KT-461-735

SWANSEA PSYCHIATRIC EDUCATION
LIBRARY

The Medical Directory 2002

158th edition

Volume One

Published by Informa Professional, a division of Informa Group plc
Informa House
30-32 Mortimer Street
London W1W 7RE
Tel: +44 (0)20 7017 5375
Fax: +44 (0)20 7017 5221
Email: liz.godden@informa.com
Website: www.informalaw.com

First published 1845
158th edition published 2002

ISBN 1 84311 111 X

A catalogue record for this book is available from the British Library

Entry into this directory does not in any way serve as validation of a medical practitioner's fitness to practice – all such enquiries should be forwarded to the General Medical Council or the relevant registration body.

The publishers reserve the right of acceptance or rejection in respect of particulars, advertising copy, and listings submitted for insertion.

Database services and typesetting by MPG Dataworld Ltd.
Bound in Great Britain by Unwin Brothers Ltd, Old Woking.

The Medical Directory 2002

Directory of Specialist Services

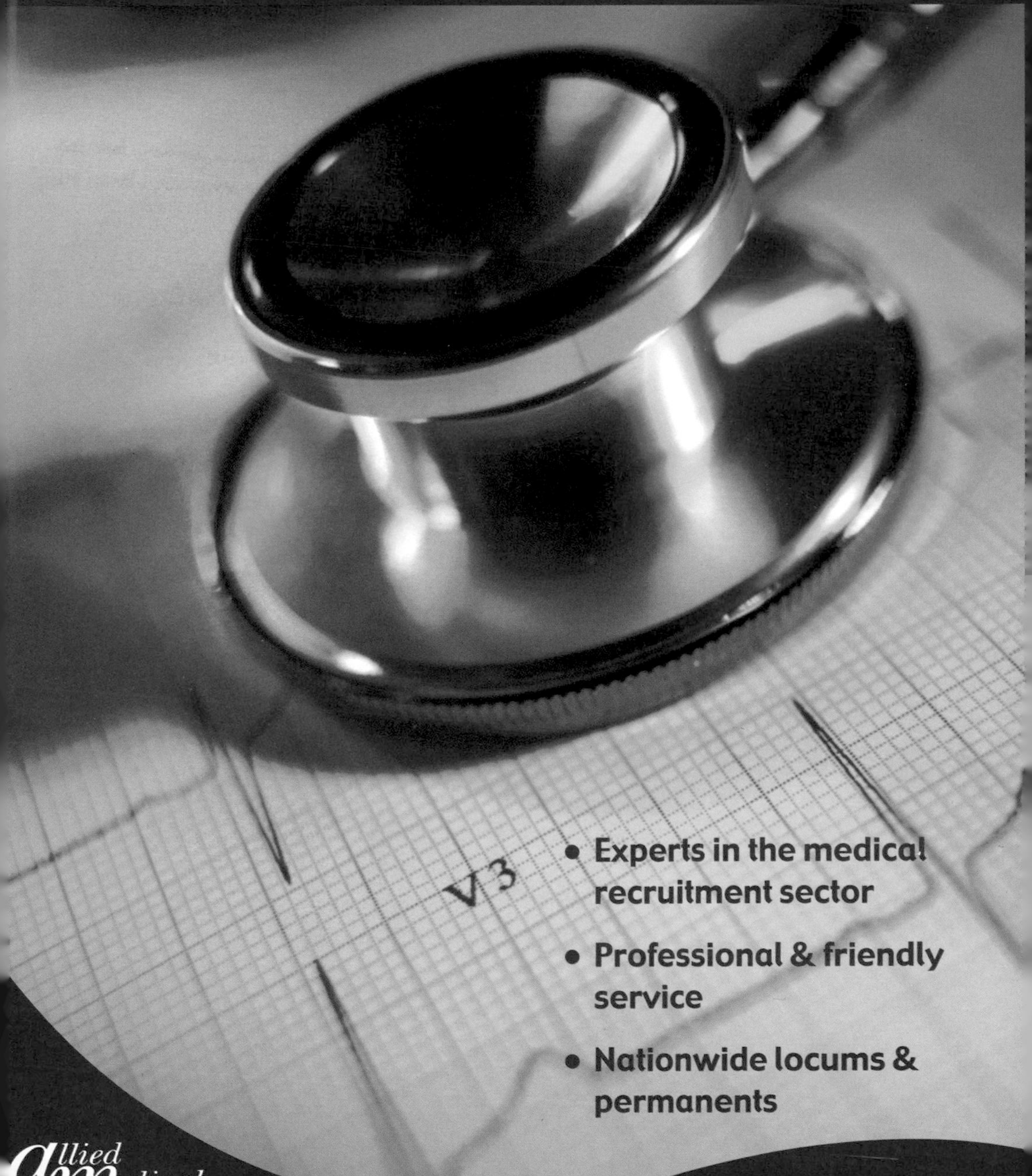

Introduction

Welcome to the 158th edition of the Medical Directory – the who's who in UK healthcare.

The Medical Directory, originally published in 1845, was the first publication of its kind to provide a comprehensive listing of those working in the medical profession and has been continuously updated ever since. It contains more detailed information on the people and organisations in the UK medical field than any other reference product available on the market today.

This year we are delighted to announce a new partnership with the *Royal Society of Medicine* and we know that over the coming year we will continue to grow this relationship to enhance the directory even further.

If you have any queries regarding the directory, or wish to update your entry, please contact me at the email or postal address below.

Thank you for your continued support.

Rosalyn Cropper
Publisher

Informa Professional
Informa House
30-32 Mortimer Street
London W1W 7RE

rosalyn.cropper@informa.com

Other healthcare titles available from Informa Professional:

- The Medical Directory Database 2002 (CD-ROM)
- Directory of Hospitals & Trusts 2002/03
- Directory of Primary Care 2003
- Database of Primary Care (CD-ROM)

Foreword

I am delighted to have this opportunity to write a Foreword to the 2002 edition of *The Medical Directory*. The *Directory*, first published in 1845, and the Royal Society of Medicine (RSM), founded forty years earlier in 1805, are both prestigious and well-recognised features of the medical landscape in the UK and overseas. For the first time, there is now an official association between the two, which I hope will continue for many years.

The RSM and the publishers of the *Directory* plan to work together in a number of ways, including joint marketing activities, promotion of the *Directory* to members of the RSM at a special price, and the development of new ideas to enhance the publication in the future.

The RSM is an independent, non-political charitable organization, with a flourishing international membership of nearly 18,000. It provides a forum for an exchange of views on topical and educational healthcare issues in an environment where they can be discussed frankly and constructively.

The aims of the Society are essentially twofold:

- to provide a broad range of educational activities and opportunities for doctors, dentists, veterinary surgeons and allied healthcare professionals, including students of these disciplines.
- to promote an exchange of information and ideas on the science, practice and organisation of medicine, both within the health professions and with responsible and informed public opinion.

The Medical Directory is recognised as the leading and best-established source of information on doctors practising in the UK. Published both in paper and CD-ROM format, it contains the full biographical profiles of over 132,000 medical practitioners and the details of over 5,000 healthcare organisations, including an alphabetical listing of all NHS trusts and hospitals.

At a time when patients and healthcare professionals are seeking greater information about individual doctors, such as their particular area of specialisation or research, this joint collaboration between *The Medical Directory* and the Royal Society of Medicine could not be a more appropriate venture.

Deirdre Hine

Dame Deirdre Hine DBE FFPHM FRCP Hon FRCS Hon FRCA
President
The Royal Society of Medicine
March 2002

Contents

Volume One

Volume Two

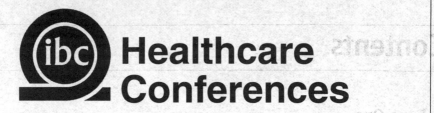

Abbreviations

AB	Bachelor of Arts
ABPsS	Associate British Psychological Society
ADMS	Assistant Director Medical Services
AE	Air Efficiency Award
AFC	Air Force Cross
AFOM	Associate Faculty of Occupational Medicine
AFPM	Associate Faculty Pharmaceutical Medicine
AHA	Associate Institute of Hospital Administrators
AKC	Associate King's College (London)
AM	Albert Medal
AMQ	American Medical Qualification
AMS	Army Medical Service
AO	Officer Order of Australia
ARIC	Associate Royal Institute of Chemistry
BA	Bachelor of Arts
BAc	Bachelor of Acupuncture
BAO	Bachelor of the Arts of Obstetrics
BASc	Bachelor of Applied Science
BC, BCh	Bachelor of Surgery
BChir	Bachelor of Surgery
BChD	Bachelor of Dental Surgery
BDA	British Dental Association
BDS	Bachelor of Dental Surgery
BDSc	Bachelor of Dental Science
BDentSc	Bachelor of Dental Science
BEM	British Empire Medal
BHy	Bachelor of Hygiene
BHyg	Bachelor of Hygiene
BM	Bachelor of Medicine
BMA	British Medical Association
BMedBiol	Bachelor of Medical Biology
BMedSc	Bachelor Medical Science
BMedSci	Bachelor of Medical Science
BPharm	Bachelor of Pharmacy
BS	Bachelor of Surgery
BSc	Bachelor of Science
BSc (MedSci)	Bachelor of Science (Medical Sciences)
Bt	Baronet
BVMS	Bachelor of Veterinary Medicine & Surgery
CAA	Civil Aviation Authority
CAS Applied Immunol	Certificate of Advance Study in Applied Immunology
CB	Companion Order of the Bath
CBE	Commander Order of British Empire
CC	County Council
CCFP	Certificate College of Family Physicians
CChem	Chartered Chemist
CD	Canadian Forces Decoration
Cert AvMed	Certificate in Aviation Medicine
CH	Companion of Honour
ChB	Bachelor of Surgery
CIH	Certificate in Industrial Health
CM, ChM	Master of Surgery
CMF	Christian Medical Fellowship
CMG	Companion Order of St Michael & St George
CMS	Church Missionary Society
CPH	Certificate in Publich Health
CRAMC	Commander Royal Army Medical Corps
CRCP	Certificant Royal College of Physicians
CRCS	Certificant Royal College of Surgeons
CStJ	Commander Order of St John
CTCM&H	Certificate in Tropical Community Medicine & Hygiene
CVO	Commander Royal Victorian Order
DA	Diploma in Anaesthetics
DADMS	Deputy Assistant Director Medical Services
DADH	Deputy Assistant Director of Health
DAP & E	Diploma in Applied Parasitology & Entomology
DAvMed	Diploma in Aviation Medicine
DBE	Dame Commander Order of British Empire
DipBMS	Diploma in Basic Medical Sciences
DC	District Council
DCC	Diploma of Chelsea College
DCCH	Diploma in Child & Community Health
DCD	Diploma in Chest Diseases
DCDH	Diploma in Community Dental Health
DCh	Doctor of Surgery
DCH	Diploma in Child Health
DChD	Doctor of Dental Surgery
DCHT	Diploma in Community Health in the Tropics
DCL	Doctor of Civil Law
DCM	Distinguished Conduct Medal
DCMT	Diploma in Clinical Medicine of Tropics
DCP	Diploma in Clinical Pathology
DCPath	Diploma College of Pathologists
DDerm	Diploma in Dermatology
DDM	Diploma in Dermatological Medicine
DDMS	Deputy Director Medical Services
DDO	Diploma in Dental Orthopaedics
DDR	Diploma in Diagnostic Radiology
DDS	Doctor of Dental Surgery
DDSc	Doctor of Dental Science
DFC	Distinguished Flying Cross
DFHom	Diploma Faculty of Homoeopathy
DFM	Distinguished Flying Medal
DFM	Diploma in Forensic Medicine
DGDP	Diploma in General Dental Practice
DGM	Diploma in Geriatric Medicine
DGMS	Director-General Medical Services
DGO	Diploma in Gynaecology & Obstetrics
Dip GU Med	Diploma in Genitourinary Medicine
DHA	District Health Authority
DHMSA	Diploma in History of Medicine, Society of Apothecaries
DHyg	Doctor of Hygiene
DIC	Diploma of Membership of Imperial College of Science & Technology (London)
DIH	Diploma in Industrial Health
Dip IMC RCS Ed	Diploma in Immediate Medical Care, Royal College of Surgeons, Edinburgh
DL	Deputy Lieutenant
DLO	Diploma in Laryngology & Otology
DM	Doctor of Medicine
DMC	District Medical Committee
DMD	Director of Dental Medicine
DMedRehab	Diploma Medical Rehabilitation
DMHS	Director Medical & Health Services
DMJ	Diploma in Medical Jurisprudence
DMO	District Medical Officer
DMR	Diploma in Medical Radiology
DMRD	Diploma in Medical Radio-Diagnosis
DMRE	Diploma in Medical Radiology & Electrolysis

DMRT Diploma in Medical Radio-Therapy
DMS Director Medical Services or Doctor of Medicine & Surgery
DMSA Diploma in Medical Services Administration
DMSS Director Medical & Sanitary Services
DMV Doctor of Veterinary Medicine
DO Diploma in Ophthalmology
DObst Diploma Obstetrics
Dobst RCOG Diploma Royal College Obstetrics & Gynaecology
DOMS Diploma in Ophthalmic Medicine & Surgery
DOrth Diploma in Orthodontics
DPA Diploma in Public Administration
DPath Diploma in Pathology
DPD Diploma in Public Dentistry
DPhil Doctor of Philosophy
DPhilMed Diploma in Philosophy of Medicine
DPhysMed Diploma in Physical Medicine
Dip Pract Derm Diploma of Practical Dermatology
DPH Diploma in Public Health
DPM Diploma in Psychological Medicine
DPMSA Diploma in Philosophy of Medicine Society of Apothecaries
DrAc Doctor of Acupuncture
DR Diploma in Radiology
DRACOG Diploma Royal Australian College of Obstetrics & Gynaecology
DFACR Diploma Royal Australasian College of Radiologists
DRCOG Diploma Royal College of Obstetrics & Gynaecology
DRCPath Diploma Royal College of Pathologists
DRM Diploma in Radiation Medicine
DRS Doctorandus
DS Doctor of Surgery
DSC Distinguished Service Cross
DSc Doctor of Science
DSM Diploma in Social Medicine
DSO Companion Distinguished Service Order
DSSc Diploma in Sanitary Science
DStJ Dame Order of St John
DTCD Diploma in Tuberculosis & Chest Diseases
DTCH Diploma in Tropical Child Health
DTD Diploma in Tuberculous Diseases
DTM & H Diploma in Tropical Medicine & Hygiene
DTPH Diploma in Tropical Public Health
DV & D Diploma in Venereology & Dermatology
ECFMG Education Council for Foreign Medical Graduates
ED Efficiency Decoration
EMAS Employment Medical Advisory Service
EMS Emergency Medical Service
ENT Ear, Nose & Throat
ERD Emergency Reserve Decoration
ESMI Elderly Subnormal Mentally Infirm
FACA Fellow American College of Anesthetists
FACC Fellow American College of Cardiologists
FACDS Fellow Australian College of Dental Surgeons
FACG Fellow American College of Gastroenterology
FACMA Fellow Australian College of Medical Administrators
FACO Fellow American College of Otolaryngology
FACOG Fellow American College of Obstetrics & Gynecology
FACP Fellow American College of Physicians
FACR Fellow American College of Radiologists
FACS Fellow American College of Surgeons
FACTM Fellow American College of Tropical Medicine
FAGO Fellow in Australia in Obstetrics & Gynaecology
FANZCP Fellow Australian & New Zealand College of Psychiatrists
FBIM Fellow British Institute of Management
FBCO Fellow British College of Ophthalmic Opticians
FBPsS Fellow British Psychological Society
FCAP Fellow College of American Pathologists
FCCP Fellow American College of Chest Physicians
FCGP Fellow College of General Practitioners
FCOphth Fellow College of Ophthalmology
FCMS Fellow College of Medicine & Surgery
FCPath Fellow College of Pathologists
FCP Fellow College of Clinical Pharmacology or Fellow College Physicians
FCPS Fellow College of Physicians & Surgeons
FCS Fellow Chemical Society
FCRA Fellow College of Radiologists of Australia
FDS Fellow in Dental Surgery
FFA Fellow Faculty of Anaesthetists
FFCM Fellow Faculty of Community Medicine
FFCMI Fellow Faculty of Community Medicine in Ireland
FFDS Fellow Faculty of Dental Surgery
FFFP Fellow Faculty of Family Planning
FFHom Fellow Faculty of Homeopathy
FFOM Fellow Faculty of Occupational Medicine
FFPath Fellow Faculty of Pathology
FFPHM Fellow Faculty of Public Health Medicine
FFPM RCP (UK) Fellow Faculty of Pharmaceutical Medicine Royal College of Physicians UK
FFR Fellow Faculty of Radiologists
FIHA Fellow Institute of Hospital Administrators
FIBiol Fellow Institute of Biology
FICS Fellow International College of Surgeons
FKC Fellow King's College London
FLCO Fellow London College of Osteopathy
FLCOM Fellow London College of Osteopathic Medicine
FLEXLic(USA) Federal Licensing Examination (USA)
FLS Fellow Linnean Society
FMC Fellow Medical Council
FMCGP (Nigeria) Fellow Medical Council of General Practitioners (Nigeria)
FOM Faculty of Occupational Medicine
FPA Family Planning Association
FPC Family Practitioner Committee
FPHM Faculty of Public Health Medicine
FPS Fellow Pharmaceutical Society
FRACDS Fellow Royal Australasian College of Dental Surgery
FRACGP Fellow Royal Australian College of General Practitioners
FRACO Fellow Royal Australasian College of Ophthalmologists
FRACOG Fellow Royal Australian College of Obstetricians & Gynaecologists
FRACP Fellow Royal Australasian College of Physicians
FRACR Fellow Royal Australasian College of Radiologists
FRACS Fellow Royal Australasian College of Surgeons
FRAI Fellow Royal Anthropological Institute
FRANZCP Fellow Royal Australian & New Zealand College of Psychiatrists
FRCA Fellow Royal College of Anaesthetists
FRCD Fellow Royal College of Dentists
FRCGP Fellow Royal College of General Practitioners
FRCOG Fellow Royal College of Obstetricians & Gynaecologists
FRCP Fellow Royal College of Physicians
FRCPA Fellow Royal College of Pathologists Australasia
FRCPath Fellow Royal College of Pathologists
FRCPC Fellow Royal College of Physicians of Canada
FRCPI Fellow Royal College of Physicians of Ireland
FRCPS Fellow Royal College of Physicians & Surgeons
FRCPsych Fellow Royal College of Psychiatrists
FRCR Fellow Royal College of Radiologists
FRCRA Fellow Royal College of Radiologists of Australasia
FRCS Fellow Royal College of Surgeons
FRCSI Fellow Royal College of Surgeons of Ireland
FRES Fellow Royal Entomological Society

FRFPS	Fellow Royal Faculty of Physicians & Surgeons
FRIC	Fellow Royal Institute of Chemistry
FRIPHH	Fellow Royal Institute of Public Health & Hygiene
FRMS	Fellow Royal Microscopical Society
FRS	Fellow Royal Society
FRSC	Fellow Royal Society of Chemistry
FRSE	Fellow Royal Society of Edinburgh
FRSH	Fellow Royal Society of Health
FSS	Fellow Royal Statistical Society
FZS	Fellow Zoological Society
GBE	Knight/Dame Grand Cross Order of the British Empire
GC	George Cross
GCB	Knight/Dame Grand Cross Order of the Bath
GCMG	Knight Grand Cross Order of St Michael and St George
GCSI	Knight Grand Commander Order of the Star of India
GCStJ	Knight Grand Cross Venerable Order of St John of Jerusalem
GCVO	Knight/Dame Grand Cross Royal Victorian Order
GM	George Medal
GMC	General Medical Council
GP	General Practitioner
HA	Health Authority
HDD	Higher Dental Diploma
HSE	Health & Safety Executive
IAMC	Indian Army Medical Corps
i/c	In Charge
IC	Intensive Care
ICRF	Imperial Cancer Research Fund
ICU	Intensive Care Unit
IMA	Irish Medical Association
IMS	Indian Medical Service
ISO	Imperial Service Order
JCC	Joint Committee on Contraception
JCHMT	Joint Committee for Higher Medical Training
JCPTGP	Joint Committee on Postgraduate Training in General Practice
JHMO	Junior Hospital Medical Officer
JP	Justice of the Peace
KBE	Knight Commander British Empire
KCB	Knight Commander Order of the Bath
KCMG	Knight Commander Order of St Michael and St George
KCSI	Knight Commander Order of the Star of India
KCVO	Knight Commander Royal Victorian Order
KCSG	Knight Commander Order St Gregory the Great
KM	Knight of Malta
KStJ	Knight of Justice Order of St John
LAH	Licentiate Apothecaries Hall, Dublin
LCPS	Licentiate College of Physicians & Surgeons
LDSc	Licentiate in Dental Science
LDS	Licentiate in Dental Surgery
LicAc	Licentiate in Acupuncture
LIHSM	Licentiate of Institute of Health Services Management
LLB	Bachelor of Laws
LLCO	Licentiate London College of Osteopathy
LLCOM	Licentiate London College of Osteopathic Medicine
LLD	Doctor of Laws
LLM	Master of Laws
LM	Licentiate in Midwifery
LMC	Local Medical Committee
LMCC	Licentiate Medical Council of Canada
LMS	Licentiate in Medicine & Surgery
LMSSA	Licentiate in Medicine & Surgery Society of Apothecaries London
LRCP	Licentiate Royal College of Physicians
LRCPI	Licentiate Royal College of Physicians of Ireland
LRCPS	Licentiate Royal College Physicians & Surgeons
LRCS	Licentiate Royal College of Surgeons
LRCSI	Licentiate Royal College of Surgeons of Ireland
LRFPS	Licentiate Royal Faculty of Physicians & Surgeons
LSA	Licentiate Society of Apothecaries London
LSM	Licentiate School of Medicine
LVO	Lieutenant Royal Victorian Order
M	Member
MA	Master of Arts
MACD	Member Australasian College of Dermatology
MACGP	Member Australasian College of General Practitioners
MACO	Member Australian College of Ophthalmologists
MACR	Member American College of Radiology
MANZCP	Member Australian & New Zealand College of Psychiatrists
MAO	Master of the Art of Obstetrics
MAustCOG	Member Australian College Obstetrics & Gynaecology
MB	Bachelor of Medicine
MBA	Master in Business Administration
MBAcA	Member British Acupuncture Association
MBE	Member Order of British Empire
MC	Military Cross
M-C	Medico-Chirurgical
MC, MCh, MChir	Master of Surgery
MCB	Master of Clinical Biochemistry
MCCM	Member College of Community Medicine (New Zealand)
MCCP	Member Ceylon College of Physicians
MCDH	Mastership in Community Dental Health
MCFP	Member College of Family Practitioners
MCh	Master of Surgery
MChir	Master of Surgery
MChD	Master of Dental Surgery
MChOrth	Master of Orthopaedic Surgery
MChOtol	Master of Otology
MClSc	Master of Clinical Science
MClinPsychol	Master of Clinical Psychology
MCommH	Master of Community Health
MCPA	Member College of Pathologists of Australia
MCPath	Member College of Pathologists
MCPS	Member College of Physicians & Surgeons
MCRA	Member College of Radiologists of Australia
MD	Doctor of Medicine
MDD	Doctor of Dental Science
MDentSc	Master of Dental Surgery
MDS	Master of Dental Surgery
MDSc	Master of Dental Science
MFCM	Member Faculty of Community Medicine
MFCMI	Member Faculty of Community Medicine, Ireland
MFFP	Member Faculty of Family Planning
MFHom	Member Faculty of Homoeopathy
MFOM	Member Faculty of Occupational Medicine
MFPaedRCPI	Member Faculty of Paediatrics, Royal College of Physicians of Ireland
MFPM	Member Faculty Pharmaceutical Medicine
MFPHM	Member Faculty Public Health Medicine
MFPM RCP (UK)	Member Faculty Pharmaceutical Medicine Royal College Physicians UK
MGDS	Member in General Dental Surgery
MHyg	Master of Hygiene
MIBiol	Member Institute of Biology
MICGP	Member of Irish College of General Practitioners
MIH	Master of Industrial Health
MLCO	Member London College of Osteopathy
MLCOM	Member London College of Osteopathic Medicine
MM	Military Medal
MMed	Master of Medicine
MMedSc	Master of Medical Science
MMF	Member Medical Faculty
MMSA	Master of Midwifery Society of Apothecaries

ABBREVIATIONS

MMSc	Master of Medical Science
MO	Master of Obstetrics
MOD	Ministry of Defence
MO & G. MObstG	Master Obstetrics & Gynaecology
MOH	Medical Officer of Health
MPhil	Master of Philosophy
MPH	Master of Public Health
MPS	Member Pharmaceutical Society
MPSI	Member Pharmaceutical Society of Ireland
MPsy	Master of Psychiatry
MPsychMed	Master of Psychological Medicine
MRACGP	Member Royal Australasian College of General Practitioners
MRACO	Member Royal Australasian College of Ophthalmologists
MRACP	Member Royal Australasian College of Physicians
MRACR	Member Royal Australasian College of Radiologists
MRad(D)	Master of Radiodiagnosis
MRad(T)	Master of Radiotherapy
MRANZCP	Member Royal Australian & New Zealand College of Psychiatrists
MRC	Medical Research Council
MRCGP	Member Royal College of General Practitioners
MRCOG	Member Royal College of Obstetricians & Gynaecologists
MRCP	Member Royal College of Physicians
MRCPA	Member Royal College of Pathologists Australasia
MRCPath	Member Royal College of Pathologists
MRCPI	Member of Royal College of Physicians of Ireland
MRCPsych	Member Royal College of Psychiatrists
MRCS	Member Royal College of Surgeons
MRCVS	Member Royal College of Veterinary Surgeons
MRNZCGP	Member Royal New Zealand College General Practitioners
MRO	Member Register of Osteopaths
MRSH	Member Royal Society of Health
MS	Master of Surgery
MSc	Master of Science
MScD	Master of Dental Science
MSSc	Master of Surgical Science
MSMF	Member of State Medical Faculty
MVO	Member Royal Victorian Order
NHI	National Health Insurance
NHS	National Health Service
NUI	National University of Ireland
OBE	Officer Order of British Empire
OM	Order of Merit
OSJ	Knight Sovereign Order of St John
OStJ	Brother Officer Order of St John
PAMC	Pakistan Army Medical Corps
PC	Privy Councillor, Pharmaceutical Chemist
PhD	Doctor of Philosophy
PHLS	Public Health Laboratory Service
PMO	Principal Medical Officer
QC	Queen's Counsel
QGM	Queen's Gallantry Medal
QHP	Queen's Honorary Physician
QHS	Queen's Honorary Surgeon
QJM	Queen's Jubilee Medal
QSM	Queen's Service Medal
QSO	Queen's Service Order
RADC	Royal Army Dental Corps
RAMC	Royal Army Medical Corps
RAuxAF	Royal Auxiliary Air Force
RCAMC	Royal Canadian Army Medical Corps
RCOG	Royal College of Obstetricians & Gynaecologists
RCP	Royal College of Physicians
RCS	Royal College of Surgeons
RD	Reserve Decoration
RNVR	Royal Naval Volunteer Reserve
SA	College of Medicine of South Africa
SBStJ	Serving Brother Order of St John
ScD	Doctor of Science
SHO	Senior House Officer
SHMO	Senior Hospital Medical Officer
SJM	Silver Jubilee Medal
SSStJ	Serving Sister Order of St John
SMO	Sovereign Military Order
TAVR	Territorial & Army Volunteer Reserve
TC Dub	Trinity College Dublin
TD	Territorial Decoration
TDD	Tuberculosis Diseases Diploma
UGM	Unit General Manager
VAD	Voluntary Aid Detachment
VC	Victoria Cross
VD	Volunteer Decoration
VQE	Visa Qualifying Examination USA
VRD	Volunteer Reserve Decoration
VTS	Vocational Training Scheme
VTSO	Vocational Training Scheme Organiser
WHO	World Health Organisation

Obituary List

Listed below are the names of those medical practitioners whose deaths were notified during the period March 2001–March 2002. Actual dates of death are shown where such information was made available.

ABBEY, Joseph Edward
ABEL, Arthur Robert Lawrence 25/12/2001
ADAMS, Rowan Hopwood
ADAMS, William Greig Fettes 16/04/2001
ADAMSON, James Wylie
ADAMSON, Robert John Wallace
AHMED, Iqbal
AL SAMARRAI, Qahtan
ALLCHIN, William Henry
ALLCOCK, John Michael
ALLEN, Sidney George 15/04/2000
ALLISON, Andrew 20/05/2001
ANDERSON, Hazley
ANDERSON, Janet Watson
ANDERSON, John Cleghorn
ANDERSON, Patricia Frances Desiree
ANDREWS, John Laurence 28/05/1999
ANDREWS, Mabel Louisa Violet 18/10/2000
ANDREWS, Robin John 09/03/2001
ANNAN, William George Taylor 31/03/2001
ANSELL, Barbara Mary, CBE 14/09/2001
ANTHONY, David
ARDLEY, John 03/02/2001
ASHKEN, Joseph John
ASHRAF, Muhammad
ASHTON, Leigh Perry
ASSINDER, Mary Louise 11/02/2001
BADMINTON, Robert Michael
BAIDOO, Solomon Kwabena
BAKATHIR, Ahmad Abdulrahman
BAKER, Alex Anthony, CBE
BALL, Godfrey Dacre Jennings
BALLON, Leslie 28/09/2001
BALMER, Charles Hill
BANKIER, James Douglas Haig 18/07/2001
BARBER, Frederick 29/03/2000
BARKER, Alan Humphrey
BARLOW, Douglas McWilliam
BARLOW, Kenneth Elliott 09/12/2000
BARMANROY, Pranab Kumar
BARNE, Islay Cecil 23/01/2001
BARR, Marjorie Marie 11/09/2000
BARRON, Margaret Coupland
BARRY, Richard Garrett George
BATEMAN, Anthony Rex Michael
BAZELEY, Ralph Whitfield, VRD
BEATON, Donald Rose, TD 10/05/2001
BEATTIE, William Martin 31/07/2001
BEDFORD, Samuel Geoffrey 19/01/2001
BEG, Mohammad Akram
BELASCO, David George
BENJAFIELD, Peter John Derrick
BENSTED, John Patrick Macrae 08/10/2000
BERRY, David 05/07/2001
BICKFORD, Bertram John 26/04/2001
BIGBY, Mary Ardelice Murray
BINNS, Charles Herbert Bryan
BIRCH, James William 22/10/2000
BIRCH, Margaret Hilary 28/12/2000
BLACK, James
BLACKBURNE, John Robert
BLAIKLOCK, Thomas Snowdon
BLUES, Roy Gibb
BOATMAN, David Wilson
BOLGER, Brendan Stephen
BOURSIN, Edward Clement
BOWEN, John James
BOWEN, Philip Douglas 25/02/2002
BOYDELL, Stanley
BOYLE, Iain Thomson
BOYLE, Michael Maurice 27/11/2000
BOYLE, Thomas Finlayson
BRADLEY, James Moyes
BRAIN, Anthony Thomas
BRAINE, George Ian Hector
BREWIN, Thurstan Berkeley 25/02/2001
BRIDGER, Elizabeth Jane
BRISCOE, Arnold Daly, TD 25/01/2002
BRITTAIN, Thomas
BROADBENT, Thomas Edwin
BROOK, Stanley Gordon
BROWN, Donald Cyrus
BROWN, Julia Margaret
BROWN, William Aiken
BROWSE, Clarence Mervyn
BRUCE-MITFORD, Margaret Theodore Callender
BUCHAN, Thomas Wilson, ISO 19/09/1999
BUCKLER, John Warwick 06/02/2001
BUGAIGHIS, Abdulla Mohamed
BULLOUGH, Arthur Stanley 10/09/2000
BUNTING, Charles Frederic
BURCH, Jean Lowrie
BURCHER, Lydia Anne 16/10/2000
BURGESS, Jerrold Ross 04/01/2001
BURN, Rollin Arthur
BURNS, James Neilson Golder

BURNS, James Ruddell Alexander
BURNS, Thomas Augustine
BURRIDGE, Peter Michael
CALAM, John
CALDER, Andrew Todd 15/03/2000
CALLANDER, Eric Milligan
CAMERON, Alastair Ross
CAMPBELL, Agnes Urquhart 17/10/2000
CAMPBELL, Angus Murdo
CAMPBELL, Margery Neville
CAMPBELL, Ronald William Fearnley 13/06/1998
CANTLAY, Leslie Stuart 05/01/2001
CAPE, James Chalmers
CAPSTICK, Alan 05/1996
CARMICHAEL, Robert
CARR, Stella Maud
CARTER, William Irving
CASEY, Denis
CASSELLS-SMITH, Alan James
CAUDWELL, Cedric Eustace 25/11/2000
CAVE, A J E 17/05/2001
CHAMBERLAIN, N
CHANDLER, Elizabeth Margaret
CHAPMAN, Margaret Joyce 07/1997
CHAPMAN, William Adam Wylie
CHASE, Rosemary Ann 01/03/2001
CHILDS, John Peter
CHOYCE, David Peter 08/08/2001
CHRISTIE, David Edward
CHUNG, Chuk Yin Lisette
CHURIN, Rochelle
CLARK, Charles Denley 27/01/2001
CLARK, Donald Walter 09/2001
CLARK, James Robert 20/12/2001
CLARK, John Derwent
CLARK, John Stuart Gibson
CLARKE, Helen Susanna
CLELAND, John Keir
CLEMENTS, Edmund Michael Baverstock
CLEMENTS, Michael William Leitrim 01/09/2001
CLYNES, Eva
COHEN, Alan Geoffrey
COLENBRANDER, Johan Cornelius Alphons Lawrence
COLTART, Wilfrid Seymour 08/02/2001
CONNELL, John Gardner
CONNELL, William Muir 11/02/2001
CONSTANT, Olivia Christine Anne O'Connor
CONYNGHAM, Mary Auderiah
COOK, John Wylie 18/08/2001
COOKE, David Alexander Pealing
COOKE, William George
CORBETT, Anthony Ralph
COSGROVE, Peter John
COX, John Anthony
COYNE, Felix Claude McConville
CRABTREE, James Wright Anderton, OBE, TD
CRANER, Alan Stanley
CRITCHLEY, Julian Arthur John Hall
CROCKETT, Gerard Samuel
CROFT, John Lawrence
CROME, Leonard, MC 05/05/2001
CROWE, Arthur James
CROWSON, Michael Christopher 17/12/1998
CROWTHER, Donald Ineson 10/01/2002
CULLEN, Helen Bernadette 06/10/1999
CUMMING, Gordon
CURLEY, John 16/08/2000
CUSSEN, William Terence
DALLY, Wilfred John
DALTON, Eileen Mary 28/02/2002
DALTON, Marguerite Jane 22/11/2001
DALY, Richard Aloysius
DAVEY, Charles James Constantine 16/09/2001
DAVIDSON, Chalmers Hunter 05/08/2001
DAVIDSON, Robert Murray
DAVIDSON, Robert Wallace
DAVIDSON, William Armstrong
DAVIDSON, William Marshall Burns
DAVIES, David Walford
DAVIES, Edward Beresford 13/08/2001
DAVIES, Hilary Janet
DAVIES, Trevor 13/09/2001
DAVIS, Herbert 29/11/2000
DAWES, Alfred Henry
DAWSON, David Andrew
DE FREYNE, Kevin John
DE KEYSER, Geoffrey Michael
DEADY, Stephen Patrick
DEEBLE, John Frederick Henry
DEMPSTER, Kenneth Robertson 06/03/2001
DEMPSTER, Margaret Balfour
DERRINGTON, Margaret Mary
DESMOND, Jean McGregor
DEVLIN, Henry Richard Tarleton
DICKSON, John Wanless 16/06/2001
DINGWALL, Ian Macdonald 15/06/2001
DITTMAR, Ralph Bryon
DIXON, George Edward
DONALDSON, George Gregor 29/07/2000
DORRELL, Edmund Were 18/11/2000
DOUGLAS-JONES, Arthur Percy 10/03/2001
DOYLE, Joseph Ignatius
DOYLE, Leslie 22/12/2000
DRINKWATER, Peter Derrick, OStJ 12/10/2000
DRURY, Kathleen Agnes Dru
DUCKWORTH, Sylvia Irene
DUNN, Denis Michael
DUPRE, Pierre Vincent Charles Waldemar 30/10/2000
DURAN, Francis
DUVAL, Howard Roderick 04/01/2001
EADIE, Douglas George Arnott
EBBING, Robert Nissim
EDWARDS, David Arthur Wright 16/10/2001
EDWARDS, Moire Elizabeth 19/02/2001
ELLENBOGEN, Saul
ELLIOTT, Ian Michael 20/07/2001
EMSON, Daksha Pravin
EVANS, Benjamin Ifor 14/01/2000

EVANS, Philip
EVANS, Sinclair Morris
FAITHFULL, Stephen Theodore, DFC
FARMER, Alexander Russell
FEGGETTER, Helen Winchester
FEINGOLD, Maurice
FINGLAND, Margaret Joan 25/12/2001
FITCH-HOLDEN, Grace Joan Veronica
FITZGERALD, Desmond Finbar, SBStJ
FLACKS, Benjamin 03/02/2001
FLOOD, Charles Mackintosh, VRD, KCSG
FLUCK, David Charles, TD
FLYNN, Kevin Leo Henry
FOGGITT, Kenneth Dudley
FOSTER, Douglas Benjamin Evan 1992
FOTHERINGHAM, William Milne
FOULDS, Tom
FRANCE, William Gordon
FRASER, Clara Jean 04/07/2001
FREEMAN, Anthony George 01/02/2001
FREEMAN, Granville
FULTON, Marjorie Stephens
GALLA, Thomas 11/02/2001
GALLOWAY, Walter Brown Frame
GANDHI, Abhayakumar Gulabchand
GANTLEY, William
GARDINER, Robert John Terrance
GARDNER, Thomas, MBE 01/01/2001
GARRETT, James Allan
GARROW, Donald Hugh 25/02/2001
GAY, Joseph
GEBERTT, Stanislaw
GEE, David John, OBE
GELL KNIGHT, Pakalapti Devanandam
GEOGHEGAN, Vincent Patrick
GERMAN, Monica Vanessa
GIBSON, John Hammond 10/10/2001
GILBERT, Sydney Filvar 12/10/2000
GILCHRIST, Thomas Reid
GILL, James Munro Christie
GILLESPIE, Walter McLean
GILLESPIE, William Hewitt
GILMOUR, Alan Breck, CVO, CBE 07/2001
GLANVILLE, Frank Harold 20/03/2002
GLASSER, Mervin 09/11/2000
GLASSETT, Michael Clifton
GLEDHILL, Doreen Edith
GLEESON-WHITE, Myles Hemingway
GLENDINNING, Robert Hereward, OBE 08/03/2001
GODBOLE, D D
GOLDIE, Robert Bruce James
GOLTEN, Mark Anthony
GORDON, Thomas
GOTTLIEB, Sydney
GOULD, Donald William 13/02/2002
GOW, Ian Menzies 03/04/2001
GRAHAM, Daphne Mary Nur Mahal 08/05/2000
GRAHAM-STEWART, Colin Woodward 08/10/2000
GRAY, Noel Atherton
GREEN, Colin Michael
GREEN, John Herbert 25/08/2000
GREEN, Walter Peter Douglas
GREENING, Wilfred Peter
GREENWOOD, Edward
GREGORY, Beatrice Alicia Joan
GRIFFIN, Joseph 03/10/2001
GRIFFITH, John 30/10/2001
GRIFFITHS, Glaslyn John 02/05/2001
GRIFFITHS, John Daniel 10/04/2001
GRIFFITHS, Lawrence
GRIMES, Daphne Joan
GROVE-WHITE, Robert John
GRYSPEERDT, Michael John 15/08/2000
GURNEY, Norman James Stratton
GUROWSKI, Boleslaw Jozef
HALFORD, Jeffrey
HALLETT, James Thomas 07/11/2001
HALLIDAY, Charles Edwin 02/06/2001
HALLINAN, Francis John 01/08/2000
HAMILTON, Margaret Dorothy Winspear
HAMILTON, Pamela Helen Lindsay
HAMILTON, Roderick Rogerson 11/2000
HAMILTON, Ursula Helena
HAMMICK, Penelope Katherine
HANDOLL, Maurice Henry 23/03/2001
HANLEY, Howard Granville, CBE 18/02/2001
HANNA, Thomas Moore
HARAN, Thomas Mary Joseph 15/04/1999
HARDIE, Leslie Allan
HARDING, Frances Anne 07/2001
HARDING, Patricia Ann 01/10/2001
HARDMAN, Andrew Patrick
HARGREAVES, Jill 25/04/2001
HARPER, Ernest Harold Carr
HARRIS, Michael Benjamin
HARVEY, Raymond John
HASHMI, Altaf-Ur-Rahman
HASKELL, Alexander
HASKELL, Richard 12/06/2000
HASLAM, George Charles
HATTERSLEY, Francis George
HEALD, Patrick Robin
HEILPERN, Ernest Henry
HENDRY, Neil Geddes Clarkson, CBE 21/12/2000
HENDRY, William Gordon 22/11/2000
HEWAT, Richard Middleton
HICKMAN, Alan Dudley
HICKS, Josephine Elaine
HIERONS, Raymond 07/03/2001
HILL, Adrian Graham Warren 06/09/2001
HILL, Rowland Nicholas 12/05/2001
HILLIS, Barclay Renfrew 23/03/2001
HINDLE, Keith Longsworth
HIRSCHMANN, Samuel Wolfe
HIRST, William James Richard
HOFFMANN, Arthur Dunstan
HOLDEN, Rupert James
HOLTBY, Gerald Rookledge 22/03/2001

HOLZER, Emil Mendel 06/12/2000
HOOTON, William Frederick
HOPE, Peter Lawrence
HOPKIRK, Kenneth Dewar
HORNE, Kathleen
HOROWITZ, Michael Simon
HORROCKS, Sidney
HORTON, John
HOULSTON, Nigel Ravenscroft
HOULT, John Graham
HOUSE, Robert Joseph
HOUSEMAN, Rodney John
HOUSTON, Thomas
HOWARD, Richard Corfield 06/2001
HOWARTH, Eric Colin
HOWELLS, Denys Elwyn 07/04/2001
HOWITT, Harold Geoffrey 08/12/2000
HUCKBODY, James Allan
HUGHES, Eluned Margaret
HUGHES, Margaret Winifred
HUNT, Charles William John
HUNT, Wilfrid Estridge
HUSSAIN, Khateeb Khasim
HUTCHISON, David 02/06/2001
INGMAN, William 22/08/2001
IRELAND, Dudley Aubrey 1997
ISINKAYE, Helen Feyisetan
JACKSON, Harry
JACKSON, Ian Martin
JACKSON, John Dill
JACKSON, John Littler 16/01/2001
JACOBS, Dorothy 22/05/2001
JACOBS, Leslie Joseph
JAMES, Frank
JAMES, Herbert 07/03/2001
JAMES, John Ivor Pulsford 11/07/2001
JEFFREE, Gladys Irene 12/07/2001
JENKINS, David Graham Watts
JENKINS, Hugh Llewellyn
JENNER, Eric Greenwood, MBE
JOHN, Alan Oakley, CStJ
JOHNSTONE, George
JONES, Derrol Clifford
JONES, Harold Witcomb Everley, OBE 09/01/2001
JONES, John Stephen Phillips 07/12/2000
JONES, Philip Ernest Henry
JONES, Philip Malcolm Pryce
JONES, Richard Wynne
JONES, Roland Norman
JUMAILY, Dhiaa
JUNOR, James Winton
KEDIA, Nawal Kishore
KEE, Frederick Thomas
KEEBLE, Margaret Brown 02/05/2001
KELLEHER, Thomas Daniel
KENYON, Ida Eileen 20/07/2000
KENYON, Keith Brian
KERR, Esther Selkirk
KERR, Lilian 28/09/2001

KERSHAW, Damian James Edward
KEYWORTH, Edmund Roland
KHAN, Aman Ullah
KHAN, Rafiq Ullah
KING, Barbara Cunningham
KING, Robert Ernest, VRD
KIPLING, Joan Winifred
KNAPPETT, Charles Richard
KNIGHT, Geoffrey Clinton Hewett 18/05/2001
KNOWLES, Colin Henry Rylands 08/09/1998
KNOWLES, Joan
KONSTAM, Michaela
KULKARNI, Krishna Bhagwan
KWAN, David Ching Yuen
LACE, Margaret Elizabeth 01/06/2001
LAIDLAW, Matthew
LAIRD, Sydney Mander
LAMB, Douglas Watson 11/12/2001
LAMB, Henry Harold Brian 1997
LANKESTER, Lionel William Archibald 14/02/2002
LAUSTE, Leslie Wallace, MBE, TD 03/01/2001
LAWSON, Hugh Montagu
LAWSON, John
LAWSON, John Alexander Reid, OBE
LAWTON, James Kenneth
LE VAY, David
LEASK, Alan Rennie
LEE, Edward Stanley
LEE, Sheila Millar
LEES, James Corson 08/06/2001
LEESE, Thomas Kenneth James
LEHANE, Sarah
LEIGH, Richard 04/10/2001
LESSINGTON-SMITH, Carolina Mathilda
LEUNG, Kwan Lai
LEVANTINE, Nicholas Stewart
LEVOI, Richard Keyes
LEWARS, Peter Henry Dalziel, TD 01/04/2001
LEWIS, Cyril Vernon
LEWIS, David Owen 07/01/2000
LEWIS, John David 19/08/1999
LEWIS, Mair Elizabeth
LEWIS, Thomas Morgan Archibald
LEWTHWAITE, Christopher
LIGHT, Albert Lawson 1992
LINDSAY, Susan Lesley
LINLEY-ADAMS, John Charles 08/05/2001
LINTON, John Steuart Alexander
LISTER, Jessica Charlotte
LIVINGSTON, Douglas Ronald
LIVINGSTONE, Robert
LLOYD-DAVIES, David Gerald
LODGE, Frank Edmanson 09/02/2002
LOGIE, Alexander Wylie 16/02/2001
LOGUE, Valentine 28/12/2000
LONG, Charles
LOW, Maurice Gerald
LUCAS, Victor Levy
LUNN, Marion Taylor

LUNT, Henry Randle Wybunbury, TD
LUTWYCHE, Violet Lesley 12/03/2001
LUTWYCHE, Vivien Ursula 13/03/2001
MCALL, Robert Kenneth
MACASKILL, Angus Stewart
MACAULAY, Mary Hope
MCCLINTOCK, Joseph
MCCOMB, Samuel Gerald
MCDOWALL, Margaret Burnside Woods 11/02/2001
MCDOWELL, Leslie Alexander
MCENTEGART, Michael Gerard 19/08/2001
MCEVOY, Edward Noel 04/05/2001
MCEWEN, William Gray 13/06/2001
MCGOWAN, Gregory Patrick, MC 31/08/2000
MCHATTIE, Anne Margaret Hume
MCINERNEY, Francis Patrick
MCINTOSH, Donald
MACINTYRE, Hugh McCallum
MCKELLAR, William
MCKEOWN, Maureen Patricia
MACKINLAY, Cecil John, TD
MCKIRDY, David
MCKIRDY, Thomas Carl Gustaf 30/05/2000
MCLAUGHLIN, Margaret Elisabeth
MCLELLAND, James 01/09/2000
MCLEOD, Andrew Jeremy
MACLEOD, Hugh Robert
MACNEISH, William Thomas Moore
MCPHILLIPS, Kathleen Mary
MCQUAKER, William
MCQUILLAN, Dermot Leo
MCRAE, Duncan Alexander
MCVEIGH, James Anthony
MAGILL, Betty Emma Anna
MAINGAY, Hugh Courtney 10/09/2001
MALIK, Nasim Ahmad
MALLOCH, John Alexander
MALLON, John Michael
MANDERSON, William Scott
MANN, Evelyn Margaret Fortune
MANN, William Neville 25/06/2001
MANNERS, Stella Margaret
MANSON, William John 07/1998
MARSDEN, Pamela Jill
MARSHALL, George Hay
MARSHALL, John Pascal
MARSHALL, Kenneth George
MARSHALL, William Robert
MARTIN, Hugh Thomas Plunkett
MARTIN, James Gerard
MARTIN, Joseph Barnett Hicks 18/12/2001
MARTIN, (Margaret) Doreen (Cuthbert)
MASSIE, Francis Edward
MATHES, Cecil John
MATHIAS, David 23/03/2000
MAUGHAN, Matthew Michael James
MAUNSELL, Eileen Dorothea
MAXWELL, William Russell
MAY, George Bruce 10/1998
MELDRUM, William James Gillan
MELINEK, Arnold
MENDICK, Norman 03/11/2000
MEREDITH, David Eryl, OBE 17/03/2001
MERRY, John Johnstone Fergus 28/7/2001
METCALF, Valerie Joyce
MIBASHAN, Reuben Sougin 20/01/2001
MICHAELS, Barry Stanley
MICHAELSON, Harold Montague
MICHIE, Joanne Ray 26/08/2001
MILEY, Robert Arnold
MILLAR, Robert James
MILLER, Barrie 02/07/2001
MILLER, Hugh
MILLINGTON, Gertrude Olga Walker
MILNE, Douglas Blyth
MILNE, Elizabeth Honor
MILNE, Valerie MacAra
MINDHAM, Brian Aubrey Edwin 16/06/2000
MISRA, Sisir Kumar
MITCHELL, Logan
MITTING, Alison Kennard 12/11/2000
MOLES, Thomas Michael 20/03/2001
MONAGHAN, Laurence
MONTAGNON, John Langlois 30/04/2001
MORGAN, Samir Sadek
MORRISON, Eleanor 04/2001
MORRISON, Janet Faulds 05/05/2000
MORTON, Helen Elizabeth Mary
MORTON, James Dougall Kent, TD
MUIR, William
MULLIGAN, James Brendan
MUMMERY, Michael Browning
MUNK, Magdalena Krystyna
MURFIN, Walter John
MURPHY, Martin James, MC
MURPHY, Thomas
MURRAY, David Sinclair
MUSGRAVE, Evelyn Marcelle
MUTVALLI, Maqbul Ebrahim Ismail 01/02/2002
NABNEY, John Beresford Cotter
NADDELL, Alexander Walker, ERD, QHS, KStJ 04/2000
NAIK, Baiju Ishwarlal 07/2001
NATHWANI, Ashokkumar Morarji 26/01/2001
NELSON, Clifford
NEVELOS, A'kos Bela
NEWMAN, Charles Richard
NEYLON, John Patrick 12/06/1999
NICHOLLS, Nevill Armstrong
NICHOLSON, Thomas Wilson
NIGHTINGALE, Jean Muriel
NIPPS, Noel James
NORMAN-TAYLOR, William
NORWELL, Henry
O'CONNELL, John Eugene Anthony
O'CONNOR, Patrick Joseph, CB, OBE
O'CONNOR, Thomas Christopher
O'NEILL, John
O'SHEA, Bridget Jane

O'SULLIVAN, John Thomas
O'SULLIVAN, Maeve
O'SULLIVAN, William
OGILVIE, Leonard Alexander
OKOLSKI, Stefan
OLLIFF, Donald Edwin 07/02/2001
ORR, John Archibald 23/04/2001
ORR, Mary Watson
PAGE, Nancy Margaret 06/01/2002
PALMER, John William Bryan
PANDYA, Govindlal Jatashanker
PANTIN, Charles Guy, OBE 25/02/2001
PARKES, William Edgar 23/09/2001
PARRY-JONES, Owen 26/11/2000
PEACOCK, David Barnes
PEARCE, Alfred
PEARSON, Norman Goundry
PEARSON, Robert Antony O'Grady
PEBERDY, Geoffrey Robert
PEDDER, Bridget Mary
PERKINS, Irwyn Morse, MBE
PERRY, Francis Stephen 12/04/2001
PETRIE, James Colquhoun, CBE
PETRIE, Patrick William Roy 1999
PETTICREW, Robert
PHILLIPS, Terence Talbot
PICKETT, David Harry 09/09/2000
PICTON, Arthur Dyce, MBE, MC 12/01/2002
PIRIE, Ian Fordyce
PITTS, Robert MacLaren
PLEYDELL, Malcolm James, MC
POLLARD, Constance Joyce
POULTON, Eustace Christopher 11/12/2000
POWER, Denis John, TD
PRESHAD, N
PRESTON, Nigel David Bentley
PRICE, Derek Lionel
PRINGLE, George Morgan 24/10/2001
QAZI, Iftikhar-Ud-Din
QUANTRILL, Douglas Walter 26/08/2001
QUEENBOROUGH, Jeremy Hugh Crossley
RABBS, Cyril 17/03/2001
RACKOW, Aubrey Maurice
RADHA, Tirvmalai Gopalaswami
RAJJAYABUN, Phimol 31/03/2001
RAMADAN, Soliman Abdel Aziz
RANDALL, Zoe Christine 02/09/2001
RANDERIA, Phiroze Kawashah
RAO, Rudravajhala Visveswara 08/08/2001
RASHID, Abdul 16/11/2000
RAY, William Turner Densham
READ, Robert Alexander, TD
READER, Ann
REAY, Paul
REES, Gordon Jackson
REES-ROBERTS, Ivor Bailey
REID, James 25/06/2001
REID, Robert Kenneth
REID, Sylvia Mary 13/06/2001

REILLY, Lilian Violet
RENDLE-SHORT, Coralie Winifrede, OBE 20/03/2001
REVIE, Archibald MacDonald 13/07/2000
REYNOLDS, Denis Buckley
RICHARDS, Lionel Dyer
RICHARDSON, Robert Alan 1999
RICHARDSON, Robert Edmund 22/09/2001
RIGBY, Edward Pim, MBE
RIGG-MILNER, Alfred John
ROBERTS, Anne Patricia 09/12/2000
ROBERTS, Sarah Diane
ROBIN, Ashley Arnold 26/06/2001
ROBINSON, Anthony
ROBINSON, Joseph 26/08/2001
ROBSON, John Harvey
ROCHE, Aileen Campbell 11/11/2000
ROCHE, John William Joseph
RODGERS, Harold William, OBE, OStJ 24/06/2001
ROGERS, Richard Douglas, MBE
ROWSON, Alan Horace
ROY, Suhas Kumar 05/02/2001
ROYALL, Cecil Peter
RUSHFORD, William Armstrong Innes
RUSHWORTH, Geoffrey
RUSSELL, Christina 03/04/2001
RUSSELL, Patrick Morries Gordon 22/08/2001
RUSSELL, Stanley Farrant 12/01/2001
RYAN, John Valentine 04/01/2001
RYCROFT, Richard Noel, MC
RYDER, George Jeffrey
SAHAY, Sarojini
SAINSBURY, Hugh Stewart Kerr 17/02/2001
SALAMA, Salama Fakhry 26/12/2000
SANERKIN, Nedjdet Gurgen
SCOTT, John Kemp 15/09/2000
SCOTT, Kathleen
SCOTT-CLARKE, Mary Winifred
SCOWEN, Eric Frank
SCRIVENER, Eric Ralph Ravenscroft
SEAGER, Anna Violet 16/05/2001
SEARLE, James Gordon 22/08/2001
SENTER, George William
SEYMOUR, Francis 16/03/2001
SHARP, John Leicester
SHAW, George Harold
SHAW, James Brian, OBE 06/01/2001
SHAW, Robert Macdonald, CB 09/11/2000
SHEARER, John Alexander 21/02/2001
SHELMERDINE, Barry Anthony 26/10/2001
SHENKIN, Percy
SHEPPARD, James Golding Harding, GM
SHERLOCK, Sheila Patricia Violet, DBE 09/02/2002
SHERMAN, Alan George 15/05/2001
SHERWOOD, Leslie Maurice
SHIPMAN, John Jeffrey 01/04/2001
SIMMONS, Eileen Mary
SIMPSON, William 21/11/2001
SINCLAIR, David Refson
SINCLAIR, Isobel Alexander

SINGER, Geoffrey Everett
SITTAMPALAM, Arumugam
SIVALINGAM, Thambipillai
SKINNER, Edward Michael 09/09/1998
SLOAN, David Graham
SLOPER, John Chaplin 14/06/2000
SLOSS, John David Grant
SMALL, Anthony Robert Alexander
SMITH, Esther 24/11/2000
SMITH, Jamie William Jarvie 09/10/2001
SMITH, Margaret Anne
SMITH, William Davidson Livingstone
SMYTH, Patrick McIlroy 29/09/2001
SNAPE, Geoffrey
SORRELL, Frances 05/11/2001
SOUTHGATE, Kenneth 12/03/2001
SPEAKE, Jacqueline Jill
SPEER, William George 07/01/2002
SPENCE, Ernest Edward 07/12/2000
SPENCER, Anthony Maurice 1994
SQUIRE, John 20/08/2001
STAMM, Temple Theodore 18/10/2001
STARRITT, Alexander
STATHERS, Douglas Nicholson
STEPHEN, Gita 04/06/2001
STEPHEN, John Low
STEVEN, Ranald Fyfe Findlay
STEVENS, John Douglas 20/12/2000
STEWART, Hamish Alexander 08/1998
STEWART-HESS, Charles Henry 17/04/2001
STONE, Jeffrey
STORRIER, Shirley 10/06/2001
STOTT, Hector John
STOUT, Geoffrey
STOWERS, John Marcus 30/07/2001
STRATON, James 20/02/2001
STREET, Walter John, TD
SUTCLIFFE, John Duncan
SUTHERLAND, Isabel Frances
SUTTIE, Alastair Mackintosh
SUTTON, Simon
SWANSTON, John Lawson, TD
TAIT, Angus McInnes
TATE, Norman 25/03/2001
TATTERSALL, Ian 10/1999
TAYLOR, Bruce Drummond
TAYLOR, Cyril 11/12/2000
TAYLOR, Hermon 10/01/2001
THICK, Gordon Caton
THIRD, Alastair Joseph
THOMAS, David Robert
THOMAS, Irene Barbara
THOMSON, Edward Laidlaw, VRD
THOMSON, William
THORNHILL, Stephen Niall
THURSTON, Crawford John 22/03/2001
TILLY, Clifford Rickard, MC
TOMLINS, David Corbett 28/03/2001
TOMLINSON, Michael Richard 03/03/2002
TORRANCE, Henry Bruce
TOWERS, Sheila Mary
TOWN, Jonathan Peter
TOWNSLEY, Norman Joyce 11/03/2001
TRAILL, Raymond
TUDDENHAM, Harry Malcolm, MBE
TURNER, Winifred Lucy
TWISS, Eric Frank
TWOMEY, James Golden
TYAGI, Jagraj Singh
TYSER, Peter Anthony
UNDERWOOD, John Elphinstone 13/09/2001
URQUHART, David Robert Hannah
VAHL, Stephen Peter
VAN ESSEN, William 27/07/2001
VANSTONE, Derrick Richard David
VINCENT, Alan 24/06/2001
VIRET, John Benjamin
WADLOW, Anne Yvonne Mary 18/04/2001
WAINE, Theodore Edward
WAINWRIGHT, Angela Patricia 12/08/2001
WALDRON, Dennis Harry
WALKER, Arthur Harold Colyear 03/03/2001
WALKER, Donald Oliphant
WALKER, Elizabeth Peta
WALL-CLARKE, John Garrett
WALLACE, Gordon Profeit
WALLACE, James Meighan 28/08/2001
WALLBRIDGE, David Christopher
WALLER, Caroline Mary
WALLEY, Ronald Victor
WALLIS, Ralph Wilson Gray Ransome, DSC 13/04/2001
WALLS, John 01/03/2001
WALMSLEY, Robert, TD 24/08/1998
WARNOCK, Grizel
WASSEF, Boulos Adib Yacoub
WATERFALL, William Blair
WATSON, Alan Albert
WATSON, Edgar Stewart, OBE
WATSON, Hamish, TD
WATSON, Jean Lorraine 28/06/2001
WATSON, Leonard Alex
WATT, Barbara Stalker
WEST, Albert 20/08/2001
WEST, Gerald Andrew
WEST, Harry Fortescue
WEST, Iain Eric
WEST, Roger, OBE, TD, OStJ
WESTCOMBE, Rosemary Elizabeth
WHITE, John Edward 19/12/2000
WHITE, John Ronald
WHITELAW, Michael Newton 13/09/2000
WHITEWRIGHT, Arthur
WHITNEY, Freda Bury
WHITNEY, Rupert Underwood
WHYTE, David Fairweather 04/12/2000
WICKHAM, Basil Felix
WIGHTMAN, James
WILCOX, Graeme Jackson

OBITUARY LIST

WILDGRUBE, Christiane
WILKINSON, Cecil Henry 25/07/2001
WILKINSON, John Battle 12/09/2000
WILLIAMS, David Christopher 17/10/2000
WILLIAMS, Gregory Cain
WILLIAMS, Jonathan Alun 26/07/2001
WILSON, Cecil Trevor Marshall
WILSON, Christine Helen 06/07/2001
WILSON, Derek 13/10/2000
WILSON, John Logan 05/05/2001
WILSON, Martha Neill Algie 24/04/2001
WILSON, Scott Nigel John
WILSON, Thomas
WILTON, Roy
WINSLEY-STOLZ, Henry 20/03/2001
WINSTONE, Norman Edward 22/03/2001
WISEMAN, Gerald 08/12/2000
WITHEY, James Lewis
WOLFFE, Paul Simon
WOODRUFF, Michael Francis Addison
WOOLLEY, John William 04/05/2000
WOTHERSPOON, John Gavin
WRAITH, Rachel
WRAY, George Arthur
WRIGHT, Basil Martin 04/03/2001
WRIGHT, Dorothy
YATES, Peter Owen
YOUNG, Arnold
ZAIDI, Syed Karamat Husain 08/01/2001
ZONDEK, Lilly H
ZONDEK, Theodor

The Medical Directory 2002

Part One

Medical Practitioners in the UK

A-L

A-ALI, Nuzhet 5 Ellis Avenue, Slough SL1 2RD — MB ChB 1992 Leic.

A'COURT, Christine Hannah Dorothy Wilkinson and Partners, Carterton Surgery, 17 Alvescot Road, Carterton OX18 3JL Tel: 01993 844567 Fax: 01993 841551; Longlands, 48 Millwood End, Long Hanborough, Witney OX29 8BY Tel: 01993 883702 Fax: 01993 883702 Email: chdacourt@aol.com — MB BS 1985 Lond.; BA Oxf. 1982, MA 1989; MRCP (UK) 1989; MRCGP 1996. (Oxford & St Thomas Hosp.) GP Carterton, Oxon; GP Co-ordinator Oxon. Multi-disciplinary Audit Advis. Gp. (MAAG). Socs: BMA. Prev: Research Fell. (Intens. Ther.) John Radcliffe Hosp. Oxf.; Regist. (Haemat., Intens. Care & Emerg. Med.) & SHO (Accid. Serv.) Freemantle Hosp. W. Austral.

A'HARA, Lynne June Mary Esslemont Group, Foresterhill Health Centre, Westburn Road, Aberdeen AB25 2AY Tel: 01224 559666; Woodhaven, Cowstones, Hatton of Fintray, Aberdeen AB21 0HY — MB ChB 1992 Aberd.; MRCGP 1996; DFFP 1997; DRCOG 1995. (Aberd.)

A'NESS, Tina Louise 7 Poole Road, Bournemouth BH2 5QR; 43 Old Pound Close, Lytchett Matravers, Poole BH16 6BW Tel: 01202 621487 — MB ChB 1990 Leic.; BSc Lond. 1988; MRCGP 1995; DRCOG 1994; DGM RCP Lond. 1993; Cert Family Plann. 1995; IUCD Cert 1995. p/t GP Bournemouth. Socs: BMA; Young Princip. Gp.; MDU. Prev: SHO (Elderly Care) Dorset Co. Hosp.; SHO (O & G & Paediat.) W. Dorset Hosp. Dorchester; SHO (Cas.) Weymouth & Dist. Hosp.

AALAMANI, Professor Hossain London Bridge Hospital, 27 Tooley St., Waterloo, London SE1 2PR Tel: 01836 545409; Institute of Psychiatry, De Crespigny Park, Denmark Hill, London SE5 8AF — MD 1973 Tehran. Phys. Lond. Bridge Hosp.; GP Attend. Train. Guy's Hosp. Lakeside Health Centre Lond.; Observer Moorfields Eye Hosp.; Hon. Phys. Postgrad. Dept. Roy. N. Hosp. Lond.; Clin. Asst. Inst. Psychiat. & Hon. Regist. (Psychiat.) Guy's Hosp. Lond.; Phys. Min. Health Iran; Surg. Min. Health Iran; Pres. Iranian Med. Assn. UK; GP Min. Health Iran; Prof. & Pres. Hippocratic Iranian-Internat. GMC (Lond.). Socs: Fell. Roy. Soc. Med.; Assoc. Mem. Irish Coll. Gen. Pract. & RCGP; World Psychiat. Assn. Prev: Cons. Psychiat. Roy. Free Hosp. Lond.; Sen. Psychiat. William Harvey Hosp. Kent; Regist. (Psychiat.) P.ss Alexandra Hosp. Harlow.

AAL, Bronwen 85 Fern Avenue, Jesmond, Newcastle upon Tyne NE2 2RA — MB BS 1972 Newc.; MRCGP 1976; DObst RCOG 1975.

AALI, Sayyed Adnan Ealing Hospital NHS Trust, Uxbridge Road, Southall UB1 3HW Tel: 020 8967 5401; 209 The Ridgeway, Harrow HA2 7DE Tel: 020 8930 8770 Fax: 020 8427 7037 Email: saali@dircon.co.uk — MB BS 1982 Punjab; PhD Lond. 1992, MSc 1987. Staff Grade Pract. (Microbiol.) Ealing Hosp. NHS Trust. Socs: Hosp. Infec. Soc.; Amer. Soc. Microbiol. Prev: Regist. (Microbiol.) Norwich PHLS; Regist. (Ophth.) Rawalpindi Med. Coll., Pakistan; Med. Off. Samli Sanat.

AARON, Mr David Azariah Rajan (retired) Ross Hall Hospital, Crookston Road, Glasgow G52 3NQ Tel: 0141 810 3151 — MB ChB 1963 Glas.; FRCS Ed. 1968; Cert. Orthop. Surg.1975. Vis. Cons. Orthopaedic Surg. Ross Hall Hosp. Glas. Prev: Cons. Orthop. Surg. Roy. Alexandra Hosp. Paisley.

AARON, John (retired) 1 Church View, Burton Latimer, Kettering NN15 5LG Tel: 01536 725783 — MB BS 1955 Lond.; MRCS Eng. LRCP Lond. 1955; FDS RCPS Glas. 1976; FRCR 1981; DMRD Eng. 1979; LDS RCS Eng. 1963. Prev: Cons. Radiol. St. Cross Hosp. Rugby.

AARONRICKS, Paul James Frederic (retired) 1 Barton Road, Canterbury CT1 1YG — MB ChB 1953 Birm.; FRCPsych. 1982, M 1973; DPM Eng. 1957. Hon. Cons. Psychiat. Canterbury-Thanet HA; Mem. Ment. Health Rev. Tribunal. Prev: Cons. Psychiat. Canterbury-Thanet & Medway HAs.

AARONS, Brian Michael The Surgery, 4 Disraeli Road, London SW15 2DS Tel: 020 8788 4836 Fax: 020 8780 2961; 11 Cambridge Road, West Wimbledon, London SW20 0SQ Tel: 020 8946 5984 — MB BS 1975 Lond.; MRCGP 1997; MRCP (UK) 1978. (Middlesex) GP Lond.; Hosp. Pract. Roy. Hosp. & Home for Incurables Lond.; Local Med. Off. Civil Serv.; Hon. Med. Off. Wimbledon Football Club. Prev: Clin. Asst. Marks & Spencer plc; Clin. Asst. Diabetic Clinic Qu. Mary's Hosp. Roehampton.

AARONS, Emma Julia Department of Microbiology, John Radcliffe Hospital, Level 7, Headley Way, Headington, Oxford OX3 9DU Tel: 01865 741166 Fax: 01865 220890; 32 Demesne Furze, Headington OX3 7XF Email: emmaaarons@hotmail.com — MB BS 1988 Lond.; MD 1997; BSc Lond. 1985; MRCP (UK) 1992. Specialist Regist. Infec. Dis. & Med. Microbiol. Oxf. Radcliffe Hosp.

AARONS, Stephen David St Johns Way Medical Centre, 96 St. Johns Way, London N19 3RN Tel: 020 7272 1585 Fax: 020 7561 1237; 9 Gloucester Gardens, Golders Green, London NW11 9AB Tel: 020 8458 1190 Email: aarons@btinternet.com — MB BS 1980 Lond.; DRCOG 1983; Dip. Dermat. Wales 1998. (Middlx.) GP Princip. Lond.; Trainer (Gen. Pract.) Lond. Prev: Ho. Phys. Centr. Middlx. Hosp.; Ho. Surg. Barnet Gen. Hosp.; Trainee GP Barnet VTS.

AARONSON, Rosa B (retired) 1 The Leadings, Wembley Park, Wembley HA9 9DT — MD 1938 Vienna. Prev: Med. Off. Lond. Boro. Brent.

AAS, Ole George Barkenas Suite 350, 27 Colemore Row, Birmingham B3 2EW — Cand Med 1982 Oslo.

AAWAR, Mr Omar Amine 11 Denmark Road, Portslade, Brighton BN41 1GJ Tel: 01273 424868 — MB BChir 1976 Cairo; FRCS Ed. 1987.

ABABIO, Samuel Ntim 29 Hamilton Crescent, Warley, Brentwood CM14 5ES — MD 1970 Szeged; MD (Child Health) Budapest 1977.

ABAD ALEJANDRE, Javier 177 Queen Edith's Way, Cambridge CB1 8NJ — LMS 1982 Saragossa.

ABADI, Dennis Isaac The Surgery, 22 St. Anne's Terrace, London NW8 6PH Tel: 020 7722 7389; 23 Linden Lea, Hampstead Garden Suburb, London N2 0RF Tel: 020 8455 9521 Fax: 020 8458 0329 Email: carolden@compuserve.com — MB BS 1988 Lond.; BSc (Hons.) Lond. 1985; DRCOG 1991. (Middlx. Hosp. Med. Sch.) Chairm. Marylebone PCG. Prev: Trainee GP Temple Fortune Health Centre; SHO (Paediat.) Edgware Gen. Hosp.; SHO (Cas.) King's Coll. Hosp. Lond.

ABADIR, Wedad Faltas 40 Mount Avenue, London W5 2QJ Tel: 020 8998 5434 Fax: 020 8991 1548 — MB BCh 1958 Cairo; FRCS 1973 Eng.; LMSSA 1969 Lond.; DLO 1963 Eng. (Ain Shams Univ.) Assoc. Specialist Otorhinolaryng. W. Middlx. Univ. Hosp. Socs: Fell. Roy. Soc. Med.; Brit. Assn. Otol. Prev: Regist. (ENT) Centr. Middlx. Hosp.; SHO (ENT) Chase Farm Hosp. Enfield; ENT Specialist MoH, Egypt.

ABADJIAN, Maksoud (Max) Stepping Hill Hospital, Stockport SK2 7JE Tel: 0161 483 1010; 271 Dialstone Lane, Stockport SK2 7NA — Vrach 1965 Erevan. SCMO (O & G) Stockport HA.

ABAECHETA, Anne-Marie Ngosi 3 Ground Floor, 33 Kay Road, Clapham North, London SW9 9DF — MB BS 1991 Lond. Regist. (Adult Psychiat.) Guys Hosp. Lond.

ABAECHETA, Honor Cheyne 51 Edithna Street, London SW9 9JR — MB BS 1994 Lond.

ABANG MOHAMMED, Dayang Kusnah 45 Earle Road, Liverpool L7 6AD — MB ChB 1994 Liverp.

ABANG-TAHA, Abang Bennett 5 Scrooby Street, Catford, London SE6 4JB — MB BS 1979 Malaya.

ABANIWO, Mr Ndalai Majiyebo Five Elms Medical Practice, Five Elms Road, Dagenham RM10 5TT — MB BS 1979 Ahmadu Bello Univ. Nigeria; DFFP 1995; FRCS Ed. 1991. GP Partner, Dagenham; Locum Cons. Surg. Socs: MDU. Prev: Locum Cons. Surg. (various specialties).

ABAS, Melanie Amna Section of Old Age, Institute of Psychiatry, De Crespigny Park, London SE5 8AF Tel: 020 7919 3550 Fax: 020 7701 0167 — MB ChB 1982 Birm.; MPhil Lond. 1990; MRCP (UK) 1985; MRCPsych 1988. Lect. Inst. Psychiat. Lond. Prev: Lect. (Psychiat.) Univ. Zimbabwe; Sen. Regist. Maudsley Hosp. Lond.

ABAYA, Venumbaka Child & Adolescent Services, Severn NHS Trust, Cleeve House, Horton Road, Gloucester GL1 3PX Tel: 01452 308757; 10 Gorse Close, Bourton-on-the-Water, Cheltenham GL54 2EG — MB BS 1979 Madras; MRCPsych 1989. Cons. Child Adolesc. Psychiat. (Child & Adolesc. Servs.) Severn NHS Trust Glos. Prev: Sen. Regist. (Child Adolesc. Psychiat.) Sheff.; Regist. (Adult Psychiat.) Carlisle.

ABAYASIRIWARDANA, June Maduka 52 Kenley Road, Kingston upon Thames KT1 3RS — BM 1990 Soton.; MRCP (UK) 1996. Specialist Regist. Wessex Region Soton.

ABAYAWARDANA, Ruvina Dias The Heritage, 110 Fishponds Road, London SW17 7LF — MB BS 1998 Lond.

ABAYAWICKRAMA, Pothutuwe Chandra Kumari Jayanthika 14 Ashcombe Road, Merstham, Redhill RH1 3BY — MB BS 1981 Colombo; MRCP (UK) 1994.

ABAYOMI, Ekundayo Maria-Juliette Crawley Hospital, West Green Drive, Crawley RH11 7DH Tel: 01293 600300; 44 April Close, Horsham RH12 2LN Tel: 01403 251296 Fax: 01403 251296 — MB BS 1976 Ibadan; MSc Lond. 1996; MRCS Eng., LRCP Lond. 1979; FRCOG 1997, M 1982; Dip. Ven. 1982; Dip. Clin. Pharm. (Fertil. Regulat. WHO) 1982. Cons. O & G Crawley Hosp. Socs: Fell. Roy. Soc. Med. Prev: Lect. & Cons. O & G & Dir. Vitro Fertil Unit. Univ. Coll. Hosp. Ibadan, Nigeria; Sen. Clin. (In-Vitro Fertil.) Thomson Med. Centre, Singapore; Sen. Regist. (O & G) Nat. Guards Hosp. Riyadh, Saudi Arabia.

ABAYOMI, Emmanuel Akinola School of Clinical Medicine and Research, Queen Elizabeth Hospital, Bridgetown, Barbados, West Indies Tel: 001 246 432 8202 Fax: 001 246 429 6738 Email: babawura@hotmail.com; Flat 23, 18 Thorn Tree Court, Parkview Road, Ealing, London W5 2JB Tel: 020 8810 5919 Fax: 020 8810 5919 — MB BS 1983 Lond.; MRCP (UK) 1990; FCPath 1996. (St. Bart.) Lect. (Haemat.) Univ. Zimbabwe Harare, Zimbabwe.; Lect. (Haemat.) Univ. of the W. Indies Barbados. Prev: Sen. Regist. (Clin. Haemat.) Univ. Coll. Hosp. Ibadan, Nigeria; Regist. (Haemat.) St. Bart. Hosp. Lond.; Regist. (Med.) Oxf. HA.

ABAYSIRIWARDENA, Chandrasiri Hemapala Leelaratne 219 Rutland Avenue, High Wycombe HP12 3LN Tel: 01494 29782 — MB BS 1968 Ceylon; DRCOG 1981.

ABBAS, Abdul Mohsen Abdullah 161 Old Church Road, Romford RM7 0BE Tel: 01708 753146 — MB ChB 1972 Mosul; MRCPI 1983; Dip. Clin. Neurol. Lond. 1983; DTCD Wales 1982. Research Fell. Neurol. Dept. Old Ch. Hosp. Romford. Socs: Brit. Neuropath. Soc.; Assoc. Mem. Assn. Brit. Neurols.

ABBAS, Adel Mohamed Aly Department of Microbiology, District General Hospital, Moorgate Road, Rotherham S60 2UD; 3 Middle Drive, Rotherham S60 3DL — MB BCh 1955 Ain-Shams; PhD (Med. Microbiol.) Sheff. 1965; MPH Alexandria 1961; CBiol. 1985, MIBiol 1978. Cons. Microbiol. Rotherham HA; Hon. Clin. Lect. Dept. Med. Microbiol. Univ. Sheff.; Mem. Rotherham HA. Prev: Asst. Prof. Head Dept. Med. Microbiol. & Parasitol. Tanta Fac. Med. Egypt; Hon. Cons. to Teachg. Hosps. Tanta Egypt.

ABBAS, Ahmed Charif 15 Kensington Gate, Glasgow G12 9LG — MB ChB 1989 Manch.; MRCGP 1995; DRCOG 1993.

ABBAS, Andrea 15 Kensington Gate, Glasgow G12 9LG — State Exam Med 1993 Ulm. SHO (Geriats.) Gartnaval Gen. Hosp. Glas. Prev: SHO (Med.) Monklands Hosp. Airdrie; SHO (Med.) W.ern Infirm. Glas..

ABBAS, Anthony 68 Rodwell Road, E. Dulwich, London SE22 9LE — MD 1986 Amer. Univ. Beirut.

ABBAS, Badi Kamil 23 Pelham Close, Sudbrooke, Lincoln LN2 2SQ — MB ChB 1967 Mosul.

ABBAS, Edgar Munir Saxilby Health Centre, 85 Syres Lane, Saxilby, Lincoln LN1 2NU Tel: 01522 702236 Fax: 01522 703132 — MB ChB 1972 Bristol. Hosp. Pract. (Chest & Allergy Med.) Lincoln Chest Clinic. Socs: Thoracic Soc.; N. Lincs. Research Ethics (Mem. Comm.).

ABBAS, Mr Ghulam 9 Roddinghead Road, Glasgow G46 6TW — MB BS 1981 Punjab; FRCS Glas. 1988.

ABBAS, Hajera 11 Illetson Drive, Churwell, Morley, Leeds LS27 7TZ — MB ChB 1993 Sheff.

ABBAS, Kamran 11 Vancouver Quay, Salford Quays, Manchester M5 2TT Tel: 07930 327321 — MB ChB 1993 Manch. Specialist Regist. Anaesth. Rotat. Manch. Socs: MPS; Manch. Med. Soc.; Assoc. of Anaesth.s. Prev: SHO (Anaesth.) Halifax Roy. Inf.; SHO (ICU) St. Jas. Univ. Hosp.; SHO (Anaesth.) Qu.s Hosp. Burton.

ABBAS, Khudair Fadhil Newham General Hospital, Glen Rd, Plaistow, London E13 8SL Tel: 020 7363 8160 Fax: 020 7363 8307; 60 Rutland Drive, Hornchurch RM11 3EN Tel: 01708 456049 Email: kf_abbas@yahoo.com — MB ChB 1972 Baghdad; FRCS Ed. 1990. Staff Grade (Gen. Surg.) King Geo. Hosp.

ABBAS, Mohammed Barnsley Road, Scawsby, Doncaster DN5 8QE — MB BS 1972 Osmania. GP Scawsby, Doncaster.

ABBAS, Nilofer Fatima Haworth Road Health Centre, Haworth Road, Bradford BD9 6LL Tel: 01274 541701 Fax: 01274 546533 — MB ChB 1990 Leeds; MRCGP 2001; DCH RCP Lond. 1997; DRCOG 1996. GP Bradford, W. Yorks. Socs: BMA; MPS.

ABBAS, Saeed Abbas and Siddeeq, Clifford Coombs Health Centre, 70 Tangmere Drive, Castle Vale, Birmingham B35 7QX Tel: 0121 747 4633 Fax: 0121 747 1587 — MB BS 1965 Punjab.

ABBAS, Sarah 18A Le More, Sutton Coldfield B74 2XY — MB BCh 1994 Wales. GP Regist. & SHO W. Midl. VTS.

ABBAS, Syed Kaukab Hanson Place Surgery, 5 Hanson Place, Wyke, Bradford BD12 8JG Tel: 01274 690661; 668-670 Halifax Road, Buttershaw, Bradford BD6 2HD Tel: 01274 690658 — MB BS 1958 Karachi. (Dow Med. Coll.) Prev: Med. Asst. Accid./Emerg. & Orthop. Dept. Beckett Hosp. Barnsley.

ABBAS, Tahir Department of Geriatric Medicine, Farnham Hospital, Hale Road, Farnham GU9 8QL — MB BS 1982 Punjab; MRCPI 1992.

ABBAS, Mr Tariq Munir (retired) 17 Dr Cranfords Close, Minchinhampton, Stroud GL6 9EZ — MB ChB 1943 Ed.; MD Ed. 1947; FRCS Ed. 1948; FRCOG 1964, M 1948. Prev: Cons. O & G S. W. RHB.

ABBAS, Wedad Soliman The Surgery, 12-14 Golborne Road, London W10 5PG Tel: 020 8969 2058 Fax: 020 8964 4156 — MB BCh 1982 Wales.

ABBAS AHMED, Omer Childrens Services Directorate, Lister Hospital, Coreys Mill Lane, Stevenage SG1 4AB Tel: 01438 781011 Fax: 01438 781437 Email: ramikoja@aol.com; 10 Harley Street, London W1N 1AA Tel: 020 7467 8408 — MB BS 1976 Khartoum; FRCP 1998; FRCPH 1997; DTCH Liverp. 1987; DCH RCP Lond. 1985; DCH Dub. 1983. Cons. (Paediat.) Childr. Directorate Lister Hosp. N. Herts. NHS Trust. Socs: BMA; Overseas Doctors Assn.; Phys. Human Rights.

ABBASI, Abdul-Hamid 22 Rowan Close, London W5 4YJ — MB ChB 1955 Baghdad; FRCP Ed. 1975.

ABBASI, Kamran Almas 63 Raleigh Court, Clarence Mews, Surrey Quays, London SE16 5GB — MB ChB 1992 Leeds.

ABBASI, Shafika (retired) 34 Priory Terrace, London NW6 4DH Tel: 020 7624 3788 — MB BChir 1967 Camb.; MRCS Eng. LRCP Lond. 1965; DPM Eng. 1973. Psychother. Sexual & Marital Therapist St. Geo. Hosp. Lond.; Mem. Lond. Centre for Psychother. Prev: Regist. Acad. Unit Psychiat. Middlx. Hosp. Lond.

ABBASI, Syed Fateh Shah (retired) 23 Brecks Road, Clayton, Bradford BD14 6DU Tel: 01274 880921 — MB BS Karachi 1967.

ABBASI, Zahir 23 Brecks Road, Clayton, Bradford BD14 6DU — MB ChB 1991 Dundee; FRCS (Ed.) 1996. Prev: SHO (Gen. Surg.) Leeds Gen. Infirm.; SHO (Cardiothoracic) Hillingbeck Leeds; SHO (Urol.) Leeds Gen. Infirm.

ABBATT, Richard James Orchard Lane Surgery, Orchard Lane, Denton, Northampton NN7 1HT Tel: 01604 890313 Email: richard.abbatt@gp-k83068.nhs.uk — MB BS 1982 Lond.; MRCGP 1986; DRCOG 1985. (Westm.)

ABBEY, Mr Herath Banda The Gables Health Centre, 26 St. Johns Road, Bedlington NE22 7DU Tel: 01670 829889 Fax: 01670 820841 — 1975 MRCS Eng. LRCP Lond.; FRCS Ed. 1974; MRCGP 1985.

ABBEY, Mr Paul (retired) The Gate House, Park Road, Stoke Poges, Slough SL2 4PA Tel: 01753 521715 — MB BS 1944 Lond.; FRCS Eng. 1953; DLO Eng. 1957. Prev: Cons. ENT Surg. Windsor Hosp. Gp.

ABBEY, Susan Jennifer 162 Wickersley Road, Rotherham S60 4JW — MB ChB 1981 Sheff.; MRCGP 1985; DRCOG 1984. p/t Gen. Practitioner, Partner.

ABBO, Salah El Din Mekki Hassan 7 Friars Field, Royal Gwent Hospital, Newport NP20 2UB Tel: 01633 52244; 7 Launcelot Crescent, Cardiff CF14 9AQ — MB BS 1980 Khartoum.

ABBOOD, Khalid Hani 13 Pine Avenue, Exwick, Exeter EX4 2DU Tel: 01392 219671 — MB ChB 1968 Baghdad.

ABBOT, Har Prakash 33 Morland Road, Croydon CR0 6HA — MB BS 1965 Delhi. GP Croydon.

ABBOTSON, Melanie Louise Royal Hallamshire Hospital, Sheffield S11 8UA; 29 Roach Road, Hunters Bar, Sheffield S11 8UA — MB ChB 1991 Sheff. Regist. (Radiol.) Sheff.

ABBOTT, Anand 334 Wickham Road, Shirley, Croydon CR0 8BH — MB BS 1996 Lond.

ABBOTT, Annette Beatrix The Surgery, Market Place, Halesworth IP19 8HP Tel: 01986 874136; Bacon's Farm, St. Michael, South Elmham, Bungay NR35 1NF Tel: 01986 782282 — MB BCh 1978

Wales; DRCOG 1991; DCH RCP Lond. 1989. Socs: BMAS. Prev: SHO (O & G) Norwich Health Dist.; SHO (Psychiat.) Norwich Health Dist.

ABBOTT, Carolyn Grace Victoria House Surgery, 228 Dewsbury Road, Leeds LS11 6HQ Tel: 0113 270 4754 Fax: 0113 272 0561 — MB ChB 1984 Bristol; DRCOG 1989. GP Princip. Socs: BMA. Prev: H. Off. Hawera Hosp. NZ; SHO (Psychiat. & Paediat.) Rotherham Dist. Gen. Hosp.; Trainee GP Sheff.

ABBOTT, Cedric Richard Department of Histopathology, Algernon Firth Institute of Pathology, Leeds Tel: 0113 292 3534; 73 Ridgeway, Leeds LS8 4DD Tel: 0113 266 8058 — MB ChB 1961 Birm.; BSc Birm. 1958; MRCPath. 1979. Cons. Histopath. Leeds Teachg. Hosps. NHS Trust; Hon. Sen. Clin. Lect. (Path.) Univ. of Leeds. Socs: Assn. Clin. Pathol.; Eur. Sch. of Cardiovasc. Pathol. Prev: Sen. Lect. (Path.) Univ. Leeds; Regist. (Clin. Path.) Gen. Infirm. Leeds; SHO Qu. Eliz. Hosp. Birm.

ABBOTT, Christopher James Alan, MBE, Wing Cdr. RAF Med. Br. Woodmans Cottage, Wendlebury, Bicester OX25 2PR — MB BS 1972 Lond.; MRCS Eng. LRCP Lond. 1972; AFOM RCP Lond. 1983; MRCGP 1979; DObst RCOG 1974; DAvMed Eng. 1980. (St. Mary's) GFMO HQ IGp. Prev: Sen. Med. Off. RAF Brawdy; Chief Instruc. RAF Aviat. Train. Centre; Sen. Med. Off. RAF Brize Norton.

ABBOTT, Claire Frances Rowan House, Denby Lane, Grange Moor, Wakefield WF4 4BJ — MB ChB 1989 Liverp.

ABBOTT, David Frederick Kingsmere Meadow, Shawford, Winchester SO21 2BL Tel: 01962 714413 Fax: 01962 713662 Email: davidfabbott@btinternet.com — MB BS 1967 Lond.; MD USA; MRCP (UK) 1971; MRCPI 1971; MRCS Eng. LRCP Lond. 1967. Socs: Amer. Med. Assn.; Brit. Med. Assn.; Amer. Coll. of Phys.s.

ABBOTT, Fionnuala Anne Aine Bayview Medical Practice, 3 Bayview Terrace, Londonderry BT48 7EE — MB ChB 1986 Manch.; MRCGP 1994. GP.

ABBOTT, Gian Thomas 3 Norfolk Drive, West Kirby, Wirral CH48 2HR — MB ChB 1984 Liverp.; BSc (Hons.) Liverp. 1981; MRCPI 1989; FRCR 1992; DMRD Liverp. 1991. Cons. Radiol. Countess of Chester Hosp. Prev: Fell. Vasc. & Interven. Radiol. Duke Univ. Med. Center N. Carolina, USA.

ABBOTT, Gillian Winifred Kirby and Partners, Charlton Group Medical Practice, Charlton Street, Oakengates, Telford TF2 6DA Tel: 01952 620138 Fax: 01952 615282 — MB BS 1968 Lond.; MRCS Eng. LRCP Lond. 1968.

ABBOTT, Graham Richard North House Surgery, 28 North Street, Ripon HG4 1HL Tel: 01765 690666 Fax: 01765 690249 Email: graham.abbott@gp-b82008.nhs.uk; High Green, Burton Leonard, Harrogate HG3 3RW Tel: 01765 677159 Email: graham@highgreenbl.freeserve.co.uk — MB ChB 1988 Leeds; MRCGP 1995. (Leeds)

ABBOTT, James Bruce Meadowbank Farm, Sugar Lane, Manley, Warrington WA6 9DZ — MB ChB 1988 Liverp.

ABBOTT, John Douglas (retired) 67 Scholars Green Lane, Lymm WA13 0PS — MB BS 1943 Lond.; MD Lond. 1950; MRCS Eng., LRCP Lond. 1943; Dip. Bact. Lond. 1950. Prev: Cons. Med. Microbiologist, Pub. Health Lab. Manch.

ABBOTT, John Malcolm (retired) Garth House, Tarn Brow, Aughton, Ormskirk L39 4SS Tel: 01695 572587 — MB ChB 1956 Liverp.; MFHom 1985; MRCGP 1963; DTM & H Liverp. 1979. Prev: Clin. Asst. (Directorate of Homeopathy) Mossey Hill Hosp. Liverp.

ABBOTT, Lee Paul 12 Coalfield Close, Sutton-in-Ashfield NG17 1JR — BM BS 1996 Nottm.

ABBOTT, Margaret Daphne Windmill Practice, Sneinton Health Centre, Beaumont Street, Sneinton, Nottingham NG2 4PJ Tel: 0115 950 5426 — MB ChB 1980 Sheff.; MRCGP 1984; DRCOG 1985; Cert. Family Plann. JCC 1984; FRCGP (Assess.) 1996. Socs: Nottm. M-C Soc. Prev: Clin. Asst. (Psychiat.) Cossham Hosp. Bristol; Trainee GP Doncaster & Gloucester VTS; SHO (Psychiat.) Glenside Hosp. Bristol.

ABBOTT, Michael Withington Hospital, Nell Lane, Manchester M20 2LR — MB ChB 1981 Liverp.; MRCP (UK) 1986; Dip. Bact. Manch. 1989; Dip. Ven. Liverp. 1991. Sen. Regist. Rotat. (Genitourin. Med.) NW RHA. Prev: Sen. Regist. (Microbiol.) Pub. Health Laborat. Serv. Manch.

ABBOTT, Michael Anthony Sean Violet Hill House, 82 St. Margaret's Street, Rochester ME1 3BJ Tel: 01634 841072 — MB BS 1973 Lond.; MRCS Eng. LRCP Lond. 1973; FFA RCS Eng. 1983. (St. Mary's) Cons. Anaesth. Darent Valley Hosp. Dartford, Kent. Prev: Sen. Regist. (Anaesth.) Inst. Urol. Lond.; Lect. Lond. Hosp.

ABBOTT, Patricia Mary Ashworth Hospital, Parkbourn, Maghull, Liverpool L31 1HW — MB ChB 1981 Liverp.; FRCPsych 2000; MRCPsych 1986; FRCP 2000 (Psych). Cons. Psychiat. Ashworth Hosp. Maghull. Prev: Cons. Rehabil. Psychiat. Rathbone Hosp. Liverp.; Sen. Regist. (Psychiat.) Liverp.

ABBOTT, Patricia Mary Brookvale Practice, Hallwood Health Centre, Hospital Way, Runcorn WA7 2UT Tel: 01928 718182 Fax: 01928 790716; 5 Horseshow Close, Kingsley, Warrington WA6 8DY — MB ChB 1983 Liverp.; MRCGP 1987. Prev: SHO (Accid. & Emerg.) Arrowe Pk. Hosp. Birkenhead; SHO (Psychiat.) Fazakerley Hosp. Liverp.; Ho. Off. (Med.) Arrowe Pk. Hosp. Birkenhead.

ABBOTT, Paul 152 Blackburn Road, Heapey, Chorley PR6 8EL — MB ChB 1981 Leeds.

ABBOTT, Paul Ralph Bottreaux Surgery, Boscastle PL35 0BG Tel: 01840 250209 Fax: 01840 250666; Millbrook, Old Road, Boscastle PL35 0AJ — BM BCh 1983 Oxf.; MRCGP 1987.

ABBOTT, Peter Harry (retired) — MRCS Eng. LRCP Lond. 1941; MB BChir 1948 Camb.; MA Camb. 1951, MD 1954; MRCP Lond. 1951; MRCGP 1965; DTM & H Eng. 1956. Prev: Med. Specialist Sudan Med. Serv.

ABBOTT, Rebecca Tamsin Mundesley Medical Centre, Munhaven Close, Mundesley, Norwich NR11 8AR Tel: 01263 724500 Fax: 01263 720165 — MB BS 1991 Lond.

ABBOTT, Richard George 8 Shadform Close, Old Shotton, Peterlee SR8 2NG — MB BS 1978 Newc.

ABBOTT, Richard John 45 Westminster Road, Stoneygate, Leicester LE2 2EH Tel: 0116 270 5784 — MB BS 1973 Lond.; MD 1983 Leic.; FRCP 1992 Lond. (St. Bart.) Cons. Neurol. Leicester Roy. Infirm. Prev: Sen. Regist. (Neurol.) Leeds; Regist. (Neurol.) Dundee Health Dist.; Ho. Phys. St. Bart. Hosp. Lond.

ABBOTT, Roger Martin Abbey Mead Surgery, Abbey Mead, Romsey SO51 8EN Tel: 01794 512218 Fax: 01794 514224; 9 The Harrage, Romsey SO51 8AE Tel: 01794 516249 — MB BS 1970 Lond.; MRCS Eng. LRCP Lond. 1970. (Univ. Coll. Hosp.)

ABBOTT, Sian Mary 6 Mallard Avenue, Groby, Leicester LE6 0GR — MB ChB 1996 Leeds.

ABBOTT, Susan Mary Family Planning and Sexual Health, Shrewsbury Centre, Shrewsbury Road, Forest Gate, London E7 8QP Tel: 020 8586 5147 Fax: 020 8586 5008 Email: sue.abbott@nchst.nthames.nhs.uk; 112 Elmstead Avenue, Wembley HA9 8NY Tel: 020 8908 4916 Fax: 020 8908 4916 — MB ChB 1980 Liverp.; MFFP 1993; DRCOG 1984. Cons. Community Gyn. Newham Community NHS Trust. Prev: Clin. Med. Off. (Family Plann.) Pk.side Community Trust.

ABBOTT, Thomas Raymond (retired) 4 Old Cottage Close, Slab Lane, West Wellow, Romsey SO51 6RL — MB ChB 1958 Birm; FFA RCS Eng. 1965; MRCS Eng. LRCP Lond. 1958. Cons. Anaesth. Soton. Gen. Hosp. Prev: Cons. Anaesth. Roy. Liverp. Childr. Hosp. & Alder Hey Childr. Hosp. & Liverp. HA.

ABBOTT, Vincent Paul, Squadron Ldr. RAF Med. Br. 5 Huntsmans Way, Badsworth, Pontefract WF9 1BE Email: abbottfamily@bigfoot.com — MB 1984 Camb.; MA Camb. 1983, MB 1984, BChir 1983; MRCGP 1990; MPH Leeds University 1998. Specialist Regist. (Pub. Health Med.). Socs: Manch. Med. Soc. Prev: GP Trainee Norf.; SHO (Orthop.) Ancoats Hosp. Manch.; SHO (Path.) Withington Hosp. Manch.

ABBOTT, Vivienne Jane Harborough Road Surgery, Harborough Road North, Northampton NN2 8LL Tel: 01604 845144 Fax: 01604 820241; 90 Cromwell Crescent, Market Harborough LE16 9JR — MB ChB 1982 Leic.

ABBOTT, William Mackenzie, Surg. Cdr. RN Retd. (retired) 87A South Beach, Troon KA10 6EQ Tel: 01292 314264 — MB ChB Glas. 1962; DObst RCOG 1969. Prev: Insp.ate Animals (Scientif. Procedures).

ABBOUD, Sahib Hadi Trafford General Hospital, Manchester M41 5SL Tel: 0161 748 4022 — MB ChB 1974 Baghdad; MRCP (UK) 1987; DTM & H RCP Lond. 1989. Staff Grade Phys. (Geriat.) Trafford HA.

ABBOUDI, Zaid Hamid Central Middlesex Hospital, London NW10 7NS Tel: 020 8453 2112 Fax: 020 8965 1115 Email: zaid@globalnet.co.uk; 29 Derwent Avenue, Kingston Vale, London SW15 3RA — MB ChB 1979 Baghdad; MRCP (UK) 1991; MRCPath

1994, D 1989. Cons. Haemat. Centr. Middlx. Hosp. Socs: BMA; Amer. Soc. Haemat.; Med. Defence Union (MDU). Prev: Sen. Regist. (Haemat.) Hammersmith Hosp. Chelsea & W.m. Hosp. & Char. Cross Hosp. Lond.

ABBS, Ian Charles Renal Unit, Guys Hospital, London SE1 9RT Tel: 020 7955 5000 Fax: 020 7955 4909 Email: i.abbs@umds.ac.uk; 111 Endlesham Road, London SW12 8JP — MB BS 1984 Lond.; BSc Lond. 1981; MRCP (UK) 1987; FRCP 1997. (St. Thos.) Cons. Renal Phys. Guy's Hosp. Lond.; Hon. Sen. Lect. Guy's, King's & St. Thos. Sch. Med., King's Coll. & Univ. Lond. Socs: Brit. Transpl. Soc. & Renal Assn. Prev: Sen. Regist. (Nephrol.) Guy's Hosp. Lond.; Lect. (Nephrol.) UMDS Univ. Lond.; Regist. Rotat. (Med.) Univ. Coll. Hosp. Lond.

ABD ALLAH, Said Ahmed Hassan Royal Brompton Hospital, Sydney Street, London SW3 6NP Tel: 020 7352 8121; 66 Queen Alexandra Mansions, Judd Street, London WC1H 9DR Tel: 020 7278 8756 — MB ChB 1968 (Hons.) Alexandria. Assoc. Specialist (Respirat. Med.) Roy. Brompton Hosp. Socs: Brit. Med. Acupunct. Soc.; Brit. Thorac. Soc. Prev: Med. Off. Wandsworth Chest Clinic, Roy. Brompton, Univ. Coll. Hosp. & Roy. Lond. Homoeop. Hosps. Lond.; Regist. (Med.) Roy. Lond. Homoeop. Hosp. & Belvidere Hosp. Glas.; Clin. Attach. Univ. Med. Dept. Roy. Infirm. Glas.

ABD EL-FATTAH, Ahmed Yehya Mohamed 6 Clwydian Park Crescent, St Asaph LL17 0BJ Tel: 01745 74570 — MB BCh 1970 Cairo; DLO RCS Eng. 1979.

ABD-EL-MASSIH, Gamal Kamel Good Hope General Hospital, Rectory Road, Sutton Coldfield B75 7RR Tel: 0121 378 2211; 264 Birmingham Road, Wylde Green, Sutton Coldfield B72 1DJ Tel: 0121 384 2231 — MB BCh 1965 Cairo; DA Eng. 1975. Assoc. Specialist Anaesth. Good Hope Hosp. NHS Trust.

ABD KARIM, Zurianah c/o P. N. Loyden, 11 Morningside Road, Annan DG12 6LB — MB ChB 1991 Glas.

ABD-MARIAM, Nassif Tawadros Morrill Street Health Centre, Morrill Street, Holderness Road, Hull HU9 2LJ Tel: 01482 323398 Fax: 01482 217957 — MB BCh 1969 Cairo. GP Hull.

ABDALLA, Abdalla Hassan 53 Prout Grove, London NW10 1PU — MB ChB 1978 Tanta; MRCPI 1989.

ABDALLA, Hayat Osman 96 Bradpole Road, Queens Park, Bournemouth BH8 9PA — Vrach 1972 1st Moscow Med Inst.

ABDALLA, Hossam Ibrahim The Lister Hospital, IVF Unit, Chelsea Bridge Road, London SW1W 8RH Tel: 020 7730 3417 Fax: 020 7259 9039 Email: sam@easynet.co.uk; Chelsea & Westminster Hospital, 369 Fulham Road, London SW10 Tel: 020 8746 8000 — MB ChB 1977 Baghdad; MRCOG 1983. Cons. Gyn. Chelsea & W.m. Hosp. Lond.; Dir. IVF Unit Lister Hosp. Lond. Socs: Brit. Fertil. Soc.; Amer. Soc. Reproduc. Med.; Eur. Soc. Human Reproduc.

ABDALLA, Mohamed Abd-El Hakam Mohamed 3 Turchill Drive, Sutton Coldfield B76 1YQ — MB BCh 1965 Alexandria.

ABDALLA, Saad Habib Haematology Department, St. Mary's Hospital, Praed Street, London W2 1PG Tel: 020 7886 6807 Fax: 020 7886 6809 — MB BS 1970 Khartoum; MRCS Eng. LRCP Lond. 1972; MRCPath Eng. 1977. Sen. Lect. Imp. Coll. Sch. Med. at St Mary's Lond.; Hon. Cons. St. Mary's Hosp. Lond. Prev: Hon. Lect. (Med.) John Radcliffe Hosp. Oxf.; Sen. Regist. (Haemat.) Oxf.

ABDALLA, Shadia Zaky Field Street, Willenhall WV13 2NY — MB BCh 1975 Assiut. GP Willenhall, W. Midl.

ABDALLAH, Hossam Mohamed Hassaballah Midland Road Surgery, Thrapston, Kettering NN14 4JR Tel: 01832 734444 Fax: 01832 734426 — MB BCh 1972 Cairo; DLO RCS Eng. 1979.

ABDEL AAL, Nadia Mohammed Yassin 18 Hanover House, St. Johns Wood High Street, London NW8 7DX — MB ChB 1993 Leic.

ABDEL-ALL, Mohamed Awad Hassan Borders General Hospital, Melrose TD6 9BS Tel: 01896 4333; Southwood, Monkswood, Gattonside, Melrose TD6 9NS Tel: 01896 822070 Fax: 01896 822070 — MB BCh 1972 Cairo; MRCOG 1991. (Cairo Med. Coll.) Assoc. Specialist (O & G) Borders Gen. Hosp. Melrose. Prev: Staff Grade (O & G) Borders Gen. Hosp. Melrose; Regist. (O & G) Borders Gen. Hosp. Melrose.

ABDEL AZIZ, Salah Ismail Ahmed Erne Hospital, Cornagrade Road, Enniskillen BT74 6AY — MB ChB 1980 Alexandria; MRCOG 1992.

ABDEL-GADIR, Ahmed Mohamed 14 Jesmond Way, Stanmore HA7 4QR — MB BS 1972 Khartoum; PhD Glas. 1978; MRCOG 1981.

ABDEL GADIR, Mr Mamoun Abdalla Queen Elizabeth Hospital, Gayton Road, King's Lynn PE30 4ET Tel: 01553 613613; Sanford House, 47 East Winch Road, Ashwilken, King's Lynn PE32 1NA Tel: 01553 630660 Fax: 01553 630660 — MB BS 1982 Khartoum. Cons. Orthop. Surg., Qu. Eliz. Hosp., King's Lynn, Norf. Socs: Brit. Orth. Soc.; Brit. Scoliosis Soc.; E. Angl. Spinal Soc.

ABDEL GAWAD, Mr Ahmed Amin 5 Ashdown Close, Haywards Heath RH16 3NR Tel: 01444 413550 — MB BCh 1968 Alexandria; FRCS Ed 1978.

ABDEL-HADI, Abdel Hamid Shehdeh Abdel Qader Medical Imaging Department, Queen Elizabeth The Queen Mother Hospital, St Peter's Road, Margate CT9 4AN Tel: 01843 225544 Fax: 01843 220049 — MB BS 1982 Jordan; FRCR 1990; T(R) (CR) 1992; DMRD Ed. 1989. Cons. Radiol. Thanet Gen. Hosp. Margate.

ABDEL-HADI, Omar Bahjat Anis 5 Fraser Road, Perivale, Greenford UB6 7AH — MB ChB 1969 Alexandria; DM Cairo 1971; MRCPI 1978; MRCP (UK) 1978; Dip. Immunol. Chelsea Coll. 1979. Cons. Phys. & Cardiol. Alfateh Hosp. Tripoli Libya; Hon. Cardiol. St. Marys Hosp. Lond. Socs: Fell. Roy. Soc. Med. Prev: Research Fell. & Sen. Regist. (Cardiol.) St. Marys Hosp. Lond.; Cons. Phys. Badanah Hosp. Tapline Saudi Arabia.

ABDEL-HADI, Salah Eldin Abdalla Mohammed 1 Blackwater Lane, Pound Hill, Crawley RH10 7RL — MB ChB 1978 Alexandria.

ABDEL KHALEK, Ahmed Ismail 40 Woodland Way, Winchmore Hill, London N21 3QA Tel: 020 8882 0424 — MB BCh 1961 Cairo; Dip. Surg. Cairo 1969. (Kasr El Eine) Med. Off. (A & E) Chase Farm Hosp. Enfield. Prev: Specialist (Trauma & Orthop.) Trauma Centre Tripoli, Libya; Surgic. Regist. Roy. Masonic Hosp. Lond.; Regist. (A & E) Pr. Wales's Hosp. Tottenham.

ABDEL KHALEK, Mr Mohamed Naguib Ahmed 134 Spilsby Road, Boston PE21 9NY Tel: 01205 369660 Fax: 01205 369660 — MB BCh 1974 Cairo; FRCS Ed. 1982; DO RCPSI 1979; FCOphth. 1989. (Al-Azhar) Cons. Ophth. Pilgrim & Assoc. Hosps. Boston. Prev: Sen. Regist. (Ophth.) N.. RHA.

ABDEL-KHALIQ, Mr Rashid Ali Ahmad 28 Braedale Avenue, Motherwell ML1 3DX Tel: 01698 261830 — MB ChB 1974 Aberd.; BMedBiol. Aberd. 1971; FRCS Ed. 1980; FRCS Glas. 1980. Locum Cons. Surg., NHS Trust Hosps. Socs: Past Fell., Assn. of Surg.s of Gt. Britain & Irel. Prev: Cons. & Surg. Lawson Memor. Hosp. Golspie, Sutherland; Asst. Prof. Yarmouk Univ. Irbid, Jordan.

ABDEL-LATIF, Mr Mohamed Mohamed Amin ENT Department, Kettering General Hospital, Rothwell Road, Kettering NN16 8UZ Tel: 01536 81141 — MB BCh 1968 Cairo; FRCS (Otol.) Eng. 1981. Cons. ENT Surg. Kettering Gen. Hosp. Prev: Sen. Regist. (ENT Surg.) Trent RHA; Regist. (ENT) Kettering Gen. Hosp.; SHO (Plastic Surg.) Newc. Gen. Hosp.

ABDEL-MALEK, Mr George Talaat Little Acre, Springbrook Lane, Earlswood, Solihull B94 5SF Tel: 01564 703926 Fax: 01564 700020 — MB ChB 1974 Tanta; MSc (Orthop.) Zagazig 1982; FRCS Ed. 1985. Clin. Assist. (Orthop) Roy. Orthop. Hosp. Birm.

ABDEL-MASSIH, Rajai Shaker The Maternity Unit, Nevill Hall Hospital, Abergavenny NP7 7EG — MB ChB 1975 Alexandria.

ABDEL-NABI, Abdel Ghani Hafiz Abdel Ghani 7 Launcelot Crescent, Cardiff CF14 9AQ — MB BCh 1979 Cairo; MRCOG 1990.

ABDEL-NASSER, Mervat Rizk Beaconfield Centre, Beacon Lane, Grantham NG31 9DF Tel: 01476 591233 Fax: 01476 591739; Woolsthorpe House, Woolsthorpe-By-Belvoir, Grantham NG32 1NZ Tel: 01476 870587 Fax: 01476 870587 Email: mnasser@compuserve.com — MB BCh 1976 Cairo; MPhil Univ Lond. 1984; DM Soton. 1992; MRCPsych 1982; DPM Eng. 1981. Cons. Psychiat. Grantham & S. Lincs.; Sen. Lect. (Brandon Ment. Health Unit) Leic. Gen. Hosp. Socs: Eur. Counc. Eating Disorders; Transcultural Psychiat. Soc. Lond.; Roy. Coll. (Sect. Social & Community Psychiat.).

ABDEL RAHMAN, Izzeldin Elsheikh 44 Southbrook Road, Countess Weir, Exeter EX2 6JE — State Exam Med 1971 Sofia.

ABDEL-SALAM, Mr Anwar Ahmad 1122 Evesham Road, Astwood Bank, Redditch B96 6EA — MB ChB 1973 Baghdad; FRCS Eng. 1984.

ABDELATTI, Mohamed Osman Dept. of Anaesthesia, Rochdale Infirmary, Whirehall Street, Rochdale OL12 9QB — MB BS 1976 Khartoum; FFA RCSI 1986; DEAA France 1987; CCSt Lond. 1997. Cons. Anaesth. Socs: BMA; BADS; AMA. Prev: Chelsea & W.minster Hosp. Lond.

ABDELAZIZ, Muntasir Mustafa Department of Respiratory Medicine & Allergy, St Bartholomew's Hospital, London EC1A 7BE Tel: 020 7601 8446 Fax: 020 7601 8060 — MB BS 1983 Khartoum; MRCP (UK) 1990.

ABDELHAMEED, Butheyna El Zahra 59 Cardigan Terrace, Newcastle upon Tyne NE6 5NU — MB ChB 1994 Glas.

ABDI, Shahram 64 Manvers Road, West Bridgford, Nottingham NG2 6DH — MB ChB 1995 Sheff.; MRCS 1998. Specialist Regist. (Radiol.) Nottm. City Hosp. Prev: SHO (Urol.) Derby City Hosp.; SHO (Gen. Surg.) Roy. Hallamshire Hosp. Sheff.; SHO (Orthop. & Plastic Surg.) N.ern Gen. Hosp. Sheff.

ABDO, Khalil Ribhi Department of Obstetrics & Gynaecology, Belfast City Hospital, 51 Lisburn Road, Belfast BT9 7AB; 7 Ludford Park, Ballinteer, Dublin 16, Republic of Ireland — MB BCh BAO 1988 NUI; LRCPSI 1988; MRCGP 1993; T(GP) 1993.

ABDO, Osman Ahmed Blackwood Health Centre, Blackwood Road, Streetly, Sutton Coldfield B74 3PL Tel: 0121 353 7558 Fax: 0121353 7056 — MB BCh 1968 Cairo.

ABDOOL RAMAN, Abdool Cader Dawood, OBE Peakfields, Gravelcastle Road, Barham, Canterbury CT4 6QF Tel: 01227 831387 Fax: 01227 831387 — LMSSA 1951 Lond.; MRCS Eng. LRCP Lond. 1952; FRCPsych 1972; DPM Eng. 1957. Cons. i/c Promise Recovery Centre Canterbury. Socs: Fell. Roy. Soc. Med.; Sec. Gen. Afr. Psychiat. Assn. Prev: Prof. Psychiat. Fac. Med., Med. Arab Univ. Benghazi, Libya; Cons. Psychiat. St. Augustine's Hosp. Chartham; Med. Supt. Broun Sequard Hosp., Mauritius.

ABDOOLCADER, Taher 33 Penrose Street, London SE17 3DW Tel: 020 7703 3677 — MB BS 1945 Bombay. (S.G.S. Med. Coll. Bombay) Socs: BMA. Prev: Cas. Off. Croydon Gen. Hosp.; Sen. Ho. Off. Kelling Hosp. Holt.

ABDOU, Michael Shoukry Blossomfield Road Surgery, 308 Blossomfield Road, Solihull B91 1TF Tel: 0121 705 5339 Fax: 0121 709 0239 — MB BCh 1970 Cairo. GP Solihull.

ABDU, Sabri Abdu Mohammed Royal Liverpool Children's Hospital, Alder Hey Child Deverlopment Centre II, Eaton Road, Liverpool L12 2AP Tel: 0151 228 4811; 318 East Prescot Road, Liverpool L14 7NH Tel: 0151 228 5676 — MB BS 1983 Khartoum, Sudan; MRCP (UK) 1994; MRCPCH 1997; DCH Lond. 1993. Specialist Regist. (Paediat.) Mersey Rotat. Socs: Roy. Coll. Phys. Lond.; MRCPCH. Prev: SHO (Paediat.) Shrewsbury.

ABDU, Tarig Abdu Mohamed Diabetes Centre, City General Hospital, Newcastle Road, Stoke-on-Trent ST4 6QG Tel: 01782 715444 Fax: 01782 553427; Flat 130C, Arrowe Park Hospital, Upton, Wirral CH49 5PE — MB BS 1985 Khartoum; MRCP (UK) 1992. Staff Phys. (Endocrinol. & Diabetes) City Gen. Hosp. Stoke-on-Trent. Socs: Brit. Endocrine Soc.; Brit. Diabetes Assn. Prev: Regist. (Endocrinol. & Diabetes) Roy. Liverp. Univ. Hosp.

ABDUL, Karim Aliff Carr 35 Sandbergh Road, Kimberworth Park, Rotherham S61 3EY — MB BS 1984 Malaya.

ABDUL, Mr Summi 50 Derby Road, Bromcote, Nottingham NG9 3FY — MB ChB 1995 Leeds; BSc 2001 CP Dip.; MRCOG 1999; BSc (Hons.) Leeds 1992; DFFP 1998. Specialist Regist. (O & G) Year 3 Oxf. Rotat. Kettering. Prev: Specialist Regist. NGH N.ington; Specialist Regist. Bradford Roy. Infirm.; Regist. Leeds Gen. Infirm.

ABDUL AZIZ, Anita Binurul Zahrina Flat 25, Royal Westminster Lodge, 3 Elverton St., London SW1P 2QW — MB ChB 1993 Glas. SHO (Obstet. & Gyn.) St. Geo.'s Hosp. Lond. Prev: SHO (Gen. Surg.) Fazakerley Hosp. Liverp.; SHO (A & E) Fazakerley Hosp. Liverp.; SHO (Obstet. & Gyn.) S. Gen. Hosp. Glas.

ABDUL AZIZ, Mr Azhar Flat 5, Florey Court, Queens Medical Centre, Nottingham NG7 2UH — MB BS 1985 Newc.; FRCS Ed. 1993.

ABDUL AZIZ, Farah Wakhida 111 Lorne Road, Leicester LE2 3AR — BM BS 1998 Nottm.

ABDUL AZIZ, Laith Abdul Sattar Royal Hospital, Haslar, Portsmouth PO12 2AA Tel: 02392 584255 Email: laith.abdul-aziz@virgin.net — MB ChB 1974 Baghdad; MRCPI 1983; DTM & H RCP Lond. 1991; FRCPI 1997; FRCP 1999. Cons. Phys. with interest in Diabetes & Endocrinol. Roy. Hosp. Haslar Hants. Socs: Fell. Roy. Soc. Trop. Med.; Soc. Endocrinol.; Diabetes UK. Prev: Cons. Phys. (Med.) Musgrave Pk. Hosp., Belf.; Sen. Lect. (Md.) Lond.; Cons. Phys. (Med.) Hong Kong, Rintein & Iserlohn.

ABDUL CADER, Aboobucker Hadjiar Mohamed 1 Star Hill, Birmingham B15 2LT — MB BS 1968 Ceylon; MRCPath 1985. (Peradeniya) Prev: SHO (Haemat.) Bradford Roy. Infirm.

ABDUL GHAFAR, Faidzal Adlee 13 Bower Avenue, Rochdale OL12 9QW — MB ChB 1998 Manch.

ABDUL-GHANI, Mr Abul Khair Mohammed 11 Hillcourt Avenue, London N12 8EY — MB BS 1976 Dacca; FRCS Ed. 1981.

ABDUL GHANI, Mr Padickal Puthiyakath Manor House Hospital, Northend Road, London NW11 7HX Tel: 020 8455 6601; 19 Kingsmere Park, London NW9 8PJ Tel: 020 8205 6224 — MB BS 1973 Kerala; FRCS Ed. 1982. Assoc. Specialist (Orthop.) Manor Hse. Hosp. Lond. Socs: Overseas Fell. BOA. Prev: Regist. (Orthop.) S. Warks. Hosp.

ABDUL-HAMID, Suhanna Nottingham City Hospital, Hucknall Road, Nottingham NG5 1PB; Flat 1, 38 Caledonia Place, Clifton, Bristol BS8 4DN — BM BS 1992 Nottm.

ABDUL-JABBAR, Tindigul Vappu Aziz Greystones, 1 Palatine Road, Birkdale, Southport PR8 2BS Tel: 01704 69145 — MB BS 1960 Madras; DCH Eng. 1962. (Stanley Med. Coll.)

ABDUL-JALIL, Dayang Norlila 132A Barnsley Road, Hemsworth, Pontefract WF9 4PG — MB ChB 1989 Leeds.

ABDUL-KADIR, Rezan Ahmed 5 Grove Gardens, Hendon, London NW4 4SA — MB ChB 1983 Baghdad; MRCOG 1993.

ABDUL KARIM, Alla Pitchai Sahib Sheik Mian Sahib Bretton Health Centre, Rightwell, Bretton, Peterborough PE3 8DT Tel: 01733 264506 Fax: 01733 266728 — MB BS 1965 Madras.

ABDUL-NABI, Mr Mohammad Jawad Burnley General Hospital, Casterton Avenue, Burnley BB1 2PQ Tel: 01282 474162; 5 Cross Bank, Skipton BD23 6AH — MB ChB 1989 Glas.; FRCS Ed. 1994; FRCOphth 1994, M 1992. (Univ. Glas.) Cons Ophth. Surg.; Sen. Regist. (Ophth.) Roy. Manch. Eye Hosp. Socs: Fell. (Vitreo-retinal Surg.). Prev: Career Regist. Rotat. (Ophth.) Glas.; SHO (Ophth.) Stobhill Hosp. Glas. & Basingstoke Dist. Hosp.; Ho. Off. Glas. Roy. Infirm.

ABDUL RAHIM, Shahnaz Whiteabbey Hospital, Doagh Road, Newtownabbey BT37 9RH — MB BCh BAO 1995 Belf.

ABDUL RAHMAN, Mohd Ramzisham 2 Lock Keepers Court, Victoria Docks, Hull HU9 1QH — MB ChB 1997 Sheff.

ABDUL-RAZAK, Nasma Abdul Jabber 268 Stradbroke Grove, Ilford IG5 0DQ — LMSSA 1991 Lond.; MSc Ed. 1981; MB ChB Basrah, Iraq 1979; Dip Clinical Neurol; DFFP. GP. Socs: Med. Protec. Soc. Prev: Clin. Asst. (Neurol.) K. Geo. & Barking Hosps. Redbridge HA.

ABDUL SALAM, Salawati Flat 201, Minister Court, Liverpool L7 3QH — MB ChB 1995 Liverp.

ABDUL WAHAB, May Abdul-Razzak Maternity Hospital, Leicester Royal Infirmary, Leicester LE1 5WW — MB ChB 1984 Al-Mustansirya U, Iraq; MD 2001; MRCOG 1994. (Leicester University) SR in Obst. & Gyn.

ABDUL WAHID, Mohamed Ibrahim 11 Windsor Close, Northwood HA6 1PD Tel: 01222 615888; 11 Hanbury Close, Millbrook, Whitchurch, Cardiff CF14 2TB Tel: 01222 520804 — MB BCh 1985 Wales. Regist. (Radiother. & Oncol.) Velindre Hosp. Cardiff. Socs: Med. Protect. Soc. Prev: SHO (Gen. Med.) Russells Hall Hosp. Dudley; SHO (Radiother. & Oncol.) Wirral HA & Clatterbridge Hosp. Bebington.

ABDULALI, Sultanali Akberali Wheatlands, Beech Hill, Reading RG7 2AZ — MRCS Eng. LRCP Lond. 1973; MRCP (UK) 1977.

ABDULEZER, Tania Ruth 57 Barcheston Road, Cheadle SK8 1LJ; Flat 14, Tudor House, Windsor Way, Brook Green, London W14 0UG Tel: 020 7602 3610 — MB ChB 1995 Manch.

ABDULLA, Ali Jawad 58 Donnington Gardens, Reading RG1 5LZ — BM 1982 Soton.

ABDULLA, Hassan Ramadan 15 Hirst Road, Retford DN22 6QN — MB BCh 1976 Al Azhar, Egypt.

ABDULLA, Usama Hillcrest, 344 Telegraph Road, Heswall, Wirral CH60 6RW Fax: 0151 342 1275 Email: uaabdulla@hotmail.com — MB ChB 1961 Baghdad; FRCOG 1983, M 1970. Cons. O & G. Univ. Hosp. Aintree Liverp.; Hon. Cons. (O & G) Liverp. Matern. Hosp. Roy. Liverp. Hosp. Wom. Hosp. & Liverp. HA. Socs: Fell. Roy. Soc. Med.; Scientif. Sec. Ospreys Gynaecol. Soc.; Pres. N. Eng. Obst. & Gynaecol. Soc. Prev: Research Fell. Inst. O & G Qu. Charlotte's Hosp. & Chelsea Hosp. Wom.; Clin. Lect. Nuff. Dept. O & G Univ. Oxf.; Sen. Lect. (O & G) Univ. Liverp.

ABDULLAH, Adel Mohsin 15 Rannock Avenue, London NW9 7JS — MB ChB 1975 Baghdad; MRCPI 1985.

ABDULLAH, Adel Ne'ma Genitourinary Medicine Department, Royal Glamorgan Hospital, Ynysmaerdy, Llantrisant CF72 8XR Tel: 01443 443597 Fax: 01443 443390 — MB ChB 1974 Basrah; LRCP LRCS Ed. LRCPS Glas. 1985; FRCPI 1995, M 1985. Cons. (Genitourin. Med.) Roy. Glam. Hosp., P.ss of Wales Hosp. Bridgend & Abedare Gen. Hosp. Socs: Assn. Genitourin. Med.; MDU; M.Soc. Study VD. Prev: Sen. Regist. (Genitourin. Med.) Cardiff Roy. Infirm.; Regist. (Genitourin. Med.) Coventry & Warwicksh. Hosp. & Roy. Lond.; Regist. (Geriat. & Dermat.) Hull Roy. Infirm.

ABDULLAH, Anthony 6 Buchan Close, Great Sankey, Warrington WA5 8XX — MB ChB 1992 Liverp.

ABDULLAH, Aza Jamal Jalal Cannock Chase Hospital, Brunswick Road, Cannock WS11 2XY — MB ChB 1979 Baghdad; MRCP (UK) 1989; MRCPI 1989.

ABDULLAH, Hajah Siti Noor 19D Westbourne Terrace, London W2 3UN — MB ChB 1995 Sheff.

ABDULLAH, Mohd Fikri Postgraduate Office, University Hospital of Wales, Heath Park, Cardiff CF4 4XN; 18 Treherbert Street, Cardiff CF24 4JN — MB BCh 1992 Wales.

ABDULLAH, Saadun Habib Furness General Hospital, Dalton Lane, Barrow-in-Furness LA14 4LF — MB ChB 1974 Baghdad; MSc (Cardiovasc. Studies) Leeds 1989; LMSSA Lond. 1989; Dip. Cardiol. Lond. 1986.

ABDULLAH, Sheila 6 Bedford Road, Oughtbridge, Sheffield S35 0FB Tel: 0114 286 2336 — MB ChB 1961 Sheff. Co-ordinator Doctor for a Wom. Choice on Abortion. Socs: Fac. Family Plann. & Reproduc. Health Care.

ABDULLAH, Suraya W.S.C.R., St. Bartholomew's Hospital Medical School, West Smithfield, London EC1A 7BE — MB BS 1994 Lond.

ABDULLAH, Victor 19 Albemarle Park, Albemarle Road, Beckenham BR3 5XG — MB BS 1985 Lond.

ABDULLAH, Wajda Simone Flat 7, Phoenix House, 4 Queen St., Newcastle upon Tyne NE1 3UG — MB BS 1991 Newc.

ABDULLAHI, Aminu Taura Flat 28 Park Hill, Moseley, Birmingham B13 8DT — MB BS 1985 Ahmadu Bello, Nigeria; MRCPsych 1992.

ABDULMAJID, Sabah Abdul Hamid 3 Oceanic Road, Liverpool L13 1BP — MB ChB 1970 Mosul; MRCOG 1981; MObstG 1985; DO RCPSI 1980.

ABDULRAHMAN, Abdulrahman Osman Ali c/o Dr. A.K. Lofty, 4 Howe Road, Onchan, Douglas Tel: 01624 626249 — MB BCh 1970 Ain Shams; DA Eng. 1979.

ABDURAHMAN, Mohamed Fouzy Sherriff The Arundel Unit, William Harvey Hospital, Ashford TN24 0LZ Tel: 01233 633331 Fax: 01233 616105; Coleman House, Brookfield Road, Dover CT16 2AH Tel: 01304 216666 Fax: 01304 216677 — MB BS 1966 Ceylon; MRCPsych 1973; FRCPsych 1994; DPM 1971 Eng. Cons. Psychiat. William Harvey Hosp. Ashford, Buckland Hosp. & Coleman Hse. Day Hosp. Dover.

ABDY, Susan Hillcrest, 11 Church Farm Road, Heacham, King's Lynn PE31 7JB — MB BS 1986 Newc.; DRCOG 1995.

ABE, Phoebe Joyce Arach 9 Leacroft Close, Yiewsley, West Drayton UB7 8AQ — MB ChB 1975 Manch.

ABECASSIS, Marc c/o Dr. Viel, 10 Harley Street, London W1G 9QQ — Laurea 1989 Rome.

ABED, Riadh Tawfiq Department of Psychiatry, Rotherham District General Hospital, Moorgate Road, Rotherham S60 2UD Tel: 01709 304331 Email: abed@globalnet.co.uk; 17 Kenwood Bank, Sheffield S7 1NU Tel: 0114 255 1976 Fax: 0114 250 7651 — MB ChB 1974 Baghdad; MRCPsych 1983; DPM Eng. 1983. Cons. Psychiat. Dist. Gen. Hosp. Rotherham; Hon. Clin. Lect. Univ. Sheff. Prev: Sen. Regist. (Psychiat.) Fulbourn Hosp. Camb.

ABEDI, Mohammed Khurram Ali 113 Wynchgate, London N14 6RJ — LMSSA 1997 Lond.

ABEDIN, Khwaja Joinul 304 Tollcross Road, Glasgow G31 4UR — MB BS 1963 Dacca. GP Glas.

ABEDIN, Mohammed Zainul Rough Hay Surgery, 44b Rough Hay, Darlaston, Wednesbury WS10 8NQ Tel: 0121 526 2233 Fax: 0121 568 8206 — MB BS 1971 Ranchi. GP Darlaston, Wednesbury, W. Midl.

ABEDIN, Sofia 47 Elliott Avenue, Ruislip HA4 9LR — MB BS 1958 Bihar.

ABEDIN, Mr Syed Shafiqul 47 Elliott Avenue, Ruislip HA4 9LR — MB BS 1958 Bihar; FRCS Ed. 1967; FRCS Eng. 1966; MRCS Eng. LRCP Lond. 1971.

ABEL, Mr Beverley John 4 Erskine Road, Whitecraigs, Glasgow G46 6TQ Tel: 0141 639 9052 — MB ChB 1966 Liverp.; FRCS Glas. 1979; FRCS Ed. 1972; FRCS Eng. 1972. Cons. Surg. Urol. S. Glas. Hosps. Univ. NHS Trust; Hon. Sen. Lect. Univ. Glas. Socs: BMA; Brit. Assn. Urol. Surg. Prev: Sen. Regist. Vict. Infirm. Glas.; Research Fell. Liverp. Regional Urol. Centre.; Ex-Pres. Scott. Neurol. Soc.

ABEL, Derek Colvin The Fairfield Centre, Fairfield Grove, Charlton, London SE7 8TX Tel: 020 8858 5738 Fax: 020 8305 3005 — MB BS 1985 Lond.; DGM. GP Charlton; GP Tutor.

ABEL, Graeme Anderson Alva Medical Practice, West Johnstone Street, Alva FK12 5BD Tel: 01259 760331 Fax: 01259 769991; Meadowpark, 3 Long Row, Menstrie FK11 7BA Tel: 01259 760673 — MB ChB 1980 Glas.; MRCGP 1984; DFFP 1994; DRCOG 1982. Socs: BMA; Brit. Soc. Med. & Dent. Hypn. Prev: SHO (O & G) Stobhill Hosp. Glas.; Ho. Off. (Surg.) Stobhill Hosp. Glas.; Ho. Off. (Med.) Gartnavel Gen. Hosp. Glas.

ABEL, Helen Bimla 11 Riefield Road, Eltham, London SE9 2QD — MB BS 1953 Punjab; LMSSA Lond. 1972. (Fatima Jinnah Med. Coll.) Prev: Gyn. Ho. Surg. Eliz. G. Anderson Hosp. Lond.

ABEL, John Victor Byways Medical Centre, Byways, 74 Pwllmelin Road, Llandaff, Cardiff CF5 2NH — MB BCh 1976 Wales; MRCGP 1981; DRCOG 1979.

ABEL, Joyce Audrey Katherine (retired) 11 Mount Heatherbank, Richmond Gardens, Bournemouth BH1 1JE Tel: 01202 551321 — MB ChB 1964 Aberd.

ABEL, Julian Charles 1 Batcombe Vale Cottages, Crows Hill, Batcombe, Shepton Mallet BA4 6BN — MB ChB 1982 Liverp.

ABEL, Kathryn Mary 41 Talfourd Road, London SE15 5PA Email: sphakma@iop.bpmf.ac.uk — MB BS 1986 Lond.; MA Oxf. 1983; MRCP (UK) 1989; MRCPsych 1994. Socs: MRC Fell. Inst. Psychiat. Prev: Lect. (Psychiat. Med.) Inst. Psychiat.; Regist. (Med.) Hammersmith Hosp. Lond.

ABEL, Kenneth William (retired) Long Cottage, Walditch, Bridport DT6 4LQ Tel: 01308 423074 — MB BS 1961 Lond.; MRCS Eng. LRCP Lond. 1961; DObst RCOG 1963.

ABEL, Marcus John Flat 2, 9 Vickers St., Nottingham NG3 4LD — MB ChB 1997 Manch.

ABEL, Margaret Elizabeth The Rookery Medical Centre, Newmarket CB8 8NW Tel: 01638 665711 Fax: 01638 561280; 4 Brookside, Exning, Newmarket CB8 7HP — MB BChir 1962 Camb.; MRCS Eng. LRCP Lond. 1962; DObst RCOG 1966. (Guy's) Socs: BMA. Prev: Ho. Phys. Addenbrooke's Hosp. Camb.; Asst. Ho. Surg. Guy's Hosp. Lond.; Ho. Surg. Matern. Hosp. Camb.

ABEL, Mr Paul David Department of Surgical Oncology & Technology, Imperial College Faculty of Medicine, B Block, Hammersmith Hospital Campus, Du Cane Road, London W12 0NN Tel: 020 8383 2430 Fax: 020 8383 2431 Email: pabel@ic.ac.uk — MB ChB 1977 Liverp.; ChM Liverp. 1987; FRCS Eng. 1982; FRCS Ed. 1981. Reader (Hon. Cons.) Urol. Imperial Coll. Sch. Med. Hammersmith Hosps. Trust Lond. & Ealing Hosp. Trust Middlx.; Head Sect. Acad. Urol. IC Fac. of Med. Socs: Brit. Assn. Urol. Surgs.; Amer. Urol. Assn.; Eur. Assn. Urol. Prev: Sen. Regist. (Urol.) S.mead Hosp. Bristol; Sen. Regist. (Urol. & Renal Transpl.) Hammersmith Hosp. Lond.; Regist. (Urol.) Freeman Hosp. Newc.

ABEL, Rhoda Agnes Orchard House Health Centre, Union Street, Stirling FK8 1PH Tel: 01786 50394 Fax: 01786 448284; Meadowpark, 3 Long Row, Menstrie FK11 7BA Tel: 01259 760673 Email: abelfam@globalnet.co.uk — MB ChB 1980 Glas.; MRCGP 1984; DCH RCPS Glas. 1983; DCCH RCP Ed. 1983; DRCOG 1982. Prev: Ho. Off. (Med.) Gartnavel Gen. Hosp. Glas.; Ho. Off. (Paediat. Surg.) Roy. Hosp. Sick Childr. Glas.; Trainee GP S.. Gen. Hosp. VTS.

ABEL, Robert John 13 Talygarn Street, Heath, Cardiff CF14 3PS Email: robert_abel@hotmail.com — MB BCh 1992 Wales; BSc Bristol 1986. Specialist Regist. Anaesth.

ABEL, Robin Michael 4 Imber Court, Greenacres, London SE9 5AX — MB BS 1988 Lond.; BSc 1985; PhD 1998; FRCS Eng. (Paed. Surg.) 1998. (University College London) Socs: Fell. Roy. Coll. Surg. Eng.

ABEL, William Jonathan (retired) 9 Birkdale, Norwich NR4 6AF Tel: 01603 455365 — MB ChB 1939 Ed.; FRCP Ed. 1969, M 1952; FRCPsych 1973, M 1972; DPM Eng. 1955. Prev: Cons. Psychiat. Hellesdon Hosp. Norwich.

ABELA, Tonio Chafford Hundred Medical Centre, Drake Road, Chafford Hundred RM17 6RS Tel: 01375 372505 Fax: 01375 394596 — MRCS Eng. LRCP Lond. 1981; DRCOG 1987. (Lond. Hosp.) Prev: Regist. (Geriat. Med.) St. Margt. Hosp. Epping; SHO (Paediat. & O & G) P.ss Alexandra Hosp. Harlow; SHO (Gen. Med.) St. Margt. Hosp. Epping.

ABELA HYZLER, Paul, CBE (retired) 2 Maxwell Drive, Datnell Park, West Byfleet, Weybridge — MD 1959 Malta; DPH RCPS Eng. 1961; MFPHM 1991. Prev: Princip. Med. Off. Internat. Relations Unit. DoH Lond.

ABELL, Christopher Adrian Theatre Royal Surgery, 27 Theatre Street, Dereham NR19 2EN Tel: 01362 852800 Fax: 01362 852819 — MB ChB 1980 Ed.; MB ChB (Hons.) Ed. 1980; MRCP (UK) 1983; DRCOG 1985.

ABELL, Debra Jane 67 Bannercross Road, Sheffield S11 9HQ — MB ChB 1987 Sheff.

ABELL, John David 85 Melton Road, West Bridgford, Nottingham NG2 6EN Tel: 0115 981 1858 Fax: 0115 982 6448; 161 Musters Road, West Bridgford, Nottingham NG2 7AF Tel: 0115 981 3057 — MB BS 1960 Lond.; DObst RCOG 1965. (St. Bart.) Hosp. Pract. (Dermat.) Univ. Hosp. Nottm.

ABELL, Shirley Ann Pamela (retired) Barton House, 45 Barton Road, Oxford OX3 9JE Tel: 01865 737309 Fax: 01865 437247 — MB BS Lond. 1958; MRCS Eng. LRCP Lond. 1958; FRCPsych 1980, M 1972; DObst RCOG 1960; DPM Eng. 1969. Hon. Assoc. Dir. Postgrad. Med. & Dent. Educat. Oxf. Univ. & Region. Prev: Assoc. Dir. Postgrad. Educat. Oxf. Univ. & Region.

ABELLAN-ANTOLIN, Francisco Javier Victoria Hospital, Whinney Heys Road, Blackpool FY3 8NR — LMS 1992 Saragossa.

ABELMAN, Walter c/o MMMR Agency, High Street House, Newmarket St., Skipton BD23 2HU — MB BCh 1992 Witwatersrand.

ABELS, John (retired) The Bungalow, Cowpen Bewley, Billingham TS23 4HU Tel: 01642 370093 — LRCS 1948 Ed.; MD Bratislava 1939; MRCGP 1957; Cert. Family Plann. RCOG, RCGP & FPA 1974. Prev: Police Surg. Stockton & Billingham.

ABENDSTERN, Robert (retired) 921 Walmersley Road, Bury BL9 5LL — MB ChB 1956 Manch.; MRCGP 1971; DObst RCOG 1960.

ABENYEKA-NUNMA, Paul Ofeoritse Kehinde Oseni 13 Durisdeer House, Lyndale, London NW2 2PA — MB BS 1985 Ibadan, Nigeria; MRCOG 1994.

ABER, Clive Peter Pine Tree Cottages, Godman Lane, Kirkella, Hull HU10 7NX Tel: 01482 653231 — MB ChB 1952 (Hons.) Leeds; BSc (Hons.) Leeds 1949, MD 1962; FRCP Lond. 1974, M 1956. Cons. Phys. Hull & E. Riding Hosp. Gps. Socs: Brit. Cardiac Soc. & Brit. Thoracic Soc. Prev: Sen. Med. Regist. Liverp. Thoracic Surgic. Centre, BRd. Green Hosp.; Regist. Med. Roy. Infirm. Liverp.; Ho. Phys. Hammersmith Hosp. Lond.

ABER, Professor Geoffrey Michael 1 Nelson Place, Newcastle ST5 1EA Tel: 01782 616811 Fax: 01782 625104; Greenleaves, Seabridge Lane, Newcastle ST5 3LS Tel: 01782 613692 — MB ChB 1952 Leeds; PhD Birm. 1964; MD (Distinc.) Leeds 1963; FRCP Lond. 1973, M 1956. Socs: Med. Res. Soc.; Renal Assn.; Internat. Soc. Hypertens. Prev: Prof. Renal Med. Univ. Keele; Cons. Renal Med. N. Staffs. Hosp. Centre Stoke-on-Trent; Dean Postgrad. Med. Sch. Postgrad. Med. & Biol. Sci. Univ. Keele.

ABERCROMBIE, Christine Anne University Hospital, Queens Medical Centre, Derby Road, Nottingham NG7 2HH Tel: 0115 924 9924 — MB ChB 1970 Manch.; FFA RCS Eng. 1975. Cons. Paediatric Anaesth., Univ. Hosp., Nottm.; Cons. Anaesth. Notts. AHA (T). Prev: Sen. Regist. & Regist. (Anaesth.) St. Thos. Hosp. Lond.; Regist. (Anaesth.) N. Staffs. Roy. Infirm. Stoke-on-Trent.

ABERCROMBIE, Mr George Forbes The Grain Store, Wenham Manor Farm, Rogate, Petersfield GU31 5AY Tel: 01730 821400 Fax: 01730 821400 — MB BChir 1960 Camb.; MA Camb. 1960; FRCS Eng. 1965. (Camb. & St. Bart.) Emerit. Cons. Urol. Surg. Portsmouth & SE Hants. Health Dist. Socs: Fell. Roy. Soc. Med.; Brit. Assn. Urol. Surgs. Prev: Sen. Regist. Rotat. Inst. Urol. Lond.; Ho. Surg. St. Bart. Hosp. Lond. & Hosp. Sick Childr. Gt. Ormond St. Lond.

ABERCROMBIE, Mr John Forbes Department of Surgery, University Hospital, Nottingham NG7 2UH Tel: 01159 249924 Ext: 43697 Email: jabercro@hgmp.mrc.ac.ul; Oakwood Lodge, Robinettes Lane, Cossall, Nottingham NG16 2RX — MB BS 1985 Lond.; FRCS Eng. 1989. Cons. Gen. Surg.

ABERCROMBIE, Mary Ruth Dunblane Medical Practice, Well Place, Dunblane FK15 9BQ Tel: 01786 822595 Fax: 0186 825298 — MB ChB 1990 Ed.; DGM RCP Lond. 1992. GP Princip. DunbLa. Med. Pract. DunbLa.; Clin. Asst. Cardiol., Stirling Roy. Infirm., Stirling.

ABERCROMBIE, Susan Mary Elisabeth 29 Barlow Moor Court, Manchester M20 2UU — MB ChB 1996 Manch.

ABERDOUR, Kenneth Robert (retired) 9 Riverside Maltings, Bridge St., Coggeshall, Colchester CO6 1NP Tel: 01376 563464 Fax: 01376 563954 Email: aberdour@dircon.co.uk/ — MB BS 1951 Lond.; FRCP Lond. 1976, M 1958; MRCS Eng. LRCP Lond. 1950; FRCR 1975; FFR 1961; DMRD Eng. 1958. Hon. Cons. Radiologist, Mid Essex Dist HA. Prev: Cons. Radiol. Mid-Essex Dist. HA.

ABERNETHY, Elizabeth Victoria Accident & Emergency Depatment, Ulster Hospital, Dundonald BT16 Fax: 02890 484511 — MB BCh BAO 1983 NUI; PSEM 1991; MRCGP 1987; DRCOG 1985; DCH Dub. 1986. Staff Grade (A & E) Ulster Hosp. Dundonald. Socs: MRCGP. Prev: SHO Flexible Trainee A & E Med. Aug 99-Jan 02; Staff Grade Orthop. Phys. Aug 94-99; Gen. Pract. Doctors Retainee Scheme 87-94.

ABERNETHY, Jacqueline Flat T/R, 25 Dalnair St., Yorkhill, Glasgow G3 8SD — MB ChB 1993 Glas.; DRCOG 1996; MRCGP 1998.

ABERNETHY, James Stuart 53 Dykes Hall Road, Hillsborough, Sheffield S6 4GP — MB ChB 1991 Sheff. Socs: BMA.

ABERNETHY, Laurence James Department of Radiology, Royal Liverpool Childrens Hospital, Alder Hey, Liverpool L12 2AP Tel: 0151 228 4811 Fax: 0151 252 5533; 29 Ryder Crescent, Aughton, Ormskirk L39 5EY Email: abernet@cybase.co.uk — MB ChB 1982 Ed.; MA Oxf. 1984, BA (Hons.) 1979; MRCP (UK) 1985; FRCR 1988; DMRD Ed. 1987. Cons. Radiol. Roy. Liverp. Childr. Hosp. & Alder Hey Hosp. Liverp. Prev: Sen. Regist. (Radiol.) Roy. Infirm. & W.. Gen. Hosp. Edin.; Fell. (Paediat. Radiol.) Roy. Childr. Hosp. Melbourne.

ABERNETHY, Pamela 4 Circus Gardens, Edinburgh EH3 6TN; 18 Heriot Row, Edinburgh EH3 — MB ChB 1974 Aberd.; LLB 1987; MRCGP 1980; DCH RCPS Glas. 1978; DObst RCOG 1976. Socs: BMA. Prev: Trainee Gen. Pract. Paisley VTS; SHO (Paediat.) S. W.. Health Dist. (Gtr. Glas.).

ABERNETHY, Mr Peter James BUPA Murrayfield Hospital, 122 Corstorphine Road, Edinburgh EH12 6UD Tel: 0131 334 0363; 10 Sunbury Place, Dean Village, Edinburgh EH4 3BY Tel: 0131 225 5648 Email: abernethy@doctors.org.uk — MB ChB 1960 Ed.; FRCS Ed. 1964. Cons. Orthop. Surg. BUPA Murrayfield Hosp. Edin.; Post Retirement Teachg. Fell. Univ. of Edin. Socs: Brit. Orthop. Assn.; Rheum. Arthritis Surg. Soc. Prev: Research Fell. Harvard Univ. 1972-73; Cons. Orthop. Surg. P.ss Margt. Rose Orthop. Hosp. Edinbugh.

ABERNETHY, Mr Robert James (retired) — MB ChB 1962 Glas.; FRCS Ed. 1966.

ABERNETHY, Veronica Elaine St. Helen's & Knowsley NHS Trust, Rheumatology Department, St. Helen's Hospital, Peasley Cross, St Helens WA9 3DA Tel: 0151 426 1600 Fax: 01744 458345 Email: rikki.abernethy@gwise.sthkh-tr.nwest.nhs.uk — MB ChB 1983 Ed.; MA Oxf. 1985; MRCP (UK) 1987. Cons. Rheum. St. Helen's & Knowsley NHS Trust. Prev: Sen. Regist. (Gen. Med. & Rheum.) Mersey RHA & Lothian HB; Regist. (Rheum. Dis.) N.. Gen. Hosp. Edin.

ABEYAKOON, Dilsiri Ranjani Flat 3, Kara Lodge, 14 Newton Grove, London W4 1LB — MB BS 1971 Ceylon.

ABEYASINGHE, Magodage Yuvaraj Department of General Surgery, The Royal Victoria Infirmary, Newcastle upon Tyne NE1 4LP Tel: 0191 232 5131 Fax: 0191 201 0155; 34 Minster Grove, North Walbottle, Newcastle upon Tyne NE15 9XA Tel: 0191 267 0160 Fax: 0191 267 0160 — MB BS 1964 Ceylon; MSc 1979 Lond.; FRCS 1989 Ed.

ABEYASINGHE, Niranjala Ishara 132 Murray Road, London W5 4DA — MB ChB 1998 Ed.; MB ChB Ed 1998.

ABEYEWARDENE, Asoka Kumarraj Orsett Road Surgery, 111 Orsett Road, Grays RM17 5HA Tel: 01375 372135 Fax: 01375 394642; 19 Wharf Road, Stanford-le-Hope SS17 0BZ Tel: 01375 676671 — MB BS 1973 Ceylon; MRCP (UK) 1981. Prev: Trainee GP Ilford VTS; Regist. (Med.) Orsett Hosp. Grays; SHO (Cardiol.) Papworth Hosp. Camb.

ABEYSINGHE, Aruni Dipamalika 67 Ondine Road, London SE15 4EA — MB BS 1998 Lond.

ABEYSINGHE, Mervyn Earle Perera 69 Fifth Lane, Kollupitiya, Colombo 3, Sri Lanka Tel: 00 94 1573230; c/o Miss A. D. Abeysinghe, 67 Ondine Road, London SE15 4EA Tel: 020 7732 4197 — MB BS 1962 Ceylon; DA RCP (Lond.) 1972; DA RCS Eng 1972. Indep. Cons. Anaesth. Colombo, Sri Lanka.

ABEYSIRI, Poorna 14 Pleasant Way, Alperton, Wembley HA0 1DF — MB BS 1996 Monash.

ABEYWARDENA, Buddhi Ranjan Yapa Ashcroft Medical Centre, 2 Ashcroft Drive, Denham, Uxbridge UB9 5JF Tel: 01895 834868 Fax: 01895 835031; Iver Heath Health Centre, Trewarden Avenue, Iver Heath, Iver SL0 0SB Tel: 01753 630340 — MB BS 1976 Sri Lanka; MRCOG 1986. Prev: Trainee GP Hemel Hempstead VTS; Regist. (O & G) N. Middlx. Hosp. Lond.; Regist. (O & G) Hemel Hempstead & St. Albans City Hosp., Crawley Hosp. & Watford Gen. Hosp.

ABHAYA KUMAR, Seetharama 4 Oakley Close, Isleworth TW7 4HZ — MB BS 1986 Mangalore, India.

ABHAYARATNE, Rohini Nimal 27 Danecourt Gardens, Croydon CR0 5JN — MB BS 1968 Ceylon. SCMO Croydon AHA. Prev: Regist. (Rheumat. & Rehabil.) St. Jas. Hosp. Lond.; SHO (Rheum.) Canad. Red Cross Memor. Hosp. Taplow.

ABID, Farzana Fairmile Hospital, Reading Road, Cholsey, Oxford OX10 9HH — MB BS 1985 Punjab; DPM RCPSI 1996; MRCPsych Lond. 1997. (Fatima Jinnah Med. Coll. Lahore, Pakistan) Cons. in Gen. Adult Psychiat. Prev: Specialist Regist. (Gen. Adult Psychiat.) W. Midl. Deanery; Regist. (Psychiat.) Rotat. Birm.; Specialist Regist. (Gen. Adult Psychiat.) Oxf. Deanery.

ABID, Muhammad Berkshire Health Authority, 57-59 Bath Road, Reading RG30 2BA Email: muhammad.abid@berkshire.nhs.com; Ambleside, Blagrave Lane, Caversham Heights, Reading RG4 7DX Email: muhammad.abid@berkshire.nhs.uk — MB BS 1975 Punjab; MFPHM RCP (UK) 1995; DTCD Vienna 1980. Cons. in Communicable Dis. Control. Prev: Sen. Regist. (Pub. Health Med.) Birm. HA; Regist. (Psychiat.) All Birm. Train. Scheme; SHO (Chest Dis.) Pulmologische Zentrum Vienna, Austria.

ABIDEEN, Sadiyah 10 Meadow Street, Cardiff CF11 9PY — MB BS 1991 Lond. SHO (Med.) P. Chas. Hosp. Merthyr Tydfil.

ABIDOGUN, Kehinde Akintola Olajide 4 Kings Gardens, Ilford IG1 4AJ — MB BS 1981 Lagos; FWACS 1990; FNMCOG 1990; MRCOG 1991. Regist. (O & G) Llandough Hosp. S. Wales. Socs: BMA.

ABILA, Bams 81 Barton Road, Canterbury CT1 1YH Tel: 01227 780776 Fax: 01227 787626 — MB BS 1977 Ibadan; PhD Wales 1984; MSc Lond. 1981; MFPM RCP (UK) 1992. Clin. Project Manager Pharmaceut. Med. Pfizer Centr. Research Sandwich, Kent. Socs: BMA. Prev: Sen. Research Phys. MMD UK; Lect. (Clin. Pharmacol.) Univ. Wales Coll. Med.; Lect. (Clin. Pharmacol.) Univ. Port HarCt. Coll. Med., Nigeria.

ABILI, Olajumoke Bodunrin Mayday University Hospital, Croydon CR7 7YE Tel: 020 8401 3000; Hawthorns, Greenway, Tatsfield, Westerham TN16 2BT — MB BChir 1976 Camb. Staff Grade, Stroke Unit. Socs: BMA; ORSM; BSG. Prev: Med. Off. (c/o Elderly) Purley Hosp.

ABLETT, Jill Catherine 152 Northampton Road, Kettering NN15 7JY — MB BS 1991 Lond.

ABLETT, John George 38 Hyde Road, Sanderstead, South Croydon CR2 9NP Tel: 020 8657 6747 — MB BCh 1964 Wales. Med. Off. Dept. Health & Social Security Lond. Prev: Mem. Staff MRC Child Nutrit. Unit Mulago, Hosp. Kampala, Uganda.

ABLETT, John James Lloyd 22 Sycamore Avenue, Scarborough Road, Filey YO14 9EF Tel: 01723 513866 — MRCS Eng. LRCP Lond. 1939; MB BS Lond. 1940; FFA RCS Eng. 1953; DA Eng. 1947. (King's Coll. Hosp.) Socs: Assn. Anaesths. & BMA. Prev: Sen. Cons. Anaesth. United Leeds Hosps.; Sen. Clin. Lect. Anaesth. Univ. Leeds; Sen. Anaesth. Regist. Roy. Free Hosp. Lond.

ABO ABOOD, Nuzhat 79 The Causeway, Potters Bar EN6 5HL — MB BS 1968 Peshawar; DA RCSI 1975.

ABOEL SAAD, Mr Adel Barsoum Springhill Cottage, Spurn Lane, Diggle, Oldham OL3 5QP — MB BCh 1964 Cairo; FRCS Ed. 1973.

ABOEL-SOOD, Abdel Aziz Mohamed Ali 22 Woodside Crescent, Sidcup DA15 7JJ — MB ChB 1977 Alexandria; FFA RCSI 1989; DA (UK) 1985.

ABOKARSH, Khaled 14B Garfield Road, London SW11 5PN — MB BCh BAO 1989 NUI; LRCPS & I 1989.

ABOLADE, Babatunde Kolawole 2 Harrison Way, Windsor Quay, Cardiff CF11 7PE — MB BS 1986 Ibadan.

ABOMELI, Doris Obianagha 215 Lansdowne Road, London N17 0NU — MB BS 1996 Lond.

ABOOBAKAR, Betty The Health Centre, High Street, Dodworth, Barnsley S75 3RF Tel: 01226 203881; 19 Kexbrough Drive, Dorton, Barnsley S75 5EY — MB BS 1974 Patna. (P. of Wales Med. Coll.) Prev: SHO (Anaesth.) Stepping Hill Hosp. Stockport.

ABOOD, Emad Abass 75 Manor Road, Guildford GU2 9NQ — MB ChB 1980 Baghdad. Socs: Roy. Coll. Phys.; Brit. Geriat. Soc.; Amer. Heart Soc.

ABOOD, Enam Amer 17 Harley Street, London W1N 1DA Tel: 020 7323 3830 Fax: 020 7323 3830; 12 Central Avenue, London N9 9RG Tel: 020 8803 3582 Fax: 020 8803 3585 — MB ChB 1978 Basrah, Iraq; BSc Basta 1978; MB ChB Lond. 1988. (St. Thos.) Private Pract. Gen. Med., Nutrit.al & Preventative Med.

ABOOD, Yasser Ali 63 Morley Crescent East, Stanmore HA7 2LG — MB ChB 1994 Manch.

ABORA, Yaw Yiadom 53 Leyton Park Road, London E10 5RL Tel: 020 8558 0439 — MB BCh Belf. 1969. Prev: Ho. Surg. Ashton-under-Lyme Hosp; Ho. Phys. Bradford Roy. Infirm. & St. Jas. Hosp. Lond.

ABOU-EL-FARAG, Mr Adel Maan ENT Department, Burnley General Hospital, Casterton Avenue, Burnley BB10 2PQ Tel: 01282 474550 Fax: 01282 474552; 8 The Rydings, Langho, Blackburn BB6 8BQ Tel: 01254 246994 Fax: 01254 246994 — MB BCh 1973 Cairo; FRCS Ed. 1985. Cons. ENT Surg. Blackburn Roy. Infirm. & Burnley Gen. Hosp.; Cons. (ENT) Beardwood Privat. Hosp. Blackburn. Socs: Brit. Assn. Otol.; Overseas Doctors Assn.; Brit. Med. Soc.

ABOU-RAGHEB, Hassan Hamdi Anis PO Box 5214, Amman, Jordan; 10 Greenfields, Highwood Park Village, Eckington, Sheffield S21 4GW — MB ChB 1973 Sheff. Prev: Ho. Off. (Gen. Med.) & Ho. Off. (Gen. Surg.) N.. Gen. Hosp. Sheff.; Resid. (Gen. Med.) Jordan Univ. Hosp.

ABOU RAYYA, Abdel Raheem Mahmoud Stoke Mandeville Hospital, Aylesbury HP21 8BD — MB BCh 1963 Cairo. (Kasr-el-Aini) Assoc. Specialist (Psychiat.) Dept. Ment. Health of Elderly Stoke Mandeville Hosp. Aylesbury.

ABOU SALEH, Mohammed Tamouh Department of Addictive Behaviour, St George's Hospital, Medical School, Cranmer Terrace, London SW17 0RE Tel: 020 8725 2802 Fax: 020 8725 2914 Email: mabousal@sghms.ac.uk — MB ChB 1975 Baghdad; PhD Surrey 1985; MPhil Ed. 1980; FRCPsych 1996, M 1980. (Baghdad Med. Coll.) Hon. Cons. Psychiat. & Reader Addictive Behaviour St Geo.'s Hosp. Lond.; Clin. Dir. Addic. Serv. St Geo. Hosp. Lond.; Hon. Cons. Psychiat. & Reader Psychiat. Roy. Liverp. Hosp. Prev: Sen. Regist. (Psychiat.) St. Geo. Hosp. Med. Sch. Lond.; Sen. Regist. (Psychopharmacol.) MRC Neuropsychiat. Laborat. W. Pk. Hosp. Epsom.

ABOU SHANAB, Komriah Sayed 68 Tower Green, Fulwood, Preston PR2 9UU — MB BCh 1972 Cairo; DTCD Wales 1978.

ABOU-ZEID, Saad Mahmoud Abdel-Hamid Wedgewood Court, Lansbury Park, Caerphilly CF83 1RB Tel: 029 2088 6006; (resid.), 4 Maes Watford, Caerphilly CF83 1LP Tel: 029 2086 9214 — MB BCh 1964 Ain Shams. Prev: Primary Care Phys. Milit. Hosp. Riyadh Saudi Arabia; Trainee GP Swansea; SHO (Urol.) Belf. City Hosp.

ABOUD, Michel Assad Aureol House, 40 Golf Side, Cheam, Sutton SM2 7EZ — MB BCh BAO 1957 NUI; FWACP 1976; MICGP 1985; FRCPI 1975; MRCPI 1963; DObst. 1961; DTM& H Lond. 1989; DTM& H Liverp. 1960; DCH 1959; LM Dubl. 1961. (Dub.) Private Practioner, Sierra Leone. Socs: BMA; Fell. Roy. Soc. Med; Fell. Roy. Acad. Med. Ire. Prev: Phys. Specialist Sierra Leone Govt.; Regist. (Med.) Centr. Middlx. Hosp.; Sen. Ho. Phys. (Chest Dis.) Walton Hosp. Liverp.

ABOUHARB, Ahmed Tareq 37 Maes-y-Coed Road, Cardiff CF14 4HB — MB BS 1993 Lond.; BSc (Hons.) Pharmacol. Lond. 1991.

ABOURAWI, Fathi Ibrahim Department of Medicine, Diana Prince of Wales Hospital, Scartho Road, Grimsby DN33 2BA Email: fathi.abourawi@nlg.nhs.uk — MB BS 1986 Al Arab Medical U, Libya; MRCP (UK) 1993. Cons. Phys. in Diabetes & Endocrinol. (Med.) Diana P.ss of Wales Hosp. Grimsby. Socs: Soc. for Endocrinol.; Diabetes UK; Brit. Thyroid Assn.

ABOUSLEIMAN, Youssif 2 Blackwood Green, Dunfermline KY11 8QG — State Exam 1993 Perugia; MRCP 2000 London; BSc (Biology) Amer. Univ. of Beirut, Lebanon 1986. SHO (Geriat. Med.) Roy. Vict. Hosp. Edin. Socs: BMA. Prev: SHO (Gen. Med.) Lincoln Co. Hosp.; SHO (Gen. Med.) Roy. Gwent Hosp. Newport; SHO (Geriat.) St. Woolos Hosp. Newport.

ABOUTALEBI, Shahriar 114 Slonk Hill Road, Shoreham-by-Sea BN43 6HY — MD 1971 Teheran.

ABRAHAM, Mr Alexander Johnston (retired) 31 Gables Court, St. Leonards Road, Eastbourne BN21 3QS Tel: 01323 729207 — MRCS Eng. LRCP Lond. 1939; FRCSC (Orthop. Surg.) 1963; FRCSC (Plast. Surg.) 1957; FRCS Eng. 1952; LMCC 1957. Prev: On Staff Sarnia Gen. Hosp. & St. Joseph's Hosp. Sarnia, Ontario, Canada & Sydenham & Dist. Hosp. Wallaceburg, Ontario.

ABRAHAM, Alison Joan 1 Cornwall Gardens, Brighton BN1 6RH — MB ChB 1958 Bristol; FRCPsych 1998; MRCPsych 1980; DPM 1979 Eng. Cons. (Psychiat.) P.ss Roy. Hosp.

ABRAHAM, Alummoottil Paul 26 Taunton Road, Ashton-on-Mersey, Sale M33; 2 Westray Crescent, Salford M5 2QZ Tel: 0161 736 4037 — MB BS 1944 Madras. Socs: Fell. Manch. Med. Soc. Prev: Med. Off. Hyderabad State; Asst. Airport Health Off. RAF & Amer. Airports Karachi; Asst. Port Health Off. Haffkine Inst. Bombay.

ABRAHAM, Alwyn Flat 8, 163 Lothian Road, Edinburgh EH3 9AA Tel: 0131 228 1321 — MB ChB 1996 Ed.; BSc (Med. Sci.) Ed. 1994. (Ed.) SHO Basic Surg. Train. Scheme SE Scotl., c/o Lister Postgrad. Inst. Edin.

ABRAHAM, Carol Marie 24 Brook Farm Road, Cobham KT11 3AX — MB ChB 1995 Birm.; ChB Birm. 1995.

ABRAHAM, Charles Alexander Calderwood (retired) The Rowans, Berwick, Polegate BN26 6SZ — MB BCh BAO 1952 Belf.; DObst RCOG 1953.

ABRAHAM, David Melville 43 Beckenham Road, Beckenham BR3 4PR; 21 Morden Hill, London SE13 7NN Tel: 020 8469 2880 Fax: 020 8692 9399 — MB BS 1980 Lond.; MA Camb. 1980; MRCGP 1985; DRCOG 1983. (Guy's)

ABRAHAM, George 28 Uplands Court, Upton Road, Norwich NR4 7PH Tel: 01603 52583 — MB BS 1985 Punjab; MRCPI 1991; MRCP (UK) 1991; MRCS Eng. LRCP Lond. 1990; Dip. GU Med. Soc. Apoth Lond. 1990.

ABRAHAM, Heather Margaret 184 Belmont Road, Belfast BT4 2AS — MB BCh BAO 1988 Belf.; DRCOG 1991; DCH RCSI 1991.

ABRAHAM, Mr John Stephen Department of Surgery, Royal Lancaster Infirmary, Ashton Road, Lancaster LA1 4RP Tel: 01524 65944 Fax: 01524 583581; Cawood House, Arkholme, Carnforth LA6 1AX Tel: 015242 21648 — MB ChB 1983 Manch.; MD Manch. 1991; FRCS (Gen.) 1995; FRCS Eng. 1987; FRCS Ed. 1987. Cons. Gen. Surg. Roy. Lancaster Infirm. & W.morland Gen. Hosp. Kendal. Prev: Sen. Regist. (Vasc. Surg.) Manch. Roy. Infirm.; Lect. (Surg.) & Research Surg. Univ. Louisville Kentucky, USA.

ABRAHAM, Kathleen (retired) Patterdale Cottage, Crook O'Lune, Caton, Lancaster LA2 9HS — MB ChB 1946 Manch. Prev: Med. Off. Oversea Civil Serv. (N. Nigeria).

ABRAHAM, Miranda Deborah Cholmley Gardens Surgery, 1 Cholmley Gardens, Mill Lane, London NW6 1EA Tel: 020 7794 6256 Fax: 020 7794 0540 — MB ChB 1985 Liverp.

ABRAHAM, Monty Alec 34 The Hollies, New Wanstead, London E11 2SL — LMSSA 1950 Lond. (Lond. Hosp.)

ABRAHAM, Nicola Jane Ash Trees Surgery, Market Street, Carnforth LA5 Tel: 015242 720000; Cawood House, Arkholme, Carnforth LA6 1AX — MB ChB 1983 Manch.; DFFP 1998; BSc St. And. 1980; MRCGP 1987; DCH RCP Ed. 1986. GP Princip. Carnforth. Prev: Trainee GP Lancaster VTS.

ABRAHAM, Peter, OStJ, Brigadier Email: peterabraham@ic24.net — MRCS Eng. LRCP Lond. 1957; FRCP 2001; MA Camb. 1975; FRCPsych 1979, M 1971; DPM 1963; DTM & H Eng. 1961. (St. Bart.) Socs: Fell. Med. Soc. Lond.; Assn. of Brit. Clin. Neurophysiologists; The Brit. Soc. for Clin. NeuroPhysiol. Prev: Exec. Dir. Med. Counc. on Alcoholism; Dir. of Army Psychiat.; Prof. Milit. Psychiat. Roy. Army Med. Coll. & Roy. Coll. Psychiat.

ABRAHAM, Philip Garden Park Surgery, Denbigh Avenue, Howdon, Wallsend NE28 0PP Tel: 0191 289 2525 Fax: 0191 289 2526 — MB BS 1974 Kerala; DFFP 1998. (Trivandrum) GP. Prev: SHO (Psychiat.) St. Geo. Hosp. Morpeth.

ABRAHAM, Ralph Richard The London Diabetes & Lipid Centre, 14 Wimpole Street, London W1G 9SX Tel: 020 7636 9901 Fax: 020 7636 9902 Email: info@londondiabetes.com; Email: info@londonbiabetes.com — BM BCh 1972 Oxf.; PhD Lond. 1971; MA Oxf. 1972; MRCP (UK) 1975. (Middlx.) Med. Dir. Lond. Diabetes & Lipid Centre. Socs: Amer. Diabetic Assn.; Endocrine Soc.; Diabetes UK. Prev: Lect. (Human Metab.) St. Mary's Hosp. Lond.; Lect. (Endocrinol.) St. Bart. Hosp. Lond.; Regist. (Gastroenterol.) Hammersmith Hosp.

ABRAHAM, Raymond Arthur Russell (retired) 1 Cornwall Gardens, Brighton BN1 6RH Tel: 01273 507677 — MB ChB 1958 Bristol; DObst RCOG 1966. Prev: GP Brighton.

ABRAHAM, Sonya Marie The Hazels, 4 Rectory Field, Harlow CM19 4HD — MB BS 1996 Lond.

ABRAHAM, Thomas Humber View, Cliff Top Lane, Hessle HU13 0EP — MB BS 1974 Kerala; MS Kerala 1983; DFFP 1994; FAIS 1994; FICS 1994; T(GP) 1992. GP, Hull. Socs: BMA.

ABRAHAM, Vallikalayil Verghese Netherley Health Centre, Middlemass Hey, Liverpool L27 7AF Tel: 0151 498 4054 Fax: 0151 487 5767 — MB BS 1962 Kerala. GP Liverp.

ABRAHAM MATHEWS, Anitha 23 Amesbury Road, Epping CM16 4HZ Tel: 01992 91 77030 — MB BS 1983 Kerala; MRCP (UK) 1986.

ABRAHAMS, Anthony Hugh Temple Cowley Health Centre, Templar House, Temple Road, Oxford OX4 2HL Tel: 01865 777024 Fax: 01865 777548 — MB BChir 1959 Camb.; MRCS Eng. LRCP Lond. 1959; DObst RCOG 1961. (Guy's) Prev: Asst. Ho. Phys Guy's Hosp.; Ho. Surg. (Obst.) Mayday Hosp. Croydon.

***ABRAHAMS, Elisabeth Maud** 57 Holdenhurst Avenue, Finchley, London N12 0JA Tel: 020 8346 7104 — MB BS 1962 Lond.

ABRAHAMS, Jacqueline Wendy 7 Penny Long Lane, Derby DE22 1AX Tel: 01332 557696 — MB ChB 1974 Glas.; MRCP (UK) 1978. SCMO (Family Plann.) Community Health Servs. NHS Trust S.. Derbysh.

ABRAHAMS, Lucille Naomi Law Medical Group Practice, 9 Wrottesley Road, London NW10 5UY Tel: 020 8965 8011 Fax: 020 8961 6239; Lydford Lodge, 25 Lydford Road, London NW2 5QY Tel: 020 8451 4888 — MB ChB 1972 Liverp.; MRCGP 1998. GP Princip.; ICLP Facilitator Imperial Coll. Med. Sch. Prev: Asst. Lect. (Path.) Middlx. Hosp. Med. Sch. Lond.; Asst. Cons. (Cas.) Centr. Middl. Hosp.

ABRAHAMS, Mark Joseph 4 Beaconsfield Terrace, Victoria Road, Cambridge CB4 3BP — MB ChB 1992 Glas.

ABRAHAMS, Professor Peter Herbert Girton College, Clarkson Road, Cambridge CB3 0EH Tel: 01223 339333 Email: pha1000@cus.com.ac.uk; Lydford Lodge, 25 Lydford Road, London NW2 5QY Tel: 020 8451 4888 — MB BS 1972 Lond.; FRCS Ed. 1993; FRCR 1994. Prof. Clin. Anat., Kigezi Internat. Sch. of Med., Camb.; WHO Cons. (Anat.) Israel; Examr. Primary FRCS RCS Eng. & RCS Edin.; Fell. Girton Coll. Camb. Socs: Fell. BACA; AACA. Prev: Vis. Asst. Prof. Univ. Iowa Coll. Med., USA; Vis. Prof. Ben-Gurion Univ. Negev, Israel; Prof. St. Geo. Med. Sch., W. Indies.

ABRAHAMS, Royce Cubitt Bridge Cottage Surgery, 41 High Street, Welwyn AL6 9EF Tel: 01438 715044 Fax: 01438 714013; Riverside, 56 Mimram Road, Welwyn AL6 9HA Tel: 0143 871 7807 — BM BCh 1975 Oxf.; MA Oxf. 1972, BM BCh 1975; DRCOG 1977; Cert. Family Plann. JCC 1977; Cert. Av. Med. 1992. Prev: Clin. Asst. (Obst.) N. Herts. Matern. Hosp.

ABRAHAMS, Sidney Isaac (retired) 44 Owlstone Road, Cambridge CB3 9JH — MB BS Lond. 1928; MD Lond. 1932; MRCS Eng., LRCP Lond. 1927; FRCGP 1967, M 1953. Prev: Obst. Resid. & Neurol. & Dermatol. Ho. Phys. Guy's Hosp.

ABRAHAMS, Mr Yusuf Lake View, Sandy Lane, Northwood HA6 3ES Tel: 020 7935 7567 Fax: 01923 841286 Email: jabrahams@compuserve.com — MB BS 1971 Lond.; MB BS (Hons.) Lond. 1971; BSc (Hons.) Lond. 1967; FRCS Eng. 1977; MRCP (UK) 1973; MRCS Eng. LRCP Lond. 1971; FRCOG 1990. (Westm.) Cons. O & G New Ealing Hosp.; Examr. Soc. Apoth. Lond.; Examr. RCOG. Prev: Sen. Regist. (O & G) Centr. Middlx. & Middlx. Hosps.; Regist. (O & G) Univ. Coll. Hosp. Lond.

ABRAHAMSON, David Community Mental Health Rehabilitation Team, 313 Shrewsbury Road, Forest Gate, London E7 8QU Tel: 020 8586 5077 Fax: 020 8970 5078; 11 Litchfield Way, London NW11 6NN Tel: 020 8455 3694 — MB BCh BAO 1960 Dub.; BA Dub. 1953, BSc (Vet.) 1953; FRCPI 1973, M 1964; MRCVS 1954; FRCPsych 1981, M 1972; DPM Lond. 1966. (TC Dub.) Cons. Psychiat. E. Lond. and The City Ment. Health NHS Trust. Socs: Fell. Roy. Soc. Med. Prev: Sen. Regist. Bethlem Roy. & Maudsley Hosps.; Regist. N. Middlx. Hosp. Lond.; Ho. Phys. & Ho. Surg. Richmond Hosp. Dub.

ABRAHAMSON, Edwin Leonard Dept. of Paediatrics, Chelsea & Westminster Hospital, Fulham Road, London SW10 9NH Tel: 020 8746 8660 Fax: 020 8746 8644 Email: doc.ed@chelwest.nhs.uk — MB BCh BAO 1985 Dub.; MRCPI 1990; DCH NUI 1986; FRCP. Cons. Paediatr. Accid. Med.

ABRAHAMSON, Gail Mathilde Department of Haematology, Ealing Hospital, Uxbridge Road, Southall UB1 3HW — MB BCh BAO 1981 Dub.; DPhil. Oxf. 1992; BA Dub. 1981; MRCPI 1984; MRCPath 1994. Cons. Haematologist Ealing Hosp. Lond. Prev: Lect. & Sen. Regist. (Haemat.) Char. Cross & W.m. Med. Sch. Lond.; Research Fell. Nuffield Dept. Med. John Radcliffe Hosp. Oxf.; Regist. (Haemat.) St. Mary's Hosp. Lond.

ABRAHEEM, Abraheem Cardiology Department, City General Hospital, Newcastle Road, Stoke-on-Trent ST4 6QG — MD 1985 Damascus.

ABRAM, William Paul Belvoir Park Hospital, Hospital Road, Belfast BT8 8JR Tel: 01232 491942; 11 Glebe Manor, Hillsborough BT26 6NS Tel: 01846 638780 Email: 106454.126@compuserve.com — MB BCh BAO 1975 Belf.; BSc. (Hons.) Physiol. Belf. 1972, MB BCh BAO 1975; FFR RCSI 1980 FRCR Lond.1980; DMRT Lond. 1979. Cons. Radiother./Oncol. N. Irel. Radiother. Centre Belvoir Pk. Hosp. Belf. Socs: BMA & Ulster Med. Soc.; Eur. Soc. of Therap. Radiol. and Oncol.; Eur. Gp. for Blood and Marrow Transpl.ation. Prev: Regist. & Sen. Regist. N.. Irel. Radiother. Centre; Hon. Sen. Regist. & Lect. Roy. Marsden Hosp. Sutton.

ABRAMCZUK, Jerzy Apoloniusz (retired) 63 Redhill Road, Rowlands Castle PO9 6DE Tel: 02392 412479 Fax: 02392 412479 Email: jabramczuk@freeserve.co.uk — MD 1956 Lodz; LAH Dub. 1969; MRCPsych 1972; DPM RCPSI 1970; Dip. Psych Warsaw 1962. Prev: Cons. Psychiat. State Sanat. for Nerv. Dis. Warsaw.

ABRAMI, George (retired) Holmglen, 66 Busby Road, Carmunnock, Glasgow G76 9BL Tel: 0141 644 3142 — MB ChB 1956 Glas.; FRCS Ed. 1961. Prev: Cons. Orthop. Surg. Vict. Infirm. Glas.

ABRAMOV, Sylvia 12 Raeburn Close, Hampstead Garden Suburb, London NW11 6UG Tel: 020 8458 7629 — MD 1992 Paris. SHO Rotat. (Med.) Whittington Hosp. Lond.

ABRAMOVICH, Mr Solomon J 97 Harley Street, London W1G 6AG Tel: 020 7935 0604 Fax: 020 7935 1022; 24 Downshire Hill, London NW3 1NT Tel: 020 7435 8342 Email: solomon@abramovichfsnet.co.uk — MB BS 1969 Kaunas; MSc Kaunas 1969; FRCS Eng. 1978; MRCS Eng. LRCP Lond. 1977. (Kaunas Med. Inst.) Cons. ENT Surg. St. Mary's Hosp. & Centr. Middlx. Hosps. Lond.; Hon. Clin. Sen. Lect. Imperial Coll.; Hon. Cons. Gibraltar; Clin. Fell. (Otolaryngol.) Univ. Toronto. Socs: Roy. Soc. Med.; Brit. Assn OtoLaryngol. and Head and Neck Surg.; Barany. & Meniere's Soc. Prev: Sen. Regist. (ENT Surg.) St. Bart. Hosp. Lond.; Sen. Regist. (ENT Surg.) Nat. Hosp. Neurol. & Neurosurg. Lond.; Regist. (ENT Surg.) Univ. Coll. Hosp. Lond.

ABRAMS, Audrey Berenice 38 Park Hall Road, London N2 9PU — MB BCh 1952 Witwatersrand; MRCP (UK) 1973; DCH Eng. 1959. Clin. Research Asst. MRC Unit Whittington Hosp. Lond. Prev: Ho. Phys. Coronation Hosp. Johannesburg, Whittington Hosp. Lond. & Whipps Cross Hosp.

ABRAMS, Dominic James Richard Ground Floor Flat, 42 Saltram Crescent, London W9 3HR — MB BS 1994 Lond.

ABRAMS, John Willoughby (retired) Heath View, Adlams Lane, Sway, Lymington SO41 6EG — MRCS Eng. LRCP Lond. 1958; MB Camb. 1959, BChir 1958; DObst RCOG 1962.

ABRAMS, Mr Joseph David Tel: 020 7806 4061; 11 Mercers Place, London W6 7BZ Tel: 020 7602 9464 Fax: 020 7603 8807 — BM BCh 1952 Oxf.; DM Oxf. 1964; FRCS Eng. 1959; FRCOphth 1989; DO Eng. 1956. (Oxf. & Middlx.) Cons. Ophth. Hosp. St. John & St. Eliz. Lond.; Hon. Cons. Roy. Free Hosp. Lond. Socs: Fell. Roy. Soc. Med. Prev: Chief Clin. Asst. Moorfields Eye Hosp. City Rd. Br.; Sen. Regist. Middlx. Hosp. Lond.; Sen. Res. Off. Moorfields Eye Hosp. High Holborn Br.

ABRAMS, Joyce Care of Elderly Office, Whiston Hospital, Dragon Lane, Prescot L35 5DR Tel: 0151 430 1245 Fax: 0151 430 1142; 9 The Meadows, Rainhill, Prescot L35 0PQ Tel: 0151 426 9455 — MB ChB 1976 Manch.; MRCP (UK) 1980; FRCP 1995. Cons. Geriat. St. Helens & Knowsley HA. Socs: Brit. Geriat. Soc.

ABRAMS, Mr Leon David (retired) 6 Grenfell Drive, Edgbaston, Birmingham B15 3LR Tel: 0121 454 1679 — MB ChB 1945 Birm.; FRCS Eng. 1951. Prev: Hon. Cons. Cardiothoracic Surg. Centr. Birm. HA.

ABRAMS, Michael Ellis, CB 97 Wood Vale, London N10 3DL — MB ChB 1956 Birm.; BSc (Hons.) Anat. & Physiol. Birm. 1953; FRCP Lond. 1972, M 1960; FFCM 1983, M 1972. Chairm. The Whittington Hosp. NHS Trust; Hon. Cons. Phys. Guy's Hosp. Lond. Prev: Dep. Chief Med. Off. DoH.

ABRAMS, Professor Paul 148 Stoke Lane, Westbury-on-Trym, Bristol BS9 3RN — MB ChB 1970 Sheff.; FRCS 1974; MD 1977 Bristol. Cons. Brit. Urological Inst. S.mead Hosp. Bristol.

ABRAMS, Sara Madeleine Louise Clinical Pharmacology, 38 Little Britain, St Bartholomews Hospital, West Smithfield, London EC1 7BE Tel: 020 7601 7423 Fax: 020 7601 8134; 50 The Pryors, E. Heath Road, Hampstead, London NW3 1BP Tel: 020 7794 1820 Fax: 020 7794 1820 — MB BS 1976 Lond.; BSc (Hons.) (Pharmacol.) Lond. 1973; FRCP (Lond.) 1997; MRCP (UK) 1980. (St. Bart.) Cons. Phys. Homerton Hosp. Lond. Socs: Roy. Soc. Med. & Brit. Pharmacol. Soc.; Brit. Hypertens. Soc. Prev: Sen. Lect. & Hon. Cons. Clin. Pharmacol. & Gen. Med. St. Bart. Hosp. Lond.; Hon. Lect. (Clin. Pharmacol. & Nephrol.) St. Bart. Hosp. Lond.; Regist. (Med.) St. Mary's Hosp. Lond.

ABRAMS, Wendy Miriam 10 Cooper House, Lyons Place, London NW8 8NJ — MB BS 1990 Lond.; DRCOG 1994; MRCGP 1997. Non Princip. GP.

ABRAR, Mr Hussain Ahmad Khan Fatima Medical Centre, Khanewal Road, Multan, Pakistan Tel: 00 1 92 61 222571; 71 Angel Hill, Sutton SM1 3EH — MB BS 1976 Punjab; FRCS Ed. 1986. Vis. Cons. & Asst. Prof. Plastic Surg. Nishtar Med. Coll. Multan, Pakistan; Hon. Cons. Combined Milit. Hosp. Multan, Pakistan.

ABRAR, Shafqat Penketh Mount Park Road, Harrow on the Hill, Harrow HA1 3LB — MB BS 1986 Karachi.

ABREW, Mr Kaluhath Meththananda Chandrasiri Royal Bournemouth Hospital, Castle Lane E., Bournemouth BH7 7DW Tel: 01202 303626; 3 Elmgate Drive, Bournemouth BH7 7EF Tel: 01202 302399 — MB BS 1976 Sri Lanka; FRCS Ed. 1986; LRCP LRCS Ed. LRCPS Glas. 1985. Staff Surg. Roy. Bournemouth Hosp. Prev: Regist. (Gen. Surg.) OldCh. Hosp. Romford; Regist Rotat. (Gastroenterol., Urol. & Vasc. Surg.) Ysbyty Gwynedd Bangor.

ABRINES, Malcolm James Danes Dyke Surgery, 463A Scalby Road, Newby, Scarborough YO12 6UB Tel: 01723 375343 Fax: 01723 501582 — BM BCh 1983 Oxf.; BA Oxf. 1980, BM BCh 1983; MRCGP 1988; DRCOG 1991. Prev: Maj. RAMC.

ABROKWAH, Mr James 72 Victoria Avenue, Westgate-on-Sea CT8 8BH Tel: 01843 33838 — LMSSA 1990 Lond.; PhD Physiol. Lond. 1986; MB BS Accra 1978; FRCS Glas. 1990.

ABROL, Vijayakar City Road Medical Centre, 5 City Road, Edgbaston, Birmingham B16 0HH Tel: 0121 454 8998 Fax: 0121 454 1151 — MB 1963 Lucknow; MB BS Lucknow 1963. (King Geo. Med. Coll.) Med. Off. Nat. Blood Serv. W. Midl.; Hosp. SP Dist. Gen. Hosp. Bromwich; Chairm. Birm. Single Handed GPs; Bd. Mem. Ladywood PCG. Socs: BMA (Post Chairm. Birm. Div.). Prev: Staff O & G Frankfurt Army (US) Regional Med. Centre; Regist. (O & G) Leicester Roy. Infirm., Newport & E. Mon. & N. Staffs. Gp. Hosps.; Family Phys. US Army Hosp. Wuerzburg, W. Germany.

ABSALOM, Henrietta Helen Rachel Darbys Green Farm, Darbys Green, Knightwick, Worcester WR6 5PU — MB ChB 1998 Leic.

ABSALOM, Stephen Richard Department of Pathology, James Paget Hospital, Lowestoft Road Gorleston, Great Yarmouth NR31 6LA Tel: 01493 452040 — MB ChB 1981 Sheff.; MRCPath (Chem. Path.) 1989. Cons. Chem. Pathol. Jas. Paget Healthcare NHS Trust Gt. Yarmouth; Clin. Director for Clin. Servs. Jas. Paget Healthcare NHS Trust. Socs: Assn. Clin. Path. & Mem. Comm. Clin. Path.; Ord. Mem. Assn. of Clin. Biochem.; FRCPath. Prev: Sen. Regist. Chem. Path. Leics. Roy. Infirm.; Lect. Dept. Chem. Path. Char. Cross & W.m. Med. Sch. Lond.; Regist. Dept. Chem. Path. St. Geo. Hosp. Lond.

ABSE, Dannie (retired) Green Hollows, Craig-yr-Eos Road, Ogmore-by-Sea, Bridgend CF32 0PG — MRCS Eng. LRCP Lond. 1950; D.Litt. Wales 1995. Prev: Vis. Sen. Fell. (Humanities) P.ton Univ. New Jersey, USA.

ABSOLOM, Michelle Ellen 13 Newcomen Court, Newcomen Road, Portsmouth PO2 8LA — MB BCh 1994 Wales.

ABSOLON, Christine Michela 18 Hobday Street, London E14 6AZ — MB BS 1983 Lond.; MRC Psych 1987; DCH RCP Lond. 1986. Sen. Regist. Child Psychiat. Rotat. Lond. Hosp. Prev: Regist. (Psychiat. Rotat.) St. Thos. Hosp. Lond.; SHO (Paediat.) P.ss Alexandra Hosp. Harlow; Ho. Off. St. Margt. Hosp. Epping.

ABSOLON, Christopher John Nightingale Practice, 10 Kenninghall Road, Clapton, London E5 8BY Tel: 020 8985 8388 Fax: 020 8986 6004; 95 Osborne Road, London E7 0PW — MB BS 1983 Lond.; MRCGP 1989; DRCOG 1988; DCH RCP Lond. 1986. (Lond. Hosp.) Socs: Christian Med. Fell.sh.; BMA. Prev: SHO (Haemat.) Lond. Hosp.; Trainee GP Newham VTS.

ABSOLON, Michael John (retired) Oakham House, Ebrington, Chipping Campden GL55 6NL Tel: 01386 593123 — MB BChir Camb. 1957; FRCS Eng. 1964; FRCOphth 1988. Hon. Cons. Ophth. Surg. Soton. Univ. Hosp. NHS Trust. Prev: Cons. Ophth. Surg. Soton. Univ. Hosps. NHS Trust.

ABSON, Charlotte Alexandra Kent Oncology Centre, Maidstone Hospital, Hermitage Lane, Maidstone ME16 9QQ Tel: 01622 225014 — MB BS 1988 Lond.; MRCP (UK) 1992; FRCR 1996. (St. Thos.) p/t Cons. (Clin. Oncol.) Kent Oncol. Centre Maidstone. Prev: Regist. (Clin. Oncol.) St. Luke's Hosp. Guildford; SHO Rotat. (Med.) King's Coll. Hosp. Lond.; Specialist Regist. (Radiother.) Roy. Marsden Hosp. Lond.

ABSON, Mr Edward Pennington (retired) The Crest, Weekes Lane, West Brabourne, Ashford TN25 5LZ — MB ChB 1941 Manch.; BA Open Univ. 1978; FRCS Eng. 1956; DObst RCOG 1948. Prev: Cons. Cas. Kent & Canterbury Hosp.

ABSOUD, Mr Edward Maurice St Giles Clinic, 67 St Giles St, Northampton NN1 1JF Tel: 01205 351193, 01604 620673 Email: edlizabsoud@doctors.org.uk — MB BCh 1964 Ain Shams; BSc Open 1994; DS Cairo 1966; FRCS Ed. 1973. Locum Cons. Surg. Gen. Surg. Socs: Fell. Internat. Coll. Angiol.; BMA; Fell. Roy. Soc. Med. Prev: Cons. Surg. Riyadh Centr. Hosp., Saudi Arabia.

ABU AISHA, Bashir Bahlul 11 Cavendish Gardens, West Didsbury, Manchester M20 1LA — MB BCh 1983 Al Fateh, Libya; MRCP (UK) 1988; MRCPI 1987.

ABU-BAKRA, Mohammed Ahmed Juma 66 Greenlee Drive, Dundee DD2 2RJ — MB ChB 1996 Dundee.

ABU HAIYYEH, Khader Jawad Ismail Saudia Medical Services, cc 507, PO Box 67, Jeddah, Saudi Arabia; 9 Sweeps Hill Close, Pembury, Tunbridge Wells TN2 4LT Tel: 01892 824564 Fax: 01892 824564 — MB BCh 1970 Cairo; MRCP (Irel.) 1981. Cons. Internist Sadia Med. Serv. Jeddah. Socs: BMA; Brit. Diabetic Assn. Prev: Cons. Internist Bakhsh Hosp. Jeddah; Regist. (Geriat. Med.) Pembury Hosp. Kent; Regist. (Geriat. Med.) Kingsmead Hosp. Stafford.

ABU-HANEEFFA, Mohamed 3 Fiske Close, St James Park, Bury St Edmunds IP32 7LX — MRCS Eng. LRCP Lond. 1980. Assoc. Specialist (ENT Surg.).

ABU-HARB, Majd Sunderland District General Hospital, Kayll Road, Sunderland SR4 7TP; Southleigh, 74 Whitburn Road, Cleadon, Sunderland SR6 7QX — MD 1981 Damascus; MRCP (UK) 1990; DCH RCPS Glas. 1990. Cons. Neonat. Paediat. Sunderland Dist. Gen. Hosp. Prev: Sen. Regist. (Paediat.) Sheff. Childr. Hosp.; Regist. (Paediat.) Roy. Vict. Infirm. Newc.; SHO (Paediat. Cardiol.) Freeman Hosp. Newc.

ABU-HEIJA, Adel Taha Hasan Khalil 51 Hogarth Crescent, Glasgow G32 6JZ — MB BS 1981 Libya; MRCOG 1987. Regist. (O & G) Inverclyde Roy. Hosp. Prev: SHO (Anaesth.) & (O & G) Univ. Hosp. Libya.

ABU KHALAF, Mr Wael Abdalla Ishaq 1122 Evesham Road, Redditch B96 6EA — MB ChB 1981 Alexandria; FRCS Glas. 1987.

ABU KMEIL, Suheib Saleh Mayyar 6 The Drive, St. Crispin Hospital, Northampton NN5 4XT; 17 Rufford Avenue, Northampton NN3 3NY — MB ChB 1983 Alexandria; MRCPsych. 1993.

ABU MAHFOUZ, Fayez Ibrahim Suliman 10 Blenheim Court, Kenton Road, Harrow HA3 8AP — MB BCh 1971 Al-Azhar Cairo.

ABU-OMAR, Yasir 2A St. Swithin Street, Aberdeen AB10 6XE — MB ChB 1997 Aberd.

ABU-RAJAB, Rashid Barakat 30 Cardinal Gardens, Darlington DL3 8SD — MB ChB 1997 Glas.

ABU SAMRA, Mamoun Ibrahim 25 Sandford Way, Dunchurch, Rugby CV22 6NB — MB BS 1971 Khartroum; MRCPI 1983.

ABU-SEIDO, Hussam-El-Din Arif Adwy Flat 264, 123 Petershill Drive, Glasgow G21 4QU — MB ChB 1994 Dundee. SHO (Paediat.) Ninewells Hosp. Dundee. Prev: Ho. Off. (Med. & Surg.) Ninewells Hosp. Dundee.

ABU SHAMS, Shawki Mohamed Said Asaid 67 St Peters Road, Margate CT9 4AL — MB BCh 1982 Ain Shams, Eygpt; MRCP (UK) 1995.

ABU-SITTA, Ghassan 2/L, 33 Cranworth Street, Glasgow G12 8AF — MB ChB 1993 Glas.

ABU ZAID, El-Hassan Ali Department of Anaesthetics, Royal United Hospital, Combe Park, Bath BA1 3NG Tel: 01225 825056 Fax: 01225 825061 — MB ChB 1980 Alexandria; FRCA 1995; DA (UK) 1992. Staff Grade (Anaesth.) Roy. United Hosp. Bath. Socs: FRCA; Obst. Anaesth. Assn.; SW Anaesth. Soc. Prev: Regist. (Anaesth.) Derriford Hosp. Plymouth; Spec. Regist. Derriford Hosp.

ABUBACKER, Mohammed Ziyad 46 Malvern Close, Mitcham CR4 1EH — MB BChir 1996 Camb.

ABUDU, Mr Adesegun Tiburaniyu 9 Claverdon Drive, Great Barr, Birmingham B43 5HR — MB BS 1987 Ibadan; MB BS Ibadan Nigeria 1987; FRCS Glas. 1992.

ABUDU, Mr Isola Adeniji 33 Westminster Gardens, Barking IG11 0BJ Tel: 020 8591 0730 — MB ChB 1966 Birm.; FRCS Ed 1972; FRCSI 1972; MRCS Eng. LRCP Lond. 1971. Cons. (Orthop. Surg.) Natl. Orthop. Hosp. Ighobi, Nigeria.

ABUDU, Titilola Omolara 37 Wood Leason Avenue, Lyppard Hanford, Worcester WR4 0EU — MB BS 1990 Lond.

ABUELELA, Hesham Mohamed Ali Khalil 49 Futherfield, Abbots Langley WD5 0PN Tel: 01923 269567 Fax: 01923 269567 — MB BCh 1983 Cairo; Cert. Prescribed Equiv. Exp. JCPTGP 1992; ECFMG 1984. Asst. GP Harold MacMillan Med. Centre Harrow Middlx.; Clin. Asst. (Gen. Med.) King Geo. Hosp. Lond. Prev: Trainee GP Aldershot Health Centre; Regist. (Geriat. & Gen. Med.) Edgware Gen. Hosp. & Brighton Gen. Hosp.

ABUHADRA, Mr Khaled Sadegh Orthopaedic Department, Luton and Dunstable Hospital, Lewsey Road, Luton LU4 0DZ Tel: 01582 491122; 14 Royce Close, Dunstable LU6 2NT Tel: 01582 475499 Fax: 01582 475499 Email: k.abuhadra@msn.com — MB BCh 1984 Al Fateh; FRCS Ed. 1991. Assoc. Specialist Orthop. Renchance Fell. (Spinal Surg.) Luton.; Research Fell. (Spinal Surg.) Luton. Socs: BMA; MDU.

ABUKHALIL, Samir Husni Department of Obstetrics & Gynaecology, Queen Elizabeth Hospital, Gayton Road, King's Lynn PE30 4ET — MB BCh 1969 Ain Shams; MRCOG 1980. Cons. O & G Qu. Eliz. Hosp. King's Lynn. Prev: Cons. O & G ARAMCO, Saudi Arabia; Sen. Regist. (O & G) Kuwait Matern. Hosp.

ABULAFI, Mr Al-Mutaz Mayday University Hospital, London Road, Croydon CR7 7YE Tel: 020 8401 3325 Fax: 020 8401 3606 Email: muti.abulafi@mhc-tr.sthames.nhs.uk; 16 Green Lane, Purley CR8 3PG — MB BCh 1980 Cairo; MS Lond. 1993; FRCS Eng. 1989; FRCS Glas. 1988. Cons. Surg. Mayday Univ. Hosp. Croydon. Socs: Assn. of ColoProctol. of GB & Ire; Assn. of Surg.s of GB & Ire; Assn. of Endoscopic Surg.s of GB & Ire. Prev: Sen. Regist. (Gen. Surg.) St. Thos. Hosp. Lond.; Research Fell. Lond. Hosp. Med. Coll. Univ. Lond.; Regist. (Surg.) Roy. Lond. Hosp. Whitechapel.

ABUMAHLULA, Mr Musa Abdussalam Flat 9, Donne Court, Orpington Hospital, Sevenoaks Road, Orpington BR6 9JU — MB BCh 1983 Al Fateh; FRCS Glas. 1994.

ABUOWN, Mr Abdussalam Abubakr 288 Prittlewell Chase, Westcliff on Sea SS0 0PN — MB BS 1981 Libya; FRCS Glas. 1986. Clin. Research Fell. (Surg.) Middlx. Hosp. Lond. Socs: Fell. Roy. Soc. Med. Prev: Regist. (Gen. Surg.) Harrogate Dist. Hosp., Inverclyde Roy. Hosp. & Monklands Dist. Gen. Hosp.

ABURIZIQ, Issa Said Department of Orthopaedics, North Tyneside General Hospital, Rake Lane, North Shields NE29 8NH; PO Box 5615, Birmingham B37 5EF — MB BS 1981 Al Fateh.

ABURN, Simon Peter Devon Road Surgery, 32 Devon Road, South Darenth, Dartford DA4 9AB Tel: 01322 862121 Fax: 01322 868794 — MB BS 1986 Lond.

ABUSREWIL, Fayrus Mansur 12 Brynteg, Rhiwbina, Cardiff CF14 6TS — MB BS 1996 Lond. SHO Rotat. (Paediat.) Whipps Cross Hosp. Socs: Med. Protec. Soc.; MSS.

ACELLAM-ODONG, Charles Casan 473 Dunstable Road, Luton LU4 8DG — MB ChB 1976 Makerere; MRCOG 1983 (Lond.). GP Luton.

ACERINI, Carlo Lorenzo Department of Paediatrics, Addenbrooke's Hospital, Cambridge CB2 2QQ Tel: 01223 336805 Fax: 01223 336996 — MB ChB 1988 Dundee; MD Dundee 2000; MRCPCH 1990; BSc Dundee 1984; MRCP (UK) 1993; DCH RCPS Glas. 1990. Univ. Lect. & Cons. Paediat. (Paediat. Endocrinol. & Diabetes) Univ. of Camb. Addenbrooke's Hosp. Camb. Prev: SHO (Paediat.) Tayside & Lanarksh. HB.; SHO & Regist. (Paediat.) Roy. Hosp. Sick Childr. Glas.; Regist. (Paediat.) Roy. Alexandra Hosp. Paisley.

ACEVEDO, Isabel Astrid Mayday University Hospital, Mayday Road, Croydon CR7 7YE — MB BS 1996 Lond.; DRCOG 1999; BA 1993. (St Marys, London) SHO Elderly Care.

ACEVEDO MERINO, Mercedes Royal Cornhill Hospital, Cornhill Road, Aberdeen AB25 2ZH Email: m.acevedo@abdn.ac.uk; 10 Wallacebrae Gardens, Bridge of Don, Aberdeen AB22 8XN — MD 1984 Malaga; LMS Malaga 1981. SHO (Psychiat) Roy. Cornhill Hosp. Aberd. Prev: Lect. (Biomed. Sci.) Univ. Aberd.

ACEY, Gerald 4 Ridge Croft, Stone ST15 8PN — MB ChB 1980 Leeds. Cons. Psychiat. St. Geo. Hosp. Stafford.

ACEY, Simon John Tel: 01429 272000, 01429 274899 Fax: 01429 863877; 15 College Close, Dalton Percy, Hartlepool TS27 3JA — MB ChB 1988 Manch.; MRCGP 1992; DRCOG 1992.

ACHA GANDARIAS, Pedro 40B Gloucester Terrace, London W2 3DA — LMS 1991 Basque Provinces.

ACHAN, Mr Narayan Vasudev 3K Portman Mansions, Chiltern Street, London W1U 5AH Fax: 020 7935 8192 Email: achann.v.@aol.com — MB BS 1963 Utkal; FRCS 1970 Ed. Cons. Orthop. Surg.

ACHAN, Pramod 3K Portman Mansions, Chiltern Street, London W1U 5AH — MB BS 1993 Lond.

ACHAN, Vinod 3K Portman Mansions, Chiltern Street, London W1U 5AH — BM BCh 1993 Oxf.

ACHAR, Urmila 55 The Bramptons, Shaw, Swindon SN5 5SL — MB BS 1998 Lond.

ACHARA, Mr Ndubuisi Ikem 12 Howden Hall Drive, Liberton, Edinburgh EH16 6UJ Tel: 0131 664 7415 — BM BCh 1979 Univ. Nigeria; FRCSI 1986.

ACHARYA, Ashoka Bengathrodi Warwick Hospital, Lakin Road, Warwick CV34 5BW; 1 Tressel Croft, Heathcote, Warwick CV34 6FA — MB BS 1981 Mysore; MRCP (UK) 1992; DCH Mysore 1982; MD (Paediat.) Mysore 1985. Cons. Paediat. Warwick Hosp. S. Warks. Gen. Hosps. NHS Trust. Socs: MRCPCH; Life Mem. Indian Acad. Paediat. Prev: Sen. Regist. Leicester Roy. Infirm. & PeterBoro. Dist. Hosps.; Regist. Milton Keynes Hosp.

ACHARYA, Mr Bikash London Bridge Hospital, 27 Tooley St., London SE1 2PR Tel: 020 7407 3100 Fax: 020 7407 3162; 95 Hadley Highstone, Barnet EN5 4QQ — MB BS 1975 Utkal; MS 1977, MD Amer. Nat. Bd. Exams 1987; FRCS Ed. 1983. (S.C.B. Medical College, Orissa, India) Cons. Orthop. Surg. Lond. Bridge Hosp. Prev: Cons. Orthop. Surg. Old Ct. Hosp. Lond.; Chief Resid. (Orthop.) L. A. Weiss & Univ. Illinois Assoc. Gp. Hosps., USA; Chief Resid. & Postgrad. Fell. (Surg.) SCB Med. Coll. Hosp. Utkal Univ. Cuttack, Orissa, India.

ACHARYA, Mr Bindiganavale Srinivas Srinivas (retired) 1 Gloucester Road, Hampton TW12 2UQ Tel: 020 8979 4694 — MB BS 1938 Lond.; FRCS Eng. 1947; MRCS Eng. LRCP Lond. 1937. Prev: Ho. Surg. (ENT) St. Bart. Hosp.

ACHARYA, Dev Dinker 70 Byron Avenue, Motspur Park, New Malden KT3 6EY — MB BS 1997 Lond.

ACHARYA, Jagrati 70 Byron Avenue, New Malden KT3 6EY — MB BS 1998 Lond.; MB BS Lond 1998.

ACHARYA, Kiranroy Prutaprai 52 Orritor Road, Cookstown BT80 8BM — MB BS 1973 Gujarat. GP Cookstown, N.ern Irel.

ACHARYA, Madan Prasad 10 Sladepool Farm Road, Kings Heath, Birmingham B14 5DJ — MB BS 1973 Bangalore. GP Birm.

ACHARYA, Rajnikant Jayantilal Staunton Group Practice, 3-5 Bounds Green Road, Wood Green, London N22 8HE Tel: 020 8889 4311 Fax: 020 8826 9100 — MB BS 1969 Indore. GP Wood Green. Lond.

ACHARYA, Shambhu Prasad University Hospital Aintree, Liverpool L9 7AL Tel: 0151 529 5152 Fax: 0151 529 5155 — Vrach 1984 1st Leningrad Med Inst. USSR; FFA RCSI 1994; Dip. Europ. Acad. Anaesth 1995. Con. Anaesth. Univ. Hosp. Aintree Liverp. Socs: BMA; Nepal Med. Assn.; MPS. Prev: Regist. Rotat. (Anaesth.) Sheff.; Regist. & SHO (Anaesth.) Luton & Dunstable Hosp.; Specialist Regist. Rotat. Mersey Region.

ACHARYA, Shanti Raman Greenups Terrace, Tower Hill, Sowerby Bridge HX6 2QH — MB BS 1968 Agra. GP Sowerby Bridge, W. Yorks.

ACHARYA, Umesh Ramanikrai Southwest Centre for Reproductive Medicine, Ocean Suite, Level 06, Derriford Hospital, Plymouth PL6 8DH Tel: 01752 763683 Email: umesh.acharya@phnt.swest.nhs.uk; 1 Whiteford Road, Mannamead, Plymouth PL3 5LU — BM 1983 Soton.; DM Soton 1995; MRCOG 1989. Cons. in Obst. Gyn. & Reproductive Med. Derriford Hosp. Plymouth. Socs: Brit. Fertil. Soc.; Amer. Fertil. Soc. Prev: Sen. Lect. & Hon. Cons. Glas. Roy. Infirm.; Lect. & Sen. Regist. Univ. Dept. O & G Aberd. Matern. Hosp.; Clin. Research Fell. Assisted Reproduc. Unit Aberd. Matern. Hosp.

ACHARYA BASKERVILLE, Madhushree Torcoed Isaf, Lllangendeirne, Kidwelly SA17 5BT — MB BS 1991 Lond.; BSc (Hons.); MB BS Lond.1991; MRCPsych 1995. (Univ. Coll. Lond.) Sen. Regist. (Child & Adolesc. Psychiat.) Ty Bryn Adolesc. Unit St. Cadoc's Hosp. Gwent.; Cons. Child & Adolesc. Psychiat. Canolfan Gwili, W. Wales Hosp. Carmarthen.

ACHARYYA, Sourangshu Runwell Hospital, Runwell Chase, Wickford SS11 7XX Tel: 01268 735555 Fax: 01268 766731 — MB BS 1973 Calcutta; MPhil Psychiat. Lond. 1981; MRCPsych 1984. Cons. Psychiat. Med. Dir. S.end Community Care Servs. NHS Trust. Socs: Fell. Roy. Soc. Med. Prev: Sen. Regist. Hayes Gr. Priory Hosp. & Lect. Middlx. Hosp. Med. Sch. & Univ. Coll. Lond.; Regist. Guy's Hosp. Med. Sch.; Regist. Bethlem Roy. & Maudsley Hosp.

ACHESON, Alistair John Rosemount Medical Practice, 52 Dean Road, Bo'ness EH51 9BB Tel: 01506 822556 — MB BCh BAO 1983 Belf.; MRCGP 1989; T(GP) 1991. Socs: BMA.

ACHESON, Mr Austin George 49 Victoria Road, Northampton NN1 5ED Tel: 01604 259281 Email: aacheson@compuserve.com — MB BCh BAO 1992 Belf. (Queens Univ, Belfast) Socs: BMA; ASIT.

ACHESON, Denis James (retired) 35 Castlehill Road, Belfast BT4 3GN Tel: 01232 763717 — MB BCh BAO 1952 Belf.; MRCGP 1968. Prev: Med. Off. Campbell Coll. Belf.

ACHESON, Donald Christopher THe Surgery, 89 Gubbins Lane, Harold Wood, Romford RM3 0DR Tel: 01708 346666 Fax: 01708 381300 — MB BCh BAO 1985 Belf.

ACHESON, Elizabeth Anne 13 Greenway Road, Galmpton, Brixham TQ5 0LR — MB ChB 1993 Birm.

ACHESON, Enid Joan (retired) Braegarth, Elterwater, Ambleside LA22 9JB Email: williamacheson@compuserve.com — 1951 MB ChB Birm.; 1971 MD Birm.; 1992 FRCP Lond.; 1980 MRCP (UK). Prev: Sen. Lect. (Gen. Pract.) Univ. Manch.

ACHESON, Mrs Fiona Marigo Flat 5, 53 Millbank, London SW1P 4RL Tel: 020 7630 5258 — LRCPI & LM, LRSCI & LM 1950; FFA RCSI 1962; DA Eng. 1954. Socs: Med. Defence Union. Prev: Cons. Anaesth. St. Peter's Gp. Lond.; Instruc. Yale Univ. Sch. Med.; Attend. Anaesth. Hartford Hosp. Connecticut.

ACHESON, George Stafford (retired) — MB BChir 1967 Camb.; MA, MB Camb. 1967, BChir 1966. Chairm. N. Norf.

ACHESON, Harold William Kennedy, OBE (retired) Braegarth, Elterwater, Ambleside LA22 9JB Tel: 015394 37355 Fax: 015394 37355 Email: williamacheson@compuserve.com — MB ChB Birm.

1951; FRCGP 1970, M 1959. Prev: Sen. Lect. (Gen. Pract.) Univ. Manch.

ACHESON, Hugh Forrest 42 Dumyat Drive, Falkirk FK1 5PA — MB ChB 1950 Ed.

ACHESON, Mr James Francis 149 Harley Street, London W1G 6DE Tel: 020 7935 4444 Fax: 020 7486 1592 — BM 1980 Soton.; FRCS Glas. (Ophth.) 1985; MRCP (UK) 1984; FCOphth. 1988; DO RCS Eng. 1985. Cons. Ophth. Moorfields Eye Hosp. Lond.; Cons. Opth. Nat. Hosp. for Neurol. & Neurosurg. Lond. Prev: Cons. Ophth. W.ern Ophth. Hosp. Lond.; Regist. Moorfields Eye Hosp. Lond.

ACHESON, Nigel 7 Gilnahirk Drive, Belfast BT5 7DW — MB ChB 1989 Birm.

ACHESON, Peter 13 Green Road, Galmpton, Brixham TQ5 0LR — MB ChB 1993 Birm.

ACHESON, Peter Samuel James 11 Old Forge, Castlewellan Road, Banbridge BT32 4AH — MB ChB 1996 Dundee.

ACHESON, Mr Robert Ronald (retired) Highfield, Shoreditch, Taunton TA3 7BL Tel: 01823 284386 Fax: 01823 279848 Email: ronaldacheson@stones.com — MB BCh Belf. 1958; FRCS Ed. 1966; DO Eng. 1962; FRCOphth. Prev: Cons. Ophth. Taunton & Som. Hosp.

ACHESON, Professor Roy Malcolm 21 The Cliff, Roedean, Brighton BN2 5RF Tel: 01273 698518 — BM BCh 1951 Oxf.; ScD Dub. 1962, MA 1949, BA 1946; MA Oxf. 1951, DM 1954; Hon. MA Yale 1964; FRCP Lond. 1973, M 1962; FFOM RCP Lond. 1984; FFCM 1974. (Oxf.) Emerit. Prof. (Community Med.) Univ. Camb. Socs: Soc. Social Med.; BMA. Prev: Fell. Ch.ill Coll. Camb.; Prof. Epidemiol. Yale Univ., USA.

ACHIKE, Donald Isaac Onua 56 The Larches, London N13 5AX — MB BCh BAO 1967 Belf.; LRCP LRCS Ed. LRCPS Glas. 1966; DCH RCPSI 1970; DPH Liverp. 1974. Cons. (Paediat.) Kabwe Gen. Hosp., Zambia. Socs: BMA. Prev: SHO (Med.) Musgrave Pk. Hosp. Belf.; SHO (Paediat.) Roy. Hosp. Sick Childr. Belf.; Regist. (Paediat.) Univ. Teach. Hosp. Lusaka Zambia.

ACHKAR, Jihad Chebib 22 West Heath Gardens, Hampstead, London NW3 7TR — MB ChB 1988 Univ. Ghana; MRCP (UK) 1993.

ACHRAM, Mitri St James's University Hospital, Leeds LS9 7TF — MD 1975 Saint Joseph U, Lebanon; FRCR 1982.

ACHURCH, Suzanne Margaret Swanlow Medical Centre, 60 Swanlow Lane, Winsford CW7 1JF Tel: 01606 862868 — MB ChB 1989 Manch.

ACKAH, Mr Kwesi Osam-Pinanko, TD (retired) 5 Richmond Court, Belfast Road, Lisburn BT27 4QU Fax: 028 9266 8009 — MB BCh BAO 1963 Belf.; FRCS Ed. 1974. Prev: Med. Off. DOH N.Irel.

ACKERLEY, Diane Dapdune House Surgery, Wharf Road, Guildford GU1 4RP Tel: 01483 573336 Fax: 01483 306602; 1 Eustace Road, Merrow Park, Guildford GU4 7EB — MB BS 1981 Lond.; MA Oxf. 1978; MRCGP 1985; DCH RCP Lond. 1984; DRCOG 1985; Cert. Family Plann. JCC 1985. (Oxf. & King's Coll. Hosp.) Princip. GP Guildford.

ACKERLEY, Graham Clive Thrussington Lodge, Thrussington Road, Hoby, Melton Mowbray LE14 3EB — MB BS 1981 Lond.

ACKERLEY, Louise 15 Platt Lane, Dobcross, Oldham OL3 5AD — MB ChB 1998 Birm. MHO (Gen. Med. & Cardiol.) Walsall Manor Hosp. Prev: SHO, Gen. Surg. & Colorectal, Good Hope Hosp.

ACKERLEY, Richard George Greengate Medical Centre, 1 Greengate Lane, Birstall, Leicester LE4 3JF Tel: 0116 267 7901 — MB ChB 1983 Leic.; MRCGP 1989; DRCOG 1987.

ACKERMAN, Emily Katrina 40/3 Madeira Street, Leith, Edinburgh EH6 4AL — MB ChB 1983 Ed.

ACKERMAN, Lilian Else (retired) Old Hall Lodge, Kidderpore Gardens, London NW3 7SR — MB BS 1952 Lond.; MRCS Eng. LRCP Lond. 1950. Prev: GP.

ACKERMAN, Susan Anaesthetic Department, Royal East Glamorgan Hospital, Llantrisant, Pontypridd Tel: 01443 443443; 15 Fairwater Road, Llandaff, Cardiff CF5 2LD — MB ChB 1972 Bristol; FFA RCS Eng. 1981; DObst RCOG 1974. Cons. Anaesth. Roy. Glam. Llantrisant.

ACKERS, Brian Harry 2 Meadow Rise, Giggleswick, Settle BD24 0EF Tel: 01729 824788 — MB ChB 1958 Birm.; MRCS Eng. LRCP Lond. 1959; MRCGP 1971; DTM & H Eng. 1976. Prev: Princip. GP Guorn; Med. Dir. Jubail Indust. City Saudi Arabia; Maj. RAMC.

ACKERS, Clare Elizabeth Flat 4, 29 Brondesbury Road, Queens Park, London NW6 6BA Tel: 020 7624 6137 — MB BS 1997 Lond.; BSc 1994. SHO (Med.) Rotat. Whittington Hosp. Lond. Prev: SHO (A & E); HO (Med.).

ACKERS, Jeremy William Lloyd 34 Southfield Avenue, Paignton TQ3 1LH — BM BCh 1982 Oxf.; BA Oxf. 1982, BM BCh 1982; FFA RCS Eng. 1986. Cons. Anaesth. Torbay Hosp. Torquay. Prev: Sen. Regist. (Anaesth.) Guy's Hosp. Lond. & Brighton Gp. Hosps.

ACKFORD, Catherine Torbay Hospital, Lawes Bridge, Torquay TQ2 7AA Tel: 01803 614567; Red Lake, Dousland, Yelverton PL20 6LU Tel: 01822 855419 — MB BS 1988 Lond.; MFFP 1993. SCMO (Family Plann.) S. Devon Healthcare Trust & Plymouth Community Servs. Trust.

ACKFORD, Howard Graham Friary House Surgery, Friary House, 2a Beaumont Road, Plymouth PL4 9BH Tel: 01752 663138 Fax: 01752 675805; Redlake, Dousland, Yelverton PL20 6LU — MB BS 1987 Lond.; DRCOG 1989.

ACKLAND, Frances Mary Department of Paediatrics, Northampton General Hospital, Billing Road, Northampton NN1 5BD Tel: 01604 544591 Fax: 01604 545640 Email: fran.auckland@ngh-tr.anglox.nhs.uk — MB ChB 1979 Birm; MRCP (UK) 1984. Cons. Paediat. N.ampton Gen. Hosp.; Hon. Cons. Paediat. John Radcliffe Hosp. Oxf. Socs: Fell. Roy. Coll. Paediat. and Child Health; Fell. Roy. Coll. Phys.s. Prev: Sen. Regist. (Paediat.) Roy. Hosp. Sick Childr. Bristol; Clin. Research Fell. (Growth & Developm.) Inst. of Child Health Lond.; Hon. Sen. Regist. & Regist. (Paediat.) Hosp. for Sick Childr. Gt. Ormond St. Lond.

ACKLAND, Gareth Lewis Hillingdon Hospital, Hillingdon Field, Heath Road, Uxbridge UB8 3NN Tel: 01895 238282; Flat 23, Hart Synnot House, Leckford Road, Oxford OX2 6JL Email: gla.uk@excite.com — BM BCh 1997 Oxf.; BSc (Hons.) Lond. 1991; PhD Lond. 1994. SHO (Cardiol.) Harefield Hosp. Uxbridge; SHO (Gen. Med.) Hillingdon Hosp. Uxbridge (from December 1998). Socs: BMA; Fell. Roy. Soc. of Med. Prev: HO (Cardiol. & Gen. Med.) N.ampton Gen. Hosp.; HO (Gen. Surg.) John Radcliffe Hosp. Oxf.

ACKLAND, Penelope Woodside Health Centre, 3 Enmore Road, London SE25 5NS Tel: 020 8655 1223 Fax: 020 8656 7984 — MB BS 1983 Lond. (King's Coll.) Prev: SHO (ENT, Cas., O & G & Geriat.) Mayday Hosp. Croydon.

ACKNER, Christopher Brian (retired) Arley, 17 Gyllyngvase Terrace, Falmouth TR11 4DL Tel: 01326 219189 Email: chris.ackner@virginnet.co.uk — MRCS Eng. LRCP Lond. 1977; MRCGP 1985; DRCOG 1983. Prev: SHO (O & G & Paediat.) Roy. Cornw. Hosp. Truro.

ACKRILL, Peter Withington Hospital, Nell Lane, West Didsbury, Manchester M20 2LR Tel: 0161 445 8111; 2 Syddal Close, Bramhall, Stockport SK7 1HU Tel: 0161 440 0691 — MB ChB 1964 Manch.; FRCP Lond. 1980, M 1968; DObst RCOG 1966. Cons. Nephrol. Withington Hosp. Univ. Hosp. S. Manch. & Manch. Roy. Infirm.; Postgrad. Clin. Tutor Univ. Hosp. S. Manch.; Hon. Lect. Manch. Univ. Prev: Sen. Regist. St. Bart. Hosp. Lond.; Jun. Appts. Roy. Free Hosp. & Whittington Hosp. Lond.

ACKROYD, Alison 10A Hatherley Road, Cheltenham GL51 6DZ — MRCS Eng. LRCP Lond. 1971.

ACKROYD, Mr Christopher Edward (cons. rooms), 2 Clifton Park, Clifton, Bristol BS8 3BS Tel: 0117 9706 4207 Fax: 0117 973 0887; 4 Rodney Cottages, Clifton, Bristol BS8 4AJ Tel: 0117 974 4158 Fax: 0117 923 7672 — MB BChir 1968 Camb.; MA, MB Camb. 1968, BChir 1967; FRCS Eng. 1972. (Middlx.) Cons. Orthop. Surg. Avon Orthop. Centre S.mead Gen. Hosp. Bristol; Clin. Sen. Lect. Univ. of Bristol. Socs: Fell. (Ex-Hon. Sec.) BOA. Prev: Lect. & Clin. Reader Nuffield Dept. Orthop. Surg. Univ. Oxf.; Sen. Regist. Robt. Jones & Agnes Hunt Orthop. Hosp. OsW.ry.

ACKROYD, Clare Rebecca 91 Shropshire Street, Market Drayton TF9 3DQ — MB ChB 1992 Leic.; Dip. Immediate Care RCS Ed 1997. RMO SPBN HQ ARRC BFPOGO. Prev: SHO Frimley Pk. Hosp.; SHO QE Hosp. Gateshead; GP Trainee, Gutersloh.

ACKROYD, Douglas Findlay Winterton Previa UK Ltd, Washford House, Claybrook Drive, Redditch B98 0DU Tel: 01527 517747 Fax: 01527 525934; Stoneleigh House, West Side, North Littleton, Evesham WR11 5QP — MB BS 1977 Newc.; MMedSci Birm. 1994; MFOM RCP Lond. 1996; MRCGP 1982; DAvMed 1984; DRCOG

1983. Sen. Occ. Phys. Previa UK Ltd. Socs: Soc. Occupat. Med. Prev: Sen. Occupat.al Phys. BT plc; Med. Org. 1 (RAF); Command Med. Off. (RAF).

ACKROYD, Miss Elizabeth Briony Walsgrave Hospital, Coventry CV2 2DX; Meadowside, 14 Brook Street, Walcote, Lutterworth LE17 4JR Tel: 01455 554803 — MB BS 1981 Lond.; MSc Lond. 1972; FRCS 1986. (Middlx.) Cons. BrE. & Gen. Surg. Walsgrave Hosps. NHS Trust. Prev: Sen. Regist. (Gen. Surg.) Yorks. RHA; Regist. (Surg.) Grampian HB; Ho. Off. (Surg.) Middlx. Hosp. Lond.

ACKROYD, Miss Jenny Susan Princess Alexandra Hospital, Hamstel Road, Harlow CM20 1QX Tel: 01279 827068 Fax: 01279 827071; 3 Blakesware Manor, Wareside, Ware SG12 7RD Tel: 01920 462718 Fax: 01920 462026 — MB BChir 1975 Camb.; MChir 1986 Camb.; FRCS Eng. 1979. Cons. Surg. P.ss Alexandra Hosp. Harlow, St. Margt. Hosp. Epping & Herts. & Essex Hosp. Bishop's Stortford. Socs: Fell. Roy. Soc. Med.; Vasc. Soc. Prev: Sen. Regist. (Surg.) St. Thos. Hosp. Lond. & St. Helier Hosp. Carshalton; Research Regist. Profess. Surgic. Unit St. Thos. Hosp. Lond.

ACKROYD, John Turner Coleridge Medical Centre, Canaan Way, Ottery St Mary EX11 1EQ Tel: 01404 814447; Sandrock House, Paternoster Row, Ottery St Mary EX11 1DP Tel: 01404 814704 Fax: 01404 816716 — LRCP 1969 Lond.; MRCS Eng. LRCP Lond. 1969; MRCGP 1976; DObst RCOG 1974. (Birm.) Trainer (Gen. Pract.) Devon. Prev: Regist. (Med.) & SHO (O & G) Taunton & Som. Hosp.; SHO (Med.) Torbay Hosp. Torquay.

ACKROYD, Marguerite Anne Marie (retired) 1 Calder Vale, Whalley, Clitheroe BB7 9SR Tel: 01254 823943 Fax: 01254 823943 Email: m.ackroyd@ukgateway.net — MB Camb 1957, BChir 1956; MRCS Eng. LRCP Lond. 1956; DTM Antwerp 1960; DObst RCOG 1958. Prev: GP Blackburn, Keighley & Bedford.

ACKROYD, Peter Leslie Dawley Medical Practices, Doseley Road N., Dawley, Telford TF4 3AL Tel: 01952 505213 Fax: 01952 503089; The Briars, 29 Wood Road, Codsall, Wolverhampton WV8 1DN — MB ChB 1977 (Hons.) Manch.; DRCOG Lond. 1983. GP Dawley; Med. Off. Wolverhampton Wanderers FC; GP Tutor Birm. Med. Sch. Socs: BASM; BMA. Prev: Ho. Phys. & Ho. Surg. Stepping Hill Hosp. Stockport.

ACKROYD, Richard Simon 65 Greenhill Road, Moseley, Birmingham B13 9SU — MB BChir 1973 Camb.; MB Camb. 1973, BChir 1972; MRCP (UK) 1977; DCH Eng. 1974.

ACKROYD, Mr Roger Department of Surgery, Royal Hallamshire Hospital, Glossop Lane, Sheffield S10 2JF Tel: 0144 226 1398 Fax: 0144 226 1398 Email: r.ackroyd@sheffield.ac.uk; 14 Silkstone Close, Tankersley, Barnsley S75 3AZ — MB ChB 1989 Sheff.; FRCS 1994 Ed.; FRCS 1994 Eng.; FRCS 2000; MD 1998 Sheff. Cons. Gen. Surg. Roy. Hallamsh. Hosp. Sheff.; Specialist Regist. (Surg.) N. Trent Rotat.; Clin. Lect. (Surg.) Univ. of Sheff.; Fell. (Upper GI Surg.) Univ. Adelaide S. Austral. Socs: Fell. Roy. Coll. of Surg. of Eng.; Fell. Roy. Coll. of Surg. of Edin.; Assoc. Upper GI Surg.

ACLAND, Julian Dyke (retired) 11 Dunton Close, Sutton Coldfield B75 5QD Tel: 0121 308 6705 — BM BCh 1951 Oxf.; PhD Sheff. 1972; MA, MSc Oxf. 1949. Prev: Cons. Path. Walsall AHA.

ACLAND, Katharine Mary Ealing Hospital, Southall UB1 3HW Tel: 020 8967 5429 Fax: 020 8967 5612 — MB ChB 1989 Bristol; MRCP 1994. Dermat. Cons. & Dermatosurg. Ealing Hosp.; Cons. Dermatoncologist (St. John's Inst. of Dermat.) St. Thos. Hosp. Lambeth, Lond. Socs: Roy. Coll. of Phys.s; Brit. Assn. of Dermatol.s; Brit. Soc. of Dermatological Surg.

ACLAND, Peter Robin 20 Clarendon Road, Edgbaston, Birmingham B16 9SE — MB ChB 1976 Birm.; FRCPath 1994, M 1982; DMJ Soc. Apoth. Lond. 1981. Socs: Medico-Legal Soc.; Assoc. Mem. Assn. Police Surgs. GB. Prev: Lect. (Path.) Univ. Birm.

ACLAND-HOOD, Phyllis Lily Frances Wootton House, Glastonbury BA6 8TX Tel: 01458 42348 — MRCS Eng. LRCP Lond. 1940. (Univ. Coll. Hosp.) Socs: Affil. Roy. Coll. Psychiat.; Med. Wom. Federat. Prev: Psychiat. Mendip Hosp. Wells; Ho. Surg. Univ. Coll. Hosp. Lond.; Flight Lt. RAF Med. Serv.

ACLIMANDOS, Mr Waguih Antoun Iskander Eye Department, King's College Hospital, Denmark Hill, London SE5 9RS Tel: 020 7346 3534 Fax: 020 7346 3738 — MB BCh 1977 Ain Shams; FRCS Ed. 1985; Spec. Accredit. Ophth. RCS Eng. 1992; FCOphth 1991; DO RCS Eng. 1984. Cons. Ophth. Surg. King's Coll. Hosp. Lond.; Hon. Cons. Lewisham Univ. Hosp. Prev: Sen. Regist. King's Coll. Hosp., Moorfields & Nat. Hosp. Nerv. Dis. Lond.; Regist. Qu. Med. Centre Univ. Hosp. Nottm.; Resid. Moorfields Eye Hosp. Lond.

ACOLET, Dominique Victor Marcel Chelsea & Westminster Hospital, Fulham Road, London SW10 Tel: 020 8846 7881 Fax: 020 8846 7998 Email: d.acolet@ic.ac.uk; 10 Silver Crescent, London W4 5SE Tel: 020 8747 0834 — MD 1980 Paris; FCPCH 1997; T(M) Paediat. 1993. Cons. Paediat. Neonatol. Chelsea & W.m. Hosp.; Hon. Sen. Lect. Imperial Coll. Lond. Socs: Fell. RCPCH; Neonat. Soc.; BAPM.

ACORN, David Jan 3 Green Close, Chelmsford CM1 7SL — MB BS 1988 Lond.; T(GP) 1992; DRCOG 1991.

ACORNLEY, Alexander James 19 Fairhaven Road, St Annes, Lytham St Annes FY8 1NN — MB ChB 1996 Birm. SHO (Orthop.) Qu.s Hosp. Burton.

ACQUAAH, Victor Lartey 14 Arne Grove, Orpington BR6 9TT Tel: 01689 28121 — MD 1972 Krakow. (Med. Acad. Krakow)

ACQUAH, Edward Kwasi Department of Anaesthesia, Dudley Hospitals Group, Dudley DY1 2HQ Tel: 01384 456111; 3 Thurleigh Close, Stourbridge DY9 0AQ Tel: 01562 886900 — MB ChB 1986 Ghana; FRCA 1994. Cons. Anaesth. Dudley Gp. of Hosps. Socs: Obst. Anaesth. Assn.; Assn. Anaesths.

ACQUAH, Napoleon Enninful Loomer Road Surgery, Loomer Road, Cheaterton, Newcastle under Lyme ST5 7JS Tel: 01782 565000 Fax: 01782 565666; 52 Mount Pleasant, Harpfield Farm, Newcastle under Lyme ST5 1DP Tel: 01782 711718 — MB ChB 1972 Ghana; DRCOG 1985. Clin. Asst. (Obst. & Gyn.) N. Staffs. Matern. Hosp. Stoke-on-Trent. Socs: BMA. Prev: Regist. (O & G) Newc. Staffs.

ACQUILLA, Dilip Basant South Grange Medical Centre, Trunk Road, Eston, Middlesbrough TS6 9QG; Kilifi House, 2 Leven Close, Stokesley, Middlesbrough TS9 5AU Tel: 01642 710813 Fax: 01642 713982 — MB BS 1971 Vikram; AFOM RCP Lond. 1985; DTM & H Liverp. 1976. (Gandhi Med. Coll.) Socs: BMA; Soc. Occupat. Med.; Assn. Aviat. Med. Examr.

ACQUILLA, Sushma Dilip County Durham Health Authority, Appleton House, Lanchester Road, Durham DH1 5XZ Tel: 0191 333 3359 Fax: 0191 333 3233 Email: s.d.acquilla@newcastle.ac.uk; Kilifi House, 2 Leven Close, Stokesley, Middlesbrough TS9 5AU Tel: 01642 710813 Fax: 01642 713982 — MB BS 1971 Bhopal; MRCS Eng. LRCP Lond. 1976; FFPHM RCP (UK) 1995, M 1989; MFCM RCP (UK) 1986; DCH RCP Lond. 1975. (Gandhi Med. Coll.) Dir. Postgrad. Cont. Ed. Pub. Health. Med.; Lect. (Pub. Health Med.) Sch. of Health Care Sci. Univ. Newc. Socs: Fell. Fac. Pub. Health Med.; Soc. Social Med.; Director of Train., Fac. Pub. Health Med. Prev: Dir. of Pub. Health SW Durh. HA; Sen. Regist. (Community Med.) N.. RHA; SCMO (Child Health) S. Tees HA.

ACRES, David John N. & M. Hants Health Authority, Harness House, Aldermaster Road, Basingstoke RG24 9NB Tel: 01962 863511 Email: j.acres@soton.ac.uk; 5 Fordington Avenue, Winchester SO22 5AN — MB BS 1967 Lond.; MSc (Social Med.) Lond. 1977; DObst RCOG 1969; DCH Eng. 1972. Cons. Pub. Health Med.; Progr. Director for Pub. Health Med. Train. in Hants. and the Isle of Wight. Socs: Fell. Fac. Pub. Health Med. Prev: SCM Winchester HA.; Med. Off. Zambia Flying Doctor Serv.; SHO Bath Gp. Hosps.

ACRES, Douglas Ian, CBE, CStJ (retired) Thundersley Lodge, Runnymede Chase, Thundersley, Benfleet SS7 3DB Tel: 01268 793241 Fax: 01268 793241 — MRCS Eng. LRCP Lond. 1949; MRCGP 1968; DMJ (Clin.) Soc. Apoth. Lond. 1968. JP.; DL; Hon. Med. Adviser to Congregational Federat.; Vice-Pres. Magistrates Assn. Prev: Mem. Comm. Ment.ly Abnormal Offenders.

ACRES, Geoffrey Michael Glencairn Surgery, Glencairn, Craighouse PA60 7XG Tel: 01496 820218 Fax: 10496 820218 — MB ChB 1980 Leeds. GP Isle of Jura, Scotl.

ACRES, Peter Francis Tel: 01264 351144 Fax: 01264 358639 — MB BS 1973 Lond.; FRCGP 2000; MRCS Eng. LRCP Lond. 1973; MRCGP 1984; DRCOG 1976. (St. Bart.) Clin. Asst. in Diabetes Andover War Memor. Hosp. Prev: Trainee GP Winchester VTS.

ACTON, Gary Vanguard Medica Group plc, 2 Chancellors Court, Surrey Research Park, Guildford GU2 5SF — MB BS 1984 Lond.; MA (Hons.) Physiol. Oxf. 1981; MRCP (UK) 1987. Vice-Pres. Clin. Developm. Vanguard Medica Ltd. Prev: Dir. of Clin. Research Fujisawa Pharmaceut. Co. Lond.; Assoc. Dir. (Clin. Pharmacol.) SmithKline & French Research Ltd.

ACTON, Heather Michelle Upper Shady Farm, 74 Brighouse & Denholme Road, Denholme, Bradford BD13 4HF — MB ChB 1997 Liverp.

ACTON, Iris Ada 10 Cumnor Hill, Oxford OX2 9HA Tel: 01865 862186 — MRCS Eng. LRCP Lond. 1937. (King's Coll. Hosp.) Prev: Res. Pathol. King's Coll. Hosp. Lond.; Ho. Surg. (O & G) P.ss Beatrice Hosp. Lond.; Ho. Phys. Qu. Eliz. Hosp. Childr. Hackney.

ACTON, Joseph Daniel (retired) 43 King's Road, Belfast BT5 6JH — MB BCh BAO 1962 Belf.; MRCGP 1976; DObst RCOG 1965. Prev: Princip. Med. Off. Dept. Health & Social Servs. N. Irel.

ACTON, Mr Joseph Daniel 17 Corner Farm Close, Tadworth KT20 5SJ — MB BCh BAO 1991 Belf.; FRCS Ed. 1995. (Queen's University Belfast) Specialist Regist. (Orthop. & Trauma) St Geo.'s Hosp. Lond. Socs: Assoc. Mem. BOA. Prev: Specialist Regist. Worthing & S.heads Trust; SHO (Orthop. & Trauma) St. Helier Hosp. Carshalton; SHO Rotat. (Surg.) Belf.

ACTON, Judith Alison (retired) Melbourne House Surgery, 12 Napier Court, Queensland Crescent, Chelmsford CM1 2ED Tel: 01245 354370 — MB ChB 1969 Sheff.; DCH Eng. 1971.

ACTON, Kerry James 70 Thornlaw Road, London SE27 0SA — MB BS 1994 Lond.; BSc (Hons.) Lond. 1990, MB BS 1994.

ACTON, Patricia Margaret Stokewood Surgery, Fair Oak Road, Fair Oak, Eastleigh SO50 8AU Tel: 023 8069 2000 Fax: 023 8069 3891; Oakside House, Field Close, Compton Down, Winchester SO21 2AE Tel: 01962 713689 Fax: 01962 713689 — MB ChB 1964 Leeds; DObst RCOG 1967. Prev: SHO (O & G) Roy. Hants. Co. Hosp. Winchester; Ho. Surg. Roy. Portsmouth Hosp.; Ho. Phys. Dryburn Hosp. Durh.

ACTON, Thomas Jarlath (retired) 430 Doncaster Road, Stairfoot, Barnsley S70 3RJ Tel: 01226 282280 — MB BCh BAO 1953 NUI.

ACUYO PASTOR, Leonardo 62 Friarwood Lane, Pontefract WF8 1DX — LMS 1980 Granada.

ADAB, Naghme Walton Centre for Neurosurgery, Lower Lane, Fazakerley, Liverpool L17 8UG — MB ChB 1993 Ed.; BSc (Med. Sci.) Ed. 1991; MRCP; DTM & H Liverp. 1994. Research Regist. (Neurol.) Walton Centre for Neurol. & Neurosurg. Liverp. Prev: SHO (Gastroenterol.) Fazakerley Hosp. Liverp.; SHO (Cardiol.) Fazakerley Hosp. Liverp.; SHO (Neurol.) Walton Hosp. Liverp.

ADAB, Peymane The University of Hong Kong, Department of Community Medicine, Patrick Manson Building South Wing, 7 Sassoon Road, Hong Kong, Hong Kong Tel: 00 852 2819 9280 Fax: 00 852 2855 9528 Email: padab@hkucc.hku.hk; Milford Lodge, Green Lane, Lache Lane, Chester CH4 7NG Tel: 01244 675593 — MB ChB 1990 Liverp.; MPH Birm. 1996; Cert. Health Econ. Monash Univ. Australia 1998. Clin. Lect. (Pub. Health Med.) Univ. Hong Kong. Prev: Regist. (Pub. Health Med.) W. Midl. RHA; SHO (Gen. Med.) Kidderminster Gen. Hosp. & Aintree NHS Trust.

ADABIE, Kenneth Horn 49 Addiscombe Court Road, Croydon CR0 6TT Tel: 020 8656 3637 — MB BS 1964 Lond. (Univ. Ibadan, Nigeria) Clin. Asst. Horton Hosp. Epsom. Prev: Regist. Banstead Hosp. Sutton & St. Mary Abbots Hosp. Lond.

ADADE, Kwasi Boafo 11 Lakehall Gardens, Thornton Heath CR7 7EL Tel: 020 8689 5462; 37 Julian House, Lyall Avenue, London SE21 8PQ — MD 1973 Mainz; State Exam Med 1970; DTM & H Liverp. 1972. Socs: Med. Soc. Study Ven. Dis. Prev: Regist. O & G S.. Gen. Hosp. Glas. & W.m. Hosp. Lond.

ADAGRA, Minocher Bahadur The Surgery, 44 Nuxley Road, Belvedere DA17 5JG Tel: 01322 439707 Fax: 020 8311 5651 — MB BS 1973 Bombay. GP Belvedere, Kent.

ADAIR, Alison Ann Cwyn Tawel, Bangor Teifi, Llandysul SA44 4HY — MB BCh BAO 1989 Belf.; MRCGP 1993.

ADAIR, Andrew David 48 Studland Drive, Hart Station, Hartlepool TS24 9RX — MB ChB 1995 Manch.

ADAIR, Andrew Ian Ashgrove, Upper Mealough Road, Belfast BT8 8LR — MB BCh BAO 1995 Belf.

ADAIR, Anya 36 Grosvenor Terrace, London SE5 0NP — MB BS 1998 Lond.

ADAIR, Mr Humphry Michael Ipswich Hospital NHS Trust, Heath Road, Ipswich IP4 5PD Tel: 01473 703517 Fax: 01473 703528 Email: adair.sec@jpsh-tr.anglox.nhs.uk; 38 Anglesea Road, Ipswich 1PI 3PP Email: hmadair@btinternet.com — MChir Camb. 1979; FRCS Eng. 1973. (Westminster) Cons. Surg. Ipswich Hosp.

ADAIR, Mr Ian Victor Ashgrove, Upper Mealough Road, Carryduff, Belfast BT8 8LR Tel: 01232 812090 — MB BCh BAO 1965 Belf.; FRCS Ed. 1969. (Qu. Univ. Belf.) Cons. Orthop. Surg. Roy. Vict. Hosp. Belf. & Musgrave Pk. Hosp. Belf. Prev: Sen. Regist. (Orthop.) Musgrave Pk. Hosp. Belf.

ADAIR, John Jackson Kensington Medical Centre, 15A Donegall Road, Belfast BT12 5JJ Tel: 028 9032 5679 Fax: 028 9024 4267 — MB BCh BAO 1979 Belf.; MRCGP 1983; DRCOG 1982.

ADAIR, Margaret Geraldine May Heaton Moor Medical Centre, 32 Heaton Moor Road, Stockport SK4 4NX; 129 Bramhall Lane South, Bramhall, Stockport SK7 2PP — MB ChB 1990 Manch.; MRCGP 1994; DRCOG 1992. Prev: Trainee GP Stockport HA.

ADAIR, Norman Stanton Spence Eastern Health & Social Services Bd., Linenhall St., Belfast BT2 8 Tel: 01232 321313 — MB BCh BAO 1970 Belf.; FRCGP 1988, M 1974; DCH RCPSI 1974; DObst RCOG 1973. Med. Dir. (Primary Care) EHSSB. Socs: BMA; Ulster Med. Soc.

ADAIR, Richard John The Rock Surgery, 50 High Street, Frodsham, Warrington WA6 7HG Tel: 01928 732110 Fax: 01928 739273; Moorcroft, 75 Fluin Lane, Frodsham, Warrington WA6 7QU Tel: 01928 733076 Fax: 01928 739273 — MB ChB 1968 Liverp.; MRCGP 1974; DCH Eng. 1971; DObst RCOG 1971.

ADAIR, Mr Robin Alexander 28 Beechgrove Avenue, Belfast BT6 0NF — MB BCh BAO 1989 Belf.; FRCSI 1995.

ADAIR, Steven Richard 3 Marlborough Gardens, Malone Road, Belfast BT9 6SQ — MB BCh BAO 1993 Belf.; MRCOG RCOG 1998.

ADAIR, Teresa Helsby Health Centre, Lower Robin Hood Lane, Helsby, Warrington WA6 0BW Tel: 01928 723676 Fax: 01928 725677; 75 Fluin Lane, Frodsham, Warrington WA6 7QU Tel: 01928 733076 — MB ChB 1968 Liverp.

ADAIR, Thomas Munnis Ballavartyn House, Newtown, Santon, Douglas IM4 1HT Tel: 01624 622342 — LRCPI 1951; LRCPI & LM, LRCSI & LM 1951.

ADAIR, William David 38 Anglesea Road, Ipswich IP1 3PP — MB ChB 1997 Sheff. Resid. (Gen. Surg. & Orthop.) QE2 Jubilee Hosp. Brisbane Austral. Prev: PRHO (Gen. Med & Gastroenterol.) Roy. Hallamsh. Hosp. Sheff.; PRHO (Gen. & Hepatobiliary Surg.) Roy. Hallamsh. Hosp. Sheff.

ADAK, Anil Kumar (retired) The Surgery, 174 Rookery Road, Handsworth, Birmingham B21 9NN Tel: 0121 554 0921 — MB BS 1957 Calcutta. Prev: Regist. O & G St. Catherine's Hosp. Birkenhead.

ADAM, Mr Alexander (retired) 3 Gordondale Court, Aberdeen AB15 5GB Tel: 01224 647671 — MB ChB 1942 Aberd.; FRCS Ed. 1948. Hon. Cons. Orthop. Surg. Grampian Area HB. Prev: Sen. Regist. Roy. Nat. Orthop. Hosp.

ADAM, Alexander Hunter (retired) Wyncliffe, Rue Cohu, Castel, Guernsey GY5 7SX Tel: 01481 57311 — MB ChB 1972 Glas.; FRCOG 1992, M 1977; DCH RCPS Glas. 1975. Cons. O & G Med. Specialist Gp. Guernsey.

ADAM, Alistair Lodgehill Road Clinic, Lodgehill Road, Nairn IV12 4RF Tel: 01667 452096 Fax: 01667 456785; Craigallian, Viewfield Street, Nairn IV12 4HW Tel: 01667 454121 — MB ChB 1976 Aberd.; FRCGP 1995, M 1980. Med. Off. Nairn Town & Co. Hosp.

ADAM, Professor Andreas Ntinou Department of Radiology, 2nd Floor, Guy's Tower, Guy's Hospital, St. Thomas' Street, London SE1 9RT Tel: 020 7955 4073 Fax: 020 7955 2544 Email: andy.adam@umds.ac.uk; 31 Larpent Avenue, London SW15 6UU Tel: 020 8788 1172 — MB BS 1977 Lond.; MB BS (Hons.) Lond. 1977; FRCP Lond. 1994; MRCP (UK) 1979; FRCR 1985; FRCS 1999. (Middlx.) Prof. Interven. Radiol. United Med. Dent. Sch. of Guy's & Thos. Hosp. Lond.; Seldinger Lect. Scand.n Soc. of Interven.al Radiol. 1997. Socs: Pres. Brit. Soc. Interven. Radiol.; Pres. Brit. Inst. Radiol.; Pres. Internat. Soc. Hepatobiliary and Pancreatic Radiol. Prev: Reader (Diagn. Radiol.) Roy. Postgrad. Med. Sch. Lond.; Regist. (Med.) Univ. Coll. Hosp. Lond.; SHO (Respirat. Med.) Hammersmith Hosp. Lond.

ADAM, Andrew Ewing (retired) Kings Gatchell, Honiton Road, Trull, Taunton TA3 7EN Tel: 01823 275608 — MB BS 1969 Lond.; FRCPath 1993; MA 1963 Oxf.; MRCPath 1981. Prev: Cons. Path. RAF Inst. Path & Trop. Med. Halton.

ADAM, Brigitte Simone Flat 3, 54 The Grove, Isleworth TW7 4JA — MB BS 1987 West. Austral.

ADAM, Bruce Tel: 023 92 471 661 Fax: 023 92 498 291 — MB BS 1984 Lond.; MRCPsych 1989. (Guys) Cons. (Psychiat.).

ADAM, Catherine Kennedy (retired) Dumgoyne, 6 Sillerhole Road, Leven KY8 5NA Tel: 01333 426237 — MB ChB 1951 Aberd.; FFA RCS Eng. 1960; DA Eng. 1954. Prev: Cons. Anaesth. E. Fife Hosp. Gp.

ADAM, Mr Donald John 66 Barry Road, Kirkcaldy KY2 6HZ Tel: 01592 640968 — MB ChB 1990 Ed.; FRCS Ed. 1995. Specialist Regist. (Vasc. Surg.) Roy. Infirm. Edin. Prev: Research Fell. (Vasc. Surg.) Roy. Infirm. Edin.; SHO (Vasc. Surg.) Roy. Infirm. Edin.; SHO (Gen. Surg.) W.. Gen. Hosp. Edin.

ADAM, Edith Jane (retired) 49 Lanthorne Road, Broadstairs CT10 3NA Tel: 01843 863036 — MB ChB 1949 Ed.; MFFP 1993. Prev: SCMO Canterbury & Thanet Dist. HA.

ADAM, Edmund Ian 60 Hillview Terrace, Edinburgh EH12 8RG — MB ChB 1956 Ed.; DObst RCOG 1960. Prev: Research Fell. Dept. Med. (Migraine) W.. Gen. Hosp. Edin.; Med. Adviser Lothian Regional Counc.

ADAM, Elinor Walmsley (retired) The Gyles, Bledlow Road, Saunderton, Princes Risborough HP27 9NG — MB ChB Ed. 1959; FRCPCH 1997. Prev: Cons. Community Paediat. S. Bucks. NHS Trust.

ADAM, Elizabeth Jane Department of Radiology, St George's Hospital, Blackshaw Road, London SW17 0QT; 31 Larpent Avenue, Putney, London SW15 6UU — MB BS 1977 Lond.; MB BS (Hons.) Lond. 1977; MRCP (UK) 1979; FRCR 1982. (Middlx.) Cons. Radiol. St. Geo. Hosp. Lond. Prev: Ho. Phys. Middx. Hosp. Lond.; SHO (Cardiol.) Hammersmith Hosp. Lond.; Sen. Regist. Diagnostic Radiol. Middlx. Hosp. Lond.

ADAM, Enver Cassim The White City Health Centre, Australia Road, London W12 7PD Tel: 020 8749 4145 — MB BCh 1948 Witwatersrand.

ADAM, George The Surgery, 1 Forest Hill Road, London SE22 0SQ Tel: 020 8299 02000 — MRCS Eng. LRCP Lond. 1974; MD Geo. Washington Univ. 1971; MRCGP 1981; Dip. Amer. Bd. Intern. Med. 1975. p/t Clin. Asst. (Cardiol.) Guy's & St. Thomas' Hosp. Lond. Socs: Amer. Coll. Phys. Prev: Resid. (Med.) US Pub. Health Serv. Hosp. Staten Is., USA.

ADAM, Graeme Peter Grosvenor House Surgery, Grosvenor House, Warwick Square, Carlisle CA1 1LB Tel: 01228 536561 Fax: 01228 515786; Redlands, 54 Rae Street, Dumfries DG1 1JE Tel: 01387 268450 — MB ChB 1977 Glas.; Dip. Forens. Med. Glas 1993. GP Carlisle; Police Surg. Dumfries & Galloway. Socs: Assn. of Police Surg. Prev: GP Lockerbie.

ADAM, Henry Matthew (retired) 20 Mayfield Terrace, Edinburgh EH9 1SA Tel: 0131 667 2198 — MB ChB 1935 Ed.

ADAM, Mr Ian James Clifford Lodge, Clifford Chambers, Stratford-upon-Avon CV37 8HR — MB BS 1985 Lond.; FRCS Eng. 1989.

ADAM, James 19 Crook Log, Bexleyheath DA6 8DZ — MB ChB 1950 Glas.

ADAM, James Ian (retired) High Heatherlea, Hillside Road, Rothbury, Morpeth NE65 7PT Tel: 01669 21207 — MB ChB 1951 Glas. Prev: Ho. Surg. S.. Gen. Hosp. Glas.

ADAM, James Mills, OBE, OStJ, Col. late RAMC (retired) 3 Rope Walk Mews, Moat Sole, Sandwich CT13 9RH Tel: 01304 617992 — MB ChB Glas. 1946; PhD Fac. Med. Lond. 1966; BSc Glas. 1943; FRCP Glas. 1983, M 1980. Hon. Col. 252 (Highland) Field Ambul. RAMC (V). Prev: Cons. Physiol. MRC Div. Human Physiol. Nat. Inst. Med. Research Lond. & Army Med. Servs.

ADAM, James Stuart Hunters Hill Marie Curie Centre, 1 Belmont Road, Springburn, Glasgow G21 3AY Tel: 0141 558 2555 Fax: 0141 558 0336; 9 Firbank Avenue, Torrance, Glasgow G64 4EJ Tel: 01360 620403 — MB ChB 1974 Aberd.; FRCP Glas. 1995; FRCR 1983; DRCOG 1976. Cons. Phys. Palliat. Med. Gtr. Glas. HB; Med. Dir. Hunters Hill Marie Curie Centre Glas.; Hon. Clin. Sen. Lect. Glas. Univ.; Specialist Vis. Lect. Glas. Caledonian Univ.

ADAM, Jane Elizabeth Ross Wheatfields Hospice, Headingley, Leeds LS6 2AE Tel: 0113 278 7249 Fax: 0113 230 2778 — MB BChir 1980 Camb.; PhD Lond. 1977; MFPHM RCP (UK) 1988; MPH Leeds 1985; Dip. Palliat. Med. Wales 1994. p/t Cons. Palliat. Med. Wheatfields Hospice Leeds. Socs: Assn. Palliat. Med.; Brit. Psycho-oncol. Soc. Prev: Sen. Regist. (Palliat. Med.) N.. & Yorks. RHA.

ADAM, Janice Ann 18 St Andrew's Drive, Thurso KW14 8PY Tel: 01847 63335; First Floor Right, 11 Dowanside Road, Glasgow G12 9YB — MB ChB 1988 Ed.

ADAM, John Doig (retired) 2 Bingham Terrace, Dundee DD4 7HH Tel: 01382 459825 — MB ChB 1951 St. And.

ADAM, John Fullerton (retired) Newstead, 42 Station Road, Waddington, Lincoln LN5 9QN Tel: 01522 720334 — MB BS 1951 Lond.; DObst RCOG 1952. Prev: Cas. Off. Worcester Roy. Infirm.

ADAM, Karen Patricia Arnot House, 3 Hillpark Terrace, Wormit, Newport-on-Tay DD6 8PN — MB ChB 1979 Dundee; MFPHM 1989; MICGP 1986; MRCGP 1983; DRCOG 1984; Cert. Family Plann. JCC 1982. Cons. Pub. Health Med. Tayside HB. Prev: Sen. Regist. (Community Med.) Tayside HB; Clin. Lect. Dundee Univ.; Trainee GP Tayside VTS.

ADAM, Margaret Grace Craigalliian, Viewfield St., Nairn IV12 4HW Tel: 01667 54121 — MB ChB 1976 Aberd. Clin. Med. Off. Highlands. Prev: SHO (Cas.) Woolmanhill Hosp. Aberd.; Ho. Off. (Med.) City Hosp. Aberd.; Ho. Off. (Surg.) Raigmore Hosp. Inverness.

ADAM, Michael John Waterloo Surgery, 617 Wakefield Road, Waterloo, Huddersfield HD5 9XP Tel: 01484 531461 — MB ChB 1972 Ed.; MRCGP 1977.

ADAM, Michelle Pamela 66 Barry Road, Kirkcaldy KY2 6HZ — MB ChB 1992 Ed.

ADAM, Nazaff Shah-E Langley Health Centre, Common Road, Slough SL3 8LE Tel: 01753 544288 Fax: 01753 592415 — MB BS 1985 Adelaide. GP Slough.

ADAM, Neville Menashy (retired) 4 Brackenwood Drive, Cheadle SK8 1JX Tel: 0161 491 3313 — MB ChB 1963 Manch.; FRCR 1975; FFR 1970; DMRD Eng. 1968; DCH Eng. 1965. Prev: Cons. Radiol. Univ. Hosp. S. Manch. & Christie Hosp. Manch.

ADAM, Patrick Alan (retired) 11 Church Walk, Avonwick, South Brent TQ10 9EJ Tel: 0136 472278 — MB ChB 1941 Ed.; DPM Eng. 1948; MRCGP 1972. Prev: GP S. Brent.

ADAM, Mr Riad Faraj Ormskirk & District General Hospital, Wigan Road, Ormskirk L39 2AZ — MB ChB 1974 Basrah; MChOrth Liverp. 1988; FRCS Ed. 1985. Cons. Orthop. Surg. Ormskirk & Dist. Gen. Hosp. Socs: Brit. Trauma Soc.; Brit. Orthopaedic Assn.; Brit. Orthopaedic Sports Trauma Assn.

ADAM, Richard 56 Keswick Road, London SW15 2JE — MB ChB 1976 Dundee.

ADAM, Richard John Katharine House Hospice, East End, Adderbury, Banbury OX17 3NL Tel: 01295 811866 Fax: 01295 810953 Email: radam@khht.fsnet.co.uk; 2 Wykham Gardens, Banbury OX16 9LF Tel: 01295 252309 Email: richardadam@supanet.com — BM BCh 1959 Oxf.; MA 1960 Oxf.; FRCP 1982 Lond.; MRCP 1966 Ed.; DObst 1962 RCOG; FRCP 1998 Ed. Hon. Med. Dir. Katharine Hse. Hospice Banbury; Hon. Cons. Palliat. Med. Oxon. HA. Socs: Assn. Palliat. Med. Prev: Cons. Phys. Oxon. HA; Sen. Tutor (Therap.) Qu. Univ. Belf.; Resid. Med. Off. Brompton Hosp.

ADAM, Robert Marshall (retired) Somerset Nuffield Hospital, Taunton TA2 6AN Tel: 01823 28699l — MB BS Lond. 1954; FRCOG 1972, M 1959, DObst 1956. Cons. O & G W. Som. HA; Guest Lect. Hawkes Bay HB N.Z. Prev: Sen. Regist. Jessop Hosp. Wom. Sheff. & Hon. Clin. Tutor Univ. Sheff.

ADAM, Robert Wilson (retired) 8 Branksea Avenue, Hamworthy, Poole BH15 4DW Tel: 01202 666750 — LRCP LRCS 1942 Ed.; LRCP LRCS Ed. LRFPS Glas. 1942; LDS RFPS Glas. 1939; HDD Glas. 1941. Prev: Ho. Surg. (Dent. Dept.) Glas. Roy. Infirm.

ADAM, Ronald Henderson (retired) 17 Broomcliff, 30 Castletton Drive, Newton Mearns, Glasgow G77 5LG Tel: 0141 639 6607 — MB ChB Glas. 1934. Prev: Specialist Phys. RAMC.

ADAM, Sheila Anne 120 Wallwood Road, London E11 1AN — MB ChB 1972 Ed.; MD Ed. 1983; FRCP 1991; MRCP (UK) 1976; FFPHM 1986, M 1981; DCH Eng. 1974.

ADAM, Shiraz 27 Highway Road, Leicester LE5 5RD — MB ChB 1994 Manch.

ADAM, William James (retired) Clifford Lodge, Clifford Chambers, Stratford-upon-Avon CV37 8HR Tel: 01789 205842 — MB BS 1957 Lond.; FRCR 1975; FFR 1965; DMRD Eng. 1962. Prev: Cons. Radiol. S. Warks. HA.

ADAM, Mr William Scott (retired) Corriemar, The Shore, Aberdour, Burntisland KY3 0TY — MB BCh BAO 1958 Belf.; FRCS Ed. 1967; FRCOG 1978, M 1965. Prev: Cons. O & G Dunfermline Unit Fife HB.

ADAM, Yusuf 14 Meadland Gardens, Bolton BL1 8TQ — MB ChB 1996 Manch.

ADAMO, Soubhi Jean Crookes Valley Medical Centre, 1 Barber Road, Sheffield S10 1EA Tel: 0114 266 0703 Fax: 0114 267 8354 — MB ChB 1965 Sheff. Socs: BMA. Prev: Neurosurg. Ho. Surg. Roy. Infirm. Sheff.; Ho. Phys. Doncaster Gate Hosp. Rotherham.

ADAMS, Aileen Kirkpatrick, CBE 12 Redwood Lodge, Grange Road, Cambridge CB3 9AR Tel: 01223 356460 Fax: 01223 356460 — MB ChB 1945 Sheff.; FRCA 1991; FDS RCA 1989; 1977 MA Camb. 1977; 1988 FRCS Eng. 1988; 1954 FFA RCS Eng. 1954; 1987 Hon. FCA (SA) 1987; 1947 DA Eng. 1947. Emerit. Cons. Anaesth. Addenbrooke's Hosp. Camb. Socs: Hon. Mem. (Ex-Hon. Sec. & Vice-Pres.) Assn. Anaesth. GB & Irel.; Hon. Mem. (Ex-Pres.) Hist. of Anaesth. Soc.; Fell. Roy. Soc. Med. Prev: Dean Fac. Anaesth. RCS Eng.; Cons. Anaesth. Addenbrooke's Hosp. Camb.; Assoc. Lect. Univ. Camb.

ADAMS, Alan Sidney Danebridge Medical Centre, 29 London Road, Northwich CW9 5HR Tel: 01606 45786 Fax: 01606 331977 — MB BS 1987 Lond.

ADAMS, Alison Jane The Health Centre, Station Road, Haydock, St Helens WA11 0JN Tel: 01744 734419; Croft Cottage, 124 Heath Lane, Lowton, Warrington WA3 2SJ — MB ChB 1989 Liverp.; MRCGP 1996; DRCOG 1993. GP Princip.

ADAMS, Alison Mary 2 Walpole Gardens, Strawberry Hill, Twickenham TW2 5SJ — MB BS 1985 Lond.; MRCOG 1995. Socs: Fac. Family Plann.

ADAMS, Mr Alistair David Moray Consulting Rooms, 14 Moray Place, Edinburgh EH3 6DT Tel: 0131 225 8059 Fax: 0131 664 6998 — MB ChB 1967 Ed.; BSc (Hons.) Ed. 1964; FRCS Ed. (Ophth.) 1974; DO Eng. 1971. Cons. Eye Pavil. Edin. Roy. Infirm. Prev: SHO, Regist. & Sen. Regist. Eye Pavil. Edin. Roy. Infirm.

ADAMS, Andrew David Bulwell Health Centre, Main Street, Bulwell, Nottingham NG6 8QJ Tel: 0115 927 9119 Fax: 0115 977 1236 — MB ChB 1973 Manch.; DObst RCOG 1976.

ADAMS, Andrew de Rola (cons. rooms), 12 Sydney Place, London SW7 3NL Tel: 020 7584 8708 — MD 1938 Lvov; MB BCh 1936. Hosp. Pract. (Genitourin. Med.) St. Thos. Hosp. Lond. Socs: Med. Soc. Study VD. Prev: Sch. Lond. & Hammersmith Hosp.; Clin. Asst. Roy. Nat. Throat, Nose & Ear Hosp. Lond.; SHMO Special Treatm. Centre St. Bart. Hosp. Lond.

ADAMS, Ann Rowan Stranraer Health Centre, Edinburgh Road, Stranraer DG9 7HG Tel: 01776 706513; Ambleside, Dunragit, Stranraer, Wigtownshire DG9 8PL Tel: 01581 400656 — MB ChB 1994 Glas.; DFFP 1997; MRCGP 1998; DRCOG 1996. GP Stranraer (3/4 time). Socs: MRCGP. Prev: Overseas Locum.

ADAMS, Anthony John 7 Linkscroft Avenue, Ashford TW15 2BQ Tel: 01784 243147 — MB BS 1988 Lond.

ADAMS, Mr Anthony Michael No 2 Kay Fold Lodge, Blackburn BB1 8NG Tel: 01254 249177 Email: tadams@adrid.globalnet.co.uk — MB ChB 1990 Manch.; BSc (Med. Biochem.) Manch. 1988; FRCS Eng. 1995; FRCA Roy. Coll. Anaesth. 1999. Specialist Regist. (Anaesth.) N. W.. Deanery. Socs: Intens. Care Soc.; Ass. N. W.n. Inten. Care Univ.; Mans. Med. Soc. Prev: SHO (Anaesth.) Roy. Preston Hosp.; SHO (Anaesth.) Blackburn Roy. Infirm.; SHO (Gen. Surg.) Vict. Hosp. Blackpool.

ADAMS, Professor Anthony Peter (retired) — MB BS 1960 Lond.; PhD Lond. 1970; MRCS Eng. LRCP Lond. 1960; FRCA 1992; FANZCA 1992; FFA RACS 1987; DA Eng. 1962. Senator Europ. Acad. Anaesth.; Edr. in chief: Eur. J. of Anaesthesiology. Prev: Vis. Prof. Johns Hopkins Hosp. Baltimore, USA, 1983.

ADAMS, Astrid Elisabeth 12 Irwin Road, Guildford GU2 7PP — MB BS 1998 Lond.; MB BS Lond 1998.

ADAMS, Barbara Ruth St Nicholas Hospital, Salters Road, Newcastle upon Tyne NE3 3XT; 9 Lilburn Gardens, Newcastle upon Tyne NE3 1SU — MB BCh BAO 1979 Belf.; MRCPsych 1986. Cons. Psychiat. St. Nicholas Hosp. Gosforth. Prev: Sen. Regist. (Psychiat.) St. Nicholas Hosp. Gosforth.

ADAMS, Barbara Webster 1 Westbourne Drive, Bearsden, Glasgow G61 4BD Tel: 0141 942 0029 — MB BS 1944 Lond.; MRCS Eng. LRCP Lond. 1944; CPH Eng. 1947; FFA RCS Eng. 1954; DA Eng. 1951. (Lond. Sch. Med. Wom.) Socs: Assn. Anaesths. Prev: Asst. Anaesth. Vict. Infirm. Glas. & Hairmyres Hosp. E. Kilbride; Sen. Anaesth. Regist. Roy. N.. Hosp. Lond.; Res. Anaesth. St. Peter's Hosp. Chertsey.

ADAMS, Beata Krystyna 50 Edmonscote, Argyle Road, London W13 0HQ Tel: 020 8998 8266 — MRCS Eng. LRCP Lond. 1974.

ADAMS, Bernard George 7 Wimpole Street, London W1M 7AB Tel: 020 7436 6346 Fax: 020 8340 9879 — MB BS 1956 Lond.; MSc Lond. 1960, BSc (Hons.); FRCP Lond. 1973, M 1960; FRCPsych 1973; DPM Lond. 1963. (Lond. Hosp.) Emerit. Cons. Psychiat. Univ. Coll. Hosp. Lond.; Sen. Lect. (Psychiat.) Univ. Coll. Hosp. Med. Sch. Lond. Socs: Fell. Roy. Soc. Med.; Brit. Pharm. Soc. Prev: Sen. Regist. Bethlem Roy. & Maudsley Hosps.; Sen. Regist. (Psychol. Med.) Hammersmith Hosp. Lond.

ADAMS, Bertha Fieldhurst, Denton Road, Ben Rhydding, Ilkley LS29 8QR — MB ChB 1964 Liverp.; DCH RCP Lond. 1984. Med.ly Qualified Panel Mem., Tribunals Serv., Leeds. Prev: Sen. Med. Off. DSS Leeds; Med. Off. DHSS Leeds Reg. Off.; SCMO (Child Health) Bradford HA.

ADAMS, Beverley Jane 8 Baird Avenue, Donaghcloney, Craigavon BT66 7LP — MB BCh BAO 1997 Belf.

ADAMS, Brian Maurice, Surg. Cdr. RN (retired) 5 Russell Avenue, Hartley, Plymouth PL3 5RA Tel: 01752 786676 — MB BCh BAO Belf. 1963; DMRD Eng. 1970. Prev: Radiol. RN Hosp. Plymouth.

ADAMS, Caroline Joan X-Ray Department, Ysbyty Gwynedd, Bangor Ll57 2PW Tel: 01248 384538 — MB BCh BAO 1978 Belf.; BSc (Physiol.) Belf. 1975; FRCR 1984; T(R) (CR) 1991. Prev: Cons. Radiol. Luton & Dunstable Hosp.; Sen. Regist. (Radiol.) N.wick Pk. Hosp. Harrow; Regist. (Radiol.) Roy. Vict. Hosp. Belf.

ADAMS, Cecil Thompson Buchanan (retired) Flat 2, Gortgole Fold, 34 Riverdale Park, Portglenone, Ballymena BT44 8HX Tel: 01266 822061 — MB BCh BAO 1937 Belf.; DPH Belf. 1939. Hon. Cons. Phys. N. Health & Social Serv. Bd. N. Irel. Prev: Med. Supt. Lond.derry Chest Hosp. N. Irel.

ADAMS, Mr Christopher Bertlin Turner Department Neurological Surgery, Radcliffe Infirmary, Oxford OX2 6HE Tel: 01865 224549 Fax: 01865 224898; Felstead House, 23 Banbury Road, Oxford OX2 6NZ Tel: 01865 512433 Fax: 01865 316926 — MB BChir 1964 Camb.; MA Camb. 1964, MChir 1970; FRCS Ed. 1967; FRCS Eng. 1967; MRCS Eng. LRCP Lond. 1963. (Guy's) Head Dept. & Cons. Neurosurg. Oxon AHA (T). Socs: Brit. Neurol. Surg. Soc. Prev: Regist. (Neurol. Surg.) Radcliffe Infirm. Oxf.; Acad. Regist. Nat. Hosp. Nerv. Dis. Qu. Sq.; Sen. Regist. SE Metrop. RHB & Neurosurg. Unit Guy's, Maudsley & King's Coll. Hosps.

ADAMS, Christopher Neil Department of Anaesthesia, West Suffolk Hospital, Hardwick Lane, Bury St Edmunds IP33 2QZ Tel: 01284 713330 Email: adams118@keme.co.uk; 118 Appledown Drive, Bury St Edmunds IP32 7HQ — MB BS 1978 Lond.; MA Oxf. 1982; FRCA 1993. Cons. Anaesth. W. Suff. Hosp. Bury St Edmunds. Socs: Hon. Sec. Hist. of Anaesth. Soc. Prev: Sen. Regist. Rotat. (Anaesth.) E. Anglia Region; Ho. Surg. (Orthop.) St. Thos. Hosp. Lond.; Ho. Phys. Worthing Gen. Hosp.

ADAMS, Miss Clare 61 Weymoor Road, Harborne, Birmingham B17 0RS Email: clare@birminghamflexi.demon.co.uk — MB BChir 1992 Camb.; MA Camb. 1993; FRCS Eng. 1997. (Addenbrooke's Cambridge) Research Fell. (Gen. Surg.) Qu. Eliz. Univ. Hosp. Birm. Prev: SHO (Gen. Surg.) St. Jas. Univ. Hosp. Trust Leeds.

ADAMS, Clare Elizabeth Acheson 45 Faroe Road, London W14 0EL — MB BCh BAO 1971 Belf.; MRCPsych 1978. Sen. Regist. (Psychiat.) E. Health & Social Servs. Bd.; Seconded to Psychother. Unit Maudsley Hosp. Lond.

ADAMS, Clive Elliott 33 Bartlemas Road, Oxford OX4 1XU — MB BCh 1983 Belf.; MSc (Epidemiol.) Lond. Sch. Hyg. & Trop. Med. 1991; MRCPsych. 1989. Clin. Lect. & Hon. Sen. Regist. (Psychiat.) Oxf.

ADAMS, Mr David Alexander Department of Otolaryngology, Royal Victoria Hospital, Belfast BT12 6BA Tel: 01232 240503; 6 Deramore Park S., Belfast BT9 5JY — MB BCh BAO 1974 Belf.; MSc Manch. 1982; BSc Belf. 1971, MB BCh BAO 1974; FRCS Eng. 1999; FRCS Ed. 1979; FRCSI 1996. (Queen's University Belfast) Cons. ENT Surg. Roy. Belf. Hosp. for Sick Childr.; Sen. Lect. (Otolaryngol.) Qu. Univ. Belf. Prev: Sen. Tutor & Sen. Regist. (ENT) Roy. Vict. Hosp. Belf.

ADAMS, David Edward Newtown Surgery, 147 Lawn Avenue, Great Yarmouth NR30 1QP Tel: 01493 853191 Fax: 01493 331861 — MB ChB 1968 Ed.; DObst RCOG 1970; MRCGP 1974; LMCC 1972; DCH Eng. 1975.

ADAMS, Professor David Harvey Tel: 0121 472 1311 Fax: 0121 627 2497 Email: d.h.adams@bham.ac.uk; 5 Pinfield Drive, Barnt Green, Birmingham B45 8XA — MB ChB 1981 Birm.; MD 1990

Birm.; MRCP 1984 (UK); FMedSci 2000; FRCP 1997. Prof. (Hepatol.) Univ. Birm.; Hon. Cons. Phys. (Hepatol.) Qu. Eliz. Hosp. Liver Unit. Birm. Socs: Fell. Acad. of Med. Sci.; Assn. Phys.s of GB & Irel.; Brit. Assoc. Study of Liver. Prev: MRC Trav. Fell. Nat. Inst. Health USA; Sen. Regist. (Gastroenterol.) W. Midl.

ADAMS, David Leslie Flat 12, Swallow Court, Admiral Walk, London W9 3TX — MB BS 1998 Lond.

ADAMS, David Patterson (retired) 754 Chatsworth Road, Chesterfield S40 3PN Tel: 01246 566174 — MB ChB 1952 Sheff.; MFCM 1974; MFPHM 1989; DPH Sheff. 1958. Specialist in Community Med. (Environm. Health) Sheff. HA; Proper Off. City of Sheff.; Med. Ref. City of Sheff. Crematorium; Hon. Clin. Lect. (Community Med.) Univ. Sheff. Prev: MOH Bakewell & Chesterfield RDs & Bakewell, Clay Cross, Staveley UDs.

ADAMS, David Watson Scott Auchtermuchty Health Centre, 12 Carswell Wynd, Auchtermuchty, Cupar KY14 7AW Tel: 01337 828262 Fax: 01337 828986; 10 Eden Valley Gardens, Freuchie, Cupar KY15 7XQ Tel: 01337 858283 — MB ChB 1975 Dundee.

ADAMS, Denise Margaret Ponteland Medical Group, Thornhill Road, Ponteland, Newcastle upon Tyne NE20 9PZ Tel: 01661 825513 Fax: 01661 860755; 70 Elmfield Road, Gosforth, Newcastle upon Tyne NE3 4BD Tel: 0191 284 4208 — MB BS 1979 Newc.; MRCGP 1983; DCH RCP Lond. 1983.

ADAMS, Diana Helen Wellbourne Cottage, Cuddesdon, Oxford OX44 9GH Tel: 01865 874582 — BM BCh 1994 Oxf.; MRCP Part 1. (UMDS Guy's & St. Thos. & Oxf.) SHO (Rheum. & Renal Med.) Hammersmith Hosp. Lond. Prev: SHO Cardiol. & H/V Med., Middlx. Hosp. Lond.

ADAMS, Dorothy Pearl Little Stambridge Old Rectory, Apton Hall Road, Canewdon, Rochford SS4 3RJ Tel: 01702 258550 — MB BCh BAO 1955 NUI. (Univ. Coll. Dub.) Socs: BMA; Assoc. Mem. Inst. Psycho-Sexual Med. Prev: Ho. Off. Childr. Hosp. Temple St. Dub.; Ho. Phys. Richmond Hosp. Dub.

ADAMS, Professor Edward Barry Fernlea, Hall St., Long Melford, Sudbury CO10 9HZ Tel: 01787 378816 Fax: 01787 378816 — MB BCh 1944 Witwatersrand; BSc Oxf. 1948; MD Witwatersrand 1958; MD Hon. Causa Natal 1984; FRCP Lond. 1958, M 1947. Emerit. Prof. Med. Univ. Natal Durban, S. Afr. Prev: Prof. Head of Dept. Med. Univ. Natal Durban, S. Afr.

ADAMS, Eleri Wyn 46 St Albans Avenue, Chiswick, London W4 5JP — MB BS 1990 Lond.; MRCP (UK) 1994. (St. Mary's Hosp. Lond.) ECMO Fell. (Paediat. Intens. Care) Hosp. Childr. Gt. Ormond St. Lond. Socs: Brit. Paediat. Assn. Prev: Regist. (Paediat. Intens. Care) Hosp. Childr. Gt. Ormond St. Lond.; SHO (Paediat.) Gt. Ormond St. Hosp. Lond.

ADAMS, Elisabeth Jane 45 Garden Lane, Chester CH1 4EN Tel: 01244 381340 — MB BChir 1990 Camb.; BA Camb. 1987, MB BChir 1990. Regist. (Gyn.) Macclesfield Dist. Gen. Hosp. Prev: SHO (Gyn.) Roy. Liverp. Hosp. Preston; Ho. Off. (Surg.) Bedford Hosp.

ADAMS, Elizabeth Anne Pairman Rutherglen Health Centre, 130 Stonelaw Road, Rutherglen, Glasgow G73 2PQ Tel: 0141 531 6020 Fax: 0141 531 4130; 22 Stewarton Drive, Glasgow G72 8DF — MB ChB 1967 St. And.; DCH RCPS Glas. 1969.

ADAMS, Elizabeth Frances Maitland Tregew, Grennna Lane, Perranwell Station, Truro TR3 7LL — MB ChB 1982 Bristol; MRCGP Lond. 1989; DCH RCP Lond. 1986.

ADAMS, Elizabeth Jennifer Parkfield Day Unit, Cossham Hospital, Lodge Hill, Kingswood, Bristol BS15 1LF Tel: 0117 975 8039; Fromeshaw House, Beckspool Road, Frenchay, Bristol BS16 1NU Tel: 0117 956 7476 — MB BS 1974 Lond.; MRCS Eng. LRCP Lond. 1974; DRCOG 1976. (Westm.) Clin. Assn. (Psychogeriat.) Cossham Hosp. Bristol. Prev: Clin. Assn. (Dermat.) Frenchay Hosp. Bristol; Clin. Research Asst. Profess. Dept. Med. (c/o Elderly) Frenchay Hosp. Bristol; Regist. (Radiother.) Velindre Hosp. Cardiff.

ADAMS, Elspeth Mary Strathie 4 Newburn Road, Newcastle upon Tyne NE15 8LX — MB BS 1979 Newc.; MRCGP 1983. p/t GP Princip.; Police Surg. N.umbria Police Wom. Doctors Scheme.

ADAMS, Ferdinand Ricardo Alexander 60 Fircroft Road, London SW17 7PS — MB BS 1992 Lond.; BSc Lond. 1989; MRCP (UK) 1996. SHO (Anaesth.) Leicester Roy. Infirm. Prev: SHO (Med.) Lincoln Co. Hosp. Lincoln; SHO (A & E) Conquest Hosp. Hastings; Ho. Phys. Conquest Hosp. Hastings E. Sussex.

ADAMS, Francis Timothy, Col. The Yellow House, Godrevy Terrace, St Ives TR26 1JA Tel: 01736 793825 — MB BCh 1970 Wales; MSc (Occupat. Med.) Lond. 1990. (Cardiff) Proprietor Yellow Ho. for Retd. Med. Offs., St. Ives, Cornw. Prev: Commanding Off., Duchess of Kent's Milit. Hosp.; Cdr. Med. HQ Lond. Dist.; Cdr. Med. HQ 3 Armoured Div.

ADAMS, Frederick George Western Infirmary, Glasgow G11 6NT Tel: 0141 211 1901; 96 Fernleigh Road, Glasgow G43 2TZ — MB ChB 1961 Aberd.; 1970 FFR; 1968 DMRD Eng.; MD 1999 Aberd. Cons. Radiol. W.. Infirm. Glas.

ADAMS, Geoffrey Phillip (retired) — MB ChB 1980 Bristol; MRCPsych 1985. Prev: Regist. Bethlem & Maudsley Jt. Hosps.

ADAMS, George (retired) Dales House Farm, Sadberge, Darlington DL2 1SN Tel: 01325 380834 — MB ChB 1951 Aberd.; MRCOG 1957. Practitioner, Cleveland Area HA. Prev: Regist. (O & G) Roy. Vict. Infirm. & P.ss Mary Matern. Hosp. Newc.

ADAMS, George Fowler, CBE (retired) The Coach House, Newland Street, Eynsham, Witney OX29 4LD Tel: 01865 880116 — MD 1946 Belf.; MB BCh BAO 1938; FRCP Lond. 1961, M 1947. Prev: Vis. Prof. Univ. Manitoba.

ADAMS, Gerard 5 Firmount, Antrim Road, Belfast BT15 4HZ — MB ChB 1998 Ed.

ADAMS, Gerard Francis Adams and Partners, The Health Centre, Tavanagh Avenue, Portadown, Craigavon BT62 3BU Tel: 028 3835 1393; 19 Ballyhannon Grove, Portadown, Craigavon BT63 5SD — MB BCh BAO 1978 Belf.

ADAMS, Gillian Gwendolen Webster Department of Ophthalmology, Oldchurch Hospital, Romford RM7 0BE — MB ChB 1979 Ed.; BSc Ed. 1976, MB ChB 1979; FRCS Ed. 1984; FRCOphth 1989. Cons. Ophth. Surg. OldCh. Hosp. Romford. Prev: Fell. (Ocular Motility) Moorfields Eye Hosp. Lond.; Sen. Regist. St. Geo. Hosp. & Moorfields Eye Hosp. Lond.; Resid. Surgic. Off. Moorfields Eye Hosp. Lond.

ADAMS, Gordon James Harvey Health Clinic, Ashgrove, Blackburn, Bathgate EH47 7LL Tel: 01506 652956 — MB ChB 1964 Ed.

ADAMS, Haydn 72 Timothy Rees Close, Cardiff CF5 2AU — MB BS 1979 Lond.; MRCP (UK) 1982; FRCR 1986. Cons. Radiol. Llandough Hosp. Penarth, Cardiff & Caerphilly Dist. Miners Hosp. Prev: Sen. Regist. (Radiol.) Univ. Hosp. Wales Cardiff.

ADAMS, Hazel Grace Princess Royal Hospital, Lewes Road, Haywards Heath RH16 4EX — MB BCh 1975 Wales; BSc Wales 1971, MB BCh 1975; FFA RCS Eng. 1980. Cons. Anaesth. P.ss Roy. Hosp. Haywards Heath.

ADAMS, Helen Elizabeth 15 Lenaghan Avenue, Belfast BT8 7JF — MB BCh BAO 1972 Belf.

ADAMS, Ian Duthie St James's University Hospital, Beckett St., Leeds LS9 7TF Tel: 0113 243 3144; 1 Ancaster Road, Leeds LS16 5HH Tel: 0113 278 5318 — MB ChB 1956; MD 1973 Leeds. Cons. Phys. A & E Dept. St. Jas. Univ. Hosp. Leeds.

ADAMS, Jacqueline ICRF Cancer Medicine Research Unit, St James' University Hospital, Beckett St., Leeds LS9 7TF Tel: 0131 206 4912 — MB BS 1992 Adelaide; MRCP (UK) 1995.

ADAMS, Jacqueline Norma Crosshouse Hospital, Kilmarnock KA2 0BL Tel: 01563 521133 — MB ChB 1988 Aberd.; MRCP (UK) 1991; MD 1998. Cons. Phys. / Cardiol. Prev: Career Regist. (Cardiol.) Glas. Roy. Infirm.; Research Regist. Aberd. Roy. Infirm.; SHO Rotat. (Med.) Aberd. Hosp.

ADAMS, James (retired) 1 Low Dog Kennel, Field Broughton, Grange-over-Sands LA11 6HP — MB ChB 1955 Manch.; MRCS Eng. LRCP Lond. 1955; FRCGP 1979, M 1968. Prev: GP Cheadle.

ADAMS, James Finlayson, VRD 1 Westbourne Drive, Bearsden, Glasgow G61 4BD Tel: 0141 942 0029 — MB ChB 1951 Glas.; 1974 DSc Glas.; 1964 FRCP Ed.; 1956 FRFPS Glas.; 1965 FRCP Glas.; 1953 DObst RCOG; 1962 MRCP Glas.; 1962 MD (Hons.) Glas.; 1956 MRCP Ed. 1956. Emerit. Cons. Phys. S.. Gen. Hosp. Glas. Socs: Assn. Phys. & Scott Soc. Experim. Med. Prev: Hall Tutorial Fell. (Med.) Univ. & Roy. Infirm. Glas.; Ho. Surg. & Cas. Off. Roy N.. Hosp. Lond.; Ho. Surg. Roy. Matern. & Wom. Hosp. Glas.

ADAMS, James Frederick Renwick (Surgery) Weston House, 17 Pittville Lawn, Cheltenham GL52 2BE Tel: 01242 580582 Fax: 01242 573271; The Old Barn, Upper Dowdeswell, Andoversford, Cheltenham GL54 4LT Tel: 01242 820858 — MB BS 1958 Lond.; LMSSA Lond. 1958; DObst RCOG 1960. (Guy's) Hosp. Pract.

Delancey Hosp. Cheltenham; Med. Adviser Gulf Oil (UK). Prev: Resid. Ho. Off. (Obst.) Cheltenham Matern. Hosp.; Asst. Ho. Surg., Cas. Off. & Ho. Phys. Guy's Hosp. Lond.

ADAMS, James Henry 57 Nutfield Road, Rownhams, Southampton SO16 8JQ — BM 1991 Soton.

ADAMS, Professor James Hume 31 Burnhead Road, Newlands, Glasgow G43 2SU Tel: 0141 637 1481 Email: hume.adams@lineone.net — MB ChB 1952 (Hons.) Glas.; FRSE 1988; PhD Lond. 1962, DSc 1989, MD (Hons.) Glas. 1989; FRCP Glas. 1977, M 1973; FRCPath 1973, M 1963. Emerit. Prof. Neuropath. Univ. Dept. Neuropath. Inst. Neurol. Sci. S.. Gen. Hosp. Glas. Socs: (Ex-Pres.) Brit. Neuropath. Soc.; (Ex-Pres.) Internat. Soc. Neuropath. Prev: Reader Neuropath. Univ. Glas.; MRC Fell. Clin. Research, Dept. Neuropath. Inst. Psychiat. Lond.; Capt. RAMC, Specialist Pathol. Milit. Hosp. Wheatley.

ADAMS, Jane Christine Gourock Health Centre, 181 Shore Street, Gourock PA19 1AQ Tel: 01475 634617; 2 Upper Sutherland Crescent, Helensburgh G84 9PQ Tel: 01436 672446 — MB ChB 1971 Cape Town; MRCGP 1996; Cert. Family Plann. JCC 1977. (Cape Town) Audit Facilitator Argyll & Clyde Health Bd. Inverclyde Dist. Prev: GP Lond.; Vis. Community Med. Off. (Family Plann.) Well Woman Serv. Bowmore Hosp. Islay; Clin. Asst. (Dermat.) King's Coll. Hosp. & Glas. Roy. Infirm.

ADAMS, Janet Margaret Forest Health Care, Health Centre, Dockham Road, Cinderford GL14 2AN Tel: 01594 598030; Folly Farm, Abenhall Road, Mitcheldean GL17 0DT Tel: 01594 544993 Email: adfarm@globalnet.co.uk — MB ChB 1982 Leic. Asst. GP Retainer Scheme Cinderford & Drybrook. Prev: GP Cinderford.

ADAMS, Janette Elaine (retired) Wolverley Surgery, Wolverley, Kidderminster DY11 5TH Tel: 01562 850800 — MB ChB 1961 Manch. Prev: Fact. Apptd. Doctor Nat. Standard Co. Ltd.

ADAMS, Jennifer Anne 46 Walsingham Road, Hove BN3 4FF — MB BS 1985 Lond.

ADAMS, Jennifer Nan Waddesdon Surgery, Goss Avenue, Waddesdon, Aylesbury HP18 0LY; Moat Farm, Wotton Underwood, Aylesbury HP18 0QQ Tel: 01296 770601 Fax: 01296 770601 — MB ChB 1984 Bristol; MRCGP 1988. (Bristol) p/t Locum Gen. Practitioner. Prev: GP Hindhead Surrey; GP Hemel Hempstead VTS; Ho. Surg. Frenchay Hosp. Bristol.

ADAMS, Jill Louise Department of General Practice, The Medical School, The University of Birmingham, Vincent Drive, Edgbaston, Birmingham B15 2TT Tel: 0121 414 3330 Fax: 0121 414 3759 Email: j.l.adams@bham.ac.uk — MRCGP 1992; MB BS 1987 Lond.; DRCOG 1992; BSc 1984 Lond. (St. Bart. Hosp. Med. Sch.) Clin. Research Fell. (Gen. Pract.) Univ. Birm.; Acad. Asst. (Gen. Pract.) Birm.

ADAMS, Jocelyn William 5 Hendry Road, Oxford OX2 0DG — MB BChir 1995 Camb.; BA (Hons) Camb. 1993; MRCP (UK) 2000. (Addenbrooke's & St John's Camb.) SPR (Clin. Oncol.) Oxf. Region Rotat. Prev: LAS Oncol. N.ampton Gen. Hosp.; LAT Gen. Med. (John Radcliffe); SHO Med. Rotat. Oxf.

ADAMS, Mr John Christopher 11 Airds Court, Dumfries DG1 4EP — MB ChB 1976 Ed.; FRCS Ed. 1980.

ADAMS, Mr John Crawford, OBE 126 Harley Street, London W1 Tel: 020 7935 2030; The Old H.H. Inn, Cheriton, Alresford SO24 0PY Tel: 01962 771101 — MB BS 1937 Lond.; MD Lond. 1943, MS 1965; FRCS Eng. 1941; MRCS Eng. LRCP Lond. 1937. (St. Mary's) Hon. Cons. Orthop. Surg. St. Mary's Hosp. Lond. Socs: Fell. Roy. Soc. Med.; Hon. Fell. Amer. Acad. Orthop. Surg.; Hon. Fell. (Ex-Edit. Sec., Hon. Sec. & Vice-Pres.) Brit. Orthop. Assn. Prev: Cons. Orthop. Surg. St. Mary's Hosp. Lond.; Civil. Cons. Orthop. Surg. RAF; Produc. Edr. Jl. Bone & Jt. Surg.

ADAMS, John Drew Adams, The Health Centre, Tavanagh Avenue, Portadown, Craigavon BT62 3BU Tel: 028 3835 1393 — MB BCh BAO 1972 Belf.

ADAMS, John Hamilton (retired) 352 Lisburn Road, Belfast BT9 6GJ Tel: 02890 667283 — MD 1947 Belf.; MB BCh BAO 1942; MRCGP 1968. Prev: Sen. Med. Off. Dept. of Health & Social Servs. N. Irel.

ADAMS, John Philip 5 Stoney Lane, Horsforth, Leeds LS18 4RA — MB ChB 1992 Leeds; MRCP Lond. 1996; FRCA 1999. (Leeds) Specialist Regist. (Anaesth.) United Leeds Teachg. Hosps.

ADAMS, John Robert Cheadle Medical Practice, 1-5 Ashfield Crescent, Cheadle SK8 1BH Tel: 0161 428 7575; 15 Oakwood Avenue, Gatley, Cheadle SK8 4LR — BM BCh 1981 Oxf.; BA Camb. 1978; MSc Manch. 1998; MRCGP 1986. (Oxford) Princip. in Gen. Pract. Cheadle Med. Pract., Cheadle, Chesh.; GP Tutor for Stockport. Prev: SHO (Gen. Med.) W.morland Co. Hosp. Cumbria; Ho. Surg. Nuffield Dept. Surg. John Radcliffe Hosp. Oxf.; Ho. Phys. Roy. United Hosp. Bath.

ADAMS, Jonathan Mark St Martins Practice, 319 Chapeltown Road, Leeds LS7 3JT Tel: 0113 262 1013 Fax: 0113 237 4747 — MB ChB 1986 Sheff.; BMedSci Sheff. 1984, MB ChB 1986; MRCGP 1991. Prev: SHO St. Jas. Univ. Hosp. Leeds.

ADAMS, Jonathan Robert 14 Manister Road, Armoy, Ballymoney BT53 8UA — MB BCh 1997 Belf.

ADAMS, Joseph Paul 31 St Stephens Road, Winchester SO22 6DE — MB BS 1994 Lond.

ADAMS, Judith Ann 30 Donnington Drive, Plymouth PL3 6QS — MB BCh 1993 Wales.

ADAMS, Professor Judith Elizabeth Department of Diagnostic Radiology, Stopford Building, Oxford Road, Manchester M13 9PT Tel: 0161 275 5114 Fax: 0161 275 5594 Email: judith.adams@man.ac.uk — MB BS 1968 Lond.; FRCP Lond. 1988; MRCP (UK) 1971; MRCS Eng. LRCP Lond. 1968; FRCR 1975; DMRD Eng. 1974; T(R) (CR) 1991. (Univ. Coll. Hosp.) Prof. Radiol. & Acad. Gp. Ldr. Imaging Sci. & Biomed. Engin. Univ. Manch.; Hon. Cons. Manch. Roy. Infirm. Socs: Internat. Skeletal Soc.; (Ex Dean & Vice-Pres.) Roy. Coll. Radiol.; Nat. Osteoporosis Soc. Prev: Lect. & Sen. Lect. (Diag. Radiol.) Univ. Manch.; Sen. Regist. (Radiol.) Manch. Roy. Infirm.; Regist. (Med.) Addenbrooke's Hosp. Camb.

ADAMS, Karen Jane Mountfield, Bromhall Road, Coldharbour, Dorking RH5 6HF — MB BS 1989 Lond.; 1998 DTMH; MRCGP 1995; DRCOG 1994. Med. Doctor, Trop. Med., Medecins Sans Frontieres, Geneva, Switz.

ADAMS, Katherine Jane Ardgoil, Whitelea Road, Kilmacolm PA13 4HH — MB ChB 1992 Manch.

ADAMS, Katherine Jane 92 Hitchin Square, London E3 5QF — MB BS 1998 Lond.; MB BS Lond 1998.

ADAMS, Kathleen Margaret (retired) 100 Southbrae Drive, Glasgow G13 1UA Tel: 0141 959 2017 — MD 1965 Glas.; MB ChB 1949. Prev: Regional Med. Off. Scott. Home & Health Dept. Glas.

ADAMS, Kenneth Jack 3 Wellbridge Close, Dorchester DT1 2BJ Tel: 01305 264003 — MRCS Eng. LRCP Lond. 1947; MFCM 1974; DPH Lond. 1950; LRCP 1947 Lond. (St. Bart.) Socs: BMA. Prev: Dist. Community Phys. W. Dorset Health Dist.; Dep. Co. Med. Off. Dorset CC; Resid. Med. Off. Heritage Craft Schs. & Hosps. Chailey.

ADAMS, Kenneth John (retired) Capstone Farm House, 343 Capstone Road, Gillingham ME7 3JE Tel: 01634 841199 — MB BS Lond. 1941. Prev: Ho. Phys. Roy. Infirm. Bradford.

ADAMS, Kevin George The Granary, St Hilary, Cowbridge CF71 7DP — MB ChB 1992 Cape Town.

ADAMS, Kirsty Jane 22 Rockside Avenue, Bristol BS16 6TH — MB BS 1994 Lond.

ADAMS, Laurence Malcombe Bawtry Health Centre, Station Road, Bawtry, Doncaster DN10 6RQ — MB ChB 1975 Leeds; PhD Leeds 1987, BSc (Hons.) Leeds 1972; MRCGP 1996. (Leeds) Prev: Sen. Lect. (Anat.) Univ. Leeds.

ADAMS, Lesley Anne Orchard House Surgery, St. Marys Road, Ferndown BH22 9HB Tel: 01202 897000 Fax: 01202 897888; Cattistock, 19 Carroll Avenue, Ferndown BH22 8BW Tel: 01202 874733 Fax: 01202 874733 — BM 1983 Soton. (Soton.) Prev: Trainee GP E. Dorset VTS; SHO (Anaesth.) Poole Gen. Hosp.; Ho. Phys. Poole Gen. Hosp.

ADAMS, Lesley Jane Crewe Medical Centre, 135 Boswall Parkway, Edinburgh EH5 2LY Tel: 0131 552 5544 Fax: 0131 551 5364; 17 Goldenacre Terrace, Edinburgh EH3 5QP — MB ChB 1979 Ed.; DRCOG 1983.

ADAMS, Lesley Jayne 16 Broadmeadow Lane, Stratford-upon-Avon CV37 9FD — BM BS 1990 Nottm.

ADAMS, Leslie Albert Alfred (retired) Stacombe Farm, Doccombe, Moretonhampstead, Newton Abbot TQ13 8SS Tel: 01647 440826 Email: les_gina@msn.com — MRCS Eng. LRCP Lond. 1949.

ADAMS, Lisa Jayne 19 Rhyd-yr-Helyg, Derwen Fawr, Swansea SA2 8DH — MB BCh 1997 Wales; BPharm (Hons) Lond. 1991; MRPharm S.

ADAMS, Lucy Rachael 6 Stevenson Drive, Abingdon OX14 1SN — MB ChB 1997 Glas.

ADAMS, Mabel Gertrude 10 Cranmore Avenue, Belfast BT9 6JH — MB BCh BAO 1955 Belf.

ADAMS, Malcolm Ty-Verulam, Cardiff Road, Creigiau, Cardiff CF15 9NL — MB BCh 1970 Wales; FRCOG 1988, M 1975; FRCR 1981. Cons. (Radiother. & Oncol.) Velindre Hosp. WhitCh..

ADAMS, Malcolm Sidney Maitland (retired) Little Stambridge Old Rectory, Apton Hall Road, Canewdon, Rochford SS4 3RJ Tel: 01702 258550 — MB BS 1948 Lond.; MRCS Eng. LRCP Lond. 1948. Prev: SCMO S.end HA.

ADAMS, Margaret Elaine MacBrayne and Partners, The Oakley Surgery, Addington Way, Luton LU4 9FJ Tel: 01582 574954 Fax: 01582 561808; Pine Needles, 12 Roundwood Park, Harpenden AL5 3AB — MB BCh 1979 Wales; MRCGP 1983; DRCOG 1981.

ADAMS, Margaret Joan Hillview Lodge, Royal United Hospital, Bath BA1 3NG Tel: 01225 428331; 24 Grosvenor Place, Bath BA1 6BA Tel: 01225 311007 — MB ChB 1965 Bristol; DPM Eng. 1973. Assoc. Specialist (Psychiat.) Bath Ment. Health Care NHS Trust. Socs: Affil. RCPsych.

ADAMS, Mark 12 Hoole Road, Broomhill, Sheffield S10 5BH — MB ChB 1995 Sheff.; BSc Aston 1985; MMedSci Sheff. 1989.

ADAMS, Mark Gary 129 Rustlings Road, Sheffield S11 7AB Tel: 0114 268 4510 Email: adams@sheffielduk.u-net.com — MB ChB 1988 Stellenbosch; FRCA 1997. Cons. (Anaesth.) Sheff. Prev: Specialist Regist. (Anaesth.) Leeds.

ADAMS, Mark Stephen Medical Centre, Middle Wall Op, Stockbridge SO20 8DY Tel: 01980 674224 — MB BS 1983 Lond.; BSc 1980 (Hons.) Lond.; MFOM 1998 Lond.; DAvMed FOM RCP Lond. 1994; MSc Aberd. 1997; AFOM Lond. 1997. (St. Thos.) Cons. in Aviat. Med. MOD Stockbridge. Socs: Soc. of Occupat.al Med. Prev: Specialist (Aviat. Med.) N. Yorks.; Specialist (Aviat. Med.) Hants.; Specialist (Aviat. Med.) Suff.

ADAMS, Martin James Satchville Ct, Main Street, Thorpe, Satchville, Melton Mowbray LE14 2DQ — MB ChB 1993 Leics.

ADAMS, Mary Ann Christina (retired) 7 Ellwood Court, Shirland Road, London W9 2JX — MB BS 1934 Lond.; MRCS Eng. LRCP Lond. 1932.

ADAMS, Mary Elizabeth COA, 14 Lisson Grove, Hale, Altrincham WA15 9AE — MB ChB 1975 Birm.; DA Eng. 1978; DRCOG 1977. GP Manch.; Clin. Med. Off. & Trainer Family Plann. Prev: GP Birm.

ADAMS, Maureen Beryl (retired) Windward Cottage, 1 Days Acre, Sanderstead, South Croydon CR2 0ER Tel: 020 8657 7482 — MB BS 1948 Lond.; MRCS Eng. LRCP Lond. 1948. Prev: Chairm. Croydon HA.

ADAMS, Michael Gordon Lucarnes, Mill St., Westleton, Saxmundham IP17 3BD — BM BS 1983 Nottm.

ADAMS, Michael Shirley (retired) Alton House, Seaview PO34 5EU Tel: 01983 612102 — MRCS Eng. LRCP Lond. 1944; MA, MB BChir Camb. 1947. Prev: Cas. Off. & Ho. Surg. St. Thos. Hosp.

ADAMS, Nancy Mary 96 Carlton Road, Derby DE23 6HD Tel: 01332 21169 — MB ChB 1949 Ed. (Ed.) Sch. Med. Off.

ADAMS, Nicholas Paul 23 Bury Street, Guildford GU2 4AW — MB ChB 1993 Manch.

ADAMS, Nigel John 4 Old Steine, Brighton BN1 1EJ Tel: 01273 685588 Fax: 01273 624328; 46 Walsingham Road, Hove BN3 4FF Tel: 01273 203628 — MB BS 1985 Lond.

ADAMS, Paul John Hollytree Surgery, 42 Boundstone Road, Wrecclesham, Farnham GU10 4TG Tel: 01252 793183 Fax: 01252 795437; 2 Vine Close, Boundstone, Farnham GU10 4TE Tel: 01252 793587 — BM 1982 Soton.; MRCGP 1987. (Southampton) Socs: BMA.

ADAMS, Paul Neville Ash House, 50 Yewlands Close, Banstead SM7 3DB Tel: 01737 353313 Fax: 01737 360680 Email: ashhouse@globalnet.co.uk; Ash House, 50 Yewlands Close, Banstead SM7 3DB — MRCS Eng. LRCP Lond. 1975; MB BS Lond. 1975, BDS 1971; MFPM 1989; LDS RCS Eng. 1971. (Guy's) Cons. Pharmaceut. Med. Socs: Fell. Roy. Soc. Med. Prev: Princip. Med. Off. Med. Control Agency DoH; Regist. (Oral & Maxillo-Facial Surg.) W.m. Hosp. Lond.; Ho. Surg. Guy's Hosp. Lond.

ADAMS, Professor Peter Harold Fairholm, Hawley Lane, Hale Barns, Altrincham WA15 0DR — FRCP 1975; MB BCh 1957 Wales; PhD 1972 Camb.; MRCP 1962; MSc 1977 Manch. (Cardiff) Prof. Emerit. Univ. Manch.; Hon. Cons. Phys. Centr. Manch. Healthcare Trust; Mem. Pension Appeal Tribunals. Socs: Fell. Manch. Med. Soc. (Ex-Pres. Sect. Med.) Pres. Manch. Med. Soc. 1997-98; Assn. Phys. Prev: Prof. Med. Univ. Manch.; Mem. Scientif. Staff MRC Dunn Nutrit. Laborat. Univ. Camb.; Research Asst. Mayo Grad. Sch. Med. Univ. Minnesota, USA.

ADAMS, Peter Jameson Mount Farm Surgery, Lawson Place, Bury St Edmunds IP32 7EW Tel: 01284 769643 Fax: 01284 700833; Church Farm, Fornham All Saints, Bury St Edmunds IP28 6JW — MRCS Eng. LRCP Lond. 1975; MA Camb. 1970; DRCOG 1977. (Guy's Hosp.) Socs: BMA.

ADAMS, Peter Joseph (retired) Walnut House, Scales, Ulverston LA12 0PE Tel: 01229 869570 — MB ChB Ed. 1955; FRCOG 1975, M 1962; DObst 1959. Cons. O & G S. Cumbria Health Dist. Prev: Sen. Regist. (O & G) Jessop Hosp. Wom. Sheff.

ADAMS, Peter William 44 Wimpole Street, London W1G 8SA Tel: 020 7935 0191 Fax: 020 7224 0629; 25 Castelnau, Barnes, London SW13 9RP Tel: 020 8748 6547 — MB BChir 1962 Camb.; MA Camb. 1962; FRCP Lond. 1986, M 1969; DObst RCOG 1964; DCH Eng. 1965. (Lond. Hosp.) Cons. Phys. Ashford Hosp. Middlx. Socs: Fell. Roy. Soc. Med.; BMA; Diabetes UK. Prev: Lect. Metab. Unit. St. Mary's Hosp. Lond.; Regist. (Med.) Prospect Pk. Hosp. Reading.

ADAMS, Philip Charles Royal Victoria Infirmary, Newcastle upon Tyne NE1 4LP Tel: 0191 232 5131 Fax: 0191 261 8505; 70 Elmfield Road, Gosforth, Newcastle upon Tyne NE3 4BD Tel: 0191 284 4208 Fax: 0191 284 0924 — MB BS 1977 Newc.; FRCP 1992. Cons. Cardiol. Newc. Hosp. Prev: Research Fell. Mt. Sinai NY.; 1st Asst. Cardiol. Univ. Newc.

ADAMS, Polly Jane 99 Palewell Park, London SW14 8JJ — MB BS 1992 Lond.

ADAMS, Raymond Mark Western Avenue Medical Centre, Gordon Road, Blacon, Chester CH1 5PA Tel: 01244 390755 Fax: 01244 383955; 2 Auden Close, Hawarden, Deeside CH5 3TY — MB ChB 1987 Liverp.; MRCGP 1992. (Liverpool) GP. Prev: Sen. Med. Off. RAF Sealand; Sen. Med. Off. RAF Shawbury.

ADAMS, Richard 34 Heneage Drive, Mumbles, Swansea SA3 5BR — MB BCh 1992 Wales.

ADAMS, Richard Alexander 9 Castle Keep, Stratford Sub Castle, Salisbury SP1 3LF — BM BS 1994 Nottm.

ADAMS, Richard Derek Eden Surgery, Cavendish Road, Ilkeston DE7 5AN Tel: 0115 944 4081; 12 Pritchard Drive, Nottingham NG9 7GW Email: derekadams@msn.com — MB ChB 1982 Manch.; DRCOG.

ADAMS, Richard Edward 87 Hatch Gardens, Tadworth KT20 5LD — MB BS 1993 Lond.

ADAMS, Richard James Ashley Surgery, School Lane, Ashley, Market Drayton TF9 4LF Tel: 01630 672225 Fax: 01630 673863; Weymouth Villa, Weymouth, Market Drayton TF9 4JQ — BM BS 1977 Nottm.; MRCGP 1981. GP. Prev: Trainee Gen. Pract. Stoke-on-Trent Vocational Train. Scheme.

ADAMS, Richard James Windsor House Surgery, Corporation Street, Morley, Leeds LS27 9NB Tel: 0113 252 5223 Fax: 0113 238 1262; 1 Mostyn Villas, Stoney Lane, Batley WF17 0LR — MB ChB 1981 Leeds; MRCGP 1985; DRCOG 1984.

ADAMS, Robert David Bootham Park Hospital, Bootham, York YO30 7BY — MB BS 1983 Lond.; BSc Lond. 1979, MB BS 1983; MRCPsych 1987. (Univ. Coll. Hosp.) Cons. Psychiat. York Health Trust. Prev: Sen. Regist. (Psychiat.) Yorks. RHA; Regist. (Psychiat.) Fulbourn Hosp. Camb.

ADAMS, Robert Kingsley 9 Castle Keep, Stratford-Sub-Castle, Salisbury SP1 3LF — BM BS 1991 Nottm.

ADAMS, Robert Macindoe The County Health Centre, Nevells Road, Letchworth SG6 4TR Tel: 01462 684334 Fax: 01462 484876 — MB ChB 1969 Glas.

ADAMS, Robin Nicholas The Health Centre, Trenchard Avenue, Thornaby, Stockton-on-Tees TS17 0DD Tel: 01642 762921 Fax: 01642 760608 — MB ChB 1983 Birm.; T(GP) 1991; MRCGP 1987; DFFP 1993; Cert. Family Plann. JCC 1987. (Birmingham) Prev: Trainee GP Doncaster VTS; Ho. Off. E. Birm. Hosp. Birm.; Ho. Off. Woodlands Hosp. Birm.

ADAMS, Rodney Crompton Kings Park Community Hospital, Boscombe, Bournemouth BH7 6JE Tel: 01202 303757 Fax: 01202 391332; Hawks Hill Cottage, Hoxall Lane, Brighstone, Newport

PO30 4DT Tel: 01983 740607 Fax: 01983 740607 Email: sangom@globalnet.co.uk — MRCPsych 1974; MB BCh 1963 Witwatersrand; DPM 1973 Eng. Cons. Psychiat. Learning Disabil. Kings Paris Hosp. Bournemouth; Cons. Psychiat. Thornby Hall Therap. Community Adolesc. N.ampton. Socs: Fell. Roy. Soc. Med.; Trustee Childr. Head Injury Trust. Prev: Med. Supt. Mapumulo Mission Hosp. Natal, S. Afr.

ADAMS, Ronald William (retired) The Bargles, Main St., Mowsley, Lutterworth LE17 6NT Tel: 0116 240 2968 — MB ChB 1961 Birm.; MRCS Eng. LRCP Lond. 1961; DObst RCOG 1963. Prev: Ho. Surg. (Obst.) & Ho. Phys. Qu. Eliz. Hosp. Birm.

ADAMS, Rosemary Frances Breast Care Unit, Churchill Hospital, Headington, Oxford OX3 7LJ — BM BCh 1992 Oxon; MA Cantab.; FRCS 1999; MRCP (UK) 1995.

ADAMS, Rosemary Helen Macnaughton (retired) Park House, York Road, Beverley HU17 8DP — MB ChB 1948 Ed.; FRCS (Orl.) Eng. 1955; FRCS Ed. 1952. Prev: Cons. A & E Norf. & Norwich Hosp.

ADAMS, Ross Archibald The Health Centre, 2 The Tanyard, Cumnock KA18 1BF Tel: 01290 422723 Fax: 01290 425444 — MB ChB 1975 Glas.; MRCGP 1983; DRCOG 1978.

ADAMS, Roy Gerald (retired) Common Lane Barn, Mappleborough Green, Studley B80 7DR Tel: 01527 853207 — MB BS 1950 Lond.; MRCS Eng. LRCP Lond. 1950; AFOM RCP Lond. 1975.

ADAMS, Ruth Catherine 60 Spire Hollin, Glossop SK13 7BS — MB ChB 1996 Leeds.

ADAMS, Scott Anstey, Capt. RAMC Glebe House, Farnell, Brechin DD9 6UH — MB ChB 1993 Ed. Prev: SHO (Orthop. & A & E) Borders Gen. Hosp. Melrose.

ADAMS, Stephen John Greyfriars Surgery, 25 St. Nicholas Street, Hereford HR4 0BH Tel: 01432 265717 Fax: 01432 340150 — MB ChB 1981 Birm.; MRCGP 1987; DRCOG 1989; DA Eng. 1983.

ADAMS, Stephen Paul Renwick Five Trees, Hophurst Lane, Crawley Down, Crawley RH10 4LJ Tel: 01342 713104 — MB BS 1982 Lond.; MA Camb. 1982; MRCGP 1987; DCH RCP Lond. 1985; DRCOG 1984. GP Crawley Down; Med. Off. Qu. Vict. Hosp. E. Grinstead. Socs: Brit. Assn. Immed. Care Schemes. Prev: Trainee GP/SHO St. Richards Hosp. Chichester VTS; Ho. Phys. Roy. Hants. Co. Hosp. Winchester; Ho. Surg. Guy's Hosp.

ADAMS, Steven Mervyn 59 Elms Park, Coleraine BT52 2QF — MB BCh BAO 1991 Belf.

ADAMS, Sue 131 Knowland, Highworth, Swindon SN6 7NE — BM 1995 Soton.

ADAMS, Susan Jill Department of Dermatology, Royal Devon & Exeter Hospital, Wonford, Exeter EX2 5DW Tel: 01392 411611 — MB ChB 1975 Leeds; FRCP Lond. 1992; FRCP Ed. 1991; MRCP (UK) 1978. Prev: Cons. Dermat. Carter Bequest Hosp. Middlesbrough & S. Tees, N. Tees & N.allerton DHAs.

ADAMS, Thomas David Meurig 2 Albion Crescent, Portland DT5 1AQ Tel: 01305 820703 — MB ChB 1951 Liverp. (Liverp.)

ADAMS, Timothy John Flat 2/L, 100 Novar Drive, Hyndland, Glasgow G12 9ST Tel: 0141 334 5805 Email: tim@tadams.demon.co.uk — MB ChB 1991 Glas.; MRCP (UK) 1998. (University of Glasgow) Clin. Research Fell. (Neonatol.) Qu. Mother's Hosp. Glas. Prev: SHO III (Paediat.) Ayrsh. Centr. Hosp.; SHO III (Paediat.) CrossHo. Hosp.; SHO III (Paediat.) Ayr Hosp.

ADAMS, Timothy John The Lodge, 117 Stepney Rd, Scarborough YO12 5BT — BM 1986 Soton.; FRCA 1993; DA (UK) 1990. Cons. Anaesth., ScarBoro. Hsp. Socs: Assn. Anaesth.; Obst. Anaesth Assn.; Soc. Obst. Anaesth. & Perinatol. Prev: SR (Anaesth) S.ampton Univ. Hosp.; Fell. (Anaesth) BC's Wom hosp. Vancouver, Canada; Regist (Anaesth) St. Geo.'s Hosp. Lond.

ADAMS, Mr Titus Sam Turner Mr. TST Adams, 29 Charlbury Road, Oxford OX2 6UU — MB ChB 1995 Bristol; BSc 1993. (Bristol) SHO Plastic Surg., Dept of Plastic & Reconstruc. Surg., W Norwich hsp.

ADAMS, Wendy Elizabeth 54 Thistle Street, Dunfermline KY12 0JA — MB ChB 1994 Glas.

ADAMS, Wendy Iris Jenner Health Centre, 201 Stanstead Road, London SE23; 34 Dovercourt Road, London SE22 8ST — MB BS 1980 Lond.; DRCOG 1982.

ADAMS, William 454 Lea Bridge Road, Leyton, London E10 7DY Tel: 020 8539 3246 Fax: 020 8556 9082 — MB BChir 1971 Camb.; MA, MB Camb. 1972, BChir 1971. (Cambridge)

ADAMS, William Mark Imaging Directorate, Derriford Hosp, Plymouth PL6 8DH Tel: 01752 792099 — BM 1986 Soton.; MRCP (UK) 1992; FRCR 1995. Cons. Neuroradiologist Derriford Hosp. Prev: Spec. Reg. (NeuroRadiol.), Manch. Roy. Infirm.

ADAMS-STRUMP, Barry Jonathan Midlock Medical Centre, 7 Midlock Street, Glasgow G51 1SL Tel: 0141 427 4271 Fax: 0141 427 1405; 19 Tinto Road, Glasgow G43 2AP Email: barryjas@aol.com — MB ChB 1973 Glas.; MRCGP 1977; DFM Glas. 1987. Chairm. Glas. LME. Prev: Research Asst. Dept. Gen. Pract. Glas. Univ.

ADAMSKI, Jennifer Katherine Flat 2, 27 Everett Road, Manchester M20 3EA — MB ChB 1998 Manch.; MB ChB Manch 1998.

ADAMSON, Alison Innis West Wales General Hospital, Glangwili, Carmarthen SA31 2AF — MB ChB 1987 Liverp.

ADAMSON, Mr Andrew Stephen Department of Urology, Royal Hampshire County Hospital, Winchester SO23 — MB BS 1983 Lond.; MS Soton. 1992; FRCS (Urol.) 1993; FRCS Ed. 1987; FRCS Eng. 1987. (St. Bart.) Cons. Urol. Winchester & E.leigh NHS Trust. Socs: Brit. Assn. Urol. Surgs.; Brit. Assn. Cancer Research. Prev: Sen. Regist. (Urol.) King's Coll. & E.bourne Hosps.; Research Regist. (Urol.) St. Mary's Hosp. Lond.; Regist. (Urol.) St. Mary's Hosp. Lond.

ADAMSON, Anne Mure Manse, 9 West Road, Irvine KA12 8RE — MB ChB 1966 Glas. (Glas.) Prev: Area Med. Off. Fife Health Bd.

ADAMSON, Anthony Rattray (retired) Box Tree Farm, Gressingham, Lancaster LA2 8LW Tel: 01524 221737 — MB Camb. 1959, BChir 1958; FRCP Lond. 1975, M 1963; MRCS Eng. LRCP Lond. 1958. Prev: Sen. Regist. (Med.) St. Mary's Hosps.

ADAMSON, Brian David The Surgery, 227 Lodge Causeway, Bristol BS16 3QW Tel: 0117 958 3102 Fax: 0117 958 4272; 73 Frenchay Close, Frenchay, Bristol BS16 2QJ Tel: 01454 653102 — MB ChB 1978 Glas.; MRCGP 1983; DRCOG 1981.

ADAMSON, Clare Louise 35 Stanford Hall Crescent, Ramsbotton, Bury BL0 9FD — MB ChB 1992 Manch.

ADAMSON, Dawn Louise 21B Haldon Road, London SW18 1QD Tel: 020 8871 1876 Email: d.adamson@ic.ac.uk — MB BS 1993 Lond.; BSc (Hons.) Lond. 1990. (St. Mary's Hosp. Lond.) Brit. Heart Foundat. Jun. Fell. Nat. Heart & Lung Inst. Brompton Hosp.; Specialist Regist. N. W. Thames (Cardiol.). Socs: MDU; MRCP; BMA. Prev: SHO (Cardiol.) Roy. Brompton Hosp. Lond.; SHO Rotat. (Med.) Qu. Med. Centre Nottm.; Ho. Off. (Surg.) Wexham Pk. Hosp. Berks.

ADAMSON, Donald MacFarlane Reid 'Linden Lea', Royal Crescent, Dunoon PA23 7SB — MB ChB 1954 Glas. (Glas.) Asst. Surg. Dunoon & Dist. Gen. Hosp.; Unit Med. Off. Cowal Unit of Argyll & Clyde Health Bd. Socs: BMA. Prev: Regist. Dunoon & Dist. Gen. Hosp.; Sen. Ho. Surg. Stockton & Thornaby Hosp. Stockton-on-Tees; Ho. Surg. Ballochmyle Hosp.

ADAMSON, Douglas James Alexander Tayside Institute for Cancer Care, Ward 32, Ninewells Hospital, Dundee DD1 9SY Tel: 01382 660111 Fax: 01382 496338 Email: douglas.adamson@tuht.scot.nhs.uk; 41 Cedar Road, Broughty Ferry, Dundee DD5 3BA Tel: 01382 732515 — MB ChB 1987 Aberd.; MD Aberd. 1993; MRCP (UK) 1990; FRCR 1996. (Aberdeen) Cons. Clin. Oncologist. Socs: Eur. Soc. Therap. Radiol. & Oncol.; Scott. Radiol.l Soc. Prev: Specialist Regist., W.ern Gen. Hosp., Edin.; Fell. Clin. Research Med. Sch. Aberd.; SHO Rotat. (Med.) Aberd. Teach. Hosps.

ADAMSON, Eileen Health Centre, Brunswick Park Road, London N11 1EY Tel: 020 8368 0813 Fax: 020 8361 0288; 34 Ridgeview Road, Whetstone, London N20 0HJ — MB ChB 1971 Birm.; BSc Birm. 1968.

ADAMSON, Elizabeth Anne Community Health Services NHS Trust, Wilderslowe, 121 Osmaston Road, Derby DE1 2GA Tel: 01332 363371 Fax: 01332 341246 Email: liz.adamson@sdhchs-tr.trent.nhs.uk; 169 Harrow Road, Wollaton Park, Nottingham NG8 1FL Tel: 0115 928 1756 Fax: 0115 928 1779 Email: dr-liz@berhane-adamson.freeserve.co.uk — MB ChB 1971 Sheff.; MSc (Community Paediat.) Nottm. 1993; MSc (Clin. Trop. Med.) Lond. 1978. (Univ. Sheff.) Cons. Paediat. Community Child Health Community Health Servs. NHS Trust S.ern Derbysh.; Med. Dir., Community Health Serv. NHS Trust S.ern Derbysh. Socs: Fell. Roy.

Coll. Paediat. Child. Health. Prev: SCMO & Clin. Med. Off. (Child Health) S. Derbysh. HA; Lect. (Med.) Univ. Juba, Sudan.

ADAMSON, Frances Elizabeth (retired) 38 Oaklands, Darras Hall, Ponteland, Newcastle upon Tyne NE20 9PH — MB BS 1959 Durh. Med. Off. Univ. Health Serv. Newc.

ADAMSON, Gemma Church Grange Health Centre, Bramblys Drive, Basingstoke RG21 8QN Tel: 01256 329021 Fax: 01256 817466; Stable Cottage, Monks Sherbourne, Basingstoke RG26 5HL — MB BS 1981 Lond.; MRCGP 1987; DRCOG 1986; DCH RCP Lond. 1986.

ADAMSON, James Falsgrave Surgery, 33 Falsgrave Road, Scarborough YO12 5EA Tel: 01723 360835 Fax: 01723 503220; The Dower House, Hackness Road, Scalby, Scarborough YO13 0QY — MB ChB 1978 Sheff.; DRCOG 1980.

ADAMSON, John Gordon Sandvika, Kyle of Lochalsh, Kyle IV40 8DB Tel: 01599 534393 — DObst 1966 RCOG; MB ChB 1960 Ed. Socs: BMA; Highland Med. Soc. Prev: Ho. Phys. Dumfries & Galloway Roy. Infirm. Dumfries; Ho. Surg. Roy. Infirm. Edin. & Baerum Sykehus, Norway.

ADAMSON, Karen Ann 17 Anchorage Mews, Victoria Lock, Thornaby on Tees, Stockton-on-Tees TS17 6BG Tel: 01642 618778 — MB BS 1994 Newc.; MRCP (UK) 1997.

ADAMSON, Katharine Hope Battanropie, Station Road, Carr Bridge PH23 3AL Tel: 0147 984281 — MRCPath 1975; MB BS 1967 Lond.; MRCS 1967 Eng.; LRCP 1967 Lond. Med. Asst. Raigmore Hosp. Inverness. Prev: Cons. (Haemat.) Barking Hosp.; Sen. Regist. (Haemat.) Roy. Postgrad. Med. Sch. Hammersmith Hosp.; Lond.

ADAMSON, Margaret Isabel 30 Stag Lane, Buckhurst Hill IG9 5TD Tel: 020 8504 4061 — MB ChB 1931 Ed.; DPH Eng. 1934. (Univ. Ed.) Socs: FRSH; Fell. Roy. Soc. Med. Prev: Assoc. MOH Lond. Boro. Barking; MOH Boro. Barking, Area MOH & Div. Sch. Med. Off. Barking & Essex CC; Asst. MOH Matern. & Child Welf. & Sch. Med. Off. Warrington.

ADAMSON, Margaret Ruth Area Laboratory, Crosshouse Hospital, Kilmarnock KA2 0BE Tel: 01563 521133; Fairhaven, 14 Sarazen Drive, Troon KA10 6JP — MB ChB 1979 Glas.; FRCPath 1997; DFM Glas. 1989. Cons. Path. Ayrsh. & Arran HB.

ADAMSON, Michael Whitecross Dalmellington Clinic, Hopes Avenue, Dalmellington, Ayr KA6 7RN Tel: 01292 550238 Fax: 01292 551342 — MB ChB 1976 Glas.; DCH RCP Glas. 1978; DRCOG 1978.

ADAMSON, Patrick Butler c/o Barclays Bank, 37 High St., Knaresborough HG5 0HB — MRCS Eng. LRCP Lond. 1942; MD Lond. 1952, MB BS 1943; DTM & H Eng. 1949, DPath. 1954; DPH Cape Town 1951; DCP Lond 1953. (St. Thos.) Prev: Sen. Pathol. Natal Provin. Laborat. Serv.; Pathol. Colon. Med. Serv.; Ho. Phys. Dulwich Hosp. (LCC).

ADAMSON, Peter Michael Lyneside Cottage, Romanno Bridge, West Linton EH46 7BZ — MB BCh BAO 1988 Belf.; MB BCh Belf. 1988, BDS 1979; FDS RCPS Glas. 1984. Regist. Rotat. (Oral & Maxillofacial Surg.) Glas. Prev: SHO (Cas.) Perth Roy. Infirm.; SHO (ENT) City Hosp. Edin.; Ho. Off. (Med. & Surg.) Stirling Roy. Infirm.

ADAMSON, Rebecca Jayne 10 Baliol Square, Durham DH1 3QH — MB BS 1994 Lond.; BA (Hons.) Camb 1991. (Cambridge University, Royal London Hospital)

ADAMSON, Richard Morland 17 Anchorage Mews, Victoria Lock, Thornaby-on-Tees, Stockton-on-Tees TS17 6BG Email: rmadamson@compuserve.com — MB BS 1994 Newc.

ADAMSON, Samuel Ian Gamble Mariono Villa, Old Quay Road, Holywood BT18 0AL — MB BCh BAO 1969 Belf.; DCH RCPSI 1974; DCH RCPS Glas. 1974. Socs: Assoc. Mem. Brit. Paediat. Assn.; Ulster Paediat. Soc.

ADAMSON, Susan Jane (Surgery), 33 Falsgrve Road, Scarborough YO12 5EA Tel: 01723 360835 Fax: 01723 503220; The Dower House, Hackness Road, Scalby, Scarborough YO13 0QY Email: drsjadamson@hotmail.com — MB BS 1978 Newc.; MRCGP 1982; DRCOG 1981. GP; Clin. Asst. Braest Servs., St. James Hosp. Leeds.

ADAN, George Edward, TD (retired) Weston Villa, 6 North Road, Spennymoor DL16 6EW Tel: 01388 814896 — MB ChB 1957 Aberd.; MRCGP 1976. Prev: CO 223(D) Field Ambul. RAMC(V).

ADAPA, Uma Devi Orchard Medical Practice, Orchard Street, Ipswich IP4 2PU Tel: 01473 213261; 16 Collins, Ipswich IP2 0DS — MB BS 1973 Osmania; DGO Osmania 1975; DA Lond. Eng. 1979.

ADCOCK, Anna Valerie 16 Willow Drive, Droitwich WR9 7QE — MB ChB 1968 Ed.; MFCH 1989. (Ed.) Prev: SCMO BromsGr. & Redditch DHA.

ADCOCK, Carolyn Jane 35 Rosebarn Avenue, Pennsylvania, Exeter EX4 6DY — MB ChB 1982 Sheff.; BSc Sheff. 1977; MRCP (UK) 1990; DCH RCP Lond. 1984. p/t Cons. (Paediat.) Demiford Hosp., Plymouth. Prev: Regist. (Paediat.) John Radcliffe Hosp. Oxf.; Sen. Regist. (Paediat.) Roy. Devon & Exeter, Wonford.

ADCOCK, Craig Anthony Armley Medical Centre, 16 Church Road, Armley, Leeds LS12 1TZ Tel: 0113 295 3800 Fax: 0113 295 3810 — MB ChB 1986 Leeds. SHO (Med. of Elderly) St. Jas. Hosp. Leeds. Prev: Ho. Off. (Med./Neurol.) Pinderfields Gen. Hosp. Wakefield; Ho. Off. (Gen. Surg.) Bradford Roy. Infirm.

ADCOCK, Frederick Allen (retired) Brooklands, 72 Feering Hill, Feering, Colchester CO5 9NL Tel: 01376 570410 — MRCS Eng. LRCP Lond. 1943; DMRD Lond 1951. Prev: Cons. Radiol. Chelmsford Dist.

ADCOCK, Griselda Nicolette Friends Road Surgery, 49 Friends Road, Croydon CR0 1ED Tel: 020 8688 0532 Fax: 020 8688 2165 — BM BCh 1974 Oxf.; MRCGP 1979. (Oxford)

ADCOCK, Helen Mary 39 Station Road, Horsham RH13 5EZ — MB ChB 1990 Sheff.; MRCGP 1994; T(GP) 1994; DFFP 1993; DRCOG 1993. Regist. (Pub. Health Med.) SW Thames RHA. Prev: Trainee GP Gt. Yarmouth & Waveney VTS.

ADCOCK, Katherine Mai Tugela, 7 Hazelhurst Road, Burnham, Slough SL1 8EE — LRCP 1932 Lond.; MRCS Eng. LRCP Lond. 1932. (Lond. Sch. Med. Wom.)

ADCOCK, Richard James The Surgery, The Furlongs, Alfriston, Polegate BN26 5XT Tel: 01323 870244 Fax: 01323 870244; Milton Court Farm, Milton St., Alfriston, Polegate BN26 5RJ Tel: 01323 870342 Email: adcockalf@mistral.co.uk — MB BS 1972 Lond. (Middlx.) Prev: GP Belper, Derbysh.; Med. Off. Bermuda; Resid. (Obst.) St. Anthony Hosp. Newfld.

ADCOCK, Sidney James Patrick (retired) 4 Meadowhead Road, Bassett, Southampton SO16 7AD — MB BS Lond. 1954.

ADCOCK, Mr Stephen David Dept. of Oral & Facial Surgery, Royal Cornwall Hospital, Truro Email: stephen.adcock@nhs.swest.co.uk; Lanner Farm, Cusgarne, Truro TR4 8RW — MB ChB 1988 Bristol; FRCS Ed. 1992; FDS RCS Eng. 1992; BDS 1980. Cons. (Oral & Facial Surg.).

ADDADA, Juanah Elizabeth Linden House, 70 Liverpool Road, Hutton, Preston PR4 5SP — MB BS 1993 Lond.

ADDAGARLA-RAO, Addagarla 26 The Downs, Cuddington, Northwich CW8 2XD — MB BS 1966 Andhra; BSc Andhra India 1959, MB BS 1966; DA Andhra 1970.

ADDAI, Stephen Akwasi Newham Community Health Services NHS Trust, Samson St., Plaistow, London E13 9EH Tel: 020 8586 6223 Fax: 020 8586 6380; 18 Devalls Close, Cyprus Place, Beckton, London E6 5PL Tel: 020 7476 0858 Fax: 020 7476 0858 Email: smjaddai@globalnet.co.uk — MB ChB 1990 Ghana; MRCP (UK) 1995; DPH 1997. (Univ. of Ghana Med. Sch.) Specialist Regist. (Paediat.) Newham Community Health Servs. NHS Trust. Prev: Specialist Regist. Chase Farm Hosp. Enfield; Specialist Regist. Havering Hosps. NHS Trust.

ADDENBROOKE, Jeanne Constance Tinkers Hatch, 105 West St., Warwick CV34 6AH — MB ChB 1949 Birm. (Birm.) Clin. Med. Off. Warks. AHA.

ADDENBROOKE, Teresa Elizabeth Ann (retired) 48 Claremont Road, Highgate, London N6 5BY Tel: 020 8348 8349 — BM BCh Oxf. 1962; MA Oxf. 1962; DObst RCOG 1966. Prev: Princip. Imperial Coll. Med. Partnership.

ADDEY, Katherine Mary Regent Square Group Practice, 8-9 Regent Square, Doncaster DN1 2DS Tel: 01302 819999 Fax: 01302 369204 — MB ChB 1980 Aberd.; MRCGP 1984.

ADDICOTT, Lawrence Sinclair (retired) Coroner's Office, Central Police Station, Cathays Park, Cardiff CF31 3NN Tel: 02920 222111 Fax: 02920 220638 — MB BCh 1961 Wales; DMJ (Clin.) Soc. Apoth. Lond. 1976. p/t H.M. Coroner-Cardiff & Vale of Glam. Prev: Regist. (Anaesth.) Bridgend Gen. Hosp.

ADDIDLE, Michael 228 Orby Drive, Belfast BT5 6BE — MB ChB 1996 Ed.

ADDIE, Christine Elizabeth 28 Birkdale Drive, Ifield, Crawley RH11 0TS — MB BS 1973 Queensland.

ADDIS, Andrea 20 Sidney Gardens, Muscliff, Bournemouth BH9 3SG — BM 1992 Soton.; Summative Asessment (Gen. Pract.) 1996. Clin. Asst. (OrthoGeriats.) ChristCh. Hosp. Dorset. Prev: Trainee GP/SHO (ENT) Dorset VTS.; Clin. Asst. Oakhaven Hospice Lymington Dorset.

ADDIS, Bruce John Department of Pathology, Health Care International, Beardmore St., Clydebank G81 4HX Tel: 0141 951 5904 Fax: 0141 951 5869; Auchengare, Station Road, Rhu, Helensburgh G84 8LW Tel: 01436 820536 — MB BS 1966 Lond.; FRCPath 1989, M 1977; DCP Lond 1974. (St. Bart.) Chairm. Path. Health Care Internat. Socs: Path. Soc. Internat. Acad. Path.; Assn. Clin. Path. Prev: Cons. Histopath. Salisbury Dist. Hosp. & Brompton Hosp. Lond.; Cons. (Path.) RN Hosp. Haslar.

ADDIS, Gail Murray Kilsyth Medical Partnership, Kilsyth Health Centre, Burngreen Park, Kilsyth, Glasgow G65 0HU Tel: 01236 822081 Fax: 01236 826231; 36 Westbourne Gardens S., Glasgow G12 9PF Tel: 0141 339 5779 Fax: 01236 826231 Email: gail.addis@which.net — MB ChB 1979 Glas.; DFFP 1996; MRCGP 1986; DRCOG 1986; DCH RCPSI 1982. Prev: Regist. (Geriat. Med.) Ruchill Hosp.; SHO Rotat. (Med.) Stobhill Hosp. Glas.; SHO (Med. Paediat.) Roy. Hosp. Sick Childr. Glas.

ADDIS, George Johnston 49 Whittinghame Court, Glasgow G12 0BQ Tel: 0141 339 2140 Fax: 0141 334 4429 Email: geoaddglas@msn.com — MB ChB 1952 Glas.; MD Glas. 1968; FRCP Ed. 1974, M 1960; FRCP Glas. 1970, M 1962; FRFPS Glas. 1958. (Glas.) Cons. Phys. Glas. Socs: Brit. Thorac. Soc.; Scott. Thoracic Soc.; BMA. Prev: Cons. Phys. (Med. & Therap.) Glas. Univ.; Sen. Lect. (Mat. Med.) Univ. Glas.

ADDIS, Stephen Robert Desmond c/o Ashfield, 3 Neils Lane, Greenisland, Carrickfergus BT38 SUD — MB BCh BAO 1982 Belf.; MMedSci Belf. 1991; MRCPsych 1986. (Qu. Univ. Belf.) Cons. Psychiat. Frematle Hosp. Frematle, W.ern Austral.; Director of Clin. Train., Freemantle Hosp. Prev: Cons. Psychiat. St. Lukes & Craigavon Hosps. Co. Armagh; Cons. Psychiat. St Michaels Hosp. Warwick.

ADDIS, Vivien Patricia The Uplands Medical Practice, Bury New Road, Whitefield, Manchester M45 8GH Tel: 0161 766 8221 Fax: 0161 796 2417 — MB ChB 1976 Manch.; OFFP LOC 2001; MRCGP 1980; DRCOG 1979. Gen. Practitioner; Clin. Asst. Dermat.

ADDIS, Walter Desmond c/o Holywell Hospital, Antrim BT41 2RJ; Ashfield House, Neill's Lane, Greenisland, Carrickfergus BT38 8UD — MB BCh BAO 1950 Belf.; MRCPsych 1971; DPM Eng. 1960. (Belf.) Cons. Psychiat. Holywell Hosp. Antrim & Lagan Valley Hosp. Lisburn. Socs: BMA & Soc. Clin. Psychiatrs. Prev: Cons. Psychiat. Middlewood, Hallamshire & Yews Day Hosps. Sheff.; Sen. Regist. Liverp. RHB; Hon. Lect. Sheff. Univ.

ADDIS-JONES, Clive Dodd (retired) Green Gremlins, Hascombe Rd, Munstead, Godalming GU8 4AA Tel: 01483 414300 Fax: 01483 425974 — MB BCh 1957 Wales; BSc Wales 1952; DObst RCOG 1961. Prev: GP Guildford.

ADDIS-JONES, Margretta Eleanor (retired) Green Gremlins, Munstead, Godalming GU8 4AA Tel: 01483 414300 Fax: 01483 425974 — MB BCh 1960 Wales. Prev: GP Guildford.

ADDISCOTT, Catherine Louise 35 Bloomfield Road, Harpenden AL5 4DD — MB ChB 1996 Manch.

ADDISON, Alexander, MBE (retired) Rossland, 7 Addison Drive, Douglas, Lanark ML11 0PZ Tel: 01555 851302 — MB ChB 1954 Aberd.; FRCGP 1981, M 1966; DObst RCOG 1960. Prev: GP Douglas, Lanarksh.

ADDISON, Mr Anthony Kingsley Litchfield Greenacre, 27 Greenhill Road, Otford, Sevenoaks TN14 5RR Tel: 0195952 3210 — BM BCh 1970 Oxf.; 1970 MA Oxf. 1970, BM BCh; 1975 FRCS Eng. Cons. Orthop. Surg. Darent Valley Hosp., Dartford. Prev: Cons. Orthop. Surg. W. Cumbld. Hosp. Hensingham; Regist. Rotat. Roy. Nat. Orthop. Hosp. Lond.

ADDISON, Gerald Michael c/o Department of Chemical Pathology, Royal Manchester Children's Hospital, Pendlebury, Manchester M27 4HA Tel: 0161 727 2250 Fax: 0161 727 2249 Email: mike.addison@man.ac.uk — MB BChir Camb.; 1968 PhD Camb. 1972, MA; 1991 MSc Manch.; 1999 FRCPath. (Camb. & Univ. Coll. Hosp.) Cons. Path. Chem. Path. Roy. Manch. Childr. Hosp. Pendlebury & Booth Hall Childr. Hosp.; Hon. Assoc. Lect. (Child Health & Chem. Path.) Univ. Manch.; Dir. Regional Hypothyroid Screening Laborat. NW RHA; Chairm., Uk Neonat. Screening Laboratories Network. Socs: Soc. Study Inborn Errors of Metab. & Assn. Clin. Biochems. Prev: Sen. Regist. (Med. Biochem.) Univ. Hosp. of Wales; Sen. Tutor (Med.) Clin. Methods Welsh Nat. Sch. Med. Cardiff; MRC Jun. Research Fell.

ADDISON, John Ashby Health Centre, North Street, Ashby-de-la-Zouch LE65 1HU Tel: 01530 414131 Fax: 01530 560732 Email: addison_j@gp-c82014.nhs.uk — MB ChB 1989 Sheff.

ADDISON, John 8 Smith Drive, Elgin IV30 4NE — MB ChB 1986 Aberd.; FRCR 1993; DMRD Aberd. 1990. Cons. Radiol. Dr. Gray's Hosp. Elgin. Prev: Sen. Regist. (Radiol.) Edin. Roy. Infirm.

ADDISON, Marcus Leopold Gabriel (retired) Hoy Pa Paera, Errochty Grove, Perth PH1 2SW — MB ChB 1960 Aberd.; T(Psychiat.) 1991. Cons. Psychiat. Perthsh. Prev: Asst. Psychiat. E. Sussex Serv. (Ment. Handicap).

ADDISON, Paul Douglas Ida Darwin Hospital, Cambridge Road, Fulbourn, Cambridge CB1 5EE; Douglas House, 18B Trumpington Road, Cambridge CB2 2AH — BM BCh 1987 Oxf.

ADDISON, Rachel Lucy Sparrow Hatch, Bethersden, Ashford TN26 3ED — MB ChB 1992 Bristol.

ADDISON, Rebecca Anne 5 Beechtree Avenue, Marlow SL7 3NH — MB ChB 1994 Manch.

ADDISON, Sarah Louise 5 Morris Drive, Banbury OX16 1DD — MB ChB 1996 Birm.

ADDISON, Susan Jacqueline Taylor and Partners, Shirehampton Health Centre, Pembroke Road, Shirehampton, Bristol BS11 9SB Tel: 0117 916 2233 Fax: 0117 930 8246; 1 Debecca's Lane, Easton-in-Gordano, Bristol BS20 0LU — MB ChB 1980 Leeds; DRCOG 1984.

ADDLESON, Deborah Jessie The Spence Practice, Westcliff House, 48-50 Logan Rd, Bristol BS7 8DR Tel: 0117 944 0701, 01835 823655 Email: rebeccawilliams1@yahoo.com; Tel: 0117 924 0104 — MB BS 1991 Lond.; BSc Bristol 1986. (Kings Coll. Lond.) p/t GP on Retainer scheme. Socs: Roy. Coll. Gen. Pract.; DRCOG. Prev: GP Regist.Montpelier H/C Bristol; SHO (O & G) S.mead Hosp. Bristol; SHO (Psychiat.) FarnBoro. Hosp. Orpington Kent.

ADDLESTONE, Gerald Ralph (retired) 1 Sandmoor Chase, Alwoodley, Leeds LS17 7TB Tel: 0113 268 6283 — MB ChB 1953 Leeds; MRCGP 1966; Cert. Family Plann. JCC 1976. Prev: Ho. Phys. Gen. Hosp. Wakefield.

ADDLESTONE, Lawrence Spencer The Langworthy Medical Practice, 250 Langworthy Road, Salford M6 5WW Tel: 0161 736 7422 Fax: 0161 736 4816; 20 Danesway, Prestwich, Manchester M25 0FS Tel: 0161 740 3280 Fax: 0161 720 6887 Email: 106056.2570@compuserve.com — MB ChB 1982 Leeds; MRCGP 1986; DRCOG 1985. (Leeds) Phys. Univ. Salford. Prev: SHO (Obst. & A & E) Leeds Gen. Infirm.; SHO (Gen. Med.) St. Jas. Univ. Hosp. Leeds.

ADDLESTONE, Malcolm Bernard Gilsyke House, 212A Selby Road, Halton, Leeds LS15 0LF Tel: 0113 295 2710 Fax: 0113 295 2713 — MB ChB 1971 Leeds; MB ChB (Hons.) Leeds 1971; DObst RCOG 1974. Prev: Sen. Ho. Surg. Obst. Leeds Matern. Hosp.; Ho. Phys. & Ho. Surg. Dept. Urol. Leeds Gen. Infirm.; Ho. Phys. Dept. Med. Chapel Allerton Hosp. Leeds.

ADDLESTONE, Robert Irving New Wortley Health Centre, 15 Green Lane, Tong Road, Leeds LS12 1JE Tel: 0113 231 0626 Fax: 0113 231 9428; 94 Wigton Lane, Leeds LS17 8RZ Tel: 0113 269 6954 — MB ChB 1978 Dundee; MRCGP 1982; DRCOG 1982. Prev: SHO (Cas.) King Edwd. VII Memor. Hosp. Bermuda; SHO (Infec. Dis.) Seacroft Hosp. Leeds; Ho. Off. (Gen. Med., Surg. & Urol.) St. Jas. Univ. Hosp. Leeds.

ADDLEY, Kenneth Lincoln Building, 27-45 Great Victoria St., Belfast BT2 7AD Tel: 01232 251825 Fax: 01232 251539 Email: ken.addley@dhssni.gov.uk; Greenbank Lodge, 2 Belsize Lane, Lisburn BT27 4BG — MB BCh BAO 1979 Belf.; MD 2000; MFOM RCPI 1994, LFOM 1992; MICGP 1984; MRCGP 1983; DRCOG 1981; FFOM 1998. (Queen's University Belfast) Dir. Occupat. Health Servs. N. Irel. Civil Serv. Belf. Socs: Fell. Ulster Med. Soc.; Soc. Occupat. Med. Prev: GP Moy Co. Tyrone.

ADDLY, Freda Margaret (retired) 3/1 St Theresa Place, edinburgh EH10 5UB Tel: 0131 228 4130 — LRCP LRCS Ed. LRFPS Glas. 1948; FFCM 1985; DPH Ed. 1954. Prev: Specialist Community Med. Tayside HB.

ADDO, James Kojo Greyswood Practice, 238 Mitcham Lane, London SW16 6NT — MB BS 1985 Lond.; MRCGP 1993; DRCOG 1992. (St. Geo. Hosp. Med. Sch. Lond.) GP Princip. Socs: BMA; African & Caribbean Med. Soc.; Fell.Roy. Soc. Med. Prev: SHO (Paediat. & O & G) Whipps Cross Hosp.; SHO (A & E) King's Coll. Lond.; SHO (O & G) St. Helier Hosp. Carshalton.
ADDO, Samira Elias Clinical Investigator Unit, Bourn Hall Clinic, Bourn, Cambridge CB3 7TR; Greenacres, 110 Station Road, Over, Cambridge CB4 5NL — MB ChB 1974 Ghana; FRCOG 1996, M 1981. Clin. Dir. Clin. Investigator Unit Bourn Hall Clinic Camb. Socs: Brit. Fertil. Soc.; Eur. Soc. Human Reproduc. & Embryol.; BMA. Prev: Dir. IVF & Fertil. Unit Blessings Private Clinic Lond.; Cons. Bourn Hall Clin. Camb.; Research Fell. (Obst.) Char. Cross Hosp. Fulham.
ADDOUS, Abduljewad 31 Buckingham Road, London N1 4HY — MD 1973 Addis Ababa; MRCP (UK) 1984.
ADDY, Douglas Peter 15 Dyott Road, Moseley, Birmingham B13 9QZ Tel: 0121 449 3190 — MB ChB 1961 Leeds; FRCP Lond. 1980, M 1967; FRCPCH 1997; DCH Eng. 1964. (Univ. Leeds) Freelance Med. Jl.ist; Contrib. Edr. Med. Digest. Socs: Med. Jl.ists' Assn. Prev: Cons. Paediat. Dudley Rd. Hosp. Birm.; Regional Adviser (Paediat.) Roy. Coll. Phys. & Brit. Paediat. Assn.; Fell. (Paediat. Neurol.) Johns Hopkins Hosp. Baltimore, Maryland, USA.
ADDY, Elizabeth Vivian Nuffield Department of Anaesthesia, Radcliffe Infirmary, Woodstock Road, Oxford OX2 6HE Tel: 01865 224774 Fax: 01865 224814 — MB BS 1986 Lond.; BSc Lond. 1983; FRCA 1992; MRCP (UK) 1989. Cons. Dept. of Anaesth. Oxf. Radcliffe NHS Trust. Prev: Sen. Regist. (Anaesth.) John Radcliffe Hosp. Oxf.
ADDY, Jennifer Anne 11 Ramsden Close, Glossop SK13 7BB — MB ChB 1984 Manch.; MRCGP 1990.
ADDY, Martin George (retired) Arden House, 6 High St, Tutbury, Burton-on-Trent DE13 9LP Tel: 01283 814155 — MB ChB Bristol 1958; FRCP Lond. 1982, M 1968; MRCPCH 1997; DCH Eng. 1964. Prev: Cons. Paediat. Burton Hosps. NHS Trust.
ADDY, N C 156 Nelson Road, Gillingham ME7 4LU Tel: 01634 850943 — MB BS 1959 Calcutta.
ADDY, Niifio 119 Saint James's Lane, Muswell Hill, London N10 3RJ — MB BS 1997 Lond.
ADDY, Sourendra Nath 24 Normacot Road, Longton, Stoke-on-Trent ST3 1RL; 21 Normanton Grove, Longton, Stoke-on-Trent ST3 5BY — MB BS 1963 Calcutta; BSc, MB BS Calcutta 1963. (Calcutta Med. Coll.) SHO Leighton Hosp. Crewe. Prev: SHO (Gyn.) Camborne & Redruth Hosp. Cornw.; SHO (Orthop. & A & E) Worcester Roy. Infirm.; SHO (Obst.) P.ss Mary Matern. Hosp. Newc.
ADE, Christopher Paul Carlton Gardens Surgery, 27 Carlton Gardens, Leeds LS7 1JL Tel: 0113 295 2678 Fax: 0113 295 2679 — MB ChB 1985 Leeds; MRCGP 1992; Adv. Cert. Family Plann. JCC 1992; DRCOG 1991. Prev: Regist. Rotat. (Med.) Bradford Roy. Infirm.; SHO (Paediat.) Leeds Gen. Infirm.
ADEBAJO, Adewale Olukayode 4 Whinfell Court, Sheffield S11 9QA — MB BS 1981 Ibadan.
ADEBAYO, Adedapo Babafemi 51 Hamlet Square, London NW2 1SR — MB BCh BAO 1991 NUI; LRCPSI 1991.
ADEBAYO, Adeniyi Olugbenga 42 Belmont Avenue, Billingham TS22 5HF — MB BS 1985 Ibadan.
ADEBOYE, Mr Kayode Adesegun Oludaisi 8 Woodlands Close, Borehamwood WD6 1SX — MB BS 1987 Ibadan; FRCS Ed. 1995.
ADEBOYEKU, David Usiola 6 Ryecroft Road, London SW16 3EG — MB BS 1992 Lond.
ADEDEJI, Adedayo — MBBS 1978; MBBS, MRCOG (UK) 1992. (University of Ibadan, Nigeria) GP Princip. Socs: Roy. Coll. of Obstretrics & Gynaecologists.
ADEDEJI, Edmond Adefolu 61 Ethel Road, Custom House, London E16 3AT — MB BS 1982 Ibadan.
ADEDEJI, Mr Olufunso Adebola Department of General Surgery, Sunderland District General Hosptial, Kaylll Road, Sunderland SR4 7TD Tel: 0191 565 6256 Fax: 0191 569 9220; 59 Cheswick Drive, Gosforth, Newcastle upon Tyne NE3 5DW Tel: 0191 284 7095 Fax: 0191 284 7095 Email: noaz@town6.ncl.ac.uk — MB BS 1984 Ibadan, Nigeria; FRCS Ed. 1993. (Univ. Ibadan, Nigeria) Regist. (Gen. Surg.) Sunderland Gen. Hosp. Socs: Surgic. Research Soc.; Eur. Assn. Study Acute Abdom. Pain. Prev: Regist. (Gen. Surg.) Newc. Gen. Hosp. Newc.; Research Fell. (Surg.) N. W.. Injury Research Centre Univ. Manch.
ADEGHE, Aimua Jude-Harris Department of Obstetrics/Gynaecology, New Cross Hospital, Wednesfield Road, Wolverhampton WV10 0QP Tel: 01902 642851 Fax: 01902 643030; Green Bays, 11 Muchall Road, Penn, Wolverhampton WV4 5SE Email: judeharris@btinternet.com — MB BS 1980 Nigeria; PhD Birm. 1987; MB BS Enugu, Nigeria 1980; MRCOG 1990. Cons. Roy. Wolverhampton Hosp. Trust. Socs: Soc. Study of Fertil. (UK); Europ. Soc. of Human ReProduc. and Embryology; Brit. Fertil. Soc. Prev: Sen. Regist. & Research Fell. (O & G) Birm. Matern. Hosp.
ADEGOKE, Anthony Oladeji 73 Mayfield Road, Sanderstead, South Croydon CR2 0BJ — LMSSA 1993 Lond.; MB BS Lagos 1985.
ADEKANMI, Adeyemi Adiodun The Surgery, 167 Kingsland Road, London E2 8AL Tel: 020 7739 3600 Fax: 020 7613 5345; Tel: 01962 863511 Email: jane.bell@wessexdeanery.nhs.uk — MB BS 1987 Ibadan; DRCOG 1998; DFFP 1995. GP Princip.
ADEKUNLE, Mr Opeoluwa Oladeinde c/o 97 Finborough Road, London SW10 9DU; Department of Surgery, University College Hospital, Ibadan, Oyo State, Nigeria Tel: (00 234) (2) 714782 — FRCS 1970 Eng.; MB BS 1968 Utkal. Prof. of Surg. Univ. Coll. Hosp. Ibadan, Nigeria; Vis. Prof. of Surg. Fac. of Med. & Health Sci. Univ. of Transkei Umtata E.ern Cape RePub. of S. Africa. Socs: Nigerian Med. Assn.; Confed. of African Med. Assns & Socs; Pan Afr. Assn. Surg.
ADELMAN, Mark Ian Woodlands, Barff Road, Potterhanworth, Lincoln LN4 2DU — MB BCh 1972 Wales; MRCPath 1980. Cons. Haemat. Co. Hosp. Lincoln. Socs: Brit. Soc. Haemat. Prev: Sen. Regist. (Haemat.) King's Coll. & Lewisham Hosps. Lond.; Regist. (Haemat.) & Demonst. (Path.) King's Coll. Hosp. Lond.
ADELMAN, Simon 136A Landcroft Road, London SE22 9JW — MB BS 1996 Lond.
ADELOYE, Codanda Kalappa c/o Mrs. Kamala Adeloye, No. 6 Winchester Road, Fulwood, Sheffield S10 4EE — MB BS 1956 Madras.
ADEMOKUN, Jolaolu Adebowale Edinburgh Cancer Centre, Western General Hospital, Crewe Road, Edinburgh EH4 2XU Fax: 0131 537 1029 — MB BS 1983 Lagos; MD (Univ. of Newcastle); MRCPath; MRCP (UK) 1992. Haemat. Cons. Ipswich Hosp. Ipswich. Suff. IP4 5PD. Prev: Regist. (Haemat.) Roy. Vict. Infirm. & Sunderland Roy. Infirm.; SHO (Gen. Med.) Pilgrim Hosp. Boston.
ADENEY, Christopher Gordon Link End Surgery, 39 Pickersleigh Road, Malvern WR14 2RP Tel: 01684 568466 Fax: 01684 891064 — MB BS 1976 Lond.; MRCS Eng. LRCP Lond. 1976; DA Eng. 1981; DRCOG 1978.
ADENEY, Rev. Harold Walter, OBE (retired) 5 Coles Way, Reepham, Norwich NR10 4LW Tel: 01603 871932 — MB BChir 1938 Camb.; MCRS Eng. LRCP Lond. 1938. Prev: Hon. Curate Cranfield.
ADENIRAN, Florence Gabrielle Abiola 35 Alexandra Road, London N8 0PL — MRCS Eng. LRCP Lond. 1961.
ADENIYI-JONES, Rodney Olapeju Carlos The Regent Clinic, 21 Devonshire Place, London W1G 6HZ Tel: 020 7486 6354 Fax: 020 7486 6359 Email: rocaj@compuserve.com; 21 Devonshire Place, London W1G 6HZ Tel: 020 7486 6357 — LRCPI & LM, LRCPSI & LM 1975; LRCPI & LM, LRCSI & LM 1975; MRCP (UK) 1978. Med. Dir. The Regent Clinic Lond.
ADENWALA, Yousouf Taher 22 Cleveland Road, Stockport SK4 4BS — MB ChB 1993 Leeds.
ADEOBA, Stella Adepero 160 Moynes House, Loughborough Park, London SW9 8NN — LRCPI & LM, LRSCI & LM 1961; LRCPI & LM, LRCSI & LM 1961.
ADEOSUN, Adekule Segun 11 The Crescent, Basingstoke District Hospital, Basingstoke RG24 7LZ — MB BS 1981 Lagos.
ADEOYE, Onikepo Adetokunbo 32 Tubbenden Lane, Orpington BR6 9PN — MB BS 1980 Benin; MRCP (UK) 1995.
ADERINTO, Joseph Babatunde Flat 10, Thorness Court, Allfarthing Lane, London SW18 2AH — MB ChB 1995 Manch.
ADEROGBA, Ayodele 3 Broad Oak Drive, Stapleford, Nottingham NG9 7AX — MB ChB 1993 Bristol.
ADEROGBA, Kazeem Oladipa 3 Broad Oak Drive, Stapleford, Nottingham NG9 7AX — MB ChB 1995 Leic.
ADESIDA, Oyebode Adegboyega Child & Adolsecent Mental Health Services, Canada House, Barnsole Rd, Gillingham ME7 4JL Tel: 01634 583000; 15 Conrad Close, Gillingham ME8 9SD Tel:

01634 264120 Email: bodsida@aol.com — MB BS 1985 Ibadan; MB BS Ibadan, Nigeria 1985; MRCPsych 1992. Cons. (Child & Adolesc. Psychiat.).

ADEWALE, Lolade Adebola Department of Anaesthesia, Monteal Children's Hospital, 2300 Tupper Street, Montreal H3H 1P3, Canada — MB ChB 1987 Manch.; DA (UK) 1993; DCH RCPS Glas. 1993; FRCA Lond. 1996. (Manch.) Asst. Prof. in Paediatric Anaesth., McGill Univ., Montreal, Canada; Clin. Fell. in Paediatric Anaesth. The Hosp. for Sick Chiuldren, Toronto, Canada. Socs: Assn. Anaesth.; BMA. Prev: SHO (Anaesth.) Withington Hosp. & Wythenshawe Hosp. Manch.; SHO (Paediat. & A & E) Sheff. Childr. Hosp.; SHO (Neonat. Paediat.) St. Mary's Hosp. Manch.

ADEWOYIN, Temilade Omowonuola Ajike 19 West Kensington Mansions, Beaumont Crescent, London W14 9PE — MB ChB 1993 Leeds.

ADEY, Alistair James 158 Bridgwater Drive, Westcliff on Sea SS0 0DS Email: ali_adey@yahoo.com — MB BS 1997 Lond.; DRCOG; DFFP. (St George's) SHO (A&E), Countess of Chester Hosp.

ADEY, Colin West Road Surgery, 12 West Road, Westcliff on Sea SS0 9DA Tel: 01702 344492 Fax: 01702 437051; 18 Bovinger Way, Thorpe Bay, Southend-on-Sea SS1 3SZ Tel: 01702 586898 — DTM & H 1973 Liverp.; MB ChB 1967 Bristol; DObst 1969 RCOG. Prev: Med. Off. Nixon Memor. Methodist Hosp. Segbwema, Sierra Leone; Ho. Off. (O & G) S.mead Hosp. Bristol.

ADEY, David Francis William Spitfire Court Surgery, 39 Spitfire Court, Mitchell Close, Woolston, Southampton SO19 7TN Tel: 023 8042 0467 Fax: 023 8043 3050; Anchorage House, 191 Warsash Road, Warsash, Southampton SO31 9JE Tel: 01489 581153 Email: docadey@email.msn.com — BM 1976 Soton. (Southampton) Princip. Police Surg. Soton. Hants. Constab.; Customs & Excise Surg. Soton. HM Commiss. Customs & Excise; 12(2) Approved Doctor Ment. Health Act; Clin. Teach. (Gen. Pract.) Soton. Univ. Med. Sch.; HSE Approved Doctor Commercial Diving. Socs: Assn. Police Surg. Prev: SHO (Anat., Cas. & Orthop.) Soton. Health Dist.; Ho. Off. Roy. Portsmouth Hosp. & Roy. S. Hants. Hosp. Soton.

ADEY, Evelyn Mary 8 Aylestone Road, Cambridge CB4 1HF Tel: 01233 362731 — MB BS 1959 Lond.; MRCGP 1974. (Lond. Hosp.) Indep. Pract. Camb. Socs: Lond. Centre Psychother.

ADEY, Gillian Dalton Department Anaesthetics, Aberdeen Royal Infirmary, Foresterhill, Aberdeen Tel: 01223 681818; Burnhead Cottage, Cookney, Stonehaven AB39 3RX — MB ChB 1968 Aberd.; FRCA Eng. 1975. Cons. (Anaesth.). & Hon. Research Fell. (Biochem.) Aberd. Univ.

ADEY, John Psychotherapy Department, Wonford House Hospital, Exeter; Woodlands, Christow, Exeter EX6 7PJ Tel: 01647 252684 Email: jadey@eclipse.co.uk — MB ChB 1970 Manch.; MA (Psychother. and Conselling) City Univ. 1997. Clin. Asst. (Psychother.) Wonford Ho. Hosp. Exeter. Prev: Stud. Health Serv. Univ. Sussex.

ADEYEMI, Mercy Sijuwade 267 Newhaven Lane, Canning Town, London E16 4HJ — MB BS 1979 Lagos.

ADEYEMI, Mr Oluwole Ajibola Obstetrician and Gynaecologist, Pilgrim Hospital, Sibsey Road, Boston PE21 9QS Tel: 01205 364801; 222 London Road, Wyberton, Boston PE21 7HQ Tel: 01205 366115 Email: oluadeyemi@b-lincs.freeserve.co.uk — MB BS 1980 Ibadan; MRCOG 1991; MFFP 1993. (University College Hospital, Ibadan, Nigeria) Cons. O & G Pilgrim Hosp. Boston, Lincs. Socs: BMA; Roy. Coll. Obst. & Gynaecol.; Fac. Fam. Plann. Prev: Sen. Regist. Addenbrookes NHS Trust Camb.

ADGEY, Professor Agnes Anne Jennifer Garden Lodge, Newtownards; Mossvale House, 71 Ballyskeagh Road, Lisburn BT27 5TE Tel: 02890 629773 — MB BCh BAO 1975 Belf.; MD (Hons.) Belf. 1975; FRCP Lond. 1978, M 1967. (Qu. Univ. Belf.) Cons. Cardiol. Roy. Vict. Hosp. Belf.; Prof. Cardiol. Roy. Vict. Hosp. Belf. Socs: Assn. Phys.; Fell. Amer. Coll. Cardiol. Prev: SHO Roy. Vict. Hosp. Belf.

ADHAMI, Yassin The Surgery, 80 Hull Road, Hessle HU13 9LU Tel: 01482 646581 — LRCP LRCS 1980 Ed.; LRCP LRCS Ed. LRCPS Glas. 1980.

ADHAMI, Zubaida Naman Department of Medical Microbiology, Harold Wood Hospital, Gubbins Lane, Romford RM3 0BE Tel: 01708 345533 Fax: 01708 381486; 21 Lyndhurst Rise, Chigwell IG7 5BB — MB ChB 1973 Baghdad; MSc (Med. Microbiol.) Lond. 1980; MRCPath 1982. (Baghdad Med. Coll.) Cons. Med. Microbiol. Havering Hosps. NHS Trust; Hon. Sen. Lect. Lond. Hosp. Socs: BMA; Assn. Clin. Paths. Prev: Sen. Regist. (Microbiol.) Birm. Childr. Hosp. & Dudley Rd. Hosp.; Regist. (Bact.) Hammersmith Hosp. & Roy. Postgrad. Med. Sch.

ADHIKAREE, Shambhu Nath 24 Oak Road, Healing, Grimsby DN41 7RL — MB BS 1966 Nagpur; MRCP (UK) 1977; MRCPI 1974; DCH Eng. 1972. (Nagpur Med. Coll.) Cons. Phys. (Geriat. Med.) Grimsby & Louth DHA's. Socs: Brit. Geriat. Soc. Prev: Sen. Regist. (Geriat.) Aberd. Roy. Infirm.; Regist. (Gen. Med.) Boston Gen. Hosp.; SHO (Gen. Med.) Boston Gen. Hosp.

ADHIKARY, Manju 83A Lightfoot Lane, Fulwood, Preston PR2 3LS — MB BS 1968 Calcutta; FFA RCSI 1978. (HR Sircar Medical College, Calcutta, India) Cons. Anaesth., Blackburn Roy. Infimary, Blackburn. Socs: AAGBI; OAA; RSA.

ADHYA, Gobardhan Heaton Norris Health Centre, Cheviot Close, Heaton Norris, Stockport SK4 1JX Tel: 0161 480 3338 — MB BS 1963 Calcutta. (Calcutta) GP Stockport.

ADHYA, Nil Ratan (retired) Larkhill Health Centre, Mount Pleasant, Blackburn — MB 1948 Calcutta; 1948 MB Calcutta; 1953 LM Rotunda; 1953 DGO Dub.; 1953 DCH RCPSI; 1999 FRSM (Lond). Prev: Cons.Paediat. Bon hoogley Hosp.Calcutta.

ADIB, Mr Rafid Subhi (retired) 103B Sandy Lane, Middlestown, Wakefield WF4 4PR Tel: 01924 274789 — MB ChB 1950 Baghdad; FRCS Ed. 1957. Prev: Cons. Urol. Clayton Hosp. Pinderfields Hosp. NHS Trust.

ADIB, Tania Rafid First Floor Flat, 11 St Luke's Rd, London W11 1DB — MB BS 1992 Lond.; BSc 1987; MRCOG 1998. (Royal Free) UCH Middlx., Research Regist. Socs: RSM; BMA.

ADINKRA, Judith Peggy 81 Patterdale Avenue, Marton, Blackpool FY3 9QR — MB ChB 1995 Leeds.

ADIOTOMRE, Joseph Akpocha Diana, Princess of Wales Hospital, Scartho Road, Grimsby DN33 2BA Tel: 01472 874111; Tel: 01472 826927 — MB BS 1980 Benin, Nigeria; FRCPI 2000; FRCP 2001 Lond.; MRCPI 1988. (Univ. of Benin, Benin City Nigeria) Cons. Phys. N.. Lincs. & Govle Hosps. NHS Trust Grimsby. Socs: BMA; Brit. Geriat. Soc.; Diabetes UK. Prev: Hon. Sen. Regist. (Geriat. Med.) Leicester Teach. Hosp.; Assoc. Specialist (Gen. Med.) Bassetlaw Hosps. & Comm. Serv. NHS Trust; Regist. (Gen. Med.) Bassetlaw Dist. Hosp. Worksop.

ADIOTOMRE, Pauline Nwanyibuzor Atinuke Diana Princess of Wales Hospital, Scartho Road, Grimsby DN33 2BA Tel: 01472 874111 Fax: 01472 875570; Mount Royal, Cheapside, Waltham, Grimsby DN37 0HU Tel: 01472 826927 — MB BS 1980 Nigeria; MRCP (UK) 1991; MRCPCH. (College of Medical Sciences, University of Benin, Nigeria) Cons. Paediat. Diana P.ss of Wales Hosp. Socs: MRCPCH; Brit. Assn of Perinatal Med.; BMA. Prev: Cons. Paediat. Scunthorpe & Goole Hosps. NHS Trust; Sen. Regist. (Paediat.) W. Midl. RHA; Career Regist. Trent RHA & Lothian HB.

ADIREDDI, Venkata Surya Prakashrao Kingsmead Healthcare, 4 Kingsmead Way, London E9 5QG Tel: 020 8985 1930 Fax: 020 8533 3951 — MB BS 1974 Andhra. (Andhra) GP Lond.

ADISESH, Linganatha Anil University Hospital of Wales, Occupational Health Department, Denbigh House, Heath Park, Cardiff CF14 4XW Tel: 029 2074 3264 Fax: 029 2074 4411 Email: adisesha@cf.ac.uk; 87 Gwernrhuddi Road, Cyncoed, Cardiff CF23 6PS Tel: 02920 765464 — MB ChB 1986 Liverp.; MRCP (UK) 1992; T(GP) 1993; MSc Manch. 1997; MFOM RCP Lond. 1997. (Liverpool) Cons. Occupat. Med. Univ. Hosp. of Wales Cardiff & Vale NHS Trust; Hon. Cons. Respirat. Med. Univ. Hosp. of Wales Cardiff & Vale NHS Trust. Prev: Lect. Centre for Occupat. Health Univ. of Manch.; Sen. Regist. (Research) N. W. Lung Centre Wythenshawe Hosp.; Lect. & Hon. Sen. Regist. (Occupat. Health) UMDS Guy's & St. Thomas Hosp. Lond.

ADISESH, Linganatha Thammiam 13 Higher Road, Hunts Cross, Liverpool L25 0QG; (Surgery), 14 Eastern Avenue, Liverpool L24 2TA — MB BS 1955 Mysore; LAH Dub. 1960. Prev: Regist. Gen. Med. Barrow & Furness Hosp. Gp.

ADISESHIAH, Mr Mohankumar 149 Harley Street, London W1N 2DE Tel: 020 7380 9816 Email: m.adis@lonclin.co.uk; 32 Richborough Road, London NW2 3LX Email: adiseshiah@demon.co.uk — MB BS 1965 Lond.; MS Lond. 1978; MA Camb. 1978; FRCS Eng. 1969; MRCP Lond. 1968; FRCP Lond. 1998. (Westm.) Cons. Vasc. Surg. Univ. Coll. Lond. Hosp.; Cons. Surg. St. Luke's Hosp. Clergy Lond.; Hon. Sen. Lect. Fac. Med. Sci.

UCL. Socs: Fell. Assn. Surgs.; Fell. Internat. Cardiovasc. Soc.; Vasc. Surg. Soc. GB & Irel. Prev: Cons. Surg. Camb. Health Dist. & Assoc. Lect. Clin. (Med.) Univ. Camb.; Sen. Regist. (Surg.) Univ. Coll. Hosp. Lond.; Ho. Surg. W.m. Hosp. Lond.

ADJAYE, Nellie Turbyne Birling Ward, Preston Hall Hospital, Maidstone ME20 7NJ Tel: 01622 225640 Fax: 01622 713115; 20 St Michaels Road, Maidstone ME16 8BS — MB BS 1971 Lond; MB BS Lond. 1971; MSc Lond. 1979; FRCP Lond. 1994; MRCP (UK) 1976; MRCS Eng. LRCP Lond. 1971; FRCPCH 1997. (Royal Free) Socs: Collegiate Mem. RCP Lond.; BMA; Hon. Med. Adviser Sickle Cell Soc. (UK). Prev: Lect. & Hon. Sen. Regist. (Community Paediat.) St. Mary's Hosp. Med. Sch. Lond.; Regist. (Paediat.) St. Ann's Hosp. & N. Middlx. Hosp. Lond.; SHO (Paediat. Neurol.) Hosp. for Sick Childr. Gt. Ormond St. Lond.

ADJEI, Mr Stephen Sereboo 30 Carron Crescent, Kirkintilloch, Glasgow G66 5PJ — MB BCh BAO 1982 Belf.; MB BCh Belf. 1982; FFD RCSI 1978; FDS RCS Eng. 1977; FRCS Ed. 1991. Regist. (Oral Surg.) Altnagelvin Hosp. Lond.derry.

ADJEPONG, Kwasi 40 Glamorgan Close, Mitcham CR4 1XG — MB BS 1966 Delhi; DLO RCS Eng. 1977.

ADJEPONG, Mr Samuel Ellis 41 Mathew Walk, Danescourt, Llandaff, Cardiff CF5 2QW Tel: 029 2056 8516 — MB ChB 1975 Ghana; FRCS Ed. 1982.

ADJOGATSE, Mr James Kwasi Department of Surgery, City General Hospital, Newcastle Road, Stoke-on-Trent ST4 6QG Tel: 01782 715444; 2 Mountsorrel Close, Trenthham, Stoke-on-Trent ST4 8TL Tel: 01782 657987 Fax: 01782 657987 Email: jdjogatse@aol.com — MB ChB 1978 Ghana; MB ChB U. Ghana 1978; FRCS Eng. 1990. Staff Grade Surg. N. Staff. Hosp. Socs: Ghana Med. Assn. Prev: Regist. (Surg.) St. Mary's Hosp. Lond.; Regist. (Surg.) Roy. Vict. Infirm. Newc.

ADKIN, Dawn Elizabeth 8 Ridgewood Crescent, Newcastle upon Tyne NE3 1SQ — MB BS 1993 Newc.

ADKINS, Charlotte Tessa 35 West Grove Road, Exeter EX2 4LU — MB BS 1998 Newc.; MB BS Newc 1998.

ADKINS, Graham George Medical Department, British Nuclear Fuels Plc, Sellafield, Seascale CA20 1PG Tel: 019467 71436 Fax: 019467 71452 Email: ggal@bnfl.com; London Head, Santon Bridge, Holmrook CA19 1UY Tel: 019467 26395 Email: graham.adkins@virgin.net — BM 1981 Soton.; AFOM RCP (UK) 1992; MRCGP 1986; DRCOG 1984. (Southampton) Occupat. Phys.

ADKINS, Rupert Brian, TD Belmont Surgery, 12 Belmont Road, St Austell PL25 4UJ Tel: 01726 69444 — MB ChB 1969 Bristol; MRCS Eng. LRCP Lond. 1969; DObst RCOG 1973. (Bristol) Socs: Soc. Orthop. Med. Prev: Med. Off. RAMC.

ADKINSON, Robin Kenneth Park Drive Health Centre, 2A Park Drive, Leicester Forest East, Leicester LE3 3FN Tel: 0116 289 8111; 17 Church Street, Sapcote, Leicester LE9 4FG Tel: 01455 272736 — MB BS 1968 Lond.; MRCS Eng. LRCP Lond. 1968; DA Eng. 1970; DObst RCOG 1970. (Univ. Coll. Hosp.) Socs: BMA; SOH. Prev: Regist. (Anaesth.) & SHO (O & G) Nottm. City Hosp.

ADLAKHA, Harbans Lal 15 Dornie Place, Gowrie Park, Dundee DD2 4UD Tel: 01382 645860 — MD 1972 Rajasthan; MB BS 1968; FICA 1973. (Rabindra Nath Tagore) Regist. (Geriat. Med.) Roy. Vict. Hosp., Ninewells Hosp. & Med. Sch.

ADLAKHA, Saroj Shilpa Medical Centre, 1C Ashfield Avenue, Kings Heath, Birmingham B14 7AT Tel: 0121 444 2668; 60 Somerset Road, Edgbaston, Birmingham B15 2PD — MB BS 1969 Kanpur; Cert. FPA 1972. Med. Off. Family Plann. Assn. (Solihull); Med. Off. Old People Home Birm.; Med. Off. Child Health Sandwell HA. Prev: Res. Ho. Off. (Gen. Surg.) Selly Oak Hosp. Birm.; Res. SHO (Gyn. & Obst.) Birm. & Midl. Hosp. Wom.; Res. SHO (Paediat.) Good Hope Gen. Hosp. Sutton Coldfield.

ADLAKHA, Surjeet 15 Dornie Place, Gowrie Park, Dundee DD2 4UD Tel: 01382 645860 — MD 1974 Delhi; MD (Obst. & Gyn.) Delhi 1974, MB BS 1968; DGO Delhi 1971; DRCOG 1977. (Lady Hardinge Med. Coll.) SHO (Haemat.) Ninewells Med. Sch. & Hosp. Dundee. Prev: SHO (O & G) Lincoln Co. Hosp. & Ninewells Med. Sch. & Teach.; Hosp. Dundee.

ADLAM, David 11 Allison Avenue, Gillingham ME7 3BZ — BM BCh 1998 Oxf.; BM BCh Oxf 1998.

ADLAM, Mr David Maxwell Department of Oral & Maxillofacial Surgery, Addenbrooke's Hospital, Hills Road, Cambridge CB2 2QQ Tel: 01223 216705 Fax: 01223 216708 — MB BS 1982 Lond.; BDS Bristol 1974; FDS RCS Eng. 1977; FRCS Ed. 1986. Cons. (Oral & Maxillofacial Surg.) Addenbrooke's Hosp. Camb. Socs: Fell. Brit. Assn. Oral & Maxillofacial Surg.; Craniofacial Soc.; BMA & BDA. Prev: Sen. Regist. (Maxillofacial Surg.) Qu. Vict. Hosp. E. Grinstead, Univ. Coll. Hosp. Lond. & Hosp. Sick Childr. Gt. Ormond St.

ADLAM, Susan Ann The Haining, High St., Hildersham, Cambridge CB1 6BU — MB BS 1977 Lond.; BSc Bristol 1972.

ADLARD, Julian Weldon Cookridge Hospital, Hospital Lane, Leeds LS16 6QB Tel: 0113 267 3411; 3 The Cottages, Westend, Kirk Hammerton, York YO26 8BY Email: jools@cat-cottage.freeserve.co.uk — MB BS 1992 Newc.; MRCP (UK) 1995. Regist. (Radiother. & Oncol.) Cookridge Hosp. Leeds. Prev: SHO (Radiother. & Oncol.) Cookridge Hosp. Leeds; SHO Rotat. (Gen. Med.) Lincoln Co. Hosp.; SHO (Med.) Friarage Hosp. N.allerton.

ADLARD, Peter Department of Paediatrics, Stoke Mandeville Hospital, Aylesbury HP21 8AL Tel: 01296 315000; 18 High Street, Rickmansworth WD3 1ER Tel: 01923 778279 Fax: 01923 354037 Email: p.adlard@ich.ucl.ac.uk — MB ChB 1979 Sheff.; MD Sheff. 1994; FRCP 1997; MRCP (UK) 1983; FRCPCH 1997. (University of Sheffield) p/t Cons. Paediat. Stoke Mandeville Hosp. Aylesbury; Sen. Research Fell. Inst. Child Health Univ. Lond.; Hon. Cons. Paediat. Gt. Ormond Hosp. for childr. Socs: Brit. Soc. Paediat. Endocrinol. & Diabetes. Prev: Lect. Inst. Child Health Univ. Lond.; Lect. & Sen. Regist. Middlx. & Edgware Gen. Hosps. Lond.; Hon. Sen. Regist. Hosp. for Sick Childr. Gt. Ormond St. Lond. & Research Fell. Inst.. Child Health Univ. Lond.

ADLARD, Roger Edward 14 Morice Road, Hoddesdon EN11 9AX — MB BS 1996 Lond.

ADLER, Angela Dagmar Ariella, Christchurch Road, Virginia Water GU25 4PT — MB BS 1979 Lond.; MRCS Eng. LRCP Lond. 1979. Regist. (O & G) Heatherwood Hosp. Ascot. Prev: SHO W. Lond. Hosp.

ADLER, Benjamin Jason 21 Thornwood Avenue, Glasgow G11 7PH — MB ChB 1997 Glas.

ADLER, Beryl Rosalind Luton & Dunstable Hospital, Lewsey Road, Luton LU4 0DZ Tel: 01582 491122 Fax: 01582 497280 Email: beryl.alder@ldh-tr.anglox-nhs.uk; 25 St. Stephens Avenue, St Albans AL3 4AA Tel: 01727 833797 — MB ChB 1981 Birm.; MRCP (UK) 1988; MRCGP 1985; DCH RCP Lond. 1985; DRCOG 1983. p/t Cons. Paediat. Luton & Dunstable Hosp.; Career and Counselling Tutor, Med. Centre, Luton & Dunstable Hosp. Prev: Sen. Regist. (Paediat.) St. Mary's Hosp. Lond.; Clin. Research Fell. & Hon. Regist. (Paediat.) Brompton Hosp. Lond.; Regist. (Paediat.) Lister Hosp. Stevenage.

ADLER, Frank Peter Ashcroft Road Surgery, 26 Ashcroft Road, Stopsley Green, Luton LU2 9AU Tel: 01582 722555 Fax: 01582 418145 — MB BS 1960 Lond.; MRCS Eng. LRCP Lond. 1960; DObst RCOG 1964. (Westm.) Socs: BMA. Prev: Regist. (Med.) Chelmsford Hosp. Gp.; Med. Off. Kitwe, Zambia; Asst. (Paediat. & Internal Med.) Govt. Hosp. Hadera, Israel.

ADLER, Jonathan Lewis 5 Wychcombe Studios, Englands Lane, London NW3 4XY Tel: 020 7722 1151 Fax: 020 7722 3394 Email: jonathan.adler@marypotter.org.nz — MB BS 1990 Lond.; FAChPM 2000; BSc (Anat.) Lond. 1987; MRCP (UK) 1994; FRACP 1998. (Middlesex Medical School) Cons. in Palliat. Med., Mary Potter Hospice, Wellington, New Zealand.

ADLER, Joseph Samuel 34 Woodstock Avenue, London NW11 9SL; 682 Finchley Road, London NW11 7NP Tel: 020 8455 9994 — MB BS 1981 Lond. Prev: Fell. Oncol. & Haemat. New York, USA.

ADLER, Katharina Amanda 9 Bittacy Park Avenue, London NW7 2HA — MB ChB 1994 Bristol.

ADLER, Katherine Margaret Birch Hill Hospital, Rochdale OL12 9QB Tel: 01706 377777 Fax: 01706 755661; 2 Beatrice Road, Worsley, Manchester M28 2TN Tel: 0161 793 7841 — MB ChB 1963 Manch.; FRCP Lond. 1987; MRCP Ed. 1972; DCH Eng. 1965; ECFMG Cert. 1968; MRCPCH 1996. Cons. Paediat. & Lead Clinician in Paediat. (Matern. & Child Health) Birch Hill Hosp. Rochdale. Socs: RCPCH; (Comm.) Manch. Paediat. Club; MRCPCH. Prev: Sen. Regist. (Paediat.) NW RHA; Regist. (Paediat.) Roy. Infirm. Dundee; Sen. Resid. Hosp. Sick Childr. Toronto, Canada.

ADLER, Lawrence Martin Belmont Health Centre, 516 Kenton Lane, Kenton, Harrow HA3 7LT — MB BS 1976 London. (London) GP Harrow, Middlx.

ADLER, Matthew Alexander Flat 3, 119 King Henrys Rd, London NW3 3RB — MB BS 1996 Lond.
ADLER, Professor Michael William, CBE Department of Sexually Transmitted Diseases,Royal Free & University College Medical School, The Mortimer Market Centre, Mortimer Market, off Capper St., London WC1E 6AU Tel: 020 7380 9892 Fax: 020 7380 9778 Email: madler@gum.ucl.ac.uk — MB BS 1965 Lond.; MD Lond. 1977; FRCP Lond. 1984; MRCP (UK) 1970; FFPHM 1983, M 1977. (Middlx.) Duncan Guthrei Prof. Genitourin. Med. Roy. Free & Univ. Coll. Med. Sch. Lond.; Cons. Phys. Middlx. Hosp. Lond. Socs: Med. Soc. Study VD; Assn. Phys.; Internat. AIDS Soc. Prev: Sen. Lect. Middlx. Hosp. Lond.; Lect. (Clin. Epidemiol. & Social Med.) St. Thos. Hosp. Lond.; Regist. Centr. Middlx. Hosp. Lond.
ADLER, Salomon 682 Finchley Road, London NW11 7NP Tel: 020 8455 9994 Fax: 020 8458 9183; 20 Beechcroft Avenue, London NW11 8BL Tel: 020 8455 8822 Fax: 020 8458 0973 — MB BS 1947 Lond.; BSc 1946 Lond. (Guy's)
ADLER, Thomas Julian Evelyn Medical Centre, Marsh Avenue, Hope, Hope Valley S33 6RJ Tel: 01433 621557; Tigh-an-Duin, Coggers Lane, Hathersage, Hope Valley S32 1AL — MB ChB 1985 Aberd.; MRCGP 1990; Dip. Law (Dist.) TCU Lond. 1987.
ADLER, Vivienne Holmwood Health Centre, Tadley, Basingstoke; 78 The Avenue, Mortimer, Reading RG7 3QX — MB BS 1984 Lond.; DRCOG 1987. Prev: Trainee GP WhitCh. VTS; SHO (Med. & Geriat.) Roy. Hants. Co. Hosp. Winchester; SHO (O & G & Paediat.) Roy. Hants. Co. Hosp.
ADLER-TANZ, Mrs Pepi (retired) 3 Woodthorpe Close, Sandal, Wakefield WF2 6JA Tel: 01924 255913 — MD 1935 Vienna. Asst. Med. Off. Dept. Pub. Health Leeds. Prev: Asst. Dept Paediat. Hosp. Sick Childr. Glas.
ADLEY, Ross, Surg. Cdr. RN Airedale General Hospital, Skipton Road, Steeton, Keighley BD20 6TD Tel: 01535 651309 Fax: 01535 651309 — MRCS Eng. LRCP Lond. 1977; 1977 MB BS Lond.; 1974 BSc Lond.; 1987 FFA RCSI. (St. Bart.) Cons. Anaesth. Airedale NHS Trust. Socs: Assn. Anaesth.; Soc. Naval Anaesth.; Obst. Anaesth. Assn. Prev: Cons. Anaesth. RN; Hon. Sen. Regist. Nuffield Dept. Anaesth. Oxf. HA; Regist. Shackleton Dept. Anaesth. Soton. HA.
ADLINGTON, Mr Basil (retired) 7 Martins Close, Ferndown BH22 9SH — MRCS Eng. LRCP Lond. 1924; FRCS Ed. 1928. Prev: ENT Consult. E. Anglian RHB.
ADLINGTON, Mr Peter Hollow End, Horton, Wimborne BH21 7EP — MB BS 1956 Lond.; FRCS Eng. 1963; MRCS Eng. LRCP Lond. 1956; DLO Eng. 1962. (King's Coll. Hosp.) Cons. ENT Surg. Bournemouth & E. Dorset Hosp. Gp. Socs: Fell. Roy. Soc. Med. Prev: Sen. Regist. ENT Dept. King's Coll. Hosp. Lond.; Leverhulme Research Lect. RCS Eng.; SHO ENT Dept. W.m. Hosp. Lond.
ADLINGTON, Rebecca Jane Hollow End, Horton, Wimborne BH21 7EP — MB BS 1996 Lond.
ADLUNG, Birgit 8 Crown Road N., Glasgow G12 9DH Email: birgitadlung@compuserve.com — State Exam Med 1992 Lubeck. Specialist Regist. Radiol. W. Scotl.
ADLY HABIB, Neda Department Anaesthetics, Whipps Cross Hospital, Whipps Cross Road, Leytonstone, London E11 1NR; 6 Courtfield, Castlebar Hill, Ealing, London W5 1TA Tel: 020 8997 5568 — MD 1993 Bristol; MD Ljubljana 1978; FFA RCS Eng. 1984. Cons. Anaesth. Forrest Health Care Trust Whipps Cross Hosp. Lond. Prev: Sen. Regist. (Anaesth.) Kingston Hosp. Surrey.
ADMA, Lakshminarayan Clifton Street Surgery, Hurst Hill, Bilston WV14 9EY — MB BS 1973 Osmania. (Osmania) GP Bilston, W. Midl.
ADMANI, Abdul Karim, OBE 1 Derriman Glen, Silverdale Road, Sheffield S11 9LQ Tel: 0114 236 0465 Fax: 0114 236 0532; 15 Upper Albert Road, Sheffield S8 9HR — MB BS 1962 Karachi; BSc (1st cl. Hons.) Gujarat 1956; FRCP Lond. 1989; FRCP Glas. 1987; FRCP Ed. 1979, M 1967; DTM & H Eng. 1963. JP; Cons. Phys. (Med. Rehabil. & Stroke) N.. Gen. Hosp. Sheff.; Hon. Clin. Lect. (Med.) Univ. Sheff. Socs: Fell. Overseas Doctors Assn. (Chairm. Educat. & Postgrad. Train. Comm.); Fell. BMA; Pakistan Med. Soc. in UK (Pres. Sheff. & N Region). Prev: Sen. Regist. (Geriat. Med.) N. Sheff. Univ. Gp. Hosps.; Regist. (Gen. Med.) Birkenhead Gen. Hosp.; Regist. (Med.) Newc. Gen. Hosp.
ADNITT, David Ian Wildwood Cottage, Southend Common, Henley-on-Thames RG9 6JP — MB ChB 1988 Birm.; MRCGP 1992; DRCOG 1990. Prev: Trainee GP/SHO (O & G) Leighton Hosp. Crewe.
ADNITT, Peter Ian Wildwood Cottage, Southend Common, Henley-on-Thames RG9 6JP Tel: 01491 638671 — MB BS 1962 Lond.; MD Lond. 1968; FRCP Lond. 1979, M 1965; MRCS Eng. LRCP Lond. 1962. (St. Bart.) Med. Dir. Leo Laborat. P.s RisBoro.. Prev: Regional Dir. Clin. Research Wyeth Research Taplow Berks.; Cons. Phys. Chester Dist. Hosps.; Sen. Regist. St. Bart. Hosp. Lond.
ADOKI, Idango Ibifuro Park Practice, 12 Brodrick Close, Hampden Park, Eastbourne BN22 9NR Tel: 01323 502200/503240 Fax: 01323 500527; 18 Ashburnham Gardens, Eastbourne BN21 2NA — MB BS 1978 Ibadan; FRCS Glas. 1987; DRCOG 1992. (University of Ibadan, Nigeria) GP Princip., Pk. Pract., E.bourne, E. Sussex; GP Tutor, E.bourne, E. Sussex. Prev: Regist. (Gen. Surg.) E.bourne Dist. Gen. Hosp. & Bradford Roy. Infirm.
ADOLPH, Moir Patrick Nelham Occupational Health Department, Eastbourne Hospitals NHS Trust, King's Drive, Eastbourne BN21 2UD Tel: 01323 414913; Openwood Cottage, Whitmead Lane, Tilford, Farnham GU10 2BS — MB BCh BAO 1960 NUI; MSc (Occupat. Med.) Lond. 1976; MFOM 1981; DAvMed 1969. Cons. Occupat. Health E.bourne Hosp. NHS Trust. Prev: Research Med. Off. Army Personnel Research Estab. FarnBoro.; Sen. Specialist (Aviat. & Occupat. Med.) Roy. Saudi Air Force Aeromed. Centre & Brit. Aerospace plc.
ADOMAKOH, Nicholas Kwame Poku 6 Templars Avenue, London NW11 0PD — MB BS 1992 Lond.
ADRAIN, Alexander (retired) — MB ChB 1967 Glas.; DPH Glas. 1970.
ADRANGI, Bahbak 5 Cruden Street, London N1 8NJ — MB BS 1988 Lond.
ADRIAANS, Beverley Moira Gloucestershire Royal Hospital, Great Western Road, Gloucester GL1 3NN Tel: 01452 395584; Tel: 01452 700883 — MB ChB 1974 Cape Town; FRCP 1994 Lond; MD Cape Town 1988; MRCP (UK) 1980; FRCP Glas. 1994. Cons. Dermat. Gloucester Roy. Hosp. Prev: Cons. Dermat. Greenwich Healthcare; Sen. Regist. (Dermat.) King's Coll. Hosp. Lond.; Lect. (Microbiol.) Lond. Sch. Hyg. & Trop. Med.
ADRIAN, Crawford Kerr 2 Erith Road, Belvedere DA17 6EZ — MRCS Eng. LRCP Lond. 1967.
ADRIAN, Nicolette Sophia West London Mental Health Trust, NHS Trust, Unbridge Road, Southall UB1 3EU Tel: 0208 3548160 Email: nicky.adrian@virgin.net — MB BCh 1991 Witwatersrand; MRC Psych. Cons. child/adolesent Psychiat., Lond.
ADRIANVALA, Fali Dorabji (retired) 99 Rhyd Y Defaid Drive, Sketty, Swansea SA2 8AW Tel: 01792 204553 — MB BS 1952 Bombay; BSc Bombay 1946; DA Eng. 1957. Anaesth. W. Glam. HA; Mem. Centr. Cons. & Specialist Comm.; Mem. Welsh Cons. & Specialist Comm. Prev: Anaesth. Glantawe Hosp. Gp.
ADSHEAD, David William Butt Lane Surgery, 58 Butt Lane, Leeds LS12 5AZ Tel: 0113 263 7635 Fax: 0113 279 1781; 6 Winnipeg Place, Leeds LS7 4NR Tel: 0113 262 9337 — MB BS 1975 Lond.; BA Camb. 1964. (Lond. Hosp.) Prev: Sen. Lect. (Gen. Pract.) Univ. Leeds.
ADSHEAD, Gwynnyth Mary Johanna Department Psychotherapy, Broadmoor Hospital, Crowthorne RG45 7EG Tel: 01344 754396 Fax: 01344 754334 — MB BS 1983 Lond.; MA Med. Ethics & Law 1989; MRCPsych 1987. (King's Coll.) Cons. Psychotherapist & Hon Sen. Lect. (Forens. Psychother.) St Geo.s Hosp. (p/t); Cons. Psychiat. Traum. Stress Clinic Middlx. Hosp.
ADSHEAD, James Michael 26 Southwold Mansions, Widley Road, London W9 2LE — MB BS 1993 Lond.
ADSHEAD, Patricia Anne Hopwood Medical Centre, 1-3 Walton Street, Hopwood, Heywood OL10 2BS Tel: 01706 369886 Fax: 01706 627619; 2 Saxwood Close, Norden, Rochdale OL12 7QX Tel: 01706 638336 Email: adsheadtrisha@hotmail.com — MB ChB 1983 Manch.; DFFP 1998; Cert. Family Plann. JCC 1987; BSc (Med. Sci.) St. And. 1980. (Manchester)
ADSHEAD, Sara-Louise Bramley Court, 59 Ryegate Road, Sheffield S10 5FB — MB ChB 1998 Sheff.; MB ChB Sheff 1998.
ADU, Dwomoa The Queen Elizabeth Hospital, Edgbaston, Birmingham B15 2TH — MB BChir 1970 Camb.; MA, MB Camb. 1970, MD 1981, BChir 1969; FRCP Lond. 1986. Cons. Phys. & Nephrol. Qu. Eliz. Hosp. Birm.
ADUR, Ranjan Mohan The Surgery, 17 Berwick Road, Rainham RM13 9QU Tel: 01708 520830 Fax: 01708 521137; 6 Nelmes

Road, Emerson Park, Hornchurch RM11 3JA Tel: 01708 447965 — MB BS 1975 Bombay. (Grant Med. Coll.)

ADUSU-DONKOR, Augustine 85 Balfron Tower, St Leonards Road, London E14 0QS — MB ChB 1980 Ghana; MRCOG 1991.

ADVANI, Andrew 100 Runnymede Road, Darras Hall, Ponteland, Newcastle upon Tyne NE20 9HH — MB ChB 1996 Ed.

ADWANI, Hemendra Pessumal Carmondean Health Centre, Livingston EH54 8PT Tel: 01506 432270 Fax: 01506 434644; 620 Queensferry Road, Edinburgh EH4 6AT Tel: 0131 339 5195 Fax: 0131 339 5195 — MB BS 1971 Gujarat. (B.J. Med. Coll. Ahmedabad) Princip. & Trainer (Gen. Pract.) Blackburn & Livingston; Indust. Med. Off. Cameron Iron Works Ltd & Geo. M. Whiley Ltd. Livingston. Prev: SHO (Orthop.) Roy. United Hosp. Bath; SHO (Gen. Surg.) Hull Roy. Infirm.

ADWANI, Satish Sadanand Heart Unit, Birmingham Childrens Hospital, Ladywood, Middleway, Birmingham B16 8ET — MB BS 1986 Poona; MRCP (UK) 1992.

AEBERHARD, Penelope Jane 84 Rogers Lane, Stoke Poges, Slough SL2 4LF Tel: 01753 646747 Fax: 01753 646906; Millstones, Egypt Lane, Farnham Common, Slough SL2 3LF Tel: 01753 642739 Fax: 01753 642739 Email: penny-aeberhard@bt.internet.com — MB BS 1967 Lond.; MRCS Eng. LRCP Lond. 1967; MRCGP 1978. (Kings College Hospital, London) GP Trainer & Course Organiser Bucks.

AERTS, Saskia Lucia Francyna 76 Lindsay Road, Worcester Park KT4 8LE — MB BS 1997 Lond.

AERTSSEN, Anna Maria Gerarda 6 Blackberry Walk, Lychpit, Basingstoke RG24 8SN — MD 1990 Louvain.

AETHERIS, Phoebus Sophroniou 61 Brycedale Crescent, London N14 7EX — MB ChB 1962 Aberd.; FRCOG 1985, M 1970.

AFACAN, Ahmet Siyami Business Healthcare Ltd, The Occupational Health Centre, Leeming Lane S., Mansfield Woodhouse, Mansfield NG19 9AQ Tel: 01623 657446 Fax: 01623 423378; Brackenhurst, 201 Melton Road, Edwalton, Nottingham NG12 4BU Tel: 0115 923 1091 — Tip Doktoru 1965 Ankara; MSc (Occupat. Med.) Lond. 1970; FFOM RCP Lond. 1979, MFOM 1979; DPH Ankara 1968. (Fac. Med. Ankara) Chief Exec. & Med. Dir. Business Health Care Ltd. Mansfield. Socs: Soc. Occupat. Med. Prev: Dir. Med. Servs. Brit. Coal Corp. Mansfield WoodHo. Nottm.; Area Med. Off. Nat. Coal Bd. NE Area Gateshead & S. Yorks. Area Rotherham; Dep. Med. Off. Nat. Coal Bd. Doncaster Area.

AFAQ, Mazhar Ahmed 113 Clonmore Street, London SW18 5HD — MB BS 1996 Lond.

AFFIE, Edwina Marion West Midlands Public Health Observatory, Birmingham Research Park, Vincent Drive, Edgbaston, Birmingham B15 2SQ — MB BS 1987 Lond.; DFPHM 2001; MPH 2000; BSc (Hons.) York 1982; Dip. RCPath 1995. Specialist Regist. in Pub. Health Med., W. Midl.s Region; Hon. Clin. Lect., Div. of Pub. Health & Epidemiolog, Univ. of Birm. Prev: Regist. Rotat. (Histopath.) W. Midl. RHA.

***AFFLECK, Andrew Graeme** 4 Gillies Place, Broughty Ferry, Dundee DD5 3LE; Flat 0/1, 3 Fortingall Avenue, Kelvindale, Glasgow G12 0LR — MB ChB 1997 Glas.; BSc (Hons) Glas. 1994.

AFFLECK, Colin Cameron Tel: 01382 462222 Fax: 01382 452866 — MB ChB 1971 Ed.; BSc (Med. Sci.) Ed. 1968; FFA RCS Eng. 1977. (Edinburgh)

AFFLECK, Iain Robert Old Machar Medical Practice, 526 King Street, Aberdeen AB24 5RS Tel: 01224 480324 Fax: 01224 276121; 61 Newburgh Drive, Bridge of Don, Aberdeen AB22 8SR Tel: 01224 703912 — MB ChB 1977 Aberd.; MRCGP 1982; DRCOG 1982; DA Eng. 1980. (Aberdeen)

AFFLECK, Ronald Lindsay 22 William Street, Edinburgh EH3 7NH Tel: 0131 225 1214 — MB ChB 1988 Ed.; MRCGP 1995. Trainee GP Edin.

AFFLECK, Ruth Buchanan 61 Newburgh Drive, Bridge of Don, Aberdeen AB22 8SR Tel: 01224 703912 — MB ChB 1977 Aberd. Examg. Med. Off.

AFFLEY, Brendan Thomas 101 Llanedeyrn Road, Cyncoed, Cardiff CF23 9DU — MB BCh 1994 Wales.

AFFOLTER, Jonathan Theodore 1 Mortonhall Road, Edinburgh EH9 2HS — MB ChB 1995 Aberd.

AFGHAN, Kamaruddin The Surgery, 37 High Road, London N15 6DS Tel: 020 8809 6445 Fax: 020 8809 2640 — MD BS 1961 Sind; MB BS Sind 1961. (Sind)

AFIFI, Asad 41 Western Road, Billericay CM12 9DX Tel: 01277 651011 Fax: 01277 658119 — MD 1966 Afghanistan. (Kabul University) GP; Clin. Asst. Essex Spinal Centre, BUPA Hosp., Brentwood, Essex. Socs: BMA; Med. Protec. Soc.

AFIFI, Mr Reda Abd El Maksoud Mohamed 16 Staff Residence, Weston-Super-Mare General Hospital, Weston Super Mare BS23 4TQ — MB BCh 1976 Cairo; MS (Obst. & Gyn.) Cairo 1983, MB BCh 1976; MRCOG 1989.

AFNAN, Ali Mohammad Masoud Birmingham Womens Hospital, Edgbaston, Birmingham B15 2TG Tel: 0121 627 2699 Fax: 0121 627 2701 Email: masoud.afnan@bham-womens.thenhs.com; 3 Britannic Gardens, Yew Tree Rd, Moseley, Birmingham B13 8QX Tel: 0121 442 6272 — MB BS 1980 Lond.; MRCOG 1987. (Char. Cross Hosp.) Cons (O & G) Birm. Wom.s Hosp.; Hon. Sen. Lect. (Obst. & Gyn.) Univ. of Birm. Prev: Sen. Regist. (O & G) St. Helier Hosp. Carshalton.; Sen. Regist. (O & G) Hammersmith Hosp. 1990 - 1992.

AFOLAMI, Samuel Olubunmi 33 Emery Down Close, Martins Heron, Bracknell RG12 9FH Tel: 01384 860914 Fax: 01344 860914 Email: bunmi@dee lay.demon.co.uk — MB BS 1983 Lagos; FRCA. Sen. Specialist Regist. (Anaesth. & Intens. Care) Hammersmith Hosp. Lond. Socs: Assn. Cardioth. Anaeth.; Intens. Care Soc. Prev: Specialist Regist. (Anaesth. & Intens. Care) Hammersmith, Lond.; Specialist Regist. Roy. Brompton Hosp. Lond.; Specialist Regist. Char. Cross Hosp. Lond.

AFRIDI, Adnan Khan 22 Tresham Crescent, London NW8 8TN — MB BS 1995 Lond.

AFRIDI, Mr Khan Wali Maywood Surgery, 180 Hawthorn Road, Bognor Regis PO21 2UY Tel: 01243 829141 Fax: 01243 842115; Clarence Lodge, Clarence Road, Bognor Regis PO21 1JU Tel: 01243 864007 — MB BS 1968 Peshawar; FRCSI 1985. GP Bognor Regis.

AFRIDI, Mr Mohammed Viqar Khan 6 Sussex Close, High Wycombe HP13 6UN — MB BS 1969 Peshawar; FRCS Ed. 1977.

AFRIDI, Shazia Khan 49 Goldhurst Ter, London NW6 3HB — MB BS 1997 Lond.

AFSHAR, Mr Farhad 149 Harley Street, London W1G 6DE Tel: 020 7935 7505 Fax: 020 7935 7245 Email: fary_afshar@fsmail.net; 9 Marlborough, 38-40 Maida Vale, London W9 1RW Tel: 020 7289 6847 — MB BS 1967 Lond.; MB BS (Hons.) 1967; BSc (Hons.) (Physiol.) Lond. 1964, MD 1978; FRCS Eng. 1972; MRCS Eng. LRCP Lond. 1967. (Lond. Hosp.) Cons. i/c Dept. Neurosurg. St. Bart. Hosp. Lond. & Cons. Neurosurg. Roy. Lond. Hosp. Socs: Soc. Brit. Neurosurgs.; Amer. Congr. of Neurosurgs.; World Soc. Pituitary Surg. Prev: Neurosurgic. Fell.sh. Ohio State Univ. Colombus, Ohio, USA; Sen. Lect. & Hon. Cons. Neurosurg. Lond. Hosp. & Hon. Lect. (Neuroanat.) Univ. Lond.; Sen. Regist. (Neurosurg.) St. Bart. Hosp. Lond. & Lond. Hosp.

AFUAKWAH, Jacob Kwadwo Bridgewater Medical Centre, Bridgewater Shopping Centre, Erskine PA8 7AA Tel: 0141 812 2022 Fax: 0141 812 2023; 161 Cleveden Road, Kelvindale, Glasgow G12 0JY Tel: 0141 357 1121 — MB ChB 1964 St. And. (St. And.) Princip. Gen. Practitioner. Socs: BMA. Prev: Med. Off. Kumasi Centr. Hosp., Ghana.

AFUAKWAH, Richard James Mill Street Surgery, 81 Mill Street, Rutherglen, Glasgow G73 2LD Tel: 0141 647 6294 — MB ChB 1988 Glas.

AFZAL, Amir Duke Medical Centre, 28 Talbot Road, Sheffield S2 2TD Tel: 0114 272 0689 Fax: 0114 275 1916; 76 Montgomery Road, Nether Edge, Sheffield S7 1LR — BM BS 1986 Nottm.; BMedSci (Hons.) 1984; DRCOG 1992; DA (UK) 1991. (Nottingham)

AFZAL, Mohammad Ayr County Hospital, Ayr Tel: 01292 41110 — MB BS 1965 Punjab; MB BS Punjab (Pakistan) 1965; DLO Eng. 1969. (King Edwd. Med. Coll. Lahore) Assoc. Specialist (ENT) Ayr Co. Hosp. Prev: SHO (ENT) Roy. Halifax Infirm. & Kingston Hosp.; Ho. Phys. Caerns. & Anglesey Gen. Hosp. Bangor.

AFZAL, Mubeen Mohamed The Rowans Surgery, 1 Windermere Road, Streatham, London SW16 5HF Tel: 020 8764 0407; 87 Fishponds Road, Tooting, London SW17 7LJ Tel: 020 8488 0143 — MB BS 1993 Lond.; DRCOG 1996; MRCGP 1998. (St George's) Princip. GP.

AFZAL, Mr Muhammad 74 Belle Vue Road, London E17 4DG — MB BS 1978 Punjab; BSc Punjab 1974; FRCS Ed. 1986; FRCS Glas. 1986.

AFZAL, Mr Muhammad c/o S. Mahmood, 48 Gordon Road, Ilford IG1 1SP — MB BS 1987 Bahauddin Zakariya Univ.; FRCS Ed. 1993.

AFZAL, Mr Naveed Flat 8, Tamarisk, Heatherwood Hospital, Ascot SL5 8AA — MB BS 1984 Peshawar; FRCS Glas. 1993.

AFZAL, Shahid 166 New Mills Street, Walsall WS1 4LQ; 25 Borage Close, Pontprennau, Cardiff CF23 853 — MB BCh 1997 Wales.

AFZAL, Tahiraa 22 Shalloch Park, Ayr KA7 4HL — MB ChB 1994 Glas.

AG HJ MOHD HASSAN, Dy Haslinda 3 Abbey Court, Abbey Grove, Eccles, Manchester M30 9QN; Room 124, Parkstone House, Poole General Hospital, Longfleet Road, Poole BH15 2JB — BM 1990 Soton.

AGABABIAN, Armand Arshavir 20 Ash Tree Gardens, Bolton le Sands, Carnforth LA5 8BD — MB ChB 1972 Baghdad; MRCP (UK) 1983; DCH RCP Lond. 1979.

AGARWAL, Mr Anil Kumar Flat 5, McRobert House, Hartlepool General Hospital, Hartlepool TS24 9AH — MB BS 1987 Calcutta; FRCS Glas. 1992; FRCS Ed. 1992. Regist. (Surg.) Hartlepool Gen. Hosp.

AGARWAL, Anjila Brook Hill Surgery, 30 Brook Hill, Little Waltham, Chelmsford CM3 3LL Tel: 01245 360253 Fax: 01245 361343; 1 Old Vicarage Close, High Easter, Chelmsford CM1 4RW Tel: 01245 231084 — MB BS 1992 London; MB BS Lond. 1992; DRCOG 1995. (London) GP Chelmsford; Clin. Asst. c/o Elderly St Michael's Hosp. Braintree.

AGARWAL, Gopal Chandra The Medical Centre, Gun Lane, Strood, Rochester ME2 4UW Tel: 01634 726555 Fax: 01634 296404; 11 The Shades, Strood, Rochester ME2 2UD Tel: 01634 710145 Fax: 01634 296404 — MB BS 1958 Lucknow; DMRE 1965; DTM & H Liverp. 1967. (K.G. Med. Coll. Lucknow) Socs: BMA. Prev: Regist. (Geriat. Med.) All St.s Hosp. Chatham; SHO (Med.) Wilson Hosp. Mitcham; Cas. Off. St. Bart. Hosp. Rochester.

AGARWAL, Ishwar Chand Hillfields Health Centre, 1 Howard St., Coventry CV1 4GH Tel: 024 76 224363; 27 Bispham Close, Bury BL8 2TJ — MB BS 1973 Jiwaji. (G.R. Med. Coll. Gwalior)

AGARWAL, Kailash Narain High Street Surgery, 87-89 High Street, Rishton, Blackburn BB1 4LD Tel: 01254 884424 Fax: 01254 884424 — MB BS 1970 Agra. (Sarojini Naidu Med. Coll., Agra, India) GP Blackburn. Prev: SHO (Orthop.) Mansfield Gen. Hosp.; SHO (Paediat. & O & G) King's Mill Hosp. Sutton-in-Ashfield.; SHO A & E Hosp. St. Cross, Rugby.

AGARWAL, Kaushik 98 St George's Terrace, Jesmond, Newcastle upon Tyne NE2 2DL — MB BS 1992 Newc.; BMedSci. 1991; MRCP UK 1995. (Newcastle) Research Fell., Freeman Hosp. Socs: RCP; RSM. Prev: Specialist Regist. Gastroenterol.

AGARWAL, Krishna Kumar, MBE The Village Surgery, 49 High Street, Wolstanton, Newcastle ST5 0ET Tel: 01782 626172 — MB BS 1961 Lucknow; FRCGP 1992, M 1976; DCH RCPSI 1969; DMRE Lucknow 1964. (King Geo. Med. Coll.) Prev: Regist. (Infec. Dis. & Geriat.) Bucknall Hosp. Stoke-on-Trent; Regist. (Med.) Coleraine Hosp.

AGARWAL, Meena Holly House, Flat 7, Stepping Hill Hospital, Stockport SK2 7JE — MB BS 1981 Kanpur; MS (Surg.) Kanpur 1984; FRCS Glas. 1993; Dip. Urol. Lond 1991.

AGARWAL, Meena Red Oak, Piccadilly, Scotforth, Lancaster LA1 4PW Tel: 01524 842322 Fax: 01524 841270; 3 The Woodlands, Old Langho, Blackburn BB6 8BH Tel: 01254 248685 — MB BS 1973 Lucknow; MRCPsych 1992. Cons. Child & Adolesc. Psychiat. Morcambe Bay Primary Care Trust Lancaster. Prev: Sen. Regist. Child Psychiat. Newc.; Regist. (Psychiat.) Walsgrave Hosp. Coventry; Assoc. Specialist (Psychiat.) Knowle Hosp. Fareham Hants.

AGARWAL, Mr Murli Dhar Clifton Lane Surgery, Stone Cross, West Bromwich B71 3AS Tel: 0121 766 6113 — MB BS 1972 Lucknow; FRCS Ed. 1981.

AGARWAL, Narendra Kumar Singleton Hospital, Sketty, Swansea SA2 8QA Tel: 01792 205666; 81 Rhyd-y-Defaid Drive, Sketty, Swansea SA2 8AN Tel: 01792 20155 — MB BS 1958 Lucknow; 1991 FRCP Lond. 1991; 1967 MRCP (Lond) 1967; 1961 DCH Eng. 1961; 1996 FRCPCH. Cons. Paediat. Base Hosp. Singleton Swansea.; Hon. Clin. Teach. Univ. Wales Coll. Med. Socs: Brit. Paediat. Assn. Prev: Cons. Paediat. P.ss Margt. Hosp. Nassau, Bahamas; Sen. Regist. (Paediat.) Childr. Hosp. Sheff.; Regist. (Paediat.) Leicester Roy. Infirm. & Leicester Gen Hosp.

AGARWAL, Neel Kamal The Surgery, Clifton Lane, Stone Cross, West Bromwich B71 3AS Tel: 0121 588 7989 Fax: 0121 567 5418 — MB BS 1970 Lucknow. (Lucknow) GP W. Bromwich.

AGARWAL, Prabodh Chandra 10 Prince Consort Drive, Chislehurst BR7 5SB — MB BS 1994 Lond.

AGARWAL, Prem Swarup (retired) 128 Henrietta Street, Ashton-under-Lyne OL6 8PH Tel: 0161 330 6741 Fax: 0161 339 6117 — MB BS 1955 Lucknow; DCH Eng. 1957. Prev: Regist. (Paediat.) Ashton-under-Lyne Gen. Hosp.

AGARWAL, Ragini Kalpana 106 Greencroft Road, Hounslow TW5 0BH — MB BS 1992 Lond.

AGARWAL, Rajendra Prasad Old Swan Health Centre, St. Oswalds Street, Liverpool L13 2BY Tel: 0151 228 2216 Fax: 0151 228 2216; 8 Calder Grange, Calderstones, Liverpool L18 3LW Tel: 0151 428 9595 — MB BS 1972 Calcutta; BSc Calcutta 1965, MB BS 1972; MFFP 1993. (Calcutta Med. Coll.) GP & GP Trainer Liverp.; Sen. Clin. Med. Off. Family Plann. (Community Health) Liverp. Prev: SHO (Gen. Med.) Scartho Rd.Hosp. Grimsby; Sen. Resid. Med. Off. (Surg. & Med.) Univ. Teach. Hosp. Lusaka; SHO (Med.) Calcutta Med. Coll. & Hosps., India.

AGARWAL, Mr Ramesh Chandra Cwm y Dwr House, Cwm y Dwr Road, Briton Ferry, Neath SA11 2YT — MB BS 1971 Allahabad; FRCS Ed. 1980; FICS 1991.

AGARWAL, Roshan 6 Northfold Road, South Knighton, Leicester LE2 3YG — MB ChB 1995 Leic.; BSc Leic. 1993. (Univ. Leic.)

AGARWAL, Sangita 54 Rochford Road, Bishop's Stortford CM23 5EX — MB BS 1997 Lond.

AGARWAL, Saumya 39 Naples Drive, Newcastle ST5 2QD — MB BCh 1994 Wales.

AGARWAL, Seema 39 Naples Drive, The Westlands, Newcastle ST5 2QD — BM BS 1996 Nottm.

AGARWAL, Vasantika The Medical Centre, Gun Lane, Strood, Rochester ME2 4UW Tel: 01634 726555 Fax: 01634 296404; 11 The Shades, Strood, Rochester ME2 2UD Tel: 01634 710145 Fax: 01634 296404 — MB BS 1961 Lucknow; DObst RCOG 1970. (G.S.V.M Med. Coll. Kanpur) Clin. Asst. (O & G) All St.s' Hosp. Chatham. Socs: BMA. Prev: Regist. (O & G) All St.s' Hosp. Chatham; SHO (O & G) W. Kent Gen. Hosp. Maidstone; Ho. Surg. (Gen. Surg.) Medway Hosp. Gillingham.

AGARWAL, Veena The Mound Medical Centre, 4-6 The Mound, William Barefoot Drive, Eltham, London SE9 3AZ Tel: 020 8857 1957 Fax: 020 8857 0386 — MB BS 1967 Lucknow. (Lucknow) GP Eltham, Lond.

AGARWAL, Mr Virendra Kumar Beaumont Leys Health Centre, 1 Little Wood Close, Beaumont Leys, Leicester LE4 0UZ Tel: 0116 235 0435; 8 Iona Road, Tudor Lodge, Syston, Leicester LE7 1QP Tel: 0116 260 1525 — MB BS 1967 Lucknow; MS (Orthop.) All India Inst. Med. Scs. 1971. (G.S.V.M. Med. Coll. Kanpur) Med. Off. H.M. Young Offenders Centre Glen Parva Leics. & Leics. Prison. Socs: Assoc. Mem. Brit. Orthop. Assn. Prev: Regist. (Orthop.) Brighton Health Dist. & Fife Area Health Bd.

AGARWALA, Mr Raseswar Prasad (retired) 1 Ballylloughan Brow, Ballymena BT43 6PW — MB BS 1960 Calcutta; FRCS Ed. 1969; DLO Eng. 1963. Cons. ENT Surg. N. Area Health Bd. Prev: SHO (ENT) Roy.Hosp. Wolverhampton.

AGARWALA, Simon 1 Ballyloughan Brow, Ballymena BT43 6PW Tel: 01266 43270 — MB ChB 1997 Ed.; BSc (Hons.) Ed. 1995.

AGARWALA, Vijaya Kumar 47 Newlands Road, Crumpsall, Manchester M23 9BQ — MB ChB 1979 Manch.

AGARWALLA, Mr Balachand c/o Dr M.L. Agarwal, The Surgery, 8 Ashburnham Road, Bedford MK40 1DS — MB BS 1957 Univ. Utkal; FRCS Eng. 1964.

AGASS, Martyn John Benjamin Berinsfield Health Centre, Fane Drive, Berinsfield, Wallingford OX10 7NE Tel: 01865 340558 Fax: 01865 341973; Hampden House, Clifton Hampden, Abingdon OX14 3EG Tel: 01865 407928 Fax: 01865 407164 Email: martyn.agass@talk21.com — MB BChir 1974 Camb.; MA (1st cl. Hons.) 1974; MRCP (UK) 1976; MRCGP 1978; DCH Eng. 1975; FRCGP 1997. (Camb. & King's Coll. Hosp.) GP Trainer Oxf. Prev: SHO (Gen. Med.) Radcliffe Infirm. Oxf. & St. Nicholas Hosp. Plumstead; SHO (Paediat.) King's Coll. Hosp. Lond.

AGATHANGELOU, Cristina Olivia 9 Newton Avenue, Caversham Park Village, Reading RG4 6PX — MB BS 1996 Lond.

AGATHOKLEOUS, Konstantinos 35 Bruges Place, Baynes St., London NW1 0TJ Tel: 020 7482 6058 Fax: 020 7482 6058 — Ptychio Iatrikes 1984 Athens; MRCPsych 1995. Sen. Regist. Alcohol & Subst. Misuse, Maudsley Hosp. Prev: Sen. Regist. (Gen. Adult Psychiat.) Maudsley Hosp.

AGATHONIKOU, Alexander Flat 2W7, 3 Gassiot House, St Thomas' Hospital, 2 Lambeth Palace Road, London SE1 7EH — Ptychio Iatrikes 1987 Thessalinka; Ptychio Iatrikes Thessalonika 1987.

AGBAJE, Ishola Michael 277 London Road, Portsmouth PO2 9HE — MB BCh BAO 1997 Belf.

AGBAJE, Olumeni Akin Robert Frew Medical Centre, Silva Island Way, Salcott Crescent, Wickford SS12 9NR Tel: 01268 578800 Fax: 01268 578825; 31 Riverdale Walk, Wickford SS12 0DU Tel: 01268 472785 Email: oagbaje@aol.com — MB BS 1979 Ahmadu Bello U. (Ahmadu Bello U) GP Wickford, Essex. Socs: MDU; R.C.O.G.

AGBAMU, David Akpo'ovy Department of Histopathology, Arrowe Park Hospital, Upton, Wirral CM49 5PE Tel: 0151 678 5111 Ext: 2563 Fax: 0151 604 1733 Email: meddir@pathport.org.uk — MB BChir 1989 Camb.; 1989 MB BChir Camb.; 1989 MA Camb.; 1994 DipRCPath; 1997 MRCpath. Cons. Histopath., Wirral Hosp.NHS Trust (Arrowe Pk.).

AGBASI, Nwogo Nnunwa Dept of Obstetrics and Gynaecology, Peterborough District Hospital, Thorpe Road, Peterborough PE3 6DA — MB BS 1982 Univ. Nigeria; MRCOG 1994.

AGBEJA, Aderonke Mojisola 92 Candlemas Lane, Beaconsfield HP9 1AE — MB BS 1979 Ibadan; FRCS Glas. 1985; FCOphth 1988; DO RCPSI 1982.

AGBIM, Mr Osita Godfrey The Surgery, 99 High Road, Willesden Green, London NW10 2SL Tel: 020 8459 0579 Fax: 020 8830 1992; (Surgery) 131 High Road, Willesden Green, London NW10 Tel: 020 8459 0579 & 071 486 3499 — MB BCh BAO 1961 NUI; MRCS Eng. LRCP Lond. 1961; FRCS Eng. 1968. (Univ. Coll. Dub.) Research Asst. Med. Research Counc. N.wick Pk.; Cons. Nigeria High Commiss.. Prev: Lect. (Anat.) Lagos Univ. Teach. Hosp.

AGEED, Adil Bashir Mohamed Ahmed 45 Hospital Close, Leicester LE5 4WQ — MB BS 1986 Gezira U, Sudan; MB BS Gezira Univ. Sudan 1986.

AGELL ARGILES, Ignacio Flat 57, Block 19, Ysbyty Glan Clwyd, Rhuddlan Road, Bodelwyddan, Rhyl LL18 5UJ — LMS 1992 Barcelona.

AGER, David Alexander The Old Sawmill, 3A Cock St, Wymondham NR18 0BX Tel: 01953 604835 — MRCS Eng. LRCP Lond. 1948; FDS RCS Eng. 1969. (Guy's) Socs: (Emerit.) BMA; (Emerit.) Assn. Sc. Educat. Prev: Col. late RADC.

AGER, John Alfred Moore (retired) 3 Bowling Green Lane, Swindon SN1 4EU Tel: 01793 522423 — MB BS 1951 Lond.; MD Lond. 1960; FRCPath 1974, M 1963. Prev: Cons. Path. P.ss Margt. Hosp. Swindon.

AGER, Peter William Eastleigh Surgery, Station Road, Westbury BA13 3JD Tel: 01373 822807 Fax: 01373 828904; The Orchard, Wellhead Drove, Westbury BA13 3RD — MB BS 1963 Lond.; MRCS 1962 Eng.; LRCP 1962 Lond. (St. Geo.) Sec. Wilts. LMC; Chairm. Wilts. HA Primary Care Quality Gp.; Assoc. Tutor Bath Postgrad. Educat. Foundat. Socs: Assoc. Mem. Soc. Occupat. Med.; BMA; Assoc. Mem. RCGP. Prev: Clin. Asst. Eye Dept. Roy. United Hosp. Bath; Regist. (Ophth.) Salisbury Gen. Infirm.; Surg. Lt-Cdr. RNR.

AGGARWAL, Anil Meltham Road Surgery, 9 Meltham Road, Lockwood, Huddersfield HD1 3UP Tel: 01484 432940 Fax: 01484 451423; 17 The Ghyll, Fixby, Huddersfield HD2 2FE Tel: 01484 424708 — MB ChB 1979 Manch.; MBA 1995; MRCGP 1984. (Manchester) GP Huddersfield.; Vice-Chairm. S. Huddersfield PCG. Socs: Huddersfield Med. Soc.; Local Med. Comm. Prev: Trainee GP Huddersfield VTS; SHO (Path.) Withington Hosp. Manch.

AGGARWAL, Anjna Kumari 199 Oxford Gardens, Stafford ST16 3JD Tel: 01785 42560 — MB ChB 1992 Leeds; DRCOG 1994. SHO (Paediat.) Leicester Roy. Infirm. Prev: SHO (Med.) Russells Hall Dudley Hosp.; SHO (O & G) Wordsley Hosp. Dudley; SHO (Paediat.) New Cross Hosp. Wolverhampton.

AGGARWAL, Arjan Dass South Humber Health Authority, Wrawby Road, Brigg DN20 8GS Tel: 01652 659659; 8 Woodrow Park, Grimsby DN33 2EF — MB BS 1957 Bombay; MFPHM RCP (UK) 1989; MFCM RCP (UK) 1982; Cert. Family Plann. JCC 1975; DPH Liverp. 1963. (Grant Med. Coll.) Cons. Pub. Health Med. S. Humber HA; Cons. Communicable Dis. Control; Med. Off. (Environm. Health) N. Lincs. & NE Lincs. Councs.; Port Med. Off. Immingham, Hull & Goole & Grimsby Ports HAs. Socs: Pub. Health Med. Environm. Gp.; Overseas Doctors Assn.; BMA. Prev: Sen. Regist. (Community Med.) Yorks. RHA; SCMO Humberside AHA; Asst. Dir. Med. Servs. MoH, Kenya.

AGGARWAL, Arun Kumar Rainbow Surgery, Stocking Fen Road, Ramsey, Huntingdon PE26 1SA Tel: 01487 710980 Fax: 01487 710982; Ambleside, Upwood Road, Ramsey, Huntingdon PE26 2PE — BM BCh 1984 Oxf.; MA Camb. 1985; MRCP (UK) 1987; MRCGP 1988; DRCOG 1986. (Oxf.) Med. Audit Facilitator; Chairm. Audit GP. Camb. & Huntingdon EQUIP.

AGGARWAL, Ashok Kumar 18 Oakwood Avenue, Southall UB1 3QB Tel: 020 8571 5583 — MB ChB 1989 Liverp.; DCH RCP Lond. 1993; T(GP) 1993; DFFP 1993.

AGGARWAL, Atul Maylands Healthcare, 300 Upper Rainham Road, Hornchurch RM12 4EQ Tel: 01708 476411 Fax: 01708 620039; 52 Sylvan Avenue, Emerson Park, Hornchurch RM11 2PW Tel: 01708 441373 Fax: 01708 620039 — MB BCh 1988 Wales; MRCGP 1993; DCH RCP Lond. 1991; DRCOG 1991. Div. Surg. St. John Ambul.; Chairm. HornCh. PCG. Prev: SHO (Orthop.) Roy. Gwent Hosp.; SHO (Paediat.) Basildon Hosp.; Trainee GP Laindon.

AGGARWAL, Dhan Raj Thameside Community Healthcare NHS Trust, Thurrock Hospital, Long Lane, Grays RM16 2PX Tel: 01375 390044 Fax: 01375 364400; Orsett Hospital, 5 Imperial Avenue, Westcliff on Sea SS0 8NE Email: dhanraj.aggarwal@btinternet.com — MB BS 1980 Guru Nanak Dev. Assoc. Specialist (Med. for the Elderly) Thameside Community Healthcare NHS Trust, Thurrock Hos. & Orsett Hosp. Socs: BMA; BGS.

AGGARWAL, Elizabeth Krishna Louise No75, The Crosspath, Radlett WD7 8HP — MB ChB 1995 Manch.; BSc (Hons.) Manch. 1994; Dip Family planning; DRCOG 1999. (Manchester) SHO Paediat., Hemel Hempstead. Prev: GP Regist. Centr. Manch.; SHO (O & G) St. Mary's Hosp. Manch.

AGGARWAL, Mr Jawahar Lal (retired) 7 The Ghyll, Fixby, Huddersfield HD2 2FE Tel: 01484 537686 Fax: 01484 311377 — MB BS 1964 Punjab; MB BS Punjab (India) 1964; FRCS Eng. 1978; FRCOphth 1988; DO Eng. 1969. Prev: Cons. Ophth. Roy. Infirm. Huddersfield.

AGGARWAL, Krishna (retired) Pinderfields Hospital, Wakefield Tel: 01924 375217 — MB BS 1959 Bombay; FFA RCS Eng. 1965; DA Eng. 1965. Cons. Anaesth. Wakefield Hosp. Gp. Prev: SHO Walton Hosp. Liverp.

AGGARWAL, Mohanlal Wexham Road Surgery, 242 Wexham Road, Slough SL2 5JP Tel: 01753 552255 Fax: 01753 219100 — MB BS 1968 Punjab. (Punjab) GP Slough.

AGGARWAL, Murari Lal Orchard Cottage, Washingwell Lane, Wickham, Newcastle upon Tyne NE16 4HJ — MB BS 1967 Punjab.

AGGARWAL, Naresh Kumar Southchurch Boulevard Surgery, 27 Southchurch Boulevard, Southend-on-Sea SS2 4UA Tel: 01702 468443 Fax: 01702 603281 — BM 1984 Soton.; T(GP) 1991. Prev: SHO (O & G & Psychiat.) Roy. Childr. Hosp. Bristol; Trainee GP Swanage.

AGGARWAL, Neeru 8 Woodrow Park, Grimsby DN33 2EF — MB ChB 1987 Leeds. Trainee GP Grimsby.

AGGARWAL, Om Parkash City Surgery, 187 City Road, Roath, Cardiff CF24 3WD Tel: 029 2049 4250 Fax: 029 2049 1968 — MB BS 1967 Gujarat; MRCGP 1978. (B.J. Med. Coll. Ahmedabad) Mem. Gen. Practitioner Comm., Wales; Mem. BMA Welsh Counc.; Bd. Mem. Cardiff Local Health Gp.; Mem. Brutaf Local Med. Comm. Socs: BMA (Ex-Chairm. S. Glam. Div.).; Treas., Cardiff Med. Soc. Prev: Trainee GP Welsh Nat. Sch. Med. VTS Cardiff; Police Surg. Nairobi, Kenya; Regist. (Surg.) Kenyatta Nat. Hosp. Nairobi, Kenya.

AGGARWAL, Parveen The Barley Lea, Coventry CV3 1EG — MB BS 1980 Jammu and Kashmir; MB BS 1980 Jammu and Kashmir; LRCPS Glas. 1988.

AGGARWAL, Rajeev St Peter's Hospital, Guildford Road, Chertsey KT16 0PZ Tel: 01932 872000; 12 Lampeter House, Mount Hermon Road, Woking GU22 7TF Tel: 01483 772848 — MB BS 1994 Lond. (Univ. Coll. Lond. Med. Sch.) SHO (Paediat.) St. Peter's Hosp. Chertsey. Prev: SHO (O & G & Cas.) St. Peter's Hosp. Chertsey; Ho. Off. (Surg.) Luton & Dunstable Hosp.

AGGARWAL, Rajesh Kumar 16 First Avenue, London NW4 2RJ — MB ChB 1987 Ed.; MRCP (UK) 1991.

AGGARWAL, Mr Rajesh Kumar Department of Ophthalmology, Southend General Hospital, Prittlewell Chase, Westcliff on Sea SS0 0RY Tel: 01702 435555 Fax: 01702 221279; 31 Queen's Road, Southend-on-Sea SS1 1LT — BM 1983 Soton.; BM Soton 1983; FRCS Ed. 1990; MRCP (UK) 1988; FRCOphth 1990. (University Southampton) Cons. Ophth. S.end Gen. Hosp. & Basildon Hosp. Essex; Hon. Vis. Ophth. Moorfields Eye Hosp. Lond. Prev: Anterior Segment, Cataract & Excimer Fell. Moorfields Eye Hosp. Lond.; Sen. Regist. & Regist. (Ophth.) Birm. & Midl. Eye Hosp.; SHO (Ophth.) Addenbrooke's Hosp. Camb.

AGGARWAL, Ram Paul Char and Aggarwal, Plumstead Health Centre, Tewson Road, Plumstead, London SE18 1BH Tel: 020 8854 8027 Fax: 020 8317 3030; 62 Birchwood Road, Wilmington, Dartford DA2 7HG Tel: 01322 613877 Fax: 01322 613877 — MB BS 1974 Guru Nanak Dev U; FRCS Ed. 1982; MS PGI Chandigarh 1978. (Guru Nanak Dev U) GP Plumstead, Lond.

AGGARWAL, Rita Rainbow Surgery, Stocking Fen Road, Ramsey, Huntingdon PE26 1SA Tel: 01487 710980 Fax: 01487 710982; Ambleside, Upwood Road, Bury, Ramsey, Huntingdon PE26 2PE — MB BS 1985 Lond.; MA Camb. 1985; MRCGP 1989; DRCOG 1987.

AGGARWAL, Rohini 17 Buttermere Road, Gatley, Cheadle SK8 4RQ — MB ChB 1998 Manch.; MB ChB Manch 1998.

AGGARWAL, Sabita Westbourne Surgery, 11A St. James Road, Marsh, Huddersfield HD1 4QR Tel: 01484 531672 Fax: 01484 456463; 17 The Ghyll, Fixby, Huddersfield HD2 2FE — MB ChB 1982 Sheff.; MRCGP 1986; DRCOG 1985. Princip. GP. Prev: SHO (O & G) Nether Edge Hosp. Sheff..; SHO (Geriat.) St. Lukes Hosp. Huddersfield; SHO (Paediat.) Huddersfield Roy. Infirm.

AGGARWAL, Sanjay Kumar 199 Oxford Gardens, Stafford ST16 3JD — BChir 1996 Camb.

AGGARWAL, Mr Shashi Pal 56 Oakham Road, Harborne, Birmingham B17 9DG Tel: 0121 427 9557 Fax: 0121 427 9557 — MB BS 1976 Lond.; FRCS Ed. (Ophth.) 1982; FCOphth 1989. (University College Hospital London) Cons. Ophth. Dudley & Sandwell HAs.

AGGARWAL, Ved Parkash 70 Tyrone Road, Southend-on-Sea SS1 3HB — MB BS 1971 Panjab; FRCOG 1989, M 1976.

AGGARWAL, Vimal Tel: 0161 223 0637 Fax: 0161 220 7220; 52 Spath Road, Didsbury, Manchester M20 2GT Tel: 0161 434 7127 — MB BS 1974 Bangalore; MFHom 1992; RSHom 1989; DRCOG 1978. (Bangalore Med. Coll.) GP; Homeopathic Practitioner. Socs: Fac. Homoeopaths; Brit. Assn. Sexual & Marital Ther. Prev: Clin. Med. Off. (Community Health) S. Manch. Health Dist.

AGGETT, Professor Peter John Lancashire Postgraduate School of Medicine & Health, Preston PR1 2HE Tel: 01772 892791 Fax: 01772 892992 Email: pjaggett@uclan.ac.uk; 194 Upper Malone Road, Dunmurry, Belfast BT17 9JZ — MB ChB 1967 Sheff.; MSc Lond. 1977; FRCP Ed. 1989; FRCP Lond. 1987; FRCP Glas. 1987; MRCP (UK) 1973; MRCS Eng. LRCP Lond. 1967; FRCPCH 1997; DCH Eng. 1974. (Sheff.) Head of Sch., Lancs. Postgrad. Sch. of Med. & Health (U. of C.L., Preston); Hon. Cons. Paediat.: Roy. Preston Hosp., Blackpool Vict. Hosp & Burnley Gen. Hosp. Prev: Sen. Lect. (Child Health & Nutrit.) Aberd.; Asst. Dir. Inst. Food Research Norwich; Surg. Lt. RN Med. Specialist.

AGHA, Dr 99 Tyrone Road, Thorpe Bay, Southend-on-Sea SS1 3HD — MB BS 1967 Dacca. (Dacca) GP S.end-on-Sea.

AGHADIUNO, Mabel — MB ChB 1983 Glas.; MRCGP 1990; DGM RCP Lond. 1989; MFHom 1997; MSc. Liverp. (Glas.) p/t Gen. Practioner; Assoc. Specialist. In Homoeop. Socs: BMA; Roy. Coll. Gen. Pract.; Fac. Homoeop. Prev: SHO Homoepathic Med.; Assoc. GP; Clin. Asst. in Homoeopathy.

AGHAHOSEINI, Assad Mohammad Reza 125 Woodgreen Road, Leicester LE4 9UD — MB ChB 1992 Leic.

AGHEL, Matoug Moh 108 Victoria Road, Pinxton, Nottingham NG16 6NH — MB BS 1976 Garyounis; MRCP (UK) 1986; T(GP) 1991; DCH Dub. 1979. GP Princip. Socs: MDU.

AGIUS, Erika Veronika 19 Argyle Place, London W6 0RQ — BM BS 1992 Flinders.

AGIUS, Mark (retired) Bedfordshire & Luton Community NHS Trusts, Charter House, Alma St., Luton LU1 2P — MD 1975 Malta. Staff Grade Psychiat., Beds. & Luton Community Health Care Trust; Facilitator (Ment. Health) Primary Care S. Beds.; Med. Adviser S. Beds. Community Health Care Trust. Prev: GP Luton.

AGIUS, Professor Raymond Martin Centre for Occupational and Environmental Health, University of Manchester, Stopford Building, Oxford Road, Manchester M13 9PL; Email: raymond@agius.com — MRCS Eng. LRCP Lond. 1977; DM 1999 Soton; AFOM 1987 RCP, Lond; MFOM 1990 RCP, Lond; FRCP 1997 Lond; FFOM 1994 RCP, Lond.; MD 1989 Malta; FRCP 1992 Ed; MRCP 1979 UK. Prof. (Occup. & Environ. Med.) Med. Fac., Manch.; Hon. Cons. Manch. Roy. Infirm. & Wythenshawe Hosp..; Dir, centre for Occupat.al and Environm. Health, Univ. of Manch. Socs: (Ex-Pres.) Brit. Occupat. Hyg. Soc.; Soc. Occupat. Med.; BMA. Prev: Prof. of Occupat.al & Environm. Med., Univ. of Manch.; Dir. of Med. Servs. & Cons. Occupat. Phys. Inst. Occupat. Med. Edin.; Clin. Research Fell. & Regist. Soton. Gen. Hosp.

AGIUS, Richard (retired) 55 Horseshoe Crescent, Beaconsfield HP9 1LJ Tel: 01494 674220 — MB BS Lond. 1954.

AGIUS-FERNANDEZ, Adriana 2 Lytham Close, Aintree, Liverpool L10 1NF — MRCS Eng. LRCP Lond. 1981; MRCP (UK). SHO (Ophth.) Wolverhampton Eye Infirm. & N.ampton Gen. Hosp. Socs: BMA. Prev: SHO (Chest Med. & Rheum.) Broomfield Hosp. Chelmsford; Ho. Off. (Surg.) S.end HA; Ho. Off. (Med.) Amersham Gen. Hosp.

AGIUS-FERRANTE, Marie-Therese Blossoms Inn Medical Centre, 21/26 Garlick Hill, London EC4 2AU Tel: 020 7606 6159; 104 Queens Avenue, London N3 2NP — MB BS 1972 Lond.; MRCS Eng. LRCP Lond. 1972. (St. Bart. Lond.) Prev: Sen. Part. GP Finchley.

AGLAN, Magdy Yassin Abd El Azim Anaesthetic Department / Pain Clinic, Macclesfield District G.H., Victoria Rd, Macclesfield SK10 3BL Tel: 01625 661348 Fax: 01625 661092; 1 Byre Close, Sale, Manchester M33 2LB — MB BCh 1981 Alexandria; FFA RCSI 1990; 1984 MSc Alexandria; 1991 FRCA.; 1992 DEAA. (Alexandria Univ. Egypt) p/t Cons. Pain Managem. and Anaesth., Macclesfield DG Hosp. 1997. Socs: Eur. Acad. Anaesthesiol.; Internat. Assn. Study of Pain; Pain Soc. Prev: Cons. (Locum) N. Manch. G.H. 1996; Clin. Instruc. UCI Med. Centre, CA, USA 1995; Sen. Regist. (Anaesth.) NWRHA Rotat. 1992.

AGNEW, Alan Norman David Andrew House Surgery, 2 South Terrace, Camborne TR14 8ST Tel: 01209 714876 Fax: 01209 612334 — MB BCh BAO 1980 Belf.; MRCGP 1994; MRCPath 1989; T(GP) 1994; DFFP 1993; DRCOG 1992; T(M) 1991; T(Path) 1991; FRCPath 1998. (Qu. Univ. Belf.) GP Princip. & Partner Andrew Ho. Surg. Camborne; Clin. Asst. (Haemat.) Treliske Hosp. Truro. Socs: Assn. Clin. Path.; Brit. Soc. Haematol.; Diplomates Assn. RCOG. Prev: GP Asst. Co. Armagh; Gen. Manager, Occupat. Health Consultancy, Belf.; Sen. Regist. (Haemat.) Belf. City & Roy. Vict. Hosps.

AGNEW, Elizabeth Marguerite Helsby Health Centre, Lower Robin Hood Lane, Helsby, Warrington WA6 0BW Tel: 01928 723676 Fax: 01928 725677; Southbank, Alvanley Road, Helsby, Warrington WA6 9PU — MB ChB 1983 Bristol; MRCGP 1988; DRCOG 1986. GP Helsby.

AGNEW, Iris Preston Grove Medical Centre, Preston Grove, Yeovil BA20 2BQ Tel: 01935 474353 Fax: 01935 425171; 3 Court Gardens, Yeovil BA21 3LZ Tel: 01935 479233 Fax: 01935 479233 — MB BCh BAO 1973 Belf.; DRCOG 1978. (Belf.) Prev: SHO S.mead Hosp. Bristol; SHO Roy. Belf. Hosp. Sick Childr.; Ho. Off. Belf. City Hosp.

AGNEW, John Frederick (retired) Whitehaven, The Green, Whiston, Rotherham S60 4JD — MB ChB 1960 St. And. Prev: Ho. Surg. & Ho. Phys. Roy. Infirm. Derby.

AGNEW, Linda Mary Dunluce Health Centre, 1 Dunluce Avenue, Belfast BT9 7HR — MB BCh BAO 1987 Belf.; MRCGP 1991; DCH RCPS Glas. 1990; DGM RCP Lond. 1989. p/t Retainee in Gen. Pract.

AGNEW, Maureen 8 Inveresk Place, Coatbridge ML5 2DA Tel: 01236 424466 — LRCP LRCS Ed. LRFPS Glas. 1950; Exams Edin. 1950. (Anderson College Glasgow) Examr. St And.Ambul. Scotl.

AGNEW, Maurice Norman Hollins Park, Hollins Lane, Winwick, Warrington WA2 8WA Tel: 01925 664124 Fax: 01925 664117 — MB BCh BAO 1980 Belf.; MRCPsych 1984. Cons. Psychiat. Warrington Community Health Care, NHS Trust. Prev: Cons. Psychiat. Halton Gen. Hosp. Runcorn.; Cons. Psyhiat. Tameside & Glossop community & Priority NHS Trust.

AGNEW, Neil Murray Karibu, Stockcross, Newbury RG20 8LH — MB BS 1993 Lond.

AGNEW, Robin Alan Leslie 69 Greetby Hill, Ormskirk L39 2DR Tel: 01695 574877 — MB BCh BAO 1950 Dub.; MD Dub. 1955; FRCPI 1971, M 1956. (TC Dub.) Emerit. Cons. Chest Phys. Liverp. HA. Socs: Fell. Roy. Soc. Med.; Brit. Thorac. Soc.; Liverp. Med. Hist. Soc. Prev: Cons. Mem. Med. Appeal Tribunals NW Region; Cons. Phys. Mersey RHA & Regional Thoracic Unit Fazakerley & BRd.green Hosps. Liverp.; Regist. (Med.) St. Richard's Hosp. Chichester.

AGNEW, Sydney Alexander (retired) Roachill Farm, Knowstone, South Molton EX36 4EB Tel: 013984 341248 Fax: 01398 341678 — MB BCh BAO 1950 Belf.; Cert Family Plann JCC 1980; Cert. Av Med. 1975.

AGNIHOTRI, Sangeeta 17 Cleanthus Road, London SE18 3DE — MB BS 1992 Lond.; BSc (Hons.) Biochem. Lond. 1989. (Char. Cross and Westm.) SHO (O & G) John Radcliffe Hosp. Oxf. Prev: Sen. RMO (O & G) King Edwd. Memor. Hosp., W. Australia; SHO (O & G) St. Thos. Hosp. Lond.; SHO (O & G) Guy's Hosp. Lond.

AGOMBAR, Andrew Charles 13 Spenders Close, Basildon SS14 2NX — MB BS 1990 Lond.

AGOSTON, Stephen Anthony 15 Winterburn Road, Worcester WR2 6DW Tel: 0973 392030 Email: sagoston@aol.com — MB ChB 1988 Cape Town; MBA 1995.

AGRANOFF, Daniel David 58 Endymion Road, London SW2 2BT — MB BChir 1990 Camb.

AGRANOFF, Jonathan 27 Oman Avenue, London NW2 6AX Email: 100712.2274@compuserve.com — BM 1994 Soton.

AGRAWAL, Aloke Tel: 01245 513261 Fax: 01245 513032; 1 Honeypots, Beehive Lane, Chelmsford CM2 9ST Tel: 01245 350509 Email: alokeagrawak@yahoo.co.uk — MB BS 1981 Delhi; MRCP (UK) 1990. Cons. Paediat. St. John's Hosp. Chelmsford. Socs: Fell. Roy. Coll. Paediat. & Child Health (FRCPCH); BMA. Prev: Sen. Regist. (Paediat.) Basildon Hosp.; Regist. (Paediat.) Roy. Hosps. NHS Trust Lond.

AGRAWAL, Anupama Dolly Flat 1 Up Right, 63 Lymburn St., Glasgow G3 8PD — MB ChB 1998 Glas.; MB ChB Glas 1998.

AGRAWAL, Archana Tina 22 Hartop Close, Bedford MK41 8HE — MB BS 1998 Lond.; MB BS Lond 1998.

AGRAWAL, Mr Avinash 15 Furrowfelde, Basildon SS16 5HB Tel: 01268 281223 — MB BS 1993 Lond.; MSc Surgical Science, 1998; FRCS (Ed) 1999. (The Lond. Hosp. Med. Coll.) Res. Fell. Gen. Surg., UCL. Socs: Roy. Soc. Med.; Assoc. of Surg.s in Train. Prev: SHO (Gen. Surg.) OldCh. Hosp. Romford; SHO (Neurosurg. & Orthop.) OldCh. Hosp. Romford; SHO (A & E) S.end Gen. Hosp.

AGRAWAL, Bella Gopal 3 Charlemont Close, Walsall WS5 3ND — MB BS 1994 Lond.

AGRAWAL, Dwarka Lall Adwick Road, Mexborough S64 0BY — MB BS 1972 Calcutta. (Calcutta) GP MexBoro.

AGRAWAL, Gaurav Shanker 13 Appleton Drive, Greasby, Wirral CH49 1SJ — MB ChB 1995 Manch.

AGRAWAL, Gopal Krishna Oakwood Health Centre, 40 Izons Road, West Bromwich B70 8PG; 57 Hail Close, Kettering NN15 7LQ Tel: 01536 204849 — MB BS 1966 Vikram; MB BS Vikram l966.

AGRAWAL, Kishori Gopal 3 Charlement Close, Walsall WS5 3ND — MB BS 1965 Poona; MB BS Poona l965; FRCOG 1989, M 1973.

AGRAWAL, Kusum The Surgery, 1A Red Lion Road, Tolworth, Surbiton KT6 7QG Tel: 020 8399 1779; 1A Red Lion Road, Tolworth, Surbiton KT6 7QG Tel: 020 8399 1779 Fax: 020 8390 0817 — MB BS 1970 Rajasthan. (S.M.S. Med. Coll. Jaipur)

AGRAWAL, Lila Holmhurst Park Rise, Wolverhampton WV3 9JQ — MB ChB 1991 Dundee; MRCP (UK) 1995; MRCPCH Lond. 1997; DCH RCP Lond. 1994. Specialist Regist. (Paediat.) Soton. Gen. Hosp.

AGRAWAL, Meena Ram Department Paediatric Surgery, Guy's Hospital, St Thomas St., London SE1 9RT Tel: 020 8955 5000 — MB BS 1967 Bombay; MS Bombay 1970, MB BS 1967; FRCS Eng. 1975; FRCS Ed. 1975. (Grant Med. Coll. Bombay) Cons. Paediat. Surg. Guy's Hosp. & Childr. Hosp. Lewisham. Prev: Acting Cons. Paediat. Surg. Hosp. Sick Childr. Gt. Ormond St. Lond. & Qu. Mary's Hosp. for Childr. Carshalton; Sen. Regist. (Paediat. Surg.) Qu. Mary's Hosp. for Childr. Carshalton; Sen. Regist. (Paediat. Surg.) Hosp. for Sick Childr. Gt. Ormond St. Lond.

AGRAWAL, Murari Lal Ashburnham Road, 8 Ashburnham Road, Bedford MK40 1DS Tel: 01234 358411 Fax: 01234 273202 — MB BS 1972 Jiwaji. (Jiwaji)

***AGRAWAL, Nidhi** Raghu Kamal, Horseshoe La, Ash Vale, Aldershot GU12 5LJ — MB BS 1997 Lond.

AGRAWAL, Prabha Ashburnham Road, 8 Ashburnham Road, Bedford MK40 1DS Tel: 01234 358411 Fax: 01234 273202 — MB BS 1970 Inore; MB BS Indore 1970. (Indore)

AGRAWAL, Rajendra Kumar The Surgery, 1A Red Lion Road, Tolworth, Surbiton KT6 7QG Tel: 020 8399 1779; 94 Alexandra Drive, Surbiton KT5 9AG Tel: 020 8390 8444 — MB BS 1971 Banaras; MS Banaras 1973. (Inst. Med. Scs. Varanasi) Forens. Med. Examr. Surbiton.

AGRAWAL, Ratan Lal Southview ParkSurgery, Southview Park, London Road, Vange, Basildon SS16 4QX Tel: 01268 553292 Fax: 01268 559805; 8 Lingcroft, Basildon SS16 5EZ Tel: 01268 553292 — MB BS 1960 Rajasthan; DCH Calcutta 1961. (S.M.S. Med. Coll. Jaipur)

AGRAWAL, Samir Gupt 2 Windrush Avenue, Bedford MK41 7BS; 240 South Lane, New Malden KT3 5RW — MB ChB 1988 Bristol; MRCP 1991; MRCPath Part11994; PhD Immunology (uni of Paris) 1999. SR.

AGRAWAL, Sanjay 25 Sybil Road, Leicester LE3 2EY — MB ChB 1991 Dundee.

AGRAWAL, Sanjay Kumar Bobby Apartment K, 3 Magdala Road, Nottingham NG3 5DD — BM BS 1992 Nottm.; BMedSci. (Hons.) Nottm. 1990.

AGRAWAL, Shailesh Holmhurst, Park Rise, Wolverhampton WV3 9JQ — MB ChB 1997 Manch.

AGRAWAL, Shiva Ram Tudor Road Surgery, Tudor Road, Heath Town, Wolverhampton WV10 0LT Tel: 01902 731330 Fax: 01902 306406 — MB BS 1963 Lucknow.

AGRAWAL, Tapan 22 Hartop Close, Bedford MK41 8HE — MB BS 1995 Lond.

AGRAWAL, Vijay Kumar Stockingford Medical Centre, 13 Northumberland Avenue, Stockingford, Nuneaton CV10 8EJ Tel: 024 7638 6344 Fax: 024 7638 4512 — MB BS 1969 Bihar.

AGRAWAL, Mr Vijay Kumar 258 Broadway N., Walsall WS1 2PT — MB BS 1969 Indore; FRCS Ed. 1978.

AGU, Kenneth Chukwudi 24 Brook Road, Newbury Park, Ilford IG2 7EY — MB BCh 1979 Univ. Nigeria; BM BCh Univ. Nigeria 1979; MRCOG 1994; MFFP 1994.

AGUADO SAGARRIBAY, Mercedes 34 Leeward Gardens, Wimbledon, London SW19 7QR — LMS 1970 Madrid.

AGUILERA ROIG, Xavier Department of Orthopaedics, Southampton General Hospital, Tremona Road, Southampton SO16 6YD — LMS 1989 U Autonoma Barcelona.

AGULNIK, Peter Leopold Littlemore Mental Health Centre, Oxford OX4 4XN — FRCPsych 1985; MB BS 1960 Lond.; MRCPsych 1972; DPM 1965 Eng. (Lond. Hosp.) Cons. Psychiat. Littlemore Hosp. Oxf. Prev: Asst. Psychiat. & Sen. Regist. Littlemore Hosp. Oxf.; Instruc. (Psychiat.) Boston Univ. Sch. Med.; Reseaarch Fell. (Psychiat.) Tufts Univ. Med. Sch. Boston State Hosp., Mass.

AGUNWA, Mr William Chukurere Raphael Tel: 01420 588574 Fax: 01420 577019; Kitcombe Farmhouse, Kitcombe Lane, Farringdon, Alton GU34 3ND — MB ChB 1970 Glas.; FRCS 1978 Eng. Cons. Orthopaedic & Trauma St Helen & Knowsley Hosps. Trust.; Cons. trauma and orthopaedic Surg., St Helens Hosp. And Whiston Hosp., Merseyside. Socs: Fell. Roy. Soc. of Med.; Elected Mem.Brit. Orthopaedic Foot Surg. Soc.; Elected Mem. SICOT (Brussels). Prev: Research Regist. (Surg.) Oxf. HA; SHO (Orthop.) Roy. Nat. Orthop. Hosp. Lond.; SHO (Surg.) Farnham Hosp.

AGUSTSSON, Pall Department of Obst. & Gyn., Ward 37 & 38 Level 6, Ninewells Hospital, Dundee DD1 9SY Tel: 01382 60111 — Cand. Med. & Chir. Iceland 1978; MRCOG 1987. Cons. Tayside HB.

AGWU, Samson Chukwuma 49 Christchurch Close, Birmingham B15 3NE — MB BS 1980 Nigeria; MFFP 1995; MRCOG Lond. 1991. Staff Gyn. & Obst. Kidderminster NHS Health Care Trust. Socs: Fell. W. Afr. Coll. Surgs.; Brit. Med. Ultrasound Soc.

AGWUNOBI, Mr Anselm Onyemauche 18 Lytton Avenue, Enfield EN3 6EN — MB BS 1987 Nigeria; MB BS U Nigeria 1987; FRCS Glas. 1994.

AGYARE, Kofi The Royal National Orthopaedic Hosp. NHS Trust, Brockley Hill, Stanmore HA7 4LP; 14 Bell Close, Pinner HA5 2AQ — MB ChB 1986 Ghana; FRCA 1993; FFA RCSI 1993; DA (UK) 1991. (Univ of Ghana med School) Cons. Anaesth. Roy. Nat. Orthop. Hosp. NHS Trust Stanmore. Prev: Sen. Regist. (Anaesth.) Middlx. Hosp. Rotat.s Lond.

AGYEI, Senyo Kwame 110 Sherwood Avenue, London SW16 5EJ Tel: 020 8 765 0436 — MB ChB 1985 Ghana; LRCP LRCS Ed. LRCPS Glas. 1993. Locum GP. Prev: Trainee GP Lond.; SHO (Obst. & Gyn. & Geriat. Med.) Mayday Univ. Hosp.

AGYEMAN, Albert 18 Pilgrims Way, Standish, Wigan WN6 0AJ — MB ChB 1973 Ghana; MRCP (UK) 1985.

AGYEMAN, Kwado 581 High Road, Tottenham, London N17 6SB — MB BS 1977 London; MB BS Lond. 1977. (London) GP Tottenham.

AH CHONG, Ah Kian 9 Eastwood Street, London SW16 6PT — MB ChB 1981 Sheff.

AH-FAT, Mr Frank Gaetan St Paul's Eye Unit, Royal Liverpool University Hospital, Prescot St., Liverpool L7 8XP Tel: 0151 706 2000; 223 Minster Court, Liverpool L7 3QH — MB ChB 1989 Leeds; FRCS Ed. 1994; FRCOphth 1994. Specialist Regist. St. Paul's Eye Unit Liverp.

AH-FAT, Lim Nian Chow 65 Redwood Drive, Bradley Manor, Huddersfield HD2 1PW — MB ChB 1978 Manch.; MRCP (UK) 1982; FRCR 1986.

AH-KINE, Desiree Royal Victoria Infirmary, Queen Victoria Rd, Newcastle-upon-Tyne NE1 4LP — MB BS 1993 Newc.; FRCOphth 1998.

AH KINE, Phi Kian 171 New Road, West Parley, Ferndown BH22 8ED — MB ChB 1988 Manch. Prev: SHO (Anaesth.) Univ. Hosp. Wales Cardiff.

AH-MOYE, Guy René The Surgery, 4 Hardell Rise, Tulse Hill, London SW2 3DX Tel: 020 8674 6586; 9 Crescent Way, Norbury, London SW16 3AL — MB BS 1966 Lond.; MRCP (UK) 1970; MRCS Eng. LRCP Lond. 1966; MRCGP 1983; FRCGP 1994. (St. Bart.) Clin. Asst. Cardiol. Mayday Hosp.; GP Trainer Lond.; Hon. GP Tutor KCH; Tutor 1991 GP Gp.; Med. Manager (SELDOC GP Co-op.). Socs: Roy. Coll. Gen. Pract.(Lond. Fac.); Local Med. Comm. Prev: Comm. Mem. & Mem. Educat. Sub Comm. S. Lond. Fac. Roy. Coll. Gen. Pract.; Cons. Phys. Seychelles Gen. Hosp. Acting Chief Med. Off., Seychelles.

AH-MOYE, Michael Holly House Hospital, High Road, Buckhurst Hill IG9 5HX Tel: 020 8505 3315 Fax: 020 8504 7688; 14 Ossulton Way, London N2 0DS Tel: 020 8201 8819 Fax: 020 8455 4973 Email: m_ahmoye@compuserve.com — MB BS 1976 Lond.; MRCOG 1982; FRCOG 1998. (Lond. Hosp. Med. Coll.) Med. Dir. Fertil. & IVF Unit Holly Hse. Hosp. Buckhurst Hill. Socs: Fell. Roy. Soc. Med.; Eur. Soc. Human Reproduc. & Embryol.; Amer. Soc. Reproduc. Med. Prev: Cons. Gyn. Fertil. & IVF Unit, Humana Hosp. Wellington, Lond.; Lect. & Hon. Sen. Regist. (O & G) Oxf. Univ. & John Radcliffe Hosp. Oxf.; Regist. (O & G) St. Mary's Hosp. Lond.

AH-SEE, Mr Antoine Kim-nen Consultant General Surgeon, Ward 34, Aberdeen Royal Infirmary, Foresterhill, Aberdeen AB25 2ZN Tel: 01224 552106 Fax: 01224 403658 Email: akas@doctors.net.uk — MB ChB 1965 Aberd.; ChM Aberd. 1975, MB ChB 1965; FRCS Ed. 1970. (Aberd.) Sen. Lect. in Surg. Univ. Aberd. & Hon. Cons. Surg. Aberd. Roy. Prev: Ho. Surg. Hosp. Sick Childr. Aberd.; Ho. Phys. City Hosp. Aberd.; Regist. Aberd. Roy. Infirm.

AH-SEE, Mr Kim Wong Department of Otolaryngology - Head and Neck Surgery, Aberdeen Royal Infirmary, Aberdeen AB25 2ZN Tel: 01224 681818 Email: kim.ah-see@arh.grampion.scot.nhs.uk; Tel: 01224 863301 — MB ChB 1986 Aberd.; MD Aberd. 1994; FRCS Ed. 1991; FRCS Glas. 1991; FRCS (ORL) 1998. (Aberd.) Cons. Otolaryngologist - Head and Neck Surg., Aberd. Roy. Infirm., Aberd. Socs: Mem. Brit. Assn. Otorhinolaryng. Head & Neck Surgs. Prev: Regist. (Surg.) Glas. Roy. Infirm.; Clin. Research Fell. (Surg.) Glas. Roy. Infirm.; SHO III (ENT) Glas. Roy. Infirm.

AH-SEE, Mei Lin Wong St Ronan's House, St Ronan's Circle, Peterculter AB14 0NE; 9 Ridley Avenue, West Ealing, London W13 9XW Tel: 020 8567 7281 — MB BChir 1994 Camb.; MRCP (UK) 1996; BA Camb. 1991. (Cambridge University) Specialist Regist. (Clin. Oncol.) Roy. Free Hosp. Lond. Socs: Roy. Coll. Phys.; Roy. Coll. Radiol. (Home Assn. Oncol.). Prev: SHO Rotat. (Med.) St. Mary's Hosp. Lond.

AH-SEE, Sui-Yen W Lensfield Medical Practice, 48 Lensfield Road, Cambridge CB2 1EH Tel: 01223 352779 Fax: 01223 566930 — MB ChB 1989 Aberd.; MRCGP 1995. Prev: GP Regist. Camb.

AH-WENG, Allan 86 Herondale Road, Liverpool L18 1LB — MB ChB 1993 Dundee.

AH-WENG, Frank Prospect House Medical Centre, 84 Orrell Road, Orrell, Wigan WN5 8HA Tel: 01942 222321 Fax: 01942 620327; Tel: 01704 220493 — MB ChB 1993 Liverp.; BSc (Hons.) Anat. Aberd. 1988; DRPM 1999. (Liverpool) GP Princip., Orrell, Wigan; GP Regist. Socs: BMA. Prev: SHO (Obst. & Gyn.) Blackburn Qu.'s Rd., Hosp.; SHO (Gen. Med.) S.port DGH; SHO (Acute & Emerg. Med.) Roy. Liverp. Hosp.

AHAD, George Wadie Station Surgery, 8 Golden Hill Lane, Leyland, Preston PR25 3NP Tel: 01772 622505 Fax: 01772 457718 — MB BCh 1969 Cairo; MRCS Eng. LRCP Lond. 1978; DO RCPSI 1983; DHMSA 1984; DRCOG 1985.

AHAD, Mohammed Fazle Rubby 80 Claremont Road, Luton LU4 8LZ — MB ChB 1992 Dundee.

AHAD, Nurul Islam 58 Wynter Street, London SW11 2TZ — MB BS 1994 Lond.

AHAMED, Hosne Ara The Surgery, 113 Church Lane, Stechford, Birmingham B33 9EJ Tel: 0121 783 2861 — MB BS 1970 Dacca. (Dacca)

AHAMED, Masud The Surgery, 107 Warren Road, Kingstanding, Birmingham B44 8QL Tel: 0121 373 1511 — MB BS 1967 Dacca. (Dacca) GP Birm.

AHAMED, Mohamed Tel: 0151 426 5253 Fax: 0151 431 0652 — MB BS 1966 Mysore. (Kasturba Medical College Mangalore) GP Prescot, Merseyside. Socs: Med. Protec. Agency.

AHEARN, Raymond Stephen 11 Harthill Road, Calderstones, Liverpool L18 6HU Tel: 0151 724 1118 — MB BS 1959 Sydney; 1959 MB BS Sydney; 1964 FFA RACS; 1967 FFA RCS Eng.; 1992 FANZCA; FRCA 1993. Cons, Emerit., Roy. Liverp. Hosp. Socs: Fell. Roy. Soc. Med.; Assn. Anaesth. & BMA. Prev: Cons. Anaesth. Roy. Liverp. Hosp.

AHEARNE, David Anthony Jerome 13 Richmond Road, Manchester M14 6YW — MB ChB 1997 Manch.

AHEE, Mr Peter Robert Department of Accident & Emergency Medicine, City Hospital, Dudley Road, Birmingham B18 7QH Tel: 0121 507 5502 Fax: 0121 507 5182 — MB BS 1986 West Indies; FRCS Ed. 1992. (Univ. W. Indies) Cons., (A&E), Med., City Hosp. Birm.

AHERN, Michael Douglas 264 Maidstone Road, Chatham ME4 6JL — MB BCh BAO 1968 Dub.; DObst RCOG 1976. Prev: Ho. Surg. Dr. Steevens' Hosp. Dub.

AHERNE, John Joseph Aloysius Weavers Medical Centre, 50 School Lane, Kettering NN16 0DH Tel: 01536 513494 Fax: 01536 416521; Glanmire, 213 Deeble Road, Kettering NN15 5HL Tel: 01536 481201 — MB BCh BAO 1976 NUI; MRCGP 1980; DCH NUI 1980; DRCOG 1980. (Univ. Coll. Cork Irel.) Trainer (Gen. Pract.) Kettering VTS. Socs: Kettering Med. Soc.

AHIAKU, Mr Ernest Komla Nenonenemako 21 Alleyn Gardens, Plymouth PL3 5RS; 2 Blagen y Wawr, Bangor LL57 4TR Tel: 01248 384637 Email: ernest.ahiaku@nww.nhs.uk — MB ChB 1980 Ghana; FRCS Eng. 1990; Dip Urology 1994. (Ghana Med School) Cons. Urol., Gwynedd Hsp, Bangor.

AHILAN, Ratnajothi 30 Ramsthorn Close, Woodhill Park, Swindon SN2 2TZ Tel: 01793 701391 — MB BS 1995 Lond. (United Medical & Dental School of Guys & St Thomas' Hospitals) SHO Anaesth., P.ss Margt. Hosp., Swindon. Socs: BMA; MDU. Prev: Resid.ial MO, Ridgeway Hosp, Wroughton. Anat. Demos, Oxf. Uni; SHO Orthop, P.ss Margt. Hosp; SHO A&E, Watford Gen Hosp.

AHLING-SMITH, Helena Edith Maria, Surg. Lt. RN 42 Fore Street, Praze-An-Beeble, Camborne TR14 0JX Tel: 01209 831630 — MB BS 1994 Lond. Doctor in Roy. Navy. Socs: MDU; BMA.

AHLQUIST, James Alan Olof Southend Hospital, Prittlewell Chase, Westcliff on Sea SS0 0RY Tel: 01702 221204 Fax: 01702 221259 Email: dr.ahlquist@hospital.southend.nhs.uk — MB ChB 1982 Bristol; PhD Birm. 1991; BSc Bristol 1979; MRCP (UK) 1985. Cons. Phys. & Endocrinol. S.end Hosp.; Hon. Cons. Phys. & Endocrinol. Nat. Hosp. for Neurol. & Neurosurg. Lond. Socs: Soc. Endocrinol.; Diabetes UK. Prev: Sen. Regist. (Endocrinol. & Diabetes) Radcliffe Infirm. Oxf.; Research Fell. Harvard Univ. Mass. Gen. Hosp., USA; MRC Train. Fell. Univ. Birm.

AHLQUIST, Patricia Yvonne Ashley 95 Marine Parade, Leigh-on-Sea SS9 2NL Tel: 01702 716041 — MB ChB 1982 Bristol; BSc Bristol 1979; MRCP (UK) 1985; MRCGP 1987; DRCOG 1986. Specialist Regist., Palliat. Med. Socs: BMA; Christ. Med. Fell.sh. Prev: SHO (Med.) Manor Hosp. Walsall; SHO (Paediat.) Childr. Hosp. Birm.; GP Leigh-On-Sea.

AHLUWALIA, Anjali Consultant O&G, Wythenshawe Hospital, Manchester M23 9LT Tel: 0161 291 2954 Fax: 0161 291 2560 Email: anjali.ahluwalia@smuht.nwest.nhs.uk — MB BS 1980 Delhi; Dip Obst 1995 (RCOG/RCR) Ultrasound; MD Manch. 1995; MRCOG 1987. Cons. (O & G) SMUHT, Manch. Socs: BSCCP (Brit. Soc. of Colposcopy & Clin. Pathologists); Brit. Soc. of Fetal & Matern. Med.

AHLUWALIA, Ashvinderjit Singh 135 College Road, Manchester M16 0AA — MB ChB 1997 Liverp. SHO Med. for the Elderly.

AHLUWALIA, Jagjit Singh Neonatal Intensive Care Unit, Box 226, Addenbrookes Hospital, Cambridge CB2 2QQ Email: jag.ahluwalia@addenbrooks.nhs.uk; 83 High Street, Little Shelford, Cambridge CB2 5ES Tel: 01223 843443 — MB BChir 1987 Camb.; FRCPCH 1996; BA Camb. 1983, MA 1987; MRCP (UK) 1991; MRCGP 1990; DRCOG 1988; DCH RCP Lond. 1988. Cons. Neonatologist Addenbrookes Hosp. NHS Trust, Hill Rd. Camb.; Trainee GP Sch. La. Surg. Huntingdon. Socs: Neonat. Soc. (Mem.); Brit. Assn. of Perinatal Med. (Dep. Represen., Exec. Comm.). Prev: Trainee GP/SHO Hinchingbrooke Hosp. Huntingdon VTS; Ho. Phys. Middlx. Hosp. & Univ. Coll. Hosp. Lond.; Ho. Surg. Edgware Gen. Hosp. Middlx.

AHLUWALIA, Jagmohan Singh 1 Whitehall Road, Rugby CV21 2AE — MB BS 1975 Punjabi U. (Punjabi U) GP Rugby.

AHLUWALIA, Mandeep Singh 11 Kingsmead Close, Sidcup DA15 7LA — MB ChB 1997 Aberd.

AHLUWALIA, Navjot Singh 25 Findhorn Avenue, Hayes UB4 0DG — BM BS 1992 Nottm.

AHLUWALIA, Navneet Kumar Stockport Acute Services NHS Trust, Department of Gastroenterology, Stepping Hill Hospital, Stockport SK2 7JE Tel: 0161 419 5640 Fax: 0161 419 5944 Email: nka@man.ac.uk — MB BS 1978 Delhi; 1991 PhD Manch.; 1981 MD (Intern. Med.) Delhi; 1983 MRCPI; 1997 FRCP (I); 1983 MRCP (UK); 1994 MHSM; 1991 T(M); FRCP 1999 Lond.; 1999 Dip. EU Gastroenterology. Cons. Phys. & Gastroenterol. Stepping Hill Hosp. Stockport. Socs: Amer. Gastroenterol. Assn.; Brit. Soc. Gastroenterol.; Europ. Soc. of Gastroenterol. & Hepat. Prev: Sen. Regist. (Gastroenterol.) Manch. Roy. Infirm. & Hope Hosp. Salford; Regist. (Gastroenterol.) Univ. Hosp. Nottm. & Mansfield Dist. Gen. Hosp.

AHLUWALIA, Nirmal Singh 12A Frithwood Avenue, Northwood HA6 3LX Tel: 01923 835271 — MB ChB 1964 Ed.; FRCP Glas. 1987; MRCP (UK) 1970.

AHLUWALIA, Rajpal Singh 42 Kingscliffe Street, Harpurhey, Manchester M9 4PG Tel: 0161 205 9602 — MB ChB 1979 Manch.; BSc (Distinc.) (Biol.) Malawi 1974.

AHLUWALIA, Sanjiv Mohan Singh 23 Canons Drive, Edgware HA8 7RB Tel: 020 8958 3294 — MB BS 1994 Lond.; BMedSci (Experim. Path.) Lond. 1991.

AHLUWALIA, Sapna 43 Pinner Road, Harrow HA1 4ES — MB BS 1994 Lond.

AHLUWALIA, Sukhbir 65 Chichester Road, Cleethorpes DN35 0HY — MB BS 1997 Lond.

AHLUWALIA, Usha c/o Dr D. Raj, 5 Kindlewood Drive, Chilwell, Nottingham NG9 6NE — MB BS 1972 Delhi.

AHMAD, Abu Muzaffar 32 Brickfield Farm Gardens, Farnborough, Orpington BR6 7TE — MB BS 1963 Dacca; Dip. Addic. Lond. 1993; Dip. Psychiat. Lond. 1986; MSc. Univ. Lond. 1998. Assoc. Specialist, Oxleas NHS Trust.

AHMAD, Mr Aftab 3 Oakridge Close, Fulwood, Preston PR2 9PT Tel: 01772 774222 — MB BS 1966 Agra 1963; FRCS Ed. 1975 (SN Medical College, Agra India,) Locum Cons. Roy. Oldham Hosp.; Loc.cons. A & E Sunderland Roy Hosp. Socs: Med. Protec. Soc. Prev: Cons. Surg. Min. of Health, Zambia.

AHMAD, Mr Afzal 30 Hammond Avenue, Brown Edge, Stoke-on-Trent ST6 8QU — MB BS 1985 Punjab; FRCS Glas. 1991. (Rawalpindi Med. Coll., Pakistan) Clin. Fell. (Vasc. Surg.) Providence Hosp. Seattle, USA. Prev: Regist. (Gen. Surg.) Bradford Roy. Infirm.

AHMAD, Alfi Bin 68 Merches Gardens, Grangetown, Cardiff CF11 6RE — MB ChB 1998 Bristol.

AHMAD, Athar 8 Cressy House, Queens Ride, London SW13 0HZ; 60 Albert Road, New Malden KT3 6BS — MB BS 1989 Lond.; BSc (Hons.) Lond. 1986; MRCP (UK) 1992. Regist. & Research Fell. (Med. Oncol.) UMDS Guy's & St. Thos. Hosp. Lond.

***AHMAD, Ayesha** Tree Tops, Parsons Hill, Colchester CO3 4DT — MB BS 1998 Lond.; MB BS Lond 1998.

AHMAD, Aziz 27 Staveley Road, Luton LU4 0DG Tel: 01582 594714 — MB BS 1965 Peshawar; DTM & H Liverp. 1969. (Khyber Med. Coll.)

AHMAD, Aziz The Health Centre, Rose Tree Avenue, Cudworth, Barnsley S72 8UA Tel: 01226 710326 Fax: 01226 780627 — MB BS 1965 Peshawar. (Peshawar) GP Barnsley, S. Yorks.

AHMAD, Bashir, Lt.-Col. RAMC (retired) 3 The Pastures, Kingsworthy, Winchester SO23 7LU Tel: 01962 881124 — MB BS 1940 Punjab; DPM Eng. 1968; DPH Eng. 1949. Prev: Assoc. Specialist Psychiat. Basingstoke Dist. Hosp.

AHMAD, Bilquis Radnor Place Surgery, 2 Radnor Place, Liverpool L6 4BD Tel: 0151 263 3100; Shalamar, Woolton Park, Liverpool L25 6DU — MB BS 1969 Punjab; MB BS Punjab (Pakistan) 1969; DFFP 1993. (Fatima Jinnah Med. Coll. Lahore) Prev: Med. Off. Walton Hosp. Liverp.; Asst. Med. Off. Sahiwal, Pakistan.

AHMAD, Bushra 90 Fenham Hall Drive, Newcastle upon Tyne NE4 9XA — MB BS 1994 Newc.

AHMAD, Fahima Bano Shamima 114A Burnway, Hornchurch RM11 3SQ Tel: 01708 52786 — MB BS 1962 Dacca; DRCOG 1971. Sessional GP & Med. Off. Barking & Havering HA. Socs: BMA & BDMA. Prev: Regist. (Gyn. & Obst.) Centr. Hosp. Abu Dhabi; SHO (Gyn. & Obst.) St. Peters Hosp. Chertsey.

AHMAD, Farhan Syed 24 Long Drive, Burnham, Slough SL1 8AL; 34 Walton Heath Drive, Macclesfield SK10 2QN — MB BS 1998 Lond.; MB BS Lond 1998.

***AHMAD, Farida Sajjad Ali** 60 Elm Avenue, Eastcote, Ruislip HA4 8PB — MB BS 1998 Lond.; MB BS Lond 1998.

AHMAD, Farooq The Medical Centre, Tanhouse Lane, Church Hill, Redditch B98 9AA Tel: 01527 59192 Fax: 01527 597679 — MB BS 1972 Jammu & Kashmir. (Govt. Med. Coll. Srinagar) Trainee GP Burnham-on-Sea VTS. Prev: SHO/Regist. (Gen. Med. Rotat.) Wrexham Gp. Hosps.; SHO (Cardiol.) Regional Cardiac Centre Sefton Gen. Hosp. Liverp.; SHO (Coronary Care Med. & Cas.) Roy. Liverp. Teach Hosp.

AHMAD, Hasina Khatoon Branch Surgery, Old Ashby Road, Loughborough LE11 4 Tel: 01509 234101; 42 Cotes Road, Barrow-on-Soar, Loughborough LE12 8JS Tel: 01509 412375 — MB BS 1949 Punjab; MB BS Punjab (Pakistan) 1949; DObst RCOG 1965; DGO Dub. 1964; LM, DObst RCPI 1964. (King Edwd. Med. Coll. Lahore) Clin. Asst. Gyn., LoughBoro. Gen. Hosp. Prev: Asst. MOH Doncaster Co. Boro.; Dep. Obst. Off. St. Mary's Hosp. Leeds; Cons. Obstetr. & Gynaecol. Seventh Day Adventist Hosp. Karachi.

AHMAD, Hassina Begum 43 Lon-y-Gors, Caerphilly CF83 1DP — MB ChB 1998 Bristol.

AHMAD, Humayun 130 Upney Lane, Barking IG11 9LT Tel: 020 8594 4353 Fax: 020 8591 4686; 37 Lincoln Gardens, Ilford IG1 3NF — MB BS 1982 Karachi; MRCP (UK) 1990; MRCGP 1992. Med. Stud. Teach. in Primary Care; GP Trainer. Prev: Regist. (Med.) Roy. Oldham Hosp.

AHMAD, Imran 37 Longley Road, London SW17 9LA — MB BS 1996 Lond.

AHMAD, Irshad 1 Bronte View, Gravesend DA12 1PX — MB BS 1986 Pakistan.

AHMAD, Ishfaq 7 Broadwell Court, Castledene, Gosforth, Newcastle upon Tyne NE3 1YS — MS BS 1988 Punjab; MB BS Punjab 1988.

AHMAD, Izma Homa Harold Wood Hospital, Harold Wood, Romford RM3 0BE Tel: 01708 345533; 114A Burnway, Hornchurch RM11 3SQ Tel: 01708 452786 — MB BS 1990 Lond.; DRCOG 1993.

AHMAD, Jamil 4 Cayton Road, Greenford UB6 8BJ — MB BS 1978 Punjab.

AHMAD, Jarhat Jabeen 34 Kensington Road, Oldham OL8 4BZ — MB ChB 1966 Baghdad; FRCPath 1991, M 1978; DCP Lond 1974. Cons. (Microbiol.) Ealing Hosp. S.all.

AHMAD, Johan 56 Brunswick Street, Sheffield S10 2FL — MB ChB 1997 Sheff.

AHMAD, Kamran Saeed 37 Glebe Road, London N8 7DA — BM BS 1990 Nottm.; FRCA 1997.

AHMAD, Karim Zafar Flat 176, Lea View House, Springfield, London E5 9EA — MB BS 1998 Lond.; MB BS Lond 1998.

AHMAD, Khurshed (retired) 15 Holmston Road, Ayr KA7 3JH Tel: 01292 262522 — MB BS 1962 Punjab; MB BS Punjab (Pakistan) 1962; DO RCS Eng. 1972. Prev: Assoc. Specialist (Ophth.) Ayrsh. & Arran Health Bd.

AHMAD, Mahmud The Shalimar, 53 Sheepwalk Lane, Ravenshead, Nottingham NG15 9FD Tel: 01623 792531 — MB BS 1966 Punjab; MRCP (UK) 1976.

AHMAD, Mansoor Dewsbury District and General Hospital, Dewsbury Health Care NHS Trust, Healds Road, Dewsbury WF13 4SA Tel: 01924 465105 Ext: 3417 Fax: 01924 816087; 47 Chadwick Crescent, Oxford Park, Oxford Road, Dewsbury WF13 4SP Tel: 01924 502215 — MB BS 1980 Punjab; BSc MBBS MCPS Pakistan; DPM RCPSI; MMedSci (Clin. Psychiat.) Leeds. (Lahore, Pakistan) Assoc. Specialist.

AHMAD, Mr Mansur (retired) Dr Merali & Partners, GP Direct, 43 Butler Avenue, Harrow HA1 4EJ Tel: 0208 515 9300 — MB BS 1955 Punjab; FRCS Glas. 1966. Prev: Sen. Regist. (Thoracic) Harefield Hosp.

AHMAD, Manzur Ingrebourne Medical Centre, 135 Straight Road, Harold Hill, Romford RM3 7JJ Tel: 01708 372021 Fax: 01708 378161 — MB BS 1964 Dacca.

AHMAD, Maqsood 67 Brackenbury Road, Middle Floor, Hammersmith, London W6 0BG — MB BS 1981 Punjab.

AHMAD, Masood Nork Way Surgery, 63 Nork Way, Banstead SM7 1HL Tel: 01737 362211 Fax: 01737 362980 — MB BS 1964 Lucknow; MS Lucknow 1968, MB BS 1964; FRCS Ed. 1974.

AHMAD, Md Matin Uddin Villa 1, Hollins Lane, Winwick, Warrington WA2 8RT Tel: 01925 573129 — MB BS 1968 Dacca; MB BS Dacca, Bangladesh 1968.

AHMAD, Mr Mohammad Hafeez-Uddin General Hospital, Hartlepool TS24 9AH Tel: 01429 266654; 21 Warkworth Drive, Hartlepool TS26 0EW Tel: 01429 263871 Email: m.ahmad@virgin.net — MB BS 1971 Aligarh; MB BS Aligarh Muslim India 1971; FRCS Glas. 1983. (J.N. Med. Coll.) Assoc. Specialist (Orthop.) Gen. Hosp. Hartlepool. Prev: Staff Grade (Orthop.) Gen. Hosp. Hartlepool; Regist. (Orthop.) Batley Gen. Hosp., W. Suff. Hosp. Bury St. Edmunds & Friarage Hosp.; SHO (Gen. Surg.) Friarage Hosp.

AHMAD, Mohammed Taliquir 316/69 James Watt Street, Glasgow G2 8NF — MB ChB 1993 Glas.

AHMAD, Mohd Azhar 66 Dundas Street, Stockton-on-Tees TS19 0EX — MB BS 1997 Newc.

AHMAD, Muaaze Zamir 8 Netherwood Road, Manchester M22 4BQ — MB ChB 1996 Manch.

AHMAD, Mubashshar 90 Fenham Hall Drive, Newcastle upon Tyne NE4 9XA — MB BS 1997 Lond.

AHMAD, Mumtaz The Surgery, 2 Chatham Road, Bradford BD3 0JG Tel: 01274 636434 Fax: 01274 776522; 5 Upper Lombard Street, Rawdon, Leeds LS19 6BP Tel: 0113 239 1974 Email: mumtazahmad47@hotmail.com — MB BS 1972 Calcutta; DCH 1974 DCH 1974. (NRS Medical College Calcutta, India) GP Asst.; Staff Grade, Psychiat. Prev: RMO Fulford Grange Hosp. Leeds; Med. Off. Jamia Univ. New Delhi, India; Clin. Asst. (Haemat.) Seacroft Hosp. Leeds.

AHMAD, Munawar Christchurch Hospital, Fairmile Road, Christchurch BH23 2JX Tel: 01202 486361; 22 Emily Close, Christchurch BH23 2NN Tel: 01202 480967 — MB BS 1962 Punjab. (Nishtar Medical College, Multan, Pakistan) Clin. Asst., c/o the Elderly, ChristCh. Hosp., ChristCh., Dorset. Prev: Med. Miss. Ghana, The Gambia & Nigeria.

AHMAD, Mushtaq Aqueduct Surgery, Majestic Way, Aqueduct, Telford TF4 3RB Tel: 01952 591555; 5 Glade Way, Shawbirch, Telford TF5 0LD — MB BS 1965 Rajshahi, Bangladesh.

AHMAD, Mushtaq Clarkson Street Surgery, 42 Clarkson Street, Ravensthorpe, Dewsbury WF13 3DR Tel: 01924 491096; 15 Ashcroft Close, Sycamore Court, Batley WF17 7DP Tel: 01924 519630 — MB BS 1974 Kashmir. Socs: Med. Protec. Soc.

AHMAD, Muzaffar Mahmoud Bollington Road Surgery, 126 Bollington Road, Ancoats, Manchester M40 7HD Tel: 0161 205 2979 Fax: 0161 205 6368; 55 Cavendish Road, Ellesmere Road, Eccles, Manchester M30 9EE Tel: 0161 707 6864 — MB ChB 1966 Manch.

AHMAD, Nadeem 24 Radinden Manor Road, Hove BN3 6NH — MB BS 1994 Lond.

AHMAD, Naeem Child Health Department, Mansfield Community Hospital, Stockwell Gate, Mansfield NG18 5QJ; 38 Haddon Road, Ravenshead, Mansfield NG19 7BS Tel: 01623 478464 — MB BS 1983 Delhi; MRCP (UK) 1992; DCH 1985; FRCPCH 1997. (Univ. Coll. of Med. Sci, Delhi)

AHMAD, Naeem Anaesthetic Department, James Paget Hospitwal, Lowestoft Road, Gorleston, Great Yarmouth NR31 6LA — MB BS 1973 Punjab.

AHMAD, Nafis Panteg Health Centre, Kemys Street, Griffithstown, Pontypool NP4 5DJ Tel: 01495 763608 Fax: 01495 753925 — MB BS 1968 Jammu & Kasmir.

AHMAD, Nargis Shehnaz 65 Gibbon Road, Kingston upon Thames KT2 6AD; First Floor Flat, 95 Savernake Rd, Hampstead, London NW3 2LG Tel: 020 7485 5299 — BChir 1993 Camb.

AHMAD, Naseer 22 Armitage Close, Oldham OL8 4LG — MB BS 1968 Punjab; MRCP (UK) 1980.

AHMAD, Niaz The Homoeopathic Clinic, 7 Rickmansworth Road, Pinner HA5 3TF Tel: 020 8866 3712 Fax: 020 8866 9970 — MB ChB 1960 Glas.; MFHom 1962. (Glas.) Socs: Fell. Roy. Soc. Med.

AHMAD, Mr Niaz Department of Transplant Surgery, St James University Hospital, Leeds LS9 7TF Tel: 0113 244 8182; 10 St. James' Court, St. James' University Hospital, Leeds LS9 7TF Tel: 0113 243 3144 Email: mrpna@leeds.ac.uk — MB BS 1986 Karachi; FRCS Ed. 1992. (Dow Med. Coll. Karachi, Pakistan) Clin. Research Fell. (Transpl. Surg.) St. Jas. Univ. Hosp. Leeds. Socs: Brit. Transpl. Soc. Prev: Regist. (Gen. Surg.) RN Hosp. Plymouth; SHO Rotat. (Surg.) Derriford Hosp. Plymouth; Ho. Off. (Gen. Med. & Gen. Surg.) Civil Hosp. Karachi, Pakistan.

AHMAD, Mr Nisar Treetops, Parsons Hill, Lexden, Colchester CO3 4DT Tel: 01206 561670 Fax: 01206 561670 — MB BS 1965 Punjab; FRCS Ed. 1977; FRCSI 1977; FRCOphth 1988; DO RCPSI 1971. (King Edwd. Med. Coll. Lahore) Cons. Ophth. Essex Co. Hosp. Colchester. Socs: Oxf. Ophth. Congr. Prev: Sen. Regist. Addenbrooke's Hosp. Camb.; Sen. Regist. & Regist. Norwich Health Dist.

AHMAD, Nishat Glebe Farm Road Surgery, 37-39 Glebe Farm Road, Stetchford, Birmingham B33 9LY — MB ChB 1992 Dundee. Prev: SHO (c/o Elderly) Burton Hosp.; Ho. Off. (Gen. Med.) Walsgrave Hosp. Coventry.

AHMAD, Noor 48 Hindemith Gardens, Old Farm Park, Milton Keynes MK7 8PW — MB ChB 1996 Dundee.

AHMAD, Norezalee 4 The Fosseway, Bristol BS8 4EN — MB ChB 1994 Bristol.

AHMAD, Nuzhat 2 Grove Shaw, Kingswood, Tadworth KT20 6QL Tel: 01737 362211 — MB BS 1968 Lucknow; DA Eng. 1972. (GSVM Med. Coll. Kanpur)

AHMAD, Omar Abdul Fattah BUPA Alexandra Hospital, Impton Lane, Walderslade, Chatham ME5 9PG — MB ChB 1972 Baghdad, Iraq; MRCPsych 1980.

AHMAD, Qamar 3 Oakridge Close, Fulwood, Preston PR2 9PT Tel: 01772 774222 — MB ChB 1990 Dundee.

AHMAD, Qutubuddin Department of Paediatrics, Luton and Dunstable Hospital, Lewsey Road, Luton LU4 0DZ — MB BS 1970 Dacca; DTCH Liverp. 1979.

AHMAD, Rajai Ali Shahin 27 Eynham Road, London W12 0HD — MB ChB 1981 Sheff.

AHMAD, Rasheed Renal Unit, Royal Liverpool University Hospital, Prescot St., Liverpool L7 8XP Tel: 0151 706 2000 Fax: 0151 706 5841; Shalamar, Woolton Park, Liverpool L25 6DU Tel: 0151 428 4042 Fax: 0151 428 4475 Email: theahmads@aol.com — MB BS 1966 Sind; MSc Manch. 1973; DTM Hamburg 1969. (Liaquat Med. Coll.) Cons. Renal Phys. Roy. Liverp. Univ. Hosp.; Hon. Lect. (Med.) Univ. Liverp. Socs: Eur. Dialysis & Transpl. Assn., Merseyside Assn. Kidney; Res. & Liverp. Med. Inst. Prev: Wellcome Research Schol. in Clin. Pharmacol.; Asst. Med. Dir. Nat. Kidney Centre Lond.; German Acad. Exchange Schol. Univ. Berlin.

AHMAD, Mr Rasheeque Fulford Grange Hospital, Micklefield Lane, Rawdon, Leeds LS19 6BA — MB BS 1964 Agra; FRCS Ed. 1977. Prev: Sen. Lect. (Cardiothoracic Surg.) Roy. Vict. Hosp. Belf.;

Sen. Regist. (Cardiothoracic Surg.) Univ. Hosp. Wales; Regist. (Cardiothoracic Surg.) Killingbeck Hosp. Leeds.

AHMAD, Rizvana Shaheen 5 Bunten Meade, Cippenham Lane, Slough SL1 2YJ Tel: 01753 715043; 318 Cavendish Road, London SW12 0PJ — MB BS 1991 Lond.; MRCP (UK) 1995. (Char. Cross & Westm.) Regist. (Clin. Oncol.) Roy. Marsden Hosp. NHS Trust. Prev: Regist. (Clin. Oncol.) St. Barts & Roy. Lond. Hosps.; SHO Rotat. (Gen. Med.) Char. Cross Hosp. & W. Middlx. Hosp.; Ho. Off. (Gen. & Vasc. Surg.) Mayday Univ. Hosp. Croydon.

AHMAD, Rizwan Saeed 4 The Beeches, Brookfield, Johnstone PA5 8UZ — MB ChB 1998 Glas.; MB ChB Glas 1998.

AHMAD, Rosemina 50 Peel Pl, Ilford IG5 0PS — MB BS 1997 Lond.

AHMAD, Rukhshunda Naheed 59 Rowfant Road, London SW17 7AP — MB BS 1992 Lond.; DRCOG 1995; MRCGP 1997. (UCH)

AHMAD, Sabah 30 Bedford Road, Orpington BR6 0QH; 34 Clevedon Gardens, Hounslow TW5 9TS — MB BS 1994 Lond.

AHMAD, Saeed Westfield Surgery, Westfield, Graham Street, Johnstone PA5 8QY Tel: 01505 337888 Fax: 01505 337700 — MB BS 1965 Punjab; MB BS Punjab (Pakistan) 1965. (King Edwd. Med. Coll.) Regist. Dykebar Hosp. Paisley.

AHMAD, Saeeda 54 Parkfield Road, Ickenham, Uxbridge UB10 8LW Tel: 01895 673391 — MB BS 1963 Punjab. Prev: Staff Psychiat. St. Thos. Psych. Hosp. Canada; Regist. Ealing Hosp. Lond.

AHMAD, Sajjad 92 Reddings Road, Moseley, Birmingham B13 8LR; 53 Moorcroft Road, Birmingham B13 8LT — MB BS 1997 Lond.

AHMAD, Sajjad 95 Sutherland Avenue, Newcastle upon Tyne NE4 9NR — MB BS 1997 Newc.

AHMAD, Sakhina Louise Monta Rosa, 15 Vicarage Lane, Shrivenham, Swindon SN6 8DT — MB BS 1996 Lond.

AHMAD, Salma 46 Wansunt Road, Bexley DA5 2DH Tel: 01322 521790 — MB BS 1975 Osmania.

***AHMAD, Samarina** 12 Oakway, Southgate, London N14 5NN — MB BS 1997 Lond.

AHMAD, Sameena Isobel Bolton Centre for Sexual Health, Royal Bolton Hospital, Minerva Road, Farnworth, Bolton BL4 0JR Tel: 01204 390777 Fax: 01204 390779; Winterbrook, The Courtyard, 16 Olde Stoneheath Court, Heath Charnock, Chorley PR6 9EH Tel: 01257 272553 — MB ChB 1990 Glas.; BSc (Hons.) Glas. 1987; MRCP (UK) 1993; Dip. GU Med. Soc. Apoth. Lond 1995; DTM & H RCP Lond. 1994; DFFP 1994. Cons. (Genitourin. Med.) Bolton Centre for Sexual Health. Socs: Assoc. Mem. Inst. Psychosexual Med; Assn. Genitourin. Med.; Soc. Study VD. Prev: Sen. Regist. Whittall St. Clinic, Birm.

AHMAD, Shabbir The Armthorpe Surgery, Church Street, Armthorpe, Doncaster DN3 3AH Tel: 01302 831437 Fax: 01302 300623; 178 Stoops Lane, Bessacarr, Doncaster DN4 7RA Tel: 01302 371426 — MB BS 1976 Punjab; DFFP 1996; DRCOG 1992; DCH RCPS Glas. 1986; DCH Dub. 1983. (Nishtar Medical College Pakistan) Socs: BMA. Prev: Regist. (Paediat.) Doncaster Roy. Infirm.; Community Med. Off. Doncaster; SHO (O & G) Doncaster Roy. Infirm.

AHMAD, Shagufta 57 Rashleigh House, Thanet St., London WC1H 9ER — MB BS 1996 Lond.

AHMAD, Shahed Nizam 196 South Lodge Drive, London N14 4XN — MB BChir 1993 Camb.

AHMAD, Shahid Munir Burnley General Hospital - Mary Burbury Unit, Casterton Avenue, Burnley BB10 2PQ Tel: 01282 474800 — MB BS 1974 Punjab; MRCPsych. 1987; DPM 1986. Cons. Child & Adolesc. Psychiat. Burnley Gen. Hosp.

AHMAD, Shahla GP Direct, 5/7 Welback Road, West Harrow, Harrow HA2 0RH Tel: 020 8515 9300 Fax: 020 8515 9300 — MB BS 1994 Lond.

AHMAD, Shahnaz 17 Askill Drive, London SW15 2HX — MB BS 1996 Lond.

AHMAD, Shahreen 32 Westmoreland Avenue, Hornchurch RM11 2EE — MB BS 1994 Lond.; BSc (Hons.) Lond. 1991; MRCP (UK) 1998. (Univ. Coll. Lond. Med. Sch.) Specialist Regist. in (Clin. Oncol.), St. Bart. Hosp., Lond. EC1. Socs: Jun. Oncol. Club. Prev: SHO (Gen. Med.) Havering Hosps. Trust Romford; SHO (A & E) King Geo. Hosp. Ilford.

AHMAD, Shahzad 20 Walford Place, Chelmsford CM2 6PG — MB ChB 1998 Sheff.; MB ChB Sheff 1998.

AHMAD, Shakeel 58A Hodford Road, London NW11 8NJ — MB BS 1984 Punjab; MRCPsych 1991.

AHMAD, Shakeel 5 Oakwood Avenue, Cynoed, Cardiff CF23 9EY — MB ChB 1996 Leeds.

AHMAD, Shamim Department of Community Child Health, York House, Cleveland St., Doncaster DN1 3EH; 3 Newman Court, Spinneyfield, Rotherham S60 3JA — MB BS 1976 Kashmir. Clin. Med. Off. Community Child Health Doncaster HA. Prev: Community Med. Off. (Community Child Health) Rotherham HA.

AHMAD, Shamsun Nahar 32 Westmoreland Avenue, Hornchurch RM11 2EE — MB BS 1968 Dacca. (Dacca) Gen. Practitioner, Barking & Havering Health Auth. Prev: Regist. (Gyn. & Obst.) OldCh. & Rush Green Hosps. Romford.

AHMAD, Sohaib Mahmud Ali 13 Empress Avenue, Ilford IG1 3DE — MB BS 1989 Lond.

AHMAD, Syed Hazelmere Surgery, 58 Lutterworth Road, Blaby, Leicester LE8 4DN Tel: 0116 247 7828 Fax: 0116 277 2416; 5 Station Road, Countesthorpe, Leicester LE8 5TA Email: syed@srma.epula.net — MB BS 1962 Karachi. (DOW Medical College) GP Leicester. Prev: Regist. (ENT) City Hosp. Edin.

AHMAD, Syed Farooq Flat 10, Burvill Court, 21 Langham Road, London SW20 8TP — MB ChB 1993 Manch. SHO (A & E) Qu. Med. Centre Nottm. Prev: Resid. Med. Off. & Demonst. (Anat.) UMDS Guy's Campus Lond.; Ho. Off. (Gen. Surg.) Tameside Gen. Hosp.; Ho. Off. (Gen. Med.) Wigan Infirm.

AHMAD, Mr Syed Shafique A/E, West Middlesex University Hospital, Twickenham Road, Isleworth TW7 6AF; Flat 3, 23 Ladbroke Crescent, Notting Hill, London W11 1PS — MB ChB 1992 Liverp.; FRCS (Ed) 1997. A & E Specialist Reg., Chelsea & W.minster Hosp. Prev: W.MM.U.H. A & E Dept; St Mary's Hosp., Paddington, A&E Dept.

AHMAD, Syed Z Mabarak Health Centre, 8-12 Cannon Hill Road, Balsall Heath, Birmingham B12 9NN Tel: 0121 440 4666 Fax: 0121 446 5986 — MB BS 1974 Patna.

AHMAD, Tamizuddin Health Centre, Beech Avenue, Rhosslanerchrugog, Wrexham LL14 1AA Tel: 01978 840054 Fax: 01978 843344 — MB BS 1959 Dacca.

AHMAD, Mr Tariq Department of Plastic Surgery, St Johns Hospital, Howden, Livingston EH54 6PP Tel: 01506 419666 Ext: 4151 Fax: 01506 460592 Email: tariq.ahmad@luht.scot.nhs.uk, tariq.ahmad@wlt.scot.nhs.uk — MB BChir 1983 Camb.; FRCS 1987 Eng.; FRCS 1997 Eng. (Plast.); FRCS 1999 Ed. (Hon.); MA 1984 Oxford; BA 1980 Oxford. (Preclinical: Oxford, Clinical School:Cambridge) Cons. Plastic & Reconstruc. Surg. St Johns Hosp. Howden, Livingston; Cons. Plastic & Reconstruc. Surg. Roy. Hosp. For Sick Childr. Sciennes Rd, Edin., EH9 1LF; Cons. Plastic Surg.,Qu. Market Hosp., Dunfermline, Fife; Cons. plastic Surg. Raicmore Hosp., Inverness; Cons. Plastic Surg., Bupa Murrayfield Hosp., Edin. Socs: Brit. Assn. of Plastic Surgs.; Craniofacial Soc. of Gt. Britain & Irel.; Brit. Burns Assn. Prev: Sen. Regist., SE Scotl. Regional plastic Surg. Unit 1995 - 1997; Regist., plastic Surg. Addenbrookes Hosp., Camb., 1992- 1995; Research Regist., MRC Addenbrookes Site, Camb. 1990 - 1992.

AHMAD, Tariq Dept of Gastroenterology, Radcliffe Infirmary, Oxford OX2 6HE Tel: 01203 351351; Elfordleigh, 81 Hampton Lane, Solihull B91 2QD — BM 1981 Soton.

AHMAD, Tasneem 147 Titwood Road, Glasgow G41 4BN — MB ChB 1994 Glas.

AHMAD, Taufiq Uddin 18 Swallowfields, Blackburn BB1 8NR Tel: 01254 691394 Fax: 01254 691394 — MB ChB 1995 Manch. SHO (Gen. Med.) Roy. Lancaster Infirm.

AHMAD, Wieam Khaleel Cullford House, Coombe Park, Kingston upon Thames KT2 7JB Tel: 020 8546 3666 Fax: 020 8903 3371 — MB ChB 1974 Baghdad; MSc Med. Microbiol. Lond. 1983; Cert. Managem. Kingston 1994. Socs: Assoc. Mem. Brit. Soc. Antimicrobial Chemother. & BMA. Prev: Regist. (Med. Microbiol.) Roy. Hallamsh. Hosp. Sheff. & Centr. W. Middlx. Hosp. Lond.; SHO (Path.) Ealing Hosp. Lond.

AHMAD, Yasmeen Akhtar 69 Croydon Road, Newcastle upon Tyne NE4 5LP — MB ChB 1991 Manch.

AHMAD, Yasmin Coventry Road Medical Centre, 448 Coventry Road, Small Heath, Birmingham B10 0UG Tel: 0121 773 5390 Fax: 0121 771 2703 — MB ChB 1991 Glas.; BSc Glas. 1989.

AHMAD, Zile Huma 243 Kingsway, Manchester M19 2NB — MB ChB 1996 Liverp.

AHMAD, Zulfquar Talbot, Ward, Seery and Ahmad, Gardenia Surgery, 2A Gardenia Avenue, Luton LU3 2NS Tel: 01582 572612 Fax: 01582 494553 — BM BS 1987 Nottm.

AHMAD FAROUK, Ahmad Ridzuvan Royal Berkshire and Battle Hospitals, London Road, Reading RG1 5AW — MB BCh 1986 Wales.

AHMAD MOHD ZAIN, Zahiah 74 Humphrey Road, Old Trafford, Manchester M16 9DF — MB ChB 1998 Manch.; MB ChB Manch 1998.

AHMAD-SALEM, Mr Mahmoud Issa Mahmoud Abdel Rahim Summerfield House, Station Road, Holton-Le-Clay, Grimsby DN36 5HR Tel: 01472 824210 — MD 1974 Aleppo; FRCS Glas. 1981.

AHMAD TURKISTANI, Ibrahim Yaqub 19 Holme Crescent, Castle Park, Cottingham HU16 5LH — MB BS 1984 Punjab, Pakistan.

AHMADANI, Mr Hidayatullah 4 Twickenham Close, Croydon CR0 4SZ — MB BS 1980 Sind; MB BS Sind Pakistan 1980; FRCS Ed. 1984.

AHMADO, Abdul Rahman The Women's Hospital, Catharine St., Liverpool L8 7NG Tel: 0151 709 1000 — MD 1969 Damascus; DGO Dub. 1981; MRCOG 1981; DObst RCPSI 1974; LM Rotunda Hosp. 1981. (Damascus Univ.) Regist. (O & G) Wom. Hosp. & Liverp. Matern. Hosp.

AHMADOUK, Naim Azzam Crosshouse Hospital, Crosshouse, Kilmarnock KA2 0BE Tel: 01563 521133; 11 Glen Affric Place, Kilmarnock KA1 1QE Tel: 01563 537585 — MD 1982 Aleppo; MD Aleppo Syria 1982; MRCP (UK) 1990. Staff Grade (Nephrol.) CrossHo. Hosp. Kilmarnock. Prev: Regist. (Gen. Med.) CrossHo. Hosp. Kilmarnock; SHO (Gen. Med.) Darlington Memor. Hosp. Co. Durh.

AHMED, Aamer Bashir The Highfield, Barrowfield Lane, Kenilworth CV8 1EP — BM BS 1989 Nottm.; BMedSci (Hons.) 1987; DCH RCP Lond. 1991. SHO (Gen. Med.) Derby City Hosp. Socs: BMA. Prev: SHO (A & E) Derbysh. Roy. Infirm.; SHO (Paediat.) Derbysh. Childr. Hosp.

AHMED, Abdel Hak Sabir X-Ray Department, Sandwell Health Care NHS Trust, Lyndon, West Bromwich B71 4HJ Tel: 0121 607 3264 Fax: 0121 607 3403; 112 Knightlow Road, Harborne, Birmingham B17 8QA — MB BCh 1969 Ain Shams; FRCR 1985; DMRD Eng. 1978. (Ain Shams) Cons. Radiol. (Radiodiagn.) Sandwell Health Care NHS Trust. Socs: BMA; Cons. & Specialists Assn. Prev: Sen. Regist. W. Midl. Rotat Scheme; Regist. Enfield Dist. Hosp.; Trainee Regist. Bristol Roy. Infirm.

AHMED, Abdel Mutaal Mohamed Institute of Liver Studies, King's College Hospital, Denmark Hill, London SE5 9PJ Tel: 020 7737 4000; 119 South Park Crescent, London SE6 1JP Tel: 020 8473 7060 Fax: 020 8473 7060 — MB BS 1978 Khartoum; MRCP (UK) 1986. Clin. Research Fell. (Liver Dis.) & Hon. Lect. Inst. Liver Dis. Lond. Socs: Brit. Soc. Gastroenterol. Prev: Sen. Regist. Milit. Hosp. Riyadh, Saudi Arabia; Regist. Lewisham & Hither Green Hosp.; SHO Pontefract Gen. Infirm.

AHMED, Abdul Baten Jalal 30 Adeliza Close, Barking IG11 8BQ — MB BS 1962 Calcutta.

AHMED, Abu Bakr Mohamed Elamin Northumberland Community Health, The Health Centre, Civic Precinct, Forum Way, Cramlington NE23 6QN Tel: 01670 714581 Fax: 01670 730386 — MB BS 1980 Khartoum; MRCP (UK) 1990. GP Cramlington, N.d.

AHMED, Mr Abu Imad Hasib Medway Maritime Hospital, Medway NHS Trust, Gillingham ME7 5NY Tel: 01634 8251531 Ext: 5471 Fax: 01634 811250 Email: lowe.rosamed@mcdway-tr.sthamcs.nhs.uk; St Clement, 100 Berstal Road, Rochester ME1 3BD Tel: 01634 843133 Fax: 01634 843133 Email: hormoneace@aol.com — MB BS 1986 Lond.; MRCOG 1992. (Charing Cross & Westminster) Cons. (O & G). Socs: Fell. Roy. Soc. Med.; Ex-Chairm. & Scientif. Sec. Victor Bonney Soc.; Medway Surgic. Soc. Prev: Sen. Regist. (O & G) Guy's & St. Thomas Hosps. Lond.; Research Regist. (O & G) Guy's Hosp. Lond.; Lect. & Regist. St. Thos. Hosp. Lond.

AHMED, Afsaruddin 131 Fishponds Road, Tooting, London SW17 7LL Tel: 020 8672 6641 — MB BS 1967 Dacca; MRCOphth. 1990; DOMS 1973; DO RCPSI 1983. Clin. Asst. (Ophth.) Ashford Hosp. Middlx. Prev: SHO (Ophth.) Torbay Hosp., Ashford Hosp. & Vict. Eye Hosp.

AHMED, Aftab 45 Cressey Avenue, Shenley Brook End, Milton Keynes MK5 7EL — MB ChB 1994 Sheff.

AHMED, Aftabuddin Adam Avenue Medical Centre, 1 Adam Avenue, Airdrie ML6 6DN Tel: 01236 763581 Fax: 01236 750507 — MB BS 1967 Dibrugarh. Socs: Chairperson of Airdrie LHCC.

AHMED, Ahmed Abdel Salam Moneeb 96 Fox Lane, London N13 4AX — MB BCh 1976 Cairo.

AHMED, Ahmed Rashid 16a Moss Hall Grove, Finchley, London N12 8PB — MB BS 1996 Lond.

AHMED, Aijaz Eqbal 733 Holderness Road, Hull HU8 9AR — MB ChB 1994 Leeds.

AHMED, Akhtar 21 Whernside, Marton, Middlesbrough TS7 8PJ — MB BS 1958 Karachi; FRCP Ed. 1976, M 1962. (Dow Med. Coll.) Prof. Neurol. Dow Med. Coll. & Civil Hosp. Karachi.

AHMED, Al Wali 29 Ashley Avenue, Lower Weston, Bath BA1 3DS — MB BS 1994 Lond.; DRCOG 1998. (Kings College, London) Prev: GP Reg.

AHMED, Alaadin Hassan Department of Respiratory Medicine, Birmingham Heartlands Hospital, Birmingham B9 5SS Tel: 0121 766 6611 Fax: 0121 772 0292; 47 Lincoln House, Birmingham Heartlands Hospital, Birmingham B9 5SS — MB BS 1981 Khartoum, Sudan; MRCP (UK) 1990; MD 1997. Sen. Regist. (Respirat. Med.) Birm. Heartlands Hosp.; Hon Lect. Sch. of Postgrad. Med., Keele Univ. Socs: Brit. Thorac. Soc.; Amer. Thoracic Soc.; Affil. Mem. Amer. Coll. of Chest Phys. Prev: Clin. Research Fell. (Microbiol. & Immunol.) Leicester Univ.; Regist. (Respirat. Med.) W.. Infirm. Glas.; Regist. (Gen. Med. & Chest Med.) Wrexham Maelor Hosp.

AHMED, Alauddin The Surgery, 45 Westbury Road, Forest Gate, London E7 8BU Tel: 020 8472 4123 Fax: 020 8552 5329 — MB BS 1968 Dacca.

AHMED, Mr Alhassan Mustafa 53 Glynderi, Tanerdy, Carmarthen SA31 2EX Tel: 01267 235151 Fax: 01267 220764 — MB BCh 1972 Cairo; FRCS Ed. 1989; DLO RCS Eng. 1989. Assoc. Specialist (Otolaryngol.) Carmarthen & Dist. NHS Trust. Prev: Regist. (Otolaryng.) Sandwell HA.

AHMED, Aliya 9 Hertford Court, Green Lanes, London N13 4DD — MB BS 1985 Karachi; FFA RCSI 1992; DA (UK) 1990.

AHMED, Altaf Uddin Newham Medical Centre, 576 Green Street, London E13 9DA Tel: 020 8470 7859 Fax: 020 8552 2161 — MB BS 1972 Gauhati.

AHMED, Amar Rauf 312 Wilbraham Road, Chorlton-cum-Hardy, Manchester M21 0UU — MB BS 1996 Lond.

AHMED, Andleeb 13 Kings Drive, Wembley HA9 9HP — MB BS 1993 Lond.

AHMED, Anjum 8 Coachmans Lane, Baldock SG7 5BN — MB BS 1993 Lond.; DFFP 1998; BSc Lond. 1990; DRCOG 1996. (UCL) GP Locum, N Herts. Socs: Mem. Nat. Assn. of Non-Princip.s; Brit. Med. Assn. Prev: Clin. Asst., Garden Ho. Hospice; GP Regist., Arlesey & Stotfold; SHO Lister Hosp. Stevenage.

AHMED, Asfack Uddin 7 Caspian House, Shandy St., London E1 3LU — MB BS 1996 Lond.

AHMED, Ashfaque Uddin 2 Well Cottage Close, London E11 2NB — MB BS 1967 Dacca; FRCR 1980.

AHMED, Ayesha Ali Flat 2E2, Cassiot House, St Thomas's Hospital, Lambeth Palace Road, London SE1 7EH — MB BS 1997 Lond.

AHMED, Babus Sama 6 Octavia Drive, Witham CM8 1HQ — MB BS 1998 Lond.; MB BS Lond 1998.

AHMED, Badr Eldeen Ibrahim 1 Beech Court, North Tyneside General Hospital, North Shields NE29 8NH — MB BCh 1981 Ain Shams; MRCOG 1994.

AHMED, Bashir The Surgery, 1 Newport Road, Balsall Heath, Birmingham B12 8QE Tel: 0121 449 1327 — MRCS Eng. LRCP Lond. 1981.

AHMED, Basir Abiodun 54 Boddens Hill Road, Stockport SK4 2DG — MB BS 1981 Lagos; MRCOG 1992.

AHMED, Chowdhary Munir 41 Waldram Park Road, London SE23 2PW — LRCP LRCS 1954 Ed.; LRCP LRCS Ed. LRFPS Glas. 1954.

AHMED, Ehsan Union Street, Darwen BB3 0DA Tel: 01254 778392 Fax: 01254 778388; Bridge End Surgery, Sudell Road, Darwen BB3 3HD Tel: 01254 706345 Fax: 01254 706819 — MB BS 1975 Osmania. Gen. Practitioner.

AHMED, Eleanor Rosemary Maywood Surgery, 180 Hawthorn Road, Bognor Regis PO21 2UY Tel: 01243 829141 Fax: 01243 842115 — MB BS 1964 Durh.; DA Eng. 1967.

AHMED, Faheem Bobby 3 Castle Mews, Nottingham NG7 1EA — BM BS 1993 Nottm.

AHMED, Farah Bashir The Highfield, Barrowfield Lane, Kenilworth CV8 1EP — MB BChir 1994 Camb.; MA Camb. 1995, BA (Hons.) 1991; MRCP 1997. (Univ. Camb.) SHO (Anaesth.) Chase Farm Hosp. Enfield Middlx. Prev: SHO (Anaesth.) Whittington Hosp. Lond.; SHO (Med. Rotat.) N.wick Pk. Hosp. Middlx.

AHMED, Fasihuddin Luqman Medical Centre, 75 Countess Street, Walsall WS1 4JZ Tel: 01922 621659 Fax: 01922 621702 — MB BS 1971 Patna.

AHMED, Mr Golam Moula Shahid Uddin 22 Roe Green, London NW9 0NY — MB BS 1970 Dhaka; FRCS Glas. 1982; DLO RCS Eng. 1980. Cons. ENT Surg. Armed Forces Hosp. Saudi Arabia. Socs: Gen. Sec. Soc. Otolaryngol. Prev: Assoc. Prof. ENT Dhaka Med. Coll. Bangladesh.

AHMED, Hajira Sabah 246 Heaton Road, Heaton, Newcastle upon Tyne NE6 5QE; 84 Manor Road, Rugby CV21 2TQ — MB ChB 1998 Leeds.

AHMED, Ibrar 55 Tarry Road, Birmingham B8 3JN — MB ChB 1997 Birm.

AHMED, Iftikhar Mersey Medical Centre, First Floor, Port of Liverpool Building, Liverpool L3 1BZ Tel: 0151 236 6031; Bridge Manor, Wheathill Road, Huyton, Liverpool L36 5UR Tel: 0151 480 7411 — MB BS 1968 Panjab; MRCS Eng. LRCP Lond. 1983; DIH Eng. 1980; AFOM RCP Lond. 1980. (Nishtar Med. Coll. Multan) Socs: Soc. Occupat. Med.; BMA; Soc. Occup. Med. Prev: Med. Regist. Clwyd Health Auth.

AHMED, Ilyas Park Surgery, 60 Ilkeston Road, Heanor DE75 7DX Tel: 01773 531011 Fax: 01773 534440 — MB BS 1974 Bhopal; LMSSA Lond. 1977. (Gandhi Med. Bhopal) Clin. Asst. (Ophth.) Derbysh. Roy. Infirm. Prev: SHO (Gen. Med. & Coronary Care) Scartho Rd. Hosp. Grimsby; SHO (Paediat. & Neonat.) Copthorne Hosp. Shrewsbury; SHO (Thoracic Med.) Bury Gen. Hosp.

AHMED, Imran Stamford and Rutland Hospital, Ryhall Road, Stamford PE9 1UA Tel: 01780 764151 Fax: 01780 763385; 2 Park View, Thurlby, Bourne PE10 0EU Tel: 01778 393016 Email: 1ahmed3@compuserve.com — MB BS 1981 Punjab; BSc Punjab 1975; MRCP (UK) 1991. (King Edwd. Med. Coll. Lahore) Assoc. Specialist Stamford & Rutland Hosp. Prev: Regist. (Gen. Med.) Borders Gen. Hosp. Melrose; Regist. (Acute Med. for Elderly) Sunderland Dist. Gen. Hosp.; SHO (Dermat.) Roy. Hosp. Wolverhampton.

AHMED, Imran 120 Lwer Rushton Road, Thornbury, Bradford BD3 8PZ — MB BS 1996 Lond.

AHMED, Imtiaz 11 Roby House, Broadgreen Hospital, Liverpool L14 3LB Tel: 0151 228 4878 — MB BS 1985 Karachi; MRCP (UK) 1991.

AHMED, Imtiaz Dept. of Dermatology, Univ. Hospitals, Coventry CV2 2DX — MB BS 1987 Punjab; MRCP (UK) 1994. Cons. Dermat.Dept. Univ. Hosps. Coventry and Warks. Socs: BMA; Brit. Assn. Dermat. Prev: Specialist Regist. (Dermat.), W.Midl.s Rotat.; Research Regist. (Dermat.) Walsgrave Hosp. Coventry; SHO (Med.) Good Hope Hosp. Sutton Coldfield.

AHMED, Iqbal Rothwell Health Centre, Stonebrig Lane, Rothwell, Leeds LS26 0UE Tel: 0113 282 1938 Fax: 0113 282 9195 — MB ChB 1989 Sheff.; MRCGP 1994; T(GP) 1994.

AHMED, Irfan 57 Chiltern Road, Lincoln LN5 8SB — MB ChB 1994 Sheff.

AHMED, Mr Irfan Greenwich District Hospital, Vanbrugh Hill, Greenwich, London SE10 9HE — MB BS 1987 Punjab, Pakistan; FRCS Glas. 1993.

***AHMED, Ishtiaq Mehmood** 60 Boswell Road, Doncaster DN4 7DD Tel: 01302 531909 — MB ChB 1995 Leeds; BSc (Hons. Anat.) Leeds 1994.

•**AHMED, Jalaluddin** (retired) 21 Lumley Road, Chester CH2 2AQ — MB BS 1961 Dhaka; PhD Lond. 1971; MSc Karachi 1964; FRCPath 1988, M 1976. Prev: Cons. Chem. Path. Countess of Chester Hosp.

AHMED, Jamshed 9 Tudor Gardens, Calverton End, Milton Keynes MK11 1HX — MB ChB 1985 Manch.

AHMED, Javed Mansoor Flat 25 Block Q5, Northern General Hospital, Harries Road, Sheffield S5 7AU Tel: 0114 243 4343; 75 Yardley Wood Road, Moseley, Birmingham B13 9JF Tel: 0121 449 2295 — MB BS 1983 Punjab; MRCP (UK) 1989. Specialist Regist. (Cardiol.) N. Gen. Hosp. Sheff. Socs: Manch. Med. Soc.; Overseas Doctors Assn.; BMA.

AHMED, Kafeel Prince Philip Hospital, Bryngwyn Mawr, Dafen, Llanelli SA14 8QF — MB BS 1966 Ranchi.

AHMED, Mr Kafeel c/o Dr S. Mukherji, Flat 5, Charnock House, Lancaster Court, Chorley PR7 1PB — MB BS 1981 Calcutta; FRCS Ed. 1989.

AHMED, Mr Kamal Department Eye & ENT, North West Armed Forces Hospital, PO Box 100, Tabuk, Saudi Arabia Tel: 00 966 44233988 Fax: 00 966 44232795; 2 Goldsmith Road, Rainham, Gillingham ME8 9JG Tel: 01634 378405 — MB BS 1968 Karachi; FRCS Eng. 1983; DLO RCS Eng. 1977. Sen. Cons. ENT Surg. NW Armed Forces Hosp. Tabuk, Saudi Arabia. Prev: Sen. Lect. & Co-ordinator (Otolaryngol.) Univ. Sains, Malaysia; Cons. ENT Surg. Penang Gen. Hosp. Malaysia.

AHMED, Kamal Abdel Gadir 12 Sparkford Close, Bournemouth BH7 7HY — MB BS 1980 Khartoun.

AHMED, Khaja Azizuddin North Wingfield Road Surgery, 186 North Wingfield Road, Grassmoor, Chesterfield S42 5ED Tel: 01246 852995 — MB BS 1967 Osmania.

AHMED, Khalid 5 Fountains Way, Wakefield WF1 4TQ Email: kahmed1741@aol.com — MB BS 1985 Karachi; PhD Univ. Lond. 1990; MRCP Royal Coll. Phys. Ireland 1995. (Dow Medical College, Karachi) Sen. Regist. Rheum. Dept. Leeds Gen. Infirm., York Dist. Hosp. Socs: BMA; BSR (Brit. Soc. Rheumatol.). Prev: Regist. Gen. Med./Rheum., Pinderfields Hosp. Wakefield; Regist. Gen. Med. Glan Clywd Hosp. N. Wales.

AHMED, Khursh Department of Anaesthetics, Pinderfields General Hospital, Aberford Road, Wakefield WF1 4DG Tel: 01924 212348 Fax: 01924 814574 — MB BS 1987 Lond.; FRCA 1994; DA (UK) 1991. (The Middlesex Hospital Medical School) Cons. Anaesth. Pinderfields Hosp. Wakefield. Socs: Yorks. Soc. Anaesth.; Assoc of Anaesth.s; Brit. Opthalmic Anaesth.s Soc. Prev: Sen. Regist. Rotat. (Anaesth.) Leeds Gen. Infirm.; Regist. (Anaesth.) Nat. Hosp. for Neurosurg. & Neurol. & St. Mary's Hosp. Lond.; SHO Rotat. (Anaesth.) Char. Cross Hosp. Lond. & Ealing Hosp. Middlx.

AHMED, Khurshed Anwar Health Centre, Gloucester Road, Wolverton, Milton Keynes MK12 5DF — MB BS 1958 Dacca.

AHMED, Mahmoud 43 Kelmscott Gardens, London W12 9DB — MB BChir 1978 Camb.

AHMED, Mamdouh Mohamed St Huberts Road Surgery, 153-155 St Huberts Road, Great Harwood, Blackburn BB6 7ED Tel: 01254 889376 Fax: 01254 877413 Email: mamdouh.ahmed@gp-p81682.nhs.uk — MB BCh 1976 Mansoura. GP Gt. Harwood.; PCG Bd. Mem. (Hyndburn PCG).

AHMED, Mr Mazharuddin (retired) 35 Langley Drive, London E11 2LN Tel: 020 8530 3975 — MB BS 1958 Dacca; FRCS Ed. 1972; DLO RCS Eng. 1964. Prev: Cons. Surg. (ENT) Min. Health, Saudi Arabia.

AHMED, Merina 20A Danehurst Street, London SW6 6SD — MB BS 1994 Lond.

AHMED, Mir Mesbahuddin Tel: 020 8593 7141 — MB BS 1964 Dacca. (Dacca Med. Coll.) Prev: GP Newc.; SHO (Chest Med.) Markfield Hosp. Leicester; Med. Off. E. Pakistan Indust. Developm. Corp. Dacca, Bangladesh.

AHMED, Mirza Shahid Nadim 93 Bradford Road, Fartown, Huddersfield HD1 6DZ Tel: 01484 452250; 80 Parsonage Road, Heaton Road, Stockport SK4 4JL Tel: 0161 431 6846 — MB ChB 1984 Manch.; DRCOG 1987. Socs: BMA; Overseas Doctors Assn. Prev: SHO (Paediat.) Salford HA; SHO (Geriat.) Blackpool HA; SHO (A & E) Oldham HA.

AHMED, Misbah-ud-Din 58 Durnford Road, Wigston, Little Hill, Leicester LE18 2RG Tel: 0116 281 1199 — MB BS 1965 Peshawar; MRCOG 1976.

AHMED, Mr Mohamed Atif Ibrahim Flat C, Block 2, North Flats, Royal Shrewsbury Hospital, Mytton Oak Road, Shrewsbury SY3 8XF — MB BS 1985 Khartoum; FRCSI 1992.

AHMED, Mohammad Amin The North Whitehouse, Great Leighs, Chelmsford CM3 1PU — MB BS 1961 Karachi; BSc Karachi 1955, MB BS 1961; FRCPath 1985, M 1973. (Dow Med. Coll.) Cons. Histopath. Chelmsford & Essex Hosp. Socs: Assn. Clin. Path. & Internat. Acad. Path. Prev: Ho. Surg. Huddersfield Roy. Infirm.; Regist. (Path.) Roy. Berks. Hosp. Reading; Sen. Regist. (Morbid Anat. & Histopath.) St. Mary's Hosp. Lond.

AHMED, Mohammed Ali 190 Lynwood Drive, Wimborne BH21 1UU Tel: 01202 59865 — MB BS 1954 Calcutta; DO Eng. 1964. (Med. Coll. Calcutta) Med. Off. Sch. Eye Clinics ChristCh. & Lymington. Prev: SHO (Ophth.) Kent Co. Ophth. & Aural Hosp. Maidstone; Ophth. Regist. LLa.lli Hosp.; Clin. Asst. Soton. Eye Hosp.

AHMED, Mohammed Arfan Southwood Medical Centre, Links Way, Farnborough GU14 0NA — MB ChB 1991 Dundee; MRCGP 1996; DFFP 1997; DRCOG 1995.

AHMED, Mohammed Monzur 27 Poplar Road, Sparkhill, Birmingham B11 1UH — MB ChB 1987 Birm.

AHMED, Mukhtar 14 Pilgrims Hill, Linlithgow EH49 7LN — MB ChB 1984 Dundee; MRCP (UK) 1993; MRCPI 1992.

AHMED, Mukhtiar 5 Plumpton Terrace, Westgate, Wakefield WF2 9RB — MB ChB 1996 Leic.

AHMED, Mushtaq 24 Streatham Common N., London SW16 3HP — MB BS 1962 Karachi; DA (UK) 1966. Prev: Regist. Dudley Rd. Hosp. Birm.; Sen. Regist. Mubarakel Kabir Hosp., Kuwait; Assoc. Specialist AGA Khan Univ. Hosp. Karachi.

AHMED, Mushtaq 407 Stapleton Road, Eastville, Bristol BS5 6NE Tel: 0117 951 1477 Fax: 0117 951 1477 — MB BS 1983 Lond.

AHMED, Mustafa Jamal 174 Crystal Palace Road, London SE22 9EP — MB BS 1996 Lond.

AHMED, Muzaffar Doctor's House No. 1, Louth County Hospital, High Holme Road, Louth LN11 0EU — MB BS 1986 Sind; MB BS Sind Pakistan 1986; MRCP (UK) 1993. Staff Grade Phys. (Gen. Med.) Lincoln & Louth NHS Trust Louth.

AHMED, Muzzaffara Irum 213 Burntwood Lane, London SW17 0AL — MB BS 1998 Lond.; MB BS Lond 1998.

AHMED, Nadeem 64 Havelock Street, Aylesbury HP20 2NX Tel: 01296 86389 — MB ChB 1994 Dundee; BMSc Dund 1991; MRCP 1997. (University of Dundee) SHO (Orthop.) Warwick Hosp. Warwick. Prev: SHO (Respirat. Med.) Walsgrave Hosp. Coventry; SHO (Gastroenterol.) Walsgrave Hosp.; SHO (Haemat.) Walsgrave Hosp.

AHMED, Najib 19 Micklefield Road, Liverpool L15 5BT Tel: 0151 733 4605 — MB ChB 1992 Liverp.; BSc (Hons.) Physiol. Liverp. 1989. SHO (A & E) Fazakerley Hosp. Liverp.

AHMED, Nasiruddin 17 Farndale Avenue, Southbents, Sunderland SR6 8BH Tel: 0191 529 5517 — MB BS 1962 Dhaka; BSc Dhaka 1956, MB BS 1962, Dhaka; DPM Eng. 1972. (Dhaka) Cons. Psychiat. Gen. Hosp. S. Shields. Socs: BMA; RCPsych Assn.; Roy. Soc. Med. (Fell.).

AHMED, Nazeer Ahmed, Queens Park Health Centre, Dart Street, London W10 4LD Tel: 020 8964 9990 Fax: 020 8964 0436 — BM 1982 Soton.; DCH RCP Lond. 1988. GP Princp. Prev: Clin. Med. Off. (Community Paediat.) Char. Cross Hosp. Lond.; Regist. (Paediat.) Qu. Eliz II Hosp. Welwyn Garden City; SHO (Paediat./Paediat. Cardiol.) Leic. Hosps.

AHMED, Nazia The Market Surgery, 26 Norwich Road, Aylsham, Norwich NR11 6BW Tel: 01263 733331 Fax: 01263 735829; Bridge Cottage, Birds Lane, Cawston, Norwich NR10 4JB — MB ChB 1985 Leic.; MRCGP 1989; DRCOG 1988. (Univ. of Leicester)

AHMED, Nazir 12 Arden Road, Nuneaton CV11 6PT Tel: 01203 383282 — MB BS 1951 Dacca; FFA RCS Eng. 1959. (Med. Coll. Dacca) Cons. Anaesth. Nuneaton (N. Warks.) Health Dist.

AHMED, Nazir 52 Halfway Avenue, Luton LU4 8RB — MB ChB 1990 Cape Town.

AHMED, Nomy Waseem 268 Gayfield Avenue, Brierley Hill DY5 2SU — MB ChB 1994 Liverp.

AHMED, Mr Nooruddin Kidderminster General Hospital, Bewdley Road, Kidderminster DY11 6RJ Tel: 01562 823424 — MB BCh 1980 Cairo; FRCS Ed. 1985. (Cairo University) Cons. Orthop. Surg. Worchestershire Acute NHS Trust. Socs: Fell. BOA; BASK. Prev: Cons. Orthop. Surg. Kidderminster Gen. Hosp.; Regist. SW Metrop. & St. Geo. Hosp. Orthop. Train. Scheme; Sen. Instruc. & Asst. Prof. Orthop. Surg. Aga Khan Univ. Karachi, Pakistan.

AHMED, Nour El Din Abdel-Fattah Homestead, Garstang Road, Bilsborrow, Preston PR3 0RD — MB BCh 1976 Ain Shams; MRCOG 1987.

AHMED, Omer Nazir 6 Lethington Road, Giffnock, Glasgow G46 6TB Email: omer@albus.demon.co.uk — MB ChB 1990 Glas.; MRCGP 1994. (Univ. Glas.) Princip. GP; Clin. Asst. (A & E) Law Hosp. Carluke.

AHMED, Parveen Rehana Mersey Medical Centre, Strand St., Mann Island, Liverpool L3 1DQ Tel: 0151 236 6031; Bridge Manor, Wheathill Road, Huyton, Liverpool L36 5UR Tel: 0151 480 7411 — MB BS 1971 Punjab; MRCS Eng. LRCP Lond. 1983.

AHMED, Qazi Wasim 149 Stanmore Road, Edgbaston, Birmingham B16 0SX — MB BS 1998 Lond.; MB BS Lond 1998.

AHMED, Quazi Zaffar 49 Cameron Road, Bromley BR2 9AY — MB BS 1957 Calcutta.

AHMED, Rashid Townhead Health Centre, 16 Alexandra Parade, Glasgow G31 2ES Tel: 0141 531 8940 Fax: 0141 531 8935 — MB ChB 1976 Glas.; MSc Strathclyde 1972.

AHMED, Riaz Eqbal The Laurels, 733 Holderness Road, Hull HU8 9AR — BChir 1992 Camb.

AHMED, Riaz Iftikhar H-5 Norton Court, Metchley Park Road, Birmingham B15 2TL — MB BS 1982 Punjab.

AHMED, Riyaz The Surgery, 13 Lozells Street, Lozells, Birmingham B19 2AU Tel: 0121 554 3386 Fax: 0121 523 8439 — MB BS 1965 Rajasthan.

AHMED, Miss Rosina University Department of Surgery, Royal Hallamshire Hospital, Sheffield Tel: 0114 276 6222; 4 Crabtree Drive, Norwood, Sheffield S5 7AZ Tel: 0114 243 6681 — MB BS 1988 Calcutta; FRCS Eng. 1991; MD Univ. Sheffield 1999. Specialist Regist. (Gen. Surg.) Roy. Hallamsh. Hosp. Sheff. Prev: Research Assoc. Univ. Dept. Surg. Sheff. Univ.; Regist. (Gen. Surg.) N.. RHA.

AHMED, Rukhsana Yousufi 18 Rowland Lane, Thornton-Cleveleys FY5 2QU — MB BS 1976 Karachi; MRCP (UK) 1988; DCH RCP Lond. 1983; FRPCH 1997. Cons. (Community Paediat.) Child Developm. Unit Birch Hill Hosp. Rochdale. Socs: BAACH; MRCPCH. Prev: Sen. Regist. (Community Paediat.) Roy. Lancaster Infirm.; Sen. Regist. (Community Paediat.) Roy. Preston Hosp.

AHMED, Saad Kamal Amberstone Hospital, Carters Corner, Hailsham BN27 4HU Tel: 01323 440022; 15 Burton Road, Eastbourne BN21 2RD — MB ChB 1971 Baghdad; MRCPsych 1982; DPM Eng. 1981. Cons. Psychiat. Amberstone Hosp. Hailsham & E.bourne Dist. Gen. Hosp.

AHMED, Saeed 64 Tanfield Road, Birkby, Huddersfield HD1 5HD — MB ChB 1995 Leeds.

AHMED, Sahid 339 Iffley Road, Oxford OX4 4DP Email: sahid@drl.ox.ac.uk — MB BS 1987 Lond.; MRCP (UK) 1991. (St. Geo. Hosp. Med. Sch. Lond.) Research Regist. (Diabetes & Endocrinol.) Radcliffe Infirm. Oxf.; Novo Nordisk Jun. Fell. Clin. Diabetes Harris Manch. Coll. Oxf. Socs: Brit. Diabetic Assn.; Brit. Endocrine Soc. Prev: Regist. (Diabetes & Endocrinol.) Radcliffe Infirm. Oxf.; Regist. (Gen. Med., Diabetes & Endocrinol.) Battle & Roy. Berks. Hosp. Reading; SHO (Med.) Stoke Mandeville Hosp. & Joyce Green Hosp.

AHMED, Saif Uddin 72 Taylor Street, Tunbridge Wells TN4 0DX — MB BS 1989 Lond.

AHMED, Salim 1 Laburnum Grove, Ruislip HA4 7XF Tel: 01895 622488 — MB BS 1962 Lucknow. Dir. Roy. Med. Agency.

AHMED, Salim Telford House, Hulse Rd, Southampton SO15 2JW — BM 1997 Soton.

AHMED, Mr Salim Uddin Villa Estella, 15 Ben Wyvis Drive, Hawkhead Estate, Paisley PA2 7LB — MB BS 1950 Punjab; MB BS Punjab (Pakistan) 1950; FRCS Ed. 1967.

AHMED, Salma 19 Wolfe Crescent, London SE16 6SF — MB BS 1991 Lond.; 2000 MSC Lond; MRCGP 1996; DCH RCP Lond. 1994. Trainee GP/SHO Roy. Lond. Hosp. VTS.

AHMED, Salwa Ali 17 Sheringham Covert, Beaconside, Stafford ST16 3YL — MB BS 1980 Khartoum; MRCP (UK) 1987.

AHMED, Samina 249 Addington Road, South Croydon CR2 8LR; 174 Crystal Palace Road, Dulwich, London SE22 9EP — MB BS 1994 Lond.; MRCGP 1998; DRCOG 1999.

AHMED, Samreen Iram 2 Somerby Court, Bramcote, Nottingham NG9 3NB Email: siahmed@innotts.co.uk — MB BS 1994 Lond.; MRCP (UK) 1997. (Royal Free Hospital School of Medicine) Regist. (Med. Oncol.).

AHMED, Sanjeeda 3 Whitby Gardens, London NW9 9TU — MB BS 1991 Lond.

AHMED, Mr Sarfraz 138 Pershore Road, Edgbaston, Birmingham B5 7QY — MB BS 1982 Punjab; FRCS Glas. 1990; FRCSI 1989.

AHMED, Sayeed Abubaker Department of Psychiatry, District General Hospital, Kiwas Drive, Eastbourne BN21 2UD Tel: 01323 417400; The Courtyard, New Road, Hellingly, Hailsham BN27 4EW Tel: 01323 847681 — MB BS 1970 Mysore.

AHMED, Shabaz 18 Westgate Avenue, Bury BL9 0TJ — MB ChB 1991 Liverp.

AHMED, Shabbir 113 Heath Avenue, Rode Heath, Stoke-on-Trent ST7 3TH — BM 1992 Soton.

AHMED, Mr Shafi 54 Roxy Avenue, Romford RM6 4AY — MB BS 1993 Lond.; FRCS Ed. 1997; FRCS Eng. 1997; FRCSI 1997. (Kings College London) Basic Surgic. Trainee.

AHMED, Shaheed Darwen Health Centre, Union Street, Darwen BB3 0DA Tel: 01254 778377 Fax: 01254 778372; Kusumalaya, 14 Chestnut Grove, Whitehall, Darwen BB3 2NQ Tel: 01254 702266 — MB BS 1973 Dacca; MRCS Eng. LRCP Lond. 1978. (Mymensingh Med. Coll. Dhaka)

AHMED, Shahid Nazir 30 Farrer Road, Manchester M13 0QX — MB ChB 1994 Liverp.

AHMED, Shahla Mumtaz Dept of Immunology, Royal Free Hospital School of Medicine, Pond St, London NW3 2QG Tel: 020 7794 0500 Ext: 942; Flat 19, Pemberton Court, 39 Portelet Road, London E1 4EN Tel: 020 7790 7741 — MB BS 1987 Lond.; MRCOG 1993. Clin. Res. Fell.

***AHMED, Shahzada Khuram** 5 Croome Close, Sparkhill, Birmingham B11 4JG Email: sahmed@dial.pipex.com — MB ChB 1997 Birm.; BSc (Hons.) Birm. 1994.

AHMED, Shakeel Imam Hunter Health Centre, Andrew Street, East Kilbride, Glasgow G74 1AD Tel: 01355 906611 Fax: 01355 906615 — MB ChB 1988 Glas.; MRCGP 1993; DRCOG 1992.

AHMED, Shamsuddin Medical Centre, 3 Strouts Place, London E2 7QU Tel: 020 7739 1972; 4 Cleveland Road, South Woodford, London E18 2AN — MB BS 1972 Dacca; MRCP (UK) 1984.

AHMED, Mr Sheikh Jaliluddin 479 Cranbrook Road, Gants Hill, Ilford IG2 6ER — MB BS 1957 Dacca; FRCS Eng. 1982; DO Eng. 1968; DOMS Vienna 1965. Sen. Regist. (Ophth.) Roy. Free Hosp. Lond.; Clin. Asst. (Ophth.) Moorfield's Eye Hosp. Lond. Socs: BMA. Prev: Regist. (Ophth.) Roy. N.. & Whittington Hosp. & N. Middlx. Hosp.; Lond.

AHMED, Mr Shibhan Ali 97 Merchants Quay, Salford Quays, Salford M5 2XQ — MB BS 1994 Gorakhpur, India; FRCS Ed. 1992.

AHMED, Shoaib Shahnaz Manzil, 17 Woodend Drive, Stalybridge SK15 2SF — MB BS 1969 Bihar.

AHMED, Sirajuddin 58 Buchanan Drive, Bearsden, Glasgow G61 2EP — MB BS 1972 Bangalore.

AHMED, Soaleha 221 Bilton Road, Perivale, Greenford UB6 7HQ Tel: 020 8997 4570 — MB BS 1965 Punjab; MB BS Punjab (Pakistan) 1965; MRCOG 1976. (Fatima Jinnha Med. Coll. Lahore)

AHMED, Sohail Imam — MB ChB 1984 Glas. GP Locum, Glas. Socs: Med. and Dent. Defence Union Scotl. Prev: GP Princip., Glas.; Trainee GP Dumfries VTS.

AHMED, Syed 17Laurel Park Gardens, Jordanhill, Glasgow G13 1RD Tel: 0141 201 4917 Fax: 0141 201 4950 — MB ChB 1984 Dundee; FRCP 2001 (Glasgow); FFPHM 1999 RCP (UK); MRCP (UK) 1989; MFPHM RCP (UK) 1992. Cons. (Pub. Health Med.) Gt.er Glas. Health Bd.; Hon. Sen. Lect. Univ. Glas. Prev: Cons. (Pub. Health Med.) Lanarksh. Health Auth.; Sen. Regist. (Pub. Health Med.) Tayside HB; Regist. (Med.) Ipswich.

AHMED, Syed Health Centre, Beech Avenue, Rhosslanerchrugog, Wrexham LL14 1AA Tel: 01978 840054 Fax: 01978 843344 — MB BS 1970 Rajshahi; MB BS Rajshahi, Bangladesh 1970.

AHMED, Syed Anees Wrafton House Surgery, 24 The Common, Hatfield AL10 0NB Tel: 01707 265454; 2 Lowlands, Hatfield AL9 5DY Tel: 01707 266611 — MB BS 1953 Osmania; DTM & H Eng. 1959.

AHMED, Syed Ayaz 96 Crankhall Lane, Friar Park, Wednesbury WS10 0EQ; 27 Lake Avenue, Walsall WS5 3PA — MB BS 1986 Lond.; DRCOG 1990. Med. Adviser to Healthcall Forens. Med. Servs.; Bd. Mem. LMC.; Clin. Asst. Compton Hospice Wolverhampton. Prev: SHO (A & E) St. Bart. Hosp. Lond.

AHMED, Syed Faisal Department Child Life & Health, University Edinburgh, 17 Hatton Place, Edinburgh EH9 1UW Tel: 0131 667 2617; TFL, 6 Newhaven Road, Edinburgh EH6 5PU Tel: 0131 555 1115 — MB ChB 1987 Ed.; MRCP (UK) 1991. Clin. Research Fell. Univ. Edin. Prev: Regist. Rotat. (Paediat.) Lothian & Borders; SHO (Neonat..) Rosie Matern. Hosp. & Addenbrooke's Hosp. Camb.; Regist. Neonat. Unit Simpson Memor. Matern. Pavil. Roy. Infirm. Edin.

AHMED, Syed Irfan 21 Abbeystead Drive, Hala, Lancaster LA1 4QS Tel: 01524 843206 — MB BS 1976 Karachi; BSc Ranchi 1967; MB BS (Hons.) Karachi 1976.

AHMED, Syed Mahmood 6 Glenoven Court, Searle St, Cambridge CB4 3DW Tel: 01223 367432 Email: sma1000@cus.cam.ac.uk — BChir 1994 Camb.; MB BChir Camb. 1994; MA Camb. 1996; BA (Hons.) Camb. 1992; FRCS Section A, RCSI 1999. (Camb. Univ.) SHO Surgic. Rotat.: Guy's & Thomas Hosp./Qu. Mary's Sidcup. Prev: ENT SHO, Ipswich Hosp.; ENT SHO, Addenbrooke's Hosp. Camb.

AHMED, Syed Razi (retired) Abbotts Royd, Barkisland, Halifax HX4 0BZ Tel: 01422 822489 — MB BS 1961 Karachi; BSc Karachi 1954. Prev: Clin. Asst. (Psychiat.) Halifax Gen. Hosp.

AHMED, Syed Shahabuddin 60 Eastbrook Road, Blackheath, London SE3 8BT Tel: 020 8265 6559 — MB BS 1973 Patna. (Patna Med. Coll. Bihar, India) Staff Grade Doctor Greenwich Healthcare. Prev: Clin. Asst. (A & E) Greenwich Healthcare.

AHMED, Tariq Mahmoud The Health Centre, Magna Lane, Dalton, Rotherham S65 4HH Tel: 01709 851414 — MB ChB 1985 Glas.; MRCGP 1992; DRCOG 1991. Prev: Trainee GP/SHO (Med. Elderly) P'boro.; SHO (O & G) Selly Oak Hosp. Birm.; SHO (A & E) P'boro.

AHMED, Tosaddak King Fahad Hospital, Madinah Al Munawara, Saudi Arabia Tel: 823 7146; 27 View Close, Chigwell IG7 5JU Tel: 020 8 500 7876 — MB BS 1964 Calcutta; FRCP Lond. 1990; MRCP (UK) 1972; DTM & H RCP Lond. 1970. Cons. Gen. & Chest Phys. King Fahad Hosp., Saudi Arabia. Prev: Assoc. Asst. Prof. Med. Al Arab Med. Univ. Benghazi, Libya.

AHMED, Waqar Swanmore, Staplehay, Trull, Taunton TA3 7HF Tel: 01823 327090 — MB ChB 1978 Manch.; MRCPsych 1983; MHM Lond. 1995. (Manchester) Cons. Psychiat. Avalon Trust Som.; Hon. Lect. Bristol Univ. Socs: MRCPsych.

AHMED, Waqar 32 Colemere Drive, Thingwall, Wirral CH61 7XS Tel: 0151 648 2090 — MB BS 1981 Peshawar; MRCP(UK) 1986.

AHMED, Waseem High Street, 16 High Street, Great Baddow, Chelmsford CM2 7HQ Tel: 01245 473251 Fax: 01245 478394; Langford Cross, Holloway Road, Heybridge, Maldon CM9 4SW — MB BCh 1985 Wales; MRCGP 1992. Prev: SHO Rotat. (O & G) Rush Green Hosp. Romford; SHO Rotat. (Paediat.) Rush Green & OldCh. Hosps. Romford.

AHMED, Mr Yahya Shihab 2 Talbot Court, Leeds LS8 1LT — MB ChB 1970 Baghdad; FRCS Glas. 1979.

AHMED, Yusuf 7 Balfour Place, London SW15 6XR — BM 1985 Soton.; BSc Manch. 1980; MRCOG 1992. (Soton.) Sen. Lect. (O & G) Sch. Med. Univ. Zambia. Prev: Lect. Sch. Med. Univ. Zambia.

AHMED, Zahed 12 Pugh Road, Birmingham B6 5LL — MB ChB 1997 Liverp.

AHMED, Zahida Perween 8 Sullivan Road, Courthouse Green, Coventry CV6 7JR — MB BS 1966 Karachi; DA Eng. 1970. (Dow Med. Coll.) Clin. Med. Off. Coventry AHA.

AHMED, Zahir 50 Gwendoline Avenue, London E13 0RD — MB BCh 1988 Wales.

AHMED, Mr Zubair 8 Britnal Avenue, Longsight, Manchester M12 4DS — MB BS 1986 Karachi; FRCS Glas. 1994; FRCS Ed. 1993.

AHMED, Zuber Alexandra Group Medical Practice, Glodwick Health Centre, Glodwick Road, Oldham OL4 1YN Tel: 0161 909 8350 Fax: 0161 909 8354 — BM BS 1989 Nottm.; BMedSci (Hons.) Nottm. 1987; MRCGP 1994; T(GP) 1994; DFFP 1994.

AHMED-JUSHUF, Imtyazali Hasanali Department of Genitourinary Medicine, City Hospital Nottingham, Hucknall Road, Nottingham NG5 1PB Tel: 0115 962 7746 Fax: 0115 962 7684 —

MB ChB 1977 Manch.; MRCP (UK) 1981. (Manch.) Cons. Genitourin. Med. City Hosp. Nottm.; Mem. (Vice-Pres.) Genitourin. Phys. Colposcopy GP. Socs: Fell. RCP. Prev: Cons. Genitourin. Med. Roy. Liverp. Hosp.; Lect. (Genitourin. Med.) Univ. of Liverp.

AHMED-SHUAIB, Ali 9 Fairmead Gardens, Redbridge, Ilford IG4 5BP — MB BS 1996 Lond.; BMedSci (Hons.) 1995. (St. Bartholomew's Hospital Medical College)

AHMEDZAI, Professor Sam Hjelmeland Department of Palliative Medicine, University of Sheffield, K Floor, Royal Hallamshire Hospital, Sheffield S10 2JF Tel: 0114 271 2950 Fax: 0114 271 3991 Email: pallmed@sheffield.ac.uk; Trent Palliative Care Centre, Sykes House, Little Common Lane, Sheffield S11 9NE Tel: 0114 262 0174 Fax: 0114 236 2516 — MB ChB 1976 Manch.; BSc (Hons.) St. And. 1973; FRCP Lond. 1993; FRCP Glas. 1992; MRCP (UK) 1980. Prof. Palliat. Med. Dept. Surgic. & Anaesth. Scs. Roy. Hallamsh. Hosp. Sheff.; Dir. Trent Palliat. Care Centre. Socs: Brit. Thorac. Soc. Prev: Med. Dir. Leics. Hospice; Sen. Regist. (Respirat. Med.) Glas. Roy. Infirm.; SHO (Oncol.) Gartnavel Gen. Hosp. Glas.

AHMMED, Mr Ansar Uddin Tel: 01772 401310; 17 Fareham Cl, Fulwood, Preston PR2 8FH — MB BS 1983 Dhaka; 1992 FRCS Ed.; 1990 DLO RCS Eng.; MSc 1995 Manchester. Cons. Audiological Phys.; Hon. Sen. Lect. Centre for Human Communication & Deafness, Manch. Socs: Brit. Assoc. of Audiological Phys.s; Brit. Soc. of Audiol.; BMA. Prev: Sen. Regist. (Audiol. Med.) MRI; Regist. (ENT Surg.) Roy. Preston Hosp.; SHO (ENT Surg.) Leicester Roy. Infirm.

AHRENS, Caroline Louise 29 Kelvin Road, Nottingham NG3 2PR — MB ChB 1992 Birm.

AHRENS, Gustav Nils Fulham Medical Centre, 446 Fulham Road, London SW6 1BG Tel: 020 7385 6001 — MB BS 1987 Lond.

AHRENS, Philip Michael 10 Ernle Road, London SW20 0HJ — MB BS 1992 Lond.

AHSAN, Arif Jamal Department of Cardiology, Nottingham City Hospital, Hucknall Road, Nottingham NG5 3HZ Tel: 0115 969 1169 Fax: 0115 962 8097 — MB BS 1981 Lond.; MA Oxf. 1982; MD Lond. 1992; MRCP (UK) 1984; FRCP 1998. (Merton Coll. Oxf. & Lond. Hosp. Med. Sch.) Cons. Cardiol. Nottm. City Hosp.; Lect. Peoples Coll. Nottm.; Vis. Cons. Cardio., Lincoln Co. Hosp. Socs: Brit. Pacing & Electrophysiol. Gp.; Brit. Soc. Echocardiogr.; BMA. Prev: Sen. Regist. (Cardiol.) N.. Gen. Hosp. Sheff.; Regist. (Cardiol.) Roy. Brompton & Nat. Heart & Lung Hosp. Lond.; Research Fell. Nat. Heart Hosp. Lond.

AHSAN, Ayesha Nazish 65 Aktins Road, London SW12 0AH — MB BS 1995 Lond.

AHSAN, Syed Farhan 191 Cornhill Drive, Aberdeen AB16 5HN — LMSSA 1997; LMSSA Lond. 1997.

AHSON, Agha Atiya Creswell Road Health Centre, Creswell Road, Clowne, Chesterfield S43 4UL Tel: 01246 811555; 71 Ringer Lane, Clowne, Chesterfield S43 4BX Tel: 01246 811555 — MB BS 1965 Punjab; MB BS Punjab (Pakistan) 1965. (Fatima Jinnah Med. Coll. Lahore)

AHUJA, Mrs Amarjeet 25 Garth Road, Child's Hill, London NW2 2NH Tel: 020 8455 8540 — MB BS 1966 Patna. (Patna) Gyn. Ho. Surg. Eliz. G. Anderson Hosp. Lond. Prev: SHO Obst. Shrodells Wing Watford Gen. Hosp.

AHUJA, Anand Sheel Royal Albert Edward Infirmary, Wigan Lane, Wigan WN1 2NN Tel: 01942 822548 Fax: 01942 822301; Redthorn, 888 Plodder Lane, Over Hulton, Bolton BL5 1AJ Tel: 01942 822548 Fax: 01942 822301 Email: anandahuja@mail.com — MB BS 1966 Patna; FRCP Lond. 1989; MRCP (UK) 1974; FRCPH, 1997; DCH Eng. 1970. (Prince of Wales Med. Coll., Batna, India) Cons. (Paediat.) Roy. Albert Edwd. Infirm. Wigan. Socs: Manch. Paediat. Club (Ex-Pres.); Vice Pres. Overseas Doctors' Assn. UK; Roy. Coll. Phys.s Lond. (Mem. of Internat. Comm.). Prev: Sen. Regist. (Paediat.) Wigan AHA & Salford AHA (T); Regist. Paediat. Duchess of York Hosp. for Babies Manch.; SHO (Paediat.) Shrodells Hosp. Watford.

AHUJA, Devendra Kumar The Surgery, 153 Bearwood Road, Smethwick, Warley B66 4LN Tel: 0121 558 1840 Fax: 0121 565 0422 — MB BS 1974 Lucknow.

AHUJA, Jyoti The Surgery, 153 Bearwood Road, Smethwick, Warley B66 4LN Tel: 0121 558 1840 Fax: 0121 565 0422; 222 St Pauls Road, Smethwick, Smethwick B66 4LD Tel: 0121 558 0549 — MB BS 1967 Lucknow.

AHUJA, Murli Tejbhandas 208 Bagnall Road, Light Oaks, Stoke-on-Trent ST2 7NE Tel: 01782 534860 — MB BS 1951 Madras; MRCGP 1968. (Madras Med. Coll.) Clin. Asst. Minor Cas. Dept. Haywood Hosp. Burslem; Med. Off. Local Auth. Family Plann. Clinic. Prev: Med. Regist. Groby Rd. Hosp. Leicester; Clin. Asst. (Rheum.) Hartshill Stoke-on-Trent.

AHUJA, Rajkumari The Surgery, 1 Wrightington St., Wigan WN1 2AZ Tel: 01942 231965 Fax: 01942 826427; 11 Brookland Road, Wigan WN1 2QG Tel: 01942 248184 — MB BS 1962 Vikram; DTM & H Liverp. 1974. Family Plann. Off. Wigan; Clin. Asst. (Obst. & Gyn.) Billinge Hosp. Wigan; Family Plann. & IUCD Cert. Socs: Fell. Overseas Doctors Assn.; BMA; (Pres.) Wigan Overseas Doctors Assn. Prev: SHO (Psychiat. & O & G) Billinge Hosp. Wigan.

AHUJA, Satish Kumar Wrightington Street Surgery, 1 Wrightington Street, Wigan WN1 2AZ Tel: 01942 231965 Fax: 01942 826427; 11 Brookland Road, Wigan WN1 2QG Tel: 01942 248184 — MB BS 1961 Lucknow; FRIPHH 1989; DTM & H Liverp. 1967; DA Eng. 1966. Assoc. Specialist (Anaesth. & Psychiat.) Roy. Albert Edwd. Hosp. Wigan; Dir. Wigan Metro Med. Servs.; Mem. LMC. Socs: BMA (Treas. & Ex-Sec. Wigan Br.); (Treas. & Ex Vice-Pres.) Overseas Doctors Assn. (Nat.). Prev: Mem. BMA (Ex-Pres. Wigan); Assoc. Specialist (Anaesth.) Roy. Albert Edwd. Infirm. Wigan.

AICHINGER, Gerald Department of Immunology, RPMS, Hammersmith Hospital, Du Cane Road, London W12 0NN — MD 1980 Innsbruck.

AICHROTH, Mr Paul Michael (retired) Wellington Hospital, London NW8 9LE Tel: 020 7586 5959 Fax: 020 7483 5241 — MB BS 1959 Lond.; MS Lond. 1973; FRCS Eng. 1964; MRCS Eng. LRCP Lond. 1959; DObst RCOG 1961. p/t Emerit. Cons. Orthop. Surg. Wellington Hosp. Lond.; Hon. Cons. Hosp. Sick Childr. Gt. Ormond St. Lond.; Emer. Surg. Teach. Imperial Coll. Lond. Prev: Cons. Orthop. Surg. Chelsea & W.m. Hosp.

AICKIN, Celia Patricia (retired) Dumbletons, Overthorpe, Banbury OX17 2AE Tel: 01295 710322 — MB BS Lond. 1947; MRCS Eng., LRCP Lond. 1941. Prev: Capt. RAMC.

AICKIN, Jennifer Carole N. West Anglia HA, St James, Extons Road, King's Lynn PE30 5NU Tel: 01553 773951; Church House, Church Lane, Heacham, King's Lynn PE31 7HJ — MB BCh BAO 1966 Belf.; FFPHM RCP (UK) 1990; DObst RCOG 1968; Dip. Community. Med. Ed. 1975. (Qu. Univ. Belf.) Cons. Pub. Health Med. & Cons. Communicable Dis. Control NW Anglia HA. Socs: BMA & Soc. for Social Med. Prev: Med. Off. DHSS N.. Irel.; Sen. Tutor Qu. Univ. Belf.; Sen. Regist. EHSS Bd.

AIHIE SAYER, Avan Penelope Tel: 02380 777624 Email: aas@mrc.soton.ac.uk — MB BS 1987 Lond.; PhD Soton. 1997; MSc Lond. 1993, BSc 1984; MRCP (UK) 1990. (Lond. Hosp. Med. Coll.) MRC Clin. Scientist, MRC Environm. Epidemiol. Unit, Univ. of Soton.; Hon. Cons. in Geriat. Med. & Hon. Sen. Lect. in Geriat. Med., Elderly Care Unit, Soton. Univ. Hosps. NHS Trust. Prev: Sen. Regist. Rotat. (Geriat. Med.) Soton. Univ. Hosp. Trust Portsmouth Healthcare Trust; Wellcome Research Fell. (Clin. Epidemiol.) Univ. of Soton.; Regist. Rotat. (Med.) Guy's Hosp. Lond.

AIKEN, Christopher Geoffrey Alexander Department of Paediatrics, Addenbrooke's Hospital, Hills Road, Cambridge CB2 2QQ — MB 1978 Camb.; BChir 1977.

AIKEN, David Alexander (retired) 2 Karen Court, Denbigh LL16 4RB Tel: 01745 812841 — MB BCh BAO 1952 Belf.; FRCOG 1977, M 1964, DObst 1954. Cons. (O & G) Clwyd AHA. Prev: Sen. Regist. United Manch. Hosps.

AIKEN, Robert Adshead (retired) 86 Walton Road, Chesterfield S40 3BY Tel: 01246 273638 — MB BChir 1958 Camb.; MA Camb. 1958; FRCOG 1980, M 1967, DObst 1959. Prev: Cons. O & G Chesterfield Gp. Hosps.

AIKEN, Yvonne Brimmond Medical Group, 106 Inverurie Road, Bucksburn, Aberdeen AB21 9AT Tel: 01224 713869 Fax: 01224 716317 — MB BS 1979 Lond.

AIKMAN, Andrew Niven Tildesley, SBStJ (retired) 8 Hamilton Drive, Melton Mowbray LE13 0QY Tel: 01664 62576 — MB ChB 1939 Leeds; BSc (Hons.), MB ChB Leeds 1939. Prev: Surg. Lt. RNVR.

AIKMAN, Ann Sanderson (retired) The Gables, Corra Meadows, Calverhall, Whitchurch SY13 4QB Tel: 01252 25505 — MB ChB 1952 Ed.

AIKMAN, Mubina 53 Sandielands Avenue, Erskine PA8 7BS — MB ChB 1982 Glas. (Glasgow) MB ChB Glas. 1982.

AINGER, Margaret Clare Page Hall Medical Centre, 101 Owler Lane, Sheffield S4 8GB Tel: 0114 261 7245 Fax: 0114 261 1643 — MB ChB 1983 Bristol; BSc 1980 Bristol; MRCGP 1987; DRCOG 1987. (Bristol)

AINLEY, Colin Clifford 7 Whistlers Avenue, London SW11 3TS Tel: 020 7585 0938 — MB BChir 1977 Camb.; BA Camb. 1973, MD Camb. 1989; FRCP Lond. 1995; MRCP (UK) 1979. (Middlx.) Cons. Gastroenterol. Barts & The Lond. and Newham Healthcare NHS Trusts; Sen. Lect. (Gastroenterol.) Med. & Dent. Coll. St. Bart. & Roy. Lond. Hosp.

AINLEY, Eric John Village Surgery, Gillett Road, Poole BH12 5BF Tel: 01202 525252 Fax: 01202 533956 — MB BCh 1976 Wales; MRCGP 1982. GP Bournemouth.

AINLEY, Margaret Isabel (retired) — MB BCh BAO 1946 Belf.; DPH Belf. 1949. Prev: Clin. Med. Off. Lisburn Health Centre.

AINLEY, Neil Jonathan 1 Windsor Road, Formby, Liverpool L37 6DU — MB BS 1992 Lond.

AINLEY, Nicholas Christopher William 26 London Road S., Merstham, Redhill RH1 3DT Tel: 01737 643856 — MB BS 1989 Lond.; BSc Lond. 1986, MB BS 1989.

AINLEY, Rhoda Margaret (retired) 49 Woodgrange Avenue, Kenton, Harrow HA3 0XG — M.B., Ch.B. Glas. 1945. Prev: Ho. Dermatol. & Ho. Phys. (O & G) S.. Gen. Hosp. Glas.

AINLEY, Tina Caroline Flat 2, 20 Lime Grove, London W12 9OA — MB BS 1986 Lond.

AINLEY-WALKER, John Chalie Skrine (retired) Mere Lodge, Old College Lane, Windermere LA23 1BY — BM BCh 1949 Oxf.; BM BCh Oxon. 1949; FFA RCS Eng. 1956; DA Eng. 1954. Cons. Anaesth. S.W. Cumbria Health Dist. Prev: Cons. Anaesth. Canterbury & Thanet Health Dist.

AINLEY-WALKER, Patricia Frances Halliwell Child Development Centre, Aylesford Walk, Bolton BL1 3SQ Tel: 01204 366641; Hill House, 120 Markland Hill, Bolton BL1 5EJ Tel: 01204 431493 — MB BS 1987 Lond.; FRCPCH 1997; MRCP (UK) 1991; BA Camb. 1979. (Charing Cross & Westminster) Cons. Community Paediat. Bolton. Prev: Lect. (Child Health) & Hon. Sen. Regist. Univ. Manch.; Research Fell. MRC Environm. Epidemiol. Unit Soton.; Paediat. Mekane Hiwet Hosp. Asmara, Eritrea.

AINSCOW, Cuthbert Blundell 8 Overdale Gardens, Dore, Sheffield S17 3HE Tel: 0114 362092 — MB ChB 1932 Manch.; BSc Manch. 1928, MB ChB 1932; FRCP Glas. 1977, M 1962; FRFPS Glas. 1943. Prev: Maj. RAMC (Specialist Venereol.); Res. Med. Off. Pk. Hosp. Davyhulme; Cas. Off. Warneford Hosp. Leamington Spa.

AINSCOW, Mr Donald Arthur Paul Daisy Bank House, Leckhampton, Cheltenham GL53 9QQ — MB ChB 1972 Bristol; FRCS Ed. 1977; FRCS (Orthop.) Ed. 1982. Cons. Orthop. Surg. Cheltenham Gen. Hosp. & Standish Orthop. Hosp. Prev: Sen. Orthop. Regist. Soton Gen. Hosp., Qu. Alexandra Hosp. Portsmouth; & Lord Mayor Treloar Hosp. Alton.

AINSCOW, Donald Mason Chalmers (retired) Grange Court, Temple-Sowerby, Penrith CA10 1SA — MB BChir 1946 Camb.; MA Camb. 1948, MB BChir. 1946; MRCS Eng., LRCP Lond. 1946. Prev: RAMC 1947-9.

AINSCOW, Glyn 27 Grange Road, Winton, Eccles, Manchester M30 8JW — MD 1977 Manch.; MB ChB 1968; MRCOG 1974. Regist. (O & G) Univ. Hosp. S. Manch. Prev: Ho. Off. (O & G) Withington Hosp. Manch.; Asst. Res. Surg. Off. Salford Roy. Hosp.; SHO (O & G) Univ. Hosp. S. Manch.

AINSLEIGH-JONES, Mari (retired) Rose Garth, Ordsall Park Close, Retford DN22 7PE Tel: 01777 702395 — MRCS Eng. LRCP Lond. 1949; DA Eng. 1954. Prev: Assoc. Specialist Doncaster Roy. Infirm.

AINSLEY, Jacqueline 9 Caractacus Green, Watford WD18 6JU — BM BS 1997 Nottm.

AINSLEY, Roberta Frances Dunbar (retired) Graystones, 2A Renton Avenue, Guiseley, Leeds LS20 8EE — MB ChB 1936 Ed. Prev: Res. Med. Off. Howbeck Infirm. W. Hartlepool.

AINSLIE, Mr Derek Fairways, 11 Claremont Drive, Esher KT10 9LU Tel: 01372 462466 — MB BChir 1944 Camb.; MA Camb. 1944, MD 1954; FRCS Eng. 1949; FRCOphth 1993; DOMS Eng. 1945. (Camb. & Middlx.) Emerit. Ophth. Surg. Middlx. Hosp. Lond.; Hon. Cons. Surg. Moorfields Eye Hosp. Socs: Fell. Roy. Soc. Med. Prev: Cons. Ophth. Surg. Middlx. Hosp. Lond.; Cons. Surg. & Sen. Resid. Off. Moorfields Eye Hosp.

AINSLIE, Dorothy Beechgrove, Tweedmount Road, Melrose TD6 9ST; Roxburgh Street Surgery, 10 Roxburgh St, Galashiels TD1 1PF Tel: 01896 752557 Fax: 01896 755374 — MB ChB 1976 Ed.

AINSLIE, John Archibald (retired) 10 St Dunstans Terrace, Canterbury CT2 8AX — MRCS Eng. LRCP Lond. 1942; BSc (Hons. Phys.) Lond. 1938; DPM Eng. 1945; MRCPsych 1971. Prev: Cons. Psychiat. Kent AHA (S.E. Kent).

AINSLIE, Robina Susan Long Thatch, The Green, Hook Norton, Banbury OX15 5LE — MB BS 1953 Lond. (Middlx.) Clin. Asst. Contact Lens Dept. Moorfields Eye Hosp. Lond. Prev: Ho. Surg. Sussex Co. Hosp. Brighton; Ho. Surg. (ENT Dept.) & Ho. Phys. Skins & Eyes Dept. Middlx. Hosp.; Lond.

AINSLIE, William George 18 Watermill Avenue, Kirkintilloch, Glasgow G66 5QS — MB ChB 1993 Glas.

AINSWORTH, Anthony Francis Curtin 38 Mirfield Road, Solihull B91 1JD — MB ChB 1973 Birm.

AINSWORTH, Anthony Joseph Avondale Surgery, 5 Avondale Road, Chesterfield S40 4TF Tel: 01246 232946 Fax: 01246 556246 — MB ChB 1980 Sheff.; MA Camb. 1981; MRCGP 1984; DRCOG 1984; DCH RCPS Glas. 1982. GP Chesterfield.

AINSWORTH, Barbara Beechwood, Waddington Road, Clitheroe BB7 2HJ Tel: 01200 23413 — MB ChB 1960 St. And.; MFFP 1993. SCMO (Family Plann.) Communicare NHS Trust Blackburn.

AINSWORTH, Carol Ann Mellow End, Littleworth Cross, Seale, Farnham GU10 1JN — MB BS 1985 Lond.

AINSWORTH, Christopher James St. James Medical Centre, Burnley Road, Rawtenstall, Rossendale BB4 8HH — MB ChB 1987 Manch.; MRCGP 1992; DRCOG 1990. Socs: GP Writers Assn.; Assoc. Mem. Med. Jl.ists Assn.

AINSWORTH, David Philip The Surgery, Rockleigh Court, 136 Hutton Road, Shenfield, Brentwood CM15 8NN Tel: 01277 223844 Fax: 01277 230136; 29 Covenbrook, Brentwood CM13 2TR Tel: 01277 221367 Email: dainsworth@btinternet.com — MB BS 1978 Lond. (Roy. Free) Prev: SHO (Paediat.) OldCh. Hosp. Romford; SHO (Obst.) Rush Green Hosp. Romford; SHO (Psychiat.) Warley Hosp. Brentwood.

AINSWORTH, Edgar Seymour (retired) Roxford, Brookes Ln, Whalley, Clitheroe BB7 9RG Tel: 01254 822166 — MB ChB 1955 Manch.; MRCS Eng. LRCP Lond. 1956; FRCGP 1990, M 1972. Prev: GP Blackburn.

AINSWORTH, Gerard 15 Beech Avenue, The Brecks, Rotherham S65 3HN — MB ChB 1995 Manch.

AINSWORTH, John Healy Wilmslow Health Centre, Chapel Lane, Wilmslow SK9 5HX Tel: 01625 548555 Fax: 01625 548287; 95 Moor Lane, Wilmslow SK9 6BR Tel: 01625 522373 — MB ChB 1960 Manch.; MRCS Eng. LRCP Lond. 1960; MRCGP 1975; DObst RCOG 1963. (Manch.) Socs: Fell. Manch. Med. Soc. Prev: SHO (O & G) Ashton-under-Lyne Gen. Hosp.; SHO (Paediat.) Wythenshawe Hosp. Manch.; Ho. Surg. Ancoats Hosp. Manch.

AINSWORTH, John Hugh Stephen The Surgery, Bank Street, Slamannan, Falkirk FK1 3EZ Tel: 01324 851288 Fax: 01324 851622 — MB ChB 1990 Dundee; BSc (Hons.) Dund 1985; DFFP 1994. (Dundee) Trainee GP Tayside VTS. Socs: BMA.

AINSWORTH, John Ross Birmingham Children's Hospital, Steelhouse Lane, Birmingham B4 6NH Tel: 0121 333 9465 Fax: 0121 333 9461 — MB BS 1982 Nottm.; BMedSci Nottm. 1980; FRCS Ed. 1987; FRCOphth 1989. Socs: Amer. Assn. of Ophth., Mem.; Amer. Assn. of Paediatric Ophth., Mem.; Internat. Soc. of Genetic Eye Dis.s. Prev: Phys. Hosp. for Sick Childr. Toronto, Canada; Sen. Regist. Tennent Inst. Glas. & Roy. Hosp. Sick Childr. Glas.

AINSWORTH, Jonathan Grieve 44 Doyle Gardens, Kensal Rise, London NW10 3DA Tel: 020 8964 5011 — MB BS 1984 Lond.; MRCP (UK) 1988. Cons. HIV, N. Middlx. Hosp. Lond. Prev: MRC Research Hon. Sen. Regist. St. Mary's Hosp. Lond.; Regist. (Genitourin. Med. & AIDS) St. Mary's Hosp. Lond.

AINSWORTH, Liam Frederick 3 School Avenue, Norwich NR7 0QU — MB ChB 1985 Liverp.

AINSWORTH, Miriam Kay Graham Road Surgery, 22 Graham Road, Weston Super Mare BS23 1YA Tel: 01934 62811 Fax: 01934 645842 — MB ChB 1986 Aberd.; BSc Aberd. 1982, MB ChB 1986.

AINSWORTH, Patricia Red Oak House, Piccadilly, Scotforth, Lancaster LA1 4PW Tel: 01524 842322; Westholme, Westbourne Drive, Lancaster LA1 5EE Tel: 01524 32322 — MB ChB 1963 Bristol; FRCPsych 1985, M 1972; DPM Manch. 1970; DCH Eng. 1967; DObst RCOG 1965. Cons. Child & Adolesc. Psychiat. Bay Community NHS Trust. Socs: Assn. Psychiat. Study Adolesc. & Assn. Child Psychiat. Psychol. & Allied Disciplines. Prev: Lect. (Child & Adolesc. Psychiat.) Univ. Manch.; Hon. Cons. Adolesc. Psych. Salford HA; Cons. Child Psychiat. Roy. Manch. Childrs. Hosp.

AINSWORTH, Paul Sherbourne Medical Centre, 40 Oxford Street, Leamington Spa CV32 4RA Tel: 01926 424736 Fax: 01926 470884; The Firs, Butt Hill, Mapton, Warwick CV47 8NE Email: drpainlis@hotmail.com — MB BCh 1983 Witwatersrand; MRCP (UK) 1988. Clin. Asst. ENT Warwick Hosp.

AINSWORTH, Paul 10 Belvedere Drive, Chorley PR7 1LY — MB ChB 1998 Leeds.

AINSWORTH, Quentin Paul Yew Tree Cottage, Ardley Road, Somerton, Bicester OX25 6LP — MB ChB 1984 Liverp.; FRCA. 1990. Cons. Anaesth. Oxf. Radcliffe NHS Trust. Prev: Sen. Regist. (Anaesth.) Middlx. Hosp. Lond.; Regist. (Anaesth.) Harefield Hosp. Middlx.

AINSWORTH, Roger William Mellow End, Littleworth Cross, Seale, Farnham GU10 1JN — MB 1955 Camb.; BChir 1954; MRCP Ed. 1962; DMJ Soc. Apoth. Lond. 1971; MCPath. 1963. Cons. Pathol. Frimley Pk. Hosp.

AINSWORTH, Sean Brian 13 Hanover Place, Cramlington NE23 3QX — MB ChB 1988 Ed.

AIONO, Semisi 11B Milman Road, Reading RG2 0AZ — MB ChB 1986 Otago.

AIRD, Mr David Weir 10 Bethany Lane, West Cross, Swansea SA3 5TL — MB ChB 1972 St. And.; MMSc Dundee 1980; FRCS Glas. 1980. Cons. Surg. (Otolaryngol.) Singleton Hosp. Swansea. Prev: TWJ Fell. 1981 Univ. Calif. San Francisco, USA; Sen. Regist. Dept. of Otolaryng. Univ. Hosp. Wales Cardiff; Regist. Dept. Otolaryng. Ninewells Hosp., Dundee.

***AIRD, Fiona Katherine** 8 Spinners Wynd, Dundee DD2 1AY; 8 Spinners Wynd, Dundee DD2 1AY — MB ChB 1997 Glas.; MB ChB(hons) Glas. 1997.

AIRD, Ian Alexander Queen Elizabeth Hospital, Ssheriff Hill, Gateshead NE9 6SX Tel: 01914820000; 21 Lintzford Road, Hamsterley Mill, Rowlands Gill NE39 1HG Email: docaird@aol.com — MB ChB 1987 Liverp.; MRCOG 1993; DA (UK) 1990. Cons. (Obst & Gyn). Qu. Eliz. Hosp., Gateshead. Prev: Lect. Univ. of Liverp. (Dept. of O & G); Research Fell. - Liverp. Wom.'s Hosp.; Regist. (O & G) Arrowe Pk. & Fazakerley Hosps. Wirral +Vhester Hosp.

AIRD, Irene Ann 10 Bethany Lane, West Cross, Swansea SA3 5TL — MB ChB 1972 St. And.; DObst RCOG 1976; DCH RCPS Glas. 1974.

AIRD, Peter Malcolm East Quay Medical Centre, East Quay, Bridgwater TA6 5YB Tel: 01278 444666 Fax: 01278 445448; 40 Oakfield Park, Wellington TA21 8EY Tel: 01823 664610 — MB ChB 1991 Bristol; BSc (Hons.) Bristol 1989; MRCGP 1995; DRCOG 1994; DCH RCP Lond. 1993. (Univ. Bristol) GP Princip. Prev: Trainee GP Taunton VTS.

AIREY, Carolyn Lois 66 Cunningham Drive, Bromborough, Wirral CH63 0JZ — MB ChB 1995 Leeds.

AIREY, Faith Margaret — MB ChB 1994 Manch. p/t GP Retainer, Keswick. Prev: GP Asst., Silloth; GP Regist. E. Cumbrian VTS; SHO (A & E) Blackpool Vict. Hosp.

AIREY, George Oswald (retired) 10 Barclay Hall, Hall Lane, Mobberley, Knutsford WA16 7DZ Tel: 01565 872068 — MB ChB Ed. 1937. Prev: Med. Off. Regional Office, Dept. of Health & Social Security.

AIREY, Margaret (retired) 75 The Causeway, Potters Bar EN6 5HL Tel: 01707 655267 — MB BCh BAO 1946 NUI. Prev: Clin. Med. Off. E. Herts. HA.

AIREY, Mildred Susan (retired) 7 Manor Court, Grange Road, Cambridge CB3 9BE Tel: 01223 323248 — MB ChB Leeds 1942. Prev: Clin. Med. Off. E. Herts & W. Essex HA's.

AIREY, Nicholas John Beech Court, 2-4 Taunton Road, Bridgwater TA6 3LS Tel: 01278 444737 Email: nick.airey@sompar.nhs.uk — MB ChB 1985 Bristol; MRCPsych 1998; MRCGP 1993; MSc 2000 (Distinction). Cons., Som. Partnership, NHS & Social Care Trust, Bridgwater. Prev: Specialist Regist., SW Peninsular Train. Scheme.

AIREY, Timothy Peter Redlands, Rickmansworth Lane, Chalfont St Peter, Gerrards Cross SL9 0LY — MB BS 1983 Lond.; BSc (Physiol.) Lond. 1980; DRCOG 1988; DCH RCP Lond. 1987.

AIRLIE, Ian (retired) 91 Kenton Road, Newcastle upon Tyne NE3 4NL Tel: 0191 285 8811 — MB ChB 1956 Glas.; FRCGP 1986, M 1974.

AIRLIE, Kenneth Russell Auckland Medical Group, 54 Cockton Hill Road, Bishop Auckland DL14 6BB Tel: 01388 602728; 3 Etherley Lane, Bishop Auckland DL14 7QR Tel: 01388 601949 — MB ChB 1985 Dundee; MRCGP 1989; DRCOG 1989. (Dundee)

AIRLIE, Maureen Agnes Anne Department of Community Child Health, Iochalmers Crescent, Edinburgh EH9 1TS Tel: 0131 536 0470; 61 Barnton Park Avenue, Edinburgh EH4 6HD — MB ChB 1979 Aberd.; BMedBiol 1976; MRCP (UK) 1983; MRCGP 1990; DCCH RCGP & FCM 1989. Staff Grade (Community Paediat.) Edin. Sick Childr.'s Trust.

AISBITT, Michael Richard St Peter's Vicarage, Northgate, Horbury, Wakefield WF4 6AS — MB ChB 1997 Liverp.

AITCHESON, Patricia Elaine Park Avenue Medical Centre, 166-168 Park Avenue North, Northampton NN3 2HZ Tel: 01604 716500 Fax: 01604 721685; Beechwood, 7 Mears Ashby Road, Earls Barton, Northampton NN6 0HQ — MB ChB 1985 Leic.; BSc (Med. Sci.) Leic. 1982; MRCGP 1990; DRCOG 1989. (Leic.) Secondment to Pub. Health Directorate N.ampton. Prev: Secondment to Pub. Health N.ampton; Trainee GP Kettering; SHO Rotat. (Med.) Leics.

AITCHISON, Charles Ingram (retired) Underfell, 13 Greenside, Kendal LA9 5DU Tel: 01539 722195 — MB ChB 1960 Ed.; MRCGP 1979; DObst RCOG 1964; DCH Eng. 1963.

AITCHISON, David John McDonald New Road Surgery, 109 York Road, Chingford, London E4 8LF Tel: 020 8524 8124 Fax: 020 8529 8655 — MB ChB 1978 Dundee; DRCOG 1981.

AITCHISON, Edda Inge Milton House Surgery, Doctors Commons Road, Berkhamsted HP4 3BY Tel: 01442 874784 Fax: 01442 877694; Ivymead, Ivy House Lane, Berkhamsted HP4 2PP — MB BS 1971 Lond.; DCH Eng. 1974; DObst RCOG 1973. (Char. Cross)

AITCHISON, Elizabeth Anne Milburn The Brow, Wylam NE41 8DQ Tel: 01661 853888 Fax: 01661 853888 Email: anne@gemini.plasma.uk — MB BS 1964 Durh. (Newc. Univ.) GP Wylam; Pract. Complementary Therapies N.d.; Examr. Various Insur. Cos. Socs: BMA & Brit. Med. & Dent. Hypn. Soc.; Anglo-German Med. Soc. Prev: Civil Med. Pract. RAF; Ho. Off. (Paediat). & Ho. Phys. Med. Unit Newc. Gen. Hosp. Newc. u. Tyne.

AITCHISON, Frances Anne XRay Department, City Hospital, Dudley Road, Birmingham B18 7QH — MB ChB 1985 Ed.; MRCP (UK) 1989; FRCR 1992. (Edin.) Cons. Radiol. City Hosp. NHS Trust Birm.

AITCHISON, Helen Tor'Edin, Old Edinburgh Road, Minnigaff, Newton Stewart DG8 6PL Tel: 01671 402196 — MB ChB 1963 Ed. (Ed.) Prev: GP Newton Stewart; Ho. Surg. Craigtoun Hosp. St. And.; Ho. Phys. Cumbld. Infirm. Carlisle.

AITCHISON, Ian (retired) 8 Kensington Close, Savile Park, Halifax HX3 0HX Tel: 01422 353564 — MB ChB 1936 Glas.

AITCHISON, Mr James Douglas Freeman Hospital, Freeman Road, Newcastle upon Tyne NE7 7DN Tel: 0191 284 3111 Fax: 0191 222 1177 Email: j.d.aitchison@ncl.ac.uk; 7 Treherne Road, High West Jesmond, Newcastle upon Tyne NE2 3NP — MB BS 1993 Newc.; BMedSci 1992; FRCS Lond. 1997; FRCS Ed. 1997. Fell. (Transpl. & Cardiothoracic Surg.).

AITCHISON, Katherine Jean Department of Psychological Medicine, Institute of Psychiatry, De Crespigny Park, Denmark Hill, London SE5 8AF Tel: 020 7919 3536 Fax: 020 7701 9044 Email: spmakja@iop.bpmf.ac.uk — BM BCh 1990 Oxf.; MA Oxf. 1990, BA (1st cl. Hons.) Physiol Sc. 1987; MRCPsych 1996. Wellcome Clin. Train. Fell. Inst. Psychiat. Lond.; Hon. Sen. Regist. Maudsley Hosp. Lond. Socs: BMA; Med. Defence Union. Prev: Regist. (Psychiat.) & SHO (Gen. Psychiat.) Maudsley Hosp. Lond.; SHO (Neurol.) Radcliffe Infirm. Oxf.

AITCHISON, Kenneth James Dornoch Medical Practice, Shore Road, Dornoch IV25 3LS Tel: 01862 810213 Fax: 01862 811066 — MB ChB 1978 Aberd.; MRCGP 1983; DRCOG 1983.

AITCHISON, Michael 8 Kensington Road, Downahill, Glasgow G12 9LF — MB ChB 1982 Glas. Socs: Fell. RCS (Urol.) Doctor of Med.

AITCHISON, Philip James McDonald Wilson Street Surgery, 11 Wilson Street, Derby DE1 1PG; Meadowbrook, 4 Flagshaw Lane, Kirk Langley, Derby DE6 4NW — MB ChB 1977 Ed.; MRCGP 1981; DRCOG 1980.

AITCHISON, Robin Graeme McDonald Department of Haematology, Wycombe General Hospital, High Wycombe HP11 2TT — MB ChB 1980 Dundee; FRCPath. 1999; FRCP Lond. 1998; MRCPath 1990; MRCP (UK) 1984. Cons. Haemat. Wycombe Gen. Hosp. Prev: Lect. (Haemat.) Roy. Lond. Hosp.

AITCHISON, Valerie Anne Calsayseat Medical Group, 2 Calsayseat Road, Aberdeen AB25 3UY Tel: 01224 634345 — MB ChB 1989 Aberd.; MRCGP 1993. (Aberdeen) Gen. Practitioner Aberd. Socs: BMA; Aberd. M-C Soc. Prev: Trainee GP/SHO Aberd. VTS.

AITCHISON, Rev. William Kenneth (retired) 45 Grange Road, Fenham, Newcastle upon Tyne NE4 9LB — MB BS 1954 Durh.; DObst RCOG 1956. Chairm. Prostrate Cancer Suppport Gp. N.ern Region. Prev: GP Dunston.

AITCHISON, William Robb Cameron The Surgery, Station Road, Bridge of Weir PA11 3LH Tel: 01505 612555 Fax: 01505 615032 — MB ChB 1965 Ed. (Ed.)

AITKEN, Adam George Frederick The Radiology Department, Raigmore Hospital NHS Trust, Perth Road, Inverness IV2 3UJ — MB ChB 1975 Aberd.; FRCR Lond. 1981.

AITKEN, Angela Christine Kirtlands Cottage, Weston Road, Bletchingdon, Kidlington OX5 3DH — MB BS 1991 Lond.; BSc Biochem. (1st cl. Hons.) Lond. 1986. SHO (Dermat.) Nuffield Orthop. Centre Oxf. Prev: SHO Rotat. (Med.) Lond.

AITKEN, Carol The Coach House, 48 Headingley Lane, Leeds LS6 2EL — MB ChB 1994 Leeds.

AITKEN, Catherine Hay 52a North Hill, London N6 4RH Tel: 020 8340 5914 — MB ChB 1945 Aberd.; DCH Eng. 1948. (Aberd.) Clin. Asst. (Dermat.) N. Middlx. Hosp. Lond.; Clin. Asst. (p/t) Dermat. Whittington Hosp. Lond.

AITKEN, Catherine Mary Eardley and Partners, Biddulph Medical Centre, Well Street, Biddulph, Stoke-on-Trent ST8 6HD Tel: 01782 512822 Fax: 01782 510331; 104 Biddulph Road, Congleton CW12 3LY — MB ChB 1986 Liverp.; DRCOG 1990.

AITKEN, Celia Cameron St Bartholomew's Hospital, London EC1A 7BE Tel: 020 7601 7356; 62 Agamemnon Road, London NW6 1EH — MB BS 1987 Lond.; MRCP (UK) 1990. Lect. & Sen. Regist. (Virol.) St. Bart. Hosp. Lond. Prev: Lect. (Med. Microbiol.) Roy. Lond. Hosp. Trust; Regist. (Med. Microbiol.) Roy. Lond. Hosp. Trust; SHO (Med.) Roy. Free Hosp. Lond.

AITKEN, Colin James Dow The Lomond Practice, Napier Road, Glenrothes KY6 1HL Tel: 01592 611000 Fax: 01592 611639 — MB ChB 1962 Ed.; DObst RCOG 1968. (Ed.) Prev: Regist. (Med.) Leith Hosp. Edin.; SHO City Hosp. Edin.; SHO (Virol.) Wellcome Laborat. Edin. City Hosp.

AITKEN, David Ian (retired) Hillcrest Cottage, 34 Bon Accord Road, Swanage BH19 2DU Tel: 01929 422046 — BM BCh Oxf. 1957; DObst RCOG 1959; DA Eng. 1963.

AITKEN, Delia Montgomery (retired) Hillcrest Cottage, 34 Bon Accord Road, Swanage BH19 2DU Tel: 01929 422046 — MB BS Lond. 1958; MRCS Eng. LRCP Lond. 1958; DObst RCOG 1960. Prev: SCMO E. Dorset HA.

AITKEN, Dianne Marie The New Surgery, 31-35 Linom Road, London SW4 7PB Tel: 020 7274 4220 Fax: 020 7737 0205 — MB BS 1988 Lond.; MRCGP 1992; DRCOG 1992; Dip. Ther. (Lond.) 1998. (Lond. Hosp. Med. Sch.) Socs: Treas. African-Caribbean Soc. Prev: Trainee GP/SHO Lond. Hosp. VTS.

AITKEN, Donald Andrew (retired) 38 Ranmoor Crescent, Sheffield S10 3GW Tel: 0114 230 7315 — MB ChB (Commend.) Aberd. 1954; FRCOG 1976, M 1963; DObst RCOG 1957. Prev: Cons. O & G Nether Edge Hosp. Sheff.

AITKEN, Elizabeth Madge Department of Medicine for the Elderly, Waterloo Block, Lewisham Hospital, Lewisham High St., London SE13 6LH Tel: 020 8333 3000; 2 Forster Road, Beckenham BR3 4LJ — MB BS 1988 Lond.; MRCP (UK) 1992. Cons. Phys. (Gen. & Geriatr. Med) Lewisham Hosp. Prev: Sen. Regist. King's Coll. & Bromley Hosps.

AITKEN, Elizabeth Margaret (retired) 21 Tannoch Drive, Milngavie, Glasgow G62 8AY Tel: 0141 956 1451 — M.B., Ch.B. Glas. 1936.

AITKEN, Ethel Burleigh Medical Practice, Loch Leven Health Centre, Kinross KY13 8SY Tel: 01577 862112 Fax: 01577 862515; Iona, Nether Tillyrie, Kinross KY13 0RW Tel: 01577 862418 Email: paitken@compuserve.com — MB ChB 1987 Ed.; DRCOG 1991; DCH RCPS Glas. 1990. Socs: Assoc. Mem. BMAS.

AITKEN, Fiona Jean Balmore Park Surgery, 59A Hemdean Road, Caversham, Reading RG4 7SS Tel: 0118 947 1455 Fax: 0118 946 1766; 2A Kidmore Road, Caversham, Reading RG4 7LU Tel: 0118 947 7722 — MB BS 1966 Lond.; MRCS Eng. LRCP Lond. 1966; MRCGP 1975; DCH Eng. 1969; DObst RCOG 1969. (Roy. Free)

AITKEN, Gordon James Aitken, Thorniley-Walker, Lombard and Booth, Medical Centre, Gibson Court, Boldon Colliery NE35 9AN Tel: 0191 519 3000 Fax: 0191 519 2020 — MB BS 1967 Newc.; MRCGP 1977.

AITKEN, Hamish Willsoun (retired) Ashdown Forest Health Centre, Lewes Road, Forest Row RH18 5AQ Tel: 01342 822131 Fax: 01342 826015 — MB BS 1971 Lond.; MRCS Eng. LRCP Lond. 1971. Prev: SHO (Psychiat.) Oakwood Hosp. Maidstone.

AITKEN, Henry Chance 9 Beechgrove Heights, Mullaghboy Hill, Magherafelt BT45 5EF — MB BCh BAO 1967 Belf.; FRCOG 1986, M 1972, DObst 1969. Cons. (O & G) Mid Ulster Hosp. Magherafelt. Socs: Ulster Obst. & Gyn. Soc. Prev: Sen. Regist. & Sen. Tutor (O & G) Ulster Hosp. Dundonald; SHO Roy. Matern. Hosp. Belf.; Ho. Off. Roy. Vict. Hosp. Belf.

AITKEN, Hilda (retired) 293 Westburn Road, Aberdeen AB25 2QZ Tel: 01224 315011 — MB ChB Aberd. 1947; DPH Aberd. 1965. Prev: Staff Community Med. Dept. Grampian Health Bd.

AITKEN, Ian Clark Crail Medical Practice, 245 Tollcross Road, Glasgow G31 4UW Tel: 0141 554 3199 Fax: 0141 551 9950 Email: ian.aitken@gp46131.glasgow-hb.scot.nhs.uk — MB ChB 1981 Aberd. GP Glas.

AITKEN, Jacquilyn 19 Coverley Rise, Yeadon, Leeds LS19 7WB — MB ChB 1995 Leeds; MB ChB (Hons.) Leeds 1995; BSc (Hons.) Leeds 1990.

AITKEN, James 8B Morningside Place, Edinburgh EH10 5ER Tel: 0131 447 7413 — MB ChB 1966 Ed. Prev: on Staff MRC Clin. & Populat. Cytogenetic Unit, W.. Gen. Hosp. Edin.; Ho. Surg. Dunfermline & W. Fife Hosp.; Ho. Phys. W.. Gen. Hosp. Edin.

AITKEN, Jane 25 Khartoum Road, Ipswich IP4 4EX — MB BS 1997 Lond.

AITKEN, Jane Elizabeth Barbara (retired) Altacraig, Leighton Gardens, Ellon AB41 9BH Tel: 01358 720442 Fax: 01358 725236 — DObst 1968 RCOG; MB ChB 1966 Glas.; DCH 1968 Eng. Hosp. Pract. Aberd. Roy. Infirm., Roy. Hosp. Sick Childr. Aberd. Prev: Ho. Off. (Surg.) Vict. Infirm. Glas.

AITKEN, John, Wing Cdr. RAF Med. Br. Command Medical Officer (Occupational Health), Royal Airforce, Directorate of Health Services, Head Quarter Personnel Training, RAF Innswater, Gloucester GL3 1EZ Tel: 01452 712612; Thornhall, Dyke, Forres IV36 2TL Tel: 01309 641283 — MB ChB 1982 Ed.; BSc (Med. Sci.) Ed. 1979; AFOM 2000; DAvMed FOM RCP Lond. 1994. (Edinburgh) Command Med. Off. (Occupat.al Health), Roy. Air Force, HQ Personnel & Train., RAF Innswater, Gloucester. Socs: Soc. Occup. Med.; Assoc. Mem. Fac. of Occupat.al Med. Prev: Sen. Med. Off. RAF Kinloss; Sen. Med. Off. RAF Valley; Specialist Regist., Occupat. Med.Policy Surg., Gen. Dept. MOD Whitehall Lond.

AITKEN, John Alexander (retired) 11 Lingdale Road, West Kirby, Wirral CH48 5DG Tel: 0151 632 2255 — MB ChB 1952 Ed.; FRCP Ed. 1975, M 1961; DTM & H Liverp. 1959; MTh Chest. Coll. Of Liverp. Univ. Prev: Cons. Phys. (Geriat.) Clatterbridge Hosp. Bebington.

AITKEN, John Mark Northfields, 59 High Road, Leavenheath, Colchester CO6 4PB — MB BChir 1963 Camb.; MD Camb. 1974, MA, MB 1963, BChir 1962; FRCP Lond. 1981, M 1966. Cons. Phys. Colchester Gen. Hosp. Socs: Fell. Roy. Soc. Med. Prev: Chief Asst. Med. Profess. Unit St. Bart. Hosp. Lond.; Research Fell. Univ. Dept. Med. W.. Infirm. Glas.

AITKEN, Kirsty Elizabeth 11 Hazelton Road, Bishopston, Bristol BS7 8ER Tel: 0117 924 0811 — BM BS 1990 Nottm.; MRCGP 1996; DRCOG 1995. GP Princip. Prev: GP. Regist. Bristol.

AITKEN, Muriel (retired) 38 Ranmoor Crescent, Sheffield S10 3GW — MB ChB Aberd. 1957. Prev: Research/Clin. Asst. (Clin. Oncol.) W.on Pk. Hosp. Sheff.

AITKEN, Murray James 3 Pennethorne Close, Victoria Park Road, London E9 7HF — MB ChB 1987 Bristol.

AITKEN, Peter (retired) Leemount, 83 Lady Nairn Avenue, Kirkcaldy KY1 2AR Tel: 01592 652223 — MB ChB Ed. 1944; FRCR 1982; DMR 1946. Prev: Cons. Radiol. Vict. Hosp. Kirkcaldy.

AITKEN, Peter Henry Lowry Liaison Psychiatry Clinic, Clare House, St George's Hospital, Blackshaw Road, London SW17 0QT Tel: 020 8725 5288 Fax: 020 8725 3094 Email: paitken@sghms.ac.uk — MB ChB 1987 Glas.; MRCGP 1993; MRCPsych 1995; DRCOG 1992; DCH RCP Lond. 1992. Cons. Liaison Psychiat. S. W. Lond. & St Geo.s Ment. Health Trust, St Geo.'s Hosp., Lond.; Sen. Lect. in Med. Educat. St Geo. Hosp. Med. Sch. Prev: Trainee GP Morden Surrey; Regist. Rotat. (Psychiat.) St. Geo. Hosp.; Clin. Lect. (Adult Psychiat.) St. Geo.s' Hosp. Med. Sch. Lond.

AITKEN, Professor Robert Cairns Brown, CBE (retired) 11 Succoth Place, Edinburgh EH12 6BJ — MB ChB 1957 Glas.; MB ChB 1957 Glasgow; 1992 DSc (Hon.) CNAA; 1965 MD (Commend.) Glas.; 1965 FRCP Ed. 1971, M; 1971 FRCPsych 1975, M; 1965 DPM Eng. Prev: Sen. Lect. & Hon. Cons. Psychiat. Roy. Infirm. & Roy. Edin. Hosp.

AITKEN, Robert Hector 57 Hemingford Gardens, Yarm TS15 9ST — MB ChB 1976 Ed.; MRCOG 1981.

AITKEN, Robert Jack Gibson (retired) Avon Park Nursing Home, Gallowhill, Lesmahagow Road, Strathaven ML10 6BZ — LRCP LRCS 1945 Ed.; LRCP LRCS Ed. LRFPS Glas. 1945.

AITKEN, Robert James Royal Infirmary, Department of General Surgery, Lauriston Place, Edinburgh EH3 9YW Tel: 0131 536 1609 Fax: 0131 536 1509; 1 Dalrymple Crescent, Edinburgh EH9 2NU Tel: 0131 667 6212 — MB BS 1977 Lond.; MS Lond. 1994; FRCS Ed. 1982; MRCS Eng. LRCP Lond. 1977; FCS(SA) 1984. (Charing Cross Hospital London) Cons. Surg. Roy. Infirm. Edin. Socs: Fell. Roy. Soc. Med. (Proctol. Sect.); Assn. Col. Proctol. GB & Irel.; Assn. Surg. Prev: Lect. Univ. Dept. Surg. Edin.; Regist. & Sen. Regist. Groote Schuur Hosp. Cape Town, SA.

AITKEN, Robert MacGregor (retired) 27 Cleyhall Drive, Spalding PE11 2EZ Tel: 01775 722055 Email: royait@btinternet.com — MB ChB 1947 Ed.; FRCGP 1972, M 1954; DObst RCOG 1951. Prev: Ho. Surg. (O & G) Simpson Memor. Matern. Pavil. & Roy. Infirm. Edin.

AITKEN, Robin Elliot Guild, TD The Hollies, 4 Woodhall Road, Colinton, Edinburgh EH13 0DX Tel: 0131 441 2615 — MB ChB 1963 Aberd.; MSc Ed. 1982; MFCM RCP (UK) 1984. Sen. Med. Off. Scott. Home & Health Dept. Prev: SCM Hosp. Admin. Grampian Health Bd. Aberd.; CO 252 Field Ambul. RAMC (TA); Regtl. Med. Off. 23 Parachute Field Ambul.

AITKEN, Sarah Jane Department of Public Health Medicine, Gwent Health Authority, Mamhilad, Pontypool NP4 0YP Tel: 01495 765119 Fax: 01495 769201 — MB BS 1984 Lond.; BSc 1981 Lond.; DRCOG 1990; DCH RCP Lond. 1987; MFPHM, Faculty of Public Medicine; CCST Public Health Med 1997; GMC Specialist Reg for Public Health 98. (St. Thos.) p/t Cons. (Pub. Health Med.) Gwent HA.

AITKEN, William Blackwood Vinegarth, Chirnside, Duns TD11 3UH Tel: 0189081 8998 Email: vinegarth@aol.com — MB ChB 1956 Ed.

AITKENHEAD, Alan Robert University Department Anaesthetics, Queen's Medical Centre, Clifton Boulevard, Nottingham NG7 2UH Tel: 0115 970 9231 Fax: 0115 970 0739 — MB ChB 1972 Ed.; BSc (Med. Scs.) Ed. 1969, MD 1986; FFA Eng. 1976. Prof. Anaesth. Univ. Nottm. Socs: (Counc.) Med. Defence Union; (Pres.) Europ. Soc. Anaesthesiol. (Mem. Counc. & Bd. Directors).; (Vice-Pres.) Assn. Anaesth. GB & Irel. Prev: Sen. Lect. (Anaesth.) Univ. Leicester; Sen. Regist. (Anaesth.) Radcliffe Infirm. Oxf.; Hon. Sen. Regist. Shock Study Gp. W.. Infirm. Glas.

AITMAN, Timothy John Molecular Medicine Group, Hammersmith Hospital, Du Cane Road, London W12 0NN Fax: 020 8383 2028 Email: taitman@rpms.ac.uk — MB ChB 1982 Birm.; BSc (Physiol.) Birm. 1979; DPhil Oxf. 1992; MSc (Biochem.) Lond. 1988; MRCP (UK) 1985. MRC Clin. Scientist, Hons. Sen. Lect. & Cons. Phys. Hammersmith Hosp. Lond. Prev: Sen. Regist. St. Bart. Hosp. Lond.; Wellcome Research Fell. & Hon. Sen. Regist. John Radcliffe Hosp. Oxf.; Clin. Scientist & Regist. (Med.) Clin. Research Centre & N.wick Pk. Hosp. Harrow.

AITON, Clive Grierson 10 Field Close, Hilton, Derby DE65 5GL — MB BS 1993 Lond.

AITON, Neil Robert Trevor Mann Baby Unit, Royal Sussex County Hospital, Eastern Road, Brighton BN2 5BE — MB BS 1987 Lond.; 1987 MB BS Lond.; 1998 MD Lond.; 1991 MRCPI; FRCP 1998. Cons. Neonatologist Trevor Mann Baby Unit Roy. Sussex Co. Hosp. Brighton. Prev: Lect. (Neonat. Med.) Univ. Bristol.

AITON-MACBEAN, David Ralph Department of Obstetrics & Gynaecology, New Cross Hospital, Wolverhampton WV10 0QP Tel: 01902 732255; Freshfield, The Drive, Tettenhall, Wolverhampton WV6 8SE — MB BS 1980 Newc.; MRCOG 1988. Prev: Acting Regist. (O & G) New Cross Hosp. Wolverhampton; SHO (O & G) St. Geo. Hosp. Lond.; SHO (Sexual Dis.) Newc. Gen. Hosp.

AIYAPPA, Kumbera Somaiah Keighley Road Surgery, Keighley Road, Illingworth, Halifax HX2 9LL Tel: 01422 244397/248308 Fax: 01422 241101; The Hollies, Rawson Avenue, Savile Park, Halifax HX3 0JP Tel: 01422 356454 Email: 106302.2422@compuserve.com — MB BS 1971 Mysore. (Mysore Medical, India)

AIYEGBUSI, Modupe c/o Drive Ambrose Togobo, 59 Kings Road, Leytonstone, London E11 1AU — MB BCh 1983 Ain Shams; MRCOG 1988.

AJAI-AJAGBE, Emmanuel Kunnuji Oluyinka Ajai-Ajagbe, Outgang Barn, Outgang Road, Aspatria, Wigton CA7 3HW Tel: 016973 20367 Fax: 016973 23230 — MB ChB 1968 Bristol; MRCP (UK) 1973; FT Cert 1986 Lond. Gen. Practitioner. Socs: FRSM; MRCP.

AJAM, Goolam Saber Cornmarket Surgery, 6 Newry Health Village, Monaghan St., Newry BT35 6BW; 34 Derryleckagh Road, Newry BT34 2NL — LRCPI & LM, LRSCI & LM 1972; LRCPI & LM, LRCSI & LM 1972. (Royal College of Surgeons in Dublin, Ireland) Socs: RCS. Prev: GP.

AJAM-OGHLI, Abdul Rahman 8 Hartsbourne Drive, Halesowen B62 8ST Tel: 0121 550 0545 — MD 1971 Damascus.

AJAYI, Adeleye Afolabi 1 Chapel Terrace, Kemp Town, Brighton BN2 1HB — MB BS 1993 Lond. (King's Coll. Sch. Med. & Dent.) Prev: SHO (Urol.) Roy. Sussex Co. Hosp. Brighton.

AJAYI, Mr Benedict Adedayo 40 Ffordd Cwellym, Sovereign Chase, Cyncoed, Cardiff CF23 5NB Tel: 029 2049 1906 Fax: 029 2049 1906 — MB BS 1978 Ibadan; FRCS Ed. 1990. Staff Grade (Surg.) Bridgend NHS Trust.

AJAYI, Mr James Dehinde 1 Hazel Walk, Broadstairs CT10 2LX — MB BS 1975 Ibadan, Nigeria; FRCS Glas. 1989.

AJAYI, Johnson Folorunso District General Hospital, Town Lane, Kew, Southport PR8 6PN Tel: 01704 547471 Fax: 01704 502131; 4 Norwood Crescent, Southport PR9 7DU Tel: 01704 212244 Fax: 01704 212244 Email: ajayi@premiumuk.com — MB BS 1979 Ibadan; MRCOG 1991. (Univ. Ibadan) Staff Grade (O & G) S.port & Formby NHS Trust. Socs: Obst. & Gyn. Soc.; BMA. Prev: Regist. (O & G) Mill Rd. Matern. Hosp., Fazakerley Hosp. Liverp. & S.port & Formby HA.

AJAYI, Richardson Adedayo 18A Marmora Road, E. Dulwich, London SE22 0RX Tel: 020 8299 0847 — MB BS 1988 Lond.; MRCOG 1993. Regist. Lewisham Hosp. Lond. Prev: SHO (Obst.) King's Coll. Hosp. Lond.; SHO (Gyn.) Hammersmith Hosp. Lond.; SHO (Obst.) Ealing Hosp. Lond.

AJAYI-OBE, Olayinka 4 Brant Road, Scunthorpe DN15 7BS — MB BS 1983 Lagos; MB BS Lagos 983.

AJAZ, Mazhar Adnan Roslyn, 51A Westridge Road, Southampton SO17 2HP — BM 1997 Soton.; BSc Soton. 1996. (Southampton)

AJDUKIEWICZ, Katherine Mary Brzechwa 36 St Gabriels Road, London NW2 4SA — MB ChB 1997 Dundee. Ho. Off. (Gen. Surg.) Perth Roy. Infirm.

AJEKIGBE, Mr Olanrewaju Lawrence Department of Plastic Surgery, Middlesbrough General Hospital, Ayresome Green Lane, Middlesbrough TS5 5AZ Tel: 01642 850222; 28 Dewberry, Coulby Newham, Middlesbrough TS8 0XH — MB BS 1987 Ibadan; FRCS Glas. 1992. Staff Grade Surg. (Plastic Surg.) Middlesbrough Gen. Hosp.; Clin. Asst (A & E) Gen. Hosp. Middlesbrough.

AJIMAL, Sarbjit Kaur 107 Sandwell Road, Birmingham B21 8NG — MB ChB 1996 Leic.

AJIMOKO, Bolajoko Anike 1 Montaigne Gardens, Lincoln LN2 4RL — MB BS 1980 Ibadan; MB BS Ibadan Nigeria 1980; FCOphth 1991; DO RCS Glas. 1988.

AJINA, Isam Abid Ali Hassoon 76 Regal Way, Harrow HA3 0RY Tel: 020 8907 7114 — MB ChB 1976 Baghdad. Staff Psychiat. Belvedere Ho. Day Hosp. Lond. Prev: Regist. (Psychiat.) Runwell Hosp. Wickford.

AJITSARIA, Richa 56 Edgwarebury Lane, Edgware HA8 8LW — MB BS 1997 Lond.

AJMAL, Mr Muhammad 11 Barrow Meadow, Cheadle Hulme, Cheadle SK8 6SF — MB BS 1986 Bahauddin Zakariya U; MB BS Bahauddin Zakariya U, Pakistan 1986; FRCS Glas. 1993.

AJUIED, Adil 56A Albion Drive, London E8 4LX — MB BS 1998 Lond.; MB BS Lond 1998.

AKA, Albert Kolawole 237 Green Lane, London SW16 3LY — Vrach 1983 Crimea Med Inst USSR.

AKAGBOSU, Lilian Chizomam 35 Ashvale, Cambridge CB4 2SZ — MB BS 1986 Benin; MB BS 1986 Benin.

AKAGI, Hiroko St James' University Hospital, Beckett St, Leeds LS9 7TF — BM BCh 1983 Oxf.; MSc (Med.) Lond. 1989; MA Oxf. 1985; MRCP (UK) 1987; MRCPath 1992; MRCPsych 1998. (Oxford) Specialist Regist.Gen. Psych. Prev: Lect. & Sen. Regist. (Chem. Path.) Gt. Ormond St. Hosp. for Childr.; Regist. (Chem. Path.) Roy. Free Hosp. Lond.

AKAH, Mrs Frances Bernardine Chinwe 50 Tantallon Road, London SW12 8DG — MB BCh BAO 1978 NUI; LRCPI & LM, LRCSI & LM 1978.

AKAK, Abubaker Mohamed 4 Beech Court, North Tyneside General Hospital, North Shields NE29 8NH; 35 Broadwell Court, South Gosforth, Newcastle upon Tyne NE3 1YS — MB BS 1979 Libya; MRCP (UK) 1986.

AKAM, Robert Maurice Elmwood Health Centre, Huddersfield Road, Holmfirth, Huddersfield HD9 3TR Tel: 01484 681777 Fax: 01484 689603; Carr House, Hightown Lane, Holmfirth, Huddersfield HD9 3HY — BM 1985 Soton.; MRCGP 1992.

AKANDE, Olufemi 111 Warwick Road, Scunthorpe DN16 1ES — MB BS 1974 Mysore; FRCSI 2001.

AKANGA, John Moses Cytos 19 Salem Place, Croydon CR0 1AQ — MB ChB 1991 Makerer; MSc Lond. 1991; LMSSA Lond. 1993. SHO (Gen. Med.) S. Warks. Gen. Hosp. Prev: SHO (A & E) St. Geo. Hosp. Lond.; Ho. Surg. Mayday Hosp.; Ho.Phys. Char. Cross Hosp. Lond.

AKAR, Mr Patrick Eric Accident & Emergency Department, Scarborough Hospital, Scalby Road, Scarborough YO12 6QL Tel: 01723 368111 Fax: 01723 342155 Email: akarp@mail.scarney.northy.nhs.uk; Akwaba Lodge, 25 Racecourse Road, E. Ayton, Scarborough YO13 9HP Tel: 01723 864108 Email: pat.akar@lineone.net — Lekarz 1970 Warsaw; FRCS Ed. 1977; FFAEM 1995. (Warsaw Medical Academy, Poland) Cons. A & E ScarBoro. & NE NHS Trust. Socs: Assn. Police Surg.; Brit. Assn. Accid. & Emerg. Med.; BMA. Prev: Cons. Traumatol. & Orthop. Nat. Orthop. Hosp. Kano, Nigeria; Stanley Johnson Research Fell.sh. (Microsurg.) Clin. Research Centre N.wick Pk. Hosp. Harrow.

AKASHA, Mr Kamal Shawgi Kalil c/o Dr Khalil, Warrington District Hospital, Lovely Lane, Warrington WA5 1QG — MB BS 1983 Khartoum; FRCSI 1991.

AKASHEH, Khalil N. Wales Medical Centre, Queens Road, Llandudno LL30 1UE — BM 1978 Soton.

AKBANY, Jaffar 18 Brudenell Road, London SW17 8DA — MB BS 1995 Lond.

AKBAR, Abdullah Victoria Hospital, Mansfield NG18 5QJ — MB BS 1960 Dacca; MRCP Glas. 1969. Cons. Phys. i/c Geriat. Servs. Mansfield Area Sheff. RHB. Prev: Sen. Regist. (Geriat.) King's Coll. Hosp. Lond.; Asst. in Geriat. Foresthall, Ruchill & Robroyston Hosps. Glas.

AKBAR, Ali Department of Paediatrics, The City Hospital NHS Trust, Dudley Road, Birmingham B18 7QH Tel: 0121 507 5572 Fax: 0121 507 5587 Email: drakbar@hotmail.com; Email: drakbar@hotmail.com — MB ChB 1985 Dundee; MRCP (UK) 1993; MRCPCH 1997; T(GP) 1992; DCH RCPS Glas. 1989. (Dundee) Cons. Paediat., Dept. of Paediat., The City Hosp. NHS Trust, Birm.; Hon. Cons. Respirat. Paediat., Birm. Childr.'s Hosp., Birm.; Hon. Sen. Clin. Lect., The Univ. of Birm., Birm. Prev: Regist. & SHO Rotat. (Higher Profess. Train.) Birm. Childr. Hosp.; Clin. Research Fell. (Paediat. Respirat. Med.) Birm. Childr. Hosp.; Paediat. Specialist Regist., Walsgrave Hosp., Coventry.

AKBAR, Ayesha 6 Higher Croft, Whitefield, Manchester M45 7LY — MB ChB 1997 Manch.

AKBAR, Fazal Ali 7 The Briars, Warren wood, High Wycombe HP11 1ED Tel: 01494 20103 — MB BS 1953 Punjab; MB BS Punjab (Pakistan) 1953; FRCP Glas. 1972, M 1962; FFPM 1990; FCCP 1962. (King Edw. Med. Coll. Lahore) Dir. GD Searle UK High Wycombe. Socs: Fell. Roy Soc. Med.; Assn. Antimicrobial Chemother. Prev: Regist. (Med.) Roy. Bucks. Gp. Hosps.; Cons. Phys. Karachi; Sen. Research Phys. Roussel Lond.

AKBAR, Naseem Balham Health Centre, 120 Bedford Hill, London SW12 9HS — MB ChB 1966 Liverp.; DObst 1968 RCOG.

***AKBAR, Syed Ali** 1 Long Meadow, Moss Pit, Stafford ST17 9DP — MB BS 1996 Lond.

AKBAR, Mr Syed Shahzad c/o Department of Accident & Emergency, Kingston Hospital, Glasworthy Rd,., Kingston upon Thames KT2 7QB — LMS 1986 Cordoba Univ.; FRCSI 1994.

AKBERALI, Azim Fazal 13 Shere Avenue, Cheam, Sutton SM2 7JX — MB BS 1985 Lond.

AKERELE, Miss Olatokumboh Folawuyo 13 Belsize Park Gardens, London NW3 4JG — MB BS 1992 Lond.; FRCOphth 1998. (St Mary;s Paddington)

AKERELE, Oluremilikun Flat 2, Avenue House, 1 The Avenue, London NW6 7YH; 1A Rectory Grove, Basement Flat, London SW4 0DX — MB BS 1997 Lond.

AKERMAN, Frank MacDonald Alma Road Surgery, Alma Road, Romsey SO51 8ED Tel: 01794 513422 Fax: 01794 518668; 7 The Harrage, Romsey SO51 8AE Tel: 01794 513981 — MB BS 1964 Lond.; DPH 1968; DCH Eng. 1968; DObst RCOG 1967. (St. Thos.) Prev: SHO (Gen. Med.) St. Richard's Hosp. Chichester; Ho. Off. (O & G) St. Thos. Hosp. Lond.; Ho. Phys. Roy. Alexandra Hosp. Sick Childr. Brighton.

AKERMAN, Henry Frank 7 The Harrage, Romsey SO51 8AE — MB BS 1997 Lond.

AKERMAN, Nicholas Halfway, London Rd, Adlington, Macclesfield SK10 4NA — MB ChB 1997 Leeds.

AKERMAN, Pamela Lesley NHS Executive South & West, Westward House, Lime Kiln Close, Stoke Gifford, Bristol BS34 8SR Tel: 0117 984 1750 Fax: 0117 984 1751 — BM BCh 1980 Oxf.; MA Oxf. 1981, BA 1977; MRCGP 1985; MFPHM RCP (UK) 1992; DRCOG 1983; DFFP 1997. Cons. Pub. Health Med. NHS Exec. S.-W. Prev: Sen. Regist. (Pub. Health Med.) S. & W. RHA; Trainee GP Bath VTS.

AKERS, Patricia Sylvia (retired) Two Yews, Netherfield Hill, Battle TN33 0LE Tel: 01424 772352 — MB BS Lond. 1953; MRCS Eng. LRCP Lond. 1953.

AKESTER, Helen Alexandra Ashfield House Surgery, Main Street, Kirkby Malzeard, Ripon HG4 3SE Tel: 01765 658298 Fax: 01765 658846 — BM BS 1989 Nottm. Trainee GP Boston VTS.

AKHRASS, Aktham Orthopaedic Department, Grantham and District Hospital NHS Trust, Grantham Tel: 01476 565232 Fax: 01476 590441; 7 Brecon Close, Gonerby Hill Foot, Grantham NG31 8FX Tel: 01476 562491 Fax: 01476 562491 — MD 1978 Damascus; FRCS Glas. 1990. Assoc. Specialist Grantham & Dist. Hosp. NHS Trust. Socs: Brit. Orthop. Assn. Prev: Staff Surg. (Orthop.) P'boro. Hosps.

AKHTAR, Mr Ahmed Shahzad 25 Trossach's Drive, Belfast BT10 0HS — MB BCh BAO 1989 Belf.; MB BCh Belf. 1989; FRCSI 1993.

AKHTAR, Aleem Alum Rock Medical Centre, 27-29 Highfield Road, Alum Rock, Birmingham B8 3QD Tel: 0121 328 9579 Fax: 0121 328 7495 — MB BS 1976 Karachi; MRCGP 1981; LRCP Ed.; LRCS Ed. (Dow Medical College Karami) Socs: BMA.

AKHTAR, Aslam 57 King Street, Southall UB2 4DQ — MB BS 1983 Lond.

AKHTAR, Mr Javed 52 Crescent Road, Reading RG1 5SP — MB BS 1979 Peshawar; FRCSI 1989.

AKHTAR, Mr Khurshid 27 Langdale Road, Bramhall, Stockport SK7 1DH Tel: 0161 440 8555 — MB BS 1983 Karachi; FRCS Eng. 1989. Socs: Assn. Surg.; Assn. Endoscopic Surgs.

AKHTAR, Mr Mahammoud Eglinton Street Surgery, 658-660 Eglinton Street, Glasgow G5 9RP Tel: 0141 429 1421 Fax: 0141 429 8394; 156 Titwood Road, Glasgow G41 4DB Tel: 0141 424 3270 — MB ChB 1976 Glas.; FRCS Glas. 1982.

AKHTAR, Muhammad City General Hospital, Newcastle Road, Stoke-on-Trent ST4 6QG Tel: 01782 715444; Silverwood, 16 Beechfield Road, Trentham, Stoke-on-Trent ST4 8HG Tel: 01782 643313 — MB BS 1965 Peshawar; FFARCS Eng. 1970; DA (UK) 1967. Cons. Anaesth. N. Staffs. HA. Prev: Sen. Regist. (Anaesth.) W. Midl. RHA; Regist. (Anaesth.) S.end-on-Sea.

AKHTAR, Muhammad Azeem Department of Psychiatry, Green Lane Hospital, Devizes SN10 5DS — MB BS 1984 Punjab, Pakistan.

AKHTAR, Muhammad Samee 13 Convent Way, Southall UB2 5UB — MB BS 1978 Punjab; MRCOG 1983.

AKHTAR, Nadeem 45 Glebe Crescent, Kenton, Harrow HA3 9LB — MB BS 1996 Lond.

AKHTAR, Naim Haematology Department, King George Hospital, Barley La, Goodmayes, Ilford IG3 8YB Tel: 020 8970 8251 Fax: 020 8970 5747 — MB BCh BAO 1979 NUI; MD Leic. 1992; FRCP (UK) 1999; MRCP (UK) 1984; MRCPath 1991; T(M) 1992; T(Path.) 1991. Cons. Haemat. Redbridge Health Care. Socs: Brit. Soc. Haematol. Prev: Sen. Regist. (Haemat.) W. Midl. Train Scheme; Lect. (Molecular Haemat.) Univ. Leicester; Regist. (Haemat., Gen. Med. & Neurol.) Leicester Roy. Infirm.

AKHTAR, Naveed 1 Lynch Court, Voorhees NJ 08043, USA; 32 Carey Park, Lower Reddanick, Truro TR1 2LD Tel: 01872 74242 — MB BS 1982 Karachi; FRCR 1990; T(R) (CR) 1991.

AKHTAR, Mr Raja Pervez 68 Glenfrith Close, Leicester LE3 9QQ Tel: 0116 287 5993 — MB BS 1984 Punjab; FRCS Ed. 1989.

AKHTAR, Rashid 52 Westminster Road, Handsworth, Birmingham B20 3LJ — MB ChB 1996 Leic.

AKHTAR, Razia Littleton, Queens Road, Maidstone ME16 0HX — MB BS 1969 Jammu & Kashmir.

AKHTAR, Shaheen 28 Dorset Avenue, Leeds LS8 3RA — BM 1992 Soton.; MRCGP 1996; DRCOG 1995. (Soton.) Socs: MDU. Prev: Trainee GP/SHO Derriford Hosp. Plymouth VTS.

AKHTAR, Shamim Shaftesbury Medical Centre, 39 Shaftesbury Pardae, South Harrow, Harrow HA2 0AH Tel: 020 8423 5500 — MB BS 1962 Punjab.

AKHTAR, Shamim Ali 11 Horton Grange Road, Bradford BD7 3AH — MB BS 1998 Lond.; MB BS Lond 1998.

AKHTAR, Sohail 27 Geraldton Avenue, Kings Park, Bradford BD2 1EG — MB ChB 1996 Liverp.

AKHTAR, Syed Amir Arshad 42 Beechwood Avenue, Kew, Richmond TW9 4DE — MB BS 1987 Lond.; BSc Lond. 1984, MB BS 1987.

AKHTER, Hassan Max Road Surgery, 4-6 Max Road, Liverpool L14 4BH Tel: 0151 259 2549 — MB BS 1970 Bangalore.

AKHTER, Ribena Flat T/R, 3 Bower St., Glasgow G12 8PT — MB ChB 1998 Glas.; MB ChB Glas 1998.

AKHTER, Saleem 5 Poynt Chase, Worsley, Manchester M28 1FQ — MB ChB 1990 Manch. SHO (Paediat.) Qu.'s Pk. Hosp. Blackburn VTS. Prev: SHO (O & G & Psychiat.) Qu.'s Pk. Hosp. Blackburn; Ho. Off. (Phys.) Blackburn Roy. Infirm.

AKHTER, Zubeida 20 Merryton Avenue, Giffnock, Glasgow G46 6DT — MB BS 1958 Punjab.

AKHURST, Mrs Jessamine Mary (retired) Bay Cottage, Birchwood Road, Cock Clarks, Chelmsford CM3 6RF Tel: 01621 828240 — MB BS 1953 Lond.; DObst RCOG 1955. Prev: SHO Cromer & Dist. Hosp.

AKIL, Mohammed Rheumatology Department, Royal Hallamshire Hospital, Glossop Road, Sheffield S10 2JF Tel: 0114 271 1932 Fax: 0114 271 1844 Email: m.akil@sheffield.ac.uk — MD 1986 Damascus; MRCP (UK) 1991; MRCS Eng. LRCP Lond. 1992. Cons. Rheum. Roy. Hallamsh. Hosp. Sheff. Socs: Brit. Soc. Rheum. Prev: Sen. Regist. (Gen. Med. & Rheum.) Leicester Roy. Infirm.; Regist. (Rheum.) Nether Edge Hosp. Sheff.; Regist. (Med.) Chesterfield Roy. Hosp.

AKIN-OLUGBADE, Oluyemi 4 St Augustine's Court, Mornington Road, London E11 3BQ; 2A Sandringham Avenue, West Bridgeford, Nottingham NG2 7QS — MB BS 1996 Lond.

AKINBOLUE, Oladele Samuel c/o Mr. J. O. Fayemi, 19B Bellingham Road, London SE6 2PN — MB BS 1984 Ibadan; FRCA 1996.

AKINDOLIE, Omowunmi Dryburn Hall, Dryburn Hospital, North Road, Durham DH1 5TW — MB BS 1998 Newc.; MB BS Newc 1998.

AKINFENWA, Olayinka Oyegbade 10 Kingsleigh Place, Mitcham CR4 4NS Email: a.akinfenwa@virgin.net — MB BS 1987 Ibadan; MRCOG 1995. Research Fell. (Fetal Med.) Fetal Med. Foundat. Lond.

AKINGBA, Morella Adekemi Flat 74, Jarrom Court, 40 Deacon St., Leicester LE2 7EF; 18 Thomas North Terrace, Barking Road, London E16 1EL Email: morella_akingba@yahoo.com — MB ChB 1998 Leic.; MB ChB Leic 1998. (Univ. of Leicester) Socs: BMA; Med. Protec. Soc.; Med. Sickness Soc. Prev: Ho. Off. (Haematol.); Ho. Off. (Gen. Med.); Ho. Off. (Surg.).

AKINGBEHIN, Mr Akintayo Olusola Drayton House Clinic, 2 Lulworth Road, Southport PR8 2AT Tel: 01704 563279 Fax: 01704 550057 Email: tayo@draytonhouseclinic.com; Charles Adam Clinic, Green Farm, Rayrigg Road, Bowness on Windermere, Windermere LA23 3DN Tel: 01539 447401 Fax: 01539 447401 — MB ChB 1975 Manch.; MD Manch. 1983; FRCS Eng. 1980; FRCOphth 1989. (Manchester University) Cons. Ophth. Surg. & Med. Dir. Drayton Hse. Clinic S.port & Chas. Adam Clinic Bowness. Socs: Fell. Roy. Coll. Surgs. Eng.; UKISCRS; Fac. Mem. ESCRS (Europ. Soc. of cataract and refractive Surg. Prev: Lect. (Ophth.) Univ. Liverp.

AKINKUNMI, Akintunde Camlet Lodge Regional Secure Unit, Chase Farm Hospital, The Ridgeway, Enfield EN2 8JL Tel: 020 8967 1056 Fax: 020 8342 0806 — MB BS 1986 Ibadan; LLM 2000 Cardiff; MRCPsych 1994. Cons. Forens. Psychiat. Prev: Sen. Regist. (Forens. Psychiat.) Chase Farm Hosp. Middlx.

AKINLOYE, Olufunmilayo Tokunbo 7A Avenue Road, London E7 0LA — MB BCh BAO 1975 NUI; FRCSI 1983; LRCPSI 1975.

AKINMADE, Olukayode 44 Acre Lane, Carshalton SM5 3AB — MB BS 1981 Ibadan; DCH RCP Lond. 1994.

AKINOLA, Samuel Ebun 15 Sisley Road, Barking IG11 9SR — MB BS 1977 Ibadan, Nigeria; MRCOG 1986.

AKINOLA, Mary Kennington Health Centre, 250, Kennington Rd., Oxford OX1 5PY Tel: 01865 730911 Fax: 01865 327759 Email: mary.akinola@gp-k84005.nhs.uk — MBBS 1988; DFFP 2000. (Univ. of Benin Sch. of Med.) Clin. Asst., Addic.s Servs., Chilton Clinic Warneford Hosp., Oxf.; GP Cover (Hosp. Practitioner) Oxf. Community Hosp. & The Linden Unit Ch.ill Hosp., Oxf.

AKINOSHO, Babafunke Olayide 8 Baskerville Gardens, Dog Lane, London NW10 1PF — LRCPI & LM, LRSCI & LM 1962; LRCPI & LM, LRCSI & LM 1962; DPH Liverp. 1968. (Univ. Liverp. & Roy. Coll. Surgs. Irel.)

AKINSOLA, Sunday Adeyemi 92 Burnham, Fellows Road, London NW3 3JP — Vrach 1981 Kiev Medical Institute; MRCOG 1993.

AKINTADE, Latify Kolawole 69 Chepstow Way, Camden Estate, Peckam, London SE15 5LU — MB BS 1996 Lond.

AKINWUNMI, James Olakunle 194B Harrow View, Harrow HA1 4TN — MB BS 1987 Ibadan.

AKINYANJU, Olufemi Owolabi 192 Clarence Gate Gardens, Glentworth St., London NW1 6AU — MRCS Eng. LRCP Lond. 1963; MD Lond. 1982, MB BS 1963; FRCP Lond. 1980, M 1967; FRCP Ed. 1979, M 1966. Prof. Med. Univ. Lagos, Nigeria; Cons. Phys. & Haemat. Lagos Univ. Teach. Hosp. Socs: Internat. Soc. Haemat.

AKIRI, Andrew Obaro Casualty Department, Queen Mary's Hospital, Swarp, London SE13 Tel: 020 8302 2678; 22 Admirals Place, Lakender Dock, Rotherhithe, London SE14 5NW — MB BS 1996 Lond.; BSc (Hons.) Lond. (UMDS) SHO (Cas.) Qu. Mary's Sidcup. Prev: Ho. Off. Bromley Hosp.; Ho. Off. Guy's Hosp. Lond.

AKITA, Abigail Gifty Merley 158 Old Farm Road, Strawberry Vale, London N2 9RQ — MB ChB 1987 Ghana; FRCA 1995.

AKIWUMI, Benjamin Olufemi 8 Maltfield Road, Northway, Headington, Oxford OX3 9RG — MB ChB 1982 Ghana.

AKLE, Anne 9 Devonshire Mews W., London W1G 6QE Tel: 020 7935 6241 — MB BS 1982 Lond.; FCAnaesth 1990; FFARCSI 1987. Sen. Regist. (Anaesth.) St. Mary's Hosp. Lond. Prev: SHO (A & E & Anaesth.) Lewisham Hosp. Lond.; Regist.(Anaesth.) St. Mary's Hosp. Lond. W2.

AKLE, Mr Charles Assad Nightingale House, 90A Harley St., London W1G 7HT Tel: 020 7935 6241 Fax: 020 7224 2805 Email:

charlesakle@dial.pipex.com — MB BS 1976 Lond.; MB BS (Hons. Surg.) Lond. 1976; BSc (Hons.) Lond. 1973, MS 1983; FRCS Eng. 1980; MRCS Eng. LRCP Lond. 1976. (Guy's) Indep. Cons. Surg. Lond. Socs: Fell. Roy. Soc. Med.; Fell. Assn. Surgs. Of GB & I; Fell. Assn. Endoscopic Surgs. GB & Irel. Prev: Lect. & Hon. Regist. (Surg.) Guy's Hosp. Lond.; Cas. Off. Guy's Hosp. Lond.; SHO (Surg.) St. Luke's Hosp. Guildford.

AKMAL, Mohammed 4 Buchanan Gardens, London NW10 5AE Tel: 020 8969 9166 — MB BS 1992 Lond.; BSc (Hons.) Lond. 1991, MB BS 1992. SHO (A & E) Roy. Lond. Hosp. Trust. Prev: Ho. Off. (Gen. Med. & Cardiol.) Roy. Lond. Hosp.; Ho. Off. (Gen. Surg.) St. Marys Hosp. Lond.

AKOH, Mr Jacob Attah 18 Barry Close, St Albans AL2 3HN — MB BS 1980 Ahmadu Bello Univ. Nigeria; MB BS Ahmadu Bello U. Nigeria 1980; FRCS Ed. 1990.

AKOMEA-AGYIN, Mr Clement 52 Ravensbourne Park Crescent, London SE6 4YP Tel: 020 83145 619 — MB ChB 1983 Ghana; MB ChB U. Ghana 1983; FRCS Eng. 1992. Specialist Regist. (Cardiothoracic Surg.) Guy's Hosp. Lond.

AKOO, Mahomed Shiraz 3 Stanley Gardens, Mitcham CR4 2BS — MB ChB 1990 Natal.

AKOOJEE, Ebrahim 74 Woodfield Avenue, London SW16 1LD — MRCS Eng. LRCP Lond. 1983.

AKOTIA, William Yao Sewu 8 Annsmuir Place, Kirkcaldy KY2 6HS Tel: 01592 593929 — Vrach 1968 Kalinin Med. Inst. Anaesth. Posts.

AKOWUAH, Enoch Francis 11 Bonnington Road, Leicester LE2 3DB — MB ChB 1997 Leic.

AKPOBOME, Gibson 104 Grove Vale, London SE22 8DR — MB BS 1981 Ibadan.

AKRAM, Abdah Parveen 44 Raeburn Place, Stockbridge, Edinburgh EH4 1HL — MB ChB 1991 Aberd.; MRCGP 1995; DRCOG 1994; DFFP 1996. (Aberd.) Clin. Asst. (Palliat. Med.) Qu. Marg. Hosp. Dunfermline. Socs: BMA. Prev: Trainee GP Glas.

AKRAM, Ashrif 73 Broom Valley Road, Rotherham S60 2QT — MB ChB 1998 Manch.; MB ChB Manch 1998.

AKRAM, Asif Pervez 11 Craven Terrace, Hopwood Lane, Halifax HX1 4DY — MB ChB 1997 Manch.

AKRAM, Fazli 45 Beechcroft Road, London SW17 7BZ — MB BS 1962 Peshawar.

AKRAM, Nuzhat Saleem 8 Downs Side, Sutton SM2 7EQ — MB BS 1995 Lond.

AKRAM, Mr Salim 31 Eden House, Alexandra Hospital, Woodrow Drive, Redditch B98 7UB — MB BS 1985 Punjab; FRCS Eng. 1993.

AKRAM CHAUDHRY, Tahra Melanie 31 Pine Grove, Maidstone ME14 2AJ — MB ChB 1995 Birm.

AKRAMUL HAQ, Abu Khaled Muhammed Havering Hospitals NHS Trust, Haroldwood Hospital, Gubbins Lane, Romford RM3 0BE Tel: 01708 746090; 2 Pilgrims Way, Dartford DA1 1QA Tel: 01322 221123 Fax: 01322 227369 — MB BS 1965 Dacca; FFA RCS Eng. 1973; DA Eng. 1969. (Chittagong Med. Coll.) Cons. Anaesth. Havering Hosps. NHS Trust Haroldwood Hosp. Romford. Socs: (Ex-Pres.) Bangladesh Med. Assn. UK. Prev: Cons. Anaesth. Qu. Mary's Hosp. Sidcup.; Sen. Regist. (Anaesth.) Char. Cross Hosp.; Regist. (Anaesth.) St. Peter's Hosp. Chertsey, Roy. Free & Brompton Hosps. Lond.

AKRAMUZZAMAN, Mizra 28 New Wanstead, London E11 2SN Tel: 020 8989 7503 — MB BS 1962 Dacca.

AKROYD, Ian Harrison Wisteria Lodge, 41 Beaumont Avenue, St Albans AL1 4TW Tel: 01727 760782; Wisteria Lodge, 41 Beaumont Avenue, St Albans AL1 4TW Tel: 01727 760782 — MB BChir 1975 Camb.; MB Camb. 1975, BChir 1974; MCOphth. 1989; DO Eng. 1978. (Middlx.) SCMO S. Beds. HA; Clin. Asst. Luton & Dunstable Hosp.; Clin. Asst. Moorfields Eye Hosp. Lond.; Sen. Clin. Med. Off. W Herts HA. Prev: SHO (Ophth.) Bradford Roy. Infirm.

AKROYD, Simon Andrew Flat 3/5, Deanpath, Dean Village, Edinburgh EH4 3BG — MB ChB 1991 Ed. SHO (Gen. Med.) Roy. Infirm. Edin.

AKUFFO, Emmanuel Owusu Forest Healthcare Trust, Coleridge Road, London E17 6QU Tel: 020 8521 0337 — MB ChB 1969 Ghana; FRCPsych 1993, M 1980; DPH Otago 1974. Cons. Psychiat. Forest Healthcare Trust Lond.; Sen. Lect. (Ment. Handicap & Learning Disabil.) St. Bart. Hosp. Med.Coll Lond. Socs: Fell. Roy. Soc. Med. Prev: Sen. Regist. (Psychiat.) St. Lawrence's Hosp. Caterham & St. Thos. Hosp. Lond.; Regist. (Psychiat.) Char. Cross Hosp. Lond.

AKUFO-TETTEH, Humphrey Narh Coombswood and Hawned Surgery, 146-148 Coombs Road, Halesowen B62 8AF Tel: 0121 561 4275 Fax: 0121 561 4275 — MB BCh 1980 Wales.

AKUM LUM, Jinai 67 Cherry Crescent, Westmoorings, Trinidad & Tobago Tel: 00 1 809 868 637 3469 Fax: 00 1 809 868 623 5277; 43 Alfred Hill, Bristol BS2 8HN — MB BS 1997 W. Indies. SHO.

AKYOL, Mr A. Murat Transplant Unit & Univ. Department of Surgery, Edinburgh Royal Infirmary, Lauriston Place, Edinburgh EH3 9YW Tel: 0131 536 3452 Fax: 0131 5361520/5364194 Email: muratakyol@luht.scot.nhs.uk; Ty'n Llechwedd, Dinbren, Llangollen LL20 8EB Tel: 0131 667 9087, 01987 869364 — MD 1980 Ankara; MD Glas. 1990; FRCS Glas. 1987. Cons. Gen. Surg. Roy. Infirm. of Edin.; Hon. Clin. Sen. Lect., Med. Sch., Univ. of Edin. Socs: Brit. Transpl. Soc. - Counc. Membr and Educat. Sec.; Scott. Soc. Experim. Med.; Scott. Renal Assn. (Counc. Mem.). Prev: Cons. Surg. W.ern Infirm. Glas.; Sen. Regist. (Surg.) Gt.er Glas. Health Bd.; Research Fell. & Hon. Regist. (Surg.) Univ. Glas.

AL-AARAJI, Yassir Mohamed Shaker 32 Shooters Close, Birmingham B5 7LN — MB BCh BAO 1987 NUI; LRCPSI 1987.

AL-ABADY, Ali Flat 6, 19 Raleigh Close, Lapwing Lane, Manchester M20 2BY — MB ChB 1992 Glas.

AL-ABDEL RAHMAN, Anwar Moh'd Al-Nofan West Cumberland Hospital, Whitehaven CA28 8JG — Medic 1983 Cluj, Romania.

AL-ABDULLAH, Anees Farhan Ibraheem 1 Lon Y Plas, Johnstown, Carmarthen SA31 3NJ — MB ChB 1977 Baghdad; MRCPath 1990.

AL-ADNANI, Mohammed Sadik Department of Histopath./F.B.H., Unilabs UK, London NW1 7BY Tel: 020 7333 0585 Fax: 020 7333 0586; 2 Woodway Crescent, Harrow HA1 2NQ Tel: 020 8907 6966 Fax: 020 8357 9384 — MB ChB 1963 Baghdad; PhD (Path.) Glas. 1975; FRCP Glas. 1990; FRCPath 1989, M 1977. Cons. Histopath. F.B.H. Histopath. Socs: Brit. Soc. Gastroenterol.; Path. Soc.; Internat. Acad. Path. (Brit. Div.). Prev: Assoc. Prof. & Prof. (Hon. Cons.) Path. Kuwait Univ.; Cons. Centr. Middlx. Hosp. Lond. 1992-1997.

AL-ADNANI, Mudher 2 Woodway Crescent, Harrow HA1 2NQ — MB ChB 1997 Aberd.

AL-ADWANI, Andrew Aziz Scunthorpe District General Hospital, Scunthorpe — MB BCh BAO 1987 NUI; LRCPSI 1987; BSc; MRCPsych. (Roy. Coll. Surgs. Irel.) Cons. Socs: Mem. BMA; MDU; SSA.

AL-AHMAD, Suhaila Kadhim Yousef 19 Grasmere Avenue, Kingston Vale, London SW15 3RB — MB ChB 1972 Baghdad; MRCP (UK) 1983; MRCPI 1983.

AL-ALI, Mohammed Saleh Moustafa Accident & Emergery Department, Hexham General Hospital, Hexham NE46 1QJ Tel: 01434 606161 — MB BCh 1975 Ain-Shams.

AL-ALI, Mr Safa Hussain Abbass 23 Barlich Way, Redditch B98 7JR — MB ChB 1971 Baghdad; FRCS Ed. 1985; FCOphth 1989.

AL-ALLAF, Abdul Wahab Younis Saleem Rheumatic Disease Unit, Ward 1 and 2, Ninewells Hospital, PO Box 120, Dundee DD1 9SY — MB ChB 1982 Mosul.

AL-ALOUL, Mohamed Boldfarm, Asmall Lane, Scarisbrick, Ormskirk L40 8JL — MB ChB 1996 Dundee.

AL-ALOUSI, Louay Muhi Eldden Department of Forensic Medicine & Science, University of Glasgow, University Avenue, Glasgow G12 8QQ Tel: 0141 330 4574 Fax: 0141 330 4602 Email: l.m.al-alousi@formed.gla.ac.uk — FRCPath 2000; MB ChB 1976 Baghdad; FRCP Glas 2001; 2000 MACFE; 2001 DABFM; PhD (Path.) Glas. 1987; MRCPath 1992; DMJ(Path) Soc. Apoth. Lond. 1989. (Univ of Baghdad) Sen. Lect. & Cons. Forens. Med. Univ. Glas. Socs: Am. Acad. Forens. Sci. AAFS; Assn. Clin. Path.; Brit. Acad. Forens. Sci. Prev: Sen. Lect. & Hon. Cons. Forens. Med. Char. Cross & W.m. Med. Sch. Lond.; Regist. (Histopath.) Hairmyers Hosp.; Sen. Med. Off. Medico-Legal Inst. Baghdad.

AL-AMIN, Muhammad 19 Gordon Street, Burnley BB12 0AZ Tel: 01282 425389 — MB ChB 1996 Manch. (Manch.) SHO (Gen. Med.) Burnley Healthcare NHS Trust. Prev: Ho. Off. (Gen. Surg. & Med.) Burnley Gen. Hosp. Healthcare NHS Trust.

AL ANI, Fouad Sadik Saied Endoscopy Unit, Blackburn Royal Infirmary, Bolton Road, Blackburn BB2 3LR Tel: 01254 263555; 9

Walton Crescent, Blackburn BB2 3TQ — MB ChB 1969 Baghdad; MD Baghdad 1973; MRCP (UK) 1976. Assoc. Specialist (Med.) Blackburn HA. Prev: Regist. (Med.) Blackburn HA; Regist. (Med.) E. Yorks. & Hull HA.

AL-ANI, Hashim Muhsin The Medical Centre, 50 Wimpole St., London W1M 7DG Tel: 0207 573 8888 Fax: 0207 573 8801 — MB ChB 1971 Baghdad; MSc Lond. 1979. (Royal Free Hosp.) Assoc. Cons. The Heart Hosp. Lond. Prev: Phys. i/c Lond. Heart Clinic; Research Fell. Acad. Dept. Roy. Free Hosp.

AL ANI, Khalil Ibraheem Jasim 6 Main Street, Carlton, Wakefield WF3 3RW — MB ChB 1976 Baghdad; MRCPI 1989; LMSSA Lond. 1988.

AL-ANI, Sami-Ali Abdulhaq 72 Heathcroft Ave, Sunbury-on-Thames TW16 7TN — MB BS 1997 Lond.

AL-ANSARI, Intesar Khalid Birmingham Childrens Hsp, NHS Trust, Park House Child & Family Cntre, Park Rd, Spark hill, Birmingham B11 Tel: 0121 773 8400; 63 Moorcroft Road, Birmingham B13 8LS Tel: 0121 449 0279 — MB ChB 1981 Baghdad; Dip of Child Health, Warwick; MRCP (UK) 1990; MSc in Community Child Health. (MBChB Uni of Baghdad) Cons. Community Paediat. Socs: MRCPCH; BACCH; BMA.

AL-ANSARY, Yahaya The Surgery, 7 Buckhurst Road, Bexhill-on-Sea TN40 1QF Tel: 01424 214757 Fax: 01424 733811 — MB ChB 1964 Bagdad; FRCS 1972 Ed.; LMSSA Lond. 1981. (Baghdad) GP Bexhill-on-Sea, E. Sussex. Prev: Former Cons. Paediatric Surg., Sen. Lect. in Surg., Basrah Med. Coll. and Univ. Hosp., Basrah, Iraq.

AL-ASADI, Mr Ali Dakheel 116 Hollin Lane, Middleton, Manchester M24 5LB; Blairhill, Main St, Thornhill FK8 3PL — MB ChB 1970 Baghdad; FRCS Eng. 1983. Cons. Vasc .Gen. Surg. Falkirk & Dist. Roy. Infirm. NHS Trust. Socs: Vasc. Surgic. Soc. GB & Irel.; Scott. Vasc. Audit Gp. Prev: Cons. Vasc. & Gen. Surg. King Fahd Specialist Hosp., Buraidah, Saudi Arabia; Regist. (Gen. Surg.) Highland HB Caithness Gen. Wick. & Roy. Albert Edwd. Infirm. Wigan; Cons. Gen. Surg. Falkirk & Dist. Roy. Infirm. NHS Trust.

AL ASADY, Mazin Hyder Saleem c/o 63 Lee Road, Perivale, Greenford UB6 7DA Tel: 020 8991 1787 — MB ChB 1972 Mosul; MRCP (UK) 1983; DPM Eng. 1980; DTM & H RCP Lond. 1984.

AL-ASHBAL, Saleh 29 Aller Park Road, Newton Abbot TQ12 4NG — MB ChB 1970 Baghdad, Iraq; MRCP (UK) 1983.

AL-ASLAN, Salih Mohammed Ali Kadim East Glamorgan General Hospital, Church Village, Pontypridd CF38 1AB Tel: 01443 218218 Fax: 01443 217213; 24 Rhydhelig Avenue, Cardiff CF14 4DD — MB ChB 1971 Baghdad; PhD Lond. 1979; FRCP Glas. 1994; MRCP (UK) 1980; T(M) 1991. Cons. Phys. (Gen. Med.) E. Glam. NHS Trust. Prev: Sen. Regist. (Gen. Med. & Med. for Elderly) Univ. Hosp. Wales & P.ss of Wales Hosp. Bridgend; Regist. (Med.) Falkirk & Dist. Roy. Infirm. NHS Trust.

AL-ATRAKCHI, Mr Sabah Lynfield House, 42 Church Lane, Stallingborough, Grimsby DN41 8AA Tel: 01472 883282 — MB ChB 1961 Baghdad; FRCS Ed. 1970. (Baghdad) Cons. Surg. A & E Grimsby Dist. Gen. Hosp. Socs: BMA; Brit. Assn. Accid. & Emerg. Med.; Brit. Assn. Sport & Med. Prev: Assoc. Specialist A & E Dept. Leeds Gen. Infirm.; Cons. Surg. Lect. Basrah Med. Sch., Iraq.

AL-AUMMRAN, Monna Essa 18 Roman Road, Ayr KA7 3SZ — MB ChB 1974 Baghdad.

AL-AWA, Mr Arfan Ousama Gwynedd District General Hospital, Bangor LL57 2PW — MD 1985 Damascus; FRCS Ed. 1993. Staff Gen. & BrE. Surg. Llandudno Gen. Hosp. Gwynedd.

AL-AZZAWI, Farouk Abdul Latif Muhyeldin Department of Obstetrics & Gynaecology, Leicester Royal Infirmary, Leicester LE2 7LX Tel: 0116 252 3165 Fax: 0116 252 5850 Email: fa2@leicester.ac.uk — MB ChB 1974 Baghdad; PhD Strathclyde 1988; MA Camb. 1988; MRCOG 1983; FRCOG 1997. Sen. Lect. & Cons. O & G Leic. Univ. Sch. Med. Socs: Counc. Brit. Menopause Soc.; Eur. Soc. Human Reprod. & Embryol.; Internat. Menopause Soc. Prev: Clin. Lect. & Sen. Regist. Camb. Univ. Sch. Med. Addenbrooke's Hosp.; Research Fell. & Hon. Regist. (O & G) Glas. HB.

AL-BADRAN, Leith 45 Kelvin Court, Glasgow G12 0AE — MB ChB 1996 Glas.

AL-BADRAN, Resan Hmood 45 Kelvin Court, Kelvinside, Glasgow G12 0AE Tel: 0141 357 1213 — MB ChB 1963 Glas.; FRCP Ed. 1987; FRCP Lond. 1986; FRCP Glas. 1982; MRCP (UK) 1972. (Glas.) Dir. Mohammed bin Khalifa bin Sulman Al Khalifa Cardiol. Centre, Bahrain; Assoc. Prof. Med. Arabian Gulf Univ. Bahrain.

AL-BADRI, Adnan Mohsin Tahir Department of Pathology, Huddersfield Royal Infirmary, Huddersfield HD3 3HE Tel: 01484 482425 — MB ChB 1982 Al-Mustansirya U, Iraq; PhD Glas. 1995, MSc 1988; MRCPath 1995. Cons. Histopath. Huddersfield Roy. Infirm. Prev: Sen. Regist. SHO Roy. Hants. Hosp.; Regist. Roy. Hallamshire Hosp. Sheff.

AL BAHNASAWY, Lubna Mahmoud Said 2/L 12 Baliol Street, Glasgow G3 6UU Tel: 0141 564 5564 — MB ChB 1995 Glas. SHO (Paediat. Surg.) Roy. Hosp. Sick Childr. Glas.; SHO (ENT) Gantnavel Gen. Hosp. Glas. Socs: BMA; MDDUS. Prev: Ho. Off. (Med.) Stobhill NHS Trust Glas.; Ho. Off. (Surg.) Gartnavel Gen. Hosp. Glas.; SHO (ENT) Roy. Hosp. Sick Childr. Glas.

AL-BARAZANCHI, Ali Jawad Hadi Prospect House, Peace Drive, Watford WD17 3XE — MB ChB 1973 Baghdad; MRCPsych 1983; DPM Eng. 1982. Cons. Psychiat. Old Age, W. Herts Community Trust. Watford. Prev: Cons. Psychiat. D.M.H.E. High Wycombe.

AL-BARAZI, Sinan Adrian 36 Trinity Street, St Ebbes, Oxford OX1 1TY Tel: 01865 240980 Fax: 01865 240980 — MB BS 1996 Lond.; BSc (Hons.) Lond. 1993. (King's Coll. Hosp. Sch. of Med.) Prev: Ho. Surg. Cheltenham Gen. Hosp.

AL-BARJAS, Hamad Soud A 17 Stockleigh Hall, 51 Prince Albert Rd, London NW8 7LA — MB ChB 1997 Leeds.

AL-BARJAS, Mohammad 69 Jubilee Road, Gosforth, Newcastle upon Tyne NE3 3EX — MB BS 1998 Newc.; MB BS Newc 1998.

AL-BASRI, Mr Isam Abid Issa Safa House, Church Lane, Wexham, Slough SL3 6LH — MB ChB 1972 Baghdad; FRCS Glas. 1987.

AL-BASSAM, Abdul Husain (retired) Old Kiln Farm, Allonby, Maryport CA15 6QH — MB ChB 1964 Baghdad; MRCS Eng. LRCP Lond. 1974; DCH RCPSI 1967. Prev: Cons. Psychiat. (Learning Disabil.) W. Cumbria Health Care NHS Trust.

AL-BAYATI, Mr Abdul Hamid Abdul Redha 128 Humber Avenue, Coventry CV1 2AT — MB ChB 1963 Bahgdad; MB ChB Baghdad 1963; FRCS Ed. 1972.

AL-BAZZAZ, Mohammad Khalil Ibrahim Mahdi Barnsley District General Hospital, Gawber Road, Barnsley S75 2EP Tel: 01226 777705 Email: khalil.albazzaz@bdgh-tr.trent.nhs.uk; 15 Nottingham Road, Radcliffe-on-Trent, Nottingham NG12 2DW Tel: 0115 912 3194 Fax: 0115 912 3194 — MB ChB 1974 Baghdad; MRCP 1983 UK; FRCP 2000 UK. Cons. Phys. (Integrated Med.) Barnsley Dist. Gen. Hosp. Socs: Brit. Geriat. Soc.; Brit. Assn. of Stroke Phys.s; BMA. Prev: Cons. Phys. (Integrated Med.) Grantham & Dist. Hosp.; Sen. Regist. (Health c/o Elderly) Univ. Hosp. Nottm.

AL-BENNA, Sammy 2 The Avenue, Bedford Park, Chiswick, London W4 1HT — MB ChB 1997 Ed.

AL-BITAR, Mohamed Ziad 8 River Road, West Walton, Wisbech PE14 7EX Tel: 01945 587512 — MB BCh 1970 Ain Shams; LRCP LRCS Ed. LRCPS Glas. 1981.

AL-BUSAIDY, Saqar Zaid Academic Department of Radiology, Aberdeen Royal Infirmary, Foresterhill, Aberdeen AB25 2ZN — MB ChB 1991 Dundee. SHO (Med.) Armed Forces Hosp., Muscat, Sultanate of Oman.

AL-CHALABI, Mr Ali Nadhim Coventry & Warwickshire Hospital, Stoney Stanton Road, Coventry CV1 4FH Tel: 024 76 224055; 33 Beechnut Lane, Solihull B91 2NN — MB ChB 1969 Baghdad; FRCS Ed. 1982; FFAEM 1994. (Baghdad Coll. Med.) Specialist (Orthop. & A & E) Coventry & Warks Hosp.

AL-CHALABI, Ammar King's MND Clinic, Institute of Psychiatry, Denmark Hill, London SE5 8AF Tel: 020 7346 5172 Fax: 020 7346 5190 Email: ammar@iop.bpmf.ac.uk — MB ChB 1989 Leic.; MRCP 1993. Specialist Regist. (Neurol.) S. Thames Deanery; Hon. Lect. Clin. Neurosci.s Inst. of Psychiat. Socs: Roy. Coll. Phys.; Jun. Mem. Assn. Brit. Neurol.; Jun. Mem. Amer. Assn. Neurol.

AL-CHALABI, Nadia 2 Tangleberry Close, Bickley, Bromley BR1 2WJ — MB BS 1996 Lond.

AL-CHALABI, Thawab 25 Prince Consort Drive, Ascot SL5 8AW — BM BS 1996 Nottm.

AL-DABBAGH, Ali Salim Kasim Kings Cross Hospital, Clepington Rd, Dundee DD3 8EA; 73 Meadowview Drive, Inchture, Perth PH14 9TQ — MB ChB 1982 Mosul; MRCP (UK) 1993. Staff Grade Phys. (Respirat. & Infec. Dis.) Dundee & King's Cross Hosp. Prev:

Regist. in Gen. Med. & Gastroenterol., Kettering; Regist. in Gen. Med. & Resp. Med, Kettering.

AL-DABBAGH, Amir Khudhir Razzoki Lincoln Wing, Breast Unit, St James Hospital, Becket St., Leeds LS9 7TF; c/o Mrs M. Furber, 20 Clifton Drive, Marple, Stockport SK6 6PP Tel: 0161 427 2339 — MB ChB 1970 Mosul, Iraq; FRCS Eng. 1979; FRCS Ed. 1978. Specialist Regist. (Gen. Surg.) Pontefract Gen. Infirm. Socs: Fell. Internat. Coll. Surgs.; BMA. Prev: Cons. Gen. Surg. & Clin. Lect. Arbil, Kurdistan, Iraq; Dean of Med. Coll. & Sen. Lect. Med. Coll. Arbil, Kurdistan, Iraq.

AL-DABBAGH, Lamia Taki 4 Watermill Lane, London N18 1SU — MB ChB 1978 Baghdad.

AL-DABBAGH, Mohammed Ahmed Taha 10 Marlowe Way, Lexden, Colchester CO3 4JP — MB ChB 1974 Mosul; FRCR 1983; DMRD Eng. 1983. Cons. Radiol. Colchester Gen. Hosp.

AL-DABBAGH, Mr Zaid Taki Naki 5 Grove Gardens, Hendon, London NW4 4SA — MB ChB 1983 Baghdad, Iraq; FRCS Glas. 1994.

AL-DAHHAN, Mrs Jinan Abdul Hammed 80 Robin Hood Lane, Kingston Vale, London SW15 3QS Tel: 020 8789 1094 Fax: 020 8546 1292 — MB ChB 1972 Baghdad; PhD Lond. 1984; MSc Baghdad 1977; DCH NUI 1984; FRCPH 1998. (Baghdad medical School) Cons. Paediat. Socs: Roy. Coll. Paediat. & Child Health; Brit. Soc. of Paediatric Nephrol.; Brit. Paediatric Assn.

AL-DAMLUJI, Saad Department of Endocrinology, Royal Free Hospital and University College Medical School, Rowland Hill St., London NW3 2PF — MB BS 1977 Lond.; BSc Lond. 1974; MD Lond. 1991; FRCP Lond. 1994; MRCP (UK) 1980. (Middlx. Hosp. Med. Sch.) Sen. Lect. (Endocrinol.) Roy. Free and Univ. Coll. Med. Sch. Socs: Endocrine Soc.; Neurosci. Soc.; Amer. Physiol. Soc. Prev: Vis. Sci. NIH Bethesda, USA; Lect. (Endocrinol.) St. Bart. Hosp. Lond.; MRC Train. Fell. St. Bart. Hosp. Lond.

AL-DAWOUD, Abdul Amir Faraj Pathology Department, Burnley General Hospital, Casterton Avenue, Burnley BB10 2PQ Tel: 01282 474305 — MB ChB 1977 Basrah; MRCPath 1988; Dip. Forens. Med. Glas 1992. Cons. Path. Burnley, Pendle & Rossendale HA. Prev: Sen. Regist. (Path.) Glas. Roy. Infirm.; Regist. (Path.) W.. Gen. Hosp. Edin. & Monklands Dist. Gen. Hosp.

AL-DEIRI, Mohamad 74 Linkside, London N12 7LG Tel: 020 8346 2588 — MD 1965 Damascus; DO RCPSI 1978. Ophth. Med. Practitioner (Self employed).

AL-DOORI, Asaad Abed Al-Muhsin Black Torrington, Beaworthy EX21 5QE — MB ChB 1974 Baghdad.

AL-DOORI, Mr Munther Ibrahim Huddersfield Royal Infirmary, Acre St., Huddersfield HD3 3EA Tel: 01484 422191 Fax: 01484 482888 Email: m.i.aldoori@aol.com; 33 Norwood Park, Birkby, Huddersfield HD2 2DU Tel: 01484 535350 Fax: 01484 517317 — MB ChB 1971 Baghdad; PhD Bristol 1986; FRCS Eng. 1994; FRCS Glas. 1979; FACS 1998; T(S) 1991. (Baghdad) Sen. Clin. Lect. Univ. Leeds; Hon. Lect. Univ. Huddersfield. Socs: Vasc. Soc. GB & Irel.; Surgic. Research Soc.; Assn. Endoscopic Surgs. Prev: Cons. Gen. & Vasc. Surg. & Hon. Lect. (Surg.) Univ. Leeds & Pontefract Gen. Infirm.; Cons. Transpl. Surg. St. Jas. Univ. Hosp. Leeds; Tutor & Sen. Regist. (Surg.) Univ. Bristol & Bristol Roy. Infirm.

AL-DUJAILY, Mr Saad Shakir Mohamed Doctor's Residence, Mayday Hospital, Mayday Road, Thornton Heath CR7 7YE — MB ChB 1973 Baghdad; FRCS Ed. 1986.

AL-DURI, Zaid Abdul Aziz Abdul Karim The Wellington Knee Surgery Unit, The Wellington Hospital, Wellington Place, London NW8 9LE Tel: 020 7586 5959 Fax: 020 7483 0297; 55 Replingham Road, Southfields, London SW18 5LU — MB BCh 1975 Cairo; MSc (Orthop.) Lond. 1990. Assoc. Specialist Orthop. Surg. The Wellington Knee Surg. Unit. Lond.; Hon. Research Fell. Orthop. Socs: Brit. Assn. Surg. Knee; Roy. Soc. Med. Prev: Hon. Clin. Asst. Orthop. & Clin Research W.m. Hosp.

AL-DURRAH, Faisal Mustafa Ibrahim Gateshead and South Tyneside H.A, Ingham House, Horsley Hill Road, South Shields NE33 3BN Tel: 0191 401 4551 Fax: 0191 401 4520; 17 East Street, North Shields NE30 4EB Tel: 0191 296 2512 — MB ChB 1977 Baghdad; MB ChB Baghdad, Iraq 1977; DCM, Iraq, 1989; MFPHM, UK, 1998. Cons. in Pub. Health Med. Socs: BMA - Mem.; FPHM - Mem.

AL-EGAILY, Safwat Salman Moortop Farm, Slaithwaite Road, Meltham, Huddersfield HD9 5PT — MB ChB 1964 Baghdad; Dip. Dermat. Lond 1971; Dip. Ven. Liverp. 1969. (Baghdad) Ons. Genitourin. Med. Huddersfield & Halifax Roy. Infirm. Socs: Med. Soc. Study VD; Hudds. Med. Soc.

AL-ESSA, Safaa Essa Jaafar 16 Willow Drive, Kirkcaldy KY1 2LF — MB ChB 1976 Basrah; MRCP (UK) 1985; DCH RCPS Glas. 1983; DCH RCP Lond. 1983; DCH Dub. 1984; DCCH RCP Ed. 1984.

AL-FALLOUJI, Mr Mohannad Abdul Razzak Pilgrim Hospital, Boston PE21 9QS Tel: 01205 364801 Fax: 01205 354395 Email: alfallouji@hotmail.com; Woodlands Cottage, Owlet Hurst Lane, Liversedge WF15 7AJ — MB ChB 1976 Baghdad; MB ChB Baghdad, 1976; PhD Lond. 1988; LRCP LRCS Ed. LRCPS Glas. 1981; FRCS Ed. 1981; FRCS Glas. 1981; FRCSI 1981. Cons. Gastrointestinal. Surg. Pilgrim Hosp. Boston, Lincs.; Prof. Surg. Arab Univ. Baenghazi; Asst. Prof. Surg. UAE Univ. Al-Ain, UAE; Sen. Regist. (Surg.) Belf. Teach. Hosps.; LIPHA Research Fell. Dept. Surg. Roy. Postgrad. Med. Sch. Hammersmith Hosp Lond; Trainer Laparoscopic Surg. RCS Eng. (Lond.). Socs: Fell. Assn. Surgs.; Assn. Coloproctol.; Internat. Hepato-Pancreato-Biliary Assn. Prev: Examr. Surg. Arab Bd. Med. Specialties Damascus Riyadh; Elect. Examr. Surg. RCS Irel.; Regist. (Surg.) E. Anglian RHA.

AL-FATTAL, Mr Saad Mohammed Ali Saleh 14 The Wraglings, Bedlams Lane, Bishop's Stortford CM23 5TB Tel: 01279 505739 — MB ChB 1972 Baghdad; MChOrth Liverp. 1983; FRCS Eng. 1981; FRCS Glas. 1981.

AL FULAIJ, Saleh 40 West Street, Ashburton, Newton Abbot TQ13 7DU — MB BS 1994 Lond.

AL-GAILANI, Mr Mohamad Abdul-Munim Abdul-Rahman Trafford General Hospital, Moorside Road, Davyhulme, Manchester M41 5SL Tel: 0161 748 4022 Fax: 0161 746 2025; 136 Woodland Lane, Sale M33 4LL Email: mohamad@gailani.freeserve.co.uk — MB ChB 1993 Baghdad; MB ChB Baghdad 1979; MSc Baghdad 1986; FRCS Eng. 1993; FICS 1995. (Baghdad College of Medicine) Staff Grade. (Gen. Surg.) Trafford Gen. Hosp. Manch.; Cons. Surg. Med. City Teachg. Hsp, Baghdad, Iraq; Regist. (Gen. Surg.) Trafford Gen. Hosp. Manch. Socs: BMA. Prev: Regist. (Gen. Surg.) Wythenshawe Hosp. Manch.; SHO (Gen. Surg.) Barnsley Dist. Gen. Hosp.; SHO (Orthop.) Pontefract Gen. Infirm.

AL-GHITA, Haider 2 Kiltongue Cottages, Monks Court, Airdrie ML6 0JS Tel: 01236 748748 — MB ChB 1982 Al Mustansirya U, Iraq.

AL-GHONAIMI, Ghada Shaker 1/2 Welland House, St Annes Close, Lincoln LN2 5RB — MB ChB 1994 Dundee.

AL-HABOUBI, Nadim Ya'cub Ali East Birmingham Hospital, Arden Lodge, Yardley Green Road, Birmingham B9 — MB ChB 1974 Baghdad; MRCP (UK) 1982; MRCPI 1982; LRCP LRCS Ed. LRCPS Glas. 1982.

***AL-HABSI, Hamdan Ahmed** Flat 10, 14 Cleveland St., Glasgow G3 7AE — MB ChB 1992 Glas.

AL-HADDAD, Mr Hassan Buchinger Cromwell Hospital, Cromwell Road, London SW5 0TU Tel: 020 7460 5914 Fax: 020 7460 5709 Email: hassanalhaddad@hotmail.com — MD 1961 Duesseldorf; State Exam Med Goettingen 1961; Facharzt (FRCS) Univ. Hannover Germary 1969. Cons. Orthop. & Traumatol. Surg. Cromwell Hosp. Lond. & P.ss Grace Hosp. Lond. Socs: AO Internat.; Germ. Assn. for Traumatol.; BMA. Prev: Head Orthop. & Traumatol. Surg. Siloah Teach. Hosp. Univ. Hannover, W.Germany; Guest Lect. (Surg.) Univ. Hannover, W. Germany.

AL-HADI, Hisham Parkside Health - NHS Trust, Wembley Hospital, Fairvie Avenue, Wembley HA0 4UH Tel: 020 8451 8353 Fax: 020 8451 8369; 37 West Hill, Wembley HA9 9RN Tel: 020 8357 5838 — MB ChB 1972 Baghdad; DCH, Dub 1981. Staff Grade Paediatr. Socs: BMA; RCPaed.; BACDA. Prev: Staff Grade Paediatr., Optimum Health, Lewisham; Clin. Med. Off., Medway NHS Trust.

AL-HADITHI, Mr Bara Ahmed Kamel 294 Grange Road, London SE19 3DF — MB ChB 1981 Baghdad, Iraq; PhD Soton. 1988; FRCS Ed. 1993. Regist. & Research Fell. (Orthop.) Char. Cross & Hammersmith Hosp. Lond. Prev: Acting Regist. (Orthop.) Mayday Univ. Hosp. Croydon; Regist. Rotat. (Surg.) Soton. Gen. Hosp. & Poole Hosp.

AL HAJAJ, Wathik Hamed 10 Magdalen Close, Langney, Eastbourne BN23 8JF Tel: 01323 760889 — MB ChB 1973 Basrah; LMSSA Lond. 1986; FRCA 1991; DEAA 1993; DA (UK) 1988; Dip. Respirat. Med. RCSI 1988. Specialist (Anaesth.) E. Sussex.

AL-HAKIM, Ali Husain Ali 74 The Avenue, Sale M33 4WA — MB ChB 1969 Alexandria; DLO RCS Eng. 1975.

AL-HAMALI, Mr Salem Ali 189A Weedon House, Du Cane Road, London W12 0TZ — MB BS 1986 Libya; MB BS Al-Arab Medical U. Libya 1986; FRCS Ed. 1991.

***AL-HAMAR, Emad** 23 Thirston Way, Kenton Bar Estate, Newcastle upon Tyne NE3 3EQ — MB BS 1995 Newc.

AL-HAMED, Mohammed Hamed Northampton General Hospital, Northampton NN1 5BD Tel: 01604 34700; 4 Stratton Close, Northampton NN3 3HQ — MB ChB 1983 Cairo; DA (UK) 1990.

AL-HARBI, Obaid Mohammad Abdullah Mosaid 33 Windmill Court, Claremont Road, Newcastle upon Tyne NE2 4BA — MB BS 1995 Newc. (Newcastle-upon-Tyne) Ho. Off. (Med.) S. Tyneside Hosp.; Ho. Off. (Surg.) Shotley Bridge; SHO (Gen. Surg.) Mubark Kuwait; SHO (ICU) Kuwait. Socs: MDU; BMA. Prev: SHO (IC Med.) Amiro Hosp. Kuwait.

AL-HASANI, Aimen Jafar 2 Chestnuts, Hutton Mount, Brentwood CM13 2PA — MB ChB 1982 Baghdad; FRCA 1992. Cons. Anaesth & Intens. Care Brentwood.

AL-HASANI, Haider Hasan Mohamad Ali 105 Elmstead Gardens, Worcester Park KT4 7BG — MB ChB 1969 Baghdad; MSc Immunol. Lond. 1988; DMedRehab RCP Lond. 1980. Prev: Hon. Med. Regist. Rheum. & Lupus Research Unit St. Thos. Hosp. Lond.

AL-HASANI, Latif Jamad c/o Mr & Mrs A Hawkins, 30 The Dell, Tonteg, Pontypridd CF38 1TG — MD 1964 Istanbul; MRCPsych 1974; DPM Eng. 1972. (Istanbul Univ.)

AL-HASANI, Mohammad Khier Al-Kaber Kent At Canterbury Hospital, Ethelbert Rd, Canterbury CT1 3NG Tel: 01227 766877; Malt Farm, Bossingham Rd, Stelling Minnis, Canterbury CT4 6BD Tel: 01227 709251 — MD 1972 Damascus; MRCP (UK) 1983. Cons. Nephrol. Head Nephrol. Dept. Roy. Hosp. Muscat, Oman. Prev: Clin. Ass. (Nephrol.) Kent & Canterbury Hosp.; Cons. Nephrol. Riyadh Armed Forces Hosp., Saudi Arabia.

AL-HASSAN, Saad Hamad Department of Obstetrics & Gynaecology, Floor B, East Block, University Hospital, Queens Medical Centre, Nottingham NG7 2UH — MB BS 1983 King Faisal U, Saudi Arabia; MRCOG 1991.

AL-HILALI, Mahir Mohamad Ali Department of Pathology, Dorset County Hospital, Williams Avenue, Dorchester DT1 2JY Tel: 01305 254327 Fax: 01305 254319; 7 Berwick Road, Talbot Woods, Bournemouth BH3 7BB Tel: 01202 555806 — MB ChB 1974 Basrah; DM Soton. 1991; FRCPath 1995, M 1983. Cons. Haemat. W. Dorset Gen. Hosps. NHS Trust. Socs: Brit. Soc. Haematol. Prev: Sen. Regist. Dorchester & W.m. Hosps.; Regist. Roy. Devon & Exeter Hosp.; SHO Glas. Roy. Infirm.

AL-HILALY, Mr Mushrik Abdul Latif Doctors Mess, Nottingham City Hospital, Hucknall Road, Nottingham NG5 1PB — Vrach 1967 Crimean Med Inst. USSR; FRCS Ed. 1980.

AL-HILALY, Nasir Hussain Dhaiem 2 Rushton Avenue, South Godstone, Godstone RH9 8LA Tel: 01342 893457 — MB ChB 1974 Baghdad; MRCPI 1986; DCH RCP Lond. 1983; DCH RCPS Glas. 1983. Cons. (Paediat.) E. Surrey Hosp. Redhill. Prev: Sen. Regist. (Paediat.) John Radcliffe Hosp. Oxf. & Wexham Pk. Hosp. Slough.

AL HILLAWI, Abdul Hadi Sadiq Wycombe General Hospital,, Queen Alexandra Rd, High Wycombe HP11 2TT — MB BS 1977 Lond.; MD Lond. 1987; FRCP Lond. 1994; MRCP (UK) 1980. (Middlesex) Cons. Gen. & Geriat. Med. Wycombe & Amersham Hosp.s. Socs: Brit. Geriat. Soc.; Brit. Thorac. Soc. Prev: Regist. (Med. Unit.) Middlx. Hosp. Lond.; Research Regist. (Pulm. Physiol.) Brompton Hosp. Lond.; Sen. Regist. (Gen. & Geriat. Med.) United Oxf. & Amersham Hosp.

AL-HUSEIN, Muaweih Omar Mustafa 59 Trenchard Avenue, Stafford ST16 3RD Tel: 01785 52600 — Medic Timisoara Romania 1982; DA (UK) 1990.

AL-HUSSAINI, Ala Sahib 20 Rutland Gardens, Hove BN3 5PB Tel: 01273 738070 — MB ChB 1972 Baghdad; MRCP (UK) 1979.

AL-IBRAHIM, Mr Jalil 55 Knightlow Road, Harborne, Birmingham B17 8PX Tel: 0121 420 4929 — MD 1973 Tehran; FRCS (Ophth.) Ed. 1985; DO RCPSI 1977.

AL-ISA, Akeel Abdul Hussein Ibrahim 60 Gayhurst, Hopwood Road, London SE17 2BL Tel: 020 7703 4263 Fax: 020 7460 5558 — MB BChir 1994 Camb.; MRCP London 1998. (University of Cambridge) Clin. Research Regist. - Liver Unit - Cromwell Hosp. - Lond. Prev: 1995-1998 Kings Coll. Hosp. (SHO Med. Rotat.); 1995 St Geo.'s Hosp. (SHO AAE); 1994 St Bartholomews Hosp. (Ho. Off. Med.).

AL-ISMAIL, Saad Abdul Daim Abdul Razak Singleton Hospital, Swansea NHS Trust, Sketty, Swansea SA2 8QA Tel: 01792 285024 Fax: 01792 285537 Email: saad.al-ismail@swansea-tr.wales.nhs.uk; Morriston Hospital, Heol Maes Eglwys, Swansea SA6 6NL Tel: 01792 703055 — MB ChB 1970 Baghdad; FRCP Lond. 1992; MRCP (UK) 1976; MRCPI 1975; FRCPath 1992, M 1980. Cons. Haemat. Swansea NHS Trust. Socs: Brit. Soc. Haematol.; Internat. Soc. Haematol.; Brit. Soc. Transfus. Prev: Lect. (Haemat.) Welsh Nat. Sch. Med. Cardiff; Sen. Regist. (Haemat.) Univ. Hosp. Wales Cardiff; Research Fell. (Haemat.) Welsh Nat. Sch. Med.

***AL-ISMAILY, Abla** Flat 14, 14 Cleveland St., Glasgow G3 7AE — MB ChB 1992 Glas.

AL-IZZI, Moutaiz Shakir Saleh Department of Pathology, Queen Elizabeth II Hospital, Welwyn Garden City AL7 4HQ Tel: 01707 328111 — MB ChB 1978 Baghdad; MRCPath 1986. Cons. Histopath. Qu. Eliz. II Hosp. Welwyn Gdn. City. Prev: Sen. Regist. (Path). Roy. Berks. Hosp. Reading.

AL-JABIRY, Mr Hashim Hassan Shibib ENT Department, Aberdeen Royal Infirmary, Aberdeen AB25 2ZN; 48 Camperdown Road, Aberdeen AB15 5NU — MB ChB 1973 Mosul; FRCS Ed. 1989; DLO RCS Eng. 1989.

AL-JADER, Layla Naman University of Wales College of Medicine, Department of Epidemiology and Public Health, Health Park, Cardiff CF14 4XN Tel: 029 2074 2119, 029 2074 2321 Fax: 029 2074 2898 Email: al-jader@cf.ac.uk; 14 Altmauer Road, Cyncoed, Cardiff CF23 6NQ Tel: 029 2075 8482 Fax: 01222 758482 Email: alfaham@compuserve.com — MB ChB 1974; MFPHM (UK) 1996; MD (Wales) 1991; DA (UK) 1980. (Baghdad Medical Society Baghdad University) Clin. Sen. Lect. in Pub. Health Genetics, Epidemiol. & Pub. Health Univ. of Wales Coll. of Med. Cardiff; Hon. Cons. in Pub. Health Genetics at the Univ. Hosp. of Wales; Cons. in Pub. Health Genetics at Bro Taf HA Cardiff. Socs: Coun. Mem. of the Clin. Genetics Soc. UK; Brit. Soc. Human Genetics; Fac. Pub. Health Med. Prev: Train. in Pub. Health in S. Wales; Clin. Asst./ Research Off. in Med. Genetics (Inst., Cardiff); Train. in Anaesth., Regist. in S.-W. Wales.

AL-JAFARI, Mohammad Sali Pathology Directorate, North Cheshire Hospitals NHS Trust, Lovely Lane, Warrington WA5 1QG Tel: 01925 662540 — MB ChB 1972 Baghdad; MSc (Path.) Baghdad 1977; FRCPath 1993, M 1983. (Baghdad Med. Sch.) Cons. Histopath. N. Chesh. Hosp.s NHS Trust, Warrington, Chesh.; Clin. Dir. Warrington NHS Trust Hosp. Socs: BMA; ACP; Internat. Acad. Path. Prev: Sen. Regist. (Histopath.) Mersey RHA; Regist. (Histopath.) Nottm. HA; Lect. (Path.) Baghdad Univ.

AL JANABI, Khalid J S Department of Histopathology, Chelmsford & Essex Hospital, New Writtle St., Chelmsford CM2 0PT Tel: 01245 513479 — MB ChB 1977 Mosul; MRCPath 1990; FRCPath 1999. Cons. Histopath., Mid Essex Hosps., Chelmsford, Essex. Socs: Internat. Acad. of Cytol.; Chelmsford Med. Soc.; Brit. Soc. of Clin. Cytologists.

AL-JANABI, Mazin Ahmad Mahmood Department of Nuclear Medicine, Royal Liverpool Hospital, Prescot St., Liverpool L7 8XP Tel: 0151 706 2000 Fax: 0151 706 5844; 26 Varley Road, Mossley Hill, Liverpool L19 3PU Tel: 0151 724 3056 — MB ChB 1978 Baghdad; PhD Univ. Lond. 1992, MSc 1985. Sen. Regist. (Nuclear Med.) Roy. Liverp. Univ. Hosp. Socs: Brit. Nuclear Med. Soc. & Europ. Assn. Nuclear Med.

AL-JANABI, Sabiha The Tannahill Centre, 76 Blackstown Road, Paisley PA3 1NT Tel: 0141 889 7631 Fax: 0141 889 6819; 188 Hawkhead Road, Paisley PA2 7BS Tel: 0141 581 9964 — MB ChB 1967 Baghdad; DCH 1973 Glas. (Bagdad) GP Paisley, Renfrewsh.

AL-JANABI, Mr Tarik Abdul Jalil Department of Accident & Emergency, University Hospital Lewisham, Lewisham High St., London SE13 6LH; 6 Selhurst Close, Wimbledon Park Side, Wimbledon, London SW19 6AZ Tel: 020 8789 7036 Email: tarik@acgnet.co.uk — MB ChB 1984 Baghdad, Iraq; FRCS Ed. 1996. (Univ. Baghdad Med. Sch.) Regist. (A & E) St. Thos. Hosp. Lond. Socs: Fac. Accid. & Emerg. Med.; Brit. Assn. Accid. & Emerg. Med. Prev: SHO (A & E) Newc. Gen. Hosp. & Treliske Hosp. Truro; SHO (Gen. Surg.) Furness Gen. Hosp.

AL-JASSIM, Mr Abdul Hadi Hussain 35 The Park, St Albans AL1 4RU; 35 The Park, St. Albans AL1 4RU Fax: 01224 559597 Email: sarh.mackenzie@westburn.grampian.scot.nhs.uk — MB ChB 1971 Baghdad; FRCS. Assoc. Specialist (ENT) Univ. Hosp. Hintree NHS Trust Liverp. Socs: Fell. Of the RCS Irel.; Pres. Of the Brit. Assn. of Arabic Otolaryngol., Head & Neck Surg.; Mem. Of Brit. Ass. Of Otolaryngol. Head & Neck Surg.s. Prev: SHO (ENT) Qu. Eliz. II Hosp. Welwyn Garden City; SHO (ENT) Lister Hosp. Stevenage.; Regist. (ENT) Whiston Hosp. Prescot.

AL-JEZAIRY, Mr Abdul Ilah Kadhum Blue Hills, Esher Close, Esher KT10 9LL Tel: 01372 470296 — MB ChB 1968 Baghdad; FRCS Glas. 1976; FRCS Ed. 1975.

AL-JILAIHAWI, Mr Ali Nagim Abid Hairmyres Hospital, East Kilbride, Glasgow G75 8RG Tel: 0141 20292 Fax: 0141 34064; 9 Dukes Gate, Castle Avenue, Bothwell, Glasgow G71 8SN Tel: 01698 812718 — MB ChB 1970 Baghdad; FRCS Cardiothor Ed. 1985; FRCS Ed. 1978. Cons. Thoracic Surg. Lanarksh. HB. Socs: Soc. Cardiothoracic Surg. GB & Irel.; Scott. Thoracic Soc. Prev: Regist. (Cardiothoracic Surg.) Brook Hosp. Lond.; Sen. Regist. (Cardiothoracic Surg.) Bristol; Clin. Research Fell. Univ. Toronto Univ., Canada.

AL-JUBOURI, Mohammad Alaywi Mahmood Department of Clinical Biochemistry, Rotherham General Hospital, Moorgate Road, Rotherham S60 2UD — MB ChB 1980 Baghdad; MRCPath 1993; T(Path) 1994.

AL-KAABI, Juma Khalfan Abdullah 43 Colintraive Avenue, Glasgow G33 1BW — MB ChB 1992 Dundee.

AL-KADHIMI, Mr Abdul Rahim Jaffar Hussain AMI Ross Hall Hospital, 221 Crookston Road, Glasgow G52 3NQ Tel: 0141 810 3151 — MB ChB 1974 Baghdad; FRCS Glas. 1984; MRCPI 1983.

AL-KADI, Khoshnaf 1 Beech Court, 130 Middleton Hall Road, Kings Norton, Birmingham B30 1DH — State Exam Med 1973 Magdeburg.

AL-KALAI, Darwisha 2 Church Hill, Ingham, Lincoln LN1 2YE — MB BCh 1979 Wales; PhD (Health Serv. Managem.) Calif. 1991; Dip. Pract. Dermat. Wales 1990; MFCH Lond. GP Emirates Airline, U.A.E.; ATLS Cert. Amer. Coll. Surg. Socs: BMA; Fac. Community Health; Soc. Pub. Health. Prev: Primary Care Phys. (A & E); King Khalid Hosp. Nat. Guard Hosp. Jeddah K.S.A.

AL-KASSIM, Nawal Consultant Anaesthetist, Department of Anaesthesia, Benenden Hospital, Cranbrook TN17 4AX — MB ChB 1967 Baghdad. Cons. Anaesth., Benenden Hosp. Socs: FFARCS.

AL-KHABORI, Mr Mazin awad Jafar 75 Melville Gardens, Bishopbriggs, Glasgow G64 3DB Tel: 0141 772 2670 — MB BCh 1981 Ain Shams; FRCS Glas. 1990.

AL-KHAFAJI, Mohammed Naji Mohammed Vale of Leven, District General Hospital, Alexandria G83 0UA Tel: 01389 754121 Fax: 01389 755948; 3 Thorn Road, Bearsden, Glasgow G61 4PP Tel: 0141 942 7566 — MB ChB 1971 Mosul, Iraq; MRCPI 1980; FACC 1988. Cons. Phys. Vale of Leven Dist. Gen. Hosp. Alexandria. Socs: Brit. Cardiac Soc.; Amer. Coll. Cardiol.; BMA. Prev: Assoc. Specialist (Cardiol.) King Geo. Hosp. Lond.; Head Cardiol. Amiri Teachg. Hosp., Kuwait.

AL-KHAFFAF, Mr Haytham Shareef 58 Ash Lane, Hale, Altrincham WA15 8PD — MB ChB 1976 Mosul; FRCS Ed. 1982. Cons. Gen. & Vasc. Surg. Burnley Gen. Hosp. Socs: Vasc. Surgic. Soc.; Assn. of Surg.s of GB & Irel.; Europ. Soc. of Vasc. Surg. Prev: Regist. (Vasc. Surg.) Univ. Hosp. S. Manch.

AL KHALAF, Saad Said Issa Ridgewood Centre, Old Bisley Road, Camberley GU16 9QE Tel: 01276 605366 Fax: 01276 605388; Little Coneyhurst, Cove Road, Fleet GU51 2RT Tel: 01252 614708 Fax: 01252 614708 — MB ChB 1971 Baghdad; DPM Eng. 1980; Dip. Psychiat. 1984; MRCPsych 1985; T(Psychiat.) 1992. Cons. Psychiat. Camberley.

AL-KHALIDI, Basim Gamal Othman Pallion Health Centre, Hylton Road, Sunderland SR4 7XF Tel: 0191 565 8598 Fax: 0191 514 7467; 47 Beechwood Terrace, Sunderland SR2 7LY Tel: 0191 564 1677 — MB ChB 1978 Ain Shams; DFFP (Diploma in Clinical Hypnosis) Sheffield University; DRCOG. (Ain Shams University, Cairo, Egypt) GP Sunderland. Prev: Staff Grade in Obstet. & Gyn., William Snellie Hosp., Lanark, Lanarksh., Scotl.

AL-KHAN, Jalal Abdulla Mohamed 2/2, 12 Melrose Gardens, North Kelvinside, Glasgow G20 6RA — MB ChB 1995 Glas.

AL-KHATIB, Falah Abdel Hamid 128 Guildford Park Avenue, Guildford GU2 7NN — MB ChB 1969 Ain Shams; FFR RCSI 1984; DMRT Eng. 1980. Cons. & Chief Radiother. Tawain Hosp., UAE.

AL-KHATIB, Muhieddin Orthopaedic Department, Doncaster Royal Infirmary, Doncaster DN2 5LA Tel: 01302 366666; 6 Dublin Road, Doncaster DN2 5HE — MD 1980 Damascus; FRCS Glas. 1990. Cons. Orthop. Surg. Doncaster Roy. Infirm.

AL-KHAWAJA, Imad Mahmoud Shihadeh Suite 5077, 19 Cheval Place, London SW7 1EW — MB ChB 1980 Mosul; PhD Surrey 1989; MSc (Nuclear Med.) NUI 1983; LRCP LRCS Ed. LRCPS Glas. 1984; MRCPI 1987. Cons. Neurol. Disabil. & Rehabil. Lond. Socs: Brit. Soc. Rehabil. Med.; Soc. Research in Rehabil.; Med. Res. Soc. Prev: Sen. Regist. Rivermead & Radcliffe Infirm. Oxf & Roy. Berks. & Battle Hosp. Reading.

AL-KHAYAT, Mahmoud Abdul Rahman Mahmoud Areley Kings Surgery, The Bridge, Dunley Road, Stourport-on-Severn DY13 0AA Tel: 01299 822103 Fax: 01299 827350 — MB ChB 1971 Baghdad; MRCP (UK) 1980.

AL-KHAZRAJI, Mr Mohammed Ridha Abdul Hussain 10 Churchfield Road, Poole BH15 2QN — MB ChB 1969 Baghdad; FRCS Ed. 1983.

AL-KHUDHAIRI, Mr Maan Subhi Muhyee 26 Grafton Park Road, Worcester Park KT4 7QP Tel: 020 8337 2192; 5 Auriol Close, Worcester Park KT4 7DR Tel: 020 8337 2192 — MB ChB 1973 Baghdad; FRCS Ed. 1982. Assoc. Specialist ENT Surg. Lewisham Hosp.

AL-KHULAIFI, Mr Abdul Aziz Mohd 80 St Mary's Mansions, St Mary's Terrace, London W2 1SY — MB BCh BAO 1984 NUI; MCh NUI 1994; FRCS Eng. 1991; FRCS Ed. 1989; MCh NUI 1993. (Roy. Coll. Surgs. Irel.) Prev: Sen. Regist. Harefield Hosp.; Sen. Regist. (Cardiothoracic) Hammersmith Hosp. Lond.; Regist. (Cardiothoracic Surg.) The Lond. Chest Hosp.

***AL-KHURAISHI, Amir Rasheed Ahmed** The Cage, Ninewells Hospital, PO Box 120, Dundee DD1 9SY — MB ChB 1997 Dundee.

AL-KHYATT, Mr Muzahim Kassim Hamo Flat 19, Linton House, Holland Park Avenue, London W11 3RL — MB ChB 1977 Mosul; FRCSI 1984.

AL-KURDI, Mr Mousa Department of Obstetrics & Gynaecology, Hinchingbrooke Hospital, Huntingdon PE29 6NT Email: mousa@al-kurdi.demon.net — MD 1972 Damascus; 1972 MD Damascus; 1979 FRCOG 1991, M. Cons. Obst. & Gynecologist.

AL-KUREISHI, Talib Wishaw Health Centre, Kenilworth Avenue, Wishaw ML2 7BQ Tel: 01698 372888 Fax: 01698 376289 — Vrach 1968 Volgograd Med. Inst.; Vrach 1968 Vogograd Med. Inst.

***AL-MA'WALY, Fatma Juma** 1/R 45 Milnbank Road, Dundee DD1 5PY — MB ChB 1996 Dundee.

AL-MAAROF, Majida Said Magied 38 Ripley Road, Willesborough, Ashford TN24 0UX — MB ChB 1982 Al-Mustansirya U, Iraq; MRCOG 1995.

AL-MAHARZI, Abdulaziz Mahmood Flat 1 (Right), 314 St Georges Road, Glasgow G3 6JR — MB ChB 1992 Glas.

AL MAHDY, Husayn 15 Reed House, Totland Square, London SW15 5PE — BM 1980 Soton.

AL-MASKARI, Mr Sultan Mohammed 123 London Road, Stockton Heath, Warrington WA4 6LG; 123 London Road, Stockton Heath, Warrington WA4 6LG — MB ChB 1990 Glas.; FRCS Ed. 1995; FRCSI 1995. SR in Orthop & Trauma, Mersey Deanery, Liverp.

AL-MASRI, Amal Abdul-Kader 9 Cavendish Avenue, Sudbury Hill, Harrow HA1 3RD Tel: 020 8422 6098 — MB ChB 1967 Mosul; DO RCPSI 1977.

AL-MAWALI, Sulieman Hamdan 38 Fairford Court, Hestia Drive, Selly Oak Hospital, Birmingham B29 6JD — MB ChB 1991 Glas.

AL-MEMAR, Ali Yousif Muhammad Jawad 5 Sutton Mews, Mariners Court, Plymouth PL4 0BU — MB ChB 1981 Baghdad; MRCP (UK) 1994.

AL-MITWALLI, Mr Kutaiba Abdul Haleem Ibrahim 28 Melbourne Way, Newport NP20 3RF — MB ChB 1976 Baghdad; MPhil Lond. 1984; FRCS Glas. 1986. Regist. (Urol.) St. Woolos Hosp. Newport, Gwent. Prev: Regist. (Gen. Surg.) Medway Hosp. Gillingham & St. Bart. Hosp. Rochester; Regist. (Surg.) Llandudno Gen. Hosp.

AL-MITWALLY, Qussay Abdul Haleem 28 Melbourne Way, Newport NP20 3RF — MB ChB 1974 Baghdad.

AL-MOHAMMAD, Abdallah 29 Station Road W., Peterculter AB14 0US — MD 1985 Damascus; MRCP (UK) 1990. Regist. (Cardiol. & Gen. Med.) Riverside HA. Prev: Regist. (Gen. Med.) W.m. Hosp. Lond.; Regist. (Gen. Med.) Qu. Mary's Univ. Hosp. Roehampton; SHO (Gen. Med.) Nevill Hall Hosp.

AL-MOOMEN, Mr Abdul Hameed Abdulhadi Flat 10 Didsbury Lodge Service Flats, 132 Palatine Road, West Didsbury, Manchester M20 9XA — MB BCh BAO 1983 NUI; FRCSI 1987; LRCPI & LM, LRCSI & LM 1983.

AL MOUDARIS, Muhamed Muhi Al Dean University Hospitals, Coventry & Warwickshire NHS Trust, St Cross Hospital, Barby Road, Rugby CV22 5PX Tel: 01788 572831; 227 Hillmorton Road, Rugby CV22 5BA Tel: 01788 546314 — MB ChB 1969 Baghdad; MRCP (UK) 1984. Cons. Paediat. Univ. Hosps. Coventry and Warks. NHS Trust. Prev: SCMO E. Birm. HA; Regist. (Paediat.) Kingston Gen. Hosp. Hull; Regist. (Paediat.) Redhill Hosp. Surrey.

AL-MOUSAWI, Adil Hashim Fakhir Mental Health Unit, Northwick Park Hospital, Watford Road, Harrow HA1 3UJ — MB ChB 1977 Basrah; MRCPsych 1987.

AL-MRAYAT, Ma'en Abdul-Jalil Khalil Endocrinology Department, Northwick Park Hospital, Watford Road, Harrow HA1 3UJ Tel: 020 8864 3232; 29 Byron Hill Road, Harrow HA2 0JD — MB BS 1992 Lond.; MRCP (UK) 1995. (St. Mary's Hosp. Lond.) Regist. (Med. & Endocrinol.) N.wick Pk. Hosp. Middlx. Socs: BMA; BDA. Prev: Regist. (Med. & Endocrinol.) Lond.; SHO Rotat. (Med.) Nottm.; SHO (Haemat.) Guy's Hosp. Lond.

AL-MUDALLAL, Ghassan Basim The Surgery, 113 Balaam Street, London E13 8AF Tel: 020 8472 1238 Fax: 020 8470 1739 — MB ChB 1974 Baghdad; LMSSA Lond. 1987; DLO RCS Eng. 1986.

AL-MUFTI, Raghad Abdul Wahab Mohammed Latif Flat 6, Shortland House, Beaufort Road, Clifton, Bristol BS8 2JT — MB ChB 1989 Bristol.

AL-MUFTI, Mr Ragheed Abdul-Wahab Mohamed-Latif Tel: 0207 601 7032 Fax: 0207 7601 7034 — MB BCh BAO 1984 Belf.; MD Belfast 1996; MSc Lond. 1995; FRCS Eng. 1993; FRCS Ed. 1990; FRCS Ed (Gen) 1998. (Queen's Univ. Belfast) Cons. Surg. St Barts Hosp. Lond.; Cons.Gen. Surg. St John, St Eliz. Hosp.s, Lond.; Cons.Gen. Surg. Wellington Hosp., Lond. Socs: Ulster Med. Soc. & Qu.s Univ. Assn.; Fell. Assn. Surgs. Of GB & Irel.; Fell. Roy. Soc. Med. Prev: Cons. Surg. & Sen. Lect.Univ.Coll. Lond. & Whittington Hosp. Lond.; Sen. Regist. & Lect. (surg.)Univ. Coll. Lond. & Roy. Free Hosp.s, Lond.; Career Regist. (Surg.) Middlx. & Univ. Coll. Hosps. Lond.

AL-MUHANDIS, Waleed Majeed Department of Anaesthetics, Airedale General Hospital, Skipton Road, Steeton, Keighley BD20 6TD; Buckley Farm, Buckley Green, Stanbury, Keighley BD22 0HL Tel: 01535 646081 — MB ChB 1974 Baghdad; MSc Manch. 1990; FFA RCSI 1986.

AL-MUKHTAR, Mr Abdul Amir Mahmoud Abbas Balfour Hospital, New Scapa Road, Kirkwall KW15 1BD Tel: 01856 885400 Fax: 01856 885413; 46 Barn Way, Wembley HA9 9NW Tel: 020 8933 2412 Fax: 020 8933 2412 Email: almq@hotmail.com — MB ChB 1974 Baghdad; FRCS Glas. 1985. Cons. Surg. Balfour Hosp. Kirkwall, Scot. Socs: BMA; Assoc. Endoscopic Surgs.; Assn. Surg. Prev: Regist. (Surg.) Stirling Roy. Infirm., Roy. Alexandria Hosp. Paisley & Inverclyde Roy. Hosp. Greenock.

AL-MULLA, Asmahan Flat 6, 19 Raleigh Close, Lapwing Lane, Manchester M20 2BY — MB ChB 1992 Glas.

AL-MULLA, Fahd Rashed 35/37 Craigieburn Gardens, Glasgow G20 0NU Tel: 0141 945 1332 — MB ChB 1993 Glas.; BSc (Hons.) Glas. 1991, MB ChB 1993.

AL-MUSAWI, Mr Dhia Mohammed Mir 85 Chatsworth Road, London NW2 4BH — MB ChB 1979 Baghdad; FRCS Eng. 1992.

AL-NAHHAS, Adil Mosa Mohammed Department of Nuclear Medicine, Derriford Hospital, Plymouth PL6 8DH Tel: 01752 792277 Fax: 01752 517587 — MB ChB 1974 Baghdad; FRCPI 1997; MRCPI 1991; MSc Nuclear Med. Lond. 1981. Cons. Nuclear Med. Derriford Hosp. Plymouth & Roy. Cornw. Hosp. Truro. Socs: Nuclear Med. Soc.; BMA; Eur. Assn. Nuclear Med. Prev: Sen. Regist. (Nuclear Med.) Roy. Marsden Hosp. Sutton; Regist. (Rheum.) Odstock Hosp. Salisbury.

AL-NAJAR, Mohammed Abdul Wahid Abdul Hussain 142 Bawtry Road, Doncaster DN4 7BP — MB ChB 1973 Baghdad; MRCP (UK) 1984.

AL-NASHI, Mr Munther Ezzut 52 Rectory Lane, Bury BL9 7TA Tel: 0161 797 4511 — MB ChB 1972 Baghdad; FRCS Glas. 1985.

AL-NASIRI, Nazar Department of Histopathology, The Royal Marsden Hospital, Fulham Road, London SW3 6JJ — MB ChB 1970 Baghdad; MB ChB Baghdad, Iraq 1970; MRCPath 1980.

AL-NAWAB, Mashal Dhia Al-Deen Dept. of Histopathology, King's College Hospital, Denmark Hill, London SE5 Tel: 020 7346 3190 Fax: 020 7346 3670 Email: mashal-al-nawab@kcl.ac.uk; 20 Wellington Court, 116 Knightsbridge, London SW1X 7PL Tel: 020 7584 8757 Fax: 020 7581 1379 Email: mashalalnawab@netscapeonline.co.uk — MB ChB 1983 Al-Mustansirya Univ. Iraq; 1983 MB ChB Al-Mustansurya Univ. Iraq; 1991 PhD (Histopath.) Lond. 1991; 1997 DRCPath; 1997 MRCPAth. Hon. Sen. Lect. Pathol. Kings Coll. Hosp.; Cons. Histopath. / Cytopathologist, King's Coll. Hosp. Socs: Roy. Coll. Pathol. Prev: Sen. Regist. (Histopath.) N.wick Pk. Hosp.; Regist. (Histopath.) Greenwich Dist. Hosp. & Conquest Hosp. Hastings; Sen. Reg. (Histopath.), Roy. Brompton Hosp.

AL-OBAIDI, Mohamed Kadhim 47 Spencer Road, Isleworth TW7 4BN — MB ChB 1989 Al-Mustansirya U; MRCP (UK) 1995.

AL-OKATI, Dhafir Abdul Karim Abdul Ghafoor Department of Histopathology, Harold Wood Hospital, Gubbins Lane, Romford RM3 0BE — MB ChB 1981 Baghdad; MRCPath 1993. Cons. Path. Harold Wood Hosp. Romford. Prev: Cons. Path. Roy. Liverp. & BRd.green Univ. Hosps. NHS Trust; Staff Grade Path. Fife Area Laborat. Kirkcaldy; Regist. (Histopath.) Frenchay Hosp. Bristol.

AL-OMARI, Mr Abdullah Muayyad Mustafa Flat A2, Doctor's Residence, Sunderland District General Hospital, Sunderland SR4 7TP — MB ChB 1985 Baghdad; FRCS Glas. 1994.

AL-ONAIZY, Ziad Yasin Flat 2, 29 Craven Road, London W2 3BX — MB ChB 1994 Dundee.

AL-OTAIBI, Ibrahim Mohammed Department of Psychiatry, Royal Victoria Infirmary, Newcastle upon Tyne NE1 4LP; 10 Warbeck Close, Kingston Park, Newcastle upon Tyne NE3 2FG — MD 1989 King Abdulaziz Univ.; DPM (RCPSI) 1996. SHO (Liaison Psychiat. of Psychother.) Roy. Vict. Infirm. Newc. U. Tyne. Socs: MRCPsych. (Incept.); Med. Protec. Soc. Prev: Research Regist. (Psychiat.).

AL-QADRI, Mohammed Abdus Salam 1/2 219 Berkeley Street, Glasgow G3 7HH — MB ChB 1993 Glas.

AL-QASSAB, Hisham Kamil King George Hospital, Barley Ln, Ilford IG3 8YB Tel: 0208 970 8283 Fax: 0208 970 8191 Email: hal_qassab@hotmail.com; Tel: 0208 597 8676 Email: alg-uassab@zetnet.co.uk — MB ChB 1972 (Distinc.) Baghdad; MRCPI 1983. (Univ. Baghdad) Cons. Phys. Geviatrician, King Geo. Hosp., Goodmayes, Essex. Socs: BGS. Prev: Cons. Phys. Al-Hammadi Hosp., Riyadh; Asst. Prof. Med. Jordan Univ. of Sci. & Technol.; Research Assoc. (Clin. Pharmacol.) St. Bart. Hosp. Med. Coll. Lond.

AL-QUISI, Mrs Najlaa Khalil Salman Huddersfield Royal Infirmary, Lindley, Huddersfield; 5 Larchdale, Fixby, Huddersfield HD2 2FB Tel: 01484 422413 — MB ChB 1976 Baghdad; FFA RCS Eng. 1982; DA Eng. 1981; DCH RCPSI 1985. Cons. Anaesth. Huddersfield Roy. Infirm. Prev: Sen. Regist. Dept. Clin. Anaesth. Roy. Vict. Hosp. Belf.; SHO (Anaesth.) N. Manch. Gen. Hosp. (T); Rotat. Regist. (Anaesth.) Centr. Middlx., N.wick Pk. & Brompton Hosps. Lond.

AL-QURAINY, Isam Abdullah Royal Eye Infirmary, Apsley Road, Plymouth PL4 6PL Tel: 01752 203123 Fax: 01752 254162 — MB ChB 1969 Baghdad; PhD Ophth. Glas. 1993; MRCOphth 1988; DO RCPSI 1980. Assoc. Specialist (Ophth.) Roy. Eye Infirm. Plymouth. Socs: SW Ophth. Soc.; Med. Contact Lens and Ocular Surface Assn. (MCLOSA). Prev: Research fell. Hon. Regist. (Ophth.) Tennent Inst. of Ophth. Glas.; SHO (Ophth.) Qu. Mary's Hosp. Sidcup Kent; Sen. Ho. Off. (Ophth.) Roy. Eye Infirm. Plymouth.

AL-RABBAN, Mr Sabah Francis Brook Street Surgery, 7 Brook Street, Woodsetton, Dudley DY3 1AD Tel: 01902 883346 Fax: 01902 673757; Meadows End, Brindley Brae, Dunsley, Kinver, Stourbridge DY7 6LR — Vrach 1967 Crimean Med. Inst. USSR; FRCS Glas. 1982. Clin. Asst., providing Vasc. access Surg. to Pat.s in Renal Failure.

AL-RAIS, Mr Sanharib Hermiz (retired) 55 Stag Lane, Burnt Oak, Edgware HA8 5LH — MB ChB 1960 Baghdad; LMSSA Lond. 1977; FRCS Ed. 1970. Cons. Surg. & Head Surg. Dept. Al-Jazeira Hosp., UAE.

AL-RAWAF, Salman Abbas Aziz 17 Lowry Close, College Farm, Camberley GU15 Tel: 01276 32126 Fax: 01276 33215 Email: rawaf@compuserve.com — MB ChB 1971 Baghdad; PhD (Community Paediat.) Lond. 1982; DCH 1974; FFPHM RCP (UK) 1992, M 1989; MFCM RCP (UK) 1984; MPH NUI 1976; DCH Dub. 1981. Dir. of Clin. Standards Merton Sutton & Wandsworth HA; Hon. Sen. Lect. St. Geo. Hosp. Med. Sch. Lond. Prev: Dir. of Pub. Health Merton & Sutton HA; Specialist Community Med. (Child Health) W. Surrey & NE Hants. HA; Surrey Co. Med. Adviser (Child Health) Surrey Co. Counc.

AL-RAWI, Mr Sadir Jumaa Allawi Department of Surgery, Royal Cornwall Hospital, Treliske Hospital, Truro TR1 3LJ — MB ChB 1985 Baghdad; FRCS Eng. 1994.

AL-RIFAI, Hilal Amin 12 St Denis Road, Selly Oak, Birmingham B29 4LP — MB ChB 1967 Baghdad; MRCP (UK) 1984; MRCPI 1983.

AL-ROOMI, Layla 68 Dumgoyne Drive, Bearsden, Glasgow G61 3AW — Lekarz 1969 Warsaw; FRCP Glas. 1987; FRCPC 1997; DCH Eng. 1972; DTM & H Liverp. 1972. (Warsaw) Cons. Paediat. Glas. Roy. Matern. Hosp. & Roy. Hosp. Sick Childr. Glas.; Lect. Child Health Glas. Univ.

AL RUBEYI, Bushra Ibrahim Queen Elizabeth Hospital, Woolwich, London SE18 Tel: 020 8858 8141 Fax: 020 8312 6174; 200 Rotherhithe Street, London SE16 7RB Tel: 020 7252 3202 Email: alrubeyi@freeserve.co.uk — MB BCh 1979 Ain Shams, Egypt; MRCP (UK) 1989; T(M) (Paed.) 1994; FRCPCH 1998. Cons. Paediat. Qu. Eliz. Hosp. Prev: Sen. Regist. (Neonat.) Univ. Coll. Hosp. Lond.; Sen. Regist. (Paediat.) Edgware Gen. Hosp.; Research Regist. Hammersmith Hosp.

AL-SAAB, Mr Jaamal Jasim Mohammad 8 Shepherds Way, Castledean, Bournemouth BH7 7JY — MB ChB 1973 Baghdad; FRCSI 1994. Staff Grade (A & E) Roy. Bournemouth Hosp. Prev: Regist. (A & E) CrossHo. Hosp. Kilmarnock; Regist. (Paediat. Surg.) Roy. Hosp. for Sick Chilr. Edin.; Regist. (Gen. Surg. & Paediat. Surg.) Ailsa Hosp. Ayr.

AL-SAADY, Naab Mejble Mohmmed Department of Cardiological Sciences, St George's Hospital Medical School, Cranmer Terrace, London SW17 0RE Tel: 020 8672 9944 Fax: 020 8767 7141; 15 Park Hill Road, Epsom KT17 1LQ Tel: 020 8393 3248 — MB ChB 1972 Baghdad; PhD Med. Lond. 1987; MSc Baghdad 1978; Dip. Thoracic Med. Lond 1985. Lect. & Hon. Sen. Regist. (Cardiological Scis.) St. Geo. Hosp. & Med. Sch. Lond. Socs: Med. Res. Soc. UK. Prev: Lect. Baghdad Med. Sch.; SHO & Regist. (Med.) Baghdad; Regist. (Med. & ITU) St. Geo. Hosp. Lond.

AL-SABTI, Mr Ali Hamed Abdul-Razak Old Church Hospital, Waterloo Road, Romford RM7 0BE Tel: 01708 708466; 136 North End House, Fitz James Avenue, London W14 0RZ Tel: 020 7603 7107 Fax: 020 7602 2981 — MB BCh 1977 Ain Shams; FRCS Ed. 1983. Cons. Orthop. Surg. OldCh. Hosp. Romford. Prev: Cons. Orthop. Surg. Armed Forces Hosp. Riyadh, Saudi Arabia.

AL-SAD, Heidar Mahmoud Hajatieh Heidar Essex County Hospital, Lexden Road, Colchester CO3 3NB Tel: 01206 853536; The Firs, Long Road W., Dedham, Colchester CO7 6ES Tel: 01206 322931 — MB ChB 1972 Alexandria; DMRT Liverp. 1984. Clin. Asst. Radiother. Oncol. Centre Colchester.

AL-SAFAR, Jan Ahmed Brightside, Shay Lane, Halebarnes, Altrincham WA15 8UE Tel: 0161 980 7285 — MB ChB 1966 Baghdad; DPM Eng. 1972. (Univ. Baghdad) Cons. Psychiat. Cheadle Roy. Hosp. Socs: Bahrain Med. Soc. Prev: Chairm. Dept. Psychiat. Min. Health, Bahrain.

AL-SAFFAR, Anwar Aziz Radiotherapy Department, Old Church Hospital, Waterloo Road, Romford RM7 0BE Tel: 01708 746090; 46 Long Meadow, Hutton, Brentwood CM13 2HJ — MB ChB 1972 Baghdad; DMRT Eng. 1985. Staff Grade (Clin. Oncol.) Old Ch. Hosp. Romford. Prev: Staff Grade (Clin. Oncol.) Cumbld. Infirm. Carlisle.

AL-SAFFAR, Zaid Salah Aldeen 28 Heathfield Drive, Swinton, Manchester M27 5LW — MB ChB 1986 Mosul; MRCP (UK) 1993.

AL-SAFI, Mr Walid Sabri Ahmad 3 Kintyre Road, Portsmouth PO6 3UH — MB ChB 1973 Baghdad; FRCSI 1982.

AL-SAGER, Abdul Hamid Jasem 7 Windermere Road, Kinston Vale, London SW15 3QP Tel: 020 8974 9696 — MB ChB 1968 Baghdad; MRCP Lond. 1984; DCH RCP Lond. 1983; DTCH Liverp. 1974.

AL-SAHAB, Ahmed Naji Abbod c/o Doctor's Mess, City Hospital, Hucknall Road, Nottingham NG5 1PB — MB ChB 1969 Baghdad.

AL SAHLANI, Ubaid Yasir Abdullah 54 Cedar Road, London NW2 6SP — State DMS 1987 Parma.

AL-SAIDI, Nidhal Hasun Muhammad 56 Baronsmede, Ealing, London W5 4LT Tel: 020 8576 4262 — MB ChB 1972 Baghdad.

AL SAIDI, Thamir Kadim Jassim 18 Skipton Avenue, Chadderton, Oldham OL9 0QA — MB ChB 1973 Baghdad; MBCHb Baghdad 1973.

AL-SAIGH, Ghiath Salim 20 Grimescar Meadows, Birkby, Huddersfield HD2 2DZ — MB ChB 1976 Mosul; MB ChB Mosul Iraq 1976.

AL-SALEEM, Mr Muthanna Abdul Wahed South Saxon House Surgery, 150A Bexhill Road, St Leonards-on-Sea TN38 8BL Tel: 01424 441361 Fax: 01424 461799; Clavering, 195 Cooden Sea Road, Cooden, Bexhill-on-Sea TN39 4TR Tel: 01424 846071 — MB ChB 1967 Baghdad; FRCS Eng. 1978.

AL-SALIHI, Omar Nejdet 7 Buckingham Cl, Orpington BR5 1SA — MB BS 1997 Lond.

AL-SALIHI, Tara Westwind, 101 Moor Hall Drive, Four Oaks, Sutton Coldfield B75 6LS — BM BS 1996 Nottm.

AL-SALMI, Hilal Nasser Yousuf Flat 1/R, 63 Dorset St., Glasgow G3 7AG — MB ChB 1994 Glas.

AL-SAMARRAIE, Mohamed Tawfiq Kamal Tawfiq Department of Obstetrics & Gynaecology, Princess Alexandra Hospital, Harlow CM20 1QX Tel: 01279 444455 — MB ChB 1974 Baghdad; FRCOG 1993, M 1983. Cons. O & G P.ss Alexandra Hosp. Harlow, Essex. Prev: Cons. O & G Neath Gen. Hosp. W. Glam.

AL-SANJARI, Nazar Abdul Ghafoor Ali Department of Histopathology, Ninewells Hospital, PO Box 120, Dundee DD1 9SY — MB ChB 1977 Mosul; MRCPath 1991.

***AL-SARIRI, Basem Said** 2H Garnet Court, Glasgow G4 9NT — MB ChB 1992 Glas.

AL-SARRAJ, Safa Taha Department of Neuropathology (Institute of Psychiatry), Kings' College Hospital, De Crespigny Park, London SE5 8AF Tel: 020 7848 0269 Fax: 020 7708 3395 Email: s.al-sarraj@iop.kcl.ac.uk; 54 Pollyhaugh, Eynsford, Dartford DA4 0HF Tel: 01322 866210 Email: safa@alsarral.freeserve.co.uk — MB ChB 1981 Baghdad; MS 1987 Glasgow; MRCP 1990; FRCP 1999. (Medical College, University of Baghdad) Cons. Neuropath. Kings Coll. Hosp. / Inst. of Psychiat.; Clin. Sen. Lect. (Neuropathol.) IOP, Kings Coll. Lon. Socs: Brit. Neuropath. Soc.; Internat. NeuroPath. Soc. Prev: Clin. Lect. Lond.

AL-SAYER, Mr Hilal Musaed Mill Dam House, Murtle Den, Milltimber AB13 0HS Tel: 01224 861123; PO Box 889 (Safat), State of Kuwait, Arabian Gulf 13009, Kuwait — MB BCh 1972 Cairo; ChM Aberd. 1984; FRCS Ed. 1978. Chairm. Dept. Surg. Fac. of Med., Kuwait Univ.; Chairm. Fac. Surg. Kuwait Inst. Med. Specialisations; Vice-Dean Postrgrad. Clin. Studies Fac. Med. Kuwait Univ.; Assoc. Prof. Dept. Surg. Fac. Med. Kuwait Univ; Dean Fac. Med. Kuwait Univ. 1991-94. Socs: Kuwait Med. Assn.; Brit. Med. Assn.; Fell. Roy. Coll. Surg. Edin. Prev: Lect. (Surg.) Univ. Aberd.; Research Fell. (Surg.) Univ. Aberd.; Cons. Surg. Amiri Hosp. Kuwait.

AL-SEBAI, Mohamed Azmy Hassanein Dept. of Obstetrics and Gynaecology, George Elliot Hospital, Nuneaton CV10 7DJ Tel: 02476 351351 Fax: 02476 865014 — MB BCh 1977 Cairo; MRCOG 1990; Mobst (Liverpool)1992; MD (Liverpool) 1996. Cons. (O & G), Geo. Eliot Hosp. Nuneaton, Warwicks. Socs: Mem. of the Brit. Soc. for Colposcopy & Cervical Path.; Mem. of the Birm. & Midl.s Obstetric & Gyn. Soc.; Mem. of the Midl.s UroGyn. Soc. Prev: Sen. Regist. (Obst. & Gynaecolagist), Leicester Roy. Infirm.

AL-SHABENDER, Muna Holyrood Avenue, Colwyn Bay LL29 8BG Tel: 01492 513636 Fax: 01492 515837; Ablett Unit, Glan Clwyd Hospital, Bodelwyddan, Rhyl LL18 5UJ Tel: 01745 583910 — MD 1975 Aleppo; MD Aleppo, Syria 1975; D.C.P. Ireland 1999. (Aleppo Med. Sch.) Staff Grade in Psychiat. Glanlwyd Hosp. Rhyl Clwyd. Prev: Regist. in Psychiat. N. Wales Hosp. Denbigh, Clwyd.

AL-SHAFI, Khalid Mehdi Khalaf Microbiology Department, Royal Gwent Hospital, Newport — MB ChB 1978 Baghdad; 1986 PhD Lond.; 1982 MSc Trop. Med. Lond.; 1993 MRCPath. Cons. Microbiol. Roy. Gwent Hosp. Newport.

AL-SHAHI, Rustam Department of Clinical Neurosciences, Western General Hospital, Edinburgh EH4 2XU Tel: 0131 537 2944 Email: ras@skull.den.ed.ac.uk; 84 Middle Way, Summertown, Oxford

OX2 7LQ — MB BChir 1994 Camb.; MA Camb. 1995; MRCP (UK) 1997. (Camb.) MRC, Clin. Train. Fell., (Neurol.) Dept. of Clin. Neurosci.s, Edinb. Socs: BMA; Assoc. Mem. Assoc. Brit. NeUrol.s; Assoc. Mem. of the Brit. Assn. Stroke Phys.s. Prev: SHO (Neurol.) Nat. Hosp. for Neurol. Qu. Sq. Lond.; SHO (Gen. Med.) Hammersmith Hosp. Lond.; SHO (Gen. Med.) Whittington Hosp. Lond.

AL-SHAIKH, Baha Zeki Taha 7 Lovelace Court, Bethersden, Ashford TN26 3AY — MB ChB 1977 Baghdad; FFA RCSI 1989. Cons. Anaesth. William Harvey Hosp. Ashford; Univ. Clin. Tutor. Prev: Sen. Regist. (Anaesth.) NE Thames RHA.

AL-SHAKARCHI, Bashir Ali Bashir 7 Purdy Close, Old Hall, Warrington WA5 9QU — MB ChB 1978 Baghdad.

AL-SHAKARCHI, Basil Nima Jawad 1 White Knights Road, Reading RG6 7BY — MB ChB 1981 Baghdad.

AL-SHAKIR, Amal Mahmood 11 Nero Court, Augustus Close, Brentford TW8 8QA Tel: 020 8560 0521 — MB ChB 1969 Mosul; MRCOG 1983.

AL SHAMMA, Fatin Adbel Sahib Montfort House, Parkgate Road, Mollington, Chester CH1 6JS Tel: 01244 880401 — MB ChB 1976 Baghdad; DCH Dub. 1982; DCCH RCP Ed. 1987.

AL-SHAMMA, Musa Radhi Rashid 22 Hallydown Drive, Glasgow G13 1UF Tel: 0141 950 1751 — MB ChB 1973 Baghdad; MSc Glas. 1982; MRCP (UK) 1982; FRCP Glas. 1991. Cons. Phys. Gen. & Resp. Med. Vale of Leven Hosp. Dunbartonsh.; Hon. Clin. Sen. Lect. Glas. Univ. Socs: Scott. Thoracic Soc.

AL-SHAMMARI, Mr Amir Abbas ENT Department, Southend Hospital, Prittlewell Chase, Westcliff on Sea SS0 0RY Tel: 01702 435555 Fax: 01702 221300; 36 Woodside, Leigh-on-Sea SS9 4QU Tel: 01702 523283 — MB ChB 1975 Basrah; FRCS Dub. 1995; DLO RCS Eng. 1985. Staff Grade (ENT Surg.) S.end Gen. Hosp.

AL-SHEIKHLI, Mr Abdul Razzak Jasim Mayday University Hospital, London Road, Thornton Heath, Croydon CR7 7YE — MB ChB 1961 Baghdad; FRCS Eng. 1976; FRCS Ed. 1968; DLO Eng. 1976. Cons. ENT Surg. S.W. Thames RHA. Socs: Fell. Roy. Soc. Med.; Brit. Assoc. Otolaeryngol. Prev: Sen. Regist. Otolaryng. Grampian Health Bd.

AL-SHIHABI, Mr Basil Adam Lister Hospital, Stevenage SG1 4RY Tel: 01438 781291 Fax: 01438 781218; Tel: 01438 356363 Fax: 01438 356363 Email: bas@shihabi.demon.co.uk — MB ChB 1970 Mosul; MSc Lond. 1991; FRCS Ed. 1983; DLO RCS Eng. 1983. Cons.Ent Dept.Lister Hosp. Stevenage; Cons.Ent Dept. Qu. Eliz. Hosp.welwyn Garden city. Socs: Fell. Internat. Coll. Surgs. USA; Fell. Roy. Soc. Med.; Brit. Assn. of Audiological Phys.s. Prev: Sen. Reg. (Audiol.Med) St. Geo.'s Hosp., Lond.; Cons. ENT Surg. Fujairah Hosp., UAE; Regist. (Audiol. Med.) Roy. Nat. ENT Hosp. Lond.

AL-SHIRAWI, Ali Hamdan 1A Pentwyn Court, Heol Pentwyn, Cardiff CF14 7BY — MB ChB 1989 Glas.

AL-SHUKRI, Sultan Jaber Aziz 95 Mallowdale, Marton-in-Cleveland, Middlesbrough TS7 8PP — MB ChB 1981 Baghdad; FRCS Edinb. Staff Grade, ENT.

AL-SIMAANI, Mariam Tawfik St John & St Elizabeth Hospital, 60 Grove End Road, London NW8 9NH Tel: 020 7286 5126 — MB ChB 1969 Baghdad; DCH Dub. 1982. Clin. Supt. St. John & St. Eliz. Hosp. Lond.

AL-SINAWI, Mr Azim Abdul Halim Sulaiman Medway Maritime Hospital, Windmill Road, Gillingham ME7 5NY — MB ChB 1973 Baghdad; FRCS Ed. 1988. Socs: Assoc. Mem. Brit. Assn. Otolaryngol. Prev: Regist. (ENT) Kent. Co. Ophth. & Aural Hosp. Maidstone.

AL-SUDANI, Mr Mohammed Lazim Dept. Of Orology, St. Bartholomew's Hospital, West Smithfield, London EC1A 7BE; Monksfield, Sawbridgeworth Rd, Hatfield Heath, Bishop's Stortford CM22 7DR — MB ChB 1973 Baghdad, Iraq; FRCS Ed. 1992; FRCS Glas. 1983; DHMSA london 1989; FRCS urol 2000. Cons. Urological Surg. St Barts/ Roy. Lond. Hosp.s Lond.. Socs: BAUS. Prev: Staff Urol. St. Margt. Hosp. Epping, Essex; Sen. Regist. Lister Hosp. Stevenage; Sen. Regist. Urol., WalsGr. Hosp, Coventry.

AL-TAI, Saqar Hamed Issa Department of Clinical Radiology, Bristol Royal Infirmary, Bristol BS2 8HW Tel: 0117 928304 Fax: 0117 928 3267 — MB ChB 1990 Dundee; FRCR 1998. SR in Clin. Radiol., Bristol Roy. Infirm. Prev: Regist. Radiol., St Vincents Hsp, Sydney, Australia; SHO Surg., Th Roy. Hsp, Oman.

AL-TURKI, Siham Abdulaziz Penn House, Rudall Crescent, London NW3 1RR — MB BS 1980 Lond.

AL-TURKI, Wajdi Al-Hadi 38 Haycock Close, Mottram Rise, Stalybridge SK15 2UD Tel: 01457 65408 — MB BS 1977 Garyounis.

AL-UBAID, Mr Kamal Salman Health Centre, 73 Main Street, Stoneyburn, Bathgate EH47 8BY Tel: 01501 762515 Fax: 01501 763174 — LMSSA 1964 Lond.; FRCS Ed. 1969.

AL-UBAIDI, Firial Fadhel Harestock, 182 Epsom Road, Guildford GU1 2RR — MB ChB 1971 Baghdad.

AL-WAFI, Mr Ali Abouzeid Regional Centre for Paediatric Surgery, Univeristy Hospital Wales, Heath Park, Cardiff CF4 4XW — MB BCh 1981 Tripoli; FRCS Ed. 1985; FRCS Glas. 1985.

AL-WAGGA, Mr Muflih Ammar D162 Armed Forces Hospital, PO Box 7897, Riyadh 11159, Saudi Arabia Tel: 477 7714; Cefn, Bannerdown Road, Batheaston, Bath BA1 7LA Tel: 01225 858524 — MB ChB 1969 Baghdad; FRCS Eng. 1978; FRCS Ed. 1978. (Baghdad) Cons. Orthop. Surg. Armed Forces Hosp. Riyadh, Saudi Arabia. Socs: Brit. Scoliosis Soc.; Fell. Brit. Orthop. Assn. Prev: Sen. Regist. (Orthop.) Armed Forces Hosp. Riyadh, Saudi Arabia; Regist. (Orthop.) St. Geo. Hosp. Lond.

AL-WAKEEL, Baha Abdul Razzak Accident & Emergency Department, Kingston Hospital, Kingston upon Thames KT2 7QB Tel: 020 8546 7711 Fax: 020 8810 6883; 4 Beaufort Road, Ealing, London W5 3EA Tel: 020 8810 6883 Fax: 020 8810 6883 — MB ChB 1972 Baghdad; MRCPI 1984; FFAEM 1997; Dip. Cardiol. Lond 1984. (Baghdad, Iraq) Cons. A & E Med. Kingston Hosp. Surrey. Socs: BMA; BAEM; Med. Protec. Soc. Prev: Sen. Regist. (A & E) Chelsea & W.m. Hosp. Lond.; Regist. (Gen. Med. for the Elderly) Newham AHA; Regist. (Cardiol. & Gen. Med.) Roy. Liverp. Hosp.

AL WAKEEL, Gwendolen Margaret Department of Haematology, Frenchay Hospital, Bristol BS16 1LE; 91 Dovercourt Road, Horfield, Bristol BS7 9SG — MB BS 1982 Lond.; BSc Lond. 1979; MRCP (UK) 1985. (Roy. Free) Assoc. Specialist (Haemat.) Frenchay Hosp. N. Bristol NHS Trust. Socs: Brit. Soc. Haematol. Prev: Regist. (Haemat.) Leic. Roy. Infirm.; SHO (Haemat.) City Hosp. Nottm.; SHO (Med.) Freeman Hosp. Newc.

AL-WALI, Walid Ibrahim Ali 219 Crimicar Lane, Sheffield S10 4EH — MB ChB 1980 Baghdad; MRCPath 1992. Sen. Regist. & Hon. Clin. Tutor. N. Gen. Hosp. Socs: BMA; Assn. Med. Microbiol. Prev: Sen. Regist. & Hon. Clin. Tutor Roy. Hallamsh. Hosp. Sheff.; Lect. & Hon. Sen. Regist. Roy. Free Hosp. Med. Sch. Lond.

AL-YAQUBI, Nabil Najib The Surgery, 157 High Street, New Malden KT3 4BH Tel: 020 8942 0094 Fax: 020 8269 0065; Cornerways, Coombe Park, Kingston upon Thames KT2 7JD — MB ChB 1968 Baghdad.

AL-YASSIRI, Majid Mohammed Hussain Barnes Hospital, South Worple Way, London SW14 8SU Tel: 020 8878 4981 Fax: 020 8876 5471 Email: alyassiri@aol.com — MB ChB 1969 Baghdad; MRCPsych 1976; DPM 1976 Eng. Cons. Psychiat. Old Age Barnes Hosp. Lond.

AL-ZAIDY, Abdul Karim Abbey Wood Surgery, 9 Godstow Road, Abbey Wood, London SE2 9AT Tel: 020 8310 7066 Fax: 020 8311 8867 — MB ChB 1967 Baghdad; MRCPI 1977. Clin. Asst. (Chest Med.) Lond. Prev: Regist. (Radiol.) Lond. Hosp. Whitechapel; Regist. (Geriat. Med.) W. Norwich Hosp.

AL-ZIDGALI, Faisal The Mews, Gorleston, Great Yarmouth NR31 6TW — MB ChB 1990 Glas.

ALA, Abul Jamil Khursheed The Surgery, 514 Wandsworth Road, London SW8 3LT Tel: 020 7622 5642 Fax: 020 7978 1927 — MB BS 1963 Patna; DObst RCOG 1970.

ALA, Aftab 142 Trinity Road, London SW17 7HS Tel: 020 8672 6827 — MB BS 1992 Lond.; MRCP (UK) 1996. Specialist Regist. (Gastroenterol. & Gen. Med.) N. Thames Deanery Lond. Prev: SHO (Intens. Care) Whittington Hosp. Lond.; SHO (Gen. Med. & Hepat.) KCH Lond.; SHO (Neurol. & Med. Ophth.) St. Thomas' Hosp. Lond.

ALA, Fereydoun Abolghassem National Blood Service, West Midlands Centre, Edgbaston, Birmingham B15 2SG Tel: 0121 253 4013 Fax: 0121 253 4003; Hall Farm, Weather Oak Hill, Alvechurch, Birmingham B48 7EG Email: faala@aol.com — MB ChB 1960 Ed.; FRCP Ed 1971, M 1964; FRCPath 1996, M 1992. p/t Cons. Haemat. Nat. Blood Serv., W. Midl. Centre; Hon. Sen. research Fell., divicion of Med. Sci.s, univ. Birm; Hon. Pres.y, Iranian haemophilia comprehension care centre, Iran. Socs: Internat. Soc. Blood Transfus.; World Federat. of Haemophilia; Brit. Soc. Haematol.

ALABASTER, Charlotte Jane 11 Holland Road, Larkhall, Bath BA1 6QG Tel: 01225 330948; Professional Medical Associates, 550 Main St. N., Moose Jaw SK S6H 3K3, Canada — MB BS 1982 Lond.; DRCOG 1988. (Char. Cross) GP Moose Jaw, Saskatchewan, Canada. Prev: GP Gibraltar.

ALADERUN, Samuel Ayodele 71 Springwell Road, Heston, Hounslow TW5 9BW — State DMS 1984 Milan.

ALADIN, Abizar 105 Drayton, South Bretton, Peterborough PE3 9XW — BM BS 1995 Nottm.

ALAGAR, Shunmugam Pillai 91 Cairn Hill Road, Airdrie ML6 9HA — MB BS 1977 Madras.

ALAGELI, Nabil Abduruahman Spinal Injuries Unit, Robert Jones & Agnes Hunt Orthopaedic Hospital, Oswestry SY10 7AG Tel: 01691 404000 Email: ageli@msn.com; 1 The Maltings, West Felton, Oswestry SY11 4EL Tel: 01691 610770 Email: 100305.2430@compuserve.com — MB BCh 1983 Al Fateh; MMedSci Birm. 1996. (Univ. Birm.) Regist. (Spinal Injuries) Robt. Jones & Agnes Hunt Orthop. Hosp. OsW.ry; Dip. Surgic. Resusc. Inst. Accid. Surg. Birm. 1996. Socs: BMA; BOA. Prev: Tutor (Trauma & Orthop.) Al Fateh Univ., Tripoli, Libya.

ALAGESAN, Kandasamy Department of Anaesthesia, City Hospital, Nottingham NG5 1PB — MB BS 1973 Ceylon; FFA RCS Eng. 1983. Cons. Critical Care Med. & Anaesth. Nottm. Prev: Miss. Doctor PCEA Hosp. Tumu, Kenya; Regist. (Anaesth.) N.wick Pk. Hosp. Harrow & Clin. Research Centre; Sen. Regist. (Anaesth.) Nottm.

ALAGHBAND ZADEH, Jamshid Department Chemical Pathology, Imperial College Medical School, Charing Cross School Campus, London W6 8RP Tel: 020 8846 7065 Fax: 020 8846 7007 Email: j.zadeh@ic.ac.uk; 19 Gatwick Road, London SW18 5UF Tel: 020 8874 0580 — LMSSA 1963 Lond.; PhD Univ. Lond. 1979; FRCPath 1983, M 1971. (Guy's Hospital) Reader in Chem. Path., Imperial Coll. Med. Sch. Prev: Sen. Lect. & Hon. Cons. Chem. Endocrinol. Char. Cross. & W.m. Med. Sch. Lond.

ALAGNA, Nicholas 43 Harbour Road, Southbourne, Bournemouth BH6 4DE Tel: 01202 423302 — MB ChB 1997 Sheff. Ho. Off. (Vasc. Surg. & Gen. Surg., Gen. Med. & Gastroenterol., Orthop. & Trauma Surg. & Cardiol.).

ALAGRAJAH, Perrumal The Surgery, 151 Byron Avenue, London E12 6NQ Tel: 020 8471 5037 Fax: 020 8552 3322; 13A Fair View Road, Chigwell IG7 6HN Tel: 020 8500 6660 Fax: 0208 501 5455 — MB BS 1962 Madras. (Stanley Med. Coll. Madras) Socs: BMA.

ALAIBAC, Mauro Salvatore Alessandro Via Trieste 11, Lequile, Lecce 73010, Italy; 28 Vellacott House, Du Can Road, London W12 — State Exam 1986 Florence. Research Fell. (Dermat.) Roy. Postgrad. Med. Sch. Lond.

ALAILY, Aly Bashir El Maynards Oast, Leigh Green, Tenterden TN30 7DE — MB ChB 1968 Alexandria; PhD Manch. 1977; FRCOG 1986, M 1974. (Alexandria) Cons. & Clin. Dir. (O & G) Hastings & Rother NHS Trust; Hon. Tutor St. Mary's Hosp. Med. Sch. Lond. Socs: BMA. Prev: Regist. & Clin. Tutor (O & G) Wythenshawe Hosp. Manch. & Manch. Univ.

***ALAKESON, Renuka** 57 Bournemouth Road, London SW19 3AR — MB BS 1996 Lond.

ALAM, Abu Taher Mohammed Shamsul Abbeydale Road Surgery, 267 Abbeydale Road, Sheffield S7 1FJ Tel: 0114 255 0383 — MB BS 1963 Dacca.

ALAM, Arif 57 Winter Avenue, London E6 1NZ — MB BS 1994 Lond. (Lond. Hosp. Med. Coll.) Socs: BMA.

ALAM, Mr Ashar Nazir 4 Broomfield Crescent, Wivenhoe, Colchester CO7 9PZ — MB BS 1984 Punjab; FRCS Ed. 1987; FRCS Glas. 1987; Dip. Urol. Lond 1989.

ALAM, Danish Kamal 3 Lynford Gardens, Edgware HA8 8TX — MB BS 1998 Lond.; MB BS Lond 1998.

ALAM, Farrukh Brent, Kensington, chelsea & Westminster NHS Trust, Uxbridge Road, Southall UB1 3EU Tel: 020 8354 8005 — MB ChB 1989 Manch.; BSc St. And. 1986; MRCPsych 1993. Cons. Psychiat. Brent Kensington & Chelsea NHS Trust, Lond.; Hon. Tutor - Inst. of Psychiat., Denamrk Hill, Lond., SE5. Prev: Sen. Regist. (Psychiat.) Maudsley Hosp. Lond.; Regist. (Psychiat.) St. Mary's Hosp. Lond.

ALAM, Khursheed c/o Mr Ali, Cultural Centre, 146 Park Road, London NW8 7RG — MB BS 1954 Bihar. (Darbhanga Med. Coll.) GP Leeds; Clin. Asst. (Dermat.) Wakefield HA. Socs: Pres. Bihar Med. Grad. Assn.; BMA. Prev: Med. Regist. Manch. RHB.

ALAM, Mr Mahbubul 18 Vernon Avenue, Handsworth Wood, Birmingham B20 1DE Tel: 0121 554 8841 — MB BS 1964 Dacca; FRCS Glas. 1976. GP Smethwick; Clin. Asst. Orthop. Rehabil. Unit W. Heath Hosp. Birm. Prev: SHO Selly Oak Hosp. Birm.; Surg. Regist. Bignold Hosp. Wick; Med. Asst. W. Bromwich & Dist. Gen. Hosp.

ALAM, Malik Mahmood 14 Westfield Road, Bishop Auckland DL14 6AE — MB BS 1978 Peshawar; MRCP (UK) 1993.

ALAM, Manzoor 28 Kingscroft Road, Sutton Coldfield B74 2HG — MB BS 1966 Patna. (Patna)

ALAM, Maswood Heaton Norris Health Centre, Cheviot Close, Heaton Norris, Stockport SK4 1JX Tel: 0161 480 3338 — MB BS 1958 Bihar.

ALAM, Mirza Moshih-Ul (retired) 9 Osborne Crescent, Baswich, Stafford ST17 0AD Tel: 01785 603621 — MB BS 1958 Dacca. Prev: Assoc. Specialist (Psychiat.) St. Geo. Hosp. Stafford.

ALAM, Mohamed Samsul The Surgery, 48 Wilberforce Road, London N4 2SR — LMSSA 1968 Lond.; DPH Eng. 1963.

ALAM, Mohammad Mansoor 14 Bleadon Mill, Bleadon, Weston Super Mare BS24 0BE Tel: 01934 813470 — MB BS 1966 Bihar; MB BA Bihar 1966. (Darbhaga Med. Coll. Bihar, India) Examg. Med. Pract. Benefit Agency Bristol. Socs: Med. Protec. Soc. Prev: Assoc. Specialist (A & E) Gen. Hosp. W.on-super-Mare.

ALAM, Mohammed Ashraful 8 Compton Drive, Poole BH14 8PW — MB BS 1994 Lond.

ALAM, Mr Mohammed Imran 90 Chelwood Avenue, Childwall, Liverpool L16 3NW — MB BS 1980 Patna; FRCS Ed. 1994.

ALAM, Muhammad Fazlul Mull, Admiral Road Surgery, 36 Admiral Road, Glasgow G41 1HU Tel: 0141 429 0943 — MB BS 1967 Dacca; LRCP LRCS Ed. LRCPS Glas. 1979.

ALAM, Mr Muhammad Munir Chesterfield & N. Derbyshire Royal Hospital, Calow, Chesterfield S44 5BL Tel: 01246 277271 — MB BS 1965 Panjab; BSc Panjab 1959; FRCS Ed. 1977; FFAEM 1993. (Nishtar Med. Coll.) Cons. A & E Chesterfield & N. Derbysh. Roy. Hosp.

ALAM, Naaz Afrina 5 Watson Close, Bury St Edmunds IP33 2PG — MB BS 1996 Lond.

ALAM, Rinku 802 Eccleshall Road, Hunters Bar, Sheffield S11 8TD; 71 Lthrop Street, London N10 7JD — MB ChB 1996 Sheff.

ALAM, Saddaf Chadderton Town Health Centre, Middleton Road, Oldham OL9 0LH Fax: 0161 284 2923 — MB ChB 1991 Manch. Socs: Chairm. Mediconcern.

ALAM, Saeed Shams 27 Burnt Stones Drive, Sheffield S10 5TT — MB BS 1998 Lond.; MB BS Lond 1998.

ALAM, Sardar Muhammad 37 Trinty Courtyard, Newcastle upon Tyne NE6 1TS — MB BS 1980 Peshawar; MRCP Ed. 1987.

ALAM, Shadan Khurshid 3 Lynford Gardens, Edgware HA8 8TX — MB BS 1997 Lond.

ALAM, Shah Zafar Station Road Surgery, 45 Station Road, Atherstone CV9 1DB Tel: 01827 718631 Fax: 01827 712944 — MB BS 1965 Sind; MB BS Sind. 1965.

ALAM, Sharmin 2 St Cyprians Street, London SW17 8SZ — MB BS 1997 Lond.

ALAM, Syed Khursheed Springfield Surgery, 102 Bolton Road, Darwen BB3 1BZ Tel: 01254 701000 Fax: 01254 761160 — MB BS 1962 Osmania; BSc Osmania 1956, MB BS 1962; MRCGP 1972; DA Eng. 1967. (Osmania Med. Coll. Hyderabad) Prev: Regist. (Anaesth.) Reading & Dist. Gp. Hosps.

ALAM, Tahsin Adnan 2 Oronsay Cr, Bearsden, Glasgow G61 2EX — MB ChB 1997 Ed.

ALAMIN, Mutah Ismail The Therapy Centre, Birchley Mill House, St Mary's Avenue, Billinge, Wigan WN5 7QL Tel: 01744 895666 Email: mial@activemail.co.uk — MB ChB 1975 Ain Shams; MRCPsych 1981; M. Inst. G.A. 1988. (Ain Shams Univ.) Cons. (Psychiat.). Socs: Amer. Gp. Psychother. Assn.; Internat. Gp. Psychother. Assn.

ALAN, Tanya Sian 11 Hillary Rise, Barnet EN5 5AZ — MB ChB 1997 Liverp.; BSc (Microbiol.) Liverp. 1995. (Univ. of Liverpool)

ALANI, Abdel Amir 1 St Christopher's, Warren Drive, Tadworth KT20 6PY — MD 1956 Istanbul; LAH Dub. 1963; MRCPsych 1974; DPM Eng. 1973. (Istanbul) Prev: Med. Asst. Hill End Hosp. St. Albans; Regist. (Surg.) Sligo Co. Hosp.; Regist. (Psychiat.) Centr. Hosp. Warwick.

ALAPONT PEREZ, Eduardo 6 Pineways Drive, Wolverhampton WV6 0LL — LMS 1987 Valencia.

ALARCON PALOMO, Gonzalo EEG Department, Maudlsey Hospital, Denmark Hill, London SE5 8AZ Tel: 020 7703 6333; 38 Rutland Court, Denmark Hill, London SE5 8ED Tel: 020 7274 2214 — LMS 1984 U Complutense Madrid; PhD U Complutense Madrid 1987. Research Regist. Maudsley Hosp. Lond.

ALAUDDIN, Khalida Old Chester Road Surgery, 241 Old Chester Road, Lower Tranmere, Birkenhead CH42 3TD Tel: 0151 645 2306 — MB BS 1968 Punjab.

ALAUDDIN, Mr Mohammed 18 Gainsborough Road, Great Barr, Birmingham B42 1NA — MB BS 1968 Dacca; FRCS Glas. 1978.

ALAWATTEGAMA, Anura Bandara Royal Liverpool University Hospital, Prescot St., Liverpool L7 8XP Tel: 0151 706 2629 Fax: 0151 706 5821; 138 Brookdale Avenue S., Greasby, Wirral CH49 1SS Tel: 0151 604 0242 Email: anuraba@aol.com — MB BS 1969 Ceylon; MB BS Peradeniya, Ceylon 1969; MFFP 1994; FRCOG 1992, M 1977. Cons. Genitourin. Phys. Roy. Liverp. Univ. Hosp.; Clin. Lect. Univ. Liverp. Socs: Founder Mem. Genitourin. Phys. Colposc. GP; Ex. Hon. Pres., Hon. Sec. & Audit Co-ordinator, Genitourin. Phys. Colpose GP. Prev: Sen. Regist. (Genitourin. Med.) Roy. Hallamsh. Hosp. Sheff.; Sen. Lect. & Hon. Cons. O & G Univ. Peradeniya, Sri-Lanka; Regist. (O & G) St. Jas. Univ. Hosp. Leeds.

ALAWATTEGAMA, Hemantha Dinuka Bandara 138 Brookdale Avenue S., Greasby, Wirral CH49 1SS — MB BS 1996 Lond.

ALAWI, Mr Michael Hassan Elm Road Surgery, 84 Elm Road, Leigh-on-Sea SS9 1SJ Tel: 01702 711559 Fax: 01702 471447 — MB ChB 1972 Baghdad; FRCS Eng. 1979; FRCS Ed. 1979; DRCOG 1986. (Baghdad) GP Leigh-on-Sea.; Clin. Asst., GU Med. Socs: Med. Protec. Soc.; S. Essex LMC.

ALBAN, Mark Timothy The Old Vicarage, Sedbergh LA10 5AL — MB BS 1997 Lond.

ALBAN DAVIES, Huw West Hill Hospital, Dartford DA1 2HF Tel: 01322 223223; Troutbeck, Otford, Sevenoaks TN14 5PH Tel: 01959 525439 — BM BCh 1974 Oxf.; MA Oxf. 1973, DM 1986, BM BCh 1974; FRCP Lond. 1993. (Univ. Coll. Hosp.) Cons. Phys. Dartford & Gravesham HA Kent. Prev: SHO Taunton; Regist. Cardiff; Sen. Regist. E. Anglia.

ALBANESE, Assunta Institute of Child Health, Medical Unit, 30 Guildford St., London WC1N 1EH Tel: 020 7242 9789 Fax: 020 7831 0488 — State Exam Med 1988 Florence.

ALBERMAN, Eva Dorothea 3 Millfield Place, London N6 6JP Tel: 020 8340 3122 — MB BChir 1955 Camb.; MD Camb. 1965; FRCP Lond. 1985, M 1976; FRCOG 1989; FFCM 1977; DPH Lond. 1960. (Lond. Hosp.) Prof. Emerit. Lond. Univ.; Med. Adviser Office Populat. Censuses & Surveys. Socs: Fell. Roy. Soc. Med.

***ALBERT, Anna Maya** 17 Richmond Avenue, London N1 0NE — MB BS 1996 Lond.

ALBERT, Daniel John The Whitfield Practice, Hunslet Health Centre, 24 Church Street, Leeds LS10 2PE Tel: 0113 270 5194 Fax: 0113 270 2795 — MB BChir 1990 Camb.; MPhil (Med. Physics) Leeds 1985; MSc (Med. Physics) Aberd. 1979; MA (Med. Sci.) Camb. 1990; BSc (App. Physics) Hull 1978; DFFP 1994. (Camb. & Leeds) Clin. Asst. (A & E) St. Jas. Univ. Hosp. Leeds. Socs: BASICS.

ALBERT, Mr David Martin Hospital for Children, Great Ormond St., London WC1N 3JH Tel: 020 7829 8632 Fax: 020 7829 8635; Portland Hospital for Women and Children, Great Portland St, London W1N 6AH Tel: 020 7390 8300 Fax: 020 7383 4269 Email: albert@easynet.co.uk — MB BS 1979 Lond.; FRCS 1984 Eng. Cons. Paediat. (ENT Surg.) Hosp. Childr. Gt. Ormond St. & Portland Hosp. Wom. & Childr. Lond.; Sen. Lect. Inst. Child Health. Socs: Fell. Roy. Soc. Med.; (Sec.) Brit. Assn. Paediat. Otolaryngol. Prev: Dir. Research Otolaryngol. Childr. Hosp. Med. Center Cincinnati, USA; Sen. Regist. Hosp. Sick Childr. Lond.; Regist. Kings Coll. Hosp. Lond.

ALBERT, Edmund George 75 Church Road, Woolton, Liverpool L25 6DA — MB ChB 1991 Ed.

ALBERT, Mr John Stephen 77 Newmarket Road, Norwich NR2 2HW Tel: 01603 612538; Duke's Head, Shotesham All Saints, Norwich NR15 1AP — MB BS 1974 Lond.; BSc Lond. 1971, MB BS 1974; FRCS Eng. 1980. (St. Bart.) Cons. Trauma & Orthop. Norf. & Norwich Hosp. Socs: Fell. Brit. Orthop. Assn. Prev: Sen. Regist., Orthop. St. Bart. Train. Progr.; Regist. (Surg.) Qu. Eliz. Hosp. Birm.; Ho. Surg. St. Bart. Hosp. Lond.

ALBERT, Paul Stuart 3 Beach Bank, Liverpool L22 7RL — MB ChB 1997 Ed.

ALBERT, Peter Julian Raymond 3 Holmdene Avenue, London NW7 2LY — MB BS 1994 Lond.; BSc (Anat.) Lond. 1991.

ALBERT-RECHT, Frank Department of Chemical Pathology, Royal Infirmary, Medical School Forresterhill, Aberdeen Tel: 01224 23423 — MB ChB 1955 Ed.; FRCPath 1977, M 1965. (Ed.) Sen. Lect. Dept. Chem. Path. & Hon. Consult. Roy Infirm. Aberd. Socs: Assn. Clin. Biochems. Prev: Research Asst. Roy. Infirm. Edin.; Lect. Dept. Chem. Path. Ibadan; Lect. Dept. Clin. Chem. Roy. Infirm. Edin.

ALBERTI, Professor Kurt George Matthew Mayer 11 St Andrews Place, Regent Park, London NW1 4LE Tel: 020 7935 1174 Fax: 020 7224 1398 Email: professor.alberti@replondon.ac.uk — BM BCh 1965 Oxf.; DPhil Oxf. 1964; FRCP Ed. 1988; FRCP Lond. 1978, M 1975; FRCPath 1985, M 1973. Pres. Roy. Coll. of Phys.; Prof. Med. Univ. Newc. Socs: Assn. Phys.; Pres. Elect Internat. Diabetes Federat. Prev: Prof. Clin. Biochem. Univ. Newc.; Prof. Chem. Path. & Human Metab. Soton. Univ. Med. Sch.; Research Off. Radcliffe Infirm. Oxf.

ALBERTI MARONO, Javier University Hospital of Wales, Heath Park, Glamorgan House, Cardiff CF14 4XW — LMS 1992 Santiago de Compostela.

ALBERTS, Mr Justin Charles John 4 Brookside, Exning, Newmarket CB8 7HP Tel: 01638 577449 Email: jalberts@albie.demon.co.uk — MB BS 1990 Lond.; BSc (Hons.) Lond. 1987, MB BS 1990; FRCS (Eng.) 1995. (Roy. Free Hosp. Sch. Med. Lond.) Specialist Regist. (Gen. Surg.) Wessex Region. Socs: Assn. Surg. Train.; Affil. Fell. Assn. Surg. GB & Irel.; Fell. (Jun.) Roy. Soc. Med. Prev: Research Regist. (Gen. Surg.) Tenovus Inst. Soton. Univ. Hosp.; Sen. SHO (Gen. Surg.) Horton Gen. Hosp. Banbury; SHO (Cardiothorac Surg.) Roy. Brompton Hosp. Banbury.

ALBERTYN, Ryck Daniel 81 Netheravon Road, London W4 2NB — MB BCh 1989 Witwatersrand.

ALBIN, Malgorzata Westminster Hospital, Page St., London SW1 — Lekarz 1970 Warsaw; FFA RCS Eng. 1979; DA Eng. 1975. (Acad. Med. Warsaw) Cons. Anaesth. W.minster Hosp. Prev: Sen. Regist. (Anaesth.) Char. Cross Hosp. Lond.

ALBISTON, Elizabeth Malcolm Maryhill Practice, Elgin Health Centre, Maryhill, Elgin IV30 1AT Tel: 01343 543788 Fax: 01343 551604 — MB ChB 1983 Dundee; MRCGP 1987; DRCOG 1985. (Dundee)

ALBON, Lorraine Iris Mary 20 Torrington Gardens, London N11 2AB — MB BS 1992 Lond.; BSc (Hons.) Lond. 1987; MRCP (UK) 1995.

ALBOROUGH, Elizabeth Anne Barton Surgery, Barton Terrace, Dawlish EX7 9QH Tel: 01626 888877 Fax: 01626 888360; 2 The College, Ide, Exeter EX2 9RH — MB BS 1986 Lond.; MRCGP 1992; DGM RCP Lond. 1990. Prev: SHO (Cas.) Roy. Surrey Co. Hosp.; SHO (Geriat.) W. Middlx. Hosp.; SHO (Psychiat.) Torbay Hosp.

ALBRECHT, Thomas Hammersmith Hospital, Department of Diagnostic Radiology, Du Cane Road, London W12 0NN Tel: 020 8743 2030 Fax: 020 8743 5409; 34A Ainger Road, London NW3 3AT Tel: 020 7483 0150 — MD 1991 Berlin; State Exam. Med. 1990. Regist. (Diag. Radiol.) Hammersmith Hosp. Lond.

ALBRIGHT, Elizabeth Jessie Wolverhampton Road Surgery, 13 Wolverhampton Road, Stafford ST17 4BP Tel: 01785 258161 Fax: 01785 224140 — MB ChB 1978 Birm.; AFOM RCP Lond. 1990. (Birmingham) Occupat. Health Phys. GEC Stafford.

ALBRIGHT, Stuart Whitlark 51 Somerville Road, Sutton Coldfield B73 6HH Tel: 0121 354 8829 Fax: 0121 321 1933 — MB BS 1951 Lond.; MRCS Eng. LRCP Lond. 1951; DObst RCOG 1957. (St. Bart.)

ALBUQUERQUE, Kevin Vincent de Paul c/o Mr A. P. Barlow, Department of Surgery, Lincoln COunty Hospital, Lincoln LN2 5QY — MB BS 1986 Bombay.

ALBUQUERQUE, Selwyn Romeo Jude Cefn Coed Hospital, Waunarlwydd Road, Cockett, Swansea SA2 0Gh — MB BS 1986 Bombay; MS Bombay 1988; MRCPsych 1996; MSc 1998. Cons. Psychiat., Swansea NHS Trust. Socs: RCP; Life Mem. Brit. Indian Psych. Assn.; BMA.

ALBUQUERQUE, Wendy 28 Littleheath Road, South Croydon CR2 7SA Tel: 020 8657 4913 — MB ChB 1993 Manch.; MSc (Audiological Medicine) London Univ. 2000; MRCP (Paediatrics) March 1997. (Manchester UK) Specialist Regist. Dept. of Neuro-otol., Nat. Hosp. of Neurol. and Neurosurg., Qu. Sq. Lond. Prev: SpR (Audiol Med) Roy. Nat. Throat, Nose and Ear Hosp., Lond.; SpR (Audiol Med) Gt. Ormond St. Hosp.

ALBUQUERQUE, Wilfred John 52 Waltham Road, Grimsby DN33 2NA — MB BCh BAO 1963 NUI.

ALCALAY, Marco 53 Westmount Road, Eltham Park, London SE9 1JF Tel: 020 8850 7796 Fax: 020 8265 1101; No.7 Gilston Park House, Gilston CM20 2SF Tel: 01279 444296, 0208 850 7796 Fax: 0208 265 1101 — MB BS 1974 Lond.; BDS Lond. 1962; MRCS Eng. LRCP Lond. 1973; FDS RCS Lond. 1968; FDS RCPS Glas. 1968. Endodont. Specialist Belgravia Lond. Socs: Internat. Coll. Dent.; Lond. Dent. Fell.; Dent. & Cons. Restorat. Dent. Gp. Prev: Cons. (Dent. Surg.) Roy. Masonic Hosp. Lond.; Hon. Cons. & Sen. Lect. Kings Coll. Dent. Sch. Lond.

ALCIDE, Julia Marie 100 York Avenue, Huddersfield HD2 2PP — MB ChB 1992 Manch.

ALCOCK, Angela Michelle Riverside Lodge, Lower Foxdale, Douglas IM4 3AZ — MB ChB 1998 Sheff.; MB ChB Sheff 1998.

ALCOCK, Christopher John Department of Clinical Oncology, The Churchill, Old Road, Headington, Oxford OX3 7LJ Tel: 01865 225653 Fax: 01865 225660; Pettiwell House, Garsington, Oxford OX44 9DB — MB BS 1974 Lond.; FRCP Lond. 1996; MRCP (UK) 1978; MRCS Eng. LRCP Lond. 1974; FRCR 1982. (Roy. Free Hosp. Lond.) Cons. Clin. Oncol. Oxf. Radcliffe Hosp. Socs: BMA; BOA; BIR.

ALCOCK, David John 35 Castle View, Witton-Le-Wear, Bishop Auckland DL14 0DH — MB 1969 Camb.; BChir 1968; MRCGP 1978.

ALCOCK, Duncan Gordon Bootham Park Hospital, Bootham, York YO30 7BY Tel: 01904 631313; Bootham Park Hospital, Bootham, York YO30 7BY Tel: 01904 631313 — MB ChB 1997 Aberd. (Aberdeen) SHO in Psychiat. Socs: BMA.

ALCOCK, Emma Louise Flat 1, 25 Broadwall, London SE1 9PL Email: emalcock@doctors.org.uk — MB BS 1992 Lond.; FRCA 1998. (London Hosp Med Sch) Specialist Regist. Anaesth. Kings Coll. Hosp Lond.

ALCOCK, Frank (retired) 19 Holly Road, Uttoxeter ST14 7NX Tel: 01889 563604 Email: frank@the-alcocks.freeserve.co.uk — MB ChB 1960 Ed.; BA Manch. 1950; DObst RCOG 1962.

ALCOCK, Gary Stuart Camjay, Little Stambridge Hall Lane, Rochford SS4 1EN — MB ChB 1989 Ed.; MRCP (UK) 1994.

ALCOCK, Ian Stephen Tel: 01242 580511; PO Box 400, Cheltenham GL53 7YY Tel: 07770 511711 Email: ian@box400.com — MB BS 1993 Lond. GP. Socs: BMA.

ALCOCK, James, MBE Cowdenbeath Medical Practice, 173 Stenhouse Street, Cowdenbeath KY4 9DH Tel: 01383 518500 Fax: 01383 518509; Bowood, Cleish, Kinross KY13 0LQ Tel: 01577 850213 Fax: 01577 850213 — MB ChB 1969 Ed.; MRCGP 1976. Chairm. Fife LMC; Mem. (Agenda Comm.) Conf. of Scott. LMCs. Socs: SGCP. Prev: SHO (Obst.) Dunfermline Matern. Hosp.; SHO (Paediat.) Vict. Hosp. Kirkcaldy; Ho. Surg. W.. Gen. Hosp. Edin.

ALCOCK, Katherine Maria Pinderfields Gen. Hospital, Aberford Rd, Wakefield WF1 4DG; 15 Mickleton Road, Solihull B92 7EH — MB ChB 1993 Sheff.; MRCP (UK) 1996; Dip. IMC RCS (Ed) 1999. SHO (Paed) Pinderfields Hosp. Socs: BAAEM; BASICS. Prev: SHO (Anaesth.) Pinderfields Hosp.; Sen. SHO (A&E) Leeds Gen. Infirm.; SHO (Gen. Med.) Leeds Gen. Infirm.

ALCOCK, Nathaniel Scott (retired) The Old Rectory, Sowton, Exeter EX5 2AG Tel: 01392 367423 — MB ChB 1931 Ed.; FRCP 1948 Lond; MD 1944 Ed.; MRCP 1937 Lond. Prev: Neurol. Roy. Devon & Exeter Hosp. & Torbay Hosp. Torquay.

ALCOCK, Robert Julian Robert Jones & Agnes Hunt Orthopaedic & District Hospital, Oswestry — MB BS 1986 Lond.; FCAnaesth 1991. Cons. Anaesth. Robt. Jones & Agnes Hunt Orthop. & Dist. Hosp. OsW.ry Shrops. Prev: Sen. Regist. (Anaesth.) Gt. Ormond St. Hosp. Lond.; Sen. Regist. & Regist. (Anaesth.) Roy. Free Hosp. Lond.; SHO (Anaesth.) St. Geo. Hosp. Lond.

ALCOCK, Roger Douglas 8 Roxburgh St, Edinburgh EH8 9TA — MB ChB 1997 Ed.; BSc (Hons) Immunol Ed 1995. (Edinburgh) SHO in Neurosci.s, Ninewells hosp.; Tayside Univ. Teachg. Hosp. NHS Trust. Prev: SHO A&E Med., Roy. Liverp. Uni Hosp; SHO A&E Med., Ninewells Uni Hosp, Dundee; Jun. Ho. Off. in Med., Borders Gen Hosp, Melrose.

ALCOCK, Stephen Robert c/o Deptartment of Clinical Microbiology, University of Glasgow, Western Infirmary, Glasgow G11 6NT Tel: 0141 211 2246 Fax: 0141 211 2138 — MB ChB 1969 Aberd.; PhD Aberd. 1979; T(Path) 1991. (Aberd.) Sen. Lect. (Bact.) Univ. Glas.; Cons. Bact. Gtr. Glas. HB; Head of Dept. of Clin. Microbiol. Socs: Soc. Gen. Microbiol.; BMA. Prev: Lect. (Bact.) Univ. Aberd.; Ho. Off. Aberd. Roy. Infirm.

ALCOLADO, Juan Carlos Department of Medicine, University of Wales College of Medicine, Heath Park, Cardiff CF14 4XN Tel: 029 2074 7747; 151 Lake Road W., Roath Park, Cardiff CF2 5EQ Tel: 029 2074 7247 Email: alcoladojc@cardiff.ac.uk — BM 1986 Soton.; DM Soton. 1992, BM (Hons.) (Distinc. Clin. Med. & Med. Scs.) 1986; MRCP (UK) 1989. Sen. Lect. & Cons. Phys. (Diabetes & Endocrinol.) Univ. Wales Coll. Med. Cardiff. Prev: Lect. (Diabetes & Endocrinol.) Univ. Hosp. Wales Cardiff.; Regist. (Diabetes & Endocrinol.) E. Birm. Hosp.; Research Regist. St. Bart. Hosp. Lond.

ALCOLADO, Ruth Singleton Hospital, Sketty, Swansea SA2 8QA Tel: 01792 205666 Fax: 01792 208647; 151 Lake Road W., Cardiff CF23 5PJ — BM 1987 Soton.; BM (Hons. Distinc. Clin. Med.) Soton. 1987; MRCP (UK) 1991. Cons. Phys. (Gastroenterol.) Singleton Hosp. Swansea. Prev: Clin. Lect. (Med.) Univ. Wales Coll. Med. Cardiff; Regist. (Gastroenterol.) Soton. & Research Regist. Univ. Med. Soton.

ALCOREZA OLIVA, Maria Isabel 52 Clare Court, Judd St., London WC1H 9QW Tel: 020 8693 3377 — MD 1972 Chile; MRCPysch 1980.

ALCORN, Ann Shaw The Old School House, Dinnington, Newcastle upon Tyne NE13 7JS — MB ChB 1985 Glas.; MRCPsych 1992; DRCOG 1987. Sen. Regist. (Child & Adolesc. Psychiat.) N. RHA.

ALCORN, David Lindsay 2 James Watt Road, Milngavie, Glasgow G62 7JY — MB ChB 1990 Glas.; FRCA (Lond.) 1998. Specialist Regist. Anaesth. W. of Scot. Train. Scheme.

ALCORN, Mr Desmond Joseph 109 Stockiemuir Avenue, Bearsden, Glasgow G61 3LX; X-Ray Department, Law Hospital, Carluke ML8 5ER Tel: 01698 361100 — MB ChB 1988 Glasg.; FRCS Glas. 1993; FRCR Lond. 1997. Cons. (Radiol.) Law Hosp.

ALCORN, James Ronald Mackey Shankill Health Centre, 135 Shankill Parade, Belfast BT13 1SD — MB BCh BAO 1977 Belf.; BSc Belf. 1974; MRCGP 1982.

ALCORN, Nicola Jane 13 Finnick Glen, Ayr KA7 4RF — MB ChB 1995 Glas.

ALCORN, Ronald James Margarete Centre, 108 Hampstead Rd, London NW1 2LS Tel: 020 7380 9692 — MB ChB 1981 Otago; FRANZCP 1989. Cons. Psychiat. Camden & Islington Community Health Servs. NHS Trust Lond.; Hon. Sen. Lect. Roy. Free & Univ. Coll. Lond. Med. Sch.

ALCORN, Thomas Sunnyside, Carman Hill, Renton, Dumbarton G82 4LZ Tel: 01389 52404 — MB ChB 1960 Glas.; DObst RCOG 1962.

ALCROFT, John Edmonds Mayfield Medical Centre, 37 Totnes Road, Paignton TQ4 5LA; Court Farm, Little Hempston, Totnes TQ9 6LU — LRCPI & LM, LRSCI & LM 1970; LRCPI & LM, LRCSI & LM 1970; BSc (Eng.) Lond. 1963; MRCGP 1979; DObst RCOG 1972.

ALCROFT, Penelope Anne Lower Court, Littlehempston, Totnes TQ9 6LU — MB BS 1992 Lond.

ALDABBAGH, Ameer 24 Whitehill Road, Halifax HX2 9HD — MB ChB 1998 Liverp.; MB ChB Liverp 1998.

ALDAM, Mr Charles Heaton 76 Pishiobury Drive, Sawbridgeworth CM21 0AF — MB BS 1976 Lond.; FRCS Eng. 1981. Cons. Orthop. Surg. P.ss Alexandra Hosp. Harlow, Herts & Essex Hosp. & St. Margt. Hosp. Epping. Prev: Sen. Regist. (Orthop. Surg.) St. Bart. Hosp. Lond.

ALDAYA LORENZO, Jose Maria 18 Park Crescent, Boston Road, Sleaford NG34 7HY — LMS 1991 Basque.

ALDEAN, Mr Isamiel Mohammed Ali 8 Normanby Chase, Altrincham WA14 4QP — MB ChB 1968 Baghdad; FRCS Ed. 1975; T(S) 1994. Cons. Surg. Trafford Gen. Hosp. Manch. Socs: BMA; Brit. Assn. Surgic. Oncol.; Assn. Surg. Prev: Cons. Surg. Iraq.

ALDEGHATHER, Jehad Taha The Portmill Surgery, 114 Queen Street, Hitchin SG4 9TH Tel: 01462 434246 — MB BS 1986

Lond.(Royal Free); MRCP (UK) 1989; 1999 DOccMed; DRCOG 1994; DCH 1995; MRCGP 1996. (Roy. Free) Prev: Regist. (Cardiol.) St. Mary's Hosp. Lond.; SHO & Regist. Rotat. (Gen. Med.) St. Bart. Hosp. Lond.; Ho. Phys. Roy. Free Hosp. Lond.

ALDEN, Anna Elizabeth Wickham Market Medical Centre, Chapel Lane, Wickham Market, Woodbridge IP13 0SB Tel: 01728 747101 Fax: 01728 747580 — MB BS 1972 Lond.

ALDEN, Mr David John The Surgery, 61 Wroxham Road, Sprowston, Norwich NR7 8TT Tel: 01603 427153 Fax: 01603 787341 — MB BChir 1972 Camb.; LMSSA Lond. 1972; FRCS Eng. 1979.

ALDEN, Stephen Robert The Medical Centre, High Street, Lindfield, Haywards Heath RH16 2HX Tel: 01444 457666; Bridge Cottage, Sheffield Park, Uckfield TN22 3QU Tel: 01825 722788 — MB BS 1985 Lond.

ALDER, David Edmund (retired) Moredon Surgery, 25/27 Moredon Road, Swindon SN25 3DF Tel: 01793 487394 — MB BS 1961 Lond.; LMSSA Lond. 1960; DObst RCOG 1962. Prev: Ho. Phys. & Ho. Surg. Warneford Hosp. Leamington Spa.

ALDER, Hermione Park Cottage, Bromley Road, Ardleigh, Colchester CO7 7SJ — MB ChB 1993 Leic.

***ALDER, Janette Louise** 35 Marlowe Road, Hartlepool TS25 4PF — MB ChB 1997 Manch.

ALDER, Sydney 48 Park Crescent, Brighton BN2 3HB Tel: 01273 606237 — MB BS 1929 Durh.; MCPS Sask. 1957. (Univ. Durh.) Prev: Resid. Med. Off. Dudley Rd. Hosp. Birm.; Ho. Phys (Anaesth.) New Cross Hosp. Wolverhampton; Vis. Surg. Balcarres Hosp. Sask., Canada.

ALDER, Timothy Andrew Poole Road Medical Centre, 7 Poole Road, Bournemouth BH2 5QR Tel: 01202 761120 Email: timothy.alder@gp-t81004.nhs.uk; 34 Parkstone Avenue, Lower Parkstone, Poole BH14 9LR Tel: 01202 721726 Email: timsuealder@care4free.net — MB BS 1991 Lond.; MRCGP 1997; DRCOG 1996; DCH RCP Lond. 1995. (Char. Cross & Westm. Med. Sch.) GP Poole, Dorset.

ALDERDICE, David King 11 Ireton Street, Belfast BT7 1LH — MB BCh BAO 1989 Belf.; MB BCh Belf. 1989.

ALDERDICE, Lady Joan Margaret The Laboratory, Antrim Hospital, Antrim BT41 2RL Tel: 02894 424131 Fax: 02894 424214 Email: joan.alderdice@uh.n-i.nhs.uk; 55 Knock Road, Belfast BT5 6LB Tel: 02890 793097 Fax: 02890 225276 — MB BCh BAO 1979 Belf.; FRCPath 1997, M 1986. (Queen's Belfast) Cons. Histopath. & Cytopath. Antrim Hosp. Socs: Assn. Clin. Path.; Brit. Soc. Clin. Cytol.; BMA.

ALDERDICE, Rt. Hon. Lord John Thomas Rosebank House, Department of Psychotherapy, 100 Kings Road, Belfast BT4 3EU Tel: 02890 401141 Fax: 02890 705869 Email: alderdicej@parliament.uk; 55 Knock Road, Belfast BT5 6LB Tel: 02890 793097 Fax: 02890 225276 Email: alderdicej@parliament.uk — MB BCh BAO 1978 Belf.; FRCPsych. 1997, M 1982. (Qu. Univ. Belf.) p/t Cons. Psychother. Belf. Socs: Fell. Ulster Med. Soc.; Assn. for Psychoanal. Psychother. in NHS; Peruvian Psychiatric Assn. Prev: Hon. Sen. Lect. (Psychother.) Qu. Univ. Belf.; Exec. Med. Dir. S & E Belf. H & SS Trust; Sen. Tutor (Ment. Health) Qu. Univ. Belf.

ALDERMAN, Brian Arrowe Park Hospital, Upton, Wirral CH9 5PE Tel: 0151 678 5111 Fax: 0151 604 1552 Email: brianalderman@e.c.mail.wirral-tr.n.west.nhs.uk; Hessle Moor, 31 Dawstone Road, Heswall, Wirral CH60 0BT Tel: 0151 342 5469 Fax: 0151 342 5469 — MB ChB 1965 Liverp.; FRCOG 1982, M 1970, DObst 1967. Cons. O & G Arrowe Pk. Hosp. Upton Merseyside; Clin. Lect. Liverp. Univ.; Dist. Tutor & Roy. Coll. Obst. & Gyn. Socs: BMA & Gyn. Vis. Soc. GB & Irel.; N Eng. Obst. & Gyn. Soc. Pres. Prev: Lect. (Obst.) Liverp. Univ.; Regist. Wom. Hosp. Liverp.; Regist. (Obst.) Liverp. Matern. Hosp.

ALDERMAN, Edward William Richard 91 St Asaph Road, Brockley, London SE4 2EB — MRCS Eng. LRCP Lond. 1944. (Camb. & Guy's) Prev: Ho. Surg. & Ho. Phys. Norf. & Norwich Hosp.; Ho. Phys. Guy's Hosp.; Ho. Phys. (Paediat.) Osterhills Hosp. St. Albans.

ALDERMAN, Peter Robert 36 Old Lansdowne Road, Manchester M20 2WU — BM BS 1987 Nottm.

ALDERMAN, Mr Phillip Martyn St Joseph's Private Hospital, Harding Avenue, Malpas, Newport NP20 6ZE Tel: 01633 857975 Fax: 01633 857975 — MB ChB 1982 Bristol; FRCS Ed. 1987. Cons. Trauma & Orthop. Surg. Roy. Gwent Hosp. Newport.; Hon. orthopaedic Surg. to Newport RFC and Welsh Dist.s Rugby Union. Prev: SHO (Orthop.) Univ. Hosp. Nottm.; Ho. Phys. Bristol Gen. Hosp.; Ho. Surg. Bristol Roy. Infirm.

ALDERS, Frances Mary (retired) 25A Elgin Road, Talbot Woods, Bournemouth BH3 7DQ — MB BS 1950 Lond.; MRCS Eng. LRCP Lond. 1950; DObst RCOG 1954; DCH Eng. 1952. JP. Prev: Ho. Phys. Roy. Free Hosp. Lond.

ALDERSLEY, Mark Andrew Walsgrave Hospital, Clifford Bridge Rd, Coventry CV2 2DX Email: markaldo@msn.com — BM 1987 Soton.; MRCP (UK) 1990. Cons. Phys. & Gastroenterol. Prev: MRC Clin. Research Fell. (Liver Dis. & Gastroenterol.) St. Jas. Univ. Hosp. Leeds; Regist. (Liver. Dis. & Gastroenterol.) St. Jas. Hosp. Leeds.

ALDERSON, Charles Lynford (retired) 1 St Matthews Court, Northowram, Halifax HX3 7HE Tel: 01422 206942 — MB ChB 1941 Leeds. Prev: Regist. (Med.) Leeds Gen. Infirm. & St. Luke's Hosp. Bradford.

ALDERSON, Mr David John Department of Otolaryngology, Torbay Hospital, Lanes Br, Torquay TQ2 7AA — MB BS 1989 Lond.; FRCS (ORC-HNS) 1998; FRCS Eng. 1995. Cons. (ENT) Torbay. Prev: Regist. (Gen. Surg.) New Plymouth, NZ; SHO (ENT) Sheff.; Regist. (ENT) Liverp.

ALDERSON, David Michael 32 Cornhill Road, Urmston, Manchester M41 5TD — MB BS 1977 Lond.; MRCS Eng. LRCP Lond. 1974; MRCPath 1984. (Char. Cross) Cons. (Haemat.) Trafford Gen. Hosp. Socs: Assoc. Clin. Path. Prev: Sen. Regist. (Rotat.) (Haemat.) NWRHA.

ALDERSON, Professor Derek University Department of Surgery, Bristol Royal Infirmary, Bristol BS2 8HW Tel: 0117 928 3153 Fax: 0117 925 2736 Email: derek.alderson@bristol.ac.uk — MB BS 1976 Newc.; MD Newc. 1987; FRCS Eng. 1980. Prof. Gastro-Intestinal Surg. & Cons. Surg. Bristol Roy. Infirm.; Arris & Gale Lect. RCS 1985. Socs: Surgic. Research Soc.; Assn. Upper G.I. Surg. (Pres. 2000 - 2002); Brit. Soc. Gastroenterol. Prev: Sen. Regist. NRHA; Research Fell. Washington Univ, St. Louis, Missouri 1985-86; Wellcome Surg. Train. Fell. 1981-83.

ALDERSON, Esther Helen 83 Lexham Gardens, London W8 6JN — MB BS 1997 Lond.

ALDERSON, James William, Surg. Cdr. RN 8 Little Fancy Close, Roborough, Plymouth PL6 7DR — MB BS 1955 Durh. Prev: Ho. Phys. & Ho. Surg. Darlington Memor. Hosp.

ALDERSON, John David 36 Stone Delf, Fulwood, Sheffield S10 3QX Tel: 0114 230 7197 — MB ChB 1969 Sheff.; FFA RCSI 1974. Cons. Anaesth. N. Gen. Hosp. Trust Sheff. Prev: Sen. Regist. Sheff. AHA; Regist. (Anaesth.) N.. Gen. Hosp. Sheff.

ALDERSON, Margaret Lorraine 65 Barn Hey Crescent, Meols, Wirral L47 9RW Tel: 0151 632 1949; Middle Farm House, Long Crichel, Wimborne BH21 5JU — MB ChB 1992 Sheff.; MRCP (UK) 1995; FRCA 1997. (Sheffield) p/t Specialist Regist. in Anaesth. in S. W. Prev: SHO (Anaesth.) Roy. Hallamsh. Hosp. Sheff.; SHO (Anaesth.) Arrowe Pk. Hosp. Wirral; Specialist Regist. (Anaesth.) Merseyside.

ALDERSON, Marianne Louise East Barnwell Health Centre, Ditton Lane, Cambridge CB5 8SP — MB ChB 1990 Bristol; MRCGP 1996; T(GP) 1996; DFFP 1996. (Bristol) Prev: GP/Regist. Camb.

ALDERSON, Pamela Moira 71 Cairnfield Place, Aberdeen AB15 5LX — MB ChB 1990 Aberd.; MRCGP 1996. Trainee GP/SHO Inverness VTS.

ALDERSON, Peter John Royal Halifax Infirmary, Free School Lane, Halifax HX1 2YP; 2 Falcon Street, Halifax HX3 0QZ — MB BS 1985 Lond.; MBA Open. 1995; MA Oxf. 1986; DA (UK) 1987. Staff (Anaesth.) Calderdale Healthcare Trust. Prev: Fell. (Anaesth.) HSC, Toronto; Regist. (Anaesth.) St. Mary's Hosp. Lond.

ALDERSON, Philip Robert 13 St Annes Road, Headington, Oxford OX3 8NN — MB ChB 1988 Leeds.

ALDERSON, Rosemary Anne 8 Sully Terrace, Penarth CF64 3DS Tel: 01222 700829 — MB BS 1967 Lond.; DA Eng. 1969; Dip Occ Med RCP Lond. 1997. (Univ. Coll. Hosp.) Company Doctor Dow Corning Ltd. Barry; Asst. Brig. Med. Adviser S. Wales Fire & Rescue Serv.

ALDERSON, Thomas St John Nuffield Road Medical Centre, Nuffield Road, Chesterton, Cambridge CB4 1GL Tel: 01223 423424 Fax: 01223 566450 — BM BCh 1986 Oxf.; 2001 ILTM; MA Camb. 1987; MRCGP 1991; T(GP) 1991; DCH RCP Lond. 1990; DRCOG 1989; DGM RCP Lond. 1988; MSc (GP)1998; DFFP 1996. Princip. in

Gen. Pract., Nuffield Rd Med Ctre, Camb.; Asst. Dir. Of Gen. Pract. Shidies, Univ. Of Camb. Prev: Clin. Lect. (Gen. Pract.) Camb. Univ.

ALDERTON, Daniel Arthur (retired) 122 High Street, Melbourn, Royston SG8 6AL — MB BS Lond. 1961; DObst RCOG 1965; DA Eng. 1963. Prev: Gen. Practitioner.

ALDERTON, Margaret Joyce (retired) Tideways, 3 Victoria Esplanade, West Mersea, Colchester CO5 8AT — MB BS 1959 Lond.; MRCS Eng. LRCP Lond. 1959; FFA RCS Eng. 1965; DA Eng 1962. Prev: Cons. Anaesth. Barking & Havering AHA.

ALDINGTON, Dominic Joseph Stable House, Innings Lane, White Waltham, Maidenhead SL6 3RU — MB BS 1994 Lond.; BSc (Hons.) Lond. 1988, MB BS 1994.

ALDINGTON, Sarah Craigmor, Fulshaw Park, Wilmslow SK9 1QQ — BM BS 1998 Nottm.; BM BS Nottm 1998.

ALDIS, James Stuart 356 Wyld's Lane, Worcester WR5 1EF — MB BS 1979 Lond.; MRCS Eng. LRCP Lond. 1978.

ALDOURI, Elham Abid Salo Runwell Hospital, The Chase, Wickford SS11 7QE Tel: 01268 366272; 45 Silver Birch Close, London N11 3NW — MB ChB 1974 Mosul, Iraq; MRCPsych 1987; Dip. Psych. 1985; DPM 1983. (Mosul Med. Sch. Iraq) Cons. Psychiat. (Gen. Adult Psychiat.) S.end Community Care Serv. NHS Trust Runwell Hosp. Wickford, Essex. Socs: BMA; Med. Protec. Soc.; Eur. Psychiat. Assn. Prev: Hon. Sen. Regist., The Bethlem Roy. & Maudsley Hosp. Inst. of Psychiat.; Sen. Regist. Gr.lands Priory Hosp. Lond.; Regist. Bexley Hosp. Kent.

ALDOURI, Maadh Abdul Wahab Department of Haematology, Royal Free Hospital, Hampstead, London NW3 2QG Tel: 020 7794 0500 — MB ChB 1978 Baghdad; MRCPath (UK) 1988.

ALDOUS, Brian Charles Edward (retired) Severn View, David's Lane, Alveston, Bristol BS35 3LN Tel: 01454 413119 — MRCS Eng. LRCP Lond. 1942.

ALDOUS, Caroline Anne Langley Medical Practice, Oak Hill Health Centre, Oak Hill Road, Surbiton KT6 6EN — MB BS 1982 Lond.; BSc Psychol. Lond. 1979; DRCOG 1987. Prev: Trainee GP Qu. Mary's Univ. Roehampton VTS.

ALDOUS, Inez Rosemary (retired) Church Cottage, Church Lane, Hitcham, Ipswich IP7 7NN — MRCS Eng. LRCP Lond. 1954; MB Camb. 1955, BChir 1954; MFCM 1973; DPH Lond. 1964; DCH Eng. 1957.

ALDOUS, John Christopher 59 Church Road, Ashford TW15 2TU Tel: 01784 254041 — MB BS 1982 Lond.; BA Camb. 1979; DRCOG 1988; DCH RCP Lond. 1988. (Char. Cross) Trainee GP Ashford VTS. Prev: SHO (Path.) Univ. Coll. Hosp. Lond.; SHO (Paediat.) Lewisham Hosp.; SHO (Obst.) St. Helier Hosp.

ALDOUS, Margaret Desiree Elizabeth (retired) The Little House, Marine Drive, Hannafore, Looe PL13 2DH Tel: 01503 263926 — MB ChB Birm. 1948; MRCS Eng. LRCP Lond. 1948; DObst RCOG 1951. Prev: SCMO Cornw. & I. of Scilly DHA.

ALDOUS, Michael Radcliffe Fiveways Cottage, Shutford, Banbury OX15 6HA — MB BS 1958 Lond. (St. Thos.) Socs: BMA. Prev: Ho. Phys. Burton-on-Trent Gen. Hosp.; Ho. Surg. Salisbury Gen. Hosp.; Ho. Surg. O & G Odstock Hosp.

***ALDOUS, Sally** Debden Lodge, Harlow Road, Roydon, Harlow CM19 5HE — MB ChB 1998 Sheff.; MB ChB Sheff 1998.

ALDRED, Judith Elizabeth Spring Gable Surgery, Clint Bank, Birstwith, Harrogate HG3 2DW Tel: 01423 770202; 21 Gainsborough Court, Skipton BD23 1QG — BM BCh 1986 Oxf.; MRCGP 1990; DRCOG 1988. GP Harrogate Retainer Scheme. Prev: Asst. GP Birtstwith Harrogate; Trainee GP Camb. VTS.

ALDRED, Philip Robert High Street Medical Centre, 19 High Street, Staveley, Chesterfield S43 3UU Tel: 01246 472296 Fax: 01246 471665 — MB ChB 1977 Sheff.; MRCGP 1982. Prev: Trainee GP Boston Lincs. VTS.

ALDREN, Mr Christopher Philip Department of Otolaryngology, Wexham Park Hospital, Slough SL2 4HL Tel: 01753 633000 Fax: 01753 634848 — MB BS 1986 Lond.; MA Camb. 1987; FRCS (Orl.) 1995; FRCS (Orl.) Eng. 1991; FRCS Eng. 1990; CCST Otolaryngol 1997. (Camb.) Cons. Otolaryngol. & Head & Neck Surg. Socs: Brit. Assn. Otol. Head & Neck Surg.; BMA; RSM. Prev: Sen. Regist. (Otolaryngol.) Freeman Hosp. Newc.; SHO (Head & Neck Unit) Roy. Marsden Hosp. Lond.; Demonst. (Anat.) Camb. Univ.

ALDREN, John Townshend (retired) 10 Combe Rocke, West Rocke Avenue, Bristol BS9 2AN — MB ChB Ed. 1940. Prev: Ho. Surg. Edin. Roy. Infirm.

ALDRICH, Clive Jeffrey 24 Priest Hill, Caversham, Reading RG4 7RZ — BM 1988 Soton. SHO (O & G) St. Geo. Hosp. Lond.

ALDRICH, Ian David Morris and Partners, 93 Queens Drive, Bedford MK41 9JE Tel: 01234 360482 Fax: 01234 219361; 53 Falcon Avenue, Brickhill, Bedford MK41 7DY — MB BS 1974 Lond.; MRCS Eng. LRCP Lond. 1974; DFFP 1996; DRCOG 1977. (Roy. Free) Med. Off. Texas Instruments, Granada TV Rental & Binney & Smith Bedford.

ALDRIDGE, Mr Andrew James Blengdale Cottage, 10 Peakfield, Frensham, Farnham GU10 3DX — MB BS 1989 Lond.; FRCS Eng. 1994. Regist. (Gen. Surg.) SW Thames RHA.

ALDRIDGE, Christian Ronald 48 Australia Road, Cardiff CF14 3DB — MB BCh 1998 Wales.

ALDRIDGE, Christine Stella Vivienne Hope 5 Pilford Road, Leckhampton, Cheltenham GL53 9AG — MB BS 1975 Lond.

ALDRIDGE, Frances Joyce 27 Willian Way, Letchworth SG6 2HQ Tel: 01462 686196 — MB ChB 1964 St. And.; Dip. Palliat. Med. Cardiff 1993. (St. And.) Med. Off. Garden Hse. Hospice Letchworth. Socs: BMA; Christ. Med. Fell.sh. Prev: Family Plann. Assn. Med. Off. Tanzania.

ALDRIDGE, Francis Robert 923 Bristol Road, Selly Oak, Birmingham B29 6ND — MB ChB 1998 Birm.; ChB Birm. 1998.

ALDRIDGE, Graham Richard Riverside Medical Centre, Savile Road, Castleford WF10 1PH Tel: 01977 554831 Fax: 01977 603057 — MB ChB 1974 Leeds; DCH Eng. 1979. GP Castleford.

ALDRIDGE, John Frederick Lewis, OBE East House, Charlton, Chichester PO18 0HU Tel: 01243 811392 — MB BS 1951 Lond.; FRCP Lond. 1984; FRCP Ed. 1980, M 1956; FFOM RCP Lond. 1981, MFOM 1978; DIH Eng. 1963. (St. Thos.) Emerit. Civil. Cons. (Occupat. Med.) RN. Prev: Cons. Occupat. Phys. Med. & Indust. Servs. Ltd. E.bourne; Dean. Fac. Occupat. Med. RCP Lond.; Chief Med. Off. IBM UK Ltd.

ALDRIDGE, Jonathan Peter 7/3 Sienna Gardens, Edinburgh EH9 1PG — MB ChB 1997 Ed. SHO (A&E), St. John's Hosp., W. Lothian.

ALDRIDGE, Louise McCulloch 64 Polwarth Terrace, Edinburgh EH11 1NJ — MB ChB 1975 Aberd.; FFARCS 1981; DCH Eng. 1982. Cons. Paediat. Anaesth., Roy. Hsp of Sick Childr., Edin.

ALDRIDGE, Mr Malcolm Charles Queen Elizabeth II Hospital, Howlands, Welwyn Garden City AL7 4HQ Tel: 01707 328111 Fax: 01707 365127; Clunie Cottage, Ayot St Lawrence, Welwyn AL6 9BX Fax: 01438 718712 — MB BS 1977 Lond.; MS Lond. 1987; FRCS Eng. 1982; FRCS Ed. 1982; MRCS Eng. LRCP Lond. 1977. (St. Mary's) Cons. Surg. Qu. Eliz. II Hosp. Welwyn Gdn. City. E. & N. Herts. NHS Trust. Socs: Fell. Roy. Soc. Med. (Mem. Surg. Sect. & Sect. Colo-Proctol.); Pancreatic Soc.; Internat. Hepato Pancreato Biliary Assn. Prev: Sen. Regist. (Surg.) Hammersmith Hosp. Lond.; Chef de Clin. Asst. Hosp. Paul Brousse Villejuif, France; Sen. Regist. (Surg.) St. Mary's Hosp. Lond.

ALDRIDGE, Mr Michael John Coventry & Warwickshire Hospital, Stoney Stanton Road, Coventry CV1 4FH Tel: 024 76 224055 Fax: 024 76 221655; 29 Westfield Road, Rugby CV22 6AS Tel: 01788 576583 — MB ChB 1968 Birm.; BSc (Anat. Studies) Birm. 1965; FRCS Ed. 1973. Cons. Orthop. Surg. Coventry & Warks. Hosp. Socs: Fell. BOA; BMA.

ALDRIDGE, Michael Staples Little Crouches Farm, Flitterbrook Lane, Rushlake Green, Heathfield TN21 9PL Tel: 01435 830633 — MB BChir 1950 Camb.; MRCS Eng. LRCP Lond. 1942; DPM Eng. 1959. (Univ. Coll. Hosp.) Prev: Cons. Psychiat. Worthing Child Guid. Clinic; Jun. Hosp. Med. Off. (Psychiat.) Brookwood Hosp.; Psychiat. Regist. Oakwood Hosp. Maidstone.

ALDRIDGE, Nicholas Anthony 48 Barnfield, Penkhull, Stoke-on-Trent ST4 5JE — MB BS 1986 Lond.; DCH RCP Lond. 1993.

ALDRIDGE, Oliver Rupert Vincent Medical Centre, Rattray's Lane, Tomintoul, Ballindalloch AB37 9HF Tel: 01807 580219; Ballmorlich, Bridge of Avon, Tomintoul, Ballindalloch AB37 9HD Tel: 01807 580388 — MB BCh 1988 Witwatersrand; DRCOG 1994; MRCGP 1994. Assoc. GP.

ALDRIDGE, Rachel Philippa 27 Willian Way, Letchworth SG6 2HQ — MB ChB 1996 Leic.

ALDRIDGE, Richard Vincent Hope Six Acre Cottage, Scounslow Green, Uttoxeter ST14 8RE — MB BS 1974 Lond.; BSc (Hons. Anat.) Lond. 1971, MB BS 1974; MRCP (UK) 1979; DCH Eng. 1978; DRCOG 1977. (St. Thos.)

ALDRIDGE, Roger Dennis 64 Polwarth Terrace, Edinburgh EH11 1NJ — MB BS 1974 Lond.; PhD 1987; MRCP (UK) 1977; AFOM RCP Lond. 1989; DCH Eng. 1982.

ALDRIDGE, Ruth Elizabeth 17 Bates Street, Crookes, Sheffield S10 1NP — MB ChB 1989 Sheff.; MRCP (UK) 1993.

ALDRIDGE, Shirley Ann 32 Thingwall Avenue, Knotty Ash, Liverpool L14 5PD Tel: 0151 220 0411 — MB ChB 1984 Liverp.; BSc (Hons.) Liverp. 1981, MB ChB 1984; MRCP (UK) 1987. Regist. (Paediat.) P. Wales Childr. Hosp. Sydney, Aust. Prev: SHO (Paediat.) Guys Hosp Lond.; SHO (Neonatol.) Bristol Matern. Hosp.; SHO (Paediat.) Aldery Hey Childr. Hosp. Liverp.

ALDRIDGE, Stephen John Child & Family Unit, St Jame's University Hospital, Beckett St, Leeds LS9 7TF — BM BS 1981 Nottm.; BSc Bristol 1974; BMedSci Nottm. 1979, BM BS 1981; MRCPsych 1990. Cons. & Hon. Sen. Clin. Lect. (Child & Adolesc. Psychiat.) St. Jas. Univ. Hosp.

ALDRIDGE, Sylvia May 51 Steepside, Collegefields, Radbrook, Shrewsbury SY3 6DS; 50 Shelton Road, Shrewsbury SY3 8SP — MB ChB 1979 Liverp.; BSc (Hons.) (Physiol.) Liverp. 1976; MRCS Eng. LRCP Lond. 1979; MRCP (UK) 1982; FRCR 1985. Rohan Williams Medal Radiol. 1985; Cons. Radiol. Roy. Shrewsbury Hosp. Prev: Sen. Regist. Radiol. Bristol Roy. Infirm.; Regist. (Radiol.) Bristol Roy. Infirm.; SHO (Med.) BRd.green & Walton Hosps. Liverp.

ALDULAIMI, David Michael 1C Earlham Grove, London N22 5HJ — MB BS 1992 Lond.

ALDWINCKLE, Robin James 242 Muscliffe Lane, Bournemouth BH9 3NW — BM BS 1994 Nottm.

ALDWINCKLE, Timothy James 9 Scholars Walk, Gerrards Cross SL9 0EJ — MB ChB 1986 Bristol; PhD Lond. 1981, BSc (Hons.) 1977; Dip. Pharm. Med. RCP (UK) 1996. Sen. Med. Adviser, Leo Pharmaceut., P.s RisBoro., Bucks. Socs: Brit. Assn. Pharmaceut. Phys. Prev: Phys. Glaxo Research & Developm. Ltd. Stockley Pk.; Research Phys. Boots Pharmaceut. Nottm.; SHO (Paediat. Surg.) Childr. Hosp. Birm.

ALEEM, Mahmood University Hospital, Heath Park, Cardiff CF14 4XW; 58 North Lonsdale Street, Gorse Hill, Stretford, Manchester M32 0PG — MB BS 1979 Punjab; MRCOG 1988.

ALEESON, Rebecca 72 Ridgeway Road, Long Ashton, Bristol BS41 9HA — MB BCh 1992 Wales; MRCP (UK) Lond. 1995; DCH . Otago New Zealand 1997. (University of Wales College of Medicine) Socs: Med. Protec. Soc.; BMA. Prev: Regist. (Paediat.) Dunedin Pub. Hosp. New Zealand; Ho. Off. Univ. Hosp. Wales, Cardiff Roy. Infirm. & Llandough Hosp.; SHO Nottm. City Hosp.

ALEMI, Ali Akbar Frizinghall Medical Centre, 274 Keighley Road, Frizinghall, Bradford BD9 4LH Tel: 01274 495577 Fax: 01274 480703 — MD 1964 Tehran. (Tehran) GP Bradford, W. Yorks.

ALEMI, Caroline Mary Frizinghall Medical Centre, 274 Keighley Road, Bradford BD9 4LH Tel: 01274 495577 Fax: 01274 480703; 86 Prospect Walk, Windhill, Shipley BD18 2LR Tel: 01274 532999 — MB ChB 1968 Leeds; DRCOG 1971; DCH Eng. 1970. (Leeds)

ALEMI, Zholia 39 Common Road, Chandlers Ford, Southampton SO53 1HJ — MB ChB 1992 Auckland.

ALESCI, Giuseppe Department of Surgery, St Mark's Hospital, City Road, London EC1V 2PS — State Exam 1988 Messina.

ALEXANDER, Alan Crawford Adam, MBE Nethertown Surgery, Elliot Street, Dunfermline KY11 4TF Tel: 01383 623516 Fax: 01383 624254; 36 The Heathery, Golf View, Dunfermline KY11 8TS — MB ChB 1959 Ed. (Edin.) Non-Exec. Mem. Fife HB (Retd. Sept. 01). Prev: Ho. Off. Dunfermline Matern. Hosp.; Ho. Surg. Dunfermline & W. Fife Hosp.; Ho. Phys. N.. Hosp. Dunfermline.

ALEXANDER, Andreas 415 Burnley Lane, Chadderton, Oldham OL9 0BP — MB ChB 1977 Manch.

ALEXANDER, Andrew George Respiratory Unit, Royal United Hospital, Combe Park, Bath BA1 3NG — MB BS 1983 Lond.; FRCP 1999; MRCP (UK) 1988; MA Oxf. 1984, BA 1980. (Lond. Hosp.) Cons. Phys. (Respirat. & Gen. Med.) Roy. United Hosp. Bath. Prev: Sen. Regist. (Chest & Gen. Med.) Roy. Lond. Hosp. & Lond. Chest Hosp.; Clin. Research Fell. Brompton Hosp. Lond.; Regist. (Med.) Lond. Hosp. & Broomfield Hosp. Chelmsford.

ALEXANDER, Mr Angus Fraser (retired) Roselea, Elrick, Westhill AB32 6TJ Tel: 01244 743752 — MB ChB 1942 Ed.; FRCS Ed. 1948. Prev: Assoc. Chief Surg. & Med. Dir. Centr. Newfld. Health Centre Grand Falls Newfld., Canada.

ALEXANDER, Anita Mary 105 Underhill Road, London SE22 0QS — BM 1994 Soton.

ALEXANDER, Ann Mckinnon 191 Maxwell Avenue, Westerton, Bearsden, Glasgow G61 1HS Tel: 0141 942 6437 — MB ChB 1959 Glas.

ALEXANDER, Barbara Kathleen 61 Drumagrove Road, Clough, Ballymena BT44 9RZ Tel: 01266 758612; 37 Kilnford Crescent, Dundonald, Kilmarnock KA2 9DN — MB ChB 1990 Aberd.; MRCGP 1995; DCH RCPS Glas. 1993.

ALEXANDER, Betty (retired) 5 Westernmoor Road, Neath SA11 1BJ — MB BCh 1952 Wales; BSc Wales 1949, MB BCh 1952.

ALEXANDER, Carole Anne 2 Virginia Gardens, Milngavie, Glasgow G62 6LG — MB ChB 1977 Glas.; FRCR 1983; DMRD 1981. Cons. (Radiol.) Roy. Alexandra Infirm. Paisley.

ALEXANDER, Catherine Maria Nightingale Practice, 10 Kenninghall Road, Clapton, London E5 8BY Tel: 020 8985 8388 Fax: 020 8986 6004 — MB BS 1990 Lond.; BSc (Hons.) Lond. 1987; MRCGP 1995; DFFP 1995; DCCH RCP Ed. 1993. (St. Bart. Hosp. Med. Coll. Lond.) Prev: Asst. GP Lond.

ALEXANDER, Catriona Claire Ground Floor Flat, 32 Stuart St., Leicester LE3 0DU — MB ChB 1997 Leic.

ALEXANDER, Claire Isobel Glasgow Royal Maternity Hospital, Rottenrow, Glasgow G4 0NA Tel: 0141 211 5400; 34 Polwarth Street (2/2), Hyndland, Glasgow G12 9ST — MB ChB 1990 Glas.; MRCOG 1996. (Univ. Glas.) Specialist Regist. (O & G) Glas. Roy. Matern.. Hosp. Glas.

ALEXANDER, Clare Department of Allergy and Clinical Immunology, National Heart and Lung Institute, Dovehouse Street, London SW3 6LY Email: c.alexander@ic.ac.uk — MB BS 1992 Lond.; BSc (Hons.) Lond. 1989; MRCP (UK) 1994. (King's Coll. Hosp. Lond.) Clin. Research Fell. Roy. Brompton Hosp. Socs: BMA; RCP. Prev: SWT SpR Rotat.

ALEXANDER, Colin Arthur Haskards, St Thomas St., Winchelsea TN36 4EB Tel: 01797 226423 — MB BS 1966 Lond.; MRCS Eng. LRCP Lond. 1966; FFA RCS Eng. 1973; DA Eng. 1971. (Roy. Free) Cons. Anaesth. Hastings Health Dist.; Adviser in Anaesth., The Horder Centre, CrowBoro., E. Sussex.

ALEXANDER, Colin Menzies The Menston & Guisley Practice, Kirklands, 119 Main St., Menston, Ilkley LS29 6HT Tel: 01943 872113 Fax: 01943 878294 — MB ChB 1971 Birm. Prev: Med. Supt. Bonda Miss. Hosp. Zimbabwe.

ALEXANDER, Colleen Alston Stone Croft, The Nook, Bitteswell, Lutterworth LE17 4RY — MB ChB 1987 Stellenbosch.

ALEXANDER, Damon James 33 Montrose Avenue, Twickenham TW2 6HE — MB BS 1996 Lond.

ALEXANDER, David Nethertown Surgery, Elliot Street, Dunfermline KY11 4TF Tel: 01383 623516 Fax: 01383 624254 — MB ChB 1974 Ed.; MRCGP 1978.

ALEXANDER, Mr David John 8 Alstone Road, Heaton Chapel, Stockport SK4 5AH — MB BS 1983 Lond.; FRCS Eng. 1987.

ALEXANDER, David Morgan (retired) 3 Highfield Close, Kenilworth CV8 1QR Tel: 01926 858877 Fax: 01926 858877 — MB ChB 1952 St. And.; FRCR 1975; FFR 1963; DMRD Eng. 1958. Prev: Cons. Radiol. Coventry & N. Warks. DHA.

ALEXANDER, Denis I'Anson (retired) 8 Parkwood, Elmley Castle, Pershore WR10 3HT Tel: 01386 710566 — MA, BM BCh Oxf. 1952. Prev: G.P.

ALEXANDER, Dolores Frances (retired) 8 Parkwood, Elmley Castle, Pershore WR10 3HT Tel: 01386 710566 — MB ChB Aberd. 1950. Prev: G.P.

ALEXANDER, Eliza May 12 Lily Avenue, Jesmond, Newcastle upon Tyne NE2 2SQ Tel: 0191 281 2539; 80A Stockwell Park Road, London SW9 0BX Tel: 020 7274 3040 Email: e.alexander@ucl.ac.uk — MB BS 1991 Lond.; MRCP (UK) 1995. Clin. Research Fell. (Molec. Path.) UCL Lond. Prev: Regist. (Paediat.) Kent & Canterbury Hosp.; SHO (Paediat.) Guy's Hosp. Lond.; SHO (Neonat.) Roy. Sussex Co. Hosp. Brighton.

ALEXANDER, Elizabeth Anne (retired) 3 Highfield Close, Kenilworth CV8 1QR Tel: 01926 858877 Fax: 01926 858877 — MB ChB 1955 Liverp. Med. Off. DSS. Prev: Med. Off. DSS.

ALEXANDER, Eric Richardson 14 Woodend Place, Aberdeen AB15 6AL Tel: 01224 37465 — MD 1973 Aberd.; MB ChB 1957;

MRCPsych 1972; DPM Eng. 1970. (Aberd.) Cons. Psychiat. Grampian Health Bd.

ALEXANDER, Erica June Blackpark Farm, Westhill, Inverness IV2 5BP — MB ChB 1995 Glas.

ALEXANDER, Fiona Mary Victoria Medical Centre, Victoria Medical Centre, 7-11 Longmoore Street, London SW1V 1JH Tel: 020 7821 1531 Fax: 020 7233 5995 — MB BS 1985 Lond.; DFFP 1999; MRCGP 1995; DCH RCP Lond. 1994; DRCOG 1993. ((St. Mary's)) GP Princip. Lond.

ALEXANDER, Francis George (retired) 157 Viceroy Close, Bristol Road, Birmingham B5 7UX Tel: 0121 440 3452 — MB ChB Ed. 1941.

ALEXANDER, Fraser William 16 Beverley Gardens, North Shields NE30 4NS Tel: 01207 549954 — MB BChir Camb.; 1978 MD Camb.; 1968 FRCP Lond. 1981, M; 1988 FRCP Ed.; 1965 DCH Eng.; 1996 FRCPCH. (St. Thos.) Cons. Paediat. & Hon. Lect. Newc. Univ. Hosps.; Postgrad. Clin. Tutor Newc. Gen. Hosp.; Paediat. Adviser N. Region RCP Lond.; Regional Special Adviser in Paediat.; CALMAN Program Director. Socs: Brit. Paediat. Assn. Prev: Sen. Regist. & Research Fell. Inst. Child Health & Hosp. Sick Childr. Gt. Ormond St. Lond.; Regist. (Med.) Salisbury Gen. Hosp.; SHO (Paediat.) St. Peter's Hosp.

ALEXANDER, Gilbertha Angela c/o Department of Obstetrics & Gynaecology, Mayday Hospital, Mayday Road, Thornton Heath CR7 7YE — MB BS 1983 W. Indies.

ALEXANDER, Gillian Susan Kingsway Surgery, 655 Kingsway, Burnage, Manchester M19 1RD Tel: 0161 432 2725 Fax: 0161 947 9192; Mill Cottage, Old Mill Lane, Hazel Grove, Stockport SK7 6DP Tel: 01625 859897 — MB ChB 1976 Manch. Hosp. Specialist Gastroenterol., S. Manch. Univ. Hosp.s Trust. Prev: Tutor (Child Health) Univ. Manch.

ALEXANDER, Graeme James Mackay Department of Medicine, Addenbrooke's Hospital, Hills Road, Cambridge CB2 2QQ Tel: 01223 217456 Fax: 01223 242474 — MB ChB 1976 Bristol; MRCP (UK) 1979. Cons. Hepatol. Addenbrooke's Hosp. Camb.

ALEXANDER, Graham Newton Port Surgery, Newton Port, Haddington EH41 3NF Tel: 01620 825497 Fax: 01620 824622 — MB ChB 1977 Ed.; MRCGP 1981; DRCOG 1980.

ALEXANDER, Hanh Phuoc Minh National Westminster Bank PLC, 26 Spring St., London W2 1JA — MB BS 1989 Lond.

ALEXANDER, Helen Ceinwen Bowley Farm, Sandway, Maidstone ME17 2BG Tel: 01622 858348 — MB ChB 1996 Bristol.

ALEXANDER, Helen Mary Brannam Medical Centre, Kiln Lane, Barnstaple EX32 8GP Tel: 01271 329004; The Old Chapel, Alswear, South Molton EX36 4LH Tel: 01769 550625 — MB BChir 1988 Camb.; MA Camb. 1988; MRCP (UK) 1991; MRCGP 1995. GP Retainer Barnstaple. Prev: Trainee GP Barnstaple; SHO (Histopath.) S.mead Hosp. Bristol.

ALEXANDER, Ian Department of Genitourinary Medicine, Derriford Hospital, Plymouth EX2; Department of Genitourinary Medicine, Royal Devon & Exeter Hospital, Barrack Road, Exeter EX2 — MRCS Eng. LRCP Lond. 1971; BSc Lond. 1968, MB BS 1971; FRCOG 1994, M 1978; T(OG) 1991; Dip. Venereol. 1985; DObst 1973. Cons. Genitourin. Med. Plymouth Hosp. NHS Trust & Roy. Devon & Exeter Hosp. NHS Trust. Prev: Cons. Genitourin. Med. Tayside HB & Hon. Sen. Lect. Dundee Univ.; Sen. Regist. (Genitourin. Med.) Bristol Roy. Infirm.; Sen. Regist. (O & G) RAMC.

ALEXANDER, Isobel Anne Craig (retired) 19 Great Stuart Street, Edinburgh EH3 7TP — MB ChB 1954 Ed.; DPH Ed. 1962; DObst RCOG 1958. Prev: GP Univ. Edin. Health Serv.

ALEXANDER, Isobel Bisset (retired) 23 Queen's Close, Lancaster Road, Harrogate HG2 0HG Tel: 01423 560915 — MB ChB 1949 Aberd.; MFCM 1972; DPH Leeds 1965. Prev: SCMO Harrogate HA.

ALEXANDER, James Leonard Stewart (retired) 42 Silverdale Road, Ecclesall, Sheffield S11 9JL Tel: 0114 368889 — MB ChB 1959 Ed.; FRCR 1974; DMRD Eng. 1972; DObst RCOG 1961. Prev: Cons., Diagnostic Radiol., Rotherham Dist. Gen. Hosp.s.

ALEXANDER, John Bennett 11 Damgate Street, Wymondham NR18 0BG Tel: 01953 606235 — LMSSA 1937 Lond.; MA Camb. 1941. (Camb. & Westm.) Prev: Chief Med. Off. MacRobt. Hosp. Dhariwal, Punjab.

ALEXANDER, John Gordon Uvedale Okeden (retired) Appledene, 6 Nunburnholme Avenue, North Ferriby HU14 3AN Tel: 01482 632184 Fax: 01482 632184 — MB BS 1948 Lond.; MRCS Eng. LRCP Lond. 1942; DPath. Eng. 1951; FRCPath 1964. Prev: Cons. Bacteriol. Hull & E. Yorks. Health Auth. Hosps.

ALEXANDER, John Innis Sir Humphry Davy Department of Anaesthesia, Bristol Royal Infirmary, Bristol BS2 8HW Tel: 0117 923 0000 Fax: 0117 928 4964 Email: john.alexander@ubht.swest.nhs.uk; 278 Church Road, Frampton Cotterell, Bristol BS36 2BH Tel: 01454 778260 Fax: 01454 778260 — MB BS 1965 Lond.; MRCS Eng. LRCP Lond. 1965; FRCA 1969; DObst RCOG 1967. (Univ. Coll. Hosp.) Cons. Anaesth. & Pain Managem. United Bristol Healthcare (NHS) Trust; Clin. Sen. Lect. Univ. Bristol. Socs: Anaesth. Res. Soc.; Assn. Anaesths.; Internat. Assn. Study of Pain. Prev: Sen. Regist. (Anaesth.) United Bristol Hosps.; Research Fell. (Anaesth.) Univ. Glas.; Regist. (Anaesth.) Roy. Free Hosp. Lond.

ALEXANDER, John Lindsay Rental Unit, Link6C, Royal Liverpool University, Liverpool l7; 52 Nightingale Road, Liverpool L12 0QN Tel: 0151 706 2000 — MB ChB 1993 Glas.; BSc (Hons) Glasgow 1990; MRCP (UK) 1996. SR in Nephrol., RLU Hosp NHS Trust, Liverp.

ALEXANDER, John Milne Taylor (retired) Daleside, Willow Lane, Clifford, Wetherby LS23 6JN Tel: 01937 842121 — MB ChB 1965 Ed.; MRCP (UK) 1972; FRCP 1990; DCH Eng. 1969; FRCPCH 1997. Prev: Cons. Paediat. Pontefract Gen. Infirm.

ALEXANDER, John O'Donel (retired) Redcliffe, 13 Keir St., Bridge of Allan, Stirling FK9 4AY — MB ChB 1938 Birm.; FRCP Glas. 1968, M 1962; FRFPS Glas. 1950. Prev: Cons. Dermat. Glas. Roy. Infirm.

ALEXANDER, John Pentland (retired) 18 Cranmore Avenue, Belfast BT9 6JH — MB BCh BAO 1954 Belf.; FRCPI 1977, M 1957; FFA RCSI 1962; FFA Eng. 1960; DA RCPSI 1957. Cons. Anaesth. Belf. City Hosp.

ALEXANDER, Joyce Oliver The Manse, Newton Road, Bishopton PA7 5J Tel: 01505 862161 — MB ChB 1958 Glas. Assoc. Specialist (Haemat.) CrossHo. Hosp. Ayrsh.

ALEXANDER, Julia Mary Chapeloak Practice, 347 Oakwood Lane, Leeds LS8 3HA Tel: 0113 240 9999 Fax: 0113 235 9233 — MB BS 1983 Lond.; MRCGP 1987.

ALEXANDER, Julie Helston, Radford Lane, Lower Penn, Wolverhampton WV3 8JT — MB BCh 1988 Wales.

ALEXANDER, Katharine Laura Pinderfields & Pontefract NHS Trust, Pontefract General Infirmary, Friarwood Lane, Pontefract WF8 1PL — MB BChir 1983 Camb.; MA Oxf. 1987, BA 1981; DRCOG 1988. (Addenbrookes) p/t GP Twyford Retainer Scheme. Prev: GP Twyford.

ALEXANDER, Kevin 62 Cotswold Avenue, Chester-le-Street DH2 3BP — MB ChB 1976 Sheff.; DRCOG 1979.

ALEXANDER, Kirsteen Mary Mackenzie 32 Ravenswood Road, Redland, Bristol BS6 6BW — MB ChB 1996 Bristol.

ALEXANDER, Loraine Leslie (retired) Crooked Rigg, Whittinghame, Haddington EH41 4QA Tel: 01368 850234 — MB BS Lond. 1945; DMRT Eng. 1948. Prev: MRC Scientif. Off. Clin. & Populat. Cytogenetics Unit W.. Gen. Hosp.Edin.

ALEXANDER, Malcolm The Surgery, John St., Stromness KW16 3AD Tel: 01856 850205 — MB ChB 1980 Ed.

ALEXANDER, Malikayil Skaria Department of Psychiatry, St James University Hospital, Leeds LS9 7TF Tel: 0113 206 5802 Fax: 0113 206 5803 Email: alex4121@aol.com; 21 Dunstarn Drive, Leeds LS16 8EH Tel: 0113 267 4121 Fax: 0113 225 9599 — MB BS 1972 Kerala; MRCPsych 1975; DPM Eng. 1974. Hon. Sen. Clin. Lect. (Psychiat.) Univ. Leeds; Cons. Psych. St James Univ.Hosp. Socs: BMA; Expert Witness Inst. Prev: Sen. Regist. (Psychiat.) Wessex Train. Scheme.

ALEXANDER, Mark Salkeld McClintock X-Ray Department, Luton & Dunstable Hospital NHS Trust, Dunstable Road, Luton LU4 0DZ — MB BS 1980 Lond.; FRCS 1988; MA 1977 Oxf.; MA Oxf. 1977; FRCR 1988. Cons. Radiol. & Clin. Dir. of Imaging Luton & Dunstable Hosp. NHS Trust. Prev: Hon. Cons. & Sen. Regist. (Diag. Radiol.) Hammersmith & Qu. Charlottes Hosp. Lond.; Admitting Med. Off. Middlx. Hosp. Lond.; Resid. Med. Off. (Cardiac Surg.) Nat. Heart Hosp. Lond.

ALEXANDER, Mathew Changatharayil Parkgate Medical Centre, Netherfield Lane, Parkgate, Rotherham S62 6AW Tel: 01709 514500 Fax: 01709 514490 — MB BS 1971 Kerala.

ALEXANDER, Matthew Kenyon (retired) 27 Banbury Road, Stratford-upon-Avon CV37 7HN Tel: 01789 292562 — MB ChB 1944 Liverp.; FRCP Lond. 1975, M 1954; DPath Eng. 1951; FRCPath 1967, M 1963. Prev: Path. S. Warks. HA.

ALEXANDER, Murdo James Clarence House, 14 Russell Road, Rhyl LL18 3BY Tel: 01745 350680 Fax: 01745 353293 — MB ChB 1982 Dundee.

ALEXANDER, Nabih Highbury Grange Health Centre, Highbury Grange, London N5 2QB Tel: 020 7226 9966; 120 Powys Lane, Palmers Green, London N13 4HR — MB BCh 1954 Cairo; LAH Dub. 1960; MRCS Eng. LRCP Lond. 1965. (Cairo & Dub.) Hon. Clin. Asst. Dept. Surg. St. Chas. Hosp. Lond. Prev: Surg. Regist. Lond. Chest Hosp.; Sen. Surg. Regist. St. Luke's Hosp. Dub.; Thoracic Surg. Regist. Regional Thoracic Centre S. W. RHB.

ALEXANDER, Nicholas Calder Stones, Westella Road, Westella, Hull HU10 7SD Tel: 01482 632207 Fax: 01482 632207 — MB BS 1966 Kerala; FRCGP 1994, M 1974; Dip. Pract. Dermat. Wales 1990; Dip. Ven. Liverp. 1974. (Kerala Trivandrum, India) Regist. (Chest Med., Endocrinol. & Gen. Med.) Hull; Trainer Humberside VTS; Tutor Undergrad. Leeds Med. Sch. Socs: Fell. Hull Med. Soc.; BMA; MMA Pres., Vice-Pres. & Sec.

ALEXANDER, Pamela June Appledene, 6 Nunburnholme Avenue, North Ferriby HU14 3AN Tel: 01482 632184 Fax: 01482 632154 — MB ChB 1947 Liverp. Socs: Hull Med. Soc. Prev: Geo. Holt Fell. Physiol. Univ. Liverp.

ALEXANDER, Peter David 60A Cornwall Gardens, London SW7 4BE — MB ChB 1989 Cape Town.

ALEXANDER, Pothen 218 Ifield Drive, Ifield, Crawley RH11 0EP; Old Court, Rusper Road, Ifield, Crawley RH11 0LN Tel: 01293 28422 Email: palexander@workmail.com — MB BS 1974 Mysore; DFFP 1996; MRCGP 1981; DCH RCPSI 1978; DRCOG 1978. GP Trainer; Tutor Dept. Gen. Pract. St. Geo. Med. Sch. Lond.; Occupat.al Health Phys.

ALEXANDER, Rachel Kanjirathara 18 Newbold Way, Nantwich CW5 7AX — MB ChB 1998 Bristol.

ALEXANDER, Rebecca Child Development Centre, Town Barn Road, West Green, Crawley RH11 7EL Tel: 01293 615050 Fax: 01293 538695; Old Court, Rusper Road, Ifield, Crawley RH11 0LN Tel: 01293 528422 — MB BS 1973 Kerala; DCH Madras 1976. (Kottayam Medical College Kerala, India) Assoc. Specialist (Community Child Health) Surrey & Sussex Health Care. Socs: BACCH; MRCPCH; Fell. Roy. Inst. Pub. Health and Hyg.

ALEXANDER, Richard Finlay (retired) 3 Tenniel Close, London W2 3LE — MB BS 1943 Lond.; MD Lond. 1962; FRCPath 1975, M 1963. Prev: Cons. Path. Newham Health Dist.

ALEXANDER, Richard Ian (retired) Little Firs, Jiggs Lane South, Bracknell RG42 3DP Tel: 01344 483608 — MB ChB 1951 Glas. Prev: Ho. Phys. & Ho. Surg. Vict. Infirm. Glas.

ALEXANDER, Robert Gray Cornhill Surgery, Kincaidston, Ayr KA7 3YF Tel: 01292 264080 Fax: 01292 269731 — MB ChB 1962 Glas.

ALEXANDER, Mr Ronald James Thomas 117 Moss Side Road, Glasgow G41 3UP — MB ChB 1987 Manch.; FRCS Ed. 1992.

ALEXANDER, Rosemary Elaine Edgeware Community Hospital, Edgware HA8 0AD Tel: 020 8952 2318; 5 Dehar Crescent, West Hendon, London NW9 7BD — MB ChB 1974 Liverp.; MRCP (UK) 1980; Dip. Acupunc. WHO 1983 (Hosp. Pract.). Clin. Asst. (Rheum.) Rheum. & Acupunc. Clinic Edgware & Barnet Gen. Hosp. Socs: Brit. Holistic Med. Assn.; Brit. Med. Acupunc. Assn. (Regional Represen.). Prev: Regist. (Gen. Med. & Geriat.) Lond. Hosp.; Regist. (Rheum.) King's Coll. Hosp. Lond.; Ho. Off. Profess. Med. Unit. Leeds Gen. Infirm.

ALEXANDER, Sebastian John Campbell 14 Home End, Fulbourn, Cambridge CB1 5BS; 14 Home End, Fulbourn, Cambridge CB1 5BE — MB ChB 1982 Birm.; MRCGP 1988; DRCOG 1985.

ALEXANDER, Shanet Anne Eisner, Goldman and Ship, Shipley Health Centre, Alexandra Road, Shipley BD18 3EG Tel: 01274 589160; 84 Bachelor Lane, Horsforth, Leeds LS18 5NF — MB ChB 1985 Leeds; DCH RCP Lond. 1990.

ALEXANDER, Shirley Marie St Mary's Hospital, Paddington, London W2 1BL Tel: 0207 886 6666; Moorfield, Sheild Hill, Haltwhistle NE49 9NN — MB ChB 1987 Ed.; MRCP (UK) 1992; DCH RCP Lond. 1990. (Univ. Ed.) p/t Locum Cons. PICU, St Mary's Hosp., Paddington, Lond. Socs: Mem. of BMA; Mem. of PICS.

ALEXANDER, Susan 43 Winslow Road, London W6 9SF — MB BS 1996 Lond.

ALEXANDER, Suzanne Liselotte 3 Tenniel Close, London W2 3LE Tel: 020 7229 0926 — MB BS 1950 Lond.; MRCS Eng. LRCP Lond. 1949. (W. Lond.) Emerit. Cons. St. Marks Hosp. Lond. Socs: Brit. Assn. Dermat. Prev: Cons. Dermat. NE Thames RHA; Hon. Cons. St. Marks Hosp. Lond.; Hon. Cons. Guy's Hosp. Lond.

ALEXANDER, Timothy John David The Health Centre, Leypark Walk, Estover, Plymouth PL6 8UE Tel: 01752 776772 Fax: 01752 785108 — MB ChB 1987 Bristol; BSc Bristol 1984; MRCGP 1995; DFFP 1994; DRCOG 1991; DCH RCP Glas. 1989. (Bristol) Prev: Trainee GP Bere Alston Devon; Sen. Med. Off. Manguzi Hosp. Kwazulu, S. Afr.; SHO (O & G) Bristol Matern. & Gen. Hosp.

ALEXANDER, Victoria Alice Lilian Priory Farmhouse, Gauldry, Newport-on-Tay DD6 8RU Tel: 01382 330579 — MB ChB 1983 Aberd.; MRCP (UK) 1989. Assoc. Specialist (Paediat.) Ninewells Hosp. Dundee. Prev: Regist. (Paediat.) Roy. Aberd. Childr. Hosp.; Staff Grade (Paediat.) Ninewells Hosp. Dundee; SHO (Neonat. Med.) St. Mary's Hosp. Manch.

ALEXANDER, Mr W. Leslie Rettendon Place, Church Chase, Rettendon Common, Chelmsford CM3 8DR Tel: 01702 221271 Fax: 01702 221279; Rettendon Place, Church Chase, Rettendon Common, Chelmsford CM3 8DR Tel: 01268 573372 Fax: 01268 764479 — MB ChB 1974 Aberd.; FRCS Eng. 1982; FRCOphth. 1988; DA Eng. 1977. (Univ. Aberd.) Cons. Ophth. Surg. NE Thames RHA; Cons. Ophth. Surg., Bupa Wellesley Hosp., S.end on Sea. Socs: Fell. Roy. Soc. Med. (ex Mem. Counc. Ophth. Sect.); BMA. Prev: Sen. Regist. Moorfields Eye Hosp. & Roy. Lond. Hosp. Whitechapel; Regist. (Ophth.) W.m. Hosp. Lond.; SHO (Ophth.) Aberd. Roy. Infirm.

ALEXANDER, William Bryce (retired) Playden, Walpole Avenue, Chipstead, Coulsdon CR5 3PQ — MB BChir 1942 Camb.; MRCS Eng. LRCP Lond. 1942; MRCP Lond. 1947. Prev: Ho. Phys. & Regist. (Neurol.) Middlx. Hosp.

ALEXANDER, William David 31A Heriot Row, Edinburgh EH3 6ES — MB BS 1968 Lond.; FRCP Lond. 1989; MRCP (UK) 1972; FRCP (Ed.) 1999. (St. Thos.) Cons. Phys. (Diabetes) W.ern Gen. Hosp. Edin. Prev: Cons. Phys. (Diabetes) Qu. Mary's Hosp. Sidcup; Sen. Regist. (Med.) Univ. Hosp. Wales Cardiff; Regist. (Med.) St. Mary's Hosp. Portsmouth & Bristol Roy. Infirm.

ALEXANDER, William Donald Carsaig, Mount Pleasant Drive, Old Kilpatrick, Glasgow G60 5HJ Tel: 01389 73140 — MB ChB 1951 Glas.; MD (Hons.) Glas. 1964; FRCP Ed. 1966, M 1959; FRFPS Glas. 1959; FRCP Glas. 1966, M 1962. (Glas.) Consulatant Med. Office, Abbey Nat. Life plc, Abbey Nat. Hse, 301 St. Vincent St,, Glas., G2 5HN. Socs: Endocrine Soc. & Scott. Soc. Experim. Med. Prev: Reader (Med.) Univ. Glas.; US Pub. Health Serv. Post Doctoral Fell. N.I.H. Bethesda, MD.; Vis. Prof. Med. Harvard Univ. Camb. Mass. & New Eng. Med. Center Boston, USA.

ALEXANDER, Zoe Staff and Partners, Queensway Medical Centre, Olympic Way, Wellingborough NN8 3EP Tel: 01933 678767 Fax: 01933 676657; 18 Park Close, Sywell, Northampton NN6 0AX — BM BS 1985 Nottm.; BMedSci Nottm. 1983; MRCGP 1990; Cert. Family Plann. JCC 1989; DA (UK) 1988. (Nottm.) GP WellingBoro. Prev: SHO (Anaesth.) Kettering HA; SHO (Paediat.) Bedford HA; SHO (O & G) Huntingdon HA.

ALEXANDER-SEFRE, Farhad Flat 9, Somerset Court, 136-138 Queens Road, Buckhurst Hill IG9 5AT — MB ChB 1992 Leeds.

ALEXANDER-WHITE, Sian The Westmoreland GP Centre, Fazakerley Hospital, Aintree, Liverpool L9 7AL Tel: 0151 525 6286 — MB ChB 1979 Liverp.

ALEXANDER-WILLIAMS, Jeremy Mark Leicester Royal Infirmary, Infirmary Square, Leicester LE1 5WW; 25 North Avenue, Leicester LE2 1TL — MB BS 1987 Lond.; FRCA 1994. Sen. Regist. (Anaesth.) Leicester Roy. Infirm. Socs: Anaesth. Res. Soc.; MRCAnaesth.; Assn. Anaesth. Prev: Regist. Roy. Lond. Hosp.

ALEXANDER-WILLIAMS, Professor John (retired) 5 Farquhar Road E., Edgbaston, Birmingham B15 3RD Tel: 0121 454 1279 Fax: 0121 454 1279 — MRCS Eng. LRCP Lond. 1950; MD Birm. 1969, ChM 1961, MB ChB (Hons.) 1950; FRCS Eng. 1955; FACS 1975. Prev: Prof. Gastrointestinal Gen. Hosp. Birm.

ALEXANDROU, Dionisios Flat 4, 39 Gunterstone Road, London W14 9BS — Ptychio Iatrikes 1985 Athens.

ALEXANDROU, Kyriacos Andreou Flat 4, 21 Peel Moat Road, Heaton Moor, Stockport SK4 4PL — MB ChB 1992 Manch.; FRCS 1996 Ed. Research Fell. (Urol.) Stepping Hill Hosp. Stockport.

ALEXOPOULOU, Alexandra Department of Medicine (10th Floor), St Mary's Hospital, London W2 1PG — Ptychio Iatrikes 1985 Athens.

ALEY, Mark Christopher Millers Dale Surgery, 9 Ormesby Drive, Chandlers Ford, Eastleigh SO53 1SH — MB ChB 1982 Leeds; DRCOG 1986.

ALFAHAM, Mazin Department Child Health, Llandough Hospital & Community NHS Trust, Penlan Road, Penarth CF64 2XX Tel: 01222 715308 Fax: 01222 708064; 14 Alltmawr Road, Cyncocd, Cardiff CF23 6NQ Tel: 01222 758482 Email: mazin.alfaham@lhct_tr.wales.nhs.uk — MB ChB 1974 Baghdad; MD Wales 1996; MRCP Lond. 1983; FRCP Lond. 1995; FRCPCH Lond. 1997. (College of Medicine, University of Baghdad) Cons. Paediat. Dept. Child Health Llandough Hosp. Penarth. Socs: BMA; Brit. Paediatric Respirat. Soc.; Brit. Soc. of Allergy & Clin. Immunol. Prev: Lect. (Child Health) Univ. Wales.

ALFAKIH, Khaled Mohamed Ali South Tyneside District Hospital, Harton Lane, South Shields NE34 0PL — MB BS 1993 Lond.

ALFARO ADRIAN, Jesus Worcester College, Oxford OX1 2HB; Flat 7, Girdlestone Close, Headington, Oxford OX3 7NS — LMS 1990 Navarve.

ALFARO GARCIA, Gonzalo Maria Anaesthetics Department, Nevill Hall Hospital, Abergavenny NP7 7EG — LMS 1993 Navarre.

ALFONSI, Vincent Paul 2 Churchward Close, Eversley Park, Chester CH2 2BG — MB ChB 1987 Manch.; MRCP (UK) 1992.

ALFONZO-NGWENYA, Annette Verna Marie Top Floor Flat, 20 Manor Race, Edinburgh EH3 7DS Tel: 0131 226 6255 — MB ChB 1993 Ed.; MRCP (UK) 1997. (University of Edinburgh) SHO III (Renal Unit) W.ern Infirm. Glas. Socs: Roy. Coll. Phys. Ed.; Scot. Renal Assn. Prev: Med. Falkirk Roy. Infirm.; Geriat. Med. City Hosp.; Med. Roy. Infirm. of Edin.

ALFORD, Antony Mark 22 Walton Road, Sheffield S11 8RE — MB ChB 1982 Bristol; FCAnaesth. 1989. Regist. (Anaesth.) Sheff. Area Hosps.

ALFORD, Gail 7 Crosscombe Terrace, Cwm, Ebbw Vale NP23 7SP — MB BCh 1981 Wales.

ALFORD, Paul Frederick 918 Garratt Lane, London SW17 0ND — MB BS 1992 Lond.

ALGAWI, Mr Kais Diab Mohammed 16 Rhodfar Grug, Colwyn Bay LL29 6DJ — MB ChB 1981 Baghdad, Iraq; FRCS Ed. 1992.

ALGIE, Thomas Alexander 9 Milverton Avenue, Bearsden, Glasgow G61 4BE — MB ChB 1978 Glas.; FFA RCS Eng. 1982.

ALGUERO, Luis Woodside Health Centre, Barr Street, Glasgow G20 7LR Tel: 0141 531 9585 Fax: 0141 531 9339 — LMS 1983 Oviedo; T(GP) 1994. (Oviedo, Spain) Prev: SHO (A & E) Perth Roy. Infirm.; SHO (Paediat., O & G & Orthop.) Perth Roy. Infirm.; SHO (Med.) Arbroath Infirm.

ALHADEFF, Benjamin Dundrum, Cotmaton Road, Sidmouth EX10 8ST — MB BS 1943 Lond.; MRCS Eng. LRCP Lond. 1940. (Guy's) Socs: BMA. Prev: Flight Lt. RAFVR.

ALHADI, Ban Ziad Raouf 11 Henley Drive, Coombe Hill, Kingston upon Thames KT2 7EB — Artsexamen 1992 Leiden.

ALHADI, Hafidh Aqeel Ahmed 29 Buckstone Court, Edinburgh EH10 6UL — MB ChB 1992 Dundee.

ALHASSAN, Salah El-Din Abdalla Kent and Canterbury Hospital, Ethelbert Road, Canterbury CT1 3NG — MB BCh 1983 Cairo. SCMO (Haemat.) Kent & Canterbury Hosp. Prev: Staff Grade Doctor (Haemat.) Bromley Hosps. NHS Trust; Regist. (Haemat.) Barnsley & Glas.; SHO (Haemat.) Portsmouth.

ALHEJAZI, Mr Muhammad Basim Rajab Hamzeh 121 Harley Street, London W1N 1DH Tel: 020 7224 4088 Fax: 020 7935 6655; 55 Vyner Road, London W3 7LZ Tel: 020 8932 7380 — MB BS 1975 Karachi; FRCS Ed. 1982. (Dow Med. Coll.) Indep. Cons. Surgic. Harley St. Lond.; Cons., Gen. and brE. Surg. at Newham G.H., Lond. Socs: Med. Soc. Lond.; Brit. Assn. Surg. Oncol.; Brit. Oncol. Assn. Prev: Surg. Research Fell. St. Geo.'s Hosp. Lond.; Sen. Regist. (Gen. Surg.) Roy. Marsden Hosp.; Regist. (Gen. Surg. & Urol.) Fife HB.

ALI, Abad Zuckerman, Felderhof and Ali, Northfield Health Centre, 15 St Heliers Road, Northfield, Birmingham B31 1QU Tel: 0121 478 0220 Fax: 0121 476 0931 — MB BS 1990 Newc.; MRCGP 1998; DCH RCPS Glas. 1994; DRCOG 1993. (Newc. u. Tyne) GP N.field Birm. Prev: GP Regist. Warley; SHO Gladstone Hosp. Qu.sland, Austral.; SHO (A & E) Sandwell Hosp.

ALI, Abdelgalil Abdelrahman Department of Nephrology & Renal Transplantation, The Royal Free Hospital, Pond Street, Hampstead, London NW3 2QG Tel: 020 7794 0500 Fax: 020 7431 3189; 26 Alder Grove, London NW2 7DB — MB BS 1976 Khartoum; MRCPI 1986. Research Fell. (Nephrol. & Transpl.) Roy. Free Hosp. Lond.

ALI, Abdelmoniem Abdelbagi Dept of Psychiatry, Leazes Wing, Royal Victoria Infirmary, Richardson Rd, Newcastle upon Tyne NE1 4LP Tel: 0191 282 5706 Fax: 0191 227 5281 — MB BCh 1980 Ain Shams; MRCPsych 1991; DPM RCPSI 1990; DCAP 1993; BCPsych 1991; CET-CBT 1997. Cons. in acute adult Psychiat.; Hon. Lect., Newc. Univ. Med. Coll. Socs: BMA; RCPsych.

ALI, Abdul Khier M Seymour Grove Health Centre, 70 Seymour Grove, Old Trafford, Manchester M16 0LW Tel: 01612 877 9230 Fax: 0161 848 0478 — MB BS 1961 Dacca.

ALI, Mr Ahmed Said Mohamed Darlington Memorial Hospital, Hollyhurst Road, Darlington DL3 6HX Tel: 01325 380100 Fax: 01325 743518; 20 St. Roberts Road, Knaresborough HG5 8EQ Tel: 01423 863152 — MB BCh 1976 Cairo; MRCOG 1991. Cons. O & G Darlington Memor. Hosp. Prev: Staff Grade (O & G) St. James' Univ. Hosp. Leeds; Regist. (O & G) Airdale Gen. Hosp. & Jersey Gen. Hosp.

ALI, Akhtar Hoylake Road Surgery, 314 Hoylake Road, Wirral CH46 6DE Tel: 0151 677 2425 Fax: 0151 604 0482 — MB BS 1977 Punjab; LMSSA Lond. 1987; DLO RCS Eng. 1983.

ALI, Mr Amjad 25 Glendhu Manor, Garnerville Road, Belfast BT4 2RJ — MB BS 1981 Peshawar; FRCSI 1995.

ALI, Amjed Bootle Health Centre, Park Street, Bootle L20 3RF Tel: 0151 922 1600; Southside, Vicarage Lane, Altrincham WA14 3AS — MB ChB 1985 Manch.; MRCGP 1991.

ALI, Amjid Ashraf 14 Cherry Street, Blackburn BB1 1NR — MB ChB 1996 Sheff.

ALI, Anwar Hussain Mohemmad Sarfaraz 66 Finnemore Road, Birmingham B9 5XT — MB BS 1970 Dacca.

ALI, Ashfaq Bridgeton Health Centre, 210 Abercromby St., Glasgow G40 2DA Tel: 0141 531 6620 Fax: 0141 531 6626 Email: ashali@hotmail.com; 198 Terregles Avenue, Pollokshields, Glasgow G41 4RR Tel: 0141 427 4348 — MB ChB 1975 Glas.

ALI, Ashiya 10 Sporhams, Basildon SS16 5TT — MB BS 1994 Lond.

ALI, Assif Nawaz 8 Shakespeare Road, Eynsham, Witney OX29 4PY; 84 Aller Place, Eliburn, Livingston EH54 6RG Tel: 01506 496596 Email: assif nablia@hotmail.co.uk — MB ChB 1992 Leeds; MRCGP 1997; DRCOG 1995. SHO O & G St Johns Hosp. Livingston. Prev: Clin. Med. Off., Emerg. Off., Maitland Hosp. N S Wales, Austral. (Apr. 98 - Jan. 99); GP. Regist. Wetmore Rd Surg., Burton-on-Trent (Sep. 96 - Sep. 97).

ALI, Aulfat Rusool Adam House Medical Centre, 85-91 Derby Road, Sandiacre, Nottingham NG10 5HZ Tel: 0115 949 1102 Fax: 0115 949 1522; Hillside Medical Centre, 162 Nottingham Road, Stapleford, Nottingham NG9 8AR Tel: 0115 949 1550 Fax: 0115 949 7720 — MB BS 1976 Lond.; MRCP (UK) 1981; MRCS Eng. LRCP Lond. 1976; MRCGP 1980.

ALI, Ayyaz Anwar 10 Sandringham Drive, Stockport SK4 2DD — MB ChB 1998 Leic.; MB ChB Leic 1998.

ALI, Azhar 3 Borland Road, Bearsden, Glasgow G61 2NB — MB ChB 1997 Glas.

ALI, Azhar 51 Longlands, Hemel Hempstead HP2 4DD — MB BS 1997 Lond.

ALI, Mr Baqar Hassness, Redhill Lane, Redhill, Worcester WR5 2JL Tel: 01905 354430; 11 Greensvalley Drive, Hartburn, Stockton-on-Tees TS18 5QH Tel: 01642 860950 — MB BS 1984 Karachi; FRCS Glas. 1991; FRCS Ed. 1990. Staff Grade (Urol. & Gen. Surg.) N. Tees Gen. Hosp. Stockton-on-Tees. Socs: BMA. Prev: Regist. (Urol.) Burnby Gen. Hosp.; Regist. (Urol.) Bolton Roy. Infirm.; Regist. (Gen. Surg.) N. Manch. Gen. Hosptial.

***ALI, Daud Reza** 39 Braeside, Dunstan, Gateshead NE11 9RD — LMSSA 1996 Lond.

ALI, Faisal Sonny Manzoor 9 Lodge Lane, Dukinfield SK16 5HY Tel: 01426 639004 — MB ChB 1996 Manch. (Manch.) Prev: Ho. Off. Gen. Surg. Tameside Gen. Hosp.; Ho. Off. Gen. Med. Tameside Gen. Hosp.

ALI, Farida Sadiq 54 Wigton Lane, Leeds LS17 8SJ — MB ChB 1994 Birm.

ALI, Fawzia Runa 2 Ontario Close, Blackburn BB2 7DZ Tel: 01254 56976 Email: runaali@aol.com — MB BS 1992 Lond.; BSc Lond. 1989; MRCP (UK) 1996. (Univ. Coll. & Middlx Sch. Med. Lond.) Specialist Regist. (Respirat. Med.) Roy. Free Hosp. Lond. Prev: SHO Hammersmith Hosp. & Lond. Chest Hosp.

ALI, Ghazanfar 18 Spring Lane, Radcliffe, Manchester M26 2TQ — MB BS 1984 Bahauddin Zakariyau; MB BS Bahauddin Zakariyau, Pakistan 1984.

ALI, Hassan Omer Mohammed 17 Willow Street, Anniesland, Glasgow G13 1DA Tel: 0141 958 0428 — MB BS 1976 Khartoum; MRCOG 1991.

ALI, Haythem Mahmoud Mohamed Dehman Alsheikh 214 Wingrove Road, Newcastle upon Tyne NE4 9DD — MB ChB 1992 Aberd.

ALI, Hiam Hussain Haj Department of Pathology, Trafford General Hospital, Moorside Rd, Manchester M41 5SL Tel: 0161 746 2475 — MB ChB 1973 Baghdad; MRCPath 1982. Cons. Histopath / lyopath.Traff. Gen. Hosp. Manch. Socs: Brit. Soc. Gastroenterol.; Brit. Soc. Clin. Cytol.

ALI, Huda Elgurani Abdelrahman Learning Assessment Centre, 48-50 Springfield Road, Horsham RH12 2PD — MB BS 1998 Khartoum.

ALI, Imad Mohammed Coity Clinic, Bro Morgannwg NHS Trust, Princess of Wales Hospital, Bridgend CF31 1RQ Tel: 01656 752752 Fax: 01656 752664 Email: imad.ali@bromer-te.wales.nhs.uk — BM BS 1986 Nottm.; 1995 MSc (Psychiat.) Cardiff; 1984 BMedSci Nottm.; 1994 MRCPsych; 1998 CCST (gen. adult psychiat); 1998 CCST (old age psychiat). (Univ. Nottm.) Cons. in Gen. Adult Psychiat., Bro Morgannwg NHS Trust, P.ss of Wales Hosp., Bridgend; Clin. Tutor, Bro Morgannwg NHS Trust. Prev: Sen. Regist. Rotat. (Adult Psychiat.) S. Wales.

ALI, Javaid Bramhall Health Centre, 66 Bramhall Lane South, Bramhall, Stockport SK7 2DY Tel: 0161 439 8213 Fax: 0161 439 6398 — MB BChir 1991 Camb.

ALI, Kauser Mahmud 11 Oakthorpe Road, London N13 5HY — MB BS 1994 Lond.

ALI, Liaquat Lime Tree Surgery, 38 Cann Hall Road, Leytonstone, London E11 3HZ Tel: 020 8519 9914 Fax: 020 855 7109; 17 Basildon Avenue, Ilford IG5 0QE — MB ChB 1992 Leeds; MRCGP 1998.

ALI, Mr Mahar Liaqat 27 St Johns Road, Ilford IG2 7BB — MB BS 1977 Punjab; MB BS Punjab, Pakistan 1977; FRCSI 1981.

ALI, Mahnaz 100 Peregrine Road, Sunbury-on-Thames TW16 6JP — MB ChB 1990 Manch.

ALI, Mark Intikhab Zaman 20 Royal Crescent, London W11 0XX — MB BS 1989 Lond.

ALI, Mir Ahmed Derwen Deg, Wrexham Road, Pontblyddyn, Mold CH7 4HG Tel: 01352 770494 — MB BS 1942 Osmania; LAH Dub. 1955; MRCGP 1965; TDD Wales 1948. (Osmania Univ. Med. Coll. India)

ALI, Mir Azmal — MB BS 1965 Dacca; FFA RCSI 1974; FFA RCS Eng. 1974. (Sir Salimullah Med. Coll. Dacca) Cons. Anaesth. Centr. Middlx. Hosp. Lond. Socs: Assn. Anaesth.; Intens. Care Soc.; Life-Mem. Soc. Anaesthesiol., Bangladesh. Prev: Sen. Regist. (Anaesth.) RCS Lond.; Sen. Regist. (Anaesth.) Whittington Hosp. Lond.

ALI, Mir Mahmood Scourfield and Partners, The Surgery, Oakfield Street, Ystrad Mynach, Hengoed CF82 7WX Tel: 01443 813248 Fax: 01443 862283; 3 Aspen Avenue, Blackwood NP12 1WW — MB BS 1974 Osmania.

ALI, Mohammad Faiz 11 Abbotswood Close, Belvedere DA17 5RN — MB ChB 1994 Liverp.

ALI, Mohammad Omar 2 Ontario Close, Lammack, Blackburn BB2 7DZ — MB BS 1959 Dacca; DTM & H Ed. 1969. (Dacca Med. Coll.)

ALI, Mohammad Shaukat Greenwich District Hospital, Vanbrugh Hill, London SE10 9HE Tel: 020 8312 6013 Fax: 020 8312 6218; Kyrle House, Orpington Road, Chislehurst BR7 6RA Tel: 01689 74890 — MB BS 1962 Dacca; FRCP Lond. 1994; FRCP Glas. 1984; FRCP Ed. 1984; FRCPI 1984, M 1971; MRCP (UK) 1973; DTM & H Liverp. 1966. (Dacca) Cons. Phys. (Geriat. & Gen. Med.) Greenwich Dist. Hosp. Lond.; Indep. Cons. Assessor of the NHS Exec.; Trainer (Med.) Overseas Doctors Dual Sponsorship Scheme; Mem. SE Thames Regional Cons. Specialists Comm.; Mem. NHS Health Advis. Serv. Panel. Socs: Brit. Geriat. Soc.; (Ex-Pres.) Bangladesh Med. Assn. UK; BMA (Ex-Chairm. Greenwich & Bexley Div.). Prev: Sen. Regist. (Geriat.) King's Coll. Hosp. Lond. & Bromley Gp. Hosps.; Regist. (Med.) Profess. Unit Chittagong Med. Coll. Hosp.; Regist. (Geriat.) Ipswich Gp. Hosps.

ALI, Mohammed Muazzam 28 Priory Road, Barking IG11 9XL — MB BS 1994 Lond.

ALI, Mr Mohammed Salman Corbett Hospital, Stourbridge DY8 4JB — MB BS 1971 Aligarh; FRCS Ed. 1976. (Jawaharlal Nehru) Cons. Orthop. Surg. Russells Hall Hosp. Dudley W. Midl. Socs: Brit. Orth. Assn.; Brit. Soc. Shoulder Surg.; BASK. Prev: Sen. Regist. (Orthop.) Robt. Jones & Agnes Hunt Orthop. Hosp. OsW.ry; Hand Fell. P.ss Margt. Rose Hosp. Edin.; Regist. (Orthop.) Robt. Jones & Agnes Hunt Orthop. Hosp. OsW.ry.

ALI, Mohammed Tariq Dept Anaesthesia, John Radcliffe Hsp, Oxford — MB ChB 1986 Leeds; FRCA 1993. Cons., John Radcliffe Hsp, Oxfrd. Prev: Sen. Regist. (Anaesth. & IC) Univ. Coll. Lond. Hosps.

ALI, Mousa Saber Asaad Haj 32 Clos Nanr Glaswg, Conway Park, Pontprennau, Cardiff CF23 8NB; 32 Clos Nanr Glaswg, Conway Park, Pontprennau, Cardiff CF23 8NB Tel: 01222 731277 Fax: 01222 731277 — MB BCh 1975 Al-Azhar; MB BCh Al-Azhar, Egypt 1975; Jordanian Board in Anaesthesiology 1987. (Azhar Uni, Egypt) Staff Anaesth., Uni Hosp of Wales. Socs: Jordanian Med Assn. Full Mem. Prev: SR Anaes. King Khalid Uni Hsp, Riyadh, Saudi Arabia.

ALI, Muhammad 1 Tollington Court, Tollington Park, London N4 3QT Tel: 020 7272 2121; 4 Merrivale, London N14 4SH Tel: 020 8882 1656 — MB BS 1957 Punjab; DTCD Wales 1963; DTM & H Liverp. 1963. (King Edwd. Med. Coll. Lahore)

ALI, Muhammad Asif 26 Alexandra Drive, Beverley HU17 8PG — MB BS 1988 Karachi.

ALI, Muhammad Matleb Roles Grove Surgery, 18 Roles Grove, Marks Gate, Chadwell Heath, Romford RM6 5LT Tel: 020 8590 4030; Grasmere, 154 Manor Road, Chigwell IG7 5PX Tel: 020 8500 2940 — MB BS 1960 Dacca; DCH RCPS Glas. 1968. (Med. Coll. Dacca) Prev: Research Phys. CDDR Dhaka, Bangladesh; Cons. Paediat. Holly Family Hosp. Dhaka, Bangladesh.

ALI, Mr Muhammad Sadiq 90 Oxford Street, Oldham OL9 7SL Tel: 0161 284 0607; 11 Jami Road, Rawalpindi Cantt, Pakistan, Pakistan Tel: 00 92 51 564413 — MB BS 1962 Punjab; FRCS Ed. 1971. Specialist (Surg.) Milt. Hosp. & Cons. Surg. Hearts Internat. Clinic Rawalpindi Cantt, Pakistan; Cons. Surg. Roy. Palace Clinic King Khalid Bin Asdul Aziz, Riyadh. Prev: Assoc. Prof. Surg. Rawalpindi Med. Coll. Rawalpindi, Pakistan; Sen. Regist. (Paediat. & Urol.) Sheff.; Regist. (Gen. Surg. & Urol.) N.. Gen. Hosp. Sheff.

ALI, Muhammed Mukabber Red Gables, 608 Garstang Road, Barton, Preston PR3 5DR — MB BS 1965 Rajshahi; MRCP (UK) 1991; DTM & H Liverp. 1975; DCH Dub. 1971. Staff Grade Paediat. Preston HA. Prev: Regist. (Paediat.) N. Middlx. Hosp. Lond.

ALI, Mr Muwaffaq Abdul-Sahib Orthopaedic Department, Southport & Formby District Hospital, Town Lane, Kew, Southport PR8 6NJ Tel: 01704 547471; Tel: 01704 547471 Fax: 01704 550779 — MB ChB 1973 Baghdad; MChOrth Liverp. 1984; FRCS Ed. 1983. (Baghdad Med. Sch. - IRAQ) Cons. Orthop. & Trauma S.port & Formby Dist. Hosp. Socs: Fell. BOA; Mem. of SICOT.

ALI, Nabeel Jawad 25 Westgate, Southwell NG25 0JN Tel: 01623 816689 — BM 1982 Soton.; MRCP (UK) 1987. Cons. Gen. & Thoracic Med. King's Mill Hosp. Sutton in Ashfield, Notts. Prev: Research Regist. Osler Chest Unit Ch.ill Hosp. Headington Oxf.; Sen. Regist. Addenbrooke's & Papworth Hosp. Camb.; Regist. (Chest Med.) Llandough Hosp. Cardiff.

ALI, Nadia Sadiq 72 Parkfield Street, Manchester M14 4BW — MB ChB 1993 Manch. Prev: PhD (O & G) Ipswich Gen. Hosp. Ipswich Qu.sland, Australia; SHO (O & G); SHO (Urol.).

ALI, Nasir Craig Dunain Hospital, Inverness IV3 8JU Tel: 01463 234101; Balmachree House, Dalcross, Inverness IV2 7JQ Tel: 01463 790602 Fax: 0870 055 2892 Email: nasir@balma.demon.co.uk — MB BS 1965 Karachi; MRCPsych 1972; DPM 1970 Eng.; FRCPsych 1995. (Dow Med. Coll.) Cons. Highland HB Inverness; Hon. Sen. Lect. Aberd. Univ. Prev: Cons. Salford & Prestwich Gp. Hosps.; Sen. Regist. (Psychol. Med.) Univ. Gp. Hosps. Newc.

ALI, Nasreen 36 Farnborough Drive, Shirley, Solihull B90 4TB — MB ChB 1995 Sheff.

ALI, Nayeem Tarak 9 Wighton Tarak, Isleworth TW7 6ST — MB BS 1994 Lond.; BDS (Hons.) Lond. 1988. SHO (Oral & Maxillofacial Surg.) Univ. Coll. Lond. Hosp.

ALI, Nayyar Rukhsana 13 Stuart Close, Great Baddow, Chelmsford CM2 7AR Tel: 01245 74041 — MB BS 1967 Kashmir; DObst RCOG 1975.

ALI, Nazaarkut Sultan 102 Twycross Street, Highfields, Leicester LE2 0DW — MB ChB 1995 Leeds.

ALI, Nehas Aktar Jahan The Broadway Surgery, 3 Broadway Gardens, Woodford Green IG8 0HF Tel: 020 8491 3344 — MB BS 1984 Lond. GP. Prev: Ex. Dir. Sanibel Coun. Centre.

ALI, Mr Osman Ahmed Ear Nose & Throat Department, Wrexham Maelor Hospital, Croesnewydd Road, Wrexham LL13 7TD — MB BCh 1976 Cairo; FRCS Ed. 1993.

ALI, Playiparambil Mohamed The Surgery, 32 Knights, Basildon SS15 5LE Tel: 01268 415888 Fax: 01268 491318 — MB BS 1966 Kerala; MRCP (UK) 1972.

ALI, Mr Qazi Khalid 7 Haytons Lane, Appleby, Scunthorpe DN15 0AP — MB BS 1986 Punjab; FRCS Ed. 1993. (Rawalpindi Medical College) Cons. Ophth. Surg. Scunthorpe Gen. Hosp. Socs: Amer. Acad. of Ophth. (Intl Mem.); Roy. Coll. Ophth.

ALI, Rosena 103 Monmouth Drive, Sutton Coldfield B73 6JJ — MB ChB 1996 Liverp.

ALI, Miss Rozina Shahzady 140 Stoke Poges Lane, Slough SL1 3LH — MB BS 1992 Lond.; FRCS Eng. 1996. (St. Thos. Hosp. Med. Sch.) Prev: SHO Rotat. (Surg.) Qu. Mary's Hosp. Sidcup Kent.

ALI, Saadi Ahmad Community Mental Health Team, Manor Road, Beverley HU17 7BZ Tel: 01482 872462 — MB ChB 1971 Baghdad; MRCPsych 1982; DPM Eng. 1980. Cons. Psychiat. Community Ment. Health Team Beverley. Prev: Sen. Regist. High Royd Hosp. Menston.

ALI, Sabah Husain 38 Corfton Road, Ealing, London W5 2HT Tel: 020 8997 6646 Fax: 020 8961 6661 — MB ChB 1974 Basrah; MRCP (UK) 1985; MRCPI 1985. (Basrah University Medical School) Prev: Regist. (Community Med.) King's Coll. Hosp. Lond.; Regist. (Gen. Med.) Furness Gen. Hosp. Cumbria.; SHO (Chest Med.) St And.Hosp. Lond.

ALI, Sadiq Ahmed Church Street Surgery, 57 Church Street, Hunslet, Leeds LS10 2PE Tel: 0113 271 1884 Fax: 0113 272 0008 — MB ChB 1969 Leeds; MRCS Eng. LRCP Lond. 1969 DTM & H Eng. 1971. (Leeds) Prev: SHO (Gen. Surg.) Airedale Gen. Hosp. Steeton; SHO (Gen. Surg.) Maryfield Hosp. Dundee; SHO (Orthop.) Dundee Roy. Infirm.

ALI, Saima Karamat 163 Maxwell Drive, Pollokshields, Glasgow G41 5AE — MB ChB 1996 Glas. (Glas.) SHO Dept. of Med. of the Elderly, Stobhill Hosp. Glas. Prev: SHO (O & G) Stobhill Hosp. Glas.; SHO (c/o the Elderly) Inverclyde; Jun. Ho. Off. (Surg.) Hairmyres Hosp., E. Kilbride.

ALI, Sajjad Aziz 4 Merrivale, London N14 4SH — MB BS 1990 Lond.

ALI, Shahid Mahmood Phoenix Medical Practice, Auerton Health Centre, 33 Heaton Grove, Bradford BD15 7PA Tel: 01274 544749 Email: ashalhid@bradford-ha.nhs.uk — MB ChB 1994 Leeds; PhD Open 1988; BSc (Hons.) Hatfield 1985. Gen. Pract.; Sen. Lect. in Primary Care CRPC Univ. of Leeds. Leeds. Socs: BMA; Biochem. Soc.; Brain Res. Assn.

ALI, Shaikh Shawkat 18 Langley Road, Sunderland SR3 1AH — MB BS 1960 Dacca. (Dacca Med. Coll.) Med. Asst. N. RHA. Prev: SHO (Anaesth.) Gen. Hosp. Harrogate & Newc. Gen. Hosp.; Regist. (Anaesth.) Sunderland Gp. Hosps.

ALI, Mr Shaukat ENT Department, King's Mill Hospital, Mansfield Road, Sutton-in-Ashfield NG17 4JL Tel: 01623 672328 Fax: 01623 672305 — MB BS 1972 Punjab; FRCS Ed. 1979; DLO Eng. 1980. (Nishter Pakistan) Cons. ENT Surg. Kings Mill Hosp. Notts.; Speciality co-ordinator. Socs: Brit. Assn. Laryngol.; Brit. Assn. Head & Neck Oncol.; Midl. Assn. Otolaryngol. Prev: Sen. Regist. (ENT) N.. RH; Regist. (ENT) W. Glam. AHA; Fell. (Head & Neck Surg.) Free Univ. Hosp. Amsterdam, Holland.

ALI, Simone Feiza 114 Colwith Road, London W6 9EZ Tel: 020 8748 8093; 26 Woodcote Valley Road, Purley CR8 3AJ Tel: 020 8668 0305 — MB BS 1993 Lond.; MRCP (UK) 1998. (Charing Cross & Westminster, University of London) SHO (Clin. Oncol.) St. Thomas' Hosp. Lond. Prev: SHO (Gen. Med.) St. Peter's Hosp. Chortsey; SHO (Oncol. & Haemat.) Qu. Eliz. Hosp. Woolwich; SHO (Neurol.) Maudsley/King's Lond.

ALI, Soghra 3 Finch Avenue, Pledwick, Wakefield WF2 6SE — MB ChB 1987 Sheff.

ALI, Sophia 9 Station Avenue, Tile Hill, Coventry CV4 9HR — MB ChB 1995 Leic.

ALI, Sumbal Irshad 22 Crosslands Meadow, Riverview Park, Colwick, Nottingham NG4 2DJ — MB BS 1994 Lond.; DRCOG 1997; DFFP 1998. Trainee GP/SHO Mansfield VTS. Prev: GP Regist., Nottm. VTS.

ALI, Syed Anwar Cwmaman Health Centre, 6-14 Glanaman Road, Aberdare CF44 6HY Tel: 01685 873002 Fax: 01685 872179 — MB BS 1964 Agra.

ALI, Syed Irshad 97 Minster Court, Crown St., Liverpool L7 3QD — MB ChB 1989 Liverp.; MRCP (UK) 1994; DMRD Liverp. 1996; FRCR 1998. (Liverp.) Regist. Rotat. (Radiol.) Liverp. Socs: Roy. Coll. Radiol. Prev: Regist. Rotat. (Med.) Merseyside.

ALI, Syed Liaquat The Health Centre, Marmaduke St., Hull HU3 3BH Tel: 01482 27708; 163 Cottingham Road, Hull HU5 2EG — MB BS 1958 Osmania; MRCP Glas. 1963. (Osmania Med. Coll. Hyderabad) Prev: Clin. Asst. BRd.gate Hosp. Beverley; Ho. Phys. Bolton Dist. Gen. Hosp.; SHO Hillend Hosp. St. Albans.

ALI, Syed Maqbool Fleetwood Health Centre, London Street, Fleetwood FY7 6HD Tel: 01253 875305 Fax: 01253 878417 — MB BS 1967 Karachi. (Dow Med. Coll.)

ALI, Syed Masroor SMA Medical Centre, 693-695 High Road, Leyton, London E10 6AA Tel: 020 8539 2078 Fax: 020 8558 3833 — MB BS 1972 Sind. (Liaquat Med. Coll. Hyderabad) Regist. (Med.) Wanstead Hosp. Lond.

ALI, Syed Nasim 158 Tudor Crescent, Ilford IG6 2SE — MB BS 1993 Lond.

ALI, Syed Osaf Northolt Family Practice, (surgery), 330/322 Ruislip Road, Northolt UB5 6BG Tel: 020 8575 8620 Fax: 020 8813 0471; 11 Lowswood Close, Northwood HA6 2XE — MB ChB 1982 Leic.

ALI, Syed Shuja 27 Camborne Road, Morden SM4 4JL Tel: 020 8540 5476 — MB BS 1990 Lond.

ALI, Syed Toufeeq Briercliffe Road Surgery, 357 Briercliffe Road, Burnley BB10 1TX Tel: 01282 424720 Fax: 01282 429055 — MB BS 1973 Marathwada, India; LMSSA Lond. 1977. (Govt. Med. Coll. Aurangabad, India) Clin. Med. Off. Family Plann. Clinic. Blackburn, Hyndburn & Ribble Valley AHA.

ALI, Syeda Farhat Nasreen 18 Carmarthen Green, Leegomery, Telford TF1 6UF — MB BCh 1997 Wales.

ALI, Tahir 9 Station Avenue, Tilehill Village, Coventry CV4 9HR — MB ChB 1998 Leic.; MB ChB Leic 1998.

ALI, Tasneem 16 Hawthorn Avenue, London N13 4JT — MB BS 1994 Lond.

ALI, Thamer Tawfik 4 Watermill Lane, London N18 1SU — MB ChB 1978 Baghdad.

ALI, Tuhin Mohammed Mominul Islam 14A Fairfield Road, London N8 9HG — BM BCh 1990 Oxf.

ALI, Zahir 56A Trinity Road, Birmingham B6 6AL — MB ChB 1998 Sheff.; MB ChB Sheff 1998.

ALI, Zahra Asad Medical Centre, 100, Lavender Hill, London SW11 Tel: 020 8673 7140; 45 Elmbourne Road, London SW17 8JS Tel: 8772 1822 — MB BS 1964 Karachi; DRCOG 1968. (Dow Med. Coll. Karachi, Pakistan) Prev: GP Lond.; O & G, Saudi Arabia.

ALI-KHAN, Adil Sundon Park Clinic, Tenth Avenue, Sundon Park, Luton LU3 3EP — MB BS 1988 Lond.

ALI-KHAN, Ahmed Shubho 2A Pennine Road, Oldland Common, Bristol BS30 8QD — MB ChB 1995 Birm.; ChB Birm. 1995.

ALI-KHAN, Ghazanfar Lamorna Surgery, 55A Thomas Drive, Gravesend DA12 5PY Tel: 01474 363217/534367; Wrotham Lodge, 137 Wrotham Road, Gravesend DA11 0QP Tel: 01474 362636 — MB BS 1956 Karachi. (Dow Med. Coll.) Prev: Specialist (Orthop.) RAF; Regist. (Orthop.) Gloucester Roy. Infirm. & Lewisham Gen. Hosp.

ALI-KHAN, Mir Askar 22 Bankfold, Barrowford, Nelson BB9 6JW — MB BS 1954 Osmania. (Osmania Med. Coll.) Med. Asst. (Med. & Chest Dis.) Burnley Gp. Hosps. Socs: BMA. Prev: Ho. Phys. City Gen. Hosp. Edin.; Sen. Ho. Phys. Sheff. Roy. Infirm.; Regist. Burnley Gp. Hosps.

ALI-KHAN, Mir Vizarath Ali-Khan and Partners, 128 High Street, Bentley, Doncaster DN5 0AT Tel: 01302 874551 Fax: 01302 820920 — MB BS 1965 Osmania. Gen. Practioner, 128 High St., Bentley, Doncaster.

ALI KHAN, Mohamed Fasihuddin Siddique 115A Burdon Lane, South Cheam, Sutton SM2 7DB Tel: 020 8642 4045; 181 Carshalton Road, Sutton SM1 4NG Tel: 020 8661 1505 — MB BS 1964 Osmania; ECFMG Cert. 1970; DCH Eng. 1970. Mem. LMC. Socs: BMA. Prev: Regist. (Med.) Lond. Jewish Hosp.; SHO (Paediat.) Roy. Manch. Childr. Hosp.; Phys. Nat. Iranian Oil Company Iran.

ALI KHAN, Nuzhat Fatima Doctors Surgery, 181 Carshalton Road, Carshalton SM1 4NG Tel: 020 8661 1505; 181 Carshalton Road, Sutton SM1 4NG Tel: 020 8661 1505 — MB BS 1972 Osmania; MB BS Osmania 1971; Cert. Family Plann. JCC 1980. (Osmania) GP Sutton. Prev: SHO St. Benedict's Hosp. Lond.; Ho. Surg. (Surg.) Pk. Hosp. Manch.; Ho. Phys. (Med.) Lond. Jewish Hosp.

ALI-NAJA, Saad Wajih St James's Hospital, Beckett St., Leeds LS9 — MB ChB 1974 Baghdad; MRCOG 1983. Sen. Regist. (O & G) St. Jas. Hosp. Leeds.

***ALI-ZUBAIR, Munir** 73 Glenarm Road, London E5 0LY Tel: 020 8985 5858 — MB BS 1997 Lond.

ALIBHAI, Ali Amijee Dental Centre, 3 Gower Place, London WC1E 6BN Tel: 020 7387 6306; 118 Cranley Gardens, Muswell Hill, London N10 3AH Tel: 020 8365 2212 — MB BS 1979 Lond.; BSc (Hons.) Lond. 1976; DRCOG 1984. (St. Bart.) Clin. Asst. Sports Injury Clinic UCLH Lond.; LMC Mem. Camden & Islington; Hon. Stud. Health Phys. UCL; Med. Off. Brit. Athletic Federat.; Med. Off. Hampstead & W.m. Hockey Club.; Exec. & Counc. Mem. Nat. Assn. Fundholding Pract.; Chairm. Nat. Assn. Fundholding Pract. Lond. Region. Socs: Brit. Assn. Sport & Med.; Chairm. Football Assn. Regional Med. Soc. (SE). Prev: SHO (O & G) St. Bart. Hosp. Lond.; SHO (A & E) Guy's Hosp. Lond.; Ho. Off. (Surg.) St. Bart. Hosp. Lond.

ALIEF, Lie Robert Jonathan 21 Whitemeadows, Darlington DL3 8SR — MB BS 1983 Newc.; MRCOG 1990. Regist. (O & G) Hillingdon Hosp. Middlx. Prev: SHO (Gen. Surg.) Newc. Gen. Hosp.; SHO (A & E) Roy. Vict. Infirm. Newc.; SHO (O & G) Sunderland HA.

ALIER LAPLANA, Carlos Rochdale Infirmary, Whitehall St., Rochdale OL12 0NB — LMS 1992 Barcelona.

ALIFIERI, Evangelia 5 Peterborough Road, Durham DH1 5QX Tel: 0191 384 3354 Email: evangelia.alifieri@ncl.ac.uk — Ptychio Iatrikes 1991 Crete. (University of Crete, Greece) Specialist Regist. (Paediat.) Newc. u. Tyne.

ALIJANI, Afshin 12 South Inch Park, Perth PH2 8BU — MB ChB 1993 Dundee.

ALIJANI, Mandana 21 Wheatley Close, London NW4 4LG — MB BS 1998 Lond.; MB BS Lond 1998.

ALIKHAN, Raza 347 Clapham Road, London SW9 9BT — MB BS 1996 Lond.; BSc Lond. 1993. Research Fell. Vasc. Med., Guys, Kings, St Thomas' Med Sch., Lond.

ALIKHANI, Sharon Flat 11, 9-10 Colville Terrace, London W11 2BE Tel: 020 7229 8404 Fax: 020 7792 2619 Email: sharonalikhani@hotmail.com — MB BS 1993 Lond.

ALIM, Shaik Abdul Alim and Partners, 151 North Street, Keighley BD21 3AU Tel: 01535 607444 Fax: 01535 691201 — MB BS 1972 Utkal.

ALIMO, Mr Ethan Barclay Dennis 59 Claremont Road, London N6 5DA — MB BS 1967 Lond.; MSc Lond. 1971, MB BS 1967; FRCS Eng. 1980; MRCP (UK) 1974. (Middlx.) Resid. Surg. Off. Lond. Chest Hosp. Prev: Regist. (Surg.) W.m. Hosp.; Resid. Surg. Off. Brompton Hosp.; Resid. Med. Off. Nat. Heart Hosp. Lond.

ALIPOUR-ALMACHAVAN, Karim 105 Cairncry Road, Aberdeen AB16 5NF — MB ChB 1993 Aberdeen.

ALISHAHI, Siamack Flat 48, Lister Court, Dundee DD2 1UY — MB ChB 1992 Bristol.

ALISON, Annie Cameron (retired) Midway, Weddells Lane, Berwick-upon-Tweed TD15 1HG — MB ChB 1942 Glas.; DCH Eng. 1945. Prev: Clin. Med. Off. Croydon HA.

ALISON, Dawn Louise St James University Hospital, Beckett St., Leeds LS9 7TF Email: meddladleeds@ac.uk; Beech House, High St, Bramham, Wetherby LS23 6QQ — MB ChB 1978 Glas.; MSc Lond. 1983; MD (Hons.) Glas. 1985; FRCP Lond. 1996; MRCP Lond. 1981. Sen. Lect. & Hon. Cons. Oncol. & Palliat. Med. Univ. Leeds & St. Jas. Univ. Hosp. Prev: Med. Dir. & Cons. Palliat. Med. Wheatfields Hospice Leeds; Sen. Regist. (Med. Oncol.) Leeds; Hon. Regist., Clin. Fell. Inst. Cancer Research & Roy. Marsden Hosp.

ALISON, Lilias Helen The Childrens Hospital, Western Bank, Sheffield S10 2TH Tel: 0114 271 7149 — MB BS 1982 Newc.; MRCP (UK) 1987; DRCOG 1985; MMed Sc 1999 Leeds. Cons. Community Paediat. Socs: Fell. Roy. Coll. of Paediat. & Child Health. Prev: Regist. (Paeds) Sheff. HA; Regional Paediat. Roy. New Zealand Plunket Soc. Dunedin, NZ.; Sen. Regist. (Community Paediat.) Leeds.

ALISTER, Marilyn Eileen Hill and Partners, 36 Belmont Hill, London SE13 5AY Tel: 020 8852 8357 Fax: 020 8297 2011; 100 Kidbrooke Grove, Blackheath, London SE3 0LG Tel: 020 8858 1576 — MB BS 1969 Lond.; MRCS Eng. LRCP Lond. 1969; T(GP) 1991; DObst RCOG 1972; DA Eng. 1971. (King's Coll. Hosp.) GP; Clin. Med. Off. Greenwich HA. Socs: W. Kent M-C Soc.; BMA (Greenwich & Bexley Br.); Med. Wom. Federat. Prev: Clin. Asst. (Paediat.) Kent & Canterbury Hosp.; SHO (Anaesth.) King's Coll. Hosp. Lond.; SHO (O & G) Dulwich Hosp. Lond.

ALKASS, Walid Abdullah Yousif The Palms, Weavering St., Weavering, Maidstone ME14 5JH — MB ChB 1969 Mosul; MSc (Audiol. Med.) Manch. 1988; DCH RCP Lond. 1980. SCMO MidKent Health. NHS Trust. Socs: Brit. Soc. Audiol.; Fac. Comm. Health; Brit. Assn. Community Drs in Audiol. Prev: Regist. (Paediat.) Shrewsbury Roy. Hosp.; SHO (Neonatol.) Whittington Hosp. Lond.; SHO (Paediat.) W.m. Childr. Hosp. Lond.

ALKATEB, Kamel Fawzy Lotfy Bungalow 2, Wexham Park Hospital, Wexham, Slough SL2 4HZ — MB BCh 1979 Cairo.

ALKATIB, Maha 2 Kingsley Drive, Adel, Leeds LS16 7PB — MB ChB 1996 Leeds; BSc (Hons.) Leeds 1993.

ALKAYALI, Rabah Mohamed Doncaster Royal Infirmary, Armthorpe Road, Doncaster DN2 5LT Tel: 01302 366666 — MB ChB 1970 Alexandria.

ALKER, Margaret Nottinghamshire Healthcare NHS Trust, Health Centre, New St., Sutton-in-Ashfield NG17 1BW Tel: 01623 558374 Fax: 01623 440842 — MB ChB 1973 Leeds; MRCPsych 1977. Cons. Psychiat. (Rehabil.) Nottm.shire Healthcare NHS Trust. Prev: Cons. Psychiat. (Rehabil. & Community) Napsbury Hosp. St. Albans.

ALL-ALLAF, Abd-Al Kareem Younis Saleem Cardiology Department, Walsall Manor Hospital, Moat Rd, Walsall WS2 9PS Tel: 01922 721172 Fax: 01922 656955 Email: kareem-alallaf@hotmail.com; 41 Skip Lane, Walsall WS5 3LW Email: susan.downes@opthalmology.oxford.ac.uk — MB ChB 1982 Mosul; MRCP 1994 UK. Cons. Cardiol. Walsall Manor Hosp.; Hon. Cons. Cardiol. Coventry & Warwick Univ. Hosp. Socs: Roy. Coll. Phys.s, Lond.; Brit. Cardiol. Soc.; Med. Protec. Soc. Prev: SpR cardiol. City Hosp. Stoke On Trent; SpR Cardiol. Walsgrave Hosp. Coventry; SpR Cardiol./Med. Walsall Manor Hosp.

ALLABY, Martin Arnold Kenworthy United Mission to Nepal, PO BOX 126, Kathmandu, Nepal Email: allaby@bigfoot.com; 6 Audon Avenue, Beeston, Nottingham NG9 4AW Tel: 0115 925 2542 — BM BCh 1986 Oxf.; BA Oxf. 1985; MFPHM RCP (UK) 1993; DRCOG 1990; DCH RCP Lond. 1989. (Oxf.) Cons. Pub. Health Med. United Mission to Nepal. Prev: Cons. Pub. Health Med. Nottm. HA; Sen. Regist. (Pub. Health Med.) N.ants. HA; Trainee GP Kettering.

ALLADI, Venkata Ramana 21 Locksley Close, Stockport SK4 2LW — MB BS 1973 Sri Venkateswara.

ALLAHABADIA, Amit 30 Locksley Avenue, Cumbernauld, Glasgow G67 4EN — MB ChB 1991 Glas.

ALLAHABADIA, Archana Alison Lea Medical Centre, Calderwood, East Kilbride, Glasgow G74 3BE Tel: 01355 233981; 18 Church Road, Giffnock, Glasgow G46 6JR — MB ChB 1989 Glas.; MRCGP 1993; DRCOG 1991.

ALLAHABADIA, Jugal Kishore Abronhill Health Centre, Pine Road, Cumbernauld, Glasgow G67 3BE Tel: 01236 723223 Fax: 01236 781426; 30 Locksley Avenue, Cumbernauld, Glasgow G67 4EN Tel: 01236 734910 Fax: 01236 734910 — MB BS 1968 Panjab; B Sc (1959); MBBS (1968); DRCOG 1978. Princip. GP. Socs: Med. Biotec. Soc.; BMA.

ALLAM, Bahgat Fathalla Biochemistry Department, Stobhill NHS Trust, Glasgow G21 3UW Tel: 0141 201 3037 Fax: 0141 201 3047 — MB BCh 1957 Cairo; PhD (Clin. Chem.) Ed. 1964; DMSc Cairo 1961. (Kasr El-Aini) Cons. Clin. Biochem. Gtr. Glas. HB. Socs: Assn. Clin. Biochem.; Roy. M-C Soc. Glas. Prev: Sen. Regist. & Regist.

(Path. Biochem.) Glas. Roy. Infirm.; SHO (Path.) N. Staffs. Roy. Infirm.

ALLAM, Charlotte Louise 32 Fairway, Guildford GU1 2XJ — BM BCh 1997 Oxf.

ALLAM, Joanna 28 Ridgmount Street, London WC1E 7AQ — MB BS 1998 Lond.; MB BS Lond 1998.

ALLAM, Marina 28 Ridgemount Street, London WC1E 7AA — MB BS 1996 Lond.

ALLAM, Sonia Flat 2/L 5 Cathkin Road, Langside, Glasgow G42 9UB — MB ChB 1995 Glas.

ALLAMBY, Mr David Lister 99 Albert Road W., Heaton, Bolton BL1 5ED — MB ChB 1987 Sheff.; FRCS Ed. 1993; FRCOphth 1994. Wellcome Trust Research Fell. Manch. Roy. Eye Hosp.

ALLAMBY, Peter Russell Gomersal Lane Surgery, 2 Gomersal Lane, Dronfield, Dronfield S18 1RU Tel: 01332 290120 Fax: 01332 291737 — MB ChB 1982 Sheff.; BMedSci 1979; MRCGP 1989. Prev: Regist. (Histopath.) Barnsley VTS.

ALLAN, Agnes Whitelaw (retired) 2 Page Furlong, Dorchester-on-Thames, Wallingford OX10 7PU Tel: 01865 340726 — MB ChB 1942 Aberd.

ALLAN, Alexandra Jane 46 Peel Street, London W8 7PD — MB BS 1994 Lond.

ALLAN, Alison Jane Anaesthetic Department, Queen Alexandra Hospital, Portsmouth PO6 2LY — BM 1987 Soton.; FRCA 1994; DA (UK) 1991. (Southampton) Cons. Anaesth. Prev: Regist. (Anaesth.) Portsmouth Hosps. NHS Trust.

ALLAN, Mr Andrew 18 Starling Close, Aylsham, Norwich NR11 6XG — MB ChB 1979 Glas.; FRCS Glas. 1983.

ALLAN, Andrew Nicholas Health Centre, Midland Street, Long Eaton, Nottingham NG10 1NY Tel: 0115 973 2157 Fax: 0115 946 5420 — MB ChB 1985 Sheff.; MRCGP 1989; DRCOG 1988. (Sheffield) GP Princip. Nott.; Clin. Tutor Nottm. Univ. Med. Sch.; Chairm. Trent Immediate Med. Emerg. Serv.; Clin. Governance Lead Erewash PCT. Socs: BASICS; BMA. Prev: Trainer (Gen. Pract.) Nottm. VTS; GP Med. Adviser Derbysh. Ambul. Serv. NHS Trust.

ALLAN, Ann-Marie Teresa Woodgate Valley Practice, 61 Stevens Avenue, Woodgate Valley, Birmingham B32 3SD Tel: 0121 427 6174 Fax: 0121 428 4146; 5 Carpenter Road, Edgbaston, Birmingham B15 2JT Tel: 0121 454 1943 — MB ChB 1978 Birm.; MA Camb. 1978. (Camb. & Birm.)

ALLAN, Anne Eirlys Heath House, Knowsley Grange, Chorley New Road, Bolton BL1 5DQ Tel: 01204 41801 — MB ChB 1955 Manch. Socs: Fell. Manch. Med. Soc. & Roy. Soc. Med.; Roy. Soc. Med. Prev: Clin. Asst. Blair Hosp. Bolton; Sen. Ho. Off. (Anaesth.) Manch. Roy. Infirm.

ALLAN, Anthony Campbell Newtown Surgery, 147 Lawn Avenue, Great Yarmouth NR30 1QP Tel: 01493 853191 Fax: 01493 331861; 147 Lawn Avenue, Great Yarmouth NR30 1QP Tel: 01493 853191 — MB BS 1980 Lond.; MRCP (UK) 1985; MRCGP 1986; DCH RCP Lond. 1985.

ALLAN, Anthony Graham Lloyd 11 Crarae Avenue, Edinburgh EH4 3JD — MB ChB 1995 Manch.

ALLAN, Mr Arthur Candlemas Croft, 18 Footherley Road, Shenstone, Lichfield WS14 0NJ Tel: 01543 481769 — MB BS 1971 Lond.; MD Lond. 1982; FRCS Eng. 1977. (St. Bart.) Cons. Surg. Gen. & Colorectal Surg. Good Hope Hosp. Trust Sutton Coldfield & Vict. Hosp. Lichfield; Fell WHO.; Hon. Sen. Clin. Lect. Univ. Birm.

ALLAN, Barbara Kathryn The Docs, 55-59 Bloom Street, Manchester M1 3LY Tel: 0161 237 9490 Fax: 0161 228 3164 — MB ChB 1987 Manch.; MRCGP 1992.

ALLAN, Belinda Jayne Scarborough General Hospital, Scalby Road, Scarborough YO12 6QL Tel: 01723 368111; The Masons Arms, Hopperton, Knaresborough HG5 8NX — MB ChB 1991 Leeds; MRCP (UK) 1995. Regist. (Med.) ScarBoro. Gen. Hosp. Prev: Regist. (Diabetes & Endocrinol.) ScarBoro. Gen. Hosp.; SHO (Cardiol., Med. & Med. for Elderly) Bradford Roy. Infirm.

ALLAN, Mr Bruce Duncan Samuel 1 Cromwell Gardens, Scarborough YO11 2DS — MD 1993 Camb.; MB BChir 1985; FRCS Eng. 1989. Sen. Regist. (Ophth.) Moorfields Eye Hosp. Lond. Prev: SHO (Ophth.) St Thos. Hosp. Lond.

ALLAN, Catherine Mary 7 Archibald St NE3 1EB Tel: 0191 477 2243 Fax: 0191 478 6728 — MB ChB 1989 Ed. GP Sunderland; Clin. Asst., GUM Clinic, Newc. Gen. Hosp.

ALLAN, Christopher George 36 Henderson Drive, Skene, Westhill AB32 6RA — MB ChB 1997 Aberd.

ALLAN, Mr David Furness General Hospital, Barrow-in-Furness LA14 4LF Tel: 01229 870870; 19 Mayfield Road, Ulverston LA12 0DU Tel: 01229 584154 Email: david@allan-ulv.freeserve.co.uk — MB ChB 1964 Manch.; BSc Manch. 1961; FRCS Eng. 1970; FRCS Ed. 1968. (Manch.) Cons. Surg. Morecambe Bay Hosp. NHS Trust. Socs: Fell. Manch. Med. Soc.; Pres. Surg. Sect. Manch. Med. Soc. 2001-2002. Prev: Sen. Regist. (Surg.) Manch. Roy. Infirm.; Sen. Regist. (Surg.) Preston & Chorley Gp. Hosps.; Res. Surg. Off. Salford Roy. Hosp.

ALLAN, Mr David Birnie 37 Whittingehame Court, Daventry Drive, Kelvinside, Glasgow G12 0BQ — MB ChB 1975 Glas.; FRCS Glas. 1979 RCPS Glas. Cons. Orthop. Surg. Qu. Eliz. Nat. Spinal Injuries Unit; Hon. Sen. Lect. Glas. Univ. Prev: Sen. Regist. Gtr. Glas. HB & Wrightington Hosp. Lancs.; Regist. Robt. Jones & Agnes Hunt Orthop. Hosp. OsW.ry.

ALLAN, David John (retired) Oak Lattice, Kewferry Drive, Northwood HA6 2NT Tel: 01923 823602 — MB BChir 1963 Camb.; MSc Lond. 1968; MA, MB Camb. 1963, BChir 1962; MRCS Eng. LRCP Lond. 1962; FRCPath 1981 M 1969. Prev: Cons. Chem. Pathol. Harefield & Mt. Vernon Hosp.

ALLAN, David John Anaesthetic Department, Royal Albert Edward Infirmary, Wigan Ln, Wigan WN1 2NN Tel: 01942 822088 Fax: 01942 822089; 595 Knowsley Ln., Knowsley Village, Prescot L34 9EA Tel: 0151 549 0858 Email: alland@abbeygroud.net — MB ChB 1967 Liverp.; DObst RCOG 1969; FFA RCS Eng. 1975. (Liverp.) Cons. Anaesth. Wigan AHA. Socs: Hosp. Cons. & Specialists Assn. & Assn. Anaesths.; Brit. Soc. Med. and Dent. Hypn.; Brit. Opthalmic Anaesth.s Assn. Prev: Sen. Regist. (Anaesth.) Manch. AHA (T); Regist. (Anaesth.) Wigan AHA.

ALLAN, David Macintosh Tel: 01322 428100 Fax: 01322 428554 Email: david.allan@dag-tr.sthames.nhs.uk — MB ChB 1968 Ed.; FRCR 1977; DMRD Ed. 1973. (Ed.) Cons. Radiol. Dartford & Gravesham Health Dist. Prev: Sen. Regist. Radiol. Radcliffe Infirm. Oxf.

ALLAN, Deborah Elizabeth Ty Bryn Surgery, The Bryn, Trethomas, Caerphilly CF83 8DQ; 4 The Acorns, Thornhill, Cardiff CF14 9HZ Tel: 01222 765535 — MB BS 1988 Lond.; DObst RCPI 1992; DCH RCP Lond. 1991. (St. Geo.) GP Retainer Ty Bryn Surg. Gwent.

ALLAN, Donald James Morrison 29 Stirling Road, Edinburgh EH5 3JA Tel: 0131 552 2012 — MB ChB 1971 St. And.

ALLAN, Doreen Peggy (retired) Grey House, Cnwce, Cilgerran, Cardigan SA43 2SR Tel: 01239 614139 — MB BS Lond. 1950; MRCS Eng. LRCP Lond. 1950; DIH Eng. 1956; DPH Lond. 1954. Prev: Ho. Phys. & Dep. Res. Med. Off. & Ho. Phys. Diabetic Dept. Roy. Free Hosp. Lond.

ALLAN, Duncan Shearer Kinorth Medical Centre, 26 Abbotswell Crescent, Aberdeen AB12 5JW Tel: 01224 876000 Fax: 01224 899182; 12 Whitehills Way, Cove Bay, Aberdeen AB12 3UJ Tel: 01224 894913 — MB ChB 1966 Aberd. Socs: BMA.

ALLAN, Eileen Mary Woodside Health Centre, 3 Enmore Road, London SE25 5NS Tel: 020 8656 5790 Fax: 020 8656 7984 Email: administratoragp-h83025.sthames.nhs.uk — MB ChB 1976 Otago; DRCOG 1980; DCH NUI 1978. (Otago) Prev: SHO Bolingbroke Hosp.; SHO St. Ultan's Infant Hosp. Dub.

ALLAN, Elizabeth Rosemary 2 The Staddlestone, Perton, Wolverhampton WV6 7UH — MB BS 1981 Lond.; FRCR Lond. 1987.

ALLAN, Elspeth Anne Long Furlong Medical Centre, 45 Loyd Close, Abingdon OX14 1XR Tel: 01235 522379 — MB ChB 1981 Glas.; BSc Ed. 1978; DRCOG 1984.

ALLAN, Emily Blythe 30 Brockleaze, Neston, Corsham SN13 9TW — MB ChB 1996 Sheff.

ALLAN, Mr Ernest The Manse, 55 Higher Lane, Lymm WA13 0BE — MB ChB 1963 Manch.; FRCS Ed. 1969; MRCS Eng. LRCP Lond. 1963; FRCR 1976; DObst RCOG 1965.

ALLAN, Frances Glencroft, Lower Mains Road, Dollar FK14 7LN — MB ChB 1953 Aberd.; MRCPsych 1973; DPM Eng. 1970; DCH Eng. 1956; DPH Liverp. 1957. (Aberd.) Socs: BMA & Liverp. Med. Inst. Prev: Phys. Supt. Lynebank Hosp. Dunfermline; Cons. Psychiat. Roy. Scott. Nat. Hosp. Larbert; Sen. Med. Off. (Ment. Health) Stirling CC.

ALLAN, Gavin David Lapraik 73 Sutherland Av, Orpington BR5 1QY — MB BS 1997 Lond.

ALLAN, Geoffrey Walter (retired) 20 Northbank Road, Kirkintilloch, Glasgow G66 1EU Tel: 0141 776 1145 — MB ChB 1948 Glas.; FRCP Ed. 1978, M 1953; FRCP Glas. 1984, M 1983. Prev: Cons. Phys. Stobhill Hosp. Glas.

ALLAN, Gillian Bedford House Medical Centre, Glebe Street, Ashton-under-Lyne OL6 6HD Tel: 0161 330 9880 Fax: 0161 330 9393; 39 Beech Lane, Romiley, Stockport SK6 4AF — MB ChB 1979 Liverp.

ALLAN, Gina Calcot Medical Centre, Hampden Road, Chalfont St. Peter, Gerrards Cross SL9 9SA Tel: 01753 887311 Fax: 01753 891933 — MB ChB 1987 Manch.; MRCGP 1992; T(GP) 1992.

ALLAN, Gordon Robert Tel: 01333 426913 Fax: 01333 422300; 78 Leven Road, Lundin Links, Leven KY8 5JB — MB ChB 1981 Ed.; MRCGP 1988; DRCOG 1986.

ALLAN, Graeme Muir Church Street Practice, 8 Church Street, Southport PR9 0QT Tel: 01704 533666 Fax: 01704 539239; 14 Gloucester Road, Southport PR8 2AU — MB ChB 1982 Liverp.; MRCGP 1987; DCH RCP Lond. 1989; DRCOG 1988. Prev: SMO Garrison Med. Pract. BFPO 24.

ALLAN, Hilary Frances Greenwood Surgery, Tylers Ride, South Woodham Ferrers, Chelmsford CM3 5XD Tel: 01245 322443 Fax: 01245 321844; Woodford, Elm Green Lane, Danbury, Chelmsford CM3 4DW Tel: 01245 222515 — MB BS 1984 Lond.; DCH RCP Lond. 1988; MRCGP 1989.

ALLAN, Isobel Campbell (retired) The Anchorage, Hall Road, Rhu, Helensburgh G84 8RR Tel: 01436 215 — MB ChB 1925 Glas.

ALLAN, James Dillwyn Douglas Heath House, Knowsley Grange, Chorley New Road, Bolton BL1 5DQ — MB BS 1988 Lond.

ALLAN, James Gordon Level 8, Gartnavel Gen. Hospital, 1053 Gt. Western Rd, Glasgow G12 0YN Tel: 0141 211 3283 Email: jgallan@emailmsn.com; 5 Redlands Road, Glasgow G12 0SJ Tel: 0141 357 1669 Email: allanjg@hotmail.com — MB ChB 1966 Glas.; MRCP (UK) 1970. (Glas.) Cons. Phys. Gartnavel Gen. Hosp. Glas. Socs: BMA; Brit. Soc. Gastroenterol.; Scott. Soc. Phys.

ALLAN, James Robertson 33 Kinnear Road, Edinburgh EH3 5PG Tel: 0131 552 3698 — MB ChB 1939 Ed. (Ed.)

ALLAN, Janet Mary Mowbray House Surgery, Malpas Road, Northallerton DL7 8FW Tel: 01609 775281 — MB ChB 1986 Ed.; DRCOG 1988.

ALLAN, Janette Marie 11 Rivington Drive, Burscough, Ormskirk L40 7RN — MB ChB 1993 Dundee.

ALLAN, Jean Houston Budhill Medical Practice, 2 Budhill Avenue, Glasgow G32 0PN Tel: 0141 211 1585 Fax: 0141 211 1583; 5 Redlands Road, Glasgow G12 0SJ Tel: 0141 357 1669 — MB ChB 1966 Glas. (Glas.)

ALLAN, John James Inverkeithing Medical Group, 5 Friary Court, Inverkeithing KY11 1NU Tel: 01383 413234 Fax: 01383 410098; Inverkeithing Medical Group, 5 Friary Court, Inverkeithing KY11 1NU Tel: 01383 413234 Fax: 01383 410098 — MB ChB 1977 Aberd.

ALLAN, John Muir (retired) Sandiholme, Sandy Lane, Lathom, Ormskirk L40 5TU Tel: 01695 575203 — MB ChB 1956 Glas.; DObst RCOG 1960. Prev: Ho. Surg. Law Hosp. Carluke.

ALLAN, Julian Richard (retired) The Spinney, Parkside, Upper Hale, Farnham GU9 0JP Tel: 01252 726250 Fax: 01252 393982 — MB BS 1958 Lond.; FRCP Lond. 1993; MRCS Eng. LRCP Lond. 1958; FFOM RCP 1992, MFOM 1980. Prev: Chief Scientist Centre for Human Scis. Defence Research Agency.

ALLAN, Kathryn Margaret Maidencraig, Woodend Hospital, Eday Road, Aberdeen AB15 6LS — MB ChB 1986 Ed.; BSc Ed. 1984. Clin. Asst. (Rehabil.) Woodend Hosp. Aberd.

ALLAN, Lauren Glenister Northwick Park and St Marks NHS Trust, Watford Road, Harrow HA1 3UJ Tel: 020 8869 3976 Fax: 020 8869 3975 Email: laurie.allan@datacom.net; Tel: 01923 897735 Fax: 01923 897735 — MB BS 1978 Lond.; MRCS Eng. LRCP Lond. 1978; FFA RCS Eng. 1983. (Char. Cross) Cons. Anaesth. N.wick Pk. & St. Mark's NHS Trust & Dir. Chronic Pain Serv. Socs: BMA (Ex-Mem. Counc.); Assn. Anaesth. (Ex-Mem. Counc.); Hosp. Cons. & Spec. Assn. (Co. Chairm., Lond. W.). Prev: Sen. Regist. (Anaesth.) Roy. Infirm. Edin.; SHO N.wick Pk. Hosp.

ALLAN, Louise Marie 26 Little Sutton Lane, Sutton Coldfield B75 6PB Tel: 0121 354 7937 — BM BCh 1994 Oxf.; MA Oxf. 1996; BA Oxf. 1991; MRCP UK 1999. (Oxf.) SHO Gen. Med. Freeman Hosp. Newc. Socs: BMA. Prev: Ho. Off. (Gen. Surg.) W. Cumbld. Hosp. Whitehaven; Ho. Off. (Gen. Surg. & Orthop.) W. Cumbld. Hosp. Whitehaven; Ho. Off. (Med.) John Radcliffe Hosp. Oxf.

ALLAN, Margaret Pirie (retired) 90 Hurlingham Court, Ranelagh Gardens, London SW6 3UR Tel: 020 7731 0357 — MB ChB 1938 Aberd.

ALLAN, Mrs Marianne St Lukes Medical Centre, 53 Cainscross Road, Stroud GL5 4EX Tel: 01453 763755 Fax: 01453 756573; 10 Tuffley Lane, Gloucester GL4 0DT Tel: 01452 525660 — LRCP LRCS 1967 Ed.; LRCP LRCS Ed. LRCPS Glas. 1967. Socs: Anthroposophical Med. Assn.

ALLAN, Mark Dunlop Accident & Emergency Department, Royal United Hospital, Combe Park, Bath BA1 3NG Email: mark-allan@msn.com — MB ChB 1989 Glas.; MRCP (UK) 1993. Specialist Regist. A & E. Roy. United Hosp. Combe Pk., Bath.

ALLAN, Martin William Bell Department Anaesthesia, Hope Hospital, University Manchester School of Medicine, Stott Lane, Salford M6 8HD Tel: 0161 787 5107 Fax: 0161 787 4677 Email: mallan@hope.srht.nwest.nhs.uk; 23 Grange Avenue, Hale, Altrincham WA15 8ED Tel: 07970 699201 — MB ChB 1980 Dundee; FRCA. 1984. Cons. (Anaesth.) Salford Roy. Hosps. NHS Trust; Hon. Clin. Lect. (Anaesth.) Univ. Manch.; Lead Clin. for Audit & Clin. Governance (Anaesth.). Socs: Anaesth. Res. Soc.; Assn. Anaesths.; Difficult Airway Soc. Prev: Sen. Regist. (Anaesth.) N. W. RHA; Regist. (Anaesth.) W.. Infirm. Glas.; Regist. (Anaesth.) Ninewells Hosp. Dundee.

ALLAN, Michael James The Health Centre, Charlton Road, Andover SP10 Tel: 01264 65031 — LMSSA 1957 Lond.

ALLAN, Norman Colvin (retired) 7 St Andrews Close, Hope Bowdler, Church Stretton SY6 7EN Tel: 01694 720080 Fax: 01694 724927 Email: allanne77@netscapeonline.co.uk — MB ChB 1952 Ed.; FRCP Ed. 1968; FRCPath 1975, M 1964. Co-ordinator MRC Chronic Myeloid Leukaemia III Trial W.. Gen. Hosp. Edin. Prev: Cons. Haemat. W.. Gen. Hosp. Edin.

ALLAN, Norman James Wilson 2 Campbell Street, Banff AB45 1JR Tel: 01261 815291 — LRCP LRCS Ed. LRFPS Glas. 1945; MA Aberd. 1986; FRCOG 1973, M 1957; FRCSC 1966. (Glas.) Emerit. Assoc. Prof. O & G Univ. Ottawa, Canada. Prev: Assoc. Prof. O & G Univ. Ottawa, Canada; Cons. Matern. Welf. Govt., Ontario; O & G Ottawa Gen. Hosp. Canada.

ALLAN, Patricia Mary 11 Hampshire Drive, Edgbaston, Birmingham B15 3NY — MB ChB 1980 Bristol; BA, MB ChB Bristol 1980. Prev: Research Fell. Bristol Brain Tumor Research Laborat. & Hon. SHO Histopath. (Neuropath.) Frenchay Hosp. Bristol.

ALLAN, Paul 30 Hangleton Road, Hove BN3 7GE — MB ChB 1984 Glas.

ALLAN, Paul Lindsay Peter Royal Infirmary, Edinburgh EH3 9YW Tel: 0131 536 2809 Fax: 0131 229 9106 Email: p.l.allan@ed.ac.uk; 12 Cluny Terrace, Morningside, Edinburgh EH10 4SW — MB BS 1974 Lond.; BSc (Hons.) (Anat.) Lond. 1971; FRCP Ed. 1990; MRCP (UK) 1978; FRCR 1982; DMRD Ed. 1980. (Westm.) Cons. Radiologist, Roy. Infirm., Edin. Socs: Scott. Radiol. Soc.; Former Pres. BMUS; Roy. Coll. Radiol. (Chairm. Train. Accreditation Comm.). Prev: SHO Rotat. (A & E & Med.) Soton. Gen. Hosp.; Ho. Off. (Surg.) W.m. Hosp.

ALLAN, Penelope Elizabeth Mary Perry Hill Surgery, 225 Perry Hill, Catford, London SE6 4HD Tel: 0208 699 1062; 21 Barnmead Road, Beckenham BR3 1JF Tel: 020 8402 1966 — MB BS 1967 Newc. (Newc.) Socs: BMA. Prev: Ho. Off. (Med. & Surg.) S. Shields Gen. Hosp.

ALLAN, Philip James Beech House Group Practice, Beech House, Beech Avenue Hazel Grove, Stockport SK7 4QR Tel: 0161 483 6222 Fax: 0161 419 9244 — MB ChB 1977 Manch.; DCH Eng. 1979; DRCOG 1980.

ALLAN, Poopathy Sriskandab Department of Genitourinary Medicine, Coventry and Warwickshire Hospital, Stoney Stanton Road, Coventry CV1 4FH Tel: 024 76 224055 Fax: 024 76 844199 — MB BS 1981 Colombo; MRCS Eng. LRCP Lond. 1988; MRCOG 1990. (University of Colombo) Cons. (Genitoruinary Med.) Coventry & Warks. Hosp. Socs: Soc. Study VD; Assn. Genitourin. Med.

ALLAN, Robert (retired) 7 Wheatland Drive, Lanark ML11 7QG Tel: 01555 662121 — MB ChB 1944 Ed. Prev: Phys. St. Mary's Hosp. Lanark.

ALLAN, Robert Blair Priory Fields Surgery, Nursery Road, Huntingdon PE29 3RL Tel: 01480 52361 Fax: 01480 434640 — MB ChB 1968 Glas.; DObst RCOG 1971.

ALLAN, Professor Robert Norman Queen Elizabeth Hospital, Edgbaston, Birmingham B15 2TH Tel: 0121 472 1311 Fax: 0121 472 8135 Email: robert.allan@university-b.wmids.nhs.uk; 5 Carpenter Road, Edgbaston, Birmingham B15 2JT Tel: 0121 454 1943 Email: robertnallan@aol.com — MB ChB 1964 Birm.; PhD Birm. 1978, MD 1973; FRCP Lond. 1980, M 1967. Cons. Phys. (Gastroenterol.) Univ. Hosp. Birm. NHS Trust; Dir. of Med. Educat. Univ. Hosp. Birm. NHS Trust; Dep. Med. Director Univ. Hosp. Birm. NHS Trust. Socs: Brit. Soc. Gastroenterol.; Pres. 2002-2003; Chairm. RCP Gastroenterol. and Hepat. Comm. Prev: Cons. Phys. S. Birm. Health Dist. (T); NIH Research Fell. Mayo Grad. Sch. Med. Rochester, USA; Sen. Regist. (Med.) United Birm. Hosps.

ALLAN, Roger Charles Saundersfoot Medical Centre, Westfield Road, Saundersfoot SA69 9JW Tel: 01834 812407 Fax: 01834 811131; Cilrhiw Farm, Princes Gate, Narberth SA67 8TG — MB BS 1987 Lond.; MRCGP 1992; DCH RCP Lond. 1991; DRCOG 1991.

ALLAN, Rosemary Anne Tel: 020 8725 1481 Fax: 020 8725 2936 Email: rosemary.allan@stgn-tr.sthames.nhs.uk — MB BS 1984 Lond.; MSc (Nuclear Med.) Lond. 1993; MA Camb. 1985; MRCP (UK) 1987; FRCR 1994; T(R)(CR) 1995. Cons. Radiol., St. Geo.s Hosp., Lond. Socs: BNMS; Brit. Inst. Radiol. & Roy. Coll. Radiol.; Soc. Paediatric Radiol. Prev: Sen. Regist. (Diag. Radiol.), St Mary's; Regist. (Diag. Radiol.) Hammersmith Hosp. Lond.; Regist. (Nuclear Med.) Guy's Hosp. Med. Sch. Lond.

ALLAN, Sheena Jacqueline Reside Queen Margaret Hospital, Dunfermline KY12 0SU Tel: 01383 623623; 78 Leven Road, Lundin Links, Leven KY8 6AJ Tel: 01333 320958 — MB ChB 1981 Ed.; MRCP (UK) 1985. Cons. Dermatol. (PT).

ALLAN, Mr Simon Michael Eastbourne District General Hospital, Eastbourne BN21 2UD Tel: 01323 413744 — MB BS 1982 Lond.; MS Lond. 1994; FRCS Eng. 1987. (Lond. Hosp.) Cons. Gen. Surg. & BrE. Specialist E.bourne Hosps. NHS Trust. Socs: Brit. Assn. Surg. Oncol. Prev: Sen. Regist. (Surg.) Poole Hosp. NHS Trust & Roy. Bournemouth Hosp. NHS Trust; Sen. Regist. & Regist. (Surg.) Roy. Marsden NHS Trust.

ALLAN, Steven Robert 18A Moray Place, Edinburgh EH3 6DT Tel: 0131 225 5089 — MB ChB 1992 Glas.; MRCGP 1997. SHO (Pychogeriats.) Roy. Vict. Infirm. Edin. Prev: SHO (ENT) City Hosp. Edin.; SHO (O & G) E.ern Gen. Hosp. Edin.; SHO (Geriat.) Roy. Vict. Infirm. Edin.

ALLAN, Stuart James West Cumberland Hospital, Homewood, Whitehaven CA28 8JG — BM BS 1992 Nottm.

ALLAN, Susan Elizabeth The Surgery, 6 Queens Walk, Ealing, London W5 1TP Tel: 020 8997 3041 Fax: 020 8566 9100 — MB BChir 1971 Camb.; MB Camb. 1971, BChir 1970; DObst RCOG 1974; DCH Eng. 1973. (Camb.)

ALLAN, Terence Corduff Bosmere Medical Practice, PO Box 41, Civic Centre Road, Havant PO9 2AJ Tel: 023 9245 1300 Fax: 023 9249 2524 Email: bosmeremedical@cs.com — MB BS 1978 Lond.; MRCGP 1982 DRCOG 1980.

ALLAN, Theodore Martin (retired) 127 Broomhill Road, Aberdeen AB10 6JB Tel: 01224 586105 — MB ChB 1941 Aberd. Prev: Asst. Dir. NE Scotl. Blood Transfus. Serv.

ALLAN, Thomas Lindsay Haematology Department, Wishaw General Hospital, Netherton St., Wishaw ML2 Tel: 01698 361100; 25 Garngaber Avenue, Lenzie, Glasgow G66 4LL Tel: 0141 776 6538 — MB ChB 1968 Glas.; PhD Glas. 1983; FRCPath 1994, M 1982. (Glas.) Cons. (Haemat.) Wishaw Gen. Hosp. Wishaw. Prev: Sen. Regist. (Haemat.) Hammersmith Hosp. Lond. & W. Middlx. Hosp. Lond.; Regist. (Haemat.) Stobhill Gen. Hosp. Glas.

ALLAN, Thomas William Bruce 18 Robin Lane, Edgmond, Newport TF10 8JN — MB BS 1991 Lond. (St. Thomas's Hospital)

ALLAN, Walter Morison (retired) Gowanea, 74 Bo'ness Road, Grangemouth FK3 9BL Tel: 01324 482536 — MB ChB 1942 Glas. Prev: Clin. Asst. Stoneyetts Ment. Hosp.

ALLAN, Mr Walter Ramsay Heath House, Knowsley Grange, Chorley New Road, Bolton BL1 5DQ — MB ChB 1951 Ed.; BA Oxf. 1948; FRCS Eng. 1959; FRCS Ed. 1958. Cons. Surg. Bolton Roy. Infirm. & Bolton Dist. Hosp. Socs: Assoc. Mem. Brit. Assn. Urol. Surgs; Fell. Manch. Med. Soc.

ALLAN, William The Health Centre, Gosber Road, Eckington, Sheffield S21 4BZ Tel: 01246 432131; 11 Ambleside Close, Halfway, Sheffield S20 4GA — MB ChB 1957 Glas. (Glas.)

ALLAN, Yvonne D. Yellow Practice, Drumhar Health Centre, North Methven Street, Perth PH1 5PD Fax: 01738 643757 — MB ChB 1989 Glas.; MFFP 1995; BSc (Hons.) Glas. 1986; MRCOG 1995. (Glasgow University) GP Princip.s. Prev: Regist. (O & G) Qu. Charlottes & Ealing Hosps.

ALLANBY, Charles Williamson Clifton Surgery, 151-153 Newport Road, Roath, Cardiff CF24 1AG Tel: 029 2049 4539/2049 0944 Fax: 029 2049 4657 Email: charles.allanby@gp-w97060.wales.nhs.uk; 22 Ty Draw Road, Roath, Cardiff CF23 5HB Fax: 01222 494657 — MB BS 1979 Lond.; DRCOG 1982; Cert FPA IUD 1982. (Guy's) Treas. Brotaf LMC. Socs: Cardiff Med. Soc. Prev: SHO (Paediat., O & G & Gen. Med.) Guy's Hosp. Lewisham & N. S.wark HA.

ALLANBY, Kenneth Derwent (retired) Staddle Barn, Back Lane, Morcott, Oakham LE15 9DG — MB BS 1945 Lond.; MD (Univ. Medal) Lond. 1951; FRCP Lond. 1969, M 1947. Prev: Cons. Phys. P'boro. DHA.

ALLANSON, Judith Rivermead Rehabilitation Centre, Abingdon Road, Oxford OX1 4XD Tel: 01865 240321 Fax: 01865 200185; Rimes Cottage, Rimes Farm Lane, Kingston Bagpuize, Abingdon OX13 5AY — BM BCh 1986 Oxf.; PhD (Ceremony Awarded) Camb. 1995; BA Camb. 1983; MRCP (UK) 1992. (Camb. Oxf.) Sen. Regist. Rehabil. Rivermead Rehabil. Centre Abingdon Rd. Oxf./Recliffe Infirm. NHS Trust. Socs: Assn. ABN; BSRM; Brain Res. Assn. Prev: Regist. (Neurol.) The Roy. Lond. Hosp.; Wellcome Foundat. Med. Grad. Fell. MRC Research Centre Camb.

ALLANSON, Mavis Jean (retired) 'Hedgeways', 66 Newhall Lane, Bolton BL1 5LG Tel: 01204 40508 — MB ChB 1952 Glas.; DObst RCOG 1954. Prev: Sen. Med. Off. (Social Security) Manch.

ALLANSON, Nicola Kay 23 Hanover Road, Norwich NR2 2HD — MB BS 1990 Lond.

ALLAQABAND, Ghulam Qadir 3 Newman Court, Spinneyfield, Rotherham S60 3JA — MB BS 1960 Madras; FRCP Ed. 1981; MRCP Ed. 1964.

ALLARD, Louise Lilian Charcoal House, Market Place, Colerne, Chippenham SN14 8DF — MB ChB 1990 Bristol; Dip. Geriatric Med. Clin. Asst. Rheum., RNHRD Bath; Clin. Asst. Cardiol. RUH Bath. Socs: Assoc. Mem. Research & Rehabil. Soc. Prev: SHO (O & G) Roy. United Hosp. Bath; SHO (Geriat. Med.) Manor Pk. Hosp. Bristol; Staff Grade (A & E) RUH Bath.

ALLARD, Sally Anne Doctors Surgery, Newton Way, Baildon, Shipley BD17 5NH Tel: 01274 582506 Fax: 01274 532426; 36 Bromley Road, Shipley BD18 4DT Tel: 01274 587665 — MB ChB 1986 Manch.; DRCOG 1991.

ALLARD, Shubha Northwick Park & St Marks NHS Trust, Watford Road, Harrow HA1 3UJ Tel: 020 8864 3232 Fax: 020 869 2745 Email: haem.nph@pipex.com — MRCP UK; MRCP 1993; FRCP 1999 UK. Cons. Haemat. N.wick Pk. & St Mark's Hosp. Trust Harrow. Prev: Sen. Regist. (Haemat.) St. Geo. Hosp. Lond. & Roy. Marsden Hosp. Sutton; Clin. Research Fell. Dept. Med. Univ. Leeds.

ALLARD, Simon Andrew Department of Medicine, West Middlesex University Hospital, Twickenham Road, Isleworth TW7 6AF Tel: 020 8565 5370 Fax: 020 8565 5371 Email: simon.allard@wmuh-tr.nthames.nhs.uk; Tel: 020 8997 7087 Fax: 020 8991 1433 Email: drsallard@aol.com — MB BS 1979 Lond.; MD 1992; FRCP Lond. 1995; MRCP (UK) 1983. Cons. (Med. & Rheum.) W. Middlx. Univ. Hosp. Isleworth; Hon. Sen. Lect. Imperial Coll. Sch. Med. Lond. Socs: Fell. Roy. Soc. Med.; Brit. Soc. Rheum.; Roy. Coll. of Phys.s. Prev: Sen. Regist. (Med. & Rheum.) St. Geo.s Hosp. Lond.; ARC Research Fell. & Hon. Regist. Kennedy Inst. Rheum. & Char. Cross Hosp. Lond.; Regist. (Med. & Rheum.) Char. Cross Hosp. Lond.

ALLARDICE, James Todd Tara Cottage, Brookbottom, Strines, High Peak SK22 3AY Tel: 0161 427 1849 — MB ChB 1952 St. And.; MFOM 1980; DIH Eng. 1964. Employm. Med. Adviser N. & W. Yorks.

ALLARDICE, Mr James Todd Little Grove Clinic, Rue De Haut, St Lawrence, Jersey JE3 1JZ Tel: 01534 625000 Fax: 01534 625575; Briville, Rue Du Tas De Geon, Trinity, Jersey JE3 5AN Tel: 01534

866800 Fax: 01534 866811 — MB BS 1980 Lond.; BSc Lond. 1977, MS 1991; FRCS Eng. 1985; FRCS Ed. 1984. (Lond. Hosp.) Cons. Surg. (Gen. Surg.) Gen. Hosp. St. Helier, Jersey. Socs: Brit. Assn. Surg. Oncol; Eur. Soc. Mastol.; Assn. Coloproctol. Prev: Sen. Regist. (Gen. Surg.) Roy. Lond. Hosp.; Clin. Lect. (Surg.) Lond. Hosp. Med. Centre Lond.

ALLARDICE, Sheena Malloch 4 Hermitager Road, Broughty Ferry, Dundee DD5 2HY Tel: 01382 776710 — MB ChB 1943 St. And.; DPH 1948. (Dundee) Prev: Coll. of Educat. Dundee; Asst. Med. Off. Matern. & Child Welf. Dept. Dundee.

ALLARDYCE, Judith Grace Shankland 28 Inchgotrick Road, Kilmarnock KA1 4UJ — MB ChB 1989 Aberd.

ALLARDYCE, Kenneth David (retired) 4 Vicarage Gardens, Scunthorpe DN15 7AZ Tel: 01724 843041 Email: ken.allardyce@virgin.net — MB ChB 1957 Glas.; DObst RCOG 1959. Prev: GP Scunthorpe.

ALLASON-JONES, Erica Department of Genitourinary Medicine, Mortimer Market, (Off Capper Street), London WC1E 6AU Tel: 020 7530 5055 Fax: 020 7530 5044 — MB ChB 1978 Liverp.; MD Liverp. 1993; FRCP Lond. 1995; MRCP (UK) 1981. Cons. Genitourin. Med. Camden & Islington Community Health Servs. NHS Trust Lond.; Hon. Sen. Lect. (Genitourin. Med.) UCL. Socs: Med. Soc. Study VD; Assn. Genitourin. Med. Prev: Lect. & Hon. Sen. Regist. (Genitourin. Med.) Middlx. Hosp. Med. Sch. Lond.

ALLATT, Jillian Margaret CMHT(E), Kildean Hospital, Drip Road, Stirling FK8 1RW Tel: 01786 446615 — MB ChB 1984 Ed.; MRCGP 1988. (University of Edinburgh) Staff Grade Psychogeriat. CMHT (E) Stirling. Prev: Regist. (Psychiat.) Dingleton Hosp. Melrose; Trainee GP Borders HB VTS.

ALLAUN, David Henry Monton Medical Centre, Canal Side, Monton Green, Eccles, Manchester M30 8AR; 6 The Downs, Schools Hill, Cheadle SK8 1JL Tel: 0161 428 9950 — MB ChB 1967 Manch.; DA Eng. 1971; DObst RCOG 1969. (Manch.) Socs: Brit. Soc. Med. & Dent. Hypn. Prev: Ho. Off. Surg. Manch. Roy. Infirm.; SHO (Anaesth.) Crumpsall Hosp. Manch.; Ho. Off. O & G Withington Hosp. Manch.

ALLAWAY, Mr Adrian John Drove House, Hamsey, Lewes BN8 5TA Tel: 01273 487331 Fax: 01273 487331 Email: adrian_allaway@dial.pipex.com — MB BS 1966 Lond.; FRCS Eng. 1974; FRCS Ed. 1972; MRCS Eng. LRCP Lond. 1966. (Roy. Free) Cons. Paediat. Surg. Roy. Alexandra Hosp. Sick Childr. Brighton.

ALLAWAY, Ernest John 10 Kinghtlow Road, Birmingham B17 8QB Tel: 0121 429 3200 — MB ChB 1946 Birm.; MRCS Eng. LRCP Lond. 1946. (Birm.) Prev: Cas. Off. Walsall Gen. Hosp.; Ho. Surg. Qu. Eliz. Hosp. Birm.

ALLAWAY, Glen William Lower Lodge, Springrove, Milverton, Taunton TA4 1NL — MB BS 1996 Lond.; BSc Lond. 1993. (Kings London)

ALLBESON, Michael Penkridge Medical Practice, St. Michael's Road, Penkridge, Stafford ST19 5AJ Tel: 01785 712300 Fax: 01785 713696; Tarnside, Dunston Heath, Stafford ST18 9AN Tel: 01785 712300 — MB ChB 1970 Manch.; MRCGP 1979; MRCP (UK) 1975. (Manch.) Research Fell. Keele Univ.; Hosp. Pract. (Chest Med.) Stafford; GP Trainer. Socs: Eur. Respirat. Soc. Prev: Ho. Off. Manch. Roy. Infirm.; Resid. Med. Off. St. Barnabas Hosp. Dogura, Papua New Guinea; Regist. (Med.) P.ss Alexandra Hosp. Brisbane, Austral.

ALLBRIGHT, Martin 6 Cockshot Road, Malvern WR14 2TT Tel: 01684 893393 — MB BS 1981 Lond.; AcM CTA 1993; BAc CTA 1990; LicAc 1986; DRCOG 1986; DA Eng. 1983. Clinic Traditional Chinese Acupunc. Malvern. Prev: Dir. W.. Sci. Coll. of Traditional Acupunc. Leamington.

ALLBRIGHT, Susan Elizabeth Little Applecroft, 6 Cockshot Road, Malvern WR14 2TT — MB ChB 1984 Birm.; DRCOG 1986. p/t Clin. Asst. - Child & Adolesc. Psychiat. Worcester; Clin. Asst. - Antenatal Clinic Worcester. Prev: Sch. Med. Off. Malvern Girls Sch.; Clin. Asst. (Psychogeriat.) Kidderminster Gen. Hosp.; Clin. Asst. Palliat. med. St Richards Hospice Worcs.

ALLCHIN, Mr Robert William 8 Grange Terrace, Sunderland SR2 7DF Tel: 0191 510 0555 Fax: 0191 656 5998 — MB BChir 1972 Camb.; MA Camb. 1973; FRCS Eng. 1977; FRCOphth. 1988; DO RCS Eng. 1976. Cons. Ophth. Surg. Sunderland Eye Infirm. & Hartlepool Dist. Gen. Hosp. Socs: Coll. Ophth. & Intra-Ocular Implant Soc.; N. of Engl. Ophth. (Pres. Elect 2000-1); Oxf. Ophth. Congr. Prev: Regist. & Sen. Regist. Moorfields Eye Hosp. Lond.

ALLCOCK, Alan Charles The Health House, 1 Wootton Street, Cosham, Portsmouth PO6 3AP Tel: 023 9238 1118 Fax: 023 9232 6379 — MB BChir 1975 Camb.; MA, MB BChir Camb. 1975; DRCOG 1978.

ALLCOCK, Catherine Green Bank, Lowes Lane, Gawsworth, Macclesfield SK11 9QR — MB ChB 1997 Glas.

ALLCOCK, Damian Michael 8 Egerton Road S., Manchester M21 0YP — MB ChB 1989 Manch.

ALLCOCK, Helen Hebden Bridge Health Centre, Hangingroyd Lane, Hebden Bridge HX7 6AG Tel: 01422 842333 Fax: 01422 842404 — MB ChB 1985 Sheff.; MRCGP 1989.

ALLCOCK, Jonathan Nicholas Flat 7 Honeybee Cottages, Wells Close, Husbands Bosworth, Lutterworth — BM BS 1985 Nottm.

ALLCOCK, Liesl Marie Department of Geriatrics, Royal Victoria Infirmary, Newcastle upon Tyne — BM BCh 1992 Oxf.; BA Camb. 1989; MRCP (UK) 1995. Regist. (Elderly Care), Roy. Vict. Infirm., Newc. Socs: BGS. Prev: Regist. (Med) Tauranga Hosp., New Zealand; SHO (Med.) Newc. HA.; Ho. Off. (Med.) John Radcliffe Hosp. Oxf.

ALLCOCK, Mr Paul Alexander Department of Orthopaedics, Ninewells Hospital, Dundee DD1 9SY — MB ChB 1991 Glas.; FRCS Glas. 1995. Regist. (Orthop.) Dundee Teachg. Hosps. Prev: SHO (Orthop.) Roy. Alexandra Hosp. Paisley.

ALLCOCK, Robert John Royal Victoria Infirmary, Victoria Road, Newcastle upon Tyne NE44 6EJ Tel: 0191 2325131 Email: r.j.allcock@ncl.ac.uk; Low Shilford House, Riding Mill, nr Stocksfield NE43 7HW Email: r.j.allcock@ncl.ac.uk — BM BCh 1992 Oxf.; BA Camb. 1989; MRCP (UK) 1995. Res. Fell (Pulm. Vasc.) Freeman Hosp., Newc.; Specialist Regist. Respiratary Med. Socs: Brit. Thoracic Soc.; Europ. Respirat. Soc.; Amer. Thoracic Soc. Prev: Regist. (Gen. Pract.), Corbridge, N.umberland; Regist. (Respirat. Med.) S. Tynside Trust; Regist. (Gen. Med.) Tauranga Hosp., New Zealand.

ALLCOCK, Steven 32 Scofield Road, Peel Green, Eccles, Manchester M30 7LG Tel: 0161 707 4569 — MB ChB 1986 Liverp.; FRCPS Glas. 1991.

ALLDAY, Richard Kime (retired) 80 Sleaford Road, Boston PE21 8EU Tel: 01205 353231 — MB BS 1952 Lond.; MRCS Eng. LRCP Lond. 1952. Prev: Ho. Surg. (O & G) Ipswich Hosp. Gp.

ALLDRICK, Arthur Richard Health Clinic, 407 Main Road, Dovercourt, Harwich CO12 4ET Tel: 01255 201299 Fax: 01255 201270 — MB BCh 1975 Wales; FFA RCS Eng. 1982.

ALLDRICK, Margaret Delyth Martyr Worthy, Main Road, Peterston-Super-Ely, Vale of Glamorgan, Cardiff CF5 6LH Tel: 01446 760295 Email: hurley@geofflexlex.u-net.com; Whitchurch Hospital, Park Road, Whitchurch, Cardiff CF14 7XB Tel: 029 2033 6479 Fax: 029 206 2103 — MB BCh 1975 Wales; MRCPsych. 1982; FRCPsych 1998. Cons. Psychiat. with special responsibil. for Psychogeriat. WhitCh. Hosp. Cardiff.; Assoc. Med. Director of the Ment. Health Serv. Gp. of Cardiff & Vale NHS Trust.

ALLDRIDGE, Douglas George Edward (retired) 158 Station Road, Redhill RH1 1HF Tel: 01737 765205 — MB BS Lond. 1950; MRCS Eng. LRCP Lond. 1950. Prev: GP Redhill.

ALLEBONE, Philip (retired) Fourth House, 227 Newton Road, Burton-on-Trent DE15 0TU Tel: 01283 561824 — MB BChir 1948 Camb.; MA Camb. 1948; MRCS Eng. LRCP Lond. 1944; MRCGP 1952; DObst RCOG 1949. Prev: Clin. Asst. (Med.) St. Thos. Hosp.

ALLELY, Peter Robert 8 Merron Mews, Dungannon BT71 6FD — MB BCh BAO 1997 Belf.

ALLEN, Agnes Josephine 68 Dublin Road, Omagh BT78 1HQ Tel: 01662 243686 — MRCS Eng. LRCP Lond. 1964; DA RCPSI 1969; DObst RCOG 1965. (Manch.) Med. Assessor Indep. Tribunal Serv. (N.I.).

ALLEN, Alison Rosalind 9 Fairway Avenue, Belfast BT9 5NL — MB BCh BAO 1991 Belf.; MB BCh Belf. 1991.

ALLEN, Amy Mary 24 Crabmill Close, Knowle, Solihull B93 0NP Tel: 01564 776642 — MB ChB 1950 Birm. Prev: Ho. Phys. Gen. Hosp. Birm.

ALLEN, Andrew James Park Surgery, 25 The Park, Yeovil BA20 1DG Tel: 01935 474196 Fax: 01935 411429; West Wing, Ham Hill House, Stoke-sub-Hamdon TA14 6RQ — MB ChB 1987 Birm.; MRCGP 1991; DCH RCP Lond. 1991. Prev: Dist. Med. Off. Commonw. of Dominica; GP SE Lond.

ALLEN, Andrew Roger Renal Unit, Hammersmith Hospital, Du Cane Road, Acton, London W12 0NN Tel: 020 8383 2310 Fax: 020 8746 2410 Email: a.allen@rpms.ac.uk; Flat 2, 4 Prince Albert Road, London NW1 7SN — BM BCh 1990 Oxf.; BA Oxf. 1987; MRCP (UK) 1993. Research Fell./Hon. Sen. Regist. (Renal Med.) Hammersmith Hosp. Socs: Renal Assn. Prev: Lect. (Renal Med.) Hammersmith Hosp. Lond.; Sen. Regist. (Renal Med.) King's Coll. Hosp. Lond.

ALLEN, Anthony James Chestnut Cottage, The Green, Claverdon, Warwick CV35 8LL Tel: 01926 842780 Fax: 01926 842874 Email: aajallen@aol.com — MB ChB 1951 Birm.; MRCS Eng. LRCP Lond. 1951; MRCGP 1963. Socs: Sands Cox Med. Soc.

ALLEN, Anthony Phillip The Green Practice, Waterside Health Centre, Beaulieu Road, Hythe SO45 4WX Tel: 023 8084 5955 — MB BS 1979 Lond.; BA Camb. 1976; MRCP (UK) 1982; MRCGP 1985; DRCOG 1985. (Camb. & St. Bart.) Clin. Lead Coronary Heart Dis., New Forest PCT; Clin. Lead, Coronary Heart Dis. for New Forest PCT. Socs: BMA. Prev: Regist. (Med.) Soton. HA.

ALLEN, Arthur Walter Shaftesbury Medical Centre, 480 Harehills Lane, Leeds LS9 6DE Tel: 0113 248 5631 Fax: 0113 235 0658; Greenacres, Wetherby Road, Scarcroft, Leeds LS14 3AS Tel: 0113 892698 — MB ChB 1965 Leeds; MRCGP 1975. (Leeds)

ALLEN, Barbara Dorothy (retired) 16 Thornhill, Banbridge BT32 4LT — BA Open 1989; MB BCh BAO Belf. 1952; DCH Eng. 1955; DObst RCOG 1954. Prev: Clin. Med. Off. S.. Health & Social Serv. Bd.

ALLEN, Bernard Roger 11 Regent Street, Nottingham NG1 5BS Tel: 0115 947 5475 Fax: 0115 924 1606; Vinetree Cottage, 9 Main St., Bunny, Nottingham NG11 6QU Tel: 0115 921 3404 Fax: 0115 984 3408 Email: brallen@aol.com — MB ChB 1964 Bristol; FRCP Lond. 1983, M 1970. Cons. Dermat. Univ. Hosp. Nottm.

ALLEN, Catherine Clare Tollbar House, 107 Ashover Road, Old Tupton, Chesterfield S42 6HQ — MB ChB 1998 Manch.; MB ChB Manch 1998.

ALLEN, Christina Helen 60 Willow Road, Bournville, Birmingham B30 2AS — MB ChB 1985 Birm.

ALLEN, Christine Margaret Halton General Hospital, Hospital Way, Runcorn WA7 2DA Tel: 01928 714567; 55 The Croft, Halton Brow, Runcorn WA7 2EX Tel: 01928 575197 — MB BS 1983 Newc. Staff Grade Pract. (Gen. Med. & c/o Elderly) Halton Gen. Hosp.

ALLEN, Christopher 50 Micklehome Drive, Burton-on-Trent DE13 7AU — MB ChB 1995 Bristol.

ALLEN, Christopher Andrew Manor Hospital, Moat Road, Walsall WS2 9PS Tel: 01922 721172 Email: chris-allen@isses3.freeserve.co.uk; 14 Archers Close, Heron Water, Droitwich WR9 9LH Tel: 01905 770970 — MB ChB 1983 Birm.; BSc Birm. 1980; MRCP (UK) 1986; MRCPath 1991; FRCP 2000 (path). Cons. Histopath. Manor Hosp. Walsall. Prev: Sen. Regist. (Histopath.) Russells Hall Hosp. Dudley; Regist. Rotat. (Histopath.) W. Midl. RHA; SHO Rotat. (Gen. Path.) Gen. Hosp. Birm.

ALLEN, Christopher John Fownhope Medical Centre, Commonhill Lane, Fownhope, Hereford HR1 4PZ Tel: 01432 860235 Fax: 01432 860900 — MRCS Eng. LRCP Lond. 1974.

ALLEN, Christopher Michael Colquhoun Department of Neurology, Addenbrooke's Hospital, Cambridge CB2 2QQ Tel: 01223 216759 Fax: 01223 336941 Email: cmca100@cam.ac.uk; 232 Hills Road, Cambridge CB2 2QE Tel: 01223 247694 Fax: 01223 414904 Email: chrisallen@doctors.org.uk — MB BChir 1974 Camb.; 1973 BChir Camb.; 1974 MB Camb.; 1974 MA Camb.; 1984 MD Camb.; 1991 FRCP Lond.; 1975 MRCP (UK). (Univ. Camb. (Christ's College) and Guy's) Cons. Neurol. Addenbrooke's Hosp. Camb.; Dean Univ. Camb. Clin. Sch. Socs: Assn. Brit. Neurol.; BMA. Prev: Sen. Regist. (Neurol.) Char. Cross Hosp. Lond.; Regist. (Neurol.) Middlx. Hosp. Lond.; Research Asst. & Hon. Sen. Regist. (Neurol.) Guy's Hosp. Lond.

ALLEN, Claire Suzanne 122 Gloucseter Road, Bishopston, Bristol BS7 8NL Tel: 0117 942 5315 — MB ChB 1983 Bristol; MRCGP 1987. Asst. GP Bristol. Prev: Ho. Phys. Ham Green Hosp.; Ho. Surg. Gloucester Roy. Hosp.; Cheltenham & Gloucester HA. VTS.

ALLEN, Clare Mary 15 The Common, Ealing, London W5 3TR — BM BCh 1985 Oxf.; FRCR 1991. Cons. (Radiol.) Centr. Middlx. Hosp. Lond. Prev: Sen. Regist. (Diag. Radiol.) Univ. Coll. & Middlx. Hosp. Lond.; Regist. (Diag. Radiol.) St. Geo. Hosp. Lond.

ALLEN, Colin Douglas 31 Chailey Avenue, Rottingdean, Brighton BN2 7GH — MRCS Eng. LRCP Lond. 1961; MD Lond. 1971, MB BS 1961; FRCP Lond. 1985; MRCP (UK) 1964. Assoc. Prof. & Staff Neurol. Dartmouth-Hitchcock Med. Center Lebanon, New Hants., USA; Assoc. Prof. Med. Dartmouth Med. Sch., USA. Socs: Assn. Brit. Neurols. & Amer. Acad. Neurol.; Amer. Med. Assn. Prev: Cons. Neurol. Univ. Hosp. S. Manch. & Salford Roy. Hosps.; Regist. Nat. Hosp. Nerv. Dis. Lond.; Regist. Lond. Hosp.

ALLEN, Mr Colin Laurence Owen Saxon Well, Causeway, Garth Lane, Old Thorpe, Audlin, Pontefract WF8 3HD Tel: 01977 620108 — MRCS Eng. LRCP Lond. 1966; FRCS Eng. 1976.

ALLEN, Daniel Stephen 1 Cedar Avenue, Hazlemere, High Wycombe HP15 7DW Tel: 01494 711130 Fax: 01494 713383 Email: dsallen@globalnet.co.uk — MB BS 1979 Lond.; MRCPsych 1990; MRCGP 1987. (Middl. Hosp. Med. Sch.) Cons. Psychiat. Bucks. Ment. Health NHS Trust, High Wycombe. Prev: Sen. Regist. Rotat (Psychiat.) Bristol; Regist. (Psychiat.) Basingstoke HA; Trainee GP Basingstoke.

ALLEN, Daphne Elizabeth Airedale General Hospital, Skipton Road, Steeton, Keighley BD20 6TD Tel: 01535 652511 — BM BCh 1971 Oxf.; FRCP Lond. 1994; DCH Eng. 1975; DObst RCOG 1974. (Oxf. Univ. Med. Sch.) Cons. Phys. (Med. for the Elderly) Airedale Gen. Hosp. Keighley.

ALLEN, Daphne Mary (retired) Fairhaven, Beach Road, Port St Mary IM9 5NG — MB ChB 1958 Bristol; DObst RCOG 1973.

ALLEN, David James Cullybackey Health Centre, Tober Park, Cullybackey, Ballymena BT42 1NR Tel: 028 2588 0505 Fax: 028 2588 1916 — MB BCh BAO 1974 Belf.; MRCGP 1978; DRCOG 1977.

ALLEN, David John Omega, Lowes Lane, Gawsworth, Macclesfield SK11 9QR; 11 Orchard St, West Didsbury, Manchester M20 2LP Tel: 0161 434 1792 Email: dj.allen@btinternet.com — MB ChB 1994 Manch. SHO Med., S. Manch. Univ. Hosp. Prev: SHO Preston.

ALLEN, David John 4 Ainsdale Court, Kilwinning KA13 6QD — MB ChB 1994 Dundee.

ALLEN, David Julian Lowesmoor Medical Centre, 93 Lowesmoor, Worcester WR1 2SA Tel: 01905 727874 Fax: 01905 724987 — MB BS 1980 Lond.; MRCGP 1985; DRCOG 1985; DCH RCP Lond. 1984.

ALLEN, David Leslie 20 Bankfield Drive, Worsley, Manchester M28 1GA — MB BS 1986 Monash.

ALLEN, Mr David Robyn Royal West Sussex Hospital, St Richards, Spitafield Lane, Chichester PO19 4SE Tel: 01243 788122; Stanes Cottage, Adsdean, Nr. Funtington, Chichester PO18 9DW Tel: 01243 576178 — MB BS 1978 Lond.; MS Lond. 1988; FRCS Eng. 1982. (Char. Cross) Cons. Surg. St. Richards Hosp. Chichester. Prev: Sen. Regist. Soton. & Bath; Lect. (Surg.) St. Thos. Hosp. Lond.

ALLEN, Dawn Beverley Penkridge Medical Practice, St. Michael's Road, Penkridge, Stafford ST19 5AJ Tel: 01785 712300 Fax: 01785 713696; Dorcas, Mitton Road, Bradley, Stafford ST18 9EA — BM BS 1982 Nottm.; BMedSci 1980. Prev: Regist. (Med.) Norwich Hosp.

ALLEN, Deborah Manor Cottage, Main St., Heath, Chesterfield S44 5RX — MB ChB 1988 Sheff.

ALLEN, Deborah Karen 496 Chester Way, London SE11 4UR — MB BS 1992 Lond.

ALLEN, Denis John 65 Towngate, Silkstone, Barnsley S75 4SW — MB ChB 1985 Sheff.

ALLEN, Derek Creswell Histopathology Laboratory, Belfast City Hospital, Belfast BT9 7AD Tel: 01232 329241 — MD 1988 Belf.; MB BCh BAO 1980; MRCPath 1986; T(Path) 1991. Cons. Histopath. & Cytopath. Belf. City Hosp.

ALLEN, Duncan Kirk 27 Carmichael Place, Langside, Glasgow G42 9UE — MB ChB 1989 Dundee; FRCA. Specialist Regist. (Anaesth.) Vict. Infirm. Glas. Socs: BMA; Assn. Anaesth.

ALLEN, Edgar David Baylis (retired) Arboretum Cottage, 46 Barton Common Lane, New Milton BH25 5PS Tel: 01425 619157 — MB BS 1952 Lond. Prev: Clin. Asst. (Cardiol.) Hastings Hosp. Gp.

ALLEN, Edmond Brewster Fircroft, Bagshot Road, Englefield Green, Egham TW20 0BS Tel: 01784 432933 — MRCS Eng. LRCP Lond. 1942; MRCGP 1953. (St. Thos.) Med. Examr. various Insur. Cos. Socs: (Pres. Woking & Chertsey Div. & Div. Represen.) BMA. Prev: Clin. Asst. (ENT & VD) St. Thos. Hosp.; Med. Adviser Pk.e-

Davis & Co. Hounslow; Assoc. Mem. World Med. Assn.; (Delegate of Brit. Support Gp. to the Assembly).

ALLEN, Elizabeth Aileen (retired) 21 Letchmore Road, Radlett WD7 8HU Tel: 01923 855579 — MB ChB Ed. 1955.

ALLEN, Elizabeth Kathryn Sandbanks, 3 Compton Road, Kinver, Stourbridge DY7 6DL — MB BS 1997 Lond.

ALLEN, Mr Eric David City Hospitals NHS Trust, Sunderland Royal Hospital, Kayll Road, Sunderland SR4 7TP Tel: 0191 560 9110 Email: david.allen@chs.northy.nhs.uk; 55 The Generals Wood, Washington NE38 9BN Tel: 0191 416 0565 Email: david@allen50.fsnet.co.uk — MB BS 1972 Newc.; BSc (Hons.) Newc. 1969, MB BS 1972; FRCS Eng. 1979; FRCOphth 1988; DO Eng. 1978. Cons. Ophth. Sunderland Eye Infirm.; Med. Dir. City Hosp. Sunderland. Socs: Eur. Soc. Ophth. Plastic & Reconstruc. Surg.; Amer. Soc. Cataract & Refractive Surg.; Eur. Soc. Cataract & Refractive Surg. Prev: Sen. Regist. Norwich & Addenbrooke's Hosp. Camb.; Regist. (Ophth.) Soton. Eye Hosp.; Ho. Off. Roy. Vict. Infirm. Newc.

ALLEN, Fiona Jane The Surgery, East Grinstead Road, Lingfield RH7 6ER Tel: 01342 833456 Fax: 01342 836347; Greenfields, Rabies Heath Road, Bletchingley, Redhill RH1 4LZ Tel: 01883 743266 — MB BS 1980 Lond.; DRCOG 1985; DCH RCP Lond. 1984. (Char. Cross)

ALLEN, Fraser Stewart Greenacres, Wetherby Road, Scarcroft, Leeds LS14 3AS — BM BS 1990 Nottm.

ALLEN, Gareth Bennett Gayton Road Health and Surgical Centre, Gayton Road, King's Lynn PE30 4DY Tel: 01553 762726 Fax: 01553 696819 — MB BS 1983 Lond.

ALLEN, Gareth John 22 Sunningdale Park, Ballymena BT43 5NG — MB BCh 1998 Belf.; MB BCh Belf 1998.

ALLEN, Geoffrey Cannon Street, Oldham OL9 6EP; The Old Lodge, Denshaw Road, Delph, Oldham OL3 5EY Tel: 0161 909 8228 — MB ChB 1970 Manch. Prev: Clin. Asst. (Ophth.) Oldham HA; Ho. Phys. & Ho. Surg. Stepping Hill Hosp. Stockport.

ALLEN, Geoffrey Robert Allen, Moore, Jackson and Ferrer, Wellside Medical Centre, 3 Burton Road, Derby DE1 1TH Tel: 01332 737777 Fax: 01332 737778 — MB ChB 1977 Leeds; MRCGP 1982; DRCOG 1979. Undergrad. Clin. Tutor Nottm. Univ. Med. Sch.

ALLEN, Geoffrey Samuel Skegoneill Health Centre, 195 Skegoneill Avenue, Belfast BT15 3LL Tel: 01232 772471; 23 Connor Road, Parkgate, Templepatrick, Ballyclare BT39 0DY Tel: 01849 433814 — MB BCh BAO 1990 Belf.; MRCGP 1994; DFFP 1995; DRCOG 1993; DGM RCP Lond. 1992.

ALLEN, Geoffrey Thomas Christmas Cottage, 474 Unthank Road, Norwich NR4 7QJ — MRCS Eng. LRCP Lond. 1931; MD Lond. 1949, MB BS 1947; DTM & H Eng. 1947. (Univ. Coll. Lond. & St. Thos.) Prev: Clin. Asst. St. And. Hosp. Norwich; Cons. Pathol. St. James Hosp. Lond.

ALLEN, Georgia Mary 21 Park Place, London W5 5NQ — BM BS 1991 Nottm.

ALLEN, Georgina Marian Castell Mal, Llangynin, St Clears, Carmarthen SA33 4JU — BM 1985 Soton.; MRCP (UK) 1991; FRCR 1996; MRCGP 1989; DCH RCP Lond. 1988.

ALLEN, Geraint The Maples Medical Centre, 2 Scout Drive, Newall Green, Manchester M23 2SY Tel: 0161 498 8484 Fax: 0161 428 9411 — MB ChB 1988 Manch.; MRCGP 1994. (Univ. Manch.)

ALLEN, Giles Matthew 10 Furse Close, Camberley GU15 1BF — MB BS 1996 Lond.

ALLEN, Grace Elvira Department of Dermatology, Belfast City Hospital, Belfast BT9 7AB Tel: 01232 329241 Fax: 01232 326614; The Old Manse, Annahilt, 147 Ballynahinch Road, Hillsborough BT26 6BD — MB BCh BAO 1958 Belf.; MD Belf. 1971; FRCP Ed. 1995; FRCPI 1973; MRCPI 1963. Cons. Dermat. Belf. City Hosp. & Ulster Hosp.

ALLEN, Harry Cochrane White House, 73A Hagley Road, Hayley Green, Halesowen B63 1DR — MB ChB 1952 Ed.; DObst RCOG 1955. Prev: Ho. Phys. Chalmers Hosp. Edin.; Ho. Surg. Marston Green Matern. Hosp. Birm.

ALLEN, Helen Ruth 9 Main Street, Bunny, Nottingham NG11 6QU — MB ChB 1994 Ed.; MRCP 1998; MRCPCH 1999. (Edinburgh) SHO in Paediat. IC. Socs: RCPLond; RCPaed.

ALLEN, Hilary Mavis Brent House Surgery, 14 King Street, Bridgwater TA6 3ND Tel: 01278 458551 Fax: 01278 431116; 17 Queenswood Road, Bridgwater TA6 7NB — MB ChB 1978 Leeds; MRCGP 1982; DRCOG 1981; Cert. Family Plann. JCC 1981. (Leeds) GP Trainer Bridgwater. Prev: Trainee GP Bradford VTS.

ALLEN, Howard Accident & Emergency Department, Morriston Hospital, Swansea SA6 6NL; Pentwyn, Gwynfe, Llangadog SA19 9PG — MB BCh 1981 Wales; MRCP (UK) 1986; DRCOG 1984. Cons. A & E Med. Morriston Hosp. Swansea.

ALLEN, Ian Chisholm Wishaw General Hospital, 50 Netherton Street, Wishaw ML2 0DP Tel: 01698 366349 Fax: 01698 366347 Email: ian.allan@laht.scot.nhs.uk; Tollie, 11 Hagholm Road, Cleghorn, Lanark ML11 7SG Tel: 01555 661975 Email: ian_c_allen@hotmail.com — MB ChB 1968 Glas.; FRCOG 1989, M 1973. (Glas.) Cons. O & G Wishaw Gen. Hosp. Wishaw. Socs: BMA; Glas. Obst. & Gyn. Soc.; (Exec. Treas.) BSPOGA (Brit. Soc. of Psychosomatic Obst., Gyn. and Andrology). Prev: Sen. Regist. (O & G) Qu. Mother's Hosp. & W.. Infirm. Glas.; Regist. (O & G) S.. Gen. Hosp. Glas.; Regist. (Path.) Stobhill Gen. Hosp. Glas.

ALLEN, Ingrid Victoria, CBE Department of Neuropathology, Royal Victoria Hospital, Grosvenor Road, Belfast BT12 6BA Tel: 01232 894742 Fax: 01232 438024 — MB BCh BAO 1957 Belf.; MB BCh BAO (Hons.) Belf. 1957; DSc Belf. 1983, MD (Hons.) 1963; FRCP Ed. 1995; FRCP Glas. 1987; FRCPI 1985; MRCP (UK) 1985; FRCPath 1975, M 1965. (Qu. Univ. Belf.) Prof. Neuropath. Qu. Univ. Belf.; DL; Cons. Neuropath. Roy. Vict. Hosp. Belf. Socs: Path. Soc.; Brit. Neuropath. Soc.; Roy. Irish Acad. 1993. Prev: Tutor (Path.) Qu. Univ. Belf.; Ho. Surg. Roy. Vict. Hosp. Belf.; Musgrave Research Fell. in Path.

ALLEN, James Christopher c/o Department of Anaesthesia, Grampian University NHS Trust, Forestmill Road, Aberdeen AB25 2ZN Tel: 01224 840644 Fax: 01224 685307 Email: j.c.j.allen@abdn.ac.uk; 13 Kettock's Mill Road, Bridge of Don, Aberdeen AB22 8WR — MB ChB 1988 Aberd.; BMedBiol. (Commend.) Aberd. 1986; DA (UK) 1990. (Aberd.) Staff Grade. (Anaesth.) Aberd. Roy. Infirm.; Hon. Clin. Tutor Univ. Aberd. Socs: NE Scotl. Soc. Anaesth.; BMA; Scott. Soc. Anaesth. Prev: Regist. (Anaesth.) Raigmore Hosp. NHS Trust Inverness; Regist. & SHO (Anaesth.) Aberd. Roy. Infirm.; Resid. Ho. Off. (Med., Gen. Surg. & Orthop.) Aberd. Hosps.

ALLEN, James Taylour Doyle (retired) 5 Flacca Court, Field Lane, Tattenhall, Chester CH3 9PW — MB ChB 1944 Liverp. Prev: Clin. Asst. (Allergy) Liverp. Clinic & Alder Hey Childr. Hosp. Liverp.

ALLEN, Jane Margaret Shaw The Surgery, 35A High Street, Wimbledon, London SW19 5BY Tel: 020 8946 4820 Fax: 020 8944 9794; 23 Selwyn Road, New Malden KT3 5AU Tel: 020 8942 7216 — MB BS 1976 Lond.; MRCGP 1981; DRCOG 1978. (Middlx.)

ALLEN, Janet Frances Old Basing Surgery, 2 Linden Court, Linden Avenue, Old Basing, Basingstoke RG24 7HS Tel: 01256 57754; Marlefield, Shalden Green Road, Shalden, Alton GU34 4DT Tel: 01420 83009 — BM 1987 Soton.; MRCGP 1992. Socs: Med. Protec. Soc.; BMA.

ALLEN, Professor Janet Marjorie Div. Biochemistry & Molecular Biology, University of Glasgow, Glasgow G12 8QQ Tel: 0141 330 5189 Fax: 0141 330 4620 Email: j.allen@bio.gla.ac.uk — MB BS 1977 Lond.; BSc (Hons.) Lond. 1974, MD 1986; MRCP (UK) 1980. (Roy. Free) Dir. of Molecular & Cellular Biol. Jouveinal/Pk.e-Davis; Prof. Molecular Med. Univ. Glas.; Hon. Cons. Phys. Med. & Therap. W.ern Infirm. Glas. Prev: Lect. (Physiol.) Univ. Camb.; Wellcome Sen. Fell. Research Clin. Hammersmith Hosp. Lond.; Wellcome Research Fell. Harvard & Mass. Gen. Boston Mass., USA.

ALLEN, Jennifer Alexis Devonshire Lodge Practice, Eastcote Health Centre, Abbotsbury Gardens, Eastcote, Pinner, Ruislip HA5 1TG Tel: 020 8866 0200 Fax: 020 8429 3087 — MB ChB 1975 Birm.; MRCGP 1980. GP Princip.; Jt. Course Organizer Hillingdon VTS.

ALLEN, Mr John Charles 7 Victoria Court, Albert Road, Leicester LE2 2AA — MB BS 1972 Newc.; FRCS Glas. 1985.

ALLEN, John Desmond Physiology, The Queen's University, 97 Lisburn Road, Belfast BT9 7BL Tel: 01232 245133 Fax: 01232 247895; 40 Malone Heights, Belfast BT9 5PG Tel: 01232 615263 — MD 1972 Belf.; MB BCh BAO 1966. Reader in Physiol. Qu. Univ. Belf.; Cons. (Physiol.) E. Health & Social Servs. Bd. N. Irel.

ALLEN, John Patrick Link Cottage, Ship St., East Grinstead RH19 4EF Tel: 01342 325170 — MB BS 1981 Lond.; MRCPath 1988. (St. Thos.) Cons. Histopath. Qu. Vict. Hosp. E. Grinstead.

Prev: Sen. Regist. (Histopath.) King's Coll. Hosp. Lond. & Kingston Hosp. Surrey.

ALLEN, John Pendrell (retired) 172 High Street, Hook, Goole DN14 5PL Tel: 01405 763369 Fax: 01405 718661 Email: john@jpallen30.freeserve.co.uk — MB ChB 1954 Sheff. Prev: Princip. GP N. Humberside.

ALLEN, John Raymond Holly Tree House, 3 The Flags, Yew Tree Avenue, Cartmel, Grange-over-Sands LA11 6PN Tel: 015395 36497 Fax: 015395 36797 Email: medicolegal@bizonline.co.uk — MB ChB 1967 Liverp.; FFAEM 1994. (Liverp.) Director, Cartmel Medicolegal Cons.s; Police Surg. Cumbria Constab. Socs: Fell. Inst. Cert. Ambul. Personnel; Fell. Ambul. Serv. Inst.; Merseyside Medico-Legal Soc. Prev: Cons. A & E Med. BRd.green Hosp. Liverp.; Cons. Emerg. Servs. Hull Roy. Infirm. & Mersey RHA; Med. Asst. (A & E) BRd.green Hosp. Liverp.

ALLEN, John Stephen Daryl 8 Mount Pleasant Park, Newtownabbey BT37 0NJ — MB BCh BAO 1993 Belf.

ALLEN, John Sydney Marine Medical, Blyth Health Centre, Thoroton Street, Blyth NE24 1DX Tel: 01670 396520 Fax: 01670 396537; 1 Wellridge Park, Red House Farm, Whitley Bay NE25 9PQ Tel: 0191 252 5638 — MB ChB 1979 Leeds; DGM RCP Lond. 1990; DRCOG 1982. Hosp. Pract. (Gen. Med.) Blyth Community Hosp. Socs: Roy. Coll. Gen. Pract. & Brit. Geriat. Soc.

ALLEN, John William 4 Leachfield Road, Galgate, Lancaster LA2 0NX — MB ChB 1972 Manch.; MSc Manch. 1977, MB ChB 1972. (Manch.)

ALLEN, Jonathan Andrew Dale Old Forge Surgery, 14 Kilkeel Road, Annalong, Newry BT34 4TH Tel: 028 4376 8218; 16 Mission Road, Ballymartin, Kilkeel, Newry BT34 4PR Tel: 013967 68218 — MB BCh BAO 1983 Belf.; MRCGP 1988; DRCOG 1987.

ALLEN, Jonathan Mark 28 Machin Grove, Gateford, Worksop S81 8TB — MB ChB 1994 Leic.

ALLEN, Jonathan Mark 4A Links Road, Budleigh Salterton EX9 6DF — MB BS 1986 Lond.; MRCGP 1994; DCH RCP Lond. 1990.

ALLEN, Judith Ann Physiology Department, Medical Biology Centre, 97 Lisburn Road, Belfast BT9 7BL Tel: 01232 245133 ext. 2075 Fax: 02890 235483 — MD 1972 Belf.; BSc Belf. 1964, MD 1972, MB BCh BAO 1967. (Belf.) Sen. Lect. Physiol. Qu. Univ. Belf. Socs: Physiol. Soc.

ALLEN, Judith Margaret Deansbridge, Armagh — MB BCh BAO 1984 Dub.

ALLEN, Julian Peter Dyneley House Surgery, Newmarket Street, Skipton BD23 2HZ Tel: 01756 799311 Fax: 01756 707203 — MB BS 1974 Lond.; BSc (Hons. Biochem.) Lond. 1971; MRCP (UK) 1978; MRCS Eng. LRCP Lond. 1974. (St. Bart.)

ALLEN, Justin Norman Bertram Central Street Health Centre, Central Street, Countesthorpe, Leicester LE8 5QJ Tel: 0116 277 6336; The Firs, Main St, Bruntingthorpe, Lutterworth LE17 5QF — MB BS 1969 Lond.; MRCS Eng. LRCP Lond. 1969; FRCGP 1985, M 1977; DObst RCOG 1973. (Guy's) Dep. Dir. of Postgrad. GP Educat., S. Trent Region; Hon. Jt. Sec. Jt. Comm. Postgrad. Train. Gen. Pract. Socs: (Counc.) RCGP.; (Exec. Bd.) Europ. Acad. of Teach.s in Gen. Pract. Prev: Ho. Surg. Guy's Hosp. Lond.; Ho. Phys. Lewisham Hosp.; Intern Pittsfield Gen. Hosp., USA.

ALLEN, Justine Claire 38 Blunts Wood Road, Haywards Heath RH16 1NB — MB ChB 1998 Bristol.

ALLEN, Karen Diana Microbiology Department, Whiston Hospital, Dragon Lane, Prescot L35 5DR — MB ChB 1981 Manch.; FRCPath 1987; Dip. Health Managem. Keele 1993. Cons. Med. Microbiol. St. Helens & Knowsley Hosp. Trust. Prev: Sen. Regist. (Med. Microbiol.) Mersey Regional HA; Regist. (Microbiol.) Roy. Liverp. Hosp.; SHO (Path.) N. Manch. Gen. Hosp.

ALLEN, Karen Heather Church Langley Health Centre, Harlow CM17 9TG Tel: 01279 629707 — MB ChB 1992 Aberd.; DFFP 1996.

ALLEN, Kate Victoria Varclin House, Le Varclin, St Martin's, Guernsey GY4 6AL — BM 1996 Soton.

ALLEN, Katharine Elizabeth Mary (retired) 120 Heathcroft Road, Sutton Coldfield B75 6NJ — MRCS Eng. LRCP Lond. 1934; MA Camb. 1950. Prev: Asst. Co. Med. Off. Glos. CC.

ALLEN, Katherine Mary Department of Public Health, Leicestershire Health, Gwendolen Road, Leicester LE5 4QF Tel: 0116 273 1173 Fax: 0116 258 8722 Email: kate.allen@leics-ha.nhs.uk — MB ChB 1987 Leeds; 1984 BSc (Hons. Psychol.) Leeds; 1995 MPH Nottm.; 1990 DTM & H Liverp.; MFPHM 2000. (Leeds Univ. Med. Sch.) Cons. (Pub. Health Med.), Leics. Health Auth., Leicester. Socs: BMA. Prev: SPR (pub. Health. Med) Leics. Health; SHO (Paediat.) St. Luke's Bradford; Regist. (Pub. Health Med.) Lincolnsh. Health.

ALLEN, Kathryn Elizabeth The New Surgery, 128 Canterbury Road, Folkestone CT19 5NR Tel: 01303 243516 Fax: 01303 244633; Orbost House, 23 Julian Road, Folkestone CT19 5HW — MB BS 1979 Lond.; MRCS Eng. LRCP Lond. 1976; DRCOG 1981. (Guy's)

ALLEN, Kathryn Patricia 20 Ilsham Road, Torquay TQ1 2JQ — MB ChB 1991 Manch.

ALLEN, Katrina Ruth Wells Park Road Surgery, 1 Wells Park Road, London SE26 6JQ Tel: 020 8699 2840 Fax: 020 8699 2552 — MB BS 1980 Adelaide; BA (Hons.) Lond. 1975; DObst. RCOG 1983.

ALLEN, Keith Henry Tel: 01382 461588 Fax: 01382 452121 — MB ChB 1987 Dundee; MRCGP 1991; Dip Occ Med 1999.

ALLEN, Kenneth William Barnsley Health Authority, Hillder House, 49-51 Sawber Road, Barnsley S75 2PY Tel: 01226 777013 Fax: 01226 777013 Email: kenallen@barnsley-ha.nhs.uk; 2 Whirlowdale Crescent, Millhouses, Sheffield S7 2NA Tel: 0114 236 9819 Fax: 0114 236 9819 — MB ChB 1966 Sheff.; MA Camb. 1967; FFPHM RCP (UK) 1995, M 1989; DPH Manch. 1972; DObst RCOG 1969. (Sheff.) Cons. Pub. Health Med. (Communicable Dis. Control) Doncaster & Barnsley HAs; Mem. Inst. promotion Ed; Mem. (Pres.) Pub. Health Med. Environm. GP. Socs: Fell. Soc. Pub. Health Med.; BMA; Aesculapian.Soc. Prev: Regional Epidemiol. (Infec. Dis.) Trent; Dist. Med. Off. Bassetlaw HA; Specialist Community Med. (Health Care Plann. & Monitoring) Trent RHA.

ALLEN, Mr Leonard Norman (retired) 21 Letchmore Road, Radlett WD7 8HU Tel: 01923 855579 Fax: 01923 855579 — MB BS 1954 Lond.; FRCS Eng. 1959; MRCS Eng. LRCP Lond. 1954. Prev: Cons. Urol., WillHo. NHS Trust.

ALLEN, Miss Louise Elizabeth Opthamology Department, Box 41, Addenbrooks Hspital, Hills Rd, Cambridge CB2 2QQ Tel: 01223 216700 — MB BS 1989 Lond.; FRCOphth. 1994. (St. Thomas Hosp. Med. Sch.) Regist. (Ophth.) Addenbrookes Hosp. - Cons. Ophth Surg. Addenbrooks Hosp. Camb. Prev: Clin. Research Fell. Inst. of child health and Gt. Ormond St. Hosp. for Childr. NHS Trust; Sen. Registra (Ophth) Addenbrooks Hosp.; Registra (opth) Birm. Eye Hosp.

ALLEN, Louise Jayne 42 Darley Abbey Dr, Darley Abbey, Derby DE22 1EF — MB ChB 1997 Leeds.

ALLEN, Lucy-Claire Department of Paediatrics, Friarage Hospital, Northallerton DL6 1JG; Flat 19, Castle Hill Court, 72 Bournemouth Road, Poole BH14 0EY — BM BS 1994 Nottm.; BMedSci Nottm. 1992. GP Regist. Cleveland VTS.

ALLEN, Lucy Mary Cwmbran Village Surgery, Victoria Street, Cwmbran NP44 3JS Tel: 01633 871177 Fax: 01633 860234 — MB BS 1987 Lond.; MRCGP 1995; DRCOG 1992. (Lond. Hosp. Med. Coll.) Prev: Regist. (Med.) Chase Farm Hosp.; SHO (O & G) Nevill Hall Hosp.; SHO (Med.) Chelmsford Hosp. & Roy. Lond. Hosp.

ALLEN, Margaret Elizabeth Department of Rheumatology, Univ. Hospital of Coventry & Warwickshire, Clifford Bridge Road, Coventry CV2 2DX Tel: 024 76 602020 Fax: 024 76 538778 Email: magsallen@aol.com; White Cottage, Coventry Road, Kenilworth CV8 2FU Tel: 01926 777784 Fax: 01926 777785 — BM 1986 Soton.; 1986 BM Soton; 1997 PhD Birm.; 1982 BSc (Hons.) Lond.; 1989 MRCP (UK). Cons. Rheum. Univ. Hosp. of Coventry & Warks. NHS Trust. Socs: Brit. Soc. Rheum.; Brit. Soc. Immunol.; BMA. Prev: Clin. Research Fell. Univ. Birm.; Regist. (Rheum.) Bloomsbury Rheum. Unit. Lond.; Clin. Lect. (Rheum.) Univ. Birm.

ALLEN, Maria Jane 28 Machin Grove, Gateford, Worksop S81 8TB — MB ChB 1994 Leic. Socs: Insp., Roy. Coll. Psychiatr.

ALLEN, Mark James Royal Marsden Hospital, Fulham Road, London SW3 6JJ Tel: 020 7352 8171; Flat C, 255 Hackney Road, London E2 8NA — MB ChB 1992 Ed.; MRCP (UK) 1997. Specialist Regist. (Med. Oncol.) Roy. Marsden Hosp. Lond. Prev: SHO (Oncol.) Roy. Marsden Hosp. Lond.; SHO (Oncol.) Middlx. Hosp. Lond.; SHO Harefield Hosp. Middlx.

ALLEN, Mark William Maltings Surgery, 8 Victoria Street, St Albans AL1 3JB Tel: 01727 855500 Fax: 01727 845537 — MB BS

1982 Lond.; MA Camb. 1983; MRCP (UK) 1986; MRCGP 1989. GP Tutor St. Albans City Hosp. Prev: Regist. (Med.) N.lands Base Hosp. Whangare, NZ.

ALLEN, Martin Brent Department Respiratory Medicine, City General Hospital, London Road, Stoke-on-Trent ST4 6QG Tel: 01782 553055 Fax: 01782 552323 — MB ChB 1979 Birm.; FRCP Lond. 1997; MRCP (UK) 1982; FCCP 1996. (Birm.) Cons. Phys. N. Staffs. NHS Trust. Socs: Brit. Thorac. Soc.; Brit. Sleep Soc.; Amer. Thoracic Soc. Prev: Cons. Phys. St. Luke's Hosp. Bradford; Sen. Regist. (Respirat. & Gen. Med.) Yorks. RHA; Regist. Chest Unit City Hosp. Edin.

ALLEN, Martin Paul Woodland Road Surgery, 57 Woodland Road, Northfield, Birmingham B31 2HZ Tel: 0121 475 1065 Fax: 0121 475 6179 — MB ChB 1983 Leic.; MRCGP 1987; DRCOG 1987. Prev: SHO (Paediat) S. Derbysh. HA.; Trainee GP Boston VTS; Ho. (Cardiol. & Gen. Med.) Groby Rd. Hosp. Leics.

ALLEN, Mary-Elizabeth Ancrum Medical Centre, 12-14 Ancrum Road, Dundee DD2 2HZ Tel: 01382 669316 Fax: 01382 660787 — MB ChB 1987 Dundee.

ALLEN, Mary Theresa Allen, Crossmaglen Health Centre, McCormick Place, Crossmaglen, Newry BT35 9HD Tel: 028 3086 1226 Fax: 028 3086 8552 — MB BCh BAO 1975 Belf.

ALLEN, Matthew James Flat 8, 96 Rope Street, Surrey Quays, London SE16 7TQ — MB BS 1996 Lond.

ALLEN, Mr Michael James The Ulster Hospital, Dundonald, Belfast BT16 1RH Tel: 01232 484511 — MB BCh BAO 1983 NUI; MS 1991; BSc (Hons.) NUI 1985; FRCSI 1987. (Univ. Coll. Dub.) Cons. Gen. & Vasc. Surg. The Ulster Hosp. Dundonald, Belf.; Hon. Cons. Vasc. Surg.; Roy. Vict. Hosp., Belf. Prev: Research Fell. (Vasc. Surg.) New Eng. Med. Center Hosps. Boston, USA.

ALLEN, Mr Michael John Cinnibar Cottage, 25/27 High St., Hallaton, Market Harborough LE16 8UD — MB BS 1973 Lond.; FRCS Eng. 1979; MRCS Eng. LRCP Lond. 1973. (St. Bart.)

ALLEN, Michael John Pfizer Central Research, Ramsgate Road, Sandwich CT13 9NJ Tel: 01304 618532 Fax: 01304 618159; Courts Cottage, Alrise, Folkestone CT18 8LJ — MB ChB 1979 Bristol; MD Bristol 1990; MRCP (UK) 1982; MFPM RCP (UK) 1994. Dir., Early Clin. Research Gp. Pfizer Centr. Research Sandwich.

ALLEN, Mureen Cressida 15 Meadowview Road, Catford, London SE6 3NL Tel: 020 8698 9686 — MB BS 1989 West Indies.

ALLEN, Nicholas Anthony Southampton & South West, Hampshire Health Authority, Oakley Road, Southampton SO16 4GX Tel: 02380 725458 Fax: 02380 725509; 8 Sparrowgrove, Otterbourne, Winchester SO21 2DL Tel: 01962 714736 — BM BCh 1977 Oxf.; MPhil Bath 1986; MA Oxf. 1977, BA (Animal Physiol.) 1970; FFPHM RCP (UK) 1993; MFCM RCP (UK) 1986; MRCGP 1982. (Oxf. Uni.) Dir. Pub. Health & Health Strategy.

ALLEN, Nicholas John Gudgeheath Lane Surgery, 187 Gudgeheath Lane, Fareham PO15 6QA Tel: 01329 280887 Fax: 01329 231321 — MB BS 1987 Lond.; BSc Lond. 1984, MB BS 1987; MRCGP 1992; DObst. Auckland 1991. Socs: BMA.

ALLEN, Nicholas John Charles Street Surgery, Charles Street, Otley LS21 1BJ Tel: 01943 466124; Beech House, Birdcage Walk, Otley LS21 3HB Tel: 01943 462498 — MB BS 1974 Lond.; MRCS Eng. LRCP Lond. 1973; MRCGP 1977; DRCOG 1976. (Guy's)

ALLEN, Nigel Harry Philip Manchester Mental Health Partnership., Manchester Royal Infirmary, Manchester M13 9WL Tel: 0161 276 5316 Fax: 0161 276 5316 Email: hallen@psy.cmht.nwest.nhs.uk; Beech Trees, Trouthall Lane, Plumley, Knutsford WA16 0UN — MB BS 1986 Lond.; BA Camb. 1983; MRCPsych 1991. (Lond. Hosp. Med. Coll.) Cons. Old Age Psychiat. Manch. Ment. health Partnership. Prev: Sen. Regist. (Psychiat. of Old Age) Manch.; Regist. Rotat. Soton.

ALLEN, Mr Nigel Horace Alexandra House, Ruette Braye, St Martin's, Guernsey GY1 3EX Tel: 01481 238565 Fax: 01481 237782 Email: sallyd@medspec.demon.co.uk; Les Vinaires D'Amont, Rue Des Vinaires, St. Pierre Du Bois, Guernsey GY7 9EZ Tel: 01481 265728 Fax: 01481 265803 Email: nige@gtonline.net — MB ChB 1971 Sheff.; MS Soton. 1982; FRCS Eng. 1976; T(S) 1991. Cons. Urol. P.ss Eliz. Hosp. Guernsey. Socs: Brit. Assn. Urol. Surgs.; Assn. Surg.; Brit. Transpl. Soc. Prev: Clin. Lect. Nuffield Dept. Surg. John Radcliffe Hosp. Oxf.; Lect. Wessex Regional Transpl. Unit. St. Mary's Hosp. Portsmouth; Research Fell. Univ. Dept. Surg. Soton. Gen. Hosp.

ALLEN, Olwen Bessie 293 Castle Road, Salisbury SP1 3SB — MB BS 1937 Lond.; MB BS (Hnrs. Med. Foren. Med. & Hyg.) Lond. 1937; MRCS Eng. LRCP Lond. 1937. (Lond. Sch. Med. Wom.) Prev: Capt. RAMC; Med. Regist. & Ho. Phys. Roy. Free Hosp.

ALLEN, Pamela Sangita Flat 8, 96 Rope Street, Surrey Quays, London SE16 7TQ — MB BS 1996 Lond.

ALLEN, Patricia Anne Spring Gardens Health Centre, Providence Street, Worcester WR1 2BS Tel: 01905 681681 Fax: 01905 681699; 14 Archers Close, Heron Water, Droitwich WR9 9LH Tel: 01905 770970 — MB ChB 1974 Birm. Princip. Gen. Practitioner, The Health Centre, Spring Gdns., Worcester; Clin. Asst. (Rheum.) Newton Hosp. Worcester. Prev: Clin. Asst. (Rheum.) BromsGr. & Redditch HA.; Clin. Asst. (Rheum.) Hereford & Worcester HA.

ALLEN, Patricia Elizabeth 31 Ravenswood Road, Redland, Bristol BS6 6BW — MB ChB 1988 Birm.; FRCS Eng. 1992; FRCS (Orth.) 1997. Regist. Rotat. (Orthop.) Bristol.

ALLEN, Patricia Kathryn Meddygfa Rhiannon, Northfield Road, Narberth SA67 7AA Tel: 01834 860237 Fax: 01834 861625; Northfield House, Northfield Road, Narberth SA67 7EP Tel: 01834 860110 — MB BCh 1979 Wales; MRCGP 1983; DRCOG 1982; DCH RCP Lond. 1981.

ALLEN, Paul Watchfield, 31 Rowden Hill, Chippenham SN15 2AQ — MB BS 1986 Lond.; BDS Lond. 1976; LDS RCS Eng. 1977; FDS RCPS Glas. 1981. Assoc. Specialist (Oral Surg.) P.ss Margt. Hosp. Swindon.

ALLEN, Mr Paul Richard Department of Orthopaediac Surgery, Bromley Hospital, Cromwell Avenue, Bromley BR2 9AJ Tel: 020 8289 7000 Fax: 020 8289 7127; Bowzell Place, Bowzell Road, Weald, Sevenoaks TN14 6NF Tel: 01732 463382 Fax: 01732 463649 — MB BS 1970 Lond.; FRCS Eng. 1975; MRCS Eng. LRCP Lond. 1970. (King's Coll. Hosp.) Cons. Orthop. Surg. Bromley Hosps. NHS Trust; Vis. Lect. Surrey Univ. Socs: Fell. BOA; Brit. Assn Knee Surg. Prev: Cons. Orthop. Surg. Guys & Lewisham Hosp. Lond.; Sen. Regist. & Regist. (Orthop.) St. Thos. Hosp. Lond.

ALLEN, Mr Paul William Department of Orthopaedics, Princess Alexandra Hospital, Harlow CM20 1QX Tel: 01279 444455 — MB BS 1980 Lond.; BSc Lond. 1977; FRCS Eng. 1984. Cons. Trauma & Orthop. P.ss Alexandra Hosp. Harlow.

ALLEN, Pauline Hope House, Gloucestershire Royal Hospital, Great Western Road, Gloucester GL1 3NN Tel: 01452 394805 Fax: 01452 394808; Brook Cottage, Churchend, Eastington, Stonehouse GL10 3SB Tel: 01453 822068 Email: p.allen@saqnet.co.uk — MB BS 1968 Lond.; Membership of Institute of Psychosexual Med. 1987; MRCS Eng. LRCP Lond. 1968; MFFP 1993; DRCOG 1979. (Westm.) Cons. (Family Plann. Reproduc. Health Care & Psychosexual Med.) Glos. Roy. Hosp. Cotsworld & Vale PCT. Socs: Inst. Psychosexual Med. Prev: Manager Family Plann. Serv. & SCMO (Family Plann.) Severn NHS Trust; Research SHO Metab. Unit & Ho. Phys. W.m. Hosp. Lond.; Ho. Surg. Kingston Hosp. Kingston-on-Thames.

ALLEN, Percival Louis (retired) 15 Seymour Place, Odiham, Basingstoke — MRCS Eng. LRCP Lond. 1942; DOMS Eng. 1945. Prev: Cons. Ophth. W. Surrey & N. E. Hants. Health Dist.

ALLEN, Peter (retired) Morton House, 204 Leeds Road, Bramhope, Leeds LS16 9JU Tel: 0113 261 1242 — MRCS Eng. LRCP Lond. 1963; DObst RCOG 1967.

ALLEN, Peter Northwood Cottage, 60 Warblington Road, Emsworth PO10 7HH Tel: 01243 372752 — MB BS 1969 Lond.; MRCS Eng. LRCP Lond. 1969. GP Havant; Clin. Asst. (Gen. Surg.) St. Mary's Hosp. Portsmouth.

ALLEN, Peter Leonard Charlotte Keel Health Centre, Seymour Road, Easton, Bristol BS5 0UA Tel: 0117 951 2244 Fax: 0117 935 4447 — MB BS 1985 Lond.; MA Camb. 1988; MRCGP 1989; DFFP 1996; DTM & H RCP Lond. 1992; DCH RCP Lond. 1991; DRCOG 1988.

ALLEN, Philip Graham (retired) Wythe, Cowfold, Horsham RH13 8BU Tel: 01403 864234 — MB BChir Camb. 1952; BA Camb. 1949; DCH Eng. 1957; DObst RCOG 1956. Prev: Resid. Med. Off. P.ss Louise Kens. Hosp. Childr.

ALLEN, Richard David (retired) Bramleys, 2 Dukes Meadow, Funtington, Chichester PO18 9LU Tel: 01243 575678 — MB BChir Camb. 1949; MA CAmb. 1949; MRCS Eng. LRCP Lond. 1949; MRCGP 1973; DCH Eng. 1979; DObst RCOG 1953. Prev: SCMO W. Sussex AHA.

ALLEN, Richard John Furness, Stoke Close, Stoke D'Abernon, Cobham KT11 3AE — MB BS 1990 Lond.

ALLEN, Richard William Hedley 25 Malten Close, Poringland, Norwich NR14 7RW Tel: 01508 493154 — BM BS 1996 Nottm. SHO (Paediat.) Heartlands Hosp. Birm. Prev: SHO (Paediat.) Norf. & Norwich Hosp.

ALLEN, Ricky George 1 Lanbury Road, Peckham, London SE15 3DB Tel: 020 7732 2965; 66 Bishops Way, Canterbury CT2 8DS Tel: 01227 786035 — MB BS 1986 Lond.; MRCGP 1995; DRCOG 1994. (St. Mary's Hosp. Med. Sch.) Ships Phys. P & O Cruises. Socs: Fell. Roy. Soc. Med.

ALLEN, Rosalind Tessa 63 Victoria Road, Woodbridge IP12 1EL Tel: 01394 388654 — MB BS 1964 Lond.; MRCS Eng. LRCP Lond. 1964; FRCPsych 1988, M 1972; DPM Eng. 1968.

ALLEN, Rosalyn Anne The Chapel House, Main St., Burnaston, Derby DE65 6LG — BM BS 1978 Nottm.; MRCGP 1982.

ALLEN, Rosanne Louise 1 Kingsfield Close, Bradford-on-Avon BA15 1AW — BM 1993 Soton.; DRCOG 1996; MRCGP 1997. SHO (Psychiat.) St Ann's Hosp. Dorset. Prev: GP Regist. Forrest Gate Surg. Soton.; GP Regist. N. Baddesley Health Centre Soton.; SHO (Psychiat.) Salisbury.

ALLEN, Ruth Anna 41 Balwearie Road, Kirkcaldy KY2 5LT — MB ChB 1992 Ed.

ALLEN, Ruth Elizabeth Department of Obstetrics & Gynaecology, Perth Royal Infirmary, Perth PH1 1NX Tel: 01738 623311 Fax: 01738 473212 — MB ChB 1980; MD Manch. 1989; MRCOG 1986; DCH RCP Lond. 1982; FRCOG. (St. Andrews, Manchester) Cons. O & G Perth Roy. Infirm. Prev: Sen. Regist. (O & G) Manch.

ALLEN, Ruth Lara 2 Rye Court, Brent Terrace, London NW2 1AF — MB BS 1991 Lond.; MRCPsych 1996.

ALLEN, Samuel 1 Windover, London Road, Harrow HA1 3JQ Tel: 020 8423 5720 — MB ChB 1991 Manch.; BSc (Hons.) St. And. 1988; MRCP (UK) 1996; DTM & H Liverp. 1995. Specialist Regist. (Infect. Dis. & Trop. Med.). Socs: Roy. Soc. Trop. Med. & Hyg.; Trainees Comm. Roy. Coll. Phys.(RCP). Prev: SHO (Med.) N.wick Pk. Hosp.; Ho. Off. (Med.) Profess. Med. Unit. Ninewells Hosp. & Med. Sch. Dundee; Ho. Off. (Surg.) Profess. Urol. Unit Univ. Hosp. S. Manch.

ALLEN, Sarah Margaretta Worcester Street Surgery, 24 Worcester Street, Stourbridge DY8 1AW Tel: 01384 371616; 73a Hagley Road, Halesowen B63 1DR Tel: 0121 550 1146 — MB BCh 1989 Wales; MRCP Lond. 1997. (Wales) GP Princip. Stourbridge. Socs: Roy. Coll. Paediat. & Child Health.

ALLEN, Sarah Theresa Susan Moor 74 Westwick Crescent, Sheffield S8 7DJ — MB ChB 1986 Manch.

ALLEN, Sharon Mary Abbey Mead Surgery, Abbey Mead, Romsey SO51 8EN; Tadburn House, 20 Southampton Road, Romsey SO51 8AF Tel: 01794 512806 — BM 1981 Soton.; DRCOG 1984. Prev: SHO (Orthop. & Cas.) Soton. Gen. Hosp.; SHO (O & G & Geriat.) Salisbury HA; SHO (Paediat.) Basingstoke Dist. Hosp.

ALLEN, Simon Mark 4 Winsor Villas, Plymouth PL1 2QD — MB ChB 1981 Manch.

ALLEN, Simon Michael 118 Kirkby Road, Sutton-in-Ashfield NG17 1GH — MB ChB 1994 Sheff.

ALLEN, Simonee Tara The Surgery, 36 The Avenue, Watford WD17 4NT Tel: 01923 224203 — MB BS 1987 Lond.; MRCGP 1991; DRCOG 1990.

ALLEN, Stanley 274 Green Lane, London SW16 3BA Tel: 020 8764 0019 — MB BCh BAO 1953 Dub. (TC Dub.) Hon. Phys. Battersea Miss. Varicose Clinic; Clin. Asst. (Vasc. Surg.) St. Geo. Hosp. Lond.; Med. Dir. Rank Teachg. Centre. Socs: Venous Forum Roy. Soc. Med. Prev: Sen. Cas. Off. Mayday Hosp. Croydon.

***ALLEN, Stephen** 4 Coltmuir Garden, Bishopbriggs, Glasgow G64 2SX — MB ChB 1998 Glas.; MB ChB Glas 1998.

ALLEN, Stephen Charles 9 Kennedy Gardens, Earley, Reading RG6 5RN; 9 Kennedy Gardens, Earley, Reading RG6 5RN Email: stephenallen@lineone.net — MRCS Eng. LRCP Lond. 1972; BSc (Hons.) Lond. 1969, MB BS 1972; FFA RCS Eng. 1977; DObst RCOG 1975. (Kings Coll. Lond. & Westm.) Cons. Anaesth. Roy. Berks. Hosp. Reading. Prev: Sen. Regist. (Anaesth.) Univ. Hosp. Wales Cardiff.

ALLEN, Stephen Charles Royal Bournemouth Hospital, Castle Lane East, Bournemouth BH7 7DW Tel: 01202 303626; 24 Alyth Road, Bournemouth BH3 7DG Tel: 01202 767572 Fax: 01202 704542 Email: drscallen@aol.com — MB ChB 1976 Manch.; MB ChB (Hons.) Manch. 1976; MBA (Open) 1994; FRCP Lond. 1993; FRCP Ed. 1991; MD Manch. 1981; MRCP (UK) 1978; BSc (Med. Biochem.) Manch. 1973. (Manch.) Cons. Phys. (Gen. Med.) Bournemouth & ChristCh. Hosps.; Hon. Sen. Lect. Soton. Univ. Socs: Brit. Geriat.s Soc.; Treas. BGS Respirat. Sect. Prev: Lect. & Sen. Regist. (Geriat. Med.) Univ. Hosp. S. Manch.; Sen. Regist. (Med.) Univ. Teach. Hosp. Lusaka; Research Fell. (Med.) Manch. Roy. Infirm.

ALLEN, Stephen James Edward Graylingwell Hospital, 9 College Lane, Chichester PO19 4FX Tel: 01243 787970 — MB BCh BAO 1986 NUI; LRCPSI 1986; MRCPsych 1995. (Royal College of Surgeons Dublin) Cons. (Psychiat. Gen. Adult Psychiat.) Graylingwell Hosp. Chichester.

ALLEN, Stephen Michael The Surgery, 84 Rogers Lane, Stoke Poges, Slough SL2 4LF Tel: 01753 643445 Fax: 01753 646906 — MB BS 1979 Lond.; MA Camb. 1979; MRCP (UK) 1982; MRCGP (Distinc.) 1985; DRCOG 1985. GP Trainer (Windsor VTS) (Oxf. Region); Clin. Asst. Rheum. Wexham Pk. Hosp.; Clin. Governance Lead, S. Bucks. PCG. Prev: Regist. (Med.) St. Mary's Hosp. Lond.

ALLEN, Stephen Paul Brough and South Cave Medical Practice, 4 Centurion Way, Brough HU15 1AY Tel: 01482 667108 Fax: 01482 665090; 84 The Stray, South Cave, Brough HU15 2AL Tel: 01430 424511 Email: steve37doc@aol.com — MB BS 1985 Lond.; MRCGP 1990. (Camb. Univ. & King's Coll. Hosp. Lond.) Clin. Audit Fell. Hull & E. Riding Multi-disciplinary Audit Gp. Prev: SHO (Med.) Centr. Middlx. Hosp. Lond.; Ho. Surg. Bromley Hosp. Kent; Ho. Phys. King's Coll. Hosp. Lond.

ALLEN, Steven David 36 Stambourne Way, West Wickham BR4 9NF — MB BS 1997 Lond.

ALLEN, Steven James 44 Turnberry Drive, Nuneaton CV11 6TT — MB ChB 1987 Leic.

ALLEN, Susan Kathleen Gloucester Royal Hospital, Gloucester GL1 3NN; Withymoor Hill, Berkeley GL13 9EB Tel: 01454 260771 Email: susan.allen@tesco.net — MB BS 1992 Lond.; MRCGP 1997; DCH RCP Lond. 1996; DFFP 1995; DRCOG 1995; DGM RCP Lond. 1994. (Univ. Coll. & Middlx. Sch. Med.) Staff Grade A & E Gloucester Roy. Hosp. Socs: BMA. Prev: Regist. (Paediat.) Perth, Australia.

ALLEN, Suzan Child Assessment Unit, Royal Shrewsbury Hospital (South), Shrewsbury SY3 8XF Tel: 01743 231122 — BM BS 1982 Nottm.; BMedSc (2nd cl. Hons.) Nottm. 1980; DCH RCP Lond. 1989. SCMO (Child Assessm.) Shrewsbury.

ALLEN, Mr Terence Rodney 5 Thornfield Avenue, Chesterfield S40 3LG — MB ChB 1966 Liverp.; FRCS Eng. 1974. InDepend. orthopaedic Cons. 1999. Socs: Mem. Brit. Soc. Surg. of the Hand; Fell.Brit. Orthopaedic Assn. Prev: Med. Off. Brit. Antarctic Survey.; Cons.Orthop.Surg.Chesterfield&N.Derbysh..Roy.Hosp.1981-1999.

ALLEN, Thomas Paul 26 Newry Road, Crossmaglen, Newry BT35 9HH — MB BCh BAO 1997 Belf.

ALLEN, Timothy Emmanuel P&O Cruises (UK)Ltd, Richmond Hse, Terminus Terrace, Southampton SO14 3PN; 16 Edge Road, Matlock DE4 3NH — MB ChB 1991 Dundee. Ships Doctor P&O Cruises. Prev: Staff Grade A & E Hull Roy. Infirm. Kingston-upon-Hull.

ALLEN, Timothy Michael Williams Aylmer Lodge Surgery, Broomfield Road, Kidderminster DY11 5PA Tel: 01562 822015 Fax: 01562 827137; 24 Hill Grove Crescent, Kidderminster DY10 3AP Tel: 01562 829 5252 — MRCS Eng. LRCP Lond. 1975. (Roy. Free) Prev: Trainee GP Worcester & Kidderminster VTS; Ho. Phys. (Med. & Paediat.) & Ho. Surg. (Gen. Surg.) W. Suff. Hosp. Bury St. Edmunds.

ALLEN, Wallace Hugo (retired) Balmoral House, 1 Victoria Road, Deal CT14 7AS Tel: 01304 537 3444 — MB BCh 1953 Wales; BSc Wales 1950; DPH Lond. 1957; DCH Eng. 1956. Prev: Dep. Co. Med. Off. Herts. CC.

ALLEN, Walter Michael Critten 3 Jerome House, Old Bridge St., Hampton Wick, Kingston upon Thames KT1 4BJ Tel: 020 8977 8793 — MB ChB 1952 Manch.; DMRD 1956 Eng. Prev: Med. Cons. Jockey Club; Cons. Radiol. N. & Mid-Chesh., Preston & Chorley Hosp. Gps., Darlington & N.allerton DHA's & Aberd. Teachg. Hosps.; Med. Assessor Indep. Tribunal Serv.

ALLEN, Wendy Anne Beryl 14 Lansdowne Crescent, Worcester WR3 8JE Tel: 01905 26246 — MB ChB 1955 Liverp. (Liverp.) SCMO Worcester Health Dist. Prev: Clin. Med. Off. S.W. Herts. Health Dist; Civil. Med. Off. Brit. Forces Cyprus.

ALLEN-MERSH, Professor Timothy George Chelsea & Westminster Hospital, 369 Fulham Road, London SW10 9NH Tel: 020 8746 8468 Fax: 020 8746 8231 Email: t.allenmersh@ic.ac.uk; 87 Blenheim Crescent, London W11 2EQ Tel: 020 7727 7390 — MB ChB 1973 Dundee; BSc St. And. 1970; MD Dundee 1982; FRCS Eng. 1978. (St. Andrews/Dundee) Prof. Gastrointestinal Surg. & Hon. Cons. Surg.Imperial Coll. Sch. of Sci. Med. & Technol. Socs: Assn. Coloproctol.; Amer. Soc. Clin. Oncol.; Brit. Assn. Surg. Oncol. Prev: Sen. Regist. (Surg.) St. Mark's Hosp. Lond.; Fell. Surg. Oncol. Memor. Sloan-Kettering Cancer Center, NY, USA; Sen. Regist. (Surg.) Lond. Hosp.

ALLENBY, Charles Francis (retired) 34 St Andrewgate, York YO1 7BZ Tel: 01904 656413 — MB 1958 Camb.; MA Camb. 1959, MB 1958, BChir 1957; FRCP Lond. 1982, M 1961. Prev: Cons. Dermat. Lister Hosp. Stevenage.

ALLENBY, Fred Hamsey Green Surgery, 85A Limpsfield Road, Warlingham CR6 9RH Tel: 01883 625022; 14 Limekiln Place, London SE19 2RE Tel: 020 8771 8622 Email: fred.allenby@virgin.net — MB ChB 1967 Leeds; MD 1976 Leeds. GP Tutor; GP Trainer. Prev: Asst. Lect. Anat. Univ. Glas.; Research Regist. Hammersmith Hosp. Lond.; Sen. Ho. Surg. (Rotating) St. Jas. Univ. Hosp. Leeds.

ALLENBY, Mr Keith William Harvey Hospital, Kennington Road, Willesborough, Ashford TN24 0LZ Tel: 01233 633331; 116 Bridge Street, Wye, Ashford TN25 5EA Tel: 01233 813891 Email: kaisin@globalnet.co.uk — MB BS 1988 Lond.; MRCOG 1994; DRCOG 1991. (St. Geo. Hosp. Med. Sch.) Cons. O & G William Harvey Hosp. Ashford Kent. Prev: Sen. Regist. (O & G) St Jas. Univ. Hosp. Leeds.

ALLENBY, Linda Margaret The Surgery, 42 Upper Rock Gardens, Brighton BN2 1QF Tel: 01273 600103 Fax: 01273 620100 — MB BS 1976 Lond.; BSc (1st cl. Hons. Biochem.) Birm. 1971; MRCS Eng. LRCP Lond. 1976; DA Eng. 1981; DRCOG 1979; Cert. JCC Lond. 1978. (St. Thos.) Police Surg. Hove. Prev: SHO (Anaesth.) Roy. Sussex Co. Hosp. Brighton; SHO (Paediat.) Char. Cross. Hosp. Lond.; SHO (O & G) St. Thos. Hosp. Lond.

ALLENBY, Mark Ivan 308 Upper Shoreham Road, Shoreham-by-Sea BN43 6BA — MB BS 1993 Lond.

ALLENBY, William James Stannary Surgery, Abbey Rise, Whitchurch Road, Tavistock PL19 9BB Tel: 01822 613517 Fax: 01822 618294 Email: evans@stannary.fsnet.co.uk; Greenbank, Middlemoor, Tavistock PL19 9DY — MB BS 1974 Lond.; MRCS Eng. LRCP Lond. 1974; MRCGP 1979; DObst RCOG 1978. (Middlx.) Trainer (Gen. Pract.) Tavistock. Socs: (Chairm.) Med. Equestrian Assn.

ALLERA, David, SBStJ 7A Watchetts Drive, Camberley GU15 2PQ Tel: 01276 26826 — MB ChB 1966 Liverp.; MFOM RCP Lond. 1983, AFOM 1980; DIH Eng. 1982. Socs: Soc. Occupat. Med. Prev: Gp. Med. Adviser BAA plc; Squadron Ldr. RAF Med. Br.

***ALLERTON, Joanna Elizabeth** Church Farm, The Bury, Locking, Weston Super Mare BS24 8BZ — MB ChB 1998 Leeds.

ALLERTON, Kerry Edwin Glen Friarage Hospital, Northallerton DL6 1JG Tel: 01609 779911 — MB ChB 1972 Cape Town; FCS(SA) 1982. Cons. Orthop. Surg. Friarage Hosp. N.allerton.

ALLERTON-ROSS, George 415 Park Lane, Macclesfield SK11 8JR — MB BS 1992 Lond.

ALLES, Roshini Marcelle 5 George V Way, Greenford UB6 7JA Tel: 020 8998 7441 — MRCS Eng. LRCP Lond. 1978; MS (ENT) Sri Lanka 1983; FRCS (ENT) Eng. 1985; FRCS (ENT) Ed. 1985.

ALLETSON, Juliet Leigh 19 Thompson Road, Exeter EX1 2UB Tel: 01392 436617 — MB BCh 1993 Witwatersrand. A & E Staff Grade.

ALLEWAY, Paul Regimental Medical Officer, The Queen's Royal Lancers BFPO 36 — MB BS 1995 Lond.

ALLEYNE, Herbert Michael Arthur Bonchurch House, Bonchurch Shute, Bonchurch, Ventnor PO38 1NU Tel: 01983 852357 Fax: 01983 852357 Email: easyreach@isle-wight.demon.co.uk — MB ChB 1976 Aberd. Prev: GP Ottershaw, Surrey; GP Diag. Clin., Barbados.

ALLEYNE, Pamela Joan Evelyn Department of Genito Urinary Medicine, Isle of Wight Healthcare NHS Trust, St Mary's Hospital, Newport PO30 5TG Tel: 01983 821363; Woodstock, Norcott Drive, Bembridge PO35 5TX Tel: 01983 873128 Fax: 01983 873128 Email: easyreach@isle-wight.demon.co.uk — MB ChB 1977 Aberd. Clin. Asst. (Genitourin. Med.) St. Mary's Hosp. Newport, I. of Wight. Prev: Clin. Asst. (Genitourin. Med. & Colposcopy) St. Peter's Hosp. Chertsey.

ALLFORD, Sarah Lynne Department of Heamatology, University College Hospital, 25 Grafton Way, London WC1E 6DB Tel: 020 7387 9300; Yarford Cottage, Yarford, Kingston St. Mary, Taunton TA2 8AN — MB BChir 1993 Camb.; MA Camb. 1992; MRCP (UK) 1995. (Camb. & Char. Cross & Westm.) Regist. Rotat. (Haemat.) Univ. Coll. Hosp. Lond. Prev: SHO (Med.) Roy. Marsden Hosp. Sutton; SHO Rotat. (Med.) John Radcliffe Hosp. Oxf.

ALLFREE, Albert John The Mansfield Clinic, 42 Nottingham Road, Mansfield NG18 1BL Tel: 01623 641611 — MB ChB 1962 Sheff.; MLCOM 1980. Osteop./Orthop. Phys. Mansfield. Socs: Fell. Roy. Soc. Med.; Brit. Osteop. Assn.; Brit. Inst. Musculoskel. Med.

ALLFREE, John Mark 85 St Austell Dr, Nottingham NG11 7BT — BM BS 1997 Nottm.

ALLFREY, Colin Forbes (retired) 4 The Grange, Evesham Road, Cheltenham GL52 3AE Tel: 01242 579328 — MRCS Eng. LRCP Lond. 1945; MA Camb. 1946; DPM Lond. 1950. Prev: Cons. Psychiat. Warley Hosp. Brentwood.

ALLGROVE, Jeremy Newham General Hospital, Plaistow, London E13 8SL Tel: 020 7476 4000 Fax: 020 7363 8081; 18 Redbridge Lane W., Wanstead, London E11 2JU Tel: 020 8989 5944 Email: allgrove@clara.net — MB BChir 1974 Camb.; MB BChir Camb. 1973; MA, MD Camb. 1985, BA 1970; FRCP Lond. 1994; MRCP (UK) 1976; FRCPCH 1997. (Camb./Middlx.) Cons. Paediat. Newham Gen. Hosp. Lond.; Hon. Cons. Paediat. Endocrinol. Roy. Hosps. NHS Trust; Hon. Sen. Lect. (Child Health) St Bart. Hosp. & Roy. Lond. Sch. Med. & Dent. Socs: Brit. Soc. Paediat. Endocrinol. & Diabetes; Eur. Soc. Paediat. Endocrinol.; Bone & Tooth Soc. Prev: Sen. Regist. (Paediat.) W. Midl. Regional Train. Scheme; Clin. Research Asst. (Paediat.) Middlx. Hosp. Med. Sch.; Regist. (Neonatol.) Qu. Charlottes Matern. Hosp. Lond.

ALLI, Mabel Olusanu Brent and Harrow Health Authority, Grace House, Harrovian Business Village, Bessborough Road, Harrow HA1 3EX Tel: 0208 422 6644 Fax: 0208 426 8646 Email: mabel.alli@bah-ha.nthames.nhs.uk; 88 Dean Lane, Edgware HA8 9NP Tel: 0208 210 0219 Email: mblall@aol.com — MB BS 1974 Lagos; MSc Community Health Lond. 1979. (College of Medicine University of Lagos Nigeria & University of Pennsylvania Philadelphia USA) Specialist Regist. Pub. Health Med. Brent & Harrow HA. Socs: BMA. Prev: Specialist Regist. W. Herts HA; Specialist Regist. in Pub. Health Med. E. Lond. or the City HA; Specialist Regist. in Pub. Health Med. PHLS/CDSC Colindale.

ALLIBONE, Anthony, OBE, MBE (retired) Friary House, Blakeney, Holt NR25 7NJ Tel: 01263 740450 — MB BS 1954 Lond.; MRCS Eng. LRCP Lond. 1949; FRCGP 1982, M 1965; DCH Eng. 1953. Chairm. Healthwatch N. Norf. Primary Care Gp. Prev: Mem. (Chairm. Health Comm.) GMC.

ALLIBONE, Eleanor Brook (retired) 3 Dunstarn Drive, Leeds LS16 8EH Tel: 0113 267 4916 — MD 1957 Dub.; MB BCh BAO 1949; MRCPI 1952. Prev: Cons. Pathol. St. Jas. Hosp. Leeds.

ALLIBONE, James Bernard 23 Brewster House, Three Colt St., London E14 8HU — MB BS 1989 Lond.

ALLIBONE, Richard Oscar 3 Dunstarn Drive, Leeds LS16 8EH — MB ChB 1986 Liverp.

ALLIM, Alia Sharon Forensic Department, Whitchurch Hospital, Park Road, Whitchurch, Cardiff CF14 7XB Tel: 029 2069 3191 — MB BS 1983 Lond.

ALLIM, June Shazeela Shanaaz Budbrooke Medical Centre, Slade Hill, Hampton Magna, Warwick CV35 8SA Tel: 01926 403800 Fax: 01926 403855 — MB BS 1983 Lond.; BA Oxf. 1991 (Law); MRCGP 1988. (Univ. Coll. Hosp.) GP; PCG GP Postgraudate Tutor. Prev: Solicitor & Cons. Wragge & Company Solicitors.

ALLIM, Mohamed 22 Benjamin Road, High Wycombe HP13 6SR — MB BCh BAO 1966 Belf.

ALLIM, Raouf Masud Benjamin Road Surgery, 22 Benjamin Road, High Wycombe HP13 6SR Tel: 01494 534524 Fax: 01494 534524 — MB BChir 1983 Camb.; BA 1981; MA 1984 Camb.; DA (UK) 1988; DRCOG 1986. GP High Wycombe; Clin. Asst. (Psychiat.), S. Bucks NHS Trust. Prev: SHO (Anaesth.) Wycombe Gen. Hosp.; Trainee GP Beaconsfield VTS.

ALLIN, Anthony Cordeaux The Little Picket, Blackwater, Lyndhurst SO43 7FL Tel: 01703 283845 — MB ChB 1946 Birm.

ALLIN, Dennis Martin Medical Centre, Craig Croft, Chelmsley Wood, Birmingham B37 7TR Tel: 0121 770 5656 Fax: 0121 779 5619 — MB ChB 1968 Birm.; MRCS Eng. LRCP Lond. 1968.
ALLIN, Matthew Philip George Department of Psychological Medicine, Institute of Psychiatry, De Crespigny Park, London SE5 8AF; 49b Southborough Road, London E9 7EE Tel: 020 8510 9689 Email: sphamps@iop.kd.ac.uk — BM BCh 1994 Oxf.; BA Oxf 1991; MRCP 1997. (Oxford University) Clin. Research Worker.
ALLIN, Sophie Jane 17 Seacole Close, Thorpe Astley, Leicester LE3 3TX — MB ChB 1998 Leic.; MB ChB Leic 1998. GP Trainee Leicester Scheme.
ALLINGHAM, John Parry, Maj. RAMC Retd. Oliver Street Surgery, 57 Oliver Street, Ampthill, Bedford MK45 2SB Tel: 01525 402641 Fax: 01525 841107; New Road Farm, New Road, Maulden, Bedford MK45 2BG — MB BS 1987 Lond.; MRCGP 1993; DRCOG 1992. (London Hospital) Trainee GP/SHO (O & G) Duchess of Kent Milit. Hosp. Catterick VTS.; Clin. Asst. (Orthop.). Prev: SHO (O & G) Friarage Hosp. N.allerton; GP Catterick HM Forces.
ALLINGTON, Mark David 84 West View Road, Barrow-in-Furness LA14 5AW — MB ChB 1993 Liverp.
ALLINGTON, Moira Kathleen Elizabeth (retired) Whitewells, Much Birch, Hereford HR2 8HZ Tel: 01981 540364 — MB BChir 1944 Camb.; BA 1944; DPH Bristol 1967; DCH Eng. 1945. Sen. Med. Off. Hereford & Worcester AHA. Prev: Asst. MOH Worcester City.
ALLINGTON-SMITH, Patricia Flora (retired) 14 Yare Court, Yarmouth Road, Thorpe St Andrews, Norwich NR7 0EF Tel: (01603) 437185 — MB BS Lond. 1954. Prev: Cons. Ment. Handicap Lothingland Hosp. Oulton & E. Anglian RHA.
ALLINGTON-SMITH, Prudence Jane Brian Oliver Centre, Brooklands, Coleshill Road, Marston Green, Birmingham B37 7HL Tel: 0121 779 6981 Fax: 0121 788 8220 Email: pruallingtonsmith@classicfm.net — MB BS 1987 Lond.; MRCPsych 1993; DCH RCP Lond. 1991. (Royal Free) Cons. in the Psychiat. of Learning Disabil. (Child & Adolesc.). Prev: Sen. Regist. (Psychiat. of Learning Disabil.) Birm.
ALLINSON, Alexander John Ramsey Group Practice, Ramsey; Ramsey Group Practice, Ramsey — MB BChir 1991 Camb.; DGM RCP Lond. 1995; DRCOG 1995; DCH RCP Lond. 1994; MRCGP 1997. (Kings College Cambridge) GP. Prev: GP/Regist. Kentish Town Health Centre Lond.; Clin. Med. Off. City & Hackney HA; SHO Roy. Childr. Hosp. Melbourne, Austral.
ALLINSON, Andrea Marie 6 Sandringham Road, Morecambe LA4 4NE Tel: 01524 414507 — MB ChB 1995 Leeds.
ALLINSON, Fiona 25 Brooke Road, Kenilworth CV8 2BD — MB ChB 1993 Bristol.
ALLINSON, Hilary Sutherland, MBE (retired) 68 Mill Road, Abingdon OX14 5NZ Tel: 01235 532818 — MB BCh 1967 Witwatersrand; BSc Witwatersrand 1963. Prev: Sen. Partner, Long Furlong Med. Centre, Abingdon.
ALLINSON, Richard Nigel Ampthill Square Medical Centre, 219 Evershott Street, London NW1 1DE Tel: 020 7387 6161 Fax: 020 7387 0420 — MB ChB 1988 Ed.; MRCGP 1994; DFFP 1996; DCCH RCP Ed. 1991; MSc (General Practice) Lond. 1997. (Univ. Edin.) Tutor (Gen. Pract.) Roy. Free Hosp. Sch. Med. Lond.; GP Trainer N. Thames E.; Bd. Mem. S. camden PCG. Socs: BMA; RCGP; Fac. of Family Plann.
ALLIOTT, Elsa Susan The Planes, 7 Old Bury Road, Thetford IP24 3AL — MB ChB 1969 Birm. (Birm.) Staff Grade (Community Paediat.) Lifespan Healthcare (NHS Trust) Camb. Prev: Deptm. Med. Off. Mon. CC.
ALLIOTT, Robert James Grove Surgery, Grove Lane, Thetford IP24 2HY Tel: 01842 752285 Fax: 01842 751316; The Planes, 7 Old Bury Road, Thetford IP24 3AL Tel: 01842 753128 — MB ChB 1969 Birm.; MEl. Univ. E. Anglia 1997; MRCP (UK) 1973; DObst. RCOG 1974; M. Ed. UEA 1997. (Birm.) Prev: Regist. (Med.) Co. & Gen. Hosps. Hereford.
ALLIS, Dawn Elizabeth School Farm, Farlesthorpe, Alford LN13 9PQ — MB ChB 1996 Liverp.
ALLISON, Andrew George Allison and Partners, Maryhill Health Centre, 41 Shawpark Street, Glasgow G20 9DR Tel: 0141 531 8840 Fax: 0141 531 8848; 21 Ralston Road, Bearsden, Glasgow G61 3BA Tel: 0141 942 0317 — MB ChB 1971 Glas. Clin. Asst. (Anaesth.) Gartnavel Hosp. Glas. Socs: Glas. & W. Scot. Soc. Anaesth.; Scott. Soc. Anaesth. Prev: Regist. (Anaesth.) & Ho. Phys. & Ho. Surg. Glas. Roy. Infirm.
ALLISON, Mr Andrew Scott Craigrothie House, Craigrothie, Cupar KY15 5PZ — MB ChB 1989 Ed.; FRCS Ed. 1994.
ALLISON, Catherine Elizabeth 22 Lees Lane, Northallerton DL7 8DB — MB ChB 1995 Sheff.
ALLISON, Charles William Department of Anaesthesia, Stracathro Hospital, Brechin DD9 7QA Tel: 01356 647291 Fax: 01356 648165; Summerbank House, Esk Park, Brechin DD9 6HL Tel: 01356 623624 Email: drallison@angus-nhs.finix.org.uk — MB ChB 1975 Dundee; FFA RCS Eng. 1979. Cons. Anaesth. Tayside Univ. Hosps. NHS Trust; Edr. Annals Scott. Soc. Anaesth. Socs: Assn. Anaesth. & NE Scotl. Assn. Anaesth.; Hon. Sec. DMGS. Prev: Fell.sh. (Paediat. Anaesth.) Hosp. Sick Childr. Toronto; Sen. Regist. (Anaesth.) Ninewells Hosp. Dundee.
ALLISON, David Microbiology Laboratory, Dryburn Hospital, Durham DH1 5TW Tel: 0191 333 2450 Fax: 0191 333 2679; Overdale, Birches Nook, Stocksfield NE43 7NU Tel: 01661 844424 — MB BS 1981 Lond.; BSc Lond. 1978; MRCPath 1988; FRCPath 1997. (Char. Cross) Cons. Microbiol. N. Durh. Acute Hosps. NHS Trust. Prev: Sen. Regist. (Med. Microbiol.) Roy. Liverp. Hosp. Whiston Hosp.; Regist. (Med. Microbiol.) Char. Cross Hosp. Lond.
ALLISON, Professor David John Department of Imaging, Hammersmith Hospital, Du Cane Road, London W12 0NN Tel: 020 8383 3123 Fax: 020 8743 5409; 96 Alric Avenue, New Malden KT3 4JW — MB BS 1965 Lond.; MB BS (Hons.) 1965; BSc Lond. 1962, MD 1974; FRCP Lond. 1975; MRCP (UK) 1990; MRCS Eng. LRCP Lond. 1965; FRCR 1975; FFR 1974; DMRD Eng. 1972. (King's Coll. Hosp.) Prof. Diagn. Radiol. Imperial Coll. Sch. of Med. Lond. & Clin. Dir. (Imaging) Hammersmith Hosp. NHS Trust; Dir. Dept. Imaging Hammersmith Hosp. Lond.; Edr-in-Chief Jl. Interven. Radiol. Socs: (Pres.) Cardiovasc. & Interven. Soc. Europ.; Fleischner Soc.; Europ. Coll. Angiogr. Prev: Cons. Diagn. Radiol. Hammersmith Hosp. Lond.; SHO (A & E) & Ho. Off. (Gen. Med. & Surg.) King's Coll. Hosp. Lond.
ALLISON, David Kilpatrick Minto (retired) Ribigill, 2 Riverford Drive, Conon Bridge, Dingwall IV7 8HP Tel: 01349 865164 — LRCP LRCS Ed. LRFPS Glas. 1947; DA Eng. 1970. Prev: Anaesth. Belford Hosp. Fort William.
ALLISON, Elizabeth Anne, Specialist Registrar Department of Paediatrics, Leeds General Infirmary, 53 Great George Street, Leeds LSE 9NS; 38 Clifton Road, Lower Parkstone, Poole BH14 9PP Tel: 01202 745976 — MB BS 1993 Lond.; MRCP UK Lond. 1997; DCH (Royal Coll. Of Physicians) 1996. Specialist Regist. In Paediat. Med.. (Yorks. Deanery).
ALLISON, Elizabeth Claire 6 Station Drive, Hagley, Stourbridge DY9 0NX — MB ChB 1998 Sheff.; MB ChB Sheff 1998.
ALLISON, Gillian Patricia 85 Yale Court, Honeybourne Road, West Hampstead, London NW6 1JH — MB ChB 1993 Manch.; DCH RCPS Glas. 1997; DRCOG 1997; MRCGP 1998. (Manchester) G.P. Locum. Socs: BMA. Prev: Clin. Asst. (Gen. Pract.).
ALLISON, Helen Elizabeth G1R, 10 Hyndland Avenue, Glasgow G11 5BW — MB ChB 1993 Glas.
ALLISON, Helen Jane 96 Alric Avenue, New Malden KT3 4JW — MB BS 1993 Lond.
ALLISON, Howard (retired) 2 Merrow Chase, Guildford GU1 2RY Tel: 01483 300996 — MB ChB 1955 Manch.; FRCPath 1976, M 1964; DPath Eng. 1961. Prev: Cons. Pathol. Leighton Hosp. Crewe.
ALLISON, Ian Murray (retired) Crooked Acre, Ninemileburn, Penicuik EH26 9LZ Tel: 01968 660049 — MB 1954 Camb.; BChir 1953; FRCP Ed. 1971, M 1960; DObst RCOG 1958. Prev: Hosp. Pract. Roy. Infirm. Edin.
ALLISON, James Lewis 26 Langstone High Street, Langstone, Havant PO9 1RY — MB BS 1989 Lond.
ALLISON, John (retired) 121 Lanark Road, Carstairs, Lanark ML11 8QQ Tel: 01555 870498 — MB ChB Ed. 1935; DPH Glas. 1937.
ALLISON, Joy Quinque, Vicarage Lane, Yateley GU46 7QR — MB BS 1989 Lond.; FRCA 1996. Cons. Cardiothoracic Anaesth., Edin. Roy. Infirm., Edin.
ALLISON, Mr Keith Philip 271 Blossomfield Road, Solihull B91 1TA Tel: 0121 705 7050 Email: kallison@globalnet.co.uk — MB ChB 1992 Sheff.; FRCS Eng 1997; Dip. IMC RCS Ed. 1996. (Sheffield) Specialist Regist. (Burns & Plastic Surg.) W. Midl.;

Specialist Regist. Rotat. (Plastic Surg.) W. Midl.s; Mem. W. Midl. Care Team; Mem. Research Comm. Fac. of Immediate Care Res. Ed. Socs: Founder Mem. Fac. Immediate Care RCS Edin. Prev: Research Regist. (Burns & Plastic Surg.) Univ. Hosp. Sellyoak Birm.; SHO Rotat. (Surg.) N. Staffs. HA Train. Scheme; SHO (Burn & Plastics) Sellyoak.

ALLISON, Mandy Elizabeth Craigmillar Medical Group, 106 Niddrie Mains Road, Edinburgh EH16 4DT — BM 1986 Soton.; MRCGP 1996; DCH RCP Lond. 1992; DRCOG 1989. GP Princip. Craigmillar Edin.; GP Adviser in Health Promotion to Lothian Health Bd. Prev: GP/Regist. Camb. VTS; Resid. (Paediat.) Nazareth EMMS Hosp.; SHO Rotat. (Med.) Selly Oak Hosp. Birm.

ALLISON, Margaret Macausland (retired) Braemains, Barrhill Avenue, Kirkcudbright DG6 4BQ Tel: 01557 30265 — MB ChB 1924 Glas.; MRCGP 1953.

ALLISON, Marjorie Elisabeth Marion Department of Medical Education, The University of Glasgow, Glasgow Tel: 0141 211 3339; 39 Newark Drive, Pollokshields, Glasgow G41 4QA Tel: 0141 423 2047 — MB ChB 1965 Glas.; MB ChB (Hons.) Glas. 1965; BSc (Hons.) (Physiol.) Glas. 1962; MD (Hons.) 1976; FRCP Ed. 1978, M 1968; FRCP Glas. M 1978. Hon. Sen. Research Fell. Univ. Glas. Socs: Brit. Assn. Phys.; Amer. Soc. Nephrol. Prev: Hon. Cons. Nephrol. & Sen. Lect. (Med.) Glas. Roy. Infirm.

ALLISON, Mary Rose (retired) 2 Merrow Chase, Guildford GU1 2RY Tel: 01483 300996 — MB ChB 1955 Manch.; MSc Manch. 1974, MB ChB 1955; MRCGP 1965; MFCM 1972. Prev: Dir. Pub. Health Crewe HA.

ALLISON, Michael Edward Douglas 262 Queen Edith's Way, Cambridge CB1 8NL — MB BS 1989 Lond.; BSc (Hons.) Lond. 1989; MRCP (UK) 1992. Med. Research Counc. Clin. Train. Fell. Wellcome Trust Immunol. Unit Camb. Univ. Dept. Med.; Hon. Regist. (Med.) Addenbrooke's NHS Trust. Prev: Regist. (Gastroenterol.) St. Mary's & Centr. Middlx. Hosps. Lond.; Regist. (Hepatol.) Addenbrooke's Hosp. Camb.; SHO (Neurol.) Radcliffe Infirm. Oxf.

ALLISON, Michael Fidler (retired) Red House, Trotters Lane, Harlaxton, Grantham NG32 1JZ Tel: 01476 564249 — MB ChB 1961 Manch. Prev: Med. Regist. Derbysh. Roy. Infirm. & Derwent Hosp. Derby.

ALLISON, Miles Clifford The Old School House, Llangwm, Usk NP15 1HG Tel: 01291 650746 — MB BS 1979 Lond.; MD Lond. 1990; FRCP Lond. 1997; MRCP (UK) 1982. Cons. Phys. & Gastroenterol. Roy. Gwent Hosp. Newport. Prev: Sen. Regist. (Med. Gastroenterol.) Gtr. Glas. HB; Regist. (Med.) Unit Roy. Free Hosp. Lond.; SHO Rotat. (Med.) Bath HA.

ALLISON, Nicholas Laerdal, Cokes Lane, Chalfont St Giles HP8 4TX — MB BS 1965 Punjab; BSc Punjab (Pakistan) 1969, MB BS 1965; FFA RCS Eng. 1970. (King Edwd. Med. Coll. Lahore) Cons. Anaesth. Wycombe Gen. Hosp. High Wycombe & Amersham Gen. Hosp.

ALLISON, Nicholas Quentin Orchard Surgery, Cope Road, Banbury OX16 2EJ Tel: 01295 256201, 01295 277220 Fax: 01295 277783 — MB BS 1984 Lond. (Char. Cross)

ALLISON, Rhoda Mary (retired) Weatherhill, Woodhouse Lane, Brighouse HD6 3TP Tel: 01484 3867 — MD 1953 Leeds; MB ChB 1945. Prev: Cons. Pathol. Huddersfield Roy. Infirm.

ALLISON, Robert Hector Department Anaesthesia, Ninewells Hospital, Dundee Tel: 01382 660111; Vinebank, 78 Tay St, Newport-on-Tay DD6 8AP Tel: 01382 541415 — MB ChB 1972 St. And.; FFA RCSI 1977. Cons. (Anaesth.) Ninewells Hosp. Dundee & Dundee Roy. Infirm.; Hon. Lect. (Anaesth.) Univ. Dundee. Socs: NE (Pres. 1998-99) E. Scotl. Soc. Anaesth.; Scott. Soc. Anaesth.; Assn. Anaesth. Prev: Ho. Surg. Maryfield Hosp. Dundee; Ho. Phys. Bridge of Earn Hosp. Perth; Sen. Regist. (Anaesth.) W.. Infirm. Glas.

ALLISON, Robert John Mount Pleasant Practice, The Health Centre, Tempest Way, Chepstow NP16 5XR Tel: 01291 636500 Fax: 01291 636518; The Trees, Devauden, Chepstow NP16 6PE Tel: 01291 650273 — MB ChB 1980 Birm.; DCH RCP Lond. 1984.

ALLISON, Samuel (retired) 7 Stedham Hall, Stedham, Midhurst GU29 0PS — MB BCh Belf. 1940.

ALLISON, Sarah Clare 1a Darnley Road, Leeds LS16 5JF — MB ChB 1996 Dundee.

ALLISON, Professor Simon Philip University Hospital, Clinical Nutrition Unit, Queens Medical Centre, Nottingham NG7 2UH Tel: 01159 194427 Fax: 01159 194427 Email: simonallison@mail.qmc.uh-tr.trent.nhs.uk; Old manor Farm, 19 Shelford Road, Radcliffe on Trent, Nottingham NG12 2AE Tel: 0115 933 2663 Fax: 0115 933 2663 — MB BChir 1963 Camb.; MD (Hons.) Birm. 1970; FRCP Lond. 1977, M 1964. Prof. Clin. Nutrit., Univ. Hosp. Qu.s Med. Centre Nottm.; Med. Dir. Clin. Nutrit. Unit Univ. Hosp. Nottm.; Mem. Advis. Comm. on Borderline Subst.s. Socs: Chairm. Europ. Soc. Parenteral and Enteral Nutrit. 1998-2002; Counc. Mem. Brit. Assn Parenteral and Enteral Nutrit. 1992-98; Assn of Phys.s. Prev: Regist. Dept. Med. Qu. Eliz. Hosp. Birm.; MRC Clin. Research Fell. Univs. Birm. & Bristol; Wellcome Sen. Res. Fell. & Hon. Lect. Dept. Med. Bristol Roy. Infirm.

ALLISON, Stuart Norwood Radiodiagnostic Department, Princess Elizabeth Hospital, Le Vauquiedor, St Martin, Jersey Tel: 01481 725241 Fax: 01481 724272; De Beauvoir, La Rue de la Grande Maison, St. Pierre du Bois, Guernsey GY7 9AL — MB ChB 1969 Aberd.; FRCR 1977; DMRD Aberd. 1974. (Aberd.) Cons. Radiol. P.ss Eliz. Hosp. Guernsey. Prev: Diag. Radiol. Gemeente Ziekenhius Arnhem & Rotterdam Radiother. Inst., Netherlands; Sen. Regist. (Diag. Radiol.) Aberd. Roy. Infirm.

ALLISON-BOLGER, Victoria Yvonne The Carleton Clinic, Cumwhinton Drive, Carlisle CA1 3SX Tel: 01228 602451 — MB ChB 1984 Bristol; MRCPsych 1991. Cons. Psychiat. Garlands Hosp. Carlisle.

ALLISTER, Alison Herriot Rocklea, Bonar Crescent, Bridge of Weir PA11 3EH — MB ChB 1979 Glas.; MRCGP 1983; DRCOG 1982.

ALLISTER, Anne Hamilton Young and Partners, The Ryan Medical Centre, St. Marys Road, Bamber Bridge, Preston PR5 6JD Tel: 01772 335136 Fax: 01772 626701; 30 Studholme Crescent, Penwortham, Preston PR1 9NE — MB ChB 1977 Sheff.; MRCGP 1981.

ALLISTER, Janice Wendy Brinnington Health Centre, Brinnington Road, Stockport SK5 8BS Tel: 0161 430 4002 Fax: 0161 430 7918; 1 Depleach Road, Cheadle SK8 1DZ Tel: 0161 428 3440 — MB BS 1971 Lond.; MRCGP 1975; DCH Eng. 1974; DObst RCOG 1973. (Royal Free)

ALLISTON, Joanne Elizabeth The Surgery, Chestnut Walk, Stratford-upon-Avon CV37 6HQ Tel: 01789 292895 Fax: 01789 414721 Email: joalliston@stratford-gp.org.uk — MB ChB 1989 Bristol; MRCGP 1993; DRCOG 1992. Prev: Trainee GP Stratford-upon-Avon; SHO (Psychiat.) Rubery Hosp.; SHO (O & G) Marston Green Hosp. Birm.

ALLISTONE, Anne Catherine Grange Street Surgery, 2 Grange Street, St Albans AL3 5NF Tel: 01727 851136 Fax: 01727 847961; Wood End House, Lime Avenue, Blackmore End, St Albans AL4 8LG Tel: 01438 833735 Fax: 01438 833872 — MB BS 1986 Lond.; BSc Lond. 1983; Cert. Family Plann. JCC 1991; DCH RCP Lond. 1990. (St. Geo. Hosp. Med. Sch.) GP Princip. Grange St. Surg. Socs: BMA. Prev: SHO (O & G) St. Albans City Hosp.; SHO (Paediat. & Gen. Med.) Watford Gen. Hosp.; SHO (Rheum.) Nuffield Orthop. Centre Oxf.

ALLISTONE, Jill Carolyn Lincoln House Surgery, Wolsey Road, Hemel Hempstead HP2 4TU Tel: 01442 254366 Fax: 01442 244554; Longueville, 18 Green End Road, Boxmoor, Hemel Hempstead HP1 1QW Tel: 01442 392333 Fax: 01442 262725 Email: barry.banks@btinternet.com — MB BS 1979 Lond.; BSc (1st cl. Hons.) Lond. 1976. (Royal Free) Clin. Asst. (Dermat.) Barnet Gen. Hosp. Socs: BMA. Prev: Trainee GP St. Albans; SHO (O & G) N.wick Pk. Hosp. Lond.; SHO (Gen. Med.) Hammersmith Hosp. Lond.

ALLKINS, Mr James Allan Flat 8, Stonecroft, Parkfield Road S., Didsbury, Manchester M20 6DA Tel: 0161 434 3782 — MB ChB 1991 Manch.; BSc St. Andr. 1988; FRCS Ed. 1997. (St. Andrews University and Manchester University) SHO (Cardiothoracic Surg.) Manch. Roy. Infirm. Prev: SHO (Cardiothoracic Surg.) Wythenshawe Hosp. Manch.

ALLMAN, Andrew Christopher John Ty Draw Farmhouse, Colwinstone, Cowbridge CF71 7NL — MB BCh 1984 Wales.

ALLMAN, Ian Graham Burton Croft Surgery, 5 Burton Crescent, Leeds LS6 4DN Tel: 0113 274 4777 Fax: 0113 230 4219 — MB ChB 1979 Birm; MRCGP 1984; Cert. Family Plann. JCC 1984. Chairm. NW Leeds PCG.

ALLMAN, Michael Benjamin 115 Norcliffe Road, Blackpool FY2 9ES — MB ChB 1970 Birm; MBA Keele 1990.

ALLMAND, Celia Anne 111 Menlove Avenue, Liverpool L18 3HP — MB ChB 1994 Sheff.

ALLMARK, Anthony Howard 2c Southdale Gardens, Ossett WF5 8BB Tel: 01924 267989 — MB BChir 1976 Camb.; MFPHM 1989. Prev: Cons. Pub. Health Med. Wakefield HA.; Sen. Regist. (Community Med.) Shropsh. HA; Regist. Chem. Path. Sefton AHA.

ALLONBY-NEVE, Claire Louise 7 Chaseley Road, Chaseley Gardens, Salford M6 7DZ — MB ChB 1996 Manch.

ALLOTT, Helen Anne Department of Obstetrics & Gynaecology, Royal Berkshire Hospital, Reading RG1 5AN Tel: 01189 875111 Fax: 01189 878954 — MB ChB 1980 Sheff.; MRCOG 1986. Cons. Feto-Matern. Med. Roy. Berks. Hosp. Reading.

ALLOUB, Mr Mohamed Ibrahim Amin Bassetlaw District General Hospital, Kilton, Worksop S81 0BD — MB BCh 1978 Ain Shams; FRCOG 1998; FRCS Ed. 1985; FRCS Glas. 1985; MRCOG 1985. Cons. O & G Bassetlaw Dist. Gen. Hosp.; Chairm. Audit Strategy Gp. Socs: Med. Protec. Soc.; Brit. Soc. Colposc. & Clin. Pathol.; Brit. Soc. Gyn. Endoscopy.

ALLOUNI, Sabah 9 Tymynydd Close, Radyr, Cardiff CF15 8AS — MD 1970 Damascus; DFFP 1993; DGO 1976; DObst RCPI 1976; LM 1975.

ALLOWAY, Lara Judith 63 Claudian Place, St Albans AL3 4JQ — BM 1995 Soton.

ALLOWAY, Ruth Dorking Child and Adolescent Mental HealthService (CAMHS), The Dene Centre, Dorking Hospital, Horsham Road, Dorking RH4 2AA Tel: 01306 502708 — MB BS 1979 Lond.; MA Oxon; MRCPsych 1984. Cons. Child & Adolesc. Psychiat. Surrey Oaklands NHS Trust. Prev: Sen. Regist. (Child & Adolesc. Psychiat.) Maudsley Hosp. Lond.

ALLPORT, Simon John Wheelgate House, Market Square, Bampton OX18 2JH — MB BS 1992 Lond.; BSc Lond. 1983.

ALLPORT, Thomas Denison 21 Lathbury Road, Oxford OX2 7AT — MB BChir 1993 Camb.; MRCP 1995.

ALLRED, Jane Patricia St Johns Medical Centre, St Johns Rd, Altrincham WA14 2PJ Tel: 0161 928 8727 — MB ChB 1978 Manch.; MRCGP 1983; DRCOG 1984. (Manchester) Gen. Practitioner.

ALLRED, Josephine Elizabeth Island Health, 145 East Ferry Road, London E14 3BQ Tel: 020 7363 1111 Fax: 020 7363 1112 — MB BS 1984 Lond.; MRCGP 1991; DCH RCP Lond. 1990; DGM RCP Lond. 1988; DRCOG 1987. Prev: SHO (Med. for Elderly & Paediat.) Whipps Cross Hosp. Lond.; SHO (O & G) Mid Essex HA; SHO (Gen. Med.) NE Essex HA.

ALLROGGEN, Holger University Hospital of Birmingham, Queen Elizabeth Neuroscience Centre, Birmingham B15 2TH Tel: 0121 472 1311; Damson Cottage, 134 Lodge Road, Knowle, Solihull B93 0HF Tel: 01564 771985 — State Exam Med 1991 Frankfurt; MD Frankfurt 1992; MRCP (UK) 1996. (Univ. Frankfurt, Germany) Specialist Regist. (Neurol.) Leic. Roy. Hosp. Prev: SHO (Neurosurg.) Qu. Eliz. Hosp. Birm.; SHO (Neurol.) Qu. Med. Centre Nottm.; SHO (Gen. Med.) Good Hope Hosp. Sutton Coldfield.

ALLSAGER, Christopher Mark 95 Knutsford Road, Wilmslow SK9 6JH — MB ChB 1994 Leic.

ALLSEBROOK, Ian Harrowby Lane Surgery, Harrowby Lane, Grantham NG31 9NS Tel: 01476 579494 Fax: 01476 579694 — MB BS 1992 Lond.

ALLSOP, Alistair Roos Lonsdale 3 Shute Court, Shute Hill, Bishopsteignton, Teignmouth TQ14 9QL Tel: 01626 772799 Email: roosallsop@compuserve.com — MB ChB 1997 Manch.; BSc 1994. (Manchester) Doctor in Roy. Navy.

ALLSOP, Christopher John 3 Rivington Avenue, Washford Park, Meole Brace, Shrewsbury SY3 9QL — BM 1980 Soton. SCMO Shrops. Community & Ment. Health NHS Trust.

ALLSOP, Elaine Janet Tremanis 1 Straits, Easton, Portland DT5 1HG — BM 1982 Soton.

ALLSOP, Paul 1 Beacon Road, Rolleston-on-Dove, Burton-on-Trent DE13 9EF — MB BS 1980 Lond.

ALLSOP, Susan Mary (retired) 18 Green Lane, Dronfield, Sheffield S18 6LJ — MB ChB 1968 Sheff.

ALLSOPP, Allan Whaddon Way Surgery, 293 Whaddon Way, Bletchley, Milton Keynes MK3 7LW Tel: 01908 375341 Fax: 01908 374975; 27 Byron Close, Bletchley, Milton Keynes MK3 5BD Tel: 01908 367773 — MB BS 1977 Lond.; BA Oxf. 1974; MRCGP 1983; DRCOG 1979. Prev: Trainee GP N.ampton VTS; Ho. Surg. N.ampton Gen. Hosp.; Ho. Phys. Liverp. Roy. Infirm.

ALLSOPP, Elizabeth Sarah Devonshire Green Medical Centre, 126 Devonshire Street, Sheffield S3 7SF Tel: 0114 272 1626 — MB ChB 1989 Sheff.; MRCGP 1994. Prev: Trainee GP Sheff. VTS.

ALLSOPP, Emma Jane 9 Elizabeth Way, Kenilworth CV8 1QP Tel: 01926 512227 Email: emmaallsopp@doctors.org.uk; 3 Shute Court, Shute Hill, Bishop Steignton, Teignmouth TQ14 9QL Tel: 01626 772799 Email: roosallsop@compuserve.com — MB ChB 1997 Manch. (Manchester) Res. Asst., Warwick Univ. Community Paediat. & Social Policy Dept.; Locum (Ho. Off. & SHO). Socs: BMA; MDU; BMAS. Prev: SHO - Paediat., Roy. Devon & Exeter Hosp.; Surg. HO, Blackburn Roy. Infirm.; Med. HO, N. Manch Gen. Hosp.

ALLSOPP, Gail Marie 33 Chapel St, Bishops Itchington, Leamington Spa CV47 2RB Tel: 09588 786820 Email: gma@doctors.org.uk — MB ChB 1997 Birm. Basic Surgic. Train. Rotat. Warks & Worcs.

ALLSOPP, Kathleen Mary (retired) Little Busto House, West Marden, Chichester PO18 9EQ Tel: 01705 631494 — MB BS Lond. 1961; MRCS Eng. LRCP Lond. 1961.

ALLSOPP, Lesley Barbara 13 Bryn-y-Coed, Holywell CH8 7AU — MB ChB 1994 Leeds. SHO (Med. for Elderly) St. Jas. Univ. Hosp. Leeds. Prev: Ho. Off. (Med.) St. Jas. Univ. Hosp.; Ho. Off. (Surg.) Hull Roy. Infirm.

ALLSOPP, Lucy Ellen Bridge Farm, Bridge Sollars, Hereford HR4 7JH — MB BS 1991 Lond.

ALLSOPP, Mark Richard Berkshire Adolescent Unit, Wokingham Hospital, Barkham Road, Wokingham RG41 2RE Tel: 0118 949 5019 Fax: 0118 949 5026 — MB BS 1979 Lond.; BSc Lond. 1976; MRCPsych 1985; DCH RCP Lond. 1981. Cons. Child & Adolesc. Psychiat. Berks. Healthcare NHS Trust. Prev: Cons. Child & Adolesc. Psychiat. Swindon & MarlBoro. Hosps.; Sen. Regist. (Child & Adolesc. Psychiat.) Oxf. RHA.

ALLSOPP, Mr Roger Henry Princess Elizabeth Hospital, St Martin's, Guernsey GY4 6UU Tel: 01481 725241; Le Douit Farm, Grande Rue, St. Saviours, Guernsey GY7 9JP Tel: 01481 65029 Fax: 01481 66463 — MB BS 1964 Durh.; LLM Cardiff 1993; FRCS Eng. 1970; FRCS Ed. 1970; Spec. Accredit. Gen. Surg. RCS Eng. 1975. Cons. Surg. P.ss Eliz. Hosp. Le Vauquiedor; Cons. Surg., Soton. Univ. Trust; BrE. unit at Roy. S.ants Hosp. Socs: Fell. Assn. Surgs.; Brit. Assn. Surg. Oncol.; Vasc. Surgic. Soc. GB & N. Irel. Prev: Sen. Research Fell. (Surg.) Univ. Newc.; Sen. Regist. (Vasc. Surg. & Renal Transpl.) Roy. Vict. Infirm. Newc.; Sen. Regist. Profess. Surg. Unit Roy. Vict. Infirm. Newc.

ALLSUP, David John Royal Liverpool University Hospital, Prescot St., Liverpool L7 8XP; 3 The Pastures, West Kirby, Wirral CH48 9XT — MB ChB 1992 Leic.; MRCP (UK) 1996. Regist. (Haemat.) Roy. Liverp. Univ. Lond.

ALLSUP, Stephen James 184 Brownedge Road, Lostock Hall, Preston PR5 5AJ — MB ChB 1994 Sheff.

ALLT, Julius Edward 1008 Pershore Road, Selly Park, Birmingham B29 7PX — MB ChB 1994 Birm.

ALLT-GRAHAM, John 56 Clapham Common West Side, London SW4 9AT Tel: 020 7223 1521 — MB BS 1971 Melbourne; BSc (Statistics) Melbourne 1967; FANZCA 1992; FRCA 1990; FFA RACS 1977. (Melb.) Cons. Anaesth. & Intens. Care St. Geo. Hosp. Tooting Lond. Prev: Cons. Anaesth. St. Jas. Hosp. Lond.

ALLTREE, Margaret Joyce (retired) Kenyon Cottage, Castle Streeet, Holt, Wrexham LL13 9YL Tel: 01829 270941 Fax: 01829 270941 — MB ChB 1953 Liverp.

ALLTREE, Michael, TD (retired) Scots Pines, Church Lane, Hargrave, Chester CH3 7RN Tel: 01829 781206 — MB ChB Liverp. 1960; FRCR Lond. 1988; DMRD Liverp. 1968; DObst RCOG 1963. Prev: Cons. Radiol. Macclesfield HA.

ALLTREE, Samuel John (retired) Kenyon Cottage, Castle St, Holt, Wrexham LL13 9YL Tel: 01829 270941 Fax: 01829 270941 Email: johnalltree@btinternet.com — MB ChB 1953 Liverp.

***ALLUM, Alaster Malcolm** Cornwood, Westland Green, Little Hadham, Ware SG11 2AH Tel: 01279 842198 — MB BS 1994 Lond.; BA Camb. 1991.

ALLUM, Caroline Ann Royal Free Hospital, Dept. of Radiology, Pond Street, London NW3 2QG Tel: 07970 047741 Email: caroline@royalfree.co.uk; 4 Glasslyn Road, London N8 8RH Tel: 07970 047741 Email: caroline@royalfree.co.uk — MB BS 1991

Lond.; 1999 FRCR; MRCP (UK) 1993. (Roy. Free Hosp. Sch. Med.) Specialist Regist. (Radiol.) Roy. Free Hosp. Lond. Prev: Regist. Chelsea & W.minster Hosp. Lond.; SHO Roy. Brompton Hosp.; SHO Rotat. Harefield & Hillingdon Hosps.

ALLUM, Gerald John (retired) The Old School House, Hilton, Blandford Forum DT11 0DB Tel: 01258 880074 — MB BS Lond. 1951; BSc Lond. 1947. Prev: Hosp. Pract. Occupat. Health Dept. Whipps Cross Hosp. Lond.

ALLUM, Mr Robin Leslie 15 Heatherside Gardens, Farnham Common, Slough SL2 3RR — MB ChB 1972 Bristol; FRCS Eng. 1977. Brit. Orthop. Assn. Europ. Trav. Schol. 1984; Cons. Orthop. Surg. Heatherwood Hosp. Ascot, Wexham Pk. Hosp. & King Edwd. VII Hosp. Windsor. Socs: Fell. Brit. Orthop. Assn.; Brit. Orthop. Res. Soc. Prev: Sen. Orthop. Regist. Roy.Nat. Orthop. Hosp. Stanmore; Sen. Orthop. Regist. N.wick Pk. Hosp. & Clin. Res. Centre Harrow; Clin. Fell. Dept. Orthop. Univ. Toronto.

ALLUM, Timothy Gerald Lown 191 Queens Road, Buckhurst Hill IG9 5AZ Tel: 020 8505 1560 — MB BS 1957 Lond.; FFA RCS Eng. 1964. (Lond. Hosp.) Cons. Anaesth. Whipps Cross Hosp. Lond.

ALLUM, Wendy Elizabeth Berkeley Place Surgery, 11 High Street, Cheltenham GL52 6DA Tel: 01242 513975 Fax: 01242 563787 — MB BS 1975 Lond.; BSc Lond. 1972; DRCOG Lond. 1981. (Lond. Hosp.) GP Partner; Clin. Asst. BrE. Clin.

ALLUM, Mr William Herbert Epsom & St. Helier NHS Trust, Dorking Road, Epsom KT18 7EG Tel: 01372 735114 Fax: 01372 735159 — MB ChB 1977 Birm.; BSc (Physiol.) Birm. 1974, MD 1986; FRCS Eng. 1982. Cons. Surg. Epsom & St. Helier NHS Trust; Hon. Cons. Surg. (Gastrointestinal) Roy. Marsden Hosp. Lond.; Mem. Ct. Examrs. RCS Eng.; Mem. Physiotherapists Bd. (Counc. Profess. Suppl. Med.); RCS Regional Adviser Surg. (S. Thames W.); Mem. Intercollegiate Bd. in Gen. Surg. Socs: Surgic. Research Soc.; Brit. Assn. Surgic. Oncol. (Nat. Comm. Mem.); (Hon. Sec.) Assn. Upper Gastrointestinal Surg. Prev: Cons. Surg. St. Bart. Hosp. Lond.; Sen. Lect. (Surg.) Univ. Leicester & Hon. Cons. Surg. Leicester Roy. Infirm.; Observer Surg. Oncol. MD Anderson Hosp. & Cancer Centre Houston, Texas.

ALLUM LAI-FOOK, Janet Theresa 30 Pendarves Road, London SW20 8TS — MB BCh BAO 1973 NUI.

ALLWEIS, Barry St Andrews Medical Centre, 30 Russell Street, Eccles, Manchester M30 0NU Tel: 0161 707 5500 — MB ChB 1973 Manch.

ALLWOOD, Alexander Charles Lewis Rochford Tower House, Rochford Tower Lane, Boston PE21 9RH — MB ChB 1992 Birm.

ALLWOOD, Christopher Roy Lewis Parkside Surgery, Tawney Street, Boston PE21 6PF Tel: 01205 365881; Rochford Tower House, Rochford Tower Lane, Fishtoft, Boston PE21 9RH Tel: 01205 361414 — MB ChB 1965 Bristol. (Bristol) Med. Off. (Prison Serv.) HMP N. Sea Camp Boston. Prev: Ho. Surg. Roy. Infirm. Bristol; Ho. Off. (Obst. & Paediat.) S.mead Hosp. Bristol.

ALLWOOD, Ian Justin Bridge House Medical Centre, Scholars Lane, Stratford-upon-Avon CV37 6HE Tel: 01789 292201 Fax: 01789 262087 Email: ian.allwood@bhmlb.warwick-ha.wmids.nhs.uk; 20 Old Town Mews, Stratford-upon-Avon CV37 6GP Tel: 01789 414906 Email: ian.allwood@virgin.net — MB BS 1987 Lond.; DRCOG 1991; DCH RCP Lond. 1989. (Char. Cross & Westm.) Clin. Asst. (Gastroenterol. & Endoscopy) Warwick Hosp.

ALLWOOD, Michael John, VRD (retired) Ridge Barn, Ufton Fields, Leamington Spa CV33 9PE Tel: 01926 613844 — MRCS Eng. LRCP Lond. 1948; MA Wales 1991; PhD Lond. 1959, MD 1971, MB BS 1950; AFOM RCP Lond. 1980; AKC. Hon. Surg. Capt. RNR UK Represen. & Ex-Pres. CIOMR (NATO). Prev: Cons. Clin. Physiol. Cardiothoracic Unit Walsgrave Hosp. Coventry.

ALLWRIGHT, Graham John The Village Surgery, Elbow Lane, Liverpool L37 4AW Tel: 01704 878661 Fax: 01704 832488 — MB BS 1977 Lond.

ALLYBOCUS, Sheik Abdool Hamid 20 Dunedin Road, Leyton, London E10 5PE — MB ChB 1982 Leeds. SHO Dept. Elderly Newton Green Hosp. Leeds.

ALMAN, Richard James Pasture Rd. Health Centre, Pasture Road, Moreton, Wirral CU46 85A Tel: 0151 678 0993 — MB ChB 1985 Manch.; DRCOG 1991.

ALMASSI, Maryam 11 Maple Road, Loughborough LE11 2JL — MD 1994 Brussels.

ALMEIDA, Mr Anthony Zino 15 Endersleigh Gardens, London NW4 4RX — MB BS 1955 Bombay; FRCS Ed. 1962. (Grant Med. Coll. Bombay) Cons. Surg. Manor Ho. Hosp. Golders Green.

ALMEIDA, Antonio Medina 23 Collingham Place, London SW5 0QF — BChir 1993 Camb.

ALMEIDA, Bernice Martha Department of Histopathology, St George's Hospital, Blackshaw Rd, London SW17 0QT; 240 Norbury Avenue, London SW16 3RN — MB ChB 1979 Nairobi; PhD Lond. 1997; MSc (Cytopathology), Lond., 1998. Specialist Regist. (Histopath.), PT. Prev: Research Assoc. & Regist. UMDS Guy's & St. Thos. Hosp. Lond. .

ALMEIDA, Eli John Joseph The New Surgery, 296 Queens Road, London SE14 5JN Tel: 020 7639 5528 — MB BS 1961 Lond.; MRCS Eng. LRCP Lond. 1960; DObst RCOG 1963; DCH Eng. 1967. (Lond. Hosp.) GP New Cross Gate Lond. Prev: Regist. Dept. Child Health St. Bart. Hosp. Lond.; Med. Regist. Bethnal Green Hosp. Lond.

ALMEIDA, Joyce Hart The Priory Cottage, Tottingworth Park, Heathfield TN21 8UN Tel: 01435 864545 Fax: 01435 869084 Email: dr.almeida@virgin.net; Email: dr.almeida@virgin.net — MB BS 1983 Lond.; MRCPsych 1987. Cons. Psychiat., The Priory Grange, Heathfield, Sussex; Cons. Pschiatrist, The Priory, Ticehurst Hse, Ticehurst, E. Sussex. Prev: Lect. (Psychogeriat.) Guy's & St. Thos. Hosps. Lond.; Sen. Regist. (Psychiat.) Guy's Hosp. Lond.; Sen. Regist. (Psychogeriat.) Tooting Bec Hosp. Lond.

ALMEIDA, Nalini Margaret The New Surgery, 296 Queens Road, London SE14 5JN Tel: 020 7639 5528; (Surgery), 397 Queens Road, London SE14 — MB BS 1966 Bombay; MB BS (Hons.) Bombay 1966. (Seth G.S. Med. Coll.) GP New Cross Gate Lond. Prev: Clin. Asst. (Geriat.) New Cross Hosp. Lond.; Ho. Phys. Bethnal Green Hosp.; Ho. Surg. St. Giles Hosp. Lond.

ALMENT, Sir (Edward) Anthony (John) (retired) Winston House, Boughton, Northampton NN2 8RR — MRCS Eng. LRCP Lond. 1945; DSc Leic. 1982; Hon. FRCP Ed. 1981; Hon. FRCPI 1979; Hon. FRCGP 1982; FRCOG 1967, M 1951; Hon. FRACOG 1985; Hon. FRCPCH 1997. Prev: Cons. O & G N.ampton Health Dist.

ALMEYDA, John James Ryan 111 Harley Street, London W1N 1DG Tel: 020 7935 4013 Fax: 020 7935 0728; The Old Rectory, Ayot St Peter, Welwyn AL6 9BG Tel: 01438 714347 — MB BS 1960 Lond.; FRCP Lond. 1988; MRCP (UK) 1966; MRCS Eng. LRCP Lond. 1960. (St. Bart.) Cons. Dermat. Enfield Health Dist.; Asst. Prof. Med. St. Geos. Univ. Sch. Med. Socs: Fell. Roy. Soc. Med. (Mem. Sect. Dermat.); Fell. St. John's Hosp. Dermat. Soc. Prev: Sen. Regist. (Dermat.) Lond. Hosp.

ALMEYDA, Mr John Stephen The Old Rectory, Ayot St Peter, Welwyn AL6 9BG Fax: 01438 714347 — MB BS 1990 Lond.; FRCS Lond. 1996; FRCS Ed. 1994. (St. Bart. Med. Sch.) Socs: Roy. Soc. Med.; Brit. Assn. Otol. & Head & Neck Surg.

ALMEYDA, Robert Victor The Old Rectory, Ayot Saint Peter, Welwyn AL6 9BG — MB BS 1997 Lond.

ALMOND, Adrian John Kingsteignton Surgery, Whiteway Road, Kingsteignton, Newton Abbot TQ12 3HN Tel: 01626 883312 Fax: 01626 336406; Barn Close, Broadway Road, Kingsteignton, Newton Abbot TQ12 3EH Tel: 01626 63556 — MB BChir 1963 Camb.; BA Camb. 1960; MRCS Eng. LRCP Lond. 1963. (Camb. & St. Mary's) GP Adviser S. Devon Health Care Trust. Socs: Torquay & Dist. Med. Soc. Prev: SHO (Surg.) St. Ann's Gen. Hosp. Tottenham; SHO (Obst.) Perivale Matern. Hosp. Greenford; SHO (Gyn.) King Edwd. Memor. Hosp. Ealing.

ALMOND, Mr David James 8 West End, Walkington, Beverley HU17 8SX Tel: 01482 88220 Fax: 01482 679513 Email: david@suryalmo.demon.co.uk — MD 1987 Leeds; MB ChB 1975; FRCS Eng. 1981. Cons. Urol. Roy. Hull Hosps. Trust.

ALMOND, David Laurence (retired) St Just, Coopers Lane, Northaw, Potters Bar EN6 4NJ Tel: 01707 655222 Fax: 01707 646888 Email: davidalmond@msn.com — MB BChir Camb. 1954; DObst RCOG 1959; MRCGP 1966. Prev: GP Potters Bar.

ALMOND, David Soloman 43 Woodview Road, Liverpool L25 6HY — MB ChB 1991 Leeds; BSc (1st cl. Hons.) Psychol. in Relation to Med. Leeds 1988. SHO Rotat. (Med.) Roy. Liverp. Univ. Hosp.

ALMOND, Diana Patricia 11 Firs Road, Gatley, Cheadle SK8 4JT Tel: 0161 428 5954 — MRCS Eng. LRCP Lond. 1957.

ALMOND, Esther (retired) 50 Gerard Road, Barnes, London SW13 9QQ Tel: 020 8 748 5431 Fax: 020 7748 5431 — MB ChB Manch. 1954; DCH Eng. 1956. Sen. Clin. Med. Off. (Family Plann.) Riverside Community Health Care NHS Trust. Prev: Ho. Phys. (Paediat.) Woolwich Memor. Hosp.

ALMOND, Francis Anthony 12 Malham Court, Silsden, Keighley BD20 0QB Tel: 01535 658676 Fax: 01535 658676 — MB BS 1951 Lond. (St. Bart.) Med. Adviser Health Servs. Appeal Auth. Socs: BMA. Prev: Ho. Surg. Orthop. & Anaesth. Ho. Off. St. Bart. Hosp. Lond.

ALMOND, Ian David Gameslea House, Glossop Road, Hayfield, High Peak SK22 2NF Tel: 01663 744604 Fax: 01663 744604 — MB BS 1971 Lond.; MRCGP 1976; AFOM RCP Lond. 1995; DRCOG 1977. (Middlx. Hosp. Med. Sch.) Occupat. Med. Off. Manch. City Counc.; Lead Apptd. Doctor Health & Safety Exec. Socs: Soc. Occupat. Med. Prev: Asst. Med. Dir. BUPA Med. Centre; Ho. Phys. & Ho. Surg. St. Albans City Hosp.; RAMC.

ALMOND, Isabella Margaret (retired) 4 Acacia Avenue, Chapel-St Leonards, Skegness PE24 5RE Tel: 01754 872657 — MB ChB 1944 Sheff.; DCH Eng. 1947. Prev: Lady Med. Off. Colonial Med. Serv. Malaya.

ALMOND, Janet Anne BMI Health Services, The Newcastle Clinic, Towers Ave, Jesmond NE2 3Qe Tel: 0191 2815031 Fax: 0191 2815035 Email: jalmond@bmihs.co.uk; 26 Fellside, Darras Hall, Ponteland, Newcastle upon Tyne NE2 9JP Tel: 01661 821540 Fax: 01661 820599 Email: jalmond304@aol.com — MB ChB 1979 Manch.; MRCGP 1985; DRCOG 1983; DOCC Med 2000. Occupat.al Phys. (Specialist Regist.) BMI Health Serv.s, Newc. Upon Tyne. Prev: GP Cramlington; SHO (O & G) Preston Hosp. N. Shields; SHO (Psychiat.) St. Geo. Hosp. Morpeth.

ALMOND, Michael Kevin Cannonbury, Potash Road, Billericay CM11 1HH — BM BS 1982 Nottm.; BMedSci Nottm. 1980; DM Nottm. 1991, BMedSci (Hons.) 1980; MRCP (UK) 1985; FRCP Lond. 1998. Cons. Phys. & Nephrol. S.end Hosp. Socs: Internat. Soc. Nephrol.; Eur. Dialysis & Transpl. Assn.; Amer. Soc. Nephrol. Prev: Lect. (Med.) & Hon. Sen. Regist. Lond. Hosp. Med. Coll.

ALMOND, Richard George Patrick (retired) 8 Charlbury Road, Oxford OX2 6UT Tel: 01865 55529 — BM BCh 1940 Oxf.; BA Oxf. 1937, BM BCh 1940. Prev: Childr. Ho. Phys. Middlx. Hosp. & Mt. Vernon Hosp. EMS.

ALMOND, Sarah Louise 5 Burnside Way, Penwortham, Preston PR1 9JT — MB ChB 1998 Liverp.

ALMOND, William Richard Library House Surgery, Avondale Road, Chorley PR7 2AD Tel: 01257 262081 Fax: 01257 232114 — MB ChB 1965 Manch.; MRCOG 1971; MRCGP 1975; FRCOG 1987.

ALMUTAIRI, Salem Flat 2/5, 170 Elmbank St., Glasgow G2 4NY — MB ChB 1992 Glas.

ALNAES-KATJAVIVI, Patji Haakon 51 Raglan Street, London NW5 3BU — MB BS 1998 Lond.; MB BS Lond 1998.

ALNER, Mark Richard 47 Dorchester Road, Lytchett Minister, Poole BH16 6JE; 47 Dorchester Road, Lytchett Minister, Poole BH16 6JE — MB BS 1987 Lond.; MRCP (UK) 1990; FRCR 1994. Cons. Radiologist, Dorset Co. Hosp., Dorchester, Dorset. Prev: Cons. Radiologist, Selly Oak Hosp., Birm.; Regist. (Diagn. Radiol.) John Radcliffe Hosp. Oxf.; Regist. (Clin. Oncol.) Roy. S. Hants. Hosp. Soton.

ALNUAMAANI, Timothy Mark 26 Woodbourne Road, Brooklands, Manchester M33 3SY — MB ChB 1991 Sheff. SHO (Psychiat.) Manch. Roy. Infirm.

ALO, Mr Gabriel Olaseinde Walsall NHS Trust, Manor Hospital, Moat Road, Walsall WS2 9PS Tel: 01922 721172 Ext: 7137; 5 Amelas Close, Clockfields Estate, Brierley Hill DY5 3FD Tel: 01384 482288 Fax: 01384 482288 — MB ChB 1978 Ife; FRCS (Glasgow); FRCS (Orth.); FMCS (Nigeria), MMedSci (Tr). (Obafenu Awolono Univ, Coll. of Health Sci., Nigeria) Specialist Regist., Robt. Jones & Agnes Hunt Orthop. Hosp.; Cons. Orthopaedic Surg., Manor Hosp., Walsall. Socs: BMA.

ALONSO MADRAZO, Carlos Wings Medical Centre, 238 Broomhill Road, Brislington, Bristol BS4 5RG Tel: 0117 972 0999 Fax: 0117 972 0888; Flat 2, 23 Park St, Bath BA1 2TE Tel: 01225 338277 Email: drcalonso@cs.com — LMS 1989 Cantabria. Sen. Med. Off. Air Ambul. Company (Wings AeroMed. Servs.); Clin. Asst. (A & E) Roy. United Hosp. Bath. Prev: SHO (Cardiac Surg.) Bristol; SHO (Orthop.) Bath.

ALONSO URRUTIA, Ana Maria Flat 4, 297 Brownhill Road, London SE6 1AG — LMS 1990 Basque Provinces. SHO (Geriats.) Joyce Green Hosp. Dartford, Kent. Prev: SHO (Med./Geriat.s); SHO (Psychogeriat.) Joyce Green; SHO (Geriat.) Whipps Gross.

ALONSO VICENTE, Maria Jose Stepping Hill Hospital, Doctor's Mess, Poplar Grove, Stockport SK2 7JE — LMS 1993 U Complutense Madrid.

***ALONZI, Roberto** 18 Connaught Way, Tunbridge Wells TN4 9QL — MB BS 1997 Lond.; BSc Lond. 1994.

ALONZO, Karl Hilario Reloj Coopers Road Surgery, 51 Coopers Road, Handsworth Wood, Birmingham B20 2JU Tel: 0121 554 1812 — MB ChB 1983 Birm.

ALORDA BOSCANA, Maria Magdalena Room 17, 3 Broadhurst Gardens, London NW8 3QS — LMS 1993 Valencia.

ALOZAIRI, Ous 28 Primrosehill Drive, Aberdeen AB24 4HY Tel: 01224 486599 Email: ous@xrated.demon.co.uk — MB ChB 1995 Aberd.

ALP, Nicholas John Stable Cottage, 160 Old Road, Headington, Oxford OX3 8SY Tel: 01865 750066 Fax: 01865 750066 Email: 101323.2347@compuserve.com — BM BCh 1994 Oxf.; PhD Camb. 1991; BSc Lond. 1988; MRCP UK 1997. (Oxf.) Specialist Regist. (Cardiol.) Oxf. Reg. Prev: L.A.T. (Gen. Med.) John Radcliffe Hosp. Oxf.; SHO (Gen. Med.) John Radcliffe Hosp. Oxf.; Ho. Off. (Med.) John Radcliffe Hosp. Oxf.

ALPER, Jonathan 2 Pembroke Hall, Mulberry Close, Hendon, London NW4 1QW — MB BCh 1985 Witwatersrand; DA (UK) 1993.

ALPIN, Harry Rodney, MBE The Garden House, Lands Lane, Knaresborough HG5 9DE Tel: 01423 863261 — MRCS Eng. LRCP Lond. 1952; FFOM RCP Lond. 1987, MFOM 1982; DIH Eng. 1973; DIH Soc. Apoth. Lond. 1973. Hon. Lect. (Occupat. Health) Newc. Univ. Prev: Chief Med. Off. Powergen plc; Chief Med. Off. Yorksh. Electricity plc Leeds.

ALPIN, Helen Rachel Bellbrooke Surgery, 395-397 Harehills Lane, Leeds LS9 6AP Tel: 0113 249 4848 Fax: 0113 248 4993; 20 Baronsmead, Leeds LS15 7AR Tel: 0113 264 6432 Email: kcg02@dial.pipex.com — MB BS 1983 Lond.; MRCGP 1987; Dip. Sports Med. Lond. 1988; DRCOG 1987; DFFP 1987. (Roy. Free Hosp. Sch. Med.) GP Leeds. Socs: Brit. Assn. Sport & Med. Prev: Trainee GP Dewsbury VTS.

ALPREN, Charles Gideon 16 Sunningdale Gardens, Kingsbury, London NW9 9NB — MB ChB 1997 Leeds.

ALSADI, Mohamad Rida Hamied Virgina Waters, 67 Huntly Road, Bournemouth BH3 7HQ Tel: 01202 518331 — MB ChB 1977 Baghdad; FFA RCSI 1986.

ALSAIDY, Ahmed 1 Willow Close, Bath BA2 2DZ — MB ChB 1989 Glas.

ALSFORD, Lesley Joyce North Middlesex Hospital, Sterling Way, Edmondon, London N18 1QX Email: lesley.alsford@nmh.nhs.uk — MB ChB 1979 Sheff.; FRCPCH 1997; MRCP (UK) 1985. Cons. Paediat. N. Middlx. Hosp. Lond. Socs: RCPCH. Prev: Sen. Regist. (Paediat.) Roy. Free Hosp. Lond.

ALSHABAN, Mr Natik Abdul Wahab Abdul Razak 2 Churchill Avenue, Scaltback, Newmarket CB8 0BU Tel: 01638 665225 — MB ChB 1968 Baghdad; ChM Baghdad 1977, MB ChB 1968; FRCS Ed. 1982; FICS 1998. Cons. Trauma. Surg. St Richards Hosp. Sussex; Staff Grade Surg. (A & E) St Cross Hosp. Rugby. Prev: Clin. Asst. (A & E) Grimsby Hosp. S. Humberside.

ALSHARIF, Mahnaz 37 Holloway, Bath BA2 4PT Tel: 01225 333385 — MB ChB 1996 Bristol; BSc (Biochem.) Sussex 1983; PhD (Biochem.) Bath 1988. (Bristol) BTS. Socs: BMA. Prev: SHO (Paediat. & O & G); Ho. Off. (Med. & Surg.).

ALSMEIER, Christa Johanne Joyce Green Hospital, Joyce Green Lane, Dartford DA1 5PL — State Exam Med 1990 Frankfurt.

ALSOP, Katharine Ruth Bristol General Hospital, Guinea St., Bristol BS1 6SY Tel: 0117 926 5001; 23 Cricklade Road, Bishopston, Bristol BS7 9EW Tel: 0117 944 1758 — MB ChB 1987 Bristol; MRCGP 1992; DRCOG 1991; DGM RCP Lond. 1990. (Bristol) Staff Phys. (c/o Elderly Med.) Bristol Gen. Hosp.

ALSOS, Bjorn Gold Street Surgery, Gold Street, Saffron Walden CB10 1EJ Tel: 01799 525325 Fax: 01799 524042 — MB BS 1981 Newc.; MB BS (Hons.) Newc. 1981; MRCP (UK) 1985.

ALSTAD, Karl Severin (retired) Shuna, Bullwood Road, Innellan, Dunoon PA23 7QN Tel: 01369 830401 — BSc Glas. 1933, MD

1944, MB ChB 1936; FRCP Ed. 1973, M 1946; DPH Glas. 1938. Prev: Manager Marketing Servs. Div. & Dep. to Gp. Marketing Dir., Wellcome Foundat. Ltd.

ALSTEAD, Elspeth Mary Dept. of Gastroenterology, Whipps Cross Hospital, London E11 1NR — MD 1988 Liverp.; FRCP 1994; MB ChB 1978; MRCP (UK) 1980. Cons. Gastroenterol. & Sen. Lect. Whipps Cross Hosp. & St. Bart. Hosp. Lond. Prev: Sen. Regist. (Gastroenterol.) St. Bart. Hosp. Lond.

ALSTEAD, Jane Ann Doctors Surgery, 40 St. Georges Crescent, Wrexham LL13 8DB Tel: 01978 290708 — MB ChB 1984 Liverp.; Cert. Family Plann. JCC 1986.

ALSTEAD, Phillip Doctors Surgery, 40 St. Georges Crescent, Wrexham LL13 8DB Tel: 01978 290708 — MB ChB 1984 Liverp.; Cert. Family Plann. JCC 1987. Ho. Off. Walton Hosp. Liverp.

ALSTON, Aileen Bell 42 Glenpatrick Road, Elderslie, Johnstone PA5 9AE — MB ChB 1993 Glas.

ALSTON, Anne Kathryn Anaesthetic Department, Torbay Hospital, Lawes Bridge, Torquay TQ1 7AA; Thorns Orchard, Combeinteignhead, Newton Abbot TQ12 4RD Tel: 01626 873585 — MB ChB 1978 Dundee; FFA RCSI 1984. Assoc. Specialist (Anaesth.) Torbay Hosp. Torquay. Socs: Assn. Anaesths.; BMA; Brit. Soc. Med. & Dent. Hypn. Prev: Regist. (Anaesth.) Torbay Hosp.

ALSTON, David Joseph Pytchley Court Health Centre, 5 Northampton Road, Brixworth, Northampton NN6 9DX Tel: 01604 880228; Cottesloe, Golf Lane, Church Brampton, Northampton NN6 8AY — MB BS 1976 Lond.; MRCS Eng. LRCP Lond. 1975; MRCGP 1987; DRCOG 1987; Cert. Family Plann. JCC 1986. Socs: Fell. Roy. Soc. Med.; BMA. Prev: Occupat. Health Phys. Brit. Petroleum Plc.; Med. Off. Abu Dhabi Gas Liquefaction Co. Abu Dhabi, UAE.

ALSTON, Robert Henry Quintins Medical Centre, Hawkswood Road, Hailsham BN27 1UG Tel: 01323 845669 Fax: 01323 846653; Spring Pastures, Spring Hill, Punnett's Town, Heathfield TN21 9PE Tel: 01435 830860 — MB BS 1965 Lond. (Univ. Coll. Hosp.)

ALSTON, Robin Peter Royal Infirmary of Edinburgh, 1 Lauriston Place, Edinburgh EH3 9YW Tel: 0131 536 3672 Email: p.alston@ed.ac.uk — MB ChB 1977 Glas.; MD Glas. 1990; FFA RCS Eng. 1982; T(Anaes.) 1991. (Glasgow) Cons. Anaesth. Roy. Infirm. Edin.; Sen. Lect. Edin. Univ. 1997-. Socs: Fell. Roy. Coll. Anaesth.; Assn. Anaesth. Prev: Asst. Prof. Anaesth. Univ. Washington 1990-92; Lect. (Anaesth.) Univ. of Glas. 1985-90.

ALSTON, William Connell Department of Chemical Pathology, Frimley Park Hospital, Frimley, Camberley GU16 5UJ; 2 Woodend, Pirbright Road, Farnborough GU14 7BA — MB ChB 1958 Glas.; PhD Glas. 1966, BSc (Hons.) 1962; FRCPath 1983, M 1971. (Glas.) Emerit. Cons. Chem. Path. Frimley Pk. Hosp. NHS Trust. Socs: Nutrit. Soc.; BMA; Biochem. Soc. Prev: Asst. Lect. (Biochem.) Univ. Glas.; Sen. Regist. (Biochem.) W.. Infirm. Glas.; Regist. (Biochem.) Roy. Infirm. Glas.

ALTERMAN, Julius (retired) 3 Birch Court, 8 Woodside Grange Road, London N12 8SW Tel: 020 8446 3786 — MB BS 1944 Lond.; MRCS Eng. LRCP Lond. 1944. Prev: Asst. Med. Off. N. W.. Hosp. Hampstead & Colindale Hosp.

ALTMAN, Mr Keith Department of Oral & Maxillofacial Surgery, The Royal Sussex County Hospital, Eastern Road, Brighton BN1 5BE Tel: 01273 696955 Fax: 01273 628517; 24 Mytten Close, Cuckfield, Haywards Heath RH17 5LN — MB BS 1989 Lond.; BDS 1981; FRCS Eng. 1992; FRCS (Max Fac.) 1995; FDS RCS Eng. 1984. Cons. Maxillofacial Surg. Roy. Sussex C. Hosp., E.bourne Dist. Gen. Hosp. Socs: Fell. Brit. Assn. Oral & Maxillofacial Surg.; BMA. Prev: Sen. Regist. (Maxillofacial Surg.) Qu. Mary's Hosp. Roehampton & Roy. Surrey Co. Hosp. Guildford; SHO (Plastic Surg., Gen. Surg. & A & E) Lister Hosp. Stevenage; SHO (Oral & Maxillofacial Surg.) Mt. Vernon Hosp.

ALTMAN, Michael 7 Totteridge Park, London N20 8NH — MRCS Eng. LRCP Lond. 1951; MRCGP 1960. (St. Mary's Hosp. Lond) GP Locum. N. Lond. Locums. Socs: BMA. Prev: Flight Lt. RAF Med. Br.; Vasectomy Surg. Lond.; Vasectomy Surg. Marie Stopes Hse. Lond.

ALTMANN, Paul Nicholas Sebastian Oxford Renal Unit, The Churchill Hospital, Headington, Oxford OX3 7LJ Tel: 01865 226091 Fax: 01865 225773 — MB BS 1979 Lond.; MD Lond. 1991; FRCP (UK) 1982. (Univ. Coll. Lond.) Cons. Nephrol. Ch.ill Hosp. Oxf. Prev: Cons. Nephrol. & Phys. Portsmouth.

ALTON, Helen Mary 11 Moorcroft Road, Moseley, Birmingham B13 8LT — MB ChB 1976 Birm.; MRCP (UK) 1980; FRCR 1984. Cons. Radiol. Childr. Hosp. Birm.

ALTON, Peter Anthony Frimley Park hosp, NHS Trust, Portsmouth Rd, Frimley, Camberley GU10 5AP Tel: 01276 604494 Fax: 01279 604924 Email: peter.alton@fph-n.nhs.uk; Corner Cottage, The Hollow, Ewshot, Farnham GU10 5AP — MB BS 1985 Lond.; BSc Lond. 1981; MRCP (UK) 1988; MRCPath 1996. (Roy. Free Hosp. Lond.) Cons. Haematologist & Dir., Haemophelia Cntre. Socs: BSFHaematol. Prev: Clin. Lect., St Geo.s Hsp Med Sch. & Ryl Marsden Hsp.

ALTSCHULOVA, Herta Julie c/o National Westminster Bank, Swiss Cottage Branch, 106 Finchley Road, London NW3 5JN — MD 1944 Czechoslovakia; MRCPsych 1971. (Prague, Vienna & Roy. Free) Hon. Psychiat. (Dermat.) Univ. Coll. & Middlx. Hosp. Med. Schs. Lond. Socs: Fell. Roy. Soc. Med.; Soc. For Psychosomatic. Research. Prev: Psychiat. (Dermat.) Univ. Coll. Hosp. Lond.; Cons. Psychiat. E.man Dent. Hosp. Lond.; Cons. Psychiat. Child Guid. Clinic Ilford.

ALTY, Henry Myers (retired) 27 Rodney Street, Liverpool L1 9EH — MB ChB MB ChB Liverp. 1958; BDS Liverp. 1952; FDS RCS Eng. 1954, LDS 1952. Prev: Cons. Oral Surg. Liverp. & Chester HA & Isle of Man.

ALTY, Margaret Rock Court Surgery, Rock Court, Old Swan, Liverpool L13 2BY Tel: 0151 228 0672 Fax: 0151 228 0298 — MB ChB 1983 Liverp.; MRCGP 1987; DObst RCOG 1986. (Liverp.) Prev: SHO Alder Hey Childr. Hosp. Liverp.; SHO (O & G) Fazakerley & Walton Hosps. Liverp.; SHO (Geriat.) Fazakerley Hosp. Liverp.

ALUN-JONES, Jane Elizabeth Maples Family Medical Practice, 35 Hill Street, Hinckley LE10 1DS Tel: 01455 234576 Fax: 01455 250506 — MB ChB 1981 Liverp.; MRCP (UK) 1985; MRCGP 1986.

ALUN ROBERTS, Gwerfyl (retired) Bridle Cottage, Pownall Park, Wilmslow SK9 5PZ Tel: 01625 524488 — MB ChB Liverp. 1952. Prev: Clin. Asst. (Ultrasound) Wythenshawe Matern. Hosp. S. Manch.

ALUSI, Mr Ghassan Flat 110, Thomas Moore House, Barbican, London EC2Y 8BU — MB ChB 1987 Leic.; FRCS Ed. 1992.

ALUSI, Sundus Husni Charing Cross Hospital, Fulham Palace Road, London W6 8RF Tel: 020 8846 7631 Fax: 020 8846 7135 Email: s.alusi@ic.ac.uk; 13 Westpoint, 49 Putney Hill, Putney, London SW15 6RU Tel: 020 8780 0090 — MB ChB 1992 Leic.; MRCP (Lond.) 1995. Research Fell. (Clin. Neurol.); Hon. Regist. (Neurol.). Socs: Roy. Coll. Phys.; BMA; MDU. Prev: SHO (Neurol.) Char. Cross Hosp.; SHO (Psychiat.) Amersham Gen. Hosp.; SHO (Gen. Med.) Leicester Roy. Infirm.

ALUVIHARE, Varuna Romesh 3 Ashbourne Road, London W5 3ED — MB BS 1987 Lond.

ALUWIHARE, Mr Arjuna Panchkori Ram c/o Ms D. Aluwihare, Flat 2, Sutton Lodge, Clandon Road, Guildford GU1 2DS — MB BChir 1963 Camb.; MChir Camb. 1970; FRCS Eng. 1967; MRCS Eng. LRCP Lond. 1963.

ALUWIHARE, Nedra Priyanthi 83 Wood Lane, Harborne, Birmingham B17 9AY — MB BS 1986 Lond.; MRCPath 1993. Sen. Regist. (Neuropath.) W. Midl. RHA; Sen. Regist. (Neuropath.) Med. Sch. Univ. Birm.

ALVARES, Caroline Lilian 324 Monega Road, London E12 6TY — MB BS 1996 Lond. (United Medical & Dental Schools of Guy's & St. Thomas' Hosp.)

ALVAREZ, Arthur Sinclair 3 Northwick Terrace, London NW8 8JJ Tel: 020 7286 1812; 3 Northwick Terrace, London NW8 8JJ Tel: 0121 459 6742 Email: arthur@alvarez3.demon.co.uk, d.j.dsouza@amserve.net — MB ChB Birm. 1954; FRCP Lond. 1976; MRCP (Lond) 1959; MRCS Eng. LRCP Lond. 1954; T(M) 1991. (Birm.) Emerit. Cons. Physiciain in Geriat. Med., Leics HA, 1992. Socs: Fell. Roy. Soc. Med.; Leic. Med. Soc. Prev: Cons. Geriat. Leic. HA.

ALVAREZ, Mr Emilio Venancio 1 Brookside Avenue, Fulwood, Preston PR2 9TR — MB BS 1980 Lond.; FRCS Glas. 1985; FCOphth 1991.

ALVAREZ ESCURRA, Moises Fernando Mapplewell Health Centre, 276 Darton Lane, Mapplewell, Barnsley S75 6AJ Tel: 01226 233777 Fax: 01226 233773 — LMS 1984 Barcelona. (Barcelona) GP Barnsley, S.Yorks.

ALVAREZ IGLESIAS, Montserrat Barnsley District General Hospital, Gawber Road, Barnsley S75 2EP — LMS 1993 Oviedo.

ALVAREZ PARRA, Mr Gabriel Elias Private Consulting Rooms, University College Hospital, 25 Grafton Way, London WC1E 6DB Tel: 020 7387 9709 Fax: 020 7380 9816 Email: gea@plastsurg.demon.co.uk — Medico Cirujano Nat. Autonomous Mexico 1971; FRCS Eng. 1997. Cons. Plastic Surg. P.ss Alexandra NHS Trust, Harlow, Essex. Socs: Fell. RSM (Plastic Surg.); BAPS. Prev: Cons. Plastic Surg. Hosp. Gen. de Mexico.

ALVAREZ-UDE, Jose Maria 33 Beech Hill, Haywards Heath RH16 3RY — LMS 1973 Barcelona; DPM Eng. 1980.

ALVES, Crawford Baxter 14 Queensberry Avenue, Bearsden, Glasgow G61 3LR Tel: 0141 943 1007; 3A Killermont View Bearsden, Glasgow G20 0TZ Tel: 0141 945 3739 Email: crawford.a@virgin.net — MB ChB 1995 Glas.; BSc (Hons) Glas. 1992. (Glasgow) SHO (A & E) W.ern Infirm. Glas.

ALVES TEIXEIRA, Jeronima Maria 14 Romulus Court, 1 Justin Close, Brentford TW8 8QR — Lic Med 1987 Oporto; Lic. Med. Oporto 1987.

ALVEY, Mr Peter Leonard 3 Sunleigh Court, Mount Pleasant, Alperton, Wembley HA0 4PH Tel: 020 8903 9883 — MB BChir 1971 Camb.; PhD Lond. 1982; MA, MB Camb. 1971, BChir 1970; FRCS Eng. 1976; MRCS Eng. LRCP Lond. 1970. (Camb. & St. Bart. Lond.) Sen. Software Engineer, Advanced Recognition Ltd, Winsor. Socs: Harv. Soc. Prev: research fell. Imperial Cancer Research Fund; Regist. (Surg.) N.ampton Gen. Hosp.; Sen. Ho. Off. (Surg.) St. Bartholemews Hosp. Lond.

ALVEYN, Christopher George Totton Health Centre, Testwood Lane, Totton, Southampton SO40 3ZN — MB BS 1981 Lond.; MRCP (UK) 1984; MRCGP 1995. (St. Bart.) GP; Clin. Asst. (GI Endoscopy). Socs: BMA. Prev: Med. Regist. Profess. Med. Unit Soton Gen. Hosp.; SHO (Med. Rotat.) Soton HA; Ho. Phys. Whipps Cross Hosp. Lond.

ALVI, Mr Abdur Rab (retired) 31 Eyebrook Road, Bowdon, Altrincham WA14 3LH Tel: 0161 928 2686 Fax: 0161 929 1617 — MB BS 1952 Punjab; MB BS Punjab (Pakistan) 1952; FRCOphth 1991; DTM & H Liverp. 1956; DO Eng. 1966. Prev: Sen. Regist. & Regist. (Ophth.) Manch. Roy. Eye Hosp.

ALVI, Farhan-Ul-Haq 59 Egerton Road N., Chorlton, Manchester M21 0GX — MB BS 1995 Lond. (King's Coll. Lond.)

ALVI, Nurus-Sabah Fatima 160 Oaksford, Ty-Gwyn Road, Cwmbran NP44 6UN — MB ChB 1988 Manch. SHO (Paediat.) Booth Hall Childr. Hosp. Manch.; SHO (Paediat. Cardiol.) Birm. Childr. Hosp. Prev: Ho. Phys. Withington Hosp. Manch.; Ho. Surg. Tameside Gen. Hosp.

ALVI, Roohi 734 Great West Road, Osterley, Isleworth TW7 5LT Tel: 020 8232 8473 Email: dralvi@compuserve.com — MB BCh 1995 NUI; LRCPS 1995; DRCOG 1998; BAO 1995; DFFP 1998; DCH 1999. (Royal College of Surgeons Dublin) GP Regist. N.wood, Middlx.

ALVI, Samir Ahmed 734 Great West Road, Osterley, Isleworth TW7 5LT Fax: 020 8232 8473 Email: dralvi@compuserve.com — MB BS 1992 Lond.; BSc (Hons.) Path & Basic Med. Sci. Lond. 1989; PhD 1998; DFFO 1999. (Univ. Coll. Lond.) Well Being (RCOG) Research Fell. Imperial Coll. Sch. of Med. Hammersmith Hosp.; GP Regist., Wimbledon. Socs: Roy. Soc. Med. Prev: SHO (Gyn. & Urol.) Hammersmith Hosp. Lond.; SHO (A & E) Univ. Coll. Hosp. Lond.; Ho. Off. (Plastic & Vasc. Surg. & ENT) Univ. Coll. & Middlx. Hosps. Lond.

ALVIS, Stephen John The Street Surgery, 42 The Street, Uley, Dursley GL11 5SY Tel: 01453 860459; Woodmancote Farm, Nunnery Lane, Woodmancote, Dursley GL11 4AL Tel: 01453 545776 — MB ChB 1982 Bristol; MRCGP 1987; DRCOG 1986; Cert. Family Plann. JCC 1986.

ALWAIL, Ali Nagi Cardiology Department, City General Hospital, Newcastle Road, Stoke-on-Trent ST4 6QG — MB BCh 1980 Cairo; MRCP Lond. 1992.

ALWAN, Ali Hussain 6 Hampshire Close, Edmonton, London N18 2LG — MB ChB 1969 Baghdad; DCH Eng. 1978.

ALWAN, Mr Mohammad Abdul Rutha 2 Dumbrock Road, Milngavie, Glasgow G62 7RB — MB ChB 1972 Baghdad; FRCS Glas. 1988. Regist. (Urol.) W.. Infirm. Glas.

ALWITRY, Amar Roseden, La Rue a Don, Grouville JE3 9GD — BM BS 1996 Nottm.

ALWYN SMITH, Alison Helen Collier (retired) Orchard Cottage, Newton, Porthcawl CF36 5NP Tel: 01656 783455 — MRCS Eng. LRCP Lond. 1945; DPH Wales 1952. Prev: Clin. Med. Off. Mid. Glam. HA.

ALWYN-SMITH, Peter, KStJ (retired) Orchard Cottage, Newton, Porthcawl CF36 5NP Tel: 01656 783455 — MB BS 1946 Lond.; MRCS Eng. LRCP Lond. 1942; FRCP Lond. 1977; MRCP Lond. 1972; FFPHM RCP (UK) 1990; FFCM 1972. Prev: Sen. Admin. Med. Off. Welsh Hosp. Bd.

ALY, Fatima Zahra c/o 1 Gregory Av, Romiley, Stockport SK6 3JZ — MB ChB 1997 Leic.

ALY, Mr Hassan El Banna Mahmoud 12 Albany Street, Edinburgh EH1 3QB — MB BCh 1975 Cairo; FRCS Ed. 1986.

ALY, Mr Sayed Awad Abdel Fattah 95 Byron Way, Northolt UB5 6AZ — MB BCh 1983 Ain Shams; FRCSI 1990.

ALYAS, Faisal 146 Friary Road, London SE15 5UW — MB BS 1998 Lond.; MB BS Lond 1998.

ALZUA BLANCO, Juan Maria 6 East Street, Bodicote, Banbury OX15 4DN — LMS 1990 Basque Provinces.

AMADI, Ahamefula Aintree Cardiac Centre, University Hospital Aintree, Lower Lane, Liverpool L9 7AL Tel: 0151 529 2722 Fax: 0151 529 2724 — MB BS 1983 Lond.; MSc Lond. 1987; MRCP (UK) 1986; DTM & H Lond. 1987. (St. George's Hospital Medical School) Cons. Cardiol. and Phys. Univ. Hosp. Aintree Liverp.; Hon. Lect. Dept of Med. Univ. of Liverp. Socs: Fell. Roy. Soc. of Med. Brit. Cardiac Soc. Expert Witness Inst. Prev: Sen. Regist. Char. Cross & Hammersmith Hosps.; Research Fell. Nat. Heart & Lung Inst. Lond.; Regist. (Cardiol.) Harefield Hosp. Middlx.

AMAKU, Eddys Elizabeth 99 Crab Lane, Harrogate HG1 3BQ — MB ChB 1959 Leeds.

AMAKU, Mr Erete Offiong 99 Crab Lane, Harrogate HG1 3BQ — MB ChB 1960 Leeds; ChM Leeds, 1974; FRCS Glas. 1964. Prof. Surg. & Urol. Dept. Surg. Univ. Lagos, Nigeria. Socs: Nigeria Med. Assn. & Internat. Urol. Assn. Prev: Sen. Lect. (Surg.) Univ. Lagos, Nigeria; Chief Resid. (Urol.) Instruc. & Fell. Urol. Surg. Univ. Rochester, USA.

AMAKYE, Christine Ama 61 Dryburgh Gardens, Kingsbury, London NW9 9TY — MB ChB 1983 Ghana.

AMAKYE, Janet 95-97 Crawford Street, London W1H 2HJ — MB BS 1984 Lond.; Diploma in Acupunc. & Traditional Chinese Med.; DCM Beijing; BSc (Hons.) Newc. 1978; Cert. Family Plann. JCC 1988; DRCOG 1986. (Roy. Free Hosp. Sch. Med.) Prev: GP Centr. Middlx. Hosp. VTS Lond.

AMALADOSS, Aloysius Stephen Prakash 1 Victoria Mews, Victoria Drive, Bognor Regis PO21 2EP — BM BCh 1987 Oxf.; MRCPsych. 1992. Regist. Rotat. (Psychiat.) Wessex Train. Scheme. Prev: Ho. Surg. St. Richard's Hosp. Chichester; Ho. Phys. Qu. Eliz. Hosp. Birm.

AMANAT, Mr Liaquat Ali c/o James Paget Healthcare (NHS Trust), Lowestoft Road, Gorleston, Great Yarmouth NR31 6LA Tel: 01493 452452 Fax: 01493 453190; Tel: 01493 662404 — MB BS 1971 Punjab; BSc Punjab 1970; FRCS Ed. 1977; FRCOphth 1989; DO Eng. 1974. (Lahore) Cons. Ophth. James Paget Healthcare NHS Trust Gorleston, Gt. Yarmouth NR31 6LA. Socs: Oxf. Ophth. Congr.; UK & Irel. Soc. Cataract & Refractive Surg.; Amer. Acad. Ophth. Prev: Cons. Ophth. Argyll & Clyde HB; Sen. Regist. (Ophth.) Gtr. Glas. HB; Regist. (Ophth.) Addenbrooke's Hosp. Camb.

AMANN, Michaela Elisabeth The Health Centre, North Road, Stokesley, Middlesbrough TS9 5DY Tel: 01642 710748 Fax: 01642 713037; Glenside, Great Broughton, Stokesley, Middlesbrough TS9 7EG Tel: 01642 712202 — MB BS 1983 Newc.; MRCGP 1988.

AMAR, Khaled Abdel Kawi Ahmed 155 Badminton Road, Downend, Bristol BS16 6NF — MB BCh 1980 Ain Shams; MRCP (UK) 1988.

AMAR, Satya Swarup 6 Cragmoor Road, Burton Joyce, Nottingham NG14 5AR Tel: 01602 313139 — MB ChB 1965 Aberd.; FFR 1971; DMRD Aberd. 1969; DMRD Eng. 1969. (Aberd.) Cons. Radiol. Gen. Hosp. Nottm. Prev: Res. Ho. Off., SHO (Neurosurg.) & Sen. Regist. (Radiol.) Aberd. Roy.; Infirm.

AMARA, Mr Sameer Nasir Orthopaedic Department, Hinchingbrooke Hospital, Hinchingbrooke Park, Huntingdon PE29 6NT Tel: 01480 416416 Fax: 01480 416561; Glen Eden, Eyensbury Hardwick, St. Neots, Huntingdon PE19 6XJ Tel: 01480 473457 Fax: 01480 210182 — MB ChB 1970 Baghdad; FRCS Glas. 1990. p/t Cons. Trauma & Orthop. Hinchingbrooke Hosp. Huntington. Socs: Med. Protec. Soc.; BMA. Prev: Sen. Regist.

(Trauma & Orthop.) P'boro. Hosps. NHS Trust; Regist. (Trauma & Orthop.) P.ss of Wales Hosp. Bridgend.

AMARASEKARA, Ruwanpura Nandasena de Silva Parkway Health Centre, 1 Parkway, New Addington, Croydon CR0 0JA Tel: 01689 846642 Fax: 01689 849729 — MB BS 1971 Ceylon.

AMARASENA, Mr Gallege Aruna Chandima 90 Vale Road, London N4 1PZ — MB BS 1985 Colombo; FRCS Eng 1992; FRCS Ed. 1992.

AMARASINGHE, Amidinie Rashika 7 Churchill Close, Feltham TW14 9XF; 79/18 Alexandra Place, Colombo 7, Sri Lanka Tel: 00 941 699769 — MB ChB 1994 Leic. Ho. Off. (Med.) Leicester Roy. Infirm. NHS Trust. Prev: Ho. Off. (Gen. Surg. & Orthop.) Leicester Roy. Infirm.

AMARASINGHE, Gongala Punchihewage Wansapala 20 Frederick Row, Blackburn BB1 1NS Tel: 01254 580986 — MB BS 1955 Ceylon.

AMARASINGHE, Lalantha Migara c/o Mike Amarasinghe, 86 Minchenden Crescent, London N14 7EN — MB BS 1967 Ceylon.

AMARASINGHE, Mr Maithriya Ananda 86 Minchenden Crescent, London N14 7EN — MB BS 1974 Ceylon; MRCS Eng. LRCP Lond. 1981; FRCS Ed. 1985.

AMARENDRA, Vasireddy 6 Lynton Villas, Bradford BD9 5JU — MB BS 1973 Madras.

AMARIN, Jarir Odeh Carlton House Surgery, 28 Tenniswood Road, Enfield EN1 3LL Tel: 020 8363 7575 Fax: 020 8366 8228; 14 William Covell Close, The Ridgeway, Enfield EN2 8HP Tel: 020 8366 7755 — State Exam Med 1979 Sofia; PhD 1982; MRCP 1989; MRCGP 1993; DRCOG 1993. (Medical Academy Sofia Bulgaria) GP Enfield; Clin. Tutor Roy. Free Hosp. Hampstead; Clin. Asst. Cardiol. N. Middlx. Hosp.; Clin. Tutor UCL. Prev: Regist. (Med.) York Dist. Hosp.

AMARNANI, Aarti 21 Bennett Way, South Wigston, Leicester LE18 4SF — MB BCh 1995 Wales.

AMASANTI, Daniela Barnet General Hospital, Wellhouse Lane, Barnet EN5 3DJ — MB ChB 1994 Manch. (Manchester)

AMATO, Gino Antonio Morris House Surgery, Waltheof Gardens, Tottenham, London N17 7EB Tel: 020 8801 1277 Fax: 020 8801 8228 — MB BS 1983 Lond.; BSc Lond. 1980; DRCOG 1987. Clin. Asst. (Dermat. & Cardiol.) N. Middlx. NHS Trust. Prev: SHO N. Middlx. Hosp. Lond. VTS; Ho. Surg. (Gen. Surg. & Orthop.) Orsett Hosp. Essex; Ho. Phys. (Gen. Med. & Endocrinol.) Centr. Middlx. Hosp. Lond.

AMATYA, Mr Birendra Kumar Annapurna, 14 Green Pastures, Stockport SK4 3RA Tel: 0161 442 9012 — MB BS 1966 Patna; FRCS Ed. 1983; DO RCS Eng. 1975.

AMBACHE, Nachman (retired) Clifton, Royal Parade, Chislehurst BR7 6NW Tel: 020 8467 3609 — MRCS Eng. LRCP Lond. 1943; MA Camb. 1942. Prev: MRC Extern. Scientif. Staff RCS Eng.

AMBACHE, Stella Maude Ellen Clifton Royal Parade, Chislehurst BR7 6NW; Email: sambache@lineone.net — MB BChir 1943 Camb.; MRCS Eng. LRCP Lond. 1942; MRCGP 1953. (Camb. & Lond. Sch. Med. Wom.) Socs: Brit. Psychoanal Soc.

AMBASHT, Dinesh Prasad The Surgery, 134 Newton Road, Great Barr, Birmingham B43 6BT Tel: 0121 357 3309 — MB BS 1963 Patna.

AMBEGAOKAR, Sangeeta 47 Allt-Yr-Yn Avenue, Newport NP20 5DB — MB ChB 1995 Birm.; ChB Birm. 1995. SHO (Gen. Psychiat.) Solihull Hosp. Prev: SHO (Psychiat. of Old Age) Qu. Eliz. Psychiat. Hosp. Birm.; SHO (Gen. Psychiat.) Solihull Hosp.; SHO (Gen. Psychiat.) All St.s Hosp. Birm.

AMBEKAR, Anjali Ajit 161 Knightlow Road, Birmingham B17 8PY — MB BS 1972 Bombay.

AMBEKAR, Madhukar Desford Surgery, 19 Manor Road, Desford, Leicester LE9 9HD Tel: 01445 828176 — MB BS 1971 Osmania.

AMBELAS, Aristides Child & Family Psychiatric Service, Westcotes House, Westcotes Drive, Leicester LE3 0QU Tel: 0116 225 2900 Fax: 0116 225 2899 — Ptychio Iatrikes 1968 Thessalonika; MD Thessalonika 1985; FRCPsych 1993, M 1977. Cons. Child & Adolesc. Psychiat. W.cotes Hse. Leicester; Clin. Teach. Univ. Leicester Med. Sch. Prev: Cons. Child & Adolesc. Psychiat. Coventry HA.

AMBERY, Philip Duncan Gloucestershire Royal Hospital, Great Western Road, Gloucester GL1 3P; 28 Collum End Rise, Cheltenham GL53 0PB Tel: 01242 252632 Email: philip.ambery@virgin.net — MB ChB 1994 Bristol; MRCP Lond. 1997. Specialist Regist. (Gen. Med. & Elderly Care) S. W.ern Region. Socs: Roy. Coll Phys.; Brit. Soc. of Geriat. Prev: SHO Med. Rotat. Gloucester Roy. Hosp.; SHO (A & E) Cheltenham Gen. Hosp.

AMBIAVAGAR, Indra Nalini 2 The Court, Billington Manor, Billington, Leighton Buzzard LU7 9BJ — MB BCh BAO 1988 NUI; LRCPSI 1988.

AMBIKAPATHY, Parameswaraiyer The Primary Health Care Centre, Crockenhill Vale Surgery (Village Surg.) 2 James Cottages, Eynsford Road, Crockenhill, Swanley BR8 8JT Tel: 01322 667447; Gokulum, 71 Glendale, Swanley BR8 8TP Tel: 01322 666330 Fax: 01322 666330 — MB BS 1972 Ceylon. (Univ. Ceylon) Clin. Asst. (Cas.) Gravesend Hosp.; Mem. Kent. LMC. Socs: BMA & Overseas Doctors Assn. Prev: Clin. Asst. (Rheum.) Basildon Hosp.; Clin. Asst. (Chest Med.) W.hill Hosp. Dartford; Regist. & SHO (Psychiat.) Fairfield Hosp. Stotfold, Hitchin.

AMBLER, Jonathan James Selwood The Cedars, Moorgreen, Newthorpe, Nottingham NG16 2FB — MB BS 1993 Lond.

AMBLER, Lucy Clare The Howdah, Castle Road, Woking GU21 4EU — MB BS 1993 Lond.; DRCOG 1996; DCH 1997. (St Thomas')

AMBLER, Phillip John Wantage Health Centre, Church Street, Wantage OX12 Tel: 01235 770245 Fax: 01235 770727; Barnards Farm House, Charlton Village Road, Chanton, Wantage OX12 7HQ Tel: 01235 770167 — MB BS 1975 Lond.; BSc (Hons.) Lond. 1972; DO Eng. 1980. (St. Thos.) Clin. Asst. (Ophth.) Oxf. Eye Hosp.

AMBRIS, Mary Gilbertha 16 Warwick Road, London E12 6QP — MB BS 1979 W. Indies; MB BS Univ. W. Indies 1979.

AMBROSE, Anne (retired) Brick Kiln Farm, Brick Kiln Lane, Swainsthorpe, Norwich NR14 8PY Tel: 01508 470389 — MB BS 1955 Lond.; MRCS Eng. LRCP Lond. 1955; MRCPsych 1973; DPM Eng. 1960. Prev: Cons. Psychiat. in Ment. Defic. Little Plumstead Hosp.

AMBROSE, Elizabeth Rita Finches, Lower Road, Stuntney, Ely CB7 5TN — MB BS 1967 Lond.; MRCS Eng. LRCP Lond. 1967; DObst RCOG 1970. (Roy. Free) Prev: Ho. Phys. S. Lond. Hosp. Wom. & Childr.; Ho. Surg. Camb. Matern. Hosp.

AMBROSE, Geoffrey Crosby Hockering Gate, Hockering Road, Woking GU22 7HG Tel: 01483 760637 — MB BS 1947 Lond.; MRCP (UK) 1971; MRCPsych 1975; DPM Eng. 1974. (Guy's) Socs: BMA. Prev: Cons. Child & Adolesc. Psychiat. Mt. Alvernia Hosp. Guildford; Cons. Child & Adolesc. Psychiat. St. Luke's Hosp. Guildford & Guilford & Godalming Child Guid. Clinics.

AMBROSE, James Abraham Edward (retired) Badgers Rake, North Connel, Oban PA37 1QZ Tel: 01631 710534 — MB ChB 1952 Cape Town; FRCP Lond. 1977; FRACR (Hon.) 1986; FFR 1959; DMRD Eng. 1956. Prev: Cons. Radiol. Atkinson Morley's Hosp. Wimbledon.

AMBROSE, Janet Ann Portland Lodge, West Road, Hexham NE46 3JU — MB BCh 1976 Wales.

AMBROSE, Judith Sarah 87A Wilsthorpe Road, Breaston, Derby DE72 3EA — BM BS 1987 Nottm.

AMBROSE, Lucy Jane Badgers Rake, North Connel, Oban PA37 1QZ — MB BS 1994 Lond.

AMBROSE, Mr Neil Simon St James's University Hospital, Becket St., Leeds LS9 7TH Tel: 0113 243 3144; Rigton Gates, Scarsdale Lane, Bardsey, Leeds LS17 9BH Tel: 01937 74463 — MB BS 1974 Lond.; MS Lond. 1983; FRCS Eng. 1979. Cons. Surg. & Hon. Lect. Univ. Leeds.; Clin. Dir. Surgic. Servs. Prev: Lect. (Surg.) Univ. Birm.

AMBROSS, Audrey Margaret (retired) Lyndhurst, Toppesfield Road, Great Yeldham, Halstead CO9 4HG Tel: 01787 237434 — MB BS 1962 Lond. Prev: GP Braintree.

AMBUS, Ivor Ashby Winstanley Drive Surgery, 138 Winstanley Drive, Leicester LE3 1PB Tel: 0116 285 8435 Fax: 0116 275 5416 — MB ChB 1979 Sheff.; BDS Lond. 1969; FDS RCS Eng. 1973; MRCGP 1983. GP Leicester.

AMDURER, Michael Antony 105 Bow Lane, Finchley, London N12 0JL Tel: 020 8346 6364 Email: mikeydur@aol.com; Lister Hospital, Corey's Mill Lane, Stevenage SG1 4AB Tel: 01438 781082 — MB BCh 1976 Wales. Cons. (Psychiat. of Old Age) Lister Hosp. Stevenage. Socs: MRCPsych. Prev: Locum Cons. (Psychiat. of Old Age) Clambory Hosp. Essex.

AMEEN, Mr Ameen Abbas Department of Neurosurgery, Royal Free Hospital, Pond St., London NW3 2QG Tel: 020 7830 2097

Fax: 020 7830 2560; 19 Grasmere Avenue, London SW15 3RB Tel: 020 8546 9958 Fax: 020 8546 9958 — LMSSA 1978 Lond.; MB ChB Baghdad 1970; FRCS Eng. 1977; FRCS Ed. 1977. Cons. Neurosurg. Roy. Free Hosp. Lond. Prev: Cons. Neurosurg. Jordan Univ. Hosp.; Assoc. Prof. Amman & Basrah Univ. Iraq; Regist. Centr. Middlx. Hosp. Lond.

AMEEN, Mahreen 14A Heatherbank, London SE9 1NN — MB BS 1994 Lond.

AMEEN, Mohammad Department of Pathology, New East Surrey Hospital, Redhill RH1 5RH Tel: 01737 768511 — MB ChB 1976 Basrah; MRCPath 1987. Cons. Histopath. New E. Surrey Hosp. Redhill. Socs: Assn. Clin. Path.; Brit. Soc. Clin Cytol. Prev: Regist. (Histopath.) Soton Gen. Hosp.

AMEERALLY, Phillip Javed 55 Willow Wood Crescent, London SE25 5PZ — MB BS 1998 Lond.; MB BS Lond 1998.

AMEGAVIE, Festus Laweh Whiston Hospital, Prescot L35 5DR Tel: 0151 426 1600 Fax: 0151 430 1902 Email: laweh.amegavie@gwise.stnk-tr.nwest.nhs.uk — MB ChB 1973 Ghana; MSc Lond. 1982; MRCPI 1991; DTCH Liverp. 1984; DCH RCPS Glas. 1984; FRCP 1993 CH. Cons. Paediat. Whiston Hosp. Merseyside; Hon. Clin. Lect. (Child Health) Liverp. Univ. Socs: Liverp. Paediat. Club; Brit. paediatric Repiratory Soc.; St Helens Med. Soc. Prev: Sen. Regist. Roy. Albert Edwd. Infirm. Wigan; Regist. Alder Hey Childr. Hosp.

AMEKE, Ifeoma Nkechikwunyelu 21 Louvaine Road, London SW11 2AG — MB BS 1993 Lond.

AMEN, Mr Amer Abdul Aziz St Margarets's Hospital, Epping CM16 6TN Tel: 01279 444455; Flat 18, Poseidon Court, Homer Drive, London E14 3UG Tel: 020 7536 8444 Fax: 020 7536 8440 Email: amer_amen@msn.com — MB ChB 1967 Baghdad; FRCS 1978 Eng.; DLO 1974 Baghdad. Cons. ENT Surg. St. Margt. Hosp. Epping. Prev: Sen. Regist. (ENT) Roy. Vict. Eye & Ear Hosp. Dub.; Regist. (ENT) Wexham Pk. Hosp. Slough; Regist. (ENT) St. Bart. Hosp. Lond.

AMENDY, Ulrich 11 Spring Vale, Wallasey CH45 3HR — State Exam Med 1992 Berlin.

AMER, Katherine Jane 762 Liverpool Road, Southport PR8 3QF — MB ChB 1998 Birm.

AMER, Mr Khalid Mohamed Ali University Hsp of Wales, Heath Park, Cardiff CF14 4XW Tel: 029 20747 747 Fax: 029 20745 439 Email: kmamer@globalnet.co.uk; 57 Lakeside Drive, Cardiff CF23 6DE — MB BS 1980 Khartoum; FRCS Eng. 1994. (Faculty of medicine, Uni of Khartoum) Specialist Regist. in Cardiothoracic Surg., Uni Hsp, Wales.

AMERASINGHE, Cyrille Nissanka Department Histopathology, Central Middlesex Hospital, London NW10 7NS Tel: 020 8453 2172 Fax: 020 8453 2532 Email: c.amerasinghe@cmh-tr.nthames.nhs.uk; 28 Claremont Road, London W13 0DQ Tel: 020 8997 7024 Fax: 020 8930 0488 Email: missannka@classic.msn.co — MB BS 1964 Ceylon; FRCPath 1989, M 1977; DMJ Soc. Apoth. Lond. 1973. (Colombo) Cons. Histopath. Centr. Middlx. Hosp. Lond. Socs: Assn. Clin. Paths.; Brit. Assn. Forens. Med.; Brit. Assn. of Clin. Cytol. Prev: Sen. Regist. (Histopath.) Centr. Middlx. Hosp.; Regist. (Histopath.) Centr. Middlx. Hosp.; Asst. (Forens. Med.) Guy's Hosp. Lond.

***AMERASINGHE, Nishani** Flat 6 Hambledon Court, The Grove, London W5 3SW — MB BS 1998 Lond.; MB BS Lond 1998.

AMERY, Anthony Henry Crows Farm, Crows Lane, Upper Farringdon, Alton GU34 3ED Tel: 01420 587223 Fax: 01420 587223 — MB BS 1963 Lond.; BSc (Anat.) Lond. 1959; FRCS Eng. 1969; MRCS Eng. LRCP Lond. 1962. (Char. Cross.) Med. Dir. Frimley Pk. NHS Trust; Cons. Surg. Frimley Pk.; Hon. Clin. Tutor Char. Cross Hosp. Lond. Socs: Brit. Soc. Gastroenterol. & Europ. Soc. Surg. Oncol.; Assn. Surg. Prev: Cons. Surg. Univ. Basel, Switz.; Sen. Regist. (Surg.) Char. Cross Hosp.

AMERY, Caroline Mary Diabetes Centre, The General Infirmary, Great George Street, Leeds LS1 3EX Email: carol.amery@leedsth.nhs.uk — MB ChB 1989 Liverp.; MRCP (UK) 1992; MMed Sc 1998 Keele. (Liverp.) Cons. (Diabetes & Gen. Med.) Leeds Teachg. Hosp.s NHS Trust. Socs: Fell. Roy. Soc. Med. Prev: Research Fell. (Diabetes) Selly Oak Hosp. Birm.; Regist. (Diabetes & Endocrinol.) New Cross Hosp. Wolverhampton; Regist. (Gen. Med.) Leighton Hosp. Crewe.

AMERY, Jennifer Elisabeth Dept. For International Development, 94 Victoria St, London SW1E 5JL Tel: 020 7917 7000 Fax: 020 7917 0363; 114 Uplands, Welwyn Garden City AL8 7EQ — MB ChB 1976 Bristol; MSc Lond. 1989; FFPHM 1999; MFPHM 1991; DCH RCP Lond. 1978. Prev: Cons. (Pub. Health Med.), Beds. Health Auth.; Regional Sen. Regist. (Pub. Health Med.) NW Thames; Primary Health & Child Care & Health Educat. in Peru & Chile.

AMERY, Justin Mark Bury Knowle Health Centre, 207 London Road, Headington, Oxford OX3 9JA Tel: 01865 761651 Fax: 01865 768559 — MB BS 1989 Lond.; MRCGP 1996; DFFP 1993; DRCOG 1993; DCH RCP Lond. 1991. (Char. Cross & Westm.) Med. Dir. Helen Ho. Hospice, Oxf.

AMES, Anthony Cyril (retired) Tyn-y-Cwm House, Rhos, Pontardawe, Swansea SA8 3EY Tel: 01792 862513 — MRCS Eng. LRCP Lond. 1958; MB BS Lond. 1958; BSc (Hons.) Lond. 1955; FRCPath 1979, M 1967. Prev: Sen. Regist. (Chem. Path.) King's Coll. Hosp. Lond. & Lewisham Hosp.

AMES, David John 76c Fairhazel Gardens, London NW6 3SR — MB BS 1978 Melbourne; MRCPsych 1985. Research Fell./ Hon. Lect. Roy. Free Hosp. Sch. Med. Lond. Prev: Regist./Jun. Resid. Med. Off. Roy. Melbourne Hosp.

AMES, David Samuel The Surgery, Pickering Road, West Ayton, Scarborough YO13 9JF Tel: 01723 863100 — MB ChB 1982 Leeds; MRCGP 1988; DA (UK) 1984; Dip. Therap. (Newc.) 1998.

AMES, Diane Edna Coombe Parva, Warren Road, Kingston upon Thames KT2 7HN — MB BS 1984 Lond.; BPharm Queensland 1963; MRCP (UK) 1989.

AMES, Judith Anne Suilven Cottage, Buckland Monachorum, Yelverton PL20 6ES — MB ChB 1983 Brist.; MRCGP 1996; DA (UK) 1993; DRCOG 1986; DCH RCP Lond. 1985. (Bristol University) Prev: GP Plymstock; SHO (O & G, Paediat. & Anaesth.) Plymouth.

AMES, Paul Richard Julian Bloomsbury Rheumatology Unit, 40-50 Tottenham St., London W1T 4RN — State Exam Med 1983 Naples.

AMES, Samantha Jane Neath Child & Family Clinic, Dyfed Road, Neath SA11 3AR Tel: 01639 652927; Email: clairegooding@doctors.org.uk — MB BS 1988 Lond.; MRCGP 1992; MRCPsych 1995. (St. Mary's Hosp. Med. Sch. Lond.) p/t Cons. In Child & Adolesc. Psychiat. Prev: Trainee GP/SHO (Psychiat.) Cefn Coed Hosp. Swansea VTS; Ho. Phys. Centr. Middlx. Hosp. Lond.; Ho. Surg. St. Mary's Hosp. Lond.

AMES, Warwick Aubrey 2B Woodbourne Avenue, Brighton BN1 8EQ Email: w.ames@virgin.net — MB BS 1991 Lond.; FRCA 1996. Liver Transpl.ion Team King's Coll. Hosp. Dulwich Lond. on Rotat. from St. Thos. Hosp. Lond. Socs: Assn. Anaesth.; MRCAnaesth.

AMESBURY, Brendan Douglas William St Wilfrid's Hospice, Grosvenor Road, Chichester PO19 2FP Tel: 01243 755 813 Fax: 01243 538 171 Email: brendanamesbury@stwilfridshospice.org — MB ChB 1983 Leic.; MRCGP 1988; DRCOG 1986. (Univ.Leic.) Med. Dir. & Cons. Palliat. Med. St. Wilfrid's Hospice Chichester; Cons. Palliat. Med. St. Richard's Hosp. Chichester. Prev: Resid. Med. Off. (Oncol. & Palliat. Med.) ChristCh. Hosp., NZ; Regist. St. Joseph's Hospice Lond.; Trainee GP Mansfield VTS.

AMESS, John Alfred Lechmere 46 Shire Ln, Chorleywood, Rickmansworth WD3 5NP — MB BS 1967 Lond.; MRCP (UK) 1973; FRCP Lond. 1988; FRCPath. 1988, M 1975. (St. Geo.) Cons. Haemat. St. Bart. Hosp. Lond.

AMESS, Philip Nicholas Trevor Mann Baby Unit, Royal Sussex County Hospital, Eastern Road, Brighton BN2 5BE Tel: 01273 696955 Fax: 01273 664795 Email: philip.amess@brighton.healthcare.nhs.uk — MB BS 1988 Lond.; MRCP (UK) 1992. (St. Bartholomew's Medical School) Cons. Neonatologist, Brighton Healthcare NHS Trust.

AMESS, Rachel Margaret 46 Shire Lane, Chorleywood, Rickmansworth WD3 5NP; Highlands, Crewe Road, Wistaston, Crewe CW2 6PS Tel: 01293 416604 Email: rswonnacott@lineone.net — MB BS 1994 Lond.; MRCGP 1998; DFFP 2000; BSc (1st cl. Hons.) Lond. 1991; DRCOG 1997. (Univ. Coll. Lond.) GP, Clin. Asst., Saxonbrook Med., Maidenbower, Crawley. Prev: GP Locum, Aylesbury, Bucks; Staff Grade Palliat. Care, Florence Nightingale Hospice, Stoke Mandeville; Med. Miss. in rural Nepal.

AMEY, Helena 55 Melville Road, Edgbaston, Birmingham B16 9JR — MB ChB 1980 Birm.

AMIAS, Mr Alan Gerald (retired) Flat 5, 72 Courtfield Gardens, London SW5 0NL Tel: 020 7373 3810 Fax: 020 7341 0065 — MB BS 1952 Lond.; FRCS Eng. 1957; FRCOG 1974, M 1961, DObst 1953. Hon. Sen. Lect. St. Geo. Hosp. Med. Sch. Lond.; Cons. Obst. & Gyn. St. Geo. Hosp. Lond. Prev: 1st Asst. Dept. O & G & SHO Surg. Unit. St. Geo. Hosp. Lond.

AMIEL, Professor Stephanie Anne Diabetes, Endrocrinology & Internal Medicine, Guy's, King's & St. Thomas' School of Medicine, King's College, Denmark Hill Campus, London SE5 9PJ Tel: 020 7737 4000 Fax: 020 7346 3685 Email: stephanie.amiel@kcl.ac.uk; Tel: 020 8766 7132 — MB BS 1978 Lond.; BSc (Hons.) Path. Lond. 1975, MD 1988; FRCP Lond. 1993; MRCP (UK) 1980. (Guy's Hosp.) RD Lawrence Prof. Diabetic Med.; Hon. Cons. KCH Lond. Prev: Sen. Lect. UMDS Guy's & St. Thos. Hosp. Lond.; Clin. Research Asst. St. Bart. Hosp. Lond.; JDF Fell. Yale Univ. Sch. Med., USA.

AMIEL, Stephen Michael Caversham Practice, 4 Peckwater Street, London NW5 2UP Tel: 020 7530 6500 Fax: 020 7530 6530 — MB BChir 1975 Camb.; MA Camb. 1975; MRCGP 1981; DRCOG 1977. (Univ. Coll. Hosp.) GP Princip. Caversham Gp. Pract.; Hon. Sen. Lect. (Gen. Pract.) Sch. Med. UCL. Prev: Trainee GP N.wick Pk. (Harrow) VTS; Ho. Surg. N. Middlx. Hosp.; Ho. Phys. Univ. Coll. Hosp. Lond.

AMIES, Peter Lowell Kingshill House, Kingshill Rd, Swindon SN1 4LG Tel: 01793 491917 Fax: 01793 491047 Email: amiesp@doctors.org.uk — MB BS 1973 Queensland; MSc Surrey 1976; MRCPsych 1979. (Queensland University) p/t Cons. Psychother. Avon & Wilts. Ment. Health Partnership NHS Trust; Med. Dir., E. Wilts. Health Care and Wilts. and Swindon Health Care, 1996 - 2000 (p/t); Hon. Cons. Psychotherapist, Warneford Hosp., Oxf. Prev: Cons. Psychother. Barrett Centre Brisbane, Austral.; Research Psychiat. & Sen. Regist. (Psychiat.) Univ. Oxf.; Regist. Rotat. Psychiat. Oxf. Train. Scheme.

AMIES, Victoria Mary 123 Newmarket Street, Norwich NR2 2DR — MB BS 1992 Lond.

AMILY, Ghassan Sabbah 48 Kylemore Drive, Heswall, Birkenhead CH61 6XZ; 48 Kylemore Drive, Heswall, Birkenhead CH6 6XZ — MRCS Eng. LRCP Lond. 1966. (Guy's) Clin. Asst. (A & E) Whiston Hosp. Socs: BMA; Brit. Soc. Med. & Dent. Hypn.; Med. Protec. Soc. Prev: Clin. Med. Off. (Child Health) St. Helens & Knowsley HA; Asst. Surg. Aramco Hosp. Dharan, Saudi Arabia; Med. Dir. On Call Ltd. St. Helens.

AMIN, Ahmed Wagih Abdel Kader Chester Royal Infirmary, Nicholas St., Chester CH1 2 Tel: 01244 315500; 70 Ballacrink Drive, Onchan, Douglas — MB ChB 1973 Cairo; DLO RCS Eng. 1985.

AMIN, Mr Ali Abbass Grimsby District Hospital, Grimsby DN33 2BY Tel: 01472 74111 — MB ChB 1968 Baghdad; FRCS Ed. 1982; FRCS Glas. 1981.

AMIN, Mr Amin Ibrahim Borders General Hospital NHS Trust, Melrose TD6 9BS Tel: 01896 754333; Oakes, High Cross Avenue, Melrose TD6 9SX Tel: 01896 823834 — MB BCh 1978 Cairo; FRCSI 1985. Assoc. Specialist (Gen. Surg.) Borders Gen. Hosp. NHS Trust. Prev: Staff Grade Surg. Borders Gen. Hosp.

***AMIN, Anita Nagendra** 95 High Street, Teversham, Cambridge CB1 5AG — BChir 1996 Camb.

AMIN, Ashok Jashbhai Spinney Hill Medical Centre, 143 St. Saviours Road, Leicester LE5 3HX Tel: 0116 251 7870 Fax: 0116 242 1701 — MB BS 1977 Mysore; MRCS Eng. LRCP Lond. 1979; T(GP) 1991. (Kasturba Med. Coll. Manipal) Prev: Trainee GP Newham VTS; SHO (Geriat. Med.) Manor Hosp. Walsall; Clin. Asst. (Gen. Med.) Leicester Roy. Infirm.

AMIN, Bipin Chimanbhai 4 Marsham Close, Grotton, Oldham OL4 5RB — LRCPI & LM, LRSCI & LM 1974; LRCPI & LM, LRCSI & LM 1974; MRCGP 1978. (RCSI)

AMIN, Claire Louise 8 Furzefield Avenue, Beaconsfield HP9 1PQ — MB BS 1992 Lond.; MRCP (UK) 1995. (St. Thos. Hosp. Med. Sch.) SHO (O & G) Roy. Free Hosp. Lond.

AMIN, Dilipkumar Jashbhai Andover Medical Centre, 270-282 Hornsey Road, London N7 7QZ Tel: 020 7281 6956 — MB BS 1975 Gujarat.

AMIN, Dipti Mahendra Guy's Drug Research Unit, 6 Newcomen St., London SE1 1YR Tel: 020 7378 1772 — MB BS 1987 Lond.; MRCGP 1991; DCH RCP Lond. 1991; DGM RCP Lond. 1991; DRCOG 1990; DCPSA 1997. Vice-Pres. Phase 1 Servs. & Unit Head, GDRU Ltd.; Hon. Lect. (Clin. Pharmacol.) UMDS Lond. Socs: Fell. Roy. Soc. Med. Prev: Research Phys. Guy's Drug Research Unit Lond.

AMIN, Mr Hazem Hashem Sid Grimsby District Hospital, Scartho Road, Grimsby DN33 2BA — MB BCh 1980 Ain Shams; FRCS Glas. 1985. Cons. ENT Surg. Grimsby Dist. Hosp.

AMIN, Jawad 16 Eskdale Drive, Aspley, Nottingham NG8 5GZ — MB ChB 1996 Manch.

AMIN, Kiritkumar Manibhai 33 Pinner View, Harrow HA1 4QG Tel: 020 8427 1246 Fax: 020 8861 1490 — MB BS 1973 Bombay; DA (UK) 1976.

AMIN, Kiritray Ambalal 11 Malvern Terrace, Edmonton, London N9 9PP Tel: 020 8803 4962 — MB BS 1972 Baroda.

AMIN, Lisa Irwani 1 Tatlow Court, West Heath Av, London NW11 7QU — MB ChB 1997 Leic.

AMIN, Mahendra Babubhai Hazeldene Medical Centre, Hazeldene, 1B Wyld Way, Wembley HA9 6PW Tel: 020 8902 4792 — MB BS 1963 Bombay.

AMIN, Malika Rameshchandra 27 Grove Park, Wanstead, London E11 2DN Tel: 020 8989 9254 — MB BS 1961 Bombay; MRCOG 1973, DObst 1968; FRCOG 1993, M 1973; DObst 1968. Clin. Asst. (O & G) Whipps Cross & Wanstead Hosps. Lond. Prev: SHO (Gyn. & Obst.) Wanstead Hosp. Lond.; SHO (Gyn.) & Regist. (Gyn. & Obst.) Whipps Cross Hosp. Lond.

AMIN, Margaret Anne 10 Hart Road, St Albans AL1 1NF — MB BS 1990 Lond.; MRCP (UK) 1993.

AMIN, Michael Anthony 24 Sunnsyside Road, London W5 5HU — MB BS 1996 Lond.

AMIN, Mohammed Ruhul 6 Blenheim Crescent, Luton LU3 1HA — MB ChB 1996 Leic.

AMIN, Mukund 4 Becmead Avenue, Streatham, London SW16 1UQ — MRCS Eng. LRCP Lond. 1979; MB BS Indore 1976.

AMIN, Naseem Sajjid 52 Edward Avenue, London E4 9DN — MB BS 1987 Lond.

AMIN, Nipulkumar White Lodge Medical Practice, 68 Silver Street, Enfield EN1 3EW Tel: 020 8363 4156 Fax: 020 8364 6295; 150 The Avenue, West Wickham BR4 0EA Tel: 020 8777 3414 — MB BS 1983 Lond.; BSc Lond. 1980; MRCGP 1988; DRCOG 1987; Cert. Family Plann. JCC 1987. (King's Coll Hosp. Med. Sch.) Prev: Trainee GP/SHO Middlx. Hosp. Lond. VTS.

AMIN, Rajni Exeter Oncology Centre, Royal Devon & Exeter Hospital (Wonford), Barrack Road, Exeter EX2 5DW Tel: 01392 411611 Fax: 01392 402112 — MB BS 1962 Calcutta; FRCP Lond. 1991; MRCP (UK) 1970; MRCS Eng. LRCP Lond. 1973; FRCR 1975; FFR 1974; DMRT Eng. 1973. (Calcutta Nat. Med. Inst.) Cons. Radiat. Oncol. Roy. Devon & Exeter Hosp. Wonford. Socs: Fell. Roy. Soc. Med.; Fell. Roy. Coll. Radiol.; Fell. Roy. Coll. Phys. Prev: Sen. Regist. (Radiother.) Univ. Coll. Hosp. Lond.; SHO (Med.) Leicester Gen. Hosp.; Ho. Surg. Makerere Univ. Uganda.

AMIN, Rakesh 37 Birchwood Avenue, Sidcup DA14 4JZ — MB ChB 1991 Leeds.

AMIN, Mr Rameshchandra Tulsidas 1 Pretoria Road, Leytonstone, London E11 4BB Tel: 020 8539 5232; The Pink House, 27 Grove Park, Wanstead, London E11 2DN Tel: 020 8989 9254 Fax: 020 8556 4149 — MB BS 1959 Bombay; FRCS Ed. 1965. (Grant Med. Coll.) Prev: Regist. (Surg.) Hertford Co. Hosp., E. Ham Memor. Hosp. Lond. & Poplar Hosp. Lond.

AMIN, Rashida 12 Coachmans Drive, Parklands, West Derby, Liverpool L12 0HX — MB BS 1992 Lond.

AMIN, Rizkar Aziz Mohammad Waterlow Unit, Whittington Hospital, Highgate Hill, London N19 Tel: 020 7272 3070; Flat C, 77 Sotheby Road, London N5 2UT Tel: 020 7704 0990 — MB ChB 1983 Mosul; MRCPsych 1994. Sen. Regist. (Psychiat.) Whittington Hosp. Lond. Prev: Clin. Research Fell. Roy. Free Hosp. Med. Sch. Lond.; Regist. (Psychiat.) N. Trent RHA; SHO (Psychiat.) Sheff. HA.

AMIN, Sandipkumar 150 The Avenue, West Wickham BR4 0EA — MB BS 1988 Lond.

AMIN, Sepideh BCM Northpole, London WC1N 3XX Tel: 0411 801464 Email: sepamin@mcmail.com — MB ChB 1991 Leic.; FRCOphth. 1998.

AMIN, Shahid Lynton House Surgery, 43 London Road, High Wycombe HP11 1BP Tel: 01494 558811 Fax: 01494 447070; Rectory House, Locas Road, High Wycombe HP13 6QG Tel: 01494 527321 — MB BS 1980 Lond.; BSc (Hons.) Lond. 1977; MRCGP 1985; DRCOG - RCOG 1985; DA (UK) 1986. (St. Mary's Hosp.) Socs: B.A.S.M. Mem.

AMIN, Shahid Flat 4 Block B, Bellgarth Residences, Bellgarth, Carlisle CA2 7PH — MB BS 1983 Punjab.

AMIN, Sharuddin Mohammad 9 St Christophers Close, Ashington NE63 9DG; Medical Personnel Department, Dryburn Hospital, Durham DH1 5TW — MB ChB 1993 Sheff.

AMIN, Shazad 16 Eskdale Drive, Aspley, Nottingham NG8 5GZ Tel: 0115 970 9292 Email: shazad.amin@nottingham.ac.uk — MB ChB 1990 Manch.; MRCPsych 1994. (Manch.) Specialist Regist. (Psychiat.) Nottm. Healthcare NHS Trust. Prev: Clin. Research Fell. Dept. Psychiat. Univ. Nottm.

AMIN, Shazia Naz 60 Pickmere Road, Sheffield S10 1GZ — MB ChB 1997 Sheff.

AMIN, Sheela Oxnead, Marsham Way, Gerrards Cross SL9 8 Tel: 01753 882492 — MB BS 1962 Lond.; MRCS Eng. LRCP Lond. 1962; FRCPath 1985, M 1973. (Guy's) Cons. (Haemat.) Mt. Vernon & Harefield Hosps. Prev: Regist. (Haemat.) Hammersmith Hosp. Lond.; Sen. Regist. (Haemat.) Hammersmith & W. Middlx. Hosps.

AMIN, Shobha Manubhai 18 Burdon Lane, Sutton SM2 7PT — MB BS 1965 Panjab; FRCOG 1989, M 1971.

AMIN, Shwan Niazi Omar 9 March Court, Warwick Drive, London SW15 6LE — MB ChB 1985 Al-Mustansirya U, Iraq.

AMIN, Sumant Purushottam c/o Miten Patel, 203 Edgwarebury Lane, Edgware HA8 8QJ — LAH 1962 Dub.

AMIN, Urmila Ravjibhai West Midlands Duty Services, Nestor Medical Duty Services, Peugeot House, Birmingham B19 3ND Fax: 0121 359 6492; 16 Chattock Avenue, Solihull B91 2QX — MB BS 1974 Bombay. (Grant Med. Coll.) Socs: Birm. Med. Inst.; Overseas Doctors Assn.; BMA. Prev: GP Birm.; Regist. (Anaesth.) Stafford.

AMIN, Vimal Sharad Nithsdale Road Surgery, 162 Nithsdale Road, Glasgow G41 5RU Tel: 0141 424 1831 Fax: 0141 423 7422; 18 Church Road, Glasgow G46 6JR Tel: 0141 638 3311 — MB ChB 1989 Glas.; MRCGP 1993; DRCOG 1993.

AMIN, Yogen Kunj 442 Finchley Road, London NW2 2HY — MB ChB 1993 Manch.

AMIN, Yogesh Yeshvantlal Central Surgery, 86 Cheriton Road, Folkestone CT20 2QH Tel: 01303 220707 Fax: 01303 254292; 83 Harcourt Road, Folkestone CT19 4AE — MB BS 1979 Mysore; MRCS Eng. LRCP Lond. 1981; LRCP LRCS Ed. LRCPS Glas. 1981. Prev: Trainee GP Maidstone HA; SHO (A & E) Maidstone Hosp.; SHO (Geriat.) Med. Linton Hosp. Maidstone.

AMIN, Zahir Department of Diagnostic Imaging, Chelsea & Westminster Hospital, 369 Fulham Road, London SW10 9NH Tel: 020 8746 8570 Fax: 020 8746 8588; 41 Bodley Road, New Malden KT3 5QD Email: zahir.amin@ic.ac.uk — MB BS 1986 Lond.; MD Lond. 1994; MRCP (UK) 1989; FRCR 1994. (University College London) Cons. Radiol. Chelsea & W.m. Hosp. Lond. Socs: BMA; Roy. Coll. Radiol.; Brit. Instit. Radiol. Prev: Sen. Regist. (Radiol.) Univ. Coll. Lond. Hosps.; Research Fell. & Regist. (Radiol.) Univ. Coll. Lond. Hosps.; Hon. Regist. & Research Fell. (Gastroenterol.) Centr. Middlx. Hosp. Lond.

AMINI, Mr Alexander 37 Carnarvon Road, South Woodford, London E18 2NT — MRCS Eng. LRCP Lond. 1981; MA Camb. 1981, MB 1981, BChir 1980; FRCS Eng. 1986.

AMINU, A'Ishatu Kingi 26 Burnley Road, London NW10 1EJ — MB BCh 1992 Wales; BMed Sci. 1992. SHO (Paediat.) S. Glam. HA.

AMIR, Willem Pieter 60 Greswolde Road, Sparkhill, Birmingham B11 4DL — Artsexamen 1987 Utrecht.

AMIR-ANSARI, Behzad King's College Hospital, (Dulwich) Renal Unit, East Dulwich Grove, London SE22 8PT Tel: 020 7737 4000 Fax: 020 7346 6472; Upper Flat, 8 Lansdowne Road, London N3 1ES Tel: 020 8343 1475 — MD 1975 Nat. Univ. Iran; MD Nat. Univ. Iran 1975 1974. Assoc. Specialist (Renal) KCH Lond. Socs: Brit. Transpl. Soc.; Brit. Renal Assn.; Iranian Assn. Nephrol. & Transpl. Prev: Assoc. Prof. Behshti Univ. Tehran, Iran; Research Regist. Inst. Urol. Lond.

AMIR-ANSARI, Katayon 74 Copleston Road, London SE15 4AG — MB ChB 1987 Aberd.; FRCA Lond. 1995. (Aberdeen) Cons. Mayday Hosp., Croydon; Specialist Regist. Rotat. (Anaesth.), Middlx. Hosp.

***AMIRCHETTY RAO, Sandya Rani** 596 Derby Road, Adams Hill, Nottingham NG7 2GZ Tel: 0115 942 4816 — BM BS 1996 Nottm.; B.Med.Sci (Physiol.& Pharmacol.) Nottm. 1994.

AMIRUDDIN, Mr Kallolikkal Meeran 33 Selworthy Road, Catford, London SE6 4DP Tel: 020 8291 1974 — MB BS 1970 Kerala; MS (Gen. Surg.) Kerala 1975, MB BS 1970; FRCSI 1983.

AMIS, Shamim Jahan 51 Abbey Road, St John's Wood, London NW8 0AD Email: shamim@btinternet.com — LMSSA 1990 Lond.; MB BS Bangladesh 1985; MRCOG 1994. Specialist Regist. in O & G Colchester Gen. Hosp.

AMISSAH-ARTHUR, Justice Brookman The Royal Shrewsbury Hospital, Shrewsbury SY3 8XQ Tel: 01432 268161; 3 The Broadwell, Radbrook Grove, Shrewsbury SY3 6AD — MB ChB 1978 Ghana; MRCOG 1987.

AMLOT, Nicholas 270 Ferme Pk Road, London N8 9BL — BM 1997 Soton.

AMLOT, Peter Lloyd 118A Avenue Mansions, Alexandra Park Road, London N10 2AH Tel: 020 8883 5444 — MB BS 1967 Lond.; MRCP (U.K.) 1972. (Guy's) Lect. Dept. Med. Guy's Hosp. Lond. Prev: Ho. Phys. & Ho. Surg. Orpington Hosp.; SHO Roy. N.. Hosp. Lond; Research Assoc. Dept. Clin. Pharmacol. Guy's Hosp. Lond.

AMMAR, Katy Musa 1 Avocet Wharf, Castle Marina, Nottingham NG7 1TH — BM BS 1996 Nottm.

AMMAR, Mohamed Abdel Wahed 10 North Drive, Aylesbury HP21 9AN — MB BCh 1979 Cairo.

AMMAR, Thoraya 13 Oldacres, Maidenhead SL6 1XH — MB BS 1997 Lond.

AMMIR, Tarig Fath El Rahman Flat 41, Coniston, Fazakerley Hospital, Liverpool L9 7AL — MB BS 1981 Khartoum; MRCP (UK) 1992.

AMMURI, Mr Basil Jaser Ibrahim Flat 2, 38 Clarendon Road, Leeds LS2 9PJ — MB ChB 1986 Baghdad; FRCS Ed. 1992; FRCS Eng. 1992.

AMOAKU, Mr Winfried Mawutor Kwaku Department of Opthalmology, B Floor, South Block, Queens Medical Centre, University Hospital NHS Trust, Nottingham NG7 2UH Tel: 0115 924 9924 Fax: 0115 970 9963 Email: jennie.phillips@nottingham.ac.uk, wma@nottingham.ac.uk; 22 Wasdale Close, Edwalton Park, West Bridgford, Nottingham NG2 6RG — MB ChB 1979 Ghana; PhD Belf. 1990; FRCS Ed. 1985; FCOphth 1988. Hon. Cons. (Ophth.) Qu. Med. Centre Nottm.; Sen. Lect. (Ophth.) Univ. Nottm. Socs: Fluorescein Angiogr. Club Europe; Amer. Acad. Ophth.; Oxf. Ophth. Congr. Prev: Sen. Regist. (Ophth.) Yorks. RHA; Brit. Counc. Research Fell. Qu. Univ. Belf.; Regist. & SHO (Ophth.) Roy. Vict. Hosp. Belf.

AMOBI, Carole Ann Ebiwari Brentfield Medical Centre, 10 Kingfisher Way, London NW10 8TF Tel: 020 8459 8833 Fax: 020 8459 1374 — MB BS 1979 Lond.

AMODEO, Paolo Alexander 7A Crystalwood Road, Cardiff CF14 4HU — MB ChB 1989 Sheff.

AMOILS, Shann Flat B, 10 Rona Road, London NW3 2JA — MB BCh 1988 Witwatersrand.

AMOLE, Mr Adeniyi Adeyemi Bronglais General Hospital, Aberystwyth SY23 1ER — MB BS 1977 Lagos, Nigeria; MB BS Lagos, Nigeria; FRCS Glas. 1986.

AMONKAR, Jayant Anant Kelvin Grove Surgery, Kelvin Grove, Wombwell, Barnsley S73 0DL Tel: 01226 752361 Fax: 01226 341577 — MB BS 1969 Poona.

AMONOO-KUOFI, Kwamena 9 Dering Road, Croydon CR0 1DS — MB BS 1998 Lond.; MB BS Lond 1998.

AMOR, Timothy James Barron 1 Ward, Ealing Hospital, Uxbridge Road, Southall UB1 3EU Tel: 020 8354 8691 Fax: 020 8354 8685 Email: timamor@doctors.org.uk; 38 Wintersbrook Road, Herne Hill, London SE24 9JA — MB ChB 1980 Leeds; MRCPsych 1987. Cons. Psychiat. Ealing, Hammersmith and Fulham NHS Trust.

AMOROSO, Peter St Bartholomews Hospital, West Smithfield, London EC1; 66 Lullington Garth, Finchley, London N12 7BY Tel: 020 8445 6696 — MB BS 1983 Lond.; FFA RCS Eng. 1988; DA (UK) 1985. (King's Coll.) Cons. Anaesth. St. Bart. Hosp. Lond. Prev: Regist. (Anaesth.) Roy. Free Hosp. Lond.; SHO (Anaesth.) St. Geo. Hosp. Lond.; SHO (Renal) St. Bart. Hosp. Lond.

AMOS, Alison Mary The Station Medical Centre, RAF Bruggen BFPO 25 — MB BCh 1983 Wales; DRCOG 1986.

AMOS, Carol Elizabeth Nelson Street Surgery, 18 Nelson Street, Dalton-in-Furness LA15 8AF Tel: 01229 463999; Moorcroft, Cross-a-Moor, Ulverston LA12 0RT Tel: 01229 583423 — MB BS 1974 Newc.; BSc (Hons.) Newc. 1971, MB BS 1974; MRCGP 1978; DRCOG 1976. Clin. Asst. (Ophth.) Furness Gen. Hosp.

AMOS, Catherine Frances 52 Dene Road, Northwood HA6 2DE Tel: 020 896 57700 — MB BS 1977 Lond.; 1974 BSc. (Hons.) Lond; 1995 FFOM RCP Lond.; 1984 DIH Eng. (St. Bart.) Gp. Head, Occupat.al Health Diageo. Socs: Internat. Forum Organizational Health; .Anglo-Amer. Med. Soc.; Roy. Soc. Med. Prev: Sen. Regional Med. Off. Lucas Indust. plc; Area Med. Adviser Post Off.; Med. Off. Lond. Regional Transport.

AMOS, Clare Newbridge Surgery, 129 Newbridge Hill, Bath BA1 3PT; 2nd Floor Flat, 4 St James Square, Bath BA1 2TR Tel: 01225 339212 — MB ChB 1990 Bristol; MRCGP 1995. p/t Asst. G.P Newbridge Surg., Bath; Asst. G.P Catharine Cottage Surg., Bath.

AMOS, Harry Edmund Libra, Cartside Quay, Galampton Greek, Brixham TQ5 0EH — MB BS 1963 Lond.; PhD Camb. 1968; FIBiol 1976. Med. Dir. Pharmaco UK. Socs: Path. Soc.; Brit. Soc. Immunol. Prev: Sen. Med. Advisor ICI; Sen. Lect. & Hon. Cons. Inst. Dermat. St. John's Hosp. Dis. Skin Lond.

AMOS, Hugh Timothy University Department of Psychiatry, Withington Hospital, Manchester M20 2LR Tel: 0161 291 4358 Fax: 0161 291 4358 Email: tim.amos@tsl.with.man.ac.uk; Bradshaw Head Farm, Watling St, Affetside, Bury BL8 3QJ — MB BS 1992 Lond.; MA Oxf. 1984; MRCPsych 1996. (St. Thos. Hosp. Med. Sch. Lond.) Clin. Research Fell. Nat. Inquiry into Suicide & Homicide in People with Ment. Illness Withington Hosp. Manch. Prev: Regist. (Psychiat.) & SHO Univ. Hosp. S. Manch. & Manch. Roy. Infirm.

AMOS, Matthew William Central Surgery, Welfare Road, Thurnscoe, Rotherham S63 0JZ Tel: 01709 890501 Fax: 01709 898595 (Call before faxing); 19 Spa Well Grove, Brierley, Barnsley S72 9LS Tel: 01226 717418 — MB ChB 1990 Sheff.

AMOS, Rodney Stephen 20 Totley Brook Road, Sheffield S17 3QS — MB ChB 1972 Birm.; BSc (Hons.) Birm. 1969; FRCP 1990. Cons. Phys. (Rheum.) Centr. Sheff. Univ. Hosps. & Roy. Hallamsh. Hosp. Sheff. Prev: Sen. Regist. Leeds; Sheldon Research Fell. Dudley Rd. Hosp. Birm.; Regist. Selly Oak Hosp. Birm.

AMOS, Roger James Department of Haematology, Homerton Hospital, Homerton Row, London E9 6SR Tel: 020 8510 7900 Fax: 020 8510 7555; 226 Alexandra Park Road, London N22 7BH — MB BChir 1979 Camb.; MD Camb. 1985, MA 1978; MRCPath 1985. (St. Bart's) Cons. Haematologist, Homerton Hosp. Prev: Sen. Lect. St. Bart. & the Roy. Lond. Sch. of Med. & Dent.; Hon. Cons. Haemat. Homerton Hosp.

AMOS, Thomas Andrew Scott 463A London Road, Carlisle CA1 3DL — MB BS 1982 Lond.; MRCS Eng. LRCP Lond. 1982; MRCP (UK) 1986; MRCPath 1997; DTM & H RCP Lond. 1992. (St. Bart.)

AMOUR, Ahmed Abdulla 6 Coombe Grove, Combe Park, Bath BA1 — LMSSA 1978 Lond.

AMR, Mr Mohammed Amr Yasir 9 Dellcot Close, Salford M6 7PE — MB BS 1988 Jordan; FRCS Glas. 1994.

AMRAN BIN MARZUKI, Dr Doctors Mess, Blackburn Royal Infirmary, Blackburn BB2 3LP — MB ChB 1996 Manch.

AMRANI, Mohamed Department of Cardiac Surgery, Harefield Hospital, Hill End Road, Harefield, Uxbridge UB9 6JH — MD 1987 Louvain; PhD Lond. Sen. Lect. & Cons. (Cardiac Surg.) Harefield Uxbridge.

AMROLIA, Persis Jal 70a Fellows Road, London NW3 3LJ — MB BS 1989 Lond.

AMROLIWALLA, Fredoon Kaikhushro, Air Commodore RAF Med. Br. (retired) MDHU Peterborough, Peterborough District Hospital, Thorpe Road, Peterborough PE3 6DA Tel: 01733 875780 Fax: 01773 874939 — MB BS 1957 Bombay; BSc (1st cl. Hons.) Bombay 1952; FRCP Lond. 1978, M 1964; DAvMed Eng. 1978; DIH Eng. 1960; DPH Lond. 1959. Cons. Phys., Defence Med. Serv.s, Brit. Forces, Cyprus. Prev: Defense Med. Serv.s, Speciality Director of Med.

AMSO, Nazar Najib Jarmanos Department of Obstetrics and Gynaecology, University Hospital of Wales, Heath Park, Cardiff CF14 4XN Tel: 029 2074 4448 Fax: 029 2074 3722 Email: amsonn@cardiff.ac.uk — MB ChB 1974 Baghdad; PhD Lond. 1996; MRCOG 1985; FRCOG 1999. Sen. Lect. O & G Univ. of Wales Coll. of Med. Cardiff; Hon. Cons. Obst. & Gyn. Univ. Hosp. of Wales. Socs: BMA; Roy. Soc. Med.; Brit. Med. Ultrasound Soc. Prev: Cons. O & G Qu. Eliz. Hosp. Gateshead; Sen. Regist. Roy. Vict. Infirm. Newc. u. Tyne & Newc. Gen. Hosp.; Lect. & Sen. Regist. Roy. Free Hosp. Lond.

AMU, Sunday Olubusola 57 Ryder Road, Kirby Frith, Leicester LE3 6UJ — MB BS 1986 Lagos.

AMUA-QUARSHIE, Nee (retired) 1 Chertsey Walk, Drill Hall Road, Chertsey KT16 8ES Tel: 01932 565254 — MRCS Eng. LRCP Lond. 1961.

AMURE, Adebayo Olawole 39 Strathyre Avenue, Norbury, London SW16 4RF — LRCPI & LM, LRSCI & LM 1965; LRCPI & LM, LRCSI & LM 1965.

AMURE, Bamidele Olusola Drings Close Surgery, 1 Drings Close, Over, Cambridge CB4 5NZ Tel: 01954 231550 Fax: 01954 231573 — BChir 1984 Camb.; BSc (Hons.) Bristol 1976; PhD Camb. 1979, BChir 1984; DO RCS Glas. 1989. (Camb.) SHO (Ophth.) Qu. Med. Centre Nottm.; GP Cleveland VTS. Prev: SHO (Neurosurg.) Qu. Med. Centre Nottm.; Cas. Off. Bedford Gen. Hosp.; Res. Med. Off. Biddenham Manor Hosp. Bedford.

AMURE, Yetunde Olayinka 45 Druid Woods, Stoke Bishop, Bristol BS9 1SZ — MB ChB 1988 Bristol; BSc (Hons.) Physiol. Manch. 1982, MSc Pharmacol. 1983. Prev: SHO (A & E) Frenchay Hosp. Bristol; SHO (Med., Rheumat. & Geriat.) Newport Gwent.

AMUSAN, Kehinde Adedapo 28 Colbert, Sceaux Gardens, Camberwell, London SE5 7DE Tel: 020 7701 1497; 123 Kent House Road, Beckenham BR3 1JJ Tel: 020 8325 2842 — MB BS 1975 Lagos; MB BS Lagos, Nigeria 1975; MRCOG 1992. GP. Socs: BMA. Prev: Regist. (O & G) Buchanan Hosp. Hastings & Maidstone Hosp.

ANA, Joseph Enebieni 84 Bishopscote Road, Luton LU3 1PB Tel: 01582 583507 Fax: 01525 853319 — BM BCh 1978 Nigeria; FRCS Ed. 1989; Dip. Urol. Lond 1991; DFFP (UK) 1993. (Univ. Nigeria, Nsukka) Partner & GP Princip. Europa Ho. Surg. Leighton Buzzard. Socs: Assoc. Mem. BAUS; (Sec. Gen.) Nigerian Med. Forum UK & Irel.; Assoc. Mem. Roy. Coll. Gen. Pract. Prev: Regist. (Gen. Surg. & Urol.) Qu. Eliz. Hosp. Kings Lynn & Nevill Hall Hosp. Abergavenny; GP Regist. Luton & Dunstable Heaton; Regist. (Surg. & Urol.) Bedford Gen. Hosp.

ANAFI, Raymont Ferempong 8 Lingmoor Drive, Burnley BB12 8UY Tel: 01282 456038; 8 Lingmoor Drive, Burnley BB12 8UY Tel: 01282 456038 — MD 1972 Leningrad. Staff Surg. (Orthop. & Trauma). Socs: Med. Protec. Soc. Prev: SHO (Trauma & Orthop.) Burnley Gen. Hosp.; SHO. Off. (Gen. Surg.) Burnley Gp. Hosps.; SHO. Off. (Trauma & Orthop.) Batley Gen. Hosp.

ANAGNOSTOPOULOS, Afendra-Vassiliki The National Hospital for Neurology & Neurosurgey, Queen Square, Pain Clinic, London WC1N 3BG Tel: 020 7837 3611 — State Exam Med 1983 Munich; PhD Munich 1989; T(Anaesth) 1994. (Univ. Ludwig-Maximilian, Munich) Cons. Anaesth. & Chronic Pain Specialist Nat. Hosp. Neurol. & Neurosurg. Lond. Socs: Neuroanaesth. Soc.; Difficult Airway Soc.; Internat. Assn. Study of Pain.

ANAGNOSTOU, Efthimios Cardiology Department, Northern General Hospital, Herries Road, Sheffield S5 7AU Tel: 0114 243 4343 — Ptychio Iatrikes 1982 Athens. Staff Grade (Cardiol.) Cardiothoracic Unit N. Gen. Hosp. Sheff.; Cardiovasc. Specialist (Europ. Specialist Med.) Qualification Order 1995; Mem. BSE; Mem. ASE.

ANAKWE, Mr Geoffrey Nnaebue 8 Rawcliffe Croft, York YO30 5UT — MD 1971 Kalinin; FRCS Ed. 1984; MRCOG 1982.

ANAM, Khairul Abul Kassem Mohammed Wheatfield Surgery, 60 Wheatfield Road, Lewsey Farm, Luton LU4 0TR Tel: 01582 601116 Fax: 01582 666421 — MB BS 1968 Dacca.

ANAM, Zarina York Road Surgery, 127 York Road, Hartlepool TS26 9DN Tel: 01429 234646 Fax: 01429 861559 — MB BS 1968 Dacca.

ANAMAN, Stephen Simon The Grove Surgery, Farthing Grove, Netherfield, Milton Keynes MK6 4NG Tel: 01908 668453 Fax: 01908 695064 — Lekarz 1972 Krakow. (Cracow Univ. Med. Sch.)

ANAND, Dr Elmfield Health Group, 18 Elmfield Road, Gosforth, Newcastle upon Tyne NE3 4BP Tel: 0191 285 1663 Fax: 0191 284 7015 — MB BS 1974 Patna; MRCGP 1983. (P. of Wales Med.

Coll.) Hon. Tutor (Family Med.) Newc. Univ.; Trainer N.d. VTS; Clin. Asst. (Alcohol & Drug Addic.) Regional Unit Newc.

ANAND, Anthea Elmfield Health Group, 18 Elmfield Road, Gosforth, Newcastle upon Tyne NE3 4AY Email: anandji@aol.com — MB BS 1980 Newc. Wom.'s Ret. (GP). Prev: Trainee GP N.umbria VTS.

ANAND, Chaman Lal St George's Medical Centre, 137 St George's Road, Glasgow G3 6JB Tel: 0141 332 5553 Fax: 0141 332 5557 — MB BS 1956 Punjab.

ANAND, Chandra 9 Cheadle Avenue, Cramlington NE23 3YT — MB ChB 1995 Birm.

ANAND, Harkirat Anand and Anand, The Health Centre, Bilston Street, Darlaston, Walsall WS10 8EY Tel: 0121 526 2845 Fax: 0121 568 8034 — MB BS 1962 Poona; DA Eng. 1965. (B.J. Med. Coll.) Clin. Asst. (Anaesth.) Walsall Gp. Hosps. Prev: Regist. (Anaesth.) Walsall Gp. Hosps.

ANAND, Joginder Kumar 68 Ledbury Road, Peterborough PE3 9PJ Tel: 01733 264219; 68 Ledbury Road, Peterborough PE3 9PJ Tel: 01733 264219 — MB BS 1958 Punjab (India); BSc Punjab (India) 1958; FFCM 1978, M 1972; DPH Eng. 1970. (Med. Coll. Amritsar) Hon. Med. Off. Med. Foundat. for Care Victims of Torture Lond. Socs: FRSM. Prev: Med. Mem., Disabil. Appeal Tribunal, InDepend. Tribunal Serv.; Dist. Med. Dir. P'boro. HA; MOEH Fenland, Huntingdon Dist. & P'boro. Councs.

ANAND, Kamni 70 Ballywillan Road, Portrush BT56 8JN — MB BCh BAO 1978 Belf.

ANAND, Kuki Flat 3, Tyrone County Hospital, Hospital Road, Omagh BT79 0AP — MB BCh BAO 1975 Belf.

ANAND, Mr Makhan Singh Anand and Anand, The Health Centre, Bilston Street, Darlaston, Walsall WS10 8EY Tel: 0121 526 2845 Fax: 0121 568 8034 — MB BS 1955 Nagpur; FRCS Eng. 1961. (Nagpur) Hosp. Pract. (Gen. Surg.) Walsall Hosp. Gp.

ANAND, Premkarran The Lakeside Health Centre, Tavy Bridge, Thamesmead, London SE2 9UQ Tel: 020 8310 3281; 57 Lamorbey Close, Sidcup DA15 8BA — MB BS 1985 Lond.; BSc Basic Med. Scs. & Biochem. 1981.

ANAND, Raj 3 Moor Park, Nunthorpe, Middlesbrough TS7 0JJ — MB BS 1950 Delhi.

ANAND, Rajiv 17 Lizban Street, London SE3 8SS — MB BS 1998 Lond.; MB BS Lond 1998.

ANAND, Sanjay 28 Fenmere Cl, Wolverhampton WV4 5EN — MB ChB 1997 Manch.

ANAND, Sumit 21 Shakespeare Avenue, Hayes UB4 0BB — MB BS 1992 Lond.

ANAND, Usha Rashid and Partners, Havercroft Health Centre, Cow Lane, Ryhill, Wakefield WF4 2AX Tel: 01226 725555 Fax: 01226 700051 — MB BS 1965 Delhi. (Delhi) GP Wakefield, W. Yorks.

ANAND, Mr Vellore Thiruvengaden 221 King George V Drive E., Cardiff CF14 4ER — MB BS 1984 Madras; FRCS Glas. 1991.

ANAND, Vijay Kumar 28 Elmfield Terrace, Halifax HX1 3EB Tel: 01422 346135 Fax: 01422 346135 Email: vanand@aol.com; 86 Vasant Vihar, New Delhi 110057, India — MB BS 1978 Delhi; DTCD 1981; MRCP (UK) 1984; FRCP Lond. 1998. Assoc. Specialist (Med.) Halifax Gen. Hosp.

ANAND, Vikram 50 Canning Road, London N5 2JS Tel: 020 7354 3957 — MB BS 1973 Kanpur; MS (Ophth.) Kanpur 1978; DO Glas. 1987. Assoc. Specialist Moorfields Eye Hosp. Lond.; Ophth. Med. Pract. N. Lond. & Herts. Socs: Med. Protec. Soc. Prev: Ophth. Chase Farm Hosp., N. Middlx. Hosp. & W.. Ophth. Hosp. Lond.

ANANDA BALENDRAN, Velupillai 6 Underwood Close, Nackington Road, Canterbury CT4 7BS — MB BS 1971 Ceylon.

ANANDA RAJAN, Mr Rohan 112, Riverside, Milk Yard, Wapping, London E1W 3TA Tel: 020 7790 8098 Email: rohan20@aol.com — MB BS 1990 Lond.; FRCS (Eng). (The London Hospital) Orthomedic Regist.

ANANDAKUMAR, Padmini Bushyfields Hospital, Bushyfields Road, Dudley DY1 — MB BS 1982 Sri Lanka; MRCS Eng. LRCP Lond. 1990. Clin. Med. Off. Bushyfields Hosp. Dudley. Prev: SHO (Psychiat.) Bushyfields Hosp. Dudley & Barnsley Hall Hosp. BromsGr.; SHO (Psychiat.) Burton Rd. Hosp. Dudley W. Midl.

ANANDAKUMAR, Perumal Alpha House Surgery, 32-34 Avenue Road, Coseley, Bilston WV14 9DL Tel: 01902 882070; 26 Terrace Street, Brierley Hill DY5 1HT — MB BS 1982 Peradeniya; MB BS Univ. Peradeniya, Sri Lanka 1982; MRCS Eng. LRCP Lond. 1987; DRCOG 1993. Prev: SHO (Psychiat.) Burton Rd. Hosp. Dudley W. Midl.; SHO (Paediat.) Wordsley Hosp. W. Midl.; SHO (ENT Surg.) Russells Hall Hosp. Dudley W. Midl.

ANANDAN, Mr Nellickal Appukutty Stamford & Rutland Hospital, Stamford PE9 1UA Tel: 01780 764151 Fax: 01780 763385; St Giles, First Drift, Wothorpe, Stamford PE9 3JL Email: anandan@globalnet.co.uk — MB BS 1978 Madras; MS (Surg.) Madras 1982; FRCS Glas. 1988. (Jipmer Pondicherry) Assoc. Specialist (Surg.) Stamford & Rutland Hosp. Socs: Assn. Surg. Prev: Staff Surg. Stamford & Rutland Hosp. Lincs.; Regist. (Surg.) P'boro. Dist. Gen. Hosp.; SHO (Surg.) Dewsbury HA.

ANANDAPPA, Anthony Joseph Augustus 169 Cavendish Road, Bispham, Blackpool FY2 9EG Tel: 01253 356571 Fax: 01253 352229 — MB BS 1960 Ceylon. (Ceylon) Div. Police Surg. Lancs. Constab. Blackpool.

ANANDARAJAH, Mr Thambirajah 25 Thurleston Avenue, Morden SM4 4BN — MB BS 1975 Colombo; FRCS Ed. 1984; LMSSA Lond. 1985.

ANANI, Abder Rahman Ahmed 8 Maes-y-Gwernen Drive, Cwmrhydceirw, Swansea SA6 6LN — MB ChB 1976 Alexandria.

ANANTA, Marikanti Potha Parakrama 4A Hardwick Road, Streetly, Sutton Coldfield B74 3BU — MB BS 1987 Osmania.

ANANTHAKRISHNA RAO, Aparna 22 Ramilies Road, Liverpool L18 1ED — MB BS 1994 Newc.

ANANTHANARAYANAN, Héma Department of Psychiatry, Royal Free Hospital, Pond St., London NW3 Tel: 020 7794 0500; 6 Ash Lodge, Chester Road, Poyntor, Stockport SK12 1EU Tel: 01625 871109 — MB BS 1994 Lond.; BSc (Nutrit.) Lond. 1991. (UCMSM) SHO (Neuropsychiat.) Nat. Hosp. Au. Sa. Lond. Prev: SHO (Gen. Adult Psychiat.) Chase Farm Hosp.; SHO (Gen. Adult Rehabil. Psychiat.) St. Ann's Hosp.; SHO (Liaison Psychiat.) Roy. Free Hosp. Lond.

ANANTHANARAYANAN, Tinnevely Subramanian City General Hospital, Newcastle Road, Stoke-on-Trent ST4 6QG Tel: 01782 718826; 6 Ash Lodge, Chester Road, Poynton, Stockport SK12 1EU — MB BS 1970 Kerala; FRCPsych 1991, M 1978; DPM Eng. 1976; DPM RCSI 1976. Cons. Psychiat. City Gen. Hosp. Stoke-on-Trent.

ANANTHANARAYANAN, Vimala Central Clinic, Hall St., Dudley DY2 7BX — MB BS 1966 Kerala. (Med. Coll. Trivandrum) Clin. Med. Off. (Child Health) Dudley AHA.

ANANTHRAM, Sabarathnam Woodrow Medical Centre, Woodrow, Redditch B98 7RY Tel: 01527 526824 Fax: 01527 501787; Branch Surgery, Millstream Surgery, Cherry Tree Walk, Batchley, Redditch B97 6PB Tel: 01527 591871 Fax: 01527 501787 — MB BS 1975 Bombay; DRCOG. (Grant Medical College) Dir.Millstream Pharmacy Lyric Ltd. & Saltley Ltd. Wolverhampton; E.realm Ltd. Tudor Hall Nursery (pre-Sch.), Redditch; Proprietor: Chiltern Ho. Nursing Home, Redditch; Dir. Greenrose Ltd. Acorn Care Nursing Agency. Prev: Exec.: UREC (Worcs); Exevutive: Community Relations Counc., Redditch.

ANASTASIOU, Nikolaos Department of Cardiothoracic Surgery, Glenfield Hospital, Leicester LE3 9QP — Ptychio Iatrikes 1986 Athens.

ANATHHANAM, Annamma Joseph Department of Histopathology, Bassetlaw District General Hospital, Kilton, Worksop S81 0BD — MB BS 1977 Kerala; MRCPath 1987; FRCPath 1997. Cons. Histopath. Bassetlaw Dist. Gen. Hosp. Worksop. Socs: Assn. Clin. Pathol.; Brit. Soc. Clin. Cytol.; BMA.

ANATHHANAM, Joseph Jacob Kallarackkal Department of Anaesthesia, Huddersfield Royal Infirmary, Lindley, Huddersfield HD3 3EA — MB BS 1975 Kerala; FFA RCSI 1983. Cons. Anaesth. Huddersfield Roy. Infirm.; Huddersfield Roy. Infirm.; Director of Anaesth. Socs: Assn. Anaesth.; BMA; Fell. Roy. Soc. Med.

ANCHOR, Stephen Charles 20 East View, Barnet EN5 5TN — MB BS 1966 Newc.; FRCR 1978; DMRD 1976 Eng. Cons. Radiol. Chase Farm &Barnet NHS Hosp.s Trust, Enfield, Middx. Prev: Sen. Regist. (Radiol.) Sheff. AHA; Regist. (Gen. Surg.) Kettering Hosp. Gp.; SHO Roy. Nat. Orthop. Hosp. Stanmore.

ANCILL, Bernice Rendle Yeovil District Hospital, Higher Kingston, Yeovil BA21 4AT — MB ChB 1984 Dundee. Staff Anaesth. Yeovil Dist. Hosp. Prev: Regist. (Anaesth.) Yeovil Dist. Hosp.; SHO (Anaesth.) Weymouth & Dist. Hosp.; SHO (Anaesth.) Univ. Coll. & Middlx. Hosps. Lond.

ANCILL, Mr Paul Kendrick Yarley Hill Farm, Yarley, Wells BA5 1PA — MB ChB 1979 Manch.; BSc (Med. Sci.) St. And. 1976; FRCS Ed. 1986. Cons. A & E Dewsbury Dist. Hosp.

ANCLIFF, Helen Mary 8 Nunwick Way, Newcastle upon Tyne NE7 7GB — MB BS 1991 Newc. ((Newc.)) GP Regist. NVTS.

ANCLIFF, Jane Elizabeth 55 Ancroft Garth, High Shincliffe, Durham DH1 2UD — MB BS 1993 Newc.

ANCLIFF, Neville Bowness The Health Centre, Midland St., Long Eaton, Nottingham NG10 1NY Tel: 0115 973 2370 Fax: 0115 946 3894 — MB BS 1974 Lond.; MRCGP 1978. (Univ. Coll. Hosp.) Socs: Brit. Med. Acupunct. Soc.; Brit. Soc. Med. & Dent. Hypn.; Soc. Orthop. Med. Prev: Trainee GP Lincoln VTS; Ho. Phys. St. Pancras Hosp. Lond.; Ho. Surg. Leicester Roy. Infirm.

ANCLIFF, Patricia Mary 37 Derby Road, Risley, Draycott, Derby DE72 3SY — MB BS 1974 Lond.; DRCOG 1976. (Univ. Coll. Hosp.) Clin. Asst. Nottm. City Hosp. Prev: Ho. Surg. Univ. Coll. Hosp. Lond.; Ho. Phys. Geo. Eliott Hosp. Nuneaton; Trainee Gen. Pract. Nottm. Vocational Train. Scheme.

ANCLIFF, Philip James Great Ormond St Hospital, Dept of Haematology, London WC1N Email: anclip@gosh.nhs.uk — MB BChir 1993 Camb.; MRCP (UK) 1995; Dip RCPath, 1997. (Camb.) Specialist Regist. Haemat. Gt. Ormond St. Socs: BSHaematol.

ANDELIC, Steven Harry Kendal Road, Hartlepool TS25 1QU Tel: 01429 233611 — MB BS 1983 Newc.; DRCOG 1985. Gen. Practitioner, Hartlepool; Forens. Med. Examr., Cleveland Constab.; Chairm. of Hartlepool, RCT Exec. Comm.

ANDER, Patrick Gustav McDonald Radiology Department, Staffordshire General Hospital, Weston Road, Stafford ST16 3SA Tel: 01785 257731; Bakers Croft, 1 High St, Gnosall, Stafford ST20 0EX Tel: 01785 822340 Fax: 01785 822340 — MB ChB 1974 Bristol; FRCR 1984; DMRD Eng. 1983; DCH Eng. 1977. Cons. Radiol. Mid Staffs. Gen. Hosps. NHS Trust.

ANDERMAN, Janet Elizabeth Freda 179 Bilton Road, Greenford UB6 7HG — MB BS 1971 Lond.; MRCS Eng. LRCP Lond. 1971; DCH Eng. 1976. Prev: Ho. Phys. St. Anne's Gen. Hosp. Tottenham; Ho. Surg. Soton. Gen. Hosp.

ANDERS, Mr Christopher John (retired) Hollesley, Heath Road, Woking GU21 4DX Tel: 01483 773245 — MB ChB Cape Town 1951; FRCS Eng. 1956. Prev: Cons. Surg. NW Surrey HA.

ANDERSEN, John Anthony Royal Liverpool University Hospital, Prescot St., Liverpool L7 8XP — MB BS 1980 Queensland.

ANDERSEN, Peter Anthony Dental Centre, 3 Gower Place, London WC1E 6BN Tel: 020 7387 6306; 118 Albert Street, London NW1 7NE Tel: 020 7267 4656 — MB BS 1966 Lond.; MRCS Eng. LRCP Lond. 1966; DCH Eng. 1970. (Univ. Coll. Lond. & Oxf.) Stud. Health Phys. Health Centre UCL. Socs: BMA. Prev: Clin. Asst. Paddington Green Childr. Hosp.; Ho. Surg. Radcliffe Infirm. Oxf.; Dep. Edr. Brit. Jl. Hosp. Med.

ANDERSEN, Rosalind Muriel Tay Court Surgery, 50 South Tay Street, Dundee DD1 1PF Tel: 01382 228228 Fax: 01382 202606 — MB ChB 1966 St. And.; DA Eng. 1969; DObst RCOG 1967.

ANDERSEN, Sarah Liv 118 Albert Street, London NW1 7NE — MB BS 1997 Lond.

ANDERSEN, Siow Yen 49 High Ash Crescent, Leeds LS17 8RH — MB ChB 1991 Leeds.

ANDERSEN, Ulla Holm 113 Ember Lane, Esher KT10 8EQ — MD 1993 Odense; FRCS Ed. 1999.

ANDERSON, Adrian Robert Crown House Surgery, Chapelgate, Retford DN22 6NX Tel: 01777 703672 Fax: 01777 710534; Wesley Court, Main St, Hayton, Retford DN22 9LA — MB ChB 1976 Sheff.; MRCGP 1981; DCH Eng. 1980; DRCOG 1978.

ANDERSON, Alan Jeffrey Royal Hallamshire Hospital, Glossop Road, Sheffield S10 2JF Tel: 0114 271 1769 Fax: 0114 271 3689 — BM BCh 1970 Oxf.; MA Oxf. 1970; FRCP Lond. 1989; MRCP (UK) 1974. Cons. Phys. Centr. Sheff. Univ. Hosps. NHS Trust. Socs: Brit. Soc. Gastroenterol.; Brit. Geriat. Soc. Prev: Sen. Regist. (Med.) Newc. AHA (T).

ANDERSON, Alexander Caldwell (retired) 10 Northbeck Lane, Spilsby PE23 5NB Tel: 01790 53655 — MB ChB Glas 1947; DObst RCOG 1952. Prev: Ho. Surg. & Ho. Phys. Vict. Infirm. Glas.

ANDERSON, Alexander Douglas Gray 7 Baberton Mains Farm, Westburn Avenue, Edinburgh EH14 2SR — MB ChB 1998 Ed.; MB ChB Ed 1998.

ANDERSON, Alexander George (retired) 11 Househill Meadows, Nairn IV12 5SQ Tel: 01667 56582 — MB ChB 1949 Glas. Prev: Ho. Phys. & Ho. Surg. Roy. Infirm. Glas.

ANDERSON, Alexander James Hill House, Walpole Rd, Halesworth IP19 8DJ — MB BS 1996 Newc.

ANDERSON, Alexander Mark Reid Renfrew Health Centre, 103 Paisley Road, Renfrew PA4 8LL Tel: 0141 886 2012 Fax: 0141 886 2092; 3 Westbourne Drive, Bearsden, Glasgow G61 4BD — MB ChB 1975 Glas.; DRCOG 1977.

ANDERSON, Alexander Ritchie 63 Herbertshire Street, Denny FK6 6HG — MB ChB 1982 Aberd.; DRCOG 1984.

ANDERSON, Alexander Victor (retired) 5 Allanshaw Gardens, Hamilton ML3 8NT Tel: 01698 282246 — MB ChB 1957 Glas.; LRCP LRCS Ed. LRFPS Glas. 1956. Prev: GP Hamilton.

ANDERSON, Alexander William Microbiology Department, District Pathology, York District Hospital, Wigginton Road, York YO31 8HE — LMSSA 1976 Lond.; MA Camb. 1979, MB 1977, BChir 1976; MRCPath 1983; FRCP 1999. Cons. Microbiol. York Dist. Hosp.

ANDERSON, Alison Mary 100 Woodfield Lane, Ashtead KT21 2DP — MB BS 1988 Newc.; MRCGP 1993; DRCOG 1991. GP Asst. Stoneleigh, Epsom, Surrey.

ANDERSON, Andrew (retired) Seafield, Hunters Quay, 173 Marine Parade, Dunoon PA23 8HJ Tel: 01369 704353 — MB ChB Glas. 1942; BSc Glas. 1939.

ANDERSON, Andrew Alexander Turners Lane, Whittlesey, Peterborough PE7 1EJ Tel: 01733 203601 Email: andrew.anderson@gp-d81039.nhs.uk — MB ChB 1980 Manch. Clin. Governance Lead, S. PeterBoro. PCT. Prev: SHO (O & G) Hull HA; Trainee GP/SHO Lancaster HA VTS.

ANDERSON, Andrew McInnes (retired) 6 Barnshot Road, Edinburgh EH13 0DH Tel: 0131 441 2093 — MB ChB 1953 Ed.; DPH Ed. 1959; FFCM 1981 M 1972. Prev: SCM Lothian HB.

ANDERSON, Angela Astrid Synnove 3 North Dean Park Avenue, Bothwell, Glasgow G71 8HH Tel: 0141 852177 — MB ChB 1971 Dundee; MRCGP 1986; MPH 1988; MFPHM 1990; MBA 1994. (Glas.)

ANDERSON, Angela Lesley Harvey House Surgery, 13-15 Russell Avenue, St Albans AL3 5ES Tel: 01727 831888 Fax: 01727 845520 — MB BChir 1983 Camb.; BSc Bristol 1979; MRCGP 2000; DRCOG 1986; Cert. Family Plann. JCC 1986. Prev: SHO (Med.) Rotat. Addenbrooke's Hosp. Camb.

ANDERSON, Angela Mary Woodstock, Alkham Valley Road, Alkham, Dover CT15 7BX — MB ChB 1989 Glas.; DCH RCPS Glas. 1992. Trainee GP Aldershot.

ANDERSON, Ann Stirling Farne Drive Surgery, 59 Farne Drive, Glasgow G44 5DQ Tel: 0141 637 9828 Fax: 0141 633 5284; 37 Lubnaig Road, Newlands, Glasgow G43 2RY Tel: 0141 637 9828 — MB ChB 1977 Glas.; DRCOG 1979.

ANDERSON, Anthony Colin Clifton Surgery, Victoria Place, 35 Victoria Road, Dartmouth TQ6 9RT Tel: 01803 832212 Fax: 01803 837917 — MB BS 1975 Newc.; MRCGP 1979. (Newc-u-Tyne) Med. Off. GB Jun. Rowing Team.

ANDERSON, Archibald Ray (retired) 9 Ferrings, London SE21 7LU — MRCS Eng. LRCP Lond. 1943.

ANDERSON, Arucha Linda 45 Oakley Avenue, London W5 3SA — MB BS 1997 Lond. SHO Gen. Med. Kent & Canterbury Hosp.

ANDERSON, Barbara Tucker (retired) 10a Bower Gardens, Salisbury SP1 2RL Tel: 01722 321270 — MB BS 1964 Lond.; MRCS Eng. LRCP Lond. 1964; MRCGP 1980; DCH RCPSI 1969; DObst RCOG 1967; DTM & H Liverp. 1967. Univ. Health Phys. Univ. Lond. Centr. Insts. Prev: SHO (Paediat.) Mulago Hosp., Uganda.

ANDERSON, Beverley Elaine 30 Admirals Court, Rose Kiln Lane, Reading RG1 6SW — MB ChB 1996 Birm.; ChB Birm. 1996.

ANDERSON, Brian David 36 Oakfield Grove, Bradford BD9 4PY — MB BCh BAO 1984 Belf.

ANDERSON, Brian George Bo'ness Road Medical Practice, 31-33 Bo'ness Road, Grangemouth FK3 8AN Tel: 01324 482653; 112 Bo'ness Road, Grangemouth FK3 9BL Tel: 01324 666482 — MB ChB 1978 Glas.; AFOM RCP Lond. 1993; DRCOG 1984. (Glas.) Socs: Soc. Occupat. Med.

ANDERSON, Brian Grant Kenilworth Medical Centre, 1 Kenilworth Court, Greenfields, Cumbernauld, Glasgow G67 1BP Tel:

01236 727816 Fax: 01236 726306; Faskine, 3 Locksley Crescent, Cumbernauld, Glasgow G67 4EL — MB ChB 1978 Ed.; MRCGP 1988.

ANDERSON, Bruce Lancaster (retired) Scyld, Horsemere Green Lane, Clymping, Littlehampton BN17 5QZ Tel: 01903 716050 — MB BS 1953 Lond.; MRCS Eng. LRCP Lond. 1953.

ANDERSON, Bruce Mark McClintock 19 Manilla Road, Birmingham B29 7PZ — MB ChB 1992 Birm.

ANDERSON, Bryan Leslie Beacon Medical Practice, 40 Algitha Road, Skegness PE25 2AJ Tel: 01754 897000 Fax: 01754 761024 — MB ChB 1974 Dundee; MRCGP 1982; DRCOG 1978. Med. Adviser Pilgrim Hosp. Trust. Prev: Trainee GP Perth VTS; Ho. Phys. (Paediat.) Ninewells Hosp. Dundee; Ho. Surg. Perth Roy. Infirm.

ANDERSON, Caroline Mary Orchard Surgery, The Dragwell, Kegworth, Derby DE74 2EL Tel: 01509 672419 Fax: 01509 674196; 34 Leake Road, Gotham, Nottingham NG11 0JL Tel: 0115 983 0249 — MB BChir 1982 Camb.; MA Camb. 1983, MB 1982, BChir 1981; MRCGP 1986; DCH RCP Lond. 1985; DObst RCPI 1985. Lect. Gen. Pract. Univ. Nottm. Socs: Nottm. M-C Soc. Prev: Trainee GP Nottm. VTS; Ho. Phys. Newmarket Gen. Hosp.; Ho. Surg. Addenbrookes Hosp. Camb.

ANDERSON, Catherine Hare Cottage, New Buildings, Sandford, Crediton EX17 4PW — MB BS 1991 Lond.; DRCOG 1994; MRCGP 1995. Assoc. GP Wembury.

ANDERSON, Catherine Clare Whipps Cross Hospital, Whipps Cross Road, London E11 1NR Tel: 020 8539 5522 — MD 1988 Ed.; MB ChB 1974; FRCP Ed. 1994; MRCP (UK) 1978; FRCPath 1994, M 1982; FRCP Ed. 1994; FRCP 1995. Cons. Haemat. Whipps Cross Hosp. Lond. Socs: Counc. Mem. Brit. Blood Transfus. Soc. Prev: Sen. Regist. (Haemat.) Univ. Coll. Hosp. Lond.

ANDERSON, Catherine Margaret Scott Keighley Road Surgery, Keighley Road, Illingworth, Halifax HX2 9LL Tel: 01422 244397/248308 Fax: 01422 241101; Whitegate Lodge, Whitegate, Siddal, Halifax HX3 9AE Tel: 01422 344348 — MB ChB 1975 Dundee; BSc St. And. 1972. (St. And. & Dundee)

ANDERSON, Catriona Eleanor 131/9 Gylemuir Road, Edinburgh EH12 7DL — MB ChB 1997 Ed.; BSc Ed. 1995. (Edinburgh)

ANDERSON, Catriona Susan 190 Jarrom Street, Leicester LE2 7DF — MB ChB 1997 Leic.

ANDERSON, Charles Esler (retired) 1C Melbourne Court, Braid Park Drive, Giffnock, Glasgow G46 6LA Tel: 0141 637 7258 — MB ChB 1954 Glas. Prev: GP Glas.

ANDERSON, Mr Charles James Barton Southbank, Arbirlot Road, Arbroath DD11 Tel: 01241 3333 — MB ChB 1940 Aberd.; FRCS Ed. 1946. Surg. Consult. Arbroath Infirm. Socs: Fell. Assn. Surgs. Gt. Brit. & Irel. Prev: Sen. Surg. Regist. Aberd. Roy. Infirm.; Clin. Tutor Edin. Roy. Infirm.; Surg. Consult. Shetland Gp. Hosps.

ANDERSON, Charles Keith (retired) 11 Dunstarn Lane, Adel, Leeds LS16 8EN Tel: 0113 267 8397 — MB ChB 1948 St. And.; FRCPath 1976, M 1964. Prev: Reader (Path.) Univ. Leeds.

ANDERSON, Charles Morrison Carstairs Health Centre, The School House, School Road, Carstairs, Lanark ML11 8QF Tel: 01555 870512 — MB ChB 1971 Glas.; DObst RCOG 1973. Prev: Ho. Surg. Vict. Infirm. Glas.; Sen. Med. Ho. Off. Law Hosp. Carluke; Sen. Obst. Ho. Off. William Smellie Memor. Matern. Hosp. Lanark.

ANDERSON, Charles Robin Swift The Tavistock Clinic, Belsize Lane, London NW3 5BA Tel: 020 7435 7111; 77 Kelvin Road, London N5 2PL Tel: 020 7226 7327 — MB BS 1965 Lond.; MRCP (UK) 1970; FRCPsych 1993, M 1974. (St. Bart.) Cons. Psychiat. Adolesc. Dept. Tavistock Clinic; Hon. Sen. Lect. (Community Paediat.) Roy. Free Hosp. Sch. Med. Univ Lond. Socs: Brit. Psychoanal Soc. Prev: Cons. Vale Drive Child Guid. Clinic & Barnet Gen. Hosp.

ANDERSON, Charlotte Rachel Sunset Cottages, 23 Meldreth Road, Shepreth, Royston SG8 6PS — MB BChir 1993 Camb.; BSc Lond. 1991. SHO (Psychiat.) Addenbrooke's & Fulbourn Hosp. Camb.

ANDERSON, Christopher Hugh Owls Barn, Whittlesford, Cambridge CB2 4NL Tel: 01223 833430 Fax: 01223 833430 — MB BChir 1969 Camb.; MA Camb. 1969; MRCGP 1974. (Camb. & Lond. Hosp.) Prev: GP Sawston Med. Pract. Camb.

ANDERSON, Christopher John St Georges NHS Trust, Blackshaw Road, Tooting, London SW17 0QT; 3 Harman Road, Claremont, Cape Town 7700, South Africa Tel: 00 27 021 612297 — MB ChB 1985 Stellenbosch.

ANDERSON, Clare Michelle 23 Lammas Road, Godalming GU7 1YL — BChir 1991 Camb.

ANDERSON, Colette Catherine Pauline Ethel Street Surgery, 88/90 Ethel Street, Benwell, Newcastle upon Tyne NE4 8QA Tel: 0191 219 5456 Fax: 0191 226 0300 — MB BS 1986 Newc.

ANDERSON, Colin Fenwick (retired) Health Centre, Lawson St., Stockton-on-Tees TS18 1HX Tel: 01642 672351 — MB BS 1949 Durh. Prev: Ho. Phys. Roy. Vict. Infirm. Newc. & Childr. Dept. Middlesbrough Gen.

ANDERSON, Constance Heaton Moor Medical Centre, 32 Heaton Moor Road, Stockport SK4 4NX Tel: 0161 432 0671 — BM BCh 1966 Oxf.

ANDERSON, Craig Stuart Mid-Essex Community & Mental Health Trust, The Linden Centre, Woodlands Way, Chelmsford CM1 7LF — MB BS 1983 Lond.; MRCPsych 1988. Cons. Psychiat. Mid-Essex Community & Ment. Health Trust. Prev: Sen. Regist. (Psychiat.) N.wick Pk. Hosp. Harrow.

ANDERSON, David Alexander Robertson (retired) Garroch, Hillside Road, Stromness KW16 3HR Tel: 01856 850617 — MB ChB 1940 St. And. Prev: Sen. Med. Off. H.M. Prison, Barlinnie.

ANDERSON, David Edwin Webb (retired) Seagulls, 7 Greenacres, Birdham, Chichester PO20 7HL Tel: 01243 512188 — MRCS Eng. LRCP Lond. 1935; MRCPsych 1972; DPM Eng. 1940. Prev: Phys. Supt. & Cons. Psychiat. Roy. Earlswood Gp. Hosps.

ANDERSON, David Frederick 5 The Maples, Chandlers Ford, Eastleigh SO53 1DZ Tel: 01703 274670 Email: dfa@soton.ac.uk — MB BS 1989 Lond.; FRCOphth 1994. (St Thos. Hosp.) Specialist Regist. (Ophth.) Soton. Eye Unit. Prev: MRC Clin. Research Fell. Soton. Univ.; SHO (Ophth.) Soton. Eye Unit & St. Bart. Hosp. Lond.; SHO (Neurosurg.) St. Bart. Hosp. Lond.

ANDERSON, David Gavin Henrietta Street Health Centre, Henrietta Street, Girvan KA26 9AN Tel: 01465 712281 Fax: 01465 712187; 24 Ainslie Road, Girvan KA26 0AY Tel: 01465 714946 Email: daveg.anderson@argonet.co.uk — MB ChB 1979 Dundee; MRCGP 1983.

ANDERSON, David George The Health Centre, Spaines Road, Fartown, Huddersfield HD2 2QA Tel: 01484 544318; 20 Cumberland Avenue, Fixby, Huddersfield HD2 2JJ Tel: 01484 531591 — MB BS 1979 Lond.

ANDERSON, David Gibb (retired) Hillside, Allstretton, Church Stretton SY6 6AN — MB ChB 1923 Ed.; DPH Ed. & Glas. 1925. Prev: Div. MOH Cheadle & Wilmslow Div. Chesh. CC.

ANDERSON, David Graeme 44 St Quivox Road, Prestwick KA9 1LU — MB ChB 1997 Glas.

ANDERSON, David Guy William Brown Centre, Manor Way, Peterlee SR8 5TW Tel: 0191 554 4544 Fax: 0191 554 4552 Email: dave.anderson@gp_a83012.nhs.uk; 7 Clifton Square, Peterlee SR8 5HQ Tel: 0191 586 3298 Email: david@theandersons.force9.co.uk — MB BS 1983 Newc.; MRCGP 1988; Dip. Ther. Newc. 1994. (Newcastle) Course Organiser Cleveland VTS; GP Vocational Trainer with Cleveland VTS; Summative Assessm. 1st Line Audit Assessor. Socs: Assn. Course Organisers. Prev: Trainee GP Cleveland VTS; SHO (Gen. Med.) Dryburn Hosp. Durh.; Ho. Off. (Gen. Med.) Roy. Vict. Infirm. Newc.

ANDERSON, David Ian Avenue House Surgery, 109 Saltergate, Chesterfield S40 1LE Tel: 01246 272139 Fax: 01246 556336; Press Farm, Press, Tupton, Chesterfield S42 6AZ — MB ChB 1972 Ed.; MRCGP 1976; DCH Eng. 1976; DObst RCOG 1975. Prev: SHO (Med.) Walton Hosp. Chesterfield; Ho. Off. (Med.) Sefton Gen. Hosp. Liverp.; Ho. Off. (Surg.) St. Mary's Gen. Hosp. Portsmouth.

ANDERSON, David John 6 The Lane, Sedgefield, Stockton-on-Tees TS21 3BH; Cleaves Barn, Thirlby, Thirsk YO7 2DQ — MB ChB 1991 Sheff. SHO (Gen. Med.) Bishop Auckland Gen. Hosp.

ANDERSON, Mr David John Scott Department of Orthopaedics, Dr Gray's Hospital, Elgin IV30 1SN Tel: 01343 543131 Fax: 01343 552612; East Lodge, Westerton, Pluscarden, Elgin IV30 8TZ Tel: 01343 890321 — MB BS 1979 Lond.; FRCS Eng. 1985; FRCS Ed. 1983; MRCS Eng. LRCP Lond. 1979. (St. Bart.) Cons. Orthop. Surg. Dr Gray's Hosp. Elgin. Prev: Sen. Fell. Heatherwood & Wexham Pk. Hosps.; Surg. (Orthop.) Nacka Hosp., Stockholm, Sweden; Sen. Regist. (Orthop.) Karolinska Hosp., Stockholm.

ANDERSON, David Laurence 27 Viewpark Dr, Rutherglen, Glasgow G73 3QE — MB ChB 1997 Glas.
ANDERSON, David Malcolm 57 Hamilton Drive, Elgin IV30 4NL — MB ChB 1988 Aberd.
ANDERSON, David Nicholas 612 Warrington Road, Rainhill, Prescot L35 0NS — MB ChB 1979 Manch.; MRCPsych 1985. Sen. Regist. (Psychiat.) Mersey RHA.
ANDERSON, Mr David Nicholls 8 Birch Brae, Silvertonhill, Hamilton ML3 7LJ — MB ChB 1982 Dundee; FRCS Ed. 1987.
ANDERSON, David Nigel The Chesterfield Hospital, 3 Clifton Hill, Bristol BS8 1BP Tel: 07000 779362 Fax: 0117 973 8918 Email: da779362@aol.com; 23 Milner Green, Warmley, Bristol BS30 7BF Tel: 07000 779362 — MB BS 1970 Lond.; MRCS Eng. LRCP Lond. 1970. (Guy's) Specialit. Regist. (Musculo Skeletal Med.) Chesterfield Hosp. Bristol. Socs: Brit. Inst. Musculoskeletal Med.; Brit. Assn. Sport & Med.; BSM.
ANDERSON, Mr David Robert Department Cardiac Surgery, Guy's Hospital, London SE1 9RT Tel: 020 7955 4065 Fax: 020 7955 4858 Email: david.anderson@gstt.sthames.nhs.uk — MB BChir 1980 Camb.; MA Camb. 1979; FRCS Eng. 1983; FRCS Ed. 1983. Cons. Cardiothoracic Surg. Adult & Paediat. Guy's Hosp. Lond. Prev: Sen. Regist. (Cardiothoracic Surg.) W. Midl. RHA; Regist. (Cardiothoracic Surg.) Guy's Hosp. Lond.; Research Fell. Univ. Pennsylvania, USA.
ANDERSON, David Robert The Health Centre, Wharf Rd, Ash Vale, Aldershot GU12 5BA Tel: 01252 317551 — MB BS 1986 Lond.; BSc (1st cl. Hons.) Lond. 1983; MRCGP 1995; DRCOG 1992. (King's Coll. Hosp.) Socs: BMA; Med. Protec. Soc.; Brit. Med. Acupunct. Soc. Prev: Trainee GP Medway HA VTS; SHO Rotat. (Med.) Qu. Eliz. Gen. Hosp. Birm.; Ho. Surg. (Gen. & Vasc. Surg.) & Ho. Phys. (Gen. Med.) & Gastroenterol.) N.wick Pk. Hosp. Harrow.
ANDERSON, Denise Maree Britannia Pharmaceuticals Ltd., 41-51 Brighton Road, Redhill RH1 6YS Tel: 01737 773741 Fax: 01737 764351 — MB BS 1983 Lond.; BSc Lond. 1980; DFFP 1994; Dip. Pharm. Med. RCP (UK) 1989; Dip. Management 1998. Developm. Dir. Britannia Pharmaceut. Ltd. Redhill. Socs: FFPM. Prev: Med. Adviser Lilly Industries Ltd.; Clin. Research Phys. Roche Products Ltd. Welwyn Garden City; Research Phys. Glaxo Gp. Research.
ANDERSON, Derek Pitcairn Pitcairn Cottage, 44 Stirling Road, Milnathort, Kinross KY13 9XG Tel: 01577 863554 Fax: 01577 863554 Email: derek_anderson@talk.21.com — MB ChB 1955 Ed.; Dip IMC RCS Ed. 1995. Authorised Med. Examr. to Civil Aviat. Auth. Socs: Fell. (Ex-Sen. Pres.) Roy. Med. Soc. Edin.; Brit. Assn. Immed. Care Schemes; Fac. Pre Hosp. Care. Prev: Ho. Off. (Gen. Surg. & Med.) Simpson Memor. Matern. Pavil. & Roy. Infirm. Edin.
ANDERSON, Dick Wardrop (retired) Holme Bank, Cark-in-Cartmel, Grange-over-Sands LA11 7NX — MB ChB 1947 Ed. Prev: Ho. Surg. Coventry & Warw. Hosp.
ANDERSON, Donald James Woodroffe 158 Lake Road E., Cardiff CF23 5NQ Tel: 029 2075 3695 — MB BCh 1957 Wales; DPH (Distinc.) 1960; FFPHM 1972. (Cardiff) Socs: Cardiff Med. Soc. & Rhondda Med. Soc. Prev: Cons. Pub. Health Med. S. Glam. HA; Sen. Med. Off. Welsh Office; MOH, Port Med. Off. & Princip. Sch. Med. Off. City & Port of Cardiff.
ANDERSON, Doreen May Mowatt Holme Bank, Cark-in-Cartmel, Grange-over-Sands LA11 7NX Tel: 0153 95 58216 — MB ChB 1949 Aberd. (Aberd.) Socs: Inst. Psychosexual Med. Prev: SCMO Wakefield HA; Staff Surg. W. Yorks. Police.
ANDERSON, Dorothy Elizabeth Consultant Radiologist, X-Ray Department, Glasgow royal Infirmary, 8-16 Alexandra Parade, Glasgow G31 2ER Tel: 0141 211 5565 Email: dorothy.anderson@northglasgow.scot.nhs.uk; 18 Milverton Avenue, Bearsden G61 4BE Tel: 0141 942 7510 — MB ChB 1974 Glas.; BSc (Hons.) Glas. 1972; FRCP Glas. 1988; MRCP (UK) 1976; FRCR 1979; DMRD Eng. 1978. Cons. Radiol. Glas. Roy. Infirm. Socs: Scott. Radiol. Soc. & BMA. Prev: Sen. Regist. & Regist. (Radiol.) W.. Infirm. Glas.; SHO (Respirat. Med.) Kt.swood Hosp. Glas. & W.. Infirm. Glas.
ANDERSON, Dorothy Joan (retired) 4 North Road, Hertford SG14 1LR Tel: 01992 589116 — MB BS Lond. 1953; MRCS Eng. LRCP Lond. 1953. Prev: Indep. GP Hertford.
ANDERSON, Duncan John 110 Oxford Gardens, London W10 6NG — MB BS 1982 Lond.; BSc Lond. 1979. Neurophys. Research Fell. Hammersmith Hosp. Lond.
ANDERSON, Edward (retired) Torridon, 14 Findhorn rd, Forres IV36 3TP Tel: 01309 673442 — MB ChB 1946 Aberd.; MRCGP 1968. JP. Prev: GP, Glenlivet.
ANDERSON, Edward Gerald (retired) Mayhill, Glasllwch Lane, Newport NP20 3PT — MD Lond. 1971, MB BS 1960; FRCP Lond. 1977, M 1963; MRCS Eng. LRCP Lond. 1960. Prev: Lead Clin. Comer Serv. Gwent Health Care.
ANDERSON, Edward John Box Lodge, Upper Cheddon, Kingston St Mary, Taunton TA2 8LB Tel: 01823 45403 — MB BChir 1962 Camb.; BA Camb. 1961; FFA RCS Eng. 1970; DTM & H Eng. 1966; DObst RCOG 1964. (Middlx.) Prev: Ho. Surg. Middlx. Hosp. Lond.; Maj. RAMC; Anaesth. Regist. Soton. Gen. Hosp.
ANDERSON, Edwin (retired) Bloors Place, 542 Lower Rainham Road, Gillingham ME8 7TP Tel: 01637 321221 — MB ChB 1942 Aberd. Prev: Ho. Surg. Aberd. Roy. Infirm.
ANDERSON, Eileen Margaret Hillhouse, Braehead, Avoch IV9 8QL — MB BS 1983 Newc.; DFFP 1983 UK; MRCGP 1999 UK; DRCOG 1996; DA (UK) 1989. GP/Regist. Inverness; LOCUM GP, Highlands; Occasional Pollice Surg., Highlands; Part Time Hospice Doctor, Highlands. Socs: BMA. Prev: SHO (O & G) Gen. Hosp. Newc.; LOCUM GP; Hospice Doctor.
ANDERSON, Eileen Margaret (Surgery) 3 Cannonside, Fetcham, Leatherhead KT22 9LE Tel: 01372 379941 Fax: 01372 361178; 148 Kingston Road, Leatherhead KT22 7PZ Tel: 01372 362099 — MB BCh BAO 1956 Dub.; Dip. FPA 1959. Prev: Clin. Asst. Skin Dept. Epsom Dist. Hosp.
ANDERSON, Elaine Dougal Cowe Edinburgh Breast Unit, Western General Hospital, Crewe Road, Edinburgh Tel: 0131 537 1614 Fax: 0131 537 1004 — MB ChB 1982 Ed.; 1979 BSc (1st cl. Hons.) Ed.; 1986 FRCS Ed.; 1992 Ed.; 1991 MD Ed. (Ed.) Cons. Surg. Edin. BrE. Unit W.. Gen. Hosp. Edin.; Mem. WIST (Regional Represen.); Sen. Lect. Socs: Brit. Assn. Surg. Oncol; Brit. BrE. Gp.
ANDERSON, Elaine Gladys Frome Valley Medical Centre, 2 Court Road, Frampton Cotterell, Bristol BS36 2DE Tel: 01454 772153 Fax: 01454 250078; The Nuttage, 54 Chapel Lane, Old Sodbury, Bristol BS37 6NG Tel: 01454 312380 — MB ChB 1977 Bristol; MRCGP 1983; DFFP 1993; DRCOG 1982. (Bristol)
ANDERSON, Elaine Jane Derwent Clinic, Shotley Bridge Hospital, Shotley Bridge, Consett DH8 0NB Tel: 01207 214667 — MB ChB 1988 Aberd.; MRCPsych 1995; MRCPsych 1995. Cons. in Gen. Adult Psychiat. Prev: Sen. Regist., Roy. Cornhill Hosp. Aberd.
ANDERSON, Eleanor Mary Shettleston Health Centre, 420 Old Shettleston Road, Glasgow G32 7JZ Tel: 0141 531 6220 Fax: 0141 531 6206 — MB ChB 1989 Glas.
ANDERSON, Elizabeth Fox Cottage, School La, Blymhill, Shifnal TF11 8LJ — MB BCh 1997 Wales.
ANDERSON, Elizabeth Ann 5 Highfield Drive, Lexden Road, Colchester CO3 3QA Tel: 01206 512577 — MB BS 1983 Lond. Clin. Asst. (Pychogeriats.) Mid-Essex Community & Ment. Health Trust. Prev: SHO (Paediat.) Ealing Hosp. Lond.; SHO (Cas.) Ealing Hosp. Lond.; Ho. Off. (Surg.) & SHO (Gyn.) St. Jas. Hosp. Lond.
ANDERSON, Elizabeth Jane The Health Centre, Commercial Road, Skelmanthorpe, Huddersfield HD8 9DA Tel: 01484 863542 — MB ChB 1985 Leeds; DRCOG 1989.
ANDERSON, Elizabeth Jean Fraser (retired) 100 Southbrae Drive, Glasgow G13 1TZ — MB ChB 1950 Glas.; DCH RCPS Glas. 1959; DObst RCOG 1952.
ANDERSON, Elizabeth Marian (retired) 6 Barnshot Road, Edinburgh EH13 0DH Tel: 0131 441 2093 — MB BS 1956 Lond.; MB BS (Hons.) Lond. 1956; DObst RCOG 1959. SCMO Lothian HB. Prev: SHO Cumbld. Infirm. Carlisle.
ANDERSON, Elizabeth Rachel 1 Gill Beck Close, Baildon, Shipley BD17 6TJ — MB BS 1993 Lond.; MA Camb. 1994, BA 1990; DTM & H Lond. 1995; DRCOG 1996; DFFP 1998; Part 1 MRCOG 1999. SHO (O & G) Qu.s Med. Centre, Nottm.; Assoc. RCM Lond. Socs: BMA & Med. Protec. Soc. Prev: SHO (Community Gynae.) Edin.; Med. Off., Hlabisa Hosp., Kwazulu-Natal; SHO (Cardiol.), Airedale Hosp.
ANDERSON, Ephraim Saul, CBE 10 Rosecroft Avenue, London NW3 7QB — MD 1953 Durh.; FRS; MB BS 1934; Hon. DSc Newc. 1975; FRCP Lond. 1975; FRCPath 1963; FIBiol. 1973; Dip. Bact. Lond. 1948. (Durh.) Chairm. Internat. Federat. Enteric Phage Typing. Socs: Fell. Roy. Soc. Med.; Soc. Gen. Microbiol. Prev: Dir. Enteric

Ref. Laborat. Lond.; Dir. Internat. Ref. Laborat. For Enteric Phage Typing; Vis. Prof. Applied Biol. Sch. Biol. Sc. Brunel Univ.

ANDERSON, Eric George Western Infirmary, Glasgow G11 6NT Tel: 0141 211 1853 Fax: 0141 339 0462; 102 Prestonfield, Milngavie, Glasgow G62 7PZ Tel: 0141 956 3594 Fax: 0141 955 0324 — MB ChB 1964 St. And.; MSc (Med. Eng.) Salford 1974; FRCS Glas. 1981; FRCS Ed. 1971. Cons. Orthop. Foot Surg. W.. Infirm. Glas. & Gartnavel Gen. Hosp. Glas.; Sen. Clin. Lect. Univ. Glas.; Lect. (Surg.) Glas. Caledonian Univ.; Vis. Lect. Glas. Caledonian Univ.; Dep. Edr. & Mem. Exec. Bd. Injury; Mem. Edit. Bd. Foot Dis.; Mem. Edit. Comm. Foot; Clin. Assoc. Nat. Centre Prosth.s & Orthotics; Sec.-Gen. Internat. Federat. Foot & Ankle Socs. Socs: Fell. Roy. Soc. Med.; (Ex-Pres.) Brit. Orthop. Foot Surg. Soc.; Counc. Europ. Federat. Foot & Ankle Socs. Prev: Sen. Regist. Birm. Accid. Hosp. & Robt. Jones & Agnes Hunt Orthop. Hosp. OsW.ry; Research Fell. (Orthop.) Salford Gp. Hosps.

ANDERSON, Evelyn Andrae Monique 73 Haymarket Terrace (1FR), Edinburgh EH12 5HD Tel: 0131 337 9385 — MB ChB 1990 Ed.; DRCOG 1995; MRCGP 1997. (Edinburgh)

ANDERSON, Felicity Mary 24 Fairfax Road, London W4 1EW Tel: 020 8995 2039; Microbiology Department, St Helier NHS Trust, Wrythe Lane, Carshalton SM5 1AA Tel: 020 8296 2779 Fax: 020 8644 6317 — MB BS 1966 Lond.; MRCS Eng. LRCP Lond. 1966; FRCPath 1986, M 1974; T(Path.) 1991. (St. Geo.) Cons. Microbiol. St. Helier NHS Trust Carshalton, Surrey. Socs: Brit. Soc. Antimicrob. Chemother & Hosp. Infec. Soc. Prev: Sen. Lect. (Bacteriol.) Univ. Edin.; Sen. Regist. (Bact.) Hammersmith Hosp. Lond.; SHO (Path.) Radcliffe Infirm. Oxf.

ANDERSON, Fiona Margaret 5 Kindleton, Great Linford, Milton Keynes MK14 5EA — MB ChB 1980 Glas.; MRCOG 1985.

ANDERSON, Fionn Mary Mercer 4 Nungate Road, North Berwick EH39 4PD — MB ChB 1986 Ed.; BSc Ed. 1985; DRCOG 1989. Trainee GP Inverness VTS.

ANDERSON, Frances Elizabeth (Surgery) Rosemead, River Road, Taplow, Maidenhead SL6 0AT Tel: 01628 22023; Eastbank, River Road, Taplow, Maidenhead SL6 0BG Tel: 01628 23139 — MB 1955 Camb.; BChir 1954; DObst RCOG 1956. (Camb. & St. Bart.) Socs: BMA. Prev: Sen. Ho. Off. (O & G) Freedom Fields Hosp. Plymouth; Ho. Surg. (O & G) St. Mary Abbots Hosp.; Ho. Surg. & Ho. Phys. St. Bart. Hosp. Lond.

ANDERSON, Frazer Hunter University Department of Geriatric Medicine, Southampton General Hospital, Tremona Road, Southampton SO16 6YD Tel: 02380 796132 Fax: 02380 796134 — MB ChB 1986 Ed.; MRCP (UK) 1989. Sen. Lect. (Geriat. Med.) Soton. Gen. Hosp. Prev: Action Research Train. Fell. Freeman Hosp. Newc.; Sen. Regist. (Geriat.) Newc. Gen. Hosp.

ANDERSON, Mr Geoffrey Hunter Plymouth Nuffield Hospital, Derriford Road, Plymouth PL6 8BG Tel: 01752 761818; Long Barn, Court Barton, Down Thomas, Plymouth PL9 0AQ — MB ChB 1982 Birm.; FRCS (Orth.) 1994; FRCS Eng. 1987. Cons. Orthop. Surg. Plymouth Hosps. NHS Trust. Prev: Sen. Regist. (Orthop. Surg.) Leicester Hosps.; Lect. (Orthop. Surg.) Univ. Leicester.

ANDERSON, George Henry Irwin (retired) 13 Ashley Park, Bangor BT20 5RQ Tel: 01247 468980 — MB BCh BAO Belf. 1947; FRCGP 1985; DObst RCOG 1950.

ANDERSON, Gerry Flat 11, 7 Belgrave Gardens, London NW8 0QY Tel: 020 7372 7996 Email: gander@dircon.co.uk — MB BS 1992 Lond.; Mphil (Cantab) 1993; MRCP 99. (Lond. Hosp. Med. Coll.)

ANDERSON, Glenn McBain Plas Cerrig, Station Road, Whittington, Oswestry SY11 4DA — MB ChB 1990 Birm.; MRCGP 1995; T(GP) 1995; DRCOG 1994. Prev: Trainee GP/SHO (ENT & O & G) Wrexham Maelor Hosp.

ANDERSON, Gordon Edmonston (retired) 23 Wearside Drive, The Sands, Durham DH1 1LE Tel: 0191 386 1878 — MB ChB 1964 Glas.; FRCOG 1982. Prev: Cons. O & G Dryburn Hosp. Durh.

ANDERSON, Gordon Gregor James 33 Shaw Road, Prestwick KA9 2LW — MB ChB 1990 Glas.

ANDERSON, Graham Herbert (retired) 8 Marlton Way, Lancaster LA1 5BW Tel: 01524 32089 — MB ChB Glas. 1940; FRFPS Glas. 1947; FRCP Glas. 1981, M 1962; FRCGP 1977. Prev: RAF Med. Br. 1942-46.

ANDERSON, Halina Ewa Wyndhurst, 17 Red Row, Limekilns, Dunfermline KY11 3HU — MB ChB 1972 Ed.; FFA RCS Eng. 1981. Cons. (Anaesth.) Dunfermline & W. Fife Hosp.

ANDERSON, Heather 21 Elmsway, Bramhall, Stockport SK7 2AE — MD 1984 Manch.; MB ChB 1976; MRCP (UK) 1980; FRCP Lond. 1987. Cons. Med. Oncol. Wythenshawe & Christie Hosps. S. Manch. AHA.

ANDERSON, Heather Emily The Mote Medical Practice, St Saviours Road, Maidstone ME15 9FL Tel: 01622 756888 Fax: 01622 672573 — MB BCh BAO Dub. 1968; DCH S Afr 1975.

ANDERSON, Heather Marjorie 18 Dalboyne Gardens, Lisburn BT28 3BX — MB ChB 1989 Manch.

ANDERSON, Hector John The Churchill Clinic, 80 Lambeth Road, London SE1 7PW Tel: 020 7928 5633; 102 Lambeth Road, London SE1 7PT — MB BChir 1940 Camb.; MA (cl. 2 Nat. Sc. Trip. Pt. 1) Camb. 1940; FRCP Lond. 1950, M 1941; MRCS Eng. LRCP Lond. 1940. (Camb. & St. Thos.) Phys. & Phys. i/c Dept. Thoracic Med. St. Thos. Hosp.; Phys. Lambeth Hosp., Disp. Français Lond. & S. W.. Hosp. Lond.; Examr. in Med. RCP Lond. & Univ. Lond.; Examr. MRCP Lond. Socs: Assn. Phys. GB & Thoracic Soc. Prev: Resid. Asst. Phys. & Regist. St. Thos. Hosp.; Hon. Lt.-Col. RAMC.

ANDERSON, Helen Margaret Department of Psychiatry, Southern General Hospital, Glasgow G41 4TF Tel: 0141 201 1100 Fax: 0141 201 1920 — MB ChB 1981 Aberd.; MRCPsych 1986; T(Psych) 1991. Cons. Psychiat. S.. Gen. Hosp. Glas. Prev: Cons. Psychiat. Bellsdyke Hosp. Stirlingsh.; Sen. Regist. Gtr. Glas. HB; Regist. & SHO Gartnavel Roy. Hosp. Glas.

ANDERSON, Henry Hasted Dale (retired) 14 Corby Gate, Ashbrooke, Sunderland SR2 7JB Tel: 0191 528 3535 — MB BS 1930 Durh.; BHyg., DPH 1932. Prev: Ho. Phys. Roy. Infirm. Sunderland.

ANDERSON, Hugh John X-Ray Department, Eastbourne District General Hospital, King's Drive, Eastbourne BN21 2UD Tel: 01323 417400; 14 Keere Street, Lewes BN7 1TY — MB BS 1978 Lond.; FRCR 1984. Cons. Radiol. E.bourne Dist. Gen. Hosp. Prev: Sen. Regist. & Regist. (Diagn. Radiol.) King's Coll. Hosp. Lond.

ANDERSON, Iain Wellfield, Acomb, Hexham NE46 4RD — MB BS 1970 Newc.; FFA RCS Eng. 1977; MRCGP 1974; DObst RCOG 1974. Cons. Anaesth. Hexham Gen. Hosp.

ANDERSON, Mr Iain David B1/2 Offices, Hope Hospital, Stott Lane, Salford M6 8HD Tel: 0161 787 5129 Fax: 0161 787 1276 Email: iain.anderson@srht.nhs.uk; 8 Greenleas, Bolton BL6 4PL — MB ChB 1983 Manch.; MB ChB (Hons.) Manch. 1983; BSc St. And. 1980; MD Manch. 1989; FRCS (Gen.) 1994; FRCS Eng. 1987. Cons. Surg./ Hon. Sen. Lect. Hope Hosp. Manch.; HillsBoro. Tutor (Critical Care) RCS Eng. Socs: Assn. Coloproctol.; Assn. Surg.; Brit. Assn. Endocrine Surg.s. Prev: Sen. Regist. (Surg.) Edin. Hosp.; Research Fell. (Surg.) Hope Hosp. Univ. Manch.; Regist. (Surg.) Manch. Hosps.

ANDERSON, Ian Medical Centre, Fallingbostel BFPO 38; 22 St Ninians Road, Moffat DG10 9BE — MB ChB 1985 Aberd.; MRCGP 1989; DRCOG 1991.

ANDERSON, Ian (retired) 23 St Johns Road, Leicester LE2 2BL Tel: 0116 270 6181 — B.Sc. (Hnrs. Physiol.) Sheff. 1942, M.B., Ch.B; FRCP Lond. 1973, M 1948. Cons. Dermat. Leicester Roy. Infirm. Prev: Sen. Regist. (Dermat.) Roy. Infirm. Sheff.

ANDERSON, Ian Frank (retired) The Surgery, 5 Kidgate, Louth LN11 9HA Tel: 01507 602421 — MRCS Eng. LRCP Lond. 1956; BSc Lond. 1953, MB BS 1958; DA Eng. 1966; DObst RCOG 1961. Prev: Cas. Off. Hillingdon Hosp.

ANDERSON, Ian George Greengate Medical Centre, 1 Greengate Lane, Birstall, Leicester LE4 3JF Tel: 0116 267 7901 — MB ChB 1979 Birm.; MRCGP 1983; DRCOG 1983.

ANDERSON, Ian Kennedy (retired) 15 Marine Parade, Gorleston, Great Yarmouth NR31 6DX Tel: 01493 662057 — BM BCh 1949 Oxf.; MA Oxf. 1987; AFOM RCP Lond. 1982; MRCGP 1968. Med. Ref. Gt. Yarmouth Crematorium. Prev: Capt. RAMC.

ANDERSON, Ian Muir University of Manchester, Department of Psychiatry, Rawnsley Building, Manchester Royal Infirmary, Oxford Road, Manchester M13 9WL Tel: 0161 276 5396 Fax: 0161 273 2315 Email: ian.anderson@man.ac.uk; Overlea Farm, Eccles Road, Whaley Bridge, High Peak SK23 7EL — MB BS 1980 Lond.; MA Camb. 1981, BA 1977; MD Lond. 1992; MRCP (UK) 1983; MRCPsych 1986. (Univ. Coll. Hosp.) Sen. Lect. & Hon. Cons. Psychiat. Univ. Manch. Socs: Fell. Roy. Soc. Med.; Brit. Assn.

Psychopharmacol.; Roy. Coll. Psychiat. Prev: Sen. Regist. (Psychiat.) Fairmile Hosp. Wallingford; MRC Train. Fell., Hon. Sen. Regist., Regist. & SHO (Psychiat.) Littlemore Hosp. Oxf.; SHO (Gen. Med.) Cornw. & Isles of Scilly HA.

ANDERSON, Ian Paul Saxonbrook Medical, Maidenbower Square, Crawley RH10 7QH Tel: 01293 450400 Fax: 01293 450401 Email: admin@saxonbrook.co.uk; Rivers Farm, Borde Hill Lane, Haywards Heath RH16 1XS — MB BS 1986 Lond.; MRCGP 1991; T(GP) 1991; DRCOG 1991; DTM & H RCP Lond 1988. (St. Thomas Hospital) Princip., Gen. Pracitce; Clin. Asst. (Gastroenterol.) W. Sussex. Socs: Primary Care Gastroenterol. Soc.

ANDERSON, Ian Robert 32 Queens Way, Feltham TW13 7NS — MB ChB 1992 Leic.

ANDERSON, Ian Roger MacDonald The White House, Brenchley, Tonbridge TN12 7NQ Tel: 01892 722007; Wrangling Green, Castle Hill, Brenchley, Tonbridge TN12 7BX Tel: 01892 723757 — MB BS 1964 Lond.; MRCS Eng. LRCP Lond. 1964. Prev: Phys. i/c Exercise Testing Unit PPP Med. Centre Lond.; Phys. i/c Roy. Ward, Roy. Hosp. Muscat, Oman; Squadron Ldr. RAF Hosp. Halton Ely.

ANDERSON, Ian Vernon Ash Grange, Hilderstone, Stone ST15 8RT — MB ChB 1955 Aberd.; DPH Aberd. 1969.

ANDERSON, Mr Ian Wilson Russell Accident & Emergency Department, Victoria Infirmary, Glasgow G42 9TY Tel: 0141 201 5305 Fax: 0141 636 5608; 58 Newton Grove, Glasgow G77 5QJ Tel: 0141 639 6133 Fax: 0141 639 6133 — MB ChB 1975 Glas.; MB ChB (Commend.) Glas. 1975; FRCS Ed. 1999; FRCS Eng. 1998; FFAEM 1993; FRCS Glas. 1979. (Univ. Glas.) Cons. i/c A & E Vict. Infirm. Glas.; Hon. Clin. Sen. Lect. Univ. Glas. Prev: Sen. Regist. W.. Infirm. Glas.

ANDERSON, Isabella McDonald (retired) 5 Coles Way, Reepham, Norwich NR10 4LW Tel: 01603 871932 — MB ChB 1938 St. And. Prev: Med. Miss. Burundi & Rwanda.

ANDERSON, Jack (retired) 37 Moorbank Road, Sandygate, Sheffield S10 5TQ Tel: 0114 230 1100 — MB ChB 1942 Leeds. Prev: Asst. Med. Off. Boro. Gen. Hosp. Ipswich.

ANDERSON, Jacqueline Elizabeth 21 Milford Gardens, Edgware HA8 6EY — MB BS 1991 Lond.

ANDERSON, Jacqueline Mary Parkhead Hospital, 81 Salamanca St, Glasgow G31 5ES Tel: 0141 211 8424 — MB ChB 1988 Dundee. Cons. Psych. Pk.head Hosp. Glas.

ANDERSON, James, Col. late RAMC Pangkor, Colburn, Catterick Garrison DL9 4PD Tel: 01748 832439 — MB ChB 1963 Ed.; 1963 MB ChB Ed.; 1983 MSc (Occupat. Med.) Lond.; 1988 MFOM RCP Lond.; 1987 AFOM Lon.; 1998 FFOM. (Ed.) Socs: Soc. of Occupat.al Med.; Mem. BMA.

ANDERSON, James Ards Hospital, Church Street, Newtownards BT23 4AS Tel: 028 9151 0106 Fax: 028 9151 0119 Email: jim.anderson@nda.n-i.nhs.uk — MB BCh BAO 1988 Belf.; MA (Med. Ethics & Law) 1997; MRCPsych 1994; DMH Belf. 1991. Cons. Psych old age Ards Hosp. Socs: Ulster Med. Soc.

ANDERSON, James Adam Castlehill Health Centre, Castlehill, Forres IV36 1QF Tel: 01309 672233 — MB ChB 1968 Ed.; MRCOG 1973. (Edin.) Socs: Highland Med. Soc.; Moray Med. Soc. Prev: Regist. (O & G) W.. Gen. Hosp. Edin.

ANDERSON, James Adams (retired) 11 Precinct Crescent, Skegness PE25 3AL — MB ChB 1951 Aberd. Prev: Res. Ho. Surg. Aberd. Roy. Infirm.

ANDERSON, Mr James Ainslie Department of Surgery, Arrowe Park Hospital, Arrowe Park Road, Upton CH49 5PE Tel: 0151 678 5111; The Towers, Chester High Road, Neston CH64 7TA Tel: 0151 336 2024 Email: jim.anderson3@btinternet.com — FRCS 1999; BM 1987 Soton.; BSc (2nd cl. Hons.) (Physiol.) Aberd. 1982; FRCS Ed. 1992. (Southampton) Cons. Colorectal Surg., Arrowe Pk. Hosp., Upton. Prev: Regist. (Gen. Surg.) Sheff. Roy. Hosps.; Research Fell. Univ. Kentucky, Louisville; SHO (Surg.) Roy. Hallamsh. Hosp. Sheff.

ANDERSON, James Barclay Barclay's Bank, 15 Bene't St., Cambridge CB2; Barclay's Bank, Kirkdale, Sydenham, London SE26 — MB BChir 1976 Camb.; MA, MB Camb. 1976, BChir 1976; MRCP (UK) 1980.

ANDERSON, James David Baysley, 179 Rolleston Road, Burton-on-Trent DE13 0LD Tel: 01283 567076 Email: jola@burtaihosh.com — MB BS 1963 Lond.; FFA RCS Eng. 1969; DA Eng. 1965; DObst RCOG 1965. (St. Thos.) Chief Exec. & Cons. Anaesth. Burton Hosps. NHS Trust. Socs: BMA & Assn. Anaesth. Prev: Sen. Regist. (Anaesth.) Coventry Hosp. Gp.; Regist. Derby Hosp. Gp.; SHO Intens. Ther. Unit St. Thos. Hosp. Lond.

ANDERSON, James Edward Burnhope Surgery, The Haven, Burnhope, Durham DH7 0BD Tel: 01207 214707; Satley Grove, Satley, Bishop Auckland DL13 4HY — MB ChB 1974 Leeds; BSc (Hons.) (Anat.) 1971; MRCGP 1982. GP Bishop Auckland.

ANDERSON, James Gebbie Ferguson Shelley Surgery, 23 Shelley Road, Worthing BN11 4BS Tel: 01903 234844 Fax: 01903 219744; 36 Oval Waye, Ferring, Worthing BN12 5RA Tel: 01903 506908 — MB ChB 1975 Glas.; MRCGP 1979; DRCOG 1978. Socs: BMA; RCGP; Brit. Soc. of Allergy, Environm. & Nutrit.al Med.

ANDERSON, James Killoch, OBE (retired) 15 Kenilworth Avenue, Helensburgh G84 7JR Tel: 01436 673739 — MB ChB 1946 Glas.; FFCM 1982, M 1972. JP.; Dist. Med. Off. E. Health Dist. Prev: Gp. Med. Supt. Glas. Roy. Infirm. & Assoc. Hosps.

ANDERSON, James Lyle (retired) 8 Smugglers Close, Alfriston, Polegate BN26 5TG Tel: 01323 870499 — MB BS 1946 Lond.; FFA RCS Eng. 1956. Prev: Cons. Anaesth. Edgware Gen. Hosp. & Colindale Hosp.

ANDERSON, James Michael Perch Heights, CArlton Road, Felmersham, Bedford MK43 7JH — MB ChB 1994 Leeds.

ANDERSON, James Storey 1 Cranbourne Grove, North Shields NE30 3NB — MB BS 1993 Newc. Specialist Regist. Dundee Teachg. Hosps. NHS Trust. Prev: SHO (Gen. Med.) Roy. Wolverhampton Hosps. NHS Trust.

ANDERSON, James Tardrew (retired) 66 Firgrove Hill, Farnham GU9 8LW Tel: 01252 713509 — MB ChB 1943 St. And.; FFA RCS Eng. 1955; DA Eng. 1947. Prev: Cons. Anaesth. W. Surrey & NE Hants. Dist.

ANDERSON, Jane St Bartholemew's Hospital, Andrewes Unit, West Smithfield, London EC1A 7BE Tel: 020 7601 8032 Fax: 020 7601 8057 Email: j.anderson@mds.qmw.nc.uk — MB BS 1984 Lond.; PhD Lond. 1980; FRCP Lond. 1994; MRCP (UK) 1987. (St. Mary's) p/t Sen. Lect. & Hon. Cons. HIV Infec. St. Bart. Hosp. Lond.; Hon. Cons., Dept. of Sexual Health, Homerlan Hosp., NHS Trust, Lond. E9. Socs: Brit. Assn., Exec. Comm.; Internat. AIDS Soc.; Med. Soc. for Study of Venereal Dis. Prev: Sen. Regist. (Genitourin. Med.) Middlx. Hosp. Lond.; Regist. (Genitourin. Med.) St. Mary's Hosp. Lond.; SHO (Med.) N.wick Pk. Hosp.

ANDERSON, Jane Margaret 82 Speldhurst Road, London W4 1BZ — MB ChB 1976 Manch. SHO (Anaesth.) Ninewells Hosp. Dundee. Prev: SHO (Gen. Med.) Yeovil Dist. Hosp; SHO (Paediat. Med. & Surg.) Booth Hall Childr. Hosp. Manch.; Ho. Off. (Surg.) Manch. Roy. Infirm.

ANDERSON, Janet Elizabeth Deveron Medical Group, Banff Health Centre, Clunie Street, Banff AB45 1HY Tel: 01261 812027 Fax: 01261 818455; 7 Shand Terrace, Macduff AB44 1XH — MB ChB 1976 Dundee; DA Eng. 1981.

ANDERSON, Janet Linda The Surgery, 2 Gregson Avenue, Gosport PO13 0HR Tel: 01329 232446 Fax: 01329 282624 — MRCS Eng. LRCP Lond. 1967 London; MB BS; MRCP Eng. LRCP Lond. 1967 London.

ANDERSON, Janet Marjorie New Cross Hospital, Wolverhampton WV10 0QP Tel: 01902 307999 Fax: 01902 643082; The Crofts, 32 Church Hill, Penn, Wolverhampton WV4 5PN Tel: 01902 337404 Fax: 01902 337404 — MB BS 1965 Lond.; FRCP Lond. 1990; MRCP (UK) 1969; MRCS Eng. LRCP Lond. 1965; FRCPCH 1997; DObst RCOG 1967. (Char. Cross) Cons. Paediat. Roy. Wolverhampton NHS Trust; Hon. Sen. Lect. Univ. Wolverhampton; Hon. Sen. Clin. Lect. Univ. Birm.; Donald Ct. Fell. Off. Cor. Gen.; Professional Train. RCPCH 1997. Socs: BMA; Fell. Roy. Coll. Paediat. & Child Health; BDA. Prev: Regist. (Paediat.) Char. Cross Hosp. Gp.; SHO Whittington Hosp. Lond.; Ho. Phys. & Ho. Surg. Char. Cross Hosp. Lond.

ANDERSON, Janice Rosemary Department of Histopathology, Addenbrooke's Hospital, Cambridge CB2 2QQ Tel: 01223 217170 Fax: 01223 216980; Owls Barn, Whittlesford, Cambridge CB2 4NL Tel: 01223 833430 Fax: 01223 833430 — MB BS 1968 Lond.; BSc Lond. 1965; MRCS Eng. LRCP Lond. 1968; FRCPath 1987, M 1975. (Lond. Hosp.) Cons. Neuropath. Addenbrooke's Hosp. Camb.; Assoc. Lect. Univ. Camb. Socs: (Past Sec. Gen.) Internat. Soc. Neuropath. Prev: Cons. Histopath. Addenbrooke's Hosp. Camb.

ANDERSON, Janie Sarah T/L 12 Colebrooke Street, Kelvinbridge, Glasgow G12 8HD — MB ChB 1996 Glas.

ANDERSON, Jennifer Mary Addenbrookes NHS Trust, Adrian House, Fulbourn Hospital, Cambridge CB1 5EF; 29 Downs Road, Epsom KT18 5JF — MB BS 1997 Lond. Psychiat. SHO, Addenbrookes NHS Trust, Camb.

ANDERSON, Jessie Isabel (retired) Ladycot, The Bwlch, Llanbedr D.C., Ruthin LL15 1YG Tel: 01824 702122 — MB ChB Liverp. 1947, DPH 1955. Prev: Cas. Off. & Ho. Phys. David Lewis N.. Hosp. Liverp.

ANDERSON, Joanna Elizabeth The Surgery, The Common, Parbold, Wigan WN8 7DG Tel: 012576 3126; Blue Slates Farm, Leyland Lane, Ulnes Walton, Leyland, Preston PR26 8LB Tel: 01257 452594 Fax: 01257 453519 — BM BCh 1969 Oxf.; MA Oxf. 1969.

ANDERSON, Mr John (retired) The Steadings, The Street, Westward, Wigton CA7 8AF Tel: 0169 73 43909 — MB ChB 1964 Aberd.; FRCS Ed. 1968. Cons. Orthop. Surg. Cumbld. Infirm. Carlisle. Prev: Sen. Lect. (Orthop. Surg.) Univ. Nairobi.

ANDERSON, Professor John (retired) 6 Wilson Gardens, Gosforth, Newcastle upon Tyne NE3 4JA Tel: 0191 285 4745 Email: andersgos@jander.demon.co.uk — MB BS (2nd cl. Hons. Distinc. Surg.) Durh. 1958; FRCP Glas. 1992; FRCP Lond. 1973, M 1961; FRCOG 1983. Prev: Postgrad. Dean N.. & Prof. Med. Educat. Univ. Newc. u. Tyne.

ANDERSON, Professor John 14 Styles Way, Park Langley, Beckenham BR3 3AJ Email: km92@bcs.org.uk — MB BS 1950 Durh.; MA (Mod. Hist.) Durh., BSc (1st cl. Hons. Physiol.) 1952, MD; 1956, MB BS (Hons.) 1950; FRCP Lond. 1962, M 1954. (Durh.) Socs: Fell. Brit. Computer Soc.; Med. Res. Soc.; Club Med. Educat. Prev: Prof. Med. & Hon. Phys. King's Coll. Hosp. Med. Sch. Lond. 1954-85; Prof. Emerit. 1988 King's Coll.; Fell. Clin. Research Med. Research Counc. Univ. Coll. Hosp.

ANDERSON, John Alan Richard The Queen Elizabeth Hospital, Gayton Road, King's Lynn PE30 4ET Tel: 01553 613677 Fax: 01553 613700; 4 Wodehouse Road, Old Hunstanton, Hunstanton PE36 6JD Tel: 01485 532351 Fax: 01485 532351 Email: jar.anderson@qenie.co.uk — MB BS 1967 Lond.; FRCP Lond. 1991; MRCP (UK) 1974; MRCS Eng. LRCP Lond. 1967; T(M) 1991. (Westm.) Cons. Dermat. King's Lynn & Wisbech NHS Trust; AKC. Socs: Brit. Assn. Dermat.; Dowling Club. Prev: Sen. Regist. (Dermat.) Ninewells Hosp. Dundee; Hon. Lect. (Dermat.) Univ. Dundee; Ho. Surg. W.m. Hosp. Lond.

ANDERSON, John Anthony (retired) Torre Garda, Shildon DL4 1DH — M.B., B.S. Durh. 1949. Prev: Res. Ho. Phys. Roy. Vict. Infirm. Newc.-On-Tyne.

ANDERSON, Mr John Barry Department of Urology, Royal Hallamshire Hospital, Glossop Road, Sheffield S10 2JF Tel: 0114 271 3482 Fax: 0114 271 3425; 387 Fulwood Road, Ranmoor, Sheffield S10 3GA Tel: 0114 230 6004 — MB ChB 1979 Bristol; ChM Bristol 1988; FRCS Eng. 1983. (University of Bristol) Cons. Urol. Surg. Roy. Hallamsh. Hosp. Sheff.; Chair. Of Med. Advisery Comm., Thornbury Hosp. Sheff.; Chair. Basic Surg. Train. Comm., Sheff. Socs: Brit. Assn. Urol. Surgs.; Soc. Internat. d'Urol.; Sec. BAUS Sect. of Oncol. Prev: Sen. Regist. (Urol.) Sheff.; Research Fell. (Surg.) Bristol; Regist. (Gen. Surg.) Plymouth Gen. Hosp.

ANDERSON, John Campbell Heatherleigh, Coreway, Sidmouth EX10 9SD — MB BS 1963 Lond.; FRCPC 1976; MRCP Lond. 1968; MRCS Eng. LRCP Lond. 1963; MRCGP 1978; DA Eng. 1972; DObst. RCOG 1965. Socs: New Zealand Med. Assn. Prev: Surg. Union Castle Steamship Co.; Regist. (Med.) Roy. Free Hosp.; Ho. Surg. Lond. Hosp.

ANDERSON, John Christopher (retired) Millicent House, Linton, Cambridge CB1 6JY — BM BCh 1958 Oxf. Prev: GP Camb.

ANDERSON, John Colquhoun (retired) Finiterre, 71 South St, Tillingham, Southminster CM0 7TH Tel: 01621 778108 Email: tuandoc@eggconnect.net — MB ChB St. And. 1958; MRCGP 1981; DPH Aberd. 1966. Prev: Dir. Health & Med. Servs. RePub. of Nauru.

ANDERSON, Mr John Douglas Chalmers, OBE (retired) 9 Radcliffe Road, Salisbury SP2 8EH Tel: 01722 324936 Email: jock@auntie.demon.co.uk — MB BChir Camb. 1952; BSc Lond. 1946; MA Camb. 1951; FRCS Eng. 1967; DO Eng. 1960; DCEH 1988 (Hon. Causa) Inst. Ophth. Lond. Prev: Sen. Lect. Inst. Ophth. Lond.

ANDERSON, John Edward 6 Antrim Avenue, Sheffield S10 2DZ — MB BS 1998 Lond.; MB BS Lond 1998.

ANDERSON, John Ferguson (retired) Rosemount, Riggs Place, Cupar KY15 5JA — MB ChB 1960 Glas.; MRCPsych 1972; DPM Ed. & Glas. 1964. Prev: Cons. Psychiat. Stratheden Hosp. Cupar.

ANDERSON, John Grant St Pauls Medical Centre, St. Pauls Square, Carlisle CA1 1DG Tel: 01228 524354 Fax: 01228 616660 — MD 1979 Brussels. (Brussels) GP Carlisle.

ANDERSON, Mr John Hilton Department of Coloproctology, Glasgow Royal Infirmary, Glasgow G31 2ER Tel: 0141 211 4000; 16 Coltmuir Drive, Bishopbriggs, Glasgow G64 2SU Tel: 0141 762 2017 — MB ChB 1983 Dundee; MD Dundee 1993; FRCS (Gen.) 1995; FRCS Glas. 1987. (Dundee) Cons. Colorectal Surg.Glas. Roy. Infirm. Prev: Cancer Research Campaign Research Fell. Glas. Roy. Infirm.; Vis. Lect. Chinese Univ. Hong Kong; Regist. W. of Scotl. Higher Surgic. Train. Scheme.

ANDERSON, John Hughes, Col. late RAMC Retd. Lakeside, Little Anglesey Road, Alverstoke, Gosport PO12 2JA — MRCS Eng. LRCP Lond. 1926. (Guy's) Socs: BMA.

ANDERSON, John Mackenzie (retired) 2 Panmure Terrace, Broughty Ferry, Dundee DD5 2QP Tel: 01382 778358 — MB ChB St. And. 1958; FRCPath 1977, M 1965; DPath Eng. 1963. Hon. Sen. Lect. (Path.) Univ. Dundee. Prev: Cons. Histopath. Dundee Teach. Hosps. Trust.

ANDERSON, John McClure (retired) 3 Craigbet Crescent, Bridge of Weir PA11 3QY — MB ChB 1985 Glas. Asst. GP I. of Cumbrae.

ANDERSON, John Michael Ewart Newcombes Surgery, Crediton EX17 2AR Tel: 01363 772263 Fax: 01363 775906 Email: mandersond@cix.co.uk; Hare Cottage, New Buildings, Crediton EX17 4PW Tel: 01363 84868 Fax: 01363 84868 — MB BChir 1963 Camb.; MA Camb. 1964; MRCGP 1978; DObst RCOG 1966. (St. Thos.) Course Organiser Exeter VTS; Trainer (Gen. Pract.) Devon; Hon. Research Fell. Inst. of Gen. Pract. Exeter Univ.; Chairm. N. & E. Devon, Local Med. Comm. Socs: BMA. Prev: Ho. Surg. Qu. Alexandra Hosp. Portsmouth; Ho. Phys. Clatterbridge Hosp. Bebington; Ho. Surg. (O & G) St. Thos. Hosp. Lond.

ANDERSON, John Milne (retired) 35 Hyndford Street, Dundee DD2 1HX Tel: 01382 667309 — MB ChB St. And. 1956. Prev: Ho. Surg. & Ho. Phys. Dundee Roy. Infirm.

ANDERSON, John Noel (retired) Brookfield, 124 Chester Road, Helsby, Warrington WA6 0QT Tel: 01925 3760 — MB BS 1942 Durh. Prev: GP Helsby.

ANDERSON, John Patrick (retired) Greenlands, Ash Thomas, Tiverton EX16 4NP Tel: 01884 821257 — MB BS (Hons.) Durh. 1947; MD Durh. 1953; FRCP Ed. 1970, M 1957; DTM & H RCP Lond. 1989; DCH Eng. 1951. Prev: Vis. Med. Off. St. Francis Hosp., Katete, Zambia.

ANDERSON, Mr John Richard Department of Surgery, Southern General Hospital, Glasgow G51 4TF Tel: 0141 201 1100; Low Borland, Glasgow Road, Eaglesham, Glasgow G76 0DN Tel: 01355 302991 — MB ChB 1973 Glas.; BSc Ed. 1970; FRCS Glas. 1993; FRCS Ed. 1978; T(S) 1991. (Univ. Ed.) Cons. Surg. (Gen. Surg.) S.. Gen. Hosp. Glas. Prev: Sen. Lect. Univ. Dept. Surg. Roy. Infirm. Glas.; Sen. Regist. Roy. Vict. Hosp. & City Hosp. Belf.

ANDERSON, John Rognvald (retired) The Manor House, 13 Kingsholm Square, Gloucester GL1 2QJ Tel: 01452 524303 — MB ChB 1943 Aberd. Prev: SHO Neurosurg. Unit Chase Farm Hosp. Enfield.

ANDERSON, John Russell, CBE (retired) 3 Connell Crescent, Milngavie, Glasgow G62 6AR — MB ChB 1942 St. And.; FRSE; LLD Dundee 1981; BSc St. And. 1939, MD (Hons. & Univ. Gold Medal); 1955, MB ChB (Commend.) 1942; FRCP Lond. 1979, M 1961; FRCP Glas. 1965, M 1962; FRCPath 1966, M 1964; Hon. FRCPI 1981. Prev: Prof. Path. Univ. Glas. & Path. W. Infirm. Glas.

ANDERSON, John Stewart Nicholas Woodlands Health Centre, Paddock Wood, Tonbridge TN12 6AR Tel: 01892 833331 Fax: 01892 838269; Mascalls Pound Cottage, Maidstone Road, Paddock Wood, Tonbridge TN12 6LT Tel: 01892 832043 Email: dr_nick@talk21.com — MB BChir 1972 Camb.; MA, MB Camb. 1972, BChir 1971; MRCGP 1989; DObst RCOG 1975. (Camb./Guy's Hosp.) Socs: BMA; MRCGP. Prev: Ho. Surg. Guy's Hosp.; Ho. Phys. Pembury Hosp.; Cas. Off. Kent & Sussex Hosp. Tunbridge Wells.

ANDERSON, John Stuart 5 Newlands Road, Glasgow G43 2JB — MB ChB 1988 Glasg.

ANDERSON, Mr John Thomas 41 Cambridge Road, Linthorpe, Middlesbrough TS5 5NL Tel: 01642 823801 Fax: 01642 250196

Email: john.anderson@btinternet.com — MB BS 1965 Lond.; FRCS Ed. 1970; MRCS Eng. LRCP Lond. 1965. (Univ. Coll. Hosp.) Cons. Orthop. Surg. Middlesbrough Gen. Hosp.; Chief of Serv. Trauma Div. S.Tees Acute Hosps. Trust; Hon. Lect. Clin. Orthop. Univ. of Teesside. Socs: Fell. BOA; (Sec.) N.. Regional Advis. Subcomm. in Orthop. Prev: Sen. Regist. (Orthop. Surg.) Newc. RHA; Regist. (Accid. & Orthop. Surg.) Gen. Infirm. Leeds; Flight. Lt. RAF Med. Br., Surg. Specialist RAF Hosp. Cosford.

ANDERSON, John Thomas Cheltenham General Hospital, Sandford Road, Cheltenham GL53 7AN Tel: 01242 222222 Fax: 01242 273664; Crudens Barn, Ashleworth, Gloucester GL19 4HT — MB ChB 1988 Liverp.; BSc Liverp. 1985, MB ChB 1988; MRCP (UK) 1991. Cons. (Phys. Gastroenterol.) Cheltenham Gen. Hosp. Prev: Sen. Regist. (Gen. Med. & Gastroenterol.) Ninewells Hosp. Dund.; Reg. (Gen. Med. Gastroenterol.) Ninewells Hosp. Dund.; SHO (Gen. Med.) Thanet Dist. Gen. Hosp. Margate.

ANDERSON, John Thomas Hughes The Surgery, 2 Gregson Avenue, Gosport PO13 0HR Tel: 01329 232446 Fax: 01329 282624; 2 Dolphin House, Green Lane, Alverstoke, Gosport PO12 3QB — MRCS Eng. LRCP Lond. 1967; DObst RCOG 1975; DA Eng. 1972. (Guy's) Maj. RAMC T & AVR. Socs: BMA. Prev: Ho. Surg. Roy. Free Hosp. Lond. (New End. Hosp.); Ho. Phys. Ashford Hosp., Middlx.; Maj. RAMC.

ANDERSON, John Venner Department of Medicine, St Bartholomew's Hospital, West Smithfield, London EC1A 7BE Tel: 020 7601 7450 Fax: 020 7601 7449 Email: j.v.anderson@mds.qmw.ac.uk; 61 West Street, Hertford SG13 8EZ Tel: 01992 552632 Fax: 020 7601 7449 — MB BS 1979 Lond.; MA Camb. 1980, BA (Hons.) 1976, MD 1989; FRCP Lond. 1991; MRCP (UK) 1982. (Univ. Coll. Hosp.) Cons. Phys. (Med.) Roy. Hosps. NHS Trust & Homerton Hosp. Lond. Socs: Brit. Diabetic Assn. (Med. & Scientif. Sect.); Med. Res. Soc. Prev: Sen. Regist. (Endocrinol./Diabetes & Gen. Med.) St. Bart. Hosp. Lond.; Brit. Heart Foundat. Research Fell. Roy. Postgrad. Med. Sch. Lond.; Regist. Rotating (Med.) Ealing Hosp. S.all & Hammersmith Hosp. Lond.

ANDERSON, Johnston Morris (retired) Fixby Croft, Grimscar Road, Fixby, Huddersfield HD2 2EF Tel: 01422 373745 — MB ChB 1944 St. And. Prev: GP Huddersfield.

ANDERSON, Mr Jonathan Robert Hammersmith Hospital, Du Cane Rd, London W12 0HS Tel: 020 8383 2277 Fax: 020 8383 2725 Email: jranderson@hhnt.org; 6 Park Road, Hampton Wick, Kingston upon Thames KT1 4AS Tel: 020 8943 3581 Email: jon@jonanderson.demon.co.uk — MB ChB 1987 (Hons) Birm.; 1987 MB ChB (Hons) Birm.; 1991 FRCS Eng.; 1996 FRCS (CTH). (Birm. Univ.) Cons. Cardiothoracic Surg. Hammersmith Hosp. Lond. Socs: BMA; Ulster Med. Soc.; Soc. Cardiothoracic Surgs. GB & Irel. Prev: Cons. Cardiothoracic Surg. St Marys Hosp. Lond.

ANDERSON, Jonathan Roger 18 Redcliffe Gardens, London SW10 9EX — MB BS 1987 Lond.; MSc Lond. 1992, MB BS 1987. Sen. Regist. (Microbiol.) St. Bart. Hosp. Lond. Prev: Regist. & SHO (Microbiol.) Univ. Coll. Hosp. Lond.; SHO Whittington Hosp. Lond.; Ho. Off. (Med.) Medway Hosp.

ANDERSON, Joseph Milne 72 Launceston Road, Park Hall, Walsall WS5 3EE — MB ChB 1965 St. And.; FRCP Lond. 1983; FRCP Ed. 1982, M 1969; MRCP (UK) 1969. Cons. Neurol. Qu. Eliz. Neurosci. Centre Birm.; Hon Sen. Clin. Lect. (Neurol.) Univ. Birm. Prev: Assoc. Prof. Neurol. King Saud Univ. Riyadh, Saudi Arabia.

ANDERSON, Judith Helen 48 Grove St,, Leamington Spa CV32 5AG Tel: 01926 421524 Fax: 01926 421525 — MB ChB 1975 Aberd.; MRCPsych 1980. Indep. Cons. Psychiat.; Registered Therap. UK Counc. Psychother.; Jungian Analyst. Psychother. W. Midl. Inst. Psychother. 1996; Assoc. Prof. Mem. W. Midl. Inst. Psychother. Prev: Cons. Psychiat. S. Lincs. HA; Sen. Lect. (Psychiat.) Univ. Leicester; Sen. Regist. (Psychiat.) Mapperley Hosp. Trent RHA.

ANDERSON, Judith Margaret 27 Acacia Drive, Paisley PA2 9LS — MB ChB 1995 Glas.

ANDERSON, Judith Mary 113 Crabtree Close, Firvale, Sheffield S5 7AQ — MB ChB 1986 Ed.

ANDERSON, Julia 99 Pelham Avenue, Scartho, Grimsby DN33 3NG — MB 1969 Camb.; BChir 1968; MRCP (U.K.) 1974. (St. Thos.)

ANDERSON, Julia Anne Mary 14 Pentland Crescent, Edinburgh EH10 6NP — MB ChB 1988 Ed.; BSc (Hons.) Ed. 1986; MRCP (UK) 1993; DRCPath 1995; MRCPath 1999, RC of Pathologists; MD, Uni of Edinburgh 1999. Regist. Rotat. (Haemat.) Lothian VTS.

ANDERSON, Julian Patrick Hannay 5 Red Rose Close, Alderton, Woodbridge IP12 3DG — BM BCh 1956 Oxf.; MRCS Eng. LRCP Lond. 1955. (St. Geo.)

ANDERSON, Julie Ann Ardler Surgery, Turnberry Avenue, Dundee DD2 3TP Tel: 01382 833399 Fax: 01382 832484; 6 Balmyle Road, West Ferry, Dundee DD5 1JJ Tel: 01382 477133 — MB BS 1981 Lond.; MRCGP 1990; FFA RCSI 1987; DRCOG 1983. Prev: Trainee GP Glas.; Regist. (Anaesth.) Stobhill Gen. Hosp. Glas.

ANDERSON, Julie Anne Berinsfield Health Centre, Fane Drive, Berinsfield, Wallingford OX10 7NE Tel: 01865 340558 Fax: 01865 341973; 93 Church Road, Sandford-on-Thames, Oxford OX4 4YA Tel: 01865 774178 — BM BCh 1979 Oxf.; MRCGP 1983; DTM & H RCP Lond. 1988; DObst 1982.

ANDERSON, Karen Jean 118-120 Stanford Avenue, Brighton BN1 6FE Tel: 01273 506361; 19 Seymour Square, Kemp Town, Brighton BN2 1DW — BM 1988 Soton.; MRCGP 1994; DCH RCP Lond. 1995; DRCOG 1993. (Univ. Soton.) GP Partner.

ANDERSON, Karen Lorraine 38 Brookhill, Woodstock, Oxford OX20 1JE — MB ChB 1991 Bristol; MRCP 1995. (Bristol) Clin. Research Fell. (Nephrol.) S.mead Hosp. Bristol. Socs: BMA. Prev: Renal Regist. Waikato Hosp. Hamilton New Zealand; Respirat. Regist. Wakato Hosp. Hamilton New Zealand; Cardiol. SHO Nencross Hosp. Wolverhampton.

ANDERSON, Katharine Jane Royal Alexandra Hospital for Sick Children, Dyke Rd, Brighton BN1 3JN Tel: 01273 328145; Scalands House, Brightling Road, Robertsbridge TN32 5EU Tel: 01580 880215 Email: katharine.anderson@doctors.org.uk — MB BS 1982 Lond.; MRCP (UK) 1986; DRCOG 1984; MSc 2000. p/t Locum Cons. Paediat. (Community) S. Downs Health NHS Trust. Prev: Sen. Regist. (Paediat.) Conquest Hosp. St Leonards-on-Sea.

ANDERSON, Kay Margaret Royal Edinburgh Hospital, Morningside Park, Edinburgh EH10 5HF; Flat 2F2, 92 East Claremont St, Edinburgh EH7 4JZ — MB ChB 1994 Aberd.; BSc (Hons.) Med. Sci. Aberd. 1993. SHO Rotat. (Psychiat.) Roy. Edin. Hosp.

ANDERSON, Keith Arthur (retired) 3 Becket Wood, Mill Lane, Newdigate, Dorking RH5 5AQ Tel: 01306 631178 — MB BS Lond. 1957; MRCS Eng. LRCP Lond. 1957; DA Eng. 1961. Prev: Hon. Accredit. (Anaesth.) St. Anthony's Hosp. Cheam, Ashtead Hosp. & Sturt & Priory Hosp.

ANDERSON, Keith Derek 16 Broomhall Place, Edinburgh EH12 7PE — MB ChB 1993 Dundee.

ANDERSON, Keith John c/o Nuffield Department of Anaesthetics, Oxford Radcliffe Hospital, Headleyway, Headington, Oxford OX3 9OU — MB ChB 1994 Glas.; BSc (Hons) Glas. Pharm. 1991; FRCA (Lond.) 1999. (Glasgow) Specialist Regist. (Anaesth. & IC), Stoke Mandeville. Socs: Assoc. of Anaesth.s. Prev: SHO (Anaesth. & IC) S.ern Gen. NHS Trust.; Specialist Regist. (Anaesth. & IC) Nuffield Dept. Anaesth. Oxf..

ANDERSON, Kenneth Department of Respiratory Medicine, Level 3 Eastwing, Crosshouse Hospital, Kilmarnock KA2 0BE Tel: 01563 521183 Fax: 01698 376671 Email: kenneth.anderson@aaaht.nhs.scot.uk; Fairhaven, 14 Sarazen Drive, Troon KA10 6JP Email: drknderson@aol.com — MB ChB 1979 Glas.; MD Glas. 1989; MRCP (UK) 1982; FRCP (Glas.) 1996; FRCP 2000 (Edin). (Glas.) Cons. Phys. (Gen. & Respirat. Med.) CrossHo. Hosp., Kilmarnock; Hon. Lect. (Environm. Health) Strathclyde Univ.; Chairm. W. of Scotl. Environm. Lung GP.; Hon. Sen. Lect. Univ. Glas.; Chairm., Brit. Lung Foundat. Socs: Scott. Thoracic Soc.; Brit. Thoracic Soc.; Amer. Thoracic Soc. Prev: Sen. Regist. Vict. & W.. Infirm. Glas.; Vis. Fell. NJCRD Univ. Colorado.

ANDERSON, Kirstie Nicola 18 Rosedale Terrace, North Shields NE30 2HP — MB BS 1994 Newc.; BMedSc. Newc. 1991; MRCP (UK) 1997. Wellcome Clin. Train. Fell. Research Regist., Dept. of Human Anat. & Genetics, Univ. of Oxf.; Specialist Regist. (Neurol) Middlesbrough Gen Hosp; Specialist Regist. (Neurol) Newc Gen Hosp; SHO (Neurol) Nat Hosp for Neurol & Neurosurg.; Wellcome Clin. Train. Fell. Research Regist., Dept. of Human Anat. & Genetics, Univ. of Oxf. Socs: BMA. Prev: SHO Rotat. (Med.) Camb.; Ho. Off. (Surg.) Roy. Hosp. Sick. Childr. Edin.; Ho. Off. (Med.) Roy. Vict. Infirm. Newc. u. Tyne.

ANDERSON, Laura Margaret Adderlane Surgery, Adderlane Road, Prudhoe NE42 5EU Tel: 01661 836361; 23 Tyne Green, Hexham NG64 3HF Tel: 01434 609912 — MB ChB 1992 Leeds.

ANDERSON, Lisa Deborah Heathfield Medical Centre, Lyttelton Road, Hampstead Garden Suburb, London N2 0EE Tel: 020 8458 9262 Fax: 020 8458 0300; 22 Tenterden Gardens, Hendon, London NW4 1TE — MB BS 1986 Lond.; MRCGP 1992; DCH RCP Lond. 1991; DRCOG 1990. (St. Mary's Hosp. Lond.) Occupat. Health Doctor Wembley plc.

ANDERSON, Lisa Judith 5 Ham Street, Richmond TW10 7HR — MB ChB 1990 Liverp.

ANDERSON, Lorraine Catherine 32 Harberton Park, Belfast BT9 6TS — MB BCh BAO 1993 Belf.; MB BCh Belf. 1993.

ANDERSON, Louisa Ellen Countess of Chester Hospital, Liverpool Rd, Chester CH2 1BA Tel: 0161 748 4022; 11 Orchard Street, West Didsbury, Manchester M20 2LP Tel: 0161 434 1792 — MB ChB 1995 Manch.; MRCP 1999. SHO (Gen. Med.). Socs: BMA. Prev: SHO (Gen. Med.) Trafford Gen. Hosp. Manch.; SHO (Gen. Med.) Roy. Preston Hosp. Fullwood Preston.

ANDERSON, Louise Parkhill Medical Practice, Parkhill Road, Torquay TQ1 2AR — MB ChB 1985 Leic.; MRCGP 1990; DRCOG 1990. GP Princip.

ANDERSON, Lynda Jane Wellwood, Kettle Road, Ladybank, Cupar KY15 7PA; Hollydene, Dykeside, Freuchie, Cupar KY15 7ES — MB ChB 1982 Ed.

ANDERSON, Margaret (retired) 16 Glenhurst Road, Henley-in-Arden, Solihull B95 5HZ — MB BS 1961 Lond.; DObst RCOG 1963. Prev: Sen. Clin. Med. Off. S. Warks. HA.

ANDERSON, Margaret Elizabeth 36 Brighton Place, Edinburgh EH15 1LT — MB ChB 1965 Ed.

ANDERSON, Margaret Elizabeth Fixby Croft, Huddersfield HD2 2EF — MB ChB 1948 St. And. (St. And.) Socs: Huddersfield Med. Soc. Prev: Asst. MOH Halifax Co. Boro.; Ho. Surg. & Ho. Phys. Bridge of Earn Hosp.; Res. Surg. Off. Matern. Unit, Roy. Infirm. Perth.

ANDERSON, Margaret Grace (retired) 14 Northumberland Street, Edinburgh EH3 6LS Email: andersonaag@aol.com — MB BS 1954 Lond.; FFPHM RCP (UK) 1989; FFCM 1984, M 1974; DPH Singapore 1969. Prev: Sen. Clin. Community Med. Off. (Child Health) W. Dorset Health Dist.

ANDERSON, Margaret Hogg Gardner (retired) 13 Baird Terrace, Haddington EH41 3AX — MB ChB 1933 Glas.; DPH Glas. 1937; LM Rotunda 1937. Prev: Dep. Co. Med. Off. E. Lothian CC.

ANDERSON, Margaret Joyce 1 Kinnear Square, Laurencekirk AB30 1UL — MB ChB 1982 Aberd.; DRCOG 1987.

ANDERSON, Margaret Ritchie (retired) Homescott House, Flat 56, 6 Goldenacre Terrace, Edinburgh EH13 5RE — MB ChB 1926 Ed.

ANDERSON, Margaret Winifred (retired) West Dualt, Stockiemuir Road, Killearn, Glasgow G63 9QW Tel: 01360 55943 — MB ChB 1929 Glas.

ANDERSON, Marina Ellen Rheumatic Diseases Centre, Clinical Sciences Building, Hope Hospital, Eccles Old Road, Salford M6 8HD Tel: 0161 789 7373 Fax: 0161 787 4367 Email: manderson@fsl.ho.man.ac.uk; 40 Rushgreen Road, Lymm WA13 9PW Tel: 01925 755402 Email: chris.marina@btinternet.com — MB ChB 1991 Ed.; MSc (Rheum.) Manch. 1995; MRCP (UK)1997. (Ed.) Clin. Research Fell., Arthritis Research Campaign. Prev: Specialist Regist. (Rheum) N. W.; Sen. SHO (Med.) Trafford Gen. Hosp. Manch.; MSc Research Stud. (Rheum.) Hope Hosp. Manch.

ANDERSON, Mark Hayes Cardiology Department, Morriston Hospital, Swansea SA6 6NL Tel: 01792 704118 Fax: 01792 704140; 88 Westport Avenue, Mayals, Swansea SA3 5EF Tel: 01792 516799 — MB BS 1982 Lond.; 2001 FRCP Lond.; BSc Lond. 1979, MD 1994; MRCP (UK) 1985. (Middlx. Hosp.) Cons. (Cardiol.) Morriston Hosp. Swansea. Socs: Brit. Cardiac Soc.; N. Amer. Soc. Pacing & Electrophys. Prev: Sen. Regist. (Cardiol.) St. Mary's Hosp. Lond.; Sen. Regist. (Cardiol.) Hammersmith Hosp. Lond.; Research Regist. (Cardiol.) St. Geo. Hosp. Lond.

ANDERSON, Mark Robert 14 Hatley Drive, Burwell, Cambridge CB5 0AY — BChir 1994 Camb.

ANDERSON, Mary (retired) 6 Wilson Gardens, Kenton Park, Newcastle upon Tyne NE3 4JA — MB BS Durh. 1958. Prev: Assoc. Rheum. Freeman Hosp. Newc.

ANDERSON, Mary Elizabeth Margaret Old Distillery Surgery, Ardronie Park, Kingussie PH21 1ET Tel: 01540 661233 Fax: 01540 661277 — MB ChB 1981 Aberd.; MRCGP 1986.

ANDERSON, Mary Margaret, CBE (retired) Green Roof Cottage, 1 Heathway, Blackheath, London SE3 7AN Tel: 020 8858 2330 — MB ChB Ed. 1956; FRCOG 1974, M 1962; DObst RCOG 1959. Prev: Cons. O & G Lewisham Hosp.

ANDERSON, Maryan Gordon (retired) Field House Stud, Little Saxham, Bury St Edmunds IP29 5LH — MB ChB 1946 St. And.; DObst RCOG 1952. Prev: Ho. Surg. & Ho. Phys. ScarBoro. Hosp.

ANDERSON, Marylynne Isabel McColl 21 Hillcrest Avenue, Hardgate, Clydebank G81 6PD — MB ChB 1988 Glasg.

ANDERSON, Methven Campbell (retired) 1 Fairway, Bramhall, Stockport SK7 1DB — MB ChB 1943 Glas.; BSc Glas. 1940; DO Eng. 1966.

ANDERSON, Michael Archibald John 27 Acacia Dr, Paisley PA2 9LS — MB ChB 1997 Glas.

ANDERSON, Michael George West Middlesex University Hospital, Isleworth TW7 6AF Tel: 020 8565 5351 Fax: 020 8565 5152; 4 Golden Cross Mews, Portobello Rd, London W11 1DZ Tel: 020 7229 0567 Fax: 020 229 0567 — MB BS 1975 Lond.; MD Lond. 1990; FRCP Lond. 1995; MRCP (UK) 1979; MRCS Eng. LRCP Lond. 1975. (St. Bart.) Cons. Phys. Gastroenterol. W. Middlx. Univ. Hosp.; Hon. Cons. Phys. Chelsea & W.m. Hosp. Lond. Prev: Sen. Regist. Char. Cross & W.m. Hosps. Lond.

ANDERSON, Monique Infrid Widcombe Manor, Church St., Bath BA2 6AZ — MB BS 1996 Lond.

ANDERSON, Morris 9 Carrick Gardens, Livingston EH54 9ET Tel: 01506 461458 — MB ChB 1977 Ed.; BSc (Med Sci) Ed. 1974. Socs: Brit. Soc. Med. & Dent. Hypn. Prev: Lect. Gen. Pract. Fac. Med. Edin. Univ.

ANDERSON, Moyra Roberta Old School Surgery, 54 Station Road, Greenisland, Carrickfergus BT38 8TP Tel: 028 9086 4455 Fax: 028 9036 6567 Email: oldschool@pratice.dnet.co.uk; 64 Villiage Green, Doach, Ballyclare BT39 0UD Tel: 028 9335 4465 Email: moyra@mkernohan-fsnet.co.uk — MB BCh BAO 1993 Belf.; BSc (Hons.) Aberd. 1988. p/t GP. Socs: BMA. Prev: SHO (A & E) Antrim Co. Antrim N. Irel.; SHO (Med.) Antrim Area Hosp.; SHO (Surg.) Waveney Hosp.

ANDERSON, Neil Harris Department of Pathology, Institute of Pathology, Grosvenor Road, Royal Victoria Hospital, Belfast BT12 6BL; 6 Glenburn Manor, Carrickfergus BT38 7TX — MB BCh BAO 1986 Belf.; MD Belf. 1995; DRCPath (Cyto) 1995. Cons. Cytol. & Histopath. Roy. Vict. Hosp. & Belf. City Hosp.; Hon. Sen. Lect. Qu.'s Univ. Belf. Socs: Assn. Clin. Paths.; Brit. Soc. Clin. Cytol.

ANDERSON, Neil James Laurencekirk Medical Group, Blackiemuir Avenue, Laurencekirk AB30 1DX Tel: 01561 377258 Fax: 01561 378270 — MB ChB 1985 Aberd.; MRCGP 1989; DRCOG 1988.

ANDERSON, Neil Wilson 57 Lough Road, Boardmills, Lisburn BT27 6TS — MB BCh BAO 1995 Belf.; DRCOG RCObst&Gyn 1998.

ANDERSON, Neill Haig Royal Edinburgh Hospital, Morningside Terrace, Edinburgh EH10 5HF Tel: 0131 537 6632 Fax: 0131 537 6105 — MB ChB 1990 Ed.; MRCPsych 1994. Cons. Psychiat. Ryl Edin. Hsp. Prev: Regist. (Psychiat.) Roy. Edin. Hosp.; Ho. Phys. Roy. Infirm. Edin.; Sen. Regist. (Old Age Psychiat.) Roy. Edin. Hosp. Lothian Train. Scheme.

***ANDERSON, Nicola Louise** 83 Salcombe Gardens, Low Fell, Gateshead NE9 6UD Tel: 0191 482 1360 — MB ChB 1998 Leeds.

ANDERSON, Norman Fraser (retired) Struan, Bogsbank Road, West Linton EH46 7EN Tel: 01968 660209 — MB ChB 1956 Ed.

ANDERSON, Norman McLennan The Red House Surgery, 241 Queensway, Bletchley, Milton Keynes MK2 2EH Tel: 01908 375111; The Old Rectory, Church Green Road, Bletchley, Milton Keynes MK3 6BJ — MB BCh 1972 Wales.

ANDERSON, Norman Wilson Officers Mess, BMH Munster BFPO 17 — MB BCh BAO 1978 Belf.

ANDERSON, Patrick Campbell Whately (retired) 12 St John's Hill, Shrewsbury SY1 1JJ Tel: 01743 351652 Fax: 01743 351652 — MB Camb. 1955, BChir 1954; MRCGP 1968; DObst RCOG 1959. Prev: GP Shrewsbury.

ANDERSON, Patrick McCormick Donald Balmore Park Surgery, 59A Hemdean Road, Caversham, Reading RG4 7SS Tel: 0118 947 1455 Fax: 0118 946 1766 — MRCS Eng. LRCP Lond. 1962; FRCGP 1978, M 1972; DObst RCOG 1966; DCH Eng. 1965. (Guy's) Prev: Chairm. Berks. MAAG; GP Tutor Postgrad. Med. Educat. Centre Roy. Berks. Hosp.; Course Organiser (Gen. Pract.) Postgrad. Med. Educat. Centre.

ANDERSON, Paul Bryan Department of Respiratory Medicine, Sheffield Chest Clinic, Northern General Hospital, Herries Road, Sheffield S5 7AU Tel: 0114 271 4661 Fax: 0114 271 5745 Email: paulbry1@aol.com; 624 Abbey Lane, Sheffield S11 9NA Tel: 0114 236 4568 Fax: 0114 235 2919 — BM BCh 1970 Oxf.; MA Oxf. 1970; FRCP Lond. 1988; MRCP (UK) 1974. Cons. Phys. Gen. Med. & Chest Dis. N. Gen. NHS Trust Sheff. Socs: Fell. BMA; Brit. Thorac. Soc. Prev: Lect. (Med.) Acad. Div. Med. Univ. Sheff.; Regist. (Med.) United Sheff. Hosps.; Research Asst. Profess. Med. Unit Roy. Hosp. Sheff.

ANDERSON, Mr Paul Craig Bull 22 Finchley Road, Hale, Altrincham WA15 9RD — MB ChB 1994 Manch.; MB ChB (Hons.) Manch. 1994; BSc (Hons.) Manch. 1992; MRCS (Eng) 1998. (Manch.) SHO (Gen. Surg.) Warrington. Prev: SHO (Orthop.) Warrington; SHO (A & E) Whiston.

ANDERSON, Paula Margaret 77 Elkington Road, Burry Port SA16 0AB — MB BS 1996 Lond.

ANDERSON, Mr Peter (retired) 16A Foxholes Road, Horwich, Bolton BL6 6AP — MB ChB 1960 Birm.; FRCS Eng. 1967; MRCS Eng. LRCP Lond. 1960. Prev: Cons. Otolaryngol. Bolton Gp. Hosps.

ANDERSON, Peter Wellway Medical Group, The Surgery, Wellway, Morpeth NE61 6TB Tel: 01670 517300 Fax: 01670 511931; The Surgery, West View, Pegswood, Morpeth NE61 6TB Tel: 01670 515326 — MB BS 1975 Lond.; MRCGP 1979.

ANDERSON, Peter Gordon 237 Clarendon Pk Road, Leicester LE2 3AN — MB ChB 1997 Leic.

ANDERSON, Peter Ian Priory Medical Group, Cornlands Road, Acomb, York YO24 3WX Tel: 01904 781423 Fax: 01904 784886; 22 The Vale, Skelton, York YO30 1YH — MB ChB 1987 Leeds; MRCGP 1993.

ANDERSON, Mr Peter John Department of Plastic Surgery, Cannimburn Hospital, Glasgow G66 1QL — MB ChB 1989 Ed.; MD 1998 Ed.; BDS Ed. 1983; FRCS Eng. 1993; FDS RCS Ed. 1988. (Ed.) Specialist Regist. (Plastic Surg.) Cannimburn Hosp., Glas.; Sub-Specialist Train. March to June 2001; Craniofacial Fell., Austral. Cranofacial Unit, Adelaide; Specialist Regist. (Oral & Cranilofacial Surgury), Cannimburn Hosp. Glas. Jan to May 2001. Socs: Craniofacial Soc.; Brit. Assn. of Head & Neck Surg.s; Brit. Assn. of Oral & Maxillofacial Surg.s. Prev: Fell. (Craniofacial Surg.) Gt. Ormond St. Hosp. for Childr. Lond.; Regist. (Paediat. Surg.) Roy. Hosp. Sick Childr. Edin.; SHO (Plastic Surg.) Mt. Vernon Hosp. N.wood.

ANDERSON, Peter Marchmont (retired) 61 St Asaph Road, Dyserth, Rhyl LL18 6HG Tel: 01745 570166 — MRCS Eng. LRCP Lond. 1944; MRCGP 1974. Prev: Squadron Ldr. RAF Med. Br., Graded Orthop. Specialist.

ANDERSON, Philip England 1A Dalrymple Crescent, Edinburgh EH9 2NU Tel: 01795 1288 — MB ChB 1944 Ed.

ANDERSON, Rachel Louise N. Tees General Hospital, Hardwick, Stockton-on-Tees Tel: 01642 617617 — MB BS 1997 Newc. SHO Gen. Med.

ANDERSON, Richard Alexander Department of Obstetrics & Gynaecology, Centre for Reproductive Biology, 37 Chalmers St., Edinburgh EH3 9EW Tel: 0131 229 2575 Fax: 0131 229 2408; 28 Greenhill Gardens, Edinburgh EH10 4BP — MB ChB 1989 Ed.; PhD Ed. 1986, BSc 1982; MD Ed. 1994; MRCOG 1994. (Edinburgh) Lect. (O & G) Univ. Edin.

ANDERSON, Richard Anthony 36 Pembroke Court, Caerphilly CF83 2TN Tel: 029 2086 3701 — MB BS 1994 Lond.; BSc Lond. 1991. SHO (Cardiol.) Univ. Hosp. Wales.

ANDERSON, Richard James 44 Ravenhill Court, Belfast BT6 8FS Email: ricardo@uk.packardbell.org — MB BS 1996 Lond.; BA Oxf. 1993. (St. Geo.)

ANDERSON, Richard John 15 Wyndcote Road, Liverpool L18 2EB — MB ChB 1993 Liverp.

ANDERSON, Robert Holmleigh House, George St., Mablethorpe LN12 — LRCP LRCS 1940 Ed.; LRCP LRCS Ed. LRFPS. Glas. 1940. (Anderson Coll. Glas.)

ANDERSON, Robert George Wynn Trident Medical Services, Medical Division Atomic Weapons Establishment, Aldermaston, Reading RG7 4PR Tel: 0118 982 6868 Fax: 0118 982 6138 Email: tridentmed@msn.com; Highfield, Crevenagh Road, Omagh BT79 0EQ Tel: 01662 242086 — MRCS Eng. LRCP Lond. 1981; BSc. (Hons. Zool.) Belf. 1974; AFOM RCP Lond. 1991. (Leic.) Sen. Med. Off. Awe Aldermaston. Socs: Soc. Occupat. Med. & BMA. Prev: Maj. RAMC; Ho. Phys. St. Geos. Hosp. Lincoln; Ho. Surg. Co. Hosp. Lincoln.

ANDERSON, Professor Robert Henry Cardiac Unit, Institute of Child Health, University college London, London WC1 1EH Tel: 020 7905 2322 Fax: 020 7905 2324 Email: v.anderson.@ich.ucl.ac.uk; 60 Earlsfield Road, Wandsworth, London SW18 3DN Tel: 020 8870 4368 — MB ChB 1966 Manch.; BSc Manch. 1963, MD 1970; FRCPath 1987, M 1975. (Manch.) Joseph Levy Foundat. Prof. Paediat. Cardiac Morphol. Instit.Child Health.Univ.Coll.Lond.; Vis. Prof. Univ. Pittsburgh, USA; Vis. Prof. Child Health Univ. Liverp. Socs: Developm. Path. Soc.; Anat. Soc.; Path. Soc. Prev: MRC Trav. Fell. (Cardiol.) Wilhemina Gasthuis Univ. Amsterdam; Lect. (Anat.) Univ. Manch.; Ho. Surg. Profess. Unit & Ho. Phys. Manch. Roy. Infirm.

ANDERSON, Robert James Beacon Lane Surgery, 109 Beacon Lane, Exeter EX4 8LT Tel: 01392 73484 Fax: 01392 490135 — MB BCh BAO 1984 Belf.; MRCGP 1988; DMJ Soc. Apoth. Lond. 1993; DRCOG 1987. Prev: Trainee GP Dept. Gen. Pract. Univ. Exeter.

ANDERSON, Mr Robert James Lownie Ormskirk and District General Hospital, Wigan Road, Ormskirk L39 2AZ Tel: 01695 656165 Fax: 01695 656878 Email: pauline.appleton@mail.soh-tr.nwest.nhs.uk; 209 Prescot Road, Aughton, Ormskirk L39 5AE Tel: 01695 421918 Fax: 01695 421045 Email: rjl.anderson@virgin.net — MB ChB 1974 Dundee; BSc St. And. 1971; MD Dundee 1987; FRCS Eng. 1997; FRCS Ed. 1980; T(S) 1991. Cons. Gen. Surg. S.port & Ormskirk Hosp. NHS Trust; Tutor Manch. Univ. Socs: Assn. Coloproctol.; Assn. Endoscopic Surgs.; Assn. Upper G.I. Surg. Prev: Sen. Regist. (Surg.) N. W.. RHA; Resid Surg. Off. Christie Hosp. Manch.; Research Fell. Manch. Roy. Infirm.

ANDERSON, Robert Moir Lechmere, Col. (retired) Duchess of Kent Military Hospital, Horne Road, Catterick Garrison DL9 4 Tel: 01748873611 Fax: 01748873612 — 1967 MB ChB Aberd. 1967; 1962 MA Aberd. 1962; 1974 DPM Lond. 1974; 1975 MRC Psych. 1975; 1995 FRCPsych. 1995. Dir. of Defence Psychiat.

ANDERSON, Mr Robert Stanley St Michael's Hospital, Southwell St., Bristol BS2 8EG Tel: 0117 928 5812 Fax: 0117 928 5792; Prospect House, Chewton Keynsham, Bristol BS31 2SU — MB ChB 1974 Bristol; MD Bristol 1985; MRCOG 1980; FRACOG 1985; FRCOG 1993. Cons. O & G St. Michael's Hosp. Prev: Sen. Lect. (O & G) Univ. Sydney Austral.

ANDERSON, Ronald George (retired) Craddocks, Brock Hill, Wickford SS11 7PB Tel: 01268 710581 — MB 1956 Camb.; BA Camb. 1952, MB 1956, BChir 1955. Prev: Cas. Off., Ho. Surg. & Ho. Surg. Thoracic Unit, St. Thos. Hosp.

ANDERSON, Rosalind Beatrix Houndle Farm, Cornwood, Ivybridge PL21 9HS Tel: 01752 837877 Fax: 01752 837877 Email: david.hanley@lineone.net; Houndle Farm, Cornwood, Ivybridge PL21 9HS Tel: 01752 837877 Fax: 01752 837877 Email: david.hanley@lineone.net — MB BS 1968 Lond.; MRCS Eng. LRCP Lond. 1966. (St. Bart.) Locum Gen. Practitioner. Socs: Assoc. Mem. Inst. Psycho-Sexual Med. Prev: GP Princip. Tothill Surg. Plymouth 1996-2000; GP Princip. Havant Health Centre Havant 1982-1996.

ANDERSON, Rosemary (retired) Mayhill, Glasllwch Lane, Newport NP20 3PT — MB BS Lond. 1960; MRCS Eng. LRCP Lond. 1960; DMRD Eng. 1968; FFR 1971. Prev: Cons. Radiol. Nevill Hall Hosp. Abergavenny.

ANDERSON, Rosnah 17 Ballymoran Road, Armagh BT60 2AW — MB BCh BAO 1994 Belf.

ANDERSON, Ross Dept of Public Health Sciences, St George's Hospital Medical School, London SW17 0RE — MB ChB 1994 Aberd.

ANDERSON, Sacha May Lesley 4 Hawkridge Close, Bolton BL5 2GP — MB ChB 1998 Aberd.; MB ChB Aberd 1998.

ANDERSON, Sally Jane The Medical Centre, Cranwell Road, Driffield YO25 6UH Tel: 01377 253334 Fax: 01377 241728; 7 The Avenue, Driffield YO25 5HS Tel: 01377 253576 — MB ChB 1984 Sheff. Socs: Fam. Plann. Assn.; BMA. Prev: Resid. Med. Off. Flinders Hosp. Adelaide, S. Austral.

ANDERSON, Sarah Penelope St Leonards Hospice, Tadcaster Road, York YO24 1GL Tel: 01904 708553 Fax: 01904 704337 Email: slhyork@aol.com; Carr House, High Stittenham, Sheriff Hutton, York YO60 7TW Tel: 01347 878418 — MB BChir 1979 Camb.; 1979 MA Camb.; 1978 MB BChir Camb.; 1982 MRCGP; 1995 Dip. Palliat. Med. Wales. (King's Coll. Hosp.) Cons. Palliat. Med. & Med. Dir. St. Leonard's Hospice York. Socs: York Med. Soc.; BMA; Assn. Palliat. Med. Prev: GP York.

ANDERSON, Sarah Ruth Medical Centre, 111 Adelaide Road, London NW3 Tel: 020 7722 4135; Flat 3, 137 Sutherland Avenue, Maida Vale, London W9 2QJ Tel: 020 7286 2209 — MB BChir 1993 Camb.; MB BChir Camb. 1992; BA Camb. 1992; MRCPI 1997. (Camb. & St. Mary Hosp. Med. Sch. Lond.) GP/Regist. Lond. Prev: SHO Rotat. (Med.) N.wick Pk. Hosp. Lond.

ANDERSON, Seonaid Margaret 15 Linn Place, Kirkcaldy KY2 6JA — MB ChB 1998 Dund.; MB ChB Dund 1998.

ANDERSON, Shaun Kennedy Department of Intensive Care, Worthing Hospital, Worthing BN11 2DH Tel: 01903 285151; 25 West Avenue, Worthing BN11 5LU Email: skander@compuserve.com — MB BS 1980 Lond.; FFA RCS Eng. 1986; DRCOG 1982. (St. Mary's) Cons. Anaesth. & Dir. Intens. Care Worthing & S.lands Hosps.; Assoc. Teach. Univ. Melboure 1990-91. Socs: Intens. Care Soc.; Assn. Anaesth. Prev: Sen. Regist. (Anaesth.) Middlx. Hosp. Lond.; Regist. (Anaesth.) Bromton Hosp., Univ. Coll. Hosp. Lond. & Roy. Nat. Orthop. Hosp.; Staff Specialist Austin Hosp. Melbourne, Austral.

ANDERSON, Sheena Cameron Bonnybridge Health Centre, Larbert Road, Bonnybridge FK4 1ED Fax: 01324 814696; 8 Kirkhill, Muckhart, Dollar FK14 7JQ Tel: 01259 781391 Email: john@janders391.freeserve.co.uk — MB ChB 1975 Ed.; MRCGP 1979; Dip. Fac. Reprod. Med. 1997. (Edinburgh) GP Princip.; CMO (Family Plann.); Med. Assessor Social Security Appeal Tribunals; Clin. Ass. GUM Clinic, Falkirk Roy. Infirm.

ANDERSON, Simon Brian 17 Craighill Park, Cowpen Road, Blyth NE24 5TZ — MB BS 1983 Newc.

ANDERSON, Simon Richard Stoke Surgery, Belmont Villas, Stoke, Plymouth PL3 4DP Tel: 01752 562569 Fax: 01752 607299 — MB ChB 1987 Leeds; MRCGP 1992; DRCOG 1991.

ANDERSON, Stella Anne 3 Oldfold Place, Milltimber AB13 0JU — MB ChB 1974 Aberd.; MRCGP 1978; DRCOG 1976.

ANDERSON, Stephen William 13 Bantaskine Street, Falkirk FK1 5ES — MB ChB 1996 Ed. SHO (Psychiat.) Stratheden Hosp. Cupar. Prev: SHO (Surg.) Inverclyde Roy. NHS Trust Greenock; SHO (Med.) Monklands Hosp. Airdrie.

ANDERSON, Stewart Gray (retired) 43 Bittacy Rise, Mill Hill, London NW7 2HH — MB BS Melbourne 1942; DSc Melbourne 1962, MD Melbourne 1948; FRCPath 1975; FRCPA 1972; FRACP 1967.

ANDERSON, Stuart Hunt Kinmel Bay Medical Centre, The Square, Kinmel Bay, Rhyl LL18 5AU Tel: 01745 353965; The Gables, Denbigh Circle, Kinmel Bay, Rhyl LL18 5HW Tel: 01745 32172 — MB ChB 1972 St. And.; MRCP (UK) 1983; DTM & H Liverp. 1976. Prev: Med. Off. Bulape Hosp., Zaire.

ANDERSON, Stuart John Highbridge Medical Centre, Pepperall Road, Highbridge TA9 3YA Tel: 01278 783220 Fax: 01278 795486 — MB ChB 1988 Bristol; MRCGP 1995; DCH RCP Lond. 1994; DGM RCP Lond. 1991.

ANDERSON, Susan Lesley Leicester Royal Infirmary, Leicester LE1 5WW Tel: 0116 254 1414; Strawberry Fields, 6 Fox Pond Lane, Glen Rise, Oadby, Leicester LE2 4RY Tel: 0116 271 8186 — MB ChB 1987 Glas.; MRCGP 1992. Specialist Regist. (Anaesth.) Leicester Roy. Infirm. Socs: Assn. Anaesth.; BMA. Prev: SHO (Anaesth.) Cross Ho. Hosp. Kilmarnock.

ANDERSON, Susan Nicola Denton Park Health Centre, Denton Park Centre, West Denton Way, Newcastle upon Tyne NE5 2QZ Tel: 0191 267 2751 Fax: 0191 264 1588; 80 Darras Road, Darras Hall, Newcastle upon Tyne NE20 9PG — MB BS 1987 Newc.; MRCGP 1992; DRCOG 1991. Prev: SHO (Palliat. Med.) St. Oswalds Hosp. Gosforth; SHO (O & G) P.ss Mary Matern. Hosp.; SHO (Psychiat.) St. Geo. Hosp. Morpeth.

ANDERSON, Susan Rosemary Spitalfields Health Centre, 9-11 Brick Lane, London E1 6PU Tel: 020 7247 7070; 67 Ellesmere Road, Bow, London E3 5QU Tel: 020 8981 3140 — MB ChB 1983 Sheff.; MRCGP 1989; DRCOG 1988; DGM RCP Lond. 1986.

ANDERSON, Suzanne Theresa Belinda Academic Department of Paediatrics, St Mary's Hospital Imperial College, London W2 1NY Tel: 020 7886 1685 Email: s.anderson@ic.ac.uk — MB BS 1991 Lond.; BSc (Hons.) Lond. 1988; MRCP (UK) 1994.

ANDERSON, Sylvia Joyce Edith 20 Orken Lane, Aghalee, Craigavon BT67 0ED — MB BCh BAO 1994 Belf.

ANDERSON, Tamsyn 15 Shaws Green, Derby DE22 3HF — MB BS 1996 Newc.

ANDERSON, Thomas Barclay (retired) 14 Grantchester Road, Cambridge CB3 9ED Tel: 01223 359357 — MRCS Eng. LRCP Lond. 1944; MD Camb. 1957, MB BChir 1948; FRCGP 1979. Prev: Orthop. Ho. Surg. Horton EMS Hosp.

ANDERSON, Thomas James Nethertown Surgery, Elliot Street, Dunfermline KY11 4TF Tel: 01383 623516 Fax: 01383 624254; 3 Kincraig Place, Dunfermline KY12 7XT Tel: 01383 739724 — MB ChB 1983 Aberd.; MRCGP 1987; DRCOG 1988. (Aberdeen) GP Dunfermline. Prev: SHO (Gen. Med.) Arbroath Infirm.; Trainee GP Innerleithen Peeblesssh.; SHO (O & G) Dunfermline Matern. Hosp.

ANDERSON, Professor Thomas Johnstone Tel: 0131 537 1953 Fax: 0131 537 1013; 14 Grange Terrace, Edinburgh EH9 2LD Tel: 0131 667 4852 — MB ChB 1962 Glas.; FRCS 1995; PhD 1969 Glas.; MRCPath 1971; FRCPath 1983. Prof. Path. Univ. Edin. Socs: Brit. BrE. Gp.; Internat. Acad. Path.; Path. Soc. GB and Irel. Scott. Soc. Experim. Med. Prev: Lect. (Path.) Univ. Glas. & Aberd.; Regist. (Path.) & McGhie Cancer Research Schol. Glas. Roy. Infirm.

ANDERSON, Thomas Walter Dalziel Langford Medical Practice, 9 Nightingale Place, Bicester OX26 6XX Tel: 01869 245665 — MB ChB 1987 Bristol.

ANDERSON, Mr Timothy Donald (retired) Eastbank, River Road, Taplow, Maidenhead SL6 0BG Tel: 01628 623139 — MB BChir Camb. 1951; MA Camb. 1951; FRCS Eng. 1959; FRCOG 1975, M 1962; DObst. 1955. Prev: Cons. O & G, E. Berks Dist., Windsor.

ANDERSON, Valerie Royal Lancaster Infirmary, Ashton Road, Lancaster LA1 4RP Tel: 01524 583026 Fax: 01524 846346 — MB ChB 1960 Manch.; DTM & H Liverp. 1962. Assoc. Specialist Non-Invasive Cardiac Investig. Roy. Lancaster Infirm. Socs: Brit. Cardiac Soc.

ANDERSON, Violet (retired) 5 Kingsmills Gardens, Inverness IV2 3LU — MB ChB 1962 Aberd.

ANDERSON, Virginica 3 Valentine Crescent, Danestone, Aberdeen AB22 8DB Tel: 01224 706605 — LRCP LRCS Ed. LRCPS Glas. 1993; FRCA 1994; DA (UK) 1991.

ANDERSON, Walter Vincent 2 Beech Drive, Scalby, Scarborough YO13 0NP Tel: 01723 364648 Email: w.v.anderson@aol.uk — MB BS 1958 Durh.; MB BS (2nd cl. Hons.) Durh. 1958; BSc (Hons. Physiol) Durh. 1955; FRCGP 1978, M 1967; Family Plann. Cert 1974; DObst RCOG 1965. (Newc.) Locum GP. Socs: BMA (Ex-Pres. ScarBoro. Div.); (Ex-Provst.) Yorks. Fac. Roy. Coll. Gen. Pract. Prev: Tutor Continuing Med. Educat. for Gen. Practs. ScarBoro. Dist.; GP & Course Organiser ScarBoro. VTS; Assoc. Regional Adviser (Gen. Pract.) & Lect. Univ. Leeds & Yorks. RHA.

ANDERSON, Wendy Jane Anne 127 Upper Mealough Road, Carryduff, Belfast BT8 8JA — MB BCh BAO 1987 Belf.; MRCPI 1993; MRCGP 1993. Cons., Antrim Hosp.. Prev: Regist. (Thoracic Med.) Aberd. Roy. Infirm.

ANDERSON, Mr William Ainslie 102 Belper Road, Derby DE1 3EQ Tel: 01332 344957 Email: dadander@aol.com — MB ChB 1947 Aberd.; FRCS Ed. 1952; FRCS Eng. 1954. (Aberd.) Prev: Emerit. Surg. Derbysh. Roy. Infirm. & Childr. Hosp. Derby; Sen. Regist. (Surg.) Aberd. Gen. Hosps.; Regist., Ho. Surg. & Garden Research Fell. Roy. Infirm. Aberd.

ANDERSON, William David The Auld Kirk, Carmunnock Road, Clarkston, Glasgow G76 8SY — MB ChB 1992 Glas.

ANDERSON, Sir (William) Ferguson, OBE, KStJ 11 Craigfern Drive, Blanefield, Glasgow G63 9DP Tel: 01360 770862 — MB ChB 1936 (Hons.) Glas.; MD (Hons. & Bellahouston Gold Medal) Glas. 1942; FRCPI 1975; FRCP Lond. 1964, M 1948; FRCP Ed. 1963, M 1961; FRCP Glas. 1962; FRFPS Glas. 1939; FACP 1980;

FRCPC 1976. Emerit. Cons. Phys. Geriat. Med. S. Gen. Hosp. Glas. Socs: Assn. Phys.& Brit. Geriat. Soc. Prev: David Cargill Prof. Geriat. Med. Univ. Glas.; Phys. (Geriat.) Stobhill Hosp. Glas.; Phys. Foresthall Hosp. & W.. Dist. Hosp. Glas.

ANDERSON, William Gentles 27 Acacia Drive, Paisley PA2 9LS — MB ChB 1966 Glas.; BSc (Hons.) Glas. 1963, MB ChB (Commend.) 1966; MRCP Glas. 1969; FFA RCS Eng. 1972. (Glas.) Cons. Anaesth. Roy. Infirm. Glas. Prev: Regist. (Med.) & Regist. (Anaesth.) Glas. Roy. Infirm.; Lect. Anaesth. Univ. Glas.

ANDERSON, William James Adelaide Street Surgery, 118 Adelaide Street, Blackpool FY1 4LB Tel: 01253 620725 Fax: 01253 290765 — MB ChB 1974 Manch.

ANDERSON, William John 100 Woodfield Lane, Ashtead KT21 2DP — MB BS 1991 Newc.; BA Oxf. 1986; MRCP (UK) 1994; PhD London 1998. Lect. (Paediat. Oncol.) Inst. Child Health & Gt. Ormond St. Prev: Clin. Fell. Inst. Cancer Research & Roy. Marsden Hosp. Sutton.

ANDERSON, William Marr Kinrara, St Ronans Drive, Kinross KY13 8AF Tel: 01577 862578 — MB ChB 1951 St. And.; DObst 1954 RCOG. Prev: Ho. Phys. Dryburn Hosp. Durh.; Ho. Surg. O & G Gen Hosp. Bishop Auckland.

ANDERSON, Yvonne Doris 16 Vodar View, Lerwick ZE1 0QE Tel: 01224 633543; 47 Summerfield Terrace, Aberdeen AB24 5JE Tel: 01224 633543 — MB ChB 1995 Aberd.; DRLOG 1998; DFFP 1999. (Aberd.) GP Regist., Aberd. Socs: Med. & Dent. Defence Union Scotl.; BMA. Prev: Ho. Off. (Surg.) Raigmore NHS Hosp. Trust; Ho. Off. (Med.) Aberd. Roy. Hosps. NHS Trust; Trainee GP/SHO Aberd. Roy. Hsp, NHS Trust.

ANDERSON-SMITH, William Richard Flat 6, 297 Clifton Drive S., St Annes, Lytham St Annes FY8 1HN — MB ChB 1991 Leeds; FRCS Glas. 1997; FRCS Ed. 1997. SHO (Gen. Surg.) W. Suff. Hosp. Bury St. Edmunds. Prev: SHO (Orthop.) Bradford NHS Trust; SHO (A & E) Edin. Roy. Infirm.; SHO (Neurosurg.) Leeds Gen. Infirm.

ANDERSON-UPCOTT, Michael 68 Parkside, Shoreham-by-Sea BN43 6HA Tel: 01273 452759; 68 Parkside, Shoreham-by-Sea BN43 6HA Tel: 01273 452759 — MB BS 1973 Lond.; BSc Lond. 1960. (Middlx.) p/t Med. Advisor Adur Dist. Counc.; Examr. Health & Safety Exec.- Divers. Socs: Assoc. Mem. Fac. Occupat. Med. & Fac. Homoeop.; Eur. Undersea Biomed. Soc. Prev: Area Med. Off. BR; SHO (O & G) Roy. W. Sussex Hosp. Chichester; SHO (Anaesth. & A & E) Plymouth Gen. Hosps.

ANDERSSON, Clare Siobhan Sea Mills Surgery, 2 Riverleaze, Sea Mills, Bristol BS9 2HL Tel: 0117 968 1182 Fax: 0117 962 6408; 15 Trelawney Road, Cotham, Bristol BS6 6DX — MB ChB 1984 Bristol; MRCP (UK) 1990; MRCGP 1991; DCH RCP Lond. 1986.

ANDERSSON, Lena Christina Department of Plastic Surgery, Queen Mary's University Hospital, Roehampton Lane, London SW15 5PN; 27 Devonshire Place, London W1N 1PD — Lakarexamen Stockholm 1988.

ANDERSSON, Neil Rogan BM-HDCC, London WC1N 3XX — MRCS Eng. LRCP Lond. 1978; MPhil Lond. 1990, MSc (Epidemiol.) 1980; MFPHM 1989; MFCM 1986. Sen. Research Adviser UNICEF New York, USA; Prof. Epidemiol. & Trop. Med. Fac. of Med. Universidad Puidnoma, De Guerrero, Mexico. Prev: Dir. Centr. Trop. Dis. Research Acapulco, Mexico; Clin. Lect. Lond. Sch. Hyg. & Trop. Med.; Train. Fell. (Epidemiol.) MRC.

ANDERTON, Claire Jennifer Gale Farm Surgery, Front St., Acomb, York YO24 3BU; Delph House, 1A Scriven Road, Knaresborough HG5 9EQ Email: delphhouse.demon.co.uk — MB ChB 1988 Leeds; MRCGP 1994; DRCOG 1992.

ANDERTON, Edward Robert Graham (retired) Intack, Littledale, Lancaster LA2 9ES Tel: 01524 770857 — MB BChir 1963 Camb.; MA, MB Camb. 1963, BChir 1962; DObst RCOG 1965.

ANDERTON, Esther (retired) Flat 2, Southgate House, 15 Cannon Hill, London N14 7DJ Tel: 020 8886 5950 — MB BS Calcutta 1946. Prev: Med. Off. Camden & Islington HA & Barnet NHS Trust.

ANDERTON, John Graham Department of Medicine, The Medical School, Framlington Place, Newcastle upon Tyne NE2 4HH Tel: 0191 222 6000 Fax: 0191 222 0723 Email: j.g.anderton@ncl.ac.uk; 35 Eastlands, High Heaton, Newcastle upon Tyne NE7 7YD Tel: 0191 281 9400 — BM BCh 1990 Oxf.; MA Camb. 1991; MRCP (UK) 1993. Lect. (Nephrol.) Dept. Med. Univ. Newc. u. Tyne. Prev: Clin. Research Assoc. (Nephrol.) Dept. Med. Univ. Newc.; Regist. (Renal.) Roy. Vict. Infirm. Newc.

ANDERTON, John Michael (retired) 21 Carlton Road, Hale, Altrincham WA15 8RH Tel: 0161 980 2931 — MB ChB Manch. 1959; FFA RCS Eng. 1967; DObst RCOG 1962. Prev: Cons. Anaesth. Manch. Roy. Infirm.

ANDERTON, Mr John Michael — MB ChB 1971 Manch.; MChOrth Liverp. 1978; FRCS Ed. 1977. Cons. Orthop. Countess of Chester Hosp. Socs: Fell. BOA; Liverp. Med. Inst. Prev: Sen. Regist. (Orthop.) Liverp. AHA; Regist. (Orthop.) Warrington Dist. Hosps. & Roy. Infirm. Chester.

ANDERTON, Kenneth John (retired) Department of Obstetrics & Gynaecology, Rotherham District General Hospital, Moorgate Road, Rotherham S60 2UD Tel: 01709 820000 — MB BCh 1964 Wales; FRCOG 1982, M 1969; DObst RCOG 1966. Clin. Dir. & Cons. O & G Rotherham Dist. Gen. Hosp. Prev: Lect. (O & G) Jessop Hosp. Wom. Univ. Sheff.

ANDERTON, Miss Lorraine Claire Summerhill Cottage, Denshaw Road, Delph, Oldham OL3 5TS — MB ChB 1988 Liverp.; FRCOphth 1993. (Liverpool) Cons. Ophth. Plastic & Rewnstructure Surg., Qu. Med. Centre Nottm. 2000; Fell. in Oculoplastic, Orbital & Reconstruc. Surg. Roy. Vict. Hosp. Newc.-upon-Tyne. Prev: Fell. Orbital Reconstructure Surg.; Manch. Roy. Eye Hosp; Fell. Orbital Reconstruc. Surg. Vict. Hosp. Newc.-upon-Tyne.

ANDERTON, Mark 79 Green Oak Road, Sheffield S17 4FR — MB ChB 1993 Liverp.

ANDERTON, Philippa Mary Little Greenway, Greenway Lane, Sidmouth EX10 0LZ Email: p@sheaf.demon.co.uk — MB ChB 1993 Liverp. Socs: Ass. Mem. RCGP.

ANDLAW, Mildred Rosemary The Surgery, 93 Streatham Hill, London SW2 4UD Tel: 020 8671 9424 — MB BS 1963 Lond. (Lond. Hosp. Med. Sch.) Socs: BMA. Prev: SHO Qu. Eliz. Hosp. Childr. Hackney; Ho. Phys. & Ho. Surg. Lond. Hosp.

ANDRADE, Mr Antonio Jose Martin Dias — MB BS 1990 Lond.; FRSC 2000 (Tr & Orth); FRCS Ed. 1995. (Lond. Hosp. Med. Coll.) Specialist Regist. (Orthop.) Wessex Region. Socs: Brit. Orthop. Train. Assn.; ESSKA (Europ. Soc. Of Sports Traumatol., Knee Surg. & Arthro.); Assoc. Mem. BOA. Prev: SHO (Orthop.) Portsmouth Hosp. NHS Trust; SHO Rotat. (Surg.) Portsmouth Hosp.; SHO (Cardiothoracic Surg.) St. Bart. Hosp. Lond.

ANDRADE, Elizabeth June Yasmin 138 Harrowdene Road, North Wembley, Wembley HA0 2JF — MB BS 1985 Lond.; MSc (Gen. Pract.) Lond. 1996; BSc Bristol 1979; MRCGP 1992; DRCOG 1991.

ANDRADE, Gerard George Savio 114 Harrison Road, Leicester LE4 6BS — MB ChB 1996 Leic.

ANDRAKA, Dorota Department of Anaesthetics, Hexham Park Hospital, Slough SL2 4HL — Lekarz 1982 Warsaw.

ANDRAWIS, Nabeel Fouad Greenfield Medical Centre, 143-145 Cricklewood Lane, London NW2 1HS Tel: 020 8450 5454; 71 Hodford Road, London NW11 8NH Tel: 020 8455 0145 — MB BCh 1958 Cairo; LMSSA Lond. 1965; AMQ 1960. (Kasr El Aini Hosp.) Socs: (Pres.) Hampstead Med. Soc. Prev: Regist. (Surg. & Accid.) Connaught Hosp. Lond.

ANDREA-BARRON, Diana Ruth Flat 65, Braithwaite House, Bunhill Row, London EC1Y 8NQ — MB BS 1998 Lond.; MB BS Lond 1998. (Uni College Hsp, London) PRHO Gen Surg.

ANDREASEN, Marie-Josée 46 Harvey Goodwin Avenue, Cambridge CB4 3EU — MB BChir 1980 Camb.; MA Camb. 1981, BA 1977; MRCS Eng. LRCP Lond. 1980; Dip. Ven. Soc. Apoth. Lond. 1983.

ANDREN, Sheila Marion Quadriga Health & Safety Ltd, 18A Bridge St, Reading RG4 8AA Tel: 0118 947 5870 Fax: 0118 947 5801 Email: Sheilaandren@quadriga.demon.co.uk; 121 Gresham Road, Staines TW18 2FB Tel: 01784 452677 Fax: 01784 457160 — MB ChB 1965 Glas.; 1971 MRCP (UK); AFOM RCP Lond. 1991; DObst RCOG 1967. Med. Director Quadriga Heaths Safety Ltd Readings; Occupat. Med. Adviser Thames Water & Roy. Boro. Kingston u. Thames. Socs: Soc. of Occupat.al Med. Prev: Med. Off. Hounslow & Spelthorne DHA; Regist. Harefield Hosp.; SHO (Paediat.) W. Middlx. Hosp. Isleworth.

ANDREOU, Basil Andreas Oldbury Health Centre, Albert Street, Oldbury B69 4DE Tel: 0121 552 6747 Fax: 0121 552 2999; 30 Lodge Road, Park Hall, Walsall WS5 3JY — LMSSA 1979 Lond.; Med. Dip. Athens 1973. (Athens) Hosp. Pract. (Dermat.) Sandwell Dist. Gen. Hosp. W. Bromwich. Prev: Regist. (Med.) Sandwell Dist.

Gen. Hosp. W. Bromwich; Ho. Surg. Wordsley Hosp. Stourbridge; Ho. Phys. Burton Rd. Hosp. Dudley.

ANDREOU, Petros Steliou Moorfields Eye Hsp, London EC1U 2PD Tel: 020 7253 3411; 13 Frances Road, Basingstoke RG21 3DB — BM 1990 Soton. SHO (Ophth.) Roy. Vict. Infirm. NHS Trust Newc. u. Tyne; Special Regist., Moorfields Eye Hsp, Lond. Socs: Med. Protec. Soc.; FRCOphth. Prev: SHO (Ophth.) N. Middlx. Hosp. & Roy. United Hosp. Bath; SHO (A & E) Centr. Middlx. Hosp.; Ho. Off. Roy. S. Hants. Hosp. Soton.

ANDREW, Alison Catriona Department of Histopathology, Leeds General Infirmary, Great George St., Leeds LS1 3EX — MB BS 1982 Nottm.; MRCPath 1992.

ANDREW, Bernice DHME, Stoke Mandeville Hospital, Aylesbury HP21 8AL — MB BS 1970 Lond.; MRCS Eng. LRCP Lond. 1969; MRCPsych 1979; DObst RCOG 1972. (Roy. Free) Cons. Psychogeriat. Wycombe Dist. Hosp. Socs: BMA. Prev: Research Asst. Oxf. RHA; Sen. Regist. Rotat. (Psychiat.) Oxf. Train. Scheme.

ANDREW, Charles Ian (retired) Ridgeway, Sutton Road, Newton, Wisbech PE13 5EB Tel: 01945 870581 — MRCS Eng. LRCP Lond. 1967; MRCGP 1972; DObst RCOG 1971.

ANDREW, Christopher John St Andrew's Centre, St Andrew's Road, Plaistow, London E13 8QD Tel: 020 7511 6011 Fax: 020 7511 6011 Email: chris@capa2000.freeserve.co.uk; 122 Hunter Av, Shenfield, Brentwood CM15 8PG Tel: 01277 226121 Fax: 01277 226121 Email: capa@compuserve.com — MB BS 1966 Lond.; MRCS Eng. LRCP Lond. 1966; FFA RCS Eng. 1972; MRC Psych. 1975; T(GP) 1991; T(Psych) 1991. (Char. Cross) Private Cons. Psychiat., Lond.; Specialist Regist. (Psychiat.) Lond. Prev: Sen. Regist. (Child Guid.) Clwyd HA; Sen. Regist. (Psychiat.) Mapperley Hosp. Nottm.; Regist. (Psychiat.) Glenside Hosp. Bristol.

ANDREW, David Christopher Anstey Surgery, 21A The Nook, Anstey, Leicester LE7 7AZ Tel: 0116 236 2531 Fax: 0116 235 7867; Oldfield Farm House, Ellistown Lane, Stanton-under-Bardon, Leicester Tel: 01530 245952 — MB ChB 1986 Manch.; MRCGP 1991.

ANDREW, Mr David Robertson Grantham & District Hospital, Grantham NG31 8DG Tel: 01476 565232 Fax: 01476 590441 — MB ChB 1981 Glas.; FRCS Glas. 1988. Cons. Surg. Grantham & Dist. Hosp.; Cons. Surg. United Lincs. Hosps. NHS Trust. Socs: Assn. Surg.; Vasc. Surgic. Soc.; Assn. of Endoscopic Surg.s of GB & Ire. Prev: Cons. Surg. P.ss Alexandra's Hosp. RAF Wroughton Swindon; Sen. Regist. P'boro. Dist. Hosp. & Leicester Gen. Hosp.

ANDREW, David Smith (retired) East Cruxton, Cruxton, Dorchester DT2 0DZ Tel: 01300 321595 — BM BCh Oxf. 1965; MA Oxf. 1965; FFA RCS Eng. 1970; DObst RCOG 1968. Prev: Cons. Anaesth. W. Dorset Gen. Hosps. NHS Trust.

ANDREW, Douglas Stuart (retired) 11 Seafield Avenue, Bearsden, Glasgow G61 3LB Email: douglas.andrew@beeb.net — MB ChB 1948 Glas.; FFR 1969; DMRT Eng. 1960. Hon. Cons. Radiotherap. Glas. Inst. Radiother.

ANDREW, James Darby (retired) Pentlands Cottage, 12 Gatton Road, Reigate RH2 0EX Tel: 01737 242824 — MRCS Eng. LRCP Lond. 1944; MA, MB BChir Camb. 1945; FRCOG 1966, M 1950, DObst 1948. Prev: Cons. O & G E. Surrey Health Dist.

ANDREW, James Harvey 22 Langley Drive, Camberley GU15 3TB Tel: 01276 64316 — MB ChB 1951 Ed.; FRCOG 1975, M 1961. (Ed.) Prev: Med. Off. DHSS Her Majesty's Insp. Anat.; Asst. Dir. Med. Servs. S.E. Dist. RAMC; CO Brit. Milit. Hosp. Iserlohn.

ANDREW, John Douglas (retired) Whinwood, 41 Cradock St., Bishop Auckland DL14 6HB Tel: 01388 602630 — MB ChB 1947 St. And.; FRCP Ed. 1971, M 1953; DCH Eng. 1951. Prev: Cons. Paediatr. SW Durh. & Darlington Health Dists.

ANDREW, Mr John Glynne Department Orthopaedics, Clinical Sciences Building, Hope Hospital, Eccles Old Road, Salford M6 8HD Tel: 0161 789 7373 — MB ChB 1980 Sheff.; FRCS (Orth.) Eng. 1991; FRCS Eng. 1984; MD 1994. Sen. Lect. & Hon. Cons. Hope Hosp. Manch. Socs: Brit. Orthopaedic research soc (Hon sec 1997-2000; Brit. Orthopaedic Assn.; Brit. Hip Soc. Prev: Sen. Regist. Rotat. (Orthop.) S. Manch.; Regist. Rotat. (Orthop.) Roy. Hallamsh. Hosp. Sheff.; Regist. (Orthop.) Roy. Lancaster Infirm.

ANDREW, Lorna Jean Department of Anaesthetics, Kingston Hospital, Galsworthy Road, Kingston upon Thames KT2 7QB — MB ChB 1981 Manch.; FFA RCS 1988. Cons. Anaesth. Kingston Hosp. Surrey. Prev: Sen. Regist. (Anaesth.) W.m. & Char. Cross Hosps. Lond.

ANDREW, Lucy Authville, Aislaby Road, Eaglescliffe, Stockton-on-Tees TS16 0JJ — MB BS 1997 Newc.

ANDREW, Margot 95 Bridge Lane, London NW11 0EE Tel: 020 8455 7131 — MD 1936 Siena. (Siena)

ANDREW, Martin 248 Heathwood Road, Cardiff CF14 4BS — MB BCh 1987 Wales.

ANDREW, Martin Fergusson Avondale Surgery, 5 Avondale Road, Chesterfield S40 4TF Tel: 01246 232946 Fax: 01246 556246 — MB ChB 1983 Sheff.; MA Camb. 1984; MRCGP 1987. Prev: GP Leyland Lancs.; Trainee GP Chesterfield VTS.

ANDREW, Megan Calder (retired) Whinwood, 41 Cradock St., Bishop Auckland DL14 6HB Tel: 01388 602630 — MB ChB 1948 St. And.; DCH Eng. 1952. Prev: Clin. Asst. (Dermat.) Bishop Auckland Gen. Hosp.

ANDREW, Mr Nigel Carmichael Kent and Canterbury Hospital, Canterbury CT1 3NG Tel: 01227 455466; Cornerways, Stodmarsh, Canterbury CT3 4BD Tel: 01227 721051 Email: nigel.andrew@freeuk.com — MB BS 1975 Lond.; FRCS Eng. 1984; FRCOphth 1989. (London Hospital) Cons. (Opthalmology) Kent & Canterbury Dist. Gen. Hosp. Socs: Liveryman Worshipful Soc. Apoth. Lond.; Roy. Soc. of Med. Prev: Sen. Regist. (Opthalmology) Lond. Hosp. & Moorfields Eye Hosp. Lond.; Resid. Moorfields Eye Hosp.

ANDREW, Richard (retired) 12 Waterloo Road, Edgmond, Newport TF10 8EW Tel: 01952 820018 — MRCS Eng. LRCP Lond. 1945; Lic. Acupunc. Acad. West. Acupunc. 1980. Prev: Ho. Surg. Middlx. Hosp.

ANDREW, Robert Alexander (retired) Croftlands, Colthouse, Ambleside LA22 0JT Tel: 015394 36511 — MB ChB 1951 Aberd. Prev: GP Middleton St. Geo.

ANDREW, Robert Lawrance (retired) 25 Marquis Drive, Clackmannan FK10 4EZ Tel: 01259 213036 — MB ChB 1956 Glas.

ANDREW, Rosalind 321 Jersey Road, Isleworth TW7 5PJ Tel: 020 8574 4454 — MB BS 1961 Madras. (Stanley Med. Coll.)

ANDREW, Susan Louise 38 Farm Road, Beeston, Nottingham NG9 5BZ — BM BS 1983 Nottm.; BMedSci (Hons.) Nottm. 1981, BM BS 1983; MRCGP 1987. Asst. GP Doctors Retainer Scheme Nottm.

ANDREW, Susan May Department Histopathology, Hope Hospital, Stott Lane, Salford M6 8HD — MB ChB 1981 Sheff.; BA Camb. 1977; MSc Trop. Med. Liverp. 1984; MRCPath 1988. Cons. Histopath. Hope Hosp. Salford. Prev: Lect. (Histopath.) Manch. Univ.; Sen. Regist. (Histopath.) Roy. Hallamsh. Hosp. Sheff.; Sen. Regist. (Histopath.) Heath Hosp. Cardiff.

ANDREW, Mr Terence Alec 19 Greenfield Avenue, Stourbridge DY8 1SX Tel: 01384 378584 Fax: 01384 443797 — MB BS 1974 Newc.; BSc (Anat.) Newc. 1971, MSc 1978, MB BS (1st cl.; Hons.) 1974; FRCS Eng. 1979; FRCS Ed. 1979. Cons. Orthop. Surg. Stowlbridge. Socs: Fell. BOA; Brit. Anat. Soc. Prev: Sen. Regist. (Orthop. Surg.) Roy. Orthop. Hosp. Birm.; Con. Orhop Surg. Russell Hall Hosp. & Corbett Hosp. Dudley 1984 - 1999.

ANDREW, Tina Yvonne 18 Bannerman Road, Petersfield GU32 2HQ Tel: 01730 67940 — MB BS 1983 Lond.; DRCOG 1986. Trainee GP Liphook. Prev: SHO (Med. & Geriat., A & E & O & G) Portsmouth HA.

ANDREWES, David Anthony (retired) Orchard Hill, Salterns Lane, Old Bursledon, Southampton SO31 8DH Tel: 01703 403311 — MB BS 1954 Lond.; DObst RCOG 1959. Prev: Ho. Phys. St. Bart. Hosp.

ANDREWES, Helen 22 Ainsley Street, Bethnal Green, London E2 0DL Tel: 020 7729 1557 — MB BS 1997 Lond.

ANDREWES, John Frederick (retired) Whitehill House, Bridge Road, Lower Hardres, Canterbury CT4 7AG Tel: 01227 464968 — MB BChir 1952 Camb.; DCH Eng. 1956; DObst RCOG 1959.

ANDREWS, Mr Brian George Lister Hospital, Chelsea Bridge Road, London SW1W 8RH Tel: 020 7730 6036 Fax: 020 7730 2837; 7 Lauriston Road, Wimbledon, London SW19 4TJ Tel: 020 8946 4705 — MB BS 1955 Lond.; FRCS Eng. 1960; MRCS Eng. LRCP Lond. 1955. (Westm.) Hon. Cons. Orthop. Surg. Chelsea & W.m. Hosp. Lond. & Qu. Mary's Hosp. Roehampton. Socs: Fell. BOA; Fell. Roy Soc. Med. Prev: Mem. Ct. Examrs. RCS Eng.; Sen. Regist. (Orthop.) W.m. Hosp. Lond.; Regist. (Orthop.) Roy. Nat. Orthop. Hosp.

ANDREWS, Brian Terence Edward 85 Hill View Road, Ensbury Park, Bournemouth BH10 5BL — MB BS 1982 Lond.

ANDREWS, Catherine Anne Gables Barn, Ollerton Road, Little Carlton, Newark NG23 6BP — MB BS 1986 Lond.; MRCPsych 1996; MRCGP 1991; DGM RCP Lond. 1990; DRCOG 1989. Sen. Regist. (Psychiat.) Trent. Prev: SHO Rotat. (Psychiat.) Trent; Trainee GP/SHO Norf. & Norwich Hosp. VTS; SHO (Paediat.) Tadworth Hosp. Surrey.

ANDREWS, Catherine Margaret 368 Old Bath Road, Cheltenham GL53 9AD Tel: 01242 522372 — MB ChB 1958 Birm. (Birm.) Assoc. Specialist (Geriat.) Delancey Hosp. Cheltenham.

ANDREWS, Charles Whitford Healthcare Group, Rohais Health Centre, Rohais, St Peter Port, Guernsey GY1 1FF Tel: 01481 723322; La Tourelle, La Ruette de la Generotte, Castel, Guernsey GY5 7PG Tel: 01481 52511 — MB ChB 1974 Bristol. Locum GP, Healthcare Gp. Guernsey.

ANDREWS, Christopher John Antony East Cowes Health Centre, Down House, York Avenue, East Cowes PO32 6RR Tel: 01983 295611 Fax: 01983 280815; Long Meadow, Gravel Pit Road, Ryde PO33 4RB Tel: 01983 884161 — MB BS 1985 Lond.; MRCGP 1989; DRCOG 1988.

ANDREWS, Christopher John Horner The Anaesthetic Department, Derriford Hospital, Plymouth PL6 8DH Tel: 01752 792691; 21 Seymour Park, Mannamead, Plymouth PL3 5BQ Tel: 01752 664830 — MB BS 1971 Lond.; FRCP 2001 Ed.; LMSSA Lond. 1971; PhD Lond. 1976; FFA RCS Eng. 1980. (St. Mary's) Cons. (Anaesth.) Derriford Hosp. Plymouth. Prev: Sen. Regist. (Anaesth.) Bristol Roy. Hosp.

ANDREWS, Mr Christopher Mark The Adela Shaw Orthopaedic Unit, Scarborough Hospital, Scarborough YO12 5QL Tel: 01723 342488 Email: cmandrews@btinternet.com — MB BS 1985 Lond.; FRCS (Onth) 1997.

ANDREWS, Mr Christopher Thomas Royal Victoria Hospital, Orosvenor Road, Belfast BT12 6BA Tel: 02890 240503 Ext: 4036 — MB ChB 1987 Ed.; FRCSI 1991; FRCS Glas. 1989; FRCS (Traum. and Orth.) Glas. 1998. (Intercollegiate Bd. of Examiners in Trauma and Orthop. Surg.) Cons. Trauma & Orthopaedic Surg., Belf.; Roy. Vict. Hosp. and Mlesgrave Pk. Hosps., Belf. Prev: Anat. Demonst. Glas. Univ.

ANDREWS, Colin J Red and White House Surgery, Suite 6, 113-115 High Street, Berkhamsted HP4 2DJ Tel: 01442 866148.

ANDREWS, David Mark Darwen Health Centre, Union Street, Darwen BB3 0DA Tel: 01254 778366 Fax: 01254 778367 — MB ChB 1979 Manch.; 2000 Occ. Med. Diploma Occupational Health Manchester; MRCGP 1983; DObst RCOG 1982. (Manch.) Gen. Practitioner Princip. Health Centre, Union St., Darwen, Lancs. BB3 0DA; Various Occupat.al Health Appts. Socs: Soc. of Occupat.al Health.

ANDREWS, David Michael 12 Raglan Close, Frimley, Camberley GU16 8YL — BM 1998 Southampton; BM Soton 1998.

ANDREWS, Diane Pentland Medical Centre, 44 Pentland View, Currie EH14 5QB Tel: 0131 449 2142 Fax: 0131 451 5855; West Acres Cottage, Lanark Road W., Balerno, Edinburgh EH14 7BL — MB ChB 1981 Ed.; BSc Ed. 1978, MB ChB 1981; MRCGP 1985; DCCH RCP Ed. 1986; DRCOG 1985.

ANDREWS, Elizabeth Caroline 43 Moor Edge, Harden, Bingley BD16 1LB — MB ChB 1994 Bristol.

ANDREWS, Elizabeth Napier (retired) 18 Castle Street, Brechin DD9 6JU — MB ChB 1958 Ed. Prev: Gen. Practitioner - Brechin.

ANDREWS, Fiona Dr Polkinhorn and Partners, The Surgery, Boyden Close, Nunnery Green, Wickhambrook, Newmarket CB8 8XU Tel: 01440 820140 Fax: 01440 820534; Wiggins Farm, Wiggens Green, Helions Bumpstead, Haverhill CB9 7AD — MB BS 1988 Lond.; MRCGP 1996; DCH RCP Lond. 1990. GP Retainer. Prev: GP Lond. Sat. Thos. Hosp. Retainer Scheme.

ANDREWS, Francis John Dept of Intensive Care Medicine, Whiston Hospital, Warrington Rd, Prescot L35 5DS Tel: 0151 426 1600 Email: f.andrews@talk21.com; 55 Eskdale Road, Ashton-in-Makerfield, Wigan WN4 8BG Tel: 01942 717035 — MB ChB 1990 Leeds; BSc (Hons.) Med. Microbiol. Leeds 1987; MRCP (UK) 1994; DCH RCP Lond. 1994; FRCS (A&E) Ed. 1996; FFAEM 1999. (Leeds) Lect. IC Med.; Hon. Specialist Regist., Whiston Hosp. Socs: BMA; Brit. Assn. Accid. & Emerg. Med. Prev: Specialist Regist. (Accid. & Med. Emerg.) St. Ja. Univ. Hosp. Leeds; SHO (Gen. Med.) Dudley HA; Ho. Off. (Profess. Med. & Surg. Units) St. Jas. Univ. Hosp. Leeds.

ANDREWS, Francis Michael (retired) 2A Woodlands Road, Sonning Common, Reading RG4 9TE Tel: 0118 972 2354 — MB BS 1954 Lond.; FRCP Lond. 1979, M 1962. Prev: Phys. Dept. Rheum. W. Berks. AHA.

ANDREWS, Geoffrey Samuel (retired) 1 Beauchamps, Southminster Rd, Burnham-on-Crouch CM0 8PR Tel: 01621 784669 — MB ChB 1941 Bristol (1st Cl. Hons.); FRCP 1963; MD 1950 Bristol. Prev: Home Off. Pathol.

ANDREWS, Gilbert Priory Hospital Woking, Knaphill, Woking GU21 2QF; 175 Oatlands Drive, Weybridge KT13 9JY Tel: 01932 845797 Fax: 01932 853815 — MB BS 1968 Madras; DPM Eng. 1972; FRCPsych 1974. (Thanjavoor Med. Coll.) Cons. Psychiat. Priory Hosp. Woking Knaphill. Socs: Fell., Roy. Soc. of Med. Prev: Med. Director, Heathlands NHS Trust; Med. Director, Priory Hosp.

ANDREWS, Gwendoline Robertson (retired) 26 Ardgowan Square, Greenock PA16 8NJ Tel: 01475 21673 — LRCP LRCS 1926 Ed.; LRCP LRCS Ed. LRFPS Glas. 1926. Prev: Clin. Asst. Glas. Eye Infirm.

ANDREWS, Harry Bertram Rehabilitation Services, Sandringham Suite, Windsor House Humberstone Lane, Leicester LE4 9HA Tel: 0116 225 6868 Fax: 0116 225 6855 Email: harry.andrews@dmhs_tr.trent.nhs.uk; The Willows, Cordelia Close, Leicester LE5 0LE Tel: 0116 246 0988 — MB ChB 1978 Glas.; MA Nottm. 1983, DM 1988; MRCPsych 1982. Cons. Psychiat. Rehabil. Leics. Ment. Health Serv. Trust; Hon. Sen. Lect. (Psychiat.) Leicester Unit. Med. Sch. Prev: Research Psychiat. (Clin. Neurophysiol.) Maudsley Hosp.; Lect. (Psychiat.) Univ. Nottm.

ANDREWS, Heather Stephanie Edgecumbe House, 15 Southfield Road, Cotham, Bristol BS6 6AX — MB BS 1970 Lond.; MRCP (U.K.) 1975; MRCS Eng. LRCP Lond. 1970; FRCR 1976; DMRD Eng. 1974. (St. Bart.) Cons. Radiodiag. Bristol & W.on HA; Hon. Clin. Lect. (Radiodiag.) Univ. Bristol. Socs: Brit. Med. Ultrasound Soc. & Brit. Inst. Radiol. Prev: Ho. Surg. St. Bart. Hosp. Lond.; Sen. Regist. (Radiol.) St. Bart. Hosp. & Hosp. Sick. Childr. Gt. Ormond St. Lond.

ANDREWS, Henry Thomas Tertius Mental Health Unit, Chase Farm Hospital, The Ridgeway, Enfield EN2 8JL Tel: 020 8366 6600 Fax: 020 8364 6711 Email: henry.andrews@enfieldcc-tr.nrthames.nhs.uk — MB BChir 1990 Camb.; MA Camb. 1991; MRCPsych 1995. (Univ. Camb.) Cons. Gen. Adult Psych. Enfield Community Care Trust, Lond. Socs: CAIUS Med. Assoc. Prev: Sen. Regist. (Psychiat.) Roy. Free Hosp. Lond.; Regist. (Psychiat.) Roy. Free Hosp. Train. Scheme Lond.; Regist. (Psychiat.) St. Mary's Hosp. Lond.

ANDREWS, Hilary Anne c/o Lloyds Bank Plc, University of Birmingham Branch, 142 Edgbaston Park Road, Birmingham B15 2TY — MB ChB 1963 Birm.; LMCC 1974; MRCGP 1988; DFFP 1994; Dip. Ven. Soc. Apoth. Lond. 1986. Staff Grade Med. Off. (Genitourin Med.) Birm. Gen. Hosp. Prev: Research Asst. Birm. Gen. Hosp.; Dip. Ascertainment & Phys. & Ment. Handicap Birm.

ANDREWS, Hilary June (retired) Yew Cottage, 20 The Crescent, Reigate RH2 0PB Tel: 01737 246910 — BSc Lond. 1950, MB BS 1955; FRCP Lond. 1987, M 1960; FRCPath 1977, M 1965; MRCS Eng. LRCP Lond. 1955. Prev: Cons. (Microbiol.) Wexham Pk. Hosp. Slough & King Edwd VII Hosp. Windsor.

ANDREWS, Iain Malcolm 26 James Street, Dalry KA24 5ET — MB ChB 1997 Glas.

ANDREWS, Jacqueline — MB ChB 1993 (Hons) Dundee; MD 2001 Dundee; MRCP (UK) 1996. Rheum. SpR Hammersmith Hosital Lond. Socs: Brit. Soc. of Rheum. Prev: Regist. (Cardiol.) Roy. Infirm. Edin.; Cardiovasc. Research Fell. GreenLa. Hosp., Auckland, NZ; Rheum. SpR Wexham Pk. Hosp. Slough SL7.

ANDREWS, James Alexander Brough 2 Priory Avenue, Reading RG4 7SE; 3 Coley Park Road, Reading RG1 6AH Tel: 0118 957 1843 — MB BS 1976 Lond.; MRCS Eng. LRCP Lond. 1975; MRCGP 1979; DRCOG 1978.

ANDREWS, James David Bruyn Thames Side, Felix Lane, Shepperton TW17 8NG Tel: 01932 220760 — MB BS 1950 Lond.; MD Lond. 1952. (St. Bart.) Clin. Edr. Gerontology. Socs: Brit. Geriat. Soc.; Eur. Assn. Sci. Eds.; Med. Leg. Soc. Prev: Cons. Geriat. W. Middlx. Hosp. & Sen. Lect. (Geriat.) Lond. Univ.; Cons. & Geriat. W. Middlx. Hosp. Isleworth & St. Tydfils Hosp. Merthyr Tydfil.

ANDREWS, James Douglas Benefit Agency Medical Services, Government Buildings, Gabalea, Cardiff CF14 4YJ Tel: 029 2058 6408; 5 The Woodlands, Lisvane, Cardiff CF14 0SW Tel: 029 2075 6004 — MB ChB 1973 Ed.; T(GP) 1991; DCH Eng. 1978; DRCOG 1976. (Ed.) Med. Adviser Benefits Agency Med. Serv.; Depty Health Care. Prev: GP Newbury & Bishop's Waltham; Med. Adviser Welsh Off.

ANDREWS, James Ian The Intensive Care Unit, South Tyneside District Hospital, Harton Lane, South Shields NE34 0PL — MB ChB 1973 Birm.; FFA RCS Eng. 1981.

ANDREWS, Janet Mary Regional Infectious Diseases Unit, Western General Hospital, Crewe Road, Edinburgh EH4 2XU Tel: 0131 537 2843 Fax: 0131 537 2887; 111 Trinity Road, Edinburgh EH5 3JY Tel: 0131 552 5391 — MB ChB 1975 Birm.; MRCGP 1980; DCH Eng. 1979. (Birmingham) Staff Grade (Infec. Dis.s) Reg. Infec. Dis.s Unit W.ern Gen. Hosp. Edin.

ANDREWS, Jean Romer (retired) 36 St Bernards Road, Oxford OX2 6EH — MRCS Eng. LRCP Lond. 1938; DA Eng. 1942.

ANDREWS, Joan (retired) Rothbury Cottage, Mill Road, Dinas Powys CF64 4BT Tel: 01222 512402 — MRCS Eng. LRCP Lond. 1956; MSc Wales 1994; MD Lond. 1973, MB BS 1956; FRCS Ed. 1964; FRCOG 1975, M 1962, DObst 1958. Prev: Cons. O & G St. David's & Llandough Hosps.

ANDREWS, John 40 Brompton Square, London SW3 2AF — MB BS 1968 Lond.; MRCP (UK) 1973.

ANDREWS, John Henry Lockstone, 58 Station Road, Shirehampton, Bristol BS11 9TY Tel: 0117 93034 — MB ChB 1956 Bristol.

ANDREWS, John Nathaniel Highmore The Old House, 44 Long St., Tetbury GL8 8AH Tel: 01666 502335 — MRCS Eng. LRCP Lond. 1942. (St. Bart.) Socs: BMA. Prev: Med. Off. Tetbury & Dist. Hosp., Avening Ho. Childr. Home; Gloucester & Stroud Matern. Hosp.

ANDREWS, Jonathan Tel: 01323 744644 Fax: 01323 736094 — MB BS 1990 Lond.; BSc Lond. 1987; MRCGP 1994; DFFP 1994; DRCOG 1994; DCH RCP Lond. 1993. (University College Middlesex) GP Princip. E.bourne; Bd. Mem. E.bourne Downs PCG; Clin. Cancer Lead for E.bourne Downs PCG. Prev: Trainee GP E.bourne VTS; Ho. Phys. (Med.) E.bourne DGH; Ho. Surg. (Orthop.) Univ. Coll. Hosp. Lond.

ANDREWS, Jonathan Lionel 24 Camac Road, Twickenham TW2 6NY Tel: 020 8893 4590 Email: jandrews@doctors.org.uk — MB BS 1992 Lond.; FRCA 1999. (Charing Cross & Westminister) Specialist Regist. (Anaesth.) Ealing Hosp. Prev: Specialist Regist. (Anaesth.) Watford Gen. Hosp.; Specialist Regist. (Anaesth.) Chelsea & W.minister Hosp.; Specialist Regist. (Anaesth.) Char. Cross Hosp.

ANDREWS, Jonathon Tristan Dept of Radiology, Royal London Hospital, Whitechapel, London E1 1BB — MB BS 1992 Lond.; FRCS Ed. 1996; FRCS Eng. 1996. (Univ. College London) Specialist Regist., Roy. Lond. Hosp., Lond.

ANDREWS, Keith Royal Hospital for Neurodisability, West Hill, Putney, London SW15 3SW Tel: 020 8780 4534 Fax: 020 8780 4503 — MB BS 1969 Newc.; MD Newc. 1983; FRCP Lond. 1986; MRCP (UK) 1973. Med. & Research Dir. Roy. Hosp. for Nerurodisabil. Lond. Socs: Med. Disabil. Soc.; Fell. Roy. Soc. Med.; Chairm. UK Acquired Brain Injury Forum. Prev: Sen. & Hon. Lect. (Geriat. Med.) Univ. Manch.; Cons. (Geriat. Med.) Univ. Hosp. S. Manch.

ANDREWS, Laura Jane Marshall 2 Marchmont Gardens, Richmond TW10 6ET — BM 1996 Soton.

ANDREWS, Lea Martyn 158 Whitehorn Avenue, West Drayton UB7 8LD — MB BS 1994 Lond.

ANDREWS, Lucy Henrietta The Highgate Group Practice, 44 North Hill, London N6 4QA Tel: 020 8340 6628 — MB BS 1992 Lond.; BSc Lond. 1989. Socs: BMA. Prev: Trainee GP/SHO Whittington Hosp. VTS.

ANDREWS, Margaret Sheila 13 Heatherwood, Midhurst GU29 9LH — MB BS 1987 Lond.

ANDREWS, Mark Limes Surgery, 8-14 Limes Court, Conduit Lane, Hoddesdon EN11 8EP Tel: 01992 464533 Email: mark.andrews5@virgin.net — MB BS 1980 Melbourne; Dip RACOG 1983; DObst. 1983. (University of Melbourne) GP Hoddesdon.; Exec. Mem. Herts. and Beds. L:ocal Med. Comm.; Exec. Mem. S. E. Herts. Primary Care Trust.

ANDREWS, Mark Johnathan 172 Henley Road, Ipswich IP1 4NT; 6 Enfield Street, Beeston, Nottingham NG9 1AL — MB ChB 1987 Birm.; MRCP (UK) 1991. (Birm. Univ.) Specialist Regist. Renal & Gen. Med. Nottm. Teach. Hosps. Prev: Research Fell. (Renal Med.) Nottm. City Hosp.; Regist. Rotat. (Renal Med.) N. Staffs. & Wolverhampton Dist. HAs.; SHO Rotat. (Med.) Leicester Teach. Hosp.

ANDREWS, Mark Justin Daniel 55 Ditton Lane, Cambridge CB5 8SR — MB BS 1991 Lond.

ANDREWS, Michael (retired) 18 Castle Street, Brechin DD9 6JU Tel: 01356 622635 Fax: 01356 622635 Email: michaelandrews@compuserve.com — MB ChB 1958 Ed.; DObst RCOG 1963.

ANDREWS, Michael Ian James Uplands, White Dirt Lane, Catherington, Waterlooville PO8 0TL — MB BChir 1960 Camb.; MA, MB BChir Camb. 1960; FRCPath 1980, M 1968. (King's Coll. Hosp.) Cons. Path. Portsmouth & S.E. Hants. Health Dist. Socs: BMA & Path. Soc. Prev: Sen. Regist. (Path.) St. Thos. Hosp. Lond.; Demonst. (Path.) Univ. Bristol.

ANDREWS, Michael John (retired) 20 Warren Road, Bexleyheath DA6 7LU Tel: 020 8303 9966 — MB BS 1956 Lond.; MRCS Eng. LRCP Lond. 1956; FFOM RCP Lond. 1991, M 1978. Prev: Dir. Occupat. Health & Safety Brit. Rail Lond.

ANDREWS, Muriel Constance (retired) 75 Calderstones Court, Liverpool L18 3JA Tel: 0151 724 4319 — MB ChB Liverp. 1943; MFCM 1972; DPH Manch. 1947; DCH Eng. 1946. Prev: SCMO Liverp. AHA (T).

ANDREWS, Neil Peter Royal Hospital haslar, Gosport PO12 2AA Tel: 02392 762117 Fax: 02392 762150 Email: neilandr@dsca.gov.uk; 4 Leigh Road, Havant PO9 2ET Tel: 02392 477212 Fax: 02392 475974 — BM BS 1986 Nottm.; BMedSci Nottm. 1984; MRCP (UK) 1990. (Nottm.) Cons. (Cardiol.), Dept. of Cardiol., Portsmouth NHS Trust. Prev: Specialist Regist. (Cardiol.) Univ. Hosp. Wales Cardiff; Electrophysiol. Fell. St. Vincent's Hosp. Indianapolis, USA.

ANDREWS, Mr Nigel John The Pilgrim Hospital, Boston PE21 9QS Tel: 01205 64801; 134 Woodville Road, Boston PE21 8BT Tel: 01205 351227 — MB ChB 1971; MD 1984 Manch.; FRCS Eng. 1977. (Manch.) Cons. Gen. Surg. Pilgrim Hosp. Boston Lincs. Socs: N. Eng. Gastroenterol. Soc.; Brit. Soc. Gastroenterol. Prev: Sen. Regist. (Surg. Gastoenterol.) Manch. Roy. Infirm.; Tutor Clin. Surg. Manch. Roy. Infirm.; Regist. (Surg.) Manch. Roy. Infirm.

ANDREWS, Patrick Yiewsley Health Centre, High Street, Yiewsley, West Drayton UB7 7DP Tel: 01895 422292 Fax: 01895 422134 — MB BS 1978 Lond.; MRCGP 1984; DRCOG 1983. (Roy. Free) Clin. Asst. (GI Endosc.) Hillingdon Hosp. Prev: Trainee GP Luton & Dunstable VTS; SHO (Surg. & Radiother.) Roy. Marsden Hosp. Lond.; Ho. Surg. Roy. Free Hosp. Lond.

ANDREWS, Peter Antony Renal Unit, St Helier Hospital, Wrythe Lane, Carshalton SM5 1AA Tel: 020 8296 3696 Fax: 020 8644 6191 — MB BS 1986 Lond.; MA Oxf. 1990, BA 1983; MD Lond. 1996; MRCP (UK) 1989. (Oxford and London) Cons. (Nephrol.) St. Helier Hosp. Carshalton & Frimley Pk. Hosp. Frimley. Socs: Brit. Transpl. Soc.; Renal Assn.; Eur. Dialysis & Transpl. Assn. Prev: Sen. Regist. (Nephrol.) St. Helier Hosp. Carshalton; Sen. Regist. (Nephrol. & Gen. Med.) St. Geo. Hosp. Lond.; Lect. (Renal Med.) Guy's Hosp. Lond.

ANDREWS, Peter James 38 Bellfield Avenue, Harrow HA3 6SX — MB BS 1993 Lond.

ANDREWS, Peter Searell (retired) Vines Cottage, Little Addington, Kettering NN14 4AY — MB BChir 1948 Camb.; MA, MD Camb. 1957, BA, MB BChir 1948; FRCPath 1970; DMJ Soc. Apoth. Lond. 1970. Cons. Pathol. Kettering & Dist. Hosp. Gp.; Home Office Path. E. Midl. Area. Prev: Asst. Pathol. Bland-Sutton Inst. Middlx. Hosp.

ANDREWS, Rachel Elizabeth Guy's Hospital, St Thomas' St., London SE1; 11 Madeira Park, 18B Benhall Mill Road, Tunbridge Wells TN2 5JH — MB BS 1993 Lond.; BA (Hons.) Oxf. 1990; MRCP (UK) 1996. (St. Mary's) Specialist Regist. (Paediat.)Guy's Hosp. Socs: Christian Med. Fell.sh.; Fell. Med. Soc. Lond. Prev: SHO (Paediat.) Pembury Hosp. Tunbridge Wells; SHO (Paediat.) St. Mary's Hosp. Lond.; Specialist Regist. (Paediat.) Pembury Hosp. Tunbridge Wells.

ANDREWS, Raymond Horace (retired) 5 St Mildred's Avenue, Ramsgate CT11 0EE Tel: 01843 593514 — MRCS Eng. LRCP Lond.

1941; MD Lond. 1948, MB BS 1941; FRCP Lond. 1972, M 1948. Prev: Cons. Chest Phys. Thanet & S.E. Kent Hosp. Gps.

ANDREWS, Richard The Gables Barn, Ollerton Road, Little Carlton, Newark NG23 6BP — MB BS 1986 Lond.; MRCP (UK) 1989. Regist. (Cardiol.) Groby Rd. Hosp. Leicester.

ANDREWS, Richard Baylis (retired) The Hollies, Colemere, Ellesmere SY12 0QW Tel: 01939 270569 — MRCS Eng. LRCP Lond. 1960; DObst RCOG 1963.

ANDREWS, Richard Michael 18 Deuchar Street, Newcastle upon Tyne NE2 1JX — MB BS 1990 Newc.

ANDREWS, Robert 30 Richmond Road, Sedgley, Dudley DY3 1BA — MB ChB 1993 Ed.

ANDREWS, Robert Charles Flat 6, 28 Barony St., Edinburgh EH3 6NY — MB ChB 1991 Birm.; ChB Birm. 1991; MRCP (UK) 1995. Regist. (Endocrinol.) Qu. Eliz. Hosp. Gateshead. Prev: SHO Rotat. (Med.) Burton Dist. Hosp.; SHO (A & E) Redditch Hosp.; SHO (Geriat.) Sandwell Hosp.

ANDREWS, Roger Michael John Westrop Surgery, Newbeigh Place, Highworth, Swindon SN6 7DN — MRCS Eng. LRCP Lond. 1959. (Guy's) Prev: Ho. Phys. & Ho. Surg. New Cross Gen. Hosp.; Ho. Surg. (Obst.) Brighton Gen. Hosp.

ANDREWS, Ronald Douglas (retired) 28 Sharps Lane, Ruislip HA4 7JQ — MB BS 1951 Lond.; BSc Lond. 1937, PhD 1940, MB BS 1951. Prev: Sen. Med. Off. Dept. of Health.

ANDREWS, Mr Samuel Moores Maidstone Hospital, Hermitage Lane, Maidstone ME16 9QQ Tel: 01622 224985 Fax: 01622 224984 Email: sam.andrews@lineone.net — MB BS 1987 Lond.; BA (Hons.) Camb. 1984; MS Lond. 1996; FRCS Eng. 1992; FRCS (Gen.) 1997. (Char. Cross & Westm. Med. Sch.) Cons. Gen. Surg. Maidstone Hosp. Prev: Specialist Regist. (Vasc. Surg.) St. Thos. Hosp. Lond.; Lect. (Surg.) Char. Cross Hosp. & W.m. Med. Sch. Lond.; Fell. in Vasc. Surg, Flinders Med. Centre, Adelaide, SA.

ANDREWS, Sarah Jane The Fort House Surgery, 32 Hersham Road, Walton-on-Thames KT12 1JX Tel: 01932 253055; 47 Mayfield Gardens, Walton-on-Thames KT12 5PP — MB BS 1987 Lond.; DRCOG 1989.

ANDREWS, Simon James High Pastures Surgery, 138 Liverpool Road N., Maghull, Liverpool L31 2HW Tel: 0151 526 2161 Fax: 0151 527 2377 — MB ChB 1981 Sheff.; BMedSci (Hons.) Sheff. 1980; DRCOG 1985; MRCGP 1988. (Sheffield University) GP Maghull; GP Bd. Mem. Crosby & Maghill PCG. Socs: BMA.

ANDREWS, Mr Stephen John 19 Trinity Road, East Finchley, London N2 8JJ Email: stephen.vikki@which.net — MB BS 1990 Lond.; BSc Lond. 1987; FRCS Eng. 1995. (Guy's Hosp.) Specialist Regist. (Urol.) Inst. of Urol., Meddlesex Hosp., Lond. Prev: Specialist Regist. (Urol), Lister, Stevenage; Specialist Regist. (Urol), Hammersmith Hosp., Lond.; Specialist Regist. (Urol), Guy's Hosp., Lond.

ANDREWS, Thomas Campbell Maynard (retired) Church House, Sidestrand, Cromer NR27 0LT — MRCS Eng. LRCP Lond. 1961; MB Camb. 1961, BChir 1960; DObst RCOG 1962; DA Eng. 1963. Prev: GP Cromer.

ANDREWS, Thomasin Catharine Flat 2, 67 Whitehall Park, London N19 3TW — MB BS 1991 Lond.; BSc (Physiol.) Lond. 1988; MRCP (UK) 1994. (UCL) Specialist Regist. Neurol., S. Lond. Prev: Research Regist. (Neurol.) MR Cyclotran Unit; Regist. (Gen. Med.) St. Peter's Hosp. Chertsey; SHO (Neurol.) Roy. Free Hosp. Lond.

ANDREWS, Timothy Martin Slade House, Horspath Driftway, Headington, Oxford OX3 7JH Tel: 01865 228101 Email: tim.andrews@oldt.anglox.nhs.uk — MB ChB 1989 Manch.; MSc Manch. 1997; MRCPsych 1994. (Manchester) Cons. Oxon. Leaming Disabil. NHS Trust (from Aug 99). Socs: Penrose Soc.; Brit. Neuropsychiatric Assn.

ANDREWS, Vasanth 11 Melford Court, Fendall St., London SE1 3DX — MB BS 1996 Lond.

ANDREWS, Vivienne Elizabeth Darent Valley hospital, Darenth Wood Rd, Dartford DA2 8DA Tel: 01322 428100 Fax: 01322 428493 — MB BS 1975 Lond.; FRCPath 1994, M 1982. Cons. Haemat. Dartford & Gravesham HA. Socs: Brit. Soc. Haematol. Prev: Sen. Regist. (Haemat.) King's Coll. Hosp.; Regist. (Haemat.) St. Geo. Hosp. Tooting.

ANDREWS, William John Ruthmount, 64 Hillhead Road, Ballycarry, Carrickfergus BT38 9JF Tel: 019603 73386 Fax: 01232 73386 Email: andrewsjohn@aol.com — MB BCh BAO 1973 Belf.; MD Belf. 1980; MRCP (UK) 1976; DCH RCPSI 1975; FRCP 1991; FRCP 1998; FRCP 1999. (Queens Univ Belfast) Cons. Phys. Whiteabbey Hosp. Co. Antrim. Socs: Amer. Diabetes Assn. & Brit Diabetic Assn; BDA; Assn. of Brit. Clin. Diabetologists. Prev: Endocrinol Fell. Univ. Texas at Dallas, USA; Sen. Regist. Belf. City Hosp.; Sen. Regist. Mater Infirm. Hosp. Belf.

ANDREYEV, Hubert Jervoise Nicholas 19 Meynell Crescent, London E9 7AS — MB BS 1987 Lond.; MA Camb. 1985; MRCP (UK) 1991.

ANDRZEJOWSKI, Antoni Zbigniew 61 Station Road, Woodhouse, Sheffield S13 7RA — MB ChB 1956 Sheff.; FRCGP 1987, M 1976; DA Eng. 1960; DObst RCOG 1959. Asst. Adviser (Gen. Pract.) Univ. Sheff.

ANDRZEJOWSKI, Antony Richard Mark The Medical Centre, Crystal Peaks, 15 Peaks Mount, Sheffield S20 7HZ Tel: 0114 251 0040 Fax: 0114 251 0954 — MB ChB 1984 Sheff.; MRCGP 1988. GP Sheff. Prev: Sen. Trainer RkH Progr., Riyadh; GP Trainer, Sheff. VTS; Trainee, Barnsley VTS.

ANDRZEJOWSKI, John Christopher 61 Station Road, Woodhouse, Sheffield S13 7RA Email: johnaski@msn.com — MB ChB 1989 Sheff.; FRCA 1996. Regist. Rotat. (Anaesth.) Sheff. Prev: SHO (Anaesth.) Roy. Hallamsh. Hosp. Sheff.; Fell. (Anaesth.) Waikato Hosp. New Zealand; Med. Off. Gosford Hosp. NSW, Austral.

ANDUVAN, Sarangapani Department of Anaesthesia, Warwick Hospital, Lakin Road, Warwick CV34 5BW Tel: 01926 495321 Email: sand@doctors.org.uk; 5D Aragon Drive, Warwick CV34 6NB Tel: 01926 885085 Email: mazhavarayar@mail.com — MB BS 1975 Madurai; FFA RCSI 1990. (Madurai medical college) Assoc. Specialist (Anaesth.).

ANEES, Nabil Nagy Gemini House, Wolverhampton Health Care NHS Trust, 31 Compton Road, Wolverhampton WV3 9QP Tel: 01902 645011 Fax: 01902 645012; 3 Cooke Close, Penkridge, Stafford ST19 5SL Tel: 01785 715595 — MB BCh 1978 Assiut; MSc Psychoanalysis, UCL. Specialist Psychotherapist Gemini Ho. Wolverhampton; Psychiat. Train. Course W. Midl. Inst. Psychother.; Hon. Lect. (Psychother.) Wolverhampton Univ. Prev: Assoc. Specialist Psychiat. & Psychother. St. Geo. Hosp. Stafford; Mem. W. Midl. Inst. Psychother.

ANEES, Naheed Wasif 102 Parkhall Crescent, Castle Bromwich, Birmingham B36 9SU — MB ChB 1993 Leeds.

ANEES, Wasif Mohammed 4 Mersey Way, Newbury RG18 3DL — MB BS 1990 Lond.

ANEIROS-GUERRERO, Angel 1st Floor Dental Institute, The London Hospital, London E1 Tel: 020 7377 7000; 84 Balfron Tower, St. Leonards Road, London E14 0QS — MD 1984 Granada.

ANFIELD, Anita Corinne Dorothy Little Blakes, Southview Road, Danbury, Chelmsford CM3 4DX — MB BCh 1987 Wales.

ANFILOGOFF, Michael Ernest 143 Ingrebourne Gardens, Upminster RM14 1BJ Tel: 014022 28888; Mithril, Stanley Road, Bulphan, Upminster RM14 3RX Tel: 01375 892222 — MB BS 1953 Lond.; MRCS Eng. LRCP Lond. 1953; MRCGP 1963. (Univ. Coll. Hosp.) Clin. Asst. Dermat. Harold Wood Hosp. Prev: Ho. Phys. Univ. Coll. Hosp.

ANFILOGOFF, Nicholas Harry Cofton Medical Centre, 2 Robinsfield Drive, Off Longbridge Lane, West Heath, Birmingham B31 4TU Tel: 0121 693 4414 Email: nic.anfilogoff@p.c.birminghamha.wmids.nhs.uk — MB ChB 1981 Birm.; MRCP (UK) 1984. (Birm.) Hon. Lect. (Gen. Pract.) Univ. Birm.; Clin. Sub. Dean., Univ. Birm. Prev: Hon. Regist. (Cardiovasc. Med.) E. Birm. Hosp.; Regist. (Med.) Sandwell Hosp. W. Bromwich; SHO (Med.) E. Birm. Hosp. Bordesley Green.

ANFILOGOFF, Rosalind 93 Northbrook Road, Shirley, Solihull B90 3LX Tel: 0121 746 5000 Fax: 0121 746 5020 Email: wlod.holweger@nhcb3.ms.solihull-ha.wmids.nhs.uk — MB ChB 1985 Birm.; BA Oxf. 1982; MRCP (UK) 1988. GP Birm.

ANG, Choon Kiat Flat 6, 2 Sutcliffe Court, Sutcliffe Road, Glasgow G13 1AP — MB ChB 1994 Aberd. SHO Tretiske Hosp. Roy. Cornw. Hosp. Socs: MDU & BMA.

ANG, Christine Wan-May Flat 2, 169 Palatine Road, Manchester M20 2GH — MB ChB 1995 Glas.

ANG, Ms Swee Chai Royal London Hospital, Whitechapel, London E1 1BB Tel: 020 7377 7198 Fax: 020 7377 7198; Tel: 020 7729 3994 — MB BS 1973 Singapore; MSc (Occupat. Med.) Singapore

1976; FRCS Eng. 1980. (Singapore) Cons. Orthop. Surg. Roy. Lond. Hosp. Socs: Brit. Soc. for Surg. of the Hand; Hon. Mem., Jordan Orthopeadic Assn.; Fell. BOA. Prev: Sen. Cons. Orthop. Surg. Newham Gen. Hosp. Lond.; Cons. Orthop. Surg. Bishop Auckland Gen. Hosp.; Sen. Regist. (Orthop.) Roy. Vict. Infirm. Newc.

ANG WAN-MING, Claire Oak Day Cottage, 26 Wood Lane, Leeds LS7 3QF — MB ChB 1992 Glas.; MRCP (UK) 1996. (Univ. Glas.) SHO III (Paediat.) Yorkhill NHS Trust. Prev: SHO (Paediat.) Roy. Brompton Hosp. Lond., King's Coll. Hosp. Lond. & Addenbrooke's NHS Trust Camb.

ANGEL, Anthony Maurice 16 Martlett Lodge, Oak Hill Park, Hampstead, London NW3 7LE Tel: 020 7794 6103 — MB BS 1948 Lond. (Middlx.) Socs: Nuffield Trav. Fell. 1971; Fell. BMA. Prev: Ho. Phys. W. Middlx. Co. Hosp.; Ho. Surg. (O & G) Roy. Bucks. Hosp. Aylesbury.

ANGEL, Carole Ann Department of Pathology, The University of Sheffield Medical School, Beech Hill Road, Sheffield S10 2RX Tel: 0114 276 6222 Fax: 0114 278 0059 Email: c.a.angel@sheffield.ac.uk — MB ChB 1981 Leic.; MRCPath 1989; FRCPath 1998. (University of Leicester) Sen. Lect. (Path.) Univ. Sheff. Socs: Roy. Coll. Path.; Path. Soc. Gt. Brit. & Irel. Prev: Lect. (Path.) Univ. Leicester; Regist. (Histopath.) Leics. HA.

ANGEL, Helen Rose Maria Alexandra Cottage, 129 Findhorn, Findhorn, Forres IV36 3YJ Tel: 01309 690488 — MB BCh BAO 1976 Belf.; MSc Lond. 1988; MRCGP Lond. 1981; DTM & H Liverp. 1980; DCH Dub. 1979; DRCOG 1979. (Qu. Univ. Belf.) Prev: Project Off. UNICEF Bangladesh & Udaipur Rajastan, India; PMO Solomon Is.

ANGEL, Mr John Charles 26 The Grove, Radlett WD7 7NF Tel: 01923 857442 Fax: 01923 857442 Email: jcangel@compuserve.com; 26 The Grove, Radlett WD7 7NF — MB BS 1963 Lond.; FRCS Eng. 1970; MRCS Eng. LRCP Lond. 1963. Cons. Orthop. Surg. Roy. Nat. Orthop. Hosp. Socs: Fell. BOA; Brit. Orthop. Foot Surg. Soc. Prev: Regist. Surg. Unit Qu. Mary's Hosp. Roehampton; Sen. Regist. Orthop. Surg. Lond. Hosp. Whitechapel; Vis. Fell. Rancho Los Amigos Hosp. Downey, Calif.

ANGEL, Joseph Harold 33 Grove Wood Close, Chorleywood, Rickmansworth WD3 5PX Tel: 01923 283595 — MB BChir 1948 Camb.; BA Camb. 1944, MD 1959; FRCP Lond. 1973, M 1954. (Univ. Coll. Hosp.) p/t Cons. Phys. Bishopswood Hosp. N.wood; Hon. Cons. Phys. Watford Gen. & Harefield Hosps. Socs: Eur. Respirat. Soc.; Brit. Thorac. Soc. & Soc. Francaise des Maladies Respiratoires. Prev: Regist. (Med.) Univ. Coll. Hosp.; Mem. Tuberc. Research Unit Med. Research Counc.; Asst. Prof. (Med.) State Univ., New York.

ANGEL, Ralph Jonathan Europ Assistance, Sussex House, Perrymount Road, Haywards Heath RH16 1DN Tel: 01444 442800 Fax: 01444 410164 Email: jon-angel@europ.assistance.co.uk; Tidebrook House, Tidebrook, Wadhurst TN5 6PQ Tel: 01892 784102 Fax: 01892 783664 — MB BCh 1976 Oxf.; MA, MB BCh Oxf. 1976. (The Royal London) Sen. Med. Advisor Europ Assistance Haywards Heath Sussex; Police Surg. Kent.

ANGELERI-RAND, Elisabetta Maria Teresa Stroud Road Surgery, 102 Stroud Road, Gloucester GL1 5JN Tel: 01452 524506 — State Exam 1983 Pavia. (Pavia) GP Gloucester.

ANGELL, Cecil Leonard 2 Ruskin Close, Hampstead Gardens Suburb, London NW11 7AU — MRCS Eng. LRCP Lond. 1938; Cert JCC Lond. 1978. (Guy's) Socs: Fell. Roy. Soc. Med. & Roy. Soc. Trop. Med.

ANGELL, Mr Graham Richard Bounds End, Shepards Close, Coombe Bissett, Salisbury SP5 4LX — MB BChir 1967 Camb.; MA, MB Camb. 1967, BChir 1966; FRCS Eng. 1973. (Camb. & Lond. Hosp.)

ANGELL, Matthew Price 6B London Road, Petersfield GU31 4BD — BM 1994 Soton.

ANGELL-JAMES, Jennifer Evelyn Department of Clinical Pharmacology, St Bartholemew's Hospital, Medical College, University of London, London EC1A 7BE Tel: 020 7601 7423 Fax: 020 7601 8134; Coney Cottage, Rignall Road, Little Hampden, Great Missenden HP16 9PE Tel: 01494 862866 — MB BS 1962 Lond.; PhD Lond. 1969, MD 1975; MRCS Eng. LRCP Lond. 1962. (St. Bart.) Emerit. Reader Physiol. St. Bart. & the Roy. Lond. Sch. of Med. & Dent. Qu. Mary & W.field Coll. Univ. of Lond.; Hon. Cons. Phys. Med. St. Bart. Hosp. Lond.; Hon. Cons. Phys. St. Mary's Hosp. Lond. Socs: Internat. Soc. Hypertens.; Brit. Hypertens. Soc.; Roy. Soc. Med. Prev: Ho. Surg., Lect. & Sen. Lect. Reader (Physiol.) St. Bart. Hosp. Med. Coll.Lond.

ANGELL-JAMES, Mr John, CBE (retired) The Leaze, Sundays Hill Lane, Falfield, Wotton-under-Edge GL12 8DQ Tel: 01454 260351 — MB ChB 1924 Bristol; MB BS (Hons. & Distinc. Med.) Lond. 1924; MD Lond. 1927; FRCP Lond. 1965, M 1927; FRCS Eng. 1928; Hon. FRCS Ed. 1971. Hon. Cons. Surg. (Otolaryngol.) United Bristol Hosps.; Colles Lect. RCSI 1963. Prev: Lect. & Head (Otolaryngol.) Univ. Bristol.

ANGELOGLOU, Myrto The Surgery, Chippenham Gardens, 4 Malvern Road, London NW6 5PP Tel: 020 7328 3836 Fax: 020 7328 3839; 59 Llanvanaor Road, London NW2 2AR — MB BS 1973 Newc.; MRCGP 1979. GP Princip. Lond. NW6 5PP; Locum Med. Off. to Pk.side Health Auth. Family Plann. Clinics. Socs: HMS Hellenic Med. Soc.; (BMA); WMF Wom.'s Med. Federat.

ANGIER, Elizabeth Ann 39 Matlock Road, Crookes, Sheffield S6 3RQ Tel: 0114 232 1833 — MB ChB 1989 Sheff. (Sheff.) SHO Rotat. New S. Wales, Austral. Prev: SHO St. Peter's Hosp. Bristol & Mildmay Miss. Hospice Lond.

ANGIOR, Penelope Grace Pemberton Surgery, 388 Ormskirk Road, Pemberton, Wigan WN5 9DD Tel: 01942 222246 Fax: 01942 620125; The Gables, 16 Spencer Road, Wigan WN1 2PW Tel: 01942 241640 — MB ChB 1969 Liverp. (Liverpool)

ANGLIN, James Timothy The Stables, Brooklyn Avenue, Rochdale OL16 2SG — MB BS 1983 Lond.

ANGLIN, Mary 49 Rawreth Lane, Rayleigh SS6 9QD; 1 Claybrick Avenue, Hockley SS5 4PS — MB BCh BAO 1968 NUI. (Cork) Prev: Regist. (Surg.) St. Joseph's Hosp. Ijebu-Igbo, Nigeria; SHO (O & G) Leicester Gen. Hosp.; Ho. Phys. & Ho. Surg. Bon Secours Hosp. Cork.

ANGRIS, Suneel Waterhouses Medical Practice, Waterfall Lane, Waterhouses, Stoke-on-Trent ST10 3HT Tel: 01538 308207 Fax: 01538 308653 — BM BS 1986 Nottm.

ANGUNAWELA, Romesh Indika Kismet, 4A Sandbanks Rd, Poole BH14 8AQ — BM 1997 Soton.

ANGUS, Andrew Robert The Surgery, High Street West, Anstruther KY10 3DJ Tel: 01333 310352 Fax: 01333 312525; 17 Nethergate, Crail, Anstruther KY10 3TU — MB ChB 1979 Ed.

ANGUS, Brian John Department of Tropical Medicine, John Radcliffe Hospital, Headington, Oxford; T/L 146 Onslow Drive, Dennistown, Glasgow G31 2PZ Email: brianangus@yahoo.com — MB ChB 1989 Glas.; BSc (Hons.) Glas. 1987; MRCP (UK) 1992; DTM & H 1993. (Glasgow) Clin. Lect. Nuffield Dept. ofMed.John Radcliffe Hosp. Oxf. Prev: Clin. Lect. Wellcome Mahidol Oxf. Univ.; Trop. Med. Research Progr. Bangkok Thailand.

ANGUS, Charles William Gregor The Surgery, 195 Queensferry Road, Rosyth, Dunfermline KY11 2LQ Tel: 01383 414874 Fax: 01383 410616; 21 The Wynd, Dalgety Bay, Dunfermline KY11 9SJ Tel: 01383 822860 Email: willieandgina@bigfoot.com — MB BCh BAO 1967 Dub.; FRCGP 1987, M 1977; DObst RCOG 1972. (T.C. Dub.) Trainer (Gen. Pract.) Fife. Socs: BMA; SE Scotl. Fac. Bd.; Irish Coll. Gen. Pract. Prev: Med. Intern & Surg. Intern Adelaide Hosp. Dub.; Capt. RAMC.

ANGUS, Duncan Anthony Peter 21 Whitebeam Close, Caldwell St., London SW9 0EG — MB ChB 1990 Bristol.

ANGUS, Graeme 61 Woodlands, Seaham SR7 0ER — MB BS 1993 Lond.

ANGUS, M Margaret 22 Woodlands Grove, Edinburgh EH15 3PP Tel: 0131 661 4238 — MB ChB 1965 Ed.; MRCP (U.K.) 1972; DObst RCOG 1969; DCH Eng. 1968.

ANGUS, Margaret Muir McLean Chapelhall Practice, 30 Lauchope Street, Chapelhall, Airdrie ML6 8SR — MB ChB 1986 Glas.; BSc (Med. Sci.) St. And. 1984; DRCOG 1991. (Glasgow) p/t Clin. Asst. (Endoscopy) Monklands Hosp. Airdrie. Prev: SHO (Cas.) Dundee Roy. Infirm.; SHO (Opthop.) Stracathro Hosp. Breckon; SHO (Surg.) W.. Infirm. Glas.

ANGUS, Mr Peter Dewar Dewsbury District Hospitals, Healds Road, Dewsbury WF13 4HS Tel: 01924 499861 — MB ChB 1974 Ed.; BSc 1971 (Hons.) Ed.; FRCS Ed. 1979. Cons. Orthop. Surg. Dewsbury & Dist. Hosp.

ANGUS, Rachel Jean Huddersfield Royal Infirmary, Lindley, Huddersfield HD3 3EA — BM BCh 1975 Oxf.; FRCP Lond. 1995; FRCP Ed. 1994.

ANGUS, Robert Martin Aintree Chest Centre, University Hospital Aintree, Liverpool L9 7AL — MB ChB 1985 Glas.; MRCP (UK) 1989. Regist. (Respirat. Med.) W.. Infirm. & Kt.swood Hosp. Glas. Prev: Regist. (Gen. Med.) Inverclyde Roy. Hosp. Greenock.

ANGUS, Susan Lyle Easter Clevage Farm, Dunning, Perth PH2 9BZ — MB ChB 1998 Glas.; MB ChB Glas 1998.

ANGUS, William Hector Ninian 10 The Parkway, Bassett, Southampton SO16 3PQ — MB ChB 1941 Glas.; FRCGP 1970. (Glas.) Hon. Clin. Teach. Soton. Univ. Socs: Fell. BMA. Prev: Ho. Surg & Ho. Phys. Roy. Vict. Infirm. Glas.; Res. Pathol. Roy. Berks. Hosp. Reading; Med. Off. RAF Med. Br.

ANGUS-LEPPAN, Heather Neurology Department, Royal Free Hospital, Pond St., London NW3 Tel: 020 7794 0500 Fax: 020 7431 1577 — MB BS 1984 New South Wales; MD New South Wales 1994; FRACP 1993. (Univ. New South Wales, Austral.) Cons. Neurol. Roy. Free Hosp.; Hon. Sen. Lect. (Neurol.) Roy. Free Hosp. Socs: Roy. Soc. Med.; Fell. Roy. Austral. Coll. Phys.; Assn. Brit. Neurol. Prev: Sen. Regist. Univ. Hosp. Wales, Cardiff; Vis. Australasian Regist. Oxf.; Speciality Regist. (Neurol.) Inst. Neurol. Sci. P. of Wales Hosp. Austral.

ANGWIN, Hilary Vivien 8 Homerfield, Welwyn Garden City AL8 6QZ — MB BS 1991 Lond.; MRCGP 1995; DRCOG 1993.

ANGWIN, John Richard (retired) September Cottage, 5 Firs Close, Bledington, Chipping Norton OX7 6UA Tel: 01608 658621 — MRCS Eng. LRCP Lond. 1951; MRCGP 1972; DObst RCOG 1953. Prev: GP Basildon.

ANGWIN, Mr Richard Adrian Pentreath c/o St Andrews Vicarage, Parsonage St., Halstead CO9 2LD — MB BS 1977 Lond.; FRCS Eng. 1982. (St. Bart.)

ANHAL, Arun Lata Wenlock Street Surgery, 40 Wenlock Street, Luton LU2 0NN Tel: 01582 27094 — MB BS 1961 Rajasthan.

ANIFOWOSHE, Sadiq Oladele 22 Gulliver Street, Surrey Quays, London SE16 7LT — MB BS 1980 Ibadan; MRCOG 1995.

ANIKIN, Mr Vladimir Alexandrovich Thoracic Surgical Department, Bradford Royal Infirmary, Duckworth Lane, Bradford BD9 6RJ Tel: 01274 364624; 2 Gosvenor Mews, Little London, Rawdon, Leeds LS19 6SD — Vrach 1979 USSR, N.O.M. Inst; 1985 MD (Oncology); 1995 FRCS Ed.; 1999 FRCS; 1998 FEBTS. (N. Ossetian Med. Inst. USSR 1979) Cons.

ANIM-ADDO, Alfred Bentley Health Centre, Askern Road, Bentley, Doncaster DN5 0JX Tel: 01302 874416 Fax: 01302 875820 — MB BS 1961 Durh.

ANIS, Abu Bakr John Street Medical Centre, Colbourne, Warrington WA3 3AS — MBBS 1969. G. P.

ANIS, Mohammed Ashraf Ibrahim Frimley Park Hospital, Frimley, Camberley GU16 7UJ; Ridgewood Centre, Old Bisley Road, Frimley, Camberley GU16 5QF — MB BCh 1975 Ain Shams.

ANISKOWICZ, Jan Stefan The Surgery, The Green, Haddenham, Ely CB6 3TA Tel: 01353 740205 — MB ChB 1976 Leeds; FFARCS Eng. 1981; DA Eng. 1980. Socs: LMC Cambridghsire.

ANJANEYULU, Kandukuri 651 Lea Bridge Road, London E10 6AJ — MB BS 1974 Andhra.

ANJARWALLA, Naffis Kaiyumali Abbasbha Hammersmith Hospital, 150 Du Cane Road, London W12 0HS Tel: 020 8743 2030; 215 Wandsworth Road, London SW6 2TT — MB BS 1993 Lond.; MA Oxf. 1994.

ANJUM, Iftikhar Ahmad Walmersley Road Surgery, 110 Walmersley Road, Bury BL9 6DX Tel: 0161 764 6100 Fax: 0161 764 0100; 6 Higher Croft, Whitefield, Manchester M45 7LY Tel: 0161 766 2299 — MB BS 1965 Punjab. (King Edwd. Med. Coll. Lahore) Prev: SHO (O & G) Fairfield Gen. Hosp. Bury; Regist. (Gen. Med.) Law Hosp. Carluke & Roy. Salop. Infirm Shrewsbury; Regist. (Clin. Haemat. & Med.) Walsgrave Hosp. Coventry.

ANJUM, Mr Javed Iqbal Mater Hospital Trust, Crumlin Road, Belfast BT14 6AB — MB BS 1981 Punjab; FRCS Ed. 1989; FRCSI 1989.

ANJUM, Shazad 8 Angram Drive, Grangedown, Sunderland SR2 7RD Tel: 0191 551 3219 — MB BS 1981 Punjab.

ANKCORN, Christopher Thomas Woodlands Road Surgery, 6 Woodlands Road, Middlesbrough TS1 3BE Tel: 01642 247982 Fax: 01642 241636; Mount House Farm, Pinchinthorpe, Great Ayton, Middlesbrough TS9 6QX — MB ChB 1984 Birm.; MRCGP 1996; DA (UK) 1986; Dip. Coll. Radiogr. 1974. (Birm.) GP. Prev: Trainee GP Nottm. VTS; Vis. Lect. (Anaesth.) Univ. Sci. & Tech. & Komfo Anokye Teach. Hosp. Kumasi, Ghana.

ANKENBAUER, Martin Rainer 27 Longdale Avenue, Ravenshead, Nottingham NG15 9AG — State Exam Med 1986 Wurzburg.

ANKLESARIA, Rita Phiroz Flat 15, Hazel Court, The Avenue, Hitchin SG4 9SJ — MB BS 1949 Bombay; FFA RCS Eng. 1965. (G.S. Med. Sch.) Cons. Anaesth. Lister Hosp. Stevenage.

ANKRAH, Theophilus Commey Department of Medicine, School of Medical Sciences, University of Science and Technology, Kumasi, Ghana Tel: 00 233 51 53515360; 11 Upper Blantyre Walk, World's End Estate, King's Road, London SW10 0DX Tel: 020 7352 9771 — MB ChB 1969 Ghana; MRCP (UK) 1978; DTCD Wales 1975. Sen. Lect. (Gen. Med.) Univ. of Sci. & Technol. Kumasi, Ghana; Hon. Cons. Phys. Komfo Amokye Teachg. Hosp. Kumasi, Ghana. Prev: Lect. (Med.) Med. SMS, UST; Med. Off. Ghana.

ANKRETT, Vivienne Owen Beacon Surgery, Beacon Road, Crowborough TN6 1AH Tel: 01892 652233 Fax: 01892 668840 — MB BCh 1982 Wales; MRCGP 1986; DRCOG 1986. p/t GP. Socs: NL.

ANNADANI, Sherbanoo Roshanali Uxbridge Road Surgery, 337 Uxbridge Road, Acton, London W3 9RA Tel: 020 8993 0912 — MB BS 1962 Vikram.

ANNAL, David John (retired) 109A Park Avenue, Mitcham CR4 2ES — MB BS 1958 Lond.; DObst RCOG 1960. Prev: GP Lond.

ANNAMALAI, Mr Ganesan 30 Edenderry Cottages, Edenderry, Belfast BT8 8RY Tel: 01232 491516 — MB BCh BAO 1993 Belf.; FRCSI 1997. Specialist Regist. (Vasc. Surg.) Roy. Vict. Hosp. Belf. Prev: SHO Rotat. (Gen., Orthop., Vasc. Surg.) Belf.; SHO (A & E) & Demonst. (Anat.) Belf. City Hosp.; Ho. Off. Roy. Vict. Hosp.

ANNAN, Dimitrios Pericles (retired) 2 Hunard Drive, Lexden, Colchester CO3 3SH Tel: 01206 562828 — MD Athens 1961; LAH Dub. 1967. Prev: Research Asst. Karolinska Inst. Stockholm, Sweden.

ANNAN, Fiona Jane Ravensrood, 171 Colinton Road, Edinburgh EH14 1BE — MB ChB 1977 Ed.; FFA RCS Eng. 1982.

ANNAN, George Polighan House, Hermitage Farm, Fenay Bridge, Huddersfield HD8 0JG — Lekarz 1971 Warsaw. (Warsaw) Assoc. Specialist St. Luke's Hosp. Huddersfield. Prev: Clin. Asst. St. Luke's Hosp. Huddersfield.

ANNAN, Mr Henry George Department of Obstetrics & Gynaecology, Whipps Cross University Hospital, Leytonstone, London E11 1NR Tel: 020 8539 5522 Fax: 020 8508 9349; Bachelors Hall, York Hill, Loughton IG10 1HZ Tel: 020 8508 5388 Fax: 020 8502 0185 Email: henryannan@lineone.net — MB BChir 1973 Camb.; MA Camb. 1973; MFFP 1993; FRCOG 1992, M 1978. (Camb. & St. Bart.) p/t Cons. O & G Whipps Cross Univ. Hosp. Lond.; Hon. Sen. Lect. (Obst. & Gyn.) St. Bart. Hosp. Lond.; Examr. RCOG; Recognised Teach. Univ. Lond.; Examr. MBBS; Examr. for PLAB (GMC). Socs: Fell. Roy. Soc. Med.; Brit. Soc. Gyn. Endoscopy; Brit. Soc. Colposc. & Cervic. Pathol. Prev: Sen. Regist. Rotat. (O & G) Addenbrooke's Hosp. Camb. & St. Mary's Hosp. Lond.; Regist. (O & G) St. Mary's & St. Geo. Hosps. Lond.

ANNAN, Iain Hunter Ravensrood, 171 Colinton Road, Edinburgh EH14 1BE — MB ChB 1974 Ed.; FRCS Ed. (Orth.) 1986; FRCS Ed. 1979. Cons. Orthop. Surg. P.ss Margt. Rose Orthop. Hosp. Edin. & Roy. Hosp. for Sick Childr. Edin. Prev: Cons. Orthop. Surg. St. John's Hosp. Livingston.

ANNAN, Mr John Hunter (retired) 1B Napier Road, Edinburgh EH10 5BE Tel: 0131 447 1281 — MB ChB 1938 Ed.; FRCS Ed. 1947. Prev: Cons. Orthop. Surg. Huddersfield GP. Hosps.

ANNAN, Mary Heather Steyning Health Centre, Tanyard Lane, Steyning BN44 3RJ; 3 Balfour Place, Putney, London SW15 6XR Tel: 020 8789 7259 — MB BS 1993 Lond.; DRCOG 1997; DFFP 1999. (UMDS) Main GP Regist., Steyning, W Sussex. Socs: Med. Protec. Soc.; MSS. Prev: SHO (Med. for Elderly) Worthing Hosp.; SHO (ENT & O & G) Worthing Hosp. W. Sussex; SHO (A & E) St. Richard's Hosp. Chichester.

ANNAN, Naa Torshie 19 Shakespeare Crescent, London NW10 8NS — MB BS 1998 Lond.; MB BS Lond 1998. PRHO Gen. Med., Whipps Cross Hosp. Prev: PRHO - Surg., OldCh. Hosp.

ANNAND, John Carmichael (retired) Murrayfield House, 66 Murrayfield Avenue, Edinburgh EH12 6AY — MB ChB 1937 Aberd.; MA, MB ChB Aberd. 1937.

ANNARADNAM, Rajendran John Southgate Surgery, 270 Chase Side, Southgate, London N14 4PR Tel: 020 8440 9301 Fax: 020 8449 9349; 20 South Lodge Crescent, Enfield EN2 7NP Tel: 020 8366 8788 — MB BS 1973 Wales. (Madras) Prev: Regist. (Psychiat.) Enfield Dist. Hosps.; Regist. (Psychiat.) Goodmayes Hosp.; Regist. (Psychiat.) Claybury Hosp.

ANNAS, Mr Edward Guirguis 6 Moore Close, Wroughton, Swindon SN4 9BE Tel: 01793 813651 — MB BCh 1966 Cairo; FRCS Ed. 1983.

ANNEAR, John Marshall Barnet Community Healthcare NHS Trust, Edgeware Community Hospital, Burnt Oak Broadway, Edgware HA8 0AD Tel: 020 8954 2381 Fax: 020 8732 6983 — MB BS 1966 Lond.; MRCP (UK) 1972; FRCP Ed. 1999; MRCS Eng. LRCP Lond. 1966; MRCPsych 1972; FRCPsych, 1995; DPM Eng. 1972; DCH Eng. 1969; DTM & H Eng. 1969; DObst RCOG 1968. (St. Geo.) Cons. In Gen. Psychiat. with s/i in Forens. Psychiat., Barnet Comm Hlthcare NHS Trust. Socs: Brit. Assn. Behavioural Psychother.; BMA; Roy. Soc. Med. Prev: Sen. Regist. Bethlem Roy. & Maudsley Hosps. Lond.; Sen. Regist. Guy's Hosp. Lond.; Cons. (Psychiat.) Croydon Health Auth.

ANNEAR, Richard O'Donovan 308 Mumbles Road, West Cross, Swansea SA3 5AA — MB BS 1975 Lond.; MRCS Eng. LRCP Lond. 1975; MRCPsych. 1981; DRCOG 1977; DPM 1982; Cert Family Plann JCC 1977. (St. Geo.) Cons. Psychiat. Cefncoed Hosp. Swansea. Prev: Sen. Regist. (Psychiat.) Banstead Hosp., W.m. Hosp. Lond. & St. Geo.; Hosp. Lond.

ANNESLEY, Samuel Erl The Health Centre, Bunny Lane, Keyworth, Nottingham NG12 5JU Tel: 0115 937 3527 Fax: 0115 937 6781; 9 Cherrytree Lane, Edwalton, Nottingham NG12 4AL Tel: 0115 923 5966 — MB BCh BAO Belf. 1958.

ANNESLEY-WILLIAMS, Deborah Jane 43 Ormes Lane, Wolverhampton WV6 8LL — State Exam Med 1990 Cologne; States Exam Med Cologne 1990.

ANNESS, Valerie Rose Hensol Hospital, Pontyclun CF72 8YS Tel: 01656 753083 Fax: 01656 753093 Email: val.anness@bromor-tr.wales.nhs.uk — MB ChB 1976 Liverp.; MB ChB (Hons.) Liverp. 1976; FRCPsych 1996, M 1981. Cons. Psychiat. (Learning Disabilities) Bro Morgannwg NHS Trust. Prev: Cons. Psychiat. (Ment. Handicap.) Liverp. DHA; Lect. (Psychiat. Ment. Handicap.) St. Geo. Hosp. Med. Sch. Lond.; Regist. (Psychiat.) Guy's Health Dist.

ANNETTS, Sarah Elizabeth 30 Westbourne Road, Solihull B92 8AU — MB ChB 1997 Bristol.

ANNIS, Mr David Little Hey, Dibbinsdale Road, Bromborough, Wirral CH63 0HQ Tel: 0151 334 3422 — MB ChB 1942 Liverp.; MD Liverp. 1959, ChM 1953; FRCS Eng. 1946; MRCS Eng. LRCP Lond. 1942. (Liverp.) Sen. Research Fell. (Med. Engin.) Univ. Liverp. Prev: Cons. Surg. Roy. Liverp. Hosp.; Mem. Physiol. Systems & Disorders Bd. Med. Research Counc.; Fell. Mayo Foundat. Rochester Minn.

ANNIS, Helen Miriam 63A Netherhall Gardens, London NW3 5RE Tel: 020 7435 7952 Email: helenannis@btinternet.com — MD 1960 Detroit, USA; MD Wayne State, Detroit 1960; MRCPsych 1985. (Leeds Univ. Wayne State U.) p/t Cons. Psychiat., Ealing, Hammersmith & Fulham NHS Trust. Prev: Cons. Psychiat. S. Downs Health NHS Trust.

ANNIS, Jonathan Arthur David 70 Castle Road, Salisbury SP1 3RL — MB BS 1981 Lond.

ANNS, Jonathan Paul Littleford, Newent GL18 1EB — MB BS 1998 Lond.; MB BS Lond 1998.

ANREP, Igor Jaraslave (retired) 42 Southwood Lane, London N6 5EB Tel: 020 8340 8154 — MRCS Eng. LRCP Lond. 1941.

ANSARI, Mr Abdul Saleem 32 Woodcock Close, Bamford, Rochdale OL11 5QA — MB BS 1979 Sind; FRCSI 1991.

ANSARI, Anwar Rauf Coombe Farm, Oaks Road, Croydon CR0 5HL — MB BS 1983 Lond.

ANSARI, Ejaz Akhtar 11 Pinewood Grove, Coventry CV5 6QB — MB BCh 1990 Wales; BSc (Hons.) Wales 1987; FRCOphth 1995. (Univ. Wales Coll. Med., Cardiff) Cons. Ophth. Dept. Roy. Glam. Hosp. CF72 8XR. Socs: Med. Protec. Soc.; ARVO; BMA. Prev: Clin. Fell. Glaucoma Serv. Moorfields Eye Hosp.; Research Fell., Dept. Ophth. Uni of Wales Coll. of Med. Cardiff.

ANSARI, Hina Naila Rauf 225 Rosendale Road, London SE21 8LW — MB BS 1991 Lond.

ANSARI, Iqbal Ahmed Primary Care Health Care Centre, South Road, Chopwell, Newcastle upon Tyne NE17 7BU Tel: 01207 561736 Fax: 01207 563824; 35 Springhouse Lane, Consett DH8 0QF Tel: 01207 560488 — MB BS 1966 Bihar; BSc Benaras Hindu Univ. 1960; DCH NUI 1978. (Darbhanga Med. Coll. Laheriasarai) Prev: SHO (Paediat.) Roy. Manch. Childr. Hosp. Pendlebury, Maelor Gen.; Hosp. Wrexham & Stepping Hill Hosp. Stockport.

ANSARI, Jauwad Karim 7 Oak Croft, Stalybridge SK15 2UQ — MB BS 1969 Ranchi.

ANSARI, Mohammad Idris Birch Lane Medical Centre, Birch Lane, Bradford BD5 8BH Tel: 01274 393392; 6 Colston Close, Bradford BD8 0BN Tel: 01274 820579 — MB BS 1968 Aligarh; MB BS Alifarh 1968; MS Aligarh 1974. (J. N. Med. Coll. AMU Aligarh, India)

ANSARI, Mohammed Aslam 47 Grove Farm Park, Northwood HA6 2BQ — MB BS 1968 Sind; FRCOphth 1992, M 1988; DO RCPSI 1976. (Liaquat Med. Coll.) Ophth. Comm. Health Hillingdon AHA. Prev: Out-pat. Off. Moorfields Eye Hosp. Lond.; Assoc. Ophth. Surg. Spencer's Eye Hosp. Karachi, Pakistan; Ho. Off. (Surg.) St. Bart. Hops. Lond.

ANSARI, Mr Mohammed Zubair Rasheedul Haq City Hospital NHS Trust, Dudley Road, Birmingham B18 7QH Tel: 0121 507 5522 Fax: 0121 507 5182; 1A Alderbrook Road, Solihull B91 1NH Tel: 0121 682 7388 — MB BS 1971 Alig.; MB BS Alig 1971; BSc Alig. 1964; LRCP LRCS Ed. LRCPS Glas. 1979; FRCS Ed. 1979; Dip. IMC RCS Ed. 1992. (JN Medical College, Aligarh, India) Cons. (A & E) City Hosp. NHS Trust, Birm.; Sen. Lect. in Med. (Hon.), Univ. of Birm. Socs: Fell. Fac. Accid. & Emerg. Med.; Brit. Assn. Emerg. Med. Prev: Cons. (A & E) Alexandra Healthcare NHS Trust, Redditch; Dep. Head (A & E) King Khalid Nat. Guard Hosp., Jeddah, Saudi Arabia.

ANSARI, Muhammad Zaimul Akhtar Walsgrave Road Surgery, 59 Walsgrave Road, Coventry CV2 4HF Tel: 024 7622 2094 Fax: 024 7663 3860; 11 Pinewood Grove, Earlsdon, Coventry CV5 6QB Tel: 024 76 678176 — MB BS 1966 Bihar; DLO Eng. 1973. (Darbhanga Med. Coll.)

ANSARI, Nadeem Andrew 45 Langford Green, Champion Hill, Dulwich, London SE5 8BX — MB BS 1984 Lond.

ANSARI, Namir Abbas Cleome, Wood Green, Rackheath, Norwich NR13 6NS — MB ChB 1977 Baghdad; MRCP (UK) 1994.

ANSARI, Naseem Akhtar 11 Pinewood Grove, Coventry CV5 6QB — MB BS 1992 Lond.

ANSARI, Nasim-ul-Haq 7 The Laurels, Providence St., Earlsheaton, Dewsbury WF12 8JN Tel: 01924 466609 — MB BS 1968 Karachi. Clin. Asst. (ENT) Dewsbury Dist. Hosp. & St. Jas. Hosp. Leeds.

ANSARI, Nina Zareen 12 Langford Green, London SE5 8BX — MB BCh BAO 1987 NUI; LRCPSI 1987.

ANSARI, Roshan 180 Bury Street, Ruislip HA4 7TJ Tel: 01895 636414 — MB BS 1969 Karachi; DRCOG 1978. Clin. Med. Off. Hillingdon HA.

ANSARI, Samia The Surgery, 112 Princedale Road, Holland Park, London W11 4NH — MB BS 1994 Lond.; DFFP; MRCGP 2001. (London) Gen. Practitioner, Lond.; PCG IT lead for Kennington and Chelsea PCG; A/E GP.

ANSARI, Shaheen Ashfaq 21 Mount Plesant Road, Chigwell IG7 5EP — MB BS 1972 Karachi.

ANSARI, Shahid Mahmood Burton Road Surgery, 82 Burton Road, Lincoln LN1 3LJ Tel: 01522 513895 Fax: 01522 525660; Tillbridge Cottage, Tillbridge Lane, Sturton-by-Stow, Lincoln LN1 2BP Tel: 01427 787007 Fax: 01427 787007 — MB BS 1979 Punjab; DA (UK) 1987. (Nishtar Medical College Multan Pakistan) Clin. Asst. (Anaesth.) Lincoln Co. Hosp.; BA Med. Off. Socs: MDU. Prev: GP Regist. E. Cumbria VTS.

ANSARI, Shaukat Hussain South Tyneside Health Care Trust, Flagg Court Health Centre, Flagg Court, South Shields NE33 2PG Tel: 0191 456 2612 Fax: 0191 454 9131 — MB BS 1968 Karachi. GP S. Shields Tyne & Wear.

ANSARI, Mr Sher Mohammed Mohammed Jaffer (retired) 3 Dalebrook Road, Sale M33 3LD — MB BS 1948 Bombay; FRCS Ed. 1953; FICS. Prev: Assoc. Prof. Plastic Surg. Dow Med. Coll. Karachi.

ANSARI, Sohail Ipswich Hospital, Heath Road, Ipswich IP4 5PD — MB BS 1983 Karachi; MRCP (UK) 1991. Assoc. Specialist (Respirat. Med.) Ipswich Hosp. Socs: Brit. Thorac. Soc. Prev: Regist. (Respirat.

Med.) Heatherwood Hosp. Ascot; Regist. (Gen. Med.) Arrowe Pk. Hosp. Wirral & Walton Hosp. Liverp.

ANSARI, Mr Suhail Akhter Abdul Hamid Flat 2 Wylie House, Salisbury District Hospital, Odstock Road, Salisbury SP2 8DL — MB BS 1983 Bombay; FRCS Glas. 1991.

ANSCOMBE, Allen Maxwell Department of Histopathology, Dorset County Hospital, Williams Avenue, Dorchester DT1 2JY Tel: 01305 254301 — MB BChir 1977 Camb.; MA, MB Bchir 1977 Camb.; DMJ (Path.) Soc. Apoth. 1989 Lond.; MRCPath 1983; MA Camb. 1977; MRCPath 1983; DMJ (Path.) Soc. Apoth. Lond. 1989. Cons. (Histopath.) W. Dorset Hosp. Dorchester; Hon. Cons. & Sen. Lect. (Forens. Med.) Guy's Hosp. Lond. Socs: Assn. Clin. Path.; Medico-legal Soc. Prev: Sen. Regist. (Morbid Anat.) Soton. Gen. Hosp.

ANSCOMBE, Beryl Georgina (retired) 4 Hunters Court, Little Heath Road, Littleton, Chester CH3 7DW — MB ChB 1945 Liverp.; MRCPsych 1971; DPM Eng. 1959; DObst RCOG 1948. Prev: Cons. Psychiat. Child & Family Psychiat. Kingston Hosp. Surrey.

ANSCOMBE, Marion Katharine Donnington Health Centre, 1 Henley Avenue, Oxford OX4 4DH Tel: 01865 771313 — MB BChir 1976 Camb.; MA Camb. 1976; MRCGP 1980; DRCOG 1980. (King's College Hospital) Prev: SHO (A & E) Plymouth Gen. Hosp.; SHO (O & G) Plymouth Gen. Hosp.; SHO (Paediat. & Med.) Plymouth Gen. Hosp.

ANSDELL-SMITH, Margaret 15 Francis Road, Frodsham, Warrington WA6 7JR — MB ChB 1976 Sheff.; BSc Nottm. 1971.

ANSELL, David Bernard Renal Registry, Southmead Hospital, Southmead Road, Bristol BS10 5NB Tel: 0117 959 5665 Fax: 0117 959 5664 Email: ansell@renalreg.com; 8 Victoria Walk, Bristol BS6 5SR — MB ChB 1980 Liverp.; MRCS Eng. LRCP Lond. 1980. Dir., UK Renal Registry, S.mead Hsp, Bristol; Clin. Fell. in Nephrol., S.mead Hsp, Bristol.

ANSELL, Eric Cholmley Gardens Surgery, 1 Cholmley Gardens, Mill Lane, London NW6 1EA Tel: 020 7794 6256 Fax: 020 7794 0540; 12A Salisbury Court, Salisbury Avenue, London N3 3AH Tel: 020 8349 0870 — MB ChB 1978 Liverp. Clin. Asst. (Cardiol.) Roy. Free Hosp. Lond.; Primary Care Phys. & Clin. Asst. (A & E) Roy. Free Hosp. Lond.; Hon. Lect. & Research Fell. (Primary Care) Roy. Free Hosp. Lond.; Mem. Camden & Islington LMC; Mem. Med. Audit Advis. GP. Socs: Brit. Assn. Sport & Med. Prev: Regist. (A & E) Whipps Cross Hosp. Lond.; Regist. (Neurol.) Char. Cross Hosp. Lond. & Hon. Research Fell/Regist. (Med.) Migraine Clin. St. Bart. Hosp. & Hackney HA Lond.; SHO (Respirat. Med.) N. Manch. Gen. Hosp.

ANSELL, Gavin James Horsefair Practice, Horse Fair, Rugeley WS15 2EL Tel: 01889 582244 Fax: 01899 582244 — MB ChB 1993 Sheff. SHO Rotat. Roy. & Newcross Hosps. Wolverhampton VTS. Prev: Ho. Off. (Gen. Med. & Gen. Surg.) Doncaster Roy. Infirm.

ANSELL, George (retired) 101 Childwall Park Avenue, Liverpool L16 0JF Tel: 0151 722 2675 — MB ChB Liverp. 1945; MD Liverp. 1949; FRCP Lond. 1972, M 1947; FRCR 1975; FFR 1955; DMRD Eng. 1953; DMRD Liverp. 1953. Prev: Cons. Radiol. i/c Whiston Hosp. & Lect. (Radiodiag.) Univ. Liverp.

ANSELL, Gillian Lindsay 20 Shelley Close, Ashley Heath, Ringwood BH24 2JA Tel: 01425 472612 — MB BS 1996 Lond.; BSc Lond. 1993. (St Geos. Hosp. Med. Sch.)

ANSELL, Gregory Douglas 20 Shelley Close, Ashley Heath, Ringwood BH24 2JA Tel: 01425 472612 — BM BCh 1969 Oxf.; BA (Cl. II Hons., Animal Physiol.); DObst RCOG 1973; DCH Eng. 1972. (Oxf. & St. Thos.)

ANSELL, Ian David Department Histopathology, City Hospital, Hucknal Road, Nottingham NG5 1PB Tel: 0115 969 1169 Ext: 47703 Fax: 0115 962 7768; 11 Marlborough Road, Woodthorpe, Nottingham NG5 4FG Tel: 0115 926 0132 — MB BChir 1963 Camb.; MA 1963 Camb.; FRCPath. 1981 M 1969. (St. Bart./Camb.) Cons. Histopath. City Hosp. Nottm. Socs: Ex-Pres. Internat. Acad. Path. (Brit. Div.); Brit. Soc. Gastroenterol. Prev: Lect. & Hon. Cons. Histopath. Roy. Postgrad. Med. Sch. Lond.; Regist. (Path.) St. Bart. Hosp. Lond.; Lect. (Morbid Anat.) King's Coll. Hosp. Med. Sch. Lond.

ANSELL, Kenneth Stanley Shaw Heath Health Centre, Gilmore St., Stockport SK3 8DN Tel: 0161 480 2270 — MB ChB 1956 Manch. (Manch.) Prev: Ho. Surg. Manch. Roy. Infirm.; Ho. Phys. & Ho. Off. O & G Crumpsall Hosp.

ANSELL, Margaret Joan Musgrove Park Hospital, Taunton TA1 5DA Tel: 01823 3444 — MB ChB 1964 Sheff.; DA Eng. 1967; DObst RCOG 1966. (Sheff.) Prev: Med. Asst. (Anaesth.) MusGr. Pk. Hosp. Taunton; SHO (Anaesth.) Taunton Hosp. Gp.; Regist. (Anaesth.) Plymouth Gen. Hosp.

ANSELL, Peter John 1 Aldbrough Close, Ryhope, Sunderland SR2 0LD — MB BS 1974 Lond.

ANSELL, Richard William The Hawthorns, 1 Oxford Road, Redhill RH1 1DT Tel: 01737 762902 Fax: 01737 762902 — MB ChB 1981 Aberd.

ANSELL, Stephanie Faye Pheasants Crossing, Sandpits Lane, Sherston, Malmesbury SN16 0NN Tel: 01666 841127 — MB ChB 1993 Bristol. Trainee GP Bristol VTS; Mem. MDU.

ANSERMINO, John Mark Department of Anaesthesia, St Andrews Centre for Plastic Surgery, Broomfield Hospital, Broomfield, Chelmsford CM1 7ET Tel: 01245 440761 Email: plasticsurgery@dial.pipex.com — MB ChB 1985 Witwatersrand; MMed (Anaesth.) Witwatersrand 1992; FFA (S. Afr.) 1991. (University of Witwatersrand) Cons. Anaesth. St. And. Centre for Plastic Surg. & Burns.

ANSHAR, Fauzi Mohamed Dept. of Respiratory Medicine, North Manchester General Hospital, Manchester M8 5RB — MB ChB 1996 Sheff. Specialist Regist. (Respirat. Med.) N. Manch. Gen. Hosp.

ANSLEY, Douglas Gordon Howland Compass House Medical Centres, 25 Bolton Street, Brixham TQ5 9BZ Tel: 01803 855897 Fax: 01803 855613 — BM BCh 1984 Oxf.; MRCGP 1992; DA (UK) 1990.

***ANSLEY-WATSON, Michelle** 3 Lanes End, Fareham PO14 2BH — MB BS 1998 Lond.; MB BS Lond 1998.

ANSLOW, Philip Leslie Neuroradiology, Radcliffe Infirmary, Woodstock Road, Oxford OX2 6HE Tel: 01865 228441 Fax: 01865 224686; The Old Clockwork Shop, 61 Corn St, Witney OX28 6BT Tel: 01993 700874 Fax: 01993 201282 Email: panslow@quista.net — MB BChir 1977 Camb.; MA, MB Camb. 1977, BChir 1976; FRCR 1982. (Kings Coll. Hosp.) Cons. Neuroradiol. Radcliffe Infirm. Oxf. Socs: Roy. Soc. Med.; Brit. Soc. of Neuroradiologists; Brit. Soc. of Head &Neck Radiol. Prev: Sen. Regist. (Neuroradiol.) Radcliffe Infirm. Oxf.; Sen. Regist. (Radiol.) Kings Coll. Hosp. Lond.

ANSLOW, Susan Rowena Felicity Regent Street Surgery, 73 Regent Street, Stonehouse GL10 2AA Tel: 01453 822145 Fax: 01453 821663; Russell House, The Green, Frampton-on-Severn, Gloucester GL2 7EP Tel: 01452 740808 — MB ChB 1980 Bristol; MRCGP 1984; DRCOG 1982. (Bristol)

ANSON, James Joseph 23 Kingsthorne Park, Hunts Cross, Liverpool L25 0QR Tel: 0151 486 7520 — MB ChB 1988 Liverp.; DRCPath 1995. Sen. Regist. (Med. Microbiol.) Roy. Liverp. Hosp. Socs: Amer. Soc. Microbiol.; BSAC. Prev: Regist. (Med. Microbiol.) Leeds Gen. Infirm.; SHO (Med.) Fazakerley Hosp. Liverp. & Roy. Liverp. Hosp.; SHO (A & E) BRd.green Hosp. Liverp.

ANSON, John Anthony Robert (retired) 30 Tibbets Close, Inner Park Road, London SW19 6EF Tel: 020 8788 2060 — MRCS Eng. LRCP Lond. 1952; DObst RCOG 1957; DPH Lond. 1958. Prev: Cas. Off. & Ho. Phys. Roy. Hosp. Chesterfield.

ANSON, Mr Kenneth Mark Department of Urology, St George's Hospital, Blackshaw Road, Tooting, London SW17 0QT Tel: 020 8725 3305 Fax: 020 8725 1425 Email: ansonhayes@aol.com — MB BS 1985 Lond.; FRCS Eng. 1989; MS Lond. 1996; FRCS (Urol.) 1997. Cons. Urol. St Geo.'s Hosp. Lond. & Qu. Mary's Hosp. Roehampton. Socs: Brit. Assn. Urol. Surg.; Roy. Soc. Med.

ANSONS, Mr Alec Michael Lanehead House, Woodhead Road, Glossop SK13 7QE — MB BCh 1981 Wales; FRCS Ed. 1985; DO RCS Eng. 1985.

ANSONS, Christine Bents Green Surgery, 98 Bents Road, Sheffield S11 9RL Tel: 0114 236 0641 Fax: 0114 262 1069 — MB ChB 1975 Bristol; FFA RCS 1981; DRCOG 1978.

ANSORGE, Rose 117 Cazenove Road, London N16 6AX — State Exam Med 1988 Berlin; MRCGP 1996; DRCOG 1995; DFFP 1995. Asst. Gen. Pract. Lond.; Clin. Asst. Genitourin. Med. Lond.

ANSTEE, Bryan Hall Mendip, 7 Queens Road, Cheltenham GL50 2LR — MB BChir 1965 Camb.; MA Camb. 1965; FRCPsych 1985, M 1972; DPM Eng. 1968; DObst RCOG 1966. (Camb. & King's Coll. Hosp.) Cons. Psychiat. Llanarth Ct. Gwent. Prev: Cons. Psychiat. Wotton Lawn & Coney Hill Hosp. Glos.; Cons. Psychiat.

Old Manor Hosp. & Salisbury Gen. Infirm.; 1st Asst. (Psychiat.) Guy's Hosp. Lond.

ANSTEE, Quentin Mark Northwick Park and St Mark's Hospitals, Watford Road, Harrow HA1 3UJ; 33 Monmouth Close, Chiswick, London W4 5DQ — MB BS 1997 Lond.; BSc (Hons.) 1994. (University College London) SHO (Med.) N.wick Pk. & St. Mark's Hosps. Lond. Prev: Ho. Off. (Surg.) The Whittington Hosp. Lond.; Ho. Off. (Med.) The Mayday Univ. Hosp. Croydon.

ANSTEY, Alexander Vincent Royal Gwent Hospital, Department of Dermatology, Cardiff Road, Newport NP20 2UB; The Paddocks, Glascoed, Pontypool NP4 0TY Tel: 01633 785445 Fax: 01633 785230 — MB BS 1983 Lond.; MRCP (UK) 1986; DRCOG 1988; FRCP Lond. 1998. (London) Cons. Dermat. Gwent Healthcare, NHS Trust. Prev: Sen. Regist. (Dermat.) Univ. Hosp. Wales Cardiff; Regist. (Dermat.) St. Bart. Hosp. Lond. & Wycombe Gen. Hosp. Bucks.

ANSTEY, Elizabeth Jane Fishponds Health Centre, Beechwood Road, Fishponds, Bristol BS16 3TD Tel: 0117 908 2365 Fax: 0117 908 2377; 23 Northumberland Road, Redland, Bristol BS6 7AZ Tel: 0117 924 6835 — MB ChB 1973 Bristol; MRCGP 1977; DCH Eng. 1977; DObst RCOG 1975. Prev: SHO (A & E) Bristol Roy. Infirm.; SHO (Paediat.) Bristol Childr. Hosp.; SHO (Obst.) Bristol Matern. Hosp.

ANSTISS, Timothy John Occupational Health Department, West London Healthcare Trust, Uxbridge Road, Southall UB1 3EU Tel: 020 8967 5164; 95 Fern Lane, Heston, Hounslow TW5 0HH Email: timanstiss@btinternet.com — BM 1985 Soton.; Med. Viginia 1984; BM Soton 1985; Dip. Occ. Med. RCP Lond. 1996. (Univ. Soton.) Occupat. & Exercise Med. W. Lond. Healthcare NHS Trust. Socs: Amer. Coll. of Sports Med.; Soc. of Occupat. Med. Prev: SHO (Psychiat.) St. Bernard's Hosp. Lond.; Research Asst. (Acad. Psychiat.) Char. Cross Med. Sch.; Hon. Regist. Ment. Health Unit. St. Bernard's Hosp.

ANTAL, Laslo Charles (retired) 13 Salisbury Road, Cressington Park, Liverpool L19 0PH Tel: 0151 427 8168 Fax: 0151 494 2622 — MB BS Lond. 1964; MRCS Eng. LRCP Lond. 1963. Prev: Ho. Off. (Radiother. & Thoracic Surg.) United Oxf. Hosps.

ANTANI, Malini Rashmikant Harden Road, 218 Harden Road, Leamore, Walsall WS3 1BS Tel: 01922 401724 Fax: 01922 495100 — MB BS 1968 Gujarat. (M.P. Shah Med. Coll. Jamnagar) Sch. Med. Off. Walsall HA; Sen. Med. Off. (Instruc. Doctor) Family Plann. Prev: SHO (Cas.) Walsall Gen. Hosp.; SHO (O & G) Hallam Hosp. W. Bromwich; SHO (Cas.) Roy. Hosp. Wolverhampton.

ANTANI, Rashmikant Dolarrai Harden Road, 218 Harden Road, Leamore, Walsall WS3 1BS Tel: 01922 401724 Fax: 01922 495100 — MD 1966 Agra; MB BS 1963. (S.N. Med. Coll.) Sch. Med. Off. Walsall HA; Police Surg. Socs: Assn. Police Surg. Prev: SHO (Gen. Med.) Burton Rd. Hosp. Dudley; Regist. (Chest Med. & Geriat.) Heath La. Hosp. W. Bromwich.

ANTAO, Anthony Juno Orlando Renal Unit, Morriston Hospital, Swansea SA6 6NL Tel: 01792 703534 Fax: 01792 703716; 342 Gower Road, Killay, Swansea SA2 7AE Tel: 01792 205782 — MB ChB 1967 Aberd.; MSc (Ethics of Health Care) Liverp. 1992; FRCP Lond. 1997; MRCP (UK) 1972; DCMT Lond. 1969. Cons. Renal Phys. (Nephrol.) Morriston Hosp. Swansea. Socs: Renal Assn.; Eur. Dialysis & Transpl. Assn. Prev: Cons. Phys. Hamad Gen. Hosp. Doha Qatar; Regist. (Med.) & Resid. Med. Off. W.m. Hosp. Lond.; Assoc. Specialist (Nrphol.) Morrison Hosp. Swansea.

ANTAO, Vera Rita Fatima de Loyola Furtado Community Child Health, Ystradd Mynach Hospital, Hengoed CF82 7XU Tel: 01443 811385 Fax: 01443 862120 — MB BS 1972 Karnatak; MD (Paediat.) Bombay 1976; DCH Bombay 1974; MRCP (UK) 1990; MRCPCH 1997; FRCPCH 1997. (Karnatak Med. Coll. Hubli, India) Cons. Paediat. (Community Child Health) Ystradd Mynach Hosp. Wales; Mem. Europ. Acad. Childh. Disabil. Socs: BMA; Coll. of Paediat. & Child Health; Welsh Paediatric Soc. (WPS). Prev: Sen. Regist. (Community Child Health) Univ. Hosp. Wales, Cardiff; Regist. (Paediat.) Singleton Hosp. Swansea.

ANTCLIFF, Anthony Charles South Lodge, Great Bardfield, Braintree CM7 4SD — MB BS 1961 Lond. Cons. Chem. Pathol. Chelmsford & Essex Hosp. Prev: Regist. (Haemat.) W.m. Hosp. Lond.; Ho. Surg. W.m. Childr. Hosp. Lond.; Ho. Phys. St. Jas. Hosp. Balham.

ANTCLIFF, Mr Richard James Department of Ophthalmology, Royal United Hospital, Combe Park, Bath BA1 3NG; Ashlands, Belmont Road, Combe Down, Bath BA2 5JR Tel: 020 7636 7780 Fax: 020 7636 7790 — MB BS 1989 Lond.; MD 2001 Lond; FRCOphth 1994. (St. Bart.) Cons. Ophth. Surg., Roy. United Hosp. Combe Pk., Bath BA1 3NG. Prev: SHO (Ophth.) Addenbrooke's Hosp. Camb.; Regist. (Ophth.) St. Thos. Hosp. Lond.

ANTCLIFFE, Rodney Douglas Weavers Medical Centre, 50 School Lane, Kettering NN16 0DH Tel: 01536 513494 Fax: 01536 416521; 7 The Gardens, Kettering NN16 9DU — MB BS 1970 Lond.; DObst RCOG 1972.

ANTEBI, Daniel Leo Hounslow and Spelthorne Community and Mental Health Trust, Lakeside Unit, West Middlesex Hospital, Twickenham Road, Isleworth TW7 6AF — MB ChB 1982 Glas.; MSc Bristol 1991; MRCPsych 1988. Cons. (Psychiat.) Hounslow & Spelthorne Community Serv. Trust. Prev: Cons. Psychiat. Plymouth Comm. Servs. Trust.

ANTEBI, Mr David 14 Marsh Lane, Mill Hill, London NW7 4QP Tel: 020 8906 2714 — MB BS 1975 Lond.; FRCS (Eng.) 1980; MRCS Eng. LRCP Lond. 1975; DRCOG 1985. (St. Mary's) Dir. Med. Dept. Internat. Asst. Serv. Purley; Hon. Assoc. Specialist (Orthop.) Qu. Eliz. II Hosp. Welwyn Gdn. City; Chief Med. Off. Europ. Assistance Croydon. Prev: Chief Med. Off. Europ. Assistance Croyon.

ANTEBI, Raymond Picketlaw House, Montgomery House, Eaglesham, Glasgow G76 0AU Tel: 0141 303520 Fax: 0141303520 — MD Bologna 1954; FRCP Glas. 1982, M 1980; LAH Dub. 1957; FRCPsych 1979, M 1972; DPM Eng. 1961. (Bologna - Italy) Cons. Psychiat. Prev: Phys. Supt. & Clin. Surg. Manager Glas. E. Dist. Psychiat. Servs.; Hon. Cons. Psychiat. Strathclyde Univ. & All St.s' Hosp. Birm.

ANTEN, Jacqueline Lynne 21 Cwm Arian, Morriston, Swansea SA6 6GH — MB ChB 1990 Liverp.; DRCOG 1996; DCR 1996; MRCGP 1996. Med. Adviser, DVLA.

***ANTHONISZ, Gillian Minette** 9 Meldon Terrace, Newcastle upon Tyne NE6 5XP — MB BS 1998 Newc.; MB BS Newc 1998.

ANTHONY, Andrew Academic Department, Royal Free Hospital School of Medicine, Pond St., London NW3 2QG — MB BS 1987 Lond.; PhD Lond. 1982, BSc 1977; MSc Surrey 1978. Clin. Research Fell. Roy. Free Hosp. Med. Sch. Prev: Ho. Off. Liver Unit Kings Coll. Hosp. Sch. Med. & Dent.

ANTHONY, Ann 2 Trevelyan Close, Claverdon, Warwick CV35 8PA Tel: 01926 842449 — MB ChB 1982 (Hons.) Birm.; FRCP 2001 (UK); FFAEM 1997. (Birm.) p/t Cons. A & E Med. Univ. Hosp. Of Coventry & Warks. Socs: BMA; Brit. Assn. Accid. & Emerg. Med.; Sands Cox Med. Soc. Prev: Sen. Regist. (A & E) W. Midl. RHA; Regist. (A & E) W. Midl. RHA; Cons. A & E Med. Alexandra Healthcare NHS Trust Redditch.

ANTHONY, Christian Jacques Jules David L Meddyfga Taf, North Road, Whitland SA34 0AT Tel: 01994 240195 Fax: 01994 241138; The Old Vicarage, Llanddewi Velfrey, Narberth SA67 8UT Tel: 01834 860593 — MB BCh 1978 Wales; MRCGP 1990; DRCOG 1980.

ANTHONY, Edna Winifred 2 Regent Bank, Gravel Lane, Wilmslow SK9 6LE Tel: 01625 526669 — MB ChB 1955 Liverp.; DA Eng. 1957. Clin. Asst. N. BTS Manch.

ANTHONY, Edward Lyn Avenue Villa Surgery, Brynmor Road, Llanelli SA15 2TJ Tel: 01554 774401 Fax: 01554 775229; Yr Hafod, 28 Penyfai Lane, Llanelli SA15 4EN Tel: 01554 751723 — MB BS 1978 Lond.; MRCS Eng. LRCP Lond. 1977; T(GP) 1991; DRCOG 1979. (Westm.) Local Med. Off. Civil Serv. Med. Advisory Serv.; Med. Off. Marks & Spencers LLa.lli, Carmarthen & Swansea. Socs: Dyfed Local Med. Comm.; BMA. Prev: Clin. Asst. (Psychiat.) E. Dyfed AHA.; Ho. Surg. St. Stephen's Hosp. Fulham; Ho. Phys. Essex Co. Hosp. Colchester.

ANTHONY, Eric, Group Capt. RAF Med. Br. (retired) 143 Priory Road, Hungerford RG17 0AP Tel: 01488 682573 — MB ChB Birm. 1955; MD Birm. 1972; FRCPsych 1978, M 1971; DPM Eng. 1967; DCH Eng. 1962. Prev: Cons. Adviser in Psychiat. RAF.

ANTHONY, George Strathie Broomberry House, 15 Barkhill Road, Gourock PA19 1LA — MD 1983 Glas.; MB ChB 1972; FRCOG 1990, M 1978. Cons. O & G Inverclyde Roy. Hosp. & Rankin Matern. Hosp.

ANTHONY, Honor Mary 61A The Crescent, Adel, Leeds LS16 6AG Tel: 0113 267 1167 Fax: 0113 267 1167 Email: honor235@aol.com; Fairfield House, North St, Keighley BD21 3AA Tel: 01535 606881 Fax: 01535 655456 — MB ChB 1951 Leeds.

(Leeds) Socs: Brit. Soc. Allergy, Environm. & Nutrit. Med. Prev: Clin. Asst. (Allergy) Airedale Gen. Hosp., Keighley; SMO DHSS; Lect. (Immunol.) Leeds.

ANTHONY, Johanne Patricia Department of Obstetrics & Gynaecology, Northampton General Hospital, Billing Road, Northampton NN1 5BD — MB BChir 1982 Camb.; MA, MB Camb. 1982, BChir 1981; MRCOG (Gold Medal) 1986; T(OG) 1991; DRCOG 1983; FRCOG 1998. Cons. O & G s/i FetoMatern. Med. N.ampton Gen. Hosp.

ANTHONY, John Ronald Oldcastle Surgery, South Street, Bridgend CF31 3ED Tel: 01656 657131 Fax: 01656 657134; Ty Ffeiriad Farm, Blackmill, Bridgend CF35 6DN Tel: 01656 657131 — MB BS 1978 Lond.; MRCS Eng. LRCP Lond. 1978; DCH RCP Lond.1983. (Kings College Hospital) GP Bridgend; Clin. Asst. (Paediat.) Bridgend Gen. Hosp.

ANTHONY, John Roslyn Ingrebourne Gardens Medical Centre, 143 Ingrebourne Gardens, Cranham, Upminster RM14 1BJ Tel: 01708 228888 Fax: 01708 641479 — MB BS 1955 Lond.; MRCS Eng. LRCP Lond. 1956; MRCGP 1963. (Lond. Hosp.) Cons. Psychol. Med. Suttons Manor Clinic. Prev: Ho. Phys. (Radiother. & Dermat.) Lond. Hosp.; Ho. Surg. (Gyn. & Gen. Surg.) Harold Wood Hosp.

ANTHONY, Karen 61 Elmswood Road, Liverpool L17 0DH — MB BS 1994 Lond.

ANTHONY, Katherine Louise 1 Lower Road, Wirral CH62 5EG — MB ChB 1998 Liverp.; MB ChB Liverp 1998.

ANTHONY, Mary Yvonne Neonatal Unit, John Radcliffe Hospital, Headley Way, Headington, Oxford OX3 9DU — MB BS 1980 Lond.; MD Leeds 1999; MRCP (UK) 1985; FRCPCH; DCH RCP Lond. 1983. (King's Coll.) Cons. Paediat. (Neonat. Med.) Oxf. Prev: Lect. (Paediat.) Univ. Leeds; Research Fell. Dept. Paediat. Univ. Leeds; Fell. Neonat. Roy. Alexandria Hosp. for Childr. Sydney, Austral.

***ANTHONY, Nathan John** 152 Chester Close, New Inn, Pontypool NP4 0LW — MB BS 1996 Lond.; BSc Lond. 1992.

ANTHONY, Pauline Courtside Surgery, Kennedy Way, Yate, Bristol BS37 4DQ Tel: 01454 313874 Fax: 01454 327110 — MB BS 1987 Lond.; DRCOG 1991; DCH RCP Lond. 1990.

ANTHONY, Professor Peter Paul Dept Pathology Royal Devon & Exeter Hospital, Church Lane, Exeter EX2 5AD Tel: 01392 402943 Fax: 01392 402964; 2 St Leonards Place, Exeter EX2 4LZ Tel: 01392 254444 — MB BS 1961 Lond.; MRCS Eng. LRCP Lond. 1961; FRCPath 1980, M 1968. (St. Bart.) Emerit. Prof. (Clin. Histopath.) Univ. Exeter; Hons. Cons. Pathol. Exeter Health Auth. Socs: Past Mem. Counc. RCPath.; Past Pres. Assn. Clin. Pathol.; Past Mem. Counc. Internat. Acad. Pathol. Prev: Sen. Lect. & Cons. Path. Middlx. Hosp. Lond.; Sen. Lect. Makerere Univ. Coll. Uganda; Sen. Regist. Centr. Middlx. Hosp. Lond.

ANTHONY, Richard Alexander John (retired) St Brelades, The Park, Cheltenham GL50 2RP — MB BS 1951 Lond.; MRCS Eng. LRCP Lond. 1951. Prev: Ho. Phys. St. Stephen's Hosp. Chelsea.

ANTHONY, Richard Lee 197 Rednal Road, Birmingham B38 8EA — BChir 1992 Camb.

ANTHONY, Richard Ywan The Health Centre, Garden Terrace Road, Old Harlow, Harlow CM17 0AX Tel: 01279 418136 Fax: 01279 429650; 108 High Street, Roydon, Harlow CM19 5EE — MB BS 1983 Lond.; MRCGP 1987; DCH RCP Lond. 1986; DRCOG 1985. Prev: Trainee GP Epping & Harlow VTS.

ANTHONY, Susan 11 Wyndham Street, London W1H 1DB — MB BS 1992 Lond.

ANTHONY, Thomas Burns (retired) Ballencrieff, Bridge Place, Galashiels TD1 1SN Tel: 01896 753526 — MB ChB 1945 Ed. Prev: Resid. Phys. & Resid. Surg. Roy. Infirm. Edin.

ANTHONY, Ywan (retired) 16 White House Close, Solihull B91 1SL — MB ChB Birm. 1957; MRCGP 1968; DPH Lond. 1959. Prev: Retd. Gen. Practitioner.

ANTHONY-PILLAI, Indrani Roanns, 2 Trident Road, Leavesden Green, Watford WD25 7AN Tel: 01923 468237 — MB BS 1968 Ceylon; DPM Eng. 1980; AFOM 1985 London; DDA 1994 UNI. London. Sen. Med. Off. HMP Pentonville Islington; Assisstant Specialist Psychiat. (Locum) Shrodells Psychiat. Unit Watford, Gen. Hosp. Vicarage Rd Watford Herts. Socs: Fell. Roy. Soc. Med. Prev: Chief Med. Off. Ceylon Tyre Corpn. Colombo, Sri Lanka; SMO Inner Lond. Educat. Auth.; Regist. (Psychiat.) Walsgrave Hosp. Coventry.

ANTHONY-PILLAI, Rosemarie Dharshini 2 Trident Road, Watford WD25 7AN — MB BS 1996 Lond.; BSc Lond. 1993. (Royal Free Hospital School of Medicine London) SHO (Med.) Luton & Dunstable Hosp.

ANTHONYPILLAI, Pedrupillai 11 Hermitage Park, Stockwell Grove, Wrexham LL13 7HL — MB BS 1971 Ceylon; MRCOG 1983.

ANTHWAL, Vijay Mani Middlewich Road Surgery, 163-165 Middlewich Road, Northwich CW9 7DB; The Beeches, Carlton Road, Northwich CW9 5PW — MB BS 1970 Agra. Prev: SHO (Orthop.) Worcester Roy. Infirm.; SHO Rotat. (Surg., Paediat., Geriat. Med. & O & G) Hereford Co.& Gen. Hosps.

ANTO, Manfred Kwabena Westwood Surgery, 24 Westwood Lane, Welling DA16 2HE Tel: 020 8303 5353 Fax: 020 8298 0346 — MB BS 1967 Lond.; MRCP (UK) 1976; MRCS Eng. LRCP Lond. 1966.

ANTON, David James Anton, Hodges & Goodman, The Barn, Water St., Barrington, Ilminster TA19 0JR Tel: 01460 57195 Fax: 01460 55582 — MB BS 1971 Lond.; MSc Lond. 1985; MRCS Eng. LRCP Lond. 1971; FFOM RCP Lond. 1996, M 1982; DAvMed Eng. 1975. Cons. Occupat. Phys. Ilminster. Socs: Fell. Roy. Soc. Med.; Soc. Occupat. Med.; Acad. Experts. Prev: Special Lect. (Orthop. & Accid. Surg.) Univ. Nottm.; Hon. Cons. (Ocupational Phys.) Frenchay Hosp. Bristol.

ANTON-STEPHENS, Derek Pentre Lodge, Leighton, Welshpool SY21 8HN — MB BCh BAO 1946 Dub.; BA, MB BCh BAO Dub. 1946; MRCPsych 1972; DPM Lond. 1951. (T.C. Dub.) Hon. Lect. Social Admin. Dept. Univ. Birm. Socs: BMA. Prev: Cons. Psychiat. N. Birm. Hosp. Gp.; Sen. Hosp. Med. Off. & Sen. Regist. Warley Hosp. Brentwood; Res. Med. Off. Wilson Hosp. Mitcham.

ANTONIADES, Charalambos Gustav Gregory 81x Gloucester Avenue, Primrose Hill, London NW1 8LB — MB BS 1998 Lond.; MB BS Lond 1998.

ANTONIO, Susan Elizabeth 143 Stoneleigh Avenue, Worcester Park KT4 8XZ — MB ChB 1967 Aberd.; DCH Eng. 1970. SCMO Kingston Hosp. NHS Trust.

ANTONIOU, Antonios Georgiou Department of Child Health, Royal Hampshire County Hospital, Romsey Road, Winchester SO22 5DG Tel: 01962 863535 Fax: 01962 825754 Email: antonios.antoniou@weht.swest.nhs.uk; The Garden House, 15A Chilbolton Avenue, Winchester SO22 5HB Tel: 01962 856979 Fax: 01962 856979 Email: a.antoniou@hospital-docotr.net — MB ChB 1974 Manch.; FRCP Lond. 1993; MRCP (UK) 1977; FRCPCH 1997; DCH RCP Lond. 1978. (Manch.) Cons. Paediat. Roy. Hants. Co. Hosp. Winchester. Socs: BMA; Fell.Roy. Coll. Phys.; Fell. Roy. Coll. Paediat. & Child Health. Prev: Sen. Regist. (Paediat.) Char. Cross Hosp. Lond.; Regist. (Med.) N.ampton Gen. Hosp.; Regist. (Paediat.) The Childr. Hosp. Sheff. & Hammersmith Hosp. Lond.

ANTONIOU, Antonios Kyriacou Abbey Medical Centre, 87-89 Abbey Road, London NW8 0AG Tel: 020 7624 9383 Fax: 020 7328 2147 — MB BS 1964 Lond.; MRCS Eng. LRCP Lond. 1964. (Univ. Coll. Hosp.) Sen. Lect. (Gen. Pract.) Univ. Coll. Lond. Med. Sch.; GP Trainer NE Thames RHA; GP Med. Cons. Laporte Industries. Socs: Harv. Soc.; Med. Soc. Lond. Prev: Ho. Surg. Harrow Hosp.; Ho. Phys. Univ. Coll. Hosp.

ANTONIOU, Antonios Varnavas Department Obstetrics & Gynaecology, University College Hospital, Huntley Street, London WC1 — MB BS 1992 Lond.; PhD Lond. 1986; BSc (Hons) Immunol. & Biochem. Lond. 1982. (United Medical Schools of Guy's & St Thomas's London) Specialist Regist. Rotat. (O & G) Univ. Coll. Hosp. Lond.; Specialist Regist. (O&G) Whittington Hosp. Lond.; Specialist Regist. (O&G) St. Bart. Hosp. Lond.; Specialist Regist (O&G) Homerton Hosp. Lond.; Specialist Regist (O&G) Whipps Cross Hosp. Lond. Prev: Lect. (Immunol.) Med. Sch. Manch. Univ.; SHO (O & G) Whittington Hosp. & Roy. Lond. Hosp.

ANTOUN, Philip Charles Cruddas Park Surgery, 178 Westmorland Road, Cruddas Park, Newcastle upon Tyne NE4 7JT; 258 Heaton Road, Heaton, Newcastle upon Tyne NE6 5QE — MB BS 1979 Lond.; MRCGP 1984; DRCOG 1983.

ANTROBUS, James Hugh Lindsay Warwick Hospital, Lakin Road, Warwick CV34 5BW Tel: 01926 495321 Fax: 01926 482613 Email: james.antrobus@swarkhosp-tr.wmids.nhs.uk — MB BS 1981 Lond.; BSc Lond. 1978, MB BS 1981; FFA RCS Eng. 1986. (Char. Cross) Cons. Anaesth. & Pain Managem. S. Warks. Gen. Hosps. NHS Trust, Warwick. Socs: Pain Soc.; Anaesth. Res. Soc. Prev: Sen. Regist. Rotat. (Anaesth.) E. Anglian RHA; Hon. Lect. (Anaesth.) Univ. Leeds; Head Clin. Pharmacol. Hazleton Med. Research Unit Leeds.

ANTROBUS, Mr James Neale Orthopaedic Department, Queen Elizabeth Hospital, Gateshead NE9 6SX Tel: 0191 403 2441 Fax: 0191 403 2833; Willow House, Shincliffe, Durham DH1 2NJ Tel: 0191 384 3519 — MB BS 1973 Lond.; FRCS Eng. 1978. (St. Thos.) Cons. Orthop. Surg. Qu. Eliz. Hosp. Gateshead. Prev: Regist. (Orthop.) Sunderland, Durh. & Newc. (T) AHAs; Regist. (Surg.) St. Leonard's Hosp. Lond.; Ho. Off. St. Thos. Hosp. Lond.

ANTROBUS, Robert David 38 Rockwood Road, Pudsey LS28 5AA — MB ChB 1972 Leeds.

ANTRUM, Mr Ralph Manfred Hollycroft, 25 Staveley Road, Shipley BD18 4HD Tel: 01274 587747 — MRCS Eng. LRCP Lond. 1977; MS Lond. 1986, MB BS 1977; FRCS Eng. 1983; FRCS Ed. 1981. (St. Mary's) Cons. Surg. Bradford Roy. Infirm. & St. Luke's Hosp. Bradford. Socs: Vasc. Surg. Soc. GB & Irel.; Assn. Surgs. Prev: Sen. Regist. (Surg.) Yorks. RHA; Regist. Rotat. (Surg.) Yorks. RHA & Post-Fell. Regist. (Surg.) St. Jas.Univ. Hosp. & Seacroft Hosp. Leeds; Research Fell. Univ. Cincinnati Med. Center, Cincinnati, Ohio, USA.

ANTSCHERL, Henrietta Eva Larkwood Drive Surgery, Hemel Hempstead HP1 2LD Tel: 01442 250117 — MB BS 1988 Lond.; MRCGP 1993; DRCOG 1992; DCH RCP Lond. 1991. p/t Gen. Practitioner. Prev: Trainee GP/SHO (Obst.) St. Bart. Hosp. & Homerton Hosp. Lond. VTS; SHO (Paediat.) St. Bart. Hosp. Lond.; Ho. Off. (Med.) Middlx. Hosp. & Univ. Coll. Hosp. Lond.

ANTUNA CALLE, Mr Francisco Manuel 61 Overleigh Road, Hanbridge, Chester CH4 7HN — LMS 1989 Malaga; FRSCI 1996. (Malaga, Spain)

ANTWI, David Nyameasem Kofi 66 Ravenslea Road, London SW12 8RU — MB BS 1987 Lond.

ANUMBA, Dilichukwu Okeoma Chinedum 52 Alwinton Terrace, Newcastle upon Tyne NE3 1UD — MB BS 1985 Benin, Nigeria; MRCOG 1993.

ANVERALI, Juma (retired) 11 Connaught Avenue, Gorleston, Great Yarmouth NR31 7LU — MB BS Karachi 1956; DLO RCS Eng. 1962. Prev: Assoc. Specialist (Ear, Nose & Throat) Jas. Paget Hosp. NHS Trust Gt. Yarmouth.

ANWAR, Abdelraham Elawad Department of Immunology, Western Infirmary, Dumbarton Road, Glasgow G11 6NT — MB BS 1972 Khartoum.

ANWAR, Aly M G E Corporation Road Medical Centre, 4 Corporation Road, Grangetown, Cardiff CF11 7AT Tel: 029 2023 1259 Fax: 029 2064 0494.

ANWAR, Aresh Jacob 65 Hill Top Road, Oxford OX4 1PD — MB BS 1991 Lond.

ANWAR, Farrah Suhail 16 Beauvale, Ferdinand St., London NW1 8EY; 17 Brentfield Gardens, London NW2 1JP — MRCS Eng. LRCP Lond. 1987; BSc (Hons.) Lond. 1984.

ANWAR, Masud Southlands, Cresswell Drive, Hartlepool TS26 0EQ Tel: 01429 866903 — MB BS 1954 Punjab; FRCP Lond. 1995; FRCP Glas. 1984; FRCP Ed. 1983; MRCP (UK) 1972; DCMT . Lond. 1964; DPH (Hons.) Punjab (Pakistan) 1957. (King Edwd. Med. Coll. Lahore) Cons. Phys. (Geriat. Med.) Gen. Hosp. Hartlepool. Socs: Brit. Geriat. Soc.; Brit. Acupunc. Soc.; BMA. Prev: Regist. (Med.) Falkirk & Dist. Roy. Infirm. & Gateside Hosp. Greenock; Sen. Regist. (Geriat. Med.) N. Staffs. Gp. Hosps.

ANWAR, Mohammad 16 Ribble Avenue, Oadby, Leicester LE2 4NZ — MD 1987 Leicester; MB BS Newc. 1977; MRCOG 1983; MRCGP 1981; DRCOG 1982. Sen. Lect. (O & G) Univ. Leicester; Hon. Cons. Obst. & Gyn. Leicester HA. Socs: Pres. Nuffield Obst. & Gyn. Soc. Prev: Sen. Regist. (O & G) Leics. HA; Trainee GP Newc. Univ. VTS; Regist. (O & G) Leicester Gen. Hosp.

ANWAR, Mudasir 3 Queens Park Avenue, Crosshill, Glasgow G42 8BX — MB ChB 1995 Glas.

ANWAR, Mumtaz Queen Elizabeth Psychiatric Hospital, Vincent Drive, Birmingham B15 3TH Tel: 0121 678 3600; 23 Whitefields Crescent, Solihull B91 3NU — MB BS 1962 Punjab; MB BS Punjab (Pakistan) 1962. (Fatima Jinnah Med. Coll. Lahore) Assoc. Specialist Psychiat. Qu. Eliz. Psychiat. Hosp. Birm. Prev: Wom. Asst. Med. Off. W. Pakistan Govt. Hosp., Karachi; Wom. Gen. Duty Med. Off. Centr. Hosp. Al-Jof, Saudi Arabia; SHO (Geriat.) Rubery Hill Hosp. Birm.

ANWAR, Samira 22 The Loaning, Glasgow G46 6SF — MB BS 1991 Lond.

ANWAR, Zahida Riffat 364 Eastpark Road, Leicester LE5 5AY Email: zanwar@candw.ky — MB BCh 1981 Wales; FCAnaesth. Lond 1990. (Welsh National School of Medicine Cardiff) Cons. Anaesth. Geo. Town Hosp., Grand Cayman, The Cayman Is.s, Brit. W. Indies. Prev: Regist. (Anaesth.) Walsgrave Hosp. Coventry.

ANWAR-FARID, Syed Muhammad The Surgery, 348 Bearwood Road, Smethwick, Warley B66 4ES Tel: 0121 429 1345 Fax: 0121 429 2535 — MB BS 1982 Karachi.

ANWAR-UL-HAQ, Mr Mohammad Eye Department, Hairmyres Hospital, Glasgow G75 8RG Tel: 01355 584644; Norlen, 22 The Loaning, Whitecraigs, Glasgow G46 6SF Tel: 0141 639 8228 — MB BS 1965 Punjab; BSc 1962 Punjab; FRCS Ed. 1982; FCOphth 1990; FACS 1991; DO RCPSI 1971. (King Edw. Med. Coll. Lahore, Pakistan) Cons. Ophth. Surg. Hairmyres Hosp., Glas.; Cons. Ophth Surg, Wishaw Gen. Hosp., Wishaw, Lanarksh. Socs: Soc. UK & Irish Cataract & Refractive Surgs.; Amer. Acad. of Ophth.; Europ. Soc. of Cataract & REG. Surg.s. Prev: Cons. Ophth. Surg. W. Cumbld. Hosp.; Cons. Ophth. Surg. Riyadh Centr. Hosp. Riyadh, Saudi Arabia.

ANWER, Khurshid 76 Delamure Road, Levenshulme, Manchester M19 3WR Tel: 0161 248 6406 — MB BS 1964 Punjab; Cert. Family Plann. JCC 1971; DObst RCOG 1967. (Fatima Jinnah Med. Coll. Lahore, Pakistan) I/C Reproduc. Health Surgic. Centre (Populat. Plann.) Govt. Pakistan. Prev: Cons. Tabouk Saudi Arabia; Regist. (O & G) Sunderland Gen. Hosp. & N.. Gen. Hosp.; Regist. (Obst.) Hull Matern. Hosp.

ANWYL, William Evan (retired) Greenfield, Cynghordy, Llandovery SA20 0YP Tel: 01550 721058 — MRCS Eng. LRCP Lond. 1944; MFOM 1982; MFCM 1972; DIH Eng. 1965; DPH Lond. 1964. Prev: Occupat. Phys. Swindon HA & Wilts. CC.

ANYAMENE, Nicola Ann Flat 3, 34 Gloucester Drive, London N4 2LN — MB BS 1997 Lond.

ANYANWU, Adizie Lawrence Department of Obstetrics & Gynaecology, Walsgrave Hospital, Clifford Bridge Road, Coventry CV2 2DX Tel: 024 76 602020; 48 Lismose Drive, Hasborne, Birmingham B17 0TP Tel: 0121 426 1096 Fax: 0121 426 1096 — MB BCh 1978 Nigeria; MSc Birm. 1997; MRCOG 1991; FMCOG 1989. (Enugu, Nigeria) Cons. O & G Walsgrave Hosp. Coventry.

ANYANWU, Mr Anelechi Chinedu 44 Cornwallis Avenue, London N9 0JP Email: rcs@aanyanwie.freeserve.co.uk — MB BS 1991 Univ. Nigeria; FRCS Eng. 1995; FRCS Ed. 1995; MSc (Econ & QM in Health Care),City Uni. Lond. (Univ. Nigeria, Enugu) Specialist Regist. (Cardio-thoracic Surg.), N. Thames W. Lond. Rotat.

ANYANWU, Professor Humphrey Chijioke 17B Ikenga Crescent, University of Nigeria, Enugu Campus, Enugu, Nigeria Tel: 00234 42 450065 Email: chanyamwu@inforweb.abs.net; 44 Cornwallis Avenue, London N9 0JP — MB BS 1963 Lond.; FRCS Eng. 1970; FRCS Ed. 1970. (University College Hopsital (UCH) Ibadan) Prof & Cons. Cardiothoracic Surg Univ.of Nigeria Enugu.Campus & Univ. of Nigeria Teach. Hosp. Enugu; Cons Cardiothoracic surg. Nat. Orthopaedic Hosp Enugu Nigeria. Socs: Soc. Cardiothoracic Surg. GB and Irel.; Fell. Internat. Coll. of Surg.s; Fell. W. African Coll. of Surg.s. Prev: Cons. Thoracic and Vasc. Surg. Hofuf Saudi Arabia;; Sen. Regist. (Cardiothoracic Surg.) Harefield Hosp. Uxbridge Middlx.;; Regist. (Cardiothoracic Surg.) Harefield Hosp. Uxbridge Middlx..

ANZAK, Mohammed Lynton House Surgery, 43 London Road, High Wycombe HP11 1BP Tel: 01494 527036/538811/510117 Fax: 01494 447070 — MB ChB 1984 Sheff.

AP GWILYM, Elen Rhiannon Mair 12 Tydraw Road, Cardiff CF23 5HA — MB BS 1996 Lond.

AP IVOR, Trevor Denis (retired) 9 Ashurst Avenue, Saltdean, Brighton BN2 8DR Tel: 01273 301587 — MRCS Eng. LRCP Lond. 1939; FRCA 1994; FFA RCS Eng. 1954; DA Eng. 1949. Prev: Cons. Anaesth. Centr. Kent Hosp. Gp.

AP-THOMAS, Ann Humphreys Norton, 10 North Road, Grassendale Park, Liverpool L19 0LR — MB ChB 1973 Liverp.; FRCR 1979; DMRD Liverp. 1977. Cons. & Clin. Lect. Radiol. Walton & Fazakerley Hosps.; F/T Cons. Univ. Hosp. Aintree; Clin. Lect.; Hon. Cons. brE. unit,Linda McCartney centre, Roy. Liverp. Hosp., Liverp.

APAKAMA, Mr Ikechukwu Ginikanwa Department of Urology, George Eliot Hospital, College St., Nuneaton CV10 7DJ Tel: 01203 351351 Fax: 01203 865395 Email: ikeapakama@hotmail.com; 51 Woodfield Road, Earlsdon, Coventry CV5 6AJ Tel: 01203 675404 Email: ikeapakama@bigfoot.com — MB BS 1982 Lagos, Nigeria; MB BS Lagos 1982; FRCS (Urol.) 1996; FRCS Ed. 1992. (Univ. Lagos, Nigeria) Cons. Urol. Geo. Eliot Hosp. NHS Trust Nuneaton.

Socs: Brit. Assn. Urol. Surg.; BMA. Prev: Specialist Regist. Freeman Hosp. Newc.

APALOO, Edward Cuthbert Adelaide Street Surgery, 118 Adelaide Street, Blackpool FY1 4LB Tel: 01253 620725 Fax: 01253 290765 — Vrach 1968 Lvov Med Inst.

APALOO, Francis Kwasi Beeby Montague Health Centre, Oakenhurst Road, Blackburn BB2 1PP Tel: 01254 268456 Fax: 01254 268450 — Lekarz 1972 Krakow, Poland; DipMedAc Eng.; MBA 2001 Manch.; Accredit. Brit. Soc. Med. & Dent. Hypn. Accredit. Brit. Soc. Accredit. Brit. Soc. Med. & Dent.; Cert. Dent. Anaesth. Manch.; DPS Liverp.; Lekarz Krakow Poland 1972; Cert. Family Plann. JCC 1985; Cert. Prescribed Equiv. Exp. JCPTGP 1985. (Medical Academy, Krakow, Poland) Princip. Gen. Med. pratice; Clin. Asst. E. Lancs. Hospice. Socs: Brit. Med. Acupunct. Soc.; Brit. Soc. Med. & Dent. Hypn.; Inst. Health Servs. Man. Prev: Regist. (Anaesth.) Blackburn Gp. Hosps.; SHO Psychiat..Qu.s Pk. Hosp.. B'Burn; SHO Anaesth, Rochdale.

APAOLAZA CORRAL, Maria Isabel Academic Unit of Obstetrics & Gynaecology, Royal London Hospital, 4th Floor Holland Wing, London E1 1BB Tel: 020 7377 7000; Flat 3, 176 Crystal Palace Road, London SE22 9EP Tel: 020 8299 6171 — LMS 1989 Alcala de Menares. Clin. Research Fell. Acad. Unit O & G Roy. Lond. Hosp. Prev: Research Fell. (Immunol.) Roy. Lond. Hosp.; Research Fell. (Endocrinol.) Hosp. La Paz Madrid, Spain.

APARICIO, Samuel Alves Jana Rodrigues 21 Arbury Road, Cambridge CB4 2JB — BM BCh 1988 Oxf.; MA Camb. 1988. SHO (Neurol.) Radcliffe Infirm. Oxf. Prev: SHO Hammersmith Hosp. Lond.; SHO Renal Unit Oxf. RHA.

APARICIO KNORR, Carlos Flat 1, Birch House, Springwood Road, Barming, Maidstone ME16 9NF — LMS 1991 Navarre.

APARICIO LEDESMA, Javier Saint Lukes Hospital, Blackmoorfoot Road, Huddersfield HD4 5RQ; Flat 3, Woodstock, Occupation Road, Lindley, Huddersfield HD3 3WT — LMS 1993 Cordoba.

APAYA, John Andarea 4 Blyth Close, Walton, Chesterfield S40 3LN Tel: 01246 206350 — MB BS 1964 Khartoum; FRCOG 1988, M 1970; DGO TC Dub. 1968; LM Rotunda 1967. (Khartoum Univ.) Socs: Assn. Genitourin. Phys.; Med. Soc. Study VD; Brit. Soc. Colpos. & Cerv. Path. Prev: Cons. Genitourin. Med. Chesterfield & N. Derbysh. Roy. Hosp.; Sen. Regist. (Genitourin. Med.) S. Tyneside HA & Newc. HA (T); Cons. O & G Khartoum Gen. Hosp. & El Galla Matern. Hosp., Tripoli.

APILIGA, Moses Tako (Surgery), 1483 Dumbarton Road, Scotstoun, Glasgow G14 9XL Tel: 0141 211 9040 Fax: 0141 211 9043 Email: mapiliga@gps40563.domi.intersite — MB ChB 1972 Glas.; MRCP (UK) 1975; T(GP) 1991. (Glasgow University) GP Glas.; Vocat. Studies Tutor Dept. of Gen. Pract. Univ. of Glas. Socs: Roy. Coll. Phys. & Surg. Glas.; BMA. Prev: Trainer Dementia Servs. Developm. Centre Univ. of Stirling.

APLEY, Marion Susan 15 Mount Drive, Wembley HA9 9ED Tel: 020 8904 3114; 16 Kent Road, Littlehampton BN17 6LG Tel: 01903 722482 — MB BS 1969 Lond.; Cert. Family Plann. JCC 1981; Dr Med & Chir Naples 1975; Dip. Tuberc. & Chest Dis. Naples 1977; Acad. Dip. Gen. Biochem. Univ. Lond. 1964. (Univ. Coll. Hosp.) Clin. Med. Off. Child Health Servs. Community Health Br. Worthing Dist; Clin. Med. Off. Family Plann. Worthing Dist. Socs: BMA; Nat. Assn. Fam. Plann. Doctors. Prev: GP Eng. & Italy; Med. Asst. Tuberc. & Respirat. Dis. Clin. Naples Univ., Italy; Ital. Govt. Schol. Inst. Principi di Piemonte Naples, Italy.

APLIN, Carolyn Gisela Kinghorn Dermatology unit, Royal united Hospital, Combe Park, Bath BA1 3NG Tel: 01225 824524 Email: cari.aplin@virgin.net — MB BS 1982 Lond.; BSc (Hons.) Lond. 1979; MRCP (UK) 1986; MRCGP 1987. (Lond. Hosp. Med. Coll.) Specialist Regist. (Dermat.) Roy. United Hosp. Bath & Bristol Roy. Infirm. Socs: Train. Mem. Brit. Assn. Dermat.; Dowling Club. Prev: Regist. (Dermat.) St. Thos. Hosp. & Greenwich Dist. Hosp.; Company Doctor Plantation Hse. Med. Centre Lond.; Princip. GP Lond.

APOSTOLOV, Kostadin (retired) 9 Forest Ridge, Beckenham BR3 3NH — MD 1957 Skopje; PhD Lond. 1974; Dip. Microbiol. Skopje 1962. Hon. Cons. & Sen. Lect. (Clin. Virol.) Hammersmith Hosp. Lond.

APPACHI, Elumalai 14 Jackson Court, Bowfell Road, Urmston, Manchester M41 5SG — MB BS 1985 Madras; MRCP (UK) 1992.

APPADU, Balraj 39 Naseby Way, Great Glen, Leicester LE8 9GS; 43 Stoneyfield Road, Old Coulsdon, Coulsdon CR5 2HP — MD 1986 Saint-Etienne; MD Saint-Etienne France 1986; FCAnaesth. 1992.

APPADURAI, Ian Rabindranath 57 Bournemouth Road, London SW19 3AR — MRCS Eng. LRCP Lond. 1986; FCAnaesth. 1990; DA (UK) 1988. Regist. Rotat. (Anaesth.) Char. Cross, Brompton & Hillingdon Hosps. Lond. Prev: SHO (Anaesth.) Leicester Roy. Infirm.; SHO (Cardiothoracic Surg.) Groby Rd. Hosp. Leicester; Ho. Phys. (Cardiol.) Addenbrooke's Hosp. Camb.

APPAIAH, Machimada Chengapa (retired) 7 Lovain Road, Derby DE23 6DA — MB BS 1968 Mysore. Prev: GP Derby.

APPAJI GOWDA, Muttagadahalli Byanna Gowda Lambgates Doctors Surgery, 1-5 Lambgates, Hadfield, Glossop SK13 1AW Tel: 01457 869090 Fax: 01457 857367; 17 Ramsden Close, Glossop SK13 7BB — MB BS 1967 Bangalor; MB BS Bangalore 1967.

APPANNA, Ajjikuttira M Ynysangharad Road Health Centre, 70 Ynysangharad Road, Pontypridd CF37 4DA Tel: 01443 480521 Fax: 01443 400260.

APPANNA, Bhaskar c/o Dr C. N. Reddy, 39 Middleton Close, Seaton, Seaham SR7 0PQ — MB BS 1989 Mysore.

APPANNA, Nalendra 22 Upper Abbey Road, Brighton BN2 2AD — MB ChB 1985 Natal.

APPANNA, Timson Chengappa 35 The Dell, Tonteg, Pontypridd CF38 1TG — MB BCh 1993 Wales.

APPELQVIST, Ivan Patrick Huddersfield Road Surgery, 6 Huddersfield Road, Barnsley S70 2LT Tel: 01226 287589 Fax: 01226 731245 — MB ChB 1989 Birm.; DCH MRCGP. GP Princip.; Lect. Dept. GP Sheff. Univ. Prev: SHO (Obst.) Birm. Matern. Hosp.; SHO (A & E) Russells Hall Hosp. Dudley; Ho. Surg. Geo. Eliot Hosp. Nuneaton.

APPERLEY, Jane Felicity 51 Warwick Road, Beaconsfield HP9 2PL — MB ChB 1979 Birm.; MD Birm. 1988; FRCP Lond. 1995; MRCP (UK) 1982; MRCPath 1991. Sen. Lect. (Haemat.) Roy. Postgrad. Med. Sch. Socs: Brit. Soc. Haematol.; Amer. Soc. Haemat.; (Bd. Mem.) Europ. Gp. for Blood & Marrow Transpl. Prev: Hon. Cons. & Lect. (Haemat.) Univ. Camb.; Wellcome Research Fell.sh., Harvard Univ.

APPERLY, Philip Raymond (retired) West Bassetts, Higher St., Merriott TA16 5PJ Tel: 01460 73211 — MRCS Eng. LRCP Lond. 1943. Prev: on Staff Evesham Gen. Hosp.

APPIAH, Emmanuel Kwame 8 Freer Close, Blaby, Leicester LE8 4FX Tel: 0116 277 8516 — Lekarz 1972 Krakow; Lekarz Krakow Poland 1972. (Krakow Med Acad.) SCMO (Adult Learning Disabil.) Leicester Frith Hosp. Socs: MFCH. Prev: Clin. Med. Off. (Child Health) Leicester.

APPIAH, Mr Lawrence Kwarteng 39 Tanfield Avenue, London NW2 7SA — MB ChB 1969 Univ. Ghana; FRCS Ed. 1977.

APPIAH, Mr Samuel Kwasi Erdington Medical Centre, 103 Wood End Road, Erdington, Birmingham B24 8NT Tel: 0121 373 0085 Fax: 0121 386 1768; Gravelly Hill Medical Centre, 8 Wheelwright Road, Birmingham B24 8NX — MB ChB 1964 Birm.; FRCS Eng. 1971; MRCS Eng. LRCP Lond. 1964. (Birm.) Prev: Ho. Surg. Qu. Eliz. Hosp. Birm.; Regist. (Surg.) Dudley Rd. Hosp. Birm.; Lect. (Surg.) Ghana Med. Sch. Accra, Ghana.

APPLE, Michael Frank Alan Garston Medical Centre, 6a North Western Avenue, Watford WD25 9GP Tel: 01923 672086 Fax: 01923 681980; 111 Cassiobury Drive, Watford WD17 3AH Tel: 01923 236799 Email: m.apple@virgin.net — MB ChB 1978 Birm.; BA (Psychol.) Liverp. 1969. Socs: Roy. Coll. Gen. Pract.

APPLEBEE, Jacqueline Clare Globetown Surgery, 82-86 Roman Road, London E2 0PG Tel: 020 8980 3023 Fax: 020 8983 4627 — MB BS 1987 Lond.; BSc (Hons.) Lond. 1984; MRCGP 1991; DRCOG 1990; Cert. Family Plann. JCC 1989. (St. Bart.) Course Organiser (Gen. Pract.) E. Lond. VTS. Socs: BMA. Prev: Trainee GP Lond.; Trainee GP/SHO Tower Hamlets VTS; Ho. Surg. Homerton Hosp. Hackney.

APPLEBY, Alistair Brian GFL, 4 Forth Cresent, Riverside, Sterling FK8 ILE; GFL, 4Forth cresent, Riverside, Sterling FK8 ILE Tel: 01776 706375 Email: jbalmer@tinyworld.co.uk — MB ChB 1987 Ed.; MRCGP 1991; DRGOG 1996. (Edinburgh) GP, Stirling. Socs: Mem. Roy. Coll. of GPs; Mem. Brit. Med. Assoc. Prev: GP Regist., Inverness; SHO (Paediat.) Stirling; GP, Patan Hosp. Nepal.

APPLEBY, Basil Paul 111 Harley Street, London W1G 6AW Tel: 020 7486 4656 Fax: 020 7224 1756; 15 Wymondham, Queensmead, St. John's Wood Park, London NW8 6RD Tel: 020

7722 9227 Fax: 020 7224 1756 — MRCS Eng. LRCP Lond. 1947; FICS 1966; DObst RCOG 1955. (King's Coll. Hosp.) Mem. Edit. Bd. Med., Gyn. & Sociol. Socs: Fell. Roy. Soc. Med. (Mem. Sects. Obst. & Gyn. & Endocrinol.); Internat. Fertil. Assn. Prev: Asst. (O & G) Qu. Mary's Hosp. for E. End Lond.; Research Asst. City of Lond. Matern. Hosp.; Regist. E. End Matern. Hosp. Lond.

APPLEBY, Clare 74 Cavendish Drive, Birkenhead CH42 6RQ — MB ChB 1996 Manch.

APPLEBY, David Jackson Shrewsbury Road Surgery, 20 Shrewsbury Road, Craven Arms SY7 9PY Tel: 01588 672309 Fax: 01588 673943 — MB ChB 1984 Birm.; MRCGP 1991; T(GP) 1991; DA (UK) 1988. Bd. Mem. S. W. Shrops. PCG. Prev: Trainee GP Arnold, Nottm.; SHO (Paediat.) Qu. Med. Centre Nottm.; SHO (Psychiat.) Mapperley Hosp. Nottm.

APPLEBY, Esther Lee Dicker Mill House, Chalvington Road, Golden Cross, Hailsham BN27 3SS — MB BS 1996 Lond.; BSc.

APPLEBY, Ian 179 Engadine Street, Southfields, London SW18 5DU Tel: 020 8874 3602 Email: apps@dial.pipe.com — MB BS 1983 Lond. (St. Bartholomew's Medical College) Specialist Regist. (Anaesth.) Imperial Coll. Sch. of Anaesth. Prev: Med. Affairs Off. Servier Laboratories Ltd.

APPLEBY, Margaret Ann Stewart Wardrew, 48 Elmfield Road, Gosforth, Newcastle upon Tyne NE3 4BB Tel: 0191 285 2557 — MB BS 1965 Durh.; MFFP 1993. (Durh.) Med. Off. (Community Med., Child Health & Family Plann.) Newc. City Health Trust. Socs: Fac. Community Health; BACCH; Fac. Family Plann. & Reproduc. Health Care RCOG. Prev: Princip. GP Gosforth; Med. Off. Univ. Health Serv. Newc.

APPLEBY, Mark Allan Dept. Cardiology, Yorkshire Heart Centre, Leeds LS1; Old Stud Farm, Main St, Sicklinghall, Wetherby LS22 4DB — MB BChir 1985 Camb.; MA 1988, BA Camb. 1985; MRCP (UK) 1991. Cardiol. Specialist Regist., Yorks. Heart Centre, Leeds. Socs: Brit. Cardiac Soc.; Cardiovasc. Interven. Soc.; Brit. Soc. Echocardiogr. Prev: Regist. (Cardiol.) Manch. Roy. Infirm.; SHO (Cardiol.) Univ. Hosp. Wales Cardiff; Research Fell. (Cardiol.), Roy. Hosp. NHS Trust.

APPLEBY, Michael Ian Water Meadow Surgery, Red Lion Street, Chesham HP5 1ET Tel: 01494 782241 Fax: 01494 782005; Little Pendle, 215 Botley Road, Chesham HP5 1XT Tel: 01494 785075 — MRCS Eng. LRCP Lond. 1968; MB BS Lond. 1968; DObst RCOG 1971. (Guy's) Water Meadow Surg., 31A Red Lion St., Chesham, Bucks HP5 1ET.

APPLEBY, Thomas Alfred Walnut Tree Bungalow, West Beckham Road, Bodham, Holt NR25 6NW Tel: 01263 588729 — MB ChB 1945 Sheff. (Sheff.) Mem. Bd.ing Panel DHSS. Socs: BMA. Prev: Graded Orthop. Specialist RAMC; Orthop. Ho. Surg. Doncaster Roy. Infirm.; Ho. Surg. Sheff. Roy. Infirm.

APPLEFORD, James Kemp Denmark House, Queen Elizabeth Psychiatric Hospital, Mindelsohn Way, Edgbaston, Birmingham B15 2QZ Tel: 0121 697 8283 Email: jim@jimappleford.freeserve.co.uk; 112 Greenfield Road, Harborne, Birmingham B17 0EF Tel: 0121 243 6810 — MB ChB 1989 Birm.; MRCPSych 1995. (Birm.) Sen. Regist. (Psychiat.) Qu. Eliz. Psychiat. Hosp. Birm.

APPLEGATE, Eustace John 77 Elvington, Springwood Est., King's Lynn PE30 4TB Tel: 01553 775574 — MB BS 1957 Lond.; DObst RCOG 1959. (Westm.) Prev: Princip. Clin. Med. Off. W. Norf. Wisbech HA; Med. Off. Ika Christian Matern. Hosp. Nigeria; Ho. Surg. Gordon Hosp. Lond.

APPLEGATE, John Martin Acle Medical Centre, Bridewell Lane, Acle, Norwich NR13 3RA Tel: 01493 750888 Fax: 01493 751652; Acle Medical Centre, Bridewell Lane, Acle, Norwich NR13 3RA Tel: 01493 750888 — MB ChB 1989 Leic.; FIMC RCS Ed. 2000; BSc (Hons.) Loughborough 1984; Dip IMC RCS Ed. 1995; DFFP 1996. GP; Mem. Norf. Accid. Rescue Serv.; Advanced Trauma Life Support Instruc. (Camb.); Hon. Med. Adviser Norf. Br. of Brit. Red Cross. Socs: BASICS; Fac. of PreHosp. Care RCS (Ed).

APPLETON, Andrew Stewart Courtside Surgery, Kennedy Way, Yate, Bristol BS37 4DQ Tel: 01454 313874 Fax: 01454 327110; Lynnholm, 54 Goose Green, Yate, Bristol BS37 5BL Tel: 01454 311079 Email: courtside@asapple.surfaid.org — MB ChB 1991 Ed.; MRCGP 1995; DRCOG 1994; DCH RCP Glas. 1994. (Ed.) GP Princip. Yate. Prev: Trainee GP Lothian VTS; SHO (Community Paediat. & Community Child Health) Edin.

APPLETON, Anne Laura Department of Surgery (ward 46 office), Royal Victoria Infirmary, Newcastle upon Tyne NE1 4LP Tel: 0191 232 5131 Ext: 24661 Fax: 0191 232 5278; 43 Woodlands, Gosforth, Newcastle upon Tyne NE3 4YL Tel: 0191 284 7660 — MB ChB 1989 Liverp.; PhD Newc. 1996. Assoc. Specialist(BrE. Phys.), Roy. Vict. Infirm. Newc. Socs: Assn. Clin. Path. Prev: Sen. Regist. (Cytopath.) Roy. Vict. Infirm. Newc.; Sen. Demonst. & Hon. Regist. (Path.) Univ. Newc. Roy. Vict. Infirm.; Research Fell. (Path.) Univ. Newc. & Roy. Vict. Infirm.

APPLETON, Mr Barry Nigel Orchard House, 2 Foxhill Chase, Stockport SK2 5HJ Tel: 0161 427 2784 Email: barryappleton@hotmail.com — MB BChir 1992 Camb.; MA Camb. 1993; FRCS Eng. 1997. Specialist Regist., Gen. Surg., All Wales Rotat. Prev: Research Fell. Singleton Hosp. Swansea; SHO Rotat. (Gen. Surg.) Univ. Soton.

APPLETON, Cathryn Rebecca Turner, Hart, Appleton and Briggs, Woodsend Medical Centre, School Place, Corby NN18 0QP Tel: 01536 407006 Fax: 01536 401711; Tel: 01858 446813 — BChir 1990 Camb.; MA Camb. 1991; MRCGP 1995; DRCOG 1995; DCH RCP Lond. 1994. (Camb. Clin. Sch.) Gen. Practitioner, Woodsend Med. Centre, Corby.

APPLETON, Derek Frank James Department of Anaesthetics, Royal Hallamshire Hospital, Sheffield S10 Tel: 0114 276 6222; Sycamore House, Cliff Lane, Curbar, Sheffield S32 3XD Tel: 01433 630753 — BM BCh 1981 Oxf.; MA Camb. 1977; FFA RCS Eng. 1985. Cons. Anaesth. Roy. Hallamsh. Hosp. Sheff. Socs: Assn. Anaesth.; Amer. Research Soc. Prev: Sen. Regist. (Anaesth.) Sheff.; Asst. Prof. Univ. N. Carolina, USA; Regist. & SHO (Anaesth.) Sheff. VTS.

APPLETON, Derek Sidney Dept. of Radiology, Addenbrookes Hospital, Hills Rd, Cambridge CB2 2QQ Tel: 01223 216688 Fax: 01223 217847; Four Winds, 39 Fox Rd, Balsham, Cambridge CB1 6EZ Tel: 01223 216688 Fax: 01223 217847 — MB BChir 1972 Camb.; MA, MB Camb. 1972, BChir 1971; FRCR 1979; DObst RCOG 1973. Cons. Radiol. Addenbrooke's Hosp. Camb.; Cons. (Radiol.) Papworth Hosp. Camb.

APPLETON, Emma Jane 17 Piercefield Road, Liverpool L37 7DG — MB BS 1998 Newc.; MB BS Newc 1998.

APPLETON, Fiona Bryn Awelon, Llangynhafal, Denbigh LL16 4LN — MB ChB 1981 Liverp.; MRCOG 1986. Clin. Asst. (Urol.) Glan Clwyd Hosp. Bodelwyddan N Wales; Clin. Asst. (Colposcopy) Wrexham Maelor Hosp. N Wales.

APPLETON, Gillian Ann Combermere House, 148 Hospital St, Nantwich CW5 5RY Tel: 01270 624293 — MB ChB 1959 Manch.; DMJ (Clin.) Soc. Apoth. Lond. 1993.

APPLETON, Graham Victor Norman Horton General Hospital, Oxford Road, Banbury OX16 9AL Tel: 01295 229203 Fax: 01295 229203; Ridgeway Lodge, Manor Road, Adderbury, Banbury OX17 3EL Tel: 01295 811606 Fax: 01295 811609 Email: grappleton@aol.com — BM BCh 1978 Oxf.; MA Camb. 1979; BA Oxf. 1978; ChM Bristol 1990; FRCS Eng. 1982. (Camb. & Oxf.) Cons. Gen. & Colorectal Surg. Horton Gen. Hosp. Banbury & Oxf. Radcliffe NHS Trust. Socs: Assn. Coloproctol.; Roy. Soc. Med. (Coloproctol. & Oncol. Sects.); BMA. Prev: Cons. Surg. Preston; Sen. Regist. S. W. RHA; Lect. & Sen. Lect. Univ. Bristol Dept. Surg. S.mead Hosp.

APPLETON, Helen Southbury Surgery, 73 Southbury Road, Enfield EN1 1PJ Tel: 020 8363 0305 Fax: 020 8364 4288; 13 Priory Close, Totteridge, London N20 8BB Tel: 020 8446 1020 — MB BS 1983 Lond.; BSc Lond. 1980; MRCGP 1987; DCH RCP Lond. 1987. (Middlx. Hosp. Lond.) Prev: Trainee GP Barnet Gen. Hosp. VTS.

APPLETON, Mark Andrew Campbell Department of Histopathology, Worthing Hospital, Lyndhurst Road, Worthing BN11 2DH Tel: 01903 205111 Email: mark.appleton@wash-tr.sthames.nhs.uk — MB ChB 1990 Bristol; MRCPath. 1997. Cons. Histopath. Worthing Hosp. Prev: Sen. Regist. (Histopath.) Univ. Hosp. Wales Cardiff.

APPLETON, Mark Samuel Tel: 01772 433479 — MB ChB 1986 Manch.; MMedSci (Clin. Psychiat.) Leeds 1996; MRCPsych 1994. Cons. Gen. Adult Psychiat., Co. Durh. & Darlington Priority Serv.s,NHS Trust. Prev: Sen. Regist. (Psychiat) N.& Yorks HA.

APPLETON, Peter James The Brick House, Heatherlands Road, Chilworth, Southampton SO16 7JB Tel: 02380 769611 — MB BS 1962 Lond.; MRCS Eng. LRCP Lond. 1962; FFA RCS Eng. 1966.

(Westm.) Cons. (Anaesth.) Soton. & S.W. Hants. Health Dist. (T). Socs: Assn. Anaesth. Prev: Sen. Regist. Dept. Anaesth. W.m. Hosp. Lond. & Soton. Gen.; Hosp. (Jt. Appt.).

APPLETON, Peter Michael (retired) Laneside House, Church Lane, Gomersal, Cleckheaton BD19 4QL Tel: 01274 875318 — MRCS Eng. LRCP Lond. 1964. Prev: GP Cleckheaton.

APPLETON, Peter Norman John Cross Keys Practice, High Street, Princes Risborough HP27 0AX Tel: 01844 344488 Fax: 01844 274714; Three Ways Cottage, Askett, Princes Risborough HP27 9LT Tel: 01844 343704 — MB ChB 1970 Sheff.; FRCGP 1995, M 1976; DObst RCOG 1972. (Sheff.) Trainer (Gen. Pract.) Aylesbury VTS. Prev: SHO (O & G & Paediat.) St. Luke's Hosp. Guildford; Ho. Off. (Surg. & Med.) Doncaster Roy. Infirm.

APPLETON, Richard Allan Kiltearn Medical Centre, Hospital St., Nantwich CW5 5RL Tel: 01270 610200 Fax: 01270 610637; Combermere House, 148 Hospital St, Nantwich CW5 5RY Tel: 01270 624293 — MB ChB 1960 Manch. (Manch.)

APPLETON, Richard Edward The Roald Dahl EEG Unit, Alder Hey Children's Hospital, Liverpool L12 2AP Tel: 0151 252 5851 — MB BS 1980 Lond.; FRCP (UK) 1995; FRCPCH 1997; MRCP (UK) 1985; DCH RCP Lond. 1983; MRCS Eng. LRCP Lond. 1980; MA Oxf. 1977. (Oxford & Charing Cross Hospital) Cons. Paediat. Neurol. Alder Hey Childr. Hosp. & Walton Hosp. Liverp. & Clin. Lect. (Child Health) Univ. Liverp. Socs: Roy. Soc. Med.; Corr. Mem. Amer. Epilepsy Soc. Prev: Sen. Regist. (Paediat., Neonat. & Med.) Newc. HA; Fell. (Paediat. Neurol.) Childr. Hosp. Vancouver Univ. Brit. Colombia,Canada.

APPLETON, Mr Shaun Grendon 32 Fifth Cross Road, Twickenham TW2 5LE Tel: 020 8898 5913 — MB BS 1989 Lond.; FRCS Eng. 1993. Specialist Regist. Rotat. (Surg.) N. Thames (W.).

APPLEYARD, David Stuart 39 The Street, Motcombe, Shaftesbury SP7 9PE — MB ChB 1998 Birm.

APPLEYARD, Geoffrey (retired) Gable End, The Avenue, Porton, Salisbury SP4 0NT Tel: 01980 610385 — BM BCh 1954 Oxf.; MA Oxf. 1954, BSc 1952, BM BCh 1954; Dip. Bact. Lond 1959. Prev: Scientif. Staff Wellcome Research Laborat. Beckenham.

APPLEYARD, Mr Ian Department of Urology, Airedale General Hospital, Skipton Road, Steeton, Keighley BD20 6TD Tel: 01535 292136 Fax: 01535 293133 Email: iappleyard@hotmail.com; Tall Trees, Bank Lane Off Chapel St, Grassington, Skipton BD23 5BN Tel: 01759 753002 — MB ChB 1967 Birm.; MSc (Anat.) Sheff. 1970; FRCS Eng. 1974; FRCS Ed. 1972. (Birm.) Cons. Urol. Airedale Gen. Hosp. Keighley, W. Yorks.; Sen. Clin. Lect. (Surg.) Univ. of Leeds.; Director Urol. Train. Program - Yorks. Socs: Full Mem. Brit. Assn. Urol. Surgs. Prev: Sen. Regist. (Surg.) Liverp. AHA (T); Ho. Off. Dudley Rd. Hosp. Birm.; Lect. (Anat.) Univ. Sheff.

APPLEYARD, Jane Hilary (retired) Northfields, 118 Northampton Road, Rushden NN10 6AL Tel: 01933 314411 Email: janian_appleyard@hotmail.com — MB ChB St. And. 1962; DA Eng. 1965. Prev: GP, Health Centre, IrthlingBoro., WellingBoro., N.ants.

APPLEYARD, Karen Margaret Castle Medical Centre, Bertie Road, Kenilworth CV8 1 — MB ChB 1987 Sheff.; MRCGP 1992; DFFP 1993; DRCOG 1991; Cert. Family Plann. JCC 1990. (Sheffield) GP Princip. Castle Med. Centre, Kenilworth. Socs: W Midl. Assn. Family Plann. Doctors. Prev: Trainee GP Warwick; SHO (O & G) Jessops Wom. Hosp. Sheff.; SHO (Paediat. & Acute Med. Elderly) Barnsley Dist. Gen. Hosp.

APPLEYARD, Mark Neil Wooburn Lodge, Grange Drive, Wooburn Green, High Wycombe HP10 0QB — MB BS 1990 Lond.

APPLEYARD, Terence Neil 78 Chelsea Road, Sheffield S11 9BR Tel: 0114 553103 Fax: 0114 221 7099 Email: neiltappleyard@aol.com — MB ChB 1966 Leeds; FFA RCS Eng. 1971; DA Eng. 1970. (Leeds) Cons. Anaesth. N. Gen. Hosp. Sheff.; Examr. Basic Scis., RCS Eng.; Regional Educat.al Adcisor in Intens. Care Med.. N. Trent. Socs: Assn. Anaesth. Gt. Brit. & Irel.; Eur. Soc. Crit. Care Med.; IC Soc. Prev: Regist. (Anaesth.) United Sheff. Hosps.; Research Asst. & Lect. Univ. Dept. Anaesth. Sheff.

APPLEYARD, William James (retired) Kigesi International School of Medicine, 30 Regent Terrace, Cambridge CB2 1AA Tel: 01223 507110 Fax: 01223 507109 — BM BCh 1960 Oxf.; 1957 MA Oxf. 1961, BA; 1967 FRCP Lond. 1978, M; 1961 MRCS Eng. LRCP Lond.; 1962 DObst RCOG; ND (Hons.) Kent 1999; 1998 FRCPCH; 2000 DH Lett St Georges Univ. p/t Clin. Dean, KISM, 30 Regent Terr., Camb. Prev: Sen. Regist. (Paediat.) Guy's Hosp. Lond.

APPS, Anthony John Lotherington Byrne, Langham, Apps, Finnie and McIlhinney, 186 Neasham Road, Darlington DL1 4YL Tel: 01325 461128 Fax: 01325 469123 — MB BS 1982 Lond.; MRCGP 1986; DRCOG 1985.

APPS, John Michael The Street Lane Practice, 12 Devonshire Avenue, Leeds LS8 1AY Tel: 0113 295 3838 Fax: 0113 295 3842 — MB ChB 1973 Leeds; MRCGP 1977; DCH Eng. 1976; DObst RCOG 1975. Prev: Ho. Phys. & Ho. Surg. Airedale Gen. Hosp. Steeton.

APPS, Michael Charles Patrick 7 St Nicholas Grove, Ingrave, Brentwood CM13 3RA — MB BChir 1976 Camb.; MA Camb. 1976, MD 1986; FRCP Lond. 1995. Cons. Phys. Havering Hosp. Trust, Harold Wood & OldCh. Hosps. Romford, Essex. Prev: Sen. Regist. (Med.) Lond. Hosp. Whitechapel.

APPULINGAM, Kanthiah c/o Mr A Vairavamoorthy, 76 Grand Drive, London SW20 9DY — MB BS 1971 Ceylon.

APS, Christopher 77 Wickham Way, Park Langley, Beckenham BR3 3AH — MB BS 1969 Lond.; MRCS Eng. LRCP Lond. 1969; FFA RCS Eng. 1973; DObst RCOG 1971. (St. Thos.) Cons. Anaesth. St. Thos. Hosp. Lond.

APSITIS, Beryl Uplands Surgery, 48 Sketty Road, Uplands, Swansea SA2 0LJ Tel: 01792 298554 / 298555 Fax: 01792 280416; Common Close, Llanridian, Gower, Swansea SA3 1EU Tel: 01792 390987 — MB BCh 1964 Wales; DCH Eng. 1973.

APTA, Rabin Dranath The Surgery, 9 Park Road, Cannock WS11 1JN Tel: 01543 466188; Woodcroft, 72 Weeping Cross, Stafford ST17 0DL — MB BS 1974 Utkal; MSc Heriot-Watt Univ. 1985.

APTE, Prabhakar Pandurang The Health Centre, Victoria Road, Hartlepool TS26 8DB Tel: 01429 272945; 55 Hylton Road, Hartlepool TS26 0AG Tel: 01429 268298 — MB BS 1959 Poona; MRCOG 1965. Prev: Ho. Surg. Gyn. Kent & Canterbury Hosp.; Regist. O & G Cameron Hosp. Hartlepool.

APTE, Ravindra Vishwanath (retired) Liverpool Road Surgery, 523 Liverpool Road, Irlam, Manchester M44 6Z — MB BS 1964 Karnatak; MS Bombay 1970. Clin. Med. Off. Little Hulton FPC. Prev: SHO (A & E) Stockport Infirm.

APTE, Sulabha Ravindra (retired) 20 Skegness Close, Bury BL8 1EQ — MB BS 1969 Bombay; DA Bombay 1970.

APTED, Frank Ian Colclough (retired) Helm Chase, 171 Pymore Road, Bridport DT6 3AW Tel: 01308 27008 — MB BS 1939 Lond.; MRCS Eng. LRCP Lond. 1939; DTM & H Eng. 1941. Prev: Dir. Bureau Of Hyg. & Trop. Dis. Lond.

APTHOMAS, Ifan (retired) 7 Bryn Estyn Road, Wrexham LL13 9ND Tel: 01978 263807 — MB ChB Ed. 1939; DMRD Eng. 1947; FFR Lond. 1952; FRCR 1975. Prev: Cons. Radiol. Wrexham Hosps.

APTHORP, George Hugh Bentley, 8 Links Way, Northwood HA6 2XB Tel: 01923 824605 — MB BS 1951 Lond.; FRCP Lond. 1974, M 1954; MRCS Eng. LRCP Lond. 1951. (St. Bart.) Cons. Phys. St. Albans City Hosp. & W. Herts. & St. Paul's Hosps. Hemel Hempstead. Prev: Sen. Regist. Inst. Cardiol. Nat. Heart Hosp. Lond.; Sen. Regist. (Med.) St. Bart. Hosp. Lond.; Ho. Phys. Hammersmith Hosp.

APTHORP, Hugh David 8 Linksway, Northwood HA6 2XB Tel: 01923 824605 Email: hapthorp@aol.com — MB BS 1988 Lond.; FRCS (Orth.) 1997; FRCS Eng. 1992. Career Regist. (Orthop.) UMDS Train. Scheme. Socs: Brit. Orthop. Assn. Prev: Career Regist. St. Thos. Hosp. Lond.; Regist. (Orthop.) Roy. Berks. Hosp. Reading; SHO (Orthop.) Addenbrooke's Hosp. Camb.

APTHORP, Lesley Anne Conquest Hospital, The Ridge, St Leonards-on-Sea TN37 7RD Tel: 01424 755255 Fax: 01424 758013 Email: apthorp.lesley@mail.har-tr.sthames.nhs.uk; 9 Buxton Road, Eastbourne — MB BChir 1989 Camb.; MRCP (UK) 1992; FRCR 1995. Cons. Radiol. Conquest. Hosp. Hastings. Prev: Regist. (Radiol.) N.wick Pk. Hosp. Harrow.; Sen. Regist. (Radiol.) Guys & St. Thomas' NHS Trust.

APTHORP, Miles Quentin 29 Newlands Avenue, Radlett WD7 8EJ — MB BS 1989 Lond.

APTHORPE, Timothy Francis (retired) Cock Robin Green, Attleborough — MB BS 1962 Lond.; DObst RCOG 1966. Vice-Pres. Norf. Accid. Rescue Serv. Prev: Sen. Partner, Apthorpe & Partners, AttleBoro.

AQIL, Mr Shakil 8 Simpson Street, Crosshouse Hospital, Kilmarnock KA2 0BD Tel: 01563 21133; 15 Kirkdale Gardens, Leeds

LS12 6AT — MB BS 1982 Karachi; FRCS Glas. 1989; DLO RCS Eng. 1988. Regist. (ENT) CrossHo. Hosp. Kilmarnock. Socs: Med. Defence Union.

AQUILINA, Carmelo Queen's Resource Centre, Queen's Road, Croydon CR0 2PR Tel: 020 8665 6469 Fax: 020 8776 4452 Email: carmelo.aquilina@ntlworld.com; Email: carmelo.aquilina@ntlworld.com — MD 1986 Malta; MRCPsych 1992. (Univ. Malta) Cons. Cold Age Psychiat. S. Lond. & Maudsley NHS Trust. Socs: Edr. of the newsletter of theRoy. Coll. Psychiat. Fac. of Old Age Psychiat.

AQUILINA, Joseph 1 Glyn Road, London E5 0JB Tel: 020 8 533 3232 Fax: 020 8 510 7850 Email: joaquilina@hotmail.com; 121 P. Muscat Street, Rabat, Malta Tel: 00 356 456925 — MD 1987 Malta; MFFP 1995; MRCOG 1994. Research Fell & Hon. Regist. King's Coll. Hosp. Lond. Socs: BMA; Med. Ultrasound Soc.

AQUILINA, Mark Patrick Marie Yell Health Centre, Reafirth, Mid Yell, Yell, Shetland ZE2 9BX Tel: 01957 702127 Fax: 01957 702147 — MB BS 1984 Lond.; MRCGP 1990; DRCOG 1987. (University College London) GP Yell. Prev: GP Princip. Brae; Med. Off. VSO Namibia.

AQUILINA, Monica 50 Gibbon Road, Kingston upon Thames KT2 6AB — MRCS Eng. LRCP Lond. 1981.

AQUILINA, Remy John 3 Retreat Road, Wimborne BH21 1BU — MB BS 1983 Lond.; FCAnaesth 1989. Cons. Anaesth. Poole Hosp. NHS Trust.

AQUINO, Peter Jones 17 Clearwater, Londonderry BT47 6BE Tel: 01504 44779 — MB BCh BAO 1994 Belf.; MSc (Neuroscience) 1997. (King's College, University of London) SHO (Gen. Med.) Altnagelvin Hosp. Lond.derry. Prev: SHO (A & E) Roy. Surrey Co. Hosp. Guildford; Ho. Off. (Surg.) King Edwd. VII Hosp. Midhurst; Ho. Off. Med., Mater Hosp. Belf.

AR-RIKABY, Hussain Amber Neville Road Surgery, 5 Neville Road, Luton LU3 2JG Tel: 01582 563373, 01582 705085 — MB ChB 1974 Basrah; MB ChB Basrah, Iraq 1974; MRCPI 1984.

ARA, Begum Kaosar 75 Morton Way, Southgate, London N14 7AP Tel: 020 8245 5854 Fax: 020 8889 4092 — MB BS 1972 Bangladesh. (Dacca Medical College Bangladesh) Clin. Asst. Prev: Clin. Asst.

ARAEZ GUARCH, Roser Asplands Medical Centre, Wood St., Woburn Sands, Milton Keynes MK1 18QP — LMS 1992 Barcelona.

ARAFA, Mr Mohamed Aly Mohamed The Alexandra Hospital, Woodnow Drive, Redditch B98 7UB Tel: 01527 503030 Fax: 01527 518489 Email: mohamed@arafa.freeserve.co.uk; 61 Monument Lane, Lickey, Rednal, Birmingham B45 9QJ Tel: 0121 453 3588 Fax: 0121 453 3588 — MB BCh 1973 Cairo; FRCS Eng. 1978; FRCS Ed. (Orth.) 1982. (Cairo Univ.) Cons. Orthop. Surg. The Alexandra Hosp. Health Care Trust Redditch; Lect. (Orthop. Surg.) Manch. Univ.; Sen. Regist. NW RHA; AO Internat. Schol.ship W. Germany 1984. Socs: Fell. BOA; Fell. Brit. Soc. Hand Surg.; Fell. Brit. Trauma Soc. Prev: Regist. (Orthop.) Bristol United Hosps.; SHO (Orthop.) Roy. Nat. Orthop. Hosp. Stanmore.

ARAFA ALI, Khairy Abdel Latif 1 Arrowhead, Essex & Herts Hospital, Haymeads Lane, Bishop's Stortford CM23 5JH — MB ChB 1975 Alexandria, Egpyt; MB ChB Alexandria, Eygpt 1975.

ARAFAT, Qais Walid Queen Elizabeth Hospital, Gayton Road, King's Lynn PE30 4ET — MB BS 1982 Lond.; BSc Lond. 1979; FRCS Ed. 1987; FRCR 1991; T(R) (CR) 1993. (King's College Hospital Medical School) Cons. Radiol. Qu. Eliz. Hosp. King's Lynn.

ARAGONES ARROYO, Maria Luisa Marsham Street Surgery, 1 Marsham Street, Maidstone ME14 1EW Tel: 01622 752615/756129 — LMS 1990 Cadiz.

ARAIN, Araf Mahmood 36 Moorland View, Newton Abbot TQ12 4EP — MB ChB 1984 Ed.; BSc (Hons) 1982; DCH 1990; DRCOG 1991.

ARAM, Gary Eric The Health Centre, Countesthorpe, Leicester LE8 5QJ Tel: 0116 277 6336 Fax: 0116 278 0851 — MB ChB 1976 Liverp.; MRCGP 1980; DCH Eng. 1979; DRCOG 1978. (Liverpool) Lect. (Gen. Pract.) Leicester Univ.

ARAM, Julia Ann 38 Fishpool Street, St Albans AL3 4RX — MB BS 1996 Lond.

ARANA GALDOS, Miren Amaia University Hospital of Wales, Anaesthetic Department, Heath Park, Cardiff CF14 4XW — LMS 1985 Basque Provinces. SHO (Anaesth.) Newc. Gen. Hosp.

ARANDHARA, Kamini Kumar Wollaton Vale Health Centre, Wollaton Vale, Wollaton, Nottingham NG8 2GR Tel: 0115 928 2216 Fax: 0115 928 0590 — MB BS 1965 Gauhati. (Assam Med. Coll.)

ARANKI, Dima Amy 77 Alleyn Road, London SE21 8AD — MB BS 1997 Newc.

ARANKI, Sary Fuad Iskandar 77 Alleyn Road, Dulwich, London SE21 8AD — MRCS Eng. LRCP Lond. 1979.

ARAS, Stephen Francis Tel: 020 7371 7171 Fax: 020 7331 0101 Email: stephen.aras@gp-e85719.nhs.uk — BSc 1981 UEA; MRCGP 1991; MSc Dundee 1982; MB BCh; MB BCh Wales 1987. (Wales) GP Ashville Surg.

ARASARADNAM, Ramesh Pulendran 60 Luton Road, London E17 5LN — MB BCh 1996 Belf.

ARASARATNAM, Mr Royce Bertram Soundararajah Ipswich District Hospital, Heath Road, Ipswich IP4 5PD Tel: 01473 712233; 21 Berkeley Close, Ipswich IP4 2TS Tel: 01473 281482 — MB BS 1971 Ceylon; FRCS Ed. 1984; FRCS Glas. 1984; DLO Eng. 1980; FRCS (ORL-HNS) Nov 1999. (Ceylon) Assoc. Specialist (ENT) Ipswich Hosp. Socs: Brit. Assn. Otol. & Amer. Acad. Otol. Allergy. Prev: Regist. (ENT) Jas. Paget. Hosp. Gorleston, Enfield Dist. Hosp. & Ipswich Hosp.; SHO (ENT) Wexham Pk. Hosp. Slough.

ARASTU, Nilofer Firs Surgery, Stephenson Road, London E17 7JT Tel: 020 8520 9286 Fax: 020 8521 1751 — MB BS 1966 Osmania.

ARASU, Anusha 36 Jalan 1, Taman Tun Abdul Razak, 68000 Ampang, Kuala Lumpur, Malaysia Email: pta@pop7.jaring.my; 12 Ardshiel Close, Putney, London SW15 1EB Tel: 0208785 6712 Fax: 0208 785 6712 Email: anusha_a@hotmail.com/anusha@arasu.fireserve.co.uk — MB BS 1992 Lond.; MRCPCH (UK) 1999; MRCP (UK) 1996; DCH RCP Lond. 1993. (Guy's Hosp. Med. Sch. (UMDS)) Specialist Regist. in Neonatology, Neonat. Intens. Care Unit, St. Geo.'s Hosp., Tooting, Lond. SW17 0QT. Prev: Specialist Regist. in Paediat., Mayday Univ. Hosp., Lond.; Specialist Regist. in Paediat., Qu. Mary's Hosp., Sidcup; Lect. in Paediat., Univ. Hosp., Kuala Lumpur, W. Malaysia.

ARASU, Pamela Maylands Healthcare, 300 Upper Rainham Road, Hornchurch RM12 4EQ Tel: 01708 476411 Fax: 01708 620039 — MB BS 1974 Poona.

ARATARI, Carlo Cardiothoracic Department, Norhtern General Hospital, Herries Road, Sheffield S5 7AU — State DMS 1988 Rome.

ARATHOON, David Anthony Arathoon Cottage, West Knoyle, Warminster BA12 — MB BS 1983 Lond.; MRCGP 1994; Cert. Family Plann. JCC 1993. (St. Bart. Hosp. Med. Sch.) Dir. Provin. Health Servs. Lata Hosp. Santa Cruz, Temotu Province, Solomon Is.s. Prev: Med. Off. Roy. Air Force; Ho. Off (Gen. Med.) Warneford Hosp. Leamington Spa; Ho. Off. (Gen. Surg.) Harold Wood Hosp. Essex.

ARAVIND, Sarasu Pulimuttil Queen's Park Hospital, Blackburn BB2 3HH Tel: 01254 263555; Rose Tor, 29 View Rd, Keighley BD20 6JN — MB BS 1974 Kerala; BSc Kerala 1967; MRCOG 1985; DRCOG 1980. Staff Grade (O & G) Qu. Pk. Hosp Blackburn. Prev: Regist. (O & G) Barking Hosp. Essex.; Regist. (O & G) P.ss Alexandra Hosp. Harlow; Clin. Asst. (O & G) Roy. Devon & Exeter Hosp.

ARAVINDAKSHAN, Mr Kottiyattil Kunjunny The Surgery, York Road, Rotherham S65 1PW Tel: 01709 370053 Fax: 01709 371353; The Brambles, Lindrick Road, Woodsetts, Worksop S81 8RA Tel: 01909 563261 Fax: 01909 563261 Email: arvind.carbl@btinternet.com — MB BS 1962 Kerala; FRCS Ed. 1971. (Med. Coll. Trivandrum) GP Rotherham; Hon. Lect. (Clin. Hypn.) Med. Dent. Fac. Univ. Sheff. Socs: Fell. Brit. Soc. Med. & Dent. Hypn.. Prev: SHO & Regist. (Plastic Surg.) Regional Plastic & Maxillofacial Surg. Centre Bangour Gen. Hosp. Broxburn; Cons. Surg. M.C.T.M. Hosp. Rayonpuram, India.

ARAVINDHAN, Nadarajah 15 Westbrooke Close, Brampton, Huntingdon PE28 4FG — MB BS 1990 Colombo; MRCP (UK) 1993.

ARAVINDHAN, Sri Ranjini 15 Westbrooke Close, Brampton, Huntingdon PE28 4FG — MB ChB 1994 Birm.

ARAVINTHAN, Jegatheesan 145 Casterbridge Road, Blackheath, London SE3 9AD — MB BS 1996 Lond.

ARAVOT, Dah Joshua Papworth Hospital, Cambridge CB3 8RE Tel: 01480 830541 — MD 1981 Hebrew Univ. Israel.

ARAWWAWALA, Dilshan Prassana 352 Mortlake Road, Ilford IG1 2TG; Flat 1, The Hollies, 216 Eccles Old Road, Salford M6 8AL Tel: 0161 707 8241 — MB ChB 1996 Manch.; BSc (Hons) Manch. 1993. SHO (Gen. Med.) Blackburn Hyndburn & Ribble Valley Health Care Unit.

ARAYOMI, Joseph Oladeinde Department of Obstetrics & Gynaecology, Pilgrim Hospital, Sibsey Way, Boston PE21 9QS Tel: 01205 364801 Fax: 01205 354395 — MB BS 1979 Ibadan; MFFP 1993; MRCOG 1992; FRSH 1996. (Univ. Coll. Hosp. Ibadan, Nigeria) Staff O & G Pilgrim Hosp. Boston. Socs: BMA; FMCOG 1993; FWACS 1988. Prev: Regist. (O & G) Roy. Cornw. Hosp. Truro; Regist. (O & G) Vict. Infirm. Glas.

ARBAB-ZADEH, Armin Flat 3/3, 13 Lawrnece St., Glasgow G11 5HH — State Exam Med 1992 Dusseldorf.

ARBLASTER, Lachlan Andrew 17 Boniface Road, Invergowrie, Dundee DD2 5DW — MB ChB 1997 Dundee.

ARBLASTER, Peter Graeme, VRD (retired) Bywater House, Pierside, Lymington SO41 5SB Tel: 01590 677909 — MB BS 1947 Lond.; MD Lond. 1950; FRCP Lond. 1970, M 1949; MRCS Eng. LRCP Lond. 1943. Hon. Cons. Phys. UCH Lond. Prev: Assoc. Prof. Univ. Sultan Qaboos.

ARBUCKLE, Elizabeth Reedilees Farm, Auchtermuchty, Cupar KY14 7EP — MB ChB 1998 Aberd.; MB ChB Aberd 1998.

ARBUCKLE, Gillian Mary Currie Road Health Centre, Currie Road, Galashiels TD1 2UA Tel: 01896 701896 Fax: 01896 751389; 10 Monkswood, Gattonside, Melrose TD6 9NS — MB ChB 1983 Ed.; MRCGP 1987; DRCOG 1986. Med. Sec. Border LMC.

ARBUCKLE, James Duncan 34 Ennismore Avenue, Guildford GU1 1SR — MB BS 1994 Lond.

ARBUCKLE, Patricia Eliza McHardy The Hawthorns, Ormiston Terrace, Melrose TD6 9SP — MB ChB 1957 Ed.

ARBUTHNOT, Mrs Evelyn Margaret (retired) Quay Head, Sampford peverell, Tiverton EX16 7BS Tel: 01884 820275 — MB ChB Birm. 1943; DObst RCOG 1948; DCH Eng. 1950. Prev: Paediat. Regist. Qu. Charlotte's Hosp. & Portsmouth Hosp. Gp.

ARBUTHNOT, James Edmund 19 Gilberry Close, Knowle, Solihull B93 9JZ Tel: 01564 776558; 101 Dorridge Road, Dorridge, Solihull B93 8BS — MB ChB 1997 Liverp. Basic Surgic. Train., Mersey Rotat.

ARBUTHNOT, John Hugh, TD Cromer Hospital, Cromer Road, Cromer NR27 0BQ Tel: 01263 513571; Rinteln, Churchill Crescent, Sheringham NR26 8NQ Tel: 01263 822143 — MB BCh BAO NUI 1956; MRCGP 1968. Hosp. Pract. (Orthop.) Cromer Hosp.; Maj. RAMC T & AVR. Socs: BMA. Prev: Regist. (Obst. & Orthop.) OldCh. Hosp. Romford; Ho. Off. (Surg.) St. Vincent's Hosp. Dub.

ARCELUS ALONSO, Jon 155 Fox Hill Road, Sheffield S6 1HF — LMS 1990 Basque Provinces.

ARCHARD, Graham Eric Stour Surgery, 49 Barrack Road, Christchurch BH23 1PA Tel: 01202 464500 Fax: 01202 464529; Willowmarsh, St Catherines Hill Lane, Christchurch BH23 2NL Tel: 01202 470318 Fax: 01202 490718 Email: archard@eluk.co.uk — MB ChB 1981 Leeds; BSc (Hons. Physiol.) Leeds 1976; MRCGP 1985; FRCGP 1996. (Leeds) Chairm. Dorset MAAG; Mem. E. Dorset Clin. Audit Commiss.; Mem. Dorset LMC; Hon. Sec. Wessex Fac. RCGP; Clin. Governance Ldr. ChristCh. PCG.

ARCHARD, Mr Jeremy Charles 44 Canley Mews, London SW7 3BY Tel: 020 7373 5538 — MB BS 1956 Lond.; BSc Lond. 1953, MB BS 1956; FRCS Eng. 1963. (Univ. Coll. Hosp.) Prev: Cons. ENT Surg. Univ. Coll. Hosp. Lond.; Audiol. ILEA; Sen. Regist. Roy. Free Hosp. Lond.

ARCHARD, Nicholas Perry X-Ray Department, Glan Clwyd Hospital, Bodelwyddan, Rhyl LL18 5UJ — BM BS 1981 Nottm.; BMedSci Nottm. 1979; MRCP (UK) 1985; FRCR 1990; DMRD (Liverp.) 1988. Cons. Radiol. Glan Clwyd Dist. Gen. Hosp. NHS Trust. Prev: Sen. Regist. (Radiol.) Mersey RHA.

ARCHBOLD, George Pooler Rodgers 403 Antrim Road, Glengormley, Newtownabbey BT36 5ED — MB BCh BAO 1980 Belf.; MSc Surrey 1985; PhD Belf. 1974, BSc 1971, MB BCh BAO 1980; FRCP Glas. 1992; MRCP (UK) 1983; MRCPath 1988. Sen. Regist. (Chem. Path.) Belf. City Hosp.; Cons. Chem. Path. Belf. City Hosp.

ARCHBOLD, Mr James Alexander Allen Drumgooland Lodge, Seaforde, Downpatrick BT30 8NT — MB BCh BAO 1968 Dub.; BA Dub. 1966, MB BCh BAO 1968; FRCS Ed. 1974. (T.C. Dub.) Cons. Surg. Downe Hosp. Downpatrick Co. Down. Prev: Sen. Tutor (Surg.) Qu. Univ. Belf.; Sen. Reg. Roy. Vict. Hosp. Belf.; Surg. Specialist RAMC.

ARCHBOLD, Juliet Alexandra Louise 3 Mayfields, Lisburn BT28 3RP — MB BCh BAO 1992 Belf.; MB BCh Belf. 1992; MRCGP 1996; DRCOG 1995; DFFP 1995; DCH Dub. 1994; DMH Belf. 1993. Prev: Regist. (Gen. Pract.) Lisburn Health Centre Co. Antrim.

ARCHBOLD, Richard Andrew 15 Richmond Mews, Newcastle upon Tyne NE3 4BQ — MB BS 1992 Lond.; MRCP (UK) 1996. (Lond. Hosp. Med. Coll.) Specialist Researcher (Cardiol.), St. Barholomews Hosp.

ARCHER, Adrian Dale Shropshire County Council, Shirehall, Abbey Foregate, Shrewsbury SY2 6ND Tel: 01743 252833 Fax: 017443 252834 Email: dale.archer@shropshire-cc.gov.uk — MB ChB 1968 Birm.; 1991 MFOM RCP Lond; 1993 T(OM). (Birmingham) Occupat. Health Phys. Shrops. CC, Shrewsbury (occ. Med.). Socs: Soc. Occupat. Med.; Assn. Local Auth. Med. Advisors; BMA. Prev: Employm. Med. Advisor Health & Safety Exec.

ARCHER, Alan Geoffrey Chesterfield and N. Derbyshire Royal Hospital, Chesterfield S44 5BL — MB BS 1974 Lond.; MD Lond. 1987; FRCP Lond. 1995; MRCP (UK) 1979. (Roy. Free)

ARCHER, Anthony Russell (retired) Silverley, Woodland Rise, Sevenoaks TN15 0HZ Tel: 01732 761366 — MB BS Lond. 1957; DObst RCOG 1959. Prev: Gen. Pract.

ARCHER, Caroline Dawn Department of Medicine, Royal Marsden Hospital, Fulham Road, London SW3 6JJ Tel: 020 7352 8171 Fax: 020 7352 5441 Email: carcher@nthames.nhs.uk; 5 Franconia Road, Clapham, London SW4 9NB — MB BS 1990 Lond.; BSc (Pharmacol.) Lond. 1987; MRCP (UK) 1994. (Char. Cross & Westm. Lond.) SR in Med. Oncol. Socs: BMA; Roy. Soc. Med.; Assn. Cancer Phys. Prev: Clin. Lect. (Med. Oncol.) Char. Cross Hosp. Lond.; Regist. (Gen. Med. & Oncol.) Lister Hosp. Stevenage; SHO (Gen. Med.) Qu. Mary's Univ Hosp. Lond.

ARCHER, Caroline Kvetoslava Heatherbrook Surgery, Beaumont Lodge, 242 Astill Lodge Road, Leicester LE4 1EF Tel: 0116 235 6324 Fax: 0116 234 0333 — MB ChB 1977 Sheff.

ARCHER, Charlotte Christian Wellside Surgery, 45 High Street, Sawtry, Huntingdon PE28 5SU Tel: 01487 830340 Fax: 01487 832753; 15 Ivy Way, Spaldwick, Huntingdon PE28 0UN Tel: 01480 890066 — MB BS 1984 Lond.; MRCGP 1989; Cert. Family Plann. JCC 1987; DRCOG 1987. Gen. Practitioner Wellside Surg. Sawtry. Prev: Trainee GP Portsmouth VTS.; GP Camb. Retainer Scheme.

ARCHER, Christine Anne Sunnyside, California, Woodbridge IP12 4DE — MB BS 1975 Lond.; MRCS Eng. LRCP Lond. 1975; FRCA 1979. Anaesth. Ipswich Hosp. NHS Trust. Prev: Sen. Regist. Roy. Hants. Co. Hosp. Winchester; Sen. Regist. Char. Cross Hosp. Lond.; Regist. (Anaesth.) St. Bart. Hosp. Lond.

ARCHER, Clive Bruce University of Bristol, Bristol Dermatology Centre, Bristol Royal Infirmary (UBHT), Bristol BS2 8HW Tel: 0117 928 2770 Fax: 0117 928 2845 Email: clive.archer@ubht.swest.nhs.uk — MB BS 1978 Lond.; Bsc (Hons) 1975; MRCS Eng. LRCP Lond.1978; MRCP (uk) 1981; MD Lond.1986; PhD Lond.1991; FRCP Edin.1992; FRCP Lond 1995. (Guy's Lond. & Keble Coll. Oxf.) Cons. Phys. (Dermat.) Bristol Roy. Infirm.; Hon. Clin. Sen. Lect., Univ. of Bristol. Socs: Roy. Soc. Med. (Ex Counc. Mem. Dermatol.); Hon. Pres. Dowling Club 1993-94; Psoriasis Assn. Research Fell. & Brit. Assn. Dermat. Dowling Trav. Fell. 1986/87. Prev: Lect. (Dermat.) Guy's Hosp. Lond.; Sen. Regist. & Tutor St. John's Hosp for Dis. of Skin Lond. & Inst. Dermat. Lond.; Vis. Research Fell. (Dermat.) Oregon Health Sci. Univ. USA.

ARCHER, Mr Daniel James Head & Neck Unit, Royal Marsden Hospital, Fulham Road, London SW3 6JJ Fax: 020 7351 5934 — MRCS Eng. LRCP Lond. 1973; MB BS Lond. 1973, BDS 1969; FRCS Eng. 1980; FDS RCS Eng. 1977. (Kings Coll. & St. Geo. Hosps.) Cons. Oral & Maxillofacial Surg. Roy. Marsden Hosp. & Centr. Middlx. Hosp.; Hon. Cons. Oral & Maxillo-Facial Surg. Atkinson Morley's Hosp. Lond. & Roy. Brompton & Nat Heart Hosp Lond.; Hon. Sen. Lect. Inst. of Cancer Research. Socs: Fell. Brit. Assn. Oral & Maxillofacial Surg.

ARCHER, David Frederick John 228 Lichfield Road, Four Oaks, Sutton Coldfield B74 2UE Tel: 0121 308 0359 Fax: 0121 323 2682; 18 Carnoustie Close, Sutton Coldfield B75 6UW Tel: 0121

378 2379 — BM BCh 1962 Oxf.; MA Oxf. 1962; MRCP Lond. 1968. (St. Thos.) Socs: BMA.

ARCHER, David Stanley (retired) 20 Brambling Close, Offerton, Stockport SK2 5UE — MB ChB 1964 Manch.

ARCHER, Mr Desmond Brian Department of Ophthalmology, Eye & Ear Clinic, Royal Victoria Hospital, Grosvenor Road, Belfast BT12 6BA Tel: 01232 240503 Fax: 01232 330744 Email: d.archer@qub.ae.uk — MB BCh BAO 1959 Belf.; DO Lond. 1962; FRCS Eng. 1968; FRCOphth 1993. (Qu. Univ. Belfast) Sir Chas. Blackmore Chair of Ophth.; Mem. Coll. Ophth. UK; Mem. Oxf. Ophth. Congr.

ARCHER, Elizabeth 4 The Terrace, Mill Lane, Sidlesham, Chichester PO20 7NA Tel: 01243 641556 Fax: 01243 641556 Email: earc@sidle.u-net.com — MB BS 1975 Lond.; MSc Distinc. (Health Promotion) Univ. Lond. 1995; MRCGP 1981; DFFP 1993; DRCOG 1980; DCH RCP Lond. 1977. (King's Coll Hosp. Univ. Lond.) Locum in Gen. Pract. W. Sussex/Hants.; Sessional CMO Family Plann. W. Sussex/Hants. Prev: Princip. GP W. Sussex FHSA; Clin. Med. Off. Chichester HA; Princip. GP Merton Sutton & Wandsworth Family Pract. Comm.

ARCHER, Elizabeth Gladstone (retired) 50 High Street, Blakeney, Holt NR25 7AL Tel: 01263 740225 — MB ChB 1941 Ed. Clin. Med. Off. Community Health Norf. AHA Norwich Dist. Prev: Clin. Med. Off. Community Health W. Surrey & NE. Hants. HD.

ARCHER, Gilbert Micheal Diarmuid (retired) 46 Cumberland Street, London SW1V 4LZ Tel: 020 7834 0767 Fax: 020 7834 0767 — MB BChir 1957 Camb.; MRCS Eng. LRCP Lond. 1956; FFA RCS Eng. 1964. Cons. Anaesth. Roy. Marsden & St. Geo. Hosps. Lond. Prev: Sen. Regist. (Anaesth.) King's Coll. Hosp. Lond.

ARCHER, Gillian Ann, Squadron Ldr. RAF Med. Br. 89 Richmond Drive, Seacroft Fields, Skegness PE25 3SG; The Nook, Trebarber, Newquay TR8 4JT — MB BS 1987 Lond. GP RAF. Prev: Ho. Surg. St. Bart. Hosp. Lond.; Ho. Phys. Roy. Cornw. Hosp. Treliske.

ARCHER, Gillian Karen High Chimneys, Petches Bridge, Great Bradfield, Braintree CM7 4QN — MB BS 1968 Lond.; MRCS Eng. LRCP Lond. 1968; DObst RCOG 1971.

ARCHER, Gordon James Springfield, 14 Moss Lane, Bollington, Macclesfield SK10 5HJ — MB ChB 1965 Manch.; FRCP Lond. 1990, M 1969. Cons. Phys. Stepping Hill Hosp. Stockport. Socs: Brit. Thoracic Soc. & N.W. Thoracic Soc. Prev: Sen. Med. Regist. Leeds Gen. Infirm.; Regist. (Med.) Lond. Chest Hosp. & Cardiff Roy. Infirm.

ARCHER, Hayley Louise Respiratory Unit, University Hospital of Wales, Heath Park, Cardiff CF14 4XW; 3 Heathfield Road, Cardiff CF14 3JX — MB BCh 1997 Wales. Specialist Regist., Respirat. Med., Univ. Hosp. of Wales.

ARCHER, Mr Ian Angus Department of Orthopaedic Surgery, Chancellors Wing, St James' University Hospital, Beckett St., Leeds LS9 7TF Tel: 0113 243 3144; The Elders, Moorland Road, Bramhope, Leeds LS16 9HW Tel: 0113 284 3736 — MB ChB 1967 Ed.; FRCS Eng. 1977. Cons. Orthop. Surg. & Sen. Clin. Lect. St. Jas. Univ. Hosp. Leeds. Socs: Fell. Brit. Orthop. Assn.; Brit. Orthop. Research Soc. Prev: Lect. & Cons. Orthop. Surg. St. Jas. Univ. Leeds; Sen. Regist. (Orthop. Surg.) Leeds & Bradford AHA; Research Fell. & Regist. Rheum. Research Unit, Univ. Dept. Med. Gen. Infirm. Leeds.

ARCHER, James David 78 Chiltern Road, Swadlincote DE11 9SJ — MB BS 1998 Lond.; MB BS Lond 1998.

ARCHER, Keith Prospect House Medical Group, Prospect House, Prospect Place, Newcastle upon Tyne NE4 6QD Tel: 0191 273 4201 Fax: 0191 273 0129; 11 Berkley Avenue, Blaydon-on-Tyne NE21 5NN — MB BS 1971 Newc.; MRCGP 1978. Prev: Ho. Phys. & Ho. Surg. Hexham Gen. Hosp.

ARCHER, Kerry Liza 10 Sheridan Drive, Helen's Bay, Bangor BT19 1LB — MB ChB 1992 Brist.

ARCHER, Leonard Nicholas John Department of Child Health, Clinical Sciences Building, Royal Infirmary, PO Box 65, Leicester LE2 7LX — MB BChir 1975 Camb.; MA, MB Camb. 1975, BChir 1974; MRCP (UK) 1977; DCH Eng. 1977. Lect. Dept. Child Health Univ. Leic.

ARCHER, Lesley Joanne 10 Sheridan Drive, Helen's Bay, Bangor BT19 1LB — MB ChB 1995 Bristol.

ARCHER, Marilyn The Hoppit, Butts Lane, Danbury, Chelmsford CM3 4NP Tel: 01245 222518; Monkswood, Mill Lane, Little Baddow, Chelmsford CM3 4SB Tel: 01245 222316 — MB ChB 1969 Ed.; BSc Ed. 1966. (Ed.) Prev: GP Chelmsford; SHO (Psychiat.) St. Geo. Hosp. Morpeth.

ARCHER, Neil Duncan 199 Banbury Road, Stratford-upon-Avon CV37 7HT — MB ChB 1995 Birm. (Birm.)

ARCHER, Nora Emma Rose (retired) c/o Mr & Mrs O Bennett, 9 Meadow Close, Budleigh Salterton EX9 6JN — BM BCh 1935 Oxf.; DM Oxf. 1937, BM BCh 1935; DPH Eng. 1942.

ARCHER, Philip Beckington Family Practice, St Lukes Road, Beckington, Bath BA11 6SE Tel: 01372 830316 Fax: 01372 831261 Email: stlukes@globalnet.co.uk; Meadowside, 9 Linnet Way, Frome BA11 2UY Tel: 01373 472030 — MB BS 1970 Lond.; MRCGP 1984; DObst RCOG 1972; DTM & H RCP Lond. 1972. (St. Mary's) Socs: BMA & Peruvian Coll. Drs. Prev: Lect. (Family & Community Med.) San Agustin Univ., Peru; Dir. Rural Developm. Commiss. Cuzco, Peru; MO Clinica Evangelica Urcos, Peru.

ARCHER, Richard Park View Group Practice, 2 Longford Road West, Reddish, Stockport SK5 6ET Tel: 0161 431 9339 Fax: 0161 431 5140 — MB ChB 1991 Manch.; MRCGP 1996; DRCOG 1997; DFFP 1997. (St. And. & Manch.) GP Princip. Stockport. Prev: Trainee GP Stockport VTS.

ARCHER, Richard 22 Perth House, Canberra Square, Tilbury RM18 7PJ — MB ChB 1985 Liverp.

ARCHER, Richard David John Southbroom Surgery, 15 Estcourt Street, Devizes SN10 1LQ Tel: 01380 720909 — MB ChB 1989 Leeds.

ARCHER, Richard John Northern Imaging Group, PO Box 1827, Launceston Tas 7250, Australia Tel: 00 61 3 6336 6336 Fax: 00 61 3 63343335 Email: rjarcher@vision.net.au; 9 Albemarle Gate, Pittville, Cheltenham GL50 4NG Tel: 01242 239517 — MB ChB 1981 Liverp.; MRCP (UK) 1987; MRCS Eng. LRCP Lond. 1981; ECFMG Cert. 1984; FRCR 1990. (Liverp.) Radiol. N.. Imaging Gp. St. Vincents Hosp. Launceston. Socs: Austral. Soc. Ultrasound in Med. Prev: Regist. (Diagn. Radiol.) Roy. Hobart Hosp. Tasmania, Australia; Sen. Regist. (Diag. Radiol.) St. Thos. Hosp. Lond.; Regist. (Diag. Radiol.) Leicester Roy. Infirm.

ARCHER, Robert Paul Heatherbrook Surgery, Beaumont Lodge, 242 Astill Lodge Road, Leicester LE4 1EF Tel: 0116 235 6324 Fax: 0116 234 0333 — MB ChB 1975 Sheff.

ARCHER, Sally Caroline Govan Health Centre, 5 Drumoyne Road, Glasgow G51 4BJ Tel: 0141 531 8400 Fax: 0141 531 8404 — MB ChB 1980 Glas.; MRCGP 1987; MRCPsych 1986; DRCOG 1983.

ARCHER, Reverend Sarah Elizabeth St Barnabas Church, 40 Carlton Avenue, Dulwich, London SE21 7DG Tel: 020 8693 1524 Fax: 020 8693 0203 Email: searcher@fish.co.uk — MB BS 1989 Lond.; BA 1999 (oxon); MRCGP 1995. (Charing Cross and Westminster) Prev: SHO (A & E), City Hosp. Truro; GP Princip. Camborne; Trainee GP/SHO Cornw. VTS.

ARCHER, Sarah Jane Alvaston Medical Centre, 14 Boulton Lane, Alvaston, Derby DE24 0GE Tel: 01332 571322; 6 Ellastone Gardens, Alvaston, Derby DE24 0QQ — MB BS 1987 Lond.; MRCGP 1992; DRCOG 1991. (St. Mary's Hosp. Med. Sch.) Prev: Trainee GP York VTS.

ARCHER, Mr Timothy John The Ipswich Hospital NHS Trust, Heath Road, Ipswich IP4 5PD Tel: 01473 703518 Fax: 01473 703528; Sunnyside, California, Woodbridge IP12 4DE — MB BChir 1973 Camb.; MS Soton. 1986; MA Camb. 1973; FRCS Eng. 1977. (King's Coll Hosp.) Cons. Gen. Surg. Ipswich Hosp. NHS Trust. Socs: Fell. Roy. Soc. Med. (Surg. Sect.); Brit. Assn. Surg. Oncol.; Assn. Surg. Prev: Sen. Regist. (Surg.) Wessex RHA; Regist. (Surg.) Roy. Free Hosp. Lond. & Soton. Gen. Hosp.

ARCHER, Venice Rosalie 103 Grove Road, Sparkhill, Birmingham B11 4DB — MB ChB 1990 Birm.; ChB Birm. 1990; MRCP (UK) 1996.

ARCHER-HALL, Jean Frances Christina (retired) 56 Styvechale Avenue, Earlsdon, Coventry CV5 6DX Tel: 01203 674043 — MB BS 1947 Lond.; MRCS Eng. LRCP Lond. 1947. Prev: Med. Off. Marks & Spencer Ltd. Coventry.

ARCHER-KORANTENG, Ernest The Health Centre, Leypark Walk, Estover, Plymouth PL6 8UE Tel: 01752 789030 Fax: 01752 772665; 6 Woolwell Drive, Woolwell, Plymouth PL6 7JP — Vrach 1971 Kharkov Med. Inst. USSR. (Kharkhov) GP Estover. Prev: Regist. (Geriat. Med.) Roy. Devon & Exeter Hosp.; Regist. (Psychiat.) Exe Vale Hosp. Exeter; SHO (O & G) Torbay Hosp. Torquay.

ARCHIBALD, Anna Catriona Isabel Fair Mile Hospital, Wallingford OX10 9HH — MB ChB 1989 Glas. (Univ. Glas.) Staff Grade (Rehabil. Psychiat.) Fairmile Hosp. Wallingford. Socs: BMA. Prev: Clin. Asst. (Psychiat.) Fairmile Hosp. Wallingford; SHO (Psychiat.) Fairmile Hosp. Wallingford & Campbell Centre Milton Keynes.

ARCHIBALD, Catherine Acorn Cottage, 111 Worton Road, Isleworth TW7 6EG — MB BS 1996 Lond.

ARCHIBALD, Mr David Andrew Alexander Chase Farm Hospital, The Ridgeway, Enfield EN2 8 Tel: 020 8366 6600 — MB ChB 1979 Glas.; MPhil (Bio-Eng.) Strathclyde Univ. 1991; FRCS Glas. 1983. Cons. Orthop. Surg. Chase Farm Hosp. Enfield. Socs: Fell. BOA. Prev: Sen. Regist. St. Bart. Hosp. Lond.; Lect. (Orthop.) Lond. Hosp. Med. Coll.

ARCHIBALD, Fiona Louise McKay 46 Barnton Park Gardens, Edinburgh EH4 6HN — MB ChB 1998 Aberd.; MB ChB Aberd 1998.

ARCHIBALD, Lucy Jane 47 Tonacliffe Road, Whitworth, Rochdale OL12 8SS — BM BS 1998 Nottm.; BM BS Nottm 1998.

ARCHIBALD, Margaret Jean Douglas (retired) The Granary, Burnfoot Farm, Kinfauns, Perth PH2 7LB — MB ChB Ed. 1961. Clin. Asst. (Psychiat.) Murray Roy. Perth. Prev: Regist. (Psychiat.) Murray Roy. Perth.

ARCHIBALD, Roy McLellan 7 Aspen Way, High Beeches, Banstead SM7 1LE Tel: 01737 211341 — MB ChB 1944 Glas.; FFOM 1979; DIH Glas. 1948. Socs: Hon. Fell. Ergonomics Soc.; Soc. Occupat. Med. Prev: Dir. Med. Serv. Nat. Coal Bd.; Med. Off. ICI Alkali Div.; Occupat. Phys. Gen. Med. Legal Serv. Ltd.

ARCHIBONG, Eric Ime 7 Middleton House, Lawson Estate, Burge St., London SE1 4EP — MB BS 1974 Nigeria; MB BS Ahmadu Bello Univ., Nigeria 1974; MRCOG 1981.

ARDEMAN, Simon (retired) 44 Stanmore Hill, Stanmore HA7 3BN Tel: 020 8954 1462 Fax: 020 8954 1163 Email: simon@sardeman.freeserve.co.uk — PhD Lond. 1966; MA, BM BCh Oxf. 1956; MRCS Eng. LRCP Lond. 1956; FRCPath 1989, M 1977. Private Pract., BUPA Hosp. Bushey Garden Hosp., Hendon. Prev: Cons. Haemat. Edgware Gen. Hosp.

ARDEN, Christopher Donald Park Surgery, Park Surgery, Hursley Road, Chandlers Ford, Eastleigh SO53 2ZH Tel: 023 8026 7355 Fax: 023 8026 5394; 254 Sunlight Cottages, Hursley, Winchester SO21 2JL Tel: 01962 775392 — MB BS 1991 Lond.; BSc (Physiol.) Lond. 1988; MRCGP 1997; DRCOG 1996. (Char. Cross & Westm.) GP. Socs: Roy. Coll. Gen. Pract. Prev: SHO (A & E) Roy. Surrey Co. Hosp. Guildford; SHO (Med.) St. Mary's Hosp. Portsmouth; SHO (Paediat. & O & G) S.lands Hosp. Shoreham-by-Sea.

ARDEN, Geoffrey Bernard Institute of Ophthalmology, Judd St., London WC1H 9QS Tel: 020 7387 9621 Fax: 020 7388 8727 — MB BS 1956 Lond.; PhD Lond. 1953, BSc 1951, MB BS 1956. (Univ. Coll. Hosp.) Prof. Neurophysiol. Univ. Lond.; Hon. Cons. Moorfields Eye Hosp. Lond. Prev: Ho. Phys. Dept. Neurol. Univ. Coll. Hosp.

ARDEN, Margaret Lilith 16 Dealtry Road, London SW15 6NL — MB BS 1953 Lond.; DPM Eng. 1958. (Char. Cross) Socs: Assoc. Mem. Brit. Psychoanalyt. Soc. Prev: Med. Dir. Battersea Child Guid. Unit.

ARDEN, Nigel Kim MRC Unit, Southampton General Hospital, Southampton SO16 6YD — MB BS 1986 Lond.; MRCP (UK) 1989.

ARDEN-JONES, Mr Jonathan Richard Family Medical Centre, 171 Carlton Road, Nottingham NG3 2FW Tel: 0115 950 4068 Fax: 0115 950 9844; 11 Esher Grove, Nottingham NG3 5DR — MB 1974 Camb.; BChir 1973; FRCS Eng. 1978. Gen. Practitioner, Nottm.; Clin. Asst. in Dermatological Surg., Qu.s Med. Centre, Nottm.

ARDERN, Katy Dale 105 Imogen Court, Regent Park, Salford M5 4TQ — MB ChB 1986 Manch.; MSc (Epidemiol. & Health Scis.) Manch. 1995. Acting Cons. Pub. Health Med. Liverp. HA. Socs: Manch. Med. Soc. (Sect. Pub. Health Med.). Prev: Sen. Regist. (Pub. Health Med.) Manch. Health Commiss.; Regist. (Pub. Health Med.) Stockport HA; SHO (Psychiat.) Roy. Oldham Hosp.

ARDERN, Mark Howard Department of Mental Health for the Elderly, St Charles Hospital, London W10 6DZ Tel: 020 8962 4106 — MB ChB 1976 Manch.; MRCPsych. 1980; FRCPsych 1997. Cons. Psychiat. of Old Age, Brent, Kensington, Chelsea and W.minster Ment. Health NHS Trust; Hon. Sen. Lect. Imperial Coll. Lond.

***ARDERN-JONES, Michael Roger** 2 Ridgeway, Epsom KT19 8LB — MB BS 1996 Lond.; BSc (Hons) Lond. 1993.

ARDESHNA, Kirit Maganlal 234 Brecknock Road, London N19 5BQ — MB BChir 1990 Camb.; MA Camb. 1991, MB BChir 1990.

ARDILL, Alison Claire (retired) 4 Avonvale, Belfast BT4 2WA Tel: 028 9076 3550 — MB BCh BAO Belf. 1960; FFA RCSI 1973. Prev: Cons. Anaesth. Ulster Hosp. Dundonald.

ARDOUIN, Mr Alan Peter (retired) 108 New Dover Road, Canterbury CT1 3EH Tel: 01227 761151 — MB BS 1954 Lond.; FRCS Eng. 1962; DLO Eng. 1957. Prev: Cons. ENT Surg. Kent & Canterbury Hosp. & I. of Thanet Dist. Hosp.

ARDRON, Mark Ernest Elizabeth House, 6 Brooksby Road, Hoby, Melton Mowbray LE14 3EA — MB ChB 1981 Liverp.; MB ChB (Hons.) Liverp. 1981; MRCS Eng. LRCP Lond. 1981; MRCP (UK) 1984. Cons. Phys. for Elderly Glenfield & Leicester Gen. Hosps. Prev: Sen. Regist. (Geriat.) Selly Oak Hosp. Birm.; Regist. (Med.) Clatterbridge Hosp. Wirral & Walton Hosp. Liverp.

ARDUIN, Marie-Louise c/o The Practice Manager, The Queens Road Medical Practice, The Queens Road, St Peter Port, Guernsey GY1 1RH — MB ChB 1972 Bristol.

ARDUINO, Lisa Ann Bramblewood, 17 Cuddington Park Close, Banstead SM7 1RF Tel: 020 8642 9800 — MB BS 1994 Lond.

AREF-ADIB, Farhad X-Ray Department, St Mary's Hospital, Praed St., London W2 1NY; 40 Bramshill Gardens, London NW5 1JH — LMSSA 1989 Lond.; FRCR 1992. Sen. Regist. (Radiol.) St. Mary's Hosp. Lond.

ARENDS, Mark Johan Histopathology Department, Addenbrooke's Hospital NHS Trust, Hills Road, Cambridge CB2 2QQ Tel: 01223 245151; 40 Fendon Road, Cambridge CB1 7RT Tel: 01223 240647 — MB ChB 1985 (Hons.) Ed.; PhD Ed. 1992, BSc (Hons.) (Path.) 1983; MRCPath 1994; T(Path) 1994. Univ. Lect. in Clin. Path. Univ. of Camb.; Hon. Cons. in Path. Addenbrooke's. Socs: Path. Soc.; Assn. Clin. Path.; BSG. Prev: Lect. (Path.) Univ. Edin. & Hon. Sen. Regist. Univ. Edin.; MRC Train. Fell.

ARENDSE, Sean Derek 78 Warwick Road, Sutton SM1 4BL — MB BS 1997 Lond.

ARENDT, George Jerzy (retired) 16 Waverley Court, Steele's Road, London NW3 4SB Tel: 020 7586 5471 — MB ChB 1947 Polish Sch. of Med.; FRCOG 1979, M 1954; DObst 1949. Hon. Cons. O & G Newham HA; Hon. Cons. Gyn. French Disp. Lond. Prev: Charity clinic at the French Dispensaire

AREPALLI, Nandini 8 Broadway, Bramhall, Stockport SK7 3BR — MB ChB 1996 Dund.

***ARESTIS, Nikolas James** Barloch, Barloch Avenue, Milngavie, Glasgow G62 8EQ — MB ChB 1998 Aberd.; BSc (Med. Sci.), Aberd 1997.

AREY, David Keith (retired) 7 Weston Close, Woodthorpe, Nottingham NG5 4FS — MB BS 1963 Lond.; MRCS Eng. LRCP Lond. 1962; MRCOG 1968; DObst 1964. Prev: GP Nottm.

ARFAN, Aroona 76 Merrylee Road, Newlands, Glasgow G43 2QZ — MB ChB 1991 Glas.

ARFEEN, Zia-Ul 3 Stonenest Street, London N4 3BA Tel: 020 7272 6571; 22 Buckstone Howe, Edinburgh EH10 6XF Tel: 0131 445 3105 — MB BS 1981 Karachi; FFA RCSI 1990; DA (UK) 1986. Regist. (Anaesth.) Roy. Infirm. Edin.

ARFMAN, Marie Helene Josephine The Health Centre, Garden Terrace Road, Old Harlow, Harlow CM17 0AX Tel: 01279 418136 Fax: 01279 429650 — Artsexamen 1992 Amsterdam. (Univ. Amsterdam) GP Harlow.

ARGENT, Claire Joanne 84 Park Lane, Congleton CW12 3DD — MB ChB 1994 Birm.

ARGENT, Julie Dawn 321 Exeter Road, Exmouth EX8 3NP — MB BS 1984 Lond.

ARGENT, Lisa Beverley Newhaven Health Centre, Chapel Street, Newhaven BN9 9PW Tel: 01273 517000 Fax: 01273 515845; 40 Hove Park Villas, Hove BN3 6HG — MB BS 1982 Lond.; DRCOG 1986. GP Newhaven.

ARGENT, Vincent Patrick Little Friston, Jevington Road, Friston, Eastbourne BN20 0AG Tel: 01323 423131 Fax: 01323 423737 Email: vpargent@compuserve.com — MB BChir 1975 Camb.; MB Camb. 1975, BChir 1974; LLB 1985; FFA RCS Eng. 1979; DCH 1980; MRCOG 1983, D 1976; DIMC 1995. (St. Thomas' Hosp. Lond.) Cons. O & G E.bourne HA; Cons (Gyn. & Anaesth.) BPAS.

Socs: BMA; Brit. Assn. Sport & Med.; Medico-Legal Soc. Prev: Regist. (O & G) Addenbrooke's Hosp. Camb.; Regist. (Anaesth.) Plymouth Gen. Hosp.; Asst. Med. Off. Grand Bank Hosp. Newfld.

ARGIRIU, Panagiotis Eastbourne Central CMHT, St Mary's House, St Leonards Road, Eastbourne BN21 3UU Tel: 01323 747212 Fax: 01323 747206 Email: panos.argiriu@each-tr-sthames.nhs.uk.

ARGIROS, Georgios 83 Meadowbrook Road, Kibworth, Leicester LE8 0HU — Ptychio Iatrikes 1986 Thessalonika.

ARGO, John Keigwin (retired) Oakleigh, St James' Crescent, Inverurie AB51 3UD Tel: 01467 620262 — MRCS Eng. LRCP Lond. 1943. Prev: Cas. Off. & Ho. Surg. St. John's Hosp. Lond.

ARGUELLES ARIAS, Jose Antonio Flat 29 Kensington Court, 20 Kensington Road, Glasgow G12 9NX — LMS 1985 Oviedo.

ARGUMENT, Wilfred Roy (retired) 1 Dee Park Road, Gayton, Wirral CH60 3RG Tel: 0151 342 5749 — MB BS 1944 Durh.; DMRT Eng. 1949. Cons. Radiotherap. Mersey RHA & N. Wales.

ARGYLE, Catherine Mary Elms Medical Practice, 5 Stewart Road, Harpenden AL5 4QA Tel: 01582 769393 Fax: 01582 461735 — MB BS 1986 Lond.; MA Oxf. 1992, BA 1983; MRCGP 1992; DCH RCP Lond. 1991. Prev: SHO (Psychiat.) Barnet Gen. Hosp.; SHO (Paediat.) N. Middlx. Hosp. Lond.; SHO (O & G) Univ. Coll. Hosp. Lond.

ARGYROU, Nicholas Anthony Bird-In-Eye Surgery, Uckfield Community Hospital, Framfield Road, Uckfield TN22 5AW Tel: 01825 763196 Fax: 01825 760039; Romany Cottage, Lankhurst Oak, Blackboys, Uckfield TN22 5HD Tel: 01825 890347 — MB BS 1987 Lond.; DRCOG 1991. Prev: Trainee GP Tunbridge Wells VTS; Ho. Off. (Gen. Med.) Qu. Mary's Hosp. Sidcup; Ho. Off. (Gen. Surg.) Lond. Hosp. Lond.

ARIARATNAM, Gnanamala Yeovil District Hospital, Higher Kingston, Yeovil BA21 4AT — MB BCh 1992 Wales.

ARIAS ABELLAN, Margarita Maria 47 Stevenholme Crescent, Nottingham NG5 5JU — LMS 1992 U Complutense Madrid.

ARIE, Margaret Eleanor (retired) Rehabilitation Directorate, Colman Hospital, Unthank Road, Norwich NR2 2PJ Tel: 01603 288977 Fax: 01603 288922 — BM BCh 1965 Oxf.; MA Oxf. 1965; FRCP Lond. 1995; MRCP (UK) 1972; DObst RCOG 1967. Cons. Rehabil. Med. & Rheum. Norwich HA. Prev: Dep. Dir. (Med. Serv.) Roy. Hosp. & Home Putney.

ARIE, Professor Thomas Harry David, CBE Cromwell House, West Church St., Kenninghall, Norwich NR16 2EN Tel: 01953 887375 Fax: 01953 887375 Email: arie@ukgateway.net — BM BCh 1960 Oxf.; MA Oxf. 1959; FRCP Lond. 1983, M 1978; FFPHM RCP (UK) 1990; FRCPsych 1977, M 1971; FFCM RCP (UK) 1973, M 1972; DPM Eng. 1964. Emerit. Prof. Health c/o Elderly, Univ. Nottm.; Vice Chairm., (Agecare) The Roy. Surgic. Aid Soc. Socs: World Psychiat. Assn. (Ex-Chairm. Geriat. Psychiat. Sect.); Europ. Assn. Of Geriat. Psychiat. (Hon. Mem.); Soc. for Social Medicare (Hon. Mem.).

ARIF, Mohammad Haroon c/o of Department of Anaesthetics, Selly Oak Hospital, Raddlebarn Road, Birmingham B29 6JD Tel: 0121 627 1627 Fax: 0121 627 8269 — MB BS 1967 Allahabad; BSc Gorakhpur 1960; FRCA 1993; Specialist Accredit (Anaesth.) RCS Eng. 1978. (Moti Lal Nehru Med. Coll. Allahabad) Cons. Anaesth. Selly Oak Hosp. Birm. Socs: BMA; Assn. Anaesths. Prev: Sen. Regist. (Anaesth.) Birm. AHA (T); Regist. (Anaesth.) Birm. Accid. Hosp. & Dudley Rd. Hosp. Birm.

ARIF, Mohammed Rafi 102 Marsh Lane, Birmingham B23 6PL — MB ChB 1993 Leic.

ARIF, Muhammad 160 Arran Street, Roath, Cardiff CF24 3HU; 138 Wendover House, Thurlow St, Walworth, London SE17 2UG — MB BS 1988 Karachi; MRCP (UK) 1995; DTM & H 1996; MSc (Cardiol.) 1997. Cons. Asir Centr. Hosp., Abha, Kingdom of Saudi Arabia.

ARIF, Mr Muhammad Suhail 37 Woodlodge Lane, West Wickham BR4 9LY — MB BS 1982 Punjab; MSc Orthop. Lond. 1990; FRCS Ed. 1988.

ARIF, Nadeem 26 Thurston Street, Burnley BB11 3DJ — MB ChB 1998 Manch.; MB ChB Manch 1998.

ARIF, Saimah 23 The Drive, Buckhurst Hill IG9 5RB — MB BS 1998 Lond.; MB BS Lond 1998.

ARIF, Shireen 11 Upland Road, Selly Park, Birmingham B29 7JR — MB ChB 1997 Leic.

ARIFF, Ahmed Tonge Moor Road Surgery, 398 Tonge Moor Road, Bolton BL2 2LA Tel: 01204 385206 Fax: 01204 371185; 398 Tonge Moor Road, Bolton BL2 2LA Tel: 01204 385231 — MB BS 1975 Rangoon; MB BS Med Inst (I) Rangoon 1975. Med. Off. Family Plann. Clinic Bolton; Med. Mem. Disabil. Appeal Tribunal.

ARIFF, Ben Bahemia 17 Lancaster Road, London N4 4PJ — MB BS 1994 Lond.

ARIFF, Mohamed Hashir Ismail c/o Mr F Hamid, 82A Warren Road, London E10 5QA — MB BS 1998 Lond.; MB BS Lond 1998.

ARIFFIN, Sharil Azlan — BM BS 1989 Nottm.; BMedSci Nottm. 1987; FRCA 1994. Cons. Anaesth., N. Staffs Hosp. NHS Trust. Prev: Sen. Regist., Anaesthetics, Univ. Hosp. Birm. NHS Trust.

ARIJON BARAZAL, Maria Cristina 35 Bron-Y-Nant, Wrexham LL13 7TZ — LMS 1988 Santiago de Compostela.

ARISTODEMOU, Aristi 79A Linden Way, London N14 4NG — MB BS 1989 Lond.

ARIYANAYAGAM, Ithayamalar Jacintha 8 Kilmington Close, Hutton, Brentwood CM13 2JZ — LRCP LRCS 1986 Ed.; LRCP LRCS Ed. LRCPS Glas. 1986.

ARIYANAYAGAM, Sathiyakeerthy 8 Kilmington Close, Hutton, Brentwood CM13 2JZ — MB BS 1976 Ceylon; MRCOG 1987; DCH RCP Lond. 1988. Regist. (O & G) Roy. Gwent Hosp. Newport.

ARIYARATNAM, Shyamala Montague Health Centre, Oakenhurst Rd, Blackburn BB1 2PP; 5 Talbenny Close, Heaton, Bolton BL1 5FG — MRCS Eng. LRCP 1988 Lond.; MRCS Eng LRCP Lond. 1988; MRCP (UK) 1993. (Univ. Jaffna, Sri Lanka) Cons. Comm. Paediat., Blackburn. Socs: RCPCH; BACCH. Prev: Sen. Registr. Comm. Paediat.; Paediat. Neurol. Regist. Manch. Childr. Hosp.; Paediat. Regist. Nottm. Hosp.

ARIYAWANSA, Indra Birch Hill Hospital, Rochdale OL12 9QB Tel: 01706 77777; 10 Winchester Close, Rochdale OL11 5NE Tel: 01706 638477 — MB BS 1970 Ceylon; MD (Paediat.) Sri Lanka 1986; MRCP (UK) Paediat. 1983; DCH Ceylon 1978. Cons. Paediat. Birch Hill Hosp. Rochdale. Prev: Assoc. Specialist (Paediat.) Birch Hill Hosp. Rochdale.

ARJANI, Kawasji Ardeshir Doctors Mess, West Suffolk Hospital, Hardwick Lane, Bury St Edmunds IP33 2QZ Tel: 01284 713000; 39 Sebert Road, Morton Hall Estate, Bury St Edmunds IP32 7EH Tel: 01284 765768 — MB BS 1981 Karachi. (Dow Med. Coll. Karachi) Staff Grade (Psychiat. of Old Age) W. Suff. Hosp. Bury St. Edmunds.

ARJUN, Nina Vijaya Lakshmi 270 Whitehorse Lane, South Norwood, London SE25 6UW — MB BS 1986 Lond. Prev: Ho. Surg. Luton & Dunstable Hosp.; Ho. Phys. Mayday Hosp. Croydon.

ARK, Satnam Singh Booth Place Surgery, 15 Booth Place, Falkirk FK1 1BA Tel: 01324 621113 Fax: 01324 633456; 9 Ladywell Court, Larbert FK5 4HR Email: satnam@mantas.demon.co.uk — MB ChB 1980 Glas. GP Falkirk.

ARKELL, Mr David George 16 Knightlow Road, Harborne, Birmingham B17 8QB Tel: 0121 429 2772 — MB ChB 1967 Birm.; MSc Birm. 1971; FRCS Eng. 1973. (Birm.) Cons. Urol. City Hosp. NHS Trust Birm. Socs: Brit. Assn. Urol. Surgs.; BMA; Brit. Med. Laser Assn. Prev: Sen. Regist. (Surg. & Urol.) United Birm. Hosps. & Birm. RHB.

ARKELL, James Hardy Lockhart House, Greshams School, Holt NR25 6DZ Email: james.arkell@croydon-ha.sththames.nhs.uk; Croydon Health, Knollys House, 17 Addiscombe Road, Croydon CR0 6SR Tel: 020 8401 3988 — MB BS 1996 Lond.

ARKELL, Lesley Jean X-Ray Department, Russells Hall Hospital, Dudley Tel: 01384 456111; 16 Knightlow Road, Harborne, Birmingham B17 8QB Tel: 0121 429 2772 — MB ChB 1969 (Hons.) Birm.; BSc (Hons.) Birm. 1966; FRCR 1985. Cons. Radiol. Russells Hall Hosp. Dudley, W. Midl. Prev: Sen. Regist. (Radiol.) W. Midl. RHA (T).

ARKELL, Sian Marie 15 Ambra Val E., Bristol BS8 4RF — MB ChB 1991 Bristol.

ARKINSTALL, Gillian Mary Spa Road Surgery, Spa Road East, Llandrindod Wells LD1 5ES Tel: 01597 824291 / 842292 Fax: 01597 824503; Gors Barn, Cefnllys Lane, Llandrindod Wells LD1 5PD Tel: 01597 825367 — MB BS 1988 Lond.; MRCGP 1993; DRCOG 1991; DCH RCP Lond. 1990. (St. Marys) Prev: SHO (Geriat. & Psychiat.) St. Chas. Hosp. Lond.; SHO (Paediat.) St. Mary's Hosp. Lond. & (O & G) Ashford Hosp.; Ho. Off. (Med.) Ealing.

ARKLE, John Howard Roborough Surgery, 1 Eastcote Close, Southway, Plymouth PL6 6PH Tel: 01752 701659 Fax: 01752

773181; Little Orchard, 22 Powisland Drive, Plymouth PL6 6AB Tel: 01752 700280 — MB ChB 1975 Liverp.; MRCGP 1980; DRCOG 1977. Gen. Practitioner, Plymouth. Socs: Plymouth Med. Soc.

ARLETT, Peter Richard Setlands, Wellgreen Lane, Kingston, Lewes BN7 3NP — MB BS 1991 Lond.; BSc (Hons.) Lond. 1988; MRCP 1994. (University College Manchester School of Medicine) Sen. Med. Assessor Meds. Control Agency Dept. of Health.

ARLT, Regine Department of Obstetrics & Gynaecology, St Mary's Hospital, Newport — State Exam Med 1993 Berlin.

ARMAND SMITH, Nicholas Godfrey Westbury Lodge, Tarrant Gunville, Blandford Forum DT11 8JW — MB BS 1969 Lond.; 2001 Adv. Dip. Occ. Med (Manchester Univ.); MRCS Eng. LRCP Lond. 1971; FFCM 1986, M 1979; DObst RCOG 1971; Dip. Soc. Med. Ed. 1974. Cons.Occ. Phys. Stoke marobville Hosp. NHS Trust; Occ. Phys. Salisbury Health Care NHS Trust. Prev: DMO Salisbury HA; Community Med. Specialist N. Lothian Health Dist.; Epidemiol. Smallpox Eradication Progr. WHO.

ARMAR, Nii Adjeidu Department of Obst. & Gyn., Central Middlesex Hospital NHS Trust, Acton Lane, London NW10 7NS Tel: 020 8453 2409 Fax: 020 8453 2408; The End House, Cornwall Road, Pinner HA5 4LT Tel: 020 8420 2071 Fax: 020 8420 2071 — MB ChB 1975 Sheff.; MRCOG 1984. Cons. O & G Centr. Middlx. Hosp. Socs: BMA. Prev: Lect. (O & G) Univ. Coll. Hosp. Lond.; Birthright Research Fell. Reproduc. Endocrinol. Middlx. Hosp. Lond.

ARMATAGE, Robert (retired) The Rollands, 32 Norton Road, Loddon, Norwich NR14 6DU Tel: 01508 520381 — MB BS Lond. 1950; MRCS Eng. LRCP Lond. 1946; DObst RCOG 1954. Prev: Res. Med. Off. Jenny Lind Childr. Hosp. Norwich.

ARMATAGE, Mr Robert James Leighton Hospital, Middlewich Road, Leighton, Crewe CW1 4QJ Tel: 01270 612181 Fax: 01270 612176; Flaxyards Cottage, Rhuddal Heath, Tarporley CW6 9HJ Tel: 01829 733017 Email: r.j. armatage@aol.com — MB ChB 1985 Liverp.; MRCOG 1991. Cons. (O & G) Leighton Hosp. Crewe, Chesh. Prev: Sen. Regist. (O & G) Liverp. Servs. NHS Trust; Clin. Research Fell. (Reproduc. Med.) Univ. Bristol.

ARMER, Martin Lee 59 Dinerth Road, Rhos-on-Sea, Colwyn Bay LL28 4YG — MB ChB 1996 Manch.

ARMIN, Richard Hayward (retired) 43 Golf Links Road, Burnham-on-Sea TA8 2PP Tel: 01278 782275 — MB BChir 1939 Camb.; MA Camb. 1940; MRCS Eng. LRCP Lond. 1939; MRCPsych. 1971; DPM RCPSI 1949. Prev: Cons. Psychiat. St. Martin's Hosp. Bath.

ARMITAGE, Alison Jane 146 Congleton Road, Sandbach CW11 1DN — MB ChB 1994 Bristol; MRCP (UK) 1997. (Bristol) Specialist Regist. Rotat. (Nephr.) S.W. Region.

ARMITAGE, Allison The Health Centre, Byland Road, Skelton-in-Cleveland, Saltburn-by-the-Sea TS12 2NN Tel: 01287 650430 Fax: 01287 651268; Birchwood Road, 56 The Fairway, Saltburn-by-the-Sea TS12 1NG — MB BS 1988 Newc.; MRCGP 1992; DRCOG 1991.

ARMITAGE, Mr Andrew Richard 18 The Knoll, Beckenham BR3 5JW — MB BS 1992 Lond.; BSc (Hons.) Lond. 1989; FRCS Eng. 1996. (St. Thos. Hosp. Lond.) Regist. (Orthop.) Hastings.

***ARMITAGE, Catherine Marie** Northcliffe Court, 6 High Bank Lane, Shipley BD18 4LJ Tel: 01274 598230 — MB BCh 1995 Wales.

ARMITAGE, Edward Nigel (retired) Halletts Barn, Common Lane, Ditchling, Hassocks BN6 8TN Tel: 01273 844886 Fax: 01273 844886 Email: gaswiz2350@aol.com — MB BS 1960 Lond.; FFA RCS Eng. 1967; DObst RCOG 1962. Prev: Cons. Anaesth. Brighton Healthcare Trust.

ARMITAGE, Emma Louise Preston Patrick Hall, Milnthorpe LA7 7NY Tel: 015395 67200 Fax: 015395 67200 — MB BCh 1992 Wales; MRCP (UK) 1995. SHO (Gen. Med.) Hope Hosp. Manch.

ARMITAGE, Ernest (retired) Oakendean, 12 Shanter Way, Alloway, Ayr KA7 4PF Tel: 01292 441408 — MB ChB Ed. 1947; MRCP Glas. 1962. Prev: Med. Regist. Glas. Roy. Infirm.

ARMITAGE, Felicity Elizabeth The Health Centre, Main Road, Radcliffe-on-Trent, Nottingham NG12 2GD Tel: 0115 933 3737; The Surgery, Main Road, Radcliffe on Trent, Nottingham NG12 2GD — BM BS 1983 Nottm.; BMedSci Nottm. 1980, BM BS 1983; BDS (Hons.) Birm. 1976; MRCGP 1992; DRCOG 1989. Socs: BMA. Prev: SHO (O & G) City Hosp. Nottm.; SHO (Psychiat. & A & E) Univ. Hosp. Nottm.; SHO (Paediat.) Gu. Med. Centr. & Univ. Hosp. Nottm.

ARMITAGE, Francis Henderson Priory Avenue Surgery, 24-26 Priory Avenue, High Wycombe HP13 6SH Tel: 01494 448132 Fax: 01494 686407 — MB ChB 1971 Birm.

ARMITAGE, Jane Margaret Clinical Trials Service Unit, Harkness Building, Radclffe Infirmary, Oxford OX2 6HE Tel: 01865 557241 Fax: 01865 404821; 92 Southmoor Road, Oxford OX2 6RB Tel: 01865 516115 — MB BS 1979 Lond.; MRCP (UK) 1983; MFPHM RCP (UK) 1996. Sen. Research Fell. & Hon. Cons. Pub. Health Med. Clin. Trials Serv. Unit. Radcliffe Infirm. Oxf. Prev: Research Regist. Clin. Trial Serv. Unit Radcliffe Infirm Oxf.; Regist. (Thoracic Med.) Ch.ill Hosp. Oxf.

ARMITAGE, John Derrick Middlewich Road Surgery, 6 Middlewich Road, Sandbach CW11 1DL Tel: 01270 767411 Fax: 01270 759305 — MB ChB 1969 Liverp.; FRCGP 1992, M 1977; DObst RCOG 1971. Course Organiser (Gen. Pract.) S. Chesh. VTS; Lect. Dept. Gen. Pract. Univ. Liverp. Socs: BMA. Prev: Ho. Phys. & Ho. Surg. Vict. Centr. Hosp. Wallasey; SHO (O & G) Liverp. Matern. Hosp.; SHO (Paediat.) Alder Hey Childr. Hosp. Liverp.

ARMITAGE, John Philip 10 Oak Tree Lane, Cookhill, Alcester B49 5LH Tel: 01789 763616 — MB ChB 1966 Ed. (Ed.) Prev: Med. Train. Off., Benefits Agency Birm.; GP Studley Warks.; SHO (Paediat. & Obst.) Copthorne Hosp. Shrewsbury.

ARMITAGE, Jonathan Derrick 146 Congleton Road, Sandbach CW11 1DN — MB ChB 1997 Liverp.

ARMITAGE, Lesley Elizabeth HSMC, Park House, 40 Edgbaston Park Road, Birmingham B15 2RT Tel: 0121 414 7050 Fax: 0121 414 7051 Email: l.e.armitage@bham.ac.uk — MB BS 1979 Lond.; BSc Lond. 1973; MSc Community Paediat. Newc. 1990; MRCGP 1985; DRCOG 1987; DCCH RCP Ed. 1986. (St. Mary's Hosp. Med. Sch. Lond.) Hon. Research Fell. & Sen. Regist. (Pub. Health Med.) Health Servs. Managem. Centre Univ. Birm. Prev: Sen. Regist. (Pub. Health Med.) W. Midl. RHA; Clin. Med. Off. (Community Paediat.) Gateshead HA.

ARMITAGE, Mary Bournemouth General Hospital, Bournemouth; The Knoll, 9 Upper Golf Links Road, Broadstone BH18 8BT Tel: 01202 253963 Fax: 01202 658930 Email: m.armitage@rbch_tr.swest.nhs.uk — MB ChB 1980 Birm.; BSc. (Hons.) Birm. 1977, MB ChB (Hons.) 1980; DM Soton. 1988; MRCP (UK) 1983. Cons. Endocrinol. & Metab. Med. Bournemouth Gen. Hosp. Socs: Fell. Roy. Coll. Phys. Ed. & BAMM; Fell. Roy. Coll. Phys. Lond. Prev: Hon. Sen. Regist. (Endocrinol. & Diabetes) Soton Gen. Hosp.; Regist. (Med.) Poole Gen. Hosp.; SHO/Regist. Roy. Infirm. Edin.

ARMITAGE, Mr Nicholas Charles Michael 11 Regent Street, Nottingham NG1 5BS Tel: 0115 947 3772; Schoolside Farm, Main St., West Leake, Loughborough LE12 5RF Tel: 01509 856523 — MB BS 1976 Lond.; DM Nottm. 1985; FRCS Eng. 1980; MRCS Eng. LRCP Lond. 1975. (St. Bart.) Cons. Surg. Univ. Hosp. Nottm.; Examr. (Surg.) Univ. of Birm.; Examr. (MRCS) Roy. Coll. of Surg.s of Eng. Socs: Fell.Assoc. of Surg.s of Gt. Britain and Irel.; Brit. Assn. Surg. Oncol.; Assn. Coloproct. Prev: Sen. Lect. (Surg.) Univ. Nottm.; Lect. (Surg.) Univ. Nottm.; Regist. (Surg.) Hammersmith Hosp. Lond.

ARMITAGE, Paul Laurence Grange House, Lyons Gate, Dorchester DT2 7AZ — MB BS 1983 Lond.

ARMITAGE, Mr Trevor George 2-0 Grosvenor Road, South Shields NE33 3QQ — MB ChB 1976 Bristol; BSc Bristol 1973, MB ChB 1976; FRCS Eng. 1983; FRCS Ed. 1981.

ARMITSTEAD, Christopher Philip Kings Hill, Shrawley, Worcester WR6 6TD — MB BS 1997 Lond.

ARMITSTEAD, John Gerrard 19 Castle Street, High Wycombe HP13 6RU Tel: 01494 529769; 129 Sandycombe Road, Kew, Richmond TW9 2EN Tel: 020 8948 4243 Fax: 020 8940 4719 — MB 1976 Camb.; MB BChir Camb. 1976; MA Camb. 1975; MRCP (UK) 1978.

ARMITSTEAD, Margaret Maua, Newlands Drive, Leominster HR6 8PR — MB ChB 1948 Manch.; DPH 1958. (Manch.) Clin. Med. Off. Heref. & Worcs. AHA. Prev: Asst. Div. Med. Off. Lancs. CC Div. 12; Gen. Pract. Leominster.

ARMITSTEAD, Mr Philip Roy Kidderminster General Hospital, Bewdley Road, Kidderminster DY11 6RJ — MRCS Eng. LRCP Lond. 1968; MD Lond. 1976, MB BS 1968; FRCS Eng. 1973. Cons. Gen. Surg. Worcs. Acute Hosp.s NHS Trust.

ARMITT, John Michael (retired) Burton Grange, Burton, Tarporley CW6 0ES Tel: Ex Dir — MB BS 1952 Lond.; MRCGP 1965. Prev: Sen. Med. Off. DHSS.
ARMON, Kate 2 Denison Street, Beeston, Nottingham NG9 1AY Tel: 0115 917 4826 — BM BS 1989 Nottm.; MRCPCH; DM 2001; BMedSci 1987; DCH 1991; DRCOG 1992; MRCP 1993. Specialist Regist. (Paediat.) Nottm. Socs: Roy. Coll. of Paediat. and Child Health.
ARMON, Mr Matthew Philip 2 Denison Street, Beeston, Nottingham NG9 1AY Tel: 0115 917 8426 Email: mparmon@cs.com — BM BS 1989 Nottm.; BMedSci 1987; FRCS Ed. 1993.
ARMOND, Anthony Dew (retired) 36A Bittel Road, Barnt Green, Birmingham B45 8LY — MB BChir 1964 Camb.; MA Camb. 1964; MRCS Eng. LRCP Lond. 1963; MRCPsych 1976; DObst RCOG 1968. Prev: Cons. Psychiat. Dudley Priority Health W. Midl.
ARMOND, Jane Rexford (retired) The Child and Family Unit, Northbrook Clinic, 93 Northbrook Road, Shirley, Solihull B90 3LX — MB BS 1962 Lond.; MRCS Eng. LRCP Lond. 1962; MRCPsych 1977; DPM Eng. 1977. Prev: Cons. Child Psychiat. N.brook Clinic Solihull.
ARMONIS, Anastasios 35 Britten Close, London NW11 7HQ — Ptychio Iatrikes 1986 Athens.
ARMOUR, Alison Department of Histopathology, Royal Preston Hospital, Sharoe Green Lane N., Fulwood, Preston PR2 9HT Tel: 01772 710154 — MB BCh BAO 1986 Belf.; MRCPath 1992; DMJ(Path) Soc. Apoth. Lond. 1994; FRCP 2001. Cons. Path. (Forens. Path.) Dept. of Histopath. Roy. Preston Hosp. Prev: Sen. Regist. (Forens. Med.) State Path. Dept. Belf.
ARMOUR, Alison Ann 164 Finnart Street, Greenock PA16 8JB — MB ChB 1987 Glas.
ARMOUR, Andrew John 28 Victoria Avenue, Woodhall Spa LN10 6TY Tel: 01526 352396 Email: sandy-ann@armour28.freeserve.co.uk — MB BS 1957 Lond.; DObst RCOG 1962; BSc 1998; Adv.Dip.Child Develop 1997; Dip.Clin. Hyp 1999. (Guy's) p/t Clin. Med Off.. Louth& Dist. Health Trust, W. Lindsey Health Trust. Socs: Brit. Soc. Med. & Dent. Hypn.; BMA. Prev: Ho. Off. (Obst.) Surg. Kent & Canterbury Hosp.; Ho. Surg. & Ho. Phys. Pembury Hosp.
ARMOUR, Audrey Louise (retired) Birling House, 1 Abbotts Walk, Fleetwood FY7 6QF — MB BS 1955 Lond.; MRCS Eng. LRCP Lond. 1955.
ARMOUR, Bessie McCammon (retired) Flat 24, The Fold, Coleraine Road, Portstewart — MB BCh BAO 1924 Belf.
ARMOUR, James Keith Ramsey Group Practice Centre, Grove Mount South, Ramsey IM8 3EY Tel: 01624 813881 Fax: 01624 811921; Fergusiea Jurby Road, Ramsey IM7 2EA — MB BCh BAO 1986 Belf.; MRCGP 1990; DMH Belf. 1991; DRCOG 1990. (Queen's University Belfast) Clin. Asst. (Med.) Ramsey Cottage Hosp.; Ment. Health Tribunal Mem. Socs: I. of Man Med. Soc.; Brit. Soc. Med. Dent. Hypn.
ARMOUR, Mr Roger Hanif (retired) 88 Wymondley Road, Hitchin SG4 9PX Tel: 01462 459771 — MB BS 1956 Punjab; MB BS Punjab (Pakistan) 1956; ChM Liverp. 1965; FRCS Eng. 1961; FRCS Ed. 1960; MRCP Lond. 1968; DTM & H Liverp. 1965. Hon. Cons. Surg. Lister Hosp. Stevenage. Prev: Cons. Surg. Liverp. RHB (inc. Birkenhead Childr. Hosp.).
ARMSHAW, Kate Louise 17 Thorn Grove, Sale M33 3AA — MB ChB 1996 Sheff.
ARMSTEAD, Sally Patricia 1 Polecat Cottage, Polecat Corner, Tunworth, Basingstoke RG25 2LA — MB BS 1956 Lond.
ARMSTRONG, Mr Aidan Mark 88 Greystown Avenue, Upper Malone Road, Belfast BT9 6UL — MB BCh BAO 1990 Belf.; FRCSI 1994.
ARMSTRONG, Mr Alan Michael Department of Accident & Emergency Medicine, Fazakerley Hospital, Lower Lane, Fazakerley, Liverpool L9 7AL Tel: 0151 525 5980 — BM BS 1978 Nottm.; FRCS Ed. 1986; MRCP Ed. 1981; MRCGP 1984; DCH RCP Lond. 1982. Cons. A & E Med. Fazakerley Hosp. Liverp. Prev: Cons. A & E Arrowe Pk. Hosp. Wirral; Sen. Regist. (A & E Med.) Alder Hey Childr. Hosp. Liverp.
ARMSTRONG, Alexander John McNeill The Castle Practice, Health Centre, Central Street, Ludgershall, Andover SP11 9RA Tel: 01264 790356 Fax: 01264 791256; Elgin, Dauntsey Lane, Weyhill, Andover SP11 8EB — MB BS 1977 Lond.; BSc Lond. 1974; MRCGP 1984; DRCOG 1982. (London) Gen. Practitioner, Ludgershall; VTS Scheme Organiser Salisbury Dist. Hosp.; Lect. PostGrad. Med. Univ. of Bath; Stud. Tutor, UCL. Socs: Salisbury Med. Soc.; Wessex Fac. PCG.
ARMSTRONG, Miss Alison Louise Fax: 0116 258 4666; The Manor House, 70 Main St, Cossington, Leicester LE7 4UW — MB ChB 1985 Sheff.; DM Nottm. 1996; FRCS Eng. (Orthop.) 1996; FRCS Eng. 1989. Cons. Orthop. Surg. Leicester Gen. Hosp., Leicester. Socs: Brit. Orthop. Assn.; BESS; BSSH. Prev: Sen. Regist. (Orthop. Surg.) Mid Trent Train. Scheme Nottm.
ARMSTRONG, Andrew (retired) Deil's Dike, Lochmaben, Lockerbie DG11 1RN Tel: 01387 810514 — MB ChB Ed. 1952; FRCP Ed. 1971, M 1961; FRCP Glas. 1986, M 1984; DObst RCOG 1957. Prev: Cons. Phys. Dumfries & Galloway Roy. Infirm.
ARMSTRONG, Angela 25 Marsh Lane, Mill Hill, London NW7 4QN — MB ChB 1966 Glas. (Glas.) Sen. Med. Off. GLC. Socs: BMA. Prev: Anaesth. SHO Vict. Infirm. Glas.; Ho. Surg. Vict. Infirm. Glas.; Ho. Phys. Stobhill Hosp. Glas.
ARMSTRONG, Anne Caroline 43 Finchley Road, Altrincham WA15 9RE — MB ChB 1995 Bristol.
ARMSTRONG, Mr Anthony Peter Department Plastic Surgery, Northern General Hospital, Herries Road, Sheffield S5 7AU Tel: 0114 243 4343 Fax: 0114 261 9651; 4 Mountbatten Close, Shottery, Stratford-upon-Avon CV37 9ET Tel: 01789 292977 Email: tony.armstrong1@virgin.net — MB ChB 1991 Birm.; MB ChB (Hons.) Birm. 1991; BDS (Hons.) Birm. 1983; FRCS Eng. 1993; FDS RCS Ed. 1986; FRCS (Plast.) Eng. 1998. (Univ. Birm.) Specialist Regist. (Plastic & Reconstruc. Surg.) N. Gen. Hosp. & Childr. Hosps. Sheff. Socs: Fell. Roy. Coll. Surg. Ed.; Fell. Roy. Coll. Surg. Eng.; BAPS. Prev: Regist. (Plastic Surg.) Roy. Marsden Hosp. Lond.; Regist. (Plastic Surg.) Gt. Ormond St. Hosp. Lond.; Regist. (Oral Surg.) Qu. Eliz. Hosp. Birm.
ARMSTRONG, Barbara Joyce (retired) Broadview, Primrose Hill, Chartham Hatch, Canterbury CT4 7NR Tel: 01227 738243 Fax: 01227 738243 — MB ChB 1963 Birm.; T(M) RCP 1990; DCH Eng. 1974; FRCPCH 1997. Cons. Community Locum. Paediat. Child & Adolesc. Ment. Health Serv. William Harvey Hosp. Ashford Kent. Prev: Cons. Community Paediat. Thameslink NHS Trust.
ARMSTRONG, Benedict Douglas John Torrington Health Centre, New Road, Torrington EX38 8EL Tel: 01805 622247 Fax: 01805 625083 — BM BCh 1969 Oxf.; MRCGP 1980; DObst RCOG 1972. Prev: Ho. Surg. St. Bart. Hosp.; Ho. Phys. Roy. Cornw. Hosp. (Treliske) Truro; SHO (Paediat.) Torbay Hosp.
ARMSTRONG, Brian Pattison (retired) Flat No 2, St Helens, 9 Forest View, Chingford, London E4 7AY Tel: 020 8524 8136 — MRCS Eng. LRCP Lond. 1940; FFA RCS Eng. 1954; DA Eng. 1950. Prev: Cons. Anaesth. Metrop. Hosp. & Mildmay Miss. Hosp.
***ARMSTRONG, Catherine Ann** 18 Mill Close, Frindsbury, Rochester ME2 3DA — MB BS 1994 Lond.
ARMSTRONG, Charles Bruce Tulip Tree Cottage, Ash Road, Hartley, Longfield DA3 8ER — MB BS 1977 Lond.; MRCS Eng. LRCP Lond. 1977. (Middlx.)
ARMSTRONG, Christopher Joseph 26 Main Street, Glenavy, Crumlin BT29 4LW — MB BCh BAO 1988 Belf.
ARMSTRONG, Mr Christopher Paul Abbey Lodge, East St., Banwell, Weston Super Mare BS29 6BW — MD 1985 Ed.; MB ChB 1978; FRCS Ed. 1982; FRCS Eng. 1982. Sen. Regist. (Surg.) Bristol & W.on HA. Socs: Surg. Research Soc. & Brit. Soc. Gastroenterol.
ARMSTRONG, Damien Liam 44 Galwally Park, Belfast BT8 6AH — MB BCh BAO 1990 Belf.
ARMSTRONG, David James Buckrose Ward, Bridlington & District Hospital, Bessingby Road, Bridlington YO16 4QP Tel: 01262 607119 — MB ChB 1981 Birm.; MRCPsych 1987; Dip. Health Mgt. York 1997. Cons. Gen. Adult Psychiat. (Subst. Misuse) Hull & E. Riding community health NHS Trust. Prev: Cons. in Gen. Adult Psychiat. & Subst. Misuse, Hull & Holderness Community Health NHS Trust; Sen. Regist. (Psychiat.) Yorks. RHA.
ARMSTRONG, David John 4 Twinburn Hill, Newtownabbey BT37 0EJ — MB BCh BAO 1995 Belf.
ARMSTRONG, David Michael The Beacon Medical Practice, Churchill Avenue, Skegness PE25 2AN Tel: 01754 897000 Fax: 01754 761024 — MB BS 1980 Lond.; Cert. Family Plann. JCC 1985; DA Eng. 1982. (Roy. Lond. Hosp. Med. Coll.) GP; Phys. i/c

Animal Ho. Skegness. Prev: Trainee GP Chelmsford VTS; SHO (A & E) Broomfield Hosp. Chelmsford; SHO (Anaesth.) Lond. Hosp. Whitechapel.

ARMSTRONG, Dermot Keith Brown Department of Dermatology, Craigavon Area Hospital, 68 Lurgan Rd, Belfast BT63 5QQ; 40 Cadogan Park, Belfast BT9 6HH Tel: 02890 683728 — MB BCh BAO 1989 Belf.; MRCP (UK) 1992; MD 1999. (Queen's University Belfast) Cons. Dermatol., Craigavon Area Hosp., Co. Armagh.

ARMSTRONG, Ernest McAlpine Scottish Executive Health Department, St Andrews House, Edinburgh EU1 3DG Tel: 0131 244 2264 Fax: 0131 244 2835 Email: cmo@scotland.gsi.gov.uk — MB ChB 1970 (Hons.) Glas.; FFPHM 2001; BSc (Hons.) Glas. 1968; FRCP Ed. 1997; FRCP Glas. 1988; MRCP (UK) 1975; FRCGP 1987, M 1978. Chief Med. Off., Scotl. Socs: (Sec.) BMA. Prev: Princip. GP Argyll; Lect. (Path.) Univ. Glas. & W.. Infirm. Glas.; Sec., BMA Lond.

ARMSTRONG, Euan McAlpine Craiglora, Connel, Oban PA37 1PH — BChir 1995 Camb.

ARMSTRONG, Ferghal Timothy 136 Agincourt Avenue, Belfast BT7 1QD — MB BCh 1998 Belf.; MB BCh Belf 1998.

ARMSTRONG, Fiona Jane Alexandra Villa, 19 Marine Parade, Sheerness ME12 2PQ Tel: 01795 585058 Fax: 01795 585158; 99 High Street, Queenborough ME11 5AG Tel: 01795 665847 — MB ChB 1981 Manch.; Cert. Family Plann. RCGP 1985; Cert. Prescribed Equiv. Exp. JCPTGP 1985; DRCOG 1984.

ARMSTRONG, Fiona Mary High Street Surgery, 26 High Street, Erdington, Birmingham B23 6RN Tel: 0121 373 0086 — MB ChB 1991 Birm.; MRCGP 1999; DCH RCP Lond. 1996; DRCOG 1993; DFFP 1993. GP Princip. Prev: GP assist. Sutton Coalfield; GP registra Poplars Surg., Erdington; SHO (GP minor specialities Rotat.) City Hosp. Birm.

ARMSTRONG, Francis Craigmyle (retired) 9 Creswick Lane, Grenoside, Sheffield S35 8NL — MB ChB 1955 St. And.; DPH 1959; MFCM 1974. Prev: Dist. Community Phys. N.. Dist. Sheff.

ARMSTRONG, Frank Murdoch Bayer AG, Geschäftsbereich Pharma, D-42096 Wuppertal, Germany Tel: 00 49 202 368337 Fax: 0049 202368338 Email: frank.armstrong.fa@bayer-ag.de; Kingston, 2 Hawthorn Park, Wilmslow SK9 5BP Tel: 01625 528009 — MB ChB 1981 Ed.; BSc (Hons.) Ed. 1978; FRCP Ed. 1993; MRCP (UK) 1984; FFPM RCP (UK) 1994, M 1992. Exec. Vice-Pres. (Product Developm.). Prev: Vice-Pres. (Clin. & Med. Affairs) Zeneca Inc.; Head (Med. Research) Zeneca Pharmaceuts. Macclesfield; Sen. Vice-Pres., Zeneca Pharm.

ARMSTRONG, Giles Hugh 30 Vicars Cl, London E9 7HT — MB BS 1997 Lond.

ARMSTRONG, Gordon Roger Department of Histopathology, Hope Hospital, Salford M6 8HD Tel: 0161 787 5013 Fax: 0161 787 4654 Email: gordon.armstrong@srht.nhs.uk — BM BS 1982 Nottm.; MRCPath. 1989. Cons. Histopath. Salford Roy. Hosps. Trust.

ARMSTRONG, Graham Colin 12 Streamside Close, Penkridge, Stafford ST19 5ES — MB ChB 1978 Birm.

ARMSTRONG, Heather Evelyn Dumfries and Galloway Royal Infirmary, Bank End, Dumfries DG2 8LA Tel: 01387 246246; Linnfield, Torthorwald, Dumfries DG1 3SA — MB ChB 1984 Glas. Clin. Asst. (Paediat.) Dumfies & Galloway Roy. Infirm. Dumfies. Prev: Regist. (Paed.) Dumfries & Gallaway Roy. Infirm. Dumfies; SHO (Paed.) Dumfies & Galloway Roy. Infirm. Dumfies; GP Asst. Greyfnors Med. Centre, Dumfies.

ARMSTRONG, Helen Joan University Medical Practice, Elms Road, Birmingham B15 2SE Tel: 0121 414 5112 — MB ChB 1979 Manch.; MRCP (UK) 1983; DRCOG 1984.

ARMSTRONG, Helene Elizabeth The Surgery, Chilton Place, Ash, Canterbury CT3 2HD Tel: 01304 812227 Fax: 01304 813788; The Old Rectory, Church Lane, Kingston, Canterbury CT4 6HY — MB BS 1983 Lond.; DA (UK) 1987.

ARMSTRONG, Henry Angus The Rothbury Practice, 3 Market Place, Rothbury, Morpeth NE65 7UW Tel: 01669 620339 Fax: 01669 620583; Hall Hill Farm, Logfraulington, Morpeth NE65 8AD Tel: 01665 570388 Fax: 01665 570557 — MB BChir 1964 Camb.; MA Camb. 1964; MRCS Eng. LRCP Lond. 1964; FRCGP 1994, M 1980; DCH Eng. 1967. (Guy's) Prev: Asst. Ho. Phys. & Cas. Off. Guy's Hosp.; Ho. Surg. Roy. Surrey Co. Hosp. Guildford; Ho. Phys. (Paediat.) Gen Hosp. Newc. u. Tyne.

ARMSTRONG, Hilary Margaret 7 Academy Street, Gracehill, Ballymena BT42 2NJ — MB BCh BAO 1993 Belf.

ARMSTRONG, Ian Ross Royal Infirmary of Edinburgh, Lauriston Place, Edinburgh Tel: 0131 536 1000, 0131 536 3251; 43 Malbet Park, Liberton, Midlothian, Edinburgh EH16 6SY Email: i.r.armstrong@btinternet.com — MB ChB 1979 Ed.; FFA RCS Eng. 1983. Cons. Anaesth. Intens. Ther. Unit. Roy. Infirm. Edin.

ARMSTRONG, Irene Ann Govanhill Health Centre, 233 Calder St., Glasgow G42 7DR Tel: 0141 424 3003; 25 Larch Road, Glasgow G41 5DA Tel: 0141 427 2222 — MB ChB 1959 St. And. (St. And.) Prev: Ho. Phys. Stobhill Hosp. Glas.; Ho. Surg. Vict. Infirm. Glas.

ARMSTRONG, James Davison Health Centre, Cornagrade Road, Enniskillen BT74 6AY Tel: 028 6632 7190; Glencar, 20 Cooper Crescent, Enniskillen BT74 6DQ Tel: 02866 326399 — MB BCh BAO 1978 Belf.; MRCGP Ed. 1982; DRCOG Lond. 1981. (The Queen's Univ., Belf.) GP Enniskillen. Prev: Trainee GP Salisbury Med. Centre; Ho. Off. Roy. Belf. Hosp. for Sick Childr.; Ho. Off. Whiteabbey Hosp. Co. Antrim.

ARMSTRONG, James Henry (retired) 19 Collingwood Close, Coniston LA21 8DZ Tel: 0153 94 41242 Email: chas@aunt94.freeserve.co.uk — MB BS 1950 Lond.; DObst RCOG 1953. Prev: Clin. Asst. (Dermat.) Middlesbrough Gen. Hosp.

ARMSTRONG, James Robert 18 Trevose Gardens, Nottingham NG5 3FU — MB BS 1962 Durh.; FFA RCS Eng. 1969.

ARMSTRONG, James William Old Tyles, Camp Rd, Gerrards Cross SL9 7PE — MB ChB 1997 Sheff.

ARMSTRONG, Jane Sandwell District General Hospital, West Bromwich B71 4HJ; 41 Queensway, Penwortham, Preston PR1 0DS Tel: 01772 465699 — MB ChB 1994 Leeds; MRCPCH 1997. Specialist Regist. (Paediat.) Sandwell Dist. Gen. Hosp. W. Bromwich. Prev: SHO (Cardiol., Haemat. & Oncol.) Birm. Childr.'s Hosp.; SHO (Paediat.) St James' Univ. Hosp. Leeds.

ARMSTRONG, Jane Elizabeth 73 Grosvenor Av, Newcastle upon Tyne NE2 2NQ — MB ChB 1997 Leeds.

ARMSTRONG, Janet Elizabeth The Surgery, 218 Ifield Drive, Ifield, Crawley RH11 0EP Tel: 01293 547846 — MB BCh BAO 1976 Belf.; BSc Belf. 1973, MB BCh BAO 1976. GP Crawley. Prev: SHO Ulster Hosp. Dundonald; Ho. Off. Roy. Vict. Hosp. Belf.

ARMSTRONG, Janet Kathryn 192 Windhill Old Road, Thackley, Bradford BD10 0TR — MB ChB 1991 Manch.

ARMSTRONG, Janette Suzanne Department Histopathology, Princess Margaret Hospital, Okus Road, Swindon SN1 4JU Tel: 01793 426617 Fax: 01793 426743 — MB BS 1986 Lond.; MRCPath Manch. 1996. (St. Bart.) Cons. (Histopathol.) P.ss Margt. Hosp. Swindon. Prev: Sen. Regist. (Histopathol.) Bristol Roy. Infirm.

ARMSTRONG, Jennifer Lesley Sandystones, Ancrum, Jedburgh TD8 6UP — MB ChB 1995 Dundee. Trainee GP/SHO VTS. Socs: BMA.

ARMSTRONG, Jennifer Louise 59 Fergus Drive, Top Flat Left, North Kelvinside, Glasgow G20 6AH — MB ChB 1988 Glasg. SHO (Med.) Roy. Alexandra Hosp. Paisley. Prev: SHO (Geriat.) Vict. Geriat. Unit. Glas.; Ho. Off. Glas. Roy. Infirm. & Roy. Alexandra Hosp.

ARMSTRONG, Jill Dickson Benchill Group Practice, 127 Woodhouse Lane, Manchester M22 9WP; 2 Hawthorn Avenue, Wilmslow SK9 5BP — MB ChB 1981 Ed.; MRCGP 1985.

ARMSTRONG, Joanna Frances — MB ChB 1984 Glas.; MRCGP 1991; Dip. Forens. Med. Glas. 1990; DRCOG 1989. Med. Adviser to SEMA, Med. Mem. of TAS. Socs: BMA & Med. Defence Union. Prev: Trainee GP S. Edin. VTS.; GP Partner.

ARMSTRONG, John Walton Medical Centre, 2-4 Bedford Road, Liverpool L4 5PX Tel: 0151 525 6438 Fax: 0151 530 1748 — MB ChB 1992 Liverp.

ARMSTRONG, John Bruce Ormiston, VRD (retired) Woodside Health Centre, 3 Enmore Road, South Norwood, London SE25 5NS Tel: 020 8656 0213 — MB ChB 1953 Aberd. Sen. Lect. (Gen. Pract.) Char. Cross & W.m. Med. Sch. Lond; Surg. Lt.-Cdr. RNVR. Prev: Ho. Phys. & Ho. Surg. Woodend Hosp. Aberd.

ARMSTRONG, Joseph (retired) The Old Boat House, 54 Noss Mayo, Plymouth PL8 1EE Tel: 01752 872507 — MB BChir Camb. 1949; BA Camb. 1942, MA 1946; MRCS Eng. LRCP Lond. 1944; DObst RCOG 1950. Prev: Exam. Med. Off. DHSS.

ARMSTRONG, June Treherne (retired) 18 Grimwade Avenue, Croydon CR0 5DG Tel: 020 8654 5431 Email:

junetreherne@netscapeonline.co.uk — MB BS 1952 Lond. Prev: Clin. Asst. (Haemat.) May Day Hosp.

ARMSTRONG, Katherine Mary Dickson Craiglora, Connel, Oban PA37 1PH Tel: 01631 710229 Fax: 01631 710767 Email: kmd.taynuilt_med@lineone.net — MB ChB 1970 Glas.; MRCGP 1994. Trainer (Gen. Pract.) Connel Argyll.

ARMSTRONG, Kathryn Mary 37 Yew Tree Lane, West Derby, Liverpool L12 9HG — MB ChB 1998 Sheff.; MB ChB Sheff 1998.

ARMSTRONG, Kenneth James The Ballymena Health Centre, Cushendall Road, Ballymena BT43 6HQ Tel: 01266 42181 — MB BCh BAO 1988 Belf.; MRCGP 1993; DMH Belf. 1991.

ARMSTRONG, Kirsten Anne 14 Highwayman's Ridge, Windlesham GU20 6JY Tel: 01276 475544 — MB BS 1993 Lond. (King's College London University) Gen. Med. Regist. (Cardiol. & Gastroenterol.) Frimley Pk. Surrey. Prev: Med. SHO Heatherwood Hosp.; Renal SHO King's Coll. Hosp.

ARMSTRONG, Laura Beatrice 36 Acacia Road, Birmingham B30 2AG — MB ChB 1995 Dundee.

ARMSTRONG, Lawrence 21 Kintore Place, Aberdeen AB25 2TD — MB ChB 1997 Aberd.

ARMSTRONG, Lindsey Jane 2 St Andrews Gate, Heathside Rd, Woking GU22 7LJ Email: lindsey_armstrong@gemcon.com — MB BS 1989 Lond.; MBA Stanford. Managem. Cons. Gemini Consg. Gp.

ARMSTRONG, Lucy Elizabeth 17 Birchwood Road, Binley Woods, Coventry CV3 2JH — MB ChB 1997 Birm.

ARMSTRONG, Margaret Anne 70 Glandon Drive, Cheadle Hulme, Stockport — BM BS 1986 Nottm.

ARMSTRONG, Margaret Anne 8 Wanstead Crescent, Dundonald, Belfast BT16 2EN — MB BCh BAO 1988 Belf. (Qu. Univ. Belf.) Sen. Regist. (Paediat.) Roy. Hosp. Sick Childr. Belf. Socs: BMA. Prev: SHO (Paediat.) Roy. Hosp. Sick Childr. Belf.; Sen. Regist. (Paediat.) Community Child Health N & W Belf. HSS.

ARMSTRONG, Mr Michael Francis John Church Street Surgery, 1 Church Street, Newtownards BT23 4FH Tel: 028 9181 6333 Fax: 028 9181 8805; 3 Old Belfast Road, Newtownards BT23 4SG Tel: 01247 819647 — MB BCh BAO 1979 Belf.; FRCSI 1985; MRCGP 1990. Socs: BMA.

ARMSTRONG, Michael Greig 29 Ballymoney Road, Ballymena BT43 5BS — MB BCh BAO 1989 Belf.; MRCGP 1994; DRCOG 1993; DMH Belf. 1992.

ARMSTRONG, Michael Hugh Alvanley Clinic, 1 Auburn Avenue, Bredbury, Stockport SK6 2AL Tel: 0161 430 2127; 95 Perregrine Road, Offerton, Stockport SK2 5UP — MB ChB 1981 Manch.

ARMSTRONG, Michael John (retired) 32 Clogher Road, Lisburn BT27 5PQ Tel: 02892 675023 — MB BCh BAO Belf. 1961; FRCOG 1979, M 1966; DObst RCOG 1964. Prev: Cons. O & G Belf. City & Jubilee Matern. Hosps.

ARMSTRONG, Mr Michael William Joseph 5 Rankeillor Street, Edinburgh EH8 9JA — MB ChB 1986 Ed.; FRCS Lond. 1992; FRCS Ed. 1992; FRCS 1993 (Otol) Edin.; FRCS 1998 (ORL) H&NS. (Edinburgh) Cons. Otorhinolaryngologist, Border Gen. Hosp., Melrose; Cons. Otorhinolaryngologist, Roy. Infirm. of Edin., Edin.

ARMSTRONG, Nigel Paul Ireland Portland Hospital, 209 Great Portland St., London W1W 5AH Tel: 020 7580 5754 Fax: 020 7390 8271; 20 Middleway, London NW11 6SP Tel: 020 8455 3121 — MD 1981 Manch.; MB ChB 1976; MRCOG 1982. Sen. Lect. & Cons. O & G Roy. Lond. Hosp.; Hon. Cons. Gyn. St Luke's Hosp. to the Clergy. Socs: Fell. Roy. Soc. Med.; Gyn. Res. Soc. Prev: Cons. O & G Centr. Middlx. Hosp. Lond.; Hon. Sen. Lect. (O & G) St. Mary's Hosp. Med. Sch. Lond.; Sen. Regist. The Lond. Hosp.

ARMSTRONG, Patrick John 8 Brandon Terrace, Edinburgh EH3 5EA — MB ChB 1983 Ed.

ARMSTRONG, Peter The Beeches, Oborne Road, Sherborne DT9 3RX Tel: 01935 815109 Fax: 01935 815109; 12 Comilla Court, The Avenue, Branksome Park, Poole BH13 6HD Tel: 01202 766716 Email: peter.arm@globalnet.co.uk — MB ChB 1978 Bristol; DRCOG 1981; DA Lond. 1981. (Bristol) Socs: Assn. Anaesth.; Brit. Med. Acupunct. Soc.; Assn. Dent. Anaesth.

ARMSTRONG, Professor Peter Academic Department of Radiology, Dominion House, St Bartholomews Hospital, London EC1A 7BE Tel: 020 7601 8864 Fax: 020 7601 8868 — MB BS 1963 Lond.; FRCR 1975; FFR 1968. Prof. Radiol. St. Bart. Hosp. Med. Coll. Lond.; Pres. Roy. Coll. of Radiols. Prev: Warden Roy. Coll. Radiol.; Fell. Acad. of Med. Sci.s.

ARMSTRONG, Philippa Mary Christine The Wood, Murray Court, Ascot SL5 9BP; Flat 1 8Leslie Place, Stockbridge, Edinburgh EH4 1NH Email: paulandphil@lineone.net — MB ChB 1993 Dundee.

ARMSTRONG, Phyllis Ailsie Milton House, Strathmore Road, Rowlands Gill NE39 1JD Tel: 01207 542353 — MB BS 1948 Durh.; PhD Durh. 1953. (Durh.) Prev: Demonst. Dept. Physiol. King's Coll. Newc.

ARMSTRONG, Priscilla Cruden Medical Group, The Surgery, Main St Hatton, Peterhead AB42 0QQ Tel: 01779 841208 Fax: 01779 841239; Slains School House, Collieston, Ellon AB41 8RT — MB ChB 1971 Glas.; MRCGP 1996; DFFP 1997. (Glasgow) GP. Prev: Med. Off. (Psychiat.) Roy. Cornhill Hosp. Aberd.; GP Stranraer.

ARMSTRONG, Raymond Derek Rheumatology Department, Southampton General Hospital, Tremona Road, Southampton SO16 6YD Tel: 02380 796451 Fax: 02380 794756 Email: rayarmstrong@btinternet.com; Pound House, Spearywell, Mottisfont, Romsey SO51 0LS Tel: 01794 341120 — MB BChir 1975 Camb.; MA Camb. 1975; FRCP Lond. 1992; MRCP (UK) 1977. (Camb. & Guy's) Lead Cons. Rheum. Soton Univ. Hosps. NHS Trust. Socs: Brit. Soc. Rheum.; BMIA. Prev: Sen. Regist. (Rheum.) Guy's Hosp. Lond.; Arthritis & Rheum. Counc. Research Fell. (Med.) Guy's Hosp.

ARMSTRONG, Richard Gerard Wyngarth, Main St., Ealand, Scunthorpe DN17 4JE — BM BS 1995 Nottm.

ARMSTRONG, Robert Colin 13 Elms Drive, Old Marston, Oxford OX3 0NN Tel: 01865 767150 Fax: 01865 761342 Email: bobarmstrong@supanet.com — BM BCh 1984 Oxf.; BSc (Hons.) Lond. 1976; MSc Oxf. 1978; DFFP 1994; DRCOG 1988; Cert. Occupat. Med. 1988; Dip. Occ. Med. RCPLond 1998; Dip Occ Med 1998. (Univ. Oxford Clin. Med. Sch) Sen. Med. Advisor (Occupat. Med.) & AeroMed. Phys. Oxf.; Occupat. Med. Pract. Oxf.; Clin. Asst. John Radcliffe Hosp. Oxf.; Primary Care Phys.; Occupat. Phys. Thames Valley Police; Occupat. Phys. Acland Hosp. Oxf. Prev: SHO (Cardiol. & Chest Med.) Banbury Hosp.; SHO (O & G, Geriat. & A & E) Milton Keynes Gen. Hosp.; SHO (A & E) Horton Gen. Hosp. Banbury.

ARMSTRONG, Robert Stuart Cropwell Bishop Surgery, Cropwell Bishop, Nottingham NG12 3JQ Tel: 0115 989 2287 Fax: 0115 989 2249; 100 Bingham Road, Radcliffe-on-Trent, Nottingham NG12 2GT Tel: 0115 911 8903 — MB BS 1974 Lond.; MRCS Eng. LRCP Lond. 1974; FRCGP 1992, M 1978; DRCOG 1977. (Guy's)

ARMSTRONG, Robin William Wylie Morven, Hesleden Road, Blackhall Colliery, Hartlepool TS27 4LQ Tel: 0191 586 4331; 4 Brancepeth Chase, Oakerside Park, Peterlee SR8 1LU Tel: 0191 586 4331 — MB BCh BAO 1987 Belf.; MRCGP 1991.

ARMSTRONG, Rodney Fletcher (retired) 37 Crescent W., Hadley Wood, Barnet EN4 0EQ Tel: 020 8449 5924 Email: rodarmstrong@compuserve.com — MB BS 1961 Lond.; MRCS Eng. LRCP Lond. 1961; FFA RCS Eng. 1967; DObst RCOG 1964. Prev: Asst. Burgerspital Basel, Switz.

ARMSTRONG, Ronald 11 Orchard Rise, Newtownbreda, Belfast BT8 7DA — MB BCh BAO 1955 Belf.; FFA RCS Eng. 1964; DA Eng. 1958. Cons. Anaesth. Ulster Hosp. Dundonald. Socs: Assn. Anaesth.; Intractable Pain Soc. (Linkman). Prev: Cons. Anaesth. Daisy Hill Hosp. Newry.

ARMSTRONG, Ruth 10 The Old Quarry, Quarry St., Liverpool L25 6HE — MB ChB 1997 Liverp.

ARMSTRONG, Ruth Kathryn 77 Providence Crescent, Oakworth, Keighley BD22 7QU — MB ChB 1998 Liverp.; MB ChB Liverp 1998.

ARMSTRONG, Ruth Lowri 21 Bessant Close, Cowbridge CF71 7HP — BM BS 1996 Nottm. SHO Gen. Med. P. Philip Hosp. LLa.lli.

ARMSTRONG, Sarah Elizabeth Royal Victoria Infirmary, Newcastle upon Tyne NE1 4LP; 7 Meadow Close, Ryton NE40 3RU — MB BS 1998 Newc.; MB BS Newc 1998.

ARMSTRONG, Sarah-Jane Radley 28 Arlott Court, Southampton SO15 2RZ — BM BS 1995 Nottm.

ARMSTRONG, Shona Mary 9 Clunie Bank Gardens, Braemar, Ballater AB35 5PY — MB ChB 1983 Ed. SHO (Orthop. & Cas.) CrossHo. Hosp. Kilmarnock. Socs: BMA.

ARMSTRONG, Sidney Temple 29 Ballymoney Road, Ballymena BT43 5BS — MB BCh BAO 1946 Belf.; MRCGP 1953.

ARMSTRONG, Mr Stewart Grosvenor Nuffield Hospital, Wrexham Road, Chester CH4 7QP Tel: 01244 680444 Fax: 01244 680812; Saxonbury, Rake Lane, Eccleston, Chester CH4 9JN Tel: 01244 674836 Fax: 01244 674836 Email: stewart@saxonbury.demon.co.uk — MB ChB 1973 Liverp.; FRCS Eng. 1981; FRCOphth 1988; MRCP (UK) 1978; DO RCS Eng. 1981. Cons. Ophth. Countess of Chester Hosp.; Clin. Dir. Surgic. Servs. Socs: Fell. Roy. Soc. Med.; BMA. Prev: Sen. Regist. (Ophth.) Soton. Eye Hosp.; Regist. (Ophth.) Bristol Eye Hosp.; Regist. (Med.) BRd.green Hosp. Liverp.

ARMSTRONG, Susan Jennifer Southmead Hospital, Westbury on Trym, Bristol BS10 5NB Tel: 0117 950 5050 Fax: 0117 959 0902 — MB ChB 1983 Brist.; MRCP (UK) 1986; FRCR 1990. Cons. Radiol. S.mead Hosp. Bristol. Prev: Sen. Regist. (Radiol.) SW Region.

ARMSTRONG, Thomas Morton House, Villa Road, Torrington EX38 8DZ — BM BS 1995 Nottm.

ARMSTRONG, Trevor Samuel Herbert Department of Anaesthesia, University Hospital of Wales, Cardiff CF14 4XW Tel: 02920 743107 — MB BS 1991 Newc.; FRCA 1996. Cons. (Paediat. Anaesth.) Univ. Hosp. Of Wales, Cardiff. Prev: Clin. Fell. Anaesth., Harvard Med. Sch. Boston USA; Specialist Regist. Aberd. Roy. Infirm.

ARMSTRONG, Valerie Lynne 21 Margretta Park, Portadown, Craigavon BT63 5DF — MB BCh BAO Belf.; MB BCh Belf.1991.

ARMSTRONG, Vivien Jane 84 Tinwell Road, Stamford PE9 2SD — MB BS 1972 Lond.; MRCS Eng. LRCP Lond. 1972; FFA RCS Eng. 1978; DObst RCOG 1974. (Roy. Free) Assoc. Specialist (Anaesth.) PeterBoro. Dist. Gen. Hosp. Prev: Sen. Regist. (Anaesth.) Nottm. Hosps.

ARMSTRONG, William Benthall (retired) The Barn, Paddock House, Clifford, Hereford HR3 5HB — BM BCh 1942 Oxf.; BM BCh Oxon. 1942; FRCP Lond. 1978, M 1948.

ARMSTRONG, William David (retired) Trap Farm Cottage, Trap Lane, Sheffield S11 7RG Tel: 0114 249 9898 — MB ChB 1962 Glas.; MFOM RCP Lond. 1989, AFOM 1981; DObst RCOG 1964. Cons. Occupat. Health Sheff.; Cons. Armstrong Occupat.al Health. Prev: GP Sheff.

ARMSTRONG, William Henry The Surgery, Garden Street, Gatehouse of Fleet, Castle Douglas DG7 2JU Tel: 01557 814437; Carrickstanes, 8 Mount Pleasant Avenue, Kirkcudbright DG6 4HF Tel: 01557 330060 — MB ChB 1972 Glas.; BSc (Hons.) Glas. 1970. Prev: SHO (Gyn. & Obst.) Vict. Hosp. Kirkcaldy & Craigtown Matern. Hosp. St. And.; SHO (A & E) Roy. Hosp. Sick Childr. Glas.

ARMSTRONG, William Leckie Netherhampton House, Netherhampton, Salisbury SP2 8PU Tel: 01722 742424 Fax: 01722 741395 — BM BCh 1960 Oxf.; FRCSC 1968; FRCOphth. 1989; DO RCS Eng. 1964. Med. Dir. Phys. Health Plan & Adviser Mercer Fraser Ltd.; Med. Adviser Guernsey Soc. Sec. Auth.; Med. Adviser Strasbourgeoise (UK). Socs: Fell. Roy. Soc. Med.; BMA. Prev: Asst. Prof. Dept. Surg. Univ. Connecticut, USA; Asst. Prof. & Dir. Glaucoma Unit Univ. Texas., USA; Dep. Med. Dir. Whittaker Corp. USA.

ARMSTRONG, William Neil Senior and Partners, Morrab Surgery, 2 Morrab Road, Penzance TR18 4EL Tel: 01736 363866 Fax: 01736 367809 — MB BCh BAO 1983 Dub.; MRCGP 1988; DMG RCP Lond. 1988; DCH NUI 1986; DObst RCPI 1985.

ARMSTRONG-JAMES, Darius Piers Henry 17 Hillside Gardens, London N6 5SU — BM 1996 Soton.

ARNALL-CULLIFORD, Jane Margaret 8 Grosvenor Road, Dorchester DT1 2BB — MB BS 1973 Lond.

ARNAOT, May R Z T Ocean Park Private Clinic, 29 Chandlers Drive, Erith DA8 1LL Tel: 01322 440133 Fax: 01322 440133 Mobile: 07768 054260 Email: opc@medix-uk.com — DTM Belgium; Cert. Underwater Med. UK; MD 1993 Ghent; MB Holland; PhD Lond.; DFFP RCOG Lond. (Univ. of Ghent Belgium) Priv. Gen. Med. Pract. Prev: Postdoctoral Med. Researchfell. Brown Univ. Rhode Is. USA; Lect. (Clin. Pharmacol.) Fac. of Med. ARBIL, Iraq; Dist. Med. Off. N. W. Province Zambia.

ARNEIL, Gavin Cranston Shoreland, 150 East Clyde St., Helensburgh G84 7AX Tel: 01436 674286 Fax: 01436 677570 — MB ChB 1945 Glas.; Hon. FAAP 1976; DCH Eng. 1951; PhD Glas. 1960; MD (Hons.) 1949; Hon. DSc Ankara 1980; FRCPI 1986; FRCP Lond. 1968, M 1952; FRCP Ed. 1964, M 1962; FRCP Glas. 1964, M 1962; FRFPS Glas. 1949. (Glas.) Pres. Elect. of Internat. Paediat. Assn. Prev: Titular Prof. in Child Health, Univ. Glas.; Hon. Cons. Paediat. Roy. Hosp. Sick Childr. Glas. & Qu. Mother Matern. Hosp. Glas.; Maj. RAMC.

ARNEY, Kenneth Brian Huckleberry, Undertown Lane, Compton Martin, Bristol BS40 6ND — MB ChB 1952 Bristol; MRCS Eng. LRCP Lond. 1951. (Bristol)

ARNEY, Nicolas Peter Forest Gate Surgery, Hazel Farm Road, Totton, Southampton SO40 8WU Tel: 023 8066 3839 Fax: 023 8066 7090 — MB BS 1987 Lond.; BSc Lond. 1984; MRCGP 1991; DRCOG 1994. Prev: SHO (O & G) N.wick Pk. Hosp. Harrow; Cas. Off. Torbay Hosp. Torquay; Unit Med. Off. RAF High Wycombe.

ARNISON-NEWGASS, Paul City Medical Services, 17 St Helen's Place, London EC3A 6DG Tel: 020 7638 3001 Fax: 020 7256 5295; 37 Goodhart Place, Limehouse, London E14 8EG Tel: 020 7265 8559 Fax: 020 7265 8559 Email: newgass@medmail.com — MB BS 1971 Lond.; MRCS Eng. LRCP Lond. 1971; MRCGP 1975. Indep. GP City Med. Servs. Lond. Socs: Fell. Roy. Soc. Med.; Soc. Occupat. Med. Prev: Surg. Chief Off. Roy. Fleet Auxil.; Diplomatic Serv. Med. Adviser FCO; Med. Adviser Civil Serv. Occupat. Health Serv. (Lond. Fire Brig.).

ARNO, Jeanne Department of Pathology, Tennis Court Road, Cambridge CB2 1QP — BM BCh 1962 Oxf.; MRCPath 1972. Lect. Path. Univ. Camb. & Hon. Consult. Camb. AHA.

ARNOLD, Mr Andrew James Department of Urology, Queen Elizabeth Hospital, Queen Elizabeth Medical Centre, Birmingham B15 2TH Tel: 0121 472 1311 Fax: 0121 471 2625; 410 Gillott Road, Edgbaston, Birmingham B16 9LP — MB BS 1978 Lond.; BSc Lond. 1975; ChM Liverp. 1991; FRCS Eng. 1984; FRCS Ed. 1982. Cons. Urol. Qu. Eliz. Hosp. Birm.; Sen. Clin. Lect. (Surg.) Univ. Birm. Prev: Sen. Regist. (Urol.) Roy. Liverp. Hosp.; Herbert Johnston Research Fell. Univ. Liverp.; Regist. (Urol.) BRd.green Hosp. Liverp.

ARNOLD, Ann Elaine Mental Health Unit, Central Middlesex Hospital, Acton Lane, London NW10 7NS Tel: 020 8965 5733 Fax: 020 8961 6339 — MB ChB 1979 Manch.; MRCPsych 1983; T(Psychiat.) 1991. Cons. Psychiat. Centr. Middlx. Hosp. Lond. Prev: Sen. Regist. (Psychiat.) St. Chas. Hosp. Lond.

ARNOLD, Annabel Jane Chawton House, St. Thomas Street, Lymington SO41 9ND — MB BS 1992 Lond.; BSc Lond. 1989; MRCGP 1996. (Univ. Coll. & Middlx. Sch. Med. Lond.)

ARNOLD, Anne Margaret The Taylor Practice, Hornsey Rise Health Centre, Hornsey Rise, London N19 3XU — MB BS 1987 Lond.; MRCGP 1993; DRCOG 1992; DCH RCP Lond. 1991.

ARNOLD, Anthony Graham 67 Ferriby Road, Hessle HU13 0HU — MD 1984 Manch.; MB ChB 1973; FRCP 1992. Cons. Gen. & Respirat. Med. Hull & E. Yorks. HAs.

ARNOLD, Audrey Kathleen (retired) 32 The Ridgeway, Radlett WD7 8PS — MB BCh BAO 1948 Belf.; MFPHM 1989; MFCM 1972; DPH Belf. 1953; DObst RCOG 1951. Prev: Dist. Med. Off. Enfield Health Dist.

ARNOLD, Barry David Charles AstraZeneca, Alderley Park, Macclesfield SK10 4TG Tel: 01625 512169 Fax: 01625 586874 Email: barry.arnold@alderley.zeneca.com; 2 Kershaw Grove, Macclesfield SK11 8TN Tel: 01625 501401 — MB BCh 1980 Wales; FRCA Eng. 1985; DA Eng. 1982; FFPM RCP UK 1997. (Welsh National Sch. Med., Cardiff) Head Drug Safety AstraZeneca. Macclesfield. Socs: Brit. Assn. Pharmaceut. Phys.; Soc. Pharmaceut. Med. Prev: Med. Adviser SmithKline Beecham Pharmaceuts. Welwyn; Clin. Pharmacol. Beecham Med. Research Centre Harlow; Regist. (Anaesth.) Roy. Free Hosp. Lond.

ARNOLD, Christine Joanna 28 Linkfield Street, Redhill RH1 6BW — MB BS 1983 Lond.; LMSSA Lond. 1982; MRCGP 1988; DRCOG 1985. Clin. Med. Off. (Community Child Health) E. Surrey HA.

ARNOLD, Christine Lesley The Surgery, 16 George St., Alderley Edge SK9 7EP; Kershaw House, 2 Kershaw Grove, Macclesfield SK11 8TN — MB BCh 1980 Wales; MFFP 1994; DCH RCP Lond. 1985. (Welsh National School of Medicine) Asst. GP; CMO Family Plann. Macclesfield Hosp. Socs: Nat. Assn. Family Plann. Doctors. Prev: Trainee GP St. Albans VTS.

ARNOLD, Christine Sabina 51 St Peters Court, Broadstairs CT10 2UU — MB BS 1985 Lond.

ARNOLD, Christopher William Bentham Postgraduate Office, Ninewells Hospital & Medical School, Dundee; East Cottage, Errol, Perth PH2 7RF — MB BS 1982 Lond. (Roy. Free) Educat. Facilitator

Med. Audit & Resource Managem. Project Doctor Ninewells Hosp. Dundee. Prev: Regist. (ENT Surg.) Raigmore Hosp. Inverness.

ARNOLD, Colin Leslie Carnelly 8 Queens Road, Buckland, Portsmouth PO2 7NX Tel: 023 92 665134 — MRCS Eng. LRCP Lond. 1959; MB Camb. 1960, BChir 1959; DObst. RCOG 1961. (St. Mary's) Socs: Soc. Apoth. Lond.

ARNOLD, Elizabeth Jane 1 St Brelades, 24 Blake Hill Avenue, Poole BH14 8QA — MB BCh 1998 Wales.

ARNOLD, Elizabeth Sarah 4 Top Right South Oxford Street, Edinburgh EH8 9QF — MB ChB 1998 Ed.; MB ChB Ed 1998.

ARNOLD, Fiona Jane Lempriere 7 Holland Park Avenue, London W11 3RH — MB BChir 1995 Camb.; MB BChir Camb. 1994; MA Camb. 1995. SHO (A & E) & Anat. Demonst. King's Coll. Hosp. Lond.

ARNOLD, Mr Francis William 136 Sandy Lane, Manchester M21 8TZ — MB 1976 Camb.; BChir 1975; FRCS Eng. 1980. Dir. Hunter Med. Research Ltd. Prev: Research Fell. Clin. Research Dept. Christie Hosp. Manch.; Regist. Surg. N. Manch. Hosps.

ARNOLD, Ian Robert Oxford Radcliffe Hospitals NHS Trust, Horton Hospital, Oxford Road, Banbury OX16 9AL Tel: 01295 275500; Elton House, The Green, Adderbury, Banbury OX17 3ND — MB BS 1979 Lond.; MA Oxf. 1980, BA 1976; MD Leic. 1994; FRCP (Lond.) 1997, M (UK) 1982. Cons. Phys. & Cardiol., Horton Hosp., Oxf. Radcliffe NHS Trust, Banbury; Hon. Cons. Cardiol. John Radcliffe Hosp. Oxf.

ARNOLD, Jane Katherine 22 Bingham Avenue, Lilliput, Poole BH14 8NE Tel: 01202 701540 Fax: 01202 701541 — MB BS 1982 Lond.; MRCGP 1990; DRCOG 1986. GP Retainer, Quanterjach Surg., Wimbone, Dorset; Clin. Asst., Dermat. Poole Hosp. NHS Trust; GP Specialist Dermat. Roy. Vict. Hosp. Wimbone. Socs: BMA; Lond. Soc. Family Plann. Doctors.; Primary Care Dermat. Soc. Prev: GP Hampton Wick; SHO (A & E) Qu. Mary's Hosp. Roehampton Lond.; SHO (Psychiat.) Ashford Gen. Hosp. Middlx.

ARNOLD, Jayantha Dharmananthan Ealing Hospital NHS Trust, Uxbridge Road, Southall UB1 3HW Tel: 020 8967 5513 Fax: 020 8967 5083 — MB BS 1980 Colombo; MRCP (UK) 1984; MRCS Eng. LRCP Lond. 1983. Cons. Phys. & Gastroenterol. Ealing Hosp. S.all, Middx; Hon. Sen. Lect. (Med.) Imperial Med. Sch., Univ. of Lond. Socs: Brit. Soc. Gastroenterol. Prev: Sen. Regist. (Med.) Univ. Hosp. Wales Cardiff & P.ss of Wales Hosp. Bridgend; Research Fell. (Med.) King's Coll. Hosp. Lond.

ARNOLD, Jennifer Ann Chase Farm Hospital, The Ridgeway, Enfield EN2 8JL Tel: 020 8366 6600 Ext: 5455 — MB BS 1990 Lond.; MRCP (UK) 1993; MRCPath 1999. (Univ. Coll. Hosp.) Cons. Haemat. Chase Farm Hosp. Socs: Brit. Soc. Haematol. Prev: Regist. (Haemat.) N.wick Pk. Hosp. Harrow; Regist. (Haemat.) Hammersmith Hosp. Lond.; Specialist Regist. (Haemat.) St Mary's Hosp. Lond.

ARNOLD, Jillian Margaret Royal Glamorgan Hospital, Ynysyplwm, Llanstrisant, Pontyclun CF72 8XR; Brewery Cottage, Llanquian Rd, Aberithin, Cowbridge CF71 7HB — MB BCh 1975 Wales; 1980 MRCOG; 1997 FRCOG. (Welsh National School of Medicine) Cons. O & G E. Roy. Glam. Hosp., Ynysyplwm, Llantrisant. Socs: BMA; Roy. Coll. Obst. & Gyn.; Brit. Fertil. Soc.

ARNOLD, June Pope Crud y Gwynt, Tremeirchion, St Asaph LL17 0UB Tel: 01745 710224 — MB ChB 1948 Liverp.; MD Liverp. 1953; FRCP Lond. 1976, M 1960; MRCPI 1960; DCH Eng. 1953. Prev: Cons. Phys. Geriat. Dept. Clwyd HA.

ARNOLD, Kim Gordon St Pancras Hospital, 4 St Pancras Way, London NW1 0PE Tel: 020 7530 3348 Fax: 020 7530 3386; 2 Romney Drive, Sundridge Avenue, Bromley BR1 2TE Tel: 020 8289 3908 — MB BS 1972 Lond.; BSc Lond. 1969; FRCP Lond. 1991; MRCP (UK) 1975. (St. Thos.) Cons. Phys. (Geriat. Med.) Univ. Coll. Hosp. Lond.; Hon. Sen. Lect. Univ. Coll. & Roy. Free Sch. Med. Lond. Socs: Brit. Geriat. Soc. Prev: Lect. (Geriat. Med.) Univ. Coll. Lond.

ARNOLD, Malcolm Murdoch Trafford General Hospital, Moorside Road, Davyhulme, Manchester M41 5SL Tel: 0161 748 4022; 35 Ferryman Park, Paull, Hull HU12 8PS — MB ChB 1984 Glas.; MRCP (UK) 1990. Prev: Clin. Research Fell. Trafford Gen. Hosp. & Hon. Regist. Hope Hosp. Salford & Univ. Manch.; Regist. (Cardiol. & Rheum.) Hull Roy. Infirm.; Regist. (Gastroenterol. & Gen. Med.) Qu. Alexandra Hosp. Portsmouth.

ARNOLD, Natasha St Pancras Hospital, St Pancras Way, London NW1 0PE; 23 Tavistock Terrace, London N19 4BZ Email: tasha@familyrobins.demon.co.uk — MB BS 1985 Lond.; MRCP (UK) 1994. p/t Sen. Regist. Geriat. UCLH/ St Pancras. Socs: Brit. Geriat. Soc. Prev: Sen. Regist. GIM - Chase Farm Hosp.; Sen. Regist. (Geriat.s) / Rehabil., regional Rehabil. unit, Homerton Hosp..; Regist. (c/o Elderly) Whipps Cross Hosp. Lond.

ARNOLD, Patricia Ann Torridon Medical Practice, Torridon, Achnasheen IV22 2EZ Tel: 01445 791223 Fax: 01445 791401; Glenariff, Lochcarron, Strathcarron IV54 8YQ Tel: 01520 722388 — MB BCh BAO 1968 Belf.; T(GP) 1991. (Belf.) Prev: CMO EHSSB N. Irel.; Clin. Asst. (Psychogeriat.) Crichton Roy. Hosp. Dumfries; Assoc. GP lochcarrow.

ARNOLD, Penelope Clare Greystone House Medical Centre, 99 Station Road, Redhill, Dorking RH1 1EB Tel: 01737 761201; 1 Deepdene Park Road, Dorking RH5 4AL Tel: 01306 876132 — MB BS 1981 Lond.; MFFP 1995; MRCGP 1985; DRCOG 1987; DCH RCP Lond. 1987. (Royal Free Hospital) p/t GP Partner Greystone Ho. Med. Centre, Redhill. Prev: GP Asst. Priory Med. Centre Warwick; Dist. Health Off. Malawi.

ARNOLD, Peter Frederick Walton Health Centre, Rodney Road, Walton-on-Thames KT12 3LB Tel: 01932 228999 Fax: 01932 225586; Oakmead, Blundel Lane, Stoke D'Abernon, Cobham KT11 2SF — MB BS 1980 Lond.; MRCS Eng. LRCP Lond. 1980; DRCOG 1984. (Char. Cross Hosp.)

ARNOLD, Philip (retired) 28 Lander Close, Poole BH15 1UN Tel: 01202 680573 — MRCS Eng. LRCP Lond. 1942; MB BS Lond. 1942; MD Lond. 1949; FRCP Lond. 1972, M 1948; MB BS 1942 Lond. Prev: Cons. Phys. Geriat. Poole Gen. Hosp.

ARNOLD, Philip David 32 Manor Park, Nether Heyford, Northampton NN7 3NN — BM 1991 Soton.; BM Soton 1991.

ARNOLD, Philip David Ossian, 5 Heather Gardens, off Monks Lane, Newbury RG14 7RG Tel: 01635 230192 — MB BS 1953 Lond.; MRCS Eng. LRCP Lond. 1953. (King's Coll. Hosp.) Indep. Manip. Pract. Berks. Socs: Newbury Med. Soc. Pres. Prev: Ho. Phys. (Paediat.) King's Coll. Hosp.; Squadron Ldr. RAF Med. Br.; Ho. Surg. (Obst.) Qu. Mary's Hosp. E. End.

ARNOLD, Rachel Teresa City Walls Medical Centre, St. Martin's Way, Chester CH1 2NR — MB BS 1986 Lond.; MRCP (UK) 1990; MRCGP 1992; DCH RCP Lond. 1991. (Lond. Hosp.) p/t GP Chester. Prev: Trainee GP Sheff. VTS.

ARNOLD, Rachelle Ann Flat G/L, 42 Edgehill Road, Broomhill, Glasgow G11 7JD — MB ChB 1993 Glas.

ARNOLD, Ralph Hodby (retired) Sundale, Odun Rd, Appledore, Bideford EX39 1PT — MB ChB 1952 St. And. Prev: Gen. Practitioner, Camb.

ARNOLD, Ranjana Chandravathany 41A Maytree Close, Winchester SO22 4JE — MB BS 1969 Madras.

ARNOLD, Richard Charles Willowbrook Health Centre, 81 Birch Grove, Llanmartin, Newport NP18 2JB; Wychwood, 5 Cowleaze, Magor, Newport NP26 3LE — MB BCh 1983 Wales.

ARNOLD, Richard Graham 6 The Orchard, Old Cultra Road, Holywood BT18 0BD — MB BCh 1998 Belf.; MB BCh Belf 1998.

ARNOLD, Richard William 189 Shooters Hill Road, London SE3 8UL — MB BS 1976 Lond.; FFA RCS Eng. 1982. Cons. Anaesth. Sydenham Childr. & Lewisham Hosps. Lond. Prev: Sen. Regist. (Anaesth.) Lond. Hosp.

ARNOLD, Robert — MB ChB 1964 Ed.; FRCPCH 1997; FRCP Lond. 1986, M 1970; FRCP Ed. 1985. (Ed.) Cons. Paediat. Cardiol. Roy. Liverp. Childr. Hosp. & Community Trust; Lect. (Child Health) Univ. Liverp.; Hon. Cons. Nobles Hosp. IOM; Hon. Cons. Cardiol. Centre Liverp. Socs: Brit. Cardiac Soc.; Assn. Europ. Paediat. Cardiol.; Brit. Paediat. Cardiac Assn. Prev: Sen. Regist. (Paediat. Cardiol.) Roy. Liverp. Childr. Hosp.; Regist. (Med. Paediat.) W.. Gen. Hosp. Edin.; Clin. Fell., Hosp. For Sick Childr., Toronto.

ARNOLD, Robert Windsor House Surgery, Corporation Street, Morley, Leeds LS27 9NB Tel: 0113 252 5223 Fax: 0113 238 1262; 4 Hill Top Grove, West Ardsley, Wakefield WF3 1DZ Tel: 0113 238 1399 — MB ChB 1988 Leeds; DRCOG 1992. Prev: Trainee GP Hull VTS.

ARNOLD, Robin Pierce Southmead Hospital, Westbury-on-Trym, Bristol BS10 5NB Tel: 0117 959 5882 Fax: 0117 959 5804 — MB BS 1979 Lond.; MRCPsych 1985. Cons. Psychiat. i/c Rehabil. S.mead Dist. Hosp. Bristol. Socs: Roy. Coll. Psychiat. Prev: Sen. Regist. Rotat. (Psychiat.) Bristol & W.on HA; Regist. Rotat. (Psychiat.) Oxf. HA.

ARNOLD, Sally Mary (retired) 27 Springfield Park, North Parade, Horsham RH12 2BF Tel: 01403 248355 — MB BS 1971 Lond.; D.Occ.Med. RCP Lond. 1995.

ARNOLD, Sheila May Robin Hill, 18 Murdoch Road, Wokingham RG40 2DE Tel: 01189 787027 — LRCPI & LM, LRSCI & LM 1954; FRCS Eng. 1971; DLO Eng. 1964. (RCSI) Cons. ENT Surg. Frimley Pk. Hosp. Camberley. Prev: Sen. Regist. (ENT) Guy's Hosp. Lond. & Lewisham Hosp.; Regist. ENT Dept. Metrop. ENT Hosp. Kensington; SHO ENT Dept. Roy. Vict. Infirm. Newc. upon Tyne.

ARNOLD, Steven James 14 Ridgeway Drive, Bromley BR1 5DQ Tel: 020 8857 6174 — MB BS 1997 Lond.; BSc Lond. 1994. (UMDS Guy's and St Thomas') SHO (Orthop.) Greenwich Hsp. Socs: BMA; MPS; MDU. Prev: PRHO (Oncol.) Guys Hosp.; PRHO (Urol.) Kent & Canterbury Hosp.; PRHO (Surg.) Kent & Canterbury Hosp.

ARNOLD, Susan Jennifer 68 Eastgate, Deeping St James, Peterborough PE6 8HJ — MB BS 1975 Lond.; MRCS Eng. LRCP Lond. 1975; DRCOG 1977.

ARNOLD, Timothy David Fairlands Medical Centre, Fairlands Avenue, Worplesdon, Guildford GU3 3NA Tel: 01483 594250 Fax: 01483 598767 — MB BS 1987 Lond.; MRCGP 1992.

ARNOLD, Timothy James Michael 13 St Helen's Close, Southsea PO4 0NN — MB BS 1992 Lond.

ARNOT, Angela Margaret Wallace The Mead, Blackford, Yeovil BA22 7EF — MB BS 1967 Lond.; MRCS Eng. LRCP Lond. 1967; Cert. FPA 1978. (St. Bart.) Adjudicating Med. Pract. & Exam. Med. Pract. Benefits Agency Med. Serv.; Non-Exec. Dir. E. Som. NHS Trust. Socs: Med. Wom. Federat. Prev: GP Castle Cary & Milborne Port; Ho. Phys. (Child Health) St. Bart. Hosp. Lond.

ARNOT, Arthur David Warden Ardgillian, Prieston Road, Bridge of Weir PA11 3DG — MB ChB 1968 Ed.

ARNOTT, Alec Hughes Meiklemyre Farm, Hindog Road, Dalry KA24 5LG — MB ChB 1977 Glas.; BSc Alberta 1970; FFA RCSI 1983.

ARNOTT, Alison Susan Globetown Surgery, 82-86 Roman Road, London E2 0PG Tel: 020 8980 3023 Fax: 020 8983 4627; 9 Mountgrove Road, London N5 2LU — MB BS 1986 Newc.; MRCGP 1990; DCCH RCP Ed. 1991. (Univ. Newc. u. Tyne)

ARNOTT, Professor Eric John Trottsford, Headley, Bordon GU35 8TF Tel: 01420 472136 Fax: 01420 473477 Email: arnottev@compuserve.com — MB BCh BAO 1954 Dub; MB BCh BAO Dub. 1954; BA Dub. 1952; FRCS Eng. 1962; DO Eng. 1956; MA Dub 2000. (TC Dub.) Med. Dir. FAA Internat. Eye Institue, Gibraltar; Vis. Prof. Indore Univ. India; Hon. Facilites Cromwell Hosp., Wellington Hosp. Lond. & King Edw. VII Hosp. Midhurst; Hon. Research Asst. Inst. of Ophth.; Dir. Internat. Phacoemulsificat. & Cataract Methodology Soc. Socs: (Ex-Sec.) UK Intraocular Implant Soc.; Amer. Soc. Ophth.; Internat. Soc. Refractive Surg. Prev: Cons. Surg. Char. Cross Hosp. Lond. & Roy. Eye Hosp. Lond. & Masonic Hosp. Lond.; Sen. Regist. (Ophth.) Moorfields Eye Hosp. Lond. & Univ. Coll. Hosp. Lond.

ARNOTT, Gail Liddell Vennel Street Health Centre, 50 Vennel Street, Dalry KA24 4AG Tel: 01294 832523 Fax: 01294 835771 — MB ChB 1979 Glas.

ARNOTT, Ian David Ramsay 30 Midmar Gardens, Edinburgh EH10 6DZ Tel: 0131 447 6533 — MB ChB 1992 Manch.; BSc (Med. Sci.) St. And. 1989; MRCP (UK) 1995; MD 1998. Specialist Regist. (Gastroenterol. & Gen. Med.), S. E. Scot. Socs: BMA; Caledonian Soc. Gastroenterol. Prev: Clin. Research Fell. (Gastroenterol.) W.. Gen. Hosp. Edin.; SHO (Gastroenterol.) Manch. Roy. Infirm.; SHO Rotat. (Med.) Blackburn Hosp.

***ARNOTT, Jennifer Mary** 20 Priory Gardens, St Andrews KY16 8XX — MB ChB 1996 Dundee.

ARNOTT, Michael Stephen McMillan Southmead Hospital, Westbury on Trym, Bristol BS10 5NB Tel: 0117 959 5834 — MB BS 1983 Lond.; MRCPsych 1992; MRCGP 1987; DRCOG 1986. Hon. Sen. Lect. (Ment. Health) Univ. Bristol.

ARNOTT, Neil 7 Bay Road, Wormit, Newport-on-Tay DD6 8LU Email: n.arnott@talk21.com — MB ChB 1991 Dundee; DGM 1993; DRCOG 1994; MRCOG 1996. Sen. Specialist Regist. Obst. Gyn. Tayside Univ. NHS Trust. Dundee; Hon. Clin. Teach. Univ. Dundee. Socs: Brit. Soc. Colpos. & Cerv. Path.; Brit. Soc. Gyn. Endoscopy.; MRCOG.

ARNOTT, Neil David Amherst Medical Practice, 21 St. Botolphs Road, Sevenoaks TN13 3AQ Tel: 01732 459255 Fax: 01732 450751; Guzzlers Wood, Ide Hill, Sevenoaks TN14 6JT Tel: 01732 750221 Fax: 01732 750590 Email: Neil.D.Arnott@btinternet.com — MB BS 1973 Lond.; LMCC 1977; FRCGP 1993, M 1980; DObst RCOG 1976. (St. Thos.) p/t Gen. Pract.; Sch. Med. Off. Sevenoaks; Clin. Asst. (Cas. & Geriat.) Tunbridge Wells HA; Trainer (Gen. Pract.) Sevenoaks; Police Surg. Sevenoaks; Examr. RCGP; Sec. of MOSA. Socs: Roy. Soc. Med.; BMA. Prev: SHO (O & G) Odstock Hosp. Salisbury; SHO (Paediat.) St. Mary's Hosp. Portsmouth; Ho. Surg. (Gen. Surg.) St. Thos. Hosp. Lond.

ARNOTT, Mr Sidney John (retired) 81 Harley Street, London W1G 8PP Tel: 020 7299 9410 Fax: 020 7299 9414 — MB ChB Ed. 1962; FRCS Ed. 1966; FRCR 1975; FFR 1970; DMRT Ed. 1968. Cons. Clin. Oncologist. Prev: Sen. Lect. Radiother. Univ. Edin. W.. Gen. Hosp. Edin. & Roy.

ARNOTT, Susan Health Centre, 14 Market Place, Carluke ML8 4AZ Tel: 01555 752150 Fax: 01555 751703 — MB ChB 1992 Glas.

ARNOULD, Kathryn Marian 9 Howe of Enzie, Buckie AB56 5BF Tel: 01542 850415 Email: angus@enzie.freeserve.co.uk — MB ChB 1987 Birm.; MRCGP 1992. Indep. GP Banffsh. Prev: GP Argyll; Cas. Off. Dumfries; Trainee GP Inverness.

ARNSTEIN, Francis Emmanuel Department of Anaesthesia, Edinburgh Royal Infirmary, Lauristone Place, Edinburgh EH3 9YW — MB ChB 1983 Leeds; FRCA. 1989; DAvMed FOM RCP Lond. 1992; DA (UK) 1986. Socs: Brit. Aeromed. Practs. Soc.

ARNSTEIN, Mr Peter Michael Cherry Cottage, Furnace Farm Road, Furnace Wood, East Grinstead RH19 2PU Tel: 01342 714578 Fax: 01342 716293 — MB ChB 1979 Manch.; FRCS (Plast Surg.) Eng. 1994; FRCS Lond. 1987; FRCS Ed. 1986. (Manchester) Cons. Plastic Surg. E. Grinstead. Socs: Brit. Assn. Plastic Surg.; Brit. Soc. Surg. Hand; Brit. Assn. Microsurg. Prev: Sen. Regist. (Plastic Surg.) E. Grinstead; Regist. (Plastic Surg.) Guy's Hosp. Lond. & Slough.

ARNTSEN, Kenneth Walter (retired) Balglaze, 51 Trevaunance Road, St Agnes TR5 0NB Tel: 01872 553529 — MB ChB 1958 Cape Town; MSc (Biochem.) Lond. 1981; MMed (Path.) Cape Town 1965; MRCPath. 1980. Cons. Chem Path. Roy. Cornw. Hosp. Truro. Prev: Cons. Chem. Path. P.ss Alexandra Hosp. Harlow.

AROKIANATHAN, Dunstan Surendra 13 Hawkhead Avenue, Paisley PA2 7BT — MB ChB 1994 Glas.

AROKIANATHAN, Moyna Chitra 13 Hawkhead Avenue, Paisley PA2 7BT — MB ChB 1996 Aberd.

AROKIANATHAN, Timothy Ravindra 13 Hawkhead Avenue, Paisley PA2 7BT — MB ChB 1991 Ed.

AROMOLARAN, Aderemi Adenrele 7C Wakefield House, Lovely Lane, Warrington WA5 1QG — MB BS 1981 Lagos, Nigeria; MRCOG 1995.

ARON, Peter Michael Leavesden Road Surgery, 141A Leavesden Road, Watford WD2 5EP Tel: 01923 225128 — MB BS 1981 Lond.; MRCGP 1990. Prev: Regist. (Gen. Surg. & Urol.) Watford Gen. Hosp.

ARON, Usha Rowan Tree Surgery, Rowan Tree Road, Tunbridge Wells TN2 5PX Tel: 01892 515658 Fax: 01892 526271; Tidebrook House, Tidebrook, Wadhurst TN5 6PQ Tel: 01892 784102 Fax: 01892 783662 — MB BS 1971 Calcutta. (Nat. Med. Coll.) Clin. Asst. c/o the Elderly Med.; Police Surg. to Kent Co. Constab.

ARONICA, Guiseppe Franco 30 Sydney Grove, London NW4 2EH — MB BS 1994 Lond.

ARONSON, Jeffrey Kenneth University Department of Clinical Pharmacology, Radcliffe Infirmary, Woodstock Road, Oxford OX2 6HE Tel: 01865 241091 Fax: 01865 791712 Email: jeffrey.aronson@clinpharm.ox.ac.uk — MB ChB 1970 Glas.; MA Oxf. 1984; DPhil Oxf. 1977; FRCP Lond. 1985; MRCP (UK) 1973. Clin. Reader (Clin. Pharmacol.) Univ. Oxf.; Hon. Cons. Phys. Oxf. Radcliffe Hosp.s Trust. Socs: Assn. Phys.; Med. Res. Soc.; Brit. Pharm. Soc. Chairm., Edr.ial Bd. Prev: Vis. Prof. Clin. Pharmacol. Univ. Ceara Brazil 1991; Austral. Vis. Brit. Pharmacol. Soc. 1986; Vis. Prof. Clin. Pharmacol.Univ. Colombo, Sri Lanka 2000.

ARONSTAM, Anthony N. Hampshire Hospital, Basingstoke RG24 9NA Tel: 01256 473202 Fax: 01256 484769 — MB ChB 1957 Cape Town; DM Soton. 1981; FRCPath 1981 M 1969. (Cape Town) Cons. Haemat. N. Hants. Gp.; Dir. Treloar Haemophilia Centre Alton. Socs: Assn. Clin. Path. & Brit. Soc. Haemat. Prev: Research Fell. (Med.) Univ. W.. Ont. Canada; Sen. Regist. (Haemat.)

St. Helier's Hosp. Carshalton; Lect. (Haemat.) St. Geo. Hosp. Med. Sch. Tooting.
ARORA, Amit Kumar 2 Mornington Close, Woodford Green IG8 0TT — MB BS 1990 Lond.
***ARORA, Anita** 1 Farmadine, Trentham, Stoke-on-Trent ST4 8DZ Tel: 01782 658454 Fax: 01782 658454 — MB ChB 1997 Birm.; BSc (Hons.) Birm. 1994.
ARORA, Ashoni Royal North Shore Hospital, St Leonards, Sydney 2065, Australia Tel: 00 61 2 9267521 Fax: 00 61 2 9065142; 110 Spackmans Way, Chalvey, Slough SL1 2SA — MB ChB 1989 Leic. Regist. (Emerg. Med.) Roy. N. Shore Hosp. Sydney, Austral. Socs: BMA. Prev: Regist. (Obst. & Gyn.) Bunderberg, Austral.; SHO (Emerg. Med.) Berlin, Germany; SHO (Emerg. Med.) Wrexham.
ARORA, Asit Kundan, 43 Green Pastures, Stockport SK4 3RB — MB ChB 1998 Manch.; MB ChB Manch 1998.
ARORA, Atul The Surgery, Bromley North Clinic, Station Road, Bromley BR1 3LP Tel: 020 8466 8844 Fax: 020 8466 8465; Acacia, Walden Road, Chislehurst BR7 5DH Tel: 020 8467 6717 — MB BS 1977 Delhi; MRCP (UK) 1983; MRCS Eng. LRCP Lond. 1982. Clin. Asst. (Diabetes Med.) Dist. Diabetic Centre FarnBoro. Hosp. Kent. Prev: Regist. (Gen. Med.) Orsett Hosp. Grays; Regist. (Geriat. Med.) St. Geo. Hosp. Med. Sch. Lond.
ARORA, Gulshan Rai The Surgery, 179 Alvechurch Road, West Heath, Birmingham B31 3PN Tel: 0121 475 1550; 7 Earlsmere, Valley Rd, Solihull B94 6AA — MB BS 1966 Patna; MRCP (U.K.) 1974; DCH RCPS Glas. 1972; DA Eng. 1970. (P.W.Med. Coll. Patna)
ARORA, Gurcharan Singh 36A Cowper Road, London W3 6PZ — MB ChB 1991 Liverp.
ARORA, Kamal Jeet Perry Park Surgery, 291 Walsall Road, Perry Barr, Birmingham B42 1TY Tel: 0121 356 4131 — MB BS 1974 Jiwaji.
ARORA, Mahesh Kumar Lister Street Surgery, 10 Lister Street, Nuneaton CV11 4NX Tel: 024 7638 3784 Fax: 024 7635 4958; 4 Meadow Close, Wolvey, Hinckley LE10 3LW Tel: 01455 220464 Fax: 01455 220464 — MB BS 1975 Punjab; Dip. Addict Behaviour Med St. George's Lond 1991. (Govt. Med. Sch. Patiala) SHO A & E Dept. Manor Hosp. Nuneaton. Socs: Conserv. Med. Soc.; Brit. Assn. Sexual & Marital Ther.; Soc. of Performing Arts Med. Trust.
ARORA, Nirmal Barnet Healthcare Trust, Mill Hill Clinic, Hartley Avenue, London NW7 2HX Tel: 020 8959 3005 Fax: 020 8906 3510; 2 Lodge Avenue, Elstree, Borehamwood WD6 3ND Tel: 020 8207 5497 — MB ChB 1979 Glas. Clin. Med. Off. Barnet HA.
ARORA, Nupur 43 Green Pastures, Stockport SK4 3RB — MB BS 1998 Lond.; MB BS Lond 1998.
ARORA, Pramod Rock Court Surgery, Rock Court, Old Swan, Liverpool L13 2BY Tel: 0151 228 0672 Fax: 0151 228 0298 — MB BS 1975 Panjab; MRCP (UK) 1978.
ARORA, Puneet Paul 144 Selly Park Road, Birmingham B29 7LH — MB BCh 1995 Wales.
ARORA, R M Rock Court Surgery, Rock Court, Old Swan, Liverpool L13 2BY Tel: 0151 228 0672 Fax: 0151 228 0298.
ARORA, Sheila 32 Connaught Square, London W2 2HL Tel: 020 7402 1777 — MB BS 1959 Delhi. p/t GP NHS Asst. & Private Pract. Socs: Med. Soc. Lond. Prev: Med. Off. Family Plann. Clinic, Hendon; Ho. Phys. & Ho. Surg. Chase Farm Hosp. Enfield.
ARORA, Mr Subhash Chandra Ashcroft Surgery, 803 Stockport Road, Levenshulme, Manchester M19 3BS Tel: 0161 224 1329 Fax: 0161 224 0094; Kundan, 43 Green Pastures, Heaton Mersey, Stockport SK4 3RB — MB BS 1967 Panjab; MS (ENT) Lucknow 1972; DLO Lucknow 1969. (Christian Med. Coll. Ludhiana)
ARORA, Surinderjit Kaur 3 Lansdowne Avenue, Slough SL1 3SG — MB BS 1977 Meerut; MRCP (UK) 1985; DCH RCPS Glas. 1984; DCH 1980.
AROWOJOLU, Ayodele Olatunji Hull Maternity Hospital, Hedon Road, Hull HU9 5LX Tel: 01482 76215 — MB BS 1978 Ibadan; MRCOG 1992.
ARRAND, Ruth Mavis Firs Health Centre, Firs Lane, Smethwick, Smethwick B67 6AE Tel: 0121 558 0105 — MB ChB 1983 Sheff. Socs: BMA. Prev: Trainee GP Walkley Sheff. VTS; SHO (O & G) Doncaster Roy. Infirm.; SHO (Psychiat.) Pontefract Gen. Infirm.
ARRANDALE, Lindsay Anne Church Road Farm, Church Road, Mellor, Stockport SK6 5LY — MB BS 1998 Lond.; MB BS Lond 1998.
ARRAZOLA BERRIZBEITIA, Maria Teresa 9B Lancaster House, Whiston Hospital, Warrington Road, Prescot L35 5DR Tel: 0151 426 1600 Email: maitearrazola@compuserve.com — LMS Basque Provinces 1990; T(GP) 1994; MSc (Community Eye Health) Lond. 1997. Socs: Train. Mem. ESCRS; BMA.
ARRIGONI, Peter Bruce Charing Cross Hospital, Fulham Palace Road, London W6 8RF Tel: 020 8846 7017 Fax: 020 8846 7013 — MB ChB 1982 Manch.; FFA RCS (Eng.) 1988. Cons. Anaesth. Char. Cross Hosp., Lond. Prev: Cons. Anaesth. Qu. Mary's Univ. Hosp. Roehampton; Sen. Regist. (Anaesth.) Char. Cross & W.m. Hosp. Lond.; Regist. (Anaesth.) Char. Cross Hosp. Lond.
ARRINDELL, Angelica Patricia 50 Berkley Close, Highwoods, Colchester CO4 4RR — Artsexamen 1992 Amsterdam.
ARROWSMITH, Alice Eleanor 6 Hanby Gardens, Sunderland SR3 1UQ Tel: 0191 522 7339 — MB BS 1966 Durh.; FRCA 1970. Cons. Anaesth. Sunderland Hosps.
ARROWSMITH, Janet Mary Trafford General Hospital, Moorside Road, Manchester M41 5SL Tel: 0161 948 4022; Convent of St. Emilie, Grange Road, Bowdon Vale,, Altrincham WA14 3HA Tel: 0161 928 2119 Fax: 0161 928 2119 — MB ChB 1971 Leeds. Clin. Asst. (Geriat.) Trafford HA. Prev: GP Yorks.
ARROWSMITH, Jill Susan 17 Blackburn Avenue, Brough HU15 1BD Tel: 01482 668379 — BM BCh 1990 Oxf.
ARROWSMITH, Joseph Edmund Department of Anaesthesia, Papworth Hospital, Papworth Evarard, Cambridge CB3 8RE Tel: 01480 830541 Ext: 4406/4381 Fax: 01480 831143 Email: joe.arrowsmith@papworth-tr.anglox.nhs.uk; Email: jarrowsmith@doctors.org.uk — MBBS 1985 Lond.; CCST 1997; MRCP 1991 (UK); MD 2001 Lond.; DA (UK) 1987; FRCA 1992. (St. Georges, London) Cons. Anaesth. Papworth Hosp. Camb.; Cons. Anaesth. Lea Hosp., Camb.; Cons. Anaesth. Evelyn Hosp., Camb.; Cons. Anaesth. Cromwell Clinic, Huntingdon. Socs: BMA; AM Soc. Anaesth.; Assn. Anaesth. Prev: Snr. Regist. (Anaesth.) St. Geo.s's Hosp. Lond.; VIS. Assoc. (Anaesth.) Duke Univ. Med. Center Durh. NC. USA; Research Fell. (Anaesth) Middlex. Hosp. Lond.
ARROWSMITH, Paul (retired) 27 Whinmoor Gardens, Leeds LS14 1AF — MB ChB 1957 Liverp. Prev: Princip. Med. Off. HM Home Off. Prison Dept.
ARROWSMITH, Peter John Room 6225, War Pensions society, Dept. of Social Security, Blackpool FY5 0WP; Lamplight, Horse Park Lane, Pilling, Preston PR3 6AS Tel: 01253 790743 — MB ChB 1968 Sheff. Med. Adviser War Pens. Agency DSS.
ARROWSMITH, William Alfred (retired) 76 Wilfrid's Road, Bessacarr, Doncaster DN4 6AE Tel: 01302 535317 Email: bill.arrowsmith@dial.pipex.com — FRCP Lond. 1984; MRCP (UK) 1971; MRCS Eng. LRCP Lond. 1966; DCH Eng. 1969. Prev: Cons. Dept. Paediat. Doncaster Roy. Infirm.
ARROYO VIVAR, Miguel Angel Room 15 Block A, Arrowe Park Hospital, Arrowe Park Road, Wirral CH49 5PE — LMS 1992 Basque Provinces.
ARSANIOUS, Mr Nasr Hizkial Nasr 50 St David's Crescent, Newport NP20 3AW — MB BCh 1978 Cairo; FRCS Ed. 1993.
ARSCOTT, Joyce 8 Bell Hill, Histon, Cambridge CB4 9JQ Tel: 01223 233164 — MB BS 1951 Lond.; MRCS Eng. LRCP Lond. 1951. (Roy. Free)
ARSCOTT-BARBER, Julian Andrew 26 Frere Avenue, Fleet GU51 5AP — MB ChB 1989 Leeds.
ARSENOPOULOU, Ioanna 53 Heathcroft, Hampstead Way, London NW11 7HJ — Ptychio Iatrikes 1992 Thessalonika.
ARSHAD, Sikander Ali 9 Carlisle Close, Whitefield, Manchester M45 6TH; House 15-A, Street 17, F-7/2, Islamabad 44000, Pakistan — MB BCh 1985 Wales; MRCP (UK) 1993. Specialist Regist. in Rehabil. Med., Yorks. Socs: Brit. Geriat. Soc. (NW Br.).; Brit Soc of Rehab Med. Prev: Regist. (Gen. Med. & Geriat.) N. Manch. Gen. Hosp.
ARSHAD, Syed Hasan The David Hide, Asthma and Allergy Centre, St Mary's Hospital, Newport Tel: 01983 534359 Fax: 01983 822928 Email: sha@soton.ac.uk; 28 Hickory Gardens, West End, Southampton SO30 3RN Tel: 01703 470164 Fax: 01703 701711 — MB BS 1979 Karachi; MRCP (UK) 1986; DM Soton. 1993. (Karachi Pakistan) Specialist (Allergy) & Dir., The David Hide Asthma & Allergy Centre, St . Mary's Hosp., Newport, Isle of Wight; Sen. Fell. (Med.) Univ. of Soton., Soton. Gen. Hosp. 1997. Socs: Brit. Allergy Soc. Prev: Assoc. Prof. & Hon. Cons. Phys. in Chest Med.

Aga Khan Univ. Hosp. Karachi, Pakistan; Sen. Fell. John Hopkins Asthma & Allergy Centre Baltimore, USA.

ARSHI, Harpreet St Thomas Health Centre, Cowick Street, St. Thomas, Exeter EX4 1HJ Tel: 01392 676677 Fax: 01392 676677 — MB ChB 1983 Bristol; MRCGP 1988; DRCOG 1986; E. (Bristol) Med Off. Univ. Exeter; Hon. Treas. Tamar Fac. RCGP. Prev: Princip. Topsham Surg. Exeter; Princip. NW Surg. Plymouth; Trainee GP Cornw. VTS.

ARTAMENDI LARRANAGA, Pablo Gloucester Royal Hospital, Great Western Road, Gloucester GL1 3NN; Kingsgate, 3 Hamilton Square, Easy Row, Worcester WR1 3HL Tel: 01905 617848 — LMS 1993 Basque Provinces. SHO (Ophth.) Gloucester Gen. Hosp. Socs: BMA; Med. Protec. Soc. Prev: SHO (Ophth.) Kidderminster Gen. Hosp., Worcester Roy. Infirm. & Alexandre Hosp. Redditch.

ARTARAZ BEOBIDE, Joseba Inaki N. Riding Infirmary, Newport Road, Middlesbrough TS1 5JE — LMS 1990 Basque Provinces.

ARTEEN, Mr Petrus Bedo 77 Helston Road, Parkhall Est., Walsall WS5 3HX — LMSSA 1966 Lond.; FRCS Ed. 1968. (Bagdad) Med. Asst. (Emerg. & Trauma Surg.) Walsall Gen. Hosp. Socs: BMA. Prev: Sen. Regist. (Orthop.) P.ss Alexandra Hosp. Harlow; Cas. Surg. A & E Dept. Walsall Gen. Hosp.; Neurosurg. Regist. Brook Gen. & Whittington Hosps. Lond.

ARTHUR, Alasdair Gordon 99 Lanark Road W., Currie, Edinburgh EH14 5LB Tel: 0131 449 4610 Fax: 0131 449 4610 — MB ChB 1993 Glas.

ARTHUR, Aline Lucy Tindal Sunnyside, Battlehill, Huntly AB54 6HX — MB ChB 1989 Aberd.; MSc Newc. 1991.

ARTHUR, Angus Euan Bank Cottage, 99 Lanark Road W., Currie EH14 5LB — MB ChB 1997 Glas.

ARTHUR, Charles Peter Claughton Medical Centre, 161 Park Road North, Birkenhead CH41 0DD Tel: 0151 652 1688 Fax: 0151 670 0565; West Lawn, 12 Reservoir Road N., Prenton CH42 8LU Tel: 0151 512 7656 Email: petercpa@epulse.net — MB BS 1985 Lond.; MRCGP 1989; DRCOG 1988. Chairm. Birkenhead PCG.

ARTHUR, David Kilpatrick Toft Road Surgery, Toft Road, Knutsford WA16 9DX Tel: 01565 632681; Heath Lodge, Parkgate Lane, Knutsford WA16 8EZ Tel: 01565 632681 Fax: 01565 633298 — MB BS 1973 Lond.; MRCS Eng. LRCP Lond. 1973; DObst RCOG 1976. (St. Mary's) Prev: SHO (A & E) Derbysh. Roy. Infirm.; Demonst. (Anat.) Nottm. Univ.; Ho. Surg. Chelmsford & Essex Hosp.

ARTHUR, Douglas Salmond (retired) 31 New Endrick Road, Killearn, Glasgow G63 9QD — MB ChB 1966 Glas.; FRCA 1970. Prev: Cons. Annaesth.

ARTHUR, Eleanor Joy 301 Reading Road, Henley-on-Thames RG9 1EL — MB BS 1983 Lond.; DCH RCP Lond. 1987; DRCOG 1985.

ARTHUR, George David (retired) Cannon Heath, Rock, Wadebridge PL27 6LP Tel: 01208 862563 — MRCS Eng. LRCP Lond. 1944. Prev: Med. Off. Falkland Is.s.

ARTHUR, Mr Godfrey William (retired) Stratton, 15 Coastal Road, East Preston, Littlehampton BN16 1SJ Tel: 01903 782099 — MB BChir 1957 Camb.; MA, MB Camb. 1957, BChir 1956; FRCS Eng. 1962; MRCS Eng. LRCP Lond. 1956. Cons. Surg. Worthing & Shoreham Hosp. Gp. Prev: Sen. Surg. Regist. Leicester Roy. Infirm.

ARTHUR, Iain Douglas Ancrum Road Surgery, 12-14 Ancrum Road, Dundee DD2 2HZ Tel: 01382 669316 Fax: 01382 660787 — MB ChB 1987 Aberd.; MRCGP 1994.

ARTHUR, Mr Ian Hugh 77 St Georges Drive, Ickenham, Uxbridge UB10 8HP Tel: 01895 634430 — MB BS 1981 Lond.; FRCS Eng. 1990. (Roy. Free) Prev: Regist. (Gen. Surg. & Orthop.) St. Albans City Hosp.; SHO Surgic. Rotat. Basingstoke Dist. Hosp.; Ho. Phys. & Ho. Surg. Roy. Free Hosp. Lond.

ARTHUR, Ian Sinclair Mistral, Slamannan, Falkirk FK1 3BA Tel: 01324 851967 — LRCP LRCS Ed. LRFPS Glas. 1952. (St. Mungo's Coll. & Univ. Glas.)

ARTHUR, James Brown 6 Central Avenue, Harton, South Shields NE34 6AZ Tel: 0191 455 2965 — MB ChB 1931 Ed.; MRCP Lond. 1941. (Ed.) Hon. Cons. Phys. S. Shields Gp. Hosps. Socs: Roy. Med. Soc. Edin. & BMA. Prev: SHO (Surg.) Childr. Hosp. Newc.; Clin. Path. Roy. Infirm. Manch., Lt.-Col. RAMC, OC Med. Div. & Med.; Specialist 1941-46.

ARTHUR, James Bryant George (retired) Denewell House, Low Fell, Gateshead Tel: 01632 876123 & 876246 — MB BS 1956 Durh.; MRCS Eng. LRCP Lond. 1957. Prev: Ho. Surg. Roy. Vict. Infirm. Newc.

ARTHUR, James Lynn (retired) Cobblecote, 127 Marine Drive, Rhos-on-Sea, Colwyn Bay LL28 4HY Tel: 01492 548023 — LRCPI & LM, LRSCI & LM 1942; LRCPI & LM, LRCSI & LM 1942; LAH Dub. 1941. Prev: RAMC 1942-6.

ARTHUR, James Philip Buckthought (retired) 34 The Avenue, Andover SP10 3EW Tel: 01264 50451 — MRCS Eng. LRCP Lond. 1942; LM Rotunda 1947. Prev: Ho. Phys. Roy. Cornw. Infirm. Truro.

ARTHUR, John Kilpatrick (retired) The Lodge, Uplands Park, Sheringham NR26 8NE Tel: 01344 622160, 01263 824672 — MRCS Eng. LRCP Lond. 1956. Prev: Capt. RAMC.

ARTHUR, John Maxwell McKenzie Department of Family Medicine, King Faisal Specialist Hospital, PO Box 3352, MBC62, Riyadh 1121, Saudi Arabia Email: jkarthur@naseej.com.sa; 45/8 West Bryson Road, Pollwarth, Edinburgh EH11 1BQ Tel: 0131 313 2697 — MB BS 1974 Newc.; AFOM RCP Lond. 1989; MRCGP 1980.

ARTHUR, Julie 15 Main Street, Springfield, Cupar KY15 5SQ — MB ChB 1998 Glas.; MB ChB Glas 1998.

ARTHUR, Linda Marie Email: lmarthur@waitrose.com; Ryall Lawn, Ryall Grove, Upton-upon-Severn, Worcester WR8 0PL Email: lmarthur@waitrose.com — BM 1991 Soton.; DGM RCP Lond. 1995. (Soton.) Prev: GP/Regist. The Surg. Upton-upon-Severn; SHO (Cas., Med., Surg. & Elderly Med.) Cirencester Hosp.; GP Albany Ho. Surg., Worcester.

ARTHUR, Michael 63 Falcons Way, Shrewsbury SY3 8ZG — MB BChir 1994 Camb.; BA Camb. 1991, MB 1994, BChir 1993. Ho. Off. (Gen. Surg.) Ipswich Hosp. NHS Trust. Prev: Ho. Off. (Gen. Med.) Ipswich Hosp. NHS Trust.

ARTHUR, Professor Michael James Paul University Medicine (South Block), Southampton General Hospital, Southampton SO16 6YD Tel: 02380 796886 Fax: 02380 794154 Email: mja1@soton.ac.uk; Slab Farm, Slab Lane, West Wellow, Romsey SO51 6BY — BM 1977 Soton.; DM Soton. 1986; FRCP Lond. 1993; MRCP (UK) 1979. (Univ. Soton. Sch. Med.) Prof. Med. Univ. Soton.; Hon. Cons. Phys. Soton. Univ. Hosps. Trust. Socs: (Counc.) Brit. Soc. Gastroenterol.; Eur. & Internat. Assns. Study Liver; Amer. Assn. Study Liver Dis. Prev: Sen. Lect. Univ. Soton.; Fogarty/NIH Internat. Fell. UCSF, USA.

ARTHUR, Nicholas Simon Oakfield Surgery, Vicarage Road, Newmarket CB8 8JF Tel: 01638 662018 Fax: 01638 660294; 30 Ditton Green, Wood Ditton, Newmarket CB8 9SQ Tel: 01638 731029 — MB BS 1977 Lond. (Westm.) Med. Off. Tattersalls (UK) Ltd.; Med. Assessor (Incapcity Benefit) Indep. Tribunal Serv. Suff. Prev: Trainee GP Guildford.; Regist Rotat. (Anaesth.) Char. Cross Hosp., Nat. Hosp. Nerv. Dis. Lond. & Roy. Surrey Co. Hosp. Guildford.

ARTHUR, Norma Agnes Standish Medical Practice, Rodenhurst, Church Street, Standish, Wigan WN6 0JP Tel: 01257 421909 Fax: 01257 424259; Lakewood, Brandreth Delph, Lancaster Lane, Parbold, Wigan WN8 7AQ Tel: 01257 464125 — MB ChB 1974 Dundee.

ARTHUR, Philip James Douglas Kingsteignton Surgery, Whiteway Road, Kingsteignton, Newton Abbot TQ12 3HN Tel: 01626 883312 Fax: 01626 336406; Gibhay, Teign View Road, Bishopsteignton, Teignmouth TQ14 9SZ Tel: 01626 775497 — MB BS 1972 Lond.; DObst RCOG 1974. (St. Thomas' Hospital Medical School) Prev: SHO. (O & G) St. Thos. Hosp. Lond.; Ho. Surg. St. Thos. Hosp. Lond.; Med. Off. Save The Childr. Fund. Algeria & Nepal.

ARTHUR, Rachel Mary Fleming 2 Festing Road, Putney, London SW15 1LP Tel: 020 8788 8850 Fax: 020 8788 8850 — MB BS 1979 Lond. Prev: Edr., The Practitioner.

***ARTHUR, Rebecca Margaret** 192 Turney Road, London SE21 7JL Tel: 020 7733 3329 Fax: 020 7733 5302 — BM BS 1997 Nottm.

ARTHUR, Richard Carson Bard (retired) 1 Grant Close, Osmotherley, Northallerton DL6 3BD — MB BS 1949 Lond.; MRCS Eng. LRCP Lond. 1945. Prev: Ho. Phys. Middlx. Hosp.

ARTHUR, Roger Alan, TD, Maj. RAMC (retired) 5 Bodley Road, New Malden KT3 5QD Tel: 020 8942 8236 — MRCS Eng. LRCP Lond. 1950; MRCGP 1962. JP.; Dep. Dir. GPFC; Maj. RAMC RARO. Prev: GP Lond.

ARTHUR, Rosemary Joan The XRay and Ultrasound Department, The Clarendon Wing, The General Infirmary, Belmont Grove, Leeds LS2 9NS Tel: 0113 243 2799; Rose Cottage, 54 Town St, Guiseley, Leeds LS20 9DT Tel: 01943 77397 — MB ChB 1976 Leeds; BSc Leeds 1973, MB ChB (Hons.) 1976; MRCP (UK) 1979; FRCR 1983; DMRD 1982. Cons. Paediat. Radiol. Leeds W.. HA.

ARTHUR, Ruth Gilly Royal Oak Cottage, Church Broughton, Derby DE65 5AS — BM BS 1990 Nottm.

ARTHUR, Sarah Jane Ancrum Road Surgery, 12-14 Ancrum Road, Dundee DD2 2HZ Tel: 01382 669316 Fax: 01382 660787 — MB ChB 1988 Leeds; FPC 1993; MRCGP 1994. GP Partner; Tutor in Univ. Dept of GP.

ARTHUR, Timothy Ieuan Francis (retired) Crud-y-Gwynt, 70 Deganwy Road, Deganwy, Conwy LL31 9DN Tel: 01492 593941 — MB BS Lond. 1955. Prev: Ho. Surg. W. Norwich Hosp.

ARTHUR, Valerie-Margaret Keir Stockwell Road Surgery, 21 Stockwell Road, Knaresborough HG5 0JY Tel: 01423 867433 Fax: 01423 869633; 11 Whiteway Head, Knaresborough HG5 8LE — MB ChB 1967 Glas.; MRCGP 1981; DCH RCPS Glas. 1970; DObst RCOG 1969. (Glas.)

ARTHUR, Wayne Roy 8 Ellenglaze Meadow, Cubert, Newquay TR8 5QU — MB BS 1993 Newc.

ARTHURE, John Edgar The Medical Centre, Upper Green Road, St Helens, Ryde PO33 1UG Tel: 01983 872772 Fax: 01983 874800 — LMSSA 1962 Lond.; MA, BM BCh Oxf. 1962; DObst RCOG 1964. (Oxf. & King's Coll. Hosp.) Med. Off. RNLI Bembridge. Socs: BMA & N. of Eng. Obst. & Gyn. Soc. Prev: Ho. Phys. & Ho. Surg. (O & G) Radcliffe Infirm. Oxf; Regist. (O & G) Mill Rd. Matern. Hosp. Liverp.

ARTHURS, David Forest Health Care, The Health Centre, Dockham Road, Cinderford GL14 2AN Tel: 01594 598030 — MB BS 1969 Lond.; DObst RCOG 1973; DA Eng. 1973.

ARTHURS, Graham John, OBE Maelor Hospital, Wrexham LL13 7TD Tel: 01978 291100; 40 Trem Yr Eglwys, Wrexham LL13 7QE Tel: 01978 359398 — MB ChB 1969 Leeds; FRCA 1975. Cons. Anaesth. Maelor Hosp. Socs: Soc. Anaesth of Wales; Internat. Assn. for the Study of Pain; Assn. of Anaesthesia.

ARTHURS, Yvonne Mary Constance 39 Beaufort Avenue, Langland, Swansea SA3 4PB — MB BCh BAO 1973 NUI.

ARTHURSON, Iain Hayden Benefits Agency Medical Services, Argyle House, 3 Lady Lawson St., Edinburgh EH3 9SH Tel: 0131 229 9191; 91 Craigleith Crescent, Edinburgh EH4 3JX — MB ChB 1962 Ed.; DA Eng. 1965; DObst RCOG 1965. Med. Adviser Benefits Agency DSS. Socs: BMA. Prev: GP Ladywell Med. Centre Edin.; Ho. Phys. (Paediat.) W. Middlx. Hosp. Isleworth.

ARTHURTON, Malcolm William (retired) Easdale, Aynsome Road, Cartmel, Grange-over-Sands LA11 6PR Tel: 015395 36363 — MD Lond. 1952, MB BS 1941; FRCP Lond. 1969, M 1948; MRCS Eng. LRCP Lond. 1941; DCH Eng. 1947. Prev: Cons. (Paediat.) Bradford Health Dist.

ARTLEY, Malcolm Leonard 25 Rochelle Close, London SW11 2RU — MB BCh 1992 Camb.

ARTUS, Joan Marie 8 Mercers Place, Brook Green, London W6 7BZ — MB BCh BAO NUI 1948; MD NUI 1950; FRCPI 1960; FRCPath 1969; FRCOphth 1988.

ARUL, Mr Arangannal 22 Dryburgh Walk, Moodiesburn, Glasgow G69 0HH Tel: 0141 875900 Fax: 0141 875900 — MB BS 1986 Madras; FRCS Ed. 1992; DTM & H Liverp. 1987. Staff Grade Surg. Glas. Roy. Infirm. Glas.

ARUL, Dhilanthy Rasini Yew Cottage, 142 Blackbrook Lane, Bromley BR1 2HP — MB ChB 1995 Bristol.

ARUL, Mr Gularaj Suren Department of Paediatric Surgery, Bristol Royal Hospital for Sick Children, Bristol; 148 Cranbrook Road, Bristol BS6 7DG — MB ChB 1992 Bristol; BSc (Hons.) Bristol 1989; FRCS Eng. 1994. (Bristol) Clin. Research Fell. (Paediat. Surg.) Bristol Roy. Hosp. Sick Childr. Socs: Med. Defence Union; BMA.

ARULAMBALAM, Kamalini Jayawathy Farnborough Hospital, Farnborough Common, Orpington BR6 8ND Tel: 01689 814290 Fax: 01689 814041 — MB BS 1965 Ceylon; FRCPath 1975, D 1971. Cons. Histopath. FarnBoro. Hosp. Kent. Prev: Sen. Regist. (Histopath.) & Regist. (Path.) Roy. Berks. Hosp. Reading; SHO St. Helier Hosp. Carshalton.

ARULAMPALAM, Mr Thanjakumar Hermon Arichandran 3 Riverside Close, Clapton, London E5 9SP — MB BS 1992 Lond.; FRCS Eng. 1996. (St. Bart. Hosp.) Specialist Regist. NE Thames. Prev: SHO (Gen. Surg.) St. Bart. Hosp. Lond.; SHO (Orthop.) Homerton Hosp.; SHO (Gen. Surg.) Whipps Cross Hosp.

ARULANANTHAM, Nirmalan Yohan 3 St John's Church Road, Folkestone CT19 5BQ — MB ChB 1994 Birm. SHO (Gen. Med.) Solihull Hosp. Socs: MDU and BMA. Prev: SHO (Gen. Med.), Staffs. Gen. Hosp.; SHO (A & E Med.), Staffs. Gen. Hosp.; Ho. Off. (Med.) Staffs. Gen. Hosp.

ARULEFELA, Muibat Mojisola 129 Cavendish Drive, London E11 1DJ — MB BS 1990 Ibadan.

ARULKUMARAN, Sabaratnam Department of Obstetrics, Midwifery & Gynaecology, Derby City General Hospital, Uttoxeter Road, Derby DE22 3NE Tel: 01332 34013 Ext: 5991 Fax: 01332 625633 Email: arulkumaran@nottingham.ac.uk; 516 Burton Road, Derby DE23 6FN Tel: 01332 297359 Email: arulkamaran@nottingham.ac.uk — MB BS 1972 Sri Lanka; PhD Singapore 1992; MD Singapore 1997; MRCS Eng. LRCP Lond. 1979; FRCS Ed. 1979; MRCOG 1980. (Univ. Ceylon) Prof. O & G The Univ. of Nottm.; Vis. Prof. Dept. of Obst. & Gyn. Nat. Univ. of Singapore. Socs: Internat. Federat. Obst. & Gyn. (Treas.). Prev: Prof. & Head Dept. of O & G Nat. Univ. of Singapore.

ARULLENDRAN, Puveendran 22 Motspur Park, New Malden KT3 6PL — MB BS 1991 Lond.

ARULRAJAH, Selvaratnam Arulraja and Partners, 161 Wandle Road, Morden SM4 Tel: 020 8648 1877 Fax: 020 8648 4737 — MB BS 1969 Ceylon.

ARULRAJAN, Arumainayagam Ebanezar Hawthorn Lodge, Moorgreen Hospital, Botley Road, West End, Southampton SO30 3JB Tel: 02380 475157 Fax: 02380 475160; 18 Eden Road, West End, Southampton SO18 3QX Email: ae@arulrajan.fsnet.co.uk — MB BS 1978 Sri Lanka; LRCP LRCS Ed. LRCPS Glas. 1985; MRCPsych 1986. Cons. Psychiat. Moorgreen Hosp. Soton. Prev: Sen. Regist. (Psychiat. of Ment. Handicap.) Tatchbury Mt. Hosp.

ARUMAINAYAGAM, Joseph Thiruthuvakumar Department of HIV & Genitourinary Medicine, Manor Hospital, Moat Road, Walsall WS2 9PS Tel: 01922 633341 — MB BS 1975 Sri Lanka; 1998 FRCOG; 1995 MFFP; 1985 MRCOG; 1981 LRCP LRCS Ed. LRCPS Glas. (University of Colombu, Sri-Lanka) Cons. HIV & Genitourin. Med. Manor Hosp. Walsall. Socs: Med. Soc. Study VD; Brit. Soc. Colpos. & Cerv. Path.

ARUMUGAM, Chitra 8 Ardrossan Road, Seamill, West Kilbride KA23 9LR — MB ChB 1992 Glas.

ARUMUGAM RATNAM, Lakshmi 23 Turnstone Close, London E13 0HN — MB ChB 1998 Sheff.; MB ChB Sheff 1998.

ARUMUGASAMY, Aarani 31 Clonallan Road, Warrenpoint, Newry BT34 3RP — MB BCh BAO 1987 NUI; LRCPSI 1987; MRCPI 1992.

ARUNA PRASAD, Gokaraju Patience Lane Surgery, Patience Lane, Altofts, Normanton WF6 2JZ Tel: 01924 890729 Fax: 01924 896546 — MB BS 1974 Madras.

ARUNACHALAM, Nagappan 47 Brampton Drive, Liverpool L8 7SU — MB ChB 1998 Liverp.; MB ChB Liverp 1998.

ARUNACHALAM, Somaskantha Barnet Hospital, Wellhouse NHS Trust, Wellhouse Lane, Barnet EN5 3JD Tel: 020 8216 5494 Fax: 020 8216 5495; 57 Sudbury Court Drive, Harrow HA1 3ST — MB BS 1964 Ceylon; MRCP (UK) 1976; FRCP (Lond) 1994. Cons. Phys. Wellhse. NHS Trust Barnet Hosp. Socs: Fell. Roy. Soc. Med.; BMA.

ARUNASALAM, Premila First Floor Flat, 45 Woodlawn Road, London SW6 6NQ — MB BS 1992 Lond.; FRCA 1997. (Charing Cross & Westminister, Univ. of Lond.) Specialist Regist. In Anaesth. On N. Thames Rotat. Socs: Roy. Coll. Obst. & Gyns.; Assn. Anaesth.; Brit. Soc. of Orthopaedic Anaesth.

ARUNDALE, Diana Elizabeth The Holt, Hutton Buscel, Scarborough YO13 9LN Tel: 01723 862045; Rose Cottage, 2 Butts Lane, Tibthorpe, Driffield YO25 9LE Tel: 01377 229235 — MCRS Eng. LRCP Lond. 1979. (Cardiff) Clin. Asst. Humberside brE. screening unit Kingston Gen.Hosp.Hull. Socs: BMA. Prev: GP Regist.; SHO Gen. Internal Med.; SHO (A & E).

ARUNDALE, Nicholas Northlands Wood Surgery, 7 Walnut Park, Haywards Heath RH16 3TG Tel: 01444 458022 Fax: 01444 415960; 36 Perryfields, Burgess Hill RH15 8TU — MB BCh 1984 Wales; MRCGP 1988; DRCOG 1987; DGM RCP Lond. 1986.

ARUNDEL, Paul 18A Tinshill Road, Cookridge, Leeds LS16 7DU — MB BS 1996 Newc.

ARUNDELL, Lewis Ernest (retired) Beaks Hill House, 19 Beaks Hill Road, King's Norton, Birmingham B38 8BJ Tel: 0121 458 3369 — MB ChB 1943 Birm.; MRCP Lond. 1949; MRCS Eng. LRCP Lond. 1943. Med. Examr. Norwich Union. Prev: Med. Regist. Gen. Hosp. Birm.

ARUNDELL, Peter William (retired) 14 Third Avenue, Worthing BN14 9NZ Tel: 01903 36714 — MRCS Eng. LRCP Lond. 1945; DOMS Eng. 1949. Prev: Asst. Ophth. St. Richards Hosp. Chichester & Worthing Hosp.

ARVANITIS, Andreas Tel: 01253 853992 — Ptychio Iatrikes 1977 Athens; MRCP 1988 (UK). Gen. Practitioner, Cleveleys Gp. Pract., Kelso Ave. Cheveleys, Lancs. FY5 3CF. Socs: Brit. Med. Acupunc. Soc.; Primary Care Cardiovasc. Soc. Prev: Clin. Asst., Cardiol. Dept., Vict. Hosp., Blackpool; Gen. Med. Regist., Maccelesfield Gen. Hosp., Maccelesfield, Chesh.; Clin. Asst., Accid. and Emerg., Grimsby Gen. Hosp., Grimsby, S. Humberside.

ARVIN, Babak 32 Waddington Way, London SE19 3XJ — MB BS 1997 Lond.

ARVIND, Attiganal Shankara Rao West Wales General Hospital, Carmarthen SA31 2AF Tel: 01267 235151 Fax: 01267 227740 — MB BS 1977 Bangalore; MD Bangalore 1981; FRCP Glas. 1995; MRCP (UK) 1984. Cons. Phys. W. Wales Gen. Hosp. Carmarthen. Socs: BMA; Indian Med. Assn.; Indian Soc. Gastroenterol. Prev: Med. Dir., Cons. Phys. (Gastroenterol.) & Med. Admin. Mallya Hosp. Bangalore, India; Cons. Phys. & Gastroenterol. Dasappa Hosp.

ARYA, Anita 56 Kelvin Grove, Sandyford, Newcastle upon Tyne NE2 1RL — MB BS 1997 Newc.

ARYA, Elvira Cecilia Speke Health Centre, North Parade, Speke, Liverpool L24 2XP Tel: 0151 486 1695 — MB BS 1955 Panjab (India); FFA RCSI 1977; DA Eng. 1967; DObst RCOG 1961. (Med. Coll. Amritsar) GP Liverp. Family Pract. Comm. Prev: Regist. (Anaesth.) Liverp. AHA (T); Med. Off. Uganda Med. Serv.; SHO Dept. Anaesth. E.. Gen. Hosp. Edin.

ARYA, Manit 2 StClements Avenue, Blackpool FY3 8LT Tel: 01253 302615; 2 St. Clements Avenue, Blackpool FY3 8LT Tel: 01253 302615 — MB ChB 1992 Manch.; FRCS Glas 1998. Socs: BMA. Prev: Ho. Phys. Withington Hosp. Manch.; Ho. surg. Withington & Christie Hosps. Manch.

ARYA, Pratibha Flat 6, Sharoe Green Hospital, Sharow Green Lane, Fulwood, Preston PR2 8DU — MB BS 1978 Lucknow; MRCOG 1992.

ARYA, Raj Pal Park House Consulting Rooms, Haigh Road, Waterloo, Liverpool L32 3XS Tel: 0151 257 6702 Fax: 01704 506056; Arya Niwas, 3 Skipton Avenue, Crossens, Southport PR9 8JP Tel: 01704 506056 Fax: 01704 506056 — MB BS 1965 Punjabi; FRCPsych 1985, M 1973; DPM Eng. 1973. (Govt. Med. Coll. Patiala) Cons. Psychiat. Pack Ho. Consg. Rooms. Socs: (Ex-Pres.) Liverp. Psychiat. Soc.; BMA (Ex-Pres. Sefton Div.). Prev: Cons. Psychiat. Greaves Hall Hosp.

ARYA, Renu Tameside General Hospital, Fountain St., Ashton-under-Lyne OL6 9RW Tel: 0161 331 5151 Email: renu.arya@exchange.tgcps-tr.nwest.nhs.uk; 6 Wensley Drive, Withington, Manchester M20 3DD — MB ChB 1987 Liverp.; FRCPCH 1998; MRCP (UK) 1991; DCH RCP Lond. 1991. Cons. Paediat. Tameside Gen. Hosp. Prev: Sen. Regist. Rotat. Manch.; Regist. (Paediat.) N. Staffs. Hosp. Centre Stoke-on-Trent.

ARYA, Rita 17 Haydock Park Gardens, Newton-le-Willows WA12 0JF Tel: 01942 718760 — MB ChB 1995 Manch.; MRCOG Part I 1998. (Manchester) Sen. SHO (O & G) Fairfield OGH, Bury. Prev: SHO (O & G) Hope Hosp. Salford; SHO (O & G) Wythenshawe Hosp. Manch.; SHO (O & G) St. Mary's Hosp. Manch.

ARYA, Roopen 19 Cavendish Drive, Marston, Oxford OX3 0SD — BM BCh 1986 Oxf.

ARYA, Sanjay Dept. of Cardiology, Manchester Royal Infirmary, Oxford Rd, Manchester M13 9WL Tel: 0161 276 1234; Plummers Cottage, Wythenshawe Hospital, South Moor Road, Manchester M23 9LT Tel: 0161 291 2677 Fax: 0161 291 2677 Email: sarya@compuserve.com — MB BS 1990 Magadh U; MRCP (UK) 1994. (Nalanda Medical College, Patna) Specialist Regist. (Cardiol.). Prev: Specialist Regist. (Cardiol.) Wythenshawe Hosp.; Specialist Regist. (Cardiol.) Vict. Hosp.

ARYA, Saroj Oxford Medical Centre, 406 Waterloo Road, Blackpool FY4 4BL Tel: 01253 764444 Fax: 01253 838552 — MB BS 1967 Panjab.

ARYA, Subhash Chandra Oxford Medical Centre, 406 Waterloo Road, Blackpool FY4 4BL Tel: 01253 764444 Fax: 01253 838552 — MB BS 1962 Punjab.

ARYA, Tarun 8 Bank Hill, Woodborough, Nottingham NG14 6EF — MB BChir 1994 Camb.

AS, Alok Kumar Department of Obstetrics & Gynaecology, Princess Anne Hospital, Coxford Road, Southampton SO16 5YA Tel: 02380 777222 Fax: 02380 794243; 3 Chapman Road, Stevenage SG1 4RJ Tel: 01438 216215 — MB BS 1977 Calcutta; MD Calcutta 1980; MRCOG 1991; Dip. NBE (New Delhi) 1984. Specialist Regist. (Obst. & Gynaecol.) P.ss Anne Hosp. Soton. Socs: BMA, Brit. Soc. Gynaecol. Endoscopy & Brit. Soc. Colposcopy & Cervical+Pathol. Prev: Clin. Lect. Hon. Sen. Regist. Rosie Matern. Hosp. Cambs.

AS'AD, Mr Sheharyar Mubarik 107C Dartmouth Road, London NW2 4ES — MB BS 1983 Lond.; FRCS Glas. 1992.

ASAAD, Issa Jennyfield Health Centre, Grantley Drive, Harrogate HG3 2XT Tel: 01423 524605 Fax: 01423 524605; The Cedars, 45 Ripon Road, Killinghall, Harrogate HG3 2DG Tel: 01423 884476 — MD 1968 Damascus. (Damascus) GP Harrogate. Prev: Regist. (Surg.) Harrogate Health Dist.; Mem. Brit. Soc. Gastroenterol.; Trainee GP Harrogate Hosps. VTS.

ASAAD, Kamal Asaad Botros — MB BCh 1978 Ain Shams; MRCOG 1988. Cons. O & G P. Chas. Hosp. Mid Glam. Socs: MDU; BMA; Welsh Soc. of OCG. Prev: Lect. (Hon. Sen. Regist.) O & G Dept. Univ. of Wales Coll. of Med. Cardiff.

ASAAD, Lillian Jennyfield Health Centre, Grantley Drive, Harrogate HG3 2XT Tel: 01423 524605 Fax: 01423 524605 — MD 1970 Damascus. Clin. Asst. Harrogate HA.

ASAAD, Naeim Michael Bungalow 3, Wexham Park Hospital, Slough SL2 4HL — MB ChB 1982 Alexandria. GP Regist. Wexham Pk. Hosp. Slough.

ASADULLAH, Hamida The Surgery, 221 High Street, Hornchurch RM10 9BA Tel: 01708 447747 Fax: 01708 451408 — MB BS 1963 Dacca.

ASADULLAH, Mohammad 2 Third Avenue, Dagenham RM10 9BA Tel: 020 8592 0346 Fax: 020 8984 8619; 2A Berther Road, Emerson Park, Hornchurch RM11 3HS Tel: 01708 479743 Fax: 020 8984 8619 — MB BS 1963 Dacca; DA Eng. 1976. Socs: BMA & Med. Protec. Soc.

ASAFU-ADJAYE, Derek Sarpong 74 Cotleigh Road, London NW6 2NP — MRCS Eng. LRCP Lond. 1977. (Univ. Coll. Hosp.)

ASAFU-ADJAYE, Henry Boaten 10 Malthus Path, Thamesmead, London SE28 8AJ Tel: 020 8310 6427 — MB ChB 1960 Liverp.; MRCS Eng. LRCP Lond. 1960.

ASAMOAH, Daniel Kwaku 4 Beechwood Lane, Culcheth, Warrington WA3 4HJ — MB ChB 1970 Ghana; FRCR 1976; DMRD Liverp. 1975. (Ghana Med. Sch.) Cons. Mersey RHA. Socs: Liverp. Med. Inst.; Brit. Inst. Radiol.

ASANTE, Maxwell Asiedu Department of Gastroenterology, Bromley Hospital, Cromwell Ave, Bromley BR2 9AJ Tel: 020 8289 7000 Fax: 020 8289 7155 Email: asantem@hotmail.com — MB ChB 1987 Ghana; PhD 1999 (Med) U. Lond.; BSc (Biochem.) U. Ghana 1982; MRCP (UK) 1991. (Univ. Ghana) Cons. Phys. and Gastroenterologist, Bromley Hosp., Kent. Socs: RCP; BMA; Brit. Soc. of Gastroenterol. Prev: Clin. Research Fell. (Gastroenterol.) & Regist. (Med.) St. Geo. Hosp. Med. Sch. Lond.; Sen. Regist. (Gen. Med. & Gastroenterol.) St. Geo. Hosp. Lond.; Sen. Regist. (Med & Gastroenterol.) Mayday Univ. Hosp, Croydon.

ASANTE-SIAW, Julius 203 Harrow View, Harrow HA1 4SS — BM BCh 1994 Oxf.

ASAR, Aliasghar Hasanali 102 Kings Drive, Mickleover, Derby DE3 5AW — MB BS 1979 Karachi; MRCPI 1989.

ASARIA, Riaz Hassan Yusuf 25 Dunston Road, London NW11 8AG — BM 1989 Soton.

ASBOE, David Chelsea & Westminster Hospital, 369 Fulham Road, London SW10 9TH Tel: 020 8746 8000 Fax: 020 8846 6198 Email: dasboe@crusaid-star.co.uk — MB ChB 1986 Otago; MRCP (UK) 1993.

ASBRIDGE, Gerald Stone Barrow, Dry Hill, Crockerton, Warminster BA12 8AT — MB ChB 1958 St. And.; DObst RCOG 1970. Prev: GP Trowbridge; Civil Med., Pract. to HM Forces Singapore & Germany; Ho. Surg. (Surg. & Obst.) Dundee Roy. Infirm.

ASBRIDGE, Martin Scott The Surgery, 2 Gregson Avenue, Gosport PO13 0HR Tel: 01329 232446 Fax: 01329 282624 — BM

BCh 1984 Oxf.; MA Oxf. 1986, BM BCh 1984. Trainee GP Bournemouth & Poole VTS.

ASBURY, Adrian John University Department of Anaesthesia, Western Infirmary, Dumbarton Road, Glasgow G11 6NT Tel: 0141 211 2698 — MB ChB 1971 Birm.; PhD Sheff. 1982; MD Sheff. 1995; FRCA 1975. (Birmingham) Reader & Hon. Cons. Anaesth. Glas. Univ. Socs: BMA & Assn. Anaesth. Prev: Sen. Regist. (Anaesth.) Qu. Eliz. Hosp. Birm.; Regist. (Anaesth.) Dudley Rd. Hosp. Birm.; Lect. (Anaesth.) Harari Centr. Hosp. Salisbury, Rhodesia.

ASBURY, David Leonard — MB ChB 1964 Ed.; DMRD 1969; FFR 1971. Cons. Radiol. Univ. Hosp. S. Manch.

ASBURY, Jolyon Frank Percy (retired) 145 Lydalls Road, Didcot OX11 7EA Tel: 01235 815583 — MB BS Lond. 1949; MRCGP 1963; DObst RCOG 1956. Prev: Princip. GP Didcot, Oxf.

ASBURY, Michael John 13 Holly Road N., Wilmslow SK9 1LX — MB BCh BAO 1969 Dub.; MRCP (U.K.) 1973. (TC Dub.) ICI Pharmaceut. Div., Alderley Pk., Macclesfield.

ASCROFT, Norman Osborne 5 Lovell Garth, Foxholes, Driffield YO25 3QP; Peake House, Southside, Kilham, Driffield YO25 4ST Tel: 01262 420170 — MB ChB 1948 Liverp.; MRCS Eng. LRCP Lond. 1948. Prev: RAF Med. Div.; Regist. Chest Med. Ipswich Sanat.

ASEN, Karl Michael 36 Lady Somerset Road, London NW5 1TU Tel: 020 7485 6451 — State Exam Med 1971 Berlin; MRCPsych 1978. Clin. Asst. MarlBoro. Hosp. Lond.

ASFOURY, Zakaria M 56 Ivanhoe Road, Camberwell, London SE5 Tel: 0207 274 6877 — MRCS Eng. LRCP Lond. 1949; MB BCh Cairo 1946; PhD Heliopolis & Georgia USA 1965; MSc Lond. 1952; BSc (Hons.) Cairo 1944. (Lond. Hosp. & Liverp.) Cons. Phys. Lond. Socs: Fell. Roy. Soc. Med.; Renal Assn.; Hunt. Soc. Prev: Cons. Phys. Schs. Hosp. & Coptic Hosp. Cairo, Egypt; Regist. (Med.) N. Middlx. Hosp. & St. Ann's Hosp. Lond.; Research Fell. & Hon. Demonst. Lond. Hosp.

***ASGARI-JIRHANDEH, Nima** St Thomas's Hospital, Lambeth Palace Rd, London SE1 7EH Tel: 020 7928 9292 Email: nimaasgari@cwcom.net — MB ChB 1996 Ed.; BMedSci Ed. 1994.

ASGHAR, Basharat 55 Millbrae Road, Langside, Glasgow G42 9UF — MB ChB 1996 Glas.

ASGHAR, Muhammad Maasum c/o Erne Hospital, Enniskillen BT74 6AY — MB BS 1975 Punjab, Pakistan; MRCPI 1993.

ASGHAR, Nasir Mahmood 19 Ravens Grove, Burnley BB10 2RD — MB ChB 1998 Birm.

ASGHAR, Ramzana B 4 Ormes Meadow, Owlthorpe, Sheffield S20 6TE — MB ChB 1994 Sheff.; MRCP. Specialist Registr. (Neph. & Gen. Med.) W. Midl. Rot. Prev: Specialist Regist. (Lat.): Neph. & Med., Leeds Gen. Infirm.; SHO, Oxf. Renal Unit; A&E Med & SHO, Rotherham Gen. Hosp.

ASH, Catherine Elizabeth Glebe House Surgery, Church Road, Saxilby, Lincoln LN1 2HJ Tel: 01522 702236 Fax: 01522 703132 — MB ChB 1991 Leic.

ASH, Daniel Victor 10 Oakwood Park, Leeds LS8 2PJ Tel: 0113 267 3411 — MB BS 1968 Lond.; FRCP Lond. 1992; MRCP (UK) 1971; MRCS Eng. LRCP Lond. 1968; FRCR 1976. Cons. Radiother & Oncol. Cookridge Hosp. Leeds.; Sen. Lect. Univ. Leeds. Socs: (Pres.) Brit. Oncol. Assn.

ASH, Elizabeth Caroline 118 Albert Road, Jarrow NE32 5AG Tel: 0191 489 7915 — MB BS 1983 Newc.; MRCGP 1987.

ASH, Graham Martin Scarisbrick Centre, West Lancashire NHS Trust, Ormskirk & District General Hospital, Ormskirk L39 2AZ Tel: 01695 57711 — MB ChB 1982 Manch.; Msc Psychiat. Manch. 1994, BSc (Hons.) Pharmacol. 1979; MRCP (UK) 1986; MRCPsych 1989. Cons. Gen. Psychiat. W. Lancs. NHS Trust; Co-ordinator NW Liason Psychiat. Interest GP. Socs: Roy. Coll. Phys. Edin.; Finchleian Med. Club. Prev: Sen. Regist. (Psychiat.) N. W.. RHA; Research Regist. (Psychiat.) Manch. Roy. Infirm.; Tutor (Psychiat.) Univ. Manch.

ASH, Helen Clare 59 Dale Road, Marple, Stockport SK6 6NF — MB ChB 1988 Leeds.

ASH, Isidore (retired) Tana, 28 Kingsmoor Rd, Harlow CM19 4HP Tel: 01279 427676 — MD 1938 Rome; MFCM 1974; DPH Lond. 1953. Prev: Dist. Community Phys. Harlow Health Dist.

ASH, Jane Victoria Oakfield, Alcester Road, Studley B80 7PD Tel: 01527 852985 — MB ChB 1995 Manch. SHO GP VTS Redditch Worcs. Prev: SHO (Med.) Nuneaton; SHO (Geriat.) Worthing W. Sussex; SHO (A & E) Worthing W. Sussex.

ASH, Stephen Adrian The Pasteur Suite, Ealing Hospital, Uxbridge Road, Southall UB1 3HW Tel: 020 8354 5454 Fax: 020 8354 5448 Email: aids_ealing@compuserve.com; 17 The Drive, Banstead SM7 1DF Fax: 01737 210491 Email: ash_elkss@compuserve.com — MB BS 1978 Lond.; BSc Lond. 1975; FRCP Lond. 1994; MRCP (UK) 1981. (St. Geo. Hosp. Med. Sch.) Cons. Phys. Ealing Hosp. Lond.; Sen. Lect. (Infec. Dis.) Roy. Postgrad. Med. Sch. Hammersmith Hosp. Lond.; Hon. Clin. Sen. Lect. St. Mary's Hosp. Med. Sch. Lond.; Dep. Clin. Tutor Brit. Postgrad. Med. Federat. Prev: Sen. Regist. St. Geo. Hosp. Lond.; Hon. Lect. St. Geo. Hosp. Med. Sch. Lond.; MRC Special Train. Fell.

ASH-MILES, Janice Angela Muller House, 7 Cotham Park, Bristol BS6 6DA — MB ChB 1998 Bristol.

ASHAR, Karin Nina The Ross Practice, Keats House, Bush Fair, Harlow CM18 6LY Tel: 01279 692747 Fax: 01279 692737 — MB ChB 1989 Manch.; MRCGP 1993; DRCOG 1992. Prev: Trainee GP/SHO (Med.) Birch Hill Hosp. Rochdale.

ASHAYE, Olakunle Adebisi Mental health Unit, St Margarets Hosp, Epping Email: oashaye@aol.com; 16 Sparrow Drive, Stevenage SG2 9FD — MB BS 1983 Ibadan; MRCPsych 1995; Fell GP Nigerian Post Grad Med Coll. Sen. Regist. (Adult/Old Age Psychiat.) Higher Psychiat. Train. Middlx./UCH Scheme. Prev: Regist. (Gen. Psychiat.) Char. Cross Train. Scheme; SHO (Gen. Psychiat.) Char. Cross Train. Scheme; Sen. Regist., Regist. & SHO (Gen. Pract.) Univ. Coll. Hosp. Ibadan, Nigeria.

ASHBEE, Christopher Richard Neville (retired) 164 Spixworth Road, Old Catton, Norwich NR6 7EH Tel: 01603 408984 — MB BS 1956 Lond.; DObst RCOG 1959. Prev: GP Norwich.

ASHBRIDGE, Kevan Bredon Hill Surgery, Main Road, Bredon, Tewkesbury GL20 7QN Tel: 01684 773444 Fax: 01684 772315; Halfway Cottage, Bredons Hardwicke, Tewkesbury GL20 7EE Tel: 01684 772452 — MB BS 1976 Lond.; DRCOG 1978. (Westm.) Prev: SHO (Obst.) Cheltenham Matern. Hosp.; Ho. Phys. Cheltenham Gen. Hosp.; Ho. Surg. W.m. Hosp.

ASHBROOKE, Avis Beatrice Frimley Park Hospital NHS Trust, Portsmouth Road, Frimley, Camberley GU16 7UJ Tel: 01276 604458 Fax: 01276 604457; Darby Green House, Stroud Lane, Blackwater, Camberley GU17 0BL Tel: 01252 861813 Email: avisashbrooke@doctors.org.uk — MB BS 1980 Lond.; FRCS 1984 Ed.; FRCS Ed. 1984. (King's Coll. Hosp.) Cons. Orthop. & Trauma Surg. Frimley Pk. Hosp.

ASHBURN, Ann Elizabeth Alexandra Manor Crescent Surgery, 7 Manor Crescent, Bursledon, Southampton SO31 8DQ Tel: 023 8040 4671 Fax: 023 8040 7417 — MB ChB 1976 Leeds; MRCGP 1981; MRCPsych. 1980. GP Bursledon; Clin. Asst. (Rheum.) Soton. Gen. Hosp. Prev: Sen. Regist. ColdE. Hosp. Hants.; Regist. (Psychiat.) Graylingwell & Knole Hosps.; Regist. (Psychiat.) Warlingham Pk. Hosp.

ASHBY, Amanda Fleur 32 Aldred Road, Sheffield S10 1PD Tel: 0114 268 5847 — MB ChB 1994 Sheff.

ASHBY, Mr Brian Sterry (retired) Keigwin, Mousehole, Penzance TR19 7TS Tel: 01736 731688 — MB BChir 1955 Camb.; MA Camb. 1965, MChir 1970; FRCS Eng. 1961. Hon. Cons. Surg. S.end Gen. Hosp. 1991. Prev: Cons. Surg. S.end Gen. Hosp.

ASHBY, Caroline Rosemary 29 The Avenue, Chichester PO19 4PX — MB BS 1996 Lond.; BSc 1993, MB BS Lond. 1996. (St. Geo. Hosp.) SHO O & G (GP trainee) Soton. Prev: SHO (c/o the Elderly) Worthing & S.lands Hosp. NHS Trust; Ho. Surg. St. Geo. Hosp.; SHO (Med/c/o the Elderly) Winch.

ASHBY, Christopher Philip Medical & Industrial Services Ltd., MIS House, 53-59 Seaside, Eastbourne BN22 7NE; Honeysuckle Cottage, Cinderford Lane, Cowbeech, Herstmonceux, Hailsham BN27 4HL Tel: 01323 833051 — MRCS Eng. LRCP Lond. 1969. (St. Bart.) Company Med. Adviser Med. & Indust. Servs. Ltd. E.bourne.

ASHBY, Clare Bethan 28 Linden Way, Ponteland, Newcastle upon Tyne NE20 9DP — MB ChB 1994 Leeds.

ASHBY, Damien Raphael Flat 2, Denham Lodge, 2 Westbury Road, London W5 2LF — MB BS 1998 Lond.; MB BS Lond 1998.

ASHBY, David Julian — MB BS 1994 Lond.; MRCGP 1999; BSc 1991; DRCOG 1997; DCH 1998. (Royal London Hosp.) GP Cathedral Med. Gp., Chichester.

ASHBY, Desmond William Ronald (retired) 4 Middleton Hall, Belford NE70 7LF — MRCS Eng. LRCP Lond. 1939; MD Lond.

1948, MB BS 1939; FRCP Lond. 1964, M 1941. Prev: Cons. Phys. & Clin. Tutor in Postgrad. Med. Gateshead AHA.

ASHBY, Edwin Charles The Sherburne Hospital, Broyle Road, Chichester PO19 4BE Tel: 01243 530600 Fax: 01243 532244; 29 The Avenue, Chichester PO19 4PX Tel: 01243 782294 Fax: 01243 782294 — MB BChir 1959 Camb.; MChir Camb. 1967; FRCS Eng. 1963; MRCS Eng. LRCP Lond. 1958. (Camb. & Westm.) Cons. Surg. King. Edwd. VII Hosp. Midhurst & Sherburne Hosp. Chichester. Socs: Fell. (Ex-Mem. Counc.) Assn. Surg.; Sen. Mem. BAUS. Prev: Cons. Surg. St. Richard's Hosp. Chichester; Sen. Regist. (Surg.) W.m. Hosp. Gp. & St. Mark's Hosp.; Former Examr. (Path.) Primary FRCS.

ASHBY, Gillian Helen Lee on Solent Health Centre, Manor Way, Lee-on-the-Solent PO13 9JG Tel: 023 9255 0220 — MB BS 1981 Lond.; MRCP (UK) 1985; MRCGP 1989; DCH RCP Lond. 1985. (St. Bart. Hosp. Lond.) Prev: Trainee GP Soton. VTS.

ASHBY, James Benedict Bothwell Gorley Vale Farm, Furze Hill, Fordingbridge SP6 2PX — MB BS 1987 Lond.; MRCGP 1992.

ASHBY, Jane Helen Alvaston Medical Centre, 14 Boulton Lane, Alvaston, Derby DE24 0GE Tel: 01332 571322 — MB BS 1988 Lond.; BSc (Hons.) Biochem. Soton. 1982; MRCGP 1995; DCH RCP Lond. 1991; DRCOG 1991. (St. Geo. Hosp. Med. Sch.) GP. Prev: Trainee GP Herne Bay; GP, Canterbury.

ASHBY, John McKinley 72 Hillmorton Road, Rugby CV22 5AF — MB ChB 1964 Ed.; MRCPsych 1974; DPM Eng. 1971.

ASHBY, Lesley Marion Bethel Child & Family Centre, Mary Chapman House, Hotblack Road, Norwich NR2 4HN Tel: 01603 421421 — MB BS 1981 Lond.; MRCPsych 1986. Cons. Child & Family Psychiat. Norwich DHA.

ASHBY, Martin 286 London Road, Slough SL3 7HT — MB BS 1994 Lond.; BSc (Hons.) Lond. 1991. SHO (c/o Elderly) Lond.

ASHBY, Michael Anthony 9 Durfold Drive, Reigate RH2 0QA Tel: 01737 44718 — MB BS 1978 Lond.; MRCP (UK) 1981; MRCS Eng. LRCP Lond. 1978; FRCR 1986. (St. Bart.) Asst. Inst. Curie, Paris, France. Socs: Fell. Roy. Soc. Med.; Brit. Oncol. Assn. & BMA. Prev: Lect. & Hon. Sen. Regist. Dept. Clin. Oncol. & Radiother. Univ. Camb. Sch. Clin. Med.; Fell. (Radiat. Oncol.) & Staff Specialist Peter MacCallum Cancer Inst. Melbourne, Australia; Regist. Radiotherap. & Oncol. Roy. Marsden Hosp. Lond.

ASHBY, Michael George Corbett (retired) Wickens, Birch Grove, Horsted Keynes, Haywards Heath RH17 7BT Tel: 01825 740264 — BM BCh 1941 Oxf.; MA, BM BCh Oxon. 1941; FRCP Lond. 1965, M. 1942. Prev: Hon. Cons. Neurol. Whittington Hosp. Regional Neurol. & Neurosurg.

ASHBY, Michael William 21 Tredegar Square, London E3 5AD — MB ChB 1978 Birm.; FFA RCS Eng. 1984. Cons. St. Barts. Hosp. Lond. Prev: Sen. Regist. Nuffield Dept. Anaesth. Oxf.; Vis. Asst. Prof. Dept. Anaesth. Univ. Maryland Baltimore USA; Regist. Nuffield Dept. Anaesth. Oxf.

ASHBY, Pamela Mary St Richard's Hospital, The Royal West Sussex Trust, Chichester PO19 4SE Tel: 01243 788122; Middlefield, The Avenue, Chichester PO19 4PX Tel: 01243 527661 — MB ChB 1964 Bristol. (Bristol) Clin. Asst. (Haemat.) St. Richard's Hosp. Chichester. Prev: Ho. Surg. Upton Hosp. Slough; Ho. Phys. Childr. Hosp. Sheff.

ASHBY, Peter Anthony The Bell Surgery, York Road, Henley-on-Thames RG9 2DR Tel: 01491 843250 Fax: 01491 411295; Cedarwood House, Nettlebed, Henley-on-Thames RG9 5AX Tel: 01491 843250 Fax: 01491 411295 — MB BS 1968 Lond.; DObst RCOG 1976. (St. Bart. Hosp. Lond.) Prev: Ho. Surg. St. Bart. Hosp. Lond.; Ho. Phys. Gen. Hosp. Rochford; Med. Off. RAMC.

ASHBY, Peter Hereward Newick Health Centre, Marbles Road, Newick, Lewes BN8 4LR Tel: 01825 722272 Fax: 01825 724391; Wickhurst, 29 Allington Road, Newick, Lewes BN8 4NB Tel: 01825 723604 — MB BS 1976 Lond.; DRCOG Lond. 1979. (Middlx.) Clin. Asst. (Gen. Surg.) Vict. Hosp. Lewes. Socs: Brighton & Sussex M-C Soc. Prev: Trainee GP Brighton VTS.

ASHBY, Mr Peter Hugh 51 Harley Street, London W1N 1DD Tel: 020 7580 6449 — MB ChB 1974 Birm.; FRCS Eng. 1982. Cosmetic Plastic Surg. Lond. Socs: Profess. Assoc. Brit. Assn. Plastic Surgs.; Amer. Acad. Cosmetic Surg. Prev: Regist. (Plastic Surg.) St. Geo. & St. Jas. Hosps. Roehampton; Regist. (Plastic Surg.) NW Durh. HA.; Regist. (Gen. Surg.) Groote Schuur Hosp., Capetown.

ASHBY, Peter Maxted The Surgery, 1-4 The High Parade, Streatham High Road, London SW16 1EX Tel: 020 8769 8753 Fax: 020 8769 8704; 8 Giles Coppice, Dulwich Wood Park, London SE19 1XF Tel: 020 8761 6144 Fax: 020 8761 6144 Email: peterm@doctors.net — MB BS 1960 Lond.; DObst RCOG 1963. (St. Bart.) Dir. of IT LSL Multifund; Chairm. LSL Multifund Ltd. Socs: Fell. Inst. Analysts & Progr.rs; Fell. Roy. Soc. Med. Prev: SHO (Surg.) & Ho. Phys. St. Bart. Hosp. Lond.; Ho. Off. (O & G) Lewisham Hosp.

ASHBY, Sheena Mary The Surgery, 24 Albert Road, Bexhill-on-Sea TN40 1DG Tel: 01424 730456/734430 Fax: 01424 225615; Peach Cottage, The Twitten, Bexhill-on-Sea TN39 4PJ — MB BS 1974 Lond.; MRCGP 1980; DRCOG 1978. (Lond. Hosp.)

ASHCROFT, Albert Edward (retired) Hillside, Helton, Penrith CA10 2QA Tel: 019312 517 — MB 1957 Camb.; BChir 1956; DObst RCOG 1958. Prev: Sen. Med. Off. W.ern Div. Med. Off. Birm.

ASHCROFT, Andrew John 13 Dorcas Avenue, Barrow-in-Furness LA13 9NB — BChir 1992 Camb. SHO Rotat. (Cardiol.) Leeds Gen. Infirm. Prev: Ho. Off. Addenbrooke's Hosp. Camb.; Ho. Off. Norwich.

ASHCROFT, Anthony (retired) 15 Avondale Court, Rectory Road, Newcastle upon Tyne NE3 1XQ Tel: 0191 285 6356 — MB BS 1947 Durh.; MD Durh. 1951; FRCGP 1982, M 1963. Prev: Lect. (Family Med.) Univ. Newc.

ASHCROFT, Christopher Nigel Norwood Medical Centre, 99 Abbey Road, Barrow-in-Furness LA14 5ES Tel: 01229 822024 Fax: 01229 823949; 37 Croslands Park, Barrow-in-Furness LA13 9NH Tel: 22505 — MB ChB 1959 Liverp. (Liverp.) Socs: BMA. Prev: Ho. Surg. & Ho. Phys. Liverp. Stanley Hosp.; Med. Off. Brit. Milit. Hosp. Nairobi.

ASHCROFT, David (retired) Bridgnorth Medical Practices, Northgate House, 7 High Street, Bridgnorth WV16 4BU Tel: 01746 767121 Fax: 01746 765433 — MB ChB Manch. 1960; DIH Soc. Apoth. Lond. 1967.

ASHCROFT, David Alexander 7 France Street, Redcar TS10 3HJ — MB ChB 1994 Ed.

ASHCROFT, Debbie Gail Cedar Lodge, Burgage Lane, Southwell NG25 0ER — MB ChB 1990 Sheff.

ASHCROFT, George Patrick 2 Fassiefern Avenue, Denmore Park, Bridge of Don, Aberdeen AB23 8BZ — MB ChB 1981 Manch.

ASHCROFT, Professor George Warburton 2 Fassiefern Avenue, Bridge of Don, Aberdeen AB23 8BZ Tel: 01224 702266 — MB ChB 1953 Manch.; DSc Manch. 1971, MB ChB 1953; FRCP Ed. 1968, M 1958; DPM Eng. 1959; DObst RCOG 1955; FRCPsych. (Manch.) Emerit. Prof. Ment. Health Univ. Aberd.

ASHCROFT, Gillian Sarah 3 Canal Bank, Appley Bridge, Wigan WN6 9AW — MB BChir 1989 Camb.

ASHCROFT, Joanne Lynne Fullarton Street Surgery, 24 Fullarton Street, Ayr KA7 1UB Tel: 01292 264260 Fax: 01292 283284; 11 Barns Terrace, Ayr KA7 2DB — MB ChB 1988 Glas.; MRCGP 1992; DFFP 1996. (Glasgow University)

ASHCROFT, John Stanley 108 Stevens Lane, Breaston, Derby DE72 3BW Tel: 01332 872508 — BM BS 1987 Nottm.; BMedSci Nottm. 1985, BM BS 1987; MRCGP 1993.

ASHCROFT, Keith (retired) Gorsehill, Hafodty Lane, Upper Colwyn Bay, Colwyn Bay LL28 5YN Tel: 01492 532900 — MB BS 1954 Lond.; DMRD Eng. 1957. Prev: Cons. Radiol. Glan Clwyd Hosp.

ASHCROFT, Linda Park West Meetings, Milton Road, Windygates, Leven KY8 5DF — MB ChB 1995 Manch.

ASHCROFT, Margaret Mary The Landscape Surgery, High Street, Garstang, Preston PR3 1FA Tel: 01995 603355 Fax: 01995 601810; Landscape, High St, Garstang, Preston PR3 1FA Tel: 01995 3355 — MB ChB 1980 Manch.; DRCOG 1983. Socs: BMA. Prev: Trainee GP Preston VTS; Ho. Off. (Surg. & Med.) Preston HA.

ASHCROFT, Mary Elizabeth Public Health Laboratory, Heartlands Hospital, Bordesley Green, Birmingham B9 5SS; 12 Imperial Avenue, Kidderminster DY10 2RA — MB BS 1994 Lond. (Lond. Hosp. Med. Coll.) Regist. (Virol.) Birm. Heartlands Hosp.

ASHCROFT, Michael Walker Yew Tree Cottage, Compton St., Compton, Winchester SO21 2AT Tel: 01962 715500 — MB BS 1995 Lond.; BSc (Path.) Lond. 1992; MRCS Core Modules Paper. (Roy. Free Hosp. Sch. Med.) SHO Rotat. (Orthop.) Salisbury Dist. Hosp. Prev: SHO (A & E) N.wick Pk. Hosp.; Ho. Off. (Med.) Derriford Hosp. Plymouth; Anat. Demonst. UMDS Guys Hosp.

ASHCROFT, Mr Peter Blair Yew Tree Cottage, Compton St., Winchester SO21 2AT — MB BS 1967 Lond.; FRCS Eng. 1973; MRCS Eng. LRCP Lond. 1966; Specialist Accredit. (Orl.) RCS Eng.

1977. (Guy's) Cons. ENT Surg. Roy. Hants. Co. Hosp. Winchester; Cons. Otol. MRC Inst. Hearing Research Soton.; Cons. Otol. S. Eng. Cochlear Implant Centre, Soton. Socs: Fell. Roy. Soc. Med. Prev: Sen. Regist. (ENT) Guy's Hosp. Lond.; Asst. Prof. Dept. Otolaryngol. Univ. Washington Seattle, USA; Sen. Regist. Roy. Nat. Throat, Nose & Ear Hosp. Lond.

ASHCROFT, Thomas (retired) 10 Mitchell Avenue, Jesmond, Newcastle upon Tyne NE2 3LA Tel: 0191 281 2745 — MB ChB Aberd. 1957; MD Aberd. 1971; FRCPath 1984, M 1972. Prev: Cons. Path. Freeman Hosp. Newc.

ASHDOWN, Andrew Charles 155 Cholmley Gardens, London NW6 1AD — MB BS 1994 Lond.

ASHE, Antony Granville Rowse 51 Sloane Street, London SW1X 9SW Tel: 020 7235 5151 Fax: 020 7259 5409; 13 Anhalt Road, Battersea, London SW11 4NZ Tel: 020 7223 3577 Fax: 020 7228 2124 — MB BS 1979 Lond.; Cert. Family Plann. JCC 1984. (St. Thos.) Socs: Brit. Soc. Allergy, Environm. & Nutrit. Med.; Sloane Soc.; St. Albans Med. Club. Prev: Regist. (Surg.) Roy. Masonic Hosp. Lond.; SHO (Cas. & Orthop.) Qu. Eliz. Hosp. Barbados; Ho. Surg. (Orthop.) St. Thos. Hosp. Lond.

ASHE, Edward Samuel Armstrong 12 Southbourne Road, Sheffield S10 2QN — LM 1934 Rotunda; MA, MB BCh BAO Dub. 1933. (T.C. Dub.) Prev: Resid. Med. Off. Walton Hosp. Liverp.; Ships Surg. Blue Funnel Line; Lt.-Col. RAMC.

ASHE, Mr Norman Desmond (retired) 38 Drax Avenue, Wimbledon, London SW20 0EJ Tel: 020 8946 5554 — BM BCh 1945 Oxf.; MA, BM BCh Oxf. 1945; FRCS Eng. 1953. Prev: Ho. Surg. Radcliffe Infirm. Oxf. & Hammersmith Hosp.

ASHE, Philip John St Georges Surgery, 46A Preston New Road, Blackburn BB2 6AH Tel: 01254 53791 Fax: 01254 697221; Spring Bank Cottage, Lovely Hall Lane, Salesbury, Blackburn BB1 9EQ — MB ChB 1986 Manch.; MRCGP 1990.

ASHE, Robert George Antrim Hospital, 45 Bush Road, Antrim BT41 2RL; 2 Ben Madigan Park, Upper Antrim Road, Newtownabbey BT36 7PZ Tel: 01232 775206 Email: robinashe@dnet.co.uk — MB BCh BAO 1976 Dub.; MAO Dub. 1993; MRCOG 1983; DRCOG 1979; DCH RCPSI 1979. (Dub) Cons. O & G Antrim Area Hosp. Socs: Chairmain Obstretics & Gyn. Urol. Soc.; Exec. Counc. Inst. Obst. & Gyn. RCPI; Ulster Obst. & Gyn. Soc. Prev: Sen. Tutor Roy. Matern. Hosp. Belf.

ASHELFORD, David John 18 Farrar Lane, Leeds LS16 7AA Tel: 0113 267 7196 — MB ChB 1961 Leeds. Prev: Ho. Phys. Gen. Infirm. Leeds.

ASHENHURST, Elma Margaret Waterside Health Centre, Glendermott Road, Londonderry BT47 6AU Tel: 028 7132 0100 Fax: 028 7132 0117 — MB BCh BAO 1978 Belf.; MRCGP 1982; DCH Dub. 1981; DRCOG 1980.

ASHER, Janaksinh Navnitdas 279 Ashgate Road, Chesterfield S40 4DB — MB BS 1961 Bombay; MRCP Glas. 1968.

ASHER, Peter Neville 94 Holloway Road, London N7 8JG Tel: 020 7607 2323 — MB BCh 1949 Witwatersrand. Clin. Asst. Dept. Gyn. Barking Hosp.

ASHER, Robert Uxbridge Health Centre, George St., Uxbridge UB8 1UB Tel: 01895 231925 Fax: 01895 813190; 72 Yeldham Road, London W6 8JG Tel: 020 8748 2239 Fax: 020 8741 5671 Email: robertasher@easynet.co.uk — MB BS 1980 Lond.; MA Camb. 1972, BA (Mechanical Scs.) 1969; Cert. Family Plann. JCC 1985. Socs: Fell. Med. Soc. Lond. Prev: SHO (Cas. & Ophth.) & Demonst. (Anat.) Middlx. Hosp. Lond.; SHO (Gyn.) Glas. Roy. Infirm.; SHO (Obst.) Wexham Pk. Hosp. Slough.

ASHER, Ruth Grace 5 Hillside Road, Mossley Hill, Liverpool L18 2ED — MB ChB 1997 Liverp.

ASHERSON, Geoffrey Lister (retired) 8 Wigmore Place, London W1U 2LR Tel: 020 7580 3197 Fax: 020 7580 3197 Email: glasherson@cs.com — BM BCh Oxf. 1953; MSc CNAA 1984; MA Oxf. 1953, BA 1951; DM Oxf. 1963; FRCP Lond. 1973, M 1957; FRCP Ed. 1971, M 1956; FRCPath 1973, M 1964; DCH Eng. 1957. Brit. Coordinator John Humphrey Advanced Summer Schs. in Immunol., Russia. Prev: Head Div. Immunol. Med. Clin. Research Centre & Hon. Cons. Immunol. N.wick Pk. Hosps.

ASHERSON, Philip John Elliot SGDP, Institute of Psychiatry, De Crespigny Park, London SE4 8AF Tel: 020 7919 3873 Fax: 020 7919 3407 Email: p.asherson@iop.t.cd.ac.uk; Hazeldene, Highgate Road, Forest Row RH18 5AZ Tel: 01342 824337 Email: p.asherson@iop.bpmf.ac.uk — MB BS 1984 Lond.; MRCPsych 1988; Phd Wales 1998. (The Royal London Hospital) Sen. Lect. (Molecular Psychiat.) Social Genetic & Developm. Psychiat. Research Centre (SGDP) Lond. Prev: MRC Train. Fell. Psychol. Med. Univ. of Wales Coll. of Med.

ASHFAQ, Imran 122 Viewforth, Edinburgh EH10 4LN — MB ChB 1996 Dundee.

ASHFIELD, Richard Pengelley (retired) 15 Herringston Road, Dorchester DT1 2BS Tel: 01305 264434 Fax: 01305 264434 — MB BS 1955 Lond.; FRCP Lond. 1977, M 1961; MRCS Eng. LRCP Lond. 1957. Prev: Cons. Phys. W. Dorset HA.

ASHFORD, Andrew Livingstone Limes Medical Centre, The Plain, Epping CM16 6TL Tel: 01992 572727 Fax: 01992 574889; Oaks & Bushes, Sawbridgeworth Road, Little Hallingbury, Bishop's Stortford CM22 7QU — MB BS 1981 Lond.; MA Camb. 1982; MRCGP 1985; DRCOG 1984.

ASHFORD, Anthony Charles Copping Manor Road Surgery, 33 Manor Road, Caddington, Luton LU1 4EE Tel: 01582 25673 Fax: 01582 726672; Christmas Cottage, Pipers Lane, Aley Green, Luton LU1 4DS — MB BChir 1982 Camb.; MA Camb. 1982, MB BChir 1982; MRCGP 1986. GP Luton. Prev: Trainee GP Luton & Dunstable Hosp. VTS.; Med. Rotat. Roy. Cornw. Hosp. Treliske.

ASHFORD, Neil Philip Nicholas Norfolk Mental Health Care NHS Trust, Julian Hospital, Bowthrorpe Road, Norwich NR2 3TD Tel: 01603 421421 Fax: 01603 421831 — BM BCh 1984 Oxf.; MRCPsych. 1991; MA (Contab) 1985; BA (Cantab) 1981; Dip HSc U.E.A. 2000. (Camb. Oxf.) Staff Grade Psychiat. Of Old Age Norwich.

ASHFORD, Nicholas Stephen Department Radiology, St Richards Hospital, Chichester PO19 4SE Tel: 01243 788122; 10 Church Lane, Funtington, Chichester PO18 9LH Tel: 01243 575585 — MB BS 1976 Lond.; BSc (1st cl. Hons.) (Anat.) Lond. 1973, MB BS 1976; FRCR 1985. (Univ. Coll. Hosp.) Cons. Radiol. St. Richard's Hosp. Chichester.; Cons. Radiol. King Edwd. VII Hosp. Midhurst; Cons. Radiol. Sherburne Hosp. Chichester. Socs: Brit. Soc. Interven.al Radiologist; Brit. Nuclear Med. Soc.; Brit. Paediat. Radiol. & Imaging GP. Prev: Sen. Regist. (Diag. Radiol.) Addenbrookes Hosp. Camb.

ASHFORD, Peter Manchester Children's Hospitals, Hospital Rd, Pendlebury, Manchester M27 4; 3 Valley Road, Cheadle SK8 1HY Fax: 0161 291 1929 Email: peter@ashfordnet.com — MB ChB 1975 Manch.; FFA RCS Eng. 1979. (Manchester) Cons. Paediat. Anaesth. Manch. Childr. Hosps.; Cons. Anaesth. N. Manch. Gen. Hosp. Socs: SCATA (Comm. Mem.); Manch. Med. Soc. Comm.; Assn. of Paediatric Anaesth.s. Prev: Cons. Intensivist, Manch. Childr.'s Hosp.; Cons. Anaesth., N.M. G. Hosp.

ASHFORD, Peter David Bell Lane Surgery, 22 Bell Lane, Kesgrave, Ipswich IP5 1JF Tel: 01473 624800 Fax: 01473 612269; Chevington House, Melton, Woodbridge IP12 1PX Tel: 01394 383190 — MB BS 1968 Lond.; MRCS Eng. LRCP Lond. 1968. (Guy's) Socs: BMA; Ipswich Clin. Soc. Prev: SHO (A & E) St. Geo. Hosp. Lond.; Ho. Phys. St. Stephen's Hosp. Chelsea; Ho. Surg. (O & G) St. Mary Abbots Hosp. Lond.

ASHFORD, Richard Francis Urquhart Mount Vernon Centre For Cancer Treatment, Mount Vernon Hospital, Northwood HA6 2RN Tel: 01923 844323 Fax: 01923 844138 — MB BChir 1971 Camb.; MA Camb. 1972; MRCP (UK) 1975; FRCR 1983; DMRT 1981. (St. Thos.) Cons. Radiother. & Oncol. Mt. Vernon Hosp. N.wood. Socs: Brit. Oncological Assn.; Brit Assn. Surg. Oncol. Prev: Sen. Regist. (Radiother.) W.m. Hosp. Lond.; Lect. (Therap.) W.m. Hosp. Lond.

ASHFORD, Richard Paul 29 Keele Road, Newcastle ST5 2JT — MB BS 1992 Newc.; DRCOG 1995; MRCGP 1996. Socs: Roy. Coll. Gen. Pract.

ASHFORD, Robert Urquhart Sheffield Metabolism Bone Unit, University of Sheffield Medical School, Beech Hill Road, Sheffield S10 2RX Tel: 0114 271 1725 Fax: 0114 273 9176 Email: r.u.ashford@sheffield.ac.uk; 23 Fernside Road, Bournemouth BH9 2LB Email: robert.ashford@virgin.net — MB BS 1992 Lond. (LHMC) Clin. Research Fell., WHO Bone Metab. Unit, Univ. of Sheff.

ASHFORD-BROWN, William Hay (retired) The Old Vicarage, Marden, Devizes SN10 2LA Tel: 01380 84207 — MB ChB 1939 Glas.; BSc 1936, MB ChB Glas. 1939.

ASHFORD-HODGES, Mr William Anthony Herons Reach, Herringfleet Road, St Olaves, Great Yarmouth NR31 9HW — MB BChir 1946 Camb.; FRCS Eng. 1950; MRCS Eng. LRCP Lond. 1944.

ASHFORTH, Marion Muriel (retired) 1C Clovelly, Blackwater Road, Eastbourne BN21 4JQ Tel: 01323 727205 — MB BS 1948 Lond.; MRCS Eng. LRCP Lond. 1948; DCH Eng. 1952. Prev: SCMO (Community Child Health/Community Health) E.bourne HA.

ASHKAN, Keyoumars Department of Neurosurgery, Hurstwood Park Neurological Centre, Haywards Heath RH16 4EX — MB BCh 1993 Wales.

ASHKEN, Iris Constance (retired) Tasburgh House, Tasburgh, Norwich NR15 1NS — MB BS Lond. 1956; BSc (Hons.) Lond. 1953; BA (Hons.) E. Anglia 1988; MRCS Eng. LRCP Lond. 1956. Clin Asst. (Family Plann.) Matern. Dept. Norf. & Norwich Hosp. Prev: SCMO Norf. AHA.

ASHKEN, Julia Vera Little Bullington, Sutton Scotney, Winchester SO21 3QQ Tel: 01962 760233 Email: juliavt@globalnet.co.uk — MB ChB 1977 Manch.; BSc Open 1995. (Manch.) Clin. Med. Off. Family Plann. Hants. Prev: GP Hants.; Clin. Audit Asst. W. Hants. HA.

ASHKEN, Mr Michael Ralph Handley Tasburgh House, Tasburgh, Norwich NR15 1NS Tel: 01508 470456 Fax: 01508 471902 Email: miris@gn.apc.org — MB BS 1955 Lond.; BSc (Physiol.) Lond. 1952, MS 1967; FRCS Eng. 1959; MRCS Eng. LRCP Lond. 1955. (Middlx.) Hon. Cons. Urol. Norf. & Norwich Hosp.; Examr. FRCS Eng.; Examr. Intercoll. (Urol.) FRCS. Socs: Fell. Roy. Soc. Med. (Pres. Urol. Sect. 1990-91); (Ex-Pres. 1994-96) Brit. Assn. Urol. Surgs.; RCS Eng. (Invited Counc. 1993-96). Prev: Sen. Regist. (Surg.) Middlx. Hosp. Lond.; Asst. Path. Bland Sutton Inst. Path Middlx. Hosp. Lond.; Act. Maj. RAMC (Nat. Serv.).

ASHLEIGH, Mr Raymond Joel Department of Diagnostic Radiology, Wythenshawe Hospital, South Manchester University Hospitals Trust, Southmoor Road,Wythenshawe, Manchester M23 9LT Tel: 0161 291 6239 Fax: 0161 291 6201 Email: Ray.ashleigh@smuht.nwest.nhs.uk; Email: ray@radiologist.net — MB BS 1980 Lond.; BSc (1st cl. Hons.) Anat. Lond. 1977; FRCS Ed. 1985; FRCR 1988. (Univ. Coll. Hosp.) Cons. Vasc. Radiol S. Manch. Univ. Hosp. NHS Trust; Hon. Clin. Lect. in Radiol., Univ. of Manch.

ASHLEY, Angus McAlpine Drymen Road Surgery, 160 Drymen Road, Bearsden, Glasgow G61 3RD Tel: 0141 942 6644; 7 Lochend Road, Bearsden, Glasgow G61 1DX Tel: 0141 942 6644 Email: ashley@cgm.co.uk — MB ChB 1961 Glas.; MRCGP 1974; DObst RCOG 1963. Prev: Assoc. Specialist (Cytol.) Vale of Leven Hosp. Alexandria; Ho. Phys. Belvidere Hosp. Glas.; Ho. Surg. S.. Gen. Hosp. Glas.

ASHLEY, Barbara Dawn James Cook University Hospital, Middlesbrough; Email: dawn@dawnashley.demon.co.uk — BM BS 1995 Nottm.; BMedSci Nottm. 1993; MRCP 1998. (Nottm.) SPR Gastroentrology, Newc. Upon Tyne. Prev: Jun. Ho. Off. (Med.) Derby City Gen. Hosp.; SHO (Med.) Derby City Gen. Hosp.; Jun. Ho. Off. (Surg.) Qus. Med. Centre Nottm.

ASHLEY, Beatrice Kate 4 Newburn Road, Newcastle upon Tyne NE15 8LX Tel: 0191 229 0090 Fax: 0191 267 4830 — MB BS 1981 Newcastle; MB BS Newc. 1981. (Newcastle) GP Newc.

ASHLEY, David Arthur (retired) (Surgery) Walnut Lodge, Walnut Road, Chelston, Torquay TQ2 6HP Tel: 01803 605359 Fax: 01803 605772 — MRCS Eng. LRCP Lond. 1970; MRCGP 1977; DObst RCOG 1975. Prev: Squadron Ldr. RAF Med. Br.

ASHLEY, Deborah Louise 31 Westbury Drive, Macclesfield SK11 8LR — MB ChB 1992 Manch. Trainee GP/SHO Stockport VTS.

ASHLEY, Edwin Raymond William Wareham Health Centre, Streche Road, Wareham BH20 4PG Tel: 01929 553444 Fax: 01929 550703 — MB BS 1959 Lond. (St. Thos.) Socs: BMA. Prev: Regist. (Surg.) Gen. Hosp. Jersey; Ho. Surg. (Ophth.) & Jun. Res. (Anaesth.) St. Thos. Hosp. Lond.

ASHLEY, Elizabeth Anne 62 Fitzjames Avenue, Croydon CR0 5DD Tel: 020 8654 2456 — MB BS 1994 Lond.; BSc (Hons.) Lond. 1991; MRCP (UK) 1997. (UMDS) SHO (Neurol.) St. Jas. Univ. Hosp. Leeds. Prev: SHO Cardiol. St. Mary's Hosp. Lond.; SHO Renal St. Mary's Hosp. Lond.; Ho. Surg. St. Thos. Hosp. Lond.

ASHLEY, Elizabeth Joan High Street Surgery, 26 High Street, Wanstead, London E11 2AQ Tel: 020 8989 0407 Fax: 020 8518 8435 — MB BCh 1984 Wales; BSc 1991 (Hons. Physiol.) Wales; DRCOG 1988; DCH RCP Lond. 1986. GP. Prev: SHO (O & G) P.ss Alexandra Hosp. Harlow; SHO (A & E) Centr. Middlx. Hosp. Lond.; SHO (Med. & Geriat.) St. Margt. Hosp. Epping.

ASHLEY, Elizabeth Mary Christine King's College Hospital, Denmark Hill, London SE5 9RS Tel: 020 7737 4000; 19 Mustard Road, London W6 8NR — MB ChB 1990 Birm.; BSc (Hons.) Birm. 1986; FRCA 1994; DA (UK) 1991. (Birm.) Cons. (Anaesth.) King's Coll. Hosp. Lond. Socs: BMA; Assn. Anaesth.; Roy. Soc. Med. Prev: Sen. Regist. (Anaesth.) Gt. Ormond St. Hosp. & St. Geo.s Hosp.; Regist. (Anaesth.) Middlx. & Roy. Free Hosp. Lond.; Regist. (Anaesth.) Flinders Hosp. Adelaide, S. Australia.

ASHLEY, Euan Angus 7 Lochend Road, Bearsden, Glasgow G61 1DX — MB ChB 1996 Glas.

ASHLEY, Joan (retired) 23 Northumberland Road, Leamington Spa CV32 6HE Tel: 01926 426854 — MB ChB Bristol 1950; DCH Eng. 1953. Prev: SCMO Coventry HA.

ASHLEY, John Selwyn Alford 157 Jersey Road, Osterley, Isleworth TW7 4QJ Tel: 020 8572 0067 — MB ChB 1957 Bristol; FFCM 1977, M 1974. Sen. Research Fell. & Hon. Sen. Lect. Med. Care Lond. Sch. Hyg. & Trop. Med. Prev: Mem. Scientif. Staff Social Med. Research Unit Med. Research Counc.; Jun. Hosp. Med. Off. Manor Pk. Hosp. Bristol; Ho. Surg. & Dermat. Ho. Phys. Bristol Roy. Infirm.

ASHLEY, Jonathan Robert Department of Anaesthesia, Field House, Bradford Royal Infirmary, Bradford BD9 6RJ Tel: 01274 542200; 38B Cornmill Lane, Liversedge WF15 7DZ Tel: 01924 412692 — MB ChB 1990 Leeds. SHO (Anaesth.) Bradford Hosp. NHS Trust. Prev: Ho. Off. (Med.) Calderdale HA.

ASHLEY, Keith Francis, OBE, Group Capt. RAF Dent. Br. Retd. (retired) Vineyard Croft, 36 Hampton Park Road, Hereford HR1 1TH — MRCS Eng. LRCP Lond. 1975; 1958 BDS, LDS Manc.; 1968 FDS RCS Ed.; 1969 FDS RCS Eng.; 1985 FRCS Ed. Private Pract. in Oral and Maxillofacial Surg. and Oral Med. at home address and Wye Valley Nuffield Hosp. Hereford. Prev: Cons. Oral Surg. Hereford Co. Hosp.

ASHLEY, Martin Hugh 12 Cambrian Close, York Hill, West Norwood, London SE27 0BS Tel: 020 8670 2803 — MB BS 1978 Lond.; MRCS Eng. LRCP Lond. 1978; FFA RCS Eng. 1983.

ASHLEY, Philippa Mary 12 Cambrian Close, York Hill, West Norwood, London SE27 0BS Tel: 020 8670 2803 — MB BS 1978 Lond.; DCH Eng. 1980; DRCOG 1980; MRCGP 1982.

ASHLEY, Richard Hollis Department of Biochemistry, University of Edinburgh, George Square, Edinburgh EH8 9XD — MB BS 1975 Lond.; PhD Lond. 1984; MSc (Distinc.) Neurochem. Lond. 1978, MB BS 1975; MRCP (UK) 1980. (St. Thos.)

ASHLEY, Mr Simon Derriford Hospital, Derriford Road, Plymouth PL6 8DH Tel: 01752 792155 Fax: 01752 792537 Email: simona.ashley@phnt.swest.nhs.uk; Email: as@vascular.co.uk — BM 1983 Soton.; MS Soton. 1992; FRCS Eng. 1987. Cons. Vasc. Surg. Derriford Hosp. Plymouth; RCS Inc. New York Trav. Fell. 1992. Socs: Vasc. Surg. Soc. GB & Irel.; Eur. Soc. Vasc. Surg. Prev: Sen. Regist. (Gen. Surg.) St. Jas. Univ. Hosp. Leeds.

ASHLEY, Stephen David The Hull Nurfield Hospital, Enterance 3, Castle Hill Hospital, Cartle Road, Cottingham HU12 8JR Tel: 01482 623500 Fax: 01482 623510 Email: lynn.kilkenny@nuffieldhospitals.org.uk; Souttergate House, 59 Souttergate, Hedon, Hull HU12 8JR Email: stephen.ashley@dial.pipex.com — MB ChB 1976 Manch.; MIOSH 2001; BSc (Hons.) St. And. 1973; AFOM RCP Lond. 1988; MFPM 1989; Dip. Pharm. Med. RCP(UK) 1981. Occupat. Health Phys. & Cons. Pharmaceut. Med. Hull. Socs: Fell. Roy. Soc. Med.; Med. Defence Union; Soc. Occupat. Med. Prev: Tutor Med., Salford; Med. Advis. Reckitt & Colman; Med. Advis. & Occupat. Phys. Smith & Nephew.

ASHLEY-MILLER, Michael, CBE (retired) 28 Fitzwarren Gardens, Highgate, London N19 3TP Tel: 020 7272 7017 — BM BCh Oxf. 1955; MA Oxf. 1959; FRCP Lond. 1990; FRCP Ed. 1985; MRCP (UK) 1986; FFCM 1977, M 1973; Hon. FRCGP 1994; DPH Lond. 1962; DObst RCOG 1957. Research Fell. Brookes Univ. Oxf. Prev: Sec. Nuffield Provin. Hosps. Trust Lond.

ASHMAN, Anthony George 10 Blackthorn Road, Welwyn Garden City AL7 3JS — MB BS 1981 Lond.

ASHMAN, Eric (retired) Domus, 95 New St., Ash, Canterbury CT3 2BW — MRCS Eng. LRCP Lond. 1935. Prev: Cons. Phys. (Chest Dis.) Plymouth Chest Clinic.

ASHMAN, Lorraine Mary Lynfield Mount Hospital, Daisy Hill, Bradford BD12 9NS — MB ChB 1987 Sheff.; MRCPsych 1997; MMedSci Clin Psych 1998.

ASHMAN, Roger Wells Health Centre, Glastonbury Road, Wells BA5 1XJ Tel: 01749 672137 Fax: 01749 679833 Email: roger.ashman@wellshc.nhs.uk; Gollege, Pen Hill, Wells BA5 3EJ Tel: 01749 675411 Email: roger.ashman@ukgateway.net — MB BS 1972 Lond.; MRCS Eng. LRCP Lond. 1972; DA Eng. 1978; DObst RCOG 1976. (Guy's) Princip. in Gen. Pract. Socs: Roy. Soc. Med.

ASHMAN, Stanley Gabriel (retired) 29 Hadrian Court, Darras Hall, Ponteland, Newcastle upon Tyne NE20 9JU Tel: 01661 824866 Fax: 01661 824866 — MRCS Eng. LRCP Lond. 1959. Prev: Ho. Phys. & Ho. Surg. Memor. Hosp. Darlington.

ASHMAN, Virginia Frances 6 Morland Avenue, Leicester LE2 2PE — MB ChB 1991 Leic.

ASHMEAD, Jennifer Dawn Caledonia House, Department of Child Adolescent Psychiatry, Royal Hospital for Sick Children, Yorkhill NHS Trust, Glasgow G3 8SJ — MB ChB 1988 Glas.; MRCPsych. Cons. Child Psychiat., Kt.swood Clinic, Yorkhill NHS Trust.

ASHMORE, Alexander Maurice 20 Brighton Place, Portobello, Edinburgh EH15 1LJ Tel: 0131 669 8007 — MB ChB 1998 Bristol; BSc Bristol 1995.

ASHMORE, Gordon Timothy Woodmans Cottage Farm, Onesmoor Road, High Bradfield, Sheffield S6 6LJ — MB ChB 1964 Sheff. (Sheff.) Hon. Clin. Teach. in Gen. Pract. Univ. Sheff.; Clin. Asst. (Geriat.) St. Geo. Hosp. Sheff.; Clin. Asst. (Psychiat.) St. Josephs Hosp. Sheff. Socs: BMA. Prev: Ho. Phys. City Gen. Hosp. Sheff.; Ho. Surg. Sheff. Roy. Infirm; Sen. Med. Off. Mafeteng Hosp., Lesotho.

ASHMORE, Michael William Clarendon Lodge Medical Practice, 16 Clarendon Street, Leamington Spa CV32 5SS Tel: 01926 422094 Fax: 01926 331400 — MRCS Eng. LRCP Lond. 1969; MB Camb. 1970, BChir 1969; DObst RCOG 1972. (Camb. & Birm.)

ASHOK KUMAR, Janardhanan Mohan Flat 10 Roby House, Broadgreen Hospital, Thomas Drive, Liverpool L14 3LB — MB BS 1975 Kerala, India; MRCP (UK) 1993.

ASHOK KUMAR, Tirunelveli Lakshmanaswamy Highwoods Square Surgery, Highwoods Square, Colchester CO4 4SR Tel: 01206 752010 Fax: 01206 843280; Tel: 01206 231451 — MB BS 1976 Madras; LRCP LRCS Ed. LRCPS Glas. 1982. Clin. Asst. Learning Disabil. Med. for Elderly. Socs: Med. Defence Union.

ASHOUR, Fatma Aly Abd El-Magid 3 Repton Avenue, Sudbury, Wembley HA0 3BX Tel: 020 8902 4900 — MB ChB 1979 Alexandria.

ASHOUR, Mr Hamdy Yousef Hafez Queen Elizabeth Hospital, Sheriff Hill, Gateshead NE9 6SX Tel: 0191 487 8989; 28 The Rise, Darras Hall, Ponteland, Newcastle upon Tyne NE20 9LH Tel: 01661 821855 Email: h.ashour@virgin.net — MB ChB 1982 Ain Shams; FRCS Ed. 1990. Cons. Gen. & Vasc. Surg. Qu. Eliz. Hosp. Gateshead. Socs: BMA; MDU; Vasc. Soc. GB & N.. Irel.

ASHPOLE, Emma Jane Oaks Medical Centre, Villa St., Beeston, Nottingham NG9 2NY — MB ChB 1989 Bristol; MRCGP 1994; T(GP) 1995; DA (UK) 1993. GP Retainer Beeston. Prev: Staff Grade (c/o Elderly) Lings Bar Hosp. Nottm.; Regist. (Med.) N.W. Hosp. Melb., Austral.; Trainee GP N.d. VTS.

ASHPOLE, Keri Jane West Wing, Osmore Mill Farm House, The Schwyll, Ogmore-by-Sea, Bridgend CF32 0QP — MB BS 1996 Lond.

ASHPOLE, Mr Richard David Department of Neurosurgery, Queens Medical Centre, Nottingham NG7 2UH Tel: 0115 970 9075 Fax: 0115 970 9075 Email: www.neurosurgeon.co.uk — MB BS 1984 Lond.; BSc (Hons.) Neurosci. Lond. 1981; FRCS (SN) 1994; FRCS Eng. 1988. (St. Thos.) Cons. Neurosurg. Qu. Med. Centre Nottm. Socs: Soc. Brit. Neurosurg.; Soc. Research into Hydrocephalus & Spina Bifida; Internat. Soc. Neurosurg. Instrument Invention. Prev: Sen. Regist. (Neurosurg.) Austin Hosp. Melbourne, Austral.; Regist. (Neurosurg.) Addenbrooke's Hosp. Camb.; Sen. Regist. (Neurosurg.) Newc. Gen. Hosp.

ASHRAF, Aisha Siddiqua 5 Athlone Road, Walsall WS5 3QU Tel: 01922 626553 — MB BS 1996 Lond. (Univ. Coll. Lond. Med. Sch.)

ASHRAF, Ali 8 Roxby Avenue, Kemplah Park, Guisborough TS14 8LF Tel: 01287 636697 — LMSSA 1971 Lond.; FRCP Lond. 1995; FRCP Ed. 1992; FRCP Glas. 1983, M 1967; MRCP Ed. 1967; DTM & H Liverp. 1961. (Dhaka Med. Coll., Bangladesh) Cons. Phys., N. Tys & Hartlepool NHS Trust, Stockton-on-Tees; Sen. Tutor Univ. Coll. Galway; Assoc. Prof. Gerontol. Roy. Univ. Saskatchewan, Canada. Socs: BMA; Brit. Geriat. Soc.; Overseas Doctors Assn. Prev: Cons. Phys. N.allerton & Darlington HA.

ASHRAF, Dilshad 178 Chamer Road, Oldham OL8 4BU — MB ChB 1997 Leeds.

ASHRAF, Makiya Tayyiba Humaria Beechfield House, 27 Kings Hill, Hengoed CF82 7NH — MB BS 1989 Kashmir.

ASHRAF, Masooma High Street Health Centre, High Street, Aberdare CF44 7DD Tel: 01685 874614 Fax: 01685 877485.

ASHRAF, Mobeen 415 High Street, Newarthill, Motherwell ML1 5SP — MB ChB 1996 Glas.

ASHRAF, Mr Mohammad 1 Wren Avenue, Norwood Green, Southall UB2 4EJ Tel: 020 8843 9283 — MB BS 1976 Punjab; FRCSI 1984; Dip. Urol. Lond 1988.

ASHRAF, Muhammad The Surgery, 9 Wellesley Street, Shelton, Stoke-on-Trent ST1 4NF Tel: 01782 286812; 2 Ambrose Place, Turnhurst Road, Stoke-on-Trent ST6 6XB — MB BS 1976 Punjab; MRCS Eng. LRCP Lond. 1979. (Lahore) SHO (Ophth.) E. Reach Hosp. Taunton. Prev: SHO (Obst.) Bellshill Matern. Hosp.; SHO (O & G) City Hosp. Nottm.

ASHRAF, Samina 74 Green Lane, Acklam, Middlesbrough TS5 7SL Tel: 01042 812932 — MB BS 1997 Lond. (Char. Cross & Westm.)

ASHRAF, Shazad 8 Frank Street, Bury BL9 0RY — MB ChB 1997 Manch.

ASHRAF, Sohail 46 Bentinck Street, Glasgow G3 7TT — MB ChB 1982 Glas.

ASHRAF, Syed M S H Tel: 01685 874614 Fax: 01685 877485 — BSc 1953 M.U.Aligarh, India. (Dacca Medical College, Dacca University, East Pakistan, 1960) Socs: Mem. Local Health Gp., Cynan Valley Primary Care.

ASHRAF, Mr Syed Saeed Department of Cardiothoracic Surgery, Killingbeck Hospital, York Road, Leeds LS14 6UH — MB BS 1981 Karachi; FRCS Ed. 1986.

ASHRAF, Waseem Department of Gastroenterology, King George Hospital, Barley Lane, Ilford IG3 8YB Tel: 020 8970 8054 Fax: 020 8970 8124 Email: waseemashraf@sbhe_ts.nthames.nhs.uk — MB BS 1982 Punjab; FRCP 2001; 1988 MRCP (UK); 1976 BSc Punjab. (King Edward Medical College, Lahore) Cons. Gastroenterol., King Geo. Hsp, Essex. Socs: Amer. Gastroenterol. Assoc; Roy. Soc. Med.; Brit. Soc. of Gastroenterol.

ASHRAFF, Nina Nazneen 283 Woodlands Road, Wilton Park, Batley WF17 0QJ — MB ChB 1995 Leeds. (Univ. Leeds)

ASHRAFF, Syed Mohammed Matinuddin The Surgery, 585 Heathway, Dagenham RM9 5AZ Tel: 020 8593 1771 Fax: 020 8593 1751 — MB BS 1958 Bihar.

ASHRAFF, Yasmin Nina 283 Woodlands Road, Batley WF17 0QJ — MB BS 1991 Lond.; FRCS (Eng.) 1996. (Charing Cross and Westminster) SHO (A&E) St Geo.'s Hosp. Lond. Prev: SHO (Paediat.) Ealing Hosp. Lond.; SHO (Gen. & Vasc. Surg.) Char. Cross Hosp. Lond.; SHO (Gen. Surg.) Roy. Marsden Hosp. Lond.

ASHRAFUZZAMAN, Baharul Mulk Kazi Ahmed 17 Crawford Avenue, Lenzie, Glasgow G66 5HW Tel: 0141 777 7225 — MB BS 1964 Dacca. (Med. Coll. Dacca)

ASHTON, Alison Elizabeth 40 Greystones Close, Sheffield S11 7JU — MB BS 1988 Lond.; DCH RCP Lond. 1993. (St. Geo. Hosp. Med. Sch. Lond.)

ASHTON, Andrew John Edward Flat 5, 29 Dee Banks, Chester CH3 5UU — MB BS 1996 Lond.

ASHTON, Carol Ann Soulton Hall, Soulton Road, Wem, Shrewsbury SY4 5RS — MB ChB 1994 Leic.

ASHTON, Charles Edward Brighton House, 14 Droitwich Road, Worcester WR3 7LJ Tel: 01905 26300 — MB BS 1981 Lond.; MRCP (UK) 1986. (Middlx. Hosp.) Cons. Phys. (Elderly) Worcester Roy. Infirm.; Med. Dir. Worcester Roy. Infirm. Socs: Brit. Geriat. Soc.; Roy. Coll. Phys.

ASHTON, Christopher John 25 Odell Place, Priory Road, Edgbaston, Birmingham B15 2RG — MB ChB 1979 Birm.

ASHTON, Professor Chrystal Heather (retired) Department of Psychiatry, Newcastle upon Tyne NE1 4LP Tel: 0191 222 6000 Ext: 6978 Fax: 0191 227 5108 Email: c.h.ashton@ncl.ac.uk — BM BCh 1954 Oxf.; DM Oxf. 1961, MA 1954; FRCP Lond. 1975, M 1958. Prof. Clin. Psychopharmacol. Univ. Newc. Prev: Cons. Clin. Pharmacol. Newc. AHA (T).

ASHTON, Claire Tracey 71B Redlake Drive, Pedmore, Stourbridge DY9 0RX — BM BS 1995 Nottm.

ASHTON, Eleanor Kay (retired) 1 Hawthorne Villas, Mount Murray, Santon, Douglas IM4 1JF Tel: 01624 628923 — MB ChB 1954 Liverp.; 1954 MB ChB Liverp.; 1968 DPM Eng.; 1997 Dip. Acu. BMAS; 1997 Med. Ac. Indep. Acupunc. & Homoeop. I. of Man.

ASHTON, Elizabeth Joy Glat 7, Dunwan Residences, Blarbuie Road, Lochgilphead PA31 8LD — MB ChB 1993 Leeds. SHO (Psychiat.) Argyll & Bute Hosp.

ASHTON, Elizabeth Margaret Scotstown Medical Centre, Cairnfold Road, Bridge of Don, Aberdeen AB22 8LD Tel: 01224 702149 Fax: 01224 706688; 7 Migvie Avenue, Kingswells, Aberdeen AB15 8GF Tel: 01224 744528 — MB ChB 1984 Birm.; DRCOG 1988. Prev: GP Birm.

ASHTON, Eric George (retired) Lauriston, Riverside Road, Dittisham, Dartmouth TQ6 0HS — MB BCh BAO 1933 Dub.

ASHTON, Mr Frank Piper's Hill Farm, Hanbury, Bromsgrove B60 4AU Tel: 01527 84353 — MRCS Eng. LRCP Lond. 1948; ChM Birm. 1960, MB ChB 1948; FRCS Eng. 1955. (Birm.) Emerit. Prof. Surg. Univ. Birm.

ASHTON, Frederick John Valentine 200 Leigham Court Road, London SW16 2RB — MB BS 1968 Lond.; MRCS Eng. LRCP Lond. 1968. (St. Bart.)

ASHTON, Helen Alwyn House, Burgh-by-Sands, Carlisle CA5 6AX — MB BS 1979 Lond.; DA Eng. 1981.

ASHTON, Helen Ruth Flat E, 30 Willowbank Road, Aberdeen AB11 6YH — MB ChB 1998 Aberd.; MB ChB Aberd 1998.

ASHTON, John 2 Princess House, 42 Farquhar Road, Edgbaston, Birmingham B15 3RE Tel: 0121 455 7018 — MB ChB 1958 Birm.; DA Eng. 1963. Indep. Med. Adviser Birm.; Med. Panel Mem., The Appeals Serv. Socs: BMA; Birm. Med. Inst. Prev: Sen. Med. Off. DSS Benefits Agency; Princip. Leic. FPC; Regist (Anaesth.) Leicester Roy. Infirm.

ASHTON, John Bradley Kent L.M.C, Oast Wing, Tenacre Court, Harrietsham ME17 1AM Tel: 01622 851197 Fax: 01622 851198; Springfield House, 59 The St, Mereworth, Maidstone ME18 5NA Tel: 01622 812626 Fax: 01622 817938 — MB BS 1963 Lond.; MRCS Eng. LRCP Lond. 1963; MRCGP 1973; DObst RCOG 1965. (King's Coll. Hosp.) Med. Sec., Kent local Med. Comm. Prev: Ho. Phys. (Neurol. & Dermat.) King's Coll. Hosp. Lond.; Ho. Surg. Roy. Cornw. Infirm. Truro; Ho. Off. (Obst.) Taunton & Som. Hosp.

ASHTON, John Grant Stonecroft Medical Centre, 871 Gleadless Road, Sheffield S12 2LJ Tel: 0114 398575 Fax: 0114 265 0001; (Surgery), 200 Ridgeway Road, Sheffield S12 2TA — MB ChB 1973 Sheff. Prev: Police Surg. S. Yorks. Metrop. Police; Rotating Regist. (Med.) Sheff. AHA (T); SHO (Med.) United Sheff. Hosps.

ASHTON, Professor John Richard, CBE Hale Cottage, 15 church Road, Much Woolton, Liverpool L25 5JE Tel: 0151 428 1563 Fax: 0151 428 0977 Email: j.ashton@btinternet.com — MB BS 1970 Newc.; MSc (Social Med., with Merit) Lond. 1978; MFFP 1993; FRCPsych 1993, M 1975; FFPHM RCP (UK) 1986; T(Psych.) 1993; T(GP) 1991; T(PHM) 1991; Cert. JCC Lond. 1975. (newcastle upon Tyne) Regional Dir. & Regional Med. Off. (Pub. Health) NW NHS Exec.; Vis. Prof. Inst. Pub. Health Univ. Valencia, Spain; Prof. Pub. Health Policy & Strategy Univ. Liverp.; Prof. Fell. Liverp. Sch. Trop. Med.; Vis. Prof. John Moores Univ. Liverp.; Mem. of the N. W. Regional Assembly Extern. Examr., Trinity Coll., Dub.; Jt. Edr., Jl. of Epidemiol. and Community Health; Vis Prof. Univ. Manch. Socs: Liverp. Med. Inst.; Manch. Med. Soc.; Duncan Soc. Prev: Regional Dir. and Regional Med. Off. (Pub. Health) Mersey RHA; Head (Pub. Health) Univ. Liverp.; Sen. Lect. (Community Health) Lond. Sch. Hyg. & Trop. Med.

ASHTON, Jonathan Richard The Surgery, Grosvenor House, 6 Warwick Square, Carlisle CA1 1LB Tel: 01228 525041 Fax: 01228 525041; Alwyn House, Carlisle CA5 6AX Tel: 01228 576014 — MB ChB 1979 Leeds; FRCS Ed. 1985. (Leeds) Surg. Cdr. RNR, HMS Calliope.

ASHTON, Kathryn Louise Roslea Surgery, 51 Station Road, Bamber Bridge, Preston PR5 6PE Tel: 01772 335128 Fax: 01772 492248 — MB ChB 1984 Liverp.; MRCGP 1991; T (GP) 1991; DRCOG 1988. GP.

ASHTON, Kirsty Louise 519 Pontins, Shore Road, Ainsdale, Southport PR8 2PX — MB ChB 1993 Liverp.

ASHTON, Lesley Carolyn 43 Cavendish Road, Jesmond, Newcastle upon Tyne NE2 2NJ Tel: 0191 281 7390 — MB BS 1994 Newc. GP Regist. Newc.; SHO (Obst. & Gyn.) QEH Newc. Prev: SHO (A & E) Dryburn Hosp. Durh.; Trainee GP Croft Surg. Wrekenton, Gateshead; SHO (Med.) Hexham Gen. Hosp.

ASHTON, Leslie Arthur Saffron Group Practice, 509 Saffron Lane, Leicester LE2 6UL Tel: 0116 244 0888 Fax: 01162 831405 — MB ChB 1982 Leic.; BSc MedSci Leic. 1980; MRCP (UK) 1986; DRCOG 1988. Mem. Edit. Bd. Ambulatory Child Health Jl.

ASHTON, Mark Andrew Grimsby Hospital, North East Lincolnshire Trust, Grimsby DN33 2BA Tel: 01472 875438 Fax: 01472 875333 Email: mark.ashton@nlg.nhs.uk — MB BS 1980 Lond.; FRCPath 1997. (Char. Cross Hosp.) Cons. Histopath. Pathlinks Path. Serv. Socs: Assn. Clin. Path.; Brit. Soc. Clin. Cytol.; Brit. Assn. Forens. Med. Prev: Cons. Path. (BrE. & Gyn. Path.) Armed Forces Inst. of Path. Washington DC, USA; Cons. Histopath. RAF Med. Br.; Hon. Cons,. Histopath. Stoke Mandeville Hosp. Aylesbury.

ASHTON, Mark Richard Department of Paediatrics, St Mary's Hospital, Portsmouth Hospitals NHS Trust, Milton Road, Portsmouth PO3 6 — BM BCh 1984 Oxf.; MA Oxf. 1981. BM BCh 1984; MRCP (UK) 1988. Cons. Paediat. St. Mary's Hosp. Portsmouth Hosps. NHS Trust. Socs: Brit. Paediat. Assn. Prev: Sen. Regist. (Paediat.) Poole Hosp.; Clin. Research Fell. Univ. Soton.; Regist. (Paediat.) Soton. Gen. Hosp.

ASHTON, Michael Blair The Surgery, Faraday Avenue, Tuxford, Newark NG22 0HT Tel: 01777 870203 Fax: 01777 872221 — MB ChB 1970 Glas.; MRCP (U.K.) 1973. Prev: SHO (Gen. Med.) Foresterhill & Assoc. Hosps. Aberd.; Regist. (Haemat.) Nottm. Gen. Hosp.

ASHTON, Michael George 53 Fairview, Pilton, Barnstaple EX31 1JS — MB BS 1970 Lond.; MRCS Eng. LRCP Lond. 1970; DO Eng. 1977.

ASHTON, Michael Graham The White House, Eaton Hill, Baslow, Bakewell DE45 1SB — MB ChB 1971 Leeds; FRCP Lond. 1991; MRCP (UK) 1974. Cons. Phys. Gastroenterol. Chesterfield & N. Derbysh. Roy. Hosp. Prev: Cons. Phys. Gastroenterol. Sunderland Roy. Infirm.; Sen. Regist. (Gen. Med.) Sheff. AHA; Hon. Lect. (Physiol.) Univ. Sheff.

ASHTON, Pamela Susan Courtyard Surgery, 1 Poynders Road, London SW4 8NL Tel: 020 8673 1386 Fax: 020 8673 3312 — BM BCh 1974 Oxf.; MA Oxf. 1975; MRCP (UK) 1980); MRCGP 1983; Cert. Family Plann. JCC 1981; DCH RCP Lond. 1980. (St. Bart.) GP Clapham Pk.; Sen. Clin. Med. Off. (Housing) Wandsworth HA. Prev: SHO (Paediat.) W.. Hosp. Lond.; SHO (Neonatol.) Hammersmith Hosp. Lond.; SHO (Paediat.) Qu. Mary's Hosp. Roehampton.

ASHTON, Paul Cristopher Bernard 20 Springfield Crescent, West Kirby, Wirral CH48 9UZ — MRCS Eng. LRCP Lond. 1974. (Liverp.) Attend. Phys. Swift Curr. Union Hosp. Canada. Prev: Regist. (Anaesth.) Wirral HA; SHO (Anaesth.) Roy. S.. Hosp. Liverp.; SHO (Anaesth.) Clatterbridge Hosp. Bebington.

ASHTON, Peter Jervis (retired) Plas Du, Montgomery SY15 6QR — MB BS 1954 Lond.; DObst RCOG 1958. Prev: GP Montgomery.

ASHTON, Rebecca Julianna Angela The Surgeries, Lombard St., Newark NG24 1XG Tel: 01636 702363; Blairmore, 3 Sandfield Way, Newark NG24 4QL — MB ChB 1981 Leics.; BSc (Hons.) Hull 1976; DRCOG 1985.

ASHTON, Richard Eric, Surg. Cdr. RN Bridge House, Mill St., Titchfield, Fareham PO14 4AB Tel: 01329 842441 — MB BChir 1974 Camb.; MA Camb. 1973, MD 1991; FRCP Lond. 1994. Cons. Dermat. Roy. Hosp. Haslar Gosport Hants. Prev: Hon. Cons. Dermat. Roy. S. Hants Hosp. Soton.; Assoc. Prof. Div. Dermat. UCLA; Hon. Sen. Regist. St. John's Hosp. for Dis. of the Skin.

ASHTON, Robert Michael (retired) 6 Andrews Drive, Evesham WR11 6JN — MB ChB Manch. 1950. Prev: Asst. Chest Phys. Sheff. Chest Serv.

ASHTON, Roderic The Rogerstone Practice, Chapel Wood, Western Valley Road, Rogerstone, Newport NP10 9DU Tel: 01633 893272 Fax: 01633 895079 — MB BCh 1981 Wales; MRCGP 1985; DRCOG 1984. Prev: S. Gwent Trainer Grp Co-Ordinator.

ASHTON, Shirley Gwyneth (retired) 10 Briar Close, Knutsford WA16 6TL Tel: 01565 3528 — MB ChB 1942 Manch.; BSc MB ChB Manch. 1942.

ASHTON, William Bernard c/o Anaesthetic Department, Poole Hospital NHS Trust, Longfleet Road, Poole BH15 2JB; 2 Ormonde

Road, Branicsome Park, Poole BH13 6DF — MB ChB 1983 Zimbabwe; LRCP LRCS Ed. LRCPS Glas. 1983; FCAnaesth. 1989.

ASHTON, William David 44 Chancellors Close, Birmingham B15 3UJ — MB ChB 1977 Manch.

ASHTON-JENNINGS, Carole Ann Montalto Medical Centre, 2 Dromore Road, Ballynahinch BT24 8AY Tel: 028 9756 2929; Hillhead House, 27 Cargagh Road, Annacloy, Downpatrick BT30 9AG Tel: 0139 683 0517 — MB BCh 1973 Wales; MRCGP 1977.

ASHTON-KEY, Margaret Rose Department of Histopathology, Royal Sussex County Hospital, Eastern Road, Brighton BN2 6BE Tel: 01273 664411 Fax: 01273 664412 Email: margaret.ashton-key@brighton-healthcare.nhs.uk; 44 Hove Park Villas, Hove BN3 6HG Email: meg.ak@doctors.org.uk — BM 1989 Soton.; MRCPath 1995, D 1994; DM Soton. 1997. Cons. Histopath. Roy. Sussex Co. Hosp. Brighton. Prev: Lect. (Histopath.) Univ. Coll. Lond.; Research Fell. (Histopath.) Univ. Coll. Lond.; Regist. (Histopath.) John Radcliffe Hosp. Oxf.

ASHTON-KEY, Martin Charter Medical Centre, 88 Davigdor Road, Hove BN3 1RF Tel: 01273 738070 Fax: 01273 220883 — BM 1990 Soton.; BM Soton 1990; MRCGP 1996; DCH RCP Lond. 1994; DRCOG 1994. Prev: Trainee GP Banbury; SHO Horton Gen. Hosp. Banbury VTS; SHO (Surg.) Leicester Roy. Infirm.

ASHURST, Neil Harry Anaesthetre Dept., Bradford Roy. Infirm., Dackworth Lane, Bradford BD9 6RJ Tel: 01274 364066; Email: harry@ashurstn.fsnet.co.uk — MB ChB 1987 Leeds; FRCA 1992. Cons. Anaesth. Bradford.

ASHURST, Nigel James 10 The Rustons, Duxford, Cambridge CB2 4SG — MB ChB 1998 Leeds.

ASHURST, Pamela Margaret (retired) 130 Highfield Lane, Southampton SO17 1NR Tel: 02380 553773 Fax: 023 80 555024 — MB ChB 1964 Bristol; FRCPsych 1987, M 1973. Prev: Cons. Psychother. Head of Dept. Psychother. Soton. Health Dist.

ASHWELL, Colin Stuart (retired) 30 Pledwick Lane, Sandal, Wakefield WF2 6DN Tel: 01924 257786 — MB ChB 1938 Birm.; MRCS Eng. LRCP Lond. 1938. Prev: Med. Off. St.Ho. Child Welf. Clinic.

ASHWELL, Simon Guy 37 Burnett Road, Streetly, Sutton Coldfield B74 3EL Tel: 0121 353 8260 — MB ChB 1995 Leeds. SHO (Med. Rotat.) York Dist. Hosp.

ASHWOOD, Christopher George Birchwood Surgery, 232-240 Nevells Road, Letchworth SG6 4UB Tel: 01462 683456; 2 Parker Close, Letchworth SG6 3RT Tel: 01462 683456 — MB BS 1982 Lond.; MRCGP 1991; DRCOG 1987. Trainer (Gen. Pract.) Letchworth.

ASHWOOD, Neil 7 Manor Lea, Haslemere GU27 1PD — MB BS 1992 Lond.

ASHWORTH, Albert Norman 3 St Helens Close, Southsea PO4 0NN Tel: 01705 733538 — MB ChB 1942 Manch.; MD Manch. 1954, MB ChB 1942; MRCS Eng. LRCP Lond. 1942; FRCOphth 1988; DOMS Eng. 1948. (Vict. Univ. Manch.) Hons. Cons. Ophth. Surg. Portsmouth & Chichester Gp. Hosps.

ASHWORTH, Alison Jane Dept. Diagnostic Radiology, QMC, Nottingham; Cross Lane Farm, Cross Lane, Starkholmes, Matlock DE4 5JD Email: alison ashworth@lineone.net — BM BS 1992 Nottm.; MRCP (UK) 1996. (Nottingham) Specialist Regist. (Radiol.) Nottm. Prev: Regist. (Med.) Macclesfield Dist. Gen. Hosp.; SHO Derby City Hosp.

ASHWORTH, Andrew John, Surg. Lt.-Cdr. RN Retd. 22 Springfield Lea, South Queensferry EH30 9XD — MB ChB 1980 Leeds; MRCGP 1985; Dip. Occ. Med. RCP Lond. 1996. (Leeds) Clin. Asst. Centr. Scotl. Community Addic. Team; Prospective Conserv. Parlimentary Candidate for Staffs. Moorlands. Socs: (Counc.) BMA. Prev: Med. Off. HMS Vigilant.

ASHWORTH, Bryan (retired) 13/5 Eildon Terrace, Edinburgh EH3 5NL Tel: 0131 556 0547 — MB ChB 1952 St. And.; MA Wales 1993; MD St. And. 1969; FRCP Lond. 1975, M 1960; FRCP Ed. 1971, M 1960. Hon. Sen. Lect. Univ. of St Andrews. Prev: Cons. Neurol. Roy. Infirm. Edin.

ASHWORTH, Caroline 21 Grosvenor Road, East Grinstead RH19 1HS — MB BS 1978 Lond.

ASHWORTH, Catherine Selby Louise Hill Cottage, West St., Llantwit Major CF61 1SP — MB BS 1996 Lond.

ASHWORTH, Daniel Robert 54 Homelands Road, Cardiff CF14 1UJ — MB BCh 1997 Wales.

ASHWORTH, David Arnold (retired) Solway, Willowmead Drive, Prestbury, Macclesfield SK10 4BU Tel: 01233 633331 Ext: 86693, 01625 828717 Fax: 01233 616019 Email: nagesh.rao@virgin.net — MB ChB Manch. 1959. Prev: SHO Accid. Serv. Radcliffe Infirm. Oxf.

ASHWORTH, Francis Joseph 18 Buttercross Close, Burnley BB11 5HB — MB ChB 1993 Liverp.

ASHWORTH, Frank Leonard (retired) 92 South Mossley Hill Road, Liverpool L19 9BJ Tel: 0151 427 6027 — MB BS 1950 Lond.; MRCGP 1957; FFA RCS Eng. 1972; DTM & H Eng. 1954. Prev: Cons. Anaesth. Roy. Liverp. Teach. Hosp.

ASHWORTH, Geraldine Jasmine Oxford Craniofacial Unit, Radcliffe Infirmary, Woodstock Road, Oxford OX2 6HE; 4 Duke Street, Oxford OX2 0HX Tel: 01865 250874 — BM BCh 1979 Oxf.

ASHWORTH, Helen Lesley 69 Bayham Road, Sevenoaks TN13 3XD Tel: 01732 461970 — BM BS 1991 Nottm.; FRCA 1997. (Nottm.) Specialist Regist. (Anaesth.) St. Thos. Hosp. Lond. Socs: MRCAnaesth. Prev: Specialist Regist. (Anaesth.) Bromley Hosp.; SHO (Anaesth.) Whittington Hosp. Lond.; SHO (Anaesth.) Middlx. Hosp. Lond.

ASHWORTH, Henry Mark Didsbury Medical Centre, 645 Wilmslow Road, Didsbury, Manchester M20 6BA Tel: 0161 445 1957 Fax: 0161 434 9931; 4 Dene Park, Didsbury, Manchester M20 2GF Tel: 0161 445 0195 — MB ChB 1976 Manch.; BSc St. And. 1973; MRCGP 1980; DRCOG 1978. Civil. Med. Off. RAC Co. Manch.; Adjudicating Med. Pract. DSS; Attached Med. Pract. BBC Manch.; Med. Adviser Norweb. Socs: (Hon. Treas.) Manch. Medico Ethical Assn. Prev: SHO (Paediat.) Pk. Hosp. Davyhulme; SHO (O & G) St. Mary's Hosp. Manch.; Ho. Surg. Manch. Roy. Infirm.

ASHWORTH, Henry Wilkinson (retired) 2 Dene Park, Manchester M20 2GF Tel: 0161 434 4093 — MB ChB 1944 Manch.; BSc Manch. 1941, MD 1960; FRCGP 1974. Prev: Hon. Lect. (Gen. Pract.) Vict. Univ. Manch.

ASHWORTH, Iain Richard Barrowford Surgery, Ridgeway, Barrowford, Nelson BB9 8QP Tel: 01282 612621 Fax: 01282 611958 Email: iain@medix-uk.com — MB ChB 1987 Sheff.; T(GP) 1992; Cert. Family Plann. JCC 1990. (Sheffield)

ASHWORTH, Ian Andrew Holderness Road Surgery, 445 Holderness Road, Hull HU8 8JS Tel: 01482 374255 Fax: 01482 790301 — MB BS 1984 Newc.; MRCGP 1988.

ASHWORTH, Ian Newton Strathmore Medical Practice, 26-28 Chester Road, Wrexham LL11 2SA Tel: 01978 352055 Fax: 01978 310689; Sunnyside, 10 Rhosnesni Lane, Wrexham LL12 7LY Tel: 01978 352123 — MB ChB 1961 Manch.; MRCS Eng. LRCP Lond. 1962; DObst RCOG 1963. (Manch.) Socs: Fell. Roy. Soc. Med.; Assur. Med. Soc.

ASHWORTH, Mr James Pear Tree Cottage, Church St., Well, Bedale DL8 2QA — MB ChB 1951 Manch.; FRCS Eng. 1963; MRCS Eng. LRCP Lond. 1951. (Manch.) Cons. Surg. (Orthop.) Darlington & N.allerton Health Dists. Mem. Socs: Brit. Orthop. Assn. & N. Eng. Surg. Soc. Prev: Sen. Regist. (Orthop. Surg.) United Leeds Hosps.; Regist. Nuffield Orthop. Centre Oxf.; Ho. Surg. Manch. Roy. Infirm.

ASHWORTH, Miss Jane Louise Department of Ophthalmology, Manchester Royal Eye Hospital, Oxford Road, Manchester M13 9WH Tel: 0161 276 1234 Email: jashwort@fs1.scg.man.ac.uk; 9 York Drive, Grappenhall, Warrington WA4 2EJ Tel: 01925 861696 — BM BCh 1992 Oxf. (Oxford) Clin. Research Fell. Univ. of Manch.; Hon. Regist. Manch. Roy. Eye Hosp. Prev: SHO Manch. Roy. Eye Hosp.; Ho. Off. (Med.) Roy. United Hosp. Bath; Ho. Off. (Surg.) Nuffield Dept. of Surg. John Radcliffe Hosp. Oxf.

ASHWORTH, Janet Ruth Rectory Cottage, Atlow, Ashbourne DE6 1NS — BM BS 1990 Nottm.

ASHWORTH, Jennifer Mary 1 Walnut Close, Barrow on Trent, Derby DE73 1JL — BM BS 1985 Nottm.; MRCGP 1989; DRCOG 1990. (Nottingham)

ASHWORTH, John Department of Dermatology, Stepping Hill Hospital, Stockport SK2 7JE — MB ChB 1979 Manch.; MD Manch. 1989; FRCP Lond. 1997; MRCP (UK) 1983. Cons. Dermat. Hope Hosp. Salford & Stepping Hill Hosp. Stockport. Prev: Cons. Dermat. Roy. Liverp. Hosp.; Sen. Regist. St. John's Hosp. Dis. Skin Lond.

ASHWORTH, John Spencer Gillies and Overbridge Medical Partnership, Brighton Hill, Sullivan Road, Basingstoke RG22 4EH Tel:

01256 479747; Oakfield Farm House, Scures Hill, Nateley Scures, Basingstoke RG27 9JR Tel: 01256 762694 — MB BS 1968 Lond.; MRCS Eng. LRCP Lond. 1968; DObst 1974. (Guy's) Socs: BMA. Prev: Ho. Off. (Orthop.) Guy's Hosp.; SHO (Gyn.) Mt. Vernon Hosp. N.wood.

ASHWORTH, Julie N. Staffordshire Hospital, Department of Anaesthesia, City General, Newcastle Road, Stoke-on-Trent ST4 6QG Tel: 01782 552732; 31 Church Lane, Oulton, Stone ST15 8UB Tel: 01785 814297 — BSc (Med. Sci.) St. And. 1987; DA (UK) 1992; FRCA 1995. (St. And. & Manch.) Cons. Anaesth. N. Staffs Hosp. Stoke-on-Trent. Socs: Assn. Anaesth.; Assn. Cardiothoracic Anaesth.s; Soc. for Educat. in Anaesth. (SEA UK). Prev: Specialist Regist. Anaesth. Qu.s Hosp., Burton on Trent; Specialist Regist. Anaesth. N. Staffs Hosp., Stoke on Trent; Regist. Anaesth. P.ss Roy. Hosp. Telford.

ASHWORTH, Karen Lindsay 36 Holdbrook Way, Romford RM3 0JD — MB ChB 1991 Liverp.; MRCP (UK) 1994.

ASHWORTH, Lesley Barbara (retired) Carr Croft, 144 Wheatley Lane Road, Barrowford, Nelson BB9 6QJ Tel: 01282 603658 Email: lesbilash@easicom.com — MB BS 1961 Lond.; MRCS Eng. LRCP Lond. 1961; MFFP 1993. JP.; Med. Off. Family Plann. Clinic Burnley & Nelson. Prev: Resid. Ho. Off. (Obst.) Bank Hall Matern. Hosp. Burnley.

ASHWORTH, Linda Jane Moss View, Plover Drive, Heysham, Lancaster LA1 3JR Tel: 01524 865900; 88 Sycamore Road, Brookhouse, Lancaster LA2 9PE Email: linda.ashworth@virgin.net — MB ChB 1987 Leeds; BSc 1984 Leeds; MRCPsych 1991; MRCPsych. 1991. Cons. (Old Age Psychiartry) Morecambe Bay Primary Care Trust.

ASHWORTH, Margaret Little Steading, Church Walk, Crowton, Northwich CW8 2SA Tel: 01928 88690 — MB ChB 1962 Liverp.

ASHWORTH, Mark Hurley Clinic, Kennington Lane, London SE11 4HJ — BM 1979 Soton.; MRCP (UK) 1982; MRCGP 1986; DTM & H RCP Lond. 1983.

ASHWORTH, Mr Mark Julian Torbay Hospital, Torquay TQ2 7AA — MB ChB 1986 Manch.; BSc (Hons.) Physiol. Manch. 1983; FRCS Eng. 1991; FRCS (Orth.) 1997. Cons. Trauma Orthopaedic Surg. Prev: Regist. (Orthop.) Wexham Pk. & Heatherwood Hosp.; Regist. (Trauma & Orthop.) N. Staffs. Roy. Infirm.; SHO Rotat. (Surg.) Manch. Roy. Infirm.

ASHWORTH, Mary Felicity Department of Obstetrics & Gynaecology, Stoke Mandeville Hospital, Aylesbury HP21 8AL — BM BCh 1978 Oxf.; BA Camb. 1975; FRCS Eng. 1982; MRCOG 1984; T(OG) 1991. (Cambridge and Oxford) Cons. O & G Stoke Mandeville Hosp. Aylesbury. Prev: Lect. (O & G) The Lond. Hosp. Med. Coll.; Lect. (O & G) Univ. Zimbabwe.

ASHWORTH, Maureen Elizabeth Church Grange Health Centre, Bramblys Drive, Basingstoke RG21 8QN Tel: 01256 329021 Fax: 01256 817466; Oakfield Farm House, Scures Hill, Nateley Scures, Hook RG27 9JR Tel: 01256 722694 — MB BS 1967 Lond.; MRCS Eng. LRCP Lond. 1967. (Roy. Free) Socs: BMA. Prev: Regist. Rheum. Stoke Mandeville Hosp. Aylesbury; Ho. Surg. Roy. Free Hosp.; Ho. Phys. King Edwd. Hosp. Windsor.

ASHWORTH, Michael Robert Wigan Road Surgery, 246 Wigan Road, Bryn, Ashton-in-Makerfield, Wigan WN4 0AR Tel: 01942 727270 Fax: 01942 272197 — MB ChB 1979 Manch. GP Wigan FPC.

ASHWORTH, Michael Thomas 48 St Matthews Road, Bristol BS6 5TU — MB BCh BAO 1980 NUI; MRCPath 1989.

ASHWORTH, Nigel Paul Dr Dow and Partners, 87-89 Prince of Wales Road, London NW5 3NT; Flat 1 New River Head, 173 Rosebery Avenue, London EC1R 4UJ Tel: 020 7278 9972 — MB BS 1984 Lond.; MRCGP 1990; DA (UK) 1986; DRCOG 1989. Prev: Research Fell. & Regist. (HIV & Genitourin. Med.) Char. Cross Hosp. Lond.; Trainee GP Lond VTS.

ASHWORTH, Robert Neil 33 Sawley Avenue, Blackpool FY4 2NB — MB ChB 1978 Leeds.

ASHWORTH, Robin Neil Cricketfield Surgery, Cricketfield Road, Newton Abbot TQ12 2AS Tel: 01626 208020 Fax: 01626 333356 — MB BChir 1966 Camb.

ASHWORTH, Shura Louise Warwick House Medical Centre, Upper Holway Road, Taunton TA1 2QA Tel: 01823 282147 Fax: 01823 338181; Chestnut House, 23 Mount St, Taunton TA1 3QF Tel: 01823 331643 — MB BS 1990 Lond.; DRCOG 1994; MRCGP 1996. (Med. Coll. St Barts. Hosp.) GP Princip. Prev: GP Taunton.

ASHWORTH, Simon Francis Dept of Anaesthetics, St Marys Hospital, Praed St., London W2 Email: simon@rosebud.dircon.co.uk; 31 Glenfield Road, London W13 9JZ — BM 1991 Soton.; BSc (1st cl. Hons.) Psychol. 1990; MRCP (UK) 1995; FRCA 1998. Specialist Regist. Anaesth. Imperial Coll. Socs: BMA; SCCM. Prev: SHO Anaesth. (Hammersmith, Char. Cross, Chelsea & W.minister Hosps.); SHO (PCU) Univ. Hosp. QMC Nottm.

ASHWORTH, Walter Donald The Smithy, 4 Market Street, Hollingworth, Hyde SK14 8LJ Tel: 01457 763558 Fax: 01457 766429; 64a Mottram Old Road, Stalybridge SK15 2TE — MB ChB 1958 Manch. Prev: Ho. Surg. Manch. Roy. Infirm. & St. Mary's Hosp. Manch.; Res. Med. Off. Oldham Roy. Infirm.

ASIAIN URRIZOLA, Jesus Maria Rowan House Wing, 72 Room 50, Medway Hospital, Windmill Road, Gillingham ME7 5NY — LMS 1991 Navarre.

ASIEDU-OFEI, Emmanuel Samuel Avenue Crescent Surgery, 47 Avenue Crescent, Leeds LS8 4HD Tel: 0113 262 4630; 23 Adel Towers Close, Long Causeway, Adel, Leeds LS16 8ES Tel: 0113 267 1995 — MRCS Eng. LRCP Lond. 1969. (Birm.) Hosp. Pract. (Rheum.) St. Jas. Univ. Hosp. Leeds. Socs: BMA & Brit. Soc. Rheum.; Primary Care Rheum. Soc. Prev: Regist. (Rheum.) Leeds Gen. Infirm.; Ho. Surg. Gen. Hosp. Birm.; Ho. Phys. Selly Oak Hosp. Birm.

ASIF, Mohammed 261 Malmesbury Road, Birmingham B10 0JE Email: m.asif@shef.ac.uk — BM BCh 1993 Oxf.; BA Camb. 1990; MA Camb. 1994; FRCS Glas 1997; FRCS Ed 1997. (Oxford)

ASIF, Muhammad 57 Carlye Road, Edgbaston, Birmingham B16 9BH — MB BS 1985 Punjab.

ASIRDAS, Sharmila Rachel Niranjana 58 Brighton Road, Coulsdon CR5 2BB — MB BS 1990 Lond.

ASIRVATHAM, Rajan Department of Orthopaedics, Lincoln County Hospital, Greetwell Road, Lincoln LN2 5QY Tel: 01522 512512, 01522 573830; 30 Lee Road, Lincoln LN2 4BH Email: rajan@bonedoc.freeserve.co.uk — MB BS 1980 Madras; FRCS (Ed.) Orth 1989; FRCS Glas. 1984; T(S) 1991. (Kilpauk Medical College, Madras) Cons. Orthop. & Trauma Lincoln Co. Hosp. Socs: Fell. BOA; Hosp. Cons. & Spec. Assn.; Fell. Brit. Childr.'s Soc. Orthop. Prev: Fell. Paediat. Orthop. Salt Lake City, USA.

ASIRWATHAM, Jeanne Sharmini 34 Grosvenor Road, Wallington SM6 0EF — MB BS 1981 Lond.; MRCGP 1986; DCH RCP Lond. 1984.

***ASK, Jodie Anne** 68 Milden Road, Sheffield S6 4AU Tel: 0114 234 7900 Fax: 0114 285 4837 — MB BS 1997 Lond.

ASKARI, S H Max Road Surgery, 4-6 Max Road, Liverpool L14 4BH Tel: 0151 259 2549.

ASKER, Diane Claire 16 Hawthorne Drive, Hollywood Grange, Wythall, Birmingham B47 5QT — MB ChB 1981 Birm.; MRCGP 1985; MFFP 1993.

ASKEW, Alison Elizabeth 43 Campion Hill, Castle Donnington, Derby DE74 2XH — MB ChB 1987 Birm.; MRCGP 1993.

ASKEW, Linda Janet 19 Richmond Road, Sheffield S13 8TB — MB ChB 1982 Sheff.

ASKEW, Michael Frederick Colyton Health Centre, Grove Hill, Colyton EX24 6ET Tel: 01297 552728; Sevenoaks, Harepath Hill, Seaton EX12 2TA — MB BS 1966 Lond.; Cert. Family Plann. JCC 1974. (St. Geo.) Community Hosp. Pract. Seaton Hosp. Devon. Prev: Flight Lt. Med. Off. RAF.

ASKEW, Michael Gerald (retired) Seafield House, 14 Anglesey Road, Alverstoke, Gosport PO12 2EQ Tel: 023 9258 0917 — MB BS Lond. 1959; MRCS Eng. LRCP Lond. 1959; FRCGP 1993, M 1975. Prev: Ho. Phys. (Cardiol.) & Ho. Surg. (Orthop.) St. Geo. Hosp. Lond.

ASKEW, Michael Raymond 109 A Leicester Road, Ashby De La Zouch, Leicester LE65 1DF — MB BChir 1968 Camb.; BA Camb. 1965. (Camb. & King's Coll. Hosp.)

ASKEY, Andrew Timothy The Surgery, Beech Tree Road, Walsall Wood, Walsall WS9 9LT Tel: 01543 375457 Fax: 01543 458484; 53A Allens Lane, Pelsall, Walsall WS3 4JR Tel: 01922 692739 — MB BS 1985 Lond.

ASKHAM, Robert Norman Hugh 2-4 Bedford Road, Liverpool L4 5PG Tel: 0151 525 6438 — MB BS 1948 Lond. (Middlx.) Prev:

Paediat. Ho. Phys. & O & G Ho. Surg. Hereford Co. Hosp.; Surg. Lt. RN.

ASKILL, Colin Stanley Radiotherapy Department, Singleton Hospital, Sketty, Swansea SA2 8QA — MB ChB 1973 Liverp.; FRCR 1980; DMRT Eng. 1978. Cons. Radiother. & Oncol. Singleton Hosp. Swansea.

ASKWITH, Jacqueline Hazel 13 Peri Court, St Mildreds Place, Canterbury CT1 3TH — MB BS 1986 Lond.

ASLAM, Aamik Flat 3/2, 605 Great Western Road, Glasgow G12 8HX — MB ChB 1998 Glas.; MB ChB Glas 1998.

ASLAM, Mr Adil 1 Aversley Road, Birmingham B38 8PD — MB BS 1984 Punjab; FRCS Eng. 1990.

ASLAM, Mr Habib Ben Haider Department of Accident & Emergency, Princess Margaret Hospital, Okus Road, Swindon SN1 4JU Tel: 01793 536231 Fax: 01793 426636 Email: aslamae@yahoo.com — MB BS 1982 Peshawar; 1982 MB BS Peshawar; 1987 FRCSI; FFAEM 1996; FRCS 1987. Cons. Accd. & Emerg. P.ss Margt. Hosp. Swindon. Prev: Sen. Regist. Chelsea & W.m. Hosp. Lond.

ASLAM, Javed 7 Harbourne Ave, Walkden, Manchester M28 7UD — MB ChB 1978 Manch.; FFA RCS Eng. 1985. Cons. Anaesth. Wigan & Leigh NHS Health Trust. Socs: Assn. N.W. Intens. Care Units; Obst. Anaesth. Assn. Prev: Sen. Regist. N. W.. Regional Scheme; Cons. Anaesth. Bury HA; Trainee GP Rochdale VTS.

ASLAM, Mansoor 3 Dunearn Street, Broughty Ferry, Dundee DD5 3NP — MB BS 1976 Punjab; FRCR 1994.

ASLAM, Masood 39 Suffolk Street, Werneth, Oldham OL9 7DS — MB ChB 1996 Aberd.

ASLAM, Mian Naeem c/o Dr H Aslam, Accident & Emergency Department, Princess Margaret Hospital, Okus Road, Swindon SN1 4JU — MB BS 1984 Peshawar; MRCP (UK) 1990.

ASLAM, Mohamed 6 Bristow Close, Warrington WA5 8EU — MB ChB 1977 Manch.

ASLAM, Mohammad 15 Beveland Road, Canvey Island SS8 7QU — MB BS 1975 Peshawar.

ASLAM, Mohammed 93 Lincoln Road, Ruskington, Sleaford NG34 9AR — MB BS 1968 Dacca. (Sir Salimullah Med. Coll.) Assoc. Specialist Rauceby Hosp. Sleaford.

ASLAM, Naaila Compton Vectis, 49 Marlow Road, High Wycombe HP11 1TG — MB ChB 1994 Leeds.

ASLAM, Nadim Compton Vectis, 49 Marlow Road, High Wycombe HP11 1TG — MB ChB 1994 Dundee; BMSc Dund 1991. Sen. SHO (Orthop. & Trauma) High Wycombe; SHO Trauma/Orthg. Oxf.; SHO A & E Slough.; SHO (Plastic Surg.) Radcliffe Infirm. Oxf.; SHO (Gen. Surg.) High Wycombe. Socs: BOTA; ASIT; BMA.

ASLAM, Najmus-Sehar 93 Lincoln Road, Ruskington, Sleaford NG34 9AR — MB ChB 1994 Leic.

ASLAM, Neelo Farhat 5 Westend Avenue, Gatley, Cheadle SK8 4DR — MB BS 1993 Lond.

ASLAM, Rizwan 1 Northdene Drive, Rochdale OL11 5NH — MB ChB 1991 Aberd.

ASLAM, Shahzeena 31 Stratford Way, Cassiobury Estate, Watford WD17 3DL — MB BS 1996 Lond. (Kings Coll. Lond.)

ASLAM, Tariq Mehmood 31 Wollaton Hall Drive, Wollaton Park, Nottingham NG8 1AF Tel: 0115 978 6754 Fax: 0115 978 6754 — MB ChB 1994 Birm.; MA (Physiol. Sci.) Oxf. 1991. (Oxf. & Birm. Med. Sch.) SHO, Opth., Qu. Margt. Hosp. NHS Trust. Socs: Med. Defence Union; BMA. Prev: SHO Opth. Roy. United Hosp. Bath.

ASLAM, Toqeer Princes Park Medical Centre, Dove Close, Walderslade, Chatham ME5 7TD Tel: 01634 201272 Fax: 01634 868159; 58 Priestfields, Rochester ME1 3AE Tel: 01634 843411 — MB ChB 1981 Bristol.

ASLAM, Waseem Soaper House, Coley Road, Halifax HX3 7SA — MB BS 1986 Punjab.

ASLAN, Tom 54 Flower Lane, London NW7 2JL — MB BS 1992 Lond.

ASLETT, David John Station Road Surgery, 99 Station Road, Redhill RH1 1EB Tel: 01737 761201 Fax: 01737 780510; Cherry Trees, 35 London Road S., Merstham, Redhill RH1 3AX Tel: 01737 645424 — MB BS 1979 Lond.; DRCOG 1982.

ASMAL, Yunus Yakub Valli 6 Headfield Road, Savile Town, Dewsbury WF12 9JE — MB BS 1997 Lond.

ASMAR, Mr Muhsin Abdulla Abdulruhman Abdulla Doctors Residence, Staincliffe General Hospital, Healds Road, Dewsbury WF13 4HS — MB ChB 1979 Baghdad; FRCS Ed. 1986.

ASMUSSEN, Tilo 2 Megagissey House, Royal Cornwall Hospital, Treliske, Truro TR1 3LD — State Exam Med 1992 Greifswald.

ASOPA, Vipin 23 Wilderness Heights, West End, Southampton SO18 3PS — MB ChB 1998 Bristol.

ASPBURY, John Noel Royal Bolton Hospital, Minerva Road, Farnworth, Bolton BL4 0JR Tel: 01204 390762 Fax: 01204 390640; 13 Dimple Park, Egerton, Bolton BL7 9QE Tel: 01204 593929 Email: jnaspbury@cs.com — MB ChB 1972 Manch.; FFA RCS Eng. 1979. Cons. Anaesth. Bolton. Socs: Bolton & Dist. Med. Soc.; Intens. Care Soc.; Assn. NW Intens. Care Units.

ASPEL, Johanna Louise 70 Eastfield Close, Horspath Meadows, Headington, Oxford OX3 7SH — MB BS 1998 Lond.; MB BS Lond 1998. (Imp College of Science, Tech & Medicine (Charing Cross Campus)) Surgic. Ho. Off.

ASPIN, Andrew James Dales Outpatient Centre, Skipton Road, Steeton, Keighley BD20 6TD Tel: 01535 652511 — BM BCh 1984 Oxf.; MRCPsych 1989. Cons. Psychiat. (Subst. Abuse) Airedale Gen. Hosp. W. Yorks.

ASPIN, John David Department of Family Psychiatry, St John's Hospital, Livingston EH54 6PP; 4 Kirkhill Court, Broxburn EH52 6HS — MRCS Eng. LRCP Lond. 1969; MRCPsych 1976; DPM Ed. & Glas. 1974. (Birm.) Cons. Child. & Adolesc. Psychiat. W. Lothian Health Dist. Prev: Sen. Regist. (Adolesc. Psychiat.) Roy. Edin. Hosp.

ASPINAL, Robert John (retired) Belwood Cottage, Emery Down, Lyndhurst SO43 7FH Tel: 01703 283705 — MB BS Lond. 1946; MRCS Eng. LRCP Lond. 1945.

ASPINALL, Darren James 21 Redwood Avenue, Liverpool L31 2PE — BM BS 1998 Nottm.; BM BS Nottm 1998.

ASPINALL, Gillian Rebecca 3 Blakefield Drive, Walkden, Manchester M28 7DW — MB ChB 1995 Sheff.

ASPINALL, John William Ivy Grove Surgery, 1 Ivy Grove, Ripley DE5 3HN Tel: 01773 742286 Fax: 01773 749812; Amber Rigg, Pentrich, Ripley, Derby DE5 3RE Tel: 01773 742622 — MB ChB 1958 Manch.; DObst RCOG 1961. Socs: Derby Med. Soc. & Derbysh. Obst. Gp.

ASPINALL, Rebecca Louise 3 Kingsley Road, Cotham, Bristol BS6 6AF — MB BS 1988 Lond.; FRCA 1995. Regist. (Anaesth.) Bristol Roy. Infirm.

ASPINALL, Richard James 13 Woodland Avenue, Bolton BL3 2LR Email: r.j.aspinall@ic.ac.uk — MB ChB 1992 Liverp.; MB ChB (Hons.) Liverp. 1992; BSc (Hons.) Physiol. Liverp. 1989; MRCP (UK) 1995. (Liverpool) DDF Research Fell., Centre for Molecular MicroBiol. & Infec., Imperial Coll., Lond.; SR, NW Thames. Socs: Mem. Brit. Assn. for the Study of Liver. Prev: Lect. (Gastroenterol.) Roy. Postgrad. Med. Sch. Lond.; SHO (Med.) Addenbrooke's Hosp. Camb.; Ho. Off. Roy. Liverp. Univ. Hosp.

ASPINALL, Richard William Chadwell Heath Hospital, Grove Road, Chadwell Heath, Romford RM6 4XH Tel: 020 8924 6553 Fax: 020 8924 6535; 39 Broadstrood, Loughton IG10 2SB Tel: 020 8508 3452 Email: richard@bstrood.freeserve.co.uk — MB BS 1983 Lond.; Cert. Av. Med. 1989; DRCOG 1987; DCCH 1998. (London) Staff Grade (Community Child Health) Redbridge Healthcare Essex.; Med. Adviser Barnardos Lond. Div. Socs: Assoc. Mem. Roy. Coll. Paediat. Child Health. Prev: Ho. Phys. Lond. Hosp.; Ho. Surg. P.ss Alexandra Hosp. Harlow.

ASPINALL, Sebastian Rupert 2 Highland Ville, Halifax HX3 8AG — MB ChB 1994 Bristol.

ASPINALL, William Paul The Old Bakehouse, 6 Corby Road, Cottingham, Market Harborough LE16 8XH — MB ChB 1982 Manch.; MRCGP 1986; DFFP 1993; DRCOG 1984. Prev: Trainee GP Sudden Health Centre Rochdale VTS; Trainee GP/SHO & Ho. Off. (Gen. Med. & Gen. Surg.) Birch Hill Hosp. Rochdale.

ASPLIN, Christopher Michael Royal Cornwall Hospitals Trust, Treliske Hospital, Truro TR1 3LJ — MB ChB 1970 Bristol; MD Bristol 1979; MRCP (UK) 1973.

ASPLIN, Eamon James 18 Barn Owl Close, Langtoft, Peterborough PE6 9RG — MB ChB 1989 Leeds.

ASPLUND, Olof Arne Olle Charing Cross Hospital, Fulham Palace Road, London W6 8RF Tel: 020 8846 1723 Fax: 020 8846 1719; 24 The Riverside, Graburn Way, East Molesey KT8 9BF Tel: 020 8224 3777 Fax: 020 8224 3888 — Med Lic 1971 Stockholm; Med.

Lic. Stockholm 1971; PhD (Plastic Surg.) Sweden 1984; T(S) 1994. Assoc. Specialist (Plastic & Reconstruc. Surg.) Char. Cross Hosp. Lond.; Mem. Edit. Advis. Bd. Jl. Long Term Effects of Med. Implants. Socs: Swedish & Nordic Assn. Plastic Surg.; Profess. Assoc. Brit. Assn. Plastic Surgs. Prev: Plastic Surg. Dept. Karolinska Hosp., Sweden.

ASPOAS, Mr Arthur Robert Regional Neuroscience Centre, Oldchurch Hospital, Waterloo Road, Romford RM7 0BE Tel: 01708 746090 — MB BCh 1980 Witwatersrand; FRCS (Surg. Neurol.) Eng. 1993; FCS(SA) 1989; M Med. (Neurosurg.) Cape Town 1990. (University of the Witwatersrand) Cons. Neurosurg. OldCh. Hosp. Romford. Prev: Cons. Neurosurg. Goote Schur Hosp., Cape Town; Sen. Regist. & Vis. Regist. (Neurosurg.) Newc. u. Tyne.

ASPREY, Juliette Claire East Whinfel, Sheep Plain, East Sussex, Crowborough TN6 3ST — MB BS 1984 Lond.

ASQUITH, Charlotte Elaine London Road Surgery, 46-48 London Road, Carlisle CA1 2EL Tel: 01228 27559 Fax: 01228 594434; Ivy House, Temple Sowerby, Penrith CA10 1SB — MB BCh BAO 1983 Belf.; MB BCh Belf. 1983; MRCGP 1987.

ASQUITH, John Richard 24 Antringham Gardens, Edgbaston, Birmingham B15 3QL — MB ChB 1992 Manch.; MRCP (UK) 1995. Specialist Regist. (Diagnostic Radiol.) Manch.

ASQUITH, Peter (retired) Heartlands Hospital, Bordesley Green E., Birmingham B9 5ST Tel: 0121 766 6611 — MB ChB 1960 Manch.; MD Birm. 1971; FRCP Lond. 1979, M 1965. Hon. Sen. Lect. Univ. Birm. Prev: Cons. Phys. (Gastroenterol.) Heartlands Hosp. Birm.

ASSADOURIAN, Raffi Odiham Health Centre, Deer Park View, Odiham, Basingstoke RG29 1JY — MB BS 1993 Lond.; BSc (Hons.) Lond. 1988, MB BS 1993; MRCGP 1998; DRCOG; DFFP.

ASSAF, Mr Ahmad Abdel-Rahman Sulieman c/o Department of Ophthalmology, Milton Keynes General Hospital, Standing Way, Eaglestone, Milton Keynes MK6 5LD — MD 1984 Sheff.; MD Ophth. Sheff. 1984; MB ChB Baghdad 1971; FRCS Ed. 1977; DO Eng. 1975; Cert. Higher Surgic. Train. Ophth. Ed. 1980. (Baghdad) Lect. Ophth. Univ. Sheff. Socs: Internat. Strabismol. Assn. & Europ. Strabismol Assn. Prev: SHO St. Paul's Eye Hosp. Liverp. AHA (T); Regist. (Ophth.) Roy. Hallamshire Childr. Hosp. Sheff..

ASSAF, Anna Krystina Denham Medical Centre, Tilehouse Way, Denham, Uxbridge UB9 5JD Tel: 01895 832012 Fax: 01895 834704; 145 Ashford Road, Iver SL0 0QE Tel: 01753 630522 Fax: 01753 630522 Email: assaf@vossnet.co.uk — MB ChB 1975 Manch.; DRCOG 1978. (Manch.) Socs: BMA; MDU. Prev: Cons. Primary Care, Saudi Arabia; Family Pract. Newfld., Canada; GP Manch.

ASSASSA, Richard Philip The Coach House, Osbaston Hall, Gotham Lane, Nuneaton CV13 0DR — MB ChB 1988 Leic.

ASSCHER, Professor Sir Adolf William Chairman's Office, Morriston NHS Trust, Morriston Hospital, Morriston, Swansea SA6 6NL Tel: 01792 703332 Fax: 01792 799574; The Old Rectory, Llangan, Bridgend CF35 5DW Tel: 01656 646351 Fax: 01656 646351 — MB BS 1957 Lond.; MB BS (Hons.) 1957; BSc (Anat., Hons.) Lond. 1954, MD 1963; FRCP Lond. 1971, M 1959; MRCS Eng. LRCP Lond. 1957; FFPM RCP (UK) 1994; Hon D.Univ. (Kingston Univ.) 1996. (Lond. Hosp.) Chairm. Morriston Hosp. NHS Trust Swansea; Pres. Fac. Pharmaceut. Med. RCP (UK); Chairm. Coordinating Comm. Cancer Research; Chairm. Bd Sci & Educat. BMA; Non-Exec. Dir. Vanguard Med. Plc; Chairm. Welsh Med. Technol. Forum. Socs: (Ex-Counc.lor) Med. Res. Soc.; (Ex-Sec. & Ex.Pres.) Renal Assn.; Assn. Phys. Prev: Princip. St. Geo. Hosp. Med. Sch. (Univ. Lond.); Vis. Prof. Austral. Soc. Nephrol. 1986; Hon. Cons. Phys. & Prof. Med. St. Geo. Hosp. Lond.

ASSEM, El-Sayed Khalil El-Sayed Ahmad 25 Heath View, London N2 0QD Tel: 020 8883 9484 — LMSSA 1966 Lond.; PhD Lond. 1964; Dip. Med. Cairo 1959, MB BCh 1955; FRCP Ed. 1975, M 1966; FRCP Lond. 1966, M 1997; FRCP Glas. 1981, M 1965; FRCPath. 1982, M 1974; DCH Cairo 1960. Hon. Cons. Phys. Clin. Immunol. & Allergy Univ. Coll. Lond. Hosps. Trust; Reader (Immunopharmacol.) UCL. Socs: Internat. Soc. Immunopharmacol.; Eur. Histamine Research Soc.; Brit. Pharm. Soc. Prev: Hon. Sen. Regist. (Med.) Univ. Coll. Hosp. Lond.; Sen. Research Fell. Univ. Coll. Lond.

ASSERSOHN, Laura Claire 11 Pickwick Road, London SE21 7JN — MB ChB 1993 Manch.

ASSHETON, David Christopher Bungalows, Brown Heath Rd, Christleton, Chester CH3 7PN — MB ChB 1996 Ed.

ASSHETON, Sarah Jane 19 Julian Court, 150 Camden Road, London NW1 9HU — MB BS 1998 Lond.; MB BS Lond 1998.

ASSI, Alexandre Moorfields Eye Hospital, City Road, London EC1V 2PD Tel: 020 7253 3411; Flat 14, Pavilion Court, 17 Thurlow Road, London NW3 5PL Email: alexassi@hotmail.com — MB BS 1991 Lond.; CCST 2001; BSc 1986; FRCOphth 1995. (Univ. Coll. Lond.) Fell. in Vitreoretinal Surg. Prev: Specialist Regist. (Ophth.) N. Thames Lond.

ASSI, Ghassan Cromer Street Surgery, 76 Cromer Street, London WC1H 8DR Tel: 020 7916 4638 Fax: 020 7916 4638 — MB BS 1972 Lond.; BSc Amer. Univ. Beirut 1964.

ASSIN, Mandy c/o Mill New Hospital, Wevill Avenue, Hove BN3 7HZ Tel: 01273 696011 Fax: 01273 242046 — MB BS 1986 Lond.; MRCPsych 1990. (St. Bart. Hosp. Lond.) Cons. (Psychiatric), S.downs Health NHS Trust. Brighton. Prev: Sen. Regist. & Regist. (Psychiat.) St. Geo. Hosp. Lond.; Regist. & SHO Rotat. (Psychiat.) Mid-Downs HA.; Cons. (Psychiatric), S.downs Health NHS Trust. Brighton.

ASSIN, Wilfred David Mill View Hospital, Nevill Avenue, Hove BN3 7HZ Tel: 01273 242052 Fax: 01273 242037 Email: wilfred.assin@southdowns.nhs.uk — MB ChB 1983 Cape Town; MRCPsych 1989. (Univ. Cape Town, S. Afr.) p/t Cons. Psychiat. Mill View Hosp., Hove; Cons. Psychiat., Priory Clinic, Hove. Prev: Cons. Psychiat. Epsom Gen. Hosp.; Sen. & Regist. Rotat. (Psychiat.) St. Geo. Hosp. Lond.

ASSINDER, Frank Rea St Clair, VRD 3 Pine Crescent, Carshalton Beeches, Carshalton SM5 4HQ Tel: 020 8642 0771 — MB BS 1949 Lond.; MRCS Eng. LRCP Lond. 1943; FRCGP 1975, M 1953. (St. Thos.) Prev: Asst. Med. Off. St. Raphael's Hospice Cheam; Chairm. Med. Bds. DHSS; Surg. Lt.-Cdr. RNR (Ret.).

ASSING, Joseph Michael Gaston 93 Knowle Lane, Ecclesall, Sheffield S11 9SN — LAH Dub. 1969.

ASSOGBAKPE-TEVI, Cecile 50 Percy Road, London W12 9QA — MD 1990 Paris. SHO Edgware Gen. Hosp.

ASSOUFI, Basil Khudher Royal Brompton National Heart & Lung Hospital, Sydney St., London SW3 6HP Tel: 020 7352 8121 — MB ChB 1974 Mosul; PhD Lond. 1989; Dip. Cardiac Med. Lond. 1984; Dip. Thoracic Med. Lond. 1983.

ASTALL, Elizabeth Constance South West Lodge, Rede Road, Whepstead, Bury St Edmunds IP29 4ST — MB BChir 1994 Camb.

ASTBURY, Mr Nicholas John West Norwich Hospital, Bowthorpe Road, Norwich NR2 3TU Tel: 01603 288374 Fax: 01603 288261 — MB BS 1972 Lond.; FRCS Eng. 1978; MRCS Eng. LRCP Lond. 1972; FRCOphth 1987; DO Eng. 1974. (Guy's) Cons. Ophth. W. Norwich Hosp.; Vice-Pres., Roy. Coll. of Ophth.s. Prev: Resid. Moorfields Eye Hosp. Lond.; Sen. Regist. Kings Coll. Hosp. Lond.

ASTBURY, Philip Harlestone Road Surgery, 117 Harlestone Road, Northampton NN5 7AQ Tel: 01604 751832 Fax: 01604 586065; 117 Harlestone Road, Northampton NN5 7AQ Tel: 01604 751832 — MB BS 1974 Lond.; MRCGP 1984; D.Occ.Med. RCP Lond. 1995; DRCOG 1978. (Middlx.) Sen. Clin. Med. Off. (Family Plann.) N.ampton HA.

ASTELL, Susan Linda 17 Simpson Street, Stanley DH9 0PF — MB BS 1994 Newc.; BSc (Hons.) Leic. 1983. SHO (Paediat. Emerg.) Starship Hosp. Auckland, NZ. Prev: SHO (Paediat.) & Ho. Off. (Surg.) Bishop Auckland Gen. Hosp.; SHO (A & E) Sunderland Dist. Gen. Hosp.

ASTERIADES, Helen Elizabeth River Place Group Practice, River Place, Essex Road, London N1 2DE Tel: 020 7530 2100 Fax: 020 7530 2102 — MB BS 1984 Lond.; LMSSA Lond. 1984.

ASTHANA, Aruna Town Hall Surgery, 112 King Street, Dukinfield SK16 4LD Tel: 0161 330 2125 Fax: 0161 330 6899; 20 Hunters Court, Stalybridge SK15 2UH Tel: 0161 303 1882 — MB BS 1969 Jiwaji; MS (Gen. Surg.) Delhi 1973.

ASTHANA, Jagdish Chandra 20 Hunters Court, Stalybridge SK15 2UH Tel: 0161 303 1882 — MB BS 1973 Poona; BSc Allahabad 1964; DCH RCP Lond. 1978; DCCH RCP Ed. 1984. SCMO (Child Health) Tameside & Glossop HA.

ASTHANA, Kiaran Church Road, Perton, Wolverhampton WV6 7PD — MB ChB 1981 Birm.; MRCGP 1985; DGM 1989; DRCOG 1983. GP Perton. Prev: GP Highley.

ASTILL, Philip Howard (retired) 67 Macclesfield Road, Buxton SK17 9AG — MB ChB 1954 Birm. Prev: Ho. Off. (Surg.) Gen Hosp. Birm.

ASTIN, Kathryn Joan Surgery, 18 Compton Avenue, Luton LU4 9AZ; 40 Tring Road, Dunstable LU6 2PT — MB ChB 1969 Sheff.; MB ChB (Hons.) Sheff. 1969; MRCP (U.K.) 1972; DObst RCOG 1971. (Sheff.) Prev: Research Asst. Dept. Neurol. United Sheff. Hosps.; SHO (Med.) Aberd. Roy. Infirm.; SHO. Phys. Roy. Hosp. Sheff.

ASTIN, Trevor Walter (retired) 40 Tring Road, Dunstable LU6 2PT Tel: 01582 664996 — MB BS Lond. 1958; MD Lond. 1970; MRCP Lond. 1966; DTM & H Eng. 1963. Prev: Lect. (Med.) Univ. Sheff.

ASTLE, Diane Louise 1 Haigh Cr, Chorley PR7 2QS — BM BS 1997 Nottm.

ASTLE, Lisa Margaret 16 St Johns Close, Woodley, Reading RG5 4RD — MB ChB 1995 Birm.; ChB Birm. 1995. SHO Paediat. Orthop., Alderhey Childr.s Hsp, Lvrpl.

ASTLES, John Graham Willowbrook Medical Centre, 195, Thurncout Road, Leicester LE5 2NL Tel: 0116 262 8368; 34 Westminster Road, Stonegate, Leicester LE2 2EG Tel: 0116 270 7828 — MB ChB 1978 Liverp.; DRCOG 1981. Princip. in Gen. Pract., Leicester; Family Plann. Clinic Doctor, Coalville, Leics. Prev: Ho. Surg. Leicester Roy. Infirm.; Ho. Phys. Groby Rd. Hosp. Leicester.

ASTLEY, Beverley Anne The Middlesex Hospital, Mortimer St., London W1T 3AA Tel: 020 7636 8333; 80 Park Road, London W4 3HL Tel: 020 8994 8327 — MB BS 1975 Lond.; MD Lond. 1988; FFA RCS Eng. 1979. Cons. Anaesth. Univ. Coll. Middlx. Hosp. Lond. Prev: Sen. Regist. (Anaesth.) Univ. Coll. Hosp. Lond.; Regist. (Anaesth.) Roy. Infirm. Edin.

ASTLEY, David Adrian Leadgate Surgery, George Ewen House, Watling Street, Consett DH8 6DP Tel: 01207 583555 Fax: 01207 583585; 64 Queens Road, Blackhill, Consett DH8 0BW — MB ChB 1980 Sheff.; MRCGP (Distinc.) 1987; DCH RCP Lond. 1986; DRCOG 1985. (Sheff.) Durh. Sub-Fac. Represen. N.. Region Coll. Gen. Pract. Prev: Surg. Lt. RN.

ASTLEY, Joan Tawny End, The Ridgeway, Fetcham, Leatherhead KT22 9BA — MRCS Eng. LRCP Lond. 1942.

ASTLEY, William Constantine (retired) Wickhamford, Evesham WR11 6SA Tel: 01386 832728 — MB ChB 1944 Manch.; DObst RCOG 1947. Prev: Sen. Ho. Surg. Manch. Roy. Infirm.

ASTON, Anthony Robin Old Road Surgery, Old Road, Llanelli SA15 3HR Tel: 01554 775555 Fax: 01554 778868 — MB BS 1983 Lond.; MRCGP 1988; DRCOG 1985.

ASTON, Catherine Elizabeth Department of Obstetrics & Gynaecology, Family Services Division, Royal Hampshire County Hospital, Romsey Road, Winchester SO22 5DG — MB ChB 1986 Bristol; MRCOG 1991. Cons. (O & G) Roy. Hants. Co. Hosp. Winchester.

ASTON, Clifford Ellis (retired) Wayside, Carrlane, Great Ouseburn, York YO26 9RW Tel: 01423 330133 — MB BS Lond. 1938; MRCS Eng. LRCP Lond. 1937. Prev: Med. Supt. Ackton Isolat. Hosp.

ASTON, David Lynn Department of Haematology, North Hampshire Hospital, Aldermaston Road, Basingstoke RG24 9NA Tel: 01256 313279 Fax: 01256 313905 — MB BChir 1969 Camb.; MRCPath 1978. (Univ. Coll. Hosp.) Cons. Haemat. N. Hants. Hosp. Prev: Cons. Haemat. Dist. Hosp. Basingstoke.; Ho. Phys. & Regist. Clin. Haemat. Univ. Coll. Hosp. Lond.; Sen. Regist. Clin. Haemat. Roy. Perth Hosp. W.. Austral.

ASTON, Ian Robert Nottingham Occupational Health, Queen's Medical Centre, Nottingham NG7 2UH Tel: 0115 970 9268 Fax: 0115 970 9704; 5 Eagle Close, Beeston, Nottingham NG9 3DY Tel: 0115 922 9582 — MB BS 1977 Lond.; FRCP 2001; BSc Lond. 1974; MRCP (UK) 1981; FFOM RCP Lond. 1997, AFOM 1985, MFOM 1987; T(OM) 1991. (St Mary's Hosp. Lond.) Cons. Occupat. Phys. Qu. Med. Centre Nottm. Socs: Soc. Occupat. Med. Prev: Head Occupat. Health Glaxo Manufacturing Servs. Ltd. Ware Herts.; Med. Off. The Boots Co. plc Nottm.; Regist. (Med.) Leics. HA.

ASTON, Judith Elizabeth The Surgery, 4 Old Steine, Brighton BN1 1EJ Tel: 01273 685588 Fax: 01273 624328; 20 Clifton Street, Brighton BN1 3PH Tel: 01273 710005 — MB BS 1987 Lond.; DRCOG 1991.

ASTON, Mr Niall Oliver Fenn Queen Elizabeth Hospital, London SE18 4QH Tel: 020 8836 5489 Fax: 020 8836 5436 — MB BChir 1976 Camb.; MA Camb. 1975, MChir 1992; FRCS Eng. 1980; MRCS Eng. LRCP Lond. 1975. (St. Thos.) Cons. Gen. and Vasc. Surg., Qu. Eliz.s Hosp. NHS Trust. Prev: Sen. Regist. (Gen. Surg.) Guy's Hosp. Lond.; Regist. (Vasc. Surg.) St. Thos. Hosp. Lond.; Regist. (Paediat. Surg.) Childr. Hosp. Birm.

ASTON, Peter Lennard Bunbury Medical Practice, Bunbury, Tarporley CW6 9PJ Tel: 01829 260168 Fax: 01829 260411; Birchfield, Bunbury, Tarporley CW6 9PJ Tel: 01829 260218 Fax: 01829 260190 — MRCS Eng. LRCP Lond. 1955; FRCGP 1988, M 1970; Dip IMC RCS Ed. 1995; DCH Eng. 1959. (Liverp.) Med. Adviser Hope. Hse. Childr. Hospice OsW.ry.

ASTON, Ralph Harry Richmond (retired) Woodrow, 9 Plymouth Road, Barnt Green, Birmingham B45 8JE Tel: 0121 445 3893 — MB ChB 1948 Birm; MB ChB Birm. 1948; MD Birm 1963; FRCP Lond. 1985; MRCS Eng. LRCP Lond. 1948; FFOM RCP Lond. 1978; DIH Soc. Apoth. Lond. 1955. Prev: Chief Med. Off. Lucas Industries.

ASTON, Robert Communicable Disease Unit, Wigan & Bolton Health Authority, The Pikes Lane Centre, Deane Road, Bolton BL3 5HP Tel: 01204 874374 Fax: 01204 874375 Email: robertaston@yahoo.co.uk; Stoneyacre, Foxholes Road, Horwich, Bolton BL6 6AL Tel: 01204 468896 Email: robert.aston@wab-ha.nwest.nhs.uk — MB ChB 1969 Ed.; MSc Manch. 1988; BSc Ed. 1966; MFPHM RCP (UK) 1990; MRCGP 1978. Cons. Communicable Dis. Control Wigan & Bolton HA.

ASTON, Sarah Jane 19 Charmouth Road, Bath BA1 3LJ — BM BS 1994 Nottm.; DCH RCP Lond. 1998.

ASTON, William John Spicer 20 Longdon Croft, Warwick Road, Knowle, Solihull B93 9LJ — MB BS 1997 Lond.

ASTROULAKIS, Zoe Maria Jane 11 Lansdowne Gardens, London SW8 2EQ — MB BS 1997 Lond.

ASTRUC, Dominique Marion Nicole 30 Limes Av, London N12 8QN — MB BS 1997 Lond.

ASUMU, Theophilus Osiregbheme 2 Woodlea, Worsley, Manchester M28 2BJ Tel: 0161 799 4915 Email: theo@asumu.freeserve.co.uk — MB BS 1988 Benin, Nigeria; FRCS Eng. 1993; FRCS (Tr. & Orth.), 1998. (Univ. Benin, Nigeria) Specialist Regist. (Orthop. Surg.) N. W. Region. Socs: Fell. Manch. Med. Soc.; BMA; Assoc. Mem. BOA. Prev: Regist. (Orthop. Surg.) Roy. Lancaster Infirm.; Regist. (Orthop. Surg.) Roy. Oldham Hosp.; Regist. (Orthop. Surg.) Hope Hosp. Salford.

ASVER, Mohamed Auffer Acute Psychiatry Unit, Bronllys Hospital, Bromllys, Brecon LD3 0LY Tel: 01874 711671 Fax: 01874 712045; 12 Gorse Farm, Llandrindod Wells LD1 5SH Tel: 01597 825578 Fax: 01597 825578 Email: laara@asver.freeserve.co.uk — MB BS 1982 Colombo. Staff Grade Phys. (Age Care) Llandrindod Wells Hosp. Powys; Mem. Sri Lanka Med. Counc. Socs: BMA. Prev: SHO (Elderly Care) Mayday Hosp. Thornton Heath, Surrey; SHO (Elderly Care) Worthing & S.lands Hosps.; SHO (Elderly Care) Norwich Healthcare Trust.

ASWANI, Daulatram 16 St James Road, Heaton Moor, Stockport SK4 4RE Tel: 0161 443 1283 Fax: 0161 443 1283 — MB BS 1973 Sind; MB BS Sind, Pakistan 1973.

ASWANI, Girdhari Tulsiram The Surgery, 12 Hanworth Road, Feltham TW12 5AB Tel: 020 8890 2208 Fax: 020 8893 1399; 4 Shepherds Close, Shepperton TW17 9AL — MB BS 1963 Gujarat; DA Eng. 1972. GP Feltham. Prev: Regist. (Anaesth.) Harefield Hosp. & Ashford Hosp. Middlx. & Mt. Vernon Hosp. N.wood; SHO (Cas.) Greenwich Hosp. Lond.

ASWANI, Kanyalal Allum Medical Centre, Fairlop Road, Leytonstone, London E11 1BN Tel: 020 8539 2513 Fax: 020 8558 0525 — MB BS 1986 Newc.; MRCGP 1990. Chair. Redbridge Waltham Forest MAAG.

ASWANI, Nivedita Margaret Springfield Farmhouse, Whitwell Lane, Stocksbridge, Sheffield S36 1GB — MB ChB 1996 Sheff.

ASZKENASY, Odet Mark The Barn, Back Lane, Osmotherley, Northallerton DL6 3BJ — MB BS 1982 Lond.; MRCP (UK) 1985; MFPHM RCP (UK) 1993; DCH RCP Lond. 1989; DA, FARCS 1987; MRCPCH. (Roy. Free Hosp.) Cons. Community Phys. for Child Health S. Tees Community & Ment. Health Trust Middlesbrough; Cons. Pub. Health Med. Tees Health Cleveland. Prev: Sen. Regist. (Pub. Health Med.) N.. RHA; SHO (Paediat.) Roy. Free Hosp. Lond.; Trainee GP Borehamwood Herts. VTS.

ASZTALOS, Anthony Ludwig Mario Binbrook, Lincoln — MD 1953 Budapest; LAH Dub. 1959. Socs: BMA.

ATACK, Judith Ann Bank Street Surgery, 9 Bank Street, Keswick CA12 5JY Tel: 017687 72438 Fax: 017687 72454; Tweedsmuir, Rogerfield, Keswick CA12 4BL — MB ChB 1971 Aberd.; MRCGP 1981; DRCOG 1979. GP Clin. Asst. Keswick Hosp. Prev: Trainee GP E. Cumbria VTS; SHO (A & E) Cumbld. Infirm. Carlisle.

ATALAR, Mr Ali Tekin Fullwell Cross Health Centre, 1 Tomswood Hill, Barkingside, Ilford IG6 2HG Tel: 020 8500 0231 Fax: 020 8491 1598; Oak Lodge, 33 Hillcrest Road, Loughton IG10 4QH Tel: 020 8532 0230 — MD 1970 Istanbul; FRCS Ed. 1978; MRCS Eng. LRCP Lond. 1979. (Istanbul) Socs: Roy. Soc. Med. Prev: Regist. (Surg.) Hackney Hosp. Lond.

ATALLA, Albert Estasy, Lt.-Col. RAMC Retd. Luxor, 9 Carrick Gardens, Middleton, Manchester M24 6TB — MB BCh 1969 Cairo; MFFP 1995; FRCOG 1992, M 1979. Cons. O & G Birch Hill Hosp. Rochdale. Socs: Brit. Fertil. Soc.; Brit. Soc. Colpos. & Cerv. Path.; Brit. Menopause Soc. Prev: Cons. O & G Louise Margt. Matern. Wing Camb. Milit. Hosp. Aldershot; Cons. O & G RAMC.

ATALLA, Rami Kamal 80B South Ealing Road, South Ealing, London W5 4QB — MB BCh 1987 Ain Shams; MRCOG 1994.

ATALLAH, Magdy George Department of Genitourinary Medicine, St Helier Hospital, Carshalton SM5 1AA Tel: 020 8296 2505; 70 Mostyn Road, Wimbledon, London SW19 3LN Tel: 020 8543 1029 Fax: 020 8543 3744 — MB ChB 1970 Cairo; Dip. Dermat. Lond 1978; Dip. GU Med. Soc. Apoth. Lond. 1978. Staff Phys. (Genitourin.) St. Helier Hosp. Carshalton. Socs: Med. Soc. Study VD. Prev: Staff Phys. (Genitourin. Med.) St. Thos. Hosp. Lond. & Upton Hosp. Slough.

ATAN, Deniz Taunton and Somerset Hospital, Musgrove Park, Taunton TA1 5DA Tel: 01823 333444; 11 Parkfield Drive, Taunton TA1 5BX Tel: 01823 326428 Email: atand@usa.net — BM BCh 1996 Oxf.; BA Cantab 1993, MA 1997. (Cambridge and Oxford) SHO (Gen. Med.) Taunton & Som. Hosp. Socs: BMA; MDU. Prev: Jun. Ho. Off. (Med.) Freeman Hosp. Newc.; Jun. Ho. Off. (Surg.) Roy. Devon & Exeter Hosp. (Wonford) Exeter.

ATANDO, Seth Wellington 73 Whipps Cross Road, Leytonstone, London E11 1NJ Tel: 020 8530 3962 — Vrach 1965 1st Moscow Med. Inst.; DTM & H Liverp. 1969. (Moscow) Staff Grade Phys. (c/o Elderly) Upton Hosp. Slough. Socs: MDU. Prev: Locum UCL Lond.; Regist. (Geriat.) St. Baths Homeeton.

ATANG, Fonawah Martyn 30 Park Grove, York YO31 8LG Tel: 01904 632774 Email: fonawah@hotmail.com; Email: fonawah@hotmail.com — MB ChB 1997 Sheff. (Sheff.) Roy. Preston Hosp.

ATAULLAH, Ifat Jabin 36 Watford Road, Northwood HA6 3NY — MB BS 1987 Lond.

ATAULLAH, Mr Sajid Mahmood Manchester Royal Eye Hospital, Oxford Road, Manchester M13 9WH Tel: 0161 276 1234 Email: saj789@hotmail.com — MB BS 1991 Lond.; FRCOphth 1996. Specialist Regist. Manch. Roy. Eye Hosp. (MREH). Prev: SHO (Ophth.) Croydon Eye Unit.; SHO MREH.

ATAYI, Michael Attiogbe 16 Kitchener Road, Thornton Heath, Croydon CR7 8QL — MB ChB 1986 Ghana.

ATCHA, Abdul Wahid 25 Peace Street, Bolton BL3 5LJ — MB ChB 1998 Manch.; MB ChB Manch 1998.

ATCHA, Sabiha 25 Peace Street, Bolton BL3 5LJ — MB BChir 1994 Camb.

ATCHA, Zaheda Idris Green Fields, Beaumont Road, Lostock, Bolton BL6 4JJ — MB ChB 1994 Manch.

ATCHA, Zakyeya Cornwall and Isles of Scilly HA, John Keay House, Tregonissey Road, St Austell PL25 4NQ Tel: 01726 77777 Fax: 01726 71777; 50 Carrine Road, Newbridge, Truro TR1 3XB Tel: 01872 240625 Email: zakyeya.atcha@ho.cios-ha.swest.nhs.uk — MB ChB 1990 Liverp.; MB ChB Liverp.1990; MPH Liverp. 1997. Trainee Regist. (Pub. Health) Cornw. & Isles of Scilly HA. Prev: SHO (Infec. Dis.) Fazakerley Hosp. Liverp.; SHO Rotat. (Med.) Ormskirk & Wrighton Hosps.; RMO & Admitting Off. Goulburn Valley Base Hosp. Shepparton Vict. Austral.

ATCHESON, Robert 48 Latimer Road, Cropston, Leicester LE7 7GN — MB BS 1985 Lond.; MD Lond. 1994; FCAnaesth 1991.

ATCHESON, Susan Fiona 75 Whitehall Road, Aberdeen AB25 2PQ — MB ChB 1997 Aberd.

ATCHISON, David Gerald The Surgery, 56 Northern Road, Portsmouth PO6 3DS Tel: 023 9237 3321 — MB BCh BAO 1988 Belf. (Qu. Univ. Belf.) Police Surg. Hants. Constab. Prev: GP Mid Ulster Hosp. Magherafelt VTS.

ATCHISON, Eileen Maude Gallows Street Surgery, 50 Gallows Street, Dromore BT25 1BD Tel: 028 9269 2758; 50 Ballymacormick Road, Dromore BT25 1OR Tel: 01846 692294 — MB BCh BAO 1980 Belf.; MRCGP 1984; DCCH RCP Ed. 1985; DRCOG 1983; DCH RCPSI 1982. (Qu. Univ. Belf.) Clin. Med. Off. (Family Plann.) N. & W.. EHSSB. Prev: Clin. Med. Off. S.. Health & Social Servs. Bd.

ATCHISON, Robert Keith c/o Fulwell Medical Practice, Ebdon Lane, Fulwell, Sunderland SR6 8 Tel: 0191 548 3635; 13 Bywell Road, Cleadon, Sunderland SR6 7QT — MB BCh BAO 1983 Belf.; Cert. Family Plann. JCC 1990; DCH RCPI Dub. 1988. Socs: BMA.

ATCHLEY, Julian Thomas Martin 44 Nuns Road, Winchester SO23 7EF Tel: 01962 620398 Email: jtma@mcmail.com — MB BS 1986 Lond.; MA Camb. 1987, BA 1983; MRCP (UK) 1990; FRCR 1996. Specialist Regist. (Radiol.) Soton. Univ. Hosps. Prev: Regist. (Med.) Roy. S. Hants. Hosp. Soton.; SHO (Renal) St. Thos. Hosp. Lond.; SHO (Med.) Broomfield Hosp. Chelmsford.

ATEAQUE, Asif 24 Brunel Street, Burnley BB12 8AE — MB BCh 1995 Wales.

ATENSTAEDT, Robert Leslie Worcester College, Walton St., Oxford OX1 2HB — MB BS 1995 Lond.

ATEWAH, Mr Ramadan Mohamed Doctors' Residence, Birmingham Heartlands Hospital, 51 Bordesley Green East, Bordesley Green, Birmingham B9 5SS — MB BCh 1983 Garyounis, Libya; FRCS Ed. 1989.

ATHA, Patricia (retired) 12 Outwoods Road, Loughborough LE11 3LY Tel: 01509 212450 — MB ChB 1952 Leeds; DA Eng. 1957.

ATHALE, Dinor Madhusudan The Health Centre, Rose Tree Avenue, Cudworth, Barnsley S72 8UA Tel: 01226 710326 Fax: 01226 780627 — MB BS 1971 Rajasthan. (Rajasthan) GP Barnsley, S. Yorks.

ATHANASSIOU, Evangelos Lister Hospital, IVF Unit, Chelsea Bridge Road, London SW1W 8RH Tel: 020 7730 3417; 6 Wealden Court, Constitution Road, Chatham ME5 7EG Tel: 01634 817944 — Ptychio Iatrikes 1992 Thessalonika; DFFP 1995. (Aristotle Univ. Greece) Regist. Roy. Sussex Co. Hosp. Brighton. Socs: MDU; BMUS; MDU. Prev: SHO Greenwich Gen. Hosp. Lond.; SHO (O & G) S.mead Hosp. Bristol; SHO (O & G) King's Mill Hosp. Sutton in Ashfield.

ATHANASSIOU, Stavros 35A Dulwich Village, London SE21 7BN — Ptychio Iatrikes 1987 Athens.

ATHAWES, Richard William Bridger Dept. Old Age Psychiatry, Royal Cornhill Hospital, 26 Cornhill Road, Aberdeen AB10 6TJ Tel: 01224 557031 Fax: 01224 403024; 9 Gladstone Place, Queen's Cross, Aberdeen AB10 6UX Tel: 01244 322895 — MB ChB 1988 Aberd.; MRCPsych 1993. Cons., Dept. of Old Age Psychiat., Roy. Conrnhill Hosp. Aberd. Prev: Sen. Regist. Old Age Psychiat., Grampian Health Bd.

ATHERLEY, Carolyn Elizabeth Dept. of Ophthalmology, St James' University Hospital, Leeds LS9 7TF — MB ChB 1986 Sheff.; FCOphth. 1992. Specialist Regist. Ophth. St Jas. Univ. Hosp. Leeds.

ATHERLEY, David Bryan Health Centre, Curtis St., Hucknall, Nottingham NG15 7JE Tel: 0115 963 3580 Fax: 0115 963 3733; 180 Moor Road, Papplewick, Nottingham NG15 8EQ — MB ChB 1960 Sheff. (Sheff.) Prev: SHO (Anaesth.) Nottm. City Hosp.

ATHERTON, Anthony Mark Joseph 3 Farriers Way, Wirral CH48 1QJ — MB BS 1989 Newc.; FRCA 1995. Cons. Anaesthatist, Wirral Hosps, NHS Trust.

ATHERTON, David Allen 54A Manchester Road, Greenfield, Oldham OL3 7HH — MB ChB 1974 Manch. Prev: SHO (A & E) Oldham Roy. Infirm.; SHO (O & G) & Ho. Off. (Surg.) Oldham & Dist. Gen. Hosp.

ATHERTON, David John Great Ormond Street Hospital for Children, London WC1N 3JH Tel: 020 7405 9200 Fax: 020 7813 8174 — MB 1974 Camb.; BChir 1973; FRCP Lond. 1985; MRCP (UK) 1975. Cons. Dermat. Hosp. for Childr. Gt. Ormond St. & St. Johns Inst. Dermat. Centre St. Thos. Hosp. Lond.; Sen. Lect. Inst. Child Health Lond. Prev: Sen. Regist. (Dermat.) Guys Hosp. Lond.; Research Fell. (Paediat. Dermat.) Inst. Child Health Lond.; MRC Research Train. Fell. (Paediat. Immunol.) Inst. Child Health Lond.

ATHERTON, Desmond Joseph, Capt. RAMC (retired) 32 The Firs, Coventry CV5 6QD Tel: 01203 672360 — MB ChB 1944 Manch.;

MRCS Eng. LRCP Lond. 1945; DObst RCOG 1948. Prev: GP Coventry.

ATHERTON, Desmond Paul Lindsay Dept of Anaesthesia, Whiston Hospital, Prescot L35 5DR Tel: 0151 430 1267 Fax: 0151 430 1155 Email: dplath@globnet.co.uk; 45 Charles Berrington Road, Liverpool L15 9HG — MB ChB 1989 Liverp.; FRCA 1995. (Liverpool) Cons. Anaesth. St Helens & Knowsley NHS Trust.

ATHERTON, Edward Nicholas 106 Birch Avenue, Penwortham, Preston PR1 0LP — MB ChB 1993 Dundee.

ATHERTON, Ewa Anna 26 New Road, Lymm WA13 9DY — MB BS 1988 Lond.; DCH RCP Lond. 1993. SHO (Paediat.) Birm. Matern. Hosp. Prev: SHO (Histopath.) Dudley Rd. Hosp. Birm.

ATHERTON, Francis DFID (Bangladesh), c/o FCO, King Charles St., London SW1A 2AH Tel: 00 880 288 2705 Fax: 00 880 288 3474 Email: f-atherton@dfid.gov.uk; British High Commission, U.N. Road, Baridhara, Dhaka, Bangladesh — MB ChB 1982 Leeds; MPH Leeds 1993; MFPHM RCP (UK) 1993; MRCGP 1988; DCH RCP Lond. 1988. Sen. Adviser, Health & Populat. - Dept. for Internat. Developm. Prev: Dist. Health Off. Dowa Dist., Malawi; Sen. Regist. (Pub. Health Med.) Bradford HA.; Director, Tranzanic family health project.

ATHERTON, James Bernard Oaklands, Middlewich Medical Centre, St. Anns Walk, Middlewich CW10 9BE Tel: 01606 836481; Newlands, Oak Tree Lane, Cranage, Crewe CW3 9AB Tel: 01477 33326 — MB ChB 1977 Manch.; PhD Manch. 1972, BSc (Chem.) 1969, MB ChB 1977. Socs: BMA & Family Plann. Assn. Prev: Trainee GP S. Manch. VTS.

ATHERTON, Janet 3 Farriers Way, Wirral CH48 1QJ — MB BS 1986 Newc.; MSc Newc. 1991; MFPHM RCP (UK) 1993. Cons. Pub. Health Med. Wirral Health.

ATHERTON, Professor John Christopher Division of Gastroenterology, University Hospital, Nottingham NG7 2UH Tel: 0115 924 9924 Fax: 0115 942 2232 — BM BCh 1986 Oxf.; FRCP (UK) 2001; MA Camb. 1987, BA 1983; MRCP (UK) 1990; MD Camb 1999. (Univ. Camb. & Oxf.) MRC Sen. Clinic. Fell. Div. of Gastroenterol. & Inst. Infec. & Immunity Univ. Nottm.; Prof. (Gastroenterol.) & Hon. Cons. Phys. Socs: Brit. Soc. Gastroenterol.; Soc. Gen. Microbiol.; Nottm. Gut Gp. Prev: MRC Clinican Scientist Fell. Div. Of Gastroenterol. & Inst. Infetc. & Immunity , Univ. Nottm.; Post-Doctoral Research Fell. (Infec. Dis.) Vanderbilt Univ. Nashville, Tennessee, USA; Clin. Research Fell. (Therap.) Univ. Nottm.

ATHERTON, Lesley Ann Department of Anaesthetics, 12th Floor, Royal Liverpool University Hospital, Prescot Street, Liverpool L7 8XP — MB ChB 1998 Liverp.; MB ChB Liverp 1998.

ATHERTON, Martin Tristram Colin Park Road Surgery, 17 Park Road, St. Annes on Sea, Lytham St Annes FY8 1PW Tel: 01253 727938 — MB ChB 1982 Leeds; MRCGP 1987; DRCOG 1986; DCH RCP Lond. 1985.

ATHERTON, Mary Theresa The Garden Flat, 26 Lower Redland Road, Bristol BS6 6SU — MB ChB 1994 Leic.; BSc Biol. Chem. 1989; DRCOG 1996; DFFP 1997. SHO Geriat. S.mead Hosp. Bristol.

ATHERTON, Neil Anthony — MB ChB 1994 Leeds; MRCP 1998. (Leeds) Regist. Paediat. Special Care, Sydney, Australia. Socs: BMA. Prev: SHO (Paediat. Neurol.) Leeds Gen. Infirm.; SHO (Paediat. Oncol.) St. James' Univ. Hosp. Leeds; SHO (Paediat.) St. James' Univ. Hosp.

ATHERTON, Pauline Anne 36 Swann Lane, Cheale Hume, Cheadle SK8 7HR — MB ChB 1996 Birm.

ATHERTON, Philip James Sunnybank House Medical Centre, 506 Huddersfield Road, Towngate, Wyke, Bradford BD12 9NG Tel: 01274 424111 Fax: 01274 691256; Lake View, 90 Pk Road, Low Moor, Bradford BD12 0DJ Tel: 01274 673889 — MB ChB 1977 Leeds; MRCGP 1987; DRCOG 1982.

ATHERTON, Philip James Institute for Cancer Studies, Clinical Research Block, Queen Elizabeth Hospital, Edgbaston, Birmingham B15 2TH Tel: 0121 414 3291 Fax: 0121 414 3700 Email: p.j.atherton@bham.ac.uk; 26 New Road, Lymm WA13 9DY — MB BS 1985 Lond.; MRCP (UK) 1992; FRCR 1996. Clin. Research Fell. (Clin. Oncol.) Qu. Eliz. Hosp. Birm. Prev: Regist. (Clin. Oncol.) Qu. Eliz. Hosp. Birm.

ATHERTON, Sarah Jane Riversdale Surgery, 59 Bridge Street, Belper DE56 1AY Tel: 01773 822386 — BM BS 1989 Nottm.; BMedSci Nottm. 1987; MRCGP 1995; DRCOG 1994.

ATHERTON, Stephen Thomas 44 View Road, Rainhill, Prescot L35 0LS — MB ChB 1970 Liverp.; FRCP Lond. 1991; MRCP (UK) 1975. Cons. Phys. Internal Med. & IC. Socs: IC Soc. & Europ. Respirat. Soc.; BMA.

ATHERTON, William 16 Higham Court, Wigan WN1 3ND — MB 1955 Camb.; BChir 1954.

ATHERTON, William Guy Riverside, East Mills, Fordingbridge SP6 2JS — MB BChir 1993 Camb.

ATHEY, Geoffrey Norman 36 Greenacres, Wetheral, Carlisle CA4 8LD Tel: 01228 561049 — MB ChB 1967 Manch.; FRCR 1975; FFR 1974; DMRD Eng. 1973. Cons. Radiol. E. Cumbria Health Dist. Socs: Brit. Med. Ultrasound Soc.; Brit. Inst. Radiol. Prev: Sen. Regist. (Radiol.) N. W.. RHA; SHO (Surg.) Manch. Roy. Infirm.; Asst. Lect. Anat. Manch. Univ.

ATHEY, Richard James 36 Greenacres, Wetheral, Carlisle CA4 8LD — MB BS 1997 Newc.

ATHOW, Mrs Anna Christine 23 Letchford Gardens, London NW10 6AD — MB BS 1971 Lond.; FRCS Eng. 1979.

ATHOW-FROST, Theresa Anne Margaret Chudleigh Woods Farm, Chudleigh, Newton Abbot TQ13 0NE; Royal Devon & Exeter Hospital, Barrack Road, Exeter EX2 5DW — MB BS 1968 Lond.; MRCP 1971; MRCS Eng. LRCP Lond. 1968; DTM & H Liverp. 1973. Assoc. Specialist (Dermat.).

ATHREYA, Kannan 26D Grosvenor Road, London E11 2EP — MB BS 1992 Lond.

ATHWAL, Balwindar Singh 10 Royal Crescent, Edinburgh EH3 6PZ Tel: 0131 556 0996 — MB ChB 1989 Ed.; BSc (Hons.) Ed. 1988, MB ChB 1989; MRCP Ed. 1992. (Univ. Edin.)

ATHWAL, Shivinder Singh 9 Early Bank, Stalybridge SK15 2RU — MB BS 1977 Poona; LRCP LRCS Ed. LRCPS Glas 1985.

ATIA, Waheeb Atalla Whittington Hospital, Archway Wing, (ASHC), London N19 5NF Tel: 020 7530 5812 Fax: 020 7530 5823; 40 Constantine Road, Hampstead, London NW3 2NG — MB BCh 1957 Cairo; MSc (Steroid Endocrinol.) Leeds 1971; LMSSA Lond. 1966; FRCP Ed. 1994; FRCP Lond. 1987; MRCP (UK) 1970; MRCP Ed. 1964. Cons. Phys. (Genitourin. Med.) Camden & Islington Community Trust.

ATIBA, Olanrewaju Emmanuel 8 Pintail Close, Haresfinch, St Helens WA11 9YN — MB BS 1980 Lagos; MRCOG 1994.

ATINE, Mr George Isaac Ojok Orthopaedic Unit, Gloucester Royal Hospital, Great Western Road, Gloucester GL1 3NL Tel: 01452 528555; 34 Beaumont Road, Longlevens, Gloucester GL2 0EP Tel: 01452 527959 — MB ChB 1974 Makerere; FRCS Ed. 1981; FRCS Glas. 1981. (Makerere) Assoc. Specialist (Orthop. & Trauma) Glos. Hosp. NHS Trust. Socs: BMA; Brit. Orthop. Assn. Prev: Regist. (Orthop. & Trauma) Glos. HA; Regist. (Surg.) EHSSB N. Irel.; Regist. (Traum. & Orthop. Surg.) E. Glam. Gen. Hosp. Pontypridd.

ATINE-OKELLO, Mr Martin Luther 28 Fishbourne Lane, Ryde PO33 4EZ; St. Mary's Hospital, Newport PO30 5TG — MB ChB 1975 Kampala; FRCS Ed. 1988. Assoc. Specialist (Orthop.) St. Mary's Hosp. Newport.

ATIOMO, Pippa-Louise 18 Greenways, Holt NR25 6RX — MB BChir 1991 Camb.; BA Oxf. 1988; MRCP (UK) 1994. (Oxf. & Camb.) Trainee GP Saltash, Plymouth. Prev: Hon. Clin. Research Fell. BRACE Centre, Blackberry Hill Hosp. Bristol; SHO (Gen. Med.) Frenchay Hosp. Bristol.

ATKIN, Christine Elizabeth Valley Medical Centre, Johnson Street, Stocksbridge, Sheffield S36 1BX Tel: 0114 288 3841 Fax: 0114 288 7897; Huthwaite Hall, Huthwaite Lane, Thurgoland, Sheffield S35 7AF — MB ChB 1983 Sheff.; MRCGP 1988; DCH RCP Lond. 1986; DRCOG 1985. (Sheffield) Socs: RCGP.

ATKIN, Claire Mary Shepperton Health Centre, Shepperton Court Drive, Laleham Road, Shepperton TW17 8EJ Tel: 01932 220524 Fax: 01932 244948 — MB BS 1990 Lond.; BSc Lond. 1982; MRCGP 1995; DCH RCP Lond. 1992. (Char. Cross & Westm.)

ATKIN, Gary Keith 33 Cumberland Avenue, Leyland, Preston PR25 1BH — MB ChB 1996 Manch.

ATKIN, Helen Susan 115 Cassiobury Drive, Watford WD17 3AH Tel: 01923 220318 — MB ChB 1960 Birm.; MRCS Eng. LRCP Lond. 1960. (Birm.) Sch. Med. Off. S.W. Herts. Health Dist. Prev: Ho. Phys. Little Bromwich Gen. Hosp. Birm.; Ho. Surg. (Obst.) St. Paul's Hosp. Hemel Hempstead.

ATKIN, Karen Jane Newlands, 36 Park Lane, Congleton CW12 3DG — MB BS 1989 Lond.; MRCP (UK) 1992; Dip. Pharm. Med. RCP (UK) 1994. Med. Adviser Zeneca Pharmaceuts. (Internat.) Lond. Prev: Sen. Med. Adviser Sandoz Pharmaceut. Surrey; Med. Adviser Lederle Laborats. Lond.

ATKIN, Mark Valley Medical Centre, Johnson Street, Stocksbridge, Sheffield S36 1BX Tel: 0114 288 3841 Fax: 0114 288 7897; Huthwaite Hall, Huthwaite Lane, Thurgoland, Sheffield S35 7AF — MB ChB 1983 Sheff.; MRCGP 1988; DRCOG 1988. Prev: SHO (A & E) Roy. Hallamsh. Hosp. Sheff.; Ho. Off. Lodge Moor Hosp. Sheff.; Ho. Off. Roy. Hallamsh. Hosp. & N. Gen. Hosp. Sheff.

ATKIN, Mark Paul 14 Oaks Road, Willington, Derby DE65 6DU — BM 1997 Soton.

ATKIN, Niels Bentzen 37 Woodstock Avenue, London NW11 9RG — MRCS Eng. LRCP Lond. 1939; MD Camb. 1974, MB BChir 1950; DMRT Eng. 1948. (Camb. & Middlx.) Cytogeneticist, Mt. Vernon Hosp. N.wood. Socs: Fell. Roy. Soc. Med; Brit. Assn. Cancer Research. Prev: Flight Lt. RAF Med. Br.; Asst. Radiotherap. & Ho. Surg. Middlx. Hosp.

ATKIN, Paul Damian Plas y Bryn Surgery, Chapel Street, Wrexham LL13 7DE Tel: 01978 351308 Fax: 01978 312324; Min-yr-Afon Cottage, Overton Bridge, Erbistock, Wrexham LL13 0DS — MB ChB 1983 Manch.; BSc St. And. 1980; MRCGP 1988; DRCOG 1988. Prev: Trainee GP Rochdale VTS; SHO N. Manch. GPVTS; SHO (Gen. & Geriat. Med.) Birch Hill Hosp. Rochdale.

ATKIN, Philip Alan 19 Mallory House, Teviot St., London E14 6QF — MB BS 1998 Lond.; MB BS Lond 1998; BDS Lond 1989; MSc Lond 1995. (King's College London) Ho. Off. Surg. Prev: Ho. Off. Med., Greenwich; Lect. (PT), Oral & Maxillofacial Surg.

ATKIN, Stephen Lawrence Michael White Diabetes Centre, Brocklehurst Building, 220-236 Anlaby Road, Hull HU3 2RW Tel: 01482 675365 Fax: 01482 675370 Email: s.l.atkin@medschool.hull.ac.uk; Towerhurst, 75 Ferriby Rd, Hessle HU13 0HU Tel: 01482 640657 — MB BS 1984 Newc.; BSc (Biochem.) Newc. 1979; PhD Liverp. 1993; MRCP (UK) 1987; FRCP 1999. (Newc upon Tyne) Reader in Med., Acad. Head, Diabetes and Endocrinol.; Sen. Lect. (Hon. Cons.) Dept. Med. Roy. Hull Hosp. Trust. Prev: Sen. Regist. Hull Roy. Infirm. & Kingston Gen. Hosp. Hull; MRC Train. Fell. (Med.) Roy. Liverp. Hosp.; Regist. Hope Hosp. Salford.

ATKINS, Atheling Fennell John 1 Scugdale Road, Swainby, Northallerton DL6 3DP — MB BS 1960 Lond.; MRCS Eng. LRCP Lond. 1960; FRCOG 1984, M 1971. (Lond. Hosp.) Hon. Cons. Fetal Med. S. Tees AC. Hosps. NHS Trust. Prev: Sen. Regist. (O & G) Birm. AHA (T); Regist. (O & G) Hammersmith Hosp. Lond.

ATKINS, Catherine Mary (retired) King's Garn, Fritham, Lyndhurst SO43 7HH — M.B., Ch.B. Aberd. 1943; MFCM 1972. Prev: SCM Dorset AHA.

ATKINS, Catherine Sara 3 Weavers Walk, Swynnerton, Stone ST15 0QZ — MB ChB 1997 Leic.

ATKINS, Christopher John Graystones Medical Centre, 33 Graystones Road, Sheffield S11 7BJ Tel: 0114 266 6528; 51 Glebe Road, Sheffield S10 1FB — MB BS 1981 Lond.; DRCOG 1984.

ATKINS, David Ferrybridge Medical Centre, 8-10 High St., Ferrybridge, Knottingley WF11 9NQ Tel: 01977 672109 Fax: 01977 671107 — MRCS Eng. LRCP Lond. 1959.

ATKINS, Donald Roger (retired) Greenhoe, Norwich Road, Swaffham PE37 8DD Tel: 01760 721348 — MB 1967 Camb.; BChir 1966; FRCGP 1993, M 1983; DObst RCOG 1968.

ATKINS, Frances Elizabeth 4 Old Mill Close, Burley-in-Wharfedale, Ilkley LS29 7RU Tel: 01223 217141, 01943 865087; 4 Old Mill Close, Burley-in-Wharfedale, Ilkley LS29 7RU — MB ChB 1989 Leeds. p/t GP Retainee, Sataire Med. Centre, Bradford; Clin. Asst., Dermat. Dept. Wharfedale Gen. Hosp., Otley, Leeds.

ATKINS, George (retired) Georgian, 2B Plymouth Road, Barnt Green, Birmingham B45 8JA — MB ChB 1955 Birm.; MRCS Eng. LRCP Lond. 1955.; MRCGP 1968; DObst RCOG 1960. Prev: GP Birm.

ATKINS, James Leon The Surgery, Alexandra Road, Lowestoft NR32 1PL Tel: 01502 574524 Fax: 01502 531526 — MB BS 1984 Lond. (The Royal London Hosp.) GP.

ATKINS, Jane Louise 18 Charterhouse Close, Nailsea, Bristol BS48 4PU — MB BCh 1995 Wales.

ATKINS, Jo-Anne Lesley 155 Longedge Lane, Wingerworth, Chesterfield S42 6PR — MB ChB 1994 Manch.

ATKINS, Mr John (retired) The Pound, Harley, Shrewsbury SY5 6LP Tel: 01743 263 — MB ChB Birm. 1954; FRCS Eng. 1961; FRCS Ed. 1961; MRCS Eng. LRCP Lond. 1954; DLO Eng. 1960. Prev: Cons. Surg. (Otorhinolaryngol.) Dudley Rd. Gp. Hosps.

ATKINS, Maria Cecilia Cranbourne Centre, Mutton Lane, Potters Bar EN6 3AA Tel: 01707 657630 — MB BS 1988 Lond.; 1992 MRCPsych. Cons. (Gen. Adult Psychiat.), Barnet.

ATKINS, Mark Charles 100 Southwood Avenue, Knaphill, Woking GU21 2EY Tel: 01483 486597 — MB BS 1986 Lond.; MB BS Lobd, 1983; BSc Lond. 1983, MSc 1993; MRCPath 1993. Research Fell. Roy. Free Hosp. Lond. Socs: Soc. Gen. Microbiol.; Assn. Clin. Path. Prev: Sen. Regist. (Virol.) St. Mary's Hosp. Lond.

ATKINS, Martin Roderick Department of Psychiatry of Later Life, Mental Health Services of Salford, Meadowbrook, Stott Lane, Salford M6 8DD Tel: 0161 772 3767 Fax: 0161 772 3772 — MB ChB 1984 Zimbabwe; LRCP LRCS Ed. LRCPS Glas. 1987; MRCPsych 1993. Cons. Psychogeriat. Ment. Health Servs. Salford. Prev: Sen. Regist. (Psychiat. of Old Age) NW RHA; Regist. (Psychiat.) Stoke-on-Trent N. Staffs. HA.

ATKINS, Maurice 47 Alma Road, Windsor SL4 3HH Tel: 01753 863724 Fax: 01753 858569 — BA Dub. 1963, MB BCh BAO 1965; FRCPsych 1991, M 1972; DPM Eng. 1971; DCH Dub. 1967. (TC Dub.) Full Time Private Practise, Cardinal Clinic, Oakley Grn., Windsor. Socs: Roy. Soc. Med. Prev: Sen. Regist. Prof.ial Unit United Newc. Hosps.; Research Regist. Nuffield Unit Child Psychiat. Newc. upon Tyne.

ATKINS, Michael John Trinity Phareceuticals Ltd, The Old Exchange, 12 Compton Rd, Wimbledon, London SW19 7QD Tel: 020 8947 Ext: 9443 Fax: 020 8947 9325 Email: matkins@trinityp.co.uk; Porthill Lodge, Porthill, Nettlebed, Henley-on-Thames RG9 5RL Tel: 01491 641452 Fax: 01491 641452 — MB BS 1979 Lond.; BSc (Hons.) Lond. 1973; Dip. Pharm. Med. (RCP UK) 1986. (Roy. Free) Med. Dir. Socs: FFPM; Fell. Roy. Soc. Med./Counc. Mem. - Phareceutical Med. & Research; BMA. Prev: Managing director, Health Focus (HF) Ltd; Med. Director, Loylex Synthelabo; Locum ENT Cons.

ATKINS, Michele Louise Highbury House, 94 High St., Boston Spa, Wetherby LS23 6EA Tel: 01937 541304 — MB ChB 1990 Leic. (Leicester) Specialist Regist. (Anaesth.) W. & N. Yorks. Yorks. Deanery. Prev: SHO (Anaesth.) York Dist. Hosp.; SHO (Paediat.) Leeds Gen. Infirm.; SHO (Gen. Med.) Roy. Hallamshire Hosp. Sheff.

ATKINS, Mullion 23 St Paul's Road, Chichester PO19 3BH — MB ChB 1998 Ed.; MB ChB Ed 1998.

ATKINS, Patricia Coppywood, Curly Hill, Ilkley LS29 0BA — MB ChB 1976 Bristol.

ATKINS, Mr Paul Abbey Sefton Hospital, Park Road, Waterloo, Liverpool L22 3XE Tel: 0151 257 6702/03; 48 Warren Road, Liverpool L23 6UF Tel: 0151 924 4617 — MB BS 1957 Lond.; 1967 MS Lond.; 1961 FRCS Eng.; 1957 MRCS Eng. LRCP Lond. (King's Coll. Hosp.) Cons. Surg. Abbey Sefton Hosp. Socs: Assn. Surg.; Liverp. Med. Inst.; Sen. Fell. Roy. Soc. Med. & Assn. Surgs. Prev: Cons. Surg. Roy. Liverp. Hosp. & Walton Hosp.

ATKINS, Paula Mary (retired) Tullens Toat, Pulborough RH20 1DA Tel: 01798 872664 — MB BS 1950 Lond.; MRCS Eng. LRCP Lond. 1950; DObst RCOG 1952.

ATKINS, Peter Francis Nettleham Medical Practice, 14 Lodge Lane, Nettleham, Lincoln LN2 2RS Tel: 01522 751717 Fax: 01522 754474 — MB BS 1978 Lond.; MRCGP 1982; DCH RCP Lond. 1982; DRCOG 1980. GP Nettleham; Med. Dir. St. Barnabas Hospice, Lincoln. Prev: Trainee Gen. Pract. Lincoln Vocational Train. Scheme.

ATKINS, Peter John 1 Lavington Lane, Little Panell, Devizes SN10 4EY — MB BCh 1959 Wales.

ATKINS, Mr Roger Michael Department of Orthopaedic Surgery, Bristol Royal Infirmary, Bristol BS2 8HW Tel: 0117 928 2242 Fax: 0117 928 4206 Email: roger-atkins@sneydwood.demon.co.uk; Sneydwood, 9 Avon Grove, Sneyd Park, Bristol BS9 1PJ Tel: 0117 968 5912 Fax: 0117 968 6245 — MB BS 1978 Lond.; DM Oxf. 1988, MA 1975; FRCS Eng. 1983. (Guy's) Cons. Orthop. Surg., Bristol Roy. Infirm. & Avon Orthop. Centre, Bristol; Reader, Univ. of Bristol. Socs: BOA; Brit. Limb Reconstruction Soc. (Sec.); Brit.

Orthopaedic Foot Soc. Prev: Cons. Sen. Lect. (Orthop. Surg.) Univ. Bristol; Clin. Lect. (Orthop. Surg.) Univ. Oxf.; Hunt. Prof.

ATKINS, Roy Leonard William (retired) Thorneywood Child & Adolescent Psychiatry Unit, Porchester Road, Nottingham NG3 6LF Tel: 0115 969 1300 — MB ChB Ed. 1963; MRCPsych 1973; DPM Ed. 1972. Prev: Sen. Regist. (Psychiat.) Childr. Hosp. Birm.

ATKINS, Sarah Jane 170 Clive Street, Cardiff CF11 7JF — MB BCh 1990 Wales.

ATKINS, Sarah Louise 1 Coppemhall Grove, Crewe CW2 7UQ — MB ChB 1991 Aberd. SHO (Orthop.) Leighton Hosp. Crewe. Prev: SHO (A & E & Paediat.) Leighton Hosp. Crewe; RMO Mackay Base Hosp. Mackay Qu.sland, Austral.

ATKINS, Simon Edward Fishponds Health Centre, Beechwood Road, Fishponds, Bristol BS16 3TD Tel: 0117 908 2365 Fax: 0117 908 2377 — MB ChB 1995 Bristol; BSc (Hons) Physiology with Psychology Soton. 1990. (Bristol) GP Regist. Bishopsworth Bristol.

ATKINSON, Alan Geoffrey Eastwood Lodge, 48 Spixworth Road, Old Catton, Norwich NR6 7NF Tel: 01603 425518 — MRCS Eng. LRCP Lond. 1947. (Guy's) Med. Ref. Norf. & Norwich Crematorium. Socs: Governor Roy. Humane Soc.; Norwich M.-C. Soc. Prev: Cas. Off. St. John's Hosp. Lewisham; Ho. Surg. Maidenhead Hosp.; Capt. RAMC, Sen. Med. Off. Winchester Area.

ATKINSON, Professor Albert Brew 43 Richmond Court, Lisburn BT27 4QU Tel: 01846 671848 — MB BCh BAO 1973 Belf.; BSc (1st cl. Hons.) 1970, DSc 1993, MD 1980; FRCPI 1993; FRCP Ed. 1990; FRCP Lond. 1990; FRCP Glas. 1987; MRCP (UK) 1976. Cons. Phys. & Endocrinol. Roy. Vict. Hosp. Belf., 1980; Hon. Prof. Endocrinol. Qu. Univ. Belf. 1993. Socs: Fell. RCP Lond., Edin., Glas. & Irel.; Amer. Endocrine Soc., Brit. Hypertens. Soc. & Assn. Phys. GB & Irel.; (Ex-Pres.) Irish Endocrine Soc. Prev: Fell. (Endocrinol.) Vanderbilt Univ. Nashville, USA; Clin. Scientist MRC Blood Pressure Unit W.. Infirm. Glas.; Sen. Regist. (Endocrinol. & Diabetes) Roy. Vict. Hosp. Belf.

***ATKINSON, Alexander Mark** 6 The Beeches, 43 Queens Road, Leicester LE2 1WQ — MB ChB 1990 Leic.

ATKINSON, Alison Ann 36 Mount Drive, Nantwich CW5 6JG — MB ChB 1983 Ed.; DA (UK) 1987. Clin. Asst. (Anaesth.) Watford Gen. Hosp.

ATKINSON, Alison Clare Abbotswood Medical Centre, Defford Road, Pershore WR10 1HZ Tel: 01386 552424 — MB ChB 1985 Birm.; MRCP (UK) 1990; MRCGP 1993; DRCOG 1992. Prev: Regist. (Gen. Med.) Sandwell Dist. Gen. Hosp. Birm.; SHO (Gen. Med.) N. Staffs. Med. Centre Stoke-on-Trent; Ho. Phys. Qu. Eliz. Hosp. Birm.

ATKINSON, Alison Diane The Surgery, 7 Barmby Road, Pockington, York YO4 2DN Tel: 0175 302500 — MB ChB 1985 Sheff.

ATKINSON, Allan Alfred (retired) 23 Brampton Road, St Albans AL1 4PP Tel: 01727 857100 — MB ChB 1956 Glas.; DObst RCOG 1963.

ATKINSON, Anna Catherine White House Surgery, Weston Lane, Weston, Southampton SO19 9HJ; 57 Station Road, Netley Abbey, Southampton SO31 5AE Tel: 02380 457501 — MB BS 1989 Lond.; DRCOG 1992. (St. Geo.)

ATKINSON, Anna Maria 296 Twentywell Lane, Bradway, Sheffield S17 4QH — MB ChB 1995 Birm.

ATKINSON, Mr Anthony Julian Three Shires Hospital, Cliftonville, Northampton NN1 5DR Tel: 01604 620311 — MB BS 1966 Lond.; BSc (Anat.) Lond. 1962; FRCS Eng. 1974; MRCS Eng. LRCP Lond. 1965; DO Eng. 1971; FRCOphth 1994. (Univ. Coll. Hosp.) Cons. Surg. (Ophth.) N.ampton Gen. Hosp. Prev: Res. Surg. Off. Moorfields Eye Hosp. Lond.; Ho. Surg. & Ho. Phys. Univ. Coll. Hosp. Lond.

ATKINSON, Cecil Noel (retired) 14 Avenue Road, Teddington TW11 0BT — MB BS 1945 Lond. Med. Off. & GP Anaesth. Teddington & Hampton Wick Memor. Hosp. Prev: Resid. Surg. Off. Memor. Hosp. P'boro.

ATKINSON, Charlotte Joan 3 Marsham Drive, Marple, Stockport SK6 7DP — MB BS 1997 Newc.

ATKINSON, Charlotte Louise 42 Bridgefoot Path, Emsworth PO10 7EB — MB BS 1997 Lond.

ATKINSON, Claude Mackenzie (retired) Silver Birches, Harmanswater Road, Bracknell RG12 9PT Tel: 01344 425721 — MRCS Eng. LRCP Lond. 1957. Prev: Civil. Med. Off. RAF Staff Coll. Bracknell.

ATKINSON, Clea Victoria 3 Church Road, Flamstead, St Albans AL3 8BN — BM 1995 Soton.

ATKINSON, Sir David, KBE (retired) Rosedene, Woodside Lane, Lymington SO41 8FJ Tel: 01590 670438 — MB ChB Ed. 1948; FRCP Ed. 1983; FFCM 1976, M 1973; FFOM RCP Lond. 1983, MFOM 1978; DPH Lond. 1962; DIH Eng. 1963. Prev: Dir. Gen. RAF Med. Servs.

***ATKINSON, David** The Grange, 17 Smithy Close, Acton, Wrexham LL12 8AQ — MB ChB 1996 Liverp.

ATKINSON, Mr David Worthington (retired) 54 Wellington Road, Enfield EN1 2PH Tel: 020 8372 2387 — MB BChir 1954 Camb.; FRCS Eng. 1960; MRCS Eng. LRCP Lond. 1954. Prev: Regist. (Thoracic Surg.) Guy's Hosp. Lond.

ATKINSON, Deborah Carole 38 Carden Crescent, Brighton BN1 8TQ — MB BS 1991 Lond.

ATKINSON, Derek Orchard End, 182A Liverpool Road, Longton, Preston PR4 5ZE Tel: 01772 612926 — MB ChB 1958 Birm.; MRCGP 1968; DObst RCOG 1960.

ATKINSON, Edmund Clegg (retired) 2 Conalan Avenue, Sheffield S17 4PG Tel: 0114 236 4125 — MB BS 1935 Lond.; MRCS Eng. LRCP Lond. 1935; DLO Eng. 1952. Prev: Resid. Aural Regist. Hosp. Sick Childr. Gt. Ormond St.

ATKINSON, Eileen 38 North View Avenue, Bideford EX39 3LJ — MB ChB 1950 Leeds; MRCPsych 1972; DPM Eng. 1960; DObst RCOG 1952. (Leeds)

ATKINSON, Elizabeth Shiach (retired) 10 Wentworth Drive, Ipswich IP8 3RX Tel: 01473 683371 — MB BS 1961 Durh.; Cert FPA (I.U.D. Trained) 1972. Prev: GP Ipswich.

ATKINSON, Fiona Margaret East Parade Surgery, East Parade, Harrogate HG1 5LW Tel: 01423 566574 Fax: 01423 568015 — MB BS 1988 Newc.

ATKINSON, Frank Gordon The Surgery, 22 Woods Mews, London W1K 7DS Tel: 020 7499 1338 Fax: 020 7495 0768 — MB ChB 1958 Sheff.; ECFMG Cert 1972; DObst RCOG 1960. Socs: BMA. Prev: Ho. Surg. Roy. Hosp. Sheff.; Ho. Surg. Univ. O & G Unit United Sheff. Hosps.

ATKINSON, Harold Glenn 10 Belvedere View, Leeds LS17 8BR — MB BS 1983 Lond.; MRCOG 1990. Sen. Regist. (Reproductive Med.).

ATKINSON, Henry Dushan Edward 9 Sutcliffe Close, London NW11 6NT Tel: 0973 824953 Email: duscha@hotmail.com — MB ChB 1998 Ed.; MB ChB Ed 1998; BSc Med. Sci Biochemistry 1996. (Edinburgh University medical School) Edin. Roy. Infirm.

ATKINSON, James Dominic St James University Hospital, Beckett St., Leeds LS9 7TF Tel: 0113 243 3144; 7 Masham Court, Headingley, Leeds LS6 4DT Email: jdatkinson@yahoo.co.uk — MB ChB 1996 Leeds; BSc (Hons.) Leeds 1993. SHO Rheumat. St. Jame's Hosp. Leeds. Prev: SHO Med. Oncol., St. Jas. Hosp. Leeds; SHO Med. Elderly, Seacroft Hosp. Leeds; SHO (Gen. Med.) St. Jas. Hosp. Leeds.

ATKINSON, James Navarre Crammond 88 High Street, Barton, Cambridge CB3 7BG Tel: 0144 761690 Email: jamesatkinson@cwcom.net — MRCS Eng. LRCP Lond. 1963; PhD (Biochem.) Bristol 1973; MSc (Biochem.) Lond. 1966, MB BS 1963; MRCPsych 1976. (Guy's) Prof. Mem. Soc. Anal. Psychol. Prev: Sen. Regist. (Psychother.) Camb.; Lect. (Psychiat.) Univ. Soton.; Research Fell. (Brit. Diabetic Assn.) Univ. Bristol.

ATKINSON, Jayne 1 Whinfell Cottages, Eccleshall Road S., Sheffield S11 9QB — MB ChB 1996 Sheff.

ATKINSON, Joan Margaret (retired) 72 Broadway, Lincoln LN2 1SR Tel: 01522 519031 — MB BS Lond. 1954. Prev: Clin. Med. Off. (Child Health) NW Durh. HA.

ATKINSON, John Airdrie Health Centre, Monkscourt Avenue, Airdrie ML6 0JU Tel: 01236 769333; 81 Meldrum Main, Glenmavis, Airdrie ML6 0QQ Tel: 01236 475 5017 — MB ChB 1977 Glas.; MRCP (UK) 1981; MRCGP 1982; DRCOG 1980; DCH Glas. 1980.

ATKINSON, John Frazer Dougal Summerfield, Low St., East Drayton, Retford DN22 0LN — MB BS 1997 Newc.

ATKINSON, John Norman (retired) Lyndhurst, 21 Allerton Park, Leeds LS7 4ND Tel: 0113 268 6799 — MB ChB 1954 Leeds; MRCGP 1969. Prev: Hosp. Pract. (Geriat.) St. Jas. Univ. Hosp. Leeds.

ATKINSON, Judith Anne Hurlingham Road Surgery, 34A Hurlingham Road, Fulham, London SW6 3RF Tel: 020 7371 8472;

42 Ennismore Avenue, London W4 1SF Tel: 020 8994 2892 — MB BS 1963 Lond. (Roy. Free)

ATKINSON, Kathryn Student Health Service, 315 Cavendish Road, Leeds LS1 3EW; 5 Hawksworth Avenue, Guiseley, Leeds LS20 8EJ — MB ChB 1976 Liverp.; DRCOG 1978. Prev: SHO (Psychiat.) Lynfield Mt. Hosp. Bradford; SHO (O & G) Fazakerley & Walton Hosps. Liverp.; Ho. Off. Fazakerley Hosp. Liverp.

ATKINSON, Laurence Kingsley Southgates Medical Centre, 41 Goodwins Road, King's Lynn PE30 5QX Tel: 01553 692333 Fax: 01553 692555 — MB BS 1983 Newc.; BMedSc (Hons.) Newc. 1980, MB BS 1983; MRCP (UK) 1986; MRCGP 1989; Cert. Family Plann. JCC 1989. Prev: Regist. (Med.) Char. Cross Hosp. Lond.; SHO (Med.) Roy. Vict. Infirm. Newc.

ATKINSON, Lawrence Wishart (retired) 155 Blackpool Road, Ansdell, Lytham St Annes FY8 4AA Tel: 01253 734187 — MB ChB 1951 St. And. Prev: Authorised Med. Examr. Civil Aviat. Auth.

ATKINSON, Leonard René Nicholas (retired) Little Paddock, Elm Crescent, Charlbury, Oxford OX7 3PZ Tel: 01608 810977 — MB BS Durh. 1943; MRCGP 1958. Prev: Med. Off. DHSS.

ATKINSON, Leslie John (retired) Lindens, Milton, Brampton CA8 1HR Tel: 0169 77 41170 Email: lesliejohn@cwcom.net — BM BCh 1954 Oxf.; MA 1951, BM BCh Oxf. 1954. Prev: Ho. Surg. & Dep. Res. Med. Off. Manch. Roy. Infirm.

ATKINSON, Lucinda Eastwood Lodge, 48 Spixworth Road, Old Catton, Norwich NR6 7NF Tel: 01603 425518 — MB ChB 1991 Aberd.; MRCP (UK) 1998. (Aberdeen) Psychiat. SHO, Duchess of Kent Hosp, N Yorks. Prev: SHO (Intens. Care) Roy. Brompton Hosp. Lond.; SHO (Med.) Roy. Hosp. Haslar Gosport; SHO (Med.) Frimley Pk Hosp. Frimley Surrey.

***ATKINSON, Mark** Gloucestershire Royal Hospital, Gloucester GL1 3NN Tel: 01420 561871; 2 Drummond Cl, Four Marks, Alton GU34 5BQ Tel: 01420 561871 — MB BS 1997 Lond.; BSc (Hons.) 1994.

ATKINSON, Mark William Histopathology Department, The Royal Oldham Hospital, Rochdale Road, Oldham OL1 2JH Tel: 0161 627 8390 Email: mark.atkinson@oldham-tr.nwest.nhs.uk — MB ChB 1981 Sheff.; MRCPath 1989. Cons. Histopath. & Cytopath. Roy. Oldham Hosp.

ATKINSON, Martin Guy Wickham Yoxall Health Centre, Savey Lane, Yoxall, Burton-on-Trent DE13 8PD Tel: 01543 472202 Fax: 01543 472362 — MB ChB 1979 Birm.; DRCOG 1983.

ATKINSON, Melanie Jane Brook Green, Halloughton, Southwell NG25 0QP — BM BS 1982 Nottm.; BMedSci Nottm. 1980, BM BS 1982; DRCOG 1986. Med. Off. (Family Plann.) Centr. Notts. Healthcare (NHS) Trust.

ATKINSON, Mervyn Charles 82 Laing Gardens, Broxburn EH52 6XT — MB ChB 1994 Ed.

ATKINSON, Professor Michael (retired) Far Well, Mill Side, Witherslack, Grange-over-Sands LA11 6SG Tel: 015395 52423 — MB BS 1946 Lond.; MA Lancaster 1992; MD Lond. 1950; FRCP Lond. 1966, M 1949. Prev: Special Prof. Gastroenterol. Univ. Nottm. & Cons. Phys. Univ. Hosp. Nottm.

ATKINSON, Noel Harry 4 Firs Road, Gatley, Cheadle SK8 4JT — MRCS Eng. LRCP Lond. 1960. Hosp. Pract. (Haemat.) N. Manch. Gen. Hosp. Clin. Asst. (Med.); Ancoats Hosp. Manch.

ATKINSON, Patricia Isabella Crawley Hospital, West Green Drive, Crawley RH11 7DA Tel: 01293 600300 Fax: 01293 565587; Email: nmemon@globalnet.co.uk — MB BCh BAO Dub. 1980; DCH Dub. 1982; DCCH RCP Ed. 1985; FRCPCH 1997. (Trinity College Dublin) Cons. Community Paediat. Crawley Hosp. W. Sussex. Socs: RCPCH; Brit. Assn. Community Child Health; Internat. Child Health Gp. Prev: Med. Dir. (Community Child Health) Renfrewsh.; Clin. Med. Off. Paisley & Belf.; SHO (Paediat.) Roy. Belf. Hosp. Sick Childr.

ATKINSON, Paul Robert Thomas A & E Dept, Bedford Hospital, Bedford MK41 9DJ; 44 Sun Hill, Royston SG8 9AX — MB BCh BAO 1995 Belf.; BSc 1992; MRCP 1998. (Belfast) Specialist Regist. A & E Bedford Hosp. Socs: Fac. Accid. & Emerg. Med.

ATKINSON, Paul Simon The Surgery, 2 Heathcote Street, Newcastle ST5 7EB Tel: 01782 561057 Fax: 01782 563907 — MB ChB 1983 Manch. Trainee GP Runcorn VTS. Prev: SHO (Geriat. Med.) Stepping Hill Hosp. Stockport; SHO (A & E) Oldham Roy. Infirm.

ATKINSON, Penelope Ann, Surg. Lt.-Cdr. RN 79 Beaconfield Road, Beacon Park, Plymouth PL2 3LG — MB BCh 1995 Wales; DRCOG 2001; DFFP 2001. (Cardiff) GP Train. Roy. Navy.

ATKINSON, Peter Department of Pathology, Southend Hospital, Prittlewell Chase, Westcliff on Sea SS0 0RY Email: patkinson@southend.nhs.uk — MB ChB 1982 Liverp.; MRCPath 1995. Cons. Histopath. S.end Hosp. Essex. Prev: Lect. (Path.) Univ. Aberd.

ATKINSON, Peter James 63 Lyncombe Hill, Bath BA2 4PH — MB BS 1962 Lond. (Char. Cross) Socs: Med. Assur. Soc. & Mem. BMA. Prev: Clin. Teach. Gen. Pract. Univs. Soton. & Bristol.; Ho. Phys. Char. Cross Hosp.; Ho. Surg. Wembley Hosp.

ATKINSON, Mr Peter Leonard Department of Ophthalmology, Bradford Royal Infirmary, Duckworth Lane, Bradford BD9 6RJ Tel: 01274 542200 — MB ChB 1983 Leic.; FRCS Eng. 1987; FRCOphth 1988; DO RCS Eng. 1986. Cons. Ophth. Surg. Bradford Roy. Infirm. Prev: Sen. Regist. (Ophth.) King's Coll. Hosp. Lond.; Regist. (Ophth.) St. Paul's Eye Hosp. Liverp.

ATKINSON, Mr Peter Miles St. John of God Hospital, Scorton, Richmond DL10 6EB Tel: 01748 811535; The Old Rectory, Croft on Tees, Darlington DL2 2SF — MB BS 1962 Lond.; MS Lond. 1978; FRCS Ed. 1967; FRCS Eng. 1967; DObst RCOG 1964. (Middlx.) Private Pract.; Private Pract. Socs: Assoc. Mem. BAUS; BMA. Prev: Consul Surg Gen Surg Urol. Memor. Hosp. Darllington; Consul Surg Gen Surg Urol. Friarage Hosp. N.allerton; Sen. Regist. St. Mary's Hosp. Lond.

ATKINSON, Philip Andrew Department of Occupational Health, Blackpool Victoria Hospital NHS Trust, Trust Headquarters, Furness Drive, Poulton-le-Fylde FY6 8JT Tel: 01253 303003 Fax: 01253 303002 Email: philip.atkinson1@btinternet.com; 134 Newton Drive, Blackpool FY3 8JB Tel: 01253 399583 Email: philatki@globalnet.co.uk — MB BS 1978 Newc.; MFOM RCP Lond. 1996. (Newcastle upon Tyne) Cons. (Occupat. Health) Blackpool Vict. Hosp. NHS Trust. Socs: Soc. Occup. Med.; Associaiton of Nat. Health Occupat.al Phys.s; Assn. of Local Auth. Med. Advisers. Prev: Cons. (Occupat. Health) King's Coll. Hosp. Lond.

ATKINSON, Philip George (retired) Crosscombe, Southway, Sidmouth EX10 8JL — MB ChB Sheff. 1955; DCH Eng. 1960; DObst RCOG 1961.

ATKINSON, Phillip Howard Mitchell Road Surgery, 9 Mitchell Road, Canford Heath, Poole BH17 8UE — MB ChB 1973 Manch.; FRCS Ed. 1978; MRCGP 1984; DRCOG 1982.

ATKINSON, Rachel Barbara Elms Surgery, 5 Derby Street, Ormskirk L39 2BJ Tel: 01695 571560 Fax: 01695 578300; Ashford House, Back Lane, Newburgh, Wigan WN8 7XB — MB ChB 1985 Liverp.; MRCGP 1989. Prev: GP Preston.

ATKINSON, Rachel Elizabeth 1 Barcombe Close, Seaford BN25 4DP — BM BS 1986 Nottm.; BMedSci (Hons.) Nottm. 1984; MRCP (UK) 1990; MPH Nottm. 1996. Prev: Sen. Regist. (Pub. Health Med.), N.ampton HA; Research Fell. (Child Health) Univ. of Leicester; Regist. Rotat. (Paediat.) St. Geo.'s Hosp. Lond. & St. Peter's Hosp. Chertsey.

ATKINSON, Ravell Shaw 5 Northumberland Avenue, Gosforth, Newcastle upon Tyne NE3 4XE — MB BS 1963 Durh.; DMRT Eng. 1970.

ATKINSON, Richard Edmund Pain Management Clinic, Royal Hallamshire Hospital, Sheffield S10 2JF Tel: 0114 271 3713, 0114 279 8314 Email: richard.atkinson@csuh.nhs.uk; 296 Twentywell Lane, Bradway, Sheffield S17 4QH Tel: 0114 236 0355 Fax: 0114 235 1544 Email: reatkinson@talk24.com — MB BS 1966 Lond.; MRCS Eng. LRCP Lond. 1966; FRCA 1992; FFA RCS Eng. 1971; DObst RCOG 1968. (St. Bart.) Cons. Pain Managem. & Pall. Care Serv. Centr. Sheff. Univ. Trust; Hon. Lect. (Pain Managem.) Sheff. Univ.; Asst. Edr. Pain Reviews. Socs: (Ex Vice-Pres.) Assn. Anaesth.; (Ex-Treas.) Brit. Pain Soc.; Internat. Assn. Study of Pain (Chairm. s/i Gp.). Prev: Med. Dir. Ashgate Hospice Chesterfield; Asst. Prof. Anaesth. McGill Univ. Roy. Vict. Hosp. Montreal, Canada; Sen. Regist. & Regist. (Anaesth.) Sheff. AHA.

ATKINSON, Robert 106 Lumley Street, Castleford WF10 5LU — MB ChB 1986 Birm.

ATKINSON, Robert James 9 Waldeck Street, Lincoln LN1 3JB — MB ChB 1996 Leic.

ATKINSON, Robert Michael (retired) 7 Cavendish Avenue, Dore, Sheffield S17 3NJ Tel: 0114 235 2003 Email:

rm@kinson30.fsnet.co.uk — MB ChB 1952 Sheff.; PhD Sheff. 1955, BSc 1949, MB ChB 1952; BA (Open Univ.) 1983. Prev: Med. Research Worker Glaxo Gp. Research Ltd.

ATKINSON, Ronald James Oncology Department, University Floor Belfast City Hospital Tower, 97 Lisburn Road, Belfast BT9 7AB Tel: 02890 263911 Fax: 02890 314055 Email: r.j.atkinson@qub.ac.uk; 29A Carnreagh, Hillsborough BT26 6LJ Tel: 02890 689144 — MB BCh BAO 1971 Belf.; MD Belf. 1979; FRCS Glas. 1978; FRCOG 1989, M 1976. (Qu. Univ. Belf.) Sen. Lect. & Cons. Oncol. Qu. Univ. Belf. Socs: Ulster Med. Soc.; Ulster Obst. & Gyn. Soc.; Brit. Gyn. Cancer Soc. (Mem. & Past Sec.). Prev: Acting-Head Oncol. Qu.'s Univ. Belf.

ATKINSON, Rosemary Wyn West Wales community drug team, Jobs well house, Jobs well Road, Carmarthen SA31 3HB Tel: 01267 223483 Fax: 01796 301576 — MB BS 1968 Lond.; BSc (Anat.) Lond. 1965; MRCS Eng. LRCP Lond. 1968; MRCPsych 1974; FRCPsych 1999. (Roy. Free) Cons. Psychiat. Subst. Misuse Swansea. Prev: Cons. Psychiat. P'boro. Dist. Hosp. (Old Age Psychiat.); Cons. Psychiat. P'boro Dist. Hosp. (Gen. Psychiat).

ATKINSON, Sarah Helen 8 Heldar Court, Kipling Estate, London SE1 3RH — MB BS 1997 Lond.

ATKINSON, Sarah Rosemary Parkstone Health Centre, Mansfield Road, Poole BH14 0DJ Tel: 01202 741370 Fax: 01202 730952 — MB BS 1971 Lond. (London University) GP Partner; Police Surg. Socs: Assn. Police Surg.; Diplomate Mem. Fac. Family Plann. Prev: SHO (Gen. Med.) Poole Gen. Hosp.; SHO (Paediat.) Soton. Univ. Hosp.; Ho. Phys. Middlx. Hosp. Lond.

ATKINSON, Shona Mary Chappelle Lodge, Cliff Road, Wooldale, Holmfirth, Huddersfield HD9 1QP Tel: 01484 689832 — MB ChB 1992 Sheff. (Sheffield) p/t GP Regist. (Gen. Pract.), Gen. Practitioner Huddersfield; Clin. Asst. (GU Med. & Dermat.); Clin. Asst. Dermat.; Clin. Asst. Colposcopy. Prev: GP Regist. & SHO (O & G).

ATKINSON, Mr Simon William 18 Downs Road, Beckenham BR3 5JY Email: 101464.1266@compuserve.com — MB BS 1987 Lond.; BSc Lond. 1984; MS Lond. 1996; FRCS Eng. 1991. (Univ. Lond.) Sen. Regist. (Gen. Surg.) Roy. Perth Hosp., W.. Austral. Prev: Regist. & Lect. (Surg.) Guy's Hosp. Lond.

ATKINSON, Stephanie Anne Iveagh House Surgery, Iveagh House, Loughborough Road, Brixton, London SW9 7SF; 72 Thornlaw Road, London SE27 0SA — MB ChB 1983 Leic.; DRCOG 1987; DCH RCP Lond. 1986. Prev: GP Retainer Spital Wirral VTS.; SHO (Psychiat.) Arrowe Pk. Hosp. Wirral.

ATKINSON, Stuart Norman Medical Department, Pfizer Ltd., Sandwich CT13 9NJ Tel: 01304 643963 Fax: 01304 655564 Email: atkins@pfizer.com — MB ChB 1983 Liverp.; MFPM RCP (UK) 1993; Dip. Pharm. Med. RCP (UK) 1993; DRCOG 1988; Cert. Family Plann. JCC 1988. (Liverp.) Princip. Med. Adviser, Viagra, Pfizer Ltd. Socs: Assoc. Mem. BAUS. Prev: Med. Advisor Duphar Laborats. Ltd. Soton.; Off. Commanding ACE Mobile Force Detachment 16 Field Ambul.; Regtl. Med. Off. 1st Bn. Devonsh. & Dorset Regts.

ATKINSON, Susan Department Anaesthetics, The Royal Hospitals Trust, Grosvenor Road, Belfast BT12 6BA Fax: 01232 325725; 5 Garland Hill, Manse Rd, Belfast BT8 6YL — MB BCh BAO 1981 Belf.; MD Belf. 1994; FFA RCSI 1987. Cons. Anaesth. Roy. Gp. Hosps. Belf.

ATKINSON, Sue Department of Health, London, 40 Eastbourne Terrace, London W2 3QR Tel: 0207 725 5418 Fax: 0207 723 0087 Email: sue.atkinson@doh.gst.gov.uk — MB BChir 1975 Camb.; BSc Zoology, 1968; FFPHM RCP (UK) 1989; DCH RCP Lond. 1977. (University of Cambridge, & Middlesex Hosp. Medical School) Regional Dir. Pub. Med. Director; Health Adviser to Mayor Lond. & Gt.er Lond. Auth. Prev: Dir. (Pub.Health & Chief Ex. SE Lond. Lewisham & N.S.wark Has; Regional Director Pub hlth/ Med. Dir, S. Thames RHA/RO; Regional Director Pub. Health/Med. Director Wessex/S & W RHA.

ATKINSON, Timothy David 9 Palm Court Cottages, South Strand, E. Preston, Littlehampton BN16 1NZ — MB BS 1989 Lond.; MRCP (UK) 1992.

ATKINSON, William John Eshwood Lodge, New Brancepeth, Durham DH7 7HG Tel: 01525 730380 — MB BS 1959 Durh.; DA Eng. 1967; DObst RCOG 1961. (Newc.) Socs: Durh. Med. Soc. Prev: Ho. Off. (Surg.) Roy. Vict. Infirm. Newc.; Ho. Phys. Fleming Memor. Hosp. Newc.; Sen. Ho. Off. Obst. Unit Dryburn Hosp. Durh.

ATLAY, Robert David (retired) 35 Rodney Street, Liverpool L1 9EN Tel: 0151 708 9528 — MB ChB Liverp. 1960; FRCOG 1981, M 1966. Clin. Lect. Univ. Liverp. (Chairm. Bd. Fac. Med.); Examr. Univs. Liverp., Manch., Birm., Camb., Glas., Univ. W. Indies & Univ. Lond (St Mary's) & Amman, Jordan; Examr. RCOG & RACOG; Examr. Centr. Midw. Bd.; Chairm. CME Comm. & Roy. Coll. Obst. & Gyn. (Fell. Represen. Counc.); Cons. Gyn. Liverp. Obst. & Gyn. Servs. Trust. Prev: Cons. O & G Mill Rd. Matern. Hosp. Liverp., Liverp. Wom. Hosp., Liverp. Matern. Hosp. & Roy. Liverp. Univ. Hosp.

ATOYEBI, Oyewale Ishola 3 Holland Place, Headington, Oxford OX3 8QT Tel: 01865 750364 — MB BS 1988 Benin; MRCP (UK) 1993. Regist. Rotat. (Haemat.) St. Mary's & Hammersmith Hosps. Lond. Prev: Research Regist. (Haemat.) John Radcliffe Hosp. Oxf.; SHO Rotat. (Gen. Med.) Ipswich Hosp.; SHO (Haemat.) John Radcliffe Hosp. Oxf.

ATRA, Ayad Alawi Abdulhussian The Royal Marsden Hospital, Downs Road, Sutton SM2 5PT Tel: 020 8642 6011 Fax: 020 8661 3617 Email: ayad.atra@rmh.nthames.nhs.uk; 10 Effingham Close, Sutton SM2 6AG Tel: 020 8643 8488 — MB ChB 1977 Baghdad; 1977 MB ChB Baghdad; 1987 MD Baghdad; 1988 MRCP (UK); 1997 MRCPath; FRCP 1999. Cons. Paediat. Haematol./Oncol. Roy. Marsden Hosp. NHS Trust Sutton. Prev: Regist. (Paediat.) Qu. Mary's Univ. Hosp. Roehampton; Clin. Research Fell. (Haemat. & Oncol.) Hosp. Sick Childr. Gt. Ormond St. Lond.; Regist. & Sen. Regist. (Paediat.) Med. Teach. Hosp. Baghdad, Iraq.

ATRAH, Hasan Ibrahim Abdul Rasool Department of Haematology, Bronglais Hospital, Cardoc Road, Aberystwyth SY23 1ER Tel: 01970 623131 Fax: 01970 635923 — MB ChB 1978 Baghdad; 1995 MBA Keele; 1996 FRCP Ed.; 1997 FRCP; 1997 FRCPath. Cons. Haemat. Bronglais Hosp. Aberystwyth. Socs: BMA; Assn. Clin. Path; Brit. Soc. Haematol. Prev: Cons. Transfus. Med. W. Midl. Regional Blood Transfus. Serv.

ATRAH, Mr Salah Ghani Khudhair The Hillingdon Hospital, Uxbridge UB8 3NN Tel: 01895 279512; Little Acorns, 35 Holm Grove, Uxbridge UB10 9LZ Tel: 01895 259212 — MB ChB 1973 Baghdad; MSc Orthop. Lond. 1987; FRCSI 1984; FRCS Ed. 1984. (Coll. Med. Baghdad, Iraq) Cons. Orthop. Surg. (Orthop. & Trauma) Hillingdon Hosp. Middlx. Socs: Fell. BOA. Prev: Sen. Regist. Roy. Lond. Hosp.

ATREY, Ashok Kumar The Surgery, Meadowview Medical Centre, 3 Formby Avenue, Atherton, Manchester M46 0HX Tel: 01942 883330 Fax: 01942 877748 — MB BS 1971 Punjab.

ATREY, Neela The Surgery, Meadowview Medical Centre, 3 Formby Avenue, Atherton, Manchester M46 0HX Tel: 01942 883330 Fax: 01942 877748 — MB BS 1973 Himachal Pradesh; DA Eng. 1981.

ATTA, Mr Hatem Riad Sunningdale, Sunert Road, Milltimber AB13 0JQ Tel: 01224 861849 Fax: 01224 861849 Email: h.atta@btinternet.com — MB ChB 1974 Tanta; MB ChB Tanta Egypt 1974; FRCS Ed. 1982; FRCOphth 1988; DO Eng. 1979. Cons. Ophth. Aberd. Roy. Hosps. NHS Trust; Hon. Sen. Lect. Univ. Aberd. Socs: Internat. Soc. Ophth. Ultrasound (SIDUO); Oxf. Congr. Prev: Sen. Regist. (Ophth.) W. Midl. RHA; Regist. (Ophth.) Gtr. Glas. HB.

ATTAH, Anthony Bassey Celyn House, Weston Rhyn, Oswestry SY10 7RP Tel: 01691 774327 — MB BCh BAO 1963 NUI. (University College, Galway, Eire)

ATTAIS, Michael 163 Dunstable Road, Luton LU1 1BW — MBBS 1986 Lond. (Univ. College London) GP Princip., Luton; Final Examg. Med. Officier, H.M. Forces. Socs: Primary Care Cardiol. Gp. Prev: Clin. Assisitant, Pasque Hospice; Former Panel Doctor to Austral. Immergation Serv.

ATTALLA, Fadia Erian 31 Whitehorn Gardens, Enfield EN2 6HF Tel: 020 8366 0194 Fax: 020 8366 0194 — MB BCh 1967 Cairo; FFA RCS Eng. 1980; DA Eng. 1976. (Cairo Univ.) Assoc. Specialist (Anaesth.) Moorfields Eye Hosp. Lond.

ATTALLA, Youssef Awad 1 Thrivithick Close, Kingsmead Eaglescliffe, Stockton-on-Tees TS16 0RY — MB BCh 1980 AiN Shams.

ATTAR, Mr Gulamdastagir Sultansaheb 4 The Spinney, Marlow Hill, High Wycombe HP11 1QE — MB BS 1974 Karnatak; FRCS Glas. 1993; FRCS Ed. 1993.

ATTARA, Mr George Antoine 7 Wellfield Road, Folkestone CT20 2PJ — MB BCh 1970 Cairo; FRCS Eng. 1980; MRCS Eng.

LRCP Lond. 1980. Cons. Orthop. Surg. P.ss Alexandra's RAF Hosp. Swindon. Socs: Fell. BOA. Prev: Chief of Orthop. King Abdul Aziz Hosp. (Teachg.) Jeddah, Saudia Arabia; Sen. Cons. Orthop. N.. Armed Forces Hosp. MoD, Saudia Arabia; Sen. Cons. Orthop. Surg. Min. Health Sharjah, UAE.

ATTARD, Adrian Carmel South Norwood Hill Surgery, 103a South Norwood Hill, London SE25 6XN Tel: 020 8771 0742 Fax: 020 8771 6097; 171 Banstead Road, Carshalton Beeches, Carshalton SM5 4DP — MRCS Eng. LRCP Lond. 1978. Prev: Clin. Asst. (Orthop.) Mayday Hosp. Croydon.

ATTARD, Alexandra 28 Westminster Road, Stoneygate, Leicester LE2 2EG — MB ChB 1982 Leeds.

ATTARD, Diana Jeanne (retired) 1 Hepscott Terrace, South Shields NE33 4TH Tel: 0191 422 0821 — MB BS Adelaide 1949. Med. Ref. S. Tyneside Boro. Counc. Prev: Clin. Med. Off. S. Tyneside.

ATTARD, Henry William 2 Warrington Road, Richmond TW10 6SJ — MB ChB 1998 Manch.; MB ChB Manch 1998.

ATTARD, Marie Therese 171 Banstead Road, Carshalton SM5 4DP Tel: 020 8642 9869 — MRCS Eng. LRCP Lond. 1978; MRCPsych 1982.

ATTARD, Mr Raphael (retired) 1 Hepscott Terrace, South Shields NE33 4TH — MD Malta 1952; BSc Malta 1949; FRCS Eng. 1958. Prev: Sen. Cons. Surg. S. Tyneside Dist. Hosp.

ATTARD-MONTALTO, Simon Paul Tel: 00356 241251 — MB ChB 1985 Liverp.; MRCP (UK) 1988; DCH RCP Lond. 1988. Lect. (Paediat. Oncol.) St. Bart. Med. Coll. Hosp. Lond. Prev: Regist. (Paediat.) Guy's Hosp. Lond.

ATTARWALA, Mr Umakant c/o Mr P Shukla, Cumberland Infirmary, Carlisle CA2 7HY — MB BS 1973 Rajasthan; FRCS Glas. 1980. (R.N.T. Med. Coll. Udaipur)

ATTENBOROUGH, John, TD (retired) Heatherglade House, Crawley Drive, Camberley GU15 2AA Tel: 01276 64741 — MB BChir 1943 Camb.; MA Camb. 1943; MRCS Eng. LRCP Lond. 1943. Prev: Gen. Practitioner, Camberley, 1946 - 1980.

ATTENBURROW, Averil Anne (retired) Department of Paediatrics, Dr Gray's Hospital, Elgin IV30 1SN Tel: 01343 543131 Fax: 01343 552612 — MB ChB 1976 Birm.; BSc (Hons.) Birm. 1973; FRCP Lond. 1994; FRCP Glas. 1993; FRCPCH 1997; DCH Eng. 1978. Prev: Cons. Paediat. Moray Health Servs.

ATTENBURROW, Mary Elizabeth Jane University of Oxford Dept of Psychopharmacology, Warneford Hospital, Warneford Lane, Headington, Oxford OX3 7JX — MB BS 1987 Lond.; BA Oxf. 1984. Hon. Cons. Res.

ATTER, Cheryl Clare Cadbury Heath Health Centre, Parkwall Road, Bristol BS30 8HS Tel: 0117 980 5706 Fax: 0117 980 5707 — MB ChB 1988 Bristol; MRCGP 1994; DFFP 1993; DRCOG 1991. p/t GP Princip. Prev: Trainee GP Newport.

ATTER, Michael 218A Harrogate Road, Leeds LS7 4QD — MB ChB 1994 Leeds.

ATTIA, Mr Fawzi Fadlalla 3 Bindon Abbey, Bedford MK41 0AZ — MB BS 1979 Garyounis; FRCS Glas. 1991.

ATTIAS, Michael Dunstable Road Surgery, 163 Dunstable Road, Luton LU1 1BW — MB BS 1986 Lond. (Univ. Coll. Hosp.) GP Princip. Luton; Fnal Examg. Med. Off. HM Forces; JP. Socs: Primary Care Cardiol. Gp. Prev: Clin. Asst. Pasque Hospice; Panel Doctor Austral. Immigr. Serv.

ATTLEE, Bridget Kathleen (retired) 18/20 St Peter's Close, Church Rd, Goodworth, Clatford SP11 7SF Tel: 01264 354679 — MB BS 1953 Lond.; MRCS Eng. LRCP Lond. 1952; LMSSA Lond. 1952. p/t JP. Prev: GP Clin. Asst. Woodside Day Hosp. Maidstone.

ATTLEE, Wilfrid Ormiston The Granary, Whitton, Ludlow SY8 3DB Tel: 01584 890333 — MRCS Eng. LRCP Lond. 1942; MA Camb. (Camb. & St. Bart.) Prev: Maj. RAMC.

ATTOCK, Brian North Devon Dist. Hospital, Barnstaple EX31 4JB — MB ChB 1968 Bristol; MRCPath 1975; DCH Eng. 1970. Cons. Haemat. N. Devon Dist. Hosp. Prev: Sen. Regist. (Haemat.) Roy. Free Hosp. & N. Middlx. Hosp. Lond.; Fell. Paediat. Path. Childr. Hosp. Los Angeles USA.

ATTREE, Robert Christopher Buckley Health Centre, Padeswood Road, Buckley CH7 2JL Tel: 01224 550555 Fax: 01224 545712; The Cherries, 7 Main Road, Higher Kinnerton, Chester CH4 9AJ — MB ChB 1980 Birm.; MRCGP 1987; DRCOG 1984.

ATTRUP, Mrs Bronwen Hainton House, Wigsley Road, Harby, Newark NG23 7EF Tel: 01522 702347 — MB BS 1987 Lond.; FRCOphth 1991; DO RCS Eng. 1990. Clin. Asst. Ophth. Lincoln Co. Hosp. Prev: SHO (Ophth.) Odstock Hosp. Salisbury, St. Geo. Hosp. Lond. & Roy. Vict. Eye Hosp. Bournemouth; Clin. Asst. Soton. Eye Hosp.

ATTRUP, Martin Glebe House Surgery, Church Road, Saxilby, Lincoln LN1 2HJ Tel: 01522 702236 Fax: 01522 703132 — MB BS 1987 Lond. Trainee GP Salisbury VTS.

***ATTWELL, Ruth Mary** 31 Adlington Road, Wilmslow SK9 2BJ — MB ChB 1998 Ed.; MB ChB Ed 1998.

ATTWOOD, Mr Anthony Ian, Wing Cdr. RAF Med. Br. Retd. 50 Northumberland Avenue, Aylesbury HP21 7HJ Tel: 01296 415156 Fax: 01296 415156 Email: tony.attwood@dial.pipex.com — MB BS 1971 Lond.; FRCS Ed. 1977; MRCS Eng. LRCP Lond. 1971. (Guy's) Cons. Plastic Surg. (Private Pract.); Hon. (Cons. in Plastic Surg.), Milton Keynes Gen. Hosp. Socs: Brit. Assn. Plastic Surg.; Brit. Assn. Aesthetic Plastic Surgs.; Brit. Burns Assn. Prev: Cons. Burns & Plastic Surg. RAF.

ATTWOOD, Charles Matthew (retired) 9 Mill Lane, Linton, Cambridge CB1 6JY Tel: 01223 891488 — MRCS Eng. LRCP Lond. 1945. Prev: Ho. Surg. St. Thos. Hosp.

ATTWOOD, Kathryn 17 Hanwood Close, Woodley, Reading RG5 3AB — MB ChB 1990 Aberd.

ATTWOOD, Margaret Denise 357 Bentley Road, Doncaster DN5 9TJ — MB ChB 1998 Glas.; MB ChB Glas 1998.

ATTWOOD, Michael Vauxhall Health Centre, Limekiln Lane, Liverpool L8 5XR — MB BCh BAO 1941 NUI; MB BCh NUI 1941.

ATTWOOD, Paul Robert Arthur Wickham Surgery, 1 Wickham Avenue, Ramsgate CT11 8AY Tel: 01843 593420 Fax: 01843 591799 — BM 1979 Soton.; DRCOG 1983. Clin. Asst. (A & E) Thanet Gen. Hosp. Prev: Trainee. GP Ashford VTS; Ho. Surg. Qu. Alexandra's Hosp. Portsmouth; Ho. Phys. Weymouth & Dist. Hosp.

ATTWOOD, Mr Stephen Edwin Arthur Hope Hospital, Stott Lane, Salford M6 8HD Tel: 0161 787 5472 Fax: 0161 787 5992 — MB BCh BAO 1981 Dub.; BA MoD (Physiol.) Dub. 1978; MCh Dub. 1990; FRCSI 1992; FRCS 1987; FRCSI 1985. Cons. Hope. Hosp. Shalford, Manch.; Cons., BUPA Hosp., Manch.; Hon. Sen. Lect. Manch. Univ.; Chairm. of Gtr. Manch. and Chesh. Cancer Network, Oesophago-Gastric SubGp. Socs: Surg. Research Soc.; Internat. Soc. Dis. Oesophagus; Brit. Soc. of Gastroenterol. Prev: Sen. Regist. (Surg.) St. Jas. Hosp. Dub.; Research Regist. Roy. Lancs. Infirm.

ATTWOOD, Stephen John 12 Kingwood Close, Cardiff CF23 9HE — MB BCh 1989 Wales.

ATTWOOD, Stephen Paul Bicester Health Centre, Coker Close, Bicester OX26 6AT Tel: 01869 249333 Fax: 01869 320314; Field House, Bileste Road, Marsh Gibbon, Bicester OX27 0EU — MB BS 1983 Lond.; BSc Lond. 1980, MB BS 1983; MRCGP 1987; DRCOG 1986; DCH RCP Lond. 1986. GP Bicester. Prev: Trainee GP Stoke Mandeville Hosp. VTS Aylesbury; Ho. Off. (Gen. Med.) Char. Cross Hosp. Lond.; Ho. Surg. (Gen. Surg.) Stoke Mandeville Hosp. Aylesbury.

ATUBRA, David Kwasi 10 Cheyney Close, Saintbridge, Gloucester GL4 4PR — MB ChB 1970 Ghana; MRCOG 1982.

ATUKORALA, Ananda Wijetilaka X-Ray Department, Bradford Royal Infirmary, Bradford BD9 6RJ Tel: 01274 542200 — MB BS 1951 Ceylon; FRCR 1987; DMRD Eng. 1956. (Ceylon) Cons. Radiol. Bradford Roy. Infirm.

ATUN, Ayla Ruth 9 Onslow Road, Endcliffe Park, Sheffield S11 7AF — MB ChB 1998 Sheff.; MB ChB Sheff 1998.

ATUN, Rifat Ali High Road Surgery, 114 High Road, South Woodford, London E18 2QS Tel: 020 8491 3310 Fax: 020 8491 3307 — MB BS 1985 Lond.; MBA Lond. 1993; MRCGP 1990; DIC 1993. Lect. (Health Managem.) Imperial Coll. Sci. Technol. & Med.; Postgrad. Tutor (Gen. Pract.) Brit. Postgrad. Med. Federat. Univ. Lond. Prev: Trainee GP/SHO (Paediat.) St. Bart. Hosp. Lond. VTS; SHO (Cardiothoracic Unit) Harefield Hosp. Middlx.; Ho. Phys. Guy's Hosp. Lond.

ATURU, Bhaskara Reddy The Surgery, 85 Stopford Road, Plaistow, London E13 0NA Tel: 020 8472 3901 Fax: 020 8503 4818; 32 Ratcliffe Road, Forestgate, London E7 8DD Tel: 020 8470 3285 Fax: 020 8470 3285 — State Exam 1983 Bologna; State DMS Messina 1988. GP Lond. Prev: SHO (A & E) Leigh Infirm.; Med. Off. (Radiother.) Italy; SHO (Orthop. Surg.) Burnley Gen. Hosp. & Lincoln Co. Hosp.

ATWAL, Mr Amarjit Singh 5 West End Lane, Horsforth, Leeds LS18 5JP Tel: 0113 281 9689 Email: amaratwal@compuserve.com — BM BS 1987 Nottm.; BMedSci (Hons.) Nottm. 1985; FRCS Ed. 1995; MRCP (UK) 1992; DA (UK) 1994. (Nottm.)

ATWAL, Arminder Singh 30 Squires Croft, Coventry CV2 2RQ Tel: 024 76 621734 — MB ChB 1997 Leic. Socs: MPS; BMA.

***ATWAL, Gurprit Singh** 31 Collingwood Road, Westpoint, Levenshulme, Manchester M19 2AP — MB ChB 1997 Manch.

ATWAL, Sarvbinder Singh 3 Greenhill Road, Handsworth, Birmingham B21 8DX — MB ChB 1998 Sheff.; MB ChB Sheff 1998.

ATWAL, Tejpal Singh 140 Murray Road, Rugby CV21 3JR — MB ChB 1993 Leeds.

ATWELL, Beryl May 16 Middlefield Close, Dore, Sheffield S17 3AR Tel: 0114 236 5710 — MB ChB 1940 Liverp.

ATWELL, Mr John David Church Cottage, Common Road, Whiteparish, Salisbury SP5 2SU Tel: 01794 884152 — MB ChB 1955 Leeds; FRCS Eng. 1959; MRCS Eng. LRCP Lond. 1956. Emerit. Cons. Paediat. Surg. Wessex Regional Centre for Paediat. Surg. Soton. Gen. Hosp. Tremona Rd. Soton. Socs: Fell. Roy. Soc. Med.; (Ex-Pres.) Brit. Assn. Paediat. Surgs. Prev: Paediat. & Neonat. Surg. Wessex Regional Centre for Paediat. Surg. at Soton. Gen. Hosp.; Sen. Lect. (Paediat. Surg.) Inst. Child Health Lond.; Paediat. Surg. W.m. Hosp. & St. Thomas' Hosp.

ATWELL, John Derrick (retired) 16 Middlefield Close, Dore, Sheffield S17 3AR — MB BChir Camb. 1942.

ATWELL, Sarah Ann Wye Valley Surgery, 2 Desborough Avenue, High Wycombe HP11 2RN Tel: 01494 521044 Fax: 01494 472770; 5 Brackenwood, Naphill, High Wycombe HP14 4TD Tel: 01494 563668 — MB BS 1987 Lond.; MA Camb. 1987, BA 1984; DRCOG 1991. Prev: Trainee GP Cookham Med. Centre; Trainee GP/SHO (Paediat.) Amersham Gen. Hosp.

ATWICK, Deborah Louise 4 Cypress Road, Walton Cardiff, Tewkesbury GL20 7RB — BM 1993 Soton. (Soton.) SHO (Paediat.) MusGr. Pk. Hosp. Taunton. Prev: SHO (Obst./Gyn.) R.D. & E Hosp. Exeter; SHO (Med. For the Elderly) Roy. Bournemouth Hosp.; Ho. Off. (Gen. Surg.) W. Dorset Hosp.

ATWILL, Kathryn Nicole 100 Ware Road, Hertford SG13 7HN — MB BS 1983 Lond.; DCH RCP Lond. 1989; DRCOG 1986.

AU, Boo Tee Kingsbridge Medical Practice, Kingsbridge Avenue, Clayton, Newcastle ST5 3HP Tel: 01782 427361 Fax: 01782 427369 — LMS 1988 Oviedo; LMS 1988 Oviedo.

AU, Gillian Taylor Queensway Medical Centre, Doctors Surgery, Queensway, Poulton-le-Fylde FY6 7ST — MB ChB 1986 Ed.; 1991 FP Cert; 2001 Dip Primary care Rheumatology; MRCGP 1991; DRCOG 1992. Prev: Trainee GP/SHO (Psychiat.) W. Lothian VTS.

AU, Mr John Kwok Keung Department of Cardiothoracic Surgery, Victoria Hospital, Whinney Heys Road, Blackpool FY3 8NR Tel: 01253 303668 Fax: 01253 303669 Email: jkkau@onetel.net.uk — MB ChB 1980 Ed.; BSc (Hons.) Ed. 1978; FRCS (Cth) 1994; FRCS Ed. 1986; MRCP (UK) 1983; FRCP 1999. (Univ. Ed.) Cons. Cardiothoracic Surg. Vict. Hosp. Blackpool. Socs: Soc. Cardiothoracic Surg. GB & Irel. Prev: Sen. Regist. (Cardiothoracic Surg.) Wythenshawe Hosp. Manch.; 1st Asst. (Surg.) Univ. Newc. Freeman Hosp.; Regist. (Cardiothoracic Surg.) Roy. Infirm. Edin.

AU, Kevin How-Kok St Johns Street Surgery, 16 St. Johns Street, Kempston, Bedford MK42 8EP Tel: 01234 851323 Fax: 01234 843293; 34 Wood End Road, Kempston, Bedford MK43 9BB — MB BS 1973 Lond.; MRCS Eng. LRCP Lond. 1973; DObst RCOG 1976. (King's Coll. Hosp.) Prev: Trainee GP Dartford & Gravesham VTS; Ho. Phys. Joyce Green Hosp. Dartford; Ho. Surg. King's Health Dist. (T) Lond.

AU, Leon 38 Heron Drive, Lenton, Nottingham NG7 2DE — BM BS 1998 Nottm.; BM BS Nottm 1998.

AU, Patrick Wing Hei Royal Liverpool University Hospital, Prescot St, Liverpool L7 8XP Tel: 0151 708 0647 Email: mercedes 888@hotmail.com; 10 Lancashire Road, 2nd Floor, Kowloon, Hong Kong — MB ChB 1994 Liverp.; DLO (RCS) Eng 1998; MRCS 1999. SHO (ENT) Roy. Liverp. Univ. Hosp.; SHO (Surg.), Wigan. Prev: Sen. Demonst. Liverp. Univ.; SHO (Orthop.) Wigan; SHO (ENT) Qu.s Med. Centre.

AU, Yiu Chung Bath Street Health Centre, 60 Bath St., London EC1V; 5 Wood Vale, London N10 3DJ — MB BS 1958 Calcutta. (Calcutta Med. Coll.) Prev: Ho. Off. Nat. Temperance Hosp. Lond.; Paediat. Ho. Off. City Gen. Hosp. Stoke-on-Trent; Sen. Ho. Off. Wimbledon Hosp. Lond.

AU-YONG, Robert Chee Loong St Peter's Health Centre, Sparkenhoe Street, Leicester LE2 0TA Tel: 0116 251 8276 Fax: 0116 251 8276; 3 holmfield Road, Leicester LE2 1SD Tel: 0116 270 5862 Email: robert@auyong.freeserve.co.uk — MB ChB 1969 Sheff.; MRCS Eng. LRCP Lond. 1970; BA (Law) De Montfort Univ. 1984. (Univ. Sheff.) Occup. Phys. Socs: BMA; Assn. Police Surg.; Soc. Occupat. Med. Prev: Regis. (Gen. Med.) Roy. Infirm. & Roy. Hosp. Sheff.

AUBIN, Anne Institute of Psychiatry, De Crespigny Park, London SE5 Tel: 020 7919 3346 — BM 1989 Soton.; MRCPsych 1994. Clin. Research Worker (Child Psychiat.) Inst. Psychiat. Lond.; Hon. Sen. Regist. Maudsley Hosp. Prev: Regist. (Psychiat.) Maudsley Hosp. Lond.

AUBIN, Susan Dorothy Department of Psychiatry, Level 5, Clinical Sciences Building, St James' University Hospital, Leeds; 10 Cross Green Avenue, Leeds LS9 0DE — MB ChB 1988 Leeds. Teachg. Fell. (Psychiat.) St. Jas. Univ. Hosp. Prev: Regist. (Psychiat. of Old Age & Transcultural Psychiat.) Lynfield Mt. Hosp. Bradford; Regist. (Psychiat.) Airedale Hosp. Keighley.

AUBREY, Daniel Roland Burnside Surgery, 41 Connaught Road, Fleet GU51 3LR Tel: 01252 613327 Fax: 01252 815156 — MB BChir 1961 Camb.; MA, MB Camb. 1962, BChir 1961; DObst RCOG 1964. (Camb. & Westm.) Prev: Ho. Off. (Surg.) W.m. Childr. Hosp. Lond.; Cas. Off. W.m. Hosp.; Ho. Phys. St. Stephen's Hosp. Chelsea.

AUBREY, Mr David Alan The Surgery, Bonvilston cottage, Bonvilston, Vale of Glamorgan, Cardiff CF5 6TR — MB BS 1961 Lond.; MD Lond. 1974, MS 1970; FRCS Eng. 1964; MRCS Eng. LRCP Lond. 1961; MEWI (Founder Member). (King's Coll. Hosp.) Indep. Cons. Cardiff. Prev: Buswell Fell. Univ. New York, USA; Author of over 100 Pub.ations and presentations to Med. Jl.s and learned societies on a wide range of subjects.; Sen. Regist. Univ. Hosp. of Wales.

AUBREY, Keith John Howard (retired) Lorien, Haverbreaks Road, Lancaster LA1 5BJ Tel: 01524 69558 — MB ChB 1961 Ed. Prev: GP Lancaster.

AUBREY, Nia 2 Rhyd-Y-Gwern Lane, Lower Machen, Newport NP10 8GH — MB BS 1994 Lond.

AUBREY, Roger John (retired) Bridge Cottage, 41 High St., Welwyn AL6 9EF — MB BS Lond. 1963; FRCS Eng. 1968; MRCS Eng. LRCP Lond. 1963; MRCGP 1972; DObst RCOG 1970. Hon. Cons. Colonoscopy Lister Hosp. Stevenage; Hosp. Pract. (Endoscopy) Qu. Eliz. II Hosp. Welwyn Gdn. City; Med. Off. Brit. Red Cross Welwyn Div.; Trustee Isabel Hospice, E. Herts.; Endoscopy Specialist Welwyn Hatfield PCG. Prev: Clin. Asst. (Med. & Endoscopy) St. Marks Hosp. Lond.

AUBREY, Sadie Eleanor Sempers, Front St., Dunston, Lincoln LN4 2ES — MB BS 1996 Lond.

AUCHINCLOSS, Mr Jeremy Macgregor The BUPA Regency Hospital, West St., Macclesfield SK11 8DW Tel: 01625 501150 Fax: 01625 501800; Arley, 10 Beech Hall Drive, Tytherington, Macclesfield SK10 2EF — MB ChB 1969 St. And.; FRCS Ed. (Orth.) 1982; FRCS Eng. 1976; FRCS Ed. 1976; DA Eng. 1974. Cons. (Orthop. Surg.) Macclesfield Dist. Gen. Hosp. Socs: Fell. Brit. Orthop. Assn.; Brit. Soc. for Surg. of Hand.; Fell. Brit. Soc. Of Surg. Of the Hand. Prev: Hand Res. Fell. Univ. Ed. P.ss Margt. Rose Orthop. Hosp. Ed.; Sen. Regist. (Orthop. & Trauma Surg.) Bristol United Hosps.; Surg. Regist. Mpilo Centr. Hosp. Bulawayo, Rhodesia.

AUCHTERLONIE, Ian Adrian 9 Church Road, Potterton, Aberdeen AB23 8UW — MB ChB 1971 Glas.; MRCP (UK) 1977. Cons. Paediat. Roy. Aberd. Childr. Hosp.

AUCKLAND, Cressida Rachel Homefarm House, Longworth, Abingdon OX13 5EB Tel: 01865 821151 — MB BS 1993 Lond. Prev: SHO (A & E) Roy. United Hosp. Bath; SHO (Geriat.) Canterbury Hosp.

AUCKLAND, Geoffrey Douglas Parade Surgery, The Parade, Liskeard PL14 6AF Tel: 01579 342667 Fax: 01579 340650; Ramsland, St. Cleer, Liskeard PL14 5DF Tel: 01579 342133 — MB BS 1976 Lond.; MRCS Eng. LRCP Lond. 1976; MRCGP 1980; DCH Eng. 1980; DRCOG 1979. (Guy's)

AUCKLAND, Katherine Margaret (retired) Normanston, Cliff Hill Lane, Aslockton, Nottingham NG13 9AP Tel: 01949 850052 — MB ChB Birm. 1951.

AUCKLAND, Kathryn Jane CFMHS, 3 Rillbank Terrace, Edinburgh EH9 1LL; Email: kjauckland@doctors.org.uk — MB ChB 1987 Ed.; MRCPsych 1994; MRCGP 1991; DRCOG 1990. p/t SpR in Child & Adolscent Psychiat.

AUCOTT, Doreen Joyce (retired) 6 Knowle Road, Budleigh Salterton EX9 6AR Tel: 01395 445166 — MB BCh BAO 1961 Dub.; DCH Eng. 1965. SCMO (Child Health) Exeter Dist.

AUCOTT, Mr William Rivers 301 Brimington Road, Chesterfield S41 0TD Tel: 01246 558417 — MB BChir 1979 Camb.; FRCS Ed. 1985; FRCS (ORL-HNS)1999.

AUDAH, Subhy Ahmed Queen Elizabeth the Queen Mother's Hospital, St Peters Road, Margate CT9 4AN — MB ChB 1961 Ain Shams; MRCPI 1983; LRCP LRCS Ed. LRCPS Glas. 1991.

AUDEN, Rita Romola 43 Thurloe Square, London SW7 2SR — BM BCh 1967 Oxf.; FRCS Eng. 1972. (Lond. Hosp.)

AUER, Rebecca Louise Haematology Dept, The Royal London Hosp, Turner St, London E1 2AD Email: rauer@hgmp.mrc.ac.uk; 4 Rye Field, Ashtead Woods Road, Ashtead KT21 2EH — MB ChB 1993 Birm.; ChB Birm. 1993; MRCP (UK) 1996. Research Regist. (Haemat.) Birm. Heartlands Hosp.; Clin. Research Fell.; Haemat., Roy. Lond. Hosp. Prev: SHO (Med.) Birm. Heartlands Hosp.; Research Reg, Haemat., Birm. Heartlands Hsp.

AUERBACH, Mr Ronald (cons. rooms), 22 Gerard Road, Harrow HA1 2NE Tel: 020 8907 5000 Fax: 020 8909 1030 Email: auerbach.ent@jmi.org.uk; 22 Gerard Road, Harrow HA1 2NE Tel: 020 8907 1905 Email: auerbach.ent@jmi.org.uk — MB BCh 1960 Witwatersrand; FRCS Eng. 1966. (Witwatersrand) Cons. ENT Surg. Socs: Fell. Roy. Soc. Med.; Mem. Watford & W. Herts. Med. Soc. Prev: N.wick Pk. Hosp., Harrow; Cons. Ent Surg. N.wick Pk. Hosp Harrow, Watford Gen. Hosp. Watford; Watford Gen. Hosp., Watford.

AUF, Mr Ihab Abd El-Hamid Glan Clwyd Hospital, Block 4, Flat 22, Bodelwyddan, Rhyl LL18 5UJ — MB BCh 1982 Ain Shams; FRCS Glas. 1994.

AUGER, Bernadette Maria 2 The Sandholes, Mansfield Road, Farnsfield, Newark NG22 8HQ — MB ChB 1980 Liverp.; MRCP (UK) 1987; DTM & H Liverp. 1982. Staff Grade (Palliat. Med.) John E.wood Hospice, Sutton-in-Ashfield.

AUGER, Martin John Department of Haematology, King's Mill Hospital, Mansfield Road, Nottingham NG17 4JL Tel: 01623 622515 Fax: 01623 421071 — MD 1989 Liverp.; MB ChB 1979; MRCP (UK) 1982; MRCPath. 1989. Cons. Haemat. N. Notts. HA. Socs: Brit. Soc. Haemat. Prev: Sen. Regist. (Haemat.) W.. Gen. Hosp. Edin.; Research Fell. (Haemat.) Roy. Liverp. Hosp.; Regist. (Haemat.) Roy. Liverp. Hosp.

AUGHEY, Trevor Thomas Adelaide Street Surgery, 20 Adelaide Street, Stonehouse, Plymouth PL1 3JF Tel: 01752 667623 Fax: 01752 667623; Tredis Farm House, Polbathic, Torpoint PL11 3ER — MB BS 1976 Lond.; MRCS Eng. LRCP Lond. 1976. (St. Mary's) Team Mem. Plymouth Locality Team S & W Devon HA. Prev: GP Lond.; SHO (Obst.) Roy. Free Hosp. Lond.; Clin. Asst. (Dermat.) Univ. Coll. Hosp. Lond.

AUGUST, Mr Adrian Charles West Barn, Golden Lane, Lawshall, Bury St Edmunds IP29 4PS — MB BS 1975 Lond.; FRCS Eng. 1980. Cons. Orthop. Surg. W. Suff. Hosp. Bury St. Edmunds. Prev: Sen. Orthop. Regist. St. Barts. Hosp. Lond.

AUGUST, Paul Jeffrey 19 St John Street, Manchester M3 4DT Tel: 0161 834 0363 Fax: 0161 834 4205; Tel: 01925 730337 Fax: 01925 730217 — MB BS 1967 Lond.; FRCP Lond. 1988; MRCP (UK) 1970. (St. Thos.) Cons. Dermat. Salford Roy. Hosp. Trust; Med. Appeal Tribunal Manch. 1986-1996. Socs: Brit. Assn. Dermat.; Roy. Soc. of Med.; Brit. Med. Laser Assn. Prev: Sen. Regist. & Regist. St. Thos. Hosp. Lond.; Regist. United Liverp. Hosps.

AUGUSTINE, Antionette Sunitha 1 South Park Crescent, London SE6 1JJ — MB BS 1994 Lond.

AUGUSTT, Alfred Godfrey 8 Horsham Court, Lansdowne Road, London N17 0LP — LRCPI & LM, LRSCI & LM 1963; LRCPI & LM, LRCSI & LM 1963.

AUJLA, Kashmir Singh 105 Somerset Road, Southall UB1 2UE — MB ChB 1989 Aberd. Specialist Regist. (A & E) Aberd. Roy. Infirm. Prev: Regist. (Emerg. Med.) Roy. N. Shore Hosp. Sydney, Australia; SHO (A & E) Aberd. Roy. Infirm.

AUKETT, Maureen Anne Childrens Directorite, Carnegie, Hunts Road, Hockley B19 1DR Tel: 0121 255 7510 Fax: 0121 255 7519 Email: anneaukett@bscht.wmids.nhs.uk — MB ChB 1975 Birm.; BSc (Biochem.) Birm. 1971; FRCP Lond. 1993; MRCP (UK) 1982; Dip. Community Paediat. Warwick 1983; DCH RCP Lond. 1980; DRCOG 1979. (Birm.) Cons. Paediat. (Community & Child Health) W. Birm. HA; Hon. Clin. Sen. Lect. Univ. Birm.; Clin. director Childr.s Serv.s, Birm specialist community health NHS trust. Socs: Fell. Roy. Coll. Paediat. and Child Health. Prev: Sen. Regist. (Paediat.) Sheff. Childr. Hosp.; SCMO (Child Health) E. Birm. HA; Med. Off. (Matern. & Child Health) The Gambia W. Africa.

AUKLAND, Mr Andrew 45 Knightlow Road, Harborne, Birmingham B17 8PX Tel: 0121 429 9961 — MB ChB 1970 Liverp.; FRCS Eng. 1976; FRCS Ed. 1976. Cons. Surg. Sandwell Dist. Gen. Hosp. W. Bromwich.

AUKLAND, John (retired) Y Bwthyn, 15 Oakhill Drive, Prestatyn LL19 9PU Tel: 01745 888698 — MB ChB 1962 Liverp.; BSc (Hons.) Liverp. 1959, MB ChB 1962. Med. Off. St. Kentigern Hospice St. Asaph. Prev: G.P. Prestatyn.

AULAKH, Harnam Singh Adelaide Street Surgery, 118 Adelaide Street, Blackpool FY1 4LB Tel: 01253 620725 Fax: 01253 290765 — MB ChB 1983 Bristol. GP Blackpool. Prev: Regist. (Med.) Bundeberg Gen Hosp. Qu.sland, Austral.

AULAKH, Jagat Mohan Singh Hawthorne Gardens, Church Road, Long Itchington, Rugby CV47 9PR Tel: 01926 817554 — MB BS 1976 Poona; FFA RCS Eng. 1980. Cons. Anaesth. & Dir. ICU Warwick Hosp. Prev: Cons. Anaesth. W. Middlx. Univ. Hosp. Isleworth Middlx.; Sen. Regist. (Anaesth.) St. Mary's Hosp. Lond. W2; Regist. (Anaesth.) Middlx. Hosp. Lond. & Qu. Charlotte's Matern. Hosp. Lond.

AULAKH, Ravinder The Oaklands Practice, Yateley Medical Centre, Oaklands, Yateley GU46 7LS Tel: 01252 872333 Fax: 01252 890084; 65 Nine Mile Ride, Finchampstead, Wokingham RG40 4ND Tel: 01734 733355 — BM 1979 Soton.; MRCGP 1988. (Southampton)

AULAQI, Mr Adel Abdulla Mohammad 16 Wykeridge Close, Chesham HP5 2LJ Tel: 01494 776341 Fax: 01494 773798 — MB ChB 1967 Ed.; FRCS Ed. 1972; MFPM RCP (UK) 1989; DTM & H Ed. 1969. (Ed.) Clin. Asst. (A & E) Wexham Pk. Hosp. Slough; GP & Cons. Pharmaceut. Phys. Bucks. Socs: Fell. Roy. Soc. Trop. Med. & Hyg. Prev: Med. Adviser Wellcome Internat. Ltd.; Head Clin. Trials Phase IV, The Wellcome Foundat. Ltd. Beckenham; Surg. i/c & Sen. Med. Off. Aden Refinery Hosp., Aden.

AULD, Andrew Clark and Partners, 20 Aitken Street, Largs KA30 8AU Tel: 01475 674545 Fax: 01475 689645; 1 Buchanan Street, Largs KA30 8PP Tel: 01475 674545 Fax: 01475 685649 — MB ChB 1976 Glas.

AULD, Andrew (retired) 1 Woodside Gardens, Craigsheen Est., Clarkston, Carmunnock, Glasgow G76 9AD Tel: 0141 644 2204 — MB ChB 1957 Glas.; FRCOG 1980, M 1964. Cons. O & G Vict. Infirm. Glas. & Rutherglen Matern. Hosp. Glas. Prev: Cons. O & G Roy. Samarit. Hosp. Wom. & Robroyston Hosp. Glas.

AULD, Ann Robertson Summerlands, 1 St Cuthbert's Avenue, Dumfries DG2 7NZ — MB ChB 1985 Ed.; BSc Hons (Med. Sci.) 1983.

AULD, Mr Barry John Conquest Hospital, The Ridge, St Leonards-on-Sea TN37 7RD Tel: 01424 755255 Email: auld.barry@mail.nar-tr.sthames.nhs.uk — MB BChir 1983 Camb.; MRCOG 1991. (Camb. & St. Thos.) Cons. O & G Conquest Hosp. St. Leonards-on-Sea. Socs: BSGE. Prev: Sen. Regist. Guy's Hosp. Lond.; Regist. St. Geo. Hosp.

AULD, Bruce Milner Duns Medical Practice, The Knoll, Station Road, Duns TD11 3EL Tel: 01361 883322 Fax: 01361 882186 — MB ChB 1981 Birm. (Birm.) Socs: Roy. Coll. Gen. Pract.

AULD, Mr Charles David Department of Surgery, Dumfries & Galloway Royal Infirmary, Bankend Road, Dumfries DG1 4AP Tel: 01387 246246; Summerlands, 1 St Cuthbert's Avenue, Dumfries DG2 7NZ Tel: 01387 250127 — MD 1983 Aberd.; MB ChB 1975; FRCS Ed. 1980; DA (UK) 1980. Cons. Gen. Surg. Dumfries & Galloway Roy. Infirm. Socs: Fell. Assn. Surgs. Prev: Regist. (Surg.) Aberd. Teachg. Hosps.; Regist. (Surg.) Roy. Infirm. Edin.; Sen. Regist. (Surg.) Glas. Teachg. Hosps.

AULD, Christine Margaret Portland Street Surgery, 101 Portland Street, Troon KA10 6QN Tel: 01292 313593 Fax: 01292 312020; 5 Fairhaven, Barassie, Troon KA10 6UA — MB ChB 1981 Glas.; MRCGP 1985; DRCOG 1984.

AULD, Jacqueline Elizabeth Banbridge Medical Group Centre, Linenhall Street, Banbridge BT32 3EG; 9 Castle Lodge, Banbridge BT32 4RN — MB BCh BAO 1989 Belf.; MRCGP 1993; DCH RCPS Glas. 1992; DRCOG 1992; DGM RCP Lond. 1991.

AULD, James Calzieveg, Braco, Dunblane FK15 9RD — MB ChB 1981 Glas.

AULD, Jason William Whim Lodge, Hill Road, Gullane EH31 2BE Tel: 01620 842161 — MB BS 1992 Lond.; BSc Lond. 1989. SHO (Orthop.) Roy. Bournemouth Hosp. Socs: Med. Protec. Soc.; BMA. Prev: SHO (A & E Surg., Orthop. & Anaesth.) Redcliffe Hosp. Qu.sland, Austral.; Ho. Off. (Med.) W. Cumbria HA; Ho. Off. (Surg.) Whittington Hosp. NHS Lond.

AULD, Mary Hendry 3 Dalziel Drive, Glasgow G41 4JA Tel: 0141 427 1720 — MB ChB 1958 Glas.

AULD, Mary Innes Ruxton (retired) Granville Lodge, Charleston Road, Aboyne AB34 5EL Tel: 0133 98 87106 — MB ChB Aberd. 1951; DPH Aberd. 1956. Prev: Clin. Med. Off. Grampian HB.

AULD, William Harry Ruxton (retired) Normanhurst, 56 Midton Road, Ayr KA7 2TP — MB ChB 1944 Aberd.; MD Aberd. 1954; FRCPath 1968; FRCP Glas. 1975, M 1972. Prev: Cons. Med. Biochem. Ayrsh. & Arran HB.

AULT, Elizabeth Ann 25 Thames Reach, 80 Rainville Rd, London W6 9HS — MB BS 1996 Lond.

AUMEERALLY, Zeennat Banu 21 Kelso Gardens, Leeds LS2 9PS — MB ChB 1992 Leeds.

AUMONIER, Frederic John (retired) Wake, Heatherdene, West Horsley, Leatherhead KT24 6LH — MRCS Eng. LRCP Lond. 1944; MSc. Lond. 1936; DA Eng. 1946. Prev: Asst. Venereol. Frimley Pk. Hosp. Guildford.

AUNG, Maung Gyaw (retired) 1 Main Street, Burton Salmon, Leeds LS25 5JS Tel: 01977 675261 — MB ChB 1963 Aberd. Prev: Regist. (Path.) Mayfield Hosp. Dundee.

AUNG, Soe Homerton Hospital, Homerton Row, London E9 6SR Tel: 020 8919 7361; 16 Forest Approach, Woodford Green IG8 9BW — MB BS 1984 Med. Inst. (I) Rangoon; MRCP (UK) 1992. Sen. Regist. (Neonat.) Homerton Hosp. Lond.

AUNG, T M Cedar Cross Medical Centre, 42 Cedar Road, Prescot L35 2XA Tel: 0151 426 5569 Fax: 0151 426 5969.

AUNG, Tayza Damian Jude 85 Long Road, Canvey Island SS8 0JB — MB BS 1994 Lond.

AUNG, Tin Tun Woolpit Health Centre, Woolpit Bury St., Bury St Edmunds IP30 9QU Tel: 01359 240298 — LMSSA 1988 Lond.; MB BS Med. Inst. (I) Rangoon, Burma 1979; MSc 2001 (Sch. of Health Policy & Pract., Univ. of E. Anglia). Prev: Trainee GP Bury St. Edmunds; SHO (Ophth.) W. Suff. Hosp.; SHO (Neurosurg.) Char. Cross. Hosp. Lond.

AUNG HPYOE, Dr Flat 3, Lowlands, 2-8 Eton Avenue, London NW3 3EJ — MB BS 1981 Rangoon; MB BS Med. Inst. (I) Rangoon 1981.

AUNG MYINT KYAW, Dr c/o Dr K. Aye, 69 Sutherland Avenue, Petts Wood, Orpington BR5 1QY Tel: 01689 600486; 10F Tettenhall Road, Wolverhampton WV1 4SA Tel: 01902 427469 — MB BS 1971 Med. Inst. (I) Rangoon. (Inst. Med. (I) Rangoon) SHO New Cross Hosp. Wolverhampton.

AUNG THU, Dr 24 Jasmin Way, Up Hatherley, Cheltenham GL51 3HZ — MB BS 1980 Rangoon; MB BS Rangoon, Burma 1980; MRCP (UK) 1992.

AUNGLE, Jean Clare (retired) 97 Strips of Craigie Road, Dundee DD4 7QQ Tel: 01382 459386 — MB ChB 1948 Ed.; DPM Ed. & Glas. 1973.

AUNGLE, Peter George (retired) 97 Strips of Craigie Road, Dundee DD4 7QQ Tel: 01382 459386 — MB ChB 1949 Ed.; FRCP Ed. 1964, M 1952; FRCPsych 1971; DPM Lond. 1951.

AUPLISH, Mr Rajinder Nath 22 Copthorne Road, Croxley Green, Rickmansworth WD3 4AQ — MB BS 1960 Panjab; MB BS Panjab (India) 1960; FRCS Ed. 1970; DO Aligarh 1962. (Patiala Med. Coll.) Ophth. Surg. Watford Gen. Hosp.

***AUPLISH, Sunil** 22 Copthorne Road, Croxley Green, Rickmansworth WD3 4AQ — MB BS 1997 Lond.; BSc (Hons.) 1995.

AURAS, Alfred 11 Cairn Grove, Crossford, Dunfermline KY12 8YD — MB ChB 1971 Ed.

AURORA, Monique Baldwins Lane Surgery, 266 Baldwins Lane, Croxley Green WD3 3LG.

AURORA, Paul 27A Forty Lane, Wembley HA9 9EU — MB BS 1990 Lond.; MRCP (UK) 1994. (Univ. Coll. Lond.) Clin. Fell. (Intens. Care) Roy. Liverp. Childr. Hosp. Prev: Med. Co-ordinator Med. Emerg. Relief Internat., Afghanistan; Regist. (Paediat.) Oxf. Radcliffe Hosps.

AURORA, Ravinder Paul Medical Centre, 1 Oxford Drive, Eastcote, Ruislip HA4 9EY Tel: 020 8866 6589 Fax: 020 8868 3317; 37 St. Mary's Avenue, Northwood HA6 3AY Tel: 01923 826354 Email: rmaurora@epulse.net — MB BS 1985 Lond.; MRCGP 1991; DRCOG 1991; DCCH RCGP 1990; DCH RCP Lond. 1990. (Guy's & St. Thom.) GP Princip.

AUST, Thomas Richard 31 Meadow Road, Catshill, Bromsgrove B61 0JJ — MB ChB 1998 Liverp.; MB ChB Liverp 1998.

AUST, William John Park View Surgery, 24-28 Leicester Road, Loughborough LE11 2AG Tel: 01509 230717 Fax: 01509 236891 — MB ChB 1976 Liverp.

AUSTEN, Belinda Louise 8 Banister Gardens, Southampton SO15 2LX — BM BCh 1996 Oxf.

AUSTEN, Janet Christine Lygon Croft, Sandy Way, Cobham KT11 2EY — MB BS 1980 Lond. Socs: Roy. Coll. Gen. Pract.

AUSTEN, Jennifer Margaret Westwood, 4 Burrell Road, Prenton, Birkenhead CH42 8NH Tel: 0151 608 1221 — BM 1983 Soton.; DRCOG 1987; Dip. GU Med 1997. Clin. Asst. (Genitourin. Med.) Arrowe Pk. Hosp. Upton. Prev: Clin. Asst. (Genitourin. Med.) Birm.; Clin. Asst. (A & E) Wirral; Trainee GP Melksham VTS.

AUSTEN, Judith Caroline 44 Matlock Way, New Malden KT3 3AY Tel: 020 8942 5597 — BM BCh 1971 Oxf. (St. Geo.) Prev: Ho. Phys. Chase Farm Hosp. Enfield; Ho. Surg. Wembley Hosp.; Resid. (Med.) Veterans' Admin. Hosp. Sepulveda, U.S.A.

AUSTERA, Jan The Health Centre, University of Sussex, Falmer, Brighton BN1 9RW Tel: 01273 679434 Fax: 01273 675689 — MRCS Eng. LRCP Lond. 1986; T(GP) 1991.

AUSTIN, Aileen Veronica 12 Eastwood Avenue, Giffnock, Glasgow G46 6LR — LM 1945 Dub.; BSc Glas. 1942, MB ChB 1944; DObst RCOG 1949. (Glas.) Prev: Asst. Area Med. Off. Area 4 Middlx.; Res. Obst. Off. Matern. Hosp. Luton; Ho. Surg. Vict. Infirm. Glas.

AUSTIN, Alison Elizabeth New Park Medical Practice, 163 Robertson Road, Dunfermline KY12 0BL Tel: 01383 629200 Fax: 01383 629203; South Holme, 5 Pitbauchlie Bank, Dunfermline KY11 8DP — MB ChB 1988 Ed.; BSc (Hons.) Ed. 1986; MRCGP 1992; DRCOG 1991; DCH RCPS Glas. 1990.

AUSTIN, Andrew Simon 64 Woodhall Road, Wollaton, Nottingham NG8 1LE — MB ChB 1992 Birm.; MRCP (UK) 1995. (Birm.) Regist. (Gastroenterol. & Gen. Med.) Univ. Hosp. Qu. Med. Centre Nottm. Socs: Med. Research Soc.; Brit. Soc. of E.rognterologists. Prev: SHO (c/o Elderly) Roy. Wolverhampton Hosps. NHS Trust; Specialist Regist. Gastro, Derby City Gen.; Specialist Regist. Gastro, Derbysh. Roy. Infirm.

AUSTIN, Angela Helen Central Gateshead Medical Group, Prince Consort Road, Gateshead NE8 1NB — MB BS 1984 Newc.; MRCGP 1988; DRCOG 1987. (Newc.)

AUSTIN, Anthony John Farnham Health Centre, Brightwells, Farnham GU9 7SA Tel: 01252 723122 Fax: 01252 728302; 7 Old Compton Lane, Farnham GU9 8BS Tel: 01252 727412 — MB BS 1963 Lond.; MRCS Eng. LRCP Lond. 1963; MRCGP 1974; DObst RCOG 1965. (St. Bart.) Prev: SHO (Paediat.) Salisbury Hosp.

AUSTIN, Antony David Leigh North Street Surgery, 22 North Street, Ilminster TA19 0DG Tel: 01460 52284 Fax: 01460 57233; The Rockery, North St, Ilminster TA19 0DG — MB ChB 1983 Sheff.; DRCOG 1988; DCH RCP Lond. 1987. (Sheffield) GP Ilminster. Socs: BMA; MDU. Prev: Trainee GP Langport; SHO (Psychiat.) Mendip Hosp. Wells; SHO (O & G) Dorset Hosp.

AUSTIN, Mr Brian McConnell The Dell, 17 Lawrie Park Crescent, London SE26 6HH — MB BCh BAO 1986 Belf.; MB BCh Belf. 1986. Cons. Paediat. & Adult Cardiac Surg., Guys Hsp, Lond.

AUSTIN, Bryan Newns Glannrafon Surgery, Glannrafon, Amlwch LL68 9AG Tel: 01407 830878 Fax: 01407 832512; Y Ddeudir, Bull Bay, Amlwch LL68 9SU Tel: 01407 830878 Fax: 01407 832512 — MB BS 1962 Lond.; DRCOG 1978. (Univ. Coll. Hosp.) Prev: Ho. Surg. Surgic. Unit Univ. Coll. Hosp.; Ho. Phys. Caern. & Anglesey Hosp. Bangor; Ho. Surg. St. David's Hosp. Bangor.

AUSTIN, Christopher Arthur Northern General Sheffield Teaching Hospital NHS Trust, Herries Road, Sheffield S5 7AU Tel: 0114 271 4046; 2 Stumperlowe Park Road, Sheffield S10 3QP Tel: 0114 230 5549 — MB BChir 1978 Camb.; MA Camb. 1978; FRCP Lond. 1993; MRCP (UK) 1979. (Univ. Camb. & Middlx. Hosp. Lond.) Cons. Phys. & Geriat. N. Gen.Sheff. Teachg. Hosp. NHS Trust Sheff.; Hon. Sen.Clin. Lect. Univ. Sheff. Prev: Cons. Phys. (Elderly) Centr. Sheff. Univ. Hosps. NHS Trust; Sen. Regist.(Gen. Internal & Geriat. Med.) Roy. Hallamsh. Hosp. & Nether Edge Hosp. Sheff.

AUSTIN, Danielle Joanna 113A Gravelly Hill North, Birmingham B23 6BJ — MB ChB 1996 Leic.

AUSTIN, Daphne Isabelle Worcestershire Health Authority, Isaac Raddox House, Shrub Hill Road, Worcester WR4 9RW — MB ChB 1985 Otago, NZ; BSc Vict. Univ., NZ 1979; MFPHM RCP (UK) 1994. Cons. Pub. Health Worcs. HA.

AUSTIN, Mr David John BUPA Hospital, Gartree Road, Oadby, Leicester LE2 2FF Tel: 0116 265 3652 Fax: 0116 272 0666; Field View Cottage, Shearsby, Lutterworth LE17 6PL Tel: 0116 247 8398 — LRCPI & LM, LRSCI & LM 1968; FRCS Ed. 1974; FRCOphth 1990; DO Eng. 1972. (RCSI) Cons. Ophth. Leicester Roy. Infirm. Socs: F.R.C.Opthalmologists. Prev: Sen. Regist. (Ophth.) Birm. & Midl. Eye Hosp.; Ho. Off. Our Lady of Lourdes, Drogheda.

AUSTIN, David Nicholas 1 Hamfield Cottages, Lower Road, Cookham, Maidenhead SL6 9HQ Tel: 01628 531139 Email: dnaus@aol.com — BM BS 1990 Nottm.; MRCP 1993. (Nottingham) Res. Fell. in Gastroenterol., Cent. Middlx. Hosp. Lond. Prev: Special. Regist. Gen. Med. & Gastroenterol. St. Mary's Hosp. Lond.; Special. Regist. Gen. Med. & Gastroenterol. Hemel Hempstead Hosp.; Special. Regist. Gen. Med. & Gastroenterol. Chelsea & W.minister Hosp.

AUSTIN, Deborah Jane Thornbrook Surgery, Chapel-en-le-frith, High Peak SK23 7RS Tel: 01298 812725 — MB ChB 1994 Manch.; DRCOG 1996. p/t GP Princip., Thornbrook Surg. Prev: GP Retainer, Macclesfield.

AUSTIN, Gerard Louis Raymond 4A High Street, Great Ayton, Middlesbrough TS9 6NJ — MB ChB 1992 Dundee.

AUSTIN, Giles Roland, Maj. RAMC Department of Aviation Medicine, School of Army Aviation, Middle Wallop; 31 Vine Close, Aldershot GU11 2HG Tel: 01252 345862 — MB BS 1995 Lond.; BSc Lond. 1993. (St. Mary's Hosp. Med. Sch.) Prev: SHO (A & E) Wexham Pk. Hosp.; Ho. Phys. Centr. Middlx. Hosp.

AUSTIN, Gregory Steven c/o Anaesthetic Department, Taunton & Somerset Hospital, Musgrove Park, Taunton TA1 5DA — MB BS 1988 Tasmania.

AUSTIN, James David Raymond 23 Yelverton Drive, Edgbaston, Birmingham B15 3NT Tel: 0121 455 8205 — MB BCh BAO 1950 NUI; CPH 1954. (NUI) Cons. Phys. Birm. Chest Clin. & E. Birm. Hosp. Prev: Cons. Phys. Romsley Hill Hosp. Halesowen. Asst. Chest Phys. Chest; Servs. of Hants. & Poole Chest Clinic; Med. Regist. Baguley Sanat. Manch.

AUSTIN, Jane Burdon Department of Child Health, Royal Northern Infirmary, Inverness IV3 5SF Tel: 01463 704000 Fax: 01463 713844; Candide, Ardersier, Inverness IV2 7RR — MB BS 1975 Lond.; MRCS Eng. LRCP Lond. 1975; DCH RCPS Glas. 1978. (Charing Cross, Lond.) Assoc. Specialist (Community Paediat.) Highland Primary Care NHS Trust. Socs: (Comm. Mem.) Scott. Assn. Community Child Health; MRCPCH; BMA. Prev: SHO (Paediat.) Roy. Hosp. Sick Childr. Edin.; SHO (Neonat.) Simpson Memor. Matern. Pavil. Edin.; Ho. Off. Char. Cross Hosp. Lond.

AUSTIN, Kingsley David (retired) 5 Beechfield, Westbourne Road, Lancaster LA1 5LH Tel: 01524 68087 — MB BChir 1956 Camb.; 1953 BA Camb.; 1958 DCH Eng.; 1959 DObst. RCOG UK. Mem. Lancaster and Morecambe Community Health Counc. Prev: Princip. GP Crewkerne.

AUSTIN, Letitia-Jane Scudamore 5 Star Lane, Avening, Tetbury GL8 8NT Tel: 0145383 4478 — MB BS 1978 Lond.

AUSTIN, Manuela Lisa Corner Place Surgery, 46a Dartmouth Road, Paignton TQ4 5AH Tel: 01803 557458; 12 Long Rydon, Stoke Gabriel, Totnes TQ9 6QH Tel: 01803 782714 — MB BS 1988 Lond.; DRGOG; MRCGP.

AUSTIN, Margaret Aureol 20 Coombe Street, Lyme Regis DT7 3PR — MB BS 1950 Lond.; FRCOG 1972, M 1959. (King's Coll. Hosp.) Cons. O & G Qu. Mary's Hosp. Sidcup. Prev: Sen. Regist. (O & G) Lewisham Hosp.; Regist. (O & G) St. Luke's Hosp. Guildford & King's Coll. Hosp.

AUSTIN, Margaret Sylvia (retired) 38 Queen Street, Stirling FK8 1HN Tel: 01786 474997 — MB ChB Birm. 1942. Prev: GP Poynton.

AUSTIN, Margaret Wendy Elizabeth Whiteley and Partners, 4 Market Place, Billesdon, Leicester LE7 9AJ Tel: 0116 259 6206 Fax: 0116 259 6388; The Manor House, Illston-on-The Hill, Leicester LE7 9EG — LRCPI & LM, LRSCI & LM 1969; LRCPI & LM, LRCSI & LM 1969. (RCSI) Prev: Clin. Asst. (Anaesth.) Dudley Rd. Hosp. Birm.; Ho. Phys. Sharoe Green Hosp. Preston; Ho. Surg. Corbett Hosp. Stourbridge.

AUSTIN, Mark Andrew Claremont Medical Centre, 91 Claremont Road, Salford M6 7GP Tel: 0161 743 0453 Fax: 0161 743 9141; 20 Sandgate Road, Whitefield, Manchester M45 6WG — MB ChB 1984 Leeds; MRCGP 1989.

AUSTIN, Mark John 57 Chyngton Way, Seaford BN25 4JE — MB ChB 1998 Liverp.; MB ChB Liverp 1998.

AUSTIN, Martin William Masonic House Surgery, 26 High Street, Buckingham MK18 1NU Tel: 01280 816450 Fax: 01280 823885 — MB BS 1985 Lond.; MRCGP 1994; T(GP) 1991.

AUSTIN, Mr Michael William Consultant Ophthalmologist, Singleton Hospital, Sketty Lane, Swansea SA2 8QA Tel: 01792 205666 Fax: 01792 285362; Roseville, Mayals Green, Swansea SA3 5JR Tel: 01792 402126 — MB BCh 1983 Wales; FRCS Ed. (Ophth.) 1988; FRCOphth 1989. Cons. Ophth. Singleton Hosp. Swansea. Socs: Internat. Perimetric Soc.; UK & Eire Glaucoma Soc. Prev: Sen. Regist. (Ophth.) Univ. Hosp. Nottm.; Research Regist. St. Paul's Eye Hosp. Liverp.; Regist. (Ophth.) Aberd. Roy. Infirm.

AUSTIN, Peter Graham The Surgery, Hill Terrace, Middleton-in-Teesdale, Barnard Castle DL12 0QE Tel: 01833 640217 Fax: 01833 640961; Low Thatch lea, Laneside, Middleton in Teesdale, Barnard Castle DL12 0RY Tel: 01833 640217 Fax: 01833 640961 — MB ChB 1973 Dundee; DRCOG 1976.

AUSTIN, Phyllis Margaret (retired) Ferrand, Broadmead, Woodbury, Exeter EX5 1HR Tel: 01395 32248 — MA Oxf. 1941; MB BS Lond. 1952; DObst RCOG 1954.

AUSTIN, Mr Ralph Charles Tilston 46 Ratcliffe Road, Stoneygate, Leicester LE2 3TD Tel: 0116 270 4609 — MB BS 1987 Lond.; FRCS Eng. 1991.

AUSTIN, Mr Roger Tilston (retired) BUPA Hospital, Gartree Road, Oadby, Leicester LE2 2FF Tel: 0116 272 0888 Fax: 0116 272 0666 — MB BS 1962 Lond.; FRCS Ed. 1968. Prev: Cons. Orthop. Surg. Leicester Roy. Infirm., Leicester Gen. Hosp. & Hinckley & Dist. Hosp.

AUSTIN, Shaun Occupational Health Department, British Vita plc, Oldham Road, Middleton, Manchester M24 2DB Tel: 0161 643 1133 Fax: 0161 653 5411; Mount Pleasant, East Lee Lane, Higher Eastwood, Todmorden OL14 8RW Tel: 01706 814557 Email: shaunaust@aol.com — MB ChB 1985 Ed.; AFOM 2001; MRCGP 1990; DRCOG 1990; Dip. IMC RCS Ed. 1990. Occupat.al Phys. Prev: GP Princip., Todmorden Gp. Pract.; Trainee GP Leicester VTS.

AUSTIN, Simon Flat E, 25 Taylors Lane, Dundee DD2 1AP — MB ChB 1998 Dund.; MB ChB Dund 1998. (Dundee)

AUSTIN, Stephen John 28 Waterloo Park, Belfast BT15 5HU — MB BCh BAO 1993 Belf.

AUSTIN, Thomas Raymond, TD (retired) Star House, Star Lane, Capel Llaniltern, Cardiff CF5 6JH Tel: 01222 890332 Fax: 01222 890332 Email: tomaust@compuserve.com — MB ChB Birm. 1954; FFA RCS Eng. 1967; DTM & H Eng. 1963. Prev: Cons. Anaesth. Univ. Hosp. Wales.

AUSTIN, Vera Maria Arruda Godspiece Leaze, Trowbridge Road, Norton St Philip, Bath BA2 7NG — MRCS Eng. LRCP Lond. 1986.

AUSTIN-PUGH, Christopher Kenneth William Flaxlands House, Hook, Swindon SN4 8DZ — MB BS 1971 Lond.; MRCS Eng. LRCP Lond. 1971; FRCOG 1993, M 1978.

AUSTWICK, Mr David Harwood Orthopaedic Department, Luton & Dunstable Hospital, Luton LU4 0DZ Tel: 01524 497068 Fax: 01524 883639 Email: daustwick@aol.com; The Old Orchard, Village St, Hexton, Hitchin SG5 3JB Tel: 01582 883639 — MB BS 1970

Lond.; FRCS Eng. 1975; MRCS Eng. LRCP Lond. 1970. (Roy. Free) Cons. Orthop. & Trauma Surg. Luton & Dunstable Hosp.; Clin. Dir. (Trauma & Orthop.) Luton & Dunstable Hosp.. Socs: Exec. HCSA; Fell. BOA; BMA. Prev: Sen. Regist. (Orthop.) Addenbrooke's Hosp. Camb.; Regist. (Orthop.) Roy. Free Hosp. Lond.; Regist. (Thoracic & Gen. Surg.) Broomfield Hosp. Chelmsford.

AUTERSON, Thomas Norman Erne Hospital, Cornagrade Road, Enniskillen BT74 6AY Tel: 02866 327411 Fax: 02866 326131; 22 Castle Wood, Castlecoole Road, Enniskillen BT74 6BF Tel: 02866 327885 — MB BCh BAO 1977 Belf.; FFA RCSI 1987. (Queen's Belfast) Cons. Anaesth. Erne Hosp. Enniskillen. Socs: Assn. Anaesth. GB & N. Irel. & N.. Irel. Soc. Anaesth.

AUTH, Marcus Karl-Heinz 14 Pritchatts Road, Birmingham B15 2QT — State Exam Med 1992 Frankfurt.

AUTY, Frank Thomas Southfields Group Practice, 7 Revelstoke Road, London SW18 5NJ Tel: 020 8947 0061 Fax: 020 8944 8694; White Chimneys, Elm Grove Road, Cobham KT11 3HB — BM BS 1990 Nottm.

AUTY, Richard Maitland Zeneca Pharmaceuticals, Alderley Park, Macclesfield SK10 4TG Tel: 01625 582828 Fax: 01625 584058 Email: richard.auty@alderley.zeneca.com — MB ChB 1971 Bristol; MB ChB (Hons.) Bristol 1971; BSc (Hons. Physiol.) Bristol 1968, MD 1975; FRCP Lond. 1991; MRCP (UK) 1974; FFPM 1991. Research & Developm. Dir., Zeneca Pharmaceut. Macclesfield; Non-Exec. Dir. Cantab Pharamceut. plc, Camb.; Mem. Meds. Commiss. UK. Prev: Head Med. Research Dept. ICI Pharmaceut. Macclesfield; Dep. R & D Dir. Fisons Pl Pharmaceut. Div.; Sen. Regist. (Med.) Ahmadu Bello Univ. Hosp. Zaria, Nigeria.

AUTY, Simon Joseph 36 High House Road, Bradford BD2 4EX — MB ChB 1990 Ed.; BSc (Hons.) Anat. Ed. 1988. SHO Rotat. (Gen. Med., Haemat., Renal Med. & Gastroenterol.) Hope Hosp. Salford; SHO III Profess. Cardiol. Unit Glas. Roy. Infirm. Prev: Ho. Off. (Surg.) Roy. Infirm. Edin.; Ho. Off. (Med.) Roy. Infirm. Edin.

AVANN, Helen Jane Eaton Road Surgery, 276 Eaton Road, West Derby, Liverpool L12 2AW Tel: 0151 531 0675 — MB ChB 1991 Liverp. p/t GP Liverp. Socs: BMA; Liverp. Med. Inst.

AVASTHI, Anil Lone Pines, Old Watling St., Rochester ME2 3UF — MB BS 1993 Lond.

AVASTHI, Ram Bandhu (retired) Lytham Road Surgery, 194 Lytham Road, Blackpool FY1 6EU Tel: 01253 349710 — MB BS 1964 Punjab (India); FRCS Ed. 1969; FRCS Eng. 1970; MRCS Eng. LRCP Lond. 1973; ECFMG Cert 1972. JP. Prev: Regist. (Cardiothoracic Surg.) Roy. Infirm. & City Hosp. Edin.

AVELINE, Anna Jennet Dudley Bassetlan Hospital, Worksop, Nottingham S81 0BD Tel: 01909 500990; The Foundry, 1 High St, Solva, Haverfordwest SA62 6TF Tel: 0115 960888, 01437 720169 — MB BS 1965 Lond.; FRCPath 1996, M 1984. (St. Bart.) Cons. Microbiol. Bassetlaw Hosp. Worksop. Prev: Sen. Regist. (Microbiol.) Univ. Hosp. Nottm.

AVELINE, Mark Oxenford Nottingham Psychotherapy Unit, 114 Thorneywood Mount, Nottingham NG3 2PZ Tel: 0115 952 9453 Fax: 0115 952 9459 Email: maveline@nadt.org.uk; The End House, Pembroke Drive, Nottingham NG3 5BG Tel: 0115 960 6888 Email: dr.m.aveline@btinternet.com — MB BS 1965 Lond.; MD Lond. 1990; FRCPsych 1983, M 1972; DPM Eng. 1969. (St. Bart.) Cons. Psychother. Nottm.shire Healthcare NHS Trust. Socs: Chairm. PTSAC RCPsych; Bd. Mem. UK Counc. Psychother.; (Pres.) Brit. Assn. Counselling and Psychother. Prev: Ed. Neurosis & Personality Disorder Sect., Curr. Opin. in Psychiat. 1994-97; Sen. Regist. Roy. Ed. Hosp.; Regist. Guy's Hosp. Lond.

AVELING, Wynne Sylvan Lodge, 3 Sylvan Road, Wanstead, London E11 1QL Tel: 020 8530 3982 — MB BChir 1971 Camb.; MA Camb. 1971, MB BChir 1971; FRCA 1978; DObst RCOG 1973. Cons. Anaesth. Middlx. Hosp. Lond.; Hon. Cons. Anaesth. St. Luke's Hosp. for Clergy. Lond. Prev: Regist. & Lect. (Anaesth.) Lond. Hosp.

AVENELL, Alison Health Services Research Unit, Aberdeen Medical School, Foresterhill, Aberdeen AB25 2ZD Tel: 01224 554336 Fax: 01224 663087 Email: a.avenell@abdn.ac.uk — MB BS 1985 Lond.; MSc 1999; BSc (Nutrit.) Lond. 1981; MD Aberd. 1996; MRCP (UK) 1988; MRCPath 1997. (St. Bart.) MRC Train. Fell. in Health Servs. Research; Lect. in Pub. Health 1998-. Socs: Nutrit. Soc.; Assn. Clin. Biochem. Prev: Regist. Grampian HB; MRC Train. Fell. (Nutrit.) Rowett Research Inst. Aberd.; Sen. Regist. (Clin. Biochem.) Roy. Infirm. Ed.

AVERNS, Henry Lloyd Rock House, Landkey Newlands, Barnstaple EX32 0NA — MB ChB 1988 Sheff.; MRCP (UK) 1991. Cons. Rheum. N. Devon Dist. Hosp.

AVERY, Alan Frederick Purlieu House, Lyncombe Vale Road, Bath BA2 4LP — MB ChB 1967 Bristol; FFA RCS Eng. 1972. Cons. Anaesth. & Intens. Care Roy. United Hosp. NHS Trust Bath. Prev: Sen. Regist. (Anaesth.) Bristol Health Dist. (T).

AVERY, Anthony John The Valley Surgery, 81 Bramcote Lane, Chilwell, Nottingham NG9 4ET Tel: 0115 943 0530 Fax: 0115 943 1958 — MB ChB 1986 Sheff.; FRCGP 1999; DM Nottm 1996; MRCGP 1990; DGH RCP Lond. 1989; DGM RCP Lond. 1988. Reader in Primary Health Care (Gen. Pract.) Nottm. Univ. Med. Sch.

AVERY, Mr Brian Stuart Department of Oral & Maxillofacial Surgery, Middlesbrough General Hospital, Ayresome Green Lane, Middlesbrough TS5 5AZ Tel: 01642 850850 Fax: 01642 824727; Mordon House, Mordon, Sedgefield, Stockton-on-Tees TS21 2EY Tel: 01740 620634 Fax: 01740 623702 Email: avery@mordonhouse.demon.co.uk — MB BS 1974 Lond.; BDS (Hons.) Lond. 1970; FRCS Ed. 1985; MRCS Eng. LRCP Lond. 1974; LDS RCS Eng. 1970; FDS RCS Eng. 1976, LDS 1970. (Guy's) Cons. Oral Surg. Middlesbrough Gen. Hosp., N. Tees Gen. Hosp. & Hartlepool Gen. Hosp.; Hon. Cons. to the Army at Catterick. Socs: Fell. Brit. Assn. Oral & Maxillofacial Surg.; BMA; BDA. Prev: Sen. Regist. (Oral Surg.) Canniesburn Hosp. Bearsden; Regist. (Oral Surg.) Qu. Mary's Hosp. Roehampton & W.m. Hosp. Lond.

AVERY, Brice Johnson 4 Millerfield Place, Morningside, Edinburgh EH9 1LW — BM 1986 Soton.

AVERY, Charles Malcolm Kingsteignton Surgery, Whiteway Road, Kingsteignton, Newton Abbot TQ12 3HN Fax: 01626 336406 — LMS 1988 Spain. (Ovieno, Spain) p/t GP Kingsteignton Med. Pract., Clin. Asst. Cardiol. Dept. Socs: PCCS. Prev: VTS Tonbay Hosp.

AVERY, Mr Christopher Martin Edward The Queens Victoria Hospital, Holtye Road, East Grinstead RH19 3DZ Tel: 01342 410210; 28 Paul's Place, Farm Lane, Ashtead KT21 1HN — MB BChir 1991 Camb.; MB BChir Camb. 1992; BDS Bristol 1985; FRCS Eng. 1994; FDS RCS Eng. 1988. Sen. Regist. (Oral & Maxillofacial Surg.) Qu. Vict. Hosp. E. Grinstead. Socs: BMA; BAOMS; Eur. Assn. Cranio-Maxillo. Surg. Prev: Sen. Regist. (Oral & Maxillofacial Surg.) King's Coll. Hosp. Lond.; Regist. (Oral & Maxillofacial Surg.) Roy. Surrey Hosp. Guildford; SHO (Transpl. Surg.) Addenbrooke's Hosp. Camb.

AVERY, David Joel (retired) 1 Highfield Court, St Margarets Road, Manor Park, London E12 5DW Tel: 020 8989 6159 Email: davery7468@aol.com — MRCS Eng. LRCP Lond. 1942; MRCGP 1959. Prev: Med. Insp. Aliens & Commonw. Immigrants.

AVERY, Deborah Anne Mayfield Medical Centre, 37 Totnes Road, Paignton TQ4 5LA Tel: 01803 558257 Fax: 01803 663353; 6 Langdon Lane, Galmpton, Brixham TQ5 0PG — MB ChB 1985 Bristol; MRCGP 1990; DCH RCP Lond. 1989.

AVERY, Geoffrey Charles Blyth Road Medical Centre, 8 Blyth Road, Maltby, Rotherham S66 8JD Tel: 01709 812827; The Maples, Woodside Court, ickersly, Rotherham S66 1FB Tel: 01709 702962 — MB ChB 1987 Sheff.

AVERY, Gerard Richard Castle Hill Hospital, Castle Road, Cottingham HU16 5JQ; 29 Ferriby Road, Hessle HU13 0HS — MB BS 1982 Nottm.; BMedSci Nottm. 1980; FRCR 1989; MSc Lond. 1997. Cons. Radiol. Hull & E. Yorks. Prev: Sen. Regist. (Radiol.) Newc.; Regist. (Radiol.) Hull.

AVERY, James Gordon Iechyd Morgannwg Health, 41 High St, Swansea SA 1 1LT Tel: 01792 458066 Fax: 01792 607533 Email: gordon.avery@morgannwg_ha.wales.nhs.uk; The Beeches, 56 Kenilworth Road, Leamington Spa CV32 6JW Tel: 01926 431034 Fax: 01926 431034 Email: pennyandgordon@yahoo.co.uk — MB ChB 1963 Sheff.; FFPHM 1981; 1973 M; MD (Distinc.) Sheff. 1978; FFCM 1981, M 1973; DTM & H Liverp. 1968. Cons. Pub. Health Med. Iechyd Morgannwg Health Swansea; Mem. (Counc.) Managem. Child Accid. Prevent. Trust. Socs: Fell. Roy. Soc. Trop. Med. & Hyg.; Brit. Travel Health Assn.; BMA Chairm. S. Warks Br. 1986-90. Prev: Govt. Malariol. & Chief Med. Off. Brit. Solomon Is.s; Chiff Med. Off., Montserrat; Dpu S. Warks Ha.

AVERY, Jill Patricia Tel: 01293 523383 Fax: 01293 553560 — MB BS 1981 Lond.; MRCGP 1985.

AVERY, Michael John BUPA Murrayfield Hospital, Holmwood Dr, Thingwall, Wirral CH61 1AU Tel: 0151 648 7000 Fax: 0151 648

7684; Copper Folly, Well Lane, Mollington, Chester CH1 6LD — MB ChB 1963 Sheff.; BSc Lond. 1950; FRCPsych 1997, M 1976; DPM Eng. 1967; CChem; MRSC 1980. Cons. Psychiat. BUPA Murrayfield Hosp. Socs: Chester & N. Wales Med. Soc.; Liverp. Psychiatric Soc. (Past Pres.); Soc. of Clin. Psychiat.s. Prev: Cons. W. Chesh. Hosp., Chester; Sen. Reg. Inst. of Family Psychiat., Ipswich; Reg. Cane Hill Hosp., Coulsdon, Surrey.

AVERY, Nicholas Robert The Centre for the Study of Complementary Medicine, 14 Harley House, Brunswick Place, London NW1 4PR Tel: 020 7935 7848 Fax: 020 7224 4159 Email: harley@complemed.co.uk; Little Dene, 14 Denton Road, Eastbourne BN20 7SU Tel: 01323 727474 Fax: 01323 729159 Email: nickavery@tiscali.co.uk — MB BS 1975 Lond.; MFHom 1999; MRCS Eng. LRCP Lond. 1975. (Guy's) Complementary Med. Specialist, the Centre for the Study of Complementary Med., Lond.; Clin. Fell. (Homoeop. & Acupunc.), Director of Educat., Homoeop. Hosp., Tunbridge Wells. Socs: Fac. of Homeopathy; Brit. Med. Acupunc. Soc.; Brit. Soc. for Allergy, Environm. and Nutrit.al Med. Prev: Clin. Asst. (Diabetes) Conquest Hosp. Hastings; Gen. Practitioner, Heathfield.

AVERY, Peter Jonathan Compass House Medical Centres, 25 Bolton Street, Brixham TQ5 9BZ Tel: 01803 855897 Fax: 01803 855613; 6 Langdon Lane, Galmpton, Brixham TQ5 0PG — MB ChB 1986 Bristol; MA Camb. 1981; MRCGP 1990; DCH RCP Lond. 1990; DRCOG 1989.

AVERY, Philip George Aneddfa, Bethel Lane, Penclawdd, Swansea SA4 3FP — MB BS 1983 Lond.; MD Leicester 1992; MRCP (UK) 1986. Cons. Phys. & Cardiol. P. Philip Hosp. LLa.lli; Hon. Cons. Cardiol. Univ. Hosp. Wales Cardiff. Prev: Regist. (Cardiol.) Univ. Hosp. Wales Cardiff; Research Regist. (Cardiol.), Groby Rd. Hosp., Leicester; Regist. (Gen. Med. & Cardiol.) Roy. Devon & Exeter Hosp.

AVEYARD, Paul Nicholas Department of Public Health & Epidemiology, University of Birmingham, Birmingham B15 2TT Tel: 0121 414 4532 Fax: 0121 414 7692; Japonica Cottage, 18 Birmingham Road, Stoneleigh, Coventry CV8 3DD Tel: 024 76 415303 — MB BS 1990 Lond.; MPH Birmingham 1996; BSc Lond. 1987; MRCP (UK) 1994. Lect. in Pub. Health Med., Pub. Health, Univ. of Birm., Birm.

AVEYARD, Sarah Catherine 20 St Georges Dr, Bransgore, Christchurch BH23 8EZ — MB ChB 1997 Ed.

AVILL, Mr Roger Bassetlaw District General Hospital, Kilton Hill, Worksop S81 0BD; 6 Woodall House Farm, Dowcarr Lane, Harthill, Sheffield S26 7XN Tel: 01909 515330 — MB ChB 1974 Sheff.; ChM Sheff. 1989, MB ChB 1974; FRCS Eng. 1980. Cons. Surg. Bassetlaw HA.

AVIS, Rebecca Claire 12 The Paddock, Guildford GU1 2RQ — MB ChB 1991 Sheff.

AVISON, Mr Geoffrey Gillies 69 Simpson Avenue, Ninewells, Dundee DD2 1UZ — MB BCh 1985 Cairo; MRCS Eng. LRCP Lond. 1990; FRCS Eng. 1991.

AVISON, John Derek (Surgery), 1A Ullswater Crescent, Kingston Vale, London SW15 3RG Tel: 020 8546 1190 Fax: 020 8541 5652 Email: avidocj@aol.com; Summer House, The Drive, Kingston upon Thames KT2 7NY Tel: 020 8942 9540 — MB BChir 1954 Camb.; MA Camb. 1953; DObst RCOG 1956. (Camb. & Westm.) Med. Off. New Vict. Hosp. Kingston; Med. Off. Bentalls Ltd. Kingston-upon-Thames, Mansell plc Croydon, Unichem plc Chessington & other companies. Socs: Assur. Med. Soc.; Affil. Fac. Occupat. Med. RCP Lond; Soc. Occupat. Med. Prev: Jun. Cas. Off. W.m. Hosp.; Ho. Surg. & Ho. Surg. Obst. Kingston Hosp.

AVIV, Richard Ivan Doctors Residence, St James' University Hospital, Beckett St., Leeds LS9 7TF Tel: 0113 243 3144; PO Box 32162, Camps Bay, Cape Town 8040, South Africa Tel: 01027 21 4389850 Fax: 01027 21 4382641 — MB ChB 1993 Cape Town.

AVIVAR FERNANDEZ, Manuel Bartolome Doctors Residence, Burnley General Hospital, Casterton Avenue, Burnley BB10 2PQ; 98 Leamington Avenue, Burnley BB10 3EY Tel: 01282 432922 — LMS 1989 Granada. SHO (O & G) GP VTS.

AVRAAMIDES, Panayiotis Costa 11 Coleraine Road, London N8 0QJ — MB BS 1984 Lond.

AVRANE, Jean-Jacques SOS Doctors, 15 Berghem Mews, Blythe Road, London W14 0HN — MD 1982 Paris.

AW, Jacky Flat 2f1, 139 Bucclench St., Edinburgh EH8 9NE; 99 Ottrelles Mead, Bradley Stoke North, Bristol BS32 0AL — MB ChB 1998 Ed.; MB ChB Ed 1998. (Edinburgh)

AW, Tar-Ching Institute of Occupational Health, University Birmingham, Edgbaston, Birmingham B15 2TT Tel: 0121 414 6026 Fax: 0121 414 6217 Email: t.c.aw@bham.ac.uk — MB BS 1971 Malaya; 1980 PhD Lond.; 1974 MSc (Pub. Health) Singapore; 1993 FRCP Lond.; 1990 FRCPC; 1987 FFOM RCP Lond.; 1975 DIH Eng.; 1975 MSc (Occupat. Med.). Sen. Lect. Inst. (Occupat. Health) Univ. Birm.; Vis. Prof. Univ. of Malaysia, Sarawak. Socs: Fell. Amer. Coll Preven. Med.; Soc. Occupat. Med.; Counc. Mem. Roy. Inst. Pub. Health and Hyg. Prev: Lect. (Dept. Social Med. & Pub. Health) Univ. Singapore; Employm. Med. Adviser Health & Safety Exec.; Epidemic Intelligence Serv. Off. CDC, Atlanta.

AW, Tuan Chen 40 Burnham Court, Burnham St., Bethnal Green, London E2 0JF Tel: 020 8983 0933 Email: geckod@clara.net — MB BS 1996 Lond. SHO (Anaesth.) Newham Gen. Hosp. Lond. Socs: BMA; MPS; RCA.

AW YONG, Yew Meng 468 Fulham Palace Road, London SW6 6HY — MB BS 1992 Lond.; BSc (Hons.) Lond. 1988. Police Surg., Met. Police; Med. Off. Fulham Football Club. Socs: FRSM. Prev: SHO (A & E) Qu. Mary Hosp. Lond.; SHO (Orthop.) St. Geo. Hosp. Lond.; SHO (Cardiothoracic & Vasc. Surg.) Roy. Brompton Hosp. Lond.

AWAAD, Mohamed Osman Mohamed Ahmed The Alexandra Hospital, Woodrow Drive, Redditch B98 7UB Tel: 01527 503030; 28 Prince Harry Road, Henley-In-Arden, Solihull B95 5DD Tel: 01564 794786 — MB BS 1972 Khartoum Sudan; MRCP (UK) 1979.

AWAD, Abbas Helmy General Medical Centre, Surgery Lane, Hartlepool TS24 9DN — MB BCh 1981 Zagazig, Egypt; MRCOG 1992.

AWAD, Hani Hassan Fikri, Squadron Ldr. RAF Med. Br. The Princess Mary's Hospital, RAF Akrotiri BFPO 57 Tel: 00357 25965590 Fax: 00357 25952844 Email: haniawad@dsca.gov.uk — MB ChB 1975 Alexandria; 1975 MB ChB Alexandria; 1986 MRCOG; 1998 FRCOG. (Faculty of Medicine, Alexandria University, Egypt) Cons. obs. & gyn., P.ss Mary's Hosp., RAF Akrotiri; Defence Med. Serv.s adviser in Obst. & gyn. Socs: N. Eng. Obst. & Gyn. Soc.; Brit. Med. Ultrasound Soc. Prev: Hon. Sen. Regist. Obst. & gyn., Glas. HB, Q. Mother,s Hosp, & Glas. W. Infirm. (seconded by RAF); Sen. Regist (O&G) RAF Hosp., Weybeng; Regist (O & G) Boplou G>H> & St Peter's Hosp, chertsey.

AWAD, Mr Reda William Ibrahim Watford General Hospital, Vicarage Road, Watford WD18 0HB Tel: 01923 217397; 3 Gayton Close, Chesham Bois, Amersham HP6 6DW Tel: 01494 723175 Fax: 01494 723174 Email: reda@dial.pipex.com — MB ChB 1976 Ain Shams; MD Leic. 1988; FRCS Ed. 1983. (Univ. Ain Shams Cairo, Egypt) p/t Cons. Surg. (Gen. & Vasc. Surg.) W. Herts. NHS Trust Watford Gen. Hosps. Socs: Roy. Soc. Med.; BMA; Vasc. Surg. Soc. GB & Irel. Prev: Sen. Regist. (Surg.) W. Midl. RHA.

AWAD, Mr Said Ahmed Mostafa Mohamed Bronglais General Hospital, Carodoc Road, Aberystwyth SY23 1ER Tel: 01970 635636; Mousadekeen, 21 Cefn Llan, Waunfawr, Aberystwyth SY23 3TF Tel: 01970 610112 Fax: 01970 610112 — MB BCh 1978 Cairo; MRCOG 1988. (Med. Sch. Cairo Univ., Egypt) Regist. (O & G) Torbay Gen. Hosp. & Torbay Gen. Hosp. Socs: Welsh Soc. Obst. & Gyn.; Eur. Soc. Obst. & Gyn.; Brit. Soc. Colpos. & Cerv. Path. Prev: Regist. (O & G) Wom. Hosp. Liverp.

AWAD, Mr Wael Ibrahim Issa Flat 71, Dorset House, Gloucester Place, London NW1 5AF — MB BS 1988 Lond.; FRCS Eng. 1994; FRCS Ed. 1993; MD 1999. (Char. Cross & Westm. Univ. Lond.) Sp. Regist. (Cardiothoracic Surg.) St. Bart's. Hosp. Lond. Socs: Internat. Soc. Heart Research; Brit. Soc. Cardiovasc. Research. Prev: Res. Regist. (Cardiothoracic Surg.) St Thomas's Hosp.; Regist. (Cardiothoracic Surg.) Lond. Chest Hosp.; SHO (Cardiothoracic Surg.) Guy's Hosp. & Roy. Brompton Hosp. Lond.

AWADH, Mekhled 3 Aylith Place, Newcastle upon Tyne NE3 4PT; Lancaster Moor Hospital, Quernmore Rd, Lancaster LA1 3JR — MB BS 1998 Newc.; MB BS Newc 1998.

AWADZI, Gabriel 19 Ellicks Close, Bradley Stoke N., Bristol BS32 0EP Tel: 01454 613267 — MB BS 1984 Ibadan; MRCOG 1992. (Ibadan Nigeria) Staff Grade Doctor (Gyn.) Frenchay Healthcare Trust Bristol; Staff Grade Doctor (Obst.) S.mead Hosp.

Bristol. Socs: BMA; Brit. Menopause Soc. Prev: Regist. (O & G) Wordsley Hosp. Stourbridge; Regist. New Cross Hosp. Wolverhampton.

AWAN, Abdul Wahid Queens Road Surgery, 252 Queens Road, Halifax HX1 4NJ Tel: 01422 330636 — MB BS 1962 Karachi.

AWAN, Bismillah The Surgery, 200a Upminster Road South, Rainham RM13 9BH Tel: 01708 552896 Fax: 01708 552285 — MB BS 1965 Punjab.

AWAN, Mohammed Tahir Sultan Neston Surgery, Mellock Lane, Little Neston, South Wirral CH64 4BN Tel: 0151 336 3951 Fax: 0151 353 0173 — MB ChB 1985 Manch.; MRCGP 1989; DCH RCP Lond. 1989; DRCOG 1988. PCG Bd. Mem.; Trainer in GP since 96.

AWAN, Mr Muhammad Yousaf E-4 Kingstor House, Derriford Hospital, Derriford Road, Plymouth PL6 8DH — MB BS 1986 Bahauddin Zakariya Univ. Pakistan; FRCS Glas. 1993.

AWAN, Rachel Jane 134 Pimlico Road, Clitheroe BB7 4PT — MB BS 1994 Newc.

AWAN, Ramzan Khan Orchard 2000 Medical Centre, 480 Hall Road, Hull HU6 9BS Tel: 01482 854552 Fax: 01482 859900 — LRCP LRCS 1983 Ed.; LRCP LRCS Ed. LRCPS Glas. 1983. GP Hull.

AWAN, Shahnaz Kusar 4 Beeston Avenue, Timperley, Altrincham WA15 7RX Tel: 0161 941 6680 — MB ChB 1986 Leeds. Prev: SHO (O & G & Paediat.) Trafford Gen. Hosp.; SHO (Anaesth.) Stepping Hill Hosp. Stockport; SHO (A & E) Stockport Infirm.

AWAN, Tayyaba Tasnim Eric Moore Health Centre, Tanners lane, Warrington WA2 7LY Tel: 01925 417252 Fax: 01925 417729 — MB BS 1970 Newc.

AWBERY, David Eric Ash Tree House, Church St., Kirkham, Preston PR4 2SE Tel: 01772 686688 Fax: 01772 672054; Beardwood Farm House, Beardwood Fold, Blackburn BB2 7AS Tel: 01254 689511 — MB ChB 1972 Liverp.

AWBERY, Sylvia Margaret War Pensions Agency, Norcross, Blackpool, Blackpool Tel: 01772 332562; The Old Mill House, Mill Lane, Wrea Green, Preston PR4 2WP Tel: 01772 683149 — MB ChB 1973 Liverp.; AFOM RCP Lond. 1984. Med. Off. War Pens. Agency. Socs: Soc. Occupat. Med. Prev: Clin. Asst. (A & E) Vict. Hosp. Blackpool; Med. Off. (Occupat. Health) Blackpool, Wyre & Fylde DHA.

AWDRY, Mr Philip Neville (retired) Felstead House, 23 Banbury Road, Oxford OX2 6NX Tel: 01865 55036 — MB 1958 Camb.; MB BChir 1958; MA Camb. 1968; FRCS Eng. 1966; FRCOphth 1989; DO Eng. 1963. Prev: Cons. Ophth. Surg. United Oxf. Hosps. & Oxf. RHA.

AWEID, Mr Adil Mehdi Saleh Department of Orthopaedics, Ashford Hospital &St. Peter's Hosp, Ashford; 27 Stornaway Road, Slough SL3 8YB — MB ChB 1973 Baghdad; FRCS Ed. 1982. Staff Grade (Orthop.) Ashford Hosp. Middlx. & St. Peter's Hosp. Chertsey. Prev: Cons. Orthop. Surg. As-Salama Hosp. Saudi Arabia; Regist. (Orthop. & Trauma) Maidstone Hosp. & Manor Hosp. Nuneaton.

AWI, Michael Mang 3 Redwood Road, Gateacre, Liverpool L25 2QR Tel: 0151 487 5414 — MB BS 1972 Mingaladon; DO RCPSI 1983.

AWONUGA, Awoniyi Olumide 151 Coombe Park Road, Binley, Coventry CV3 2PD Tel: 01922 55911 Fax: 01922 59020; 151 Coombe Park Road, Binley, Coventry CV3 2PD Tel: 024 76 635714 Fax: 01203 635714 — MB BS 1979 Ibadan; MRCOG 1989. Gyn. Midl. Fertil. Servs. Walsall. Socs: Eur. Soc. Human Reproduc. & Embryol.; Amer. Fertil. Soc.; Eur. Assn. Gyn. & Obst. Prev: Hon. Research Fell. Asst. Concep. Unit King's Coll. Hosp. Lond.; Regist. (O & G) York. Dist. Hosp.

AWTY, Malcolm Wilson The Woodside Medical Practice, The New Surgery, Wensley Green, Woodside, Telford TF7 5NR Tel: 01952 586691; 36 Pageant Drive, Aqueduct, Telford TF4 3RF — MB ChB 1981 Manch.; BSc (Hons.) Manch. (Pharmacol. & Physiol.) 1978; MRCGP 1986; DRCOG 1984. Prev: SHO (Med.) Manch. Roy. Infirm.; SHO (Geriat.) Barnes Hosp. Manch.; SHO (O & G) & (Paediat.) St. Mary's Hosp. Manch.

AWTY, Michael David (retired) 11 Harcourt House, 19A Cavendish Square, London W1M 9AD Tel: 020 7499 0891 Fax: 020 7499 0889 — MRCS Eng. LRCP Lond. 1961; FDS RCS Eng. 1964, L 1953. Prev: Hon. Cons. Oral Surg. Qu. Vict. Hosp. E. Grinstead.

AWWAD, Mr Awad M Cromwell Hospital, Cromwell Road, London SW5 0TU Tel: 020 7460 5663 Fax: 020 7460 5555; 64 Warwick Gardens, Kensington, London W14 8PP Tel: 020 7603 8305 Fax: 020 7602 6692 — MB BCh 1971 Ain Shams; MB BCh (Hons.) Ain Shams 1971; MSc (Bioengineering) Glas. 1983; FRCS Glas. 1980. (Univ. Ain Shams) Cons. Plastic & Reconstruc. Surg. Cromwell Hosp. Lond. Socs: Fell. Roy. Soc. Med.; Assn. Brit. Plastic Surg. Prev: Vis. Cons. Plastic & Reconstruc. Surg. Mermaid Clinic Ebeltoft, Denmark; Sen. Regist. (Plastic Surg.) Arhus Univ. Hosp., Denmark; Regist. (Plastic Surg.) & Research Fell. (Microsurg.) Canniesburn Hosp. Glas.

AWWAD, Saif Taher Radiotherapy Department, Royal Shrewsbury Hospital, Shrewsbury SY3 8XQ Tel: 01743 261103 Fax: 01743 261100; 16 Westwood Drive, The Mount, Shrewsbury SY3 8YB Tel: 01743 363740 Email: awwad@cwcom.net — MB BS 1980 Jordan; FFR RCSI 1991; DMRT Ed. 1986. (Univ. Jordan) Cons. Clin. Oncol. Roy. Shrewsbury Hosp. Socs: Roy. Coll. Radiol.; Eur. Soc. Radiother. & Oncol.; Scott. Radiol. Soc. Prev: Sen. Regist. (Radiother. & Oncol.) Univ. Newc.; Regist. (Clin. Oncol.) Lothian HB.

AXFORD, Alan Thomas Bronglais Hosp, Caradog Rd, Aberystwyth SY23 1ER Tel: 01970 623131 Fax: 01970 635998; Nant-y-Benglog Isaf Farm, Capel Seion, Aberystwyth SY23 4EE Tel: 01970 880697 Fax: 01970 880456 Email: benglos@compuserve.com — MRCS Eng. LRCP Lond. 1965; BSc (Physiol.) Lond. 1962, MB BS 1965; MRCP (UK) 1974; FRCP Lond. 1987. (Univ. Coll. Hosp.) Cons. Phys. Bronglais Gen. Hosp. Aberystwyth.; Med. Director, Ceredigion & Mid Wales Nhs Trust, Bronglais Hosp. Aberystwyth. Socs: Brit. Thoracic Soc. Prev: Med. Regist. Med. Research Coun. Pneumoconiosis Unit, Llandough Hosp.; Penarth; Med. Regist. FarnBoro. Hosp. Kent; Ho. Phys. FarnBoro. Hosp. Kent.

AXFORD, John Stewart St George's Hospital Medical School, Cranmer Terrace, London SW17 0RE Tel: 020 8725 5795 Fax: 020 8725 5758 Email: j.axford@sghms.ac.uk — MB BS 1981 Lond.; BSc CNAA 1975; MD Lond. 1990; FRCP Lond. 1995; MRCP (UK) 1985; T(M) 1991. (Univ. Coll. Hosp.) Cons. Rheum. & Reader (Rheum. & Clin. Immunol.) St. Geo. Hosp. Med. Sch. Lond. Socs: Fell. Roy. Geogr. Soc.; Brit. Soc. Rheum.; Fell. RSM. Prev: Clin. Lect. (Rheum.) & Hon. Sen. Regist. Bloomsbury Rheum. Unit Univ. Coll. & Middlx. Sch. Med. Lond.; Regist. (Rheum.) King's Coll. Hosp. Lond.; Ho. Phys. Univ. Coll. Hosp., Hammersmith Hosp, Nat. Hosp. Nerv. Dis. & Brompton Hosp. Lond.

AXFORD, Shelagh Lesley 37 Lodge Breck, Drayton, Norwich NR8 6AR — BM BCh 1974 Oxf.; DRCOG 1978.

AXON, Andrew David 23 Kingsway, Liverpool L22 4RG — MB ChB 1994 Ed.

AXON, Professor Anthony Thomas Roger Upwood, Woodlands Drive, Rawdon, Leeds LS19 6JZ; The General Infirmary, Great George St, Leeds LS1 3EX Tel: 0113 392 2125 Fax: 0113 392 6968 Email: anthony.axon@leedsth.nhs.uk — MB BS 1965 (Hons.); MD Lond. 1973; FRCP Lond. 1980, M 1968. (St. Barts. Hosp. Medical College) p/t Cons. Phys. Leeds Gen. Infirm.; Hon. Prof. Gastroenterol. Univ. Leeds. Socs: Past Pres. Brit. Soc. of Gastroenterol.; Past Pres. N. of Eng. Gastroenterol. Soc.; Pres. Europ. Soc. of Gastrointestinoe Endoscopy. Prev: Sen. Regist. St. Thos. Hosp. Lond.; Ho. Phys. Med. Profess. Unit St. Bart. Lond.

AXON, Emma Jane 2A Coalway Road, Renn, Wolverhampton WV3 7LR Tel: 0121 426 3221; Cornerways, South View Road, Pinner, Pinner HA5 3YB Tel: 0121 426 3221 — MB ChB 1994 Birm.; DFFP 1999; DRCOG 1997. (Univ. Birm.) p/t GP Princip.

AXON, Jeremy Michael Charles Queen Elizabeth II Hospital, Welwyn Garden City AL7 4HQ Tel: 01707 365083 Fax: 01707 365058; Plummers Cottage, Sally Deards Lane, Rabley Heath, Welwyn AL6 9UE Tel: 01438 820596 — MB BS 1984 Lond.; MRCP 1987 (UK); FRCP 2000. (Char. Cross) Cons. Rheum. & Rehabil. Qu. Eliz. II Hosp. Welwyn Gdn. City. Prev: Sen. Regist. (Rheum. & Rehabil.) Nuffield Orthop. Centre Oxf.; Hon. Regist. (Rheum. & Med.) St. Bart. Hosp. Lond.; SHO Rotat. (Med.) OldCh. Hosp. Romford.

AXON, Patrick Robert ENT Unit, Hope Hospital, Stott Lane, Salford M6 8HD Tel: 0161 789 7373 — MB ChB 1990 Leeds.

AXSON, Dorothy May 2 The Colonnade, 418 Hotwells Rd, Bristol BS8 4NU — MB ChB 1966 Bristol; DPM Eng. 1970. Cons. Psychiat. in Ment. Handicap. & Family Psychiat. Farleigh Hosp.

AXTON, John Henry Michael 91 Belper Road, Derby DE1 3ER Tel: 01332 384084 Email: john-axton@hotmail.com — MB BS 1962 Lond.; MD Rhodesia 1975; FRCP Glas. 1984, M 1967; FRCP Lond. 1981, M 1968; DCH Eng. 1966; DObst RCOG 1966. Socs:

Brit. Paediat. Assn. Prev: Dean Fac. Med. & Prof. Paediat. & Child Health Univ. Zimbabwe, Harare; Cons. Paediatritian, Derbysh. Childr.s Hosp.; Vis. Lect., Mbarara Med. Sch., Uganda.

AYALA GONZALEZ, Angel 93 Harlington Road W., Feltham TW13 3JW — LMS 1988 Barcelona.

AYALA ORTEGA, Jose Luis Scunthorpe General Hospital, Cliff Gardens, Scunthorpe DN15 7BH — LMS 1992 U Autonoma Madrid.

AYANA, Aster Ergate 1 Auchneagh Avenue, Greenock PA16 9EP — MB ChB 1998 Glas.; MB ChB Glas 1998.

***AYANA, Gamada Ergate** 1 Auchneagh Avenue, Greenock PA16 9EP Email: gamayana@hotmail.com; Flat 8E, 33 Cleveden Drive, Glasgow G12 0SD — MB ChB 1995 Glas.; MRCS Glas. 1999.

AYANA, Margaret Simpson Ravenscraig Hospital, Greenock PA16 9HA Tel: 01475 633777; 1 Auchneagh Avenue, Greenock PA16 9EP Tel: 01475 783101 — MB ChB 1959 Glas.; DObst RCOG 1963. Assoc. Specialist (Psychiat.) Ravenscraig Hosp. Greenock. Socs: BMA; Greenock & Dist. Fac. Med.

AYCART VALDES, Enrique Ricardo 6 Montague Flats, Eugene St., St James, Bristol BS2 8EU — LMS 1992 Seville.

AYE, Cho Cho Dunelm Medical Practice, 1-2 Victor Terrace, Bearpark, Durham DH7 7DF Tel: 0191 373 2077 Fax: 0191 373 6216 — MB BS 1982 Med. Inst. (I) Rangoon. (Med. Inst.) GP Durh.

AYE, Omma Trent View Medical Practice, 45 Trent View, Keadby, Scunthorpe DN17 3DR Tel: 01724 782209 Fax: 01724 784472 — MB ChB 1993 Ed. Trainee GP Humberside. Socs: Med. Protec. Soc.

AYEKO, Michael Olusegun c/o Mrs Adegboye, 58 Fordel Road, Catford, London SE6 1XP — MB BS 1982 Lagos, Nigeria; FRCA 1994.

AYERS, Anthony Brian 4 Broomcroft Close, Pyrford, Woking GU22 8NR Tel: 01932 353347 — MB BS 1966 Lond.; MD Lond. 1974; MRCS Eng. LRCP Lond. 1966; FRCR 1975; FFR 1974. Radiol. & Med. Dir. Guy's & St. Thos. Hosp. Trust Lond.; Hon. Sen. Lect. United Med. & Dent. Sch. Lond. Socs: Roy. Soc. Med. (Counc. Mem. Sect. Radiol.). Prev: Sen. Regist. Hammersmith Hosp. Lond.

AYERS, Dominic Edwin 46 Mackenders Lane, Eccles, Aylesford ME20 7HZ — MB BChir 1995 Camb.

AYERS, Richard James Briton Ferry Health Centre, Hunter Street, Briton Ferry, Neath SA11 5SF Tel: 01639 812270 Fax: 01639 813019; 59 Daphne Road, Rhyddings, Neath SA10 8DU Tel: 01639 642963 — BM 1987 Soton.; MRCGP 1991.

AYERS, Sarah Jane 24 Hill Rise, Potters Bar EN6 2RR Tel: 01707 642327 — MB BS 1992 Lond.; BSc Lond. 1987; MRCP (UK) 1996. Regist. (Med. Oncol.) Guy's Hosp. Lond. Prev: SHO (Oncol.) Roy. Marsden Hosp. Lond.; SHO (Med.) P.ss Margt. Hosp. Swindon; SHO Medway Hosp. Gillingham.

AYIDA, Miss Gubby Anire Chelsea and Westminster Hospital, London SW10 9NH Email: gubby.ayida@chelwest.nhs.uk — MB BS 1985 Lond.; BA Oxf. 1982; MRCOG 1991; MA Oxon 1996; DM Oxon 1999. (Somerville Coll. Oxford; St Thomas's Hosp., London) Cons. Obst. Chelsea and W.m. Hosp. Socs: BMA; Brit. Fertil. Soc.; BMUS. Prev: Sen. Regist. Chelsea & W.minster Hosp.; Res. Fell. John Radcliffe Hosp.

AYLARD, Ann Pauline Heath House Priory Hospital, Heath House Lane, Off Bell Hill, Stapleton, Bristol BS16 1EQ Tel: 01179 525255 — MB ChB 1978 Leeds; MRCPsych 1982. p/t Vis. Cons. in Child & Adolesc. Psychiat. Heath Ho. Priory Hosp., Bristol. Prev: Cons. Child Psychiat. Swindon HA.

AYLARD, Paul Robert Heath House Priory Hospital, Heath House Lane, Off Bell Hill, Bristol BS16 1EQ Tel: 0117 952 5255 Fax: 0117 952 5552; 2 Clifton Park, Clifton, Bristol BS8 3BS Tel: 0117 973 7371 — MB ChB 1978 Leeds; MRCPsych 1982; Dip Psychother Leeds 1985; FRCPsych 1995. Cons. Psychiat. Heath Ho. Priory Hosp.; Hon. Sen. Clin. Lect. (Ment. Health) Univ. Bristol. Prev: Cons. Psychiat. Psychother. S.mead HA; Cons. Psychiat. Psychother. Bath HA; Research Fell. Leeds Univ.

AYLES, Anthony Charles Murray The Hermitages Medical Practice, 5 Hermitage Terrace, Edinburgh EH10 4RP Tel: 0131 447 6277 Fax: 0131 447 9866; 10 Church Hill, Edinburgh EH10 4BQ Tel: 0131 447 9960 Fax: 0131 447 9960 — MB BChir 1980 Camb.; Dip. Occupat. Med. Lond. 1998; BSc (Med. Sci.) St. And. 1978. Sen. Med. Adviser Bank of Scotl.; Area Treas. Med. Off; Area DVLA Med. Off. Socs: BMA & Soc.Occup. Med. Prev: Regist. Rotat. (Surg.) Lothian HA.

AYLES, Helen Mary 3 Purves Road, London NW10 5ST — MB BS 1989 Lond. Socs: MRCP.

AYLESBURY, Heidi Elisabeth 31 Harvest Hill, East Grinstead RH19 4BU — MB BS 1992 Lond.

AYLETT, Malcolm John (retired) Stone Martin, Haugh Head, Wooler NE71 6QL Tel: 01668 282268 Fax: 01668 281675 Email: malcolm.aylett@newcastle.ac.uk — 1955 MB BS Lond.; 1955 MRCS Eng. LRCP Lond.; 1971 FRCGP 1987, M; 1966 DObst RCOG; MD 2000 Newcastl upon Tyne. Prev: GP Wooler, N.umberland.

AYLETT, Mary Rosamund 14 Weybridge Park, Weybridge KT13 8SQ — MB BS 1979 Lond.; BSc (Hons.) Lond. 1976, MB BS 1979; MRCGP 1985; DRCOG 1984; DCH RCP Lond. 1983. (Univ. Coll. Hosp.) Clin. Med. Off. (Community Paediat.) N. Downs Community Health. Prev: Trainee GP Orkney; SHO (Paediat.) Roy. Albert Edwd. Infirm. Wigan; SHO (Med. Rotat.) Gen. Infirm. Leeds.

AYLETT, Pamela Eileen (retired) 4 Nepean Street, Roehampton, London SW15 5DW Tel: 020 8788 0704 Email: peter.aylett@owcom.net — MB BS 1947 Lond.; PhD (Med.) Lond. 1967; MD Lond. 1963; FRCPsych 1985; DPM Eng. 1971; DCH Eng. 1950. Prev: Cons. Psychiat. W.m. & St. Stephens Hosps. Lond. & Qu. Mary's Univ. Hosp. Roehampton.

AYLETT, Sarah Elizabeth 5 Virginia Close, Egerton Road, Weybridge KT13 0TR; The Epilepsy Unit, Southwood Building, Great Ormond St. Hospital for Children NHS Trust, London WC1N 3JH Tel: 020 7405 9200 Fax: 020 7813 8356 — MB BS 1982 Lond.; MRCP (UK) 1986; DCH RCP Lond. 1985; FRCPCH 1997. (Roy. Free) Cons. Paediat. Neurol. Gt. Ormond St. Hosp. for Childr. NHS Trust & Hon. Sen. Lect. Inst. of Child Health Univ. Coll. Lond. Socs: Europ. Paediat. Neurol. Soc. (normal Mem.ship). Prev: Sen. Regist. St. Geo.'s Hosp. Tooting Lond.; Clin. Research Fell. Inst. of Child Health Lond.

AYLETT, Mr Stanley Osborn, MBE (retired) 54 Viceroy Road, London SW8 2EZ Tel: 020 7622 1564 — MRCS Eng. LRCP Lond. 1935; BSc (1st cl. Hons.) Lond. 1932, MB BS (Hons. Med.) 1935; FRCS Eng. 1936. Prev: Surg. W.m. Hosp. Teach. Gp. (Gordon Hosp.) & Potters Bar & Dist.

AYLETT, Virginia Philippa 8 Kirklands, Carr Lane, Thorner, Leeds LS14 3HB — MB ChB 1992 Leeds; MRCP (UK) 1995. Specialist Regist. (c/o Elderly) St. Jas. Univ. Hosp. Leeds. Prev: Regist. (c/o Elderly) St. Lukes Hosp. Bradford.

AYLIFFE, Professor Graham Arthur John 50 Halesowen Road, Halesowen B62 9BA Tel: 0121 422 4233 — MB ChB 1954 Bristol; Hon. Dip HIC 1999; BSc (Hons.) Bristol 1951, MD 1963; FRCPath 1977, M 1965. Emerit. Prof. Med. Microbiol. Univ. Birm.; Hon. Cons. Hosp. Infec. Research Laborat. City Hosp. Birm. Socs: (Ex-Pres.) Hosp. Infec. Soc.; Hon. Mem. (Ex-Pres.) Infec. Control Nurses Assn.; Hon. Fell. (Ex-Pres.) Inst. Sterile Servs. Managem. Prev: Hon. Dir. Hosp. Infec. Research Laborat. City Hosp. Birm.; Prof. Med. Microbiol. Birm. Univ.; Research Asst. & Regist. (Bact.) Postgrad. Med. Sch. Hammersmith Hosp. Lond.

AYLIFFE, Mr Peter Roland Dept. of Facial Surgery, Grampian University Hospital, Foresterhill, Aberdeen AB25 2ZN — MB BS 1992 Lond.; FRCS Eng. 1994; FDS RCS Eng. 1994; FRCS OMFS Eng. 1999. (St. Geo. Hosp. Lond.) Cons. Surg. Maxillofacial Surg. Grampian Uni. Hosp. Aberd.; Hon. Sen. Lect. Prev: Sen. Regist. (Oral & Maxillofacial Surg.) Roy. Surrey Co. Hosp. Guildford; Fell. Dept. of Plastic Surg., Qu. Vic. Hosp. E. Grinstead; Sen. Regist., Maxillofacial Surg. Qu. Vic. Hosp. E. Grinstead.

AYLIFFE, Mr William Harold Reginald The Croydon Eye Unit, 33 Mayday Road, Thornton Heath, Croydon CR7 7YE Tel: 020 8401 3130 Fax: 020 8401 3489; Shirley Oaks Hospital, Poppy Lane, Shirley, Croydon CR9 8AB Tel: 020 8655 2255 — MB BS 1982 Lond.; PhD Lond. 1993; BSc (Hons.) Lond. 1979; FRCS Ed. 1987; FRCS Lond. 1987; FRCOphth 1989; DO RCS Eng. 1986. (St. Bart.) Cons. Croydon Eye Unit. Prev: Corneal & Immunol. Fell Harvard Univ. Mass., USA; SHO & Regist. Rotat. Bristol Eye Hosp.; Research Fell. (Ophth.) Oxf. Univ.

AYLIN, David Raymond The Swan Medical Centre, 4 Willard Road, Yardley, Birmingham B25 8AA Tel: 0121 706 0216 Fax: 0121 707 3105; 4 Ferndown Road, Solihull B91 2AT Tel: 0121 704 4721 — LRCPI & LM, LRSCI & LM 1968; LRCPI & LM, LRCSI & LM 1968; MRCGP 1983; DObst RCOG 1970. (RCSI) Prev: SHO

(Paediat.) Good Hope Hosp. Sutton Coldfield; SHO (Gen. Med.) Doncaster Roy. Infirm.; SHO (Obst.) N. Tees Gen. Hosp. Stockton-on-Tees.

AYLIN, Paul Philip Department Epidemiology and Public Health, Imperial College of Medicine at St Mary's, Norfolk Place, London W2W 1PG Tel: 020 7594 3334 Fax: 020 7402 2150 Email: p.aylin@ic.ac.uk; 170 Hartfield Road, Wimbledon, London SW19 3TQ Tel: 020 8543 3057 — MB ChB 1986 Dundee; MFPHM 1995. (Dundee) Clin. Sen. Lect. (Epidemioloy) Imperial Coll. Lond.; Hon. Cons. in Pub. Health Med. Kensington, Chelsea & W.m. HA. Socs: Fac. Publ. Health Med. Prev: Med. Statistician Office for Nat. Statistics; Sen. Regist. (Pub. Health Med.) Wandsworth HA; Regist. (Pub. Health Med.) SW Thames HA.

AYLING, Christopher Jeremy 11 Cousins Grove, Southsea PO4 9RP Tel: 01705 811442 — MB 1963 Camb.; BChir 1962; DObst RCOG 1967.

AYLING, Geraldine Zoe 36 The Green, Southwick, Brighton BN42 4FR — MB BS 1996 Lond.; BSc Lond. 1996. SHO (Med.) Ulster Hosp. Dundonald, Belf. Prev: SHO (A & E) Mater Infirmorium Hosp. Belf.; Jun. Ho. Off. (Surg.) Mater Infirmorium Hosp. Belf.; Jun. Ho. Off. (Med.) Mater Infirmorium Hosp. Belf.

AYLING, John Christopher Charles (retired) 4 Crichton Avenue, Wallington SM6 8HL — MB BS Lond. 1961; MRCS Eng. LRCP Lond. 1960. Prev: SHO (Paediat. & Cas.) Univ. Coll. Hosp. W. Indies, Jamaica.

AYLING, Lesley Ann 18 Broad Elms Lane, Sheffield S11 9RQ — BM BCh 1983 Oxf.; MRCP (UK) 1991; MRCGP 1994; DCH RCP Lond. 1990. GP Retainee Sheff. Prev: Trainee GP Sheff.; SHO (Paediat.) Sheff. Childr. Hosp. & Leeds Gen. Infirm.

AYLING, Penelope Jane 28 Lymbourne Road, Havant PO9 2SL — MB BS 1997 Lond.

AYLING, Ruth Margaret Department of Clinical Biochemistry, Kings College Hospital, Denmark Hill, London SE5 9RD Tel: 020 7737 4000 Fax: 020 7737 7434 Email: ruthayling@clinicalbiochemistry.org.uk; 23 Farmaby Road, Bromley BR1 4BL — MB BS 1985 Lond.; BSc 1982 Lond.; MSc 1993 Lond.; MRCP (UK) 1991; PhD Lond. 1997; MRCPath 1998; MRCPCH 1997. (Guy's) Cons. Chem. Pathol. King's Coll. Hosp.

AYLMER, Albert Thomson 33 Marlborough Avenue, Glasgow G11 7BP Tel: 0141 339 2046 — MB ChB 1936 Glas.; DMRD Eng. 1946. (Glas.) Socs: BMA. Prev: Cons. Radiol. Kt.swood Hosp. Glas.; Maj. RAMC.

AYLMER, David Alexander c/o Department of Anaesthesia, Stobhill NHS Trust Hospital, 133 Balornock Road, Glasgow G21 3UW — MB ChB 1975 Glas.; FFA RCSI 1982.

AYLOTT, Caroline Lorna Chetwynd Lodge, Chettisham, Ely CB6 1SB — BM BS 1988 Nottm.

AYLOTT, Caspar Edward William 21 The Close, Norwich NR1 4DZ — MB ChB 1998 Leic.; MB ChB Leic 1998.

AYLWARD, Catherina Madeleine 6 Clevedon House, Ferry Rd, Oxford OX3 0HA — MB BS 1997 Lond. (UCLMS)

AYLWARD, George William 114 Harley Street, London W1N 1AG Tel: 020 7935 1565 Fax: 020 7224 1752; Moorfields Eye Hospital, City Road, London EC1V 2PD Tel: 020 7253 3411 Fax: 020 7253 4696 — MD 1989 Camb.; MA Camb. 1980; FRCS Glas. 1987; FRCOphth 1989; DO RCS Eng. 1987. (Cambridge) Cons. Ophth. Surg. Moorfields Eye Hosp. Lond. Socs: Mem. Club Jules Gonin; Fell. Vitreous Soc. Prev: Fell. Med. Retina Bascom Palmer Eye Inst. Miami, Florida; Fell. Vitreoretinal Surg. Moorfields Eye Hosp. Lond.; Sen. Regist. Moorfields Eye Hosp. Lond.

AYLWARD, James Gerard Oliver Street Surgery, 57 Oliver Street, Ampthill, Bedford MK45 2SB Tel: 01525 402641 Fax: 01525 841107 — MB BCh BAO 1971 Dub.; MRCGP 1975; DObst RCOG 1974; DCH NUI 1973. (Trinity Coll. Dub.)

AYLWARD, Mansel Corporate Medical Group, Dept for Work and Pensions, The Adelphi, 1-11 John Adam St., London WC2N 6HT Tel: 020 7962 8702 Fax: 020 7712 2330 Email: mansel.aylward@dwp.gsi.gov.uk; Cefn Cottage, Cefn Coed, Merthyr Tydfil CF48 2PH Tel: 01685 722324 Fax: 01685 375009 — MB BS 1967 Lond.; 2001 DDAM RCP(UK); MB BS (Hons. Distinc. Obst. & Gyn.) Lond. 1967; BSc (Hons.) Lond. 1964, MD 1972; MRCS Eng. LRCP Lond. 1967; FFPM RCP (UK) 1989. (Lond. Hosp.) Chief Med. Adviser & Med. Director, Dept for Work and Pens. Lond.; Expert Internat. Med., French Min. Health; Med. Adviser, Wom.'s Health Concern, Lond.; Chief Med. Adviser, The War Pens. Agency, Min. of Defence, Lond.; Hon Dean (Wales) Roy. Soc. of Med. Socs: Fell. Roy. Soc. Med.; Fell. Med. Assur. Soc.; Fell. Amer. Acad. Insur. Med. Prev: Princip. Med. Off., DSS & Benefits Agency, Lond.; Dir. (Experim. Med.) Simbec Research Inst. Merthyr Tydfil; Ho. Phys. (Cardiac & Gen. Med.) & Ho. Surg. Surgic Unit & Plastic Surg. Lond. Hosp.

AYLWARD, Martin John Bridge Road Surgery, 1A Bridge Road, Oufton Broad, Lowestoft NR32 3LJ Tel: 01502 565936 Fax: 01502 531539; Forton House, 7 St Peter's Road, Lowestoft NR33 0LH Tel: 01502 514975 — BM BCh 1982 Oxf.; BA Oxf. 1979, BM BCh 1982; MRCGP 1986; DRCOG 1985.

AYLWARD, Rebecca Lucia Margaret Department of Clinical Neurosciences, Western General Hospital, Crewe Road, Edinburgh EH4 2XU Tel: 0131 537 1000 Fax: 0131 332 7886 Email: rlmzeman@aol.com; Tel: 0131 315 2046 — BM BCh 1983 Oxf.; MA Oxf. 1989, DM 1993; MRCP (UK) 1986. (Oxford) Cons. Epileptologist (Neurol.) W.. Gen. Hosp. NHS Trust Edin.; Locum Cons. NeUrol., Falkirk & Dist. Ryl Inf. Socs: BMA. Prev: Sen. Reg. (Neurol.) W.. Gen. Hosp. NHS Trust Edin.; Sen. Regist. (Paediat. Neurol.) Addenbrooke's Hosp. Camb. & Hosp. Childr. Gt. Ormomd St. Lond.; Regist. (Paediat. Neurol.) Addenbrooke's Hosp. Camb.

AYLWIN, Anthony Charles Barton 25C Lady Somerset Road, London NW5 1TX — MB ChB 1995 Manch. (Manchester)

AYLWIN, Simon John Byng 2 Pennels Close, Milland, Liphook GU30 7NL — BChir 1990 Camb.

AYMAT TORRENTE, Antonio 7 Baltimore Close, Cardiff CF23 8PX — LMS 1990 Barcelona; LMS Autonoma Barcelona 1990; FRCS 1997. Specialist Regist. (Ototryugol) S.W Region.; Research Fell. Gt Ormond St Hosp.

AYNSLEY-GREEN, Professor Albert Institute of Child Health, University of London, 30 Guilford St., London WC1N 1EH Tel: 020 7813 8391 Fax: 020 7813 0387 Email: a.aynsley-green@ich.ucl.ac.uk — MB BS 1967 Lond.; MA Oxf. 1981, DPhil 1973; FRCP Ed. 1987; FRCP Lond. 1982, M 1970; MRCS Eng. LRCP Lond. 1967; FRCPCH 1997; F.Med.Sci 1998; Dhc 1998. (Guy's) Nuffield Prof. Child Health Univ. Lond.; Cons. Paediat. Gt. Ormond St. Hosp. for Childr. NHS Trust & UCL Hosps. Lond. Socs: Fell. Roy. Soc. Med.; (Ex-Pres.) Europ. Soc. Paediat. Endocrinol. Prev: Jas. Spence Prof. Child Health Univ. Newc.; Univ. Lect. (Paediat.) Univ. Oxf.; Wellcome Research Fell. Radcliffe Infirm. Oxf.

AYNSWORTH, Sydney Herbert (retired) 10 Beechcroft Road, Alverstoke, Gosport PO12 2ER Tel: 023 92 580544 — MB BS 1957 Lond.; DObst RCOG 1960. Prev: Regist. (Path.) St. Mary's Hosp. Portsmouth.

AYODELE, Solomon Oluwole 105 Walkford Way, London SE15 6EY — MB BS 1964 Lond.

AYOUB, Abdel-Wahab Ayoub Ahmad Mount Vernon Hospital, Northwood HA6 2RN Tel: 01923 896563 — MB BCh 1964 Alexandria; FRCS Eng. 1977; FRCR 1983. (Alexandria) Cons. (Radiol.) Mt. Vernon Hosp. N.wood. Socs: Roy. Soc. Med. Prev: Sen. Regist. (Diag. Radiol.) Lond. Hosp. Whitechapel.

AYOUBBEY, Mohamed Ahmed Mustafa The Cromwell Hospital, London SW5 Tel: 020 7370 4233 exts. 5357 & 5024; 91 Bedford Road, East Finchley, London N2 9DB — MB BS 1963 Khartoum; FRCR 1977; FFR RCSI 1977; DMRT Eng. 1973. (Khartoum) Cons. (Radiother. & Oncol.) Cromwell Hosp. Lond. Prev: Cons. (Radiother. & Oncol.) Leics. HA (T); Sen. Regist. Univ. Coll. Hosp. Lond.; Regist. Roy. Free Hosp. Lond. & Middlx. Hosp. Lond.

AYRE, Andrew Norman The Surgery, 9A Bullpit Road, Balderton, Newark NG24 3PT Tel: 01636 705826 Fax: 01636 605222; Hamilton Lodge, The Avenue, Newark NG24 1ST Tel: 01636 673923 — BM BCh 1975 Oxf.

AYRE, Malcolm Anthony The Health Centre, Victoria Road, Hartlepool TS26 8DB Tel: 01429 272000/274899 Fax: 01429 863877 — MB BS 1968 Newc.; DObst RCOG 1971.

AYRES, Cameron Michael Forest Gate Surgery, Hazel Farm Road, Totton, Southampton SO40 8WU Tel: 023 8066 3839 Fax: 023 8066 7090 — MB BS 1975 London; MB BS Lond. 1975. (London) GP Soton.

AYRES, Janet Priorslegh Group Medical Practice, Civic Centre, off Park Lane, Poynton, Stockport SK12 1GP Tel: 01625 872299; 19 Hardwicke Road, Poynton, Stockport SK12 1BJ Tel: 01625 876681 — MB ChB 1979 Leeds.

AYRES, John Francis 35 Hall Park, Lancaster LA1 4SH — BM 1997 Soton.

AYRES, Professor Jonathan Geoffrey Department of Respiratory Medicine, Birmingham Heartlands Hospital, Birmingham B9 5SS Tel: 0121 424 2746 Fax: 0121 772 0292 Email: ayresj@heartscl.wmids.nhs.uk — MB BS 1974 Lond.; BSc Lond. 1971, MD 1984; FRCP Lond. 1989; MRCP (UK) 1977; MRCS Eng. LRCP Lond. 1974. Cons. Respirat. Birm. Heartlands Hosp.; Prof. Respirat. Med. Univ.Birm., 2000. Socs: Brit. Thorac. Soc.; Internat. Epidemiol Assn.; Amer. Thoracic Soc. Prev: Sen. Regist. (Thoracic Med.) E. Birm. Hosp.; Regist. & Ho. Off. Guy's Hosp.; Prof. of Respirat. Med., Univ. of Warwick.

AYRES, Julie Elizabeth Ayrdale, 11 Ladywood Road, Leeds LS8 2QF Tel: 0113 265 8045 — MB ChB 1984 Leeds; DRCOG 1987. (Leeds) Regional Phys. i/c BUPA Health Screening; Clin. Asst. Menopause & PMS Clinic Clarendon Wing Leeds Gen. Infirm.; Sessional Phys. BUPA Health Screening Leeds. Socs: Diplomate RCOG; Diplomate FFP (RCOG). Prev: GP. Asst. Leeds.

AYRES, Mr Michael Leonard (retired) Old Barn, Junction Road, Churchill, Chipping Norton OX7 6NW Tel: 01608 658401 — MB BS 1963 Lond.; FRCS Ed. 1968. Prev: Cons. A & E ScarBoro. Hosp.

AYRES, Reuben Christopher Simon Royal Devon & Exter Hospital (Wonford), Barrack Road, Exeter EX2 5DW Tel: 01392 402818 Fax: 01392 822044 Email: reuben@rull.demon.co.uk — BM 1982 Soton.; DM Soton. 1994, BM 1982; MRCP (UK) 1985; FRCP 1998. Cons. Phys. & Gastroenterol. Roy. Devon & Exeter Hosp. Socs: Brit. Soc. Gastroenterol. & Amer. Gastroenterol. Assn.; Fell. Roy. Soc. Med. Prev: Sen. Regist. (Gastroenterol. & Gen. Med.) W. Midl. RHA; Research Fell. Liver Unit Birm.; Regist. (Med.) Soton. Gen. Hosp. & Roy. Vict. Hosp. Bournemouth.

AYRES, Richard George N. Devon District Hospital, Raleigh Park, Barnstaple EX31 4JB; 1 Abyssinia Terrace, Barnstaple EX32 9BH Tel: 01271 327765 — MB ChB 1980 Ed.; MRCGP 1984; DCH RCP Lond. 1990; DTM & H Liverp. 1987; DRCOG 1984; MRCP 1998. SHO Med. Prev: Med. Dir. Exeter Community Trust; GP S. Molten N. Devon.

AYSHA, Marei Hassan Ali PO Box 685, Sohar 311, Oman Tel: 00 968 840287 Fax: 00 968 840287; 264 Bannerdale Road, Sheffield S11 9FE Tel: 0114 258 8071 — MB BCh 1969 Ain Shams; MB BCh Ain Shams Egypt 1969; FRCPI 1991, M 1980. Sen. Cons. Phys. & Head Internal Med. Dept. Sohar Hosp. Sultanate of Oman. Socs: Brit. Soc. Echocardiogr. Prev: Cons. Phys., Sen. Regist. & Regist. Al-Jahra Hosp., Kuwait.

AYSHFORD, Christopher Andrew 3 The Hop Kilns, Broughton Hackett, Worcester WR7 4BB — MB BS 1992 Lond.

AYTO, Robert Michael 452 Hurst Road, Bexley DA5 3JR — MB BS 1998 Lond.; MB BS Lond 1998.

AYTON, Paul Richard Stanley Bridge House, Desborough Rd, Braybrooke, Market Harborough LE16 8LE Tel: 01858 468051; Jordans End, Jordans, Beaconsfield HP9 2SW — MB ChB 1987 Birm.; ChB Birm. 1987.

AYUB, Aamir Flat 5, Holly House, Stepping Hill Hospital, Poplar Grove, Stockport SK2 7JE Tel: 0161 4195 176 Email: aayub89151@aol.com — MB BS 1986 Punjab; Dip. (Cardio.) Roy. Post Grad.Med. Sch. Lond.1995; MD Uni. Mans. (Mans.) Staff Grade (Cardio.) stepping Hill Hosp. Stockport.

AYUB, Mr Ghayyur Hussain 58 Duke Street, Rochdale OL12 0LT — MB BS 1968 Pakistan; FRCS Ed. 1979.

AYUB, Mohammed Saqib Colliers Wood Surgery, 58 High Street Colliers Wood, London SW19 2BY Tel: 020 8540 6303 — MB BS 1993 Lond.; DRCOG 1995; MRCGP 1998; Cert. JCPTGP 1998. (King's Coll. Lond.) Trainee GP. Socs: BMA. Prev: SHO (Geriat.s) Mayday Hosp. Croydon; SHO (Paediat.) St Helier Hosp. Corshalton; SHO (O & G) St Helier Hosp. Corshalton.

AYUB, Muhammad 41A Caiystane Gardens, Edinburgh EH10 6TB — MB BS 1985 Bahauddin Zakariya U Pakistan.

AYUB, Naeem Anjum 524 Kingston Road, London SW20 8DT — MB BS 1983 Benin, Nigeria.

AYUB, Waqar Flat 35A Block 6 Phase 111, Walsgrave General Hospital, Clifford Bridge Road, Coventry CV2 2DX — MB BS 1985 Karachi. Staff Grade (Renal Med.) Raigmore Hosp. Inverness. Prev: Regist. (Med.) Boston (UK) & Swindon; SHO (Med.) Norf. & Norwich.

AYUK, Tabe-Yang Paul 6 Elmwood, Sale M33 5RN — MB ChB 1994 Manch.; MB ChB (Hons.) Manch. 1994; BSc (Hons.) Manch. 1991. Research Fell. (Child Health) St Mary's Hosp. Manch. Prev: Ho. Off. (Surg.) Hope Hosp. Salford; Ho. Off. (Med.) N. Manch. Gen. Hosp.

AYYASH, Hani Yew Court, Chesterfield & North Derbyshire Royal Hospital, Calow, Chesterfield S44 5BL; Department of Paediatrics, Royal Hospital, Chesterfield and North Derbyshire Royal Hospital, Chesterfield S44 5BL Tel: 01246 277271 Fax: 01246 552620 — Ptychio Iatrikes 1981 Thessalonika; Medical Diploma Thessaloniki 1981; PhD Athens 1987; Directorate Health Athens 1987. Staff Grade Paediat. Dept. of Paediat. Roy. Hosp. Chesterfield Derbysh. Socs: MRCPCH; BMA. Prev: Locum Staff Grade Paediat. N. Derbysh. Community Health Care Servs. Walton Hosp. Saltergate Centre.

AYYUB, Mohammad Wheelerstreet Healthcare, Wheeler Street, Anlaby Road, Hull HU3 5QE Tel: 01482 354933 Fax: 01482 355090; Tel: 01482 354933 — MB BS 1965 Panjab; DPD 1990 Univ. of Wales Sch. of Med. Cardiff (Dip. In P. Derm.); DCH Eng. 1979. (King Edwd. Med. Coll.) Princip. Gen. Pract. Hull. Socs: Hull Med. Soc. Prev: SHO (Paediat.) Hull Roy. Infirm.; SHO (Paediat.) Boothhall Childr. Hosp. Manch.; SHO (A & E) Hull Roy. Infirm.

AZAD, Ajith 31 Vaughan Gardens, Ilford IG1 3PA — MB BS 1994 Lond.

AZADIAN, Berge Sarkis Microbiology Department, Charing Cross Hospital, Fulham Palace Road, London W6 8RF Tel: 020 8846 1234 — MB BCh 1973 Cairo; BSc Beirut 1966; FRCPath 1992, M 1979. (Cairo) Cons. Med. Microbiol. Char. Cross Hosp. Lond.; Hon. Sen. Lect. (Med. Microbiol.) Char. Cross & W.m. Med. Sch. Lond. Prev: Lect. (Med. Microbiol.) Char. Cross Hosp. Med. Sch. Lond.

AZAM, Anwer 9 Pemberton Drive, Bradford BD7 1RA Tel: 01274 721621 — MB BS 1967 Bihar. (Bihar) GP Bradford, W. Yorks.

AZAM, Farrah Shabana 210 Stretford Road, Urmston, Manchester M41 9NT — MB ChB 1996 Sheff.

AZAM, Hashim Uddin Ninewells Hospital, Dundee DD1 9SY — MB BS 1989 Peshawar, Pakistan; MRCP (UK) 1994.

AZAM, Mr Mahmood 248 Kings Road, Old Trafford, Manchester M16 0JE — MB BS 1965 Patna; MS (Gen. Surg.) Patna 1973, MB BS 1965. Mem. Manch. FPC & Pld Trafford FPC; Mem. Salford Family Pract. Comm.

AZAM, Mohammad The Bungalow, 153 Silverhill Road, Bradford BD3 7JH — MB BS 1983 Punjab; LRCP LRCS Ed. LRCPS Glas. 1985.

AZAM, Mr Muhammad Fareedul Alberta Street Surgery, 22 Alberta Street, Longton, Stoke-on-Trent ST3 4LF Tel: 01782 319397; 3 Lansdowne Crescent, Werrington, Stoke-on-Trent ST9 0LL — MB BS 1987 Lond.; FRCS Eng. 1992; FRCPS Glas. 1992. Regist. (Orthop.) Selly Oak Hosp. Birm. Prev: SHO (Orthop. Surg.) Frimley Pk. Hosp.; Demonst. (Anat.) St. Geo. Med. Sch. Lond.

AZAM, Muhammed Usman 69 Stanley Street, Rochdale OL12 6JX — MB ChB 1992 Liverp.

AZAM, Sheba 25 Frederick Road, Selly Oak, Birmingham B29 6NX — MB BS 1997 Lond.

AZAMI, John 2 Powys Close, Dinas Powys CF64 4LQ — MB BCh 1985 Wales.

AZAR, Nadim Efteem Saba 152 Nottingham Road, Burton Joyce, Nottingham NG14 5BD — BM BS 1994 Nottm.

AZAZ, Amer Masaud Abdullah 54A Victoria Park Road, London E9 7NB — MB BCh 1986 Al Fateh; MRCP (UK) 1993. Tutor & Regist. (Paediat. Gastroenterol.) Booth Hall Childr. Hosp. Manch. Prev: SHO (Gen. Paediat., Nephrol. & Neonat.) St. Jas. Hosp. Leeds.

AZAZ, Simon Yehu Self-Realization Meditation Healing Centre, Laurel Lane, Queen Camel, Yeovil BA22 7NU Tel: 01935 850266 Fax: 01935 850234 — BM BS 1981 Nottm.; BMedSci Nottm. 1979; MRCP (UK) 1985; DCH RCP Lond. 1985. Healer & Counsellor Self-Realization Meditation Healing Centre. Prev: Regist. (Paediat.) MusGr. Pk. Hosp. Taunton; Research Fell. (Child Health) Matern. Hosp. Bristol & Hosp. Sick Childr. Bristol.

AZEEM, Tariq 78 Countess Street, Stockport SK2 6HD — MB BS 1987 Punjab, Pakistan; MRCP (UK) 1995.

AZFAR, Sikandar Siraj Redlam Surgery, 62 Redlam, Blackburn BB2 1UW Tel: 01254 260051 Fax: 01254 691937 Email: saj.azfar@gp-p81061.nhs.uk — MB ChB 1988 Leic.; MRCGP 1994; DFFP 1993. (Leic.) Socs: Med. Protec. Soc.; Med. Sickness Soc.;

BMA N. W. Div. Prev: GP/Regist. Burnley; SHO (Anaesth.) Qu. Med. Centre Nottm.

AZIMUDDIN, Mr Khawaja No. 1 Kipling House, North Devon District Hospital, Raleigh Park, Barnstaple EX31 4JB Tel: 01271 22577 — MB BS 1988 Karachi; FRCS Eng. 1992; FRCS Ed. 1992.

AZIZ, Adel Isaac — MB BCh 1984 Assiut; FRCS Ed. 1991; MRCOG 1995. L. Cons., Dewsbury & Dist. Hosp., W. Yorks. Socs: Roy. Soc. Med.; Soc. Minimal Invasive Surg.; BMA. Prev: Regist. (O & G) Crawley Hosp., Mayday Hosp. & St. Helier Hosp., Kingston, St Thomas', St Guy's.

AZIZ, Ghazala 36 Folly Bridge Court, Shirelake Close, Oxford OX1 1SW — BM BCh 1991 Oxf.

AZIZ, Kashaf Ahmar 31 Moorholme, Woking GU22 7QZ — MB BS 1997 Lond.

AZIZ, Khalid 7 Alder Drive, Timperley, Altrincham WA15 7YG — MB ChB 1986 Leeds; FRCOphth 1993. Community Eye Phys. Manch. Roy. Eye Hosp.

AZIZ, Mehroo (retired) 3 Radnor Close, Homewood Crescent, Chislehurst BR7 6SH Tel: 0208 467 7868 — MB BS 1952 Bombay; DObst. RCOG 1956. Prev: Med. Off. Lewisham & N. S.wark HA.

AZIZ, Michael Mahmud 26 Dunstall Road, London SW20 0HR Tel: 020 8946 3081; 19 Alexandra Road, Wesham, Preston PR4 3JE Tel: 01772 681807 — MB BS 1992 W. Indies. (University of the West Indies, Mona, Jamaica, West Indies) SHO GP Trainee (Paediat.) Blackpool Vict. Hosp. Blackpool. Socs: Med. Protec. Soc. Prev: SHO (O & G) Blackpool Vict. Hosp.; SHO (Ophth.) Burton Dist. Hosp.; SHO (Ophth.) P.ss Margt. Hosp. Swindon.

AZIZ, Michael Nissan North Middlesex Hospital NHS Trust, Sterling Way, Edmonton, London N18 1QX; 4 Westchester Drive, Hendon, London NW4 1RD Tel: 020 8202 8261 — MB BS 1991 Lond.; BSc (Pharmacol.) Lond. 1988; MRCP (UK) 1995. Regist. (Gen. Med. & Elderly Care) Hamerton Hosp. Hackney; Cons. (Elderly Care), N. Middlx. Hosp., Sterling Way, Edmonton N18 1QX. Socs: BMA; MDU. Prev: SPR (Elderly Care) P.ss Alexandra Harlow; SPR (Elderly Care) N. Middlx. Hosp.; SPR (Integrated Med.) Homerton, Hackney.

AZIZ, Monica Vijay 24 Chester Court, Albany St., London NW1 4BU — MB BS 1990 Lond. SHO Rotat. (Psychiat.) UMDS St. Thos. Hosp. Socs: Inceptor Roy. Coll. Psychiat. Prev: SHO (Psychiat.) Guy's Hosp. Lond. & Canterbury; Ho. Off. (Med.) Brighton.

AZIZ, Moussa Raouf Antoun 80B South Ealing Road, London W5 4QB — MB BCh 1983 Ain Shams, Egypt.

AZIZ, Nabil Fahim Liverpool Womens Hospital NHS Trust, Crown Street, Liverpool L8 7SS Tel: 44151 7089988 Email: naziz@liv.ac.uk — MB BCh 1977 Ain Shams; MD 1999 Univ. Liverpool; MRCOG 1988. (Ain Shams University, Cairo) Cons. (O&G) Liverp. Wom.s Hosp.

AZIZ, Mr Nabil Habib Avondale, 6 Hillside Drive, Walton, Chesterfield S40 2DB Tel: 01246 233558 — MB BCh 1977 Ain Shams, Egypt; FRCS Glas. 1987. Cons. A & E Med. Chesterfield Roy. Hosp. Socs: RCS Glas.; BMA; Fac. A & E Med.

AZIZ, Nagui Lewis Royal Oldham Hospital, Rochdale Road, Oldham OL1 2JH Tel: 0161 627 8161; 64 Oulder Hill Drive, Bamford, Rochdale OL11 5LB Tel: 01706 868957 — MB ChB 1978 Alexandria, Egypt; MRCOG 1987. Cons. O & G Roy. Oldham Hosp. Prev: Sen. Regist. King Khalid Nat. Guard Hosp. Jeddah, Saudi Arabia.

AZIZ, Nasreen 9 Brooklands Avenue, London SW19 8EP — MB BS 1988 Lond.

AZIZ, Omar Munim Khalil Premier House, 43-48 New St., Birmingham B2 4LL — MB ChB 1971 Mosul.

AZIZ, Shahid 46 Lomeshaye Road, Nelson BB9 7AR — MB ChB 1994 Leeds.

AZIZ, Talat Saeed 8 Northumberland Street, NewTown, Edinburgh EH3 6LW Tel: 0131 556 3266 Fax: 0131 537 1025 Email: talat@freeserve.co.uk — MB ChB 1987 Glas.; MRCGP 1992; FRCA 1994; DRCOG 1991. (Glasgow) Career Regist. (Anaesth.) Edin. Roy. Infirm.; Cons. Anaesth. W.ern Gen., Edin.

AZIZ, Tipu Zahed 22 Watkin Avenue, Hadfield, Hyde SK13 1QD — MB BS 1983 Lond.; BSc (1st cl. Hons.) (Physiol.) Lond. 1978, MB BS 1983. SHO (Orthop.) Winford Hosp. Bristol. Prev: Demonst. in Path. Univ. Bristol Med. Sch.; SHO Neurosurg. Frenchay Hosp. Bristol.

AZIZ, Victoria Murad The Surgery, 4 Raleigh Close, Hendon, London NW4 2TA Tel: 020 8202 8302 Fax: 020 8203 7295 — Vrach 1966 1st Moscow Med. Inst. GP Hendon.

AZIZ, Waseem Ahmed 31 Moorholme, Guildford Road, Woking GU22 7QZ — MB ChB 1991 Aberd.

AZMI, Mr Abu Hakim c/o Royal Albert Edward Infirmary, Wigan Lane, Wigan WN1 2NN — MB BS 1974 Aligarh; MB BS Aligarh Muslim, India 1974; FRCSI 1979.

AZMY, Ahmed Amir Mohamed Fouad Royal Hospital for Sick Children, Yorkhill, Glasgow G3 8SJ Tel: 0141 201 0000 Fax: 0141 201 0858; Flat 8 Block2, Barcapel Avenue, Newton Meadows, Glasgow G77 6QJ Tel: 0141 636 0191 — MB BCh 1964 Ain Shams; DS Ain Shams 1966; FRCS Ed. 1994; FRCS Glas. 1985; FRCS Eng. 1975. Cons. Paediat. Surg. Roy. Hosp. Sick Childr. Glas.; Clin. Sen. Lect. Univ. Glas. Socs: Brit. Assn. Paediat. Surg.; Brit. Assn. Urol. Surg.; Brit. Assn. Paediat. Urol. Prev: Sen. Regist. Hosp. Sick Childr. Lond.; Regist. W.m. Childr. Hosp. Lond.; Regist. Roy. Hosp. Sick Childr. Glas.

AZMY, Hany Helmy Brinnington Road Surgery, 30 Brinnington Road, Stockport SK1 2EX Tel: 0161 480 4164 Fax: 0161 476 1996; 7 Foxhill Chase, Stockport SK2 5HJ Tel: 0161 427 4083 — MB ChB 1977 Ain Shams, Cairo; MRCS Eng. LRCP Lond. 1984; Dip. Ven. Liverp. 1988; 1997 Dip. Med. Acupunc. GP Stockport; Hosp. Practitioner (Genitourin. Med.) Macclesfield. Socs: Brit. Med. Acupunct. Soc. Prev: Clin. Asst. (Anaesth.) Blackburn; RMO AMI Alexandra Hosp. Cheadle.

AZMY, Iman Ahmed Fouad 28 Botanical Road, Botanical Gardens, Sheffield S11 8RP — MB ChB 1991 Glas.; FRCS (Ed.) 1996. Specialist Regist. (Gen. Surg.) N. Trent Reg. Rotat.

AZMY, Medhat Aly Labib 609a Denby Dale Road, Calder Grove, Crigglestone, Wakefield WF4 3DJ Tel: 01924 275627 — MB BCh 1969 Ain Shams; MRCPI 1978.

AZOO, Nazar Michael 98 Argyle Road, London W13 8EL — MB ChB 1966 Baghdad; MRCPsych 1984; DCH Dub. 1978.

AZRA, Sajda Mandeville Road Surgery, 141 Mandeville Road, Northolt UB5 4LZ Tel: 020 8422 3181 Fax: 020 8621 3437 — MB BS 1958 Karachi.

AZUH, Victor Ijoma 33 Peters Hill Drive, Glasgow G21 4QQ — MB BS 1979 Lagos; MRCOG 1994.

AZULAY, Arnold Asher Tel: 01702 466340 Fax: 01702 603179; Tel: 01702 479797 Fax: 01702 471359 — MB ChB 1960 Leeds; MRCS Eng. LRCP Lond. 1960; DCH Eng. 1963; DObst RCOG 1962. (Leeds) Clin. Asst. S.end Gen. Hosp.; Med. Audit Adviser. Socs: Roy. Soc. Med.; BMA (Ex-Chairm. S.end & Basildon Br.). Prev: Regist. (Med.) S.end Gen. Hosp.

AZUONYE, Ikechukwu Obialo South London & Maudsley NHS Trust, Lambeth Hospital, 108 Landor Road, Stockwell, London SW9 9NT Tel: 020 7411 6380 Fax: 020 7411 6126 Email: ike.azuonye@slam-tr.nhs.uk — BM BCh 1976 Nigeria; MRCPsych 1983. (Univ. Nigeria) Cons. Psychiat. & Sen. Lect. Lambeth & St. Thos. Hosps. Lond. & Research Unit Roy. Coll. Psychiat. Guy's, King's Coll. & St. Thomas' Hosp. Med. Sch.; Vis. Cons. Psychiat. The Priory Hosp. Hates Gr., Hayes, Bromley, Kent. Socs: Fell. Roy. Soc. Med.; BMA.

AZURDIA, Carlos Michael, OStJ Azurdia and Partners, Bebington Health Centre, Civic Way, Bebington, Wirral CH63 7RX Tel: 0151 645 6936 Fax: 0151 643 1698; Avondale, 24 Reservoir Road N., Prenton, Birkenhead CH42 8LU Tel: 0151 608 2228 Fax: 0151 643 1698 — MB ChB 1963 Liverp.; MRCGP 1972; DObst RCOG 1969. (Liverp. Univ.) Div. Surg. St. John Ambul. Brig.; Med. Off. Tranmere Rovers FC. Socs: Birkenhead Med. Soc.; BMA; Liverp. Med. Inst. Prev: SHO (Obst.) Mill Rd. Matern. Hosp. Liverp.; Demonst. (Anat.) Univ. Liverp. Med. Sch.; Ho. Surg. & Ho. Phys. Liverp. Roy. Infirm.

AZURDIA, Michelle Rosalind 4 Ripplesmore Close, Sandhurst GU47 8PE — MB BS 1998 Newc.; MB BS Newc 1998.

AZURDIA, Richard Michael Royal Liverpool University Hospital, Prescot Street, Liverpool L7 8XP Email: mitch@eggconnectinet, richard.azurdia@rlbuh-tr.nwest.nhs.uk; 4 Poplar Road, Oxton Village, Birkenhead, Wirral CH43 5TB Tel: 0151 651 2056 Email: richardsarah@azurdia.freeserve.co.uk — BM BS 1990 Nottm.; BMedSci Nottm. 1988; MRCPI 1994. Cons. Dermatol., Roy. Liverp., Univ. Hospital and BRd.green Hosp., Liverp. Prev: Regist. (Dermat.) Roy. Liverp. Univ. Hosp.

AZURMENDI SASTRE, Victor Tyndall House, Southmead Hospital, Southmead Road, Westbury-on-Trym, Bristol BS10 5NB — LMS 1994 Basque Provinces.

AZURZA SORRONDEGUI, Mr Koldo Mirena 72 School Road, Thornton-Cleveleys FY5 5AP Tel: 01253 851270 Email: koldo@talk21.com; Zumalakarregi 9, Sixth Floor, Donostia, Gipuzkoa 20008, Spain Tel: 00 349 43216068 — LMS 1991 Basque Provinces; FRCS Ed. SHO (Orthop.) W.morland Gen. Hosp. Kendal.

AZZAM, Khalid 1 Barony Court, Nantwich CW5 5RD — State Exam Med 1989 Frankfurt.

AZZAM, Yasser Mahmound Abdou 26 Central Road, Wembley HA0 2LH — MB BCh 1983 Cairo; LRCP LRCS Ed. LRCPS Glas. 1994.

AZZOPARDI, Denis 21 Summerlands Avenue, London W3 6EW — MD 1975 Malta; FRCP Lond. 1996; MRCP (UK) 1979. Sen. Lect. (Paediat. & Neonat. Med.) Roy. Postgrad. Med. Sch. Hammersmith Hosp. Lond.

AZZOPARDI, John Gerald 7 Gordon Road, London W5 2AD — MD 1949 Malta; BSc Malta 1946, MD 1949; FRCPath 1973, M 1963; DPath Eng. 1955; DCP Lond 1951. (Malta) Prof. of Oncol. Roy. Postgrad. Med. Sch. Lond. Socs: Path. Soc.; Fell. Roy. Soc. Med. Prev: Reader in Oncol. Roy. Postgrad. Med. Sch. Lond.; Sen. Lect. & Lect. Morbid Anat. Postgrad. Med. Sch. Lond.

AZZOPARDI, Joseph (retired) 46a mansfield Court, Riverside Close, Bridge, Canterbury CT4 5TN Tel: 01227 830701 — MD 1946 Malta; PhC Malta 1942, BSc 1943, MD 1946. Prev: Cons. Phys. Geriat. St. Michael's Hosp. Enfield.

AZZU, Mr Ahmed Ali 4 Pencisely Rise, Llandaff, Cardiff CF5 1DX — Laurea Pavia 1977; FRCS Eng. 1985.

BAAKO, Mr Benjamin Narh Inverleith, 13 Lime Tree Road, Norwich NR2 2NQ — MB ChB 1975 Ghana; FRCS Eng. 1983; FRCS Ed. 1982.

BAAS, Avinus Antonius Gijsberthus 14 Kingfisher Way (Kings Court), Bishop's Stortford CM23 2AZ — Artsexamen 1990 Rotterdam.

BAATH, Lars-Erik Swedish Medical Centre Ltd., 15 Harley St., London W1N 1DA — Lakarexamen 1973 Goteburg; T(M) (Paed) 1994.

BABAJEWS, Mr Alexander Victor 6 Homefield Close, Leatherhead KT22 8RW — MB BS 1976 Lond.; BDS Sydney 1969; FRCS Ed. 1986; MRCS Eng. LRCP Lond. 1976; FDS RCPS Glas. 1980; FFD RCSI 1981. (King's Coll. Hosp.) Cons. Oral & Maxillofacial Surg. Roy. Devon & Exeter Hosp. Socs: BMA & Brit. Assn. Oral & Maxillofacial Surg. Prev: Sen. Regist. (Maxillofacial Surg.) St. Richards Hosp. Chichester & St. Thos. Hosp. Lond. & Roy. Surrey Co. Hosp. Guildford.

BABAN, Mr Serok Dhair Azmi c/o 26 Blackshots Lane, Grays RM16 2JU — MB ChB 1974 Baghdad; FRCS Ed. 1992.

BABAN, Vian 71 Heathfield Road, Gabalfa, Cardiff CF14 3JX Email: hurle@internet-projects.cymru.net — MB BCh 1995 Wales; DCH 1998; DRCOG 1998. (University of Wales College of Medicine)

***BABAR, Humera** Flat 5, 31 Rosslyn Hill, London NW3 5UJ — MB BS 1998 Lond.; MB BS Lond 1998.

BABAR, Inayat Khan Baillie Street Health Centre, Baille Street, Rochdale OL16 1XS Tel: 01706 525322, 01706 640950 Fax: 01706 713246; 42 Wordsworth Way, Bamford, Rochdale OL11 5JE — MB BS 1969; 1982 (Fell. Paediatrics) Vienna, Austria; 1996 (MRCPCH Foundation) London; 1999 (Registered Nutritionist) UK; DCH Ireland (1974), Glasgow (1982); MSc 1991 (Community Paediatrics) Univ. of Warwick, UK; PhD 1985 (Nutrition/ Paed. Nutrition) Columbia Pacific Univ. California, USA. (Khyber Medical College, Peshawar, Pakistan) GP Princip., Baille St. Health Centre, Rochdale, Lancs; Clin. Asst. in Dermat. N.Manch. Gen. Hosp. Delawney Rd., Crumpsall, Manch., M8 5RB. Socs: Roy. Coll. of Paediat. & Child Health; Nutrit. Soc.; Fell. Roy. Inst. of Pub. Health. Prev: Sen. Regist. Paediat. St Luke's Hosp. Bradford, W.Yorks '88; Sen. Paediat./ Chief Paediat. Sevices, M. Dossary Hosp. Al-Kabar, Saudi Arabia '82-'86; Assoc. Specialist Paediat. Arrow Pk. Hosp. Upton, Merseyside '82.

BABAR, Izhar Ullah 59A Balmoral Road, Westcliff on Sea SS0 7DB — MB BS 1981 Peshawar; MRCPI 1988.

BABATOLA, Francis Dada Opeyemi Department of Anaesthetics, Manor Hospital, Moat Road, Walsall WS2 9PS Tel: 01922 721172; 8 Broadfields Road, Wylde Green, Birmingham B23 5TL Fax: 0121 682 7159 Email: yembab@aol.com — MB BS 1978 Ibadan; FRCA 1994; Dip. Anaesth. Ibadan 1987; PhD (Physiol.) Wales 1985; BSc (Physiol.) Ibadan 1972. (Ibadan, Nigeria) Cons. Anaesth. Manor Hosp. Walsall. Socs: Pain Soc.; Assn. Anaesth.; Obs. Anaesth. Assoc. Prev: Sen. Regist. (Anaesth.) W. Midl. RHA; Regist. Hammersmith Hosp. Lond.; Lect. (Physiol.) Univ. Ibadan, Nigeria.

BABB, Anna Genevieve John Radcliffe Hospital, Headington, Oxford OX3 9DU Tel: 01865 741166; 15 Norman Avenue, Twickenham TW1 2LY — BM BCh 1997 Oxf.; BA (First Class)Physiological Sciences (Oxford) 1994; Dip. In Child Health (London) 1999. (Oxford) Sen. Ho. Off., John Radcliffe Hosp. Oxf. Socs: BMA. Prev: SHO, ASE, Caring Cross Hosp.; SHO Paediat., W. Middx. Hosp.

BABB, Margaret Anne — MB BS 1992 Newc.; FRCA 1997. p/t SpR Yr4 (Anaesth) John Radcliff Hosp. Oxf.

BABBINGTON, Susan Patricia Eaton Socon Health Centre, 274 North Road, Eaton Socon, St. Neots, Huntingdon PE19 8BB Tel: 01480 477111 Fax: 01480 403524 — MB BS 1976 Lond.; MRCS Eng. LRCP Lond. 1976; MFFP 1993; DRCOG 1980.

BABBS, Christopher Department of Gastroenterology, Hope Hospital, Salford M6 8HD Tel: 0161 787 5142 Fax: 0161 787 5366; 13 Pargate Chase, Norden, Rochdale OL11 5DZ Tel: 01706 869163 Fax: 01706 869163 Email: cbabbs@doctors.org.uk — MB BS 1981 Lond.; MD Lond. 1993; FRCP 1997. (St. Mary's) Cons. Phys., Hope Hosp. Salford; Director, springhill hospice, Rochdale. Socs: Brit. Soc. Gastroenterol. & Brit. Assn. Study Liver; Manch. Med. Soc.; Amer. gastroenterological assoc. Prev: Cons. Phys., Roy. Oldham Hosp.; Sen. Regist. Rotat. (Med.) Manch. Roy. Infirm. & N. Manch. Gen. Hosp.

BABBS, David John St Marys Medical Centre, Wharf Road, Stamford PE9 2DH Tel: 01780 764121 Fax: 01780 756515 — MB BS 1981 Lond.; MRCS Eng. LRCP Lond. 1981; MRCGP 1989; Dip Sports Med. . Lond. 1986; DRCOG 1984. (Char. Cross) Head Doctor, Brit. Internat. Rowing. Socs: Brit. Assn. Of Sport and Exercise Med. Prev: SHO (Paediat.) Pilgrim Hosp. Boston; SHO (Obst.) N.wick Pk. Hosp. Harrow; SHO (A & E) St. Stephens Hosp. Chelsea.

BABBS, Susan Linda 1 Oakenrod Mews, Oakenrod Hill, Rochdale OL11 4ED — MB BS 1982 Nottm. Clin. Asst. Renal Unit, Sird Hill Hosp. Rochdale.

BABER, Fiona Ruth Old Fire Station Surgery, 68A Portsmouth Road, Woolston, Southampton SO19 9AN Tel: 023 8044 8558/8901 Fax: 023 8043 5569; 234 Highlands Road, Fareham PO15 5BG Tel: 01329 511282 — MB BS 1985 Lond.; MB BS (Hons.) Lond. 1985; MRCGP 1989; DRCOG 1987. Prev: Trainee GP Portsmouth VTS.

BABER, Patricia Margaret Acton Health Centre, 35-61 Church Road, London W3 8QE Tel: 020 8992 6768 — MB BS 1977 Lond.; MRCS Eng. LRCP Lond. 1977; DRCOG 1982; Cert. Family Plann. JCC 1982. (Roy. Free Hosp. Sch. Med.) Sen. Partner GP Princip. Lond.; Med. Adviser PDSA Charity.

BABICKI, Joseph Wladyslaw High Croft, Haslingdon Old Road, Rawstenstall, Rossendale BB4 8RR — MB BS 1996 Lond.; BSc (Hons) 1995. (St Bartholomew's Hospital)

BABIKER, Isam Eltayeb 11 Pembroke Road, Clifton, Bristol BS8 3AU — MB BS 1967 Khartoum; PhD Ed. 1977; FRCPsych 1987, M 1973. Emerit. Cons. Psychiat., S.mead Hosp., Bristol. Prev: Clin. Lect. (Ment. Health) Univ. Bristol; Cons. Psychiat. Glenside Hosp. Bristol; Cons. Psychiat. S.mead Hosp. Bristol.

BABIKER, Mohamed Mohi El Din County Hospital, Park Lodge Lane, Wakefield WF1 4JH; 14 Conrad Close, Hillside, Rugby CV22 5RX — MB BS 1977 Khartoum.

BABIKER, Salih Khalafalla 11 Newheath Close, New Cross Hospital, Wolverhampton WV11 1XX — MB BCh 1982 Mansourah Fac. Med. Cairo.

BABIKER, Seif El Din Mohd Nevill Hall Hospital, Staff House 5, Abergavenny NP7 7EG — MB BS 1978 Khartoum; MRCP (UK) 1993.

BABINGTON, Anthony Harrie William (retired) 4 Mount House Close, Hythe, Southampton SO45 6AE Tel: 023 8084 3743 — MRCS Eng. LRCP Lond. 1940; MRCGP 1953. Prev: Sen. Med. Off. DHSS Limb Fitting Centre, Portsmouth.

BABINGTON, Peter Cleary Boswell Princess Margaret Hospital, Swindon SN1 4JU — MB BS 1964 Lond.; FFA RCS Eng. 1969; DObst RCOG 1966; DA Eng. 1966. (St. Thos.) Cons. Anaesth. P.ss Margt. Hosp. Swindon.

BABINGTON, William Scott Flat 3, 148 Barry Road, East Dulwich, London SE22 0HW Tel: 020 8299 6673 — MB ChB 1990 Otago; Dip. Obst. Otago 1992. Socs: BMA.

BABINSKYJ, Roman Mark Shephall Way Surgery, 29 Shephall Way, Stevenage SG2 9QN Tel: 01438 312097 — MB BS 1984 Lond.

BABIRECKI, Matthew 14 North Grove, Duckmanton, Chesterfield S44 5HA — BM BS 1995 Nottm.

BABLA, Himadri Jeramdas Department of Anaesthesia, Arrowe Park Hospital, Arrowe Park Road, Wirral CH49 5PE — MB BS 1973 Bombay.

BABLADI, Mahalingappa Neelakantappa 9 Clough House Drive, Leigh WN7 2GD — MB BS 1972 Mysore.

BABOOLAL, Anthony Weldon Wellhall Medical Centre, 4 Hillhouse Road, Hamilton ML3 9TZ Tel: 01698 285818 — MB ChB 1970 St. And.; DCH Eng. 1975.

BABOR, Barbara Emmy Tivoli, Cow Lane, Inchbrook, Stroud GL5 5HN Tel: 01453 832074 — MB ChB 1996 Dundee; BMSc (Hons.) Dund. 1993. (Dundee) SHO (A&S) Stirling Roy. Infirm. Prev: RMO I (Emerg.) The Canberra Hosp., Australia; RMO I (Emerg. & Anaesth.) Bathurst Base Hosp. New S. Wales, Australia; SHO (Surg.) Stirling Roy. Infirm.

BABU, Ramesh 1 Goodwood Close, Stratford-upon-Avon CV37 9FP — MB BS 1973 Kerala.

BABU MANOHAR, Mr Munirajulu 2 New Heath Close, New Cross Hospital, Wolverhampton Road, Heath Town, Wolverhampton WV10 0QP — MB BS 1986 Madras; FRCS Ed. 1991.

BABU-NARAYAN, Ramakrishna Kadayam N. Bushey Medical Centre, 122 Park Avenue, North Bushey, Watford WD23 2BB Tel: 01923 226446; Fryent Medical Centre, 331 Church Lane, London NW9 8JD Tel: 020 8205 6262 Fax: 020 8205 1687 — MB BS 1962 Poona; FRCS Ed. 1967. (B.J. Med. Coll. Poona) Med. Dir. Healthcall Plc, Ruislip, Middlx.; Vice-Chairm. Brent & Harrow LMC. Socs: Fell. Roy. Soc. Med. Prev: Regist. (Orthop.) Gen. Hosp. Nottm.; Regist. (Surg.) LLa.lli Hosp.; Regist. (Orthop.) Wexham Pk. Hosp. & Hammersmith Hosp. Lond.

BABU-NARAYAN, Sonya Vidya 9 Woburn Mansions, Torrington Place, London WC1E 7HL — MB BS 1998 Lond.; MB BS Lond 1998.

BABU RAO, Eladasari c/o Drive V Sriramulu, 10 Downing St., Rectory Garth, Hemsworth, Pontefract WF9 9NB — MB BS 1975 Osmania. (Gandhi Med. Coll. Hyderabad)

BACALL, Laurence Higher Broughton Health Centre, Bevendon Square, Salford M7 4TP Tel: 0161 792 2142 Fax: 0161 792 9203 — MB ChB 1985 Manch.; MRCGP 1990; DRCOG 1991. (Manchester)

BACARESE-HAMILTON, Mr Ian Anthony Department of Orthopaedic Surgery, The Whittington Hospital, Highgate Hill, London N19 5NF Tel: 020 7272 3070 Fax: 020 7288 3147 — MB BS 1984 Lond.; FRCS Ed. (Orth.) 1994; FRCS Ed. 1988. (Charing Cross and Westminster) Cons. Orthop. & Trauma Surg. Whittington Hosp. Lond. Prev: Sen. Regist. (Orthop. Surg.) Roy. Nat. Orthop. Hosp. Stanmore, Chelsea & W.m. & Univ. Coll. Lond. Hosps.

BACCHUS, Robby Ahmad Eastlodge, 15 Lime Avenue, Wheathampstead, St Albans AL4 8LQ — LRCPI & LM, LRSCI & LM 1963.

BACH, Clive David c/o Denyer, 10 Redwood Ct., St Flora's Road, Littlehampton BN17 6BB — MB BS 1973 Lond.; MRCS Eng. LRCP Lond. 1973.

BACH, Simon Parkinson 9B Otterburn Terrace, Newcastle upon Tyne NE2 3AP — MB BS 1992 Newc.

BACHE, Christopher Edward 109 Wood Lane, Harborne, Birmingham B17 9AY — MB ChB 1990 Birm.; ChB Birm. 1990.

BACHE, James Christopher Wychbury Medical Centre, 121 Oakfield Road, Wollescote, Stourbridge DY9 9DS Tel: 01562 882277 — MB ChB 1965 Birm.

BACHE, Mr Jonathan Beesley Leighton Hospital, Crewe CW1 4QJ Tel: 01270 255141 Fax: 01270 612004; Helmsdale House, 326 Crewe Road, Wistaston, Nantwich CW5 6NN Tel: 01270 663220 — MB ChB 1974 Liverp.; FRCS Ed. 1979; FRCS Eng. 1997; FFAEM 1993. (Liverp.) Cons. Surg. (A & E) Leighton Hosp. Crewe & Vict. Infirm. N.wich; Dep. Postgrad. Dean, Mersy Deanery; JP. Socs: Fell. Fac. Accid. & Emerg. Med.; Fell. Roy. Soc. Med. - Hon. Sec & Pres. Elect, Sect. of A&E Med.; Mem. Brit. Assn. Emerg. Med. Prev: Sen. Regist. (A & E) W. Midl. RHA; Regist. (Surg.) Liverp. AHA (T); Demonst. (Human Morphol.) Univ. Nottm.

BACHE, Xenia Jane Samantha 143A Ashley Gardens, Thirleby Rd, London SW1P 1HN Email: xbache@hotmail.com — MB ChB 1997 Birm.

BACHELANI, Ahmed 130 Valley Drive, London NW9 9NS — MB BS 1997 Lond.

BACHH, Zeenat Jalal 17 Devonshire Place, Newcastle upon Tyne NE2 2NB — MB BS 1998 Newc.; MB BS Newc 1998.

BACHLANI, Mehdi Mohammed 22 Park Avenue, Broadstairs CT10 2EY Tel: 01843 867430 — MB BS 1970 Karachi; MRCOphth 1989; DO RCPSI 1973. (Dow Med. Coll.) Clin. Asst. (Ophth.) I. of Thanet Dist. Hosp. Margate. Socs: BMA. Prev: Regist. (Ophth.) Glas. Eye Infirm., Roy. Vict. Eye & Ear Hosp. Dub. & Roy. Halifax Infirm.

BACHRA SINGH, Permjit Queens Medical Centre, Derby Rd, Nottingham NG7 2UH Tel: 0115 924 9924; Tel: 0115 878 0488 — MB ChB 1984 Birm.; FRCA 1992; DA (UK) 1988. Cons. Anaesth. Qu. Med. Centre Nottm. Prev: Sen. Regist. Rotat. (Anaesth.) E. Midl.

BACHTALIA, Panagoula Princess Alexandra Hospital, Hamstel Road, Harlow CM20 1QX — Ptychio Iatrikes 1989 Thessalonika.

BACK, Christopher Peter Niall 43 Thropton Terrace, Newcastle upon Tyne NE7 7HT — MB BS 1997 Newc. SHO (Gen. Surg.), N. Tees Hosp., Stockton.

BACK, Diane Lesley 2 Shrawley Road, Fernhill Heath, Worcester WR3 7UQ Email: preston.wilson@virgin.net — MB BS 1992 Lond.; BSc (Hons.) Immunol. 1989; FRCS Ed. (UCH & Middlesex) Research Fell. RNOU Stanmore.

BACK, Gary Wayne 37 Greenways, Thorpe Bay, Southend-on-Sea SS1 3BS — Artsexamen 1991 Nijmegen.

BACK, Ian Nicholas Holme Tower, Marie Curie Centre, Bridgeman Road, Penarth CF64 3YR Tel: 02920 426000; 20 Triscombe Drive, Llandaff, Cardiff CF5 2PN Tel: 02920 554530 — MB BChir 1982 Camb.; MA Camb.; MRCGP 1989; DA (UK) 1988; DRCOG 1987. (Cambridge) Cons. Palliat. Med. Holme Tower Marie Curie Centre.; Cons. Paediat. Med. Pontypridd & Rhondda NHS Trust.

BACKER, Hana 44 The Cathedral Green, Llandaff, Cardiff CF5 2EB Tel: 029 2055 4271; 44 The Cathedral Green, Llandaff, Cardiff CF5 2EB Tel: 029 2055 4271 — LMSSA 1954 Lond. (Welsh Nat. Sch. Med.) Private Pract. Socs: Founder Mem. Inst. Psychosexual Med.; Roy. Coll. Psychiat. Prev: Assoc. Specialist (Psychiat.) WhitCh. Hosp. Cardiff; Hon. Clin. Tutor (Psychosexual Med.) Univ. Wales Coll. Med. Cardiff.

BACKETT, Edward Maurice Harvey Cottage, R/O 53 Fore St, Totnes TQ9 5NJ Tel: 01803 865241 Email: maurice.backett@btinternet.com — MB BS 1944 Lond.; BSc Lond. 1940; FRCP Lond. 1965, M 1950; FFCM 1975, M 1974; DPH Eng. 1955. (Westm.) Socs: Hon. Mem. Soc. for Social Med.; Hon. Mem. Internat. Epidemiol. Assn. Prev: Prof. Emerit. Community Health Univ. Nottm.; Prof. Social Med. Univ. Aberd.; Sen. Lect. (Social Med. & Pub. Health) Guy's Hosp. & Lond. Sch. Hyg. & Trop. Med.

BACKETT, Simon Anthony St Johns Hospital, Livingston EH54 6PP Tel: 01506 419666 — MB ChB 1973 Ed.; BSc. Ed. 1970, M Phil. 1981; MRCGP 1977; FRCPsych 1997, M 1979. (Edinburgh University) Cons. Psychiat. St. John's Hosp. W. Lothian; Hon. Lect. (Psychiat.) Roy. Edin. Hosp. Prev: Research Psychiat. MRC Unit Epidemiol. Studies in Psychiat. Roy. Edin. Hosp.; Cons. Psychiat. Gtr. Glas. HB; Sen. Regist. (Psychiat.) Roy. Edin. Hosp.

BACKHOUSE, Catherine Ann 2 Lime Tree Paddock, Scothern, Lincoln LN2 2XD — MB ChB 1995 Birm. (Birm.) GP Regist. Lincoln VTS.

BACKHOUSE, Charles Ivan (retired) Boscawen Cottage, E. Clandon, Guildford GU4 7SD Tel: 01483 223389 Fax: 01483 223389 Email: cibackhouse@talk21.com — MB BChir 1959 Camb.; BA Camb. 1955; DObst RCOG 1964. Prev: Med. Off. HM Detention Centre Send.

BACKHOUSE, Mr Christopher Morley The Oaks Hospital, Mile End Road, Colchester CO4 5XR Tel: 01206 753203 Fax: 01206 753240; The Trellis House, Copford Green, Colchester CO6 1BZ — MB BS 1976 Lond.; MD Lond. 1989; FRCS Eng. 1981; MRCS Eng.

LRCP Lond. 1976. Cons. Surg. Gen. & Vasc. Surg. Essex Rivers Healthcare Trust, Colchester G.H. Socs: BMA; Assn. Surg.; Vasc. Surg. Soc. Prev: Sen. Regist (Surg.) W. Midl. RHA; Regist. & Lect. (Surg.) Char. Cross Hosp. Lond.

BACKHOUSE, Henry Lewis (retired) 136 Malvern Road, Cherry Hinton, Cambridge CB1 9LH Tel: 01223 247246 Fax: 01223 247246 — BA, BM BCh Oxon. 1946; DO Eng. 1950. Prev: Ho. Surg. (Orthop.) Guy's Hosp.

BACKHOUSE, Joseph Edwin 51 Richard Hesketh Drive, Westvale, Kirkby, Liverpool L32 0TX — MB ChB 1953 Leeds.

BACKHOUSE, Kenneth Morley, OBE, VRD The Old Tannery, Sternfield, Saxmundham IP17 1RS Tel: 01728 602414 Fax: 01728 602414 — MB BS 1952 Lond.; MRCS Eng. LRCP Lond. 1946. (St. Bart.) Emerit. Reader in Applied Anat. Univ. Lond.; Clin. Anatomist Inst. Laryngol. & Otol. Univ. Lond.; Hon. Clin. Anat. Roy. Nat. Throat Nose & Ear Hosp. Lond.; Surg. Capt. RNR. Socs: Fell. Roy. Soc. Med.; Sen. Mem. (Ex-Pres.) Brit. Soc. Surg. Hand. Prev: Reader Applied Anat. Roy. Coll. Surg. Eng.; Hon. Research Assoc. Hand Surg. Chelsea & Kensington & Roy. Lond. Homoepath. Hosps.; Sen. Lect. Char. Cross Hosp. Med. Sch. Lond.

BACKHOUSE, Mary Frances Tower House Medical Centre, Stockway South, Bristol BS48 2XX Tel: 01275 866700 Fax: 01275 866711 Email: mary.backhouse@nailsea.net — BM 1980 Soton.; MRCP (UK) 1984; MRCGP 1987; DRCOG 1986. (Southampton) GP Nailsea Bristol. Prev: GP Chingford.

BACKHOUSE, Oliver Charles Edward van Millingen Boscawen Cottage, Back Lane, E. Clandon, Guildford GU4 7SD Tel: 01483 223389 Fax: 01483 223389 — MB BS 1992 Lond.; BSc (Immunol. & Biochem.) Lond. 1990; FRCOphth 1997; CTCM & H (UK) 1993. (Char. Cross & Westm.) Specialist Regist. Rotat. (Ophth.) N. Yorks.; Founder MOSS (Madagascan Organisation for Saving Sight) 1993. Socs: BMA; Fell. Roy. Coll. Ophth.s. Prev: Paediat., Ophth. & Eye Research Madagascar; SHO (Ophth.) Leeds Gen. Infirm. & Gt. Ormond St. Hosp. Lond.; Gen. Ophth. Andranomadio, Madagascar.

BACKHOUSE, Paul Jonathan Bampton Medical Practice, The Surgery, Barnhay, Bampton, Tiverton EX16 9NB Tel: 01398 331304 Fax: 01398 332067; Forde House, Bampton, Tiverton EX16 9LN — MB ChB 1983 Leeds; MRCGP 1989; DRCOG 1988; DCH RCP Lond. 1988; DA (UK) 1985. GP Tiverton. Prev: Trainee GP S. Glam. VTS.

BACKHOUSE, Polly Kate Dallow Cottage, Grantley, Ripon HG4 3PU — MB BS 1994 Lond.

BACKHOUSE, Rupert Henry 10 South Street, Wareham BH20 5LL — BM 1989 Soton.

BACKHOUSE, Mr Steven Steel 1 Mount Melville Crescent, Strathkinness, St Andrews KY16 9XS — MB ChB 1991 Dundee; BMSc (Hons) Dundee 1988; FRCS ENT Ed. 1998. (Dundee) Specialist Regist. (ENT), All Wales Train. Scheme.

BACKHOUSE, Thomas Wynter (retired) Abbeyfield Lodge, Castle Road, Kenilworth CV8 1NG Tel: 01926 853730 — MA Camb. 1947; MB BChir Camb. 1947; MRCS Eng. LRCP Lond. 1946; FRCR 1975; FFR 1956; DMRT Eng. 1953. Prev: Asst. Radiotherap. Middlx. Hosp.

BACON, Annette Susan Rupert's Bell, Bell Lane, 4 Northfield End, Henley-on-Thames RG9 2HN Tel: 01491 572951 — MB BChir 1984 Camb.; MA Camb. 1985; FRCS Lond. 1989; FRCOphth 1989. (St. Thos.) Cons. Ophth. Roy. Berks. Hosp. Reading. Prev: Sen. Regist. Moorfields Eye Hosp. Lond.

BACON, Anthony Peter Coats (retired) 10 Buccleuch Road, Branksome Park, Poole BH13 6LE Tel: 01202 767356 — MB BChir Camb. 1947; MA Camb. 1950, MD 1961; FRCP Lond. 1973; MRCP (UK) 1950; MRCS Eng. LRCP Lond. 1947. Prev: Phys. ScarBoro. Health Dist.

BACON, Christopher John Glebe House, Danby Wiske, Northallerton DL7 0LY — MB BChir 1971 Camb.; MA, MB BChir Camb. 1971; FRCP Lond. 1984, M 1974. Cons. (Paediat.) Friarage Hosp. N.allerton.

BACON, David Haydon Farm Cottage, Hatch La, Windsor SL4 3QY — MB BS 1997 Lond.; BSc. (University College, London)

BACON, Helen Annette (retired) 10 Buccleuch Road, Branksome Park, Poole BH13 6LE Tel: 01202 767356 — MB BChir Camb. 1947; MRCS Eng. LRCP Lond. 1947.

BACON, Mr Hugh Francis 64A Hauteville, St Peter Port, Guernsey GY1 1DQ Tel: 01481 720679 Fax: 01481 716443; Les Ruettes Farm, Le Gron, St. Saviour, Guernsey GY7 9FT Tel: 01481 63621 Email: bacon@guernsey.net — MB 1977 Camb.; MB BChir 1976; MA Cantab. 1977; FRCS Glas. 1984; FRCOphth 1992; DO RCS Eng. 1983. (Cambridge & St. Thomas' Hospital London) Cons. Ophth. Guernsey. Socs: S. W.. Ophth. Soc.; Oxf. Ophth. Congr.; UK & Irel. Soc. Cataract & Refractive Surg. Prev: Regist. (Ophth.) Roy. Berks. Hosp. Reading; Research Reg. Diabetic Retinopathy Exeter HA.

BACON, Joanna Mary 10 St Albans's Road, Westbury Park, Bristol BS6 7SJ — MB ChB 1989 Bristol; MRCGP 1993. No longer employed.

BACON, Lesley Elizabeth Community Health S. London, St Giles, St Giles Road, London SE5 7RN Tel: 0207 771 3330 Fax: 0207 771 3338; 21 Papillons Walk, Blackheath Park, London SE3 9SF Tel: 020 8852 7355 — MB BChir 1973 Camb.; MA Camb. 1973; MFFP 1993; MRCGP 1976; Dip. Ven. Soc. Apoth. Lond. 1980; DCH RCPS Glas. 1975; DObst RCOG 1974. (Camb. & Univ. Coll. Hosp.) Cons. Family Plann. & Reproductive Health Care Community Health S. Lond.; Hon. Sen. Lect. GKT Med. Sch., 1998. Socs: Med. Soc. Study VD; Lond. Soc. Family Plann. Doctors; Soc. Cons. Reproductive Health Care. Prev: SCMO (Family Plann.) SE Lond.; Clin. Asst. (Genitourin.) Beckenham Hosp.; Regist. (Genitourin. Med.) Univ. Coll. Hosp. Lond.

BACON, Margaret Mary Clare 36 Gallowhill, Peebles EH45 9BG — MB BCh BAO 1975 NUI; FFA RCSI 1983; DA Eng. 1978. (Univ. Coll. Dub.) Prev: Regist. (Anaesth.) P.ss Alexandra Hosp. Essex; Intern (Surg.) & Intern (Med.) Dr. Steevens' Hosp. Dub.

BACON, Michael Arthur (retired) 2 Victor Road, Dore, Sheffield S17 3NH Email: mabacon@lineone.net — MB ChB Sheff. 1960; DObst. RCOG 1962. Prev: SHO (O & G) City Gen. Hosp. Sheff.

BACON, Michael Terence Rosedale, 79 Redhill Road, Rowlands Castle PO9 6DE — MB ChB 1989 Ed.; MRCP (UK) 1993. Specialist Regist. (Gen. & Elderly Med.) Roy. Hants. Co. Hosp. Winchester. Prev: SHO Wessex Renal Unit Portsmouth Hosps.; SHO Rotat.

BACON, Neil Colin Michael The Bungalow, Hill Farm, Barnard Gate, Witney OX8 2UY — BM BS 1990 Nottm.; BM BS (Hons.) Nottm. 1990; MRCP (UK) 1993; ECFMG Cert. 1993. Prev: Renal Fell. Beth Israel Hosp. Harvard Boston, USA; Regist. (Renal Med.) Oxf.

BACON, Niall Antony Almond Road Surgery, Almond Road, St. Neots, Huntingdon PE19 1DZ Tel: 01480 473413 Fax: 01480 406906 — MB ChB 1984 Ed.; MRCGP 1989. (Edinburgh University) Prev: Clin. Asst. (Laser Dermat.) Bedford Gen. Hosp.

BACON, Nigel Francis Priory Avenue Surgery, 24-26 Priory Avenue, High Wycombe HP13 6SH Tel: 01494 448132 Fax: 01494 686407 — MB BS 1977 Lond.; MRCGP 1982; DRCOG 1981. (Middlx.) GP High Wycombe. Prev: Trainee Gen. Pract. Cinque Ports Vocational Train. Scheme (Dover); Ho. Surg. & SHO (A & E) Salisbury Gen. Infirm.

BACON, Professor Paul Anthony Department of Rheumatology, The Medical School, University of Birmingham, Edgbaston, Birmingham B15 2TT Tel: 0121 414 6777 Fax: 0121 414 6794 Email: p.a.bacon@bham.ac.uk; 44 Westfield Road, Edgbaston, Birmingham B15 3QG Tel: 0121 454 9071 — MB 1963 Camb.; BChir 1962; FRCP Lond. 1979, M 1966. (Camb. & St. Bart.) Prof. Rheum. Med. Sch. Birm. Univ.; Hon. Cons. Rheumatologist. Socs: Brit. Rheum. Soc.; Brit. Soc. Immunol.; Amer. Coll. of Rheum. Prev: Cons. Rheum. Roy. Nat. Hosp. Rheum. Dis. Bath; Research Fell. (Rheum.) Univ. Calif. Los Angeles, USA; Sen. Regist. St. Bart. Hosp. Lond.

BACON, Mr Peter Jaques Bupa Belvedere Hospital, Consulting Rooms, Lonsdale Road, Scarborough YO11 2QY Tel: 01723 361072; 3 Weaponness House, 31 Deepdale Avenue, Scarborough YO11 2UF Tel: 01723 507983 — MB BS 1978 Lond.; FRCS Eng. 1985; MRCP (UK) 1981; FRCOphth 1989; DO RCS Eng. 1984. (St. Thos.) Cons. Ophth. ScarBoro. & NE Yorks. Health Care. Prev: Sen. Regist. (Ophth.) Univ. Hosp. Wales Cardiff; Research Fell. (Ophth. & Clin. Pharmacol.) United Med. & Dent. Sch. St. Thos. Hosp. Lond.; Regist. (Med.) Eye Unit St. Thos. Hosp. Lond.

BACON, Robert William Brecon Medical Group Practice, Ty Henry Vaughan, Bridge Street, Brecon LD3 8AH Tel: 01874 622121 Fax: 01874 623742; Lower Argoed, Talachddu, Brecon LD3 0UG Tel: 01874 622715 — MB BCh 1980 Wales; FFA RCSI 1987. (Cardiff) Clin. Asst. (Anaesth.) Brecon & Nevill Hall Hosp. Abergavenny. Socs: Assn. Anaesth. GB & Irel.; BMA. Prev: GP Glos.; Trainee GP Birm.; Regist. (Anaesth.) E. Birm. & Leicester.

BACON, Rosalind Clare 31 Mayfield Road, London W12 9LT — MB BS 1988 Lond.

BACON, Sallie Elizabeth Park Surgery, Park Surgery, Hursley Road, Chandlers Ford, Eastleigh SO53 2ZH Tel: 023 8026 7355 Fax: 023 8026 5394 — BM BS 1983 Nottm.; MRCGP 1989; DCH RCP Lond. 1987. (Nottingham) Prev: GP Willesden.

BACON KINSELLA, Clare Elaine Central Surgery, King Street, Barton-upon-Humber DN18 5ER Tel: 01652 635435 Fax: 01652 636122; 11 Birchdale, Barton-upon-Humber DN18 5ED Tel: 01652 634787 — MB BCh BAO 1991 Belf.; Dip. Asth. Warwick 1998; MRCGP 1997; DFFP 1996; DRCOG 1996; DCH RCP Lond. 1995. (Qu. Univ. Belf.) GP Princip. Barton u. Humber; Co. Surg. St John Ambul. Brigage Humberside. Prev: GP/Regist. Letchworth; Trainee GP Stevenage; SHO City Hosp. Belf.

BACSICH, Paul (retired) 11 Ashton Road, Glasgow G12 8SP Tel: 0141 339 6696 — MD 1931 Szeged; FRS Ed. 1938; DSc Glas. 1948; DMedSc (Hon. Causa) Szeged 1971, MD 1931; FRFPS Glas. 1957. Prev: Sen. Lect. Anat. Univ. Birm.

BADAL-BIT, Ashour 30 Flag Court, Kings Way, Hove BN3 2WG — LAH Dub. 1966.

BADAMI, Ashok Jayantilal 6 Hillcrest Close, Epsom KT18 5JY Tel: 01372 40611 — MB BS 1963 Karnatak; DA Eng. 1969. (Kasturba Med. Coll.) Clin. Asst. Anaesth. Dept. Epsom Dist. Hosp. Prev: Regist. St. Geo. Hosp. Bombay, India & E. Birm. Hosp.

BADAT, Ahamed Adamjee The Surgery, 336 Uxbridge Road, London W12 7LL Tel: 020 8743 5153 Fax: 020 8742 9070; 88 Park Road, Chiswick, London W4 3HL Tel: 020 8994 2189 — MRCS Eng. LRCP Lond. 1977. (Univ. Coll. Hosp.)

BADAWI, Horiah Ibrahim 16 Woodleigh Avenue, Birmingham B17 0NJ — LRCP LRCS 1985 Ed.; LRCP LRCS Ed. LRCPS Glas. 1985.

BADCOCK, Diana Jane 8 Bossetts Way, Highfields, Caldecote, Cambridge CB3 7NY — MB BS 1986 Lond.

BADCOCK, Diana Jane Curtis Chilworth, High St., Cranbrook TN17 3DT Tel: 01580 713202 — BM BCh 1965 Oxf.; MA, BM BCh Oxf. 1965; DFFP 1993. Med. Off. (Family Plann. & Health Educat.) Kent. Prev: Ho. Surg. & Ho. Phys. Univ. Coll. Hosp.

BADCOCK, Kathleen (Kate) Gable House, 46 High Street, Malmesbury SN16 9AT Tel: 01666 825825; Perry Green Cottage, Charlton, Malmesbury SN16 9DP Tel: 01666 822252 — BM BCh 1971 Oxf.; MA; DCH Eng. 1974.

BADCOCK, Louisa Jane Staffordshire Rheumatology Centre, Haywood Hospital, High Lane, Burslem, Stoke-on-Trent Tel: 01782 835721 — MB BS 1990 Lond.; BSc Lond. 1987; MRCP (UK) 1993. (Uni Coll of London) Specialist Regist. (Rheum.) Staffs. Rheum. Centre. Socs: Brit. Soc. Rheum. Prev: Regist. (Rheum.) Mid. Staffs. & Roy. Shrewsbury Hosp.; SHO (Neurol. Rehabil.) Hope Hosp. Manch.; SHO (Gen. Med.) Mid. Staffs. HA.

BADCOCK, Richard John Rampron Hospital, Retford DN22 0PD Tel: 01777 247720 Fax: 01777 247737 — MB BChir 1973 Camb.; MPhil Ed. 1982; MA, MB Camb. 1973, BChir 1972; MRCPsych 1980. Cons. Forens. Psychiat. Rampton Hosp. Auth., Retford, Notts; Sen. Clin. Lect. Leeds Univ. Prev: Cons. Forens. Psychiat. Yorks RHA; Sen. Regist. (Psychiat.) Gtr. Glas. HB; Psychiat. Train. Scheme Edin.

BADCOCK, Stephen Felixstowe Road Surgery, 235 Felixstowe Road, Ipswich IP3 9BN Tel: 01473 719112 — MB BS 1982 Newc.; MRCGP 1986; DMJ(Clin) Soc. Apoth. Lond. 1991; DRCOG 1985; DPD Wales 1998. (Newcastle-upon-Tyne) Police Surg. Ipswich Div. Socs: Assn. Police Surg. Gt. Brit. Prev: Trainee GP Ipswich VTS; Ho. Off. (Surg.) Tynemouth Vict. Jubilee Infirm. N. Shields; Ho. Off. (Med.) Roy. Infirm. Sunderland.

BADDELEY, Hiram Scanner Centre, Mount Vernon Hospital, Northwood HA6 2RN Tel: 01923 844283 Fax: 01923 844600 — MB BS 1961 Lond.; FRACR Sydney 1979; FRCR Lond. 1975; FFR Lond. 1969. Cons. Radiol. Mt. Vernon Hosp. N.wood Middlx. Socs: Fell. Roy. Soc. Med.; Soc. Magnetic Resonance in Med. Prev: Prof. Radiol. Univ. Qu.sland, Austral.; Cons. Radiol. United Bristol Hosps.; Sen. Lect. Univ. Liverp.

BADDELEY, Peter Grosvenor Beacon Medical Practice, Stepping Stone Lane, Painswick, Stroud GL6 6RU Tel: 01452 814050 Fax: 01452 812070 Email: drbad@beacor-medical.co.uk; The Little Bridge House, Steppingstone Lane, Painswick, Stroud GL6 6RU Tel: 01452 812070 Fax: 01452 812070 — MB BS 1970 Lond.; MRCP (UK) 1974; MRCS Eng. LRCP Lond. 1970; MRCGP 1988; DGM RCP Lond. 1991; DObst RCOG 1973. (Kings Coll. Hosp) Consg. Gen. Med. Pract. Glos.; Staff Grade Phys. (Med. Oncol.) E. Glos. NHS Trust.

BADDON, Andrew Christopher James The Red House, Pendreich Road, Bridge of Allan, Stirling FK9 4LY — MB ChB 1995 Manch.

BADDOO, Mr Henry Hood Kpakpo 54 Balmoral Crescent, Dronfield_Woodhouse, Dronfield S18 8ZY — MB ChB 1978 Ghana; FRCS Ed. 1989; FFA RCS Eng. 1985.

BADDOO, Michael Allotey 32 Hallowes Court, Dronfield, Sheffield S18 6WG — MB BChir 1952 Camb.; MRCS Eng. LRCP Lond. 1950; DPH RCPS Eng. 1961.

BADDOO, Winifred Adukwei Doncaster Royal Infirmary & Montague Hopsitals NHS Trust, Armthorpe Road, Doncaster DN2 5LT Tel: 01302 796246 Fax: 01302 320098; 156 Coniston Road, Dronfield Wood House, Dronfield S18 8NZ Tel: 01246 413247 Fax: 01246 555938 — MB BS 1981 Ghana; DCH RCP Lond. 1987. (Univ. Ghana Med. Sch.) Staff Grade (Paediat. & Child Health) Doncaster Roy. Infirm. & Montague Hosp. NHS Trust. Socs: Assoc. Mem. RCPCh. Prev: SHO (Child Health & Paediat.) Doncaster Roy. Infirm. & Montague Hosps. NHS Trust; SHO (O & G & Paediat.) Rotherham Dist. Gen. Hosp.

BADEN FULLER, Joanna Jane 4 Eastdown Gardens, Preston, Weymouth DT3 6QP — MB BS 1996 Lond.

BADENOCH, Mr David Fraser 123 Harley Street, London Tel: 020 7935 3881 Fax: 020 7224 6481 Email: david.badenoch@dial.pipex.com; Fernwood, 54 North Hill, Highgate, London N6 4RH Tel: 020 8341 5622 — BM BCh 1975 Oxf.; MA (Animal Physiol.) Oxf. 1984, DM 1987, BA 1970, MCh 1987; FRCS (Urol.) 1987; FRCS Eng. 1979; FEBU 1996. (St. Bart.) Hons.Cons. Urol. Surg. St. Bart. Hosps. Lond.; Hon. Cons. Surg. King Edwd. VII Hosp. Offs. Lond. Socs: Sect. Urol. RSM, Hon Treas. (ex Hon. Sec.); Chelsea Clin. Soc. Hon. Sec. 2000 to date; Brit. Assn. Urol. Surg. Prev: Sen. Regist. (Urol.) Lond. Hosp.; Lect. (Surg.), Regist. & Ho. Surg. St. Bart. Hosp. Lond.; Lect. (Anat.) St. Bart. Hosp. Med. Coll. Lond.

BADENOCH, Jean McKinnell (retired) Church Hayes, Lea, Malmesbury SN16 9PF Tel: 01666 822289 — MB ChB Ed. 1937. Liveryman Worshipful Soc. Apoth. Prev: Ho. Surg. Edin. Hosp. Wom. & Childr.

BADENOCH, Michele Patricia Blossoms Inn Medical Centre, Garlick Hill, London EC1; 54 North Hill, London N6 4RH Tel: 020 8341 5622 — MB BS 1982 Lond.; BSc (Psychol.) Lond. 1979; MRCGP 1986; DRCOG 1985; DCH RCP Lond. 1985. (St. Barts.) Socs: Fell. Roy. Soc. Med. Prev: GP Bounds Green; Hon. Clin. Asst. (Diabetes) Whittington Hosp. Lond.; Trainee GP/SHO Reading VTS.

BADER, Mr Muzahim Salih Surgery of Light, Hungerhill Lane, Whiston, Rotherham S60 4BD Tel: 01709 820400 Fax: 01709 820400; 50 Broom Lane, Rotherham S60 3EL Tel: 01709 364606 — MB ChB 1974 Mosul; FRCS Ed. 1981. GP Rotherham. Socs: MDU Scotl.; BMA.

BADER, Roxana 66 Charles Crescent, Bathgate EH48 1JG — MB ChB 1994 Aberd.

BADERIN, Mr Andrew Ademoye Stafford Street Surgery, 21 Stafford Street, Liverpool L3 8LX Tel: 0151 207 0921 Fax: 0151 207 0921; Maryville, 16 Floral Wood, Liverpool L17 7HR Tel: 0151 728 9623 — MB BS 1980 Nigeria; FRCS Glas. 1988; Dip. Clin. Hypn. Sheff. 1995. (College of Medicine University of Ibadan) GP Princip. Prev: Assoc. Phys. Liverp. HA; Regist. (Gen. Surg.) Burnley Gen. Hosp.

BADERMAN, Howard, OBE (retired) 21 Churchill Road, London NW5 1AN Tel: 020 7267 4281 — MB BS 1959 Lond.; BSc Lond. 1957; FRCP Lond. 1974, M 1967; MRCS Eng. LRCP Lond. 1959; FFAEM 1994; FRCS Ed. 1999. Hon. Clin. Sen. Lect. Med., Roy. Free & Univ. Coll. Lond. Med. Sch. 2000 to Present; Vice Pres. Child Accid. Preven. Trust; Scientif. Fell. Zool. Soc. Lond.; Fell. UCL; Fell. UCL Hosp. Prev: Cons. Phys. & Cons. A & E & Hon.Sen. Lect. Fac. Clin. Univ. Coll.Hosp. Lond.

BADGER, Mr Frederick George (retired) Marlow, Holyford Lane, Colyford, Colyton EX24 6HW Tel: 01297 552520 — MRCS Eng. LRCP Lond. 1930; BSc Wales 1927; FRCS Ed. 1938. Prev: Sen. Cons. Surg. Birm. Accid. Hosp. & Rehabil. Centre.

BADGER, Geraldine Whitchurch Health Centre, Armada Road, Bristol BS14 0SU Tel: 01275 832285 Fax: 01275 540035; Wellington Back, 21 Canynge Road, Clifton, Bristol BS8 3JZ — MB ChB 1978 Bristol; BSc (Hons.) Bristol 1975; MRCP (UK) 1981; Cert. Family Plann. JCC 1983. (Univ. Bristol)

BADGER, Mr Ian Laurence Russell 70 Lomaine Drive, Birmingham B30 1AJ — MB ChB 1983 Birm.; FRCS Eng. 1988.

BADGER, Janet Lorraine Dept. Of Orthopaedics, St Hellier Hospital, Wrtha Lane, Carshalton SM1 5AA Tel: 01633 871177, 020 8296 2581 Fax: 01633 860234 — BM 1995 Soton.; MRCGP 1999; DFFP 2000; MRCP, 1999; DCH, 1998; DRCOG, 1997. p/t GP, Cwmbran village Surg., Gwent.

BADGER, Katharine Mary Mary Sheridan Centre for Child Health, 405 Kennington Road, London SE11 4QW Tel: 020 7346 5400; 154 Burbage Road, Dulwich, London SE21 7AG Tel: 020 7274 8126 Fax: 020 7274 8126 — MB BS 1965 Lond.; MRCS Eng. LRCP Lond. 1965; DCH RCP Lond. 1994; DObst RCOG 1967. (Char. Cross) Assoc. Specialist W. Lambeth Community Care NHS Trust.

BADGER, Thomas Reginald Dunbar Medical Centre, Abbey Road, Dunbar EH42 1JP Tel: 01368 862327 Fax: 01368 865646; 3 The Doon, Spott, Dunbar EH42 1RJ Tel: 01368 864085 — MB ChB 1974 Ed.; DRCOG 1979; DCH Eng. 1977. (Ed.) Prev: SHO (Geriat. Med.) Norf. AHA; Capt. RAMC Regtl. Med. Off.

BADGETT, William John Lyth St Margaret's Practices, 237 St. Margarets Road, Twickenham TW1 1NE Tel: 020 8892 1986 Fax: 020 8891 6466 — MB BS 1974 Lond.; MRCS Eng. LRCP Lond. 1973. (Middlx.)

BADH, Charanjit Singh 45 Marshall Road, Willenhall WV13 3PB — MB BS 1998 Lond.; MB BS Lond 1998.

BADHAM, David Peter, Surg. Lt.-Cdr. RN Taunton and Somerset Hospital, Musgrove Park, Taunton TA1 5DA Tel: 01823 333444; Gwinere, West Buckland, Wellington TA21 9LD Tel: 01823 662130 Fax: 01823 664459 — MB BS 1991 Lond.; BSc Lond. 1987, MB BS 1991. (St. Mary's) GP Regist. Taunton. Socs: BMA.

BADHAM, David Stephen The Health Centre, Sea Road, Lymington SO41 0PG Tel: 01590 643022 Fax: 01590 644950; Broad Reach, Barnes Lane, Milford on Sea, Lymington SO41 0RR Tel: 01590 645291 — MB BS 1970 Lond.; MRCGP 1978; DObst RCOG 1974; DCH Eng. 1974. (St. Bart.) Socs: BMA.

BADIA VALLRIBERA, Lidia 25 Thornhill Bridge Wharf, Caledonian Road, London N1 0RU Tel: 020 7837 9456 — LMS 1989 U Autonoma Barcelona; FRCS (Orl.) Glas. 1993. Regist. Rotat. (ENT) Char. Cross Lond. Prev: SHO (ENT) Roy. Nat. Throat, Nose & Ear Hosp. Hosp. Lond.

BADIANI, Dinesh 28 Lewis Crescent, Neasden, London NW10 0NR — MB ChB 1980 Sheff.; MRCS LRCP 1980.

BADIANI, Kamlesh Nanji Forest House Surgery, 25 Leicester Road, Shepshed, Loughborough LE12 9DF Tel: 01509 508412; 2 Homeway Close, Shepshed, Loughborough LE12 9DX Tel: 01509 508452 — MB ChB 1982 Leic.

BADIE, Mr Farouk Yahya Royal Berkshire Hospital, Anaesthetics Department, London Road, Reading RG1 5AN Tel: 0118 987 7065; Menton, Madeira Road, West Byfleet, Weybridge Tel: 01932 340446 — MD Istanbul 1965; DA (UK) 1972; FFA FRCSI 1978. Assoc. Specialist Anaesth. Anaesth. Roy. Berks. & Battle Hosps. NH Trust Reading Berks.

BADIGER, Rekha Vijaykumar 17 Bronington Close, Chatham ME5 7RA — MB BS 1998 Lond.; MB BS Lond 1998.

BADKOUBEI, Shahrokh Thanet District General Hospital, St Peter's Road, Margate CT9 4AN Tel: 01843 225544 Fax: 01843 220048; 16 Magnolia Avenue, Cliftonville, Margate CT9 3DS Tel: 01843 294660 — MB BS 1972 Karachi. Staff Grade (O & G) Thanet Dist. Gen. Hosp.

BADMAN, Michael 21 Brandon Grove, Newcastle upon Tyne NE2 1PA — MB BS 1998 Newc.; MB BS Newc 1998.

BADMINTON, Michael Norman Department of Medical Biochemistry, University Hospital of Wales, Heath Park, Cardiff CF14 4WZ Tel: 029 2074 7747 — MB ChB 1987 Cape Town; BSc Cape Town 1981, BSc (Hons.) Med. Biochem. 1982.

BADO, William John Francis 7 Lingfield Close, Northwood HA6 2FP — BM 1984 Soton.

BADOCK, Geoffrey Boughey (retired) Hollywood, 40 The Esplanade, Frinton-on-Sea CO13 9JD Tel: 01255 2998 — MRCS Eng. LRCP Lond. 1943; FFA RCS Eng. 1954; DA Eng. 1948. Prev: Surg. Lt. RNVR.

BADR, Adil Abdel Gadir Mohamed Wexham Park Hospital, Slough SL2 4HL Tel: 01753 364506 Fax: 01753 691343 — MB BCh 1965 Ain Shams.

BADR ELDIN, Salah Eldin Ahmed Fathalla 2 Rush Bank, High Crompton, Shaw, Oldham OL2 7QP — MB ChB 1976 Alexandria; MB ChB (Hons.) Alexandria 1976; MRCP (UK) 1991.

BADRASHI, Falah-V-Din (retired) Church Street, Ruddington, Nottingham NG11 6HD.

BADRAWY, Galal Akasha 121 Harley Street, London W1G 6AX Tel: 020 7935 6875 Fax: 020 7224 0651 — MB BCh 1970 Cairo; MRCPsych 1983. Cons. Psychiat. Surrey Hants. NHS Trust, The Ridgewood centre, Old Birley Rd., Frimley, Surrey; Vis. Cons. P.ss Grace Hosp, Lond.; Cardinal Clinic, Windsor; Priory Gp. Hosps., Charter Clinic, Wellington Hosp.Lond & Cromwell Hosp. Socs: Fell. Roy. Soc. Med.; Amer. Psychiat. Assn.; Mem. Brit. Med. Assn.

BADREK-AMOUDI, Ahmed 55 Northend House, Fitzjames Avenue, London W14 0RT — MB BS 1993 Lond.

BADRINATH, Manikundalam Ramanatha Department of Anaesthetics, Medway Hospital, Gillingham ME7 5NY; 33 Hickory Dell, Hempstead, Gillingham ME7 3SL Tel: 01634 376263 — MB BS 1979 Bangalore; MD Manipal (India) 1989; FFA RCSI 1995. Staff Grade (Anaesth.) Medway Hosp. Kent. Socs: Assn. Anaesth. GB & Irel. Prev: Regist. (Anaesth.) NW Region; SHO (Anaesth.) Medway Hosp.

BADVE, Michael Ian Primrose Cottage, off Spar Lane, Illogan, Redruth TR16 4RG Tel: 01209 843649 Fax: 01209 843649 — MB BCh BAO 1989 NUI; LRCPSI 1989. GP & Police Surg. Cornw.; SHO (Psychiat.) Trengweath Hosp. Redruth. Socs: BMA & Med. Protec. Soc. Prev: Trainee GP Torpoint VTS; SHO (A & E) Derriford Hosp. Plymouth; SHO (O & G) Treliske Hosp. Truro.

BADVE, Sunil Shankar Department of Histopathology, Royal Marsden Hospital, Sutton SM2 5PT Tel: 020 8643 8901; 33 Bavent Road, Camberwell, London SE5 9RY Tel: 020 7733 2157 — MD 1986 Bombay; MB BS 1982; MRCPath 1993. Regist. (Histopath.) Roy. Marsden Hosp. Sutton. Socs: Assn. Clin. Path. Prev: Lect. Sir. J. J. Hosp. Bombay, India; Sen. Regist. Tata Memor. Hosp. & Research Centre Bombay, India.

BADWAN, Mr Derar Ali Husein The Royal Leamington Spa Rehabilitation Hospital, Heathcote Lane, Warwick CV34 6SR Tel: 01926 317700 Fax: 01926 317710 Email: mblgo4@dial.pipex.com — MB ChB 1974 Basrah; FRCS Ed. 1983; FRCP 2000. Cons. Rehabil. Med. Roy. Leamington Spa Rehabil. Hosp. Socs: BSRM. Prev: Sen. Regist. Midl. Centre for Spinal Injuries OsW.ry; Lect. & Hon. Regist. (Rehabil.) Univ. Soton. & Soton. Gen. Hosp.; Regist. (Neurosurg.) Atkinson Morley's Hosp. & The Maudsley Kings Coll. & Guy's Hosp. NeuroSurgic. Unit.

BADYAL, Satinder Kaur Weardale Practice, Stanhope Health Centre, Dale Street OL13 2XD Tel: 01388 528555; Redgate House, Redgate Bank, Wolsingham, Bishop Auckland DL13 3HH — MB BCh 1991 Wales; DRCOG. p/t GP.

BAECKER, Tadeusz Edward Culag House, Kiltarlity, Beauly IV4 7JH — MB ChB 1968 St. And.; FRCPsych 1995; DPM Ed. & Glas. 1973. (St. And.) Cons. Psychiat. Craig Phadrig Hosp. Inverness.

BAER, Geoffrey Maurice Lionel (retired) Court End, Kintbury Square, Kintbury, Hungerford RG17 9US — MB BS 1953 Lond.; FFA RCS Eng. 1963; DA Eng. 1957. Prev: Cons. Anaesth. Horton Gen. Hosp. Banbury.

BAER, Mr Roger Max The Bath Clinic, Combe Down, Bath BA2 7BR Tel: 01225 840555 Ext: 274 Fax: 01225 840708 Email: www.cataract-surgeon.co.uk; 17 Macaulay Buildings, Widcombe Hill, Bath BA2 6AT Tel: 01225 336741 Email: aer@onetel.net.uk — MB BS 1984 Lond.; FRCS Eng. 1989; FRCOphth 1989. (St. Mary's Hosp.) Cons. Ophth. Roy. United Hosp. Bath. Socs: Europ. Soc. of Cateract and Refractive Surg. Prev: Resid. Surg. Off. Moorfields Eye Hosp. Lond.

BAER, Mr Simon Thomas Conquest Hospital, The Ridge, St Leonards-on-Sea TN37 7RD Tel: 01424 755255; Luxford House, Standard Hill, Ninfield, Battle TN33 9NJ — MB BS 1981 Lond.; FRCS (Orl.) Eng. 1987. (St. Mary's) Cons. Otolaryngol. Hastings & Rother NHS Trust. Prev: Sen. Regist. (Otolaryngol.) Bristol & Bath

Hosps.; Regist. St. Geo. Hosp. Lond.; SHO (Otolaryngol.) St. Mary's Hosp. Lond.

BAERSELMAN, Gillian Margaret 22 Woodlands Park, Merrow, Guildford GU1 2TH Tel: 01483 301632 Fax: 01483 301632 Email: gilliebee@msn.com — MB BS 1964 Lond. (St. Bart.) Socs: BMA. Prev: Med. Off. Plymouth HA; Ho. Phys. & Ho. Surg. Bedford Gen. Hosp.

BAEZ GANDIA, Jose Antonio 9 Carey Close, Aylesbury HP21 9JP — LMS 1989 Seville.

BAFADHEL, Zain Ahmed William Harvey Hospital, Kennington Road, Willesborough, Ashford TN24 0LY — MB ChB 1974 Baghdad; MRCPI 1987.

BAFFOUR-KODUA, Margaret Ofobi Amoayiwah 31 Whitwell Road, Plaistow, London E13 8BP — MB BS 1992 Lond.; MRCGP 2000; DRCOG 2000; BSc Hons. (Pharm.) Lond. 1989, MB BS 1992; DFFP 1994. (Lond. Hosp. Med. Coll.) GP. Prev: SHO (O & G) Homerton Hosp. & Hammersmith Hosp. Lond.; Specialist Regist. (O & G) FarnBoro. Hosp. Bromley.

BAGARY, Davinder Singh The Health Centre, Alfred Squire Road, Wednesfield, Wolverhampton WV11 1XU Tel: 01902 575033 Fax: 01902 575013 — MB ChB 1990 Sheff.; MRCGP 1996; DRCOG 1993.

BAGARY, Manjinder Singh Institute of Neurology, Department of Neuropsychiatry, Queen Square, London WC1N 3BG Tel: 020 7837 3611 Email: m.bagary@ion.ucl.ac.uk — MB BS 1990 Lond.; MRCPsych 1997; BSc (Hons.) Lond. 1987. (St Mary's (Imperial Coll. Lond)) Clin. Research Fell., Dept. Of NeuroPsychiat., Inst. Of Neurol., Qu. Sq., Lond.; Hon. SpR, Maudsey Hosp. Socs: Roy. Coll. Psychiat.; BMA; Brit. NeuroPsychiat. Assn. Prev: Wellcome Research Fell. Hammersmith Hosp. Lond.

BAGCHI, Dinendra Narayan Brookfield Surgery, 29 Clivedon Place, Longton, Stoke-on-Trent ST3 4JB Tel: 01782 598211 Fax: 01782 598211; 9 Deansberry Close, Trentham, Stoke-on-Trent ST4 8JH Tel: 01782 643197 — MB BS 1965 Calcutta; 1987 (FPC) RCOG, RCGP, FP Assoc. & National Assoc. of Fam. Plan. (Nat. Med. Coll. Calcutta) Prev: Regist. (Psychiat.) Lennox Castle Hosp. Glas.; Trainee GP Kemnay Aberd.sh.; Trainee Middlemass Hey Liverp.

BAGCHI, Rita 588 Linnet Drive, Chelmsford CM2 8AW — MB ChB 1990 Sheff.

BAGCHI, Mr Saral Kumar Scissett Health Centre, Wakefield Road, Scissett, Huddersfield HD8 9JL Tel: 01484 862793; Greystones, Bank End Lane, High Hoyland, Barnsley S75 4BB Tel: 01226 382337 — MB 1947 Calcutta; FRCS Ed. 1965. (Calcutta Med. Coll.) Prev: Regist. Gen. Surg. Huddersfield Roy. Infirm. & Clayton Hosp.; Wakefield.

BAGCHI, Shiv Prasad Pallion Health Centre, Hylton Road, Sunderland SR4 7XF Tel: 0191 567 2995 — MB BS 1973 Patna. (Patna) GP Sunderland.

BAGG, Charles Ernest (retired) — MRCS Eng. LRCP Lond. 1946; MA Camb. 1946; Hon. DSc Malta MGS Internat. University Fundation 1987; FRCPsych 1983, M 1971; DPM Eng. 1951. Prev: Cons. Psychiat. St. John's Hosp. Aylesbury.

BAGG, Leonard Robert King George Hospital, Barley Lane, Goodmayes, Ilford IG3 8YB Tel: 020 8970 8068 Email: robert.bagg@rbhc-tr.nthames.nhs.uk — MB BS 1971 Lond.; BSc Lond. 1968; FRCP Lond. 1992; MRCP (UK) 1974. Cons. Phys. King Geo. Hosp. Goodmayes. Socs: Brit. Thorac. Soc.; Brit. Soc. Allergy & Clin. Immunol. Prev: Sen. Regist. (Gen. & Thoracic Med.) Lond. Hosp.; Lect. Fac. Med. Univ. Nairobi; Wellcome Clin. Research Fell. Lond. Hosp.

BAGGA, Arun Kumar 19 Sherborne Avenue, Southall UB2 4HX — BM 1993 Soton.

BAGGA, Poonam Golden Pond, Main Road, Brigsley, Grimsby DN37 0RF — MB BS 1981 Delhi; FRCS Ed. 1985; FCOphth 1989.

BAGGA, Mr Tajesh Kumar Golden Pond, Main Road, Brisley, Grimsby DN37 0RF — MB BS 1978 Delhi; FRCS Glas. 1984.

BAGGALLAY, Alison Janet Caol Clinic, Kilmalhe Road, Fort William PH33 7DZ Tel: 01397 700883; Inverlair Lodge, Roy Bridge PH31 4AR — MB BS 1972 Lond. (St. Thos.) Clin. Med. Off., Community Child health, Highland Primary Care trust.

BAGGETT, Clare Jane Royal Bournemouth Hospital, Bournemouth BH7 7DW; 9 The Moorings, 2 Willow Way, Christchurch BH23 1JJ Tel: 01202 486748 — MB BS 1991 Lond. SHO (Card of Elderly) Roy. Bournemouth Hosp. Prev: Trainee GP Roy. Bournemouth Hosp. VTS.

BAGGOTT, Jonathan Norman 3 Sherard Way, Thorpe Astley, Braunstone, Leicester LE3 3TN — MB ChB 1998 Leic.; MB ChB Leic 1998.

BAGGULEY, Katrina Anne Forest Rise, Debden Road, Loughton IG10 2NY — MB ChB 1994 Manch.

BAGHAI-RAVARY, Ramin 4 Henson Avenue, London NW2 4AR — MB BS 1996 Lond.

BAGHDADI, Sabah Hassen Nasser Birmingham Women's Hospital, Edgbaston, Birmingham B15; 56 Heathleigh Road, Birmingham B38 8HH Tel: 0121 608 9629 Fax: 0121 458 3186 Email: sbaghdadi@compuserve.com — LMSSA 1995 Lond.; LRCP, LRCS 1995; M. Med. Sc. Obst. & Gyn. Birm. 1992; Dip Obst. & Gyn. Spec. Obst. & Gyn. Romania 1986; Dip. Med. Romania 1983. Regist. (O & G) Birm. Wom.'s Hosp. Socs: Brit. Fertil. Soc.; Brit. Soc. Colposcopy and Clin. Path. Prev: Research Fell. (IVF) Priory Hosp. Birm.; Princip. Specialist. in O & G, Romania.

BAGHDJIAN, Raffi Boghos Chorley Health Centre, Collison Avenue, Chorley PR7 2TH Tel: 01257 265080 Fax: 01257 232285 — MB ChB 1980 Manch.; BSc (Hons. Anat.) Manch. 1977; DRCOG 1985.

BAGHLA, Davindar Paul Singh 18 St Erkenwald Road, Barking IG11 7XA — MB BS 1997 Lond.

BAGHOMIAN, Aram 144 Heath Park Avenue, Heath, Cardiff CF14 3RJ — MB BCh 1996 Wales. SHO Rotat. (Gen. Med.) Walsgrave Hosp. Coventry.

BAGLEY, Andree Marie Pinfold Medical Practice, The Health Centre, Pinfold Gate, Loughborough LE11 1DQ Tel: 01509 263753 Fax: 01509 264124; The Willows, 46 Derby Road, Hathern, Loughborough LE12 5LD Tel: 01509 842364 — MB BS 1967 Lond. (Roy. Free) Socs: BMA. Prev: Ho. Surg. & Ho. Phys. Nottm. Gen. Hosp.

BAGLEY, Gerard Carters Lane House, 41 Brunswick Road, Shoreham-by-Sea BN43 5WA Tel: 01273 440950 Fax: 01273 440962 — MB BS 1983 Lond.; MA Camb. 1980; MRCPsych 1988. Cons. Old Age Psychiat. Worthing Priority Care NHS Trust. Socs: BMA. Prev: Sen. Regist. Rotat. (Old Age Psychiat.) Wessex RHA.

BAGLEY, Mr John Sorrell 38 Hillside Avenue, Sutton-on-Sea, Mablethorpe LN12 2JH — MB BS 1981 Lond.; MD Aberd. 1992; FRCS Ed. 1988.

BAGLEY, Simon Richard Vaughan c/o Barron Grove, The Mead, Timsbury, Bath BA2 0NS — MB ChB 1992 Ed.

BAGLIN, Trevor Patrick Dept of Haematology, Addenbrookes NHS Trust, Cambridge CB2 2QQ Tel: 01223 216748 Fax: 01223 217017 Email: tpb20@cam.ac.uk — MB ChB 1981 Manch.; PhD Birm. 1989; MRCP (UK) 1984; MRCPath 1990; FRCP 1995; MA 1996; FRCPath 1998. (Manch) Cons. Haemat. Addenbrooke's Hosp. Camb. Prev: Sen. Regist. (Haemat.) Addenbrooke's Hosp. Camb.; Leukaemia Research Fund Train. Fell. Dept. Haemat. Univ. Birm.; Regist. Birm. Gen. Hosp. & Qu. Eliz. Hosp. Birm.

BAGNALL, Alan James 6 Burghley Close, Market Harborough LE16 8BW — MB ChB 1994 Leeds.

BAGNALL, Julie Joy The Old Post Office, Main St., Aldborough, York YO51 9ES Tel: 01423 322232; The Old Post Office, Main St, Aldborough, York YO51 9ES Tel: 01423 322232 — MB BS 1966 Lond.; MRCS Eng. LRCP Lond. 1966; FFPHM 1990, M 1979.

BAGNALL, Mark John Charles High Quarry, Harcourt Hill, Oxford OX2 9AS — MB BS 1992 Lond. SHO Rotat. (Med.) N.wick Pk. Hosp. Harrow.

BAGNALL, Mr Philip Jeffrey Department of Orthopaedics, Royal Bournemouth Hospital, Castle Lane E., Bournemouth Tel: 01202 303626; 59 Granby Grove, Highfield, Southampton SO17 3RY — BM 1986 Soton.; FRCS Lond. 1990. Staff Grade Orthop. Surg. Roy. Bournemouth Hosp.

BAGNALL, Robert Alexander 9 West Ed., Elgin IV30 1SA — MB ChB 1996 Glas.

BAGNALL, William Eric St James's & Seacroft University Hospitals Trust, Beckett St., Leeds LS9 7TF Tel: 0113 243 3144 — MB ChB 1971 Leeds; MB ChB (Hons. Distinc. Obst. & Gyn.) Lond. 1971; BSc (Hons.) Leeds 1968; FRCP Lond. 1987; MRCP (UK) 1973. Cons. Phys. (Med. of Elderly) Leeds (St. Jas.) Univ. Hosp.; Div.al Dir. (Med.) St. Jas. Hosp. Trust. Socs: Brit. Geriat. Soc.; BMA. Prev: Sen. Regist. (Geriat. Med.) Hull Roy. Infirm.; Tutor (Med.) & Regist. (Gen.

Med.) St. Jas. Hosp. Leeds; SHO (Gen. Med.) Chapel Allerton Hosp. Leeds.

BAGOTT, Mark James Child Health Centre, John St., Ashington NE63 0SE Tel: 01670 395706 Fax: 0670 395717; 30 Eastlands, Newcastle upon Tyne NE7 7YE — MB BS 1986 Lond.; MRCP Ed. 1993; DTCH Liverp. 1990. (Roy. Free) Cons., Community Child Health, Ashington. Socs: Christian Med. Fell.ship; Roy. Coll. Of Paediat. & Child Health; BMA. Prev: Sen.Regist. (community Child Health) N.umberland; Sen.Regist.(Community Child Health) N. Tyneside; Sen.Regist.(Community Child Health) Gateshead.

BAGSHAW, Mr Hillary Ashton The Surgery, 274 Havant Road, Drayton, Portsmouth PO6 1PA Tel: 023 9237 0422 Fax: 023 9261 8383; 35 Drayton Lane, Drayton, Portsmouth PO6 1HG Tel: 023 92 377880 — MB BS 1969 Lond.; FRCS Eng. 1976; MRCS Eng. LRCP Lond. 1969. (St. Bart.) Prev: Regist. (Surg.) St. Mary's & Roy. Hosps. Portsmouth; Regist. (Urol.) Inst. Urol. Lond.; Research Fell. (Paediat. Urol.) Inst. Child Health Lond.

BAGSHAW, Ian Michael Murray, MBE The Surgery, Rockcliffe Court, Hurworth Place, Darlington DL2 2DS Tel: 01325 720605; 29 The Green, Hurworth on Tees, Darlington DL2 2AA Fax: 01325 722700 — MB ChB 1968 Glas.; FRCGP 1983, M 1974; DCH Eng. 1974; DObst RCOG 1974. Med. Adviser Hydro Polymers; Med. Dir. Cleveland Health Call. Prev: Lt. Col. RAMC; Chief Med. Off. Brunei & Catterick Garrison.

BAGSHAW, Melanie Jeana Margaret 37 Stallcourt Avenue, Penylan, Cardiff CF23 5AL — MB BS 1987 Lond.; MRCGP 1992; DGM RCP Lond. 1990.

BAGSHAW, Michael British Airways Health Services, Waterside (HMAG), Harmondsworth UB7 0GB; 3 Bramley Grove, Crowthorne RG45 6EB — MB BCh 1973 Wales; MRCS Eng. LRCP Lond. 1973; AFOM RCP 1982; DFFP 1996; DAvMed Eng. 1980; FRAes 1995, M 1977; MFOM RCP 2000. (Welsh Nat. Sch. Med.) Head of Occupat.al & Aviat. Med., Brit. Airways. Socs: Assoc. of Authorised Med. Examr.s (Chairm. Elect); Internat. Acad. Aerospace Med.; Fell. Aerospace Med. Assn. (Chairm., Air Transport Med. Comm.). Prev: GP Crowthorne; Cons. Neuro-otol. St. Geo. Hosp. Lond.; Sen. Med. Off. Pilot & Specialist Aviat. Med. RAF Inst. Aviat. Med. FarnBoro.

BAGSHAW, Oliver Neil Turner Birmingham Childrens Hospital, Steelhouse Lane, Birmingham B4 6NH Tel: 0121 333 9999 Fax: 0121 333 9998; 45 Grange Road, Solihull B91 1BY Tel: 0121 706 0347 Email: oliver@bagsh.softnet.co.uk — MB ChB 1984 Birm.; FCAnaesth 1989; DA (UK) 1986. Cons. Anaesth. Birm. Childr. Hosp. Prev: Sen. Regist. (Sheff.) Hosps.; Regist. (Anaesth.) Lincoln Co. Hosp. & Nottm.

BAGSHAW, Peter James Whitchurch Health Centre, Armada Road, Bristol BS14 0SU Tel: 01275 832285 Fax: 01275 540035 — MB ChB 1977 Birm.

BAGSHAW, Stanley Alfred Church Street Surgery, 27-28 Church St, Whitehaven CA28 7EB Tel: 01946 693660 — MB ChB 1972 Aberd.

BAGSHAWE, Kenneth Dawson, CBE Department of Surgery, Charing Cross Hospital, London W6 8RF Tel: 020 8846 7517 Fax: 020 8846 1443 Email: k.bagshawe@cxwms.ac.uk; 115 George Street, London W1H 7HF Tel: 020 7262 6033 Fax: 020 7262 6033 — MB BS 1952 Lond.; FRS 1989; Hon. DSc Bradford 1990; MD Lond. 1964; FRCP Lond. 1969, M 1954; FRCR 1983; FRCOG 1979. (St. Mary's) Emerit. Prof. Med. Oncol. Char. Cross Hosp. Lond. Socs: Hon. Fell. Roy. Soc. Med.; Pres. Brit. Assn. Cancer Research; Brit. Soc. Immunol. Prev: Chairm. Scientif. & Exec. Comms. CRC; Sen. Regist. (Med.) St. Mary's Hosp. Lond.; Fell. Johns Hopkins Hosp. Baltimore, USA.

BAGUANT, Nirmal Kishore 19 Oxenden Way, Coventry CV3 2HR — LRCP LRCS 1981 Ed.; LRCP LRCS Ed. LRCPS Glas. 1981.

BAGULEY, Ian Lea Hall, Lea Cross, Shrewsbury SY5 8HY — MB ChB 1980 Aberd.; FFA RCS Eng. 1984. Cons. Anaesth. Shrops. HA. Prev: Sen. Regist. (Anaesth.) W. Midl. RHA.; Regist. (Anaesth.) Birm HA; SHO Shrewsbury HA.

BAGULEY, Stephen David Kenneth Derriford Hospital, Derriford, Plymouth PL6 8DH Tel: 01752 763919 Email: stevebaguley@bigfoot.com; Ash Cottage, Brentor, Tavistock PL19 0LU Tel: 01822 810713 Fax: 01822 810713 — MB ChB 1994 Glas.; BSc Glas. 1992; MRCP (UK) 1998. (Glasgow) Specialist Regist. (Genito-Urin.). Socs: Med. Soc. Study VD. Prev: SHO (O & G); SHO Med. Rotat. Trelstr Hosp. Turo.

BAGUNEID, Mohamed Saeed 14 Highfield Gardens, Hollingworth, Hyde SK14 8NF Tel: 01457 763231 Email: dolmu@btinternet.com — MB ChB 1993 Manch.; FRCS Ed. 1997. Research Fell. (Vasc. Surg.) Manch. Roy. Infirm. Prev: SHO Rotat. (Surg.) Manch. Roy. Infirm.; Demonst. (Anat.) Univ. Cardiff.

BAGWELL, Andrew David Squirrels, Hillside Close, Mitchel Troy, Monmouth NP25 4JR — BM 1995 Soton.

BAHADUR, Tej The Buckland Medical Centre, Brookfield Place, Buckland Avenue, Dover CT16 2AE Tel: 01304 206353 Fax: 01304 209522 — MB BS GSVM Med. Sch. Kanpur WP India; BSc. GP Partner Dover Kent. Socs: Med. Protec. Soc.

BAHAL, Mr Vijay Laurus, 79 Warkron Lane, Kettering NN15 5AB — MB BS 1979 Delhi; MS Delhi 1982; FRCS Glas. 1986. Prev: Research Regist. (Vasc. Surg.) Wordsley Hosp.

BAHARANI, Jyoti Balram 18A Taylors Lane, Dundee DD2 1AQ Tel: 01382 660111 Email: jyoti-baharani@compuserve.com; 18A Taylors Lane, Dundee DD2 1AQ Tel: 01382 660111 — MB ChB 1992 Dundee; MRCP, 1996. JPR Gen. Med & Nephrol.

BAHGAT, Mr Mahmoud Salama 39 Napier Road, Monton, Eccles, Manchester M30 8BF — MB ChB 1966 Alexandria; FRCS Eng. 1982; FRCS Ed. 1982; DLO 1970.

BAHIA, Balbinder Singh Burdwood Surgery, Wheelers Greenway, Thatcham RG19 4YF Tel: 01635 868006 Fax: 01635 867484 — MB BS 1989 Lond.; MRCGP 1993; DRCOG 1992. (St. George's Hospital)

BAHIA, Hilal Isam 33 Furness Avenue, Blackburn BB1 5SE — MB BCh BAO 1991 NUI; LRCPSI 1991.

BAHIA, Sarbjit Singh 37 Morris Street, Swindon SN2 2HU — MB BS 1997 Lond.

BAHIA, Sukhdip Singh 72 Parkfield Street, Manchester M14 4BW — MB ChB 1993 Manch.

BAHIA, Sundus Omran Thames Pathology Services, 12 Mill St., Slough SL2 5DH Tel: 01753 522677 Fax: 01753 574142; Tall Timbers, Church Lane, Stoke Poges, Slough SL2 4PB Tel: 01753 647588 — MB ChB 1972 Baghdad; DCP Baghdad 1976; FRCPath (Haemat.) 1984. Med. Dir. Thames Path. Servs. Slough. Socs: BMA; Assn. Clin. Paths. Prev: Cons. Haemat. & Clin. Path. Cromwell Hosp. Lond.; Regist. (Haemat.) Greenwich Dist. Hosp. Lond.; Regist. (Path.) W. Middlx. Univ. Hosp. Isleworth.

BAHINIPATY, Lingaraj 8 Rose Gardens, Eythorne, Dover CT15 4BS — MRCS Eng. LRCP Lond. 1974; MB BS Utkal 1965.

BAHL, Madan Ramlal Camden & Islington Health Authority, 110 Hampstead Road, London NW1 2LJ Tel: 020 7853 5364 Fax: 020 7853 5369; 79 Cuckoo Hill Road, Pinner HA5 1AU — MB BS 1961 Baroda; FFPHM RCPI 1993; FFPHM RCP (UK) 1990; MFCM RCPI 1979; FFCM 1989, M 1974; DCH Eng. 1970; DPH Toronto 1964. (Baroda) Cons. Pub. Health Med. Communicable Dis. Control Camden & Islington HA; Hon. Sen. Lect. Roy. Free Hosp. Med. Sch. And Univ. Coll. Med. Sch. Socs: Fell. Roy. Soc. Health; Fell. Soc. Community Med./FRIHPH; BMA. Prev: Cons. Pub. Health Phys. Lewisham & N. S.wark HA & Hampstead HA; Specialist (Community Med.) Lambeth, S.wark & Lewisham HA (T); Hon. Lect. (Community Med.) Sch. Med. Univ. Zambia, City of Lusaka.

BAHL, Shailini Department of Paediatrics, St Georges Hospital, Blackshaw Road, London SW17 0QT Tel: 020 8672 1255; 5 St Pauls Road, Richmond TW9 2HH Tel: 020 8940 9503 Email: shailininbahl@hotmail.com — BM BS 1990 Nottm.; BMedSci Nottm. 1988; MRCP (UK) 1995. Regist. (Paediat. Endocrinol.) St. Geo.s Hosp. Tooting, Lond. Socs: Med. Protec. Soc.; MRCPCH; Brit. Soc. Paediatric Endocrinol. and Diabetes. Prev: Regist. (Paediat.) St. Peter's Hosp. Chertsey; Regist. (Paediat.) St. Richards Hosp. Chichester; SHO (Paediat.) Chelsea & W.m. Hosp. & King's Coll. Hosp. Lond.

BAHMAIE, Arash 29 Bray Road, Guildford GU2 7LH Email: abahmaie@hotmail.com — MB BS 1989 Lond.; MRCOG 1996. (Char. Cross & Westm.)

BAHRA, Anish 99 Howards Lane, Rowtown, Weybridge KT13 1ES Tel: 01932 858067 — MB ChB 1990 Bristol; MRCP (UK) 1995. (Bristol Univ.) Research Fell. Neurol. Inst. Neurol. Lond. Prev: Regist. (Med. & Neurol.) Wellington Hosp., NZ; Regist. (HIV & Respirat. Med.) Roy. Free Hosp. Lond.

BAHRA, Ranjit Singh 9 Burnmoor Street, Leicester LE2 7FW — MB ChB 1994 Leic. (Univ. Leicester) SHO Rotat. (Gen. Med.) Leicester. Socs: BMA.

BAHRAMI, Jamshid Department for NHS Postgraduate Medical & Dental Education, Willow Terrace Rd., University of Leeds, Leeds LS2 9JT Tel: 01132 331501 Fax: 01132 331530 Email: drjbahrami@compuserve.com; Clarence Field Cottage, 13 Townend Court, Great Ouseburn, York YO26 9RD Tel: 01423 331880 — MB ChB 1965 Leeds; FRCGP 1988, M 1977; FRCOG 1983, M 1970; DObst RCOG 1968. Dir. Postgrad. GP Educat. Assoc. Dean (Yorks.) Univ. of Leeds; Mem. of Jt. Comm. on PostGrad. Train. for Gen. Pract.; Mem. Nat. Summative Assessm. Bd. for Gen. Pract.; Mem. Exec. Counc. of the UK Conf. of PostGrad. Advisers & Universities of the UK; Mem. N.ern & Yorks. Regional Educat. Developm. Gp. Prev: Sec. of UK Conf. of Postgrad. Advisers & Universities of the UK; Examr. RCGP & RCOG; Mem. Nat. Assn. of Course Organisers.

BAHRI, Mr Adil Habib Lewisham Hospital, Lewisham High St., Lewisham, London SE13 6LE Fax: 020 8333 3000; 18 Albyfield, Bromley BR1 2HZ — MB ChB 1966 Baghdad; FRCS Ed. 1977; FRCS Glas. 1977; FICS 1980. Assoc. Specialist (ENT) Lewisham Hosp. Prev: Cons. ENT Al-Sabah Hosp., Kuwait.

BAHRI, Anoop Kumar 225A Finchley Road, London NW3 6LP — MB BS 1984 Lond.; MSc (Toxicol.) Lond. 1979, BSc (Pharmacol.) 1977. (Guy's) Research Regist. (Cardiol.) Mayday Hosp. Croydon.

BAHRIN, Natalia Rosalind 61D New City Road, Glasgow G4 9DF — MB ChB 1997 Glas.

BAHT, Hardeep Singh 79 City Way, Rochester ME1 2BA — MB BS 1993 Lond.

BAICHOO, Shivcoomar Anaesthetic Department, Stafford District General Hospital, Weston Road, Stafford ST16 3SA — MB BS 1969 Lucknow.

BAIDWAN, Jatinder Singh, Capt. Chalfont, 258 Norwood Road, Northwood UB2 4JH — MB BS 1994 Lond.; BSc (Hons) Lond. 1993. Specialist Regist., Dept. of Radiol., Oxf. Hosps. Socs: Fell.of The Roy. Soc. of Trop. Med. and Hyg.; MRCRadiol.

BAIDWAN, Manpreet Kaur 258 Norwood Road, Norwood Green, Southall UB2 4JH — MB BS 1996 Lond.; BSc (Hons.) Lond. 1993; DFFP 1999; DRCOG 1999. (The Royal London Hospital Medical College) SHO (GP Vocational Trainee) High Wycombe Bucks.

BAIER, Sigrun Helga Gertrud Orrell Road Practice, 84 Orrell Road, Orrell, Wigan WN5 8HB Tel: 01942 222321 Fax: 01942 620327 — State Exam Med 1989 Tubingen.

BAIG, Akhthar 61 Laurel Drive, Eccleston, St Helens WA10 5JB — MB BS 1949 Madras; DTM & H Liverp. 1956.

BAIG, Akram St Brides Way Surgery, St. Brides Way, Gibbonsdown, Barry CF63 1DU Tel: 01446 744877 Fax: 01446 744900 — LMSSA 1978 Lond.; MB BS 1971; DRCOG 1979.

BAIG, Kamran Azam 1 York Road, New Barnet, Barnet EN5 1LL — MB BS 1997 Lond.

BAIG, Lubna Flat 12, Imperial Court, 36 Sheperds Hill, London N6 5WA — MB ChB 1991 Leeds; DRCOG 1994.

BAIG, M A A Priory Road Surgery, 117 Priory Road, Liverpool L4 2SG Tel: 0151 263 1081 Fax: 0151 260 7470.

BAIG, Mirza Farrukh Akram c/o 8 Eastlands, Stafford ST17 9BB; 9 Essex Chase, Priorslee, Telford TF2 9ST Email: fab7@bigfoot.com — MB BS 1987 Punjab; MRCP (UK) 1994. (King Edward Medical College, Lahore, Pakistan) Specialist Regist. (Respirat. Med.), P.ss Roy. Hosp., Telford. Socs: BMA. Prev: Specialist Regist. N. Staffs. Gen. Hosp. Stoke on Trent; Clin. Research Fell. (Respirat. Med.) The Manor Hosp. Walsall; Regist. P.ss Roy. Hosp. Telford.

BAIG, Mirza Hafeez 30 Tibbermore Road, Glasgow G11 7QG — MB BS 1976 W. Indies.

BAIG, Mirza Ilyas The Medical Centre, 10 Richmond Road, Pevensey Bay, Pevensey BN24 6AQ Tel: 01323 762054 Fax: 01323 461180 — MB BS 1967 Karachi.

BAIG, Mirza Kamran 4 Brookside Close, Holcombe Brook, Ramsbottom, Bury BL0 9TZ Tel: 01204 885744 — MB ChB 1989 Manch.; MRCP (UK) 1993. Brit. Heart Foundat. Research Fell. St. Geo Hosp. Med. Sch. Lond. Prev: Regist. Rotat. Mersey; SHO (Med.) Hope Hosp. Manch.; SHO (Cardiothoracic Med.) Wythenshawe Hosp. Manch.

BAIG, Mirza Kamran Ali-Khan and Partners, 128 High Street, Bentley, Doncaster DN5 0AT Tel: 01302 874551 Fax: 01302 820920 — MB BS 1969 Osmania.

BAIG, Mirza Mohammed Abid 1 Fenbourne Close, Walsall WS4 1XD — MB ChB 1994 Sheff.

BAIG, Mirza Mustafa St Marys Lane Health Centre, 226 St. Marys Lane, Upminster RM14 3DH Tel: 01708 251407 Fax: 01708 221878 — MB BS 1955 Osmania; DA Eng. 1973; DCH Osmania 1962. (Osmania Med. Coll. Hyderabad) Clin. Asst. (Anaesth.) Bolton Roy. Infirm. Prev: Asst. Surg. Andhra Pradesh State Govt. Serv., India; Regist (Anaesth.) Pk. Hosp. Davyhulme & Bolton Roy. Infirm. & Bolton; Dist. Gen. Hosp.

BAIG, Mirza Wazir Doncaster Royal Infirmary, Armthorpe Road, Doncaster DN2 5LT Tel: 01302 366666 Fax: 01302 761208; 105 Bawtry Road, Bessacarr, Doncaster DN4 7AG Tel: 01302 370578 Fax: 01302 531043 — MB BS 1981 Lond.; MD Lond. 1994; MRCP (UK) 1985; FRCP Lond. 1997. (Westminster Medical School) Cons. Phys. & Cardiol. Doncaster Roy. Infirm. Socs: Brit. Cardiac Soc. Prev: Lect. (Cardiovasc. Studies) Univ. Leeds.

BAIG, Mirza Zahoor The Surgery, Stuart St., Pontlottyn, Bargoed CF81 9QE Tel: 01685 841356; 31 Bryn Rhosyn, Tredegar NP22 3BE Tel: 01495 717820 — MB BS 1963 Karachi. (Dow Med. Coll.) Socs: BMA. Prev: Ho. Surg. & Ho. Phys. St. Helen's Hosp. Hastings; Ho. Phys. (Med. & Paediat.) Swansea Gen. Hosp.; Ho. Phys. (Gen. Med.) Llwynpia Hosp.

BAIG, Mohammed Naveed River House Surgery, East Road, London SW19 1YG Tel: 020 8543 4037 Fax: 020 7544 1126 — MB BCh 1986 Wales; MRCP (UK) 1990; MRCGP 1993. Prev: Regist. (Gastroenterol.) Qu. Mary & W.m. Hosp. Lond.; SHO (Med.) Jas. Paget Hosp. Gt. Yarmouth & Roy. Marsden Hosp. Lond.; Ho. Off. (Med.) Withybush Hosp. HaverfordW.

BAIG, Sabiha Sultana St Marys Lane Health Centre, 226 St. Marys Lane, Upminster RM14 3DH Tel: 01708 251407 Fax: 01708 221878.

BAIG, Shakila Ramsbottom Health Centre, Carr Street, Ramsbottom, Bury BL0 9DD — MBBS 1961. (Osmania Medical School, Hyderabad, India) Princip. in Gen. Pract., Rochdale & Bury Health Trust. Socs: SPA.

BAIG, Shela Naz Flat 1, 47 Park Hill, Carshalton SM5 3SD — MB BS 1993 Lond.

BAIGEL, Sydney (retired) 4 Danesway, Bury Old Road, Prestwich, Manchester M25 0FS Tel: 0161 740 2521 Fax: 0161 740 2521 — MB BCh BAO Dub. 1953; BA Dub. 1950; FFPHM RCP (UK) 1989; FFCM 1980, M 1972; DA Eng. 1956. Bd. Mem. Spring Hill Hospice Rochdale; Mem. (Exec) Alcohol & Drug Serv.s (formerly GMLA). Prev: Cons. Pub. Health Med NW RHA.

BAIGENT, Colin Nigel Clinical Trial Service Unit, Harkness Building, Radcliffe Infirmary, Oxford OX2 6HE Tel: 01865 557241 Fax: 01865 558817 Email: colin.baigent@ctsu.ox.ac.uk — BM BCh 1989 Oxf.; MSc Lond. 1995; MA Oxf. 1991, BA 1983. MRC Scientist Clin. Trial Serv. Unit. Oxf. Socs: Brit. Cardiac Soc.; Brit. Atherosclerosis Soc. Prev: Research Off. Clin. Trial Serv. Unit Radcliffe Infirm. Oxf.; SHO (Gen. Med.) Centr. Birm. HA.

BAIGENT, David Frederick 5 Wimborne Road, Stoneygate, Leicester LE2 3RQ Tel: 0116 270 5070 Email: dfbaigent@hotmail.com — MB ChB 1962 Bristol; FFA RCS Eng. 1968; DA Eng. 1965; DObst RCOG 1964. Socs: Assn. Anaesths. Gt. Brit. & Irel.; Leics. Med. Soc. (Ex Pres.); Sheff. & E. Midl. Soc. Anaesth. Prev: Emerit. (Leicester Roy. Infirm.) Cons. Anaesth. Leics. Dist. HA; Regist. (Anaesth.) Cardiff Roy. Infirm.; Regist. (Anaesth.) Luton & Dunstable Hosp.

BAIGENT, John Keith Bridge Medical Centre, Wassand Close, Three Bridges Road, Crawley RH10 1LL Tel: 01293 526025 — MB ChB 1968 Leeds.

BAIGRIE, Carolyn Frances 34 Northfield Road, Oxford OX3 9EW — MB ChB 1983 Cape Town.

BAIJAL, Eric Paul Department of Public Health, Highland Health Board, Inverness IV2 3HG Tel: 01463 704926 Fax: 01463 235189 — MB ChB 1981 Birm.; MSc Ed. 1986; FFPHM RCP (UK) 1996. Dir. of Pub. Health Highland Health Bd. Prev: Dir. Pub. Health Fife Health Bd.; Trainee GP Dudley HA VTS; Ho. Surg. Roy. Hosp. Wolverhampton.

BAIJU, Dean Steven 2 Kings Road, East Ham, London E6 1DY — MB BS 1994 West Indies.

BAIKIE, Mary Lindsay North of Scotland Blood Transfusion Service, Raigmore Hospital, Inverness IV2 3UJ Tel: 01463 704212; Airdrie Farm, Glenferness, Nairn IV12 5XB Tel: 01309 651248 — MB ChB 1966 Ed. Med. Off. Blood Transfus. Serv. Raigmore Hosp. Inverness; Clin. Asst. Diabetic Clinic Gray's Hosp. Elgin.

BAIL, Mr Harish Chandra Kumar Kodial Kingcroft, 15 Grange Court Road, Harpenden AL5 1BY — MB BS 1965 Madras; FRCS Ed. 1973; DLO Eng. 1970. Cons. Surg. (ENT) St. Albans City Hosp. & Hemel Hempstead Gen. Hosp. Socs: Fell. Roy. Soc. Med.; BMA. Prev: Sen. Regist. (ENT) Nottm. Gen. Hosp. & Sheff. Gen. Hosp.; Regist. (Otolaryng.) Law Hosp. Carluke.

BAILDAM, Mr Andrew David University Hospital of South Manchester, West Didsbury, Manchester M20 8LR Tel: 0161 291 3185 Fax: 0161 291 3846 Email: andrew.baildam@smuht.nwest.nhs.uk; Heath Lodge, Elm Grove, Alderley Edge SK9 7PD — MB ChB 1978 Manch.; BSc (Hons. Med. Biochem.) Manch. 1975, MD 1987; FRCS Eng. 1982; T(S) 1992. (University of Manchester) Cons. Surg. & Hon. Sen. Lect. (BrE. & Surgic. Oncol. & Gen. Surg.) Univ. Hosp. S. Manch. Socs: Surgic. Research Soc.; Brit. Assn. Surgic. Oncol.; Brit. Assn. Plastic Surgs.

BAILDAM, Eileen Marion Booth Hall Childrens Hospital, Charlestown, Blackley, Manchester M9 7AA Tel: 0161 220 5597 Fax: 0161 220 5421 — MB ChB 1980 Manch.; MRCP (UK) 1985; MRCGP 1984; DRCOG 1983; DCH RCP Lond. 1983; FRCP 1997; FRCPCH 1997. Cons. Paediat. (Paediat. Rheum. & Ambulatory) Booth Hall Childr. Hosp. Manch.; Hon. Lect. (Child Health) Manch. Socs: Brit. Paediat. Rheumatol. Gp.; Brit. Soc. Rheum.; Brit. Assn. Community Child Health.

BAILEY, Alan Richard The Limes, Charfield, Wotton-under-Edge GL12 8SR Tel: 01453 843084 Fax: 01453 844180 Email: abailey@netcomuk.co.uk — MB BS 1966 Lond.; FRCP Lond. 1991; MRCP (UK) 1971. (St. Bart.) p/t Chief Med. Adviser Prime Health; Med. Adviser Commonw. & Brit. Minerals. Socs: Fell. Roy. Soc. Med.; Soc. Occupat. Med. (Treas.). Prev: Med. Directror BUPA Health Servs.; Regist. (Med.) Roy. N.. Hosp. Holloway; Ho. Phys. St. Bart. Hosp. Lond.

BAILEY, Alison Margaret 17 The Glebe, Thorverton, Exeter EX5 5LS — MB BS 1977 Lond.; DRCOG 1979.

BAILEY, Alistair Dennis White House Surgery, 1 Cheriton High Street, Folkestone CT19 4PU Tel: 01303 275434 Fax: 01303 271921 — MB BS 1983 Lond.; BSc Lond 1980; DRCOG 1987. Prev: Trainee GP Ashford VTS; Ho. Surg. Dorset Co. Hosp. Dorchester; Ho. Phys. Roy. Vict. Hosp. Bournemouth.

BAILEY, Andrew John Marshall (retired) The Surgery, 82 Lillie Road, London SW6 1TN Tel: 020 7386 9299 Fax: 020 7610 0635 — MB BS 1956 Lond.; FRCGP 1986, M 1977; DObst RCOG 1963. p/t Assoc. Dean Postgrad. Gen. Pract. Lond. Univ. Prev: Clin. Tutor W.m. Hosp. Lond.

BAILEY, Andrew Philip Ash Tree Close, Puddletown, Dorchester DT2 8UZ — MB BS 1992 Lond.; MRCGP 1996. (St. Geo. Hosp. Med. Sch. Lond.) GP Regist. Weymouth.

BAILEY, Andrew Richard Department of Anaesthetics, Addenbrooke's Hospital, Cambridge CB2 2QQ — MB BS 1988 Lond.; BSc Lond. 1985; FRCA 1995; DA (UK) 1993. Cons. (Anaesth.), Addenbrookes Hosp., Camb. Socs: Assn. Anaesth.; Obst. Anaesth. Assn.; Soc. Naval Anaesth. Prev: Specialist Regist. (Anaesth.), E. Anglian Rotat.; Regist. (Anaesth.) Qu. Eliz. Hosp. King's Lynn; SHO (Anaesth.) RNH Haslar.

BAILEY, Anthony James The Institute of Psychiatry, De Crespigny Park, London SE5 8AF Tel: 020 7252 5756 Fax: 020 7252 5107 — MB BS 1982 Lond.; BSc Lond. 1980; MRCPsych 1987; DCH RCP Lond. 1984. (The London Hospital) MRC Sen. Clin. Sci. & Hon. Cons. Child Psychiat. The Maudsley Hosp.; Hon. Sen. Lect. (Child & Adolesc. Pschiatry & Neuropathol.) Inst. of Psychiat. Lond. Prev: Hon. Lect. (Child & Adolesc. Psychiat. & Neuropath.) Inst. Psychiat. Lond.

BAILEY, Mr Basil Malcolm Wheatcroft Ashford and St. Peter's Hospital Trust, London Road, Ashford TW15 3AA, 01784 884168 Fax: 01784 884168 Email: bmwb@mcmail.com; 51 Oakfield Road, Ashford CT21 2RB — MRCS Eng. LRCP Lond. 1976; MB BS Lond. 1976, BDS 1971; FRCS Ed. 1985; FDS RCS Eng. 1979, L 1970. (Guy's) Cons. Oral & Maxillofacial Surg. Ashford & St. Peter's Hosp. Trust, Surrey; Kingston Hosp. Trust, Surrey. Socs: BMA; Brit. Assoc. oral & Maxillofacial Surg. Prev: Sen. Regist. (Oral & Maxillofacial) St. Thos. Hosp. Lond.; Regist. (Maxillofacial Surg.) St. Richard's Hosp. Chichester & Univ. Coll. Hosp. Lond.

BAILEY, Mr Bruce Noel (retired) 81A New Road, Weston Turville, Aylesbury HP22 5QT Tel: 01296 29099 — MB BS 1949 Lond.; MB BS (Hons.) Pub. Health Lond. 1949; FRCS Eng. 1956. Prev: Cons. plastic Surg., Stoke Mandeville.

BAILEY, Caroline Elizabeth 50 The Droveway, Hove BN3 6PP — MB BS 1992 Lond.; MRCP (UK) 1995.

BAILEY, Catherine Gilray (retired) c/o M Bailey, 45 Compton Avenue, Lilliput, Poole BH14 8PU — BSc Glas. 1940, MB ChB 1944; DPH Birm. 1948.

BAILEY, Catherine Sheila 20 Silverdale Avenue, Oxshott, Leatherhead KT22 0LB — MB ChB 1998 Leic.; MB ChB Leic 1998.

BAILEY, Cheryl 31 Ferndown Close, Bloxwich, Walsall WS3 3XH Tel: 01922 710695 Email: cheryl@cbailey.demon.co.uk — MB ChB 1984 Manch.; MSc Warwick 1996; DMJ Soc Apoth 1999. Assoc. Specialist in Community Child Health, Wolverhampton Health Care; Police Surg. Staffs. Socs: Assn. Police Surg.; Brit. Paediat. Assn.; Roy. Coll. Paediat. and Child health. Prev: SCMO (Child Health) 1st Community Health Staffs.; Regist. (Pub. Health Med.) Walsall HA.

BAILEY, Mr Christian Martin 55 Harley Street, London W1G 8QR Tel: 020 7580 2426 Fax: 020 7436 1645 Email: cbq@uk-consultants.co.uk; 7 Heathgate, Hampstead Garden Suburb, London NW11 7AR Tel: 020 8455 8628 Fax: 020 8381 4292 Email: cmbailey@compuserve.com — MB BS 1973 Lond.; BSc Lond. 1970; FRCS Eng. (Orl.) 1978; MRCS Eng. LRCP Lond. 1973. (Royal Free Hospital) Cons. ENT Surg. Gt. Ormond St. Hosp. for Childr. Lond.; Hon. Cons. ENT Surg. St Luke's Hosp. for the Clergy Lond.; Hon. Sen. Lect. Inst. Child Health & Inst. Laryngol. & Otol. Lond.; Hon. Cons. ENT Surg. Roy. Nat. Throat, Nose & Ear Hosp. Lond.; Hon. Cons. ENT Surg. King Edwd. VII Hosp. For Off. Lond. Socs: Fell. Roy. Soc. Med.; Brit. Assn. Otorhinol. Head & Neck Surg.; Counc. Mem. Brit. Assn. Paediat. Otorhinolaryng. Prev: Cons. ENT Surg. Roy. Nat. Throat, Nose & Ear Hosp. Lond.; TWJ Foundat. Clin. & Research Fell. Univ. Michigan, USA; Sen. Regist. Roy. Nat. Throat, Nose & Ear Hosp. Lond. & Sussex +Throat & Ear Hosp. Brighton.

BAILEY, Christine Cottage in the Woods, Littleheath Lane, Cobham KT11 2QF — MB BS 1969 Lond.; FFA RCS Eng. 1974.

BAILEY, Mr Christopher Steven 99 Harley Street, London W1G 6AQ Tel: 07973 691727 Fax: 020 7431 8131 Email: csb@compuserve.com — MB BS 1976 Lond.; BSc (Physiol.) Lond. 1973; FRCS Eng. 1987; MRCS Eng. LRCP Lond. 1976; FRCOphth 1989; T(Ophth) 1992; ECFMG Cert. 1976; DO Lond. 1981. (Roy. Free) Prev: Sen. Regist. Moorfields Eye Hosp. Lond.; Assoc. Specialist (Ophth.) Moorfields Eye Hosp. Lond.

BAILEY, Claire Louise Maybury House, Orchard Lane, Helford Village, Helston TR12 6JX Tel: 01326 231251 — MB BS 1995 Lond. SHO (Anaesth.) Treliske Hosp. Truro; Mem. Advanced Trauma & Life Support.

BAILEY, Miss Clare Catherine Bristol Eye Hospital, Lower Maudlin Street, Bristol BS1 2LX Tel: 0117 928 4653 Fax: 0117 928 4686 Email: clare.bailey@ubht.swest.nhs.uk — BM BCh 1988 Oxf.; FRCOphth 1993; MRCP 1991; MD 1999. (Cambridge/Oxford) Cons. Ophth. Bristol Eye Hosp., Bristol. Prev: Med. Retina Fell., Moorfields Eye Hosp., Lond.; Specialist Regist. in Ophth., St Thomas' Hosp., Lond.

BAILEY, Clare Frances 38 Finlay Street, London SW6 6HD — MB BS 1986; BSc (Hons.) 1983; MRCGP 1991; DCH RCP Lond. 1990. GP Doctors Retainer Scheme Lond.

BAILEY, Clare Susannah 66 Camberwell New Road, London SE5 0RS — MB BS 1997 Lond.

BAILEY, Clive Vincent 59 Addiscombe Road, East Croydon CR0 6SD Tel: 020 8688 5929 Fax: 020 8686 5818 Email: c.bailey@doctors.org.uk; Email: c.bailey@doctors.org.uk — MB ChB 1977 Bristol; BSc (Hons.) Bristol 1974; MRCGP 1983; D.Occ.Med. RCP Lond. 1995; DFFP 1994; Dip. Addic. Behaviour Lond. 1992; DRCOG 1980. (Bristol) GP Trainer & Tutor Undergrad. Teach. & Clin. Asst. (Cardiol.) Croydon Gen. Hosp.; Occupat. Phys. Local NHS Trusts. Prev: SHO (Obst.) S.mead Hosp. Bristol; SHO (Geriat. Med.) Plymouth Gen. Hosp.; SHO (A & E) Bristol Roy. Infirm.

BAILEY, Craig Richard 5 Burstock Road, London SW15 2PW Tel: 020 8789 5444 Fax: 020 8785 3444 — MB BS 1985 Lond.; FRCA 1991; DA (UK) 1988. (Westm. Lond.) Cons. Anaesth. Guy's & St. Thos. NHS Trust; Hon. Sen. Lect. GKT Sch. of Med. Socs: Coun. Membr, Sect. of Anasethetics, Roy. Soc. of Med.

BAILEY, David (retired) 44 St Michaels Terrace, Stoke, Plymouth PL1 4QG — MB BS 1946 Lond. Prev: SCMO Plymouth DHA.

BAILEY, David Alan 1a Wells Road, Chilcompton, Bath BA3 4EX — MB BCh 1993 Wales. (Univ. Wales Coll. Med.)

BAILEY, Mr David Alan Tamarin, 31A Uphill Road, Mill Hill, London NW7 4RA Tel: 020 8959 2373 — MB BChir 1945 Camb.; MA Camb. 1947, MChir 1956; FRCS Eng. 1950; MRCS Eng. LRCP Lond. 1945. (Camb. & Univ. Coll. Hosp.) Socs: Fell. Roy. Soc. Med.; BMA. Prev: Cons. Surg. Univ. Coll. Hosp. Lond., Roy. N.. Hosp. Lond. & Barnet Gen. Hosp.; Emerit. Cons. Surg. Bloomsbury Health Dist. Lond.

BAILEY, David James Elizabeth Place Surgery, 8 Elizabeth Place, St Helier, Jersey JE2 3PN Tel: 01534 25824; La Ferme, Le Clos de la Porte, Sion, St John, Jersey JE3 4FL Tel: 01534 862678 — MB BCh 1989 Wales; MRCGP 1993; DCH RCP Lond. 1993. Socs: BMA. Prev: GP Clin. Asst. (A & E) St Helier; Trainee GP St Helier Jersey.

BAILEY, David John Godfrey Hanham Surgery, 33 Whittucks Road, Hanham, Bristol BS15 3HY Tel: 0117 967 5201 Fax: 0117 947 7749; Westover House, Bath Road, Bitton, Bristol BS30 6HT Tel: 0117 932 8949 — MB BS 1980 Lond.; PhD (Physiol.) Lond. 1977; MRCGP 1984; DCH RCP Lond. 1983; DRCOG 1980. (King's Coll. Lond. & Char. Cross) Clin. Tutor (Gen. Pract.) Frenchay Hosp. Socs: Fac. Mem. RCGP (Severn); GP Educat. SubComm. Prev: Chair Avon MAAG.

BAILEY, David John Osbert 209 Oakington Manor Drive, Wembley HA9 6NA — MB BS 1991 Lond.

BAILEY, David John Whitburn The Royal Hospital Haslar, Gosport PO12 2AA Tel: 01705 762508 Fax: 01705 762400 Email: 101660.1310@compuserve.com — MB BS 1986 Lond.; FRCR 1992. Cons. Radiol. Roy. Hosp. Haslar. Prev: Hon. Sen. Regist. (Radiol.) Oxf. Radcliffe Hosps.

BAILEY, David Martin 20 Eastwick Row, Hemel Hempstead HP2 4JF — MB BS 1989 Lond.

BAILEY, David Michael Pain Management Clinic, The Ipswich Hospital, Heath Road, Ipswich IP4 5PD Tel: 01473 702162 Fax: 01473 703400 Email: m.bailey@lpsh-tr.anglox.nhs.uk; 49 Graham Road, Ipswich IP1 3QF — MB BS 1976 Lond.; FRCA 1982. (UCHM8, Lond.) Cons. Anaesth. Chronic Pain Managem. Ipswich Hosp. NHS Trust. Socs: Anaesth. Assn.; Pain Soc. Prev: Cons. Anaesth. Barnet Gen. Hosp.

BAILEY, David Rex (retired) Cedar House, Brumstead Road, Stalham, Norwich NR12 9DQ Tel: 01692 580955 — MB BChir 1961 Camb.; MA Camb. 1961; DTM & H Liverp. 1966; DObst RCOG 1962. Prev: GP Stalham.

BAILEY, David Stephen The Conifers, 9 Pentwyn Isaf, Energlyn, Caerphilly CF83 2NR — MB BCh 1981 Wales; DRCOG 1985. GP Trethomas.

BAILEY, David William Thursby Surgery, 2 Browhead Road, Burnley BB10 3BF Tel: 01282 422447 Fax: 01282 832575; 30 George Lane, Read, Burnley BB12 7RH — MB ChB 1984 Manch.; MRCGP 1991; DRCOG 1994.

BAILEY, Derek Sidney George Montgomery (retired) Hollybush, Densome Wood, Woodgreen, Fordingbridge SP6 2BE — MB BS 1948 Lond.; MRCPsych. 1971; DPM Roy. Med. Psych. Assn. 1952. Prev: Cons. Psychait. Poole Gen Hosp.

BAILEY, Edward Vincent 12 Hollins Close, Astley, Tyldesley, Manchester M29 7QD — MB ChB 1977 Aberd.

BAILEY, Elizabeth Anne 72 Clarence Avenue, London SW4 8JP; 54 Killyon Road, London SW8 2XT — MB BS 1980 Lond.; MRCGP 1985; DCH RCP Lond. 1984; DRCOG 1984. Princip. GP Roy. Preston Hosp.

BAILEY, Elizabeth Anne Dialysis Unit, Royal Preston Hospital, Sharoe Green Lane, Fulwood, Preston PR2 9HT Tel: 01772 710520; 55 Melrose Avenue, Fulwood, Preston PR2 8DE — BM BS 1980 Nottm.; BMedSci (Hons.) Nottm. 1978, BM BS 1980; DRCOG 1982. Staff Grade (Nephrol.) Roy. Preston Hosp. Prev: GP Walkden; SHO (Paediat. & O & G) Qu. Pk. Hosp.Blackburn.

BAILEY, Eric Haynes (retired) Wyndelis, 14 Egdon Glen, Crossways, Dorchester DT2 8BQ Tel: 01305 852634 — MRCS Eng. LRCP Lond. 1939; FRCPath 1963. Prev: Cons. Path. S.. Gp. Laborat. Hither Green Hosp.

BAILEY, Erica Warde Ella Ilkeston Health Centre, South St, Ilkeston DE7 5PZ Tel: 0115 932 2968 — MB ChB 1991 Sheff.; MRCGP 1997; DRCOG 1995. (Sheff.)

BAILEY, Gillian Mary The Surgery, 1 Goodrest Croft, Yardley Wood, Birmingham B14 4JL Tel: 0121 474 2059 — BM BCh 1970 Oxf.

BAILEY, Gillian Ruth 20 Park Lane, Allestree, Derby DE22 2DT — BM BS 1975 Nottm.

BAILEY, Grenfell Moyle (retired) Thatched Cottage, Sonning Lane, Sonning-on-Thames, Reading RG4 6ST Tel: 0118 969 2372 Fax: 0118 969 2372 — MRCS Eng. LRCP Lond. 1945; MD Lond. 1949, MB BS 1945; MRCP Lond. 1949. Prev: Sen. Med. Off. Pruden. Assur. Co.

BAILEY, Helen Ruth Plas Tyno, Llandegla, Wrexham LL11 3AW — MB ChB 1982 Sheff.; DFFP 1998; DLO RCS Eng. 1984. (Sheffield) Clin. Asst. GUM Ysbyty Glan Clwyd. Prev: GP Sheff.; GP Liverp.; Ho. Off. Univ. Surg. & Med. Units Roy. Hallamsh. Hosp. Sheff.

BAILEY, Helena Bozena Marie (retired) Staunton Lodge, Whitchurch, Bristol BS14 0QG — MB ChB 1952 Bristol.

BAILEY, Hermione Jane 30 Alderney Street, London SW1V 4EU — MB BS 1993 Lond. (King's College School of Medicine & Dentistry London) Specialist Regist. Kent & Canterbury Hosp. Prev: SHO (O & G) King's Coll. Hosp. Lond.; SHO (O & G) Roy. Sussex Co. Hosp. Brighton; SHO (A & E) King's Coll. Hosp. Lond.

BAILEY, Horace 71 Grove Road, Millhouses, Sheffield S7 2GY — MB ChB 1950 Sheff.; MFCM 1972; DPH Manch. 1958. (Sheff.) Specialist (Community Med.) Sheff. AHA (T); Fell. Soc. Community Med. Socs: BMA. Prev: MOH & Chief Welf. Off. Boro. Chesterfield; Dep. MOH & Dep. Princip. Sch. Med. Off. City Stoke-on-Trent; Ho. Phys. & Cas. Off. Sheff. Roy. Hosp.

BAILEY, Hugh Brewis (retired) Hillcrest, 214 Newmarket Road, Eaton, Norwich NR4 7LA Tel: 01603 54843 — MRCS Eng. LRCP Lond. 1958. Prev: Ho. Surg. Ho. Phys. & SHO in Midw. & Gyn. Norf. & Norwich Hosp.

BAILEY, Mr Ian Campbell 13 Ulsterville Avenue, Belfast BT9 7AS Tel: 028 9066 7741; The Black Stone House, Magheragall, Lisburn BT28 2TB Tel: 028 9262 1333 — MB BCh BAO 1953 Dub.; BA Dub. 1951, MB BCh BAO 1953; FRCS Eng. 1963; FRCSI 1959. (Univ. Dub.) Cons. Neurol. Surg. Roy. Vict. Hosp. Belf. Socs: Soc. Brit. Neurol. Surgs.; Fell. Assn. Surgs. E. Afr.; Irish Neurol. Assn. Prev: Sen. Regist. Roy. Vict. Hosp. Belf. & Guy's-Maudsley Neurosurg. Dept. Lond.; Cons. Neurosurg. Mulago Hosp. Kampala & Makere Univ., Uganda.

BAILEY, Ian Gordon (retired) 22 Woodthorne Road, Tettenhall, Wolverhampton WV6 8TT Tel: 01902 275 1009 — MB ChB Manch. 1961. Prev: Ho. Phys. & Ho. Surg. Withington Hosp. Manch.

BAILEY, Ian Richard Department Chemical Pathology, Farnborough Hospital, Farnborough Common, Orpington BR6 8ND Tel: 01689 814042 Fax: 01689 814041 Email: ibailey@bromley.tcom.co.uk — MB ChB 1983 Bristol; BSc Bristol 1980; MRCPath 1990; T(Path) 1991. Cons. Chem. Path. Bromley Hosps. NHS Trust. Socs: Assn. Clin. Biochem.; Brit. Med. Informat. Soc. Prev: Sen. Regist. (Chem. Path.) Yorks. RHA; Regist. (Chem. Path.) John Radcliffe Hosp. Oxf.; Ho. Phys. Yeovil Dist. Hosp.

BAILEY, Ian Stuart Orchard Surgery, Knypersley Road, Norton-in-the-Moors, Stoke-on-Trent ST6 8HY Fax: 01782 541068; Byways, Denford Road, Longsdon, Stoke-on-Trent ST9 9QG — MB ChB 1979 Birm.; MRCGP 1983; DRCOG 1983. Police Surg. Stoke-on-Trent. Socs: Assn. of Police Surg.s. Prev: SHO (O & G) Dudley Rd. Hosp. Birm.; SHO (Paediat.) Wordsley Hosp. Stourbridge; Ho. Phys. Qu. Eliz. Hosp. Birm.

BAILEY, Mr Ian Stuart Department of Surgery, Southampton General Hospital, E Level, Tremona Road, Southampton SO16 6YD Tel: 02380 798535 Fax: 02380 798509 Email: ian.bailey@suht.swest.nhs.uk — MB ChB 1983 Leic.; MS Soton. 1993; FRCS Eng. 1988; FRCS Ed. 1988; CCST Gen Surg 1997. Cons. Upper GI & Gen. Surg., Soton. Gen. Hosp.; Hon. Cons., Roy. Hants. Co. Hosp., Winchester; Hon. Cons., N. Hants. Hosp., Basingstoke. Socs: Fell. ASGBI; Fell AUGIS; Fell AESGI. Prev: Sen. Regist. Rotat., Wessex; Regist., Rotat., Wessex; Fell.sh. Regist., S. Wales.

BAILEY, Irene Sargent (retired) Windy How, Colthouse, Hawkshead, Ambleside LA22 0JU Tel: 015394 36385 — MRCS Eng. LRCP Lond. 1943; MA Camb.; DPH Manch. 1958. Prev: Dep. Co. Med. Off. W.mld.

BAILEY, James Stewart Block Lane Surgery, 158 Block Lane, Chadderton, Oldham OL9 7SG Tel: 0161 620 2321 Fax: 0161 628 5604; 17 Turf Park Road, Royton, Oldham OL2 6EP Tel: 0161 620 2321 — MRCS Eng. LRCP Lond. 1966; FRCGP 1990, M 1975. (Leeds) Assoc. Dir. (Gen. Pract.) Univ. Manch. Prev: Trainee GP Course Organiser; Regist. (Gen. Med.) Oldham & Dist. Gen. Hosp.

BAILEY, Jana Susanne Helena Medical Services, Government Buildings, Flowers Hill, Brislington BS4 5LA — MB ChB 1973 Bristol; MRCGP 1978; DObst RCOG 1975. Socs: Disabil. Med.

BAILEY, Jane Anne Meopham Medical Centre, Wrotham Road, Meopham, Gravesend DA13 0AH Tel: 01474 814811/814068 Fax: 01474 814699 — MB BS 1982 Lond.; DCH RCP Lond. 1989.

BAILEY, Jane Nicola Rotha Dermatology Department, Clinic 6, Royal Free Hospital, Pond St., London NW3 2QG Tel: 020 7794 0500 Ext: 3508 Fax: 020 7830 2247; 7 Heathgate, London NW11 7AR Tel: 020 8455 8628 Fax: 020 8381 4292 — MB BS 1972 Lond.; DObst RCOG 1974. (Roy. Free) Clin. Asst. (Dermat.) Roy. Free Hosp. Lond. Socs: BMA. Prev: Trainee GP Camden & Islington HA & Brighton Health Dist.; SHO (Paediat.) & Ho. Surg. (Obst.) Roy. Free Hosp. Lond.

BAILEY, Janet Sunset Cottage, Ramsey IM7 4HE — MB ChB 1996 Leeds.

BAILEY, Janet Margaret 172 Sandy Lane, Cheam, Sutton SM2 7EU Tel: 020 8642 8039 — MB BS 1962 Lond.; MRCS Eng. LRCP Lond. 1961; DCH Eng. 1967; DObst RCOG 1963. (Middlx.) Med. Off. Dept. Soc. Security.

BAILEY, Jean Eynsham Medical Centre, Conduit Lane, Eynsham, Oxford; 5 Lakeside, Oxford OX2 8JF — MB BS 1981 Lond.; MA Oxf. 1982; MRCGP 1985. (Middlx.) Trainer GP. Socs: Oxf. Med. Soc.

BAILEY, Jennifer Shernhall Street Surgery, 103 Shernhall Street, Walthamstow, London E17 9HS Tel: 020 8520 5138 — MB BS 1976 Lond.

BAILEY, Jennifer Jane Clifton Lodge, Sheinton Rd, Cressage, Shrewsbury SY5 6DH Tel: 01952 510318 Fax: 01952 510760 — MB BCh 1988 Wales; MRCGP 1995. Gen. Practitioner; Clin. Asst. in ENT, Pricess Roy. Hosp. Telford.

BAILEY, Joanna Elizabeth Mill Stream Medical Centre, North Street, Storrington, Pulborough RH20 4DH Tel: 01903 743083 — MB BS 1978 Lond.; MRCS Eng. LRCP Lond. 1978.

BAILEY, Joanne Lesley Sunderland Royal Hospitsl, Kayll Rd, Sunderland SR4 7TP; 24C Eslington Terrace, Jesmond, Newcastle upon Tyne NE2 4RL Tel: 0191 281 8405 — MB ChB 1993 Glas.; FRCS Ed. 1997; MRCOG 1999. Specialist Regist. O & G Sunderland Roual Hosp.

BAILEY, John Anthony Whiteladies Health Centre, Whatley Road, Clifton, Bristol BS8 2PU Tel: 0117 973 1201 Fax: 0117 946 7031 — MB BChir 1973 Camb.; MA, MB Camb. 1973, BChir 1972; MRCGP 1983; LMCC 1979; FLEX Lic. (USA) 1978; VQE Lic. 1981; DObst RCOG 1976. (Camb. & Middlx.) Rolleston Schol. St. Johns Coll. Camb.; Med. Off. Courage Ltd.; Clin. Teach. (Gen. Pract.) Bristol Univ. Med. Sch.; Med. Off. John Lewis Partnership. Socs: BMA; Soc. Occupat. Med. Prev: Ho. Surg. Middlx. Hosp. Lond.; SHO (Med.) St. Mary's Hosp. Lond.; Med. Dir. Union Hosp. Cabri, Saskatchewan, Canada.

BAILEY, John Christopher (retired) Hunter's Lodge, 494 Bath Road, Saltford, Bristol BS31 3HG — MB ChB 1956 Bristol; DObst RCOG 1962.

BAILEY, John Ridley St Andrews House, Thorpe St Andrew, Norwich NR10 5QQ Fax: 01603 307111 Email: john.bailey@norfolk.nhs.uk — MB BS 1971 Lond.; FFPHM 2002; MFPHM 1987. (Royal London Hospital Medical School) Cons. in Communicable Dis. control, Norf. HA. Prev: Cons. Pub. Health Med. Gt. Yarmouth & Waveney HA.; Gen. Manager, Health Promotion Serv.s.

BAILEY, Mr John Stuart (retired) 43 Chaveney Road, Quorn, Loughborough LE12 8AB Tel: 01509 413674 — MB BChir 1959 Camb.; MB Camb. 1959, BChir 1958; FRCS Eng. 1964; MRCS Eng. LRCP Lond. 1958; DTM & H Eng. 1960. Cons. Cardiothoracic Surg. Groby Rd. Hosp. Leicester. Prev: Sen. Regist. (Thoracic Surg.) W.m. Hosp. Lond.

BAILEY, Joseph Henry Lewis Summerlands Surgery, Starts Hill Road, Farnborough, Orpington BR6 7AR — MB BS 1985 Lond.; MRCGP 1989; DRCOG 1987.

BAILEY, Julia Elizabeth Barrow Hospital, Barrow Gurney, Bristol BS48 3SG — MB BS 1986 Lond.; MRCPsych. 1991.

BAILEY, Julia Vivian 1 Durwent Close, Mount Batten, Turnchapel, Plymouth PL9 9TP Tel: 01752 480688; Hoxton Health Collective, 12 Rushton St., London N1 5DR Tel: 020 7729 4704 Email: hhc@dircon.co.uk — MB BS 1989 Lond.; BSc Lond. 1988; MRCGP 1995; DCH RCP Lond. 1993. (St Marys Hospital) GP Hoxton Health Collective. Prev: Trainee GP NE Thames Region VTS.

BAILEY, Kathryn Mary Thicknall Farm House, Thicknall Lane, Clent, Stourbridge DY9 0HP Tel: 01562 883108 Fax: 01562 883108 Email: roger.bailey@which.net.uk — MB BS 1989 Lond.; DCH; MRCP (UK)1997. (St Georges) Specialist Regist. (Paediat.) Birm. Childr.s Hosp., Birm. Socs: MRCPCH; Roy. Coll. Phys. Prev: SHO (Paediat.) Kingston Dist. Gen.; SHO (Paediat.) N.wick Pk. NHS Trust; SHO (Paediat. & Infec. Dis.) St Mary's Paddington.

BAILEY, Katie Louise 32 Prince's Road, Burnham-on-Crouch CM0 8BX — MB BS 1994 Lond.

BAILEY, Keith 24 Upper Stonyfield, Harlow CM19 4BD — MB ChB 1990 Leic.

BAILEY, Louise 24 Inverleith Terrace, Edinburgh EH3 5NU — MB ChB 1989 Ed.

BAILEY, Martin Alexander Mcleod (retired) Stocks Farm, Harescombe, Gloucester GL4 0XD Tel: 01452 813393 Fax: 01452 813393 — MB BS Lond. 1959; MRCS Eng. LRCP Lond. 1959; MRCGP 1976; DObst RCOG 1962. JP.; Sec. Glos. LMC.

BAILEY, Mary Clare Homefirst Community&Social Services Trust, Whiteabby Hospital, Doagh Rd, Newtownabbey Tel: 01232 865181 Fax: 01232 364015 — MB BCh BAO 1980 Belf.; DCCH RCP Ed. 1986; DCH RCPSI 1983. SCMO Home1st Community Trust. Prev: Clin. Med. Off. N.. & W. Belf.; Clin. Med. Off. Lewisham & N. S.wark HA; Clin. Med. Off. NHSSB.

BAILEY, Michael Brian (retired) 108A Moorland Road, Poulton-le-Fylde FY6 7EU Tel: 01253 885411 — MB ChB Manch. 1956; MRCGP 1977; DObst RCOG 1965. Prev: SCMO (Community Med.) Blackpool.

BAILEY, Michael Charles The Writtle Surgery, 16A Lordship Road, Writtle, Chelmsford CM1 3EH Tel: 01245 421205 Fax: 01245 422094; Kitts Croft, 16 Lordship Road, Writtle, Chelmsford CM1 3EH — MB BS 1976 Lond.; DRCOG 1980. (Univ. Coll. Hosp.) Clin. Asst. (Dermat.) St. Andrews Centre, Broomfield Hosp. Chelmsford; Pre-Hosp. Trauma Life Support Course RCS Eng. 1999. Socs: Mid Essex Doctors Immediate Care Scheme. Prev: Med. Off. Chelmsford Sports Injuries Centre.

BAILEY, Professor Michael Edward The Royal Surrey County Hospital, Guildford GU2 7XX Tel: 01483 406688 Fax: 01483 304698; Court Farm, Church Lane, Hambledon, Godalming GU8 4DS Tel: 01428 685575 Email: mebailey@uk-consultants.co.uk — MB BS 1966 Lond.; FRCS Ed. 1994; FRCS Eng. 1971; MRCS Eng. LRCP Lond. 1966. (King's Coll. Hosp.) Dir. Minimal Access Ther. Train. Unit Roy. Surrey Co. Hosp.; Prof. of Surg., Univ. of Surrey; Cons. Surg. - Roy. Surrey Co. Hosp., Guildford; Mem. Edit. Bd. Jl. Surgic. Laparoscopy & Endoscopy; Examr. Intercollegiate Bd. Gen. Surg. Socs: Fell. Roy. Soc. Med. (Ex-Pres. Surg. Sect.); Vice Pres., Assn. of Endoscopic Surg.s of Gt. Brit & Ire. Prev: Sen. Examr. & Sec. Ct. of Examrs. RCS Eng.; Examr. Primary FRCS (Physiol.) RCS Eng.; Sen. Regist. (Surg.) King's Coll. Hosp. Lond.

BAILEY, Mr Michael John The Ashtead Hospital, Ashtead KT21 2SB Tel: 01372 277494; Cottage in the Woods, Littleheath Lane, Cobham KT11 2QF Tel: 01372 843878 Fax: 01372 844640 Email: mikebailey@doctors.org.uk — MRCS Eng. LRCP Lond. 1971; MS Lond. 1983, MB BS 1971; FRCS Eng. 1976. Cons. Urol. St Geo.s Hosp. Lond. & Epsom Gen. Hosp. Epsom; Program Dir. S. W. Thames Urological Train.; Surgic. Director, St. Geo.'s Hosp.,; Hon. Sen. Lect. Univ. Coll. Hosp., Lond. Socs: Brit. Assn. of Urol. Surgs. (Comm. Mem. Sect. of Oncol.); Roy. Soc. Med. (Counc. Mem. Sect. of Urol.); Corr. Mem. Amer. Urol. Assn. Prev: Sen. Surgic. Regist. St. Geo. Hosp. Lond.; Sen. Regist. (Urol.) Inst. Urol. & St. Peter's Gp.; Research Fell. Inst. Cancer Research.

BAILEY, Michelle 111 Chapelview, Bower Hinton, Martock TA12 6LA — MB ChB 1997 Birm. Surg. Ho. Off. Univ. Hosp. Birm. Prev: SHO (Med.) S. Warks. Hosp.

BAILEY, Neil Anthony 3 Hardings Meadow, Kidsgrove, Stoke-on-Trent ST7 1DY — MB ChB 1986 Ed.

BAILEY, Neville 22 Ripon Close, Whitfield, Manchester M45 8PF — MB BS 1988 Queensland; BSc (Hons.) Lond. 1979.

BAILEY, Neville Martin (retired) The Grey Tower, Silverdale Glen, Ballasalla IM9 3DT — MB ChB Manch. 1954; MSc Lond. 1967, BSc (Hons.) 1958; MD Manch. 1967; MRCS Eng. LRCP Lond. 1955; MFPHM 1989; MFCM 1974; DPH Lond. 1964; MRCGP 1963; DObst RCOG 1956. Prev: Community Phys. I. of Man.

BAILEY, Nicola Jane St Neot's Surgery, 47 Wolseley Road, Milehouse, Plymouth PL2 3BJ Tel: 01752 561305; 88 Durnford Street, Plymouth PL1 3QW Tel: 01752 228114 — BM 1983 Soton.; MRCGP 1988; DRCOG 1986. (Southampton University Medical School) p/t GP Plymouth Retainer Scheme. Prev: GP Norwich; SHO (ENT) Barnet Gen. Hosp.; GP Traniee Potters Bar Herts.

BAILEY, Nicola Margaret — MB BS 1991 Lond.; BA Oxf. 1988, MA 1997; MRCPsych 1996. Cons. in Psychiat. of Learning Disabil. (from Jan 2002). Prev: Regist. & SHO (Psychiat.) Oxf. Train. Scheme; Specialist Regist. (Learning Disabil. & Psychiat.) Oxf. Higher Train. Scheme.

BAILEY, Nigel Peter Torbay Hospital, Department of Oncology, Lawes Bridge, Torquay TQ2 7AA Tel: 01803 655052 Email: nigel.bailey@sdevonhc-tr.swest.nhs.uk; 16 Townsend, Stratton, Bude EX23 9DL — BM 1982 Soton.; DM Soton. 1994; MRCP (UK) 1989; FRCP 1999 Edin. (Soton.) Cons. Med. Oncol. Torbay & Plymouth Hosps. Prev: Cons. Med. Oncol. NCCT Newc. Gen. & Qu. Eliz. Hosp. Gateshead; Lect. & Hon. Sen. Regist. (Med. Oncol.) Univ. Newc.; CRC Research Fell. (Oncol.) Clin. Trials Unit Qu. Eliz. Med. Centre Birm.

BAILEY, Patrick David 51 Gwendolen Road, Leicester LE5 5FL — MB BCh BAO 1993 NUI. SHO (Surg. & A & E) Irel.

BAILEY, Paul Edward Michael Roselands Resource Centre, 163B Kingston Road, New Malden KT3 3NN Tel: 020 8336 2848 Fax: 020 8336 2839 — MB BS 1982 Lond.; MRCPsych 1989. Cons. Psychiat. Kingston & Dist. Community NHS Trust. Prev: Sen. Regist. Rotat. (Psychiat.) St. Geo. Hosp. Lond.; Hon. Sen. Regist. Bethlem Roy. & Maudsley Hosps Lond.; Clin. Research Fell. Inst. Psychiat. Lond.

BAILEY, Paul Julian 69 High Elm Road, Hale Barns, Altrincham WA15 0RN — MB ChB 1990 Manch.

BAILEY, Paul Martin Royal National Throat, Nose & Ear Hospital, Grays Inn Road, London WC1 Tel: 020 7837 8855 — MB BS 1976 Lond.; FFA RCS Eng. 1980. Cons. Anaesth. Roy. Nat. Throat, Nose & Ear Hosp. Trust. Prev: Sen. Regist. (Anaesth.) Univ. Coll. Hosp. & Hosp. Sick Childr. Gt. Ormond St. Lond.

BAILEY, Pauline Audrey Margaret (retired) 40 Moffat Road, Dumfries DG1 1NY Tel: 01387 254408 — MB BCh BAO 1956 Dub.; BA Dub. 1954; MRCPath 1964; DPath Eng. 1962. Prev: Cons. Haemat. Dumfries & Galloway HB.

BAILEY, Peter The Medical Centre, Hall Close, Marske-by-the-Sea, Redcar TS11 6BW Tel: 01642 482725 Fax: 01642 483334; Dundonald, 4 Woodbrook Close, New Marske, Redcar TS11 8HP Tel: 01642 488414 — MB ChB 1971 Ed.; MRCGP 1979; DFFP 1993; Cert. JCC Lond. 1978; DObst RCOG 1974. (Ed.) Socs: BMA.

BAILEY, Peter Anthony 96 Chesterton Road, Cambridge CB4 1ER Tel: 01223 365555 Fax: 01223 356848; 31 De Freville Avenue, Cambridge CB4 1HW Tel: 01223 327311 Fax: 01223 503130 Email: pabailey@compuserve.com — MB BS 1978 Lond.; BSc (1st cl. Hons.) (Pharmacol.) Lond. 1975; MRCGP 1983; DCH RCP Lond. 1983; DRCOG 1983. (St. Bart.) Clin. Asst. (Geriat.) Chesterton Hosp. Camb.; Med. Off. Childr. Hospice E.. Region Cambs. Prev: Trainee GP Camb. VTS.

BAILEY, Peter Bryan (retired) Staunton Lodge, Whitchurch, Bristol BS32 4PR — MB ChB 1954 Bristol; MRCGP 1958; DObst RCOG 1956.

BAILEY, Peter Stefan Radiology Department, St John's Hospital at Howden, Livingston EH54 6PP Tel: 01506 419666; 5 Ramsay Dr, Dunblane FK15 0NG — MB ChB 1977 Ed. Cons. Radiol. St. John's Hosp. Howden Livingston.

BAILEY, Philip James 224 Ruskin Park House, Champion Hill, London SE5 8TG — MB BS 1994 Lond.; BSc Lond. 1991, MB BS 1994.

BAILEY, Philip Wellesley (retired) 38 Riverhead, Sprotborough, Doncaster DN5 7QR Tel: 01302 851680 Email: philbailey@doctors.org.uk — MB Camb. 1965, BChir 1964; FFA RCS Eng. 1976; DA Eng. 1968; DObst RCOG 1967. Prev: Cons. (Anaesth.) Doncaster HA.

BAILEY, Psyche 43 Honeysuckle Lane, Creekmore, Poole BH17 7YY — MB ChB 1998 Birm.; ChB Birm. 1998.

BAILEY, Rachael Claire 41 Kingscroft Road, Hucclecote, Gloucester GL3 3RG Tel: 01452 616322 — MB ChB 1997 Birm. SHO (Psychiat.), Basteyfields Hosp., Dudley. Prev: SHO (A&E), Russells Hall Hosp., Dudley; HO. (Haemat.), Qu. Eliz. Hosp. Birm.; Ho. Off. (Med.), Selly Oak Hosp.

BAILEY, Rachel Clare Langford Surgery, Peregrine Way, Bicester OX26 6; 5 Lakeside, Oxford OX2 8JF — MB BS 1986 Lond.; BSc Lond. 1982, MB BS 1986; Cert. Prescribed Equiv. Exp. JCPTGP 1990; DRCOG 1989; Cert. Family Plann. JCC 1988. Prev: Trainee GP Luton & Dunstable Hosps.

BAILEY, Rachel Gay Child Health, Rikenel, Montpellier, Gloucester GL1 1LY Tel: 01452 891000; The Limes, Charfield, Wotton-under-Edge GL12 8SR Tel: 01453 843084 — MB BS 1964 Lond.; FFA RCS Eng. 1970. Community Med. Off. (Community Paediat.) Severn NHS Trust.

BAILEY, Reginald Donald (retired) 1 The Mount, Ewell, Epsom KT17 1LZ — MB BS 1955 Lond.; DPH Lond. 1961.

BAILEY, Mr Richard Conrad Department of Accident and Emergency, Chesterfield and North Derbyshire Royal Hospital, Calow, Chesterfield Tel: 01246 277271; 26 Highfield Road, Little Eaton, Derby DE21 5AG Tel: 01332 833621 Fax: 01332 833621 Email: billbailey@cndrh.fsnet.co.uk — MB BS 1987 Lond.; 1988 MA Camb.; 1987 MB BS Lond.; 1992 FRCS Ed.; 1994 DA (UK); 1998 FFAEM. (Cambridge and St. Mary's Hospital Medical School) Cons. (A & E) Chesterfield Roy. Hosp. Socs: BAEM; Fell. Fac.of A & E Med.; Brit. Med. Assn. Prev: Sen. Regist. (A & E) Qu. Med. Centre Nottm.; Regist. (A & E) Derbysh. Roy. Infirm.; SHO (Anaesth.) P.ss Margt. Hosp. Swindon.

BAILEY, Richard John Allens, Turners Hill Road, Crawley Down, Crawley RH10 4EY Tel: 01342 714926 — MB 1973 Camb.; MA Camb. 1972, MB 1973, BChir 1972; FRCP Lond. 1993; MRCP (UK) 1977. (St. Thos.) Cons. Phys. Geriat. Med. Crawley & Horsham Hosps. Prev: Sen. Regist. (Geriat. Med.) St. Geo. Hosp. Lond.; Regist. St. Thos. Hosp. Lond.

BAILEY, Mr Robert George Minster Precincts Surgery, 27 Minster Precincts, Peterborough PE1 1XZ Tel: 01733 554478; 49 Thorpe Park Road, Peterborough PE3 6LJ — MB BChir 1980 Camb.; MA Camb. 1982, MB BChir 1980; FRCS Eng. 1986; MRCGP 1989. (Cambridge and Addenbrooke's) Clin. Asst. (Surg.) Edith Cavell Hosp. P'boro.; Hosp. Practitioner (BrE. Imaging) PeterBoro. Socs: Sec. E. Anglia Fac. RCGP; Sec. PeterBoro. GP Forum. Prev: Regist. (Surg.) Leicester Roy. Infirm.

BAILEY, Robin Leslie 33 St Marys Road, Southampton SO14 0BG — BM 1986 Soton.; MRCP (UK) 1989.

BAILEY, Roger David Northampton Lane North Surgery, 120 Northampton Lane North, Moulton, Northampton NN3 7QP Tel: 01604 790108 Fax: 01604 670827 — MB BS 1985 Lond.; BSc (Hons.) Durham. 1980; MRCGP 1991; DRCOG 1990; DCH RCP Lond. 1990; DCCH RCP Ed. 1990. (Char. Cross & Westm.) Socs: Exec. Mem. BMA (N.ampton Br.).; Pres. BMA (N.ampton Br.) 2000-2001. Prev: GP Dunstable; Trainee GP N.ants. VTS; SHO (O & G) Qu. Eliz. Hosp. Gateshead.

BAILEY, Sally Anne The Hedges Medical Centre, Pasley Road, Eyres Monsell, Leicester LE2 9BU Tel: 0116 225 1277 Fax: 0116 225 1477; 23 Green Lane, Countesthorpe, Leicester LE8 5QQ Tel: 0116 277 4092 — MB ChB 1982 Leic.; DRCOG 1986. Prev: Trainee GP Leicester VTS.

BAILEY, Sally Kathryn 25 Stokesay Road, Telford TF1 3NX — MB ChB 1982 Birm.

BAILEY, Sarah Louise 48 Napier Road, Southsea PO5 2RB — MB BCh 1996 Wales. (University of Wales College of Medicine) SHO (Paediat.) Qu. Alexandra Hosp. Cosham.

BAILEY, Sheila Hammond Ground, George Lane, Read, Burnley BB12 7RB — MB ChB 1984 Manch.; MRCGP 1995; DRCOG 1994. GP. Prev: Trainee GP Clitheroe Health Centre; SHO (O & G) Preston Roy. Hosp.

BAILEY, Simon 11 Blenheim Close, Heywood OL10 1QF — MB ChB 1996 Manch.

BAILEY, Simon James 37 Manor Gardens, Kewstoke, Weston Super Mare BS22 9XU — MB ChB 1992 Leic.

BAILEY, Steven Ross 36 Marlborough Avenue, Bromsgrove B60 2PD — MB ChB 1983 Birm.; FRCR 1990. Cons. Radiol. Worcester Roy. Infirm. NHS Trust; Cons. Radiol. Co. BrE. Screening Unit Worcester. Prev: Sen. Regist. (Radiol.) W. Midl. RHA.

BAILEY, Susan Carolyn Pavilion Family Doctors, 153A Stroud Road, Gloucester GL1 5JJ Tel: 01452 385555 Fax: 01452 387905; 7 Court Farm, Huntley Road, Tibberton, Gloucester GL19 3AF Tel: 01452 790709 — MB BS 1973 Lond.; MRCP (UK) 1978; MRCGP 1982. (St Geos. Hosp. Med. Sch.)

BAILEY, Susan Margaret 12/14 Waldeck Road, London W13 8LY — MB BS 1983 Lond.

BAILEY, Miss Susan Margaret James Cook University Hospital, Marton Road, Middlesbrough TS4 3BW Tel: 01642 850850 Email: sue.bailey@email.stahnhst.northy.nhs.uk; Email: simon-helen.gullirer@virgin.net — MB ChB 1981 Birm.; MRCGP 1999; MRCOG 1987; FRCOG 1999. Cons. O & G Middlesbrough. Socs: Brit. Med. Ultrasound Soc. Prev: Lect. (O & G) Univ. Wales Coll. Med.; Research Regist. Bellshill Matern. Hosp. Lanarksh.

BAILEY, Susan Mary Adolescent Forensic Service, Mental Health Unit, Bury New Road, Prestwich, Manchester M25 3BL Tel: 0161 772 3590 Fax: 0161 772 3443 — MB ChB 1973 Manch.; FRCPsych 1996. Cons. Forens. Psychiat. Adolesc. Secure Unit Prestwich.; Cons. Forens. Psychiat. Adolesc. S. Lond. & Maudsley NHS Trust; Hon. Sec. Research Fell. Univ. of Manch.

BAILEY, Susan Yvonne (retired) 108A Moorland Road, Poulton-le-Fylde FY6 7EU Tel: 01253 885411 — BSc Lond. 1956, MB BS 1959; MRCS Eng. LRCP Lond. 1959.

BAILEY, Theodore Robert Simon Orchard House Surgery, Fred Archer Way, Newmarket CB8 8NU; Tel: 01638 663792 — MB BS 1971 Lond.; BSc Lond. 1968; MRCS Eng. LRCP Lond. 1971; FRCGP 1992, M 1976; DObst RCOG 1974. (Univ. Coll. Hosp.) Approved Clin. Teach. Univ. Camb; Assoc. Dir. E. Anglian Deanery PGME. Prev: SHO (Obst.) Univ. Coll. Hosp.; Ho. Phys. Univ. Coll. Hosp. Lond.; Ho. Surg. St. Chas. Hosp. Lond.

BAILEY, Veira Frances Alexandra 1 Park Close, Knightsbridge, London SW1X 7PQ Tel: 020 7351 3069 Email: veira.bailey@virgin.net; 2 Redcliffe Road, London SW10 9NR Tel: 020 7351 3069 Email: veira.bailey@virgin.net — MB BS 1957 Lond.; FRCPsych 1992; MRCS Eng. LRCP Lond. 1957; MRCPsych 1972; DPM Eng. 1970. (Roy. Free) Prev: Cons. Child Psychiat. W. Middlx. Univ. Hosp.

BAILEY, Vivienne Elizabeth Sanofi Winthrop Ltd, One Onslow St., Guildford GU1 4YS Tel: 01483 554282 Fax: 01483 554804 Email: vivienne.bailey@sanofi.com; 4 Greypoint House, The Square, Findon Village, Worthing BN14 0TE Tel: 01903 877226 — MB BS 1984 Lond. (St. Bart. Hosp.) Med. Manager, CNS Bus. Unit, Sanfi Winthrop Ltd. Surrey. Socs: Assoc. Mem. Brit. Med. Acupunc. Soc. Prev: GP Findon Valley; Clin. Med. Off. MoH, Barbados.

BAILEY-SMITH, Robin The Health Centre, Alloa FK10 1AB — MB ChB 1973 Aberd.

BAILHACHE, Nicola Ann Halkett Place Surgery, 84 Halkett Place, St Helier, Jersey JE1 4XL Tel: 01534 36301 Fax: 01534 887793; Roselea Barn, Rue de la Mare Ballam, St John, Jersey JE3 4EJ — MB ChB 1986 Bristol; DRCOG 1990. Socs: Roy. Coll. Gen. Pract.

BAILIE, Mr Alan George 154 Kings Road, Belfast BT5 7EL — MB BCh BAO 1988 Belf.; FRCS Glas. 1993; FRCS Ed. 1992. Specialist Regist. Paediat. Surg. Socs: Assoc. Mem. Brit. Assn. Paediat. Surgs.

BAILIE, Alexander Graham 3 The Drumlins, Ballynahinch BT24 8HW — MB BCh BAO 1994 Belf.

BAILIE, Carolyn Anne Louise 39 Malone Heights, Belfast BT9 5PG — MB BCh BAO 1987 Belf.; MRCGP 1991; MRCOG 1996; DRCOG 1990.

BAILIE, Miss Fiona Buckston (retired) — MB BCh BAO Belf. 1969; FRCS Ed. 1974. Prev: Cons. Plastic Surg. City Hosp. Nottm.

BAILIE, Helen Christina 16 Mill Road, Mattishall, Dereham NR20 3RN — MB ChB 1998 Bristol.

BAILIE, James Stephen Portrush Medical Centre, Dunlace Avenue, Portrush BT56 8DW Tel: 028 7082 3767 Fax: 028 7082 3413; Glenwillan House, 110 Gateside Road, Portrush BT56 8NP Tel: 01265 822262 Fax: 01265 822262 Email: stephenbailie@6tinternet.com — MB BCh BAO 1978 Belf.; MRCGP 1982; DPH Belf. 1996; DRCOG 1984; Cert. Family Plann. JCC 1983. Asst. Med. Adviser NHSSB. Socs: BMA; Roy. Coll. Occupat. Health; Ulster Med. Soc.

BAILIE, John Charles Thompson The Health Centre, 24 High St., Draperstown, Magherafelt BT45 7AA Tel: 01648 28201; 6 Slievegallion Park, Draperstown, Magherafelt BT45 7JS Tel: 01648 28201 — MB BCh BAO 1977 Belf.

BAILIE, Karen Elizabeth Margaret Mater Hospital Trust, Crumlin Road, Belfast BT14 6AB Tel: 01232 741211 Fax: 01232 741342 Email: k.bailie@qub.ac.uk; 48 Drumfad Road, Millisle, Newtownards BT22 2JA — MB BCh BAO 1983 Belf.; MSc (Epidemiol.) Lond. 1995; MD Belf. 1993; MRCP (UK) 1986; MRCPath 1993. (The Queen's University of Belfast) Cons Haematologist, Mater Hsp Trust, Belf. Socs: Brit. Soc. Haematol.; BMA. Prev: Sen. Regist. (Haemat.) Roy. Vict. Hosp.; Regist. (Haemat.) Roy. Vict. Hosp. Belf.; MRC Health Servs. Research Train. Fell.

BAILIE, Lorraine Muriel 15 Ilford Drive, Belfast BT6 9SW — MB BCh BAO 1990 Belf.; MB BCh Belf. 1990; MRCGP 1995; DCH RCPSI 1994; DRCOG 1992. (Qu. Univ. Belf.) Socs: Med. Defence Union; BMA. Prev: Trainee GP N. Irel.

BAILIE, Mr Neil Alexander 51 Earlsfort, Moira, Craigavon BT67 0LY Email: nbailie@aol.com — MB BCh BAO 1994 Belf.; BSc (Hons.) Pathol. Belf. 1992; MB BChir BAO Belf. 1994; FRCS (Eng.) 1998; FRCSI 1998. (Queen's University Belfast) SHO (OtorhinoLaryngol.) Roy. Vicotria Hosp. Belf.; SPR (Otorhinolryngology) N.ern Irel. Rotat. Prev: SHO (Centr. Surg.) Rotat. Belf.; Anat. Demonst. Qu.s Univ. Belf.; SHO (OtorhinoLaryngol.) N.ern Irel. Rotat.

BAILIE, Nicola 154 Kings Road, Belfast BT5 7EL; 154 Kings Road, Belfast BT5 7EL — MB BCh BAO 1991 Belf.; MRCPCH 1995. Specialist Regist. Paediat.

BAILIE, Richard William Adam Castlederg Surgery, 13A Lower Strabane Road, Castlederg BT81 7AZ Tel: 028 8167 1211 Fax: 028 8167 9700; 30 Ferguson Crescent, Castlederg BT81 7AG Tel: 016626 71179 — MB ChB 1984 Manch.; BSc (Med. Sci.) St. And. 1981; MRCGP 1990; T(GP) 1991; Cert. Family Plann. JCC 1989; DCH Dub. 1988; DRCOG 1987. Socs: BMA & Med. Dent. Defence Union Scotl.

BAILIE, Robert Keith 4 Station Walk, Bangor BT19 1EX — MB BCh BAO 1996 Belf.

BAILIE, Ronald Royal Halifax Infirmary, Free School Lane, Halifax HX1 2YP Tel: 01422 357222; Stonehurst, Linden Road, Halifax HX3 0BS Tel: 01422 363713 — MB BCh BAO 1981 Belf.; FFA RCSI 1985. Cons. Anaesth. & Intens. Care Calderdale NHS Trust.

BAILIE, William Thompson Health Centre, Townaill Road, Portglenone, Ballymena Tel: 01266 84551; Green Gables, Portglenone, Ballymena Tel: 01266 821078 — MB BCh BAO 1946 Belf.

BAILLIE, Alastair Thomas Kerr 145 Heene Road, Worthing BN11 4NY Tel: 01903 235344 — MB ChB 1957 Glas.; DObst RCOG 1962.

BAILLIE, Christopher John d'Anyers 27 Queens Road, Wimbledon, London SW19 8NW Tel: 020 8946 1172; 45 Galveston Road, London SW15 2RZ Tel: 020 8870 5708 — MB BS 1987 Lond.; MA (Hons.) Zool. Oxf. 1982; MRCGP 1991; DRCOG 1990. Prev: SHO (Geriat.) Qu. Mary's Hosp. Roehampton; SHO (Paediat.) Centr. Middlx. Hosp. Lond.; SHO (A & E & O & G) Centr. Middlx. Hosp.

BAILLIE, Colin Tennent Ground Floor Flat, Residence 8, Whipps Cross Hospital, Whipps Cross Road, Leytonstone, London E11 1NR — MB ChB 1984 Liverp.

BAILLIE, David Maryhill Health Centre, 41 Shawpark Street, Glasgow G20 9DR Tel: 0141 531 8811 Fax: 0141 531 8808; 293 Southbrae Drive, Glasgow G13 1TR — MB ChB 1978 Ed.; MRCGP 1982.

BAILLIE, David William Hunter Flat 10, Selwyn Court, Blackheath Village, London SE3 9SZ — MB ChB 1997 Birm.

BAILLIE, Elizabeth Susan 13 Calverley Park Crescent, Tunbridge Wells TN1 2NB — MB BS 1953 Lond.; MRCS Eng. LRCP Lond. 1953; DTM & H Eng. 1957. (St. Mary's)

BAILLIE, Marjorie Tyndale Child & Adolescent Mental Health Service, Chad House, Hexham General Hospital, Corbridge Road, Hexham NE46 1QJ Tel: 01434 656285 Fax: 01434 656286 Email: marjorie.baillie@ncl.ac.uk — MB BS 1975 Newc.; MRCPsych 1993; MRCGP 1979. (Newcastle) Cons. (Child & Adolesc. Psychiat.); Hon. Lect. (Child Health), Univ. of Newc. Prev: Sen. Regist. (Psychiat.) Newc.; GP Skelton Cleveland.

BAILLIE, Michael St Olaf, Eastgate, Moffat DG10 9AE — MB ChB 1996 Manch.

BAILLIE, Mrs Moira Patricia (retired) 82 Coombe Lane W., Kingston upon Thames KT2 7DA Tel: 020 8949 5008 — MB BCh BAO 1948 Belf. Prev: Phys. i/c Psoriasis Uva Ltd. Lond.

BAILLIE, Nicola Ann 23 Kimmeter Place, Annan DG12 6JU — MB ChB 1994 Glas.

BAILLIE, Noreen Meredith Brinnington Clinic, Brinnington, Stockport SK5 8BS Tel: 0161 430 4002 Fax: 0161 430 2918; 12 Green Lane, Heaton Moor, Stockport SK4 3LE Tel: 0161 431 3211 — MB ChB 1958 Aberd. (Aberd.)

BAILLIE-HAMILTON, Alexander Buchanan Cedars Surgery, 8 Cookham Road, Maidenhead SL6 8AJ Tel: 01628 20458 Fax: 01628 33270; Knowle Croft, Shoppenhangers, Maidenhead SL6 2PZ Tel: 01628 27547 Fax: 01628 33270 — MB ChB 1956 Aberd.; DIH Soc. Apoth. Lond. 1959.

BAILLIE-HAMILTON, Paula Frances The Gart, Callender FK17 8LE — MB BS 1987 Lond.; DPhil Oxf. 1995. Prev: Hon. Regist. (Radiol.) ICRF Med. Research Fell. Univ. Oxf.

BAILLIE-JOHNSON, Hugo Roger Alclutha, Old Park Avenue, Dover CT16 2DY — MB BS 1971 Lond.; MRCP (UK) 1974.

BAILLOD, Rosemarie Andree 21 Belsize Court, Hampstead, London NW3 5QN Tel: 020 7435 6285 — MB BS 1961 Lond.; MRCS Eng. LRCP Lond. 1961. (Roy. Free) Emer. Cons. Roy. Free Hosp. Lond.; Hon. Cons. Hosp. Sick Childr. Gt. Ormond St. Lond. Socs: Europ. Dialysis & Transpl. Assn.; Renal Assn. Prev: 1st. Asst. Dept. Nephrol. Roy. Free Hosp. Lond.

BAILLON, Bernard Richard Fellowes (retired) Meadow End, Little Houghton, Northampton NN7 1AH Tel: 01604 890050 Email: brfbaillon@telinco.co.uk — MB BCh BAO NUI 1957; FRCGP 1983, M 1974. Prev: Assoc. Adviser (Gen. Pract.) Oxf.

BAILWARD, Thomas Alexander Montpelier Health Centre, Bath Buildings, Bristol BS6 5PT Tel: 0117 942 6811 Fax: 0117 944 4182; 45 Waverley Road, Bristol BS6 6ET Tel: 0117 973 0105 Email: bailward@compuserve.com — MB BS 1987 Lond.; MA Oxf. 1992, BA (Hons) 1984; MRCGP 1994; MRCPCH 1996. (Oxf. & Univ. Coll. Hosp. Middlx.) Clin. Tutor Bristol Univ. Socs: BMA; Co-opted Exec. Mem. BACCH; RCPCH. Prev: Sen. Community Med. Off. (Community Paediat.) Bristol; SHO (O & G) Roy. United Hosp. Bath; SHO (Paediat.) Bristol Childr. Hosp.

BAIN, Angus Howard Weir (retired) Gowancroft, 1 Wolds Drive, Orpington BR6 8NS Tel: 01689 850096 — MB BS 1952 Lond.; MRCS Eng. LRCP Lond. 1949. Sen. Forens. Examr. Metrop. Police. Prev: Ho. Surg. Grimsby Gen. Hosp.

BAIN, Mr Archibald Kennedy (retired) 155 Old Castle Road, Cathcart, Glasgow G44 5TJ Tel: 0141 637 6426 Fax: 0141 637 6426 — LRCP LRCS Ed. LRFPS Glas. 1948; FRCS Glas. 1962; FRFPS Glas. 1960; DLO Eng. 1954. Prev: Cons. Surg. (ENT) Gartnavel Gen. Hosp. & Roy. Hosp. Sick Childr. Glas.

BAIN, Barbara Jane 54 Hemingford Road, London N1 1DB — MB BS 1965 Queensland; FRACP 1980, M 1969 MRCPath 1976. (Queensland) Sen. Lect. (Haemat.) St. Mary's Hosp. Med. Sch. Lond.

BAIN, Catrina Alison Lynch Flat 3/1, 22 Oban Drive, Glasgow G20 6AF — MB ChB 1994 Glas.

BAIN, Christine The Cardiothoracic Centre, Thomas Drive, Liverpool L14 3PE Tel: 01224 869794, 0151 228 1616 Fax: 0151 293 2331; Fax: 0151 293 2331 — MB ChB 1987 Aberd.; MFFP 2000; MRCOG 1994. Cons. (O&G) Aberd.

BAIN, Christopher Norman 64 Main Street, Woodborough, Nottingham NG14 6EA — MB BS 1965 Lond.; MRCS Eng. LRCP Lond. 1965; FRCOG 1984, M 1972. (St. Mary's) Cons. O & G Nottm. City Hosp. Socs: Fell. Roy. Soc. Med. Prev: Sen. Regist. & Lect. Univ. Coll. Hosp. Lond.; Resid. Med. Off. Qu. Charlotte's Matern. Hosp. Lond. & Samarit. Hosp. Wom. Lond.

BAIN, David Austin 10 Shore Road, Killyleagh, Downpatrick BT30 9UE Tel: 01396 828251 — MB BCh BAO 1945 Belf.

BAIN, Donald Ladywell Medical Centre (West), Ladywell Road, Edinburgh EH12 7TB Tel: 0131 334 3602 Fax: 0131 316 4816; 3 Campbell Avenue, Edinburgh EH12 6DS Tel: 0131 337 1670 — MB BS 1974 Lond.; BSc (Hons.) Ed. 1965; MRCGP 1979; DRCOG 1978. (St. Bart.) GP Princip.

BAIN, Donald John 37 Dunellan Road, Milngavie, Glasgow G62 7RE — MB ChB 1991 Glas.

BAIN, Douglas John Geddes Tayside Centre for General Practice, Kirsty Semple Way, Dundee DD2 4BF Tel: 01382 632771 Fax: 01382 633839 Email: tcep@ninewells.dundee.ac.uk — MB ChB 1964 Aberd.; PhD Aberd. 1986, MD 1974; FRCP Ed. 1987; FRCGP 1979, M 1969. Prof. Gen. Pract. Tayside Centre for Gen. Pract. Univ. Dundee. Socs: Chairm. Assn. Univ. Depts. Gen. Pract. Prev: Prof. Primary Med. Care Univ. Soton.; GP Livingston.

BAIN, Elizabeth Maria Royal Edinburgh Hospital, Morningside Park, Edinburgh EH10 5HF — MB ChB 1994 Ed. Sen. Ho. Off. S. E. Scotl. Psychiat. Train. Scheme. Socs: BMA; RC Psych - Inceptor.

BAIN, Gillian Allison Central Middlesex Hospital, Acton Lane, London NW10 7NS Email: gillian.bain@cmh-tr.nthames.nhs.uk; 55 Rusthall Av, London W4 1BN Tel: 020 8742 0284 — MB ChB 1989 Bristol; MRCP (UK) 1992; FRCR 1996. (Bristol University) Cons. (Radiol.), Centr. Middlx. Hosp. Prev: Specialist Regist. (Radiol.) St Geo.'s Hosp. Lond.; Specialist Regist. (Radiol.) Addenbrooke's Hosp. Camb.; SHO (Med.) Stoke Maudeville Hosp.

BAIN, Helen Margaret Heaton Norris Health Centre, Cheviot Close, Heaton Norris, Stockport SK4 1JX Tel: 0161 480 3338 — MB ChB 1986 Aberd.

BAIN, Hugh Hall 44 Oakfield Road, Gosforth, Newcastle upon Tyne NE3 4HS — MB ChB 1963 Ed.; MRCP (UK) 1971.

BAIN, Iain Matheson 66 Vicarage Road, Harbourne, Birmingham B17 0SP — MB BS 1986 Lond.

BAIN, John Coldside Medical Practice, 129 Strathmartine Road, Dundee DD3 8DB Tel: 01382 826724 Fax: 01382 884129 — MB ChB 1972 Glas.; MRCGP 1976; DFM Glas. 1989; DObst RCOG 1974. Dep. Force Med. Off. Tayside Police; Clin. Asst. (Geriat. Psychiat.) Roy. Dundee Liff Hosp. Prev: GP Princip. Tayside Health Bd.; Regist. (Psychiat.) Garnavel Roy. Hosp. Glas.; Research Asst. (Geriat. Med.) Stobhill Hosp. Glas.

BAIN, Karen Elizabeth Ground Right Flat, 103 Queensborough Gardens, Glasgow G12 9RS Tel: 0141 357 0811; Ground Right Flat, 103 Queensborough Gardens, Glasgow G12 9RS Tel: 0141 357 0811 — MB ChB 1993 Glas.; FRCophth 1999. SHO (Ophth.) Manch. Roy. Eye Hosp. Socs: BMA. Prev: SHO (Ophth.) Ayr Hosp.; SHO (Neurosurg.) S.ern Gen. Hosp. Glas.; SHO (O & G) Qu. Mother's Hosp. & W.ern Infirm. Glas.

BAIN, Lindsey Anne Southend Hospital, Prittlewell Chase, Westcliff on Sea SS0 0RY Tel: 01702 221069 Fax: 01702 221059 — MB ChB 1979 Liverp.; MSc (Clin. Microbiol.) 1990 Lond.; MRCPath 1990. (Liverpool) Cons. Microbiol. S.end Healthcare Trust. Prev: Sen. Regist. (Microbiol.) Hosp. Sick Childr. Lond.

BAIN, Marion Ruth Sloan Information & Statistics Division, Common Services Agency, Trinity Park House, South Trinity Road, Edinburgh EH5 3SQ Tel: 0131 552 6255 Email: marion.bain@isd.csa.scot.nhs.uk — MB ChB 1988 Ed.; MSc (Community Health) Ed. 1993, BSc (Hons.) Pharmacol. 1986; MFPHM RCP (UK) 1995. (Edinburgh) Cons. Pub. Health Med. (Informat. & Statistics Div.) Common Servs. Agency Edin.; Mem. Fac. Pub. Health Med. Socs: BMA. Prev: Sen. Regist. & Regist. (Pub. Health Med.) Health Systems Div. Common Servs. Agency Edin.; Regist. & SHO (Bact.) City Hosp. Edin.

BAIN, Murray Douglas Department of Child Health, St George's Hospital, Cranmer Terrace, London SW17 0RE — MB ChB 1976 Ed.; MD Ed. 1991; MRCP (UK) 1980. Cons. & Sen. Lect. (Child Health) St. Geo. Hosp. Med. Sch. Lond.

BAIN, Raymond Roy Langley Health Centre, Common Road, Slough SL3 8LE Tel: 01753 544288 Fax: 01753 592415; Acorns, Church Lane, Wexham, Slough SL3 6LE — MB BS 1962 Lond.; LMSSA Lond. 1962; DO Eng. 1965. (St. Mary's) p/t Hosp. Pract. (Ophth.) P. Chas. Eye Unit Windsor.

BAIN, Robert 4C Victoria Mansions, Victoria Park, Ayr KA7 2TR Tel: 01292 289262 — MB ChB 1948 Glas.; DObst RCOG 1953.

BAIN, Robert John Iain Mentmore, 34 Park Drive, Grimsby DN32 0EG Tel: 01472 751185 Fax: 01472 278922 — MB ChB 1980 Liverp.; MSc Manch. 1977; BSc (Hons.) Bristol 1974; MD Liverp. 1991; FRCP Lond. 1996; MRCP (UK) 1984. (Liverp.) Cons. Phys. & Cardiol. Grimsby Dist. Gen. Hosp. Socs: Brit. Cardiac Soc. & Med. Research Soc. Prev: Lect. (Med.) Liverp. Univ. & Sen. Regist. (Cardiol.) Roy. Liverp. Hosp.; Research Fell. (Cardiol.) E. Birm. Hosp.; Regist. Rotat. Liverp.

BAIN, Roderic Bruce Stannary House, Stainland Road, Stainland, Halifax HX4 9HA Tel: 01422 374109 — MB ChB 1972 Aberd.

BAIN, Roderick McLean (retired) 4 Firthview Terrace, Alness IV17 0QX Tel: 01349 882486 — MB ChB 1947 Aberd.; MFCM 1972; DPH Aberd. 1951. Prev: SCMO Wigan HA.

BAIN, Sheila Stewart Robertson (retired) 70 Craiglockhart Road, Edinburgh EH14 1EW — MB ChB 1965 St. And.; FRCOG 1985, M 1971. Cons. Genitourin. Med. Roy. Infirm. Edin. & Hon. Sen. Lect. Univ. Edin. Prev: Cons. (Venereol.) Roy. Infirm. Edin.

BAIN, Mr Walter Edward Spencer (retired) 401 Upper Richmond Road, London SW15 5QW Tel: 020 8876 0229 — MB BChir 1942 Camb.; MA Camb. 1942; FRCS Eng. 1947; MRCS Eng. LRCP Lond. 1942. Prev: Ophth. Surg. King Edwd. VII Hosp. Windsor & Heatherwood Hosp. Ascot.

BAIN, Professor William Herbert (retired) 37 Dunellan Road, Milngavie, Glasgow G62 7RE Tel: 0141 956 3218 — MB ChB 1950 Glas.; MD (Commend.) Glas. 1967; FRCS Glas. 1969; FRCS Ed. 1955; FCCP 1962. Prev: Prof. Cardiac Surg. Univ. Glas.

BAINBRIDGE, Anthony Douglas 2 Cavendish Court, Cardigan Road, Richmond TW10 6BL — MD 1991 Manch.; MB ChB 1980; MRCP (UK) 1985. Lect. & Hon. Sen. Regist. Char. Cross Med. Sch.

BAINBRIDGE, Barbara Anne Rainbow Medical Centre, 333 Robins Lane, St Helens WA9 3PN Tel: 01744 811211 — MB ChB 1973 Leeds; MRCGP 1979. GP Merseyside. Prev: Chairm. St. Helens & Knowsley LMC.

BAINBRIDGE, Beatrice Mary Lordshill Health Centre, Lordshill District Centre, Lordshill, Southampton SO16 8HY Tel: 023 8073 8144 Fax: 023 8073 0722; 121 Botley Road, Whitenap, Romsey SO51 5RQ Tel: 01794 513227 — MB BS 1970 Lond.; MRCS Eng. LRCP Lond. 1970; Cert. Family Plann. JCC 1974; DObst RCOG 1973. (Roy. Free) Prev: Clin. Med. Off. (Child Health) Soton & SW Hants. Health Dist. (T); SHO (O & G & Paediat.) Soton. Childr. Hosp.; Ho. Phys. Whipps Cross Hosp. Lond.

BAINBRIDGE, David Robert Moatfield Surgery, St. Michaels Road, East Grinstead RH19 3GW Tel: 01342 327555 Fax: 01342 316240; Copyhold House, Copyhold Lane, Haywards Heath RH17 5ED Email: dbainbridge@ntcworld.com — MB 1965 Camb.; Bchir 1964; FRCS Eng. 1970. (Univ. Camb.) Prev: Demonst. (Anat.) Univ. Edin.; Regist. (Surg.), Ho. Phys. & Ho. Surg. Lond. Hosp.

BAINBRIDGE, Derek (retired) 43 Stamford Road, Bowdon, Altrincham WA14 2JR — MB ChB 1962 Birm.; FRCP Lond. 1982, M 1966. Prev: Cons. Phys. Trafford Gen. Hosp. Davyhulme Manch.

BAINBRIDGE, Douglas Robert (retired) Alderford House, Sible Hedingham, Halstead CO9 3HX — MB BChir 1960 Camb.; MB Camb. 1961, BChir 1960.

BAINBRIDGE, Mr Edward Thomas 91 Reddings Road, Moseley, Birmingham B13 8LP Tel: 0121 449 4119 — MB ChB 1970 Birm.; FRCS Eng. 1975. Cons. Gen. Vasc. Surg. Sandwell Gen. Hosp. W. Bromwich. Socs: Fell. Assn. Surgs.; Vasc. Surg. Soc. GB & Irel. Prev: Regist. (Surg.) Hereford Co. Hosp.

BAINBRIDGE, Elizabeth Anne Stoneycroft Medical Centre, Stoneville Road, Liverpool L13 6QD Tel: 0151 228 1138 Fax: 0151 228 1653 — MB ChB 1986 Liverp.; BSc (Hons.) Birm. 1981; DRCOG 1989.

BAINBRIDGE, Grace 27 Westfield Park, Ryde PO33 3AB Tel: 01983 65867 — MB BS 1933 Lond.; MRCS Eng. LRCP Lond. 1931; MRCPsych 1972; DPM Eng. 1957. (King's Coll. Hosp.) Socs: BMA. Prev: Cons. Vis. Psychotherap. H.M. Prisons Pk.hurst, Camphill & Albany; Cons. Psychotherap. Friern & Whittington Hosps.; Asst. Resid. Neuro-Psychiat. Dept. Albany Hosp. New York.

BAINBRIDGE, Irene Malkah Falcon Square Surgery, 9-10 Falcon Square, Castle Hedingham, Halstead CO9 3BY Tel: 01787 460436 Fax: 01787 462829; Alderford House, Sible Hedingham, Halstead CO9 3HZ Fax: 01787 462088 — BM BCh 1960 Oxf.; MA Oxf. 1960; DFFP 1995; DObst RCOG 1976. Clin. Med. Off. (Family Plann.) Essex Rivers Health Care Trust. Socs: Brit. Soc. Med. & Dent. Hypn.; Diplomate Fac. Reproduc. Health Care RCOG; Treas. Dispensing Doctors Ltd.

BAINBRIDGE, Mr James William Braithwaite 34 Cheriton Square, London SW17 8AE — MB BChir 1993 Camb.; MA Camb. 1993; FRCOphth 1996. Specialist Regist. (Ophth.) Moorfields Eye Hosp. Lond. Prev: SHO (Ophth.) St Geo.s Lond.; SHO (Neurosurg.) Nat. Hosp. Lond.; Ho. Phys. (Med.) St Mary's Lond.

BAINBRIDGE, Jean Miller (retired) 1 Pierremont Drive, Darlington DL3 9LZ Tel: 01325 252203 — MB BS 1949 Durh.; LLB Lond. 1961; FFCM 1986, M 1973; DPH Durh. 1958; DObst RCOG 1951. Prev: Dir. Pub. Health Med. & Clin. Policy Darlington HA.

BAINBRIDGE, Mr Lionel Christopher Pulvertaft Hand Centre, Derbyshire Royal Infirmary, London Road, Derby DE1 2QY Tel: 01332 254751; 33 Broadway, Duffield, Belper DE56 4BU Tel: 01332 840128 — MB ChB 1981 Aberd.; FRCS Ed. 1986. Cons. Plastic & Hand Surg. Pulvertaft Hand Centre Derby.

BAINBRIDGE, Mary Anne 17 Crossway, Didsbury, Manchester M20 6TU — MB ChB 1994 Manch.; BSc St. And. 1991.

BAINBRIDGE, Michael Alan 49 Bondgate, Castle Donnington, Derby DE74 2NS — BM BS 1980 Nottm.; MRCGP 1985.

BAINES, Alastair Graham Portland House, Portland Place, Helsby, Warrington WA6 9LD — MB ChB 1987 Leeds.

BAINES, Andrew John 115 Coulby Manor Farm, Coulby Newham, Middlesbrough TS8 0RZ — MB BS 1992 Lond.

BAINES, Arthur Raymond (retired) 9 Stour Court, Stour St., Canterbury CT1 2PG — MB BS 1948 Lond.; MRCS Eng. LRCP Lond. 1947. Prev: Research Phys. F Hoffman- La Roche Basle, Switz.

BAINES, Dianne Lesley 21 St Bede's, East Boldon NE36 0LF — MB BChir 1984 Camb.; BSc (Hons.) Med. Biol. St. And. 1981.

BAINES, Duncan Alexander The Old Mill, Cubley, Ashbourne DE6 2EZ — MB ChB 1997 Birm.

BAINES, Geoffrey Fielden The Cottage, Main St., Great Addington, Kettering NN14 4BJ Tel: 01536 330223 — MB ChB 1956 St. And.; FRCP Lond. 1978, M 1965; FRCP Ed. 1977, M 1963. Cons. Cardiol. Colchester Gen. Hosp. Socs: Brit. Cardiac Soc.; Brit. Soc. Echocardiogr. Prev: Regional Adviser (Med.) Oxf.; Cons. Phys. (Cardiol.) Kettering, N.ants; Sen. Regist. Profess. Med. Unit Roy. Infirm. Dundee.

BAINES, John David US Naval Medical Clinics UK, 88 Blenheim Crescent, Ruislip HA4 7EG Tel: 01895 616317 Fax: 01895 616323 Email: jdbaines@med.navy.mil; 15 Winkfield Road, Windsor SL4 4BA Tel: 01753 858815 Fax: 01753 858815 Email: jd.baines@which.net — MRCS Eng. LRCP Lond. 1964; T(GP) 1991. (Leeds) Brit. Liaison Phys & Clin. Med. Off. (Family Pract.) US Naval Med. Clinics UK. Socs: BMA (Vice-Pres. E. Berks. Div.); Fac. Pre-Hosp. Care RCS (Ed.). Prev: GP Windsor; Clin. Asst. (Thoracic Surg.) King Edwd. VII Hosp. Windsor.

BAINES, Julian H E 7 Villiers Crescent, St Helens WA10 5HP Tel: 01744 26484 — MB ChB 1956 Manch.; FFCM RCP (UK) 1981, M 1972; DPH Liverp. 1961. (Manch.) Prev: Dir. (Pub. Health) Warrington HA; Area Med. Off. Sefton AHA.; MOH & Princip. Sch. Med. Off. St. Helens Co. Boro.

BAINES, Laura Anne 40 Denewell Avenue, High Heaton, Newcastle upon Tyne NE7 7YB Tel: 0191 281 5888 Email: i.a.baines@ncl.ac.uk — MB BS 1992 Newc.; BMedSc Newc. 1991; MRCP (UK) 1995. Specialist Regist. (Nephrol.). Prev: Clin. Research Assoc. (Med.) Newc.; Regist. (Diabetes) Newc.

BAINES, Mary Jean, OBE Ellenor Foundation, East Hill, Dartford DA1 1SA Tel: 01322 221315 Fax: 01322 626503; 10 Bromley Avenue, Bromley BR1 4BQ Tel: 020 8460 8256 — MB BChir 1958 Camb.; MRCP (UK) 1992; FRCP (UK) 1997. (St. Thos.) Cons. Phys. Ellenor Foundat. Dartford; Hon. Cons. Phys. Dartford & Gravesham NHS Trust. Socs: Founder Mem. Europ. Assn. Palliat. Care. Prev: Cons. Phys. St. Christopher's Hospice Lond.

BAINES, Paul Bruce Royal Liverpool Childrens NHS Trust, Eaton Road, West Derby, Liverpool L12 2AP Email: p.baines@liverpool.ac.uk; 8 St Anthony's Road, Crosby, Liverpool L23 8TP — BM BCh 1984 Oxf.; BA (Hons.) Oxf. 1981; MRCP (UK) 1990; FCAnaesth 1991. Cons. Intens. Care Unit & Anaesth. Roy. Liverp. Childr. Hosp. Prev: Regist. (Anaesth.) Addenbrooke's Hosp. Camb.; SHO (Anaesth.) Hinchingbrooke Hosp. Huntingdon; SHO (Neonat. Paediat.) Liverp. Matern. Hosp.

BAINES, Paul Ian Bailey 9 Bryn Terrace, Mumbles, Swansea SA3 4HD — MB BCh 1994 Wales. Socs: Brit. Assn. Accid. & Emerg. Med.

BAINES, Peter Scott Clerkenwell Medical Practice, Finsbury Health Centre, Pine Street, London EC1R 0HJ; Flat 1, 36-38 Mildmay Park, London N1 4PH — MB ChB 1991 Manch.; BSc St. And. 1988.

BAINES, Phyllis Cawburn Sheild Farm, Haltwhistle NE49 9PW Tel: 01434 321247 — MB ChB 1965 Sheff.; DCH Eng. 1968. (Sheff.) Staff Grade Community Paediat., Community Paediat., Newc. City Health Trust. Socs: BACCH; ACRP. Prev: Sen. Med. Off. (Physical

Handicap) Leeds HA; Sen. Med. Off. Berks. AHA; Dept.al Med. Off. Leeds Pub. Health Dept.

BAINES, Rebecca 17 Rews Park Drive, Pinhoe, Exeter EX1 3QL — MB BS 1996 Lond.

BAINES, Richard John Twin Oaks, Acaster Selby La, Acaster Malbis, York YO23 2PY — MB ChB 1997 Leic.

BAINS, Harinder Singh 369 Burton Road, Derby DE23 6AH — MB ChB 1988 Manch.; MRCGP 1993.

BAINS, Jatinder Jit Singh 55 Begbie Road, London SE3 8DA — MB BS 1992 Lond.

BAINS, Joginder 1 Fitzroy Avenue, Harborne, Birmingham B17 8RL Tel: 0121 420 4991 — BM 1979 Soton.; DRCOG 1984.

BAINTON, Cynthia Adela Ruth (retired) 32 Higher Lincombe Road, Torquay TQ1 2EY Tel: 01803 212652 — MB ChB 1954 Birm.; MRCPsych 1971; DPM Eng. 1962; DCH Eng. 1959; DObst RCOG 1956. Prev: Cons. Psychiat. (Learning Disabil.) S. Devon Healthcare Trust.

BAINTON, David Sun Inn, Longtown, Hereford HR2 0LD — MB BChir 1965 Camb.; MSc Lond. 1975; MRCP Lond. 1969; FFPHM RCP (UK) 1991, M 1976; FRCP 1998. (Univ. Coll. Hosp.) Sen. Lect. Centre for Applied Pub. Health Med. UWCM. Prev: SCM Huddersfield, Bristol, W.on & Avon HAs.

BAINTON, Mr Roger The Beeches, Keithall, Inverurie AB51 0LJ — MB ChB 1976 Liverp.; BDS Wales 1969; FDS RCS Eng. 1984; FRCS Ed. 1980. Cons. Oral. & Maxillofacial Surg. Aberd. Roy. Infirm.

BAINTON, Rowena Dawn Royal Hallamshire Hospital, Guossop Road, Sheffield NN7 3PA; 64 Murray Road, Banner Cross, Sheffield S11 7GG Email: rdbainton@doctors.org.uk — BM BCh 1994 Oxf.; MRCP (UK) 1998. Specialist Regist. Haemat. Roy. Hallamshire Hosp., Sheff..

BAINTON, Vernon Christian The Old Bakehouse, 20 High St., Bugbrooke, Northampton NN7 3PA Email: vcbainton@doctors.org.uk — MB ChB 1998 Birm.; ChB Birm. 1998.

BAIRD, Affra Mary (retired) 23 Old Sneed Park, Bristol BS9 1RG Tel: 0117 968 5523 — MB ChB 1967 Ed.; DMRD Ed. 1972. Cons. Radiol. Avon BrE. Screening Serv. United Bristol Healthcare NHS Trust. Prev: Sen. Regist. (Radiol.) Bristol Roy. Infirm.

BAIRD, Alastair Gordon Tel: 01776 830262 Fax: 01776 830440 — MB ChB 1976 Glas.; FRCGP 1998; MRCOG 1992. Rural GP., RCGP; HMA & Chairm. Portpatrick RNLI; Mem. of RCGP Rural Gp. Socs: MRCOG; FRCGP. Prev: Regist. (O & G) King Edwd. VIII Hosp. Durban, S. Afr.; SHO (Obst.) Glas. Roy. Matern. Hosp.

BAIRD, Amy Mary Heywood House, 3 Cliff St., Whitby YO21 3DD — LRCPI & LM, LRSCI & LM 1946; LRCPI & LM, LRCSI & LM 1946; DPH Bristol 1962. Sen. Med. Off. ScarBoro. Health Dist.

BAIRD, Angela Mary The Stannington Health Centre, Uppergate Road, Stannington, Sheffield S6 6BX Tel: 0114 234 8779 Fax: 0114 285 4778 — MB ChB 1981 Sheff.

BAIRD, Anne Elizabeth (retired) Cairnsmore, Port Isaac PL29 3SQ Tel: 01208 880249 — MB ChB Glas. 1951.

BAIRD, Ayanda Elizabeth 250 Moira Road, Lisburn BT28 2TU — MB BCh BAO 1996 Belf.

BAIRD, Miss Barbara Jean Mackenzie (retired) 76 Little Meadow, Writtle, Chelmsford CM1 3LG Tel: 01245 421069 — MB ChB 1972 Glas.; MA Glas. 1964; FRCS Glas. 1977; FFAEM 1993. Prev: Clin. Asst. (Orthop.) Orsett Hosp.

***BAIRD, Christopher Donalbain** 25 Thornbury, Harpenden AL5 5SN Tel: 07957 257082; 25 Thornbury, Harpenden AL5 5SN Tel: 07957 257082 — MB BS 1998 Lond.; MB BS Lond 1998.

BAIRD, Clive Henry 48 Ottoline Drive, Troon KA10 7AW Tel: 01292 312322 — MB ChB 1973 Glas.; FRCOG 1990, M 1980. Cons. O & G Ayrsh. & Arran.

***BAIRD, Colin Robert Wilson** 50 Munro Road, Jordanhill, Glasgow G13 1SF — MB ChB 1998 Aberd.; MB ChB Aberd 1998; BSc Med Sci (2nd Class Honours).

BAIRD, David Orchard Bank (Lower), Frankscroft, Peebles EH45 9DX Tel: 01721 720275 — MB ChB 1962 Ed.; MRCGP 1974; DCH Eng. 1966; DObst RCOG 1965. Med. Off. Blood Transf. Serv.; Civil. Med. Off. MOD. Prev: GP Bathgate; SHO (Paediat.) Alder Hey Hosp. Liverp.; Ho. Off. (Surg.) Edin. Roy. Infirm.

BAIRD, David James Ronald Eastside Surgery, 56 Templemore Avenue, Belfast BT5 4FT Tel: 028 9045 1000 Fax: 028 9043 2483; 32 Cyprus Avenue, Belfast BT5 5NT — MB BCh BAO 1974 Belf.; BSc Physiol. (Hons.) Belf. 1971; MRCGP 1978; DRCOG 1976; DCH Dub. 1975. Socs: AUTGP 1981.

BAIRD, David Macdonald The Surgery, St. Couan Crescent, Kirkcowan, Newton Stewart DG8 0HH Tel: 01671 830206 Fax: 01671 404163; Corrib, Main St, Kirkcowan, Newton Stewart DG8 0HG Tel: 01671 830497 — MB ChB 1982 Ed.; DRCOG 1987. Prev: Clin. Med. Off. Dalrymple Hosp. Stranraer; Regist. (O & G) Cresswell Matern. Hosp. Dumfries; Ho. Surg. Roodlands Gen. Hosp.

BAIRD, Mr David St Clair 10 Carmoney Road, Campsie, Londonderry BT47 3JH Tel: 01504 860568 — MB BCh BAO 1956 Belf.; FRCS Ed. 1961. (Belf.) Socs: Fell. Ulster Med. Soc.; Fell. BOA. Prev: Cons. Orthop. Surg. Altnagelvin Hosp. Lond.derry; Sen. Regist. (Orthop.) Musgrave Pk. Hosp. Belf.; Regist. Harlow Wood Hosp.

BAIRD, Professor David Tennent, CBE Department of Obstetrics & Gynaecology, Centre for Reproductive Biology, University of Edinburgh, 37 Chalmers St., Edinburgh EH3 9EW Tel: 0131 229 2575 Fax: 0131 229 2408 Email: dtbaird@ed.ac.uk; 22 India Street, Edinburgh EH3 6HB Tel: 0131 225 3962 — MB ChB 1959 Ed.; DSc Ed. 1976; BA Camb. 1956; FRCP Lond. 1996; FRCP Ed. 1972, M 1962; FRCOG 1973, M 1964; FRSE 1990. MRC Clin. Research Prof. of Reproduc. Endocrinol. Univ. Edin.; Hon. Cons. Gyn. Roy. Infirm. & Simpson Memor. Matern. Pavil. Edin. Socs: Endocrine Soc. & Soc. Study Fertil. Prev: Prof. O & G Univ. Edin.; Dep. Dir. MRC Unit Reproduc. Biol.; Worcester Foundat. Experim. Biol. Shrewsbury Mass., USA.

BAIRD, Dugald Reid Department of Microbiology, Hairmyres Hospital, East Kilbride, Glasgow G75 8RG; 9 Stuarton Park, East Kilbride, Glasgow G74 4LA Tel: 01355 220115 — BM BCh 1970 Oxf.; MA Oxf. 1968; MRCP (UK) 1973; FRCPath 1994; Dip. Bact. Manch. 1981. (Oxf. & Middlx.) Prev: Cons. Bact. Roy. Infirm. Glas.; Asst. Med. Microbiol. Pub. Health Laborat. Serv.; Sen. Regist. (Med.) Ahmadu Bello Univ. Hosp. Zaria, Nigeria.

BAIRD, Gareth Vernon 21 Lismenary Road, Ballynure, Ballyclare BT39 9UE — MB BCh BAO 1997 Belf.

BAIRD, Gilbert Maurice (retired) Corrish, Stuckenduff, Shandon, Helensburgh G84 8NN Tel: 01436 820917 — MB ChB Ed. 1942; FRCP Ed. 1971, M 1953; FRCPsych 1988, M 1971; DPM Eng. 1959. Prev: Cons. Psychiat. Vale of Leven Hosp. Alexandria & Argyll & Bute Hosp. Lochgilphead.

BAIRD, Herbert The Health Centre, George Avenue, Ballyclare Tel: 01960 322575; 21 Lismenary Road, Ballynure, Ballyclare BT39 9UE Tel: 01960 322640 — MB BCh BAO 1959 Belf.; FRCGP 1975, M 1968. (Qu. Univ. Belf.) Socs: (Ex-Pres.) Ulster Med. Soc. Prev: Res. Med. Off. Roy. Vict. Hosp. Belf. & Roy. Matern. Hosp. Belf. & Roy. Belf. Hosp. Sick Childr.

BAIRD, Hugh Macdonald (retired) Greenhead of Troquhain, Balmaclellan, Castle Douglas DG7 3QJ Tel: 01644 440653 — MB BS (Hons.) Lond. 1950; DObst RCOG 1952. Prev: Ho. Off., Res. Obstetr. & Res. Med. Off. Guy's Hosp. Lond.

BAIRD, Ian McLean (retired) Pine Court, Fairbourne, Cobham KT11 2BT Tel: 01932 868778 Fax: 01932 863954 Email: iandoc@btopenworld.com — MB ChB 1945 St. And.; MB ChB (Merit in Path.) 1945; MD (1st cl. Hons. & Silver Medal) St. And. 1957; FRCP Lond. 1973, M 1950. Hon. Cons. Phys. W. Middlx. Univ. Hosp. Isleworth. Prev: Hon. Sen. Lect. (Med.) W.m. & Char. Cross Hosp. Lond. Med. Sch.

BAIRD, James Brown Barnett (retired) 39 Coates Gardens, Edinburgh EH12 5LF Tel: 0131 337 2588 — LRCP LRCS Ed. LRFPS Glas. 1952. Prev: GP Edin.

BAIRD, James Ettrick 9 Lynwood Avenue, Epsom KT17 4LQ — BM 1998 Soton.

BAIRD, James Wiseman (retired) The Beeches, Kirklington, Bedale DL8 2LX Tel: 01845 567354 — MB ChB 1948 Glas.; MRCGP 1962.

BAIRD, Janis MRC Environmental Epidemology Unit, University of Southampton, Southampton General Hospital, Southampton SO16 6YD; 21 Fordington Avenue, Winchester SO22 5AN — MB BCh 1987 Wales; MFPHM 2001; DRCOG 1991; DCH RCP Lond. 1990. Sen. Regist. (Pub. Health) MRC Envioronm. Epidemiol. Unit Soton.; Trainee Mem. Fac. Pub. Health Med. Socs: BMA; Soc. for Social Med. Prev: Regist. (Pub. Health Med.) Basingstoke Dist. Hosp.

BAIRD, Jesme Wilson 25C Herbert Street, Kelvinbridge, Glasgow G20 6NB — MB ChB 1989 Glas. Staff Grade (Med. Oncol.).

BAIRD, Jessie Elizabeth Crichton (retired) 18 Garngaber Avenue, Lenzie, Kirkintilloch, Glasgow G66 4LJ — MB ChB 1939 Aberd.; FRCOG 1978, M 1949. Prev: Cons. (O & G) Robroyston Hosp. Glas.

BAIRD, Sir John Alexander, KBE, Air Marshal RAF Med. Br. (retired) Braeburn, Barway, Ely CB7 5UA Tel: 01353 624968 Email: sirjbaird@ukonline.co.uk — MB ChB Ed. 1961; FFOM RCP Lond. 1994, MFOM 1981; DAvMed Eng. 1968; FRCP Ed 1998; FRCS Ed 1998. Prev: Surg. Gen., Defence Med. Serv.s.

BAIRD, John Alexander Leverndale Hospital, 510 Crookston Road, Glasgow G53 7TU Tel: 0141 211 6400 — MB ChB 1971 Ed.; MD Ed. 1984; FRCPsych 1978; DObst RCOG 1974; DCH RCPS Glas. 1974. Cons. Forens. Psychiat. Leverndale Hosp. Glas.; Hon. Clin. Sen. Lect. Univ. Glas.; Mem. Parole Bd. for Scotl. Socs: Sec. Exec. Forens. Fac. of the RCBych; Bd. Mem., SACRO; Trustee, Ment. Health Foundat., Scotl. Prev: Phys. Supt. State Hosp.; Cons. Forens. Psychiat. State Hosp.; Mem. Advisory Comm. on Prison Managem.

BAIRD, John Lewis Brae Health Centre, Brae, Shetland ZE2 9QJ Tel: 01806 522543 — MB ChB 1971 Aberd.; MRCP (UK) 1974; MRCGP 1979.

BAIRD, Joyce Deans (retired) Department of Diabetes, The Royal Infirmary, Edinburgh EH3 9YW Tel: 0131 552 2030 Fax: 0131 552 3637 — MB ChB Aberd. 1954; MA Aberd. 1948; FRCP Ed. 1980, M 1973. Hon. Research Fell. Univ. Edin. Dept. Med. Roy. Infirm. Edin. Prev: Reader & Sen. Lect. (Med.) Univ. Edin. W.. Gen. Hosp. Edin.

BAIRD, Mr Kevin Scott University Department of Orthopaedic Surgery, Level 2, Western Infirmary, Glasgow G11 6NT Tel: 0141 211 2264 Fax: 0141 339 0462; 34 Dunglass Avenue, Glasgow G14 9EJ Tel: 0141 954 9728 — MB ChB 1984 Aberd.; BMedBiol 1981; FRCS Ed. 1988. Lect. & Hon. Sen. Regist. (Orthop. Surg.) Univ. Glas. Socs: Assoc. Fell. BOA. Prev: Regist. (Orthop. Surg.) W.m. Infirm. Glas.; Regist. (Surg.) Aberd. Roy. Infirm.

BAIRD, Maria Elizabeth 12 Marden Terrace, Cullercoats, North Shields NE30 4PD Tel: 0191 251 1843 — MB BS 1996 Newc. (Newcastle upon Tyne) SHO (Psychiat.) N. Tyneside Gen. Hosp. N. Shields.

BAIRD, Michael Spencer Wake Green Surgery, 7 Wake Green Road, Moseley, Birmingham B13 9HD Tel: 0121 449 0300 — MB ChB 1971 Birm.; MRCGP 1976. (Birm.) Prev: Intern Danbury Hosp., U.S.A.; SHO (Anaesth.) Harari Hosp. Salisbury, Rhodesia; Resid. Sydney Hosp., Australia.

BAIRD, Moira Ann Green Lane Medical Centre, 15 Green Lane, Stoneycroft, Liverpool L13 7DY Tel: 0151 228 9101 Fax: 0151 228 2472 — MB ChB 1979 Manch.; Dip. Pract Dermat. Univ. of Wales 1999; FRCGP 1997; MRCGP 1984; Cert. Family Plann. JCC 1984; DCH RCP Lond. 1983; DRCOG 1983. GP Trainer; Chairm. Liverp. LMC.

BAIRD, Monica Birgit Department of Anaesthesia, Royal United Hospital, Combe Park, Bath BA1 3NG Tel: 01225 825057 — BM 1988 Soton.; MRCP (UK) 1993; FRCA 1994. Cons. Anaesth., Roy. United Hosp., Bath. Socs: FRCA & Assn. Anaesth. Prev: Regist. (Anaesth.) Bristol Roy. Infirm.; Regist. (Anaesth.) Frenchay Hosp. S.mead; SHO (Med.) Glos.

BAIRD, Paul Wayne Long Bredy Surgery, Long Bredy, Dorchester DT2 9HW Tel: 01308 482488 Fax: 01308 482650 — MB BS 1983 Lond.; BSc Lond. 1980, MB BS 1983; MRCGP 1990; DGM RCP Lond. 1989.

BAIRD, Peter James Templehill Surgery, 23 Templehill, Troon KA10 6BQ Tel: 01292 312012 Fax: 01292 317594 — MB ChB 1977 Ed.; MRCGP 1981; DRCOG 1979.

BAIRD, Mr Peter R Ettrick 1A Pennant Mews, London W8 5JN Tel: 020 7370 4233 Fax: 020 7460 5548 Email: pbaird@uk-consultants.co.uk — MB BChir 1969 Camb.; MA, MB Camb. 1969, BChir 1968; FRCS Eng. 1973. (Camb. & St. Thos.) Cons. Surg. Chelsea Hospice, Lond. Prev: Sen. Regist. (Orthop.) Univ. Coll. Hosp. Lond. & W.m. Hosp. Lond.

BAIRD, Richard Douglas 23 Old Sneed Park, Stoke Bishop, Bristol BS9 1RG — MB BS 1997 Lond.

BAIRD, Robert Boyd (retired) The Coppice, 42 Lindeth Road, Silverdale, Carnforth LA5 0TX — MB ChB 1938 Ed.; CPH Ed. 1955; FRCP Ed. 1967; MRCP (UK) 1949; FRCPath 1963. Prev: Cons. Path. Walsall AHA.

BAIRD, Mr Robert Hamilton 20 Broomhill Park, Belfast BT9 5JB — MB BCh BAO 1939 Belf.; FRCS Eng. 1955; DO Eng. 1950. Cons. Ophth. Surg. Roy. Vict. Hosp. Belf.

BAIRD, Mr Roger Neale Litfield House, Clifton Down, Bristol BS8 3LS Tel: 0117 973 1323 Fax: 0117 973 3303; 23 Old Sneed Park, Bristol BS9 1RG Tel: 0117 968 5523 Email: rnbaird@btinternet.com — MB ChB 1966 Ed.; BSc (Hons.) Ed. 1963, ChM 1977; FRCS Eng. 1978; FRCS Ed. 1970. Cons. Surg. Bristol Roy. Infirm. & Clin. Reader in Surg., Bristol Univ. Socs: Corresp. Mem. Soc. Vasc. Surg. (USA); (Pres.) Bristol M-C Soc.; Pres. (2000-01) Vasc. Surgic. Soc. Of GB & Irel. Prev: Med. Dir., United Bristol Healthcare NHS Trust; Sen. Lect. (Surg.) Bristol Univ.; Fulbright Sen. Research Schol. Harvard Med. Sch. Boston USA.

BAIRD, Ruth Margaret 29 Windsor Avenue, Whitefield, Manchester M45 6AZ — MB ChB 1973 Aberd.

BAIRD, Simon Herbert 21 Lismeanry Road, Ballynure, Ballyclare BT39 9UE — MB BCh BAO 1991 Belf.

BAIRD, Stephen Ross Five Elms Medical Practice, Five Elms Health Centre, Five Elms Road, Dagenham RM9 5TT Tel: 020 8517 1175 Fax: 020 8592 0114; 54 Billet Road, Little Heath, Romford RM6 5SU — MB BS 1983 Lond.; MRCGP 1988. GP Dagenham.

BAIRD, Stuart Hugh 22 Hope Crescent, Larkhall ML9 2EL — MB ChB 1998 Dund.; MB ChB Dund 1998.

BAIRD, Thomas James Whitehaven, 2 Dunclare Park, Mullaghanagh, Dungannon BT71 7RY — MB BCh BAO 1972 Belf.; BSc (Hons.) Physiol. Belf. 1969; FRCP Lond. 1995; FRCP Glas. 1991; MRCP (UK) 1977. Cons. Phys. S. Tyrone Hosp. Dungannon Co Tyrone. Prev: Sen. Regist. (Gen. Med.) Craigavon Area Hosp.; Sen. Regist. (Rheum.) Belf. City & Musgrave Pk. Hosps.

BAIRD, Tracey Anne 16 Fairview Park, Carrickfergus BT38 7JG Tel: 01960 369830; 63 Belvedere Park, Belfast BT9 5GT — MB ChB 1993 Dundee; BMSc (Physiol.) Dund 1990; MRCP (UK) 1996. Specialist Regist. (Neurol.). Prev: SHO Rotat. (Med.) W.. Infirm. Glas.; SHO (Neurol.) Roy. Vict. Hosp. Belf.

BAIRD, William Alexander, MBE (retired) 'Gleniffer', Sandhead, Stranraer DG9 9JA Tel: 01776830332 Fax: 01776830332 — MB ChB 1943 Glas.; FRCGP 1980, M 1958. Prev: Ho. Surg. Roy. Vict. Hosp. Belf.

BAIRD, William James Stewart Bangor Health Centre, Newtownards Road, Bangor BT20 4LD Tel: 028 9146 9111; 16 Maralin Avenue, Bangor BT20 4RQ — MB BCh 1970 Belf.

BAIRD, William Leslie Macgregor (retired) Pedraces, 8 Kilmardinny Crescent, Bearsden, Glasgow G61 3NR Tel: 0141 942 5566 — MB ChB Glas. 1956; FRCP Glas. 1986, M 1984; FFA RCS Eng. 1962; DA Eng. 1960. Hon. Clin. Sen. Lect. Univ. Glas. Prev: Cons. Anaesth. Glas. Roy. Infirm.

BAIRD, William Macdonald (retired) Cairnsmore, Port Gaverne, Port Isaac PL29 3SQ Tel: 01208 880249 — MB ChB Glas. 1951; DObst RCOG 1954.

BAIRD, William Walker (retired) 15A Main Road, Castlehead, Paisley PA2 6AJ — MB ChB 1955 Glas.; MRCGP 1968; MRCPsych 1977; DTM & H Ed. 1961; DPM Eng. 1978. Cons. Psychiat. Dykebar Hosp. Paisley. Prev: Sen. Med. Off. Sandakan Med. Gp. Sabah, Malaysia.

BAIRD-SMITH, Sarah Valentine Bedwell Medical Centre, Sinfield Close, Bedwell Crescent, Stevenage SG1 1LQ Tel: 01438 355551 Fax: 01438 749704 — MRCS Eng. LRCP Lond. 1977; BSc Lond. 1974, MB BS 1978.

BAIROLIYA, Mr Ramautar Prasad 22 Tedder Road, Hemel Hempstead HP2 4HA Tel: 01442 63099 — MB BS 1962 Patna; MS Bihar 1972; Primary FRCS 1978. (P. of Wales Med. Coll. Patna) SHO (Gen. Surg./Urol.) Surgic. Rotat. York Dist. Hosp. Prev: SHO (Cas.) W. Wales Gen. Hosp. Carmarthen & Whittington Hosp. Lond; SHO (Orthop.) Enfield Dist. Hosp. (Highlands Wing) & Hemel Hemstead; Gen. Hosp.

BAIRSTOW, John Anthony 11A St. James Road, Marsh, Huddersfield HD1 4QR — MB ChB 1981 Leeds.

BAIRSTOW, Paul Douglas N. Tyneside General Hospital, Rake Lane, North Shields NE29 8HN — MB BS 1993 Newc.

BAIRSTOW, Thomas Edward 22 Carnoustie Grove, Cottingley, Bingley BD16 1QF Tel: 01274 779679 — MB ChB 1942 Leeds; MRCS Eng. LRCP Lond. 1943. (Leeds) Prev: Ho. Surg. Leeds Gen. Infirm.; Sen. Ho. Surg. Dewsbury & Dist. Gen. Infirm.

BAISHNAB, Rai Mohan Langworthy Road Surgery, 195 Langworthy Road, Salford M6 5PW Tel: 0161 736 2338 Fax: 0161 737 2415 — MB BS 1967 Dacca.

BAITHUN, Suhail Ibrahim Aziz Department of Morbid Anatomy, The Royal London Hospital, Whitechapel, London E1 1BB Tel: 020 7377 7348 Fax: 020 7377 7030 Email: s.i.baithun@mds.gmw.ac.uk — MB ChB 1976 Baghdad; MRCPath 1983; FRCPath 1996. Sen. Lect./Cons. Tower Hamlets & Newham HAs. Socs: Worshipful Soc. of Apoth.; Roy. Soc. Med.

BAJAJ, Balwinder Paul Singh 2B Hayfield Road, Moseley, Birmingham B13 9LF — MB BS 1987 Lond.

BAJAJ, Narinder Paul Singh Email: narinderbajaj@compuserve.com — BM BCh 1991 Oxf.; 1999 PHD, London; MA Camb. 1992; MRCP Lond. 1994. Specialist Regist. Neurol., S. Thames; Hon. Lect. in Neurol., Inst of Psychiat., Lond. Prev: Regist. (HIV Med.) Chelsea & W.m. Hosp. Lond.; Regist. (Chest Med.) Qu. Mary's Univ. Hosp. Lond.

BAJAJ, R K Blue Bell Lane Surgery, 2 Blue Bell Lane, Huyton, Liverpool L36 7TN Tel: 0151 489 1422 — MBBS; D Occ Med (Lon.); CIH (Dundee); DA (Lon.). (Maulana Azad (Delhi) India) Socs: BMA; SPA; ODA.

BAJAJ, Mr Raj Kumar Kirkdale Medical Centre, 63 Walton Road, Liverpool L4 4AF Tel: 0151 207 0950 — MB BS 1969 Punjab; MS Delhi 1973; MB BS Punjabi 1969; FRCS Ed. 1978. (Govt. Med. Coll. Patiala) GP Liverp. Prev: Regist. (Surg.) Clatterbridge Hosp. Bebington.

BAJAJ, Sanjeev 34 Forty Avenue, Wembley HA9 8JP; 34 Forty Avenue, Wembley HA9 8JP Tel: 020 8908 6694 — MB BS 1981 Delhi; MRCS Eng. LRCP Lond. 1989; T (GP) 1991; DGM RCP Lond. 1989. (Maulana Azad Medical College, New Delhi, India) Trainee GP Dorset.; Deput. GP Healthcall Ltd Bournemouth. Socs: MDU. Prev: SHO (A & E) Maidstone Hosp.; SHO (Acute Geriat. Med.) Poole Gen. Hosp.; SHO (Acute Geriat. Med.) N. Devon Dist. Hosp. Barnstaple.

BAJAJ, Subhash The Surgery, 35 Herbert Street, West Bromwich B70 6HZ Tel: 0121 525 1481 — MB BS 1970 Rajasthan; MS (Obst. & Gyn.) Rajasthan 1975, MB BS 1970. (S.M.S. Med. Coll. Jaipur)

BAJAJ, Veena Kirkdale Medical Centre, 63 Walton Road, Liverpool L4 4AF Tel: 0151 207 0950 — MB BS 1970 Panjab; MRCP (UK) 1982.

BAJALAN, Ahmad Abdulla Aziz Clinical Neurophysiology, Hill Royal Infirmary, Anlaby, Hull HU2 3JZ Tel: 01482 674423 — MB ChB 1972 Baghdad; FRCP London; MRCP (UK) 1979. (Baghdad) p/t Cons. (Clin. Neurophysiol.) Hull Roy. Infirm. Socs: Brit. Soc. of Clin. NeuroPhysiol. (BSCN); Assn. of Brit. Clin. Neurophysiologists (ABCN); N. Eng. Neurol. Assn. (NENA). Prev: Sen. Regist. Clin. Neurophysiol. Dudley Rd. Hosp. & Midl. Centre; for Neurol. & Neurosurg. Birm.; Contract Research Fell. Univ. Aston; Med. Regist. Morriston Hosp. Swansea.

BAJALLAN, Nabil Muhammed Salih Pathology Department, George Eliot Hospital NHS Trust, College St., Nuneaton CV10 7DJ Tel: 02476 865196 Fax: 02476 865196; 8 Gibbett Hill Road, Coventry CV4 7AJ Tel: 01203 418738 Email: nbajallan@teco.net — MB ChB 1973 Baghdad; FRCPath 1996, M 1985. (Baghdad) Cons. Histopath. Geo. Eliot Hosp. NHS Trust. Socs: Internat. Acad. Path.; Assn. Clin. Paths. Prev: Sen. Regist. E. Anglia RHA; SHO Roy. Berks. Hosp. Reading.

BAJEK, Genowefa The Health Centre, High Street, Arnold, Nottingham NG5 7BG Tel: 0115 926 7257; 6 Cocker Beck, Lambley, Nottingham NG4 4QP — BM BS 1982 Nottm.; MRCGP 1986; DRCOG 1986.

BAJEN, Jose Maria Flat 33, Pointer Court II, Royal Lancaster Infirmary, Ashton Road, Lancaster LA1 4RP — LMS 1992 Saragossa.

BAJKOWSKI, Adam Orrell Road Practice, 84 Orrell Road, Orrell, Wigan WN5 8HB Tel: 01942 222321 Fax: 01942 620327; 7 Briarly, Standish, Wigan WN6 0BY Tel: 01257 426982 — MB ChB 1982 Manch.; Cert. Family Plann. JCC 1986. (Manch.) Socs: (Hon. Sec.) Primary Care Rheum. Soc.

BAJOREK, Marian Feliks Walerian 2B Brompton Road, Sprotbrough, Doncaster DN5 7LB Tel: 01302 855723 — Med. Dipl. Lwow 1937.

BAJOREK, Piotr Kazimierz Marian Anaesthetic Dept, East Surrey Hospital, Canada Drive, Redhill RH1 5RH; 33 Woodcote Avenue, Wallington SM6 0QU — MB BS 1979 Lond.; BSc (Hons.) Lond. 1976, MB BS 1979; FFA RCSI 1986. Cons. Anaesth., Surrey & Sussex Healthcare NHS Trust, E. Surrey Hosp., Redhill.

BAJORIA, Rekha 4 St Stephens Road, Hounslow TW3 2AX Tel: 020 8570 3428 — MB BS 1980 Calcutta; MRCOG 1985.

BAJORIA, Mr Shyam Sunder (retired) 46 White Ox Way, Penrith CA11 8QP Tel: 0114 268 5289, 01768 891272 Email: sarah.gowlett@talk21.com — MB BS 1957 Agra; FRCS Eng. 1964; DA Eng. 1965. Prev: Cons. Wrexham Limb Fitting Centre.

BAJORIA, Mr Suresh Kumar Kenwood, 2 Kribyn Lane, Swiss Valley Road, Llanelli SA14 8BU — MB BS 1982 Utkal; FRCS Glas. 1987; Dip. Urol. Lond 1991. Regist. (Urol. & Renal Transpl.) Hammersmith Hosp. Lond. Prev: Regist. (Urol.) BRd.green Hosp. Liverp.; Regist. (Urol.) Law Hosp. Carluke.

BAJPAI, Anup Chandra Saltley Centre for Health Care, Craddock Road, Saltley, Birmingham B8 1RZ Tel: 0121 327 6444 Fax: 0121 327 2413; 12 Lady Byron Lane, Knowle, Solihull B93 9AU Tel: 0121 704 2676 — MD 1969 Lucknow; MB BS 1966. (G.S.V.M. Med. Coll. Kanpur)

BAJPAI, Sheela Julia Engwell Health Centre, 153 Woodward Road, Dagenham RM9 4SU Tel: 020 8592 5500 Fax: 020 8592 1127 — MB BS 1958 Bihar.

BAJWA, Narinder Paul Singh Park Road Surgery, Park Road, Camberley GU15 2NN Tel: 01276 26171; Flat 10, Ruskin Court, Champion Hill, London SE5 8AH Tel: 020 7274 6291 Email: narinder@orangenet.com — MB BS 1993 Lond.

BAJWA, Miss Raj (retired) N. Hants Hospital, Aldermaston Road, Basingstoke RG24 9NA Tel: 01256 473202 Fax: 01256 313553 — MB BS Panjab (India) 1956; FRCS Ed. 1970; FRCS Eng. 1965. Prev: Cons. Surg. (ENT) N. Hants Hosp.

BAJWA, Saba X-Ray Department COP D, North Staffordshire Hospitals, Stoke-on-Trent ST4 7PA Tel: 01782 554156 Fax: 01782 555057; 2 Allensway, Newcastle under Lyme, Newcastle ST5 3SY — MB BS 1987 Punjab; FRCR 1995; FFR Dub. 1994. Cons. COP D, N. Staffs. Hosp.; Cons. Radiologist, N. Staffs Nuffield. Socs: Roy. Coll. Radiol.; RCR BrE. Gp.; W Midl.Radiol. Gp.

BAK, Julie Ellen 127 Acre Road, Kingston upon Thames KT2 6EZ — MB BS 1986 Lond.; FRCS Ed. 1994.

***BAKAEEN, Faisal Ghazi Saleh** c/o Trinity College, Cambridge CB2 1TQ; D Ahiet Al Ameer Rashid, PO Box 21, Amman, Jordan Tel: 00 962 6815121 — BChir 1994 Camb.

BAKAJ, Peter Oakwood Surgery, Church Street, Mansfield Woodhouse, Mansfield NG19 8BL Tel: 01623 633111 Fax: 01623 423480 — MB ChB 1973 Sheff.; FRCGP 1994, M 1977; DRCOG 1976. CME Course Organiser N. Notts.; Mem. N. Notts. LMC; Mem. Clin. Govtrnance Sub-Comm. Mansfield Dist. PCT; Exec. Mem. Mansfield Dist. PCT; Educat.al Lead, Mansfield Dist. PCT. Socs: Mansfield Med. Soc.

BAKALA, Alina Irena 7 Balfour Road, London W3 0DQ — MB BS 1996 Lond.

BAKAR, Ida Ratnawati c/o Mr Paul Bell, 11 Dundonald Street, Edinburgh EH3 6RZ — MB ChB 1998 Bristol.

BAKAR, Normi Binte Abu 31 Highbury Place, London N5 1QP — MB BS 1979 Lond.; MRCGP 1984; T(GP) 1991; DCH RCP Lond. 1987; DCCH RCP Ed. 1985. Prev: GP Lond.

BAKAR, Shilpi Jakia St Cuthberts Lodge, Steep Hill, Lincoln LN2 1LR — MB ChB 1998 Leic.; MB ChB Leic 1998.

BAKARE, Rotimi Olusegun North Croydon Medical Centre, 518 London Road, Thornton Heath CR7 7HQ Tel: 020 7476 2255 Fax: 020 7511 8980 — MB ChB 1986 Ife; B.Tech (Brunel) 1977; MSc Newc. 1979; BSc Ife 1982; DFFP 1993; T (GP) 1996. GP Regist. Lond.

BAKAYA, Ramala Rosemaen, Anglesey Drive, Poynton, Stockport SK12 Tel: 0161 874434 — MB BS 1955 Bombay; FRCOG 1989, M 1963; DObst 1960.

BAKE, Alan John The Village Practice, Mere Lane, Armthorpe, Doncaster DN3 2DB Tel: 01302 300322 Fax: 01302 300737; 1 Armthorpe Lane, Barnby Dun, Doncaster DN3 1LZ Tel: 01302 886844 — MB ChB 1980 Leeds; MRCGP 1986; DRCOG 1985. Socs: Brit. Med. Acupunct. Soc.

BAKEER, Giumma Mohamed Orthopedic Department - Scarborough General Hospital, Woodlands Drive, Scarborough

YO12 5DX Tel: 01723 368111; 45 Hovingham Drive, Woodlands Vale, Scarborough YO12 5XT Tel: 01723 379559 — MB ChB 1983 Garyounis, Libya; MSc (Orthop.) Lond. 1992; FRCS 1997. Assoc. Specialist (Orthop. & Trauma) ScarBoro. Hosp. Prev: Clin. Fell. (Orthop. & Trauma) Kettering Gen. Hosp.

BAKER, Abu Strathmore Medical Practice, 26-28 Chester Road, Wrexham LL11 7SA Tel: 01978 352055 Fax: 01978 310689 — MB BS 1976 Mysore.

BAKER, Adel 56 Manor Road, Great Crosby, Liverpool L23 7XL — MB BCh 1966 Ain Shams; DLO RCS Eng. 1974. (Ein Shams)

BAKER, Adrian Bruce 2 Freedom Villas, Launceston Road, Tavistock PL19 8NG — MB ChB 1980 Birm.

BAKER, Adrian William Thomas Erin, Copley Dr, Barnstaple EX31 2BH — MB ChB 1989 Birm.; MRCGP 1996; DRCOG 1994; DTM & H Liverp. 1991; DCH RCP Lond. 1991. (Birm.)

BAKER, Alan Murray (retired) Barn Close, Combe Bank Drive, Sundridge, Sevenoaks TN14 6AD Tel: 01959 562514 Fax: 01959 562514 — MRCS Eng. LRCP Lond. 1950; MA Camb. 1950; DPH Lond. 1961; DTM & H Liverp. 1957. Prev: Princip. Med. Adviser Overseas Devel. Admin.

BAKER, Alastair James 29 Downs Hill, Beckenham BR3 5HA — MB ChB 1980 Glas.

***BAKER, Alicia Clare** 54 Hazelwood Road, Sutton Coldfield B74 3RW — MB ChB 1997 Bristol.

BAKER, Alison Katharine Severn Surgery, 159 Uplands Road, Oadby, Leicester LE2 4NW Tel: 0116 271 9042 — MB ChB 1976 Sheff.; DRCOG 1978.

BAKER, Alison Margaret Saltaire Medical Centre, Richmond Road, Shipley BD18 4RX Tel: 01274 593101 Fax: 01274 772588; 9 The Orchards, Lady Lane, Bingley BD16 4AZ — MB ChB 1988 Manch.; MRCGP 1993. Prev: Trainee GP Airedale VTS.

BAKER, Mr Allen Stanley (retired) 123 Tavistock St, Bedford MK40 2SB Tel: 01234 358223 Fax: 01234 349656 Email: allenbaker@uk_consultants.co.uk — MB ChB 1974 Leeds; BSc (Hons.) Leeds 1971; FRCS Ed. (Orth.) 1983; FRCS Eng. 1978. Cons. Orthop. Surg. Prev: Cons. Orthop. Surg. Bedford Gen. Hosp.

BAKER, Andrew Kenneth Mount Cottage, Little Shore Lane, Bishops Waltham, Southampton SO32 1ED — MB BCh BAO 1993 NUI; LRCPSI 1993.

BAKER, Andrew Reuben Mark Purton Surgery, High Street, Purton, Swindon SN5 4BD Tel: 01793 770207 Fax: 01793 772662 — MB BS 1980 Lond.; BSc Engin 1970, MB BS Lond. 1980; MRCGP 1985; T(GP) 1991. Prev: Project Dir. Primary Health Care Project, Sidi Bouzid, Tunisia; Trainee GP St. Thos. Lond. VTS.

BAKER, Mr Andrew Robert 9 Broad-Dykes Crescent, Kingswells, Aberdeen AB15 8UJ; 435 Marine Drive, Brighton Beach, Durban 4052, South Africa Tel: 0131 478130 — MB ChB 1985 Cape Town; FRCS Glas. 1993. Prev: Regist. (Surg.) King Edwd. Hosp. Durban, SA.

BAKER, Andrew William 2 Arundell Close, Cheshunt, Waltham Cross EN8 0EE — MB ChB 1990 Bristol.

BAKER, Anthony Searle Greenbank, Old Tiverton Road, Bampton, Tiverton EX16 9DP Tel: 01398 331601 — MB BS 1954 Lond. (St. Bart.) Ref. Min. of Health. Prev: Ho. Phys. & Ho. Surg. Whipps Cross Hosp.; Gyn. & Obst. Ho. Surg. Lambeth Hosp.

BAKER, Anthony William Ashwood Centre, Stonemason's Court, Cemetery Dales, Brookwood, Woking GU24 0BL Tel: 01483 487979 Fax: 01483 486464; the Cottage, Pinewood Road, Ash, Aldershot GU12 6DQ Tel: 01252 231 8777 — MB BS 1974 Lond.; MRCS Eng. LRCP Lond. 1974; MRCPsych 1980. Cons. Indep. Child Care Consultancy Pract. Ashwood Centre Brookwood. Socs: Fell. Roy. Soc. Med. Prev: Cons. Psychiat. St. Joseph's Holy Cross Haslemere & Child & Family Kingston & Esher HA; Sen. Regist. (Child & Adolesc. Psychiat.) St. Geo. Hosp. Lond.

BAKER, Mr Antony Richard Department of General Surgery, Frenchay Hospital, Bristol BS16 1LE Tel: 0117 918 6505 Fax: 0117 975 3765 — MB BChir 1978 Camb.; MA Camb. 1978; MD Leic. 1986; FRCS Eng. 1982. Cons. Surg. Gen. & Vasc. Frenchay Hosp. Bristol. Socs: Surgic. Research Soc.; Vasc. Surgic. Soc.; Assn. Surg. Prev: Sen. Regist. (Surg.) Trent RHA; Lect. (Surg.) Leic. Roy. Infirm.; SHO Roy. Nat. Orthop. Hosp. Stanmore.

BAKER, Brian Flat 2, Rann Lea, Mill Lane, Rainhill, Prescot L35 6NH — MRCS Eng. LRCP Lond. 1981; MRCGP 1986.

BAKER, Brian Rowden 200 Ridgeway Road, Sheffield S12 2TA Tel: 0114398575 — MB BS 1958 Lond.; MRCS Eng. LRCP Lond. 1957. (King's Coll. Hosp.) Prev: Ho. Surg. St. Giles' Hosp. Lond.; Ho. Phys. Bedford Gen. Hosp.; Obst. Ho. Surg. Qu. Mary's Hosp. For E. End. Lond.

BAKER, Brian Sidney, OStJ (retired) 300 Dyke Road, Brighton BN1 5BB Tel: 01273 501970 — MB BS 1954 Lond.; FFOM RCP Lond. 1994. Surg. St. John Ambul. Prev: Regional Med. Off. Brit. Telecom.

BAKER, Carey Denis (retired) 28 Oaks Park, Canterbury CT2 9DP Tel: 01227 457203 — MRCS Eng. LRCP Lond. 1941; FRCGP 1967. Prev: Upjohn Trav. Fell.

BAKER, Caroline Gorsley Lodge, Woodgate, Bishopsbourne, Canterbury CT4 5JL — MB BS 1998 Lond.; MB BS Lond 1998.

BAKER, Caroline Blanche House 12, 7 Steele Road, London W4 5AE — MB BS 1985 Melbourne.

BAKER, Caroline Jill 60 Plymouth Wharf, Isle of Dogs, London E14 3EL — MB BS 1994 Lond.

BAKER, Catharine Mary Boggs Farm, Westlinton, Carlisle CA6 6AW — MB BS 1980 Lond.

BAKER, Charles Eric North Staffordshire Hospitals, Stoke-on-Trent — MB BCh 1990 Wales; FRCA.

BAKER, Christine de Chair Bemerton Heath Surgery, Pembroke Road, Salisbury SP2 9DJ Tel: 01722 411691 Fax: 01722 415047; Bodnant, 56 Hulse Road, Salisbury SP1 3LY Tel: 01722 325933 — MB BS 1983 Lond.; MRCGP 1987; DRCOG 1986.

BAKER, Christopher David Baker and Rose, The Surgery, Bowholm, Canonbie DG14 0UX Tel: 01387 371313 Fax: 01387 371244 — MB BS 1979 Lond.; MRCGP 1987. (St Mary's Hospital Medical School) Med. Direct. Dumfries & Galloway Prim. Care Trust Dumfries; Care Mem. Coronary Heart Dis. Task Force for Scotl. (2 year appointment). Prev: Regist. (Gen. Med.) Ipswich E. Anglian RHA.

BAKER, Christopher Stephen Rainald 30 Ufton Road, London N1 5BX Tel: 020 7254 3053 Fax: 020 7684 1861 Email: ccbaker6751@aol.com — MB BS 1990 Lond.; BSc (Physiol.) Lond. 1987; MRCP (UK) 1993. (Char. Cross & Westm. Lond.) Card. Research Regist. Roy. Postgrad. Med. Sch. Hammersmith Hosp. Prev: Ho. Off. Med. W.m. Hosp. Lond.; Regist. Rotat. (Cardiol. & Gen. Med.) Chase Farm Hosp., Roy. Free Hosp. & Lond. Chest Hosp.; SHO Rotat. (Med. & Renal Med.) Guy's Hosp. Lond.

BAKER, Claire Marie 56 Hockenhull Lane, Tarvin, Chester CH3 8LR — MB ChB 1996 Liverp.

BAKER, Cyril Leon 8 Ellenborough Place, London SW15 5LZ — MB BS 1949 Lond.

BAKER, Mr Daryll Marc Royal Free Hospital, Pond St., London NW3 2QG Tel: 020 7794 0500 Fax: 020 7431 5437 Email: baker@freevas.demon.co.uk — BM BCh 1987 Oxf.; PhD Wales 1988, BSc 1981; FRCS (Gen.) 1996; FRCS (Ed.) 1992. (Oxford University) Cons. Surg. Roy. Free Hosp. Lond.

BAKER, David, Maj. RAMC Medical Branch, HQ 1 (UK) Armoured Division, Hereford, BFPO 15 — MB ChB 1984 Dundee; PhD Aston 1982, BSc 1976; MRCGP 1988.

BAKER, David Bryntirion, Park Hill, Tredegar NP22 3PG — MB ChB 1994 Leic.; BSc (Hons.) Wales 1989; FRCS (Eng) 1998. Specialist Regist. (Orthop & trauma), Welsh Orthop. Train. Progr. Prev: Lect. (Anat.) Univ. Birm.; Ho. Off. (Surg. & Trauma) Leicester Roy. Infirm.; Ho. Off. (Med.) Nevill Hall Hosp. Abergavenny.

BAKER, David Alan 2 Park Row, Sutton-in-Craven, Keighley BD20 7BU — MB BS 1984 Lond.

BAKER, David Antony (retired) Hallfield Manor, Water Lane, Bassingham, Lincoln LN5 9LA Tel: 01522 788079 Email: drdavidbaker@cs.com — MB BS Lond. 1970; MRCS Eng. LRCP Lond. 1970. Locum GP Lincs.

BAKER, David James Saxmu 75, Hopital Necker-Enfants Malades, 149 rue de Sèvres 75743, Paris Cedex 15, France Tel: 33 1 44 492323 Fax: 33 1 44 492325; 6 Addingham Road, Eastbourne BN22 7DY — MB BS 1972 Lond.; MRCS Eng. LRCP Lond. 1972; DM Soton. 1987; FFA RCS Eng. 1979. (St. Bart.) Medecin Vacataire Serv. D'Anesthesie/Reanimation Hôpital Necker-Enfants Malades Paris; Hon. Cons. Clin. Neurophysiol. Soton. Gen. Hosp.; Attached Cons. in Anaesth.; Serv. D'anesthesie et Reanimation SAMU de PARIS; Hoptal Necker Enfants Malades, Paris; Cons. Adviser in trauma Anaesth. to the Roy. Navy. Socs: Internat. Trauma Anaesth.

& Critical Care Soc. (Toxic trauma comm.); Europ. Emerg. Care Train. organisation (sec.); Roy. Soc. Med. Prev: Cons. Med. Off. RN; Anaesth. & applied Physiol. (Roy. Navy).

BAKER, David John Vine House Surgery, Vine Street, Grantham NG31 6RQ Tel: 01476 576851 Fax: 01476 591732 — MB ChB 1990 Leic.; MRCGP. (Leicester) GP Vine Ho. Surg. Grantham.

BAKER, David Lindsay Middlewich Road Surgery, 6 Middlewich Road, Sandbach CW11 1DL Tel: 01270 767411 Fax: 01270 759305; Wheelock Farm, Mill Lane, Wheelock, Sandbach CW11 4RD Tel: 01270 766877 — MB ChB 1980 Manch.; MRCGP 1986; DRCOG 1986. Prev: SHO Rotat. Train. Scheme Gen. Pract. Wythenshawe Hosp. Manch.; SHO Cardiothoracic Med. Regional Cardiothoracic Unit Wythenshawe; Hosp. Manch.; Ho. Surg. (Gen. & Vasc. Surg.) Manch. Roy. Infirm.

BAKER, David Michael Haymeads, Dunheved Road, Launceston PL15 9JQ — MB BS 1980 Lond.; DRCOG 1983. (St. Bart.) GP Launceston Health Centre Cornw.

BAKER, Dhia Salih 12 Cottom Mill Spinney, Cubbington, Leamington Spa CV32 7XH — MB ChB 1968 Mosul; MRCP (UK) 1991.

BAKER, Diane Margaret Belbury End, Toadpit Lane, West Hill, Ottery St Mary EX11 1TR — MB ChB 1977 Birm.; DRCOG 1979.

BAKER, Dorothy Joan Mary (retired) The Green, Woogates Green, Knighton-on-Teme, Tenbury Wells WR15 8LX — MB ChB 1943 Birm.

BAKER, Edward James Department of Paediatric Cardiology, Guy's Hospital, St Thomas St., London SE1 9RT Tel: 020 7955 4617 Fax: 020 7955 4614 Email: edward.baker@gstt.thames.nhs.uk — MB BChir 1979 Camb.; MD Camb. 1986, MA 1979.; FRCP Lond. 1994; MRCP (UK) 1982; FRCPCH 1997. (St. Thos.) Hon. Cons. Paediat. Cardiol. Guy's and St. Thomas's Hosp. Lond.; Sen. Lect. (Paediat.) King's Coll. Lond.; Asst. Med. Director, Guy's and St. Thomas's Hosp. Trust.; Exec. Edr., "Cardiol. in the Young", Greenwich Med. Media, Lond. Socs: Fell., Roy. Coll. of Phys.s, Lond.; Fell., Roy. Coll. of Paediat. and Child Health; Mem. Brit. Cardiac Soc. Prev: Vis. Prof. Pittsburgh Childr. Hosp., USA.; Gp. Dir. Wom. & Childr. Servs. Guy's & St Thos. Hosp. Trust; Assoc. Edr. Paediat. Cardiol. Springer, N.Y.

BAKER, Emma Harriet First Floor Flat, 115 Knolly's Road, Streatham, London SW16 2JP Email: ebaker@sghms.ac.uk — MB ChB 1988 Ed.; PhD Manch. 1996; MRCP (UK) 1991. (Ed.) Sen. Regist. (Clin. Pharmacol. & Gen. Med.) St. Geo. Hosp. Med. Sch. Lond. Socs: Med. Res. Soc. Prev: Research Fell. (Gen. Med.) & Hon. Regist. Univ. Manch.; SHO (Med.) Hope Hosp. Salford & Roy. Lancaster Infirm.

BAKER, Emma Jane 21 Laburnum Grove, Horbury, Wakefield WF4 6HG — MB BS 1998 Lond.; MB BS Lond 1998.

BAKER, Eurgain Tramways Medical Centre, 54a Holme Lane, Sheffield S6 4JQ Tel: 0114 233 9462; 383 Redmires Road, Sheffield S10 4LE Tel: 01472 304087 — MB BS 1975 Lond.; BSc Lond. 1972, MB BS 1975; MRCGP 1981.

BAKER, Fiona Margaret Ardmhor, Kyleakin, Isle of Skye IV41 8PR Tel: 01599 534509; 15 Bishopsgate Road, Colston, Glasgow G21 1XD Tel: 0141 772 2345 — MB ChB 1992 Ed.; MRCGP 1998; DRCOG 1997. GP Locum.

BAKER, Frances Anne Nuffield Health Centre, Welch Way, Witney OX28 6JQ Tel: 01993 703641; 80 Woodstock Road, Witney, Oxford OX28 1DY Tel: 01993 779413 — MB BS 1988 Lond. GP Sessions; Clin. Asst. (Genitourin.) Oxf.; Family Plann. Sessions. Socs: DFFP; MSSVD. Prev: Clin. Asst. (Genitourin.) Wycombe; Research GP Oxf. Depression Study; Family Plann. sessions.

BAKER, Frank George Medical Centre, Cambridge Avenue, Bottesford, Scunthorpe DN16 3LG Tel: 01724 842415 Fax: 01724 271437; 6 Old Brumby Street, Scunthorpe DN16 2DB Tel: 01724 842415 — MB BS 1981 Lond.; MRCGP 1987; DRCOG 1985.

BAKER, Franklyn Newlands Medical Centre, 315 Chorley New Road, Bolton BL1 5BP Tel: 01204 840342 Mobile: 07947 102281 — MB ChB 1971 Manch.; MRCGP 1976. (Manchester) GP; Apptd. Med. Mem. Counc. for Gen. Med. Counc. Fitness to Practise Comm.s, Lond.; Med. Mem. for the Appeals Serv. Manch.; Examr. for Medico-Legal Reporting; Dent. Anaesth. Socs: Bolton Med. Soc. Prev: Clin. Asst. (Accid. & Emerg.) Hope Hosp. Salford; Clin. Asst. (O & G) Hope Hosp. Salford; Med. Off. Manch. Regional Blood Transfus. Serv.

BAKER, Gemma Mary 8 Shootersway Park, Berkhamsted HP4 3NX — MB BCh BAO 1973 NUI.

BAKER, Geoffrey Arthur Evelyn (retired) Lych Gate, Bakeham Lane, Englefield Green, Egham TW20 9TZ Tel: 01784 432724 — MB BS (Hnrs.) Lond. 1951; MRCS Eng. LRCP Lond. 1951; DObst RCOG 1957; MRCGP 1965. Consg. Med. Off. Hanover Life. Prev: Squadron Ldr. RAF Med. Br.

BAKER, Mr Geoffrey Cecil Winchester Somerset House Farm, Calow, Chesterfield S44 5AF Tel: 01246 271994 Email: gcwbaker@btinternet.com — MB BS 1955 Lond.; FRCS Eng. 1960; MRCS Eng. LRCP Lond. 1955. (Guy's) Socs: Fell. BOA; BMA. Prev: Cons. Orthop. Surg. Chesterfield & N. Derbysh. Roy. Hosp.; Cons. Orthop. Surg. Harlow Wood Orthop. Hosp. Mansfield; Lect. (Orthop.) Surg. Univ. Edin.

BAKER, George Hugh Barrington 152 Harley Street, London W1G 7LH Tel: 020 7935 3834 Fax: 020 8643 4494 — MB BCh BAO 1957 Belfast; 1962 MD Belf.; 1981 FRCPI, M 1964; 1980 FRCPsych, M 1971; 1965 DPM Eng. (Belf.) Hon. Cons. Psychiat. Chelsea & W.m. Hosp. Lond. Socs: Fell. Roy. Soc. Med. Prev: Sen. Regist. Bethlem Roy. & Maudsley Hosps.; Supervis. Psychiat. Syracuse Psychiat. Hosp. New York, USA; Sen. Regist. St. Bart. Hosp.

BAKER, George Peter 5 Harland Avenue, Croydon CR0 5QB Tel: 020 8654 6762 — MB BChir 1942 Camb.; MSc 1939, MA 1940; MD Camb. 1950; FRCP Lond. 1964, M 1948. (Camb. & Guy's) Cons. Phys. Emerit. Croydon HA. Socs: Fell. Roy. Soc. Med. Prev: Med. 1st Asst. St. Geo. Hosp.; Chief Med. Off. Hill Samuel Life Assur. Ltd.; Squadron Ldr. RAFVR.

BAKER, Gillian Boyne Avenue Surgery, 57 Boyne Avenue, Hendon, London NW4 2JL Tel: 020 8203 2230 Fax: 020 8202 7980 — MB ChB 1968 Liverp.; DCH Eng. 1971. (Liverp.) GP; SCMO Psychosexual Med. St. Albans & Hemel Hempstead NHS Trust Barnethealth Care Trust. Socs: BMA.

BAKER, Glynn Raymond Curtis The Haven, Cobbs Hill, Old Wives Lees, Canterbury CT4 8AL — BM 1992 Soton.

BAKER, Guy Richard Hamilton The Surgery, West End, Herstmonceux, Hailsham BN27 4NN Tel: 01323 833535 Fax: 01323 833998; The Sanatorium, Eastbourne College, Eastbourne Tel: 01323 723194 Fax: 01323 412218 — MB BS 1969 Lond.; MRCS Eng. LRCP Lond. 1969.

BAKER, Harvey 152 Harley Street, London W1G 7LH Tel: 020 7935 8868 Fax: 020 7224 2574; 16 Sheldon Avenue, Highgate, London N6 4JT Tel: 020 8340 5970 Fax: 020 8347 7017 — MB ChB 1954 Leeds; MD Leeds 1965; FRCP Lond. 1973, M 1959. Socs: Fell. (Ex-Pres.) St. John's Hosp. Dermat. Soc.; (Ex-Pres.) Brit. Assn. Dermat. Prev: Cons. Dermat. Lond. Hosp.; Sen. Lect. Inst. Dermat. Lond.; Vis. Research Assoc. Univ., Pennsylvania.

BAKER, Hazel Bertha (retired) 18 Gaialand's Crescent, Lichfield WS13 7LU Tel: 01543 263502 Email: hazelbaker@talk21.com — MB BS Lond. 1943; MRCS Eng. LRCP Lond. 1943; MRCPsych 1972; DPM Eng. 1961. Prev: Hon. Cons. Good Hope Hosp. Sutton Coldfield.

BAKER, Heather Elizabeth Porch Surgery, Beechfield Road, Corsham SN13 9DL Tel: 01249 712232 Fax: 01249 701389 — MB ChB 1982 Birm.; MRCGP 1986; DRCOG 1985. (Birmingham) GP Corsham. Prev: Trainee GP Pboro. VTS.

BAKER, Helen Jane Whiston Corner Surgery, 99 Coldharbour Lane, London SE5 9NS Tel: 020 7274 4507 Fax: 020 7733 6545 Email: helen.baker@kcl.ac.uk — MB BChir 1990 Camb.; MA Camb. 1990; MRCGP 1996; DRCOG 1994. p/t GP Partner, The Corner Surg. 99 Coldharbour La. Lond. SE5 9NS. Prev: Trainee GP/SHO Lewisham Trust.

BAKER, Henry de Chair (retired) Sea Winds, Orford, Woodbridge IP12 2NG Tel: 01394 450302 — MD 1957 Manch.; MB ChB 1948; FRCPath 1970, M 1964. Prev: Cons. Histopath. Norwich Health Dist.

BAKER, Hilary Ann Falklands Surgery, Falkland Way, Bradwell, Great Yarmouth NR31 8RW Tel: 01493 442233 — MB BS 1982 Lond.; MRCGP 1987.

BAKER, Iain Richardson Sanquhar Health Centre, Station Road, Sanquhar DG4 6BT Tel: 01659 50221 Fax: 01659 58116 — MB ChB 1974 Aberd.; MRCGP 1984; DObst RCOG 1976. Prev: Squadron Ldr. RAF Med. Br.

BAKER, Ian Alfred c/o Avon HA, 10 Dighton St., Bristol BS2 8EE Tel: 0117 976 6600 Fax: 0117 976 6601 — MB BS 1965 Lond.; BSc Lond. 1962, MSc (Soc. Med.) 1976; FRCP Lond. 1991; MRCP Lond. 1969; MRCS Eng. LRCP Lond. 1964; FFPHM RCP (UK) 1990; MFCM 1987. (Guy's) Cons. Pub. Health Med. Avon HA; Hon. Reader in Epidemiol., Univ. of Bristol. Socs: Soc. Social Med. Prev: Mem. Scientif. Staff MRC Epidemiol. Unit Cardiff; Dir. Britain Nepal Med. Unit; Regist. (Med.) Guy's Hosp. Lond.

BAKER, Ian Hunter Staploe Medical Centre, Brewhouse Lane, Soham, Ely CB7 5JD Tel: 01353 624121 Fax: 01353 624203; 8 The Oaks, Soham, Ely CB7 5FF Tel: 01353 723123 Email: ianhbaker@aol.com — MB BS 1972 Lond.; BSc Lond. 1966; MRCS Eng. LRCP Lond. 1973. (St. Bart. Med. Coll.) Socs: Mid. Anglia Gp. Accid. Serv.; Newmarket Med. Soc. Prev: SHO (Trauma & Orthop.) P.ss Margt. Hosp. Swindon; Ho. Phys. St. Bart. Hosp. Lond.; Ho. Surg. Addenbrooke's Hosp. Camb.

BAKER, Jack Richmond (retired) 39 School Lane, Hagley, Stourbridge DY9 9LD Tel: 01562 882094 — MB ChB 1946 Birm. Prev: Ho. Surg. (Cas.) Birm. Gen. Hosp.

BAKER, Professor James Bernard Ellis Hustyn Mill, Burlawn, Wadebridge PL27 7LD Tel: 01208 813345 — BM BCh 1945 Oxf.; BSc Oxf. 1947, MA 1947. (Oxf.) Emerit. Prof. Univ. Lond. Socs: Brit. Pharm. Soc.; Physiol. Soc. Prev: Prof. Pharmacol. Char. Cross Hosp. & W.m. Med. Sch.

BAKER, Janet Whitwick Road Surgery, Whitwick Road, Coalville LE67 3FA Tel: 01530 836507 — MB BS 1963 Durh.; MRCOG 1977, DObst 1965. (Durh.) Clin. Asst. Hysteroscopy Leicester Roy. Infirm. Socs: BMA & Leicester Med. Soc.; Brit. Colposcopy Soc. Prev: Regist. (Obst.) Hull Matern. Hosp.; SHO (Obst.) Dryburn Hosp. Durh.; SHO (O & G & Gen. Surg.) W.wood Hosp. Beverley.

BAKER, Janet Ruth Whitelands, Raikeswood Crescent, Skipton BD23 1ND Tel: 01756 798324; Airedale General Hospital, Skipton Road, Steeton, Keighley BD20 6TD Tel: 01535 652511 — MB ChB 1980 Leeds; BSc (Hons.) Leeds 1977; FFA RCS Eng. 1984. (Leeds) Cons. Anaesth. Airedale HA. Prev: Sen. Regist. (Anaesth.) Nottm.; Regist. (Anaesth.) Gt. Ormond St. Hosp. Sick Childr. Lond.; Regist. (Anaesth.) St. Jas. Hosp. Leeds.

BAKER, Jeremy Paul c/o 29 The Bevers, Mortimer Common, Reading RG7 3SP — MB BS 1991 Lond.

BAKER, Jillian Glenda 47 Perry Orchard, Upton St Leonards, Gloucester GL4 8EH Tel: 01452 618960 — BM BS 1996 Nottm.; BMedSci Nottm. 1994; MRCP 1999. (Nottm.) SHO (Med.) Qu.'s Med. Centre Nottm. Socs: BMA & MPS. Prev: Jun. Ho. Off. (Surg.) Nottm. City Hosp.; Jun. Ho. Off. (Med.) Derbysh. Roy. Infirm.

BAKER, Joanne Lisa The Byre, Barn Courtyard, Palstone, South Brent TQ10 9JR — BM 1990 Soton.; MRCP (UK) 1996; DCH RCP Lond. 1993; DRCOG 1992. SHO (Paediat.) Bristol Childr. Hosp. Prev: SHO (Paediat.) Roy. Devon & Exeter Hosp. Exeter.

BAKER, Joanne Louise 119 Pringle Street, Brinsworth, Rotherham S60 5AZ — MB ChB 1994 Manch.; BSc (Hons.) Psychol. Manch. 1989. Ho. Off. (Gen. Surg. & Orthop.) Withington Hosp. Manch. Prev: Ho. Off. (Gen. Med.) Leighton Hosp. Crewe.

BAKER, John Beresford (retired) Hampden House, Sturdy Close, Hythe CT21 6AG Tel: 01303 265698 — MB BS 1957 Lond. Prev: GP Kent.

BAKER, John Harry Edmund Rookwood Hospital, Fairwater Road, Cardiff CF5 2YN Tel: 029 2056 6281; 5 Bridge Road, Llandaff, Cardiff CF5 2PT Tel: 029 2057 8091 Fax: 0122 560729 — MB BS 1973 Lond.; BSc Lond. 1970, MB BS (Hons) 1973; MRCP (U.K.) 1976; Bayer Prize 1984; FRCP Lond. 1998. (Middlesex) Cons. Spinal Injuries Rookwood Hosp. Cardiff; Cons. Rehabil. Med. & Spinal Injuries Univ. Hosp. of Wales; Asst. Chief Surg. St. John Ambul. Prev: Sen. Regist. Midl. Spinal Injuries Centre OsW.y & Nat. Spinal Injuries Centre Stoke Mandeville; Regist. Gough Cooper Deptartment Neurosurg. Studies Nat. Hosp. for Nerv. Disorders Qu.'s Sq. Lond.

BAKER, John Timothy Wrexham Maelor Hospital, Wrexham LL13 7OT Tel: 01978 725514 Fax: 01978 715141 — MB BS 1962 Lond.; MSc (Nuclear Med.) Lond. 1971; FRCP Lond. 1981, M 1967. (St. Geo.) Cons. (Gen. Med. & Chest Dis.) Ass. Med. Director N.E. Wales Trust; p/t Med. Mem. InDepend. Appeals Tribunal. Socs: Brit. Nuclear Med. Soc. & Brit. Brit. Thoracic Soc.; Brit. Thoracic Soc. Prev: Postgrad. Tutor Wrexham Hosp.; Lect. Dept. TB & Chest Dis. Welsh Nat. Sch. Med. Cardiff.

BAKER, John Walter 2 Richil Court, Ayston Road, Uppingham, Oakham LE15 9RL — MB ChB 1947 Birm.; MRCGP 1953. (Birm.) Barrister-at-Law.

BAKER, John Winskill The Surgery, The Pond, East Peckam, Tonbridge TN12 8LP Tel: 01622 871540; Friars' Coach House, Matfield, Tonbridge TN12 7LG Tel: 01892 722406 Fax: 01892 722406 — BM BCh 1960 Oxf.; FRCGP 1981, M 1972; DObst RCOG 1963. (Lond. Hosp.) Prev: Med. Off. Mbale Hosp. Uganda; Ho. Phys. & Ho. Surg. Lond. Hosp.; Ho. Off. Brit. Hosp. Mothers & Babies Woolwich.

BAKER, Jon 3 Argyle Road, London N12 7NU — MB BS 1996 Lond.

BAKER, Julie Anita Overleat, Lake Lane, Dousland, Yelverton PL20 6LZ — MB ChB 1981 Bristol; FFARCS Lond. 1987.

BAKER, Mr Justin George Diboll Scarborough Hospital, Scalby Road, Scarborough YO12 6QL Tel: 01723 368111; 135 Stepney Road, Scarborough YO12 5NJ Tel: 01723 374880 — MB BS 1968 Lond.; FRCS Eng. 1976; FRCS Ed. 1974; MRCS Eng. LRCP Lond. 1968. Cons. Otolaryngol. ScarBoro. Gen. Hosp. Mem. Brit. Assn. Socs: Fell. Roy. Soc. Med.

BAKER, Karen Ann 45 Rothesay Avenue, Lenton, Nottingham NG7 1PU — BM BS 1984 Nottm.

BAKER, Katherine Louise 102 Ninian Road, Roath Park, Cardiff CF23 5ER — MB BCh 1998 Wales.

BAKER, Keith Wigston Central Surgery, 48 Leicester Road, Wigston, Leicester LE18 1DR Tel: 0116 288 2566 — MB ChB 1976 Sheff.; FRCGP 1998; MRCGP 1980; DRCOG 1979. Chair Oadby & Wigston PCG. Socs: Pres. Leics. & Rutland BMA (1997).

BAKER, Keith Warren Enfield and Haringey Health Authority, Holbrook House, Cockfosters Road, Barnet EN4 0DR Tel: 020 8272 5551 Fax: 020 8272 5582 Email: keith.baker@enhar-ha.nthames.nhs.uk; 22 Murray Road, Northwood HA6 2YJ Tel: 01923 823867 Fax: 01923 823867 Email: baker@behamlet.demon.co.uk — MB BS 1975 Lond.; BDS Lond. 1969; MRCS Eng. LRCP Lond. 1975; LDS RCS Eng. 1970; FFPHM RCP (UK) 1995, M 1989. (St. Mary's) Dir. of Pub. Health Enfield & Haringey Health Auth. Prev: Cosn. Pub. Health Med. E. & N. Herts. HA; Dir. (Pub. Health) Enfield HA; Sen. Regist. (Community Med.) NW Thames RHA.

BAKER, Mr Kenneth (retired) Lyndhurst, 14 Harrowby Drive, Westlands, Newcastle ST5 3JE Tel: 01782 614265 — MB ChB 1945 Liverp.; MD Liverp. 1956; FRCOG 1966, M 1951; FRCS Canada 1959; FACS 1960. Prev: Cons. O & G N. Staffs. Roy. Infirm. & City Gen. Hosp. Stoke-on-Trent.

BAKER, Mr Kevin Francis 3 Earls Garden, St John St., Lewes BN7 2QE Tel: 01273 471367; 3 Earls Garden, St. John St, Lewes BN7 2QE Tel: 01273 471367 — MB BChir 1980 Camb.; MA Camb. 1979; FRCS Ed. 1986; MRCP (UK) 1983. (Camb. & St. Geo.) Indep. GP Lewes. Prev: Sen. Regist. (A & E) Roy. Sussex Co. Hosp. Brighton.

BAKER, Kristina Mary, MBE Queensway Day Hospital, Yeovil District Hospital, Higher Kingston, Yeovil BA21 4AT Tel: 01935 384 824 Fax: 01935 426850; 99 Southway Drive, Yeovil BA21 3EB Tel: 01935 424911 Email: stephen.baker4@virgin.net — MB ChB 1978 Zambia; MRCS Eng. LRCP 1978 Lond; DGM 1999; MRCGP 1986. (Univ. Zambia) Clin. Asst. (Geriat.) Qu.sway Day Hosp. Yeovil. Socs: BMA & Roy. Coll. GPs; Christ. Med. Fell.sh. Prev: Ho. Off. Yeovil Dist. Hosp.; Organiser Anti AIDS Project Lusaka, Zambia; GP, Minibank Med. Serv., Lusaka, Zambia.

BAKER, Laurence David 4 Heath View, London N2 0QA Tel: 020 8883 4113 — MB BS 1985 Lond.; BSc Lond. 1982. (Lond. Hosp. Med. Coll.) Freelance Med. Sub Edr. & Proof Reader Lond.; Freelance SubEdr.ial, BMJ. Prev: Trainee GP Barnet Gen. Hosp.; SHO (Psychiat.) St. Thos. Hosp. Lond.; Assoc. Research Asst. Inst. Laryngol. & Otol. Lond.

BAKER, Laurence Rainald Ian 149 Harley Street, London W1G 6DE Tel: 020 7935 4444 Fax: 020 7486 8706 Email: lrib@londin.co.uk — MB BChir 1963 Camb.; FRCP Lond. 1978, M 1965; MA Camb. 1965, MD 1970; FRCP Ed. 1993 (Westm.) Cons. Phys. & Nephrol. St. Bart. & Roy. Lond. Hosps.; Examr. RCP; Mem. (Counc.) RCP; Mem. (Exec commi) RCP. Socs: Med. Res. Soc.; Renal Assn.; Amer. Soc. Nephrol. Prev: CME Advisor N. Thames E RCP; Regional Adviser N Thames E. RCP; Postgrad. Dean St. Bart's. Hosp. & Med. Coll.

BAKER, Lesley (retired) The Nottingham Nuffield Hospital, 748 Mansfield Road, Woodthorpe, Nottingham NG5 3FZ Tel: 0115 993 2001 — MB ChB 1954 Sheff.; FRCOG 1974, M 1961; DObst 1956. Cons. Obst & Gyn. Nottm. City Hosp. Prev: Lect. (O & G) Univ. Sheff.

BAKER, Liesl 9 Broad-Dykes Crescent, Kingswells, Aberdeen AB15 8UJ — MB ChB 1989 Orange Free State.

BAKER, Lisa Clare 9 Otterburn Terrace, Newcastle upon Tyne NE2 3AP — MB BS 1996 Newc.

BAKER, Lucy Victoria Flat L, 23 Warwick Square, London SW1V 2AB — BM BCh 1991 Oxf.; BA Oxf. 1988, MA 1997; MRCP (UK) 1994. Specialist Regist. (Gen. Med. & Chest Med.) SE Thames.

BAKER, Marianne Ruth 199A Nine Mile Ride, Wokingham RG40 4JD — MB BCh 1997 Wales.

BAKER, Mark Arden House, Regent Farm Road, Newcastle upon Tyne NE3 3JN Tel: 0191 223 3086; Wardle Cottage, Front St, Wall, Hexham NE46 4EB Tel: 01434 681796 — MB ChB 1982 Leeds; MRCGP 1986; DRCOG 1985. Med. Adviser Benefits Agency Newc. u. Tyne. Prev: Trainee GP Cockermouth VTS; SHO (Geriat.) Cumbld. Infirm. Carlisle; SHO (O & G) City Gen. Hosp. Carlisle.

BAKER, Professor Mark Ronald 2 Alder Carr, West Lane, Baildon, Shipley BD17 5TE — MB BS 1973 Newc.; MSc Manch. 1979; MD Newc. 1980; FRCP Lond. 1994; MRCP (UK) 1977; FFCM 1985, M 1980. Med. Dir. N. Yorks. DHA; Ext. Prof. Pub. Health Univ. Leeds; Hon. Prof. Pub. Health Bradford Univ. Prev: Dir. of Research & Developm. Yorks. RHA; Chief Exec. Bradford Hosps. NHS Trust.

BAKER, Maureen Newark Road Surgery, 501 Newark Road, South Hykeham, Lincoln LN6 8RT Tel: 01522 537944 Fax: 01522 510932; 501A Newark Road, Lincoln LN6 8RT Tel: 01522 537943 — MB ChB 1981 Dundee. Assoc. Adviser (Gen. Pract.) Univ. Nottm.; Lect. (Gen. Pract.) Univ. Nottm.

BAKER, Melanie Milton Farm, Milton of Buchanan, Drymen, Glasgow G63 0JE — MB ChB 1994 Dundee.

BAKER, Michael (retired) 117 Dysart Road, Kirkcaldy KY1 2BB — MB BS Lond. 1962; MRCS Eng. LRCP Lond. 1962. Med. Assessor Fife Indep. Tribunal Servs. UK. Prev: GP Kirkcaldy.

BAKER, Michael Alexander Hallam Lawnswood, 40 Curzon Park N., Chester CH4 8AR Tel: 01244 675334 — MB ChB 1997 Birm.

BAKER, Michael Raymond Greensands Medical Practice, Brook End Surgery, Potton, Sandy SG19 2QS Tel: 01767 260260 Fax: 01767 261777 — MB ChB 1977 Sheff.; MRCGP 1983; DRCOG 1982. Prev: Regist. (Med.) ChristCh. Hosp. New Zealand; Ho. Off. (Paediat. Surg.) Sheff. Childr. Hosp.; Ho. Off. (Med.) Sheff. Roy. Infirm.

BAKER, Monica Joan Hallfield Manor, Water Lane, Bassingham, Lincoln LN5 9HF Tel: 01522 788079 — MB BS 1972 Lond.; MRCS Eng. LRCP Lond. 1972. (Roy. Free) Clin. Med. Off. (Community Child Health) Lincoln Dist. Healthcare Trust (p/t). Socs: BMA. Prev: Partner The Bassingham Surg. Lincoln; Ho. Phys. & Ho. Surg. W. Norf. & King's Lynn Gen. Hosp.; Clin. Med. Off. Norf. AHA.

BAKER, Mr Nicholas James 50 Horndean Road, Emsworth PO10 7PT — MB BS 1989 Lond.; FDS RCS Eng. 1991, LDS 1981; BDS Sheff. 1981; FRCS Ed. 1993. (Charing Cross and Westminster) Cons. (Oral & Maxillofacial Surg.) Soton Univ. & Roy. Hants. Co. Hosp. Winchester. Socs: Fell. Brit. Assn. Oral & Maxillofacial Surg.; Eur. Assn. Cranio-Maxillo. Surg.

BAKER, Patricia Bernadette (retired) Petra, 16 Oak Close, Ottery St Mary EX11 1BB Tel: 01404 813922 Email: patricia.petra@eclipse.co.uk — MB BS Lond. 1963; MRCS Eng. LRCP Lond. 1963; MRCGP 1976; DTM & H Eng. 1973. Prev: Med. Off. Save the Childr. Fund (Jordan, Bangladesh & S. Vietnam).

BAKER, Patricia Marjorie (retired) 1 Bailey Close, Woodbrook, Loughborough LE11 3PB Tel: 01509 263558 — MB BS 1954 Lond.; DObst RCOG 1956; DCH Eng. 1957. Prev: Med. Off. Univ. LoughBoro.

BAKER, Paul Bolton Hospitals NHS Trust, Royal Bolton Hospital, Minerva Road, Farnworth, Bolton BL4 0JR Tel: 01204 390991 Fax: 01204 390933; Lurden House, 149 Wigan Road, Standish, Wigan WN6 0AG Tel: 01257 427571 — MB ChB 1980 Liverp.; MRCP (UK) 1983; 2001 FRCGP; FRCP Lond. 1997. Cons. Phys. Bolton HA. Socs: Brit. Geriat. Soc.; Brit. Diabetic Assn. Prev: Lect. Univ. Hosp. S. Manch.; Sen. Regist. (Med.) Manch. Roy. Infirm.; Sen. Regist. (Geriat. Med.) Bolton Gen. Hosp.

BAKER, Paul David Royal mail, Dawson Rd, Mount Farm, Milton Keynes MK1 1AA — MB BS 1989 Lond.; 1989 MA Oxf.; 1992 MRCGP; 1996 AFOM RCP Lond.; 1991 DRCOG; 1999 MFOM RCP Lond. (Lond. Hosp.) Cons. Occupat.al Phys., Consignia Employee Health Serv.s. Socs: Brit. Holistic Med. Assn.; Soc. Occupat. Med.; Brit. Assn. of Musculoskeletal Med. Prev: Hon. Sen. Reg. & Res. Fell. In Occ. Med. S.ampton Univ. Hosp. NHS Trust; Sen. Occupat.al Phys., The Post Office, E. Territory.

BAKER, Penelope Ann 23 De Parys Avenue, Bedford MK40 2TX Tel: 01234 350022 Fax: 01234 213402; 2 Nevern Gardens, Biddenham, Bedford MK40 4RW Tel: 01234 328218 — MB ChB 1975 Birm. GP. Prev: GP Asst. Backwell; GP Plympton; Trainee GP Plymouth VTS.

BAKER, Peter John Samuel 38 Denmark Road, Flat 1, Exeter EX1 1SE Tel: 01392 275366 Email: peterbaker@doctors.net.uk; 38 Denmark Road, Flat 1, Exeter EX1 1SE Email: peterbaker@doctors.net.uk — MB BCh BAO 1967 Belf.; MLCOM (Member London College Osteopathic Medicine); DMS Med 1999; DRCOG 1971; DCH RCP Glas. 1969; D.Occ Med. 1996. GP Locum. Socs: BMA. Prev: Ships. Surg., GP Princip. Cullompton.

BAKER, Peter Michael Department of Anaesthesia, Peterborough District Hospital, Thorpe Road, Peterborough PE3 6DA Tel: 01733 67451; 34 Stamford Road, Market Deeping, Peterborough PE6 8AB — MB BS 1978 Newc.; FFA RCS Eng. 1984. Cons. Anaesth. P'boro. Hosps. NHS Trust. Socs: Assn. Anaesth. of GB & Irel.; BMA. Prev: Cons. Anaesth. City Hosps. Sunderland; Sen. Regist. (Anaesth.) Sheff. HPT Progr.; Pre-Fell.sh. SHO (Anaesth.) Killingbeck Hosp. Leeds.

BAKER, Peter Richard, MBE 5 The Paddocks, Prestbury, Macclesfield SK10 4DB — MB ChB 1955 St. And.; MRCGP 1974. Prev: Ho. Phys. & Ho. Surg. Dundee Roy. Infirm.; Sen. Ho. Off. Ross Memor. Hosp. Paisley.

BAKER, Professor Philip Newton Department of Obstetrics and Gynaecology, City Hospital, Hucknall Road, Nottingham NG5 1PB Tel: 01559 962 7670 — BM BS 1985 Nottm.; DM Nottm. 1991; MRCOG 1990. (Nottingham) Prof. (O & G) Nottm. Univ. Socs: Internat. Soc. Study of Hypertens. in Pregn.; Blair Bell Res. Soc.; (Pres.) Nuffield Obst. & Gyn. Soc. Prev: Sen. Lect. Nottm. Univ.; Lect. Nottm. Univ.

BAKER, Philippa Jane Haymeads, Dunheved Road, Launceston PL15 9JQ — MB BS 1980 Lond.; BSc (Hons.) Lond. 1977, MB BS 1980; DRCOG 1985. (St. Bart.)

BAKER, Raymond Francis Baker, Greenwood and Gammack, 110 King's Road, Harrogate HG1 5HW Tel: 01423 503035 Fax: 01423 562665 — MB ChB 1973 Birm.; BSc Biochem. (Hons.) 1970.

BAKER, Mr Raymond Harry 1 Beech Hill Road, Sheffield S10 2SA Tel: 0114 268424; Springwell Cottage, Pinfold Hill, Curbar, Calver, Hope Valley S32 3YL Tel: 01433 639364 — MB ChB 1960 Sheff.; FRCS Eng. 1966. Cons. Orthop. Surg. Roy. Hallamsh. Hosp., Sheff. Childr. Hosp. & King; Fell. Brit. Orthop. Assn. Prev: Sen. Regist. Roy. Infirm. Sheff.; Clin. Research Fell. Sick Childr. Hosp.; Regist. (Orthop.) Robt. Jones & Agnes Hunt Hosp. OsW.ry.

BAKER, Richard Harold Drs. Lervy, Pincott, Baker, Buck & Lloyd, Llys Meddy G, The Surgery, 65 Sway Rd, Morriston, Swansea SA6 6JA Tel: 01792 771392, 01792 773150 Fax: 01792 790880; Tel: 01792 206355 — MB ChB 1977 Auckland, New Zealand; 1974 BSc Auckland, New Zealand. Gen. Practitioner, Princip., Swansea. Socs: Brit. Med. Assn.; Med. Defence Union.

BAKER, Richard Henry Department of General Practice and Primary Health Care, University of Leicester, Gwendolen Road, Leicester LE5 4PW Tel: 0116 258 4873 Fax: 0116 258 4982 Email: rb14@ie.ac.uk; Brooke Court, Main St, Brooke, Oakham LE15 8DE — MB BS 1975 Lond.; MD Lond. 1996; FRCGP 1992, M 1980. (Royal Free) Dir. Clin. Governance Research & Dev. Unit. Prev: Princip. GP Glos.; Research Fell. (Gen. Pract.) Dept. Epidemiol. & Pub. Health Med. Univ. Bristol.

BAKER, Richard James 32 Orchard Lisle House, Talbot's Yard, Guy's Hospital, London SE1 1XY Tel: 020 7378 0814 — MB BChir 1990 Camb.; MA Camb. 1991, MB BChir 1990. SHO (Med.) Guy's Hosp. Lond.

BAKER, Richard John Nicholas Rushbottom Lane Surgery, 91 Rushbottom Lane, Benfleet SS7 4EA Tel: 01268 754311 Fax: 01268 795150 Email: richard.baker@gp-f81142.nhs.uk; 2 Apeldoorn, Benfleet SS7 4EH Tel: 01268 757479 Email:

jackandsarah@talk21.com — MB BS 1978 Lond. (St. Geo. Hosp. Med. Sch. Lond.) GP Essex.

BAKER, Richard Paul 3 Castlemere Drive, Shaw, Oldham OL2 8TQ — MB ChB 1996 Leeds. (Leeds)

BAKER, Mr Richard Volant Vashon (retired) Maybank, 20 Island Bank Road, Inverness IV2 4QS Tel: 01463 233695 — MB BS 1959 Lond.; FRCS Ed. 1986; FRCS Eng. 1967; MRCS Eng. LRCP Lond. 1959. Prev: Cons. Surg. S.. Inverness Health Dist.

BAKER, Richard William Clement's Surgery, Greenfields Way, Haverhill CB9 8LU Tel: 01440 702462 Fax: 01440 712112 — MB ChB 1983 Glas.; Cert. Family Plann. JCC 1988; Dip. Ther. Cardiff 1997. (Glasgow) Dir. Suff. Doctors on Call.

BAKER, Robert Clarke 9 The Fort, Helens Bay, Bangor BT19 1PU — MB BCh BAO 1993 Belf.

BAKER, Robert William Swanage Health Centre, Railway Station Approach, Station Road, Swanage BH19 1HB Tel: 01929 422231 — MB BS 1982 Lond.; MRCP (UK) 1986; MRCGP 1994; DCH RCP Lond. 1989; DRCOG 1988. Prev: Regist. (Med.) Bristol Roy. Infirm.; SHO (O & G) Bristol Gen. Hosp.; SHO (Paediat.) Roy. Cornw. Hosp.

BAKER, Robert William Rowleigh House, Evington Lane, Leicester LE5 6DJ; 31 Tantallon Road, Balham, London SW12 8DF Tel: 020 8673 9409 Fax: 020 7636 8175 Email: robert.baker@ucl.ac.uk — MB ChB 1988 Bristol; MRCP Glas. 1992. (Bristol) Hon. Research Fell. (Infec. Dis.) Univ. Coll. Hosp. Lond.; Lect. & Hon. Research Fell. Imperial Coll. Lond.; Clin. Asst. Hosp. for Trop. Dis. Prev: Hon. Research Fell. NHLI (St. Mary's Campus); Wellcme Research Fell. UCL; Hon. Research Fell. Univ. of Bristol.

BAKER, Ronald Stewart 12 Southwood Lawn Road, Highgate, London N6 5SF Tel: 020 8348 2343 Fax: 020 8348 2343 Email: ronaldbaker@clara.co.uk — LRCPI & LM, LRSCI & LM 1963; LRCPI & LM, LRCSI & LM 1963; MRCPsych 1974; DPM Eng. 1966. (RCSI) Indep. Psychoanalyst & Psychother. Lond. Socs: Brit. Psychoanal. Soc. Prev: Sen. Regist. (Child Psychiat.) Paddington Green Childr. Hosp. (St. Mary's Hosp.) Lond.; Regist (Psychiat.) Shenley Hosp.; Hon. Cons. Lond. Clin. Psychoanal.

BAKER, Rosemary Anne Tamarind, New Road, Littleton, Winchester SO22 6QR — MB ChB 1974 Dundee; MRCPsych 1983; MRCGP 1979. Cons. Psychiat. Ment. Handicap. Basingstoke & N.ants HA. Prev: Cons. Psychiat. Ment. Handicap Basingstoke & Winchester HA's; Sen. Regist. (Ment. Handicap.) Hortham & Brentry Hosps.; Regist. (Psychiat.) Basingstoke Dist. Hosp.

BAKER, Sarah Jane 15 Little Bornes, London SE21 8SD — MB BS 1991 Lond.

BAKER, Sarah Jane Leeds Health Authority, Blenheim House, West One, Duncombe St., Leeds LS1 4PL Tel: 01132 952000 Fax: 01132 952222; 12 Ingswell Drive, Notton, Wakefield WF4 2NF Tel: 01226 728336 — MB BS 1982 Lond.; DRCOG 1987; DFPHM 1999. (St. Bart.) Dir. (Primary & Community Care) Leeds HA; Research Fell. (Gen. Pract.) Sheff. Univ. Socs: Brit. Assn. Med. Managers. Prev: GP Barnsley & Aylesbury; Lect. (Gen. Pract.) Sheff. Univ.

BAKER, Simon Charles Mill View Hospital, Nevill Avenue, Hove BN3 7HZ Tel: 01273 696011 — MB BS 1982 Lond.; PhD Lond. 1994; BA Oxf. 1978; MRCP (UK) 1985; MRCPsych 1992. (Guy's) Cons. Psychiat. S. Downs Health NHS Trust. Prev: Sen. Regist. Maudsley Hosp. Lond.; Research Fell. Inst. Neurol. Qu. Sq. Lond.

BAKER, Simon Mark Railway Corner, Low Road, Wenhaston, Halesworth IP19 9BU; 18 Invermay Avenue, Balmoral, Auckland, New Zealand Tel: 09 629 0373 — BM 1988 Soton.; MRCGP 1995; DFFP 1995; Dip. Obst. Auckland 1993; Dip. Paediat. Auckland 1993; DPH, Auckland 1998. (Soton.) Regist. (Pub. health Med.), Auckland Healthcare Pub. Health Protec., Auckland, New Zealand. Prev: GP Locum, New Zealand; GP/Regist. Portishead Avon; SHO (Obst. & Paediat.) Auckland.

BAKER, Simon Scott 16A Ashfield Lane, Chislehurst BR7 6LQ — MB ChB 1991 Leic.

BAKER, Stephen Broughton de Chair (retired) Ballanarran, Surby, Port Erin IM9 6TE Tel: 01624 833111 — MB ChB 1952 MB ChB Manch.; MD 1960 MD Manch.; 1976 FRCPath. Prev: Cons. Pathol. Nobles Isle of Man Hosp.

BAKER, Susan Frances Brenkley Avenue Health Centre, Brenkley Avenue, Shiremoor, Newcastle upon Tyne NE27 0PR Tel: 0191 251 6151 — MB BS 1976 Newc.; BA (Hons.) Durham. 1969.

BAKER, Susan Phrenda Shelton Hospital, Bilton Heath, Shrewsbury — MB BCh 1990 Wales; MRCGP 1994; MRCPsych 1998.

BAKER, Susan Samantha 320 Calmore Road, Calmore, Southampton SO40 2RH — MB BS 1994 Lond.

BAKER, Timothy Holland Readesmoor Medical Group Practice, 29-29A West Street, Congleton CW12 1JP Tel: 01260 276161 Fax: 01260 297340; Old School House, School Lane, Marton, Macclesfield SK11 9HD Tel: 01260 224424 — MB BS 1972 Lond.; FRCP 2001; MRCP (UK) 1975; MRCS Eng. LRCP Lond. 1972. (Roy. Free) Hosp. Pract. (Cardiol.) Dist. Gen. Hosp. Macclesfield. Socs: Brit. Soc. Echocardiogr. Prev: SHO (Gen. Med. & O & G) N.ampton Gen. Hosp.; SHO (Cas. & ENT) Orsett Hosp.

BAKER, Timothy John Stuart Pool Health Centre, Station Road, Pool, Redruth TR15 3DU Tel: 01209 717471 Fax: 01209 612160; Wheal Britain Farm, Blackwater, Truro TR4 8HJ Tel: 01209 891213 — MB ChB 1985 Bristol; MRCGP 1996; DObst RACOG 1994; DCH RCP Lond. 1991; DA (UK) 1988.

BAKER, Timothy Martyn Cripps Health Centre, University Park, Nottingham NG7 2QW — BM BS 1996 Nottm.; DRCOG; MRCGP; DFFP. (Nottm.) GP Princip. Socs: BMA & MPS; RCGP Roy. Coll. of GP's; BAHSHE Brit. Assn. Of Health Serv.s in Higher Educat. Prev: SHO GP Pract. Nottm.; Jun. Ho. Off. City Hosp. Nottm.; Jun. Ho. Off. Derby Roy. Infirm.

BAKER, Valerie Neilson (retired) 18 Westway, Clevedon BS21 7XN Tel: 0117 987 2677 — MB ChB (Commend.) St. And. 1946; MFCM 1973; DPH Bristol 1962; DObst RCOG 1948. Prev: Sen. Med. Off. Avon AHA (T).

BAKER, William Harrison Jessop (retired) White Rose Cottage, Lugwardine, Hereford HR1 4DS Tel: 01432 850242 — MB BS 1938 Lond.; MB BS (Distinc. Path.) Lond. 1938; MRCS Eng. LRCP Lond. 1938; FRCPath 1963. Prev: Cons. Pathol. Hereford Co. & Gen. Hosps.

BAKER, Mr William Nigel Whiston 77 Elers Road, Ealing, London W13 9QB Tel: 020 8567 8817 — MB BS 1958 Lond.; MS Lond. 1975; FRCS Eng. 1966. (Middlx.) Cons. (Gen. Surg.) Ashford Hosp. Middlx.; Fell. Roy. Soc. Med. Prev: Sen. Regist. W.m. Hosp. Gp.; Res. Surg. Off. St. Mark's Hosp.; Ho. Off., SHO & Surg. Regist. Middlx. Hosp.

BAKER, Winston Joseph Sunrise, Brownlow Drive, Bracknell RG42 2LL — MRCS Eng. LRCP Lond. 1966. (St. Geo.) Prev: Ho. Surg. (Surg.) & (O & G) St. Mary Abbots Hosp. Lond.; SHO (O & G) Cheltenham Matern. Hosp.

BAKER, Zoe Charlotte 39 Hilperton Road, Trowbridge BA14 7JG — BM 1998 Soton.

BAKER-GLENN, Emily Jane Spinola, 26 Tennyson Avenue, Hitchin SG4 0PY — MB BS 1997 Lond.

BAKEWELL, Sarah Elizabeth Charlton Farm, Hartlebury, Kidderminster DY11 7YE — MB ChB 1989 Bristol.

BAKEWELL, Sarah Michelle Brook Hill Surgery, 30 Brook Hill, Little Waltham, Chelmsford CM3 3LL Tel: 01245 360253 Fax: 01245 361343; Hyde Cottage, Hyde Hall Lane, Great Waltham, Chelmsford CM3 1BY Tel: 01245 362702 — BM 1978 Soton.; MRCGP 1982; DRCOG 1981; DMJ (Clin.) Soc. Apoth Lond. 1998. (Southampton) GP; Police Surg. Essex Constab. (p/t).

BAKHAI, Ameet Shashikant — MB BS 1990 Lond.; MRCP (UK) 1993. (St Bartholomew's Hosp.) Specialist Regist. Roy Brompton Hosp. Lond. Socs: Roy. Coll. Phys.s; Fell. Roy. Soc. Med.; Brit. Soc. Cardiol. Prev: Specialist Regist. St Marys Hosp. Lond.

BAKHAI, Mr Jayant Abhechand, SBStJ, Surg. Cdr. RN (retired) 4 St Francis Road, Alverstoke, Gosport PO12 2UG Tel: 02392 643582 Fax: 02392 643285 Email: jayant bakhai@supanet.com — MB ChB 1966 St. And.; FRCS Ed. 1980; FRCOphth 1985; DO Eng. 1974. Cons. Ophth. Surg. Portsmouth; Mem. Portsmouth & SE Hants. LMC. Prev: Med. Off. HMS Nelson.

BAKHAI, Rameshchandra Premjibhai Eastern Avenue Surgery, 167 Eastern Avenue, Redbridge, Ilford IG4 5AW Tel: 020 8550 4532 Fax: 020 8551 2199 — MB BS 1974 Bombay.

BAKHAT, Ashraf Ali 219 Withington Road, Manchester M16 8LU — MB ChB 1992 Manch.

BAKHEIT, Professor Abdel Magid Osman The Academic Department of Rehabilitation Medicine, Stroke Unit, Mount Gould Hospital, Plymouth PL4 7QD Tel: 01752 272481 Fax: 01752 272483; 10 Romilly Gardens, Plympton, Plymouth PL7 2FF —

Vrach 1975 Lvov Med. Inst. USSR; MRCP; PhD Glas. 1990; MSc Lond. 1987; MD Glas. 1993; Dip. Neurol. Lond. 1983; DPhysMed 1993. Prof. Neurol. Rehabil. Univ. of Plymouth; Hon. Cons. Phys. Socs: Brit. Soc. Rehabil. Med. Prev: Sen. Lect. (Rehabil. Med.) Soton.; Lect. (Neurol.) Univ. Glas.; Regist. (Neurol.) S.. Gen. Hosp. Glas..

BAKHEIT, Mr Naim Zaki 5 Glebe Road, Cogenhoe, Northampton NN7 1NR — MB BCh 1965 Ain Shams; FRCS Ed. 1979.

BAKHRU, Mr Moti Naraindas The Garden City Practice, 185 Knightsfield, Welwyn Garden City AL8 7QG Tel: 01707 330522 Fax: 01707 391629; 3 Nut Grove, Welwyn Garden City AL8 7SQ Tel: 01831 321932 — MB BS 1958 Bombay; MS Bombay 1962; FRCS Ed. 1964; FRCS Eng. 1963. Socs: BMA; Assn. Surgs. India.

BAKHSH, Nadia 14 Canterbury Av, Ilford IG1 3NA — MB BS 1997 Lond.

BAKHSHI, Krishna Nath Stoke Mandeville Hospital, Mandeville Road, Aylesbury HP21 8AL; Mulberry Cottage, Ellesborough Road, Butlers Cross, Ellesborough, Aylesbury HP17 0XA — BM 1983 Soton.; FRCA 1991. (Soton.) Sen. Regist. (Anaesth.) St Bart & St. Ormond St. Hosps. Lond.; Cons. Anaesth. & Pain Managem. Stoke Mandeville Hosp. Aylesbury Bucks. Prev: Sen. Regist. (Anaesth.) St Bart Hosp. Lond.; Clin. Research Fell. & Regist. (Anaesth.) St. Bart. Hosp. Lond.; Regist. Whipps Cross Hosp. Lond.

BAKHSHI, Surinderjit Singh 48 Vernon Avenue, Handsworth Wood, Birmingham B20 1DF Tel: 0121 554 9846 — MB ChB 1965 E. Africa; FFPHM RCP (UK) 1985, M 1974; DIH Dund 1977; MPH Univ. Michigan 1971. (Makerere Med. Sch. Kampala) Cons. Communicable Dis. Control Birm. HA; JP.; Hon. Sen. Clin. Lect. Med. Sch. Birm. Univ. Prev: SCM (Environm. Health) Centr. Birm. HA; SCMO (Occupat. Health) Glos. AHA; Provin. Med. Off. & Matern. & Child Health Specialist MoH, Zambia.

BAKHT, Tarek 29A Queens Road, Oldham OL8 2AX — MB ChB 1997 Manch.

BAKHTYARI-NEJAD-ESFAHANI, Arash 1 Deanstone Place, Coatbridge ML5 4AY — MB ChB 1993 Aberd.

BAKKER, Adam Antoni Bakker, Brown, Jacobs and Wormell, Lisson Grove Health Centre, Gateforth Street, London NW8 8EF Tel: 020 7723 2213; 49 Bankside, London SE1 9JE — Artsexamen 1985 Leiden; Cert. Prescribed Equiv. Exp. JCPTGP 1992. Prev: Ho. Off. (Gen. Surg.) Dewsbury HA.

BAKKER, Adriaan Hendrik (retired) Halsewater House, Cotford St Luke, Taunton TA4 1DD — MB BCh BAO Dub. 1957; MRCPsych 1971; DPM Eng. 1963. Prev: Cons. Psychiat. Merriefield Unit Tone Vale Hosp. Taunton.

BAKKER, Philip Adriaan Gerard Lawrence Hill Health Centre, Hassell Drive, Bristol BS2 0AN Tel: 0117 955 5241 Fax: 0117 941 1162; 136 Abbots Road, Hanham, Bristol BS15 3NS — MB ChB 1984 Brist.; MRCGP 1994; DRCOG 1988.

BAKO, Angelina Mary St Davids Medical Centre, Pentwyn Drive, Pentwyn, Cardiff CF23 7SD Tel: 029 2073 3032 Fax: 029 2054 1392; 60 Heol Cefn On, Lisvane, Cardiff CF14 0TQ — MB BCh 1967 Wales.

BAKOWSKA, Anna Janina Colliers Wood Surgery, 58 High Street Colliers Wood, London SW19 2BY Tel: 020 8540 6303; Elysium, 1A Daybrook Road, London SW19 3DJ — MB BS 1963 Med. Acad. Warsaw; PhD Lond. 1969; LMSSA Lond. 1974. Hosp. Pract. Horton Hosp. Epsom. Socs: BMA. Prev: Clin. Asst. Horton Hosp. Epsom; Research Fell. (Experiment. Path.) Kennedy Inst. Rheumatol. Lond.; Regist. (Geriat. Med.) St. Geo. Hosp. Lond.

BAKOWSKI, Marie Theodora Solvay Healthcare Ltd., Mansbridge Road, West End, Southampton SO18 3JD Tel: 02380 467029 Fax: 02380 465350 Email: marie.bakowsk@soluay.com — MB BS 1972 Lond.; BSc Lond. 1969, MD 1983; MRCP (UK) 1975; FFPM RCP (UK) 1994. (King's Coll. Hosp.) Med. Dir. Solvay Healthcare Ltd. Soton. Prev: Dir. Med. Operat. Boehringer Ingelheim Ltd.; Med. Adviser Eli Lilly & Co. Ltd.; Lect. (Med.) & Hon. Sen. Regist. Guy's Hosp. Lond.

BAKRAN, Mr Ali 9C Link Unit, The Royal Liverpool Hospital, Prescot St., Liverpool L7 8XP Tel: 0151 706 3492 Fax: 0151 706 5819 — MB ChB 1973 Leeds; BSc (Anat.) Bristol 1970; FRCS Ed. 1978; FRCS Eng. 1978. (Leeds) Cons. Surg. (Transpl. & Vasc. Surg.) Roy. Liverp. Hosp. Socs: Internat. Transpl. Soc. & Vasc. Soc. GB & Irel.; Eur. Soc. Vasc. Surg.; Brit. Transpl. Soc. Prev: Tutor (Surg.) Manch. Roy. Infirm.; Regist. (Surg.) Hull Roy. Infirm. & Leeds Gen. Infirm.; Research Asst. (Surg.) Leeds Gen. Infirm.

BAKRI, Sophie Jane 71 Victoria Park, Colwyn Bay LL29 7YY Tel: 01492 533696 Email: sbakri@doctors.org.uk — BM BS 1998 Nottm.; BM BS Nottm 1998; BMedSci 1996. (notts.Univ) Res.med.Ophth. Albany.Med.Centre. Prev: Ho..Phys.Univ.hosp.Qu.s.med.Centre.Notts; Ho..Surg.Taunton & Som. hosp.Taunton.

BAKRY, Mohamed Ahmed Ahmed 8 Ballyregan Road, Dundonald, Belfast BT16 1HY — MB ChB 1980 Alexandria; MRCOG 1994.

BAKSH, Madhu The Coldharbour Surgery, 79 William Barefoot Drive, Eltham, London SE9 3JD Tel: 020 8857 3472 Fax: 020 8851 6471 — MB BS 1966 Lucknow.

BAKSHI, Aparna Hemel Hempstead General Hospital, Hillfield Road, Hemel Hempstead HP2 4AD; 28 Ebrington Road, Harrow HA3 0LR — MB BS 1971 Calcutta.

BAKSHI, Jitender Mohan 33 Wyre Grove, Hayes UB3 4PH — MB BS 1979 Patna.

BAKSHI, Jogindra Jaybee Medical Centre, 25 Charnwood Street, Derby DE1 2GU Tel: 01332 342711 Fax: 01322 349004 — MB BS 1970 Rajasthan.

BAKSHI, Neelam University College Hospital, National Temperance Hospital, 112 Hampstead Road, London NW1 2LT Tel: 020 7387 9541 — MB BS 1975 Rajasthan; MS (Obst. & Gyn.) Rajasthan 1984; MRCPsych 1986; DRCOG 1981. (S.M.S. Med. Coll. Jaipur) Cons. Psychiat. Camden & Islington Health Trust; Hon. Sen. Lect. Univ. Coll. & Middlx. Med. Sch. Lond.; Cons. Psychiat. Charter Nightingale Hosp. Lond. Socs: RCPsych. Prev: Sen. Regist. Guy's & St. Thos. Hosp. Lond.

BAKSHI, Prem Gillingham Medical Centre, Woodlands Road, Gillingham ME7 2BU Tel: 01634 854431 — MB BS 1966 Agra; BSc Agra 1961, MB BS 1966; DA Eng. 1972. (Agra Med. Coll.)

BAKSI, Arun Kalyan St Mary's Hospital NHS Trust, Newport PO30 5TG Tel: 01983 524081 Fax: 01983 534910 Email: baksi@baksi.demon.co.uk; Stable Cottage, Ashlake Park Lane, Wootton Bridge, Ryde PO33 4LF Tel: 01983 883853 Fax: 01983 884778 — MB BS 1962 Calcutta; FRCP Lond. 1983, M 1968. (Calcutta Med. Coll.) Cons. Phys. I. of Wight HA; Hon. Clin. Teach. (Gen. Med.) Soton. Univ.; Chairm. ASEC Diabetes & Endocrinol. Wessex; Hon. Cons. Ed. Practical Diabetes Internat. Socs: Brit. Diabetic Assn. (Ex-Hon. Sec. Educat. Sect.); BMA; Internat. Diabetes Federat. Prev: Chairm. I. of Wight Postgrad. Med. Federat.; Cons. Phys. Wesley Guild Hosp. Ilesha, Nigeria; Sen. Regist. (Med.) Liverp. Roy. Infirm. & Mersey RHA.

BAKY, Emad Shawky Department of Obstetrics & Gynaecology, Royal Shrewsbury Hospital NHS Trust, Mytton Oak Road, Shrewsbury SY3 8XQ; 50 Upton Drive, Chester CH2 1BX Tel: 01244 378911 — MB BCh 1980 Ain Shams; MRCOG 1992. Prev: Regist. (O & G) Fazakerley Hosp. Liverp. & Countess of Chester Hosp.

BAL, Amarjit Singh 40 Buckingham Drive, Loughborough LE11 4TE — MB ChB 1997 Sheff.

BAL, Harjot Singh 17B Whiteknights Road, Reading RG6 7BY — MB BS 1997 Lond.

BAL, Vininder Singh 42 Holly Bush Lane, Hampton TW12 2QS — MB BS 1988 Lond.; BSc (Hons. Psychol.) Lond. 1984; Cert. Family Plann. JCC 1992; T(GP) 1993; DFFP 1995. Socs: RCP Osler Soc.; BMA; Assoc. Mem. Roy. Coll. Gen. Pract. Prev: GP Molesey, Surrey; SHO (Acute Adult Psychiat.) Medway Hosp.; A & E Off. Roy. Lond. Hosp.

BALA, Deepa 1a Leigh Road, London E10 6JH — MB BS 1998 Newc.; MB BS Newc 1998.

BALA, Kuma 135 Park Road, Camberley GU15 2LL — MB ChB 1990 Manch.; MRCGP 1996.

BALA-POWELL, Meena 5 Brookfield Road, Wirral CH48 4EJ — MB ChB 1997 Dundee.

BALA SUBRAMANIAN, Venkateswaran 10 Hillside Grove, London NW7 2LR Email: balasub@aol.com — MB BS 1964 All India Inst. Med. Scs.; MD Poona 1970. (All India Inst. Med. Sci.) Dir. Complete Cardiac Care Centre. Socs: Fell. Amer. Coll. Cardiol.; Brit. Cardiac Soc.; Int. Fell. Amer. Heart Assn. Prev: Cons. Clin. Physiol. & Sen. Regist. (Cardiol.) N.wick Pk. Hosp. Harrow; Sen. Research Fell. (Cardiol.) Brit. Heart Foundat.

BALAC, Nikola Mapplewell Health Centre, 276 Darton Lane, Mapplewell, Barnsley S75 6AJ Tel: 01226 233777 Fax: 01226 233773 — MB ChB 1987 Sheff.; MRCGP 1991.

BALACHANDAR, Chandrika Department of Obstetrics & Gynaecology, Walsall Hospital NHS Trust, Walsall WS2 9PS Tel: 01922 721172 Fax: 01922 656695; Woodside House, Woodside Drive, Little Aston, Sutton Coldfield B74 3BB Tel: 0121 353 4240 Fax: 0121 353 5200 — MB BS 1980 Madras; MRCOG 1986. (Stanley Medical College Madras) Cons. O & G Manor Hosp. Walsall. Socs: BMOGS; Brit. Soc. Colpos. & Cerv. Path.; Brit. Menopause Soc.

BALACHANDAR, Krishna Department of Anaesthesia, Manor Hospital, Moat Road, Walsall WS2 9PS Tel: 01922 721172; Woodside House, Woodside Drive, Little Aston, Sutton Coldfield B74 3BB — MB BS 1974 Bangalore; FFA RCSI 1986. Cons. (Anaesth.) Walsall Hosps. NHS Trust.

BALACHANDER, Chidambaram Sundram The Surgery, 25 Wouldham Road, Borstal, Rochester ME1 3JY Tel: 01634 408765 — MB BS 1975 Madras; Dip. Sports Med. Lond 1990; DRCOG 1982; DA (UK) 1977.

BALACHANDRA, Kumaraswamy 38 Guildford Drive, Seymour Court, Chandlers Ford, Eastleigh SO53 3PT Tel: 01703 252222 Fax: 02380 252222; Suite 35, Circus Lodge, Circus Road, St. Johns - Wood, London NW8 9JN Tel: 020 7266 2232 — MB BS 1968 Ceylon. (Colombo) Cons. Psychiat. Rehabil. St. Bart. Hosp. Lond. Socs: Fell. Roy. Soc. Ment. Health.; Fell. Roy. Soc. Med.; BMA. Prev: Cons. Psychiat. Learning Disabil. & Gen. Psychiat. Oxf. RHA (T); Assoc. Specialist (Psychiat. & Developm. Paediat.) Soton. HA (T); Regist. (Psychiat. Med.) Cane Hill Hosp. Coulsdon.

BALACHANDRAN, Mr Chandrasekharan 2 Aspen Road, Ayr KA7 3QR Tel: 01292 282533 — MB BS 1982 Kerala; FRCS Ed. 1992. Staff Grade Urol. Ayr Hosp.

BALACHANDRAN, Govindasamy Doncaster Drive Surgery, 45 Doncaster Drive, Northolt UB5 4AT; Cedar Heights, Lincoln Road, Gerrards Cross SL9 9TQ — MB BS 1978 Madras; LRCP LRCS Ed. LRCPS Glas. 1986; MRCPI 1990; MRCGP 1990; T(GP) 1990.

BALACHANDRAN, Krishnan (retired) The Elms, Cowley Hill Lane, Helens, St Helens WA10 2AW Tel: 01744 28098 Fax: 01744 604084 — MB BS Madras 1970; DCH RCPS Glas. 1976; MRCPCH 1996; T(M) (Paed) 1991. Cons. Community Paediat., St Helens & Knowsley Community Health NHS Trust. Prev: Cons. Community Paediat. Merseyside.

BALACHANDRAN, Nanthini 21 Bellamy Drive, Stanmore HA7 2DD — LMSSA 1996 Lond.

BALACHANDRAN, Sivarajah Cartref, 29 Balder Rise, Grove Park, London SE12 9PF Tel: 020 8857 7100 — MB BS 1972 Sri Lanka; MRCOG 1989; DRCOG 1988; LMSSA Lond. 1986. Trainee GP Dover VTS. Prev: Regist. (O & G) Thanet Dist. Gen. Hosp. Margate; SHO (O & G) Geo. Eliot Hosp. Nuneaton; SHO (O & G) Greenwich Dist. Hosp.

BALACHANDRAN, Thangaraj c/o Dr J. De, 30 Park Road, Walsall WS5 3JU — MB BS 1979 Madras.

BALACHANDRAN, Thirunavukarasu 5 Gudgeon Court, Draper Road, Enfield EN2 8LZ — MB BS 1972 Madras; DPM Eng. 1978. (Madras) Prev: Regist. (Psychiat.) N. Wales Hosp. Denbigh.

BALAGGAN, Kamaljit Singh 575 Parkfield Road, Wolverhampton WV4 6EL Tel: 01902 354800 — MB BS 1997 Lond.; BSc (Hons) 1994. (St. Georges Medical School, Tooting) SHO (Opthalmology), Vict. Hosp., Blackpool. Prev: SHO (A & E), New Cross Hosp., Wolverhampton; PRHO (Surg.), St. Helier's Hosp., Carshalton, Surrey; PRHO (Med.), Walsall Manor Hosp., Walsall, W. Midl.

BALAGOPAL, Viswanatha Pai Manor Hospital, Moat Road, Walsall WS2 9PS — MB BS 1990 Madras; MB BS Madras 1980; MRCP (UK) 1990.

BALAI, Richard Richards and Partners, The Surgery, North Street, Langport TA10 9RH Tel: 01458 250464 Fax: 01458 253246; Pitts Farm, Pitney, Langport TA10 9AS Tel: 01458 250314 — MB BS 1983 Lond.; MRCP (UK) 1987; MRCGP 1990; DRCOG 1989. Prev: SHO (O & G) W. Middlx. Hosp.; Trainee GP Langport Som. VTS; Regist. & SHO (Geriat.) W. Middlx. Hosp. Isleworth.

BALAJI, Meena 55 Clarence Gardens, Hyndland, Glasgow G11 7JW — MB BS 1990 Baroda; FRCS Ed. 1994.

BALAJI, Mr Venugopal No 8 Doctors Residences, Ysbyty Glan Clwyd, Rhuddlan Road, Bodelwyddan, Rhyl LL18 5UJ — MB BS 1986 Madras; MS Madras 1989, MB BS 1986; FRCS Eng. 1990; FRCS Ed. 1990. Prev: Regist. Rotat. (Surg.) Portsmouth Hosps.

BALAKRISHNA, Jeyabala John Howard Centre, 2 Crozier Terrace, Hackney, London E9 6AT — MB BS 1987 Singapore; MRCPsych 1994; LLM 1998. Cons. (Forens. Psychiat.) City of Hackney NHS Trust. Prev: Sen. Regist. (Forens. Psychiat.) Springfield Univ. Hosp. Lond.; Cons. (Forens. Psychiat.) Addenbrooke's, Camb.

BALAKRISHNAN, Indran Academic Department Medical Microbiology, Royal Free Hospital School Medicine, Rowland Hill St., London NW3 2PF Tel: 020 7794 0500 Fax: 020 7794 0433 Email: indranb@rfhsm.ac.uk; 84 The Fairway, Southgate, London N14 4NU Tel: 020 8440 9839 Email: indran@nyhavn.simplyonline.co.uk — MB BS 1989 Lond.; MB BS (Hons.) Lond. 1989; MSc Lond. 1996; BSc (Hons.) Lond. 1986; MSc Lond. 1996; MRCP (UK) 1993; DRCPath 1998. (Roy. Free Hosp. Sch. Med. Lond.) Clin. Lect. & Hon. Regist. (Med. Microbiol.) Roy. Free Hosp. Sch. Med. Lond. Prev: SHO Rotat. (Med.) Qu. Eliz. II Hosp. Welwyn Garden City; SHO Rotat. (Med.) Enfield Dist. Hosp.; Ho. Surg. St. Albans City Hosp.

BALAKRISHNAN, Juliette Ann Flat 11, 55 Lancaster Gate, London W2 3NA — MB BS 1994 Lond.

BALAKUMAR, Thulasi 123 Longwood Gardens, Ilford IG5 0EG — MB BS 1983 Colombo; MB BS Colombo Sri Lanka 1983; MRCP (UK) 1993.

BALANCE, Rosalind Jane Forest Lodge, Staple Fitzpaine, Taunton TA3 5BL — BM 1993 Soton.; DFFP 1999.

BALAPASKARAN, Mahendrany 108 Taunton Way, Stanmore HA7 1DG Tel: 020 8204 3281 — MB BS 1975 Colombo; LMSSA Lond. 1989; DO RCS Eng. 1986. Clin. Asst. (Ophth.) Merton & Sutton HA.

BALARATNAM, Nimal 1 Mont Clair, Lisvane Road, Cardiff CF14 0SA Tel: 01222 753080 Email: nimbala@msn.com — BM 1991 Nottm.

BALARATNAM, Sherina 37 Waldale Drive, Leicester LE2 2AR — MB ChB 1998 Leic.; MB ChB Leic 1998.

BALASANTHIRAN, Sinnathurai Ashby Clinic, Collum Lane, Scunthorpe DN16 2SZ Tel: 01724 271877; 4 Avenue Vivian, Scunthorpe DN15 8JE Tel: 01724 860329 — MB BS 1969 Ceylon. (Ceylon) Prev: Med. Off. i/c Gen. Hosp. Kaduna State Nigeria; Clin. Asst. (Gen. Med. & c/o Elderly) Goole & Dist. Hosp. N. Humberside.

BALASEGARAM, Manica Vasagar 52 Julien Road, Ealing, London W5 4XA — MB BS 1996 Lond.

BALASEGARAM, Uthayasoori 52 Julien Road, Ealing, London W5 4XA — MB BChir 1993 Camb.; MRCOG 1997. (Camb.)

BALASINGAM, Velupillai 25 Grasmere Avenue, London SW19 3DY — MB BS 1978 Sri Lanka.

BALASSA, George 34 Wildcroft Manor, Wildcroft Road, London SW15 3TT Tel: 020 8789 0165 — MD Budapest 1937; MA Oxf. 1947. Socs: BMA.

BALASUBRAMANIAM, Chelliah Hadley Health Centre, High Street, Hadley, Telford TF1 5NG Tel: 01952 249251 Fax: 01952 250013 Email: balachellia@shrpha.38.nhs.com — MB BS 1970 (per GMC) Mysore. GP. Socs: Med. Defence Union.

BALASUBRAMANIAM, Krishnapillai Calnwood Court (1st Floor), Luton & Dunstable Hospital, Calnwood Road, Luton LU4 0DZ Tel: 01582 709152 — MB BS 1972 Ceylon; MRCS Eng. LRCP Lond. 1981; FRCPsych. Cons. Psychiat. Luton & Dunstable Hosp. (Gen. Adult/Forens.); Hon. Cons. Forens. Psychiat., W. Lond. NHS Trust.

***BALASUBRAMANIAM, Richard Navaratnum** 29 Blackwell Road, Barnt Green, Birmingham B45 8BT — MB ChB 1996 Birm.; BSc Birm. 1993.

BALASUBRAMANIAM, Tamboo Shanmugampillai 1 Whitehall Road, Rugby CV21 3AE Tel: 01788 561319; 10 Tennants Close, Rugby CV21 3NH — MB BS 1972 Sri Lanka. (Univ. Ceylon)

BALASUBRAMANIAN, Mariyappan Blackburn Royal Infirmary, Blackburn BB2 3LR — MB BS 1973 Mysore.

BALASUNDERAM, Sabaratnam North Road Surgery, 27 North Road, Ravensthorpe, Dewsbury WF13 3AA Tel: 01924 464492; Greenbanks, 50 Whitley Road, Thornhill Edge, Dewsbury WF12 0LR Tel: 01924 457406 — MB BS 1972 Mysore; BSc Univ. Madras 1964. (Kasturba Med. Coll. Mangalore) Occupat. Health Med. Adviser Dewsbury & Huddersfield HA; Brig. Med. Adviser W. Yorks. Fire Serv. Bradford. Socs: BMA & Med. Protec. Soc. Prev: Regist. (Gen. Med.) Scartho Rd. Hosp. Grimsby; SHO (Gen. Med. & Paediat.) Louth Co. Hosp. Louth Lincs.

BALASUNDERAM, Subathra Greenbanks, 50 Whitley Road, Thornhill, Dewsbury WF12 0LR — MB BS 1970 Ceylon. (Med. Coll. Colombo) Clin. Med. Off. Dewsbury HA. Prev: Regist. Pontefract Gen. Infirm.; SHO St. Luke's Hosp. Huddersfield; SHO Scartho Rd. Hosp. Grimsby.

BALAYOGI, Komakula K Balayogi, Hussain and Sreenivasan, Doctors Surgery, 76 Market Street, Droylsden, Manchester M43 7UD Tel: 0161 370 2626 Fax: 0161 371 3577 — MB BS 1973 Andhra.

BALAZS, John Robert The Surgery, 1 Binfield Road, London SW4 6TB Tel: 020 7622 1424 Fax: 020 7978 1436 — MB BS 1982 Lond.; BSc 1979 Lond.; MRCGP 1986; DRCOG 1986; DCH RCP Lond. 1985. (Guy's) Chairm. N. Lambeth Primary Care Gp. Prev: GP (Single Homeless) City & E. Lond.

BALBES, Dean Ivor Grosvenor Street Surgery, 4 Grosvenor Street, St Helier, Jersey JE1 4HB Tel: 01534 30541 Fax: 01534 887948 — MB ChB 1986 Dund.; BSc 1982 Dund.; MRCGP 1990. Prev: Trainee GP Grantham VTS; Ho. Phys. & Ho. Surg. Hairmyres Hosp. E. Kilbride.

BALBOA, Stephanie 34 Gavenny Way, Abergavenny NP7 5LX — MB BS 1991 Lond.

BALCH, Katherine Jane Morthen Road Surgery, 2 Morthen Road, Wickersley, Rotherham S66 1EU Tel: 01709 549711; Highfields Pinchwell View, Wickersley, Rotherham S66 1FP — MB ChB 1993 Sheff.; DFFP 1997; DROG 1996; DRCOG 1996; MRCGP 1997. (Sheff.) p/t GP. Prev: Trainee GP/SHO Doncaster Roy. Infirm.; Ho. Off. (Surg.) Roy. Hallamsh. Hosp. Sheff.; Trainee GP Doncaster VTS.

BALCH, Nicola Joyce Wedderhill House, Blairs, Aberdeen AB12 5YX — MB ChB 1975 Aberd.; MRCP (UK) 1978.

BALCOMBE, Jonathan Noah 4 Elm Walk, London NW3 7UP — MB BS 1998 Lond.; MB BS Lond 1998.

BALCOMBE, Nicholas Roger Queens Hospital, Burton Hospital NHS Trust, Belverdere Road, Burton-on-Trent DE13 0RB; 1 Brewers Close, Binley, Coventry CV3 2UP — MB BS 1991 Lond.; MRCP (UK) 1995. (St. Georges Hospital London) Specialist Regist. (Geriats.) Qu.s Hosp., Burton. Socs: Brit. Geriat. Soc.; W Midl. Brit. Geriat. Soc.; Inst. Ageing & Health. Prev: Regist. (Med.) Walsgrave Hosp. Coventry.

BALCON, Raphael 22 Upper Wimpole Street, London W1G 6NB Tel: 020 7486 8964 Fax: 020 7486 7918 — MB BS 1960 Lond.; MD Lond. 1969; FRCP Lond. 1977, M 1965; MRCS Eng. LRCP Lond. 1960. (King's Coll. Hosp.) Cons. Cardiol. Nat. Heart & Chest Hosps. Lond.; Hon. Sen. Lect. Cardiothoracic Inst. Socs: (Pres. & Ex-Treas.) Brit. Cardiac Soc. Prev: Sen. Regist. Nat. Heart Hosp. Lond.; Regist. (Med.) King's Coll. Hosp. Lond.; Pub. Health Serv. Fell. (Cardiol.) Wayne State Univ. Detroit, USA.

BALDACCHINO, Alexander Mario Department of Addictive Behaviour and Psychological Medicine, St George's Hosptial Medical School, Cranmer Terrace, Level 6, London SW17 0RE Tel: 020 8725 5476 Fax: 020 8725 2914 Email: a.baldacchino@sghms.ac.uk; 6 Eltisley Avenue, Newnham, Cambridge CB3 9JG Tel: 01223 573642 — MD 1987 Malta; MPhil Ed. 1996; MRCPsych 1994; Dip. Addic. Behaviour Lond. 1990. (Univ. Malta Med. Sch.) Sen. Lect. St. Geo.'s Hosp. Med. Sch. Lond.; Hon. Cons. Psychiat., N. E. Essex Ment. Health Trust. Socs: Brit. Assn. Psychopharmacol. Prev: Sen. Regist. (Gen. Psychiat.) Addenbrooke's Hosp. Camb.

BALDAM, Amanda Louise 30 Moorland Road, Poulton-le-Fylde, Blackpool — BM 1985 Soton.; DA (UK) 1988. Staff. Anaesth.Vict. Hosp.Blackpool. Prev: SHO (A & E) Roy. Lancaster Infirm.; Regist. (O & G) Bundaberg Qld, Australia.; Anaesth.Reg.Hope hosp.Salford.

BALDAS, Mr Aristides 337 Goffs Lane, Goffs Oak, Waltham Cross EN7 5QH Tel: 01992 23949 — Ptychio Iatrikes 1972 Athens; FRCS Glas. 1984. Assoc. Specialist (Orthop. Surg.) Harold Wood Hosp. Romford. Prev: Staff Orthop. Surg. Harold Wood Hosp. Essex.

BALDASERA, Martin Anthony 21 Dean's Walk, Gilesgate, Durham DH1 1HA — MRCS Eng. LRCP Lond. 1979.

BALDEO, Dindial Leigh Infirmary, The Avenue, Leigh WN7 1HS — MB BS 1981 West Indies.

BALDERAMOS-PRICE, Josephine Mary 69 Chesterton Avenue, Harpenden AL5 5SU Tel: 01582 769643 — MB BS 1985 West Indies; MRCGP 1994.

BALDEWEG, Stefanie Department of Medicine UCL, Whittington Hospital, Archway Road, Archway Camp, London N19 3UA Tel: 020 7288 5301 Fax: 020 7288 5302 Email: s.baldeweg@ucl.ac.uk; 38 Summerlee Avenue, London N2 9QP — State Exam Med 1990 Humboldt U Berlin; State Exam Med. Humboldt U Berlin 1990; MSc Berlin 1987; MRCP 1997. Research Regist. (Diabetes & Endocrinol.). Prev: SHO (Diabetes, Gen. Med. & Cardiol.) Whittington Hosp. Lond.; SHO (Gen. Med., Dermat. & Rheum.) OldCh. Hosp. Romford.

BALDING, Jane The Medical Centre, Kingston Avenue, East Horsley, Leatherhead KT24 6QT Tel: 01483 284151 Fax: 01483 285814 — BM 1992 Soton.; MRCGP 1998; DFFP 1997; DRCOG 1997; DRCOG 1997; DGM 1998; DPD 1999. GP Princip. Socs: Roy. Coll. Gen. Pract.

***BALDOCK, Alice Marieke** 9 Parkwood Avenue, Esher KT10 8DE Tel: 020 8398 3759; 9 Parkwood Avenue, Esher KT10 8DE Tel: 020 8398 3759 — MB BS 1998 Lond.; MB BS Lond 1998.

BALDOCK, Charles Anthony Richard The Health Centre, Iveldale Drive, Shefford SG17 5AU Tel: 01462 814899 Fax: 01462 752161; Uplands, 24 Elston Road, Kempston, Bedford MK42 8HB Tel: 01234 740280 — MB BChir 1974 Camb.; MA Camb. 1976; MRCGP 1979.

BALDOCK, Graham John Department of Anaesthetics, Hammersmith Hospital, Du Cane Road, London W12 0NN Tel: 020 8383 4521 Fax: 020 8383 4524 Email: g.baldock@ic.ac.uk; 116B Church Road, Hanwell, London W7 3BE Tel: 020 8840 9755 Email: graham.baldock3@which.net — MB BS 1973 Lond.; FFA RCS Eng. 1977. (King's Coll Hosp.) Cons. Anaesth. Hammersmith Hosp. Lond. Socs: Intens. Care Soc.; Assn. Anaesth. GB & Irel.; Eur. Soc. Intens. Care Med. Prev: Cons. Anaesth. Lewisham Hosp. Lond.; Sen. Regist. (Anaesth.) Guy's & Lewisham Hosps.; Regist. (Anaesth.) Guy's Hosp. Lond.

BALDOCK, Janet Elizabeth Cuckoo Lane Surgery, 14 Cuckoo Lane, Hanwell, London W7 3EY — MB BChir 1970 Camb.; MA Camb. 1971; MRCGP 1985. (Univ. Coll. Hosp.) Prev: SHO (Paediat.), Ho. Surg. & Ho. Phys. W. Middlx. Hosp. Isleworth.

BALDOCK, Nicolas Edwin, Surg. Cdr. RN 17 Osborne View Road, Hillhead, Fareham PO14 3JW Tel: 01329 662640 — MB ChB 1969 Bristol; MRCP (UK) 1975; MRCS Eng. LRCP Lond. 1968; FFOM RCP Lond. 1995, MFOM 1980; DAvMed Eng. 1972; FRCP 1997 UK. (Bristol) Med. Off.-in-Charge, Inst. of Naval Med., Alverstoke; Edr., Jl. of Roy. Naval Serv. Prev: Chief Staff Off. Health & Safety to Flag Off. Naval Aviat.; Pres. Centr. Air & Admiralty Med. Bd.; Dir. of Health (Navy).

BALDOCK, Nigel John Douglas The Grayshott Surgery, Boundary Road, Grayshott, Hindhead GU26 6TY Tel: 01428 604343 Fax: 01428 604899; 4 The Rowans, Crossways Road, Grayshott, Hindhead GU26 6EW Tel: 01428 604063 — MB BChir 1976 Camb.; MA Camb. 1976; MRCP (UK) 1978. (Camb. (St. Johns) & Middlx Hosp.) Prev: Regist. (Med.) N. Staffs. Roy. Infirm. Stoke-on-Trent.

BALDOCK GRIMES, Suzanne Mary Wetmore Road Surgery, 12 Wetmore Road, Burton-on-Trent DE14 1SL — MB ChB 1990 Leic.; MRCGP 1995; DRCOG 1994; DFFP 1994. (Leicester) p/t 3/4 Time Partner in Gen. Pract.; Clin. Med. Off. (Family Plann.) Leicester. Prev: Asst. GP S.wigston Leicester.

BALDOTA, Sanjay Zumberlal Department of General Surgery, Central Middlesex Hospital, Acton Lane, Park Royal, London NW10 7NS; 12 West End Lane, Pinner HA5 1EE — MB BS 1988 Bombay.

BALDRY, Peter Edward Millstream House, Fladbury, Pershore WR10 2QX Tel: 01386 860107 Fax: 01386 861228 — MB BS 1944 Lond.; FRCP Lond. 1972, M 1949; MRCS Eng. LRCP Lond. 1943. (St. Bart.) Socs: Fell. Roy. Soc. Med.; Ex-Chairm. Brit. Med. Acupunc. Soc.; (Ex-Pres.) Acupunc. Assn. Chartered Soc. of Physiother. Prev: Cons. Phys. Ashford Hosp. Middlx. & St. Mary's Hosp. Hampton; Sen. Regist. (Med.) Harefield Hosp.; Ho. Phys. St. Bart. Hosp. & Brompton Hosp.

BALDRY, Sarah Jillian THe Surgery, 89 Gubbins Lane, Harold Wood, Romford RM3 0DR Tel: 01708 346666 Fax: 01708 381300; 59 Merriefield Avenue, Broadstone BH18 8DB Tel: 01202 696896 — MB BS 1981 Newc.; MRCGP 1985; DRCOG 1985. (Newcastle upon Tyne)

BALDWICK, Cheryl Mary Flat 2/2, 121 Kilmarnock Road, Shawlands, Glasgow G41 3YT — MB BS 1994 Lond.

BALDWIN, Alison Mary Jenifer Flat 1, 2 Empress Road, Lyndhurst SO43 7AE — MB BS 1994 Lond.

BALDWIN, Anna Louise The Rowans, Portsmouth Area Hospice, Purbrook Heath Road, Purbrook, Portsmouth PO7 5RU; Tanners,

Love Lane, Petersfield GU31 4BW — MB BS 1978 Lond.; MSc Lond. 1989, MD 1993; MRCP (UK) 1980; MRCPath 1991. (King's Coll. Hosp.) Cons. in Palliat. Med., Portsmouth Healthcare NHS Trust, Portsmouth; Lead Cons. in The Rowans, Portsmouth Area Hospice. Socs: Assn. Palliat. Med. Prev: Cons. Chem. Path. Mt. Vernon & Watford Hosps. NHS Trust; Lect. (Chem. Path.) Univ. Coll. & Middlx. Hosp. Med. Sch. Lond.; Specialist Regist. (Palliat. Med.) S. Thames.

BALDWIN, Anthony David 27 Lodge Road, Pelsall, Walsall WS4 1DE — MB BS 1992 Newc.

BALDWIN, Ashley Christopher 38 Croftson Avenue, Ormskirk L39 1NJ — MB ChB 1990 Sheff.

BALDWIN, Christopher Donald Hergest Unit, Ysbyty Gwynedd, Bangor Tel: 01248 384384 — MB BS 1977 Newc.; BA Open 1991; MA Newc. 1993; MRCPsych 1997; DGM (RCP, Lond) 1998. Cons., N. W. Wales NHS Trust Psychiat., Bangor. Socs: Brit. Geriat. Soc. Prev: Sen. Med. Off. (Respirat. Dis.) Benefits Agency; Med. Off. DSS; GP BrigHo., W. Yorks.

BALDWIN, Christopher Jon 74 Western Avenue, Newport NP20 3SN — MB BS 1998 Lond.; MB BS Lond 1998.

BALDWIN, Mr David Lionel Department of Otolaryngology, Southmead Hospital, Westbury on Trym, Bristol BS10 5NB Tel: 0117 959 5160 Fax: 0117 959 5158 — BM 1979 Sthamptn; FRCS 1984 Otolaryngology, London. (Southampton) Cons. ENT Surg. S.mead Hosp. Bristol.; Cons. OtoLaryngol. Head & Neck Surg., N. Bristol Trust. Prev: Cons. Sen. Lect. S.mead Hosp. Univ. Bristol; Sen. Regist. (Otolaryng.) Lond. Hosp.; Regist. (Otolaryng.) St. Bart. Hosp. Lond.

BALDWIN, David Raymond Department of Respiratory Medicine, City Hospital, Nottingham NG5 1PB Tel: 0115 969 1169 Fax: 0115 962 7723 Email: david.baldwin@nottingham.ac.uk — MB ChB 1984 Birm.; FRCP 1999; MD Birm. 1991; MRCP (UK) 1987. (Birmingham) Cons. Phys. (Respirat. & Gen. Med.) City Hosp. Nottm.; Clin. Teach. Univ. of Nottm.; Roy. Coll. Phys.s Tutor. Socs: Brit. Thorac. Soc.; BMA; MDU. Prev: Sen. Regist. (Respirat. & Gen. Med.) City Gen. Hosp. Stoke-on-Trent; Research Fell. (Respirat. Med.) Dudley Rd. Hosp. Birm. & City Hosp. Nottm.; Regist. (Med.) Sandwell Dist. Gen. Hosp.

BALDWIN, David Stewart Royal South Hampshire Hospital, Brintons Terrace, Southampton SO14 0YG Tel: 02380 825533 Fax: 02380 234243 — MB BS 1984 Lond.; MRCPsych 1988. (Char. Cross Hosp. Med. Sch.) Sen. Lect. (Psychiat.) Fac. Med. Univ. Soton.; Hon. Cons. Psychiat. Soton. Community Servs. NHS Trust. Socs: Coun. Mem. Brit. Assn. Psychopharmacol.; Eur. Coll. Neuropsychopharm.; Pres. Depression Alliance. Prev: Cons. Gen. & Community Psychiat. John Conolly Wing. W. Lond. Healthcare NHS Trust; Sen. Regist. (Emerg. Psychiat.) Maudsley Hosp. Lond.; Sen. Regist. (Gen. Psychiat.) St. Mary's Hosp. Med. Sch. Lond.

BALDWIN, David Victor Trevor (retired) Woodford Cottage, Tittleshall, King's Lynn PE32 2PF — MRCS Eng. LRCP Lond. 1946. Prev: RNVR 1947-9.

BALDWIN, Donald Walter 27 Kerver Lane, Dunnington, York YO19 5SL Tel: 01904 489918 — MB ChB 1951 St. And. Med. Mem. Disabil. Appeal Tribunals & Med. Assessor Social Security Appeal Tribunals. Prev: GP BrigHo.; Surg. Lt. RNVR.

BALDWIN, Elizabeth Sarah 22 Sands Avenue, Chadderton, Oldham OL9 0NU — MB ChB 1996 Leeds.

BALDWIN, Emma Clare 11 Lantree Crescent, Cambridge CB2 2NJ — MB BS 1991 Lond. Trainee GP/SHO (Psychiat.) OldCh. Hosp. Romford VTS. Prev: SHO (O & G) Rush Green Hosp. Romford; Ho. Off. Harold Wood Hosp. N. Middlx. Hosp.

BALDWIN, Eric Thomas (retired) 11 Tudor Avenue, Maidstone ME14 5HH — MB BCh BAO 1952 Dub.; BDent Sc 1958.

BALDWIN, Fiona Jane 15 Burnaby Road, Bournemouth BH4 8JF Email: fionabaldwin@yahoo.com — MB BS 1992 Lond.; FRCA. 1998. (St Georges Hosp Med School)

BALDWIN, Heather Catherine 29 Rectory Close, Carlton, Bedford MK43 7JT Email: hcgreaney@aol.com — MB BS 1992 Lond.; FRCOphth 1996; BSc (1st. cl. Hons.) Anthropol. Lond. 1989. (Med. Coll. St. Bart. Hosp. Lond.) Research Assoc. (Ophth.) St. Thomas' Hosp. Lond. Prev: SHO Soton. Eye Unit.

BALDWIN, Helen Louise 1 Dairy Close, Corfe Mullen, Wimborne BH21 3UX Tel: 01202 658451 — MB BS 1984 Lond.; MRCGP 1992; DCH RCP Lond. 1987. Staff Grade Community Paediat. (p/t), Poole; Clin. Asst. Dermat. Poole NHS Trust Hosp. Dorset. Prev: GP Morris Manitoba, Canada; Regist. (Paediat.) Waikato Hosp. Hamilton, NZ; Regist. & SHO (Paediat. & Anaesth.) Freedom Fields Hosp. Plymouth.

BALDWIN, Jane Elizabeth Radiology Department, Yeovil District Hospital, Yeovil BA21 4AT; Tel: 01935 881345 — MB BS 1981 Lond.; MRCP (UK) 1984; FRCR 1988. Cons. Radiol. Yeovil Dist. Hosp. Som. Prev: Sen. Regist. (Diag. Radiol.) Addenbrooke's Hosp. Camb.

BALDWIN, Janet Mary 29 Park Road, Hampton Hill, Hampton TW12 1HG Tel: 020 8979 0046 — MB BS 1972 Lond.; MB BS (Hons.) Lond. 1972; MRCP (UK) 1977; MRCS Eng. LRCP Lond. 1972; FRCOG 1990, M 1977; DCH Eng. 1976; MBA Keele 1996. (Univ. Coll. Hosp.) Cons. O & G W. Middlx. Hosp. Isleworth; Hon. Sen. Lect. Char. Cross Hosp. Med. Sch. Prev: Sen. Regist. (O & G) Char. Cross & W. Middlx. Hosps.; Regist. (O & G) St. Helier Hosp. Carshalton.

BALDWIN, John Richard The Health Centre, The Quay, Kingsbridge TQ7 1HR Tel: 01548 853551; The Millers House, Bowcombe Road, Kingsbridge TQ7 2DL Tel: 01548 854271 — MB BS 1982 Lond.; MRCGP 1989.

BALDWIN, Kathryn Joanne Park House, 177 London Road, Appleton, Warrington WA4 5BJ Tel: 01925 850818 — MB ChB 1990 Liverp.; MRCOG 1995. Specialist Regist. (O & G), Roy Hartley Matern. Hosp., Wigan & Leigh NHS Trust. Socs: Brit. Matern. & Fetal Med. Soc.; Brit. Med. Ultrasound Soc.; Brit. Soc. Colposc. & Cervic. Pathol. Prev: Specialist Regist. (O & G) N. Staffs. Hosp. Stoke; Research Regist. (Dermat.) N. Staffs. Hosp.; Regist. (O & G) St. Mary's Hosp. Manch.

BALDWIN, Kirsty Anne 26 Moorlands Drive, Brierfield, Nelson BB9 5ER — MB BS 1993 Lond.; MRCGP. (Knig's College, London)

BALDWIN, Lee Nigel East Whinfel, Sheep Plain, East Sussex, Crowborough TN6 3ST — MB BS 1984 Lond.; BSc Lond. 1981, MB BS 1984; MRCP (UK) 1987; FCAnaesth 1991. Regist. Rotat. (Anaesth.) Avon HA.

BALDWIN, Lindsay Jane Pineview, Bedmond Rd, Abbots Langley WD5 0RS — MB ChB 1997 Manch.

BALDWIN, Marjorie Joy Tattenham Health Centre, Tattenham Crescent, Epsom KT18 5NU Tel: 01737 371011 Fax: 01737 359641; 3 Ladbroke Road, Epsom KT18 5BG — MB BS 1979 Lond.; DCH RCP Lond. 1984.

BALDWIN, Mary Josephine 539 Fulwood Road, Sheffield S10 3QG — MB ChB 1964 Leeds. (Leeds) Prev: Regist. (Path.) Roy. Free Hosp. Lond.; Regist. Clin. Haemat. & Oncol. N. Middlx. Hosp. Lond.; GP Sheff..

BALDWIN, Mr Peter John William Rosie Maternity Hospital, Robinson Way, Cambridge CB2 2SW Tel: 01223 245151; 11 Lantree Lane, Cambridge CB2 2NJ — MB BS 1992 Lond.; MRCOG, 1998. Specialist Regist. Obsst. & Gyn., Anglia Robihan; Specialist Regist. (Obst. & Gyn.), Qu Eliz. Hosp., Kingslynn.

BALDWIN, Peter Martin Baldwin and Partners, Hucknall Road Medical Centre, off Kibworth Close, Nottingham NG5 1FX Tel: 0115 960 6652 Fax: 0115 969 1746; East Lodge, Burntstump Hill, Arnold, Nottingham NG5 8PQ Tel: 0115 963 6490 — MB ChB 1972 Sheff.

BALDWIN, Robert Charles York House, Manchester Royal Infirmary, Oxford Road, Manchester M13 7BX Tel: 0161 276 5321 Fax: 0161 276 5303; 11 Ballbrook Avenue, Didsbury, Manchester M20 6AB — BM 1976 Soton.; BSc Manch. 1970; FRCP Lond. 1997; FRCP 1979; FRCPsych 1994, M 1981. Cons. Psychiat. for Elderly York Ho., Manch. Roy. Infirm.; Hon. Clin. Sen. Lect. Prev: Sen. Regist. (Psychiat.) Soton. & Basingstoke DHAs; Regist. (Psychiat.) Soton. Univ. Hosp.; SHO (Med.) Soton. Univ. Hosp.

BALDWIN, Robert James Courtside Surgery, Kennedy Way, Yate, Bristol BS37 4D2 Tel: 01454 313874 Email: davidmcd@doctors; 14 Brins Close, Stoke Gifford, Bristol BS34 8XU Tel: 0117 931 5137 Email: robert-baldwin@lineone.net — MB BCh 1977 Wales. Prev: GP Bristol; Police Surg. Gwent Constab.

BALDWIN, Robert Neil Gloucestershire Royal Hospital, Great Western Road, Gloucester GL1 3NN Tel: 01452 528555 Fax: 01452 394321 Email: nbaldw@aol.com; Vell Mill, Ryton Road, Dymock GL18 2DG Tel: 01531 890829 Email: neil@nbaldw.demon.co.uk — BM BS 1981 Nottm.; BMedSci (Hons.) Nottm. 1979; MRCP (UK) 1984; FRCP 1996. Cons. Phys. Gloucester Roy. Hosp. Socs: Brit. Geriat. Soc.; Brit. Assn. of Stroke Phys.s. Prev: Sen. Regist. (Gen. &

Geriat. Med.) Clatterbridge Hosp. Wirral & Roy. Liverp. Hosp.; Research Fell. Radcliffe Infirm. Oxf.

BALDWIN, Roger Walter Middleton 13 Meadow Way, Farnborough Park, Orpington BR6 8LN — MB BS 1966 Lond.; MRCS Eng. LRCP Lond. 1966; FRCOG 1984, MRCOG 1971, DObst 1968; DA Eng. 1969. (Char. Cross) Cons. O & G Whipps Cross, Wanstead, & Jubilee Hosps. Lond. Socs: Fell. Roy. Soc. Med. Prev: Regist. (O & G) Roy. Free Hosp.; SHO (Obst.) City of Lond. Matern. Hosp.

BALDWIN, Russell John Thomas Oak Street Surgery, Oak Street, Cwmbran NP44 3LT Tel: 01633 866719 Fax: 01633 838208; Lyndhurst, Abergavenny Road, Penperlleni, Pontypool NP4 0AH — MB BCh 1963 Wales.

BALDWIN, Sam Henri George Doctors Residences, Law Hospital, Carluke ML8 5ER — MB ChB 1998 Dund.; MB ChB Dund 1998.

BALDWIN, Samuel Joseph (retired) 2 Copse Edge Avenue, Epsom KT17 4HS Tel: 01372 728676 — MRCS Eng. LRCP Lond. 1951; MRCGP 1961. Prev: Demonst. Chem. Path. Univ. Leeds.

BALDWIN, Stuart Peter North Hill Surgery, 18 North Hill, Colchester CO1 1DZ Tel: 01206 578070 Fax: 01206 769880; 21 Chapel Road, West Bergholt, Colchester CO6 3JB Tel: 01206 241443 — MB 1977 Camb.; MA (Hons.) Camb. 1977, MB 1977, BChir 1976; MRCGP 1980; DRCOG 1980. (Camb. & St. Thos.) GP Colchester. Prev: Ho. Surg. (ENT) St. Thos. Hosp.; Ho. Phys. (Gen. Med.) St. Helier Hosp. Carshalton.

BALE, Catherine Jane Parklands, Second Avenue, Newcastle ST5 8NU — MB BS 1993 Lond.

BALE, Charles Geoffrey The Green House, 83 High St., Godstone RH9 8DT Tel: 01883 744624 Fax: 01883 740005 — MB BS 1969 Lond.; MRCS Eng. LRCP Lond. 1969; DObst RCOG 1975. (Lond. Hosp.) Semi Cosmetic Surg. Private Work; Self Employed for respect of Med. Insur. Meds., Accid. & Health Examrs. & Reporters, Personal Injury Accid, Indust. Injuries, Prescribed Disablem.s, Loss of earnings, Exams. & Reports. Socs: BMA. Prev: Police Surg. for Dorking & Leatherhead; Maj. RAMC; Ho. Surg. Surgic. Unit & Ho. Phys. Lond. Hosp.

BALE, Mr Richard Stephen Department of Orthopaedics, Royal Preston Hospital, Sharoe Green Lane, Preston PR2 9HT Tel: 01772 716565; The Mount, Stanmore Drive, Haverbreaks, Lancaster LA1 5BL Tel: 01524 32675 Fax: 01524 32675 — MB ChB 1986 Manch.; BSc St. And. 1983; FRCS Eng. 1990; FRCS (Orth.) 1995. Cons. Orthop. Surg. Preston Acute Hosps. Socs: Brit. Orthop. Assn.; Assoc. Mem. Brit. Soc. Surg. Hand; Brit. Elbow & Shoulder Soc. Prev: Lect. & Tutor (Orthop. Surg.) Univ. Manch.; Regist. (Orthop.) Bolton Roy. Infirm.

BALE, Robert John Putney Community Mental ealth Team, Queen Mary's University Hospital, Roehampton Lane, London SW15 5PN — MB BS 1990 Lond.; MRCPsych 1995. (St Georges London) Cons. Psychiat. N. Sector Team Rookery Resource Centre Qu. Mary's Hosp. Lond.

BALE, Roderick Norman 45 Warblington Road, Emsworth PO10 7HG — MB BS 1961 Lond.; FRCP Ed. 1981, M 1966; MRCS Eng. LRCP Lond. 1961; FRCPsych 1985, M 1971; DPM Eng. 1967. (St. Mary's) Cons. Psychiat. & Head Psychiat. Dept., Kuwait Hosp. for Psychol. Med. Prev: Cons. Psychiat. St. Jas. Hosp. Portsmouth.; Sen. Regist. (Psychiat.) United Birm. Hosps.; Regist. (Psychiat.) John Conolly Hosp. Birm.

BALEN, Adam Henry Dept Obstetics Gynaecology, Clarendon Wing, Leeds General Infirmary, Leeds LS2 9NS Tel: 0113 392 2728 Fax: 0113 392 2446 Email: abalen@ulth.northy.nhs.uk; Email: abalen@ulth.northy.nhs.uk — MB BS 1983 Lond.; MD Lond. 1995; MFFP 1993; MRCOG 1990. (St Barts) Cons. Reproduc. Med. (O & G) Leeds Gen. Infirm. Socs: Amer..Soc. Reprod. Med; (Counc.) Brit. Fertil. Soc. (Treas.); Eur. Soc. Human Reproduc. & Embryol. Prev: Sen. Regist. (Reproduc. Med.) John Radcliffe Hosp. Oxf.; Regist. (O & G) Hillingdon Hosp. Lond.; Research Fell. (Reproduc. Endocrinol.) Middlx. Hosp. Lond.

BALEN, Frances Gwenllian The Department of Radiology, Main X-Ray, Pinderfields Hospital, Aberford Road, Wakefield WF1 4DG Tel: 01924 212464 Fax: 01924 212103 — MB BS 1987 Lond.; BSc (Hons.) Lond. 1984; MRCP (UK) 1990; FRCR Lond. 1995; DObst 1995; DCH RCP Lond. 1990. (St. Bart.) p/t Cons. Radiol. Pinderfield Hosp. Wakefield (p/t). Prev: Sen. Regist. (Radiol.) St Ja. Hosp. Leeds; Sen. Regist. (Radiol.) Middlx. & Univ. Coll. Hosp. Lond.; SHO (Paediat.) Qu. Eliz. Hosp. Lond.

BALENDRA, Padma Rani Forth Valley Health Board, 33 Spittal St., Stirling FK8 1DX Tel: 01786 457262 Fax: 01786 446327; 28 Stirling Drive, Bearsden, Glasgow G61 4NU Tel: 0141 942 0294 — MB BCh BAO 1975 Belf.; MD Belf. 1991; MFPHM RCP (UK) 1995; MPH Glas. 1992. (Qu. Univ. Belf.) Cons. Pub. Health Med. Forth Valley Health Bd. Socs: (Counc.)(Ex-Pres.) Med. Woms. Federat. Scott. W.. Assoc. Prev: Sen. Regist. (Pub. Health Med.) Lothian HB Edin.; Princip. GP Clin. Research Asst. Univ Glas.

BALENDRAN, Nadarajah Westbourne Road Surgery, 42 Westbourne Road, Marsh, Huddersfield HD1 4LE Tel: 01484 426044 Fax: 01484 454541 — MB BS 1969 Mysore.

BALENDRAN, Nalini 42 Sandpits Road, Surrey, Croydon CR0 5HG — BM BCh 1993 Oxf.

BALENDRAN, Poopalasingam Department of Anaesthetics, King's College Hospital, Denmark Hill, London SE5 9RS — MB BS 1975 Colombo; 1980 MRCS Eng. LRCP Lond. 1980; 1987 FFA RCSI 1987; 1999 Ph D South Bank Univ. Cons. Anaesth. King's Coll. Hosp. Lond. Socs: Assn. Anaesth. GB & Irel.; Roy. Soc. Med. Prev: Cons. Anaesth. Hull Roy. Infirm.; Sen. Regist. (Anaesth.) Guy's Hosp. Lond.; Clin. Fell. (Anaesth.) McGill Univ. Montreal, Canada.

BALENDRAN, Rakulan 69 Manor Drive N., New Malden KT3 5PA — MB BS 1996 Lond.

BALET, Richard St Bartholomew's Hospital, West Smithfield, London EC1 Tel: 020 7601 7176 Fax: 020 7601 7182; 26 Sutherland Grove, London SW18 5PU Tel: 020 8789 6775 — MD 1977 Paris. Clin. Asst. (O & G) St. Bart. Hosp. Lond. Prev: Clin. Research Fell. Roy. Lond. Hosp.

BALFOUR, Alison Elizabeth Department of Microbiology, Yorkhill NHS Trust, Glasgow G3 8SJ Tel: 0141 201 0421 Fax: 0141 201 0413 Email: alison.balfour@yorkhill.scot.nhs.uk — MB ChB 1987 Glas.; BSc (Microbiol.) Glas. 1985; MRC Path 1998. p/t Locum Cons. Microbiologist, Yorkhill NHS Trust, Glas. Prev: Sen. Regist. (Microbiol.) S.. Gen. NHS Trust Glas.; Regist. (Microbiol.) Roy. Infirm. Glas.; SHO (Infec. Dis.) Fazakerley Hosp. Liverp.

BALFOUR, Alistair Melville Balholm, Pikes Hill Avenue, Lyndhurst SO43 7AX; 52 Coopers Close, Stepney, London E1 4BB Tel: 020 7366 9778 Email: alistair@sushibalfour.freeserve.co.uk — MB BS 1997 Lond.; BSc. (London hosp.med.Coll)

BALFOUR, Anthony John Chetwynd, CBE 43A Ellesborough Road, Wendover, Aylesbury HP22 6EL Tel: 01296 622442 Email: tonybalfour@aol.com — LMSSA 1952 Lond.; MB BChir Camb. 1960; MA Camb. 1960; DCP Lond 1961; DTM & H Liverp. 1962; FRCPath 1975, M 1963; MRAeS 1980. (Camb. & Oxf.) Socs: Fell. Brit. Assn. Forens. Med.; Fell. Roy. Soc. Med. Prev: Cons. Advisor Path. & Trop. Med. & Advisor Aviat. Path. to DGMS (RAF), RAF Inst. Path & Trop. Med. Aylesbury; Resid. Path. Ch.ill Hosp. Oxf.; Ho. Phys. Neurol. Dept. Stoke Mandeville Hosp. Bucks.

BALFOUR, Catriona Eleanor 43 Rodney Road, West Bridgford, Nottingham NG2 6JH — MB ChB 1996 Liverp.

BALFOUR, David Melville Lyndhurst Surgery, 2 Church Lane, Lyndhurst SO43 7EW Tel: 023 8028 2689 Fax: 023 8028 2918 — MB BS 1969 Lond. (Lond. Hosp.) PCT Exec. Chair. New Forest PCT. Prev: Med. Off. Nchanga Consolidated Copper Mines Ltd., Zambia; Med. Adviser (Matern. & Child Health & Family Plann.) Govt. of Seychelles.

BALFOUR, Juliet Ann The Park Road Medical Practice, Park Road, Shepton Mallet BA4 5BP Tel: 01749 342350 Fax: 01749 346859; Beryl Cottage, Hawkers Lane, Wells BA5 3JP Tel: 01749 676915 — MB BS 1987 Lond.; BSc Lond. 1984; MRCGP 1991; DRCOG 1990. (St. Bart.) GP.

BALFOUR, Leith Leeds General Infirmary, Department of Surgery, Clarendon Wing, Leeds LS1 3EX Tel: 0113 3923557; 45 Stonebridge House, Cobourg Street, Manchester M1 3GB Tel: 0161 236 0852 Email: leith.a@virgin.net — MB ChB 1994 Liverp.; BClinSci (Hons.) Liverp. 1993; FRCS 1999; FRCS (Ed) 1999. Clin. Research Fell., (Gen. Surg.), Leeds Gen. Infirm. Prev: SHO Rotat. (Gen. Surg.) Countess of Chester Hosp.; SHO Rotat. (A & E) Whiston Hosp.

BALFOUR, Peter John Torquil c/o Cymbeline, 43A Ellesborough Road, Wendover, Aylesbury HP22 6EL Tel: 01296 622442; 237 Oldham Road, Ashton-under-Lyne OL7 9AT Tel: 0161 339 0032 — MB ChB 1983 Birm.; MSc Birm. 1991, BSc 1980. (Birm.) Socs:

BMA. Prev: Clin. Research Fell. Sch. Med. Sci. Bristol; Regist. (Histopath.) Edgware Gen. Hosp.; SHO (Psychiat.) N. Manch. HA.

BALFOUR, Mr Robert Peter Dept of O&G, Princess of Wales Hospital, Coity Rd, Bridgend CF31 1RQ Tel: 01656 752465 Fax: 01656 752294; 7 Marine Walk, Ogmore-By-Sea, Bridgend CF32 0PQ Tel: 01656 880034 — MB ChB 1966 Liverp.; FRCOG 1986, M 1974; DObst RCOG 1968; DTM & H Liverp. 1967. (Liverp.) Cons. O & G P.ss of Wales Hosp. Bridgend; Hon. Vis. Prof. (Obst. & Gyn.) Univ. Oradea, Romania. Socs: Internat. Soc. Gynaecol. Endoscopy; Brit. Soc. Gyn. Endoscopy; Welsh Obst. & Gyn. Soc. Prev: Sen. Regist. (O & G) St. David's Hosp. Bangor & Cardiff; Regist. (O & G) Fazakerley & Walton Hosps. Liverp.; Med. Off. Vom Christian Hosp. Nigeria.

BALFOUR, Robin Francis Murrayfield Medical Practice, 8 Corstorphine Road, Edinburgh EH12 6HN Tel: 0131 337 6151 Fax: 0131 313 3450; Westor Dalmeny Farm House, Dalmeny, South Queensferry EH30 9TT Tel: 0131 337 6151 Fax: 0131 313 5450 — MB BChir 1985 Camb.; MRCGP; DRCOG. (St Andrews, Cambridge)

BALFOUR, Ross Owen Clunie Lodge, Isla Road, Perth PH2 7HG — MB ChB 1998 Dund.; MB ChB Dund 1998.

BALFOUR, Mr Tom Wyles (retired) 43 Rodney Road, Nottingham NG2 6JH Tel: 0115 923 2897 — MB ChB 1965 Ed.; FRCS Ed. 1969. Cons. Surg. & Sen. Lect. (Surg.) Univ. Nottm. Prev: Clin. Dean Univ. Nottm. Med. Sch.

BALFOUR, William Deas (retired) 'Hollybush', 51 New Abbey Road, Dumfries DG2 7LZ Tel: 01387 253696 — MB ChB 1956 Glas. Prev: Ho. Phys. W.. Dist. Hosp. Glas.

BALFOUR-LYNN, Ian Michael Royal Brompton Hospital, Sydney St., London SW3 6NP Tel: 020 7351 8509 Fax: 020 7351 8763 Email: i.balfourlynn@ic.ac.uk — MB BS 1982 Lond.; BSc (Hons.) Lond. 1979, MD 1994; FRCS Ed. 1987; MRCP (UK) 1986; FRCPCH 1997; DHMSA 1981. (Westm.) Cons. Paediat. Respirat. Med. Roy. Brompton Hosp. & Chelsea & W.m. Hosp.; Hon. Sen. Lect. - Imperial Coll. Sch. of Med. Socs: Fell. Roy. Soc. Med.; BMA; Brit. Paediat. Respirat. Soc. Prev: Sen. Regist. (Paediat.) Gt. Ormond St. Hosp. for childr.; Research Regist. N.wick Pk. Hosp. Clin. Research Centre & Roy. Postgrad. Meds.ch.; Regist. (Paediat.) N.wick Pk. Hosp.

BALFOUR-LYNN, Lionel Peter 120 Harley Street, London W1N 1AG Tel: 020 7935 2220; 543 Finchley Road, London NW3 7BJ Tel: 020 7435 5400 Fax: 0207 431 4663 — MB BChir 1952 Camb.; MA Camb. 1953, MD 1984; FRCPCH 1997; MRCS Eng. LRCP Lond. 1952; DCH Eng. 1957. (Camb. & Guy's) Hon. Cons. Paediat. Hammersmith Hosp. Lond.; Hon. Lect. (Paediat.) Roy. Postgrad. Med. Sch. Lond. Socs: Fell. Roy. Soc. Med.; Hosp. Cons. & Spec. Assn.; Hampstead Med. Soc. Prev: Hon. Lect. (Paediat.) Brompton Hosp. Lond.; Cons. Paediat. Amer. Hosp. Ruislip; Regist. (Paediat.) Hillingdon Hosp.

BALHETCHET, Marguerite Sheila (retired) Kechil, 6 Glenrose Avenue, Ravensden, Bedford MK44 2SB Tel: 01234 772283 — MB BS 1956 Lond.

BALI, Anu Flat 7 Monument Court, 1 Lower Canal Walk, Town Quay, Southampton SO14 3AN — MB BCh 1995 Wales.

BALI, Bindu 19 Lee Road, Lincoln LN2 4BJ — BM BS 1995 Nottm.

BALI, Mr Harbajan Singh 34 Newland, Lincoln LN1 1XP Tel: 01522 543573 Fax: 01522 569699; Portland Medical Centre, 60 Portland St, Lincoln LN5 7LD Tel: 01522 876800 Fax: 01522 876803 — MB BS 1963 Uktal; FRCS Ed. 1971. Princip. Gen. Med. Practitioner; Surg. for waiting list initiative scheme, Train. of GP's & referral taken from GPs. Socs: Local Med. Comm.; BMA; Lincoln Med. Soc. (Comm. Mem.) Pres. Elect for 2002/3. Prev: Surg. Vasectomy Clinic Lincoln.

BALI, Mr Inder Mohan 2 Murob Park, Ballymena BT43 6JG — MB BS 1963 Punjab; PhD Belf. 1974; MS (Gen. Surg.) Punjab 1968, MS (Anaesth.) 1970; FFA RCSI 1973.

BALI, Mr Padam Lal 32 Hest Bank Lane, Hest Bank, Lancaster LA2 6DB — MB BS 1959 Punjab; MS Ophth, Lucknow, (India) 1964; MB BS Punjab (India) 1959; FRCS Eng. 1974; MRCS Eng. LRCP Lond. 1975; DO Eng. 1969; DOMS Punjab (India) 1964. Cons. Ophth. Surg. Lancaster Moor Hosp.

BALI, Sanjeev 4 The Willows, Ballymena BT42 1QN — MB ChB 1993 Ed.

BALI, Satish 151 Clasemont Road, Morriston, Swansea SA6 6AH — MB BS 1971 Utkal.

BALI, Ved Parkash Greenfield Surgery, 12 Porth Street, Porth CF39 9RP Tel: 01443 682644 Fax: 01443 682291 — MB BS 1968 Punjabi.

BALI, Vishan 12 Porth Street, Porth CF39 9RP Tel: 01443 682644 Fax: 01443 682291 Email: greenfield@nice.wales.nhs.uk — MBBS Punjab; LLM (Medical aspects) Cardiff; DObst RCOG Lond. Gen. Practitioner, Porth; Clin. Asst. Obst. & Gynae. Roy. Glamoral Hosp.

BALIAN, Berge Hagop Rosser and Partners, Crewkerne Health Centre, Middle Path, Crewkerne TA18 8BX Tel: 01460 72435 Fax: 01460 77957; The Stables, Woolminstone Manor Court, Woolminstone, Crewkerne TA18 8QP Tel: 01460 73868 — MB BS 1990 Lond.; BSc (Neurosci.) Lond. 1987; DRCOG 1995; DFFP 1995. (St. Thos. Hosp. Med. Sch.) Full-time Gen. Practitioner; Vice-Chair., Som. Local Med. Comm. Prev: Trainee GP/SHO (O & G, Paediat. & Psychiat.) Yeovil Dist. Hosp.

BALIDIS, Miltiadis 27 Hale Lane, London NW7 3NU — Ptychio Iatrikes 1991 Thrace.

BALIGA, Kallyanpur Vidya Surendra General Hospital, Cockton Hill Road, Bishop Auckland DL14 6AD Tel: 01388 604040; Robin Dyke, 38 Northumberland Avenue, Bishop Auckland DL14 6NP Tel: 01388 600058 — MB BS 1979 Bangalore; BSc 1972; MRCS Eng. LRCP Lond. 1982; DGM RCP Lond. 1994. Staff Phys. (Gen. & Geriat. Med.) SW Durh. HA. Socs: Brit. Geriat. Soc. Prev: SHO (Geriat. Med.) Halton Gen. Hosp. Runcorn; Clin. Asst. (Gen. & Geriat. Med.) SW Durh. HA; SHO (Gen. & Geriat. Med.) S. Shields Gen. Hosp.

BALIGA, Surendra Kallianpur Shildon Health Clinic, Church Street, Shildon DL4 1AH Tel: 01388 772829 Fax: 01388 775118 Email: surendrabaliga@gp_a83638.nhs.uk; Robin Dyke, 38 Northumberland Avenue, Bishop Auckland DL14 6NP Tel: 01388 600058 — MB BS 1974 Mysore; DFFP Lond. 1998; FME (Forensic Medical Examiner) 1997; BSc Mysore 1967. (Kasturba Med. Coll. Mangalore, India) GP; Police Surg. Durh. Constab. Durh. Co. Durh. Socs: NE Hypertens. Soc.; Newc. Hypertens. Soc.; GP Asthma Gp. Prev: Clin. Asst. Sunderland Dist. Gen. Hosp. A & E Dept.; Clin. Asst. Diabetic Sunderland Dist. Gen. Hosp.

BALIGH, Helmy Mohamed Aly 58 Cedar House, Frimley Park Hospital, Portsmouth Road, Frimley, Camberley GU16 7UJ — MB BCh 1980 Cairo; MRCP (UK) 1994.

BALIN, Graham Victor Harewood Surgery, Harwich Road, Great Oakley, Harwich CO12 9AD Tel: 01255 880341 Fax: 01255 880815 — MB BS 1978 Lond.; BSc (Hons.) Lond. 1975, MB BS 1978; DRCOG 1981; Cert. Family Plann. JCC 1981. (Univ. Coll. Hosp.)

BALIS, Nicholas Flat 2, Royal Preston Hospital, Sharoe Green Lane, Fulwood, Preston PR2 9HT — MB BS 1986 Melbourne.

BALKIND, Jack 5 Hermon Hill, London E11 2AR Tel: 020 8989 3800 — LRCP LRCS 1940 Ed.; LRCP LRCS Ed. LRFPS Glas. 1940. (Glas.) Prev: Sen. Asst. Med. Off. Middlx. CC & Dep. MOH Willesden; Asst. Med. Off. LCC; Res. Med. Off. Isolat. Hosp. & Sanat. Leicester.

BALKRISHNA, Naresh Flat 9, 14 Cleveland St., Glasgow G3 7AE Tel: 0141 221 0639; Gallowhill Medical Centre, 4/6 Gallowhill, Larkhall ML9 1EX Tel: 01698 884082 Fax: 01698 889211 — MB ChB 1987 Glas.; MRCGP 1991; DCCH RCGP 1993. GP.

BALKWILL, Judith Mary Timbrils, Oakside Way, Shinfield, Reading RG2 9BJ Tel: 01734 871498 — MB ChB 1952 Birm. (Birm)

BALKWILL, Peter Hugh 44 Shayer Road, Southampton SO15 5JZ Tel: 02380 787531 — BM 1994 Soton.; DPhil Oxf. 1989. GP Regist., St. Clements Partnership, Winchester. Prev: Ho. Off. (Gen. Surg.) Soton.

BALL, Mr Adrian Bernard Shervington Department of Surgery, Surrey and Sussex NHS Trust G.H., West Green Drive, Crawley RH11 7DH Tel: 01293 600300 Fax: 01293 600341 — MB BChir 1979 Camb.; MA Camb. 1980, MChir 1989; FRCS Eng. 1983; FICS 1991. (Middlx. Hosp.) Lead Clinician Cancer Serv.s, Surrey and Sussex NHS Trust. Socs: Fell. Assn. Surgs.; Eur. Soc. Mastol.; Fell. Roy. Soc. Med. Prev: Regist. & Hon. Lect. (Surg.) Lond. Hosp.; Lect. Acad. Surgic. Unit Roy. Marsden Hosp. Lond.; Cons. Gen. Surg. & Mem. BrE. Unit Surrey & Sussex Health Care Trust, Crawley adn E.

BALL, Adrian Peter (retired) 6 Gilchrist Row, St Andrews KY16 8XU Fax: 01334 476637 Email: peterball1@aol.com — MB

ChB 1969 Ed.; FRCP Ed. 1983; MRCP (UK) 1973. Prev: Cons. Infec. Vict. Hosp. Kirkcaldy.

BALL, Adrian Rowland High Pastures, 138 Liverpool Road North, Liverpool L31 2HW Tel: 0151 531 9420 Fax: 0151 527 2377; 31 Ryder Crescent, Aughton, Ormskirk L39 5EY Tel: 01695 421579 — MB ChB 1969 Liverp.; FRCGP 1992, M 1976; DObst RCOG 1971. Assoc. Regional Advis. Gen. Pract. Univ. Liverp. Socs: W Lancs. Med. Soc. Prev: SHO (Paediat.) Alder Hey Childr. Hosp. Liverp.; Ho. Phys. & Ho. Surg. Birkenhead Gen. Hosp.; Ho. Surg. (O & G) Sefton Gen. Hosp. Liverp.

BALL, Mrs Adrianne Cartref, Broadford, Isle of Skye IV49 9AA — MB BS 1961 Lond.; MRCS Eng. LRCP Lond. 1961; DObst RCOG 1964. (Roy. Free) Surgic. Clin. Asst. Dr. Mackinnon Memor. Hosp. BRd.ford.

BALL, Alexandra Karin 73 Grimshaw Lane, Bollington, Macclesfield SK10 5LY — MB ChB 1994 Birm.; DGM RCP Lond. 1997. SHO Medic. Socs: BMA. Prev: SHO (Elderly Care Med.); SHO (A & E); Staff Grade Rehabil. Medic.

BALL, Andrew James Dorset County hospital, Williams Avenue, Dorchester DT1 2JY Tel: 01305 25444 Email: andy.ball@dorch.mdgh.swest.nhs.uk; 67 Parkstone Avenue, Parkstone, Poole BH14 9LW Tel: 01202 748165 — BM 1986 Soton.; BM Soton 1986; FRCA. 1992; DRCOG 1990; DCH RCP Lond. 1988. Cons. Anaesth. + ICU, Dorset Co. Hosp. Prev: Sen. Regist. (Anaesth.) Soton. Gen. Hosp.; Vis. Instruc. Pediat. Anaesthesiol. Univ. Michigan, USA; Regist. (Anaesth.) Salisbury Gen. Hosp.

BALL, Mr Andrew Justin Department of Urology, Southend Hospital, Prittlewell Chase, Westcliff on Sea SS0 0RY Tel: 01702 435555 Fax: 01702 221209 — MB ChB 1972 Bristol; MD Bristol 1984; FRCS Eng. 1977. (Bristol) Cons. Urol. S.end Hosp. Essex. Socs: Fell. Roy. Soc. Med.; Eur. Assn. Urol.; Brit. Assn. Urol. Surg. Prev: Sen. Regist. (Urol.) Bristol Roy. Infirm. & S.mead Hosp.; Research Hon. Sen. Regist. (Urol.) Avon HA; Regist. (Surg.) Univ. Hosp Wales Cardiff & Roy. Gwent Hosp. Newport.

BALL, Andrew Robert 70 Spital Road, Wirral CH62 2AH — MB ChB 1993 Leic.

BALL, Campbell Mowat (retired) 8 Glenochil Road, Falkirk FK1 5LT Tel: 01324 23463 — MB ChB 1946 Glas.

BALL, Christopher John 11 Cricklewood Drive, Halesowen B62 8SN — MB ChB 1973 Birm.; DObst RCOG 1976.

BALL, Christopher John Hither Green Hospital, Hither Green, London SE13 6RU Tel: 020 8698 4611 — MB BS 1983 Lond.

BALL, Christopher Mark 93 Avenue Road, Dorridge, Solihull B93 8JL — BM BCh 1996 Oxf.

BALL, Mr Christopher Sydney Department of Surgery, Furness General Hospital, Dalton Lane, Barrow-in-Furness LA14 4LF Tel: 01229 870870 Fax: 01229 871182; The Old Vicarage, Colton, Ulverston LA12 8HF Tel: 01229 861361 — MB ChB 1979 Manch.; MD Manch. 1990; FRCS Eng. 1984; FRCS Ed. 1983. Cons. Gen. Surg. Furness Gen. Morecambe Bay Hosps. NHS Trust. Socs: Brit. Soc. Gastroenterol.; Assn. Upper G.I. Surg.; Manch. Med. Soc.

BALL, Claire Joanne Kingston Hospital, Galsworthy Road, Kingston upon Thames KT2 7QB; The Old Farm House, Epsom Road, Merrow, Guildford GU4 7AB Tel: 01483 568659 — MB BS 1996 Lond. (Kings College London) Basic Surgic. Trainee (SHO Grade). Prev: SHO (A & E) Kings Coll. Hosp.

BALL, Colin Stuart Department of Child Health, King's College Hospital, Denmark Hill, London SE5 9RS — MB BS 1979 Lond.; BSc (Hons.) Physiol. Lond. 1976; MRCP (UK) 1982. (Univ. Lond.) Cons. Paediat. & Hepatol. KCH Lond. Prev: Lect. Child Health (Hepatol.) King's Coll. Sch. Med. & Dent. Lond.

BALL, David Hamilton (retired) High Forest, Manchester Road, Sway, Lymington SO41 6AS — MB 1956 Camb.; BChir 1955; MRCGP 1966; DObst RCOG 1960; DIH Soc. Apoth. Lond. 1959. Prev: GP New Milton, Hants.

BALL, David Mark Institute of Psychiatry, De Crespigny Park, London SE5 8AF Email: dball@iop.bpmf.ac.uk — BM BCh 1984 Oxf.; MA Oxf. 1987; MRCPsych. 1989. Sen. Lect. & Cons. Prev: Peacock Train. Fell. (Inst. of Psychiat. Lond.); Clin. Res. Off. (Med. Genetics) Coleg Meddygaeth Prifysgol Cymru; Regist. (Psychiat.) Barrow Hosp. Bristol.

BALL, David Raymond Department of Anaesthetics, Dumfries & Galloway Royal Infirmary, Bankend Road, Dumfries DG1 4AP; Drumpark Mains, Irongray, Dumfries DG2 9TX — MB BS 1984 Lond.; FRCA. Cons. (Anaesth.) Dumfries & Galloway Roy. Infirm.

BALL, David Reginald (retired) The Island Cottage, Kelly Park, St Mabyn, Bodmin PL30 3BL — MB ChB 1953 Leeds; FFA RCS Eng. 1959; DA Eng. 1956. Prev: Cons. Anaesth. Bradford Dist. Hosps.

BALL, David Richard Roslea Surgery, 51 Station Road, Bamber Bridge, Preston PR5 6PE Tel: 01772 335128 Fax: 01772 492248; 6 Brookside, Church Park, Euxton, Chorley PR7 6HR — MB ChB 1973 Manch.; MRCGP 1977; DObst RCOG 1975. Prev: Trainee GP Preston VTS; Ho. Off. (Med.) Manch. Roy. Infirm.; Ho. Off. (Surg.) Macclesfield Infirm.

BALL, Doreen Sheila (retired) 18A Knighton Park Road, Leicester LE2 1ZA — LRCP LRCS 1947 Ed.; 1947 LRCP LRCS Ed. LRFPS Glas.; 1953 DObst RCOG; LRCP LRCS Ed. LRFPS Glas. 1951 Lond. Prev: Clin. Biochem. Char. Cross Hosp.

BALL, Dorothea Helen (retired) 19 Clare Court, Grosvenor Hill, Wimbledon, London SW19 4RZ Tel: 020 8946 6627 — MB ChB Glas. 1939; MRCPsych 1973. Prev: Asst. Psychiat. (Psychol. Med.) Univ. Coll. Hosp.

BALL, Elizabeth Louise Vardo House, 25 Billington Road E., Elmesthorpe, Leicester LE9 7SB — MB BCh 1998 Wales.

BALL, Elizabeth Susan Prestwood Road West Surgery, 81 Prestwood Road West, Wednesfield, Wolverhampton WV11 1HT Tel: 01902 721021 Fax: 01902 306225 — MB ChB 1985 Sheff.; DRCOG 1991. Prev: GP Lond. Retainer Scheme; SHO (O & G) Roy. Free Hosp. Lond.; Trainee GP Wolverhampton VTS.

BALL, Emma Felicity 93 Avenue Road, Dorridge, Solihull B93 8JU — MB BS 1996 Newc.

BALL, Eric Michael Prestige 3 Rowcliffe Avenue, Chester CH4 7PN — MRCS Eng. LRCP Lond. 1947; MRCPath 1963; FRCPath 1970; FRCPA 1971.

BALL, Esmond William (retired) Orchard House, 20A Fiery Hill Road, Barnt Green, Birmingham B45 8LG Tel: 0121 445 1942 — MB BS 1944 Lond.; MD Lond. 1962; MCPath 1965. Prev: Cons. Haematol. Selly Oak Hosp. Birm.

BALL, Lady Florine Isabel Flat 30, Homesearle House, Goring Road, Worthing BN12 4PW — MB BCh BAO 1922 Dub.; LM Rotunda Hosp. Dub. 1922. (TC Dub.)

BALL, Gail Victoria 4 Wallner Way, Wokingham RG40 2JY — MB BS 1994 Lond.

BALL, Geoffrey Michael Bangor Examination Centre, (Rear of Benefits Centre), Ty Glyder, High St., Bangor Tel: 01248 362660 — MB BS 1984 Queensland; FRACGP 1991. Med. Adviser Benefits Agency.

BALL, Hadrian Neil Norfolk Mental Health Care NHS Trust, Drayton Old Lodge, Drayton High Road, Norwich NR8 6AN Tel: 01603 421147 — MB ChB 1984 Liverp.; MRCPsych. 1988. Med. Dir., Norf. Ment. Health Care, NHS Trust; Cons. Forens. Psychiat.s, Norvic Clinic, Norwich Hon. Sen. Lect., Univ. of E. Anglia. Prev: Cons. Forens. Psychiat. Norvic Clinic Norwich; Sen. Regist. (Forens. Psychiat.) Prestwich Hosp. Manch.; Clin. Dir. E. Anglian Regional Forens. Serv.

BALL, Howard John Tregony Road Surgery, Tregony Road, Probus, Truro TR2 4JZ — MB ChB 1985 Cape Town.

BALL, James Leslie 67 Albemarle Road, South Bank, York YO23 1EP — BChir 1995 Camb.

BALL, Jeffrey Bernard Whiston Hospital, Warrington Road, Prescot L35 5DR Tel: 0151 430 1905 Fax: 0151 430 1913 — MB ChB 1987 Liverp.; FRCP 2001 UK; BSc Liverp. 1984; MRCP (UK) 1991. Cons. Cardio. & Gen. Phys. Whiston Hosp. Prescot.

BALL, Jennifer Claire 11 Fieldlands, Southport Road, Southport PR8 5HO — MB ChB 1997 Liverp.

BALL, Joanna Ann St Mary's Hospital, Praed St., London W2 1NY Tel: 020 7886 1216 Fax: 020 7886 1422; National Hospital for Neurology & Neurosurgery, Queen Square, London WC1N 3BG — MB BS 1981 Lond.; BA (Hons.) Lond. 1975, MD 1989; MRCP (UK) 1984; FRCP 1997. Cons. Neurol. St. Mary's Hosp. & Nat. Hosp. Neurol. & Neurosurg. Lond.

BALL, John Albert Campbell (retired) 27 Rugby Road, Belfast BT7 1PT — BSc Belf. 1944, MD 1958, MB BCh BAO 1953; FRCP Ed. 1971, M 1962. Hon. Phys. (Geriat.) Belf. City Hosp., Musgrave Pk. Hosp. & Lagan Valley Hosp.

BALL, John Anthony Woodacre Surgery, 324 Holly Lane, Erdington, Birmingham B24 9LN Tel: 0121 350 9927; 22 Greenside

Road, Birmingham B24 0DJ Tel: 0121 373 0467 Email: tony@balja.demon.co.uk — MB ChB 1963 Birm.; MRCS Eng. LRCP Lond. 1972; DA Eng. 1972. (Birm.) Socs: BMA (Hon. Sec. N. Birm., Tamworth & Lichfield Div.); Reg. Coord. Prim. Health Care Specialist Gp.; Brit. Computer Soc. Prev: Med. Off. Brit. Antarctic Survey; Regist. (Anaesth.) Warneford Gen. Hosp. Leamington Spa; Ho. Surg. (Thoracic & Gen. Surg.) Qu. Eliz. Hosp. Birm.

BALL, John Blatchford 58 Brigg Road, Barton-upon-Humber DN18 5DR Tel: 01652 632354 — MB BS 1957 Durh.; DObst RCOG 1958. (Newc.) JP. Prev: Ho. Surg. (Paediat.) Newc. Gen. Hosp.; Ho. Surg. (O & G) Ho. Phys. (Med.) Preston Roy. Infirm.; Squadron Ldr. RAF Med. Br.

BALL, John Godfrey, CBE (retired) Dundas, Rosenhurst Drive, Bewdley DY12 2ES Tel: 01299 403421 Fax: 01299 402691 Email: jgodball@aol.com — MB ChB Birm. 1952; FRCGP 1978; DObst RCOG 1956. Prev: Chairm. Med. Pract. Comm. & Gen. Med. Serv. Comm.

BALL, Mr John Robert Cartref, Broadford, Isle of Skye IV49 9AA — MB BS 1958 Lond.; FRCS Ed. 1964; FRCS Eng. 1964; MRCS Eng. LRCP Lond. 1958; FICS 1990. (St. Mary's) Cons. Surg. & Surg. Supt. Dr. Mackinnon Memor. Hosp. BRd.ford; Fell. Assn. Surg. Gt. Brit. & Irel. Socs: Fell. Roy. Soc. Med. Prev: Surg. Research Fell. Qu. Mary's Hosp. Carshalton; Surg. Regist. St. Mary's Hosp. Harrow Rd.; Ho. Off. St. Mary's Hosp. Lond.

BALL, Jonathan Arthur Selwyn Dept. Anaesthesia and Intensive Care, 1st Floor, Grosvenor Wing, St. George's Hospital, Blackshaw Road, London SW17 0QT Tel: 020 8725 3316 Fax: 020 8725 3135 — MB BS 1993 Lond.; BSc Lond. 1990; MRCP (UK) 1996. (UMDS) Lect. in Intens. Care Med., St. Geo.'s Hosp. Med. Sch., Univ. of Lond.

BALL, Jonathan Edward Bridge House, Hele, Taunton TA4 1AH — MB BS 1996 Lond.

BALL, Jonathan Lewis Ardersier Medical Practice, 142 Manse Road, Ardersier, Inverness IV2 7SR; Tel: 01667 462255 — MB ChB 1993 Ed.; MRCGP 1997; DFFP 1998. (Edinburgh)

BALL, Katherine Ellen Ashbrook House, Brook St., Kingston Blount, Chinnor OX39 4RZ — MB ChB 1998 Bristol.

BALL, Mr Keith John The Old School Surgery, Hinckley Road, Stoney Stanton, Leicester LE9 4LJ Tel: 01455 271445 Fax: 01445 274526; Greencroft Surgery, Carey Hill Road, Stoney Stanton, Leicester LE9 4LA Tel: 01455 272279 Fax: 01455 274526 — MB ChB 1967 St. And.; FRCS Ed. 1972. Prev: Surg. Regist. Profess. Surg. Unit. Dundee Roy. Infirm.

BALL, Keith Percy, OBE (retired) The Studio, Mount Park Road, Ealing, London W5 2RP Tel: 020 8997 4765 Fax: 020 8997 4765 Email: kfball@aol.com — MB BS 1938 Lond.; MB BS (Hons.) Lond. 1938; MD Lond. 1940; FRCP Lond. 1962, M 1940; FFCM 1981. Hon. Phys. Centr. Middlx. Hosp. Prev: Sen. Lect. (Preven. Med.) Univ. Coll. & Middlx. Hosp. Med. Sch.

BALL, Linsey Margaret Cona Mheall, Ardersier Mains, Ardersier, Inverness IV2 7QN — MB ChB 1993 Ed.

BALL, Luke John Robins Cottage, Blackborough, Cullompton EX15 2HH — MB BS 1968 Lond. (Univ. Coll. Hosp.)

BALL, Madeleine Joyce 10 Jessops Close, Marston, Oxford OX3 0NU — MD 1986 Wales; BSc (Hons.) Wales 1975, MD 1986, MB BCh 1979; MRCP (UK) 1982. Clin. Lect. John Radcliffe Hosp. Oxf.

BALL, Mary Elizabeth North Glen Medical Practice, 1 Huntsmans Court, Glenrothes KY7 6SX Tel: 01592 620062 Fax: 01592 620465; 6 Gilchrist Row, St Andrews KY16 8XU — MB ChB 1970 Ed.

BALL, Maxwell James Hendford Lodge Medical Centre, 74 Hendford, Yeovil BA20 1UJ Tel: 01935 470200 Fax: 01935 470202; 82 Combe Street Lane, Yeovil BA21 3PG Tel: 01935 427678 Email: max.ball@gp-85022.nhs.uk — MB BS 1981 Lond.; BSc (Hons.) Lond. 1978; MRCGP 1985; Cert. Family Plann. JCC 1984; DRCOG 1983; Dip. Occ. Med. 1997. (Univ. Coll. Hosp.) Socs: Soc. of Occupat.al Med.

BALL, Mr Michael Joseph (retired) The Private Clinic, 14 Woodhouse Road, Mansfield NG18 2AD Tel: 01623 624137 — MA, MB BChir Camb. 1950; FRCS Eng. 1958; MRCS Eng. LRCP Lond. 1949. Prev: Cons. Gen. Surg. Mansfield Hosp. Gp.

BALL, Neil Antony Havant Health Centre Suite B, PO Box 43, Civic Centre Road, Havant PO9 2AQ Tel: 023 9248 2124 Fax: 023 9247 5515 — BM 1982 Soton.; MRCGP 1987; DRCOG 1987.

BALL, Neville Tel: 01254 262121 Fax: 01254 265969; 8 Hollow Head Lane, Wilpshire, Blackburn BB1 9JX — MB ChB 1978 Manch.

BALL, Nicholas Stewart Cohen and Partners, West Lodge Surgery, New Street, Farsley, Pudsey LS28 5DL Tel: 0113 257 0295 Fax: 0113 236 2509; Beechwood, 18 Rockwood Road, Calverley, Pudsey LS28 5AA — BM BS 1983 Nottm.; BMedSci Nottm. 1981, BM BS 1983; DA (UK) 1985. GP Princip. Prev: SHO (Anaesth.) Huddersfield Roy. Infirm.; Ho. Phys. City Hosp. Nottm.; Ho. Surg. Roy. Preston Hosp.

BALL, Norman John (retired) The Old Moorings, The Lake, Kirkcudbright DG6 4XL Tel: 01557 330388 — MD 1956 Dub.; MB BCh BAO 1953; CRCP Canada 1968. Prev: Cons. Histopath. Jas. Paget Hosp. Gorleston Gt. Yarmouth.

BALL, Pamela Margaret (retired) Dundas, Rosenhurst Drive, Bewdley DY12 2ES Tel: 01299 403421 Fax: 01299 402691 — MB ChB Birm. 1950; MRCS Eng. LRCP Lond. 1950; FRCS Eng. 1954; MSc (Mathmatics) Open University 1991. Prev: Clin. Asst. Regional Plastic Surg. Unit Wordsley Hosp. Stourbridge.

BALL, Peter Andrew 22 Harberton Drive, Belfast BT9 6PF — MB BCh BAO 1995 Belf. SHO Gen. Med.

BALL, Peter John (retired) 11 Nevill Park, Tunbridge Wells TN4 8NN Tel: 01892 523074 — MB BChir 1958 Camb.; MA Camb. 1958; DA Eng. 1963; DObst RCOG 1960. Prev: Clin Asst. (Anaesth.) Kent. & Sussex Hosp. Tunbridge Wells.

BALL, Rebecca Hatfield Road Surgery, 70 Hatfield Road, Ipswich IP3 9AF Tel: 01473 723373 — MB ChB Sheff.

BALL, Miss Rebecca Jane Leeds General Infirmary, Great George St., Leeds LS1 3EX; 9 Broomfield Road, Headingley, Leeds LS6 3DE — MB ChB 1997 Leeds. SHO (Med), LGI.

BALL, Reena Gupta and Ball, 10 Sandmere Road, London SW4 7QJ Tel: 020 7274 6366 Fax: 020 7738 5172 — MB BS 1971 Calcutta.

BALL, Professor Richard Yardley Department of Histopathology & Cytopathology, Norfolk and Norwich University Hospital, Colney Lane, Norwich NR4 7UY Tel: 01603 286014 Fax: 01603 286017 Email: richard.ball@norfolk-norwich.thenhs.com — BM BCh 1979 Oxf.; PhD Camb. 1984, MA 1980, MD 1987; MA Oxf. 1979; FRCPath 1997, M 1989. Cons. Path. Norf. & Norwich Univ. Hosp. NHS Trust; Hon. Prof. Univ. E. Anglia. Socs: Path Soc.; BMA; Roy. Soc. Med. Prev: Wellcome Trust Fell. Camb. Univ.; Elmore Med. Research Stud. Camb. Univ.; Ho. Phys. John Radcliffe Hosp. Oxf.

BALL, Robin Jeffrey Department of Paediatrics, York District Hospital, Wigginton Road, York YO31 8HE Tel: 01904 454729 Fax: 01904 453995 — MB ChB 1980 Bristol; MRCP (UK) 1984; DRCOG 1993. Cons. Paediat. York. Dist. Hosp.

BALL, Rosemary Ann Maddison Centre, 140 Church Road, Teddington TW11 8QL Tel: 020 8977 3156 Fax: 020 8977 3270 — MB ChB 1977 Leeds; MPhil Lond. 1988; MRCPsych. 1982. Cons. Psychiat. Qu. Mary's Univ. Hosp. Lond.

BALL, Sarah Elizabeth Department of Haematology, St George's Hospital Medical School, Cranmer Terrace, London SW17 0RE — MB BS 1980 Lond.; BA Oxf. 1977, DM 1990; FRCP Lond. 1996; MRCP (UK) 1983; FRCPCH 1997; MRCPath 1989; FRCPath 1998. Sen. Lect. & Hon. Cons. (Haemat.) St. Geo. Hosp. Med. Sch. Lond.

BALL, Sarah Molly 67 Nursery Lane, Hockwold, Thetford IP26 4ND — MB ChB 1998 Birm.; ChB Birm. 1998.

BALL, Sidney Graham Clinical Chemistry, Chelsea and Westminster Hospital, 369 Fulham Rd, London SW10 9NH Tel: 020 8746 8091, 02879 301575 Fax: 020 8746 8085 — MRCS Eng. LRCP Lond. 1972; MSc (Clin. Biochem.) Lond. 1977, MB BS 1972; FRCPath 1991, M 1979. (Middlx.) Sen. Cons. (Chem. Path.) Hammersmith Hosp. NHS Trust. Lond.; Hon.Sen. Lect. Imperial Coll. Lond. Prev: Sen. Lect. (Chem. Path.) W.m. Med. Sch.; Sen. Regist. (Chem. Path.) Univ. Coll. Hosp. & Whittington Hosp. Lond.

BALL, Simon Christopher Church Farm, Victoria Road, Aldeburgh IP15 5EB Tel: 01728 452027 Fax: 01728 452041; Gable End Cottage, Warren Hill, Leiston Road, Aldeburgh IP15 5QA Tel: 0172 845 3095 — MB BS 1980 Lond.; MRCGP 1984; DRCOG 1983; DCH RCP Lond. 1983.

BALL, Simon James Arden Sawston Health Centre, Link Road, Sawston, Cambridge CB2 4LB Tel: 01223 832711 Fax: 01223 836096; 102 Thoday Street, Cambridge CB1 3AX Tel: 01223 245311 — MB BChir 1993 Camb.; MA Camb. 1994; MRCGP 1997; DRCOG 1995. Prev: Trainee GP/SHO Camb. VTS.

BALL, Simon Thomas 31 Monson Road, London NW10 5UR — MB BS 1989 Lond.; BA Oxf. 1986; MRCP (UK) 1992.

BALL, Stephen Edward Penistone Group Practice, 19 High St., Penistone, Sheffield S36 6BR Tel: 01226 762257 — MB ChB 1981 Sheff.; MRCGP 1986; DCCH RCP Ed. 1985; DRCOG 1984; FRCGP 1997. Assoc. Adviser (Gen. Pract.) Univ. Sheff.

BALL, Stephen Geoffrey Institute for Cardiovascular Research, The University, Leeds LS2 9JT Tel: 0113 233 4821 Fax: 0113 233 4803 Email: cvssgb@leeds.ac.uk — MB 1972 Camb.; BChir 1971; PhD Leeds 1979; MA Camb. 1972; MRCP (UK) 1973; FRCP Lond. 1988. Brit. Heart Foundat. Prof. Cardiol. & Hon. Cons. Cardiol. Inst. Cardiovasc. Research.

BALL, Stephen Gerard Department of Medicine, University of Newcastle, The Medical School, Framlington Place, Newcastle upon Tyne NE2 4HH — MB BS 1987 Lond.

BALL, Stephen Peter The Surgery, Mill Hoo, Alderton, Woodbridge IP12 3DA Tel: 01394 411641 Fax: 01394 410183; Tel: 01394 450303 — MB BS 1983 Lond.; BSc Lond. 1980; MRCGP 1990; DRCOG 1990. (Westm.) GP Princip., Alderton, Woodbridge. Prev: Asst. GP Needham Market Suff.; SHO (O & G) Ipswich Hosp.; SHO (Paediat.) Ipswich Hosp.

BALL, Susan Ann 28 Wynmore Avenue, Bramhope, Leeds LS16 9DE — MB BS 1967 Lond.; MRCS Eng. LRCP Lond. 1967; DObst RCOG 1969. (Roy. Free)

BALL, Susan Elizabeth Forston Clinic, Herrison, Dorchester DT2 9TB Tel: 01305 251812; 82 Combe Street Lane, Yeovil BA21 3PG — BM 1982 Soton.; MRCPsych 1989. (Soton.) Staff Grade Psychiat. Forston Clinic, Dorchester. Prev: Clin. Asst. (Psychiat.) Furston Clinic Dorchester.

BALL, Susan Patricia 116 Norwood Road, Tulse Hill, London SE24 9BB Tel: 020 8674 4623; 49 Streatham Common N., London SW16 3HS — MB BS 1980 Lond.

BALLAH, Nina Devi 64 Hyde Park Av, London N21 2PP — MB ChB 1997 Bristol.

BALLAM, Judith Margaret Deirdre Nansawsan Mews, Ladock, Truro TR2 4PW — MB BS 1981 Lond.; MFFP 1995; MRCGP 1986; DRCOG 1985.

BALLANCE, Gerard Alaric (retired) 44 Queen Edith's Way, Cambridge CB1 8PW Tel: 01223 246319 — MB BChir 1940 Camb.; MA Camb. 1940. Prev: Ho. Phys. St. Thos. Hosp. Lond.

BALLANCE, John Howard William Orchid Bank, Woolhope, Hereford HR1 4RQ Tel: 01432 364080 Fax: 01432 364164 Email: john@ballances.net — MB ChB 1968 Liverp.; FFA RCS Eng. 1977. Cons. Anaesth. Hereford Hosp.

BALLANCE, Peter Gerard The Old Farmhouse, Lower Westerland, Marldon, Paignton TQ3 1RU — BM BCh 1970 Oxf.; DA S. Afr. 1976; DCH S. Afr. 1974; FFA RCS Eng. 1979. Cons. Anaesth. Torbay Hosp. Torquay.

BALLANTINE, Donald Ingram Health Centre, Kersiebank Avenue, Grangemouth FK3 9EW Tel: 01324 471511 — MB ChB 1970 Sheff.

BALLANTINE, Duncan Maclean 62 Grantchester Meadows, Cambridge CB3 9JL — MRCS Eng. LRCP Lond. 1964. (Sheff.) Dir. Camb. Med. Systems Consult.; Cons. Med. Software AAH Meditel BromsGr. Prev: Regist. (Anaesth.) Addenbrooke's Hosp. Camb.

BALLANTINE, Karen The Pound, Eastbury, Hungerford RG17 7JL — BM 1988 Soton. Clin. Asst. Psychiat. Community Alcohol Serv. Reading.

BALLANTINE, Richard James Allesley Park Medical Centre, Whitaker Road No.2, Coventry CV5 9JE Tel: 024 7667 4123 Fax: 024 7667 2196; Allesley Park Medical Centre, Coventry CV5 9JE Tel: 024 76 674123 Fax: 01203 672196 — MB BS 1975 Lond.; MRCS Eng. LRCP Lond. 1975; DRCOG 1979. Med. Off. Univ. Warwick.

BALLANTINE, Trudy Jane Garrett 39 Gilmore Place, Edinburgh EH3 9NG Tel: 0131 228 1443 Email: trudy@doctors.org.uk — MB ChB 1993 Ed.; BSc (Hons.) Med. Sci. Ed. 1991. (Univ. Ed.) Specialist Regist. (Anaesth.) S. E. Scotl. of Anaesth. Socs: Train. Mem RCA; Train. Mem. Assn. AnE.h.; BMA. Prev: SHO (Anaesth.) Penine Sch. Anaesth., Airedale Gen. Hosp. & Bradford Roy. Infirm.; SHO Mackay Base Hosp. Qu.sland, Austral.; Experienced SHO (Anaesth.) S. E. Scotl. of Anaesth.

BALLANTYNE, Archibald The Surgery, Springwell House, Ardmillan Terrace, Edinburgh EH11 2JL — MB ChB 1975 Ed.; MRCGP 1980; DCH RCPS Glas. 1979; DRCOG 1979.

BALLANTYNE, David 34 Ralston Road, Glasgow G61 3BA Tel: 0141 942 9136 Email: d.ballantyne@task21.com; 34 Ralston Road, Bearsdien, Glasgow G61 3BA — MB ChB 1966 Glas.; MD Glas. 1977; FRCP Lond. 1990; FRCP Glas. 1980; MRCP (UK) 1970. Cons. Phys & Cardiol, S. Glas. Univ. NHS Trust &. Vict. Infirm. NHS Trust Glas. Socs: Brit. Med Assoc.; Brit. Card. Soc.

BALLANTYNE, Mr Eric Sinclair Department of Neurosurg, Walton Centre for Neurology & Neurosurgery, Rice Lane, Liverpool L9 1AE — MB ChB 1987 Glas.; BSc (Hons.) Glas. 1984, MB ChB 1987; FRCS Ed. 1991. Regist. (Neurosurg.) Walton Centre for Neurol. & Neurosurg. Liverp. Prev: Regist. Rotat. (Surg.) Lothian; SHO (Neurosurg.) S.. Gen. Hosp. Glas.

BALLANTYNE, James Anderson TFL, 25 Jordan Lane, Morningside, Edinburgh EH10 4QZ Tel: 0131 447 3933 — MB ChB 1994 Ed.; BSc (Med. Sci.) Hons. Ed. 1992. SHO (A & E) St. John's Hosp. Livingston.

BALLANTYNE, James Hamilton The Surgery, High St., Clive, Shrewsbury SY4 5PS — MB ChB 1989 Sheff.; MRCGP 1994; DFFP 1995. (Sheff.) Prev: Trainee GP Roy. Shrewsbury Hosp. VTS; SHO (ENT) Shrewsbury; SHO (A & E) P.ss Roy. Hosp. Telford.

BALLANTYNE, James Rollo 16 Wolds End, Chipping Campden GL55 6JW Tel: 01386 840027 — MB BS 1948 Lond.; MRCS Eng. LRCP Lond. 1942; DObst RCOG 1947. (St. Mary's) Prev: Gyn. Regist. Surg. Regist. & Clin. Asst. Dept. Neurol. St. Mary's; Hosp. Lond.

BALLANTYNE, Jennette Frances The Surgery, Highfield Road, North Thoresby, Grimsby DN36 5RT Tel: 01472 840202; Manor House, Covenham, Louth LN11 0PB — MB BS 1986 Lond.; MRCGP 1990; DGM RCP Lond. 1989. Prev: Trainee GP/SHO Barnsley VTS; Dist. Health Off. Mchinji Dist. Hosp. Centr. Malawi.

BALLANTYNE, Mr John Chalmers, CBE 11 Holland Park Road, London W14 8NA Tel: 020 7602 3095 — MRCS Eng. LRCP Lond. 1942; FRCS Eng. 1950; Hon. FCS (SA) 1989; Hon. FRCPSG 1987; Hon. FRCSI 1975; DLO Eng. 1947. (St. Mary's) Emerit. Cons. ENT Surg. Roy. Free Hosp. Lond. Socs: Hon. Fell. Roy. Soc. Med. (Ex-Pres. Sect. Otol.); (Ex-Hon. Sec.) Brit. Assn. Otolaryngols. Prev: ENT Surg. King Edwd. VII Hosp. for Offs.; Hon. Cons. Adviser in Otolaryngol. to the Army; Asst. Dir. Audiol. Unit. Roy. Nat. Throat, Nose & Ear Hosp. Lond.

BALLANTYNE, John Pithie Burnside Cottage, 100 Crosshill St., Lennoxtown, Glasgow G66 7HQ Tel: 0141312451 — MB ChB 1962 Glas.; BSc (Physiol. Hons.) Glas. 1959; FRCP Glas. 1976; MRCP Glas. 1966. Cons. Neurol. & Hon. Clin. Sen. Lect. Inst. Neurol. Sci. S.. Gen. Hosp. Glas.

BALLANTYNE, John Pithie 100 Crosshill Street, Lennoxtown, Glasgow G66 7HQ Tel: 0141 312451; 8 Whittinge Lane Gardens, Glasgow G12 0AA Tel: 0141 357 1168 — MB ChB 1993 Glas.; DRCOG 1996; MRCOG 1997. (Glasgow University) GP Princip. Socs: BMA; Roy. Coll. Gen. Pract.

BALLANTYNE, Mr Kenneth Campbell Victoria Hospital, Hayfield Road, Kirkcaldy KY2 5AH Tel: 01592 643355; 99 Milton Terrace, Kirkcaldy KY1 1RY Tel: 01592 261075 — MB ChB 1978 Glas.; FRCS Glas. 1982. Cons. Surg. Vict. Hosp. Kirkcaldy. Prev: Lect. (Surg.) & Hon. Sen. Regist. Univ. Nottm.; Research Fell. (Gen. Surg.) Univ. Nottm.; Regist. (Gen. Surg.) Univ. Hosp. Nottm.

BALLANTYNE, Mark Jensen Department of Gastroenterology, Salisbury District Hospital, Odstock Road, Salisbury SP2 8BJ — MB ChB 1996 Dundee; BMSc Dund 1994. (Dund.) SHO Med. Qu. Med. Centre Nottm.

BALLANTYNE, Mary Harrison (retired) Stoneways, 11 School Hill, Middleton, Market Harborough LE16 8YZ Tel: 01536 771201 — MB ChB Glas. 1950. Prev: Asst. MOH N.ants.

BALLANTYNE, Philip Taylor (retired) Three Horseshoes, Meadle, Aylesbury HP17 9UD Tel: 0184 443946 — MB BS 1946 Lond.

BALLANTYNE, Robert Turner and Partners, 201 Main Street, Barrhead, Glasgow G78 1SA Tel: 0141 880 6161 Fax: 0141 881 5636 — MB ChB 1993 Glas.; BSc Glas. 1990. SHO (c/o Elderly) W. Glas. Hosps. Univ. NHS Trust. Prev: SHO (Radiother. & Oncol.) Beatson Oncol. Centre; Ho. Off. (Med.) Stirling Roy. Infirm.; Ho. Off. (Surg.) Monklands Dist. Gen. Hosp.

BALLANTYNE, Russell Wood (retired) Stoneways, 11 School Hill, Middleton, Market Harborough LE16 8YZ Tel: 01536 771201 — MB ChB Glas. 1950; FRCGP 1978, M 1962. Prev: Squadron Ldr. RAF.

BALLANTYNE, Sandra Lynn Geriatric Department, City Hospital NHS Trust, Dudley Road, Birmingham B18 7QH Tel: 0121 507 4908 Fax: 0121 507 5488 — MB ChB 1976 Birm.; FRCP Lond. 1995. (Birmingham) Cons. Phys. and Geriat.ian, City Hosp., Dudley Rd, Birm.

BALLARD, Clive Gerald 47 Lakeside Drive, Cardiff CF23 6DE — MB ChB 1987 Leic.; MD Leic. 1995; MMedSci. Birm. 1992; MRCPsych. 1991. (Leic.) MRC Clin. Scientist Newc.; Hon. Cons. Old Age Psychiat. & Hon. Sen. Lect. (Old Age Psychiat.) Newc. Prev: Lect. (Psychiat.) Univ. Birm.

BALLARD, James David 13 Hampton Drive, Bangor BT19 7GH — MB BCh BAO 1997 Belf. SHO Fract.s, Roy. Vict. Hosp.; Orthop. Musgrave Pk. Hosp. Prev: SHO (Gen. Surg. & A & E) Antrim Area Hosp. Antrim.

BALLARD, Janet 322 Greenford Avenue, Hanwell, London W7 3AH — MB BS 1986 Lond.; BSc Lond. 1972, MB BS 1986; DRCOG 1988.

BALLARD, Paul Anthony Seamus — MB ChB 1988 Leeds; 2000 PGDip Law, Leeds Met.; MD 2000 Hull; MRCOG 1994. (O & G) Leeds Gen. Infirm.; Cons. Ohs & Gynae., Friarage Hosp., N.allerton, N. Yorks.

BALLARD, Paul Knowlton 3 Mount Rise, Kenn, Exeter EX6 7XE — MB BS 1967 Lond.; MRCP (U.K.) 1971; FFA RCS Eng. 1973; DCH Eng. 1972. (St. Thos.) Cons. (Anaesth.) Roy. Devon & Exeter Hosp.

BALLARD, Philip The Peel Medical Practice, Peel Croft, 2 Aldergate, Tamworth B79 7DS Tel: 01827 50575 Fax: 01827 318911 — MB ChB 1977 Birm.; MBA (Open) 1997; DRCOG 1979; Cert. Family Plann. JCC 1979. (Birm.)

BALLARD, Mr Robin Meiklejohn Queen Mary's Hospital, Roehampton Lane, London SW15 5PN Tel: 020 8355 2024 Fax: 020 8355 2871 — MB BS 1966 Lond.; BSc (Physiol.) Lond. 1963; FRCS Ed. 1971; FRCOG 1985, M 1973. (St. Thos.) Cons. O & G Qu. Mary's Hosp. Roehampton. Prev: Sen. Regist. (O & G) St. Thos. Hosp. Lond.; Res. Surg. Off. (Gyn.) Chelsea Hosp. Wom. Lond.; Res. Med. Off. (Obst.) Qu. Charlotte's Matern. Hosp. Lond.

BALLARD, Timothy Harold The Old School Surgery, Church Street, Great Bedwyn, Marlborough SN8 3PF Tel: 01672 870388 Fax: 01672 870664 — MB ChB 1983 Leic. Prev: GP Redlam Surg. Blackburn.

BALLARDIE, Francis Westwood Manchester Royal Infirmary, Oxford Road, Manchester M13 9WL Tel: 0161 276 4148 Fax: 0161 276 4196 Email: francisballardie@mail.com — MB ChB 1979 Manch.; PhD Glas. 1973, BSc (Hons) 1970; MB ChB (Hons.) Manch. 1979; FRCP Lond. 1991; MRCP (UK) 1982. (Manchester) Cons. Phys. Gen. & Renal Med. Centr. Manch. HA; Sen. Lect. (Med.) Univ. Manch. Prev: Sen. Regist. (Renal & Gen. Med.) Hammersmith Hosp. Lond.

BALLARO, Andrew Peter Carmelo Flat 2, 143 Abbey Road, London NW6 4SL — MB BS 1993 Lond.

BALLESTEROS JERONIMO, Maria Salome Department of Pharmaceutical Sciences, Aston University, Aston Triangle, Birmingham B4 7ET — LMS 1987 U Complutense Madrid.

BALLESTEROS JIMENEZ, Juan Antonio Pinderfields General Hospital, Aberford Road, Wakefield WF1 4DG Tel: 01924 212422 Fax: 01924 814840; 12 Old Garth Croft, Fairburn, Knottingley WF11 9HD Email: juanb@ings.demon.co.uk — LMS 1988 U Complutense Madrid. Staff Grade (A & E) Pinderfields Gen. Hosp. Wakefield. Socs: Med. Protec. Soc.; Assoc. Mem. Fac. Accid. & Emerg. Med.; Fell. Brit. Assoc. Accid. & Emerg. Med. Prev: SHO (Gen. & Neonat. Paediat.) Hull Roy. Infirm.; SHO (A & E) Pinderfields Gen. Hosp.; SHO Rotat. (Surg.) Pontefract Gen. Infirm.

BALLHAM, Mr Andrew Accident and Emergency Department, General Hospital, Nelson St., Hereford HR1 2PA Tel: 01432 355444 Fax: 01432 264840 Email: aballam@aol.com; Tel: 01432 830527 — MB BS 1974 Lond.; FRCS Eng. 1979; MRCS Eng. LRCP Lond. 1975; FFAEM. (St. Thos.) Cons. A & E Hereford Gen. Hosp. Socs: FFAEM. Prev: Sen. Regist. (A & E) Leicester Roy. Infirm.; Regist. (Orthop.) Mansfield Gen. Hosp. & Harlow Wood Orthop. Hosp.

BALLIN, Ian Andrew Pendlebury Health Centre, The Lowry Medical Centre, 659 Bolton Road, Pendlebury, Manchester M27 8HP Tel: 0161 793 8686 Fax: 0161 727 8011; 126 Hilton Lane, Prestwich, Manchester M25 9QX Tel: 0161 798 8065 — MB ChB 1987 Manch.; MRCGP 1991; DFFP 1993; DRCOG 1991; Cert. Family Plann. JCC 1989. Mem. LMC. Prev: Trainee GP Farnworth; SHO (Paediat. & Med.) Bolton Gen. Hosp.

BALLIN, Mark Steven Stepping Hill Hospital, Department of Anaesthesia, Stockport SK2 7JE Tel: 0161 419 5869 — MB ChB 1990 Manch.; FRCA 1996; DA (UK) 1993. Cons. (Anaesth. & IC). Socs: Manch. Med. Soc. (Anaesth. Sect.); Assn. Anaesth.; Obst. Anaesth. Assn.

BALLIN, Neville Constantine 4 Wellington Villas, Arundel St., Nottingham NG7 1NP Tel: 0115 947 0386 Email: nevbal@infochan.com — MB ChB 1976 Aberd.; FFA RCSI Aberd. 1980. (Aberdeen University) Cons. Anaesth. Kingston Pub. Hosp., Jamaica; Lect. (Anaesth. & IC) Univ. W. Indies, Mona Kingston, Jamaica. Socs: Assn. Anaesths.; Internat. Trauma Anaesth. & Critical Care Soc.; Bahamas Med. Assn. Prev: Cons. Anaesth. P.ss Margt. Hosp. Nassau, Bahamas; Regist. (Anaesth. & Intens. Care) Dudley Rd. Hosp. Birm.; Sen. Regist. (Anaesth.) Qu. Eliz. Hosp. Barbados.

BALLINGALL, Clare Garden Flat, 28 Huntly Gardens, Dowanhill, Glasgow G12 9AU — MB ChB 1995 Dundee.

BALLINGALL, David Andrew Turner 9 Round Hill, Darton, Barnsley S75 5QJ — MB ChB 1987 Aberd.; DA (UK) 1992.

BALLINGALL, Thomas Allan Gardiners Cottage, Balbirnie Park, Markinch, Glenrothes — MB ChB 1950 Ed. (Ed.)

BALLINGER, Anne Barbara Digestive Diseases Research Centre, 3rd Floor, 2 Newark St., Whitechapel, London E1 Tel: 020 882 7191 Fax: 020 882 7192 Email: a.b.ballinger@mds.gmw.ac.uk; 5 Oldfield Mews, Highgate, London N6 5XA — MB BS 1986 Lond.; FRCP 2001; MD Lond. 1996; MRCP (UK) 1989; MD Lond. 1996. (Univ. Coll. Hosp. Lond.) Sen. Lect. & Hon. Cons. Phys. (Gastroenterol. & Gen. Med.)St Barth. & Roy. Lond. Hosp. Socs: BMA; Brit. Soc. Gastroenterol.; Amer. Gastroenterol. Assn.

BALLINGER, Brian Richard (retired) 5 Shaftesbury Park, Dundee DD2 1LB — BM BCh 1961 Oxf.; MA Oxf. 1961; FRCP Ed. 1981 M 1965; FRCPsych 1981 M 1971; DPM Eng. 1968. Prev: Cons. Psychiat. Roy. Dundee Liff Hosp.

BALLINGER, Constance Barbara (retired) 5 Shaftesbury Park, Dundee DD2 1LB — BSc Sheff. 1962, MB ChB 1965; FRCPsych 1984, M 1972; MRCP Lond. 1968; DPM Ed. & Glas. 1972. Prev: Cons. Psychiat. Dundee Psychiat. Serv.

BALLINGER, Fiona Carol Longfleet Road Surgery, 4 Longfleet Road, Poole BH15 2HT Tel: 01202 676111 — MB BS 1978 Lond.; DCH RCP Lond. 1982; DRCOG 1981. (Char. Cross)

BALLINGER, Jonathan Peter Mansion House Surgery, Abbey Street, Stone ST15 8YE Tel: 01785 815555 Fax: 01785 815541; 14 The Woodlands, Cold Meele, Stone ST15 0YA Tel: 01785 760611 — MB BS 1990 Lond.; MRCGP 1995. (St. Bart.) Gen. Practitioner. Prev: SHO (A & E) Manor Hosp. Nuneaton; Ho. Phys. Staffs. Gen. Infirm. & Stafford Dist. Gen. Hosp.; SHO (Med/GP Rotat.) Staffs. Gen. Hosp.

BALLINGER, Marion Beatrice (retired) Leathercote, The Droveway, St Margaret's Bay, Dover CT15 6DD Tel: 01304 852492 — MB BS 1948 Sydney; MRCP Lond. 1957; DCH Eng. 1954. Prev: SCMO SE Kent HA.

BALLINGER, Paul Martin Heonesford Street Surgery, 60 Heonesford Street, Cannock, Cannock Ws11 1DJ Tel: 01543 503121; 3 Grange Court, Hixon, Stafford ST18 0GQ Tel: 01889 270545 Email: pballin440@aol.com — MB ChB 1985 Manch.; DCH 1995; DRCOG 1994; MRCGP 1996; MRCP (UK) 1989. GP Cannock, Staffs.; Clin. Asst. Endoscopy, Mid Staffs. NHS Trust. Prev: SHO (Med.) Tameside Gen. Hosp.; SHO (Med.) Hope Hosp. Salford.; GP Train. Scheme N. Staffs. Hosp. Stoke-on-Trent.

BALLOCH, Clark Balfour Weavers Medical Centre, 50 School Lane, Kettering NN16 0DH Tel: 01536 513494 Fax: 01536 416521; 154 Northampton Road, Kettering NN15 7JY Tel: 01536 523695 — MB ChB 1980 Ed.; BSc Ed. 1977; MRCGP 1986; DRCOG 1984.

BALLON, Milton David Levenshulme Health Centre, Dunstable Street, Manchester M19 3BX Tel: 0161 225 4033 Fax: 0161 248 8020; 8 Woodcote View, Wilmslow SK9 2DT Tel: 01625 522660 — MB ChB 1971 Manch.; DObst RCOG 1974; DCH RCPS Glas. 1974.

BALLS, Jennifer Louise Patea, Les Varendes, Castel GY5 7RG — MB BS 1997 Lond.

BALLS, Margaret Ann 33 Moseley Wood Avenue, Leeds LS16 7HL Tel: 0113 281 7011 — MB ChB 1976 Leeds; DRCOG 1978; M.Psychother. 1997. (Leeds) SCMO (Family Plann.) Med. Off. Leeds Community & Ment. Health Trust; Clin. Asst. (Obst. & Gyn.) United Leeds Teach. Hosp. Trust. Socs: Fac. Fam. Plann. & Reproduc. Health Care.

BALLSDON, Janette Christina 1 Brockley Gardens, Brockley, London SE4 1SZ — MB BS 1993 Lond.

BALMAIN, Sean 30 Hamilton Park Avenue, Glasgow G12 8DT — MB ChB 1997 Glas.

BALME, Emily Jane The Red House, Ufford, Woodbridge IP13 6EL — MB ChB 1990 Bristol; BSc Bristol 1987.

BALME, George Maxwell The Surgery, Roman Way, Billingshurst RH14 9QZ Tel: 01403 782931 Fax: 01403 785505 — MB BS 1978 Lond.; MRCGP 1984; DCH RCP Lond. 1981. (Lond. Hosp.) GP Trainer W. Sussex. Prev: GP Havant; GP Train. Scheme Portsmouth Hosps.; SHO (Paediat.) St. Mary's Hosp. Portsmouth.

BALME, Richard Hugh (retired) 13 Fair Mile Court, Henley-on-Thames RG9 2JG Tel: 01491 572305 — BM BCh 1947 Oxf.; DM Oxf. 1958, BM BCh 1947; FRCP Lond. 1970, M 1951. Cons. Phys. Geriat. Med. E. Berks. Health Dist. Prev: Sen. Lect. (Med.) Lond. Hosp. Med. Coll.

BALMER, Brian David Essex Local Medical Committees, 70 High St., Great Baddon, Chelmsford CM2 7HH Tel: 01245 473488 Fax: 01245 473489 Email: brian.balmer@btinternet.com; 55 Church Street, Maldon CM9 5HW Tel: 01621 841908 — MB ChB 1980 Manch.; BSc (Hons.) Manch. 1977; MBA Anglia Univ. 1996. Chief Exec. Essex Local Med. Comm.s. Socs: BMA; Brit. Assn Med. Managers. Prev: GP Lond.; HA Med. Adviser.

BALMER, Francis 8 Eglinton Terrace, Skelmorlie PA17 5ER — MB ChB 1996 Glas.

BALMER, Francis Joseph 8 Eglinton Terrace, Skelmorlie PA17 5ER Tel: 01475 521959 — MB ChB 1971 Glas. Prev: Ho. Off. (O & G) Paisley Matern. Hosp.; Ho. Phys. Stobhill Gen. Hosp. Glas.; Ho. Surg. Roy. Alexandra Infirm. Paisley.

BALMER, Mr George Alwyn Sheyboygan, Haverbreaks Road, Lancaster LA1 5BJ Tel: 01524 68763 — MB BCh BAO 1952 Belf.; FRCS Ed. 1963. Cons. Orthop. Surg. N. Lancs. & S. W.morland Hosp. Gp. Socs: Fell. Manch. Med. Soc.; Brit. Orthop. Assn. Prev: Sen. Regist. (Orthop.) Manch. Roy. Infirm.; Regist. Robt. Jones & Agnes Hunt Orthop. Hosp.; Resid. Alfred I. DuPont Inst. Delaware, USA.

BALMER, George James Tramways Medical Centre, Farmley Road, Newtownabbey BT36 7XX Tel: 028 9034 2131 Fax: 028 9083 9111 — MB BCh BAO 1970 Belf.; MRCGP 1975.

BALMER, Herbert George Rea Department of Anaesthetics, Level 04 Derriford Hospital, Derriford Road, Plymouth PL6 8DH Tel: 0175 279 2691; Brackenfield, The Crescent, Crapstone, Yelverton PL20 7PS Tel: 0182 285 2421 — MB BChir 1966 Camb.; MD Camb. 1973; FFA RCS Eng. 1973. Cons. Anaesth. Derriford Hosp. Plymouth.

BALMER, Isabella Mary 8 Eglinton Terrace, Skelmorlie PA17 5ER — MB ChB 1998 Glas.; MB ChB Glas 1998.

BALMER, Jonathan Niall Walton Stranraer Health Centre, Edinburgh Road, Stranraer DG9 7HG; Beechill, Sun St, Stranraer DG9 7JH Tel: 01776 706375 Email: nbalmer@argonet.co.uk — MB BCh BAO 1983 Belf.; DCH RCP Lond. 1987; DRCOG 1986. (Qu's Univ. Belf.)

BALMER, Robin Lockie Beech House, 5 The Avenue, Norton, Malton YO17 9EF — MB ChB 1985 Bristol.

BALMER, Simon Leslie 5 The Avenue, Norton, Malton YO17 9EF — MB BS 1987 Lond.

BALMFORD, Sarah Emma 91 Highbury Road, Headingley, Leeds LS6 4EX Tel: 0113 274 6193 — MB ChB 1997 Leeds; MRCP paediat.part 1 1999.

BALMFORTH, James Richard 50 Burkes Road, Beaconsfield HP9 1PN — MB BS 1993 Lond.

BALNAVE, Kenneth 47 Richmond Court, Lisburn BT27 4QX — MB BCh BAO 1972 Belf.; FRCP Lond. 1991; MRCP (UK) 1976. (Queen's Belfast) Cons. Phys. Cardiol. Craigavon Area Hosp. Socs: Irish Cardiac Soc.; Ulster Soc. Internal Med.

BALNAVE, Susan Elizabeth Department of Pathology, Stirling Royal Infirmary, Livilands, Stirling FK8 2AU; Gartmore Home Farm, Gartmore, Stirling FK8 3RU — MB ChB 1986 Glas.; MRCPath 1995. Cons. Cytopath. & Histopath.Stirling Roy. Infirm. Prev: Cons. Cytopath. & Histopath.Inverclyde Roy. NHS Trust.

BALOCH, Abdul Ghafoor c/o Victoria Hospital, Blackpool FY3 8NR — MB BS 1958 Punjab; MB BS Punjab (Pakistan) 1958; FRCP Ed. 1995; FRCP Glas. 1986; MRCP (UK) 1974; MRCS Eng. LRCP Lond. 1972; TDD Punjab (Pakistan) 1962. (Nishtar Med. Coll. Multan) Cons. Phys. Geriat. Med. Blackpool & Fylde Hosps. Socs: Brit. Geriat. Soc. & Pakistan Med. Soc. Prev: Med. Asst. (Geriat Med.) N. Gen. Hosp. Sheff.; Regist. (Gen. Med. & Geriat.) Durh. Gp. Hosps.; Cons. Phys. Internal Med. Makkah (Saudi Arabia) Hosps.

BALOCH, Mr Anwer Hussain 2 Bergholt Avenue, Ilford IG4 5NE — MB BS 1972 Sind; MB BS Sind. 1972; FRCSI 1991.

BALOCH, Khadim Hussain Little Court, Long Road, Dedham, Colchester CO7 6BW Tel: 01206 322302 — MB BS 1964 Sind; MRCGP 1976. (Liaquat Med. Coll. Hyderabad)

BALOCH, Mr Khalid Ghafoor 20 Sir Johns Road, Selly Park, Birmingham B29 7ER Tel: 0121 415 5539 — MB ChB 1986 Manch.; FRCS Glas. 1994. SHO (Gen. Surg.) Manch. Roy. Infirm. Prev: Ho. Off. (Gen. Surg.) Manch. Roy. Infirm.; Ho. Off. (Gen. Med.) N. Manch. Gen. Hosp.

BALOCH, Nusrat The Lakes Mental Health Centre, Colchester General Hospital, Turner Road, Colchester CO4 5JL Tel: 01206 228375; 18A Thornwood, Colchester CO4 5LR Tel: 01206 852731 — MB BS 1967 Sind; FRCPsych 1986; MRCPsych 1972; DPM Eng. 1970; DObst RCOG 1968. (Liaquat Med. Coll. Hyderabad) Cons. Psychiat. NE Essex Ment. Health Servs. Colchester. Prev: Ho. Phys. (Gen. Med.) & Ho. Surg. (Gyn. & Obst.) Gen. Hosp.; Ashton-under-Lyne; Ho. Off. (Obst.) Forest Gate Hosp. Lond.; Regist. Sen. Regist. (Psychiat.) Severalls Hosp. Colchester.

BALRAJ, Vinohar 84 Stainforth Road, Newbury Park, Ilford IG2 7EL — MB BS 1978 Madras.

BALSHAW, John Hedon Group Practice, 4 Market Hill, Hedon, Hull HU12 8JD Tel: 01482 899111 Fax: 01482 890967 — MB ChB 1975 Dundee; DRCOG 1979; DA Eng. 1978.

BALSHAW, Margaret Esthonia, Main Road, Camerton, Hull HU12 9NQ — MB ChB 1975 Dundee; DA Eng. 1979.

BALSINGHAM, Sivadevi 25 Grasmere Avenue, London SW19 3DY Tel: 020 8543 0298 — MB BS 1980 Colombo; MRCS Eng. LRCP Lond. 1986; DCH RCP Lond. 1985.

BALSITIS, Margaret Department of Histopathology, Northern General Hospital, Sheffield S5 7AU Tel: 0114 271 4941 Fax: 0114 261 1034; 620 Abbey Lane, Whirlow, Sheffield S11 9NA — MB ChB 1984 Glas.; MRCPath 1993. Cons. Path. N. Gen. Hosp. Sheff. Socs: Brit. Soc. Gastroenterol. Prev: Lect. & Sen. Regist. (Path.) Nottm.; Regist. (Path.) Glas.

BALTHAZOR, David Paul Jonathon 11 Granville Close, Havant PO9 2TR — ChB Birm. 1996.

BALUCH, Catherine Jane 46 Princes Road, Felixstowe IP11 7QZ — MB BS 1996 Lond.

BALUCH, Mohammad Aslam Sanghar, Cliff Farm Barns, Old Hunstanton Road, Hunstanton PE36 6QA — MB BS 1964 Karachi; BSc Sind 1958; DRCOG 1972; DA Eng. 1968. (Dow Med. Coll.)

BALUCH, Nasrullah Whitehouse, Eccles, Aylesford, Maidstone Tel: 01622 718558 — MB BS 1965 Sind; DA Eng. 1972. (Liaquat Med. Coll.)

BALUCH, Shakira Whitehouse, Eccles, Aylesford, Maidstone Tel: 01622 718558 — MB BS 1965 Sind. (Liaquat Med. Coll.)

***BALUCHI, Professor Brion** Kimia Health Clinic, 62 Gloucester Place, London W1U 8HW Tel: 020 7224 2211 Fax: 020 72242442 Email: bsbkimia.co.uk — MB ChB 1989 Leeds; 1983 LMS (MD), Madrid.

BALY, Peter Leonard Nickson Long Cottage, East Ilsley, Newbury RG20 7LH — MRCS Eng. LRCP Lond. 1941. (St. Mary's) Prev: Med. Off. Infec. Dis. Unit. St. John's Hosp. Uxbridge; Surg. Lt. RNVR; Ho. Surg. Gynaecol. & Obst. Dept. St. Mary's Hosp.

BAMBAWALE, Ajit Kumar Bhargav Family Doctor Unit Surgery, 92 Bath Road, Hounslow TW3 3LN Tel: 020 8570 5908 Fax: 020 8577 0692 — MB BS 1955 Bombay.

BAMBER, Catherine Sarah Strawberry Place Surgery, 5 Strawberry Place, Morriston, Swansea SA6 7AQ Tel: 01792 522526

Fax: 01792 411020 — MB BCh 1991 Wales; DRCOG 1995. Trainee GP Swansea VTS.

BAMBER, Claude Charles (retired) Greys Farm, Canterton Green, Brook, Lyndhurst SO43 7HF Tel: 01703 813679 Fax: 01703 814658 — MB BCh BAO 1959 Dub.; LAH Dub. 1959. Prev: GP Soton.

BAMBER, David Bruce 74 Littleton Street, London SW18 3SY — MB BS 1965 Lond.; MRCS Eng. LRCP Lond. 1965; FFA RCS Eng. 1969. (Char. Cross) Cons. Anaesth. Char. Cross Hosp. Lond.

BAMBER, James Henry 19 Olde Forge Manor, Upper Malone Road, Belfast BT10 0HY — MB ChB 1986 Glas.

BAMBER, Lily Henry (retired) Bembury Lodge, Thornford, Sherborne DT9 6QE Tel: 01935 872200 — MB BCh BAO 1940 Dub.

BAMBER, Martin John Department of Anaesthesia, Aintree Hospitals NHS Trust, Fazakerley Hospital, Lower Lane, Liverpool L9 7AL Tel: 0151 529 5152/3 Fax: 0151 529 5155; 4 Kirklake Bank, Formby, Liverpool L37 2YJ — MB ChB 1984 Liverp.; FRCA 1992; FFA RCSI 1991; DA (UK) 1988. (Univ. Liverp.) Cons. Anaesth. Aintree Hosp. NHS Trust Fazakerley Hosp. Liverp.; Cons. NeuroAnaesth., Walton Centre for Neurol. & Neurosurg., Lower La., Liverp. Socs: Assn. Anaesth. GB & Irel.; Neuroinaesth. Soc. Prev: Sen. Regist. Rotat. (Anaesth.) Mersey; Regist. Rotat. (Anaesth.) Mersey Region; Regist. (Anaesth.) Whiston & St. Helens Hosp.

BAMBER, Maurice Desmond 21 Finaghy Park Central, Belfast BT10 0HP Tel: 028 612749 — MB BCh BAO 1948 Dub.; MRCGP 1964.

BAMBER, Michael Gervase Back Lane Surgery, Back Lane, Colsterworth, Grantham NG33 5NJ Tel: 01476 860243 Fax: 01476 860200; The Old Rectory, North Witham, Grantham NG33 5LQ — MB BS 1977 Lond.; MRCP (UK) 1980; MRCS Eng. LRCP Lond. 1976; MRCGP 1986. (St. And. & Liverp.) Socs: Fell. Roy. Soc. Med.

BAMBER, Peter Anthony Department of Anaesthesia, Royal Halifax Infirmary, Free School Lane, Halifax HX1 2YP Tel: 01422 357171 Fax: 01422 342581 — MB ChB 1981 Liverp.; FRCA 1986. Cons. Anaesth. Calderdale Healthcare NHS Trust. Socs: Assn. Anaesth. GB & Irel.; Soc. Computing & Technol. in Anaesth.; Obst. Anaesth. Assn. Prev: Sen. Regist. (Anaesth.) Leeds Gp. Hosps.; Lect. (Anaesth.) Univ. Sheff.; Regist. (Anaesth.) Sheff. Hosps.

BAMBER, Richard William Kevin c/o St Martins Hospital, Little Bourne Road, Canterbury CT1 1TD Tel: 01227 597111 — MB BCh BAO 1975 Dub.; MRCPsych 1979; FRCPsych 1998. (Trinity College University of Dublin) Cons. Psychiat.E. Kent Community NHS Trust; Cons. Psychiat. E. Kent Community NHS Trust; Hon. Cons. St. Lukes Hosp. Lond. Prev: Sen. Regist. & Regist. Guy's Hosp. Lond.; Ho. Off. Sir Patrick Dunns Hosp. Dub.

BAMBER, Stephen Christopher Long Stratton Health Centre, Flowerpot Lane, Long Stratton, Norwich NR15 2TS Tel: 01508 530781 Fax: 01508 533030 — MB ChB 1984 Birm.; MA Camb. 1976; DRCOG 1987. Prev: Ho. Phys. Selly Oak Hosp. Birm.; Ho. Surg. Gen. Hosp. Birm.

BAMBERGER, Diane Clare 151 Woodyates Road, London SE12 9JJ — MB BS 1988 Lond.; MRCGP 1994; DObst 1993; DGM RCP Lond. 1992.

BAMBRICK, Marie Kneesworth House Hospital, Bassingbourn, Kneesworth, Royston SG8 5JP Tel: 01763 255600 — MB BCh BAO 1977 NUI; MRCPsych 1986; DO RCPSI 1982; DCH NUI 1981. Cons. Psychiat.Forens. Learning Disabil.) Kneesworth Hosp. Prev: Sen. Lect. (Learning Disabil.) & Hon. Cons. Psychiat. Nottm. Univ. & S. Derbysh. HA; Cons. Psychiat. (Learning Disab.) Lifespan NHS Trust, Camb.

BAMBRIDGE, Emma Jane Charlotte Farnham Road Surgery, 301 Farnham Road, Slough SL2 1HD Tel: 01753 520917 Fax: 01753 550680 — MB BS 1985 Lond.; MRCGP 1993; DRCOG 1990. Princip. in Gen. Pract. Slough.

BAMBRIDGE, Peter Robert Newlands, Tamworth Road, Keresley End, Coventry CV7 8JJ — MB BS 1956 Lond.; DObst RCOG 1961. (Middlx.)

BAMDAD, Samad 41 Elmcroft Crescent, Harrow HA2 6HL — MD 1971 Azarabadegan, Iran; Dip. (Thoracic Med.) Univ. Lond. 1982. Clin. Asst. Roy. Brompton & Nat. Heart Hosp. Lond.

BAMFORD, Colin St Annes Road East, 24 St. Annes Road East, Lytham St Annes FY8 1UR Tel: 01253 722121 Fax: 01253 781121 — MB ChB 1980 Manch. Prev: Trainee GP Lancaster VTS.

BAMFORD, Mr David James Ryley Mount, 432 Buxton Road, Stockport SK2 7JQ Tel: 0161 483 9333 Fax: 0161 419 9913; Dingle Hey, Brookledge Lane, Adlington, Macclesfield SK10 4JU Tel: 01625 828318 — MB ChB 1983 Manch.; FRCS (Orth.) 1995; FRCS Eng. 1988. Cons. Orthop. Surg. Stockport Acute Servs. Health Trust, Stepping Hill Hosp. Socs: Brit. Orthop. Assn.; BMA; Brit. Orthop. Train. Assn. Prev: Sen. Regist. (Orthop.) N. W.. RHA; Clin. Research Fell. & Regist. (Orthop.) Hope Hosp. Salford.

BAMFORD, Diana Helen (retired) 29 Hawthornden Road, Knock, Belfast BT4 3JU — MB ChB 1959 Manch. GP Anaesth. Ards Hosp. Newtownards.

BAMFORD, Mr Douglas Sladen (retired) The Garth, 151 Church Road, Combe Down, Bath BA2 5JN Tel: 01225 833206 — MRCS Eng. LRCP Lond. 1959; MA Camb. 1960, MB BChir 1959; FRCS Ed. 1968; FRCOG 1978, M 1965, DObst 1961. Cons. O & G Bath Clin. Area. Prev: Ho. Phys., Ho. Surg. & Regist. Lond. Hosp.

BAMFORD, Frank Noel (retired) Dolphin's Green, 8 Broughton Road, Adlington, Macclesfield SK10 4ND Tel: 01625 828544 — MB ChB Manch. 1951MB ChB Manch. 1951; MD Manch. 1968; FRCP Lond. 1986, M 1979; FFCM 1980 M 1972; Hon. FRCPCH 1996; DCH Eng. 1956; DPH Leeds 1959. Prev: Reader (Developm. Paediat.) Manch. Univ. & Hon. Cons. (DeveReader (Developm. Paediat.) Manch. Univ. & Hons. Cons. (Developm. Paediat.) Manch. HA.

BAMFORD, John Michael Department of Neurology, St James's University Hospital, Beckett St., Leeds LS9 7TF Tel: 0113 206 5437 Fax: 0113 246 5231 — MD 1986 Manch.; MB ChB (Hons.) 1979; FRCP Lond. 1994; MRCP (UK) 1982. Cons. Neurol. & Phys. Cerebrovasc. Med. St. Jas. Univ. Hosp. Leeds; Hon. Sen. Lect. Univ. Leeds. Socs: Assn. Brit. Neurol.; Brit. Stroke Research Gp.; Assn. Brit. Stroke Phys. Prev: Regist. & Acting Clin. Lect. Univ. Dept. Clin. Neurol. Radcliffe Infirm. Oxf.; Sen. Regist. (Neurol.) Yorks. RHA.

BAMFORD, Kathleen Branigan 36 Beechwood Grove, Belfast BT8 7UR — MB BCh BAO 1982 Belf.

***BAMFORD, Louise Catherine** 34 Castlehill, Comber, Newtownards BT23 5XA Tel: 01247 873276 — MB BCh BAO 1997 Belf.

BAMFORD, Mark Richard Bewick Crescent Surgery, 27 Bewick Crescent, Newton Aycliffe DL5 5LH Tel: 01325 313289 Fax: 01325 301428; 20 Pierremont Crescent, Darlington DL3 9PB — MB BS 1988 Newc.; MRCGP 1993; DRCOG 1993.

BAMFORD, Michael Frank Manley Ipswich Hospital, Heath Road, Ipswich IP4 5PD Tel: 01473 702170 Fax: 01473 702180; Bentley Old Hall, Bentley, Ipswich IP9 2LW Email: michael.bamford@talk21.com — MB BChir 1971 Camb.; MB Camb. 1971, BChir 1970; FRCP Lond. 1992; MRCP (UK) 1975; DCH Eng. 1974; FRCPCH 1997. (Guy's) Cons. Paediat. Ipswich & E. Suff. Health Dist. Prev: Sen. Regist. (Paediat.) Soton. Gen. Hosp.; Regist. (Paediat.) Radcliffe Infirm. Oxf.; Ho. Off. (Paediat.) & Ho. Surg. Guy's Hosp. Lond.

BAMFORD, Neil John The Earlsfield Practice, 2-4 Steerforth St., London SW18 4HH Tel: 020 8946 5681; 123 Gladstone Road, Wimbledon, London SW19 1QS Tel: 020 8583 3663 Email: bamford@cableinet.co.uk — MB BCh BAO 1980 Dub.; MSc Public Health 1999; MRCGP 1985. PCG Bd. Mem. Prev: Trainee GP Maidstone VTS.

BAMFORD, Nicola Jane 45 pennine Rise, Scissett, Huddersfield HD8 9JE — MB ChB 1995 Manch.; MRCP 1998. (Manchester University) Specialist Regist. Paediat. Leeds Deanery. Prev: SHO (Paediat.) N. Staffs. Gen. Hosp. Stoke on Trent.

BAMFORD, Norman Alfred 26 Astor Drive, Moseley, Birmingham B13 9QR Tel: 0121 778 3129 — LMSSA 1948 Lond.; MRCGP 1963. (King's Coll. Lond. & Ed.) Socs: BMA & Roy. Med. Soc. Edin. Prev: Ho. Phys. & Cas. Off. Dist. Hosp. Lymington.

BAMFORD, Norman Edmund Collins, OBE, TD, OStJ (retired) Pooks Hill Cottage, Crossways Road, Grayshott, Hindhead GU26 6HD Tel: 01428 607317 Fax: 01428 607317 — MB BCh BAO 1955 Belf. Prev: Hosp. Pract. (Psychiat.) Purdysburn Hosp. Belf.

BAMFORD, Peter Alexander Collins Tel: 01257 265080 Fax: 01257 232285 — MB ChB 1984 Manch.; MRCGP 1988. Prev: Ho. Off. (Gen. Surg. & Urol.) Preston; Ho. Off. (Gen. Med.) Oldham Dist. Gen. Hosp.

BAMFORD, Philip Noel Pembury Hospital, Tunbridge Wells TN2 4TJ Tel: 01892 514110 — MB BS 1973 Lond.; MD Lond.

1984; FRCOG 1991. p/t Cons. Pembury Hosp. Maidstone and Tunbridge Wells NHS Trust. Prev: Lect. Univ. Soton.; Regist. Middlx. Hosp. Lond.; SHO Qu. Charlottes Hosp. Lond.

BAMFORD, Sarah Louise 23 Knatchball Close, Romsey SO51 8WJ — BM BS 1995 Nottm.

BAMFORD, William Mark 7 Poole Avenue, Baddeley Green, Stoke-on-Trent ST2 7JJ Tel: 01782 543319 — MB ChB 1995 Bristol; BSc Bristol 1991. SHO (Med.) N. Staffs. Hosps. Stoke-on-Trent.

BAMFORTH, Charles Ian 19 Alder Road, Newlands, Glasgow G43 2UU — MB ChB 1982 Glas.

BAMFORTH, John BUPA Chalybeate Hospital, Tremona Road, Southampton SO16 6UY Tel: 02380 775544 Fax: 02380 701160 Email: jbamforth@onetel.net.uk; Pine Trees, Bassett Green Road, Southampton SO16 3NF Tel: 02380 768687 Fax: 01703 766010 — MB BChir 1954 Camb.; FAMS 1994; FRCP Lond. 1974, M 1960. Emerit. Cons. Phys. Soton. Gen. Hosp.; Chief Med. Off., Skandia Life Uk. S.ampton. Socs: Brit. Soc. Gastroenterol. & Roy. Soc. Med.; Assur. Med. Soc. Prev: Ho. Phys. (Gen. Med. & Neurol.) & Sen. Regist. (Med.) St. Thos. Hosp. Lond.; Research Fell. Mayo Clinic Rochester, USA.

BAMFORTH, Malcolm Manor Mead, Manor Heath Road, Halifax HX3 0BG Tel: 01422 355909 — MB ChB 1957 Aberd. Socs: Fell. Roy. Soc. Med.; Drug Inform. Assn. & Assur. Med. Assn. Prev: Med. Dir. Sterling Health Products Surbiton; Med. Dir. Berk Pharmaceuts. Ltd. Godalming; Med. Adviser Bayer Products Co. Surbiton.

BAMFORTH, Margaret Anne 24 Elm Tree Road, Lymm WA13 0NH — MB ChB 1974 Liverp.; MRCPsych 1981; DCH RCPS Glas. 1977. Cons. Child & Adolesc. Psychiat. Halton HA & Mersey RHA. Prev: Sen. Regist. (Child & Adolesc. Psychiat.) N. W.. RHA.

BAMFORTH, Rosemary Margaret Warren Pine Trees, 210 Bassett Green Road, Southampton SO16 3NF Tel: 02380 768687 — MB ChB 1951 Glas. (Glas.) Prev: Lect. Cytol. St. Thos. Hosp. Lond.; Research Asst. Mayo Clinic Rochester USA; Cons. Path. Roy. Hants. Co. Hosp. Winchester.

BAMGBALA, Ademola Mabayoje 106 Lonsdale Avenue, London E6 3JX — MB BS 1980 Ibadan; MB BS Ibadan Nigeria 1980; MRCOG 1993.

BAMIAS, Aristotle St Bartholomew's Hospital, Smithfields, London EC1 Tel: 020 7601 8888; 1 Woodlands Road, Harold Wood, Romford RM3 0QX Tel: 01708 346221 — Ptychio Iatrikes 1987 Athens; PhD Lond. 1994. Lect. & Hon. Regist. (Med. Oncol.) St. Bart. Hosp. Prev: SHO (Neurol.) OldCh. Hosp.; SHO (Med.) Roy. Marsden Hosp. & N.. Gen. Hosp.

BAMIGBADE, Timothy Adewale 8 Slindon Road, Worthing BN14 9LJ — MB BS 1989 Lond.

BAMJI, Andrew Nariman Queen Mary's Hospital, Frognal Avenue, Sidcup DA14 6LT Tel: 020 8308 3070 Fax: 020 8308 3058 Email: andrew_bamji@compuserve.com; Torphins, 14 Burntwood Road, Sevenoaks TN13 1PT Tel: 01732 463200 — MB BS 1973 Lond.; MB BS (Hons.) Lond. 1973; FRCP Lond. 1989; MRCP (UK) 1975. (Middlx.) Cons. Rheum. & Rehabil. Qu. Mary's Hosp. Sidcup & Erith Dist. Hosp.; Dir. Elmstead Younger Disabled Unit Qu. Mary's Hosp. Sidcup; Assoc. Med. Dir. Clin. Support Care Gp. Socs: Allied Assoc. Brit. Assn. of Plastic Surg.s; Brit. Soc. Rheum. (Chairm., Clin. Affairs Comm.); Brit. Soc. Rehabil. Med. Prev: Sen. Regist. (Rheum.) Middlx. Hosp. Lond.; Regist. (Med.) Bath Health Dist.; SHO (Med.) Hammersmith Hosp. Lond.

BAMJI, Joan Elizabeth (retired) Tracey House, Haytor Road, Bovey Tracey, Newton Abbot TQ13 9LE Tel: 01626 832757 — BSc (1st cl. Hons.) Lond. 1937, MB BS (Hons. &; Distinc. Med. 1948; MRCS Eng. LRCP Lond. 1948; DTM & H Eng. 1948. Prev: GP Lond.

BAMPOE, Samuel Addo 5 Essex House, Harold Wood Hospital, Gubbins Lane, Harold Wood, Romford RM3 0BE — Vrach 1969 Kharkov Med. Inst.

BANAIT, Gurvinderjit Singh 12 Sandwell Drive, Sale M33 6JL Tel: 0161 905 3461 — MB ChB 1989 Manch.; MRCP (UK) 1993.

BANAN, Mr Homayoun Old Church Hospital, Waterloo Road, Romford RM7 0BE Tel: 01708 708152 Fax: 01708 708152; 8 Greystone Gardens, Barkingside, Ilford IG6 2HH Tel: 020 8550 1615 Fax: 020 8924 4321 — MD 1974 Iran; FRCS Glas. 1986. (Nat. Univ. Iran) Cons. Orthop. Surg. Socs: Fell. BOA; BMA.

BANASZKIEWICZ, Paul Anthony 249 Every Street, Nelson BB9 7BZ Tel: 01282 601063 — MB ChB 1990 Glas.; FRCS Eng. 1996; FRCS Ed. 1995; FRCS Glas. 1994. Specialist Regist. (Orthop.) Grampian region.

BANAT, Joseph John Park House Surgery, 55 Higher Parr Street, St Helens WA9 1BP Tel: 01744 23705 Fax: 01744 454601; 8 Rainford Road, Dentons Green, St Helens WA10 6BS — MB ChB 1982 Liverp.

BANATI, Richard Bela 156 Hammersmith Grove, London W6 7HE — State Exam 1987 Mainz.

BANATVALA, Professor Jangu Edalji, CBE Little Acre, Church End, Henham, Bishop's Stortford CM22 6AN Tel: 01279 850386 Fax: 01279 851181 Email: jangu@church-end.henham.co.uk — MB BChir 1959 Camb.; MA, MD Camb. 1964; FRCP Lond. 1995; MRCP (UK) 1986; FRCPath 1977, M 1965; DPH (Distinc.) Lond. 1961; DCH Eng. 1960; F Med Sci (Founder & Fell.) 1998. (Camb. & Lond. Hosp.) Emerit. Prof. Clin. Virol. St. Thos. Campus, Guy's, King's Coll. & St Thos. Sch. of Med. Lond.; Mem. Med. Defence Union Counc. & Cases Comm.; Mem.Bd. Pub. health Lab. Serv. (PHLS); Mem. Bd. & Chief Lab. Accreditation (CPA); Mem. Chief Med Off. stategic working party on communicable Dis.s. Socs: Fell. Roy. Soc. Med.; (Ex-Pres.) Europ. Assn. Against Virus Dis.; Roy. Coll. Phys & Roy. Coll. Pathologists Jt. Comm. on Infec. & Trop. Med. Prev: Prof. Clin. Virol. St. Thos. Campus, Guy's, King's Coll. & St Thomas' Sch. of Med. Lond.; Regist. / Counc. Mem. / Vice Pres. Roy. Coll. Of Path.s; DOH: Chairm. of Advisery Gp. hepatitis (c/c 1998).

BANATVALA, Nicholas Department of Epidemiology & Medical Statistics, London Hospital Medical College (QMW), Mile End Road, London E1 4NS Tel: 020 7982 6391 Fax: 020 7982 6396; 48 Tyler Street, Greenwich, London SE10 9EX Tel: 020 8853 0885 — MB BS 1986 Lond.; MSc Med. Microbiol. Lond. 1993; MRCP (UK) 1989. Lect. (Epidemiol.) Lond. Hosp. Med. Coll. Socs: Worshipful Apoth. of Lond. Prev: Regist. (Infec. Dis.) Monklands Dist. Gen. Hosp. Airdrie; SHO (Med. Paediat.) Roy. Hosp. Sick Childr. Glas.; SHO Hosp. Sick Childr. Lond.

BANBERY, Joanna Kay 30 Willow Crescent, St Albans AL1 5DB — MB BS 1982 Lond.; MRCPsych. 1987.

BANBURY, Jacqueline Elizabeth 7 Snelston Crescent, Littleover, Derby DE23 6BL — MB BS 1954 Lond.; MRCS Eng. LRCP Lond. 1954.

BANCE, Hans Raj Elizabeth Court Surgery, Elizabeth Drive, Airedale, Castleford WF10 3TG Tel: 01977 515203 Fax: 01977 519652 — MB ChB 1983 Leeds; MRCGP 1987; 1997 Dip. Occ. Med. RCP Lond.; DFFP 1993; Cert. Family Plann. JCC 1987; DRCOG 1987. (Leeds)

BANCEWICZ, Desmond Eskdale, 140 Brownside Road, Cambuslang, Glasgow G72 8AH — MB ChB 1970 Glas.

BANCEWICZ, John Hope Hospital, Eccles Old Road, Salford M6 8HD Tel: 0161 789 7373 Fax: 0161 787 5992; 10 Syddal Road, Bramhall, Stockport SK7 1AD Tel: 0161 439 2508 — MB ChB 1969 Glas.; BSc (Hons.) Glas. 1967; ChM Manch. 1984; FRCS Eng. 1995; FRCS Glas. 1973. Reader (Surg.) Univ. Manch.; Hon. Cons. Hope Hosp. Salford. Socs: Brit. Soc. Gastroenterol.; Assn. of Surg.s of Gt. Britain & Irel.; Internat. Soc. Dis. of Oesophagus. Prev: Sen. Lect. (Surg.) Univ. Manch.; Hon. Sen. Regist. & Lect. (Surg.) W.. Infirm. Glas.; Research Fell. (Surg.) Harvard Med. Sch. Boston, USA.

BANCILHON, Marie Louis Augustin Bernard 1 Bournehall Lane, Bushey, Watford WD23 3NQ Tel: 020 8950 4480 — MB BS 1960 Lond.; LMSSA Lond. 1957. (Guy's)

BANCROFT, Carol Tel: 0115 978 1231 Fax: 0115 979 0419; 11 Arnos Grove, Reynards Park, Nuthall, Nottingham NG16 1QA Tel: 0115 976 1722 Fax: 0115 919 5962 Email: carol.bancroft@ntlworld.com — BM BS 1982 Nottm.; BMedSci (Hons.) Nottm. 1980; MRCGP 1988; DRCOG 1988. (Nottingham) Princip. (Gen. Pract.).

BANCROFT, Douglas George (retired) Briarwood, 85 Middle Gordon Road, Camberley GU15 2JA — MB BS 1963 Lond.; MRCS Eng. LRCP Lond. 1963; DObst RCOG 1965. Prev: Ho. Off. (O & G) Guy's Hosp.

BANCROFT, Geoffrey Neil Kingshurst Medical Practice, 40 Gilson Way, Kingshurst, Birmingham B37 6BE Tel: 0121 788 8674 — MB ChB 1986 Birm. Prev: Trainee GP/SHO Birm. HA VTS.

BANCROFT, Julie Swanswell Medical Centre, 370 Gospel Lane, Acocks Green, Birmingham B27 7AL Tel: 0121 706 5676 — MB

ChB 1986 Birm.; MRCGP 1990; DRCOG 1990. Prev: Trainee GP Solihull HA VTS.

BANCROFT, Karen Royal Bolton Hospital, Minerva Rd, Bolton BL4 0JR — MB ChB 1983 Manch.; MD Manch. 1991; MRCOG 1993. Cons. Obst. & Gyn., Roy. Bolton Hosp. Prev: Sen. Regist. Leeds Gen. Infirm.

BANCROFT, Philip James 26 Carlton Hill, Edinburgh EH1 3BJ — MB ChB 1992 Ed.

BANCROFT, Rebecca Jane Flat 16C, Lanhill Road, Maida Vale, London W9 2BP Tel: 020 7289 7451 — MB BCh 1998 Wales. (UWCM Cardiff)

BANCROFT, Ruth Mary (retired) 2 Bishops Road, Tewin Wood, Welwyn AL6 0NS Tel: 01438 79 385 — MB ChB Manch. 1953. Prev: Ho. Surg. (Orthop.) Manch. Roy. Infirm.

BANCROFT, Thomas Peter 26 Calton Hull, Edinburgh EH1 3BJ — BChir 1992 Camb.

BANCROFT-LIVINGSTON, George Henry The White House, Ickleford, Hitchin SG5 3RN Tel: 01462 432006 — MB BS 1944 Lond.; MD Lond. 1946; FRCS Eng. 1951; MRCS Eng. LRCP Lond. 1944; FRCOG 1960, M 1947. (Middlx.) Cons. O & G Luton & Hitchin Gp. Hosps. Socs: Fell. Roy. Soc. Med. & Ulster Obst. & Gyn. Soc.; E. Anglia Obst. & Gyn. Soc. Prev: Lect. (O & G) Qu. Univ. Belf.; Research Asst. & Sen. Regist. (O & G) Middlx. Hosp.; Squadron Ldr. RAFVR.

BANCROFT-LIVINGSTON, Mark Kilsyth Pavilion Family Doctors, 153A Stroud Road, Gloucester GL1 5JJ Tel: 01452 385555 Fax: 01452 387905; Beaconsfield House, New St, Painswick, Stroud GL6 6UN — MB BChir 1978 Camb.; MA Camb. 1978; MRCP (UK) 1981; MRCGP 1985. (Guy's) Postgrad. Clin. Tutor (Gen. Pract.) Univ. Bristol. Prev: Sen. Regist. (Med.) Al Quassimi Hosp., Sharjah; Regist. (Med.) Mayday Hosp. Croydon.

BAND, Jessica Susan Glengaur, Main Street, Bankfoot, Perth PH1 4AA — MB ChB 1973 Manch.

BANDAK, Raja Sutton Hill Medical Practice, Maythorne Close, Sutton Hill, Telford TF7 4DH Tel: 01952 586471 Fax: 01952 588029 — BM 1978 Soton.; MRCGP 1983; DRCOG 1983; DCH RCP Lond. 1983.

BANDARA, Deshal Sanatha Pallawala Kapurupastha 23 Weycroft Road, Birmingham B23 5AD — MB BS 1972 Ceylon.

BANDARA, Dudley Jayawardene Department of Community Services, Oldham NHS Trust, Westhulme Avenue, Oldham OL1 2PN Tel: 0161 627 8754; 13 Polperro Close, Heyside, Royton, Oldham OL2 6LA Tel: 01706 882693 Email: dudleyb@btinternet.com — MB BS 1969 Ceylon; DFFP 1994. (Peradeniya Medical School Sri Lanka) Clin. Med. Off. (Child Health) Dept. Community Serv. Oldham HA. Socs: Fell. Roy. Inst. Pub. Health and Hyg. Prev: SHO (c/o Elderly) Roy. Oldham Hosp.

BANDARA, Induja Sarangi 2 Wellington Lane, Heath End, Farnham GU9 9BA Tel: 01252 22338 — MB BS 1990 Lond.; MRCGP 1995; DRCOG 1993. (St. Geo. Hosp. Med. Sch.) Prev: Trainee GP Woking; Trainee GP/SHO (A & E) St. Peter's Hosp. Chertsey.

BANDEKAR, Mars Silva 9 Khartoum Road, Sheffield S11 8RD — MB ChB 1998 Sheff.; MB ChB Sheff 1998.

BANDESHA, Gunjit 11 Dorset Avenue, Wigston, Leicester LE3 8BD — MB ChB 1993 Leeds.

BANDOPADHYAY, Sumitra All Saints Hospital, Lodge Road, Hockley, Birmingham B18 5SD Tel: 0121 523 5151 — MB BS 1971 Calcutta. Clin. Asst. Black Country Ment. Health NHS Trust. Prev: SHO Rotat. (Psychiat.) New Cross Hosp. Lond.

BANDYOPADHYAY, Mr Birendra Chandra 16 Pavenham Drive, Birmingham B5 7TW — MB BS 1976 Calcutta; MSC Birm. Univ. 1996; FRCS Glas. 1987. (Calcutta Medical College and Hospital) Cons. Orthop. Surg. Good Hope Hosp. Birm. Socs: Brit. Orthop. Assn.

BANDYOPADHYAY, Pradipta Kumar 108 Victoria Road, Pinxton, Nottingham NG16 6NH Tel: 01773 810207 — MB BS 1974 Calcutta; DA Eng. 1978. (Calcutta Nat. Med. Coll.) Socs: Fac. Anaesth. Lond. Prev: Regist. & SHO (Anaesth.) Leighton Hosp. Crewe, Chesh., Glam. Hosps. & Roy. Alexandra Hosp. Rhyl.

BANDYOPADHYAY, Shyamli (Surgery), 220-222 Warwick Road, Sparkhill, Birmingham B11 4RA Tel: 0121 766 6113 — MB BS 1977 Calcutta; MPhil Bradford 1985; FRCS Ed. 1983.

BANDYOPADHYAY, Syamalendu 3 McVeigh Court, The Avenue, Healing, Grimsby DN41 7NB Tel: 01472 883224; 70 Winslow Drive, Immingham, Immingham DN40 2DL Tel: 01469 574197 — MB BS 1974 Calcutta. (R.G.Kar Med. Coll. Calcutta) GP Immingham. Socs: MDU.

BANDYOPADHYAY, Tapas Kumar BD-131, Sector 1, Salt Lake, Calcutta 700064, India Tel: (00 91) (33) 359 6004 Email: tkban@cal.vsnl.net.in; 20 Holly Park, Finchley, London N3 3JD Tel: (01703) 796286 — MBBS 1980 Calcutta; MD Calcutta 1983; MRCP (UK) 1989. Cons. NeUrol. Nat.Neurosci. Centre Peerless Hosp. & BK Roy. Research Centre Calcutta, India. Socs: Assoc. Brit. Neurol.; Brit. Soc. Clin. NeuroPhysiol.; Neurolog. Soc. India. Prev: Clin. Assoc. Neurol. Nat. Inst.s of Health Bethesda, USA; Sen. Regist. Clin. NeuroPhysiol. S.ampton Gen. Hosp.; Regist. in Neurol. W.wood Pk. Neurol. Centre.

BANDYOPADHYAY, Mr Uttiya 29 Riddlesdown Road, Purley CR8 1DJ — MB BS 1974 Calcutta; FRCS Ed. 1984.

BANERJEA, Benoy Lal The Surgery, 149 Chester Road, Streetly, Sutton Coldfield B74 3NE Tel: 0121 352 0570 — MB BS 1964 Calcutta.

BANERJEA, Parthasarathi 58 Huntingdon Street, London N1 1BX — MB ChB 1990 Birm.; ChB Birm. 1990.

BANERJEE, Aleya 2 Pilling Field, Egerton, Bolton BL7 9UG Tel: 01204 305482 — MB BS 1958 Calcutta; DA Eng. 1965. (Calcutta) Clin. Med. Off. (Community Med.) Bolton AHA; Mem. Fac. Anaesths. RCS Eng. Prev: Regist. (Anaesth.) Portsmouth Hosp. Gp.; Lect. (Anaesth.) Univ. Malaya, Kuala Lumpur; SHO (Anaesth.) N.ampton Gen. Hosp.

BANERJEE, Amalendu (retired) 2 Belvedere Drive, Bromsgrove B61 0AJ Tel: 01527 876859 — MB BS Calcutta 1964. Staff Med. Off. (Learning Disabil.) Lea Castle Centre Kidderminster.

BANERJEE, Amit Kumar 43 Gatesden Road, Fetcham, Leatherhead KT22 9QW; 1 School Close, Thorpe Thewles, Stockton-on-Tees TS21 3JE Tel: 01740 30126 — MB BS 1970 Calcutta; PhD Ranchi 1982.

BANERJEE, Anil Kumar (retired) North View, Bells Meadow, Necton, Swaffham PE37 8NE — MMF W. Bengal 1955. Prev: Ho. Phys. & Cas. Off. Gen. Hosp. King's Lynn.

BANERJEE, Anil Robin The Willows, Manor Road, Kirton, Boston PE20 1PH — MB BS 1987 Newc.; FRCPS Glas. 1992.

BANERJEE, Anindo Kumar Red House, 4 Wheatbottom, Crook DL15 9HB Tel: 01388 762537 Fax: 01388 768726 Email: aindobanerjee@ — MB BS 1991 Newc.; MRCP (UK) 1995; ALS Instruc. RC (UK) 1997. (Newcastle-upon-Tyne) Specialist Regist. Rotat. (Thoracic & Gen. Med.) SE Thames. Prev: SHO Rotat. S. Cleveland Hosp. & Middlesbrough Gen. Hosp.

BANERJEE, Mr Anjan Kumar Consultant Surgeon, Royal Halifax Infirmary, Free School Lane, Halifax HX3 8SD Tel: 01422 357222 Fax: 01422 342581; Hopewell House, Leeds Road, Lightcliffe, Halifax HX3 8SD Tel: 01422 203048 — MB BS 1985 Lond.; MB BS (Hons.) (Distinc. Med. & Path.) Lond. 1985; CBiol 1989; MSc (Distinc.) Lond. 1991, MS 1991; DM Nottm. 1996; FRCS (Gen.) 1995; FRCS Eng. 1989; FRCP Ed. 1998, MRCP (UK) 1988; FICS 1994; T(S) 1994; MIBiol 1989. (Guy's & St. Thos.) Cons. Surg. (Gen. & Colorectal) Roy. Halifax Infirm.; Sen. Clin. Lect. (Surg.) Univ. Leeds; Lytle Fell. (Univ. Sheff. & RCS Eng.); Ethicon Trav. Fell. RCS Eng; Davis & Geck/ASIT Trav. Fell.; ATLS Instruc. RCS Eng. Socs: Fell.(Counc. Mem.) Assn. Coloproctol. & Endoscopic Surgs. (Ed.); Fell. Manch. Med. Soc. & Assn. Surg. GB & Irel.; Surgic. Research Soc. Prev: Regist. (Gen. Surg.) Profess. Unit, Hon. Lect. & MRC Train. Fell. King's Coll. Hosp. Med. Sch. Lond. & Trent RHA; Sen. Regist. (Gen. Surg.) Trent RHA; Sen. Regist. (Surg.) St. Mark's Hosp. Lond.

BANERJEE, Anjan Kumar Red House, 4 Wheatbottom, Crook DL15 9HB Tel: 01388 762537 Fax: 01388 765826 Email: ak.banerjee@onyxnet.co.uk — MB ChB 1995 Dundee. SHO Surg. Rotat. Newc.; SHO (A & E), N. Tyneside Gen. Hosp.

BANERJEE, Arpan Kumar 11 Greswolde Road, Solihull B91 1DZ; Department of Radiology, Birmingham Heartlands Hospital, Bordesley Green E., Birmingham B9 5SS Tel: 0121 766 6611 Ext: 4406 Fax: 0121 685 5543 — MB BS 1983 Lond.; MRCP (UK) 1986; FRCR 1992; T(R)(CR) 1994; FRCP (Lond.) 1999. (St. Thos.) Cons. Radiol. Birm. Heartlands & Solihull Hosp. (Teach.) NHS Trust; Hon. Clin. Sen. Lect. Univ. Birm.; Brit. Inst. Radiol. Travel Bursary

1993; Mem. Brit. Inst. Radiol. (Mem. Library Comm.); Postgrad. Clin Tutor (Radiol.) Birm. Heartlands & Solihull Hosp.; Lead Tutor (Research & Audit) Birm. Radiol. Train. Progr.; Undergrad. Clin Tutor (Radiol.) Birm. Heartlands & Solihull Hosp.; Dep. Edr. Clin. MRI; RCP Lond. Travel Fell. Toronto Gen. Hosp., Canada 1987. Socs: Brit. Med. Ultrasound Soc.; Brit. Inst. Radiol.; Hist. Comm. Radiol. Hist. & Heritage Charitable Trust. Prev: Sen. Regist. Guy's & St. Thos. Hosps. NHS Trust Lond.; Regist. (Radiol.) W.m. Hosp., Char. Cross & W.m. Med. Sch.; Regist. (Med.) St. Thos. Hosp. Lond.

BANERJEE, Arun Kumar Red House, 4 Wheatbottom, Crook DL15 9HB Tel: 01338 762537 — MB BS 1964 Calcutta. (Calcutta)

BANERJEE, Arup Kumar, OBE 2 Pilling Field, Egerton, Bolton BL7 9UG Tel: 01204 305482 — MB BS 1958 Calcutta; FRCPI 1997; FRCP Lond. 1982, M 1967; FRCP Ed. 1980, M 1967; FRCP Glas. 1979, M 1965. (Calcutta) Clin. Director Wigan & Leigh Hosp. Trust; JP; Hon. Lect. (Geriat.) Univ. Manch.; Mem. Registered N. Home Tribunal Panel; Regional Specialist Advisor in ger. Med (N.W.). Socs: (Pres.) Brit. Geriat. Soc. 1996 -1998; Mem. Brit. Med. Assn. Prev: Med. Dir. Bolton Hosp. Trust Sen. Regist. (Geriat. Med.) Portsmouth & Soton. Hosp. Gps.; Lect. (Med.) Univ. Malaya; Cons. Phys. (Geriat.) Bolton Hosp. Trust Univ. Hosp. S. Manch.

BANERJEE, Ashis Department of Accident & Emergency, Whittington Hospital, Highgate Hill, London N19 5NF Tel: 020 7288 5699; 23 Brook Meadow, London N12 7DB — MB BS 1978 Madras; MS Madras 1981; FRCS Eng. 1983; FRCS Ed. 1983; FFAEM 1996; MRCS Eng. LRCP Lond. 1986; DTM & H RCP Lond. 1992. Cons. A & E Whittington Hosp. Lond.; Hon. Sen. Lect. UCL Med. Sch. Socs: Brit. Assn. Sport & Med.; Brit. Assn. Accid. & Emerg. Med. Prev: Sen. Regist. (A & E) W. Midl. RHA; Regist. (A & E) Walsall HA; SHO (A & E) Wexham Pk. Hosp. Slough.

BANERJEE, Ashis 68 Crofton Av, Bexley DA5 3AT — MB BS 1997 Lond.

BANERJEE, Ashis Kumar Bridgeton Health Centre, 201 Abercromby Street, Glasgow G40 2DA Tel: 0141 531 6500 Fax: 0141 531 6505 — MB BS 1959 Calcutta.

BANERJEE, Bela 21 St Christopher Close, Isleworth TW7 4NP — MB BS 1965 Calcutta; DA Eng. 1970; Cert. Family Plann. RCOG & RCGP 1975. Med. Off. (Family Plann. Clin.) Hammersmith. Socs: Med. Protec. Soc. Prev: Med. Off. (Community Child Health) Wandsworth HA.

BANERJEE, Bibek 8 Nunwick Way, Haydon Grange, Newcastle upon Tyne NE7 7GB Tel: 0191 240 2334 — MB BS 1991 Newc.; FRCS Ed. 1996. (Newcastle) Vasc. Research Fell. Newc. Univ. Socs: MDU.

BANERJEE, Binayendra Group Practice Centre, Howard Street, Glossop SK13 7DE Tel: 01457 854321; 43 Heath Road, Glossop SK13 7BA Tel: 01457 852043 — MB BS 1954 Calcutta; FRCP Ed. 1994; MRCP Ed. 1963; DTM & H Liverp. 1958. (R.G. Kar. Med. Coll. Calcutta) Prev: Regist. (Gen. Med.) Gen. Hosp. Otley & Wordsley Hosp. Stourbridge; Med. Asst. (Gen. Med. & Infec. Dis.) Lodge Moor Hosp. Sheff.; Hon. Clin. Tutor (Infec. Dis.) Univ. Sheff.

BANERJEE, Mr Biswapati 47 Spring Grve., Loughton IG10 4QD Tel: 020 8508 8754 — MB BS 1957 Calcutta; FRCS Eng. 1970. (Calcutta Nat. Med. Coll.) Indep. Cons. Gen. & Cosmetic Surg. Socs: Brit. Assn. Cosmetic Surg. Prev: Regist. (Gen. Surg.) E. Ham Memor. Hosp. Lond.; Regist. (Surg.) King Geo. Hosp. Ilford.

BANERJEE, Mr Biswaranjan West Brook, 35 Marple Hall Drive, Marple, Stockport SK6 6JN — MB BS 1966 Calcutta; FRCS Eng. 1974; FRCR 1981; DMRD Liverp. 1979. Cons. Radiol. (Diagn. Radiol. & Imaging) Tameside & Glossop Acute Servs. NHS Trust. Socs: Amer. Ulstrasound Soc.; Brit. Soc. Nuclear Med.; Brit. Ultrasound Soc. Prev: Sen. Regist. & Regist. (Radiol.) Roy. Liverp. Hosp.

BANERJEE, Bratati Netherne Hospital, Coulsdon CR5 1YE Tel: 01737 556700 Fax: 01737 556701; 42 Russel Green Close, Purley CR8 2NR — MB BS 1963 Calcutta; DPM Eng. 1975. (Nilratan Sircar Med. Coll. Calcutta)

BANERJEE, Chitralekha 47 Ravenscroft Avenue, Wembley HA9 9TE — MB BS 1964 Calcutta; MRCOG 1977.

BANERJEE, Devtosh Jonathan Birmingham Heartlands Hospital, Bordesley Green E., Birmingham B9 5SS; 26 Gordon Road, Harborne, Birmingham B17 9HB Tel: 0121 242 2763 Email: dev.banerjee@virgin.net — MB ChB 1992 Leeds; BSc (Hons.) Leeds 1989; MRCP (UK) 1995. (Leeds) Regist. Rotat. (Thoracic Med.) Birm. Socs: Brit. Thorac. Soc. Prev: SHO (Med.) St. Jas. & Seacroft NHS Trust.

BANERJEE, Dilip Kumar 188 Banstead Road, Banstead SM7 1QG Tel: 020 8393 8105 & profess. 081 672 9944 — MD 1966 All India Inst.; PhD Lond. 1972; MD All India Inst. Med. Scs. 1966; MB BS Calcutta 1960; FRCPath 1988. (Nat. Med. Coll. Calcutta) Sen. Lect. (Med. Microbiol.) St. Geo. Hosp. Med. Sch. Lond.; Hon. Cons. (Microbiol.) St. Geo. Hosp. Lond.

BANERJEE, Mr Dipak Kumar Ophthamology Department, Royal Albert Edward Infirmary, Wigan Lane, Wigan WN1 2NN Tel: 01942 241538 Email: dipak.banerjee@hotmail.com; Crofthill, 351 Wigan Lane, Wigan WN1 2RD Tel: 01942 241538 Email: depakkbanerjee@yahoo.com — MB BS 1966 Calcutta; MD (Ophth.) All India Inst. Med. Scs. 1973; FRCS Glas. 1981; FCOphth. 1989; DOMS Calcutta 1969. (Calcutta Medical College) Cons. Ophth. Surg. Roy. Albert Edwd. Infirm. Wigan. Socs: BMA ODA. Prev: Sen Regist. (Ophth.) W. Midl. RHA.

***BANERJEE, Kathryn Jane** 26 Gordon Road, Harborne, Birmingham B17 9HB — MB ChB 1996 Birm.

BANERJEE, Keya Twynham Croft, 42 Park Rd, Walsall WS5 3JU — MB BS 1996 Lond.

BANERJEE, Kunal (Surgery), 1A Gold St., Barnsley S70 1TT — MB BS 1965 Calcutta.

BANERJEE, Lalita 91 Stradbroke Grove, Clayhall, Ilford IG5 0DW — MB BS 1997 Lond.

BANERJEE, Neena c/o Miss Chakraborty, 290 Horns Road, Barkingside, Ilford IG6 1BS — MB BS 1965 Rajasthan. (Sardar Patel Med. Coll. Bikaner)

BANERJEE, Nina Lalita 7 Victoria Street, Cannock WS11 1AG — MB BS 1969 Lond.; MRCS Eng. LRCP Lond. 1969. (King's Coll. Hosp.)

BANERJEE, Penelope Jane Mansel 3 The Square, Glenfield, Leicester LE3 8DQ — MB BS 1988 Newc.

BANERJEE, Mr Pinaki Wexham Park Hospital, Wexham St., Wexham, Slough SL2 4HL — MB BS 1987 Calcutta; FRCS Eng. 1993; FRCS Ed. 1992.

BANERJEE, Piu 132 Squires Lane, London N3 2QT — MB BS 1989 Lond.; MRCP (UK) 1992. Research Regist. (Dermat.) Roy. Free Hosp. Lond. Prev: SHO (Neurol. & Dermat.) St. Mary's Hosp. Lond.; SHO (Med.) Lister Hosp. Stevenage.

BANERJEE, Probal Ferndale Road Surgery, Ferndale Road, Tylorstown, Ferndale CF43 3HB Tel: 01443 730169.

BANERJEE, Rajasi 22 Holly Drive, Aylesbury HP21 8TZ — MB BS 1988 Calcutta; MRCP (UK) 1994.

BANERJEE, Raka Sandwell District General Hospital, Lyndon, West Bromwich B71 4HJ Tel: 0121 553 1831 — MB BS 1966 Calcutta; MS Calcutta 1970, MB BS 1966; FRCS Ed. 1979. (Calcutta Med. Coll.) Clin. Asst. (A & E) Sandwell AHA.

BANERJEE, Mr Ram Krishna, OBE, TD, Col. (retired) — MB BS 1960 Calcutta; FRCS Ed. 1966; LLD (Hon.) Honorary Doctorate in Law. S/Lond.Univ. 1993.; FFAEM. Prev: ADC to HM The Qu.

BANERJEE, Saikat 49 Bloomhall Road, Gipsy Hill, London SE19 1JH — MB BS 1994 Lond.; BSc (Hons.) Lond. 1991. Research Fell.(O & G), King's Coll. Hosp., Lond. Socs: BMA; MDU; RSM. Prev: SHO (O & G) King's Coll. Hosp. Lond.; Ho. Off. (Gen. Med.) Lewisham Hosp. Lond.; Ho. Off. (Gen. Surg.) Guy's Hosp. Lond.

BANERJEE, Sandra Tina 11 Greswolde Road, Solihull B91 1DZ — MB ChB 1989 Leeds; DFFP 1994; DRCOG 1993.

BANERJEE, Shanti Priya 33 Durham Road, Walsall WS2 9TF — MB BS 1973 Ranchi; MD Mithila 1980; DGM RCP Lond. 1994. Clin. Asst. (Geriat. Med.) Manor Hosp. Walsall. Socs: Med. Protec. Soc. Prev: Regist. & SHO Harrogate Dist. Gen. Hosp.; SHO (Elderly Med.) High Roys Hosp. Menston; SHO Rotat. (Med. for Elderly & Gen. Med.) Tameside Gen. Hosp. Ashton under Lyne.

BANERJEE, Shramana Mitul 14 Green Park, Erddig, Wrexham LL13 7YE — MB BS 1996 Lond.

BANERJEE, Shrilla 188 Banstead Road, Banstead SM7 1QG — MB ChB 1993 Birm.; MRCP (UK) 1996. (Birm.) Regist. (Cardiol.) Lond. Chest Hosp. Socs: Med. Defence Union; BMA; Fell. Roy. Soc. Med. Prev: SHO (Renal) Guy's Hosp. Lond.; SHO Rotat. (Med.) St. Geo. Hosp. Lond.

BANERJEE, Shyamal The Surgery, Leeswood, Mold CH7 4SA Tel: 01352 770212 Fax: 01352 770212; Ty-Lila, County Road,

Leeswood, Mold CH7 4RF Tel: 01352 770212 — MB BS 1962 Calcutta.

BANERJEE, Soma 47 Ravenscroft Av, Wembley HA9 9TE — MB BS 1997 Lond.

BANERJEE, Somen Ranjan 300 Banbury Road, Oxford OX2 7ED — MB BS 1992 Lond. Prev: SHO Nat. Spinal Injuries Centre Stoke Mandeville Hosp.

BANERJEE, Somnath 2 Belvedere Drive, Bromsgrove B61 0AJ — MB BS 1992 Lond.

BANERJEE, Mr Soumitra Lister Hospital, Corey's Mill Lane, Stevenage SG1 4AB Tel: 01438 781101 Fax: 01462 634879 Email: judi.martin@lister.org.uk; 5 Grace Avenue, Shenley, Radlett WD7 9DN Tel: 07951 005708 — MB BS 1984 Calcutta; MB BS 1984 Calcutta; MRCOG. Cons. Obst. and Gynaecologist, Lister Hosp.. Prev: Sen. Regist., Hammersmith Hosp..

BANERJEE, Subhabrata c/o Dr S. K. Ghosh, Plumstead Medical Centre, 110 Sandy Hill Road, London SE18 7BA — MB BS 1969 Calcutta.

BANERJEE, Mr Subharun Bolland, Lawrence Road, Halifax HX3 0LW — MB BS 1967 Calcutta; FRCS Glas. 1984; FRCS Ed. 1975; DLO RCS Eng. 1983.

BANERJEE, Subhas Gastrointestinal Centre, Southern General Hospital, Govan Road, Glasgow G51 4TF — MB BS 1986 Poona; MRCP (UK) 1988.

BANERJEE, Subir Kumar 42 Hamilton Avenue, Birmingham B17 8AJ Tel: 0121 429 1913 — MB BS 1966 Calcutta.

BANERJEE, Mr Subir Kumar Sandwell District General Hospital, Lyndon, West Bromwich B71 4HJ — MB BS 1965 Calcutta; MS Calcutta 1969, MB BS 1965. Clin. Asst. (A & E) Sandwell Dist. Gen. Hosp.

BANERJEE, Subrata Sekhar Section of Old Age Psychiatry, Institute of Psychiatry, Decrespigny Park, London SE5 8AF — MB BS 1987 Lond., MSc Epidemiol. Lond. 1993; MD Lond. 1995; MRCPsych 1991. (St Thos. Hosp. Med. Sch.) Sen. Lect. (Old Age Psychiat.) Inst. of Psychiat. & Hon. Cons. Psychiat. Bethlem & Maudsley NHS Trust. Prev: Lect. (Psychiat.) Inst. Psychiat. Lond.; Research Fell. UMDS (Guy's Campus) Lond.; Regist. Rotat. (Psychiat.) Guy's Hosp. Lond.

BANERJEE, Sudipta Flat 3, 109 Clyde Road, West Didsbury, Manchester M20 2WW — MB ChB 1994 Manch. Surgic. SHO Manch. Roy. Infirm.

BANERJEE, Mr Sunil Kumar University Hospital Birmingham NHS Trust, Selly Oak Hospital, Birmingham B29 6JD Tel: 0121 627 1627 Fax: 0121 627 8294; 33 Falstaff Close, Walmley, Sutton Coldfield B76 1YG Tel: 0121 351 4053 Fax: 0121 240 2614 — MB BS 1966 Calcutta; FRCS Ed. 1978; FFAEM 1993. Cons. (A & E) Selly Oak Hosp. Birm. Socs: BMA; Brit. Assn. Accid. & Emerg. Med.; Fac. Accid. & Emerg. Med. Prev: Sen. Regist. (A & E) Derby & Nottm. Rotat.; Regist. (Trauma & Orthop.) Dudley Rd. Hosp. Birm.; RSO (Gen. Surg.) St. Cross Hosp. Rugby.

BANERJEE, Surja Sekhar, Maj. RAMC Point Gribbin, 67 Sea Road, Carlyon Bay, St Austell PL25 3SQ Tel: 01726 814815; Point Gribbin, 67 Sea Road, Carlyon Bay, St Austell PL25 3SQ Tel: 01762 814815 — MB BS 1956 Calcutta. p/t Locum GP HMP Dorset & Devon; RMO Cornw. Light Infantry; Divisonal Surg. St Johns Ambul. Socs: MDU. Prev: GP Cricklade.

BANERJEE, Tarun Kumar The Surgery, 68 Crofton Avenue, Bexley DA5 3AT Tel: 020 8303 1662 Fax: 020 8309 7773; 30 Canadian Avenue, Catford, London SE6 3AS Tel: 020 8690 3896 — MB BS 1960 Calcutta.

BANERJI, Arnab Kumar Woodridge, Nettleden Road, Little Gaddesden, Berkhamsted HP4 1PP — BM BCh 1980 Oxf.

BANERJI, Ashis 10 Front Street, Winlaton, Blaydon-on-Tyne NE21 4RD Tel: 0191 414 2339; 23 Barlow Road, Barlow, Blaydon-on-Tyne NE21 6JU Tel: 0120 74 542506 — MB BS 1953 Calcutta; DCH Eng. 1959. (R.G. Kar Med. Coll.) Socs: BMA. Prev: Regist. Geriat. Unit Newc. Gen. Hosp. & Cowley Rd. Hosp. Oxf.; Regist. (Med.) Hull A Gp. Hosps.

BANERJI, Chandana Princess of Wales Hospital, City Road, Bridgend CF31 1RQ — MB BS 1979 Calcutta; MRCPath. 1993. Cons. Microbiologist Bridgend & Dist. NHS Trust.

BANERJI, Kumaran Southlands Hospital, Shoreham-by-Sea BN43 6TQ Tel: 01273 455622 — MB BS 1965 All India Inst. Med. Scs.; DPM Eng. 1978. (All India Inst. Med. Scs.) Assoc. Specialist (Psychiat.) S.lands Hosp. Shoreham.

BANERJI, Mr Sandip 29 Broomhill Road, Ilford IG3 9SH — MB BS 1971 Delhi; FRCS Eng. 1982; FRCS Ed. 1981.

BANERJI, Susheela Flat D, 13 Benvie Rd, Dundee DD2 2LG — MB ChB 1996 Dundee.

BANFIELD, Cedric Charles Immunobiology Unit, Institute of Child Health, 30 Giulford St., London WC1N 1EH — MB BS 1991 Lond.; MSC Molecular Biol. & Biochem. (Distinc.) Lond. 1986; BSc Chem. (1st cl. Hons) Lond. 1985; MRCP (UK) 1994.

BANFIELD, Graham Kaye 7 Monck's Row, West Hill Road, London SW18 1LW — MB BS 1989 Birm.

BANFIELD, James Martin Flat 4, 14 Church Road, St Leonards-on-Sea TN37 6EF — BM 1996 Soton.

BANFIELD, Peter John, Surg. Cdr. RN Hill Land Farmhouse, Birdham, Chichester PO20 7LJ — MB BS 1959 Lond.; MRCS Eng. LRCP Lond. 1957; Dip. Ven. Liverp. 1969. (Westm.) Adviser in Venereol. to Med. Dir. Gen. (Naval). Socs: Med. Soc. Study VD. Prev: Specialist in Genitourin. Med. RN; Vice-Pres. Inst. Technicians in Venereol.; Med. Off. HMS Terror Singapore.

BANFIELD, Philip James Glan Clwyd District General Hospital NHS Trust, Bodelwyddan, Rhyl LL18 5UJ Tel: 01745 583910 Fax: 01745 583143; Dolhaiarn, Llanfair Talhaiarn, Abergele LL22 8SW Tel: 01745 720711 Fax: 01745 720711 Email: philipbanfield@hotmail.com — MB BS 1984 Lond.; MD Lond. 1994; MRCOG 1989; DA (UK) 1988. (St. Geo.) Cons. O & G Glan Clwyd Dist. Gen. Hosp. NHS Trust. Prev: Sen. Regist. (O & G) Addenbrooke's Hosp. Camb.; Research Fell. Obst. St. Mary's Hosp. Lond.; Regist. Rotat. (O & G) Basingstoke Dist. Hosp. & W.m. Hosp. Lond.

BANGA, Mr Balwant Singh 26 Ridings Close, Doncaster DN4 6UZ — MB BS 1971 Punjab; FRCS Glas. 1981; FRCS Ed. 1981; T(GP) 1993.

BANGA, Rupan 26 Ridings Close, Doncaster DN4 6UZ — MB ChB 1998 Sheff.; MB ChB Sheff 1998.

BANGAR, Vijay Calderdale Royal Infirmary, Halifax — MB ChB 1991 Birm.; MRCP UK 1995; MRCP (UK) 1995. Cons. Calderdale Roy. Infirm. Halifax W. Yorks. Prev: Specialist Regist. (Endocrinol. & Diabetes) Newcross Hosp. Wolverhampton; Specialist Regist. (Endocrinol. & Diabetes) N. Staffs. Hosp. Stoke-on-Trent; SHO (Med.) Edin. Roy. Infirm.

BANGASH, Iftikhar Hussain 42 The Blossoms, Fulwood, Preston PR2 9RF — MB BS 1974 Peshawar; MRCP (UK) 1982.

BANGAY, Arthur Paul Dorrington Castle Hill Surgery, Castle Hill Gardens, Torrington EX38 8EU Tel: 01805 623222 Fax: 01805 625069; Torridge House, Torrington EX38 8AG Tel: 01805 22562 — MRCS Eng. LRCP Lond. 1970; MRCGP 1978.

BANGERT, Stephen Keith Clinical Chemistry Department, Eastbourne General District Hospital, Kings Drive, Eastbourne BN21 2UD Tel: 01323 413742 Fax: 01323 414924 Email: stephen.bangert@virgin.net — BChir 1980 Camb.; BA 1977; MBA Keele 1997; MSc Lond. 1986; MA MB Camb. 1981; FRCPath 1997, M 1988. Cons. Chem. Path. E.bourne Hosp. NHS Trust.; Clin. Dir. (Pathol.). Socs: Fell. Roy. Soc. Med.; Assn. Clin. Biochems.; Comm. Mem. Med. Writers Gp. of the Soc. of Authors. Prev: Sen. Regist. (Chem. Path.) King's Coll. Hosp. Lond.; Sen. Regist. (Chem. Path.) Lewisham Hosp. Lond.; Regist. (Chem. Path.) & SHO (Path.) W.m. Hosp. Lond.

BANGHAM, Alec Douglas (retired) 17 High Green, Great Shelford, Cambridge CB2 5EG — MRCS Eng. LRCP Lond. 1944; FRS; MD Lond. 1966, MB BS 1946; FRCP 1997. Prev: Sen. Princip. Scientif. Off. Agric. Research Counc. Inst. of Animal.

BANGHAM, Alison Mary 4 Crown Close, Highwood Hill, London NW7 4HN Tel: 020 8959 6166 — MB BChir 1952 Camb. (Univ. Coll. Hosp.) Med. Off. Brit. Pregn. Advis. Serv. Prev: Sen. Clin. Off. Barnet DHA; Med. Off. Family Plann. Assn.; Research Asst. Hosp. Sick Childr. Gt. Ormond St. Lond.

BANGHAM, Catharine Hamilton 26 Park Lane, Norwich NR2 3EE — MB BS 1972 Lond.; DObst. RCOG 1974.

BANGHAM, Celia Elizabeth Cornwall House Surgery, Cornwall Avenue, London N3 1LD Tel: 020 8346 1976 Fax: 020 8343 3809 — MB ChB 1977 Bristol; MRCGP 1984; DFFP 1993; DRCOG 1982.

BANGHAM, Professor Charles Richard Mark River View, The Walk, Islip, Kidlington OX5 2SD — BM BCh 1980 Oxf.; PhD Counc.

Nat. Acad. Awards 1987; MA Camb. 1980; MRCP (UK) 1983; MRCPath 1992. Prof. Immunol. Imperial Coll. St. Mary's Hosp. Lond.; Hon. Cons. St. Mary's Hosp. Med. Trust. Lond. Prev: Dir. Pub. Health Laborat. John Radcliffe Hosp. Oxf.; Wellcome Trust Sen. Research Fell. Inst. Molecular Med. John Radcliffe Hosp. Oxf.; MRC Train. Fell. Nat. Inst. Med. Research Mill Hill Lond.

BANGHAM, Derek Raymond (retired) 4 Crown Close, Mill Hill, London NW7 4HN Tel: 0208 959 6166 — MB BS 1948 Lond.; FRCP Lond. 1981 M 1975. Prev: Head, Div. Hormones Nat. Inst. Biol. Standards.

BANGHAM, Lietta Caron Department of Palliative Care, The Furze, The Hillingdon Hospital, Pield Heath Road, Uxbridge UB8 3NN Tel: 01895 279412 Fax: 01895 279452 — MB ChB 1978 Bristol; MRCP (UK) 1984; FRCP Lond. 1996. Cons. Phys. Palliat. Med. The Hillingdon Hosp. Trust Mt. Vernon Hosp. & Harefield Hosp. Socs: Assn. Palliat. Med. Prev: Sen. Regist. (Palliat. Med.) Michael Sobell Hse. Mt. Vernon Hosp. Middlx.; Sen. Regist. (Haemat.) N. Middlx. Hosp. Lond.

BANGHAM, Mrs Rosalind Barbara (retired) 17 High Green, Great Shelford, Cambridge CB2 5EG Tel: 01223 843192 — MB BS 1946 Lond.

BANHAM, Michael John Fort House Surgery, 32 Hersham Road, Walton-on-Thames KT12 1JX Tel: 01932 253055 Fax: 01932 225910; 25 Rivermount, Walton-on-Thames KT12 2PR — MB BS 1969 Lond.; MRCP (UK) 1971. (St. Thos.) Prev: Ho. Surg. St. Thos. Hosp.; Ho. Off. (O & G) Lambeth Hosp.; Resid. (Med.) Toronto E. Gen. Hosp. Canada.

BANHAM, Stephen Walter 4 Heather Place, Lenzie, Glasgow G66 4UJ — MD 1987 Ed.; MB ChB 1974; FRCP Ed. 1986; MRCP (UK) 1977. Cons. Phys. Gen. & Respirat. Med. Glas. Roy. Infirm.; Hon. Clin. Lect. Univ. Glas. Socs: Brit. Thorac. Soc.; Chairm. W. Scotl. Lung Cancer Gp. Prev: Cons. Phys. Respirat. Med. Glas. Roy. Infirm. & Belvidere Hosps.

BANHATTI, Rajeev Gopal 87 Bootham Park Court, off Clarence St., York YO31 8JT — MB BS 1983 Poona; MRCPsych 1995.

BANI, Rashid Habib 35 Tudor Av, Watford WD24 7NU — MB BS 1997 Lond.

BANI-HANI, Mr Kamal Ed-Din Hussein Ali Abdulla Surgical Department, Blackburn Royal Infirmary, Blackburn BB2 3LR — MB ChB 1984 Baghdad; FRCS Glas. 1992.

BANIEGHBAL, Mr Behrouz 28 Dyke Road, Brighton BN1 3JB — MB BCh BAO 1987 NUI; FRCSI 1991.

BANIK, Jitendra Lall (retired) Royal Preston Hospital, Sharoe Green Lane, Fulwood, Preston PR2 9HT Tel: 01772 716565 — MB BS 1957 Calcutta; MCOphth 1989; DO Eng. 1960. Prev: Assoc. Specialist (Ophth.) Roy. Preston Hosp.

BANIK, Samiran Department of Pathology, Blackburn Royal Infirmary, Bolton Road, Blackburn BB2 3LR — MB BS 1961 Calcutta; FRCPath 1986, M 1975, DPath Eng. 1971. (Calcutta Med. Coll.) Cons. (Morbid Anat. & Histopath.) N. W.. RHA. Socs: Assn. Clin. Pathols. & Brit. Div. Internat. Acad. Path. Prev: Sen. Regist. (Path.) David Lewis N.. Hosp. Liverp.; Regist. (Path.) & SHO (Path.) Birch Hill Hosp. Rochdale.

BANIM, Ronan Henry 175 Winchmore Hill Road, London N21 1QN — MB BS 1993 Lond.; BSc (Hons.) Lond. 1990, MB BS 1993.

BANIM, Seamus Oliver (cons. rooms), 50 Wimpole St., London W1M 7DG Tel: 020 7486 1813 Fax: 020 7224 3282; 175 Winchmore Hill Road, London N21 1QN Tel: 020 8882 5863 Email: sbanim@cableinet.co.uk — MB BCh BAO NUI 1967; FRCP Lond. 1983; MRCP (UK) 1970. Cons. Cardiol. St. Bart. Hosp. & N. Middlx. Hosp. Lond. Socs: Fell. Roy. Soc. Med.; Brit. Cardiac Soc.; BCIS. Prev: Sen. Regist. (Cardiac) Lond. Chest Hosp.; Regist. (Med.) Char. Cross Hosp. Lond.; SHO (Cardiol.) Hammersmith Hosp. Lond.

BANISTER, Ann Downton (retired) 15 Colletts Walk, Woodbridge IP12 4HS — MB BS 1959 Lond.; MB BS (Hons. Obst. & Gyn.) 1959; MD Lond. 1973; FRCP Lond. 1983, M 1965; DObst RCOG 1960; DCH Eng. 1961. Prev: Cons. Paediat. Basildon & Thurrock Health Dist.

BANISTER, Edmund Hugo D'Alvetham (retired) The Moorings, 72 The Lynch, Winscombe BS25 1AR Tel: 01934 842120 — MRCS Eng. LRCP Lond. 1943; MA Camb.; DA Eng. 1967. Med. Asst. (Anaesth.) Winford Orthop. Hosp. & Orthop. Dept. Bristol Roy. Infirm. Prev: Ho. Surg. Roy. Surrey Co. Hosp. Guildford.

BANJEREE, Gitika Silksworth Health Centre, Silksworth, Sunderland SR3 2AN Tel: 0191 521 2282 — MB BS 1960 Calcutta. (Calcutta) GP Sunderland.

BANJO, Adeyemi Adeyinka 79 Kings Grove, London SE15 2NA — MB BS 1996 Lond.

BANKES, Mr Marcus James Kennerley Dept. of Orthopaedics, First Floor, Thomas Guy House, Guy's Hospital, St. Thomas' Street, London SE1 9RT Tel: 020 7955 5000 Ext: 5605 Fax: 020 7955 2759; 18 Howard Walk, London N2 0HB Tel: 020 8381 4551 Email: marcus@bankes.org.uk — MB BS 1991 Lond.; FRCS 1999 (Ortho.); BSc (1st. cl. Hons.) Lond. 1988; FRCS Eng. 1995. Specialist Regist. (Orthop.) Roy. Nat. Orthop. Hosp. Stanmore, Rotat. - Cons. Orthop. Surg., Guy's & St. Thomas' NHS Turst, Lond. Socs: Brit. Orthop. Assn.; Roy. Soc. of Med. Prev: SHO Rotat. (Surg.) St. Mary's Hosp.; Specialist Regist. (Orthop) Chasefarm Hosp., Enfield; Specialist Regist. (Orthop) Watford Gen. Hosp.

BANKES-PAGE CHAPMAN, Cordelia Anjali 194 Coldhams Lane, Cambridge CB1 3HH — MB ChB 1997 Leic.; BSc (Hons) Leicester 1994. (Leicester)

BANKHEAD, Keith Brian Bridge Street Medical Centre, 30 Bridge Street, Londonderry BT48 6LA Tel: 02871 261137 Fax: 02871 370723 — MB BCh BAO 1986 Belf.; MRCGP 1990; DCH Dub. 1989. (QUB) Socs: BMA; BMAS.

BANKOLE, Claire Adebolanle 39 Hazeltree Road, Hertfordshire, Watford WD2 5RH — MB ChB 1996 Leic.

BANKOLE, Michael Akintayo 119 Chalkhill Road, Wembley HA9 9AL — MB BS 1960 Lond.; MB BS (Hons.) Lond. 1960; FACS 1974. (Univ. Coll. Ibadan) Prof. Surg. Univ. Ife; Chief Cons. Paediat. Surg. Ile-Ife Univ. Hosps. Socs: Brit. Assn. Paediat. Surgs.; Fell. W. Afr. Coll. Surgs. Prev: Sen. Lect. Paediat. Surg. Univ. Ibadan & Cons. Paediat. Surg. U.C.H.; Ibadan Nigeria; Instruc. Paediat. Surg. Ohio State Univ. & Chief Resid. Paediat.

BANKOWSKA, Urszula Zofia Centre for Family Planning and Reproductive Health Sandyford init, 6 Sandyford Place, Glasgow G3 7NB Tel: 0141 211 8135 Fax: 0141 211 8139 — MB ChB 1973 Ed.; MFFP. Cons. in Family Plann. & Sexual Health; Assoc. Dir. Sandyford Initiative, Quality & Governance.

BANKS, Alan James West Pennine HA, Selbourne House, Union St., Hyde SK14 1NG Tel: 0161 368 4464; 20 The Crescent, Davenport, Stockport SK3 8SN Tel: 0161 419 9773 — MRCS Eng. LRCP Lond. 1973; Dip. Prescribing Sci Liverp. 1997. Primary Care Med. Adviser W. Pennine HA. Prev: GP Norwich.

BANKS, Alison Amanda 1 Ebenezer Road, Paignton TQ3 3RL — BM 1994 Soton.

BANKS, Amelia Candida Cottage, Heyford Road, Kirtlington, Kidlington OX5 3HL — MB BS 1996 Lond.

BANKS, Annabelle Jennifer Cynthia Dalunna — MB BS 1994 Lond.; MRCPsych 2000; BSc (Hons.) Lond. 1991. (UCMSM Lond.) SpR Gen. Adult Psychiat., Herts Partnership Trust. Prev: Psychiat. SHO Learning Disabil. (St Mary's Rotat.); Psychiat. SHO Forens., St Barth. Hosp. Lond.; Psychiat. SHO (UCH Rotat.) Various posts.

BANKS, Mr Anthony James Bank Cottage, Bolton Road, Edgworth, Turton, Bolton BL7 0DR — MRCS Eng. LRCP Lond. 1971; MSc Salford 1981; FRCS Ed. 1977. (Manch.) Cons. Orthop. Surg. Bolton Roy. Infirm.; Hon. Clin. Lect. Univ. Manch. Prev: Lect. (Orthop. Surg.) & Hon. Sen. Regist. Manch. Univ.; Regist. (Orthop.) & Regist. (Gen. Surg.) Manch. Roy. Infirm.

BANKS, Mr Archibald Walker (retired) 5 Slayleigh Avenue, Sheffield S10 3RA Tel: 0114 230 4814 — MB BS Lond. 1947; FRCS Ed. 1963; LMSSA Lond. 1944; FRCOG 1980, M 1954. Prev: Capt. RAMC E. Afr. Command.

BANKS, Arthur (retired) 16 Palmerston Lodge, Great Baddow, Chelmsford CM2 7HF Tel: 01245 472049 — MB ChB 1952 Ed.; DTM & H Eng. 1961. Prev: Princip. GP Chelmsford.

BANKS, David (retired) 28 Ashley Way, Westone, Northampton NN3 3DZ Tel: 01604 401881 Fax: 01604 408432 Email: david.banks@btinternet.com — MB BCh Wales 1960. Prev: GP N.ants.

BANKS, David Charles The Park Hospital, Nottingham NG5 8RX Tel: 0115 967 0670 Fax: 0115 967 0381; The Mill House, Caythorpe, Nottingham NG14 7ED Tel: 0115 966 3092 — MB BS 1962 Lond.; MD Lond. 1973; FRCP Lond. 1979, M 1966; MRCS Eng. LRCP Lond. 1962. (Lond. Hosp.) Emerit. Cons. Phys. Nottm. City Hosp. Trust; Fell. Univ. Nottm.; JP. Socs: Brit. Cardiac Soc.;

Hon. Mem. Ceylon Coll. Phys.; Assn. Phys. Prev: Cons. Phys. City Hosp. Nottm. & Dist. Gen. Manager Nottm. HA; Cons. Phys. & Unit Gen. Manager City Hosp. Nottm.; Sen. Lect. (Therap.) Nottm. Univ.

BANKS, David Shewell Arrowe Park General Hospital, Arrowe Park Road, Upton, Wirral CH49 5PE Tel: 0151 678 5111 Email: banksey@pyteeoh.demon.co.uk; Flat 14, Heathfield, Croft Avenue E., Bromborough, Wirral CH62 2HE Tel: 0151 343 1101 Fax: 0870 161 7209 — MB BChir 1992 Camb.; MA Camb. 1993; MRCP (UK) 1997; DA (UK) 1994. (Addenbrooke's Camb.) SHO Anaesth., Countess of Chester Hosp. Chester. Prev: SHO Med. Rotat. N. Manch. Gen. Hosp.; SHO (Anaesth.) Leighton Hosp. Crewe; SHO (A & E) Roy. Preston Hosp.

BANKS, Desmond Clifton Fyers Dromore House, 3 Laburnum Grove, Cleadon Village, Sunderland SR6 7RJ Tel: 0191 536 7864 — MB BCh BAO 1957 Dub.; MA, MD (Anaesth.) Dub. 1957, MB BCh BAO 1946; DA Eng. 1956. (T.C. Dub.) Cons. Anaesth. S. Shields Hosp. Gp. Socs: Fell. Assn. Anaesths.; BMA. Prev: Attend. Anaesth. Univ. Hosp. Bellvue Med. Centre, New York; Regist. (Anaesth.) Hammersmith Hosp. Postgrad. Med. Sch. Lond. & Dulwich Hosp. Gp.

BANKS, Emily Imperial Cancer Research Fund, Cancer Epidemiology Unit, Gibson Building, Radcliffe Infirmary, Oxford OX2 6HE Tel: 01865 311933 Fax: 01865 310545; 108 Hurst Street, Oxford OX4 1HG — MB BS 1993 Monash. Clin. Research Fell. (Epidemiol.) Imperial Cancer Research Fund Oxf.

BANKS, Ian Christopher 38 Briony Avenue, Hale, Altrincham WA15 8QD — MB BS 1987 Lond.; FRCA. 1992.

BANKS, Ian George 40 Grove Road, Ballynahinch BT24 8PW — MB BCh BAO 1987 Belf.

BANKS, Mr James Gillies Accident & Emergency Department, University Hospital of North Durham, North Road, Durham DH1 5TW Tel: 0191 333 2333 Fax: 0191 333 2697; 1 Crossgate Moor Gardens, Durham DH1 4HS Tel: 0191 384 1885 — MB ChB 1972 Ed.; FRCS Ed. 1977; FRCS Glas. 1977; FFAEM 1993. (Edinburgh) Cons. A & E Med., Univ. Hosp. of N. Durh., Durh. City N. RHA. Prev: Lect. Surg. (A & E) Univ. Manch.; Research Regist. Shock Study Gp.; Univ. Dept. Surg. W.. Infirm. Glas.

BANKS, James Noel (retired) Kelsale Court Home, Kelsale, Saxmundham IP17 2QU Tel: 01728 603439 — MB ChB 1923 Ed.; DTM & H Eng. 1925. Prev: Flight Lt. RAFVR.

BANKS, Janet 68 Brougham Road, Marsden, Huddersfield HD7 6BJ — MB BS 1963 Lond.; MRCS Eng. LRCP Lond. 1963.

BANKS, John Singleton Hospital, Swansea SA2 8QA Tel: 01792 205666 Fax: 01792 285329 — MB ChB 1975 Manch.; MD Manch 1988; FRCP Lond. 1997. (Manch.) Cons. Phys. (Gen. & Respirat. Med.) Singleton Hosp. Swansea. Socs: BMA; Brit. Thorac. Soc.; Welsh Thoracic Soc. Prev: Sen. Regist. (Gen. & Thoracic Med. & HIV) Llandough Hosp. Cardiff, Univ. Hosp. Wales Cardiff, Roy. Gwent & St. Woolos Hosp. Newport.

BANKS, John Christopher 8 Whitefield Neuk, Dunfermline KY12 0RJ — MB ChB 1998 Ed.; MB ChB Ed 1998.

BANKS, John Crispin Dunlop Eastgate Surgery, York Place, Knaresborough HG5 0AD Tel: 01423 557200 Fax: 01423 557201; 1A Scriven Road, Knaresborough HG5 9EQ — MB ChB 1988 Leeds; MRCGP 1994; DRCOG 1992.

BANKS, Judith Claire Anaesthetic Dept., William Harvey Hospital, Kennington Road, Asmford, Ashford TN24 0LZ Tel: 01233 616041; Email: judith@newbank.demon.co.uk — MB BS 1989 Lond.; FRCA 1996; DA (UK) 1994. Cons. Anaesth. William Harvey Hosp. Ashford. Prev: Regist. (Anaesth.) N.. & Yorks. RHA; Specialist Regis. (Anaesth) S.E. Thames.

BANKS, Judith Elizabeth (retired) Medical Centre, Main St., E. Bridgford, Nottingham NG13 8NH Tel: 01949 20216 — MB BS 1962 Lond.; MRCS Eng. LRCP Lond. 1962.

BANKS, Lionel Claude, OBE, Surg. Capt. RN 15 Carthew Villas, Hammersmith, London W6 0BS Tel: 020 8741 3070 — MB BCh BAO 1954 Belf.; FFCM 1987, M 1974. Assoc. Prof. Community Med. Quaboos Univ., Oman. Socs: Fell. Roy. Soc. Med. Prev: Dir. Med. Serv. Sultan of Oman's Forces Muscat; Dir. Med. Organisation (NAVAL) & Dep. Dir. Med. Policy & Plans MoD.

BANKS, Matthew John 6 Topsham Croft, Topsham, Birmingham B14 6UF — MB ChB 1990 Birm.; ChB Birm. 1990.

BANKS, Matthew Rupert Flat 1, 255 Goldhurst Terrace, London NW6 3EP Tel: 020 7624 3237 — MB BS 1992 Lond.; BSc Hons Lond. 1990; MRCP Lond. 1995. (University College London) Specialist Regist. The Homerton & St. Bartholomews Hosp. Prev: Specialist Regist. S.end Gen. Hosp.

BANKS, Paul Alan 84 Erlanger Road, Telegraph Hill, London SE14 5TH Tel: 020 7639 0500 — MB BS 1988 Lond.

BANKS, Mr Peter Falconwood House, Groombridge, Tunbridge Wells TN3 9SH Tel: 01892 861532 Email: peter.bank@btinternet.com — MB BS 1964 Lond.; MRCS Eng. LRCP Lond. 1964; FDS RCS Eng. 1961; FRCS Ed. 1991. (Guy's) p/t Cons. Oral Surg. Qu. Vict. Hosp. Grinstead & E.man Dent. Hosp. Lond. Socs: IADMS (Past Pres.); BDA. Prev: Sen. Regist. Qu. Vict. Hosp. E. Grinstead; Regist. E.man Dent. Hosp.; Cons. Dent. Surg. PeterBoro. Dist. & United Camb. Hosp. Gp.

BANKS, Peter Charles The Leeds Road Practice, 49-51 Leeds Road, Harrogate HG2; 14 Kenilworth Avenue, Harrogate HG2 8DB — MB BS 1988 Lond.; MRCGP 1995; DRCOG. (Roy. Free Sch. Med. Lond.) Prev: Trainee GP Harrogate VTS.

BANKS, Rebecca Helen 14 Pennine Close, Manchester M9 6HR — MB ChB 1997 Liverp.

BANKS, Richard Anthony Gloucester Royal Hospital, Great Western Road, Gloucester GL1 3NN Tel: 01452 528555; Verona, Pirton Lane, Churchdown, Gloucester GL3 2QE Tel: 01452 713892 Email: r.banks@virgin.net — MRCS Eng. LRCP Lond. 1971; MD Lond. 1983, BSc (Hons.) 1967, MB BS 1971; FRCP Lond. 1991; MRCP (UK) 1975. Cons. Phys. Gloucester Roy. Hosp. Socs: Renal Assn.; Brit. Hypertens. Soc. Prev: Sen. Regist. (Renal Med. & Gen. Med.) S.mead Hosp. & Bristol Roy. Infirm.

BANKS, Robert Alan Kent & Sussex Hospital, Mount Ephraim, Tunbridge Wells TN4 8AT Tel: 01892 526111 Fax: 01892 520088 — MB BS 1972 Lond.; BSc Lond. 1969; FRCP Lond. 1993; MRCP (UK) 1975. (Middlesex Hosp. Medical School.) Cons. Phys. Maidstone and Kent and Sussex NHS Trust, Pembury Hosp., Pembury, Kent; CONS Phys. Qu. Vict. NHS Trust, Holtye Rd, E. Grinstead, W. Sussex. Socs: Brit. Thorac. Soc.; Intens. Ther. Soc. Prev: Lect. & Regist. (Med.) Middlx. Hosp. Lond.; SHO (Med.) Dudley Rd. Hosp. Brim.

BANKS, Roger Conwy and Denbighshire (NHS) Trust, Gwynfryn Unit, Nantglyn Road, Denbigh LL16 5SS Tel: 01745 815291 Email: rogerbanks@doctors.org.uk — MB ChB 1982 Sheff.; MRCPsych 1987. Cons. Psychiat. (Learn. Disabil.) Conwy & Denbighsh. (NHS) Trust. Socs: BMA. Prev: Cons. Psychiat (Learn. Disabil.) N. Mersey Community (NHS) Trust; Cons. Psychiat (Learn. Disabil.) Serv. Sheff.; Lect. & Sen. Regist. (Psychiat.) Ment. Handicap Univ. Sheff.

BANKS, Thomas Wilson Forrest Dunvegan Medical Practice, Tullochard, Dunvegan, Isle of Skye IV55 8GU Tel: 01470 521203 — MB ChB 1978 Aberd.; MRCGP 1987.

BANKS, Victoria Anne Gosport War Memorial Hospital, Bury Road, Gosport PO12 3PW Tel: 02392 603267 Fax: 02392 584062 — MB BS 1981 Lond.; MRCGP 1986; MRCPsych 1989. Cons. Psychiat. of Old Age Gosport War Memor. Hosp.

BANKS-SMITH, Heather Ruth, MBE (retired) Mill Cottage, Rushden, Buntingford SG9 0TA Tel: 01763 288231 — MB BS 1952 Lond.; MRCS Eng. LRCP Lond. 1952.

BANKY, Eva Judith East Surrey Hospital, & Community Health Care NHS Trust, Maple House, Three Arch Road, Redhill RH1 5RH; 10 The Chase, Reigate RH2 7DH Tel: 01737 765859 — MB BS 1963 Lond.; MRCS Eng. LRCP Lond. 1961; DPH Eng. 1970. (St. Bart.) Sen. Med. Off. (Audiol.) Surrey AHA. Socs: Fac. Pub. Health Med. & Brit. Soc. Audiol. Prev: Clin. Med. Off. E. Surrey Health Dist.; SHO & Ho. Surg. Redhill Gen. Hosp.; JHMO Netherne Hosp. Coulsdon.

BANKY, Peter Ivan, SBStJ (retired) 10 The Chase, Reigate RH2 7DH Email: pbanky2821@aol.com — MB BS 1961 Lond.; MRCS Eng. LRCP Lond. 1961; MRCGP 1970; DHMSA Lond. 1979; DObst RCOG 1965. Disabil. Analyst; Surg., HQ Staff. Prev: Manager (Med. Servs.) DSS (BAMS).

BANN, Richard Frank Yeomans Cottage, Paddle Lake Lane, Bugford, Dartmouth — MB ChB 1962 Sheff.; DObst RCOG 1964; MRCGP 1968. (Sheff.)

BANN, Simon David 20 Ainsley Street, London E2 0DL — MB BS 1993 Lond.; BSc (Hons.) Pharmacol. Lond. 1988, MB BS 1993.

BANNA, Mr Antoine Layer Road Surgery, Colchester CO2 9LA Tel: 01206 546494 Fax: 01206 369912 Email: antoine.banna@gp_fp1109.nhs.uk; Toftwood, Layer Rd, Colchester

CO2 9LA Tel: 01206 760860 — MD 1971. (Damascas University 1971) Principal Gen. Pract., Colchester. Prev: Clin. Asst. Obst. & Gyn.

BANNAR-MARTIN, Brian Rawdon St Mary's Medical Centre, Vicarage Road, Strood, Rochester ME2 4DG Tel: 01634 291299/291266 Fax: 01634 295752; 132 Gravesend Road, Strood, Rochester ME2 3QT Tel: 01634 716070 — MB BCh BAO 1971 Dub.; MRCGP 1979; DObst RCOG 1974; DCH Eng. 1975. (TC Dub.)

BANNATYNE, Douglas Finlay The Surgery, 54 Church Avenue, Harrogate HG1 4HG Tel: 01432 564168 Fax: 01432 501102; 40 Westminster Crescent, Burnbridge, Harrogate HG3 1LY — MB ChB 1980 Ed.; MRCP (UK) 1983; MRCGP 1985. Prev: SHO (Med.) Dist. Hosp. Gorleston; SHO Rotat. (Med.) Dudley Rd. Hosp. Birm.

BANNATYNE, Robert Alexander Henry (retired) 3 Glasgow Road, Paisley PA1 3QS Tel: 0141 2604 — MB ChB 1945 Glas.

BANNATYNE, William (retired) 69 Moston Lane E., Manchester M40 0JP Tel: 0161 681 7287 — LRCP LRCS 1913 Ed.; LRCP LRCS Ed. LRFPS Glas. 1913.

BANNELL, Kathryn Judith Flat 2, 28 Villiers Road, Southsea PO5 2HQ — BM 1993 Soton. SHO (Med.) Roy. Bournemouth Hosp. Socs: BMA; Med. Protec. Soc. Prev: Ho. Off. (Surg.) Qu. Alexandra Hosp. Portsmouth; Ho. Off. (Med.) Roy. Hants. Co. Hosp. Winchester.

BANNER, Anne Veronica Old Fletton Surgery, Rectory Gardens, Old Fletton, Peterborough PE2 8AY Tel: 01733 343137 Fax: 01733 894739; Virginia Cottage, 6 Glinton Road, Helpston, Peterborough PE6 7DQ Tel: 01733 252294 — BM BS 1986 Nottm.; BMedSci Nottm. 1984; MRCGP 1990. (Nottm.) GP Asst.,. Prev: Trainee GP P'boro. VTS; Ho. Surg. Derbysh. Roy. Infirm.; Ho. Off. (Med.) Nottm. City Hosp.

BANNER, Beryl Hefina Ty Rhosyn, 64 Bathurst Wk., Iver SL0 9EQ Tel: 01753 818406 — MB BCh 1957 Wales; DPH Eng. 1967; DCH Eng. 1961; DObst RCOG 1960. (Cardiff) SCMO Hillingdon Health Auth. Prev: Ho. Phys. St. David's Hosp. Cardiff; Ho. Surg. (O & G) Bridgend Gen. Hosp.; Regist. (Paediat.) Edgware Gen. Hosp.

BANNER, Claire Victoria Park Lane House Medical Centre, 187 Park Lane, Macclesfield SK11 6UD Tel: 01625 422893 Fax: 01625 424870 — MB ChB 1980 Manch.; MRCGP 1988; DCH RCP Lond. 1983; DRCOG 1983.

BANNER, John Victor (retired) Bramble Cottage, Retirement Home, 18 Carden Avenue, Patcham, Brighton BN1 8NA Tel: 01273 553484 — MRCS Eng. LRCP Lond. 1925; MRCGP 1953. Prev: Ho. Surg. & Cas. Ho. Surg. Gen. Hosp. Croydon.

BANNER, Nicholas Robert Harefield Hospital, Harefield, Uxbridge UB9 6JH Tel: 01895 823737 Fax: 01895 828556 — BM 1980 Soton.; BM (Hons.) Soton. 1980; FRCP Lond. 1996; MRCP (UK) 1983; FESC 1997. Cons. Roy. Brompton & Harefield NHS Trust. Prev: Sen. Lect. Imperial Coll. Sch. of Med.; Lect. Nat. Heart & Lung Inst. Lond.; Regist. (Cardiol. & Med.) Harefield Hosp.

BANNER, Rosemary Weetman 9 Arlington Drive, Mapperly Park, Nottingham NG3 5EN — MB BS 1965 Lond.; MRCS Eng. LRCP Lond. 1965; DO Eng. 1968. (St. Geo.)

BANNERJEE, Dave Bratt 10 Rectory Park, Morpeth NE61 2SZ — MB BS 1958 Lucknow; FRCP Lond. 1979, M 1967; DCH Eng. 1961. (K.G. Med. Coll. Lucknow) Cons. Phys. Wansbeck Gp. Hosps.

BANNERMAN-LLOYD, Frank Rushton Medical Centre, 6 Rushton St., London N1 5DR Tel: 020 7739 5164 Fax: 020 7329 5166; 12 Dale Lodge, Shepherds Hill, Highgate, London N6 5RL Tel: 020 8348 8026 Fax: 020 8374 2915 Email: fbanner@ibm.net — MB BS 1958 Lond.; MRCS Eng. LRCP Lond. 1958. (St. Bart.)

BANNING, Adrian Paul Department of Cardiology, John Radcliffe Hospital, Headington, Oxford Tel: 01865 228934 Fax: 01865 220585 Email: adrianbanning@orh.uk — MB BS 1987 Lond.; FESC (Fellow Europ. Soc. Of Cardiology) 2001; MD Lond. 1995; MRCP (UK) 1990. Cons. Cardiol. John Radcliffe Hosp. Oxf. Socs: Brit. Cardiac Soc.; Brit. Cardiac Interven. Soc.; Europ. Cardiac Soc. Working Gp. Valvular Heart Diosease. Prev: Sen. Regist. John Radcliffe Hosp, Oxf.; SHO (Med.) Ashford Hosp. Middx.; SHO (Nephrol.) Roy. Free Hosp. Lond.

BANNING, Michael Derek Brimington Surgery, Church Street, Brimington, Chesterfield S43 1JG Tel: 01246 273224 Fax: 01246 556616 — MB ChB 1984 Sheff. SHO (Geriat.) Huddersfield Roy. Infirm. Prev: SHO (Gen. Med.) Huddersfield Roy. Infirm.; SHO (ENT) & Ho. Phys. Barnsley Dist. Gen. Hosp.

BANNISTER, Miss Barbara Ann Royal Free Department Infection & Tropical Disease, Royal Free Hospital, Pond St, London NW3 2QG Tel: 020 8883 9792 Fax: 020 8444 3207 — MRCS Eng. LRCP Lond. 1972; MB BS Lond. 1972; MSc Lond. 1984, BSc 1969; FRCP Lond. 1990; MRCP (UK) 1975. (Roy. Free) Cons. Phys. Roy. Free Hosp. Lond; Hon. Cons. Communicable Dis. Surveillance Centre Lond. Socs: (Ex.-Hon. Treas.) Brit. Infec. Soc.; Internat. Soc. Infec. Dis.; Eur. Soc. Clin. Virol. Prev: Lect. (Med. Microbiol.) Lond. Hosp. Med. Coll. & St. Bart. Hosp. Lond.; Sen. Regist. (Med.) Roy. Free Hosp.; Mem. Edit. Bd. Jl. Infec.

BANNISTER, Carol Lesley 9 Elmwood Court, Poplar Road, Stretford, Manchester M32 9AN — MB ChB 1986 Leic.

BANNISTER, Carys Margaret Department of Neurological Surgery, Manchester Royal Infirmary, Manchester M13 Tel: 0161 276 1234 — MB BS 1958 (Hons. Surg.) Lond.; BSc Oxf. 1966; FRCS Ed. 1966. (Char. Cross) Cons. Neurol. Surg. N. Manch. Gen. Hosp. Socs: Soc. Brit. Neurol. Surgs. Prev: Sen. Regist. (Neurosurg.) Leeds Gen. Infirm.; Ho. Surg. Char. Cross Hosp. Lond.; SHO Birm. Accid. Hosp.

BANNISTER, Mr Gordon Campbell Harry Griffiths Room, Southmead Hospital, Westbury-on-Trym, Bristol BS10 5NB Tel: 0117 959 5195 Fax: 0117 950 0297; 19 Cranbrook Road, Redland, Bristol BS6 7BL — MB ChB 1974 Birm.; MD Bristol 1994; MChOrth. Liverp. 1983; FRCS Ed. (Orth.) 1985; FRCS Eng. 1979; FRCS Ed. 1979. Cons. S.mead Hosp. Bristol. Socs: Fell. BOA; Eur. Hip Soc. (Sec. Gen.); Brit. Hip Soc. Prev: Resid. (Orthop. Surg.) Vancouver Gen. Hosp., Canada; Sen. Lect. & Lect. (Orthop.) Univ. Bristol.

BANNISTER, Mr Jeremy James Barnsley District General Hospital, Gawber Road, Barnsley S75 2EP Tel: 01226 777888 Fax: 01226 777873; Langkawi, 121 Manchester Rd, Ranmoor, Sheffield S10 5DN — MB BS 1977 Lond.; BA (Hons.) (Nat. Sc.) Camb. 1971, MA 1976; MD Lond. 1988; FRCS Eng. 1982. (St Thomas' University of London) Cons. Gen. Surg. Barnsley Dist. Gen. Hosp.; Lead Clinician (Cancer Serv.) Barnsley Dist.; Dep. Lead Clinician (Cancer Serv.s) N. Trent Cancer Network; Mem. Bd. of Trustees, Barnsley Hospice. Socs: Fell. Roy. Soc. Med.; Brit. Soc. Gastroenterol.; Assn. Coloproctol. Prev: Sen. Regist. (Gen. Surg.) Sheff. & Chesterfield Hosps.; Resid. Surg. Off. St. Marks Hosp. Lond.; Regist. (Surg.) St. Thos. Hosp. Lond.

BANNISTER, Jonathan Department of Anaesthetics, Ninewells Hospital and Medical School, Dundee DD1 9SY Tel: 01382 660111 Fax: 01382 644914 Email: j.bannister@tuht.scot.nhs.uk — MB ChB 1980 Sheff.; FFA RCS Eng. 1987. Cons. Anaesth. Ninewells Hosp. Dundee. Socs: Assn. Anaesth. GB & Irel.; NE Scotl. Soc. Anaesth.; Amer. Soc. Regional Anaesth. Prev: Clin. Research Fell. (Anaesth.) Roy. Infirm. Edin.; Regist. (Anaesth.) Edin. Roy. Infirm.; SHO (Med. & Anaesth.) Sheff. HA.

BANNISTER, Mark Careitha, Lower Loxhore, Barnstaple EX31 4SY Tel: 01271 850547; 37 St. Augustine Road, Heath, Cardiff CF14 4BE Tel: 01222 521604 Fax: 01222 521604 — MB ChB 1990 Liverp.; FRCA, 1998; MRCGP 1994. Specialist Regist. (Anaesth.) Univ. Hosp. of Wales Cardiff.

BANNISTER, Nicolette Joan 249 Thorpe Hall Av., Southend-on-Sea SS1 3SG — MB ChB 1980 Dundee; MRCP (UK) 1984. Regist. (Geriat. Med.) Addenbrooke's Hosp. Camb.

BANNISTER, Paul Dept. of Medicine, Manchester Royal Infirmary, Manchester M13 9WL; 34 Morningside Drive, Manchester M20 5PL — MB ChB 1979 Leeds; BSc Leeds 1976; MRCP (UK) 1982. Cons. Gen. Med. Manch. Roy. Infirm.; Research Fell. Dept. Med. St. Jas. Univ. Hosp. Leeds.

BANNISTER, Ralph Victor (retired) 174 Ansley Road, Stockingford, Nuneaton CV10 8NU Tel: 01203 388555 — MB ChB 1942 Glas. Prev: Ho. Surg. Glas. Eye Infirm.

BANNISTER, Sir Roger (Gilbert), CBE (retired) 21 Bardwell Road, Oxford OX2 6SU Tel: 01865 511413 — MRCS Eng. LRCP Lond. 1954; MA Oxf. 1953, MSc 1952; Hon. DSc Jyvaskyla, Finland 1982; Hon. DSc Sheff. 1978; Hon. LLD Liverp. 1973; Hon. D Laws Victoria, Canada 1994; Hon. DMed Pavia 1986; FRCP Lond. 1969, M 1957; DM Oxf. 1963, BM BCh 1955; Hon. DSc E. Anglia Univ. 1997; Hon. DSc Loughborough 1996; Hon. DSc Univ. Wales 1994; Hon. DSc Williams Coll. USA 1987; Hon. DSc Rochester USA 1985; Hon. DSc Grinnell USA 1984; Hon. DSc Bath 1984. Hon. Cons. Phys. Nat. Hosp. Qu. Sq. & Hon. Cons. Nerv. Dis. St. Mary's Hosp.

Lond.; Hon. Cons. Neurol. Oxf. Regional & Dist. HA; Fell. Imperial Coll. Sci. Technol. & Med.; Hon. Fell. Merton Coll. Oxf. 1986; Hon. Fell. Manch. Inst. Sc. & Technol. & Exeter Coll. Oxf. Prev: Resid. Med. Off. & Sen. Regist. Univ. Dept. Clin. Neurol. Nat. Hosp. Qu. Sq. Lond.

BANNOCK, Anne Elizabeth Audrey 10 Sefton Street, Southport PR8 6SL — MB ChB 1990 Manch.

BANNON, Colin Francis Stoke Hill Cottage, Stoke Hill Lane, Crapstone, Yelverton PL20 7PP Tel: 01822 855169 — MB ChB 1985 Sheff.

BANNON, Dominick 20 Lismoyle Park, Belfast BT15 5HF — MB BCh BAO 1955 NUI.

BANNON, John Joseph Edward Penketh Health Centre, Honiton Way, Penketh, Warrington WA5 2EY Tel: 01925 725644 Fax: 01925 791017 — MB BCh BAO 1988 NUI; MRCGP 1995; DRCOG 1993; DCH RCP Lond. 1991. (Trinity Coll. Dub.)

BANNON, Luke 7 The Woodlands, Pudding Wood Lane, Broomfield, Chelmsford CM1 7ES Fax: 01245 514507 Email: lukebannon@hotmail.com; 7 The Woodlands, Pudding Wood Lane, Broomfield, Chelmsford CM1 7ES Fax: 01245 514507 — MB BS 1996 Lond. (London) SHO (Anaesth.) Chelmsford Hosp. Prev: Ho. Off. (Med.) S.end Hosp.; Ho. Off. (Surgic.) Roy. Lond. Hosp.

BANNON, Michael John Patrick — MB BS 1992 Lond.; DRCOG 1995; MRCGP 1996. (Charing Cross & Westm.) Salaried PMS GP, Morden Hill Surg., Lewisham. Socs: BMA & Med. Defence Union. Prev: GP Assoc., Lambeth S.wark & Lewisham; GP Regist. Clapham Pk. Surg.; SHO (O & G & Psych.) Chelsea & W.. Hosp.

BANNON, Michael Joseph 25 Thames Crescent, Chiswick, London W4 2RU — MA Dub. 1992, MB BCh BAO 1978; FRCPI 1993, M 1983; DCH Dub. 1979. Cons. Community Paediat. S. Warks.; Sen. Lect. Univ. Warwick. Prev: SCMO Warrington HA.

BANNON, Roy Peter 79 Raingate Street, Bury St Edmunds IP33 2AR — MB BS 1973 Lond.; BSc Hull 1968; MRCS Eng. LRCP Lond. 1973; FRCR 1982; DCH Eng. 1975; DMRD 1981. (Lond. Hosp.) Cons. Radiol. The W. Suff. Hosp. Bury St. Edmonds. Prev: Radiol. RAF Hosp. Ely.

BANNOURRAH, Faiz Elias Abdalleh 10 Wollescote Drive, Solihull B91 3YN — MB ChB 1978 Mosul; FFA RCSI 1987.

BANSAL, Amolak Singh Department of Immunology, St Helier NHS Trust, Carshalton SM5 1AA Tel: 0208 8296 2805 Fax: 0208 641 9193; 33 Tadorne Road, Tadworth KT20 5TF — BM 1982 Soton.; DM 1998; FRACP 1996; FRCPA 1996; MRCPath 1993; MRCP (UK) 1986; MRCGP 1986; DCH RCP Lond. 1986; DRCOG 1985. Cons. Clin. Immunol. & Immunopath.; Cons. Clin. Immunol. and ImmunoPath., Immunol. & Allergy, Kingston Hosp., Kingston, Surrey. Prev: Sen. Lect. Univ. of Qu.sland Aust.

BANSAL, Anil Balfour Medical Centre, 2 Balfour Road, Grays RM17 5NS Tel: 01375 373366 Fax: 01375 394562; Rivendell, Albert Road, Bulphan, Upminster RM14 3SB Tel: 01375 891007 Fax: 01375 890121 — MB BS 1973 Lucknow. (King Geo. Med. Coll.) LMC Mem. Prev: GP Trainee Chorlton-on-Medlock; SHO (Cas.) Orsett Hosp. Grays Essex; SHO (Psychiat.) Gen. Hosp. St. Helier.

BANSAL, Anita 1 Saint Peters Road, Bury BL9 9RA — MB ChB 1996 Leeds. SHO (A & E) Pinderfields Gen. Hosp. Wakefield Yorks. Prev: SHO (c/o the Elderly); Ho. Off. (Gen. Med./Cardiol.); Ho. Off. (Gen. Surg.).

BANSAL, Bina 38 The Birches, Priory Lane, South Wootton, King's Lynn PE30 3JG Tel: 01553 673284 — MB BS 1969 Rajasthan; MS Rajasthan 1972, MB BS 1969. (S.M.S. Med. Coll. Jaipur) SHO (Cas.) N. Cambs. Hosp. Wisbech.

BANSAL, Narinder 7 Old Quarry Drive, Upper Gornal, Dudley DY3 3XS — MB ChB 1995 Leic.

BANSAL, Om Prakash Arrowe Park Hospital, Upton, Wirral CH49 5PE Tel: 0151 678 5111; 3 Woodbank Park, Oxton, Birkenhead CH43 9WN — MB BS 1971 Rajasthan; FFA RCSI 1984; DA (UK) 1981. Assoc. Specialist Arrowe Pk. Hosp. Wirral. Socs: BMA (Sec. Mersey NCCGD's Sub Comm.); BMA (CCSC Anaesthetic Sub Comm.). Prev: Cons. Anaesth. Dammam KSA.

BANSAL, Mr Parvin 35 Parklands Way, Hartlepool TS26 0AP Tel: 0976 614907 Email: parvin.bansal@ncl.ac.uk — MB BS 1994 Newc.; FRCS Eng. 1998. Specialist Regist. Trauma & Orthop. N.ern. Deanery. Prev: SHO (Gen. Surg.) RVI Newc.; SHO (Orthop. & Trauma) Sunderland DGH; SHO (Paediat. Surg.) RVI Newc. uponTyne.

BANSAL, Rajinder Knowle Green Surgery, Staines Health Centre, Knowle Green, Staines TW18 1XD Tel: 01784 883654 Fax: 01784 441244; Deepwaters, 22 Thameside, Staines TW18 2HA Tel: 01784 883650 — MB BS 1963 Panjab; MB BS Panjab (India) 1963; DObst 1969; FRCOG 1997. (Govt. Med. Coll. Patiala) Socs: Fell. Roy. Coll. Obst. & Gyn. Prev: SHO (Gen. Surg.) E. Birm. Gp. Hosps.; Regist. (O & G) Walsgrave Hosp. Coventry & PeterBoro. Dist. Hosp.

BANSAL, Sajive Nuffield House Surgery, The Stow, Harlow CM20 3AX Tel: 01279 425661 Fax: 01279 427116; 90 Copse Hill, Harlow CM19 4PP Tel: 01279 419377 Fax: 01279 419377 Email: sajivebansal@compuserve.com — MB ChB 1989 Manch.; MRCGP 1994; DRCOG 1993.

BANSAL, Sushil Kumar Sunderland Royal Hospital, Kayll Road, Sunderland SR4 7TP Tel: 0191 565 6256 — MD 1972 Allahabad; BSc Agra 1964; FRCP Lond. 1992; FRCP Ed. 1988; MRCP (UK) 1977; MRCPI 1977. (MLN Medical College, Allahabad) Cons. Phys. (Med. for Elderly) Sunderland HA; Clin. Lect. (Geriat. Med.) Univ. Newc. u Tyne.; Vis. Prof. (Med.), Himalayan Inst., Dehradun, India; Princip. Lect. (HON) Sunderland Univ.

BANSAL, Vijay Kumar Penketh Health Centre, Honiton Way, Penketh, Warrington WA5 2EY Tel: 01925 725644 Fax: 01925 791017; 14 Hilltop Road, Grappenhall, Warrington WA4 2ED Tel: 01925 63390 Fax: 01925 791017 — MB BS 1968 Delhi. (M.A. Med. Coll.)

BANSEL, Ajaib The Medical Centre, 10 Richmond Road, Pevensey Bay, Pevensey BN24 6AQ Tel: 01323 465100 Fax: 01323 465108; 243 Eastbourne Road, Polegate BN26 5DL — MB BS 1976 Lond.; BSc (Hons.) Biochem. Lond. 1973; MRCS Eng. LRCP Lond. 1976; MRCGP 1983; Dip. Pract. Dermat. Wales 1994; DCH RCP Lond. 1983; DRCOG 1982; DA (UK) 1980. (St. Bart.) Prev: Trainee GP E.bourne VTS.

BANSEL, Jatindar Kaur 107 College Road, London NW10 5EY — MB BS 1992 Lond.

BANSEL, Jerbinder Kaur The Surgery, 153 Grove Lane, Handsworth, Birmingham B20 2HE Tel: 0121 554 2493 — MB BS 1973 Banaras Hindu; DObst RCOG 1976. (Inst. Med. Sc. Varanasi)

BANSEL, Jernail Singh The Surgery, 153 Grove Lane, Handsworth, Birmingham B20 2HE Tel: 0121 554 2493 — MB BS 1973 Banaras.

BANSI, Devinder Singh Flat 3 Pinehurst Court, Bassett Row, Bassett, Southampton SO16 7FT — BM 1988 Soton.; MRCP (UK) 1992. Research Regist. (Gastroenterol.) John Radcliffe Hosp. Oxf. Prev: Regist. (Med.) Roy. Hants. Co. Hosp. Winchester; SHO Rotat. (Med.) Soton. Gen. Hosp.

BANSTEAD, Catherine Ann 5 Toy Lane, Worcester Road, Chipping Norton OX7 5FH — MB BCh 1985 Wales.

BANT, Wendy Pamela (retired) Overdale, 2 Harrison Lane, Sheffield S10 4PA Tel: 0114 305896 — MD Sheff. 1977, MB ChB 1967; MRCPsych 1972; DPM Eng. 1970; DObst RCOG 1969. Prev: Cons. Psychiat. for the Elderly N. Gen. Hosp. Sheff..

BANTICK, Mr Giles Lawrence Longstone, High Drive, Woldingham, Caterham CR3 7ED Tel: 0188 365 3307 — MB BS 1989 Lond.; FRCS Eng. 1993. Research Fell. (Plastic Surg.) Mass. Gen. Hosp. & Shriners Burns Inst. Boston, Mass., USA. Prev: SHO Rotat. (Surg.) Frenchay Hosp. Bristol; SHO (A & E) S.end Hosp.; Demonst. (Anat.) Qu. Mary & W.field Coll. Lond.

BANTICK, Ralph Alexander Imperial College of Medicine, PET Neuroscience Group, Cyclotron Unit, The Hammersmith Hospital, Du Cane Road, London W12 0NN Tel: 020 8383 3162 Fax: 020 8383 2029 Email: rabantick@doctors.org.uk — MB BS 1992 Lond.; MRCPsych 1999; BSc Lond. 1989; MRCP (UK) 1995. Wellcome Clin. Research Train. Fell., The Cyclotron Unit, The Hammersmith Hosp., Lond.; Hon. Specialist Regist. in Gen. Adult Psychiat., The Warneford Hosp., Oxf. Prev: Fulbourn Hosp. Camb.

BANTOCK, Alastair Munro Granville (retired) 78 High Street, Ecton, Northampton NN6 0QB — BM BCh Oxf. 1959; MA Oxf. 1959; DObst RCOG 1962. Prev: Clin. Asst. Cynthia Spencer Hse.

BANTOCK, Helen Martha Elizabeth The Northern Health Centre, 580 Holloway Road, London N7 6LB; 101 Crouch Hill, London N8 9RD — MB BS 1971 Lond.; FRCPCH 1998; BSc Lond. 1968; FRCP Lond. 1996; MRCP (UK) 1973. Sen. Lect. (Paediat.) Roy. Free and Univ. Med. Sch., Univ. Coll. Lond.; Hon. Cons. Paediat. Camden & Islington Community NHS Trust. Prev: Sen. Regist. (Paediat.) Univ. Coll. Hosp. Lond.; Mem. Scientif. Staff, MRC

Statistical Research & Servs. Unit; Hon. Lect. (Paediat.) Univ. Coll. Hosp. Med. Sch. Lond.

BANTON, John George (retired) Quarry Bank, Church Road, Watnall, Nottingham NG16 1JA Tel: 0115 938 2968 — MB ChB Leeds 1953; MRCGP 1977; DObst RCOG 1956. Prev: Ho. Surg. (O & G) St. Luke's Hosp. Bradford.

BANU, Sabiha Parvin Flat A, 105 Thorpedale Road, London N4 3BD — MB BS 1973 Bangalore.

BANU, Sayyideh Zohra 18 Western Road, Southall UB2 5DU Tel: 020 8574 0137 Fax: 020 8571 9683; 13 Marlborough Road, Southall UB2 5LW — MB BS 1973 All India Inst. Med. Sc.-; Cert. Family Plann. JCC 1984. (All-India Instit. of Med. Sciences New Delhi) Mem. Malaysian Coll. Gen. Practs. (Founder Mem.); Dip. Clin. Forens. Med. UK 1994.

BANULS PATTARELLI, Miguel 17 Aberdare Close, St Richards Hospital, Chichester PO19 4UG — LMS 1989 Valencia.

BANWELL, Miles Edwin Lower Manor Farmhouse, Main St., East Hanney, Wantage OX12 0HX — MB BS 1994 Lond.; BSc (Human Genetics) Lond. 1992. SHO (Surg.) St. Geo. Hosp. Lond. Prev: Demonst. (Anat.) Camb.; SHO (A & E) Univ. Coll. Hosp. Lond.

BANWELL, Mr Paul Edward Department of Plastic Surgery, Stoke Mandeville Hospital, Aylesbury HP21 8AL Tel: 01296 315906 Fax: 01296 315183 Email: pbanwell@aol.com; 17A Downside Crescent, Stoke Mandeville Hospital, London NW3 2AN Tel: 020 7794 3602 — MB BS 1992 Lond.; BSc (Hons.) Lond. 1991; FRCS Eng. 1996. (St. Mary's Hosp. Med. Sch.) Duke of Kent Research Fell. Dept. of Plastic Surg. Stoke Mandeville Hosp. Aylesbury; Med. Off. Brit. Boxing Bd. Control (S.. Area) & Counc. Mem. Socs: Fell. Roy. Soc. Med.; Eur. Tissue Repair Soc.; Brit. Burns Assn. Prev: SHO (Plastic Surg.) St Geo.'s Hosp.; SHO (Plastic Sugery) Qu. Mary's Hosp.; SHO Rotat. (Surg.) St. Mary's Hosp. Lond.

BANYARD, Barbara Dilys 13 St Jude Close, Colchester CO4 4PP Tel: 01206 842335 — MB BS 1956 Lond.; DObst RCOG 1959; DCH Eng. 1959. (Roy. Free) Socs: Med. Adviser NE Essex Adoption Panel Essex Social Servs. Prev: SCMO Essex Rivers Healthcare Trust; Asst. GP Ipswich; Jun. Asst. Resid. Kingston Gen. Hosp. Ont.

BANYARD, Jean Euphemia 20 Park Road, Edinburgh EH6 4LD — MB ChB 1958 Ed.

BANYARD, Peter John Bewsey Street Medical Centre, 40-42 Bewsey Street, Warrington WA2 7JE Tel: 01925 635837 Fax: 01925 630353 — MB ChB 1977 Bristol; BSc (Hons. Med. Microbiol.) Bristol 1977; MRCGP 1984; DRCOG 1982; Cert. Family Plann. JCC 1982. (Bristol) Civil Serv. Local Med. Off.; Tutor (Gen. Pract.) Warrington Dist. Prev: Trainee GP Windsor VTS; Ho. Surg. Bristol Roy. Infirm. & Bristol Radiother. & Oncol. Centre; Ho. Phys. Bristol Gen. Hosp.

BAPNA, Govind Katherine Road Medical Centre, 511 Katherine Road, London E7 8DR Tel: 020 8472 7029 — MB BS 1969 Rajastjan; MB BS Rajasthan 1969.

BAPODRA, Sarman Vajshi Severn Street Health Centre, 25 Severn Street, Leicester LE2 0NN Tel: 0116 254 3253; 33 New Street, Oadby, Leicester LE2 4LJ — MB BS 1978 Saurashtra; LRCP LRCS Ed. LRCPS Glas. 1982.

BAPTIE, Julie Anne, Capt. Cademuir 31 Letham Mains, Haddington EH41 4NW Tel: 01620 822349 Email: jbaptie@aol.com — MB ChB 1997 Ed.; BSc (Hons) 1995. (Edinburgh) Med. Off., Hohne Garrison.

BAPTIST, Gerard Philip 17 Loch Road, Dumfries DG2 9JE — MB ChB 1995 Birm.; ChB Birm. 1995.

BAPTISTE, Carlton Eustace Department of Anaesthesia, General Hospital, Middlesbrough TS1 5JE — MRCS Eng. LRCP Lond. 1963; FFA RCS Eng. 1972; DA Eng. 1966. Cons. Anaesth. S. Tees Gp. Hosps.

BAPTY, Arthur Allan (retired) Grasmere, Old Exeter St., Chudleigh, Newton Abbot TQ13 0LD Tel: 01626 853448 — MB BS 1951 Lond.; MRCS Eng. LRCP Lond. 1951; DObst RCOG 1953; DTM & H Antwerp 1955. Prev: GP Exeter.

BAPUJI RAO, Velagapudi Gwent Health Care NHS Trust, Maindiff Court Hospital, Abergavenny NP7 8NF Tel: 01873 735548 Fax: 01873 735529 Email: bvelaga@aol.com; The Gables, Harold Road, Abergavenny NP7 7DG Tel: 01873 852374 — MB BS 1968 Andhra; MRCPsych 1974; FRC 1999. Cons. Psychiat. Abergavenny. Socs: Welsh Psychiat. Soc.; Brit. Geriat. Soc.; BMA (Chairm. Gwent Div.). Prev: Cons. Psychiat. W. Suff. Hosp. Bury St. Edmunds; Sen. Regist. (Psychiat.) Roy. Free, Friern & Whittington Hosps.

BAQAI, Mr Ahmad Nadeem Furness General Hospital, Dalton Lane, Barrow-in-Furness LA14 4LF Tel: 01229 870870; Meadow Croft, 25 Fell View, Swarthmoor, Ulverston LA12 0XF — MB BS 1981 Karachi; 1981 MB BS Karachi; 1986 FRCS Ed; 1999 FRCS Tr. & Orth. (Dow Medical College) Cons. Orthop & trauma Surg., Furness G.H. Prev: Cons. Orthop. Surg. Sports Med. Hosp. Riyadh, Saudi Arabia.

BAQAI, Andrea 85 Blunts Hall Road, Witham CM8 1LY — MB BS 1986 Lond.; DRCOG 1990; DGM RCP Lond. 1988.

BAQAI, Azhar Central Surgery, 23 Boston Avenue, Southend-on-Sea SS2 6JH Tel: 01702 342589 Fax: 01702 437015; 45 Dungannon Chase, Thorpe Bay, Southend-on-Sea SS1 3NJ Tel: 01702 584361 — MB BS 1969 Karachi; DA Eng. 1972.

BAQAI, Manzoor Ahmad 129 Newland Street, Witham CM8 1BH; 85 Blunts Hall Road, Witham CM8 1LY — MB BS 1953 Punjab; MB BS Punjab (Pakistan) 1953. (King Edwd. Med. Coll.) Prev: Asst. Phys. Notley Hosp. Braintree; Ho. Phys. (Chest & Paediat.) W. Middlx. Hosp.; Med. Regist. Highwood Hosp. Brentwood.

BARABAS, Mr Andras Little Welnetham Hall, Bury St Edmunds IP30 0DA Tel: 01284 386305 Fax: 01284 388345 Email: aalwhall@aol.com — MB ChB 1960 Manchester; FRCS (Eng.) 1961; MD Manchester 1967. (Manchester) Cons.Vasc. & Gen. Surg. W. Suff. Hosp. Bury St Edmunds.; Teach. in Surg. Fac. of Med. Camb. Univ. Socs: Venous Forum; Roy. Soc. Med.; Vasc. Surg. Soc. GB. Prev: Tutor (Dept. Surg.) Manch.; Regist., Norf. & Norwich Hosp.; Sen. Regist. Roy. Postgrad. Med. Sch. Hammersmith Lond.

BARAGWANATH, Mr Philip Mole End, Old Mill Road, Broughton Astley, Leicester LE9 6PQ — MB ChB 1989 Birm.; FRCS Gen. Surg. 2001; MD Birm. 2000; FRCS Eng. 1993. Specialist Regist. (Surg.) S. Trent. Prev: Research Regist. (Surg.) Wound Healing Research Unit Univ. Wales Coll. Med.

BARAITSER, Michael The Institute of Child Health, Guilford St., London WC1; 38 Chalcot Crescent, London NW1 — MB ChB 1963 Stellenbosch; MB ChB Stellenbosch 1958; BSc (Agric.) Stellenbosch 1958; FRCP Lond. 1981. (Stellenbosch) Cons. Clin. Geneticist Hosp. Sick Childr. Lond. Prev: Cons. Clin. Geneticist Kennedy Galton Centre Radlett; Hon. Cons. N.wick Pk. Hosp. Harrow; Sen. Neurol. Univ. Stellenbosch Med. Sch. Bellville, S. Africa.

BARAITSER, Paula 38 Chalcot Crescent, London NW1 8YD — MB BS 1990 Lond.

BARAKA, Mr Mohamed El Fatih Magdoub ENT Department, Royal Lancaster Infirmary, Ashton Road, Lancaster LA1 4RP Tel: 01524 65944 Fax: 01524 583581; Willow Hayne, 61A Lancaster Road, Cabus, Preston PR3 1JD Tel: 01995 601105 Fax: 01995 601105 Email: baraka@btinternet.com — MB BS 1972 Khartoum; FRCSI 1979. Cons. ENT Surg. Roy. Lancaster Infirm. Socs: Irish Otolaryngol. Soc.; (Exec. Bd. Mem.) Saudi Otolaryngol. Soc.; Brit. Assn. Paediat. Otol. Prev: Prof. Otorhinolaryg. & Cons. ENT Surg. King Faisal Univ., Saudi Arabia.

BARAKAT, Mr Ahmed Abdel Azim Staff Residences, James Paget Hospital, Lowestoft Road, Gorleston, Great Yarmouth NR31 6LA — MB BCh 1981 Ain Shams; FRCS Ed. 1994; MRCOG 1992.

BARAKAT, Khalid 65 Seymour Road, Slough SL1 2NT Tel: 01753 570007 Email: khalidbarakat@compuserve.com — MB BS 1991 Lond.; BA Oxf. 1988; MA Oxf. 1992; MRCP(UK) 1994. (Guy's Hosp. Lond.) Specialist Regist. Rotat. The Roy. Hosps. Trust.

BARAKAT, Maha Taysir Endocrine Unit, Hammersmith Hospital, Du Cane Road, London W12 0NN — MB BChir 1994 Camb.; PHd Camb. 1993; MRCP Lond. (Cambridge) Specialist Regist. (Diabetes & Endocrinol.) Hammersmith Hosp. Lond.

BARAL, Syamal Seymour Grove Health Centre, 70 Seymour Grove, Old Trafford, Manchester M16 0LW Tel: 0161 848 7563 Fax: 0161 876 7805.

BARALLE, Diana Department of Medical Genetics, Box 134, Addenbrookes Hospital, Cambridge CB2 2QQ Tel: 01223 274568 Fax: 01223 217054 Email: dbaralle@hgmp.mrc.ac.uk — MB BS 1993 Lond.; BSc Lond. 1990; MRCP (UK) 1997. (Univ. Coll. & Middlx. Lond.) Specialist Regist. (Med. Genetics) Addenbrookes Hosp. Camb. Socs: Brit. Soc. of Human Genetics. Prev: Regist. (Genetics) Gt. Ormond St. Hosp. for Sick Childr. Lond.

BARANAUSKAS, Christine Valerie 62 Ling Forest Road, Mansfield NG18 3NJ — MB ChB 1992 Sheff.

BARANIECKA, Vera Teresa 78 Waldemar Avenue, London SW6 5LU Tel: 020 7736 7262 — MB BS 1965 Sydney; MRCPsych 1972; DPM Eng. 1970. (Sydney) Cons. Psychiat. Ashford Hosp.

BARANOWSKI, Andrew Paul The Pain Management Department, UCL Hospitals Trust, The National Hospital for Neurology and Neurosurgery, Queen Square, London WC1N 3BG Tel: 020 7419 1714 — MB BS 1983 Lond.; BSc Lond. 1980, MD 1993; FFA RCS Eng. 1988. (Guy's) Cons. Pain Managem. & Anaesth. UCLH Trust Lond.; Hon. Sen. Lect. UCL; Hon. Sen. Lect. Inst. of Neurol. Socs: Internat. Assn. Study of Pain; Assn. Anaesth. GB & Irel.; Pain Soc. Prev: Sen. Regist. (Anaesth.) St. Thos. Hosp. Lond.; MRC Research Fell. (Neurophysiol.) Univ. Coll. & St. Thos. Hosp. Lond.; Regist. (Anaesth.) St. Thos. Hosp. Lond.

BARASI, Faibes West Lodge, Porters End, Kimpton, Hitchin SG4 8ER Tel: 01462 832633 — MRCS Eng. LRCP Lond. 1941; MFCM 1974; DPH Lond. 1947. (St. Bart.) Prev: Sen. Med. Off. Herts. AHA; Dep. MOH Watford.

BARATA, Luis ManuelTaborda Department of Allergy & Clinical Immunology, National Heart & Lung Institute/Imperial College, Royal Brompton Hospital, Dovehouse St., London SW3 6LY Tel: 020 7351 8181 Fax: 020 7376 3138 Email: l.barata@ic.ac.uk; 2C Neville Street, London SW7 3AR — Lic Med 1987 Coimbra; Lic. Med. Coimbra 1987; MSc Porto 1993; PhD Lond. 1998. Hon. Regist. (Clin. Immunol.) Nat. Heart & Lung Inst. Roy. Brompton Hosp. Lond. Socs: Brit. Soc. Allergy & Clin. Immunol.; Portuguese Soc. Respirat. Dis.; Brit. Soc. Immunol. Prev: Regist. (Clin. Immunol. & Allergol.) & SHO (Internal Med.) Coimbra Univ. Hosp., Portugal.

BARATHAN, Indra 7 Coltsfoot, Welwyn Garden City AL7 3HZ — MB BS 1997 Lond.

BARBARY, Nagy Shafik 26A Highfield Road, Chislehurst BR7 6QZ — MB ChB 1973 Alexandria.

BARBEN, Margaret Rosanel (retired) Kearsley Medical Centre, Jackson St., Kearsley, Bolton BL4 8EP Tel: 01204 573164 Fax: 01204 792161 — MB BS 1964 Lond.; DFFP 1998 London; MRCS Eng. LRCP Lond. 1963; DA Eng. 1966. p/t Clin. Med. Off. (Gynae), Bolton Hosp. NHS Trust. Prev: Clin. Asst. (Anaesth.) Bolton Dist. Gp. Hosps.

BARBENEL, David Magnus 64 Oakfield Road, London N4 4LB — MB BChir 1991 Camb.

BARBER, Alexander Buchan Woodside Medical Centre, 80 Western Road, Aberdeen AB24 4SU Tel: 01224 492828 Fax: 01224 276173; 20 Parkhill Avenue, Dyce, Aberdeen AB21 7FP Tel: 01224 723589 — MB ChB 1971 Aberd. (Aberd.) Clin. Asst. (A & E) Aberd. Roy. Infirm. Prev: Res. Surg. Off. Woodend Gen. Hosp. Aberd.; Res. Med. Off. Aberd. Roy. Infirm.; Trainee GP Aberd. VTS.

BARBER, Alfred Desmond c/o National & Grindlays Bank, 13 St James Square, London SW1Y 4LB — MB BCh BAO 1931 Dub. (Dub.)

BARBER, Anne Satterthwaite (retired) Kestrels, 18 Stoke Row Road, Peppard Common, Henley-on-Thames RG9 5EP Tel: 0118 972 3165 — BM BCh 1950 Oxf. Prev: Med. Asst. Roy. Berks. Hosp. Reading.

BARBER, Anthony Robert (retired) White Gables, 26 Elstow Road, Kempston, Bedford MK42 8HB Tel: 01234 851109 — MB BS 1953 Lond.; MRCGP 1975; DObst RCOG 1957. Prev: Ho. Phys. & Ho. Surg. King's Coll. Hosp. Lond.

BARBER, Barrington Pasley Road Health Centre, Pasley Road, Leicester LE2 9BU Tel: 0116 278 5182; Peppercorn, 132 Saffron Road, South Wigston, Leicester LE18 4UP Tel: 0116 278 5627 — MB ChB 1976 Liverp.; BSc (Hons.) Anat. Liverp. 1970; Cert JCPTGP 1983; Cert. FPA 1980. Socs: BMA & Leicester Med. Soc. Prev: Maj. RAMC; Trainee GP Munster Gp. Pract.; Regtl. Med. Off. 1st Bn. Qu.'s Own Highlanders.

BARBER, Charles Gethyn The Surgery, Station Road, Great Massingham, King's Lynn PE32 2JQ Tel: 01485 518336 Fax: 01485 518725; Peddars Way, Fring, King's Lynn PE31 6SD Tel: 01485 518695 Fax: 01485 518950 — MB BChir 1969 Camb.; MA Camb. 1969; MRCGP 1972; DObst RCOG 1971. (Camb. & Guy's) Socs: BMA. Prev: Trainee GP Ipswich VTS; Ho. Phys. Kent & Canterbury Hosp.; Ho. Surg. Guy's Hosp. Lond.

BARBER, Mr Christopher John Princess Alexandra Hospital, Department of Radiology, Harlow CM20 1QX Tel: 01279 444455 — MB BS 1977 Lond.; FRCS Eng. 1982; FRCS Ed. 1981; FRCR 1987. (Westminster) Cons. Radiol. P.ss Alexandra Hosp. NHS Trust. Socs: Fell. of The Roy. Soc. of Med. Prev: Sen. Regist. (Radiol.) St. Mary's Hosp. Lond.

BARBER, Christopher Michael 174 Carter Knowle Road, Sheffield S7 2EA — BM BS 1993 Nottm.

BARBER, Mr David Thomas Cecil (retired) 121 Glebe Road, Cambridge CB1 7TE — MB BS 1952 Lond.; FRCS Ed. 1961; MRCS Eng. LRCP Lond. 1952; FRCOG 1972, M 1958, DObst 1955. Cons. O & G Hexham & Newc. Hosp. Gps. Prev: Sen. Regist. (O & G) Norwich, LoW.oft & Gt. Yarmouth Hosp. Gp.

BARBER, Douglas Norman (retired) 2A Ireland Avenue, Beeston, Nottingham NG9 1JD Tel: 0115 922 8028 — MB ChB 1954 Manch.; BDS 1946. Prev: Dent. Off. RADC Hosp. Ship 'El Nil'.

BARBER, Elizabeth Anne Email: chris@lizmoore.freeserve.co.uk — MB ChB 1989 Leic.; MRCOG 1998. Regist. in Gen. Pract. Socs: Yorks. Regional Regist.s Comm. (Comm. Memb.). Prev: Specialist Regist. (O & G) St. Jas. Univ. Hosp. Leeds; Specialist Regist. (O & G) Huddersfield Roy. Infirm.

BARBER, Mr Hugh Michael Old Grove, Linstock, Carlisle CA6 4QD Tel: 01228 21312 — MB BS 1964 Durh.; FRCS Eng. 1970; FRCS Ed. 1970. (Newc.) Cons. Orthop. Surg. Cumbld. Infirm. Carlisle. Socs: Fell. Brit. Orthop. Assn. Prev: Ho. Phys. & Ho. Surg. Roy. Vict. Infirm. Newc.; Regist. & Sen. Regist. Accid. Serv. Radcliffe Infirm. & Nuffield; Orthop. Centre Oxf.

BARBER, Isobel Blanche Armitage (retired) Northfield, Newstead, Melrose TD6 9RN Tel: 0189 682 2643 — MB ChB Aberd. 1951; DA Eng. 1955.

BARBER, Professor James Hill (retired) Windyedge, 12 Baldernock Road, Milngavie, Glasgow G62 8DU Tel: 0141 956 5920 — MB ChB 1957 Ed.; MD Ed. 1966; FRCP Glas. 1981, M 1977; FHKCGP 1992; FRCGP 1976, M 1970; DObst RCOG 1964. Prev: Norie-Miller Prof. Gen. Pract. Univ. Glas.

BARBER, Jane Mary Moorcroft Medical Centre, 10 Botteslow Street, Hanley, Stoke-on-Trent ST1 3NJ Tel: 01782 281806 Fax: 01782 205755; 88 Basford Park Road, Newcastle ST5 0PP — MB BS 1981 Lond.; BSc Lond. 1978; MRCGP 1985; DRCOG 1984.

BARBER, Joan Mary Garnock Day Hospital, Ayrshire Central Hospital, Kilwinning Road, Irvine KA12 8SS Tel: 01294 323050 Fax: 01294 311747 — MB ChB 1989 Glas.; MRCPsych 1995. Cons. Old Age Psychiat.

BARBER, Joanna Mary Paterson 28 Manor House Lane, Birmingham B26 1PG Tel: 0121 743 2455 — BM BCh 1983 Oxf.; MSc Oxf. 1980, BA 1978, BM BCh 1983.

BARBER, Jonathan Mark 70 Lismore Place, Newton Mearns, Glasgow G77 6UQ Email: mark.barber@btinternet.com — MB ChB 1991 Glas.; MRCP (UK) 1996. Specialist Regist. Rotat. (Geriat. & Gen. Med.) W. of Scotl. Socs: Brit. Geriat. Soc. Prev: SHO (Gen. Med.) CrossHo. Hosp. Kilmarnock.

BARBER, Jonathan Michael Leeds General Infirmary, Great George St., Leeds LS1 3EX — MB ChB 1992 Leeds; MRCP (UK) 1996. Specialist Regist. (Diagn. Radiol.) St. Jas. Univ. Hosp. Leeds.

BARBER, Julian Charles Peddars Way, Fring, King's Lynn PE31 6SD — MB BS 1998 Lond.; MB BS Lond 1998.

BARBER, Julie 18 Old School Lane, Pleasley, Mansfield NG19 7PW — MB BChir 1992 Camb.

BARBER, Katherine Janet 29 Woodfield Road, Kings Heath, Birmingham B13 9UL — MB ChB 1991 Birm.

BARBER, Mr Kenneth Walcot Farm, Walcot Lane, Drakes Broughton, Pershore WR10 2AL Tel: 01905 840606 — MB ChB 1977 Birm.; FRCS Ed. 1982; FCOphth 1988. Cons. Ophth. Worcester Roy. Infirm. Newtown Br. Prev: Sen. Regist. (Ophth.) Roy. Hallamsh. Hosp. Sheff.; Regist. (Ophth.) Birm. & Midl. Eye Hosp.

BARBER, Kevin William Woodside Health Centre, 3 Enmore Road, London SE25 5NS Tel: 020 8655 1410; Beam Ends Cottage, 2 Grimwade Avenue, Croydon CR0 5DG — MB BS 1970 Lond.; MRCS Eng. LRCP Lond. 1970; DObst RCOG 1973. (Char. Cross) Socs: Fell. Roy. Soc. Med.; Croydon Medico-Legal Soc. Prev: SHO Char. Cross Hosp. Lond.; SHO (Obst.) Roy. Free Hosp. Lond.

BARBER, Linda Margaret The Old Grove, Linstock, Carlisle CA6 4QD Tel: 01228 21312 — MB BS 1965 Durh.; MRCPsych 1972; DPM Newc. 1969. Cons. (Child Psychiat.) E. Cumbria Health Dist. Socs: Assn. Child Psychol. & Psychiat. & Assn. Psychiat. Study.

Prev: Regist. Dept. Psychol. Med. Roy. Vict. Infirm. Newc.; Sen. Regist. Warneford Hosp. Oxf. & BoroCt. Hosp. Reading.

BARBER, Margaret Amy Breffney, 77 Buxton Road, High Lane, Stockport SK6 8DX Tel: 016632 2551 — MB ChB 1943 Manch.; DObst RCOG 1949. (Manch.) Prev: Med. Regist. Dept. Neurol. & Gen. Med. Centr. Middlx. Hosp. Lond.; Obst. Ho. Surg. & Paediat. Ho. Phys. St. Mary's Hosp. Manch.; Ho. Surg. Manch. Roy. Infirm.

BARBER, Mark Daison Hill Farm, Tarrington Common, Hereford HR1 4HR — MB BS 1990 Lond.; MSc Lond. 1982, MB BS 1990; BSc Bristol 1982.

BARBER, Mr Matthew David 31/7 Rankeillor Street, Edinburgh EH8 9JA — MB ChB 1992 Glas.; MB ChB (Hons.) Glas. 1992; BSc (Hons) Glas. 1989; FRCS Glas. 1996; FRCS Ed. 1996. Research Fell. (Surg.) Univ. Edin. Prev: SHO Basic Surgic. Train. Scheme Edin.; SHO Rotat. (Surg.) St John's Hosp. Livingston.

BARBER, Matthew Joseph Lawrence Hill Health Centre, Hassell Drive, Bristol BS2 0AN Tel: 0117 955 5241 Fax: 0117 941 1162 — MB ChB 1986 Liverp.; BSc Med. Scs. & Biochem. Liverp. 1981; DTM & H Liverp. 1989; DCH 1989; MRCGP 1993. (Liverp.)

BARBER, Michelle Ann 224 Heol Hir, Thornhill, Cardiff CF14 9LA — MB BCh 1986 Wales; MRCP (Paediat.) (UK) 1994.

BARBER, Neil James Cheesemans, Brick Kiln Common, Wisborough Green, Billingshurst RH14 0HZ — MB BS 1993 Lond.

BARBER, Nicola Andrea 14 Broadacre, Stalybridge SK15 2TX — BM BCh 1994 Oxf.

BARBER, Nigel Christopher York Road Group Practice Surgery, York Road, Ellesmere Port, South Wirral CH65 0DB Tel: 0151 355 2112 Fax: 0151 356 5512; Stonegarth, Well Lane, Mollington, Chester CH1 6LD Tel: 01244 851394 — MB ChB 1966 Liverp.; BSc (Hons.) Liverp. 1963. GP Trainer S. Wirral. Prev: Regist. (Cas.) David Lewis N.. Hosp. Liverp.; Ho. Surg. (O & G) & Ho. Phys. BRd.green Hosp. Liverp.

BARBER, Nigel Peter Durnford Medical Centre, 113 Long Street, Middleton, Manchester M24 6DL Tel: 0161 643 2011 Fax: 0161 653 6570 — MB ChB 1983 Manch.

BARBER, Paul Crispin The Surgery, Marlpits Road, Honiton EX14 2DD; Lucerhayes Farm, Stoney Lane, Honiton EX14 9TS Tel: 01404 44847 — MB BS 1975 Lond.; MRCGP 1983; DObst. Auckland 1981.

BARBER, Peter Middleton Lodge Surgery, New Ollerton, Newark NG22 9SZ Tel: 01623 860668 Fax: 01623 836073 — MB ChB 1974 Manch.; DA RCPSI 1976.

BARBER, Peter John Swan Medical Centre, 17 Willard Road, Birmingham B25 8AB Tel: 0121 706 0216; 28 Manor House. Lane, Birmingham B26 1PG Tel: 0121 743 2455 — BM BCh 1952 Oxf.; MA Oxf. 1954, BA 1949, BM BCh 1952. (Oxf. & St. Bart.) Prev: Ho. Off. St. Bart. Hosp.

BARBER, Peter John (retired) Goodlands Farmhouse, Terrington, York YO60 6PU Tel: 01653 648434 — MB ChB Manch. 1956. JP. Prev: GP Warrington.

BARBER, Philip Andrew Northern General Hospital, Herries Road, Sheffield S5 7AU; 48 Bower Road, Sheffield S10 1ER — MB ChB 1991 Sheff.

BARBER, Philip Vernon North West Lung Centre, Wythenshawe Hospital, Manchester M23 9LT Tel: 0161 291 2721 Fax: 0161 291 2919; 135 Palatine Road, Didsbury, Manchester M20 3YA Tel: 0161 445 0127 Fax: 0161 946 0690 — MB ChB 1968 Manch.; FRCP Lond. 1990; MRCP (UK) 1972. (Manch.) Cons. Phys. (Respirat. Med.) S. Manch. HA. Socs: Hon. Fell. RCP.

BARBER, Rex Tyson (retired) Silvanus, Woodside Hill, Gerrards Cross SL9 9TB Tel: 01753 891219 — MB BS 1955 Lond.; MRCS Eng. LRCP Lond. 1956. Prev: Clin. Asst. (Orthop.) Highlands Hosp. Lond.

BARBER, Robert 26 Thornleigh Road, Jesmond, Newcastle upon Tyne NE2 3ET — BM BS 1987 Nottm.; MSc Nottm. 1993; MRCPsych 1991. Sen. Regist. (Adult & Gen. Psychiat.) Manch.

BARBER, Robin Norman Summervale Medical Centre, Wharf Lane, Ilminster TA19 0DT Tel: 01460 52354 Fax: 01460 52652 Email: robinbarber@doctors.org.uk; The Chantry, Stocklinch, Ilminster TA19 9JH Tel: 01460 57819 — MB BS 1974 Lond.; MRCGP 1978; DRCOG 1978; DCH Eng. 1977. Prev: SHO (O & G, Paediat., Gen. Med. & Geriat.) Salisbury Gen. Hosp.

BARBER, Ronald Dan Frenchay Hospital, Frenchay, Bristol BS16 1LE Tel: 0117 970 1212 Fax: 0117 975 3944 — MB BS 1974 Lond.; MB BS (Hons.) Lond. 1974; FRCP Lond. 1992; MRCP (UK) 1976; MRCS Eng. LRCP Lond. 1974. (Westm.) Cons. Phys. & Geriat. Frenchay Hosp. Bristol. Prev: Sen. Regist. (Med. & Geriat.) W. Midl. RHA; Regist. (Cardiol.) & (Med.) Univ. Hosp. Wales Cardiff; SHO (Med.) Radcliffe Infirm. Oxon.

BARBER, Sophie Louise 47 Eastville Terrace, Harrogate HG1 3HJ — MB ChB 1997 Birm.

BARBER, Stephen George Solway, Ashford, Barnstaple EX31 4BY — MB ChB 1969 Birm.; BSc; FRCP; DTM & H Liverp. 1971.

BARBER, Thomas Michael 20 Richmond Road, Stockton-on-Tees TS18 4DT — MB BS 1998 Newc.; MB BS Newc 1998.

BARBER, Timothy Sean, Lt.-Col. RAMC Retd. Department of Anaesthetics, Vale of Leven District General Hospital, Alexandria G83 0UA Tel: 01389 754121 Fax: 01389 603915 Email: timothy barber@vol.scot.nhs.uk; Fax: 01389 603915 — LRCPI & LM, LRSCI & LM 1971; LRCPI & LM, LRCSI & LM 1971; FFA RCSI 1978; DA RCPSI 1976. (Royal College of Surgeons in Ireland) Cons. Anaesth.Vale of Leven Dist. Gen. Hosp. Socs: W Scotl. Anaesth. Soc.; Obst. Anaesth. Assn.; W. of Scotl. Intens. Care Soc. Prev: Cons. Anaesth. HM Forces (Army).; Hon. Sen. Regist. (Anaesth.) Addenbrookes & Papworth Hosps.; Regist. (Anaesth.) Manch. Roy. Infirm.

BARBER, Victor Everall Bodreinallt Surgery, Bodreinallt, Conwy LL32 8AT Tel: 01492 593385 Fax: 01492 573715; Plas Dolydd, Sychnant Pass, Conwy LL32 8BJ Tel: 01492 593812 — MRCS Eng. LRCP Lond. 1964; DObst RCOG 1969; MRCGP 1974. (Liverp.) Prev: SHO (O & G & Paediat.) & Ho. Phys. & Ho. Surg. Clatterbridge Gen. Hosp. Bebington.

BARBER, Victoria Elizabeth Parklands Surgery, Wymington Road, Rushden NN10 9EB Tel: 01933 396000 Fax: 01933 396001 — MB BS 1991 Lond.; MRCGP 1996; DRCOG 1996; DCH RCP Lond. 1995; DFFP 1995. (Char. Cross & Westm. Hosp. Lond.) GP Princip. Prev: GP Asst. BromsGr. Worcs.; GP/Regist. S.wick, W. Sussex.; SHO (Paediat. & O & G) St. Richards Hosp. Chichester.

BARBER, Wendy Elizabeth Uplands, Ellerncroft Road, Wotton-under-Edge GL12 7AY Tel: 01453 842612 — MB ChB 1978 Bristol; BSc Bristol 1975; MRCPsych 1988. Staff Grade (Child & Adolesc. Psychiat.) Gwent Healthcare NHS Trust. Prev: Sen. Regist. (Child & Adolesc. Psychiat.) Bristol Roy. Hosp. for Sick Childr.; Regist. (Psychiat.) Glenside Hosp. Bristol.; Clin. Ast (Child & Adolesc. Psychiat.) Severn NHS Trust.

BARBER, Zoe Estelle Aries, Hadrian Way, Chilworth, Southampton SO16 7HY — MB ChB 1994 Bristol.

BARBER-LOMAX, Charles Arthur Davenport House Surgery, Bowers Way, Harpenden AL5 4HX Tel: 01582 767821 Fax: 01582 769285; Ruscombe, Spring Road, Kinsbourne Green, Harpenden AL5 3PP Tel: 01582 762734 — MB BS 1974 Lond.; FRCGP 1993, M 1979.

BARBIER, Brian Francis Trent View Medical Practice, 45 Trent View, Keadby, Scunthorpe DN17 3DR Tel: 01724 782209 Fax: 01724 784472; Oaktree Lodge, Epworth Road, Haxey, Doncaster DN9 2LF Email: bfbarbier@aol.com — MB BS 1969 Lond.; MRCS Eng. LRCP Lond. 1969; FFA RCS Eng. 1976; BSc. (Anat) Lond; DA (Eng); Dobst SRCOG Eng. (Westminster) Princip. in Gen. Pract.

BARBIERI, Mark 12 Dillotford Avenue, Styvechale, Coventry CV3 5DQ Tel: 024 76 415395 — MB ChB 1996 Leic. (Leicester) Prev: SHO (A & E) Ryde Hosp. Sydney, Australia; Jun. Ho. Off. (Gen. Surg./Orthop.) Leicester Roy. Infirm.; Jun. Ho. Off. (Med.) Warwick Hosp.

BARBIR, Mahmud Royal Brompton and Harfield NHS Trust, Harefield Hospital, Harefield, Uxbridge UB9 6JH Tel: 020 8998 0045 Fax: 01895 828896; 3 Goldcrest Mews, Montpelier Road, Ealing, London W5 2QH Tel: 020 8997 8708 Fax: 020 8991 0736 — MB BCh BAO 1980 NUI; MRCP (UK) 1985; LRCPI & LM, LRCSI & LM 1980; Dip. Clin. Cardiol. Lond 1984; FRCP 1998. Cons. Cardiol. Hairfield Hosp. Socs: Irish Cardiac Soc.; Brit. Hyperlipid. Assn. Prev: Hon. Sen. Regist. (Cardiac Transpl.) Harefield Hosp.; Regist. (Cardiol.) Hammersmith Hosp. Lond.

BARBOUR, Alison Farquharson Hillcrest, Quinneys Lane, Redditch B98 7WG — MB ChB 1982 Aberd.; MRCGP 1986; DRCOG 1985. (Aberdeen) GP Grampian HB.

BARBOUR, Catherine Dummigan (retired) 21 St Ninian's Road, Prestwick KA9 1SL Tel: 01292 77458 — MB ChB 1959 Ed. Prev: Assoc. Specialist (Geriat. Med.) N. Ayrsh. Dist. Gen. Hosp.

BARBOUR, James (retired) 65 Arrowe Road, Greasby, Wirral CH49 1RY Tel: 0151 677 3009 — LRCP LRCS Ed. LRFPS Glas. 1955. Prev: Ho. Phys. & Ho. Surg. Vict. Gen. Hosp. Wallasey.

BARBOUR, James Vevers Redman Springfield Medical Practice, 463 Springfield Road, Belfast BT12 7DN Tel: 028 9032 7126 Fax: 028 9032 5976 — MB BChir 1975 Camb.; MA Camb. 1975; MRCP (UK) 1977; MRCGP 1982; Dip Occ. Med. RCP Lond. 1996. (Lond. Hosp.) GP Princip. Socs: Ulster Med. Soc.; Soc. Occupat. Med.

BARBOUR, Jamie Arthur 27 Fairfield Road, West Jesmond, Newcastle upon Tyne NE2 3BY — MB BS 1996 Newc.

BARBOUR, Leon Aldous Andrew New Inn Surgery, 202 London Road, Burpham, Guildford GU4 7JS Tel: 01483 301091 Fax: 01483 453232; 4 Green Lane, Guildford GU1 2LZ Tel: 01483 572113 — MB BS 1979 Lond.; MSc Manch. 1971; MRCGP 1984; DRCOG 1984. (St. Thos.) Med. Pract. Surrey FHSA; Princip. Forens. Phys. Surrey Constab. Guildford; Vis. Med. Pract. Home Off. Guildford. Socs: Assn. Police Surg.; Guildford Med. Soc.

BARBOUR, Linda Patricia Ruth Beaconsfield, Wolverton Fields, Norton Lindsey, Warwick CV35 8JN Tel: 01926 842178 Fax: 01926 842178 Email: ruth.barbour@tesco.net — MB ChB 1971 Birm.; FRCGP 1986, M 1976; DCH Eng. 1975; DObst RCOG 1973; Dip. Prescribing Sci Liverp 1999; Postgrad. Dip 1999. (Birm.) Prev: Primary Care Med. Adviser Warks. HA; GP Wolverhampton; SHO (A & E & O & G) Barnet Gen. Hosp.

BARBOUR, Margaret Isabella (retired) 20 Crosshill Road, Strathaven ML10 6DS Tel: 01357 20377 — MB ChB 1961 Glas.

BARBOUR, Maureen Patricia (retired) 8 Blairtum Drive, Burnside, Rutherglen, Glasgow G73 3RY — MB BCh BAO Belf. 1958.

BARBOUR, Patricia The Medical Centre, 2 Francis Street, Doncaster DN1 1JS Tel: 01302 349431 Fax: 01302 364558 — MB ChB 1984 Manch.; MRCGP 1988; DRCOG 1987. GP; Tutor Hon. Clin. Teach. Sheff. Univ.

BARBOUR, Pauline Margaret 27 Grange Road, Dungannon BT71 7EJ — MB BCh BAO 1977 Dub.

BARBOUR, William Gordon (retired) 21 St Ninians Road, Prestwick KA9 1SL Tel: 01292 77458 — MB ChB 1953 Glas. Prev: Clin. Asst. (Haemat.) Ayrsh. & Arran HB.

BARCELLOS, Albert Anthony Glenmoor Road Surgery, Corbin Avenue, Ferndown BH22 8AZ Tel: 01202 897989 Fax: 01202 877743 — MB ChB 1976 Bristol.

BARCHARD, Marguerite Claire The Mount, Woodgates Lane, North Ferriby HU14 3JY Tel: 01482 631628 Fax: 01482 634845 — MB BS 1971 Lond. (Westminster) Prev: GP Partner Brough & S. Cave Med. Pract.

BARCLAY, Alexander Patrick (retired) 1 Oxenden Drive, Hoddesdon EN11 8QF Tel: 01992 463825 — MB BChir 1951 Camb.; MRCS Eng. LRCP Lond. 1951; DO Eng. 1958; DObst RCOG 1953. Prev: GP Hoddesdon.

BARCLAY, Alistair David McLennan Fourwinds, East Lambrook, South Petherton TA13 5HF — MB BS 1985 Lond.; BSc Lond. 1980, MB BS 1985.

BARCLAY, Allan Alexander (retired) 23 Stanely Crescent, Paisley PA2 9LF Tel: 0141 581 1691 — MB BCh BAO 1960 Dub.; BA Dub. 1957, MB BCh BAO 1960; DObst RCOG 1962. Prev: Ho. Surg. Moyle Hosp. Larne.

BARCLAY, Andrew George Tillingham Medical Centre, 61 South Street, Tillingham, Southminster CM0 7TH Tel: 01621 778383 Fax: 01621 778034 — MB ChB 1978 Glas.; MRCGP 1982.

BARCLAY, Andrew James Hillside, Bircham Road, Snettisham, King's Lynn PE31 7NG — MB BS 1969 Lond.; MRCS Eng. LRCP Lond. 1968; FFA (SA) 1976; DA Eng. 1973. Cons. (Anaesth.) Qu. Eliz. Hosp. Kings Lynn. Prev: Princip. Anaesth./ Sen. Lect. Univ. Natal Durban.

BARCLAY, Andrew James Gurney Sunnyrose Surgery, Sunnyrose, 75-77 Wheelwright Lane, Coventry CV6 4HN Tel: 024 7636 6775 Fax: 024 7636 5793; 37 St. Martins Road, Finham, Coventry CV3 6FE Tel: 024 76 412932 — BM BCh 1977 Oxf.; MRCGP 1993; DTCH Liverp. 1985; DRCOG 1978. Prev: Med. Superintend. Mvumi Hosp., Tanzania.

BARCLAY, Andrew Robert 33 Mousebank Road, Lanark ML11 7PE — MB ChB 1997 Aberd.

BARCLAY, Christopher Stewart Nethergreen Road Surgery, 34-36 Nethergreen Road, Sheffield S11 7EJ Tel: 0114 230 2952 — MB ChB 1978 Sheff.; MRCOG 1986.

BARCLAY, Claire Anne 1 Ormonde Road, Chester CH2 2AH — MB ChB 1996 Ed.

BARCLAY, David Alan The Millfield, 39 Glenlyon Road, Leven KY8 4AA — MB ChB 1994 Aberd.

BARCLAY, Derek George Banchory Group Practice, The Surgery, Bellfield, Banchory AB31 5XS Tel: 01330 822121 Fax: 01330 825265; Tom-na-Faire, Woodside Road, Banchory AB31 4EN Tel: 01330 823616 — MB ChB 1975 Aberd.

BARCLAY, Douglas Jon 96C St Michaels Hill, Bristol BS2 8BQ — MB BS 1998 Newc.; MB BS Newc 1998.

BARCLAY, Gail Suzanne 7 Ferntower Place, Inverness IV2 7TL — MB ChB 1998 Aberd.; MB ChB Aberd 1998.

BARCLAY, George Peter Thompson 14 Moray Place, Edinburgh EH3 6DT Tel: 0131 226 2846 Fax: 0131 225 6749; 79/7 Braid Avenue, Edinburgh EH10 6ED Tel: 0131 446 9738 Fax: 0131 446 0757 — MB ChB 1951 Ed.; MD 1961; FRCPath. 1976. Clin. Direct. Moray Pl.. Edin. Prev: Managing Dir. Health Managem. Serv. Ltd.; Cons. Path. N.. Regional Hosp. Bd.; Prof. Path. Univ. Rhodesia.

BARCLAY, Gillian 37 St Martins Road, Finham, Coventry CV3 6FE Tel: 024 76 412932 — MB BS 1976 Lond.; DCH RCP Lond. 1979; DRCOG 1978. Clin. Research Asst. (Dermat.) Walsgrave Hosp. Coventry.

BARCLAY, Gillian Anne Wilson Tait and Partners, 68 Pipeland Road, St Andrews KY16 8JZ Tel: 01334 476840 Fax: 01334 472295; St. Fold Farm, Elie, Leven KY9 1JT Tel: 01333 330406 — MB ChB 1989 Manch.; BSc St. And. 1986; MRCGP 1995; DCH RCPS Glas. 1996; DGM RCPS Glas. 1993; DObst Glas. 1992. Socs: BMA; Diplomate Fac. Family Plann. Prev: Trainee GP/SHO (Paediat.) Roy. Hosp. Sick Childr. Edin.; SHO Sunshine State HA Qu.sland, Austral.; SHO (Geriat. Med.) Gartnavel Hosp. & Stobhill Hosp. Glas.

BARCLAY, Gordon Barking & Havering Health Authority, The Clockhouse, East St., Barking IG11 8EY Tel: 020 8532 6375 Fax: 020 8532 6354; 24 Glanville Drive, Hornchurch RM11 3SY — MB ChB 1967 Aberd.; MRCGP 1972; Cert. Family Plann. JCC 1984; DObst RCOG 1969. (Aberd.) Med. Advisor Barking & Havering HA; Hon. Lect. (Gen. Pract.) St. Geo. Hosp. Lond. Socs: Roy. Coll. Gen. Pract.; BMA. Prev: Med. Advisor Merton, Sutton & Wandsworth FHSA; GP Braintree & Lond.; Ho. Phys. Roy. Aberd. Childr. Hosp.

BARCLAY, Mr Gordon Andrew 77 Maze Hill, Greenwich, London SE10 8XQ Tel: 020 8858 4968 Fax: 020 8333 5183 Email: barcvier@aol.com — 1941 MRCS Eng. LRCP Lond.; MB BChir 1942 Camb.; 1947 FRCS Eng.; 1993 BSc (Hons.) O.U. ec. 31st. (Camb. & Lond. Hosp.) Hon.Examg. & Consg. Surg. Med. Foundat. for the c/o Victims of Torture, Lond. Socs: Sen. Fell. Assn. Surgs.; Sen. Mem. Brit. Assn. Urol. Surgs.; Med. Soc. Lond. Prev: Surg. St. And. Hosp. Bow, E. Ham Memor. Hosp. & Qu. Mary's Hosp. Stratford; Hon. Lect. (Surgic. Unit) Lond. Hosp. Med. Coll.; Surg. Brit. Paediat. Team Saigon, S. Vietnam.

BARCLAY, Gordon James Lothian Flat 1/2, 11 Kirklee Quadrant, Glasgow G12 0TS Tel: 0141 357 2392 Fax: 0141 357 2392 — MB ChB 1992 Glas.; MA (Hons.) Ed. 1985; MRCGP 1996; DRCOG 1996. (Glas.) SHO (Gen. Med.) S. Gen. Hosp. Glas. Socs: BMA; Anthroposop. Med. Assn.; Assoc. Mem. Fac. Homoeop. Prev: GP Locum.

BARCLAY, Guy Alexander 84 August Road, Liverpool L6 4DF — MB ChB 1994 Liverp.

BARCLAY, Helene 8 Winstanley Road, Thorpe St Andrew, Norwich NR7 0YH — BM 1989 Soton. Staff Grade (Learning Disabil.) Little Plumstead Hosp. Norwich.

BARCLAY, Iain Medical Protection Society, Granary Wharf House, Leeds LS11 5PY Tel: 0113 243 6436 Fax: 0113 241 0500; 3 Leadhall Avenue, Harrogate HG2 9NH Tel: 01423 871837 — MB ChB 1976 Aberd.; MRCGP 1981; DRCOG 1980; LLB 1998. Medico-Legal Adviser Med. Protec. Soc. Leeds. Socs: BMA. Prev: GP Edin.; Med. Adviser Avon FHSA.

BARCLAY, Ian Hamilton Woodlands, Hindon Lane, Tisbury, Salisbury SP3 6QQ Tel: 01722 870489 — MB BS 1938 Durh.; DTM & H McGill 1954. Prev: Commandant Canad. Forces Med. Train. Centre; Regional Surg. RCAF Europe; Gp. Capt. RCAF.

BARCLAY, James Alexander 5 Hillcrest, Peasedown St John, Bath BA2 8JL Tel: 01761 439556 — MB ChB 1937 Aberd.

BARCLAY, Jennifer Menzies 82/8 Pleasance, Edinburgh EH8 9TJ Tel: 0131 667 7688 — MB ChB 1983 Ed.; MRCGP 1988; DGM RCP Lond. 1990; DRCOG 1986. Prev: Regist. (Geriat. Med.) Roy. Vict. Hosp. Edin.

BARCLAY, John Herbert 5 Sandbeck Place, Sheffield S11 8XP Tel: 0114 268 3414 Email: john.barclay@virgin.net — MB ChB 1987 Sheff.; FRCA 1996. SHO (A & E) Sheff. Childr.s Hosp. Prev: SHO O & G Rotherham Gen. Hosp.; SHO Doncaster Roy. Inf.; SHO Paediat. Sheff. Childr. Hosp.

BARCLAY, Karen 8 West Harwood Crofts, West Calder EH55 8LF — MB ChB 1990 Aberd.

BARCLAY, Katharine Elisabeth (retired) Denny Abbey, Waterbeach, Cambridge CB5 9PQ Tel: 01223 860282 — MB BS 1959 Lond. Prev: Clin. Med. Off. Camb. HA.

BARCLAY, Laurance 5 Kinnoull Hill Place, Kinnoull, Perth PH2 7DD — MB ChB 1956 St. And.; MRCPsych 1973; DPM Eng. 1960.

BARCLAY, Patrick Melvin (retired) 16 Knaresborough Avenue, Marton, Middlesbrough TS7 8LN Tel: 01642 318502 — MB ChB 1935 Ed.

BARCLAY, Paul Linden Medical Group, Linden Medical Centre, Linden Avenue, Kettering NN15 7NX Tel: 01536 512104 Fax: 01536 415930 — MB ChB 1992 Leic.; MRCGP. GP; GP Tutor. Socs: Roy. Coll. Gen. Pract.

BARCLAY, Paul Stuart, MC, TD (retired) Rede's House, 15 Overstrand Road, Cromer NR27 0AH Tel: 01263 512060 — MRCS Eng. LRCP Lond. 1940; MA Camb.; DA Eng. 1954. Prev: GP, Cromer 1947-79.

BARCLAY, Philip Michael Liverpool Women's Hospital, Crown St., Liverpool L8 7SS Tel: 0151 702 4134 — MB ChB 1987 Leeds; FRCA 1996. Cons. Anaesth. Liverp. Wom.'s Hosp. NHS Trust; Hon. Lect., Univ. of Liverp. Socs: Obst. Anaesth. Assn.; Brit. Ophthabis Anaesth. Assoc. Prev: Specialist Regist. (Anaesth.) NW RHA; Regist. (Anaesth.) NW RHA; SHO (Anaesth.) Hope Hosp. Salford.

BARCLAY, René Fordyce (retired) 2 Richmond Mews, Clifton, Bristol BS8 3DH — MB BS Lond. 1945; MFCM 1972; DPH Lond. 1949. Prev: Sen. Med. Off. Frenchay & S.mead HAs.

BARCLAY, Robert Peter Clarkson 33 Mousebank Road, Lanark ML11 7PE — MB ChB 1966 Ed.; FRCP Glas. 1984; FRCP Ed. 1983; DCH RCPS Glas. 1971. Cons. Paediat. Lanarksh. Health Bd.

BARCLAY, Roderick Paul Manor Farm Close Surgery, 8 Manor Farm Close, Drayton, Norwich NR8 6DN Tel: 01603 867532 — MB BS 1974 Lond.; MRCS Eng. LRCP Lond. 1973; DRCOG 1980. (St. Bart.)

BARCLAY, Seana Rowan Sherwood, Bridge of Weir PA11 3AW Tel: 01505 612361 — MB ChB 1957 Glas.; DObst RCOG 1959. (Glas.) Sessional SCMO Family Plann. Clinics Argyll & Clyde HB. Prev: Med. Off. Marks & Spencer Ltd.

BARCLAY, Stephen Ian Gurney East Barnwell Health Centre, Ditton Lane, Cambridge CB5 8SP Tel: 01223 728900 Fax: 01223 728901 — BM BCh 1981 Oxf.; MA Camb. 1978; MRCGP 1987; Dip. Palliat. Med. Wales 1997; DRCOG 1983. GP Camb.; Hon Cons. Phys. (Palliat. Med. (Primary Care)) Camb.

BARCLAY, Mr Thomas Laird (retired) 3 Taverngate, Hawksworth, Guiseley, Leeds LS20 8NX Tel: 01943 879750 — MB ChB 1947 Ed.; ChM Ed. 1970; FRCS Eng. 1982; FRCS Ed. 1951. Prev: Cons. Plastic Surg. Bradford Roy. Infirm., Huddersfield Roy. Infirm. & Halifax Roy. Infirm.

BARCLAY, William Hugh Tel: 020 8688 0333 Fax: 020 8688 9707; 30 Brancaster Lane, Purley CR8 1HF Tel: 020 8660 4552 — MB BChir 1980 Camb.; MRCGP 1988; DFFP 1997. Managem. Gp. Mem. Centr. Croydon Commiss.ing Gp. Prev: Clin. Asst. (Rheum.) Purley Hosp.

BARCO MARCELLAN, Jesus Maria Flat 14, Lancaster Hall, 3-4 Wesley Avenue, London E16 1SN — LMS 1994 Saragossa.

BARCO MARCELLAN, Maria Pilar James Paget Hospital NHS Trust, Lowestoft Road, Gorleston, Great Yarmouth NR31 6LA — LMS 1991 Saragossa.

BARCROFT, John 11 Melior Court, 79 Shepherds Hill, London N6 5RQ Tel: 020 8341 0928 Fax: 020 8341 0928 Email: jbarcroft@hotmail.com — MB BChir 1963 Camb.; MPhil Lond. 1970; MRCPsych 1972; DCH Eng. 1965. (Univ. Coll. Hosp.) p/t Volunteer Med. Found. for c/o victims of torture, Kentish Town, Lond. Socs: Assn. Child Psychol. & Psychiat.; Brit. Assn. Of Behav. & Cognit. Psycother. Prev: Cons.child Psychiat. Dept.child & family Psychiat., Camb.; Cons. Child Psychiat. Roy. Belf. Hosp. Sick Childr. & Ulster Hosp. Belf.; Sen. Regist. Childr. Dept. Bethlem Roy. & Maudsley Hosp. Lond.

BARCROFT, John Pim RNOH NHS Trust, Brockley Hill, Stanmore HA7 4LP Tel: 020 8909 5463 Email: jbarcroft@rnoh-tr.ore; 28 Chestnut Drive, Pinner HA5 1LY — MB 1977 Camb.; 1977 MB Camb; 1983 FFA RCS Eng. 1983; BChir 1976 Camb.; FRCA; 1973 BA. (Cambridge & Barts) Cons. Anaesth. Roy. Nat. Orthop. Hosp. Lond.; Cons. Anaesth., UCLH Lond.; Cons. Anaesth., Nat. Hosp. for Nerv. Dis.s, Lond. Socs: Assn. of Anaesth.s; Brit. Soc. of Orthopaedic Anaesth.; Europ. Soc. of Regional Anaesth. Prev: Sen. Regist. (Anaesth.) Research Dept. Anaesth. RCS & St. Peter's Hosp. Lond.

BARCZAK, Paul Jan Nigel 13 Greetwell Road, Lincoln LN2 4AQ — MB BS 1979 Lond.

BARCZAK, Stella Margaret 13 Greetwell Road, Lincoln LN2 4AQ; 1 Hall Lane, Branston, Lincoln LN4 1PZ Tel: 01522 791934 — MB BS 1979 Lond.; FFA RCS Eng. 1983.

BARD, Valerie Penshurst Gardens Surgery, 39 Penshurst Gardens, Edgware HA8 9TN Tel: 020 8958 3141 Fax: 020 8905 4638; Tile Croft, 22 Aylmer Drive, Stanmore HA7 3EG Tel: 020 8954 2640 — MB BS 1963 Lond.; MRCGP 1976. (Roy. Free) Prev: Course Organiser Edgware Gen. Hosp.; Ho. Phys. Eliz. G. Anderson Hosp. Lond.; Ho. Surg. New End Hosp. Lond.

BARDANI, Irini 41 Glasslyn Road, Crouch End, London N8 8RJ — Ptychio Iatrikes 1981 Athens.

BARDEN, Andrea Louise Northern General Hospital, Herries Rd, Sheffield S5 7AU; Flat 27 Block 1, 5 Beech Hill Road, Sheffield S10 2RA — MB ChB 1997 Sheff.

BARDEN, M Elizabeth Highwood, Tweeddale Avenue, Gifford, Haddington EH41 4QN — MB ChB 1960 Bristol; MB ChB (Hnrs.) Bristol 1960; DObst RCOG 1963.

BARDEN, Robert Keith Alscot Farmhouse, Alscot Lane, Princes Risborough HP27 9RU — MB BCh BAO 1978 NUI; LRCPI & LM, LRCSI & LM 1978; DRCOG 1984; Cert. Family Plann. JCC 1981. Med. Dir. Ashbourne Pharmaceut. Ltd. Socs: BMA. Prev: Med. Adviser Abbott Laborat. Ltd.; GP RAF.

BARDEN, Sarah Delyth 48 Quintin Gurney House, Keswick Hall, Norwich NR4 6RP — MB BS 1996 Lond.

BARDGETT, Dorothy Margaret Mary Department Anaesthesia, Macclesfield District General Hospital, Victoria Road, Macclesfield SK10 3BL Tel: 01625 421000; 27 Park Lane, Congleton CW12 3DG Tel: 01260 275270 — MB ChB 1965 Liverp.; DA Eng. 1970; FFA RCS Eng. 1981. (Liverp.) Cons. Anaesth. Macclesfield Dist. Gen. Hosp. Socs: Assn. Anaesth. Intens. Care Soc. Prev: Sen. Regist. (Anaesth.) Mersey RHA; Regist. (Anaesth.) Leighton Hosp. Crewe; Clin. Asst. (Anaesth.) Leighton Hosp. Crewe.

BARDGETT, Harry Paul — MB ChB 1994 Liverp.; MRCP; Dip Trop. Med.health 1997. SPR Med. Oncol., St James Hosp., Leeds. Prev: Ho. Off. (Med. & Surg.) Walton & Fazakerley Hosp. Liverp.

BARDGETT, Rebecca Jane Mayson — MB ChB 1992 Liverp.; MRCP 1996. St James Hosp., Leeds Gen. Infirm. & Bradford Roy. Infirm.

BARDHA, Harbhajan Singh The Surgery, 1A Cordley Street, West Bromwich B70 9NQ Tel: 0121 553 3646 Fax: 0121 580 1908; 297 Lordswood Road, Harborne, Birmingham B17 8PR Tel: 0121 429 2150 — MB BS 1966 Calcutta. (Nat. Med. Coll. Calcutta)

BARDHAN, Gouri Haematology Department, Doncaster Royal Infirmary, Doncaster DN2 5LT Tel: 01302 366666; 26 Melrose Grove, Rotherham S60 3NA Tel: 01709 372288 — MB BS 1966 Madras; LF Hom. (Med.) 1998; Lic. Ac 1983; FRCP Lond. 1996; MRCP (UK) 1972; FRCPath 1988, M 1976; DCH Madras 1968. (Christian Med. Coll. Vellore) Cons. Haemat. Doncaster Roy. Infirm.; Tutor Coll. of Paths. Socs: Brit. Soc. Haematol. (Regional Represen.).

BARDHAN, Karna Dev Rotherham General Hospital NHS Trust, Moorgate Road, Rotherham S60 2UD Tel: 01709 820000 Fax: 01709 304168 Email: bardhan.sec@rgh-tr.trent.nhs.uk; 26 Melrose Grove, Rotherham S60 3NA Tel: 01709 372288 Fax: 01709 304168 — MB BS 1964 Madras; DPhil Oxf. 1968; FRCP Ed. 1990; FRCP Lond. 1981; MRCP (UK) 1970; FACP 1992; FACG 1991. (Christian Med. Coll. Vellore) Cons. Phys. & Gastroenterol. Rotherham Gen. Hosps. NHS Trust; Hon. Lect. (Gastroenterol.) Univ.

Sheff. Socs: Amer. Gastroenterol. Assn.; Brit. Soc. Gastroenterol.; Assn. Phys.

BARDNER, Duncan James 5 Mount Beacon, Bath BA1 5QP; 5 Waldon Court, St. Lukes Road S., Torquay TQ2 5PB Tel: 01803 380115 — MB ChB 1992 Birm.; MRCGP 1997; DFFP 1996; DCH 1995. (Birm. Univ.)

BARDSLEY, Mr Allan Frank Plastic Surgery Associates, Hill House, BUPA Hospital, Norwich NR4 7TD Tel: 01603 255505 Fax: 01603 250404 Email: plasticsurgery@enterprise.net — MB ChB 1976 Manch.; FRCS Eng. 1981; FRCS (Plast Surg.) Eng. 1990. (Manch.) Cons. Plastic & Reconstruc. Surg. BUPA Hosp. Norwich. Socs: Brit. Assn. Plastic Surg.; Brit. Assn. Aesth. Plastic Surg.; Brit. Assn. Head & Neck Oncol. Prev: Sen. Regist. Adelaide, S. Australia; Sen. Regist. Canniesburn Glas..

BARDSLEY, Mr David Chesterfield and North, Derbyshire Royal Hospital, Chesterfield Tel: 01246 277271 Fax: 01246 550171 Email: david.bardsley@cndrh-tr.trent.nhs.uk; Glenthorne, 228 Handley Road, New Whittington, Chesterfield S43 2ER Tel: 01246 452959 Email: davidbardsley@handleyroad.fsnet.co.uk — MB ChB BAO 1962 Sheffield; MB ChB Sheff. 1962; FRCS Eng. 1967. (Sheff.) Cons. Surg. Chesterfield & N. Derbysh. Roy. Hosp. Socs: Fell. Assn. Surg.; BMA; Assn. Upper G.I. Surg. Prev: Sen. Regist. (Surg.) Roy. Infirm. Sheff.; SHO Surg. Manch. Roy. Infirm.; Ho. Surg. (Urol.) Hammersmith Hosp. Lond.

BARDSLEY, Elizabeth Mary Royal Free Hospital, Pond St., London NW3 2QG; 86 Sutton Road, Muswell Hill, London N10 1HG — MB ChB 1978 Birm.; MRCPsych 1983.

BARDSLEY, Isabel Maria 4F Bishopswood Road, London N6 4NY — Lic Med 1974 Laurenco Marques; Lic Med. Laurenco Marques 1974.

BARDSLEY, Philip Andrew The Cottage, Hooton Lane, Slade Hooton, Laughton en le Morthern, Sheffield S25 1YQ — MD 1988 Manch.; MB ChB Manch. 1981; MRCP (UK) 1985; FRCP 1999 Lond. Cons. Gen. & Respirat. Med. Rotherham Gen. Hosp. Socs: Brit. Thorac. Soc.; BMA. Prev: Sen. Regist. (Gen. & Respirat. Med.) Glenfield Gen. Hosp. Leicester; Research Fell. Dept. Med. Roy. Hallamsh. Hosp. Sheff.; Regist. (Gen. Med.) Lodge Moor Hosp. Sheff.

BARDSLEY, Stella Jane 216 Compstall Road, Romiley, Stockport SK6 4JG — MB ChB 1990 Manch.

BARDSLEY, Victoria 60A Mount Peasant, Norwich NR2 2DQ — MB BChir 1994 Camb.

BARE, Laurent Marcel Jacqueline 142 Beverley Road, Kirk Ella, Hull HU10 7HA — Artsexamen 1994 Maastricht.

BAREFORD, David, RD Department of Haematology, City Hospital, Dudley Road, Birmingham B18 7QH Tel: 0121 507 4234 Fax: 0121 523 7990 Email: d.bareford@bham.ac.uk — MB ChB 1973 Bristol; MD Bristol 1988; FRCP Lond. 1996; MRCP (UK) 1977; FRCPath 1994, M 1982. Cons. Haemat. City Hosp. Birm. Socs: Brit. Soc. Haematol.; Assn. Clin. Path. Prev: Lect. (Haemat.) Univ. Birm.; Sen. Regist. (Haemat.) St. Jas. Hosp. Leeds; Regist. (Haemat.) Groote Schuur Hosp., Cape Town.

BAREILLE, Jean-Philippe Medicare Francais, 3 Harrington Gardens, London SW7 4JJ — MD 1994 Paris.

BARENDT, Andrew Basil Tower House Practice, St. Pauls Health Centre, High Street, Runcorn WA7 1AB Tel: 01928 567404 — MB ChB 1984 Liverp.; MRCGP 1989; DCH RCP Lond. 1987. Prev: SHO (Thoracic) Clatterbridge Hosp. Wirral.

BARENDT, Geoffrey Harold (retired) 4 Brookvale Road, Portswood, Southampton SO17 2QL — MRCS Eng. LRCP Lond. 1927; BA Camb. (Hons.) 1924, MB BChir 1928. Prev: Ho. Phys. Roy. S. Hants. & Soton. Hosp.

BARER, David Howard Stroke Research Team, Queen Elizabeth Hospital, Gateshead NE9 6SX Tel: 0191 403 2840 Fax: 0191 403 2842 Email: d.h.barer@ncl.ac.uk — MB BS 1977 Lond.; MSc Birm. 1979; DM Nottm. 1988; FRCP Lond. 1994; MRCP (UK) 1979. Hon. Cons. Phys. Qu. Eliz. Hosp. Gateshead; Prof. Stroke Med. & Elderly Care Univ. of Newc. upon Tyne. Prev: Sen. Lect. (Geriat. Med.) Univ. Liverp.; Prof. (Clin. Geriat. Med.).

BARER, Gwendoline Rachel (retired) 76 Dene Road, Wylam NE41 8HB Tel: 01661 853021 Email: o.r.barer@ncl.ac.uk — MA Oxf. 1961; BSc Lond. 1939, MB BS (Hons.) 1942. Prev: Reader (Med.) Univ. Sheff.

BARER, Michael Richard Department of Microbiology, The Medical School, Framlington Place, Newcastle upon Tyne NE2 4HH Tel: 0191 222 8264 Fax: 0191 222 7736 Email: m.r.barer@nel.ac.uk; 36 Castle View, Ovingham, Prudhoe NE42 6AU — MB BS 1978 Lond.; PhD Lond. 1987, MSc 1982, BSc 1975, MB BS 1978; FRCPath 1998; MRCPath 1989. Sen. Lect. (Microbiol.) Univ. Newc. u. Tyne; Reader. Prev: Lect. (Clin. Trop. Med.) Lond. Sch. Hyg. & Trop. Med.; Wellcome Fell. Path. Dept. Med. Microbiol. Lond. Sch. Hyg. & Trop. Med.; Regist. (Med. Microbiol.) St. Geo. Hosp. Lond.

BARETTO, Jennifer Maria 11 Copthorne Avenue, London SW12 0JZ — MB BS 1987 Lond.; DRCOG 1991.

BARETTO, Richard Lawrence 11 Copthorne Avenue, London SW12 0JZ — MB BS 1992 Lond.; MSc (Immunol.) Lond. 1995.

BARFF, Deborah Margaret Childrens Centre, Drove Road, Weston Super Mare BS23 6NT Tel: 01934 647265 Fax: 01934 613256 Email: deborah.barff@waht.swest.nhs.uk; 10 Cote Park, Westbury-on-Trym, Bristol BS9 2AD Tel: 0117 968 5889 — MB BChir 1971 Camb. Cons. Community Paediat. W.on Area Health Trust. Prev: SCMO W.on Area Health Trust.; Clin. Med. Off. Bristol & W.on HA.

BARFIELD, Lisa Jayne The Surgery, 2 Bennetts Road N., Kersley, Coventry CV7 8LA; 43 James Dawson Drive, Allesley, Coventry CV5 9QJ — MB ChB 1986 Sheff.

BARFIELD, Sandra Teglwyn, 28 North Road, Aberaeron SA46 0JG; 59 Riversdale, Llandaff, Cardiff CF5 2QL — MB BCh 1993 Wales; BSc (Hons.) Pharmacol. 1992; MRCP (UK) 1996. (Univ. Wales Coll. Med. Cardiff) SHO (A & E) Roy. Gwent Hosp. Newport. Socs: Med. Sickness Soc. Prev: SHO (Anaesth.) Singleton Hosp. Swansea; SHO (Med.) P.ss Wales Hosp. Bridgend.

BARFOOT, Louise Carolyn 19 Beresford Dr, Woodford Green IG8 0JJ — BM 1997 Soton. SHO Med.

BARFORD, Derek John Northfield Health Centre, 15 St. Heliers Road, Northfield, Birmingham B31 1QT Tel: 0121 478 1850 Fax: 0121 476 0931 — MB ChB 1978 Birm.

BARFORD, Mai The Surgery, Fairacre, 17 Lower Road, Fetcham, Leatherhead KT23 9EL Tel: 01372 374734; Waterloo Farm Cottage, 97 East Lane, West Horsley, Leatherhead KT24 6LR Tel: 01483 282109 — MB ChB 1960 Liverp. (Liverp.) Med. Off. (Paediat.) Surrey Co. Counc. Prev: Ho. Surg. & Ho. Phys. Sefton Gen. Hosp. Liverp.; Cas. Off. Roy. Surrey Co. Hosp. Guildford.

BARGE, Alan John Astra Zeneca, Alderley House, Alderley Park, Macclesfield SK10 4TF; Withinlee Brow, Withinlee Rd, Mottram St Andrew, Macclesfield SK10 4QE — MB BS 1982 Lond.; MRCP (UK) 1986. Med. Dir.

BARGER, Jennifer Isobel Health Unit, Canadian High Commission, Diplomatic Enclave, Sector G-5, PO Box 1042, Islamabad, Pakistan; Flat 3, South Hill Mansions, South Hill Park, London NW3 2SL Tel: 020 7435 2748 — MB BS 1973 Lond.; MRCS Eng. LRCP Lond. 1973. (Roy. Free)

BARGERY, Andrew Brannams Medical Centre, Brannams Square, Kiln Lane, Barnstaple EX32 8AP Tel: 01271 329004 Fax: 01271 346785; The Red House, Pilton St, Pilton, Barnstaple EX31 1PJ Tel: 01271 45569 — MB BS 1979 Lond.; MA Camb. (Hist.) 1972; MRCS Eng. LRCP Lond. 1979; MRCGP 1983; DRCOG 1983. (St. Bart.) Prev: Trainee GP/SHO N. Devon Dist. Hosp. Barnstaple VTS; Ho. Surg. St. Bart. Hosp. Lond.; Ho. Phys. Roy. Berks. Hosp. Reading.

BARGH, Donald Miles Barton Surgery, 1 Edmunds Close, Barton Court Avenue, Barton-on-Sea, New Milton BH25 7EH Tel: 01425 620830 Fax: 01425 629812 — MB BS 1981 Lond.; MA Camb. 1982; MRCGP 1985; DCH RCP Lond. 1985; DRCOG 1984. (King's Coll. Hosp.) Med. Off. Ballard Schs. & Durlston Ct. Sch. Hants.; Trainer Med. Stud. Teach. Hants.

BARGH, Ian Andrew The Surgery, 54 Church Avenue, Harrogate HG1 4HG Tel: 01423 564168 Fax: 01423 501102 Email: bilton.surg@btinternet.com; Graythwaite House, 12 Barnwell Crescent, Yew Tree Grange, Harrogate HG2 9EY Tel: 01423 528772 Email: ian.bargh@virgin.net — MB ChB 1986 Manch.; MRCGP 1991. (Manch.) Partner with Drs Jones, Thromton & Partners; Police Surg. with N. Yorks. Police.

BARGH, John Howard Farrow Medical Centre, 177 Otley Road, Bradford BD3 0HX Tel: 01274 637031; 5 Southlands, Town Close,

Town St, Horsforth, Leeds LS18 5BR Tel: 0113 258 2530 — MB ChB 1985 Leeds; DRCOG 1989. Prev: Trainee GP Leeds & Otley.

BARGHOUTI, Waddah Yousef 92 Devonport, Southwick St., London W2 2QF Tel: 020 7402 7802 — MB ChB 1978 Birm.

BARHAM, Christine (Channon) — MB BS 1983 Newc.; MB BS Newc.1983; MRCGP 1987; DRCOG 1987. p/t GP.

BARHAM, Christopher John The Queen Victoria Hospital, Holyte Road, East Grinstead RH19 3DZ Tel: 01342 410210 Fax: 01342 323420 Email: chris.barham@gvh-tr.sthames.nhs.uk; Spyways, Hartfield TN7 4DN Tel: 01892 770256 Fax: 01892 770887 Email: chris_barham@compuserve.com — MB BS 1972 Lond.; MRCS Eng. LRCP Lond. 1972; FFA RCS Eng. 1977. (King's Coll. Hosp.) Cons. Anaesth. Qu. Vict. Hosp. E. Grinstead; Med. Adviser Kent Electronic Pat. Record Project. Socs: Fell. Roy. Soc. Med.; Assn. Anaesth. GB & Irel. Chairm. Counc.; (Vice-Chairm.) Soc. Computing & Technol. Anaesth. Prev: Med. Dir. Qu. Vict. Hosp. NHS Trust; Sen. Regist. (Anaesth.) Roy. Sussex Co. Hosp. Brighton; Sen. Regist. (Anaesth.) King's Coll. Hosp. Lond.

BARHAM, Mr Christopher Paul Department of Surgery, Bristol Royal Infirmary, Marlborough St., Bristol BS2 8HW Tel: 0117 928 4942 Email: paul.barham@ubht.swest.nhs.uk, paul.barham@ublt.swest.nhs.uk; 34 South Croft, Henleaze, Bristol BS9 4PR — MB ChB 1985 Bristol; MD Bristol 1994; FRCS Ed. 1989; FRCS (Gen.) 1997. (Bristol) Cons. Gen. Surg. (Upper Gastrointestinal). Prev: Sen. Regist. Bristol Roy. Infirm.; Sen. Regist. S.mead Hosp. Bristol; Sen. Regist. Gloucester Roy. Hosp.

BARHAM, Derald Herbert (retired) 8 Stanbury Avenue, Watford WD17 3HW Tel: 01923 227010 — MB BS 1958 Lond.; LMSSA Lond. 1958; DTM & H Eng. 1962, DA 1963. Prev: Med. Off. Kwahu Hosp. Mpraeso, Ghana.

BARHAM, John Percival (retired) Wimblehurst, Church Road, Hythe CT21 5DP Tel: 01303 266005 — MB BS 1949 Lond.; MRCS Eng. LRCP Lond. 1944.

BARHAM, Nicola Jayne Anaesthesai Dept, South Cleveland Hospital, Martn rd, Middlesbrough TS4 3BW — MB ChB 1987 Birm.; FRCA 1993; MRCP (UK) 1990. Cons. S. Cleveland Anaesth. Dept. Socs: Assn. Anaesth.; Linkman for Anaesth. in Train. Prev: SHO (Anaesth.) Dudley Rd. Hosp. Birm.; SHO (Med.) Corbett Hosp. Stourbridge; SHO (Med.) Wordesley Hosp. Stourbridge.

BARHEY, Jagtar Singh Central Surgery, Corporation St., Rugby CV21 3SP Tel: 01788 574335; Tel: 01788 817299 — MB ChB 1994 Dundee. (Dundee) GP Princip. Centr. Surg., Rugby. Socs: BMA; MDU. Prev: Trainee GP/SHO (Gen. Med. & Psychiat.) Walsgrave Hosp. Coventry VTS; Trainee GP/SHO (O & G) Walsgrave Hosp. Coventry VTS; GP Regist., Centr. Surg., Rugby.

BARHEY, Manraj Bradley and Partners, 30 Woodland Avenue, Luton LU3 1RW Tel: 01582 572239 Fax: 01582 494227; Tel: 01582 619066 — MB BS 1988 Newc.; MRCGP 1994. Prev: Trainee GP/SHO Luton & Dunstable Hosp. VTS.

BARHEY, Narinda Kaur 6 Pinfold Street, Rugby CV21 2JD — MB ChB 1998 Birm.

BARI, Nabeela 25 Harold Road, London E11 4QX — MB BS 1998 Lond.; MB BS Lond 1998.

BARIK, Sukumar Department of Obstetrics & Gynaecology, Northern General Hospital, Herries Road, Sheffield S5 7AU; Flat 6, 282 Herries Road, Sheffield S5 7HA Tel: 0114 242 6967 — MB BS 1983 Calcutta; MRCOG 1990; MD 1985; DNB 1987; MFFP 1993. Staff O & G N.ern Gen. Hosp. Sheff. Socs: Life Mem. SOFIGO; Brit. Soc. Colpos. & Cerv. Path.

BARK, Christopher Michael 55 The Ridings, London W5 3DP — MB ChB 1992 Leic.

BARK, Oliver Geoffrey (retired) Cedar Lodge, West St., South Petherton TA13 5DQ Tel: 01460 240261 — MB ChB 1936 Liverp.; MA Camb. 1939; MRCGP 1953; DObst RCOG 1938. Prev: Ho. Surg. & Ho. Phys. Roy. S.. Hosp. Liverp.

BARK, Roger Michael (retired) Webb and Partners, Cox's Yard, West Street, Somerton TA11 7PR Tel: 01458 272473 Fax: 01458 274461 — MB BChir Camb. 1965; DObst RCOG 1966. Prev: Ho. Phys. Roy. Portsmouth Hosp.

BARK-JONES, Elizabeth Mary Havard 49 Denning Road, London NW3 1ST Tel: 020 7794 7431 — MB BS 1969 Lond.; DA Eng. 1971. (Middlx.)

BARKATAKI, Hirendra Chandra The Surgery, Church Walk, Eastwood, Nottingham NG16 3BH Tel: 01773 712951 Fax: 01773 534160 — MB BS 1966 Gauhati. (Assam Med. Coll.)

BARKATAKI, Nripen The Surgery, Marlborough, Seaham SR7 7TS Tel: 0191 581 2866 Fax: 0191 513 0393 — MB BS 1970 Dibrugarh. (Dibrugarh) GP Seaham, Co. Durh.

BARKBY, Grahame David St Catherines Hospice, Lostock Lane, Lostock Hall, Preston PR5 5XU Tel: 01772 629171; 121 Preston Road, Whittle-le-Woods, Chorley PR6 7PJ Tel: 01257 274978 — MB ChB 1976 Manch.; BSc (Hons.) St. And. 1973. Med. Dir. St. Catherine Hospice Preston; Clin. Asst. (Oncol.) Chorley & S. Ribble NHS Trust; Assoc. Specialist (Palliat. Med.) Chorley & S. Rebble NHS Trust & Roy. Preston Hosp NHS Acute Trust. Prev: GP Lancs. FHSA.

BARKEL, Jeanette Margot 22 Victoria Road, Hitchin SG5 2LS — MB BS 1979 Lond.; DRCOG 1982.

BARKELL, Eleanor Margaret 82 Bryanston Road, Solihull B91 1BS — MB BS 1997 Lond.

BARKER, Agnes Duff (retired) Laxmi House, 86 Station Road, Wem, Shrewsbury SY4 5BL Tel: 01939 232247 — MB ChB 1942 Glas.

BARKER, Alan Marcus Newhaven Health Centre, Chapel Street, Newhaven BN9 9PW Tel: 01273 615000 Fax: 01273 611527 — MB BS 1980 Lond.; BA (Physics) Oxf. 1975; MRCS Eng. LRCP Lond. 1980; MRCGP 1985; DRCOG 1984; DCH Eng. 1982. (Guy's)

BARKER, Andrew John Redwood House, Harracott, Barnstaple EX31 3JN — MB ChB 1995 Birm.

BARKER, Andrew Simon The Becton Centre, The Fairway, Barton on Sea, New Milton BH25 7AE — MB ChB 1986 Leic.; MSc Lond. 1988, MD 1994; MBA Keele 1997; MRCPsych 1992. (Univ. Leic.) Cons. Psychiat. of Old Age, Salisbury Healthcare NHS Trust. Prev: Sen. Regist. (Psychiat.) Wessex RHA; Research Fell. (c/o Elderly) St. Martin's Hosp. Bath; SHO Rotat. (Psychiat.) Oxf.

BARKER, Ann Faith Bracton Clinic, Bexley Hospital, Old Bexley Lane, Bexley DA5 2BW — MB BS 1971 Lond.; MPhil Lond. 1990, MB BS 1971; MRCPsych 1986. Cons. Forens. Psychiat. Bracton Clinic Bexley Hosp.

BARKER, Anthony Peter (retired) — MB ChB 1977 Liverp.; BSc (Hons. Anat.) Liverp. 1974; MRCS Eng. LRCP Lond. 1977. Univ. Community Clin. Teach. (Health Care Educat.).

BARKER, Brian Michael, Capt. RAMC Retd. Fernhall, 4 Collingwood Road, Horsham RH12 2QW Tel: 01403 326 6052; 57A Wimpole Street, London W1 — MB ChB 1965; BSc (1st cl. Hons.) Birm. 1962; MRCS Eng. LRCP Lond. 1965; FRSH Lond. 1975. (Birm.) GP Wimpole St., Lond. Socs: Fell. Roy. Soc. Med.; BMA; Fell. Roy. Soc. Health. Prev: Clin. Asst. Surg. Windsor Hosp. Gp.; Dir. Med. Affairs Johnson & Johnson UK; Med. Dir. Lond. & Med.

BARKER, Carol Ruth Brunswick Surgery, 18/19 Western Road, Hove BN3 1AE — MB BS 1988 Lond.; BA (Hons.) Lond. 1972. Prev: Trainee GP Brighton HA VTS.

BARKER, Caroline 33 Burnside Road, Newcastle upon Tyne NE3 2DU — MB BS 1993 Lond.; DRCOG 1996; MRCGP 1997. GP Asst.

BARKER, Caroline Elizabeth Merston, Green Farm Lane, Shorne, Gravesend DA12 3HL; 17 Whitehall Terrace, Aberdeen AB25 2RY — BM 1984 Soton. Sen. Regist. (Virol.) Aberd. Roy. Infirm.; Clin. Lect. Univ. Aberd. Socs: Hosp. Infec. Soc.; Assoc. Mem. Roy. Coll. Path.; Assn. Clin. Path. Prev: Regist. (Med. Microbiol.) Addenbrooke's Hosp. Camb.; Regist. & SHO (Path.) Ipswich Hosp.

BARKER, Professor Charles Philip Geoffrey, Surg. Cdr. RN Department Surgery, Royal Hospital Haslar, Alverstoke, Gosport PO12 2AA Tel: 01705 762116 Fax: 01705 762116; 13 Residence, Royal Hospital Haslar, Gosport PO12 2AA Tel: 01705 762562 — MB BS 1975 Lond.; MS Lond. 1992; FRCS Eng. 1980; FICS 1991. (Middlx.) Cons. Surg. RH Haslar, Gosport; Defence Med. Serv. Prof. Clin. Surg. Socs: Fell. Assn. Surgs.; Assoc. Fell. Brit. Assn. Paediat. Surg.; Vasc. Surgic. Soc. GB & Irel.

BARKER, Charles Simon Neuroradiology Department, Wessex Neurological Centre, Southampton General Hospital, Southampton SO16 6YD Tel: 02380 796983 Fax: 02380 794621 — MB ChB 1980 Bristol; MRCP (UK) 1984; T(R) (CR) 1991; FRCR 1987. Cons. Neuroradiol. Wessex Neurol. Centre Soton. Gen. Hosp. Socs: Brit. Soc. of Neuroradiologists (Treas); UK NeuroInterven.al Gp.; Brit. Inst. Of Radiol. Prev: Sen. Regist. (Neuroradiol.) Radcliffe Infirm.

Oxf.; Regist. (Med.) Qu. Eliz. Hosp. Birm.; Ho. Surg. & Phys. Bristol Roy. Infirm.

BARKER, Christopher 29 Spencers Lane, Melling, Liverpool L31 1HA — MB BS 1994 Lond.

BARKER, Christopher Thomas, Maj. RAMC Defence Services Psychiatric Centre, Duchess of Kent Hospital, Horne Road, Catterick Garrison DL9 3AP Tel: 01748 873173 — MB BS 1993 Lond. (Royal Free Hospital School of Medicine) SHO (Psychiat.), Brit. Forces Health Servs., Germany. Prev: Med. Off., 23 Para Field Ambul.

BARKER, Claire Louise Farfield, 200 Crewe Road, Alsager, Stoke-on-Trent ST7 2JF — MB BS 1998 Lond.; MB BS Lond 1998.

BARKER, Claire Nicola 21 Hawthorn Grove, Heaton Moor, Stockport SK4 4HZ Tel: 0161 442 4152 — MB ChB 1994 Manch. SHO Rotat. Diagnostic Radiol., N. W. Region.

BARKER, Clive Library House Surgery, Avondale Road, Chorley PR7 2AD Tel: 01257 262081; Euxton Lodge, 95A Wigan Road, Euxton, Chorley PR7 6JU — MB ChB 1982 Manch.; DRCOG 1985; MRCGP 1986.

BARKER, Craig Scott Touchwood 2 Howgate Cl, Bembridge PO35 5TG — MB ChB 1997 Aberd.

BARKER, Dave Alexander 32 Belsize Park, Hampstead, London NW3 4DX Tel: 020 7431 3362 — BM 1991 Soton. Regist. (Gen. Psychiat.) St. Lukes Woodside Hosp. Lond.

BARKER, David Alan (retired) New Leaze, Tincleton, Dorchester DT2 8QP — MRCS Eng. LRCP Lond. 1944. Prev: Ho. Phys. & Ho. Surg. Lond. Hosp.

BARKER, David Charles Grange Road Welfare Centre, Grange Road, Widdrington, Morpeth NE61 5LX Tel: 01670 790229 Fax: 01670 791312; The Granary, 6 Manor Farm, Ulgham, Morpeth NE61 3BH Tel: 01670 790133 Fax: 01670 791406 Email: dcbarker@manor-farm.demon.co.uk — MB BS 1982 Newc.; MRCGP 1986; T(GP) 1991; Cert. Family Plann. JCC 1987. (Newcastle)

BARKER, Professor David James Purslove MRC Environmental Epidemiology Unit, Southampton General Hospital, Southampton SO16 6YD Tel: 02380 777624 Fax: 02380 704021; Manor Farm, East Dean, Salisbury SP5 1HB Tel: 01794 340016 — MB BS 1962 Lond.; MD 1973 Lond; PhD Birm. 1966; BSc (1st cl. Hons.) Lond. 1959; FRCP Lond. 1979, M 1968; FRCOG 1993; FFPHM RCP (UK) 1979, M 1974; FRS 1998. (Guy's) Prof. (Clin. Epidemiol.) Univ. Soton.; Dir. MRC Environmt. Epidemiol. Unit; Hon. Cons. Phys. Soton. Univ. Hosps. Trust. Prev: Research Fell. (Social Med.) & Lect. (Med.) Univ. Birm.; Hon. Lect. (Epidemiol.) Makerere Univ., Uganda.

BARKER, David Lawrence Charles 17 Granville Park, Aughton, Ormskirk L39 5DS — MB ChB 1987 Dundee; MRCPath 1997. Cons. Histopath. Wigan & Leigh NHS Trust. Prev: Specialist Regist. (Histopath.) Glas. Sch. Path.; Regist. (Histopath.) Stobhill Gen. Hosp. Glas.; SHO (Histopath. & Cytol.) Wycombe Gen. Hosp.

BARKER, David Philip Department of Paediatrics St Mary's Hospital, Milton Road, Portsmouth PO3 6AD — MB ChB 1984 Liverp.; DM (Nottm.) 1997; MRCP (UK) 1990; DCH RCP Lond. 1989. Cons. Paediat. St. Mary's Hosp. Portsmouth. Prev: Lect. & Hon. Sen. Regist. (Child Health) Univ. Nottm.; Regist. (Paediat.) S. W. RHA; Ho. Phys. Hosp. Sick Childr. Gt. Ormond St. Lond.

BARKER, David Rodney Wellington House Surgery, Henrietta Street, Batley WF17 5DN Tel: 01924 470333 Fax: 01924 420981; 64 Moorside Crescent, Drighlington, Bradford BD11 1HS — MB ChB 1975 Leeds.

BARKER, Davnet Adrienne Veronica The Limes Medical Centre, The Plain, Epping CM16 6TL Tel: 01992 572727 Fax: 01992 574889; Stepping Stones, Kendal Avenue, Epping CM16 4PW Tel: 01992 573865 — MB BS 1958 Lond.; MRCS Eng. LRCP Lond. 1958; DObst RCOG 1961. (Roy. Free) Prev: SHO (O & G) Herts. & Essex Gen. Hosp. Bishop's Stortford; Resid. Anaesth. Roy. Free Hosp. Lond.

BARKER, Debra Stephanie 91 Robinson Road, London SW17 9DN; 26 Princes Road, Heaton Moor, Stockport SK4 3NQ Email: debra.barker@roche.com — MB 1987 Camb.; BA (Hons.) Camb. 1984; MSc Lond. 1990; BChir 1986. Internat. Med. Manager F. Hoffman La Roche Ltd. Socs: Assoc. Mem. Fac. Pharmaceut. Med.

BARKER, Denis Castledawson Surgery, Station Road, Castledawson, Magherafelt BT45 8AZ Tel: 028 7938 6237 Fax: 028 7946 9613; Castledown Surgery, Station Road, Castledown, Magherafelt BT45 2AA Tel: 01648 468294 — MB BCh BAO 1970 Belf.; FRCGP 1993, M 1974.

BARKER, Derek Charles (retired) The Old Stable, Crapstone Road, Yelverton PL20 6BT Tel: 01822 853557 — MRCS Eng. LRCP Lond. 1947; DObst RCOG 1950.

BARKER, Derek John Skin Deptartment, St Luke's Hospital, Little Horton Lane, Bradford BD5 0NA — MB BChir 1973 Camb.; MB Camb. 1973, BChir 1972; FRCP Lond. 1991. Cons. Dermat. Bradford Roy. Infirm. Prev: Lect. (Dermat.) Leeds Univ.

BARKER, Dudley (retired) September House, Lewes Road, Blackboys, Uckfield TN22 5LF Tel: 01825 890876 Email: dr-dudley@21.com — MRCS Eng. LRCP Lond. 1950; DOrth RCS 1965; LDS (Leeds). 1939.

BARKER, Elizabeth Anne 27 Alexandra Road, Reading RG1 5PE — MB BS 1972 Newc. Sen. Regist. (Community Med.) Oxf. RHA.

BARKER, Elizabeth Sandys (retired) Pine Corner, Elmstead Road, West Byfleet KT14 6JB Tel: 01932 345031 — MB BS 1957 Lond. Prev: Clin. Asst. (Med.) St. Peter's Hosp. Chertsey.

BARKER, Emma Victoria Orchard House, Moulton, Richmond DL10 6QJ — MB ChB 1995 Dundee.

BARKER, Eric Manor Cottage, Bradley Common, Whitchurch SY13 4QZ Tel: 01948 860305 — MB BS 1961 Lond.; MRCS Eng. LRCP Lond. 1961; MFOM RCP Lond. 1979; DIH Soc. Apoth. Lond. 1971. (Guy's) Prev: Sen. Med. Off. Brit. Nuclear Fuels Plc Capenhurst Works Chester & HeadOff. Risley Warrington; Med. Off. Brit. Leyland Castle Bromwich Body Plant & Brit. Leyland Assembly Plant Cowley.

BARKER, Faye Louise Chapel House, 5 The Green, Brompton, Northallerton DL6 2QT Tel: 0411 395584 — MB ChB 1996 Leeds.

BARKER, Frederick George Pathology Laboratory, Hillingdon Hospital, Uxbridge UB8 3NN — MB ChB 1979 Birm.; MA Oxon. 1976.

BARKER, Gary George Health Centre, Whyteman's Brae, Kirkcaldy KY1 2NA Tel: 01592 642902 Fax: 01592 644814; 14 West Albert Road, Kirkcaldy KY1 1DL Tel: 01592 260506 — MB ChB 1980 Ed.; MRCGP 1984.

BARKER, Geoffrey Battersby (retired) 9 Beresford Avenue, Twickenham TW1 2PY — MRCS Eng. LRCP Lond. 1943; MA Cantab. 1945, MB BChir 1948; FRCPsych 1973; DPM Eng. 1948. Hon. Cons. Psychiat. St. Thos. Hosp. Lond. Prev: Cons. & Med. Admin. Tooting Bec Hosp. Lond.

BARKER, Mr Geoffrey Neish Cotswold Cottage, Mill Lane, Winchcombe, Cheltenham GL54 5LT Tel: 01242 602357 — MB BS 1933 Lond.; FRCS Ed. 1935; MRCS Eng., LRCP Lond. 1932; DLO Eng. 1937. (St. Thos.) Prev: Surg. ENT Dept. Cheltenham Hosp. Gp.; Ho. Surg. ENT Dept. St. Thos. Hosp.; Clin. Tutor Ear & Throat Dept. Roy. Infirm. Edin.

BARKER, Geoffrey Robin Green Street Green Medical Centre, 21A High Street, Green Street Green, Orpington BR6 6BG Tel: 01689 850012 Fax: 01689 862247; The Old Rectory, Knockholt, Sevenoaks TN14 7PP — MB BS 1975 Lond.; MRCS Eng. LRCP Lond. 1975; DRCOG 1976. Prev: SHO (O & G) FarnBoro. Hosp.; Ho. Surg. Guy's Hosp.; Ho. Phys. Orpington Hosp.

BARKER, Professor Geoffrey Ronald 12 Wordsworth Place, Southampton Road, London NW5 4HG Tel: 020 7428 0274 Fax: 020 7428 0274; Fax: 01993 880580 — MB BS 1973 Lond.; MSc Manch. 1985; BSc (Physiol., 1st cl. Hons.) Lond. 1966; BDS (Hons., Distinc. Dent. Surg.) Lond. 1969; FRCS Ed. 1985; MRCS Eng. LRCP Lond. 1972; FFPM RCP (UK) 1996; FDS RCS Eng. 1979, LDS RCS 1969; Cert. Av Med. MoD (Air) & CAA 1975. (Guy's) Cons. Oral & Maxillofacial Surg. The Roy. Free Hosp. Lond.; Managing Dir. MENTOR Assoc. Ltd (Med. Dent. & Pharmaceut. Cons. Serv.); Sen. Med. Assessor, Meds. Control Agency. Socs: Expert Witness Inst. Prev: Med. Dir. Astra Pharmaceut. King's Langley; Prof. & Head of Dept. Oral Surg. Med. & Path. Univ. Wales Coll. Med. & Hon. Cons. Oral & Maxillofacial Surg. & Oral Med.; Sen. Lect. & Hon. Cons. Oral Surg. & Med. Univ. Manch.

BARKER, Gillian Margaret 55 Woodville Road, Harborne, Birmingham B17 9AR — MB ChB 1982 Aberd.; FRCS Ed. 1987. Regist. (Paediat. Surg.) Birm. Childr. Hosp. Prev: Career Regist. (Surg.) Kidderminster Gen. Hosp.; Research Regist. (Surg.) Qu. Eliz. Hosp. Edgbaston; Regist. (Gen. Surg.) Sandwell Dist. Gen. Hosp. Birm.

BARKER, Gordon Kinsman, MBE (retired) 75 Egloshayle Road, Wadebridge PL27 6AF Tel: 01208 812403 — MRCS Eng. LRCP

Lond. 1949; BA (Nat.Sc.Trip. 2nd cl.) Camb. 1942, MA 1950, MB BChir 1949.

BARKER, Mr Graham Harold, TD 12 Wolsey Close, Kingston upon Thames KT2 7ER Tel: 020 8942 2614 Email: grahambarker@colposcopy.org.uk — MB BS 1973 Lond.; MD Lond. 1991; FRCS Ed. 1980; FRCOG 1993, M 1978; AKC 1973. (King's Coll. Lond. & St. Geo.) Hon. Sen. Lect. (O & G) St. Geo. Hosp. Lond.; Astor Fell. Harvard Hosps., Boston 1984. Socs: Brit. Gyn. Cancer Soc.; Brit. Soc. Colpos. & Cerv. Path. Prev: Sen. Regist. (O & G) Middlx., Hosp. for Wom. Soho & Univ. Coll. Hosp. Lond.; Lect. Inst. Cancer Research & Regist. Qu. Charlotte's & Chelsea Hosps. for Wom. Lond.; Hon. Regist. Roy. Marsden Hosp. Lond.

BARKER, Graham John 5 St Nicholas Close, Tingrith, Milton Keynes MK17 9EL — MRCS Eng. LRCP Lond. 1981.

BARKER, Graham Leslie 23 Colney Lane, Cringleford, Norwich NR4 7RF — MRCS Eng. LRCP Lond. 1973; BSc (Hons.) Lond. 1970, MB BS 1973; FFA RCS Eng. 1978; DObst RCOG 1974. (Guy's) Cons. (Anaesth.) Norf. & Norwich Hosp. Norwich. Prev: Sen. Regist. (Anaesth.) Addenbrooke's Hosp. Camb.

BARKER, Graham Macmillan Schering Health Care Ltd, The Brow, Burgess Hill RH15 9NE Tel: 01444 465610 Email: gbarker@schering.co.uk; 22 Willow Park, Haywards Heath RH16 3UA Tel: 01444 458567 — MB ChB 1981 Manch.; BSc (Hons.) St. And. 1978; DipAvMed. (RCP) 1992; AFOM (RCP) 1993; AFPM 1999 (RCP). (St Andrews and Manchester) Assoc. Med. Director, Schering Health Care Ltd. Prev: Sen. Specialist in Aviat. Med. Roy. Navy.

BARKER, Graham Milton Hollies Medical Practice, Tamworth Health Centre, Upper Gungate, Tamworth B79 7EA Tel: 01827 68511 Fax: 01827 51163; School House, Main Road, Newton Regis, Tamworth B79 0NF Tel: 01827 830297 — MB ChB 1974 Leeds; BSc St. And. 1970.

BARKER, Harry Acroyd (retired) 22 Daleside Road, Riddlesden, Keighley BD20 5ES Tel: 01535 603265 — MB ChB 1937 Ed.; DPH 1946. Prev: Cons. Phys. Infec. Dis. Leeds RHB.

BARKER, Helen Carol The Red House, 78 Manchester Rd, Swinton, Manchester M27 5FG Tel: 0161 794 0875; 90 Northampton Road, Broughton, Kettering NN14 1NS Email: helen.barker@cwcom.net — MB ChB 1991 Manch.; MRCPsych 1996. Specialist Regist. (Psychother.) The Red Ho. Manch.

BARKER, Helen Edwina 48 Woodthorpe Park Drive, Sandal, Wakefield WF2 6NE — MB ChB 1976 Birm.

BARKER, Helen Frances Department of Haematology, Rotherham General Hospital, Moorgate Road, Rotherham S60 2UD Tel: 01709 820000 Fax: 01709 830694 Email: helenbarker@rgh-tr.nhs.uk — MB ChB 1984 Manch.; BSc Manch. 1982; MRCP (UK) 1988; MRCPath 1994. (Manch.) Cons. Haemat. Rotherham Gen. Hosp. Prev: Sen. Regist. (Haemat.) Birm. Childr. Hosp.; Sheldon Research Fell. (Haemat.) Qu. Eliz. Hosp. Birm.; Regist. (Haemat.) E. Birm. Hosp.

BARKER, Ian 32 Moorside, Blackbrook Road, Sheffield S10 4LN — MB ChB 1977 Dundee; FFA RCS 1981. Cons. Anaesth. Sheff. Childr. Hosp.

BARKER, Ian Anthony Hammond Holsworthy Health Centre, Western Road, Holsworthy EX22 6DH Tel: 01409 253692 Fax: 01409 254184; Sanctuary, Diddies Road, Stratton, Bude EX23 9DW Tel: 01288 353435 — MB BS 1964 Lond.; MRCS Eng. LRCP Lond. 1964; FRCGP 1984, M 1974; DCH Eng. 1967; DObst RCOG 1967. (Char. Cross) Princip. Holsworthy GP. Prev: Ho. Surg. (ENT) & Ho. Phys. (Paediat.) Char. Cross Hosp. Lond.; Ho. Phys. Fulham Hosp. Lond.

BARKER, Jack Anthony, Wing Cdr. RAF Med. Br. Retd. Pairc Medical Centre, The Surgery, Gravir, Isle of Lewis HS2 9QX Tel: 01851 880272 Fax: 01851 880201 — MB ChB 1962 Liverp.; AFOM RCP Lond. 1982; DLO Eng. 1967; MRAeS 1980. (Liverp.) GP Pairc Med. Pract., Isle of Lewis. Socs: Fell. Roy. Soc. Health. Prev: Sen. Med. Off. RAF Kinloss; Off. i/c Med. Wing PM RAF Hosp. Halton Aylesbury.

BARKER, James Michael The Health Centre, Front St., Hetton-le-Hole, Houghton-le-Spring DH5 9NX Tel: 0191 526 1177 Fax: 0191 517 3859; Bretton, Gillas Lane W., Houghton-le-Spring DH5 8JX Tel: 01783 842126 — MB BS 1959 Durh.; MRCGP 1974.

BARKER, Jean Elizabeth Dr J E Barker and Partners, 85 Ross Road, Maidenhead SL6 2SR Tel: 01628 623767 Fax: 01628 789623; Flat 34, Riverine, Grosvenor Drive, Maidenhead SL6 8PF Tel: 01628 23767 — MRCS Eng. LRCP Lond. 1965; BSc Birm. 1962, MB ChB 1965; MRCGP 1981. (Birm.) Prev: Ho. Phys. Birm. Childr. Hosp.; Ho. Surg. (Neurosurg.) Qu. Eliz. Hosp. Birm.

BARKER, Jean Valerie (retired) Ashenhurst, Rectory Lane, Stevenage SG1 4BX Tel: 01438 314823 — MD 1948 Toronto; LMS PEI 1949; Dip. Bact. Lond 1951. Prev: Sen. Med. Off. (Family Plann.) N. Herts. HA.

BARKER, Jennifer Anne 14 West Albert Road, Kirkcaldy KY1 1DL — MB ChB 1980 Ed.; MRCPsych 1984. (University of Edinburgh) Clin. Asst. (Child & Family Psychiat.) Stratheden Hosp. Cupar Fife.

BARKER, John 2 Kirkhouse Avenue, Blanefield, Glasgow G63 9BT — MB ChB 1950 Glas.; FRCA. 1992; FFA RCS Eng. 1961. Emerit. Cons. Neuroanaesth. Inst. Neurol. Sci. Glas. Socs: (Ex-Pres.) Glas. & W. Scotl. Soc. Anaesth.; Assn. Anaesth. Gt. Brit. & Irel. Prev: Vis. Assoc. Prof. Anaesth. Univ. of W.. Ontario; Cons. Anaesth. Paisley & Dist. Hosps.; Sen. Regist. (Anaesth.) Glas. Roy. Infirm.

BARKER, John Michael Blount The Surgery, Hillson Close, Port Isaac PL29 3TR Tel: 01208 880222 Fax: 01208 880633; Littlewood Mill, Trevisquite, St Mabyn, Bodmin PL30 3DF — MRCS Eng. LRCP Lond. 1964; BA Camb. 1961, MB 1965, BChir 1964; DA Eng. 1966. (Univ. Coll. Hosp.)

BARKER, John Philip 4 Selwyn Court, Queens Road, London E17 8XE Tel: 0208 520 2184 Email: john.barker15@virgin.net; 6 High Street, Burnham-on-Crouch CM0 8AA Tel: 01621784209 — MB BS 1961 Lond.; MRCS Eng. LRCP Lond. 1961; DMJ Soc. Apoth. Lond. 1970; DObst RCOG 1963. (Guy's) Medico-Legal Cons.; JP; Chartered Insur. Pract. Assoc. Chartered Insur. Inst. Socs: Fell. Roy. Soc. Med.; Medico-Legal Soc. Prev: HM Coroner E. Dist. Gtr. Lond.; GP Woodford Green; Dep. Med. Dir. Med. Protec. Soc.

BARKER, Mr John Robert Redwood House, Harracott, Barnstaple EX31 3JN Tel: 01271 858325 — MB ChB 1962 Birm.; FRCS Eng. 1969; FRCS Ed. 1967. Cons. Surg. N. Devon Dist. Hosp. Socs: Fell. Assn. Surgs.; Brit. Soc. Gastroenterol.; Vasc. Surg. Soc. GB & Irel. Prev: Sen. Regist. (Surg.) United Birm. Hosps.; Regist. (Surg.) Hammersmith Hosp. & Roy. Postgrad. Med. Sch.; Surg. Lt. RN.

BARKER, John Stuart 34 Well Ridge Close, Whitley Bay NE25 9PN — MB BS 1988 Newc.; MRCP (UK) 1992. Regist. (Cardiol.) Freeman Hosp. Newc. u. Tyne.

BARKER, Professor Jonathan Nicholas William Noel St John's Institute of Dermatology, St Thomas' Hospital, London SE1 7EH Tel: 020 7928 9292 Fax: 020 7620 0369 Email: jonathan.barker@kcl.ac.uk — MB BS 1981 Lond.; BSc Lond. 1978; FRCP Lond. 1995; MRCP (UK) 1985; MD 1999; FrcPath 2000. (Guy's Hosp. Lond.) Prof. Clin. Dermat., St. John's Inst. of Dermat., GKT Sch. of Med., King's Coll., Lond..; Hon. Cons. Guy's & St. Thos. Hosps. NHS Trust; Dir. Skin Ther. Research Unit St. John's Inst. Dermat.; Dean, St Johns Inst. of Dermat. Socs: (Bd. Mem.) Europ. Immunodermat. Soc.; Brit. Assn. Dermat.; (Bd. Med.) Brit. Soc. Investigative Dermat.

BARKER, Joseph Paul 2 East Ascent, St Leonards-on-Sea TN38 0DS — LMSSA 1979 Lond.

BARKER, Julia Margaret Pine Cottage, 29 The Evers, Saves Lane, Ireleth, Askam-in-Furness LA16 7EB — MD 1985 Nantes.

BARKER, Julian Michael 21 Hawthorn Grove, Heaton Moor, Stockport SK4 4HZ Tel: 0161 442 4152 — MB ChB 1993 Manch.; MRCP (UK) 1997. SHO Rotat. (Anaesth.) N. W. Region. Socs: Med. Defence Union; BMA. Prev: SHO (Anaesth.) Roy. Oldham Hosp.; SHO Rotat. (Med.) Mcclesfield Dist. Gen. Hosp.

BARKER, Julie Anne de Gay and Partners, The Surgery, 50 Barnaby Gate, Newark NG24 1QD Tel: 01636 815234 Fax: 01636 613044 Email: juliebarker@gp-c84009.nhs.uk — BM BS 1987 Nottm.; BMedSci Nottm. 1985; Dip. Psychosexual Med. 1997. (Univ. Nottm.)

BARKER, Karen The Fairfield Centre, Fairfield Grove, Charlton, London SE7 8TX Tel: 020 8858 5738 Fax: 020 8305 3005 — MB BS 1989 Lond.; DRCOG 1993.

BARKER, Keith Frank Glaxosmithkline, Harlow CM19 5AW; 28 Westbourne Terrace, London W2 3UP — MB BS 1985 Lond.; MA, BA Oxf. 1982; MSc Lond. 1991; MRCPath 1992. Prev: Med. Assessor Med. Control Agency Lond.; Cons. Microbiol. Pub. Health Laborat. Centr. Middlx. Hosp. Lond.; Sen. Regist. (Med. Microbiol.) PHLS Dulwich Hosp. Lond.

BARKER, Keith Michael The Health Centre, Coatham Road, Redcar TS10 1SX Tel: 01642 475157 Fax: 01642 470885; 30 Green Lane, Redcar TS10 3RW Tel: 01642 475157 Fax: 01642 470885 — MB BS 1972 Newc.; MRCGP 1976; DFFP 1996; DObst RCOG 1974.

BARKER, Kenneth Fitch Dormer Cottage, Whitehills Farm, Abernyte, Perth PH14 9RD — MB ChB 1990 Glas. SHO (Anaesth.) Ninewells Hosp. Dundee.

BARKER, Lindsey Carol Mark Ash, 116 Shinfield Road, Reading RG2 7DA Tel: 0118 986 8671 — MB ChB 1979 Bristol; MRCP (UK) 1982. Assoc. Specialist Roy. Berks. Hosp. Reading. Socs: Med. Res. Soc.; Renal Assn. Prev: Sen. Regist. (Geriat. Med.) John Radcliffe Hosp. & Radcliffe Infirm.; Regist. (Med.) Roy. Berks. Hosp. Reading.

BARKER, Miss Lindsey Gay — MB ChB 1990 Manch.; FRCS Glas. 1995. Specialist Regist. (Gen. Surg.) SE Thames Higher Surgic. Train. Regional Rotat.

BARKER, Lucie Helen 30 Coombe Road, Sheffield S10 1FF — MB ChB 1996 Sheff.

BARKER, Margaret Anne Camden and Islington Health Authority, 110 Hampstead Road, London NW1 2LJ Tel: 020 7380 9935 Fax: 020 7380 9675; 5 West Temple Sheen, East Sheen, London SW14 7RT Tel: 020 8876 6768 Fax: 020 8876 6768 — MB BS 1982 Lond.; MSc Lond. 1988, BSc 1975, MD 1995; MFPHM RCP (UK) 1989; FFPHM RCP (UK) 1998. Dir. Pub. Health Camden & Islington HA; Hon. Sen. Lect. Inst. of Child Health Lond. Socs: BMA; Soc. Social Med. Prev: Cons. Pub Health Brent & Harrow HA.

BARKER, Margaret Rose Stevenson Children's Centre, Damers Road, Dorchester DT1 2LB Tel: 01305 251150; 45 Bridport Road, Dorchester DT1 2NG Tel: 01305 260959 — MB ChB 1966 Birm.; FRCP Lond. 1992, M 1979; MRCS Eng. LRCP Lond. 1966; DCH Eng. 1968. (Birm.) Cons. Community Paediat. W. Dorset Gen. Hosps. Trust.

BARKER, Martin Elliott The Surgery, The Sheepmarket, Stamford PE9 2SL Tel: 01780 753151 Fax: 01780 757536; 12 Austin Street, Stamford PE9 2QP Tel: 01780 764616 Fax: 01780 757536 — MB ChB 1961 St. And.; FRCGP 1982, M 1972; DObst RCOG 1963. (St Andrews Univ. Hosp.) Socs: BMA & Brit. Assn. Manip. Med. Prev: Regist. (Med.) Dist. Hosp. P'boro.; Asst. Phys. Sherwood Hosp. Nottm.

BARKER, Michael John Mowbray Hardwicke House Surgery, Hardwicke House, Stour Street, Sudbury CO10 2AY Tel: 01787 370011 Fax: 01787 376521; Tel: 01787 370011 Fax: 01787 376521 — MB BS 1967 Lond. (St. Bart. Hosp.) Mem. Local Med. Off. Suff. Socs: BMA & Colchester Med. Soc. Prev: Research Fell. Nuffield Inst. Comparative Med. Lond.; Clin. Asst. (Ment. Handicap.) Bridge Hosp. Witham.

BARKER, Miriam Sarah Anne 6 Selside Court, Beeston, Nottingham NG9 5NF — MB BS 1986 Lond.

BARKER, Montagu Gordon (retired) — MB ChB 1960 St. And.; FRCP Ed. 1972, M 1964; FRCPsych 1979, M 1971; DPM Ed. & Glas. 1963. Prev: Cons. Psychiat. & Med. Dir. Heath Hse. Priory Hosp. Bristol.

BARKER, Nicola Jane Thorner Cottage, The Green, Pirbright, Woking GU24 0JT — MB BS 1988 Lond.; MRCGP 1995; DRCOG 1995; Cert. Family Plann. JCC 1990. Asst. GP Lond. Prev: Trainee GP/SHO Barnet Gen. Hosp. VTS.

BARKER, Nigel Ian 8 Dorchester Avenue, Prestwich, Manchester M25 0LH — MB ChB 1997 Sheff.

BARKER, Pamela Margaret Wentworth (retired) Burnside, Leachkin Road, Inverness IV3 8NW — BSc Leeds 1951, MB ChB 1957; MRCPsych 1976; DPM Eng. 1965. Cons. (Psychiat.) Craig Dunain Hosp. Inverness. Prev: Ho. Phys. & Ho. Surg. Leeds Gen. Infirm.

BARKER, Paul Norfolk & Norwich Hospital, St Stephens Road, Norwich NR1 3; The Far End Claxton Mill, Mill Lane, Norwich NR14 7AU — MB BS 1984 Lond.; FCAnaesth. 1989. Cons. Anaesth. Norf. & Norwich Hosp. Prev: Cons. Anaesth. Leicester Gen. Hosp.; Sen. Regist. (Anaesth.) Leicester Roy. Infirm.; Lect. (Anaesth.) Univ. Leicester.

BARKER, Paul Geoffrey Ground Floor Flat, 55 The Avenue, Moordown, Bournemouth BH9 2UP — MB BS 1998 Lond.; MB BS Lond 1998.

BARKER, Peter Anthony The Health Centre, Albany Road, Invergordon IV18 0DH Tel: 01349 852522 Fax: 01349 852530 — MB BS 1971 Lond.; MRCS Eng. LRCP Lond. 1971.

BARKER, Peter Gerard Sidcup MRI Centre, Queen Mary's Hospital, Frognal Avenue, Sidcup DA14 6LT Tel: 020 8309 4720 Fax: 020 8309 4721 Email: pbarker@mri-scan.demon.co.uk; Belltrees, Sandown Road, Sandwich CT13 9NY Fax: 01304 613352 — MB BS 1983 Lond.; FRCR 1990. (Guy's Hospital, London) Cons. (Radiol.), E. Kent Hosp. NHS Trust; Dir., Magnetic Resonance Imaging, Qu. Mary's Hosp. Kent; Hon. Cons. St Bart's Hosp. Lond. Socs: Fell. Roy. Coll. Radiol.; BMA; Radiol. Soc. N. Amer.

BARKER, Peter James Coventry HA, Christchurch House, Greyfriars Lane, Coventry CV1; Apple Tree Cottage, MainST, Bruntingthorpe, Leicester LE17 5QF — MB ChB 1981 Leic.; MFPHM RCP (UK) 1994; DGM RCP Lond. 1987; DRCOG 1985. Cons. Pub. Health Coventry HA. Prev: Sen. Regist. (Pub. Health) Solihull HA.

BARKER, Peter Ralph Green Street Green Medical Centre, 21A High Street, Green Street Green, Orpington BR6 6BG Tel: 01689 850012 Fax: 01689 862247; Copperkins, Stonehouse Road, Halstead, Sevenoaks TN14 7HW — MB BS 1982 Lond.; MRCP (UK) 1985; MRCGP 1989. (Westm.) Clin. Asst. (Ophth.) High Wycombe Gen. Hosp. Socs: (Hon. Sec.) Chiltern Med. Soc. Prev: Princip. GP Gt. Missenden, Bucks.; Clin. Asst. (Neurol.) Kent & Sussex Hosp. Tunbridge Wells; SHO (Gen. Med.) St. Stephen's Hosp. Lond.

BARKER, Philip Nigel The Almshouse Surgery, Trinity Medical Centre, Thornhill Street, Wakefield WF1 1PG Tel: 01924 327150 Fax: 01924 327165; 23 Willow Park, Newton Hill, Wakefield WF1 2JP — MB BS 1976 Newc.; MRCP (UK) 1982; MRCGP 1984.

BARKER, Richard John — MB ChB 1990 Leeds; BA (Hons.) Camb. 1987.

BARKER, Richard Michael Southampton & South West Hampshire Health Authority, Oakley Road, Southampton SO16 4GX Tel: 02380 725400 Fax: 02380 725457 — MB BS 1977 Lond.; MPH 1988; MFPHM 1990. (Middlx.) Cons. Communicable Dis. Control Soton. & SW Hants. HA. Prev: Cons. Pub. Health Med. Herefordsh. HA; Sen. Regist. (Community Med.) Bradford HA; Regist. (Anaesth.) N.ampton Gen. Hosp.

BARKER, Richard William Francis The Queens Road Medical Practice, The Grange, St. Peter Port, Guernsey GY1 1RH Tel: 01481 724184 Fax: 01481 716431; Le Motet, Rue Motet, St. Martins, Guernsey GY4 6ED Tel: 01481 234111 Email: billy.barker@ukgateway.net — MB BS 1986 Lond.; MSc (Sports Med.) Lond. 1994; DA (UK) 1990. (Lond. Hosp. Med. Coll.) Socs: Brit. Assn. Sport & Med.; BMA; RCGP.

BARKER, Robert Fraser Fairhaven, 1 The Dene, Beardwood, Blackburn BB2 7QS — MB BChir 1978 Camb.; MA, MB Camb. 1979, BChir 1978; FRCR 1984. Cons. Diag. Radiol. Blackburn, Hyndburn & Ribble Valley HA; FRCR; Fell Manch. Med. Soc. Prev: Sen. Regist. Diag. Radiol. Manch. HA.

BARKER, Robert James 39 Calverley Road, Epsom KT17 2NX — BM 1993 Soton.

BARKER, Rodney William 17/18 Toddington Road, Tingrith, Milton Keynes MK17 9EQ Tel: 01582 594607; Hand Post Cottage, Tingrith, Milton Keynes MK17 9EQ Tel: 01582 594607 Fax: 01582 594607 — MB BS 1967 Lond.; MRCS Eng. LRCP Lond. 1967; DObst RCOG 1971. (Univ. Lond., King's Coll. Hosp.) Indep. Cons. Med. Pract. Beds. Prev: Princip. Beds. FMSA; Ho. Phys. & Regist. i/c Cas. Dept. King's Coll. Hosp. Lond.; Ho. Surg. Guy's-Maudsley Neurosurg. Unit Lond.

BARKER, Roger Alistair National Hospital for Neurology & Neurosurgery, Queen Square, London WC1N 3BG Tel: 020 7837 3611 Fax: 020 7829 8720; 4 High Street, Foxton, Cambridge CB2 6SP — MB BS 1986 Lond.; PhD Camb. 1994; BA Oxf. 1983; MRCP (UK) 1989. Regist. Nat. Hosp. Neurol. & Neurosurg. Lond. Prev: Regist. (Neurol.) Addenbrooke's Hosp. Camb.; Research Regist. (Experim. Psychol.) Camb.; Regist. St. Thos. Hosp. Lond.

BARKER, Rosalind Margaret 34 Montefiore Street, London SW8 3TP — MB BChir 1995 Camb.; MRCP I + II.

BARKER, Rosetta Catherine (retired) 234 Ballyveely Road, Cloughmills, Ballymena BT44 9NW — MB BCh BAO 1935 Belf.; MFCM 1974; DPH Lond. 1939. Prev: Sen. Med. Off. (Community Med.) W. Sussex AHA.

BARKER, Ross Lyndon 24 Burn Bridge Oval, Burn Bridge, Harrogate HG3 1LP — MB BS 1997 Lond. (University College and

Middlesex School of Medicine) Surg Train. Rotat. Lancaster Roy Infirm. Prev: HO.(Med.) Nobles IOM Hosp; HO.(Surg.) Whittington Hosp. Lond.

BARKER, Samantha Jane 8 Yarmouth Av, Grantham NG31 7LJ — MB ChB 1997 Leic.

BARKER, Samuel Stanley 16 Bowenhurst Road, Church Crookham, Fleet GU52 6HS Tel: 01252 629099 Fax: 01252 629099 — MB BS 1952 Lond.; FFA RCS Eng. 1959; DA Eng. 1957. (Guy's) Cons. Anaesth. Roy. Surrey Hosp. & St. Luke's Hosp. Guildford. Prev: Sen. Regist. Anaesth. Guy's Hosp. Lond.; Sen. Ho. Off. (Anaesth.) Walton Hosp. Liverp.; Ho. Phys. King Edwd. Memor. Hosp. Ealing.

BARKER, Sarah Elizabeth Camberley Health Centre, 159 Frimley Road, Camberley GU15 2QA Tel: 01276 20101 Fax: 01276 21661; Wanborough Barn, Wanborough, Guildford GU3 2JR Tel: 01483 810198 — MB BS 1963 Lond.; MRCS Eng. LRCP Lond. 1963. (Roy. Free) GP Camberley.

BARKER, Mr Simon Brand 6 Wolsey Court, Stanley Road, Felixstowe IP11 7DJ — MB ChB 1973 Birm.; FRCS Eng. 1979. Urol. & Renal Transpl. Surg. Ibn Al Bitar Hosp. Baghdad, Iraq.

BARKER, Simon Lee 5 High Street, Aberdeen AB24 3EE Tel: 01224 487246 Email: slbarker@rcsed.ac.uk — MB BS 1994 Lond.; BSc Lond. 1991; FRCS (Ed) 1998. (Guy's and St. Thomas' Hospitals) Research Fell./Lect. in Orthop. Surg., Univ. of Aberd. Med. Sch., Aberd. Socs: Chairm., Grampian Jun. Doctors Comm. Prev: SHO (Orthop. Surg.) Aberd. Roy. Infirm.

BARKER, Simon Stanley Hellesdon Hospital, Drayton High Road, Norwich NR6 5BE Tel: 01603 421616 — MB ChB 1983 Leic.; MRCPsych 1987.

BARKER, Sophie Joanna 7 Burdenshott Avenue, Richmond TW10 5EE — BM 1998 Soton.

BARKER, Stanley Raymond 36 Airedale Avenue, Tickhill, Doncaster DN11 9UD — MB ChB 1967 Sheff.; MB ChB 1967 Sheff; DObst. RCOG 1969. Regional Med. Off. DHSS (EMDMO Nottm.).

BARKER, Mr Stephen George Edward The Vascular Laboratory, The Middlesex Hospital, Mortimer Street, London W1N 8AA Tel: 020 7813 9972 Fax: 020 7813 9971 Email: stephen.barker@ucl.ac.uk; 16 Wilks Gardens, Shirley CR0 8UJ — MB BS 1984 Lond.; BSc (Hons.) Lond. 1981, MS 1992; FRCS Eng. 1988. (St. Thos.) Sen. Lect. Univ. Coll. Lond. Cons. Vasc. Surg. UCLH. Socs: Vasc. Surg. Soc.; Eur. Vasc. Surg. Soc.; Assn. Surg. Prev: Sen. Regist. (Vasc. Surg.) King's Coll. Hosp. Lond.; Sen. Regist. Roy. Adelaide Hosp., S. Austral.

BARKER, Susan Andrea 50 Faber Avenue, Singapore 129552, Singapore Tel: 00 65 7736801; The Garden Flat, 21 The Park, Ealing, London W5 5NL — BM BS 1991 Nottm.; BMedSci Nottm. 1989. GP Singapore. Socs: MDU & BMA. Prev: GP Assist. Ealing; Trainee GP/SHO Hillingdon Hosp. VTS; SHO (Paediat.) Hemel Hempstead.

BARKER, Susan Gwendolen Ingham House, Church Hill, Ingham, Lincoln LN1 2YE — MB BS 1976 Lond.; MRCS Eng. LRCP Lond. 1976; DRCOG 1978; FFARCS Eng. 1981. (Guy's)

BARKER, Teresa Maria Burnley Health Care Trust, Reedley Hall, Colne Road, Burnley BB10 2LW Tel: 01282 602754 Fax: 01282 619673; Fairhaven, 1 The Dene, Beardwood, Blackburn BB2 7QS — MB BChir 1979 Camb.; MA, MB Camb. 1979, BChir 1978; MRCPCH 1997; DCH Eng. 1980. (Kings College London & Newham College, Cambs) Assoc. Specialist (Community Child Health) Burnley Healthcare NHS Trust Burnley. Socs: MRCPCH; BACCH. Prev: SCMO (Child Health) Communicare NHS Trust Blackburn; Clin. Med. Off. (Child Health) Burnley, Pendle & Rossendale HA.

BARKER, Timothy Huw Wilson Norfolk & Norwich Hospital, Brunswick Road, Norwich Tel: 01603 280020 Fax: 01603 286017 Email: tim.barker@norfolk-norwich.thenhs.com — MB 1977 Camb.; 1976 B Chir; 1982 MRCPath; 1992 FRCPath. Cons. Histopath. Norf. & Norwich Hosp. Prev: Sen. Regist. Addenbrookes Hosp. Camb.

BARKER, Victor Charles Joseph 10 New River Avenue, Stanstead Abbotts, Ware SG12 8BL — MB BS 1954 Lond. Prev: GP Essex.

BARKER, Vira (retired) 82 Darwin Court, Gloucester Avenue, London NW1 7BQ Tel: 020 7911 0570 Fax: 020 7911 0570 — MB BS Bombay 1945. Prev: Clin. Asst. (Cytol.) Papworth Hosp. Camb.

BARKER, Wendy Elisabeth Arundel Street Surgery, 10 Arundel Street, Treeton, Rotherham S60 5PW Tel: 0114 269 2600 Fax: 0114 269 3296; 46 Conduit Road, Crookes, Sheffield S10 1EW Tel: 0114 268 5033 — MB ChB 1984 Sheff.

BARKER, William Anthony Hartside Unit, St. Nicholas' Hospital, Jubilee Rd, Gosforth, Newcastle upon Tyne NE3 3XT Tel: 0191 273 6666 Fax: 0191 223 2537; 19 Longmeadows, Darras Hill, Ponteland, Newcastle upon Tyne NE20 9DX Email: mail@barkerworld.fsnet.co.uk — MB BS 1976 Newc.; MRCP (UK) 1979; MRCPsych 1982; FRCP 2000; FRCP 1996 (Psych). Cons. Neuropsychiat. Newc. City Health NHS Trust; Hon. Clin. Lect. Univ. Newc.; Hon. Cons. NeuroPsychiat., Dept. of Med. Genetics, N.ern Region Genetics Serv., Newc. upon Tyne. Prev: Cons. Psychiat. N.. RHA; Lect. (Psychiat.) Univ. Newc. u. Tyne.

BARKER, William Hawksworth (retired) Ashenhurst, Rectory Lane, Stevenage SG1 4BX Tel: 01438 314823 — MB BChir 1947 Camb.; MA (Hons.) Camb. 1948. Prev: GP Stevenage.

BARKHAM, David William, OBE 15 Colebrooke Row, London N1 8DB Tel: 020 7837 3733 — MB BChir 1958 Camb.; FRCP Lond. 1975, M 1960. Prev: Sen. Govt. Phys. Uganda Med. Serv.; Cons. Phys. Specialist Hosp. Riyadh, Saudi Arabia; Chief Med. Al-Salam Hosp. Sadah, N. Yemen.

BARKHAM, Justin David Titus Coggeshall Surgery, Stoneham Street, Coggeshall, Colchester CO6 1UH Tel: 01376 561242 Fax: 01376 563486 — MB BS 1988 Lond.; T(GP) 1992; DRCOG 1991.

BARKHAM, Magnus Nichol 2B Berry Street, Aberdeen AB25 1DL — MB ChB 1993 Aberd.

BARKHAM, Miranda Helen 65 Hall Farm Road, Duffield, Belper DE56 4FJ — MB ChB 1995 Aberd.

BARKLEY, Alastair Simon John Po Box 30076, London SE1 4FP Tel: 07769 292386 Fax: 020 72885831 Email: epid@globalnet.co.uk; Tel: 020 747072568 — MB BS 1978 Lond.; DHMSA 2002; FRCP Lond. 1997; MRCP (UK) 1982. (Roy. Free) p/t Cons. (Dermat.) The Whittington NHS Trust. Prev: Cons. (Dermat.) The Medway NHS Trusts; Sen. Regist. (Dermat.) Qu. Med. Centre & Univ. Hosp. Nottm.; Regist. (Dermat.) Roy. Infirm. Edin.

BARKLEY, Andrea Mary Eastgates, Main St., Swardeston, Norwich NR14 8AD — MB BS 1991 Lond.

BARKLEY, Anna Charlotte Frenchay Hospital, Frenchay Park Rd, Bristol BS16 1LE; Mill House, Rookery Drive, Wescott, Dorking RH4 3LQ Tel: 01306 882720 — MB ChB 1994 Bristol; MRCP/MRCPCH 1998. SHO (Paed)Bristol; SHO (A & E) Norwich. Prev: Ho. Off. (Med.) S.mead Hosp. Bristol; Ho. Off. (Surg.) Torbay.

BARKLEY, Claire The Foundation NHS Trust, Corporation St., Stafford ST16 3AG Tel: 01785 257888 Fax: 01785 221371 — MB ChB 1983 Ed.; MRCPsych 1988. Cons. Forens. Psychiat. The Foundat. NHS Trust. Prev: Sen. Regist. (Forens. Psychiat.) Prestwich Hosp. Manch.; Sen. Regist. (Forens. Psychiat.) Maudsley Hosp.; Research Assoc. & Hon. Sen. Regist. (Psychiat.) Camb. Univ.

BARKLEY, Diana Elizabeth Helen 54 Primrose Gardens, London NW3 4TP — MB BS 1982 Lond.; BSc (Hons.) Lond. 1979, MB BS 1982; MRCP (UK) 1985.

BARKWORTH, Frederic Basil Stileman (retired) 17 Clifton Close, Park Avenue, Eastbourne BN22 9QQ Tel: 01523 506517 Email: barkworthb@aol.com — MB BS Lond. 1945. Prev: Res. Med. Off. Mildmay Miss. Hosp. Bethnal Green.

BARLAS, John Alexander, TD (retired) Higlers, Shipbourne, Tonbridge TN11 9PP Tel: 01732 810463 — MB BS 1944 Lond.; MRCS Eng. LRCP Lond. 1944; MRCGP 1968. Clin. Asst. Geriat. Dept. Pembury Hosp. Prev: Childr. Ho. Phys. St. Helier Co. Hosp. Carshalton.

BARLEE, Rosemary Jane 6 Werberside Mews, Edinburgh EH4 1SW — MB ChB 1987 Aberd.; MRCPsych 1993. Staff Grade (Psychiat.) Kettering. Prev: Clin. Asst. (Psychiat.) Kettering; Regist. & SHO (Psychiat.) St. Crispin Hosp. N.ampton.

BARLEY, Janet 8 Chestnut Grove, Clevedon BS21 7LA — MB BChir 1967 Camb.; MRCS Eng. LRCP Lond. 1966; MRCPsych. 1979.

BARLEY, John Albert (Surgery), New St., Dinnington, Sheffield S25 2QD; The Manor House, South Anston, Sheffield S25 5FS — MB ChB 1973 Sheff.; MRCGP 1980; DRCOG 1976.

BARLEY, Michael Gordon, RD Church Surgery, Saunders Park Rise, Lewes Road, Brighton BN2 4ES; 10 Queen Alexandra Avenue, Hove BN3 6XH Tel: 01273 505239 — MB BS 1964 Lond. (Guy's) Socs: BMA (Hon. Sec. Brighton Div.).

BARLEY, Penelope Elizabeth 10 New Dover Road, Canterbury CT1 3AP Tel: 01227462197 Fax: 01227786041 — MB ChB 1979 Sheff.; MRCGP 1984 London; DRCOG 1983 London. Partner in Gen. Pract.

BARLEY, Simon Learmonth (retired) Hollow Barn, Woodhead Road, Wortley, Sheffield S35 7DS Tel: 0114 246 7093 Fax: 0114 246 7093 — MB BS Lond. 1966.

BARLEY, Victor Laurence Bristol Haematology & Oncology Centre, Horfield Road, Bristol BS2 8ED Tel: 0117 928 2415 Fax: 0117 928 3572 Email: victor.barley@ubht.swest.nhs.uk; 11 Barrow Court Mews, Barrow Gurney, Bristol BS48 3RW Tel: 01275 463006 — MB BChir 1970 Camb.; MRCS Eng. LRCP Lond. 1966; DObst RCOG 1968; DPhil Oxf. 1973; DMRT Eng. 1974; FRCS Ed. 1975; FRCR 1976. Cons. Clin. Oncol. United Bristol Healthcare NHS Trust; Macmillan Lead Clinicain for User Involvem. Avon Som. & Wilts. Cancer Servs. Socs: Brit. Inst. of Radiol., Dep. Edr. of Brit. Jl. of Radiol. Prev: Sen. Regist. (Radiother.) Ch.ill Hosp. Oxf.; Research Assoc. Nuffield Dept. O & G Univ. Oxf.; Demonst. (Human Anat.) Univ. Oxf.

BARLIN, Carol Ann Berrylands Surgery, Howard Road, Surbiton KT5 8SA Tel: 020 8399 6362 Fax: 020 8339 5700 — MB BCh 1969 Witwatersrand. (Witwatersrand)

BARLING, Jason Michael 31 Greyhound Road, London W6 8NH — MB BS 1996 Lond.

BARLING, Peter Seymour Lorraine Willow Street Medical Centre, 81-83 Willow Street, Oswestry SY11 1AJ Tel: 01691 653143 Fax: 01691 679130; Vron Lodge, Pant Glas, Oswestry SY10 7HR Tel: 01691 658827 Fax: 01691661709 — MB ChB 1972 Birm.; LMCC 1976; DA (UK) 1975; DObst RCOG 1974. Clin. Asst. (Anaesth.) Shropsh. Orthop. Hosp.; Hosp. Practitioner; Clin. Tutor; Police Surg. Prev: on Med. Staff Banff Mineral Springs Hosp. Alberta & Vict. Gen. Hosp. Brit. Columbia, Canada.

BARLING, Rosemary Willow Street Medical Centre, 81-83 Willow Street, Oswestry SY11 1AJ Tel: 01691 653143 Fax: 01691 679130 — MB BS 1973 Lond.; LMCC 1976; DObst RCOG 1975. (Middlx. Hosp. Univ. Lond.) Clin. Asst. Terminal care & palliat. med. Shrops. & Mid Wales Hospice.

BARLING, Rosemary Gillian (Jill) Mann Cottage Surgery, Oxford Street, Moreton-in-Marsh GL56 0LA Tel: 01608 650764 Fax: 01608 650996; The Walnuts, Paxford, Chipping Campden GL55 6XP Tel: 01386 78544 — MB ChB 1970 Birm.; DA Eng. 1973; Cert FPA. 1979.

BARLING, Timothy Charles Moorfield House Surgery, 35 Edgar Street, Hereford HR4 9JP Tel: 01432 272175 Fax: 01432 341942; Kington Cottage, Burghill, Hereford HR4 7RX — MB ChB 1979 Birm.; Diploma of Muscoloskeletal Medicine 1998; DRCOG 1984. Musculoskeletal Phys.,Heref. Musculoskeletal clinic, Beaumont, Hereford. Prev: Trainee GP/SHO Droitwich & BromsGr. Gen. Hosp. VTS.

BARLOW, Alan Marsh (retired) Corner House, Stainton, Penrith CA11 0ES Tel: 01768 866782 Email: albarlow@lineone.net — MD 1959 Manch.; MB ChB 1954; FRCP Ed. 1973, M 1961; FRCPath 1975, M 1963. Prev: Cons. Pathol. Roy. Infirm. Huddersfield.

BARLOW, Alan Robert The Health Centre, Gotham Lane, East Leake, Loughborough LE12 6JG Tel: 01509 852181 Fax: 01509 852099 — MB ChB 1967 Ed.; FRCGP 1992, M 1978; DObst RCOG 1972; DCH RCPS Glas. 1969. (Ed.) Lect. (Gen. Pract.) Univ. Nottm. Socs: BMA & Nottm. M-C Soc.; Assn. Aviat. Med. Examrs. Prev: Ho. Surg. & Ho. Phys. Edin. Roy. Infirm.; Med. Off. Zambia Flying Doctor Serv.; Med. Off. Internat. Grenfell Assn. Labrador, Canada.

BARLOW, Alexander John Elliott (retired) 152 Penistone Road, Shelley, Huddersfield HD8 8JQ Tel: 01484 602993 — MD 1943 Leeds; MB ChB 1935. Prev: Cons. Dermatol. Huddersfield & Halifax Hosp. Gps.

BARLOW, Alexander Paul Alma Street Medical Centre, Alma Street, Stockton-on-Tees TS18 2AP Tel: 01642 607248 Fax: 01642 612968 — MB ChB 1991 Liverp. Prev: Trainee GP/SHO (A & E) St. Helens & Knowsley Hosp. Trust.

BARLOW, Alison Frances The Old School House, Pannal, Harrogate HG3 1NN — MB ChB 1995 Bristol; DRCOG 1997; MRCPCH 1999. (Bristol) SHO (Paediat.) Unified Bristol Healthcare NHS Trust. Prev: SHO (O & G) Roy. Hants. Co. Hosp. Winchester; SHO (Paediat.) Roy. Hants. Co. Hosp. Winchester; SHO (Paediat.) St. Helier NHS Trust Carshalton Surrey.

BARLOW, Andrew Bryan Timothy 20 Carr Cottage, Carrybrook, Stalybridge SK15 3NS — MB ChB 1996 Sheff.

BARLOW, Andrew Dalmahoy 10 Wimpole Street, London W1G 9SS Tel: 020 7580 1242 — MB BChir 1942 Camb.; MA, MB BChir Camb. 1942; MRCP Lond. 1944; DCH Eng. 1944. (Univ. Coll. Hosp.) Prev: Cons. Paediatr. W. Middlx. Hosp. 1st Asst. Childr. Dept. Univ. Coll.; Hosp.; Med. Regist. Hosp. Childr. Gt. Ormond St.

BARLOW, Antonia (retired) Hall Farmhouse, Goodleigh, Barnstaple EX32 7NB Tel: 0271 342436 — MB ChB St. And. 1950. Prev: Ho. Surg. Obst. Mothers' Hosp. Lond.

BARLOW, Mr Antony Peter County Hosptial, Greetwell Road, Lincoln LN2 5QY Tel: 01522 573646; Northlands House, Glentworth, Gainsborough DN21 5DG Tel: 01427 667311 — BM BCh 1979 Oxf.; ChM Bristol 1991; FRCS Eng. 1985; FRCS Ed. 1984. Cons. Gen. Surg. Lincoln Hosps. NHS Trust. Socs: BMA; Brit. Soc. Gastroenterol.; Eur. Assn. Endoscopic Surg. Prev: Sen. Regist. (Surg.) S. W.. RHA.

BARLOW, Christine 30 Hallville Road, Liverpool L18 0HR — MB ChB 1992 Liverp.

BARLOW, Christopher Robert Quorn Medical Centre, 1 Station Road, Quorn, Loughborough LE12 8BP Tel: 01509 412232 Fax: 01509 620652; 38 Sanders Lane, Quorn, Loughborough LE12 8JN — MB BS 1983 Newc.; MRCGP 1987; DRCOG 1987. (Newc.) Princip. Gen. Pract. Quorn Med. Clinic Quorn Leics.; Clinicl Lect. Dept. of Gen. Pract. Univ. of Leicester. Prev: GP N.umbria VTS; Ho. Surg. Hexham Gen. Hosp.; Ho. Phys. Bishop Auckland Gen. Hosp.

BARLOW, David 18 Underhill Road, Dulwich, London SE22 0AH Tel: 020 8693 2849 — MRCS Eng. LRCP Lond. 1968; MA, BM BCh Oxf. 1969; FRCP Lond. 1986; MRCP (UK) 1973; MFFP 1993. (Oxf. & St. Thos.) Cons. Phys. Genitourin. Med. St. Thos. Hosp. Lond.; Hon. Sen. Lect. VMDS. Socs: (Counc.) Med. Soc. Study VD.; Hon. Treas. Med. Soc. Study VD. Prev: Sen. Regist. (Genitourin. Med.), Regist. (Gen. Med. & Venereol.) & SHO (Neurol. & Rheum.) St. Thos. Hosp. Lond.

BARLOW, Professor David Hearnshaw Nuffield Department of Obstetrics & Gynaecology, The Women's Centre, Oxford Radcliffe Hospital, Headington, Oxford OX3 9DU Tel: 01865 221008 Fax: 01865 69141 Email: david.barlow@obs-gyn.ox.ac.uk — MB ChB 1975 Glas.; MA Oxf. 1985; BSc (Hons.) Glas. 1971, MD 1982; FRCOG 1993, M 1980. (Glas.) Nuffield Prof. O & G Univ. Oxf.; Hon. Cons. Obst. & Gyn. John Radcliffe Hosp. Oxf.; Fell. Oriel Coll. Oxf. Prev: Clin. Reader (O & G) Univ. Oxf.; MRC Train. Fell. & Hall Tutorial Fell.(O & G) Glas. Univ.; Fell. Green Coll. Oxf. 1985-1990.

BARLOW, David John Edward Street Surgery, 2 Edward Street, Oldham OL9 7QW Tel: 0161 624 1285 Fax: 0161 620 5914 — MB ChB 1973 Manch.; BSc (Pharm. Div. 1) Manch. 1968, MB ChB 1973; DObst RCOG 1975; Cert Family Plann. RCOG RCGP & Family Plann; Assn. 1976.

BARLOW, David John South King Street Medical Centre, 25 South King Street, Blackpool FY1 4NF Tel: 01253 26637 — MB ChB 1974 Manch. GP Trainer Blackpool; Med. Off. The Hospice Fylde. Socs: Assn. Palliat. Care & Hospice Doctors.

BARLOW, Erasmus Darwin (retired) Elbrook House, Ashwell, Baldock SG7 5NE Tel: 01462 742545 — MB BChir 1941 Camb.; MRCS Eng., LRCP Lond. 1940; FRCPsych. 1981 M 1972; DPM Eng. 1951. Prev: Hon. Cons. Psychiat. & Sen. Lect. Med. & Psych. Med. St. Thos. Hosp.

BARLOW, Fiona Marie Child & Adolescent Psychiatry, Jenner Wing St. George's Hospital Medical School, Cranmer Terrace, London SW17 0RE Fax: 0208 725 3592 Email: s.allain@sghms.ac.uk; 64 Westwood Park, Forest Hill, London SE23 3QH — MB BS 1990 Lond.; MRCPsych 1995. (U M D S) Flexible trainee, Dept. child & Adolesc. Psychiat., St. Geo.'s Hosp. Lond.

BARLOW, Gavin David 3 Fford Pelydryn, Off Level Road, Hawarden, Deeside CH5 3JT Tel: 01244 533672 — MB ChB 1993 Leicester; MRCP (UK) 1996; DTM & H Liverp. 1997. Specialist Regist. in Infec. Dis & Med, Kings Cross Hosp, Dundee. Socs: Brit. Infect. Soc.; Brit. Travel Heath Assn. Prev: SHO (Infec. Dis.) Seacroft Univ. Hosp. Leeds; SHO (Med.) York Dist. Hosp.; SHO (Genitourin. Med. & Infect. Dis.) Roy. Hallamsh. Hosp. Sheff.

BARLOW, Geoffrey Ty Fair, Penybont, Llandrindod Wells LD1 5UA Tel: 01597 851216 — MB BS & LRCP Lond. 1961; MRCS Eng. 1961. (St Mary's Lond.) S.C.M.O. Occupat. Health Powys.

BARLOW, George The Crescent Medical Practice, 12 Walmer Crescent, Glasgow G51 1AT Tel: 0141 427 0191 Fax: 0141 427 1581; 76 Milverton Road, Whitecraigs, Glasgow G46 7LG — MB ChB 1973 Glas.; MRCGP 1977; DCH RCPS Glas. 1978; DObst RCOG 1976. Prev: Trainee GP Glas. VTS.

BARLOW, Gillian Margaret 26 Ashley Down Road, Horfield, Bristol BS7 9JW — MB ChB 1990 Bristol.

BARLOW, Grace Elisabeth Plowright Surgery, Market Place, Swaffham PE37 7LQ; Janet Cottages, Rougham, King's Lynn PE32 2SD Tel: 01328 838254 — MB BChir 1971 Camb.; MRCOG 1975; DObst RCOG 1973. (St. Geo.) Prev: Regist. (O & G) Oxon. AHA (T) & Centr. Middlx. Hosp. Lond.

BARLOW, Helen Chetwynd Cupar Health Centre, Bank St., Cupar KY15 4JN Tel: 01334 656812; The Steading, North Flisk, Blebo Craigs, Cupar KY15 5UQ Tel: 01334 850575 — MB BS 1982 Lond.; MRCGP 1987; DCH RCPS Glas. 1987; DRCOG 1984; AKC 1982. (Kings College Hosp, London) Staff Grade Paediat. Prev: SHO (O & G) Kings Coll. Hosp. Lond.; Trainee GP Leven VTS; SHO (Paediat.) Ninewells Hosp. Dundee.

BARLOW, Helen Jane 19 Pinfold Close, Tutbury, Burton-on-Trent DE13 9NJ — MB ChB 1991 Leic.

BARLOW, Hilary Veronica Louise Rosemount, Stapley, Taunton TA3 7QA — BM 1985 Soton. SHO (Gen. Med.) Flexible Train. Scheme MusGr. Pk. Hosp. Taunton. Prev: Trainee GP Shrewsbury; SHO (Psychiat.) Roy. Shrewsbury Hosp.; SHO (A & E) Roy. Hants. Co. Hosp. Winchester.

BARLOW, Mr Ian William Dorset County Hospital, Williams Avenue, Dorchester DT1 2JY Tel: 01305 255413; Barcombe Grange, Alton Pancras, Dorchester DT2 7RT Tel: 01300 348163 Fax: 01300 348164 — MB ChB 1985 Bristol; FRCS (Orth.) 1995; FRCS Eng. 1989. Cons. Orthop. Surg. Dorset Co. Hosp. Socs: Brit. Assn. Surg. Knee; Brit. Orthopaedic Assn. Prev: Sen. Regist. (Orthop. Surg.) Soton. Gen. Hosp.; Career Regist. (Orthop. Surg.) Soton. Gen. Hosp.; Postgrad. Train. Scheme (Surg.) St. Jas. Univ. Hosp. Leeds.

BARLOW, James Arnold (retired) Cilfach Glyd., Deuddwr, Llansantffraid SY22 6TF — MB ChB 1954 Liverp. Prev: Ho. Surg. & Ho. Phys. Maelor Gen. Hosp. Wrexham.

BARLOW, Janet Marie Barcombe Grange, Alton Pancras, Dorchester DT2 7RT Tel: 01300 348163 — MB ChB 1985 Bristol; DCH RCP Lond. 1990; DRCOG 1989. Prev: SHO (O & G) York Dist. Hosp.; SHO (Psychiat.) Bootham Pk. Hosp. York; Trainee GP York.

BARLOW, Joanne Lauretta 509 Croston Road, Farington, Preston PR26 6PJ — BM BS 1991 Nottm.

BARLOW, Mr John Sutherland Regents Park Road Surgery, 99 Regents Park Road, London NW1 8UR Tel: 020 7722 0038 Fax: 020 7722 9724; 7 Fitzroy Road, London NW1 8TU Tel: 020 7722 5527 — MB BS 1969 Lond.; FRCS Eng. 1976; MRCS Eng. LRCP Lond. 1968; ECFMG Cert 1969. (Univ. Coll. Hosp.)

BARLOW, Karen Maria 11 Rochester Close, Golborne, Warrington WA3 3XP — MB ChB 1989 Ed.; MRCP (UK) 1993.

BARLOW, Marion 1 Stable Road, Milngavie, Glasgow G62 7LY — MB ChB 1975 Dundee; BSc St. And. 1972.

BARLOW, Natasha Helen 18 Howells Crescent, Llandaff, Cardiff CF5 2AJ — MB ChB 1986 Bristol.

BARLOW, Nicholas Percy 18 Underhill Road, London SE22 0AH — BM BCh 1993 Oxf.

BARLOW, Peter William Brown Centre, Manor Way, Peterlee SR8 5TW Tel: 0191 554 4544 Fax: 0191 554 4552; 9 Berwick Chase, Oakerside Park, Peterlee SR8 1NB — MB ChB 1976 Ed.; MRCGP 1980. Prev: SHO (Obst.) Dryburn Hosp. Durh; SHO (Med.) Bishop Auckland Gen. Hosp.; SHO (Psychiat.) Cherry Knowle Hosp. Sunderland.

BARLOW, Mr Philip Department of Neurosurgery, Southern General Hospital, Glasgow G51 4TF Tel: 0141 201 1100 Fax: 0141 201 2022 — MB ChB 1975 Dundee; MPhil Glas. 1994; BSc St. And. 1972; ChM Dund 1990; FRCS Ed. 1980. Cons. Neurosurg. S.. Gen. Hosp. Glas. Socs: Soc. Brit. Neurol. Surgs.

BARLOW, Stephen Stuart The Hutton Centre, St Luke's Hospital, Marton Rd, Middlesbrugh TS4 3AF Tel: 01642 283352 Fax: 01642 283345 Email: steve.barlow@doctors.org.uk — MB ChB 1990 Liverp.; MRCPsych 1995. Cons. Forens. Psychiat., Tees and N. E. Yorks. NHS Trust, MiddlesBoro. Prev: Sen. Regist. (Forens. Psychiat.) Ashworth Hosp. Liverp.

BARLOW, Thomas Edmund (retired) 75 Cheviot View, Ponteland, Newcastle upon Tyne NE20 9BH Tel: 0191 22093 — MRCS Eng. LRCP Lond. 1937; MD Manch. 1943, MB ChB 1938. Prev: Sen. Lect. Anat. Univ. Newc.-upon-Tyne Med. Sch.

BARLOW, Thomas Harris 41 Dumbuck Crescent, Dumbarton G82 1ET — MB ChB 1966 Glas.; MRCGP 1973; DCH RCPS Glas. 1974; DObst RCOG 1969. (Glas.) Prev: Ho. Surg. Roy. Hosp. Sick Childr. Glas.; Ho. Phys. Ruchill Hosp. Glas.; SHO (Obst.) Stirling Roy. Infirm.

BARLOW-HITCHEN, Stephanie Oaklea, 298 Washway Road, Sale M33 4RU — MB ChB 1981 Manch.

BARLTROP, Mr Andrew Huw St James School House, Mildenhall Road, Shippea Hill, Ely CB7 4SU — MB BS 1989 Lond.; FRCS Ed. 1995.

BARLTROP, Professor Donald Academic Department of Child Health, Chelsea & Westminster Hospital, Fulham Road, London SW10 9NH Tel: 020 8746 8622 Fax: 020 8746 8770; 7 Grove Road, Northwood HA6 2AP Tel: 01923 826461 — MB BS 1956 Lond.; BSc Lond. 1953, MD 1966; FRCP Lond. 1974, M 1961; DCH Eng. 1959. (Char. Cross) Prof. Child Health Char. Cross & W.m. Med. Sch. Lond.; Hon. Cons. Paediat. Chelsea & W.m. & Char. Cross Hosps. Lond.; Adjunct Prof. Community Health Tufts Univ. Sch. Med. Boston, USA. Socs: Fell. Roy. Soc. Med.; Eur. Paediat. Research Soc. Prev: Asst. Dir. Paediat. Unit & Wellcome Sen. Research Fell. (Clin. Sc. Paediat.) St. Mary's Hosp. Med. Sch. Lond.; Sen. Resid. Childr. Hosp. Med. Center Boston, USA.

BARLTROP, Iwona Norfolk Mental Health Care NHS Trust, Drayton Old Lodge, 146 Drayton High Road, Norwich NR8 6AN Tel: 01603 201422; 20 Hinshalwood Way, Old Costessey, Norwich NR8 5BN — LAH Dub. 1969; MRCPsych 1977; DPM Eng. 1975; Dip. Phys. Warsaw 1964. (Med. Acad. Warsaw) Cons. Psychiat. (GP) Norf. Ment. Health Care NHS Trust, Norwich. Socs: BMA. Prev: Cons. Psychiat. Lister Hosp. Stevenage & N. Devon Dist. Hosp.; Cons. Psychiat. Qu. Eliz. Hosp. Kings Lynn.

BARLTROP, Mair Angharad (retired) 7 Grove Road, Northwood HA6 2AP Tel: 01923 826461 — MB BS Lond. 1956; DObst RCOG 1959. Prev: Assoc. Specialist (Cytol.) Mt. Vernon & Watford Hosps. NHS Trust.

BARMAN, David Nicholas Department of Anaesthesia, Manchester Royal Infirmary, Oxford Road, Manchester M13 9ES Tel: 0161 276 4551 Fax: 0161 276 8027 — MB ChB 1984 Manch.; FRCA 1990; T(Anaes.) 1994. Cons. Anaesth. Centr. Manch. Healthcare NHS Trust. Socs: Assn. Anaesth.; Assn. Paediat. Anaesth.; Paediatric Intens. Care Soc. Prev: Sen. Regist. (Anaesth.) NW Region.

BARMBY, David Stuart 4 Vicarage Close, Howden le Wear, Crook DL15 8RB — MB ChB 1992 Liverp.

BARNABAS, Archibald Jasper The Surgery, 159 Wakefield Street, East Ham, London E6 1LG Tel: 020 8472 0208 Fax: 020 8471 0794; 90 Windsor Road, Forest Gate, London E7 0QY — LRCPI & LM, LRSCI & LM 1962; LRCPI & LM, LRCSI & LM 1962.

BARNABY, Catherine Atkinson Road Clinic, St James Crescent, Benwell, Newcastle upon Tyne NE15 6JJ; 13 Grange Walk, Whickham, Newcastle upon Tyne NE16 5AL — MB BS 1970 Newc. Staff Grade Paediat. Newc. City Health Trust. Prev: Clin. Off. Newc. HA.

BARNABY, Helen Jane The Surgery, Kingswood Road, Tunbridge Wells TN2 4UJ — MB BS 1988 Lond.; MRCGP 1993.

BARNABY, Julian St John's Hill Surgery, 39 St. John's Hill, Sevenoaks TN13 3NT Tel: 01732 747202 Fax: 01732 747218 — MB BS 1988 Lond.

BARNACLE, Alex Mary 3 St Peter's Close, Lugwardine, Hereford HR1 4AT — BM 1995 Soton. SHO (Paediat.) Soton. Gen. Hosp.

BARNARD, Ann Elizabeth 21 Albert Road, Lenton, Nottingham NG7 2EX — BM BS 1993 Nottm.; BMedSci Nottm. 1991, BM BS 1993. Trainee GP Derby VTS.

BARNARD, Colin Simon 83 Main Road, Broughton, Chester CH4 0NR — MB ChB 1986 Liverp.; BSc (Physiol.) Liverp. 1983, MB ChB 1986; MRCGP 1990; DRCOG 1989. Prev: Trainee GP S. Clwyd VTS.

BARNARD, David Leslie 2 North Park Road, Leeds LS8 1JD Tel: 0113 266 7456 — BM BCh 1966 Oxf.; MA Oxf. 1966; FRCP Lond. 1987; MRCP (UK) 1970; FRCPath 1988, M 1975. (Univ. Coll. Hosp.) Cons. (Haemat.) St. Jas. Univ. Hosp. Leeds; Sen. Lect. Univ.

Leeds. Prev: Sen. Regist. (Haemat.) W.. Gen. Hosp. Edin.; Regist. (Haemat.) Bristol Roy. Infirm.; SHO (Nuclear Med.) Soton. Gen. Hosp.

BARNARD, E John W (retired) Tynwald, Upper Lane, Brighstone, Newport PO30 4BA Tel: 01983 740155 — MB BS 1937 Lond.; BA Open 1980; MRCS Eng. LRCP Lond. 1936; DA Eng. 1942. Prev: Cons. Anaesth. Hackney Hosp. Gp.

BARNARD, Eric Edmund 63 Beaconsfield Road, Blackheath, London SE3 7LG Tel: 020 8858 7680 — MB ChB 1959 Ed.; FRCOG 1979, M 1967; DObst RCOG 1961. Cons. Gyn. Blackheath Hosp. Socs: BMA. Prev: Cons. O & G Greenwich Dist. Hosp.; Sen. Regist. (O & G) St. Bart. Hosp. Lond.; Resid. Med. Off. City of Lond. Matern. Hosp.

BARNARD, Ernest Edward Peter (retired) Chesilcote, Chapel Road, Swanmore, Southampton SO32 2QA Tel: 02380 892373 Email: e.e.peterb@WHSmithnet.co.uk — MB BS Lond. 1955; DPhil Oxf. 1969; FFCM 1980; MFOM RCP Lond. 1975. Prev: Surg. Rear-Admiral (Operat.al Med. Serv.s).

BARNARD, Harry Whalebridge Practice, Health Centre, Carfax Street, Swindon SN1 1ED Tel: 01793 692933 — MB ChB 1962 Birm.; DObst RCOG 1964.

BARNARD, James Benjamin Doctors' Residence, Manchester Royal Infirmary, Oxford Road, Manchester M13 9WL — MB ChB 1998 Manch.; MB ChB Manch 1998.

BARNARD, Judith Ann 10 St Paul's Road, Richmond TW9 2HH Tel: 020 8940 9251 — MB BS 1961 Lond.; MRCS Eng. LRCP Lond. 1961; DObst RCOG 1968. (Roy Free)

BARNARD, Keith David Foxden, Drift Road, Fareham PO16 8SY Tel: 01329 280005 Fax: 01329 281180 Email: keithbarnard@zetnet.co.uk; Foxden, Drift Road, Fareham PO16 8SY Fax: 01329 281180 Email: keithbarnard@zetnet.co.uk — MB BS 1966 Lond.; MRCS Eng. LRCP Lond. 1966. (Westm.) Med. Edr., GP newspaper. Haymarket Publishing, Hmmersmith. Prev: Partner, Gen. Practitioner, The centre Pract., Fareham Health centre.

BARNARD, Maria Louise 85 Hide Road, Harrow HA1 4SE — MB ChB 1984 Bristol.

BARNARD, Matthew Jonathan The Old School, Grantchester, Cambridge CB3 9NF — MB BS 1986 Lond.

BARNARD, Maureen Elizabeth Oak Lodge Medical Centre, 234 Burnt Oak Broadway, Edgware HA8 0AP Tel: 020 8952 1202 Fax: 020 8381 1156 — MB BCh 1971 Belfast.

BARNARD, Mildred Marguerite Emily 37 The Meadway, Cuffley, Potters Bar EN6 4ET — MB BS 1952 Lond.; DPH Eng. 1959. Prev: Med. Off. Pub. Health LCC; Regist. Chest Unit Highlands Hosp. Lond.; Med. Off. Herts. CC.

BARNARD, Mr Neal Austin Department of Oral-Facial Surgery, Worcester Royal Infirmary, Castle Street Branch, Worcester WR1 3AS Tel: 01905 760215 Fax: 01905 760213; The Square House, Tunnel Hill, Upton-upon-Severn, Worcester WR8 0QL Email: nabarn@doctors.org.uk — MB ChB 1985 Aberd.; BDS Manch. 1976; FRCS Ed. 1990; FDS RCPS Glas. 1980. Cons. Oral & Maxillofacial Surg. Worcs. Socs: Brit. Assn. Oral & Maxillofacial Surg.; Internat. Assn. Oral & Maxillofacial Surgs. Prev: Sen Regist. (Oral & Maxillofacial Surg.) Bristol; Regist. (Oral & Maxillofacial Surg.) Mersey RHA; SHO (Gen. Surg.) Derby Roy. Infirm.

BARNARD, Nicholas John Brinsley Sarum House, Chilmark, Salisbury SP3 5AJ Tel: 0172 276415 — MRCS Eng. LRCP Lond. 1973; BSc Lond. 1970, MB BS 1973; FFA RCS Eng. 1977. (Guy's) Regist. (Anaesth.) Roy. Sussex Co. Hosp. Brighton.

BARNARD, Paul Bannister Newmarket Road Surgery, 7 Newmarket Road, Norwich NR2 2HL Tel: 01603 621006 — MB BS 1982 Lond.; BSc Lond 1979; DRCOG 1986.

BARNARD, Philippa Marye 433 Unthank Road, Norwich NR4 7QN — MB BS 1982 Lond.; BSc Lond. 1979; MFFP 1995; DRCOG 1987.

BARNARD, Phillip David Park Medical Centre, 2 Park Road, West Kirby, Wirral CH48 4DW Tel: 0151 625 6128 — MB ChB 1973 Liverp.

BARNARD, Rebecca Elizabeth 60 Cadnant Park, Conwy LL32 8PE — MB ChB 1989 Liverp.

BARNARD, Robert Lindsay Harbour (retired) The Crooked House, Queen St., Emsworth PO10 7BJ Tel: 01243 372699 Email: barnard@beeb.net — MB BS Lond. 1947; FRCGP 1979, M 1954. Prev: Provost. Wessex Fac. RCGP.

BARNARD, Mr Robin James (retired) 135 Palatine Road, Manchester M20 3YA Tel: 0161 445 0331 — MB BS 1958 Lond.; FRCS Ed. 1964; FRCS Eng. 1964. Prev: Cons. Urol. Univ. Hosp. S. Manch.

BARNARD, Robin Osler (retired) Beckhams, Chidding Fold, Godalming GU8 4QA Tel: 01428 682992 — MB BS 1956 Lond.; MD Lond. 1969. Neuropath. Nat. Hosps. Nerv. Dis. Prev: Sen. Regist. (Path.) Maida Vale Hosp. Nerv. Dis.

BARNARD, Sally Ann Newnham Walk Surgery, Wordsworth Grove, Cambridge CB3 9HS Tel: 01223 366811 Fax: 01223 302706 — MB BS 1987 Melbourne; MRCGP 1993; DCH RCP Lond. 1993; DFFP 1993. Princip., Gen. Pract.

BARNARD, Sally Louise Gurney Surgery, 101-103 Magdalen Street, Norwich NR3 1LN Tel: 01603 448800 — MB ChB 1989 Manch.

BARNARD, Samantha Jane 5 Viceroy Court, Wilmslow Road, Didsbury, Manchester M20 2RJ — MB ChB 1998 Manch.; MB ChB Manch 1998.

BARNARD, Sion Philip 33 Harewood Close, Whickham, Newcastle upon Tyne NE16 5SZ — MB BChir 1984 Camb.

BARNARD, Stuart Alistair 12 Church Road W., Farnborough GU14 6RT — MB BS 1996 Lond.

BARNARD, Susannah Maria 14 Foxdown Manor, Wadebridge PL27 6BD — MB BS 1996 Lond.

BARNARD, William Kenneth Harding 2 Bod Hyfryd, Flint CH6 5BE — MB ChB 1958 Liverp. (Liverp.)

BARNARD-JONES, Keith Health Centre, Park Estate Road, Easton, Portland DT5 2BJ; Old Hill House, Portland DT5 1LQ Tel: 01305 821030 Fax: 01305 824143 — MB BS 1965 Lond.; MRCS Eng. LRCP Lond. 1965; MRCGP 1972; DObst RCOG 1967. (Char. Cross) Clin. Asst. Elderly Care Unit Portland Hosp. Socs: BMA. Prev: SHO (Gen. Med. & O & G) Caerphilly & Dist. Miner's Hosp.; Ho. Off. (Radiother. & Diag.) X-Ray Dept. Char. Cross Hosp. Lond.

BARNARDO, Adrian Thomas 12 Beaconsfield Road, Claygate, Esher KT10 0PW — BM BS 1994 Nottm.; BMedSci Nottm. 1992; MRCP UK. 1998. SHO (Cas.) Medway A & E Centre. Prev: Ho. Off. (Gen. Med.) Nottm. City Hosp.; Ho. Off. (Gen. Surg.) Stafford Dist. Gen. Hosp.

BARNARDO, Alison Mary Angela 57 Lonsdale Avenue, London E6 3JZ Tel: 020 8552 0169 — MB BS 1988 Lond. Prev: SHO Poole & Newham Gen. Hosps.; Ho. Surg. Lond. Hosp.; Ho. Phys. St. Richards Hosp. Chichester.

BARNARDO, Andrew Norman Kings Avenue Surgery, 23 Kings Avenue, Buckhurst Hill IG9 5LP Tel: 020 8504 0122 Fax: 020 8559 2984; 64 Fairview Drive, Chigwell IG7 6HS Tel: 020 8500 5920 — MB BS 1961 Lond.; MRCS Eng. LRCP Lond. 1961. (Lond. Hosp.) Prev: Clin. Asst. (Colonoscopy) Whipps Cross Hosp. Lond.; Cas. Off. Centr. Middlx. Hosp.; Ho. Surg. King Geo. Hosp. Ilford.

BARNARDO, Angela Elizabeth Maxwell Fulwell Cross Health Centre, 1 Tomswood Mill, Ilford IG6 2HG; 58 Spring Grove, Loughton IG10 4QE Tel: 020 8 508 4233 — MB BS 1964 Lond.; MRCS Eng. LRCP Lond. 1964. (Lond. Hosp.) Prev: Ho. Surg. & Ho. Phys. (Receiv. Room) Lond. Hosp.

BARNARDO, David Eric (retired) — MB BS Lond. 1962; BSc Lond. 1959, MD 1972; FRCP Lond. 1978, M 1965. Prev: Lect. & Sen. Regist. (Med.) Lond. Hosp.

BARNARDO, Jonathan Nicholas St Lukes Surgery, Warren Road, Guildford GU1 3JH Tel: 01483 572364 Fax: 01483 304379; 16 Longmead, Merrow, Guildford GU1 2HW Tel: 01483 835922 — MB BS 1989 Lond.; MRCGP 1994; DRCOG 1993; DGM RCP Lond. 1993. (St Thomas's and UMDS) Prev: Trainee GP/SHO Frimley VTS; SHO (A & E, Geriat. & Med.) Frimley Pk. Hosp.

BARNARDO, Philip David Basement, 77 St Georges Drive, London SW1V 4DB — MB BS 1987 Lond.; FRCA 1996.

BARNASS, Stella Juliet Microbiology Department, Farnborough Hospital, Farnborough Common, Orpington BR6 8ND Tel: 01689 814110 Fax: 01689 814031 Email: stella.barnass@bromleyh-tr.sthames.nhs.uk; 14 Mayfield Avenue, Chiswick, London W4 1PW Email: stella_barnass@epoisse.demon.co.uk — MB BS 1980 Lond.; FRCPath 1998; Dip. Pharm. Med. RCP (UK) 1993; MSC Lond. 1988, BSc (Hons.) 1977, MD 1986. (Roy. Lond. Hosp.) p/t Cons. Microbiol. Bromley Hosps. NHS Trust. Prev: Sen. Clin. Investig. Phys. SmithKline Beecham Harlow; Med. Adviser. SmithKline Beecham Brentford; Sen. Regist. (Microbiol.) St. Bart. Hosp. Lond.

BARNES, Adrian John Barnet General Hospital, Wellhouse Lane, Barnet EN5 3DJ; Kingsbury Knoll, 169 Verulam Road, St Albans AL3 4DW Tel: 01727 866833 — MB BS 1971 Lond.; BSc Soton. 1966; MD Lond. 1978; FRCP Lond. 1988; MRCP (UK) 1973; MRCS Eng. LRCP Lond. 1971. (Roy. Free) Cons. Phys. Barnet Gen. Hosp. Socs: Fell. Roy. Soc. Med. Prev: Hon. Sen. Regist. (Endocrinol) Roy. Postgrad. Med. Sch. & Hammersmith Hosp. Lond.; Regist. (Clin. Path.) Whittington Hosp. Lond.; Ho. Phys. (Neurol. & Med.) Roy. Free Hosp. (Lawn Rd. Br.).

BARNES, Alison Julia University Health Centre, 42 Old Elvet, Durham DH1 3JF; 3 Cosin's Hall, Palace Green, Durham DH1 3RL — MB BS 1982 Lond.; Cert. Family Plann. JCC 1986. (St. Bart.)

BARNES, Amanda Jane Manchester Phl., Withington Hospital, Nell Lane, Manchester M20 2LR Tel: 0161 291 3563 Fax: 0161 446 2180 Email: bernie@manphl.demon.co.uk; 17 North Houses Lane, Lytham St Annes FY8 4NT Tel: 01253 727887 Fax: 01253 727887 — MB BS 1986 Lond.; MRCP (UK) 1989; MRCPath 1998'; DTM & H RCP Lond. 1990. (The Lond. Hosp. Univ. of Lond.) Specialist Regist. (Med. Microbiol.) Withington Hosp. Manch. Socs: Manch. Med. Soc.; Brit. Infec. Soc.; Brit. Soc. Med. Mycol. Prev: Regist. (Infec. Dis.) Monsall Hosp.; Regist. (Gen. Med.) Wellington Hosp.; SHO Hosp. for Trop. Dis. Lond.

BARNES, Andrew David 7 Justice Avenue, Saltford, Bristol BS31 3DR — MB BCh 1977 Wales.

BARNES, Angela Patience Linden House, Upper Fairfield Road, Leatherhead KT22 7HH Tel: 01372 375666 Fax: 01372 360117; Milton Clere, 1 Milton Avenue, Westcott, Dorking RH4 3QA Tel: 01306 885614 — MB BS 1980 Lond.; DRCOG 1982; Cert. Family Plann. JCC 1982. Prev: Trainee GP/SHO (O & G, Psychiat. & Geriat.) Kings Coll. Hosp. VTS.

BARNES, Anne Cashfield Farmhouse, Crowhill, Dyfed, Haverfordwest SA61 2UN — MB ChB 1974 Liverp.; DObst RCOG 1976. Staff Grade (Haemat.) Withybush Hosp. HaverfordW..

BARNES, Anne Josephine 79 Ashleigh Grove, Jesmond, Newcastle upon Tyne NE2 3DJ Tel: 0191 281 7837 — MB ChB 1977 Bristol. Assoc. Specialist Hunters Moor Regional Rehabil. Centre Newc. u Tyne. Prev: Clin. Research Assoc. (Neurol.) Univ Newc.; SHO (Psychiat.) Barrow Hosp. Bristol; SHO (Psychiat.) W. Chesh. & Clatterbridge Hosp. Wirral.

BARNES, Anne Patricia (retired) 5 Bannisters Field, Newick, Lewes BN8 4JS Tel: 01825 723353 — MRCS Eng. LRCP Lond. 1957.

BARNES, Annette Paula Orchard House, Barley La, Exeter EX4 1TA — BM 1997 Soton.

BARNES, Arthur David 53 Bysing Wood Road, Faversham ME13 7RL Tel: 01795 534950 — LAH 1966 Dub.; MPH Calif. 1978; FACOG 1985. (King's Coll. Hosp.) Cons. O & G Cedars Sinai Med. Centre Los Angeles, Calif. Socs: Fell. Amer. Coll. Internat. Phys.; Fell. Los Angeles Obst. & Gyn. Soc.; FICS. Prev: Cons. O & G Midway Hosp. Med. Center Los Angeles, Beverley Hills Med. Center Calif. & Brotman Med. Center Los Angeles, USA.

BARNES, Barbara (retired) Weatherstone, 15 Lexington Court, Purley CR8 1JA Tel: 020 8660 9504 Fax: 020 8660 9504 Email: tbbarnes@tinyworld.co.uk — MB ChB 1954 Sheff. Prev: Gernal Practitioner, Ret'd.

BARNES, Barrymore William 18 Kenilworth Road, Rochdale OL16 4SF Tel: 01706 49963 — MB ChB 1957 Manch.; Fell. Manch. Med. Soc. Regional Med. Off. N. W.. Div. Prev: Ho. Surg. Crumpsall Hosp.; Ho. Phys. Birch Hill Hosp. Rochdale.

BARNES, Catherine Anne 38 Carr Bottom Road, Greengates, Bradford BD10 0BB — MB ChB 1992 Leeds. (Leeds) Staff Grade (A & E) Leeds Gen. Infirm. Prev: SHO (Med.) Huddersfield Roy. Infirm.; Med. Regist. (Med.) Wanganui Hosp. New Zealand.

BARNES, Charles Nicholas Holmcroft Surgery, Holmcroft Road, Stafford ST16 1JG Tel: 01785 242172 — MB ChB 1979 Liverp.; MRCGP 1983; DRCOG 1983.

BARNES, Christopher Francis The Surgery, Springwell Medical Centre, 39 Ardmillan Terrace, Edinburgh EH11 2JL Tel: 0131 537 7500 Fax: 0131 537 7505 — MB ChB 1966 Ed. (Ed.) Socs: Mem, Brit. Med. Acupunc. Soc.

BARNES, Clare 146 Princess Reach, Navigation Way, Ashton-on-Ribble, Preston PR2 2GB — MB ChB 1996 Manch.

BARNES, Colin Greenhill (retired) Little Hoopern, Chagford, Newton Abbot TQ13 8BZ Tel: 01647 432098 Fax: 01647 432097 Email: cgbarnes@btinternet.com — MB BS Lond. 1961; BSc Lond. 1958; FRCP Lond. 1978, M 1965. Hon. Cons. Phys. (Rheum.) Roy. Lond. Hosp.; Trustee Kennedy Inst. of Rheum. Prev: Cons. Phys. & Clin. Dir. (Rheum.) Roy. Lond. Hosp. & Hon. Sen. Lect. (Rheum.) Lond. Hosp. Med. Coll.

BARNES, David St Peter's Hospital, Guildford Road, Chertsey KT16 0PZ Tel: 01932 872000; Atkinson Morley's Hospital, Copse Hill, Wimbledon, London SW20 0NE Tel: 020 8946 7711 Email: docdave@globalnet.co.uk — MB ChB 1980 Liverp.; FRCP 1997; MD Liverp. 1987; MRCP (UK) 1983. Cons. Neurol. & Hon. Sen. Lect. St. Peters & Atkinson Morley's Hosps. Prev: Sen. Regist. (Neurol.) Nat. Hosp. Neurol. & Guy's Hosp. Lond.

BARNES, David Whites Farm Cottage, Ware Road, Widford, Ware SG12 8RE Tel: 01279 842408 Email: mpbrnsies@tinyonline.co.uk — MB BS; LLB (Hons); MRCS Eng. LRCP 1966 UCH. p/t GP. Socs: Bristish Med. Assn. Prev: Clin. Asst. E.N.T. 1982 - 1984 P.ss Alexanda Hosp., Harlow; GP 1969-1999 Hertford; Clin. Asst. G.U.M. 1991 - 1997, Hertford Hosp.

BARNES, David James The Surgery, Greenwich Avenue, Hull HU9 4UX Tel: 01482 374415 Fax: 01482 786462; 7 Park Avenue, Princes Avenue, Hull HU5 3EN — MB ChB 1984 Leeds. (Leeds)

BARNES, Dennis Joseph Kent and Sussex Hospital, Mount Ephraim, Tunbridge Wells TN4 8AT Tel: 01892 672985 Fax: 01892 520088 — MB BS 1986 Lond.; FRCP 2001; MRCP (UK) 1989. (Charing Cross and Westminster Medical School) Cons. Phys. (Diabetes, Endocrinol. & Gen. Med.). Prev: Sen. Regist. (Diabetes, Endocrinol. & Gen. Med.) Lewisham Hosp.; Research Regist. (Diabetes, Endocrinol. & Metab.) UMDS Guy's Hosp. Lond.; Regist. (Diabetes, Endocrinol & Metab.), Guy's Hosp., Lond.

BARNES, Dennis Wilberfosse 6 Castle View, Hayton, Carlisle CA8 9HH — MB BS 1952 Lond.; MRCS Eng. LRCP Lond. 1952; DObst RCOG 1954. (Univ. Coll. Hosp.) Prev: Ho. Phys. Perivale Matern. Hosp. & St. Pancras Hosp.

BARNES, Mr Douglas Grant Department of Urology, North Manchester General Hospital, Delaunays Road, Crumpsall, Manchester M8 5RB Tel: 0161 720 2468 — MB ChB 1980 Manch.; FRCS Ed. 1984. (Manchester) Cons. (Urol.), N. Manch. Gen. Hosp. & Bury Gen. Hosp. Socs: Brit. Assn. of Urol. Surg.; BMA; Corr. Amer. Urol. Assoc. Prev: Cons. (Urol.), Burnley Gen. Hosp.

BARNES, Edward 21A West Mall, Bristol BS8 4BQ; 9 Eastwick Road, Burwood Park, Walton-on-Thames KT12 5AW — MB BS 1990 Lond.; BSc Lond. 1987, MB BS 1990.

BARNES, Edward Stephen 351 Danebury Avenue, Roehampton, London SW15 4DU Tel: 020 8876 6666 Fax: 020 8878 2629 — MB BS 1978 Lond.; MRCGP 1985; DRCOG 1981. (Westm.) Prev: SHO (Geriat.) St. Johns Hosp. Lond.; SHO (Paediat.) Ealing Hosp. Lond.; SHO (O & G) Perivale Matern. Hosp. Lond.

BARNES, Edward William Darlington Memorial Hospital, Hollyhurst Road, Darlington DL3 6HX — MB ChB 1967 Ed.; BSc (Hons.) Ed. 1964, MB ChB 1967; FRCP Lond. 1987; FRCP Ed. 1982; MRCP (UK) 1971. Cons. Phys. Darlington Memor. Hosp.

BARNES, Eleanor Jane Centre for Hepatology, Royal Free & University College Medical School, London NW3 2PF — MB BS 1991 Lond.; BSc Lond. 1990; MRCP (UK) 1994.

BARNES, Elizabeth Jill Lucy Flat 107, South Quay, Wapping Dock, Liverpool L3 4BU — MB ChB 1992 Liverp. SHO (A & E) Whiston Hosp. Merseyside VTS. Prev: Trainee GP Wingate Med. Centre Kirby; SHO (Paediat.) Whiston Hosp. Merseyside; Ho. Off. (Med.) Roy. Liverp. Univ. Hosp.

BARNES, Elizabeth Shirley Millard (retired) Old Downs, Church Road, Bradford Abbas, Sherborne DT9 6RF Tel: 01935 421593 — MB BS 1954 Lond.; MRCS Eng. LRCP Lond. 1954; DObst RCOG 1956; Dip. Ven. 1980. Prev: Assoc. Specialist (Genitourin. Med.) Wycombe Gen. Hosp.

BARNES, Eric Anthony 22 Wildcroft Manor, London SW15 3TS — MB BS 1988 Lond.

BARNES, Felicity Claire The Ridge Medical Practice, 3 Paternoster Lane, Great Horton, Bradford BD7 3EE Tel: 01274 322822 — MB ChB 1994 Leeds; DRCOG; MRCGP. (Leeds) Gen. Practitioner Partner/Princip. Bradford. Socs: Mem.ship of Roy. Coll. of Gen. Practioners; Diplomat to Roy. Coll. of Obst. & Gyn.; Brit. Med. Assn.

BARNES, Fiona June 21 Kensington Gate, Glasgow G12 9LQ — MB ChB 1992 Glas. Staff Grade (Paediat.) Ayrsh. Centr. Hosp. Irvine. Socs: M-C Soc. Prev: Ho. Off. (Med.) Roy. Alexandra Hosp.

Paisley; SHO (Med. Paediat.) Roy. Hosp. Sick Childr. Glas.; SHO (Med. Paediat.) CrossHo. Hosp. Kilmarnock.

BARNES, Frances Mary (retired) Odways, Furzey Lodge, Beaulieu, Brockenhurst SO42 7WB Tel: 01590 612436 — MB BS 1938 Lond.

BARNES, Geoffrey Mark (retired) Unipart House, Cowley, Oxford OX4 2PG — MB ChB 1950 Liverp. Med. Adviser Oxf. Exhausts Plant & Unipart Gp. Ltd. Oxf. Prev: Med. Adviser Oxf. Exhausts Plant & Unipart Gp. Ltd. Oxf.

BARNES, George Howard, OStJ Rockleigh, 17 Savile Park, Halifax HX1 3EA Tel: 01422 350580 — MB ChB 1971 Aberd.; MFPHM 1989; MFCM 1987; MRCGP 1976; DCH Eng. 1975; DObst RCOG 1974; FFPHM 1998. Cons. Pub. Health Med. Calderdale & Kirklees Health Auth.; Cons. Communicable Dis. Control & Hon. Clin. Sen. Lect. (Pub. Health Med.) Leeds Univ. Socs: BMA; Fell. RSM; Fell. Roy. Inst. Pub. Health and Hygeine. Prev: SCM Calderdale HA.

BARNES, Gillian Margaret Kingston & District Community NHS Trust, Elmbridge Lodge, Weston Green Road, Thames Ditton KT7 0HY Tel: 020 8398 1834 Fax: 020 8398 9327 — MB BS 1968 Lond.; MSc (Clin. Psychother.) Lond. 1985; MRCS Eng. LRCP Lond. 1968; MRCPsych 1982; FRCPsych 1997. (Char. Cross) Cons. Psychiat. (Learning Disabil.) Kingston & Dist. Community NHS Trust. Socs: Assoc. Mem. Brit. Assn. Psychother.

BARNES, Graham Lewis (retired) Swans Nest House, Watton Road, Swaffham PE37 8HF — MB ChB 1962 Ed.; DObst RCOG 1965. Prev: Princip. GP Swaffham, Norf.

BARNES, Helena Margaret Kingsbury Knoll, 169 Verulam Road, St Albans AL3 4DW Tel: 01727 866833 Fax: 01727 866833 — MB BS 1968 Lond.; FRCP Lond. 1989; MRCP (UK) 1971; MRCS Eng. LRCP Lond. 1968; DObst RCOG 1970. (Roy. Free) Cons (Dermat) BUPA Hosp.s, Bushey & Harpenden; BMI Hosp., Kings Oak, Enfield. Socs: Fell. St. John's Hosp. Dermat. Soc.; Brit. Assn. Dermat., Mem.; Fell. Roy. Soc. Med. Prev: Cons. (Dermat.) Barnet gen. Hosp.; Sen. Regist. (Dermat.) Roy. Free Hosp. Lond.; Regist. (Respirat. Med.) Hammersmith Hosp. Lond.

BARNES, Henry Greenfield (retired) 31 Percy Gardens, Tynemouth, North Shields NE30 4HQ Tel: 0191 257 9400 — MB BS (Hons.) Durh. 1943; FRCGP 1967. Life Mem. Med. Offs. Schs. Assn. Prev: Capt. RAMC.

BARNES, Hugh Eric Department Family Psychiatry, Bristol Royal Hospital For Sick Children, St Michael's Hill, Bristol BS2 8BJ Tel: 0117 929 4530; 6 Sea Mills Lane, Stoke Bishop, Bristol BS9 1DW — MB ChB 1973 Ed.; MRCPsych 1978.

BARNES, James Edward 14 Limmer Close, Wokingham RG41 4DF — MB ChB 1996 Bristol.

BARNES, James Joseph Crookston Medical Centre, 231 Dalmellington Road G53 7FY Tel: 0141 883 8887 — MB ChB 1984 Glas.; BSc (Hons.) Glas. 1981; DRCOG 1988.

BARNES, Jayne 1/L 62 White Street, Partick, Glasgow G11 5EB Tel: 0141 334 5440 — MB ChB 1995 Glas. SHO Paediat. Socs: BMA; MDDUS. Prev: SHO Med.; SHO Geriat.; SHO O & G.

BARNES, Jennifer Margaret Nunwell Surgery, Pump St., Bromyard HR7 4BZ Tel: 01885 483412 Fax: 01885 488739 Email: jennybarnes@doctors.org.uk; Shop Cottage, Monkland, Leominster HR6 9DB Tel: 01568 720351 — MB BS 1978 Lond.; MRCGP 1985; DRCOG 1982; BA Open Univ. 1997. (Univ. Coll. Hosp. Med. Sch.) p/t GP Bromyard; GP Tutor, Heref. Prev: Trainee GP Hereford VTS.

BARNES, Joanna Lesley Cranfield Sawston Health Centre, Link Road, Sawston, Cambridge CB2 4LB Tel: 01223 832711 Fax: 01223 836096; Rhee House, Harston, Cambridge CB2 5NP Tel: 01223 871300 — MB 1964 Camb.; MA Camb. 1971, MB 1964, BChir 1963; DPM Eng. 1973. (Univ. Coll. Hosp.)

BARNES, John, TD, Lt.-Col. RAMC Retd. (retired) 7 Willow Mount, Croydon CR0 5LD Tel: 020 8680 1044 — MB BS 1951 Lond.; MSc Lond. 1962; MRCS Eng. LRCP Lond. 1951; MFCM RCO (UK) 1973; DTM & H Eng. 1959, DIH 1963; DPH Lond. 1960. Prev: Sen. Med. Off. HQ Dept. of Health Lond.

BARNES, John Ridley Court Oast, Rectory Road, Ash, Sevenoaks TN15 7EX — MB BS 1997 Lond.

BARNES, John Alan Frank (retired) 10 Parsons Hill, Colchester CO3 4DT Tel: 01206 573943 — BM BCh 1956 Oxf.; MA Oxf. 1956; DObst RCOG 1971. Locum work. Prev: Ho. Surg. (Cas. & Obst.) Battle Hosp. Reading.

BARNES, John Desborough Seaside Medical Centre, 18 Sheen Road, Eastbourne BN22 8DR Tel: 01323 725667 Fax: 01323 417169 — MB ChB 1973 Manch.; MRCGP 1977; DObst RCOG 1976.

BARNES, John Nicholas Royal Cornwall Hospital, Truro TR1 3LJ Tel: 01872 252734 Fax: 01872 253498; Pen Enys, Newmills Lane, Kenwyn, Truro TR1 3EZ — MB BChir 1978 Camb.; MA, MB Camb. 1978, MD 1986, BChir 1977; FRCP (UK) 1990. (Lond. Hosp.) Cons. Phys. (Gen. Med. & Nephrol.) Roy. Cornw. Hosp. Treliske.; Clin. Dir. Med. Prev: Lect. Med. Unit Lond. Hosp. Med. Sch.; Hon. Sen. Regist. Tower Hamlets HA.

BARNES, John Stephen Somerset Partnership NHS and Social Care Trust, Beech Court, Taunton Road, Bridgwater TA6 3LS Tel: 01278 844 4737 — MB BS 1984 Lond.; MRCPsych 1990. Cons. (Gen. Psychiat.), Som. Partnership NHS & Social Care Trust.

BARNES, Jon Clifford Phoenix House, Glastonbury Road, Wells BA5 1TH Tel: 01749 670443 Fax: 01749 679487 — MB ChB 1975 Leeds; BSc (Hons.) Leeds 1972; MRCPsych 1979; FRCPsych 1998. (Leeds) Cons. Psychiat. Som. partnership NHS Trust.

BARNES, Jonathan Andrew 20A Murray Road, Northwood HA6 2YJ — MB ChB 1993 Birm.; ChB Birm. 1993.

BARNES, Jonathan Christopher Riverside Surgery, Water Street, Port Talbot SA12 6LF Tel: 01639 891376 Fax: 01639 870163 — MB ChB 1981 Liverp.; DRCOG 1985.

BARNES, Justin Fergus Pernettya, Sinclair St., Dunblane FK15 0AH — MB BS 1988 Lond.

BARNES, Katharine Louise Little Chalfont Surgery, 200 White Lion Road, Amersham HP7 9NU — BM 1987 Soton.; MRCGP 1991; DRCOG 1991. (Southampton)

BARNES, Katherine Brook House Surgery, 98 Oakley Road, Shirley, Southampton SO16 4NZ Tel: 023 8077 4851 Fax: 023 8032 2357; 418 Winchester Road, Bassett, Southampton SO16 7DH Tel: 02380 790687 — MB BS 1976 Lond.; DCH RCP Lond. 1988. (Middlx.) Prev: Trainee GP Soton.

BARNES, Katherine Helen Queen Annes Cottage, Kings Road, Windsor SL4 2AY; 34 Ord Street, Nedlands, Perth 6009, Australia — MB BS 1988 Lond.

BARNES, Mr Keith Anthony Flat 18, The Grange, Ivy Road, Macclesfield SK11 8NA — MB ChB 1986 Leic.; BSc Leic. 1983, MB ChB 1986; FRCS Ed. 1990; FRCS Orth. 1996. (Leicester) Cons. Orthop. & Trauma Surg. Socs: BMA. Prev: Resid. (Orthop.) Mass. Gen. Hosp. Boston, USA; SHO Rotat. (Surg.) Mersey RHA; SHO (Orthop. & Cas.) Roy. Liverp. Hosp.

BARNES, Lawrence James 2 Broadway Cottages, Broadway Lane, South Cerney, Cirencester GL7 5UH — MB BS 1996 Lond.

BARNES, Louise Department of Women & Children, South Cleveland Hospital, Marton Road, Middlesbrugh TS4 3BW — MB ChB 1998 Dund.; MB ChB Dund 1998.

BARNES, Louise Michele Altair, Overstreet Lane, Stapleford, Salisbury SP3 4LR — MB BS 1988 Lond.

BARNES, Lynne Susan Castle Gardens Medical Centre, 78 East Hill, Colchester CO1 2QS Tel: 01206 866626 Fax: 01206 869575; Braiswick Farm, Braiswick Lane, Mile End, Colchester CO4 5ED Tel: 01206 823657 Fax: 01206 751168 — MB ChB 1976 Bristol; DRCOG 1979. (Bristol)

BARNES, Margaret Anne Eagle House Surgery, 291 High Street, Ponders End, Enfield EN3 4DN Tel: 020 8351 1000 Fax: 020 8351 1007; 2 Private Road, Enfield EN1 2EL — MB ChB 1970 Sheff.; MRCGP 1978; DCH RCP Lond. 1973; DRCOG 1972.

BARNES, Margaret Heather (retired) Apt. 430, The Hawthorn, 18-21 Elton Road, Clevedon BS21 7RG Tel: 01275 794418 — MB ChB Ed. 1940. Prev: Asst. Med. Off. VD (Female), Obst. Ho. Surg. & Gyn. Ho. Surg. Roy. Infirm. Edin.

BARNES, Margaret Jean 10 Parsons Hill, Colchester CO3 4DT Tel: 01206 573943 — MRCS Eng. LRCP Lond. 1960; DObst RCOG 1962. (Guy's) Sch. Med. Off. Essex AHA. Prev: Ho. Surg. St. And. Hosp. Bow; Ho. Surg. (Obst.) N. Middlx. Hosp. Lond.; Ho. Off. Evelina Childr. Hosp. of Guy's Hosp. Lond.

BARNES, Marian Nora (retired) Little Hoopern, Chagford, Newton Abbot TQ13 8BZ Tel: 01647 432098 Fax: 01647 432097 — MB BChir Camb. 1961; MA Camb 1961; MFFP 1993; DObst RCOG 1963. Prev: Assoc. Specialist (Genitourin. Med.) Newham Gen. Hosp.

BARNES, Mark David Princess Margaret Hospital, Okus Road, Swindon Wilts — BM 1991 Soton.; FRCR 1999; FRCS Eng. 1995.

BARNES, Mark Hodson Seaford Health Centre, Dane Road, Seaford BN25 1DH Tel: 01323 490022 Fax: 01323 492156 — MB BS 1983 Lond.; MRCGP 1987. Chair. E.bourne Downs PCG. Socs: E.bourne Med. Soc. Prev: Ho. Surg. Guy's Hosp. Lond.; Ho. Phys. New Cross Hosp. Lond.

BARNES, Martin Richard Fir Tree Cottage, Hutton-Le-Hole, York YO62 6UD Tel: 017515 337 — MB ChB 1991 Manch.; BSc (Physiol.) 2nd cl. Hons Manch. 1988.

BARNES, Michael Paul 236 Hexham Road, Newcastle upon Tyne NE15 9QU — MB BCh 1988 Wales.

BARNES, Professor Michael Philip Hunters Moor Regional Rehabilitation Centre, Hunters Road, Newcastle upon Tyne NE2 4NR Tel: 0191 219 5690 Fax: 0191 219 5690 Email: m.p.barnes@gtintenet.com — MB ChB 1977 Bristol; MD Bristol 1987; FRCP Lond. 1993; MRCP (UK) 1980. (Bristol) Prof. Neurol. Rehabil. Univ. Newc. u. Tyne; Hon. Cons. Neurol. And Phys.in Rehab-Med, N.gate. Socs: (Pres.) Brit. Soc. Rehabil. Med.; Founder Pres., Forum of Neutlogical Rehabil. Prev: Sen. Lect. (Neurol. Rehabil.) Univ. Newc.; Lect. Disabil. Med. (Neurol.) Soton. Gen. Hosp.; Research Regist. (Neurol.) Roy. Vict. Infirm. Newc.

BARNES, Murray Farris Lyall The Crescent Medical Practice, 12 Walmer Crescent, Glasgow G51 1AT Tel: 0141 427 0191 Fax: 0141 427 1581; 18 Newtonlea Avenue, Newton Mearns, Glasgow G77 5QA — MB ChB 1966 Glas.; FRCGP 1993, M 1971; DCH RCPS Glas. 1970; DObst RCOG 1968.

BARNES, Neil Christopher London Chest Hospital, Bonner Road, London E2 9JX Tel: 020 8983 2433 Fax: 020 8983 2279 Email: neil.barnes@bartsandthelondon.nhs.uk; Royal London Hospital, Whitechapel, London E1 1BB Tel: 020 7377 7339 Fax: 020 7377 7337 — MB BS 1979 Lond.; FRCP; MA Camb. 1980, BA 1976; MRCS Eng. LRCP Lond. 1979; MRCP (UK) 1981. (Westm.) Cons. Phys. Lond. Chest Hosp. & Roy. Lond. Hosp.; Hon. Sen. Lect. St. Bart. & Roy. Lond. Hosp. Med. Coll. Socs: Brit. Thorac. Soc. Prev: Sen. Regist. Lond. Chest Hosp.; Research Fell. King's Coll. Hosp. Lond.; Ho. Phys. & Ho. Surg. W.m. Hosp. Lond.

BARNES, Nicholas Andrew 92 Bull Cop, Formby, Liverpool L37 8BZ Tel: 01704 834432 — MB BS 1992 Newc. SHO (Paediat.) Alder Hey Liverp. Prev: SHO (Med.) N. Tees Gen. Hosp. & Cumbld. Infirm. Carlisle.

BARNES, Nicholas Delano (retired) Rhee House, Harston, Cambridge CB2 5NP Tel: 01223 871300 Email: nickdelano@aol.com — MB BChir Camb. 1963; MA Camb. 1960; FRCP Lond. 1981, M 1966; FRCPCH 1997. Prev: Cons. Paediat. Addenbrooke's Hosp. Camb.

BARNES, Nicholas Rennie 11 Brunswick Street, Walthamstow, London E17 9NB — MB BS 1991 Lond.; BSc (Biochem) 1989. (London Hospital Medical College)

BARNES, Nicholas William 7 Sturges Road, Bognor Regis PO21 2AH Tel: 01243 860139; 21A Flitton House, Sutton Est., Upper St., London N1 1UG — MB BS 1987 Lond.; BSc Basic Med. Scs. & Pharmacol. Lond. 1984. SHO (Gen. Med.) Portsmouth & S.E. Hants. Rotat.

BARNES, Nicola Louise Patricia Flat 6, Exeter Court, 378 Wilmslow Road, Manchester M20 3NA — MB ChB 1998 Manch.; MB ChB Manch 1998.

BARNES, Pamela Rosemary 100 Huntingfield, London SW15 5EU — MB BS 1988 Lond.

BARNES, Paul Marginson (retired) 7 East Hills, Cranfield, Bedford MK43 0EA Tel: 01234 750069 Fax: 01234 750069 — MB ChB 1956 Ed.; FRCP Ed. 1981 M 1967; FRCPCH 1997; DObst RCOG 1962; DCH RFPS Glas. 1961. Prev: Cons. Paediat. & Head of Dept. Al Corniche Hosp., Abu Dhabi, United Arab Emirates.

BARNES, Penelope Darell 42 East Avenue, Oxford OX4 1XP — MB BS 1992 Lond.; BSc Lond. 1989; MRCP (UK) 1995. Specialist Regist. (Infec.) Oxf. Radcliffe Hosp. Prev: SHO Rotat. (Med.) Oxf.

BARNES, Peter Halley House, High St., Pattingham, Wolverhampton WV6 7BQ — LRCPI & LM, LRSCI & LM 1954; LRCPI & LM, LRCSI & LM 1954; MA Camb. 1985, BA 1950.

BARNES, Peter Eagle House Surgery, 291 High Street, Ponders End, Enfield EN3 4DN Tel: 020 8351 1000 Fax: 020 8351 1007; 18 Slades Hill, Enfield EN2 7DH Tel: 020 8363 1868 Email: peter.barnes4@virgin.net — MB BS 1969 Lond.; MRCGP 1978. (Middlx.) GP; Chairm. Enfield N. PCG.

BARNES, Peter Andrew Westrop Surgery, Newburgh Place, Highworth, Swindon SN6 7DN Tel: 01793 762218 Fax: 01793 766073; 3 The Close, Hambidge Lane, Lechlade GL7 3EL — MB BS 1990 Lond.; MRCGP 1995.

BARNES, Peter Charles Oaklands Hospital, 19 Lancaster Road, Salford M6 8AQ Tel: 0161 787 7700; 20 Albert Square, Bowdon, Altrincham WA14 2ND Tel: 0161 941 2389 — MB ChB 1966 Manch.; MRCP (UK) 1973. Cons. Phys. & Cardiol. & Exec. Med. Dir. Salford Roy. Hosp. NHS Trust. Prev: Cons. Phys. Hope Hosp. Salford.; Postgrad. Med. Tutor Manch. Univ.; Mem. Manch. Med. Soc. (Sec. Sect. Med.).

BARNES, Professor Peter John National Heart & Lung Institute, Dovehouse St., London SW3 6LY Tel: 020 7351 8174 Fax: 020 7351 5675 Email: p.j.barnes@ic.ac.uk; 44 Woodsome Road, London NW5 1RZ — BM BCh 1972 Oxf.; F Med Sci 1999; DSc Oxf. 1987, DM 1982; MA Camb. 1973, BA (1st cl. Hons.) 1969; FRCP Lond. 1986; MRCP (UK) 1974. Prof. Thoracic Med. Nat. Heart & Lung Inst. & Hon. Cons. Phys. Roy. Brompton Hosp. Lond.; Chairm. Respirat. Scis. Imperial Coll. Sch. of Med., Lond. Socs: Brit. Thorac. Soc.; Amer. Thoracic Soc.; Brit. Pharm. Soc. Prev: Prof. Clin. Pharmacol. Cardiothoracic Inst. Lond.; Cons. Phys. Dept. Med. (Respirat. Div.) Hammersmith Hosp. Lond.; Sen. Regist. (Med.) Hammersmith Hosp. Lond.

BARNES, Peter Kenneth 85 Palewell Park, East Sheen, London SW14 8JJ — MB BS 1968 Lond.; MRCS Eng. LRCP Lond. 1968; FFA RCS Eng. 1973. (Char. Cross) Cons. Anaesth. W.m. Hosp. Lond.

BARNES, Peter Mark Fraser Hoechst Marion Roussel Ltd., Broadwater Park, Uxbridge UB9 5HP Tel: 01895 834343 Fax: 01895 837895 Email: peter.barnes@hmrag.com — MB BS 1985 Sydney; MFPM RCP (UK) 1994.

BARNES, Peter Michael Academic Centre, Dept of Community Chief Health, Llandough Hospital, Penarth Tel: 02920 716934; 1 Derwon Fawr, Cilfrow, Neath SA10 8NX — MB BCh 1991 Wales; BSc (Hons.) Wales 1990; DCH RCP Lond. 1996; MRCP (UK) 1997; MRCPCH 1998. (Cardiff) Specialist Regist.,community Health Dept., Llandough Hosp.,Cardiff. Socs: Catholic Doctors Guild; Welsh Paediat. Soc.; Brit. Assn. for Community Child Health.

BARNES, Phillip Robert John Department of Neurology, King's College Hospital, Denmark Hill, London SE5 9RS Tel: 020 7346 3667 Fax: 020 7346 3290; Piltdown House, Maidstone Road, St Mary's Platt, Sevenoaks TN15 8JE — BM BCh 1987 Oxf.; BSc 1981; PhD Lond. 1984; MRCP (UK) 1990; T(M) 1994; FRCP 1999. (King's College, Oxford) Cons. Neurol. King's Coll. Hosp. Lond. & Maidstone Gen. Hosp.; Dir. of Neurosci.s KCH Lond. Prev: Sen. Regist. (Neurol.) Qu.s Med. Centre Nottm.; Neuromuscular Research Fell. Univ. of Oxf. & EP Abraham Research Fell. Green Coll. Oxf.; Regist. (Neurol.) Qu. Eliz. Hosp. Birm.

BARNES, Richard Charles 35A Burlington Road, Southampton SO15 2FR Tel: 02380 578055 Email: rcb171152@uboot.com — MB BS 1976 Lond. GP, Non-Princip. Prev: GP, Brook Ho. Surg., S.ampton ('81-'01).; Clin. Asst. Old Age Pysch. W.ern & Moorgreen Hosps. S.ampton.

BARNES, Richard Charles Mossley Hill Hospital, Park Avenue, Liverpool L18 8BU Tel: 0151 250 3000 Fax: 0151 729 0227 Email: richard.barnes@exchange.nmc-tr.nwest.nhs.uk — MB ChB 1989 Liverp.; MRCPsych 1993. Cons. Old Age Psychiat. Liverp.; Med. Staff, St. Helens Rugby League Football Club. Socs: Liverp. Psychiat. Soc.; Rugby League Med. Assn. Prev: Cons. in Old Age Psychiat., Ormskirk DGH.

BARNES, Richard James 14 Montague Road, Cambridge CB4 1BX — MB 1971 Camb.; BChir 1970.

BARNES, Richard James Link House, Oakway, Chesham Bois, Amersham HP6 5PQ — MB ChB 1998 Manch.; MB ChB Manch 1998.

BARNES, Richard Jeremy Ashleworth Manor, Ashleworth, Gloucester GL19 4LA Tel: 01452 700350 Email: rjb@ashleworthmanor.fsnet.co.uk — MB ChB 1961 Birm.; FRCGP 1986, M 1969. Hosp. Pract. (Digestive Endoscopy) Glos. Roy. Hosp. Gloucester; Ex-Postgrad. Clin. Tutor Glos. Roy. Hosp. Gloucester. Socs: Brit. Soc. Gastroenterol.; (Ex-Sec.) Primary Care Soc. Gastroenterol.; Brit. Soc. Med. & Dent. Hypn. Prev: Ho. Phys. Qu.

Eliz. Hosp. Birm. & Childr. Hosp. Birm.; Ho. Surg. Dudley Rd. Hosp. Birm.

BARNES, Richard John Avenue Medical Practice, 7 Reney Avenue, Sheffield S8 7FH Tel: 0114 237 7649; 7 Abbey Crescent, Sheffield S7 2QX — MB ChB 1976 Sheff.

BARNES, Robert Michael 193 Wilton Road, Shirley, Southampton SO15 5JA — MB ChB 1951 Bristol; MRCP Ed. 1961; DTM & H Eng. 1960; FRCPath. 1982, M 1963. Dep. Med. Dir. Wessex Blood Transfus. Centre Soton. Socs: BMA & Assn. Clin Pathols. Prev: Lt.-Col. RAMC; Cons. Pathol. Brit. Milit. Hosp. Hong Kong.

BARNES, Roderick Martin The Spinney, Heath Rise, Camberley GU15 2ER Tel: 01276 22860; The Spinney, Heath Rise, Camberley GU15 2ER Tel: 01276 22860 — MB BS 1956 Lond.; MFOM 1980; DAvMed Eng. 1971; DObst RCOG 1960. (Middlx. Hosp. Lond.) Cons. Aviat. Med. Camberley. Prev: Sen. Med. Off. (Flight Safety & Research) Civil Aviat. Auth.; Sen. Med. Off. (Train.) Brit. Airways Med. Serv.; Asst. (Bacteriol.) Pub. Health Laborat. Manor Hosp. Bath.

BARNES, Roger Kenyon Great Eccleston Health Centre, Raikes Road, Great Eccleston, Preston PR3 0ZA Tel: 01995 670066 Fax: 01995 671054; The Cottage, Churchtown, Preston PR3 0LQ Tel: 01995 605349 Fax: 01995 605349 — MB BS 1971 Lond.; MRCS Eng. LRCP Lond. 1971; MRCGP 1975; DObst RCOG 1974. (Roy. Free) Prev: Trainee GP Carlisle Exec. Counc.; Ho. Surg. Soton. Gen. Hosp.; Ho. Phys. Roy. Shrops. Infirm. Shrewsbury.

BARNES, Professor Ronald Derek 7 Albert Park Road, Malvern WR14 1HL Tel: 01684 893612 Fax: 01684 562459 Email: drbarnes@ntlworld.com — MB BS Lond.; 1957 MRCS Eng. LRCP Lond.; 1977 DSc Lond. MD 1969; 1981 FRCPath M 1969; 1988 FIBiol M 1987; 1988 CBiol. (Guy's) Cons. Appeals Serv. & Indep. Med. Assessm. Serv.; Prof. in Med. Law (Hon.) Univ. Wolverhampton. Socs: BMA. Prev: Mem. Scientif. Staff/Cons. MRC Clin. Research Centre, N.wick Pk.; Hon. Sen. Lect. Univ. Coll. Hosp. Med. Sch.; Hon. Cons. N.wick Pk. Hosp.

BARNES, Rosalind Elizabeth 46 Hillfoot, Craigends, Houston, Johnstone PA6 7NS — MB ChB 1983 Glas. Regist. (Psychiat.) Ravenscraig Hosp. Greenock. Prev: SHO (A & E) Vale of Leven Dist. Gen. Hosp. Alexandria & Falmouth & Dist. Hosp.; SHO (Psychiat.) Roy. Cornw. Hosp. Truro.

BARNES, Rosemary Ann Department of Medical Microbiology, University of Wales College of Medicine, Heath Park, Cardiff CF14 4XN Tel: 029 2074 2166 Fax: 029 2074 2161 Email: barnesra@cardiff.ac.uk; Greenmeadow, Cefn Mably, St Mellon, Cardiff CF3 6LP — MB BS 1981 Lond.; MA Camb. 1982; MSc Lond. 1987, MD 1988; MRCP (UK) 1984; MRCPath 1989; FRCPath 1997. Sen. Lect. (Med. MicroBiol.) UWCM.

BARNES, Roy (retired) Three Gables, McFarland's Down, St Mary's TR21 0NS Tel: 01720 423141 Email: maroy@threegables.fsnet.co.uk — MRCS Eng. LRCP Lond. 1950; MA Camb. 1964; FFCM 1981, M 1972; DPH Leeds 1955. Prev: Dist. Gen. Manager & Dist. Med. Off. Airedale HA.

BARNES, Samantha Jane 8 Woburn Close, Trentham, Stoke-on-Trent ST4 8TA — MB ChB 1998 Liverp.; MB ChB Liverp 1998.

BARNES, Sandra Adeline 36 Glenarney Road, Cookstown BT80 9DZ Tel: 016487 61049 — MB BCh BAO 1992 Belf.; MRCGP 1996; DRCOG 1995. Staff Grade Paediat. S. Tyrone Hosp. Dungannon & Craigavon Area Hosp. Socs: BMA. Prev: GP/Regist. Oaks Family Pract. Cookstown; SHO (Paediat.) Craigavon Area Hosp.; SHO (O & G) S. Tyrone Hosp.

BARNES, Sarah Louise 4 Lark Close, Exeter EX4 4SL — MB BS 1987 Lond.

BARNES, Shelley Baden 15 Congreve Road, Stoke-on-Trent ST3 2HA — MB ChB 1989 Liverp.; BSc (Hons.) Liverp. 1986, MB ChB 1989. SHO N. Staffs. HA.

BARNES, Simon 11 Erskine Hill, Polmont, Falkirk FK2 0UH — MB ChB 1998 Glas.; MB ChB Glas 1998.

BARNES, Simon James 427 Harborne Road, Birmingham B15 3LB — MB BCh 1994 Wales.

BARNES, Mr Simon Nicholas 3 Willow Hey, Liverpool L31 3DL — MB ChB 1992 Liverp.; FRCS Ed. 1997. SHO (Orthop.) Roy. Liverp. Univ. Hosp. Trust; Specialist Regist. Roy. Liverp. Univ. Hosp. Trust. Socs: Assoc. BOA.

BARNES, Siobhan Station Road Surgery, 11 Station Road, Loughton IG10 4NZ Tel: 020 8508 3818 Fax: 020 8508 2539; Haslingfield, 61 Queens Road, Loughton IG10 1RR — MB BCh 1990 Wales; MRCGP 1994; DFFP 1995; DRCOG 1993.

BARNES, Stanley (retired) 7 Border Road, Sydenham, London SE26 6HB Tel: 020 8659 3339 — MB BCh BAO 1944 Dub. Prev: Resid. Surg. Off. & Resid. Orthop. Off. Clayton Hosp. Wakefield.

BARNES, Stella Kathryn Mary 52 Linden Gardens, London W4 2EH — MB BS 1994 Lond.; BSc Lond. 1991. (Univ. Coll. Lond. Hosp.)

BARNES, Mr Steven John 11 Churchfield Avenue, North Finchley, London N12 0NS Tel: 020 8343 9167 — MB BS 1983 Lond.; FRCS Eng. 1987. Regist. (Orthop.) Lister Hosp. Stevenage. Socs: Fell. Roy. Coll. Surg.; Brit. Orthop. Assn. & Brit. Soc. Surg. Hand. Prev: Regist. (Orthop.) Roy. Free Hosp. Lond.; Fell. Hand Surg. P.ss Alexandra Hosp. Brisbane, Austral.

BARNES, Susan Eileen Sherburn Surgery, Grey Avenue, Sherburn, Durham DH6 1JF — MB BS 1984 Newc.; MRCGP 1988.

BARNES, Susan Felicity Randolph Medical Centre, Green Lane, Datchet, Slough SL3 9EX Tel: 01753 541268; Queen Annes Cottage, Kings Road, Windsor SL4 2AY — MB BCh 1964 Wales.

BARNES, Susan Mary Accident and Emergency Department, Dewsbury and District Hospital, Healds Road, Dewsbury WF13 4HS Tel: 01924 465105 Fax: 01924 816079 Email: smbarnes@dial.pipex.com; Fieldhead, 12 Grovenor Road, Batley WF17 0LN Tel: 01924 420240 Fax: 01924 513843 — MB ChB 1979 Leeds; MBA Leeds 1996; MRCP (UK) 1982; Dip. Health Serv. Mgt. York 1992. Dir. Accid. & Emerency Dir. Dewsbury & Dist. Hosp.; Fell. Fac. A & E; Fell. Fac. PreHosp. Care. Socs: Fell. RCP.

BARNES, Susannah Delano Archway Medical Centre, 652 Holloway Road, London N19 3NU Tel: 020 7272 0111 — MB BS 1992 Lond.; BSc Lond. 1989; DCH RCP Lond. 1994; DRCOG 1995; MRCGP 1996; DFFP 1999. GP Partner.

BARNES, Theresa Corrinne 45 Basingbourne Road, Fleet GU52 6TG; 8 Roseland Drive, Heavitkee, Exeter EX1 2TS Tel: 01392 499427 — MB ChB 1998 Birm.; ChB Birm. 1998. SHO Med. Torbay Hosp., Torquay. Prev: PRHO Surg. Heartlands Hosp., Birm.; PRHO Med. Worcester Roy. Inf, Worcester.

BARNES, Professor Thomas Richard Edward Imperial College School of Medicine, Academic Centre, Ealing Hospital, St Bernard's Wing, London Tel: 0208 354 8892 Fax: 0208 3548 9258 Email: t.r.barnes@ic.ac.uk; 7 Grange Park Place, Thurstan Road, London SW20 0EE — MRCS Eng. LRCP Lond. 1973; MD Lond. 1990, MB BS 1973; FRCPsych 1993, M 1977. (Guy's) Prof. Clin. Psychiat. Imperial Coll. Sch. Med. Lond. Prev: Sen. Wellcome Research Fell. Univ. Camb. Clin. Sch. Addenbrooke's Hosp. Camb.; Lect. (Psychiat.) St. Geo. Hosp. Med. Sch. Lond.

BARNES, Thomas William, TD (retired) Woodfield Road, Oadby, Leicester LE2 4HQ Tel: 0116 210 0533 Fax: 0116 210 0534 — MB BS Lond. 1948; MRCS Eng. LRCP Lond. 1947. Prev: Ho. Phys. Char. Cross Hosp.

BARNES, Timothy Alexander Tel: 01506 423800 Fax: 01506 460757 — MB ChB 1991 Aberd.; DRCOG 1995; DFFP 1995; MRCGP 1995. GP; Company Doctor (Occupat.al Health), BSB, Livingston. Socs: Roy. Coll. Gen. Pract.; BMA.

BARNES, Walter Stuart Francis Conquest Hospital, The Ridge, St Leonards-on-Sea TN37 7RD Tel: 01424 758023 Fax: 01424 758121 — MB ChB 1973 Birm.; MRCP (UK) 1978; FRCPath 1996, M 1984. (Rhodesia) Cons. Histopath. Conquest Hosp. St. Leonards-on-Sea. Prev: Lect. & Demonst. (Histopath.) Roy. Vict. Infirm. Newc.

BARNET, Margaret Campbell (retired) 16 Lucombe Way, New Earswick, York YO32 4DS Tel: 01904 764360 — MB ChB 1941 St. And.; MFCM 1972.

BARNET-LAMB, Margaret West Suffolk Hospital, Hardwick Lane, Bury St Edmunds IP33 2QZ Tel: 01284 713243; The Pages, 39 Northgate Avenue, Bury St Edmunds IP32 6AZ Tel: 01284 703769 — MB 1976 Camb.; BA Camb. 1972, MB 1976, BChir 1975; MRCOG 1981, D 1977; DIP Gilmed 1997. Clin. Asst. (Genitourin. Med.) W. Suff. Hosp. Bury St Edmunds.

BARNETSON, James Kerr 9 Lonsdale Avenue, South Bents, Sunderland SR6 8AY Tel: 0191 529 3829 — LAH Dub. 1965. (Ed.) Late Intern. Flower Hosp. Toledo, USA; Anaesth. Resid. Univ. Texas Med. Br. Hosps. Galveston, USA; Path. Resid. Mercy Hosp. Toledo.

BARNETT, Adrian Anthony 9 Stamford Close, Lymm WA13 9ED — MB ChB 1990 Liverp.

BARNETT, Alicja Maria Family Planning Clinic, 4 Barnfield Hill, Exeter EX1 1SR Tel: 01392 427264 Fax: 01392 425355; 34 Station Road, Okehampton EX20 1EA Tel: 01837 53730 — MB ChB 1975 Birm.; MFFP 1994ol. Clin. Co-ordinator (Family Plann.) Exeter Community NHS Trust. Socs: Inst. Psychosexual Med.

BARNETT, Alison Mary 3 Coppice View, Weavering, Maidstone ME14 5TX — MB BS 1984 Lond.; BSc Lond. 1981; MFPHM RCP (UK) 1996; MRCGP 1989. (Univ. Coll. Hosp. Lond.) Cons. Pub. Health Med. Bexley & Greenwich. Prev: Sen. Regist. (Pub. Health Med.) S. Thames; Trainee GP Thanet VTS.

BARNETT, Amelia Louise 8 Lavant Road, Chichester PO19 4RH Tel: 01243 527264 — MB BS 1994 Lond.; DCH 1997; DRCOG 1998; MRCGP, 1998. (Royal London Hospital) p/t GP Partner.

BARNETT, Anthony Francis (retired) Owner of Cottege Gulleys, Rock St., Croscombe, Wells BA5 3QT Tel: 01749 344029 — MB BS 1947 Lond.; MD Lond. 1953; MRCP Lond. 1951. Prev: Regist. (Med.) St. Thos. Hosp. Lond.

BARNETT, Professor Anthony Howard Undergraduate Centre, Birmingham Heartlands Hospital, Birmingham B9 5SS Tel: 0121 766 6611 Fax: 0121 685 5536 Email: barneta@heartsol.wmids/nhs.uk; Meiklewood, 7 Trevelyan Close, Claverdon, Warwick CV35 8PA — MB BS 1975 Lond.; BSc (Hons) Lond. 1972, MD 1981; FRCP Lond. 1989; MRCP (UK) 1978. (King's Coll. Hosp.) Prof. Med. & Cons. Phys. Univ. Birm. & Heartlands Hosp. Socs: Assn. Phys.; Brit. Diabetic Assn.; Eur. Assn. Study Diabetes. Prev: Sen. Regist. (Gen. Med. & Diabetes) Roy. S. Hants. Hosp. Soton.; Sen. Regist. (Endocrinol.) P.ss Margt. Hosp. ChristCh., NZ; MRC Sen. Research Fell. (Diabetic) King's Coll. Hosp. Lond.

BARNETT, Arthur Lionel (retired) 17 Springfield Glen, Sheffield S7 2HL — MB ChB 1930 Glas.

BARNETT, Bernard (retired) 2 Belle Walk, Birmingham B13 9DF — LRCP LRCS 1942 Ed.; LRCP LRCS Ed. LRFPS Glas. 1942; DPM Lond. 1951. Prev: Psychiat. Adviser Childr. Dept. City Birm.

BARNETT, Carol Joan (retired) Hough Gates, Newcastle Rd, Hough, Crewe CW2 5JG Tel: 01270 567898 — MB ChB Liverp. 1967; MRCOG 1972; DObst 1970. Prev: Regist. (O & G) Liverp. RHB.

BARNETT, Clare Alison 2 Woodlands Close, Peacehaven BN10 7SF — MB BS 1998 Lond.; MB BS Lond 1998.

BARNETT, David (retired) BUPA Hospital, Jackson Avenue, Leeds LS8 1NT Tel: 0113 269 3939 — BM BCh 1960 Oxf.; MA Oxf. 1963; FRCP Lond. 1978, M 1964. Prev: Cons. Phys.St. Jas.Unii.Hosp.Leeds.

BARNETT, Professor David Braham Division of Medicine & Therapeutics, Clinical Sciences Building, PO Box 65, Leicester Royal Infirmary, Leicester LE2 7LX Tel: 01162 523126 Fax: 01162 523108 — MB ChB 1967 Sheff.; MD Sheff. 1979; FRCP 1981; MRCP (UK) 1971. Prof. Clin. Pharmacol. Univ. Leicester. & Hon. Cons. Phys., Leicester Roy. Infirm. Prev: Sen. Lect. (Clin. Pharmacol.) Leicester Roy. Infirm.; Merck Internat. Fell. Dept. Clin. Pharmacol. Univ. Calif. USA.

BARNETT, Mr David Nigel 39 Fochabers Drive, Cardonald, Glasgow G52 2LX Tel: 0141 883 9055 — MB BS 1983 W. Indies; FRCS Glas. 1991. Vis. Regist. (Orthop.) Gtr. Glas. HB.

BARNETT, Eric Jack (retired) Bronallt, Pwllglas, Mold CH7 1RA Tel: 01352 753435 — MB BS 1959 Lond.; MRCS Eng. LRCP Lond. 1959; DObst RCOG 1961. Prev: Maj. RAMC.

BARNETT, Esther Rochell (retired) 2 Belle Walk, Birmingham B13 9DF — MB BCh BAO 1948 Belf. Prev: Ho. Surg. O & G Dept. All St.s Hosp. Chatham.

BARNETT, Gillian Ceri 5 Squires Close, Kempsey, Worcester WR5 3JE — BM BCh 1998 Oxf.; BM BCh Oxf 1998.

BARNETT, Glyn Cawley Daer 78 Drive Mansions, Fulham Road, London SW6 5JH — MB BS 1996 Lond. Surg. Rotat., Kingston Hosp. Trust.

BARNETT, Helen Claire 116 Hayes Way, Beckenham BR3 6RT — MB BS 1993 Lond.

BARNETT, John Moelwyn Tel: 01263 822066 Fax: 01263 823890; 4 Montague Road, Sheringham NR26 8LN — MB BS 1969 Lond.; MRCS Eng. LRCP Lond. 1968; DObst RCOG 1972. (Char. Cross) Clin. Asst. (Post Acute Surgic. Care) Kelling Hosp. Holt. Prev: Clin. Asst. (Orthop. & Ophth.) Epsom Dist. Hosp.; Ho. Phys. (Radiother., Orthop. & Dent.) Char. Cross Hosp. Lond.; Ho. Surg. (O & G) St. Lukes Hosp. Bradford.

BARNETT, Jonathan Michael Mill Lane Medical Centre, 112 Mill Lane, London NW6 1XQ Tel: 020 7431 1588 Fax: 020 7431 8919; The Abbey Medical Centre, 87-89 Abbey Road, St. John's Wood, London NW8 0AG — MB ChB 1975 Leeds; MRCGP 1981. GP Lond. Prev: Med. Regist. St. Albans City Hosp.; SHO (Med.& Neurol.) S.end Hosp.; SHO (Paediat.) Seacroft Hosp. Leeds.

BARNETT, Julia Elizabeth 116 Street Lane, Leeds LS8 2AL — MB ChB 1991 Leeds.

BARNETT, Julian Matthew Maple Cottage, Water Lane, Somerton TA11 6RG — MB ChB 1986 Birm. SHO Rotat. (Psychiat.) Keele. Prev: Trainee GP Lydney Glos. VTS.

BARNETT, Lola Ethel (retired) 29 Greenbank Road, Liverpool L18 1HG Tel: 0151 733 3224 Fax: 0151 734 5147 — MB BS Lond. 1949; MRCS Eng. LRCP Lond. 1949. Med. Adviser Owen Owen Ltd. & Assoc. Companies. Prev: GP Liverp.

BARNETT, Mandy Mae Radiotherapy Centre, Walsgrave Hospital, Clifford Bridge Road, Coventry CV2 2DX Tel: 024 76 538779 Fax: 024 76 538900 — MB BS 1982 Lond.; BSc Lond. 1979, MB BS 1982; DMRT 1990; MRCGP 1995 - RCGP; MD 1996 (Univ. Bristol). (Univ. Coll. Hosp.) Cons. Palliat. Med. Walsgrave Hosps. MHS Trust Coventry & Myton Hamlet Hospice Warwick; Sen. Lect. (Palliat. Med.) Univ. of Warwick. Prev: Research Fell. (Palliat. Med.) Dept. Med. Univ. Bristol.; GP Regist. The Family Pract., W.ern Coll. Bristol; Reg. Clin. Oncol. Bristol Oncol. Centre.

BARNETT, Marion Betty (retired) Elm Court, Tower Road, Darlington DL3 6RU Tel: 01325 467676 — MB BS 1952 Durh.; FRCPsych 1986, M 1972; DPM Leeds 1966.

BARNETT, Mr Michael Anthony 12 Navarac Court, 21 Belle Vue Road, Poole BH14 8TW — MB BS 1960 Lond.; FRCS Eng. 1967; MRCS Eng. LRCP Lond. 1960.

BARNETT, Michael Beresford Anaesthetic Department, Guy's Hospital, London SE1 9RT Tel: 0207 955 4051 Fax: 0207 955 8844 Email: michael.barnett@gstt.sthames.nhs.uk; 39 Shearman Road, Blackheath, London SE3 9HY Tel: 020 8852 6854 — MB BS 1965 Lond.; MRCS Eng. LRCP Lond. 1965; FFA RCS Eng. 1969. (Guy' s Hospital Medical school) Cons. Anaesth. Guy's and St Thomas' Hosp. NHS Trust. Prev: Sen. Regist. (Anaesth.) Guy's Hosp. Lond. & Roy. Sussex Co. Hosp.; Brighton; Regist. (Anaesth.) Roy. N.. Hosp. Lond.

BARNETT, Paul Somerset Gardens Family Health, 4 Creighton Road, Tottenham, London N17 8NW Tel: 020 8493 9090 Fax: 020 8493 6000 — MB ChB 1983 Glas.; BSc (Hons.) Glas. 1980; MRCGP 1987; DCH RCP Lond. 1989; DRCOG 1987. Prev: Trainee GP Enfield; Regist. (Paediat.) N. Middlx. Hosp. Lond.

BARNETT, Philip Sol Tel: 020 7328 0491 — MB BCh 1977 Witwatersrand; 1993 PhD Lond; 1973 BSc Witwatersrand; 1988 MRCP (UK); FRCP 1998 UK. (Witwatersrand) Cons. Endocrinol., Diabetes, Metab. and Weight Managem., Lond.; Assoc. Prof. Med. UCLA Sch. Med. Socs: BMA; BDA; Amer. Diabetes Assn. Prev: Dir. (Diabetes & Endocrinol. & Metabol. & Internal Med.) Cedars Sinai Med. Center Los Angeles Calif., USA.

BARNETT, Phillida Alfreda Field Farm, Tillington, Hereford HR4 8LJ Tel: 01432 760206 Fax: 01432 761654 — MB ChB 1959 Birm.; MRCS Eng. LRCP Lond. 1959; DObst RCOG 1961. Clin. Asst. (Plastic Surg.) Co. Hosp. Hereford. Prev: MRC Research Asst. Surg. St. Geo. Hosp. Lond.; MRC Research Asst. Surg. & Ho. Surg. & Ho. Phys. Qu. Eliz. Hosp. Birm.

BARNETT, Richard Sunbury Health Centre Group Practice, Green Street, Sunbury-on-Thames TW16 6RH Tel: 01932 713399 Fax: 01932 713354; 125 Shaftesbury Crescent, Staines TW18 1QN — MB BS 1979 Lond.; MRCGP 1986; DRCOG 1981. Prev: Trainee GP Beaconsfield VTS.

BARNETT, Richard Jeremy Manor Surgery, Osler Road, Headington, Oxford OX3 9BP Tel: 01865 762535 — MB BS 1967 Lond.; MRCS Eng. LRCP Lond. 1967; DObst RCOG 1971. (St. Bart.) Prev: Ho. Surg. Roy. Portsmouth Hosp.; Ho. Phys. St. Bart. Hosp. Lond.

BARNETT, Robert Nigel Greenbank Road Surgery, 29 Greenbank Road, Liverpool L18 1HG Tel: 0151 733 3224 — MB ChB 1983 Liverp.; BSc (Hons.) Biochem. Liverp. 1978. (Liverp.) Med. Adviser Liverp. John Moores Univ.; Sec. Liverp. Local. Med. Comm. Socs: Liverp. Med. Inst.

BARNETT, Simon Jonathan Kneesworth House Hospital, Old North Road, Bassingbourn-cum-Kneesworth, Royston SG8 5JR Tel:

01763 255700 Fax: 01763 255718 — MB BS 1987 Lond.; BSc Lond. 1984; MRCPsych 1991. Cons. Kneesworth Hse. Hosp. Royston. Prev: Cons. NW Anglia Ment. Health Trust; Sen. Regist. & Regist. (Psychiat.) Fulbourn & Addenbrooke's Hosps.

BARNETT, Terence James (retired) 14 Hinton Wood Avenue, Highcliffe, Christchurch BH23 5AH Tel: 01425 274759 — MB ChB Liverp. 1956; BSc (1st cl. Hons.) Liverp. 1953; MRCGP 1964; DA Eng. 1965.

BARNEY, Saiyid Hasan Raza Department of Genitourinary Medicine, Charing Cross Hospital, Fulham Palace Road, London W6 8RF Tel: 020 8846 1577; 52 Pauline House, Hanbury St, London E1 5NX Tel: 020 7247 3429 — MB BS 1960 Lucknow; BSc Lucknow 1954; Dip. Ven. Soc. Apoth. Lond. 1976. (King Geo. Med. Coll.) Clin. Asst. (Genitourin. Med.) Char. Cross Hosp. Lond. Socs: Med. Soc. Study VD & BMA; Assn. Genitourin. Med. Prev: Clin. Asst. (Genitourin. Med.) Centr. Middlx. Hosp. & Guy's Hosp. Lond.

BARNFIELD, Michael Lordshill Health Centre, Lordshill District Centre, Lordshill, Southampton SO16 8HY Tel: 023 8073 8144 Fax: 023 8073 0722; 10A Grafton Gardens, Lordswood, Southampton SO16 5SQ — BM 1982 Soton.; MRCGP 1986; DGM RCP Lond. 1986; DCH RCP Lond. 1985; DRCOG 1984.

BARNHAM, Julia Jane Tel: 0121 427 5246 — MB ChB 1978 Birm.; MRCGP 1991; DO Eng. 1981.

BARNHOORN, Anna Margaretha 7 Barleycorn, Leybourne, West Malling ME19 5PR — Artsexamen 1992 Free Univ. Amsterdam.

BARNICK, Christian George William 68 Dryden Court, Renfrew Road, Kennington, London SE11 4NH — MB BS 1984 Lond.

BARNICOAT, Angela Jane Great Ormond Street Hospital for Children, NHS Trust, Great Ormond St., London WC1N 3JH; 78 Grove Avenue, London N10 2AN — MB BS 1983 Lond.; FRCP 2001; BSc (Hons.) Lond. 1980; MD Lond. 1993; MRCP (UK) 1987; DRCOG 1985. p/t Cons. Hosp. Sick Childr. Gt. Ormond St. Lond.

BARNICOAT, Ann (retired) Trefenten, Nr Pillaton, Saltash PL12 6QX Tel: 01579 350141 Fax: 01579 351520 Email: trefenten@beeb.net — MB BS Lond. 1967; MRCS Eng. LRCP Lond. 1967. Prev: Retd. Sen. Partner. Kingswood Surg. High Wycombe, Bucks.

BARNICOAT, Kenneth Thomas Newton Mapperley Lodge, Bonfire Hill, Salcombe TQ8 8EF — MB BS 1966 Lond.; MRCS Eng. LRCP Lond. 1965; FRCA 1973; FRCPC 1977.

BARNIE-ADSHEAD, Anthony Maxwell (retired) 151 Lutterworth Road, Nuneaton CV11 6PY Tel: 01203 385711 — MB BChir 1958 Camb.; MB Camb. 1958, BChir 1957; MRCS Eng. LRCP Lond. 1958; FRCGP 1987; DObst RCOG 1961. Prev: GP Nuneaton.

BARNIE-ADSHEAD, Robert Thomas All Saints Road, Lightwater GU18 5SQ Tel: 01276 72248 — MB BChir 1956 Camb.; MA, MB BChir Camb. 1956. (Camb. & Middlx.) Prev: Ho. Phys. (Med. & Neurol.) & Ho. Surg. (Surg. & ENT) Qu. Eliz. Hosp.; Birm.; Ho. Surg. (Ophth. & Dermat.) Middlx. Hosp. Lond.

BARNS, Howard Christopher Charles Hook and Hartley Wintney Medical Partnership, 1 Chapter Terrace, Hartley Wintney, Hook RG27 8QJ Tel: 01252 842087 Fax: 01252 843145; Morella Cottage, London Road, Phoenix Green, Hartley Wintney, Basingstoke RG27 8HY — MB ChB 1976 Dundee. Prev: Trainee GP. Crawley VTS; Ho. Phys. Kings Cross Hosp. Dundee; Ho. Surg. Roy. Vict. Hosp. Folkestone.

BARNS, Thomas Everard Christopher (retired) The Old Vicarage, Nether Wasdale, Gosforth, Seascale CA20 1ET Tel: 0194 67 26303 Fax: 0194 67 26303 Email: tombarns@btinternet.com — BM BCh 1943 Oxf.; MA Oxf. 1951, BA 1939, DM 1956; FRCOG 1962, M 1949; Hon. FRCP Ed. 1984. William Blair Bell Lect. RCOG; Indep. Cons. Internat. Health; Aleck Bourne Lect. St. Mary's Hosp. Prev: WHO Advisor Matern. & Child Health, SE Asia.

BARNSDALE, Christopher Alan Rectory Farm, Brandon Road, Stubton, Newark NG23 5BY — MB BS 1998 Lond.; MB BS Lond 1998.

BARNSDALE, Emily Rebecca Bescaby House, 16 Bescaby Lane, Waltham on the Wolds, Melton Mowbray LE14 4AB Tel: 01664 464124 Fax: 01664 464124 — MB ChB 1996 Leic.

BARNSDALE, Peter Hugh Bescaby House, 16 Bescaby Lane, Waltham on the Wolds, Melton Mowbray LE14 4AB Tel: 01664 464124 Fax: 01664 464124 Email: peter@barnsdale.freeserve.co.uk — MB ChB 1998 Leic.; MB ChB Leic 1998.

BARNSLEY, Christopher John 19 Lythall Avenue, Lytham St Annes FY8 4HF Tel: 01253 735654 — MB ChB 1975 Sheff.; DRCOG 1977. Med. Off. DHSS Blackpool.

BARNSLEY, Richard The Three Swans Surgery, Rollestone Street, Salisbury SP1 1DX Tel: 01722 333548 Fax: 01722 503626; 3 Bower Gardens, Salisbury SP1 2RL — MB ChB 1989 Sheff.; BMedSci Sheff. 1988; MRCGP 1997.

BARNSLEY, Richard John St Pauls Medical Centre, St. Pauls Square, Carlisle CA1 1DG Tel: 01228 524354 Fax: 01228 616660 — MB BS 1982 Newc.; MRCGP 1986; DRCOG 1985.

BARNSLEY, Mr Selwyn Layton Durrell Diamantina House, Princess Alexandra Hospital, Ipswich Road, Woolloongaba, Brisbane Qld. 4102, Australia Tel: 00 61 7 2402111 Fax: 00 61 7 2405577; 345 Barnsley Road, Wakefield WF2 6AS Tel: 01924 258239 — MB BS 1993 Lond.; FRCS Eng. 1995. SHO (Accid. & Emerg. & Orthop.) P.ss Alexandra Hosp. Brisbane, Qu.sland, Austral. Prev: SHO (Accid. & Emerg.) Pontefract Gen. Infirm. Pontefract W. Yorks.; Ho. Phys. Brook Gen. Hosp. Lond.; Ho. Surg. King's Coll. Hosp. Denmark Hill Lond.

BARNSLEY, Thomas Malcolm Health Centre, Pen y Bont, The Roe, St Asaph LL17 0LU Tel: 01745 583208 Fax: 01745 583748 — MB BS 1981 Lond.; MRCGP 1985.

BARNWAL, Anita 23 Wandle Side, Wallington SM6 7DW — MB BS 1995 Lond.

BARNWELL, Diarmuid Lepton Surgery, Highgate Lane, Lepton, Huddersfield HD8 0HH Tel: 01484 606161; Hillside House, 29 Hillside, Kirkheaton, Huddersfield HD5 0JR Tel: 01484 512934 — MB ChB 1980 Leeds; MRCGP 1986. (Leeds) Socs: Huddersfield Med. Soc. (Treas.).

BARODAWALA, Kutbuddin 14 Lime Crescent, Sandal, Wakefield WF2 6RY — MB BS 1966 Indore. (M.G.M. Med. Coll.) Prev: SHO A & E Dept. Pontefract Gen. Infirm.; SHO (Neuro-Surg.) Pinderfields Gen. Hosp. Wakefield; SHO (Gen. Med.) Clayton Hosp. Wakefield.

BARODAWALA, Shabnam St James' University Hospital, Beckett St., Leeds LS9 7TF Tel: 0113 243 3144; Croft House, 3 Chestnut Grove, Calverley, Pudsey LS28 5TN Tel: 0113 257 1274 — MB ChB 1989 Leeds; MRCP 1992. (Leeds) Sen. Regist. Yorks. Geriats. Rotat. St.James' Univ. Hosp. Leeds. Socs: Brit. Geriat.s Soc.

BARON, Charles Elliott Bryn Eurgain, Cefn Eurgain Lane, Rhosesmor, Mold CH7 6PG — MB 1978 Camb.; BChir 1977; MFOM RCP Lond. 1986, AFOM 1983; DIH Eng. 1983.

BARON, David Edward 26 Guildford Road, Leicester LE2 2RB — MB ChB 1992 Sheff.

BARON, Professor Denis Neville 47 Holne Chase, London N2 0QG Tel: 020 8458 2340 Email: d.baron@btinternet.com — MB BS 1945 Lond.; MD 1950 DSc Lond. 1966, MA (Med. Law & Ethics) 1990; FRCP Lond. 1971, M 1962; FRCPath 1963. (Middlx.) Emerit. Prof. Chem. Path. Lond. Univ. Roy. Free & Univ. Coll. Med. Sch.; Hon. Cons. Chem. Path. Roy. Free Hosp. Lond.; Assoc. Ment. Health Manager; Barnet, Enfield and Harringey Ment. Health NHS Trust. Socs: Med. & Scientif. Socs. Prev: Rockefeller Trav. Fell. Univ. Chicago 1961; Asst. (Chem. Path.) & Sen. Lect. (Clin. Biochem.) Ct.auld Inst. Biochem. Middlx. Hosp. Med. Sch. Lond.

BARON, Ivor Daniel London Bridge Hospital, Emblem House, 27 Tooley Street, London SE1 2PR Tel: 020 78153670 Fax: 020 78152930 Email: dan.baron@virgin.NET; Tel: 020 8318 7173 — MB BCh 1972 Wales; Dip. Sports Med. Lond 1990; DObst RCOG 1976. (Welsh Nat. Sch. Med.) Sports Phyician Lond. Bridge Hosp.; Knee Phys. to Lond. Knee Clinic, 126 Harley St., Lond. Socs: Europ. Soc. Sports Traumatology, Knee Surg. & Arthroscopy; Orthopaedic & Trauma Soc., Germany; Amer. Orthopaedic Soc. Sports Med. Prev: Team Phys. Millwall FC.; Team Doctor Eng Under 18 SFA; med. Off.Football Assn.

BARON, Jeremy Hugh (retired) — BM BCh Oxf. 1954; MA Oxf. 1955, BA 1951, DM 1964; FRCP Lond. 1974, M 1957; FRCS Eng. 1987; FRCP 2000 Glas. Hon. Prof. Lect. Mt. Sinai Sch. of Med. NY; Hon. Cons. Phys. & Gastroenterol. St. Mary's Hosp. Lond.; Hon. Clin. Sen. Lect. Imp. Coll. Sch. of Med. Prev: Sub-Dean St. Mary's Hosp. Med. Sch.

BARON, Julia Helen Derby Royal Infirmary, London Road, Derby Tel: 01332 347141 — BM BS 1993; BM BS (Hons.) 1993; BMedSci (Hons.) Nottm. 1991; MRCP (UK) 1996. (Nottm.) Specialist Regist. (Cardiol.) Derby Roy. Infirm. Socs: BMA. Prev: Research Fell.

(Cardiol.) Glenfield Hosp. Leicester; Specialist Regist. (Cardiol.) Glenfield Hosp. Leicester.

BARON, Louise Adelaide (retired) 6 Roefield Close, Felden, Hemel Hempstead HP3 0BZ — MB BS 1952 Lond.; MRCS Eng. LRCP Lond. 1952. Prev: Clin. Med. Off. NW Herts. HA.

BARON, Margaret (retired) 7 Brogden Drive, Gatley, Cheadle SK8 4AS — MB ChB Manch. 1959.

BARON, Margaret 19 Davidsville Road, Liverpool L18 3EL Tel: 0151 428 1084 — MB ChB 1957 Liverp.; DObst RCOG 1960. (Liverp.) Mem. Liverp. Med. Inst. Prev: Sen. Ho. Off. (Med.) & Ho. Off. (O & G) BRd.green Hosp.; Liverp.; Sen. Ho. Off. (Paediat.) Roy. Albert Edwd. Infirm. Wigan.

BARON, Rebecca Louise Bracondale House Medical Centre, 141 Buxton Road, Heaviley, Stockport SK2 6EQ Tel: 0161 483 2811 Fax: 0161 487 4221; The Dower House, Wybersley Road, High Lane, Stockport SK6 8HB — MB ChB 1984 Manch.; FRCCP 1998; MRGCP 1988; DRCOG 1987. (Manchester) GP Stockport; Fell. in Higher Professional Train.; Hon. Sen. Lect. at the Univ. of Centr. Lancs.

BARON, Robert Thomas, Squadron Ldr. RAF Med. Br. Retd. Arfryn, Gwaun Bedw, Porth CF39 9HL — MB BCh 1972 Wales; MRCGP 1978; DObst RCOG 1974. GP Tonypandy Health Centre. Socs: Brit. Soc. Med. & Dent. Hypn.. Prev: SHO (O & G) & SHO (Obst. Paediat.) E. Glam. Gen.; ypridd; Unit Med. Off. Med. Reception Station RAF Rheindahlen.

BARON, Susannah Eve Dermatology Department, The General Infirmary at Leeds, Great George Street, Leeds LS1 3EX Tel: 0113 392 3605 Fax: 0113 392 3565; Fax: 01752 894835 Email: bearmillard@btinternet.com — MB ChB 1992 Bristol; MRCP 1995. p/t Specialist Regist. in Dermat., The Gen. Infirm., Leeds. Socs: Brit. Assoc. Derm.; BMA; MDU.

BARON, Susanne 11 Barncliffe Drive, Sheffield S10 4DE — State Exam Med 1987 Freiburg.

BARONET, Philip (retired) — MD 1966 Toulouse; MD (Ophthal.) Toulouse 1966. Prev: Fell. Mass. Eye Infirm. Boston, USA.

BARONI, Marco Luigi 10 Sears Close, Flore, Northampton NN7 4NN — MB BS 1997 Lond.

BARONOS, Eleftherios 10 Gladwyn Avenue, Manchester M20 2XN; 1 Bishops Court, Pittsford NY 14534, USA Tel: 00 1 716 586 4832 Fax: 00 1 716 586 0004 — MB ChB 1993 Manch. (Univ. Manch.) Resid. (Anesth.) Univ. Rochester Strong Memor. Hosp. USA. Socs: Amer. Soc. Anesthesiol.; BMA. Prev: Intern. St. Mary's Hosp., Rochester, NY; HO Off. MRI; Ho. Off. Bolton.

BAROOAH, Kalyan MacDonald Road Medical Centre, MacDonald Road, Irlam, Manchester M44 5LH Tel: 0161 775 5421 Fax: 0161 775 2568 — MB BS 1959 Gauhati; DA Eng. 1963. (Assam Med. Coll.) Socs: BMA. Fell. Manch. Med. Soc. Prev: Regist. (Anaesth.) Manch. RHB; Regist. Anaesth. Doncaster Roy. Infirm. & City Gen. Hosp. Sheff.

BAROOAH, Philip Sanjib 8 Greenleach Lane, Worsley, Manchester M28 2RU — LMSSA 1993 Lond.

BAROUCH, Colette Alma The Roserie, Westhorpe, Sibbertoft, Market Harborough LE16 9UL — MB BCh BAO 1952 Dub.; DA Eng. 1956.

BAROUDI, Ghassan Ribble Village Surgery, 200 Miller Road, Ribbleton, Preston PR2 6NH Tel: 01772 792864 — MD 1966 Damascus. (Damascus) GP. Prev: Med. Off. Preston Community Drug Team; Regist. (Anaesth.) Preston Hosp.

BARPUJARI, Vikram Dovecot Family Health Centre, Longreach Road, Liverpool L14 0NL — MB BS 1981 Madras; LMSSA Lond. 1988.

BARR, Alan Marshall (retired) Norscot, Rosebery Road, Tokers Green, Reading RG4 9EL Tel: 01734 479646 — MB BS 1957 Adelaide; FFA RCS Eng. 1981; FFA RACS 1965. Prev: Cons. Anaesth. Roy. Berks. Hosp. Reading.

BARR, Allan John (retired) 24 Fenwick Grove, Morpeth NE61 1JW Tel: 01670 518261 — LRCP LRCS 1948 Ed.; LRCP LRCS Ed. LRFPS Glas. 1948; MRCGP 1973.

BARR, Mr Andrew David 10 Balruddery Meadows, Fowlis, Invergowrie, Dundee DD2 5LJ — MB ChB 1986 Glas.; FRCS Ed. 1992.

BARR, Andrew Davidson Brannan 8 Ledsham Park Drive, Little Sutton, South Wirral CH66 4XZ — MB ChB 1993 Aberd.

BARR, Andrew Stephen (retired) 1D Golf Court, Strathview Park, Netherlee, Glasgow G44 3LD Tel: 0141 637 8878 — MB ChB 1955 Glas.; LMCC 1960; MFOM RCP Lond. 1978; DIH St. And. 1964, DPH 1965. Prev: Dep. Sec. Med. & Dent. Defence Union Scotl.

BARR, Catriona Ann Aldborough Court Front Street, Aldborough, Boroughbridge, York YO51 9ES Tel: 01423 324950 Email: catriona.barr@virgin.net — MB ChB 1988 Manch.; BSc Med. Sci. 1984; MRCP (UK) 1991; FRCA 1995. Regist. (Anaesth.) Leeds Hosps. Socs: Train. Mem. Assn. Anaesth. Prev: Regist. (Anaesth.) Sheff. Hosps.; SHO (Anaesth.) Sheff. Hosps.

BARR, Craig Scott Department of Cardiology, University Hospital of Wales, Cardiff CF4 4XW Email: barrcs@cardiff.ac.uk; Ty Siriol Farm, Mynyddislywn, Blackwood NP12 2BG Tel: 01495 200213 — MB ChB 1989 Dundee; MRCP (UK) 1992. Career Regist. (Cardiol.) Univ. Hosp. Wales Cardiff. Prev: SHO (Gen. Med.) Ninewells Hosp. Dundee; Ho. Off. (Gen. Surg.) Roy. Infirm. Edin.

BARR, Mr David Barclay 30 Graham Avenue, Pen-y-Fai, Bridgend CF31 4NR — MB BCh 1981 Wales; FRCS Ed. 1990; FRCOphth 1991; DO RCS Eng. 1989.

BARR, David George Dryburgh Royal Hospital for Sick Children, Sciennes Road, Edinburgh EH9 1LF Tel: 0131 536 0000 Fax: 0131 536 0052; 5 Midmar Gardens, Edinburgh EH10 6DY Tel: 0131 447 6309 — MB ChB 1959 Ed.; FRCP Ed. 1973, M 1965; DCH RCPS Glas. 1962; FRCPCH (UK) 1997. Cons. Med. Paediat. Roy. Hosp. Sick Childr.; Hosp. Edin.; Sen. Lect. Dept. Child Life & Health Univ. Edin.

BARR, David Matthew 9 Ewing Court, Brackenhill Manor, Meikle Earnock, Hamilton ML3 8UX — MB ChB 1990 Glas.

BARR, Elizabeth Grace 203 Newcastle Road, Seaforde, Downpatrick BT30 8NU — MB BCh BAO 1985 Belf.; MRCP (UK) 1989. Research Fell. Qu.'s Univ. Belf.

BARR, Elizabeth Jane Forres Health Centre, Castlehill, Forres IV36 1QF Tel: 01309 672221; Ambleside, 3 Glebe Park, Dyke, Forres IV36 2WT — MB ChB 1990 Liverp.; MRCGP 1995; DROCG 1994; DFFP 1994. (Liverp.) GP Princip.; G.P. Retainer; Clin. Asst., Family Plann., Elgin.

BARR, Elizabeth Louise 9 Paddocks Way, Ashtead KT21 2QZ — MB BS 1988 Lond.; MRCGP 1992; T(GP) 1992; DRCOG 1991. Prev: Ho. Off. (Surg.) St. Geo. Hosp. Lond.; Ho. Off. (Med.) Buckland Hosp. Dover.

BARR, Gavin William Henrietta Street Health Centre, Henrietta Street, Girvan KA26 9AN Tel: 01465 712281 Fax: 01465 712187 — MB ChB 1978 Manch.; BSc (Med. Sci.) St. And. 1975; MRCGP 1982; DRCOG 1981.

BARR, Mr Geoffrey Samuel Ent Department, Ysbyty Gwynedd, Bangor LL57 2PW Tel: 01248 384238 Fax: 01248 370629 — MB ChB 1977 Dundee; ChM Dund 1990, MB ChB 1977; FRCS Ed. 1984; T(S) 1992. Cons. Otolaryngol. Head & Neck Surg. Gwynedd HA. Socs: NY Acad. Sci.; Fell. Roy. Soc. Med.; Brit. Assn. Otol. Prev: Sen. Regist. (ENT) W. Midl. RHA; Regist. Walton Hosp. Liverp., Ninewells Hosp. & Med. Sch. Dundee.

BARR, George, MBE (retired) 4 Loanhead Street, Kilmarnock KA1 3AU Tel: 01563 520775 — MB ChB 1951 Glas. Prev: Ho. Phys. Glas. W.. Infirm.

BARR, Gordon Roy MacGillivray (retired) The Coach House, 1A Chattenden Court, Boxley Road, Maidstone ME14 2AW — MB ChB 1955 Glas. Brig. Med. Adviser, Kent Fire Brig. Prev: Med. Off. Texaco Trinidad Inc. Trinidad.

BARR, Gordon Todd Dryden, Maj. RAMC Retd. (retired) 17f Mains Avenue, Giffnock, Glasgow G46 6QY Tel: 0141 638 9709 — MB ChB 1945 Glas.; FRCP Glas. 1974; FRCOG 1967, M 1954, DObst 1949. Prev: Cons. (O & G) Glas. Roy. Infirm.

BARR, Professor Hugh (retired) Gloucestershire Royal Hospital, Great Western Road, Gloucester GL1 3NN Tel: 01452 394679 Fax: 01452 394813 Email: hugh.barr@glour-tr.swest.nhs.uk — MB ChB 1977 Liverp.; ChM Liverp. 1996; MD (Distinc.) Liverp. 1991; FRCS Ed. 1982; FRCS Eng. 1982. Cons. Glos. Roy. Hosp.; Dean Fac. of Med. & BioSci. Cranfield Univ.; Hunt. Prof. RCS Eng.; Lister Prof. RCS Edin.; Prof. Cranfield PostGrad. Med. Sch. in Gloucestershire, Director of Inst. o fMed. Sci.s. Prev: Wellcome Research Fell. Univ. Coll. Lond.

BARR, John Barclay (retired) Redholm, 46 Irvine Road, Kilmaurs, Kilmarnock KA3 2RW Tel: 01563 538358 — MB ChB 1943 Glas.;

BSc Glas. 1940; FRCP Ed. 1972, M 1956; FRCP Glas. 1967, M 1962. Prev: Cons. Phys. Kilmarnock Infirm.

BARR, John Buchanan, MBE (retired) 16 West Chapelton Crescent, Bearsden, Glasgow G61 2DE Tel: 0141 942 1144 — MB ChB 1932 Glas.; MD Glas. 1938. Prev: Lt.-Col. RAMC.

BARR, John Mathieson 14 Broomhill Road, Aberdeen AB10 6HS — MB ChB 1984 Glas.; FFA RCSI 1990.

BARR, John William Richard William Street Surgery, 87 William Street, Lurgan, Craigavon BT66 6JB Tel: 028 3832 2509 Fax: 028 3834 7673 — MB BCh BAO 1982 Belf.; MRCGP 1986; DCH Dub. 1984; DRCOG 1984.

BARR, Julia Elizabeth Temple Sowerby Medical Practice, Temple Sowerby, Penrith CA10 1RZ Tel: 017683 61232 Fax: 017683 61980; Eddy House, Morland, Penrith CA10 3BJ Tel: 01931 714066 — MB ChB 1975 Manch.; DRCOG 1977.

BARR, Mr Lester Consultant Surgeon, South Manchester & Christie Hospitals, Nell Lane, Manchester M20 2LR Tel: 0161 291 4185 Fax: 0161 291 4144 — MB ChB 1978 Manch.; MB ChB (Hons.) Manch. 1978; BSc St. And. 1975; ChM Manch. 1986; FRCS Eng. 1982. Cons. Surg. S. Manch. Univ. Hosps. & Christie Hosp. Manch.; Hon. Lect. Univ. Manch.; Chairm. NW BrE. Cancer Study Gp. Socs: Connective Tissue Oncol. Soc.; (Comm.) Brit. Assn. Surgic. Oncol. Prev: Cons. Surg. Trafford Gen. Hosp. Manch.; Sen. Regist. (Surg.) W.m. Hosp. Lond.; Lect. Roy. Marsden Hosp. Lond.

BARR, Margot Christine 12 Radnor Street, Glasgow G3 7UA Tel: 0141 334 6111; 36 Moorfoot Way, Bearsden, Glasgow G61 4RL — MB ChB 1970 Glas.

BARR, Maureen Elspeth Kirkland, Dunlop, Kilmarnock KA3 4AL — MB ChB 1958 Glas.; MRCOG 1963, DObst 1960. Med. Asst. (O & G) Vict. Hosp. Rothesay. Prev: Ho. Surg. S.. Gen. Hosp. Glas.; Regist. O & G Bellshill Matern. Hosp.; Med. Asst. (Ment. Defic.) Renfrewsh. & N. Ayrsh. Ment. Defic. Hosps.

BARR, Muriel Marion Elizabeth (retired) 24 Pochins Close, Wigston Magna, Leicester LE18 2FW Tel: 0116 257 1286 — MB ChB 1953 Glas. Prev: GP Leicester.

BARR, Patrick Sheridan Ardgowan Medical Practice, 2 Finnart Street, Greenock PA16 8HW Tel: 01475 888155 Fax: 01475 785060; 113 Newton Street, Greenock PA16 8SH — MB BCh BAO 1987 Belf.; MRCGP 1991; DRCOG 1991.

BARR, Mr Reginald John The Royal Victoria Hospital, Grosvenor Road, Belfast BT12 6BA Tel: 01232 240503 Fax: 01232 234787; 1B School Lane, Brookhill, Lisburn BT28 2NT Tel: 01846 622322 Fax: 01846 622322 Email: jbarr@lineone.net — MB BCh BAO 1982 Belf.; MD Belf. 1993; FRCS Ed. 1986. (Qu. Univ. Belf.) Cons. Orthop. Surg. Roy. Vict. Hosp. Belf. Socs: Fell. BOA; Ulster Med. Soc.

BARR, Robert Birbeck Medical Group, Penrith Health Centre, Bridge Lane, Penrith CA11 8HW Tel: 01768 245200 Fax: 01768 245295; Eddy House, Morland, Penrith CA10 3BJ — MB ChB 1976 Manch.; MRCGP 1981; DRCOG 1978. Prev: Trainee GP Avon VTS; SHO (O & G) Hope Hosp. Salford; Med. Off. NW River Hosp. Labrador Canada.

BARR, Robert James (retired) 33 Coleraine Road, Ballymoney BT53 6BS Tel: 028276 63307 Email: robertbarr@genie.co.uk — MB BCh BAO 1970 Belf.; MRCGP 1976; MRCOG 1975, DObst 1972; LMCC 1973. On Staff Robinson Memor. Hosp. Ballymoney. Prev: GP Ballmoney Health Centre, Co. Antrim.

BARR, Ronald Simon Gregory The Rhonoda Primary Care Resource Centre, Llwynypia Hospital, Llwynypia, Llwynypia — MB BCh 1996 Wales. (Univ. of Wales Coll. of Med.) Gen. Practitioner - Primary Care Resource Centre for the Rhonda Llwynypia Midglamoan.

BARR, Ruth Siobhan 29 Mount Hamilton Road, Cloughmills, Ballymena BT44 9NQ — MB BCh 1998 Belf.; MB BCh Belf 1998.

BARR, St Clair Gordon (retired) Broomieknowe, Hall Crescent, Gullane EH31 2HA Tel: 01620 843101 — MB ChB 1957 Ed.

BARR, Stephen Hugh 14 Shandon Park, Galgorm Road, Ballymena BT42 2ED Tel: 01266 41244 — MB BCh BAO 1979 Belf.; MRCPI 1983; MRCGP 1990; DMH Belf. 1990.

BARR, Sybil Mary 57 Heol-y-Coed, Cardiff CF14 6HQ — MB BCh 1992 Wales; MRCP 1995. Specialist Regist. (Paediat.).

BARR, Victoria Jane 96 Gelligaer Street, Cathays, Cardiff CF24 4LB — MB BCh 1997 Wales.

BARR, Mr Wallace (retired) 65 Gartmore Road, Paisley PA1 3NG Tel: 0141 889 4385 — MB ChB 1941 Glas.; BSc Glas. 1938; MB ChB (Commend.) 1941; FRCS Glas. 1963; FRCOG 1967, M 1948. Prev: Hon. Clin. Lect. Univ. Glas.

BARR, William Stephen Ramsey Martin, Barr and Stewart, Eastwick Park Avenue, Great Bookham, Leatherhead KT23 3ND Tel: 01372 452081 Fax: 01372 451680 — MB BS 1987 Lond.; FRCS Eng. 1991; MRCGP 1996; T(GP) 1997.

BARR-TAYLOR, Peter Knighton House, 210 Castle St., Porchester, Fareham PO16 9QL — MB BS 1948 Lond.; MRCS Eng. LRCP Lond. 1947. (St. Thos.) Prev: Ho. Surg. ENT Dept. St. Thos. Hosp.; Cas. Off. St. Helier Hosp. Carshalton; Clin. Asst. ENT Dept. St. Mary's Hosp. Portsmouth.

BARRACLOUGH, Andrew Christopher Alma Partnership, 31 Alma Road, Bournemouth BH9 1BP Tel: 01202 519311 Fax: 01202 548532; 4 Coy Pond Road, Branksome, Poole BH12 1HX Tel: 01202 761697 — MB BS 1981 Lond.; MRCGP 1986; DRCOG 1985. Prev: Trainee GP Poole VTS; SHO (A & E) Guy's Hosp. Lond.; Ho. Off. New Cross & Guy's Hosps. Lond.

BARRACLOUGH, Christopher Roy Birmingham Neurosciences Centre, Queen Elizabeth Hospital, Edgbaston, Birmingham B15 2TH Tel: 0121 472 1311 — MB ChB 1970 St. And.; MD Birm. 1982; FRCP Lond. 1994; MRCP (UK) 1973. (St. And.) p/t Cons. Neurol. Univ. of Birm. NHS Trust. Socs: Roy. Soc. Med.; Assn. Brit. Neurol.; W. Midl.s Phys.s Assoc. Prev: Sen. Regist. (Neurol.) W. Midl. RHA; Hon. Sen. Clin. Lect. Neurol. Univ. Birm.; Regist. (Neurol.) Leeds Gen. Infirm.

BARRACLOUGH, Clement James 20 Newton Garth, Leeds LS7 4JZ — MB ChB 1976 Leeds.

BARRACLOUGH, Janet Elizabeth Village Surgery, Cheswick Green, Solihull B90 4JA Tel: 01564 703311 Fax: 01564 703794 — MB ChB 1983 Sheff.; MRCGP 1987; DRCOG 1987. GP Solihull Retainer Scheme. Socs: BMA.

BARRACLOUGH, Kevin Hoyland House Surgery, Hoyland House, Gyde Road, Painswick, Stroud GL6 6RD Tel: 01452 812545 — MB BS 1985 Lond.; MA Camb. 1983; MRCP (UK) 1988; MRCGP 1990; DRCOG 1990. GP.

BARRACLOUGH, Mary Hull Royal Infirmary, Anlaby Road, Hull HU3 2JZ Tel: 01482 28541; Drury House, Bainton, Driffield YO25 9NJ Tel: 01377 217568 Email: mary@barracla.globalnet.co.uk — MB ChB 1986 Manch.; BSc St. And. 1983; MRCP Paediat. (UK) 1990. Cons. (Paediat.) Hull Roy. Infirm. Prev: Sen. Regist. (Paediat.) Hull Roy. Infirm.; Clin. Research Fell. Childr.'s Hosp. Sheff.; Trainee GP N. Humberside VTS.

BARRACLOUGH, Michael Anthony River House, 56 Ferry St., Isle of Dogs, London E14 3DT Tel: 020 7987 4222 — MB BS 1957 Lond.; MB BS Lond. (Hnrs.) 1957; MRCP Lond. 1960; MRCS Eng. LRCP Lond. 1957. (St. Thos.) Sen. Lect. (Med.) & Cons. Phys. St. Thos. Hosp. Med. Sch. Prev: Ho. Phys., Ho. Phys. Childr. Dept. & Cas. Off. St. Thos. Hosp.

BARRADELL, Rosemary Paediatric Department, York District Hospital, Wigginton Road, York YO31 8HE Tel: 01904 631313 Fax: 01904 453995; 13 Gilbert Road, Bircotes, Doncaster DN11 8DL Tel: 01302 745589 — MB ChB 1984 Birm.; MRCP Paediat. (UK) 1991. Sen. Regist. (Paediat.) York Dist. Hosp. & Leeds Gen. Infirm.

BARRAGRY, Leo Francis Woodstock Bower Surgery, Rotherham S61 1AD Tel: 01709 561442; 3 Holly Mount, Wickersley, Rotherham S66 1JR — MB ChB 1980 Sheff.; DRCOG 1983.

BARRAN, Donald Austyn Nicholson (retired) 32 Kelvin Court, Great Western Road, Glasgow G12 0AE — MB BChir 1945 Camb.; MRCS Eng. LRCP Lond. 1945; FFA RCS Eng. 1954; DA Eng. 1950. Prev: Cons. Anaesth. Dunbartonsh. Dist. Anaesth. Regist. Brompton Hosp.

BARRAND, Mr Kenneth George 42 Plymouth Road, Tavistock PL19 8BU Tel: 01822 613263 — MB ChB 1967 Liverp.; FRCS Eng. 1972. Cons. Surg. Isiolo Hosp. Keyna. Prev: Cons. Surg. Vict. Hosp. Seychelles; Sen. Clin. Tutor (Surg.) Fiji Sch. Med.; Surg. Vila Base Hosp. Vanuatu.

BARRANTES GALLEGO, Raquel Scunthorpe General Hospital, Cliff Gardens, Scunthorpe DN15 7BH — LMS 1992 Extramadura.

BARRAS, Brian William (retired) Fair Beacon, 42 Carlton Road, Seaford BN25 2LP Tel: 01323 892929 Email: brian@wbarras.fsnet.co.uk — MRCS Eng. LRCP Lond. 1946. Prev: GP Newhaven & Longton Stoke-on-Trent.

BARRASS, Barnaby Jonathan Richard Gable Cottage, 13 Belle Vue Road, Henley-on-Thames RG9 1JQ — MB BS 1998 Lond.; MB BS Lond 1998.

BARRATT, Alan John (retired) 3 Manor Court, Grange Road, Cambridge CB3 9BE Tel: 01223 61056 Fax: 01223 359907 — MB BChir Camb. 1953; DObst RCOG 1958. Prev: Div. Police Surg. Metrop. Police.

BARRATT, Christopher John Danebridge Medical Centre, 29 London Road, Northwich CW9 5HR Tel: 01606 45786 Fax: 01606 331977; 7 Cartledge Close, Cuddington, Northwich CW8 2PU Tel: 01606 883991 — MB ChB 1974 Manch. (Manch.) GP; GP Trainer N.wich; GP Adviser Vict. Infirm. N.wich Chesh.; Tutor Manch. Univ. Socs: GPWA.

BARRATT, David John 15 Lynbrook Close, Hollywood, Birmingham B47 5PU — MB BS 1996 Lond.

BARRATT, David Keith 2 Hillside, Bridgetown Hill, Totnes TQ9 5BH — MB ChB 1988 Bristol; MRCGP 1993; DRCOG 1994; DFFP 1993. Socs: BMA.

BARRATT, Fiona Margaret A&E Department, St Richards Hospital, Chichester Tel: 01243 788122 — MB BS 1990 Lond.; MRCP (UK) 1993. (King's Coll. Lond.) Cons. A&E, St. Richards Hosp., Chichester. Socs: RCP; FAEM (Fell.); BMA. Prev: Regist. (A & E) King's Coll. Hosp. Lond.; Regist. (A & E) Guy's Hosp. Lond.; Specialist Regist. (A & E) Lewisham Hosp. Lond.

BARRATT, James Anthony Alma Road Surgery, Alma Road, Romsey SO51 8ED Tel: 01794 511805 Fax: 01794 518668 — MB BS 1983 Lond.; MRCGP 1987; DCCH 1990. (Westminister) Gen. Practitioner, Romsey; Police Surg. to Hants. & Wilts. Constab. Prev: Trainee GP Tidworth VTS; SHO (Paediat. & O & G) BMH Rinteln; GP, New Malden.

BARRATT, Jonathan 200 Earlham Road, Norwich NR2 3RW — MB ChB 1992 Manch.

BARRATT, Pamela Mary (retired) 'Silverdale', Long Walk, Chalfont St Giles HP8 4AN Tel: 0124 042600 — MB ChB 1977 Cape Town.

BARRATT, Sally Dawn 21 St Marys Av, Bromley BR2 0PU — MB ChB 1997 Birm.

BARRATT, Susan Ann Castle Mead Medical Centre, Hill St., Hinckley LE10 1DS Tel: 01455 635166 Fax: 01455 250506; Greens Farm, Nuneaton Road, Fillongley, Coventry CV7 8DN Tel: 01676 541987 — MB ChB 1986 Sheff.; MRCGP 1990.

BARRATT, Professor Thomas Martin, CBE 19 Clifton Road, London N8 8JA Tel: 020 8348 1735 Fax: 020 8347 5735 — MB BChir 1961 Camb.; FRCP Lond. 1977, M 1964. (St. Thos.) Emerit. Prof. (Paediat. Nephrol.) Inst. Child Health Lond.; Hon. Cons. Paediat. Hosp. Sick Childr. Gt. Ormond St. Hosp. Socs: Pres. Brit. Assn. Paediat. Nephrol. Prev: Dir. of Clin. Servs. Gt. Ormond St. Hosp. Lond.

BARRATT-JOHNSON, Malcolm Francis Roy Department of Health, Medicines Control Agency, Market Towers, 1 Nine Elms Lane, London SW8 5NQ Tel: 020 7273 0707 Email: m.j@virgin.net; 9 Kettlewell Close, Friern Barnet, London N11 3FB — MB BS 1993 Lond.; BSc (Hons.) Physiol. Lond. 1986. (St. Bart. Hosp.) Sen. Med. Off. The Dept. of Health (Meds. Control Agency) Lond. Socs: Fell. Roy. Soc. Med.; Brit. Assn. Pharmaceutical Phys.; MRCAnaesth. Prev: Regist. (Anaesth. & IC) Middlx. Univ. Coll. Lond.; SHO (Med.) Lister Hosp. Stevenage; SHO (A & E) Guy's Hosp. Lond.

BARRELL, Julian Paul The Surgery, School Lane, Upton-upon-Severn, Worcester WR8 0LF Tel: 01684 592696 Fax: 01684 593122; Hazeldene House, Worester Road, Earls Croome, Worcester WR8 9DA — MB BS 1982 Lond.; MRCGP 1989; DCH RCP Lond. 1987; DRCOG 1986. (Charing Cross) Gen. Practitioner; Clin. Asst. (Cardiol.) Worcester Roy. Infirm. Socs: Mem. of Primary Care Cardiac Soc.

BARRELL, Samantha Ruth Sanderling, Ridley Hill, Kingswear, Dartmouth TQ6 0BY Tel: 01803 752266 Fax: 01803 752266 — MB BS 1993 Lond.; BSc (Pharmacol.) Lond. 1990. SHO (Anaesth.) St. Richards Hosp. Chichester. Socs: Med. Defence Union; BMA. Prev: SHO (Anaesth. & A & E) Soton. Gen. Hosp.; Ho. Off. (Surg.) Derriford Hosp. Plymouth.

BARRERA GROBA, Casiano King's College Hospital, Denmark Hill, London SE5 Tel: 020 7737 4000 Fax: 020 7346 3632; 91 Fawnbrake Avenue, London SE24 0BG Tel: 020 7733 2487 — LMS 1987 Santiago de Compstela; LMS Santiago de Compostela 1987; DA (UK) 1993. Regist. (Anaesth.) King's Coll. Hosp. Lond. Prev: SHO (Anaesth.) Brighton Healthcare.

BARRET, Mrs Catherine Mary 39 Chamberlain Road, King's Heath, Birmingham B13 0QP Tel: 0121 441 2203; 39 Chamberlain Road, King's Heath, Birmingham B13 0QP — MB ChB 1996 Birm. SHO Rotat. (Psychiat.) Birm. Socs: BMA, MDU; Roy. Coll. Psychiatr. (Inceptor).

BARRETO, Audrey 71 Downfield Close, Amberley Road, London W9 2JH — MB ChB 1991 Leeds. Prev: SHO (A & E) Roy. Lond. Hosp.; RMO & Anat. Demonst. Nuffield Hosp. Leeds; Ho. Off. (Gen. Med.) Leeds Gen. Infirm.

BARRETT, Alexandra Anne 6 Whitland Av, Bolton BL1 5FB — MB ChB 1997 Manch.

BARRETT, Amanda Jayne Greystones, Mead Road, Stoke Gifford, Bristol BS34 8PS Tel: 01454 775393 — MB ChB 1993 Birm.; MRCGP 1999; DRCOG 1997; DCH 1998. (Birm.) GP Asst., Rowden Surg., Chippcuham; Clin. Asst., Palliahve Med., Wronghon, Swindon. Prev: GP Regist. Adam Pract, Poole; SHO Palliat. Med., Swindon; SHO Psychiahy, Poole.

BARRETT, Mr Andrew Martin Royal Victoria Infirmary, Queen Victoria Road, Newcastle upon Tyne NE1 4LP Tel: 0191 232 5131 Fax: 0191 227 5276 Email: a.m.barrett@ncl.ac.uk — MB ChB 1977; FRCS Eng. 1983; MD 1993 Birm. Cons. Paediat. Surg. Roy. Vict. Infirm. Newc. u. Tyne. Socs: Brit. Assn. of Paediatric Surg.s; UK Childr.s Cancer Study Gp.

BARRETT, Andrew Raymond (retired) Longhalves Cottage, Hooke Hill, Freshwater PO40 9GB — MB BCh BAO 1963 NUI.

BARRETT, Professor Ann Beatson Oncology Centre, Western Infirmary, Glasgow G11 6NT Tel: 0141 211 2123 Fax: 0141 211 1895 Email: ab6d@udcf.gla.ac.uk; 15 Westbourne Gardens, Glasgow G12 9XD — MB BS 1968 Lond.; MD Lond. 1983; FRCP Lond. 1991; FRCP Glas. 1989; MRCS Eng. LRCP Lond. 1968; MRCP Lond. 1985; FRCR 1975; FFR 1974. (St. Bart.) Prof. Radiat. Oncol. Univ. Glas. & Beatson Oncol. Centre Glas. Socs: Pres. Scott. Radiol. Soc.; Pres. Europ. Soc. Therap. Radiother. and Oncol.; Internat. Soc. Paediat. Oncol. (Past Mem. Scientif. comm.). Prev: Cons. (Radiother. & Oncol.) & Sen. Lect. (Radiother.) Roy. Marsden Hosp. Sutton.

BARRETT, Antony Robin Health Centre, Minniecroft Road, Burnham, Slough SL1 7DE Tel: 01628 605333 Fax: 01628 663743; Lustleigh, Poyle Lane, Burnham, Slough SL1 8LA Tel: 01628 662299 — MB BS 1976 Lond.; MRCS Eng. LRCP Lond. 1976. Prev: SHO (Surg.) Char. Cross Hosp. Lond.; SHO (Anaesth.) Wexham Pk. Hosp.

BARRETT, Brendan Gabriel Joseph 28 Cadzow Drive, Cambuslang, Glasgow G72 8NF — MB BCh BAO 1947 NUI; DObst RCOG 1952. Vis. O & G St. Francis Matern. Hosp. Glas. Socs: BMA. Prev: Regist. (O & G) Sefton Gen. Hosp. Liverp., Whiston Hosp. Liverp. & Roy. Bucks. Hosp. Aylesbury.

BARRETT, Catherine Helen Ruth Flat 13, 72 Grove Lane, London SE5 8TW — MB BS 1997 Lond.

BARRETT, Claire Ann Marie 72 Westgrove, Walton-on-Thames KT12 5PB Tel: 020 8533 7660; Homerton Hospital, Homerton Row, London E9 6SR Tel: 020 8985 5555 — MB BS 1987 Lond.; BSc Lond. 1984, MB BS 1987; MRCP (UK) 1990. Regist. (Med.) St. Bart. & Homerton Hosp. Lond. Prev: SHO (Med.) St. Bart. & Homerton Hosp. Lond.

BARRETT, Colin Francis Rutherglen Health Centre, 130 Stonelaw Road, Rutherglen, Glasgow G73 2PQ Tel: 0141 531 6020 Fax: 0141 531 6070; 4 Dryburgh Lane, West Mains, East Kilbride, Glasgow G74 1BQ Tel: 01355 904623 Fax: 01355 904624 Email: cfbarrettatccr@cableinet.co.uk — MB ChB 1984 Glas.; DCH RCPSI 1988. Med. Adviser Scott. Judo Federat.; Managing Dir. Caledonian Clin. Research Ltd Glas.; Med. Adviser St. Margt. Adopt. Soc. Scotl. Prev: SHO (Neonat. Med.) Simpson Memor. Matern. Pavil. Edin.; SHO (Paediat. & Neurol.) Roy. Hosp. Sick Childr. Edin.; SHO (Paediat., Neonat. Med. & A & E) S.. Gen. Hosp. Glas.

BARRETT, Dagmar The Thames Valley Nuffield Hospital, Wexham St., Slough SL3 6NH Tel: 01753 662241 Fax: 01753 662129; Grey House, Beeches Drive, Farnham Common, Slough SL2 3JU Tel: 01753 644198 — MRCS Eng. LRCP Lond. 1973; MUDr Prague 1957. (Chas. Univ. Prague) Socs: Brit. Inst. Musculoskel. Med.; Brit. Med. Acupunct. Soc.; Brit. Soc. Rheum. Prev: Assoc. Specialist (Rheum & Rehabil.) Heberden Unit Amersham Gen. Hosp.; Assoc. Specialist (Phys. Med.) Mt. Vernon Hosp. N.wood & Farnham Pk. Rehabil. Centre Farnham Roy.; High Wycombe Gen. Hosp.

BARRETT, David Francis 10A Langstone Avenue, Langstone, Havant PO9 1RU — MB BS 1958 Lond.; FRCP Lond. 1985; MRCP (UK) 1969. (Middlx.) Cons. Dermat. Portsmouth & I. of Wight Gps. Hosps. Socs: Scott. Dermat. Soc. & Brit. Assn. Dermat. Prev: Sen. Regist. (Dermat.) Roy. Infirm. Dundee; Regist. (Med.) OldCh. Hosp. Romford; Regist. (Dermat.) United Birm. Hosps.

BARRETT, David James 111 Priesthills Road, Hinckley LE10 1AH Tel: 01455 446466 — MB ChB 1996 Leic. (Univ. Leic. Med. Sch.) SHO (Psychiat.) Leicester Gen. Hosp. Socs: BMA; Internat. Med. Assn. Lourdes. Prev: SHO Psych.Glenfield.Gen.Hosp.Leics; Ho. Off. (Surg.) Geo. Eliot Hosp. Nuneaton; Ho. Off. (Med.) Hosp. St. Cross Rugby.

BARRETT, Mr David Stuart Orthopaedic Department, Southampton University Hospital, Tremona Road, Southampton SO16 6YD Tel: 02380 798526 Email: davidbarrett@davidbarrett.demon.co.uk; BUPA Chalybeate Hospital, Tremona Road, Southampton SO16 6UY Tel: 02380 776877 Fax: 01703 777235 — MB BS 1983 Lond.; BSc (Hons.) (Immunol.) Lond. 1980, MB BS 1983; FRCS Eng. 1987. (St. Bartholomew's London) Cons. Orthop. Surg. Soton. Univ. Hosp.; Sen. Lect. Dept. of Engin. Soton. Univ. Socs: Roy. Soc. Med. & BASK (Exec.). Prev: Knee Fell. Harvard Med. Sch. Boston; Sen. Regist. Roy. Nat. Orthop. Hosp. Lond.

BARRETT, Diana 199 East Dulwich Grove, Dulwich, London SE22 8SY — MB BS 1962 Lond.; MRCS Eng. LRCP Lond. 1962. (St. Mary's)

BARRETT, Edward Charles Alan 26 Kidderminster Road, Hagley, Stourbridge DY9 0QD — MB ChB 1998 Birm.

***BARRETT, Elizabeth Claire** 11 Croft House Lane, Marsh, Huddersfield HD1 4NX — MB ChB 1996 Sheff.

BARRETT, Emma Louise 4 Nuns Walk, Virginia Water GU25 4RT — MB ChB 1998 Manch.; MB ChB Manch 1998.

BARRETT, Mr Graham Stuart (cons. rooms), 47 Alma Road, Windsor SL4 3HH Tel: 01753 857016 Fax: 01753 858569; 16 Fairfield Road, Uxbridge UB8 1AY Tel: 01895 233535 — MB BS 1962 Lond.; FRCS Eng. 1969. p/t Cons. Surg. King Edwd. VII Hosp. Windsor, Heatherwood Hosp. Ascot & Wexham Pk. Hosp. Slough; Hon. Clin. Tutor Char. Cross & W.m. Med. Sch. Lond. Socs: Fell. Assn. Surgs. Prev: Sen. Regist. Char. Cross Hosp. Lond.; Bernard Sunley Research Fell. Roy. Coll. Surgs.; Regist. (Surg.) Mt. Vernon Hosp. N.wood.

BARRETT, Hilary Ann 28 Cadzow Drive, Cambuslang, Glasgow G72 8NF — MB ChB 1951 Liverp. Socs: BMA. Prev: Regist. (Med.) Newsham Gen. Hosp. Liverp.; SHO (Med.) & Ho. Off. (O & G) Sefton Gen. Hosp. Liverp.

BARRETT, Imke Tracey 16 Barquentine Place, Atlantic Wharf, Cardiff CF10 4NG Tel: 029 2046 2319 — MB BCh 1992 Wales; DCH RCP Lond. 1996.

BARRETT, James Alexander 2 Hawkshaw Close, Liphook GU30 7DF — MB BS 1993 Lond.

BARRETT, James Antony Clatterbridge Hospital, Bebington, Wirral CH63 4JY Tel: 0151 482 7734 Fax: 0151 482 7691 Email: james.barrett@ccmail.wirralh-tr.nwest.nhs.uk — MB ChB 1980 Liverp.; 1980 MB ChB Liverp.; 1989 MD Liverp.; 1995 FRCP Lond.; 1984 MRCP (UK). (liverpool) Cons. Phys. (Geriat. Med. & Rehabil.) Clatterbridge Hosp. Bebington; Hon. Lect. (Geriat. Med.) Liverp. Univ.; Hon snr Lect. (Pub. Health & Opidemiology), Univ. of Leicester. Socs: Expert Witness Inst.; Brit. Geriat. Soc.- Mem. of Counc. & Scientif. Comm.; Brit. Assn. Stroke Phys. Prev: Tutor & Hon. Sen. Regist. (Geriat.) Manch. Univ.; Research Regist. (Geriat. Med.) Manch. Univ.; Regist. Rotat. (Med.) Liverp.

BARRETT, James Stephen 66 Hazelwood Road, Acocks Green, Birmingham B27 7XP Email: james@barrett49.freeserve.co.uk — MB BS 1990 Lond.; MSc (Psych) 1997; BSc (Hons.) Pharm. Lond. 1986; MRCPsych 1995. (Roy. Free Hosp.) Cons. (Psychiat.), Char. Cross Hosp. Socs: Harry Benjamin Internat. Gender Dysphoria Assn.; Jl. Comm., BMA; Chair Amnesty Internat. Med. Network. Prev: Sen. Regist. Rotat. Maudsley Hosp.; Regist. Rotat. (Psychiat.) Maudsley Hosp.; SHO Rotat. (Psychiat.) Char. Cross Hosp. & S. Beds.

BARRETT, Jane Ringside, 79 High St., Bracknell RG12 1DZ; Waggoners, Great Prawls Farm, Stone-in-Oxney, Tenterden TN30 7HB — MB BS 1976 Lond.; MB BS (Hons.) Lond. 1976; AKC 1976. (King's Coll. Hosp.) Vice Pres. Med. Affairs.

BARRETT, Jane Margaret Ashbrook House, Westbrook St., Blewbury, Didcot OX11 9QA — MB ChB 1977 Bristol; BSc (Hons.) Bristol 1974; FRCP Lond. 1996; MRCP (UK) 1980; FRCR 1988. Cons. Clin. Oncol. Roy. Berks. Hosp. Reading. Prev: Sen. Regist. (Clin. Oncol.) Roy. Berks. Hosp. Reading; Regist. (Med.) Battle Hosp. Reading.

BARRETT, Jeremy William Valnet The Park Surgery, St. Flora's Road, Littlehampton BN17 6BF Tel: 01903 717154 Fax: 01903 732908; 5 Norfolk Place, Littlehampton BN17 5PD Tel: 019103 717154 Fax: 019103 732908 Email: gbyars6715@aol.com — MB BS 1963 Lond.; MRCS Eng. LRCP Lond. 1963; MRCOG 1969; DObst RCOG 1965. (Guy's) Prev: Regist. (Obst.) St. Mary's Hosp. Lond.; SHO Qu. Charlotte's Matern. Hosp. & Samarit. Hosp. Wom. Lond.

BARRETT, Joan Averil White House Barn, Hudswell, Richmond DL11 6BG — MRCS Eng. LRCP Lond. 1946; DPH Durh. 1956; DPM Dub. 1961; MRCPsych 1971. (Roy. Free) Cons. Psychiat. Whixley Hosp., Claypenny Hosp. & Allied Hosps. Socs: BMA & World Psychiat. Assn. Prev: Cons. Psychiat. Aycliffe Hosp. Darlington; Maj. RAMC, Sen. Psychiat.; SHMO Stoke Pk. Hosp. Bristol.

BARRETT, John David (retired) 3 Salisbury Avenue, Harpenden AL5 2QQ Tel: 01582 760637 — MRCS Eng. LRCP Lond. 1958; MFOM RCP Lond. 1980; DTM & H Eng. 1960. Prev: Chief Med. Off. Vauxhall Motors Ltd.

BARRETT, John Frederick 91 Kingsway, Orpington BR5 1PW — MB BS 1976 Lond.

BARRETT, John Joseph 8 Furzedown Road, Sutton SM2 5QE Tel: 020 8642 2842 — MB BCh BAO 1966 NUI; MSc Lond. 1975; FRCP Lond. 1989; MRCP (UK) 1971; DMRD Eng. 1971. (Univ. Coll. Dub.) Cons. Nuclear Med. Brook Gen. & King's Coll. Hosps. Lond. Socs: Brit. Nuclear Med. Soc. Prev: Sen. Regist. Dept. Nuclear Med. & Ultrasound Roy. Marsden Hosp. Lond.; Regist. Guy's Hosp. Lond.

BARRETT, Kenneth Haywood Hospital, High Lane, Burslem, Stoke-on-Trent ST6 7AG Tel: 01782 556001 Email: kenneth.barrett@chips.nsch-tr.wmids.nhs.uk — MD 1986 Bristol; MB BS Lond. 1976; FRCPsych. 1982. (King's College Hospital Medical School) Cons. Neuropsychiat.; Sen. Clin. (Psychiat.) Univ. Keele Staffs. Socs: Brit. Neuropsychiat. Assn.; Chair. UK Psychiat. Huntington's Dis. Gp.; UK Psychiatists Brain Injury Gp. Prev: Lect. (Ment. Health) Univ. Bristol.; Sen. Lect. (Psychiat.) Univ. of Keele Staffs.; Clin. Dir., Ment. Health Dir., N. Staffs. Combined Healthcare NHS Trust.

BARRETT, Kenneth Ernest (retired) 69 Billesley Lane, Moseley, Birmingham B13 9QX — MB BS Lond. 1953; MD Lond. 1964; MRCS Eng. LRCP Lond. 1953; FRCPath 1977, M 1965. Prev: Cons. Haemat. to RN.

BARRETT, Kevin Finbar Bridgeton Health Centre, 201 Abercromby St., Glasgow G40 2DA Tel: 0141 554 1866; 11 Beech Avenue, Dumbreck, Glasgow G41 5BY — MB BCh BAO 1946 NUI. (Univ. Coll. Dub.)

BARRETT, Kim Marie 35 Holeyn Road, Newcastle upon Tyne NE15 9PG — MB ChB 1988 Glas.

BARRETT, Leonard Middleton (retired) 'Rostellan', Summerbridge, Harrogate HG3 4JN Tel: 01423 780913 Email: barrett@rostellam.u-net.com — MRCS Eng. LRCP Lond. 1950; MA, MB BChir Camb. 1955. Prev: Ho. Surg. Roy. W. Sussex Hosp. Chichester.

BARRETT, Maeve Cecilia Frances (retired) 3 Colquhoun Court, Nithsdale Road, Pollokshields, Glasgow G41 5PY Tel: 0141 427 3464 — LRCP LRCS Ed. LRFPS Glas. 1955.

BARRETT, Mrs Margaret Shepherd (retired) 36 Hayward Road, Oxford OX2 8LW Tel: 01865 515399 — BM BCh 1952 Oxf.; BM BCh Oxon. 1952; Dip Ven. Soc. Apoth. Lond. 1978.

BARRETT, Mark Damien Anthony Top Flat, 213 Tufnell Park Road, London N7 0PX Tel: 020 7697 0161 — MB ChB 1991 Sheff.; MRCGP 1996; DRCOG 1994.

BARRETT, Martin Ernest St Peter's Surgery, Rue De L'Eglise, St Peter, Jersey JE3 7AG Tel: 01534 484533 Fax: 01534 484531 Email: meb@medhealth.co.uk; Tel: 01534 490396 — MB ChB 1979 Birm. (Birmingham) GP, St Peter's Surg., St Peter Jersey. Socs: Assur. Med. Soc.; Assoc. Police Surg.s; Forens. Sci. Soc. Prev: Sen. Med. Off. Coding Cons. NHS Centre for Coding & cl.ification LoughBoro.

BARRETT, Martina Old Fletton Surgery, Rectory Gardens, Old Fletton, Peterborough PE2 8AY Tel: 01733 343137 Fax: 01733

894739 — MB ChB 1985 Liverp.; MRCGP 1992. (Liverpool) Socs: MRCGP. Prev: SHO (Paediat.) P'boro. Dist. Hosp.; SHO (Respirat. Med.) Regional Thoracic Unit Fazakerley Hosp. Liverp.

BARRETT, Niall Dermot 46 Riviere Towans, Hayle TR27 5AF Tel: 01736 756424 — MB BCh BAO 1988 NUI.

BARRETT, Nigel Kenneth Coachmans, Netherton Park, Bradford-on-Tone, Taunton — MB BS 1980 Lond.

BARRETT, Paul David c/o Frank Noel Barrett, Hill House, 54 London Road, Buxton SK17 9NE — MB ChB 1987 Manch.

BARRETT, Paula Philomena 98 Isham Road, London SW16 4TF — MB BS 1993 Lond.

BARRETT, Peter Dept. of anaesthesia, King's Mill Hospital, Mansfield Rd, Sutton-in-Ashfield NG17 4JL Tel: 01623 22515 Email: peterbarrett7@hotmail.com — MRCS Eng. LRCP Lond. 1979; FFA RCS Eng. 1985. (Sheff.) Cons. Anaesth. King's Mill Centre for Health Care Servs. NHS Trust. Socs: BMA & Assn. Anaesth.; Intens. Care Soc. Prev: Sen. Regist. (Anaesth.) Nottm.; Regist. (Anaesth.) Centr. Notts. HA; Regist. (Anaesth.) Sheff. HA.

BARRETT, Peter James 24 Meadow Oak Drive, Oakfield Grange, Gateacre, Liverpool L25 3SZ — MB ChB 1984 Liverp.

BARRETT, Peter James The Cottage, Lambert Road, North Finchley, London N12 9ER Tel: 020 8446 1002 — MB BS 1985 Lond.; DTM & H RCP Lond. 1994. Sen. Med. Adviser to M.A.S.T.A.; Hon. Lect. (Travel Med.) Acad. Unit of Travel Med. & Vaccines Roy. Free Hosp. Med Sch. Socs: BMA; Internat. Soc. Travel Med.; Roy. Soc. Trop. Med. & Hyg.

BARRETT, Peter John The Manor Surgery, Middle Street, Beeston, Nottingham NG9 1GA Tel: 0115 925 6127 Fax: 0115 967 8612 — MB BS 1970 Lond.; MRCS Eng. LRCP Lond. 1970. (King's Coll Hosp.) Chairm. NHS Exec. Trent Region. Socs: Inst. Psycho-Sexual Med. Prev: Chairm. Nottm. Local Med. Comm.; Chairm. Nottm. Health Auth., Standard Ct., Nottm.

BARRETT, Peter Kenneth Manning (retired) 15 East Road, Bridlington YO15 3HL Tel: 01262675732 Email: pkmbarrett@hotmail.com — MB BS Lond. 1952; FRCP Lond. 1975, M 1959. Cons. Phys. ScarBoro. & E. Yorks. Health Dists. Prev: Sen. Regist. Camb. Chest Clinic & Addenbrooke's Hosp. Camb.

BARRETT, Richard Frederick Anaesthetic Dept, Salisbury District Hospital, Salisbury SP2 8BJ Tel: 01772 425050 — MB BS 1972 Lond.; FFA RCS Eng. 1979. (St. Bart.) Cons. Anaesth. Salisbury HA.

BARRETT, Richard Michael Tyn-y-Coed Surgery, 20 Merfield Close, Bryncethin, Bridgend CF32 9SW Tel: 01656 720334 Fax: 01656 721998; 76 Park Street, Bridgend CF31 4BB Tel: 01656 650176 — MB BCh 1982 Wales; DRCOG 1986. (Wales) GP Bryncethin; Mem. Morgannwg LMC.

BARRETT, Richard Victor The Forest Surgery, 2 Macdonald Road, London E17 4BA Tel: 020 8527 2569; 36 Kings Avenue, Woodford Green IG8 0JA Tel: 020 8504 6181 — MB BS 1965 Lond. (St. Geo.) Anaesth. Jubilee Hosp. Woodford Green. Prev: Regist. (Anaesth) & Ho. Phys. & Ho. Surg. Whipps Cross Hosp.; Leytonstone; SHO Anaesth. St. Margt.'s Hosp. Epping.

BARRETT, Rosemary Rutherglen Health Centre, 130 Stonelaw Road, Rutherglen, Glasgow G73 2PQ Tel: 0141 531 6020 Fax: 0141 531 6070; 4 Dryburgh Lane, E. Kilbride, Glasgow G74 1BQ Tel: 01355 904623 Fax: 01355 904624 — MB ChB 1986 Glas.; DObst RCPI 1990. (Glas.) Clin. Asst. (Geriat. Med.) Glas.; Scott. Bioethics Comm.

BARRETT, Mrs Sara Maria Liv Stonebridge Centre, Cardiff St, Carlton Road, Nottingham NG3 2FH; 31 Priory Road, West Brdeford NG2 5HU — BM BCh 1985 Oxf.; MRCPsych 1989. Cons. Psychiat., Stonebridge centre, Nottm. Socs: BMA. Prev: Sen. Regist. Mapperley Hosp. Notts.

BARRETT, Sheila 2 Pares Way, Ockbrook, Derby DE72 3TJ — BM BS 1980 Nottm.

BARRETT, Simon Robert 26 Kidderminster Road, Hagley, Stourbridge DY9 0QD — MB ChB 1990 Ed.

BARRETT, Sophie Victoria Flat 23E Roseberry Court, 23 Victoria Circus, Glasgow G12 9LB — MB BS 1994 Lond.; MA Camb. 1991; MRCP (UK) 1997.

BARRETT, Stephen Phillip Department of Medical Microbiology, Wright-Fleming Institute, St Mary's Hospital Medical School, London W6 8RF Tel: 020 88467256 Fax: 020 88467261 Email: s.barrett@ic.ac.uk; 14 Grand Drive, Leigh-on-Sea SS9 1BG — BM 1976 Soton.; DM 1987; MSc Lond. 1982; MRCPath 1984; BA Open 1995; FRCPath 1996. (Southampton) Cons. Microbiologist Char. Cross Hosp. Lond.

BARRETT, Susan Thompson The Surgery, 344 Long Lane, Hillingdon, Uxbridge UB10 9PN Tel: 01895 237411 Fax: 01895 812875 — MB BS 1964 Lond.; MRCS Eng. LRCP Lond. 1964; DObst RCOG 1966. GP Hillingdon Middlx.

BARRETT, Timothy Geoffrey Department of Endocrinology, Brimingham Children's Hospital, Steelhouse Lane, Birmingham B4 6NH Email: t.g.barrett@bham.ac.uk — MB BS 1986 Lond.; PhD Birm. 1996; MRCP (UK) 1990; DCH RCP Lond. 1988. Sen. Lect. Paediat. Endocrinol. & Diabetes; Hon. Cons.

BARRETT, Vanessa Louise Ali-Khan and Partners, 128 High Street, Bentley, Doncaster DN5 0AT Tel: 01302 874551 Fax: 01302 820920 — MB ChB 1993 Sheff.

BARRETT, William Tyrrell (retired) 36 Hayward Road, Oxford OX2 8LW — BM BCh 1951 Oxf.; BM BCh Oxon. 1951.

BARRETT-AYRES, Alexandra Marion Spital Medical Practice, 119-121 Spital, Aberdeen AB24 3HX Tel: 01224 583081 Fax: 01224 639015 — MB ChB 1971 Aberd.

BARRETT-LEE, Peter Jeffrey Velindre Hospital, Whitchurch, Cardiff CF14 2TL Tel: 029 2061 5888 Fax: 029 2052 2694; 11 Cornflower Close, Lisvane, Cardiff CF14 0BD Tel: 029 2074 7912 — MB BS 1982 Lond.; BSc (Hons.) Lond. 1979, MD 1990; MRCP (UK) 1985; FRCR 1991. Cons. Clin. Oncol. Velindre Hosp. Cardiff. Socs: MDU; Nat. Health Serv. Cons. Assn. Prev: Sen. Regist. (Clin. Oncol.) Middlx. Hosp. Lond.; Regist. (Radiother. & Oncol.) Roy. Marsden Hosp. Sutton; Research Regist. Ludwig Inst. Cancer Research St. Geo. Hosp. Lond.

BARRETTO, Christobel Josephine Thornton Heath Health Centre, 61A Gillett Road, Thornton Heath, Croydon CR7 8RL Tel: 020 8689 5797 Fax: 020 8665 1195 — MB BS 1985 Lond.; DRCOG 1997; MRCGP 1990; DCH RCP Lond. 1989; MA Med. Sci. Camb. 1982; BSC Biochem. Lond. 1980. (Char. Cross Hosp. Med. Sch.) Mem. Croydon LMC.

BARRETTO, John Harold 134 Harley Street, London W1N 1AH Tel: 020 7580 1101 Fax: 020 7487 3071; 2E Clifton Gardens, London W9 1DT Tel: 0207 286 8407 — MB BS 1965 Lond.; MRCS Eng. LRCP Lond. 1965. (St. Bart.) Socs: Fell. Roy. Soc. Med.; Chelsea Clin. Soc.

BARRICK, Deborah Naomi 35 Aldeburgh Lodge, St Peters Road, Aldeburgh IP15 5DF — MB BChir 1981 Camb. SHO (A & E) Ipswich Hosp. NHS Trust.

BARRICK, Vivienne Eileen Rosebank Surgery, 153B Stroud Road, Gloucester GL1 5JQ Tel: 01452 522767; Lystra, Paul Mead, Edge, Stroud GL6 6PG Tel: 01452 814564 — MB BS 1977 Lond.

BARRIE, Adrian Richard Plas Meddyg Surgery, Station Road, Ruthin LL15 1BP Tel: 01824 702255 Fax: 01824 707221; Pontilen, Rhewl, Ruthin LL15 1UL — MB BChir 1981 Camb.; MRCP (UK) 1984; MRCGP 1990. (Middlx. Hosp. Lond.) GP; CME Tutor for Gen. Pract. Clwyd N.

BARRIE, Agnes Anne Orr Cumbernauld Road Surgery, 144-146 Cumbernauld Road, Stepps, Glasgow G33 6HA Tel: 0141 779 2330 — MB ChB 1977 Glas.; DRCOG 1979.

BARRIE, Barbara Thomson 18 Albert Road, Stoke-on-Trent ST4 8HE — MB ChB 1989 Ed.

BARRIE, Dinah 3 Burghley Avenue, New Malden KT3 4SW Tel: 020 8942 2836 Fax: 020 8949 3350; 3 Burghley Avenue, New Malden KT3 4SW — MB BS 1959 Lond.; FRCPath 1984, M 1972. (St. Thos.) Cons. Microbiol. Pk.side & New Vict. Hosps. Lond. Socs: Brit. Soc. Antimicrob. Chemother. & Hosp. Infec. Soc. Prev: Sen. Lect. (Cons.) microBiol. Char. Cross Hosp. Lond.; Lect. (Clin. Path.) St. Thos. Hosp. Lond.; Regist.(Med.) Edgware Gen. Hosp.

BARRIE, Evelyn Frimley Children's Centre, 10 Church Road, Frimley, Camberley GU16 5AD Tel: 01483 782862; 28 Howard Drive, Cove, Farnborough GU14 9TQ Tel: 01252 371807 — MB ChB 1977 Glas.; DFFP 1980; DCH RCP Lond. 1987; MFCH 1998. Community Paediat. SCMO Surrey Hants. Borders Trust; Hon. Lct. Reading Univ. Socs: MRCPCH; Fell. Institiute of Pub. Health and Hyg.; Fell. Roy. Soc. of Med. Prev: SCMO & Family Plann. Doctor N. Downs Community Health NHS Trust.; Ho. Off. (Surg.) Falkirk & Dist. Roy. Infirm.; SHO (Orthop.) Raigmore Hosp. Inverness.

BARRIE, Fiona Mairi McDowell Colwood Farmhouse, Warninglid, Haywards Heath RH17 5TR — MB BS 1981 Lond.; MB BS Lond. 1979 DO 1981.

BARRIE, Herbert (retired) 3 Burghley Avenue, New Malden KT3 4SW Tel: 020 8942 2836 Fax: 020 8949 3350 — MB BS 1950 Lond.; MD Lond. 1952; FRCP Lond. 1972, M 1957; FRCPCH 1997. Prev: Vaccine Damage Appeals Tribunal.

BARRIE, Mr James Langlands Department of Orthopaedic Surgery, Blackburn Royal Infirmary, Blackburn BB2 3LR Tel: 01254 294584 Fax: 01254 2945 Email: jim@barries.demon.co.uk — MB ChB 1983 Ed.; FRCS (Orth.) 1994; FRCS Glas. 1987; FRCS Ed. 1987. (Ed.) Cons. Orthop. Surg. Blackburn Roy. Infirm. Socs: Fell. BOA; Brit. Orthop. Foot Surg. Soc. Prev: Sen. Regist. (Orthop. Surg.) N. W.. RHA; Tutor (Orthop.) Univ. Manch.; Regist. (Orthop.) Stockport Infirm.

BARRIE, Janet Rachel Department of Anaesthesia, Royal Oldham Hospital, Rochdale Road, Oldham OL1 2JH Tel: 0161 627 8828 — MB ChB 1986 Ed.; FCAnaesth 1991. (Ed.) Cons. Anaesth. Roy. Oldham Hosp.

BARRIE, John Darroch (retired) Tweedmount, Maxwellheugh, Kelso TD5 8AZ Tel: 01573 225835 — MD 1965 Glas.; MB ChB 1955. Prev: Head Path. King Khalid Hosp. Jeddah, Saudi Arabia.

BARRIE, Lucille Iris 13 Southernhay Road, Leicester LE2 3TN Tel: 01162 709951 — MB ChB 1968 Glas. (Glas.) Prev: Regist. Anaesth. Glas. Roy. Infirm.; Attend. Phys. E.J. Meyer Memor. Hosp. Buffalo, U.S.A.

BARRIE, Margaret Alston 29 Piercing Hill, Theydon Bois, Epping CM16 7JW Tel: 01992 813164 Fax: 01922 813164 Email: dr.m.barrie@eggconnect.net — MB BS 1955 Lond.; FRCP Lond. 1979, M 1957; MRCS Eng. LRCP Lond. 1955; DObst RCOG 1956. (Guy's) Hon Cons. Roy Lond Hosp. Socs: Assn. Brit. Neurol. & Assur. Med. Soc.; Internat. Headache Soc.; Internat. League against Epilepsy. Prev: Cons. Neurol. W. Essex HA, St. Bart. Hosp. Lond. & Roy. Lond. Hosps.; Asst. Ho. Phys. (Resid. Obst.) & Ho. Phys. (Neurol.) Guy's Hosp. Lond.

BARRIE, Michael Richmond Road Medical Centre, 95 Richmond Road, Kingston upon Thames KT2 5BT Tel: 020 8546 1961 Fax: 020 8974 9008 — MB BS 1991 Lond.; DOccMed 1999; MRCGP 1996; DRCOG 1995; DFFP 1995; DCH RCP Lond. 1994. (St. Thos.) GP; Company Med. Off. Bentalls plc, Kingston upon Thames; Company Med. Off. Rock Asphalt Ltd, Lond.; Company Med. Off. Nikon UK Ltd. Socs: Soc. of Occup. Med. Prev: Regist. GP/SHO Epsom Hosp. VTS; Ho. Phys. & Ho. Surg. Kingston Hosp. Surrey.

BARRIE, Nicholas James Cuckfield Medical Centre, Glebe Road, Cuckfield, Haywards Heath RH17 5BQ Tel: 01444 458738 Fax: 01444 416714; Colwood Farm House, Warninglid, Haywards Heath RH17 — MB BS 1979 Lond.; MRCS Eng. LRCP Lond. 1978; DRCOG 1980.

BARRIE, Nicole Pontilen, Rhewl, Ruthin LL15 1UL — MB BS 1981 Lond.; MRCGP 1988; DCH RCP Lond. 1987.

BARRIE, Pauline Jane Station Road Surgery, 2 Station Road, Prestwick KA9 1AQ Tel: 01292 671444 Fax: 01292 678023; 26 Lady Margaret Drive, Troon KA10 7AL — MB ChB 1990 Manch.; 1987 BSc (Sci. Med.); MRCGP 1994; DRCOG 1992. (St. And. & Manch.) p/t GP Prestwick. Prev: Trainee GP/SHO Inverclyde Roy. Hosp. Greenock VTS; Ho. Off. (Med.) Lancaster; Ho. Off. (Surg.) Roy. Preston Hosp.

BARRIE, Peter Mudie Church Plain Surgery, Loddon, Norwich NR14 6EX Tel: 01508 520222 Fax: 01508 528579 Email: peter@barrie21.freeserve.co.uk; 21 Mill Road, Loddon, Norwich NR14 6DR Tel: 01508 520707 — MB ChB 1982 Dundee; DRCOG 1986; DCH RCPS 1987 Glas.; DCH RCPS Glas. 1987; DRCOG 1986. (Ninewells Hosp. Med. Sch.) Hosp. Practitioner in Diabetes. Socs: Assoc. Mem. Brit. Med. Acupunc. Assn. Prev: SHO (Paediat. & O & G) Norf. & Norwich Hosp.; SHO (Med.) W. Norwich Hosp.

BARRIE, Robert (retired) Redroofs, 14 Highlands, Taunton TA1 4HP Tel: 01823 333598 — MB ChB 1939 Ed.

BARRIE, Rowena Elizabeth 21 Mill Road, Loddon, Norwich NR14 6DR Tel: 01508 520707; 21 Mill Road, Loddon, Norwich NR14 6DR Tel: 01508 520707 Email: peter@barrie21.freeserve.co.uk — MB BS 1983 Lond. (Roy. Free Hosp.) p/t GP Asst. Beccles Health Centre Beccles.

BARRIE, Ruth 75 Curtis Avenue, Kings Park, Glasgow G44 4QD — MB ChB 1995 Glas.

BARRIE, Wilhelmina Johanna 53 Tytton Lane E., Boston PE21 7HP Tel: 01205 62610 — MB ChB 1935 Ed. (Ed.)

BARRIE, William Robert Ian Clifton Lodge, 17 Cheddon Road, Taunton TA2 7BL; Hollydene, Kingston St. Mary, Taunton TA2 8HW — BM BCh 1970 Oxf.; MA; DObst RCOG 1972.

BARRIE, Mr William Wright 28 Knighton Grange Road, Leicester LE2 2LE Tel: 0116 258 4660 Fax: 0116 272009 Email: bill_barrie@msn.com — MB ChB 1968 Glas.; MD Glas. 1980; FRCS Glas. 1972; FRCS Eng 1992. Cons. Gen. Surg. Leicester Gen. Hosp. NHS Trust.

BARRINGER, John Health Control Unit, Terminal 3, Arrivals Building, London Heathrow Airport, Hounslow TW6 1NB Tel: 020 8745 7419 Email: jb@hhcu.demon.co.uk; 24 Mossy Vale, Maidenhead SL6 7RX Tel: 01628 37811 Email: john.barringer@virgin.net — MB BS 1969 Lond.; DRCOG 1971. (Lond. Hosp.) SCMO (Health Control) Heathrow Airport Hounslow. Prev: Sen. Med. Off. (Gen. & Leprosy) Borno State Nigeria.

BARRINGTON, Andrew James 1 Minterne Road, Harrow HA3 9TA — MB BS 1998 Lond.; MB BS Lond 1998.

BARRINGTON, Mr Julian Wynne — MB BChir 1986 Camb.; BA Camb. 1983, MA 1986; MRCOG 1993; MD Cambridge 1998. Cons. O & G Torbay Hosp. Torquay. Prev: Sen. Regist. (O & G) Singleton Hosp. Sketty, Swansea; Research Regist. (Urogyn.) Cardiff Roy. Infirm.; Regist. (O & G) Llandough Hosp. Cardiff.

BARRINGTON, Naomi Ann 63 Sandygate Park, Sheffield S10 5TZ — MB ChB 1970 Sheff.; FRCR 1976; DMRD Eng. 1974. Cons. (Radiol.) Sheff. AHA (T).

BARRINGTON, Patrick Colville (retired) 56 Coombe Valley Road, Preston, Weymouth DT3 6NL Tel: 01305 832367 Fax: 01305 832367 — MB BChir 1957 Camb.; MRCP Lond. 1963; MRCPsych 1973; DPM Eng. 1972; DObst RCOG 1960. Prev: Assoc. Specialist (Psychiat.) W. Dorset Ment. Health NHS Trust.

BARRINGTON, Penelope Mary Kylmorie, 48 Heathcombe Road, Bridgwater TA6 7PD Tel: 01278 458934 — MB BS 1967 Lond.; MRCS Eng. LRCP Lond. 1966; DCH RCPSI 1973; DObst RCOG 1968. (St. Mary's) Prev: Regist. (Paediat.) Our Lady of Lourdes Hosp. Drogheda; Ho. Surg. (Obst.) Canad. Red Cross Memor. Hosp. Taplow; Ho. Phys. Roy. Berks. Hosp. Reading.

BARRINGTON, Philip Clinical Pharmacology, Glaxo Wellcome Research & Development, Greenford Road, Greenford UB6 0HE Tel: 020 8966 3525 Fax: 020 8966 4363 Email: pb30746@glaxowellcome.co.uk — BM 1982 Soton.; Dip. Pharm. Med. RCP (UK) 1991. Sen.Research.Phys.CNS.Clin.Pharm.

BARRINGTON, Mr Richard Lawrence Kettering & District General Hospital, Rothwell Road, Kettering NN16 8UZ — MB BS 1972 Lond.; FRCS Eng. 1978. (Middlx.) Cons. Orthop. Surg. Kettering Gen. Hosp. Prev: Sen. Regist. (Orthop.) Leeds & Bradford Hosps.; Regist. (Orthop.) Bristol Roy. Infirm. & Winford Orthop. Hosp. Bristol; SHO Rotat. S.mead & Frenchay Hosps. Bristol.

BARRINGTON, Sally Fiona The Clinical Pet Centre, St Thomas' Hospital, Lambeth Palace Rd, London SE1 7EH Tel: 020 7922 8106 Fax: 020 7620 0790 Email: s.barrington@umds.ac.uk — MB BS 1987 Lond.; MSc (Distinc.) Nuclear Med. Lond. 1995; MRCP (UK) 1992. Clin. Lect. & Sen. Clin. Fell. (Radiol. Sci. & Nuclear Med.) Guy's KIngs & St. Thomas' Schol Of Med. & Hon. Cons. ST Thomas' NHS Trust, Lond.

BARRINGTON-WARD, Brigid Balfreish, Wester Galcantray, By Cawdor, Nairn IV12 5XY Tel: 016678 526 — MB BCh BAO 1967 NUI; DA Eng. 1972. (Galway) Prev: Clin. Asst. (Anaesth.) W. Suff. Gen. Hosp. Bury St. Edmunds; Regist. (Anaesth.) W. Suff. Gen. Hosp. Bury St. Edmunds; SHO (Anaesth.) W. Suff. Gen. Hosp. Bury St. Edmunds.

BARRINGTON-WARD, Deborah Park Lane Surgery, Park Lane, Woodstock OX20 1UD Tel: 01993 811452 — MB BCh 1983 Wales; MRCGP 1994; DFFP 1994.

BARRINGTON-WARD, Elaine Wilhelmina Balfreish, By Cawdor, Nairn IV12 5XY — MB BS 1997 Lond.

BARRINGTON-WARD, Jean Caverhill (retired) 4 Searle Street, Cambridge CB4 3DB Tel: 01223 740460 Email: sb292@cam.ac.uk — MB ChB 1951 Ed. Prev: GP Twickenham.

BARRISON, Ian Graeme Hemel Hempstead Hospital, Hillfield Road, Hemel Hempstead HP2 4AD Tel: 01442 287041 Fax: 01442 287082 — MB BS 1974 Lond.; BSc (Hons.) (Biochem.) Lond. 1970; FRCP Lond. 1993; MRCP (UK) 1977. (St. Bart.) Cons. Phys. & Gastroenterol. St. Albans & Hemel Hempstead Hosps.; Dir. of Educ. St Alban's & Hemel Hempstead NHS Trust. Socs: Brit. Soc.

Gastroenterol.; Brit. Assn. for the Study of the Liver. Prev: Sen. Regist. (Med.) St. Mary's & Centr. Middlx. Hosps. Lond.; Regist. W. Middlx. & Char. Cross Hosps.; Trustees Research Fell. Char. Cross Hosp.

BARRITT, James Michael (retired) 3 Bell's Court, Helmsley, York YO62 5BA Tel: 01904 2139 — MRCS Eng. LRCP Lond. 1947. Prev: Ho. Surg. Char. Cross Hosp.

BARRITT, Peter William Beeches Medical Practice, 1 Beeches Road, Bayston Hill, Shrewsbury SY3 0PF Tel: 01743 874565 Fax: 01743 873637; 52 Porthill Gardens, Shrewsbury SY3 8SQ Tel: 01743 241785 — MB ChB 1976 Birm.; MRCGP 1983; Cert. Family Plann. JCC 1980; DRCOG 1979; DCH Eng. 1979. (Birmingham) GP; Med. Off. to RNIB Condover Hall Sch. Prev: SHO (Paediat.) Roy. Infirm. Blackburn; Ho. Phys. City Gen. Hosp. Stoke-on-Trent; Ho. Surg. Torbay Health Dist.

BARRITT, Simon Alexander 7 Seedfield Close, Weston Favell, Northampton NN3 3PA — MB ChB 1998 Manch.; MB ChB Manch 1998.

BARRON, Agnes Montgomerie Knight (retired) 10 Golf Place, Greenock PA16 8TA Tel: 01475 721594 — MB ChB 1943 Glas.; BSc Glas. 1941; FRCP Glas. 1978, M 1962; FRFPS Glas. 1946; FCOphth 1989. Prev: Cons. Surg. Inverclyde Roy. Hosp. Greenock & Greenock Eye Infirm.

BARRON, Alan Alexander Nantwich Health Centre, Beam Street, Nantwich CW5 5NX Tel: 01270 610181 Fax: 01270 610511; 3 Lomax Road, Willaston, Nantwich CW5 6RN Tel: 01270 663733 — MB ChB 1977 Manch.; MB ChB (Hons.) Manch. 1977; MSc (Chem.) Alberta, Canada 1972; BSc (Chem.) Bristol 1969. Med. Off. Redsands Observat. & Assessm. Centre Nantwich. Prev: Clin. Asst. (ENT) Congleton War Memor. Hosp.; SHO (O & G, Paediat. & Gen. Med.) Wythenshawe Hosp. Manch.

BARRON, Bruce Morison (retired) 36 Parkstone Road, Poole BH15 2PG Tel: 01202 671532 — MB ChB 1951 Aberd. Prev: Ho. Phys. Horton Gen. Hosp. Banbury.

BARRON, Colin Murdoch Ashlea Nursing Home, Bracklinn Road, Callender FK17 8EH Tel: 01877 330325 Fax: 01877 330931; 3 Fir Road, Doune FK16 6HU Tel: 01786 841517 — MB ChB 1979 Glas.; BSc MEH Dip.1999. Med, Qual. Hypnotherap.; Chairm. SACHO. Socs: Fell. Roy. Soc. Health. Prev: Regist. (Ophth.) Gartnavel Gen. Hosp. Glas.

BARRON, Mr David James 225A Stephendale Road, London SW6 2PR — MB BS 1988 Lond.; MRCP (UK) 1993; FRCS Lond. 1992. Regist. (Cardiothoracic Surg.) Soton. Gen. Hosp. Prev: Camb. Peri-Fell.sh. Rotat.; Demonst. & Ho. (Surg. & A & E) St. Thos. Hosp.; Ho. (Phys.) Worthing Hosp.

BARRON, David Wilson (retired) Ashbrooke, 22 Millvale Road, Hillsborough BT26 6HR Tel: 02892 683938 — MB BCh BAO 1948 Belf.; PhD Belf. 1967, MD 1961; FFA RCSI 1971; FFA RCS Eng. 1954; DA Eng. 1952. Prev: Cons. Anaesth. Belf. & S. Belf. Hosp. Gps.

BARRON, Dominic Anthony 113 Locko Road, Spondon, Derby DE21 7AP — MB BS 1992 Lond.; BSc (Hons.) Lond. 1989, MB BS 1992. SHO Rotat. (Surg.) Worcester Roy. Infirm.

BARRON, Edward Kenneth c/o North Devon District Hospital, Raleigh Park, Barnstaple EX31 4JB — MB ChB 1963 Glas.; FFA RCSI 1975.

BARRON, Elizabeth Eleanor (retired) 34 Lindisfarne Close, Jesmond, Newcastle upon Tyne NE2 2HT Tel: 0191 281 8868 — MB ChB 1953 Liverp.; DObst RCOG 1959. Prev: Assoc. Specialist (Family Plann.) P.ss Mary Matern. Hosp. & Vict. Infirm. Newc.

BARRON, Elizabeth Tovani High Street, 16 High Street, Great Baddow, Chelmsford CM2 7HQ Tel: 01245 473251 Fax: 01245 478394; Rothmans, 22 High Street, Great Baddow CM2 7HQ Email: eliz_barron@excite.co.uk — MB ChB 1978 Glas.; MRCPsych 1983. Hon. Psychotherapist, N. Essex HA. Socs: Chelmsford Med. Soc. Prev: Clin. Asst. (Psychiat.) Mid-Essex HA; Research Regist. (Psycol. Med.) Univ. Glas.

BARRON, Geoffrey Corrie (retired) Boscarn, The Terrace, Port Isaac PL29 3SG — MA, MB BChir Camb. 1940; MRCS Eng. LRCP Lond. 1939. Prev: Cas. Off. & Ho. Phys. Hounslow Hosp.

BARRON, Geoffrey Robert Somers Town Health Centre, Blackfriars Close, Southsea PO5 4NJ Tel: 023 9285 1199 Fax: 023 9281 4626 — MB BS 1975 Lond.; MRCS Eng. LRCP Lond. 1975; DRCOG 1978.

BARRON, Gordon John The Smithy, Flistridge Road, Upper Minety, Malmesbury SN16 9PR — BM 1977 Soton.; DRCOG 1979.

BARRON, Hazel Leonora Queen Street Surgery, 13A Queen St., Deal CT14 6ET Tel: 01304 363181 Fax: 01304 381996 — MB BCh 1991 Witwatersrand; BA (SW) UPE 1973; BA Witwatersrand 1982.

BARRON, James Alistair Trumpets Oast, Bodle St., Hailsham BN27 4RD — MB BS 1997 Lond.; BSc Lond. 1996. (St. Bartholomew's Hospital Medical College) SHO (A & E) W. Middlx. Hosp. Lond. Prev: Ho. Off. (Med. Oncol.) St. Bart. Hosp.; Ho. Off. (Gen. Surg.) Roy. Lond. Hosp.

BARRON, Jeffrey Lawrence Department of Chemical Pathology & Metabolism, St Helier Hospital, Carshalton SM5 1AA Tel: 020 8296 2660 Fax: 020 8641 2633 Email: jbarron@sthelier.sghms.ac.uk — MB ChB 1973 Cape Town; MMed Cape Town 1978; FRCPath 1981. Cons. Chem. Path. St. Helier Hosp. Carshalton; Sen. Lect. St. Geo. Hosp. Med. Sch.; Director, S. W. Thames Regional Infant Screening Serv. Prev: Sen. Lect. Univ. Cape Town.

BARRON, Jennifer Anne (retired) 410 Gillott Road, Edgbaston, Birmingham B16 9LP — MB BS 1978 Lond.; BSc Lond. 1975; T(R) (CR) 1991; FRCR 1985; DMRD Liverp. 1983; DRCOG 1981. Prev: Cons. Radiol. Wigan HA.

BARRON, John Health Centre, Park Drive, Stenhousemuir, Larbert FK5 3BB Tel: 01324 554136 Fax: 01324 553622 — MB ChB 1977 Aberd.; T(GP) 1991.

BARRON, John (retired) 81 Rectory Lane, Thurcaston, Leicester LE7 7JR — MB ChB 1949 Aberd.; MRCPsych 1971. Prev: Cons. Psychiat. W. Sussex HA & E. Surrey Health Dist.

BARRON, Mr John Netterville (retired) Littleburn House, Manor Farm Road, Fordingbridge SP6 1DY Tel: 01425 53153 — MB ChB 1937 N.Z.; FRCS Ed. 1940; Hon. MS Soton. 1976; FRCS Eng. (ad eund.) 1975. Hon. Cons. Plastic Surg. Wessex RHA; Clin. Teach. Univ. Soton. Prev: Dir. Plastic Surg, Plastic & Maxillo-Facial Centre Odstock Hosp.

BARRON, Lesley Norwood House Surgery, Belle Vue Street, Scarborough YO12 7EJ Tel: 01723 374485 Fax: 01723 501517; Candler House, 73 Garth End Road, West Ayton, Scarborough YO13 9JJ Tel: 01723 864693 — MB ChB 1984 Dundee; MRCGP 1990; DRCOG 1990.

BARRON, Linda 114 Middle Drive, Darras Hall, Ponteland, Newcastle upon Tyne NE20 9DW Tel: 01661824205 — MB ChB 1992 Leeds. SHO (Psychiat.) Newc. Gen. Hosp.

BARRON, Morag Cecilia 6 Braid Hills Road, Edinburgh EH10 6EZ — MB ChB 1998 Aberd.; MB ChB Aberd 1998.

BARRON, Nicholas Mark 113 Locko Road, Spondon, Derby DE21 7AP — MB BS 1994 Lond.

BARRON, Owen Philip Balance Street Health Centre, Balance Street, Uttoxeter ST14 8JG Tel: 01889 562145 Fax: 01889 568164; Ashcroft, Lower St, Doveridge, Derby DE6 5NS — MB ChB 1986 Manch.; MRCGP 1992; DCH RCP Lond. 1991; T(GP) 1991. Prev: Trainee GP Burton-on-Trent VTS; SHO (Anesth.) Leics. Roy. Infirm.; Ho. Off. Roy. Vict. Hosp. Belf.

BARRON, Peter John Holmes (retired) 6A Rowlands Hill, Wimborne BH21 1AN Tel: 01202 880732 — MB BS 1946 Lond.; DObst RCOG 1950. Prev: Capt. RAMC.

BARRON, Prudence, MBE (retired) 31 Lixmount Av, Edinburgh EH5 3EW Tel: 0131 552 5971 — MB BS 1942 Lond.; FRCS Ed. 1945. Prev: Assoc. Phys. St. Columba's Hospice Edin.

BARRON, Rebecca 37 Moorfield Road, Ilkley LS29 8BL — MB BCh 1991 Wales.

BARRON, Ruth Margaret 42 Corporation Road, Redcar TS10 1PB — MB ChB 1994 Dundee.

BARRON, Mr Solomon Leonard (retired) 34 Lindisfarne Close, Jesmond, Newcastle upon Tyne NE2 2HT Tel: 0191 281 8868 — MB BS Lond. 1949; FRCS Eng. 1955; FRCOG 1970, M 1959. Prev: Chairm. Newc. upon Tyne Hosps. NHS Trust.

BARRONDO AZCORRA, Maite 25 Deva Lane, Chester CH2 1BW — LMS 1994 Basque Provinces.

BARROS D'SA, Professor Aires Agnelo Barnabe, OBE — MB BCh BAO 1965 Belf.; MD (Hons.) Belf. 1975; FRCS Eng. 1970; FRCS Ed. 1969. (Qu. Univ. Belf.) Cons. Vasc. Surg. Roy. Vict. Hosp. Belf.; Prof. Vasc. Surg. Qu. Univ. Belf. Socs: Brit. & Europ. Soc. Surgic. Research; Eur. Soc. Vasc. Surg.; Roy. Soc. Med. Prev: Vasc. Surg.Reconstruc. Cardiovasc. Research Centre Providence Med.

Centre Seattle, USA; Sen. Regist. (Vasc. & Gen. Surg.) Roy. Vict. Hosp. Belf.; Research Fell. (Surg.) Qu. Univ. Belf.

BARROS D'SA, Mr Alban Avelino John (cons. rooms), 5 Davenport Road, Coventry CV5 6QA Tel: 024 76 677838 Fax: 024 76 713822 Mobile: 07990 587505; 40 Nightingale Lane, Westwood Gardens, Coventry CV5 6AY Tel: 024 76 675181 Fax: 02476 675181 — MB ChB 1967 Bristol; FRCS Ed. 1972; MRCS Eng. LRCP Lond. 1967; FRCS ad eundem Eng. 1997. p/t Cons. Surg. Univ. Hosps. Coventry and Warks. NHS Trust; Tutor (Laparoscopic Surg.) RCS Eng.; Examr. FRCS (Gen. Surg.) Edin.; Convenor Laparoscopic Courses for MATTU, RCS Eng.; Clin. Teach., Sch. of Med., Leicester Warwick Med. Sch. Socs: Brit. Med. Assn.; Assoc. Endos. Surgs. GB& Irel.; Fell. Assn. Surgs. Of GB & Irel. Prev: Clin. Dir. (Surg.) St. Cross Hosp. Rugby; Sen. Regist. (Gen. & Vasc. Surg.) Univ. Hosp. Wales Cardiff & Singleton Hosp. Swansea; Pfizer Research Fell. & Tutor (Surg.) Roy. Postgrad. Med. Sch. Lond. & Hon. Sen. Regist. Ealing, Hammersmith & Hounslow HA (T).

BARROS D'SA, Elizabeth Anne Royal Victoria Hospital, Grosvenor Road, Belfast BT12 6BA Tel: 028 40503 — MB BCh BAO 1968 Belf. Anaesth. Roy. Vict. Hosp. Belf. & E. Health & Social Servs. Bd. N.; Irel. Socs: Ulster Med. Soc. Prev: Ho. Off. Roy. Vict. Hosp. Belf.; Anaesth. (Gen. & IC) Roy. Vict. Hosp. Belf. & Belf. City; Hosp.

BARROS D'SA, Ian James Southampton General Hospital, Tremona Road, Southampton SO16 6YD Tel: 02380 777222; 40 Nightingale Lane, Westwood Gardens, Coventry CV5 6AY — BM 1999 Soton. Rotating SHO Surg., Soton. Gen. Hosp. & Salisbury Oddstock Hosp., Orthop. & Cardiothorcac Surg. & Critical Care. Socs: Mem. BMA. Prev: HO Med., Qu. Alexandra Hosp. Portsmouth; HO Surg. S.ampton Gen. Hosp.; SHO Accid. and Emerg., S.ampton Gen. Hosp.

BARROS D'SA, Sonia Helen Royal Glamorgan Hospital, Ynysmaerdy, Llantrisant, Pontyclun CF72 8XR; 9 Tarragon Way, Pontprennau, Cardiff CF23 8SN — MB BCh 1998 Wales. (Univ Wales Coll. of Med.) SHO Trauma & Orthopeadics, Roy. Glam. Hosp. Socs: Mem. BMA. Prev: SHO in Gen. & Vasc. Surg. Llandough Hosp. Cardiff.; SHO Urol., Univ. of Wales; SHO Accid. & Emerg., Univ. of Wales.

BARROS D'SA, Vivienne Frances 14 Malone Hill Park, Belfast BT9 6RD — MB BS 1997 Lond.; BA Cantab 1994. (UMDS) SHO Gen. Med. Roy. Surrey Co. Hosp. Guildford. Socs: BMA. Prev: PRHO (Gen. Med.) St. Peter's Hosp. Chertsey, Surrey; PRHO (Gen. Surg.) Kent & Canterbury Hosp. Canterbury Kent.

BARROW, Andrea Susan 7 Lanes Close, King's Bromley, Burton-on-Trent DE13 7JS — MB ChB 1987 Dundee; MRCGP 1992; DRCOG 1991.

BARROW, Bertram Arthur Joseph, Wing Cdr. Retd. (retired) — MB BS 1953 Lond.; MRCS Eng. LRCP Lond. 1953; DPM Eng. 1967. Prev: Phys. Brit. Home & Hosp. Incurables Lond.

BARROW, David Arthur Latham House Medical Practice, Sage Cross Street, Melton Mowbray LE13 1NX Tel: 01664 854949 Fax: 01664 501825; Latham House Medical Practice, Melton Mowbray LE13 1NX — MB BS 1972 Lond.; FFA RCS Eng. 1980; DA Eng. 1975; DRCOG 1980.

BARROW, Ethel (retired) 2 Bank House, 1A Kensington High St., London W8 5NP — MB ChB 1925 Liverp.; DPH Cape Town 1939. Prev: Med. Supt. & Phys. i/c Infant Block St. Monica's Matern. Hosp., Cape Town.

BARROW, George Ian Treavon, Upper Woodford, Salisbury SP4 6PA Tel: 01722 782400 — MB ChB 1949 Glas.; MD (Commend.) Glas. 1963; Dip. Bact. Lond 1957; FRCPath 1973, M 1963. (Univ. Glas.) Clin. Common Cold Unit Harvard Hosp. Salisbury; Cons. Microbiol. & Med. Adviser to Water Auth. & Altwell Manor Pk. Runcorn. Socs: Path. Soc. & Soc. Applied Bacteriol. Prev: Dir. Ref. Laborat. Environm. Hyg. PHLS Centre Applied Microbiol. & Research Porton Down; Dir. Pub. Health Laborat. Roy. Cornw. Hosp. (City) Truro; WHO Fell. 1971.

BARROW, Ian Tilehurst Surgery, Tylers Place, Pottery Road, Tilehurst, Reading RG30 6BW Tel: 0118 942 7528 Fax: 0118 945 2405 — MB BS 1983 Lond.; BSc (Hons.) Lond. 1980, MB BS 1983; MRCGP 1987; DRCOG 1986. (St. Bart.) GP Tilehurst. Prev: Trainee GP W. Cumbria VTS; Ho. Phys. Med. Profess. Units St. Bart's Hosp. Lond.; Ho. Surg. Luton & Dunstable Hosp.

BARROW, Jack (retired) The Consulting Rooms, York House, 199 Westminster Bridge Road, London SE1 7UT Tel: 020 7928 5485 — MB BS Lond. 1947; MRCS Eng. LRCP Lond. 1941. Hon. Cons. Phys. Genitourin. Med. St. Thos. Hosp. Lond. Prev: Home Office Cons. Genitourin. Med. (Prison Serv.).

BARROW, Jane 70 Riverside Drive, Flixton, Manchester M41 9FN — MB ChB 1998 Liverp.; MB ChB Liverp 1998.

BARROW, Jennie Mair Kingsholm Surgery, Alvin Street, Gloucester GL1 3EN Tel: 01452 522902 Fax: 01452 387819; 13 Denmark Road, Gloucester GL1 3HZ — MB ChB 1978 Bristol; MRCGP 1983; DRCOG 1980; ILHOM 1997.

BARROW, Keith c/o East Surrey Hospital, Three Arch Road, Redhill RH1 5RH; 13 Earlswood Court, Earlswood Road, Redhill RH1 6HN — MB BS 1989 Lond.

BARROW, Keith Edward Meir Health Centre, Saracen Way, Meir, Stoke-on-Trent ST3 7DS — MB BS 1983 Lond.; BSc Lond. 1980; MRCGP 1989; DA (UK) 1990; DRCOG 1987. Gen. Practitioner; GP Tutor, S. Stoke Primary Care Gp. Socs: RCGP (Roy. Colege Gen. Practitairs); SPA (Small Pract.s Assn.); BMA (Brit. Med. Assn.).

BARROW, Margaret 27 Lincoln Drive, Melton Mowbray LE13 0AH — MB ChB 1974 Bristol; DCH RCP Lond. 1978. Cons. Clin. Genetics Leicester Roy. Infirm.

BARROW, Peter Michael Kingsholm Surgery, Alvin Street, Gloucester GL1 3EN Tel: 01452 522902 Fax: 01452 387819; 13 Denmark Road, Gloucester GL1 3HZ — MB ChB 1978 Bristol; MRCGP 1983.

BARROW, Philip Michael Department of Anaesthesia, Newcastle City Hospitals, Newcastle upon Tyne Tel: 0191 232 5131 — MB BS 1985 Newc.; FRCA 1990; DA (UK) 1987. Cons. Anaesth. Newc. City Hosps. Newc. u. Tyne; Hon. Clin. Lect. (Anaesth.) Univ. Newc.; Fell. IC Toronto W.. Hosp., Canada 1992-93. Prev: Sen. Regist. (Anaesth.) N.. RHA; Regist. & SHO (Anaesth.) Newc. u. Tyne Teach. Hosps.; SHO (Gen. Med. & Anaesth.) Ashington Hosp.

BARROW, Richard Brendan Sabah Clinic, PO Box 10355, 88803 Kota Kinabalu, Sabah, Borneo, Malaysia Tel: 00 60 54190 Fax: 00 60 264868 Email: aquila@pc.jaring.my; 26 Baxendale, Whetstone, London N20 0EG Tel: 020 8 445 9277 — MB BS 1967 Lond.; MRCS Eng. LRCP Lond. 1965. (Char. Cross)

BARROW, Trevor Vincent c/o Medical Centre, Pontardawe, Swansea SA8 4JU Tel: 01792 863103 — MB BS 1965 Lond.; MRCS Eng. LRCP Lond. 1965; DObst RCOG 1968.

BARROWCLIFF, Derek Ford (retired) 27 High Street, Warwick CV34 4AX Tel: 01926 491478 Fax: 01926 491478 — BM BCh 1942 Oxf.; BM BCh Oxf. 1943; FRCPath 1965. Prev: Cons. Path. Warks. HA.

BARROWCLIFFE, Dennis Graham 11 Holmesfield Road, Dronfield, Woodhouse, Dronfield S18 8WS — MB ChB 1955 Sheff.; MRCS Eng. LRCP Lond. 1955; DObst RCOG 1960. (Sheff.) Socs: BMA; Brit. Soc. Med. & Dent. Hyp. Prev: Ho. Surg. (Cas., ENT & Ophth.) Rotherham Hosp.; Ho. Phys. Derbysh. Roy. Infirm.; SHO (Obst.) Middlesbrough Matern. Hosp.

BARROWCLOUGH, Mark Derek Delapre Medical Centre, Gloucester Avenue, Northampton NN4 8QF Tel: 01604 761713 Fax: 01604 708589; 21 High Street, Weston Favell, Northampton NN3 3JS — MB BS 1983 Lond.; MRCGP 1987; DCH RCP Lond. 1986; DRCOG 1985. (King's Coll. Hosp.) Prev: Trainee GP N.ampton Dist. Gen. Hosp. VTS; Ho. Phys. & SHO (A & E) Brook Hosp.; Ho. Surg. King's Coll. Hosp. Lond.

BARROWMAN, Margaret Ordban, Ferntower Road, Crieff PH7 3DH — MB ChB 1992 Ed.

BARRY, Augustine Joseph 152 Countisbury Avenue, Llanrumney, Cardiff CF3 5RS Tel: 029 2079 2661 — MRCS Eng. LRCP Lond. 1946; BSc Wales, MB BCh 1946; MRCGP 1971. (Cardiff) Mem. (Ex-Chairm.) Local Med. Comm. & Family Pract. Comm. Socs: BMA & Cardiff Med. Soc. Prev: Surg. Regist. Llandough Hosp. Cardiff; Cas. Off. Roy. Liverp. United Hosp.; Sen. Ho. Off. Cheltenham Matern. Hosp.

BARRY, Ben Nicholas St James Hospital, Leeds LS9 7TF Tel: 0113 243 3144; Highbury House, 94 High St, Boston Spa, Wetherby LS23 6EA Tel: 01937 541304 — MB BS 1990 Lond.; BSc (Hons.) Lond. 1987. (Middlx. Hosp.) Specialist Regist. (Anaesth.) Yorks. Deanery. Prev: Research Regist. Acad. Unit Anaesth. Gen. Infirm. Leeds; Clin. Fell. (Paediat. Intens. Care) Leeds Gen. Infirm.; SHO Rotat. (Anaesth.) Sheff.

BARRY, Brenda Winefride St Winefrides Nursing Home, Romilly Crescent, Cardiff CF11 9YP Tel: 029 2022 8784 — MB BCh BAO 1970 NUI.

BARRY, Brendan Patrick 20 Appledore Avenue, Wollaton, Nottingham NG8 2RL — MB ChB 1988 Birm.; MB ChB (Hons.) Birm. 1988; BSc (Hons.) Birm. 1985; MRCP (UK) 1991; FRCR 1995; DCH RCP Lond. 1991. (Birm.)

BARRY, Christopher Neil Station House Surgery, Chiseldon, Swindon SN4 0PB Tel: 01793 740276 Fax: 01793 845526 Email: dr.barryandpartner@dial.pipex.com; 36 Draycot Road, Chisledon, Swindon SN4 0LS Tel: 01793 740403 Fax: 01793 741355 Email: christopher.barry@which.net — MB BChir 1972 Camb.; MB Camb. 1972, BChir 1971; MA Camb. 1972; FRCGP 1990, M 1976; DObst RCOG 1974. (Univ. Camb. & King's Coll. Hosp.) GP; Chairm. Ridgeway Downs Prim. Care Gp. Prev: Mem. (Counc.) RCGP; Chairm. RCGP Matern. Task Force; Chairm. & Hon. Sec. Wessex Fac. RCGP.

BARRY, Elizabeth Selina (retired) Heathgate, Great Warford, Alderley Edge SK9 7TP Tel: 0156 587 3286 — BM BCh 1951 Oxf.; BM BCh Oxon. 1951; DCH Eng. 1953.

BARRY, Gerald Peter 111 Dringthorpe Road, Tadcaster Road, Drinhouses, York YO2 — MB BCh BAO 1942 NUI; LM Coombe 1943. (NUI) Socs: (Ex-Pres.) York Med. Soc. Prev: 1st Ho. Surg. & Obst. Off. Roy. Infirm. Halifax; Ho. Surg. S. Charitable Infirm. & Co. Hosp. Cork.

BARRY, Helen Mary 25/5 Great King Street, Edinburgh EH3 6QW — MB BCh BAO 1989 NUI.

BARRY, Jayne Elizabeth Sarah 3 St Edeyrns Close, Cyncoed, Cardiff CF23 6TH — MB BCh 1981 Wales; FRCA 1987. Cons. Anaesth. Univ. Wales Coll. Med. Cardiff.

BARRY, John Joseph Gerard Department of Medicine for Elderly, St Helier Hospital, Wrythe Lane, Carshalton SM5 1AA — MB BCh BAO 1985 NUI.

BARRY, John-Sebastian 24 Greening Drive, Edgbaston, Birmingham B15 2XA — MB ChB 1996 Bristol.

BARRY, Jonathan Damian 70 Millrace Close, Lisvane, Cardiff CF14 0UQ — MB BCh 1996 Wales.

BARRY, Josephine Elizabeth Rowancrest, 8 Grange Loan, Bo'ness EH51 9DX — MB BCh BAO 1981 NUI; MRCP (UK) 1984; FRCR 1987; DMRD 1986; MBA (Healthcare Management) Stirling Univ. 1997. (Univ. Coll. Cork) Cons. Radiol. Falkirk Dist. & Roy. Infirm. Hosps.

BARRY, Kevin John Barry and Flynn, 97 Blackhalve Lane, Wednesfield, Wolverhampton WV11 1BB Tel: 01902 731902 Fax: 01902 307966; 48 Prestwood Road W., Wednesfield, Wolverhampton WV11 1HL — MB ChB 1976 Birm.

BARRY, Linda Ruth Pengarth Road Surgery, Pengarth Road, St Agnes TR5 0TN Tel: 01872 553881 Fax: 01872 553885; Wheal Butson Farm, Wheal Butson, St Agnes TR5 0PT — MB ChB 1981 Bristol; MRCGP 1986; DRCOG 1984; Cert. Family Plann. JCC 1984.

BARRY, Marian Royal Naval Hospital BFPO 52 — MRCS Eng. LRCP Lond. 1968; MB BS Lond. 1968; FFA RCS Eng. 1975. (St. Bart.)

BARRY, Martin Patrick East Lynne Medical Centre, 3-5 Wellesley Road, Clacton-on-Sea CO15 3PP Tel: 01255 220010 Fax: 01255 476350 — MB BS 1982 Lond.; MRCGP 1986; DRCOG.

BARRY, Mr Matthew John The Royal London Hospital, London E1 1BB Tel: 020 7377 7445 Fax: 020 7377 7302 Email: matthew.barry@nationwideisp.net — MB BS 1985 Lond.; MS Lond. 1996; FRCS Eng. 1989; FRCS (Orth) 1997. (Lond. Hosp.) Cons. Orthop. Surg. The Roy. Lond. Hosp.

BARRY, Michael (retired) Pitlands Farm, Hillfarrance, Taunton TA4 1AN Tel: 01823 461338 — MB 1959 Camb.; MD Camb. 1970; FRCP Lond. 1979, M 1960. Cons. Phys. Taunton & Som. Hosp. (p/t). Prev: Ho. Phys. & Ho. Surg. Lond. Hosp.

BARRY, Michael Gerard University of Liverpool, New Medical Building, Ashton St., PO Box 147, Liverpool L69 3BX Tel: 0151 794 5560 — MB BCh BAO 1983 NUI; PhD Dub. 1990; BSc NUI 1981, MB BCh BAO 1983; MRCPI 1988. Lect. (Clin. Pharmacol. & Therap.) Liverp.

BARRY, Michael Raymond Francis Priory Medical Group, Cornlands Road, Acomb, York YO24 3WX Tel: 01904 781423 Fax: 01904 784886; 11 Moor Lane, Copmanthorpe, York YO23 3TJ Tel: 01904 703366 — MB BCh BAO 1975 NUI. Socs: Brit. Med. Acupunc. Soc.; Brit. Med. Soc.

BARRY, Nigel Anthony, Col. late RAMC Retd. (retired) Coombe, Gracious St., Selborne, Alton GU34 3JE Tel: 01420 511601 — LRCPI & LM, LRCSI & LM 1956; FFA RCSI 1986. Prev: Cons. Anaesth. Camb. Milit. Hosp.

BARRY, Patricia Braeside, 26 Pwllycrochan Avenue, Colwyn Bay LL29 7BW Tel: 01492 532059 Fax: 01492 532059 Email: 26pwlly@msn.com; 26 Pwllywochan Ave, Colwyn Bay, Conwy LL29 7BW Email: pat.barry@care4free.net — MB ChB 1966 Manch.; FRFA Eng. 1971. Cons. Anaesth. Gwynedd Hosps. NHS Trust.

BARRY, Paul c/o 91 Daneville Road, Liverpool L4 9RF — MB ChB 1994 Leeds.

BARRY, Peter Walter Leicester Royal Infirmary Children's Hospitals, Leicester LE1 5WW — MB ChB 1984 Dundee; MRCPI 1991; DCH RCP Lond. 1988. Cons. Prev: Regist. (Paediat.) S. Birm. HA; Fell. (Neonat.) Brit. Columbia Childr. Hosp., Vancouver.

BARRY, Philip Hanbury 158 Brent Street, Hays, Brent Knoll, Highbridge TA9 4BE Tel: 01278 760675 — MB ChB 1955 Bristol. Prev: Ho. Surg. & Ho. Phys. Bristol Roy. Infirm.; Ho. Surg. Bristol Matern. Hosp.

BARRY, Ralph E Department of Medicine, Old Building, Bristol Royal Infirmary, Bristol BS2 8HW Tel: 0117 928 2104 Fax: 0117 928 2151; Hollytree Cottage, Badgworth, Axbridge BS26 2QN — MB ChB 1967 Bristol; BSc Bristol 1963, MD 1972; FRCP Lond. 1981; MRCP (UK) 1971. (Bristol) Cons. Sen. Lect. Univ. Bristol Dept. Med. Bristol Roy. Infirm.; Hon. Phys., Bristol Roy. Infir.; Dir. For Educ., United Bristol Healthcare Trust. Socs: Amer. Gastroenterol Assn.; Brit. Soc. Gastroenterol.; Assn. Phys. Prev: Asst. Prof. Med. Univ. Calif. Los Angeles, USA; Asst. Dir. Clin. Study Center Harbor Gen. Hosp. Torrance, USA.

BARRY, Richard John Ashton Frankley Health Centre, 125 New St., Rubery, Birmingham B45 0EU Tel: 0121 453 8211 — BM BS 1989 Nottm.; BMedSci BM BS DRCOG. (Notts)

BARRY, Simon Mark Elliot 12 Macroom Road, Maida Vale, London W9 3HY Tel: 020 8968 5535 Email: sbarry@stompi.demon.co.uk — MB BS 1991 Lond.; BSc Lond. 1986; MRCP (UK) 1995; DTM & H Lond. 1996. (University College and Middlesex) Research Regist. Dept Itoracic Med., Roy. Tree Hosp., hampstead. Prev: Regist. (Chest Med.) Roy. Free Hosp. Lond.; SHO (Trop. Med.) Hosp. Trop. Dis. Lond.; Med. Off. Hlabisa Hosp. Kwazulu, S. Africa.

BARRY, Thomas Noel 350 Sutton Road, Walsall WS5 3BB Tel: 01922 626887 — MB BCh BAO NUI 1954. (Cork) Prev: Sen. Ho. Off. (Gen. Surg.) Chorley & Dist. Hosp.; Sen. Ho. Off. (Orthop. & Cas.) Roy. Hosp. Chesterfield; Orthop. Regist. Hope Hosp. Salford.

BARRY, William Charles Wilson Queen Mary's Hospital, Sidcup DA14 6LT Tel: 020 8302 2678 Fax: 020 8308 3069; 188 Greenvale Road, Eltham, London SE9 1PQ Tel: 020 8294 1427 — MB BCh BAO 1976 NUI; FRCP Lond. 1994; MRCP (UK) 1979; DCH RCPSI 1978. Cons. Paediat. Qu. Mary's Hosp. Sidcup. Prev: Sen. Regist. (Paediat.) King's Coll. Hosp. Lond. & Roy. Alexandra Childr. Hosp. Brighton; SHO Hosp. Sick Childr. Gt. Ormond St. Lond.

BARRY-BRAUNTHAL, Julia Alice Lodgeside Surgery, 22 Lodgeside Avenue, Kingswood, Bristol BS15 1WW Tel: 0117 9615 666 — MB ChB 1986 Bristol.

BARSBY, Michael Raymond The Health Centre, Kiddrow Lane, Burnley BB12 6LH Tel: 01282 426840 — MB ChB 1993 Manch.; MRGGP 1997. GP The Heath Centre Kiddrow La. Burnley. Socs: BMA; RCGP. Prev: Trainee GP/SHO (Paediat.) Qu. Pk. Hosp. Blackburn VTS; GP Regist. Whalley, Lancs.; SHO (A & E) Blackburn Roy. Infirm.

BARSEY, Hilary 45 Banstead Road S., Sutton SM2 5LG — MB BS 1991 Lond.

BARSEY, Laurence 45 Banstead Road S., Sutton SM2 5LG Tel: 020 8642 4741 — MB BS 1954 Lond.; MRCS Eng. LRCP Lond. 1954. (King's Coll. Hosp.) Prev: Asst. Med. Regist. Metrop. Hosp. Lond.; Ho. Surg. & Ho. Phys. Sutton & Cheam Gen. Hosp.

BARSHALL, Carolyn Elizabeth The Westminster & Pimlico General Practice, 15 Denbigh St., London SW1 2HF Tel: 020 7834 6969; 18 Lamont Road, London SW10 0JE — MB BS 1986 Adelaide; MRCGP 1992; DRCOG 1991; DA (UK) 1990.

BARSHAM, Betty (retired) 4 Summerhouse Road, Godalming GU7 1PY Tel: 01483 426538 — MRCS Eng. LRCP Lond. 1945; FFA RCS Eng. 1954; DA Eng. 1947. Prev: Cons. Anaesth. W. Midl. HA.

BARSON, Anthony James Clinical Sciences Building, Manchester Royal Infirmary, Oxford Road, Manchester M13 9WL Tel: 0161 276 8813 Fax: 0161 276 6348; Lorien, 13 Pennine Drive, Altrincham WA14 4NH Tel: 0161 928 4455 Fax: 0161 928 4466 Email: lorien@barsona.freeserve.co.uk — MB ChB 1960 Manch.; MD Manch. 1965; FRCPCH 1997; FRCPath 1992, M 1981; DCH Eng. 1964. Hon. Cons. Paediat. Path. Centr. Manch. Hosp. Healthcare Trust. Socs: Brit. Paediat. Assn.; (Ex-Hon. Sec.) Paediat. Path. Soc. Prev: Reader (path) univ.Manc.; Med.Dir.N.W.. Perinatal survey unit.

BARSON, Jacqueline Karen The Health Centre, Greenside, Cleckheaton BD19 5AN; 101 Allencroft, Birkenshaw, Bradford BD11 2AB Tel: 01274 651085 Fax: 01924 422502 Email: jack-n-rog@tilbrooke.fsnet.co.uk — BM 1984 Soton.; MRCGP 1990; DCH RCP Lond. 1988. (Southampton) Prev: Trainee GP Portsmouth VTS; SHO (O & G) Roy. Sussex Co. Hosp. Brighton; SHO (Paediat. & Neonates) Leicester.

BARSOUM, Gamal Habib Guirguiss Solihull Hospital, Lode Lane, Solihull B91 2JL Tel: 0121 424 4558 Fax: 0121 424 5549; Fax: 0121 685 5539 Email: g.h.barsoum@btinternet.com — MB BCh 1978 Cairo; MD Birm. 1991; FRCS Ed. 1984; MRCS Eng. LRCP Lond. 1979. p/t Cons. Surg. (Gen. Surg.) Solihull Hosp. & Birm. Heartlands Hosp. (Teachg.); Hon. Sen. Clin. Lect. Dept. of Surg. Univ. of Birm. Socs: Assn. Surg.; Assn. Endoscopic Surgs.; Assn. Coloproctol. Prev: Sen. Regist. N. Staffs. Hosp. Centre Stoke-on-Trent; Sen. Regist. Birm. Heartlands Hosp.; Research Fell. (Surg.) Univ. Birm. Qu. Eliz. Hosp. Birm.

BARSOUM, Magdi Zaki Consultant old age Psychiatry, Minsmere house, The Ipswich Hospital, Ipswich IP4 5PD — MB BCh 1969 Cairo; MRC Psych. Cons. old age Psychiat., Local Health Partnerships, NHS Trust; Princip. Clin. Med. Off. (Old Age Psychiat.) E. Suff. HA; Sen. Clin. Med. Off. Health c/o Elderly N. Manch. HA; Clin. Research Fell. Univ. Soton.; Hon. Sen. Regist. SW Hants. Health Dist. Socs: FRSM. Prev: Resid. Med. Off. El-Fayoum, Egypt; SHO & Regist. Broomfield Hosp. Chelmsford; Clin. Asst. (Psychiat.) Warley Hosp. Brentwood.

BARSOUM, Mr Michel Kamel Middlesbrough General Hospital, Ayresome Green Lane, Middlesbrough TS5 5AZ Tel: 01642 854287; 7 Neasham Court, Stokesley, Middlesbrough TS9 5PJ — MB BCh 1967 Cairo; FRCS Ed. 1978. Cons. Rehabil. Med. S. Tees HA. Prev: Sen. Med. Off. DHSS Leeds.

BARTELLA, Lia 4 Mount Pleasant Villas, London N4 4HD — MB ChB 1994 Ed.

BARTELS, Mr Agnes Robertson Donald 31 Bute Gardens, London W6 7DR — MB BS 1951 Lond.; MRCS Eng. LRCP Lond. 1950; FRCS Eng. 1953. (W. Lond.)

***BARTENS, Miss Alison** 55 Sylvan Avenue, Bitterne, Southampton SO19 5JW Tel: 02380 440588 — MB BS 1998 Lond.; MB BS Lond 1998.

BARTER, Antony Pascal (retired) Waterfoot House, Crock Lane, Bridport DT6 4DX Tel: 01308 23381 — MB BS 1951 Lond.; MRCS Eng. LRCP Lond. 1951; MRCGP 1958; DObst RCOG 1954. Prev: Cas. Off., Obst. Off. & Med. Regist. Char. Cross Hosp.

BARTER, Dennis Antony Christopher Paediatric Department, Queen Elizabeth Hospital, Gayton Road, King's Lynn PE30 4ET Tel: 01553 613678 Fax: 01553 613909 Email: dennis.bartetr@klshosp.anglox.nhs.uk; Monkshood, Lynn Road, Gayton, King's Lynn PE32 1PA Tel: 01553 636249 Fax: 01553 636900 Email: denlynn@hospital-doctor.net — MB BS 1969 Lond.; FRCPCH; 1990 FRCP; 1973 MRCP (UK); 1969 MRCS Eng. LRCP Lond.; 1971 DCH Eng. (King's Coll. Hosp.) Cons. Paediat. Qu. Eliz. Hosp. King's Lynn. Socs: BMA. Prev: Cons. Paediat. New Cross Hosp. & Roy. Hosp. Wolverhampton; Lect. (Child Health) & Research Fell. (Paediat. Oncol.) Roy. Hosp. Sick Childr. Glas.; Ho. Phys. King's Coll. Hosp. Lond.

BARTER, Janet Audrey Department of Gynaecology, Royal Free NHS Trust, Pond St., London NW2 2QG Tel: 020 7830 2691; 325 Alexandra Park Road, London N22 7BP — MB ChB 1985 Sheff.; MRCOG 1993. (Sheff.) Cons. Community Gyn. & Wom. Reproduc. Healthcare & Hon. Sen. Lect. Roy. Free Hosp. Lond. Prev: Research Fell. (Gyn.) Whittington & Univ. Coll. Hosps. Lond.; Regist. (O & G) Univ. Coll. Hosp. Lond., Whittington Hosp. Lond. & P.ss Alexandra Hosp. Harlow; SHO (O & G) N.. Gen. Hosp. Sheff.

BARTER, John Arthur William Rowden Surgery, Rowden Hill, Chippenham SN15 2SB Tel: 01249 444343 Fax: 01249 446797; Lowden Manor House, Lowden Hill, Chippenham SN15 2BX Tel: 01249 444279 — MB BChir 1980 Camb.; MA Camb. 1978; MRCGP 1985; DRCOG 1984; DCH RCP Lond. 1983. Clin. Asst. (Geriat.) Wilts.

BARTER, Karen Lucille Home Farm House, Holton, Oxford OX33 1QA — MB ChB 1998 Manch.; MB ChB Manch 1998.

BARTER, Phillip Peter 14 Roman Meadow, Downton, Salisbury SP5 3LB — MB BS 1997 Lond.

BARTER, Richard Wade (retired) White Swan Cottage, 19 Reading St., Broadstairs CT10 3AZ Tel: 01843 861725 — MA, MD Dub. 1950, MB (Hons.) BCh BAO (Hons.) 1944; FRCPI 1961, M 1956; DPhysMed. Eng. 1955. Hon. Cons. Rheum. & Rehabil. I. of Thanet & Canterbury HA. Prev: Med. Regist. Addenbrooke's Hosp. Camb.

BARTER, Susan Joan Department of Diagnostic Radiology, Bedford Hospital NHS Trust, Kempston Road, Bedford MK42 9DJ Tel: 01234 795759; Wentworth House, 6 Ravensden Road, Renhold, Bedford MK41 0LA — MB BS 1978 Lond.; MRCP (UK) 1980; DMRD Eng. 1982; FRCR 1983. Cons. Radiol. , Beds. & Herts and Bedford Gen. Hosp., BrE. Screening Serv. Socs: Fell. Roy. Coll. Radiol. & Med. Soc. Lond.

BARTH, Colin Meeks Road Surgery, 10 Meeks Road, Falkirk FK2 7ES Tel: 01324 619930 Fax: 01324 627266; Pine Trees, Greenbank, Falkirk FK1 5PU — MB BCh BAO 1981 Dub.

BARTH, Julian Howard Department Clinical Biochemistry & Immunology, Leeds General Infirmary, Great George St., Leeds LS1 3EX Tel: 0113 392 3416 Fax: 0113 233 5672 Email: julianb@pathology.leeds.ac.uk; Tel: 0113 267 3624 — MB BS 1976 Lond.; FRCP 2001; MD Lond. 1992; MRCP (UK) 1979; MRCPath 1994. (St. Barholomews Hospital Medical School) Cons. Chem. Path. & Metab. Med. Leeds Gen. Infirm.; Director, Supraregional Assay Serv. Steroid Centre, Leeds Gen. Infirm. Prev: Sen. Regist. (Chem. Path.) Leeds Gen. Infirm.

BARTHAKUR, Anil Ranjan Eldene Health Centre, Eldene, Swindon SN3 3RZ Tel: 01793 22710; 15 The Bramptons, Shawbridge, Swindon SN5 5SJ Tel: 01793 874940 — MB BS 1954 Gauhati; DCH Eng. 1969. (Assam Med. Coll. Dibrugarh) Prev: Regist. (Geriat.) St. Margt. Hosp. Stratton St. Margt.; SHO (Paediat. Med.) St. Tydfil's Hosp. Merthyr Tydfil; SHO (O & G) Aberdare Gen. Hosp.

BARTHES-WILSON, Elizabeth Lati 28A Sudlow Road, London SW18 1HP — MB BS 1997 Lond.

BARTHOLOMEW, Alan James 21 Duthie Road, Gourock PA19 1XS — MB ChB 1980 Glas.

BARTHOLOMEW, Andrew David Goyt Valley Medical Practice, Chapel Street, Whaley Bridge, High Peak SK23 7SR Tel: 01663 732911 Fax: 01663 735702 — MB ChB 1981 Leic.; BSc Reading 1974; MRCGP 1987.

BARTHOLOMEW, Gavin John Faringdon Health Centre, Volunteer Way, Faringdon SN7 7YP Tel: 01367 242388 Fax: 01367 245401; Norham, Buckland, Faringdon SN7 8QW Tel: 01367 870601 Email: gandf.bartholomew@btinternet.com — MB ChB 1983 Dundee; MRCGP 1988; T(GP) 1991; DRCOG 1986. (Dundee University)

BARTHOLOMEW, Graham Harries 125 Ewney Road, Bridgend CF31 3ET — MB ChB 1978 Bristol.

BARTHOLOMEW, John (retired) Orchard Close, Hillcrest, Evesham WR11 6BG Tel: 01386 442400 — MB ChB 1950 St. And.

BARTHOLOMEW, Karen Marina 3 Moorbottom Farm, Rope Walk, Wainstalls, Halifax HX2 7UG — MB BChir 1987 Camb.; FRCA Eng. 1997. (Camb.) Specialist Regist. (Anaesth.) Leeds. Gen. Infirm.

BARTHOLOMEW, Madelyn Angela 65 Braiswick, Colchester CO4 5BQ Tel: 01206 842212 — MB BS 1988 Lond.

BARTHOLOMEW, Margaret Orchard Close, Hillcrest, Broadway Road, Evesham WR11 6BG Tel: 01386 442400 — MB ChB 1949 St. And. (St. And.)

BARTHOLOMEW, Noel Ian (retired) The Old Vicarage, Norton Bavant, Warminster BA12 7BD — MRCS Eng. LRCP Lond. 1943; BA Camb 1937. Hon. Surg. & Phys. Warminster Hosp. Prev: Cas. Off. W.m. Hosp. Lond.

BARTHOLOMEW, Mr Richard Shayle The Old Smiddy, Midcalder, Livingston EH53 0HT — MB BChir 1962 Camb.; BA Camb. 1958; FRCS Ed. 1967; FRCOphth 1991; DO Eng. 1965. (Middlx.) Sen. Lect. (Ophth.) Univ. Edin.; Hon. Cons. Roy. Infirm. Edin. NHS Trust. Prev: Sen. Regist. (Ophth.) Dundee Roy. Infirm.; Sen. Surg. (Ophth.) Witwatersrand Univ., Johannesburg; Regist. Oxf. Eye Hosp.

BARTHRAM, Clifford Noel 10 Lochlee Terrace, Dundee DD4 7LN — MB ChB 1987 Dundee.

BARTKIEWICZ, Adam Jan The Misbourne Surgery, Church Lane, Gerrards Cross SL9 9RR Tel: 01753 891010 — MB BS 1987 Lond.; BSc (Hons.) Anat. Lond. 1984; DRCOG 1990; Cert. Family Plann. JCC 1990. Prev: Trainee GP St Albans; SHO (Psychiat., O & G, Cas. & Paediat.) St. Albans City Hosp.

BARTLAM, Andrew Shaun Milton Surgery, Millrise Road, Milton, Stoke-on-Trent ST2 7BN Tel: 01782 545444 Fax: 01782 570135; 11 Lower Oxford Road, Basford, Newcastle ST5 0PB Tel: 01782 610102 Email: abbartlam@compuserve.com — MB ChB 1983 Manch.; MRCGP 1987; DRCOG 1986; FRCGP Nov 1996. GP Princip.; Course Organiser N. Staffs. VTS; GP Trainer. Prev: Trainee GP/SHO N. Staffs. HA VTS; Ho. Off. Pk. Hosp. Manch.

***BARTLE, David George** Broad Oaks, Old Broyle Road, West Broyle, Chichester PO19 3PR Tel: 01243 533906 — MB ChB 1997 Sheff.

BARTLE, Edward Owen Wibsey and Queensbury Medical Practice, Fair Road, Wibsey, Bradford BD6 1TB Tel: 01274 677198 Fax: 01274 693389 — MB ChB 1974 Manch. Prev: SHO (Obst.) & Ho. Phys. St. Luke's Hosp. Bradford; Ho. Surg. Bradford Roy. Infirm.

BARTLE, Margaret Rhoda Foxgloves, Back Lane, Grindleton, Clitheroe BB7 4RW — MB ChB 1973 Dundee. Sessional Med. Off. Blood Trans. Serv. Prev: Clin. Asst. (Psychiat.) Lancs. AHA.

BARTLET, Leslie Bow Sleep Disorder Service, Ashurst Hsopital, Southampton SO40 7AR; 2 St. James Terrace, Winchester SO22 4PP Tel: 01962 855026 — MB ChB 1951 Aberd.; FRCPsych 1983, M 1972; DCH Eng. 1959; DPM Eng. 1956. (Aberd.) Hon. Cons. Psychiat. Soton. City Primary Care Trust. Prev: Hon. Cons. Psychiat. Soton. Community Healthcare Trust; Cons. Psychiat. Soton. Child & Family Guid. Clin. Soton. Gen. Hosp.; Sen. Regist. Herts. Child Guid. Serv.

BARTLETT, Ann Elisabeth Adams Department of Forensic Psychiatry, St George's Hospital, Clare House, Blackshaw Road, London SW17 — MB BChir 1983 Camb.; MPhil Camb. 1987, MA 1984, MB BChir 1983; MRCPsych 1988. Clin. Research Fell. St. Geo. Hosp. Lond. Prev: Regist. (Psychiat.) St. Geo. Hosp. Lond.

BARTLETT, Calum Iain The Surgery, 118/120 Stanford Avenue, Brighton BN1 6FE Tel: 01273 506361 Fax: 01273 552483; 40 Great College Street, Brighton BN2 1HL Tel: 01273 671882 — MB BS 1983 Lond.; MRCGP 1989. (Guy's) Med. Off. Univ. Brighton. Prev: SHO (Psychiat.) Brighton Gen. Hosp.; SHO (O & G) Roy. Sussex Co. Hosp. Brighton; SHO (Paediat.) Roy. Alexandra Hosp. Brighton.

BARTLETT, Calum Iain Stewart 22 Holly Way, Blackwater, Camberley Gu1 6HP Tel: 01276 38828 — MB ChB 1949 Glas. p/t Disabil. Asst. Sutton Med. Serv.

BARTLETT, Charles Gordon West Wales General Hospital, Carmarthen SA31 2AF Tel: 01267 235151 Fax: 01267 227791 Email: charliebartlett@zetnet.co.uk; The Croft, Ferryside SA17 5SP Tel: 01267 267273 — MB BCh 1978 Wales; BSc (Hons.) Wales 1975; FRCR 1985. (Wales) Cons. Radiol. Carmarthenshire NHS Trust. Prev: Sen. Regist. (Radiol.) Univ. Hosp. Wales Cardiff; Regist. (Radiol.) N.wick Pk. Hosp. Lond.; Ho. Surg. Cardiff Roy. Infirm.

BARTLETT, Christopher Leslie Reginald 43A Oakridge Avenue, Radlett WD7 8EW — MRCS Eng. LRCP Lond. 1965; MSc Lond. 1978, MB BS 1965; FFCM 1983, M 1978. (St. Bart.) Cons. Epidemiol. & Dir. Communicable Dis. Surveillance Centre Colindale; Hon. Lect. Dept. Environm. & Preven. Med. St. Bart. Hosp. Med. Coll.; Hon. Cons. (Community Med.) NW Thames RHA. Socs: Brit. Soc. Study of Infec. & Brit. Thoracic Soc.

BARTLETT, Clare Virginia The Court House, East Meon, Petersfield GU32 1NJ Tel: 0173 087274 — MB BS 1976 Lond.; MRCS Eng. LRCP Lond. 1975.

BARTLETT, David 20 Godwin Crescent, Waterlooville PO8 0YA — BM 1991 Soton.

BARTLETT, David Child Adolecent and Family Centre, 84 Ewell Road, Surbiton KT6 6EX Tel: 020 8390 8151 Fax: 020 8390 4754 Email: swift@psionworld.net; Flat 5, Ravens Ait Hall, 24 Kings Down Road, Surbiton KT6 6LA Tel: 020 8390 2575 — MB BS 1986 Lond.; JCPTGP Certificate of Experience 1993. (Middlesex Hospital) Assoc. Specialist Child & Adolesc. Psychiat. Kingston Community NHS Trust; Clin. Asst. Adult Psychiat. N. Middlx. Hosp. Lond. Prev: Primary Care Practitioner St Geo.s Hosp. Lond.

BARTLETT, David Lewis Gayton Road Health and Surgical Centre, Gayton Road, King's Lynn PE30 4DY Tel: 01553 762726 Fax: 01553 696819; 2 St Margaret's Place, King's Lynn PE30 5DL Tel: 01553 765750 — MB BS 1969 Lond.; MRCS Eng. LRCP Lond. 1968; DO Eng. 1978; DObst RCOG 1972. (King's Coll. Hosp.) Prev: Med. Off. Anguilla, W. Indies.

BARTLETT, David Robin Cobbs Garden Surgery, West Street, Olney MK46 5QG Tel: 01234 711344; 7 Elger Close, Biddenham, Bedford MK40 4AU Tel: 01234 357825 Email: davidrbart@aol.com — MB BS 1978 Lond.; MRCS Eng. LRCP Lond. 1978; MRCGP 1983. (Westm.)

BARTLETT, David Wenyon Bartlett, Cronk and Newton, Chequers Lane, Papworth Everard, Cambridge CB3 8QQ Tel: 01480 830888 Fax: 01480 830001 — MB BS 1969 Lond.; MB BS Lond. 1969 MRCS Eng. LRCP Lond. 1969; MRCGP 1977; DObst RCOG 1972. (St.Mary's)

BARTLETT, Deborah Winifred 131 Lovibonds Avenue, Orpington BR6 8EN — MB ChB 1988 Sheff.; DFFP 1995; MRCGP 1996. GP Retainee, Ely. Prev: Sen. Med. Off., Sqn. Ldr RAF.

BARTLETT, Garry Victor Mid-Cheshire Homeopathic Group, 2 Watling Street, Northwich CW9 5EX Tel: 01606 42445; Coed-y-Cra Mill, Bryn-y-Garreg Lane, Flint Mountain, Flint CH6 5QU — MB ChB 1988 Liverp.; BSc Liverp. 1979; DRCOG 1991.

BARTLETT, Gavin Edward Westfield Farm, Shepherds Close, Weston-on-the-Green, Bicester OX25 3RF — MB BS 1996 Lond.

BARTLETT, Isabel Anne Cooper Bute House, Grove Medical Centre, Wootton Grove, Sherborne DT9 4DL Tel: 01935 810900 Fax: 01935 810901; Limerick House, North St, Milborne Port, Sherborne DT9 5EW — MB BS 1981 Lond.; MRCGP 1986; DCH RCP Lond. 1984; DRCOG 1983. (Char. Cross Hosp. Med. Sch.) Prev: Trainee GP Winchester VTS; Ho. Surg. Char. Cross Hosp. Lond.; Ho. Phys. Norf. & Norwich Hosp.

BARTLETT, James Ian Cowell Wem and Prees Medical Practice, New Street, Wem, Shrewsbury SY4 5AF Tel: 01939 232424; Castle Mound House, 67 High St, Wem, Shrewsbury SY4 5DR Tel: 01939 234932 — MB ChB 1985 Sheff.; MRCGP 1990; DRCOG 1988.

BARTLETT, James Simon William Lismore, Nightingales, West Chiltington, Pulborough RH20 2QT — MB BS 1997 Lond.

BARTLETT, Janice Marian 3 Sherard Way, Thorpe Astley, Braunstone, Leicester LE3 3TN — MB ChB 1998 Leic.; MB ChB Leic 1998.

BARTLETT, Jill Annette Midway Surgery, 93 Watford Road, St Albans AL2 3JX Tel: 01727 832125 Fax: 01727 836384; 53 Carlisle Avenue, St Albans AL3 5LX Tel: 01727 46499 — MB BS 1980 Lond.; BSc (Med. Sociol.) Lond. 1977, MB BS 1980; MRCGP 1985; DRCOG 1983. (Royal Free Hospital) Socs: Roy. Soc. Med.; Brit. Menopause Soc. Prev: Trainee GP Whipps Cross Hosp. VTS; SHO (Infec. Dis.) Coppetts Wood Hosp. Lond.

BARTLETT, Mr John Richard (retired) 28 Lee Terrace, Blackheath, London SE3 9TZ — MB 1959 Camb.; BChir 1958; FRCS Eng. 1966. Cons. Neurosurg. King's Coll. Hosp. Lond. Prev: Sen. Regist. Radcliffe Infirm. Oxf.

BARTLETT, June Mary Wake Robin, 37 The Ridgeway, Bracknell RG12 9QU Tel: 01344 55940 — MB ChB 1959 Birm.; DMRD Eng. 1970; DObst RCOG 1962. (Birm.) Clin. Med. Off. Berks. AHA. Prev: Sen. Regist. (Diag. Radiol.) Char. Cross Hosp. Lond.

BARTLETT, Katherine Louise Holman Little Grange, Pytches Road, Woodbridge IP12 1EP — MB ChB 1990 Ed.

BARTLETT, Keith (retired) Felhampton Court, Felhampton, Church Stretton SY6 6RJ Tel: 01694 781545 Fax: 01694 781587 — MB BCh 1967 Wales; FFR 1976; DMR 1972. Hon. Sen. Clin. Lect. Med. Sch. Univ. Aberd. Prev: Cons. Radiother. & Oncol. Aberd. Roy. Infirm.

BARTLETT, Louise Jane Clare Tel: 01723 863594 Fax: 01723 862902; The Kennels, Middle Lane, Hutton Buscel, Scarborough YO13 9LS — MB BS 1979 Lond.; MRCGP 1984; DRCOG 1982. (Royal Free)

BARTLETT, Margaret Hilary Wellington Medical Practice, Victoria Avenue, Wellington, Telford TF1 1PZ Tel: 01952 226000; Castle Mound House, 67 High St, Wem, Shrewsbury SY4 5DR — MB ChB 1985 Sheff.; DFFP 1995; DRCOG 1989. Gen. Practitoner, Wellington Med. Pract.; Clin. Asst. (Genitourin. Med.) Roy. Shrewsbury Hosp.; Hosp. Practitioner (GU Med.) Roy. Shrewsbury Hosp.

BARTLETT, Martin Hedley Framfield House, Woodbridge IP12 1ED Tel: 01394 382157 — MB 1961 Camb.; BChir 1960. (St. Mary's) Prev: Alexandra Hosp. Childr. Camperdown, Austral; Ho. Surg. Surgic. Unit St. Mary's Hosp. Lond.; Ho. Off. (Obst.) Whittington Hosp. Lond.

BARTLETT, Mr Matthew James 57 West Street, Harrow on The Hill, Harrow HA1 3EL — BM BCh 1991 Oxf.; BA Oxf. 1988; FRCS Eng. 1995. (Univ. Oxf.) Specialist Regist. Rotat. (Orthop. Surg.) Chelsea & W.m. Hosp. & Char. Cross Hosp. Lond.

BARTLETT, Maureen Anne Granton Medical Centre, 114 Middleton Hall Road, King's Norton, Birmingham B30 1DH Tel: 0121 459 9117 Fax: 0121 486 2889; 45 Reddings Road, Mosley, Birmingham B13 8LW — MB BS 1963 Lond.; MRCS Eng. LRCP Lond. 1963. (Roy. Free) Prev: Regist.(path.) & Sen. Ho. Phys. City Cen. Hosp. Stoke-on-Trent.

BARTLETT, Michael Department of Haematology, Withybush Hospital, Haverfordwest SA61 2PZ — MB BCh 1988 Wales; DRCOG 1994. Staff Grade (Haemat.) Withybush Gen. Hosp. HaverfordW.. Prev: SHO (A & E) Morriston Hosp. Swansea; Ho. Off. (Med. & Surg.) P.ss of Wales Hosp. Bridgend.

BARTLETT, Nicholas 3 Anglia Close, Litchard, Bridgend CF31 1QX Tel: 01656 3663 — MB BCh 1963 Wales; DA Eng. 1965. (Cardiff)

BARTLETT, Nicola Ann 24 Archway Street, Barnes, London SW13 0AR Tel: 020 8878 5154 — MB ChB 1991 Dundee. SHO (Anaesth.) Ealing Hosp. Lond.

BARTLETT, Nigel Charles Butts Road Medical Centre, Butts Road, Bakewell DE45 1ED Tel: 01629 812871 Fax: 01629 814958 — MRCS Eng. LRCP Lond. 1971; MB Camb. 1972, BChir 1971; DObst RCOG 1975.

BARTLETT, Paul Donald 20 Starboard Court, Brighton Marina Village, Brighton BN2 5UX — MB ChB 1970 Ed.

BARTLETT, Penelope Jayne 36 East Street, Alford LN13 9EH — MB ChB 1986 Birm.

BARTLETT, Peter Anthony 11 West View, Leigh Lane, Bramshall, Uttoxeter ST14 5DN Tel: 01889 564955 — MB BS 1955 Lond.; MFPHM 1980; MFOM 1980; T(OM) 1991; T(PHM) 1991; DPH Eng. 1960. Freelance Occupat. Phys. Prev: Sen. Occupat. Phys. City Bradford Metrop. Counc. Bradford; Employm. Med. Adviser EMAS.

BARTLETT, Peter George 24 Greenwood Road., Weston Super Mare BS22 6EX — MB BS 1970 Lond.; MRCS Eng. LRCP Lond. 1970.

BARTLETT, Richard John Vernon c/o X-Ray Department, Hull Royal Infirmary, Kingston-upon-Hull, Hull HU3 2JZ Tel: 01482 674083; Braidhills, 22 The Triangle, North Ferriby HU14 3AT — BM BCh 1977 Oxf.; FRCP 1999; FRCR 1984; DMRD 1982; MA Oxf. 1978. Cons. Radiol. (Neuroradiol.) N. Humberside HA. Socs: Eur. Soc. & Brit. Soc. Neuroradiol. Prev: Sen. Regist. (Neuroradiol.) Yorks. RHA.

BARTLETT, Rita Anne Lesley Oxford Housing CMHT, A. G. Palmer House, Morrell Crescent, Sandford Road, Littlemore, Oxford OX4 4SU Tel: 01865 223103; 10 Pulker Close, Cowley, Oxford OX4 3LG Tel: 01865 771665 — MRCS Eng. LRCP Lond. 1978; MRCPsych 1985. (Middlx. Hosp. Med. Sch.) Assoc. Specialist (Psychiat.) Oxf. Gp. Homes Littlemore Ment. Health Centre Oxf. Prev: Assoc. Specialist (Psychiat.) Littlemore Hosp. Oxf.; Oxf. Rotat. (Psychiat.) Train. Scheme; Ho. Phys. S. Lond. Hosp. Wom.

BARTLETT, Samuel Gregor Armson Northlands, 88 Vale Road, Ashvale, Aldershot GU12 5HS Tel: 01252 326309 Fax: 01252 312412 — MB ChB 1941 Glas.; BA (Hons.) Open 1988; BSc Glas. 1938; FRCGP 1988, M 1980; DObst RCOG 1954; DCH Eng. 1971. Socs: Brit. Soc. Med. & Dent. Hypn. (Metrop. & S.) Accredit. Mbr.

BARTLETT, Sarah 12 Hazelwood Avenue, West Jesmond, Newcastle upon Tyne NE2 3HX — MB BS 1996 Newc.

BARTLETT, Sarah Jane 2 Follett Road, Topsham, Exeter EX3 0JP; 2 Follett Road, Topsham, Exeter EX3 0JP — MB BCh 1992 Wales; MRCP (UK) 1995; DRCOG; MRCGP 1998.

BARTLETT, Thomas Paul Seymour House Surgery, 154 Sheen Road, Richmond TW9 1UU Tel: 020 8940 2802 Fax: 020 8332 7877 — MB BS 1961 Lond.; MRCS Eng. LRCP Lond. 1961; DObst RCOG 1964. (St. Geo.) Socs: BMA. Prev: Paediat. Ho. Phys. Vict. Hosp. Childr. Chelsea; Ho. Surg. Qu. Vict. Hosp. E. Grinstead; Obst. Ho. Surg. St. Nicholas' Hosp. Lond.

BARTLEY, Brian John Quilters, Black Boy Lane, Wrabness, Manningtree CO11 2TP Tel: 01255 880376 — MB BS 1955 Lond.; MRCS Eng. LRCP Lond. 1955; DObst RCOG 1959. (King's Coll.) Adjudicating Med. Pract. Socs: Colchester Med. Soc. Prev: SHO (Surg.) Brit. Hosp. Mothers & Babies, Woolwich; Ho. Phys. Dulwich Hosp. Lond.; Ho. Surg. King's Coll. Hosp.

BARTLEY, Catherine Frances Mary Laburnum Cottage, Main Road, Ovingham, Prudhoe NE42 6AA — MB ChB 1992 Bristol.

BARTLEY, Christopher William (retired) 117 Thurleigh Road, London SW12 8TY Tel: 020 8673 1312 — DM 1943 Oxf.; MD McGill 1943; DM Oxf. 1956 BM BCh 1943; FRCP Lond. 1969, M 1948. Hon. Cons. Phys. St. Thos. Hosp.; Hon. Cons. Phys. Bolingbroke Hosp. Lond.; Hon. CMO. United Friendly Insur. Co. Prev: Sen. Regist. & Regist. Lond. Hosp.

BARTMAN, Michael 2 Montrose Avenue, Datchet, Slough SL3 9NJ — MB ChB 1992 Pretoria.

BARTOLO, Mr David Charles Craig Royal Infirmary of Edinburgh NHS Trust, Lauriston Place, Edinburgh EH3 9YW Tel: 0131 536 1610 Fax: 0131 536 1510; 10A Gordon Terrace, Edinburgh EH16 5QW Tel: 0131 667 6212 Fax: 0131 662 0395 Email: dccb2107@aol.com — MB BS 1973 Lond.; MS Lond. 1985; FRCS Ed. 1991; FRCS Eng. 1977; MRCS Eng. LRCP Lond. 1973. (St. Mary's) Cons. Surg. Roy. Infirm. Edin. Socs: Brit. Soc. Gastroenterol. & Surg. Research Soc.; Assn. Coloproctol. Prev: Cons. Sen. Lect. Bristol Roy. Infirm.; Sen. Regist. St. Mark's Hosp. Lond. & S. W.. RHA; Ho. Surg. St. Mary's Hosp. Lond.

BARTON, Alan Lyle Email: abarton@doctors.org.uk — MB BCh BAO 1992 Belf.; MB BCh Belf. 1992; MRCPI 1998 Dublin. Specialist Regist. Elderly & Gen. Med. St Jas. Univ. Hosp. Leeds.

BARTON, Ann Drusilla 'Millin Ford', Millin, Rhos, Haverfordwest SA62 4AL Tel: 01437 2394 — MB ChB 1959 Sheff. (Sheff.)

BARTON, Anne Caroline 14 Wilderswood Close, Manchester M20 4XU — MB ChB 1991 Manch.

BARTON, Anthony Charles Graham 42 Gibson Square, London N1 0RB Tel: 020 7700 6761 — MB BS 1981 Lond.; MA Oxf. 1982. Solicitor (Med. Litigation) Lond. Prev: Barrister Lincoln's Inn.

BARTON, Barbara Judith Joan St Marys Surgery, St. Marys Close, Timsbury, Bath BA2 0HX Tel: 01761 470880 Fax: 01761 472492 — MB BChir 1987 Camb.; BSc St. And. 1984; MRCGP 1991; DCH RCP Lond. 1993; DRCOG 1989.

BARTON, Bernard William (retired) 8 Kingsgate, Lockington, Derby DE74 2YX Tel: 01509 674061 — MB BS 1955 Lond.; Dip. Bact. 1964; FRCPath 1976, M 1964. Prev: Dir. Regional Pub. Health Laborat. Sheff.

BARTON, Bryn William (retired) Millinford, Millin, Rhos, Haverfordwest SA62 4AL Tel: 01437 762394 — MB ChB 1962 Sheff. Prev: Hon. Clin. Teach. Univ. Wales Coll Med.

BARTON, Carol Jane (retired) Brook Cottage, North Stoke, Near Wallingford, Oxford OX10 6BL — MB 1973 Camb.; MSc (Med. Immunol.) Lond. 1988; BChir 1972; FRCP Lond. 1994; MRCP (UK) 1974; FRCPath 1990, M 1978; FRCPCH 1995. Prev: Cons. Haemat. Roy. Berks. Hosp. Reading.

BARTON, Cefin Rees 801 Clydach Road, Ynstawe, Swansea SA6 5BH — MB BCh 1996 Wales.

BARTON, Christopher Hugh 12 Comely Park, Dunfermline KY12 7HU Tel: 01383 724 4035; 12 Afton Grove, Dunfermline KY11 4LE Tel: 01383 725859 — MB ChB 1970 Ed.; DA Eng. 1972.

BARTON, Claire Melanie Department of Oncology Clinical Research, Glaxo-Wellcome, Greenford Road, Greenford UB6 0HE Tel: 020 8966 2047 Fax: 020 8966 2030; 8 Elm Avenue, Eastcote, Ruislip HA4 8PD Tel: 020 8429 2781 — MB BChir 1984 Camb.; PhD Lond. 1994; MRCP (UK) 1987. (Camb. & St. Thos.) Clin. Research Phys. (Clin. Oncol.) Glaxo-Wellcome Beckenham, Kent; Hon. Sen. Regist. (Med. Oncol.) Roy. Marsden Hosp. Sutton, Surrey. Prev: Research Fell. & Hon. Sen. Regist. (Med. Oncol.) Hammersmith Hosp. Lond.; Research Fell. & Hon. Regist. (Med. Oncol.) W. Midl.

CRC Clin. Trials Unit Qu. Eliz. Hosp. Birm.; ICRF Postgrad. Stud. & Hon. Regist. (Tumour Path.) Roy. Marsden Hosp. Lond.

BARTON, Colin Sinclair (retired) 4 Headland Avenue, Seaford BN25 4PY Tel: 01323 490717 — MB BS 1956 Lond.; LMSSA Lond. 1956; LMCC 1972; DRCOG 1959.

BARTON, Conor Michael The Hill, Castledawson, Magherafelt BT45 8AP — MB BCh 1998 Belf.; MB BCh Belf 1998.

BARTON, David Garbutt, CStJ 64 Western Esplanade, Herne Bay CT6 8DN — MB BChir 1962 Camb.; MA Camb. 1963, BA 1959; FRCS Ed. 1969; MRCS Eng. LRCP Lond. 1962; FRCGP 1976, M 1969; MFFP 1994; DCH Eng. 1967; DObst RCOG 1964. (Camb. & Univ. Coll. Hosp.) p/t Panel Mem. of the Appeals Serv.; Liveryman of Soc. Apoth.; Hon. Med. Off. Kent Co. Agricultural Soc.; Co. Med. Off. St John Kent; Locum Gen. Practitioner. Prev: Ho. Surg. Univ. Coll. Hosp. Lond.; Ho. Phys. (Obst.) St. Thos. Hosp. Lond.; Cas. Surg. St. Mary's Hosp. Lond.

BARTON, David Ian Barton and Partners, Campingland, Swaffham PE37 7RD Tel: 01760 721211 Fax: 01760 720009; Staines House, Sporle Road, Swaffham PE37 7HL Tel: 01760 723908 — MB BChir 1976 Camb.; MA Camb. 1974; MRCP (UK) 1978; MRCGP 1979; DRCOG 1977. (Westm.)

BARTON, David Michael 27 Hollybush Road, Cyncoed, Cardiff CF23 6SY — MB BChir 1994 Camb.

BARTON, Dorothy Atherton (retired) North Lodge, Rose Lane, Oxford OX1 4DT Tel: 01865 246212 — MB ChB 1922 Liverp.; DOMS Eng. 1939. Hon. Consg. Ophth. Surg. United Liverp. Hosps., Liverp. RHB & I. Of Man Health Servs. Bd. Prev: Cons. Ophth. Surg. St. Paul's Eye Hosp. Liverp., Sefton Gen. Hosp.

BARTON, Elizabeth Ann The Medical Centre, Station Avenue, Bridlington YO16 4LZ Tel: 01262 670683 Fax: 01262 401685 — MB ChB 1978 Manch.; BSc MedSci St. And. 1975; MRCGP 1988.

BARTON, Eric John Radiology Department, County Hospital, Union Walk, Hereford HR1 2ER Tel: 01432 355444; Gwynant, 21 St Margaret's Road, Hereford HR1 1TS Tel: 01432 269130 — MB BS 1977 Lond.; MRCP (UK) 1979; MRCS Eng. LRCP Lond. 1977; DMRD Eng. 1982; FRCR 1983. (Westm.) Cons. Radiol. Co. Hosp. Hereford. Prev: Sen. Regist. (Radiol.) Addenbrooke's Hosp. Camb.; Ho. Phys. W.m. Hosp. Lond.; SHO Rotat. (Med.) W.m. Hosp. Lond.

BARTON, Frances Helen 51 Leinster Avenue, E. Sheen, London SW14 7JW Tel: 020 8876 7707 — MB BS 1987 Lond.; MRCGP 1993; DRCOG 1992. GP Retainer Scheme Barnes. Prev: Trainee GP Richmond; SHO (O & G) St. Helier Hosp. Carshalton; SHO (Anaesth.) St. Thos. Hosp. Lond.

BARTON, Frederick Leslie 7 Orchard Gate, Esher KT10 8HY — MRCS Eng. LRCP Lond. 1964; FFA RCS Eng. 1971; DA Eng. 1968. (Liverp.) Anaesth. Cons. Kingston Gen. Hosp. Prev: Anaesth. Sen. Regist. N.wick Pk. Hosp. & Brompton Hosp. Lond.

BARTON, Gwendolen Margaret Gwladys (retired) Hollyville, West Grimstead, Salisbury SP5 3RQ Tel: 01722 710252 — MRCS Eng. LRCP Lond. 1940; BSc (Hons.) Lond. 1936, MD 1957, MB BS 1950; FRCPath 1968. Prev: Resid. Path. & Ho. Phys. Roy. Free Hosp.

BARTON, Hilary Ruth 34 Station Road, Stokesley, Middlesbrough TS9 5AJ Tel: 01642 711929 Fax: 01642 711929 — MB ChB 1983 Manch.; BSc St. And. 1980; MRCGP 1987. Asst. GP Cleveland; Med. Off. DSS. Prev: Trainee GP Cleveland VTS.

BARTON, Ian Kim Basildon Hospital, Nether Mayne, Basildon SS16 5NL Tel: 01268 598254 Fax: 01268 598048; 40 Blackacre Road, Theydon Bois, Epping CM16 7LU Tel: 01992 815203 Email: ian.barton@lineone.net — MB BS 1978 Lond.; FRCP 1999; MD Lond. 1989; MRCP (UK) 1980; MA Camb. 1979. (Camb. Univ. & UCHMS Lond.) Cons. Phys. & Nephrol. Basildon & Thurrock NHS Trust; Hon. Sen. Lect. (Renal Med.) Univesity Coll. Hosp. Lond. 1997. Socs: Renal Assn.; Intens. Care Soc. Prev: Cons. Intens. Care (Renal & Gen. Med.) & Clin. Dir. Med. Care Gp. Whipps Cross Hosp. Lond.; Sen. Regist. (Renal & Gen. Med.) St. Thos. Hosp. Lond.

BARTON, Mr James Reginald Searle (retired) Little Fulwood House, Trull, Taunton TA3 7PE Tel: 01823 421222 — MB BS Lond. 1953; FRCS Ed. 1966; DO Eng. 1961. Prev: Cons. Ophth. Surg. Som. HA.

BARTON, Jane Ann The Surgery, 148 Forton Road, Gosport PO12 3HH Tel: 023 9258 3333 Fax: 023 9260 1107; Clifton Corner, 11 Village Road, Alverstoke, Gosport PO12 2LD — BM BCh 1972 Oxf.; MA Oxf. 1972. Clin. Asst. (Continuing Care Elderly Servs.) Portsmouth Health Trust. Prev: Trainee GP Wessex VTS.

BARTON, Jeremy Glaxo Wellcome, Greenford Road, Greenford UB6 0HE — MB BS 1981 Lond.; MA Oxf. 1984; FRCR 1989; MRCP (UK) 1984; DMRT Liverp. 1989; EUCOR/ECPM 1995. Sen. Clin. Research Phys. (Oncol. Clin. Research) Glaxo Wellcome Middlx. Prev: Regist. (Radiother.) W.on Pk. Hosp. Sheff.; Regist. (Radiother./Oncol.) Christie Hosp. & Holt Radium Inst. Manch.; Regist. (Gen. Med./Diabetes/Endocrinol.) St. Jas. Univ. Hosp. Leeds; Leeds.

BARTON, Joanne Department of Child & Adolescent Psychiatry, Royal Hospital for Sick Children, Yorkhill, Glasgow G3 8SJ Tel: 0141 201 0228 Fax: 0141 201 9261 Email: jb11x@clinmed.gla.ac.uk; Flat 3/1, 43 Partickhill Road, Glasgow G11 5BY Tel: 0141 339 4540 Fax: 0141 201 9261 — MB ChB 1985 Aberd.; MRCPsych 1990. Sen. Lect. & Hon. Cons. Child & Adolesc. Psychiat. Univ. Glas. Prev: Lect. & Hon. Sen. Regist. (Child & Adolesc. Psychiat.) Univ. Glas.; Regist. (Psychiat.) Lothian HB Edin.; SHO & Ho. Off. (Med.) Grampian HB.

BARTON, John Roger Gastrointestinal Unit, North Tyneside Hospital, Rake Lane, North Shields NE29 8NH Tel: 0191 259 6660 Fax: 0191 293 2585 Email: j.r.barton@ncl.ac.uk — MB BS 1981 Newc.; PhD Ed. 1992; FRCP Ed. 1997; FRCP Lond. 1997; MRCP (UK) 1984; Cert Med Educat 1997. (Univ. Newc. u. Tyne) Reader (Med.) Univ. Newc. u. Tyne & Hon. Cons. N. Tyneside Hosp.; Dir. of Research & Developm. & Head Acad. Dept. N. Tyneside Hosp. Prev: Sen. Regist. (Gen. Med. & Gastroenterol.) Univ. Coll., Middlx. & Whittington Hosp. Lond.; Lect. (Med.) Univ. Edin. W.. Gen. Hosp.; Regist. Profess. Med. Unit Roy. Vict. Infirm. Newc.

BARTON, John Stephen 13 Denmark Road, Exeter EX1 1SL — MB ChB 1983 Bristol; MRCP (UK) 1986. Clin. Res. Fell. Inst. of Child Health Lond. Prev: Regist. (Paediat.) Newc. Teach. Hosps.; SHO (Paediat.) Roy. Hosp. Sick Childr. & S.mead Hosp. Bristol; SHO (Paediat.) Hosp. Sick Childr. Gt. Ormond St. Lond.

BARTON, Joseph William The New City Medical Centre, Tatham St., Sunderland SR1 2QB Tel: 0191 567 5571; Alderman Jack Cohen Health Centre, Springwell Road, Sunderland — MB BS 1961 Durh. (Newc.)

BARTON, Julie Hilda McWhirter, Barton and Silver, The Surgery, Wanbourne Lane, Nettlebed, Henley-on-Thames RG9 5AJ Tel: 01491 641204 Fax: 01491 641162; Glade House, Pishill, Henley-on-Thames RG9 6HJ Tel: 01491 638292 Fax: 01491 638709 Email: barton1000@freeserve.co.uk — MB BS 1988 Lond.; BSc (Hons.) Biol. Lond. 1983; DRCOG 1992. (St. Mary's)

BARTON, Mr Keith Moorfields Eye Hospital, City Road, London EC1V 2PD Tel: 020 7566 2256 Fax: 020 7566 2019 Email: keith.barton@moorfieldsnthants.nhs.uk — MB BCh BAO 1985 Belf.; BSc (Hons.) (Med. Microbiol.) Belf. 1982; MD Belf. 1995; FRCS Eng. 1989; MRCP (UK) 1988; FCOphth 1990; Spec. Accredit. Ophth. RCS Eng. 1995. (Qu. Univ. Belf.) Cons. Ophth. Glaucoma Serv. Moorfields Eye Hosp. Lond. Prev: Fell. (Corneal & Extern. Eye Dis.) Bascom Palmer Eye Inst. Miami, USA; Sen. Regist. & Regist. Moorfields Eye Hosp. Lond.; Clin. Lect. Inst. Ophth. Lond.

BARTON, Linda Mary Glenheath, 22 Church St., Finedon, Wellingborough NN9 5NA — MB ChB 1992 Manch.

BARTON, Margaret Elizabeth (retired) 5 Staunton House, Staunton, Coleford GL16 8NX Tel: 0159 433157 — MB BChir 1951 Camb.; MD Camb. 1964, MA, MB BChir 1951; FRCP Ed. 1971, M 1957. Cons. Paediat. E. Birm. & Solihull Hosps.; Sen. Clin. Tutor in Paediat. Univ. Birm.; Paediat. Adviser Solihull DHA. Prev: Sen. Regist. United Birm. Hosps.

BARTON, Michael (retired) 28 Harwill Avenue, Churwell, Morley, Leeds LS27 7QQ Tel: 0113 253 2693 — MB ChB 1956 Leeds. Prev: SHO (Surg.) Exeter City Hosp.

BARTON, Moyna (retired) 3 Grosvenor Road, London W4 4EJ — MB BCh BAO 1965 Belf.; BSc (Physiol.) Belf. 1962, MB BCh BAO 1965; FFA RCS Eng. 1969. Prev: Cons. Anaesth. St. Chas. Hosp. Lond.

BARTON, Nicola Veronica Yew Tree Farm Cottage, Flookburgh Road, Allithwaite, Grange-over-Sands LA11 7RH — MB ChB 1997 Manch. GP Regist., Furness Gen. Hosp., Barrow-in-Furness, Cumbria.

BARTON, Patricia Christine 134 Gresford Road, Wrexham LL12 0NW — MB ChB 1983 Leic.

BARTON, Paul Graham Warrington Hospital NHS Trust, Lovely Lane, Warrington WA5 1QG; 102 Norbreck Close, Great Sankey, Warrington WA5 2SX — MB ChB 1979 Liverp.; FRCP Lond. 1996; MRCP (UK) 1983. Cons. c/o Elderly Warrington Hosp. NHS Trust.

BARTON, Paul Michael Benson Barton Surgery, Lymington House, Barton Hill Way, Torquay TQ2 8JG Tel: 01803 323761 Fax: 01803 316920; Rowdale, Ridge Road, Maidencombe, Torquay TQ1 4TD Tel: 01803 327504 — MB BS 1985 Lond.; MRCGP 1989; DRCOG 1989.

BARTON, Penelope Ann St Keverne Health Centre, St Keverne, Helston TR12 6PB Tel: 01326 280205 Fax: 01326 280710; Stella Maris, Tregilory Lane, Gillan, Manaccan, Helston TR12 6HG Tel: 01326 231448 — MB ChB 1975 Bristol.

BARTON, Peter David 25A Flat 4, Ivanhoe Road, Aigburth, Liverpool L17 8XF — MB ChB 1996 Liverp.

BARTON, Peter John Marian Cadzow Health Centre, 187 Low Waters Road, Hamilton ML3 7QQ Tel: 01698 327028 Fax: 01698 327344 — MB ChB 1977 Glas.; MRCGP 1988; DCH RCPS Glas. 1979.

BARTON, Mr Rex Penry Edward Southfield, 37 Chapel Lane, Knighton, Leicester LE2 3WF Tel: 0116 270 7376 — MB BS 1967 Lond.; FRCS Eng. 1973. (Univ. Coll. Hosp.) Socs: Christ. Med. Fell.sh.; Leic. Med. Soc. Prev: Cons. Surg. Head & Neck Oncol. & ENT Leicester Roy. Infirm. & LoughBoro. Gen. Hosp.; Ho. Surg. & Ho. Phys. Univ. Coll. Hosp. Lond.; Sen. Regist. (ENT & Plastic Surg.) St. Mary's Hosp. Lond. & Roy. Marsden Hosp. Lond.

BARTON, Robert Curwen 91 Main Street, Ashby de la Launde, Lincoln LN4 3JG — MB BCh BAO 1960 Dub.

BARTON, Robert Oswald Barkwood Surgery, Birkwood, 31-33 Laceby Road, Grimsby DN34 5BH; 5 Cheapside, Waltham, Grimsby DN37 0LN Tel: 01472 318520 — MRCS Eng. LRCP Lond. 1970.

BARTON, Sandra 10 Trenchard Gardens, South Cerney, Cirencester GL7 6JA — MB ChB 1987 Sheff. SHO (Rheum./Gen. Med.) Highfield Hosp. Droitwich & Ronkswood Hosp. Worcester. Prev: Ho. Off. (Gen.Med.) Rotherham Dist. Gen. Hosp.; Ho. Off. (Gen. Surg.) Rotherham Dist. Gen. Hosp.

***BARTON, Sarah Jane,** Surg. Lt. RN Clifton Corner, Village Road, Alverstoke, Gosport PO12 2LD — MB BS 1998 Lond.; MB BS Lond 1998.

BARTON, Simon Everard St Stephens Centre, Chelsea & Westminster Hospital, 369 Fulham Road, London SW10 9TH Tel: 020 8846 6184 Fax: 020 8746 5611 Email: simon.barton@chelwest.nhs.uk — MB BS 1982 Lond.; 1982 MB BS Lond.; 1979 BSc Lond; 1987 MRCOG; 1990 MD; 1999 FRCOG. (Char. Cross) Clin. Dir. & Cons. Phys. Genitourin. Med. Char. Cross & Chelsea & W.m. Hosp. Lond.; Hon. Sen. Lect Imperial Coll. Sch. of Med., Lond. Socs: Fell. Roy. Soc. Med.; Med. Soc. Study VD (Hon. Treas); Eur. Acad. Dermatovenerol. (Bd. Mem.). Prev: Sen. Regist. (Genitourin. Med.) W.m. & St. Stephens Hosp. Lond.; Regist. (AIDS Med.) St. Stephen's Hosp.; Regist. (O & G) Whittington Hosp. Lond.

BARTON, Simon Roy Veor Surgery, South Terrace, Camborne TR14 8SN Tel: 01209 612626 Fax: 01209 886569; 11 Trevu Road, Camborne TR14 7AE — MB BS 1981 Lond.; MRCGP 1987; DCH RCP Lond. 1985; DRCOG 1984. Prev: GP Stanford-le-Hope; Trainee GP Harold Wood VTS.; Trainee GP Exeter VTS.

BARTON, Stephen John Cliff Road Health Centre, 4 Cliff Road, Welton, Lincoln LN2 3JH Tel: 01673 860203 Fax: 01673 862888 — MB ChB 1977 Sheff.; DRCOG 1979.

BARTON, Stuart Brian Cherry Cottage, 32 High St., Woolton, Liverpool L25 7TE — BM BCh 1979 Oxf.; DPhil Oxf. 1977, MA 1977; MRCP (UK) 1987; MRCGP 1983; DRCOG 1982; DCH RCP Lond. 1981.

BARTON, Susan 29 Picardy Court, Rose St., Aberdeen AB10 1UG — MB ChB 1993 Aberd.; BSc (Med. Sci.) Aberd. 1992. Trainee GP/SHO Aberd. Roy. Infirm. VTS.

BARTON, Susan Jane Brook Cottage, Station Road, Chacewater, Truro TR4 8NH Tel: 01872 560979 — MB BS 1980 Lond.; DIMC RCS Ed. 1997. (St. Bartholomews) Staff Grade (A & E) Roy. Cornw. Hosp. Truro.

BARTON, Tara Claire Ashby House, 14 High St., Colerne, Chippenham SN14 8DD — MB BCh 1998 Wales.

BARTON, Tessa Jane Buckfastleigh Medical Centre, 7 Bossell Road, Buckfastleigh TQ11 0DE Tel: 01364 42534 Fax: 01364 644057; Rowdale, Ridge Road, Maidencombe, Torquay TQ1 4TD Tel: 01803 327504 — MB BS 1985 Lond.; MRCGP 1989.

BARTON, William Leftwich, MBE (retired) 7 East Checkstone, 4 Douglas Avenue, Exmouth EX8 2AU — MB ChB 1945 Ed.; FRCP Ed. 1981; FFCM 1972; DPH Ed. 1954; DTM & H Ed. 1950. Prev: Dir. Med. Servs. Zanzibar.

BARTON-HANSON, Nicholas Guy c/o David Matthews & Co., Solicitors, 31/35 Cheapside, Liverpool L2 2DY — MB ChB 1989 Liverp.

BARTRAM, Professor Clive Issell Department of Radiology, 4V, St Mark's Hospital, Northwick Park, Harrow HA1 3UJ Tel: 020 8235 4180 Fax: 020 8235 4001 Email: cbartram@ic.ac.uk; Tel: 01494 766303 Fax: 01494 766303 Email: cibartram@aol.com — MB BS 1966 Lond.; FRCP Lond. 1985, M 1968; FRCR 1972; DMRD Eng. 1970; FRCS 1999. (Westm.) Cons. Radiol. St. Marks Hosp. Lond. Socs: Fell. Roy. Soc. Med.; Fell. Europ. Soc. Gastrointestinal & Abdom. Radiol.; Internat. Soc. Gastrointestinal Radiol. Prev: Cons. Radiol. St. Bart. Hosp. Lond.; Hon. Cons. St. Mary's Hosp. NHS Trust.

BARTRAM, Daniel Harry Elliott and Brixton Cottage, Ashby Parva, Lutterworth LE17 5HS — MB ChB 1997 Leic.

BARTRAM, Graham Frank 26 Clifton Road, Rugby CV21 3QF; Elliott & Brixton Cottage, Ashby Parva, Lutterworth LE17 5HS Tel: 01455 209909 — MB BS 1962 Durh.; DPM Eng. 1968. GP Rugby. Socs: BMA. Prev: Regist. (Neurol.) Hull Roy. Infirm.; Ho. Surg. Birm. Accid. Hosp. & Hosp. of St. Cross, Rugby; Ho. Phys. Bedford Gen. Hosp.

BARTRAM, Janet Wendy Pengover, Florence Rd, Callington PL17 8RB — MB BCh 1997 Wales.

BARTRAM, Sarah Alice 2 Street Houses, Wylam NE41 8BW Tel: 01661 853675 — MB ChB 1989 Leic.; MRCP (UK) 1993. Specialist Regist. (Rheumatol.) Freeman Hosp., Newc.

BARTZOKAS, Christos A (retired) Ty Ucha, Hafod Road, Gwernymynydd, Mold CH7 5JS Tel: 01352 755195 — Ptychio Iatrikes 1972 Athens. Clin. Lect. Univ. Liverp. Prev: Hon. Cons. (Med. Microbiol.) Liverp. AHA (T).

BARUA, Anadi Ranjan Donnington Medical Practice, Wrekin Drive, Donnington, Telford TF2 8EA Tel: 01952 605252 Fax: 01952 677010 — MB BS 1958 Dacca; LMSSA Lond. 1978; DTM & H Liverp. 1967 (Dacca). GP Donnington. Socs: BMA. Prev: Med. Regist. Leighton Hosp. Crewe; SHO (Paediat.) Staffs. Gen. Infirm. Stafford; SHO (O & G) Groundslow Hosp. Stoke-on-Trent.

BARUA, Basab Kumar Lee House Surgery, 84 Osborne Road, Windsor SL4 3EW Tel: 01753 861612 Fax: 01753 833695; 1 Brudenell, St. Leonards Hill, Windsor SL4 4UR Tel: 01753 868499 Fax: 01753 833695 — MB BS 1977 Lond.; MRCP (UK) 1982; MRCGP (Hons.) 1983. (St Mary's Hospital Lond.) Cons. Med. Off. Hisert (UK) Ltd.

BARUA, Ivy 36 Collier Row Lane, Collier Row, Romford RM5 3BJ.

BARUA, Mr Jayanta Malla Dept. of Neurol., Harold Wood Hospital, Gubbins Lane, Romford RM3 0BE Tel: 01708 708286; 2 Sovereign Court, Jesmond Road, Jesmond, Newcastle upon Tyne NE2 1JZ Email: jmbarua@aol.com — MB ChB 1982 Ed.; MD Ed. 1996; FRCS (Urol.) 1996; FRCS Ed. 1988; FEBU 1997. (Univ. Ed. Med. Sch.) Cons. Urol. Harold Wood & OldCh. Hosp. Romford, (Essex.); Director of Research & Developm., Redbridge NHS Trust, Romford, Essex. Socs: BMA; Brit. Assn. Urol. Surgs.; Internat. Incontinence Soc. Prev: Sen. Regist. (Urol.) Roy. Lond. & St. Bart. Hosps.; Regist. (Urol.) Dundee Roy. Infirm.; Research Fell. & Regist. Rotat. (Surg.) Ninewells Hosp. & Med. Sch. Dundee.

BARUAH, Anupom Otley Road Medical Centre, Bradford BD3 0JH Tel: 01274 632723 — MB BS 1969 Gauhati.

BARUAH, Apurba Chandra The Surgery, 73 Upper Wickham Lane, Welling DA16 3AF Tel: 020 8854 1910 Fax: 020 8317 3711 — MB BS 1966 Gauhati.

BARUAH, Mr Ashim Kanta 12 Headland Close, West Kirby, Wirral CH48 3JP Tel: 0151 625 5765 — MB BS 1959 Assam; FRCS Ed. 1968; DLO RCS Eng. 1962.

BARUAH, Probhat Chandra Ash Grove Surgery, Cow Lane, Knottingley WF11 9BZ Tel: 01977 673141 Fax: 01977 677054 — MB BS 1966 Gauhati. (Gauhati) GP Knottingley, W. Yorks.

BARUAH, Ranjit Kumar Clinical Director, Rampton Hospital, Retford DN22 0PD — MB BS 1972 Dibrugarh; MRCPsych 1977; DPM Eng. 1977. (Assam Med. Coll.) Cons. Psychiat. Univ. Hosps.

Nottm. Socs: Roy. Coll. Psychiat. (Hon. Sec. Midl. Div.). Prev: Sen. Regist. (Psychiat.) SE Thames RHA.

BARUCH, Anne Lydia Helen 1 Endsleigh Gardens, Surbiton KT6 5JL Tel: 020 8390 0735; 207 Hook Road, Chessington KT9 1EA Tel: 020 8397 6361 — MB ChB 1976 Manch.; MRCGP 1980; DRCOG 1978; DFFP 1996. (Manch.)

BARUCH, John Daniel Rickman Tindal Centre, Bierton Road, Aylesbury HP20 1HU Tel: 01296 393363 Fax: 01296 399332 — MB BS 1983 Lond.; BSc Lond. 1980; MRCPsych 1987. Cons. Psychiat. Aylesbury Vale Community Healthcare NHS Trust. Prev: Sen. Regist. (Psychiat.) E. Anglian RHA; Lect. & Hon. Sen. Regist. (Psychol. Med.) Roy. Marsden Hosp. Sutton; Train. Scheme Rotat. (Psych.) Soton.

BARUCH, Miriam Rosa 87 Pasture Lane, Clayton, Bradford BD14 6LR Tel: 01274 880333; 171 Pleasance, Edinburgh EH8 9RU Tel: 0131 667 8786 — MB ChB 1994 Ed. SHO (Cardiac Surg.) Roy. Infirm. Edin. Prev: Ho. Off. (Med. & Surg.) Borders Gen. Hosp.

BARUCH, Ury Bernard H 2 Queen's Walk, Ealing, London W5 1TP Tel: 020 8997 2900 Fax: 020 8810 9906 Email: baruchcl@tesconet; 2 Queen's Walk, Ealing, London W5 1TP Tel: 020 8997 2900 Fax: 020 8810 9906 — MD CM 1945 Ontario; 1946 LMS Nova Scotia; 1945 LMCC; 1995 FRCPsych, M 1971; 1954 DPM Roy. Med.-Psych. Assn.; 1998 M.Univ.(Honoris Causal) Brunel Univ. (Qu. Univ. Ont.) Socs: Assoc. Mem. Brit. Psychoanal. Soc.; Fell. Roy. Soc. Med.; Brit. Confederat. Psychother. Prev: Cons. Psychiat. & Psychother. Brunel Univ. Uxbridge; Cons. Psychiat. St. Bernard's Hosp. S.all & Ashford Hosp. Middlx.; Regist. W. Pk. Hosp., Espom, Surrey.

BARUYA, Munna Anaesthetic Dept., Mayday Hospital, London Rd, Croydon CR& 7YE Tel: 020 8401 3000 — MB BS 1988 Lond. Cons. (Anaesth.)Mayday Univ. Hosp. Lond. Socs: Train. Mem. Assn. Anaesth.; Assn. Of Anaesth.s; Roy. Coll. Of Anaesth. Prev: Specialist Regist. (Anaesth.) Kings Coll. Hosp. Lond.; Specialist Regist. (Anaesth.) Lewisham. Hosp. Lond.; Specialist Regist. (Anaesth.) St. Thomas. Hosp. Lond.

BARWELL, Mr James Robert 18 Belle Vue, Bristol BS8 1DB Tel: 0117 974 4792 Fax: 01179744857 Email: jamie.barwell@hotmail.com — MRCS Eng. LRCP Lond. 1991; MB BS Lond. 1991; FRCS Eng. 1996. (Guy's Hosp.) Specialist Regist. (Gen. Surg.) S. W.. Deanery.

BARWELL, Julian Grosvenor 3 Brackley, Weybridge KT13 0BJ — MB BS 1997 Lond.

BARWELL, Mr Nicholas John Royal Cornwall Hospital (Treliske), Truro TR1 6LJ Tel: 01872 274242; Loe Vean, Feock, Truro TR3 6SH Tel: 01872 862514 Fax: 01872 862514 Email: nickbarwell@msn.com — MB BChir 1962 Camb.; MA Camb. 1962; FRCS Eng. 1967. (Guy's) Cons. Gen. Surg. Roy. Cornw. Hosp. (Treliske) Truro. Socs: Fell. Roy. Soc. Med.; Surg. Club of S.W.; Assn. of Surgs. Prev: Sen. Surg. Regist. Guy's Gp. Hosps.

BARWELL, Peter James 51 Woodstock Road, Redland, Bristol BS6 7EW Tel: 0117 924 7580 Email: peterbarwell@netscapeonline.co.uk — MB BS 1972 Lond. Psychother. Bristol. Socs: Guild Psychother. Prev: Clin. Asst. (Psychiat.) S.mead HA; GP Dorchester.

BARWELL, Terence Edgar (retired) Penarrow, Six Turnings, Mylor Bridge, Falmouth TR11 5NL Tel: 01326 374041 — MB BS 1943 Lond.; MRCS Eng. LRCP Lond. 1939.

BARWELL, William Brian Andrew St Martins Surgery, 378 Wells Road, Knowle, Bristol BS4 2QR Tel: 0117 977 5641 Fax: 0117 977 5490 — MB BS 1983 Lond.; BA Camb. 1980; MRCGP 1987; DCH RCP Lond. 1985.

BARWICK, Angela Christine 22 Meadowbank, Hitchin SG4 0HX; 39 Castle Street, Luton LU1 3AG Tel: 01582 29242 Fax: 01582 25192 — MB BS 1981 Lond.; BSc Lond. 1978; DCH RCP Lond. 1984.

BARWISE, Karen Orchard End, Stoneyland, Newton Tracey, Barnstaple EX31 3PE Tel: 01271 858414 Fax: 01271 858414 — BM 1993 Soton.; BSc Lond. 1988; DCH 1996; MRCP Lond. 1998. (Southampton) Socs: MRCPH; MRCP; BMA. Prev: Specialist Regist. (Paeds), N. Hants. Co. Hosp., Basingstoke; SHO (Paediat.) Kingsmill Centre Health Care Servs. Mansfield; SHO (Paeds) Qu.s Med. Centre, Nottm.

BARWOOD, Ambrose Timothy (retired) 5 Allanhall Way, Kirk Ella, Hull HU10 7QU Tel: 01482 650548 Email: brobari@aol.com — MRCS Eng. LRCP Lond. 1949; DPH Lond. 1960. Prev: GP Cottingham.

BARWOOD, Antony John, OBE, Group Capt. RAF Med. Br. Retd. (retired) Bolton House, Burnham Market, King's Lynn PE31 8HA Tel: 01328 738256 — MRCS Eng. LRCP Lond. 1940; DPH Lond. 1958; DIH Eng. 1959. Hon. Civil Cons. to the Roy. Air Force (Accid. Investig.). Prev: Hon. Civil Cons. (Accid. Investig.) RAF Inst. Aviat. Med.

BARWOOD, Philip Fairbrother (retired) 10 School Lane, Milton, Abingdon OX14 4EH Tel: 01235 832008 — MB BChir 1937 Camb.; MD Camb. 1948; MRCS Eng. LRCP Lond. 1937. Prev: Ho. Phys. St. Bart. Hosp. & Lond. Chest Hosp.

BARZANJI, Abdul Jalil 33 Chisholm Road, Croydon CR0 6UQ — Tip Doktoru 1960 Istanbul.

BASAK, Syamali Flat 5, 75 Ravenhurst Road, Birmingham B17 9SR — MB BS 1971 Calcutta; MRCOG 1987.

BASARAB, Adriana Department of Medical Microbiology, Southampton General Hospital, Southampton SO16 6YD — MB ChB 1988 Birm.; MSc in Clin. Microbiol. Lond. 1996; MRCP 1992; DTM & H RCP Lond. 1993; MRCPath 1998. (Birm.) Regist. (Med. Microbiol.) Soton. Gen. Hosp. Socs: Assoc. of Med. microbiologists; RCP; Roy. Coll. Pathol. Prev: SHO (Infec. Dis. & Trop. Med.) Coppetts Wood Hosp. Lond.; SHO (Gen. Med.) Sandwell Dist. Gen. Hosp.

BASARAB, Anthony Omar 42 The Greenwood, Guildford GU1 2NE — LMS 1994 Basque Provinces; PhD Birm. 1966, MSc 1964.

BASARAB, Marina Hammersmith Hospital, Ducane Road, London W12 0HS; 59 Clyde Road, Alexandra Pard, London N22 7AD — MB ChB 1991 Liverp.; MRCP; DTM & H. Specialist Regist. MicroBiol./Infec. Dis.s. Prev: SHO ITU Heartlands Hosp.; SHO (Genitourin. Med.) Gen. Hosp. Birm.

BASARAB, Tamara Queen Mary's University, Hospital, Roehampton Lane, London SW15 — MB BS 1990 Lond.; MRCP (UK) 1993. (UMDS) Cons. Dermatol. Qu. Mary's Univ. Hosp. Roehampton, Chelsea & W.minister Hosp. Lond. Socs: Ord. Mem. Brit. Assn. Dermatol.; Brit. Medicla Assn.; Roy. Soc. Med. Prev: Specialist Regist. (Dermat.) Ealing Hosp., the Hammersmith Hosp. ans St. John's Inst. of Dermat., St. Thomas Hosp, Lond.; Specialist Regist. (Dermat.) St. John's Inst. of Dermat. St. Thomas's Hosp. Lond.; SHO (Oncol. & Radiotherap.) Roy. Free Hosp. Lond.

BASAVA KUMAR, Devsur Goneppa Department of Neurosurgery, Frenchay Hospital, Frenchay Park Road, Bristol BS16 1LE — MB BS 1984 Bangalore.

BASCOMBE, Michael John (retired) Abbotswell, Lyme Road, Uplyme, Lyme Regis DT7 3TJ Tel: 01297 442553 Fax: 01297 442553 Email: mjbascombe@btinternet.com — MB BS 1962 Lond.; FFA RCS Eng. 1965.

BASDEN, Ralph Duncan Edward 1 Murray Road, Northwood HA6 2Y Tel: 01923 24588 — MB BS 1956 Lond. (Middlx.) Socs: Fell. Med. Soc. Lond. Prev: Ho. Surg. Qu. Mary's Hosp. Stratford; Ho. Phys. Canad. Red Cross Memor. Hosp. Taplow; Obst. Ho. Surg. Soton. Gen. Hosp.

BASELEY, Justin Adam 14 Harcourt Road, Uckfield TN22 5DU — MB BS 1996 Lond. (St. George's)

BASHA, Mohamed Ameen 62 Woodcrest Walk, Reigate RH2 0JL Tel: 01737 69823 — MB BS 1967 Osmania; BA Madras 1959; DPM Eng. 1977.

BASHAM, Sarah Caroline Flat E, 484-488 Harrow Road, London W9 2QA — MB BS 1988 Lond.

BASHAR, Nazma Ara St Cenydd Road Surgery, 106 St. Cenydd Road, Trecenydd, Caerphilly CF83 2TE Tel: 029 2088 8118 Fax: 029 2088 8604 — MB BS 1968 Dacca.

BASHEER, Azam 8 Canada Road, Cathays, Cardiff CF14 3BW — MB ChB 1971 Baghdad.

BASHEER, Mohamed 9-Madeley Road, Kingswinford DY6 8PF Tel: 01384 273818 — MB BS 1966 Kerala; Dip. Ven. Soc. Apoth Lond. 1979. (Glaney Med. Coll., Gurunanak, Univ. Punjab, India)

BASHEER, Tarsha Soraya 30 Ivy Lane, Osler Road, Headington, Oxford OX3 9DT Tel: 01865 741166 — MB BS 1990 Adelaide.

BASHER, Michael John Samuel Birchdale, Atbara Road, Church Crookham, Fleet GU52 8JZ; Bethlem and Maudsley Hospitals, Denmark Hill, London SE5 — MB ChB 1994 Glas.; BA Oxf. 1990.

BASHEY, Asad 25C Dartmouth Road, London NW2 4ET — MB ChB 1984 Dundee; BMSc (Hons.) Dune 1981, MB ChB (Commend.) 1984; MRCP (UK) 1987. Regist. (Haemat. Med.) Hammersmith Hosp. Lond.; Clin. Scientist Inst. Cancer Research Lond. Prev: SHO (Med.) Roy. Infirm. Edin.; Ho. Off. (Med.) Profess. Unit Ninewells Hosp. Dundee.

BASHFORD, Anna Jacqueline 232 Westbourne Park Road, London W11 1EP — MB ChB 1994 Otago.

BASHFORD, James Nigel Rosslyn Trent Vale Medical Practice, 876 London Road, Trent Vale, Stoke-on-Trent ST4 5NX Tel: 01782 746898; 40 Dartmouth Avenue, Westlands, Newcastle ST5 3NY Tel: 01782 630337 — MB ChB 1979 Birm.; MRCGP 1983; DRCOG 1982. (Birm.) Lect. (Primary Care Research) Dept. Med. & Managem. Keele Univ. Staffs.

BASHFORD, Sally Elizabeth 28 Torr Rise, Tarporley CW6 0UE Tel: 01829 732170 — BM BS 1993 Nottm.; BMedSci Nottm. 1991; MRCP (UK) 1998. Specialist Regist. (Geriats. & Gen. Med.), St Mary's Lond. Socs: Brit. Geriat.s Soc. Prev: Specialist Regist. (Geriat.s & Gen Med.) Hemel Hempstead; Specialist Regist. (Geriat.s & Gen. Med.) Stevenage; SHO (Gen. Med.) Qu. Eliz. II Hosp. Welwyn Garden City.

BASHIR, Anilla Aisha 15 Wadebridge Drive, Ainsworth Chase, Bury BL8 2NN — MB BS 1994 Lond. Ho. Phys. Harold Wood Hosp. Romford. Prev: Ho. Surg. Ashford Hosp. Middlx.

BASHIR, Anjum 6 The Dingle, Ballast Quay Road, Fingringhoe, Colchester CO5 7DB — MB BS 1982 Punjab; MB BS Punjab, Pakistan 1982; MRCPsych 1988.

BASHIR, Asaf Ayub 27 Dumbreck Road, Dumbreck, Glasgow G41 5LJ Tel: 0141 427 6214 — MB ChB 1990 Glas.; MRCGP 1994; DRCOG 1993; DObst 1993. Prev: GP Glas.

BASHIR, Bashir Abdel Raheem Flat 5, Westwood Hospital, Beverley HU17 8BU — MB BS 1979 Khartoum; MB BS Khartoum Sudan 1979; MRCGO 1994.

BASHIR, Faheem Amir 10 Stenhouse Mill Crescent, Edinburgh EH11 3LP — MB ChB 1997 Manch.; BSc St. And 1994.

BASHIR, Fareed Ahmad 150 Station Road, London NW4 3SP — MB ChB 1994 Manch.

BASHIR, Khaver 75 South Lodge Drive, London N14 4XG — MB BS 1981 Lond.; MRCGP 1988; DCH RCP Lond. 1987; DRCOG 1984; MRCPsych 1998.

BASHIR, Muntazar 58 Currie Court, Block D11, Queens Medical Centre, Nottingham NG7 2UH — MB ChB 1990 Aberd.

BASHIR, Pookunju Mohamed (retired) Kumra Lodge, Ongar Road, Kelvedon Hatch, Brentwood CM15 0JX Tel: 01277 374314 Fax: 01277 374983 — MB BS 1962 Punjab; MB BS Punjab Pakistan 1962; FFA RCS Eng. 1973; DA Eng. 1970. Prev: Regist. (Anaesth.) Birm. Accid. Hosp.

BASHIR, Rihan 13 Williton Road, Luton LU2 9EH — MB ChB 1995 Aberd.

BASHIR, Saeedia 64 Tanfield Road, Birkby, Huddersfield HD1 5HD — MB ChB 1996 Manch.

BASHIR, Saqib Jawaid Department of Dermatology, University of California School of Medicine, Box 0989, Surge 110, San Francisco 94143-0989 CA, USA; 27 Dumbreck Road, Dumbreck, Glasgow G41 5LJ — MB ChB 1997 Glas.; BSc (1st cl Hons.) Biomed. Sci. Lond. 1994. (University of Glasgow) Vis. Research Fell. Univ. of Calif. Sch. of Med. San Francisco, USA. Socs: BMA. Prev: Pre-regist. Ho. Off. Dept. Orthopaedic Surg. W.ern Glas. Hosp.s; Pre-regist. Ho. Off. Dept. of Med. Roy. Infirm. Glas.

BASHIR, Waseem Amir 10 Stenhouse Mill Crescent, Edinburgh EH11 3LP — MB ChB 1995 Dundee.

BASHIR, Yaver Cardiac Department, John Radcliffe Hospital, Oxford OX3; 88 Staunton Road, Headington, Oxford OX3 7TR — BM BCh 1984 Oxf.; MRCP (UK) 1987.

BASI, Rupinder Singh Ailsworth Surgery, 32 Main Street, Ailsworth, Peterborough PE5 7AF Tel: 01733 380686 Fax: 01733 380400; 46 Merestone Road, Corby NN18 8DH — MB BS 1985 Lond. GP Princip. Peterboro. Prev: SHO (Anaesth.) Nottm. Hosp.; Trainee GP/SHO Burton-on-Trent VTS.

BASI, Susan Kamal Kaur 2 Valley Road, Littleover, Derby DE23 6HQ — MB BS 1994 Lond.

BASIL, Avo Vaughan, Lt.-Col. RAMC (retired) Beaumont House, Ty Mawr Road, Deganwy, Conwy LL31 9UD Tel: 01492 572786 Fax: 01492 572786 Email: velova@doctors.org.uk — MB ChB Liverp. 1955; MRCGP 1966; DTM & H Eng. 1963; Cert Contracep. & Family Plann. RCOG, RCGP &; Cert FPA 1975. Lect. & Examr. St. John Ambul. Brig. Prev: Ho. Phys. Roy. Liverp. Childr. Hosp.

BASIL, Edwig Alfred 28 Ford End, Woodford Green IG8 0EG Tel: 020 8505 6995 — MB ChB 1970 Baghdad; FFA RCSI 1981; DA Eng. 1973. (Univ. Baghdad)

BASIL, Kochu-Teresa Dr Law and Partners, 1 Vicarage Road, Kings Heath, Birmingham B14 7QA Tel: 0121 444 2005 Fax: 0121 441 4331 — MB BCh BAO 1978 NUI; LRCPI & LM, LRCSI & LM 1978.

BASIR, Nageeb 12 Cecil Court, 2 Acol Road, West Hampstead, London NW6 3AP — MB BS 1977 Peshawar; MRCPI 1985; Dip. Thoracic Med. Lond 1982; Dip. Cardiol. Lond 1982.

BASIT, Abdul 6 Studley Road, Forest Gate, London E7 9LX — MB BS 1988 Karachi; MRCP (UK) 1993.

BASK, Nazih Tanious 78 Old Road, Neath SA11 2BU Tel: 01639 50597 — MB BCh 1971 Ain Shams. Med. Off. Home Off. Prison Serv.; GP in TA. Prev: Trainee GP & Regist. (Psychiat.) Port Talbot Health Centre.

BASKAR, Mr Balapathiran 35 Arklow Road, Intake, Doncaster DN2 5LB — MB BS 1986 Madras; FRCS Ed. 1993.

BASKAR, Natarajan Department of Anaesthesia, Southlands Hospital, Upper Shoreham Road, Shoreham-by-Sea BN43 6TQ — MB BS 1984 Madras.

BASKARAN, Balasubramaniam Parkway Health Centre, New Addington, Croydon CR0 5JQ Tel: 01689 842554; Crossway Surgery, Crossways, Addington, Croydon Tel: 020 8657 4333 — MB BS 1978 Ceylon; LMSSA Lond. 1984; MRCGP 1989; DGM RCP Lond. 1986. Socs: BMA & Med. Protec. Soc.

BASKER, Emma Louise Little France Corner, Chalford Hill, Stroud GL6 8EL — MB BS 1990 Lond.; MRCGP 1996; DCH RCP Lond. 1993. (St. Bart.)

BASKERVILLE, Mr Paul Anthony 21 Devonshire Place, London W1G 6HZ Tel: 020 7935 5843 Fax: 020 7224 0080; Pear Tree Cottage, 87-89 Coombe Lane W., Kingston upon Thames KT2 7HB Tel: 020 8942 8074 — BM BCh 1974 Oxf.; DM Oxf. 1987, MA 1975, BA 1971; FRCS Eng. 1980. (St. Thos.) Cons. Vasc. Surg. King's Coll. Hosp. Lond.; Clin. Dir. Surg. Kings Coll. Hosp. Lond. Socs: Fell. Roy. Soc. Med.; Vasc. Surg. Soc. GB & Irel. Prev: Sen. Regist. (Surg.) St. Bart. Hosp. Lond.; Lect. (Surg.) St. Thos. Hosp. Lond.; Regist. (Surg.) Kingston Hosp. Surrey.

BASKERVILLE, Mr Richard Owls Castle, Winterslow, Salisbury SP5 1QD — MB BS 1990 Lond.; FRCS Eng. 1994.

BASKETT, David Walter Whiston Health Centre, Whiston, Prescot L35 3SX; 6 Aspinall Street, Prescot L34 5 Tel: 5253 — MB ChB 1963 Liverp.; MRCS Eng. LRCP Lond. 1963. (Liverp.) Med. Off. Brit. Pregn. Advis. Serv. & DHSS; Family Plann. Med. Off. St. Helens & Knowsley AHA (Tower Hill). Socs: BMA. Prev: Med. Off. Shell Co. of Qatar; Corkhill Research Fell. (Virol. Bact.) Univ. Liverp.; Ho. Phys. & Ho. Surg. Walton Hosp. Liverp.

BASKETT, Peter John Firth Department Anaesthesia, Frenchay Hospital, Bristol BS16 1LE Tel: 0117 970 2020 Fax: 0117 957 4414; Stanton Court, Stanton St. Quintin, Chippenham SN14 6DQ Tel: 01666 837210 Email: peterbaskett@ukgateway.net — MB BCh BAO 1958 Belf.; BA (Hons.) Camb. 1955; MB BChir Camb. 1960; FRCP 1994; FRCA 1963; Dip. IMC RCS Ed. 1996; FFAEM (Hon) 1999. (Camb. & Qu. Univ. Belf.) Emerit. Cons. Anaesth. Frenchay Hosp. Bristol Roy. Infirm.; HCons. Emerit. to the Army; Edr. in Chief Resusc. Jl. Europ. Resusc. Counc. Socs: Past (Pres.) Internat. Trauma Anaesth. & Critical Care Soc.; Roy. Soc. Med. Past Pres. United Serv.s Sect.; Past (Pres.) Soc. Anaesth. SW Region. Prev: Pres. Assn. Anaesth. GB & Irel. & World Assn. for Emerg. & Disaster Med. Europ. Resusc. Counc.; Regist. (Anaesth.) Roy. Vict. Hosp. Belf.; Sen. Regist. (Anaesth.) United Bristol Hosps. & Frenchay Hosp. Bristol.

BASKETTS, Anne Elizabeth Louie Lakenham Surgery, 24 Ninham Street, Norwich NR1 3JJ Tel: 01603 765559 Fax: 01603 766790 — MB ChB 1966 Birm.

BASKEYFIELD, Hillary Margaret Parkgreen House, Macclesfield SK11 6HW; Stonyfold Cottage, Stoneyfold Lane, Bosley, Macclesfield SK11 0PR — MB ChB 1976 Manch.; MRCGP 1982; MFHom 1987.

BASLER, Michael Howard Flat 4, 20 Oakshaw St. E., Paisley PA1 2DD — MB ChB 1989 Glas.

BASMA, Lena Culcheth Surgery, Thompson Avenue, Culcheth, Warrington WA3 4EB Tel: 01925 765101 Fax: 01925 765102; 32 Hurst Mill Lane, Glazebury, Warrington WA3 5NR — MB ChB 1985 Leic.

BASMA, Mr Nabeel 11 Beverley Road, Barming, Maidstone ME16 9DL — MB BCh 1981 Wales; FRCS Ed. 1986; DLO RCS Eng. 1985. Regist. (ENT) Kent Co. Ophth. & Aural Hosp. Maidstone.

BASNAYAKE, Prema Department of Anaesthetics, Tameside General Hospital, Ashton-under-Lyne OL6 9RW Tel: 0161 331 6357; 6 Haldane Close, Brierley, Barnsley S72 9LL Tel: 01226 715777 — MB BS 1964 Ceylon; DA Eng. 1984; DMRT Eng. 1972. (Fac. Med. Univ. Ceylon, Colombo)

BASNETT, Ian Nicholas Department of Public Health Medicine, Camden & Islington HA, 110 Hampstead Road, London NW1 2LJ Tel: 020 7380 9505; 7 Breezer Court, 20 The Highway, Wapping, London E1W 2BE Tel: 020 7480 6520 — MB BS 1982 Lond.; MSc Pub. Health Lond. 1988; MFPHM RCP (UK) 1990. (Lond. Hosp.) Cons. Pub. Health Med. Camden & Islington HA.

BASNYET, Dhurba Bahadur Brock House, Lower Lane, Longridge, Preston PR3 3SL — Lekarz 1969 Warsaw.

BASQUILL, Justin Gerard c/o Chelsea & Westminster Hospital, 369 Fulham Road, London SW10 9NH Tel: 020 8746 8330 Fax: 020 8746 8331; 23 Alexandra Mansions, 333 Kings Road, Chelsea, London SW3 5ET Tel: 020 7349 0563 — MB BCh BAO 1986 NUI; MRCPsych 1992. Sen. Regist. Gordon Hosp. Lond.; Occupat. Health Psychiat. Chelsea & W.m. Hosp. Lond. Prev: Research Regist. Chelsea & W.m. Hosp. Lond.

BASQUILL, Michael Patrick Tillicoultry Health Centre, Park Street, Tillicoultry FK13 6AG Tel: 01259 750531 Fax: 01259 752818 — MB ChB 1983 Dundee; BSc Dund 1979; MRCGP 1988.

BASRA, Mr Devinder Singh 111 Harley Street, London W1N 1DG Tel: 020 7486 8055 Fax: 020 7486 2417 — MB BS 1966 Punjab (India); FRCS Ed. 1976. Socs: Fell. Internat. Acad. Cosmetic Surg. Geneva; Japanese Assn. of Aesthetic Surg. & Internat. Soc. Aesthetic; Indian Assn. Cosmetic Surgs. Prev: SHO (Plastic Surg.) Liverp. Plastic Unit Whiston Hosp. Prescot; Regist. (Plastic Surg.) Bridge of Earn Hosp.

BASRA, Sanjiv 45 Park Road, Dundee DD3 8LB — MB ChB 1992 Ed.

BASRA, Sudesh Kumari Kismet, 12 Willowbrook Road, Stanwell, Staines TW19 7AB Tel: 01784 248936 — MB ChB 1990 Leic.

BASRA, Sukhbinder Singh 50 Aberdour Road, Goodmayes, Ilford IG3 9PG — MB BS 1996 Lond.

BASRAN, Gurnam Singh Respiratory Unit, Rotherham General Hospital, Moorgate Road, Rotherham S60 2UD Tel: 01709 304189 Fax: 01709 304189 Email: basran.gs@rgh-tr.trent.nhs.uk — MB BS 1975 Lond.; BSc (Hons.) Lond. 1972; DM Notts. 1986; FRCP Lond. 1993; MRCP (UK) 1978; MRCS Eng. LRCP Lond. 1975. (St. Mary's Hosp. Med. School) Cons. Phys. Gen. & Respirat. Med. Rotherham Gen. Hosp.; Hon. Lect. Univ. Sheff. Socs: BTS & ATS; Eur. Respirat. Soc. Prev: Sen. Regist. Rotat. Nottm. Hosp.; Clin. Lect. Bromton Hosp. & Cardiothoracic Inst.; Regist. Rotat. Centr. Middlx. Hosp.

BASS, Mr Aneil 42 Glebe Avenue, Grappenhall, Warrington WA4 2SQ — MB ChB 1988 Dundee; FRCS Glas. 1992.

BASS, Barnett Hilary (retired) 6 Riverside Mews, Bridge St., Wickham, Fareham PO17 5LL Tel: 01309 834862 — MRCS Eng. LRCP Lond. 1950; MD Lond. 1952, MB BS 1950; FRCP Lond. 1971, M 1953. Prof. Med. Amer. Univ. Caribbean. Prev: Sen. Clin. Lect. & Tutor Univ. Birm.

BASS, Catherine Sheila 41 Dryburgh Road, London SW15 1BN — MB ChB 1986 Bristol. SHO (O & G) St. Peters Hosp. Chertsey. Prev: SHO (O & G) Qu. Mary's Hosp. Roehampton & Epsom; SHO (Anaesth.) Kingston Dist. Gen. Hosp.

BASS, Christopher Maurice Department of Psychological Medicine, John Radcliffe Hospital, Oxford OX3 9DU Tel: 01865 220379 Fax: 01865 220373; 102 Cumnor Hill, Oxford OX2 9HY Tel: 01865 862004 — MB BChir 1971 Camb.; MA Camb. 1984; MD Lond. 1984; FRCPsych 1994, M 1976. (St. Thomas) Cons. Liaison Psychiat. John Radcliffe Hosp. Oxf.; Asst. Edr. Jl. Psychosomatic Research. Socs: Pres. Soc. Psychosomatic Research. Prev: Lect. & Sen. Lect. (Psychol.) Med. King's Coll. Hosp. Lond.

BASS, David James Western Road Medical Centre, 99 Western Road, Romford RM1 3LS Tel: 01708 746495 Fax: 01708 737936; 48 Heath Drive, Gidea Park, Romford RM2 5QL — MB BS 1984 Lond.; BSc 1978 Lond.

BASS, John Christopher The Ayrshire Hospice, 35 Racecourse Road, Ayr KA7 2TG Tel: 01292 269200; 79 Glenalla Crescent, Alloway, Ayr KA7 4DA — MB ChB 1980 Bristol; MRCPsych 1985; BTech. Brunel 1972. Cons. Palliat. Med. Ayr.; Med. Dir. Ayrsh. Hospice Ayr. Prev: Asst. Med. Dir. Compton Hall Hospice Wolverhampton.

BASS, Kenneth 6 Old Hall Road, Whitefield, Manchester M45 7QW Tel: 0161 766 5251 — MB ChB 1956 Manch.; DCH Eng. 1961. Prev: Ho. Phys. Booth Hall Childr. Hosp. Manch.; Sen. Ho. Off. (Paediat.) Vict. Hosp. Blackpool; Regist. Childr. Hosp. Stockton-on-Tees.

BASS, Nicholas John Royal London Hospital (St Clement's), 2A Bow Road, London E3 4LL Tel: 020 7377 7903 Fax: 020 7377 7967 Email: nick.bass@thht.org — MB BS 1987 Lond.; MRCPsych 1991. (Westminster medical School) Cons. Psychiat.; MRCPsych Course Organiser (Barts and Roy. Lond. Course). Prev: Sen. Regist. (Psychiat.) Roy. Lond. Hosp.; MRC Clin. Scientist Clin. Research Centre N.wick Pk. Harrow; Regist. Rotat. (Psychiat.) N.wick Pk. Hosp. Harrow.

BASS, Paul Steven Department of Pathology, Southampton General Hospital, Tremona Road, Southampton SO16 6YD Tel: 02380 794629 Fax: 02830 796869 — MB BS 1983 Lond.; BSc Lond. 1980, MD 1991; MRCPath 1991; 2000 FRCPath. Cons. Histopath. (Paediat. Path.) Soton. Gen. Hosp.; Ho. CLin. Sen. Lect. In Path., Univ. of S.ampton. Prev: Lect. (Path.) Soton. Gen. Hosp.; Research Regist. (Histopath.) UMDS St. Thos. Lond.

BASS, Peter George Burroughs Tylers Mead, Dereham Road, Reepham, Norwich NR10 4LA Tel: 01603 870252 — MB BS 1972 Lond.

BASS, Ranvier Singh The Climax, Langdon Hill, Basildon SS16 6HU Tel: 01268 46381 — MB BS 1957 Nagpur; DObst RCOG 1964. (Nagpur Med. Coll. India) Prev: Regist. (O & G) King's Mill Hosp. Sutton-in-Ashfield; Ho. Surg. (O & G) Centr. Middlx. Hosp. Lond.; SHO (Gen. Surg.) Acton Hosp. Lond.

BASS, Samuel Peter Department of Anaesthetics, Box 93, Addensbrooke Hospital, Cambridge CB1 6DX Tel: 01223 245151; 2 West Wratting Road, Balsham, Cambridge CB1 6DX Email: sbass@lineone.net — MB BS 1988 Lond.; BSc Lond. 1985; FRCA 1993. (St George's Hosp. London) Cons. (Anaesth.) Addenbrookes Hosp. Camb. Socs: Assn. Paedaiatic Anaesth.; Medico-Legal Soc.

BASS, Stanley Martin (retired) — MB BS 1961 Lond.; DObst RCOG 1970. Clin. Asst., Dermat. Dept. James Cook Univ. Hosp., Middlesbrough.

BASSAM, Brigid Jane Kima Mission Hospital, PO Box 416, Kisam, Kenya; c/o 93 Cranbourne Avenue, London E11 2BJ Tel: 020 8 9897408 — BM 1994 Soton.; MRCP (UK) 1998. Kima Mission Hosp. Doctor. Prev: SHO (Gen. Med.) Qu. Eliz. Hosp. King's Lynn; SHO (Med. c/o Elderly) Qu. Eliz. Hosp. King's Lynn; SHO (Accid. & Emerg.) Ipswich Hosp.

BASSAN, Lall Singh The Surgery, 19 Long Lane, Halesowen B62 9LL; 60 Moat Road, Oldbury, Oldbury B68 8ED Tel: 0121 544 5447 — MB BS 1960 Bombay. GP Dudley.

BASSAN, Tarlochan Singh Bassan, Cronehills Health Centre, Cronehills Linkway, West Bromwich B70 8TJ Tel: 0121 553 0277 Fax: 0121 580 1874 — MB BS 1968 Jiwaji; MRCOG 1976; Dip. Obst. Makerere Univ. 1972. (G.R. Med. Coll. Gwalior, India) Cons. Gyn. Brit. Pregn. Advis. Serv. Socs: BMA; Overseas Doctors Assn. Prev: Regist. (O & G) S.mead Hosp. Bristol; Clin. Fell.sh. (Infertil. & Gyn. Endocrinol.) McGill Univ., Montreal, Canada.

BASSENDINE, Professor Margaret Fiona Liver Unit, Freeman Hospital, High Heaton, Newcastle upon Tyne NE7 7DN Tel: 0191 284 3111 Fax: 0191 213 1968; Liver research, The Medical School, Framlington Place, Newcastle upon Tyne NE2 4HH Tel: 0191 222 6000 Fax: 0191 222 0723 Email: m.bassendine@ncl.ac.uk — MB BS 1971 Lond.; BSc Lond. 1968; FRCP Ed. 1989; FRCP 1989. (Roy. Free) Prof. Hepatol. Univ. Newc.; Cons. Phys. Freeman Hosp. Socs: Brit. Soc. Gastroenterol.; Assn. Phys.; Eur. Assn. Study Liver. Prev: Reader (Hepatol.) Univ. Newc.; Sen. Lect. (Molecular Med.) Univ. Newc.; 1st Asst. Med. Univ. Newc.

BASSETT, David Charles Jeremy (retired) Tygwyn Bach, Gwynfe Road, Ffairfach, Llandeilo SA19 6UY Tel: 01558 823546 — 1962 Dip. Bact. Lond; 1958 MB BS Lond.; 1971 MRCPath; 1983

FRCPath. Prev: Vis. Sen. Lect. (Dept. Microbiol.) Chinese Univ. Hong Kong.

BASSETT, Dorothy Isabella Morlich, Kirknewton EH27 8DG Tel: 01506 882034 — MB ChB 1964 Ed.; Cert. Family Plann. JCC 1987. (Ed.) Med. Off. Edin. Acad. Well Wom. Screen. Serv. Prev: Asst. MOH W. Lothian CC; Asst. MOH Stirling CC.

BASSETT, Dorothy Joyce 10 Cornford Close, Hayesford Park, Bromley BR2 9BJ Tel: 020 8464 2972 — LRCPI & LM, LRSCI & LM 1950; LRCPI & LM, LRCSI & LM 1950. Community Med. Off. Lewisham & N. S.wark HA. Prev: Med. Off. Tan Tock Seng. Hosp. Singapore.

BASSETT, Janet Isabel (retired) 8 Albany Court, Beach Road, Penarth CF64 1JU — MB ChB 1941 Glas. Prev: Med. Off. Derby City Hosp.

BASSETT, John Howard Lee on Solent Health Centre, Manor Way, Lee-on-the-Solent PO13 9JG Tel: 023 9255 0220 — MB ChB 1980 Birm.; MRCGP 1985; DCH RCP Lond. 1984; DRCOG 1983. (Birmingham University) Prev: SHO (Paediat.) Birm. Childr. Hosp.; Ho. Surg. N. Staffs. Hosp. Centre Stoke-on-Trent; Ho. Phys. Gen. Hosp. Birm.

BASSETT, John Howard Duncan Thatch Cottage, Hill Road, Hempstead, Saffron Walden CB10 2PH — BM BCh 1990 Oxf.; BA Camb. 1987, MA 1991; MRCP (UK) 1993. MRC Clin. Train. Fell. Imperial Coll. Sch. of Med. Hammersmith Hosp. Lond. Prev: Regist. (Med.) Roy. Postgrad. Med. Sch. Hammersmith Hosp. Lond.

BASSETT, Mr John Mories (retired) 38 Roland Way, London SW7 3RE Tel: 020 7373 5656 — MD Ed. (Commend.) 1929, MB ChB 1925; MRCS Eng. LRCP Lond. 1925; FRCS Ed. 1927. Prev: Mem. BMA & Med. Soc. Study VD.

BASSETT, John Waring Montalto Medical Centre, 2 Dromore Road, Ballynahinch BT24 8AY Tel: 028 9756 2929 — MB BCh BAO 1970 Belf.; MRCGP 1974.

BASSETT, Louise Christina 4 Paxton Road, Northampton NN3 3RL — MB ChB 1994 Leic.

BASSETT, Martin Robert Alexander 35 Summervale Road, Stourbridge DY9 0LX — MB BS 1990 Lond.

BASSETT, Patricia Marilyn 41 Pitman Court, Swainswick, Bath BA1 8BD — MB ChB 1968 Bristol; DObst RCOG 1971.

BASSETT, Patricia Wendy Tel: 01264 738368 Fax: 01264 738003 (office hours only); Down Farm House, The Harroway, Whitchurch RG28 7RT Tel: 01256 892490 — MB BS 1975 Lond.; MRCS Eng. LRCP Lond. 1975; DCH Eng. 1978; DRCOG 1977. (St. Geo.) Clin. Asst., Rheum., Andover. Prev: Chairm. of Andover PCG.

BASSETT, Stephen David 9 Turberville Street, Maesteg, Bridgend — MB BCh 1992 Wales.

BASSETT, William James (retired) Morlich, Kirknewton EH27 8DG Tel: 01506 882034 — MB ChB 1956 St. And.; MRCGP 1977; FRCGP 1998. Prev: Hosp. Pract. (Paediat.) St. Johns Hosp. Livingston.

BASSETT, William Lloyd Claremont Villa, 228 Sutton Park Road, Kidderminster DY11 6LA — MB BS 1988 Lond.

BASSI, Mr Chaman Lal St Pauls Clinic, Palmyra Place, Keynsham Avenue, Newport NP20 4EH Tel: 01633 266140 Fax: 01633 221655 — MB BS 1964 Punjabi; FRCS Ed. 1970.

BASSI, Narinderpal Singh 1 Normanby Road, Nottingham NG8 2TA — MB ChB 1993 Ed.

BASSI, Riva 1 Compton Close, Highcross, Rogerstone, Newport NP10 0BY — MB ChB 1995 Bristol.

BASSI, Mr Sanjeev 119 Marlborough Avenue, Princes Avenue, Hull HU5 3JU; 14 Glentworth Road, Radford, Nottingham NG7 5QL Tel: 0115 978 3453 — MB ChB 1992 Manch.; FRCS (Eng) 1997. (Manchester) Specialist Regist. (Neurosurg.) Qu.'s Med. Centre Nottm. Prev: Regist. (Neurosurg.) Hull Roy. Infirm.; SHO (ENT) Roy. Berks. Hosp.; SHO (Gen. Surg. & Orthop.) Kingston Hosp. Surrey.

BASSI, Satish Chander 18 Glenavon Park, Sneyd Park, Bristol BS9 1RW — MB ChB 1977 Bristol; MRCGP; DRCOG 1979.

BASSI, Satish Kumar The Surgery, 115 Tudway Road, Ferrier Estate, Kidbrooke, London SE3 9YX Tel: 020 8856 4167 Fax: 020 8856 1269 — MB BS 1970 All India Inst. Med. Scs.

BASSI, Shalinder 57 Loveday Road, London W13 9JT — MB BS 1993 Lond.

BASSI, Shashi Rai 234 Nottingham Road, Selston, Nottingham NG16 6AB Tel: 01773 810226; 23 The Crescent, Southall UB1 1BE — MB ChB 1984 Leic.; MRCGP 1988; DRCOG 1988; Cert. Family Plann. JCC 1987; DCH RCP Lond. 1986. Prev: SHO (A & E) Hope Hosp. Salford AHA; Manch. VTS Salford.

BASSI, Sukhbinder Kumar 124 Barrow Road, Quorn, Loughborough LE12 8DL — MB ChB 1994 Leeds.

BASSILY, Mr Ashraf Antoun Estafan East Surrey Hospital, Three Arches Road, Redhill RH1 5RH Tel: 01737 768511; 49 Briton Hill Road, Sanderstead, South Croydon CR2 0JJ Tel: 020 8657 2476 — MB ChB 1981 Ain Shams; FRCS Glas. 1992; MCh 1985; FRCS (Orth) 1999. Staff Grade Orthop. Surg. E. Surrey Hosp. Socs: BOA. Prev: Specialist Regist. & SHO (Orthop.) S.end Hosp.

BASSON, John Vincent Broadmoor Hospital, Crowthorne RG45 7EG Tel: 01344 773111 Fax: 01344 754388; Maybury, Chavey Down Road, Winkfield Row, Bracknell RG42 7NY Tel: 01344 882189 Fax: 01344 882189 — MB ChB 1970 Ed.; BSc (Hons.) Ed. 1970; MPhil Ed. 1979; FRCPsych 1990, M 1975. (Ed.) Med. Dir. (1996); Cons. Forens. Psychiat. Socs: Fell. RSM; Amer. Acad. Psychiat. & Law. Prev: Princip. Med. Off. Scott. Office Home Health Dept.; Cons. Forens. Psychiat. Roy. Edin. Hosp. & Saughton Prison.; Fell. (Community Psychiat.) S. Lothian Health Dist.

BASTABLE, Gordon James Graham Thorpe Health Centre, St William's Way, Thorpe St Andrew, Norwich NR7 0AJ; 67 Broadland Drive, Thorpe End, Norwich NR13 5BT — MB BS 1987 Lond.; MRCGP 1991; T(GP) 1991; DCH RCP Lond. 1991; DRCOG 1991; Cert. Family Plann. JCC 1991.

BASTABLE, Mr John Ralph Graham 42 St Andrewgate, York YO1 7BZ Tel: 01904 647234 — ChM Birm. 1963, MB ChB 1945; FRCS Eng. 1951. Prev: Cons. (Urol.) York Health Dist.

BASTABLE, Morag Joyce Rankine (retired) 42 St Andrewgate, York YO1 7BZ Tel: 01904 647234 — MB BS Lond. 1952; MRCS Eng. LRCP Lond. 1952; FFA RCS Eng. 1957; DA Eng. 1954. Prev: Cons. Anaesth. York Health Dist.

BASTABLE, Ruth Barbara Nuffield Road Medical Centre, Nuffield Road, Cambridge CB4 1GL Tel: 01223 423424 — MB ChB 1976 Liverp.; MRCGP 1980; DCH Eng. 1981.

BASTAWROS, Mr Salah Sarofim Glan Clwyd District General Hospital, Rhyl LL18 5UJ Tel: 01745 583910 Fax: 01745 583143 Email: sarah.bastawros@cd-tr.wales.nhs.uk; Blackthorn, 26 Pen y Bryn Rd, Colwyn Bay LL29 6AF Tel: 01492 530405 Email: sbastawros@hotmail.com — MB BCh 1970 Alexandria; FRCS Ed. 1984. Cons. Orthop. Surg.; Clin. Director, Trauma and Orthop. Socs: HCSA; Brit. Orthop. Assn.; Mem. of the Med. Protec. Soc.

BASTEN, Joanna Elizabeth Roslin Bavn, Chillerton, Newport PO30 3HG — BM BCh 1970 Oxf.; BSc Nottm. 1961; MA, BM BCh Oxf. 1970.

BASTERFIELD, Jane Elizabeth 100 Looseleigh Lane, Derriford, Plymouth PL6 5HH — MB BCh 1998 Wales.

BASTIAENEN, Henry Louis Robert North Devon District Hospital, Raleigh Park, Barnstaple EX31 4JB Tel: 01271 322577; The Croft, Lower Loxhore, Barnstaple EX31 4SX Tel: 01271 850496 — MB ChB 1973 Bristol; FFA RCS Eng. 1978; DRCOG 1976; DA Eng. 1975. Cons. Anaesth. N. Devon Dist. Hosp.

BASTIAN, Lincoln 65 Berrylands, Orpington BR6 9TF Tel: 01689 37551 — MB BS 1967 Ceylon. (Colombo)

BASTIAN, N 123 Towncourt Lane, Petts Wood, Orpington BR5 1EL.

BASTIANPILLAI, Balendran Athanasius King George Hospital, Barley Lane, Ilford IG3 8YB Tel: 020 8983 8000 Fax: 020 8970 8001; 2 Oaklands, Winchmore Hill, London N21 3DD Tel: 020 8882 1711 Fax: 020 8351 7097 Email: b.bastianpillai@virgin.net — MB BS 1979 Colombo; FFA RCSI 1988. Cons. Anaesth. King Geo. Hosp. Ilford.

BASTIANPILLAI, Loretta Shryanthi Keshini Somerset Gardens Family Health, 4 Creighton Road, Tottenham, London N17 8NW Tel: 020 8493 9090 Fax: 020 8493 6000; 2 Oaklands, London N21 3DD — MB ChB 1984 Sheff.; MRCGP 1991; DRCOG 1990.

BASTIN, Alan Charles (retired) The Health Centre, Church St., Yetminster, Sherborne DT9 6LG Tel: 01935 872530 Fax: 01935 873484 — MB ChB 1956 Leeds.

***BASTIN, Anthony John** University College Hospital, Grafton Way, London WC1E; 9 Victoria Park, Colwyn Bay LL29 7AX Tel: 01492 531059 — MB BS 1997 Lond.; BA Oxf. 1994.

BASTIN, Christopher John Seaton and Colyton Medical Practice, Seaton Health Centre, 148 Harepath Road, Seaton EX12 2DU Tel:

01297 20877 Fax: 01297 23031; Honeywood, Seaton Down Close, Seaton EX12 2JB Tel: 01297 23745 — MB BS 1970 Lond.; MRCS Eng. LRCP Lond. 1970; DObst RCOG 1973. Prev: Trainee GP Wessex RHB; Ho. Surg. (Orthop. & Urol.) Kings Coll. Hosp. Lond.; Ho. Phys. Greenbank Hosp. Plymouth.

BASTIN, Martin William 225 Tettenhall Road, Wolverhampton WV6 0DE — MB ChB 1970 Birm.

BASTOCK, Jonathan Michael, Flight Lt. RAF Med. Br. 37 Mount Nod Way, Broad Lane, Coventry CV5 7GY Tel: 024 76 468841 — MB ChB 1989 Sheff.; MRCGP 1993; DRCOG 1995; DFFP 1995. Med. Off. RAF Cranwell. Prev: SHO (O & G) Hinchinbrooke Hosp.; SHO (Paediat.) P'boro. Dist. Hosp.; SHO (Psychiat.) DCP RAF Marham.

BASTON, Daphne Marsh (retired) — MB ChB Birm. 1950; MRCGP 1967. Prev: Clin. Teach. Univ. Soton.

BASTON, John Derek (retired) Farthings, Whiteparish, Salisbury SP5 2SU Tel: 01794 884554 Email: ibastoni@ukgateway.net — MB ChB (Foxwell Memor. Prize Med.) Birm. 1950; MRCS Eng. LRCP Lond. 1950; FRCGP 1981, M 1966; DPM Eng. 1973. Prev: RAF Med. Br.

BASTOW, Katie Jane 72 Douglas Road, Bedford MK41 7YH Tel: 01234 327326 — MB ChB 1995 Leeds; Bedford BTS, 1999. (Leeds) GP Locum. Prev: GP Regist., 85 Goldincoon Ave, Bedford; SHO in A&E, Bedford Hosp.; SHO in O & G, Bedford Hosp.

BASTOW, Neil Munro 5 Madeira Croft, Chapelfields, Coventry CV5 8NX Tel: 024 7667 9585 Email: neilbastow@hotmail.com — BM BS 1996 Nottm. (Nottingham)

BASU, Amar Croft House, 51 Leylands Lane, Bradford BD9 5QT Tel: 01274 498768 — MB BS 1960 Calcutta; Dlo Eng. 1964. (Nil Ratan Sircar Med. Coll.) Prev: SHO Liverp. ENT Infirm.; Regist. (ENT Surg.) Birkenhead Gen. Hosp. & Bradford Roy. Infirm.

BASU, Amitava 74 Burnieboozle Crescent, Aberdeen AB15 8NQ — MB BS 1955 Calcutta.

BASU, Anita Sreya 1 Woodside Gardens, Gateshead NE11 9RB — MB BS 1997 Newc.

BASU, Anna Purna 6 Belle Vue Drive, Sunderland SR2 7SF — BM BCh 1997 Oxf.; MA Camb. 1998. (Oxford) SHO (Paediat.) Roy. Vict. Infirm., Newc. Socs: BMA.

BASU, Arundhati Munmun Flat 2, 53 Mauldeth Road, Manchester M20 4NF — MB ChB 1989 Manch.

BASU, Bristi Jhumku 74 Jesson Road, Walsall WS1 3AX — BM BCh 1996 Oxf.

BASU, Chitra 42 Russell Hill, Purley CR8 2JA Tel: 020 8660 7938 — MB BS 1962 Calcutta; FFA RCS Eng. 1969; DA Eng. 1964. (Calcutta Med. Coll.) Cons. Anaesth. Mayday Hosp. Thornton Heath; Cons. Pain Clin. Croydon HA. Socs: Fell. Roy. Soc. Med.; Internat. Assn. Study of Pain; Assn. Anaesths. Prev: Sen. Regist. Dept. Anaesth. Char. Cross Hosp. Lond.; Sen. Regist. (Anaesth.) Roy. Surrey Co. & St. Luke's Hosps. Guildford; Regist. Dept. Anaesth. Hammersmith Hosp. & Roy. Postgrad. Med. Sch.

BASU, Dijendra Bhushan Devereux Chambers, Devereux Court, London WC2R 3JH Tel: 020 7353 7534 Fax: 020 7353 1724 Email: basu@devchambers.co.uk — MB BS 1991 Lond.; Barrister At Law. (Guy's Hosp.) Barrister Hon. Soc. of Lincoln's Inn; Mem. of the Bar of Eng. and Wales. Prev: Ho. Off. (Surg.) W. Middx. Univ. Hosp.; Ho. Off. (Med.) Medway Hosp.

BASU, Mr Dipak Kumar The Surgery, 27 Comforts Avenue, Scunthorpe DN15 6PN Tel: 01724 842377 Fax: 01724 842350; 9A Cliff Gardens, Scunthorpe DN15 7PH Tel: 01724 872237 — MB BS 1960 Calcutta; FRCS Ed. 1975. (Nilratan Sircar Med. Coll.)

BASU, Dipendra Bhushan 11A Gloucester Road, Walsall WS5 3PL Tel: 01922 32987 — MB BS 1963 Calcutta; FFA RCS Eng. 1974. (R.G. Kar Med. Coll.)

BASU, Gautam 5 Donne Court, Orpington Hospital, Sevenoaks Road, Orpington BR6 9JU — MB BS 1985 Calcutta.

BASU, Helen 1 Mountbatten Avenue, Sandal, Wakefield WF2 6EY — MB ChB 1995 Leeds.

BASU, Mr Himansu Kumar Multicare International, 1 Harbour Exchange, Exchange Square, London E14 9GE Tel: 020 7512 2440 Fax: 020 7512 2441 Email: hbasu@gynec.abel.co.uk; Glengarry, Woodlands Lane, Shorne, Gravesend DA12 3HH Tel: 01474 822294 Fax: 01474 824019 — MB BS 1959 Calcutta; PhD Liverp. 1969; FRCS Ed. 1963; FRCOG 1984, M 1965, D 1961. Cons. O & G Dartford & Gravesham NHS Trust; Hon. Tutor Univ. Lond. Socs: Fell. Roy. Soc. Med. (Ex-Pres. Sect. Obst. & Gyn.); (Ex-Pres.) SE Gyn. Soc.; (Ex-Sec.) Ospreys Gyn. Soc. Prev: Blair-Bell Memor. Lect. RCOG; Eden Fell. RCOG; Lect. (O & G) Univ. Liverp.

BASU, Ila The Surgery, 61 Plashet Road, London E13 0QA Tel: 020 8470 8186 Fax: 020 8503 4989; 44 Raymond Avenue, London E18 2HG — MB BS 1974 Calcutta.

BASU, Jayanta Kumar Albert Place, Market St., Little Lever, Bolton Tel: 01204 72939 — MB BS 1960 Calcutta; DA Eng. 1969. (Calcutta Med. Coll.) Socs: BMA; Assoc. RCGP. Prev: Regist. Anaesth. Birm. RHB; Ho. Phys. St. Jas. Hosp. Leeds; Ho. Surg. Torbay Hosp. Torquay.

BASU, Kumar Kanti 15 Repton Road, West Bridgford, Nottingham NG2 7EP — MB ChB 1990 Leeds; BSc (Hons.) Leeds 1987. (Leeds)

BASU, Mr Manoj Kumar 30 Havenwood Road, Wigan WN1 2PA — MB BS 1965 Calcutta; MS Calcutta 1970, MB BS 1965.

BASU, Marion Beatrix Deerness Park Medical Centre, Suffolk Street, Sunderland SR2 8AD Tel: 0191 567 0961 — MB ChB 1968 Leeds; DObst RCOG 1970. (Leeds)

BASU, Mr Partha Sarathi Droylsden Road Surgery, 125 Droylsden Road, Newton Heath, Manchester M40 1NT Tel: 0161 681 1956 Fax: 0161 681 2039; 254 Brooklands Road, Brooklands, Manchester M23 9HD Tel: 0161 969 9694 — MB BS 1958 Calcutta; MS (ENT) Bihar 1967; DLO RCS Eng. 1972. Prev: GP & Hosp. Pract. ENT Dept. Withington Hosp. Manch.

BASU, Mr Parthasarathi 1 Orchard Court, Royal National Orthopaedic Hospital, Stanmore HA7 4LP — MB BS 1988 Calcutta; FRCS Glas. 1995.

BASU, Mrs Raj Ireland House, Liverpool L26 3UA Tel: 0151 487 5669 — MB BS 1950 Bombay. (Grant Med. Coll. Bombay) Assoc. Specialist (A & E) Vict. Centr. Hosp. Wallasey. & Arrowe Pk. Hosp.Upton Wirral. Prev: Ho. Surg. & O & G Ho. Surg. J.J. Hosp. Bombay.

BASU, Mr Rajat Kumar Greentops, 64 Cheerbrook Road, Willaston, Nantwich CW5 7EN Tel: 01270 67850 — MB BS 1991 Lond.; FRCS Eng. 1996; FRCS Ed. 1995. (St. Barth.)

BASU, Robin 58 High Beeches, Banstead SM7 1NB Tel: 01737 361700 — MB BS 1972 Calcutta; MRCPsych 1978; DPM Eng. 1978. Cons. Psychiat. Epsom Dist. Hosp. & Leatherhead Child & Family Centre. Prev: Sen. Regist. St. Geo. Hosp. Lond. & Qu. Mary's Hosp. Childr. Carshalton; Sen. Regist. (Adolesc. Unit) Long Gr. Hosp. Epsom.

BASU, Sachindra Nath Department of Anaesthetics, Pilgrim Hospital, Boston PE21 9QS — MB BS 1957 Calcutta; FFA RCS Eng. 1967; DA Eng. 1963. Cons. Anaesth. Pilgrim Hosp. Boston.

BASU, Mr Saradindu Shotfield Health Centre, Shotfield, Wallington SM6 0HY; 42 Russell Hill, Purley CR8 2JA Tel: 020 8647 0031 — MB BS 1962 Calcutta; FRCS Eng. 1968; MRCS Eng. LRCP Lond. 1973.

BASU, Sekhar Nath 30 Fairlands Park, Coventry CV4 7DS — MB BS 1956 Calcutta; FRCP Lond. 1992; MRCP (UK) 1969; Dip. Cardiol. Calcutta 1965. (R.G. Kar Med. Coll.) Cons. Phys. (Geriat.) Coventry Health Dist. Hosps. Prev: SHO (Chest) King Edwd. VII Memor. Chest Hosp. Warwick; Regist. (Gen. Med.) Coventry & Warks. Hosp.; Sen. Regist. (Geriat. Med.) E. Birm. Hosp.

BASU, Sheila 1 Mount Batten Avenue, Sandal, Wakefield WF2 6EY; 6 Osborne Street, Didsbury, Manchester M20 2QZ Email: shbasu@globalnet.co.uk — MB ChB 1992 Manch.; FRCA Lond. 1998. (Manch.) Specialist Regist. (Anaesth.) N. W. Region.

BASU, Subhas 22 Howard Drive, York YO30 5XB — MB BS 1969 Calcutta.

BASU, Subirendra Chandra (Surgery) 149 High Street, Connah's Quay, Deeside CH5 4DQ Tel: 01244 812217; 65 Wepre Park, Connar's Quay, Deeside CH5 4HJ — MB BS 1961 Calcutta; DTM & H Liverp. 1966. Prev: Cas. Off. Flint Community Hosp.; GP S. Wales; Med. Off. Govts. Zambia & Seychelles.

BASU, Sudhir Kumar 6 Drovers Court, Lea Road, Gainsborough DN21 1AN — MB BS 1971 Calcutta.

BASU, Sulal Krishna Wellington Road Surgery, 78 Wellington Road, Mablethorpe LN12 1HT Tel: 01507 472409 Fax: 01507 478577.

BASU, Suniti Kumar The Surgery, 61 Plashet Road, London E13 0QA Tel: 020 8470 8186 Fax: 020 8503 4989 — MB BS 1974 Calcutta.

BASU, Supratik West Middlesex University Hospital, Isleworth TW7 6AF Tel: 020 8560 2121 Fax: 020 8565 5516 — MB BS 1983 Calcutta; MD Calcutta 1986; MRCP (UK) 1988; MRCPath 1993. Sen. Regist. (Haemat.) W. Middlx. Univ. Hosp., Hammersmith Hosp. & Roy. Postgrad. Med. Sch. Lond. Prev: BMT Coordinator & Leukaemia Research Fell. Birm. Childr. Hosp.; Hon. Sen. Regist. & Clin. Research Fell. Roy. Free Hosp. Lond.; Sen. Regist. St. Helier Hosp. Carshalton.

BASU, Supriya Abbey Cottage, Horton, Wimborne BH21 7JA — MB BS 1994 Lond.; DRCOG 1997. GP Regist., Hadleigh lodge, Surrey, Corfe Mullen, Dorset. Prev: GP Trainee; Ho. Off. (Gen. Med. & Elderly Med.) Qu. Mary's Hosp. Sidcup; Ho. Off. (Gen. Surg.) Worthing Hosp. Worthing.

BASU, Tapas Kumar Strachur Rural Medical Practice, Dalnacraig, Strachur, Cairndow PA27 8BX Tel: 01369 860224 Fax: 01369 860225; Dalnacraig, Strachun, Cairndow PA27 8BX Tel: 01369 860721 Fax: 01369 860225 — MB BS 1966 Calcutta; MB BS (Univ. of Calcutta India 1966); MS (Univ. of Calcutta 1978); DA (RCS Eng. 1976). (Calcutta National Medical College) GP Cairndow, Argyll. Socs: BMA; Sec. Med. Protec. Soc. Ltd. Prev: GP Dowdis Mid Glam.; Clin. Asst. Anaesth. P. Chas. Hosp. Merthyr Tydfil; Clin. Asst. A & E Dept. Aberdare Gen. Hosp.

BASU, Uma (retired) 47 Allt-yr-yn Avenue, Newport NP20 5DB — MB BS Calcutta 1959; MRCOG Lond. 1996; FRCOG Lond. 1987. Prev: Vis. Cons. Obstretics & Gyn. Al-Zahra Hosp. Sharjah, United Arab Emirates.

BATAGOL, David Michael c/o J. Meadows, 5 Meyrick Avenue, Wash Common, Newbury RG15 6SY — MB BS 1986 Monash.

BATAILLE, Veronique 22 Aberdeen Road, London N5 2UH — MD 1985 Louvain; PhD Lond. 1995; MRCP (UK) 1988. Sen. Lect. (Dermat.) & Hon. Cons. Med. Coll. St. Bart. & Roy. Lond. Hosps. Socs: BMA; New York Acad. Sci.; Fell. Roy. Coll. Phys.s. Prev: Sen. Regist. (Dermat.) St. Geo. Hosp. Lond.

BATAREC, Alain Jean Edouard S.O.S. Doctors Ltd, 15 Berghem Mews, Blythe Road, London W14 0HN — MD 1982 Paris.

BATCH, Mr Andrew Jonathan George City Hospital NHS Trust, Dudley Road, Birmingham B18 7QH Tel: 0121 507 5110 Fax: 0121 507 4557; 83 Greenfield Road, Harborne, Birmingham B17 0EH Tel: 0121 427 9867 — MRCS Eng. LRCP Lond. 1972; BSc (Hons.) Lond. 1969, MB BS 1972; FRCS (Orl.) Eng. 1984; FRCS Eng. 1977. (Guy's) Cons. Otolaryngol. Head & Neck Surg.City Hosp. NHS Trust; Hon. Sen. Lect, Univ of Birm. Socs: Midl. Inst. Otol.; Hon. Treas., Brit. Assn. of Head & Neck Oncologists. Prev: Sen. Regist. Roy. Nat. Throat, Nose & Ear Hosp. Lond. & Roy. Sussex Co. Hosp. Brighton.

BATCHELLOR, Francis Herbert (retired) 9 Clyvedon Rise, South Shields NE34 8DL Tel: 0191 456 0062 — LRCP LRCS Ed. LRFPS Glas. 1941. Prev: J.P.

BATCHELOR, Mr Alastair David Ross (retired) 3/3 West Grange Gardens, Edinburgh EH9 2RA Tel: 0131 667 8432 — MB ChB Ed. 1945; FRCS Ed. 1950. Prev: Cons. Plastic Surg. Roy. Hosp. Sick Childr. Edin.

BATCHELOR, Mr Andrew Goolden Grant Field House, 10 Sicklinghall Road, Wetherby LS22 6AA Tel: 0113 218 5971 — MRCS Eng. LRCP Lond. 1976; MB BS Lond. 1976; BSc (Hons.) Lond. 1972; FRCS Eng. (Plast) 1986; FRCS Eng. 1981. Cons. Plastic Surg. St. Jas. Univ. Hosp. Leeds, York Dist. Hosp. & Leeds Gen. Infirm. Socs: Brit. Assoc. Plastic Surg.; Mem. of Counc.; Chairm. Private Pract. Comm. Prev: Sen. Regist. (Plastic Surg.) W. Scotl. Regional Centre Jaw & Plastic; Surg. Canniesburn Hosp. Glas.

BATCHELOR, Anna Marija IntensiveCare Unit, Royal Victoria Infirmary, Queen Victoria Road, Newcastle upon Tyne NE1 4LP Tel: 0191 282 4619 Email: a.m.batchelor@ncl.ac.uk — MB ChB 1980 Sheff.; FRCA Eng. 1985. Cons. Anaesth. & Intens. Care Med. Roy. Vict. Infirm. Newc. Socs: Intens. Care Soc.; Counc. Mem. Chairm. of Educat. & Train. Comm.

BATCHELOR, Anthony John, CBE, Group Capt. RAF Med. Br. RAF Centre of Aviation Medicine, RAF Henlow, Henlow SG16 6GN Tel: 01462 851515 x8020 Fax: 01462 816706 Email: oc@rafcam.mod.uk; 14 The Paddocks, Folksworth, Peterborough PE7 3TZ Tel: 01733 243039 Email: tbatch449@aol.com — MB BS 1971 Lond.; BSc Lond. 1968; FRCP Lond. 1992; MRCP (UK) 1976; MRCS Eng. LRCP Lond. 1971; DAvMed. Lond. 1985; DObst RCOG 1973. (Lond. Hosp.) Off. Commanding RAF Centre of Aviat. Med., RAF Henlow, Beds; Hon.cons.Phys.PeterBoro. Hosp.s trust; Whittingham Prof. of Aviat. Med.; Cons. Phys. to UK civil Aviat. Auth.,Gatwick. Socs: Brit. Soc. Gastroenterol.; Internat. Acad. of Aviat. and space Med.; Fell. Roy. Aeronautical Soc. Prev: Cons. Phys. P.ss Alexandra's RAF Hosp. Wroughton; Cons. Phys. P.ss of Wales RAF Hosp. Ely; Staff Internist. USAF Sch. Aerospace Med. San Antonio Texas, USA.

BATCHELOR, Carol Morag Forest Surgery, 11 Station Road, Loughton IG10 4NZ — MB BS 1988 Lond.; MRCGP 1992; DCH RCP Lond. 1992.

BATCHELOR, Sir Ivor Ralph Campbell, CBE 55 Hepburn Gardens, St Andrews KY16 9LS — MB ChB 1940 Ed.; FRCP Ed. 1953, M 1947; FRCPsych 1971; DPM Lond. 1948. (Ed.) Emerit. Prof. Psychiat. Univ. Dundee.

BATCHELOR, Professor John Richard (retired) Little Ambrook, Nursery Road, Walton-on-the-Hill, Tadworth KT20 7TU — MB BChir 1955 Camb.; MB BChir Camb. 1957; MD Camb. 1965; FRCP Lond. 1995; MRCS Eng. LRCP Lond. 1955; FRCPath 1991. Prof. Immunol. Roy. Postgrad. Med. Sch. Hammersmith Hosp. Lond. Prev: Prof. Immunol. Roy. Postgrad. Med. Sch. Hammersmith Hosp. Lond.

BATCHELOR, Mr John Stephen 21 Willowtree Court, Sale, Manchester M33 3QH — MB ChB 1982 Leeds; FRCSI 1990.

BATCHELOR, Moira Ann (retired) Little Ambrook, Nursery Road, Walton-on-the-Hill, Tadworth KT20 7TU Tel: 01737 812028 — MB BS Lond. 1955; MRCS Eng. LRCP Lond. 1955.

***BATCHELOR, Nicholas George** Dept of Anaesthetics, Bradford Royal Infirmary, Duckworth Lane, Bradford BD9 6RJ; 9 Broomfield Road, Headingly, Leeds LS6 3DE Email: nickbatchelor@ukgateway.net — MB ChB 1997 Leeds.

BATCHELOR, Phyllis Madeleine (retired) 8 Abbey Road, Chertsey KT16 8AL Tel: 01932 565024 — MB ChB 1948 Birm.; MRCS Eng. LRCP Lond. 1948. Prev: Ho. Phys. Roy. Infirm. Leicester.

BATCHELOR, Sarah Elizabeth 31 Brook Lane, Corfe Mullen, Wimborne BH21 3RD — MB ChB 1998 Leic.; MB ChB Leic 1998.

BATCHELOR, Yvonne Kay 33 Stoneleigh Court, Coton Road, Nuneaton CV11 5UQ — MB ChB 1992 Leic.

BATCUP, Gillian (retired) — MB BS 1966 Lond.; BSc Lond. 1963; MRCS Eng. LRCP Lond. 1966; FRCPath 1987, M 1975. Prev: Cons. Paediat. & Perinatal Path. Gen. Infirm. Leeds.

BATE, Colin Michael Royal Albert Edward Infirmary, Wigan Lane, Wigan WN1 2NN — MB ChB 1966 Manch.; MD Manch. 1978; FRCP Lond. 1989; MRCP (UK) 1975. Cons. Phys. Roy. Albert Edwd. Infirm. Wigan; Clin. Dir. Med. Specialties Directorate. Socs: Fell. Manch. Med. Soc. Prev: Cons. Phys. Al Qassimi Hosp. Sharjah, UAE; Sen. Regist. (Gen. Med.) Qu. Eliz. Milit. Hosp. Lond.; Hon. Sen. Regist. St. Bart. Hosp. Lond.

BATE, Cyril 113 Church Lane, Stechford, Birmingham B33 9EJ Tel: 0121 783 2861 Fax: 0121 785 0585; 886 Chester Road, Erdington, Birmingham B24 0EL Tel: 0121 373 0714 — MB ChB 1957 Birm.; DObst RCOG 1961. (Birm.) Police Surg. City of Birm. Socs: Birm. Medico-Legal Soc. Prev: Ho. Phys. & Ho. Surg. (Obst.) Manor Hosp. Walsall.

BATE, John Gordon 20 Dixton Close, Monmouth NP25 3PQ — MB ChB 1933 Ed.; FRCPath 1972, M 1964. (Ed.) Hon. Cons. Path. St. Mary's Hosp. Gp. Socs: Fell. Roy. Med. Soc. Edin. & Roy. Soc. Med. Prev: Squadron Ldr. RAFVR Med. Br.; Path. P.ss Louise Kensington Hosp. Childr., & Samarit. Hosp. for Wom. & W.. Ophth. Hosp. Lond.

BATE, Lauren Vanessa 29A Temple Street, Bethnal Green, London E2 6QQ — MB BS 1997 Lond.

BATE, Sara Louise 80 ELmswood Road, Liverpool L17 6DB — MB BS 1992 Newc.

***BATE, Thomas Emyr** Bryn-y-mor, Holyhead Road, Bangor LL57 2HG Tel: 01248 370787 Fax: 01248 372396 Email: 100607.3671@compuserve.com — MB ChB 1998 Ed.; MB ChB Ed 1998.

BATEMAN, Adrian Calvin Department of Histopathology, Level E., South Block, Southampton General Hospital, Tremona Road, Southampton SO16 6YD Tel: 02380 796672 Fax: 02380 796869 Email: adrian.bateman@suht.swest.nhs.uk; Tel: 02380 262627 — MB BS 1990 Lond.; BSc Lond. 1987; DRCPath 1995; MRCPath 1996; MD Lond. 1997. (Char. Cross & Westm. Lond.) Cons. (Histopath.) Soton. Gen. Hosp.; Hon. Clin. Sen. Lect. in Path., Univ. of S.ampton. Socs: Brit. Soc. of Gastroenterol. and Mem. of Path. Sect. Comm.; Assn. Clin. Path.; Internat. Acad. Path. (Brit. Div.).

Prev: Sen. Regist. (Histopath.) Soton. Gen. Hosp. & Qu. Alexandra Hosps. Portsmouth; Regist. (Histopath.) Wessex RHA; SHO (Histopath.) Soton. Gen. Hosp.

BATEMAN, Alastair Michael Scrymgoeur Stakes Lodge Surgery, 3A Lavender Road, Waterlooville PO7 8NS Tel: 023 9225 4581 Fax: 023 9235 8867; Ivy Cottage, Commonside, Emsworth PO10 8TA — MB BS 1987 Lond.; MA Oxf. 1984; MRCP (UK) 1990; MRCGP 1994; DFFP 1994. Hosp. Practitioner Cardiol., St. Richards Hosp. Chichester, W. Sussex. Prev: Regist. (Diabetes & Gen. Med.) W. Middlx. Hosp. Lond.; SHO (Paediat.) Kingston Hosp. Surrey; SHO (O & G) S.lands Hosp. Worthing.

BATEMAN, Alison Margaret Queen Square Surgery, 2 Queen Square, Lancaster LA1 1RP Tel: 01524 843333 Fax: 01524 847550 — MB ChB 1989 Sheff.; DFFP 1994.

BATEMAN, Anthony Malcolm Great Shelford Health Centre, Ashen Green, Great Shelford, Cambridge CB2 5EY Tel: 01223 843661 Fax: 01223 844569 — MB BChir 1966 Camb.; MB Camb. 1966, BChir 1965; MRCOG 1975; DA Eng. 1969; DCH Eng. 1969; DObst 1968. (St. Bart.) Prev: Ho. Off. St. Bart. Hosp. Lond.; Med. Off. Mengo Hosp., Uganda; Regist. (O & G) Roy. United Hosp. Bath.

BATEMAN, Anthony Philip 65 Alexandra Road, Ashton-in-Makerfield, Wigan WN4 8QS — MB BS 1998 Lond.; MB BS Lond 1998.

BATEMAN, Anthony Walshaw St Ann's Hospital, St Ann's Road, London N15 3TH Tel: 020 8442 6528 Fax: 020 8442 6548 — MB BS 1978 Lond.; MA Camb. 1976; FRCPsych 1996 M 1982. Cons. Psychother. St. Ann's Hosp. Lond. Prev: Cons. Psychother. Friern Hosp. Lond.; Sen. Regist. (Psychother.) Tavistock Clin. Lond.; Sen. Regist. (Psychiat.) Roy. Free Hosp. Lond.

BATEMAN, Belinda Jane David Hyde Asthma & Allergy Centre, St Mary's Hospital, Newport; 14 Holyrood Avenue, Southampton SO17 1SH — BM 1991 Soton.; MRCP Paediat. (UK) 1995. Specialist Regist. (Paediat.) Loddon Trust Basingstoke; Specialist Regist. (Paediat.); Clin. Research Fell. Asthma & Allergy Centre Isle of Wight.

BATEMAN, Caroline Jane 41 Feldon Street, London SW6 5AE Tel: 020 7736 9439 — MB BS 1990 Lond.; FRCA 1995; DA (UK) 1993. (St Thos. Hosp. Med. Sch. Lond.) Clin. Fell. (Anaes), Roy. Brompton Hosp., Lond. Prev: Regist. Rotat. (Anaesth.) St. Mary's Hosp. Lond.; SHO (Anaesth.) St. Mary's Hosp. Lond. & Frimley Pk. Hosp. Camberley; SHO (Med.) Qu. Eliz. Hosp. Gateshead.

BATEMAN, Christopher John Turner (retired) Waterleas, Watery Lane, West Ashling, Chichester PO18 9LE Tel: 01243 575484 Fax: 01243 576302 Email: waterleas@onetel.net.uk — BM BCh 1962 Oxf.; MA Oxf. 1962; FRCPath 1983, M 1971. Prev: Cons. Haemat. King Edwd. VII Hosp. Midhurst.

BATEMAN, Daniel James 64 Malting Green Road, Colchester CO2 0JJ Tel: 01206 764374 Fax: 01206 765667 — MB BS 1994 Lond.

BATEMAN, David Earl Royal United Hospital, Coombe Park, Bath BA1 3NG — MD 1985 Camb.; MA Camb. 1972, MD 1985, MB BChir 1975; MRCP (UK) 1977.

BATEMAN, David James Alexander North Hill Surgery, 18 North Hill, Colchester CO1 1DZ Tel: 01206 578070 Fax: 01206 769880; The Kiln, Brick Kiln Lane, Great Horkesley, Colchester CO6 4EU Tel: 01206 271608 — MB BS 1971 Lond.; BA Camb. 1965; DPM Eng. 1977.

BATEMAN, David Nicholas Scottish Poisons Information Bureau, 1 Lauriston Place, Edinburgh EH3 9YW Tel: 0131 536 2303 Fax: 0131 536 2304 Email: spib@compuserve.com; 63a Braid Avenue, Morninside, Edinburgh EH10 6EB — MB BS 1972 Lond.; MD Lond. 1979, BSc (Pharmacol., Hons.) 1969, MB BS 1972; FRCP Lond. 1988; MRCP (UK) 1975. (Guy's) Cons. Phys. Roy. Infirm. of Edin. & Direct. Scott. Poisons Informat. Bureau. Socs: Brit. Pharm. Soc. & Europ. Assn. Poisons Contr. Prev: Cons. Phys. & Reader (Therap.) Freeman Hosp. Newc.; Ho. Off. Guy's Hosp. Lond.; Regist. (Clin. Pharmacol.) Roy. Postgrad. Med. Sch. Lond.

BATEMAN, Frederick John Afford (retired) Broadviews, South Road, Hythe CT21 6AR Tel: 01303 260067 — MB BS 1952 Lond.; MRCS Eng. LRCP Lond. 1952. Cons. Genitourin. Med. Preston Hall Hosp. Maidstone. Prev: Med. Supt. Darwin Hosp.

BATEMAN, Jean (retired) 20 Well Head Lane, Halifax HX1 2BL Tel: 01422 355261 — MB ChB 1943 Leeds; MRCGP 1953. Prev: Res. Surg. Off. Birm. Accid. Hosp.

BATEMAN, Jeffrey Martyn Princess Royal Hospital, Apley Castle, Telford TF1 6TF Tel: 01952 641222 Fax: 01952 242218 Email: jeffrey.bateman@prh-tr.wmids.nhs.uk; Dorrington Grove, Dorrington, Shrewsbury SY5 7JX Tel: 01743 718927 — MB BS 1982 Lond.; MRCP (UK) 1987; FRCP Lond. 1998. (Lond. Hosp.) Cons. Phys. & Gastroenterol. P.ss Roy. Hosp. Telford. Prev: Cons. Phys. RAF Med. Br.; Sen. Regist. (Med.) John Radcliffe Hosp. Oxf.

BATEMAN, Jennifer Elsie 20 Woodlands Avenue, Emsworth PO10 7QE Tel: 01243 374348 — MB ChB 1967 Leeds; DCH Eng. 1975. SCMO (Family Plann. & Well Wom. Servs.) Portsmouth Health Care Trust; Asst. GP Portchester; Mem. Fac. of Family Plann. & Reproduc. Health Care RCOG. Socs: BMA; Brit. Menopause Soc.

BATEMAN, John Gordon (retired) 19 The Drive, Northwood HA6 1HW Tel: 01923 827906 — BM BCh Oxf. 1954. Prev: Cas. Off. & Orthop. Ho. Surg. Roy. E. Sussex Hosp. Hastings.

BATEMAN, John Roderick Mellor 96 Belper Road, Derby DE1 3EQ; Derby City General Hospital Trust, Uttoxeter Road, Derby DE22 3NE — MB BS 1972 Lond.; BSc Lond. 1969; MRCP (UK) 1976; MRCS Eng. LRCP Lond. 1972. (Roy. Free) Cons. Phys. (Respirat. Dis.) Derby City Hosp. Socs: Med. Research Soc. & Thoracic Soc. Prev: Sen. Med. Regist. E. Birm. Hosp.; Lect. Med. & Physiol. Roy. Free Hosp. Lond.; SHO Brompton Hosp. Lond.

BATEMAN, Karen Lesley Long Barn, The Green, Stadhampton, Oxford OX44 7UW — MB BS 1991 Lond.; DRCOG 1996; DFFP 1996. (St. Mary's)

BATEMAN, Margaret Jane Alan St John's Hospital, Livingston EH54 6PP Tel: 01506 419666; 28 Beechwood, Linlithgow EH49 6SF — MB BCh BAO 1971 Belf. (Belf.) Staff Grade Paediat. Dept. Community Child Health St. John's Hosp. Livingston. Prev: Med. Off. Dept. Community Child Health Bangour Gen. Hosp.

BATEMAN, Mary (retired) 26 Walton Street, Oxford OX1 2HQ Tel: 01865 553744 — MD Lond. 1952, MB BS 1950; FRCP Lond. 1973, M 1953; MRCS Eng. LRCP Lond. 1950. Prev: Phys. St. Geo., Bolingbroke & Eliz. G. Anderson Hosp. for Wom. Lond.

BATEMAN, Mary La Trobe (retired) Clos De Dixcart, Sark, Guernsey GY9 0SA — LRCP LRCS Ed. LRFPS Glas. 1946.

BATEMAN, Neil David 20 Woodlands Avenue, Emsworth PO10 7QE — BM BS 1993 Nottm.

BATEMAN, Nigel Turner St Thomas's Hospital, London SE1 9EH Tel: 020 7928 9292 Fax: 020 7922 8206 Email: nigel.bateman@gstt.sthames.nhs.uk; 50 Alleyn Road, Dulwich, London SE21 8AL Tel: 020 8761 5171 Fax: 020 7922 8206 — BM BCh 1969 Oxf.; MA Oxf. 1969; FRCP Lond. 1984; MRCP (UK) 1972; FRCP Glas. Cons. Phys. St. Thos. Hosp. Lond.; Hon. Sen. Lect. (Med.) Guys Kings & St Thos. Sch. Med. Socs: Chairm. MRCP UK Part 2 Written Bd.

BATEMAN, Patricia Jane 19 Ashen Green, Great Shelford, Cambridge CB2 5EY Tel: 01223 843963 Fax: 01223 843963 — MB BS 1966 Lond.; FRCS Eng. 1979; MRCS Eng. LRCP Lond. 1966; FRCOphth 1989; DO Eng. 1969; MSc Lond. 1999. (St. Bart.) Assoc. Specialist Hinchingbrooke Hosp. Huntington & Doddington Co. Hosp.; Clin. Asst. Addenbrookes Hosp. Camb. Prev: Assoc. Specialist. Doddington Co. Hosp. Cambs.; Med. Off. (Ophth.) Mulago Hosp. Kampala, Uganda.

BATEMAN, Richard Michael Poynings, The Limes, Felbridge, East Grinstead RH19 2QY — MB ChB 1994 Bristol; DMCC 1997. SHO (Anaesth.) Roy. Hosp. Haslar Gosport.

***BATEMAN, Sally Louise** Rowellen, Rushmore Hill, Orpington BR6 7NQ — MB ChB 1998 Bristol.

BATEMAN, Sandra Patricia Laisterdyke Clinic, Moorside Lane, Bradford BD3 8DH Tel: 01274 662441 — MB ChB 1983 Liverp.; DRCOG 1989; DA (UK) 1985. Prev: SHO (Psychiat.) Stanley Royd Hosp. Wakefield; SHO (Anaesth., Gyn., A & E) Leeds Gen. Infirm.

BATEMAN, Shawn Cato, DFM (retired) 28 Laneside Drive, Bramhall, Stockport SK7 3AR Tel: 0161 439 3681 — MB BCh BAO Belf. 1952; MFOM 1981; MRAeS 1981. Aviat. Med. Cons. Brit. Airways; Med. Adviser Manch. Internat. Airport Auth. Prev: Sen. Med. Off. (N.) Brit. Airways Med. Serv.

BATEMAN, Susan Georgina 5 Windsor Walk, Weybridge KT13 9AP — MB ChB 1972 Liverp.; FRCOG 1992, M 1978; DObst 1974. Cons. O & G St. Peter's Hosp. Chertsey.

BATER, Alun Smith (retired) Pinetrees, 5 The Mount, Dinas Powys CF64 4DP — MB BCh 1951 Wales; BSc Wales 1948, MB BCh

1951. Clin. Teach. (Gen. Pract.) Welsh Nat. Sch. Med.; Med. Off. Welsh Off. Prev: Ho. Surg. & Cas. Surg. Off. Cardiff Roy. Infirm.

BATER, Eric John Doctors Surgery, Hinnings Road, Distington, Workington CA14 5UR Tel: 01946 830207; The Old Vicarage, Park End Road, Workington CA14 4DG — MB ChB 1982 Bristol; MRCGP 1985; MA (Med. Educat.) Durham 1998; Dip. Palliat. Med. Wales 1998. GP; VTS Course Organiser. Prev: Trainee GP W. Cumbld. Hosp. Whitehaven VTS; Ho. Off. (Med.) W. Cumbld. Hosp.; Ho. Off. (Profess. Surg.) Bristol Roy. Infirm.

BATES, Mr Adam Charles 20 Arley Avenue, West oosqury, Manchester M20 2LQ — MB ChB 1994 Manch.; MA (Hons.) Camb. 1995; FRCOphth 1998. Specialist Regist., Ophth. Roy. Eye Hosp., Manch. Socs: BMA. Prev: SHO (Ophth.) Roy. Hallamsh. Sheff.; Demonst. (Biomed. Sci.) Univ. Sheff.

BATES, Mr Adrian Keith Taunton & Somerset Hospital, Musgrove Park, Taunton TA1 5DA Tel: 01823 342955; Orchard House, Gatchell Meadow, Trull, Taunton TA3 7HY Tel: 01823 330281 — BM BCh 1982 Oxf.; MA Oxf. 1983, BM BCh 1982; FRCS Eng. 1987; FRCOphth. 1990. (Oxford University) Cons. Ophalmic Surg. & Clin. Dir. Specialist Surg. Taunton & Som. Hosp. Prev: Sen. Regist. (Ophth.) Moorfields Eye Hosp. Lond.

BATES, Alan Bartholomew Department of Medicine, Ysbyty Gwynedd, Bangor LL57 2PW Tel: 01248 384361 Email: alan.bates@nww-tr.wales.nhs.uk; 10 Waen y Pandy, Tregarth, Bangor LL57 4RB Tel: 01248 602479 — MB BS 1979 Newc.; BMedSc (Hons.) Newc. 1978, MB BS 1979; MRCP (UK) 1982; FRCP 1996. Cons. Phys. Dept. Med. Ysbyty Gwynedd Bangor. Socs: Brit. Geriat. Soc.; Brit. Assn. of Stroke Phys.s.

BATES, Alan William Department of Morbid Anatomy and Histopathology, The Royal London Hospital, London E1 1BB Email: abates@mds.qmw.ac.uk; 100 West Road, London E15 3PY Email: awbates@globalnet.co.uk — MB BS 1989 Lond.; PhD Lond. 1992, BSc 1986; DRCPath 1998. Lect. (Path.) Qu. Mary & W.field Coll. Lond. Socs: Anat. Soc.; Fell. Roy. Soc. of Med. Prev: Demonst. (Anat.) Qu. Mary & W.field Coll. Lond.

BATES, Alexandra Louise 66 Tunis Road, London W12 7EY — MB BS 1995 Lond.

BATES, Andrew Michael Appleby Surgery, Hawkeys Lane, North Shields NE29 0SF Tel: 0191 296 1770 Fax: 0191 296 1770; 56 Grosvenor Drive, Whitley Bay NE26 2JS — MB BS 1982 Newc.; MRCGP 1986; DRCOG 1985. (Newc. u. Tyne) Clin. Asst. N. Tyneside Dist. Gen. Hosp. Prev: Trainee GP N.umbria VTS.

BATES, Andrew Stuart 43 Pulteney Drive, Boundary Farm, Tillington, Stafford ST16 1NU — MB ChB 1987 Leeds.

BATES, Andrew Tom The Old Chapel, Longstock, Stockbridge SO20 6DR Email: andrew.bates1@virgin.net — MB BS 1995 Lond.; BSc Clin Pharmacol. 1993; MRCP 1999. (Lond.) Specialist Regist. (Clin. Oncol.), Wessex Rotat.

BATES, Anthony John The Surgery, 28 Holes Lane, Woolston, Warrington WA1 4NE Tel: 01925 653218 Fax: 01925 244767; 134 London Road, Stockton Heath, Warrington WA4 6LF — MB ChB 1977 Dundee; DRCOG 1980.

BATES, Mr Arthur (retired) Phorp Farmhouse, Dunphail, Forres IV36 2QR Tel: 01309 611333 — MB BChir 1949 Camb.; MA Camb. 1959, MB BChir 1949; FRCS Eng. 1960; FRCOG 1971, M 1956, DObst 1952. Prev: Cons. (O & G) N.ants. HA.

BATES, Brenda Jean Culland Manor Farm, Culland Lane, Brailsford, Ashbourne DE6 5BW Tel: 01332 60326 — MB ChB 1980 Manch.; MRCGP 1984; DRCOG 1983.

BATES, Brian Joseph Overdale Medical Practice, 207 Victoria Avenue, Borrowash, Derby DE72 3HG Tel: 01332 280800 Fax: 01332 669256; 37 Poplar Road, Breaston, Derby DE72 3BH — MB ChB 1979 Ed.; MRCGP 1983; Dip. Pract. Dermat. Wales 1990; DRCOG 1986; Cert. Family Plann. JCC 1985.

BATES, Catherine Julia 24 Buckhurst Avenue, Sevenoaks TN13 1LZ — MB BS 1994 Lond.

BATES, Charles Patrick Urology Department, City Hospital, Nottingham NG5 1PB Tel: 0115 969 1169 Fax: 0115 962 7791; Dumbleside, 17 Bridle Road, Burton Joyce, Nottingham NG14 5FT Tel: 0115 931 3725 — BM BCh 1962 Oxf.; DM Oxf. 1974; FRCS Eng. 1967. (Middlx.) Cons. Surg. Nottm. Gps. Hosps. Socs: Brit. Assn. Urol. Surgs.; Brit. Med. Assn.; Internat. Continuance Soc. Prev: Sen. Regist. St Peter's Hosps. Lond.; Hunt. Prof. RCS Eng. 1970; Regist. Middlx. Hosp. Lond.

BATES, Charlotte Louise 9 Beechfield Road, Gosforth, Newcastle upon Tyne NE3 4DR — MB ChB 1995 Manch. SHO Rotat. (Med.) S. Cleveland Hosp. Prev: Ho. Off. (Med.) N. Manch. Gen. Hosp.; Ho. Off. (Surg.) Leeds Gen. Infirm.

BATES, Christine 3 Rectory Close, Bolton Percy, York YO23 7AX — MB ChB 1976 Leeds; MRCPath 1983. Cons. Histopath. York Dist. Hosp. Prev: Sen. Regist. (Histopath.) Leeds Gen. Infirm.; Regist. (Path.) Leeds Gen. Infirm.; Lect. Forens. Med. Univ. Leeds.

BATES, Christine Joyce Department of Microbiology, Floor F, Royal Hampshire Hospital, Sheffield S10 2SF Tel: 0114 271 3129 Email: christine.bates@csuh.nhs.uk; 14 Eyam Road, Crooks, Sheffield S10 1UU — MB ChB 1987 Sheff.; DTM & H 1997; MRCPath 1999. Cons. Microbiologist, Roy. Hallamshire Hosp., Sheff. Prev: Sen. Regist. Med. microBiol., Roy. Hallamshire & N.ern Gen. Hosp. Sheff.; Registra. Med. Microbio.; SHO med. Micro.

BATES, Christine Margaret Department of Genitourinary Medicine, Royal Liverpool University Hospital, Liverpool L7 8XP Tel: 0151 706 2000 Fax: 0151 706 5821 — MB BS 1978 Lond.; MRCP (UK) 1992; MRCGP 1982; Dip. Venereol. Liverp. 1993; DRCOG 1983; AKC Lond. 1978. (St. Geo.) Sen. Regist. (Genitourin. Med.) Roy. Liverp. Univ. Hosp. Socs: BMA & Med. Soc. for Study of VD.; Birkenhead Med. Soc. Prev: Regist. (Genitourin. Med.) Gen. Hosp. Nottm.; SHO (Obst.) City Hosp. Nottm.; SHO (Paediat.) Epsom Dist. Hosp.

BATES, Mr Christopher Arthur Department of Urology, Royal Gwent Hospital, Cardiff Road, Newport NP20 2UB Tel: 01633 234986; 5 Pen-Y-Groes Grove, Bassaleg, Newport NP10 8JD Tel: 01633 891709 Email: 100331.306@compuserve.com — MB BS 1986 Lond.; MS Lond. 1996; FRCS (Urol.) Eng. 1997; FRCS Eng. 1990. (St. Bart.) Cons. Urol. Roy. Gwent Hosp. Newport. Prev: Sen. Regist. Roy. Marsden, Hammersmith Hosp. & St. Mary's Hosps. Lond.

BATES, Christopher Charles Shepperton Health Centre, Shepperton Court Drive, Laleham Road, Shepperton TW17 8EJ Tel: 01932 220524 Fax: 01932 244948 — MB BS 1962 Lond.; MRCS Eng. LRCP Lond. 1962. (Guy's) Prev: SHO Med. Vict. Hosp. Blackpool; Ho. Off. City Gen. Hosp. Stoke-on-Trent & N. Staffs. Roy. Infirm.

BATES, Christopher Mark Winch Lane Surgery, Winch Lane, Haverfordwest SA61 1RN Tel: 01437 762333 Fax: 01437 766912 — MB BS 1976 Lond.; MRCS Eng. LRCP Lond. 1976; DRCOG 1982.

BATES, Colin Gerald Drayton Medical Practices, The Health Centre, Cheshire Street, Market Drayton TF9 3BS Tel: 01630 652158; 30 Mortimer Road, Buntingsdale, Market Drayton TF9 2EP Tel: 01630 638818 Fax: 01630 638535 — MB ChB 1974 Bristol. Chairm. N. E. Shrop. PCG.

BATES, Damian John 17 Round Head Fold, Apperley Bridge, Bradford BD10 0UG — MB ChB 1994 Leeds.

BATES, David Ward 11, Royal Victoria Infirmary, Newcastle upon Tyne NE1 4LP Tel: 0191 232 5131 Fax: 0191 261 0881; 9 Beechfield Road, Gsforth, Newcastle upon Tyne NE3 4DR Tel: 0191 285 4707 — MB BChir 1968 Camb.; MA Camb. 1969; FRCP (UK) 1982, M 1971. (Middlx.) Sen. Lect. (Neurol.) Univ. Newc.; Cons. Neurol. Newc. Hosps. NHS Trust.

BATES, Diana Thorn Craigencalt, Kinghorn, Burntisland KY3 9YG Tel: 01592 890078 Fax: 01592 890078 — MB ChB 1942 Ed.; MA Camb. 1946, BA 1939. (Univ. Ed.)

BATES, Dorothy 59 Balmammo Park, Bridge of Earn, Perth PH2 9RL — MB ChB 1977 Aberd.

BATES, Elizabeth Susan (retired) 112 Broadmead, Tunbridge Wells TN2 5RW Tel: 01892 540643 — MB BS Lond. 1958; MRCS Eng. LRCP Lond. 1958; DA Eng. 1961. Prev: Regist. Anaesth. St. Peter's Hosp. Chertsey.

BATES, Frances Mary The Surgery, 36 Pagoda Avenue, Richmond TW9 2HG Tel: 020 8948 4217 Fax: 020 8332 7639; 73 Queens Road, Richmond TW10 6HJ Tel: 020 8948 0973 — MB ChB 1969 Birm.; MRCGP 1986; MFFP 1993; FFA RCS Eng. 1974.

BATES, Gary John The Clinic, First Avenue, Gwersllt, Wrexham LL11 4E Tel: 01978 756370; Craig Felen, Mount Pleasant, Penrhos, Brymbo, Wrexham LL11 5LY Tel: 01978 750576 — MB ChB 1984 Liverp.; MRCGP 1988; DRCOG 1986. Prev: Trainee GP N. Clwyd VTS.

BATES, Georgina 17b Montagu Square, London W1H 2LE Tel: 020 7935 1241 — MB 1981 Camb.; BSc (Hons.) (Physiol.) Lond. 1978; BChir 1980. (St. Bart.) SHO (Med. Ophth.) St. Thos. Hosp. Lond. Socs: Fell. Roy. Soc. Med. Prev: SHO (Ophth.) Roy. Free Hosp. Lond.; SHO (Chest Med.) Brompton Hosp. Lond.; SHO (Neurol.) Maudsley & Kings' Coll. Hosp. Lond.

BATES, Gordon David Lyle Birmingham Childrens Hospital, Ladywood Middleway, Ladywood, Birmingham B4 6 Tel: 0121 454 4851; 72 Cambridge Road, Moseley, Birmingham B13 9UD — MB ChB 1989 Birm.; MMedSci Birm. 1996; MRCPsych 1994. Sen. Regist. (Child & Adolesc. Psychiat.) W. Midl. RHA; Hon. Lect. (Psychiat.) Univ. Birm. Socs: Brit. Neuropsychiat. Assn.; Assn. Child Psychol. & Psychiat. Prev: Regist. & SHO Rotat. (Psychiat.) Birm. HA.

BATES, Gordon Henry Nicoll 278 Wingrove Road, Newcastle upon Tyne NE4 9EE Tel: 0191 274 4401 — MB BS 1949 Durh.; DPH 1954. (Durh.)

BATES, Mr Grant James Edward Mills ENT Department, The Radcliffe Infirmary, Woodstock Road, Oxford OX2 6HE Tel: 01865 224855 Fax: 01865 224544 Email: grant.bates@nds.ox.ac.uk; Felstead House, 23 Banbury Road, Oxford OX2 6NX Tel: 01865 31105 Fax: 01865 310342 — BM BCh 1978 Oxf.; BSc Lond. 1975; FRCS Eng. 1985. Cons. Otolaryngol. Radcliffe Infirm. & Clin. Lect. Univ. Oxf. Socs: (Hon. Sec.) Roy. Soc. Med.; (Chair) Med.Staff Counc. Radcliffe Infirm.; Ass. Hon. Sec. Brit. Assn. of OtoLaryngol. & Head & Neck Surg.s. Prev: Cons. Otolaryngol. Cairns, Austral.; Head & Neck Fell. Univ. Qu.sland 1988; TWJ Research Fell. UCSF.

BATES, Helen Simpson House Medical Centre, 255 Eastcote Lane, South Harrow, Harrow HA2 8RS Tel: 020 8864 3466 Fax: 020 8864 1002 — MB BS 1989 Lond.; MRCGP 1995; DRCOG 1994; DCH RCP Lond. 1993. (St. Barts.)

BATES, James William 66 Cortsway, Greasby, Wirral CH49 2NB — MB ChB 1985 Liverp.

BATES, Janice Department of Microbiology, Worthing Hospital, Park Avenue, Worthing BN11 2DH; Downsflint, High St, Upper Beeding, Steyning BN44 3WN — MB BChir 1988 Camb.; PhD Surrey 1982; MA Camb. 1986; BSc Microbiol. Newc. 1977; MSc Virol. Reading 1978; MRCPath (Med. Microbiol.) 1993. Cons. Med. Microbiol. Worthing Hosp. W. Sussex. Prev: Clin. Lect. & Hon. Regist. (Microbiol.) John Radcliffe Hosp. Oxf.

BATES, Jean Anaesthetic Department, Warwick Hospital, Lakin Road, Warwick CV34 5; 18 Beaufort Avenue, New Cubbington, Leamington Spa CV32 7TA — MB ChB 1970 Sheff.; DA Eng. 1980. Staff Grade (Anaesth.) S. Warks. HA.

BATES, Jennifer Ann Barter Dumbleside, 17 Bridle Road, Burton Joyce, Nottingham NG14 5FT Tel: 0115 931 3725 — BM BCh 1963 Oxf.; MA Oxf. 1960; DFFP 1993. (Lond. Hosp.) Clin. Asst. Diabetes Unit Univ. Hosp. Nottm.; Med. Off. (Family Plann.) Nottm. Community Health NHS Trust. Socs: Nott. M-C Soc.; BMA. Prev: Ho. Phys. & Ho. Surg. Surgic. Unit Lond. Hosp.

BATES, Jeremy Henry James St Mary's Hospital, Upper Byron Place, Bristol BS8 1JU; 9 Southleigh Road, Bristol BS8 2BQ — MB ChB 1994 Bristol. Demonst. & RMO (Anat.) Bristol Univ. Prev: Ho. Off. (Med., Surg. & Orthop.) S.mead Hosp. Bristol.

BATES, Joanna Louise 26 Evenlode Av, Penarth CF64 3PD — MB ChB 1997 Leeds.

BATES, Karen Jayne The Surgery, Whiteway Road, Kingsteignton, Newton Abbot TQ12 3HN Tel: 01626 883312; 10 Moor Close, Teignmouth TQ14 8UG Tel: 01626 879090 — BM BS 1983 Nottm.; BMedSci 1981; MRCGP 1987; DRCOG 1986. (Nottingham)

BATES, Marie Adrienne Elisabeth Jeanne Lilian (retired) 66 North Road, Highgate Village, London N6 4AA Tel: 020 8348 1376 — MD 1934 Paris; MD (Silver Medal) Paris 1934; MRCPsych 1971; DPH 1933. Prev: Cons. Psychiat. Essex AHA & Roy. E. Co. Hosp. Colchester.

BATES, Michael 16 Corsie Hill Road, Perth PH2 7BZ — MB BCh 1981 Wales; MRCPsych 1996. Specialist Regist. (Psychiat.) Dundee. Prev: GP Lochgelly, Fife.

BATES, Milan 36 Railton Jones Close, Stoke Gifford, Bristol BS34 8BF Tel: 0117 931 5042 Fax: 0117 931 5042 — MD 1984 Manch.; Lijecnik Zagreb 1984.

BATES, Nicholas Philip Clinical Oncology Department, Oxford Radcliffe Hospitals NHS Trust, The Churchill, Headington, Oxford OX3 7LJ Tel: 01865 225601 — BM BCh 1986 Oxf.; MA Camb. 1987; MRCP (UK) 1989; FRCR (Clin. Oncol.) 1993; PhD Lond. 1997. (Oxford) Cons. (Clin. Oncol.) Oxf. Radcliffe Hosp., NHS Trust, Oxf. Socs: Brit. Oncological Assn.; Brit. Assn. for Cancer Research; Assn. of Cancer Phys.s. Prev: Specialist Regist. (Med. Oncol.) Ch.ill Hosp. Oxf.; ICRF Clin. Research Fell. & Hon. Sen. Regist. Hammersmith Hosp. Lond.; Regist. (Clin. Oncol.) Addenbrooke's Hosp. Camb.

BATES, Nicola Ann Porter Brook Medical Centre, 9 Sunderland Street, Sheffield S11 8HN Tel: 0114 263 6100; 42 Bentley Road, Walkley Bank, Sheffield S6 5DZ — BM BS 1985 Nottm.; DRCOG 1988.

BATES, Paul Ash Trees Surgery, Market Street, Carnforth LA5 9JU Tel: 01524 720000 Fax: 01524 720110 — MB BS 1974 Lond.; MRCP (UK) 1980; MRCS Eng. LRCP Lond. 1974; MRCGP 1980; DCH Eng. 1977; DRCOG 1977. (St. Bart.)

BATES, Paul Clifford The Surgery, 16 Windsor Road, Chobham, Woking GU24 8NA Tel: 01276 857117 Fax: 01276 855668; Range End, Brentmoor Road, West End, Woking GU24 9ND Tel: 01483 473046 — MB BS 1969 Lond.; DObst RCOG 1973. Socs: BMA; Roy. Soc. of Med.

BATES, Peter David 55 Thistlewaite Road, London E5 0QG Email: petebatesy@btinternet.com — MB BS 1997 Lond.; MRCS Eng. LRCP 2000 Lond. (St. Bartholomew's Hospital) SHO Orthopaed. RNOH. Prev: SHO Basic Surgic. Train., Broomfield Hosp., Chelmsford.

BATES, Mr Peter Francis 1 River Court, 82 St George's Square, London SW1V 3QX Tel: 020 7821 0768 Fax: 020 7821 0768 — MB BChir 1961 Camb.; MA 1960, BA Camb. 1956; FRCS Eng. 1969; FRCSI 1967. (Camb. & St. Mary's) Hon. Tutor (Surg.) Guy's Med. Sch. Socs: Fell. Assn. Surgs.; Fell. Roy. Soc. Med.; BMA. Prev: Cons. Surg. W. Hill & Joyce Green Hosps. Dartford; SHO (Gen. Surg.) W. Middlx. Hosp. Isleworth; Regist (Surg.) Hillingdon Hosp.

BATES, Peter Gordon 2 Squires Bridge Road, Shepperton TW17 0LB — MB BS 1992 Lond.

BATES, Peter Richard 67 Manor Crescent, Knutsford WA16 8DJ Tel: 01565 653506 — MB ChB 1991 Manch. Regist. Rotat. (Diabetes & Endocrinol.) NW RHA Train. Scheme Manch.; Regist. (Diabetes & Endocrinol.) Hope Hosp. Salford. Prev: Regist. (Gen. & Respirat. Med.) Trafford Gen. Hosp.

BATES, Polly Ann Sarah Beehive, Halfkey Road, Malvern WR14 1UP — MB ChB 1991 Bristol.

BATES, Mr Richard Adrian Department of Ophthalmology, Milton Keynes General NHS Trust, Standing Way, Milton Keynes MK6 5LD Tel: 01908 243080 Fax: 01908 669348 — MB BS 1977 Lond.; MRCS Eng. LRCP Lond. 1977; FRCS Eng. 1984; FCOphth 1988; DO Eng. 1982. (Char. Cross) Cons. Ophth. Surg. Milton Keynes NHS Trust. Socs: Fell. Roy. Soc. Med.; UK Intraocular Impl. Soc. Prev: Sen. Regist. Birm. & Midl. Eye Hosp.; Regist. St. Pauls Eye Hosp. Liverp.

BATES, Robert George The Kennet Suite, Hampshire Clinic, Basing Road, Old Basing, Basingstoke RG24 7AL Tel: 01256 364422 Fax: 01256 364422; Fair Oaks, Church Road, Tadley, Basingstoke RG26 3AU Tel: 0118 981 7501 Fax: 0118 981 7501 Email: 101351.320@compuserve.com — MB BS 1980 Lond.; MB BS (Hons.) Lond. 1980; BSc Lond. 1977, MD 1990; MRCOG 1986. (St. Geo.) Cons. O & G & Reproduc. Med. N. Hants. Hosp. Basingstoke. Socs: Amer. Soc. Reproduc. Med.; Brit. Fertil. Soc.; Roy. Soc. Med. Prev: Sen. Regist. Rotat. Hillingdon Hosp. & Qu. Charlottes Hosp. for Wom.; Research Regist. (Fertil.) Chelsea Hosp. Wom. Lond.; Regist. (O & G) Guy's Hosp. Lond. & S.lands Hosp. Shoreham-by-Sea.

BATES, Rona Caroline Elizabeth Southern Derbyshire Health Authority NHS Trust, London Road, Derby DE1 2FZ Tel: 01332 347141 — MB ChB 1987 Leic.; FRCA 1998. Cons. Anaesth., S.. Derbysh. NHS Trust, Derby. Prev: Specialist Regist. Anaesth. Nottm.

BATES, Rosalind Eva Bassetts Centre, Starts Hill Road, Farnborough, Orpington BR6 7WF Tel: 01689 853388 Fax: 01689 861232; 29 Capital Wharf, 50 Wapping High St, London E1W 1LY Tel: 020 7709 0866 — MB BCh BAO Belf. 1966; MRCPsych 1980; DPM Eng. 1977; MSc 2000 Lond. Cons. Psychiat. Learning Disabil. Servs. Ravensbourne NHS Trust Bromley; Hon. Lect. Guy's Hosp. Med. Sch.; Assoc. Cons. Bethlem Roy. & Maudsley Gp. Hosps. Socs: BMA; Roy. Coll. Psychiat.; BNPA. Prev: Sen. Regist. (Child & Adolesc. Psychiat.) Bethlem Roy. & Maudsley Hosps.

BATES, Stephen James 82A Belsize Park Gardens, London NW3 4NG — MB BS 1987 Adelaide; FRCA 1994.

BATES, Thelma Dorothy, OBE Saxonwood, Albany Close, Esher KT10 9JR Tel: 01372 464851 Email: thelma.bates@talk21.com — MB ChB 1952 Birm.; MRCS Eng. LRCP Lond. 1952; FRCR 1966; FRACR 1958; MRCP 1998. Mem. Criminal Injuries Compensation Appeals Panel. Socs: (Chairm. Health Comm.) GMC; (Ex-Vice-Pres.) Roy. Coll. Radiol.; Roy. Soc. Med. (Ex-Pres. Sect. Radiol.). Prev: Cons. Radiother. St. Thos. Hosp. Lond.

BATES, Timothy Matthew Old Pitts Farm, Langrish, Petersfield GU32 1RQ — MB BS 1994 Lond.

BATES, Mr Timothy Simon Dept. Of Urology, Royal United Hospital, Bath BA1 3NG Tel: 01225 825312 Email: tim.bates@ruh-bath.swest.nhs.uk — BM BS 1987 Nottm.; FRCS 1999 (urol); BMedSci. 1985; FRCS Eng. 1992. Cons. Urol., Roy. United Hosp., Bath.

BATES, Mr Tom Lamplands, Pilgrims Way, East Brabourne, Ashford TN25 5LU Tel: 01233 750304 Fax: 01233 750599 Email: bates.tom@virgin.net — MBBS 1996 Lond.; FRCS Eng. 1971; MRCS Eng. LRCP Lond. 1966. (St. Bart.) Cons. Surg., The BrE. Unit, William Harvey Hosp. Ashford Kent TN240LZ; Hon. Sen. Lect. Univ. Kent Canterbury 1996. Socs: (Treas.) Assn. Surgs. GB & Irel.; Vice-Chairm. Brit. Jl. of Surg. Soc.; Chair.,BrE. Gp. Of BASO. Prev: Sen. Regist. (Surg.) Guy's Hosp. Lond.; Regist. (Surg.) Luton & Dunstable Hosp.; Ho. Surg. St. Bart. Hosp. Lond.

BATES, Trevor Hambleton Park Stile Cottage Surgery, Park Stile Cottage, Church Street, Broughton-in-Furness LA20 6HJ Tel: 01229 716337 Fax: 01229 716928 — MRCS Eng. LRCP Lond. 1964. (Sheff.) Socs: BMA. Prev: SHO Obst. W.. Hosp. Doncaster; Asst. Cas. Off. Roy. Infirm. Sheff.

BATES-KREUGER, Johanna Gesina 59 Mountbatten Avenue, Sandal, Wakefield WF2 6HE — Artsexamen 1993 Amsterdam.

BATESON, Annie (retired) 89A Gores Lane, Formby, Liverpool L37 7DE Tel: 0170 48 79972 — MB ChB 1946 Manch. Prev: Med. Off. DSS.

BATESON, Malcolm Cedric 34 Low Etherley, Bishop Auckland DL14 0EU Tel: 01388 603285 — MB ChB 1968 Birm.; MD Birm. 1979; FRCP Ed. 1989; FRCP Lond. 1987; MRCP (UK) 1972. Cons. Phys. & Specialist (Gastroenterol.) Bishop Auckland Gen. Hosp.; Hon. Clin. Lect. Univ. Newc. Socs: Fell. Postgrad. Med.; Brit. Soc. Gastroenterol. Prev: Lect. (Med.) Univ. Dundee; Research Fell (Gastroenterol.) Univ. Dundee; Regist. (Med.) Gordon Hosp. Lond. & Dept. Therap. W.m. Hosp.

BATESON, Nicholas Geoffrey Robert Churchfield Surgery, Iburndale Lane, Sleights, Whitby YO22 5DP Tel: 01947 810466 Fax: 01947 811375 — MB ChB 1977 Sheff.; MRCGP 1984; DCH RCP Lond. 1983.

BATESON, Paul Michael Grassendale Medical Practice, 23 Darby Road, Liverpool L19 9BP Tel: 0151 427 1214 Fax: 0151 427 0611; 6 Gateacre Vale Road, Woolton, Liverpool L25 5NP Tel: 0151 428 1973 — MB ChB 1978 Manch.; BSc St. And. 1975. Med. Off. BAMS. Prev: SHO Roy. Manch. Childr. Hosp.

BATEY, Mr Nicholas Robin (retired) Boayl Dooin Ballavitchel Road, Crosby, Douglas IM4 2DN Tel: 01624 852366 — MB BS Durh. 1960; FRCS Eng. Ad Eundem 1983; FRCS Ed. 1966. Examr. RCS Ed. Prev: Cons. Gen. Surg. Noble's I. of Man Hosp.

BATH, Mr Andrew Paul 4 Storth Avenue, Ranmoor, Sheffield S10 3HL — BM BS 1988 Nottm.; BMedSci Nottm. 1986; FRCS Eng. 1993. Sen. Regist. (ENT Surg.) Roy. Hallamsh. Hosp. Sheff.

BATH, Desmond Sackville Gwyn 169 West Wycombe Road, High Wycombe HP12 3AF Tel: 01494 26840; Lennel Hill, 15 Lucas Road, High Wycombe HP13 6QG Tel: 01494 440476 — MB ChB 1959 Ed.; DObst RCOG 1970; DLO Eng. 1966. Socs: BMA. Prev: Ho. Phys. Roy. Vict. Hosp. Edin.; Ho. Surg. Roy. Infirm. Edin.

BATH, Eleanor Mackay 24 Priory Avenue, High Wycombe HP13 6SH Tel: 01494 448132; Lennel Hill, 15 Lucas Road, High Wycombe HP13 6QG Tel: 01494 440476 — MB ChB 1958 St. And. (St. And.)

BATH, Julian Clive John Lloyd (retired) 13 Gardenside Avenue, Uddingston, Glasgow G71 7BU Tel: 01698 813246 — MB ChB 1956 Ed.; BSc (Hons. Physiol.) Ed. 1953; FRCP Glas. 1988; FRCP Ed. 1971, M 1959. Prev: Cons. Phys. (Respirat. Dis.) Law Hosp. Carluke & Strathclyde Hosp. Motherwell.

BATH, Louise Eleanor 57 Comely Bank Avenue, Edinburgh EH4 1ET — MB ChB 1989 Leics.; DRCOG 1991; MRCGP 1993; MRCP 1995; MRCPCH 1997. Lect. Child Life & Health. Socs: MRCP; MRCPCH.

BATH, Professor Philip Michael William Division of Stroke Medicine, University of Nottingham, City Hospital Campus, Nottingham NG5 1PB Tel: 0115 840 4791 Fax: 0115 840 4790 Email: philip.bath@nottingham.ac.uk — MB BS 1982 Lond.; BSc Lond. 1979, MD 1991; MRCP (UK) 1986; FRCP Lond. 1998. (St. Thos.) Stroke Assn Prof. of Stroke Med. Univ. of Nottm.; Hon. Cons. Phys. City Hosp. Nottm. Socs: Eur. Stroke Counc.; Am. Heart Assoc. Stroke Counc.; Brit. Assoc. of stroke phys. Prev: Sen. Lect. (Stroke) & Hon. Cons. Phys. Kings Coll. Sch. of Med. & Dent.; Lect. (Med.) St. Geo. Hosp. Med. Sch. Lond.; Research Fell. Brit. Heart Foundat.

BATH, Pritpal Singh The Surgery, 49 Ashcroft Road, Stopsley, Luton LU2 9AU Tel: 01582 391831 Fax: 01582 488052 — MB BS 1976 Newc.

BATH, Rita 21 Gallosson Road, London SE18 1RD — MB BCh 1997 Wales.

BATH, Sirjit Singh Tower Hill Medical Centre, 25 Tower Hill, Great Barr, Birmingham B42 1LG Tel: 0121 357 1077; 289 Foley Road W., Streetly, Sutton Coldfield B74 3NU — MB ChB 1983 Leeds; DGM RCP Lond. 1986. Socs: BMA. Prev: Trainee GP Birm. VTS; SHO (O & G, Geriat.) Dudley Rd. Hosp. Birm.

BATHAM, Donald Richard Andover Health Centre, Charlton Road, Andover SP10 3LD Tel: 01264 350270 Fax: 01264 336701; 58 Borkum Close, Andover SP10 4LE — MB BS 1982 Lond.; MRCGP 1989; DFFP 1992; DRCOG 1986. (King's Coll. Hosp.) Socs: Brit. Assn. Sport & Med. Prev: SHO (A & E) Roy. Hosp. Plymouth; Sen. Med. Off. HMS Fawn; Med. Off. Roy. Anglian Regt.

BATHEJA, Maneka 106A Wellesley Road, Ilford IG1 4LD — MB BS 1983 Lond.

BATHER, Caroline Lisa Drum Court, Raigmore Hospital, Inverness IV2 3UJ — MB ChB 1992 Bristol.

BATHGATE, Andrew John CLDD, Royal Infimary of Edinburgh, Lauriston Place, Edinburgh EH3 9YW; 15 Frogston Avenue, Edinburgh EH10 7AQ — MB ChB 1991 Ed.; MD 2000 Ed.; MRCP 1994 (UK); MRCP (UK) 1994. (Edin.) Cons. (Gastroenterol.) Roy. Infim. Edin. Socs: Brit. Associaton for Study of Liver Dis.s; Amer. Assn. for Study of Liver Dis.s. Prev: Career Regist. (Gastroenterol.) St. John's Hosp. Livingstone; SHO Rotat. (Med.) Aberd. Roy. Hosps.

BATHGATE, James Thomas Lime Grove Medical Centre, Lime Grove Walk, Matlock DE4 3FD Tel: 01629 583223; 190 Smedley Street, Matlock DE4 3JA — MB ChB 1984 Ed.; MRCGP 1988; DCH RCP Lond. 1988; DRCOG 1986. (Edin.) GP Princip. Matlock. Prev: Trainee GP Peebles VTS.; SHO (Paediat.) Falkirk & Dist. Roy. Infirm. Falkirk; SHO (O & G) W.. Gen. Hosp. Edin.

BATHIJA, Anuradha Shyam Highland, Manor Lane, Halesowen B62 8RD Tel: 0121 550 7714 — MB BS 1966 Calcutta. (Nat. Med. Inst. Calcutta)

BATHIJA, Shyam Hariram The Surgery, Pound Close, Oldbury, Warley B68 8LZ Tel: 0121 552 1632 Fax: 0121 552 0848 — MB BS 1966 Calcutta.

BATHLA, Vijay Handsworth Medical Centre, 143 Albert Road, Handsworth, Birmingham B21 9LE Tel: 0121 554 0980 Fax: 0121 554 3025 — MB BS 1972 Banaras Hindu.

BATHOOL, Ryhana c/o Old Church Hospital, Romford RM7 0BE Tel: 01708 46090 — MB BS 1973 Madras; DGO Madras 1976.

BATHURST, Carol Elizabeth The Surgery, Ewyas Harold, Hereford HR2 0EU Tel: 01981 240320 Fax: 01981 241023; Millcroft, Enyas Harold, Hereford HR2 0EL Tel: 01981 240582 — MB ChB 1987 Liverp.; DRCOG 1991; DCH RCP Lond. 1990. p/t GP Princip. Prev: Trainee GP Cromer; Clin. Asst. (Gen. Pract.) Monmouth.

BATHURST, Mr Nicholas Charles George Yeovil District Hospital, Higher Kingston, Yeovil BA21 4AT; Pavings, The Avenue, Sherborne DT9 3AJ — MB BS 1978 Lond.; BSc. Lond. 1975, MB BS 1978; FRCS Eng. 1982; FRCR 1985. (Guy's) Cons. Radiol. Yeovil Dist. Hosp. Socs: FRCR; Brit. Inst. Radiol. Prev: Sen. Regist. (Radiol.) Bristol Roy. Infirm.; Clin. Fell. (Radiol.) McMaster Med. Centre Hamilton Ontario, Canada.

BATIN, Phillip Douglas Department of Cardiology, Pinderfield Hospital, Aberford Road, Wakefield WF1 4DG Tel: 01924 201688; Tel: 01924 213813 — MB ChB 1985 Leeds; FRCP 2001 London; DM Nottm. 1994; MRCP (UK) 1988. (Leeds) Cons. (Cardiol.). Prev:

Sen. Regist. (Cardiol.) Leeds; Regist. (Cardiol.) Leeds; Research Regist. (Cardiol.) Nottm.

BATMAN, David Christopher Nestlé UK Ltd, c/o Nestlé Rowntree, Haxby Road, York YO91 1XY Tel: 01904 602342 Fax: 01904 604413 Email: david.batman@nestlegb.nestle.com; The Firs, Front St, Tollerton, York YO61 1QQ Email: dbatma@aol.com — MB ChB 1973 Sheff.; MSc (Occupat. Med.) Lond. 1988; FFOM RCP Lond. 1997, MFOM 1991, AFOM 1986; DRCOG 1990; DIH Lond. 1985. (Sheff.) Head of Health & Safety & Gp. Chief Med. Off. Nestlé UK Ltd. Socs: MIOSH; Soc. Occupat. Med. (Ex-Chairm. Yorks. Br.); Chairm. Food Industry Med. Assn. Prev: Company Occupat. Health Adviser Rowntree Mackintosh Confectionery Ltd.; GP Felixstowe; Chief Med. Off. Port of Felixstowe.

BATMAN, Philip Anthony Bradford Royal Infirmary, Duckworth Lane, Bradford BD9 6RJ Tel: 01274 364211 Fax: 01274 364190; Ferncliffe, 7 Albany Walk, Ilkley LS29 9LZ Tel: 01943 600447 — MB BChir 1979 Camb.; MA Camb. 1979, MD 1997; FRCPath 1996, M 1986. Cons. Histopath. Bradford Roy. Infirm.; Hon. Cons. Histopath. Leeds Gen. Infirm. Prev: Sen. Regist. (Histopath.) St. Geo. Hosp. Lond.

***BATOOL, Irum** 45 Worsley Crescent, Newton Mearns, Glasgow G77 6DW Tel: 0141 639 7231 — MB ChB 1997 Glas.

BATOOL, Mr Mushahida Benstream Ltd, 246 Old Brompton Road, London SW5 0DE — MB BS 1986 Punjab; FRCS Glas. 1993.

BATOOL, Tahira c/o Dr R. M. Khokhar, Belmount, Queen's Road, Ilkley LS29 9QL — MB BS 1980 Punjab; MRCOG 1986.

BATRA, Bhupinder Kumar Waldron Health Centre, Stanley Street, London SE8 4BG Tel: 020 8691 0144 Fax: 020 8692 5094 — MB BS 1969 Aligarh Muslim; DCH Eng. 1974; DCH Delhi 1972. (Jawahar Lal Nehru) GP. Prev: GP Gr. Pk. Lond.; GP Trainee Pontefract; Regist. (Paediat.) Gulson Hosp. Coventry.

BATRA, Gaurav Surrinder 1 Langham Avenue, Accrington BB5 5BG — MB BCh 1995 Wales.

BATRA, Mr Harish Chandra Manor Hospital, Moat Road, Walsall WS2 9PS Tel: 01922 721172 — MB BS 1960 Punjab (India); MS (Orthop.) Lucknow 1964; FRCS Ed. 1971. (Christian Med. Coll. Ludhiana) Cons. Orthop. Surg. Walsall NHS Hosp. Trust. Socs: Fell. BOA; Brit. Orthop. Research Soc. Prev: Regist. Centre for Hip Surg. Wrightington Hosp. Appley Bridge; Sen. Regist. Univ. Dept. Orthop. Surg. W.. Infirm. Glas.

BATRA, Naval 155 Vale Road, Woolton, Liverpool L25 7RY — MB ChB 1991 Manch.

BATRA, Neelam 62 Westway, Garforth, Leeds LS25 1DB Tel: 0113 287 3606 — MB BS 1977 Delhi.

BATRA, Ram Paul 155 Vale Road, Woolton, Liverpool L25 7RY — MB ChB 1991 Manch.

BATRA, Ramesh Kumar The Health Centre, Gibson Lane, Kippax, Leeds LS25 7JN Tel: 0113 287 0870 Fax: 0113 232 0746 — MB BS 1975 Delhi; MB BS 1975 Delhi. (Delhi) GP Leeds.

BATRA, Sanjay Tower Medical Centre, 129 Cannon Street Road, London E1 2LX Tel: 020 7488 4240 Fax: 020 7702 2443; 38 Wanstead Park Avenue, London E12 5EN Tel: 020 8530 1128 Email: batras@bigfoot.com — MB BS 1980 Lond.; DFFP 1993. (Univ. Coll. Hosp.) Prev: Trainee GP Luton VTS; Regist. N.wick Pk. Hosp.

BATRA, Subhashini Bloomsbury Health Centre, 63 Rupert Street, Nechells, Birmingham B7 5DT Tel: 0121 678 3932 Fax: 0121 678 3925; Rowans, Streetly Wood, Streetly, Sutton Coldfield B74 3DQ Tel: 0121 353 3084 — MB BS 1963 Punjab (India); DCH RCPS Glas. 1970. (Christian Med. Coll. Ludhiana) GP; CMO in Family Plann. with N. Birm. Trust. Socs: MPS; SPA. Prev: SHO (Eye & ENT) Norf. & Norwich Hosp.; SHO (Rheum.) Wrightington Hosp. Appley Bridge; SHO (Paediat.) Roy. Hosp. Sick Childr. Glas.

BATRICK, Miss Nicola Clare Flat 7, 69 Crystal Palace Park Road, London SE26 6UT — MB BS 1988 Lond.; FRCS (Eng) 1992. (London Hospital Medical College)

BATSFORD, Paula 94 Mountcastle Road, Leicester LE3 2BX — MB ChB 1998 Leic.; MB ChB Leic 1998.

BATSON, Elizabeth Lindsay (retired) 2 The Sanctuary, Thorpeness, Leiston IP16 4PH Tel: 01728 452595 — MB BS 1951 Lond.; MRCS Eng. LRCP Lond. 1951. Prev: GP, E. Ham.

BATSON, Gerald Audley, TD (retired) Priory Farm, Kettleby, Brigg DN20 9HN — MD 1969 Aberd.; MB ChB 1960; FRCP Ed. 1984, M 1968; DObst RCOG 1962. Prev: Cons. Phys. Scunthorpe Health Dist.

BATSTONE, Professor Gifford Frank NHS Executive - South West RO, Westwood House, Lime Kiln Close, Stoke Gifford, Bristol BS34 8SR Tel: 0117 984 1835 Email: gifford.batstone@doh.gsi.gov.uk; 42 Frore Avenue, Fleet GU51 5AP — MB BS 1966 Lond.; BSc (Hons.) Bristol 1971; FRCPath 1986, M 1973; MSc (Med. Educat.) Cardiff 1995. (St. Thos.) Dir. Educat. & Train., SW NHS Exec.; Prof. PostGrad. Med. Educat. Socs: Standing Comm. Postgrad. Med. Educat.; Hon. Sec. Fell.sh. Postgrad. Med. Prev: Postgrad. Dean, Nottm. Univ. Med. Sch.; Cons. Chem. Path. & Hon. Sen. Lect. (Chem. Path.) Soton. Univ. Med. Sch.; Lect. (Chem. Path.) Soton. Univ.

BATSTONE, Griffith Richard Davies Balhan Lodge, 156 Tenison Road, Cambridge CB1 2DP — LMSSA 1993 Lond.; MA Camb. 1994, MB BChir 1993.

BATSTONE, Jane Helen Chadwell Centre, Torquay Road, Paignton TQ3 2DW — MB ChB 1979 Birm.

BATT, Bernard John (retired) St Johns, Bury Road, Kentford, Newmarket CB8 7PT Tel: 01638 552332 — MRCS Eng. LRCP Lond. 1949. Prev: Ho. Phys. & ENT Ho. Surg. St. Bart. Hosp.

BATT, Mrs Eithne Mary Bridge House Medical Centre, Scholars Lane, Stratford-upon-Avon CV37 6HE; 284 Myton Road, Warwick CV34 6PU Tel: 01926 423213 — MB BChir 1975 Camb.; MRCGP 1986; DRCOG 1979; DCH Eng. 1978.

BATT, Michael Charles 11 Cadvan Road, Ely, Cardiff CF5 4DW — MB BS 1996 Lond.

BATTA, Kapila Selly Oak Hospital, Raddlebarn Road, Selly Oak, Birmingham B29 6JD; 161 Knightlow Road, Harborne, Birmingham B17 8PY — MB ChB 1990 Birm.; MRCP Lond. 1993; MRCGP Lond. 1996. (Birmingham) Specialist Regist. Dermat., Selly Oak Hosp., Birm.; Specialist Regist. (Dermat.). Socs: Brit. Assn. of Dermatol.s; Brit. Med. Assn.

BATTCOCK, Timothy Mark Department Elderly Medicine, Poole General Hospital, Longfleet Road, Poole BH15 2JB Tel: 01202 665511 Fax: 01202 442993; 4 Brunstead Place, Poole BH12 1EW Tel: 01202 767802 — MB ChB 1981 Liverp.; FRCP Lond. 1995; MRCP (UK) 1985. Cons. Phys. (Med. for Elderly) Poole Gen. Hosp. Prev: Sen. Regist. Leicester Gen. Hosp.; Regist. (Med.) Roy. Liverp. Hosp.

BATTEN, Alison Margaret (retired) The Old Chandlery, 25A High Street, Avoch IV9 8PT Tel: 01381 621230 — MB ChB 1945 Ed.; LRCP LRCS Ed. LRFPS Glas. 1945; MFCM 1974; DPH Ed. 1954. Prev: Dist. Med. Off. N. Grampian Health Dist.

BATTEN, Anne Mary Margaret (retired) 7 Lion Gate Gardens, Kew, Richmond TW9 2DF Tel: 020 8940 3282 — BM BCh 1949 Oxf.; BM BCh Oxon. 1949; DObst RCOG 1951. Prev: Assoc. Specialist Char. Cross Gp. Hosps.

BATTEN, Brian (retired) The Barcroft Practice, Barcroft Medical Centre, Amesbury, Salisbury SP4 7AN Tel: 01980 623983 Fax: 01980 625530 — MB BS Lond. 1960; MRCS Eng. LRCP Lond. 1960; DObst RCOG 1962. Mem. Indep. Tribunal Serv. Disabil. Appeals. Prev: Local Treasury Med. Off.

BATTEN, Cecilia Hale Acre Unit, Amersham Hospital, Whielden Street, Amersham HP7 0JD Tel: 01494 734593 Fax: 01494 734506; Email: ctbatten@doctors.org.co.uk — Medico Buenos Aires 1974; MRCPsych 1986. p/t Cons. Psychiat. in Liason Obst. Socs: RC Psychiat.; MARCE Soc.; BCP, BAP, UKCP. Prev: Cons. Psychiat. S. Mead Hosp. Bristol; Cons. Psychiat. St. Michael's Hosp. Warwick.

BATTEN, Clare Oriel North Hampshire Hospital, Aldermaston Road, Basingstoke RG24 9NA Tel: 01256 313650 Fax: 01256 313634 — MB BS 1982 Lond.; MA Oxf. 1979; MRCP (UK) 1986. Cons. Rheum. N. Hants. Hosp. Basingstoke. Socs: BSR; RSM. Prev: ARC Jun. Research Fell. Roy. Free Hosp. Lond.; Sen. Regist. (Rheum.) Soton. Gen. Hosp. & Middlx. Hosp.; Regist. (Rheum.) Lond. Hosp.

BATTEN, Donald Alexander Wycombe Clinice, Child & Family Service, 2 Hamilton Wycombe HP13 5BW Tel: 01494 535727 Fax: 01494 452673 Email: dbatten@doctors.org.uk — MB ChB 1975 Sheff.; MA Univ. Wales 1994; MRCPsych 1980; FRANZCP 1989. (Sheff.) Cons. Child & Adolesc. Psychiat. Bucks. Ment. Health NHS Trust. Prev: Cons.Child Adolesc. Psychiat. Priory Hosp. Bristol; Cons. Child & Adolesc. Psychiat. E. Glos. NHS Trust; Cons. Adolesc. Psychiat. Health Dept. Vict., Austral.

BATTEN, John Moseley Avenue Surgery, 109 Moseley Avenue, Coventry CV6 1HS Tel: 024 7659 2201 Fax: 024 7660 1226 —

MB 1981 Camb.; MA Camb. 1981, MB 1981, BChir 1980; MRCP (UK) 1984.

BATTEN, Sir John Charles, KCVO (retired) 7 Lion Gate Gardens, Richmond TW9 2DF Tel: 020 8940 3282 — MB BS Lond. 1946; MD Lond. 1951; FRCP Lond. 1964, M 1950. Hon. Phys. St. Geo. & Roy. Brompton Hosps. Lond.; Pres. Cystic Fibrosis Trust. Prev: Phys. to HM the Qu. & Head of HM's Med. Ho.hold.

BATTEN, John Henry St Catherine's Surgery, St Pauls Medical Centre, 121 Swindon Road, Cheltenham GL50 4DP Tel: 01242 580668 Fax: 01242 707699; 21 Pittville Lawn, Cheltenham GL51 2BE Tel: 01242 522882 — MB BS 1978 Lond.; MRCS Eng. LRCP Lond. 1974. (Char. Cross) Prev: SHO (Paediat. & O & G) Worcester Roy. Infirm.; Ho. Surg. Char. Cross Hosp. Lond.

BATTEN, Mr Keith Leslie, CBE, KStJ Four Walls, Henrietta Villas, Bath BA2 6LX Tel: 01225 466597; Four Walls, Henrietta Villas, Bath BA2 6LX Tel: 01225 466597 — MB BS 1949 Lond.; FRCS Eng. 1972; MRCS Eng. LRCP Lond. 1948; FRCOphth 1988; DTM & H. Eng. 1952, DO 1959. (St. Bart.) Dep. Hosp.ler OStJ. Socs: Fell. Roy. Soc. Med.; BMA. Prev: Civil. Cons. P.ss Alexandra Hosp. Wroughton; Warden & Chief Surg. St. John Ophth. Hosp.; Lt.-Col. RAMC Sen. Specialist (Ophth.).

BATTEN, Sarah Frances Portsdown Group Practice, The Surgery, Crookhorn Lane, Waterlooville PO7 5XP — BM 1983 Soton.; MRCGP 1990; DRCOG 1987. Prev: Trainee GP Portsmouth; SHO (O & G & Paediat.) St. Mary's Hosp. Portsmouth; SHO Rotat. (Med. & Anaesth.) Qu. Alexandra Hosp. Portsmouth.

BATTEN, Shirley Anne (retired) Glan Culfor, Glyn Garth, Menai Bridge LL59 5PA Tel: 01248 713084 — MB ChB 1957 Manch.; MFCM 1974; DCH Eng. 1960; FRCPCH, 1997.

BATTERBURY, Mr Mark St Pauls Eye Unit, Royal Liverpool University Hospital, Prescot St., Liverpool L7 8XP Tel: 0151 706 2000 Fax: 0151 706 5861 Email: batterb@liv.ac.uk; 35 Grange Park Avenue, Wilmslow SK9 4AJ Tel: 01625 250157 Fax: 0151 706 5802 — MB BS 1984 Lond.; BSc Lond. 1981; FRCS Glas. 1988; FRCOphth. 1989; DO RCS Eng. 1988. (Guy's) Cons. Ophth. Roy. Liverp. Univ. Hosp.; Dir. Clin. Studies (Ophth.) Univ. Liverp. Prev: Lect. (Med.) Univ. Liverp.; Sen. Regist. Manch. Roy. Eye Hosp.; Regist. St. Paul's Eye Unit Liverp.

BATTERHAM, Eric John (retired) 3 Model Cottages, Poundsgate, Newton Abbot TQ13 7PF Tel: 01364 631343 — MRCS Eng. LRCP Lond. 1957. Prev: Resid. Med. Off. Roy. Devon & Exeter Hosp.

BATTERHAM, Imogen Ann Combe Down House Surgery, Combe Down House, The Avenue, Combe Down, Bath BA2 5EG Tel: 01225 832226 Fax: 01225 840757; Vineyard Cottage, Frankley Terrace, Bath BA1 6DP — MB BS 1987 Lond.; MRCGP 1991; DRCOG 1990. (King's College London) GP Princip. Socs: BMA. Prev: Trainee GP Exeter HA.

BATTERS, Walter Gordon (retired) Kingsburgh Cottage, Kingsburgh Gardens, East Linton EH40 3BJ Tel: 01620 860215 Email: batters@quista.net — MB ChB Ed. 1940. Prev: Surg. Lt. RNVR.

BATTERSBY, Alison Jane Fulbourn Hospital, Cambridge — MB BChir 1991 Camb.

BATTERSBY, Edward Fletcher (retired) The Old Rectory, 7 Flowerpot Lane, Long Stratton, Norwich NR15 2TS Tel: 01508 531253 Fax: 01508 531253 — MB ChB 1955 NZ; FFA RCS Eng. 1961; DA Eng. 1960. Prev: Cons. Anaesth. Hosp. Sick Childr. Gt. Ormond St. Lond.

BATTERSBY, John Edward ACT, BP 140, 9100 Sidi Bouzid, Tunisia Tel: 00 216 06 634339 Fax: 00 216 06 632031; c/o The Old Rectory, 7 Flowerpot Lane, Lance Stratton, Norwich NR15 2TS Tel: (01508) 531253 — MB BS 1988 Lond. Director Primary Health Care Project L'Assn. De CoOperat. Entunisie, Tunisia. Prev: Trainee GP Norwich VTS.

BATTERSBY, John McWilliam (retired) 16 Bryn Twr, Abergele LL22 8DD Tel: 01745 832578 — MRCS Eng. LRCP Lond. 1940; MA Camb. 1940. Prev: Cons. Chest Phys. Abergele Hosp.

BATTERSBY, Margaret (retired) The Old Rectory, 7 Flowerpot Lane, Long Stratton, Norwich NR15 2TS Tel: 01508 531253 Fax: 01508 531253 — MB BS 1958 Lond.; DA Eng. 1961. Prev: SCMO Lambeth Healthcare.

BATTERSBY, Nina Catherine 11 Bruce Street, Chester CH1 2DF — MB ChB 1994 Manch.

BATTERSBY, Mr Robert Douglas Eaton Department Neurosurgery, Royal Hallamshire Hospital, Glossop Road, Sheffield S10 2JF Tel: 0114 271 1900; 58 Whirlow Lane, Sheffield S11 9QF Tel: 0114 236 4901 Email: robbat@compuserve.com — MB BS 1973 Lond.; FRCS Eng. 1979; MRCS Eng. LRCP Lond. 1973. (Guy's Hospital London) Cons. Neurosurg. Roy. Hallamsh. Hosp. Sheff.; Hon. Lect. Univ. Sheff. Socs: Soc. Brit. Neurol. Surgs. & N. of Eng. Neurol. Assn. Prev: Sen. Regist. (Neurosurg.) Roy. Hallamsh. Hosp. Sheff.; Regist. (Neurosurg.) Midl. Centre Neurosurg. & Neurol. Birm.; Regist. (Surg.) St. Bart. Hosp. Lond.

BATTEY, Gillian Sheila 18 Coombe Rise, Shenfield, Brentwood CM15 8JJ — MB BS 1966 Lond.; MRCS Eng. LRCP Lond. 1966. (Roy. Free) Med. Off. St. Clare Hospice Hastingwood, Essex; Clin. Asst. (Diabetic Clinic) OldCh. Hosp. Romford. Socs: Assn. Palliat. Med. Prev: GP Romford.

BATTH, Mahinder Singh Manley's Close, Sampford Peverell, Tiverton — MB BS 1959 Nagpur; DCH Eng. 1962.

BATTIN, David Gordon John ERowan Housery, Osborne Road, Malvern, Worcester WR14 1JE Tel: 01684 612713 Fax: 01684 612790; Collitts Forge, Upper Moor, Pershore WR10 2JR Tel: 01386 860467 — MB ChB 1974 Bristol; MRCPsych 1979; 1995 FRCPsych; 1997 MA; 1979 MRCP. Cons. Psychogeriat. Newtown Hosp. Worcs. Socs: (Ex-Chairm.) W. Midl. Assn. of Psychogeriat.; Internat. Psychogeriat. Assn.; Chairm. Worcs. Div. of Brit. Med. Assn. Prev: Sen. Regist. Rotat. (Psychiat.) W. Midl.; Regist. (Psychiat.) Moorhaven Hosp. Ivybridge; Ho. Phys. & Ho. Surg. W. Cornw. Hosp. Penzance.

BATTINSON, Andree Nicola Heathcote Medical Centre, Heathcote, Tadworth KT20 5TH Tel: 01737 360202; 19 Morton, Tadworth KT20 5UA — MB ChB 1986 Sheff.; DCH; DRCOG. (Sheff.)

BATTISTESSA, Sergio Alcides Lowther Medical Centre, 1 Castle Meadows, Whitehaven CA28 7RG Tel: 01946 692241 Fax: 01946 590617; Dellcroft, Back Corkickle, Whitehaven CA28 7TS Email: battistessa@which.net — D Med Uruguay 1981; (T)GP - JCPTGO Ref. (Univ. de la Republia, Uruguay)

BATTLE, Gregory Noel Goodinge Health Centre, Goodinge Close, North Road, London N7 9EW Tel: 020 7530 4940 — MB BS 1986 Lond.; MSc Dub. 1991; DRCOG 1990. Clin. Asst. (Psychiat. & HIV) Roy. Free Hosp.; Clin. Lect. UCL Med. Sch. Lond.

BATTLE, Mark Owen Royal Cornwall Hospital Trust (Treliske), Truro TR1 2XN Tel: 01872 274242; 2 Gladstone Terrace, Long Rock, Penzance TR20 8JB — MB ChB 1994 Leeds; MRCP (UK) 1998. (Leeds) Specialist Regist. (Geriats. & Gen. Med.) Treliske Hosp. Truro Cornw.

BATTLEY, Celia Jane 43 Burntwood Grange Road, Wandsworth Common, London SW18 3JY — MB BS 1992 Lond.

BATTRAM, John William Ralph, MC, SBStJ 3 Emmbrook Court, Reading RG6 5TZ — MRCS Eng. LRCP Lond. 1941; DIH Soc. Apoth. Lond. 1960. (Cardiff) Prev: Area Med. Off. Nat. Coal Bd.

BATTU, Vijay Ram Genito, West Wales Hospital, Carmarthen SA31 2AF Tel: 01267 227557; 53 R.B.I. Colony, Anandnagar, Bangalore 560024, India Tel: 00 91 80 3330231 — MB BS 1980 Bangalore; MD New Delhi 1984; MRCP (UK) 1996; Dip. GU Med. Soc. Apoth. Lond. 1989. Cons. in Genitourin. Med., Singleton Hosp., Swansea. Socs: MSSVD; Assn. Genitourin. Med. Prev: Sen. Regist. (Genitourin. Med.) Bristol Roy. Infirm.; Locum Cons. (Genitourin. Med.), Bristol Roy. Infirm.; Staff Phys. (Genitourin. Med.) Roy. Bournemouth Hosp.

BATTY, Barbara Jean Woodlands Medical Centre, Woodland Road, Didcot OX11 0BB Tel: 01235 511355 Fax: 01235 512808; 6 Brookside, Harwell, Didcot OX11 0HG Tel: 01235 835229 — BM BS 1984 Nottm.; MRCGP 1991; DRCOG 1990. Prev: Trainee GP Wycombe Gen. Hosp. VTS & Abingdon.

BATTY, Charles Gordon, MBE, Col. late RAMC Marsh House, Howard Lane, Stratton, Bude EX23 9TE Email: cgbatty@aol.com — MB ChB 1973 Dundee; 1989 MSc (Occupat. Med.) Lond.; 1973 MB ChB Dundee; 1984 FRCS Ed.; 1984 FRCS Glas.; 1992 MFOM RCP Lond.; FFOM 2000 London; FFAEM 2000; 1989 AFOM. (Univ. Dundee) Cons. Occupat. Phys. HQ 4 Div.; Army Prof. Occupat. Med. 1997.

BATTY, Christopher John The Minster Practice, Cabourne Court, Cabourne Avenue, Lincoln LN2 2JP Tel: 01522 568838 Fax: 01522 546740; 3 The Oaks, Scothern, Lincoln LN2 2WB — MB ChB 1989

Liverp.; DRCOG 1994. Doctor Lincoln City Football Club. Prev: Trainee GP/SHO (A & E & O & G) Macclesfield VTS; SHO (A & E) Gold Coast Hosp., Austral.

BATTY, Dorothy May (retired) 104 Manor Road, Barton-le-Clay, Bedford MK45 4NS Tel: 01582 881395 — MB ChB 1948 Ed. Prev: Dist. Med. Off., N. Herts Health Auth.

BATTY, Gwenno Mair Care of the Elderly Department, Kent & Canterbury Hospital, Ethelburt Road, Canterbury CT1 3NG Tel: 01227 766877 Fax: 01227 781306 — MB BCh 1986 Wales; MRCP (UK) 1990; MD 1999. (Cardiff) Cons. Gen. Med. & Elderly Care. Prev: Sen. Regist. King's Coll. Hosp. Lond.

BATTY, Julia Ann 8 Third Avenue, Denvilles, Havant PO9 2QS — MB ChB 1992 Dundee.

BATTY, Peter Ferens York Street Medical Centre, 20-21 York Street, Stourport-on-Severn DY13 9EH Tel: 01299 827171 Fax: 01299 827910; 24 Dunley Road, Stourport-on-Severn DY13 0AX Tel: 01299 822933 Email: pbatty@argonet.co.uk — MB ChB 1971 Birm.; DObst RCOG 1973; DCH Eng. 1973. (Birmingham) Prev: Clin. Asst. (Rheum.) Kidderminster Gen. Hosp.; SHO (Paediat.) Worcester Roy. Infirm.

BATTY, Philip David Rosebank Surgery, Ashton Road, Road, Lancaster LA1 4JS Tel: 01524 842284 Fax: 01524 844839; Highfield, Main Road, Ellel, Lancaster LA2 0PU Tel: 01524 752176 — MB ChB 1987 Liverp.; MRCGP 1992; DRCOG 1991.

BATTY, Ruth 18 Devonshire Drive, Duffield, Belper DE56 4DD — MB BS 1998 Newc.; MB BS Newc 1998.

BATTY, Sari Clare 3 Westfield, Bradford-on-Avon BA15 1PS — BChir 1993 Camb.; BA Cantab. 1993; MB BChir Camb. 1995. (Cambridge University) Specialist Regist. (O & G).

BATTY, Vincent Bernard Radiology Department, Southampton General Hospital, Tremona Road, Southampton SO16 6YD Tel: 02380 796203 Fax: 02380 796927 Email: vince.batty@suht.swest.nhs.uk — MB BS 1976 Lond.; BSc Lond. 1973, MSc (Nuclear Med.) 1985; FRCR 1983; DMRD 1982. (Middlx.) Cons. Radiol. & Nuclear Med. Soton. Univ. Hosps. Socs: Brit. Nuclear Med. Soc.; The Worshipful Soc. Of Apoth. of Lond.; Soton. Med. Soc. Prev: Sen. Regist. (Nuclear Med.) Roy. Marsden Hosp.; Sen. Regist. (Radiol.) Soton. Gen. Hosp.; Regist. (Radiol.) Soton. Gen. Hosp.

BATTY SHAW, Anthony (retired) Appleacre, Barford, Norwich NR9 4BD Tel: 01603 759268 — BM BCh Oxf. 1945; MA Oxf. 1948, DM 1952; FRCP Lond. 1968, M 1946. Prev: Cons. Phys. Norf. & Norwich, W. Norwich, Cromer, Dereham, AttleBoro. & Bethel Hosps.

BATTYE, Ian Richmond Beccles Medical Centre, 7-9 St. Marys Road, St. Marys Road, Beccles NR34 9NQ Tel: 01502 712662 Fax: 01502 712906; Ivy House Farm, Gillingham, Beccles NR34 0HD — MB BS 1970 Lond.; MRCS Eng. LRCP Lond. 1970; MRCGP Lond. 1982; FFA RCSI 1976; DA Eng. 1974; MFHom 1971. (St. Bart.) Prev: Ho. Surg. Whipps Cross Hosp. Lond.; Ho. Phys. St. Bart. Hosp. Lond.

BATTYE, Joanne Elizabeth 31 Warwick Street, Crookes, Sheffield S10 1LX — MB ChB 1995 Sheff.

BATTYE, Roy 3 Station Road, Salwick, Preston PR4 0YH — MB ChB 1958 Manch.; DIH Soc. Apoth. Lond. 1963. (Manch.) Dir. Med. Research Miles Pharmaceut. W. Haven. Socs: Fell. Manch. Med. Soc. & Acad. Med. New Jersey U.S.A. Prev: SHO Rheum. Research Clinic Manch. Roy. Infirm.; SHO Med., & Ho. Surg. & Ho. Phys. Withington Hosp. Manch.

BATUWITAGE, Boyd Tilak Treharris Health Centre, Bargoed Terrace, Treharris CF46 5RB Tel: 01443 410242 Fax: 01443 413312; Laroche, Pentwyn, Treharris CF46 5BS Tel: 01443 410500 — MB BS 1968 Ceylon. (Univ. Of Ceylon, Colombo Campus)

BAUCHOP, Anne Manor Crescent Surgery, 7 Manor Crescent, Bursledon, Southampton SO31 8DQ Tel: 023 8040 4671 Fax: 023 8040 7417 — MB BCh 1969 Wales; DObst RCOG 1971. (Cardiff) LMC Represen. S.. Parishes. Socs: BMA & Soton. Med. Soc. Prev: Ho. Phys. Soton. Gp. Hosps.; Ho. Surg. Salisbury Gen. Hosp.; Ho. Off. Camb. Matern. Hosp.

BAUDON, Jean Jacques Medicare Francais, 3 Harrington Gardens, London SW7 4JJ — MD 1971 Paris.

BAUDOUIN, Christine Julie Freeman Hospital, High Heaton, Newcastle upon Tyne NE7 7DN — BM BCh 1981 Oxf.; BA Camb. 1978; MRCP (UK) 1984; FRCR 1987. Cons. Radiol. Freeman Hosp. Newc. u. Tyne.

BAUDOUIN, Simon Victor Department of Anaesthesia, Royal Victoria Infirmary, Newcastle upon Tyne NE1 4LP — MB BS 1980 Lond.; BA Oxf. 1977; MD Lond. 1980; MRCP (UK) 1983. Sen. Lect. (Intens. Care) Roy. Vict. Infirm. Newc. u. Tyne.

BAUER, Annette G (retired) Beechcroft, 75 Highlands Road, Leatherhead KT22 8NW — MB BS 1943 Lond.

BAUER, Philippe Intensive Care Unit, Guy's Hospital, St Thomas St., London SE1 9RT — MD 1984 Nancy.

BAUEROVA, Olga (retired) Morava, 5 Spencer Lane, Bamford, Rochdale OL11 5PE Tel: 01706 368261 — MD Bratislava 1934; DMR Lond 1944. Prev: Cons. Radiol. i/c Bury Gp. Hosps.

BAUGH, Olive Hazel Anne The Haematology Laboratory, Broomfield Hospital, Chelmsford CM1 7ET Tel: 01245 514160 Fax: 01245 514077 — MB BS 1966 Lond.; MRCS Eng. LRCP Lond. 1966; FRCPath 1986, M 1974. (St. Geo.) Cons. Haemat. Broomfield Hosp. Chelmsford. Socs: BMA. Prev: Lect. (Hon. Sen. Regist.) Dept. Haemat. St. Geo. Hosp. Med. Sch. Lond.; Recogn. Teach. Univ. Lond.; Regist. (Path.) St. Geo. Hosp. Lond.

BAUGH, Simon John Lynfield Mount Hospital, Heights Lane, Bradford BD9 6DP Tel: 01274 494194 Fax: 01274 363273 — MB ChB 1973 Leeds; MRCPsych 1979; DPM Leeds 1977. Cons. Psychiat. & Dir. Ment. Health Lynfield Mt. Hosp. Bradford; Med. Dir. Bradford Community Health Trust; Hon. Lect. (Psych.) Univ. Leeds. Prev: Lect. (Psychiat.) Univ. Leeds & St. Jas. Univ. Hosp. Leeds.

BAUGH, Stuart James 64 Delamere Drive, Mansfield NG18 4DF — MB ChB 1989 Leeds.

BAUGHAN, Annabelle Sara Jacqueline SCOPME, 1 Park Square W., London NW1 Tel: 020 7935 3916 Fax: 020 7935 8601 — MB BS 1974 Lond.; FRCP Lond. 1993; MRCP (UK) 1979; FRCPath 1996, M 1984. (Roy. Free) Sen. Fell. Standing Comm. (Postgrad. Med. & Dent. Educat.) Lond.; Hon. Cons. Phys. Hammersmith Hosp. Lond. Prev: Dep. Acting Dean Postgrad. Med. NW Thames; Cons. Haemat. Ashford Hosp. Middlx.; Research Fell. MRC Leukaemia Unit Roy. Postgrad. Med. Sch.

BAUGHAN, Christopher Adrian 27 Wellington Terrace, Victoria Road, Knaphill, Woking GU21 2AP — MB 1981 Camb.; BChir 1980. Regist. (Radiother. & Oncol.) W.m. Hosp. Lond. Socs: RCP.

BAUGHAN, Paul Michael Dollar Health Centre, Park Place, Dollar FK14 7AA Tel: 01259 742120 Fax: 01259 743053 — MB ChB 1992 Aberd.

BAUM, Andrew Simon 12 Malpas Drive, Pinner HA5 1DG — BM BCh 1994 Oxf.

BAUM, Geoffrey Maswell Park Health Centre, Hounslow Avenue, Hounslow TW3 2DY Tel: 020 8321 3476 Fax: 020 8893 4368; 39 Fife Road, East Sheen, London SW14 8BJ Tel: 020 8876 1832 Fax: 020 8876 1832 Email: geoffbaum@yahoo.com — MB ChB 1952 Birm.; DObst RCOG 1956. Socs: Roy. Coll. Gen. Pract.; Fell. BMA. Prev: Ho. Surg. & Ho. Phys. Qu. Eliz. Hosp. Birm.; Capt. RAMC.

BAUM, Madeline Rose Maswell Park Health Centre, Hounslow Avenue, Hounslow TW3 2DY Tel: 020 8321 3476 Fax: 020 8893 4368 — MB ChB 1991 Birm.; MRCGP 1995; DFFP 1996; DCH RCP Lond. 1994; DRCOG 1993. (Birm.) Socs: BMA.

BAUM, Professor Michael Academic Department of Surgery, University College of London, Charles Bell House, Riding House St., London W1P 7LD Tel: 020 7679 9147 Fax: 020 7679 9050 Email: m.baum@ucl.ac.uk; 2 Lothan Close, London NW11 6PT Tel: 020 8381 4263 Email: michael@mbaum.freeserve.co.uk — MB ChB 1960 Birm.; MD (Hon. Causa) Gotenburg 1986; ChM Birm. 1974; FRCS Eng. 1965; FRCR (Hon.) 1998; FRSA 1998. (Birm.) Prof. Emerit. Surg. & Vis. prof. of Med. humanities, Univ. Coll. Lond. Socs: Fell. Roy. Soc. Med.; Eur. Soc. Mastol. (Past Vice-Pres.); Brit. Oncol. Assn. Past Pres. Prev: Emerit. Prof. Surg. Inst. Cancer Research & Vis. Prof. Univ. Coll. Lond.; Hon. Dir. Cancer Research Campaign Clin. Trials Centre Lond.; Prof. Surg. King's Coll. Sch. Med. & Dent.

BAUMBER, Jill The Surgery, Trent Road, Grantham NG31 7XQ Tel: 01476 71166; 99 Manthorpe Road, Grantham NG31 8DE Tel: 01476 76362 — MB ChB 1965 St. And.; DObst RCOG 1967; Cert FPA 1969. Socs: BMA (S. Lincs. GP Comm.).

BAUMBER, Mr Richard Simon (retired) 41 Moorgate Av, Bamford, Roundacre, Rochdale OL11 5JY — MB BS 1968 Lond.;

FRCS Ed. 1977; MRCS Eng. LRCP Lond. 1968; FRCOG 1987, M 1974. Prev: Cons. (O & G) Rochdale AHA.

BAUMER, John Harry Little Luson, Near Yealmpton, Plymouth PL8 2JD Tel: 01752 830274 Email: harry.baumer@phnt.swest.nhs.uk — MB ChB 1971 Bristol; FRCP Lond. 1993; MRCP (UK) 1974. (Bristol Univ.) Cons. Paediat. Derriford Hosp. Plymouth. Socs: (Counc.) Brit. Assn. Perinatal Med.; Neonat. Soc.; Fell. Roy. Coll. Paediat. & Child Health. Prev: Lect. (Child Health) Bristol Univ.

BAUMGARTEN, Sven St Pauls Road Medical Centre, 248 St Pauls Road, London N1 2LJ — State Exam Med 1992 Berlin.

BAURA, Gurmeet Kaur 41 St Ronan's Crescent, Woodford Green IG8 9DQ — MB BS 1970 Jiwaji.

BAVALIA, Kheelna 5 Cherry Orchard, Fulbourn, Cambridge CB1 5EH — MB BS 1997 Lond.

BAVAR, Ghobad 161 Elsenham Street, London SW18 5NZ Tel: 020 8874 9288 — MD 1947 Tehran. (Tehran) Med. Asst. (Psychiat.) Brookwood Hosp. Knaphill.

BAVERSTOCK, Andrew Mark c/o Manor Road, Wantage OX12 8DP — BChir 1994 Camb.

BAVERSTOCK, Michael William John East Street Surgery, 6-7 East Street, Ware SG12 9HJ Tel: 01920 468777 Fax: 01920 484892 — MB BS 1979 Lond.; DRCOG 1982.

BAVERSTOCK, Michele Ellen 2 Wentworth Street, St John's, Wakefield WF1 2RX; The Dower House, Heath, Wakefield WF1 5SL Tel: 01924 382361 — MB BS 1965 Lond.; MRCS Eng. LRCP Lond. 1965; FFA RCS Eng. 1970; DA Eng. 1968; DObst RCOG 1967. (Roy. Free) Assoc. Specialist (Anaesth.) Leeds Gen. Infirm.; JP. Socs: Assn. Anaesth. Prev: Regist. (Anaesth.) Watford Gen. Hosp.

BAVERSTOCK, Ross Alan Selsdon Park Medical Practice, 95 Addington Road, South Croydon CR2 8LG Tel: 020 8657 0067 Fax: 020 8657 0037 — MB BS 1991 Lond.; MRCGP 1995; DFFP 1995; T(GP) 1995. (St. Geo. Hosp. Med. Sch.)

BAVETTA, Francesco 47 Shorts Gardens, London WC2H 9AA Tel: 020 7379 7209 — MD 1951 Palermo; MD (Hnrs.) Palermo 1951, TDD 1954; LAH Dub. 1959. Med. Off. King's Coll. Lond. Prev: Phys. Outpats. Italian Hosp. Lond.; Asst. Inst. Chest. Dis. Univ. Palermo; Regist. Highlands Hosp. Lond.

BAVETTA, Mr Sebastiano Department of Neurosurgery, The Royal London Hospital, Whitechapel, London E1 1BB; 3 Shirley Road, Enfield EN2 6SB — MB BS 1987 Lond.; FRCS Eng. 1993; FRCS Ed. 1993; MRCP (UK) 1990.

BAVIDGE, Kenneth John Neville (retired) South Court, Shipton by Beningbrough, York YO30 1AR Tel: 01904 470391 — MB BS Durh. 1963; FRCOG 1991, M 1970; DObst 1965. Prev: Cons. (Genitourin. Med.) York & Harrogate Health Trusts.

BAVIN, Denise Jacqueline Great Russell Street Surgery, 58 Great Russell Street, London WC1B 3BE Tel: 020 7405 2739 Fax: 020 7404 1642 — MB BS 1979 Lond.; FRCS Lond. 1984; DRCOG 1987.

BAVIN, Jack Thomas Rainsford 31 Woodland Drive, Cassiobury Park Est., Watford WD17 3BY Tel: 01923 42575 — BSc (Special) in Physiol. (Hons.) Lond. 1959, MB; BS 1955; DPM Eng. 1962; FRCPsych 1972, M 1971. (Char. Cross) Cons. Psychiat. Leavesden Hosp. Watford; Hon. Cons. Psychiat. Hammersmith Hosp. Lond.; Hon. Cons. Phys. (Subnorm.) Fulham Hosp. Lond. Socs: Fell. Roy. Soc. Med. Prev: Asst. Psychiat. S. Ockendon Hosp.; Sen. Regist. (Psychiat.) Leavesden Hosp. Watford; Regist. (Psychiat.) Harperbury Hosp. Shenley.

BAVINGTON, Alastair John Kensington Street Health Centre, Whitefield Place, Girlington, Bradford BD8 9LB Tel: 01274 499209 — MB ChB 1990 Ed.

BAVINGTON, John Trumpler (retired) 3 Ryelands Grove, Bradford BD9 6HJ Tel: 01274 403507 — MB BS 1958 Lond.; MRCPsych 1974; DPM Eng. 1971; DObst RCOG 1960. Prev: Cons. Psychiat. Lynfield Mt. Hosp.

BAVISHI, Rajnikant Khushaldas 290 Shoebury Road, Thorpe Bay, Southend-on-Sea SS1 3TT — MD 1978 Gujarat; MB BS 1970; DPM Gujarat 1973. (Smt. N.H. Laxmichand Med. Coll. Ahmedabad) Princip. GP Enfield & Haringey FPC.

BAVISTER, Anne Elizabeth St Clements Surgery, Tanner Street, Winchester SO23 8AD Tel: 01962 852211 Fax: 01962 856010 — BM BS 1981 Nottm.; Dip Occ Med; DRCOG 1984. Sen. Clinic Teach., Dept. of Primary Care, Soton. Sch. of Med.

BAVISTER, Peter Howard East Midlands Nuffield Hospital, Rykneld Road, Littleover, Derby DE23 7SN Tel: 01332 517891 Fax: 01332 512481; Chantry House, Main St, Kings Newton, Derby DE73 1BX Tel: 01332 863215 Fax: 01332 863215 — MB BS 1971 Lond.; FRCA Eng. 1975. (Lond. Hosp.) Cons. Anaesth. Derbysh. Roy. Infirm. Derby.

BAWA, Gursharan Paul Singh 80 Greygoose Park, Harlow CM19 4JL — MB ChB 1989 Manch.; FRCA. 1995. Sen. Regist.(Anaest Rotat.) UCL. Lond.

BAWA, Sarabjit Singh Centre Street Surgery, 8 Centre Street, Glenboig, Coatbridge ML5 2RY Tel: 01236 872617 Fax: 01236 875585; 8 Uddingston Road, Bothwell, Glasgow G71 8PH Tel: 01698 854417 — MB BS 1972 Jammu & Kashmir. (Govt. Med. Coll. Srinagar) Regist. (Orthop. Surg.) Monklands Dist. Gen. Hosp. Airdrie. Prev: Regist. (Orthop. Surg.) W. Cumbld. Hosp. Whitehaven.

BAWDEN, Michael John Parkfields Surgery, 1217 London Road, Derby DE24 8QJ — MB ChB 1984 Manch.; MRCGP 1989. Gen. Pract.; Ophth. Clin. Asst. Prev: GP, Wilson St. Surg., Derby.

BAWDEN, Robert Humphrey Felix Botesdale Health Centre, Back Hills, Botesdale, Diss IP22 1DW Tel: 01379 898295; Ellesmere House, Wortham, Diss IP22 1PT Tel: 01379 898310 Fax: 01379 890477 Email: bawden@ellesmere.softnet.co.uk — MB BS 1975 Lond.; MRCS Eng. LRCP Lond. 1975; MRCGP 1979; DRCOG 1978; Cert. Family Plann. JCC Lond. 1978; MSc 1998; FRCGP 1998. (Guy's) Socs: BMA; Brit. Med. Acupunct. Soc.

BAWDEN, Stella Loraine Cornwall Road Surgery, 15 Cornwall Road, Dorchester DT1 1RU Tel: 01305 251128 — BM 1982 Soton.; MFHom. 2000; MRCGP 1987; DGM RCP Lond. 1989; DRCOG 1986; DCH RCP Lond. 1985; DA (UK) 1984. Prev: Clin. Asst. Elderly Care Unit Dorset Co. Hosp.; Trainee GP Reading VTS; SHO (Anaesth.) Roy. Devon & Exeter Hosp. Wonford.

BAWDEN, Susan Elizabeth Child, Adolescent & Family Consultation Service, Ivry Lodge, 2 Ivry St., Ipswich IP1 3QW Tel: 01473 214559 Fax: 01473 222382 — BM 1976 Soton.; MRCPsych 1981; Cert JCC Lond. 1978. Cons. Child & Adolscent Psychiat. Child, Adolesc. & Family Consultation Serv. Ipswich. Prev: Sen. Regist. (Child & Adolesc. Psychiat.) Inst. Family Psychiat. Ipswich & Drummond Clinic Bury St Edmunds.

BAWN, Bridget Lesley The Surgery, Samman Road, Beverley HU17 0BS Tel: 01482 862474 — MB BS 1988 Lond.; DRCOG 1992.

BAWTREE, Mr David William, VRD, Surg. Cdr. RN Retd. (retired) Badgers Cottage, Cylinders Lane, Fernhurst, Haslemere GU27 3EL Tel: 01428 656386 — MRCS Eng. LRCP Lond. 1929; MA (Nat. Sc. Trip.), MB BChir Camb. 1930; FRCS Ed. 1931. Prev: Chief Asst. (ENT) Lond. Hosp.

BAWTREE, Helen (retired) 29 The Oaks, West Byfleet KT14 6RN Tel: 01932 347453 — MB ChB (2nd cl. Hons.) Leeds 1946; DObst RCOG 1947. Clin. Med. Off. Bournewood Community NHS Trust. Prev: Ho. Phys. Leeds Gen. Infirm. & Brompton Hosp. Lond.

BAX, Deborah Elizabeth Department of Rheumatology, Royal Hallamshire Hospital, Glossop Road, Sheffield S10 2JF Tel: 0114 271 1938 Fax: 0114 271 1844 — MB ChB 1976 Sheff.; MD Sheff. 1989; FRCP Lond. 1993; FRCP Ed. 1993; MRCP (UK) 1979. Cons. Phys. (Rheum.) Roy. Hallamshire Hosp. Sheff.; Regional Adviser RCP CME (N Trent); Clin. Director, Rheum., Sheff. Teachg. Hosp.s Trust (STHT); Hon. Sen. Clin. Lect. Univ. of Sheff. Socs: Brit. Soc. Rheum. Prev: Sen. Regist. (Rheum.) Nether Edge Hosp. Sheff.; Regist. (Gen. Med.) Roy. Hallamsh. Hosp. Sheff.; Research Fell. Univ. Dept. Therap. Sheff.

BAX, Martin Charles Owen 17 Priory Gardens, Highgate, London N6 5QY Tel: 020 8340 3566 — LMSSA 1959 Lond.; DM Oxf. 1982, BM BCh 1959; FRCP Lond. 1988; MRCP 1982. (Oxf. & Guy's) Sen. Research Fell. Child Health Char. Cross & W.m. Med. Sch. Lond.; Edr. Developm. Med. & Child Neurol. Prev: Community Paediat. St. Mary's Hosp. Med. Sch. Lond. & St. Thos. Coram Univ. Lond.

BAX, Professor Nigel Derrick Spencer Faculty of Medicine, University of Sheffield, Beech Hill Road, Sheffield S10 2RX Tel: 0114 271 3955 Fax: 0114 271 1777 — MB BS 1972 Lond.; PhD Sheff. 1985; BSc (Hons.) Lond. 1969; FRCP Ed. 1989; MRCP (UK) 1975; MRCS Eng. LRCP Lond. 1972. (Guy's) Dean Asean Sheff. Med. Coll. Malaysia & Acad. Dean of Med. SE Asia Sheff. Univ. Socs: Brit. Pharm. Soc. & Med. Research Soc. Prev: Sen. Lect. (Clin. Pharmacol.

& Therap.) & Hon. Cons. Phys. Univ. Sheff. & Roy. Hallamsh. Hosp. Sheff.; Lect. (Therap.) Roy. Hallamsh. Hosp. Sheff.; MRC Research Fell. Dept. Therap. & Pharmacol. Univ. Sheff.

BAX, Richard Peregrine Churt House, Deerleap Road, Westcott, Dorking RH4 3LE Tel: 01306 742301 & profess. 0736 366001 Email: richard.bax@transcripltd.btinternet.com — MB BS 1970 Lond.; MRCS Eng. LRCP Lond. 1970; MRCGP 1979; Dip Pharm Med RCP (Uk) 1979; FRCP 1999. (Roy. Free) Vice-Pres. & Dir. Therap. Unit (Anti Infec.) Smith Kline Beecham Pharmaceut. Reigate; Treas. Fac. Pharm. Med.; Comm. Mem. Brit. Soc. Antimicrobiol. Chemother. Socs: Amer..Soc.MicroBiol.; Fac.Pharm.med. Prev: Hon. Lect. (Microbiol.) Univ. Lond.; Hon. Sen. Regist. N.wick Pk. Hosp. Harrow; Princip. GP Shrewsbury.

BAXANDALL, John David Croft, Air Commodore RAF Med. Br. (retired) 25 Home Close, Chiseldon, Swindon SN4 0ND — MB BS 1956 Lond.; FRCOG 1980, M 1966; DObst 1957. Prev: Cons. Adviser (O & G) RAF Med. Br.

BAXANDALL, Mark Leonard Manchester Children's Hospital NHS Trust, Hospital Rd, Pendlebury, Manchester M27 4HA — MB ChB 1983 Leic.

BAXANI, Ramesh Bedwell Medical Centre, Sinfield Close, Bedwell Crescent, Stevenage SG1 1LQ Tel: 01438 355551 Fax: 01438 749704; 72 Wymondley Road, Hitchin SG4 9PT Tel: 01462 437788 Email: rbaxani@dircon.co.uk — MB BS 1969 Lucknow; DA Eng. 1978. Clin. Asst. (Anaesth.) Fairfield Hosp. Hitchin. Socs: BMA. Prev: Clin. Asst. (Anaesth.) Lister Hosp. Stevenage.

BAXBY, Mr Keith Dept of Urology, Ninewells Hospital, Dundee DD1 9SY Tel: 01382 660111 Fax: 01382 425566 Email: keithb@tuht.scot.nhs.uk; Email: kbaxby@aol.com — MB BS 1968 Durh.; BSc Newc. 1965; FRCS Ed. 1993; FRCS Eng. 1973. (Newc.) Cons. Urol. Tayside HB; Hon. Sen. Lect. Univ. Dund. Socs: Brit. Assn. Urol. Surgs.; Internat. Continence Soc. Prev: Vis. Prof. Urol. Louisiana State Univ., USA; Research Fell. N.. Counties Kidney Fund; Sen. Regist. Newc. AHA (T).

BAXENDALE, Brynley Roy 40 South Road, West Bridgford, Nottingham NG2 7AG — MB ChB 1986 Birm.; FCA 1992. Lect. & Hon. Sen. Regist. (Anaesth.) Univ. Dept. Anaesth. Qu. Med. Centre Nottm. Socs: Anaesth. Res. Soc.; Assn. Anaesth.

BAXENDALE, Helen Elizabeth Immunobiology Unit, Institute of Child Health, 30 Guildford St., London WC1N 1EH Email: h.bexenale@ich.ucl.ac.uk; 17 York House, Highbury Crescent, London N5 1RP — MB BS 1991 Lond.; BSc (Immunol.) Lond. 1988; MRCP (UK) 1995. Wellcome Clin. Research Train. Fell. Inst. Child Health Gt. Ormond St. Hosp. Lond. Prev: Research Fell. & Regist. (Paediat.) Inst. Child Health Gt. Ormond St. Lond.; Regist. (Paediat.) Auckland Childr. Hosps., NZ; SHO (Paediat.) Norf. & Norwich Hosp.

BAXENDINE, Claire Louise 321 Clarendon Park Road, Leicester LE2 3AQ — MB ChB 1998 Leic.; MB ChB Leic 1998.

BAXENDINE, David Michael 1 Pond Cottages, Gold Hill E., Chalfont St Peter, Gerrards Cross SL9 9DJ Tel: 01753 882792 Fax: 01753 891476 — MB ChB 1962 Ed.; BA Oxf. 1958; FFOM RCP Lond. 1995, M 1993; CIH Dund 1978. Occupat Health & Safety Cons. United Biscuits plc, Thames Water plc & Smith & Nephew plc; Mem. Bd. Fac. Occupat. Med. Socs: (Ex-Pres.) Soc. Occupat. Med.; BMA. Prev: Dir. Med. Servs. United Biscuits (UK) Ltd.; Chief Med. Adviser Scott. & Newc. Breweries Ltd.; Princip. GP Edin.

BAXENDINE-JONES, Julia Ann 72 Bassett Green Village, Bassett, Southampton SO16 3NB — BM 1994 Soton.

BAXI, Mr Anil Kumar c/o 4 South Croft, Old Marston, Oxford OX3 0PF — MB BS 1979 Indore; FRCS Ed. 1992.

BAXTER, Alexandra Eleanor 71 Queensway, Lisburn BT27 4QN — MB ChB 1993 Ed. SHO (A & E) Lisburn. Prev: Ho. Off. (Surg.) Qu. Margt. Hosp. Dunfermline; Ho. Off. (Med.) Dumfries & Galloway Roy. Infirm.

BAXTER, Alistair George 1 Hamilton Avenue, Tayport DD6 9BW Tel: 01382 553958 — MB ChB 1990 Dundee; FRCA 1994. Regist. (Anaesth.) Ninewells Hosp. Dundee. Socs: Assn. Anaesth. & Scott. Soc. Anaesth.; Obst. Anaesth. Assn. Prev: Fell. (Anaesth.) Roy. Wom.'s Hosp. Melbourne Vict., Australia; SHO (Anaesth.) Perth Roy. Infirm.; Ho. Off. (Med. & Surg.) Ninewells Hosp. & Med. Sch. Dundee.

BAXTER, Andrew Duncan 75 Bank Street, Alexandria G83 0NB Tel: 01389 752626 Fax: 01389 752169; Ferndell, Back Road, Clynder, Helensburgh G84 0QQ — MB ChB 1969 Glas. Prev: Lect. in Anat. Univ. Glas.

BAXTER, Andrew Duncan X-Ray Department, Macclesfield District General Hospital, Macclesfield SK10 3BL Tel: 01625 661156 Fax: 01625 663636 Email: andrew.baxter@echesh.re-tr.nwest.nhs.uk; Brook Cottage, Rainbow View, Bollington — MB ChB 1987 Liverp.; FRCR 1995. Cons. Radiol. Macclesfield Dist. Gen. Hosp. Prev: Sen. Regist. (Radiol.) Leicester Roy. Infirm.; SHO (Med.) Warrington Dist. Gen. Hosp.; SHO (Renal Med.) Roy. Liverp. Hosp.

BAXTER, Andrew John 15 Hall Farm park, Old Micklefield, Leeds LS25 4DP — MB ChB 1989 Manch.; MRCOG 1995. Lect. O & G Castle hill Hosp. E. Yorks.

BAXTER, Andrew John 20 Greystones Road, Sheffield S11 7BN — MB ChB 1991 Sheff.

BAXTER, Anthony Philip Barnsley Health Authorities, Hillder House, 49/51 Gawber Road, Barnsley S75 2PY; The Lodge, Bramwith Lane, South Bramwith, Doncaster DN7 5SJ — MB ChB 1982 Aberd.; MFPHM RCP (UK) 1995; MRCGP 1986; DRCOG 1985. Cons. Pub. Health Med. Barnsley HAs.

BAXTER, Brenda Ware Road Surgery, 59 Ware Road, Hoddesdon EN11 9AB Tel: 01992 463363 Fax: 01992 471108; Whyte House, 141 Stanstead Road, Hoddesdon EN11 0QE Tel: 01992 462730 — MB ChB 1964 Sheff. Socs: BMA. Prev: Ho. Surg., Ho. Off. (Paediat. Med.) & Ho. Surg. (O & G) Dudley; Rd. Hosp. Birm.

BAXTER, Christopher Hugh Email: cbaxter@northlondon.hospice.co.uk; 1 Marlborough Yard, Upper Holloway, London N19 4ND Tel: 020 7281 4701 — MB ChB 1980 Dundee; FRCP 1998; MRCGP 1986. Med. Dir. & Cons. Palliat. Med. N. Lond. Hospice.

BAXTER, David Loughton Clinic, 115 High Road, Loughton IG10 4JA; Mill House Farm, Theydon Road, Epping CM16 4DY — MB BS 1965 Lond. (Lond. Hosp.) Prev: Proprietor & Med. Supt. Holly Ho. Hosp. Buckhurst Hill.

BAXTER, David Neil University of Manchester, Department of Epidemiology & Health Sciences, Stopford Building, Oxford Road, Manchester M13 9PT — MB ChB 1970 Manch.; PhD Manch. 1993, MSc 1977; FFPHM RCP (UK) 1988; DTM & H Liverp. 1979. Hon. Lect. (Epidemiol. & Health Sci.) Manch.; Cons. Communicable Dis. Control Stockport Community Trust.

BAXTER, Elaine Niven Kingswood Surgery, Hollis Road, Totteridge, High Wycombe HP13 7UN Tel: 01494 474783 Fax: 01494 438424; Woodlands, 16 Terry Road, High Wycombe HP13 6QJ Tel: 01494 527757 — MB ChB 1977 Glas.

BAXTER, Fiona Jane 67 Rowan Drive, Bearsden, Glasgow G61 3HH — MB ChB 1992 Glas.

BAXTER, Grant MacDonald 7 Letham Drive, Newlands, Glasgow G43 2SL — MB ChB 1983 Dundee; FRCR 1988. Cons. Radiol. W.. Infirm. Glas.

BAXTER, Gul Ayse Medicines Control Agency, 1 Nine Elms Lane, London SW8 5NQ Tel: 020 7273 0122 Fax: 020 7273 0293; 43 Middleway, London NW11 6SH — MB BS 1984 Lond.; MRCP (UK) 1987. (Roy. Free Hosp. Sch. Med.) Sen. Med. Off. Med. Control Agency DoH Lond. Socs: BMA & Brit. Assn. Pharmaceut. Phys.; BSAC. Prev: Dir. (Clin. Developm.) SmithKline Beecham Pharmaceuts. Welwyn Gdn. City; Transpl. Off. Harefield Hosp.; SHO (Gen. Med. & Haemat.) Barnet Gen. Hosp.

BAXTER, Mrs Hazel 29 Castle Street, Killough, Downpatrick BT30 7QQ — MB ChB 1970 Birm.

BAXTER, Ian Craig (retired) 52 Woodthorpe Avenue, Boston PE21 0NP Tel: 01205 365164 — MB ChB 1960 St. And. Prev: Med. Off. Hereward Coll. of Further Educat. for Physically Handicap.

BAXTER, Ian Thomas 1 The Green, Compton Dando, Bristol BS39 4LE — MB BS 1986 Queensland.

BAXTER, Mr James Sinclair Rennick (retired) Chaucer Hospital, Nackington Road, Canterbury CT4 7AR — MB 1961 Camb.; MA Camb. 1962, MB 1961, BChir 1960; FRCS Eng. 1967. Prev: Regist. (ENT) Lond. Hosp.

BAXTER, Jane Elizabeth — MB BS 1997 Newc.; DRCOG 2000 Oct. (Newcastle upon Tyne) p/t Gen. Practitioner Newc. Upon Tyne.

BAXTER, Jane Lorimer Willow Cottage, 43 Church St., Long Bennington, Newark NG23 5ES Tel: 01400 281376; West Bridgford Health Clinic, 97 Musters Road, West Bridgeford, Nottingham NG2 7PX Tel: 0115 945 5066 Fax: 0115 945 5731 — MB ChB 1967 Leeds; MRCP (UK) 1974; DObst RCOG 1971; DCH Eng. 1970.

Clin. Med. Off. (Community Child Health) Nottm. Community Health NHS Trust. Prev: Fell. (Paediat. Endocrinol.) Hosp. Sick Childr. Toronto, Canada; Regist. (Paediat.) Alder Hey Hosp. Liverp.

BAXTER, John George Barsley St Margarets Medical Practice, 8 St Margarets Road, Solihull B92 7JS — MB ChB 1986 Birm.; DFFP 1990. Socs: BMA. Prev: Trainee GP (A & E) Selly Oak Hosp. Birm. VTS.; SHO (Geriat. Med., O & G & Paediat.) Selly Oak Hosp. Birm.; Ho. Off. (Surg.) Selly Oak Hosp. Birm.

BAXTER, Judy Anne 9 Mill Lane, Sandy SG19 1NH — BM 1982 Soton.; DRCOG 1984.

BAXTER, Kay Frances 4 Claire Court, Monkbridge Road, Headingley, Leeds LS6 4DX — MB ChB 1994 Leeds; MRCP 1998. Specialist Regist. (Dermatol.), Leeds Gen Infirm.

BAXTER, Laurelle Ann (Laurie) Parkside Farm, Sparkwell, Plymouth PL7 5AP Tel: 01752 336936 — MD 1979 Virginia; MD Virginia, USA 1979; DLO RCS Eng. 1992. Assoc. Specialist ENT Plymouth Gen. Hosp. Socs: Plymouth Med. Soc.; BMA.

BAXTER, Lawson Derek Baxter and Conway, The Surgery, Hardingham Street, Hingham, Norwich NR9 4JB Tel: 01953 850237 Fax: 01953 850581; Bullens Farm Barn, Broadmoor Road, Carbrook, Thetford IP25 6TE — MB ChB 1981 Leeds; MRCGP 1985; DRCOG 1983.

BAXTER, Leon Anthony Leslie Rookery Medical Centre, Rookery House, Newmarket CB8 8NW Tel: 01638 665711 Fax: 01638 561280; Greystones, 53 Bury Road, Newmarket CB8 7BY Tel: 01638 664366 — MRCS Eng. LRCP Lond. 1967; MB Camb. 1968, BChir 1967; DObst RCOG 1971. (Camb. & St. Thos.) Clin. Asst. Radiol. (Ultrasound) Newmarket Gen. Hosp.

BAXTER, Mark Alan 153 Hahnemann Court, Sunderland SR5 2SQ — MB ChB 1998 Dund.; MB ChB Dund 1998.

BAXTER, Mark Anthony Brooklands, Coleshill Road, Birmingham B37 7HL Tel: 0121 779 6981 — MB ChB 1984 Birm.; MRCPsych. 1989. (Birmingham) Cons. Psychiat. Learning Disabilities N. Warks. NHS Trust. Prev: Sen. Regist. (Psychiat. Ment. Handicap) W. Midl. RHA; SHO & Regist. (Psychiat.) Walsgrave Hosp. Coventry.

BAXTER, Mary Malcolm (cons. rooms), 26 Ewing St., Kilbarchan, Johnstone PA10 2JA Tel: 01505 702410; Foremount House, Kilbarchan, Johnstone PA10 2EZ Tel: 01505 702410 — MB ChB 1951 Glas.; MRCGP 1966; DObst RCOG 1954. (Univ. Glas.) Asst. MOH (Matern.) Renfrew Co. Socs: Med. Wom. Federat.; BMA. Prev: Sen. Cas. Off. Oakbank Hosp. Glas.; Ho. Off. (Obst.) Glas. Roy. Matern. & Wom. Hosp.; Ho. Off. (Gyn.) Roy. Samarit. Hosp. Wom. Glas.

BAXTER, Michael Alan St Peter's NHS Hospital Trust, Chertsey KT16 0PZ Tel: 01932 872000 — BM BS 1984 Nottm.; BM BS (Hons.) Nottm. 1984; PhD Birm. 1979, BSc 1976; BMedSci Nottm. 1982; FRCP (UK) 1997; MRCP (UK) 1987. Cons. Phys. Diabetes & Endocrinol. St. Peter's NHS Hosp. Trust Chertsey. Socs: Brit. Endocrine Soc.; Brit. Diabetic Assn. Prev: Regist. Hammersmith Hosp. Lond.; Lect. & Sen. Regist. (Med.) Univ. Birm.

BAXTER, Michael John 14 Lychmead, Clifton, Shefford SG17 5EZ — MB BS 1988 Lond.; MRCGP 1992.

BAXTER, Neil 625 Bolton Street, Brixham TQ5 9BZ Tel: 01803 855897; The Old Vicarage, Kingswear, Dartmouth TQ6 0BX Tel: 01803 752570 Fax: 01803 855613 — MB ChB 1959 Glas.; DObst RCOG 1964. (Glas.) Prev: Resid. Ho. Off. (Med., Surg. & O & G) Glas. W.. Infirm.; Asst. Dir. Clin. Research US Vit. & Pharm. Corp. New York.

BAXTER, Noel Christopher 19 Loxley Road, London SW18 3LL — MB BS 1992 Lond.

BAXTER, Peter John Addenbrooke's Hospital, Hills Road, Cambridge CB2 2QQ Tel: 01223 216767 Fax: 01223 336584; The Cottage, Green St, Little Hadham, Ware SG11 2EE Tel: 01279 505618 — MB BS 1967 Lond.; MD Lond. 1979, MSc 1974; FRCP Lond. 1991; MRCS Eng. LRCP Lond. 1967; MRCP (UK) 1970; FFOM RCP Lond. 1987, MFOM 1981; DO RCS Eng. 1973. (Univ. Coll.) Cons. Occupat. Phys. Univ. Camb. & Addenbrooke's Hosp. Trust. Socs: Fell. Roy. Soc. Med.; Soc. Occupat. Med.; BMA. Prev: Med. Epidemiol. Centres for Dis. Control, Atlanta USA; Regist. Nat. Hosp. Nerv. Dis. Qu. Sq. Lond.; SHO Univ. Coll. & King's Coll. Hosps. Lond.

BAXTER, Peter Julian Campbell North Hampshire Hospital, Basingstoke RG7 4RX Tel: 01256 473202 — MB BS 1966 Lond.; MRCS Eng. LRCP Lond. 1965; FFA RCS Eng. 1969. (Guy's) Cons. Anaesth. N. Hants. Gp. Hosps. Socs: Assn. Anaesth. & Hosp. Cons. Specialist Assn.; BMA; Assn. Orthopaedic Anaesth. Prev: Sen. Regist. (Anaesth.) Middlx. & N.wick Pk. Hosps.; Regist. (Anaesth.) Roy. N.. Hosp. Lond.; Ho. Surg. (Genitourin.) Guy's Hosp. Lond.

BAXTER, Peter Nicholas Robertson Health Centre, High Street, Alness IV17 0UN Tel: 01349 882229 Fax: 01349 884004; The House, Delny, Invergordon IV18 0NW — MB ChB 1975 Aberd.; MRCGP 1980; DRCOG 1979. Med. Dir. Highland Communities NHS Trust Inverness; Treas. N. Scotl. Fac. RCGP; Examr. for RCGP. Prev: Trainee GP Bath; SHO (A & E & Paediat.) Roy. United Hosp. Bath; SHO (O & G & Geriat.) St. Martins Hosp. Bath.

BAXTER, Peter Stuart Childrens Hospital Western Bank, Sheffield S10 2TH Tel: 0114 271 7000 Email: p.s.baxter@sheffield.ac.uk — MB BS 1978 Lond.; MA Camb. 1977, MD 1991; FRCP Ed. 1996; MRCP 1981; T(M) (Paediat.) 1991; DCH RCP Lond. 1980. Cons. Paediat. Neurol. Childr. Hosp. Sheff.; Sen. Regist. (Paediat. Neurol.) Newc. Gen. Hosp. Prev: Lect. (Paediat.) Univ. Sheff.; Regist. (Paediat.) Roy. Hosp. Sick Childr. Edin.; Medicin. Resid. Etranger, Lyon, France.

BAXTER, Prudence Wendy Morriston Hospital, Swansea SA6 6NL Tel: 01792 703572 Fax: 01792 703573 Email: j.n.baxter@swansea.ac.uk; Tuarangi, 15 The Bryn, Derwen Fawr, Swansea SA2 8DD Tel: 01792 208349 — MB ChB 1994 Glas.; MB ChB (Commedation) Glas. 1994; FRCS (Ed.) 1998. Specialist Regist. (Oral & Maxillofacial Surg.) Morriston Hosp. Swansea.

BAXTER, Richard David Lakeside Surgery, Cottingham Road, Corby NN17 2UR Tel: 01536 204154 Fax: 01536 748286; 17 Club Street, Kettering NN16 8RB — MB BS 1985 Lond.; MRCGP 1990; DRCOG 1989.

BAXTER, Richard Duncan Fax: 020 8571 9796 — MB BS 1987 Lond.; BSc Lond. 1984; MRCPsych 1992; Dip Forens Psychiat Lond. 1995. Cons. Forens. Psychiat. W. Lond. Healthcare NHS Trust.

BAXTER, Richard John 7 Clarence Gardens, Four Oaks, Sutton Coldfield B74 4AP — MB ChB 1992 Birm.; PhD Aston 1991; BA Keele 1985. SHO (Neurosurg.) Selly Oak Hosp. Birm. Prev: Ho. Off. Birm. Accid. Hosp.

BAXTER, Richard Malcolm 5 Whytingham Road, Tring HP23 5JN — MB BS 1998 Lond.; MB BS Lond 1998.

BAXTER, Robert Thomas The Commons Surgery, Sandbach CW11 1HR Tel: 01270 764151; 1 St. John's Way, Sandbach CW11 2LY — MB ChB 1970 Ed.

BAXTER, Robin 33 Grasmere, Stukeley Meadows, Huntingdon PE29 6UR Tel: 01480 433926 Fax: 0870 054 2948 Email: robin.baxter@baxte.demon.co.uk — MB BS 1994 Lond.; BSc Lond. 1991. (United Medical and Dental Schools London)

BAXTER, Ronald Henry 49 Monreith Road, Newlands, Glasgow G43 2NZ Tel: 0141 632 6096 — MB ChB 1967 Glas.; MD Glas. 1978; FRCP (Glas.) 1981; MRCP (UK) 1970; DCH RCPS Glas. 1969. Cons. Phys. & Cardiol. Law Hosp. Lanarksh.; Hon. Sen. Clin. Lect. & Postgrad. Tutor (Med.) Univ. Glas.; Dep. Dir. CME RCPS Glas. Socs: Brit. Cardiac. Soc.; Scott. Soc. Phys.; Brit. Soc. Nuclear Med. Prev: Research Fell. (Nuclear Cardiol.) Johns Hopkins Med. Inst. Baltimore; Sen. Regist. (Med.) Vict. Infirm. Glas.

BAXTER, Sally Ann Campbell Whitegates, Brimpton La, Brimpton Common, Reading RG7 4RX Tel: 0118 981 4554; Whitegates, Brimpton La, Brimpton Common, Reading RG7 4RX Tel: 0118 981 4554 — BM BCh 1997 Oxf.; BA Hons Oxf 1994. (Oxford) SHO (Med. Rotat.) Roy. United Hosps. Prev: SHO (A & E), Chelsea & W.minster; HS, John Radcliffe; HP, Derriford Hosp., Plymouth.

BAXTER, Samuel Paul (retired) St. David's Hospital, Carmarthen SA31 3HB Tel: 01267 237481 Fax: 01267 235840 — MB BChir 1966 Camb.; MPhil Lond. 1972; MRCPsych 1972; FRCPsych 1987. Cons. Psychiat. & Med. Dir. (Ment. Health) Pembrokesh. Derwen NHS Trust. Prev: Cons. Psychiat. Char. Cross Hosp. Lond. Riverside HA..

BAXTER, Sara Madeline Dept. of Anaesthetics, James Cook Univ. Hospital, 52 Cossington Road, Middlesbrugh TS4 3BW Tel: 01642 282546 Fax: 01642 274655 Email: sara.baxter@email.stahahst.northy.nhs.uk; 18 Albert Close, Pearl Street, Saltburn-by-the-Sea TS12 1DU Tel: 01202 701496, 01287 625778 Email: gasgoddess62@hotmail.com — MB BS 1986 Lond.; FRCA 1997; DA (UK) 1991. (St Mary's Hosp. Lond.) Cons. Anaesth./ Intensivist, S. Tees Hosp. MiddlesBoro. Socs: BMA; Assoc. Anaesth.s of GB & I; NeuroAnaesth. Soc. GB & I. Prev: Regist. (Intens. Care) Sydney, Austral.

BAXTER, Simon David 8 Orchard Vale, Edgeley, Stockport SK3 9RS Tel: 0161 477 2719 — MB ChB 1993 Manch.; BSc St. And. 1990. GP Princip. Prev: SHO A & E Stepping Hill Hosp.; SHO Paediat. Stepping Hill Hosp.; SHO Med. Stepping Hill Hosp.

BAXTER, Mr Stephen Tite 16 Southway, Wavertree, Liverpool L15 7JA — MB ChB 1988 Dundee; BMSc (Hons.) Dund 1985; FRCS Ed. 1993. Career Regist. Rotat. Merseyside. Prev: Research Regist. (Surg.) Univ. Liverp.

BAXTER, Terence William The Health Centre, Coatham Road, Redcar TS10 1SX Tel: 01642 482647 Fax: 01642 489166; 18 Yearby Village, Redcar TS11 8HF — MB BS 1979 Newc.

BAXTER, Timothy Schwarz Pharma Ltd., East St., Chesham HP5 1DG Tel: 01494 797500 Fax: 01494 773934 Email: tim.baxter@dial.pipex.com; Pyah, 21 Alverton, Great Linford, Milton Keynes MK14 5EF Tel: 01908 692656 Fax: 01908 692656 — MB BS 1986 Lond.; MFPM RCP (UK) 1993; Dip. Pharm. Med. RCP (UK) 1992. (Middl. Hosp. Med. Sch.) Med. Dir. Schwarz Pharma Ltd. Bucks.

BAXTER, Wendy Patricia Accord Hospice, Hospital Grounds, Hawkhead Road, Paisley PA2 7BL Tel: 0141 581 2000 Fax: 0141 581 2004; 49 Monreith Road, Newlands, Glasgow G43 2NZ — MB ChB 1969 Glas.; FRCP Glas. 1992; MRCP (UK) 1976; DA Eng. 1971. Cons. Palliat. Med. & Med. Dir. Accord Hospice Paisley.; Hon. Cons. In Palliat. Med., Roy. Alexandra Hosp. Acute NHS Trust, Paisley. Socs: Scott. Soc. of Phys.s; Roy. Medico-Chirurgical Soc. Glas.; W. of Scotl. Palliat. Phys.s Gp.

BAXTER-SMITH, Mr David Cyril Keepings, 36 Middlefield Lane, Hagley, Stourbridge DY9 0PX — MB BCh BAO 1970 Dub.; MSc Birm. 1974; FRCS Eng. 1976. Cons. Urological Surg. Kidderminster Gen. Hosp. Prev: Sen. Regist. (Surg.) Qu. Eliz. Hosp. Birm.; Lect. (Anat.) Univ. Birm.

BAYER, Antony James Academic Centre, Llandough Hospital, Penarth CF64 2XX Tel: 02920 716971 Fax: 02920 704244 Email: bayer@cf.ac.uk; 4 Heol Ty Mawr, Pendoylan CF71 7UQ — MB BCh 1977 Wales. Sen. Lect. (Geriat. Med.) Univ. of Wales Coll. of Med. Cardiff; Dir. Memory Team, Cardiff & Vale HNS Trust, Cardiff.

BAYER, Carolyn Jane 1 Bowers Way, Harpenden AL5 4EP — MB BS 1995 Lond.; MRCP (UK) 1998.

BAYER, Jacqueline Mary The Avenue Surgery, 102 The Avenue, Ealing, London W13 8LA Tel: 020 8997 2525 Fax: 020 8991 8074 — MB BCh 1975 Wales; MRCGP 1980; DCH Eng. 1980.

BAYER, Manfred (retired) 13 Wickham Way, Beckenham BR3 3AA Tel: 020 8650 9418 — LRCPI & LM, LRSCI & LM 1959; LRCP & LM LRCSI & LM 1959. Prev: GP Sidcup.

BAYER, Max Mosche Forty Willows Surgery, 46 Forty Lane, Wembley HA9 9HA Tel: 020 8385 0011 Fax: 020 8385 0411; 20 Penshurst Gardens, Edgware HA8 9TP Tel: 020 8958 6073 — MB BS 1975 Lond.; MRCGP 1980; DCH NUI 1978; DRCOG 1977; MA Univ. Westminster 1998. (Univ. Coll. Hosp.) VTS Course Organiser Centr. Middlx. Hosp.

BAYES, Anna Ruth Rachael 34 Stanbury Court, Haverstock Hill, London NW3 4RR — MB BS 1996 Lond.; BSc 1993. (UCL)

BAYES, Margaret Joyce Tel: 01534 731421 Fax: 01534 280776; La Petella, Rue Des Vignes, St Peter, Jersey JE3 7BE Tel: 01534 744780 Fax: 01534 744780 Email: docrema@hotmail.com — MB BS 1970 Lond.; DMJ (Clin.) Soc. Apoth. Lond. 1992. (Char. Cross) GP; Forens. Med. Examr. States of Jersey Police Force, CI. Socs: Fell. Roy. Soc. Med.; Assn. Police Surg.; Jersey Med. Soc. Pres. Prev: GP S.sea Hants.; Ho. Phys. & Surg. Newport I. of Wight.

BAYLES, Ian Old School Surgery, Church Street, Seaford BN25 1HH Tel: 01323 890072 Fax: 01323 492340; New Kells, Milton St, Polegate BN26 5RW — MB BChir 1974 Camb.; MRCGP 1990; DRCOG 1990; DCH RCP Lond. 1989; DA (UK) 1987.

BAYLES, Joanna Mary Old School Surgery, Church Street, Seaford BN25 1HH Tel: 01323 890072 Fax: 01323 492340 — MB BS 1984 Lond.; MRCGP 1990; DCH RCP Lond. 1988; DRCOG 1987.

BAYLEY, Anne Christine, OBE (retired) 6 Bridgeford Way, Bridge, Canterbury CT4 5LE Tel: YO62 7LA — MB BChir Camb. 1959; FRCS Ed. 1986; FRCS Eng. 1966. Prev: Prof. Surg. Univ. Zambia.

BAYLEY, Anthony Joseph (retired) Flat 7, The Manor House, 1 Earls Avenue, Folkestone CT20 2EX Tel: 01303 223323 — MB BS Lond. 1964; DObst RCOG 1967.

BAYLEY, Bethan Wyn Dept of Psychiatry, Llwyn &Groes, Wrexham Maewr Hospital, Wrexham LL13 7TD — MB ChB 1993 Manch.; PhD Wales 1987, BSc (Hons.) Biochem. 1983.

BAYLEY, Elizabeth Kathryn Flat 3, Carrington House, 39 Westwood Road, Southampton SO17 1DH — BM 1998 Soton.; BM Soton 1998.

BAYLEY, Guy Langford Department of Anaethesia, Bristol Royal Infirmary, Marlborough Street, Bristol BS2 8HW — MB BS 1989 Lond.

BAYLEY, Mr Ian Jack Lindsay Royal National Orthopaedic Hospital, Brockley Hill, Stanmore HA7 4LP Tel: 020 8954 2300 Fax: 020 8909 5620 — MRCS Eng. LRCP Lond. 1966; FRCS Eng. 1971. Cons. Orthop. Surg. Roy. Nat. Orthop. Hosp. Lond.; Pres.ial Guest Lect. Amer. Shoulder & Elbow Surgs. 1991. Socs: Fell. BOA; (Ex-Pres.) Brit. Elbow & Shoulder Soc. Prev: Sen. Regist. Roy. Nat. Orthop. Hosp. Lond.; Med. Off. RAF.

BAYLEY, Joanna Laura 8 Ninetree Hill, Bristol BS1 3SG — MB ChB 1997 Bristol.

BAYLEY, Karen Laura Windfall, Ridgway, Pyrford, Woking GU22 8PN — BM 1998 Soton.

***BAYLEY, Sarah Elizabeth,** Capt. Officers Mess, 26 Regt RA, Mansergh Barracks, BFPO 113 Tel: 005241 236828 Email: sarahbayley@doctors.org.uk — BM BS 1997 Nottm.; BMedSci 1995.

BAYLEY, Timothy Ralph Lowndes Edenbridge Medical Practice, West View, Station Road, Edenbridge TN8 5ND Tel: 01732 864442 Fax: 01732 862376 — MB ChB 1972 Bristol; MRCGP 1976; DObst RCOG 1975. Prev: Trainee GP Newc. (Cleveland) VTS; Ho. Surg. Yeovil Gen. Hosp.; Ho. Phys. S.mead Gen. Hosp. Bristol.

BAYLEY, Trevor John 83 Downhills Road, Blundellsands, Liverpool L23 8ST Tel: 0151 924 4772 — MB BCh 1958 Wales; MRCP Lond. 1962. (Cardiff) Cons. Phys. BRd.green Hosp. Liverp.; Assoc. Mem. Brit. Cardiac Soc. Socs: Med. Research Soc. Prev: SHO Profess. Med. Unit Qu. Eliz. Hosp. Birm.; Ho. Phys. Profess. Med. Unit & Ho. Surg. Profess. Surg. Unit Cardiff; Roy. Infirm.

BAYLIS, Carol Ann North House, St Bernards Wing, West London Healthcare NHS Trust, Uxbridge Road, Southall — MB BS 1988 Lond. Clin. Asst. (Child Psychiat.) W. Lond. Healthcare NHS Trust. Prev: Regist. Rotat. (Psychiat.) St. Bernard's Hosp. S.all, Char. Cross Hosp. & W.m. Hosp. Lond.; SHO Rotat. (Psychiat.) Qu. Mary's Univ. Hosp., Char. Cross & W.m. Lond.

BAYLIS, Edith Mary (retired) Clinical Chemistry, Kent & Sussex Hospital, Tunbridge Wells TN4 8AT Tel: 01892 526111 Fax: 01892 516698 — BM BCh 1963 Oxf.; MA Oxf. 1970, DM 1972. Prev: Cons. Chem. Path. Tunbridge Wells Health Dist.

BAYLIS, Elizabeth Anne Horton 62 Westbourne Road, Penarth CF64 3HB — MB BS 1985 Lond. SHO (Paediat.) Roy. Gwent Hosp. Newport.

BAYLIS, John Horton St James House, St James Green, Southwold IP18 6JL Tel: 01502 723937 Fax: 01502 725096 — MB BS 1947 Lond.; FRCP Lond. 1971, M 1951. (Guy's) Indep. Cons. Phys. Bedford. Socs: Renal Assn.; Thoracic Soc. Prev: Phys. Bedford Gen. Hosp. & Chest Clinic; Sen. Regist. (Med.) King's Coll. Hosp.; Regist. (Med.) Guy's Hosp. & Brompton Hosp.

BAYLIS, Mr Paul Michael 42 Sandhurst Drive, Belfast BT9 5AY — MB BS 1991 Lond.; FRCS Ed. 1995. Specialist Regist. (A & E) Roy. Vict. Hosp. Belf. Socs: Assoc. Fell. Fac. Accid. & Emerg. Med.; BAEM; BMA - POWAR. Prev: Surg. Chief Off. RFA; SHO (Med.) Craigavon Area Hosp.; SHO (Surg.) Downe Hosp.

BAYLIS, Professor Peter Howard The Medical School, University of Newcastle, Framlington Place, Newcastle upon Tyne NE2 4HH Tel: 0191 222 7003 Fax: 0191 222 6621 Email: dean-of-medicine@ncl.ac.uk; 53 The Rise, Darras Hall, Ponteland, Newcastle upon Tyne NE20 9LQ Tel: 01661 823244 — MB ChB 1970 Bristol; BSc (Hons.) Bristol 1967; MD Birm. 1978; FRCP Lond. 1983; MRCP (UK) 1973; 1998 F Med Sci. (Bristol) Dean of Med., Prof. of Experim. Med. Fac. of Med., Univ. of Newc.; Cons. Endocrinol., Newc. NHS Hosp.s Trust. Socs: Soc. Endocrinol.; Assn. Phys.; Founder Mem. Acad. of Med. Sci.s. Prev: Cons. Phys. & Endocrinol., Roy. Vict. Infirm., Newc.; Clin. Sub-Dean Med. Sch., Newc.; Edr. Clin. Endocrinol.

BAYLIS, Peter James BT Occupational Health Service, Telephone House, 357 Gorgie Road, Edinburgh EH11 2RP Tel: 0131 345 4067 Fax: 0131 345 4062; 12 Crookston Court, Crookston Road,

Inveresk, Musselburgh EH21 7TR Tel: 0131 653 3550 — MB ChB 1971 Ed.; FFOM RCP Lond. 1993, M 1982; DIH Eng. 1978. (Ed.) Reg. Med. Off., BT Occupat. Health Serv. Socs: Soc. Occupat. Med.; Brit. Occupat. Hyg. Soc.; Brit. Dent. Assn. Prev: Occupat. Health Manager & Princip. Med. Off. Zeneca Specialties; Gp. Occupat. Phys. The Wellcome Foundat. Ltd.; Dir. Occupat. Health & Safety Centr. Manch. Healthcare Trust.

BAYLIS, Robert Ian Nyckelbergivagen, 46A Koping, Sweden 73134, Sweden; 28 Edge Hill Road, Nether Edge, Sheffield S7 1SP — MB ChB 1979 Manch.

BAYLIS, Robert James Horton Queen Alexandra Hsp, Cosham, Portsmouth Tel: 023 92 286 000 Fax: 023 92 286 758 — MB BS 1989 Lond.; DA (UK) 1992; FRCA 1994. (RFHSM) Cons. in Pain Managem.,Portsmouth Hsp NHS Trust.

BAYLIS, Susan Mary Morpeth Health Centre, Gas House Lane, Morpeth NE61 1SR Tel: 01670 513657 Fax: 01670 511966; 53 The Rise, Darras Hall, Ponteland, Newcastle upon Tyne NE20 9LQ Tel: 01661 823244 — MB ChB 1970 Bristol; DObst RCOG 1972. GP Morpeth.

BAYLIS, Timothy Martyn Dickens Place Surgery, Dickens Place, Chelmsford CM1 4UU Tel: 01245 442628 Fax: 01245 443647 Email: timothy.baylis@gp-f81024.nhs.uk; 35 Paddock Drive, Springfield, Chelmsford CM1 6SS — MB BS 1977 Lond.; MRCS Eng. LRCP Lond. 1977.

BAYLISS, Anthony Paul School House, Drumoak, Banchory AB31 5EE Tel: 0133 08 650 — MB ChB 1969 St. And.; FRCR 1975; DMRD Eng. 1973. Cons. Radiol. Dept. Forresterhill Hosp. Aberd.. Prev: Sen. Regist. Radiol. Dept. W.. Infirm. Glas.

BAYLISS, Christopher Richard Butler Royal Devon & Exeter Hospital, Barrack Road, Exeter EX2 5DW Tel: 01392 402325 Fax: 01392 402330; Mill Down, Clyst St Mary, Exeter EX5 1DG Tel: 01392 875117 Fax: 01392 875301 — MB BChir 1970 Camb.; 1970 MB BChir Camb.; 1971 MA, Camb; 1970 MRCS Eng. LRCP Lond; 1977 FRCR; 1991 T(CR); 1976 DMRD Eng.; 1972 DObst RCOG. Cons. Radiol. Roy. Devon & Exeter Hosp. Prev: Sen. Regist. (Diagn. Radiol.) Hammersmith Hosp. Lond.; Regist. (Diagn. Radiol.) Middlx. Hosp. Lond.

BAYLISS, Helen Georgina 795 Pershore Road, Selly Oak, Birmingham B29 7LR — MB ChB 1996 Birm.; ChB Birm. 1996.

BAYLISS, Helen Jane Charlbury Surgery, Spendlove Centre, Enstone Road, Charlbury, Chipping Norton OX7 3PQ Tel: 01608 810210 Fax: 01608 811636; Clinkers, Chapel Lane, Shipton under Wychwood, Oxford OX7 6DJ Tel: 01993 832021 — MB ChB 1982 Bristol; MRCGP 1986; DCCH RCP Ed. 1985.

BAYLISS, John Francis Jerome Cardiology Department, Hemel Hempstead Hospital, Hillfield Road, Hemel Hempstead HP2 4AD Tel: 01442 287087 Fax: 01442 287091; Charnwood, 54 Holywell Road, Studham, Dunstable LU6 2PD Email: john@bayliss.nildram.co.uk — MB BChir 1978 Camb.; MA Camb. 1974; FRCP Lond. 1994; MRCP (UK) 1980. (Westm.) Cons. Cardiol. Hemel Hempstead Hosp. & St. Albans City Hosp.; Hon. Cons. Cardiol. St. Mary's Hosps. Lond. Socs: Brit. Cardiac Soc.; Eur. Soc. Cardiol.; Brit. Soc. Echocardiogr. Prev: Sen. Regist. (Cardiol.) Nat. Heart Hosp. & W.m. Hosp. Lond.; Regist. (Cardiol.) Nat. Heart Hosp. Lond.; Regist. (Med.) Hillingdon Hosp. Uxbridge.

BAYLISS, Lesley Anne Toft Road Surgery, Toft Road, Knutsford WA16 9DX Tel: 01565 632681; Manorom, Lovat Drive, Knutsford WA16 8NS Tel: 01565 750094 — MB ChB 1978 Liverp.; DCH RCP Lond. 1982; DRCOG 1980.

BAYLISS, Louise The Old Byre, The Orchard, Shrewsbury Road, Edgmond, Newport TF10 8HT — MB ChB 1997 Leeds.

BAYLISS, Margaret Anne School House, Drumoak, Banchory AB31 5EE — MB ChB 1969 St. And. (Dundee)

BAYLISS, Mark Andrew 37 Ledborough Lane, Beaconsfield HP9 2DB — MB BS 1988 Lond.; BSc (Psychol.) Lond. 1985, MB BS 1988.

BAYLISS, Patricia Ann The Haven, 3 Findhorn, Forres IV36 3YE Tel: 01309 690914 Fax: 01309 690914; Laich Medical Centre, Clifton Road, Lossiemouth IV31 6DJ Tel: 01343 812277 Fax: 01343 812396 — MB ChB 1978 Manch.; MRCGP 1988.

BAYLISS, Paul Francis Csete Flat 5, 12 The Esplanade, Scarborough YO11 2AF — MB ChB 1966 Birm.; LLB Lond. 1975; MRCP Lond. 1969; FFPM RCP (UK) 1989. Prev: Head of Internat. Regulat. Dept. ICI Pharmaceuts.; Managing Dir. Stuart Pharmaceuts. Ltd. Cheadle; Regist. (Med.) N. Staffs. Hosp. Centre Stoke-on-Trent.

BAYLISS, Sir Richard (Ian Samuel), KCVO Lister Hospital, Chelsea Bridge Road, London SW1W 8RH Tel: 020 7730 8298; Flat 7, 61 Onslow Square, London SW7 3LS Tel: 020 7589 3087 Fax: 020 7581 5937 Email: ricbayliss@dial.pipex.com — MB BChir 1941 Camb.; MA Camb. 1948, MD 1946; FRCP Lond. 1956; MRCP (UK) 1942; MRCS Eng. LRCP Lond. 1941; Hon. FRCPath 1994. (St. Thos.) Cons. Phys. Endocrinol. Lister Hosp. Lond.; Chairm. Med. Advis. Panel, ITC; Hon. Cons. Phys. King Edwd. VII Hosp.; Hon. Fell Clare Coll. Camb. Socs: Fell. Roy. Soc. Med. (Ex-Pres. Sect. Endocrinol.); (Ex-Pres.) Thyroid Club; (Ex-Pres.) Assn. Phys. Prev: Phys. to HM the Qu. & Head of HM's Med. Ho.hold; Cons. Phys. W.m. Hosp.; Lect. (Med. & Phys.) Postgrad. Med. Sch. Lond.

BAYLISS, Samuel Gordon (retired) 1 Lansdowne Avenue, Portchester, Fareham PO16 9NN — MB 1954 Camb.; MA Camb. 1960, MB 1954, BChir 1953. Prev: Cons. Neurophysiol. Roy. Surrey Co. Hosp. & Farnham Rd. Hosp. Guildford.

BAYLISS, Sarah-Jane 25 Newnham Road, Plympton, Plymouth PL7 4AW — MB BCh 1992 Wales.

BAYLISS-BROWN, Philip James Hethersett Surgery, Great Melton Road, Norwich NR9 3AB Tel: 01603 810250; Email: phil@hicomm.demon.co.uk — MB BS 1981 Lond.; MD 2000; BSc 1978 (Hons.) Lond.; MRCGP 1986; DRCOG 1984. (St Bartholomews, London) Gen. Practioner, Hethersett, Norf.; Cons. Adviser in Terminology, NHS Informat. Auth.; Hon. Sen. Lect. in Med. Informatics, St. Thomas' Hosp., Kings Coll. Lond.; Hon. Lect. in Healthcare Informatics, SYS, Univ. of E. Anglia. Socs: Mem. of the Roy. Coll. Gen. Practitioners. Prev: Sen. Med. Coding Cons. NHS Informat. Auth.; Gen. Practioner, Beccles, Suff.; Trainee GP Welwyn Garden City VTS.

BAYLY, Graham Russell Dept of Chemical Pathology, Bristol Royal Infirmary, Marlborough St, Bristol BS2 8HW Tel: 0117 928 3245 Fax: 0117 928 3107 Email: graham.bayly@ubht.swest.nhs.uk; 9 Rylestone Grove, Stoke Bishop, Bristol BS9 3UT — BM 1987 Soton.; BA Oxf. 1983; MRCP (UK) 1992; DRCPath 1994; MRCPath 1996. Cons. Chem. pathologist United Bristol Healthcare Trust.

BAYLY, Jonathan Roy Rowcroft Medical Centre, Rowcroft Retreat, Stroud GL5 3BE Tel: 01453 764471 Fax: 01453 755247; 4 Vale View, Field Road, Whiteshill, Stroud GL6 6AG Tel: 01453 764993 Email: jonathanbayly@compuserve.com — MB BS 1976 Lond.; LRCP MRCS Lond. 1976; MRCGP 1982; Dobst RCOG 1982; BA Oxf. 1971. (Guy's) GP Princip.

BAYLY, Philip James Martin Department of Anaesthesia, Freeman Hospital, Newcastle upon Tyne NE7 7DN Tel: 0191 284 3111 Fax: 0191 223 1180 Email: phil.bayly@tfu.nuth.northy.nhs.uk; 2 Fenwick Terrace, Jesmond, Newcastle upon Tyne NE2 2JQ Tel: 0191 281 8178 Email: philbayly@aol.com — MB BS 1981 Lond.; FRCA 1988. (Char. Cross Hosp. Med. Sch.) Cons. Anaesth. Head Liver Transpl. Anaesth. Freeman Hosp. Newc. u. Tyne. Socs: Chairm. of audit Comm. of Vasc. Anaesth. Soc. of Gt. Britain & Irel. Prev: Acting Asst. Prof. Univ. Washington Med. Sch. Seattle, USA.

BAYLY, Rachel Anne Hobs Moat Medical Centre, Ulleries Road, Solihull B92 8ED Tel: 0121 742 5211 Fax: 0121 743 4217; 62 Willowbank Road, Knowle, Solihull B93 9QX Tel: 01564 773172 — BM 1988 Soton.; BM Soton 1988; MRCGP 1994; DCH RCP Lond. 1993; DGM RCP Lond. 1991. (Southampton)

BAYLY, Rosemary Alison The Surgery, 34 Raymond Rd, Southampton SO15 5AL Tel: 02880 227559 — BM 1992 Soton.; MRCGP 1997; DFFP 1996; DRCOG 1995. p/t GP Shirley, Soton.; Hon. Clin. Research Fell. MRC Environm. Epidemiol. Unit, Soton. Wom.s Survey, Soton.

BAYMAN, Deborah Coutts Heathcliffe, Hanover St., Mossley, Ashton-under-Lyne OL5 0HL; Failsworth Health Centre, Ashton Road W., Failsworth, Manchester M35 0HN Tel: 0161 681 1818 — MB ChB 1979 Manch.; DRCOG 1983.

BAYMAN, Ian Walter Mansfield Medical Centre, 56 Binley Road, Coventry CV3 1JB Tel: 024 7645 7551 Fax: 024 7644 2250 — BM BCh 1974 Oxf.

BAYMAN, Robin Lincoln 9 Woodland Park, Royton, Oldham OL2 5UY Tel: 0161 624 5889 — MB ChB 1968 Manch.; DIH Eng. 1972.

BAYNE, George Murray Seaford Health Centre, Dane Road, Seaford BN25 1DH Tel: 01323 490022 Fax: 01323 492156 — MB

ChB 1968 Ed. (Ed.) Prev: SHO Roy. Edin. Hosp.; Ho. Surg. Vict. Hosp. Kirkcaldy.

BAYNE, John Burgess Manor House Surgery, Providence Place, Bridlington YO15 2QW Tel: 01262 602661 Fax: 01262 400891; 80 Cardigan Road, Bridlington YO15 3JT Tel: 01262 678327 — MB ChB 1970 Ed.; BSc (Med. Sci.) Ed. 1967. Clin. Asst. (Gyn.) Bridlington & Dist. Hosp. Prev: SHO (Cas.) Vict. Hosp. Kirkcaldy; SHO (Obst.) Forth Pk. Matern. Hosp. Kirkcaldy.

BAYNE, Michael Christopher Stubbetts, 181 Petersham Road, Petersham, Richmond TW10 7AW Tel: 020 8940 5760 — MB ChB 1993 Bristol; BSc Hons. Bristol. 1990, MB ChB 1993; MRCP. Lond.

BAYNE, Stephen (retired) Treaton, 5 Victoria Road, Lundin Links, Leven KY8 6AY — MB ChB 1944 St. And.; BSc St. And. 1941. Prev: Lect. Biochem. Univ. St. And.

BAYNES, Christopher Diabetes Centre, Chase Farm Hospital, The Ridgeway, Enfield EN2 8JL Tel: 020 8967 5967 — BM 1982 Soton.; DM Soton. 1992; MRCP (UK) 1985. Cons. Phys. Diabetes Centre Chase Farm Hosp. Enfield. Prev: Sen. Regist. & Hon. Lect. St. Mary's Hosp. Lond.

BAYNES, Derrick Benignus Pronsias Consultant Psychiatrist, Tameside General Hospital, Ashton-under-Lyne OL6 9RW, Republic of Ireland Tel: 0161 331 5386 Fax: 0161 331 5050 Email: jacqui.hanna@exchange.tgcps.tr.nwest.nhs.uk; Tel: 01482 675678 — LRCPI & LM, LRSCI & LM 1974; LRCPI & LM LRCSI & LM 1974; MRCPsych 1988; MICGP 1984. (Royal College of Surgeons of Ireland Medical School) Cons. Psychiat., Yorks. Deanery. Prev: Sen. Regist. (Psychiat.) Yorks. Deanery.

BAYNES, Kevin Charles Reginald 26 Christchurch Street, Cambridge CB1 1HT — MB BS 1989 Lond.; BA Physiol. Sci. Oxf. 1986; MRCP (UK) 1992. Wellcome Research Fell. Addenbrooke's Hosp. Camb. Socs: Brit. Diabetic Assn. Prev: Lect. Addenbrookes's Hosp. Camb.; Regist. Roy. Lond. Hosp. & Newham Gen. Hosp. Lond.; SHO St. Peters Hosp. Chertsey.

BAYNES, Stephen Charles 37A Dunvegan Drive, Lordswood, Southampton SO16 8DB — BM BS 1987 Nottm.; BMedSci Nottm. 1985, BM BS 1987; DRCOG 1989. Trainee GP Soton.

BAYNEY, Richard Deoraj 13 Birkbeck Avenue, London W3 6HX — BM BS 1986 Nottm.; BMedSci (1st cl.) Nottm. 1984, BM BS 1986.

BAYNHAM, Peter Roland Warren 39 Homelands Road, Rhiwbina, Cardiff CF14 1UH — MB BCh 1984 Wales.

BAYNHAM, Mr Timothy David Warren Bridgend General Hospital, Quarella Road, Bridgend CF31 1 — MB BCh 1980 Wales; FRCSI 1990; FCOphth 1990; DO RCPSI 1986.

BAYON, Jeanette Fort's Edge House, Kintyre Road, Portsmouth PO6 3UH; 128 Wellington Hill W., Westbury-on-Trym, Bristol BS9 4QU — MB BCh 1982 Wales; MSc MB BCh Wales 1982; MRCGP 1986. Civil. Med. Pract. (MOD) BAOR.

BAYONA BAYONA, Francesc Flat 3, 93 Oxford Road, Banbury OX16 9AJ — LMS 1990 U Autonoma Barcelona.

BAYOUMI, Abdel-Hady Mahmoud Mohamed Department of Dermatology, Queen Elizabeth II Hospital, Howlands, Welwyn Garden City AL7 4HQ Tel: 01707 365427 Fax: 01707 365239; Department of Dermatology, Hertford County Hospital, North Road, Hertford SG14 1LP Tel: 01707 365427 Fax: 01707 365239 — MB ChB 1969 Alexandria; PhD Wales 1982; DMSc Assiut 1973. Cons. Dermat. E.& N.Herts. NHS Trust. Socs: St. John's Dermat. Soc.; Brit. Assn. Dermat.; Assoc. Mem. Roy. Coll. Path. Prev: Regist. (Dermat.) York Dist. Hosp.; SHO (Gen. Med. & Dermat.) Roy. Gwent Hosp. Newport; SHO (Dermat.) Ealing Hosp. Middlx.

BAYOUMI, Hassan Mahmoud 79 Harley Street, London W1N 1DE Tel: 020 7935 1414 — MB BCh 1947 Cairo; LMSSA Lond. 1959; Dip. Surg. Cairo 1953. (Kasr El Aini) Socs: Brit. Inst. Musculoskel. Med. Prev: Clin. Asst. (Orthop.) Middlx. Hosp. Lond.; Regist. (Orthop.) W. Lond. Hosp.; Orthop. Surg. Red Cresc. Hosp. Cairo.

BAYOUMI, Mohamed Royal Glamorgan hospital, Llantrisant, Pontyclun CF72 8XL Tel: 01443 443600 Fax: 02920 2068 9488; Tel: 02920 759576 Fax: 02920 689488 Email: m.bayoumi@virgin.net — MB ChB 1975 Alexandria; FFA RCS Eng. 1983. Cons. Anaesth. Roy. Glam. Hosp., Llantrisant.

BAYREUTHER, Jane Louise 6 Temple Avenue, London N20 9EH — BM 1994 Soton. SHO (Paediat.) N. Hants. Hosp. Basingstoke. Prev: SHO (Med.) Epsom Gen. Hosp. & Portsmouth Hosps.

BAYS, Simon Martin Andrew 56B Victoria Park Road, London E9 7JJ — MB BS 1997 Lond.; BSc Hons. (St. Bartholomew's London)

BAYTON, David Howel (retired) Derlwyn, Llanarth SA47 0RG — MB BS 1952 Lond.; MRCS Eng. LRCP Lond. 1952; DObst RCOG 1958.

BAYTON, Mr Evan Aled Department of Accident and Emergency, Burnley General Hospital, Casterton Avenue, Burnley BB10 2PQ Tel: 01282 474052 Fax: 01282 474055 — MB ChB 1982 Manch.; FFAEM 1999; BSc (Hons.) Pharmacol. Manch. 1980; FRCS Ed. 1993; MRCGP 1993; DFFP 1993; T(GP) 1993; Dip IMC RCS Ed. 1989; DTM & H Liverp. 1997; CCST (Accident and Emergency Medicine) 1998. (Victoria University Manchester) Cons. in A&E, Burnley Gen. Hosp., Burnley, Lancs. Socs: Fell. Manch. Med. Soc.; Roy. Soc. Med.; Fell. Amer. Coll. Emerg. Phys. Prev: Regist. (Med.) BRd.green Hosp. Liverp.; Ho. Phys. Manch. Roy. Infirm.; Ho. Surg. Christie Hosp. Manch.

BAZARAA, Talal Ali Salim Halifax General Hospital, Huddersfield Road, Halifax HX3 0PW — MB BS 1976 Khartoum; MRCPI 1992.

BAZAZ, Moti Lal Shehjar, Number One Norwood, Carleton, Pontefract WF8 3SD — MB BS 1969 Jammu & Kashmir.

BAZELEY, Brenda Joan The Health Centre, Ampthill, Bedford MK45 2SB Tel: 01525 402302 — MB ChB 1956 Manch.

BAZELEY-WHITE, Diana Lorraine Samira, 33 Upper Cranbrook Road, Westbury Park, Bristol BS6 7UR — MB BS 1974 Lond.; MRCPsych. 1982; Dip Health Mgt 1997 Keele. Cons. Child & Adolesc. Psychiat. Bristol.

BAZETT, Michael Aldwin (retired) The Limes, Little Waltham, Chelmsford Tel: 01245 973360265 — MRCS Eng. LRCP Lond. 1944. Prev: Obst. Ho. Surg. St. John's Hosp. Chelmsford.

BAZIN, Marc Louis Francois The Princess Street Surgery, 63 Princess Street, Normanton WF6 1AB Tel: 01924 892132 Fax: 01924 898168; The Manor House, 129 High St, Normanton WF6 1NW — MB ChB 1978 Birm.

BAZLEY, Peter David 36 Delamere Road, Gatley, Cheadle SK8 4PN — MB ChB 1980 Manch.; BSc St. And. 1977; DRCOG 1983.

BDESHA, Mr Amarjit Singh Hill View, Pine Hill, Manor Road, Hazelmere, High Wycombe HP15 7QJ Tel: 020 8561 6811 Email: ab@abdesha.freeserve.co.uk; South Buckinghamshire NHS Trust, Queen Alexandra Road, High Wycombe HP11 2 Tel: 01494 526161 — MB BS 1985 Lond.; FRCS Eng. 1990; MS Lond. 1996; FRCS (Urol.) 1996. (Charing Cross Hospital) Cons. Urol. Surg. S. Bucks. NHS Trust. Prev: Sen. Regist. (Urol.) Char. Cross Hosp. Lond.; Sen. Regist. (Urol.) Hammersmith Hosp. Lond.; Clin. Research Fell. (Urol.) St. Mary's Hosp. Lond.

BEABLE, Anne Elizabeth High Street Surgery, 94 High Street, Wootton Bridge, Ryde PO33 4PR Tel: 01983 883520 Fax: 01983 883538 — MB ChB 1977 Bristol; DRCOG Lond. 1980.

BEABLE, Richard Arthur 23 Rowantree Road, Newton Abbot TQ12 4LL — MB ChB 1998 Leic.; MB ChB Leic 1998.

BEACH, Brian The Surgery, Staunton-on-Wye, Hereford HR4 7LT Tel: 01981 500227 Fax: 01981 500603 — MB ChB 1965 Birm.; MRCP (U.K.) 1971; MRCS Eng. LRCP Lond. 1965. (Birm.) Prev: Med. Off. All St.s' Hosp. Transkei; Regist. (Paediat.) Univ. Rhodesia & Nyasaland Salisbury, Rhodesia; Regist. (Med.) Heref. Gp. Hosps.

BEACH, Clive Alan David Braids Medical Practice, 6 Camus Avenue, Edinburgh EH10 6QT Tel: 0131 445 5999 — MB ChB 1976 Aberd.

BEACH, Francis Xavier Michael Barton Ridge, Rectory Lane, Horsington, Templecombe BA8 0EF Tel: 01963 370767 — MB ChB 1963 Liverp.; MD Liverp. 1972; FRCP Lond. 1980, M 1968; DTM & H Liverp. 1964. p/t Cons. Phys. E. Som. NHS Trust, Yeovil Hosp. Socs: Med. Res. Soc. & Renal Assn.; Brit. Diabetic Assn. Prev: Regist. (Med.) Intens. Care Unit Whiston Hosp. & Wessex Renal Unit Portsmouth.

BEACH, Giles Richard Balmoral, 1 Victoria Road, Deal CT14 7AU Tel: 01304 373444; 6 Wawick Road, Walmer, Deal CT14 7JF Tel: 01304 379982 Fax: 01304 381637 — BM BCh 1973 Oxf.; MA Oxf. 1974; MRCGP 1984; DCH Eng. 1979; DRCOG 1978. (St. Thos.) Med. Off. Red Cross (Deal Br.).

BEACH, Helen Isa The Surgery, Staunton-on-Wye, Hereford HR4 7LT Tel: 01981 500227 Fax: 01981 500603 — MB ChB 1969 Birm.; DCH Eng. 1971. (Birm.) Prev: SHO (Anaesth.) & SHO

(Paediat.) Heref. Gp. Hosps.; Med. Off. All St.s' Hosp. Transkei, S. Africa.

BEACH, Hilary 14 Delaporte Cl,, Epsom KT17 4AF — MB ChB 1997 Birm.

***BEACH, Jennifer Louise** Barton Ridge, Horsington, Templecombe BA8 0EF — MB BS 1997 Lond.

BEACH, Jeremy Richard The University of Birimingham, Edgbaston, Birmingham B15 2TT Tel: 0121 414 6048 Email: j.r.beach@bham.ac.uk — MB BS 1983 Newc.; MD 1996; MRCP (UK) 1986; MFOM RCP (UK) 1996. Sen. Lect. (Occupat. Health) Univ. Birm. Prev: Lect. (Occupat. Health) Univ. Birm.; Research Regist. (Thoracic Med.) Chest Clinic Newc. Gen. Hosp.; Regist. (Gen. Med. & Geriat.) Newc. HA.

BEACH, Joanna Faye Brock Cottage, Clive Ave, Church Stretton SY6 7BL — MB ChB 1997 Birm.

BEACH, Jonathan William Easthope Road Health Centre, Easthope Road, Church Stretton SY6 6BL Tel: 01694 722127 Fax: 01694 724604 — MB BS 1968 Lond.; MRCS Eng. LRCP Lond. 1968; Dip. Ven. Soc. Apoth. Lond. 1983; DObst RCOG 1974. (Middlx.) Hosp. Pract. (Genitourin. Med.) Roy. Shrewsbury Hosp. & P.ss Roy. Hosp. Telford. Prev: Ho. Phys. Middlx. Hosp. Lond.; Ho. Surg. St. And. Hosp. Billericay.

BEACH, Philip Geoffrey Landfall, 35 Corton, Warminster BA12 0SZ — MB BCh 1959 Witwatersrand; MRCP (UK) 1968.

BEACH, Richard Charles Jenny Lind Childrens Department, Norfolk & Norwich Hospital, Norwich NR1 3SR Tel: 01603 286350 Fax: 01603 287584; Hamford, Florden Road, Newton Flotman, Norwich NR15 1QX Tel: 01508 470473 — MB BS 1974 Lond.; BSc Lond. 1971, MD 1984; MRCP (UK) 1977. (St. Thos.) Cons. Paediat. Norf. & Norwich Hosp. Prev: Sen. Regist. Rotat. (Paediat.) Soton. & Portsmouth; Resid. Regist. (Paediat.) St. Thos. Hosp. Lond.; Regist. Rotat. (Paediat.) St. Thos. & Pembury.

***BEACH-THOMAS, Joanna Mary** Old Gore, Ross-on-Wye HR9 7QR; Old Gore, Ross-on-Wye HR9 7QR Tel: 01989 780280 — MB ChB 1997 Birm.

BEACHAM, Karen Jane 4 Westfield Drive, Newcastle upon Tyne NE3 4XT — MB BS 1978 Newc.; FFA RCS Eng. 1985; MRCGP 1982; DRCOG 1981. Cons. Anaesth. Freeman Hosp. Newc. u. Tyne.

BEACHAM, William Dean Shire Cottage, 399 Old Whitley Wood Lane, Reading RG2 8PY — MB BS 1997 Lond.

BEACOCK, Mr Christopher John Maxwell Royal Shrewsbury Hospital, Mytton Oak Road, Shrewsbury SY3 8XQ — MD 1988 Birm.; MB ChB 1977; FRCS Eng. 1982. Cons. Urol. Roy. Shrewsbury Hosp. & P.ss Roy. Hosp. Telford.

BEACOCK, David John 10 Penlands Walk, Leeds LS15 9DL — MB BS 1992 Lond.

BEACON, Mr Jonathan Paul The Elms, 24 Hall Place Gardens, St Albans AL1 3SF Tel: 01727 865057; Sewell Manor, Sewell, Dunstable LU6 1RP Tel: 01582 699015 Fax: 01582 663935 Email: jonathon@swgl.demon.co.ik — MB BS 1969 Lond.; FRCS Eng. 1978; MRCS Eng. LRCP Lond. 1969. (Middlx.) Cons. Orthop. Surg St. Albans City Hosp. & Hemel Hempstead Gen. Hosp. Socs: Fell. BOA; Brit. Assn. Knee Surg.; Post Cruciate Study Gp. Prev: Sen. Regist. Roy. Nat. Orthop. Hosp. Stanmore; Res. Med. Off. King Edwd. VII Hosp. for Offs. Lond.; Med. Off. Kilima Mbogo Hosp. Thika, Kenya.

BEACON, Samuel 12 Druidscross Road, Liverpool L18 3EA Tel: 0151 428 3711 — MB ChB 1945 Liverp. (Liverp.) Socs: Brit. Soc. Experim. & Clin. Hypn. Prev: Med. Off. (Cas.) Roy. Liverp. Childr. Hosp.; Flight Lt. RAFVR; Hosp. Pract. (Psychiat.) Windsor Day Hosp. Liverp.

BEACONSFIELD, Miss Michèle Moorfields Eye Hospital, City Road, London EC1V 2PD Tel: 020 7253 3411 Fax: 020 7566 2019; 62 Wimpole Street, London W1M 7DE Tel: 020 7224 0064 Fax: 020 7224 6216 — MB BS 1979 Lond.; FRCS Eng. 1986; MRCS Eng. LRCP Lond. 1979; FRCOphth 1989; DO RCS Eng. 1983. (Char. Cross) p/t Cons. Ophth. Surg. Moorfields Eye Hosp. Socs: Fell. Roy. Soc. Med.; Fell. (Hon. Sec.) Roy. Coll. Ophth. Prev: Cons. Ophth. Surg. Old Ch. Hosp. Romford; Sen. Regist. (Ophth.) Moorfields Eye Hosp. Lond.

BEACONSFIELD, Rebecca (retired) 23 Ennismore Avenue, London W4 1SE Tel: 020 8994 3278 Fax: 020 8994 9327 — MB BS 1950 Lond.; MRCS Eng. LRCP Lond. 1949.

BEACONSFIELD, Tina Radiology Department, Central Middlesex Hospital, Acton Lane, Park Royal, London NW10 7NS Tel: 020 8453 2783; 23 Ennismore Avenue, Chiswick, London W4 1SE Fax: 020 8995 0888 — MB BS 1985 Lond.; BSc Physiol & Biochem, 1980; FRCRI 1993. (St. Mary's Hospital, Paddington) Radiol. Centr. Middlx. Hosp. Lond.

BEADLE, Marcus Ronald 50 Churchill Av, Halstead CO9 2BE — MB BS 1997 Lond.

BEADLE, Rachel Marianne Royal Hallamshire Hospital Residence, 5 Beech Hill Road, Sheffield S10 2RA — MB ChB 1998 Sheff.; MB ChB Sheff 1998.

BEADLES, Wendy Iona Headmaster's House, Epsom College, College Rd, Epsom KT17 4JQ — BM 1997 Soton.

BEADMAN, Anna Mary Cottage Farm, Shackerstone, Nuneaton CV13 6NL — MB BS 1996 Lond.

BEADSMOORE, Clare Jane Toot Cottage, 33 High St., Orwell, Royston SG8 5QN — MB BS 1992 Lond.

BEADSMOORE, Emma Jane, Surg. Lt. RN Preston Farm House, Tarrant Keyneston, Blandford Forum DT11 9JQ — MB ChB 1996 Bristol. Med. Off. Roy. Navy.

BEADSWORTH, Alison Jane Vine House, 37 Main St., Middleton, Market Harborough LE16 8YU — MB BS 1997 Lond.

BEADSWORTH, Michael Barrington James 10 Norwood Avenue, Manchester M20 6EX — MB ChB 1992 Manch.

BEAGAN, Marion Marjorie Green Close Surgery, Green Close, Kirkby Lonsdale, Carnforth LA6 2BS Tel: 015242 71210 Fax: 015242 72713 — BM 1982 Soton.; MRCGP 1990; DTM & H Liverp. 1987. (Soton.)

***BEAHAN, Joanne** Accident and Emergency Department, Northern General Hospital, Sheffield S10 1SN Tel: 0114 243 4343; 50 Duncan Road, Crookes, Sheffield S10 1SN — MB ChB 1995 Sheff.; MCRP, 1999.

BEAINI, Amal Youssef Harrogate Clinic, 23 Ripon Road, Harrogate HG1 2JL Tel: 01423 500599; The Well Clinic, Cottingley Manor, Cottingley New Road, Bingley BD16 1TZ Tel: 01274 510200 Fax: 01274 510333 — MB BCh 1971 Cairo; FRCPsych. 1991, M 1978. Cons. Psychiat. Yorks. RHA; Sen. Clin. Lect. In Psychiat., Fac. of Med. (Leeds Univ.). Socs: Fell.of the Roy. Soc. of Med. Prev: Lect. (Psychiat.) Leeds Univ.

BEAINI, Youssef Amal 5 Nab Lane, Shipley BD18 4EH Email: y.a.beaini@lineone.net — MB ChB 1998 Manch.; MB ChB Manch 1998.

BEAL, John Ashley Ashleigh, Barnsley Road, Scawsby, Doncaster DN5 8QE — MRCS Eng. LRCP Lond. 1955; FFCM 1981, M 1973; DPH Liverp. 1967. (Leeds) Specialist Community Med. (Child Health) York DHA. Socs: Soc. Community Med. & Brit. Paediat. Assn. Prev: SCM (Child Health) Derbysh. AHA.; Dep. MOH Doncaster RD; RAF Med. Bd.

BEAL, Mr John Hugh Bruce (retired) Flat 12, 61 Cadogan Square, London SW1X 0HZ Tel: 020 7235 8903 — MRCS Eng. LRCP Lond. 1932; BA Lond. 1972; MA, BM BCh Oxon. 1933; FRCS Eng. 1933. Prev: Harker Smith Radium Regist. & Asst. to Surgic. Unit, Univ. Coll.

BEAL, Robin John Third Acre, Standard Hill, Ninfield, Battle TN33 9JU — MB ChB 1992 Dundee; BSc (Hons.) St And. 1988.

BEAL, Roger Morris Windermere House, Stowe-By-Chartley, Stafford ST18 0NA — MB BS 1980 Lond.

BEAL, Suzanne Elizabeth Cobbs Garden Surgery, West Street, Olney MK46 5QG Tel: 01234 711344; Sherington Place, Church End, Sherington, Newport Pagnell MK16 9PD — BM BCh 1987 Oxf.; MA (Camb.) 1988; MRCGP 1991; DRCOG 1991. (Oxf.)

BEAL, Tamsin Amanda Fimber Grange, Fimber, Driffield YO25 9LU — MB ChB 1998 Ed.; MB ChB Ed 1998.

BEAL, Vivien Elizabeth Dierdre Dr Wolfe and Dr Beal, 32 Heathfield Rd, Croydon CR0 1EU Tel: 0208 686 0708/6655 Fax: 020 8686 8436; 27 Falconwood Road, Addington, Croydon CR0 9BE Tel: 01689 842650 Email: heathfield.surgery@gp-h8300.sthames.nhs.uk — MB BS 1976 Lond. Princip. in Gen. Pract.

BEAL-PRESTON, Rosmary Margaret Clare Japps, Fitzroy Road, Fleet GU13 — MB 1974 Camb.; MA; BChir 1973.

BEALE, Alan John (retired) The Priest's House, Sissinghurst Castle, Cranbrook TN17 2AB Tel: 01580 712820 Fax: 01580 712820 Email: jbeale@dircon.co.uk — MB BS 1946 Lond.; MD (Path.)

Lond. 1951, Dipl. Bact. 1952; FRCPath 1969; F Inst. Biol. 1973. Cons. Vaccine Developm. Prev: Scientif. Dir. Wellcome BioTechnol. Ltd. Beckenham.

BEALE, Amanda Louise 61 Manor Road, Lancing BN15 0EY Tel: 01903 765485 — MB ChB 1992 Bristol; BSc (Physiol.) Hons. Bristol 1989; MRCP (UK) 1996. Regist. (Med.) W. Sussex. Prev: SHO (Med.) Frenchay Hosp. Bristol.

BEALE, Andrew Mark Radiology Dept, Princess Margaret Hospital, Okus Rd, Swindon SN1 4JU Tel: 01793 426314; 2 Kelham Gardens, Marlborough SN8 1PW Tel: 01672 516775 Email: andy@beale1.freeserve.co.uk — MB ChB 1985 Ed.; MRCP 1988; FRCR 1992; FRCP 2000. (Edinburgh) Cons. Radiol. P.ss Margt. Hosp. Swindon. Socs: Mem. Assn. Chest Radiol.; Mem. s/i Gp. in Gastrointestinal and Abdom. Radiol.

BEALE, Anthony James 21 York Avenue, Hove BN3 1PJ — MRCS Eng. LRCP Lond. 1948. (King's Coll. Hosp.) Prev: Ho. Phys. & Cas. Off. St. Mary Abbots Hosp. Lond.; Capt. RAMC.

BEALE, David James Windwood, Mill Lane, Lapworth, Solihull B94 6HX — MB ChB 1979 Birm.; FRCR 1986. Cons. Neuroradiol. MRI Centre Walsgrave Hosp. NHS Trust Coventry.

BEALE, Deborah Angharyd Eastleigh Surgery, Station Road, Westbury BA13 3JD Tel: 01373 822807 Fax: 01373 828904 — MB ChB 1983 Manch. SHO (O & G) Stepping Hill Hosp. Stockport. Prev: SHO (Psychiat.) Stepping Hill Hosp. Stockport; Ho. Off. (Orthop.) Stockport Infirm.; Ho. Off. (Med.) Withington Hosp. Manch.

BEALE, Derek John Gorbio House, 47 West Road, Bridgend CF31 4HD — MB BChir 1965 Camb.; FRCP Lond. 1987; MRCP (U.K.) 1974. (St. Thos.) Cons. Phys.P.ss of Wales Hosp., Bridgend. Prev: Sen. Regist. Nephrol. Roy. Free Hosp. Hampstead.

***BEALE, Dominic Marc** 10 Usborne Mews, Carroun Road, Vauxhall, London SW8 1LR Tel: 020 7820 9386 Email: dominic.beale@virgin.net — MB BS 1994 Lond.; BSc Univ. Lond. 1992.

BEALE, Evelyn Alice Lee on Solent Health Centre, Manor Way, Lee-on-the-Solent PO13 9JG Tel: 023 9255 3161 Fax: 023 92 554135; 9 Esmonde Close, Lee-on-the-Solent PO13 8JW — MB ChB 1982 Leic.; MRCGP 1986; DRCOG 1984. (Leicester) GP.

BEALE, Ivor Richard (retired) Malston, Woodhouse, Milnthorpe LA7 7LZ Tel: 015395 62649 — MB BS 1952 Lond.; MRCS Eng. LRCP Lond. 1952. Prev: Resid. O & G E. Gen. Hosp. Edin.

BEALE, Jacqueline Patricia Accident & Emergency Department, Ninewells Hospital, Dundee DD1 Tel: 01382 425744 — MB BS 1989 Lond.; FRCS (Ed.) 1997. (Char. Cross & Westm. Hosps. Lond.) Staff Grade (A & E) Ninewells Hosp., Dundee; Assoc. Fell.sh. Fac. A & E Med. Socs: Assoc. Mem. Brit. Assn. Accid. & Emerg. Med. Prev: Specialist Regist., Edin.; SHO (A & E) William Harvey Hosp. Ashford; SHO (A & E) Logan Hosp. Brisbane, Austral.

BEALE, John Daniel TheGrange Medical Centre, West Cliff Road, Ramsgate CT11 9LJ; 21 Royal Esplanade, Ramsgate CT11 0HA Tel: 01843 595054 — MB BS 1962 Lond.; MRCGP 1969; MFHom. 1967; DCH Eng. 1964. (St. Mary's Hosp. Lond.) p/t Fact. Med. Off. Modern Jet Support Servs. Manston. Prev: Clin. Asst. (Child & Family Psychiat.) Canterbury & Thanet Health Dist.; Ho. Phys. (Paediat.) Paddington Green Childr. Hosp. (St. Mary's Hosp.); Cas. Off. Hampstead Gen. Hosp.

BEALE, Katie Louise c/o J A Kemp, SO2 G3 Geo OPS Iplans, G3 Geo MQ ARRC, BFPO — MB BS 1988 Lond.

BEALE, Louisa Judith Treetops, 15 Endsleigh Gardens, Edwalton, Nottingham NG12 4BQ — MB BS 1983 Lond.; DFFP 1987. Staff Grade (Haemat. & Oncol.) Frimley Pk. Hosp.

BEALE, Nicola Jannet Craigclowan School, Edinburgh Road, Perth PH2 8PS — BM 1994 Soton.

BEALE, Norman Ronald Northlands Surgery, North Street, Calne SN11 0HH Tel: 01249 812091 Fax: 01249 815343; 3 Main Road, Cherhill, Calne SN11 8UX — MB BChir 1973 Camb.; MD Camb. 1989; FRCGP 1995, M 1981; DCH Eng. 1975. (St. Mary's)

BEALE, Sir Peter John, KBE, Lt.-Gen. late RAMC Retd. (retired) The Old Bakery, Avebury, Marlborough SN8 1RF Tel: 01672 539315 — MB BChir Camb. 1959; FRCP Lond. 1979, M 1965; MRCS Eng. LRCP Lond. 1958; FFOM RCP Lond. 1993; FFPHM RCP (UK) 1992, M 1987; DTM & H Eng. 1964. Prev: Chief Med. Adviser Brit. Red Cross.

BEALE, Richard John Intensive Care Unit Guy's & St. Thomas' NHS Trust, St Thomas' Hospital, Lambeth Palace Rd, London SE1 7EH Tel: 020 7955 4515 Fax: 020 7955 8828 Email: richard.beale@gstt.sthames.nhs.uk; Tel: 020 7354 2074 — MB BS 1984 Lond.; FRCA 1990. (Med. Coll. St. Bart. Hosp. Lond.) Cons. Intens. Care Guy's & St. Thom. Hosp. Trust Lond.

***BEALE, Rosemary Jane** 12 Chertsey Road, Bristol BS6 6NB — MB ChB Bristol 1997.

BEALE, Timothy John Department of Radiology, Central Middlesex Hospital, Acton Lane, London NW10 7NS Tel: 020 8965 5733; 167 Chevening Road, Kilborn, London NW6 6DT Tel: 020 8968 7731 — MB BS 1985 Lond.; FRCS Eng. 1990; FRCR 1995. Cons. Radiol. Centr. Middlx. Hosp. Socs: Brit. Soc. Head & Neck Imagery; Europ. Soc. of Head & Neck Radiol.; Radiol. Soc. N Amer. Prev: Sen. Regist. (Radiol.) St Mary's Hosp. Pk.side Trust Lond.

BEALES, Daniel Matthew Bank House, Tunley, Sapperton, Cirencester GL7 6LP — MB ChB 1995 Manch.

BEALES, David Lancelot Phoenix Surgery, 9 Chesterton Lane, Cirencester GL7 1XG Tel: 01285 652056 Fax: 01285 641562; Bank House, Tunley, Cirencester GL7 6LP Tel: 01285 760500 — MB BS 1967 Lond.; MRCP (UK) 1971; MRCS Eng. LRCP Lond. 1967; MRCGP 1977; DCH Eng. 1969; DObst RCOG 1969. (Guy's) Socs: BMA & Brit. Geriat. Soc. Prev: Hosp. Pract. Querns Hosp. Cirencester; Regist. (Rheum.) Guy's Hosp. Lond. & King's Coll. Hosp. Lond.; SHO Med. Neurol. Unit Brook Gen. Hosp. Lond.

BEALES, Ian Leonard Phillip School of Medicine, Health Policy and Practice, University of East Anglia, Norwich NR4 7TJ Tel: 01603 593061 Fax: 01603 593752 Email: i.beales@vea.ac.uk; 25 Lakefield Road, London N22 6RR Tel: 020 8888 7337 Email: ibeals@doctors.org.uk — MB BS 1989 Lond.; BSc (Hons.) Lond. 1986, MD 1997; MRCP (UK) 1992. Clin. Sen. Lect. in Cell Biol. and Gastroenterol., Sch. of Med., Health Policy and Pract., Univ. of E. Anglia, Norwich; Hon. Cons. Gastroenterologist, Norf. and Norwich Univ. Hosp., Norwich; Director of Teachg., E. Anglian Gastroenteology and Hepaldogy SpR Train. scheme. Socs: Brit. Soc. Gastroenterol.; Brit. Assn. of parental and enteral Nutrit. Prev: Gastroenterol. Fell. Dept. Internal Med. Univ. Michigan, Ann Arbor, USA; MRC Train. Fell. (Gastroenterol.) Roy. Postgrad. Med. Sch. Lond.; Clin. Lect. (Med.) Univ. Camb.

BEALES, John Stuart Maxwell (retired) Department of Diagnostic Radiology, Lister Hospital, Stevenage Tel: 01438 314333 — MB BChir 1962 Camb.; MRCP Lond. 1966; MRCS Eng. LRCP Lond. 1961; FRCR 1975; FFR 1970; DMRD Eng. 1968; DCH Eng. 1963. Cons. Radiol. Lister Hosp. N. Herts.; Cons. Radiol. Beds & Herts BrE. Screening. Prev: Med. Dir. N. Herts. NHS Trust.

BEALES, Judith Mary 4 Disraeli Road, London SW15 2DS Tel: 020 8788 4836; 104 Ormonde Court, Upper Richmond Road, London SW15 6TR — MB BS 1975 Lond.; DFFP 1995; DRCOG 1978. (Univ. Coll. Hosp.) Clin. Asst. (Family Plann.) Riveside Community Health Care Lond.

BEALES, Kenneth George (retired) — MB ChB 1961 Ed.; DA Eng. 1967. Prev: GP Nuffield Pract.

BEALES, Maire Siobhan Trinity Street Surgery, 1 Trinity Street, Norwich NR2 2BG Tel: 01603 624844 Fax: 01603 766829 — MB BCh BAO 1980 NUI.

BEALES, Mr Philip Hulme 43 Elm Bank Gardens, Barnes, London SW13 0NX Tel: 020 8876 1884 — MB BS 1941 Lond.; FRCS Ed. 1944; MRCS Eng. LRCP Lond. 1939. (Guy's) Cons. ENT Emerit. Roy. Infirm. Doncaster Vict. Hosp. Worksop & Retford & Dist. Hosp. Socs: Fell. Roy. Soc. Med. (Ex-Pres. Sect. Otol.); (Ex-Pres.) N. Eng. Otorhinolaryng. Soc. Prev: Sen. Clin. Asst. Aural Dept. Lond. Hosp.; Sen. ENT Regist. Qu. Mary's Hosp. Childr. Carshalton; Surg. Regist. Roy. Nat. Throat, Nose & Ear Hosp.

BEALES, Philip Leslie 51 Plover Way, Surrey Quays, Rotherhithe, London SE16 7TS Tel: 020 7252 0342 Email: p.beales@umds.ac.uk — LMSSA 1988 Lond.; BSc (Hons.) Lond. 1983; MRCP (UK) 1992; MRCS Eng. LRCP Lond. 1988. MRC Research Fell. & Sen. Regist. (Clin. Genetics) UMDS Guy's Hosp. Lond. Socs: Amnesty Internat.; Clin. Genetics Soc.; Assn. Study Obesity. Prev: Regist. (Paediat.) Roy. Lond. Hosp.; Research Fell. & Hon. Lect. Lond. Hosp. Med. Coll.; SHO Rotat. (Med.) Roy. Lond. Hosp.

BEALES, Sydney James 112 Burges Road, Thorpe Bay, Southend-on-Sea SS1 3JL Tel: 01702 82620 — MRCS Eng. LRCP Lond. 1948; MD Lond. 1961, MB BS 1948; FRCPath 1971, M 1963. (King's Coll. Hosp.) Cons. Pathol. S.end Gen. Hosp. Socs: Path. Soc. Gt. Brit.; Fell. Roy. Soc. Med. Prev: Asst. Clin. Pathol. Welsh Nat. Sch.

Med.; Demonst. Path. King's Coll. Hosp. Med. Sch.; Res. Asst. Pathol. Roy. Free Hosp.

BEALING, Caroline Lesley Bonda 2 Pelham Street, South Kensington, London SW7 2NG Tel: 020 7581 4222 Fax: 020 7581 4676; 69 Abingdon Villas, Kensington, London W8 6XB Fax: 020 7565 2185 — MB BS 1984 Lond.; MRCGP 1989; Dip. Sports Med. 1990; DRCOG 1987; DCH RCP Lond. 1986. (University College London) Private GP. Socs: BMA; IDF. Prev: GP Lond.; Occupat. Phys. BRd.gate Med. Centre; Trainee GP Lymington.

BEAMAN, Martin The Renal Unit, Royal Devon & Exeter Hospital, Exeter EX2 5DN Tel: 01392 402531 — MB BS 1979 Lond.; MRCP (UK) 1982; MD Lond. 1994; FRCP Lond. 1997. (King's Coll. Hosp. Lond.) Assoc, postgrad Dean (S.W.Region); Clin. Dir. of Med. Socs: Brit. Renal Assn.; Brit. Transpl. Soc.

BEAMAN, Ruth Estelle 13 Church Road, Laughton, Gainsborough DN21 3PP — MB ChB 1996 Manch.

BEAMER, Joy Elizabeth Rose The Vicarage, 99 Reading Road, Yateley GU46 7LR — MB BS 1992 Lond.; DA (UK) 1995; FRCA 1998. (St Georges hosp.) Specialist Regist. (Anaesth.) Oxf. Radcliffe Hosps.

BEAMISH, David 13 Mayfield Terrace, Edinburgh EH9 1RY Tel: 0131 667 6043 — MB ChB Ed. 1968; FFA RCS Eng. 1973; DA Eng. 1971. (Ed.) Cons. Anaesth. Roy. Infirm. Edin.; Edin. & E. of Scotl. Soc. of Anaesth. Socs: Assoc. of Anaesth. Gt. Brit. & Irel. Prev: Sen. Regist. (Anaesth.) Roy. Infirm. Edin.; SHO (Anaesth.) W.. Gen. Hosp. Edin.; Ho. Phys. Leith Hosp.

BEAN, Brenda Elizabeth Watford General Hospital, Vicarage Road, Watford WD18 0HB Tel: 01923 244366 Fax: 01923 217939; 15 The Ryde, Hatfield AL9 5DQ Tel: 01707 260352 — MB BS 1964 Lond.; MRCS Eng. LRCP Lond. 1964; MFFP 1994; DCH Eng. 1968. (St. Bart.) Assoc. Specialist (Infertil.) Watford Gen. Hosp.; Cons. Family Plann. E. Herts. HA; Regional Adviser (NW Thames) Fac. Family Plann. 1994. Socs: Brit. Fertil. Soc.; Brit. Menopause Soc.; Soc. Study Fertil.

BEAN, Jerri Nicole Broadstairs Health Centre, The Broadway, Broadstairs CT10 2AJ Tel: 01843 61014 Fax: 01843 868735; 28 Seaview Road, Broadstairs CT10 1BX Tel: 01843 61014 Fax: 01843 868735 — MB BS 1963 Lond.; MRCS Eng. LRCP Lond. 1963. (Char. Cross) Socs: BMA. Prev: SHO & Ho. Phys. (Cas.) W. Lond. Hosp.; SHO (Orthop.) Fulham Hosp. Lond.

BEAN, June (retired) 56 Spenser Road, London SE24 0NR Tel: 020 7274 6752 — MB BChir 1949 Camb.; MFCM 1972; DPH Eng. 1969. Prev: Princip. Phys. (Child Health) Newham Health Dist.

BEANEY, Ronald Philip Department of Radiotherapy & Oncology, St Thomas' Hospital, Lambeth Palace Road, London SE1 7EH Tel: 020 7928 9292 — MB ChB 1974 Glas.; BSc Glas. 1974, MD 1988; MRCP (UK) 1979; FRCR 1985. Cons. Radiother. & Oncol. St. Thos. Hosp. Lond. Prev: Sen. Lect. (Immunol.) & Hon. Cons. Radiother. Univ. Birm.; Research Fell. MRC Cyclotron Unit Hammersmith Hosp. Lond.

BEARBLOCK, Charles Henry (retired) Landstephen Cottage, Church Road, Saltash PL12 4AE Tel: 01752 842158 Fax: 01752 842158 — MB BS Lond. 1951; DObst RCOG 1953; MRCGP 1966.

BEARBLOCK, Pamela Elizabeth (retired) Landstephen Cottage, Church Road, Saltash PL12 4AE Tel: 01752 842158 Fax: 01752 842158 — BSc Lond. 1946, MB BS 1952.

BEARCROFT, Charlotte Peronel 79 Derbyshire Street, London E2 6HQ — MB BS 1985 Lond.; BSc (Hons.) Lond. 1982; MRCP (UK) 1990; CCST 1999; MD 1999. (Charing Cross and Westminster Medical School) Sen. Regist. (Gastroenterol. & Med.) Roy. Free Hosp. Lond. Prev: Regist. (Gastroenterol. & Med.) Roy. Lond. Hosp.; Regist. (Med.) OldCh. Hosp. Romford; Temp. Lect. (Physiol.) Roy. Lond. Hosp. Med. Sch.

BEARCROFT, John Stephen (retired) The Ark, Mount Ararat Road, Richmond TW10 6PA Tel: 020 8940 0346 — MD 1966 Newc.; MB BS Durh. 1950; MRCP Lond. 1956; FRCPsych 1978, M 1971; DPM Lond. 1959. Prev: Cons. Psychiat. Kingston Hosp. & Long Gr. Hosp. Epsom.

BEARCROFT, Philip William Peter Box 219, Addenbrooke's Hospital, Hills Road, Cambridge CB2 2QQ Tel: 01223 216910; 13 The Hectare, Cambridge Road, Great Shelford, Cambridge CB2 5UT Tel: 01223 509063 — MB BChir 1987 Camb.; MRCP (UK) 1990; FRCR (UK) 1993. Cons. Radiol. Addenbrooke's Hosp. NHS Trust Camb.

BEARCROFT, Rosalind Irene Barming Place, Maidstone ME16 9ED Tel: 01622 727844 Fax: 01622 727844; Barming Pl, Maidstone ME16 9ED Tel: 01622 727844 Fax: 01622 727844 — MB BS 1951 Lond.; BSc (Distinc.) Wales 1946; MA Oxf. 1955, BA (Hons.) 1948; FRCPsych 1971; DPM Eng. 1955. (Univ. Wales, Oxf. & Lond. Univ. Coll. Hosp.) Cons. Psychiat. & Admitting Cons. Godden Green Hosp. Godden Green & Ticehurst Hosp.; Guild of Catholic Doctors; Hon. Cons. Maidstone Hosp. & Kent & Sussex Hosp. Tunbridge Wells; Parliamentary & Pub. Affairs Comm. Catholic Union Of Gt. Brit. & Counc. Catholic Union. Socs: Fell. Roy. Coll. Psychiat.; BMA; Guild of Catholic Doctors. Prev: Sen. Regist. St. Ebba's Hosp. Epsom; SHMO Hill End Hosp. St. Albans; Regist. Banstead Hosp. Sutton.

BEARD, Alan Derickson The Chase Surgery, 10 The Chase, Wetherby LS22 6YU Tel: 01937 583802; Avenida José GLEZ Fortes 12, Apartment Nicole 50, Los Gigantes, Tenerife 38683, Canary Islands Tel: 00 34 922 861997 — MB BChir Camb.1945; MA Camb. 1945. (Camb. & Leeds University) Prev: Staff Leeds Gen. Infirm. & Hull Roy. Infirm.; Staff Merchant Navy.

BEARD, Catriona Ashley Scott Sheen Lane Health Centre, 70 Sheen Lane, London SW14 8LP Tel: 020 8876 3901 Fax: 020 8878 9620; 33 Castlenau, London SW13 9RS — MB BS 1981 Lond.; MRCGP 1986; DRCOG 1985; DCH RCP Lond. 1985.

BEARD, Mr David Julian Firbeck, 73 Grove Road, Ilkley LS29 9QE Tel: 01943 603176 — MB ChB 1974 Glas.; FRCS Eng. 1980. Cons. Orthop. Surg. Airedale Gen. Hosp. Steeton. Socs: Brit. Orthopaedic Assn.; Holdsworth Orthopaedic Club; Ridings Orthopaedic Club. Prev: Lect. Orthop., Sheff. Univ.; MRC Fell., Orthop.

BEARD, Gillian Alexandra Tudor House Surgery, 43 Broad Street, Wokingham RG40 1BE Tel: 0118 978 3544 Fax: 0118 977 0420; 5 The Terrace, Wokingham RG40 1BP — MB ChB 1978 Birm. GP Wokingham.

BEARD, Helen Glan Hyfryd, Llanwenarth, Abergavenny NP7 7EU — MB BCh 1981 Wales.

BEARD, Jessica Ruth 14 Grays Ter, Durham DH1 4AU — MB ChB 1997 Glas.

BEARD, Mr Jonathan David Sheffield Vascular Institute, Northern General Hospital, Sheffield S5 7AU Tel: 0114 271 5534 Fax: 0114 271 4747 Email: jonathan.beard@sth.nhs.uk; 1 Beech Hill Road, Sheffield S10 2SA Tel: 0114 268 4242 Fax: 0114 266 3608 — MB BS 1979 Lond.; ChM Bristol 1987; BSc Lond. 1976; FRCS Eng. 1984; 1999 Sheffield (Cert. Ed.). (Guy's) Cons. Vasc. Surg. Sheff. Vasc. Inst.; Sen. Edr. Europ. Jl. Vasc. & Endovasc. Surg.; Hon. Sen. Lect. Univ. of Sheff.; Progr. Director, N. Trent Higher Surgic. Train. Scheme; Chairm., Jt. Vasc. Research Gp.; Co-ordinator of Registry for EndoVasc. Treatm. of Aneurysms. Socs: Vasc. Surgic. Soc. GB & Irel.; Assn. Surg. LGB & Ire; Eur. Vasc. Surg. Soc. Prev: Lect. (Surg.) Leicester Roy. Infirm.; Regist. (Surg.) Bristol Roy. Infirm.; Tutor (Surg.) Univ. Bristol.

BEARD, Judy Conquest Hospital, The Ridge, St Leonards-on-Sea TN37; Jarmala, Hooe, Battle TN33 9EW — MB ChB 1981 Liverp.; FRCP Lond. 1996; MRCP (UK) 1984; FRCPath 1997. Cons. Haemat. Conquest Hosp. St Leonards on Sea. Prev: Cons. Haemat. Roy. E. Sussex Hosp.

BEARD, Keith 3 Castleton Crescent, Newton Mearns, Glasgow G77 5JX Tel: 0141 639 6483; 3 Castleton Crescent, Newton Mearns, Glasgow G77 5JX Tel: 0141 639 6483 — MB ChB 1977 Glas.; BSc Strathclyde 1972; FRCP Ed. 1991; FRCP Glas. 1991; MRCP (UK) 1981. Cons. Phys. (Med. for the Elderly) Vict. Infirm. Glas.; Hosp. Prescribing Adviser Gt.er Glas. Health Bd.; Hon. Clin. Sen. Lect. Univ. Glas.

BEARD, Michael John Greystones, Church St., Milnrow, Rochdale OL16 3QS — MB ChB 1972 Leeds.

BEARD, Nicolas David Owen Health Care Inernational, Beardmore St., Clydebank G81 4DY Tel: 0141 951 5017 Fax: 0141 951 5100; Deanwood, Castlehill Road, Kilmacolm PA13 4HU Tel: 01505 872271 — MB BS 1984 Lond.; MSc (Software Eng.) Lond. 1990, MB BS 1984. Dir. of Informat. Servs. Health Care Internat.

BEARD, Mr Ralph Campbell Worthing Hospital, Lyndhurst Road, Worthing BN11 2BD Tel: 01903 205111 Ext: 5559 Fax: 01903 285010; Elbourne House, Washington, Pulborough RH20 4AZ Tel: 01903 872291 — MB BChir Camb. 1970; MA Camb. 1970, MChir (Distinc.) 1982; FRCS Eng. 1974; FEBU 1995. (St. Thos.) Hon. Cons. Urol. Guys/St. Thom. Hosp. Lond.; Cons. Urol. Worthing & S.lands

NHS Hosp. Trust. Socs: Fell. Europ. Bd. Urol.; Fell. Roy. Soc. Med. (Sect. Urol.); Brit. Assn. Urol. Surg. Prev: Sen. Regist. (Surg.) Dept. Urol. St. Thos. Hosp. Lond.; Resid. Surg. Off. St. Peter's Gp. Hosp. Lond.

BEARD, Mr Randolph Gilbert Eastholme, Luston, Leominster HR6 0AR Tel: 01568 780661 Fax: 01568 780661 — MB BChir 1950 Camb.; MA Camb. 1950, MChir 1958; FRCS Eng. 1956. (Camb. & Guy's) Emerit. Cons. Surg. Guy's Hosp. Lond.

BEARD, Professor Richard William Professor. R.W. Beard, 64 Elgin Crescent, London W11 2JJ; 64 Elgin Crescent, London W11 2JJ Tel: 020 7221 1930 Fax: 020 7727 1416 Email: richard@elgin64.demon.co.uk — MA 1961; MB BChir Camb. 1956; MD Camb. 1971; FRCOG 1972, M 1963; DObst 1957. (Cambridge University/St. Bartholomew's) Prof. O & G St. Mary's Hosp. Lond.; Prof. Emerit. Imperial Coll. Sch. of Med. 1996. Socs: Fell. Roy. Soc. Med.; Gyn. Travellers Club; Acad. Roy. Med. Belgique. Prev: Pres. Europ. Bd. & Coll. O & G; Prof. O & G St. Mary's Hosp. Lond.; Director of pelvic pain clinic, N.wick Pk. & St. Mary's Hosp. Trust, Harrow.

BEARD, Mr Robert John 75 Dyke Road Avenue, Hove BN3 6DA Tel: 01273 541642 Fax: 01273 552165 — MB BS 1964 Lond.; FRCS Eng. 1969; FRCS Ed. 1968; MRCS Eng. LRCP Lond. 1964; FRCOG 1984, M (Gold Medal) 1971. (St. Geo.) Cons. O & G Brighton HA; Assoc. Med. Dir. Brighton NHS Trust. Prev: Chairm. Higher Train. Comm. (O & G) SE Thames RHA; Adviser RCOG SE Thames RHA; Sen. Regist. Qu. Charlotte's Hosp. Lond.

BEARDMORE, Charles Edward 153 Derwen Fawr Road, Swansea SA2 8ED Tel: 01792 206232 — MB BS 1989 Lond.

BEARDMORE, Charles Lee Michael The Surgery, Vicarage Lane, Walton on the Naze CO14 8PA Tel: 01255 674373 Fax: 01255 851005; Morleigh, 69 Third Avenue, Frinton-on-Sea CO13 9EF Tel: 01255 851102 — MB ChB 1969 Sheff.; MRCGP 1979. Treas. Essex LMC. Prev: Clin. Asst. (Geriat. Med.) St. Geo. Hosp. Sheff.

BEARDMORE, Hugo John Northbourne Medical Centre, Eastern Avenue, Shoreham-by-Sea BN43 6PE Tel: 01273 464640 Fax: 01273 440913 — MB BS 1986 Lond.; MRCGP 1991; DRCOG 1990.

BEARDOW, Rosemary Vera 29 Kings Road, Ealing, London W5 2SD — MB ChB 1980 Birm.; MSc Lond. 1986; FFPHM RCP (UK) 1994; MFCM RCP Lond. 1988; MRCGP 1984; DRCOG 1983. Prev: Cons. Pub. Health Med. NW Thames RHA; Sen. Regist. (Community Med.) NW Thames RHA; Trainee GP Warks. VTS.

BEARDS, Susan Caroline Intensive Care Unit, University Hospital of South Manchester, Nell Lane, Withington, Manchester M20 2LR — MB ChB 1985 Manch.; BSc (Hons.) Manch. 1983.

BEARDSALL, Kathryn Department of paediatrics, Box 116, Addenbrookes Hospital, Hills Road, Cambridge CB2 2QO Tel: 01223 763404 Email: k.beardsall@btinternet.com; 36 Hight Street, Foxton, Cambridge CB2 6RS Tel: 01223 871838, 01257 234221 Email: k.beardsall@btinternet.com — MB BS 1993 Lond.; BSc Lond. 1990; MRCP 1996; DCH Lond. 1996. (Univ. Coll. Lond.) Specialist Regist. Anglia Region, Clin. Research Fell. Socs: RCPCH; BMA.

BEARDSELL, Iain David MacDougall 3 Roslyn Road, Harrogate HG2 7SB — MB ChB 1998 Birm.

BEARDSELL, Robert Sidney Alvanley Surgery, 1 Auburn Avenue, Bredbury, Stockport SK6 2AH Tel: 0161 430 2727 Fax: 0161 406 7999 — MB ChB 1984 Manch.

BEARDSHAW, Judith Angela 26 Holland Park Gardens, London W14 8EA — MB ChB 1969 Sheff.; MRCP (UK) 1976; DObst RCOG 1971. Research Regist. Brompton Hosp. Lond.

BEARDSLEY, Fiona Jane Claremont Surgery, 56-60 Castle Road, Scarborough YO11 1XE Tel: 01723 375050 Fax: 01723 378241 — BM 1989 Soton.; MRCGP 1996; DRCOG 1993. Princip. Gen. Practician. Socs: BMA.

BEARDSLEY, Simon James Peel View Medical Centre, 45-53 Union St., Kirkintilloch, Glasgow G66 1DN Tel: 0141 776 3442 — MB ChB 1991 Glas.; MRCGP 1996; DRCOG 1996. (Glas.) GP Princip.

BEARDSMORE, Duncan Matthew 26 Worcester Street, Stourbridge DY8 1AS — MB ChB 1995 Leeds.

BEARDSMORE, John David 7 Bollington Mill, Brick Kiln Lane, Dunham Massey, Altrincham WA14 4TJ — MB ChB 1991 Manch.; BSc Med. Sci. St. And. 1988; FRCSI 1996. Specialist Regist. (Orthop.) Rotat. NW Train. Scheme.

BEARDSWORTH, Brian Smith The Health Centre, Hill St., Hinckley LE10 1DS Tel: 01455 635362; 18 Springfield Road, Hinckley LE10 1AN Tel: 01455 634367 — MB BS 1953 Lond.; MRCS Eng. LRCP Lond. 1953. (King's Coll. Hosp.) Prev: Sen. Resid. Anaesth. & Ho. Surg. (O & G) King's Coll. Hosp.; SHO (Anaesth.) Dulwich Hosp.

BEARDSWORTH, Simon Anthony De Aula The Gardens, Warter, York YO42 1XA — MB BS 1987 Lond.; MRCOG 1996. Clin. Research Fell. Centre for Metab. Bone Dis. Hull Univ. Prev: Specialist Regist. Jessop Hosp. for Wom. Sheff.

BEARDSWORTH, Stephen Frederick 23 Humber Road, North Ferriby HU14 3DN — MD 1987 Liverp.; MB ChB 1974; MRCP (UK) 1978; FRCP (UK) 1996. (Liverp. Univ.) Cons. Phys. Dept. Med. for Elderly Castle Hill Hosp. E. Yorks. Prev: Research Fell. Mersey Regional Assn. for Kidney Research.

BEARDSWORTH, Tina 17 Guest Road, Sheffield S11 8UJ — MB ChB 1990 Sheff.

BEARDWELL, Colin Gibbs (retired) 135 Palatine Road, Manchester M20 3YA Tel: 0161 445 0127 — MB BS 1961 Lond.; BSc Lond. 1957, MB BS 1961; FRCP Lond. 1976, M 1964. Hon. Cons. Phys., S. Manch. Univ. Hosp. Trust. Prev: Cons. Phys. Univ. Hosp. S. Manch. & Christie Hosp. Manch.

BEARDWELL, Norma Ann Prospect Terrace, 135 North Hill, London N6 4DP Tel: 020 8340 4588 Fax: 020 8340 4588 — MB BS 1954 Lond.; FRCP Lond. 1976, M 1958; MRCS Eng. LRCP Lond. 1954; DPhysMed Eng. 1961. (Roy. Free Hosp.) Cons. Rheum. Roding Hosp. Ilford; Mem. Pens. Appeal Tribunals (Eng. & Wales). Socs: Brit. Soc. Rheum. Prev: Cons. Rheum. Redbridge Health Trust Ilford.

BEARE, Abraham Seftel (retired) Inglewood, 57 Watford Road, St Albans AL1 2AE Tel: 01727 53671 — MD 1972 NUI; MB BCh BAO 1938; DTM & H Eng. 1954; FRCPath 1972, M 1963. Prev: Mem. MRC Scientif. Staff Common Cold Research Unit Salisbury.

BEARE, Brian Charles 8 Firfield Road, Farnham GU9 8SJ — MB BCh BAO Dub. 1968. Med. Adviser Sema Gp. Prev: GP. Farnham; SHO Nat. Matern. Hosp. Dub.; Ho. Off. Dr. Steevens Hosp. Dub.

BEARE, Mr John David Lyell Royal Eye Unit, Kingston Hospital, Galsworthy Road, Kingston upon Thames KT2 7QB Tel: 020 8546 7711 — MB BS 1976 Lond.; FRCS Eng. 1985; MRCP (UK) 1980; MRCS Eng. LRCP Lond. 1976; DO RCS Eng. 1983. (Middlx.) Cons. Ophth. Roy. Eye Unit Kingston. Socs: Roy. Soc. Med.; Eur. Soc. Ophth. Plastic & Reconstruc. Surgs. Prev: Sen. Regist. W.. Ophth. & Hammersmith Hosps. Lond.; Resid. Surg. Off. Moorfields Eye Hosp. Lond.; Regist. Oxf. Eye Hosp. & Roy. Berks. Hosp. Reading.

BEARE, John Martin (retired) Cullintraw Lodge, 36 Ballydrain Road, Comber, Newtownards BT23 5SS Tel: 01247 873376 — MB BCh BAO 1942 Belf.; MB BCh BAO (Hons. 1st pl. Jointly Gold Medal in Paediat.) Belf. 1942; MD Belf. 1946; FRCPI 1978, M 1976; FRCP Lond. 1966, M 1948. Dermat. Roy. Vict. Hosp. Belf. & Roy. Belf. Hosp Sick Childr.; Hon. Lect. (Med.) Qu. Univ. Belf. Prev: Regist. Inst. Path. Qu. Univ. Belf.

BEARE, Nicholas Alexander Venton Department of Ophthalmology, Bristol Eye Hospital, Bristol; 7 Caledonia Place, Bristol BS8 4DH — MB ChB 1994 Ed.; MA Camb. 1995, BA 1991. (Ed.) SHO (Ophth.) Bristol Eye Hosp. Prev: SHO (Ophth.) ScarBoro.; SHO (Neurosurg.) WGH, Edin.

BEARE, Mr Robin Lyell Blin (retired) Scraggs Farm, Holtye, Cowden, Edenbridge TN8 7EB Tel: 01342 850386 — MB BS 1952 Lond.; MB BS (Hons., Distinc. Surg.) Lond. 1952; FRCS Eng. 1955. Hon. Cons. Plastic Surg. Qu. Vict. Hosp. E. Grinstead; Hon. Cons. Plastic Surg. St. Mary's Hosp. Lond.; Mem. Ct. Examrs. RCS Eng. Prev: Surg. Regist. & Cas. Surg. Off. Middlx. Hosp.

BEARE-WINTER, Andrew Nigel Jarvis and Partners, Westbrook Medical Centre, 301-302 Westbrook Centre, Westbrook, Warrington WA5 8UF Tel: 01925 654152 Fax: 01925 632612 — MB ChB 1982 Liverp.; MRCP (UK) 1998; MRCP 1987; Dip. Pract. Dermat. (Distinc.) Cardiff 1993; DGM RCP Lond. 1991; DCCH RCGP & FCM 1988; DRCOG 1984. (Liverpool) Gen. Practitioner; Clin. Asst. (Dermat. & Endoscopy) Warrington Gen. Hosp.; Locum Cons. Dermatol..

BEARN, Jennifer Anne Bethlem Royal Hospital, Monks Orchard Road, Beckenham BR3 3BY Tel: 020 8776 4114 Fax: 020 8776 2026 — MB BS 1979 Lond.; BSc (Hons.) Lond. 1976; MRCP (UK) 1984; MRCPsych 1986. (Guys) Cons. Psychiat. Bethlem Roy. &

Maudsley Hosp. Lond.; Hon. Sen. Lect. Inst. Psychiat. Prev: Sen. Regist. Bethlem Roy. & Maudsley Hosp. Lond.; Regist. Maudsley Hosp. Lond.; SHO Whittington & Roy. N.. Hosps.

BEARN, Joseph Gauld 9 St Lukes Street, London SW3 3RS Tel: 020 7352 7174; Department of Anatomy, Middlesex Hospital Medical School, Windeyer Building, Cleveland St., London W1P 6DB Tel: 020 7636 8333 — MRCS Eng. LRCP Lond. 1945; MB BS Lond. 1947; FIBiol. 1969. (Middlx.) Sen. Lect. Human Anat. Middlx. Hosp. Med. Sch. Univ. Lond. Socs: Anat. Soc. Gt. Brit. & Irel.; Soc. Endocrinol. Prev: Ho. Surg. Fract. & Orthop. Dept. Middlx. Hosp.; Sen. Ho. Surg. Middlx. Hosp. Orthop. Unit Mt. Vernon Hosp. N.wood.

BEARN, Mr Michael Andrew Cumberland Infirmary, Newtown Road, Carlisle CA2 7HY Tel: 01228 523444 — MB ChB 1983 Sheff.; BMedSci Sheff. 1980; FRCS Glas. 1988; FCOphth 1989; DO RCS Eng. 1986. (Sheff.) Cons. Ophth. Cumbld. Infirm. Carlisle.

BEARN, Mr Philip Edward 55 Cambridge Street, London SW1V 4PS — MB BS 1981 Lond.; BA Camb. 1978; FRCS Eng. 1986; FRCS Ed. 1986.

BEARN, Virginia Margaret The Surgery, 327D Upper Richmond Road, London SW15 6SU Tel: 020 8788 6002 Fax: 020 8789 8568; 22 Grena Road, Richmond TW9 1XS Tel: 020 8940 1939 — BM 1984 Soton.

BEARPARK, Andrew David 9 Bridge Lane, Ilkley LS29 9HL Email: bear04@premier.co.uk — MB ChB 1994 Leeds.

BEARPARK, Annette 87 Ilkley Road, Otley LS21 3JP Tel: 01943 463237 — State Exam Med. Berlin 1989.

BEARPARK, Denis Michael (retired) 46 St Andrewgate, York YO1 7BZ — MB ChB St. And. 1957; DPM Leeds 1963. Prev: Cons. Psychiat. & Dep. Med. Dir. The Retreat York.

BEARSTED, Caroline Jane Elgin Partnership, 38 Elgin Avenue, London W9 3QT Tel: 020 7286 0747 Fax: 020 7286 9773 — MB BS 1975 Lond.; ECFMG 1974. Princip. Gen. Pract. Kensington, Chelsea & W.m. FPC. Socs: Fell. Roy. Soc. Med. Prev: SHO (Ophth.) Roy. Free Hosp. Lond.; Ho. Phys. & Ho. Surg. Hosp. St. John & Eliz. Lond.

BEARY, Michael Daniel 43 Parliament Hill, London NW3 2TA — MB BChir 1973 Camb.; MRCPsych. 1981. Cons. Psychiat. The Priory Hosp. N. Lond. Prev: Cons. Psychiat. Watford Gen. & Napsbury Hosps.; Sen. Regist., Regist. & SHO (Psychiat.) St. Geo. Hosp. Tooting.; Cons. Psychiat., Metrop. Police.

BEASLEY, Amanda Jane Wycliffe Surgery, Elliott Road, Plymouth PL4 9NH Tel: 01752 660648 Fax: 01752 261468 — MB ChB Birm. 1984; MRCGP 1989; DRCOG 1988.

BEASLEY, Catherine Lucy Pipers House, Shelfield Green, Alcester B49 6JR — MB ChB 1987 Bristol.

BEASLEY, Ian Frederick Ronald 58 Forest Drive E., London E11 1JY — MB BS 1982 Lond.

BEASLEY, James Vincent 19 Buller Road, Brighton BN2 4BH — MB BS 1991 Lond.

BEASLEY, Kirsten Sara 20 Walkers Mount, LS6 2SD — MB BS 1997 Newc.

BEASLEY, Matthew James 18 Valley Road, Lewes BN7 1LE — MB ChB 1995 Leic.; MRCP, 1999, London.

BEASLEY, Mr Nigel James Patrick Department of Otolaryngology, The Radcliffe Infirmary, Oxford OX2 6HE Tel: 01865 224544 Fax: 01865 224544 — MB BS 1989 Lond.; BSc Lond. 1986; FRCS (Otol.) 1995; FRCS Ed. 1993; FRCS 1998. (Guy's) Specialist Regist. (ENT), The Radcliffe Infirm., Oxf.; Clin. Lect. in OtoLaryngol., The Univ. of Oxf. Socs: Brit. Assn. Otol. Head & Neck Surg.; Roy. Soc. Med. Prev: Specialist Regist. (ENT) Roy. Liverp. Univ. Hosp.; Specialist Regist. (ENT) Walton Hosp. Liverp.

BEASLEY, Mr Patrick Medical Directors Office, Royal Devon & Exeter Hospital, Barrack Road, Exeter EX2 5DW Tel: 01392 411611 Fax: 01392 403911 Email: patrick.beasley@ordeehe-tr.swest.nhs.uk; 21 St. Leonard's Road, Exeter EX2 4LA Tel: 01392 272919 Fax: 01392 491238 Email: beasleyp@eurobell.co.uk — MB BS Lond. 1962; FRCS Eng. 1968; MRCS Eng. LRCP Lond. 1962; DLO Eng. 1965. (Guy's) Cons. ENT Surg. Roy. Devon & Exeter Hosp. Healthcare NHS Trust; Med. Director, Roy. Devon & Exeter Healthcare NHS Trust. Socs: Fell. Roy. Soc. Med.; BMA. Prev: Tutor (Otolaryngol.) Univ. Oxf.; Sen. Regist. (ENT) W.m. Hosp. Lond.; SHO (ENT) Roy. Surrey Co. Hosp. Guildford.

BEASLEY, Peter Alexander The Surgery, 148 Forton Road, Gosport PO12 3HH Tel: 023 9258 3333 Fax: 023 9260 1107; 14 Mound Close, Alverstoke, Gosport PO12 3QA Tel: 01705 589188 — MB BS 1970 Lond.; FFA RCS Eng. 1974. (Lond. Hosp.) Prev: Nuffield Prize (Anaesth.) RCS Eng. 1973; Regist. Nuffield Dept. Anaesth. Radcliffe Infirm. Oxf.; Ho. Off. (Obst.) Roy. Sussex Co. Hosp. Brighton.

BEASLEY, Reginald William Richardson (retired) Garden House, 2 Sarum View, Winchester SO22 5QF Tel: 01962 844595 — MB BS Lond. 1954; FFOM RCP Lond. 1982, MFOM 1978; DIH Eng. 1964; Specialist Accredit. (Occupat. Med.) RCP Lond. 1978; Fell. Amer. Acad. Occupat. Med. 1978. Indep. Cons. Occupat. Med.; Dir. Wessex Financial Managem. Ltd; Dir. Wessex Funding Ltd. Prev: Chief Med. Adviser Independant BRd.casting Auth.

BEASLEY, Roderick John Department of Child & Family Psychiatry, Raigmore Hospital, Inverness IV2 3UJ Tel: 01463 704000 — MB BChir 1980 Camb.; MRCPsych 1990; MRCGP 1985; DRCOG 1984. Cons. Child & Adolesc. Psychiat. Raigmore Hosp. Inverness.

BEASLEY, Rosemary Anne (retired) Haws Brae, Mill Road, Rosemarkie, Fortrose IV10 8UN — MRCS Eng. LRCP Lond. 1951; Dip. Community Paediat. Warwick 1983; DObst RCOG 1955. Prev: SCMO S. Warks. HA.

BEASTALL, Alison 2 Longburgh Fauld, Longburgh, Burgh-by-Sands, Carlisle CA5 6AE — MB ChB 1992 Glas.

BEASTALL, Roger Hugh, OStJ Corporate Medical Management Ltd, The Courtyard, Hall Lane, Wincham, Northwich CW9 6DG Tel: 01606 354084 Fax: 01604 351330 Email: rogerbeastall@cmm.u-net.com; 6 Village Farm, Church Minshull, Nantwich CW5 6EG Tel: 01270 522677 — MB ChB 1973 Manch.; BSc (Hons.) Manch. 1970; MFOM RCP Lond. 1985, A 1981. Med. Dir. Corporate Med. Managem. Ltd. Prev: Sen. Regional Med. Off. BT; Regional Med. Off. BT N. W.; Med. Off. Brit. Gas.

BEATH, Susan Victoria The Liver Unit, Birimingham Children's Hospital, Stellhome Lane, Birmingham B4 6NH Tel: 0121 454 4851 Fax: 0121 454 7788 Email: sue.beath@bhamchildrens.wmids.nhs.uk; 22 Greening Drive, Edgbaston, Birmingham B15 2XA — MB BS 1983 Lond.; BSc Lond. 1980; MRCP (UK) 1987; DTM & H RCP Lond. 1989. (St. Mary's) Cons. Paediat. Hepatol. Birm. Childr. Hosp. Socs: Nutrit. Soc.; ESPGAN; RCPCH. Prev: Lect. (Child Health) Univ. Birm.; Price-Hall Fell. Childr. Hosp. Birm.; Clin. Research Fell. Hepatol. Childr. Hosp. Birm.

BEATLEY, William Maurice 26 Lansdowne Walk, London W11 3AW Tel: 020 7229 7022 Fax: 020 7229 7022 — MB BChir Camb. 1952; MA Camb. 1952, MD 1964; DObst RCOG 1954. (Camb. & St. Bart.) Phys. Lond.; Regional Med. Off. Rank Hovis MacDougall Lond. & Gen. Foods Lond.; Insur. Med. Exams. Socs: Fell. Roy. Soc. Med. Prev: Phys. BUPA Med. Centre Lond.; Cons. Phys. French Consulate; Ho. Surg. St. Bart. Hosp. Lond.

BEATON, Allan The Surgery, Elham, Canterbury CT4 6UH Tel: 01303 840213 — MB ChB 1975 Aberd.

BEATON, Andrea 112 Front Lane, Cranham, Upminster RM14 1XU — MB BS 1996 Lond.

BEATON, Catriona McFadyen 87 Dougrie Road, Castlemilk, Glasgow G45 9NS — MB ChB 1976 Glas.

BEATON, Doris May (retired) Block 2, Flat 28, Pentland Drive, Edinburgh EH10 6PX Tel: 0131 445 2854 — MB ChB Ed. 1947; DCH Eng. 1954; DPH Glas. 1950. Prev: Asst. Med. Off., Edin. Pub. Health Dept.

BEATON, Francis James (retired) 203 Elgin Avenue, Paddington, London W9 1JJ Tel: 020 7286 4710 — LRCP LRCS Ed. LRFPS Glas. 1936; LRCP LRCS Ed., LRFPS Glas. 1936; CPH Eng. 1949. Prev: Resid. Med. Off. Quarriers Homes & Sanat. Bridge of Weir.

BEATON, Kevin Charles 28 Exeter Road, Felixstowe IP11 9AU — BM BS 1992 Nottm.

BEATS, Barbara Carole Canterbury & Thanet Community Healthcare, St Martins Hospital, Littlebourne Road, Canterbury CT1 1TD — MB ChB 1982 Manch.; MRCP (UK) 1985; MRCPsych 1988. Cons. Old Age Psychiat. & Hon. Sen. Lect. UMDS Lond. Prev: Lect. (Old Age Psychiat.) Inst. Psychiat. Lond.; Sen. Regist. (Psychiat.) Maudsley Hosp. & UMDS Lond.

BEATSON, Hilda Margaret Goodlands, Bradford Abbas, Sherborne DT9 6RD — MB BCh BAO Belf. 1946.

BEATSON, James McDonald Templehill Surgery, 23 Templehill, Troon KA10 6BQ Tel: 01292 312012 Fax: 01292 317594; Suilven, Monktonhill Road, Troon KA10 Tel: 01292 313302 — MB ChB 1968 Glas. (Glas.) Prev: Regist. (Gen. Med.) Roy. Alexandra Infirm. Paisley; SHO (Cardiol.) Kt.swood Hosp. Glas.

BEATSON, Stuart McDonald 60 Gladsmuir Road,, London N19 3JU — MB ChB 1997 Glas.

BEATSON, Mr Terence Richard (retired) Somerville, 12 Cronkbourne Road, Douglas IM2 3LB Tel: 01624 623372 Email: mash.birdie@talk21.com — MB BS Lond. 1951; FRCS Eng. 1957; MRCS Eng. LRCP Lond. 1951. Hon. Cons. Orthop. Surg. Nobles Hosp. Douglas Isle of Man. Prev: Cons. Orthop. Surg. I. of Man Health Serv. Bd.

BEATSON-HIRD, John Francis Hawkesley Health Centre, 375 Shannon Road, Kings Norton, Birmingham B38 9TJ Tel: 0121 459 5846 — MB ChB 1947 Birm.; FRCGP 1975. (Birm.) Prev: Squadron Ldr. RAFVR Med. Br.; Clin. Asst. Rubery Hosp. Birm.; Clin. Asst. Migraine Clinic Birm. & Midl. Eye Hosp.

BEATSON-HIRD, Philippa Clare Furnace Court, Haslemere GU27 2EJ — MB ChB 1980 Birm.; DCH RCPS Glas. 1982. Med. Assessor Benefits Agency Med. Servs. Prev: Sen. Regist. (Pub. Health Med.) SW Thames RHA.

BEATT, Kevin James Cardiology Department, Hammersmith Hosp8ital, DuCane Road, London W12 0HS Tel: 020 8383 2266 Fax: 020 8383 1777 Email: kbeatt@rpms.ac.uk — MB BS 1978 Lond.; PhD Rotterdam 1992; FRCP Lond. 1993; MRCP (UK) 1982. (Lond. Hosp. Med. Coll.) Cons. Cardiol. Hammersmith Hosp. NHS Trust. Socs: Fell Europ. Soc. Cardiol. Prev: Sen. Lect. Char. Cross & W.m. Med. Sch. Lond. Hammersmith Hosps. Trust; Brit. Heart Foundat. Fell. Thorax Centre, Rotterdam.

BEATTIE, Alan Gordon Finlayson Street Practice, 33 Finlayson Street, Fraserburgh AB43 9JW Tel: 01346 518088 Fax: 01346 510015 — MB ChB 1971 Aberd.; BMedBiol Aberd. 1968; FRCP Ed. 1991; MRCP (UK) 1974. (Univ. Aberd.) Socs: Canad. Coll. Family Pract.; BMA. Prev: GP Stornoway, Isle of Lewis; GP Brandon Manitoba, Canada; Mem. Staff (Family Med.) Brandon Gen. Hosp. Manitoba, Canada.

BEATTIE, Alan Mewett Community Paediatrics Department, Medway Maritime Hospital, Windmill Rd, Gillingham ME7 5NY Tel: 01634 830000 Fax: 01634 407342; 9 Burntwick Drive, Lower Halstow, Sittingbourne ME9 7DX Email: alan.beattie@zetnet.co.uk — MB ChB 1979 Aberd. SCMO (Community Health) Medway NHS Trust. Socs: MRCPCH. Prev: GP Medway Health Dist. Kent Train. Scheme.

BEATTIE, Alistair Duncan Gastrointestinal Centre, Southern General Hospital, Glasgow G51 4TF Tel: 0141 201 1100 Fax: 0141 201 1101; Flat 3/2 Lauderdale Mansions, 47 Novar Drive, Glasgow G12 9UB Tel: 0141 959 6639 — MB ChB Glas. 1965; MD (Hons.) Glas. 1973; FRCP Lond. 1985; FRCP Glas. 1983; MRCP (UK) 1973; FFPM RCP (UK) 1989; FRCP Ed 1997. Cons. Phys. S.. Gen. Hosp. Glas.; Hon. Treas. Med. & Dent. Defence Union of Scotl. Socs: Assn. Phys.; Brit. Soc. of Gastroenterol..; Amer. Gastoenterol. Assn. Prev: Hon. Lect. & Hon. Sen. Regist. Roy. Free Hosp. Lond.; Research Fell. Advis. Comm. on Med. Research Dept. Health Scotl.; Hon. Regist. Stobhill Hosp. Glas.

BEATTIE, Mrs Amelia Beaton (retired) 8 Carwinshoch View, Ayr KA7 4AY Tel: 01292 610919 — MB ChB 1966 Ed. Prev: Clin. Med. Off. Ayrsh. & Arran HB.

BEATTIE, Brian Edward Flinders, Dennis Lane, Padstow PL28 8DP Tel: 01841 532827 Fax: 01841 532827 — MB BCh BAO Belf. 1960; FFOM Lond. 1991 M 1980; FFOM Dub. 1985, M 1977. (Belf.) Cons. Occupat. Phys. Roy. Cornw. Hosps. Trust Truro. Socs: Fell. Ulster Med. Soc.; (Ex-Pres.) Soc. Occupat. Med.; Irish Soc. Occupat. Med.

BEATTIE, Carol Kathleen 46 Carnesure Manor, Comber, Newtownards BT23 5SJ — MB BCh BAO 1982 Belf.; MB BCh Belf. 1982; MRCGP 1987; MFPHM 1991.

BEATTIE, Cathryn Helen Breast Unit, Royal Liverpool University Hospital, Prescot Street, Liverpool L7 8XP — MB ChB 1989 Manch.; FRCR 1997; DMRD 1996; MRCP (UK) 1994.

BEATTIE, Craig Michael MacDonald 7 Johnsburn Park, Balerno EH14 7NA Email: craigbeattie@hotmail.com — MB ChB 1997 Aberd.; BSc (Med Sci) 1995. (Aberdeen)

BEATTIE, Mr David Keith 10 Archers Fields, Sandridge Road, St Albans AL1 4EL — MB BS 1990 Lond.; FRCS Eng. 1995; FRCSI 1995. Lect. (Surg.) Char. Cross Hosp. Lond. Socs: Eur. Soc. Vasc. Surg.

BEATTIE, Derek Clive Occupational Health Service, Lincoln Building, 27-45 Great Victoria St., Belfast BT2 7AD Tel: 01232 251888 — MB BCh BAO 1982 Belf.; MRCGP 1987; AFOM RCP Lond.; DRCOG 1986. Med. Off. (Occupat. Health) N. I. Civil Serv.

BEATTIE, Miss Elinor Louise Kerr-Muir Ruloe, Booths Lane, Lymm WA13 0PG — BChir 1994 Camb.; MRCS Lond. 1999. Regist.(A & E), John Hunter Hosp., NSW, Australia. Socs: BMA. Prev: SHO (A & E) Hope Hosp. Salford.

BEATTIE, Elizabeth Hall Ferryman's Farm, Northmoor, Oxford OX29 5SX — MB BCh BAO 1924 Belf. (Qu. Univ. Belf.)

BEATTIE, Garth Colin Daisy Hill Hospital, Newry BT35 8DR; Flat 2L, 24 Wesrhall Gardens, Edinburgh EH10 4JQ — MB ChB 1994 Glas. Specialist Regist., (Surg.) Daisy Hill Hosp., Co. Down. Prev: Sen. Ho. Off., Dept. Surg., Vict. Hosp. Kircaldy.

BEATTIE, Gerald John 80 Bellahouston Drive, Glasgow G52 1HJ — MB ChB 1978 Glas.

BEATTIE, Gillian Margaret 228 Queen Victoria Drive, Glasgow G13 1TN Tel: 0141 959 6639 Email: gillnal@aol.com — MB ChB Glas. 1965. (Glas.) Clin. Med. Off. Yorkhill NHS Trust Glas.

BEATTIE, Ivan Jonathan 21 Dorchester Gardens, Newtownabbey BT36 5JJ — MB BCh BAO 1994 Belf.

BEATTIE, James Alexander Gordon Inverurie Medical Group, Health Centre, 1 Constitution Street, Inverurie AB51 4SU Tel: 01467 621345 Fax: 01467 625374; Birchfield, Clovenstone, Kintore, Inverurie AB51 0YG Tel: 01467 32770 Fax: 01467 633212 Email: james@clouenstone.freeserve.co.uk — MB ChB 1967 Aberd.; FRCGP 1992, M 1976; DMRD Eng. 1972; DObst RCOG 1970. (Aberd.) Socs: FRCP Edin.; BMA. Prev: Research Fell. Health Serv. Research Unit Univ. Aberd.; Ho. Off. Dept. O & G & Regist. Dept. Radiodiag. Aberd. Roy. Infirm.

BEATTIE, James Murray Department of Cardiology, Birmingham Heartlands Hospital, Bordesley Green E., Birmingham B9 5SS Tel: 0121 766 6611 Fax: 0121 753 0608; 271 Lordswood Road, Harborne, Birmingham B17 8QL Tel: 0121 429 2924 Fax: 0121 429 5219 Email: jamesbeattie@compuserve.com — MB ChB 1976 Glas.; FRCP Lond. 1995; FRCP Glas. 1991; MRCP (UK) 1979. (Glasgow) Cons. Cardiol. Birm. Heartlands Hosp.; Hon. Sen. Clin. Lect. Fac. Med. Univ. Birm. Socs: Brit. Cardiac Soc.; Amer. Federat. Clin. Research. Prev: Clin. Lect. (Cardiovasc. Med.) Univ. Birm.; Res. Sci. Div. Cardiol. S.W. Med. Sch. Univ. Texas Health Sci. Center Dallas; Regist. Univ. Dept. Med. Cardiol. Roy. Infirm. Glas.

BEATTIE, Jane Katherine 3 Fletchers Barn, Menlove Avenue, Liverpool L25 6ET — MB ChB 1986 Ed.

BEATTIE, Joanna Mary — MB ChB 1992 Sheff. (Sheffield University Medical School) Gen. Practioner (Locum).

BEATTIE, John Allan (retired) 24 Dalmahoy Crescent, Dunnikier Park, Kirkcaldy KY2 6SZ Tel: 01592 591488 — MB ChB 1949 Ed.

BEATTIE, John Keith Church Street Surgery, Church Street, Martock TA12 6JL Tel: 01935 822541 Fax: 01935 826116; The Surgery, West St, South Petherton TA13 5DQ Tel: 01460 240707 — MB BChir 1966 Camb.; MB Camb. 1966, BChir 1965; DObst RCOG 1967. (Guy's) Prev: Dep. Med. Supt. St. Lucy's Hosp. Transkei, S. Afr.; SHO (Paediat.) Wexham Pk., Slough; SHO (Orthop.) Battle Hosp. Reading.

BEATTIE, John Ogilvie Royal Hospital for Sick Children, Yorkhill, Glasgow G3 8SJ Tel: 0141 201 0000 Fax: 0141 201 9214 Email: jackbeattie@compuserve.com; 36 Albert Place, King's Park, Stirling FK8 2RG Tel: 01786 449799 Fax: 01786 473168 — MB ChB 1976 Glas.; FRCP Glas. 1989; MRCP (UK) 1979; FRCPCH 1997; DCH RCPS Glas. 1978. (Univ. Glas.) Cons. Paediat. (Emerg. Med.) Roy. Hosp. Sick Childr. Yorkhill Glas. Socs: (Sec. & Treas.) Scott. Paediat. Soc.; BMA. Prev: Cons. Paediat. Stirling Roy. Infirm. NHS Trust; Sen. Regist. Childr. Dept. Univ. Hosp. & City Hosp. Nottm.; Regist. (Paediat.) Dept. Child Health Univ. Glas.

BEATTIE, Joyce Rosamond (retired) Flat 1,, 5 Sherfield Close, New Maden, Kingston upon Thames KT3 3RU Tel: 0208 336 2327 — MB BS 1939 Lond.; MRCS Eng. LRCP Lond. 1939; DPH Leeds 1941. Prev: Psychother. (Hon. Mem.) Lincoln Centr. & Inst. for Psychother.

BEATTIE, Julie Catherine 21 Watermill Close, Richmond TW10 7UJ — MB BS 1989 Lond.; BSc Lond. 1986, MB BS 1989.

BEATTIE, Lilian Florence Catherine (retired) Coniston House, 36 Dobbins Lane, Wendover, Aylesbury HP22 6DH Tel: 01296 622153 Email: lilian@beattie.alcom.uk — MB BS 1959 Durh. SCMO Bucks. AHA. Prev: Ho. Surg. Roy. Vict. Infirm. Newc. u. Tyne.

BEATTIE, Marie Therese Park Terrace Surgery, 7A Park Terrace, Stirling FK8 2JT Tel: 01786 445888 Fax: 01786 449154; 36 Albert Place, Stirling FK8 2RG Tel: 01786 449799 — MB ChB 1980 Glas.; BSc (Hons.) Glas. 1978, MB ChB 1980; MRCGP 1984; DRCOG 1983. GP Stirling.

BEATTIE, Neil Grant MacEachann APTLHCC Office, Ailsa Campus, Dalmellington Road, Ayr KA6 6PB Tel: 01292 886622 Fax: 01292 614303; 8 Carwinshoch View, Ayr KA7 4AY Tel: 01292 610919 — MB ChB 1966 Ed.; MRCGP 1971; MFHom 1979; DObst RCOG 1970. (Edinburgh) p/t Chairm. (PT), Ayr, Prestwick & Troon LHCC. Prev: GP Princip., 3 Racecourse Rd, Ayr.

BEATTIE, Paula Elizabeth Ninewells Hospital, Dundee DD1 9SY Tel: 01382 660111 — MB BCh BAO 1995 Belf.; 1998 MRCP (UK/Edin.); CAS Applied Immunol 1993 BSc (Hon.) Pathology Belf. (Queens University Belfast) Specialist Regist., Dermat. Dept., Dermat., Ninewells Hosp., Dundee. Socs: Brit. Soc. Paediatric Dermat.; Brit. Assn. Dermat.; Brit. PhotoBiol. Gp. Prev: Locum Regist., Dept. Dermat., Roy. Vict. Hosp., Belf.

BEATTIE, Robert Bryan Department of Fetal Medicine, University Hospital of Wales, Heath Park, Cardiff CF14 4XW Tel: 029 2074 3559 Fax: 029 2074 3559 Email: fetalmed@univ-tr.wales.nhs.uk; Julia Cottage, Stalling Down, Cowbridge CF71 7DT Tel: 01446 772866 Fax: 07967 469795 Email: bbeattie@globalnet.co.uk — MB BCh BAO 1983 Belf.; MD Belf. 1988; MRCOG 1989. (Belfast) Cons. Fetal Med. Univ. Hosp. Wales Cardiff; Hon. Sen. Lect. Univ. Wales Coll. Med. Socs: Blair Bell Res. Soc.; Roy. Coll. Obst. & Gyn.; N. Fetal Soc. Prev: Clin. Lect. (Fetal Med.) Birm. Matern. Hosp.; Clin. Fell. (Matern. Fetal Med.) Toronto, Canada.

BEATTIE, Rosaleen Margaret Glenmore Avenue Surgery, 33 Glenmore Avenue, Glasgow G42 0EH Tel: 0141 647 3020 — MB ChB 1974 Glas.

BEATTIE, Sara Catherine 14 Apsley Street, Partick, Glasgow G11 7SY Tel: 0141 339 2960; 13 Westbourne Gardens, Hyndland, Glasgow G12 9XD Tel: 0141 339 7469 — MB ChB 1982 Bristol; MRCGP 1986; DRCOG 1985.

BEATTIE, Susannah Louise Sawston Health Centre, Link Road, Sawston, Cambridge CB2 4LB Tel: 01223 832711 Fax: 01223 836096; 16 Derwent Close, Cambridge CB1 8DZ — MB BChir 1990 Camb.; BSc (Hons.) Bristol 1987; MRCGP 1994; DCH RCP Lond. 1993; DRCOG 1992.

BEATTIE, Mr Thomas Ferris Accident & Emergency Department, Royal Hospital for Sick Children, Sciennes Road, Edinburgh EH9 1LF Tel: 0131 536 0216 Fax: 0131 536 0052 — MB BCh BAO 1979 Dub.; FRCS (A&E) Ed. 1983; FFAEM 1993; DCH NUI 1980. Cons. A & E Roy. Hosp. Sick Childr. Edin.; Counc. Europ. Travel. Fell. 1991. Socs: Brit. Assn. Emerg. Med.; Assn. Study Med. Educat.; BMA. Prev: Cons. A & E Roy. Aberd. Childr. Hosp.; Sen. Regist. (A & E) N. W.. RHA.

BEATTIE, Thomas James Royal Hospital for Sick Children, Yorkhill, Glasgow G3 8SJ Tel: 0141 201 0122 Fax: 0141 201 0859 Email: jim.beattie@clinmed.glas.ac.uk — MB ChB 1975 Glas.; FRCPH 1998; FRCP Glas. 1990; MRCP (UK) 1978. (University of Glasgow) Cons. Paediat. & Nephrol. Roy. Hosp. Sick Childr. Glas.; Hon. Clin. Sen. Lect. (Child Health) Univ. Glas. Prev: Regist. (Med.) Roy. Infirm. Glas.; Regist. (Med.) Roy. Hosp. Sick Childr. Glas.; Sen. Regist. (Med.) Roy. Manch. Childr. Hosp.

BEATTIE, William Henderson 6 High Market, Ashington NE63 8PD — MB ChB Glas. 1956. (Glas.)

BEATTON, Alasdair Gillespie Emirates Airlines, PO Box 686, Dubai, United Arab Emirates Tel: 00 971 4 203 2690 Fax: 00 971 4 243980 Email: a.beatton@emirates.com; 28 St. Germains, Bearsden, Glasgow G61 2RS Tel: 0141 943 1453 Fax: 0141 943 1453 — MB ChB 1972 Glas.; MRCGP 1977; DRCOG 1974; DAvMed. FOM RCP Lond. 1974. Chief Med. Off. Emirates Internat. Airlines Dubai. Socs: Aerospace Med. Assn.; Airline Med. Directors Assn. Prev: Cons. Phys. & Specialist Aviat. Med. Family & Community Med. Saudi Arabia.

BEATTON, Peter Oliver (retired) Dunrowan Flat, Armadale Road, Rhu, Helensburgh G84 8LG Tel: 01436 820172 — MB ChB 1940 Glas.; MRCGP 1952. Prev: GP Dawley Shrops. & Salen I. of Mull.

BEATTY, Cynthia National Blood Service, East Anglic Centre, Long Road, Cambridge CB2 2PT Tel: 01223 548085 Fax: 01223 548085 Email: cynthia.beatty@nbs.nhs.uk — MB BS 1985 Lond.; MA Camb. 1982; MRCP (UK) 1990; MRCPath 1995. (University Cambridge and Westminster Hospital London) Cons. Transfus. Med. & Haemat. Camb. Transfus. Centre & Addenbrookes Hosp. Socs: Brit. Blood Transfus. Soc.; Assn. Clin. Path. Prev: Sen. Regist. (Haemat.) John Radcliffe Hosp. Oxf.; Clin. Research Regist. Qu. Eliz. Hosp. Oxf.; Regist. (Haemat.) St. Mary's Hosp. Lond.

BEATTY, David Carlyle (retired) Elizabeth Cottage, 92 High St., Wargrave, Reading RG10 8DE — MD Lond. 1952, MB BS 1943; FRCP Lond. 1972, M 1947; MRCS Eng. LRCP Lond. 1943; DPhysMed Eng. 1959. Prev: Cons. Phys. (Rheum.) St. Albans City Hosp., & Qu. Eliz. II Hosp.

BEATTY, David Eugene Fern House Surgery, 125-129 Newland Street, Witham CM8 1BH Tel: 01376 502108 — MB BS 1979 Lond.; MRCS Eng. LRCP Lond. 1979; MRCGP 1985; DRCOG 1981. (St. Mary's) Prev: Trainee GP Folkstone; SHO (Neonates) St. Mary's Lond. W2.; SHO (Paediat.) Kingston Hosp. Lond.

BEATTY, Helen Geddes 4 Lexington Chase, Saintfield, Ballynahinch BT24 7LJ — MB ChB 1978 Aberd.

BEATTY, John Hedwig c/o National Westminster Bank Ltd., 134 Front St., Arnold, Nottingham NG5 7EG — LRCP LRCS 1952 Ed.; LRCP LRCS Ed. LRCPS Glas. 1952; MRCGP 1969.

BEATTY, Olivia Louise Withers 1, Musgrave Park Hospital, Stockmans Lane, Belfast BT9 7JB; 29 Wynard Park, Belfast BT5 6NS — MD 1993 Belf.; MB BCh BAO 1986. Regist. (Rehabil. Med.) Musgrave Pk. Hosp. Belf.

BEATTY, Richard Mark 58 Burfield Road, Old Windsor, Windsor SL4 2LP Tel: 01753 864137 Email: beatty@nildram.co.uk — BM 1992 Soton.; MRCGP 1996; MRCP 1997. (Soton.) Prev: Med. Regist. The Gold Coast Hosp. Qu.sland; Med. SHO Derriford Hosp. Plymouth; GP Regist. Sawston Health Centre.

BEATUS, Daniel 10 Nether Close, Finchley, London N3 1AA — MB BS 1997 Lond.

BEAUCHAMP, Mr Colin George 40 Nethermoor Road, Wingerworth, Chesterfield S42 6LH — MB ChB Sheff. 1973; FRCS Eng. 1978. Cons. Orthop. Surg. Chesterfield Roy. Hosp. Prev: Sen. Regist. Nottm. HA; Clin. Fell. Sunnybrook Med. Centre Toronto.

BEAUCHAMP, Gerald John Patrick Camp Hill Grange, Nuneaton — MB BCh BAO 1942 NUI. (Univ. Coll. Dub.)

BEAUCHAMP, Jane Elizabeth Parsons Heath Medical Practice, 35A Parsons Heath, Colchester CO4 3HS Tel: 01206 864395 Fax: 01206 869047 — MB BS 1980 Lond.; DRCOG 1983.

BEAUCHAMP, Maureen (retired) Pump Cottage, Kings Thorn, Hereford HR2 8AL Tel: 01981 540966 — MB ChB 1961 Birm.; DObst RCOG 1963. Prev: Clin. Med. Off. (Child Health) Leics. HA.

BEAUCHAMP, Patrick Guy (retired) Pump Cottage, Kings Thorn, Hereford HR2 8AL Tel: 01981 540966 Email: pumpcott@talk21.com — MB BChir 1962 Camb.; MA Camb. 1962. Prev: Ho. Phys. N. Staffs. Roy. Infirm.

BEAUGIE, Ann Vaughan 22 Bisham Gardens, Highgate, London N6 6DD Tel: 020 8340 0191 — MB BS 1962 Lond.; FFA RCS Eng. 1967. (Lond. Hosp.) Cons. Anaesth. Roy. Free Hosp. Lond. Prev: Sen. Regist. (Anaesth.) Research Dept. Anaesth. RCS Eng.; Regist. (Anaesth.) Lond. Hosp.

BEAUGIE, Mr John McNicoll (retired) 22 Bisham Gardens, Highgate, London N6 6DD Tel: 020 8340 0191 — MB BS 1963 Lond.; MS Lond. 1972; FRCS Eng. 1967; MRCS Eng. LRCP Lond. 1963. Prev: Cons. Surg. N. Middlx. Hosp. Lond.

BEAUMONT, Mr Adrian Richard Orthopaedic Department, Salisbury District Hospital, Salisbury SP2 8BJ; Fern Hill, Homington Road, Coombe Bissett, Salisbury SP5 4LR — MB ChB 1979 Manch.; BSc Manch. (Hons.) 1976; FRCS Ed. 1984. Cons. Orthop. Surg. Salisbury Dist. Hosp. Prev: Sen. Regist. (Orthop. Surg.) Char. Cross Hosp. Lond.; Regist. (Orthop. Surg.) King's Coll. Hosp. Lond.; SHO (Plastic Surg.) Frenchay Hosp. Bristol.

BEAUMONT, Alison Grace Hilda (retired) 9 Warren Bridge, Oundle, Peterborough PE8 4DQ Tel: 01832 273863 — MB ChB 1952 Ed.; DCH Eng. 1958. Prev: Clin. Med. Off. Kettering HA.

***BEAUMONT, Andrew** medical College of Virginia, Division of Neurosurgery, MCV Station, 1101 E.marshall St, Richmond VA 232298, USA Email: abeaumon@hsc.vcu.org; 24 Penrith Ave, Thornton-Cleveleys FY5 2NA — MB ChB 1998 Ed.; MB ChB Ed 1998; PhD Virginia Commonwealth University 1999.

BEAUMONT, Anne Louise Ley Mill Surgery, 228 Lichfield Road, Sutton Coldfield B74 2UE Tel: 0121 308 0359 Fax: 0121 323 2682 Email: anne.beaumont@lhb2.birminghamha.wsmids.nhs.uk; Email: beaumontlesshalfft@hotmail.com — MB ChB 1987 Leic.; MRCGP 1993; DRCOG 1991. (Leicester) Hon. Clin. Lect., Univ. of Birm.

BEAUMONT, Anthony Charles 14 Brewery Lane, Bridge, Canterbury CT4 5LD — MB BS 1981 Lond.

BEAUMONT, Berenice Ruth The Surgery, 2 Mitchison Road, London N1 3NG Tel: 020 7226 6016 — MRCS Eng. LRCP Lond. 1971; MSc (Soc. Med.) Lond. 1976; MB Camb. 1972, BChir 1971; MRCGP 1984; MFCM 1977; DCH Eng. 1973. Sen. Lect. in Primary Health Care Univ. Coll. Lond.; GP Lond. Prev: SCM Islington HA.

BEAUMONT, Brian (retired) Timperley, Bates Lane, Solihull B94 5AP — MB ChB 1954 Leeds; FRCGP 1985, M 1961.

BEAUMONT, Christopher Guy George Street Surgery, 99 George Street, Dumfries DG1 1DS Tel: 01387 253333 Fax: 01387 253301 — MB ChB 1987 Ed.; DFMS 2001; MRCP (UK) 1990; MRCGP 1993; DRCOG 1992.

BEAUMONT, David Gordon College Lane Surgery, Barnsley Road, Ackworth, Pontefract WF7 7HZ Tel: 01977 611023 Fax: 01977 612146; 8 Badsworth Court, Badsworth, Pontefract WF9 1NW Tel: 01977 644242 — MB ChB 1984 Sheff.; MB ChB (Hons.) Sheff. 1984; MRCGP 1988; D.Occ.Med. RCP Lond. 1995; DRCOG 1987. Occupat. Health Med. Off. Pontefract Gen. Infirm. Socs: Soc. Occupat. Med.; Assn. NHS Occupat. Phys.

BEAUMONT, David Martin 48 The Links, Whitley Bay NE26 1TE — MB ChB 1979 Birm.; FRCP Lond. 1994; MRCP (UK) 1982. Cons. Phys. Med. & Geriat. Qu. Eliz. Hosp. Gateshead. Socs: Fell. Roy. Coll. Phys. Lond.; Brit. Geriat. Soc. Prev: Sen. Regist. (Med. & Geriat.) Freeman Hosp. & Gen. Hosp. Newc.; Research Regist. (Geriat.) Freeman Hosp. Newc.; Regist. (Med.) Dudley Rd. Hosp. Birm.

BEAUMONT, George (retired) 11 Dorchester Road, Hazel Grove, Stockport SK7 5HE Tel: 0161 439 5445 — MB ChB 1957 Manch.; MRCS Eng. LRCP Lond. 1957; FRCPsych 1984, M 1977; FFPM RCP (UK) 1989; DCH Eng. 1960; DObst RCOG 1958; FIBiol 1979. Med. Dir. Medad Ltd.; Dir. MGB Clin. Research. Prev: GP Stockport.

BEAUMONT, Helen Elizabeth Monkspath Surgery, 27 Farmhouse Way, Monkspath, Shirley, Solihull B90 4EH Tel: 0121 711 1414 Fax: 0121 711 3753; The Green Farm, Fanshaw Health Road, Earlswood, Solihull B94 5JV — MB ChB 1983 Birm.; MRCGP 1987; DRCOG 1986. Prev: Trainee GP Birm. HA VTS.

BEAUMONT, Joanna Michelle c/o Medical Library, High Royds Hospital, Menston, Ilkley LS29 6AQ — MB ChB 1994 Sheff.

BEAUMONT, John Malcolm 35 Littledale Road, Broohouse, Lancaster LA2 9PH — MB ChB 1966 Ed. Med. Off. Benefits Agency Med. Advis. Serv. DSS.

BEAUMONT, Jonathan David St. Nicholas Surgery, Buryfields, Guildford GU2 4AZ Tel: 01483 303200 Fax: 01483 452309 — MB 1976 Camb.; Diploma in Occupational Medicine 2001; MA Camb. 1972, BChir 1975. (Camb. & St. Thos.) Princip. St. Nicholas Surg., Guildford; Med. Adviser Ranger Oil (Canad. Natural Resources); Med. Adviser Borax Europe; Med. Adviser BOC; Med. Adviser Criterion Software. Socs: Brit. Assn. Performing Arts Med.; Brit. Assn. Health Servs. in Higher Ed. Prev: SHO (O & G) St. Thos. Hosp. Lond.; SHO (Med.) Renal Unit St. Thos. Hosp. Lond.; Ho. Surg. (Surg.) & Cas. Off. St. Thos. Hosp. Lond.

BEAUMONT, Julie Margaret Occupational Health Department, IBM UK Ltd., North Harbour, Portsmouth PO6 3AU Tel: 023 92 565080 Fax: 023 92 564892; Five Heads Farm House, 66 Five Heads Road, Horndean, Waterlooville PO8 9NZ Tel: 023 92 598665 — MB ChB 1982 Birm.; AFOM RCP (UK) 1993. Occupat. Phys. IBM United Kingdom Ltd. Portsmouth. Prev: GP Waterlooville.

BEAUMONT, Katharine Mary Pinehill Surgery, Pinehill Road, Bordon GU35 0BS; 9 Weston Lane, Weston, Petersfield GU32 3NL — BM BCh 1986 Oxf.; MA Oxf. 1986; DRCOG 1991. Prev: SHO (Geriat.) Manor Pk. Hosp. Bristol.

BEAUMONT, Neil Ivy Cottage, Patrick Brompton, Bedale DL8 1JN — MB ChB 1986 Leeds; MRCPsych 1991. Staff Grade Doctor (Psychiat.) Friarage Hosp. N.allerton.

BEAUMONT, Paul Andrew Hillsfield Health Centre, 1 Howard Street, Coventry CV1 4GH Tel: 024 7622 3446 Fax: 024 7622 5846; 6 Heyville Croft, Kenilworth CV8 2SR Tel: 01926 856305 — MB ChB 1984 Birm.

BEAUMONT, Suzanne Gratton Surgery, Gratton Close, Sutton Scotney, Winchester SO21 3LE Tel: 01962 760236; 62 Fairfield Park, Lyme Regis DT7 3DS Tel: 01297 443854 — MB BS 1994 Lond.; DRCOG 1997. GP Regist. Gratton Surg. Hants.

BEAVAN, Paul Dominic Lowther Cottage, Wymondham Road, Wreningham, Norwich NR16 1AT — MB BS 1998 Lond.; MB BS Lond 1998.

BEAVEN, John Harald Essex House Medical Centre, 59 Fore St., Chard TA20 1QA Tel: 01460 63071 Fax: 01460 66560 Email: essexmed@globalnet.co.uk; 34 Leicester Drive, Glossop SK13 8SH — MB BS 1982 Lond.; BSc (Hons.) Biochem. Lond. 1979; MRCGP 1986; DRCOG 1985. (Roy. Free) GP Partner(f/t). Socs: BMA; Anglo-French Med. Soc. Prev: Trainee GP Cornw. VTS; Former Assoc. Mem. Norwegian Soc. of Gastroenterol.; Ho. Surg. N.wick Pk. Hosp. Harrow.

BEAVEN, John Trevor St Lukes Surgery, St Lukes Road, Beckington, Bath BA11 6SE Tel: 01373 830316 Fax: 01373 831261 — MB BS 1989 Lond.; BSc Lond. 1986; MRCGP 1994; DFFP 1996. (Univ. Coll. Hosp.) Prev: SHO (Pub. Health Med.) Som.; Trainee GP Taunton VTS.

BEAVEN, Steven Robert Skerryvore Practice, Health Centre, New Scapa Road, Kirkwall KW15 1BQ Tel: 01856 885440 Fax: 01856 870043; Maple Cottage, St Rognvald Street, Kirkwall KW15 1PR Tel: 01856 885440 — MB ChB 1978 Ed.; 2001 FRCGP; DRCOG 1982. (Edinburgh) GP Health Centre Kirkwall Orkney; Assoc. Adviser Gen. Pract. Prev: Trainee GP Stockbridge Health Centre Edin.; SHO (O & G) E.ern Gen. Hosp. Edin.; SHO (Med. Paediat.) Roy. Hosp. for Sick Childr. Edin.

BEAVER, David John Foster Kingfisher Surgery, 26 Elthorne Way, Newport Pagnell MK16 0JR Tel: 01908 618265 Fax: 01908 217804; Barnstone, Bunsty Pastures, Gayhurst, Newport Pagnell MK16 8LY Email: david@beaver.powernet.co.uk — MB BS 1984 Lond.; MRCGP 1988. (King's College Hospital) Clin. Asst. Ophth, Milton Keynes Hosp.

BEAVER, Mark Richard 2 Winkfield Road, London E13 0AR — MB BS 1990 Lond.

BEAVER, Maurice William (retired) 13 Richmond Drive, Mapperley Park, Nottingham NG3 5EL Tel: 0115 960 5090 — MB BS Lond. 1954; FFCM 1981 M 1974; DPH Eng. 1960. Prev: Dir. (Pub. Health) Nottm. HA.

BEAVIS, Alan Kenneth Barnabas Road Surgery, 4 St. Barnabas Road, Woodford Green IG8 7DA Tel: 020 8504 0032 Fax: 020 8599 2247 — MB BS 1971 Lond.; MRCP (UK) 1975. (Lond. Hosp.) GP Woodford. Socs: Roy. Coll. of Phys.s. Prev: Research Fell. & Hon. Sen. Regist. (Gastroenterol.) Centr. Middlx. Hosp. Lond.; Regist. (Med.) Mt. Vernon Hosp. N.wood; Ho. Off. (Emerg. & Accid.) Lond. Hosp.

BEAVIS, Mr John Patrick Leonard Cheshire Centre of Conflict Recovery, University College London, 4 Taviton Street, London WC1H 0BT Tel: 01634 842186 — MB BS 1967 Lond.; Member Faculty Pre-Hospital Care RCS (Ed); FRCS Eng. 1974. (Univ. Coll. Hosp.) Sen. Lect. Cons. Adviser, Dep. Director, Leonard Chesh. Centre for Conflict Recovery, Acad. Dept. of Surg., Univ. Coll., Lond. Socs: Fell. Brit. Orthop. Assn.; Fell. Brit. Trauma Soc.; Fell. Roy. Socity Med. Prev: Cons. Orthop. Surg. Lewisham Hosp. & Sydenham Childr. Hosp.; Cons. Orthop. & Traum. Surg. Medway HA.

BEAVIS, Sarah Elizabeth The Old Store, 10 Swallowhouse Lane, Hayfield, High Peak SK22 2HB Tel: 01663 746495 Email: sarah.beavis@virgin.net — MB BS 1992 Lond.; BSc (Hons.) Lond. 1991; MRCP (UK) 1996; FRCA 1997. (St Mary's London) Specialist Regist. (Anaesth.) N. W. Region. Socs: Manch. Med. Soc.; Assn. Anaesths.

BEAVON, Paul (retired) Grange House, Hurley, Atherstone CV9 2HU Tel: 01827 872492 — MB ChB 1953 Birm.; DObst RCOG 1961. Prev: Med. Off. Tanganyika Govt.

BEAZER, Robert The Wychwood Surgery, 62 High St., Milton under Wychwood, Oxford OX7 6LE Tel: 01993 830260 — BM BCh

1970 Oxf.; BA Dub. 1962; MA Oxf 1966, BM BCh 1970; MRCGP 1976; DCH Eng. 1977; DRCOG 1976. (Oxf. & St. Thos.) Lect. (Med. Ethics) Oxf. RHA. Prev: Found. Sec. Med. Equestrian Assn.; SHO (Neonat. Paediat.) John Radcliffe Hosp. & Radcliffe Infirm. Oxf.

BEAZLEIGH, Timothy 1 The Grange, East Malling, West Malling ME19 6AH — MB ChB 1997 Dundee.

BEAZLEY, Professor John Milner High Rigg, Faugh, Heads Nook, Brampton CA8 9EA Tel: 01228 70353 — MB ChB 1957 Manch.; MD Manch. 1964; FRCOG 1973, M 1962; Hon. FACOG 1989; DObst RCOG 1959. Emerit. Prof. O & G Univ. Liverp.; Ordained Minister Ch. of Eng. Socs: N. Eng. Obst. & Gyn. Soc. Prev: Sen. Lect. Inst. O & G Lond.; Dean Fac. Med. Univ. Liverp.

BEAZLEY, Margaret Frances The Laurie Pike Health Centre, 95 Birchfield Road, Handsworth, Birmingham B19 1LH Tel: 0121 554 0621 Fax: 0121 554 6163; 391 Harborne Road, Edgbaston, Birmingham B15 3LB Tel: 0121 454 6708 — MB ChB 1985 Sheff.; MRCGP 1990; DObst RCPI 1987. Hon. Lect. (Gen. Pract.) Birm. Univ. Prev: Trainee GP/SHO (Dermat.) Skin Hosp. Birm. VTS.

BEAZLEY, Patricia Mary Claire Dartford East Health Centre, Pilgrims Way, Dartford DA1 1QY Tel: 01322 274211 Fax: 01322 284329 Email: clare.beazley@gp-g82006.nhs.uk; 20 Summerhill Road, Dartford DA1 2LP — MB BS 1980 Lond. (Char. Cross Hosp. Med. Sch.) Prev: Clin. Med. Off. (Family Plann.) Haringey HA.

BEBB, Charlotte Elizabeth 16 Wrigleys Lane, Formby, Liverpool L37 7DR — BChir 1994 Camb.

BEBB, Dafydd Gwyn Celyddon, Ainon Road, Bangor LL57 4LT — BM BCh 1992 Oxf.

BEBB, Nicholas James Montfort (retired) Greenbank, Landmere Lane, Ruddington, Nottingham NG11 6ND Tel: 0115 921 1537 — MB BS 1957 Lond.; MRCGP 1974; DObst RCOG 1968; DTM & H Eng. 1967. Prev: 1st Sec. (Med. Off.) Brit. High Commiss. New Delhi, India.

BEBB, Rachel Lilian 3 Blaise Hamlet, Hallen Road, Henbury, Bristol BS10 7QY — MB ChB 1996 Bristol.

BEBBINGTON, Andrew 66 Oakridge, Thornhill, Cardiff CF14 9BU — MB BCh 1996 Wales.

BEBBINGTON, Professor Paul Ernest Department of Psychiatry & Behavioural Sciences, Royal Free & University College Medical School Archway Campus, Highgate Hill, London N19 5LW Tel: 020 7288 3551 Fax: 020 7288 3411 Email: p.bebbington@ucl.ac.uk — MB BChir Camb. 1970; MA Cambridge 1971; PhD Lond. 1986, MPhil 1976; FRCP Lond. 1993; MRCP (UK) 1972; FRCPsych 1992, M 1974. (Cambridge University) Prof. of Social & Community Psychiat.; Hon. Cons. Camden & Islington Ment. Health Servs. NHS Trust; Vis. Prof. Dep. of Psychol., Inst. of Psychiat. Socs: Assn. Europ. Psychiat. Prev: Sen. Scientif. Staff, MRC Social Genetic & Developm. Psychiat. Research Centre Inst. Psychiat. Lond.; Asst. Dir. MRC Social & Community Psychiat. Unit Inst. Psychiat. Lond.; Sen. Regist. Cane Hill Hosp. Coulsdon & King's Coll. Hosp. Lond.

BECHER, Julie-Clare Department of Child Life & Health, 20 Sylvan Place, Edinburgh EH9 1UW Tel: 0131 536 4525 Fax: 0131 536 0821 Email: becherj@telemedicine.clh.ed.ac.uk; 1 Elmwood Terrace, Lochend Colonies, Edinburgh EH6 8DF — MB ChB 1991 Ed.; MRCP (UK) 1995. (Ed.) Clin. Research Fell. Dept. Child Life & Health, Univ. Edin.; Specialist Regist. (Paediat.) SE Scotl. Socs: Roy. Coll. Paediat. & Child Health. Prev: (Neonates) Simpsons Memor. Matern. Pavil. Edin.

BECHTER, Mark William Kellbrook, Slab La, Woodfalls, Salisbury SP5 2NF — BM 1997 Soton.

BECK, Alan William Coleraine Health Centre, Castlerock Road, Coleraine BT51 3HP Tel: 028 7034 4833 Fax: 028 7032 8746; 143 Mountsandel Road, Coleraine BT52 1TA Tel: 01265 44833 — MB BCh BAO Belf. 1972; DObst RCOG 1974. Prev: SHO (Gen. Med. & Cardiol.) Ulster Hosp.; Ho. Off. & SHO (O & G) Newtownards Hosp.

BECK, Mr Alfred (retired) 23 Basing Hill, London NW11 8TE Tel: 020 8455 9029 — MD Prague 1935; FRCS Eng. 1951; MRCS Eng. LRCP Lond. 1947; DA Eng. 1943. Prev: Cons. Traum. & Orthop. Surg. Accid. Unit St. David's Hosp. & Univ. Hosp. Wales (Cardiff) Gp. Hosps.

BECK, Andrew William 143 Mountsandel Road, Coleraine BT52 1TA — MB BCh BAO 1997 Belf.

BECK, Anne Josephine 29 Stoneygate Court, London Road, Leicester LE2 2AH Tel: 0116 270 1691 Fax: 0116 274 5812 Email: f.beck@science1.demon.co.uk — MB BCh 1962 Wales. (Cardiff) Regular Teach., Supervisor & Mentor with RACGP. Socs: BMA; Roy. Austral. Coll. Gen. Pract.; Austral. & NZ Assn. Psychother. Prev: Med. Off. Kensington C.H.C., Melbourne; GP Leicester; Fell. (Outpat. Med.) Johns Hopkins Hosp. Baltimore, USA.

BECK, Edwin Peter, Surg. Capt. RN Retd. 10 Avenue Road, Farnborough GU14 7BW Tel: 01252 543279 Fax: 01252 543279 — MB ChB Bristol 1956; PhD Bristol 1973; FFOM RCP Lond. 1994, MFOM 1980; MRAeS 1969. Socs: Soc. Occupat. Med. Prev: Sen. Med. Off. Civil Serv. Occupat. Health & Safety Agency Lond.; Defence Med. Serv. Directorate; Cons. Occupat. Med. RN Med. Serv.

BECK, Eric Robert 59 Glasslyn Road, London N8 8RJ Tel: 020 8340 1564 — MB BS (Hons.) Lond. 1958; BSc Lond. 1955; FRCP Lond. 1974, M 1961; FRCP Glas. 1997; FRCP Ed 1998. (Univ. Coll. Hosp.) Hon. Sen. Clin. Lect. (Med.) Univ. Coll. Middlx. Sch. Med. Lond.; Chairm. MRCP (UK) Part 2 Exam. Bd.; PDS Acad. Lead, Whittington Campus, Roy. Free & Ujiversity Coll. Med. Sch. Socs: Harv. Soc. & Brit. Soc. Gastroenterol. Prev: Phys. Whittington Hosp. Lond.; Res. Asst. Phys. Univ. Coll. Hosp. Lond.; Research Worker MRC Dept. Clin. Research Univ. Coll. Hosp. Med. Sch. Lond.

BECK, Felix Department of Biochemistry, University of Leicester, Leicester LE1 7RH Tel: 0116 252 5024 Email: f.beck@science1.demon.uk; 29 Stoneygate Court, London Road, Leicester LE2 2AH Tel: 0116 270 1691 Fax: 0116 274 5812 — MB ChB 1954 Birm.; DSc Birm. 1979, MD 1963; MRCS Eng. LRCP Lond. 1954. (Birm.) Cons. Howard Florey Inst. & Prof.ial Assoc. Univ. Melbourne, Austral.; Vis. Prof. Developm. Biol. Univ. Leic. Prev: Foundat. Prof. Anat. Univ. Leicester; Prof. Embryol. Lond. Hosp. Med. Coll.

BECK, George Norman (retired) 4 Greenhead Road, Leeds LS16 5AW Tel: 0113 275 5603 — MB ChB 1946 Glas.

BECK, Gillian S Elmhurst Surgery, Elmhurst Road, Aylesbury HP20 2AH Tel: 01296 484054 Fax: 01296 397016 — MB BS 1978 Lond.; FRCGP 1999; BSc Lond. 1975; MRCGP 1983. Gen. Practitioner.

BECK, Graham Nigel PO Box 2, Worsley, Manchester M28 2GA — MB ChB 1985 Manch.

BECK, Graham Paul 10 Coniston Drive, Priorslee, Telford TF2 9QP — MB ChB 1980 Leeds.

BECK, Ian Fernleigh, Gilstead Lane, Gilstead, Bingley BD16 3LN — MD 1987 Leeds; MB ChB Leeds 1975; MRCOG 1980. Cons. (O & G) St. Luke's Hosp. Bradford & Bradford Roy.; Infirm.; Sen. Regist. & Cons. (Obst. & Gyn.) Yorks. RHA.

BECK, Jan-Klaus Wilhelm School Cottages, Teigngrace, Newton Abbot TQ12 6QS — State Exam Med 1991 Dusseldorf.

BECK, Jane Marie Occupational Health Department, Barnsley District General Hospital, Gawber Road, Barnsley S75 2EP Tel: 01226 777942 Fax: 01226 777890 — MB BS 1986 Lond.; BSc Lond. 1982; MRCGP 1990; MFOM RCP Lond. 1997, A 1993. Cons. in Occupat. Health Barnsley Dist. Gen. Hosp., Barnsley & Rotherham Dist. Gen. Hosp., Rotherham. Socs: Fac. Occupat. Med.; Soc. Occupat. Med. Prev: Head Occupat. Med. Servs., IOM Edin.; Sen. Regist. (Occupat. Health) King's Coll. Hosp. & N.. Telecom Europe plc; Clin. Asst. (Occupat. Health) St. Thos. Hosp. Lond.

BECK, Professor John Swanson (retired) East Balloch Cottage, Kirriemuir DD8 5EY Tel: 01575 574731 Fax: 01575 575752 Email: jsbeck@clara.net — MB ChB 1953 (Hons.); FRSE 1984; FRACP 1999; Hon D. Univ Stathclyde. 1999; DSc Dund 1996; BSc (Hons.) Glas. 1950, MD (Hons.) 1964; FRCPI 1997; FRCP Glas. 1965, M 1962; FRCP Ed. 1966, M 1958; FRFPS Glas. 1956; FRCPath 1975, M 1963; FIBiol 1987; MD 1964 Glas. Progr. Convener. Roy Soc of Edin. Prev: Prof. Path. Univ. Dundee.

BECK, Joseph Michael Dr J M Beck and Partners, 21 Beaufort Road, Southbourne, Bournemouth BH6 5AJ Tel: 01202 433081 Fax: 01202 430527 — MB ChB 1962 Birm.; DObst RCOG 1964. (Birm.) Prev: Ho. Phys. & Ho. Surg. Walsall Gen. Hosp.; Ho. Surg. Roy. Vict. Hosp. Boscombe.

BECK, Marilyn 46 Ty Gwyn Road, Penylan, Cardiff CF23 5JG Tel: 01228 485982 — MB BS 1966 Lond.; FRCS Eng. 1978; MRCS Eng. LRCP Lond. 1966; FRCOphth. 1988; DO Eng. 1971. (St. Mary's) Cons. Ophth. Univ. Hosp. Wales Cardiff. Prev: Sen. Regist. (Ophth.) Univ. Hosp. Wales Cardiff; Clin. Fell. Ophth. Peter Bent Brigham Hosp. Boston, USA; Ho. Phys. St. Mary's Hosp. Lond.

BECK, Michael Hawley Dermatology Centre, Hope Hospital, Stott Lane, Salford M6 8HD Tel: 0161 787 1014 Fax: 0161 787 1018 —

MB ChB 1972 Liverp.; FRCP Lond. 1991; MRCP (UK) 1977. Cons. Dermat. Bolton & Salford Health Trusts; Cons. & Dir. of Contract Dermatitis Investig. Unit Hope Hosp. Salford; Hon. Clin. Lect. (Dermat. & Occup. Med.) Univ. Manch.; Dermat. Adviser Ileostomy Assn.; Edr.ial Bd. Jl. of Dermatological Treatm.; Mem., Nat. Soc. Steering Comm. for Surveillance of Occupat.al Dermatatoligsts (Epiderm). Socs: (Comm.) Brit. Contract Dermat. Gp.; Brit. Assn. Dermat.; N. of Engl. Dermat. Soc. Prev: Sen. Regist. Skin Hosp. Manch.; SHO (Gen. Med.) Salford Roy. Hosp. & Hope Hosp.

BECK, Mr Nicholas Edward Dept. Anaesthesia, Great Ormond St. Hospital, London WC1N 3JH Tel: 023 8077 7222 — MB BS 1987 Lond.; FRCS (Gen. Surg.) 2000 Intercollegiate exam; Ph.D. London 2001; FRCS Eng. 1991. (St. Mary's Hospital Medical School London) Cons. Gen. Surg./Coloproctologist Soton. Univ. Hosps. NHS Trust. Socs: Assn. of ColoProctol. of Gt.Britain & Irel.; BMA; Roy. Soc. of Med. Prev: S.W. Thames Regist. Rotat.; Clin. Research Fell. ICRF Lond.; Clin. Research Fell. IMM Oxf.

BECK, Nicola Anne Iveagh House Surgery, Iveagh House, Loughborough Road, London SW9 7SE Tel: 020 7274 8850 Fax: 020 7733 2102; 28 Ballingdon Road, London SW11 6AJ — MB BS 1985 Lond.; MRCGP 1997.

BECK, Nicola Jane Royal Free Hospital, Pond St., London NW3 Tel: 020 7794 0500; 35A Winchester Road, London NW3 3NR Tel: 020 7209 9750 — MB BS 1996 Lond. GP VTS.

BECK, Peter Glamorgan House, BUPA Hospital, Pentwyn, Cardiff CF23 8XL Tel: 029 2073 5825; 46 Ty Gwyn Road, Penylan, Cardiff CF23 5JG Tel: 029 2048 5982 Email: peterbeck@lineone.net — MB BS (Hons.) Lond. 1965; MA Wales 1989; MD Lond. 1976; FRCP Lond. 1980, M 1967; MRCS Eng. LRCP Lond. 1965. (St. Mary's) Cons. Phys.Cardiff & Vale NHS Trust; DL. Socs: Soc. Phys.s in Wales, Pres. 2001/2; Assn. Phys.; Diabetes UK. Prev: Wellcome Trav. Fell. Harvard Univ., USA; MRC Clin. Research Fell. & Lect. (Med.) Univ. of Wales Coll. of Med., Cardiff.

BECK, Rachel Alison 72 Marina Crescent, Bootle L30 1RR — BM BCh 1998 Oxf.; BM BCh Oxf 1998.

BECK, Rachel Susan 39 Elderberry Bank, Lychpit, Basingstoke RG24 8RY Tel: 01256 470993 — MB BS 1996 Lond. (St. Mary's London)

BECK, Mr Rupert Oliver 174 Northview Road, Hornsey, London N8 7NB Tel: 020 8340 1377 — MB BS 1986 Lond.; FRCS Ed. 1990.

BECK, Simon Charlton 10 Avenue Road, Farnborough GU14 7BW — MB ChB 1984 Birm. Socs: Lord Kitchener Nat. Schol.sh. Assn.; Soc. Occupat. Med.

BECK, Stephen 8 Alverstoke Lane, 21 Church Road, Alverstoke, Gosport PO12 2LX — MB ChB 1976 Manch.

BECK, Steven Home Farm, Church Lane, Old Ravenfield, Rotherham S65 4NG — MB ChB 1978 Sheff.; MRCPath 1984.

BECK, Walter Alexander Mount Pleasant Health Centre, Exeter EX4 7BW Tel: 01392 55722 — MB BCh BAO 1956 Belf.; MRCOG 1963, DObst 1958; Cert Av Med. MoD (Air) & CAA 1974. Authorised Examr. Civil Aviat. Auth. Socs: Devon & Exeter Med. Soc. Prev: Regist. Obst & Gyn. Roy. Berks. Hosp. Reading, Radcliffe Infirm. Oxf.; & Taunton & Som. Hosp.

BECK-SAMUELS, Peter Richard Medical Director, Rotherham General Hospitals Trust, Moorgate Road, Rotherham S60 2UD Tel: 01709 824756 Fax: 01709 824200 — MB ChB 1970 Birm.; PhD Glas. 1979; MSc Birm. 1974, BSc (Anat.) 1967, MB ChB 1970; MIBiol, CBiol; Dip. Health Mgt. Keele 1992. (Birm.) Med. Dir. Rotherham Gen. Hosps. Trust. Socs: Inst. Biol.; Brit. Assn. Med. Managers; Assn. Trust Med. Directors. Prev: Cons. Chem. Path., Rotherham HA; Sen. Regist. (Biochem.) Glas. Roy. Infirm.; SHO (Path.) & Regist. (Path.) Birm. RHB.

BECKAYA, Ashok c/o Paediatric Department, Epsom General Hospital, Dorking Road, Epsom KT18 7EG — MB BS 1977 Ranchi; DCH Agra 1981; DCH Glas 1993; DCCH Ed. 1998; MRCPH Lond. 1999; MGM India. Staff Paediat.

BECKER, Daniel Robert Henry 67 Stanfell Road, Knighton, Leicester LE2 3GE Email: dan- - becker@hotmail.com — MB ChB 1993 Leic.; FRCS A&E Ed 1999. Staff Grade A&E dept leics Roy. Infirm. Socs: Assoc. Mem. BAEM.

BECKER, Ferdinand Cromer Group Practice, 48 Overstrand Road, Cromer NR27 0AJ Tel: 01263 513148 — MB ChB 1989 Pretoria; MB ChB 1989 Pretoria.

BECKER, Giles William Doctors' Mess, Derriford Hospital, Roborough, Plymouth Tel: 01752 711111 Email: gwb33@doctors.org.uk — MB BChir Camb. 1996; MRCS 2001 Eng.; BA Camb. 1994; MA Camb. 1998. (Camb.) SHO Derriford Hosp., Plymouth. Prev: Med. Off., RAF, Cranwell; Ho. Off. Gen. Surg. Edith Cavell Hosp. PeterBoro.; Ho. Off. Gen. Med. PeterBoro. Dist. Hosp.

BECKER, Martin Georg Hinchingbrooke Hospital Health Care NHS Trust, Huntingdon PE29 6NT Tel: 01480 416464 Fax: 01480 416698 — MD 1978 Erfurt, Germany; Approbation Erfurt Germany 1971, MD 1978; MRCP (UK) 1982. Cons. Paediat. Hinchingbrooke Hosp. Huntingdon. Socs: Brit. Paediat. Assn. & Assn. Child Psychol. & Psychiat. Prev: SHO Regist. Childr. Hosp. Med. Acad. Erfurt, Germany; Regist. (Paediat.) Municip. Hosp. Dresden, Germany; Lect. (Paediat. & Child Health) Leeds Univ.

BECKER, Mr Stephen John 31 Westfield Grove, St Johns, Wakefield WF1 3RS Tel: 0831 881980 Email: steve@becker.demon.co.uk — MB ChB 1975 Liverp.; FRCS Ed. 1982.

BECKER, Walter Graham Ellis Red Hill Surgery, 11 Redhill, Chislehurst BR7 6DB Tel: 020 8467 7419 Fax: 020 8295 1270 — MRCS Eng. LRCP Lond. 1982; BSc Lond. 1978. (Westm.) Socs: Frognal Med. Soc. Prev: Trainee GP Redbridge HA VTS; Ho. Phys. William Harvey Hosp. Ashford; Ho. Surg. Tameside Gen. Hosp. Ashton-under-Lyne.

BECKERS, Martin Joseph John Littlehurst Surgery, The Street, Charmouth, Bridport DT6 6PE Tel: 01297 60872 — MB BS 1979 Newc.

BECKERS, Susan Rachel Littlehurst Surgery, The Street, Charmouth, Bridport DT6 6PE Tel: 01297 60872; The Old Engine House, Wootton Fitzpaine, Bridport DT6 6NQ Tel: 01297 560948 Email: fambeckers@eclipse.co.uk — MB BS 1983 Lond.; MRCGP 1988; DRCOG 1986. (Univ. Coll. Hosp.) Prev: SHO (Community Med., Paediat. & O & G) Dorset Co. Hosp. Dorchester.

BECKETT, Angela Kay Child & Adolescent Service, Family Services, Directorate Macclesfield District General Hospital, Victoria Road, Macclesfield SK10 3BL Tel: 01625 661241 Fax: 01625 663770; 2 Castlegate, Prestbury, Macclesfield SK10 4AZ — MB BS 1973 Newc.; Cert. Family Plann. JCC 1976. Clin. Asst. (Child & Adolesc. Ment. Health) Macclesfield HA.

BECKETT, Edmund Peter Dobbin Lane Health Centre, Dobbin Lane, Armagh BT61 7QG Tel: 028 3752 3165 — MB BCh BAO 1978 Belf.; MRCGP 1982; DRCOG 1980.

BECKETT, Mrs Elspeth Ann (retired) 3 Henley Street, Oxford OX4 1ER Tel: 01865 251579 Email: e.beckett@btinternet.com — BM BCh 1954 Oxf. Prev: GP Temple St. Surg., Oxf.

BECKETT, Eric Ivor Grosvenor Street Surgery, 8 Grosvenor Street, Mold CH7 1EJ Tel: 01352 756762 Fax: 01352 758631 — MB ChB 1967 Ed.; MRCP (UK) 1971.

BECKETT, Heather Eileen Donaghadee Health Centre, 3 Killaughey Road, Donaghadee BT21 0BU — MB BCh BAO 1978 Belf.; MRCGP 1982.

BECKETT, Henry Dale (retired) 18 Ockendon Road, Islington, London N1 3NP Tel: 020 7704 9999 Fax: 020 7354 5170 Email: dalepsych@aol.com — MRCS Eng. LRCP Lond. 1946; MRCPsych 1971; DPM Eng. 1954. Psychother. including Psychoneuroimmunol. Hypnother. Lond. Prev: Cons. Psychiat. Cane Hill Hosp. Coulsdon.

BECKETT, Joanne Pamela Hackenthorpe Medical Centre, Main Street, Hackenthorpe, Sheffield S12 4LA Fax: 0114 251 0539; 19 Thornsett Road, Kenwood, Sheffield S7 1NB Tel: 0114 255 5808 — MB BS 1985 Lond.; MRCGP 1992. (University College London) GP Sheff.

BECKETT, Marie Eleanor Mount Pleasant, Canterbury Road, Lyminge, Folkestone CT18 8JW — MB BS 1978 Lond.

BECKETT, Mary 19 Dalriada Crescent, Cushendall, Ballymena BT44 0QQ — MB BCh BAO 1975 NUI; DRCOG 1979.

BECKETT, Michael William Accident Department, West Middlesex Hospital, Isleworth TW7 6AF — MB BS 1978 Lond.; 1971 BSc Lond.; FRCP 1994 Lond.; MRCP 1982 (UK); FFAEM 1996. Cons. A & E W. Middlx. Hosp. Isleworth. Socs: Founding Fell Fac. Accid. & Emerg. Med. Prev: Sen. Regist. (A & E) Centr. Middlx. Hosp. Lond.

BECKETT, Neal 14 Maxwell Road, Bangor BT20 3SQ — MB BCh BAO 1991 Belf.

BECKETT, Nigel Stanley 37 Ridgway Road, Kettering NN15 5AQ Tel: 01536 514593 Email: n.beckett@ic.ac.uk; 63 Brent Way, Finchley, London N3 1AR Tel: 020 8346 1385 Email: nigelandbillie@amgnst.freeserve.co.uk — MB ChB 1990 Manch.; MRCP (UK) 1994. (Manchester) Brit. Heart Foundat. Research Fell., Imperial Coll. Sch. of Med., Hammersmith Hosp. Socs: Brit. Geriat.s Soc.; Lond. Hypertens. Soc.; Lond. Soc. Cardiovasc.Dis.& Ageing (Treas.). Prev: Sen. Regist. (Geriat.s), Univ. Hosp. of S. Manch.; Regist. (Gen. Med.), Bolton Hosps.; Regist. (Geriat.), Hope Hosp., Salford.

BECKETT, Paul Andrew 5 The Glen, Bryncethin, Bridgend CF32 9LX; 28 Osborne Gardens, Fair Oak, Eastleigh, Southampton SO50 7NP Tel: 01703 602907 Email: paul_beckett@lineone.net — BChir 1992 Camb.; MB BChir Camb. 1992; MRCP (UK) 1995. (Univ. Camb.) Specialist Regist. (Gen. & Respirat. Med.), Soton. Gen. Hosp.

BECKETT, Peter 10 Childwall Park Avenue, Liverpool L16 0JG Tel: 0151 722 8360 — MB ChB 1963 Liverp.

BECKETT, Peter Rene (retired) 39 Southway, Carshalton SM5 4HP Tel: 020 8643 5191 — MB BS 1962 Lond.; MRCS Eng. LRCP Lond. 1962; DMRT Eng. 1967. Clin. Med. Off. in Blood Transfus., Nat. Blood Serv., S. Thames & N. Lond. Regions. Prev: Regist. St. Bart. Hosp. Lond. & W.. Infirm. Glas.

BECKETT, Robert James The Penryn Surgery, Saracen Way, Penryn TR10 8HX Tel: 01326 372502 Fax: 01326 378126 — MB ChB 1984 Ed.; DRCOG 1989. Trainee GP Cornw. VTS.

BECKETT, Stephen Edward Park Green Surgery, Sunderland Street, Macclesfield SK11 6HW Tel: 01625 429555 Fax: 01625 502950; 2 Castlegate, Prestbury, Macclesfield SK10 4AZ Tel: 01625 827190 — MB BS 1972 Newc.; MRCGP 1976; DObst RCOG 1976; Cert Contracep. & Family Plann. RCOG RCGP &; Cert FPA 1976. (Newc.) Chairm. S. Chesh. LMC., Apr 96-Apr 00.

BECKFORD, Louisa Claire 4 Dunvegan Cl, Kenilworth CV8 2PH — MB BS 1997 Lond.

BECKHURST, Carolyn Ann 1/R 30 Hector Road, Glasgow G41 3QD — MB BS 1996 Lond.

BECKINGHAM, Mr Ian James 23 Mepperley Hall Drive, Mapperley, Park, Nottingham NG3 5EY Email: ian.beckingham@nottingham.ac.uk — BM BS 1987 Nottm.; MD Nottm. 1994, BMedSci 1985; FRCS (Gen.) 1996; FRCS Eng. 1991; L Huntarian Professor (RCS eng). (Nottm.) Cons. Hepatability & laporoscopic Surg., Qu.s Med. Centre, Derby Rd. Nottm. NG7 2UH. Socs: Brit. Soc. Gastroenterol.; Assn. Endoscopic Surgs.; Assn. Surg. Prev: Sen. Regist. (Gen. Surg.) Nottm.; Regist. Hull Roy. Infirm. & St. Jas. Univ. Hosp. Leeds; Jun.Cons.Groote Schuur Hosp. Cape Town, S.Afr.

BECKINGSALE, Mr Adrian Bernard Ophthalmic Department, Sanders Ward, Essex County Hospital, Lexden Road, Colchester CO3 3NB Tel: 01206 744626; Hope Lodge, 41 Church St, Coggeshall, Colchester CO6 1TX — MB BS 1977 Newc.; MA Camb. 1976; FRCS Eng. 1983; FRCOphth 1988; DO Lond. 1981. (Newcastle upon Tyne) Cons. Ophth. Essex Rivers Healthcare NHS Trust Colchester. Prev: Cons. Ophth. St. Mary's Hosp. Colchester; Sen. Regist. (Ophth.) Addenbrooke's Hosp. Camb. & W. Norwich Hosp.; Regist. (Ophth.) Leicester Roy. Infirm.

BECKITT, David Church Road Surgery, Crossmount, 1 Church Road, Warlingham CR6 9NW Tel: 01883 624686 Fax: 01883 625677; 10 Ridley Road, Warlingham CR6 9LR Tel: 01883 625468 — MB BS 1968 Lond.; MRCGP 1974. (King's Coll. Hosp.) Socs: BMA.

BECKITT, Timothy Adam Two Gables, Pepper St., Christleton, Chester CH3 7AG — MB ChB 1998 Bristol.

BECKLES, Don-Eyre Philip Tweedsmuir 55 Marsdale Drive, Manor Park, Nuneaton CV10 7RU Tel: 01203 346893 — MB BS 1991 West Indies. SHO (A & E) Coventry & Warks. Hosp. NHS Trust; SHO (Ophth.) P'boro. Dist. Hosp. Socs: Med. Protec. Soc.; MDU & BMA. Prev: SHO (Orthop. & A & E) Rugby NHS Trust.

BECKLES, Michael Andrew Department of Thoracic Medicine, Royal Free Hospital, Pond St., London NW3 2QG Tel: 020 7794 0500 — MB ChB 1990 Manch.; BSc (Hons.) Pharmacol. & Physiol. Manch. 1987; MRCP (UK) 1995. SHO (Gen. Med., Nephrol., Haemat., Gastroenterol. & ITU) Hope Hosp. Salford. Prev: SHO (Cardiol. & Chest Med.) Wythenshawe Hosp.; Ho. Phys. Blackburn Roy. Infirm.; Ho. Surg. Manch. Roy. Infirm.

BECKLEY, Godfrey Arthur Jefferies (retired) 151 Picardy Road, Upper Belvedere, Belvedere DA17 5QL Tel: 013224 30607 — MB BS 1959 Lond.

BECKLEY, Jane Waterloo Health Centre, 5 Lower Marsh, London SE1 7RJ Tel: 020 7928 4049 Fax: 020 7928 2644 — MB BS 1979 Lond.; MRCGP 1986; DCH RCP Lond. 1985; DRCOG 1982. (Westm.)

BECKLEY, Rachael Anne 34 Mill Green, Binfield, Bracknell RG42 4BJ — BM BS 1998 Nottm.; BM BS Nottm 1998.

BECKLEY, Sarah Louise Department of Obstetrics & Gynaecology, Derriford Hospital, Plymouth; 19 Wake Street, Pennycomequick, Plymouth PL4 6NL — MB BS 1983 Newc.; MRCOG 1989. Staff Grade (O & G), Derriford Hosp., Plymouth.

BECKLY, David Edwin Knighton, Buckland, Monachorum, Yelverton PL20 7LH — MB BS 1966 Lond.; MRCP Lond. 1968; FRCP Lond. 1988; MRCS Eng. LRCP Lond. 1966; FRCR 1975; FFR 1973; DMRD Eng. 1971. (Middlx.) Cons. Radiol. Plymouth Gen. Hosp. Socs: Brit. Soc. Gastroenterol. & BMA. Prev: Ho. Surg. Middlx. Hosp. Lond.; Ho. Phys. (Paediat.) St. Mary's Teach. Hosp. Gp.; Sen. Regist. (Diag. Radiol.) Bristol Roy. Infirm.

BECKLY, John Benjamin Knighton, Buckland Monachorum, Yelverton PL20 7LH Tel: 01822 852658 Fax: 01822 854555 Email: jbeckly@hotmail.com — MB BS 1997 Lond.; BSc (Hons) 1993; MBBS 1997. SHO (Med.), Roy. P. Alfred Hosp., Sydney, Australia. Prev: Ho. Off. (Surgic.), Dorset Co. Hosp., Dorcchester; Ho. Off. (Med.), Roy. Free Hosp., Lond.; Cas. Off. (A&E), Dorset Co. Hosp., Dorchester, Dorset.

BECKWITH, Lisa Yeadon Health Centre, 17 South View Road, Yeadon, Leeds LS19 7PS Tel: 0113 295 4040 Fax: 0113 295 4044; Yeadon Health Centre, Yeadon, Leeds LS19 — MB ChB 1989 Leeds; MRCGP 1993.

BEDDALL, Andrew Craig Haematology Department, Morriston Hospital, Swansea — MB BS 1974 Lond.; BSc Lond. 1971; MRCP (UK) 1978; MRCPath 1984; FRCP 1997; FRCPath 1995. (St. Mary's) Cons. Haemat. Morriston Hosp. Swansea & Neath Gen. Hosp. & Singleton Hosp. Swansea. Prev: Sen. Regist. (Haemat.) W. Midl. RHA; Ho. Off. St. Mary's Hosp. Lond. (Harrow Rd. Br.) & Roy. Hants. Co.; Hosp. Winchester.

BEDDIS, Ian Rowland Department of Paediatrics, Hull Royal Infirmary, Anlaby Road, Hull HU3 2JZ Tel: 01482 674039; 66 Davenport Avenue, Hessle HU13 0RW — 1973 MB Liverp.; 1981 MD Liverp.; 1994 FRCP Lond.; 1978 MRCP (UK); 1997 FRCPCH; 1975 DObst RCOG. Cons. Paediat. Hull Roy. Infirm. Socs: Neonat. Soc. Prev: Lect. (Child Health) & Hon. Sen. Regist. Roy. Hosp. Sick Childr. Bristol; Regist. (Paediat.) Roy. Hosp. Sick Childr. Bristol; Research Fell. (Paediat. & Neonat. Med.) Hammersmith Hosp. Lond.

BEDDOE, Robert John North Street Medical Centre, 274 North Street, Romford RM1 4QJ Tel: 01708 764477 Fax: 01708 757656 — MB ChB 1979 Birm.; DRCOG 1983.

BEDDOE, Vivienne Kay Moretonhampstead Health Centre, Embleford Crescent, Moretonhampstead, Newton Abbot TQ13 8LY Tel: 01647 440591 Fax: 01647 440089; Valley House, Chagford Cross, Moreton Hampstead, Newton Abbot TQ13 8LS — MB BChir 1969 Camb.; MFFP 1993; Cert. Family Plann. 1972.

BEDDOW, Emma Caroline Louise Dept of Cardiothoracic Surgery, St Bartholomew's Hospital, London EC1A 7BE Email: emmabeddow@dial.pipex.com; The Old Rectory, Rectory Road, Wivenhoe, Colchester CO7 9PQ Tel: 01206 826160 Email: emmabeddow@dial.pipex.com — MB BS 1994 Lond.; FRCS Eng 1998. Cardiothoracic Surg., RSO, Lond. Socs: MDU; BMA. Prev: Cardiothoracic Surg., RSO, Lond.; Orthop. SHO, Lond.

BEDDOW, Mr Frank Howard (retired) (cons. rooms), 72 Rodney St., Liverpool L1 9AF Tel: 0151 709 2177 — MB ChB Liverp. 1950; MChOrth Liverp. 1957; FRCS Eng. 1987; FRCS Ed. 1956. Prev: Indep. Orthop. Surg. Liverp.

BEDDOWS, Marilyn Elaine 66 Danvers Road, Leicester LE3 2AE — MB ChB 1965 Liverp.

BEDELL, John Dinmore Avenue Surgery, Grange Park, Blackpool FY3 7RW Tel: 01253 302794; 258 Hardhorn Road, Poulton, Blackpool Tel: 01253 899152 — MB ChB 1966 Ed.; BSc Ed. 1963, MB ChB 1966; DObst RCOG 1969.

BEDEN, Rushdy Shahin Ashby Rehabilitation Centre, St George's Hospital, Long Leys Road, Lincoln LN1 1FS Tel: 01522 512512 Fax: 01522 577172; 4 The Steepers, Nettleham, Lincoln LN2 2SX Tel:

01522 751968 — MB ChB 1974 Baghdad; DMedRehab RCP Lond. 1990. (University of Baghdad College of Medicine) Staff Grade (Rehabil. Med.) Lincoln Dist. Health Care NHS Trust. Socs: BSRM.

BEDFORD, Abigail Dagmar 2 Brandon Road, Southsea PO5 2LY — MB ChB 1997 Birm.

BEDFORD, Mr Alan Frederick West Suffolk Hospital, Bury St Edmunds IP33 2QZ Tel: 01284 713000 Fax: 01284 713774; Hydene Cottage, Hawkedon, Bury St Edmunds IP29 4NP Tel: 01284 789483 — MB BS 1970 Lond.; MCh (Orthop.) Liverp. 1980; FRCS Eng. 1975. (Westm.) Cons. Orthop. Surg. W. Suff. Hosp. Bury St. Edmunds. Socs: Fell. BOA; BMA. Prev: Sen. Regist. (Orthop.) Middlx. Hosp. Lond.; Regist. Roy. Nat. Orthop. Hosp. Lond. & Qu. Mary's Hosp. Roehampton.

BEDFORD, Bernard Waterside Health Centre, Beaulieu Road, Hythe, Southampton SO45 5WX Tel: 02380 845955; Whistlers, Armstrong Road, Brockenhurst SO42 7TA Tel: 01590 22052 — MB ChB 1970 Leeds; MRCGP (Dist.) 1979; DObst RCOG 1973. Socs: New Forest Med. Soc. Prev: Ho. Phys. & Ho. Surg., SHO (A & E) & SHO (Paediat.) York Gp.Hosps.

BEDFORD, C Ann The Hamilton Practice, Keats House, Bush Fair, Harlow CM18 6LY Tel: 01279 692700 Fax: 01279 692719 — MB BS 1964 Lond. (Roy. Free)

BEDFORD, Carolyn 2 Littlecote, Great Holm, Milton Keynes MK8 9EZ — MB ChB 1974 Birm.

BEDFORD, Christopher David Warrington Hospital NHS Trust, Lovely Lane, Warrington WA5 1QG Tel: 01925 635911 Fax: 01925 662009; 24 Littlecote Gardens, Appleton, Warrington WA4 5DL Tel: 01925 268022 — MB ChB 1982 Manch.; BSc (Hons.) Manch. 1979; MRCP UK 1987; DCH RCP Lond. 1984; FRCPCH. (Manch.) Cons. Paediat. Warrington Hosp. Prev: Sen. Regist. (Paediat.) Roy. Devon & Exeter Hosp.; Regist. (Paediat.) Roy. Liverp. Childr. Hosp.; Research Fell. (Cystic Fibrosis) Roy. Liverp. Childr. Hosp.

BEDFORD, Derek Frank (retired) 28 Durfold Drive, Reigate RH2 0QA Tel: 01737 248420 — MB BS 1949 Lond.; MRCS Eng. LRCP Lond. 1948; DIH Soc. Apoth. Lond. 1957. Hon. Clin. Asst. Dept. of Chem. Path. E. Surrey Hosp. Prev: Ho. Phys. St. Mary's Hosp. Lond.

BEDFORD, Eileen Mary (retired) 49 Nottingham Road, Ripley, Derby DE5 3AS Tel: 01773 742407 — MB ChB Leeds 1951. Prev: GP Ripley.

BEDFORD, Felicity Jane Bosmere Medical Practice, PO Box 41, Civic Centre Road, Havant PO9 2AJ Tel: 023 9245 1300 Fax: 023 9249 2524 Email: bosmeremedical@cs.com; 10 The Fairway, Rowlands Castle, Portsmouth Tel: 023 9241 3279 — MB ChB 1981 Dundee; BSc (Hons.) Dund 1977.

BEDFORD, Felicity Margaret (retired) Jericho Health Centre, Oxford OX2 6NW — MB BS 1954 Lond.; DObst RCOG 1957; DCH Eng. 1960.

BEDFORD, Mr Godfrey John Bateson Dumfries & Galloway Royal Infirmary, Bankend Road, Dumfries DG1 4AP Tel: 01387 246246; Zander House, Cargenbridge, Dumfries DG2 8XL Tel: 01387 263017 — MB ChB 1974 Dundee; BSc St. And. 1971; FRCS Ed. 1980; FRCOphth 1989. Cons. Ophth. Dumfries & Galloway Acute & Matern. NHS Trust. Prev: Sen. Regist. (Ophth.) Ninewells Hosp. Dundee; Temp. Lect. (Anat.) Univ. Manch. Med. Sch. & SHO (Ophth.) Manch. Roy. Eye Hosp.

BEDFORD, Janet Welstead (retired) 50 Mosspark Avenue, Dumfries DG1 4PA Tel: 01387 264770 — MB BChir 1941 Camb.; MA Camb. 1941; MRCS Eng. LRCP Lond. 1942. Prev: Resid. Surg. Off. Blackburn Roy. Infirm.

BEDFORD, John Reginald Dawson (retired) 22B Mill Brow, Marple Bridge, Stockport SK6 5LL Tel: 0161 427 5676 — MB ChB 1956 Manch.; FRCOG 1975, M 1962, DObst 1959. Cons. O & G Tameside AHA. Prev: Sen. Regist. (O & G) St. Mary's Hosp. Manch.

BEDFORD, Jonathan 1 Springfields Close, Colden Common, Winchester SO21 1SU — MB BCh BAO 1985 NUI; BSc Lond. 1978; LRCPI & LM, LRCSI & LM 1985; MRCGP 1994; DRCOG 1995. (RCSI Dub.) Med. Off. with BASMU. Socs: BMA. Prev: SHO (Paediat.) St. Mary's Hosp. Portsmouth; SHO (O & G) Plymouth Dist. Gen. Hosp.; Resid. Med. Roy. Infirm. Glas.

BEDFORD, Michael 12 Silver Birch Avenue, Fulwood, Sheffield S10 3TA — MB ChB 1981 Leeds; MRCGP 1985; DFFP 1994; DRCOG 1985; Cert. Family Plann. JCC 1985. Socs: BMA.

BEDFORD, Mr Michael Alison (retired) Oakamoor, 31 Downing Drive, Great Barton, Bury St Edmunds IP31 2RP Tel: 01284 787405 — MB BS 1956 Lond.; FRCS Eng. 1963. Hon. Cons. Oncol. Moorfields Eye Hosp. Lond.; Hon. Cons. Thos. Coram Foundat. for Childr. Prev: Cons. Surg. Moorfields Eye Hosp. Lond.

BEDFORD, Michael Ronald The Health Centre, Doctor Lane, Mirfield WF14 8DU Tel: 01924 495721 Fax: 01924 480605 — MB BS 1975 Lond.; MRCS Eng. LRCP Lond. 1975; MRCGP 1979.

BEDFORD, Mr Nicholas Alan 156 St Annes Road EaStreet, Lytham St Annes FY8 3HW — MB ChB 1970 Manch.; FRCOG 1990, M 1977. Cons. O & G Blackpool Vict. Hosp. NHS Trust. Prev: Cons. O & G Blackpool, Wyre & Fylde Health Auth.

BEDFORD, Sarah Jane 2 College of Roseisle, Elgin IV30 5YF — MB ChB 1996 Liverp.

BEDFORD, Timothy Alan 19 Grange Lane, Willingham, Gainsborough DN21 5LB — MB ChB 1985 Birm. Prev: Maj. RAMC.

BEDFORD RUSSELL, Alison Ruth Neonatal Unit, St George's Hospital, Blackshaw Road, London SW17 0QT Tel: 020 8672 1255 Ext: 2517 Fax: 020 8725 1933; 16 Huron Road, London SW17 8RB Tel: 020 8672 2002 Email: alison.bedford-russell@stgeorges.nhs.uk — MB BS 1984 Lond.; BSc (Hons.) Biochem Lond. 1981; MRCP Lond. 1987; FRCPCH. (Charing Cross) Cons. & Sen. Lect. (Paediat.) St. Geo. Hosp. Lond. Socs: Neonat. Soc.; BMA; Roy. Coll. Paediat. and Child Health. Prev: Lect. (Child Health) St. Geo. Hosp. Med. Sch. Lond.; Clin. Research Fell. Paediat. St. Mary's Lond.; SHO Rotat. Qu. Eliz. Hosp. Lond.

BEDFORD-TURNER, Christopher Mark Downlands Medical Centre, 77 High Street, Polegate BN26 6AE Tel: 01323 482323/486449 Fax: 01323 488497 — MB BS 1969 Lond.; MRCS Eng. LRCP Lond. 1968; MRCGP 1980; DObst RCOG 1970. (St. Bart.) Socs: BMA. Prev: Ho. Surg. (Gen. Surg.) & Ho. Phys. (Gen. Med.) Roy. Sussex Co. Hosp. Brighton; Ho. Surg. (O & G) Brighton Gen. Hosp.

BEDFORD-TURNER, Ernest William (retired) Lister House, 211 Eastbourne Road, Polegate BN26 5DX — MRCS Eng. LRCP Lond. 1939; MRCGP 1953. Prev: Capt. RAMC 1940-42.

BEDFORTH, Katherine Jane Tudor Square Medical Practice, Tudor Square, West Bridgford, Nottingham NG2 6BT — BM BS 1992 Nottm.; DFFP; BMedSci Nottm. 1990; DROCG Nottm. 1997; MRCGP. (Nottingham) p/t Gen. Practitioner.

BEDFORTH, Nigel Martin Queens Medical Centre, Derby Road, Nottingham NG7 2UH — BM BS 1990 Nottm.; BMedSci Nottm. 1988; FRCA 1995. Specialist Regist. (Anaesth) Nottm, Cons. Anaesth., Anaesth., Nottm.

BEDI, Ajay Kumar Mayfield Medical Centre, Park Road, Jarrow NE32 5SE Tel: 0191 489 7183 Fax: 0191 483 2001; 30 Ashtrees Gardens, Low Fell, Gateshead NE9 5BJ Tel: 0191 490 1718 Fax: 0191 483 2001 — MB BCh BAO 1988 Belf.; MRCGP 1994; DMH Belf. 1993. (QU. Univ. Belf.) GP Princip.; GP Mem. MAAG Gateshead & S. Tyneside HA; Mem. of Foll. Comms. InFertil., Assisted Conception, Appeals Tribunal; Matern. Serv. Gp., Lung Cancer Gp.; Gateshead & S. Tyneside HA; Chairm. Gateshad & S. Tyneside Commiss.ing Forum. Prev: GP Bangor; SHO Rotat. (Surg.) Belf. Gen. Hosp.; SHO (Paediat.) Roy. Belf. Hosp. Sick Childr.

BEDI, Amit The Regional Intensive Care Unit, Royal Victoria Hospital, Belfast BT12 6BA Tel: 02890 894 730; 112 Marlborough Park Central, Malone, Belfast BT9 6HP — MB ChB 1992 Manch.; MD 2001 Queen's Belfast; FRCA Lond. 1996. (Manch.) Cons. (Anaesth. & Intens. Care), Roy. Vict. Hosp. Belf.. Socs: Assn. Of Anaesth.s of GB & Irel.; Assn. For low flow Anaesth.; Anaesthetic research Soc. Prev: Specialist Regist. Roy. Vict. Hosp. Belf.; Res. Fell. Assoc. of Anaesth. Of GB & Ire.

BEDI, Carolyn Indira Flat 2, 17 Kirkvale Drive, Newton Mearns, Glasgow G77 5HD — MB ChB 1997 Bristol.

BEDI, Kulwant S R 4 Cobbet's Way, Fulshaw Park, Wilmslow SK9 6HN — MB BS 1950 Madras; BSc Punjab (India) 1944; FRCP Ed. 1973, M 1959; MRCPsych 1971; DPM Eng. 1963; DCH Eng. 1960. Cons. Psychiat. Pk.side Hosp. Macclesfield; Vis. Cons. Psychiat. Trafford AHA. Prev: Cons. Psychiat. Bristol Gp. of Hosps., Bristol.

BEDI, Mylapore Shunmukhasundaram Vasantha 4 Cobbett's Way, Fulshaw Park, Wilmslow SK9 6HN — MB BS 1959 Madras; MRCPsych 1972; DObst RCOG 1965. Med. Asst. (Psychiat.) Pk.side

Hosp. Macclesfield.; Cons. Psychiat. - Locum, E. Chesh. NHS Trust, Macclesfield, Chesh.

BEDI, Navjot Kaur Nottinghamshire Healthcare NHS Trust, Duncan Macmillan House, Porchester Rd, Nottingham NG3 Tel: 0115 969 1300 — MB ChB 1992 Sheff.; MRCPsych 1998 (UK). (Sheffield Univ. Med. Sch.) Specialist Regist.,. Prev: Regist. (Psychiat.) Nottm.

BEDI, Sarjivan Singh, Maj. RAMC Retd. Overslade Lane Surgery, 33 Overslade Lane, Rugby CV22 6DY Tel: 01788 813660 Fax: 01788 814058; 33 Overside Lane, Rugby CV22 6DY Tel: 01788 813660 Fax: 01788 335446 — MB BS 1959 Punjab; T(GP) 1992. Pres. UK Sikh Doctors Assn. Socs: Exec. Rugby & Dist. Med. Soc.; BMA (Ex-Chairm. Rugby Div.). Prev: Maj. Indian Army Med. Corps.; Med. Off. i/c Ordnance Fact. Muradnagar India; Cas. Med. Off. Irwin Hosp. New Delhi, India.

BEDI, Sheena — MB ChB 1992 Manch.; BSc (Hons.) Path. Manch. 1990; DRCOG 1995; DFFP 1995; MRCGP 1997. (Manchester) GP PMS pilot Daruzzaman Care Centre; GP in PCAP pilot in Salford. Socs: BMA. Prev: Long term Locum - Robt. Derbysh. Pract., Manch.; GP Regist., Distey; GP Regist., Sheff.

BEDI, Surjit Singh (retired) 1 The Paddock, Yarm Road, Eaglescliffe, Stockton-on-Tees TS16 9BQ Tel: 01642 782346 — MB BS 1957 Calcutta; FRCP Glas. 1981 M 1964; FRCP Ed. 1980 M 1965; DPhysMed Eng. 1968. Cons. Phys. Rheum. Cleveland Nuffield Hosp. Norton, Stockton on Tees. Prev: Med. Regist. Chester-le-St. Gen. Hosp. Durh.

BEDI, Tarlochan Singh Southern General Hospital, 1345 Govan Road, Glasgow G51 4TF Tel: 0141 201 2604; 156 Prestonfield, Milngavie, Glasgow G62 7QA — MB BS 1965 Poona; FRCPsych 1995, M 1972; DPM 1969. Cons. Psychiat. S.. Gen. Hosp. Glas. Prev: Cons. Psychiat. Woodilee Hosp. Lenzie; Sen Regist. (Psychiat.) S.. Gen. Hosp. Glas.; SHO Glenside & Barrow Hosps. Bristol.

BEDIAKO-NTIM, Kofi Apaw Pilgrim Hospital, Sibsey Road, Boston PE21 9QS — Vrach 1971 Kharkov Med. Inst. USSR; MCOphth 1989; DO RCPSI 1981.

BEDLOW, Alison Jane Department of Dermatology, Warwick Hospital, Lakin Road, Warwick CV34 5B Tel: 01926 495321 Ext: 4100 Fax: 01926 483664; 6 Canberra Close, Wellesbourne CV35 9TR Email: mcfall@virgin.net — MB BS 1990 Lond.; MRCP (UK) 1993; Dip RCPath 1999, Lond. (King's Coll. Lond.) p/t Cons., Dermatoloogy, Warwick Hosp., warwick. Prev: Regist. (Dermat.) St. Geo. Hosp. Lond.; Sen.Regist. (Dermat) St Geo.s. Hosp. Lond.

BEDNARSKI, Tadeusz (retired) Quillet Cottage, Leeds Town, Hayle TR27 6BP Tel: 01736 850577 — LRCP LRCS 1973 Ed.; LRCP LRCS Ed. LRCPS Glas. 1973; DA Eng. 1975. Prev: GP Teddington Middlx.

BEDSON, Catherine Ruth 3 Abbotswood, Guildford GU1 1UT — MB BS 1989 Lond.

BEDSON, John Mayfield Surgery, 54 Trentham Road, Longton, Stoke-on-Trent ST3 4DW Tel: 01782 315547 — MB ChB 1985 Manch.; MRCGP 1991; DRCOG 1990.

BEDWANI, Simon James 159 Bwlch Road, Cardiff CF5 3EE — BM 1997 Soton.

BEDWELL, Stephen 57 Mansfield Hill, London E4 7SS — BM 1991 Soton.; BSc Appl. Biochem. Brunel 1986. SHO (Path.) Roy. Hants. Co. Hosp. Winchester.

BEE, Alan John 65A Perry Street, Gravesend DA11 8RD Tel: 01474 356661 — MB BS 1958 Lond.; BSc Lond. 1955, MB BS 1958; DObst RCOG 1963. (Univ. Coll. Hosp.)

BEE, Anthea Louise 1 Post Paddocks, Netherend, Lydney GL15 6NJ — MB BCh 1985 Wales.

BEE, Bernard Herbert (retired) The Bakehouse, 14a The Green, Rowlands Castle PO9 6BN — MRCS Eng. LRCP Lond. 1956. Prev: Ho. Phys. Soton. Gen. Hosp.

BEE, David Edward St Brycedale Surgery, St. Brycedale Road, Kirkcaldy KY1 1ER Tel: 01592 640800 Fax: 01592 644944 — MB ChB 1978 Ed.; MRCGP 1982; DRCOG 1981.

BEE, David Lyle (retired) The Gerrards, 34 Werneth Road, Woodley, Stockport SK6 1HP Tel: 0161 430 2076 — MB BS Lond. 1954; FRCPath 1980 M 1968. Prev: Cons. Pathol. Ashton-under-Lyne Gen. Hosp.

BEE, David Michael Binbrook Surgery, Back Lane, Binbrook, Market Rasen LN8 6ED — BM BS 1984 Nottm.; Dip. IMC RCS Ed. 1989. Prev: GP Internat. HC, Portugal.

BEE, Edith May R14 St John's Road, Rowley Park, Stafford ST17 9AS — MB BS 1964 Lond.; MRCP (UK) 1972; MRCS Eng. LRCP Lond. 1964; DObst RCOG 1966; DCH Eng. 1967. (Roy. Free) SCMO Mid Staffs. HA. Prev: Cons. Paediat. Croydon AHA.

BEE, Hang Wing Department of Obstetrics & Gynaecology, George Eliot Hospital, College St., Nuneaton CV10 7DJ — MB BS 1985 Malaya.

BEE, Noel Jacques (retired) Ivy Lodge, Main Road, Wrangle, Boston PE22 9AU Tel: 01205 870216 — MRCS Eng. LRCP Lond. 1931.

BEE, Peter St Johns Medical Centre, St. Johns Road, Altrincham WA14 2NW Tel: 0161 928 8727 Fax: 0161 929 8550; 468 Hale Road, Hale Barns, Altrincham WA15 8XT Tel: 0161 980 2999 — MB ChB Manch. 1960; DObst RCOG 1962. Prev: SHO Roy. Manch. Childr. Hosp. Pendlebury; Ho. Off. Obst. St. Mary's Hosp. Manch.; Ho. Surg. Crumpsall Hosp. Manch.

BEE, Rhian Wyn Hen Furiau, Pwllheli Rd, Caernarfon LL55 2YR — MB ChB 1997 Manch. Ho. Off. (Med.) Qu.'s Pk. Hosp. Blackburn. Prev: Ho. Off. (Surg.) Lancaster Roy. Infirm.

BEEBEEJAUN, Haroon Rashid 18 Foresterhill Court, Aberdeen AB25 2WA Tel: 01224 691077 Fax: 01224 691077 Email: dr_hrb@compuserve.com; Rue Victor Hugo, Beau-Bassin, Mauritius Tel: 00 230 4546999 Fax: 00 230 4642789 Email: beau27@bow.intnet.mu — MB BCh BAO 1992 NUI; LRCPSI 1992. (Roy. Coll. Surgs. Irel.) Sen. SHO (Obstet. & Gyn.) Aberd. Roy. Infirm.

BEEBY, Andrew Richard Queen Elizabeth Hospital, Sheriff Hill, Gateshead NE9 6SX Tel: 0191 403 2202 Fax: 0191 403 6020; 3 Eighton Cottage, Galloping Green Road, Eighton Banks, Gateshead NE9 7XD Fax: 0870 0558 771 Email: arb@eightoncottage.demon.co.uk — MB BS 1985 Newc.; BMedSc (Hons.) Newc. 1982; MRCOG 1990. Cons. Obst. Gyn. Qu. Eliz. Hosp. Gateshead. Prev: Sen. Regist. (O & G) Roy. Vict. Infirm. Newc.; Sen. Regist. (O & G) Sunderland Gen. Hosp.; Regist. (O & G) Newc. Gen. Hosp.

BEEBY, Christopher Paul Princess Margaret Hospital, Swindon SN1 4JU Tel: 01793 536231 — MB 1974 Camb.; BChir 1973; FFA RCS 1980; DObst RCOG 1975. Cons. Anaesth. P.ss Margt. Hosp. Swindon. Prev: Sen. Regist. (Anaesth.) St. Geo. Hosp. Lond.; Regist. (Anaesth.) Univ. Coll. Hosp. Lond.

BEEBY, Mr Douglas Ian BUPA Alexandra Hospital, Impton Lane, Walderslade, Chatham ME5 9PG Tel: 01634 830000 Fax: 01634 815811; Two Kiln Oast, Church Lane, Newington, Sittingbourne ME9 7JX Fax: 01795 844421 Email: dibeeby@aol.com — MB BChir 1966 Camb.; M.Chir Camb. 1977; FRCS 1972 Eng.; MA 1966; BA Camb. 1962. (Camb. & St. Thos.) p/t Cons. Surg. Medway NHS Trust; Recognised Teach. Univ. Lond. Socs: Fell. Assn. Surgs.; Brit. Assn. Surg. Oncol.; Pancreatic Soc. Prev: Sen. Regist. (Surg.) St. Geo. Hosp. Lond. & Roy. Marsden Hosp. Lond.; Vandervell Research Fell. Chester Beatty Inst. Cancer Research; Regist. (Surg.) United Sheff. Hosps.

BEEBY, Karen Fingerpost Surgery, 117 Higher Parr Street, St Helens WA9 1AG Tel: 01744 21867 Fax: 01744 23342; 2 Taplow Close, Appleton, Warrington WA4 5HH Tel: 01744 813065 — MB ChB 1978 Manch.; DRCOG 1982.

BEEBY, Michael James Doctors Surgery, Great Melton Road, Hethersett, Norwich NR9 3AB Tel: 01603 810250 Fax: 01603 812402 — MB BS 1969 Lond.; MRCS Eng. LRCP Lond. 1969. (Char. Cross) Prev: Regist. (Med.) St. Stephen's Hosp. Lond.; Ho. Surg. Char. Cross Hosp. Lond.; Ho. Phys. Norf. & Norwich Hosp.

BEEBY, William James Hollowfield Surgery, 122 Hollowfield, Coulby Newham, Middlesbrough TS8 0RS Tel: 01642 598401 Fax: 01642 270055 — MB BS 1977 Newc.; MRCGP 1981. (Univ. Newc. u. Tyne) Police Surg. Cleveland Constab.; Ex-Chairm. Cleveland LMC; Ex-Mem. S. Tees Ethical Comm.

BEECH, Christopher James Risca Surgery, St. Mary Street, Risca, Newport NP11 6YS Tel: 01633 612666; 122 Cefn Road, Rogerstone, Newport NP10 9EX — MB ChB 1973 Birm. Police Surg. Gwent Police Auth. Prev: Med. Off. Tristan Da Cunha; SHO Treliske & Tehidy Hosps. Cornw.; Ho. Surg. Torbay Hosp. S. Devon.

BEECH, John (retired) 55 Chapel Lane, Navenby, Lincoln LN5 0ER Tel: 01522 810142 Email: fagus@globalnet.com — MB ChB Sheff. 1938; DMRT Eng. 1952. Prev: Med. Off. Branston Hall Hosp.

BEECH, Karen Julie 83 Woodgrove Road, Burnley BB11 3EJ — MB ChB 1998 Liverp.; MB ChB Liverp 1998.

BEECH, Lisa Dee Ella Gordon Unit, St Mary's Hosptial, Milton Road, Portsmouth PO3 6AF Tel: 023 92 866301; 8 Medlicott Way, Swanmore, Southampton SO32 2NE — MB ChB 1988 Leic.; DRCOG 1991; DFFP 1997. CMO Family Plann. Ella Gordon Unit S Mary's Hosp. Portsmouth.

BEECH, Nicholas 126 Gordon Road, Strood, Rochester ME2 3HL — MB ChB 1986 Manch.

BEECH, Paul Andrew Badgerswood Surgery, Mill Lane, Bordon GU35 8LH Tel: 01428 713511 Fax: 01428 713812; Waterlow, Linden Road, Bordon GU35 8EN Tel: 01420 472535 — MB BS 1970 Lond.; MRCGP 1974; DObst RCOG 1973.

BEECH, Susan Heather Childrens Services, Leicestershire & Ruthland Healthcare NHS Trust, Bridge Park Plaza, Bridge Park Road, Thurmaston, Leicester LE4 8PQ — MB ChB 1988 Leic. Locum Staff Grade Paediat., Community Paediat., Leicester.

BEECHAM, Karim 41 Cornel, Anington, Tamworth B77 4EF — MB ChB 1986 Birm.; ChB Birm. 1986.

BEECHER, Helen Maria Kells, Compass Hill, Taunton TA1 4EF — MB BCh 1990 Wales. Trainee GP Plymouth HA VTS.

BEECHEY, Andrew Peter Graeme Northern General Hospital, Herries Road, Sheffield S5 7AU Tel: 0114 243 4343; 28 Dover Road, Sheffield S11 8RH Tel: 0114 266 2099 — MB ChB 1977 Bristol; FFA RCS 1982. Cons. Anaesth. N. Gen. Hosp. Sheff.; Hon. Clin. Lect. (Anaesth.) Univ. Sheff. Socs: Assn. Anaesth.; Assn. Cardiothoraic Anaesth. Prev: Cons. Anaesth. Harefield Hosp.; Cons. Anaesth. Groote Schuur Hosp. Cape Town; Sen. Regist. (Anaesth.) Nottm. Trent RHA.

BEECHEY-NEWMAN, Mr Nicolas Department of Academic Oncology, Thomas Guy House, Guy's Hospital, London SE1 9RT Tel: 020 7955 5000 Fax: 020 7403 8381 Email: nbn@compuserve.com; Yew Tree Cottage, Highmoor, Nettlebed, Henley-on-Thames RG9 5DH Tel: 01491 641537 — MB BS 1983 Lond.; BSc (Hons.) Lond. 1980; FRCS Eng. 1988; FRCS (Gen.) 1997. (Guy's Hosp. Lond.) Cons. BrE. Unit Guy's Hosp. Lond.; Cons. St Thomas' Hosp. Lond. Socs: Assn. Surg.; Pancreatic Soc.; Brit. Assn. Surgic. Oncol. Prev: Sen. Regist. BrE. Unit Guy's Hosp. Lond.; Lect. (Surg.) Guy's Hosp. Lond.; Sen. Regist. Lewisham Hosp. & Greenwich Dist. Hosp.

BEECHING, Nicholas John Liverpool School of Tropical Medicine, Pembroke Place, Liverpool L3 5QA Tel: 0151 708 9393 Fax: 0151 708 8733 Email: nbeeching@aol.com; Regional Infectious Disease Unit, University Hospital Aintree, Liverpool L9 7AL Tel: 0151 529 3833 Fax: 0151 529 3762 — BM BCh 1977 Oxf.; MA Oxf. 1978; FRCP Lond. 1994; MRCP (UK) 1981; FRACP 1984; DCH RCP Lond. 1980; DTM & H Liverp. 1978. (Oxf.) Sen. Clin. Lect. (Infec. Dis.) Liverp. Sch. Trop. Med. & Hon. Cons. Phys. Infec. Dis. Unit Univ. Hosp. Aintree Liverp.; Hon. Cons. Phys., Pub. Health Auth. Serv., NW Region. Socs: Fell. Roy. Soc. Trop. Med. & Hyg.; Counc. Mem. Brit. Infect. Soc. Prev: Cons. Internal Med. Armed Forces Hosp. Khamis Mushayt, Saudi Arabia.

BEECHING, Yvonne Gladys Hughes 21 East Drive, Ham Manor, Angmering, Littlehampton BN16 4JH — MB BS 1953 Lond.; BSc Lond. 1949; MRCS Eng. LRCP Lond. 1953; DCH Eng. 1955. (Roy. Free) Med. Off. (Occupat. Health) Luton & Dunstable Hosp. & S. Beds. HA. Prev: Employm. Med. Adviser Health & Safety Exec.; Regist. (Psychiat.) Saxondale Hosp. Nottm.; SHO (Paediat. & Infec. Dis.) Roy. Free Hosp. Lond.

BEECROFT, Christina Lesley 53 Gledhow Wood Close, Roundhay, Leeds LS8 1PN — MB ChB 1998 Leeds.

BEECROFT, Nicholas Michael Psychiatry Department, Guys Hospital, London SE1 9RT — MB BS 1994 Lond.; BSc 1991. (UMDS) Specialist Regist. Psych. Guys. Hosp. Lond. Socs: MRCPsych. Prev: Reg.Maudsley.Hosp.

BEED, Martin Jeffrey 49 Lyndhurst Road, Exmouth EX8 3DS — BM BS 1994 Nottm.

BEEDEL, Anna 4F1 139 Buccleuch Street, Edinburgh EH8 9NE — MB ChB 1996 Ed.

BEEDEN, Arthur Gordon (retired) 48 Queen Alexandra Road, Bedford MK41 9SE Tel: 01234 267782 — MB BChir 1963 Camb.; FRCS Eng. 1968. Prev: Med. Dir. & Cons. ENT Surg. Bedford Hosp.

BEEDHAM, Mr Trevor Dept. of Womens Services, St. Bart's. & The London Hospital, NHS Trust, Fielden house, Whitechapel, London E1 1BB Tel: 020 7377 7000 Fax: 020 7377 7710; Department of Womens Services, St Bartholemew's Hospital, The Royal Hospitals Trust, London EC1A 7BE Tel: 020 7601 7851 Fax: 020 7601 7182 — MB BS 1972 Lond.; MB BS (Hons.) Lond. 1972; BDS Lond. 1965; FRCOG 1989, M 1977; MIBiol 1979. (Lond. Hosp.) Cons. O & G St. Bart's. & The Lond. Hosp., NHS Trust.; Assoc. Clin. Director, Gyn. Trust.; Lead Clinician, CPD. Socs: Fell. Roy. Soc. Med.; Hon. Mem. Centr. Assn. Obst. & Gyn. USA.; (Asst.) Soc. Apoth. Prev: Sen. Regist. Lond. Hosp.

BEEDIE, Elizabeth Janet Ainslie (retired) Brangan, 6 Fleurs Drive, Elgin IV30 1SS Tel: 01343 542445 — MB ChB 1948 Ed.

BEEDIE, Margaret Ann Queen Elizabeth Psychiatric Hospital, Vincent Drive, Birmingham B15 2QZ Tel: 0121 678 3359 — MB ChB 1971 Leeds; MRCP (UK) 1975; MRCPsych 1979. Cons. Psychiat. Qu. Eliz. Hosp. Birm. Prev: Cons. Psychiat. Barnsley Hall Hosp. BromsGr. & Busheyfields Hosp. Dudley; Sen. Regist. Uffculme Clinic Birm.

BEEDIE, Rosemary Margaret Humbie Cottage, Kirkliston EH29 9EG Tel: 0131 331 3839; Humbie Cottage, Kirkliston EH29 9EG Tel: 0131 331 3839 — MB ChB 1984 Dundee. (Dundee) Prev: Clin. Med. Off. (Community Child Health) Edin. Sick Childr. NHS Trust; Trainee GP Edin. VTS.

BEEHARRY, Roshni 62 Hansart Way, The Ridgeway, Enfield EN2 8ND Tel: 020 8366 8932 — MB BS 1996 Lond. (St Mary's Hospital London) Prev: Ho. Off. (Gastro & Gen. Med.) Wycombe Genreral Hosp. High Wycombe; Ho. Off. (Gen. Surg. & Urol.) Centr. Middlx. Hosp. Lond.; SHO (Geriat.) Hillingdon Hosp. Uxbridge.

BEEJAY, Nigel Umar Amaan 9 Aldridge Road Villas, London W11 1BL — MB BChir 1992 Camb.

BEEKEN, Sally Ann Oaklands Centre, Raddlebarn Rd, Selly Oak, Birmingham B29 6JB Tel: 0121 627 8231 — MB BS 1991 Newc.; BMedSc (Hons.) Newc. 1990; MRCP Psych 1996; DCH RCP Lond. 1993. Specialist Regist. (Child & Adolesc. Psychiat.), Birm. Prev: Regist. (Psychiat.) Littlemore Hosp. Oxf.; Regist. (Psychiat.) St. Crispin Hosp. & Child & Family Consultation Servs. N.ampton; Regist. (Psychother.) Leamington Spa.

BEELEY, John Michael, CBE, QHP, OStJ, Surg. Cdr. RN Retd. The Old Post Office, Stoney Middleton, Hope Valley S32 4TU Tel: 01433 631277 — MRCS Eng. LRCP Lond. 1958; FRCP Lond. 1980, M 1968; DObst RCOG 1961. Socs: Fell. Roy. Geogr. Soc. Prev: Surg. Commodore RN, Tri-Serv. Dir. Clin. Servs.; Prof. & Dir. Naval Med. RN Hosp. Haslar; Vis. Scientist Clin. Research Centre Harrow.

BEELEY, Linda 3 Newland Road, Droitwich WR9 7AF Tel: 01905 796691 — BM BCh 1966 Oxf.; FRCP Lond. 1982, M 1969. (Oxf.) Socs: Brit. Pharm. Soc.; BMA & Brit. Psychol. Soc. Prev: Cons. Clin. Pharmacol. Qu. Eliz. Hosp. Birm.; Lect. (Clin. Pharmacol.) Univ. Birm.; Ho. Off. Radcliffe Infirm. Oxf.

BEEN, Joseph Banat 80 Willifield Way, London NW11 6YJ — MB ChB 1941 Witwatersrand; DPH 1947. (Witwatersrand)

BEEN, Martin Department of Cardiology, Walsgrave Hospital, Clifford Bridge Road, Coventry CV2 2DX Tel: 024 76 538931 Email: martinbeen@aol.com — MD 1989 Dundee; MD (Commend.) Dundee 1989, MB ChB 1977; FRCP Glas. 1994; MRCP (UK) 1981. Cons. Cardiol. Walsgrave Hosp. Coventry. Socs: Brit. Cardiac Soc.; Brit. Cardiovasc. Interven. Soc.

BEENEY, Mr Michael Arthur Rees 23 Selwyn Road, Eastbourne BN21 2LE Tel: 01323 738648 Fax: 01323 416671 Email: mikebeeney@aol.com — MB BS 1972 Lond.; MB BS Lond. 1976; BSc (Hons.) (Med. Pharmacol.) Lond. 1972; FRCS Ed. 1983; MRCS Eng. LRCP Lond. 1975; MRCGP 1987; DRCOG 1979; Cert. JCC Lond. 1978. (St. Bart.) Ship's Surg. Cunard Line Ltd. Prev: Med. Off. Shell Oil Company, Nigeria; Forens. Med. Examr. City & Metrop. Police; Ship's Surg. Cunard Line Ltd.

BEENSTOCK, Norman (retired) Clarendon Medical Practice, Clarendon Street, Hyde SK14 2AQ Tel: 0161 368 5224 Fax: 0161 368 4767 — MB ChB 1955 Manch.; FRCGP 1981, M 1970; DObst RCOG 1959; DCH Eng. 1958. Clin. Tutor (Gen. Pract.) Tameside Postgrad. Med. Centre; Vice-Chairm. Tameside MAAG. Prev: GP Tutor Tameside.

BEER, Francis David Arboretum Surgery, 76 Monks Road, Lincoln LN2 5HU Tel: 01522 524274 Fax: 01522 525355; Beech Lodge, 24 Queensway, Lincoln LN2 4AH Tel: 01522 528977 — MB ChB 1962 Sheff.; DObst RCOG 1964. (Sheff.) Socs: Lincoln Med. Soc. Prev: SHO (O & G) Scarsdale Hosp. Chesterfield; SHO (Paediat.) City Gen. Hosp. Sheff.

BEER, Helen Louise 29 Ashfield Court Road, Pateley Bridge, Harrogate HG3 5JN — MB ChB 1998 Liverp.; MB ChB Liverp 1998.

BEER, Mark Henry Chulmleigh Health Centre, Three Crossways, Chulmleigh EX18 7AA Tel: 01769 580269 Fax: 01769 581131; Cowlas, Burrington, Umberleigh — MB ChB 1978 Bristol; BSc. (Hons.) Bristol 1975; MRCGP (Distinc.) 1982. GP Trainee Taunton Gen. Pract.; Train. Scheme.

BEER, Michael Dominic Bexley Hospital, Oxleas NHS Trust, Bexley DA5 2BW Tel: 01322 294300 Fax: 01322 293595; Department of Psychiatry, UMDS, Guy's Hospital, London SE1 9RT Tel: 020 7955 4247 Fax: 020 7955 2976 — MB BS 1985 Lond.; MA Oxf. 1984; MD Lond. 1993; LMSSA Lond. 1984; MRCPsych 1989. (Guy's) Sen. Lect. (Psychiat.) UMDS Guy's Hosp. Lond.; Hon. Cons. Psychiat. Bexley Hosp. Kent. Prev: Sen. Regist. Rotat. (Psychiat.) SE Thames RHA; Wellcome Research Fell. Wellcome Inst. Hist. Med.; Psychiat. Train. Rotat. Guy's Hosp. Lond. & Higher Train. Rotat. SE Thames.

BEER, Michael John Spring Gables Surgery, Clint Bank, Birstwith, Harrogate HG3 3DW — MB ChB 1980 Leeds; MRCGP 1984; DRCOG 1983.

BEER, Naomi Rosemary Steels Lane Health Centre, 384-388 Commercial Road, London E1 0LR Tel: 020 7335 4900 Fax: 020 7335 4901 — MB BS 1986 Lond.; MRCGP 1991; DRCOG 1989. (Guy's Hosp.) p/t GP Princip. Prev: GP Tutor Tower Hamlets.

BEER, Philip Anthony 6 Goodings Green, Wokingham RG40 1SB — BM BS 1996 Nottm.

BEER, Richard John Shapland Litchdon Medical Centre, Landkey Road, Barnstaple EX32 9LL Tel: 01271 23443 Fax: 01271 25979 — MB ChB 1978 Manch.; PhD Lond. 1972; BSc Lond. 1969; MRCGP 1981; DRCOG 1980. (Manch.)

BEER, Roger William Grenville 124-126 Cowbridge Road West, Ely — MB ChB 1983 Bristol; BSc (Hons.) (Pharmacol.) Bath 1977; MB ChB (Hons.) Bristol 1983; MRCPsych 1989.

BEER, Ronald Haddon (retired) New Trees, Windmill Hill, Meir Heath, Stoke-on-Trent ST3 7PQ — MRCS Eng. LRCP Lond. 1942.

BEER, Rosemary Anne 123 The Avenue, Harrogate HG1 4QG — MB BChir 1971 Camb.; MA, MB BChir Camb. 1971. (Camb. & St. Thos.)

BEER, Simon Oxford Clinic, Littlemore Mmental Health Centre, Sanford Road, Oxford NN13 5QA; 3 Lilac Farm Barns, Wappenham Rd, Heladon, Brackley NN13 5QA Tel: 01295 760139 — MB BS 1991 Lond.; MRCPsych 1995. (St. Bart. Hosp. Lond.) Locum Cons. Forens. Psychiat. Oxf. Clinic, Littlemore Ment. Heallth Centre Oxf. OX4 4XN; Jun. Mem. Doctors Comm. Socs: BMA (Chairm. Oxf. Region Jun. Doctors Comm.). Prev: Specialist Regist. (Forens. Psychiat) Oxf. Regional Rotat.; Regist. Rotat. (Psychiat.) Oxf. Train. Scheme; SHO Rotat. (Psychiat.) N.ampton Train Scheme.

BEER, Stephen Frederick Scunthorpe General Hospital, Cliff Gardens, Scunthorpe DN15 7BH Tel: 01724 282282 Fax: 01724 290414 Email: stephen.beer@nlg.nhs.uk; Parkland View, West Beck Lane, Blyborough, Gainsborough DN21 4HE Tel: 01427 667549 — MB ChB 1981 Liverp.; MD Liverp. 1993; MRCP (UK) 1984; FRCP London 1998; MBA Durham 1998. Cons. Phys. Diabetes Centre, Scunthorpe Gen. Hosp., Scunthorpe; Dep. Med. Director, N. Lincs. and Goole Hosps. Trust; Crowd Doctor, Scunthorpe United Football Club, Scunthorpe. Socs: Diabetes UK; Brit. Thyroid Foundat. Prev: Sen. Regist. (Med.) Guy's & Lewisham Hosps. Lond.; Research Fell. (Clin. Biochem.) Univ. Camb.; Ho. Phys. & Surg. BRd.green Hosp. Liverp.

BEER, Timothy Courtney Orchard House, Great Everdon, Daventry NN11 3BL Tel: 01327 361376 — MB BS 1966 Lond.; FRCP Lond. 1986; MRCP (UK) 1970; MRCS Eng. LRCP Lond. 1966. (Middlx.) Cons. Rheum. N.ampton Gen. Hosp. Trust. Socs: Brit. Soc. Rheum.; BMA. Prev: Sen. Regist. (Rheum. & Rehabil.) N.wick Pk. & Middlx. Hosps.; SHO (Rheum.) & Ho. Phys. Paediat. Middlx. Hosp. Lond.

BEERE, Deborah Mary South Tees Contraception and Reprod. Health Service, South Bank Health Shop, 23-27 Middlesbrough Road, South Bank, Middlesbrough TS6 6NW Tel: 01642 459583 Fax: 01642 467736; 79 The Grove, Marton, Middlesbrough TS7 8AN Tel: 01642 325476 — MB BS 1981 Lond.; MFFP 1993; DRCPath 1988; Cert. Family Plann. JCC 1988. Cons. Family Plann. & Reproductive Health Care Tees & N. E. Yorks. NHS Trust; Dip. Sexual Med. 1994; Mem. Fac. Community Health; S. Tees Cervical Screening Coordinator. Socs: Brit. Assn. Sexual & Marital Ther.

BEERS, Henry Teuton Burrows 52 Plantation Road, Lisburn BT27 5PH — MD 1983 Belf.; MB BCh BAO 1976; FFA RCSI 1980. Cons. (Anaesth.) Lagan Valley Hosp. Lisburn.

BEERSTECHER, Hendrik Johan The Surgery, 2 Thames Avenue, Rainham, Gillingham ME8 9BW Tel: 01634 360486 Fax: 01634 375159; 12 Lapwing Drive, Lower Halstow, Sittingbourne ME9 7DZ Tel: 01796 844068 — Artsexamen Leiden 1989. (Leiden)

BEES, Nicola Rachel Radiology Department, Mayday University Hospital, London Rd, Croydon CR7 7YE Tel: 020 8401 3054 Fax: 020 8401 3454; "Broadoaks", Cilonnen Rd, Three Crosses, Swansea SA4 3PH Tel: 01792 873983 Email: s.catling@mailcity.com — MB BS 1991 (Hons.) Lond.; BSc Hons 1986; MRCP (UK) 1994. Cons. Radiol. Prev: SHO (Oncol.) Roy. Marsden Hosp. Lond.; SHO (Med.) St. Helier Hosp. Carshalton & St. Geo. Hosp. Lond.; SPR Radiol., St. Geo. Hosp. Lond.

BEESE, Eudocie Norma Ann Morriston Hospital, Swansea SA6 6NL Tel: 01792 702222 Fax: 01792 703278 — MB BCh 1979 Wales; FFA RCS Eng. 1987. Cons. Anaesth. Morriston Hosp. Swansea. Prev: Cons. Anaesth. St. Lawrence Hosp. Chepstow.

BEESLEY, Christa Jenny 42 Montreal Road, Brighton BN2 2UY — BM 1987 Soton.

BEESLEY, Helen Sarah The Surgery, 241 Tring Road, Aylesbury HP20 1PH Tel: 01296 425858 Fax: 01296 393398 — MB ChB 1987 Bristol.

BEESLEY, John Ridehalgh 32 Rectory Terrace, Newcastle upon Tyne NE3 1YB — MB ChB 1973 Birm.; MRCP (UK) 1976. Cons. Paediat. Gateshead HA.

BEESLEY, Marie Louise Sydney 3 Inverness Mansions, Moscow Road, London W2 4BP Tel: 020 7229 8183 — BM BCh 1951 Oxf.; BA Oxf. 1946, BM BCh 1951; DPM Eng. 1956. Cons. Psychiat. Ashford Hosp. Middlx. Prev: Cons. Psychiat. Lady Chichester Hosp. Hove & Brighton Gen.; Hosp.; Sen. Regist. York Clinic Guy's Hosp. Lond.; Regist. Atkinson Morley's Hosp. Wimbledon.

BEESLEY, Sarah Anne 53 Cleveden Crescent, Kelvinside, Glasgow G12 0PD — MB ChB 1985 Aberd.; MRCPsych 1992. Lect. (Psychiat.) Glas. Univ. Gartnavel Roy. Hosp. Prev: Clin. Asst. Community Psychiat. Scotl.

BEESLEY, Sharon Harriet Kent Oncology Unit, Maidstone Hospital, Hermitage Ln, Maidstone ME16 7QQ Tel: 01622 729000 Fax: 01622 225074; 25 Redleaf Road, Tunbridge Wells TN2 3UD — MB ChB 1989 Bristol; MRCP (UK) 1993. (Bristol) Sen. Regist. (Clin. Oncol.) St. Thos. Hosp. Lond. Prev: Regist. (Clin. Oncol.) St. Thos. Hosp Lond.; SHO (Radiother.) Roy. Marsden Hosp. Sutton; SHO (Med.) Torbay Hosp. Torquay.

BEESON, Alan Alfred, TD St Peters Hospital, Chertsey KT16 0PZ; Redwych, Wych Hill Way, Woking GU22 0AE Tel: 01483 764301 — MB BS 1956 Durh.; DPH 1962; FRCP Ed. 1984; MRCP (UK) 1972; T(M) 1991. (Durh.) Emerit. Cons. Phys. St Peter's Hosp. Chertsey. Socs: Airborne Med. Soc.

BEESON, Joan (retired) 28 Balmoral Crescent, Dronfield Woodhouse, Sheffield S18 8ZY — MB ChB 1951 Sheff.

BEESON, Marina Department of General Psychiatry, 19 Billing Road, Northampton NN1 Tel: 01604 259040; 2 Sharmans Close, Church St, Cogenhoe, Northampton NN7 1LN — Diplome Federal 1983 Geneva; MRCP (UK) 1993. SHO (Psychiat.) St. Crispin Hosp. N.ampton. Prev: Regist. (Paediat.) Ealing Dist. Gen. Hosp.; SHO (Psychiat.) St. Bernard's Hosp. S.all.

BEESTON, Keren Michelle Tynyberth, Llansilin, Oswestry SY10 7PY — MB ChB 1998 Leic.; MB ChB Leic 1998.

BEET, Peter Leslie Benefits Agency, DBU, Warbreck House, Blackpool FY2 0YE Tel: 01253 336 7785; Claughton, Marine Drive, Hest Bank, Lancaster LA2 6EB — MRCS Eng. LRCP Lond. 1961. (Leeds) Med. Off. Social Security Benefits Agency Cleveleys; Company Dir. (Railways). Socs: Lancaster Med. Bk. Club. Prev: Clin. Asst. (Dermat.) Barrow, Lancaster & Kendal Hosps.; SHO (Med.) Roy. Infirm. Lancaster; Ho. Phys. (Paediat. & Dermat.) St. Jas. Hosp. Leeds.

BEETHAM, Kenneth William, MC (retired) 48 Queens Road, Southport PR9 9HB — MB ChB Ed. 1941; DMRT Eng. 1947. Prev: Capt. R.A.M.C. 1942-6.

BEETHAM, Mr Michael Douglas Consulting Suite, Thornbury Hospital, 312 Fulwood Road, Sheffield S10 3BR; 26 Strand Court, Topsham, Exeter EX3 0AZ — MB BS Lond. 1966; MRCS Eng. LRCP Lond. 1966; BChD Leeds 1956, LDS 1956; FDS RCS Eng. 1962.

(Westm.) Hon. Cons. Oral & Maxillofacial Surg. Sheff. HA. Socs: Brit. Assn. Oral & Maxillofacial Surgs.Retd. Fell.; BMA.Retd. Mem. Prev: Sen. Regist. (Oral Surg.) W.m. Hosp. Lond. & Qu. Mary's Hosp. Roehampton; Regist. (Oral Surg.) S.W. Metrop. RHB; Ho. Phys. Qu. Mary's Hosp. Roehampton.

BEETLES, Christopher 104 Randolph Avenue, Maida Vale, London W9 1PQ Tel: 020 7286 7098 — MB BS 1970 Lond. (Univ. Coll. Hosp.)

BEETLES, Esmond Arnold (retired) 36 Avalon Road, Ealing, London W13 0BN Tel: 020 8998 1904 — MB BS Madras 1938; DMRD Eng. 1950.

BEETLES, Ursula Margaret Dept. of Radiology, Trafford General Hospital, Moorside Road, Daveyhulme, Manchester SK4 3PS; 28 Cherry Hols Avenue, Heaton Mersey, Stockport SK4 3PS — MB BS 1976 Lond.; FRCR 1985; DMRD 1981; DRCOG 1979. (Univ. Coll. Hosp.) Cons. Radiol., Trafford Gen. Hosp.

BEETON, Colin 30 Thornfield Road, Darlington DL3 9TQ Tel: 01325 461063 Email: colinbeeton@compuserve.com — MB ChB 1974 Sheff.; FFA RCS Eng. 1979. Cons. (Anaesth.), Darlington Memor. Hosp.

BEETON, John Robert Old Fletton Surgery, Rectory Gardens, Old Fletton, Peterborough PE2 8AY Tel: 01733 343137 Fax: 01733 894739; 22 Cherry Orton Road, Orton Waterville, Peterborough PE2 5EF Tel: 01733 232521 — MB BS 1963 Durh.

BEEVERS, Professor David Gareth City Hospital, Dudley Road, Birmingham B18 7QH Tel: 0121 554 3801 Fax: 0121 554 4083 — MB BS Lond. 1965; MD Lond. 1979; MRCS Eng. LRCP Lond. 1965; FRCP (Lond.) 1981; MRCP (UK) 1970. (Lond. Hosp.) Prof. Med. Univ. Birm. & Cons. Phys. City Hosp. Birm.; Edr.-in-Chief Jl. Human Hypertens. Socs: Past Pres. Brit. Hypertens. Soc. Prev: Clin. Scientist MRC Blood Pressure Unit W.. Infirm. Glas.; Regist. (Med.) Chelmsford Gp. Hosps.

BEEZHOLD, Julian Neil 61 Cambridge Street, Norwich NR2 2BA — MB ChB 1986 Stellenbosch.

BEG, Gwyneth Irene 20 Deanbrook Road, Netherthong, Holmfirth, Huddersfield HD9 3UF — MB ChB 1984 Leeds.

BEG, Mr Mirza Hasan Ali Victoria Hospital, Hayfield Road, Kirkcaldy KY2 5AH Tel: 01592 643355 Fax: 01592 265777; 17 Methven Road, Kirkcaldy KY1 1TS Tel: 01592 265777 Fax: 01592 265777 Email: hasanbeg@btinternet.com — MB BS Karachi 1966; FRCS Ed. 1974; FACS 1982; FICS 1982; DLO RCS Eng. 1972. Cons. Otolaryngol. Vict. Hosp. Kirkcaldy; Edr. Pakistan J. Otolaryngol. Socs: BMA; Chinese Med. Assn.; Scott. Otolaryngol. Soc. Prev: Cons. Joyce GreenHosp. Dartford Kent; Cons. Roy. Infirm. Edin.; Cons. K. V. Site Hosp. Karachi.

BEG, Mr Mirza Shehab Afzal 4 Grasmere Gardens, Redbridge, Ilford IG4 5LF — MB BS 1985 Karachi; FRCSI 1991; Dip. Plastic Surg. 1996. Specialist Regist. (Plastic Surg.) Wordsley Hosp. Stowbridge. Socs: BMA; MDU. Prev: Regist. (Plastic Surg.) Nottm. City Hosp.; Regist. (Plastic Surg.) N.. Gen. Hosp. Sheff.

BEGBIE, Margaret Mary (retired) 33 Greenbank Crescent, Edinburgh EH10 5TE Tel: 0131 447 4321 — MB ChB 1951 Bristol; MRCS Eng. LRCP Lond. 1951. Prev: Asst. Sch. Med. Off. Edin. Corpn. Ho. Surg. Bristol Matern. Hosp.

BEGENT, Professor Richard Henry John Department of Clinical Oncology, Royal Free and University college Medical School, London NW3 2PF Tel: 020 74726151 Fax: 020 7794 3341 Email: r.begent@ucl.ac.uk; 6 St. Albans Road, London NW5 1RD Tel: 020 7267 5118 Email: r.begent@ucl.ac.uk — MB BS 1967 Lond.; MD Lond. 1978; FRCP Lond. 1986; MRCP (UK) 1972; FRCP 1999. (St. Bart.) Ronald Raven Prof. Clin. Oncol. Roy. Free Hosp. Sch. Med. Lond. & Univ. Coll. Lond. Med. Sch. Prev: Reader (Med. Oncol.) Char. Cross Hosp. Lond.; Clin. Research Fell. Imperial Cancer Research Fund; Regist. (Med.) St. Geo. Hosp. Lond.

BEGG, Agnes Campbell (retired) 7 Malta Terrace, Edinburgh EH4 1HR Tel: 0131 332 1658 — MB ChB 1952 Ed.; DA Eng. 1955. Med. Off. Family Plann. Servs. Lothian Health Bd. Prev: Jun. Hosp. Med. Off. Anaesth. Edin. Centr. Hosp. Gp.

BEGG, Alan Gordon Townhead Surgery, Townhead, Murray Lane, Montrose DD10 8LE Tel: 01674 76161 Fax: 01674 673151 — MB ChB 1975 Aberd.; MRCGP 1979; DRCOG 1977; DCH RCP Glas. 1980; DA Eng. 1980.

BEGG, Alexander Drummond Penicuik Health Centre, 37 Imrie Place, Penicuik EH26 8LF Tel: 01968 672612 — MB ChB 1992 Ed.; DRCOG 1995; MRCGP 1996. (Edinburgh) Princip. (Gen. Pract.).

BEGG, Alister Brims Golspie Medical Practice, Golspie KW10 6TL Tel: 01408 633221/633444 Fax: 01408 633303; Fairways, Ferry Road, Golspie KW10 6ST — MB ChB 1983 Aberd. Prev: SHO (Gen. Med.) Caithness Gen. Hosp. Wick; SHO (Med. Paediat.) Roy. Aberd. Childr. Hosp.; SHO (O & G) Raigmore Hosp. Inverness.

BEGG, Ayaz Hayat Princess Royal Hospital, St Francis Wing, Lewes Road, Haywards Heath RH16 4EX Tel: 01444 441881; 59 Ashenground Road, Haywards Heath RH16 4PS — MB BCh 1980 Cairo; MRCPsych 1985. Cons. Psychiat. St. Francis Hosp. Haywards Heath W. Sussex.

BEGG, Christine Margaret Scalloway Surgery, Scolloway, Shetland ZE1 0UH Tel: 01595 880219; 10 Westerloch Brae., Lerwick ZE1 0GB Tel: 01595 692833 Email: christine.begg@virgin.net — MB ChB 1982 Aberd.; MSc Glas. 1989; MRCGP 1986; DRCOG 1984. Gen. Practioner. Prev: Research Fell. (Gen. Pract.) Univ. Glas.

BEGG, Colin James 4/R 5 University Avenue, Glasgow G12 8NN — MB ChB 1997 Glas.

BEGG, David Maldwyn Penicuik Health Centre, 37 Imrie Place, Penicuik EH26 8LF Tel: 01968 672612 Fax: 01968 671543; 12 Broomhill Road, Penicuik EH26 9EE — MB ChB 1974 Ed.; MRCGP 1984; DRCOG 1977. GP Audit Facilitator Lothian Clin. Audit Dept.

BEGG, Frank Macrae (retired) Burnsyde, 21 West End, Guisborough TS14 6NN Tel: 01287 633238 — MB ChB 1952 Ed. Prev: GP GuisBoro.

BEGG, Hugh Ballantyne South Warwickshire Hospital, Lakin Road, Warwick CV34 5BW Tel: 01926 495321 — MB BS 1961 Lond.; FRCOG 1979, M 1966, DObst 1963. (Middlx.) Cons. O & G S. Warks. Hosp. Prev: Cons. O & G Warneford Gen. Hosp. Leamington Spa.

BEGG, James Andrew, MBE Cathcart Practice, 8 Cathcart Street, Ayr KA7 1BJ Tel: 01292 264051 Fax: 01292 293803; 19A Ewenfield Road, Ayr KA7 2QF Tel: 01292 269195 — MB ChB 1966 Glas. Prev: Ho. Surg. W.. Infirm. Glas.; Ho. Phys. Dumfries & Galloway Roy. Infirm.; Ho. Off. (Obst.) Ayrsh. Centr. Hosp. Irvine.

BEGG, James Drummond X-Ray Department, Royal Victoria Hospital, Jedburgh Road, Dundee DD2 1SP; Tel: 01382 42300 Ext. 26238 — MB BS 1973 Newc.; FRCR 1979. Cons. Radiol. Roy. Vict. Hosp., Dundee; Hon. Sen. Lect. (Diag. Radiol.) Univ. Dundee. Prev: Lect. (Diag. Radiol.) Univ. Edin.; Hon. Sen. Regist. (Diag. Radiol.) Roy. Inf. Edin. & W. Gen. Hosp.; Edin.; Regist. (Diag. Radiol.) Bristol Roy. Infirm.

BEGG, James Grant (retired) 30 Kingsburgh Gardens, East Linton EH40 3BJ Tel: 01620 860944 — MB ChB Ed. 1954; DPath Eng. 1962; FRCPath 1976, M 1964. Prev: Cons. Path. Fife Area Laborat. Kirkcaldy.

BEGG, John Shankland (retired) Dornal, Kilbirnie KA25 7JU Tel: 01505 683220 — MB ChB 1958 Glas.

BEGG, Louise Newmains Health Centre, 17 Manse Rd, Newmains, Wishaw ML2 9AX Tel: 01325 488075; Downholme, Darlington DL2 2RB Tel: 01325 488075 Email: louise.begg@newmdins.lanpct.scot.nhs.uk, rssdoc1@aol.com — MB ChB 1991 Glas.; MRCGP 1998. (Glasgow) p/t GP Principle, Newmdins Health Centre, Wishaw; Locum Clin. Asst., Accord Hospice, Paisley. Prev: SHO (O & G) Hairmyers Hosp. E. Kilbride.

BEGG, Norman Thorburn Building 10, Stockley Park West, Uxbridge UB11 1BT Tel: 020 8900 3684 Fax: 020 8900 2937 Email: ntb1837@gsk.com; Wild Cherries, Doggetts Wood Lane, Chalfont St Giles HP8 4TJ — MB ChB Ed. 1976; MFPHM RCP (UK) 1987; DTM & H Lond. 1980. Hon. Sen. Lect. (Epidemiol.) Lond. Sch. Hyg. & Trop. Med. Prev: Director for vaccines, Smite Kline Beecham 2000-2001, Welwyn Garden City; Cons. Epidemiol. PHLS Communicable Dis. Surveillance Centre Lond. 1987-1999.

BEGG, Robert Struthers Picken (retired) Victoria Nursing Home, 31 Kenilworth Road, Leamington Spa CV32 6JG Tel: 01926 420688 — MB ChB 1929 Glas. Prev: Phys. & Med. Supt. EMS Wembley Hosp.

BEGG, Rosemary Anne (retired) Downsfield, Pilgrims Way, Detling, Maidstone ME14 3JY — MB ChB Ed. 1950; DPH Eng. 1958.

BEGG, Thomas Ballantyne, TD (retired) 6 Ballantrae, East Kilbride, Glasgow G74 4TZ Tel: 01355 248881 Fax: 01355 248886 — MB ChB (Commend.) Glas. 1950; FRCP Lond. 1974, M 1956; FRCP Glas. 1967, M 1962. Prev: Cons. Phys. Vict. Infirm. Glas.

BEGG, William Henry Burns Medical Centre, Greggswood Road, Tunbridge Wells TN2 3JG — MB BS 1949 Lond.; MRCS Eng. LRCP Lond. 1949; DObst RCOG 1951. (King's Coll. Hosp.) Hosp. Pract. (Orthop.) Kent & Sussex Hosp. Tunbridge Wells . Prev: Ho. Surg. (O & G Dept.) & Sen. Cas. Off. King's Coll. Hosp.; Capt. RAMC.

BEGGS, Mr Fredericke David Dept. Of Anaesthesia, Dewsbury & District Hospital, Halifax Rd, Dewsbury WF13 4HS Tel: 0115 969 1169, 01924 816038 Email: dbeggs@ncht.org.uk; 36 Torvill Drive, Wollaton, Nottingham NG8 2BU Tel: 0115 928 0384 — MB BS 1973 Lond.; FETCS 2000; BDS 1967; FRCS Eng. 1978; MRCS Eng. LRCP Lond. 1973; FDS RCPS Glas. 1974; LDS RCS Eng. 1967. (Char. Cross & Lond. Hosps.) Cons. Thoracic Surg. Nottm. City Hosp. Socs: Fell. Roy. Soc. Med.; Fell. Assn. Thoracic & Cardiovasc. Surg.; Europ. Societies of Thoracic Surg.s. Prev: Assoc. Specialist (Thoracic Surg.) Nottm. City Hosp. & Univ. Hosp.; Regist. (Thoracic Surg.) City Hosp. Nottm.; Regist. (Gen. Surg.) N.wick Pk. Hosp. & Middlx. Hosp. Lond.

BEGGS, Graeme Cochrane Millyard House, Durham Rd, Ushaw Moor, Durham DH7 7QH; 19 Hallgarth Street, Durham DH1 3AT — MB ChB 1980 Aberd.; MRCGP 1985.

BEGGS, Ian Department Clinical Radiology, Royal Infirmary, Lauriston Place, Edinburgh EH3 9YW Tel: 0131 536 2881 Fax: 0131 536 2920; 33 Mortonhall Road, Edinburgh EH9 2HN Tel: 0131 668 3135 — MB ChB 1972 Glas.; MB ChB (Cullen Medal & Sclare Prize) Glas. 1972; FRCR 1979; MRCGP 1976; DMRD Ed. 1978; DRCOG 1976. (Glas.) Cons. Radiol. Roy. Infirm. Edin.; P.ss Margt. Rose Orthop. Hosp. Edin.; BUPA Murrayfield Hosp. Edin. Socs: Brit. Soc. Skeletal Radiol.; Eur. Soc. Skeletal Radiol.; Internat. Skeletal Soc. Prev: Cons. Radiol. Guy's & Lewisham Hosp. Lond.

BEGGS, Janet Isabel (retired) 5 Mullyloughran Heights, Armagh BT61 9HP Tel: 01861 522794 — MB BCh BAO 1957 Belf.; DObst RCOG 1959; DCH Eng. 1961. Prev: Gen. Pract. Armagh.

BEGGS, Lilian Heather 1 Jubilee Road, Dromore BT25 1BE — MB BCh BAO 1989 Belf.; MRCP (UK) 1992; DLO RCS Eng. 1997; FRCS Ed. 1999. (Qu. Univ. Belf.)

BEGIC, Jasna 5 Church Mews, 17 Church Road, Poole BH14 8UF — LMSSA 1995 Lond.

BEGLEY, Elizabeth Anne St Giles Surgery, 40 St. Giles Road, London SE5 7RF Tel: 020 7252 5936 — MB BS 1980 Lond.; MRCGP 1984; DRCOG 1982. (Westm. Med. Sch.) Prev: SHO (Geriat. Med.) St. Thos. Hosp. Lond.; SHO (A & E) Qu. Mary's Hosp. Roehampton; SHO (O & G) Qu. Mary's Hosp. Roehampton.

BEGLEY, Joseph Patrick Department of Biochemistry, Poole Hospital, Longfleet Road, Poole BH15 2JB Tel: 01202 442152; 9 Clifton Road, Lower Parkstone, Poole BH14 9PW — MB BCh BAO 1983 Dub.; BA Dub. 1981, MB BCh BAO 1983; MRCPath 1990. Cons. Chem. Path. Poole & Roy. Bournemouth Hosps. Prev: Sen. Regist. (Chem. Path.) Bristol Roy. Infirm.; Regist. (Chem. Path.) Roy. Hallamshire Hosp. Sheff.

BEGLEY, Malcolm David Saffron Surgery, Berkley Road, Frome BA11 2EE Tel: 01373 451256 Fax: 01373 452986; Somerleaze House, Frome BA11 3NR Tel: 01373 463563 — MB BChir 1959 Camb.; MA, MB Camb. 1959, BChir 1958; MRCS Eng. LRCP Lond. 1958; MRCGP 1977; DObst RCOG 1960. (Camb. & St. Thos.) Med. Off. Vict. Hosp. Frome. Socs: Bath Clin. Soc. & BMA. Prev: Ho. Surg. St. Thos. Hosp. Lond.; Squadron Ldr. RAF Med. Br.

BEGLEY, Pauline Jane Avon HA, King Square House, King Square, Bristol BS2 8EE Tel: 01179 002616 Fax: 01179 002571; Penny Patch, Woodside, Woolaston, Lydney GL15 6PA Tel: 01594 529245 Fax: 01594 529300 — MB ChB Birm. 1960; FFCM 1982, M 1972; DPH Eng. 1969; DCH Eng. 1963; DObst RCOG 1962. Cons. Pub. Health Med. Avon, Bristol. Prev: Dir. Pub. Health Frenchay HA.

BEGUM, Farida 2 Blair Place, Kirkcaldy KY2 5SQ Tel: 01592 263166 — MB BS 1965 Dacca.

BEGUM, Hushnara 6 Langley Road, Small Heath, Birmingham B10 0TL — MB BS 1996 Lond.

BEGUM, Jahan Ara The Surgery, 10-12 Carnbrook Road, London SE3 8AE Tel: 020 8319 3303 Fax: 020 8319 3265 — MB BS 1963 Dacca; MB BS 1963 Dacca.

BEGUM, Mosammat Jarina The Surgery, 322 High Street, St. Mary Cray, Orpington BR5 4AR; 1 Mungo Park Way, Orpington BR5 4EE — MB BS 1972 Rajshahi. (Rajshahi)

BEGUM, Nurjahan 33 Pineridge Drive, Blakebrook, Kidderminster DY11 6BQ Tel: 01562 515007 — MB BS 1969 Dacca.

BEGUM, Shahzadi 7 Sanderstead Hill, Sanderstead, South Croydon CR2 0HB Tel: 020 8651 3654 — MB BS 1981 Dacca; MB BS Dacca 1956; DPM Lond. 1981. (Dacca Med. Coll.) Assoc. Specialist Portnalls Unit FarnBoro. Hosp. Orpington.

BEGUM, Suraiya 4 Halvis Grove, Manchester M16 0DX — MB BS 1975 Dacca; MB BS Dacca, Bangladesh 1975; MRCOG 1990.

BEGUM, Zameer 4 Brookvale Grove, Olton, Solihull B92 7JH — MB ChB 1993 Bristol.

BEH, Liang Kueh Room D68, Staff Residence, St James's University Hospital, Beckett St., Leeds LS9 7TF — MB BS 1985 New South Wales; MRCP (UK) 1993.

BEHAN, Charlotte Mary Harcourt 17 South Erskine Park, Bearsden, Glasgow G61 4NA — BChir 1992 Camb.

BEHAN, Peter Oliver (retired) 17 South Erskine Park, Bearsden, Glasgow G61 4NA Tel: 0141 942 5113 — MB ChB Leeds 1964; DSc NUI 1995; MD Leeds 1979; FRCPI 1983; FRCP Lond. 1979; FRCP Glas. 1978; MRCP (UK) 1971; FACP 1972. Prev: Demonst. (Path.) Univ. Camb.

BEHAN, Professor Wilhelmina Mary Harcourt Department of Pathology, Western Infirmary, Dumbarton Road, Glasgow G11 6NT Tel: 0141 211 2208 Fax: 0141 377 2494 Email: wmblq@clinmed.gla.ac.uk; 17 South Erskine Park, Bearsden, Glasgow G61 4NA — MB ChB 1962 Bristol; 1973 Anat. Path. (Amer.) BD Path; MD Bristol 1986; MRCP Glas. 1994; FRCPath 1983, M 1970; FRCP 1996 Glas. Prof. of Muscle Path. Univ. Glas.; Hon. Cons. W. Infirm. Glas. Socs: Pres., Meluin Ramsay Soc. Prev: Chief, Laborat. Servs. Brockton Veterans' Administ. Hosp., USA.

BEHARDIEN, John Yehia St Andrews Medical Centre, 30 Russell Street, Eccles, Manchester M30 0NU Tel: 0161 707 5500; 2A Broadoak Park Road, Morton, Eccles, Manchester M4 9LQ — MB BCh 1981 Wales; MRCGP 1985; DRCOG 1984.

BEHBEHANI, Ali Mahmoud 43 Elm Hall Drive, Liverpool L18 5HX — MB ChB 1997 Liverp.

BEHENNAH, Lynne Margaret Lee Mill Unit, Lee Mill, Ivybridge PL21 9HL Tel: 01752 314800 Fax: 01752 314804 Email: lynne.behennah@pcs.swest.nhs.uk — MB BS 1982 Lond.; MRCPsych 1987. Cons.Rehabil. Psychiat., Plymouth Primary Care Trust. Prev: Regist. Rotat. (Psychiat.) St. Geo. Hosp. Lond.

BEHENNAH, Marlene Ann The New Surgery, River Street, Mevagissey, St Austell PL26 6UE Tel: 01726 843701 Fax: 01726 842565; 53 Church Street, Mevagissey, St Austell PL26 6SR Tel: 01726 843652 — BM BCh 1968 Oxf.; MA, BM BCh Oxf. 1968; MRCP (UK) 1973; DObst RCOG 1973. (Univ. Coll. Hosp.) Hosp. Pract. (Rheum.) CIty Hosp. Truro. Prev: WHO Research Fell. Dept. Pharmacol. & Therap. Univ. Dundee; Regist. (Med.) Roy. Cornw. Hosp. (Treliske) Truro.

BEHESHTI, Badiullah 39 Stone Close, Dagenham RM8 3BT — MB BS 1972 Dacca; MB BS 1972 Dacca.

BEHESHTI, Rustom Broadstairs Health Centre, The Broadway, Broadstairs CT10 2AJ Tel: 01843 861565 — MB BS 1970 Karachi.

BEHN, Alan Richard Royal Surrey County Hospital, Egerton Road, Guildford GU2 7XX Tel: 01483 571122 Fax: 01483 406668; Mead House, Station Road, Bramley, Guildford GU5 0DP Tel: 01483 892700 — BM BCh 1972 Oxf.; MA Oxf. 1969; FRCP Lond. 1993; MRCP (UK) 1975. Cons. Rheum. Roy. Surrey Co. Hosp. Guildford. Socs: Brit. Soc. Rheum. (Mem. Of Counc.). Prev: Sen. Regist. St. Thos. Hosp. Lond. & St. Peter's Hosp. Chertsey.

BEHN, Alison Pall Mall Surgery, 178 Pall Mall, Leigh-on-Sea SS9 1RB Tel: 01702 478338 Fax: 01702 471294; 26 Vernon Road, Leigh-on-Sea SS9 2NG Tel: 01702 480321 — BM 1989 Soton.; MRCGP 1995; DRCOG 1992. (Soton.) GP Princip. Leigh on Sea. Prev: Trainee GP St. Albans Soton. VTS.

BEHR, Elijah Raphael 35E Winchester Road, London NW3 3NR — MB BS 1993 Lond.; MRCP 1996. (Cambridge) Specialist Regist. (Cardiol.), St Geo.'s Hosp., Lond.

BEHR, Gerhard (retired) Marsden House, Brierfield, Nelson BB9 5EY — MRCS Eng. LRCP Lond. 1937; FRCP Lond. 1972, M 1946; FRCPath 1963. Hon. Cons. Path., Burnley, Pendle & Rossendale Hosps. Prev: Ho. Surg. (Skin & VD) St. Bart. Hosp.

BEHR, Harold Leon The North London Centre for Group Therapy, 138 Bramley Road, Oakwood, London N14 4HU Tel: 020 8440 1451 Fax: 020 8449 3847 Email: nlcent@aol.com; 81 Gordon Road, Finchley, London N3 1ER Tel: 020 8346 8323 — MB BCh Witwatersrand 1963; FRCPsych 1990, M 1972; DPM Witwatersrand 1968. (Witwatersrand) Indep. Psychiat. & Psychother. N. Lond. Centre for Gp. Ther.; Mem. Inst. Gp. Anal. Socs: Assn. Family Ther.; Assn. Child Psychol. & Psychiat. Prev: Cons. Child Psychiat. Centr. Middlx. Hosp. Lond.; Sen. Regist. (Child Psychiat.) Univ. Coll. Hosp. Lond. & Roy. Free Hosp. Lond.; Regist. (Psychiat.) Maudsley Hosp. Lond.

BEHR, Susan Bernice Sawston Health Centre, Link Road, Sawston, Cambridge CB2 4LB Tel: 01223 832711 Fax: 01223 836096 — MB BS 1981 Lond.; BSc Lond. 1978, MB BS 1981; MRCP (UK) 1985; MRCPsych 1987; MRCGP 1989. Prev: Trainee GP Sawston VTS; Staff Rotat. (Psychiat.) Maudsley Hosp. Lond.

BEHRANA, A J Blackburn Street Health Centre, Blackburn Street, Radcliffe, Manchester M26 1WS.

BEHRAZNIA-BERELIAN, Akram Ashridge, 6 St Richards Drive, Aldwick, Bognor Regis PO21 3BH — MD 1964 Tehran; DO RCPSI 1979.

BEHRENS, Judith Department of Haematology, St Helier Hospital NHS Trust, Wrythe Lane, Carshalton SM5 1AA Tel: 020 8644 4343 Fax: 020 8641 6450; 9 Southway, Carshalton Beeches, Carshalton SM5 4HP Tel: 020 8642 4964 — MB ChB 1970 Manch.; FRCP Lond. 1994; MRCP (UK) 1976; FRCPath 1992, M 1980; DObst RCOG 1972. Cons. Haemat. St. Helier NHS Trust; Hon. Sen. Lect. St. Geo. Hosp. Med. Sch. Socs: Brit. Soc. Haematol.; Brit. Assn. Med. Managers; Sutton Med. Soc. Prev: Sen. Regist. (Haemat.) St. Geo. Hosp. Lond.; Regist. (Path.) Wythenshawe Hosp.

BEHRENS, Ronald Harry Travel Clinic, Hospital for Tropical Diseases, Mortimer Market, London WC1E 6AU Tel: 020 7388 9600 Fax: 020 7388 7645 Email: ron.berens@uclh.org; Email: ron.behrens@ntlworld.com — MRCS Eng. LRCP Lond. 1977; MB ChB Zambia 1976; MD Lond. 1992; FRCP Lond. 1996. Cons. Phys. Hosp. Trop. Dis. Lond.; Sen. Lect. Lond. Sch. Hyg. & Trop. Med. 1998. Socs: Fell. Roy. Soc. Trop. Med.; Internat. Soc. Travel Med. Prev: Lect. (Nutrit.) & Clin. Trop. Med. Lond. Sch. Hyg & Trop. Med.; Alice Cory Trav. Fell.; Regist. (Gastroenterol.) Addenbrooke's Hosp. Camb.

BEHRMAN, Robert George Alexander Lea Barn, Winter Hill, Cookham, Maidenhead SL6 9TW — MB BS 1971 Lond.; BSc (Hons.) Lond. 1968, MD 1980; MRCP (UK) 1974. (Guy's)

BEHRMAN, Susan Ann Prestige House, Station Road, Elstree, Borehamwood WD6 1DF — MB BS 1977 Lond.; MRCS Eng. LRCP Lond. 1975.

BEIG, Khalida 23 Nathan's Road, Wembley HA0 3SA Tel: 020 8904 1676 — MB BS 1967 Osmania; DMRT Eng. 1973. (Osmania) Clin. Asst. Blood Transfus. Centre Edgware.

BEIGHTON, Patricia Gillian Eden Court Medical Practice, 70 Tangmere Drive, Castle Vale, Birmingham B35 7QX Tel: 0121 747 2671 — MB ChB 1988 Birm. SHO E. Birm. Hosp. GP VTS. Prev: Ho. Off. (Med.) Good Hope Hosp. Sutton Coldfield; Ho. Off. (Surg.) Walsall Gen. Hosp.

BEIGHTON, Richard Colin Borders General Hospital, Melrose TD6 9BS; Motte Linn, Ettrick Valley, Selkirk TD7 5EY — MB ChB 1962 Manch.; FFA RCS Eng. 1973. Cons. Anaesth. Borders Gen Hosp. Melrose. Prev: Cons. Anaesth. Peel Hosp. Galashiels.

BEILBY, John Oliver Wright Oriel Lodge, Hook Heath Road, Woking GU22 0LA Tel: 01483 773900 — BM BCh 1952 Oxf.; MA Oxf. 1952, DM 1965, BM BCh 1952; FRCPath 1975, M 1964. Emerit. Univ. Reader Gyn. Path. Middlx. Hosp. Med. Sch. Lond.; Asst. Sec. Brit. Soc. Clin. Cytol. Socs: Path. Soc. Prev: Hon. Cons. Pathol. Middlx. Hosp.; SHO Ch.ill Hosp. Oxf.; Med. Off. Min. of Supply.

BEIRNE, Anthony Daniel 42 Wheatsheaf Close, Northolt UB5 6YW — MB BCh BAO 1989 NUI; MRPsych 1996. (Cork) S. Thames Regional Specialist Regist. Rotat. (Psychiat.).

BEIRNE, Damien Malachy Beirne, Yoong and Cummings, 115 Falls Road, Belfast BT12 6AA Tel: 028 9032 1009 Fax: 028 9023 8166 — MB BCh BAO 1957 Belf. (Belf.)

BEIRNE, John Ailbe Francis Altnagelvin area hospital, Londonderry BT47 6SB Tel: 02871 345171 Ext: 3153, 07890815672 Fax: 02871 Email: ailbebeirne@hotmail.com — MB BCh BAO 1973 Belf.; FRCP Lond. 1995; FRCP Ed. 1991; FRCP Glas. 1989; MRCP (UK) 1978; MRCGP 1977; DObst RCPI 1975. Cons. Phys. Geriat. Med. Unit Altnagelvin Area Hosp. Lond.derry. Socs: Brit. Geriat. Soc. & Ulster Med. Soc.; BMA (Chairm. N. Irel. Cons. & Specialists Comm.). Prev: Sen. Regist. Geriat. Med. Unit Ulster Hosp. Dundonald; Regist. Geriat. Med. Unit. Roy. Vict. Hosp. Belf.; Ho. Off. Mid-Ulster Hosp. Magherafelt.

BEIRNE, Patricia Kathleen 16 Donegall Park Avenue, Antrim Road, Belfast BT15 4EH — MB BCh BAO 1980 Belf.; DRCOG 1984; DCH RCPSI 1983.

BEIRNE, Paul Adrian 34 Corrina Park, Dunmurry Lane, Belfast BT17 0HA — BChir 1995 Camb.

BEIROUTI, Mr Zeidoon Adeeb Yousef 21 St Georges Crescent, Rhyl LL18 3NN — MB BCh 1980 Cairo; FRCS Ed. 1988; FCOphth 1989.

BEISLY, Norman Lawrence 14a Chapel Street, Newport PO30 1PY Tel: 01983 529646; Nodyhill, Beacon Alley, Godshill, Ventnor PO38 3JX Tel: 01983 840286 — MB BS 1954 Lond.; MRCS Eng. LRCP Lond. 1953; DObst RCOG 1956. (King's Coll. Hosp.) Mem. Inst. Orthop. Med. Socs: Brit. Assn. Manip. Med. Prev: Clin. Asst. Orthop. I.O.W. Hosp.

BEITVERDA, Younatan 16 The Grange, The Knoll, London W13 8JJ — MB BS 1993 Lond.

BEJEKAL, Mr Rajiv Atmaram 63 Dollis Park, Church End, Finchley, London N3 1HJ — MB BS 1986 Madras, India; FRCS Glas. 1993.

BEJON, Philip Andrew 8 Heldar Court, Kipling Estate, London SE1 3RH — MB BS 1997 Lond.

BEKENN, Peter John (retired) Fir Trees, Yaldhurst Lane, Lymington SO41 8HD Tel: 01590 672349 Fax: 01509 610996 Email: gekenn@woden.com — MB BS Lond. 1956; DObst RCOG 1958. Prev: Ho. Surg. (Obst.) & Ho. Phys. (Paediat.) St. Bart. Hosp. Lond.

BEKHIT, Mohammed Taher Mohammed Sayed Mohammed 30 Humberston Road, Nottingham NG8 2SZ — MB BCh 1976 Assiut; MRCOG 1992.

BEKHIT, Sawsan Mansour 57 Harley Street, London W1N 1DD Tel: 020 7636 4424 & resid. 081 422 7179 — MB BCh 1954 Cairo; FRCSI 1966; FRCS Ed. 1966; LMSSA Lond. 1965; FRCOG 1982, M 1967. Gyn. Humana Hosp. Wellington Lond. & Clementine Ch.ill Hosp. Harrow. Socs: Fell. Hunt. Soc.; Fell. Roy. Soc. Med.; BMA. Prev: Cons. Obst. Mother's Hosp., Lond.; Cons. Gyn. Metrop. Hosp., Lond.; Cons. Gyn & Obst., Watford Gen. Hosp.

BEKIR, Jinan Siddiq Medical Director, London Women's Clinic, 113 - 115 Harley St, London W1G 6AP Tel: 020 7487 5050 Fax: 020 7487 5850 Email: lwc@lwclinic.co.uk; Blue Hills, Esher Close, Esher KT10 9LL — MB ChB 1968 Baghdad; FRCS Ed. 1976; FRCOG 1994, M 1979. Med. Dir. Hallam Med. Centre Lond. Wom. Clinic Lond.; Cons. Cromwell Hosp. Lond. Socs: Brit. Fertil. Soc.; Brit. Menopausal Soc.; ESHRE.

BEL-ELIEZER, Eldad Jeshurun Hutterian Brethren, Robertsbridge TN32 5DR — MB BS 1992 Lond. (Char. Cross & Westm. Med. Sch. Lond.)

BELAS, Reginald John, TD, Col. late RAMC (retired) The Forge, 6 High St., Catterick Village, Richmond DL10 7LJ Tel: 01748 818388 Email: rex@belas.freeserve.co.uk — MB BS Durh. 1945; FRCPsych 1979, M 1971; DPM Eng. 1969. Prev: Cons. Psychiat. NE & NW Dist. Duchess of Kent Milit. Hosp. Catterick & Brit. Milit. Hosp., Hong Kong.

BELBECK, Jacqueline Stewert Rest Harrow, Green Dene, East Horsley, Leatherhead KT24 5RE — MB BS 1998 Lond.; MB BS Lond 1998.

BELBIN, Alan Hunter 8 Melbost Borve, Isle of Lewis HS2 0RR — MB ChB 1977 Glas.; FRCR 1985.

BELBIN, David John Escrick Surgery, Escrick, York YO19 6LE Tel: 01904 728243 — MB ChB 1965 Leeds; MRCGP 1976; DA Eng. 1968; DObst RCOG 1967.

BELCH, Professor Jill Jannette Freda Department of Medicine, Ninewells Hospital, Dundee DD1 9SY Tel: 01382 660111 Fax: 01382 632333 Email: j.j.f.belch@dundee.ac.uk; Annandale, 28 Highfield Road, Scone, Perth PH2 6RL Tel: 01738 551640 Fax: 01738 551640 — MB ChB 1976 Glas.; MD (Hons.) Glas. 1987; FRCP Ed. 1992; FRCP Glas. 1988, M 1979; FRCP Lond 1999. (Glasgow) Prof. Univ. Dundee Ninewells Hosp.; Chairm. ETRO WBC working party; Mem. Acute Serv. Review Comm.; Mem. MRC Med.

Advis. Bd. Socs: Brit. Soc. Rheum.; Brit. Soc. Thrombosis & Haemostasis; Chairm. Forum of Angiol. Prev: ARC Lect. Glas.

BELCHER, Glyn Schering AG, Mullerstrasse 170-178, Berlin 65, Germany Tel: 00 49 30 4682608; 116 Bosworth Road, Measham, Swadlincote, Derby DE74 2J — MB BChir 1980 Camb.; PhD Camb. 1978; MA Oxf. 1977; MFPM 1990. Head Cardiovasc. Clin. Research Schering AG, Germany. Prev: Head of Cardiovasc. Research Europ., Schering Health Care Ltd. Burgess Hill.

BELCHER, Helen Elizabeth 3 Prospect Row, Gillingham ME7 5AL — MB ChB 1986 Leeds; MRCP (UK) 1989.

BELCHER, Mr Henry James Crispin Rashleigh Department of Plastic Surgery, Queen Victoria Hospital, Holtye Road, East Grinstead RH19 3DZ Tel: 01342 410210 Fax: 01342 317907; Basing House, Cowden, Edenbridge TN8 7JU Tel: 01342 851088 Fax: 01342 851046 Email: belcher@pncl.co.uk — MB BS 1980 Lond.; MS Lond. 1990, MB BS 1980; FRCS (Plast Surg.) Eng. 1993; FRCS Eng. 1985. Cons. Plastic Surg. Qu. Vict. Hosp. E. Grinstead. Prev: Regist. (Plastic & Reconstruc. Surg.) W. Norwich Hosp.; Sen. Regist. (Plastic & Reconstruc. Surg.) E. Grinstead; Hand Fell. Derby Roy. Infirm.

BELCHER, Mr John Rashleigh (retired) 23 Hornton Court, Hornton St., London W8 7RT Tel: 020 7937 7006 — MB BS Lond. 1939; MS Lond. 1945; FRCS Eng. 1942; MRCS Eng. LRCP Lond. 1939. Cons. Thoracic Surg. Middlx. Hosp.; Surg. Lond. Chest Hosp. Prev: Resid. Asst. Surg. St. Thos. Hosp.

BELCHER, Nicholas George Jarmala, Hooe, Battle TN33 9EW Tel: 01424 892144 — MB BS 1978 Lond.; MD Lond. 1989; MRCP (UK) 1981. (Roy. Free)

BELCHER, Ormonde Philip Paul Rashleigh University of Glasgow, Department of Cardiac Surgery, The Royal Infirmary, 10 Alexandra Parade, Glasgow G31 2ER Tel: 0141 211 4336 Fax: 0141 552 0987 Email: pbelcher@clinmed.gla.ac.uk; Torwold, 23 Ledcameroch Crescent, Bearsden, Glasgow G61 4AD Tel: 0141 931 5408 — MB BS 1973 Lond.; MD Lond. 1993; FRCS Eng. 1978; MRCS Eng. LRCP Lond. 1973. Sen. Lect. (Cardiac Surg.) Univ. Glas.; Hon. Cons. (Cardiac Surg.) Roy. Infirm. Glas. Socs: Soc. Cardiothoracic Surgs. GB & Irel.; Cardiac Surg. Research Club.; Med. Res. Soc. Prev: Sen. Regist. Nat. Hosp. Dis. Heart & Chest; Research Fell. Char. Cross. & W.m. Med. Sch.; Locum Cons. (Cardiac Surg.) Freeman Hosp. Newc. u. Tyne.

BELCHER, Pamela Elizabeth 63 Highview Road, London W13 0HA — MB BS 1994 Lond.

BELCHER, Peter David The Surgery, Worsley Road, Immingham, Immingham DN40 1BE Tel: 01469 572058 Fax: 01469 573043 Email: drbel1019@aol.com; The Health Centre, Pelham Crescent, Keelby, Grimsby DN41 8EW Tel: 01469 572058 Fax: 01469 573043 — MB ChB 1968 Manch.; DPM Leeds 1972. Trainer (Gen. Pract.) VTS Grimsby; Med. Off. Lindsey Oil Refinery Killingholme. Prev: Regist. (Psychiat. & Electrophysiol.) Pinderfields Gen. Hosp.; Ho. Phys. (Gen. Med.) & Ho. Surg. (Gen. Surg. & Ophth.) Clayton Hosp. Wakefield.

BELCHETZ, Paul Ernest Department of Endocrinology, The General Infirmary at Leeds, Great George St., Leeds LS1 3EX Tel: 0113 292 3232 Fax: 0113 292 2431; Gate Cottage, Stammergate Lane, Wetherby LS22 4JB Tel: 01937 589439 Fax: 01937 589006 — MB BChir 1969 Camb.; MSc Lond. 1973; MD Camb. 1978 (Sir Lionel Whitby Medal) MA 1969; FRCP Lond. 1983, M 1970. (Camb. & St. Bart.) Cons. Phys. & Endocrinol. Leeds Gen. Infirm.; Hon. Sen. Lect. (Med.) Univ. Leeds. Socs: Assn. Phys.; Soc. Endcrinol.; Brit. Thyroid Assn. Prev: Sen. Lect. (Med.) Univ. Liverp. & Hon. Cons. Phys. Roy. Liverp. Hosp. & Walton Hosp Liverp.; Mem. Scientif. Staff MRC Clin. Research Centre Harrow; Wellcome Sen. Research Fell. (Clin. Sc.) & Cons. Phys. St. Bart. Hosp. Lond.

BELDA BILBAO, Luis Miguel 139 Cliff Gardens, Scunthorpe General Hospital, Scunthorpe DN15 7BL — LMS 1992 La Laguna.

***BELDERBOS, Rosemary** Peace Children's Iellre, Peace Prosrect, Watford Email: rb@doctors.org.uk — MB ChB 1995 Glas.; BSc (Hons.) Psychol. & Med. Sci. Lond. 1992; MRCP 1998.

BELDERBOS, Simon Michael The Spinney, 6 High Elms, Harpenden AL5 2JU — MB ChB 1995 Glas.

BELDERSON, Linda Robin Lane Medical Centre, Robin Lane, Pudsey LS28 7DE Tel: 0113 295 1444 Fax: 0113 295 1440; 11 The Grove, Shipley BD18 4LD Tel: 01274 590486 — MB ChB 1983 Leeds; MRCGP 1988; MPH Leeds. 1987; DRCOG 1987. (Leeds) Prev: Trainee GP Leeds VTS.

BELEJ, Jan (retired) Candelaria, 7 Spinney Close, St Leonards, Ringwood BH24 2RB — MD 1931 Lwow; DTM & H Liverp. 1948; DPH Eng. 1953. Prev: MOH Accra (Colon. Med. Serv.).

BELFIELD, Jane Charlotte 61 Tasker Road, Crookes, Sheffield S10 1UY — MB ChB 1998 Sheff.; MB ChB Sheff 1998.

BELFIELD, Peter Winston General Infirmary at Leeds, Great George St., Leeds LS1 3EX Tel: 0113 292 3464; Rosedene, 14 Shaftesbury Avenue, Leeds LS8 1DT — MB ChB 1979 Leeds; BSc (Hons.) (Pharmacol.) Leeds 1976; FRCP Lond. 1994; MRCP (UK) 1982. Med. Dir. (Med. & Surg. Servs.) & Cons. Phys. (Med. of Elderly) Leeds Gen. Infirm. Socs: Brit. Assn. Med. Managers; Brit. Geriat. Soc. Prev: Cons. Phys. (Med. of Elderly) Chapel Allerton Hosp. Leeds.

BELGER, Helen Sidonie Church View Medical Centre, Silksworth Terrace, Silksworth, Sunderland SR3 2AW Tel: 0191 521 1753 Fax: 0191 521 3884; 5 St. Bede's Terrace, Sunderland SR2 8HS — MB BS 1980 Lond.; MRCGP 1985.

BELHAG, Mohamed Alhadi Ali 45 Holly Drive, Acocks Green, Birmingham B27 7NF Tel: 0121 706 5375 Fax: 0121 706 5375 — MB BCh 1980 Al Fateh; MSc Lond. 1985; MB BCh Alfateh 1980. (Alfateh Univ. Tripoli/Libya) Clin. Assessm. Gen. Med. Stroke Unit Sandwell Gen. Hosp. W. Bromich. Prev: Research Regist. - Heartlands Hosp. Birm.; Hon. Research Fell. - Birm. Univ.

BELHAM, Mr Graham John W. Herts Hospitals Trust, Mount Vernon & Watford Hospital, Vicarage Rd, Watford WD18 Tel: 01923 217030; Bishops Wood Hospital, Northwood HA6 2JW Tel: 01923 844053 Fax: 01923 844053 Email: belham.ortho@pgen.net — MB BChir Camb. 1981; MA Camb. 1981, BA 1977; FRCS Eng. 1984. (Camb. & Westm.) Cons. Orthop. Surg. Mt. Vernon & Watford Hosps. Trust. Socs: Brit. Orthop. Assn.; Roy. Soc. Med. Prev: Sen. Regist. (Orthop.) W.m. & Univ. Coll. Hosps.; Regist. Whittington & Middlx. Hosps. Lond.; SHO Nottm. Univ. & Harlow Wood Hosps.

BELHAM, Mark Ronald Downing Maidstone Hospital, Maidstone ME17 9QQ; 6 Oakwood Court, Bolsover Road, Eastbourne BN20 7JF — MB ChB 1992 Liverp.; MRCP (UK) 1995. Research Regist. Maidstone Hosp. Prev: SHO Rotat. (Gen. Med.) E.bourne Dist. Hosp. & Countess of Chester Hosp.

BELING, Genevieve Esmie Angelique The Little Willows, Lambourne Rd, Chigwell IG7 6JP — MB BS 1996 Lond.

BELK, Doreen Sylvia Family Planning and Well Woman Services, Wakefield and Pontefract Community Health, Margaret St., Wakefield Tel: 01924 327585; 4 Station Cottages, Temple Hirst, Selby YO8 8QL — MB ChB 1970 Leeds; MFFP 1993. Sen. Community Med. Off. (Family Plann. & Well Wom. Servs.) Doncaster Wakefield & Pontefract Community Health NHS Trust.

BELK, Kathleen Mary (retired) 22 Holme Close, Woodborough, Nottingham NG14 6EX Tel: 0115 965 4301 — MB ChB 1960 Leeds. Prev: Assoc. GP N. Yorks.

BELK, William Jeremy College Lane Surgery, Barnsley Road, Ackworth, Pontefract WF7 7HZ Tel: 01977 611023 Fax: 01977 612146; 5 Hemley Avenue, Rawdon, Leeds LS19 6MZ — MB ChB 1970 Leeds; MRCGP 1974; DObst RCOG 1973. (Leeds)

BELL, Alan Richard Park Street Surgery, 77 Park Street, Wombwell, Barnsley S73 0HJ Tel: 01226 752161; 113 Barnsley Road, Wombwell, Barnsley S73 8JH Tel: 01226 757991 — MRCS Eng. LRCP Lond. 1983. Socs: BMA.

BELL, Alastair Ian Price and Partners, The Surgery, Park Road, Holbeach, Spalding PE12 7EE Tel: 01406 423288 Fax: 01406 426284 — MB BS 1981 Lond.

BELL, Alexander David 10 Ellorslie Drive, Stocksbridge, Sheffield S36 2BB — MB ChB 1978 Sheff. Prev: Regist. (Histopath.), Mt. Vernon Hosp. N.wood; Clin. Fell. (Path.) Ninewells Hosp. Dundee; Regist. (Paediat. Path.) Sheff. Childr. Hosp.

***BELL, Alison Margaret** 2/1 17 Melrose Gardens, North Kelvinside, Glasgow G20 6RB — MB ChB 1996 Glas.

BELL, Alistair Middle Quarter, Yieldshields, Carluke ML8 4QE — MB ChB 1979 Aberd.; MRCGP 1983; DRCOG 1983.

BELL, Amelia Roza 40 Mendip Road, Forest Park, Bracknell RG12 0XD Tel: 01344 487994 — MB BS 1985 Lond.; BA Oxf. 1982. Regist. (Med. Microbiol.) St. Bart. Hosp. Lond. Prev: SHO (Paediat.) Wexham Pk. Hosp. Slough.

BELL, Andrew David Lintonville Medical Group, Lintonville Terrace, Ashington NE63 9UT Tel: 01670 812772 Fax: 01670 521573 — MB BS 1987 Newc.; MRCGP 1992; DRCOG 1991. GP, Lintonville Med. Gp., Ashington; Clin. Asst. (ENT) Morpeth Cottage Hosp.

BELL, Andrew James Gavin HIV Department, Chelsea & Westminster Hospital, London SW10 Tel: 020 8746 8000 — MB ChB 1991 Bristol; BSc (Hons.) Bristol 1987; MRCP (UK) 1994. Regist. (HIV & Gen. Med.) Chelsea & W.m. Hosp. Lond. Socs: BMA; Collegiate Mem. RCP Lond. & Edin. Prev: SHO (Gen. Med. & Neurol.) Qu. Med. Centre Nottm.

BELL, Andrew John Department of Haematology, Poole Hospital NHS Trust, Poole BH15 2JB; Forge Cottage, North Gorley, Fordingbridge SP6 2PE Email: andrewjbell@btinternet.com — MB 1977 Camb.; BChir 1976; FRCP (UK); FRCPath. Cons. Haemat. Poole Hosp.

BELL, Angela Hilary Ulster Hospital, Dundonald, Belfast BT16 1RH Tel: 01232 484511 — MB BCh BAO 1979 Belf.; MD Belf. 1988; MRCP (UK) 1984; DCH RCPSI 1982. Cons. Paediat. Ulster Hosp. Belf. Prev: Research Fell. Roy. Vict. Hosp. Belf.

BELL, Angela Mary Routledge 47B Fountainhall Road, Edinburgh EH9 2LN — MB ChB 1998 Ed.; MB ChB Ed 1998.

BELL, Angus James 28 Brocklesby Road, Hunter Hill, Guisborough TS14 7PX — MB BS 1986 Newc.

BELL, Anita Jane 83 Christian Court, Lawrence Wharf, 303 Rotherhithe St., London SE16 1EY — BM BS 1993 Nottm.

BELL, Anne Elisabeth 33 Scott Lane, Riddlesden, Keighley BD20 5BU — MB BS 1986 Newc.

BELL, Anne Patricia Hyde Park Surgery, Woodsley Road, Leeds LS6 1SG Tel: 0113 244 4831 Fax: 0113 295 1220; 66 West End Lane, Horsforth, Leeds LS18 5EP Tel: 0113 258 3367 — MB ChB 1962 Leeds. (Leeds)

BELL, Anthony (retired) 6 Devonshire Terrace, London W2 3DN Tel: 020 7402 9851 Fax: 020 7402 3404 Email: junebell@enterprise.net — MB BS 1947 Lond.; MRCS Eng. LRCP Lond. 1947. Prev: Gen. Pract., Petworth.

BELL, Aubrey Leathem Musgrave Park Hospital, Rheumatology Unit, Stockman's Lane, Belfast BT9 7JB Tel: 01232 669501 Email: bell@gub.ac.uk; 119 Downshire Road, Holywood BT18 9LZ — MB BCh BAO 1976 Belf.; MD Belf. 1984; FRCP Lond. 1994; FRCP Ed. 1994. Cons. Rheum. Roy. Vict. & Belf. City & Musgrave Pk. Hosps.; Sen. Lect. (Rheum.) Qu.'s Univ. Belf. Socs: Brit. Soc. Rheum.; (Pres.) Irish Soc. Rheum.; Assn. Phys.

BELL, Barbara Ann 27 Church Road, Belfast BT8 7AL — MB BCh BAO 1980 Belf.; MRCP (UK) 1983.

BELL, Blyth Taylor Tower House Practice, St. Pauls Health Centre, High Street, Runcorn WA7 1AB Tel: 01928 567404; Mill Lane House Farm, Mill Lane, Kingsley, Warrington WA6 8HZ Tel: 01928 788950 — MB ChB 1981 Aberd.; MRCGP 1985; DRCOG 1984.

BELL, Professor Bryan Anthony Department of Neurosurgery, Atkinson Morley's Hospital, 31 Copse Hill, Wimbledon, London SW20 0NE Tel: 020 8946 7711 Fax: 020 8947 8389 Email: 100335.157@compuserve.com — MB BS 1973 Newc.; MB BS News. 1973; MD Newc. 1984; FRCS Eng. 1978; FRCS Ed. 1977. Prof. Neurosurg. Univ. Lond.

BELL, Carol Ann Greenhills Health Centre, Greenhills Square, East Kilbride, Glasgow G75 8TU Tel: 0141 234325; 10 Newcraigs Drive, Carmunnock, Glasgow G76 9AX Tel: 0141 644 2639 — MB ChB 1978 Glas.; DRCOG 1980. Clin. Med. Off. (Community Health) Lanarksh. NHS Healthcare Trust. Socs: BMA.

BELL, Caroline Dervorguilla (retired) 17A Northbrook Road, London N22 8YQ Tel: 020 8888 4155 — LRCP LRCS 1952 Ed.; LRCP LRCS Ed. LRFPS Glas. 1952; DCH Eng. 1956. Prev: Regist. (Paediat.) King Edwd. VII Hosp. Windsor.

BELL, Caroline Jane Psychopharmacology Unit, Medical School, Bristol University, Bristol BS8 1TD Tel: 0117 925 3066 — BM BCh 1987 Oxf.; MRCPsych 1992. Hon. Sen. Regist. Psychopharmacol. Unit Med. Sch. Bristol Univ.

BELL, Celia Helen 9 Sealand Avenue, Formby, Liverpool L37 2HP — MB ChB 1993 Sheff. SHO Rotat. (Psychiat.) Liverp. Train. Scheme.

BELL, Charles Richard William 15 Stoke Lane, Westbury-on-Trym, Bristol BS9 3DP — MB BS 1987 Lond.

BELL, Charlotte Louise 26 Palace Court, 250 Finchley Road, London NW3 6DN — MB BS 1996 Lond.

BELL, Christa Jane c/o 32 Port Lion, Llangwm, Haverfordwest SA62 4JT — MB BCh 1991 Wales.

BELL, Christine Frances Glan Clywd Hospital, Bodelwyddan, Rhyl LL18 5UJ Tel: 01745 583910; Ty Cerrig, Tremeirchion, St Asaph LL17 0UP Tel: 01745 582923 — MB ChB 1975 Liverp.; FRCA Eng. 1980. Cons. Anaesth. Glan Clwyd Hosp. Bodelwyddan. Prev: Sen. Regist. (Anaesth.) Univ. Dept. Roy. Liverp. Hosp.; Sen. Regist. (Anaesth.) Walton Hosp. Liverp.; Regist. (Anaesth.) Alder Hey Childr. Hosp.

BELL, Clare Hazel 91 Nottingham Road, Long Eaton, Nottingham NG10 2BU Tel: 0115 973 3262; Highlands, Mill Lane, Cossall, Nottingham NG16 2RY Tel: 0115 932 6101 — MB BS 1980 Lond.; DRCOG 1982.

BELL, Colin 77 Park Street, Wombwell, Barnsley S73 0HL Tel: 01226 752161 — LMSSA 1957 Lond.; BA, BM BCh Oxf. 1958. (Oxf. & Leeds)

BELL, Colin George Squirrels Oak, Greenbanks, Llandogo, Monmouth NP25 4TG Tel: 01594 530072 — MB BS 1970 Newc.; MRCGP 1975; DA Eng. 1972. Med. Adviser Schlumberger SEMA Med. Serv.s.

BELL, David Allt Na Gleann, 1 Tofts, Dalry KA24 5AS Tel: 01294 833804 — 1966 MB BS Durh.; 1979 MSc (Comm. Med.) Ed.; 1995 FRCP Ed.; 1972 MRCP (UK); 1989 MFPHM; 1988 MFCM; 1997 Cert. Drug Alc. Studies Stirling. p/t Cons. Pub. Health Med., Argyll & Clyde Health Bd., Paisley; Clnical Med. Off. - InDepend. Med. Adviser in Housing, Argyll & Bute Counc., Lochgilpead. Socs: BMA; ASME; BSInF. Prev: Cons. Pub. Health Med. Tayside HB; Sen. Regist. (Pub. Health Med.) Lothian HB; Sen. Regist. (Rheum.) N.. Gen. Hosp. Edin.

BELL, David University Department of medicine, Level 5, Box 157, Addenbrooke's HospitalHill's Road, Cambridge CB2 2QQ Email: db252@medschl.cam.ac.uk — MB BS 1989 Lond.; BSc 1986 Lond.; MRCP (UK) 1993; DTM & H Lond. 1993. MRC Research Fell., Univ. Dept Med., Addenbrooke's Hosp., Cambs.

BELL, David Alexander Top Flat Left, 23 Lauriston Gardens, Tollcross, Edinburgh EH3 9HH — MB ChB 1996 Ed.

BELL, David James Alexander Ormeau Road Practice, 485 Ormeau Road, Belfast BT7 3GR Tel: 028 9064 1506 — MB BCh BAO 1983; Cert. Family Plann. 1987; DCH RCP Lond. 1981; DRCOG 1987.

BELL, David John Scotstown Medical Centre, Cairnfold Road, Bridge of Don, Aberdeen AB22 8LD Tel: 01224 702149 Fax: 01224 706688; Bronie House, Udny Green, Ellon AB41 7RS Tel: 01651 842294 Email: dbell_udny@compuserve.com — MB ChB 1972 Aberd.; FRCGP 1993, M 1976. Chairm. A&N LHCC.

BELL, Mr David Millar (retired) The Drumlin, 49 Ballyworphy Road, Hillsborough BT26 6LR Tel: 02892 682539 — MB BCh BAO 1945 Belf.; MSc (Surg.) Illinois 1957; FRCS Ed. 1948; FRCS Eng. 1950; FRCSI 1979. Prev: Cons. Surg. Belf. City Hosp. & Musgrave Pk. Hosp. Belf.

BELL, David Railton Clydebank Health Centre, Kilbowie Road, Clydebank G81 2TQ Tel: 0141 531 6475 Fax: 0141 531 6478; 13 Morar Drive, Bearsden, Glasgow G61 2JZ — MB ChB 1981 Glas.; DRCOG 1984.

BELL, Mr David Robert 20 Rosewood Gardens, Kenton, Newcastle upon Tyne NE3 3DH Tel: 0191 285 1812 Email: d.r.bell@ncl.ac.uk — MB BS 1992 Newc.; FRCS (Eng.) 1997. (Newc. u. Tyne)

BELL, Mr David William 'Liddesdale', 38 Lefroy St., Coatbridge ML5 1NB — MB ChB 1963 (Commend.) Glas.; FRCS Ed. 1968. (Glas.) Cons. (Orthop. & Accid. Surg.) Monklands Dist. Gen. Hosp. Socs: BMA. Prev: Sen. Regist. (Orthop.) Glas. Roy. Infirm.; Ho. Off. (Surg.) Stobhill Gen. Hosp. Glas.; Demonst. Anat. Univ. Glas.

BELL, Deborah Louise Childrens Services Directorate, Shropshire's Community & Mental Health Services NHS Trust, Cross Houses, Shrewsbury SY5 6JN Tel: 01743 761242 Fax: 01743 761601; 12 East View, Waters Upton, Telford TF6 6NS — MB BS 1977 Lond.; BA Oxf. 1974; DCP Warwick 1985; DCH RCP Lond. 1981. (Middlx.) SCMO Childr. Servs. Shrops. HA. Socs: BACCH; RCPCH & BACDA.

BELL, Deirdre Patricia Old Forge Surgery, 14 Kilkeel Road, Annalong, Newry BT34 4TH Tel: 02843 768218 Fax: 02843 767262; 129 Head Road, Ballymartin, Newry BT34 4PX Tel:

013967 68218 Email: drdeirdrebell@aol.com — MB BCh BAO 1974 Belf.; PhD Belf. 1964, BSc (Hons.) 1959; MRCGP 1981. p/t Gen. Practitioner. Socs: Downe Med. Soc.; BMA. Prev: SHO (Paediat.) Belf. City Hosp. & (Orthop.) Roy. Vict. Hosp. Belf.; SHO (Surg.) Mater Infirm. Hosp. Belf.

BELL, Dennis Campbell Mid Glamorgan Health Authority, Department of Occupational Medicine, District Headquarters, Albert Road, Pontypridd CF37 1LA Tel: 01443 485122 Fax: 01443 485068 — MB BS 1965 Durh.; FFOM RCP Lond. 1991, M 1980. Cons. Occupat. Med. Mid. Glam. HA. Socs: Soc. Occupat. Med. Prev: Sen. Employm. Med. Adviser Med. Servs. HQ.; Works Med. Off. ICI Agricultural Div. Billingham; Med. Off. (NW Coast) BSC Workington.

BELL, Derek Tel: 01900 812653 Email: derek.bell@luht.scot.nhs.uk — MB ChB 1980 Ed.; BSc (Hons.) Ed. 1977, MD 1989; FRCP Ed. 1993; MRCP (UK) 1983. (Edinburgh) Clin. Direct. Acute Med. Roy. Infirm. Edin.; Cons. Phys. (Hon. Sen. Lect.). Socs: Pres. Soc. for Acute Med. (UK). Prev: Cons. Phys. (Thoracic Med. & Intens. Care) Centr. Middlx. Hosp. Lond.; Sen. Regist. (Thoracic Med.) Centr. Middlx. Hosp. Lond.; Lect. (Med.) Univ. Edin.

BELL, Derek John Dalgleish (retired) 17 Millfield Road, Whickham, Newcastle upon Tyne NE16 4QA Tel: 0191 488 7172 — MB BS 1943 Durh. Prev: Clin. Tutor in Family Med. Univ. Newc.

BELL, Diana Mary C/o Upper Cowden, Five Ashes, Mayfield TN20 6HN — MB ChB 1982 Sheff.; MB ChB (Hons.) Sheff. 1982.

BELL, Dion Ralph (retired) 2 Clifton, York YO30 6AE Tel: 01904 651296 — MB ChB 1954 Leeds; MB ChB (Hnrs.) Leeds 1954; FRCP Lond. 1974, M 1958; MFCM 1972; FFPHM 1989; DTM & H Liverp. 1959. Reader Trop. Med. Liverp. Sch. Trop. Med. Prev: WHO Cons. Egypt, Zimbabwe, Somalia, Cameroon.

BELL, Doreen Jane 93 Fitzjohn Avenue, Barnet EN5 2HR Tel: 020 8440 2211 — MB BCh BAO 1962 Belf.; MRCGP 1976; DObst RCOG 1965. (Belf.) Clin. Asst. Old Age Psychiat. Roy. Free Hosp. Lond. Prev: GP Manch.; Resid. Ho. Surg. Roy. Vict. Hosp. Belf. & Roy. Matern. Hosp. Belf.

BELL, Douglas Thomas Samuel Heysgan Health Centre, Middleton Way, Heysham, Morecambe LA3 2LL Tel: 01524 853851 Fax: 01524 855688; 261 Heysham Road, Morecambe LA3 1PY Tel: 01524 853851 — MB BCh BAO 1971 Dub. (TC Dub.)

BELL, Edgar Frederick Herbert (retired) Wheatcroft Rose, 264 Filey Road, Scarborough YO11 3AQ — MB BS 1924 Durh. Prev: Sch. Oculist Durh. Co. Educat. Comm.

BELL, Eileen Mary (retired) 9 Maen Gwyn, Abergele LL22 7BZ — MB BS 1964 Lond.; BSc Leeds 1952; LMSSA Lond. 1963; MRCPsych 1972; DPM Eng. 1968. Prev: Cons. Psychiat. Ashworth Hosp. Maghull.

BELL, Elizabeth Ursula (retired) Spring Wood, 16 High Hamsterley Road, Hamsterley Mill, Rowlands Gill NE39 1HD Tel: 01207 542270 — MB BS Durh. 1947.

***BELL, Emma** 6 Yevele Way, Hornchurch RM11 3NB Tel: 01708 470669 — MB ChB 1996 Manch.

BELL, Eric Oriel (retired) 11 Hady Lane, Chesterfield S41 0DJ — MB ChB 1932 Ed.

BELL, Ewan 61 Earlbank Avenue, Glasgow G14 9HA — MB ChB 1990 Glas. Specialist Regist. Clin. Biochem. Glas. Roy. Infirm. Prev: SHO (Gen. Med. & Diabetes) Gartnavel Gen. Hosp. Glas.; SHO (Gen. Med.) StoneHo. Hosp. Lanarksh.; Clin. Research Fell. (Diabetes) Glas.

BELL, Fiona Jane Oving Lodge, Church Lane, Oving, Chichester PO20 6DG — BM 1985 Soton.

BELL, Francis George 14 Priory Park, Bradford-on-Avon BA15 1QU; Sheffield Childrens Hospital, Western Bank, Sheffield S10 2TH Tel: 0114 271 7000 Email: f.bell@sheffield.ac.uk — BM 1985 Soton.; MRCP (UK) 1990; DCH RCP Lond. 1989.

BELL, Gail Sybil 8 Cheyne Close, Gerrards Cross SL9 7LG — MB ChB 1979 Birm.; MRCGP 1983; DRCOG. Research Assoc. Nat. Soc. for Epilepsy Chalfont St Peter Bucks. (p/t).

BELL, Gary Thomas, OStJ Mount Vernon Hospital, Rickmansworth Road, Northwood HA6 2RN Tel: 01923 844177; Hall Place, Beaconsfield HP9 1NB Tel: 01494 674700 Fax: 01494 676710 — MB BS 1980 Queensland; BA Queensland 1974; MRCPsych 1985; FRCPsych 2000. Cons. Psychiat. Mt. Vernon Centre for Cancer Treatm. Middlx.; Psychiat. Adviser, St. John Ambul. Berks.; Examr. Jt. Examing Bd. & Roy. Coll. of Psychiat.; Vis. Cons. Psychiat. Thames Valley Nuffield Hosp. Wexham Cardinal Clinic Windsor & Priory Hosp. Woking. Socs: Liveryman Worshipful Soc. Apoth. 1992; Ct. of Asst.s 2001. Prev: Cons. Psychiat. Roy. Nat. Orthop. Hosp.; Sen. Lect. (Psychiat.) Med. Coll. St. Bart. Hosp. Lond.; Lect. (Psychiat.) Univ. Coll. & Middlx. Sch. Med. Lond.

BELL, Gaynor Susan Alpine View, Stone Read, Hill Chorlton, Newcastle ST5 5DR — MB BCh 1980 Wales.

BELL, Professor Geoffrey Duncan Endoscopy Unit, Sunderland Royal Hospital, Kayll Road, Sunderland SR4 7TP Tel: 0191 565 6256 Fax: 0191 569 9204; The Grange, Chilton Moor, Houghton-le-Spring DH4 6QB Tel: 0191 385 5332 Email: duncan_bell@compuserve.com — MB BS (Hons. Med. & Therap.) Lond. 1968; MSc (Gen. Biochem.) Lond. 1973, MD 1976; FRCP Lond. 1983; MRCP (UK) 1970; MRCS Eng. LRCP Lond. 1968; FRCP Ed 1998. (St. Bart.) Prof. Gastroenterol. Cons. Phys. Sunderland Roy. Hosp.; Vis. Prof. Sunderland Univ. Socs: Brit. Pharm. Soc.; Brit. Soc. Gastroenterol. Prev: Cons. Phys. & Gastroenterol. Ipswich Hosp.; Hon. Cons. & Sen. Lect. Univ. Dept. Therap. City Hosp. Nottm.; Hon. Sen. Regist. (Gastroenterol.) St. Bart. Hosp. Lond.

BELL, Geoffrey John Leigh View Medical Centre, Bradford Road, Tingley, Wakefield WF3 1RQ Tel: 0113 253 7629 Fax: 0113 238 1286 — MB ChB 1983 Leeds.

BELL, George Alexander (retired) 10 Heaton Grove, Bradford BD9 4DZ Tel: 01274 543903 — LRCP LRCS 1938 Ed.; LRCP LRCS Ed. LRFPS Glas. 1938; MFCM 1972. Prev: Med. Off. (Environm. Health) Bradford Boro. & Craven Local Dist.

BELL, George Armour, OBE (retired) 16 Imlach Place, Parkside Gardens, Motherwell ML1 3FD Tel: 01698 260667 — MB ChB Glas. 1942; BSc Glas. 1939. JP. Prev: Chairm. Monklands & Bellshill Hosp. NHS Trust.

BELL, Gillian Suzanne 25 Irish Hill Road, Ballyclare BT39 9NQ — MB ChB 1990 Ed.

BELL, Gordon McKenzie Link 6C, Royal Liverpool University Hospital, Prescot St., Liverpool L7 8XP Tel: 0151 706 3429 Fax: 0151 706 5841; 22 Broadmead, Heswall, Wirral CH60 1XD — MB ChB 1976 Ed.; FRCP Lond. 1993; FRCP Ed. 1992; MRCP (UK) 1979. (Edinburgh) Cons. Neurol. & Phys. Roy. Liverp. Univ. Hosp.; Lect. (Med.) Univ. Liverp. Socs: Renal Assn.; Eur. Renal Assn.; Internat. Soc. Nephrol. Prev: Lect. (Med.) Univ. Edin.; Asst. Prof. (Med.) Cornell Univ. Med. Coll. New York.

BELL, Mr Graham 11 Dalziel Drive, Glasgow G41 4JA Tel: 0141 427 0233 Fax: 0141 427 3096 — ChM Glas. 1971, MB ChB 1960; FRCS Glas. 1964. (Glas.) Cons. Surg. Inverclyde Roy. Hosp. Greenock. Socs: BMA & Clin. Research Soc.; Brit. Soc. Surg. Oncol.; Assn. Surg. Prev: Lect. in Surg. Univ. Glas., Glas. Roy. Infirm. MRC Scientif. Asst.; Dept. Surg. Glas. Roy. Infirm.; McIntyre Research Schol. Glas. Roy. Infirm.

BELL, Graham Thomas Department of Anaesthetics, Yorkhill NHS Trust, Yorkhill, Glasgow G3 8SJ Fax: 01276 675660; 16 Belford Avenue, Edinburgh EH4 3EJ Fax: 0131 332 3478 — MB ChB 1989 Aberd.; FRCA 1994. (Aberd.) Cons. Anaesth. Prev: Regist. (Anaesth.) MoD Camb. Milit. Hosp. Aldershot; Regist. (PICU) New Childr.'s Hosp. Sydney; Specialist Regist. (Anaesth.).

BELL, Harold Hervey Geoffrey (retired) Shortlands, 34 Cimla Road, Neath SA11 3TL Tel: 01639 636032 — MRCS Eng. LRCP Lond. 1950; MA Camb. 1981. Prev: SHO (Obst.) Co. Hosp. Panteg.

BELL, Harry Long Marston Manor, York YO26 7LS Tel: 01904 83417; Gale Cottage, Thorganby, York YO19 6DQ Tel: 01904 448905 — MB BS 1968 Newc.; MRCGP 1976.

BELL, Hazel Kathleen Dept of Dermatology, Royal Liverpool Hospital, Prescot St, Liverpool L7 8XP Tel: 0151 706 3478 — MB ChB 1982 Birm.; MRCP (UK) 1995; MRCGP 1987; DCCH RCP Ed. 1988; DRCOG 1985. (Birm.) p/t Specialist Regist. (Dermat.) Roy. Liverp. Univ. Hosp.

BELL, Helen Johnson (retired) 30 Carlton Gardens, Stanwix, Carlisle CA3 9NR Tel: 01228 24663 — MB BS Durh. 1961. Prev: Clin. Asst. Garlands Hosp. Carlisle.

BELL, Helen Rita 15 Heddon Banks, Heddon on the Wall, Newcastle upon Tyne NE15 0BU — BM BS 1985 Nottm.; MRCGP 1991; DRCOG 1989. Prev: GP Sheff.

BELL, Henry Edmund (retired) Benard, 44 West Moulin Road, Pitlochry PH16 5EQ — MB BCh BAO 1945 NUI; FFA RCSI 1961; DA RCPSI 1948. Prev: Cons. Anaesth. Sunderland HA & Regional Cardiothoracic Surg. Serv.

BELL, Henry James Taylor Layton Medical Centre, 200 Kingscote Drive, Blackpool FY3 7EN Tel: 01253 392403 Fax: 01253 304597 — MB ChB 1977 Manch.; BSc St. And. 1974. Prev: Sen. Med. Off. DHSS.; GP Lancs.; SHO Ulster Hosp. Belf.

BELL, Heward Ruskins, Horsham Road, Bramley, Guildford GU5 0AN Tel: 01483 893458 — MRCS Eng. LRCP Lond. 1927; MA Camb., MB BCh 1929; MRCP Lond. 1929. (Camb. & St. Thos.) Emerit. Phys. Guildford & Godalming Gp. Hosps. Prev: Phys. Roy. Surrey Co. Hosp.; Ho. Surg. W. Lond. Hosp.; Clin. Asst. Electrocardiog. Dept. St. Thos. Hosp.

BELL, Ian Frederick, Wing Cdr. RAF Med. Br. 13 Spurgeons Close, Teversham, Cambridge CB1 5AB Fax: 01223 292650 — MB ChB 1976 Bristol; MRCGP 1989; DAvMed FOM RCP Lond. 1995; DFFP 1980. Assoc. in Postgrad. Gen. Prac. Educat. Dept. Gen. Pract. Educat. RAF Inst. Health, Halton. Prev: GP Gt. Baddow.

BELL, Ian Stuart Lee on Solent Health Centre, Manor Way, Lee-on-the-Solent PO13 9JG Tel: 023 9255 0220 Email: drianbell@hotmail.com — BM BS 1987 Nottm.; BMedSci (Hons.) Nottm. 1985; DRCOG 1990. Princip. Police Surg. Hants. Constab. Prev: Trainee GP N.ants. VTS; Ho. Phys. Univ. Hosp. Nottm.; Ho. Surg. N. Staffs. Roy. Infirm.

BELL, Jacquelyn Helene 12 Seacliff Road, Old Glenarm Road, Larne BT40 1TG — MB ChB 1996 Dundee. (Univ. of Dundee)

BELL, James Allen Aghalee Dispensary, 8A Lurgan Road, Aghalee, Craigavon BT67 0DY — MB BCh BAO 1974 Belf.; MRCGP 1979; DObst RCOG 1976. Med. Pract. Aghalee Lurgan.

BELL, Mr James Crawford 70 Strangford Road, Downpatrick BT30 6SN — MB BCh BAO 1965 Belf.; FRCS Ed. 1970. Cons. Surg. Downe Hosp. Downpatrick.

BELL, James Douglas (retired) 4 Wester Coates Place, Edinburgh EH12 5YG Tel: 0131 346 1992 Email: belldouglas@talk21.com — MB ChB Ed. 1948; FRCP Ed. 1982, M 1980; FFOM RCP Lond. 1984, MFOM 1979; DIH Soc. Apoth. Lond. 1971. Prev: Former Sen. Employm. Med. Adviser (Scotl.) EMAS (Retd.).

BELL, James Francis Percy (retired) 34 Princess Mary Court, Jesmond, Newcastle upon Tyne NE2 3BG — MB BS 1948 Durh.; DObst RCOG 1951. Prev: Ho. Surg. Orthop. Dept. Roy. Vict. Infirm. Newc. & Dilston Hall.

BELL, James Graham Nut Trees, 4 Brook Farm Road, Cobham KT11 3AX Tel: 01932 867655 Fax: 01932 588867 Email: grahambell3000@aol.com — MB ChB 1974; MSc Lond. 1983; FFOM 1994; FRCP 1998; DIH 1982; DA 1977. (Glasgow) Indep. Occupat.al Phys. Prev: Chief Med. Adviser, Esso UK PLC.

BELL, James Patrick 71 Sydney Grove, Wallsend NE28 9HE — MB ChB 1993 Leeds. GP Regist. N.umbria VTS. Prev: SHO (Palliat. Med.) Newc.Med. Centre; SHO Haemat./Oncol. S. Cleveland Hosp.; SHO (Gen. Med.) N. Tyneside Gen. Hosp.

BELL, Mr James Raymond, TD South Cleveland Hospital, Marton Road, Middlesbrough TS4 3BW Tel: 01642 850850; Hill View, Tame Bridge, Stokesley, Middlesbrough TS9 5LQ Tel: 01642 710346 — MB ChB 1962 Ed.; FRCS Ed. 1968. Cons. Surg. S. Cleveland Hosp. Middlesbrough. Socs: N. Eng. Surg. Soc.; Assn. Endoscopic Surgs. Prev: Sen. Regist. (Surg.) Tayside HB; Regist. (Surg.) Roy. Infirm. Glas.; SHO (Surg.) Roy. Infirm. Edin.

BELL, James Robert George Department of Radiology, Chelsea and Westminster Hospital, 360 Fulham Road, London SW10 9NH Tel: 020 8746 8570 Fax: 020 8746 8588 Email: jamesrgbell@yahoo.com; 69 Settrington Road, Fulham, London SW6 3BA Tel: 020 7736 2695 — MB BS 1993 Lond.; BSc Basic Med. Scs. Lond. 1990; MRCP 1996. (Charing Cross and Westminster) Specialist Regist. (Radiol.) Chelsea & W.minster Hosp. Lond. Socs: BMA; Assoc. Mem. Roy. Coll. Radiol. Prev: SHO (Rheum.) W. Middlx. Hosp. Lond.; SHO (Renal) Char. Cross Hosp.

BELL, Jane Helen Thie Veg, New Road, Bamford, Hope Valley S33 0AD Tel: 01433 650826 — BM BS 1985 Nottm.; BMedSci Nottm. 1983, BM BS 1985; FCAnaesth 1990. Cons. Anaesth. N.ern Gen. Hosp. Sheff. Prev: Post-Fell.sh. Research Regist. (Anaesth.) Sheff.; Regist. (Anaesth.) Sheff. HA; SHO (Anaesth.) Trent RHA.

BELL, Jean Margery (retired) The Cottage, Otterburn Hall, Otterburn, Newcastle upon Tyne NE19 1HE Tel: 01830 520201 — MB BS 1934 Lond.; MD Lond. 1938; MRCS Eng. LRCP Lond. 1934. Prev: Clin. Pathol. Babies' Hosp. Newc.

BELL, Jeanne Elisabeth Neuropathology Laboratory, Western General Hospital, Crewe Road, Edinburgh EH4 2XU Tel: 0131 537 1955 Fax: 0131 537 1013 Email: jeanne.bell@ed.ac.uk; 29 Starbank Road, Edinburgh EH5 3BY — MB BS Durh. 1966; BSc Newc. 1963, MD 1972; FRCPath 1995, M 1983. Reader (Path.) & Hon. Cons. Neuropath. Univ. Edin. Socs: FRSE.

BELL, Jennifer Doreen Holywood Arches Health Centre, Westminster Avenue, Belfast BT4 1NS Tel: 028 9056 3354 Fax: 028 9065 3846 — MB BCh BAO 1974 Belf.

BELL, Mr John Andrew Kent & Sussex Hospital, Mount Ephraim, Tunbridge Wells TN4 8AT Tel: 01892 526111 Fax: 01892 528381 — MB BCh 1979 Wales; MD Wales 1986; FRCS Ed. 1987; FRCOphth 1989. (Welsh National School of Medicine) Cons. Ophth. Kent & Sussex Hosp. Tunbridge Wells. Socs: RSM. Prev: Sen. Regist. (Ophth.) King's Coll., Moorfields, Guy's & St. Thos. Hosps. Lond. & Maidstone Eye Hosp.; Regist. (Ophth.) Newc. Gen. Hosp.; Med. Off. Mobil Oil, Madagascar & Brit. Antarctic Survey.

BELL, John Arthur Wallingford Lodge, Streatley, Reading RG8 9LA Tel: 01734 872762 — MB BChir 1967 Camb.; FRCP Lond. 1985. (St. Thos.) Cons. Phys. Battle & Roy. Berks. Hosps. Reading. Prev: Sen. Med. Regist. St. Thos. Hosp. Lond.; Regist. IC Unit St. Thos. Hosp. Lond.; Cardiac Ho. Phys. Brompton Hosp. Lond.

BELL, John Charles George 7 Meadow Grove, Verwood BH31 6XL — BM 1996 Soton.

BELL, John David Leslie, Capt. RAMC (retired) Merryweathers, Dancers End, Tring HP23 6JY Tel: 01442 823244 Fax: 01442 823244 — MB BS 1956 Lond.; MRCS Eng. LRCP Lond. 1956; DObst RCOG 1958. Prev: Gyn. Ho. Surg. & Obst. Off. St. Mary's Hosp. Lond.

BELL, John Harold Field House, Clee St Margaret, Craven Arms SY7 9DT Tel: 0158 475242 — MB ChB 1957 Birm.; DObst RCOG 1961. Clin. Asst. (Ophth.) Good Hope Hosp. Sutton Coldfield. Prev: Ho. Surg. Birm. Matern. Hosp. & Qu. Eliz. Hosp. Birm.; Ho. Phys. Gen. Hosp. Birm.

BELL, John Irving Riverholme, Thames St., Wallingford OX10 0HD — BM BCh 1979 Oxf.

BELL, John Keith 6 Highfields, Keswick Gardens, Bookham, Leatherhead KT22 9XA Tel: 01372 57056 — MB BS 1968 Lond.; MRCS Eng. LRCP Lond. 1967; FFA RCS Eng. 1976. (Guy's) Cons. Anaesth. Mid Surrey DHA. Socs: Assn. Anaesth. Gt. Brit. & Irel.; Intractable Pain Soc. Prev: Sen. Regist. W.m. Hosp. Lond.; Fell. Anaesth. Virginia Mason Clinic Seattle, USA; Ho. Phys. & Res. Anaesth. Guy's Hosp. Lond.

BELL, John Malcolm Glamis Medical Practice, Glamis Centre, Glenrothes KY7 4RH Tel: 01592 771177 Fax: 01592 631208 — MB ChB 1972 Ed.; DRCOG 1977.

BELL, John Malcolm (retired) 1 Tukalo Drive, Strathaven ML10 6UX — MB ChB Glas. 1956; FRCR 1975; FFR 1972; DMRD Eng. 1969.

BELL, John Millar Holywood Arches Health Centre, Westminster Avenue, Belfast BT4 1NS Tel: 028 9056 3354 Fax: 028 9065 3846 — MB BCh BAO 1974 Belf.; MRCGP 1978; DRCOG 1977.

BELL, John Richard Edlesborough Surgery, 11 Cow Lane, Edlesborough, Dunstable LU6 2HT Tel: 01525 221630; Hurdles, Spring Road, Harpenden AL5 3PP — MB BS 1977 Lond.; MRCGP 1986; DA (UK) 1982; DRCOG 1980; DCH RCP Lond. 1980.

BELL, John Richard The Health Centre, 68 Pipeland Road, St Andrews KY16 8JZ Tel: 01334 473441 Fax: 01334 466508; Thornbank, Blebo Craigs, Cupar KY15 5UQ Tel: 01334 850770 — MB ChB 1967 St. And. (St. And.) Prev: Regist. (Paediat.) Ninewells Hosp. Dundee; Govt. Med. Off. Botswana.

BELL, John William 18 Grove Road, Basingstoke RG21 3BD — MB BS 1968 Newc.; BSc (1st cl. Hons.) Durham. 1965. Prev: Dir. (Clin. Research) Boehringer Ingelheim Ltd. Bracknell; Ho. Off. Roy. Vict. Infirm. Newc. upon Tyne.

BELL, Jonathan Martin Musgrove Park Branch, X-Ray Department, Taunton and Somerset Hospital, Taunton TA1 5DA — MB ChB 1978 Bristol; MRCP (UK) 1981; FRCR 1985. Cons. Radiol. MusGr. Pk. Hosp. Taunton. Socs: BMA; Brit. Inst. of Radiol.; Brit. Soc. of Interven.al Radiols. Prev: Sen. Regist. (Radiodiagn.) Bristol Roy. Infirm.

BELL, Jonathan Simon Peter 4 Worcester Road, Mustow Green, Kidderminster DY10 4LA — MB BS 1987 Lond.

BELL, Josephine Mary Kings Park Surgery, 274 Kings Park Avenue, Glasgow G44 4JE Tel: 0141 632 1824 Fax: 0141 632

0461; 16 St Brides Road, Newlands, Glasgow G43 2DU — MB ChB 1974 Glas.; MRCGP 1978. GP Glas.

BELL, Judith Anne The Moor House, Wood Lane, Uttoxeter ST14 8JR — BM 1982 Soton.; BSc Bristol 1974.

BELL, Judith Margaret The Old Brewery, Mere, Warminster BA12 6DY — MB BS 1966 Lond.; MRCS Eng. LRCP Lond. 1966; DCH Eng. 1969.

BELL, Julia Katherine 1 Waulkmill Drive, Penicuik EH26 8LA — MB ChB 1998 Glas.; MB ChB Glas 1998.

BELL, Julie-Anne 7 Cray Valley Road, Orpington BR5 2EY — MB BS 1993 Lond.

BELL, Julien Peter Grove Medical Centre, 6 Uplands Terrace, Uplands, Swansea SA2 0GU Tel: 01792 643000 Fax: 01792 472800 — MB BCh 1989 Wales.

BELL, June Drusilla (retired) 24 Leadervale Drive, Edinburgh EH16 6PA — MB BS 1949 Lond.; PhD Camb. 1956, MA 1950. Prev: Clin. Asst. Roy. Edin. Psychiat. Hosp.

BELL, Karen 20 Suffolk Road, Edinburgh EH16 5NJ — MB ChB 1979 Glas.; DRCOG 1984. Assoc. Specialist Ninewells Hosp. Dundee.

BELL, Mr Karl Martyn Alexandra Hospital, Worcs Acute NHS Trust, Woodrow Drive, Redditch B98 7UB Tel: 01527 503070 — MB ChB 1982 Ed.; FRCS (Orth.) 1995; FRCS Ed. 1987. Cons. Orthop. Surg. Alexandra Healthcare Trust Redditch. Prev: Sen. Regist. (Orthop.) Dundee Roy. Infirm.; Regist. (Orthop.) Roy. Infirm. Edin.

BELL, Lady Kathleen Ross (retired) 39 Tweskard Park, Belfast BT4 2JZ Tel: 02890 763649 — MB BCh BAO 1957 Belf. Prev: Sessional Clin. Med. Off. E. Health & Social Serv. Bd. Belf.

BELL, Kathryn Rowan Royal Victoria Infirmary, Queen Victoria Rd, Newcastle upon Tyne NE1 4LP Tel: 0191 232 5131 — MB BS 1988 Newc.; BMedSc Newc. 1987; MRCP (UK) 1991; FRCA 1995; DA (UK) 1992. cons. Anaesth., Roy. Vic., Newc. Upon Tyne. Prev: Regist. Rotat. (Anaesth.) N.. & Yorks. RHA; SHO Rotat. (Anaesth.) Newc. HA; Sen. Regist. Rotat. (Anaesth.) N. & Yorks. RHA.

BELL, Kerry Fiona 38 Station Road, Backwell, Bristol BS48 3LN — MB BS 1988 Lond.

BELL, Laurence Motherwell Health Centre, 138-144 Windmill Street, Motherwell ML1 1TB Tel: 01698 266525 Fax: 01698 252427 Email: laurence.bell@motherwell.lanpct.scot.nhs.uk; 15 Daer Way, Oakmills, Hamilton ML3 9JT Tel: 01698 283829 — MB ChB 1983 Glas.; MBA 2001 Stirling; DRCOG 1986. (Glas.) GP Princip. Motherwell Health Centre; Licensed Assoc. Fac. Homoeop.; Clin. Governance Lead, Motherwell LHCC. Socs: Brit. Soc. Med. & Dent. Hypn.; Scott. Health Advis. Serv. Prev: SHO (Psychiat.) Hartwood Hosp. Lanarksh.; Trainee GP Wishaw VTS; SHO (Orthop.) Roy. Alexandra Hosp. Paisley.

BELL, Laurence David Cassel Hospital, 1 Ham Common, Richmond TW10 7JF — MB BS 1974 Lond.; BSc (Hons.) Lond. 1971, MB BS 1974; MRCP (UK) 1980; MRCPsych 1983. Cons. Psychother. & Clin. Tutor Cassel Hosp. Richmond. Socs: Brit. Psychoanal. Soc. Prev: Sen. Regist. Maudsley Hosp. Lond.

BELL, Leslie Moyra (retired) Brenig, The Green, Tatham, Lancaster LA2 8PJ — MB ChB 1948 Liverp. Prev: Admin. Med. Off. Family Plann. Servs. Gwynedd HA.

BELL, Linda Room 560, Argyle House, 3 Lady Lawson St., Edinburgh EH3 0QL Tel: 0131 222 5967 Fax: 0131 222 5040; 5 Corpach Drive, Dunfermline KY12 7XG Tel: 01383 725702 Email: gelin98@aol.com — MB ChB 1978 Ed.; DRCOG 1982. (Ed.) Med. Adviser Benefits Agency Med. Servs. Edin. (Civil Serv.). Socs: Soc. Ocupat. Health. Prev: GP Tranent.

BELL, Linden Caroline Barnabas Medical Centre, Girton Road, Northolt UB5 4SQ; 96 Star Street, London W2 1QF — MB BS 1978 Lond.; MRCP (UK) 1983.

BELL, Lorraine Catherine Flat 6, 1 Parsonage Square, Glasgow G4 0TA — MB ChB 1989 Glas.

BELL, Malcolm McDonald The Surgery, 2 Green Lane, Belper, Derby DE56 1BZ Tel: 01773 823521 Fax: 01773 821954 — MB ChB 1961 Leeds.

BELL, Margaret Moreland (retired) 28 Cherry Tree Park, Balerno, Edinburgh EH14 5AJ Tel: 0131 449 6434 — MB BCh BAO Dub. 1951; FFCM 1983, M 1972; DPH Belf. 1956; DCH RCPSI 1953. Prev: Sen. Med. Off. DHSS Belf.

BELL, Marjorie 21 De Vere Gardens, Kensington, London W8 5AN Tel: 020 7937 5519 — MB BS 1944 Durh.; MB BS (Hons.) Durh. 1944; DCH Eng. 1947. (Newc.) GP Lond. Prev: Brit. Airways & Qantas Med. Off. Teheran United Nations Med. Off.; Res. Med. Off. Alder Hey Childr. Hosp. Liverp.

BELL, Mark Andrew Department of Emergency Medicine, Causeway Hospital, 4 Newbridge Road, Coleraine BT52 1HS Tel: 028 70346090 Fax: 028 70346293 Email: MA.bell@chsst.n-I.nhs.uk — MB ChB 1992 Ed.; MRCP (UK) 1996. (Ed.) Cons. in Emerg. Med., Causeway Hosp. Coleraine. Socs: Brit. Assn. For Accid. and Emerg. Med.; Fell. Faculty of Accid. and Emerg. Med.

BELL, Mark Hamilton Abingdon, West Lane, Lymm WA13 0TW — MB ChB 1998 Liverp.; MB ChB Liverp 1998.

BELL, Martin Peter Whitley House Surgery, Moulsham Street, Chelmsford CM2 0JJ Tel: 01245 352194 Fax: 01245 344478; Whitley House, Moulsham St, Chelmsford CM2 0JJ Tel: 01245 352194 Fax: 01245 344478 — MB BS 1982 Lond.; MRCGP 1986; DA UK 1987; DRCOG 1984. (Lond. Hosp.) Socs: GP Writers Assn. Prev: Trainee GP Avon VTS.

BELL, Mary Fiona Jean 6B Juniper Park Road, Juniper Green, Edinburgh EH14 5DX Tel: 0131 453 3692 — MB ChB 1962 Glas.; MRCPsych 1980; DPM Ed. & Glas. 1971. Cons. Psychiat. (Ment. Handicap) Lynebank Hosp. Dunfermline. Prev: Sen. Regist. (Ment. Handicap) St. Joseph's Hosp. Rosewell; Sen. Regist. (Child & Adolesc. Psychiat.) Roy. Edin. Hosp.; Sen. Regist. (Child Psychiat.) Roy. Hosp. Sick Childr. Edin.

BELL, Mary Helen (retired) Dunbartonshire Area Laboratory, Vale of Leven District General Hospital, Alexandria G83 0UA Tel: 01389 54121 — MB BS 1960 Lond.; MRCS Eng. LRCP Lond. 1959; FRCPath 1980, M 1968. Prev: Cons. Haematol. Dunbartonsh. Area Laborat. Vale of Leven Dist. Gen. Hosp. Alexandria.

BELL, Matthew Elliot 49A Downs Valley Road, Brighton BN2 6RG — MB ChB 1997 Bristol.

BELL, Mr Mervyn Stuartson 22 Railway Road, Leigh WN7 4AU; 63 The Common, Parbold, Wigaw WN8 7EA — MB BS 1961 Lond.; FRCS Eng. 1967; MRCS Eng. LRCP Lond. 1961. (Guy's) Cons. Orthop. & Traum. Surg. Wigan AHA. Socs: Fell. Brit. Orthop. Assn.; Soc. Internat. Chir. Orthop. & Traumat.; BMA, RSM.

BELL, Michael Perth Royal Infirmary, Taymount Terrace, Perth PH1 1NX Tel: 01738 623311 Fax: 01738 473267 Email: mike.bell"tuht.scot.nhs.uk — MB ChB 1979 Glas.; BSc Glas. 1977; FFA RCS Eng. 1984. (Glasgow) Cons. Anaesth. Perth Roy. Infirm. Socs: Assn. Anaesth.; Intens. Care Soc.; Scott. Intens. Care Soc. Prev: Cons. Anaesth. Dumfries Roy. Infirm.; Sen. Regist. Rotat. Mersey RHA; Regist. (Anaesth.) Roy. Infirm. Glas., Herlev Hosp. Copenhagen, Denmark.

BELL, Michael Damian Dominic 6 Woodlands Road, Whalley Range, Manchester M16 8WR — MB ChB 1979 Liverp.

BELL, Michael David Masterton Health Centre, 74 Somerville Street, Burntisland KY3 9DF Tel: 01592 872761 — MB ChB 1978 Ed.

BELL, Mr Michael John Sheffield Children's Hospital, Western Bank, Sheffield S10 Tel: 0114 271 7000 — MB BS 1974 Lond.; FRCS Eng. 1979. Cons. Orthop. Surg. Roy. Hallamsh. Hosp. & Sheff. Childr. Hosp.

BELL, Milicent Helene Sturrock (retired) 41 West St, Wivenhoe, Colchester CO7 9DA Tel: 01206 823575 — MB ChB 1939 Glas. Prev: Assoc. Specialist (Cytopath.) Vict. Infirm. Glas.

BELL, Monica Angela Caroline Hill Lodge, Hildersham, Cambridge CB1 6DB; Market Cross Surgery, 7 Market St, Mildenhall, Bury St Edmunds IP28 7EG — MB BS Lond. 1985. GP.

BELL, Nicholas James 11 Dundonald Street, Edinburgh EH3 6RZ — MB ChB 1998 Bristol.

BELL, Mr Nicholas John Vincent Poole Hospital NHS Trust, Longfleet Road, Poole BH15 2JB Tel: 01202 442323 Fax: 01202 442615 — MB BChir 1983 Camb.; MChir Camb. 1994; FRCS Ed. 1988; FRCS. (Cambridge University) Cons. Surg., Poole Hosp., NHS Trust Poole. Socs: Assoc. of Coloproctologers Roy. Soc. of Med.

BELL, Nicholas Julian 3 Old Wootton Village, Boars Hill, Oxford OX1 5JL Tel: 01865 736160 — MB BS 1976 Lond.; MRCS Eng. LRCP Lond. 1975. Socs: BMA. Prev: Med. Adviser & Edr. The Med. Gp. Oxf.; Clin. Asst. Brit. Hosp. & Resid. Amer. Hosp. Paris, France; SHO (A & E) St. Stephen's Hosp. Lond.

BELL, Nicola Jane 104 Bence Lane, Darton, Barnsley S75 5DA — BM BS 1998 Nottm.; BM BS Nottm 1998.

BELL, Pamela Frances Musgrave Park Hospital, Stockman's Lane, Belfast BT9 7JB Tel: 028 9066 9501 Fax: 028 9066 8216; Tel: 028 9185 2862 — MB BCh BAO 1980 Belf.; DP med 2001; FFA RCSI 1984; FFA RCS Eng. 1984. (Qu. Univ. Belf.) Cons. Anaesth. Musgrave Pk. Hosp. Belf. & Belf. City Hosp. Prev: Cons. Anaesth. Ulster, N. Down & Ards Hosps. Trust.

BELL, Patrick Michael Royal Victoria Hospital, Grosvenor Road, Belfast BT12 6BA Tel: 01232 894794 Fax: 01232 263161; 14 Clonevin Park, Lisburn BT28 3BL — MD 1984 Belf.; MB BCh BAO Belf. 1977; FRCP Ed. 1992; FRCPI 1991; FRCP Glas. 1988; MRCPI 1989. Cons. Phys. Roy. Vict. Hosp. Belf.; Hon. Clin. Lect. Qu. Univ. Belf. Socs: Specialist Care Sect. Diabetes UK; Irish Endocrine Soc.; Assn. Phys Prev: Mayo Foundat. Fell. (Endocrinol.) Mayo Clinic, USA.

BELL, Paul 29 Mount Eden Park, Belfast BT9 6RB — MB BCh BAO 1980 Belf.; MD Belf. 1994; MRCPsych 1985. Clin. Dir. & Head of Treatm. Servs. S & E Belf. Community Trust; Cons. Gen. Psychiat. Belf.; Sen. Tutor (Psychopharmacol.) Belf. Prev: Sen. Regist. (Psychiat.) Belf.

BELL, Peter Andrew James 10 Lyminge Gardens, Wandsworth, London SW18 3JS; Tower Hamlets Healthcare NHS Trust, Mile End Hospital, Bancroft Road, London E1 4DG Tel: 020 7377 7848 Fax: 020 7377 7848 Email: bellp.@towerhamletshealthcare.org — MB BS 1985 Newc.; MRCPsych 1990. (Old Age Psychiat.) St Bernards Wing W. Lond. Healthcare Trust.; Cons. Old Age Psychiat. Prev: Research Regist. Centr. Nottm. NHS Trust; Regist. (Psychiat.) Nottm.; SHO (Med.) Qu. Eliz. Hosp. Gateshead.

BELL, Professor Peter Robert Frank Department of Surgery, Robert Kilpatrick Building, The Leicester Royal Infirmary, PO Box 65, Leicester LE2 7LX Tel: 0116 252 3142 Fax: 0116 252 3179 Email: ra25@leicester.ac.uk; 22 Powys Avenue, Oadby, Leicester LE2 2DP Tel: 0116 270 9579 — MB ChB Sheff. 1961; MD Sheff. 1971; FRCS Glas. 1972; FRCS Eng. 1964. (Sheff.) Prof. Surg. Leicester Univ. Med. Sch.; Counc.lor RCS Eng. Socs: (Ex-Pres.) Europ. Soc. Vasc. Surg.; (Chairm.) Assn. Profs. Surg.; (Ex-Pres.) Surgic. Research Soc. Prev: Cons. Surg. & Hon. Sen. Lect. Glas.; Lect. (Surg.) W.. Infirm. Glas.; Regist. & SHO Rotat. Roy. Infirm. Sheff.

BELL, Philip Alexander Bupa Wellness, Muscoskeletal Services, No 3 White Lyon Court, London EC2Y 8EA Tel: 020 7588 3146 Fax: 020 7628 1831; 19 High Street, Long Crendon, Aylesbury HP18 9AF Tel: 01844 208453 Fax: 01844 208453 — MB ChB 1982 Sheff.; MRCGP 1987; Dip. Sports Med. (Merit) Lond. 1991; DRCOG 1988. (Sheffield) Sports & Orthop. Phys. (Accredit. Specialist) Lond. & Bucks.; Lect. MSc Sports Med. Nottm. & Roy. Lond.; Clin. Dir. (Sports Med.) Barbican Health. Socs: BIMM (Counc. Mem.); Brit. Assn. Sports Med. (Meetings Sec. Lond. & S. E.. Sect.). Prev: ECB Med. Office.

BELL, Philip Crane Armadale Group Practice, 18 North Street, Armadale, Bathgate EH48 3QD Tel: 01501 730432; 150 Bridgend Park, Bathgate EH48 2AY Tel: 01506 633713 Fax: 01501 730262 — MB ChB 1981 Edinburgh. (Edinburgh) GP Bathgate.

BELL, Philip John Reginald, MBE The Old School Surgery, 2A Station Street, Kibworth, Leicester LE8 0LN Tel: 01162 792422; Windy Ridge, Main St, E. Langton, Market Harborough LE16 7TW — MB ChB 1959 Liverp.; MRCS Eng. LRCP Lond. 1959; FRCGP 1995, M 1976; DObst RCOG 1962. (Liverp.) Trainer (Gen. Pract.) Leics.; Provost Leic. Fac. RCGP; Hon.Sec(Seico Fae RCGP) 1999-2002. Socs: Leic. Med. Soc.; Leic. Medico Legal Soc. Prev: Med. Asst. (A & E) & SHO (Orthop.) BRd.green Hosp. Liverp.; Ho. Phys. & Ho. Surg. (O & G) BRd.green Hosp. Liverp.

BELL, Rachel Elizabeth 21 Burrill Road, Bedale DL8 1ET — MB BS 1994 Lond. Ho. Off. (Gen. Med.) Kingston Hosp. Prev: Ho. Off. (Gen. Surg. & Orthop.) Guy's Hosp. Lond.

BELL, Richard Tel: 02476 224055; 13 Astill Grove, Coventry CV3 6HN Tel: 024 7650 4247 — MB ChB 1970 Bristol; FRCP 1991; MRCP (UK) 1974. Cons. Phys. (Gen. Med. & Chest Dis.) Coventry & Warks Univ Hosp Trust. Socs: Brit. Thoracic Soc. Prev: Sen. Regist. (Gen. Med. & Chest Dis.) Hope Hosp. Salford & Wythenshawe Hosp. Manch.; Regist. (Gen. Med.) MusGr. Pk. Hosp.; Taunton; Regist. (Dis. Chest) Ham Green Hosp. Bristol.

BELL, Richard Christopher Church Farm, Marksbury, Bath BA2 9HQ — MB BS 1998 Lond.; MB BS Lond 1998.

BELL, Richard Warwick 6 Ladbroke Road, Kensington, London W11 3NG Tel: 020 7727 2080 — MB BS 1946 Lond.; MRCS Eng. LRCP Lond. 1946. (King's Coll. Hosp.) Dir. Ladbroke Private Diagnostic Clinic. Socs: Fell. Roy. Soc. Med.

BELL, Robert Angus Frederick Horton General Hospital, Oxford Road, Banbury OX16 9AL Tel: 01295 275500 Fax: 01295 229219 Email: robert.bell@orh.nhs.uk; 55 St. Mary's Road, Adderbury, Banbury OX17 3HA Tel: 01295 810495 Email: rafbell@ukgateway.net — MB ChB Ed. 1967; FRCP Lond. 1987; FRCP Ed. 1984; MRCP (UK) 1971; FRCPCH 1997; DCH Eng. 1969. (Ed.) Cons. Paediat. Horton Gen. Hosp. Banbury & John Radcliffe Hosp. Oxf.; Sen. Clin. Lect. (Paediat.) Univ. Oxf. Socs: Brit. Paediat. Assn.; Brit. Soc. Paediat. Gastroenterol.; BMA. Prev: Sen. Regist. (Paediat.) Dundee Teach. Hosps. & Hon. Lect. (Child Health) Univ. Dundee; Regist. (Med. & Paediat.) Alder Hey Childr. Hosp. Liverp.; SHO (Gen. Med.) Roy. Infirm. Edin.

BELL, Mr Robert Charles (retired) 20 Linden Road, Gosforth, Newcastle upon Tyne NE3 4EY Tel: 0191 285 2755 — MB BS 1941 Lond.; FRCS Eng. 1949; MRCS Eng. LRCP Lond. 1941; LMCC 1947. Prev: Plastic Surg. Shotley Bridge Gen. Hosp. Consett.

BELL, Robert Midgley 19 Victoria Road, Alexandra Park, London N22 7XA Tel: 020 8881 3357 Email: robert.bell@ucl.ac.uk — MB BS 1994 Lond. Clin. Research Fell. (Cardiol.), Univ. Coll., Lond.

BELL, Robert William The Surgery, Abbotswood Road, Brockworth, Gloucester GL3 4PE Tel: 01452 863200 Fax: 01452 864993; 3 Cheltenham Road, Gloucester GL2 0JE — MB BS Lond. 1983; MRCGP 1988. (St. Mary's) Prev: Trainee GP Gloucester VTS.

BELL, Mr Robert William Dugald Sunderland Eye Infirmary, Queen Alexandra Road, Sunderland SR2 9HP Email: dugald.bell@virgin.net — MB BS 1988 Newc.; FRCOphth 1993, M 1992. Cons. (Opthalmology), Sunderland Eye Infirm., Sunderland Roy. NHS Trust. Prev: Regist. (Ophth.) P.ss Alexandra Eye Pavil. Roy. Infirm. Edin.; Fell. in Cornea, Extern. Dis.s & refractive Surg., Corneo Plastic Unit, Qu. Vict. Hosp., E. Grinstead.

BELL, Robin Anthony 34 Sellons Avenue, London NW10 4HH — MB BS 1985 Lond.; Dip. GU Med. Soc. Apoth. Lond. 1989. Staff Grade Phys. (Genitourin Med.) St. Mary's Hosp. Lond. Socs: Impotence Assn. (Mem. Advis. Panel). Prev: Regist. (Genitourin. Med.) St. Mary's Hosp. Lond.; SHO Rotat. Oxf. HA.

BELL, Robin Joseph Dipple Medical Centre, Wickford Avenue, Pitsea, Basildon SS13 3HQ Tel: 01268 555115 Fax: 01268 559935; 20 Downer Road, Benfleet SS7 1BQ Tel: 01268 565442 — MRCS Eng. LRCP Lond. 1976; DRCOG 1983; Dip. Clin. Hypnosis Lond. 1997.

BELL, Rory Michael Heward Hill Farm, Leafield, Oxford OX29 9PL — MB BS 1989 Lond.

BELL, Rosamund Mary Routledge Ellon Group Practice, Health Centre, Schoolhill, Ellon AB41 9AH Tel: 01358 720333 Fax: 01358 721578 Email: ros.bell@ellon.grampian.scot.nhs.uk; 13 Craigpark Place, Ellon AB41 9FG Tel: 01358 720179 — MB ChB 1971 Sheff.; DObst RCOG 1973; Cert Family Plann. RCOG, RCGP & FPA 1975. p/t Gen. Practitioner Ellon Health Centre Aberd.shire.

BELL, Roslyn Elizabeth 32 Fairhill Crescent, Carnmoney, Newtownabbey BT36 6LT — MB BCh BAO 1996 Belf.

BELL, Ruth 2 Stratford Villas, Newcastle upon Tyne NE6 5AX — MB BS 1992 Newc.

BELL, Ruth Allen (retired) A45 San Remo Towers, Sea Road, Boscombe, Bournemouth BH5 1JR — MRCS Eng. LRCP Lond. 1942.

BELL, Sally Susannah Jane 6 Devonshire Terrace, London W2 3DN Tel: 020 7402 9851 Email: sally_bell@compuserve.com; 22 Village De La Rue, Clitourps, Manche 50330, France Tel: (00) (33) 233 205885 — MB BS Lond. 1982. (St. Mary's) Ship's Surg. P & O Lines Soton. Prev: Trainee GP Fairfield Med. Centre Petworth Sussex VTS; SHO (Paediat. & Gyn.) W.m. Hosp. Lond.; SHO (Med.) & Cas. Off. St. Stephen's Hosp. Lond.

BELL, Samamtha Clare 3 Brior Avenue, Euxton, Chorley PR7 6BT Tel: 01257 249583 Email: a.gullick@freeseve.co.uk — MB ChB 1997 Manch. SHO A&E SMUHT. Socs: MPS; BMA. Prev: SHO A & E TROH; HO Surg TROH; Ho. Off. Med. TROH.

BELL, Samantha Pamela 22 Berry Park Road, Plymouth PL9 9AG — MB BS 1992 Lond.; BSc (Angiol.) Lond. 1989, MB BS 1992.

BELL, Samuel Martin (retired) Spring Wood, 16 High Hamsterley Road, Hamsterley Mill, Rowlands Gill NE39 1HD Tel: 01207 542270

— MB BS 1949 Durh.; FRCPath 1974, M 1963. Prev: Cons. Pathol. NW Durh. Health Dist.

BELL, Sarah Dilys 17 Chester Road, London N19 5DE — MB BS 1992 Lond. SHO (Cas.) Lister Hosp. Stevenage. Prev: Ho. Off. (Surg.) Barnet Gen. Hosp.; Ho. Off. (Med.) Roy. Free Hosp. Lond.

BELL, Sarah Jane 6 Birkett Drive, Ulverston LA12 9LS Tel: 01229 584580 — MB BS 1992 Newc.; FRCA 1998. Specialist Regist. (Anaesth.) N. Region. Socs: Train. Mem. Assn. Anaesth.

BELL, Sharon Margaret 61 Byker Ter, Newcastle upon Tyne NE6 3AE — MB ChB 1997 Sheff.

BELL, Sheila Margaret The Drumlin, 49 Ballyworfy Road, Hillsborough BT26 6LR Tel: 01846 682539 — MB BCh BAO 1950 Belf.; FFA RCS Eng. 1955; Hon. FFA RCSI 1971. (Belf.) Cons. Anaesth. Belf. City Hosp. & Roy. Vict. Hosp. Belf. Socs: Assn. Anaesths. & N. Irel. Soc. Anaesth. Prev: Regist. (Anaesth.) W.m. Hosp. Lond.; Research Fell. Univ. Illinois, Chicago; Sen. Regist. (Anaesth.) Roy. Matern. Hosp. Belf.

BELL, Simon John 30 Herries Drive, Sheffield S5 7HW — MB BS 1993 Lond.

BELL, Stephen Malcolm The Grantham Centre, Beckett House, Grantham Road, London SW9 Tel: 020 7733 6191 — MB BS 1982 Lond.; BChD Leeds 1976.

BELL, Susan Jane The Wessex Deanery, "Highcroft", Romsey Rd, Winchester Tel: 01962 863511 Email: jane.bell@wessexdeanery.nhs.uk; Tel: 01962 863511 Email: jane.bell@wessexdeanery.nhs.uk — MA 1999 (Distinction) Education; BM Soton 1984; FRCGP 2001; Cert. Family Plann. 1988; DRCOG 1988; DCH RCP Lond. 1987. p/t Assoc. PostGrad. Dean; GP Lead Target Portsmouth.

BELL, Susan Mary Llandough Hospital, Penlan Road, Penarth CF64 2XX; 34 Rockleigh Road, Southampton SO16 7AR — BM 1990 Soton. Regist. (O & G) Llandough Hosp. S. Glam.

BELL, Sydney John Nettleham Medical Practice, 14 Lodge Lane, Nettleham, Lincoln LN2 2RS Tel: 01522 751717 Fax: 01522 754474; Landor, Watery Lane, Dunholme, Lincoln LN2 3QW Tel: 01673 860103 — MB BCh BAO 1969 Dub.; MA Dub. 1976, BA 1967; FRCGP 1997, M 1975; DFFP 1993; Cert. Gen Av Med 1976; DCH RCPSI 1972; DObst RCOG 1971. (Trinity Coll. Dub.) Socs: Inst. Health Serv. Managers & Lincoln Med. Soc. Prev: Clin. Asst. (Palliat. Care) St. Barnabas Hospice Lincoln; Clin. Asst. (Paediat.) Lincoln Co. Hosp.

BELL, Mr Thomas Andrew Gordon Broomfield Hospital, Court Road, Broomfield, Chelmsford CM1 7ET; Mantons, Park Lane, Langham, Colchester CO4 5NJ — MB ChB 1975 Ed.; FRCS Ed. 1980; FCOphth. 1988; DO Eng. 1978. Cons. Ophth. Broomfield Hosp. Chelmsford. Socs: Oxf. Ophth. Congr. Prev: Sen. Regist. Oxf. Eye Hosp.

BELL, Thomas Richard Douglas East Street Medical Centre, East Street, Okehampton EX20 1AY Tel: 01837 52233; Ramsley Lodge, South Zeal, Okehampton EX20 2PB Fax: 01837 840424 Email: trdt@bodymind.demon.co.uk — MB BS 1976 Lond.; MRCS Eng. LRCP Lond. 1976; MRCGP 1983; DRCOG 1981. GP Okehampton Cottage Hosp. Socs: Brit. Soc. Med. & Dent. Hypn.; Eur. Soc. Hypn. Prev: SHO (Anaesth.) Roy. Devon & Exeter Hosp.; SHO (Gen. Med.) Orpington Hosp.; SHO (Paediat.) York.

BELL, Timothy 7 Peak Hill Avenue, London SE26 4LG — MB BS 1992 Newc.

BELL, Mr Timothy John 48 Dudley Road, Eastbourne BN22 8HE — MB BS 1976 Lond.; FRCS Ed. 1981; MRCS Eng. LRCP Lond. 1975.

BELL, Victoria Ann Dormer Cottage, 85 Knutsford Road, Wilmslow SK9 6JH — MB ChB 1995 Bristol.

BELL, Viola Adele 6 Baden Road, Ilford IG1 2HS — MB BS 1969 W. Indies.

BELL, Wilfred Alvyn The Brant Road Surgery, 291 Brant Road, Lincoln LN5 9AB Tel: 01522 722853 Fax: 01522 722195 — MB BCh BAO 1981 Belf.; MRCGP 1986; DRCOG 1983. (Qu. Uni. Belf.)

BELL, William Andrew Godfrey (retired) 3 Syward Road, Dorchester DT1 2AJ Tel: 01302 3427 — MRCS Eng. LRCP Lond. 1928. Prev: Temp. Capt. RAMC.

BELL, Mr William George Thompson 6 Arden Court, Bramhall, Stockport SK7 3NG — MB BCh BAO Dub. 1949; FRCS Eng. 1957. (T.C. Dub.)

BELL, Winifred Joan (retired) 34 Princess Mary Court, Jesmond, Newcastle upon Tyne NE2 3BG — MB BS 1949 Durh.

BELL-DAVIES, David Edward Hafan, Gannock Park, Deganwy, Conwy LL31 9PZ Tel: 01492 593530 — MB BS 1961 Lond.; MRCS Eng. LRCP Lond. 1961; DA Eng. 1965; DObst RCOG 1963. (Univ. Coll. Lond. & Univ. Coll. Hosp.) Gen. Practitioner, N. Wales Health Auth., Caernarfon, Gwynedd; Clin. Asst. (Anaesth.) Llandudno Hosp.; Hon. Asst. Med. Off. Football Assn. Wales. Socs: BMA; Assn. Anaesths.; Soc. Anaesth. Wales. Prev: Regist. (Anaesth.) Cardiff Roy. Infirm.; Ho. Surg. (O & G) Selly Oak Hosp. Birm.; Ho. Surg. Char. Cross Hosp. Gp. (W. Lond. Hosp.).

BELL-GAM, Hope Ilanye 82 Cedars Lawn Avenue, Barnet EN5 2LN — MB BS 1979 Ahmadu Bello U.; MB BS 1979 Ahmadu Bello U.

BELL SYER, Eileen Margaret Rutherford (retired) Bracken House, Barlow, Selby YO8 8JF Tel: 01757 618261 — MB BS 1945 Lond. SCMO N. Yorks. CC. Prev: Ho. Phys. Roy. Free Hosp.

BELL-SYER, Jonathan Wansborough Gale Farm Surgery, 109-119 Front Street, Acomb, York YO24 3BU Tel: 01904 798329 Fax: 01904 798329; The Orchard, Long Ridge Lane, Upper Poppleton, York YO26 6HA Tel: 01904 791063 — MB BS 1978 Lond. (Roy. Free) Trainer GP York VTS.

BELLAL, Shaikh (retired) 74 Longmeadow Road, Knowsley, Prescot L34 0HT — MB BS 1965 Utkal; DMRT Eng. 1971.

BELLAMY, Christopher Michael Glan Clwyd District General Hospital, Rhyl LL18 5UJ Tel: 01745 583910 Fax: 01745 583143 Email: drchris.bellamy@cd-tr.wales.nhs.uk — MB ChB 1982 Sheff.; FRCP 1999; MRCP (UK) 1985. (Sheff.) Cons. Cardiol. & Phys. Glan Clwyd Hosp. N. Wales; Vis. Cons. Cardiol. Cardiothoracic Centre Liverp. Socs: Cardiac Soc.; Roy. Coll. Phys. Ed.; Brit. Pacing & Electrophysiol. Gp. Prev: Sen. Regist. (Cardiol.) Regist. & Research Fell. Cardiothoracic Centre Liverp.; Regist. (Gen. Med.) Walton & Arrowe Pk. Hosps. Wirral.

BELLAMY, Christopher Owen Charles Department of Pathology, University Medical School, Teviot Place, Edinburgh EH8 9AG Tel: 0131 650 2879 Fax: 0131 650 6528 Email: c.bellamy@ed.ac.uk — MB BS 1988 Lond.; BSc (Hons.) Lond. 1985; DRCPath 1992; PhD 1998; MRCPath 1998. (St marys hosp.Lond) Sen. Lect./Hon. Cons. Edin. Univ. Med. Sch. Histopath. Socs: Assn. Clin.Pathol.; Pathol.Soc; Renal. Assn. Prev: CRC Gordon Hamilton Fairley Fell. Edin. Univ. Med. Sch.; Regist. (Histopath.) Edin. Roy. Infirm.; Sen. Regist. (Histopath.) Edin. Roy. Infirm. & Lect. (Path.) Edin. Univ. Med.

BELLAMY, David, MBE James Fisher Medical Centre, 4 Tolpuddle Gardens, Bournemouth BH9 3LQ Tel: 01202 522622 Fax: 01202 548480; 8 Littledown Drive, Queens Park, Bournemouth BH7 7AQ — MRCS Eng. LRCP Lond. 1971; FRCP 2001 London; MB BS Lond. 1971; BSc (Hons.) Lond. 1968; FRCP Ed. 1996; MRCP (UK) 1973; MRCGP 1986; DRCOG 1986. (Guy's) Socs: GP's in Asthma Gp.; Brit. Thorac. Soc.; Eur. Respirat. Soc. Prev: Sen. Regist. (Med.) King's Coll. & Brompton Hosps. Lond. & Roy. Sussex Co. Hosp. Brighton; Wellcome Research Fell. Chest Unit King's Coll. Hosp. Lond.; Regist. (Cardiol.) St. Bart. Hosp. Lond.

BELLAMY, David Charles, Maj. RAMC Medical Centre, Mercer Barracks BFPO 36 — MB BS 1982 Lond.; MRCGP 1987. GP/RMO Osnabruck. Socs: MDU. Prev: SHO (O & G) Qu. Eliz. Hosp. Gateshead; Sen. Med. Off. Episkopi Garrison; RMO 2 Qu's. BFPO 29.

BELLAMY, Elizabeth Anne Ashford Hospital, London Road, Ashford TW15 3AA; Shepley Wood, Shepley Drive, Wentworth, Virginia Water GU25 0LH — MB BS 1976 Lond.; MRCP (UK) 1978; FRCR Lond. 1982; DMRD Lond. 1981. Cons. Radiol. Ashford Hosp. Middlx. Prev: Sen. Lect. (CT Scanning) Roy. Marsden Hosp. Sutton.

BELLAMY, Emmanuel Philip Domnal Henley Green Medical Centre, Henley Road, Coventry CV2 1AB Tel: 024 7661 4255 Fax: 024 7660 2699; Yew Tree Farm, Long Itchington, Rugby — MB BCh BAO 1975 NUI.

BELLAMY, Jane Eleanor 8 Great Close, Culmstock, Cullompton EX15 3HQ — BM 1991 Soton.

BELLAMY, Jane Louise Holly House, Pen-y-Mynydd, Upper Colwyn Bay, Conwy LL28 5YQ — MB ChB 1985 Liverp.; MRCGP 1990; DRCOG 1988. GP N. Wales.

BELLAMY, Joan Eileen (retired) Barwood, 34 Long Lane, Framingham Earl, Norwich NR14 7RY Tel: 0150 864357 — MB ChB 1952 Birm.; MRCS Eng. LRCP Lond. 1952.

BELLAMY, John David Fothergill The Beehive, Wickham Hill, Hurstpierpoint, Hassocks BN6 9NP Tel: 01273 843827 — MB BChir Camb. 1962; MRCS Eng. LRCP Lond. 1962; DObst RCOG 1964. (Camb. & Guy's) Med. Assessor Nestor Disabil. Anal.; Mem. Social Security Appeals Serv. Prev: GP Hurstpierpoint; Princip. Med. Off. DoH.

BELLAMY, Lloyd Albert William (retired) Barwood, 34 Long Road, Framingham Earl, Norwich NR14 7RY Tel: 0150 864357 — MB ChB 1952 Birm.; MRCS Eng. LRCP Lond. 1952.

BELLAMY, Mark Carlyle St James's University Hospital, Beckett St., Leeds LS9 7TF Tel: 0113 243 3144 Fax: 0113 206 5773; Manor House, Leeds WF11 9HE Tel: 01977 672266 Fax: 0113 206 5773 Email: mark@livertransplant.org.uk — MB BS 1984 Lond.; MA, BA Camb. 1981; FRCA 1989. (Char. Cross.) Cons. Anaesth. (Intens. Care & Liver Transpl.) St. Jas. Univ. Hosp. Leeds; Hon. Sen. Clin. Lect. Univ. Leeds. Socs: Yorks. Soc. Anaesth.; Anaesth. Res. Soc. - Grants Off.; Roy. Soc. Med. Fell. Prev: Sen. Regist. Rotat. Yorks.; Specialist (Anaesth.) Univ. Uppsala, Sweden; Regist. (Anaesth.) Bristol Roy. Infirm. & Roy. Cornw. Hosp. Truro.

BELLAMY, Michael Francis 14 Victoria Cottages, Sandycombe Road, Richmond TW9 3NW — MB BS 1991 Lond.; MB BS (Hons.) Lond. 1991; BSc (Hons.) Lond. 1988; MRCP (UK) 1994. (Roy. Free Hosp. Sch. Med.) Specialist Regist. (Cardiol.) N. Thames (W.). Prev: Research Fell. & Hon. Regist. (Cardiol.) Univ. Wales Coll. Med. Cardiff; SHO (Cardiol.) Roy. Brompton Nat. Heart & Lung Hosp. Lond.; SHO Rotat. (Med.) Roy. Postgrad. Hosp. Lond.

BELLAMY, Michael John David Place Medical Practice, 56 David Place, St Helier, Jersey JE1 4HY Tel: 01534 33322; The Old School House, La Rue des Alleurs, St Martin, Jersey JE3 6AZ Tel: 01534 851482 Fax: 01534 852557 Email: bellamy@cinergy.co.uk — MB BS 1980 Lond.; BSc Lond. 1977; MRCS Eng. LRCP Lond. 1980; MRCGP 1984; DRCOG 1982; Cert. Family Plann. RCOG & RCGP 1982. (Guy's) Private GP.

BELLAMY, Peter Ashburton Surgery, 1 Eastern Road, Ashburton, Newton Abbot TQ13 7AP Tel: 01364 652731 Fax: 01364 654273; Greendown, Holne, Ashburton, Newton Abbot TQ13 7RU Tel: 01364 631323 — MB BS 1969 Lond.; MRCS Eng. LRCP Lond. 1969; DObst RCOG 1972. (St. Thos.) Prev: Trainee GP Wessex (Portsmouth) VTS; Ho. Surg. (Obst.) St. Mary's Hosp. Portsmouth; Ho. Surg. Roy. Hants. Co. Hosp. Winchester.

BELLAMY, Peter David (retired) 210 Upper Shoreham Road, Shoreham-by-Sea BN43 6BG Tel: 01273 454176 Fax: 01273 454176 — MB BS 1974 Lond.; MRCS Eng. LRCP Lond. 1974; Dip. Osteop. 1989; LFHom 1998; MA, Cantab. 1960. Prev: SHO (O & G), Ho. Surg. & Ho. Phys. S.lands Hosp. Shoreham-by-Sea.

BELLAMY, Raymond Charles Thomas (retired) Skellgarth, 4 The Crescent, Farnborough GU14 7AH Tel: 01252 541763 — MB BS 1948 Lond.; MRCS Eng. LRCP Lond. 1948. Prev: Ho. Phys. Dermat. Dept., Ho. Surg. & Cas. Med. Off. Univ. Coll. Hosp.

BELLAMY, Richard John Department of Infectious Diseases, University Hospital of Wales, Heath Park, Cardiff CF14 4XW Email: bellamrj@cardiff.ac.uk — MB BS 1992 Newc.; BMedSc Newc. 1989; MRCP (UK) 1995; DPhil. Oxf. 1998. (Newc.) Specialist Regist.(Infec. Dis.s.). Socs: Roy. Coll. Phys.s.

BELLAMY, Simon John Shepperton Health Centre, Shepperton Court Drive, Laleham Road, Shepperton TW17 8EJ Tel: 01932 220524 Fax: 01932 244948; Hunters Moon, Portnall Rise, Wentworth, Virginia Water GU25 4JZ Tel: 01344 842986 — MB BS 1976 Lond.; MRCS Eng. LRCP Lond. 1976; DRCOG 1980; DCH Eng. 1979.

BELLAMY, Stephen John Ship Street Surgery, Ship Street, East Grinstead RH19 4EE Tel: 01342 325959; Mayfield, West Lane, East Grinstead RH19 4HH Tel: 01342 300803 — MB BS 1985 Lond.; BSc Lond. 1982; MRCGP 1990; DRCOG 1988; DA (UK) 1987. Socs: BMA.

BELLAMY, Susan 13 Dunkeld Road, Talbot Woods, Bournemouth BH3 7EN — MB BS 1968 Lond.; MRCS Eng. LRCP Lond. 1968; DCH Eng. 1971. (King's Coll. Hosp.) SCMO Poole Hosp. Trust.

BELLAMY, Sydney Robert John (retired) 8 Helpston Road, Ailsworth, Peterborough PE5 7AE — MB BS Lond. 1960; DCP Lond 1971. Prev: Sen. Specialist P.ss Alexandra RAF Hosp. Wroughton.

BELLAMY, William The Bull Ring Surgery, 5 The Bull Ring, St. John's, Worcester WR2 5AA Tel: 01905 422883 Fax: 01905 423639; The Gables, Peachley Lane, Lower Broadheath, Worcester WR2 6QR Tel: 01905 640661 — MB ChB 1983 Birm.; DRCOG 1988. Prev: Trainee GP Worcester VTS.

BELLANTUONO, Ilaria 6 Borrowdale Crescent, Manchester M20 2XU — State Exam 1992 Pavia.

BELLARY, Somashekhar Veerappa c/o Dr R. V. Vibhuti, Longwood, Boxley Road, Walderslade, Chatham ME5 9JG — MB BS 1976 Karnatak, India; MRCP (UK) 1986.

BELLAS, Fiona Jayne Hale Cottage, 5 Northallerton Road, Brompton, Northallerton DL6 2QR Tel: 01609 771603 Fax: 01609 771603 — MB ChB 1994 Dundee; DRCOG 1998. N.allerton VTS.

BELLAU, Allan Raymond Grove Road Surgery, 25 Grove Road, Borehamwood WD6 5DX Tel: 020 8953 2444 Fax: 020 8207 4060; 2 Lamorna Close, Radlett WD7 7DR Tel: 01923 856357 Fax: 01923 856357 — MB BS 1961 Lond. (St. Mary's) Apptd. Dr. Health & Safety Exec. Employm. Med. Advis. Serv. Prev: Clin. Asst. (Rheum.) Barnet Gen. Hosp.; Regist. (Med.) S. W.. Hosp. Lond.; Ho. Phys. Edgware Gen. Hosp.

BELLE, Andrew Colvin 11 Manston Hill, Penkridge, Stafford ST19 5JZ — MB BS 1990 West Indies.

BELLENGER, Nicholas Gilmore Wingfield, 62 Kiln Road, Fareham PO16 7UG — MB BS 1994 Lond.; MB BS (Hons.) Lond. 1994; BSc (Hons.) Lond. 1991; MRCP (UK) 1994. Cardiol. Research Fell. Nat. Heart & Lung Inst. Roy. Brompton Hosp. Prev: SHO Rotat. (Med.) N.wick Pk. & St. Mark's Hosp. Trust; Ho. Off. (Gastroenterol.) Middlx. Hosp. Lond.; SHO (ITU) St. Thos. Hosp. Lond.

BELLENGER, Robert Arthur Fareham Health Centre, Osborn Road, Fareham PO16 7ER Tel: 01329 822111 Fax: 01329 286636; Wingfield, 62 Kiln Road, Fareham PO16 7UG — MB BS 1969 Lond.; MRCS Eng. LRCP Lond. 1969; DObst RCOG 1971. (King's Coll. Hosp.)

BELLENGER, William Stanley Tattenham Health Centre, Tattenham Crescent, Epsom KT18 5NU Tel: 017373 62345; 3 St. Martin's Avenue, Epsom KT18 5HT — MB ChB 1975 Glas.; MA Camb. 1969; DRCOG 1981; DTM & H Univ. 1980.

BELLENIS, Clio Eastleigh Child & Family Guidance Clinic, The Health Centre, Newtown Road, Eastleigh SO50 9AG Tel: 01703 610961 Fax: 01703 651611 Email: wehcmhcb@hants.gov.uk; 2 Oakbank Cottage, Oakbank Road, Bishopstoke, Eastleigh SO50 6LR Tel: 01703 641128 Fax: 01703 641128 Email: cbellenis@aol.com — BM 1981 Soton.; MRCPsych 1985. (Southampton) Cons. Child & Adolesc. Psychiat. E.leigh Child & Family Guid. Clinic & Leigh Hse. Adolesc. Unit Chandler's Ford. Socs: Assn. Child Psychol. & Psychiat. Prev: Sen. Regist. Rotat. (Child & Adolesc. Psychiat.) Wessex; Regist. (Child & Family Psychiat.) Tavistock Clinic Lond.; Regist. (Psychiat.) Roy. Free Hosp. Lond.

BELLEW, Michael Vincent Park Royal Centre for Mental Health, Central Middlesex Hospital, Acton Lane, London NW10 7NS Tel: 020 8937 6360 — MB BCh BAO 1986 NUI; MRCPsych. (University College Galway) Specialist Regist. (Psychiat.).

BELLHOUSE, John Edward 50 Dereham Avenue, Ipswich IP3 0QF — MB BS 1994 Lond.; MRCP (UK) 1997. (St. Bart. Hosp.)

BELLHOUSE, Wendy Longridge, 8 The Dingle, Gee Cross, Hyde SK14 5EP Tel: 0161 368 2811 Fax: 0161 366 7338 — MB ChB 1955 Manch. (Manch.) Socs: Fell. Manch. Med. Soc. Prev: Ho. Surg. Clayton Hosp. Wakefield; Ho. Surg. & Ho. Phys. Staincliffe Hosp. Dewsbury.

BELLI, Anna-Maria Department of Radiology, Blackshaw Road, London SW17 0QT; 36 Victoria Drive, London SW19 6BG — MB BS 1980 Lond.; FRCR 1985. Cons. Radiol. St Geo. Hosp. Lond. Prev: Sen. Lect. & Hon. Cons. Radiol. Roy. Postgrad. Med. Sch. Hammersmith Hosp. Lond.; Sen. Lect. & Hon. Cons. Roy. Hallamsh. Hosp. Sheff.

BELLI, Mr Antonio 38 Stanhorne Avenue, Higher Crumpsall, Manchester M8 4PQ Tel: 0161 795 1889 Email: antbelli@mcmail.com — State Exam 1992 Rome; MD Rome 1992; FRCS (Glas.) 1997. Specialist Regist. (Neurosurg.) Atkinson Morley Hosp. Prev: Specialist Regist. (Neurosurg.) King's Coll. Hosp. Lond.; SHO (Neurosurg.) W.ern Gen. Hosp. Edin.; SHO (Neurosurg.) Hope Hosp. Lond.

BELLIAPPA, Kandrathandra Ponnappa District General Hospital, Victoria Road, Macclesfield SK10 1BL Tel: 01625 21000; c/o

National Westminster Bank, Coney St, York YO1 1YH — MB BS 1952 Madras. Assoc. Specialist (A & E) Dist. Gen. Hosp. Macclesfield. Prev: Regist. (Orthop.) Vict. Hosp. Kirkcaldy; Regist. (Surg.) York 'A' Hosp. Gp.; Regist. (Orthop.) Memor. Hosp. Crewe.

BELLIN, Jana Marie Department of Anaesthetics, Sandwell Healthcare, Lyndon, West Bromwich B71 4HJ Tel: 0121 553 1831 Fax: 0121 607 3117; 65 Gillity Avenue, Walsall WS5 3PP Tel: 01922 635055 — MRCS Eng. LRCP Lond. 1974; FFA RCS Eng. 1986; FFA RCSI 1985. (Cambridge) Dir. (IC) & Cons. Anaesth. Sandwell Healthcare W. Bromwich. Socs: Intens. Care Soc.; BMA; Paediatric Intens. Care Soc.

BELLIN, Uta 28C South Residence, King George Hospital, 167 Barley Lane, Ilford IG3 8YB — State Exam Med 1992 Leipzig.

BELLINGAN, Geoffrey John Bloomsbury Institute of Intensive Care, Rayne Institute, University St., London WC1E 6JJ Tel: 020 7209 6208 Fax: 020 7209 6258 Email: g.bellingan@ucl.ac.uk — MB BS 1986 Lond.; MRCP 1989; PhD Ed. 1996. Sen. Lect. (IC Med.); MRC Clinician Scientist.

BELLINGHAM, Professor Alastair John, CBE Department of Haematological Medicine, King's College School of Medicine & Dentistry, Denmark Hill, London SE5 9RS Tel: 020 7346 3080 Fax: 020 7346 3514; 13 Barnmead Road, Beckenham BR3 1JF — MB BS 1962 Lond.; FRCP Glas. 1995; FRCP Lond. 1976, M 1966; FRCPath 1987; MRCS Eng. LRCP Lond. 1962; FRCP Ed 1996; FRCP (Ire.) 1996. (Univ. Coll. Hosp.) Prof. Haemat. King's Coll. Sch. Med. & Dent. Lond. Socs: Fell. (Ex-Pres.) Roy. Coll. Path.; (Ex-Pres.) Brit. Soc. Haematol.; Hon. Fell. Hong. Kong. Coll. Path. Prev: Prof. Haemat. Univ. Liverp.; Sen. Lect. (Clin. Haemat.) Univ. Coll. Hosp. Med. Sch. Lond.; Mackenzie Mackinnon Streatfeild Fell. RCPS at Univ. Coll. Hosp. Lond.

BELLINGHAM, Janet Margaret The Ross Practice, Bush Fair, Harlow CM18 6LY Tel: 01279 692747 Fax: 01279 692737; 1 Woodside Cottages, High Wych Lane, High Wych, Sawbridgeworth CM21 0JP Tel: 01279 724247 — MB BS 1980 Lond.; DRCOG 1984.

BELLINGHAM, Kathryn Margaret 10 Sneyd Avenue, Newcastle ST5 2PP — BM BS 1991 Nottm.

BELLINI, Mr Michael John The Manor House, Cooks Lane, Great Coates, Grimsby DN37 9NW Tel: 01472 232711 Fax: 01472 232718; The Manor House, Cooks Lane, Great Coates, Grimsby DN37 9NW Tel: 01472 232711 Fax: 01472 232718 — MB ChB 1978 Leeds; FRCS (Otorhinolaryng.) Ed. 1985. Cons. ENT Surg. Grimsby Dist. Gen. Hosp. & Louth Community Hosp.

BELLIS, Amanda Jane 43 Parsonage Road, Flixton, Manchester M41 6QN — MB ChB Manch. 1989; MRCOG 1996. (Manchester) Specialist Regist. (O & G) Bolton Hosp. Prev: Hon. Regist. (Med. & O & G) & Clin. Research Fell. Hope Hosp Salford; Rotat.al Specialist Regist. (O & G) NW Revion.

BELLIS, Diana Jean Princess Royal Hospital, East Wing, Lewes Road, Haywards Heath RH16 4EX Tel: 01444 441881; Kenwards, 35 Muster Green, Haywards Heath RH16 4AL — BM 1980 Soton.; FFA RCS Eng. 1985. Cons. Anaesth. P.ss Roy. Hosp. Haywards Heath. Prev: Sen. Regist. (Anaesth.) St. Geo. & W.m. Hosps. Lond.; Regist. (Anaesth.) Char. Cross Hosp. Lond.; SHO (Anaesth.) Middlx. Hosp. Lond.

BELLIS, Fionn 2 Haytor Court, Haytor, Newton Abbot TQ13 9XS Tel: 01364 661564 — MB BS 1994 Lond.; BA (Hons.) Oxf. 1991.

BELLMAN, Martin Harris Camden & Islington Community Health Services NHS Trust, childrens centre, 4 Greenland Road, London NW1 0AS Tel: 020 7530 4821 Fax: 020 7530 4825 Email: martin.bellman@cichst-tr.nthames.mhs.uk; 27 Somali Road, London NW2 3RN Tel: 020 7794 3519 Fax: 020 7813 9739 — MB BS Lond. 1970; MD Lond. 1984; FRCP Lond. 1991; DCH Eng. 1973; FRCPCH 1997. (Westminster Hospital) Cons. Paediat. Camden & Islington Community Servs. NHS Trust & Roy. Free Hosp. NHS Trust.

BELLON, Joseph Salvatore 3 Aston Mead, Windsor SL4 5PW Tel: 01753 865086 Email: castlecity@email.msn.com — LMSSA 1991 Lond.; BSc Pharmacol. Hatfield 1982. Regist. (Anaesth.) St. Peters Hosp. Chertsey. Prev: SHO (Neonat. ITU & Anaesth.) Hammersmith Hosp. Lond.; Cas. Off. Ealing Gen. Hosp.

BELLOSO UCEDA, Antonio 27 Cheam Road, Timperley, Altrincham WA15 6BQ — LMS 1992 Barcelona; LMS Autonoma Barcelona 1992.

BELLRINGER, Mr James Francis Department of Unology, West Middlesex Hospital, Isleworth TW7 6AF Tel: 020 8565 5793 Fax: 020 8565 5757 Email: urologists@incme.com; Tel: 020 8241 1637 Fax: 020 8241 1637 Email: campanologists@unforgettable.com — MB BChir 1982 Camb.; FRCS (Urol.) 1995; FRCS Eng. 1987. (Pembroke College, Cambridge and St. Thomas' , London) p/t Cons. Urol. W. Middlx. Univ. Hosp. Lond.; Cons. Urol., Hammersmith Hosp., NHS Trust, Lond. Socs: Roy. Soc. of Med.; Brit. Assn. of Urological Surg.s.

BELLWORTHY, Susan Valsa Sancta Maria Centre, Daiglen Drive, South Ockendon RM15 5SZ Tel: 01708 851888 Fax: 01708 856570; 34 Wakefield Close, Emerson Park, Hornchurch RM11 2TH Tel: 01708 450564 — MB BS 1974 Mysore. (Kasturba Med. Coll. Mangalore) Prev: Asst. Bournhall Clinic; SHO (O & G) W. Kent. Gen. Hosp. Maidstone; Clin. Asst. (Orthop.) Orsett Hosp.

BELSEY, Gillian Northam Surgery, Bayview Road, Northam, Bideford EX39 1AZ Tel: 01237 474994; Manor House Cottage, Diddywell, Northam, Bideford EX39 1NW — MB BS 1973 Lond. (St. Thos.)

BELSEY, Jonathan David 8 Poplar High Street, London E14 0DL — MB BS 1984 Lond.

BELSEY, Raymond Lusher Brookfield, Oxenhope, Keighley BD22 9HS Tel: 01535 643070 — MB BS 1956 Lond.; DO Eng. 1965. (St. Mary's) Socs: Keighley & Dist. Med. Soc. Prev: Ho. Phys. & Ho. Surg. (O & G) Keighley Vict. Hosp.

BELSHAM, Audrey Joyce (retired) 5 Syward Road, Dorchester DT1 2AJ — MB BS 1960 Lond.; MRCPsych 1971; DPM Eng. 1965, DCH 1963. Prev: Cons. Childr. Psychiat. W. Dorset Hosp. Gp.

BELSHAM, Martin Peter School Lane Surgery, School Lane, Thetford IP24 2AG Tel: 01842 753115; Jubilee Cottage, Euston Road, Barnham, Thetford IP24 2NJ Tel: 01842 890293 — MB BS 1985 Lond.; DCH RCP Lond. 1989; DA (UK) 1988. (Middlx. Hosp. Lond.)

BELSHAM, Mr Philip Alan Accident & Emergency Department, Royal Free Hospital, Hampstead, London NW3 2QG Tel: 020 7830 2126 Fax: 020 7830 2985; St. Agnes, 2 St. Giles Avenue, South Mimms, Potters Bar EN6 3PZ Tel: 01707 642214 Fax: 01707 660636 Email: pabelsham@easynet.co.uk — MB BS 1975 Lond.; FRCS Eng. 1979. Cons. A & E Roy. Free Hampstead NHS Trust; Hon. Sen. Lect. Roy. Free Sch. Med. Prev: Sen. Regist. (A & E) Roy. Free Hosp. Lond.; Regist. (Surg.) Univ. Coll. Hosp. Lond.

BELSHAW, Christopher Patrick Mount Alvernia Hospital, Waterden Road clinic, 8 Waterden Road, Guildford GU1 2AP Tel: 0800 018 9676 Email: doctor@fitness50.com; The Annexe, Ashdown, Hoe Lane, Peaslake, Guildford GU5 9SW Tel: 01306 730486 Fax: 01306 730486 Email: c.belshaw@netway.co.uk — MB BCh BAO Belf. 1969; MA Europ. Univ. 1993; MA Wales 1990; MLCOM 1974. (Belf.) Indep. Pract. Specialist in Musculoskeletal (Manual) Med. & Acupunc. Guildford. Socs: Brit. Assn. Manip. Med.; Brit. Osteop. Assn.; BMA. Prev: Asst. Med. Off. Wusasa Hosp. Zaria, Nigeria; SHO Roy. Bath Hosp. Harrogate; Clin. Asst. W.m. Hosp. Lond.

BELSHAW, Joan (retired) 3 Hardy Drive, Bramhall, Stockport SK7 2BW — LRCP LRCS Ed. LRFPS Glas. 1952. Prev: CMO Paediat., Stockport A.H.A.

BELSHAW, Mary Hazel Glencoe, 100 Mellor Brow, Mellor, Blackburn BB2 7EX — MB ChB 1982 Leeds; MRCGP 1986; Cert. Family Plann. JCC 1985; DCH RCPS Glas. 1984; DRCOG 1984. p/t GP. Prev: Partner at 293-295 Preston New Rd., Blackburn; GP Liverp.; Trainee GP Preston VTS.

BELSTEAD, Mr John Sydney Ashford & St Peters NHS Trust, Emergency Department, Ashford Hospital, London Road, Ashford TW15 3AA Tel: 01784 884404 Fax: 01784 258712 Email: john.belstead@stph-tr.sthames.nhs.uk; 6 Stanwell Road, Ashford TW15 3ER — MB ChB Leeds 1968; FRCS Ed. (Orth.) 1982; FRCS Ed. 1972; FFAEM 1994. Cons. A & E Ashford & St. Peters NHS Trust; Dir. of A & E Serv. Ashford & St Peters NHS Trust. Socs: Fell. BOA; Brit. Assn. Immed. Care Schemes; Brit. Assn. Accid. & Emerg. Med. Prev: Sen. Regist. (Orthop.) W.m. Hosp. Lond.; Surg. Manoram Christian Hosp. Thailand.

BELSTEAD, Susan Margaret Studholme Medical Centre, 50 Church Road, Ashford TW15 2TU Tel: 01784 420700 Fax: 01784 424503; 6 Stanwell Road, Ashford TW15 3ER Tel: 01784 251367 Fax: 01784 251367 — MB ChB 1969 Leeds; DObst RCOG 1971;

DA Eng. 1971. Prev: Clin. Asst. (Anaesth.) William Harvey Hosp. Ashford, Kent; Doctor Manorom Christian Hosp. Thailand.

BELT, John Derek (retired) 1 Church Street, Purton, Swindon SN5 4DS Tel: 01793 770331 — MB ChB 1950 Birm.; MRCS Eng. LRCP Lond. 1951; DObst RCOG 1952. Prev: Clin. Asst. N. View Hosp. Purton.

BELT, Mr Paul John 24 Constance Road, Worcester WR3 7NF Tel: 01905 454119 Email: pjbelt@internetnorth.com.av — BM BCh 1994 Oxf.; BA Oxf. 1991; FRCS Lond. 1996; FRCS (Gen.) 1998. Regist. (Surg.), Cairns Bsc Hosp., Cairns, Australia. Socs: RCS (Eng.); MPS. Prev: SHO (Plastic Surg.) Roy. Vict. Infirm. Newc. 1998; SHO (Gen. Surg.) Roy. Vict. Infirm. Newc.; SHO (Plastic Surg.) Ipswich Hosp. Qu.sland, Australia.

BELTON, Andrew Health Centre, Elliott St., Silsden, Keighley BD20 0DG Tel: 01535 52447 — MB ChB 1962 Leeds; BSc (Anat.) Leeds 1959, MB ChB 1962; MRCGP 1971; DObst RCOG 1964. (Leeds)

BELTON, Elaine Margaret (retired) Pebbledown, Pebblehill Road, Betchworth RH3 7BP Tel: 0173 784 3111 — MB BS 1951 Lond.; FRCP Ed. 1982, M 1960; DCH Eng. 1954. Prev: Cons. Paediatr. N.W. Surrey Hosp. Gp.

BELTON, Mollie Elizabeth Whiteley Head House, Steeton, Keighley BD20 6QS — MB ChB 1965 Leeds; DCH Eng. 1974.

BELTON, Patrick Anthony Penrhyn Surgery, 2A Penrhyn Avenue, Walthamstow, London E17 5DB Tel: 020 8527 2563 Fax: 020 8527 6583; 13 Village Park Close, Enfield EN1 2SG Tel: 020 8360 1335 — MB BCh BAO 1973 NUI; DCH Dub. 1978; MRCPI 1977; DTM & H Liverp. 1974. (University College Dub.) Socs: BMA. Prev: Trainee GP Newport.

BELTRAN DE GUEVARA MARTINEZ, Maria Luisa 25 Friary Avenue, Allenton, Derby DE24 9DD — LMS 1986 Basque Provinces.

BEM, Mr Christopher Charles 30 Foxglove Avenue, Leeds LS8 2QR — MB ChB 1977 Manch.; MD Manch. 1993; FRCS Eng. 1981.

BEM, Jerzy Ludwik 118 Albert Road, Jarrow NE32 5AG — MRCS Eng. LRCP Lond. 1975; MSc Lond. 1987; PhD Newc. 1978; MFPHM RCP (UK) 1989; Dip. Med. Warsaw 1969; Dip. Pharm. Med. RCP Ed. 1981. (Warsaw) Prev: Sen. Med. Off. DoH Lond.; Med. Dir. Kirby-Warrick Pharmaceuts. Ltd.; Ass. Med. Dir. Glaxo Pharmacol. Greenford.

BEM, Mary Jill Department of Anaesthesia, St James Hospital, Beckett St., Leeds LS9 7TF; 30 Foxglove Avenue, Roundhay, Leeds LS8 2QR Tel: 0113 265 4380 — MB ChB 1981 Leeds; FFA RCS Eng. 1987. Cons. (Anaesth.) St. James Univ. Hosp. Leeds. Socs: Assn. Anaesth.; World Federat. Soc. of Anaesth. Prev: Sen. Regist. (Anaesth.) St. James Univ. Hosp. Leeds; Lect. (Anaesth.) Univ. Zambia; Regist. (Anaesth.) St. James Univ. Hosp. Leeds.

BEMAND, Barrie Vernon Warwick Street Surgery, 18 Warwick Street, Rugby CV21 3DH Tel: 01788 540860 Fax: 01788 560988; The Mistle, Grange Farm, Biggin Hall Lane, Thurlaston, Rugby CV23 9LD Tel: 01788 811961 Email: barrieand.rynne@virgin.net — MB ChB 1970 Birm.; AFOM RCP Lond. 1989; MRCGP 1977. (Birmingham) p/t Chairm. Rugby Primary Care Gp.; Apptd. Doctor Ionising Radiat. Regulats; Med. Adviser to Isotron Plc Daventry, N.ants.; Med. Adviser to Blaulaero, Butler Leap, Rugby; Med. Adviser to Rugby High Sch.; Med. Adviser to Alstom Power Generation William Worth, Rugby. Socs: Rugby & Dist. Med. Soc; Soc. Occupat. Med. Prev: Lect. (Anat.) Univ. Birm. Med. Sch.; Ho. Phys. (Profess. Med. Unit) Qu. Eliz. Hosp. Birm.; Ho. Surg. Dudley Rd., Hosp. Birm.

BEMBRIDGE, Benjamin Albert (retired) 3/6 West Grange Gardens, Edinburgh EH9 2RA Tel: 0131 668 3809 — MB ChB Ed. 1941; MD Ed. 1956; DOMS Eng. 1948. Prev: Asst. Dir. Wellcome Trust.

BEMBRIDGE, Jane Lesley Anaesthetic Department, Bradford Royal Infirmary, Duckworth Lane, Bradford BD9 6RJ Tel: 01274 542200; 8 St. Francis Gardens, Fixby, Huddersfield HD2 2EU Tel: 01484 431002 — MB ChB 1979 Leeds; FRCA 1983. Cons. Anaesth. Bradford Hosps. NHS Trust. Socs: Assn. Anaesth. GB & Irel.; Obst. Anaesth. Assn. Prev: Sen. Regist. (Anaesth.) Yorks. Regional Scheme Leeds.

BEMBRIDGE, Michael Bradford Royal Infirmary, Duckworth Lane, Bradford BD9 6RJ Tel: 01274 542200; 8 St. Francis Gardens, Fixby, Huddersfield HD2 2EU Tel: 01484 431002 — MB ChB 1979 Leeds; FRCA 1983. Cons. Anaesth. Bradford Hosps. NHS Trust. Socs: Assn. Anaesth. GB & Irel. Prev: Cons. Anaesth. Huddersfield Roy. Infirm.; Sen. Regist. (Anaesth.) Yorks. Regional Scheme (Leeds).

BEN-SHLOMO, Yoav Dept. of Social Medicine, University of Bristol, Bristol BS8 2PR — MB BS 1985 Lond. Sen. Lect., Dept. Social Med. Univ. Bristol.

BEN-YOUNES, Mr Abdul Hakim Law Hospital NHS Trust, Carluke ML8 5ER Tel: 01698 361100 Fax: 01698 376671; Flat 2/1, 6 Walls St, Glasgow G1 1PA Tel: 0141 552 0027 Email: benyounes@aol.com — MB BCh 1983 Tripoli; FRCS Ed. 1990; FRCS (Gen Surg) 1998. (Fac. Med. Al-Fateh Univ. Tripoli, Libya) Cons. Surg. in Gen. Surg. & Interest in Upper Gastrointestinal Surg. Socs: Surg. Research Soc.; Brit. Assn. Surg. Oncol.; Assn. Surg. Prev: Specialist Regist. (Surg.) Higher Surgic. Trust N. E. of Scotl.; Research Fell. (Surg.) Aberd. Univ.; Regist. (Surg.) Higher Surgic Train. W. Scotl. Glas.

BENADY, David Roger 3 Swan Hill, Shrewsbury SY1 1NQ Tel: 01743 232167 Email: roger@rpsych.icom-web.com — MB BS 1959 Lond.; MRCS Eng. LRCP Lond. 1959; FRCPsych 1983, M 1971; DPM Eng. 1962; DCH Eng. 1961. (Lond. Hosp.) p/t Indep. Cons. Shrewsbury; Cons. Adolesc. Psychiat., Woodbourne Priory Hosp., 21 Woodbourne Rd., Birm. B17 8BY. Socs: Assn. for Family Ther. Prev: Cons. Child Psychiat. Shrops. Child & Family Serv. Shrops. NHS Ment. Health Trust; Sen. Regist. (Child Psychiat.) Mapperley Hosp.; Regist. (Psychiat.) Long Gr. Hosp. Epsom.

BENAIM, Moses Elias (retired) 12 Canterbury Close, Bamford, Rochdale OL11 5LZ Tel: 01706 648637 — MB ChB 1963 Manch.; FRCP Lond. 1986; MRCP (UK) 1969; MRCS Eng. LRCP Lond. 1965; DCH Eng. 1966; DObst RCOG 1966. Prev: Sen. Med. Regist. Roy. Vict. Infirm. Newc.

BENAIM, Silvio Edward House, Florence Nightinglae Hospital, 7 Lisson Grove, London NW1 6SH Tel: 020 7535 7901 Fax: 020 7724 8115; 30 Wood Lane, Highgate, London N6 5UB — MB BS 1948 Lond.; FRCP Lond. 1971, M 1952; MRCS Eng. LRCP Lond. 1948; FRCPsych 1971; DPM Lond. 1956. (Westm.) p/t Cons. Psychiat. Florence Nightingale Hosp.; Hon. Cons. Psychiat. Hosp. of St John & St Eliz. Socs: Fell. Roy. Soc. Med.; Mem. Hampstead Med. Soc. Prev: Cons. Psychol. Med. Roy. Free Hosp. Lond.; Cons. Psychiat. Halliwick & Friern Hosps. Lond.; Sen. Regist. Bethlem Roy. & Maudsley Hosps.

BENAMORE, Rachel Elaine 74 Rectory Road, Wanlip, Leicester LE7 4PL — BChir 1995 Camb.

BENARAN, Carlos Hairmyres Hospital, Annexe House, Eaglesham Road, E. Kilbride, Glasgow G75 8RG — LMS 1992 Basque Provinces.

BENARD, Maurice (retired) Flat 32, The Moorings, Leeds LS17 8EN Tel: 0113 268 6962 — M.B., Ch.B. Leeds 1947, BChD 1941; LDS Leeds 1940.

BENATAR-CATILLON, Jocelyne 48 The Little Boltons, London SW10 9LN — MD 1978 Paris.

BENATT, Joss Lower Allerton Farm, Dartington, Totnes TQ9 6DY — BM 1993 Soton.

BENATTAR, Karen Deborah Fyffe, Northfield Avenue, Pinner HA5 1AR — MB BS 1991 Lond.

BENAZON, Caroline Margaret (retired) The Health Centre, St Marys Road, Ferndown, Wimborne Tel: 01202 871261 — MB BS 1955 Lond.; MRCS Eng. LRCP Lond. 1955; DObst RCOG 1958. Prev: GP Wimborne.

BENAZON, David Behor (retired) Little Orchard, 12 Carroll Avenue, Ferndown, Wimborne BH22 8BP — MD Lond. 1961, MB BS 1951; MRCP Lond. 1953; MRCS Eng. LRCP Lond. 1951; FFA RCS Eng. 1959. Prev: Cons. Anaesth. Bournemouth & E. Dorset Hosp. Gp.

BENAZON, Lydia 1 Old Bakery Cottages, Charlton Marshall, Blandford Forum DT11 9NH — MB BS 1988 Lond.; DRCOG 1992; DCH RCP Lond. 1991.

BENBOW, Alastair Gerard Smithkline Beecham, Mundells, Welwyn Garden City AL7 3AY Tel: 020 8913 4628 Fax: 020 8913 4022 — MB BS 1982 Lond.; MRCP (UK) 1986; Dip. Pharm. Med. RCP (UK) 1991. (St. Thomas', London) Med. Dir. Smithkline Beecham UK. Socs: Brit. Thorac. Soc.; Eur. Respirat. Soc. Prev: Med. Dir. Lorex Synthelabo; Med. Dir. Genetech UK; Clin. Research Manager Fisons UK Operat. LoughBoro.

BENBOW, Emyr Wyn Department of Pathological Sciences, Stopford Building, The University, Oxford Road, Manchester M13 9PT Tel: 0161 276 8802, 07989 446825 Fax: 0161 276 8928 Email: ebenbow@man.ac.uk — MB ChB 1977 Manch.; BSc (Hons.) Manch. 1974; FRCPath 1995, M 1983. Sen. Lect. (Path.) Univ. Manch.; Hon. Cons. Path. Centr. Manch. HA. Prev: Regist. (Gen. Path.) Whiston Hosp. Merseyside.

BENBOW, Hilary Geraldine Brockwell Medical Group, Northumbria Road, Cramlington NE23 1XZ Tel: 01670 733700; 4 Oaklands, Darras Hall, Ponteland, Newcastle upon Tyne NE20 9PH — MB BChir 1981 Camb.; MRCGP 1990. (Camb.) Clin. Asst. (Dermat.) Roy. Vict. Infirm. Newc. Socs: BMA. Prev: Trainee GP Nottm.; SHO (O & G) St. Jas. Hosp. Leeds; SHO (Med.) Newham.

BENBOW, John Allen Yardley Green Health Centre, 75 Yardley Green Road, Birmingham B9 5PU Tel: 0121 773 3737; 15 Barnfield Drive, Solihull B92 0QB Tel: 0121 704 4745 — BM BCh 1954 Oxf.; MA, BM BCh Oxf. 1954; DObst RCOG 1956. (Oxf.) Hon. Univ. Lect. Profess. Dept. Gen. Pract. Univ. Birm. Prev: Orthop. Sen. Ho. Off. Roy. Salop Infirm. Shrewsbury; Ho. Surg. Horton Gen. Hosp.; Obst. Ho. Surg. Ch.ill Hosp. Oxf.

BENBOW, Rebecca Jane Bradeley Farm, Bourton, Much Wenlock TF13 6JN — MB ChB 1992 Birm.

BENBOW, Susan Jean Dept. of Medicine, Hairmyres Hospital, Eaglesham Rd, East Kilbride, Glasgow G75 8 Tel: 01355 220292 — MB ChB 1984 Bristol; MRCP (UK) 1988; MD 1996. (Bristol) Cons. Phys. (Diabetes & Endocrinol.); Hon. Sen. Lect., Dept. of Med., Glas. Univ. Prev: Research Fell. (Med.) Univ. Liverp.; Sen. Lect. Med. (Diabetes & Endocrinol.) Univ. of Liverp.; Hon. Cons. Phys. Whiston Hosp. Merseyside.

BENBOW, Susan Mary Penn Hospital, Penn Road, Wolverhampton WV4 5HN Tel: 01902 575151 Fax: 01902 444127 Email: dr.benbow@whc-tr.nhs.uk — MB ChB 1977 Manch.; MB ChB (Hons.) Manch. 1977; MSc Manch. 1982, BSc (Hons.) 1974; FRCPsych 1995, M 1981. Cons. Psychiat. (old age Psychiat.) Wolverhampton Health Care NHS Trust, Wolverhampton. Prev: Sen. Regist. (Psychiat.) Withington Hosp. Manch.; Cons. Psychiat. for the Elderly, Manch. Ment. Health Partnership, Manch.

BENCH, Christopher John Department of Psychiatry, Imperial College School of Medicine, St Dunstan's Road, London W6 8RP Tel: 020 8846 7387 Fax: 020 8846 7372 Email: c.bench@ic.ac.uk — MB BS 1985 Lond.; MRCPsych 1990. (St. Mary's Hosp. Med. Sch.) Sen. Lect. (Psychiat.) Char. Cross & W.m. Med. Sch. Lond.; Vis. Worker MRC Cyclotron Unit Hammermsith Hosp. Lond.; Hon. Sen. Lect. Roy. Postgrad. Med. Sch. Prev: Sen. Regist. (Psychiat.) Maudsley Hosp. Lond.; Regist. (Psychiat.) Roy. Free Hosp. Lond.; SHO Rotat. (Psychiat.) Roy. Free Hosp. Lond.

BENCH, John Tytherleigh (retired) 66 Bullocks Lane, Hertford SG13 8BT Tel: 01992 582497 — MB BS 1958 Lond.; MRCS Eng. LRCP Lond. 1958; DObst RCOG 1959. Prev: GP Hertford.

BENCH, Jonathan Justin Wells Health Centre, Glastonbury Road, Wells BA5 1XJ Tel: 01749 672137 Fax: 01749 679833 Email: jonathan.bench@wellshc.co.uk; Beryl Cottage, Hawkers Lane, Wells BA5 3JP Tel: 01749 676915 — MB BS 1987 Lond.; MRCGP 1991; DRCOG 1991; DCH RCP Lond. 1990. Prev: Trainee GP Bath VTS.

BENCH, Lucinda Jane The Westbury on Trym Surgery, 60 Falcondale Road, Westbury on Trym, Bristol BS9 3BU — MB BS 1985 Lond.; MRCGP 2000; Cert. Family Plann. JCC 1989; DRCOG 1989; DCH RCP Lond. 1988. p/t GP Bristol Retainer Scheme. Prev: Trainee GP Maidstone VTS.

BENCH, Matthew Tytherleigh Barton House Health Centre, 233 Albion Road, London N16 9JT Tel: 020 7249 5511 Fax: 020 7254 8985; 68A Burma Road, London N16 9BJ Tel: 020 7241 5253 — MB BS 1984 Lond.

BENCH, Peter Dominic The Hildenborough Medical Group, Tonbridge Road, Hildenborough, Tonbridge TN11 9HL Tel: 01732 838777 Fax: 01732 838297; 44 St. James Road, Tunbridge Wells TN1 2JZ — MB BS 1989 Lond.; MRCGP 1993; DFFP 1993; DRCOG 1993; DCH RCP Lond. 1992.

BENDALL, Anthony (retired) 402 Dorchester Road, Weymouth DT3 5AJ Tel: 01305 816116 Fax: 01305 816116 — MRCS Eng. LRCP Lond. 1951; DM Canada 1963; DAvMed, Inst. Aviat. Med. Toronto 1965. Appt. Med. Examr. for Commercial Drivers; Dir. Med. Film. Produc. (16mm). Prev: Indep. GP Weymouth.

BENDALL, Michael John Directorate of Health Care of the Elderly, Queens Medical Centre, Nottingham NG7 2UH — MB BS Lond. 1967; BSc (Anat.) Lond. 1964, MB BS 1967; DM Nottm. 1988; FRCP Lond. 1986; MRCP (UK) 1971; MRCS Eng. LRCP Lond. 1967. (Univ. Coll. Hosp.) Cons. Phys. Dept. Healthc/o the Elderly Univ. Hosp. Nottm. Socs: BMA & Mem. Brit. Geriat. Soc. Prev: Sen. Lect. Univ. Nottm.; Cons. Phys. Geriat. Med. St. Mary's Hosp. Colchester; Sen. Regist. (Geriat.) Univ. Coll. Hosp. Lond.

BENDALL, Patricia Rampton Hospital Authority, Retford DN22 0PD Tel: 01777 248321 — MB BS 1971 Lond.; BSc (Anat.) Lond. 1968; MRCS Eng. LRCP Lond. 1971; MRCPsych 1991. (Univ. Coll. Hosp.) Cons. in Forens. Learning Disabil. Psychiat. Socs: BMA. Prev: Clin. Dir. Rampton Hosp.; Cons. Psychiat. Community Trust S. Derbysh.; Clin. Dir. (Special Servs.) Forens. Learning Disabil. Psychiat.

BENDALL, Richard Pierre Truro Public Health Laboratory, Penvintinnie Lane, Treliske, Truro TR1 3LQ Tel: 01872 254940 — MB BS 1985 Lond.; BSc Lond. 1982; MRCP (UK) 1985; MRCPath 1993; DTM & H RCP Lond. 1994. Cons. Med. Microbiol. Truro Pub. Health Laborat. Prev: Regist. (Microbiol.) Addenbrooke's Hosp. Camb.

BENDALL, Mr Robin (retired) The Cider House, Allowenshay, Hinton St George TA17 8TB Tel: 01460 57268 Fax: 01460 55791 Email: ciderhouse@btinternet.com — MB BS Lond. 1956; FRCS Eng. 1964. Prev: Cons. Orthop. Surg. St. Geo. Hosp. Lond.

BENDEFY, Ilona Maria The Close, Church Lane, Bakewell DE45 1DE — MB BS 1982 Lond.; MRCP (UK) 1986. (St. Thos.) GP N. Derbysh. Health Auth.; Hon. Sen. Regist. (Paediat.) Multiple Births Foundat. Qu. Charlottes & Chelsea Hosp Lond; Staff Grade Paediat., Community Child Health, N. Derbysh. Socs: Brit. Paediat. Assn. Prev: GP Princip., Wandsworth.

BENDELOW, Keith 6 Arncliffe Avenue, Sunderland SR4 8QJ — MB BS 1979 Lond.; MRCGP 1985; DCH RCP Lond. 1988; DRCOG 1986.

BENDER, Lloyd Eric Flat 8, 16 Henrietta St., Bath BA2 6LW — MB ChB 1991 Cape Town.

BENDER, Mr Solomon Albury, 2 Lache Lane, Chester CH4 7LR Tel: 01244 678900 — MB ChB 1937 Liverp.; MD Liverp. 1947; FRCS Ed. 1948; FRCOG 1959, M 1947. Hon. Cons. O & G Chester Area. Socs: Fell. N. Eng. Obst. & Gyn. Soc. Prev: Sen. Lect. (O & G) Univ. Liverp.; Regist. (Obst. & Obst.) Liverp. Roy. Infirm.; Squadron Ldr. RAFVR.

BENDER-BACHER, Hubertus Friedrich Ferdinand Richard Hertford College, Catte St., Oxford OX1 3BW Email: rbbaker@hotmail.com — MB BS 1992 Monash; BA (Hons.) Oxf. 1997. (Alfred Hospital Melbourne Australia) SHO Spinal Unit, Stoke Mandeville Hosp. Socs: BMA. Prev: SHO (ENT) Epsom Gen. Hosp.; SHO (A & E) Mayday Univ Hosp.; Ho. Off. Leeds Gen. Infirm.

BENDIG, Justin William Allen Department of Medical Microbiology, Epsom General Hospital, Epsom — MB BS 1981 Lond.; MSc Lond. 1988; MRCPath 1990. Cons. Microbiol. Epsom and St. Helier NHS Trust, based at Epsom Gen. Hosp.

BENDING, Jeremy John District Diabetes Centre, District General Hospital, King's Drive, Eastbourne BN21 2UD Tel: 01323 414902 Fax: 01323 414964; 25 Grange Road, Eastbourne BN21 4HG Tel: 01323 648526 — MB BS 1974 Lond.; BSc Lond. 1971, MD 1985; FRCP Lond. 1993; MRCP (UK) 1977; LMCC 1981. (Westm.) Cons. Phys. (Diabetes & Endocrinol.) Dist. Gen. Hosp. E.bourne. Socs: Med. & Sci. Sect. Brit. Diabetic Assn.; Eur. Assn. for Study Diabetes.; Assn. of Brit. Clin. Diabetologists (Nat. Comm. Mem.). Prev: Wolfson Fell., Hon. Sen. Regist. & Lect. (Med.) Unit Metab. Med. United Med. & Dent Sch. Guy's Hosp. Lond.; Regist. Profess. Med. Unit Addenbrooke's Hosp. Camb.

BENDING, Michael Roy 36 Inner Park Road, Wimbledon, London SW19 6DD Tel: 020 8788 7378 & profess. 081 644 4343 — MB BChir 1970 Camb.; MSc Lond. 1975; MA Camb. 1975, MB 1970, BChir 1969; FRCP Lond. 1987, M 1972. (Camb. & Westm.) Cons. Phys. & Nephrol. St. Helier Hosp. Carshalton. Socs: Med. Research Soc. & Renal Assn. Prev: Lect. (Med.) W.m. Med. Sch.; Research Fell. Roy. Postgrad. Med. Sch. Lond.; SHO Nat. Hosp. Nerv. Dis. Qu. Sq. Lond.

BENDKOWSKI, Boleslaw (retired) 1 Burches Mead, Common Approach, Benfleet SS7 3PX Tel: 01268 779378 — MB ChB Ed.

1949; MD Ed. 1960; FRCGP 1971. Prev: Indep. Pract. (Allergy) Leigh-on-Sea.

BENDOMIR, Astrid 80 Stanley Street, Aberdeen AB10 6UQ Tel: 01224 591093; 10 Mill Court, Inverness IV2 3UJ Tel: 01463 704000 — State Exam 1989 Pavia. Career Regist. (O & G) Raigmore Hosp. Inverness. Prev: Regist. Aberd. Matern.; SHO Glas. Roy. Infirm. & Falkirk & Dist. Roy. Infirm.

BENDOR, Annette Michal The Park End Surgery, 3 Park End, South Hill Park, London NW3 2SE Tel: 020 7435 7282 — MB BS 1991 Lond.

BENE, Jacqueline 9 New Green, Harwood, Bolton BL2 4DQ — MB ChB 1988 Sheff.; MRCP (UK) 1992. Cons. Phys. (Gen. & Geriat. Med.) The Roy. Bolton Hosp. Farnworth Bolton. Socs: Brit. Geriat. Soc. Prev: Clin. Research Fell. (Geriat. Med.) Hope Hosp. Salford; Sen. Regist. (Geriat. & Gen. Med.) Oldham Roy. Infirm.; Regist. (Geriat. & Gen. Med.) Bolton Dist. & Gen. Hosp.

BENECH, Irene 7 Kendal Bank, Leeds LS3 1NR — State Exam Med 1987 Berlin.

BENEDICT, Canute Bronllwyn Surgery, Bronllwyn, Pentyrch, Cardiff CF4 8QL Tel: 029 2089 2670 Fax: 029 2089 2118; 37 Heol-y-Pentre, Pentyrch, Cardiff CF15 9QD Tel: 029 2089 2466 — MB BS 1971 Ceylon; DPD Wales 1992. (Colombo) Clin. Asst. (Psychiat.) S. Glam. HA. Socs: BMA & M. Glam. LMC. Prev: Regist. (Psychiat.), WhitCh. Hosp. Cardiff.

BENEDICT, Cleophas Bharathan 16 Parkland Avenue, Slough SL3 7LQ — MB BS 1987 Lond.

BENEDIKT, Nicholas Alexander Kingsbury Court Surgery, Church Street, Dunstable LU5 4RS Tel: 01582 663218 Fax: 01582 476488 Email: nicholas.benedikt@gp-e81045.nhs.uk; Tel: 01582 663956 — MB BS 1980 Lond.; BSc (Hons.) Lond. 1977,; DFFP 1994; DRCOG 1983. (Middlesex Hospital Medical School) GP Princip.

BENEDIKTSSON, Rafn Department for Endocrine & Metabolic Diseases, University Department of Medicine, Western General Hospital, Edinburgh EH4 2XU Tel: 0131 651 1026 Fax: 0131 651 1085 Email: r.benediktsson@ed.ac.uk; 3 Merchiston Crescent, Edinburgh EH10 5AL Tel: 0131 221 9118 — Cand Med et Chir 1987 Reyjavik; Cand Med et Chir Reykjavik 1987; PhD Ed. 1995; MRCP (UK) 1995. Lect. (Med., Endocrinol. & Diabetes) Univ. of Edin. W.ern Gen. Hosp. Edin. Socs: Soc. Endocrinol.; Brit. Diabetic Assn.; Icelandic Med. Assn. Prev: Wellcome Advanced Train. Fell. (Endocrine & Metab. Dis.) W.. Gen. Hosp. Edin.; Research Fell. (Med.) Univ. Edin.

BENEPAL, Taqdir Singh 114 Audley Road, London NW4 3HG — MB BS 1993 Lond.

BENETT, Ivan John Alexandra Practice, 365 Wilbraham Road, Manchester M16 8NG Tel: 0161 860 4400 Fax: 0161 860 7324; 29 Green Walk, Whalley Range, Manchester M16 9RE Tel: 0161 881 5786 Fax: 0161 860 7324 Email: ivanbenett@hotmail.com — MB ChB 1979 Manch.; FRCP 2000; FRCGP 2001; MMedSci Birm. 1993; MRCP (UK) 1984; MRCGP 1985; DRCOG 1983. (Manchester) GP Manch.; Chair of the Professional Excutive Comm. of Centr. Mancheter PCT.

BENETT, Marc Sylvio (retired) 9 Danescourt, Gilfach Road, Rhyddings, Neath Tel: 01639 4674 — MB BS 1957 Durh.; MRCOG 1962, DObst 1960. Cons. O & G Neath Gen. & Port Talbot Hosps. Prev: Regist. Roy. Vict. Infirm. Newc.

BENETT, Sheila Anne 34 Almondbury Close, Almondbury, Huddersfield HD5 8XX — MB ChB 1984 Manch.

BENEY, Jean Catherine Oak Lodge Medical Centre, 234 Burnt Oak Broadway, Edgware HA8 0AP Tel: 020 8952 1202 Fax: 020 8381 1156; 16 Woodcroft Avenue, Mill Hill, London NW7 2AG Tel: 020 8959 4330 Email: jbeney@aol.com — MB BS 1975 Lond.; MRCS Eng. LRCP Lond. 1975; DRCOG 1977. (St. Mary's) Bd mem. W. Barnet PCG; Trainer Edgware Middlx.; Trustee Edgware Postgrad. Centre. Prev: Ho. Surg. (Obst.) Edgware Gen. Hosp. Middlx.; Ho. Surg. Surgic. Unit St. Mary's Hosp. Lond.; Ho. Phys. Edgware Gen. Hosp. Middlx.

BENEY, John Robert Worthing Community Mental Health Team, Greenacres, Homefield Road, Worthing BN11 2HS Tel: 01903 843384; Treeview, Penton Hook Road, Staines TW18 2HU — MB BS 1986 Newc.; MRCPsych 1991; Dip.Lon.1998; (Forensic Mental Health) Dip.Lon.1998. Cons. Adult & Forens. Psychiat. Worthing Community Ment. Health Team. Socs: Roy. Coll. Psychiat. Prev: Sen. Registra, St. Geo.s, Lond.; Registra, St.Lawrences,Cornw.; SHO Exeter,Devon.

BENFIELD, Grant Frederick Allen Department of Respiratory Medicine, Ysbty Gwynedd, Penrhosgarnedd, Bangor LL57 2PW Tel: 01248 384330 Fax: 01248 384764 Email: grant.benfield@nww-tr.wales.nhs.uk; Mefus, Glyngarth, Bryn Mel Hill, Menai Bridge LL59 5PF Tel: 01248 712365 — MB ChB 1973 Bristol; MD Bristol 1989; FRCP Lond. 1996; MRCP (UK) 1977; DA Eng. 1976. (Bristol) Cons. Phys. (Gen. & Respirat. Med.) Dept. Res. Med. Dist. Gen. Hosp. Gwynedd,N.W. Wales, NHS Trust. Socs: (Treas.) Welsh Thoracic Soc.; Brit. Thorac. Soc. Prev: Sen. Regist. (Med. & Chest Dis.) E. Birm. Hosp.; Regist. (Thoracic Med.) Llandough & Sully Hosp.; Regist. (Med.) Plymouth Gen. Hosp.

BENFIELD, Helen 18 Jebb Street, London E3 2TL — MB BS 1998 Lond.; MB BS Lond 1998.

BENFIELD, John Edward Charles 97 Rosebank, Holyport Road, Fulham, London SW6 6LJ — MB BS 1981 Lond.

BENFORD, Steven Charles Friarage Hospital, Northallerton DL6 1JG Tel: 01609 779911; 61 Thirsk Road, Northallerton DL6 1PP Tel: 01609 772400 Email: steve.benford@lineone.net — MB ChB 1986 Leic.; DObst 1993; DA (UK) 1990. (Leicester) Staff Anaesth. Friarage Hosp. N.allerton; Prison Med. Off. Prev: GP Oamaru, NZ.

BENGANI, Kharag Singh 10 Great Portman Mansions, Chiltern St., London W1U 6NT Tel: 020 7224 0978 — MB BS 1965 Calcutta; FRCOG 1986, M 1972; DRCOG 1969.

BENGER, Jonathan Richard Emergency Department, Bristol Royal Infirmary, Marlborough Street, Bristol BS2 8HW Fax: 07092 249091 Email: jb@sectae.org.uk — MB ChB 1990 Bristol; FRCS Eng. 1995; DA UK 1996; DCH Lond. 1997. Specialist Regist. (A & E) Bristol Roy. Infirm., Bristol.

BENGHIAT, Albert Department of Oncology, Leicester Royal Infirmary, Leicester LE1 5WW Tel: 0116 258 5081 Fax: 0116 258 6990 — MB BChir 1977 Camb.; MA Camb. 1977; FRCP Lond. 1994; MRCP (UK) 1978; FRCR 1983. (Camb. & Middlx.) Cons. Oncologist, Univ of Leics. NHS Trust; Hon. Sen. Lec. Uni. Of Leics; Lead Clinician, Leics. Cancer Network. Prev: Sen. Regist. (Radiother.) Plymouth Gen. Hosp.; Regist. (Radiother.) Ch.ill Hosp. Oxf.; Cons. Oncologist Derbysh. Roy. Inf.

BENGOUGH, Eirwen Anne 90 Ochiltree, Dunblane FK15 0DF — MB BCh 1981 Wales.

BENHAM, Clare Louise 72 Graseley Road, Three Mile Cross, Reading RG7 1BJ — MB BS 1990 Lond.

BENHAM, Jonathan Douglas 45 Winnie Road, Selly Oak, Birmingham B29 6JU Tel: 0121 689 5128 Email: jdbenham@msn.com — MB ChB 1996 Birm. (Univ. Birm.) SHO (Med.) Good Hope Hosp. Sutton Coldfield Birm. Socs: BMA; Med. Defence Union. Prev: SHO (A & E Med.) Good Hope Hosp. Sutton Coldfield; Ho. Off. (Trauma & Gen. Surg.) Univ. Hosp. Birm.; Ho. Off. (Gen. & Liver Med.) Univ. Hosp. Birm.

BENHAM, Maria Dept. of Anaesthetics, Birmingham Heartlands Hospital, Bordesley Green East, Birmingham B9 5SS — BM BS Nottm. 1989; BMedSci (Hons.) 1987; FRCA 1994. Cons. Anaesth. Birm. Heartlands Hosp.

BENHAM, Peter (retired) 41 Long Lane, Tilehurst, Reading RG31 6YN Tel: 01734 428167 — LMSSA 1947 Lond. Assoc. Specialist Accid. & Orthop. Dept. Roy. Berks. Hosp. Reading.

BENHAM, Stuart William 27 Holyoake Road, Oxford OX3 8AF Email: stuart.benham@nda.ox.ac.uk — MB ChB 1988 Glas.; MRCP (UK) 1992; FRCA 1995. (Glas.) Sen. Regist. (Intens. Care) Oxf.

BENIANS, Richard Gore (retired) 6 Hall Park Avenue, Westcliff on Sea SS0 8NR — MD 1951 Camb.; MA Camb. 1941, MD 1951, MB BChir Camb. 1940; FRCP Lond. 1975, M 1949. Cons. Geriat. & Phys. S.end HA. Prev: Asst. Geriat. Bradford A & B Hosp. Gps.

BENIANS, Robin Christopher 11 Windermere Road, Muswell Hill, London N10 2RD Tel: 020 8883 4511 Fax: 020 8444 7998 — MB BChir 1954 Camb.; MD Camb. 1974; MRCS Eng. LRCP Lond. 1954; FRCPsych 1983, M 1971; DPM Eng. 1959. (Camb. & Mid.) Locum Cons. Child & Family Psychiat. Socs: Fell., Roy. Soc. of Med.; Assn. Child Psychol. & Psychiat.; Brit. Assn. Adoption & Fostering. Prev: Cons. Dr. Barnardo's; Cons. Psychiat. Ealing Child Guid. Serv.; Sen. Regist. (Child Psychiat.) Guy's Hosp. Lond.

BENIERAKIS, Constantin 40 Woodville Gardens, Ealing, London W5 2LQ Tel: 020 8997 3821 — MB BCh BAO 1957 Dub.; BA Dub.

1954, MB BCh BAO 1957; FRCP Canada 1972; Dip. Amer. Bd. Psychiat. & Neurol. 1968; Dip. Psych McGill 1964. (Univ. Dub.) Socs: BMA & Canad. Psychiat. Assn.

BENINGFIELD, Sheilah Antonia (retired) Hall Farm Barn, 25A Main St., Woodborough, Nottingham NG14 6EA Tel: 0115 965 5840 — MB BS 1960 Lond.; MRCP Lond. 1967; MRCS Eng. LRCP Lond. 1960; DCH Eng. 1963; DObst RCOG 1962; FRCP 1987; FRCPCH 1997. Med. Adviser to S.well Diocesan Counc. for Family Care, Notts. Prev: Cons. Paediat. Kingsmill Centre for Health Care Servs. Trust.

BENISON, Alan (retired) Tatsfield Lodge, Ricketts Hill Road, Tatsfield, Westerham TN16 2NA Tel: 01959 572654 — MB BS 1963 Lond.; MRCS Eng. LRCP Lond. 1963; DRCOG 1965.

BENISON, Patricia Margaret Department of Anaesthetics, Hinchingbrooke healthcare NHS Trust, Huntingdon PE29 6NT Tel: 01480 416416 Email: patricia.benison@hbhc-tr.anglox.nhs.uk; Lyndewode, 48 Mill Way, Grantchester, Cambridge CB3 9NB — MB BS 1971 Lond.; MRCS Eng. LRCP Lond. 1970; FRCA 1993; FFA RCS Eng. 1977; DObst RCOG 1972. (St. Bart.) Cons. Anaesth. Hinchingbrooke Hosp. Huntingdon. Socs: (Linkman) Assn. Anaesth.; BMA; Obst. Anaesth. Assn. Prev: Sen. Regist. (Anaesth.) Cambs. AHA (T); Sen. Regist. (Anaesth.) Leics. AHA (T); Regist. (Anaesth.) Addenbrooke's Hosp. Camb.

BENISTON, Mark Andrew c/o Department of Anaesthesia, South Warwickshire Hospital, Lakin Road, Warwick CV34 5BW Tel: 01926 495321; 61 Coppice Road, Whitnash, Leamington Spa CV31 2JB — MB ChB 1988 Otago. SHO (Anaesth.) S. Warks. Hosp. Warwick.

BENJAFIELD, John Gordon (retired) Slough House, China Lane, Bulphan, Upminster RM14 3RL Tel: 01375 891263 — MB BS 1954 Lond. Prev: Cons. Path. The Doctor's Laborat. Lond.

BENJAFIELD, Richard George Peverell Park Surgery, 162 Outlands Road, Peverell, Plymouth PL2 3PR Tel: 01752 791438 Fax: 01752 783623 — MB BS 1979 London; MB BS 1979 London.

BENJAMIN, Mr Albert Emanuel The Surgery, Wood Houses, Little London, Walsall WS1 3EP Tel: 01922 28280 Fax: 01922 23023 — MB BChir 1976 Camb.; FRCS Ed. 1980.

BENJAMIN, Mr Alexander, OStJ Fosse House, Brownlow Road, Berkhamsted HP4 1HD Tel: 01442 862720 Fax: 01442 864604 Email: bobbie_alec@bigfoot.com — MB BS 1946 Lond; FRCS 1953 Eng. (Lond. Hosp.) Hon. Cons. Orthop. & Traum. Surg. St. Albans & Hemel Hempstead NHS Trust; Hon. Lect. Inst. Orthop. Roy. Nat. Orthop. Hosp. Socs: Cerebral Palsy Surg. Soc.; Rheumatoid Arthritis Surg. Soc.; Brit. Soc. Surg. Hand. Prev: Cons. Orthop. & Traum. Surg. W. Herts. Hosp. Hemel Hempstead & Peace Memor. Hosp. Watford; Sen. Regist. (Orthop.) Char. Cross Hosp. Lond.

BENJAMIN, Andrea Rose 52 The Drive, London NW11 9TL — MB BS 1994 Lond.

BENJAMIN, Ann Clwydian Community Care Trust, 16 Grosvenor Road, Wrexham LL11 1BU Tel: 01978 356551; Hilbre, Wern, Weston Rhyn, Oswestry SY10 7LG — MB ChB Liverp. 1966. SCMO (Child Health) Clwydian Community Care Trust; Med. Off. (Family Plann.) Wrexham. Socs: Fac. Comm. Health; Dip. Fac. Family Plann.

BENJAMIN, Arra The Health Centre, Gilfach Goch, Porth PH1 3PF Tel: 01443 672622; 13 Green Park, Talbot Green, Pontyclun CF72 8RB — MB BS 1967 Osmania. (Osmania)

BENJAMIN, Charlotte Abigail 9 Elm Close, London NW4 2PH Tel: 020 8202 9734 Fax: 020 8202 9734 Email: elliot.benjamin@virgin.net — MB BS 1997 Lond.; BSc (Hons) Lond. 1994; DCH 1999. (UCH) GP Rotat. Whittington Hosp. Prev: Ho. Off. (Gen. Med.) Whittington Hosp.; Ho. Off. (Gen. Surg.) Luton & Dunstable Hosp.

BENJAMIN, Christopher Meyer North Tyneside Hospital, Rake Lane, North Shields NE29 8 Tel: 0191 259 6660 — MB ChB 1980 Manch.; MRCPI 1985; FRCPCH 1997. (St. And.) Cons. Paediat. & Clin. Dir. Child Health Directorate N. Tyneside Hosp. Prev: Cons. Community Paediat. W. Lancs. NHS Trust; Sen. Regist. (Community Paediat.) Mersey RHA; Tutor (Rheum.) Univ. Manch.

BENJAMIN, Elizabeth Brae House, 31 Chilbolton Avenue, Winchester SO22 5HE — MB BS 1975 Madras. (Christian Med. Coll. Vellore) Sen. Clin. Lect. (Histopath.) Univ. Coll. Lond. Med. Sch.; Hon. Cons. UCL Hosps. NHS Trust. Socs: Assn. Clin. Path.; Roy. Coll. Path.; Path. Soc. Prev: Lect. (Path.) Univ. Manch.; Regist. Soton. Gen. Hosp.

BENJAMIN, Mr Elliot Douglas 9 Elm Close, London NW4 2PH Tel: 020 8202 9734 Fax: 020 8202 9734 Email: elliot.benjamin@virgin.net — MB ChB 1995 Bristol; MB ChB (Hons.) Bristol 1995; BSc (Hons.) Bristol 1992; MRCS (Eng) 1998. (Bristol) SHO (ENT), Roy. Nat. Throat, Nose & Ear Hosp. Socs: LJMS-Jun. Doctor Rep. Prev: SHO (Neurosurg.), Nat. Hosp. for Neurol. & Neurosurg.; SHO Rotat. (Surg.) N.wick Pk. & St. Mark's Hosp.; SHO (ENT) Luton Hosp.

BENJAMIN, Mr Ernest Jai Santosh Department of Surgery, Southport & Formby District General Hospital, Town Lane, Southport PR8 6PN — MB BS 1972 Madras; FRCS Glas. 1977.

BENJAMIN, Professor Irving Stuart Department of Surgery, King's College School of Medicine & Dentistry, London SE5 9PJ Tel: 020 7346 3017 Fax: 020 7346 3438 Email: irving.benjamin@kcl.ac.uk; Taverners, 120a High St, Deal CT14 6BB Tel: 01304 367197 — MB ChB 1971 Glas.; BSc (Hons.) Glas. 1969, MD 1987; FRCS Eng. 1991; FRCS Glas. 1976. Prof. Surg. Guy's, King's & SDt. Thomas' Sch. of Med., Lond.; Vice-Chairm. Div. of Surg. Guy's King's & St.Thomas Sch. of Med., Lond. Socs: Internat. Hepato-Pancreato Biliary Assn.; Brit. Soc. Gastroenterol.; Fell. Roy. Soc. Med. (Vice-Pres. Surg. Sect.). Prev: Sen. Lect. & Hon. Cons. Surg. Roy. Postgrad. Med. Sch. & Hammersmith Hosp. Lond.; Lect. (Surg.) Roy. Infirm. Glas.; Sen. Med. Off. (Surg.) Groote Schuur Hosp. Cape Town, S. Afr.

BENJAMIN, John Amit 13 Green Park, Talbot Green, Pontyclun CF72 8RB — MB BCh 1998 Wales.

BENJAMIN, Mr Jonathan Charles Department of Neurosurgery, Oldchurch Hospital, Romford RM7 0BE Tel: 01708 708010 Fax: 01708 708124 Email: jonathan@craniolink.demon.co.uk — MB BS 1980 Lond.; FRCS Eng. 1985; FRCS Ed. 1985. (Lond. Hosp.) Cons. Neurosurg. OldCh. Hosp. Romford; Clin. director Neurosci.s Havering Hosp. NHS trust. Socs: Fell. Roy. Soc. Med.; Soc. Brit. Neurol. Surg. Prev: Lect. & Sen. Regist. (Neurosurg.) St. Bart. Hosp. Lond.; ICRF Research Fell. (Neurosurg.) Frenchay Hosp. Bristol; Regist. (Neurosurg.) The Lond. Hosp.

BENJAMIN, Joseph Gerald Avenue Medical Practice, 7 Reney Avenue, Sheffield S8 7FH Tel: 0114 237 7649 — MB ChB 1972 Sheff.; DA Eng. 1975.

BENJAMIN, Joseph Myer (retired) 964 Hertford Road, Waltham Cross EN8 7RU Tel: 01992 764336 Fax: 01992 764336 — MB ChB 1945 Leeds; MB ChB (Hons.) Leeds 1945. Mem. Gray's Inn; Clin. Research Asst. N. Middlx. Hosp. Lond.; Staff Cheshunt Cottage Hosp. Prev: Ho. Phys. Roy. Infirm. Bradford.

BENJAMIN, Larry 83 Wendover Road, Stoke Mandeville, Aylesbury HP22 5TD — MB BS 1980 Lond.; FRCOphth 1989; FRCS Ed. 1985; FCOphth 1989; DO RCS Eng. 1984. Cons. Ophth. Surg. Stoke Mandeville Hosp. Aylesbury. Socs: RSM; UKISCRS; EVER. Prev: Clin. Lect. (Ophth.) Univ. Oxf.; Regist. (Ophth.) Moorfields Eye Hosp.

BENJAMIN, Lois Deborah Brick Lane Surgery, 28 Brick Lane, Enfield EN3 5BA Tel: 020 8443 0413 Fax: 020 8805 9097; 964 Hertford Road, Waltham Cross EN8 7RU Tel: 020 8245 9580 — MB BS 1978 Lond. (St. Mary's Hosp. Med. Sch.)

BENJAMIN, Marie Suzy Moor House, Grange Road, Bromley Cross, Bolton BL7 9AX — MB ChB 1975 Manch.

BENJAMIN, Padma Dorothy Mapleton Day Hospital, Derby City General Hospital, Uttoxeter Road, Derby DE22 3NE — MB BS 1962 Kerala; MRCPsych 1975.

BENJAMIN, Sidney The Manchester Clinic, Manchester Royal Infirmary, Oxford Road, Manchester M13 9WL Tel: 0161 276 4486 Fax: 0161 276 8774 — MB BS 1964 Lond.; MPhil Lond. 1970, MD 1976; MRCS Eng. LRCP Lond. 1964; FRCPsych 1980 M 1973; DPM Eng. 1970. (Middlx.) Sen. Lect. (Psychiat.) Univ. Manch.; Hon. Cons. Manch. Roy. Infirm. Socs: Roy. Soc. Med.; Brit. Med. Assn.; Manch. Med. Soc. Prev: Sen. Regist. Bethlem Roy. & Maudsley Hosps. & Middlx. Hosp. Lond.; Research Worker Inst. Psychiat. Lond.

BENJAMIN, Sigmund Jenkins South Reddish Medical Centre, The Surgery, Reddish Road, Stockport SK5 7QU — MB ChB 1980 Manch.

BENJAMIN, Sylvia Department Haematology, St George's Hospital, Tooting, London SW17; 7A Robin Hood Lane, Sutton SM1 2RN — MB BS 1983 Lond.; BSc (Hons.) Lond. 1980; MRCP (UK) 1987. Sen. Regist. (Haemat.) St. Geo. Hosp. Lond.

BENJAMIN, Usha Bharathi Wrightington General Hospital, Hall Appley Bridge, Wigan WN6 9EP — MB BS 1972 Madras; FFA RCS Eng. 1979.

BENKE, Edward John 315 Birmingham Road, Sutton Coldfield B72 1ED — MB ChB 1994 Manch.

BENKERT, Stephan Theodor Crown Medical Practice, Tamworth Health Centre, Upper Gungate, Tamworth B79 7EA Tel: 01827 58728 Fax: 01827 63873; Crown Medical Practicer, Tamworth Heath Centre, Tamworth B79 7EA Tel: 01827 58728 — State Exam Med 1987 Mainz; MRCGP 1996; DRCOG 1991; DTM & H Liverp. 1990. (Mainz) GP Princip.

BENN, Ann (retired) The Healey Suite, The Grange, Lord Austin Drive, Bromsgrove B60 1RB Tel: 0121 445 6004 — MB ChB Birm. 1961.

BENN, Desmond Keith 16 Lily Crescent, Newcastle upon Tyne NE2 2SP — MB BCh 1976 Witwatersrand.

BENN, Helen Mary Victoria Road Health Centre, Washington NE37 2PU Tel: 0191 417 3557; The Coachman's Lodge, Greenwood, Shotley Bridge, Consett DH8 0SZ — MB BS 1979 Newc.; MRCGP 1986. Prev: Trainee GP N.ld. VTS; Regist. (O & G) Newc. VTS.

BENN, Jane Melanie 2 Pangbourne Drive, Stanmore HA7 4QT Tel: 020 8958 8557 Fax: 020 8958 2918 — MB BS 1978 Lond.; DFFP 1993; Joint Cert. Contracep. (Roy. Coll. Obst. & Gyn.) 1980. (Middlx. Hosp. Med. Sch.) Indep. GP Stanmore; Med. Examr. Norwich Union Life Assur. Soc. Socs: Brit. Med. Acupunct. Soc. & Assur. Med. Soc. Prev: Med. Off. BUPA Med. Centres; Clin. Med. Off. (Family Plann.) Barnet HA; Clin. Asst. (Venerol.) Centr. Middlx. Hosp. Lond.

BENN, Jonathan James Diabetes Centre, Queen's Hospital, Belvedere Road, Burton-on-Trent DE13 0RB Tel: 01283 566333 Fax: 01283 567579 Email: 101527.2230@compuserve.com; Draycott Mill Farm, Sudbury, Ashbourne DE6 5GX Tel: 01283 820386 — MB BChir 1978 Camb.; MB BChir Camb. 19789; MA Camb. 1975, MD 1992; FRCP Lond. 1996; MRCP (UK) 1980. Cons. Phys. (Diabetes & Endocrinol.) Burton Dist. Hosp. Burton-on-Trent. Prev: Lect. & Sen. Regist. (Med.) St. Thos. Hosp. Lond.; Regist. (Med.) St. Geo. Hosp. Lond.

BENN, Nicholas (retired) Meopham Medical Centre, Wrotham Road, Meopham, Gravesend DA13 0AH Tel: 01474 814068 — MB ChB 1960 Leeds.

BENN, Patricia Mary (retired) 47 Stonegallows, Taunton TA1 5JR Tel: 0182 346 46484 — MB ChB 1940 Bristol. Prev: Sen. Microbiol. Pub. Health Laborat. Taunton.

BENN, Paul David Flat 14, Museum Mansions, Great Russell St., London WC1B 3BJ — MB ChB 1992 Sheff.

BENN, Robin Sedley 13 Anton Street, London E8 2AD — MB BS 1974 Melbourne; BSc Melbourne 1970; DRCOG 1980.

BENN, Sarah Victoria Ann Staff Residence, Flat 18, Block 3, Pilgrim Hospital, Sibsey Road, Boston PE21 9QS — MB ChB 1990 Leic.

BENNEKERS, Johanna Elisabeth Christine Cannington Health Centre, Mill Lane, Cannington, Bridgwater TA5 2HB — Artsexamen 1991 Utrecht.

BENNET, Ailsa Cumming 60 Victoria Road, Lenzie, Glasgow G66 5AP Tel: 0141 776 1037 — MB ChB 1978 Dundee; MRCGP 1984; DRCOG 1982.

BENNET, Arthur John (retired) Knocknacroishag, Brin, Farr, Inverness IV2 6XE Tel: 01808 521383 Fax: 01808 521383 — MB ChB Ed. 1954; FRCGP 1991, M 1962.

BENNET, Edward Glin 44 Wellington Park, Clifton, Bristol BS8 2UW Tel: 0117 973 2032 Fax: 0117 973 7578 Email: glinbennet@btinternet.com — MB BCh BAO 1952 Dub.; MA Dub. 1952, MD 1971; FRCS Eng. 1958; FRCPsych 1984, M 1972; DPM Dub. 1966. (T.C. Dub.) Socs: BMA. Prev: Cons. Sen. Lect. Univ. Bristol; Cons. Psychiat. United Bristol Healthcare NHS Trust; Capt. RAMC.

BENNET, Mr George Charters Department Orthopaedic Surgery, The Royal Hospital for Sick Children, Yorkhill, Glasgow G3 8SJ — MB ChB 1970 Ed.; BSc 1967 Ed.; FRCS Ed. 1975. Cons. Orthop. Surg. Roy. Hosp. Sick Childr. & Stobhill Hosp. Glas.; Hon. Civil. Cons. in Childr.'s Orthop. and Trauma to the Army. Socs: Pres. Brit. Soc. Childr.'s Orthopaedic Surg.; Mem. Europ. Pediatric Orthopaedic Soc. Prev: Lect. Orthop. Surg. Soton. Univ.; Fell. Orthop. Surg. Hosp. for Sick Childr. Toronto; Regist. Radcliffe Infirm. & Nuffield Orthop. Centre Oxf.

BENNET, Richard Boyd (retired) 130 Cappell Lane, Stanstead Abbots, Ware SG12 8BY Tel: 01920 871010 Fax: 01920 870116 — MB BChir 1956 Camb.; BA Camb. 1956, MA 1960; MRCS Eng. LRCP Lond. 1955; MRCGP 1985; DObst RCOG 1960. Prev: GP Hoddesdon.

BENNETT, Adrian John 270 Greenway Road, Rumney, Cardiff CF3 3PL — MRCS Eng. LRCP Lond. 1973; MRCP (UK) 1979.

BENNETT, Adrian John Moberly 17 Straight Bit, Flackwell Heath, High Wycombe HP10 9LS Tel: 01628 522838 Fax: 01628 529255; Camelot, Penn St, Amersham HP7 0PY Tel: 01628 522838 Email: ajbennett_us@hotmail.com — MB BS 1965 Lond. (Roy. Free) Chairm. Bucks LMC. Prev: Ho. Off. Roy. Free Hosp. Lond. & Harrow Hosp.; Chairm. GP Advisory Comm. Wycombe HA.

BENNETT, Alan Joseph 116 Chester Road S., Kidderminster DY10 1XE — MB ChB 1980 Dundee; FFA RCSI 1987. Cons. Anaesth. Kidderminster Healthcare NHS Trust.

BENNETT, Alex Mark Donald 12 Brunswick Gardens, Cambridge CB5 8DQ — MB BS 1998 Lond.; MB BS Lond 1998.

BENNETT, Alexander Nelson 12 Ashgate Road, Broomhill, Sheffield S10 3BZ — MB ChB 1995 Sheff.

BENNETT, Mr Alfred Michael Hastin (retired) Fern Cottage, Little Wingfield, Stalisfield, Faversham ME13 0BS Tel: 01795 890737 — MRCS Eng. LRCP Lond. 1945; MA, MB BChir Camb. 1945; FRCS Eng. 1949. Prev: Isaac Wolfson Foundat. Fell.

BENNETT, Alison Maxwell 10 Church Walk, Euxton, Chorley PR7 6HL Tel: 0125 72 71977 — MB ChB 1965 Leeds; DA Eng. 1970.

BENNETT, Alistair Charles Dyfed Road Health Centre, Dyfed Road, Neath SA11 3AP Tel: 01639 635331; 12 Llwyndern Close, Mayals, Swansea SA3 5AF — MB BCh 1990 Wales; DRCOG 1992; MRCGP 1994. (Univ. Wales Coll. Med.) GP Princip.

BENNETT, Amanda Jane Alder Hey Hospital, Eaton Road, Liverpool Ll2 2AP; 40 Village Road, Oxton, Prenton CH43 6TY — MB BS 1988 Lond.; MRCP (UK) 1992; DCH RCP Lond. 1991. (Char. Cross & Westm. Hosp. Lond.) Cons. Paediat. (Community Child Health) Alder Hey Hosp. Liverp.

BENNETT, Anna Rebecca 66 Ashley Drive, Tylers Green, High Wycombe HP10 8AZ — MB BS 1998 Lond.; MB BS Lond 1998.

BENNETT, Anthony Paul Market Harborough Medical Centre, 67 Coventry Road, Market Harborough LE16 9BX Tel: 01858 464242 Fax: 01858 462929; The Limes, 9 Welham Road, Great Bowden, Market Harborough LE16 7HS — MB ChB 1968 Sheff.; DObst RCOG 1970; MRCGP 1974. (Sheff.) Clin. Asst. (Orthop.) Market HarBoro. Hosp. Prev: Trainee GP Kettering VTS; Ho. Off. (Med., Surg. & Obst.) Doncaster Roy. Infirm.

BENNETT, Astrid Camilla 6 St Albans Road, Cambridge CB4 2HG; T/L 29 Bentinck Street, Glasgow G3 7TS — MB ChB 1993 Glas.; DCH RCPhysicians; DCH Surg Glas 1996; DRCOG 1997. Gen. Pract. Regist.

BENNETT, Audra (retired) 1 Altham Road, Kew, Southport PR8 6XL — MB ChB 1990 Manch.; MRCGP 1994; DFFP 1993; DRCOG 1992. GP S.port. Prev: Trainee GP/SHO Ormskirk Dist. Gen. Hosp.

BENNETT, Augustus Glyn Werrington Village Surgery, Ash Bank Road, Werrington, Stoke-on-Trent ST13 5NW Tel: 01782 304611 — MB ChB 1981 Manch.; MRCGP 1987; DRCOG 1984.

BENNETT, Brian (retired) Forest Thatch, The Common, Woodgreen, Fordingbridge SP6 2BD Tel: 01725 512238 — MA Dub. 1965, BA, MB BCh BAO 1962; FFOM RCP Lond. 1993, MFOM 1981; FFOM RCPI 1995, MFOM 1978; DIH Eng. 1978; DObst RCOG 1964. Chief Med. Adviser Civil MoD. Prev: Med. Off. Brit. Steel Corp. (Stainless Gp.).

BENNETT, Brian Lee 42 Torquay Road, Kingsrerswell, Newton Abbot TQ12 5EZ Tel: 01803 873154; 42 Torquay Road, Kingsrerswell, Newton Abbot TQ12 5EZ Tel: 01803 873154 — MB ChB 1996 Leic. VTS SHO Totation Torbay Hosp. Torquay. Socs: BMA; MPS. Prev: Surg. SHO Rotat. Torbay Hosp. Torquay.

BENNETT, Caroline Louise Springfield Surgery, Springfield Way, Brackley NN13 6JJ Tel: 01280 703431 Fax: 01295 768624 — MB ChB 1991 Bristol; MRCGP 1996. GP Princip., Springfield Surg., Brackley. Prev: GP Trainee Exeter; GP Retainee, Washington Ho. Surg., Brackley.

BENNETT, Catherine Elisabeth 144 East Street, Corfe Castle, Wareham BH20 5EH — MB BS 1992 Lond.

BENNETT, Catherine Margaret Cornford House Surgery, 364 Cherry Hinton Road, Cambridge CB1 8BA Tel: 01223 247505 Fax: 01223 568187 — MB BCh 1986 Wales; MRCP (UK) 1992; MRCGP 1990; DRCOG 1990. (Univ. Wales) SHO (Paediat.) Dudley Rd. Hosp. Birm.; Paediat. Community Med. Off. Birm. Prev: Trainee GP Newport, Gwent; SHO (Paediat.) Roy. Gwent Hosp.

BENNETT, Charles Patrick (retired) The Red House, 1 Low Bungay Road, Loddon, Norwich NR14 6JW Tel: 01603 520525 — MB BChir 1947 Camb.; MRCS Eng. LRCP Lond. 1942; DObst RCOG 1947. Prev: Ho. Phys. Roy. Devon & Exeter Hosp.

BENNETT, Charlotte Collier Neonatal Unit, John Radcliffe Hospital, Oxford OX3 9DU Tel: 01865 221355 Fax: 01865 221366; 9 Kirby Close, South Moreton, Didcot OX11 9DT — MB BS 1989 Lond.; BSc (Hons.) Lond. 1986; MRCP (UK) 1993; DCH RCP Lond. 1991; MRCPCH 1994. (St. George's Hospital Medical School) Specialist Regist. (Gen. Paediat. & Neonates) John Radcliffe Hosp. Oxf.; Research post, follow-up studies. Socs: Brit. Assn. Perinatal Med. Prev: Regist. (Neonates) Univ. Coll. Hosp. Lond.; SHO (Neonates) Univ. Coll. Hosp. Lond.; SHO (Paediat., Haemat., Oncol. & Nephrol.) Gt. Ormond St. Hosp. Childr. Lond.

BENNETT, Cherry Naing 26 Boston Gardens, Boston Manor Rd, London W7 2AN — MB BS 1996 Lond.

BENNETT, Christine Ann 3 Meadows Road, Cheadle Hulme, Cheadle SK8 6EJ Tel: 0161 485 7419; St Annes Hospice, St Annes Road, Hearld Green, Cheadle SK8 3SZ Tel: 0161 485 7419 — MB ChB Liverp. 1965; MRCGP 1980; Dip Palliat. Med. (Liverp.) Hospice Phys., St Annes Hospice Heald Green. Prev: GP Chorlton, Manch.

BENNETT, Christopher Arthur Charles Moorlands, Chatsworth Road, Rowsley, Matlock DE4 2EH Tel: 01629 734398 — MB BS Lond. 1960; MRCS Eng. LRCP Lond. 1960; VTS Certifcate. (St. Geo.) Locum GP. Prev: Med. Dir. N.rop Corp., Saudi Arabia & Various Companies; Freelance Locum GP UK.

BENNETT, Christopher Jocelyn Cestria Health Centre, Whitehill Way, Chester-le-Street DH2 3DJ Tel: 0191 388 7771 Fax: 0191 387 1803; Springfield House, 13 Waldridge Road, Chester-le-Street DH2 3AB Tel: 0191 387 1453 — MB BS 1973 Lond.; MRCGP 1981; DGM RCP Lond. 1991; DRCOG 1976.

BENNETT, Christopher Julian North House Surgery, 28 North Street, Ripon HG4 1HL Tel: 01765 690666 Fax: 01765 690249; Green Royd, Studley Road, Ripon HG4 2QJ Tel: 01765 605291 Email: chris@ripon.demon.co.uk — MB BS 1973 Lond.; MRCS Eng. LRCP Lond. 1971; MRCGP 1990; DRCOG 1977; DCH Eng. 1976; DA Eng. 1975. (Guy's) Clin. Asst. Ripon Community Hosp. Socs: BMA; Harrogate Med. Soc.; BIMM (Brit. Inst. of Musculoskeletal Med.). Prev: SHO (O & G) Matern. Hosp. York; SHO (Paediat.) Co. Hosp. York; SHO (Gen. Med.) St. Nicholas Hosp. Lond.

BENNETT, Christopher Paul Department of Clinical Genetics, St James' University Hospital, Leeds LS9 7TF Tel: 0113 206 6969 Fax: 0113 246 7090 Email: chris.bennett@leedsth.nhs.uk — MB ChB 1981 Leeds; BSc Leeds 1978; FRCP (UK) 1997, M 1985; MD 1998. (Leeds) Cons. Clin. Genetics St. Jas. Univ. Hosp. Leeds. Prev: Sen. Regist. (Clin. Genetics.) Guy's Hosp. Lond.

BENNETT, Clare Elizabeth St Peter's Hospital, Guildford Road, Chertsey KT16 0PZ — MB BS 1976 Lond.; FRCR 1983; DMRD 1981. Cons. Radiol. St. Peter's Hosp. Chertsey.

BENNETT, Daisy Naing 26 Boston Gardens, London W7 2AN — MB BS 1998 Lond.; MB BS Lond 1998.

BENNETT, David Arthur Courtlands, Elms Road, Hook, Basingstoke RG27 9DP Tel: 01256 762677 Fax: 01256 765348 — MB BS Lond. 1954; MRCS Eng. LRCP Lond. 1954; FRCP Ed. 1978, M 1964; FRCPsych 1985, M 1971; DPM Eng. 1962. (St. Mary's) Cons. Psychiat. N. Hants. Gp. Hosps. (Emerit. Cons. since 1991). Socs: Med. -Leg. Soc. & Brit. Acad. Foren. Sc. Prev: Ho. Phys. Chase Farm Hosp. Enfield; SHO (Gen. Med.) St. Bart. Hosp. Rochester; Sen. Regist. (Psychiat.) St. Mary's Hosp. Lond.

BENNETT, David Henry Cardiology Department, Wythenshawe Hospital, Southmoor Road, Manchester M23 9LT — MD 1976 Manch.; FRCP Lond. 1986; MRCP (UK) 1982; MB ChB 1970. Cons. Cardiol. Wythenshawe Hosp. Manch. Socs: FACC; Brit. Cardiac Soc. Prev: Sen. Regist. Radcliffe Infirm. Oxf.; Regist. Manch. Roy. Infirm.; Regist. Papworth Hosp. Camb.

BENNETT, David Henry Gloucestershire Royal Hospital, Great Western Road, Gloucester GL1 3NN Tel: 01452 528555; Court View Cottage, Higher Coombe Cottages, Hannaford Road, Noss Mayo, Plymouth PL8 1EH Tel: 01752 873086 Email: dh.bennett@easynet.co.uk — MB BS 1988 Lond.; BSc (Hons.) Lond. 1985; FRCS Eng. 1992. Specialist Regist. (Gen. Surg.) Gloucestershire Roy. Hosp. Socs: BMA & Assn. Surgs. in Train.; Assn. Upper G.I. Surg. Prev: Specialist Regist. (Gen. Surg.) Derby City Gen. Hosp.; Research Regist. Univ. Nottm.

BENNETT, David James Ieuan Longlevens Surgery, 196 Church Road, Longlevens CU2 0AJ Tel: 01452 522695; 46 Winstonian Road, Cheltenham CU 52 2JE — MB BChir 1991 Camb.; MRCGP 1995; MRCP 1999; MA Camb. 1992; DCH RCP Lond. 1994. GP Gloucester.

BENNETT, David John Newland Fakenham Medical Practice, The Fakenham Medical Centre, Greenway Lane, Fakenham NR21 8ET Tel: 01328 851321 Fax: 01328 851412; Little Marsh, Little Marsh Lane, Field Dalling, Holt NR25 7LL — MB BS 1984 Lond.; MRCGP 1990; DRCOG 1989. (St. Geo.) Prev: SHO Duke of Cornw. Spinal Unit Odstock Hosp. Salisbury; SHO (Anaesth.) Roy. Hants. Hosp. Winchester; SHO (Paediat. & O & G) St. Marys Hosp. Portsmouth.

BENNETT, Davinia Gail 180 Mayals Road, Mayals, Swansea SA3 5HF Tel: 01792 402957 Email: daviniab@hotmail.com — MB ChB 1995 Bristol. SHO (A & E) Hereford & Worcester; SHO (A & E & Anaesth.) Brisbane, Australia. Socs: BMA; MDU. Prev: Ho. Off. (Med.) Cheltenham; Ho. Off. (Surg.) W.on Super Mare.

BENNETT, Denise Gloria Accident & Emergency Department, Worthing Hospital, Worthing BN11 2DH Tel: 01903 205111; Harcourt, 15 Ingram Road, Steyning BN44 3PF Tel: 01903 814895 — MB BS 1962 Durh. Assoc. Specialist (A & E) Worthing Hosp.

BENNETT, Denise Mary 19 Shirley Road, Chiswick, London W4 1DD — LMSSA 1981 Lond.; MB Camb. 1982, BChir 1981.

BENNETT, Dennis Arthur 8 Derwent Park, Wheldrake, York YO19 6AT — LMSSA 1954 Lond. (Camb. & W. Lond.) Assoc. Specialist A & E Dept. Co. Hosp. York. Prev: Ho. Phys. (Paediat.) City Hosp. Chester; Ho. Phys. Hosp. of St. Cross Rugby; Ho. Surg. Worcester Roy. Infirm.

BENNETT, Donald Louis 4 Lord Avenue, Ilford IG5 0HP Tel: 020 8550 5661 — MB BS Lond. 1946; MRCS Eng. LRCP Lond. 1938. (St. Bart.) Surg. K Div. Metrop. Police; Med. Ref. Pruden. Assur. Co. Prev: Jun. Regist. St. And. Hosp. (LCC); Ho. Surg. Kettering Gen. Hosp.; RAFVR Med. Off. F/O to Temp S/Ldr. 1940-46.

BENNETT, Douglas Harley 5 Mill Lane, Iffley, Oxford OX4 4EJ — MB BS 1941 Lond.; MD Lond. 1949; MRCS Eng. LRCP Lond. 1941; FRCPsych 1971; Hon. FRCPsych 1986; DPM Eng. 1951. (St. Bart.) Socs: Roy. Soc. Med. Prev: Emerit. Phys. Bethlem Roy. & Maudsley Hosps.; Regist. (Med.) Postgrad. Med. Sch. Lond.; Cons. Psychiat. Netherne Hosp. Coulsdon.

BENNETT, Mr Dudley Stratford Brixton Hill Group Practice, 22 Raleigh Gardens, London SW2 1AE Tel: 020 8674 6376 Fax: 020 8671 0283 — MB BS 1972 Lond.; FRCS Eng. 1976.

BENNETT, Elizabeth Jane Department of Anaesthetics, Gloucestershire Royal Hospital, Great Western Road, Gloucester GL1 3NN — MB BS 1988 Queensland.

BENNETT, Elizabeth Kathryn Anne Laurel Bank Surgery, 216B Kirkstall Lane, Headingley, Leeds LS6 3DS — MB ChB 1980 Leeds; MB ChB Leeds. 1980; MRCGP 1984; MFFP 1995; DFFP 1993.

BENNETT, Elizabeth Margaret Woodland Cottage, Aldwick, Redhill, Bristol BS40 5RF — MB ChB 1983 Dundee.

BENNETT, Emma Victoria 116 Jordanstown Road, Newtownabbey BT37 0NU — MB ChB 1998 Aberd.; MB ChB Aberd 1998.

BENNETT, Enid (retired) Old Bell Cottage, Evesham Road, Norton, Evesham WR11 4TL Tel: 01386 870344 — MRCS Eng. LRCP Lond. 1963; MB BS Lond. 1963; MD Lond. 1974. Med. Off. MRC HQ Off. Lond. Prev: Research Asst. Haemat. Dept. Univ. Coll. Hosp. Med. Sch. Lond.

BENNETT, Ephraim David 81 Lacy Road, London SW15 1NR — MB BS 1963 Lond.; FRCP Lond. 1982; MRCP (U.K.) 1970. (Middlx.) Sen. Lect. & Hon. Cons. Dept. Med. St. Geo. Hosp. Tooting. Socs: Med. Research Soc. Prev: Res. Med. Off. Nat. Heart Hosp. Lond.; Research Fell. Johns Hopkins Med. Sch., U.S.A.; Ho. Phys. Brompton Hosp. Lond.

BENNETT, Esther Rose Lynn Julian Hospital, Bowthorpe Road, Norwich NR2 3TD Tel: 01603 421421 Fax: 01603 421831; Sunnyside Cottage, 99 School Lane, Little Melton, Norwich NR9 3LA Tel: 01603 813077 — MB ChB 1985 Leic.; MRCPsych 1990. Staff Grade Psychiat. Elderly Directorate Norf. Ment. Health Care Trust. Socs: BMA. Prev: Regist. (Psychiat.) E. Anglian RHA; SHO (Psychiat.) Norwich HA; Ho. Off. (Surg. & Med.) Leic. HA.

BENNETT, Everard Patrick Talbot 38 Dartmouth Row, London SE10 8AW — MB BS 1985 Lond.

BENNETT, Fiona Melville (retired) 4 Earls Court Gardens, Aberdeen AB15 4BU Tel: 01224 318472 — MB ChB 1946 Ed.; FRCS Ed. 1960; DO Eng. 1950. Prev: Hon. Cons. Ophth. Aberd. Gen. Hosps.

BENNETT, Frederick Gade House Surgery, 99B Uxbridge Road, Rickmansworth WD3 2DJ Tel: 01923 775291 Fax: 01923 711790 — MB ChB 1977 Leeds; MRCGP 1981; DCH Eng. 1979. GP Trainer Watford VTS; Colposcopist Watford Gen. Hosp.

BENNETT, Geoffrey April Cottage, Balcombe Road, Pound Hill, Crawley RH10 3NL Tel: 01293 882653 Fax: 01293 882653 — BM BCh 1953 Oxf.; MA Oxf. 1953; FFOM RCP Lond. 1983; FRAeS 1983. (Oxf.) Cons. Aviat. Med. Socs: Internat. Acad. Aviat. & Space Med.; Fell. Aerospace Med. Assn. Prev: Reader Civil Aviat. Med. RAF Inst. of Aviat. Med.; Cons. Aviat. Med. RN & Army; Chief Med. Off. Civil Aviat. Auth.

BENNETT, Gerald Charles Joseph Department Health Care of The Elderly, Mile End Hospital, Bancroft Road, London E1 4DG Tel: 020 7377 7843 Fax: 020 7377 7844; 46 Gerrard Road, London N1 8AX Tel: 020 7359 9320 Fax: 020 7359 9320 — MB BCh 1976 Wales; FRCP Lond. 1993; MRCP (UK) 1980. Reader St. Bart. & the Lond. Sch. of Med. & Dent.; Hon. Cons. Tower Hamlets Healthcare Trust; Hon. Cons. Roy. Hosps. Trust; Pres. Action on Elder Abuse. Prev: Med. Dir. Tower Hamlets Healthcare Trust; Lect. (Geriat. Med.) St. Geo. Hosp. Med. Sch. Lond.

BENNETT, Glenis Grant The Surgery, 10 Cornwallis Gardens, Hastings TN34 1LP Tel: 01424 722666 Fax: 01424 460951; 11, Clinton Crescent, St. Leonards-on-Sea TN38 0RN — MB BS 1963 Durham; Dip Family Planning 2001; Dobst RCOG 1966; MRCOG 1968; Dip Dermat 1995. (Durham) GP Hastings, E. Sussex. Socs: BMA; RCOG.

BENNETT, Harry Gordon Butterworth 291 Devonshire Road, Blackpool FY2 0TW — MB ChB 1989 Manch.; MRCP (UK) 1992; FRCOpth 1995. Regist. (Ophth.) W. Scotl. Train. Scheme.

BENNETT, Helen Rosemary (retired) 8 Byron Mews, London NW3 2NQ Tel: 020 7485 6424 — MB ChB Manch. 1952; MRCS Eng. LRCP Lond. 1953. Prev: SCMO Bloomsbury DHA.

BENNETT, Imelda Maria Dept of community Paediactrics, Severn NHS Trust, Rikenel, Montpellier, Cheltenham GL1 1LY — BM BCh 1987 Oxf.; MSc 1997; MA Oxf. 1991, BA 1984; MRCP (UK) 1992; DCH RCP Lond. 1990. (Oxf.) Cons. Community Paediat. Severn NHS Trust. Prev: Sen. Regist. (Paediat.) Bristol Childr. Hosp.; Clin. Med. Off. (Paediat.) & Regist. Plymouth HA; SHO (Paediat.) Bristol Childr. Hosp.

BENNETT, Jacqueline (retired) Flat 6 Birnam, 56 Harborne Road, Edgbaston, Birmingham B15 3HE — MB ChB 1947 Birm.; MRCS Eng. LRCP Lond. 1947; DPH Manch. 1966. Prev: SCMO (Child Health) Birm. AHA (T).

BENNETT, Jacqueline Anne Stockwood Health Clinic, Hollway Road, Bristol BS14 8PT Tel: 01275 833103 Fax: 01275 891637; 18 Roslyn Road, Redland, Bristol BS6 6NN — MB ChB 1983 Bristol; MRCGP 1988; DRCOG 1987.

BENNETT, James Anthony Department of Anaesthesia, Frenchay Hospital, Bristol BS16 1LE Tel: 0117 970 1212 Fax: 0117 957 4414; Rose Cottage, Itchington, Alveston, Bristol BS35 3TQ Tel: 01454 419264 — MRCS Eng. LRCP Lond. 1963; FFA RCS Eng. 1969. (Bristol) Cons. Anaesth. Frenchay HC Trust; Clin. Lect. Univ. Bristol; Hon. Curator Monica Britton Exhibition Hall of Med. Hist.; Surg. Lt.-Cdr. RNR Severn Div. (Retd.). Socs: Linkman Assn. Anaesth.; SW Soc. Anaesth.; (Hon. Sec.) Hist. Anaesth. Soc. Prev: Cons. & Sen. Lect. (Anaesth.) Univ. Bristol & United Bristol Hosps.; Regist. (Anaesth.) Alder Hey Childr. Hosp. Liverp.; Leverhulme Vis. Prof. Anaesth. Univ. Khartoum.

BENNETT, James Maxwell Department of Anaesthesia, Birmingham Childrens Hospital, Steelhouse Lane, Birmingham B4 6NH — MB BS 1988 Lond.

BENNETT, James Richard Wareham Health Centre, Streche Road, Wareham BH20 4PG Tel: 01929 553444 Fax: 01929 550703 — MB BS Lond. 1990; DRCOG 1993; MRCGP 1995. (Barts) GP; Hosp. Practitioner Dermat. Poole Hosp. NHS Trust.

BENNETT, James William 205 Russell Drive, Wollaton, Nottingham NG8 2BD Tel: 0115 928 3201; 3 Brookhill Crescent, Wollaton, Nottingham NG8 2PU Tel: 0115 928 1908 — MB BCh BAO 1959 Dub.; MA Dub. 1962, BA, MB BCh BAO 1959; DObst RCOG 1965. (T.C. Dub.) Prev: Ho. Surg. Gen. Hosp. Nottm.; Ho. Phys. Little Bromwich Gen. Hosp.; Clin. Asst. A & E Dept. Roy. Infirm. Bolton.

BENNETT, Jennifer East Sussex Brighton and Hove Health Authority, 36-38 Friars Walk, Lewes BN7 2PB Tel: 01273485300 Fax: 01273485400; 9 Eastern Terrace, Kemp Town, Brighton BN2 1DJ — MRCS Eng. LRCP Lond. 1973; MA 1998; FFPHM RCP (UK) 1994; MFCM Eng. 1986; DCH Eng. 1975. (Makerere Med. Sch. Kampala) Cons. Pub. Health Med. E. Sussex HA; Assoc. Med. Adviser Caspe Research Lond; Clin. Asst.Beltlem Hosps. Prev: Sen. Regist. (Community Med.) Brighton HA.; SHO Middlx. Hosp. Lond.; Ho. Phys. Whittington Hosp. Lond.

BENNETT, Jennifer Mary Medical Centre, University of Bath, Claverton Down, Bath BA2 7AY Tel: 01225 826826; Denmede, Southstoke Road, Bath BA2 5SL Tel: 01225 832371 Fax: 01225 832371 — MB ChB 1963 Aberd. (Aberd.) Med. Off. Bath Univ. Socs: Clin. Soc. Bath. Prev: Clin. Asst. (Oncol.) Roy. United Hosp. Bath; Resid. (Med.) Woodend Hosp. Aberd.

BENNETT, John (retired) Upper Fews, 19 Fleetwood Avenue, Felixstowe IP11 9HR Tel: 01394 284823 — MB ChB 1955 Birm. Prev: GP Felixstowe.

BENNETT, John The Surgery, Balance St., Uttoxeter ST14 8JG Tel: 01889 562145 — MB BCh BAO 1958 Dub.; MA Dub. 1962, BA, MB BCh BAO 1958; DObst RCOG 1964. (T.C. Dub.) Sch. Med. Off. St. Mary & St. Anne's Abbots Bromley; Apptd. Fact. Doctor; Local Treasury Med. Off. Socs: Derby Med. Soc. & Stoke Med. Soc. Prev: Ho. Phys. Lister Hosp. Hitchin; Ho. Surg. Leicester Roy. Infirm.; SHO Leicester Roy. Matern. Hosp.

BENNETT, John Bernard Somerstown Health Centre, Blackfriars Close, Southsea PO5 4NJ Tel: 02392 820500 Fax: 02392 876606 — MB BS 1979 Lond.; BSc 1976 (Hons.) Lond.; MRCP (UK) 1982; MRCGP 1988. (St. Bart.) Socs: BMA. Prev: Research Fell. (Respirat. Med.) St. Bart. Hosp. Lond.; Regist. (Med.) St. Leonard's Hosp. Lond.; SHO Rotat. & Ho. Phys. St. Bart. Hosp. Lond.

BENNETT, John Charles Barry (retired) The Shielings, 16 Pinfold Lane, Romiley, Stockport SK6 4NP Tel: 0161 494 2692 Email: john@seapie.fsnet.co.uk — MB ChB 1957 Manch.; DObst RCOG 1964; AFOM RCP Lond. 1983. Prev: Phys. (Occupat. Health) Tameside HA.

BENNETT, John Cranston Magdalen Medical Practice, Lawson Road, Norwich NR3 4LF Tel: 01603 475555 Fax: 01603 787210 — MB BS 1973 Lond.; DFFP 1994; DObst RCOG 1976. (Char. Cross)

BENNETT, John David Courtnay 21 Wood Drive, Alsager, Stoke-on-Trent ST7 2LH — MB ChB 1979 Manch.

BENNETT, John Roderick (retired) Kingspring House, Vicarage Lane, Long Compton, Shipston-on-Stour CV36 5LH Tel: 01608 684081 Fax: 01608 684081 Email: jrbennett@dial.pipex.com — MB ChB 1957 Liverp.; MD Liverp. 1966; FRCP Lond. 1975, M 1964. Prev: Treas., Roy. Coll. of Phys.

BENNETT, John Romney Heathfield Farm, Denbury, Newton Abbot TQ12 6ES — MB BS 1980 Lond.; MRCP (UK) 1983.

BENNETT, John Walter (retired) St Helier, 21B Ermin St., Brockworth, Gloucester GL3 4EG Tel: 01452 617855 Fax: 01452 371615 Email: mavjon@talk21.com — MB BChir 1955 Camb.; MA Camb. 1955; MRCS Eng. LRCP Lond. 1955; FRCGP 1979, M 1965; DObst RCOG 1961. Prev: GP Gloucester.

BENNETT, Jonathan Andrew 101 Britannia Avenue, Basford, Nottingham NG6 0EA — MB ChB 1988 Leeds; MRCP (UK) 1991. Regist. (Respirat. & Gen. Med.) Nottm. Prev: Research Fell. Div. Respirat. Med. Nottm.; Teach. Fell. Univ. Dept. Med. Leeds Gen. Infirm.

BENNETT, Josephine Diane Greenfield Cottage, South Scarle, Newark NG23 7JH Tel: 01636 892847 — MB ChB 1973 Sheff.; FFA RCS Eng. 1978. (Sheff.) Staff Grade (Community Paediat.) Nottm. Community Health NHS Trust. Socs: Brit. Paediat. Assn. Prev: CMO (Child Health) Centr. Notts. AHA; Regist. (Anaesth.)

Frimley Pk. Hosp.; SHO (Med.) Intens. Ther. Unit & SHO (Anaesth.) Middlx. Hosp. Lond.

BENNETT, Judith Mary Behall Clinic, Cheltenham General Hospital, Sandford Road, Cheltenham GL53 7AN Tel: 01242 274279; 11 Collum End Rise, Leckhampton, Cheltenham GL53 0PA — MB BS 1984 Lond.; BSc (Hons.) Sussex 1976; MRCGP 1989; DFFP 1997; DRCOG 1987. (St. Mary's Hospital Medical School) Clin. Asst. (Genitourin. Med.) Glos. Roy. Hosp. & Cheltenham Gen. Hosp. Prev: Asst. GP Glos.

BENNETT, Judy Ann 140 Longberrys, Cricklewood Lane, London NW2 2TQ — MB BS 1983 Lond.

BENNETT, Julia Margaret Clive Surgery, Clive, Shrewsbury SY4 5PS Tel: 01939 220295 Fax: 01939 220510 — MB ChB 1976 Birm.; MFFP 1994; FRCGP 1997, M 1980; DRCOG 1979.

BENNETT, Kate Mary Eunson 48 Majors Loan, Falkirk FK1 5QG — MB ChB 1996 Ed.

BENNETT, Lesley Samantha The Cottage, West Edge, Marsh Gibbon, Bicester OX27 0HA Tel: 01869 277353 — MB ChB 1990 Bristol; MD Bristol 2000; MRCP (UK) 1993. Clin. Research Fell. Ch.ill Hosp. Oxf.; Cons. Phys. Ch.ill Hosp. Oxf. Prev: Regist. (Med.) S.mead Hosp. Bristol; Regist. (Med.) MusGr. Pk. Hosp. Taunton; SHO (Med.) Swindon HA.

BENNETT, Marco Ashley Valentine, Capt. 8 Bassett Cl, Southampton SO16 7PE Tel: 02380 769404 — MB BS 1997 Lond. GP Regist. (Army), Med. Reception Station, Talbot Barracks.

BENNETT, Margaret (retired) 486 Lea Bridge Road, Leyton, London E10 7DU Tel: 020 8558 4255 — MB BS 1940 Lond.; MRCS Eng., LRCP Lond. 1940; MRCGP 1953. Prev: Ho. Surg. (ENT & Gyn.) Chester Roy. Infirm.

BENNETT, Mark 21 Plas Ioan, Johnstown, Carmarthen SA31 3NS — MRCS Eng. LRCP Lond. 1990.

BENNETT, Mark Anthony 201 Cowick Road, London SW17 8LQ — MB BS 1998 Lond.; MB BS Lond 1998.

BENNETT, Mark Jonathan Cardiothoracic Anaesthesia, Derriford Hospital, Plymouth PL6 8DH Email: mark.bennett@nda.ox.ac.uk — MB ChB 1990 Liverp.; FRCA 1996. Cardiothoracic Anaesth., Derriford Hosp. Plymouth.

BENNETT, Mark Kirkham Department of Cellular Pathology, The Newcastle-upon-Tyne Hospitals NHS Trust, Royal Victoria Infirmary, Queen Victoria Road, Newcastle upon Tyne NE1 4LP Tel: 0191 232 5131; 2 Moor Place, Gosforth, Newcastle upon Tyne NE3 4AL Tel: 0191 285 8483 — MB BS 1975 Lond.; FRCPath 1994; MRCPath 1982. (St. Mary's) Cons. Histopath. Roy. Vict. Infirm. Newc. Prev: Sen. Regist. Histopath., John Radcliffe Hosp. Oxf.; Regist., Histopath., Hammersmith Hosp. Lond.; Regist., Histopath. St Marys Hosp. Lond.

BENNETT, Mary (retired) 29 Hamstead Hill, Birmingham B20 1BN — MB ChB Birm. 1953. Prev: Clin. Asst. (Occupat. Health) N. Birm. HA.

BENNETT, Michael Ian St. Gemmas Hospice, 329 Harrogate Road, Leeds LS17 6QD Email: m.bennett@st-gemma.co.uk; 3 St Helen's Croft, Leeds LS16 8JY — MB ChB 1988 Birm.; MRCP (UK) 1991; MD 1999. Cons./Sen. Clin. Lect. in Palliat. Med.

BENNETT, Michael William Reath Department of Anaesthetics, University Hospital, Queen's Medical Centre, Nottingham NG7 2UH — MB ChB 1984 Manch.; FRCA 1990. Cons. Anaesth. Qu. Med. Centre Nottm.

BENNETT, Muriel Leigh (retired) 6 Bollin Mews, Prestbury, Macclesfield SK10 4DP Tel: 01625 828471 — MB ChB 1937 Manch.; 1937 MB ChB Manch.; 1990 FFPHM; 1978 FFCM; 1974 MMCM. Prev: Specialist Community Med. (Child Health) Manch. AHA (T).

BENNETT, Natalie Claire Flat 2, Willow Court, Corney Reach Way, London W4 2TW — MB BS 1998 Lond.; MB BS Lond 1998.

BENNETT, Neil Lachlan Macdonald 25 Havelock Street, Flat 1/3, Glasgow G11 5JF — MB ChB 1992 Glas.; MRCP (UK) 1995. Research Fell. (Diabetes) Glas. Roy. Infirm. Socs: Brit. Diabetic Assn.; Caledonian Soc. Endocrinol. Prev: SHO III (Diabetes) Glas. Roy. Infirm.

BENNETT, Neil Rodney 29 Burnt Stones Drive, Sandygate, Sheffield S10 5TT — MB ChB 1970 St. And.; FFA RCS Eng. 1975. Regist. (Anaesth.) BRd.green Hosp. Liverp. Socs: BMA & Assn. Anaesths. Prev: Ho. Off. (Med. & Surg.) Walton Hosp. Liverp.; SHO (Anaesth.) Chester Roy. Infirm.; Regist. (Anaesth.) Walton Hosp. Liverp.

BENNETT, Mr Nicholas John Dept. of Plastic and Maxilo Facial Surgery, Salisbury District Hospital, Salisbury SP2 8BJ; Bramble Cottage, Castle Lane, Whaddon, Salisbury SP5 3EQ Tel: 01722711061 Fax: 01722 410956 Email: nickben@waitrose.com — MB BS 1988 Lond.; FRCS (Eng.). (UCH) Specialist Regist. Plastic Surg. Odstock Centre for Burns, Plastic & Maxillofacial Surg. Prev: SHO (Gen. Surg.) Duchess of Kent's Milit. Hosp. Catterick.

BENNETT, Nicola Jane Amersham Health Centre, Chiltern Avenue, Amersham HP6 5AY Tel: 01494 434344 — MB ChB 1977 Leeds; DCH Eng. 1979. Prev: Phys. i/c BUPA Hosp. Bushey Herts.

BENNETT, Norman Bruce Department of Medicine & Therapeutics, University Aberdeen, Aberdeen AB25 2ZD Tel: 01224 681818 Fax: 01224 699884; Burnhead Cottage, Cookney, Stonehaven AB39 3RX Tel: 01569 730270 — MB ChB 1963 Aberd.; MB ChB (Hons.) Aberd. 1963; MD (Hons.) Aberd. 1967; FRCP Ed. 1990; FRCP Lond. 1982; MRCP (Lond.) 1968; FRCPath 1985, M 1973. (Aberd.) Reader (Med.) Univ. Aberd. & Hon. Cons. Phys. Aberd. Roy. Infirm. Prev: Sen. Lect. (Med.) & Wellcome Research Fell. Aberd. Univ.; Lilly Research Fell. (Med.) Case W. Reserve Univ. Cleveland, Ohio.

BENNETT, Norman Osborn (retired) The Barn By The River, Dinckley, Blackburn BB6 8AN Tel: 01254 248459 — MRCS Eng. LRCP Lond. 1947. Prev: Ho. Surg. Padd. Hosp. (L.C.C.).

BENNETT, Patricia Helen 12 Priory Close, Congleton CW12 3JL — BM 1981 Soton.

BENNETT, Patrick John 38 Dartmouth Row, Greenwich, London SE10 8AW Tel: 020 8692 9330 — MB BS 1958 Lond.; BSc Lond. 1955, MB BS 1958; FFA RCS Eng. 1966; DObst RCOG 1962. (St. Thos.) Cons. Anaesth. Middlx. Hosp. Lond. Socs: Fell. Roy. Soc. Med. Prev: Instruc. in Anesth. Harvard Univ., U.S.A.; Sen. Regist. Middlx. Hosp. Lond. & Lond. Chest Hosp.

BENNETT, Patrick Michael John The Health Centre, Madeira Road, West Byfleet KT14 6DH Tel: 01932 336933 Fax: 01932 355681 — MB BChir Camb. 1959; MRCS Eng. LRCP Lond. 1959. (Camb. & St. Geo.) HM Dep. Coroner Surrey. Prev: Med. 1st Asst. & Resid. Med. Off. St. Geo. Hosp. Tooting; Regist. (Med.) Frenchay Hosp. Bristol; Resid. Med. Off. St. Teresa's Matern. Hosp. Wimbledon.

BENNETT, Paul Francis Batheaston Medical Centre, Batheaston Medical Centre, Coalpit Road, Batheaston, Bath BA1 7NP Tel: 01225 858686 Fax: 01225 852521 — MB BS 1981 Lond.; MRCGP 1987; DFFP 1993; DRCOG 1984. (St. Mary's) Socs: Nat. Assn. Family Plann. Doctors; BMA. Prev: Trainee GP Edgware Gen. Hosp. VTS.

BENNETT, Peter Emanuel Schopwick Surgery, Everett Court, Elstree, Borehamwood WD6 3BJ Tel: 020 8953 1008 Fax: 020 8905 2196; 5l Woodfield Rise, Bushey, Watford WD23 4QR Tel: 020 8953 1008 — MB BS 1971 Lond.; MRCS Eng. LRCP Lond. 1971; FRCGP 1990, M 1980. Course Organiser Beds. & Herts. Modular Train. Course; Chairm. Beds. & Herts. Fac. Roy. Coll. Gen. Pract. Prev: Clin. Asst. (Dermat.) Watford Peace Memor. Hosp.; Course Organiser Watford VTS.

BENNETT, Peter John Leal Dr Miller & Partners, Health Centre, Albert St., Lydney GL15 5NQ Tel: 01594 842167 Fax: 01594 845550; Aylands Lodge, Springfield Road, Lydney GL15 5LT Tel: 01594 843172 Email: aylands@global.co.uk — MB BCh 1974 Wales; MRCGP 1978; DRCOG 1978. Prev: Trainee GP Tunbridge Wells VTS; Ho. Off. (Gen. Med.) E. Glam. Gen. Hosp. Pontypridd; Ho. Off. (Gen. Surg.) Llandough Hosp. Cardiff.

BENNETT, Peter Norman University of Bath, Dept of Medical Sciences, Claverton Down, Bath BA2 7AY Tel: 01225 826400 Fax: 01225 837278 Email: p.n. bennett@bath.ac.uk; Denmede, Southstoke Road, Bath BA2 5SL Tel: 01225 832371 Fax: 01225 837278 — MB ChB 1963 Aberd.; MD (Hons. & Cash Medal) Aberd. 1967; FRCP Lond. 1981 M 1970. (Aberd.) Cons. Phys. & Reader Clin. Pharmacol. Roy. United Hosp. & Univ. Bath; Dep. Head, Dept. of Med. Sci.s. Socs: Brit. Pharm. Soc.; Roy. Soc. Med. Prev: Lect. (Clin. Pharm.) Roy. Postgrad. Med. Sch. & Hon. Sen. Regist. (Med.) Hammersmith Hosp.; Myers Research Fell. & Lect. (Med.) Univ. Aberd.; Wellcome Research Fell. Clin. Pharm. & Hon. Sen. Regist. Univ. Coll. Lond.

BENNETT, Peter Shepherd Mytton Oak Medical Practice, Racecourse Lane, Shrewsbury SY3 5LZ Tel: 01743 362223 Fax: 01743 244 5811; 21 St. John's Hill, Shrewsbury SY1 1JJ Tel: 01743 232756 — MRCS Eng. LRCP Lond. 1967; MA, MB BChir Camb. 1968; FRCGP 1984, M 1974. (Middlx.) Princip. GP Shrewsbury; Med. Off. The Sch. Shrewsbury. Prev: Course Organiser Shrewsbury.; GP Trainer.

BENNETT, Peter William 1 Beechwood Drive, Marple, Stockport SK6 7DG Tel: 0161 427 3205 — MB BS 1965 Lond. (Univ. Coll. Hosp.) GP Hyde, Chesh.

BENNETT, Peter William 10 Browsholme Close, Carnforth LA5 9UW — MB ChB 1990 Manch.

BENNETT, Philippa Jane 14 Ardgowan Road, London SE6 1AJ — MB ChB 1990 Leeds. Socs: Roy. Coll. Gen. Pract. Prev: Trainee GP Lond.

BENNETT, Professor Phillip Robert Queen Charlotte's Hospital, London W6 0XG Tel: 020 8383 3906 Fax: 020 8383 1838 Email: pbennett@rpms.ac.uk — MB BS 1982 Lond.; PhD Lond. 1991; BSc (Hons.) Lond. 1979, MD 1988; MRCOG 1988. (St. Geo.) Prof. O & G Qu. Charlotte's Hosp. Lond. Prev: Reader Roy. Postgrad. Med. Sch. Lond.; Regist. (O & G) St. Geo. Hosp. Lond.; Research Fell. Perinatal Inst. O & G Lond.

BENNETT, Rachel Marie Frenchay Hospital, Bristol BS16 1LE; 8 Buttlegate, Downderry, Torpoint PL11 3NQ — MB ChB 1995 Birm. SHO Frenchay Hosp. Bristol.

BENNETT, Rebecca Jane Pinfold Surgery, Pinfold Lane, Methley, Leeds LS26 9AB — MB ChB 1984 Manch.; MRCGP 1988.

BENNETT, Richard Antony (retired) 22 Foxon Close, Caterham CR3 5SY Tel: 01883 344993 Fax: 01883 342998 — MRCS Eng. LRCP Lond. 1952; MRCGP 1961. Prev: Ho. Surg. (Gen. & Orthop.) Roy. Hosp. Portsmouth.

BENNETT, Richard Ian 1 Butterleys, Dodworth, Barnsley S75 3TD — MB ChB 1983 Sheff.

BENNETT, Mr Richard James Flat 6, Birnam, 56 Harborne Road, Edgbaston, Birmingham B15 3HE Tel: 0121 454 8740 — MB ChB 1945 Birm.; FRCS Eng. 1953. Cons. ENT Surg. United Birm. Hosps. & Birm. & Midl. Ear & Throat Hosp.; Clin. Lect. (ENT) Univ. Birm. Socs: Fell. Roy. Soc. Med.; Midl. Inst. Otol. Prev: Cons. ENT Surg. Stoke-on-Trent Hosp. Gp.; Sen. ENT Surg. Durh. & NW Durh. Hosp. Gps.

BENNETT, Richard Lisle Manor Park Medical Centre, 204 Harborough Avenue, Sheffield S2 1QU Tel: 0114 239 8602; 26 Thornsett Road, Nether Edge, Sheffield S7 1NB — MB ChB 1986 Sheff.; BA (Hons.) Soton. 1979.

BENNETT, Robert John Charles Eccleston Health Centre, 20 Doctors Lane, Eccleston, Chorley PR7 5RA Tel: 01257 451221 Fax: 01257 450911 — MB ChB 1977 Manch.; DRCOG 1982. Socs: Assoc. Mem. RCGP.

BENNETT, Robert Philip 53 Doncaster Road, Newcastle upon Tyne NE2 1RB — MB ChB 1986 Sheff.; MRCGP 1990.

BENNETT, Roger John Jeremy, OStJ The Surgery, Pleasant Place, Hersham, Walton-on-Thames KT12 4HT Tel: 01932 229033 Fax: 01932 254706; 80 Hersham Road, Walton-on-Thames KT12 5NU — MB BS 1956 Lond.; DObst RCOG 1957. (St. Geo.) Med. Off. Walton-on-Thames Hosp., Whiteley Village Homes Trust, Walton-on-Thames; Charity & Felton Fleet Sch. Cobham; Area Surg. (NW Surrey) St. John Ambul. Brig. Prev: Ho. Surg. & Resid. Obst. Asst. St. Geo. Hosp.; Temp. Maj. RAMC.

BENNETT, Rowena Jennifer Marsden Road Surgery, The Health Centre, Marsden Road, South Shields NE34 6RE Tel: 0191 454 0457 Fax: 0191 427 1793; Springfield House, 13 Waldridge Road, Chester-le-Street DH2 3AB Tel: 0191 387 1453 Fax: 0870 164 1502 — MB BS 1973 Lond.; MRCGP 1981; DObst RCOG 1976.

BENNETT, Rupert Roger 5 Skipton Street, Harrogate HG1 5JF — MB BS 1992 Lond.; BSc Lond. 1989, MB BS 1992.

BENNETT, Sally Anne Microbiology Dept., Borders General Hospital, Melrose TD6 9BS — MB ChB 1979 Birm.; MRCPath 1986. Cons. Microbiol., Borders Gen. Hosp., Melrose, TD6 9BS. Prev: Cons. Microbiol. Trafford Gen. Hosp., Davyhulme; Cons. Microbiol. Blackburn, Hyndburn and Ribble Valley Health Auth., BRI, Blackburn.

***BENNETT, Sally Louise** 1F2 33 Lauderdale Street, Edinburgh EH9 1DE Tel: 0131 447 2968 Email: sbennett13@hotmail.com — MB ChB 1998 Ed.; MB ChB Ed 1998.

BENNETT, Sally Veronica 29 Franklin Place, Chichester PO19 1BL Tel: 01243 789686 — MB ChB 1992 Birm.; BSc (Hons.) Pharmacol. Birm. 1989; T(GP) 1996; DRCOG 1995; DCH RCPS Glas. 1994. SHO (Palliat. Care). Prev: Trainee GP Inverness VTS.

BENNETT, Seán Garfield Wembury Surgery, 51 Hawthorn Drive, Wembury, Plymouth PL9 0BE; Mariners, Yealm Road, Newton Ferrers, Plymouth PL8 1BL — MB BS 1972 Lond. (Middlx.) Socs: Plymouth Med. Soc.; B.M.A.S. Prev: Surg. Lt. Cdr. RN.

BENNETT, Sean Russell Beechcroft, Kemp Road, Swanland, North Ferriby HU14 3LY — MB ChB 1981 Birm.; FFA RCS Eng. 1987; DA Eng. 1985.

BENNETT, Sharon Denise Highbury New Park Surgery, 49 Highbury New Park, London N5 2ET Tel: 020 7354 1972; 30 Gibson Square, London N1 0RD — MB BS 1988 Lond.; MRCGP 1998; DRCOG 1992; FDS RCS Eng. 1983; BDS Bristol 1978. Clin. Tutor UCL Hosp. Socs: BMA; MRCGP. Prev: SHO (Paediat., O & G & c/o Elderly) Whipps Cross Hosp. Lond.

BENNETT, Shirley Joyce Orchard House, Malvern Road, Lower Wick, Worcester WR2 4BS Tel: 01905 421620 — MB ChB 1986 Manch.; MRCP (UK) 1989. Asst. GP Malvern Health Centre Worcs. Prev: SHO (Med.) Walsgrave Hosp. Coventry.

BENNETT, Sian 23 Jenson Way, Upper Norwood, London SE19 2UP — MB BCh 1980 Wales; MRCP (UK) 1984.

BENNETT, Sidney 5 Barrydene, Oakleigh Road N., London N20 9HG Tel: 020 8445 8954 — MRCS Eng. LRCP Lond. 1930. (St. Bart.) Socs: Fell. Hunt. Soc.; BMA. Prev: Cas. Off. Lond. Jewish Hosp.; R.A.M.C. 1939-45.

BENNETT, Simon Philip 31 Gresford Av, Liverpool L17 2AN — MB ChB 1997 Liverp.

BENNETT, Sophie Marie Veronique 31 Crossways, Brentwood CM15 8QY — MB BS 1998 Lond.; MB BS Lond 1998.

BENNETT, Stephen Brian 57 Lyneside Road, Knypersley, Biddulph, Stoke-on-Trent ST8 6SD — MB BChir 1947 Camb.; MRCS Eng. LRCP Lond. 1943.

***BENNETT, Stephen Peter** 54/1 Balbirnie Place, Edinburgh EH12 5JL Tel: 0131 346 4275 — MB ChB 1997 Ed.

BENNETT, Stuart 6 Fylde Road, Southport PR9 9XJ — MB ChB 1997 Sheff.

BENNETT, Stuart Mark Anthony Department of Medicine, University of Newcastle, Wellcome Research Laboratories, Royal Victoria Infirmary, Queen Victoria Road, Newcastle upon Tyne NE1 4LP Tel: 0191 282 4644 Fax: 0191 222 0723 Email: s.m.a.bennett@ncl.ac.uk; 41 Robert Westall Way, Royal Quays, North Shields NE29 6YF Tel: 0191 259 5537 Email: s.m.a.bennett@north-shields.freeserve.co.uk — MB ChB 1992 Manch.; MRCP (UK) 1995. Clin. Research Assoc. (Diabetes) Univ. Newc. Prev: Regist. (Gen. Med., Diabetes & Endocrinol.) Newc. Gen. Hosp.; SHO (Internal Med.) Qu. Med. Centre Univ. Hosp. Nottm.; SHO (Gen. & Geriat. Med.) N. Tyneside Health Care.

BENNETT, Susan Frances Dorset Health Authority, Victoria House, Princess Road, Ferndown BH22 9JR Tel: 01202 893000 Fax: 01202 870561 Email: phealth@dorset.swest.nhs.uk; 25 Sandpiper Close, Creekmoor, Poole BH17 7YE Tel: 01202 602445 Fax: 01202 602445 Email: sfbmafb@aol.com — BM BCh 1977 Oxf.; MA Oxf. 1979; MRCP (UK) 1979; MFPHM RCP Lond. 1993; MRCGP 1981. (Oxford) Cons. Pub. Health Dorset Health Commiss.; Dep. Adv. to the Fac. of Pub. Health, Wessex Deonery. Prev: GP Lond.; SHO (Cardiol.) Papworth Hosp. Camb.

BENNETT, Tamsin Jane 8 Leys Road, Oxshott, Leatherhead KT22 0QE — MB ChB 1984 Sheff.

BENNETT, Therese Horse Shoe Barn, Chunal, Glossop SK13 6JY Tel: 01457 857506 — MB BCh BAO 1978 Dub.; DCCH RCP Ed. 1990; DRCOG 1988. Clin. Med. Off. N. Manch. HA. Socs: BMA; Assoc. Mem. Nat. Assn. Family Plann. Prev: Clin. Med. Off. Mid Surrey HA.

BENNETT, Tracy Ann 85A Walton Way, Newbury RG14 2LL — MB ChB 1993 Manch.

BENNETT, Trevor Curtis Reginald 'Grove House', Melton Constable NR24 2DZ — MB ChB 1969 Sheff.; BA (Hons. French) Birm. 1960.

BENNETT, Victoria Susan 136 Straight Road, Colchester CO3 5DL — MB ChB 1998 Manch.; MB ChB Manch 1998.

BENNETT, Virginia Ruth Nethergreen Road Surgery, 34-36 Nethergreen Road, Sheffield S11 7EJ Tel: 0114 230 2952; 59

Ranmoor Crescent, Sheffield S10 3GW — MB ChB 1969 Liverp.; DObst RCOG 1971.

BENNETT, William Greig (retired) Shanty Beck, Cartmel Fell, Grange-over-Sands LA11 6NS Tel: 015395 31405 — MB ChB Manch. 1964; AFOM RCP Lond. 1983; DIH Eng. 1979.

BENNETT-JONES, David Nicholas Renal Unit, Cumberland Infirmary, Carlisle CA2 7HY Tel: 01228 814772 Fax: 01228 814857 Email: davidbj@carlh-tr.northy.nhs.uk; Scales Hall, Calthwaite, Penrith CA11 9QG Tel: 017684 84641 Email: david.bj@virgin.net — MB BChir 1979 Camb.; MA Camb. 1981; FRCP Lond. 1994; MRCP (UK) 1981. (St. Thos.) Cons. Phys. Nephrol. Cumbld. Infirm. Carlisle; Cons. Nephrol. W. Cumbld. Hosp. Whitehaven. Socs: Chairm. Med. Soc. of DGH Nephrol. Prev: Sen. Regist. (Nephrol. & Gen. Med.) N. Staffs. Roy. Infirm. Stoke on Trent.

BENNETT-RICHARDS, Katherine Jane Great Ormond Street Hospital, Department of Vascular Physiology, Great Ormond St., London WC1N Tel: 020 7813 8223; 29 Arrow Road, London E3 3HE Tel: 020 8980 5532 — MB BS 1991 Lond.; MRCP (UK) 1995. Research Fell., Unit of Vasc. Physiol., Gt. Ormond St. Hosp., Lond. Prev: Specialist Regist., Renal & Gen. Med., Basildon Hosp.; Specialst Regist., Renal, Middlx. Hosp., W1.

BENNETT-RICHARDS, Phillip John Aberfeldy Practice, 50 Aberfeldy Street, London E14 0NU Tel: 020 7515 5622 Fax: 020 7538 3462 — MB BS 1994 Lond.; BSc (Hons.) Toxicol. & Pharmacol. Lond. 1988; Dip. Ther. Wales 1998. (Univ. Coll. Middlx. Hosp. Sch. Med.) GP Regist. E. Lond. VTS. Prev: SHO (Palliat. Med.) St. Francis Hospice, Havering-at-the-Bower, Essex; SHO (Gen. Med.) Thanet Dist. Gen. Hosp. Margate.; SHO (c/o Elderly) Bancroft Unit, Mile End Hosp. Lond.

BENNETTE, John Graham (retired) Basement Flat, 1 St Martin's Road, London SW9 0SP — MB BChir 1948 Camb.; MA, MB BChir Camb. 1948. Vice-Pres. Brit. Assn. Cancer Research. Prev: Med. Servs. Sec. Roy. Soc. Med.

BENNETTO, Luke Peter Yaffle Hill, Seaway La, Torquay TQ2 6PW — BM 1997 Soton.

BENNETTS, Frank Edwin (retired) 7 bryer Place, Windsor SL4 4YL — MB BS Lond. 1953; FRCP & S Canada 1972; FFA RCS Eng. 1960; DA Eng. 1958. Prev: Cons. Anaesth. Medway Health Dist.

BENNETTS, Kae 2 The Lees, Bicton Heath, Shrewsbury SY3 5BD — MB BS 1991 Lond.

BENNETTS, Richard John The Limes Medical Centre, 65 Leicester Road, Narborough, Leicester LE9 5DU Tel: 0116 284 1347 Fax: 0116 275 2447; 140 Hinckley Road, Leicester Forest E., Leicester LE3 3JT Tel: 0116 224 9356 Email: richard.bennetts@virgin.net — MB ChB 1985 Leic.; BSc (Hons.) E. Anglia 1977; MSc (Toxicol.) Surrey 1979; MRCGP 1990; DRCOG 1989. Extern. Examr. for Dept. of GP Univ. of Leics. Undergrad. Teachg. Socs: Leic. Med. Soc.

BENNEY, Sarah Amanda Jane Langley Medical Practice, Oak Hill Health Centre, Oak Hill Road, Surbiton KT6 6EN Tel: 020 8390 9996 Fax: 020 8390 4057 — MB BS 1987 Lond.; MRCGP 1992; DRCOG 1991; DGM RCP Lond. 1990. Prev: Trainee GP Surrey.

BENNIE, Alan Michael Bishopton Health Centre, Greenock Road, Bishopton PA7 5AW Tel: 01505 863223 Fax: 01505 862798; Woodgreen, Watt Lane, Bridge of Weir PA11 3EJ Tel: 01505 612896 Email: bennieajgc@aol.com — MB ChB 1974 Ed. (Edinburgh) GP Bishopton Health Centre; Sen. Tutor (Gen. Pract.) Univ. Glas.; Voc. Studies Tutor Univ. of Glas.

BENNIE, David Blue Department of Anaesthetics, Dumfries & Galloway Royal Infirmary, Bankend Road, Dumfries DG1 4AP Tel: 01387 246246 Fax: 01387 241639; Midpark Lodge, Bankend Road, Dumfries DG1 4TN Tel: 01387 262134 Email: 113303.3307@compuserve.com — MB ChB 1967 Ed.; FFA RCS Eng. 1973. (Ed.) Cons. Anaesth. Dumfries & Galloway Roy. Infirm.; Hon Sen Lect.(Anaest.) Univ of Glasg. Socs: (Counc.) Scott. Soc. Anaesth.; Linkman Assn. Anaesth. Prev: Clin. Dir. (Anaesth., Theatres & Intens. Care) Dumfries & Galloway Acute Hosps. NHS Trust; Coll. Tutor Roy. Coll. Anaesth.; Sen. Regist. (Anaesth.) Edin. Roy. Infirm.

BENNIE, Ernest Harry Ross Hall Hospital, Glasgow G52 3NQ Tel: 0141 810 3151; 146 Terregles Avenue, Glasgow G41 4RU Fax: 0141 427 2601 Email: 101364.3011@compuserve.com — MB ChB Glas. 1962; FRCPsych 1986, M 1972; DPM Ed. & Glas. 1967; DObst RCOG 1964. Cons. Psychiat. Ailsa Hosp. Ayr. Prev: Cons. Psychiat. Leverndale Hosp. Glas.

BENNIE, Mary Jane St Thomas Hospital, Lambeth Palace Road, London SE1 7EH; 5 Ruskin Walk, North Dulwich, London SE24 9NA — MB ChB 1992 Liverp.; MB ChB (Hons.) Liverp. 1992; BSc (Hons.) Liverp. 1989; MRCP (UK) 1995. Specialist Regist. (Radiol.) St. Thos. & Guy's Hosp. Lond. Prev: SHO Rotat. (Gen. Med.) Guy's Hosp. Lond.; Ho. Surg. Profess. Surgic. Unit Roy Free Hosp. Lond.; Ho. Phys. Soton. Gen. Hosp.

BENNIE, Peter Fraser 9 Prospect Avenue, Cambuslang, Glasgow G72 8BW — MB ChB 1986 Glas.

BENNING, Amrik Singh West End Road Surgery, 62 West End Road, Bitterne, Southampton SO18 6TG Tel: 023 8044 9162 Fax: 023 8039 9742 — BM 1977 Soton.

BENNING, Ram 11 Nuffield Road, Courthouse Green, Coventry CV6 7HR — MB ChB 1996 Leic.

BENNING, Tony Bhulinder 100 Murcott Road E., Whitnash, Leamington Spa CV31 2JP — MB ChB 1995 Manch. (Manch.) Prev: Ho. Off. (Surg.) Russells Hall Hosp. W. Midl.; Ho. Off. (Med.) Roy. Oldham Hosp.

BENNINGER, Brion Leroy David 28 Chaucer Street, Leicester LE2 1HD — MB ChB 1991 Leic.

BENNISON, Dean Perry 6 Avenue Close, Queniborough, Leicester LE7 8DS — BM 1984 Soton.; MRCP (UK) 1989; MRCGP 1996.

BENNISON, Janet Marie Flat 1F2, 77 Causewayside, Edinburgh EH9 1QG — MB ChB 1996 Ed.

BENNISON, Jennifer Marion Rose Garden Medical Centre, 4 Mill Lane, Edinburgh EH6 6TL Tel: 0131 554 1274 Fax: 0131 555 2159 Email: jenny.bennison@quista.net — MB BChir 1990 Camb.; MA Camb. 1990; MRCGP (Distinc.) 1993; DFFP 1993; DCCH RCP Ed. 1993; DRCOG 1992; DGM RCP Glas. 1991. G.P Princip., director of PEP, RCGP Scotl.; Henorary Sec. of Scott. Counc.. Edin.

BENNS, John Scott Dykes Hall Medical Centre, 156 Dykes Hall Road, Sheffield S6 4GQ Tel: 0114 232 3236 — MB ChB 1976 Sheff.; BSc Sheff. 1971, MB ChB 1976; MRCGP 1985; Cert Family Plann. JCC 1985.

BENSA, Richard Mark Romeril Treliske Hospital, Truro TR1 3LJ; 3 Spencer Street, Leamington Spa CV31 3NE — MB ChB 1996 Dund.; BSc St. And. 1990; MSc Lond. 1991. (Dund.) SHO Rotat. (Gen. Med.) Treliske Hosp. Truro. Socs: BMA. Prev: SHO Ninewells Hosp. Dund.; SHO Perth Roy. Infirm.

BENSA, Robert Guy Romeril (retired) Ashton House Surgery, 15 George St., Leamington Spa CV31 1ET Tel: 01926 428321 Fax: 01926 427232 — MB ChB 1963 St. And.; DPM Eng. 1967. Prev: Sen. Regist. (Psychiat.) & Hon. Asst. Clin. Tutor United Birm. Hosps.

BENSON, Alan James (retired) 29 Coxheath Road, Church Crookham, Fleet GU52 6QQ Tel: 01252 616595 — MB ChB Manch. 1955; BSc Manch. 1951, MSc 1952. Cons. (Aviat. Med.) RAF Centre for Aviat. Med. FarnBoro. Prev: Sen. Med. Off. (Research) RAF Inst. Aviat. Med. FarnBoro.

BENSON, Alexander D'Arcy Ridgway, Harberton Mead, Headington, Oxford OX3 0DB — MB BS 1998 Lond.; MB BS Lond 1998.

BENSON, Anne Pamela (retired) 29 Coxheath Road, Church Crookham, Fleet GU52 6QQ Tel: 01252 616595 — MB ChB Manch. 1953; MRCGP 1976; DCH Eng. 1956. Prev: GP Aldershot.

BENSON, Barbara Mary 102 Carsington Crescent, Allestree, Derby DE22 2QX Tel: 01332 556600 — MB ChB 1952 Manch. (Manch.) Exam. Med. Off. DSS. Socs: Daly Med. Soc. Prev: Clin. Asst. (Geriat.) Gr. Hosp. Shardlow.

BENSON, Catharine Alice Beaumont Street Surgery, 27 Beaumont Street, Oxford City, Oxford OX1 2NR Tel: 01865 311500 Fax: 01865 311720 — MB BChir 1988 Camb.; FP Cert 1993; BSc 1985 (Hons. Med. Sci. with Biochem.); MRCS Eng. LRCP Lond. 1988; DCH RCP Lond. 1991; DRCOG 1992; MRCGP 1993. (St. Andrews and Cambridge) p/t GP; Clin. Asst. (Genito-Urin. Med.); Police Surg.; Communication Skills Tutor (Univ. of Oxf.); LMC Rep.; GP Tutor (Univ. of Cardiff).

BENSON, Charlotte Royal Marsden Hospital, Fulham Road, London SW3 6JJ Tel: 020 7352 8171; Flat 1, 12 Christchurch Road, London N8 9QL — MB ChB 1995 Liverpool. (Liverpool) SHO Med. Oncol., Roy. Marsden Hosp.; Sen. Lect. Keele Univ. Research Fell. in Gen. Pract., Regional GP Unit, Birm.; Med. Adviser to C.E. Andersons & Sons Ltd., Barclays Bank Ltd. & other Cos.; Primary Care Phys. (UK & abRd.); Vis. Cons. Learning Assessm. Centre,

Horsham, W. Sussex; HS RSCH Guildford; RAF Med. Pract. Prev: Med. SHO, Whipps Cross Hosp.; Med. SHO, Roy. Liverp. Hosp.

BENSON, Mr Edward Arthur (retired) — BM BCh 1962 Oxf.; MA Oxf. 1959; FRCS Eng. 1967. Prev: Cons. Gen. Surg. The Gen. Infirm. at Leeds & Pinderfields Gen. Hosp. Wakefield.

BENSON, Eric Nicholas Tel: 01892 546422 Fax: 01892 533987; Tel: 01892 542162 — MB BS 1977 Lond.; BSc (Biochem.) Sussex 1972; D.Occ.Med 1999 Faculty of Occupational Medicine & Royal College of Physicians of London; MRCGP 1982; DCH RCP Lond. 1982; DRCOG 1980. (King's Coll. Hosp.) Socs: Soc. Occupat. Med.

BENSON, Gillian Louise Lincoln House Surgery, Wolsey Road, Hemel Hempstead HP2 4TU; 148 Sandbridge Road, St Albans AL1 4AP Tel: 01727 838756 — MB ChB Sheff. 1986; MRCGP 1991. Asst. GP. Prev: Trainee GP/SHO (Paediat.) Tameside Gen. Hosp. Ashton VTS.

BENSON, Harold (retired) 78 waterfall Road, Southgate, London N14 7JT Tel: 020 8368 5187 — MB ChB Glas. 1946.

BENSON, Heather Graham (retired) Oak Bank, Kirkby Lonsdale, Carnforth LA6 2DE Tel: 015242 71688 — MB ChB 1951 Liverp. Prev: Obst. Ho. Surg. Sharoe Green Hosp. Preston.

BENSON, Helen Anne The Health Centre, Victoria Street, Marsden, Huddersfield HD7 6DF Tel: 01484 844332 Fax: 0148 845779; Royd House, 4 The Woodlands, Royd Road, Meltham, Holmfirth HD9 4NW — MB ChB 1988 Manch.; MRCGP 1995. p/t GP Princip. Prev: SHO (Psychiat.) Tameside Gen. Hosp. Ashton-u.-Lyne; SHO (O & G) Fairfield Hosp. Bury; SHO (A & E) Warrington Dist. Gen. Hosp.

BENSON, John Arthur 26 Greenside, Waterbeach, Cambridge CB5 9HP Tel: 01223 862643; 23 Humberside Road, Cambridge CB4 1JD — MB ChB 1981 Birm.; MRCP (UK) 1985; MRCGP 1989.

BENSON, Mr John Russell Cambridge Breast Unit, Box 97, Addenbrookes Hospital, Cambridge CB2 2QQ; 26 Millway Cl, Upper Wolvercote, Oxford OX2 8BJ Tel: 01865 553246 — BM BCh 1984 Oxf.; MA Oxf. 1985; FRCS Eng. 1990; FRCS Ed. 1989; DM (Oxf) 1997. Cons. Surg. Addenbrooke's Hosp., Camb. & Hinchinbrooke Hosp., Huntingdon. Socs: Amer. Assoc. Cancer Research; NY Acad. Sci.; Brit. Assn. Surg. Oncol. Prev: Sen. Regist. (Surg.) Chelsea & W.m. Hosp. Lond.; Sen. Regist. Acad. Dept. Surg. Roy. Marsden Hosp. & Inst. Cancer Research Lond.; SHO (Surg.) Hammersmith Hosp. Lond.

BENSON, John William Thomas Queen's Park Hospital, Blackburn BB2 3HH Tel: 01254 263555 Fax: 01254 293555; The Nook, York Lane, Langho, Blackburn BB6 8DR Tel: 01254 248543 Email: jwtbenson@aol.com — MB BChir 1972 Camb.; MA Camb. 1972; FRCP Lond. 1989; MRCP (UK) 1973; DCH Eng. 1974; FRCPCH 1997. (Camb. & St. Thom. Hosp.) Cons. Paediat. Blackburn Hyndburn & Ribble Valley DHA.; Hon. Clin. Lect. (Paediat.) Univ. of Manch. Prev: Sen. Regist. (Paediat.) Alder Hey Childr. Hosp. Liverp.; Leukaemia Research Fell. Inst. of Child Health Lond.; Regist. (Paediat.) Oxf.

BENSON, Jonathan Paul 25 Queens Drive, Stockport SK4 3JN — MB ChB 1986 Birm.; ChB Birm. 1986.

BENSON, Julian Arthur Gilpin (retired) 1 Marine Parade, Budleigh Salterton EX9 6NS — MB ChB 1960 Bristol; DObst RCOG 1961.

BENSON, Karen Judith Crouch Hall Surgery, 48 Crouch Hall Road, Hornsey, London N8 8HJ Tel: 020 8340 7736 Fax: 020 8455 0342 — MB BCh 1980 Wales; MRCP (UK) 1983; MRCGP 1987. (Univ. Wales Cardiff) Clin. Asst. (Dermat.) Lond.; GP Trainer; GP Tutor (Undergrad) Univ. Coll. & Roy. Free Hosp. Lond. Socs: Brit. Med. Acupunct. Soc. Prev: Regist. (Med.) St. Bart. Hosp. Lond.; SHO (Paediat.) Roy. Free Hosp. Lond.

BENSON, Kathryn Jane Dept of Anaesthesia, C Floor, QMC, University Hospital, Nottingham NG7 2UH; Flat B, Oakfield House, 2 Cyprus Road, Mapperley Park, Nottingham NG3 5EB — BM BS 1991 Nottm.; BMedSci Nottm. 1989; FRCA 1997. (Notts) Cons. Anaesth. Notts. Qu. Med. Centre. Prev: Specialist Regist. anaesth. Notts Qu. Med. Centre.

BENSON, Malcolm Keith 82 High Street, Wheatley, Oxford OX33 1XP Tel: 01865 3843 — MRCS Eng. LRCP Lond. 1967; MD Lond. 1976, MB BS 1967; FRCP Lond. 1984; MRCP (U.K.) 1969. (Lond. Hosp.) Cons. Phys. (Gen. & Respirat. Med.) Oxon. HA. Socs: Med. Research Soc. & Thoracic Soc. Prev: Sen. Med. Regist. Hants. HA; Fell. Cardiovasc. Research Inst. San Francisco, U.S.A.; Med. Regist. Lond. Hosp.

BENSON, Mr Mark Timothy Department of Ophthalmology, Solihull Hospital, LodeLane, Solihull B91 2JL; Birmingham and Midland Eye Centre, City Hospital NHS Trust, Dudley Road, Birmingham — MB ChB 1982 Birm.; MSc Birm. 1986; FRCS Ed. 1988; FRCOphth 1988. Cons. Ophth. Surg. Birm.& Solihull Heartlands Hospdl. Eye Hosp.; Clin. Dir. (Ophthalmol.) Birm. Heartlands & Solihull Hosp. Prev: Lect. (Ophth.) Univ. Sheff.

BENSON, Martin John St Helier Hospital, Wrythe Lane, Carshalton SM5 1AA Tel: 020 8644 4343 Fax: 020 8644 9419; 2 Cork Square, Vaughan Way, Wapping, London E1W 2NG Tel: 020 7488 1142 — MB BS 1982 Lond.; BSc (Hons. Physiol.) Lond. 1979, MD 1994, MB BS 1982; MRCP (UK) 1986. (The London Hospital Medicine College) Cons. Phys. & Gastroenterol. St Helier Hosp.; Hon Sen. Lect. (Med.) St Geo. Hosp. Med. Sch. Lond. Prev: Sen. Regist. (Gastroenterol. & Gen. Med.) St. Geo. Hosp. Lond.; Regist. (Gastroenterol. & Gen. Med.) Lond. Hosp. Whitechapel.

BENSON, Mr Michael Knox d'Arcy Nuffield Orthopaedic Trust Hospital, Headington, Oxford Tel: 01865 741155 Fax: 01865 742348; Ridgway, Harberton Mead, Oxford OX3 0DB Tel: 01865 762907 Fax: 01865 762907 — MB BS Lond. 1968; MA (Hon.) Oxf. 1977; FRCS Eng. 1973. (St. Mary's) Cons. Nuffield Orthop. Centre Oxf.; Hon. Sen. Lect. Oxf. Univ.; ABC Trav. Fell. 1980; Mem. (Sec. & Treas.) Jl. Bone & Jt. Surg. Socs: Counc. Mem. (Ex-Hon. Sec.) Brit. Orthop. Assn.; (Ex-Pres.) Brit. Soc. Childr. Orthop. Surg.; Pres. Europ. Paediat. Orthop. Soc. Prev: Sen. Regist. (Orthop.) Middlx. Hosp. Lond.; Regist. (Orthop.) St. Mary's Hosp. Lond.; SHO Roy. Nat. Orthop. Hosp. Stanmore.

BENSON, Peter John The Scott Practice, 1 Greenfield Lane, Balby, Doncaster DN4 0TG Tel: 01302 850546 Fax: 01302 855338 — MB ChB 1975 Sheff.; MRCGP 1979; DRCOG 1978. GP Doncaster.

BENSON, Rachel Clare The Nook, York Lane, Langho, Blackburn BB6 8DR — MB BCh 1998 Wales.

BENSON, Richard Anthony James Fisher Medical Centre, 4 Tolpuddle Gardens, Bournemouth BH9 3LQ Tel: 01202 522622 Fax: 01202 548480; 5 Headswell Crescent, Redhill, Bournemouth BH10 6LF Tel: 01202 510079 — MB BS 1982 Lond.; DRCOG 1986. Clin. Teach. (Primary Care) Soton. Univ. Prev: SHO (Psychiat., A & E & O & G) Bournemouth.

BENSON, Richard Fortune — MB BS 1981 Lond.; MRCGP 1986.

BENSON, Richard James 4 Oberfield Road, Brockenhurst SO42 7QF — MB BS 1988 Lond.

BENSON, Robert Gordon Linden House, 30 Upper Fairfield Road, Leatherhead KT22 7HH Tel: 01372 375666 — MB BS 1949 Lond.; DObst RCOG 1951. (St. Thos.) Prev: Ho. Phys. & Cas. Off. St. Thos. Hosp.; Gyn. Ho. Surg. St. Luke's Hosp. Guildford.

BENSON, Sarah Elizabeth 6 West End La, Horsforth, Leeds LS18 5JP — MB ChB 1997 Manch. Locum SHO in Oncol./Radiother. Prev: SHO in Emerg. Med., P.ss Alexandra Hosp.; Ho. Off. (Med), Qu.s Pk. Hosp., Blackburn; Ho. Off. Surg./Orthop., Trafford Gen. Hosp., Manch.

BENSON, Stephen Richard Charles 23 Regent Street, Stirchley, Birmingham B30 2LG — MB ChB 1991 Birm.; ChB Birm. 1991.

BENSON, William Arthur (retired) Causey Lodge, Stanley DH9 0LS Tel: 01207 232927 — LRCP LRCS 1944 Ed.; LRCP LRCS Ed. LRFPS Glas. 1944; DObst RCOG 1949. Asst. Psychiat. Durh. Health Dist. Prev: Ho. Surg. Gyn. & Gen. Surg. Depts. Roy. Cornw. Infirm. Truro.

BENSON, William Geoffrey (retired) Fentens, Upper Castle Road, St Mawes, Truro TR2 5BZ Tel: 01326 270560 — MB ChB 1951 Bristol; MFOM 1985; DIH Eng. 1979; CIH Dund 1978; DObst RCOG 1953. Prev: Res. Med. Off. King Geo. V. Memor. Hosp. Malta.

BENSTEAD, Kim Southview Cottage, The Quarry, Brockhampton, Cheltenham GL54 5XJ — MB BChir 1980 Camb.; BA Camb. 1978, MD 1989, MB BChir 1980; MRCP (UK) 1983; FRCR 1986. Sen. Regist. (Radiother.) Addenbrooke's Hosp. Camb.

BENSTEAD, Susan Elizabeth Bishopgate Medical Centre, 178 Newgate Street, Bishop Auckland DL14 7EJ Tel: 01388 603983 Fax: 01388 607782; 34 Barrington Meadows, Bishop Auckland DL14 6NT — MB BS 1984 Newc.; BSc (Hons.) Newc. 1979.

BENSTER, Barry 37-39 Lidget Street, Lindley, Huddersfield HD3 3JF Tel: 01484 658013 Fax: 01484 460020 Email: barry@hudbooks.demon.co.uk — MB ChB Manch. 1960; FRCOG

1979, M 1966; DObst RCOG 1962. (Manch.) Hon. Cons. (O & G) Roy. Infirm. Huddersfield. Prev: Sen. Regist. (O & G) Hammersmith Hosp.; Lect. (O & G) Roy. Univ., Malta.

BENSUSAN, Desiree 36 Heathhalt Road, Heath, Cardiff CF23 5QF Tel: 029 2075 6009 — MB BCh 1997 Wales.

BENT, Jennifer Ann Medical Centre, Craig Croft, Chelmsley Wood, Birmingham B37 7TR Tel: 0121 770 5656 Fax: 0121 779 5619; Barston Farm, Hob Lane, Barston, Solihull B92 0JT Tel: 01675 442977 — MB ChB Birm. 1968; DObst RCOG 1970. (Birmingham) Princip. GP Med. Centre Birm. Socs: Diplomates Assn. RCOG; Sands Cox Soc.; Brit. Menopause Soc. Prev: SHO (O & G) Marston Green Matern. Hosp. Birm.; Ho. Phys. & Ho. Surg. Selly Oak Hosp. Birm.

BENT, John Eric, OStJ Medical Centre, 106 Gold St., Wellingborough NN8 4BT Tel: 01933 223429 Fax: 01933 229240; Beechwood House, 78 Doddington Road, Earls Barton, Northampton NN6 0NQ Tel: 01604 810347 — MB ChB 1967 Birm. (Birm.)

BENTALL, Professor Hugh Henry Pyt Cottage, Marlow Road, Henley-on-Thames RG9 2JA Tel: 01491 578107 Fax: 01491 578107 — MB BS Lond. 1942; FRCS Eng. 1950; MRCS Eng. LRCP Lond. 1942. (St. Bart.) Emerit. Prof. Cardiac Surg. Roy. Postgrad. Med. Sch. Univ. Lond.; Hon. Cons. Thoracic Surg. Hammersmith Hosp.; Sen. Mem. Anat. Soc. Gt. Brit. & Irel. Socs: Sen. Mem. Brit. Cardiac Soc.; Sen. Mem. Europ. Soc. Cardiovasc. Surg. Prev: Lect. (Anat.) Char. Cross Hosp. Med. Sch.; Res. Surg. Off. Gordon Hosp.; Res. Med. Off. Lond. Chest Hosp.

BENTALL, Jean Kate Mary Cameron (retired) Pyt Cottage, Marlow Road, Henley-on-Thames RG9 2JA Tel: 01491 578107 — MB BS 1941 Lond.; MRCS Eng. LRCP Lond. 1941; DMR Lond 1952. Prev: Clin. Asst. Chest Clinic Slough.

BENTHAM, Mr John Alexander (retired) Cae Mawr, Mynydd Nefyn, Pwllheli LL53 6TN Tel: 01758 720713 — MB ChB Glas 1933; FRCS Ed. 1948; FRFPS Glas. 1948; FRCS Glas. 1962; DPH Liverp. 1937; FRCOG 1964, M 1950. Prev: Cons. Obstetr. & Gynaecol. Liverp. RHB.

BENTHAM, John Christopher Patrick Lee Health Centre, 2 Handen Road, London SE12 8NP Tel: 020 8852 2611 Fax: 020 8297 8221 — MB BS 1983 Lond.

BENTHAM, Peter William 25 Lucerne Close, Cherry Hinton, Cambridge CB1 9YR — MB ChB 1983 Leeds.

BENTLEY, Alastair James Institute of Forensic Medicine, Grosvenor Road, Belfast BT12 6BS Tel: 02890 894648 Fax: 02890 237357; Apartment 7, 14 College Gardens, Belfast BT9 6BQ Tel: 02890 667142 — MB ChB 1985 Aberd.; 1982 MSc Aberd.; 1979 BSc Glas.; 1992 MRCPath; 1994 DMJ(Path) Soc. Apoth. Lond.; FRCPath. (University of Aberdeen) Dep. State Path. Qu.'s Univ. of Belf. & N.ern Irel. Office. Prev: Lect. & Hon. Sen. Regist. (Forens. Path.) Univ. of Edin.; Sen. Regist. (Histopath.) Roy. Lond. Hosp.

BENTLEY, Andrew Mark North Manchester General Hospital, Manchester M8 5RB Tel: 0161 720 2342 Fax: 0161 720 2440; The Old Barn, Little Padfield, Glossop SK13 1ER Tel: 01457 855617 Email: andrewbentleyl@compuserve.com — MB BS 1985 Lond.; FRCP 2001; BSc Lond. 1982, MD 1995; MRCP (UK) 1988. (Kings Coll. Hosp. Med. Sch.) Cons. Phys. (ICU & Respirat. Med.) N. Manch. Gen. Hosp. Socs: Brit. Thorac. Soc.; Brit. Soc. Allergy & Clin. Immunol.; Intens. Care Soc. Prev: Sen. Regist. (Gen. & Thoracic Med.) Oxf. & Radcliffe Hosps.; Regist. (Gen. & Thoracic Med.) Wycombe Gen. Hosp. & Ch.ill Hosp. Oxf.; Clin. Researcher Fell. (Allergy & Clin. Immunol.) Nat. Heart & Lung Inst.

BENTLEY, Anthony John James The Surgery, 155 Downing Drive, Evington, Leicester LE5 6LP Tel: 0116 241 3801 — MB ChB 1990 Leic.; MRCGP 1994. Socs: Leic. Med. Soc. Prev: Trainee GP Leicester VTS.

BENTLEY, Arnold Philip, MBE (retired) 5 Roseacre Gardens, Bearsted, Maidstone ME14 4JF Tel: 01622 734510 — MB BS Lond. 1944. Prev: Cons. Phys. Roy. Brit. Legion Village Maidstone.

BENTLEY, Brian Clinical Radiology, Salisbury District Hospital, Salisbury SP2 8BJ Tel: 01722 336262 Fax: 01772 414008; Three Thatches, Bodenham, Salisbury SP5 4EU Tel: 01722 326222 — MB ChB Liverp. 1968; FRCR 1974; DMRD Liverp. 1972. Cons. Radiol. Salisbury Dist. Hosp. Prev: Sen. Regist. Soton. Gen. Hosp.; Sen. Regist. United Liverp. Hosps.

BENTLEY, Cecily Jean Macrae (retired) Ferguslie Cottage, Main St., Buchlyvie, Stirling FK8 3LP Tel: 01360 850387 — MB ChB 1948 Aberd.; MFCM 1977; DPH Glas. 1973. Prev: SCM Forth Valley HB.

BENTLEY, Christopher Charles Sheffield Hospital, 5 Old Fulwood Road, Sheffield S10 3TG Tel: 0114 271 1247 Fax: 0114 271 1101 — MB BS 1977 Lond.; MSc Lond. (Distinc.) 1989, BSc (Ist cl. Hons.) 1974; FRCP (UK) 1997; MRCP (UK) 1980; FFPHM (UK) 1997; MFPHM RCP (UK) 1991. (University College Hospital London) Dir. of Policy & Pub. Health Sheff. Health. Socs: BMA; Roy. Soc. Med. Prev: Dir. (Health Policy) W. Sussex Health Auth.; Dir. (Pub. Health) Worthing & Chichester DHA; Dir. Health Policy & Progr. W. Sussex DHAs.

BENTLEY, Christopher Richard 49 Streatham Common, North Side, London SW16 3HS Email: christopher.bentley@lineone.net — MB BS 1988 Lond.; FCOphth 1992. Specialist Regist. (Ophth.) W.. Eye Hosp. Lond. & Fell. Moorfields Eye Hosp. Lond. Socs: Fell. Roy. Soc. Med. Prev: Research Regist. (Neuro-ophth.) Nat. Hosp. Neurol. & Neurosurg. Qu. Sq. Lond.; Regist. (Ophth.) St. Geo. Hosp. Lond.; SHO (Ophth.) St. Thos. & King's Coll. Hosps. Lond.

BENTLEY, Donald (retired) Cromwell Hospital, Cromwell Road, London SW5 0TU — MB ChB 1966 Bristol; 1966 MB ChB Bristol; 1977 MSc Lond.; 1990 FRCP Lond.; 1971 MRCP (UK); 1996 MRCPCH; 1968 DCH Eng.; 1997 FRCPCH; 1996 European Specialist Qualification. Hon. Clin. Sen. Lect. Imperial Coll., Lond.; Hon. Cons. Paediat. Ealing Hosp. S.all Middlx. Prev: Fell. Paediat. Gastroenterol. Childrs. Hosp. Med. Centre Boston Mass. USA (Harvard).

BENTLEY, Douglas Paul 5 Llanedeyrn Road, Cyncoed, Cardiff CF23 9DT Tel: 029 2048 5980 — MB ChB 1967 Manch.; PhD Wales 1985; FRCP Lond. 1990; MRCP (UK) 1970; FRCPath 1988, M 1976. (Manch.) Cons. Haemat. Llandough Hosp. Penarth. Prev: Ho. Phys. & Regist. (Med.) Manch. Roy. Infirm.; Lect. (Haemat.) Welsh Nat. Sch. of Med.

BENTLEY, Geoffrey Charlton (retired) 18 Farley Road, Derby DE23 6BX Tel: 01332 343176 — MB ChB 1959 Manch.; MRCGP 1977; DObst RCOG 1961. Prev: Pincip. GP Derby.

BENTLEY, Professor George 120 Fishpool Street, St Albans AL3 4RX Tel: 01727 851600; Institute of Orthopaedics, Royal National Orthopaedic Hospital, Brockley Hill, Stanmore HA7 4LP Tel: 020 8954 2300 Ext: 532 Fax: 020 8954 3036 Email: g.bentley@ucl.ac.uk — ChM Sheff. 1972, MB ChB 1959; FRCS Eng. 1964. (Sheff.) Prof. Orthop. Surg. & Dir. Inst. Orthop. Univ. Coll. & Middlx. Sch. Med. Univ. Lond.; Vis. Prof. & Lect. Orthop. Assns. of Amer. Canada, Austral. NZ. S. Afr. Japan, India, Egypt, Greece & Italy; Hon. Cons. Orthop. Surg. Roy. Nat. Orthop. Hosp. & Middlx. Hosp. Lond. Socs: Pres. Brit. Orthop. Res. Soc.; Pres. Brit. Orthop. Assn.; Hunt. Prof. Roy. Coll. Surgs. Eng. Prev: Prof. Orthop. & Accid. Surg. Univ. Liverp.; Clin. Reader & 1st. Asst. Nuffield Dept. Orthop. Surg. Nuffield Orthop. Centre Oxf.; Regist. (Orthop.) Robt. Jones & Agnes Hunt Orthop. Hosp. OsW.ry.

BENTLEY, Henry Edward (retired) 51 Addiscombe Road, Croydon CR0 6SB Tel: 020 8688 9098 — MB BS 1939 Lond.; MRCS Eng. LRCP Lond. 1939; MRCGP 1965; DA Eng. 1961. Prev: Clin. Asst. Anaesth. Mayday Hosp. Thornton Heath.

BENTLEY, Ian Spencer Hill Lane Surgery, 162 Hill Lane, Southampton SO15 5DD Tel: 023 8022 3086 Fax: 023 8023 5487; 27 Melrose Road, Southampton SO15 7PB Tel: 02380 770863 — BM 1984 Soton.; MRCGP 1988; DGM RCP Lond. 1988; DRCOG 1986. (Soton.) Princip. GP Soton. Prev: Trainee GP Soton.; SHO (Cas. & Med.) Soton. Gen. Hosp.

BENTLEY, Mr James The Health Centre, Coatham Road, Redcar TS10 1SX Tel: 01642 482647 Fax: 01642 489166 — MB ChB 1967 Leeds; FRCS Ed. 1973.

BENTLEY, Janet Kingswood Surgery, Kingswood Avenue, Swindon SN3 2RJ Tel: 01793 534699; 21a Grove Hill, Highworth, Swindon SN6 7JL — MB BS 1983 Lond.; MRCGP 2001; DFFP 1993; DA (UK) 1986.

BENTLEY, John Ingham Longridge, 25 Holford Way, Newton-le-Willows WA12 0BZ — M.B., Ch.B. Manch. 1947. (Manch.) Prev: Ho. Surg. (Orthop. & Gen. Med.) Roy. Hosp. Salford; Med. Off. RAF.

BENTLEY, Mr John Philip (retired) 1 Victoria Esplanade, West Mersea, Colchester CO5 8AT Tel: 01206 382452 — MB BS 1938 Lond.; FRCS Eng. 1942; MB BS (Hnrs.) Lond. 1938; FACS 1954; MRCS Eng. LRCP Lond. 1938. Consg. Surg. Wanstead Hosp.; Consg. Surg. Italian Hosp. Lond.; Commonw. Fell.sh. Harkness

Fund; Moynihan Fell. Assn. Surgs. Prev: Surg. Regist. &c. Char Cross Hosp. Lond.

BENTLEY, John Trevor Long Lane Medical Centre, Long Lane, Liverpool L9 6DQ Tel: 0151 530 1009; 71 Strathcona Road, Liverpool L15 1EA — MB ChB 1991 Liverp.

BENTLEY, Judith Margaret New Cross Hospital, 124 New Heath Close, Wolverhampton WV10 0QP — MB ChB 1993 Cape Town.

BENTLEY, Karen Dorothea New Milton Health Centre, Spencer Road, New Milton, Bournemouth Tel: 01425 621188 Fax: 01425 620646; 27 Melrose Road, Southampton SO15 7PB Tel: 01703 770863 — BM 1984 Soton.; MRCGP 1989; DGM RCP Lond. 1988; DRCOG 1986. Princip. GP New Milton. Prev: Trainee GP Soton VTS; SHO (Paediat. & Cas.) Soton. Gen. Hosp.; SHO (Med.) Lymington Hosp.

BENTLEY, Kate Louise Three Thatches, Bodenham, Salisbury SP5 4EU — MB BCh 1998 Wales.

BENTLEY, Mark Russell Dr M.RR. Bentley, 3 Eaton Place, Brighton BN2 1EH Tel: 01273 570047 Email: mrbspp@aol.com — MB BS 1991 Lond.; DA (UK) 1994; DA (Dublin) 1994; FRCA Lond 1998. (St. Geo's. Hosp. Lond.) Specialist Regist. (Anaesth.) E.bourne Hosp. Socs: Train. Mem RCA; Train. Mem. Assn. AnE.h.; BMA. Prev: Specialist Regist. (Anaesth.) Kent & Sussex Hosps., Trnbridgewell; Specialist Regist. (Anaesth.) Roy. Sussex Co. Hosp. Brighton; Regist. (Anaesth.) Worthing & S.lands Hosp.s.

BENTLEY, Melissa Sarah 51 Beechwood Avenue, London N3 3BB — MB BS 1998 Lond.; MB BS Lond 1998.

BENTLEY, Paul Isenberg Northwick Park & St. Mark's NHS Trust, Harrow HA1 3UJ — MB BS 1997 Lond.; BA Camb. 194. (UCL) Sen. Ho. Off., (Rhuematology) N.wick Pk., Harrow.

BENTLEY, Peta Clare British Military Hospital Iserlöhn BFPO 24; c/o 67 Wepre Lane, Connahs Quay, Deeside CH5 4JR — MB BCh 1986 Wales; BSc Wales 1981; MRCGP 1993; DCH RCP Lond. 1992.

BENTLEY, Mr Philip Gordon Lightlands, Down Lane, Frant, Tunbridge Wells TN3 9HR Tel: 01892 530305 Fax: 01892 515689 — MRCS Eng. LRCP Lond. 1969; MS Lond. 1980, MB BS 1969; FRCS Eng. 1973. (King's Coll. Hosp.) Cons. (Gen. Surg.) Tunbridge Wells Health Dist. Prev: Sen. Regist. (Gen. Surg.) Kings Heath Dist.

BENTLEY, Robert Paul 14 Cherrydown Close, Thornhill, Cardiff CF14 9DJ — MB BCh 1992 Wales; BDS Wales 1985; FDS RCS Eng. 1988.

BENTLEY, Roger Paul Riverside Health Centre, Canton Court, Wellington Street, Cardiff CF11 9SH Tel: 029 2034 1209 Fax: 029 2034 1209; 83 Ely Road, Llandaff, Cardiff CF5 2BY Tel: 029 2055 5108 Email: thomasbentley@yahoo.com — MB BCh 1981 Wales; MRCGP 1987; MFFP 1993. Police Surg. Cardiff. Socs: Assn. Police Surg. Prev: Trainee GP Cardiff VTS; SHO (Paediat.) Univ. Hosp. Wales; SHO (Gen. Med.) Caerphilly Miners Hosp.

BENTLEY, Simon Windrush Surgery, 21 West Bar Street, Banbury OX16 9SA Tel: 01295 251491; 92 Oxford Road, Banbury OX16 9AN — MB BS 1989 Lond.; BSc (Biochem.) Hons. Lond. 1986; MRCGP 1996; DFFP 1995; DCH 1996. (Char. Cross and W. Minster. Lond.) Princip. GP Windrush Surg. Socs: Roy. Coll. Gen. Pract.; Diplomates Roy. Coll. Phys. (via DCH); Diplomates RCOG (via. DFFP). Prev: Princip. GP W. Bar Surg.; Paediat. SHO Norton Gen. Hosp. NHS Trust Brighton VTS.

BENTLEY, Stephen ASB Associates Ltd, 8 Capstan Close, Cambridge CB4 1BJ Tel: 01223 303514 Fax: 01223 302970 Email: mail@asbassociates.com — MB ChB 1971 Manch.; MIBiol 1982; FFPM RCP (UK) 1995; Dip. Pharm. Med. RCP (UK) 1983. Dir., ASB Assocs. Ltd; Dir., Manor Ho. Gp. Ltd. Prev: Dir. (R&D), Fujisawa-Fisons KK, Osaka, Japan; Dir. (R&D) Nippon Wellcome KK, Kobe, Japan; Med. Dir., Internat. Operat.s, Fisons plc.

BENTLEY, Stephen John Warrington Hospital, Lovely Lane, Warrington WA5 1QG Tel: 01925 662144 Fax: 01925 662905 Email: sjbentley@doctors.org.uk; Thackstones, Reed Lane, Antrobus, Northwich CW9 6JL Tel: 01565 777286 Fax: 01565 777493 Email: sjbentley@doctors.org.uk — MB ChB 1970 Bristol; 1989 FRCP Lond.; 1973 MRCP (UK); 1978 DTM & H Liverp. Cons. Phys. (Gen. Med.) Warrington Dist. Gen. Hosp.; Clin. Dir. Med. & Elderly Care Warrington. Prev: Sen. Regist. (Gen. Med.) Manch. Roy. Infirm.; Sen. Regist. Withington Hosp. Manch.; Cons. Phys. Unife Teach. Hosps. & Lect. Med. Univ. Ife Nigeria.

BENTLEY, Steven Charles 4 Sandhurst Drive, Beeston, Nottingham NG9 6NH — MB ChB 1989 Manch.

BENTLEY, Teresa Mary 35 Northumberland Avenue, Bishop Auckland DL14 6LW — MB ChB 1987 Leic.

BENTLEY, Timothy John 2 Agincourt Road, London NW3 2PD — MB BS 1989 Lond.

BENTLEY-THOMAS, Catherine Anne Hawthornden Surgery, Wharf Lane, Bourne End SL8 5RX Tel: 01628 522864 Fax: 01628 533226; Water Spring House, Locks Ride, Ascot SL5 8QX Tel: 01344 893216 Email: kate.bt@btinternet.com — MB BChir 1986 Camb.; BSc (Hons.) St. And. 1983; D.Occ.Med. RCP Lond. 1996. (Cambridge) GP Bourne End, Bucks. Prev: SHO (O & G) N. Devon Dist. Hosp. Barnstaple; SHO (Rheum. & Rehabil.) Qu. Eliz. Milit. Hosp. Lond.; SHO (A & E) Gen. Surg. Hosp., Saudi Arabia.

BENTON, Elizabeth Claire Department of Dermatology, Royal Infirmary of Edinburgh, Edinburgh EH3 9YW Tel: 0131 536 2050 Fax: 0131 229 8769; 6 Stirling Road, Edinburgh EH5 3HY Tel: 0131 552 4670 — MB ChB 1972 Ed.; BSc Med. Sci. Ed. 1969; FRCP Ed. 1988; MRCP (UK) 1975. (Edinburgh) Cons. Dermat. Roy. Infirm. Edin.

BENTON, Frank Miles (retired) Bullace Cottage, Kettleburgh, Woodbridge IP13 7JX Tel: 01728 723600 — MB ChB 1945 Manch.; MRCS Eng. LRCP Lond. 1945; FRCR 1975; FFR 1953; DMRT Eng. 1950.

BENTON, Ian James 70 Gelligaer Street, Cathays, Cardiff CF24 4LB — MB BCh 1998 Wales.

BENTON, Jacqueline Sarah Great Ormond Street Hospital for Sick Children, London WC1N 3JH Tel: 020 7405 9200 Fax: 020 7813 8279; 83 Lavender Grove, London E8 3LR Tel: 020 7923 3385 — MB ChB 1974 Manch.; FRCP Lond. 1996; MRCP (UK) 1977. Cons. Neurol. Gt. Ormond St. Hosp. Childr. NHS Trust. Prev: Cons. Paediat. Neurol. Qu. Eliz. Hosp. Childr. Lond.; Sen. Regist. (Neurol.) Hosp. Sick Childr. Gt. Ormond St. Lond.; Regist. (Neurol.) Lond. Hosp.

BENTON, James Leslie East Surrey Hospital, Canada Drive, Redhill RH1 5RH; 12 Shortlands Road, Kingston upon Thames KT2 6HD Tel: 020 8549 1518 — MB ChB 1995 Sheff.

BENTON, Jennifer Irene Department Anaesthetics Derriford Hospital, Plymouth PL6 8DH Tel: 01752 792692 Fax: 01752 763287 — MB BS 1990 Lond.; BSc Lond. 1989; FRCA 1996. (St. Mary's Hosp. Med. Sch.) Specialist Regist. (Anaesth.) Derriford Hosp. Plymouth.

BENTON, John James Nicholas 105 North Street, Barrow on Soar, Loughborough LE12 8PZ — MB ChB 1989 Liverp.

BENTON, Kenneth George Frank c/o Midland Bank, University Branch, 348 Oxford Road, Manchester M13 9NG — MB ChB 1972 Manch.; FRCP Ed. 1994; MRCP (UK) 1978.

BENTON, Kerry Arkendale, Dipe Lane, East Boldon NE36 0PH — MB ChB 1994 Leic.; BSc Leic. 1993, MB ChB 1994. (Leics.)

BENTON, Margaret Ann Department of Haematology, St George's Hospital, Blackshaw Road, London SW17 0QT Tel: 020 8672 1255 Email: mbenton@norf.molbiol.ox.ac.uk; 35 Chiltern View, Littelmilton, Oxford OX44 7QP — MB BS 1987 Lond.; MA Camb. 1988, BA Camb. 1984; MRCP (UK) 1990; DRCPath 1994. Research Fell. Kay Kendall Leukaemia Fund Inst. Molecular Med. John Radcliffe Hosp. Oxf. Prev: Regist. Rotat. (Haemat.) Ealing Gen. & Hammersmith Hosps.; Regist. (Med.) P.ss Alexandra Hosp. Harlow & Roy. Lond. Hosp.; SHO (Thoracic Med.) Lond. Chest Hosp.

BENTON, Margaret Dudley (retired) Fourways, Calais St., Boxford, Sudbury CO10 5JA Tel: 01787 210809 — MB ChB 1943 Birm.; MD Birm. 1949; FRCP Lond. 1983, M 1945. Prev: Mem. Staff Med. Research Counc.

BENTON, Nicholas Mark 14 The Paddock, Tickhill, Doncaster DN11 9HS — MB BS 1993 Lond.

BENTON, Nigel David Christopher 35 Station Road, Quorn, Loughborough LE12 8BP — MB ChB 1989 Sheff.; DRCOG 1993.

BENTON, Peter John 219 Lutterworth Road, Nuneaton CV11 6PX — MB ChB 1979 Bristol; MMedSc (Occupat. Health) Birm. 1992; FFOM 1999.

BENTON, Thomas Frederick St Columba's Hospice, 15 Boswall Road, Edinburgh EH5 3RW Tel: 0131 551 1381 Fax: 0131 552 3955 Email: stcol.med@dial.pipex.com; 6 Stirling Road, Edinburgh EH5 3HY — MB ChB 1972 Ed.; BSc (Hons.) Med. Sci. Ed. 1969; FRCP Ed. 1988; MRCP (UK) 1975; DMRT Ed. 1978; DObst RCOG 1976; MRCGP 1995. Med. Dir. St. Columba's Hospice Edin.

BENTOVIM, Arnon London Child & Family Consultation Service, 97 Harley St., London W1N 1DF Tel: 0207229 2800 Fax: 0207229 2888 Email: drbentouim@icfcs.com; Tel: 020 7435 2255 Fax: 020 7435 2157 — MB BS 1959 Lond.; FRCPsych 1974, M 1971; DPM (Acad.) Lond. 1965; FRCPCH 1997; BPAS 1971. (St. Thos.) Director & Cons. Psychiatrics, Lond. child & family consultation Serv., Harley St., Lond.; Hon. Cons. Child & Adolesc. Psychiat. Hosp. for Childr. Gt. Ormond St.; Hon. Cons. Psychiat. Dept. Child & Parents Tavistock Clin. Lond.; Hon. Sen. Lect. Inst. of Child Health UCL; Cons. to SWAAY Berks..; Accredit. Teach. Univ. Lond. Specialist Adviser, Selec. Comm. Ho. of Commons 1975-1979. Socs: (Ex-Chairm.) Inst. Family Ther. Lond.; Assoc. Mem. Brit. Psychoanal. Soc.; Brit. Assn. Preven. Child Abuse & Neglect. Prev: Cons. Psychiat. Child Guid. Train. Centre Lond.; Regist. Bethlem Roy. & Maudsley Hosps.; Ho. Phys. St. Thos. Hosp. Lond.

BENTSI-BARNES, Augustus 9 Rolling Mill Close, Edgbaston, Birmingham B5 7QD — MB ChB 1976 Ghana; MRCOG 1984.

BENWELL, John Bertram Surdales, Hillam Lane, Hillam, Leeds LS25 5HW Tel: 01977 684378 — MB BS 1955 Lond.; DCH Eng. 1959. (Char. Cross) Socs: Assoc. RCGP. Prev: Cas. Off. & Ho. Phys. Childr. Dept. Char. Cross Hosp.; SHO. Vict. Childr. Hosp. Hull.

BENYAMIN, Fettuh 34 St Barnabas Road, Sutton SM1 4NS — MB ChB 1966 Baghdad.

BENYON, Sarah Louise 37 West View Road, Sutton Coldfield B75 6AY — MB BS 1998 Lond.; MB BS Lond 1998.

BENZIE, Alexander Stewart Hilary Cottage Surgery, Keble Lawns, Fairford GL7 4BQ Tel: 01285 712377 Fax: 01285 713084; Beaumoor Barn House, Fairford GL7 4AP Tel: 01285 713 3395 Fax: 01285 713395 — MB ChB 1970 Aberd.; MRCGP 1976; DObst RCOG 1973. (Aberdeen) Clin. Asst. (Rheum.) Cirencester Hosp.; Mem. Authorised Aviat. Med. Examrs. Prev: Med. Off. RAF; Flight Surg. Saudi Arabian Milit. Defence & Aviat.

BENZIE, Stuart James 15 Lauderdale Street, Edinburgh EH9 1DF — MB ChB 1997 Ed.

BENZIES, Robert Alfred Owen Myrtle Cottage, Blackawton, Totnes TQ9 7BN — MB BCh BAO 1972 Belf.

BENZIMRA, Ruth Emma University Hospital of Wales, Cardiff CF14 4WZ Email: rbz@nhworld.com — MB BS 1990 Lond.; BSc (1st cl. Hons.) Pharmacol. with Basic Med. Sci. Lond. 1986; MRCP (UK) 1994. Specialist Regist. (Nephrol. & Gen. Med.) Univ. Hosp. of Wales, Cardiff. Prev: Clin. Research Fell. Inst. of Nephrol. Cardiff 1999-2001; Regist. (Nephrol.) Univ. Hosp. Wales; SHO (Cardiol.) Brompton Hosp. Lond.

BERA, Susil Kumar X-Ray Department, Walsgrave Hospital, Clifford Bridge Road, Coventry CV2 2DX — MB BS 1971 Calcutta.

BERAL, Daniel Leslie 5 Woosehill Lane, Wokingham RG41 2TT — MB ChB 1998 Leeds.

BERAL, Valerie ICRF Cancer Epidemiology Unit, Radcliffe Infirmary, Oxford OX2 6HE Tel: 01865 311933 Fax: 01865 310545; 9 Holly Lodge Gardens, London N6 6AA Tel: 020 8348 2401 Fax: 020 8348 3403 — MB BS 1969 Sydney; FRCP Lond. 1992; MRCP (UK) 1971. (Sydney) Dir. ICRF Cancer Epidemiol. Unit Oxf. Socs: Internat. Epidemiol. Assn.

BERANEK, Michael David Flat 5, Deerhurst, 15 Farnan Road, London SW16 2EX — BM 1994 Soton. Ho. Phys. (Gen. Med.) P.ss Margt. Hosp. Swindon. Prev: Ho. Off. (Surg.) RN Hosp. Haslar Gosport.

BERANEK, Paul 273 Lauderdale Road, London W9 — MB ChB 1978 Manch.; MSc Lond. 1983, PhD 1970, BSc (Hons.) 1966. (Manch.) Sterling-Withdrop. Research & Developm. Div. Guildford. Prev: Lect. Dept. Chem. Path. St. Mary's Hosp. Lond. W2.

BERARDELLI, Chiara Elizabeth Paisley Road West Surgery, 532 Paisley Road West, Glasgow G51 1RN Tel: 0141 427 2504 — MB ChB 1990 Aberd.; DRCOG 1993; DFFP 1994. (Aberd.) p/t Princip.

BERECOU, Elizabeth 7 Millennium Way, Wolston, Coventry CV8 3PE — MB ChB 1995 Birm.

BERELIAN, Siagozar Ashridge, 6 St Richards Drive, Aldwick, Bognor Regis PO21 3BH Tel: 01243 263749 — MD 1968 Tehran.

BERELOWITZ, Glen Joel Ticehurst Clinic, 22-24 Sackville Gardens, Hove BN3 4GH Tel: 01273 747464; Princess Royal Hospital, Lewes Road, Haywards Heath RH16 4EX Tel: 01444 441881 Fax: 01444 440155 — MB BS 1983 Lond.; MRCPsych 1987. Cons. Psychiat. P.ss Roy. Hosp. Haywards Heath & Ticehurst Clinic Hove. Prev: Sen. Regist. & SHO Rotat. (Psychiat.) W.m. & Char. Cross. Hosps. Lond.; Ho. Surg. Newham Gen. Hosp.

BERELOWITZ, Mark Orlin Department of Child Psychiatry, Royal Free Hospital, Pond St., London NW3 2QG Tel: 020 7830 2931 Fax: 020 7830 2810 Email: mark.berelowitz@rfh.nthames.nhs.uk — MB BCh Witwatersrand 1980; MPhil 1989; MRCPsych 1985; 1999 FRCPsych. Cons. Child Psychiat. & Hon. Sen. Lect. Roy. Free Hosp.; Hon. Sen. Lect. Inst. Child Health. Prev: Cons. Child Psychiat. Maudsley Hosp. Lond.; Sen. Regist. (Child Psychiat.) Maudsley Hosp. Lond.; Ho. Off. Tel Hashomer Hosp., Israel.

BERENDS-SHERIFF, Penelope Jane St Marys Health Centre, Cop Lane, Penwortham, Preston PR1 0SR Tel: 01772 744404 Fax: 01772 752967; 16 Castle Walk, Priory Park, Penwortham, Preston PR1 0BP Tel: 01772 747507 Fax: 01772 747507 — MB ChB 1978 Liverp.; MRCS Eng. LRCP Lond. 1978.

BERENDT, Anthony Robert 100 Victoria Road, Oxford OX2 7QE — BM BCh 1983 Oxf.; MA Camb. 1984; MRCP (UK) l986. Research Fell. (Molecular Med.) Lister Inst. John Radcliffe Hosp. Oxf. Prev: MRC Train. Fell. Nuffield Dept. Med. John Radcliffe Hosp. Oxf.; SHO (Gen. Med.) N.wick Pk. Hosp. Harrow; Regist. (Gen. Med.) Roy. Hallamsh. Hosp. Sheff.

BERENGUER PELLUS, Joaquin Vicente 179 Coniscliffe Road, Darlington DL3 8DE — LMS 1984 Alicante.

BERENS, Jurgen Friarage Hospital, Northallerton DL6 1JG — MB ChB 1976 Pretoria.

BERESFORD, Ann Patricia 16 Ragmans Close, Marlow Bottom, Marlow SL7 3QW — MB ChB 1972 Leeds. Clin. Asst. (Clin. Oncol. & Gastroenterol.) Wycombe Gen. Hosp. High Wycombe.

BERESFORD, David Nigel Lister (retired) 9 Bayham Road, London W4 1BJ — MB BS Lond. 1964; DObst RCOG 1966. Prev: Medico-legal advis.med.Defence.Union.

BERESFORD, Francis Aden Tel: 0161 231 4997 Fax: 0161 230 6227 — MB ChB 1980 Manch.; MRCGP 1986; DRCOG 1985; DCH RCP Lond. 1984.

BERESFORD, Hannah 179 Casewick Road, London SE27 0TA — MB ChB 1994 Ed. SHO Rotat. (Med.) St. Jas. Univ. Hosp. Prev: Ho. Off. Qu. Margt. Hosp. Fife.

BERESFORD, Julia Karen Wycliffe Surgery, Elliott Road, Plymouth PL4 9NH Tel: 01752 660648 Fax: 01752 261468 — BM 1988 Soton.; MRCGP 1992; DRCOG 1991.

BERESFORD, Michael William AlderHey Hospital, Eaton Road, Liverpool L12; 14 Sinclair Drive, Liverpool L18 0HN — MB ChB 1991 Ed.; MRCP (UK) 1994. (Edinburgh) Specialist Regist. Paediat.,Alder Hey Hosp., Liverp. Socs: MRCPCH; The Neonat. Soc.; Paediatric Research Soc. Prev: Research Fell., Regional Neonat. Unit, Liverp.

BERESFORD, Nicola Marie Maternity Unit, Bradford Hospitals NHS Trust, Ducksworth Lane, Bradford BD9 6RJ — MB ChB 1997 Leeds. Sen. Ho. Off., Obst. & Gyn., Bradford Hosp.s NHS Trust.

BERESFORD, Nigel William Royal Brompton & Harefield NHS Trust, Sydney St., London SW3 6NP Tel: 020 7352 8121 Fax: 020 7351 8473 Email: n.beresford@rbh.nthames.nhs.uk; 115 Thomas More House, Barbican, London EC2Y 8BU — MB ChB 1978 Manch.; LLB (Hons.) Nottm. 1997. Sen. Advisor (Clin. Risk) Roy. Brompton & Harefield NHS Trust. Prev: GP Isle of Lewis.

BERESFORD, Oswald David (retired) 84 Lodge Road, Holt, Wimborne BH21 7DW — MRCS Eng. LRCP Lond. 1938; BSc Wales 1936, MD 1950, MB BCh 1939; MRCP Lond. 1947. Prev: Cons. Chest Phys. Poole Gen. Hosp.

BERESFORD, Patrick Mark Wem and Prees Medical Practice, New Street, Wem, Shrewsbury SY4 5AU Tel: 01939 233476; Crossbank Farm, Highfields, Wem, Shrewsbury SY4 5UN Tel: 01939 233288 — MB ChB 1988 Birm.; MRCGP 1994. Prev: Trainee GP Worcs.

BERESFORD, Richard Julian Arnold Coniston Medical Practice, The Parade, Coniston Road, Patchway, Bristol BS34 5TF Tel: 0117 969 2508 Fax: 0117 969 0456 — BM 1988 Soton.; MRCGP 1994; DRCOG 1993. GP Coniston Med. Pract. Bristol.

BERESFORD, Timothy Peter 9 Barry Avenue, Windsor SL4 5JA — MB BS 1994 Lond.

BERESFORD-JONES, Paul Ruxton The Surgery, 75 Longridge Avenue, Saltdean, Brighton BN2 8LA Tel: 01273 305723 Fax: 01273 300962; 70 Lenham Avenue, Saltdean, Brighton BN2 8AG Tel: 01273 307470 — MB ChB 1983 Ed.

BERESFORD WEST, Terence Benjamin Hargreaves 26 Saunton Road, Braunton EX33 1HB Tel: 01271 812402 — MB BS 1971 Lond.; FFA RCS Eng. 1983.

BEREZA, Michal Jozef (retired) 90A Fordhook Avenue, Ealing Common, London W5 3LR Tel: 020 8992 4163 — MD 1929 Warsaw. Prev: Med. Admin. Polish Hosp. Penley & Wrexham Denbigh.

BERG, Birgit Eva Maria 27 White Road, Cowley, Oxford OX4 2JJ Tel: 01865 775338 — State Exam Med 1989 Heidelberg; MRCPsych 1993. (Heidelberg) Sen. Regist. Rotat. (Child & Adolesc. Psychiat.) Oxf. Socs: BMA.

BERG, Mr Geoffrey Alan Department of Cardiothoracic Surgery, Western Infirmary, Dumbarton Road, Glasgow G11 6NT Tel: 0141 211 2624 Fax: 0141 211 1751 Email: geoff.berg.wg"northglasgow.scot.nhs.uk — MB ChB 1980 Liverp.; ChM Liverp. 1991; FRCS Ed. 1984. (Liverpool) Cons. Cardiothoracic Surg. W.. Infirm. Glas. Prev: Sen. Regist. (Cardiothoracic Surg.) Roy. P. Alfred Hosp. Sydney, Austral.; Sen. Regist. (Cardiothoracic Surg.) Glas. Roy. Infirm.

BERG, Ian The Cottage, Rudby Hall, Hutton Rudby TS15 0JN Tel: 01642 700198 — MD 1965 Leeds; MB ChB 1956; FRCP Ed. 1979, M 1961; FRCPsych 1978, M 1971. (Leeds) Cons. Child & Adolesc. Psychiat. Leeds HA; Sen. Clin. Lect. (Psychiat.) Univ. Leeds. Prev: Sen. Regist. (Psychol. Med.) Roy. Hosp. Sick Childr. Edin.; Regist. (Psychol. Med.) Hosp. Sick Childr. Gt. Ormond St.; Sen. Asst. Resid. (Child Psychiat.) Montreal Childr. Hosp.

BERG, Jonathan Neil S.E. Scotland Regional Genetics Service, Molecular Medicine Centre, Western General Hospital, Crewe Road, Edinburgh EH4 2XU; Flat 5, 32 Castle Terrace, Edinburgh EH1 2EL Email: j.berg@ed.ac.uk — MB ChB 1989 Ed.; MSc Newc. 1991; MRCP Ed. 1993; MD Ed,1998. (Univ. Ed.) Research Fell. Edin. Univ.; Hon. Specialist Regist. Clin. Genetics.

BERG, Simon Jonathan Nuffield Department of Anaesthetics, John Radcliffe Hospital, Headley Way, Oxford OX3 9DU Tel: 08165 741166 Fax: 01865 220027 — MB BS 1981 Lond.; BSc (Immunol.) Lond. 1978, MB BS 1981; FFA RCS Eng. 1986. (University Coll London) Cons. Paediacrtric Anaesth. Oxf. Radcliffe Hosp.s NHSTrust. Prev: Sen Regist. UCL; Newman Research Fell. St. Mark's Hosp Lond.

BERG, Steven Norman Bursted Wood Surgery, 219 Erith Road, Bexleyheath DA7 6HZ Tel: 020 8303 5027 Fax: 020 8298 7735; 113 Blackbrook Lane, Bickley, Bromley BR1 2LP Tel: 020 8467 1600 Fax: 020 8295 0247 Email: 100020.602@compuserve.com — MB ChB 1973 Manch.

BERG, Valerie Gibb — MB ChB 1981 Glas.; MRCGP 1986; DCH RCPS Glas. 1985. (Univ. Glas.) Prev: SHO (O & G) Vale of Leven Hosp. Alexandria; SHO (Dermat.) CrossHo. Hosp. Kilmarnock; SHO (Paediat.) Stobhill Hosp. Glas.

BERGEL, Edith Park Lodge, Mental Health Resource Centre, Orphan Drive, Liverpool L6 7UN Tel: 0151 287 6900; 41 Menlove Gardens W., Liverpool L18 2ET Tel: 0151 722 5936 — MB BS Lond. 1955; Dip. Psychother. Liverp. 1989; DCH Eng. 1958. (Roy. Free) Clin. Med. Off. Pk. Lodge (Ment. Health Resource Centre) Liverp. Prev: Vis. Psychiat. Delamere Forest Sch. Norley; Psychotherap. on UK Counc. Psychotherap. Register; JP Liverp.

BERGEL, Richard Charles 119 Harpsden Road, Henley-on-Thames RG9 1ED — MB BS 1963 Lond.

BERGER, Abigail Jane Randolph Surgery, 235A Elgin Avenue, London W9 1NH Tel: 020 7286 6880 Fax: 020 7286 9787 — MB ChB 1990 Bristol; BSc Bristol 1987; Dip. Obst. Auckland 1992; MRCGP 1997. GP Princip.; Sci. Edr. Brit. Med. Jl. Prev: Med. Corr. New Scientist.

BERGER, Arnold Bernard Fishermead Medical Centre, Fishermead Boulevard, Fishermead, Milton Keynes MK6 2LR Tel: 01908 609240 Fax: 01908 695674 — MB BS 1975 Lond. (Royal Lond. Hosp.) Med. Examr. Meat & Livestock Commiss. City Truck Gp.; Norwegian Maritime Med. Examr.; Med. Examr. for various solicitors and Insur. cos.; Med. Adviser, St. Francis's Childr.s Soc. Socs: Milton Keynes Med. Soc. Prev: Ho. Surg. Lond. Hsop.

BERGER, Charles Paul Maurice The Surgery, Trellech, Monmouth NP5 Tel: 01600 860302; Duffryn, Catbrook Road, Catbrook, Chepstow NP16 6NQ — MB BS 1976 Lond.; MRCGP 1980; DRCOG 1978. (Middlx. Hosp.)

BERGER, David William 3 Stevenstone Court, Torrington EX38 7HY Email: tmffooluk@aol.com — MB BS 1991 Lond.; BSc (Hons.) Lond. 1988; MRCP 1995. (St. George's) GP Locum.

BERGER, Gillian Estelle 19 Springwood Park, Edinburgh EH16 6JL — MB ChB 1996 Manch.

BERGER, Jeremy Department of Radiology, Barnet General Hospital, Wellhouse Lane, Barnet EN5 3DJ Tel: 020 8216 5100 Fax: 020 8216 5104; Linden Cottage, 17 Cromer Hyde Lane, Lemsford, Welwyn Garden City AL8 7XE Tel: 01707 328242 — MA Camb. 1983; MB BS Lond. 1986; MRCP (UK) 1989; FRCR 1996. (Camb. (Middx. Hosp.)) Cons. Radiol. Barnet Gen. Hosp.; Cons. (Radiol.) Barnet Gen. Hosp. Prev: Specialist Regist. (Radiol.) Oxf. Radcliffe Hosp.; Regist. (Radiol.) John Radcliffe Hosp. Oxf.; Regist. (Paediat.) N.wick Pk. Hosp. Middlx.

BERGER, Kathleen Nina (retired) 16 Rolleston Avenue, Orpington BR5 1AH Tel: 020 8467 1182 — MB BS 1943 Lond.; MRCS Eng., LRCP Lond. 1943; DCH Eng. 1950; DObst. RCOG 1949. Prev: Med. Off. Brook La. Med. Miss.

BERGER, Leslie Alexander X-Ray Department, Royal Free Hospital, London NW3 4QH Tel: 020 7830 2170 Fax: 020 7830 2969; 40 Springfield Road, London NW8 0QN Tel: 020 7624 4067 — MB BS Sydney 1965; FRACP 1977, M 1969; FRCR 1975; FFR 1973; DMRD Eng. 1971. (Sydney) Cons. Radiol. Roy. Free Hosp. Lond.; Cons. Radiol. Garden Hosp. Lond. Socs: BMA; Brit. Inst. Radiol. Prev: Sen. Regist. (Diag. Radiol.) St. Bart. Hosp. & Hosp. Sick Childr. Gt. Ormond St.; Regist. (Diag. Radiol.) St. Bart. Hosp. Lond.; Resid. Med. Off. St. Vincent's Hosp. Sydney, Austral.

BERGER, Martin Julian (retired) 7 Dunstarn Drive, Leeds LS16 8EH Tel: 0113 267 1508 Email: regina@easicom.com — MB ChB Leeds 1952. Prev: Surg. Lt. RNVR.

BERGER, Mr Peter Lucian (retired) 12A Portman Gate, 41 Broadley Terrace, London NW1 6LQ Tel: 020 7723 5434 Fax: 020 7723 5434 Email: peterberger@compuserve.com — MRCS Eng. LRCP Lond. 1946; FRCS Ed. 1956; FRCS Eng. 1957. Prev: Hon. Cons. Surg. Good Hope Hosp. Sutton Coldfield.

BERGER, Sydney Mervyn 11 Ringley Hey, Whitefield, Manchester M45 7NU — MB BS Melbourne 1963; FFA RACS 1969; FRCA 1991; FANZCA 1992. (Melb.) Cons. Anaesth. Hope Hosp. Manch. Socs: Assn. Anaesth. & Intractable Pain Soc. Prev: Cons. Anaesth. N. Manch. Gen. Hosp.; Staff Anaesth. Hasharon Hosp. Petah Tikvah, Israel; Specialist Anaesth. Alfred Hosp. Melb., Australia.

BERGERET, Angela Mary c/o French Embassy, 49 Ba Trieu, Hanoi, Vietnam Tel: (00 84) (4) 574 0740 Fax: (00 84) (4) 869 8443 Email: angela@netnam.org.vn; 6 Garden Croft, Aldridge, Walsall WS9 8QL Tel: (01922) 451805 — MB ChB Manch. 1979; FFA RCS Eng. 1983. Director of Med. Servcies; GP/ Anaesth.

BERGIN, Adrian James Dalbeattie, Belmangate, Guisborough TS14 7BD Tel: 01287 639295 — MB BCh 1984 Wales; MRCP (UK) 1988. Cons. Phys. (Elderly Care) S. Cleveland Hosp. Middlesbrough. Prev: Sen. Regist. (Gen. & Geriat. Med.) Sheff.

BERGIN, John Howard Eversley (retired) Troy House, Meysey Hampton, Cirencester GL7 5JP Tel: 01285 851395 — MB BChir 1945 Camb.; MA Camb. 1945; MRCS Eng. LRCP Lond. 1944; DMRD Bristol 1949. Prev: Cons. Radiol. P.ss Margt. Hosp. Swindon & Assoc. Hosps.

BERGIN, John Richard 2 South Terrace, Camborne TR14 8ST Tel: 01209 714876; Trevanion, Reskadinnick Road, Camborne TR14 7LR Tel: 01209 711393 — MB ChB 1972 Liverp.; MRCGP 1988. Clin. Asst. Durgs Team Trengweath Hosp. Prev: Sen. GP. Partner Andrew Ho. Surg. Camborne.

BERGIN, Pauline Mary Dolores 26 Mountfield Road, Tunbridge Wells TN1 1SG — MB BS 1998 Lond.; MB BS Lond 1998.

BERGIN, Ronald Leslie Central Health Centre, North Carbrain Road, Cumbernauld, Glasgow G67 1BJ Tel: 01236 737214 Fax: 01236 781699; 2 Barbeth Place, Cumbernauld, Glasgow G67 4SF Tel: 01236 614131 — MB ChB 1978 Glas.

BERGIN, Stephen Peter Southern Health Board, Tower Hill, Armagh BT61 9DR — MB BCh BAO 1990 Belf.; MSc (Pub. Health Med.) Newc. 1995; DMH Belf. 1993; MFPHM RCP (UK) 1998. Cons. (Pub Health Med.) S.ern Health & Soc Serv Bd. Prev: Sen. Regist. (Pub. Health Med.) N.. RHA Newc.

BERGMAN, Beverly Patricia, Lt.-Col. RAMC c/o Army Medical Directorate, Building 21, Ministry of Defence, Keogh Barracks, Ash Vale, Aldershot GU12 5RR — MB ChB 1976 Birm.; DPH Belf.

1996. (Birm.) Med. Off. HM Forces; Sen. Lect. Roy. Defence Med. Coll. (Publ. Health Med.); Dip. Fac. Family Plann. & Reproduc. Health Care Roy. Coll. Obst. & Gyn. Socs: Fell. Roy. Soc. Health. Prev: Ho. Phys. & Ho. Surg. Camb. Milit. Hosp. Aldershot; Cdr. Med. Belize.

BERGMANN, Klaus 119 Broadhurst Gardens, London NW6 3BJ Tel: 020 7624 0916 Fax: 020 7328 7133 — MB ChB 1956 Sheff.; MD Sheff. 1970; FRCPsych 1975, M 1971; DPM Eng. 1963. (University of Sheffield) Emerit. Cons. Psychiat. The Bethlem & Maudsley Trust. Socs: Fell. Roy. Soc. Med.; Brit. Geriat. Soc. Prev: Cons. Phys. Psychol. Med. & Lect. (Psychogeriat.) Univ. Newc. & Newc. Hosp.; Sen. Research Assoc. (Psychol. Med.) Univ. Newc.; Cons. Psychiat. Bethlem Roy. Hosp., Maudsley Hosp.

BERGMANN, Maria Department of Public Health, West Kent Health Authority, Preston Hall, Aylesford ME20 7NJ Tel: 01622 710161 Fax: 01622 719802; 9 Claremont Gardens, Tunbridge Wells TN2 5DD Tel: 01892 516191 — MD 1971 Berlin; MD Berlin 1987. State Exam Med. 1971; MFPHM RCP (UK) 1985. (Free Univ. Berlin) Cons. Pub. Health Med. Tunbridge Wells HA. Socs: Fac. Comm. Med.; Pub. Health Med. Roy. Coll. Phys.s Lond. Prev: Lect. (Community Med.) Univ. Aberd.; MRC Research Fell. Med. Sociol. Unit Aberd.

BERGVALL, Ulf Erik Gottfrid X-Ray Department, Royal Hallamshire Hospital, Sheffield S10 2JF Tel: 0114 276 6222 — MD 1970 Stockholm; Med Lic 1957. Cons. Neuroradiol. Roy. Hallamsh. Sheff. Socs: Fell. Roy. Soc. Med. Prev: Prof. Radiol. Marseille, France; Vis. Prof. (Neuroradiol.) Univ. Sheff.; Head Diagn. Radiol. II Huddinge Univ. Hosp., Sweden.

BERIC, Verka 42 Stuart Road, Corby NN17 1RL — BM BS 1991 Nottm.; BMedSci Nottm. 1989. SHO (Med.) Soton. Gen. Hosp.

BERINGER, Richard Michael 92 Church La, Backwell, Bristol BS48 3JW — BM BS 1997 Nottm.

BERINGER, Timothy Richard Orr Tamnaharrie, 41 Ballyhanwood Road, Gilnahirk, Belfast BT5 7SN — MD 1985 Belf.; MB BCh BAO 1977; FRCPI 1990, M 1981; FRCP Lond. 1993; FRCP Glas. 1991; MRCP (UK) 1981. Cons. Phys. Geriat. Med. Unit Roy. Vict. Hosp. Belf.; Cons. physcian in Geriat. Med.; Musgrave Pk. Hosp., Belf. Socs: Fell. Roy. Coll. Phys.; Fell. Ulster Med. Soc. & Brit. Geriat. Soc.; Dir. of Exam.s, Roy. Coll. Phys. Irel. Prev: Sen. Regist. (Geriat. Med.) Unit Roy. Vict. Hosp. Belf.; Research Fell. (Geriat. Med.) Qu. Univ. Belf.; Sen. Regist. (Geriat. Med.) Unit Belf. City Hosp.

BERK, Cahit The Surgery, 2 Willoughby Road, Haringey, London N8 0HR — Tip Doktoru 1968 Istanbul; MD Tip Doktoru Istanbul 1968; FRCOG 1994, M 1979. Indep. Cons. O & G Lond.

BERKELEY, John Sanford (retired) Drumbeg, Coylumbridge, Aviemore PH22 1QU Tel: 01479 811055 Fax: 01479 811055 — 1949 MB ChB Ed; 1975 MD Ed.; 1989 FFPHM RCP (UK); 1967 FRCGP 1974, M; 1974 FFCM 1982, M; 1971 Dip. Soc. Med. Ed.; 1953 DObst RCOG; 1975 MD, Ed. Prev: Cons. Pub. Health Med. Grampian HB.

BERKELEY, Muriel Isobel Kathrine Drumbeg, Coylumbridge, Aviemore PH22 1QU Tel: 01479 811055 — MB ChB 1949 St. And.; MA St. And. 1944; FFPHM RCP (UK) 1989; FFCM 1983, M 1974; Dip. Soc. Med. Ed. 1967. (St. And.) Vis. Prof. Fac. Med. Aden; Hon. Specialist (Community Med.) Grampian HB.; Teach. Fell. (Community Med.) Univ. Aberd. Prev: SCM (Matern. & Child Health Serv.); Med. Adviser to NE Computer Network Project, Staff MRC Clin. & Populat. Cytogenetics Unit Edin.

BERKELEY, Peter Raymond 6 Woodvale Avenue, Glasgow G46 6RQ — MB ChB 1973 Glas.; MRCGP 1977.

BERKIN, Katharine Elizabeth St James University Hospital, Beckett St., Leeds LS9 7TF Tel: 0113 243 3144 Fax: 0113 206 4158 — MB ChB 1976 Leeds; FRCP Lond. 1995. Cons. Cardiol. St. Jas. Univ. Hosp. Leeds. Socs: Brit. Cardiac Soc.; Brit. Soc. of Echocardiography. Prev: Cons. Phys. (Gen. Med. i/c Cardiol.) Wharfedale Gen. Hosp. W. Yorks.

BERKIN, Peter Laurence Watling Vale Medical Centre, Burchard Crescent, Shenley Church End, Milton Keynes MK5 6EY Tel: 01908 501177 Fax: 01908 504916; South Barn, Northfield Barns, Deansmanger, Milton Keynes MK19 6HN Tel: 01908 263474 Email: peterberkin@southbarn.freeserve.co.uk — MB BS 1976 Lond.; MRCGP 1983; DRCOG 1981. Chairm. Mkdoc (Out of hours Co-op.).

BERKINSHAW-SMITH, Eva Marianna Inez 34 Traps Lane, New Malden KT3 4SA Tel: 020 8942 7609 — MB 1956 Camb.; BChir 1955.

BERKLEY, James Alexander Wellcome Trust Research Laboratories, PO Box 230, Kilifi, Kenya Tel: 00 254 125 22063 Fax: 00 254 125 22390 Email: kemriklf@africaonline.co.ke; Holly Hall Barn, Sandhoe, Hexham NE46 4LX Tel: 01434 632936 Fax: 01434 632936 — MB BS 1990 Newc.; MSc Trop. Med. Liverp. 1993; MRCP (UK) 1995. (New. u. Tyne) Research Fell. (Malaria & Paediat.) Wellcome Trust Research Laboratories Kilifi, Kenya. Socs: Fell. Roy. Soc. Trop. Med. & Hyg.; BMA. Prev: Doctor for Med.s Sans Frontiers Trop. Med. & Epidemiol. Worldwide; SHO Rotat. (Med.) Oxf.

BERKLEY, Michael James Peter (retired) 53 Mill Road, Lancing BN15 0PZ Tel: 01903 754551 — MB BS 1957 Lond.; LMSSA Lond. 1955; DObst RCOG 1960. Prev: Ho. Off. Harold Wood Hosp.

BERKLEY, Richard James Orchard Medical Centre, Macdonald Walk, Kingswood, Bristol BS15 8NJ Tel: 0117 980 5100 Fax: 0117 980 5104 — MB ChB 1991 Sheff.; DCH RCP Lond. 1995; Cert. Family Plann. 1996. (Sheff.)

BERKOVITCH, Ann Patricia Ship Street Surgery, Ship Street, East Grinstead RH19 4EE Tel: 01342 325959 — MB BS 1978 Lond.; MRCGP 1986; DRCOG 1981. Prev: Sen. Med. Off. RAF Chivenor; DSMO RAF Wildenrath.

BERKOVITZ, Saul Raphael 67 Fallow Court Avenue, London N12 0BE Email: saulb@doctors.org.uk — BChir 1993 Camb.; MRCP 1996; MFHOM 1997. (Cambs/Charing Cross/Westminster) Specialist Regist. Gen. Med. Homeopathic. Med. Whittington. Hosp./Roy. Lond. Homeopathic. Hosp. Lond.

BERKOWITZ, Joshua Lionel c/o Mrs. H. Ditz., 40 Dennis Lane, Stanmore HA7 4JW — MB ChB 1971 Birm.; MRCOG 1979.

BERLET, Julian Kurt 10 Mavis Avenue, Leeds LS16 7LJ — MB BS 1993 Lond.; BSc Lond. 1992, MB BS 1993. (Medical College of St. Bartholomew's Hospital) Specialist Regist. (Anaesth. & ICU) Oxf. Socs: Assn. Anaesths.; BMA. Prev: SHO (Neonat. Paediat.) Roy. Berks. Hosp.; SHO (Anaesth. & ICU) Roy. Berks. Hosp.; SHO (Anaesth. & ICU) Wycombe Gen. Hosp.

BERLIN, Anne Paule (Anita) Department of General Practice & Primary Health Care, Imperial College, School of Medicine, Norfolk Place, London W2 1PG Tel: 020 7594 3350 Fax: 020 7706 8426 Email: a.berlin@ic.ac.uk — MB BS 1984 Newc.; MRCGP 1989; DRCOG 1987; MA (Ed) 1998. Sen. Lect. (Gen. Pract.) St. Mary's Hosp. Med. Sch. Lond. 1994; GP Lond. Prev: Lect. (Gen. Pract.) St. Mary's Hosp. Med. Sch. Lond.; Research Assoc. Div. Primary Care Med. Sch. Newc.

BERLYN, Roger Andrew David Berlyn and Whitmey, Myatts Fields Health Centre, Patmos Road, London SW9 6SE Tel: 020 7411 3593 Fax: 020 7411 3583; 56 Norbury Hill, London SW16 3LB Tel: 020 8764 3082 Fax: 020 8764 8993 — MB BS 1972 Lond. (St. Thos.) Prev: SHO (O & G) Bromley Hosp.; Ho. Off. (Surg.) Brooke Gen. Hosp.; Ho. Off. (Phys.) Lewisham Gen. Hosp.

BERLYNE, Neville (retired) 53 Park Road, Prestwich, Manchester M25 0ES — MB ChB Manch. 1951; FRCP Ed. 1971, M 1958; FRCPsych 1975, M 1971; DPM Eng. 1955. Prev: Hon. Cons. Psychiat. Roy. Oldham Hosp.

BERMAN, Danielle Yona (Wolfson) — MB BS 1991 Lond.; MRCGP 1997; DRCOG 1995; DFFP 1997. (King's Coll. Lond.) GP Locum Watling Med. Centr. Burnt Oak Edgware. Socs: BMA; Med. Protec. Soc. Prev: GP/Regist. Watling Med. Centre Burnt Oak Edgware; SHO (Audiol. & Developm. Paediat.) Roy. Nat. Throat, Nose & Ear Hosp. Lond.; SHO (O & G) Qu. Eliz. II Hosp. Herts.

BERMAN, Gabrielle Lois 26 Langdon Road, Bromley BR2 9JS — MB BS 1981 Lond.; MRCGP 1986; DRCOG 1985.

BERMAN, Jeremy Warren 13 Dove Road, Bedford MK41 7AA — MB ChB 1992 Manch.

BERMAN, Jonathan Simon Anaesthetic Department, Royal National Orthopaedic Hospital, Brockley Hill, Stanmore HA7 4LP Tel: 020 8954 2300 — BM BCh 1985 Oxf.; MA Camb. 1986; FRCA 1990. Cons. Anaesth. & Chronic Pain Managem. Roy. Nat. Orthop. Hosp.

BERMAN, Laurence Herschel 2 Cross Street, London SW13 0PS — MB BS 1975 Lond.; MRCP (UK) 1978; FRCR 1985. Lect. & Cons. Addenbrooke's Hosp. Univ. Camb. Prev: Regist. (Radiol.) N.wick Pk. Hosp. Lond.; Regist. Chest Dept. St. Thos. Hosp. Lond; Regist. (Radiol.) N.wick Pk. Hosp. Lond.

BERMAN, Nerina Alison The Barns, 160 Southborough Lane, Bromley BR2 8AL — MB BS 1990 Lond.; BSc Sheff. 1985; MRCGP 1994.

BERMAN, Peter City Hospital, Hucknall Road, Nottingham NG5 1PJ Tel: 0115 969 1169; The Grange, Main St, Farnsfield, Newark NG22 8EA Tel: 01623 882903 — MB BS 1976 Lond.; FRCP Lond. 1994; MRCP (UK) 1979. (University College Hospital) Cons. Phys. City Hosp. Nottm. Prev: Cons. Phys. Health c/o Elderly City Hosp. Nottm.; Sen. Regist. (Gen. & Geriat. Med.) Radcliffe Infirm. & John Radcliffe Hosp. Oxf.; Regist. (Med.) Bristol Roy. Infirm.

BERMAN, Ralph 53 Moyser Road, London SW16 6RW — MB ChB 1975 Leeds.

BERMINGHAM, Donald Francisco 27 Parkhall Road, Somersham, Huntingdon PE28 3EU — MB BCh BAO 1977 NUI; MRCPsych 1982.

BERMINGHAM, Peter — MB BCh BAO 1966 NUI; MRCPsych 1977; DPM Eng. 1974. Cons. Psychiat. S. Downs Health NHS Trust, Brighton; Cons. Psychiat. Priory Hosp., Hove. Socs: Assoc. Mem. Soc. Analyt. Psychol. Prev: Sen. Regist. (Psychiat.) Napsbury Hosp.; Regist. (Psychiat.) Bath Hosps.; Ho. Surg. St. Vincent's Hosp. Dub.

BERNAD GONZALEZ, Maria Pilar 139 Cliff Gardens, Scunthorpe DN15 7BL — LMS 1990 Cantabria.

BERNADT, Morris William Beckenham Hospital, Croydon Rd, Beckenham BR3 3QL Tel: 0208 3256771 Fax: 0208 289 6653; Department of Psychological Medicine, King's College Hospital, 103 Denmark Hill, London SE5 9RS Tel: 020 78485135 Fax: 020 7740 5129 Email: m.bernadt@iop.kcl.ac.uk — MB ChB 1971 Cape Town; MRCPsych 1976; DPM Eng. 1976. (Cape Town) Cons. Psychiat. Beckenham Hosp. Kent; Hon. Sen. Lect. King's Coll. Sch. Med. & Dent. Lond. Prev: Sen. Regist. (Psychiat.) Hammersmith Hosp. Lond.; Clin. Lect. (Psychiat.) Inst. Psychiat. Lond.; Sen. Regist. Bethlem Roy. & Maudsley Hosps. Lond.

BERNAL, Shirley Anne 8 Rectory Hill, Cranford, Kettering NN14 4AH — MB BCh BAO 1977 NUI; Diploma Pallative Medicine 1999; MRCGP 1981; DCH RCP Lond. 1981; DRCOG 1980. Staff Grade doctor, Cythia Spencer Ho., N.ampton; Clin. Asst., Cransley Hospice, Kettering, N.hants. Prev: GP, Kettering, N.ants.

BERNAL, Susanna Jane Department of Psychiatry of Disability, St Georges Hospital Medical School, Cranmer Terrace, London SW17 0RE Tel: 020 8725 5496 Fax: 020 8725 1070; Tel: 020 8876 4169 — MB ChB 1977 Birm.; MRCPsych 1986. Sen. Lect. Psychiat. of Disabil., St. Geo.Hosp.Med.Sch.Lond; Hon. Cons. in Psychiat. of Learning Disabil.,S.W.Lond. community Health Trust. Socs: Roy. Coll. Psychiat. Prev: Clin. Lect. & Sen. Regist. (Psychiat. of Ment. Handicap) Univ. Camb.; Sen. Regist. (Psychiat.) Chase Farm. & Roy. Free Hosp. Lond.; Regist. (Psychiat.) Hosp. for Sick Childr. Lond.

BERNAL, William Magnus — MB BS 1989 Lond.; BSc 1986; MRCP 1993. (Roy.Lond.Hosp)

BERNAL CANTON, Marta Flat 1, Rannoch House, 10 Lindisfarne Road, Newcastle upon Tyne NE2 2HE — LMS 1990 Saragossa.

BERNARD, Francis Edgar Paul (retired) 29 Wix's Lane, Clapham, London SW4 0AL Tel: 020 7223 9970 — MB ChB Ed. 1956; MRCPsych 1973; DPM Eng. 1972; DTM & H Eng. 1960. Locum Cons. Child & Adolesc. Psychiat. at Surrey Oaklands Epsom. Prev: Cons. Child & Adolesc. Psychiat. Woodside Adolesc. Unit W. Pk. Hosp. Epsom & Child & Adolesc. Clinic 1996.

BERNARD, Mr Jason 21 Vivian Road, Firth Park, Sheffield S5 6WJ — MB ChB 1990 Glas.; FRCS Ed. 1994. (Glas.) Specialist Regist. Rotat. Orthop. & Trauma Surg. S.W. Thames St Geo.'s Hosp. Prev: Clin. Research Fell. Metab. Bone Unit Roy. Hallamsh. Hosp. Sheff.; SHO Rotat. (Surg.) Leeds Gen. Infirm.; Lect. (Anat.) Univ. Manch.

BERNARD, Mark Steven 6 Bulmore Road, Caerleon, Newport NP18 1QQ — MB BCh 1982 Wales; MRCP (UK) 1986; FRCR 1989. Cons. Radiol. Roy. Gwent Hosp. Newport. Prev: Sen. Regist. (Radiol.) Univ. Hosp. Wales Cardiff.

BERNARD, Paul Manuel County Durham and Darlington, Priority Services NHS Trust Hospital, Lanchester Road, Durham DH1 5RD Tel: 0191 333 6262; Box Hedge Cottage, Wharnton, Richmond DL11 7JL Tel: 01748 821430 Email: bernards@cwcom.net — MB BChir 1989 Camb.; MRCPsych 1992. Prev: Sen. Regist. (Child & Adolesc. Psychiat.) NW Thames Train. Scheme.; Regist. (Psychiat.) Roy. Free Hosp. Train. Scheme Lond.

BERNARD, Sarah Helen The Maudsley Hospital, Denmark Hill, London SE5 8AZ Tel: 020 7919 2570 — MB ChB 1983 Leic.; MD Leic. 1995; MRCPsych 1991; DRCOG 1988. (Leicester) Cons. Psychiat. (Child Learning Disabil.) Maudsley Hosp. Lond. Prev: Sen. Regist. & Regist. (Psychiat.) The Maudsley Hosp. Lond.; Research Regist. (Med. Genetics) St. Mary's Hosp. Manch.

BERNARD, Tanya Department of Haematology, 98 Chenies Mews, University College London Medical School, London WC1E 6HX Tel: 020 7380 9754 Fax: 020 7380 9597; 11 Cunard Walk, Rotherhithe, London SE16 7RH — MB BS 1987 Lond.; BSc (1st cl. Hons.) Lond. 1984; MRCP (UK) 1990. Wellcome Research Train. Fell. & Hon. Sen. Regist. (Haemat.) Univ. Coll. Hosp. Lond. Prev: Regist. (Haemat.) Roy. Lond. Hosp.; SHO (Haemat. & Gen. Med.) City Hosp. Nottm.

BERNARDI, Rachel Elsa Springwell Medical Group, Alderman Jack Cohen Health Centre, Springwell Road, Sunderland SR3 4DX Tel: 0191 528 2727 — MB BS 1994 Newc.; DFFP 2000; DRCOG 2000; MRCGP 2001. (Newc.) GP Parrtner, Sunderland. Prev: SHO (Paediat. & Adolesc.) Qu. Eliz. Hosp. Gateshead; SHO (Neonat. Unit) RVI Newc.; SHO (Paeds Surg.) RVI, Newc.

BERNARDIS, Catina Katriona 121 Lady Margaret Road, London N19 5ER — MB BS 1989 Lond.

BERNARDO, Maria Victoria The Bungalow, Merton Road, Hullbridge, Hockley SS5 6AQ — LMS 1990 Acala de Henares.

BERNAU, Frances Louise Crown House, 46 High St., Dorchester-on-Thames, Oxford OX10 7HN — BM BCh 1989 Oxf.; MA (Hons.) Oxf. 1986; MRCP (UK) 1992; FRCA (UK) 1997. (Oxf.)

BERNDT, Mrs Elizabeth (retired) 17 Moat Court, Court Road, Eltham, London SE9 5QD Tel: 020 8850 2696 — MD 1918 Berlin. Prev: Sen. Med. Off. Liverp. Psychiat. Clinic.

BERNEY, Allan George (retired) 1 Owenskerry Lane, Fivemiletown BT75 0SP Tel: 013655 31761 — LRCPI & LM, LRCSI & LM 1947; DIH Soc. Apoth. Lond. 1959; DPH Eng. 1963. Prev: Ho. Surg. Roy. City Dub. Hosp.

BERNEY, Daniel Maurice 14 St Helen's Close, Southsea PO4 0NN — MB BChir 1991 Camb.

BERNEY, Sylvia Irene Barnet General Hospital, Wellhouse Lane, Barnet EN5 3DJ Tel: 020 8216 4293 — MB ChB 1978 Bristol; FRCP; FRCPath; MRCP (UK) 1982; MRCPath 1985. Cons. Haemat. Barnet Gen. Hosp.; Dir. Med. Educat. Prev: Sen. Regist. (Haemat.) St. Bart. Hosp. Lond.

BERNEY, Thomas Peter Prudhoe Hospital, Prudhoe NE42 5NT Tel: 01661 514404 Fax: 01661 514592; Glenside House, Glen Path, Sunderland SR2 7TU Email: t.p.berney@newcastle.ac.uk — MB ChB Birm. 1969; FRCPsych 1986, M 1975; DPM Witwatersrand 1972. (Univ. Coll. Rhodesia) Cons. Child Psychiat. of Handicap Prudhoe Hosp.; Cons. Child Psychiat. Handicap, Fleming Nuffield Child Psychiat. Unit, Newc; Clin. Lect. Univ. Newc. Socs: FRCPCH; Child Psychiat. Research Soc.; Internat. Assn. Neuropsychopharm. Prev: Cons. Psychiat. Leicester Roy. Infirm.; Regist. Tara Hosp. Johannesburg, S. Afr.; Sen. Regist. Fleming Nuffield Child Psychiat. Unit. Newc.

BERNHARDT, John Richard Chrispin Bardleden Oast, Biddenden Road, Smarden, Ashford TN27 8QG — MB ChB 1984 Sheff. Prev: GP Ashford.

BERNHARDT, Mr Leslie Walter 23 Hurst Avenue, London N6 5TX — MB BCh 1970 Witwatersrand; MRCOG 1977; FRCS Eng 1982; FRCS Ed. 1981.

BERNSTEIN, Abraham Alan (retired) 124 Hilton Lane, Prestwich, Manchester M25 9QX Tel: 0161 773 2909 Fax: 0161 773 5984 Email: abandalb@aol.com — MB BCh BAO 1962 Dub.; BA, MB BCh BAO Dub. 1962; FRCP Lond. 1979, M 1967. Cons. Phys. Salford Roy. Hosps. NHS Trust; Hon. Lect. (Med.) Manch. Univ. Prev: Sen. Med. Regist., Wythenshawe Hosp., Manch.

BERNSTEIN, Cyril Aubry Bernard (retired) Side Elms, Beaufort Close, Reigate RH2 9DG Tel: 01737 41839 — MRCS Eng. LRCP Lond. 1949; MA Camb.; MFOM RCP Lond. 1979; DIH Eng. 1961. Prev: Cons. Occupat. Health Camb. HA.

BERNSTEIN, David Cyril 111 Montagu Mansions, London W1U 6LG Tel: 020 7935 0540 — BM BCh 1947 Oxf.; BM BCh Oxon. 1947; FFR 1960. (St. Thos.) Cons. Neuroradiol. Roy. Free Hosp. Lond.; Cons. Neuroradiol Whittington Hosp. Lond. Prev: Asst. Radiol. St. Thos. Hosp. Lond.; Sen. Regist. Radiol. St. Thos. Hosp. Lond.; Regist. Nat. Hosp. Nerv. Dis. Qu. Sq. Lond.

BERNSTEIN, Ian Anthony Gordon House Surgery, 78 Mattock Lane, London W13 9NZ Tel: 020 8997 9564 Fax: 020 8840 0533 — MB BS 1987 Lond.; MA Camb. 1987, BA 1984; MSc 1999 Lond.; FLCOM 2001 Lond.; 1998 Registered Osteopath; 2001 Post Grad. Cert. for teachers in primary care; MLCOM 1993; MRCGP 1992; DMS Soc. Apoth. Lond. 1993; DRCOG 1991; DCH RCP Lond. 1990. Princip. GP Practitioner; Assoc. Specialist, Musculoskeletal Phys. in Primary Care; Brit. Rowing Team Doctor. Socs: Brit. Inst. Musculoskel. Med.; Assn. For Med. Osteopathy. Prev: Clin. Asst. Lond. Coll. Osteop. Med.

BERNSTEIN, Jeffrey Merton (retired) Braemar, 24 Delahays Drive, Hale, Altrincham WA15 8DP Tel: 0161 980 7143 Email: merton.bernstein@ukgateway.net — MB ChB Manch. 1948; MRCS Eng. LRCP Lond. 1948; MRCGP 1953. Examg. Med. Practitioner NDA; Med. Bd.ing Doctor; Sect. 12 Approved Doc. (Ment. Health Act). Prev: Sect. 12 Approved Doc. (Ment. Health Act).

BERNSTEIN, Joanna Joy North Hampshire Hospital, Aldermaston Road, Basingstoke RG24 9NA Tel: 01256 313671, 01256 352544 — MB BS 1986 Lond.; MRCP (UK) 1990; CCST (Geriatric Medicine) 1998. Cons. elderly care, N. Hants.,Hosp. Socs: Med. Wom. Federat. (Pres. Lond. Assn.); BMA & BGS. Prev: Locum Cons. physcian, Gen. and Geriat. Med., S.mead Hosp. Bristol; Sen. Regist. (Geriat. Med.) Whittington Hosp. Lond.; en. Regist. (Geriat. Med.) Univ. Coll. Lond.

BERNSTEIN, Jonathan Frank The Beechcroft Medical Centre, 34 Beechcroft Gardens, Wembley HA9 8EP Tel: 0208 904 5444 Fax: 0208 904 7063 — MB ChB 1988 Birm.; MRCGP 1995; DFFP 1995; DCH RCP Lond. 1994. (Birm.) Prev: Trainee GP Lond.

BERNSTEIN, Leopold Stuart Halcyon, Hendon Wood Lane, Mill Hill, London NW7 4HS — MB ChB Birm. 1958; MRCS Eng. LRCP Lond. 1958; FFPM RCP Lond. 1989; DObst RCOG 1960. (Birmingham) Indep. Cons. Medico-Legal Affairs Lond.; Clin. Asst. (Rheum.) N.wick Pk. Hosp. Harrow. Socs: Brit. Assn. Pharmaceut. Phys. & Brit. Soc. Antimicrobial; Chemother. Prev: Sen. Staff Phys. Wellcome Research Laborat.

BERNSTEIN, Robert Michael 23 Anson Road, Manchester M14 5BZ Tel: 0161 248 2048 Fax: 0161 248 2049 Email: berstein@doctors.org.uk — MB BChir 1973 Camb.; MA Camb. 1974, MD 1984; FRCP Lond. 1990; MRCP (UK) 1975. (Camb. & Univ. Coll. Hosp.) Hon. Clin. Lect. Univ. Manch. Socs: Fell. Amer. Coll. Rheum.; Brit. Soc. Rheum.; Soc. Expert Witnesses. Prev: Sen. Regist. & Tutor (Med.) RPMS Hammersmith Hosp. & Rheum. Unit Canad. Red Cross Memor. Hosp. Taplow; Regist. (Gen. Med. & Cardiol.) Roy. Free Hosp. Lond.

BERNSTEIN, Samuel, OStJ, Col. late RAMC Retd. (retired) 4 Linden Court, Middleton Road, Camberley GU15 3TU Tel: 01276 65785 — MA Dub. 1974, BA 1954, MB BCh BAO 1957; FRCGP 1977, M 1971. Prev: GP Camberley.

BEROVIC, Marko Nicholas 138 Oakfield Road, Selly Oak, Birmingham B29 7ED — BM BS 1998 Nottm.; BM BS Nottm 1998.

BERRA, Jyoti Kana (retired) 16 Lakeside House, Eaton Drive, Kingston Hill, Kingston upon Thames KT2 7QZ Tel: 020 8546 6787 — MRCS Eng. LRCP Lond. 1944. Prev: Asst. Med. Off. Kingston & Richmond HA.

BERRAL REDONDO, Miguel Angel 85 Royal Crescent, Ruislip HA4 0PL — LMS 1990 Malaga.

BERRANGE, Eileen Jean 71 Carisbrooke High Street, Newport PO30 1NT — MB ChB Cape Town 1953. Med. Assessor/Adj. Prev: Sen. Med. Superintendent Med. Off.

BERRAONDO, Luis Manuel 56A Preston Road, Yeovil BA20 2BW — Medico 1969; Medico Tucuman 1969; MPhil (Psych.) Ed. 1976; MRCPsych 1977. (Tucuman, Argentina) Cons. Psychiat. Avalon & Som. NHS Trust. Prev: Cons. Ment. Illness. Doncaster Roy. Infirm.; Cons. Ment. Illness Brit. Milit. Hosps. Hannover & Rinteln Germany; Cons. Ment. Illness Fairfield Hosp. Hitchin & Luton & Dunstable Hosp.

BERRESFORD, Patricia Anne Department of Pathology, Princess Royal Hospital, Haywards Heath RH16 4EX Tel: 01444 441881 — BM BS 1977 Nottm.; BMedSci 1975 Nottm.; MRCPath 1986. Cons. Histopath./Cytol. P.ss Roy. Hosp. Haywards Heath.

BERRICH, Anne Smith Office Complex, Victoria Hospital Annexe, Townhead, Rothesay PA20 9JH Tel: 01700 502943 Fax: 01700 505147; 18 Crichton Road, Rothesay PA20 9JR — MB ChB 1977 Glas.; DCCH RCP Ed. 1986; DFFP 1999. Clin. Med. Off. (Community Child Health, Well Wom. & Family Plann.) Argyll & Clyde HB.

BERRIDGE, Mr David Charles Vascular Unit, St James' University Hospital, Beckett St., Leeds LS9 7TF Tel: 0113 243 3144 Fax: 0133 246 0098; 2 Wike Ridge Court, Alwoodley, Leeds LS17 9NX — BM BS 1981 Nottm.; DM Nottm. 1990; BMedSci. Nottm. 1979; FRCS Eng. 1995; FRCS Ed. 1986; T(S) 1993. Cons. Vasc. Surg. St. Jas. Univ. Hosp. Leeds; Hon. Sen. Lect. Leeds Univ. Socs: Surgic. Research Soc.; Vasc. Surg. Soc. GB & Irel.; Roy. Soc. Med. Prev: Sen. Regist. (Surg.) N.. RHA; Regist. Rotat. (Gen. Surg.) Qu. Med. Centre Nottm.; Research Regist. (Vasc. Surg.) Nottm.

BERRIDGE, Eileen Margaret Nethercote Farm, Nethercote, Rugby CV23 8AS — BM 1982 Soton.; DCH RCP Lond. 1986. (Southampton) Prev: GP & Clin. Med. Off. Corbridge Health Centre; Clin. Med. Off. (Child Health) Soton. HA; Trainee GP Romsey VTS.

BERRIDGE, John Cavers Department of Anaesthetics, Leeds General Infirmary, Great George St., Leeds LS1 3EX Tel: 0113 292 6672; Fairfax House, St. Helens Farm, Newton Kyme, Tadcaster LS24 9LY — MB ChB 1982 Ed.; MRCP (UK) 1986; FFA RCS Eng. 1987. Cons. Anaesth. & Intens. Care Gen. Infirm. Leeds. Socs: Yorks. Soc. Anaesth.; Intens. Care Soc.; Assn. Anaesth. Prev: Sen. Regist. (Anaesth.) Yorks. RHA; Regist. (Anaesth.) Camb.; SHO (Gen. Med.) Dryburn Hosp. Durh.

BERRIDGE, John Michael Beeston Village Surgery, Beeston District Centre, Town Street, Leeds LS11 8PN — MB ChB 1975 Leeds; MB ChB (Hons.) Leeds 1975. Socs: Brit. Assn. Sport & Med.; Soc. Orthop. Med.

BERRIDGE, Katherine Isabel Rawdon Surgery, 11 New Road Side, Rawdon, Leeds LS19 6DD Tel: 0113 295 4234 Fax: 0113 295 4228 — BM BS 1982 Nottm.; BMedSci Nottm. 1980. Prev: Trainee GP Mansfield VTS; GP Newc. & Leeds Retainer Schemes.

BERRIDGE, Lisa Samantha 23 Balmoral Drive, Knottingley WF11 8RQ — MB ChB 1996 Leeds.

BERRIDGE, Lynda Wellspring Medical Centre, Park Road, Risca, Newport NP11 6BJ Tel: 01633 612438 Fax: 01633 615958 — MB BCh 1979 Wales; MRCGP 1983; DRCOG 1982; Dip. Pract. Dermat. Wales 1995. Prev: Clin. Med. Off. S. Gwent; Trainee GP Newport VTS.

BERRIDGE, Michael John Burley Park Doctors, Burley Park Medical Centre, 273 Burley Road, Leeds LS4 2EL Tel: 0113 230 4111 — MB ChB 1980 Leeds; MRCGP 1984; DRCOG 1983.

BERRIDGE, Peter David Ross Rowes Farm, Colebrooke, Crediton EX17 5JH — MB BS 1993 Lond.

BERRIE, Anne Katherine 25D Hughenden Gardens, Glasgow G12 9XZ — MB ChB 1979 Manch.; BSc St. And. 1976. Dep. GP Glas.

BERRILL, Andrew John Department of Anaesthesia, St James's Hospital, Leeds LS9 7TF — MB ChB 1987 Ed.; FRCA 1993. (Edinburgh) Cons. (Anaes), St. James' Hosp., The Leeds Teachg. Hosps. NHS Trucst, Leeds; Hon. Sen. Lect. Leeds Univ. Socs: Assn. of Anaeshtetists of GB & Irel.; Hosp. Cons. & Specialists Assn.; Europ. Soc. of Reg. Anaeshesia.

BERRILL, William Trevor The Grove, Papcastle, Cockermouth CA13 0JR — MB BS 1968 Lond.; FRCP Lond. 1984; MRCP (UK) 1972. (Middlx.) Cons. Phys. W. Cumbld. Hosp. Whitehaven. Socs: BMA. Prev: Sen. Med. Regist. (Thoracic) Roy. Vict. Infirm. Newc.; Med. Regist. (Thoracic) Soton. W.. Hosp.; Research Regist. (Immunol.) Soton. Gen. Hosp.

BERRIMAN, Jo-Anne Parkview Clinic, Queensbridge Road, Moseley, Birmingham B13 8QE Tel: 0121 243 2000; Rough Park Farm House, Hamstall Ridware, Rugeley WS15 3SH Tel: 01889 504252 — MB ChB 1985 Manch.; MRCPsych 1993. Sen. Regist. (Child & Adolesc. Psychiat.) Pk.view Clinic Birm. Prev: Regist. Rotat. (Psychiat.) Keele, Stoke-on-Trent; Regist. (Psychiat.) St Matthew's Hosp. Burntwood Staffs.; SHO & Regist. Rotat. (Psychiat.) Nottm.

BERRIMAN, Timothy John The Surgery, Red Lion House, 86 Hednesford Road, Cannock WS11 2LB Tel: 01543 502391 Fax: 01543 573424; Rough Park Farm House, Rough Park, Hamstall Ridware, Rugeley WS15 3SH Tel: 01889 22252 — MB ChB 1983 Liverp.

BERRINGTON, Andrew William 4 Trinity Terrace, Corbridge NE45 5HW — BChir 1990 Camb.

BERRINGTON, Janet Elizabeth 4 Trinity Terrace, Corbridge NE45 5HW — MB BS 1992 Nottm.

BERRINGTON, Robert Michael, MBE (Surgery), School Lane, Alconbury, Huntingdon PE28 4EQ Tel: 01480 890281 Fax: 01480

414478; The Regional GP Postgrauate Office NHSE, Central Block, PO Box 650, Fulbourn Hospital, Cambridge CB1 5RB Tel: 01223 218617 Fax: 01223 218668 — MB ChB 1961 Sheff.; FRCGP 1980, M 1969; DObst RCOG 1963. (Sheff.) Regional Dir. Postgrad. Gen. Pract. Anglia & Oxf. NHSE & Univ. Camb.; Chairm. Scope Project Team (Profess. Developm. for Med. & Dent. Professions). Socs: Assn. Study Med. Educat. Prev: Mem. Standing Comm. Postgrad. Med. Educat. Lond.; Chairm. Comm. Regional Adviser (Gen. Pract.) Eng.; Mem. Jt. Comm. Postgrad. Train. Gen. Pract.

BERRINGTON, William Pye (retired) 15 Mill Lane, Sandford, Crediton EX17 4NP Tel: 0136 323342 — MD 1939 Belf.; MB BCh BAO 1931; FRCPsych 1971; DPM Lond. 1935. Prev: Dep. Med. Supt. Runwell Hosp. Wickford.

BERRIOS, German Elias 12 Pierce Lane, Fulbourn, Cambridge CB1 5DL Tel: 01223 880752 — Medico Cirujano 1966 Peru; Medico Cirujano Universidad Nacional Mayorde San Marcos, Peru 1966; MA Camb. 1977; MA Oxf. 1974, DPhil Sc 1972, BA (Psychol. & Philos.) 1970; FRCPsych 1982, M 1973; DPM Eng. 1970. Cons. Psychiat. Addenbrooke's Hosp. Camb.; Edr. Hist. Psychiat.; Univ. Lect. Psychiat. Univ. Camb.; Chairm. Camb. L.R.E.C.; Fell. Librarian, Robinson Coll., Camb. Socs: Fell. Roy. Soc. Med.; Fell. Brit. Psychol. Soc.; Fell. Acad. of Med. Sci., 2000. Prev: Regist. (Psychiat.) Littlemore Hosp. Oxf.; Lect. Psychiat. Univ. Leeds; Wellcome Fell. Hist. Med. Corpus Christi Coll. Oxf.

BERRISFORD, Charles Edward Number 18 Surgery, 18 Upper Oldfield Park, Bath BA2 3JZ Tel: 01225 427402 Fax: 01225 484627 — MB BS 1991 Lond.; BSc (Hons.) Lond. 1986, MB BS 1991.

BERRISFORD, Martyn Hugh Toft Road Surgery, Toft Road, Knutsford WA16 9DX Tel: 01565 632681; 7 Beech Close, Ollerton, Knutsford WA16 8TD — MB ChB 1969 Manch.; DObst RCOG 1972. Prev: Med. Off. Ilford Ltd. Mobberley; Ho. Surg. & Ho. Phys. Wythenshawe Hosp. Manch.; SHO (Obst.) Billinge Hosp. Orrell.

BERRISFORD, Rachel Jane 9 Clova Park, Kingswells, Aberdeen AB15 8TH — MB ChB 1996 Ed.; BSc (Hons. Bact) Ed. 1991. (Edinburgh)

BERRISFORD, Rosemary Christine 18 Castle Mount Crescent, Bakewell, Derby DE45 1AT — MB BS 1983 Lond.; MRCGP 1987; DObst. RCOG 1986. (Lond.)

BERRISFORD, Simon Bernard Haslingden Health Centre, Manchester Road, Haslingden, Rossendale BB4 5SL Tel: 01706 212518 — MB ChB 1988 Manch.; MRCGP 1992.

BERROW, Lloyd Cameron 10 Manor Place, Cults, Aberdeen AB15 9QN — MB ChB 1993 Glas.

BERROW, Paul John Linden Hall Surgery, Station Road, Newport TF10 7EN Tel: 01952 820400 — MB ChB 1982 Birm.; MRCGP 1986.

BERRY, Abraham (retired) 10 Raleigh Park, South Molton EX36 4DN Tel: 01769 573547 — MB BS Lond. 1954; MRCS Eng. LRCP Lond. 1954; DA Eng. 1957.

BERRY, Adrian David Ian Newton Lodge, Fieldhead Hospital, Wakefield WF1 3SP Tel: 01924 327000 — MB ChB 1987 Manch. Cons. Forens. Psychiat. Newton Lodge Wakefield. Socs: Roy. Coll. Psychiat. Prev: Sen. Regist. (Forens. Psychiat.) Rampton Hosp. Notts.; Regist. Rotat. (Psychait.) N. Trent Region; SHO Rotat. (Psychiat.) N. Manch.

BERRY, Mr Alan Raymond The Three Shires Hospital, The Avenue, Cliftonville, Northampton NN1 5DR Tel: 01604 885017 Fax: 01604 631711 Email: alan@aberry.fsmt.co.uk; Maryland Farm, 2 Main Road, Grendon, Northampton NN7 1JW — MB ChB 1973 Ed.; FRCS Eng. 1978; FRCS Ed. 1977. Cons. Gen. Surg. N.ampton Gen. Hosp. Prev: Clin. Tutor Nuffield Dept. Surg. John Radcliffe Hosp. Oxf.; Regist. (Surg.) Roy. Infirm. Edin.

BERRY, Anne Caroline (retired) 4 Sackville Close, Sevenoaks TN13 3QD Tel: 01732 451907 — MB BS 1961 Lond.; PhD Lond. 1972; MRCP (UK) 1987; FRCP Lond. 1991. Prev: Cons. Clin. Geneticist Guy's Hosp. Lond.

BERRY, Aubrey Winston The Surgery, 54 Thorne Road, Doncaster DN1 2JP Tel: 01302 361222 — MB ChB 1974 Sheff.

BERRY, Bharat Bhushan Maynard Court Surgery, 17-18 Maynard Court, Waltham Abbey EN9 3DU Tel: 01992 761387 Fax: 01992 716163 — MB ChB 1977 Sheff.; MRCGP 1981.

BERRY, Carol Ann 2 Adlington Close, Strensall, York YO32 5RS — MB ChB 1987 Ed.

BERRY, Carolyn Josephine 14 Kings Way Avenue, Belfast BT5 7DN — MB BCh BAO 1988 Belf.

BERRY, Christopher Maxwell Colne Road Surgery, 34-36 Colne Road, Burnley BB10 1LQ Tel: 01282 456564 Fax: 01282 451639 — MB ChB 1980 Dundee; MB ChB 1980 Dundee.

BERRY, Claire Louise 19C Shepherds Loan, Dundee DD2 1AW — MB ChB 1998 Dund.; MB ChB Dund 1998.

BERRY, Colin, TD (retired) 465 Green Lane, Coventry CV3 6EL Tel: 02476 414092 Email: cberry5148@aol.com — MB ChB Birm. 1958; MRCS Eng. LRCP Lond. 1958; FRCPsych. M 1971; DPM Eng. 1965. Mem. Ment. Health Review Tribunal; Mem. Ment. Health Act Commiss. Prev: Med. Off. HM Prison Gartree.

BERRY, Colin Nether Lolestone, Cardross, Dumbarton G82 5HQ — MB ChB 1993 Glas.

BERRY, Colin Briers Department of Anaesthetics, Royal Devon & Exeter Hospital, Wonford, Exeter EX2 5DW Tel: 01392 402474 Fax: 01392 402472 Email: cbb@eurobell.co.uk; The Cottage, Yettington, Budleigh Salterton EX9 7BW Tel: 01395 567139 Email: cbb@eurobell.co.uk — MB BS 1984 Lond.; FRCA 1991. (St. Thos.) Cons. Anaesth. Roy. Devon & Exeter Hosp. Socs: Assn. of Anaesthetics; Soc. of Anaesth. of S. W. Region; Soc. of Naval Anaesth. Prev: Asst. Prof. Anesth. Univ. Virginia, USA; Sen. Regist. Bristol. Roy. Infirm.; Provisional Fell. Alfred Hosp. Melbourne, Austral.

BERRY, Professor Sir Colin Leonard Department of Morbid Anatomy & Histopathology, The Royal London Hospital, London E1 1BB Tel: 020 7377 7349 Fax: 020 7377 0949 Email: c.l.berry@mds.qmw.ac.uk — MB BS Lond. 1961; DSc Lond. 1993, PhD 1970, MD 1968; FRCP Lond. 1993; FFOM RCP Lond. 1995; FFPM RCP (UK) 1993; FRCPath 1979, M 1967. (Charing Cross) Prof. Morbid Anat. Lond. Hosp. Med. Coll. Lond.; Warden Med. & Dent. Sch. & Vice-Princip. (Med. & Dent.) Qu. Mary & W.field Coll; Chairm. Advis. Comm. Pesticides; Mem. Med. Research Counc. Prev: Reader (Path.) Guy's Hosp. Med. Sch. Lond.; Sen. Lect. (Histopath.) Inst. Child Health Lond.; Regist. (Path.) Char. Cross Hosp. Lond.

BERRY, David Alan 20 Neville Road, Shirley, Solihull B90 2QU — MRCS Eng. LRCP Lond. 1973; MRCPsych 1982; D.P.M. Lond. 1982. (Birm.) Regist. Rotat. Highcroft Hosp. Birm.

BERRY, David John Newtown Surgery, Station Road, Liphook GU30 7DR Tel: 01428 724768 Fax: 01428 724162 — MB BS 1985 Lond.; BSc Lond. 1982; MRCGP 1990; DRCOG 1990.

BERRY, Mr David Paul Department of Surgery, Leicester General hospital, Gwendolen Road, Leicester LE5 4PW Tel: 0116 258 4446 Fax: 0116 258 4708; Reservoir House, Ratcliffe Road, Cossington, Leicester LE7 4SP Tel: 01509 812101 — MB BCh 1987 Wales; FRCS Eng. 1992; MD Wales 1997; FRCS (Gen.) 1997. (Wales) Cons. Hepatobiliary and Pancreatic Surg., Leicester Gen. Hosp., Leics. Socs: Pancreatic Soc.; Assn. of Surg.s. Prev: Sen. Regist. TQEH, Adelaide Australia; Specialist Regist., Midtrent Rotat.; Research Fell. (Surg.) Univ. of Wales Coll. of Med. Cardiff.

BERRY, Deborah Wendy 108 King Henrys Dr, New Addington, Croydon CR0 0PB — MB ChB 1997 Birm.

BERRY, Edith May (retired) The Spinney, Teversal, Sutton-in-Ashfield NG17 3JN Tel: 01623 516122 — MB ChB 1956 Sheff.; DA Eng. 1959. Prev: Regist. (Anaesth.) Mansfield Gp. Hosps.

BERRY, Edward Basil (retired) 4 West Gate Park, 28 Alumhurst Road, Bournemouth BH4 8ER — MRCS Eng. LRCP Lond. 1939. Prev: Med. Off. BUPA Med. Centre Lond.

BERRY, Eileen Patricia 18 Howards Meadow, Kings Cliffe, Peterborough PE8 6YJ — BM BS 1989 Nottm.; MRCGP 1994.

BERRY, Elisa Copper Folly, Well Lane, Mollington, Chester CH1 6LD — MB ChB 1963 Sheff.; DObst RCOG 1965.

BERRY, Elizabeth Mary (retired) The Old Sawmill, Exebridge, Dulverton TA22 9AY Tel: 01398 324004 — MB ChB 1949 Bristol.

BERRY, Freda Morisdene, Commercial Road, Barrhead, Glasgow G78 — MB ChB 1961 Glas.; MRCPsych 1972; DPM Ed. & Glas. 1964; DObst RCOG 1963. (Glas.) Cons. Psychiat. Dykebar Hosp. Paisley. Prev: Cons. Psychiat. Riccartsbar Hosp. Paisley; Med. Asst. Gartnavel Roy. Hosp. Glas.; Regist. Leverndale Hosp. Glas.

BERRY, George Harry 'Cintra', Otley Road, Bramhope, Leeds LS16 9JU Tel: 0113 267 3323 — MB ChB 1956 Birm.; FRCR 1975; FFR 1968; DMRT Eng. 1966; DObst RCOG 1958. (Birm.) Cons. Radiother. & Oncol. Leeds W.. HA; Vis. Cons. Bradford Roy. Infirm. Airedale Gen. Hosp. Keighley; Sen. Clin. Lect. Dept. Radiother. Univ.

Leeds. Prev: Sen. Regist. (Radiother.) Christie Hosp. & Holt Radium Inst. Manch.; Ho. Surg. (Obst.) Qu. Eliz. Hosp. Birm.; Ho. Phys. (Paediat.) Warwick Hosp.

BERRY, Hedley 96 Harley Street, London W1N 1AF Tel: 020 7486 0967 Fax: 020 7935 1107; 21 Dorset Drive, Edgware HA8 7NT Tel: 020 8952 5557 — BM BCh 1967 Oxf.; DM Oxf. 1973, MA, BM BCh 1967; FRCP Lond. 1985; MRCP (UK) 1970. (Guy's & Oxf.) Cons. Rheum. & Rehabil. King's Coll. Hosp. Lond. 1976- 2000. Socs: (Hon. Sec. Sect. Rheum.) Roy. Soc. Med. & BMA. Prev: Sen. Regist. (Rheum.) Lond Hosp.; Sen. Regist. St. Bart. Hosp. Lond.; Ho. Phys. Guy's Hosp. Lond.

BERRY, Mr Hedley Edward King's College Hospital, Denmark Hill, London SE5 9RS; 39 Elwill Way, Beckenham BR3 3AB Tel: 020 8650 0611 — MB BS 1960 Lond.; MB BS Lond 1960; FRCS Eng. 1964. Cons. Surg. King's Coll. Hosp. Lond. & Bromley Hosp.

BERRY, Ian Edward Ailsa Hospital, Dalmellington Road, Ayr KA6 6AB Tel: 01292 513981 — MB ChB 1984 Glas.; BSc Glas. 1973. Cons. Old Age Psychiat. Ailsa Hosp., Ayr. Prev: Cons. old age Psychiat., Crichton Roy. Hosp., Dumfries.

BERRY, Jane Frances Kingswood Surgery, Hollis Road, Totteridge, High Wycombe HP13 7UN — MB ChB 1983 Manch.; MRCGP 1987. Prev: Trainee GP Oldham VTS.

BERRY, Janet Elizabeth West Street Surgery, 89 West Street, Dunstable LU6 1SF Tel: 01582 664401 Fax: 01582 475766 — BM 1986 Soton.

BERRY, Jemima Wilson 13 Fentoun Gait, Gullane EH31 2EJ Tel: 01620 842698 — MB ChB 1944 Glas. Prev: Med. Off. Sunderland AHA; Ho. Phys. & Ho. Surg. Hairmyres Hosp. E. Kilbride.

BERRY, Mr John Burfield House, Chester Road, Penymynydd, Chester CH4 0EL; Chalet Glengarriff, Rougemont CH 1838, Switzerland — MB BS 1990 Lond.; DRCOG 1995; MRCOG, 1999. (Kings London) Specialist Regist. (O & G) Wrexnam Maelor. Socs: Med. Protec. Soc. Prev: Regist. LAT (O & G) Chesterfield, SHO (O & G) Qu. Charlottes Hosp. Lond.; GP/Regist. Twyford; SHO (Obst.) Roy. Berks. Hosp. Reading.

BERRY, John Health Centre, Victoria Road, Hartlepool TS26; 31 Coniscliffe Road, Hartlepool TS26 0BT Tel: 01429 67513 — MB ChB 1953 Leeds. (Leeds)

BERRY, John Bauvallet (retired) 20 The Island, Thames Ditton KT7 0SH Tel: 020 8398 3754 — MRCS Eng. LRCP Lond. 1946; MA Camb.; FRCP Lond. 1979, M 1952; DCH Eng. 1948. Prev: Cons. Chest Phys. St. Helier Hosp. & Merton Chest Clinic.

BERRY, Jonathan 53 Rochester Way, Darlington DL1 2XJ — MB BS 1988 Lond.

BERRY, Jonathan Mark The Princess Royal Hospital, Lewes Road, Haywards Heath RH16 4EX Tel: 01444 441881; Mill Hall Farm, Whitemans Green, Cuckfield, Haywards Heath RH17 5HX Tel: 01444 455986 — MB BS 1971 Lond.; MRCP (UK) 1973; FRCR 1976; DMRD Eng. 1975. (Middlx.) Cons. Radiol. P.ss Roy. Hosp. Haywards Heath. Prev: Cons. Radiol. Leics. HA.

BERRY, Jonathan Peter Boundary House, 462 Northenden Road, Sale M33 2RH Tel: 0161 972 9999 — MB ChB 1979 Manch.; MBA (Distinct.) Warwick 1998. Chairm. Trafford S. PCT Exec. Comm. Prev: Med. Off. St. Anns Hospice Chesh.; SHO (Orthop., Cas., O & G) Wythenshaw Hosp. Manch.

BERRY, Judith Ann 11 Juniper Close, Exeter EX4 9JT — MB ChB 1988 Bristol.

BERRY, Julian 302 Liverpool Road, London N7 8PU — MB ChB 1994 Glas.

BERRY, Kathleen A&E Department, Birmingham Children's Hospital, Steelhouse Lane, Birmingham B4 6NH Tel: 0121 333 9515 Fax: 0121 333 9501 Email: kathleen.berry@bhamchildrens.wmids.nhs.uk — MD 1982 McGill Univ. Canada; FRCP (C) 1987. (McGill Univ.) Cons. Paediat. A&E, Birm. Childr.s Hosp. Socs: Fell.Roy. Coll. Paediat. & Child Health; Fell.Roy. Coll. Phys.; Surgs. Of Canada.

BERRY, Matthew Iain 18 St Georges Place, The Mount, York YO24 1DR — BM BS 1996 Nottm.

BERRY, Maura Magdalene Govanhill Health Centre, 233 Calder Street, Glasgow G42 7DR Tel: 0141 531 8370 Fax: 0141 531 4431 — MB ChB 1974 Glas.; DObst RCOG 1976.

BERRY, Maureen (retired) 31 Coniscliffe Road, Hartlepool TS26 0BT Tel: 01429 267513 — MB ChB 1954 Leeds; MD Newc.1990; FFA RCS 1972; DA Eng. 1966. Cons. Anaesth. Hartlepool Gen. Hosp.

BERRY, Michael Anthony Ivy Cottage, Hatch Beauchamp, Taunton TA3 6TH Tel: 0121 624 0958 Email: mike@170cibbins.freeserve.co.uk; 170 Cibbins Road, Selly Oak, Birmingham B29 6NJ — MB ChB 1995 Birm.; ChB Birm. 1995; MRCP (UK). SHO A & E, Univ. Hosp., Birm. Socs: Colligate Mem., Roy. Coll. of Phys.s of Edin. Prev: SHO, Mid Staffs NHS Trust.

BERRY, Miles Gordon 4 Loveridge Road, West Hampstead, London NW6 2DT — MB BS 1991 Lond.

BERRY, Nicholas Yarnall By The Way Cottage, 18 Station Road, Cropston, Leicester LE7 7HD — BM BS 1997 Nottm.

BERRY, Patricia Margaret Ellesmere Medical Centre, 262 Stockport Road, Cheadle Heath, Stockport SK3 0RQ Tel: 0161 428 6729 Fax: 0161 428 0710; 23 Moseley Road, Cheadle Hulme, Cheadle SK8 5HJ Tel: 0161 485 3250 — MB ChB 1967 Sheff.; MRCGP 1971; FRCGP 1997, M 1971. (Sheff.) Prev: Ho. Phys. N.. Gen. Hosp. Sheff.; Ho. Surg. Salford Roy. Hosp; SHO (Paediat. Med.) Roy. Manch. Childr. Hosp.

BERRY, Paul Stanley Beccles Medical Centre, 7-9 St. Marys Road, St. Marys Road, Beccles NR34 9NQ Tel: 01502 712662 Fax: 01502 712906; Highfield, Beccles Road, Barnby, Beccles NR34 7QB — MB BChir 1979 Camb.; MA Camb. 1979; MRCGP 1984; DRCOG 1983. Prescribing Med. Adviser Suff. HA. Prev: GP Hounslow.

BERRY, Paul William Dyson Rooklyn, 52 Gledholt Road, Marsh, Huddersfield HD1 4HR — MB ChB 1959 Ed.

BERRY, Peter Derek 3 Charles Street, Stirling FK8 2HQ — MB ChB 1987 Ed.

BERRY, Professor Peter Jeremy The Bristol Royal Hospital for Sick Children, St Michaels Hill, Bristol BS2 8BJ Tel: 0117 928 5310 Fax: 0117 928 5312 — MB BChir 1975 Camb.; BA Camb. 1971; FRCP Lond. 1993; MRCP (UK) 1977; FRCPath 1993, M 1981; FRCPCH 1997. (Univ. Camb.) Prof. Paediat. Path. Univ. Bristol; Hon. Cons. Paediat. Path. Bristol Childr. Hosp. Socs: (Sec.) Paediat. Path. Soc.; (Counc.) Internat. Paediat. Path. Assn.; (Exec. Counc.) Europ. Soc. for Study & Preven. of Infant Death. Prev: Cons. Paediat. Path. Bristol Roy. Hosp. Sick Childr.; Fell. (Paediat. Path.) Childr. Hosp. Denver Colorado; Sen. Regist. (Histopath.) Addenbrooke's Hosp. Camb.

BERRY, Philip Anthony 21 Parklands Road, Chichester PO19 3DX — MB ChB 1996 Bristol.

BERRY, Phillip John 37 Livingstone Street, Norwich NR2 4HE Tel: 01603 443969; 20 Longfield Avenue, Coppull, Chorley PR7 4NT Tel: 01257 791046 Email: 106703.3166@compuserve.com — MB ChB 1994 Sheff. Specialist Regist. (Pub. Health) Norf. Health Auth. Norwich. Prev: Jun. Doctors Co-Ordinator NHS Exec. Trust Sheff.; SHO A & E N.ern Gen. Hosp. Sheff.; SHO Orthop. N.ern Gen. Hosp.

BERRY, Ralph Hugh, ERD (retired) Rockaine, Grenofen, Tavistock PL19 9ES — MRCS Eng. LRCP Lond. 1932. Prev: Res. Asst. Med. Off. Municip. Hosp. Brighton.

BERRY, Mr Robert Brookland BUPA Hospital Washington, Picktree Lane, Rickleton, Washington NE38 9JZ Tel: 0191 415 1272; Tel: 0191 388 7958 Fax: 0191 388 7958 Email: berry@castleview 15. fsnet.co.uk — MB ChB Birm. 1970; FRCS Eng. 1975. Cons. Plastic Surg. Shotley Bridge Hosp. Consett, The Dryburn Hosp. Durh. & Qu. Eliz. Hosp. Gateshead. Socs: Brit. Assn. of Plastic Surg.s; Brit. Assn. of Aesthletic Plastic Surg.s; Bristish Soc. for Surg. of the Hand. Prev: Sen. Regist. (Plastic Surg.) St. Andrews Hosp. Billericay.

BERRY, Robin David 18 Howards Meadow, Kings Cliffe, Peterborough PE8 6YJ — BM BS 1992 Nottm.

BERRY, Professor Roger Julian, RD, OStJ (retired) 109 Fairways Drive, Mount Murray, Santon, Douglas IM4 2JE Tel: 01624 617959 Fax: 01624 617959 — MD 1958 Durh. NC, USA; MD Duke Univ. Durh., NC, USA 1958; FRCP Lond. 1978, M 1971; FFOM RCP Lond. 1993, MFOM (Distinc.) 1988; FRCR 1979; MCPS Alta. 1970; Hon. FACR 1983. Vis. Prof. Univ. Lancaster. Prev: Dir. W.lakes Research Inst. Moor Row.

BERRY, Rowland Vale 2 Victoria Court, Kirkley Cliff Road, Lowestoft NR33 0DE Tel: 01502 574342; 2 Victoria Court, Kirkley Cliff Road, Lowestoft NR33 0DE Tel: 01502 574342 — MB BS 1956 Lond.; DPM Eng. 1961. (Lond. Hosp.) Psychother. (private Pract.). Prev: Cons. Psychiat. Jacques Hall Foundat.; Psychotherap. St. Bart. Hosp. Lond.; Vis. Psychiat. H.M. Prison Dept.

BERRY, Sheila Ivy (retired) 21 Willowdene Court, Brentwood CM14 5ET Tel: 01277 210676 — MRCS Eng. LRCP Lond. 1954; DPM Eng. 1965. Prev: GP Brentwood.

BERRY, Stuart Garth 18 Marnland Gr, Bolton BL3 4UJ — MB ChB 1997 Leeds.

BERRY, William Henry Charles (retired) 265 Chells Way, Stevenage SG2 0HN — MB BS 1960 Lond. Med. Off. Luton Town Football Club. Prev: Ho. Off. (Obst.) Plaistow Matern. Hosp.

BERRY, William Murray (retired) 86 Lexden Road, Colchester CO3 3SR Tel: 01206 578864 — MB BS 1955 Lond.; MRCGP 1965; DObst RCOG 1963.

BERSTOCK, Mr David Anthony BUPA Murrayfield Hospital, Holmwood Drive, Thingwall, Wirral CH61 1AU Tel: 0151 648 7000; Hesketh Hey, Manor Road, Thornton Hough, Wirral CH63 1JA — MB BS 1970 Lond.; FRCS Eng. 1975; MRCS Eng. LRCP Lond. 1969. Cons. Surg. Wirral Hosp. NHS Trust.; Clin. Lect. (Surg.) Univ. Liverp. Prev: Lect. & Sen. Regist. Kings Coll. Hosp. Lond.

BERSTOCK, Reva Leah (retired) 32A Frognal Lane, London NW3 7DT Tel: 020 7794 2351 — MB BCh BAO 1950 Dub.; DPM Eng. 1963; MRCPsych 1971. Prev: Cons. Psychiat. Child & Family Psychiat. Clinic St. Albans.

BERTENSHAW, Carol Jane 27 Trent Boulevard, Ladybay, West Bridgford, Nottingham NG2 5BB — MB BCh 1993 Wales; MRCPH (UK) 1997.

BERTFIELD, Mr Harvey (retired) 14 St John Street, Manchester M3 4DZ Tel: 0161 834 4411 Fax: 0161 835 1465 — MB ChB 1960 Ed.; MChOrth Liverp. 1970; FRCS Eng. 1967; FRCS Ed. 1966. Cons. Orthop. Surg. Univ. Hosp. S. Manch. & Wythenshawe Hosp.; Hon. Cons. Orthop. Surg. S. Manch. Hosp. Prev: Sen. Regist. (Orthop.) Roy. Infirm. Preston.

BERTH-JONES, John Department of Dermatology, Walsgrave Hospital, Coventry CV2 2DX Tel: 024 76 538884 Fax: 024 76 538766 Email: jbj@covderm.demon.co.uk; Coventry Consulting Rooms, 11 Dalton Road, Coventry CV5 6PB Tel: 024 76 677444 Fax: 01203 691436 — MB BS 1979 Lond.; MRCP (UK) 1985. (St. Bart.) Cons. Dermat. Walsgrave Hosp. Cov., Geo. Eliot Hosp. Nuneaton, Leic. Nuffield Hosp., Nuneaton Priv. Hosp.; Hon. Sen. Lect. Warwick Univ.; Clin. Teach. in Dermat. Leic. Univ. Socs: Brit. Assn. Dermatol.; Eur. Acad. Dermat. & Venercology; Brit. Soc. Investig. Dermat. Prev: Sen. Regist. (Dermat.) Leicester Roy. Infirm.

BERTHOUD, Mireille Christine Department of Anaesthesia, Royal Hallamshire Hospital, CSUH Trust,, Glossop Road,, Sheffield S10 2JF Tel: 0114 271 1900 Fax: 0114 279 8314 Email: mireille.berthoud@csuh.nhs.uk; 19 Moor Oaks Road, Sheffield S10 1BX Tel: 0114 266 0432 — BM 1982 Soton.; FCAnaesth 1990. Cons. Anaesth. Roy. Hallamsh. Hosp. Sheff. Prev: Lect. (Anaesth.) Univ. Sheff.

BERTI, Carlo Alessandro Cinical Development Centarl Research, Pfizer Ltd., Sandwich CT13 9NJ Tel: 01304 645189 Fax: 01304 658510 — State Exam Genoa 1982; FRCPI, 1998.

BERTIE, T M Friary House Surgery, Friary House, 2a Beaumont Road, Plymouth PL4 9BH Tel: 01752 663138 Fax: 01752 675805 — MB BS 1978 Lond.; DCH RCPS Glas. 1983; DRCOG 1981. (Lond. Hosp.) Socs: Plymouth Med. Soc.; Roy. Soc. Med. Prev: Trainee GP/SHO Plymouth VTS; SHO (Paediat.) Freedom Fields Hosp. Plymouth; Ho. Phys. & Ho. Surg. Lond. Hosp.

BERTONE, Raffaele Pavilion Family Doctors, 153A Stroud Road, Gloucester GL1 5JJ Tel: 01452 385555 — State Exam Rome 1986. Trainee GP Gloucester. Socs: Assoc. Mem. Brit. Med. Acupunc. Soc. Prev: SHO (O & G & Gen. Med.) Noble's Hosp. Douglas, I. of Man.

BERTORELLI, Sharon Wyn Victoria Surgery, 5 Victoria Road, Holyhead LL65 1UD; Mynyddcelyn, Mawr, Plas Road, Penryosfeilw, Holyhead LL65 2LU Tel: 01407 764892 — MB BCh 1988 Wales. (University of Wales College of Medicine) Clin. Asst. Ophth. (p/t).

BERTRAM, Alan (retired) North Cottage, 28 Locko Road, Spondon, Derby DE21 7AN Tel: 01332 673391 — MB ChB 1959 St. And.; DObst RCOG 1961. Prev: GP Derby.

BERTRAM, Amanda 8 Canning Street, Chester CH1 2AD — MB BS 1992 Lond.

BERTRAM, Mr John Lynhurst, Sydenham Damerel, Tavistock PL19 8PU — MB BS Lond. 1956; MChOrth Liverp. 1970; FRCS Eng. 1962. Socs: Fell. BOA.

BERTRAM, Robert William 24 Waterloo Place, North Shields NE29 0NA — MB ChB 1993 Liverp.

BERTRAM, Roger Charles Ricardo Coles Lane Health Centre, Coles Lane, Linton, Cambridge CB1 6JS Tel: 01223 891456 Fax: 01223 890033; Linton House, Linton, Cambridge CB1 6HS Tel: 01223 891368 — MB BChir 1980 Camb.; MA Camb. 1970, MB BChir 1980; DRCOG 1984. Sec. Camb. Med. Soc. Socs: BMA (Chairm. Camb., Ely & Huntingdon Div.). Prev: SHO (Geriat.) Newmarket Gen. Hosp.; Trainee GP Camb. VTS; SHO (O & G) Bedford Gen. Hosp.

BERWICK, Edward Patrick (retired) Oaklands, Coombe End, Kingston upon Thames KT2 7DQ Tel: 020 8942 7613 — MB BCh BAO 1954 Belf.; FFA RCS Eng. 1962; DA Eng. 1958. Prev: Sen. Regist. St. Geo. Hosp. Lond.

BERWICK, Steven James Michael 33 Willow Park Drive, Stourbridge DY8 2HL — MB ChB 1989 Liverp.; BSc (Hons.) Liverp. 1986, MB ChB 1989.

BERY, John 14 Lower Boston Road, London W7 2NR — MB BS 1991 Lond.

BERZON, David Brian 19 Harman Drive, London NW2 2ED Tel: 020 8450 4469 Fax: 020 8450 4469 — MB BS Lond. 1960; MRCS Eng. LRCP Lond. 1960; DLO Eng. 1967. (Roy. Free) Socs: Fell. Roy. Soc. Med.; Hampstead Med. Soc. Prev: Assoc. Specialist (ENT Surg.) Ealing Hosp. S.all, N.wick Pk. Hosp. Harrow & Centr. Middlx. Hosp. Lond.

BERZON, Derek (Surgery) 192 Colney Hatch Lane, Muswell Hill, London N10 1ET Tel: 020 8883 5555; 77 Holmstall Avenue, Edgware HA8 5JQ Tel: 020 8205 5900 — MB BS 1959 Lond.; MRCS Eng. LRCP Lond. 1959.

BESAG, Professor Frank Max Charles Specialist Medical Department, Bedfordshire & Luton Community NHS Trust, Milton Road, Clapham, Bedford MK41 6AT Tel: 01234 310582 Fax: 01234 310584 — MB ChB 1977 Birm.; FRCP Lond. 1997, FRCP Glas. 1990; MRCP (UK) 1980; FRCPsych 1997, M 1986; DCH RCP Lond. 1980; FRCPCH Lond. Cons.NeuroPsychiat. & Research Director,Learning Disabilities Serv., Twinwoods Health Resourses Centre,Beds & Luton Comm.NHS Trust; Hon. Sen. Lect. Inst. Psychiat. & Inst. Child Health; Vis. Prof. of NeuroPsychiat., Univ of Luton; Hon. Cons. Maudsley Hosp. Lond. KCH Lond. Socs: Brit. Paediat. Neurol. Assn.; BMA; Roy. Soc. Med. Prev: Regist. (Psychiat.) Bethlem Roy. & Maudsley Hosps. Lond.; Regist. (Paediat.) Hammersmith Hosp. Lond.; Ho. Phys. Hosp. Sick Childr. Gt. Ormond St. Lond.

BESCOBY-CHAMBERS, Nicholas John Cyril 55 Ashover Road, Old Tupton, Chesterfield S42 6HH — MB ChB 1998 Leic.; MB ChB Leic 1998.

BESHERDAS, Kalpesh 6 Coppetts Close, London N12 0AG — MB BS 1991 Lond.; MRCP (UK) 1994.

BESHR, Ahmed Shokry Mohamed Showkat 4 Kiltongue Cottages, Monkscourt Avenue, Airdrie ML6 0JS — MB ChB 1981 Alexandria.

BESHYAH, Salem Arifi Diabetes Unit, Princess Alexandra Hospital, Hamstel Road, Harlow CM20 1QX Tel: 01279 444455; 29 Elmwood, Sawbridgeworth CM21 9NN Tel: 01279 721813 Email: beshyah@yahoo.com — MB BCh 1981 Tripoli; PhD Lond. 1994; MRCPI 1987; MRCP (UK) 1987; DIC 1994; FRCP (london) 2000. Cons. Phys. (Gen. Med., Diabetes & Endocrinol.) P.ss Alexandra Hosp. Harlow. Socs: Brit. Diabetic Assn.; Brit. Endocrine Soc. Prev: Sen. Regist. & Clin. Research Fell. St. Marys. Hosp. Lond.; Regist. (Med.) Leicester Gen. Hosp.

BESKI, Shohreh Queen Charlotte Hospital, Gold Hawk Road, London W12; 40 Bramshill Gardens, London NW5 1JH — LMSSA 1988 Lond.; MRCOG 1993. Regist. (O & G) Qu. Charlotte Hosp. Lond.

BESLEY, Charles Robert Gilchrist The Red Practice, Waterside Health Centre, Beaulieu Road, Hythe SO45 4WX Tel: 023 8084 5955 Fax: 023 8084 1292; Little Gables, 9 Rollestone Road, Blackfield, Southampton SO45 2GD — BM 1992 Soton.; MRCGP 1996; DFFP 1994. (Soton.) GP Princip. Prev: Trainee GP/SHO Soton. VTS.; Med. Off., PCEA Chogoria Hosp. Chogoria, Kenya.

BESREST-BUTLER, Christopher Robert Shipley Health Centre, Alexandra Road, Shipley BD18 3EG Tel: 01274 589160; 41 Birklands Road, Shipley BD18 3BY Tel: 01274 591779 — MB BS 1977 Lond.; PhD Lond. 1966, BSc (Anat.) 1964; MRCS Eng. LRCP Lond. 1977; Dip Sports Med. . Lond. 1992; Dip. Sports Med. (Scott. Roy. Coll.) 1991. (Univ. Coll. Hosp.)

BESSANT, David Alfred Roger Moorfields Eye Hospital, City Road, London EC1 1AV Tel: 020 7253 3411 — MB ChB 1988 Manch.; FCOphth 1992.

BESSANT, Rupa 3 Gerard Road, Harrow HA1 2ND — MB ChB 1989 Manch.; MRCP (UK) 1994. Regist. (Rheum.) N.wick Pk. Hosp.

BESSE, Christopher Peter 62 Holland Park Mews, London W11 3SS Tel: 020 7727 0964 — MB BS 1981 Lond.; MRCP (UK) 1985; MRCS Eng. LRCP Lond. 1981.

BESSELL, Eric Michael Nottingham City Hospital NHS Trust, Hucknall Road, Nottingham NG5 1PB Tel: 0115 969 1169 Fax: 0115 962 7994; 13 Dovedale Road, West Bridgford, Nottingham NG2 6JB Tel: 0115 923 1864 — MB BS 1978 Lond.; PhD Lond. 1970; BSc (Hons.) (Chem.) Bristol 1967; FRCP Lond. 1993; MRCP 1980; FRCR 1984. (St. Mary's) Cons. Clin. Oncol. Nottm. City Hosp. NHS Trust. Socs: Brit. Oncol. Assn.; Eur. Soc. Therap. Radiol. & Oncol.; Radiother. Club 1951. Prev: Clin. Dir. Nottm. City Hosp. NHS Trust; Sen. Regist. (Radiother. & Oncol.) Roy. Marsden Hosp. Lond.

BESSER, Professor Gordon Michael 145 Harley Street, London W1G 6BL Tel: 020 76167790 Fax: 020 76167790 Email: endo@thelondonclinic.co.uk; White Cottage, 61A Marlborough Place, London EC1a 7BE Tel: 020 76243346 — MB BS 1960 Lond.; 1973 FRCP; MB BS (Hons., Distinc. Med. & Surg.) Lond. 1960; BSc (Special) (1st cl. Hons. Physiol.) Lond. 1957; DSc Lond. 1981; MD Lond. 1966; MD Turin (hon. causa) 1985; FRCP Lond. 1973, M 1963. (St. Bart.) p/t Prof. (Med.) emerituis St Bartholomews & Roy. Lond. Hosp. Sch. Med. & Dent. Qu. Mary W.field Coll. Lond.; Cons. Endocrinologist, Lond. Clinic centre for Endocrinol., Harley St., Lond.; Hon. Cons. Phys., Barts and the Lond. NHS Trust. Socs: Fell. (Ex. Vice-Pres. & Pres. Endocrinol Sect.) Roy. Soc. Med.; Hon. Mem. Assn. Amer. Phys.; Brit. & US Endocrinol. Socs. Prev: Ho. Phys. Med. Profess. Unit St. Bart. Hosp.; Ho. Phys. Hammersmith Hosp. & Brompton Hosp. Lond.; Prof. Of Med., St. Barts and the Roy. Lond. Sch. of Med. and Dent., Qu. Mary Univ. of Lond.

BESSON, John Alexander Owen Department of Psychiatry, St Thomas' Hospital, London SE17 7EH Tel: 020 7928 9292 Fax: 020 7922 8259 — MB ChB Ed. 1969; BSc Ed. 1966; FRCPsych 1993, M 1974; DPM Ed. 1973. Cons. Psychiat. St. Thos. Hosp., S. Lond. & Maudsley NHS Trust; Sen. Lect. UMDS St. Thos. Hosp. Lond. Prev: Wellcome Sen. Lect. Univ. Aberd.

BEST, Alison Clare Melbourne Park Medical Centre, Melbourne Road, Aspley, Nottingham NG8 5HL Tel: 0115 978 6114 Fax: 0115 924 9334 — BM BS 1988 Nottm.; BMedSci Nottm. 1986; MRCGP 1993; DFFP 1996. (Nottm.) GP Nottm.

BEST, Mr Alistair James Flat 9, Tiffany Court, Albert Road, Stonygate, Leicester LE2 2AA — MB ChB 1992 Dundee; BMSc Dund. 1989; FRCS (Eng.) 1996. (Dundee) Specialist Regist. (Orthop.).

BEST, Andrew Gregory 18 Knowsley Road, Beech Hill, Wigan WN6 7PZ Tel: 01942 43540; Unit 11/152 River Terrace, Kangaroo Point, Brisbane, Queensland 4169, Australia Tel: 017 891 2945 — MB ChB 1990 Bristol.

BEST, Mr Brian George Ulster Hospital, Dundonald, Belfast BT16 1RH Tel: 028 9048 4511 — MB BCh BAO 1975 Belf.; FRCSI 1995; FRCS Ed. 1979. Cons. Surg. Ulster Hosp. Belf.

BEST, Christopher Thomas Lyndon Rest Home, 79 Bury Road, Tottington, Bury BL8 3EU Tel: 0120 488 5124 & 7914 — MB ChB 1987 Manch. SHO (Gen. Med.) Leighton Hosp. Crewe. Prev: SHO (A & E) Leighton Hosp. Crewe.

BEST, Crispin John 14 Thorn Road, Bearsden, Glasgow G61 4PP — MB BS 1979 Lond.; MRCS Eng. LRCP Lond. 1979; FFA RCS Eng. 1984. Cons. Anaesth. Roy. Hosp. Sick Childr. Glas.

BEST, Elizabeth Anne 17 Lismore Park, Buxton SK17 9AU — MB ChB 1986 Manch.; MRCGP 1995. Med. Pract. Rural Health Alice Springs, Austral. Prev: Trainee GP W. Gorton, Manch.; Regist. (Paediat.) Alice Springs & Mater Hosp. Brisbane, Austral.

BEST, Elizabeth Anne 9 Cheveney Walk, Bromley BR2 0XZ — MB ChB 1996 Sheff. SHO (Psychiat.) Bethlem Roy. Hosp., Bethlem & Maudsley NHS Trust Beckenham.

BEST, Francis William Linhay, Forder Lane, Bishopsteignton, Teignmouth TQ14 9RZ — MB BS 1951 Lond.; MRCP Lond. 1958; FFOM RCP Lond. 1985, M 1979. (St. Thos.)

BEST, Frederick Ashley 2 Brook Road, Lytham St Annes FY8 4HY Tel: 01253 736839 — MB BCh BAO 1957 Dub.; MD Dub. 1965, BA, MB BCh BAO 1957, MAO 1961; FRCOG 1975, M 1962, DObst 1960. (T.C. Dub.) Cons. O & G Blackpool & Fylde Hosp. Gp. Socs: Fell. N. Eng. Obst. & Gyn. Soc. Prev: Lect. in O & G Univ. Sheff.; SHO (Obst.) Jessop Hosp. Wom. Sheff.; Regist. (O & G) Rotunda Hosp. Dub.

BEST, Jayne Lesley 8 Lombard Avenue, Lisburn BT28 2UP — MB BCh BAO 1995 Belf.

BEST, John Alan Aghalee House, Aghalee, Craigavon — MB BCh BAO 1955 Belf. (Belf.) Prev: Sen. Ho. Off. Belf. City Hosp.

BEST, Johnny George Weeton Way Surgery, 7 Weeton Way, Anlaby, Hull HU10 6QH Tel: 01482 658918; 7 Weeton Way, Anlaby, Hull HU10 6QH — MB ChB 1975 Leeds; DRCOG 1978. Socs: Hull Med. Soc.

BEST, Professor Jonathan James Kerle IFI, 18 Gladstone Terrace, Edinburgh EH9 1LS Tel: 0131 4663496; Level 8, The Kennedy Tower, Royal Edinburgh Hospital, Morningside Park, Edinburgh EH10 5HF Tel: 0131 537 6684 Fax: 0131 537 6684 Email: j.j.k.best@ed.ac.uk — MSc Lond. 1977; MB ChB Ed. 1967; FRCP Ed. 1982; MRCP (U.K.) 1971; FRCR 1975; DMRD Eng. 1974. Forbes Prof. (Med. Radiol.) Univ. Edin.; Hon. Cons. (Diag. Radiol.) Lothian Health Bd. Prev: Sen. Lect. (Diag. Radiol.) Univ. Manch.; Hon. Consult. (Diag. Radiol.) S. Manch. Health Dist. (T); Tutor (Diag. Radiol.) Roy. Postgrad. Med. Sch. Lond.

BEST, Julian Michael Wulf Flat 8 Oxhay Court, Oxhay View, May Bank, Newcastle ST5 0SA — MB ChB 1987 Liverp.

BEST, Margaret Elizabeth 34 Vicarage Meadow, Mirfield WF14 9JL — MB ChB 1983 Leeds.

BEST, Michael Howard Hayes Grove Priory Hospital, Prestons Road, Hayes, Bromley BR2 7AS Tel: 020 8462 7722; 10 Harley Street, London W1 Tel: 020 7935 3940 — MB BS 1973 Newc.; MRCPsych 1977; T(Psychiat.) 1991; SR 1996. (Newcastle) Staff Cons. Psychiat, Hamel Gr. Priory Hosp. Prev: Cons. Psychiat. Frenchay & Bristol & W.on HAs; Sen. Regist. Bethlem Roy. & Maudsley Hosp. Lond.; Regist. Roy. Vict. Infirm. Newc. u. Tyne.

BEST, Nicholas Roland Seymour Clinic, Kingshill Road, Swindon SN1 4LY Tel: 01793 610510; The Hawthorns, Bishopstone, Swindon SN6 8PL Tel: 01793 791121 — MB BS Lond. 1975; MRCPsych 1985; T(Psych) 1991. (St. Bart.) Cons. Psychiat. Seymour Clinic Swindon. Socs: Marcé Soc. Prev: Research Psychiat. Oxf. Univ. MRC Clin. Pharmacol. Research Unit Littlemore Hosp. Oxf.; Regist. & Sen. Regist. (Psychiat.) Warneford Gen. Hosp. & Littlemore Hosp. Oxf.; Regist. (Med.) Lond. Hosp. Whitechapel.

BEST, Nigel D'Ewes Gordon (retired) The Lodge, Les Varendes, St Andrews GY6 8TE Tel: 01481 255788 — MRCS Eng. LRCP Lond. 1958; MB BS Lond. 1962; DPM Eng. 1962; MRCPsych 1971. Prev: Cons. Psychiat. States of Guernsey.

BEST, Philip Vivian (retired) 8 Weardale Close, Reading RG2 7JD — MB ChB Birm. 1951; FRCPath 1975, M 1963. Cons. Neuropath. (Gen. Path.) Aberd. Roy. Hosps. NHS Trust; Hon. Sen. Lect. (Path.) Univ. Aberd. Prev: Research Fell. (Path.) Univ. Birm.

BEST, Richard Arthur Department of Cardiology, Burnley Healthcare NHS Trust, Burnley BB10 2PQ Tel: 01282 474161 — MB BChir 1968 Camb.; 1993 FRCP Ed.; 1972 MRCP (UK); 1994 FACC; 1990 FCCP; 2000 FRCP. (St. Thos.) Cons. Cardiol. Burnley Health Care NHS Trust. Socs: Brit. Cardiac Soc.; Primary Care Cardiovasc. Soc. Prev: Cons. Phys., Cardiol & Dir. Intens. Care Ashland Med. Centre PA, USA; Sen. Cardiac Fell. Heart Transpl. Dept. Papworth Hosp. Camb.; Regist. (Cardiol.) St. Thos. Hosp. Lond.

BEST, Richard Maxwell 20 Laganvale Manor, Stranmillis, Belfast BT9 5BE — MB BCh BAO 1988 Belf.

BEST, Richard Myles (retired) Mill House, High St., Queenborough ME11 5AQ Tel: 01795 580506 — MB BS 1958 Lond.; BA Open 1993. Prev: SHO (O & G) Leicester Gen. Hosp.

BEST, Sheena (retired) Park House, Tandragee, Portadown, Craigavon Tel: 01762 223 — MB BCh BAO 1946 Belf. Prev: Cas. Off. W. Herts. Hosp. Hemel Hempstead, Lurgan & Portadown Hosp. & Craigavon Area Hosp.

BEST, Stephen Joseph Craigavon Area Hospital, 68 Lurgan Road, Portadown, Craigavon BT63 5QQ Tel: 01762 334444; 24 Sandymount Road, Rich Hill, Armagh BT61 8QP — MB BCh BAO

1981 Belf.; MRCPsych 1985. Cons. Psychiat. Craigavon Area Hosp. Portadown.

BEST, Thomas Bernard Nicholas 126 Antil Road, London E3 5BN — MB BS 1994 Lond.

BEST, Wilma Andrea Gorbals Health Centre, 45 Pine Place, Glasgow G5 0BQ Tel: 0141 531 8290 Fax: 0141 531 8208; 596 Clarkston Road, Netherlee, Glasgow G44 3SQ — MB ChB 1986 Glas.; D.OCC.MED 1997.

BESTER, Paul De Kock Child & Family Psychiatry Unit, 5 Collingham Gardens, London SW5 0HW Tel: 020 8846 6644 Fax: 020 8846 6641 Email: nikpaul@polarbears.win-uk.net — MB BCh 1986 Witwatersrand; MRCPsych 1993. Specialist Regist. (Child & Adolesc. Psychiat.) Imperial Coll. Higher Train. Scheme for Child & Adoles. Psychiat. Socs: BMA. Prev: Research Fell. (Forens. Psychiat.) Chase Farm Hosp. Lond.; Research Regist. & Regist. (Psychiat.) Roy. Free Hosp. Lond.

BESTERMAN, Eleanor Mary Rymer (retired) 2 Calderwood Court, Montpellier Parade, Cheltenham GL50 1UA Tel: 01242 578070 — MB BS 1950 Lond.; MRCS Eng. LRCP Lond. 1950; DMRD Eng. 1958. Prev: Med. Off. (Mammographic Screening) Milton Keynes.

BESTLEY, John William 39A North Bar Without, Beverley HU17 7AG — MB ChB 1984 Leeds; MRCPsych 1989; DGM RCP Lond. 1986. Cons. Psychiat. (Old Age & Gen. Psychiat.) Hull & Holderness Community Trust. Prev: Sen. Regist. (Psychiat.) Yorks. RHA.

BESTUE, Maria de las Mercedes Dermatology Department, The Churchill Hospital, Old Road, Headington, Oxford OX3 7LJ — LMS 1989 Saragossa.

BESTWICK, John Robert Brampton Medical Practice, 4 Market Place, Brampton CA8 1NL Tel: 01697 72551 Fax: 01697 741944 — BM BS 1983 Nottingham; BM BS Nottm 1983. (Nottingham) GP Brampton, Cumbria.

BESWAL, Mr Nand Lal c/o Drive B. N. Purbey, Park Carnol Surgery, Central Park, Church Village, Pontypridd CF38 1RJ — MB BS 1972 Rajasthan; FRCS Glas. 1978.

BESWICK, David Kirkland Hall Cottages, Churchtown, Preston PR3 0HX Tel: 01995 605059 — MB BS 1978 Lond.; MA Camb. 1979; MRCS Eng. LRCP Lond. 1978; MRCGP 1984; DRCOG Lond. 1980. (Guy's)

BESWICK, Edmund (retired) 3 Larch Grove, Garstang, Preston PR3 1LE — MB BS 1949 Lond.; MRCS Eng. LRCP Lond. 1949. Prev: Ho. Surg., Ho. Phys. & ENT Ho. Surg. Roy. Infirm. Preston.

BESWICK, Francis William, CStJ (retired) Waldrons, 120 Bouverie Avenue S., Salisbury SP2 8EA Tel: 01722 322925 Email: francis.beswick2@virgin.net — PhD Wales 1964, MB ChB 1949. Prev: PMO (Research) MoD.

BESWICK, Frederic Bakewell (retired) Lea Side, 480 Burnley Lane, Chadderton, Oldham OL1 2QT Tel: 0161 624 6793 Fax: 0161 624 6793 Email: fb.b@virgin.net — MB ChB 1948 Manch.; LLD Manch. 1986.

BESWICK, Ian Cambell Adeline Road Surgery, 4 Adeline Road, Boscombe, Bournemouth BH5 1EF Tel: 01202 309421 Fax: 01202 304893 — MB BS 1974 Lond.; MRCS Eng. LRCP Lond. 1974; MRCGP 1979; DA Eng. 1980. (Lond. Hosp.) Prev: Trainee GP Swindon & Cirencester VTS; SHO (Anaesth.) Torbay Hosp. Torquay; Gen. Pract./Anaesth. Vanderhoof BC, Canada.

BESWICK, Isobel Porritt (retired) Templemore, Buxton SK17 9NA Tel: 01298 23681 — MB BS 1943 Lond.; MD Lond. 1947; MRCS Eng. LRCP Lond. 1943; FRCPath 1968. Hon. Cons. Path. Roy. Free Hosp. Lond. Prev: Sen. Lect. (Histopath.) Roy. Free Hosp. Med. Sch.

BESWICK, Rev. Joseph Hubert (retired) 38 Hallams Lane, Chilwell, Beeston, Nottingham NG9 5FH — MB ChB 1948 Birm.; Dip. Theol. Lond 1958. Prev: Ho. Phys. & Cas. Off. Kidderminster & Dist. Gen. Hosp.

BESWICK, Keith Bryan James Didcot Health Centre, Britwell Road, Didcot OX11 7JH Tel: 01235 512288 Fax: 01235 811473; Didcot Health Centre, Didcot OX11 7JH Tel: 01235 815181 — MB BS 1966 Lond.; MRCS Eng. LRCP Lond. 1966; MRCGP 1975; FFA RCS Eng. 1971. (St. Mary's) Prev: Regist. (Anaesth.) S. Warks. Hosp. Gp. & Univ. Coll. Hosp. W. Indies; Jamaica; SHO (Anaesth.) St. Mary's Hosp. Lond.

BESWICK, Kenneth Charles (retired) 4 Rosehill Close, Saxilby, Lincoln LN1 2JB Tel: 01522 702501 — MRCS Eng. LRCP Lond. 1963. Med. Adviser, War Pens. Prev: Med. Off. DSS.

BESWICK, Mary Elizabeth Yew Tree Farm House, Bickley Moss, Near Malpas SY13 4JE — MB ChB 1982 Manch.; MRCGP 1987; DCH RCPS Glas. 1986; DRCOG 1986.

BESWICK, Morilee (retired) 37 Langley Lane, Baildon, Shipley BD17 6TB Tel: 01274 585771 — MB ChB 1951 Liverp. Prev: SCMO Bradford AHA.

BESWICK, Nigel Francis St Lukes Surgery, Off Gwyddon Road, Abercarn, Newport NP11 5GX Tel: 01495 244205 Fax: 01495 249189 — BM BCh 1982 Wales.

BESWICK, Peggy Naomi 4 Rosehill Close, Saxilby, Lincoln LN1 2JB Tel: 01522 702501 — MRCS Eng. LRCP Lond. 1964. (Manch.) Clin. Med. Off. W. Lindsey NHS Trust. Prev: Ho. Surg. S.lands Hosp. Shoreham-by-Sea; Ho. Phys. Maidenhead Hosp.

BESWICK, Rachel Elizabeth North hampshire Hospital, Aldermaston Road, Basingstoke RG24 9NA Tel: 01256 473202 Email: rbeswick@doctors.net.uk — BM 1995 Soton.; MRCGP 2001. GP Loaim. Prev: GP Loaim. Bath and N. E. Som.

BESWICK, Rhona Elisabeth (retired) Waldrons, 120 Bouverie Avenue S., Salisbury SP2 8EA Tel: 01722 322925 Email: francis.beswick2@virgin.net — MB BCh Wales 1949; DObst RCOG 1951; DCH Eng. 1954. Prev: Med. Off. Wilts. HA.

BESWICK, Roger William 37 Silverwood Drive, Laverstock, Salisbury SP1 1SH — MB BCh 1984 Wales; DA (UK) 1990.

BESWICK, Samantha Jane 8 The Crescent, Preesall, Poulton-le-Fylde FY6 0EE — MB ChB 1989 Leics.; MRCGP 1993; DRCOG 1992.

BESWICK, Theresa Ann Post Office, Old Leake, Boston PE22 9NS — MB ChB 1989 Sheff.

BESWICK, Professor Thomas Spencer Leslie Fairways, Linney, Ludlow SY8 1EE Tel: 01584 872989 — MB BChir 1944 Camb.; MSc Manch. 1971; MA Camb. 1946, MD 1956; FRCP Lond. 1973, M 1946; FRCPath 1971, M 1964. (Camb. & Middlx.) Socs: BMA & Path. Soc. Prev: Emerit. Prof. Univ. Manch.; Prof. Virol. Univ. Manch.; Cons. Virol. Manch. & Salford AHAs (T).

***BETAMBEAU, Nadine** 8A Lyveden Road, Brigstock, Kettering NN14 3HE — MB BS 1998 Lond.; MB BS Lond 1998; BSc (Hons) Lond. 1968.

BETANCOR MARTINEZ, Mercedes 51B St Mary's Grove, London W4 3LW — LMS 1982 La Laguna.

BETHAM, Valerie Joan (retired) Little Thatch, Monkton, Honiton EX14 9NP Tel: 01404 43599 — MB BS Lond. 1962; FFA RCS Eng. 1971. Prev: Cons. Anaesth. Roy. Gwent Hosp. Gp.

BETHAPUDY, Susheel Rao Flat 1, 8 John Maurice Close, Balfour St., London SE17 1PY — MB BS 1996 Lond. (UMDS) SHO (Med.) OldCh. Hosp. Romford Essex.

BETHEL, Robert George Hankin Runnymede Medical Practice, The Health Centre, Bond St., Englefield Green, Egham TW20 0PF Tel: 01784 437671 Fax: 01784 434329; Newton Court Medical Centre, Burfield Road, Old Windsor, Windsor SL4 2QF Tel: 01753 863642 Fax: 01753 832180 — MB BChir 1973 Camb.; MA Camb. 1973, BA (Hons.) 1969; MRCGP 1979. (Camb. & St. Mary's) Sen. Partner Runnymede Med. Pract.; Approved Trainer (Gen. Pract.) Oxf. RHA; Assoc. Teach. Imperial Coll. Sci., Technol. & Med. Socs: Fell. Roy. Soc. Med. (Ex-Vice-Pres. Sect. Gen. Pract.); Fell. Roy. Soc. Health; Fell. Med. Soc. Lond. Prev: Regist. (Physical Med. & Rheum.) W. Middlx. Hosp.; SHO (Gen. Med. & Geriat.) N.wick Pk. Hosp. & Clin. Research Centre Harrow; Course Tutor, The Open Univ.

BETHELL, Anthony Noble Ashgate Hospice, Old Brampton, Chesterfield S42 7JE Tel: 01246 568801 Fax: 01246 569043; Ramshaw Lodge, Unstone, Sheffield S18 4AL Tel: 01246 413276 Fax: 01246 413276 Email: tonyb@ramshaw.wm.uk.net — MB ChB 1975 Sheff.; PhD Sheff. 1970; BSc Bristol 1960; Dip. Palliat. Med. Wales 1993. Med. Dir. Ashgate Hospice Chesterfield; Hon. Cons. Chesterfield Roy. Hosp. NHS Trust. Prev: Princip. GP Sheff.; Regist. (Radiol.) Sheff. AHA; Ho. Surg. Roy. Hosp. Sheff.

BETHELL, Delia Bridget 16 Chiltern View, Little Milton, Oxford OX44 7QP — BM BCh 1989 Oxf.

BETHELL, Hugh James Newton, MBE Cardial Rehabilitation Centre, Chawton Park Road, Alton GU34 IRQ Tel: 01420 544794 Fax: 01420 544825 Email: Hughbethell@netscapeonline.co.uk; Timbers, Boyneswood Road, Medstead, Alton GU34 5DY Tel: 01420

563932 Email: hughbethell@netscapeonline.co.uk — MB Camb. 1967, BChir (Distinc. Med.) 1966; MD Camb. 1995; FRCP Lond. 1996; MRCP (UK) 1970; FRCGP 1991, M 1976; DObst RCOG 1975. (Camb. & Guy's) p/t GP. Socs: Brit. Cardiac Soc.; (Founder Pres.) Brit. Assn. Cardiac Rehabil.; (Counc.) Coronary Preven. Gp. Prev: Clin. Asst. (Dermat.) Alton Gen. Hosp.; Regist. (Dermat.) Guy's Hosp. Lond.; Regist. (Cardiac.) Char. Cross Hosp. Lond.

BETHELL, Hugh William Lynch Department of Cardiology, Northwick Park Hospital, Watford Road, Harrow HA1 3UJ — MB BChir 1987 Camb.; FRCP 2001; MRCP (UK) 1990; PHD 1996. Cons. Cardiol. N.wick Pk. hosp. Socs: MRCP; FRCP. Prev: Sp Reg Cardiol.Ipswich hosp/PererBoro. hosp./Papworth hosp.

BETHELL, Jill The Health Centre, Dronfield, Sheffield S18 Tel: 01246 290882; Ramshaw Lodge, Unstone, Sheffield S18 4AL Tel: 01246 413276 — MB ChB 1967 Sheff.; DObst RCOG 1970. (Sheff.) Sen. Partner, Gen. Pract. Drs Bethell. Hawey & Sanders, Dronfield Health Centre. Prev: Matern. & Child Welf. Med. Off. Derbysh. CC.; SHO O & G Scarsdale Hosp. Chesterfield; Ho. Surg. & Ho. Phys. S.lands Hosp. Shoreham-by-Sea.

BETHELL, John Hugh 2 The Sands, Haddington EH41 3EY — MB ChB 1990 Aberd.

BETHELL, John Noble Ramshaw Lodge, Crow Lane, Unstone, Sheffield S18 5AL — MB ChB 1993 Aberd.

BETHELL, Martin John 107 Shortridge Terrace, Jesmond, Newcastle upon Tyne NE2 2JH — MB BS 1986 Newc.; MRCGP 1991; DTM Dub. 1992; DRCOG 1992.

BETHELL, Paul Anthony The Old Rectory, Cavendish, Sudbury CO10 8AZ — MB BS 1985 Lond.

BETHLEHEM, Adam Keynes Flat 3, 188 Willifield Way, London NW11 6YA — MB BCh 1985 Witwatersrand; BSc Lond. 1993.

BETHUNE, Arthur David (retired) Beechwood, 2 South Liddle St., Newcastleton TD9 0RN Tel: 013873 75406 — MB ChB Ed. 1945. Prev: Ho. Surg. Dumfries & Galloway Roy. Infirm. & Cresswell Cos. Matern.

BETHUNE, Claire Ann Department of Immunology, Royal Victoria Infirmary, Newcastle upon Tyne; 6 Wallace Terrace, Ryton NE40 3PL — MB BChir 1993 Camb.; MRCP UK 1995. p/t Specialist Regist. Immunol.

BETHUNE, Donald William, RD (retired) Brook House, 5 Newtown, Kimbolton, Huntingdon PE28 0HY Tel: 01480 860830 Email: bethune@5newtown.freeserve.co.uk — MB BS Durh. 1959; FFA RCS Eng. 1964. p/t Emerit. Cons. Anaesth. Cardiothoracic Surg. Unit Papworth Hosp. Papworth Everard; Emerit. Cons. Anaesth. Hinchingbrooke Hosp. Huntingdon; Emerit. Hon. Cons. Addenbrooke's Hosp. Camb. Prev: Sen. Regist. St. Bart. Hosp. Lond.

BETMOUNI, Mohamad Kheir 9 Studland Close, Aylesbury HP21 9UN; 9 Studland Close, Aylesbury HP21 9UN — MD 1965 Damascus.

BETMOUNI, Samar University Department of Pharmacology, Mansfield Road, Oxford OX1 3QT — MB BS 1989 Lond.; BSc Lond. 1986, MB BS 1989.

BETON, David Critchley (retired) 31 Ashford Road, Fulshaw Park, Wilmslow SK9 1QD Tel: 01625 584659 — MB ChB 1959 Manch.; BSc Manch. 1959; FRCR 1995; DMRD Eng. 1968. Prev: Cons. Radiol. Wythenshawe Hosp. & Withington Hosp. Manch.

BETON MCCULLOCH, Mary L Unity Medical Services Ltd., 552 Dereham Road, Norwich NR5 8TU Tel: 01603 250015 Fax: 01603 250747 — MB ChB 1962 Manch.; MFOM RCP (UK) 1981; DIH Eng. 1977. (Manch.) Cons. Occupat. Health Phys. Norwich; Med. Dir. Unity Med. Servs.; Med. Adviser Crane Fruehauf & Lotus Cars; Med. Adviser Norf. CC. Socs: Soc. Occupat. Med. Prev: Ho. Surg. (Thoracic Unit) & Ho. Phys. (Neurol.) Manch. Roy. Infirm.

BETT, Andrew James Old Farm, West Bourton, Gillingham SP8 5PF — MB BS 1991 Lond.

BETT, Caroline Joanne 30 Trinity Street, Taunton TA1 3JQ — MB BS 1992 Lond.

BETT, Mr Nicholas James 19 Bathgate Road, Wimbledon, London SW19 5PW — MS 1971 Lond.; MB BS Lond. 1971; MS Lond. 1982; FRCS Eng. 1976. (St. Geo.) Cons. Surg. St. Helier Hosp. Carshalton, Nelson Hosp. Lond., Pk.side Hosp. Wimbledon, St. Anthony's Hosp. N. Cheam & New Vict. Hosp. Kingston; Hon. Sen. Lect. St. Geo. Hosp. Med. Sch. Lond.; Hon. Cons. Roy. Marsden Hosp. Socs: Brit. Soc. Gastroenterol.; Pancreatic Soc.; Roy. Soc. Med.

BETTANY, George Edward Angus King George Hospital, Redbridge Healthcare, Barley Lane, Goddmayes, Ilford IG3 8YB Tel: 020 8983 8000 Ext: 8824 — MB BS 1987 Lond.; BSc Lond. 1984; MRCP (UK) 1992; MD Lond. 1996. (Lond. Hosp. Med. Coll.) Cons. Phys. & Gastroenterol., King Geo. Hosp., Illford, Essex. Prev: Specialist Regist. (Gastroenterol. & Gen. Med.) Broomfield Hosp., Chelmsford Essex; Specialist Regist. King Geoge Hosp. Ilford; Regist. (Gastroenterol & Gen. Med.) Roy. Lond. Hosp.

BETTERIDGE, Clare Louise Megan 12 Wicks House, Poplar High St., London E14 0BB — MB BS 1998 Lond.; MB BS Lond 1998.

BETTERIDGE, Professor Denis John Department of Medicine, University College London, 5th Floor Thorn Building, The Middlesex Hospital, Mortimer St., London W1T 3AA Tel: 020 7504 9443 Fax: 020 7504 9440 Email: jbetteridge@ucl.ac.uk; Willesley, Outdowns, Effingham, Leatherhead KT24 5QR Tel: 01483 283458 — MB BS 1972 Lond.; PhD Bath 1985; BSc (1st cl. Hons.) Lond. 1969, MD 1980; FRCP Lond. 1988; MRCP (UK) 1975. (King's College Hospital) Prof. Endocrinol. & Metab. Univ. Coll. Lond.; Hon. Cons. Phys. UCL Hosps. Trust; Hon. Cons. Phys. St. Luke's Hosp. for the Clergy. Socs: Assn. Phys.; Brit. Diabetic Assn. (Med. & Scientif. Sect.); (Ex-Chairm.) Brit. Hyperlipidaemia Assn. Prev: Sen. Regist. (Gen. Med. & Diabetes) Roy. United Hosp. Bath; Research Fell. (Brit. Diabetic Assn.) Dept. Lipids & Diabetes St. Bart. Hosp. Lond.; SHO (Med.) Hammersmith Hosp. Lond.

BETTERIDGE, Trevor John Sunnyside, Huish Episcopi, Langport TA10 9QT Tel: 01458 250720 — MB ChB 1957 Bristol; FRCPath 1982, M 1970; DCP Lond 1964. (Bristol) Socs: Internat. Acad. Path.; Brit. Soc. Clin. Cytol. Prev: Cons. Histopath. Security Forces Hosp. Riyadh, Saudi Arabia; Cons. Histopath. Roy. Cornw. Hosp. (Treslike) Truro & E. Som. NHS Trust Yeovil; Cons. Path. RAF Med. Br.

BETTERTON, Brian Walter 3 Belgrave Road, Minster, Sheerness ME12 3EA Tel: 01795 663943 — MRCS Eng. LRCP Lond. 1951.

BETTERTON, Michael James The Health Centre, Byland Road, Skelton-in-Cleveland, Saltburn-by-the-Sea TS12 2NN Tel: 01287 650430 Fax: 01287 651268; York House, 9 South Tce, Skelton, Saltburn TS12 2EW Tel: 01287 651897 — MB BChir 1979 Camb.; BA Hons. (Physiol. Scs.) Oxf. 1977; MRCGP 1984; DA (UK) 1985; DRCOG 1983. GP Princip. Socs: Bd. Mem. Langburgh PCT. Prev: SHO (Anaesth.) ScarBoro. Gen. Hosp.; Trainee GP ScarBoro. VTS; SHO (Orthop.) Norf. & Norwich Hosp.

BETTINSON, Henry Verden 127 High Street, Sawston, Cambridge CB2 4HJ — MB BS 1994 Lond.; MA Camb. 1995, BA 1991; MRCP (UK) 1998. (Lond. Hosp. Med. Coll.) Specialist Regist. (Respirat. & Gen. Med.), N. Thames Region, Roy. Lond. Hosp. Prev: SHO Rotat. Guy's Hosp. Lond.; SHO, ICU, Guy's Hosp., Lond.; SHO (Respirat.), Roy. Brompton Hosp., Lond.

BETTLE, Vernon Selby Tel: 01206 01206 Fax: 01206 231602; Backwaters, Bargate Lane, Dedham, Colchester CO7 6BN — MB BS 1986 Lond.; DCH RCP Lond. 1990. (Westminster) Gen. Practitioner, Ardleigh; Hosp. Pratitioner in Cardiol., Colchester Gen. Hosp. Prev: GP Felixstowe; Trainee GP Colchester VTS; Ho. Off. W.m. Hosp. Lond.

BETTRIDGE, Robert Frank Morden Hall Medical Centre, 256 Morden Road, London SW19 3DA Tel: 020 8540 0585 Fax: 020 8542 4480; 110 Graham Road, London SW19 3SS Tel: 020 8540 6298 — MB BS 1974 Lond.

BETTS, Alan Frederick Newtown Surgery, 147 Lawn Avenue, Great Yarmouth NR30 1QP Tel: 01493 853191 Fax: 01493 331861 — MB ChB 1973 Birm.

BETTS, Mr Christopher David 21 St John Street, Manchester M3 4DT Tel: 0161 834 4072; 4 Madeley Close, Hale, Altrincham WA14 3NJ — MB ChB 1981 Dundee; FRCS Ed. 1986; FRCS (Urol.) 1995; FEBU 1997. Cons. Urol. Hope Hosp. Salford. Prev: Sen. Regist. (Urol.) Chesh.; Research Regist. (Neurol.) Nat. Hosp. & The Lond. Hosp.; Regist. (Urol.) Lond. Hosp.

BETTS, Mr Jeffrey Woodrow (retired) 19 Eastgate, Lincoln LN2 4AA Tel: 01522 523615 — MB BS Lond. 1947; FRCS Eng. 1949; MRCS Eng. LRCP Lond. 1943. Prev: Cons. Surg. Lincoln Co. Hosp. & John Coupland Hosp. GainsBoro.

BETTS, Mr John Athelstan 15 North Avenue, Gosforth, Newcastle upon Tyne NE3 4DT — MB BS Lond. 1966; BSc Lond. 1963; FRCS Eng. 1971; MRCS Eng. LRCP Lond. 1966; Cert of

Accreditation of Specialist in 1978. (Univ. Coll. Hosp.) Prev: Cons. Orthop. Surg. Qu. Eliz. Hosp. Gateshead.

BETTS, John Bowring Bradworthy Surgery, The Square, Bradworthy, Holsworthy EX22 7SY Tel: 01409 241215 Fax: 01409 241086; Lower Chollaton, Abbots Bickington, Holsworthy EX22 7LG Tel: 01409 261579 — MB BS 1966 Lond.; MRCP (UK) 1971; MRCS Eng. LRCP Lond. 1966. (St. Thos.) Prev: Sen. Regist. (Med. Research) Roy. Devon & Exeter Hosp.; Regist. (Med.) Leic. Roy. Infirm.; Ho. Phys. & Ho. Surg. St. Mary's Hosp. Portsmouth.

BETTS, John Crowther 32 Grove Avenue, Muswell Hill, London N10 2AR Tel: 020 8883 7413 Fax: 020 8245 6338 Email: dr@browser.demon.co.uk — MB BS 1951 Lond.; MRCS Eng. LRCP Lond. 1950; MRCGP 1967. (Lond. Hosp.) Approved Examr. Off-shore Divers; Cons. Brit. Sub-Aqua Club Med. Comms.; Med. Ref. for UK Sport Diving Comm. Prev: Civil Serv. Local Med. Off.

BETTS, June Hampton Wick Surgery, 1 Upper Teddington Road, Kingston upon Thames KT1 4DL Tel: 020 8977 2638 Fax: 020 8977 2434; Bambatuk, Christ Church Mount, Epsom KT19 8LU Tel: 01372 812428 — MB BS 1973 Lond.; MRCOG 1979.

BETTS, Margaret Teresa (O'Donovan) Southampton General Hospital, Tremona Road, Southampton SO16; Tel: 023 8028 3084 — MB ChB 1991 Birm.; FRCR; MRCP. Specialist Regist., Clin. Radiol., Soton. Socs: RCP; Roy. Coll. of Radiol.

BETTS, Maurice Ernest Doctors Mess, County Hospital, Union Walk, Hereford HR1 2ER — MB ChB 1993 Aberd.

BETTS, Nicola Elaine 11 Barncroft Close, Tangmere, Chichester PO20 6FE — MB BS 1992 Lond.; BSc (1st cl. Hons.) Psychol. & Basic Med. Sci. Lond. 1989. (St. Mary's Hosp. Med. Sch. Lond.) GP Regist. Felpham & Middleton Health Centre Bognor Regis.

BETTS, Mr Norman Bowring (retired) Cleverdon House, Bradworthy, Holsworthy EX22 7TZ — MB BChir Camb. 1937; FRCS Ed. 1938; MRCS Eng. LRCP Lond. 1933. Prev: Ho. Surg. & Res. Med. Off. Roy. Surrey Co. Hosp. Guildford.

BETTS, Peter Rider Southampton General Hospital, Tremona Road, Southampton SO16 6YD Tel: 02380 796985 Fax: 02380 794750 Email: p.betts@soton.ac.uk — MB BS 1966 Lond.; MD Lond. 1977; FRCP Lond. 1984; FRCPCH (1997); MRCP (UK) 1970; MRCS Eng. LRCP Lond. 1966; DObst RCOG 1968. (Lond. Hosp.) Cons. Paediat. & Paediat. Endocrinol. Soton. Gen. Hosp.; Hon. Sen. Lect. (Child Health) Univ. Soton. Socs: Brit. Soc. Paediat. Endocrinol.; Fell. Roy. Coll. Paediat. & Child Health; Fell. Roy. Coll. Of Phyisicians.

BETTS, Russell John 12 Champneys Close, SM2 7AL — MB BS 1997 Lond.

BETTS, Timothy Arnold Birmingham University Seizure Clinic, Queen Elizabeth Psychiatric Hospital, Mindelsohn Way, Birmingham B15 2QZ Tel: 0121 678 2366 Fax: 0121 678 2079 Email: t.a.betts@bham.ac.uk — MB ChB Birm. 1963; FRCPsych 1986, M 1972; DPM Eng. 1967. (Birm.) Reader (psych) Univ. Birm.; Hon. Med. Adviser Brit. Epilepsy Assn.; Edr.-in-Chief Seizure; Hon. Cons. (Neuropsych), S. Birm. Ment. Health Trust. Socs: Internat. League Against Epilepsy (Pres. Brit. Br.). Prev: Sen. Lect. (Psychiat.) Univ. Birm.

BETTS, Timothy Rider Wessex Cardiothoracic Centre, Mailpoint 46, Southampton General Hospital, Tremona Road, Southampton SO16 6YD; The Loft House, Packridge Farm, Packridge Lane, Toothill, Romsey SO51 9LL — MB ChB 1991 Birm.; MRCP (UK) 1994. Specialist Regist. (Cardiol.) Wessex Rotat.

BETTS-BROWN, Andrew Kents Hill Road Family Doctors, 411 Kents Hill Road North, Benfleet SS7 4AD Tel: 01268 753591 Fax: 01268 794585; 7 Hart Road, Thundersley, Benfleet SS7 3PA Tel: 01268 566580 — BM BCh 1970 Oxf.; MA Oxf. 1972, BM BCh 1970. (Oxf. & Lond. Hosp.) Prev: Ho. Off. (Paediat.) United Oxf. Hosps.; Ho. Surg. Friarage Hosp. N.allerton; Trainee GP Edin. & Fife VTS.

BEUKES, Abraham Johannes 21 Cavendish Close, St John Wood, London NW8 9JB — MB ChB 1992 Stellenbosch.

BEUMELBURG, Neil James c/o B. Beumelburg, Flat A, 100 Gleneldon Road, Streatham, London SW16 2BZ — MB ChB 1991 Otago.

BEUZEN, Jean-Noel Lilly Research Centre Ltd, Erlwood Manor, Windlesham GU20 6PH — MD 1979 Caen.

BEVAN, Alan Bailey Annandale Surgery, 239 Mutton Lane, Potters Bar EN6 2AS Tel: 01707 644451; 42 Ladbrooke Drive, Potters Bar EN6 1QR Tel: 01707 42745 Fax: 01707 852316 Email: alanbevan@compuserve.co — MB BS 1970 Lond.; DA Eng. 1974. (Univ. Coll. Lond.) Clin. Asst. (Anaesth.) Barnet Gen. Hosp.; Chairm. Med. Staff Potters Bar Hosp.; Mem. GP's Asthma Gp. Socs: Primary Care Gp. Brit. Computer Soc.

BEVAN, Allen Trevor (retired) 17 West Lodge Road, Colchester CO3 3NL Tel: 01206 579480 — MB ChB (Hnrs.) Birm. 1957; FRCP Lond. 1977, M 1964; DObst RCOG 1960. Prev: Cons. Phys. Colchester & Dist. Hosp. Gp.

BEVAN, Ann St Bartholomew's Medical Centre, Manzil Way, Cowley Road, Cowley, Oxford OX4 1XB Tel: 01865 242334 Fax: 01865 204018 — BM BCh 1985 Oxf.; PhD Camb. 1980; BSc Biochem. Lond. 1976; MRCGP 1990. (Oxf.)

BEVAN, Catherine Anna Is-Yr-Allt, Pwll Glas, Mold CH7 1RA; 19 Littlebury Road, Clapham, London SW4 6DW Tel: 020 7627 3571 — MB BS 1991 Lond.; MRCP. (London Hospital Medical College) Specialist Regist. (Paediat.) S. Thames.

BEVAN, Cathryn Jane Kingsway Surgery, 37 The Kingsway, Swansea SA1 5LF Tel: 01792 650716 Fax: 01792 456902 — MB BCh 1991 Wales; MRCGO 1995. Socs: BMA & Med. Defence Union. Prev: Trainee GP Kingsway Surg. Swansea; SHO Neath Gen. Hosp. VTS.

BEVAN, Catrin Ann Richmonds in the Wood, Forest Road, Ascot SL5 8QU; Gardden, Dolgellau LL40 1UE Tel: 01341 423357 — MB BS 1985 Lond.; DRCOG 1987.

BEVAN, Christopher Martin Fairfield Park Health Centre, Tyning Lane, Camden Road, Bath BA1 6EA Tel: 01225 331616 Fax: 01225 482932 — MB ChB 1985 Bristol; MRCGP 1990; T(GP) 1991; DRCOG 1988. (Bristol)

BEVAN, Clifford John 2 Further Meadow, Chelmsford CM1 3LE — MB ChB 1993 Bristol.

BEVAN, Mr Colin David Department of Obstetrics and Gynaecology, Weston General Hospital, Weston Super Mare BS22 4TQ Tel: 01934 647081 Fax: 01934 647220 Email: colin.bevan@what.swest.nhs.uk — MB BS 1981 Lond.; MRCOG 1988. Cons. (O & G) W.on Gen. Hosp.; Cons (O&G) St Michaels Hosp. Bristol.

BEVAN, David Carus Peploe Hardwicke House Surgery, Hardwicke House, Stour Street, Sudbury CO10 2AY — MB BS 1976 Lond.; MRCS Eng. LRCP Lond. 1976; DRCOG 1980. Prev: Clin. Asst. Walnut Tree Hosp. Sudbury.

BEVAN, David Huw 29 Grandison Road, Battersea, London SW11 6LS Tel: 020 7223 0803 Email: dbevan@sghms.ac.uk — MB BS 1973 Newc.; FRCP Lond. 1995; MRCP (UK) 1976; FRCPath 1995, M 1983. (Newc.) Sen. Lect. & Hon. Cons. Haemat. St. Geo. Hosp. Med. Sch. Lond. Socs: Brit. Soc. Haematol. Prev: Regist. (Gen. Med.) Darlington Memor. Hosp.; Lect. & Hon. Sen. Regist. (Haemat.) St. Geo. Med. Sch. Lond.

BEVAN, David Rhys Tel: 01945 773671 Fax: 01945 773152; Tel: 01353 612324 — MB BS 1980 Lond.; MRCPG 1984; Dip. IMC RCS Ed. 1990; DRCOG 1984.

BEVAN, Mr Geoffrey Herbert (retired) 1 Mill Brae, Stanley, Perth PH1 4PE Tel: 01738 828526 — MB BS Lond. 1953; FRCS Ed. 1966; DO Eng. 1961. Prev: Cons. Ophth. Newc. Gen. Hosp.

BEVAN, Gerald Beech House, Shenley Hill, Radlett WD7 7BD — MB BS 1957 Lond.; FRCP Lond. 1980, M 1965; MRCS Eng. LRCP Lond. 1957; DObst RCOG 1959; DTM & H Eng. 1960. (King's Coll. Hosp.) Phys. and Gastroenterologist, Garden Hosp., Hendon, Lond.; Phys. and Gastroenterologist, BUPA Hosp., Bushey, Herts. Socs: Brit. Soc. Gastroenterol.; Amer. Gastroenterol. Assn. Prev: Cons. Phys. Edgware Gen. Hosp.; Asst. Prof. of Med. Univ. Calif. Los Angeles, U.S.A.; Asst.Prof of Med.Uni.Rochester, N.Y.USA.

BEVAN, Gillian Patricia Blue Bell Lane Surgery, 2 Blue Bell Lane, Huyton, Liverpool L36 7TN Tel: 0151 489 1422 — MB ChB 1979 Manch.; MRCP (UK) 1984.

BEVAN, James Stuart 6A Palace Gate, London W8 5NF Tel: 0207 589 2478 Fax: 0207 584 4595 Email: palace.gate@virgin.net; 9 Hill Road, London NW8 9QE Tel: 0207 286 8340 Fax: 0207 289 5822 — MB BChir Camb. 1955; MRCGP 1964; DObst RCOG 1960. (St. Mary's and Camb.) Sen. Med. Cons. Automobile Assn. Prev: Ho. Phys. (Med.) Supt. & Ho. Phys. (Neurol., Dermat, & VD) St. Mary's Hosp. Lond.; Jun. Specialist in Med. RAMC.

BEVAN, Jeremy Robert David Wistaton Mill, Nantwich Road, Crewe CW2 6PW — MB ChB 1984 Dundee.

BEVAN, John Clayson Lon Teify Medical Centre, 4 Lon Teify, Cockett, Swansea SA2 0YB Tel: 01792 202700 — MB BCh 1976 Wales; Cert JCC Lond. 1977. SHO (O & G) Liverp. Matern. Hosp. & Roy. Liverp. Hosp. Socs: BMA. Prev: SHO (Paediat.) Neath Gen. Hosp.; Ho. Surg. (Gen. Surg.) & Cas. Off. Singleton Hosp. Swansea; Ho. Phys. (Gen. Med.) Morriston Hosp. Swansea.

BEVAN, John Richard High Firs House, Hatch Lane, Liss Gu33 7NJ Tel: 01730 893343 Fax: 01730 890212 Email: jhnbev@aol.co.uk — MB BS 1969 Lond.; MRCS Eng. LRCP Lond. 1969; FRCOG 1988, M 1975; DCH Eng. 1979. (St. Thos.) Cons. St. Mary's Hosp. Portsmouth; Med. Dir. Portsmouth NHS Trust. Prev: Sen. Regist. Qu. Charlotte's Hosp. Lond.; Lect. Guy's Hosp. Lond.; Regist. St. Mary's Hosp. Portsmouth.

BEVAN, John Stuart Department of Endocrinology (Wards 27/28), Aberdeen Royal Infirmary, Foresterhill, Aberdeen AB25 2ZN Tel: 01224 554437 Fax: 01224 551186 Email: j.s.bevan@arh.grampian.scot.nhs.uk; The Mearns, Station Road, Milltimber, Aberdeen AB13 0DP Tel: 01224 732937 — MB ChB 1978 Ed.; MB ChB (Hons.) Ed. 1978; BSc (Hons.) Ed. 1975, MD Ed. 1987; FRCP Ed. 1993. Cons. Phys. & Endocrinol. Aberd. Roy. Infirm.; Hon. Sen. Lect. (Clin.) Univ. Aberd. Med. Sch.; Assoc. Edr. Clin. Endocrinol; SAC Mem. (DM & Endocrinol.). Socs: Eur. Neuroendocrine Assn.; Endocrine Soc.; Soc. Endocrinol. (Mem. Clin. Comm.). Prev: Sen. Regist. (Med. & Endocrinol.) Univ. Hosp. Wales Cardiff; MRC Train. Fell. Radcliffe Infirm. Oxf.; Regist. (Endocrinol. & Diabetes) Radcliffe Infirm. Oxf.

BEVAN, Jonathan David 37 Adderstone Crescent, Newcastle upon Tyne NE2 2HS — MB BS 1998 Lond.; MB BS Lond 1998.

BEVAN, Jonathan Morgan Spinney Brook Health Centre, 59 High Street, Irthlingborough, Wellingborough NN9 5GA Tel: 01933 650593 Fax: 01933 653641; Brecon House, Lower St, Great Addington, Kettering NN14 4BL Tel: 0153 678371 Fax: 0153 678371 — MB ChB 1981 Birm.; MRCGP 1985; DRCOG 1985. Prev: Trainee GP Kettering Gen. Hosp. VTS.

BEVAN, Josephine Clare (retired) 17 West Lodge Road, Colchester CO3 3NL Tel: 01206 579480 — MB ChB 1957 Birm.; FFA RCS Eng. 1971; DA Eng. 1967. Prev: Cons. Anaesth. Basildon Hosp. & St. And. Hosp. Billericay.

BEVAN, Katherine Emma 22 Constantine Road, London NW3 2NG — MB BS 1998 Lond.; MB BS Lond 1998.

BEVAN, Keith William Horsefair Practice, Horse Fair, Rugeley WS15 2EL Tel: 01889 582244 Fax: 01899 582244; Hyross, 154 Hednesford Road, Rugeley WS15 1JT Tel: 01889 576288 — MB ChB 1970 Sheff. Socs: BMA. Prev: Ho. Phys., Ho. Surg. & SHO (O & G) Scunthorpe Gen. Hosp.

BEVAN, Mr Kemal Crawley Hospital, West Green Drive, Crawley RH11 7DH Tel: 01293 600300 Fax: 01293 600341 Email: kembevan@aol.co.uk — MB BS 1977 Lond.; ChM Bristol 1990; FRCS Ed. 1985. (Royal London) Cons. (OtorhinoLaryngol.) Surrey & Sussex Health Trust. Socs: Roy. Soc. Med.; BMA; Europ. Acad. of Facial & Plastic Surg. Prev: Sen. Regist. (ENT Surg.) SW RHA Bristol & Wessex RHA; Hon. Sen. Regist. (ENT) SW RHA Bristol & Wessex.

BEVAN, Martin Anthony 3 Ryder St, Pontcanna, Cardiff CF11 9BS — MB BCh 1991 Wales; BSc (Med. Biochem.) Wales 1988; MRCP (UK) 1994. Cons. (Rheum.) Univ. Bro Morgannwg NHS Trust Wales. Socs: Hon. Sec., Welsh Soc. For Hist. Of Med.

BEVAN, Paul William Wellington Medical Centre, Bulford, Wellington TA21 8PW Tel: 01823 663551 Fax: 01823 660650; The Old School House, Bradford on Tone, Taunton TA4 1HG Tel: 01823 461572 — MB BS 1981 Lond.; MRCGP 1985; DRCOG 1984. (Lond. Hosp.)

BEVAN, Penelope Jane London Regional Office, 40 Eastbourne Terrace, London W2 3QR Tel: 020 7725 5460 Fax: 020 7725 5393; 18 Vallance Road, London N22 7UB — MB ChB 1978 Liverp.; FFPHM RCP (UK) 1995, M 1989; MPH Leeds 1987. Dep. Dir. of Pub. Health Lond. Regional Off. Socs: Roy. Soc. Med. Prev: Dir. Pub. Health Merton Sutton & Wandsworth HA; Dir. Health Strategy Hillingdon HA; Cons. Pub. Health Med. SE Lond. & Tower Hamlets HA.

BEVAN, Professor Peter Gilroy, CBE Birmingham Medical Institute, 36 Harborne Rd, Edgbaston, Birmingham B15 3AF Tel: 0121 454 5007 Fax: 0121 454 8050; 10 Russell Road, Moseley, Birmingham B13 8RD Tel: 0121 449 3055 Fax: 0121 449 3055 — MB ChB Birm. 1946; ChM Birm. 1958; FRCS Eng. 1952; Hon. FRCSI 1984; MRCS Eng. LRCP Lond. 1946. (Birmingham) Pres. Birm. Med. Inst. Socs: Fell. Assn. Surgs.; W Midl.s Surg. Soc.; Sands Cox Soc. Prev: Emerit. Prof. Surg. & Postgrad. Med. Educ. Univ. Birm.; Vice-Pres. RCS Eng.; Pres. Assn. Surgs. GB & Irel.

BEVAN, Philip Charles Department of Haematology, St Richard's Hospital, The Royal West Sussex Trust, Spitalfield Lane, Chichester PO19 4SE Tel: 01243 831651 Fax: 01243 831413 Email: phil.bevan@rws-tr.sthames.nhs.uk — MB BS 1976 Newc.; FRCP Lond. 1995; MRCP (UK) 1979; FRCPath 1994, M 1982. (Newcastle upon Tyne) Cons. Haematologist St. Richard's Hosp. Chichester. Prev: Research Assoc. & Hon. Sen. Regist. (Haemat. Med.) Univ. Camb. Addennbrooke's Hosp. Camb.; Regist. (Med. & Haemat.) Roy. Vict. Infirm. Newc.

BEVAN, Robert George Beckford (retired) 47 Marshfield Road, Chippenham SN15 1JU Tel: 01249 4466 — MB ChB 1951 St. And. Prev: Med. Off. Brit. Solomon Is.s.

BEVAN, Rosalind Anne Ty Poeth Farm, Usk Road, Pontypool NP4 8QU Tel: 01495 763801 — MB BS 1961 Durh. (Durh.) Assoc. Specialist Psychiat. Pen-y-Fal Hosp. Abergavenny. Prev: Med. Asst. St. Cadocs Hosp. Caerleon; GP Cockermouth; Ho. Surg. Roy. Vict. Infirm. Newc.

BEVAN, Rowena Kay Hammersmith Hospital, Du Cane Road, London W12 0HS; 8B Moorhouse Road, London W2 5DJ — BChir 1988 Camb.; MD Camb. 1994; MRCOG 1994. Sen. Regist. (Reproduc. Med.) Hammersmith Hosp. Lond.

BEVAN, Sally Ann St Brannocks Road Medical Centre, St. Brannocks Road, Ilfracombe EX34 8EG — MB ChB 1985 Bristol; DRCOG 1990; Cert. Family Plann. JCC 1989; DA (UK) 1987.

BEVAN, Sally Joy Delamere Street Health Centre, 45 Delamere Street, Crewe CW1 2ER Tel: 01270 214046; Wistaston Mill, Nantwich Road, Wistaston, Crewe CW2 6PW Tel: 01270 669399 — MB ChB 1982 Liverp.; DRCOG 1986; MRCGP 1988.

BEVAN, Susan Fiona, Capt. RAMC Retd. Bulby Hall, Bulby, Bourne PE10 0RU Tel: 01778 591382 Fax: 01778 591382 Email: 101364.1442@compuserve.com — MB BChir 1983 Camb.; BA Camb. 1981; MRCGP 1990; DRCOG 1988. (Univ. Camb.) Socs: BMA; Brit. Assn. Sport & Med. Prev: Trainee GP Papworth; SHO (ENT, Ophth. & A & E) Hinchingbrooke Hosp.

BEVAN, William John High Street Surgery, High Street, Pelsall, Walsall WS3 4LX Tel: 01922 682450 Fax: 01922 682644 — MB BChir 1981 Camb.; MA Camb. 1984, MB BChir 1981; MRCGP 1986; DRCOG 1984. (St. Thos.)

BEVAN-JONES, Arthur Bruce Holly House, 28 Bellhouse Crescent, Leigh-on-Sea SS9 4PT Tel: 01702 529966 — MB BChir 1968 Camb.; MA, MB Camb. 1968, BChir 1967; MRCS Eng. LRCP Lond. 1966; MRCPsych 1972; DPM Eng. 1971. (Camb. & Guy's) Cons. Psychiat. S.end-on-Sea Child Guid. Clinic & S.end Hosp. Socs: BMA & Assn. Psychiat. Study Adolesc. Prev: Cons. Psychiat. & Med. Dir. Mid. Essex Child Guid. Clinic Chelmsford & Essex Hosp.; Sen. Regist. Bethlem Roy. & Maudsley Hosps. Lond.; Regist. (Psychiat.) St. Bart. Hosp. Lond.

BEVAN JONES, Huw (retired) Pantycrauddyn, Prengwyn, Llandysul SA44 4EH — MB BS 1957 Lond.; FRCP Ed. 1981 M 1966; MRCS Eng. LRCP Lond. 1957; FRCPsych 1989, M 1972; DPM Ed. 1973; DTM & H Eng. 1963. Prev: Cons. Psychiat. St. David's Hosp. Carmarthen.

BEVAN JONES, Tessa Mair Westbourne Medical Centre, Milburn Road, Westbourne, Bournemouth BH4 9HJ Tel: 01202 752550 Fax: 01202 769700 — MB BS 1982 Lond.; DRCOG 1985; MRCGP 1986; Cert Family Planning 1985 JCC; MRCGP 1986; Cert. Family Plann. JCC 1985; DRCOG 1985. (St. Bart.) Gen. Pract. Prev: Asst. GP St. Jas. Surg. Bath; Hon. Lect. Aldermoor Health Centre Soton.; Trainee GP Jubilee Surg. Tichfield.

BEVAN-MOGG, Karen Jane Kame House, Back Lane, North Perrott, Crewkerne TA18 7SP — MB ChB 1996 Liverp.

BEVAN-THOMAS, Mary-Ann Margaret Cosham Health Centre, Vectis Way, Portsmouth PO6 3AW Tel: 023 9221 0200 Fax: 023 9223 0316; Flint Lodge, Lavant, Chichester PO18 0BH — MB BS 1958 Lond.; MRCS Eng. LRCP Lond. 1958; DRCOG 1979; DA Eng. 1960. (Roy. Free)

BEVEN, Paul Geoffrey Hassan 24 Avenue Elmers, Surbiton KT6 4SE Tel: 020 8399 1372 Fax: 020 8399 2287 — MB BS Lond. 1981; MRCGP 1988; DCH RCP Lond. 1988; DA (UK) 1987; DRCOG 1986.

BEVERIDGE, Alan James 53 The Spinnings, Waterside Road, Summer Seat, Bury BL9 5QW — MB ChB 1989 Glas.; BSc (Hons. Path.) Glas. 1987; FRCS Glas. 1994. Specialist Reg. (Surg.) NW Region (N. Manch. Gen. Hosp.). Prev: SHO (Gen. Surg.) Stirling Roy. Infirm.; Research Fell. W.. Infirm Glas.; SHO (Gen. Surg.) CrossHo. Hosp. Ayrsh.

BEVERIDGE, Brian Francis (retired) 8 The Charter Road, Woodford Green IG8 9QU Tel: 020 8504 2301 Fax: 020 8504 2301 — MB BCh BAO NUI 1958; FRCS Ed. 1970; FRCOphth 1988; DO Eng. 1967. Ophth. Med. Pract. Woodford Green & Colchester. Prev: Cons. Ophth. Holly Hse. Hosp. Buckhurst Hill BUPA Roding Hosp. Redbridge & BUPA Hartswood Hosp.

BEVERIDGE, Carolyn Janette University Department of Radiology, Royal Victoria Infirmary, Newcastle upon Tyne NE1 4LP Email: c.j.beveridge@ncl.ac.uk; 42B St. George's Terrace, Jesmond, Newcastle upon Tyne NE2 2SY — MB ChB 1987 Ed.; MA Camb. 1988, BA 1984; MRCP (UK) 1991; FRCR 1995. 1st Asst. (Diagnostic Radiol.) Univ. of Newc. Prev: Sen. Regist. (Diagnostic Radiol.) NRHA; Regist. (Diag. Radiol.) N.. RHA; SHO Rotat. (Med.) City Hosp. & Roy. Infirm. Edin.

BEVERIDGE, Emma Jane Western Infirmary, Dumbarton Road, Glasgow G11 6NT Tel: 0141 211 2000; 27B Hughenden Gardens, Glasgow G12 9XZ — MB ChB 1988 Aberd.; MRCP (UK) 1995; MRCGP 1992; DRCOG 1991. Specialist Regist. (Radiol.) W.. Infirm. Glas. Prev: Staff Grade (Gen. Med. & Geriat.) Lorn & Is.s Dist. Gen. Hosp. Oban; SHO (Gen. Med. & Med.) Co. Hosp. Oban Argyll; SHO (Cas. & O & G) Vale of Leven Hosp. Alexandria.

BEVERIDGE, George William (retired) 8 Barnton Park View, Edinburgh EH4 6HJ Tel: 0131 336 3680 — MB ChB 1956 Ed.; FRCP Ed. 1970, M 1961. Prev: Ho. Surg. Deaconess Hosp. Edin.

BEVERIDGE, Iain George St. Mary's Hosp., Prade Street, Paddington, London W2 1NY — MB BChir 1991 Camb.; MRCP UK 1994.

BEVERIDGE, James (retired) 58 Garrick Grove, Old Catton, Norwich NR6 7AN Tel: 01603 408990 — MB BS 1953 Durh.

BEVERIDGE, Jane Margaret (retired) 58 Garrick Green, Old Catton, Norwich NR6 7AN Tel: 01603 408990 — MB BS 1953 Durh. JP.

BEVERIDGE, Janice Buchan Shielhill House, Forfar DD8 3TT Tel: 0130 786209 — MB ChB 1971 St. And.

BEVERIDGE, Keith (retired) 1 Cragside, Sedgefield, Stockton-on-Tees TS21 2DU Tel: 01740 620725 — MB BS 1956 Durh.

BEVERIDGE, Margaret Edith (retired) Seaton Cottage, Bridge of Don, Aberdeen AB22 8LS Tel: 01224 703232 — MB ChB 1955 Aberd.; FFA RCS Eng. 1967; DA Eng. 1959. Prev: Sen. Regist. (Anaesth.) Aberd. Gen. Hosp. Gp.

BEVERIDGE, Robert David London Road Medical Practice, 12 London Road, Kilmarnock KA3 7AD Tel: 01563 523593 Fax: 01563 573552; 6 Charles Place, Kilmarnock KA1 2DY Tel: 01563 535330 — MB ChB 1983 Aberd.; Cert. Family Plann. JCC 1987; DRCOG 1987. Med. Ho. Off. (Occupat. Health) N. Ayshire Counc. & N. Ayrsh. Trust. Socs: SOM.

BEVERIDGE, Shona 10 Street Andrews Court, Jopps Lane, Aberdeen AB25 1BZ — MB ChB 1998 Aberd.; MB ChB Aberd 1998.

BEVERIDGE, Viven Lesley Hereward Medical Centre, Exeter Street, Bourne PE10 9NJ Tel: 01778 394188 Fax: 01778 393966; 113 North Road, Bourne PE10 9BU — MB ChB 1977 Liverp.; MRCGP 1981; DRCOG 1980.

BEVERLAND, Mr David Edward Musgrave Park Hospital, Belfast BT9 7JB Tel: 01232 669501 Fax: 01232 663222 Email: david.beverland@greenlark.n-i.nhs.uk — MD 1985 Belf.; MB BCh BAO 1978; FRCS Ed. 1982. Cons. Orthop. Surg. Musgrave Hosp. Belf.

BEVERLEY, David William York District Hospital, Wigginton Road, York YO31 8HE Tel: 01904 453735 Fax: 01904 453995 Email: david.w.beverley@excha.yhs-tr.northy.nhs.uk; Ashville Farm House, Main St, Rufforth, York YO23 3QF — MB ChB 1976 Birm.; MA Camb. 1977, BA 1973; FRCP Lond. 1994; MRCP (UK) 1979; FRCPCH 1997. Cons. Paediat. York Dist. Hosp. Prev: Sen. Regist. (Paediat.) Leeds Gen. Infirm.; Regist. (Paediat.) Birm. Childr. Hosp.; Perinatal Research Fell. Lond. Ontario, Canada.

BEVERLEY, Elisabeth Ann 4 Compton Manor, Compton, Newbury RG20 6NJ Tel: 01635 579095 — MB BS Lond. 1969. (Univ. Coll. Hosp.) Clin. Asst. (Genitourin. Med.) Homerton Hosp. Lond. Prev: Clin. Research Asst. ICR Fund; Clin. Asst. (Genitourin. Med.) Homerton Hosp. Lond.; Clin. Asst. (Colposcopy) Whittington Hosp. Lond.

BEVERLY, Mr Michael Christopher Ealing Hospital, Uxbridge Road, Southall UB1 3HW Tel: 020 8967 5407 Fax: 020 8940 0736 Email: orthomcbeverly@ukonline.co.uk; Cromwell Hospital, Cromwell Road, London SW5 0TU Tel: 020 8332 1996 Fax: 020 8940 0736 — MB BS 1976 Lond.; FRCS (Orth.) 1989; FRCS Eng. 1981; MRCS Eng. LRCP Lond. 1975; DCH Eng. 1979; DRCOG 1979. (St. Mary's) Cons. Orthop. Surg. Ealing Hosp. S.all; Hon. Cons. Orthop. Surg. Char. Cross Hosp. Socs: Fell. BOA; RSM. Prev: Sen. Regist. (Orthop.) Hammersmith Hosp. Lond.

BEVERTON, Martin James Pall Mall Surgery, 178 Pall Mall, Leigh-on-Sea SS9 1RB Tel: 01702 478338 Fax: 01702 471294; 12 Clatterfield Gardens, Westcliff on Sea SS0 0AX — MB BS 1980 Lond.; BSc (Hons.) Lond. 1977; MRCGP 1984.

BEVIN, Sheila Vivien Department Child Health, Level G, Centre Block, Southampton General Hospital, Tremona Road, Southampton SO16 6XY Tel: 02380 777222 Fax: 02380 794962; Woodside, Westwood Road, Lyndhurst SO43 7EH — MB ChB 1984 Birm.; MRCP (UK) 1989; DCH RCP Lond. 1986. Staff Grade (Paediat. Oncol.); Clin. Asst. (Paediat. Oncol.) Soton. Gen. Hosp. Prev: Regist. & Clin. Research Fell. (Paediat.) Soton. Gen. Hosp.; Regist. (Paediat.) Poole Gen. Hosp.; SHO (Paediat.) Nottm. City Hosp.

BEVINGTON, David Jeffrey Shelton Hospital, Bicton Heath, Shrewsbury SY3 8DN — MB 1968 Camb.; BChir 1967; MRCPsych 1972; DPM Eng. 1970. (Camb. & Middlx.) Cons. Psychiat. Shelton Hosp. Shrewsbury. Prev: Sen. Regist. Warneford Hosp. Oxf.; Regist. De La Pole Hosp. Willerby; SHO Shenley Hosp.

BEVINGTON, Richard Loder Shelley Flat 7, 47 Sutherland Avenue, London W9 2HF — MB BS 1992 Lond.

BEVINGTON, William Page Woodbridge Hill Surgery, 1 Deerbarn Road, Guildford GU2 8YB Tel: 01483 562230 Fax: 01483 301 132; Hill Cottage, Oakdene Road, Godalming GU7 1QF Tel: 01483 422895 Fax: 01483 422166 Email: wbevington@aol.com — MB BS 1970 Lond.; Dobst RCOG 1972; FRCGP 1992; MRCGP 1977. (Middlx.) RCGP Educat. Adviser to Kent, Surrey & Sussex GP Deanery.; Clin. Gov. Lead, Guildford PCG. Socs: BMA; Chairm., SW. Thames Fac. of the RCGP. Prev: GP Loddon Norf.; SHO Jenny Lind Hosp. Childr. Norwich; SHO (O & G) Norf. & Norwich Hosp.

BEVINGTON, William Robert Pendrice Eryl Surgery, Eryl, Station Road, Llantwit Major CF61 1ST Tel: 01446 793444 Fax: 01446 793115; 3 Orchard Close, Sigingstone, Cowbridge CF71 7LY Tel: 01446 773511 — MB ChB 1967 Bristol. (Bristol) Prev: Regist. (Gen. Pract.) Riversdale Ho. Bridgend; Ho. Phys. Bristol Roy. Infirm.; Ho. Surg. & SHO (O & G) Bridgend Gen. Hosp.

BEVIR, Thomas Anthony Dumpers House, Dumpers Lane, Chew Magna, Bristol BS40 8SS Tel: 01275 333928 Fax: 01275 333928 Email: bevir@globalnet.co.uk — MB ChB Birm. 1970; BA (Chem. Hons.) Oxf. 1964. (Birmingham) Med. Adviser, Bristol City Counc.; Med. Adviser BMI Health Serv. & Nat. W.m. Insur. Servs. Socs: Clin. Soc. Bath; Bristol M-C Soc.; Sands Cox Soc. Prev: GP Dorchester; Tutor (Gen. Pract.), Course Organiser & Princip. Univ. Sussex; SHO Barrow Hosp., Ham Green Hosp. & S.mead Hosp. Bristol.

BEVIS, Mr Christopher Richard Aitchison Victoria Hospital, St Walbegan Road, Blackpool FY3 8NR; Sowerby Hall, Sowerby Road, Inskip with Sowerby, St. Michaels, Preston PR3 0TU — MB BS 1974 Lond.; MD Lond. 1986, BSc, MB BS 1974; FRCS 1980; MRCS Eng. LRCP Lond. 1974; DA Eng. 1977. (Guy's) Cons. Urol. Vict. Hosp. Blackpool.

BEVIS, Mark Andrew Lodge Surgery, Normandy Road, St Albans AL3 5NP Tel: 01727 853107 Fax: 01727 862657; 25 Palfrey Close, St Albans AL3 5RE — MB BS 1989 Lond.; BSc Lond. 1986, MB BS 1989; MRCGP 1993; DRCOG 1993; DCH RCP Lond. 1992. Clin. Asst. Rheum. QEII Hosp. Welwyn Garden City Herts.

BEVIS, Miranda Jane Cardscroft, North St., Milverton, Taunton TA4 1LG Tel: 01823 400315 — MB BS 1981 Lond.; BSc Manch. 1974; DRCOG 1983.

BEVISS, John Eames Crabb House, Tellisford, Bath BA2 7RL Tel: 01373 830361 — MB ChB Bristol 1943; DTM & H Eng. 1973; MRCGP 1963. (Bristol) Prev: Maj. RAMC TA; Capt. RAMC.

BEW, Duncan Peter 10 The Paddock, Elwick Village, Hartlepool TS27 3DZ — MB BS 1998 Lond.; MB BS Lond 1998.

BEW, Marie Helen Hood 19 Clayton Drive, Stoughton, Guildford GU2 9TZ — MB ChB 1958 Glas.; DIH Soc. Apoth. Lond. 1975; DObst RCOG 1961.

BEW, Mary (retired) 550C Upper Newtownards Road, Belfast BT4 3HE — LRCPI & LM, LRSCI & LM 1945; LRCPI & LM, LRCSI & LM 1945.

BEW, Nigel Martin The Street Lane Practice, 12 Devonshire Avenue, Leeds LS8 1AY Tel: 0113 295 3838 Fax: 0113 295 3842; Manor House, Main St, Great Ouseburn, York YO26 9RG — MB BS 1983 Lond.; MRCGP 1988; DFFP 1996; DRCOG 1987. GP; Med. Adviser to ASDA. Prev: GP Baldock.

BEW, Stephanie Anne Anaesthetic Department, Jubilee Wing, Leeds General Infirmary, Great George St., Leeds LS1 3EX — MB BS 1987 Lond.; MA Camb. 1984; FRCA 1992. Cons. Anaesth. Leeds Gen. Infirm. Socs: Assn. of Paediat. Anaesth.s; Assn. of Anaesth.s; Paediatric Intens. Care Soc. Prev: Sen. Regist. (Anaesth.) Gt. Ormond St. Hosp.; Sen. Regist. (Anaesth.) Univ. Coll. Lond. Hosp.; Regist. (Anaesth.) St. Geo. Hosp. Lond. & Epsom Dist. Gen. Hosp.

BEWAJI, Afolake Folasade 699A Barking Road, London E13 9EU — MB BCh 1997 Wales.

BEWICK, Cecil William (retired) 39 Generals Wood, Washington NE38 9BN Tel: 0191 4165 750 — MB BS 1948 Durh.

BEWICK, Michael Beech House Group Practice, Beech House, 54 Main Street, Egremont CA22 2DB Tel: 01946 820692; Old Mill Farm House, Mill Lane, Beckermet CA21 2YE — MB BS 1980 Lond.; MRCP (UK) 1984; MRCGP 1988. (St. Mary's) Asst. Lect. Dept. Oncol. St. Bart. Hosp. Lond. Hon. Phys. St. Mary's; Hosp. Lond.; Ho. Surg. St. Mary's Hosp. Lond. Prev: SHO (Med.) Stoke Mandeville Hosp.; Sen. Regist./Regist. (Med./Oncol.) Ninewells Hosp. Dundee.

BEWICK, Mr Michael 77 Sydenham Hill, London SE26 6TQ — MB BChir 1962 Camb.; MChir Camb. 1978, MA 1962; FRCS Eng. 1967. Cons. Surg. St. Geo. Healthcare NHS Trust Lond.; Hon. Cons. Surg. S. Thames HA. Socs: Fell. Roy. Soc. Med. Prev: Regist. (Accid. & Orthop.) St. Geo. Hosp. Lond.; Regist. (Surg.) High Wycombe & Dist. Hosp. Gp.; Research Fell. RCS Eng.

BEWICKE, Richard Wentworth Yewtree Cottage, 439 Capstone Road, Gillingham ME7 3JE; 439 Capstone Road, Gillingham ME7 3JE — MB BS 1955 London. (Westm.) Socs: Fell. Roy. Soc. Med. Prev: Regist. (Med.) Croydon Gen. Hosp.

BEWLAY, Marie Anne Preston Acute NHS Trust, Sharoe Green Lane, Preston PR2 9HT; Southview Cottage, 235 Wigan Road, Euxton, Chorley PR7 6HZ — MB ChB 1988 Manch.; FRCA 1994; DA (UK) 1991. (Manch.) Sen. Regist. (Anaesth.) NW RHA. Socs: BMA; Roy. Coll. Anaesth.; Assn. Anaesth. Prev: Clin. Research Fell. & Regist. Rotat. (Anaesth.) NW RHA.

BEWLEY, Anthony Paul Department Dermatology, Whipps Cross Hospital, Leytonstone, London E11 1NR Tel: 020 8539 5522 Fax: 020 8535 6519; 4 Tavistock Chambers, Bloomsbury Way, London WC1A 2SE Email: abewley@dircon.co.uk — MB ChB 1987 Bristol; MRCP (UK) 1991. Cons. Dermat. Whipps Cross Hosp. Lond.; Hon. Cons. Dermat. Roy. Lond. Hosps. NHS Trust. Prev: Sen. Regist. (Dermat.) Soton. Univ. Hosps. NHS Trust; Regist. (Dermat.) Univ. Coll. Hosps. Lond.

BEWLEY, Dame Beulah Rosemary 4 Grosvenor Gardens Mews N., London SW1W 0JP Tel: 020 7730 9592 — MB BCh BAO 1953 Dub.; MSc Lond. 1971; MA Dub. 1966, BA 1951, MD 1974; FRCP Lond. 1992; FRCPCH (1985); FFPHM RCP (UK) 1980, M 1972. (T.C. Dub.) Emerit. Reader (Pub. Health Med.) St. Geo. Hosp. Med. Sch. Lond. Socs: Fell. Roy. Soc. Med.; GMC (Treas.). Prev: Reader (Pub. Health Med.) St. Geo. Hosp. Med. Sch. Lond.; Sen. Lect. (Community Med.) Lond. Sch. Hyg. & Trop. Med.; Sen. Research Fell. (Community Med.) St. Thos. Hosp. Med. Sch. Lond.

BEWLEY, Jeremy Stephen 5 Shutehay Drive, Cam, Dursley GL11 5UU Email: jeremyb777@aol.com; Silver Birches, Tregarn Road, Langstone, Newport NP18 2JS Tel: 01633 412114 — MB ChB 1990 Bristol; BSc Bristol 1987; MRCP (UK) 1994; FRCA 1997. (Univ. Bristol) Specialist Regist. Rotat. (Anaesth.) Bristol & SW Region. Socs: Assn. Anaesth.; Intens. Care Soc.; Roy. Coll. Phys. Prev: SHO (Anaesth.) Gloucester Roy. Hosp.; SHO (Neurol.) S.mead Hosp. Bristol; SHO (Cardiol.) Univ. Hosp Wales Cardiff.

BEWLEY, John Eric (retired) 163 Lawton Road, Alsager, Stoke-on-Trent ST7 2DD Tel: 01270 873453 — MB ChB 1958 Birm.; DObst RCOG 1960. Prev: Ho. Phys. & Ho. Surg. Copthorne Hosp. Shrewsbury.

BEWLEY, Susan Jane Womens Health Services Directorate, Guy's & St Thomas' Hospital Trust, Lambeth Palace Road, London SE1 7EH Tel: 020 7928 9292 Fax: 020 7922 8285 Email: susan.bewley@gstt.sthomas.nhs.uk — MB BS 1982 Lond.; BA Oxf. 1979; MA (Med. Law & Ethics) Lond. 1991; MD Lond. 1990; MRCOG 1987. (Oxf. & Middlx.) Dir. Obst. Guy's & St. Thos. Hosps. Lond.; Clin. Director, Wom.'s Health Serv.s, Guy's & St. Thomas' Hosp.s Trust. Socs: Soc. Perinatal Obst.; Roy. Soc. Med. Prev: Sen. Regist. & Subspeciality Trainee (Fetal Med.) Univ. Coll. Hosp. Lond.; Regist. (O & G) St. Peters Hosp. Chertsey, St. Geo. Hosp. Lond.; Research Regist. (O & G) Kings Coll. Hosp. & Dulwich Hosp. Lond.

BEWLEY, Thomas Henry, CBE 4 Grosvenor Gardens Mews N., London SW1W 0JP Tel: 020 7730 9592 — MB BCh BAO 1950 Dub.; MA Dub. 1961, BA 1948, MD (Hons.) 1987, MD 1958; FRCP Lond. 1988; FRCPI 1963, M 1954; FRCPsych (Hons.) 1989; FRCPsych 1984, M 1971; DPM 1953. (TC Dub.) Emerit. Cons. Psychiat. St. Thos. Hosp. Lond. Prev: Cons. Psychiat. St. Geo., St. Thos. & Tooting Bec Hosps.; Asst. Med. Off. St. Patrick's Hosp. Dub.; Regist. Maudsley Hosp.

BEWS, Susan Maud Mary Sanofi Winthrop Ltd., One Onslow St., Guildford GU1 4YS Tel: 01483 505515 Fax: 01483 35432; Domus, The Drive, Hook Heath, Woking GU22 0JS — MB BS 1968 Lond.; BSc (Hons) 1965; MRCS Eng. LRCP Lond. 1968; FFPM RCP (UK) 1993. (Lond. Hosp.) Med. Dir. Sanofi Winthrop. Prev: Med. Adviser Geistlich Chester; Clin. Asst. W.on-Super-Mare Gen. Hosp.

BEWSHER, Lianne Kathryn 83 Abbotshall Drive, Cults, Aberdeen AB15 9JJ Tel: 01224 868078 — MB ChB 1989 Dundee.

BEWSHER, Martin Stewart 2 Bath St, Hale WA14 2EJ — MB ChB 1991 Manch.; SCA/NBE Perioperative TEE; FRCA 1996. Clin. Fell., Cardiac Anaesth.

BEWSHER, Michael Roger Health Centre, South Croft Road, Biggar ML12 6BE; The Knoll, Biggar ML12 6HD — MB ChB 1957 Ed.; DObst RCOG 1959. Prev: SHO W.. Gen. Hosp. Edin.; Ho. Phys. Peel Hosp. Galashiels; Ho. Surg. Simpson Matern. Pavil. Roy. Infirm. Edin.

BEWSHER, Peter Dixon (retired) 83 Abbotshall Drive, Cults, Aberdeen AB15 9JJ Tel: 01224 868078 — MB ChB 1959 St. And.; MD Dundee 1971; FRCP Ed. 1975, M 1963. Prev: Reader (Med. & Therap.) Univ. Aberd.

BEXFIELD, Sherilyn Melanie 20 Barnstaple Road, Southend-on-Sea SS1 3PA — MB ChB Leeds 1991.

BEXLEY, Karl Andrew c/o Postgraduate Medical Dept, Medical School, Polwarth Building, Forresterhill, Aberdeen AB25 2ZD — MB ChB 1998 Aberd.; MB ChB Aberd 1998.

BEXON, Alice Susannah Sweetbrier, Molehill Road, Chestfield, Whitstable CT5 3PD — MB ChB 1994 Bristol.

BEXON, Martin Frances 17 Tenth Avenue, Heaton, Newcastle upon Tyne NE6 5XU — MB BS 1996 Newc.

BEXON, Wallace Harold (retired) Sherwood, South View, Meadowfield, Durham DH7 8SF Tel: 0191 378 0216 — LMSSA 1950 Lond.; MRCGP 1965. Prev: Chief Med. Off. Durh. Constab.

BEXTON, Michael David Ralph Pilgrim Hospital, Boston PE21 9QS — BM BCh Oxf. 1970; FFA RCS Eng. 1975; DA Eng. 1972. Cons. Anaesth. Pilgrim Hosp. Boston.

BEXTON, Rodney Stewart Department of Cardiology, Freeman Hospital, Freeman Road, Newcastle upon Tyne NE7 7DN Tel: 0191 284 3111 Email: r.s.bexton@ncl.ac.uk — BM BCh 1974 Oxf.; DM Oxf. 1983, MA 1974; FRCP Lond. 1991; MRCP (UK) 1977. (St. Bart.) Cons. Cardiol. Freeman Hosp. Newc. u. Tyne. Socs: Brit. Cardiac Soc. & Brit. Pacing Gp. Prev: Sen. Regist. (Cardiol.) Freeman Hosp. Newc.; Hon. Sen. Regist. (Cardiol.) St. Bart. Hosp. Lond.; Regist. (Cardiol.) Groby Rd. Hosp. Leicester.

BEYDALS, Jan c/o Dr Tom Henderson, Carswell House, Oakley Terrace, Glasgow G31 2HX — Artsexamen 1979 Groningen.

BEYER, Michael Stephen The Clinic, 4 Firs Entry, Bannockburn, Stirling FK7 0HW — MB ChB 1991 Ed.; MRCGP 1995; DRCOG 1994; DFFP 1994; DCCH RCP Ed. 1993. (Ed.) Prev: GP/Regist. Peebles.

BEYER, Pamela Mary The Surgery, 183a Woodlands Road, Sparkhill, Birmingham B11 4ER Tel: 0121 778 5439; 84 Woodlands Road, Sparkhill, Birmingham B11 4ES Tel: 0121 777 7871 — MB

BS Lond. 1964; MRCP Lond. 1969; MRCS Eng. LRCP Lond. 1964; DCH RCP Lond. 1966. (St Mary's Hospital London University)

BEYERS, Irma 29 Marlone Road, Newham, Cambridge CB3 9JW Tel: 01223 358712 Fax: 01223 303870 Email: beyers@dial.pipex.com — MB ChB 1983 Stellenbosch; MB ChB Stellembosch 1983.

BEYNON, Beryl, OBE (retired) Walkergate Surgery, 117-119 Walkergate, Beverley HU17 9BP Tel: 01482 881298 — MB ChB 1959 Manch.; DCH Eng. 1964; DObst RCOG 1960. Med. Dir. Jacob's Well Appeal Charity. Prev: Clin. Asst. (Child Psychiat.) De La Pole Hosp. Willerby.

BEYNON, David Graham 11 Tyrone Road, Thorpe Bay, Southend-on-Sea SS1 3HE Tel: 01702 587556 — MB BChir 1958 Camb.; MA, MB Camb. 1958, BChir 1957; MRCS Eng. LRCP Lond. 1957; FFA RCS Eng. 1967; DA Eng. 1966. (King's Coll. Hosp.) Cons. Anaesth. S.end Hosp. Gp. Prev: Sen. Regist. (Anaesth.) Leeds Gen. Infirm.; Regist. (Anaesth.) Portsmouth Hosp. Gp.; Ho. Phys. (Paediat.) King's Coll. Hosp.

BEYNON, Mr David William Gareth Dept of Obstetrics & Gynacology, Frimley Park Hsp, Portsmouth Rd, Camberley GU16 7UJ Tel: 01276 604268 Email: gareth.beynon@fph.th.nhs.uk — MB BS 1982 Lond.; FRCS Ed. 1987; MRCOG 1991. (St Bartholomews Hosp) Cons. (Obst & Gyna) Frimley Pk. Hsp, Surrey. Socs: Brit. Soc. Gyn. Cancer; Brit. Soc. C&C Path. Prev: Regist. (Gyn. Oncol.) Qu. Eliz. Hosp. Gateshead; Sen. Regist. (O & G) P.ss Anne Hosp. Soton.; Regist. (Surg.) Chase Farm Hosp. Enfield.

BEYNON, Gareth Philip James King Edward VII Hospital for Officers, Beaumont St., London W1G 6AA Tel: 01923 852329; 30 Elm Walk, Radlett WD7 8DP Tel: 01923 852329 — MB BChir 1964 Camb.; MA Camb. 1964; FRCP Lond. 1985; MRCP (UK) 1969. (St. Mary's) Cons. Phys. (Geriat. Med.) King Edwd. VII Hosp. Offs.; Cons. Phys. Hosp. St. John & St. Eliz. Lond.; Hon. Cons. Phys. Middlx. Hosp. Lond. Socs: Fell. Med. Soc. Lond. Prev: Cons. Phys. (Geriat. Med.) Middlx. & W.m. Hosp.

BEYNON, Gareth Wyn Amylin Europe Ltd., Magdalen Centre, The Oxford Science Park, Oxford OX4 4GA Tel: 01865 784094 Fax: 01865 787900 Email: gbeynon@amylin.com; 1 Sotwell Manor, Bakers Lane, Brightwell Cum Sotwell, Wallingford OX10 0PX — MB BChir 1979 Camb.; MA Camb. 1974, PhD 1975; MBA Cranfield 1989; MRCP (UK) 1980; Dip. Pharm. Med. RCP (UK) 1985. (Camb. & Guy's) Vice-Pres. Amylin Europ. Ltd. Oxf. Socs: Fell. Roy. Soc. Med. Prev: Marketing Dir. G.D. Searle & Co. Ltd. Paris, France; Dir. Europ. Clin. Research G.D. Searle & Co. High Wycombe; Regist. (Med.) Middlx. Hosp. Lond.

BEYNON, Huw Lewis Clarke 33 Flower Lane, London NW7 2JG — MB BS 1984 Lond.; MRCP (UK) 1987.

BEYNON, Jan Hariclia 221 Bassaleg Road, Newport NP20 3PZ Tel: 01633 263217; St. Woolos Hospital, Stowhill, Newport NP20 4SZ Tel: 01633 238289 Fax: 01633 212582 — MB BCh 1981 Wales; BSc Wales 1978, MB BCh 1981; MRCP (UK) 1988; DRCOG 1985. (Welsh National School of Medicine) Assoc. Specialist (Geriat. Med.) St. Woolos Hosp. Newport; Clin. Teach. Dept. of Geriat. Med. Univ. of Wales Coll. of Med. Socs: Brit. Geriat. Soc.; Brit. Menopause Soc.; RCP. Prev: Specialist Regist. (Geriat. Med.) St. Woolos Hosp. Newport; Assoc. Specialist Clin. Research Off. & Clin. Asst. (Geriat. Med.) S. Gwent; Regist. (Gen. Med.) Bridgend Gen. Hosp.

BEYNON, Mr John Singleton Hospital, Sketty, Swansea SA2 8QA Tel: 01792 205666; 69 Pennard Road, Southgate, Swansea SA3 2AJ — MB BS 1980 Lond.; BSc Lond. 1977; MS Lond. 1989; FRCS Eng. 1984. Cons. Surg. Singleton Hosp. Swansea. Socs: Assn. Coloproctol.; Brit. Soc. Gastroenterol.; Surgic. Research Soc. Prev: Cons. Surg. Wrexham Maelor Hosp; Resid. Surg. Off. St. Marks Hosp. Lond.; Sen. Regist. (Surg.) Univ. Hosp. Wales Cardiff.

BEYNON, Mr John Lang St Richards Hospital, Chichester PO19 4SE Tel: 01243 538411 Fax: 01243 831432; North Mundham House, North Mundham, Chichester PO20 6JU Tel: 01243 775323 Fax: 01243 775323 — MA, BM BCh Oxf. 1970; FRCS Eng. 1975; FRCOG 1992, M 1978. (Oxf. & St. Geo.) Cons. (O & G) St. Richard's Hosp. Chichester. Socs: Gynae Research Soc. Prev: Sen. Regist. St. Thos. Hosp. Lond.; Regist. John Radcliffe Hosp. Oxf.; SHO (Gyn.) Chelsea Hosp. Wom. Lond.

BEYNON, Jonathan Andrew 1B Barb Mews, London W6 7PA — MB BS 1990 Lond. Prev: Cas. Off. & Ho. Surg. Brook Hosp.; Ho. Phys. Brighton Gen. Hosp.

BEYNON, Julie Anne Flat 1/R, 53 White Street, Glasgow G11 5EQ — MB ChB 1995 Glas.

BEYNON, Paul 10 Kingston Road, Sketty, Swansea SA2 0ST — MB BS 1985 Lond.

BEYNON, Peggy (retired) Dilwara, 2 Tannersfield, Shalford, Guildford GU4 8JW Tel: 01483 563066 — MRCS Eng. LRCP Lond. 1945; MFCM 1972; DPH Bristol 1949. Prev: Dist. Med. Off. E. Surrey HA.

BEYNON, Peter John (retired) 49 Keldgate, Beverley HU17 8HU Tel: 01482 881162 Fax: 01482 865452 Email: pjbeynon@compuserve.com — MB ChB Manch. 1959; FRCPsych 1995, M 1971; DPM Eng. 1963. Prev: Cons. Child Psychiat. Hull Area.

BEYNON, Rhys Paul 17 Grove Hill, Topsham, Exeter EX3 0EG — MB ChB 1997 Ed.

BEYNON, Teresa Anne Department of Palliative Medicine, St Thomas' Hospital, Lambeth Palace Road, London SE1 7EH Tel: 020 7928 9282 Fax: 020 7922 8253 Email: t.beynon@umds.ac.uk; 27 Rowlls Road, Kingston upon Thames KT1 3ET Tel: 020 8974 5923 — MB ChB 1984 Dundee; MRCGP 1991; DA (UK) 1988. Cons. & Sen. Lect. (Palliat. Med.) Guy's & St. Thos. Trust Lond. Prev: Sen. Regist. St. Thomas' Hosp.

BEYZADE, Bengi 309 Southcroft Road, London SW16 6QT — MB BS 1996 Lond.

BEZBORUAH, Phoonoo Prasad Rosehill Surgery, 189 Manchester Road, Burnley BB11 4HP Tel: 01282 428200; 24A Rosehill Mount, Burnley BB11 4HW Tel: 01282 36423 — MB BS 1963 Gauhati; MFFP 1993; MRCOG 1970; DObst RCOG 1968; DGO Calcutta 1966. (Assam Med. Coll. Dibrugarh, Assam)

BEZEM, Mohamed Fawaz Law Hospital, Orthopaedic Department, Carluke ML8 5ER Tel: 01698 351100 — MD 1978 Damascus.

BEZUIDENHOUT, Peter Basil Torrington Park Health Centre, 16 Torrington Park, North Finchley, London N12 9SS Tel: 020 8445 7622/4127 — MB ChB 1985 Cape Town.

BEZULOWSKY, Volodia Stapleford Centre, 25A Eccleston St., London SW1W 9NP Tel: 020 7823 6840 Fax: 020 7730 3409; 31 Lynton Road, London W3 9HL Tel: 020 8993 8113 — MD 1986 Brussels. Clin. Asst. Stapleford Addic. Centre Lond.

BEZZINA, Charles L Newtown Medical Centre, 205/207 Ormskirk Road, Newtown, Wigan WN5 9DP Tel: 01942 494711 Fax: 01942 826240; 46 Boars Head Avenue, Standish, Wigan WN6 0BH Tel: 01257 427214 — MB ChB 1982 Manch.; DRCOG 1986.

BHABRA, Kalvinder Huddersfield Royal Infirmary, Huddersfield HD3 3EA Tel: 01484 422191 Fax: 01484 482888; Corby, Birkby Road, Huddersfield HD2 2DR Tel: 01484 422062 Fax: 01484 422062 — MB ChB 1979 Leeds; FRCOG 1998; MRCOG 1985. (Leeds) Cons. O & G Huddersfield Roy. Infirm. Prev: Cons. O & G Dewsbury W. Yorks.; Sen. Regist. (O & G) Yorks. RHA.

BHABRA, Mr Moninder Singh 124 St Martins Road, Coventry CV3 6ER Tel: 01203410260 — BM BS 1989 Nottm.; BMedSci Nottm. 1987; FRCS Eng. 1994. Specialist Regist. (Cardiothoracic Surg.) W. Midl. Rotat.; Hunt. Prof. 1999-2000. Prev: Regist. (Cardiothoracic Surg.) Roy. Brompton Hosp. Lond.; Research Fell. (Cardiothoracic Surg.) Wythenshawe Hosp. Manch.; SHO Rotat. (Surg.) Leics. HA.

BHABUTTA, Rakesh Kumar, Maj. RAMC Medical Centre, Queen Elizabeth Barracks, Church Crookham, Fleet GU52 8RJ Tel: 01252 355722; 4 Edy Court, Loughton, Milton Keynes MK5 8DU Tel: 01908 604391 — MB ChB 1986 Dundee; MSc (Ed.) 1995. (Univ. Ed. & Univ. Dundee) GP HM Forces; Army Health Promotion Adviser. Socs: BMA (Jun. Mem. Armed Forces Comm.).

BHACHU, Harjinder Singh Crail Medical Practice, 245 Tollcross Road, Glasgow G31 4UW Tel: 0141 554 3199 Fax: 0141 551 9950 — MB ChB 1981 Aberd.; DRCOG 1985. (Aberdeen)

BHACHU, Harjinder Singh West End Medical Centre, 102 Stockport Road, Ashton-under-Lyne OL7 0LH Tel: 0161 339 5488 Fax: 0161 330 0945; 31 Green Pastures, Heaton Mersey, Stockport SK4 3RB Tel: 0161 339 5488 — MB BS 1974 Banaras Hindu; MRCGP 1984; DRCOG 1982; FFA RCS Eng. 1980. GP Tameside FPC; Clin. Asst. (Anaesth.) Tameside HA; Dent. Anaesth. Oldham HA.

BHACHU, Jugjeet Kaur 18 Grasmere Avenue, Slough SL2 5JG Tel: 01753 525287 — MB BS 1996 Lond. (St. Geo. Hosp.) SHO (Psych.), GPVTS at W. Middlx. Hosp.; SHO (A & E and Paediat.) GPVTS at W. Middlx. Hosp. Prev: SHO (Geriat.) Gramley Pk. Hosp. Surrey; Ho. Off. (Med.) Ashford Hosp. Middlx.; Ho. Off. (Surg.) Framley Pk. Hosp.

BHADAURIA, Bhupendra Singh The Surgery, 56A Lower High Street, Wednesbury WS10 7AL Tel: 0121 502 5757 Fax: 0121 566 3361 Email: doctor.bhadauria@gp-m88627.nhs.uk — MB BS 1974 Jiwaji. Prev: Clin. Asst. A & E Dept. Sandwell DGH W. Bromwich 1981-1992; Clin. Asst. Elderly Care Sandwell DGH W. Bromwich.

BHADRA, Nirode Baran 75 Vaughan Gardens, Ilford IG1 3PB Tel: 020 8554 2403 Fax: 020 8514 5403; 86 Ballygunge Place, Flat 22, Calcutta 700019, India Tel: 408434 — MB BS 1962 Calcutta; FRCOG 1990, M 1971. (Calcutta Medical College, India) GP Doctor in Family Plann. Socs: BMA; ODA; Ilford Med. Soc.

BHADRI, Aravind Damodar Great Barr Group Practice, 912 Walsall Road, Great Barr, Birmingham B42 1TG Tel: 0121 357 1250 Fax: 0121 358 4857 — MB BS 1966 Poona; MFFP 1993; MRCOG 1978; DRCOG 1973. (BJ Med. Coll. POONA. INDIA.) Sen. Clin. Med. Off. (Family Plann.) Birm. Socs: Med. Protec. Soc.

BHADRINATH, Bindumadhava Rao Bethel Child & Family Centre, Mary Chapman House, Hotblack Road, Norwich NR2 4HN Tel: 01603 421950 Fax: 01603 421990 — MB BS 1977 Madras; MRCPsych 1982; T(Psych) 1991; DPM Bangalore 1979. Cons. Psychiat. Norf. Ment. Health Care NHS Trust Norwich.

BHADURI, Bimal Ranjan, Maj. RAMC The Maidstone Hospital, Maidstone ME16 9QQ Tel: 01622 224723 Fax: 01622 224852 Email: bim.bhaduri@lineone.net; Broadwater Farm, Broadwater Road, West Malling ME19 6HT Tel: 01732 843660 Fax: 01732 872767 Email: bim.bhaduri@lineone.net — MB BS 1979 North Bengal; BSc (Hons.) Calcutta 1971; LMSSA Lond. 1986; MRCP (UK) 1988; MRCPI 1988; DCH RCP Lond. 1988; DTM & H RCP Lond. 1982; DCH Calcutta 1981; FRCP Lond. 1998. Cons. Paediat. (Gastroenterol.) Maidstone Hosp. Kent; Sub-Dean, G.K.T. Sch. of Med., Lond.; Sen. Lect. (Hon.) (Paediat.), GKT Sch. of Med., Lond. Socs: Brit. Soc. Gastroenterol. Prev: Sen. Regist. (Paediat.) Hosp. for Sick Childr. Lond.; Research Regist. (Paediat. Liver Transpl.) King's Coll. Hosp. Lond.; Regist. York Dist. Hosp.

BHADURI, Sudip Kumar Pembroke House, 32 Albert Road, Cleethorpes DN35 8LU Tel: 01472 691033 Fax: 01472 291516; 33 Carrington Drive, Humberston, Grimsby DN36 4XQ — MRCS Eng. LRCP Lond. 1983; DRCOG 1990.

BHADURI, Sumit 3 Elm Tree Close, Leicester LE5 1UZ — MB ChB 1984 Manch.; MRCP (UK) 1991.

BHAGAT, Achal c/o Mr S. K. Nangia, 57 Headstone Lane, North Harrow, Harrow HA2 6JL — MB BS 1987 Delhi; MRCPsych 1994.

BHAGAT, Ashok Kumar Civic Centre Surgery, Main St., Shildon DL4 1AH Tel: 01388 772408 Fax: 01388 777345 — MB BS 1974 Patna; MB BS 1974 Patna. (Patna) GP Shildon, Co. Durh.

BHAGAT, Kiran 11 Queensgate Terrace, London SW7 5PR Tel: 020 7209 6616 Fax: 020 7813 2846 Email: kbhagat@ucl.ac.uk — MB ChB 1987 Univ. Zimbabwe; MB ChB; MRCP (UK) 1992; Dip. Cardiol. Lond 1993; DCH Lond. 1989; PhD Lond. 1997. Sen. Regist. & Lect. (Cardiovasc., Cardiol., Pharmacol. & Therap.) Univ. Coll. Hosp. Med. Sch. Lond. Socs: Brit. Cardiac Soc.; Amer. Heart Assn.; Brit. Hypertens. Research Gp. Prev: Brit. Heart Foundat. Research Fell. St. Geo. Hosp. Med. Sch. Lond.; Clin. Regist. (Cardiol.) Guy's Hosp. Lond.

BHAGEERUTTY, Jan Dorian Broseley Practice, Broseley TF12 5EL — MB ChB 1972 Birm.

BHAGEERUTTY, Raj Vasan The Surgery, High Street, Newnham GL14 1BE Tel: 01594 516241; 14 Foxleigh Crescent, Longlevens, Gloucester GL2 0XW Tel: 01452 309689 Fax: 01452 309689 Email: raj.bhageerutty@btinternet.com — MB BCh 1985 N U Irel.; MB BCh N U I 1985. (N U Irel.) GP Newnham, Glos.; Assoc. Specialist Psychiat. Cheltenham Gen. Hosp. Glos. Prev: Roy. Coll. of Psychiats.

BHAGRATH, Malkit Singh The Surgery, 97 Stopford Road, Plaistow, London E13 0NA Tel: 020 8472 3846 Fax: 020 8552 1442; 60 Stephens Road, London E15 3JL Tel: 020 8534 2040 Fax: 020 8534 0357 — MB BS Bombay 1962; DPH Eng. 1966. (Grant Med. Coll. Bombay) Socs: BMA & Roy. Coll. GPs. Prev: SHO Infec. Dis. Unit W.. Hosp. Lond.; Med. Off. Govt. of Kenya.

BHAGRATH, Ravi Arvinder Singh 55 Spareleaze Hill, Loughton IG10 1BS — MB BS 1992 Lond.

BHAGWANDAS, Krishnan Sai Krupa, 5 Cooper Close, Langstone, Newport NP18 2LD Tel: 01633 413962 — MB BS 1977 Madras; DDerm 1979. Trainee GP Gwent VTS; Clin. Asst. (Dermat.) Roy. Gwent Hosp. Newport. Prev: Regist. (Dermat.) Singleton Hosp. Swansea.

BHAKRI, Harbans Lal Weston General Hospital, Uphill, Weston Super Mare BS23 4TQ Tel: 01934 647156; Shaanti-Bhawan, Bridgwater Road, Winscombe BS25 1NA — MB BS 1976 Lond.; BSc Lond. 1973; MRCP (UK) 1979; FRCP Lond. 1997. (Middlesex Hosp.) Cons. Phys. W.on Gen. Hosp. W.on Super Mare; Hon. Sen. Lect. Bristol Univ.

BHAKTA, Bipinchandra Rheumatology and Rehabilitation Research Unit, School of Medicine, University of Leeds, 36 Clarendon Road, Leeds LS2 9NZ Email: b.bhakta@leeds.ac.uk — MB ChB 1985 Manch.; FRCP 2001; MD 1999; BSc (Hons.) Manch. 1982, MB ChB 1985; MRCP (UK) 1989. (University of Manchester) Sen. Lect. Rheum. & Rehabil. Research Unit Univ. Leeds; Hon. Cons. St. Jas. Univ. Hosp. & St Mary's Hosp. Leeds. Socs: Educ. Comm. Mem. of Brit. Soc. of Rehabil. Med.; Brit. Soc. of Rheum.; Mem. Jt. Specialty Comm. for Rehabil. Med. Prev: Sen. Regist. (Rheum. & Rehabil.) Research Unit Univ. Leeds.; Regist. (Gen. Med.,Neurol., Rheum & Rehabil.) Wythenshawe Hosp.; SHO (Gen. Med.) Manch. Roy. Infirm.

BHAL, Preetkiron Singh Department of Obstetrics and Gynaecology, University Hospital of Wales, Heath Park, Cardiff CF14 4XW Tel: 029 2074 7747 Email: bhalps@cf.ac.uk — MB BCh 1989 Wales; MRCOG 1995. Locum Sen. Lect. (O & G) Univ. Hosp. Wales. Socs: BMA; Brit. Fertil. Soc.; Brit. Med. Ultrasound Soc. Prev: Lect., Sen. Regist., Univ. Hosp. Cardiff; Clin. Research Fell. Assisted Reproduc. Unit Univ. Hosp. Wales Cardiff.

BHALA, Balmukund Bansilal, Maj. RAMC(V) Anaesthesia & Pain Clinic Consultant, 3 Manor Court, Little Harrowden, Wellingborough NN9 5BZ Tel: 01933 674676 Fax: 01933 674676 Mobile: 07780 606411 Email: balmbhala@yahoo.co.uk; Anaesthesia & Pain Clinic Consultant, 3 Manor court, Little Harrowden, Wellingborough NN9 5BZ Tel: 01933 674676 Fax: 01933 674676 Mobile: 07780 606411 Email: balmbhala@yahoo.co.uk — MB BS 1972 Nagpur; MBA 1998 open; Dip Med.Law UNN 2001; MD (Anaesth.) Nagpur 1975; MD (ECFMG USA) 1977; FFA RCSI 1977; DA Nagpur 1973. (Govt. Med. Coll. Nagpur) p/t Cons. Anaesth. & Resus. RAMC (V) Nottm.; Internat. Co-ordinator Hindu Intern. Med. Mission; Cons. Anaeth, BPAS. Socs: BMA Elected Memb. (1999-2000)- Med. Ethics Committe; Armed Forces Comm.; Race Relations Comm..; The Pain Soc.& Assn. Of Anaesth. Of GB. + N.I.; Founder Mem. of the Brit. Assn. Of Phys.s of Indian Origin (BAPIO). Prev: Cons. Anaesth. & Pain Clinic S. Shields; Chief Resid. (Anaesth.) Bombay Hosp., India; Clin. Fell. Pain Control Center Univ. Cincinnati, USA.

BHALERAO, Mr Vinayak Ramchandra 30 Upper Diconson Street, Wigan WN1 2AG Tel: 01947 42366; 78 Newgate Avenue, Appley Bridge, Wigan WN6 9JJ Tel: 01257 252388 — MB BS 1955 Nagpur; FRCS Ed. 1971; FRCOphth 1989; DO Eng. 1967. (Nagpur) Cons. Ophth. Surg. Roy. Albert Edwd. Infirm. Wigan. Socs: Ophth. Soc. UK. Prev: Sen. Regist. Birm. & Midl. Eye Hosp.; Regist. (Ophth.) Ipswich & E. Suff. Hosp. Ipswich; Regist. Sussex Eye Hosp. Brighton.

BHALLA, Ajay 49 Smitham Bottom Lane, Purley CR8 3DF — MB BS 1992 Lond.

BHALLA, Ashok Kumar Royal National Hospital for Rheumatic Diseases, Bath BA1 1RL Tel: 01225 473443 Fax: 01225 473437 Email: ashok.bhalla@rnhra-tr.swest.nhs.uk; Tel: 01225 318161 — MB ChB 1977 Manch.; BSc (Hons.) Manch. l974, MD 1985; FRCP Lond. 1994; MRCP (UK) 1979. (Manch.) Cons. Rheum. Roy. Nat. Hosp. for Rheum. Dis. Bath; Hon. Sen. Lect. Univ. Bath. Socs: Brit. Soc. Rheum.; Bone & Tooth Soc.; Amer. Soc. Bone & Mineral Research. Prev: Clin. & Research Fell. Mass. Gen. Hosp. & Harvard Med. Sch.; Sen. Regist. Middlx. Hosp., Univ. Coll. & N.wick Pk. Hosp.

BHALLA, Dinesh c/o Dr M. N. Zaman, 147 Somersall Lane, Chesterfield S40 3LZ — MB BS 1980 Delhi.

BHALLA, Kailash Mile Lane Health Centre, 80 Mile Lane, Bury BL8 2JR Tel: 0161 764 7804 Fax: 0161 763 1931; Elton-Vale, Elton-Vale Road, Bury BL8 2RZ — MB BS 1961 Panjab; MRCOG 1970.

BHALLA, Poonam Elton Vale, Elton Vale Road, Bury BL8 2RZ; 167 Minster Court, Myrtle St, Liverpool L7 3QE Tel: 0151 707 0306 — MB ChB 1993 Liverp. (Liverpool) Specialist Regist. Rotat. (Paediat.) Merseyside. Prev: SHO Rotat. (Paediat.) Merseyside.

BHALLA, Rajesh Wawn Street Surgery, Wawn Street, South Shields NE33 4DX Tel: 0191 454 0421 Fax: 0191 454 9428; 48 Trajan Avenue, South Shields NE33 2AN Tel: 0191 454 5381 — MB BS 1975 Newc.

BHALLA, Rajiv Kumar 65 Chaucer Avenue, Cranford, Hounslow TW4 6NA — MB ChB 1995 Leic.; BSc (Hons), 1992. Basic Surgic. Trainee. Socs: MSS; MPS; BMA.

BHALLA, Rakesh Wawn Street Surgery, Wawn Street, South Shields NE33 4DX Tel: 0191 454 0421 Fax: 0191 454 9428; 233 Sunderland Road, South Shields NE34 6AL — MB BCh 1982 Wales; MRCGP 1988.

BHALLA, Suni Kumar 54 Rosemary Hill Road, Little Aston, Sutton Coldfield B74 4HJ — MB ChB 1981 Birm.

BHAM, Anwar Yacoob 2 Grange Avenue, Batley WF17 7AW — MB BCh 1993 Wales. SHO (Gen. Med.) Huddersfield Roy. Infirm. Prev: Trainee GP/SHO (A & E) Huddersfield.

BHAM, Yacoob Gulam Mohamed 2 Grange Avenue, Batley WF17 7AW — MB BS 1961 Baroda; DO RCS Eng. 1967; DOMS Bombay 1964. Assoc. Specialist (Ophth.) Huddersfield Roy. Infirm. Prev: Ho. Off. (Gen. Med.) Chapel Allerton Hosp. Leeds; Regist. (Ophth.) & Sen. Regist. (Ophth.) St. Jas. Hosp. Leeds.

BHAMBRA, Mandeep Kaur 106 Mayflower Drive, Coventry CV2 5NP Email: mbham29@yahoo.com — MB ChB 1997 Leic.; DRCOG 2001. (Leicester) GP Locum, Swindon. Prev: GP Regist., Hinckley, Leicester.

BHAMRA, Gurpreet Singh 4 Meadow Road, Kempston, Bedford MK42 7BE — MB BS 1998 Lond.; MB BS Lond 1998.

BHAMRA, Mr Manjit Rotherham General Hospital, Moorgate Road, Rotherham S60 2UD Tel: 01709 304553 Fax: 01709 304564 Email: manjit.bhamra@rgh-tr.trent.nhs.uk — MB ChB 1981 Sheff.; FRCS Lond 1986; ChM Sheff 1990; Med Lic 2000 Sheffield. (Sheffield) Cons. (Orthop. & Trauma Surg.), Rotherham Gen. Hosps. Trust; Hon. Clin. Lect., Univ. of Sheff. Socs: Fell., Brit. Orthopaedic Surg. Assn.; Amer. Acad. of Orthopaedic Surg.; Eur. Soc. of Surg. Shoulder & Elbow.

BHAMRA, Rajinder Singh Fernville Surgery, Midland Road, Hemel Hempstead HP2 5BL Tel: 01442 213919 Fax: 01442 216433 — MB BS 1975 Lond.; MRCS Eng. LRCP Lond. 1975; MRCGP 1979.

BHAN, Angelica 221 Crofton Lane, Orpington BR6 0BL — MB BS 1984 Lond.

BHAN, Archana Opthalmology Dept, Royal Hallamshire Hospital, Sheffield S10 2JF — MB ChB 1993 Manch.

BHAN, Bushan District General Hospital, Moorgate Road, Rotherham S60 2UD Tel: 01709 62222; 82 Woodfoot Road, Moorgate, Rotherham S60 3DY — MB BS 1969 Jammu & Kashmir; MSc Lond. 1983; Dip. Cardiol. Lond 1985; DCH RCPS Glas. 1974. (Kashmir) Prev: Fell. Gastroenterol. DelHo. Univ. & Vict. Gen. Hosp. Halifax Nova Scotia, Canada; Regist. (Med. Cardiac) St. Marys Hosp. E.bourne E. Sussex.

BHAN, Girdari Lal Department of Adult Medicine, Royal Oldham Hospital, Rochdale, Oldham OL1 2JH Tel: 0161 627 8480; Camden, Dobcross New Road, Dobcross, Oldham OL3 5NP — MB BS 1967 Jammu & Kashmir; FRCP Lond. 1992; FRCPI 1991; MRCP (UK) 1978. (Govt. Med. Coll. Srinagar) Cons. Phys. Roy. Oldham Hosp.

BHANA, Vahlie 7B Sunningvale Avenue, Biggin Hill, Westerham TN16 3BU; 15 Avondale Park, Raheny, Dublin 5, Republic of Ireland — MB BCh BAO 1984 NUI; LRCPI & LM LRCSI & LM 1984; T(GP) 1994.

BHANDAL, Mandeep Singh Woodlands Surgery, 24 Woodlands, Meeting House Lane, Balsall Common, Coventry CV7 7FX Tel: 01676 532587 Fax: 01676 535154 — MB ChB 1993 Ed.

BHANDAL, Navrinder Kaur 182 Kingsway, Leicester LE3 2TW — MB ChB 1993 Leic.

BHANDAL, Sukhvinder Kaur 7 Woodhedge Drive, Thorneywood, Nottingham NG3 6LU — MB ChB 1984 Leic.

BHANDAL, Tajinder Singh Priory Medical Centre, Cape Road, Warwick CU34 4UN — MB ChB 1995; DRCOG 1998; MRCGP 2000; DFFP 1998. (Liverpool) GP.

BHANDARI, Hemant Bansilal Huddersfield Royal Infirmiary, Acre St., Lindley, Huddersfield HD3 3EA Tel: 01484 422191 Email: hbhandari@msn.com; 16 Acre House Avenue, Lindley, Huddersfield HD3 3BB Tel: 01484 422191 Ext: 2832 Email: hbhandari@email.msn.com — MB BS 1986 Bombay; MSc (Ortho.) Lond. 1998; MS (Ortho.) Bombay 1992. Staff Grade (Orthop.) Huddersfield Roy. Infirmiary. Prev: Staff Grade (Orthop.) Kingston Hosp. Surrey.

BHANDARI, Jyoti The Medical Centre, 45 Enderley Road, Harrow Weald, Harrow HA3 5HF Tel: 020 8863 3333; Highlands, Park View Road, Pinner HA5 3YF — MB ChB 1989 Manch.; MRCGP 1993; DRCOG 1992; BSc (Hons) 1985. (Mancester) GP Princ.

BHANDARI, Seema 19 Lubnaig Gardens, Bearsden, Glasgow G61 4QX — MB ChB 1998 Glas.; MB ChB Glas 1998.

BHANDARI, Sunil Renal Unit, Hull & E. Yorks. Hospital NHS Trust, Alderson House, Level 2, Hull Royal Infirmary, Kingston Upon Hull HU3 2JZ Fax: 01482 674998 Email: sunil.bhandari@medix-uk.com — MB ChB 1990 Ed.; PhD 1999 Leeds; MRCP 1993 UK. (Univ. Ed.) Cons. (Nephrol. & Gen. Med.), Hull & E. Yorks Hosp.s NHS Trust; Hon. Sen. Lect. Univ. Of Hull, Kingston - Upon - Hull. Socs: Brit. Renal Assn.; BMA; EDTA. Prev: Advanced Trainee (Nephrol.), Roy. P. Alfred Hosp., Sydney, Australia; NKRF Research Fell. & Hon. Sen. Regist. (Renal Physiol.) Univ. Leeds; Regist. (Med. Nephrol.) Leeds Gen. Inf.

BHANDARI, Vandana 15 Bristow Park, Belfast BT9 6TF — MB BCh BAO 1988 Belf.; MRCP (UK) 1991. Prev: Ho. Off. (Surg.) E. Genm. Hosp. Edin. & (Med.) Edin. Roy. Infirm.; SHO (Haemat., Rena & Cardiol.) N.. Gen. Hosp. Sheff.

BHANDARY, Lata Vasanth Shafton Lane Surgery, 20A Shafton Lane, Holbeck, Leeds LS11 9RE Tel: 0113 295 4393 Fax: 0113 295 4390 — MB BS 1972 Karnatak; DRCOG 1977. (Karnatak Med. Coll. Hubli)

BHANDARY, Panambur Vasanth Tel: 0113 2954 393; 1 Tidpr Lawns, Leeds LS8 2JR Tel: 0113 232 3588 — MB BS 1970 Mysore. (Mysore) p/t GP Leeds; Med. Off. for Burefels-Agency. Prev: GP for 22 Years.

BHANDARY, Umanath Vasanth 1 Tudor Lawns, Leeds LS8 2JR — MB BS 1996 Lond.

BHANGOO, Priya 84 Stoughton Road, Oadby, Leicester LE2 4FN Tel: 0116 271 7354 — MB ChB 1995 Leic. (Leicester) SHO Rotat. (Paediat.) Nottm. & Derby. Prev: SHO (Paediat.) Leicester Roy. Infirm.; Ho. Off. (Surg.) Kettering Gen. Hosp.; Ho. Off. (Med.) Leicester Gen. Hosp.

BHANGOO, Ranjeev Singh 84 Stoughton Road, Oadby, Leicester LE2 4FN — MB ChB 1990 Leic.

BHANGOO, Surinder Singh St Peter's Health Centre, Leicester LE2 0TA; Woodbury, 84 Stoughton Road, Oadby, Leicester LE2 4FN — MB BS 1966 Panjab; MB BS Panjab (India) 1966. (Med. Coll. Amritsar) Clin. Asst. Radiother. Dept. Leicester Roy. Infirm. Socs: BMA. Prev: Ho. Off. (Orthop.) Brighton Gen. Hosp.; Regist. (Psychiat.) Warley Hosp. Brentwood & Towers Hosp. Leicester.

BHANJI, Asgarali Bandali East Surrey Hospital, Three Arch Road, Redhill RH1 Tel: 01737 768511; 5 Furze Hill, Purley CR8 3LB Tel: 020 8668 7821 — MB BS 1969 Bombay; MRCP (UK) 1977; T(M) 1991. (Topiwalla Nat. Med. Coll.)

BHANJI, Nasheer Pyarally Willows Medical Centre, Church Street, Carlton, Nottingham NG4 1BJ Tel: 0115 940 4252 Fax: 0115 956 8876; Hill Side, 7 Cragmoor Road, Burton Joyce, Nottingham NG14 5AR Tel: 0115 931 2233 Email: nash16@bigfoot.com — MB BCh 1986 Wales; MRCGP 1991. (Welsh National School of Medicine) Prev: Trainee GP Hemel Hempstead VTS; Ho. Phys. Roy. Berks. Hosp. Reading; Ho. Surg. Mayday Hosp. Thornton Heath.

BHANJI, Sadrudin (retired) 13 Elm Grove Road, Topsham, Exeter EX3 0EQ — MB BS Lond. 1965; MD Lond. 1977; MRCS Eng. LRCP Lond. 1965; FRCPsych 1985, M 1972; DPM Eng. 1968. Prev: Sen. Lect. (Adult Ment. Illness) Univ. Exeter.

BHANOT, Mr Shiv Mohan Flat 5, Ballochmyle, Mauchline KA5 6LQ — MB BS 1981 Delhi; FRCS Glas. 1988.

BHANOT, Sunil Dutt Woodland Practice, Holmwood Health Centre, Franklin Avenue, Tadley RG26 4ER Tel: 0118 981 4166 Fax: 0118 981 1432 — MB BS 1985 Lond.; MRCGP 1989; DRCOG 1989; DCH RCP Lond. 1988. (Char. Cross & Westm.)

BHANUMATHI, Kumbakonam Srinivasachar Lambgates Doctors Surgery, 1-5 Lambgates, Hadfield, Glossop SK13 1AW Tel: 01457 869090 Fax: 01457 857367; 17 Ramsden Close, Glossop SK13 7BB

— MB BS 1966 Bangalor; MB BS Bangalore 1966; DA Eng. 1970. (Bangalore)

BHAR, G Chimene 138 High Street, Cheshunt, Waltham Cross EN8 0AP — MB BS 1988 Sydney.

BHARAJ, Harnoudeep Singh 42 Pascoe Road, London SE13 5JB — MB ChB 1985 Sheff.

BHARAL, Inderjeet K S Medical Centre, 33 Dormers Wells Lane, Southall UB1 3HY Tel: 020 8574 3986/8571 7632 Fax: 020 8893 6188; 30 Vinlake Avenue, Ickenham, Uxbridge UB10 8DS Tel: 0189 56 21563 — MB BS 1971 Delhi; DA (UK) 1977. (Maulana Azad Medical College New Delhi, India)

BHARDWA, Jeetesh Maganlal 20 Penderel Road, Hounslow TW3 3QR Tel: 020 8577 3075 — MB ChB 1994 Dundee. SHO (Surg.) Walsall Manor Hosp. Basic Surgic. Trainee. Socs: BMA. Prev: SHO (A & E) Milton Keynes Gen. Hosp. & NHS Trust; Ho. Off. (Med.) Stirling Roy. Infirm.; Ho. Off. (Surg.) Ninewells Hosp. & Med. Sch. Dundee.

BHARDWAJ, Mukesh Kumar Frankley Health Centre, 125 New Street, Rubery, Birmingham B45 0EU Tel: 0121 453 8211; 23 Beaudesert Road, Birmingham B20 3TQ — MB ChB 1989 Dundee; BSc (Hons) Dund 1986; MRCGP 1995; DRCOG 1996; DFFP 1996. (Dundee Univ. Med. Sch.) Prev: GP/Regist. Knowle Surg. Solihull; SHO (O & G) Solihull Hosp. Birm.; SHO (Paediat.) Birm. Childr. Hosp.

BHARDWAJ, Rakesh 178 Coronation Avenue, Bath BA2 2JS — MB ChB 1993 Bristol.

BHARDWAJ, Rita Bhardwaj and Mamtora, Crawford Avenue Health Centre, Crawford Avenue, Wembley HA0 2HX Tel: 020 8903 6411 — MB BS 1987 Lond.

BHARDWAJ, Shri Krishan The Hyde Surgery, 37/39 The Hyde, Stevenage SG2 9SB Tel: 01438 354582 Fax: 01438 312099; (branch Surgery), The Symonds Green Health Centre, Filey Close, Stevenage SG1 2JW Tel: 01438 351784 Fax: 01438 312099 — MB BS 1971 Panjab.

BHARDWAJ, Vipan 83 Hawkesbury Drive, Calcot, Reading RG31 7ZR — MB BS 1993 Lond.

BHARGAVA, Mr Aman 17 Berther Road, Hornchurch RM11 3HU — MB BS 1988 Lond.; FRCS Eng. 1992. Regist. (Neurosurg.) Nat. Hosp. for Nerv. Dis. Lond. Prev: SHO Rotat. (Surg.) Harrow HA; Ho. Off., SHO & Demonst. (Anat.) Roy. Free Hosp. Sch. Med. Lond.; Ho. Off. St. Albans City Hosp.

BHARGAVA, Amitabh Southgate Surgery, 2 Forester Road, Southgate, Crawley RH10 6EQ Tel: 01293 522231 Fax: 01293 515655 — MB BS 1983 Madras; LRCP Edin. LRCS Edin. LRCPS Glas. 1987. (Madras) GP Crawley, W. Sussex.

BHARGAVA, Anand 337 Caledonian Road, London N1 1DW — MB BS 1963 Rajasthan.

BHARGAVA, Jaishankar Prasad Newcastle Surgery, Llangewydd Road, Cefn Coed, Bridgend CF31 4XX Tel: 01656 652721 Fax: 01656 662864; 43 Merthyr Mawr Road, Bridgend CF31 3NN — MB BS 1963 Vikram; DLO Eng. 1971. (Mahatma Gandhi Memor. Med. Coll. Indore) Hosp. Pract. (ENT Surg.) Bridgend Gen. Hosp. Prev: Regist. (ENT Surg.) Bridgend Gen. Hosp.; SHO (ENT) Bristol Gen. Hosp.; Ho. Off. (Med.) Geo. Eliot Hosp. Nuneaton.

BHARGAVA, Jonathan Sunil 24 Clifton Pk Road, Stockport SK2 6LA — MB ChB 1997 Sheff.

BHARGAVA, Rajnish Herschel Medical Centre, 45 Osborne Street, Slough SL1 1TT Tel: 01753 520643 Fax: 01753 554964 — MB BS 1993 Lond.; DRCOG 1996; DCH RCP Lond. 1995. (St. Geo.)

BHARGAVA, Sandhya Temple Square Surgery, 2 Temple Square, Dartford DA1 5HZ Tel: 01322 226090 — MB BS 1969 Lucknow; BSc Lucknow 1963, MB BS 1969; DA Eng. 1979. (G.S.V.M. Med. Coll.) Prev: GP Lond.; GP Milton Keynes; SHO (Anaesth.) Brook Gen. Hosp. Lond. & W. Kent Gen. Hosp. Maidstone.

BHARI, Jasdeep Kaur 26 Medcroft Avenue, Birmingham B20 1NB — MB ChB 1994 Leic.

BHARMAL, Samina 22 Guilford Road, Leicester LE2 2RB — BM BS 1991 Nottm.

BHARTI, Harpreet Kaur 21 Parklands Court, Great West Road, Hounslow TW5 9AU — MB ChB 1995 Liverp.

BHARTI, Rajpreet Kaur 8 Old Mill Close, Langford, Biggleswade SG18 9QY — MB ChB 1996 Manch.

BHARTIA, Bobby Sudhir Kumar 11 West Court, West Avenue, Roundham, Leeds LS8 2JP Tel: 0113 273 2713; 21 Wharfedale Road, Pogmoor, Barnsley S75 2LJ Tel: 01226 203494 Email: bobbybhartia@hotmail.com — MB BS 1992 Lond.; MRCP 1997. (St Georges)

BHARTIA, Ramakant Ramgopal The Health Centre, 2 Duke Street, Hoyland, Barnsley S74 9QS Tel: 01226 748719 Fax: 01226 360162; 21 Wharfedale Road, Pogmoor, Barnsley S75 2LJ Tel: 01226 203494 Fax: 01226 360162 — MB BS Gauhati 1966. (Med. Coll. Gauhati) Prev: Regist. (Psychiat.) St. Crispin Hosp. N.ampton; SHO (Orthop.) Orthop. & Accid. Hosp. Sunderland; Ho. Phys. Ryhope Gen. Hosp.

BHARUCHA, Chitra (retired) 15 Richmond Court, Lisburn BT27 4QU Tel: 02892 678347 — MB BS Madras 1968; FRCPath 1990. Cons. Haemat. Belf. City Hosp.; GMC Counc. Mem.; Non Exec. Director UK Transpl. Auth.; WHO Expert Advisory Panel for Blood/Products. Prev: Dep. Chief Exec./Dep. Med. Dir. N. I. Blood Transfus. Serv. Belf.

BHARUCHA, Hoshang Institute of Pathology, Queen's University of Belfast, Grosvenor Road, Belfast BT12 6BN Tel: 028 240503 ext. 327 — MD 1970 Madras; MD (Path.) Madras 1970, MB BS 1965; FRCPath 1986, M 1973. (Christian Med. Coll. Vellore) Sen. Lect. Qu. Univ. Belf.; Cons. Pathol. Roy. Vict. Hosp. Belf. Socs: Path. Soc. Gt. Brit. & Irel. & Assn. Clin. Path. Prev: Lect. Path. Christian Med. Coll. Vellore & Ludhiana, India.

BHARUCHA, Manek-Phiroz Eddie Department of Child Psychiatry, St Mary's Hospital, Paddington Green, London W2 1LQ Tel: 020 7723 1081; 28 Ravenscroft Avenue, London NW11 0RY Tel: 020 8455 5069 — MD 1976 Bombay; DPM 1975. Princip. Child Psychother. (Child Psychiat.) St. Mary's Hosp. Lond.; Lect. Centre Psychoanalyt. Psychother.; Lect. Arbours Psychother. Socs: Assn. Child Psychother.; UK Counc. Psychother. Prev: Cons. Psychiat. L.T.M.G. Hosp., Bombay; Cons. Psychiat. Arbours Assn. Lond.

BHASIN, Bharat Bhooshan New Street Surgery, 21 New Street, Milnsbridge, Huddersfield HD3 4LB Tel: 01484 651622; 812 Manchester Road, Milnsbridge, Huddersfield HD4 5SZ Tel: 01484 644447 — MB BS 1965 Rajasthan; BSc, MB BS Rajasthan 1965. (S.M.S. Med. Coll. Jaipur) GP Huddersfield. Prev: Orthop. Regist. Orpington Hosp.; SHO Gen. Surg. Moorgate Hosp. Rotherham; SHO Orthop. & Accid. N. Staffs. Roy. Infirm. Stoke-on-Trent.

BHASIN, Neelesh 17 Concorde Close, Hounslow TW3 4DG — MB ChB 1986 Glas.; BSc (Hons) St. And. 1982.

BHASIN, Rajesh 3 Sonning Meadows, Sonning, Wokingham RG11 1XX — MRCS Eng. LRCP Lond. 1987.

BHASKAR, Vijay Ashok Paul The Surgery, 194 Sheldon Heath Road, Sheldon, Birmingham B26 2DR Tel: 0121 743 4444 — MB BS 1980 Bombay; LRCP LRCS Ed. LRCPS Glas. 1984.

BHASKARA, Rajendra Gupta Hull Royal Infirmary, Hull HU3 2JZ Tel: 01482 328541; 3 Oaklands Drive, Willerby, Hull HU10 6BJ Tel: 01482 654817 — MB BS 1972 Sri Venkateswara; DO RCPSI 1980. (Kurnool Med. Coll.) Staff Grade (Ophth.) Hull Roy. Infirm. Prev: Clin. Asst. (Ophth.) Blackburn Roy. Infirm.; Regist. (Ophth.) Altnagelvin Hosp. Lond.derry.

BHASKARA RAO, Beeraka Clinical Medical Officer, Barnsley Community & Priority Services, Kendray Hospital, Doncaster Road, Barnsley S70 3RD — MB BS 1971 Andhra.

BHASKARAN, Ann Margaret 495 Welbeck Road, Walker, Newcastle upon Tyne NE6 2PB Tel: 0191 265 5639; Guildford, Kellfield Avenue, Low Fell, Gateshead NE9 5YP Tel: 0191 491 4847 — MB BS 1961 Durh.; DA Eng. 1963. (Durh.) Socs: Fac. Anaesth. RCS Eng. Prev: Ho. Phys. & Ho. Surg. Roy. Vict. Infirm. Newc.; Regist. Anaesth. W. Cumbld. Hosp. Gp.; Specialist Anaesth. Min. of Health Libya.

BHASKARAN, Ann Radha Guildford, Kellfield Avenue, Gateshead NE9 5YP — MB BS 1994 Newc.

BHASKARAN, Nagi Chetty Barnsley District General Hospital, Gawber Road, Barnsley S75 2 Tel: 01226 730000 Fax: 0114 271 3771 Email: ncbhaskaran@shef.ac.uk — MB BS 1986 Madras; MRCP (UK) 1989; DA (UK) 1990; FFA RCSI 1994; FRCA 1994. (Stanley Med. Coll. Madras) Cons. (Anaesth.), Barnsley Dist. Gen. Hosp., Barnsley; Hon. Sen. Regist. Trent RHA Sheff. Socs: Intens. Care Soc.; Assn. Anaesth. GB & Irel. Prev: Lect. (Anaesth.) Univ.

Sheff.; Regist. (Anaesth.) Trent RHA; SHO Rotat. (Med.) Plymouth Gp. Hosps.

BHASKARAN, Mr Undiyil, Lt.-Col. RAMC Retd. (retired) Guildford, Kellfield Avenue, Low Fell, Gateshead NE9 5YP Tel: 0191 491 4847 — MB BS 1954 Madras; FRCS Glas. 1967. Prev: Cons. Surg. Vict. Hosp. Castries, St. Lucia.

BHAT, Ghullam Mohammad Stone Bridge House, Higher Heys Surgery, Heys Lane, Oswaldtwistle, Accrington BB5 3BP Tel: 01254 396265 Fax: 01254 392453 — MB BS 1968 Jammu & Kashmir; MB BS 1968 Jammu & Kashmir.

BHAT, Keshava Khandige 38 Sunningdale Park N., Belfast BT14 6RZ Tel: 028 716424 — MB BS 1970 Bangalor; MB BS Bangalore 1970; DPM Eng. 1981. (Bangalore Med. Coll.)

BHAT, Yogesh 2 Foxley Road, Thornton Heath, Croydon CR7 7DS — MB BS 1996 Lond.

BHATE, Milan Suryakant 11 Forest Rise, Oadby, Leicester LE2 4FH Tel: 0116 271 6722 — MB BS 1966 Nagpur. (Med. Coll. Nagpur)

BHATE, Shashank Madhav Hendon Health Centre, Meaburn Terrace, Sunderland SR1 2ND Tel: 0191 567 3393 Fax: 0191 510 3417 — MB BS 1975 Poona.

BHATE, Vaishali Soni 2 Park Villas, Gosforth, Newcastle upon Tyne NE3 4HU — MB BS 1992 Lond.

BHATHAL, Hari Singh Luton & Dunstable Hospital, Lewsey Road, Luton LU4 0DZ — LMS 1992 U Autonoma Madrid.

BHATI, Roy 7 Pulford Road, Bebington, Wirral CH63 2HN Tel: 0151 645 1899 Fax: 0151 645 1899 Email: 101570.262@compuserve.com — MB ChB 1993 Ed. (Ed.) SHO (Gen. Surg.) Roy. Albert Edwd. Infirm. Wigan. Prev: SHO (A & E) Roy. Albert Edwd. Infirm. Wigan; Ho. Off. (Surg. & Urol.) W.. Gen. Hosp. Edin.; Ho. Off. (Gen. Med.) Roy. Infirm. Med.

BHATIA, Ajay Singh 4 Waverton Street, London W1J 5QN — MB BS 1993 Lond.; MD (Univ. Lond.) 2001; MB BS (Distinc.) Lond. 1993; MRCP (UK) 1996. (Univ. Coll. & Middlx. Sch. Med.) Prev: SHO (Rheumatol. & Gen. Med.) Univ. Coll. Lond.; SHO (Oncol.) Roy. Marsdon NHS Trust Lond.; SHO (Cardiol. Thoracic Med.) Harefield Hosp.

BHATIA, Anu 103 Grove Vale, East Dulwich, London SE22 8EN — MB BS 1996 Lond.

BHATIA, Mr Ashok Gridharilal Department of Orthopaedics, Nevill Hall Hospital, Abergavenny NP7 7EG; 44 Malford Grove, Gilwern, Abergavenny NP7 0RN Tel: 01873 831402 — MB BS 1972 Karachi; FRCS Glas. 1984; MCh (Orth) Dundee 1998. (Dow Medical College, Karachi) Staff Orthop. Surg. Nevill Hall Hosp. Abergevanny. Prev: Asst. Prof., Orthop. Surg., Bolan Med. Coll., Quetta, Pakistan.

BHATIA, Avneesh Atul Corner Cottage, 90 Wollaton Vale, Nottingham NG8 2PN — MB BS 1996 Newc.

BHATIA, Gurbir Singh 79 Toothill Road, Loughborough LE11 1PN — MB ChB 1996 Birm.; ChB Birm. 1996.

BHATIA, Ishwar Lal Landseer Road Surgery, 478 Landseer Road, Ipswich IP3 9LU Tel: 01473 274495 Fax: 01473 727642; 4 Playford Road, Rushmere, St. Andrew, Ipswich IP4 5RH Tel: 01473 611662 Fax: 01473 611764 — MB BS 1966 Agra; MS Agra 1969. (Sarojini Naidu Med. Coll.) Clin. Asst. (Orthop.) Heath Rd. Hosp. Ipswich. Socs: MDU. Prev: Regist. (Orthop.) Ipswich Hosp.; Med. Off. Safdarjang Hosp. New Delhi, India.

BHATIA, Kunwar Surayaveer Singh 20 Broad Lane, Hampton TW12 3AW — BM BS 1996 Nottm.

BHATIA, Mahendra Shantikumar Market Cross Surgery, 103 Commercial Street, Rothwell, Leeds LS26 0QD — MB BS 1967 Nagpur; MRCGP 1972; DFFP 1993; Cert FPA 1972; DObst RCOG 1969. Hosp. Pract. (Gyn.) Leeds Univ. St. Jas. Hosp.; Occupat. Phys. Cameron Iron Works Leeds; Med. Off. DHSS. Socs: Fell. Roy. Soc. Med.; (Comm. Mem.) Leeds W. Riding M-C Soc.Mem. BMA; N. Eng. Gyn. Soc. Prev: Pres. Leeds & W. Riding M-C Soc.

BHATIA, Maya Mohandas The Surgery, 470 Stafford Road, Oxley, Wolverhampton WV10 6AR; 16 Springfield Court, Sutton Road, Walsall WS1 2PB — MB BS 1972 Gujarat; DObst RCOG 1980. (B. J. Med. Coll. Ahmedabad, India) Socs: Med. Protec. Soc.

BHATIA, Neera Northcott Farm, London Road, Whimple, Exeter EX5 2PT Tel: 01404 822367 — BM BS 1989 Nottm.; BMedSci Nottm. 1987; MRCGP 1993. (Nottm.)

BHATIA, Neil 21 Maxwell Drive, Glasgow G41 5DS — MB BS 1992 Lond.; MB BS (Hons.) Lond. 1992; MRCGP 1996; DRCOG 1995. (St. Geo. Hosp. Med. Sch.) GP Princip. Yatley. Prev: SHO A & E Thanet Gen. Hosp.

BHATIA, Prit Pal Kaur Community Child Health Department, Livingstone Hospital, East Hill, Dartford DA1 1SA Tel: 01322 292233; Preet Niwas, Church Road, Hartley, Longfield DA3 8DN Tel: 01474 702154 — MB BS 1959 Delhi; DCH Eng. 1965; DCH Delhi 1962. (Lady Hardinge Med. Coll.) SCMO Dartford & Gravesham Health Dist. Socs: Soc. Pub. Health.; Fac. Community Health; Brit. Paediat. Assn. & BMA. Prev: Regist. (Paediat.) Lady Hardinge Med. Coll. New Delhi, India; SHO (Paediat.) All St.s Hosp. Chatham Kent; CMO (Communicaty Child Health) Dartford.

BHATIA, Pritam Singh Joyce Green Hospital, Dartford DA1 5PL Tel: 01322 227242; Preet Niwas, Church Road, Hartley, Longfield DA3 8DN Tel: 01474 702154 — MB BS 1955 Punjab; MB BS Punjab (India) 1955; MRCP (UK) 1972. (Amritsar Med. Coll.) Cons. Phys. (Geriat. Med.) Joyce Green Hosp. Dartford. Socs: Brit. Geriat. Soc. & BMA. Prev: Cons. Geriat. Med. Medway HA; Sen. Regist. (Geriat. Med.) Guy's Hosp. Lond.

BHATIA, Raj Kumar 24 Charleville Road, Birmingham B19 1DA — MB ChB 1994 Manch.

BHATIA, Renu 401 Harlington Road, Hillingdon, Uxbridge UB8 3JG — MB BS 1983 Lond.

BHATIA, Sarita 40 Armada Way, Chatham ME4 6PH — MB BS 1977 Agra. Sen. Lect., Keele Univ., Staffs. Research Fell. in Gen. Pract., Regional GP Unit, Birm.; Med. Adviser to C.E. Andersons & Sons Ltd., Barclays Bank Ltd. & other Cos.; Primary Care Phys. (UK & abRd.); Vis. Cons. Learning Assessm. Centre, Horsham, W. Sussex; HS RSCH Guildford; RAF Med. Pract.

BHATIA, Shalini 159 Nether Street, London N12 8EX — MB BS 1994 Lond.

BHATIA, Surendra-Singh Jason-Smrati, Wisbech Road, Manea, March PE15 0HB Tel: 01354 680558 Email: surendra.s.bhatia.tesco.net — MB BS 1963 Vikram. (M.G.M. Med. Coll. Indore) Socs: BMA.

BHATIA, Tazeem Flat 2, 15 Grenfell Road, Manchester M20 6TG — MB ChB 1998 Manch.; MB ChB Manch 1998.

BHATIA, Vinay Kumar 110 Borstal Street, Rochester ME1 3JT — MB BS 1994 Lond.

BHATIANI, Rekha 39 Sycamore Close, St Ippolyts, Hitchin SG4 7SN — MB BS 1989 Lond.

BHATIANI, Wirinder 16 Weston Drive, Stanmore HA7 2EU — MB ChB 1976 Leeds.

BHATKAR, Rajaninath Laxmanrao Auchinleck Health Centre, Main Street, Auchinleck, Cumnock KA18 2AY Tel: 01290 421903; Shalimar, Rigg Road, Auchinleck, Cumnock KA18 1RT Tel: 01290 424055 — MB BS 1957 Nagpur; DTM & H Eng. 1962. Dep. Police Surg. Socs: BMA; Assoc. MRCGP. Prev: Lect. (Med) Med. Coll. Nagpur; Regist. (Gen. Med.) Beckett Hosp. Barnsley.

BHATNAGAR, Deepak, TD Department of Clinical Biochemistry & Metabolic Medicine, The Royal Oldham Hospital, Oldham OL1 2JH Tel: 0161 627 8384 Fax: 0161 627 8289 Email: d.bhatnagar@man.ac.uk; 4 Park Road, Cheadle Hulme, Cheadle SK8 7DA — MB BS 1975 Aligarh; MB BS Aligarh, India 1975; PhD Manch. 1991; FRCP 1997, M 1993; MRCPath 1994. Cons. (Diabetic and Clin. Biochem.ry) Roy. Oldham Hosp.; Cons. (Diabetes Metab. Med. & Clin. Biochem. Roy. Oldham Hosp.; Lect. & Hon. Cons. Metab. Med. Manch. Roy. Infirm.; Hon. Sen. Lect. & Cons. Phys., Manch. Roy. Infirm. Prev: Sen. Regist. (Clin. Biochem.) NW RHA; Regist. (Chem. Path.) Leics. Roy. Infirm.; SHO (Clin. Biochem.) Roy. Vict. Infirm. Newc. u. Tyne.

***BHATNAGAR, Drupati** 21 North Croft Rise, Bradford BD8 0BW — MB BS 1972 Rajasthan; MD 1977.

BHATNAGAR, Manisha 11A Harrod Dr, Southport PR8 2HA — MB ChB 1997 Manch.

BHATNAGAR, Pooja Medical Centre, Luton & Dunstable Hospital, Lewsey Road, Luton LU4 0DZ Tel: 01582 491122; 33 Priory Gardens, Berkhamsted HP4 2DS Tel: 01442 863481 Email: pbhatnagar_@hotmail.com — MB BS 1996 Lond.; MRCP. (United Medical and Dental Schools of Guy's and St. Thomas) SHO (Gen. Med.) Luton & Dunstable Hosp. Lewsey Rd. Luton. Socs: BMA; MDU. Prev: SHO (A & E) Luton & Dunstable Hosp. Luton; Ho. Off.

(Gen. Surg./Orthop.) Guy's Hosp. Lond.; Ho. Off. (Gen. Med.) Hereford Hosp.

BHATT, Arun 56 Stockiemuir Avenue, Bearsden, Glasgow G61 3LX — MB ChB 1995 Glas.

BHATT, Asha Mahendra 6 Wolsey Drive, Bowdon, Altrincham WA14 3QU — MB BS 1969 Baroda; MRCPsych 1986. Cons. Childs & Adolesc. Psychiat. Ment. Health Serv. Salford Manch.

BHATT, Asit Narendra 52 Ladysmith Avenue, Ilford IG2 7AY Tel: 020 8599 9089 — MB BS 1983 Bombay; MD Bombay 1985; MRCOG 1989.

BHATT, Bhanudev Mahadev, Lt.-Col. RAMC Ministry of Defence Hospital Unit (Northallerton), Northallerton Health Services NHS Trust, Friarage Hospital, Northallerton DL6 1JG Tel: 01609 763109 Fax: 01609 763126 Email: bbhatt@nahs-tr.northy.nhs.uk; 6 Carlton House, 127 Cleveland St, London W1T 6QD Tel: 020 7380 1043 — MB BS 1973 Poona; MD (Med.) Poona 1977; FRCP Lond. 1996; MRCP (UK) 1981. (Armed Forces Medical College, Pune, India) Cons. Phys. MDHU (N), Friarage Hosp. N.allerton Health Servs. NHS Trust, N.allerton, N. Yorks. Socs: Fell. Roy. Soc. Med.; Diabetes UK. Prev: Cons. Phys. The Duchess of Kent's Hosp. Catterick Garrison; Cons. Phys. TPM RAF Hosp., Akrotiri & BMH Iserlohn, Germany; Sen. Specialist (Med.) Musgrave Pk. Hosp.

BHATT, Ganga Singh (retired) Department of Psychiatry, Fairfield General Hospital, Bury BL9 7TD Tel: 0161 764 6081 — MB BS Panjab (India) 1968; MRCPsych 1975; DPM Leeds 1973. Prev: Cons. Psychiat. Fairfield Gen. Hosp. Bury.

BHATT, Gunvantrai Bhaishanker 38 Bushey Hill Road, London SE5 8QJ Tel: 020 7703 5874 — MB BS 1950 Bombay; BSc, MB BS Bombay 1950; DA Eng. 1952. Socs: BMA. Prev: SHO Dorking Gen. Hosp., Black Notley Hosp. Braintree & Roy. Bucks.; Hosp. Aylesbury.

BHATT, Gunwant Kaur 2 Wood Road, Summerseat, Bury BL9 5QA Tel: 01204 883165 — MB BS 1971 Panjab; FFA RCS Eng. 1977; DA Eng. 1973. (Ludhiana India) Assoc. Specialist (Anaesth.) Stepping Hill Hosp. Stockport. Prev: Regist. Burnley Gen. Hosp. Lancs., Hope Hosp. Salford & St. Jas. Hosp. Leeds.

BHATT, Hashmukhray B12 Metabolism Unit, Chelsea & Westminster Hospital, Fulham Road, London SW10 Tel: 020 8946 8623; 21 Rickmansworth Road, Pinner HA5 3TE Tel: 020 8866 7795 Fax: 020 8746 8860 — MB ChB 1964 Manch.; PhD Lond. 1990. Research Fell. (Child Health) Char. Cross & W.m. Med. Sch. Lond.; Assoc. Prof. Human Physiol. Jondishapour Univ., Iran. Socs: Harveian Soc. & Founder Mem. Thos. Addison Soc. Prev: SHO (Gen. Med.) Hope Hosp. Salford.

BHATT, Hemant Batukrai Burgess Road Surgery, 357a Burgess Road, Southampton SO16 3BD Tel: 023 8067 6233 Fax: 023 8067 2909 — MB BS 1985 Lond.

BHATT, Jayesh Narendra Park Medical Centre, 57 Hawkstone Rd, London SE16 2PE Tel: 0207 237 3414; Tel: 0208 599 9089 — MB BS 1973 Bombay. (Grant Med. Coll.) Princip. GP Lond. SE16. Prev: SHO (Chest Med.) Plaistow Hosp.; SHO (Geriat.) Langthorne Hosp.; Ho. Off. (Gen. Med.) St. Mary's Hosp. Plaistow.

BHATT, Kaushik Babubhai 103 Arosa Drive, Harborne, Birmingham B17 0SD — MB BS 1976 Baroda; FRCR 1982; DMRD Eng. 1981.

BHATT, Mahendraprasad Kantilal 6 Wolsey Drive, Off Eyebrook Road, Bowdon, Altrincham WA14 3QU — MB BS 1968 Baroda. Ophth. Med. Pract. Chesh.

BHATT, Nandkishor Jivanlal Villette Surgery, Suffolk Street, Hendon, Sunderland SR2 8AX Tel: 0191 567 9361 Fax: 0191 514 7476 — LRCP LRCS 1983 Ed.; BSc Saurastra 1968; MD Gujarat 1978, MB BS 1975; LRCP LRCS Ed. LRCPS Glas. 1983; DA Gujarat 1977. Socs: E. End Med. Soc. & Med. Defence Union of Scotl.

BHATT, Preetinder 15 Hall Farm Park, Micklefield, Leeds LS25 4DP — MB ChB 1996 Manch. (Manchester Medical School) SHO, O & G, St James Univ. Hosp., Leeds.

BHATT, Priya Ranu Woodmill, Wood Road, Bury BL9 5QA — MB ChB 1998 Manch.; MB ChB Manch 1998.

BHATT, Pulkit Indravadan 42 Wyvern Road, Sutton Coldfield B74 2PT — MB ChB 1997 Birm.

BHATT, Ramesh Chandra Venishanker Medical Imaging Department, Sandwell Health Care NHS Trust, Lyndon, West Bromwich B71 4HJ Tel: 0121 553 1831 — MB ChB 1977 Liverp.; MB ChB Liverp.1977; FRCR 1983; DMRD Lond. 1982. Cons. Radiol. Sandwell Healthcare NHS Trust W. Bromwich. Socs: Brit. Inst. Radiol.; BMA; RSNA. Prev: Sen. Regist. (Radiol.) W. Midl. RHA; Regist. (Radiol.) Plymouth.

BHATT, Rameshchandra Kantilal Danemead Grove Surgery, 81 Danemead Grove, Petts Hill, Northolt UB5 4NX Tel: 020 8423 8423 — MB BS 1978 Lond.; BSc Lond. (Immunol.) 1975; MRCGP 1986; DCH RCP Lond. 1982. GP Ealing, Hounslow & Hammersmith FHSA; Course Organiser New Ealing Hosp. VTS; GP Tutor Postgrad. Dept. New Ealing Hosp.

BHATT, Rupesh Indravadan 42 Wyvern Road, Sutton Coldfield B74 2PT — BChir 1994 Camb.

BHATT, Sarah Jane Department of GU Medicine, Royal South Hampshire Hospital, Brinton's Terrace, Southampton SO14 0YG; 207 Hill Lane, Bassett, Southampton SO15 7TZ — MB ChB 1986 Sheff.; Dip. GU Med. Soc. Apoth Lond. 1990. Staff Grade. (Genitourin. Med.) P/T. Roy. S. Hants. Hosp. Soton.

BHATT, Saroj Mahendra Harold Hill Centre, Gooshays Drive, Romford RM3 9JP Tel: 01708 343815 Fax: 01708 379790 — MB BS 1975 Delhi; MB BS 1975 Delhi.

BHATT, Shailendra Kumar Coleridge Crescent Surgery, 2 Coleridge Crescent, Woodhall Farm Estate, Hemel Hempstead HP2 7PQ Tel: 01442 234220 — MB BS 1974 Patna.

BHATT, Subhash Chandra Pennine Road Surgery, 15A Pennine Road, Glossop SK13 6NN Tel: 01457 862305 Fax: 01457 857010; 15A Pennine Road, Glossop SK13 6NN — MB BS 1971 Indore.

BHATT, Vikram Batukrai Chiswick Family Practice, 89 Southfield Road, Bedford Park, Chiswick, London W4 1BB Tel: 020 8995 6707; 2 Perivale Gardens, Ealing, London W13 8DH Tel: 020 8998 3048 — MB BS 1981 Lond.; BSc Lond. 1978; MRCGP Lond. 1986; DRCOG Lond. 1984.

BHATTACHAN, Mr Chitra Lal 7 Hamilton Avenue, North Cheam, Sutton SM3 9RJ — MB BS 1969 Calcutta; FRCS Glas. 1989. (R.G. Kar Med. Coll.) SHO (Orthop. Surg.) Roy. E. Sussex Hosp. Hastings.

BHATTACHARJEE, Gaur Bhusan Accrington Road Surgery, 85-91 Accrington Road, Blackburn BB1 2AF Tel: 01254 52002 Fax: 01254 265803; Netherleigh, 2 Whalley Road, Wilpshire, Blackburn BB1 9PJ Tel: 01254 246250 — MB BS 1960 Calcutta; BSc Calcutta 1954. (Nilratan Sirkar Med. Coll.) Clin. Asst. (Ment. Subn.ity) Burnley, Pendle & Rossendale HA. Prev: SHO (Orthop. & Cas.) Roy. Infirm. Blackburn; SHO (Gen. Surg.) Scotton Banks Hosp. KnaresBoro.; SHO (Plastic Surg.) St. Lawrence Hosp. Chepstow.

BHATTACHARYA, Anjan 23 Glyn Simon Close, Danescourt, Llandaff, Cardiff CF5 2RZ — MB BS 1974 Calcutta.

BHATTACHARYA, Arpita 272 Lister House, Eastbourne District General Hospital, Kings Drive, Eastbourne BN21 2UD — MB BS 1986 Calcutta.

BHATTACHARYA, Bimal Ranjan Norse Walk Surgery, 66 Norse Walk, Corby NN18 9DG Tel: 01536 743228 Fax: 01536 460092 — MB BS 1957 Calcutta; Dip. Cardiol. 1961; MRCP Lond. 1968; MRCP Ed. 1968. (Med. Coll. Calcutta)

BHATTACHARYA, Dwaipayan 31 Gladstone Street, Wednesbury WS10 8BE — MB BS 1967 Calcutta; DLO Eng. 1976. (R.G. Kar Med. Coll.) Prev: Ho. Surg. ENT. Ho. Surg. & Ho. Phys. R.G. Kar Med. Coll. Hosp.

BHATTACHARYA, Joti Jonathan Department of Neuroradiology, Institute of Neurological Sciences, Southern General Hospital, 1345 Govan Road, Glasgow G51 4TF Tel: 0141 201 2040 Fax: 0141 445 5273 Email: jobhatt@aol.com — MB BS 1986 Lond.; FRCR 1993. (Royal Free Hosp. Sch. of Med.) Cons. Neuroradiol. Inst. of Neurol. Sci. Glasg. Prev: Sen. Regist. in Neuroradiol. Newc. Gen. Hosp.; Sen. Regist. in Radiol. Lond. Hosp. & Nat. Hosp. for Neurol. & Neurosurg. Qu. Sq. Lond.; Regist. in Radiol. St Thos. Hosp. Lond.

BHATTACHARYA, Mr Kausik Apartment 12, 29 Abercorn Place, St John's Wood, London NW8 9DS Tel: 020 7624 8531; 56 Ivy Lane, Headington, Oxford OX3 9DT — MB BS 1990 Lond.; FRCS Eng. 1995. (St George's Hospital) Regist. Walsgrave Hosp. Coventry. Prev: Regist. Heartlands Hosp. Birm.; Research Regist. John Radcliffe Hosp. Oxf.; SHO (Gen. Surg.) Ysbyty Gwynedd Bangor.

BHATTACHARYA, Kaustuv University Hospital Lewisham, Lewisham High Street, London SE13 Email: www.kaustuv1@hotmail.com — MB BS 1994 Lond.; MRCPCH; MRCP. (St George's Hospital Medical School) SPR Paediat. S. Thames Rotat. Prev: Edin. Rotat. Regist.; SPR Paediat. Lewisham Univ. Hosp.; SPR William Harvey Hosp. Kent.

BHATTACHARYA, Kirsty Fiona 3 Plunkett Road, Dipton, Stanley DH9 9BJ; First Floor Flat, 99 Kennington Pk Road, London SE11 4JJ — LMSSA 1994 Lond.; MB BS 1994; BSc (Hons) Lond. 1991; LRCS Eng. 1994; MRCP (UK) 1998. (St Thomas's Hospital (UMDS)) SHO (Gen. Med.) Frimley Pk. Hosp., Camberley; Clin. Research Fell. (Neurol.), KCH, Lond. Socs: BMA. Prev: SHO (A & E) King's Coll. Hosp.; SHO (Gen.Med.), Acute Stroke Unit, King's Coll. Hosp.; SHO (Gen. Neurol. & Epileptol.) Kings Regional Neurosci. Centre.

BHATTACHARYA, Mukta 32 Oxford Drive, Eastcote, Ruislip HA4 9EZ — BM 1998 Soton.

BHATTACHARYA, Pradip Kumar 3 Plunkett Road, Dipton, Stanley DH9 9BJ — MB BS 1958 Calcutta.

BHATTACHARYA, Mr Satyajit Department of Surgery, Royal London Hospital, Whitechapel, London E1 1BB Tel: 020 7377 7439 Fax: 020 7377 7439 — MB BS 1986 Bombay; MPhil Lond. 1995; MS Bombay 1988; FRCS Ed. 1991; FRCS (Gen.) 1998. (Grant Medical College Bombay) Cons. Surg., Roy. Lond. Hosp.and St. Bartholomews Hosp., Lond.; Hepato-Biliary-Pancreatic Surg. Socs: Assn. of Surg.s of Gt. Britain & Irel.; Assn. of Upper Gastrointestinal Surg.s; Internat. HPB Assn. Prev: Research Fell. (Surg.) Roy. Free Hosp. Lond.; Regist. (Surg.) Roy. Free & Whittington Hosps. Lond.; Lect. (Surg.) Roy. Free Hosp. Sch. Med. Lond.

BHATTACHARYA, Mr Vishwanath Vivek 272 Lister House, Eastbourne District General Hospital, Kings Drive, Eastbourne BN21 2UD — MB BS 1985 Poona; FRCS Ed. 1994; FRCS Glas. 1993.

BHATTACHARYYA, Amitabha St Crispin Hospital, Duston, Northampton NN5 4UN Tel: 01604 52323 — MB BS 1959 Calcutta. (Med. Coll. Calcutta) Asst. Psychiat. St. Crispin Hosp. N.ampton.

BHATTACHARYYA, Bhanu High Trees, 124 Walsall Road, Perry Barr, Birmingham B42 1SG Tel: 0121 356 4239 — MB BS 1981 Calcutta; MRCS Eng. LRCP Lond. 1987.

BHATTACHARYYA, Binoy Kumar Marjory Warren Medical Centre, West Middlesex Hospital, Isleworth Tel: 020 8565 5450; 179 Abbotts Drive, Wembley HA0 3SH — MB BS 1964 Calcutta; MRCP (UK) 1978; MRCPI 1977. Cons. Phys. c/o Elderly W. Middlx. Hosp. Isleworth.

BHATTACHARYYA, Mr Durga Prasad c/o Dr B. N. Dey, 51 Tyninghame Avenue, Wolverhampton WV6 9PP — MB BS 1961 Calcutta; MCh Orth Liverp. 1972; FRCS Ed. 1968.

BHATTACHARYYA, Madhumita 179 Abbotts Drive, Wembley HA0 3SH — MB BS 1998 Lond.; MB BS Lond 1998.

BHATTACHARYYA, Mimi Raka 8 Hyde Park Avenue, Winchmore Hill, London N21 2PP Tel: 020 8351 8348 Email: mbhattacharya@hotmail.com — MB BS 1997 Lond.; BSc Lond. 1994. (St Marys) Socs: BMA; MPS. Prev: Jun. Ho. Off., P.ss Alexandra Hosp., Woollangabba, Australia; JHO, Qu. Eliz. II, Jubilee Hosp., Coopers Plain, Australia; Ho. Off. (Orthop./Gen. Surg.) P.ss Roy. Hosp. Haywards Heath.

BHATTACHARYYA, Mukti Nath (retired) 56 Green Pastures, Stockport SK4 3RA Tel: 0161 432 3832 Fax: 0161 432 3832 — MB BS Calcutta 1959; FRCOG 1983, M 1964; DGO Calucutta 1961. Prev: Cons. Genitourin. Med. Manch. Roy. Infirm.

BHATTACHARYYA, Pranjit Kumar Chapeltown Health Centre, Spencer Place, Leeds LS7 4BB Tel: 0113 240 9090 Fax: 0113 249 8480 — MB BS 1973 Dibrugargh; MD Dibrugargh 1977; MRCPI 1985. (Assam Med. Coll. Dibrugargh) Mem. (Treas.) Leeds LMC; Bd. Mem. PCG.

BHATTACHARYYA, Mr Rabindra Nath 4 Lindrick Gardens, Chesterfield S40 3JJ — MB BS 1963 Calcutta; MS Calcutta 1969, MB BS 1963; FRCS Glas. 1978; FRCS Ed. 1977. (Nil Ratan Sircar Med. Coll.) Clin. Asst. (Orthop. & Trauma) Shotley Bridge Gen. Hosp. Consett.

BHATTACHARYYA, Sabyasachi 'The Well House', 64 Blakes Avenue, New Malden KT3 6RF Tel: 020 8949 0906 — MB BS 1964 Calcutta; FFA RCS Eng. 1973; DA Eng. 1968; DGO Calcutta 1966. (Calcutta Nat. Med. Coll.) Cons. (Anaesth.) Epsom Dist. Hosp. Prev: Sen. Regist. (Anaesth.) Char. Cross. Hosp. Lond.

BHATTACHARYYA, Mr Samareswar Park View, Lower Eaton, Eaton Bishop, Hereford HR2 9QE Tel: 01981 250344 — MB 1945 Calcutta; FRCS Eng. 1959. (R.G. Kar Med. Coll. Calcutta) Prev: Sen. Ho. Off. P. of Wales Gen. Hosp. Lond.; Res. Surg. Off. Roy. Devon & Exeter Hosp; Surg. Regist. Hastings Hosp. Gp.

BHATTACHARYYA, Sambhu Nath (retired) 18 Ashes Lane, Foxhills, Stalybridge SK15 2RH — MB BS 1957 Calcutta; FRCP Ed. 1994, M 1965; MRCPsych 1971; DPM Eng. 1966. Prev: Cons. Psychiat. Stepping Hill Hosp. Stockport.

BHATTACHARYYA, Mr Sanjoy Royal Victoria Infirmary, Accident 2 Emergency Department, Newcastle upon Tyne NE1 4LP Tel: 0191 232 5131; 101 Green Lane, Acklam, Middlesbrough TS5 7AQ Tel: 01642 812834 — MB BS 1985 Calcutta; FRCS Eng. 1992. Sen. Regist. (A & E) N. & Yorks. RHA. Socs: BMA; Fac. Accid. & Emerg. Med. Prev: Regist. (A & E) Middlesbrough Gen. Hosp.; SHO (Surg.) P.ss Roy. Hosp. Telford & Rotherham Dist. Gen. Hosp.

BHATTACHERJEE, Janet Wynne Public Health Laboratory, Musgrove Park Hospital, Taunton TA1 5DB Tel: 01823 335557 Fax: 01823 259453; 8 Halse Manor, Halse, Taunton TA4 3AE Tel: 01823 433440 — MB BS Lond. 1963; PhD Calcutta 1980; MRCS Eng. LRCP Lond. 1963; FRCPath 1983, M 1969; Dip. Bact. Lond 1968. Cons. Pub. Health Laborat. MusGr. Pk. Hosp. Som.

BHATTACHERJEE, Shaun Newton Lodge Regional Secure Unit, Ouchthorpe Lane, Wakefield WF1 3SP Tel: 01924 201688 Fax: 01924 814970 Email: shaun@bhatty.demon.co.uk — BM BS 1990 Nottm.; MMedSc Leeds 1996; BMedSci Nottm. 1987. (Nottm.) Sen. Regist. (Forens. Psychiat.) Newton Lodge Regional Secure Unit Wakefield.

BHATTACHERJEE, Sian Flat 8, Halse Manor, Halse, Taunton TA4 3AE — MB BCh 1997 Wales.

BHATTAD, Hiralal Laxminarayan Church Avenue Surgery, 2 Church Avenue, Sidcup DA14 6BU Tel: 020 8302 1114 Fax: 020 8309 6350 — MB BS 1966 Bombay.

BHATTI, Farah Naz Kausar 4 Cargreen Road, London SE25 5AF — BChir 1989 Camb.

BHATTI, Freda 'Romford House', Goose Green, Tendring, Colchester CO16 0BT Tel: 0976 877695 — MB BS 1991 Lond.; BSc (Hons.) Lond. 1986; MRCGP 1997. (UCL London) GP Lond.

BHATTI, Graeme Cameron Gopal 1 The Rowans, Sauchie, Alloa FK10 3EU — MB ChB 1996 Glas.

***BHATTI, Mr Haleem Uddin** 769 Manchester Road, Bankfoot, Bradford BD5 8LN.

BHATTI, Manssor Ahmad 26 Kirchen Road, West Ealing, London W13 0TY — MB BS 1982 Lond.; MRCS Eng. LRCP Lond. 1993.

BHATTI, Mehboob Elahi 6 Stratford Road, Shirley, Solihull B90 3LT Tel: 0121 744 1384 — MB BS 1977 Punjab.

BHATTI, Nadeem Taj Westmuir Medical Centre, 109 Crail Street, Glasgow G31 5RA Tel: 0141 554 4253 Fax: 0141 550 0177 — MB ChB 1990 Glas.

BHATTI, Naureen 19 Lonsdale Square, London N1 1EN — MB BS 1985 Lond.; MSc Lond. 1992; MRCP (UK) 1988; MFPHM RCP (UK) 1994; MRCGP (UK) 1997.

BHATTI, Rashid Ahmed The Surgery, 13-15 Washwood Heath Road, Saltley, Birmingham B8 1SH Tel: 0121 327 3926; 13/15 Washwood Heath Road, Saltley, Birmingham B8 1SH Tel: 0121 327 3926 Fax: 0121 328 1370 — MB BS 1972 Punjab; BSc Punjab 1965; DPM RCPSI 1985.

BHATTI, Mr Shabir Ahmad c/o 18 King Street, Gillingham ME7 1EP — MRCS Eng. LRCP Lond. 1978; MB ChB Zambia 1978; FRCS Ed. 1984. Cardiothoracic Regist. Qu. Eliz. Hosp. Birm. Prev: Rotat. Surg. Regist. Bradford Roy. Infirm.; Cardiothoracic Regist. N. Staffs. Roy. Infirm. Stoke-on-Trent.

BHATTI, Shazia 14 Park Road, Sparkhill, Birmingham B11 4HB — MB BS 1994 Lond. (UCL) Socs: Pharmaceut. Soc.

BHATTI, Sohail Sharif West Lancashire Primary Care Trust, Ormskirk & District General Hospital, Wigan Road, Ormskirk L39 Email: sohail.bhatti@westlancspct.nhs.uk — MB ChB 1985 Glas.; BSc (Hons.) Glas. 1982; MSc Manch. 1994; MFPHM 1998. (Glasgow) Cons. Pub. Health Med. W. Lancs. Primary Care Trust; Mem. of the Bd. & Exec. Comm. of W. Lancaster Primary Care Trust; Hon. Research Fell., Univ. Coll. St. Matrin's, Lancaster; Clin. Reviewer, Commiss. for Health Improvement. Socs: Fac. Pub. Health Med.; Fell.Roy. Soc. of Med. Prev: Cons. Pub. Health Med. Wirral Health Auth., Birkenhead.

BHATTI, Tahir Javaid Nayeem Heston Health Centre, 25 Cranford Lane, Heston, Hounslow West, Hounslow TW5 9ER Tel: 020 8321 3414 Fax: 020 8321 3409; 42 Sunnycroft Road, Hounslow TW3 4DR Tel: 020 8570 2973 — MB BS 1987 Lond.;

MRCGP 1994; DRCOG 1991; DGM RCP Lond. 1989. (Middlx. Hosp. Lond.)

BHATTI, Mr Tahir Siddiq Royal Cornwall Hospital, Treliske, Truro TR1 3LJ — MB BS 1984 Karachi; FRCS Ed. 1991.

BHATTI, Waqar Aslam University Hospital of South Manchester, Withington Hospital, Nell Lane, West Didsbury, Manchester M21 8LR Tel: 0161 445 8111; 241 Kingsway, Cheadle SK8 1LA — MB ChB 1992 Manch. SHO Rotat. (Surg.) Withington Hosp. Manch. Prev: SHO (Gen. Surg.) Withington Hosp. & Roy. Infirm. Manch.; Temp Lect. (Anat.) Univ. Manch.

BHATTI, Zulafqar Baber Donneybrook Medical Centre, Clarendon Street, Hyde SK14 2AH; 71 Richmond Court, Lisburn BT27 4QX — MB ChB Dundee 1991; MRCGP 1997; DRCOG 1996; DCH RCP Lond. 1995. Donneybrook Med. Centre, Clarendon St., Hyde, Chesh. Prev: Trainee GP/SHO Warrington Hosp. & Halwood Health Centre Chesh. VTS.

BHAUMIK, Sabyasachi Leicester Frith Hospital, Groby Road, Leicester LE3 9QF Tel: 0116 225 5274 Fax: 0116 225 5272; Email: susmita54@hotmail.com — MB BS 1980 Calcutta; FRCPsych 2001; MRCPsych 1988; DPM Eng. 1988. (R. G. Kar Med. Coll. Calcutta India) Cons. Psychiat. Frith Leicester Hosp.; Lead Clinician, Fosse Health NHS Trust; Chairperson of Speciality Educat. Comm., Psychiat. of Learning Disabil., Trust; Train. Progr. Director and Clin. Tutor Learning Disabil. Servs.; Scheme Organiser Higher Psychiat. Train. (Learning Disabil.) Leicester; Mem. Edit. Advis. Bd.: Europ. Jl. of Clin. Hypn.; Mem. Brit. Med. Hypnother. Exam. Bd.; Sec. Trent Regional Comm. of Psychiat. (Learning Disabil.); Hon. Sen. Lect. Univ. Leicester; Sec. Trent Div. of The Roy. Coll. of Psychiat.s. Socs: BMA; POWAR Leicester Frith Hosp.; MDU. Prev: Sen. Regist. (Child & Adolesc. Psychiat.) W.cotes Hse. Leicester; Sen. Regist. Frith Leicester Hosp.; Regist. (Psychiat.) Stone Hse. Hosp. Dartford.

BHAVE, Neetin Ashok 75 College Road, Isleworth TW7 5DP — MB BS 1987 Lond.

BHAVNANI, Manju Department of Haematology, Royal Albert Edward Infirmary, Wigan WN1 2NN Tel: 01942 822140 Fax: 01924 822134 Email: mba@wigan_haem.prestel.co.uk — MB ChB 1971 Bristol; MRCPath 1983; FRCPath 1995. (Bristol) Cons. Haemat. Roy. Albert Edwd. Infirm. Wigan.

BHAWAL, Mr Rabindra 21 Alston Gardens, Bearsden, Glasgow G61 4RZ — MB BS 1975 Calcutta; MS Calcutta 1978, MB BS 1975; FRCS Ed. 1981.

BHERMI, Andrea Jane The Surgery, 118/120 Stanford Avenue, Brighton BN1 6FE Tel: 01273 506361 Fax: 01273 552483; 41 Nursery Close, Hurstpierpoint, Hassocks BN6 9WA Tel: 01273 834710 — BM 1988 Soton.; MRCGP 1994; DRCOG 1993; DFFP 1993; DCH RCP Lond. 1992. (Univ. Soton.) Prev: SHO (O & G & ENT) Roy. Sussex Co. Hosp.; SHO (Paediat.) S.lands Hosp. Shoreham-by-Sea.

BHERMI, Mr Gurpreet — MB ChB 1990 Dundee; FRCOphth 1996.

BHIDE, Alka Mahadeo Queen Mary's University Hospital, Obstetrics and Gynaecology Department, Roehampton, London SW15 5PN — MB BS 1987 Gujarat; MRCOG 1994.

BHIDE, Ashok Vishnu Central Middlesex Hospital, Acton Lane, Park Royal, London NW10 7NS Tel: 020 8453 2436 Fax: 020 8453 2404; 143 Albury Drive, Pinner HA5 3RJ Tel: 020 8428 6957 Fax: 020 8428 6957 — MB BS 1968 Nagpur; MS (Ophth.) Nagpur 1971; DO Eng. 1974; DO Nagpur 1970. (Med. Coll. Nagpur) Assoc. Specialist Centr. Eye Serv. Centr. Middlx. Hosp. Lond. Prev: Regist. Centr. Middlx. Hosp. & Regional Eye Unit OldCh. Hosp. Romford.

BHIDE, Mr Milind Royal Eye Infirmary, Dorset County Hospital, Princess St., Dorchester DT1 1TS; 1120 Sadashiv Peth, Nimbalkar Talim Chowk, Pune, Maharashtra 411030, India Tel: 010 91 212 473427 — MB BS 1986 Osmania; MS BS Osmania 1986; FRCS Ed. 1991; FCOphth 1991. Fell. Oculoplastic Moorfields Eye Hosp. Lond. Socs: UKIS & BMA. Prev: Regist. (Ophth.) Singleton Hosp. Swansea; SHO (Ophth.) Qu. Alexandra Hosp. Portsmouth & Bradford Roy. Infirm.

BHIDE, Prasad Dhondadev 25 Stane Street, Baldock SG7 6TS — MB BS 1974 Bombay. Gen. Surg. Bombay, India. Prev: Regist. Killingbeck Hosp. Leeds.

BHIDE, Supriya Ashok Northwick Park Hospital Trust, Watford Road, Harrow HA1 3UW Tel: 020 8869 2880; 143 Albury Drive, Pinner HA5 3RJ Tel: 020 8428 6957 Fax: 020 8428 6957 — MB BS 1972 Nagpur; DRCOG 1978; DObst RCPI 1977. (Govt. Med. Coll.) Clin. Asst. (O & G) N.wick Pk. Hosp. & Clin. Research Centre Harrow. Prev: SHO (Gyn. & Obst.) Rushgreen Hosp. Romford & St. Nicholas' Hosp. Lond.

BHIKHA, Alkakumari 11 Bowdler Road, Wolverhampton WV2 1EP — MB BCh 1997 Wales.

BHIMA, George Wilfred Dedan 1 Watkins Drive, Prestwich, Manchester M25 0DR — MB ChB 1975 Makerere; Makerere Univ.).

BHIMJI, Yusuf Suleman 75 Sir Richards Drive, Harborne, Birmingham B17 8SG Tel: 0121 429 2288 — MB BS 1988 Kashmir; FFA RCSI 1988; DA (UK) 1984.

BHIMPURIA, Yogesh Rajendraprasad Rosehill Medical Centre, 52 Rosehill Road, Rawmarsh, Rotherham S62 7BT Tel: 01709 522595 — MB BS 1969 Gujarat.

BHINDA, Hans Paul Outfield, Bickley Park Road, Bromley BR1 2AS — MB BS 1994 Lond.

BHOGADIA, Haider Saffron Group Practice, 509 Saffron Lane, Leicester LE2 6UL Tel: 0116 244 0888 Fax: 01162 831405 — MB ChB 1988 Leic.

BHOGAL, Harbans Singh 73 Burns Avenue, Sidcup DA15 9HT Tel: 07778 845755 Fax: 020 8306 2247 Email: drbhogal@hotmail.com — MB BS 1975 Poona; MD (Anaesth.) Shiraz 1981; FFA RCSI 1992. (Armed Forces Medical College) Socs: Med. Defence Union; BMA; LMAS. Prev: Cons. Anaesth., Gen. Hosp., Chas. Iran 1980-1981 (One year); Fac. Mem., Duke Univ., Durh., N. Carolina; Rotating Regist., Anaesthetics, USA 1998-1999 Bromley-Bexley, Lond. 1989-1991 (2 years).

BHOGAL, Julian 81 Heathmead, Heath, Cardiff CF14 3PL — MB ChB 1991 Leic.; MRCGP 1996; DRCOG 1995.

BHOJANI, Issak Hassan 2 Watersedge, Blackburn BB1 1BT — MB ChB Leeds 1993; PhD Bristol 1988; BSc (Hons.) Leeds 1985. GP Regist.; GP VTS.

BHOJANI, Jashwanti Purushottam (retired) Pear Tree House, 88 Limes Road, Hardwick, Cambridge CB3 7XN Tel: 01954 211118 — MB BS 1958 Delhi; DA Eng. 1965. Prev: Anaesth. Bourn Hall Clinic Camb.

BHOJANI, Mohammed Asghar 8 The Riding, Kenton, Newcastle upon Tyne NE3 4LQ — MB BS 1978 Newc.; MRCGP 1984.

BHOJANI, Tahera Khatun Department of Ophthalmology, Queens Medical Centre, Derby Road, Nottingham NG7 2 Tel: 0115 924 9924; 135 Nanpantan Road, Loughborough LE11 3YB Tel: 01509 231243 — MB ChB 1989 Aberd.; MRCOphth 1995. Staff Grade Ophth. Qu. Med. Centre Nottm. Socs: BMA; Midl. Ophth. Soc. Prev: Clin. Asst. & SHO (Ophth.) N. Riding Infirm. Middlesbrough; SHO (Ophth.) Worcester Eye Hosp.

BHOJWANI, Mr Shabbi Chello 37 Kingsbridge Way, Bramcote, Nottingham NG9 3LW Tel: 0115 922 4600 — MB BS 1971 Indore; MS Indore 1974, MB BS 1971; DO RCPSI 1979; DO Eng. 1979. Clin. Asst. (Ophth.) Qu.'s Med. Centre Nottm.

BHOMRA, Deedar Singh The Surgery, Aylesbury House, Warren Farm Road, Kingstanding, Birmingham B44 0DX Tel: 0121 373 1078 — MB ChB 1986 Birm.; BSc (Hons) Birm. 1983; DCH RCP Lond. 1990; DRCOG 1990. GP Birm. Prev: Trainee GP N.Birm. VTS.

BHONSLE, Ravindranath Shrinivas Tree Tops, Hill Park Crescent, St Austell PL25 5HW — MB BS 1956 Bombay. (Gordhandas Sunderdas Med. Coll.)

BHOORA, Ishan Gobardhan Department of Orthopaedics, Stafford District General Hospital, Weston Road, Stafford ST16 3SA Tel: 01785 257731 Fax: 01785 245211 — MB ChB 1986 Natal; FCS(SA) 1993. Cons. Orthop. Surg. Stafford Dist. Gen. Hosp. Socs: Brit. Orthop. Assn.; BMA; BESS.

BHOPAL, Ashwani Singh 35 Dalmeny Avenue, Giffnock, Glasgow G46 7QF — MB ChB 1993 Glas.

BHOPAL, Professor Rajinder Singh Department of Epidemiology & Public Health, Medical School, Framlington Place, Newcastle upon Tyne NE2 4HH Tel: 0191 222 7372 Fax: 0191 222 8211 Email: r.s.bhopal@ncl.ac.uk; 16 Holywell Avenue, Whitley Bay NE26 3AA Tel: 0191 252 7266 — MB ChB 1978 Ed.; BSc (Physiol., Hons.) Ed. 1975, MD 1991; MRCP (UK) 1982; FFPHM RCP (UK) 1995, M 1990; MFCM 1987; MPH Glas. 1985. Prof. Epidemiol. & Pub. Health & Hon. Cons. Pub. Health Med. Univ. Newc. u. Tyne & Newc. & N. Tyneside HA; Non-Exec. Dir. Health Educat. Auth. Prev: Sen. Lect. & SCM Univ. Newc.

BHOWAL, Mr Bhaskar The Glenfield Hospital, Groby Rd, Leicester LE3 9QP Tel: 0116 287 1471 Fax: 0116 258 3950 Email: bhaskar.bhowal@glenfield-tr.trent.nhs.uk; 34 Tower Street, Leicester LE1 6WS Tel: 0116 254 0454 — MB BS 1986 Calcutta; FRCS Ed. 1992; FRCS Ed. (Orth) 1998. Cons. Ortho. Surg, The Glenfield Hosp., Leicester.

BHOWAL, Gouri The Royal Hospital. St Bart.,The Royal London Hospital, & The London Chest Hospital NHS Trust, Whitechaple, London E1 1BB Tel: 020 8983 2412 — MB BS 1958 Calcutta. Cons. Histopath. Roy. Brompton Nat. Hosp. Vict. Pk. Socs: Fell. Roy. Coll. Path. Prev: Assoc. Specialist (Histopath.) Lond. Chest Hosp.; Regist. (Histopath.) Chelsea Hosp. for Wom.; SHO (Path.) King's Coll. Hosp.

BHOWMICK, Arnab Kanti Jamini, Allt Goch, St Asaph LL17 0BP; 61 Meltham Avenue, Withington, Manchester M20 1FE Tel: 0161 434 3865 Email: bhowmick@arnab.demon.co.uk — MB ChB 1993 Manch. Specialist Regist. (Gen. Surg.) Preston Acute Hosp. Prev: Specialist Regist. (Gen. Surg.) Furness Gen. Hosp. Cumbria; SHO (Gen. Surg., Cardiothoracic Surg., IC).

BHOWMICK, Bidisha 9 Como Road, Aylesbury HP20 1NR — MB BS 1997 Lond.

BHOWMICK, Bimal Kanti Glan Clwyd Hospital, Rhyl LL18 5UJ Tel: 01745 583910 Fax: 01745 583006; Tel: 01745 730220 — MB BS 1963 Calcutta; MD Calcutta 1969; MRCP (UK) 1972; FRCP Lond. 1987. Cons. Phys. Glan Clwyd Hosp. Bodelwyddan, Rhyl; Postgrad. Clin. Tutor RCP.; Assoc. PostGrad. Dean. UWCM; Censor Roy. Coll. of Phys.s; Counc.lor Roy. Coll. of Phys.s; Postgrad. Organizer Clwyd N. Dist. Med. Tutor; Hon. Clin. Teach. UWCM MB chB Examr.; Examr. MRCP; Chairm. Standing Comm. Postgrad. Educat. in Wales; Chairm. Dist. Med. Audit Comm. Wales; Mem. Postgrad. Steering Bd. Wales; Adviser Overseas Doctors, Wales; Assoc. PostGrad. Dean.UWCM. Socs: (Exec.) Brit. Geriat. Soc.; (Chairm.) All-Wales Med. Audit Chairms. Gp.; (Counc.) Roy. Coll. Phys. Prev: Cons. Phys. Geriat. Unit HM Stanley Hosp. St. Asaph & Glan Clwyd Hosp. Bodelwyddan; Sen. Regist. (Geriat. Med.) HM Stanley Hosp. St. Asaph; Regist. (Gen. Med.) Burton Rd. Hosp. Dudley.

BHOWMIK, Mohini Mohan 13 Vernon Street, Derby DE1 1FW Tel: 01332 332812 Fax: 01332 202608 — DTCD (UK); MBBS 1963. (Dacca, E. Pakistan) Form. Dept. Cardio Thoracic Med. & Ass. Specialist; Clin. Asst., Dept. Of Psychiat. Socs: Derby Med. Soc. Prev: Assoc. Specialist Cardio Thoracic Med.

BHOWMIK, Prasanta Ranjan The Surgery, 401 Corporation Street, London E15 3DJ Tel: 020 8555 0428 Fax: 020 8555 0641 — MB BS 1963 Calcutta.

BHOYRUL, Mr Sunil 1 Newlyn House, Benhillwood Road, Sutton SM1 4HE; 2933 Irving Street, San Francisco CA 94122, USA Tel: 415 476 6359 Fax: 415 476 9557 — MB ChB 1989 Aberd.; BMedBiol. 1987; FRCS Eng. 1993. Fell. Laparoscopic Surg. Univ. Calif., San Francisco, USA. Socs: Assoc. Mem. Soc. Minimally Invasive Ther.; Soc. Laparoendoscopic Surgs. Prev: SHO Harefield Hosp. Middlx.; SHO Rotat. (Surg.) N.wick Pk. Hosp.

BHUDIA, Sunil Kishore 24 Portland Crescent, Stanmore HA7 1ND — MB BS 1996 Lond.

BHUGRA, Dinesh Kumar Makhan Lal Institute of Psychiatry, De Crespigny Park, London SE5 8AF Tel: 020 7919 3500 Fax: 020 7277 1586 — MB BS 1976 Poona; MA Lond. 1996; MPhil Leic. 1990; LMSSA Lond. 1981; MRCPsych 1985; FRCPsych 1997; PhD 1999. (Armed Forces Med. Coll. Poona) Sen. Lect. Inst. Psychiat. Lond.; Hon. Cons. Psychiat. S. Lond. & Maudsley NHS Trust Lond.; Edr. Internat. Review of Psychiat. Socs: Chair. Fac. Gen. & Community Psychiat. Roy. Coll. Psychiat.; (Psychiat. Gp.) Roy. Soc. Med. Prev: Sen. Regist. Research MRC Social & Community Psychiat. Unit; Sen. Regist. (Psychiat.) Bethlem Roy. & Maudsley Hosps. Lond.; Regist. Rotat. (Psychiat.) Leics. HA.

BHUI, Kamaldeep Singh Dept. Psychiatry, Bart's Royal London Med. School, Queen Mary, London E1 4NS Tel: 020 7882 7727 Email: ks.bhui@mds.qmc.ac.uk — MB BS 1988 Lond.; MSc Lond. 1996, MSc 1994, BSc 1985; MRCPsych 1992; Dip. Psycother. Lond. 1993; MD 1999. (Guy's Hospital) Sen. Lect. in Social & Edipemic Psychol. Psychiat. At Bart's Roy., Lond. Socs: Roy. Soc. Med.; Roy. Coll. Psychiat. Prev: Sen. Regist. Maudsley Hosp. & UMDS & SE Thames Scheme; Wellcome Research Fell. Inst. Psychiat. Lond.; Cons. Psychiat. NHS Trust.

BHULAR, Jaspal Singh 1 Rivermount, Lower Hampton Rd, Sunbury-on-Thames TW16 5PH — MB BS 1997 Lond.

BHULLAR, Baljit Kaur Grove Village Medical Centre, 4 Cleeve Court, Grove Village, Bedfont, Feltham TW14 8SN Tel: 020 8751 6281 Fax: 020 8751 0054 — MB BS 1972 Bombay.

BHULLAR, Manjit Singh 41 Westfield Road, Edgbaston, Birmingham B15 3QE — MB BS 1966 Panjab; MB BS Panjab (India) 1966. (Med. Coll. Amritsar)

BHULLAR, Mr Tejinder Pal Singh, Wing Cdr. RAF Med. Br. Edith Cavell Hospital, Peterborough PE3 6GZ Tel: 01733 875001; Ash Cottage, 21 High St, Maxey, Peterborough PE6 9EB Tel: 01733 342122 Fax: 01733 342122 Email: bhullar@21-ash-cottage.freeserve.co.uk — MB BS 1979 Poona; FRCS (Orth.) Ed. 1988; FRCS Glas. 1983. (Armed Forces Med. Coll. Poona, India) Cons. Orthop. Surg. Edith Cavell Hosp. P'boro. Socs: Brit. Orthop. Assn.; Girdlestone Orthop. Soc.; BASK. Prev: Sen. Regist. Nuffield Orthop. Centre Oxf.

BHULLER, Amardip Singh 35 Manor Links, Bishop's Stortford CM23 5RA — MB ChB 1993 Sheff.

BHUPATHI, Vijayabharathi 1 Horton Road, Springwood, King's Lynn PE30 4XU Tel: 01553 692205 — MB BS 1983 Andhra; BM Soton. 1994. Trainee GP/SHO (Paediat.) Norf. & Norwich Hosp. Socs: MDU. Prev: Trainee GP Watlington Surg. King's Lynn; SHO (Psychiat.) Qu. ELiz. Hosp. King's Lynn; SHO (c/o Elderly) P'boro. Hosp.

BHUSARI, Gauri Sudhir Flat 4, 48 Myrdle Street, London E1 1HL — MB BS 1988 Nagpur, India; MRCP (UK) 1997; DCH RCP Lond. 1994. Trust Doctor (Paediat.) King Geo. Hosp. Ilford.

BHUSHAN, Monica 4 Wilcove, Skelmersdale WN8 8NF — MB ChB 1991 Manch.; BSc (Hons.) Pharmacol. Manch. 1988, MB ChB 1991; MRCP (UK) 1994. SHO (Neurol.) Hosp Hosp. Salford. Prev: SHO (Geriat. & Gen. Med.) Hosp. Hosp. Salford; SHO (Gen. Med. & Endocrinol.) Roy. Albert Edwd. Infirm. Wigan.

BHUSHAN, Vinay SEMA Group Medical Services, St Martin's House, Stanley Precinct, Bootle, Liverpool L69 9BN Tel: 0151 934 6162 Fax: 0151 934 6531; 4 Wilcove, Off Church Road, Skelmersdale WN8 8NF Tel: 01695 720670 Fax: 01695727738 Email: vbhul@aol.com — MB BS Punjabi 1965; MRCP (UK) 1973. (Govt. Med. Coll. Patiala, India) Med. Adviser SEMA Gp. Med. Servs. Liverp.; JP. Prev: Med. Adviser Benefit Agency Liverp.

BHUTANI, Harish Chander Enderby Surgery, 80 King Street, Enderby, Leicester LE9 5NT Tel: 0116 286 6088 — MB BS 1975 Jiwaji.

BHUVANENDRAN, Vijayaluxmy 56 Meakin Avenue, Westbury Park, Newcastle ST5 4EY — MB BS Sri Lanka 1976; LMSSA Lond. 1992.

BIADENE, Giovanni 72 Kenway Road, London SW5 0RD — State DMS 1976 Padua.

BIALAS, Ivona Bloomfield Centre, Guy's Hospital, St Thomas St., London SE1 9RT Tel: 020 7955 4583; 16 Carlingford Road, London NW3 1RX — MB BCh BAO 1986 NUI; MRCPsych 1994. Sen. Regist. (Child Psychiat.) Guy's Hosp. Lond.; Lect.

BIALAS, Michael Christopher Cheltenham General Hospital, Sandford Rd, Cheltenham GL53 7AN; 34 Mayster Grove, Rastrick, Brighouse HD6 3NU — MB ChB 1986 Sheff.; BMedSci Sheff. 1985; MRCP Ed. 1992. Cons. Gen. Med. and Geriat. Med. Prev: Regist. (Med.) Cheltenham Gen. Hosp.; Regist. (Med.) Jersey Gen. Hosp.; Lect. (Clin. Pharmacol., Therap. & Geriat. Med.) & Hon. Sen. Regist. (Med.) Cardiff.

BIANCHI, Mr Adrian Max 1 Elleray Road, Alkrington, Middleton, Manchester M24 1NY — MD Malta 1969; FRCS Ed. 1975; FRCS Eng. 1975. (Malta) Cons. Paediat. Surg. N. W.. RHA. Socs: Fell. Manch. Med. Soc.; Brit. Assn. Paediat. Surg. Prev: Research Fell. (Paediat. Surg.) Univ. Manch.

BIANCHI, Graeme Brogan and Partners, The O'Connel Street Medical Centre, 6 O'Connell Street, Hawick TD9 9HU Tel: 01450 372276 Fax: 01450 371564 — MB ChB 1982 Glasgow; MB ChB Glas. 1982. (Glasgow) GP Hawick, Roxburghsh.

BIANCHI, Stephen Mark 1 Elleray Road, Alkrington, Middleton, Manchester M24 1NY — MB ChB 1995 Manch.

BIASSONI, Lorenzo Department of Nuclear Medicine & "The Clinical Pet Centre", The Havering Hospitals NHS Trust, Oldchurch Hospital, Waterloo Rd, Romford RH7 0BE Tel: 020 7922 8106 Fax: 020 7620 0790 Email: lorenzob@gerbil.umds.ac.uk; 18 Netherhall

Gardens, London NW3 5TH Tel: 020 7431 0074 Fax: 020 7433 1276 Email: lbiassoni@doctors.org.uk — State Exam 1986 Rome; MSc (Nuclear Med.) Lond. 1995. (University of Rome) Cons. (Nuclear Med.), OldCh. Hosp. Socs: Assoc. Italiana Di Medicina Nucleare; Eur. Assn. Nuclear Med.; Med. Protec. Soc. Prev: Research Fell. Nat. Cancer Inst. Genoa, Italy; Fell.sh. Specialization Sch. Nuclear Med. Univ. Genoa, Italy; Vis. Regist. in Nuclear Med., St Bart. Hosp.

BIBBY, Cynthia Bernice Ashes House, Stanhope, Bishop Auckland DL13 2DS — MB BS 1962 Durh.

BIBBY, Joanne 27 Newton Park Road, Wirral CH48 9XE — CB Birm. 1989.

BIBBY, John Allan Windhill Green Medical Centre, 2 Thackley Old Road, Shipley BD18 1QB Tel: 01274 584223 — MB ChB 1978 Leeds; BSc (Hons.) Leeds 1975; MRCGP 1983; DRCOG 1982; DCH RCP Lond. 1981. (Leeds) GP Tutor Bradford.; PCT Clin. Governance Lead.

BIBBY, Jonathan Glover Holly Lodge Farm, 96 Sywell Road, Overstone, Northampton NN6 0AQ Tel: 01604495925 Email: jaybibby@hotmail.com — MD 1969 Otago; MD Otago 1981 MB ChB 1969; FRCOG 1990, M 1976; T(OG) 1991; FRNZCOG 1991; FRANXCOG 1997. (Otago) Cons. O & G N.ampton Gen. Hosp. Socs: Blair Bell Res. Soc. & Brit. Menopause Soc. Prev: Sen. Regist. Liverp. Teachg. Hosps.; Research Regist. Nuffield Dept. O & G Univ. Oxf.

BIBBY, Kathleen Elizabeth Sanderson (retired) Haystacks, 1 Pasture House Mews, Beverley HU17 8DR — MB ChB 1948 Sheff.

BIBBY, Miss Kim Dept of Ophthalmology, Leicester Royal infirmary, Leicester LE1 Tel: 0116 258 6198 — MB BS 1983 Lond.; BSc (Hons) Anat. Lond. 1980, MB BS 1983; FRCS Ed. 1989; FRCOphth. 1991. Cons. Ophth. Surg. Leics. Roy. Infirm. Prev: Sen. Regist. (Ophth.) Leicester Roy. Infirm.; Regist. (Ophth.) Gartnavel Gen. Hosp. Glas.

BIBBY, Richard John 19 The Avenue, Carleton, Poulton-Le-Fylde, Blackpool Tel: 01253 882401 — MB ChB 1967 Manch.; MRCP (U.K.) 1972; DObst RCOG 1969. (Manch.) Cons. Phys. Vict. Hosp. Blackpool. Socs: Fell. Manch. Med. Soc. Prev: Regist. Haemodialysis & Endocrinol. Manch. Roy. Infirm.

BIBBY, Mr Stephen Richard County Hospital, Greetwell Road, Lincoln LN2 5QY; Chenies, Stocks Lane, Faldingworth, Market Rasen LN8 3SH — MB ChB 1980 Leeds; FRCS RCPS Glas. 1989; FRCS Eng. 1989. Staff Grade (Gen. Surg.) Co. Hosp. Lincoln.

BIBI, Rajia Begum 11 Strathnairn Street, Cardiff CF24 3JL — MB BS 1997 Lond.

BICANIC, Tihana Ana Dept. of Infectious Diseases, St Georges Hospital, Blackshaw Road SW17 0QT Tel: 020 87251255; 20 Ledcameroch Road, Bearsden, Glasgow G61 4AE Tel: 0141 942 0711 Email: tihana@never.com — BM BCh 1996 Oxf.; MRCP 2000; MA Cambridge 1997. (Cambs/Oxf) Speciallist Regist., Infec. Dis. and MicroBiol.; SHO MicroBiol./Intens. care, St Thomas Hosp. Lond.; SHO Nottm. City Hosp. Socs: BMA; RCP. Prev: Resid..med.Off.Flinders.med.Centre.Adelaide.AU; SHO A&E St Thomas.Hosp.Lond; HO Med. John Radcliffe, Oxf.

BICHAN, Robert Miller Seafield, 41 Grattan Place, Fraserburgh AB43 9SD — MB ChB 1957 Aberd.

***BICK, Edward Ewart** Victoria Cottage, Holts Rd, Newent GL18 1BT Tel: 01531 821631 Email: edwardbick@hotmail.com — BM BS 1996 Nottm.

BICK, Steven Anthony Dorchester Road Surgery, 179 Dorchester Road, Weymouth DT4 7LE Tel: 01305 766472 Fax: 01305 766499; 3 Southfield Avenue, Lodmoor, Weymouth DT4 7QN Tel: 01305 761351 Fax: 01305 768322 — MB ChB 1984 Birm.; MRCGP 1988; DGM RCP Lond. 1986. (Univ. Birm.) GP; Med. Stud. Trainer Dorset; Clin. Asst. (Geriat.) Weymouth Community Hosp. Prev: Trainee GP BromsGr. & Redditch VTS.

BICKERSTAFF, Derek Richard Thornbury Hospital, 312 Fulwood Road, Sheffield S103HA Tel: 0114 2681 608 Fax: 0114 2681 608 Email: drbickerstaff@uic-consultants.co.uk; Hillcrest, Ranmoor Cliff Road, Sheffield S1U 3HA Tel: 0114 229 5846 Fax: 0114 268 1608 — MB ChB 1982 Sheff.; MD Sheff. 1992; FRCS Eng. 1986; FRCS Ed. 1986. Cons. Orthop. Surg. Sheff. Centre of Sports Med., Sheff. Univ. Socs: Fell. BOA; Treas. Brit. Assn. Surg. Knee; Brit. Orthop. Sports Trauma Assn.

BICKERSTAFF, Edwin Robert (retired) St. Helens, The Close, Trevone, Padstow PL28 8QT Tel: 01841 520061 — MB ChB 1943 Birm.; MD Birm. 1947; FRCP Lond. 1965, M 1949. Hon. Cons. Neurol. Midl. Centre Neurosurg. & Neurol. Smethwick; Hon. Cons. Neurol. Roy. Shrops. Infirm. Shrewsbury & Hereford HA; Hon. Cons. Assoc. Neurol. Birm. Centr. HA (T); Vis. Prof. Univ. Copenhagen, Detroit, Kuwait & Saudi Arabia. Prev: Cons. Adviser Neurol. DHSS.

BICKERSTAFF, Helen Elizabeth 37 Lillieshall Road, London SW4 0LN — BChir 1992 Camb.

BICKERSTAFF, Maria Catherine Michaela 2A Chestnut Drive, London E11 2TA — MB BS 1989 Lond.; BSc Hons. (Biochem.) Lond. 1986, MB BS 1989; MRCP (UK) 1992. Regist. (Rheum. & Gen. Med.) Roy. Free Hosp. Lond. & King. Geo. Hosp. Ilford. Socs: Brit. Soc. Rheum.; Roy. Soc. Med.

BICKERSTAFFE, William Edward 9 Woolton Hill Road, Liverpool L25 6HU — MB ChB 1991 Dundee; FRCA 1997. Specialist Regist. (Anaesth.) NW Regional Rotat. (Mersey). Prev: SHO (Gen. Med./Anaesth.) Wrexham; SHO Intens. Care Preston Roy. Infirm.

BICKERTON, Alex Sam Thomas 82 East Hill, London SW18 2HG — BM 1994 Soton.

BICKERTON, Mrs Delia Ann Medwyn Fellside, Pemsarmlane, Pantymwyn, Mold CH7 5EN Tel: 01352 740237; Fellside, Pemsarm Lane, Pamtymwygn, Mold CH7 5EM Tel: 01352 740237 — MRCS Eng. LRCP Lond. 1960; DFFP 1993. (Royal Free, Liverpool) Med. Off. Family Plann. & Psycho-Sexual Counsellor Clwyd HA; Clin. Med. Off. Community Med. Serv. Clwyd HA (Cerv. Cyt. & Well Wom. Clinic); JP. Socs: Assoc. Mem. Inst. Psycho-Sexual Med. 1980; BMA; Fac. Comm. Health (Regional Adviser Family Plann.). Prev: Clin. Asst. (Dermat.) W. Wales Hosp. Gp.; Ho. Surg. Roy. S.. Hosp. Liverp.; Ho. Phys. Pembroke Co. War Memor. Hosp. HaverfordW.

BICKERTON, Guy Stuart 23 Littondale, Worksop S81 0XU — MB ChB 1990 Sheff.; Dip. IMC RCS Ed. 1997; DFFP 1994. SHO (A & E Med.) Bassetlaw Dist. Gen. Hosp. Worksop. Prev: SHO (Orthop. & A & E) Qu. Med. Centre Nottm.

BICKERTON, Margaret Vera (retired) 123 Church Road, Potters Bar EN6 1EU Tel: 01707 658343 — MB BS 1949 Lond.; MRCS Eng. LRCP Lond. 1949; DLO Eng. 1956. Prev: Cons. Otol. Nuffield Centre, Roy. Nat. Throat Nose & Ear Hosp. Lond.

BICKERTON, Nigel John Department of Obstetrics & Gynaecology, Ysbyty Glan Clwyd, Bodelwyddan, Rhyl LL18 5UJ Tel: 01745 583910; North Wales Medical Centre, Queens Road, Craig-y-Don, Llandudno LL30 1UE Tel: 01492 879031 — MB BS 1978 Lond.; MRCS Eng. LRCP Lond. 1978; MRCOG 1984. (Char. Cross) Cons. O & G Glan Clwyd Dist. Gen. Hosp.; Vis. Acad. DIAS UMIST Manch. Socs: Fell. N. Eng. Obst. & Gyn. Soc.; Ospreys Gyn. Soc. Prev: Sen. Regist. (O & G) Mersey RHA (Liverp. Matern. Hosp. & Wom. Hosp.); Regist. (O & G) John Radcliffe Hosp. & Ch. Hosp. Oxf.; Lect. (Anat.) Guy's Hosp. Med. Sch. Lond.

BICKERTON, Mr Richard Charles Warwickshire Nuffield Hospital, The Chase, Leamington Spa CV32 6RW Tel: 01926 427971 Fax: 01926 428791 Email: rcb@ukgateway.net; Whitegates, Lighthorne, Warwick CV35 0AR Tel: 01926 651845 Fax: 01926 651326 Email: richardbick@lighthorne.demon.co.uk — MB ChB 1977 Dundee; FRCS Ed. 1984. (Dundee) Cons. Otolaryngol. S. Warks. Hosp. Warwick. Socs: Fell. Roy. Soc. Med.; Hon. Sec. Oriole Soc.; Hon. Treas., Draffin Soc. Prev: Sen. Regist. (ENT) Midl. Area Train. Scheme; Regist. Roy. Nat. Throat, Nose & Ear Hosp. Lond.; SHO (ENT) Gt. Ormond St. Childr. Hosp. Lond.

BICKFORD, James Arscott Raleigh (retired) Trevorswood, Church Lane, Kirk Ella, Hull HU10 7TA — MRCS Eng. LRCP Lond. 1941; FRCPsych 1972; DPM Bristol 1950. Prev: Cons. Psychiat. & Med. Supt. De La Pole Hosp. Willerby.

BICKFORD SMITH, Philip John Bradford Royal Infirmary, Duckworth Lane, Bradford BD9 6RJ Tel: 01274 364065 Fax: 01274 366548 Email: bickford.smith@bradfordhospitals.nhs.uk; Cliffe House, Cragg Wood Drive, Rawdon, Leeds LS19 6LG Tel: 0113 250 0609 — MB ChB 1975 Leeds; FFA RCS Eng. 1979. (Leeds) Cons. Anaesth. Bradford Hosps. Socs: BMA; AAGBI; YSA. Prev: Sen. Regist. Yorks. Region HA; Regist. (Anaesth.) Guy's Hosp. Lond.; SHO & Regist. (Anaesth.) Bradford Hosps.

BICKLER, Carl Brian, MBE Craigmillar Medical Group, Craigmillar Medical Centre, 106 Niddrie Mains Road, Edinburgh EH16 4DT Tel: 0131 536 9500 Fax: 0131 536 9545; 117 Craiglea Drive, Edinburgh EH10 5PL Tel: 0131 447 1405 — MB ChB 1980 Ed.; FRCGP 2001; MRCGP 1984; DRCOG 1983. (Ed.) Prev: Trainee GP N. Lothian VTS.

BICKLER, Graham Julian 36/38 Friars Walk, Lewes BN7 2PB Tel: 01273 485300 Fax: 01273 403600; 22 The Avenue, Lewes BN7 1QT — MB BS 1979 Lond.; BA Camb. 1975; MSc Community Med. Lond. 1985; FFPHM RCP (UK) 1995, M 1988; MRCGP 1984; DRCOG 1983; DCH RCP Lond. 1983. Dir. Pub. Health E. Sussex, Brighton & Hove HA. Prev: Cons. Pub. Health Med. SE Lond. HA.

BICKLEY, Christine Mary X-Ray Department, Good Hope Hospital, Rectory Road, Sutton Coldfield B75 7RR — MB ChB 1967 Liverp.; FRCR 1987; DMRD Liverp. 1970. (Liverp.) Cons. Radiol. Good Hope Hosp. W. Midl. RHA.

BICKLEY, Philip The Surgery, 190 Aston Lane, Handsworth, Birmingham B20 3HE Tel: 0121 356 4669 — MB ChB 1985 Birm.; MRCGP 1990. (Birm.) Club Doctor Aston Villa FC; Hon. Clin. Lect. Univ. Birm. Prev: Med. Off. Walsall Football Club; Occupat. Health Phys. Highcroft Hosp.

BICKNELL, Colin David 25 Northlands Avenue, Orpington BR6 9LX — BM 1996 Soton.

BICKNELL, Dorothy Joan Farthing Gate Farm, Holnest, Sherborne DT9 5PX Tel: 01963 210339 — MD 1971 Birm.; MB ChB (Hons.) 1962; DPM Eng. 1968; FRCPsych 1978. Emerit. Prof. Psychiat. Ment. Handicap. St. Geo. Hosp. Med. Sch. Lond. Prev: Regional Tutor Ment. Handicap; Hon. Cons. Psychiat. Wandsworth; Cons. Psychiat. Ment. Handicap. Merton & Sutton HA.

BICKNELL, Mr Michael Raymond (retired) Dungrianach, 115 Aghanloo Road, Limavady BT49 0HY Tel: 028 7775 0369 — MB BS 1956 Lond.; FRCS Eng. 1964; MRCS Eng. LRCP Lond. 1956; DLO Eng. 1963. Prev: Cons. ENT Surg. Altnagelvin Hosp. Lond.derry.

BICKNELL, Mr Philip George (cons. rooms), Litfield House, Clifton Down, Bristol BS8 3LS Tel: 0117 973 1323 Fax: 0117 973 3303; House of Over, Over Lane, Almondsbury, Bristol BS32 4DD Tel: 01454 612191 — MB BCh Wales 1962; FRCS Eng. 1970; FRCS Ed. 1969. (Cardiff) Cons. ENT Surg. St. Michaels Hosp., Bristol Roy. Infirm. & Roy. Hosp. Sick Childr.; Sen. Clin. Lect. (Otorhinolaryng.) Univ. Bristol. Socs: Pres. BMA Bristol 1998-99; Fell. Roy. Soc. Med. (Mem. Sect. Otol. & Laryngol.); Pres. S.W. Larngol. Soc. 1998-99. Prev: Sen. Regist. United Bristol Hosps. & S. W.. RHB; Regist. (ENT) Sheff. Roy. Infirm.; Mem. Bd. Examr. (Otolaryng.) RCS Edin.

BIDDELL, Paul Byrne, MC (retired) The Beeches, Sampford Brett, Taunton TA4 4LE Tel: 01984 32354 — MB BS 1953 Lond.; MRCS Eng. LRCP Lond. 1953; DObst RCOG 1956. Prev: GP Williton Som.

BIDDELL, Sheelagh Forcer The Beeches, Sampford Brett, Taunton TA4 4LE Tel: 01984 32354 — MRCS Eng. LRCP Lond. 1954. (Guy's) Socs: BMA; (Ex-Chairm.) Nat. Assn. of Family Plann. Drs. Prev: Sen. Med. Off. (Community Med.) som. AHA; Ho. Surg. & Ho. Phys. St. Olave's Hosp. Rotherhithe.

BIDDLE, Mrs Anna Lockswood Surgery, Centre Way, Locksheath, Southampton SO31 6DX Tel: 01489 576708; 402 Bursledon Road, Sholing, Southampton SO19 8NG Tel: 02380 405453 — MB BS 1967 Lond.; MRCS Eng. LRCP Lond. 1967.

BIDDLE, Frank Anthony Fenwick (retired) 4 Dale Hall Lane, Ipswich IP1 3RX Tel: 01473 254808 Fax: 01473 254808 — MB BS 1953 Lond.; FRCGP 1992, M 1966; MRCS Eng. LRCP Lond. 1953. Prev: Med. Off. Willis, Coroon Ltd.

BIDDLESTONE, Leigh Rachel Royal United Hospital, Combe Park, Bath BA1 3NG Tel: 01225 824705 Fax: 01225 824503 Email: leigh-biddlestone@ruh-bath.swest.nhs.uk — MB ChB 1988 Ed.; BSc (Hons.) Med. Sci. Ed. 1985; MRCPath 1997. (Univ. Ed.) Cons. (Histopath.) RUH, Bath. Socs: Path. Soc.; Assn. Clin. Paths.; IAP. Prev: Cons. (Histopath.) S.mead Hosp., Bristol; Sen. Regist. (Histopath.) Glos. Roy. Hosp.; Cons. (Histopath) Salisbury Dist. Hosp.

BIDDULPH, Desmond Rollo 3A Gilston Road, London SW10 9SJ Tel: 020 7351 3800 — MB BS 1967 Lond.

BIDDULPH, Gillian 11 Morley Square, Bishopston, Bristol BS7 9DW — MRCS Eng. LRCP Lond. 1979; DRCOG 1983.

BIDDULPH, Jean Christine 35 Lansdowne Crescent, Bayston Hill, Shrewsbury SY3 0JB — MB ChB 1976 Liverp. Clin. Asst. & Staff (Anaesth.) Shropsh. HA. Prev: Regist. (Anaesth.) Dudley Rd. Hosp. Birm.; Regist. (Anaesth.) Salop. AHA.; Ho. Surg. & Ho. Phys. David Lewis N.. Hosp. Liverp.

BIDDULPH, Michael John Patrick Tel: 01273 601122/601344 Fax: 01273 623450; 19 Goldstone Villas, Hove BN3 3RR — MB BCh BAO 1969 Dub.

BIDGOOD, Kenneth Andrew Mill House, Orchard Portman, Taunton TA3 5BW — MB BS 1978 Lond.; BSc (Hons.) Lond. 1975, MB BS 1978; MRCOG 1985. (St. Mary's) Cons. Obst. W. Som. NHS Trust. Socs: Fell. Roy. Soc. Med. Prev: Lect. & Hon. Sen. Regist. Dept. Obst. Bristol & W.on HA.

BIDGOOD, Rosalie Anne Horse Hill House, Ribbesford, Bewdley DY12 2TU Tel: 01299 403191 — MB 1977 Camb.; BChir 1976.

BIDMEAD, John Paul Department of Urogynaecology, King's College Hospital, Denmark Hill, London SE5 9RS — MB BS 1987 Lond. Specialist Regist. King's Coll. Hosp. Prev: SHO (Gyn.) Whitington Hosp. Lond.

BIDSTRUP, Patricia Lesley 11 Sloane Terrace Mansions, Sloane Terrace, London SW1X 9DG Tel: 020 7730 8720 — MB BS 1939 (Credit) Adelaide; MD Adelaide 1958; FRCP Lond. 1964, M 1947; FRACP 1954, M 1943; FFOM RCP Lond. 1981. (Adelaide & S. Austral.) p/t Med. Cons. Medico-Legal & Various Indust. Organisations. Socs: Fell. Roy. Soc. Med.; Fell. Amer. Coll. Occupat. & Environm. Med.; Brit. Occupat. Hyg. Soc. Prev: Mem. Indust. Injuries Advis. Counc. & Med. Appeal Tribunals; Med. Off. i/c Med. & Tuberc. Sects. Glyn-Hughes Hosp. Belsen; Hon. Asst. Phys. Roy. Adelaide Hosp.

BIDWELL, Catherine Mary Tanfield View Surgery, Scott Street, Stanley DH9 8AD — MB BS 1982 Newc.; MRCGP 1986; DCCH RCP Ed. 1985; DRCOG 1986. (Newc.) Principle, DRS Harbinson + Partners, Tanfield View Surg., Scott St, Stanley, Co. Durh.

BIDWELL, Mr James Peter Department of Orthopaedic Surgery, Glasgow Royal Infirmary, Castle St., Glasgow G4 Tel: 0141 211 4000 Fax: 0870 055 7830 Email: james@macbidwell.demon.co.uk — MB BS 1989 Lond.; FRCS Ed. 1993; FRCS Ed. (Tr. & Orth) 1999. (Lond. Hosp. Med. Coll.) Specialist Regist. Rotat. (Orthop.) W. Scotl. Orthop. Rotat. Socs: BMA; BOTA. Prev: Regist., S.ern Gen. Hosp. Glas.; Regist., Glas. Roy. Infirm.; Regist., CrossHo. Hosp. Kilmarnock.

BIDWELL, John Charles Darwen Health Centre, Union St., Darwen BB3 0DA Tel: 01254 778350 Fax: 01254 778347; 26 Jacks Key Drive, Darwen BB3 2LG Tel: 01254 778350 Fax: 01254 778347 — MB ChB 1974 Sheff. (Sheff.) Prev: Ho. Surg. & Ho. Phys. Doncaster Roy. Infirm.

BIDWELL, Lawrence Archibald McIlroy Dumbarton Health Centre, Station Road, Dumbarton G82 1PW Tel: 01389 602633 Fax: 01389 602623; Dumbarton Health Centre, Station Road, Dumbarton G82 1PW Tel: 01389 602662 Fax: 01389 602625 — MB ChB Glas. 1977; FRCGP 1996, M 1982; DRCOG 1980.

BIEDRZYCKI, Tadeusz Department of Histopathology, West Suffolk Hospital, Hardwick Lane, Bury St Edmunds IP33 2QZ Tel: 01284 763131; Trevone, Fornham Road, Great Barton, Bury St Edmunds IP31 2TR — Lekarz 1973 Warsaw; MRCPath 1986. Cons. Histopath. W. Suff. Hosp. Socs: Assn. Clin. Paths.; Roy. Coll. Pathol. Prev: Sen. Scientif. & Research Asst./Research Fell. Path. Maria Sklodowska-Curie Inst. Oncol. Warsaw, Poland; Sen. Regist. Rotat. (Histopath.) Mersey HA; Regist. (Histopath.) Wirral HA.

BIEKER, Martina 35 Croft Down Road, Solihull B92 9BD — MB ChB 1991 Stellenbosch; DA (UK) 1995. SHO (Anaesth.) Yeovil Dist. Hosp.

BIEL, Elzbieta Maria 3 Denbigh Road, London W13 8QA Tel: 020 8997 2865 — MB BS 1962 Lond.; MRCS Eng. LRCP Lond. 1961. (Roy. Free) Asst. MOH Lond. Boro. Ealing. Socs: BMA.

BIELAWSKA, Cecilia Ann Whittington Hospital, Highgate Hill, London N19 5NF Tel: 020 7288 5462 — MB BS 1978 Lond.; FRCP 1995 UK; MRCP 1981 UK; MRCP (UK) 1981; FRCP (UK) 1995. Cons. Phys. Geriat. & Hon. Sen. Lect. Whittington Hosp. Lond.; Undergrad. Sub Dean UCL Med. Sch. Lond. Socs: Fell. Roy. Coll. Phys.s. Prev: Sen. Regist. (Geriat.) Univ. Coll. Hosp. Lond.; Regist. (Gen. Med.) Qu. Mary's Hosp. Lond.; Regist. (Rheum.) Middlx. Hosp. Lond.

BIELENKY, Margaret Anne (retired) Tel: 01285 652056/659235 — MB BS 1970 Lond.; MRCS Eng. LRCP Lond. 1970; DObst RCOG 1974. p/t Psychotherapist. Prev: Clin. Med. Off. N.W. Surrey HA.

BIELER, Zara Anne 12 Rosetta Park, Belfast BT6 0DJ — MB BCh 1998 Belf.; MB BCh Belf 1998.

BIELINSKI, Barbara Katarzyna 30 Hazelwood Close, Kidderminster DY11 6LN — MB BS 1991 Lond.; BSc Biochem. & Basic Med. Sci. Lond. 1988; MRCP (UK) 1994. (Roy. Free Hosp. Sch. Med.) Specialist Regist. (Paediat.) W. Midl.

BIENZ, Nicola Wexham Park Hospital, Wexham, Slough SL2 4HL Tel: 01753 633000 — BM BS 1985 Nottm.; MRCP(UK) 1989; MRCPath 1997. Cons. Haematologist Wexham Pk. Hosp. Slough. Prev: Sen. Regist. (Haemat.) Nottm.; Leukaemia Research Fund Clin. Fell. Birm.

BIERER-SHARP, Deborah 6 Grange Park Place, Thurstan Road, London SW20 0EE — MB BS 1964 Lond.; DA Eng. 1966. (Char. Cross) Clin. Asst. (Anaesth.) Nelson Hosp. Wimbledon; Clin. Asst. Sutton Hosp. Prev: Ho. Surg. Harrow Hosp.; Ho. Phys., & SHO (Anaesth.) W. Lond. Hosp.

BIERVLIET, Frank Patrice 2 Wickham Gardens, Wolverhampton WV11 1SQ — Artsexamen 1989 Rotterdam.

BIETZK, Janet Elizabeth Shefford Health Centre, Iveldale Drive, Shefford SG17 5AU Tel: 01462 814899; 40 Northwood End Road, Haynes, Bedford MK45 3QB Tel: 01234 381771 — MB BS 1981 Lond.

BIETZK, Ryszard Geraint The Health Centre, Iveldale Drive, Shefford SG17 5AD Tel: 01462 814899 Fax: 01462 815322; Email: ryszbietzk@aol.com — MB BS 1981 Lond.; MRCS Eng. LRCP (Lond.) 1981; DRCOG 1985. (Charing Cross)

BIEZANEK, Anne Campbell Cluny, Manor Road, Wallasey CH45 7RG Tel: 0151 630 4000 — MB ChB 1951 Aberd.; BSc Aberd. 1947; MFHom 1989. Indep. Phys. (Homoeop). Merseyside. Socs: Hon. Mem. Wallasey Med. Soc.; Liverp. M-C Homoeop. Soc. Prev: Single Handed NHS GP Principle, 20 Years in Wallasey; Regist. Rainhill Hosp. Liverp.; Clin. Asst. (Homoeop.) Mossley Hill Hosp. Liverp.

BIGG, Andrew Russell Victoria Road Surgery, 82 Victoria Road, Oulton Broad, Lowestoft NR33 9LU Tel: 01502 572368 Fax: 01502 537035 — MB ChB 1979 Aberd.; MRCGP 1983; DRCOG 1981.

BIGGAM, Gordon James (retired) The Leys, Adderbury, Banbury OX15 Tel: 01295 810224 — MB ChB 1955 Ed.; DObst RCOG 1960; DCH Eng. 1961. Emmigration Med. Off. Govt. Austral. & Canada. Prev: Ho. Phys. Roy. Infirm. Edin. & Roy. Hosp. Sick Childr. Glas.

BIGGAR, Elizabeth Ann (retired) Whinyett, Pencaitland, Tranent EH34 5BB Tel: 01875 340407 Email: lizstacey@onetel.net.uk — MB ChB 1960 St. And. Prev: Ho. Phys. (Paediat.) Seacroft Hosp. Leeds.

BIGGART, Barbara Simmers Ravenswood Doctors Surgery, Thomson Avenue, Johnstone PA5 8SU Tel: 01505 331979 Fax: 01505 323444; Rowanknoll, Mencaun Road, Kilmacolm PA13 4PB Fax: 01505 873259 — MB ChB 1979 Ed.; Cert. Family Plann. JCC 1981; Cert. Prescribed Equiv. Exp. JCPTGP 1980. GP Glas. Job Share.

BIGGART, John Denis (retired) Histopathology Department, The Laboratories, Belfast City Hospital, Belfast BT9 7AD Tel: 01232 329241 — MB BCh BAO Belf. 1961; MD Belf. 1965; FRCPath 1982, M 1970. Sen. Lect. (Path.) Qu. Univ. Belf.

BIGGART, Matthew John Anaesthetic Department, Noble's Hospital, Douglas Tel: 01624 663322; Stoneycroft, Glen Vine Road, Glen Vine, Douglas IM4 4HF Tel: 01624 851871 Email: biggart@enterprise.net — MB BS 1978 Lond.; MRCS Eng. LRCP Lond. 1978; FFA RCS Eng. 1983. (Char. Cross) Cons. Anaesth. Noble's I. of Man. Hosp. Douglas.

BIGGART, Rosemary Jane (retired) Baker Street Surgery, 9 Baker Street, Glasgow G41 3YE Tel: 0141 632 4962 Fax: 0141 636 6651 — MB BCh BAO 1966 Belf. Prev: Ho. Off. Roy. Vict. Hosp. Belf. & Glas. Roy. Infirm.

BIGGART, Samuel Arthur (retired) Mill Croft, Millway, Reigate RH2 0RH Tel: 01737 763205 — MB BS 1947 Durh.; MRCP Lond. 1954; FRCP Ed. 1982, M 1953; DTM & H Eng. 1953.

BIGGART, Simon Andrew William Samuel Cardiac Department, St Thomas' Hospital, Lambeth Palace Road, London SE1 7EH — MB BS 1989 Lond.; BSc Lond. 1986; MRCP (UK) 1993. Cardiol. Research Fell. St. Thos. Hosp. Prev: Regist. (Cardiol.) Guy's & St. Thos. Hosp.; Regist. (Gen. Med. & Cardiol.) Roy. Sussex Co. Hosp.; SHO Rotat. Roy. Sussex Co. Hosp.

BIGGE, Thomas Leslie, RD Brannams Medical Centre, Brannams Square, Kiln Lane, Barnstaple EX32 8AP Tel: 01271 329004 Fax: 01271 346785; Marwood House, Marwood, Barnstaple EX31 4EB — MB BChir 1970 Camb.; MA Camb. 1971, MB BChir 1970; DObst RCOG 1972. Course Organiser N. Devon VTS. Prev: Surg. Lt.-Cdr. RNR; SHO (Obst.) P.ss Margt. Hosp. Swindon; SHO (Paediat.) Roy. Berks. Hosp. Reading.

BIGGIN, Alan Edward 9 Springwell, Ingleton, Darlington DL2 3JJ — MB ChB 1956 Leeds.

BIGGIN, Mr Christopher Stuart 13 Merchants Wharf, St Peter's Basin, Newcastle upon Tyne NE6 1TR Tel: 0191 224 3511 Email: chris@chriscat.demon.co.uk — MB BS 1991 Newc.; FRCS Eng. 1995. (Newc.) Research Regist. (Surg.) Cancer Research Unit Newc. Gen. Hosp.

BIGGIN, Mark Frazer Market Harborough Medical Centre, 67 Coventry Road, Market Harborough LE16 9BX Tel: 01858 64242 — MRCS Eng. LRCP Lond. 1961. (Guy's) Prev: Ho. Surg., Ho. Phys. & Jun. Hosp. Med. Off. (Anaesth.) Burton Gen. Hosp.

BIGGINS, Peter The Surgery, Clos de Carteret, Cobo GY9 3TD Tel: 01481 56404 — MB ChB 1969 Aberd. (Aberd.) Prev: Ho. Surg. & Ho. Phys. Gen. Hosp. Jersey.

BIGGS, Caroline Jane 13 Clarence Avenue, Widnes WA8 9EL — MB ChB 1998 Leeds.

BIGGS, David Thomas Cowes Health Centre, 8 Consort Road, Cowes PO31 7SH Tel: 01983 295251 Fax: 01983 280461 — MB BS 1968 Lond.; MRCS Eng. LRCP Lond. 1968; MRCGP 1974; DGM RCP Lond. 1985. (Univ. Coll. Hosp.) Prev: Ho. Phys. & Ho. Surg. St. Mary's Hosp. Newport, IOW.

BIGGS, Elizabeth Anne Cameron Department of Microbiology, Inverclyde Royal Hospital, Greenock PA16 0XN; 63 Westfield Drive, Glasgow G52 2SG — MB ChB 1977 Glas.; FRCPath (Med. Microbiol.) 1983; MRCPath (Med. Microbiol.) 1983. Cons. Microbiol. Inverclyde Roy. Hosp. Greenock.

BIGGS, John Edward Wycliffe Surgery, Elliott Road, Plymouth PL4 9NH Tel: 01752 660648 Fax: 01752 261468; Chetwode, Fernleigh Road, Mannamead, Plymouth PL3 5AN Tel: 01752 663570 Fax: 0378 591352 — MB BS 1974 Lond.; Family Plann. Cert 1976; Cert. Av Med. 1976. (Roy. Free) GP Trainer Plymouth; Hosp. Pract. (Endoscopy) Div. Radiol. Derriford Hosp. Plymouth. Socs: Plymouth Med. Soc.; Primary Care Soc. Gastroenterol.; (Chairm.) GP Educat. Comm. Plymouth. Prev: Ho. Phys. to Dean Roy. Free Hosp. Sch. Med.; SHO (O & G) & Ho. Surg. Soton Gen. Hosp.; RAF Med. Br..

BIGGS, John Sydney Grainge Regional Postgraduate Office, The Clinical School, Addenbrooke's Hospital, Hills Road, Cambridge CB2 2SP Tel: 01223 336106 Fax: 01223 415069 Email: john.biggs@lifespan-an.anglox.nhs.uk; 5 Wootton Way, Cambridge CB3 9LX Tel: 01223 323377 — MB BS 1960 Melbourne; MA Camb. 1994; MD Aberd. 1973; FRCOG 1980, M 1966; FRACOG 1979; DHMSA 1993. Postgrad. Dean Univ. Camb., Anglia & Oxf. RO NHS Exec.; Lead Dean Obst. & Gyn. Socs: (Pres Assn. Study Med. Educat.; BMA; Roy. Soc. Med. Prev: Lect. (O & G) Univ. Aberd.; Sen. Lect. & Reader (O & G) Univ. Qu.sland, Austral.; Dean of Med. & Prof. Univ. Qu.sland, Austral.

BIGGS, Mr Peter Edward Northgate Medical Practice, 1 Northgate, Canterbury CT1 1WL Tel: 01227 463570 Fax: 01227 786147; Willow Down, Harbledown, Canterbury CT2 9AJ — MB BS 1980 Lond.; FRCS Eng. 1984; MRCS Eng. LRCP Lond. 1980; MRCGP 1988; DCH RCP Lond. 1987; DRCOG 1986. Prev: Trainee GP Kent & Canterbury Hosp. VTS; SHO (A & E, Anat. & Surg.) Char. Cross Hosp. Lond.; SHO (Surg.) William Harvey Hosp. Ashford.

BIGGS, Peter Ian 20 Beech Drive, Rugby CV22 7LT — MB ChB 1971 Sheff.; BSc (Hons.) Sheff. 1967, MB ChB 1971; MRCP (UK) 1975. (Sheff) Cons. Phys. (Diabetes & Endocrinol.) Coventry & Rugby Hosps. Socs: (Med. & Scientif. Sect.) BDA. Prev: Sen. Regist. Walsgrave Hosp. Coventry & Qu. Eliz. Hosp.; arch Fell. (Dept. Med.) & SHO Med. Unit Univ. Hosp. of Wales Cardiff; SHO Dept. Tuberc. & Chest Dis. Sully Hosp.

BIGGS, Richard Creighton Gosford Hill Medical Centre, 167 Oxford Road, Kidlington OX5 2NS Tel: 01865 374242 Fax: 01865 377826; 15 Home Close, Kidlington OX5 2EA Tel: 01865 372654 — MB BS 1962 Lond.; DObst RCOG 1965. (St. Geo.) Prev: Ho. Phys. & Ho. Surg. St. Geo. Hosp. Tooting; Ho. Surg. (Obst.) Edgware Gen. Hosp.

BIGGS, Rosemary Peyton (retired) The Old Water Mill, 5 Shilbrook Manor, Black Bourton, Bampton OX18 2PD Tel: 01993 846014 — MB BS 1943 Lond.; MA Oxf. 1969; MD Lond. 1949; FRCP Lond. 1974, M 1970; MRCS Eng. LRCP Lond. 1943. Prev: Dir. Oxf. Haemophilia Centre.

BIGGS, Samantha Flat 2, Chichele Mansions, Chichele Rd, London NW2 3DG Tel: 020 8450 7091 — MB BS 1997 Lond. (St. Bartholomew's & Royal London School of Med. & Dentistry) SHO (O & G).

BIGHAM, Rhiannon Lorna Olwen Belfry House, The Old Palace, Ripon HG4 3HE — MB BS 1990 Newc.

BIGLEY, George Joseph (retired) 38 Langley Hall, Shore Road, Newtownabbey, Antrim BT37 0FB Tel: 01232 853147 — MA Dub. 1954, BA, MB BCh BAO 1952; DA Eng. 1955. Prev: Cons. Anaesth. Purdysburn Hosp.

BIGNALL, John Cockayne Victoria House, Victoria St, Laugharne, Carmarthen SA33 4SE Tel: 01994 427517 Email: j.bignall@elsevier.co.uk — MB BS Lond. 1966; MRCS Eng. LRCP Lond. 1966. (Lond. Hosp.) Med. Ed. The Lancet.

BIGNALL, Julia Amanda 23 Coed Leddyn, Caerphilly CF83 2NF — MB BCh 1997 Wales.

BIGNALL, Simon Staplegrove, 6 Church St., Hampton TW12 2EG Tel: 020 7725 6351 Fax: 020 7725 6284 Email: s.bignall@ic.ac.uk — MB BS 1977 Lond.; MD Lond. 1990; FRCP Lond. 1996; MRCP (UK) 1980; FRCPCH 1997. Cons. Neonat. Med. Lond.; Hon. Sen. Lect. Imperial Coll. Lond.

BIGNARDI, Giuseppe Enrico Microbiology Department, Sunderland Royal Hospital, Kayll Road, Sunderland SR4 7TP Tel: 0191 565 6256 Email: giuseppe.bignard@chs.nothy.nhs.uk — State Exam 1982 Bologna. Cons. Microbiologist. Socs: FRCPath.; Hosp. Infec. Soc.; Brit. Soc. for Antimicrobial Chemother. Prev: Regist. (MicroBiol.) John Radcliffe Hosp. Oxf.; SHO (Path.) Stepping Hill Hosp. Stock; Sen. Regist., Microbiologist, St. Mary's Hosp. Lond.

BIGNELL, Christopher John Nottingham City Hospital, Hucknall Road, Nottingham NG5 1PB Tel: 0115 962 7746 — MB BS 1978 Lond.; BSc Nottm. 1973; FRCP Lond. 1994; MRCP (UK) 1982. Cons. Genitourin. Phys. Nottm. HA.

BIGNELL, Julie Anne 70 Lambourne Drive, Wollaton, Nottingham NG8 1GR — MB 1979 Camb.; BChir 1978; MRCGP 1983; DRCOG 1982.

BIGNELL, Michael David 37 Northey Avenue, Cheam, Sutton SM2 7HS — MB BS 1964 Lond.; MRCS Eng. LRCP Lond. 1964; DPH Lond. 1968. (Univ. Coll. Hosp.) Clin. Med. Off. Mid Surrey Health Dist. Socs: BMA. Prev: Ho. Surg. (Paediat. & Plastic) St. Geo. Hosp. Tooting; Ho. Phys. Qu. Mary's Hosp. Sidcup.

BIGNELL, Nicola Jane Top Flat, 40 Oakhill Road, London SW15 2QR Tel: 020 8874 6397 — MB BS 1997 Lond.; MA (cantab), 1989. VTS for G. P, Roehampton & Kingston.

BIGOS, Janet Elizabeth Witley Surgery, Wheeler Lane, Witley, Godalming GU8 5QR Tel: 01483 682218 — MB BS 1981 Lond.; BSc (Hons.) Lond. 1975, MB BS 1981; Dip. Sports Med. Lond. 1987; DRCOG 1986. Smith & Nephew Bursary for Sports Med. Socs: Brit. Assn. Sport & Med.

BIGRIGG, Margaret Alison 6 Sandyford Place, Glasgow G3 7NB; 12 Sherbrooke Gardens, Glasgow G41 4HU — BM 1982 Soton.; MBA (Distinc.) 1999; MFFP 1994; DM Soton. 1992; T(OG) 1992; FRCOG 1989; FRCS Ed. 1986. Clin. Dir. & Cons. Gyn. Glas.Primary Care Trust. Prev: Cons. & Sen. Lect. (O & G) S.mead Hosp. Bristol.

BIGWOOD, Fiona Vivienne 27 Manor Road, Keynsham, Bristol BS31 1RA — MB ChB 1987 Manch.; DFFP 1994; DA (UK) 1990. Clin. Asst. (Occupat. Health) Roy. United Hosp. Bath. Prev: CMO (Community Paediat.) Frenchay Hosp. Bristol; GP/Regist. Bristol; Regist. (Anaesth.) Chester.

BIGWOOD, Mark Thomas Gunn Hanham Surgery, 33 Whittucks Road, Hanham, Bristol BS15 3HY Tel: 0117 967 5201 Fax: 0117 947 7749 — MB ChB 1989 Manch.; BDS Ed. 1980; FDS RCPS Glas. 1984; Dip Med. Sci. St. And. 1986.

BIHARI, David Julian Intensive Care Unit, Guy's Hospital, St Thomas St., London SE1 9RT Tel: 020 7955 5000 Fax: 020 7378 8621; 52 Talford Road, Peckham, London SE15 5NY Tel: 020 7703 5053 — MB BS 1978 Lond.; MRCP (UK) 1980. Dir. Intens. Care Unit. Guy's Hosp. Lond. Prev: Staff Specialist (Intens. Care) Roy. N. Shore Hosp. Sydney, Australia; Lect. (Med.) Middlx. Hosp. Med. Sch. Lond.

BIHARI, Mr Julian (retired) Melleray, 16 Beaufort Avenue, Langland, Swansea SA3 4NU Tel: 01792 368479 Fax: 01792 368479 — MB BS 1948 Lond.; FRCS Eng. 1953; MRCS Eng. LRCP Lond. 1948; DLO Eng. 1957. Hon. Med. Off. Morniston Orpheus Male Voice Choir. Prev: Cons. ENT Surg. Singleton Hosp. Swansea & Glantawe Hosp. GP.

BIHARI, Kailash 4 Uplands, Pentre CF41 7PG — MB BS 1973 Patna.

***BIJLANI, Aisha** 2 Crown Office Row, 2nd Floor, The Temple, London EC4Y 7HJ Tel: 020 7797 8000 Fax: 020 7797 8001; 29 Ponsonby Terrace, Westminster, London SW1P 4PZ Tel: 020 7821 8204 Fax: 020 7821 8204 — MB BS 1991 Lond.

BIJLANI, Natasha Women's Service, Bluebell Unit, Springfield University Hospital, 61 Glenburnie Road, London SW17 7DJ Tel: 020 8682 6941 Fax: 020 8682 6235 — MB BS 1987 Lond.; MRCPsych 1992. (St Bartholomews Hosp, London) Specialist Regist. Psychiat. (Gen. Adult) St. Geo.'s Hosp. (Lond.) Rotat. Socs: Comm. Mem., Wom. in Psyiatry s/i Gp. (WIPSIG) Roy. Coll. of Psychiat.s, Lond.; Mem., Brit. Indian Psychiatric Assn. (BIPA). Prev: Regist. (Psychiat.) St. Bart. Hosp. Lond.; Charter Research Fell. St. Geo. Hosp. Med. Sch. Lond.

BIJRAL, Harbal Singh The Doctor's House, Furnace, Inveraray PA32 8XU — MB ChB 1992 Aberd.

BIJRAL, Harkejind Singh Cumlodden House, Furnace, Inveraray PA32 8XU — MB ChB 1997 Manch.

BIJRAL, Keval Singh The Surgery, Furnace, Inveraray PA32 8XN Tel: 01499 500207 — MB BS 1967 Punjabi. (Punjabi) GP Inverary, Argyll.

BILAGI, Parineeta 4 Lancaster Court, 100 Lancaster Gate, London W2 3NY — MB BS 1997 Lond.

BILAGI, Praveen Soma Shee Kar c/o Mr Al Bayaa, 7 Greswell St., London SW6 6PR — MB BS 1996 Lond.

BILAS, Roman The Surgery, 75 Griffiths Drive, Wednesfield, Wolverhampton WV11 2JN Tel: 01902 731250 Fax: 01902 307143 — MB ChB 1985 Leic.

BILAS, Zenko The Health Centre, First Avenue, Chipstone, Mansfield NG21 9DA Tel: 01623 626132 Fax: 01623 420578 — MB ChB 1986 Leic.

BILBEY, Frank 62 Lowton Road, St Annes-on-Sea, Lytham St Annes FY8 3JG Tel: 01253 724917 — MB BS 1953 Lond.

BILBEY, Hugh Marple Road Surgery, 129 Marple Road, Offerton, Stockport SK7 5EP Tel: 0161 483 4986 — MB ChB 1987 Manch.; MRCGP 1991. (Manchester) GP Stockport.

BILBROUGH, Madeleine St James Medical Centre, St. James Street, Taunton TA20 1DB Tel: 01823 285400 Fax: 01823 285404 — MB ChB 1971 Manch.

BILCLIFFE, Elizabeth Mary Beech Tree Surgery, 68 Doncaster Road, Selby YO8 9AJ Tel: 01757 703933 — MB BS 1983 Newc.; MB BS (Hons.) Newc. 1983; DRCOG 1988; DCH RCP Lond. 1987.

BILES, Joseph Philip c/o Mr & Mrs Biles, 49 Blind End, Bourne End SL8 5TN — MB BS 1994 Newc.

BILGINER, Hasan Tahsin Laurence House, 107 Philip Lane, Tottenham, London N15 4JR Tel: 020 8801 6640; 121 Warham Road, London N4 1AS Tel: 020 8340 9586 Fax: 020 8340 1042 — MD 1963 Istanbul; LAH Dub. 1967; DCH Eng. 1968. (Istanbul) Prev: SHO Paediat. & Psychiat. Regist. Qu. Mary's Hosp. Carshalton; Paediat. Regist. St. Helier Hosp. Carshalton.

BILKHU, Jaswant Singh The Health Centre, Main Road, Radcliffe-on-Trent, Nottingham NG12 2GD Tel: 0115 933 3737; 12 Yew Tree Close, Radcliffe on Trent, Nottingham NG12 2AZ Tel: 0115 933 2948 Fax: 0115 933 2684 — MB ChB 1972 Manch.; M Med Sci (Clinical Education); FRCGP 1991, M 1976; DCH Eng. 1975; DObst RCOG 1974. (Manchester) GP Princip.; Postgrad. Med. Dean GP Nottm. Med. Sch. Socs: Notts M-C Soc. Prev: Vice-Chairm. Nottm. MAAG; Chairm. GP Educat. Sub-Comm. Trent Region; Chairm. (Vale of Trent Fac.) RCGP.

BILL, Archana 15 Windsor Hill, Hillsborough BT26 6RL — MB BCh BAO 1992 Belf.

BILL, Elizabeth Jane Mid-Cheshire Homeopathic Group, 2 Watling Street, Northwich CW9 5EX Tel: 01606 42445; The Paddocks, Ash House Lane, Little Leigh, Northwich CW8 4RG — MB BS 1984 Lond.; MRCGP 1988. GP N.wich. Socs: BMA.

BILL, Katherine Alison Fulford Surgery, 2 Fulford Park, Fulford, York YO10 4QE Tel: 01904 625566 Fax: 01904 671539; 12 St Georges Avenue, Harrogate HG2 9DP Tel: 01423 507123 — MB BS 1989 Lond.; BSc Lond. 1986, MB BS 1989; MRCGP 1993; DCH RCP Lond. 1993. (Univ. Coll. & Middlx. Hosp. Med. Sch.) Socs: RCGP.

BILL, Kathryn Moyna Department of Clinical Anaesthesia, Royal Group of Hospitals, Grosvenor Road, Belfast BT12 Tel: 01232 240503 Fax: 01232 325725 — MB ChB 1980 Ed.; FFA RCSI 1984. (Edinburgh) Cons. Anaesth. Roy. Gp. Hosps. Belf.

BILL, Richard Henry 11 Old Ballyclare Road, Templepatrick, Ballyclare BT39 0BJ — MB BCh BAO 1993 Belf.

BILL, Susan Margaret Elizabeth 4 Kiln Park, Templepatrick, Ballyclare BT39 0BB — MB BCh BAO 1993 Belf.

BILLCLIFF, Natasha 15 Cambridge Gardens, Edinburgh EH6 5DH — MB ChB 1993 Ed.

BILLETT, Anne Felicity 36 Delorme Street, London W6 8DT — MB BS 1987 Lond.

BILLETT, John Summers Wentworth House, Great Corby, Carlisle CA4 8LL — MB BS 1980 Lond.

BILLING, Mr John Stephen 40 Westland Way, Woodstock OX20 1YF — BM BCh 1990 Oxf.; FRCS Eng. 1994. Regist. (Cardiothoracic Surg.) Leeds Gen. Infirm. Prev: SHO (Cardiothoracic Surg.) Papworth Hosp. Camb.

BILLING, Valerie Christine 40 Plasturton Gardens, Cardiff CF11 9HF — MB BCh 1997 Wales.

BILLINGE, Vicki Angela 74 Church Road, Fleet GU51 4LY — BChir 1996 Camb.

BILLINGHAM, Gerald Patrick (retired) Merchiston, Stratton St Margaret, Swindon Tel: 01793 823307 — MB BS 1954 Lond. Prev: Ho. Phys. W.m. Childr. Hosp.

BILLINGHAM, Imogen Susan Department of Anaesthetics, Royal Liverpool Childrens Hospital, Alder Hey, Eaton Road, Liverpool L12 2AP Tel: 0151 228 4811 Fax: 0151 252 5460; 2 Appletree Close, Allerton, Liverpool L18 9XN — BM 1979 Soton.; FFA RCS Eng. 1986; DCH RCP Lond. 1983. Cons. Paediat. Anaesth. Roy. Liverp. Childr. Hosp. Prev: Sen. Regist. (Anaesth.) Mersey RHA.; Regist. (Paediat. Anaesth.) Roy. Liverp. Childr. Hosp.; Regist. (Anaesth.) Camb. HA.

BILLINGHAM, James William Annandale Medical Centre, Mobberley Road, Knutsford WA16 8HR Tel: 01565 755222 Fax: 01565 652049; Base Mill Cottage, Base Mill Lane, Chelford, Macclesfield SK11 9BW Tel: 01477 571313 — MB ChB Manch. 1969; MRCGP 1977; DObst RCOG 1971. Prev: Ho. Surg. Manch. Roy. Infirm.; SHO (O & G) Wythenshawe Hosp. Manch.; SHO (Paediat.) Univ. Hosp. S. Manch. Gp. Hosps.

BILLINGHAM, Jenny Ganders Green Cottage, May Hill, Longhope GL17 0NJ — MB ChB 1992 Liverp.

BILLINGHURST, John Robert (retired) 67 Marlborough Crescent, Sevenoaks TN13 2HL Tel: 01732 456384 Fax: 01732 746198 Email: john and arbell@aol.com — BM BCh 1952 Oxf.; MA Oxf. 1952; FRCP Lond. 1975, M 1960; DObst RCOG 1953. Locum Cons. Neurol. Kent & Sussex Hosp. Tunbridge Wells. Prev: Cons. Phys. Oldchuch Hosp.

BILLINGHURST, Margaret Ann (retired) The Hyde, Maidensgrove, Henley-on-Thames RG9 6EZ Tel: 01491 638238 — MB BS 1943 Lond.; MRCS Eng. LRCP Lond. 1941; DOMS Eng. 1947. Prev: Out-pat. Off. Moorfields Hosp.

BILLINGS, Anne Catherine Northgate Medical Centre, 10 Upper Northgate Street, Chester CH1 4EE Tel: 01244 379906 Fax: 01244 379703; 28 St. George's Crescent, Queens Park, Chester CH4 7AR Tel: 01244 675225 — MB BS 1977 Lond.; MRCS Eng. LRCP Lond. 1977; MRCGP 1992; DRCOG Eng. 1981. (Roy. Free Hosp.) Prev: GP Bristol.

BILLINGS, Diane Cottingham Medical Centre, 17-19 South St., Cottingham, Hull HU1 3; 4 St. Barnabas Drive, Swanland, North Ferriby HU14 3RL — MB ChB 1984 Manch.; DRCOG 1992. p/t GP, Cottingham, Hull.

BILLINGS, Mr Peter John Wrexham Maelor Hospital, Croesnewydd Road, Wrexham LL13 7TD Tel: 01978 291100; 28 St. George's Crescent, Queens Park, Chester CH4 7AR Tel: 01244 675225 Email: peter@billings.u-net.com — MB BS 1977 Lond.; MS Lond. 1987; MRCS Eng. LRCP Lond. 1977; FRCS Eng. 1981. (Roy. Free Hosp.) Cons. Surg. Wrexham Maelor Hosp. Socs: Fell. Roy. Soc. Med.; Fell. Assn. Surgs.; Assn. Coloproctol. Prev: RSO (Surg.) St. Marks Hosp. Lond.; Sen. Regist. (Surg.) Cardiff & Swansea; Regist. (Surg.) St. Geo. Hosp. Lond.

BILLINGS, Robert Andrew Berkeley Place Surgery, 11 High Street, Cheltenham GL52 6DA Tel: 01242 513975 — MB BS 1968 Lond.; MRCP (U.K.) 1972; MRCGP 1977. (Guy's) Hosp. Pract. Highfield Hosp. Rheum. Dis. Droitwich; Non Exec. Dir. Glos. HA; Brit. Inst. Musclo-Skeletal Med. Socs: Brit. Assn. Rheum. & Rehabil. & Brit. Assn. Manip. Med. Prev: Sen. Regist. (Rheum.) Guy's Hosp. Lond.; Cons. Med. Off. Morganites Ltd. Lond.; Hon. Med. Adviser Cheltenham Sports Counc.

BILLINGSLEY, Peter 46 Grandison Road, Walton, Liverpool L4 9SX — MB ChB 1990 Leeds.

BILLINGTON, Brenda May 72 Berkeley Avenue, Reading RG1 6HY Tel: 01189 955 3452 Fax: 01189 588110 — MB ChB 1974 Birm.; FRCS Eng. 1980; FRCOphth 1988; DO Eng. 1977. Cons. Ophth. Surg. Roy. Berks. Hosp. Reading. Prev: Sen. Regist. (Ophth.) St. Thos. & Moorfields Eye Hosps. Lond.; Resid. Surg. Off. Moorfields Eye Hosp. Lond.

BILLINGTON, Kim Brynffynnon, Child & Family Clinic, Pontypridd — MB BS 1980 Lond.; MRCPsych 1987; MRCGP 1984.

BILLINGTON, Margaret Teresa 24 St Johns Avenue, Churchdown GL3 2DB Tel: 01452 713036 Fax: 01452 714726; St Rose's House, Stratford Lawn, Stroud GL5 4AP Tel: 01453 762449 Fax: 01453 752617 Email: terryb@doctors.org.uk — MB ChB 1988 Bristol; MRCGP 2000; BA Open 1990; Dip. Community Paediat. Warwick 1991. GP Princip. Ch.down, Glouchester. Prev: SHO (O & G) Cheltenham Gen. Hosp.; Clin. Med. Off. Severn NHS Trust Glos.

BILLINGTON, Martin John Five Chimneys, Duck St., Child Okeford, Blandford Forum DT11 8ET — MB ChB 1993 Sheff.

BILLINGTON, Mr Peter Marton Medical Centre, 1 Glastonbury Avenue, Blackpool FY1 6SF Tel: 01253 761321 Fax: 01253 792701 — MB ChB 1975 Manch.; BSc (Hons.) Lond. 1970; FRCS Eng. 1980; Cert. Family Plann. JCC 1986. Prev: GP Blackburn, Haydock & Walkden.

BILLINGTON, Sophie Alexandra Mary West View Farm, The Raikes, Alstonefield, Ashbourne DE6 2FS — MB BS 1994 Lond.

BILLINGTON, Timothy Nicholas Heaton Moor Medical Centre, 32 Heaton Moor Road, Stockport SK4 4NX Tel: 0161 432 0671; 55 Elms Road, Stockport SK4 4PT — MB ChB 1986 Manch.; MRCGP 1990; DRCOG 1990.

BILLINGTON, Timothy Roy Markby Lordshill Health Centre, Lordshill District Centre, Lordshill, Southampton SO16 8HY Tel: 023 8073 8144 Fax: 023 8073 0722; 56 Glen Eyre Road, Bassett, Southampton SO16 3NJ — MB BS Lond. 1966; MRCS Eng, LRCP Lond. 1966; FRCGP 1988, M 1976; DTM & H Liverp. 1971; DObst RCOG 1971. (St. Bart.) p/t Hon. Lect. Soton. Med. Sch.; BRd.caster Radio Solent; Med. Writer. Prev: Asst. Phys. Stud. Health Univ. Coll. Lond.; Regist. (Med.) & SHO (Path.) St. Bart. Hosp. Lond.

BILLINGTON, Victor Leonard (retired) 24 Ashdown, Eaton Road, Hove BN3 3AQ Tel: 01273 205850 — MB BChir 1944 Camb.; MRCGP 1976. Prev: Chief Med. Off. Cayman Is.s, W. Indies.

BILLS, Geoffrey 240 Compstall Road, Romiley, Stockport SK6 4JG — MB ChB 1951 Manch.

BILLSBOROUGH, Stephen Herbert 180 King Lane, Leeds LS17 6AA — MB ChB 1983 Manch.

BILLSON, Amanda Louise Royal United Hospital NHS Trust, Combe Park, Bath BA1 3NG Tel: 01225 428331; 6 Park Street Mews, Bath BA1 2SZ Tel: 01225 447824 Email: billson@netgates.co.uk — MB BS 1986 Lond.; BA Camb. 1983; MRCP (UK) 1989; Dip. Med.Ed. Dund 1999. (St Mary's Hospital Paddington) Cons. (Paediat.) Roy. United Hosp. Bath. Socs: MRCPCH. Prev: Lect. (Child Health) Univ. Hosp. Nottm.

BILLYARD, Julian John Charles Teignbridge Medical Practice, 2 Den Crescent, Teignbridge, Teignmouth TQ14 8BG Tel: 01626 773729 Fax: 01626 777381 — BM 1984 Soton.

BILOUS, Professor Rudolf William Audrey Collins Unit, Education Centre, South Cleveland Hospital, Middlesbrough TS4 3BW Tel: 01642 854146 Fax: 01642 854148; 71 Levenside, Stokesley, Middlesbrough TS9 5BH Tel: 01642 711847 — MB BS 1976 Lond.; MD Lond. 1988, BSc 1973; FRCP Lond. 1993; MRCP (UK) 1978. (Guy's Hosp.) Regional Prof. Of Clin. Med. Univ. Newc. u. Tyne; Undergrad. Tutor S. Tees Acute Hosps. Trust; Hon. Cons. Phys. (Diabetes/Endocrinol.) S. Tees Acute Hosps. Trust; Assoc. Clin. Sub Dean Teeside, Univ. Newc. U. Tyne. Socs: Chairm., Specialist Care Sect., Diabetes UK.; Specialist Advisory Comm. Endocrinol.& Diabetes, JCHMT (Sec.); RCP Lond. (Regional Specialty Adviser Diabetes & Endocrinol. N.ern Region). Prev: Cons. Phys. Diabetes & Endocrinol. S. Tees Acute Hosps. Trust; Sen. Regist. (Diabetes &

Endocrinol.) Roy. Vic. Infirm. Newc. u. Tyne; Post-Doctoral Research Fell. Dept. Laborat. Med. Univ. Minnesota, USA.

BILSLAND, David John Southern General NHS Trust, 1345 Govan Road, Glasgow G51 4TF Tel: 0141 201 1571 — MB ChB 1983 Glas.; MRCP (UK) 1987; MRCGP 1989; DCH RCPS Glas. 1986; FRCP 1999. Cons. Dermat. S.. Gen. Hosp. NHS Trust Glas. Prev: Sen. Regist. (Dermat.) W.. Infirm. Glas.; Regist. (Photobiol.) Ninewells Hosp. Dundee.

BILSTON, Anne Elizabeth Shotfield Health Centre, Shotfield, Wallington SM6 0HY Tel: 020 8647 0916; 29 The Warren, Carshalton SM5 4EQ — MB BS 1983 Lond.; DRCOG 1988. (Roy. Free) GP. Socs: Assoc. Mem. Soc. Orthop. Med.

BILTON, Diana Papworth Hospital NHS Trust, Papworth Everard, Cambridge CB3 8RE Tel: 01480 830541 Fax: 01480 831068; Burr House, New Road, Hemingford Abbots, Huntingdon PE28 9AB Tel: 01480 460969 Fax: 01480 460969 Email: drdianabilton@cs.com — MB ChB 1984 Manch.; BSc Manch. 1981, MD 1992; FRCP Lond. 1997; MRCP (UK) 1987. Cons. (Repiratory Med.) Papworth Hosp. NHS Trust & Hinchingbrooke Hosp.; Dir. Adult Cystic Fibrosis Centre Papworth Hosp. Prev: Sen. Regist. Qu. Eliz. Hosp. Birm.; Regist. Birm. Gen. Hosp.; Fell. (Cystic Fibrosis) Regional Unit Manch.

BILTON, Kathleen 12 Northall Road, Eaton Bray, Dunstable LU6 2DQ — MB BCh 1969 Wales.

BIMBH, Karamjeet Singh 131 Park Avenue, Southall UB1 3AL — MB BS 1989 Lond.

BINCHY, Mr James Mary Ennis Derriford Hospital, Derriford Road, Plymouth PL6 8DH Tel: 01752 792511 Fax: 01752 778101 — MB BCh BAO 1985 Dub.; FRCS Ed. 1992. (Trinity Coll. Dub.) Cons. A & E Med. Derriford Hosp. Plymouth. Prev: Sen. Regist. (A & E Med.) Yorks. & N.. Region Leeds; Regist. (A & E Med.) Roy. Liverp. Childr. Hosp. Alder Hey & Countess of Chester Hosp.

BINDAL, Taruna 108 Metchley Lane, Birmingham B17 0HY — MB ChB 1998 Birm.; ChB Birm. 1998.

BINDI, Mr Francesco 29 Alric Avenue, New Malden KT3 4JL — MB BS 1988 Lond.; FRCS Eng. 1992. (Char. Cross & Westm.) Specialist Regist. Rotat. (Orthop.) NW Thames. Prev: SHO (Gen. Surg.) Roy. Marsden Hosp. Lond.; SHO (Orthop.) & Ho. Off. (Gen. Surg.) Char. Cross Hosp. Lond.; SHO (A & E) W.m. Hosp. Lond.

BINDMAN, Ellis 15 Petersham Place, Edgbaston, Birmingham B15 3RY Tel: 0121 454 5423 — MB ChB Ed. 1944; FRCPsych 1986, M 1972; DPM Eng. 1971. (Univ. Ed.) Cons. Psychother. Woodbourne Priory Hosp. Birm. Prev: Hon. Sen. Clin. Lect. (Psychiat.) Univ. Birm.

BINDMAN, Jonathan Paul Institute of Psychiatry, De Crespigny Park, London SE5 8AF Tel: 020 7919 2610 Fax: 020 7277 1462 Email: j.bindman@iop.bpmf.ac.uk; 26 Raglan Street, London NW5 3DA — BM BCh 1989 Oxford; BM BCh Oxf 1989; MRCPsych 1994. Lect. (Psychiat.) Inst. Psychiat. Lond. Prev: Regist. Maudsley Hosp. Lond.

BINDON, Carol Ianthe 94 Lawmill Gardens, St Andrews KY16 8QZ — BChir 1990 Camb.

BINDRA, Amrit Pal Singh Derry Downs Surgery, 29 Derry Downs, St. mary's Cray, Orpington BR5 4DU Tel: 01689 838207 Fax: 01689 819768 — LMSSA 1986 Lond.; DRCOG 1997; Medical Acupuncture (BMAS) 2001; DCH Panjab 1980; JCPTGP 1990. Socs: Brit. Med. Acupunc.rs Soc. Prev: Regist. (Paediat.) E. Surrey Hosp. Redhill.

BINDRA, Harjeet Singh Christchurch Road Practice, 81 Christchurch Road, Reading RG2 7BD Tel: 0118 975 5788 Fax: 0118 926 3230; 3 Sonning Meadows, Sonning on Thames, Reading RG4 6XB Tel: 0118 969 6578 — MB BS 1969 Jammu & Kashmir; DTCD Guru Nanak Univ. 1973. (Amritsar Medical College, Amritsar)

BINDRA, Renu 28 Rutland Court, Denmark Hill, London SE5 8EB — MB BS 1994 Lond.

BINDU, A The Surgery, 5 Alice Street, Off Lumb Lane, Bradford BD8 7RT Tel: 01274 736996 Fax: 01274 726956; Farwake Hill Farm, Grantley, Ripon HG4 3PT — MB BS 1968 Delhi.

BINFIELD, Mr Peter Mark 27 Albion Street, Stratton, Cirencester GL7 2HT — MB BS 1986 Lond.; BSc (Hons.) Lond. 1983, MB BS 1986; FRCS Eng. 1990.

BING, Andrew James Fill 4 Hunts Lane, Hallaton, Market Harborough LE16 8UQ — MB ChB 1995 Bristol. SHO (Orthop. & Trauma) Leicester Gen. Hosp. & Leicester Roy. Infirm.

BING, Robert Fill 17 West Hill Road, Leicester LE3 6GB Tel: 01553 858581 — MB ChB 1968 Sheff.; MB ChB (Hons.) Sheff. 1968; FRCP Lond. 1984; MRCP (U.K.) 1971. Sen. Lect. & Cons. Phys. Univ. Leic. & Leic. HA. Socs: Int. Soc. Hypertens. & Assoc. Phys. Gt. Brit. & Irel. Prev: Med. Research Counc. Clin. Research Fell. Univ. Sussex Brighton; Regist. Profess. Unit Therap. & Med. Roy. Infirm. Sheff.; Research Asst. in Hypertens. United Sheff. Hosps.

BINGE, Yvonne Nine Oaks, Grange Road, Netley Abbey, Southampton SO31 5FF Tel: 02380 452354 — MB ChB Birm. 1964; T(GP) 1991; DObst RCOG 1966.

BINGERT, Tom c/o Dr J. Howe, 68 Station Road, Burley-in-Wharfedale, Ilkley LS29 7NG — State Exam Med 1988 Berlin.

BINGHAM, Alexander Robert 2 Corby Drive, Lurgan, Craigavon BT66 7AF Tel: 01762 325891 — MB BCh BAO 1958 Belf.; DObst RCOG 1960. Prev: Med. Off. MoH & Social Serv. N. Irel.

BINGHAM, Mr Brian John Graham Dept. of ENT Surgery, Victoria Infirmary, Langside Drive, Glasgow G42 9TY Tel: 0141 201 5478 Fax: 0141 201 5093 Email: brian.bingham@civic.scot.nhs.uk — MB ChB 1980 Dundee; FRCS Ed. 1985; FRCS Glas 1994. Cons. Otolaryngol. Gtr. Glas. HB. Prev: Sen. Regist. (Otolaryngol.) Tayside HB & N.. RHA; Regist. Bristol & W.on HA; TWJ Fell. Univ. Toronto, Canada.

BINGHAM, Coralie 5 Crabtree Park, Fairford GL7 4LT — BM BCh 1989 Oxford; MRCP (UK) 1993. Specialist Regist. (Renal/Gen. Med.) Roy. Devon & Exeter Hosp. Prev: Regist. (Renal) Roy. Devon & Exeter Hosp.

BINGHAM, Elizabeth The Downland Practice, The Surgery, East Lane, Chieveley, Newbury RG20 8UY Tel: 01635 248251 Fax: 01635 247261; The Boundary House, Churn Road, Compton, Newbury RG20 6PP Tel: 01635 578925 Fax: 01635 578428 — MB ChB 1965 Birm.; BSc Birm. 1962; FRCGP 1991, M 1984; DCH Eng. 1974. (Birm.)

BINGHAM, Elizabeth Ann Department of Dermatology, Royal Hospitals Trust, Belfast BT12 6BA Tel: 01232 894635 Fax: 01232 240899; Sheena, 15 Circular Road E., Cultra, Holywood BT18 0HA Tel: 01232 422385 — MB BCh BAO 1973 Belf.; FRCP Lond. 1993; MRCP (UK) 1978. Cons. Dermat. Roy. Vict. Hosp. Belf. & Roy. Belf. Hosp. for Sick Childr. Prev: Cons. Dermat. Whiteabbey Hosp. Newtownabbey.

BINGHAM, Emma Margaret 12 The Avenue, Chobham, Woking GU24 8RU — MB BS 1992 Lond.; MRCP (UK) 1996. (Roy.Free.Hosp.Sch.Med) Hon. Clin. Research. Fell. KCH Sch. Med.

BINGHAM, Grame Paul 116 Groomsport Road, Bangor BT20 5NY — MB ChB 1991 Liverp.; MRCGP 1996; DFFP 1996; DRCOG 1995; DTM & H Liverp. 1993.

BINGHAM, James Stewart, TD The Consulting Rooms, York House, 199 Westminster Bridge Road, London SE1 7UT Tel: 020 7928 5485 Fax: 020 7620 0903 Email: james.binham@gstt.sthames.nhs.uk; 59 Park Road, London W4 3EY Tel: 020 8994 6190 — MB BCh BAO 1969 Belf.; FRCP Ed. 1994; FRCOG 1989, M 1974; DObst RCOG 1971; FRCP 1999 Lond. (Qu. Univ. Belf.) Cons. Genitourin. Med. Guy's & St. Thos. Hosps. Lond.; Edr. Continuing Med. Educat. Socs: (Ex-Pres.) Med. Soc. Study VD; (Chairm.) Assoc. for Genitourin. Med.; (Pres. Elect) Internat. Union against Sexually Transm. Infect. Prev: Cons. Genitourin. Med. Middlx. Hosp. Lond.; Sen. Regist. (Genitourin. Med.) Middlx. Hosp. Lond.; Sen. Resid. (O & G) Vancouver Gen. Hosp. Brit. Columbia, Canada.

BINGHAM, Janne Margaret Mary 31 Monument Road, Hillsborough BT26 6HT Tel: 01846 683063 — MB BCh BAO 1995 Belf.; FRCS Dub. 1997. (Queens University Belfast) SHO (Gen. Surg.). Prev: SHO (Fract.s & Orthop.); Anat. Demonst. SHO (A & E Med.).

BINGHAM, Jennifer Rosemary Macfarlane Blackthorn Medical Centre, St. Andrews Road, Barming, Maidstone ME16 9AN Tel: 01622 726277 Fax: 01622 725774; Cherry Lodge, Priory Close, East Farleigh, Maidstone ME15 0EY Tel: 01622 728498 — MB BS Lond. 1969; BSc (Special Physiol.) Lond. 1966; MRCS Eng. LRCP Lond. 1969; DObst RCOG 1972. (King's Coll. Hosp.) Socs: BMA. Prev: Ho. Phys. & Ho. Surg. (Obst.) Dulwich Hosp.; Ho. Surg. Brook Gen. Hosp. Lond.

BINGHAM, Mr John (retired) 28 Sutherland Avenue, Glasgow G41 4HQ Tel: 0141 427 0264 — MB ChB 1948 Glas.; FRCS Glas.

1983; FRCS Ed. 1956. Prev: Cons. Orthop. Surg. S.. Gen. Hosp. Glas.

BINGHAM, John Bedford Department of Radiological Sciences, 5th Floor TGH, Guy's Hospital, London SE1 9RT Tel: 020 7955 4531 Fax: 020 7955 4532 — MB BChir 1970 Camb.; MB BChir Camb. 1969; MSc (Nuclear Med.) Lond. 1976; MA Camb. 1970; FRCP Lond. 1992; FRCR 1983; Amer. Bds. in Nuclear Med. 1979; VQE 1979. (Camb. & Guy's) Cons. Radiol. Guy's & St. Thos. Hosp. Trust; Sen. Lect. Guy's Hosp. Lond. Socs: AARS; Radiol. Soc. N. Amer. & RCRadiol. Prev: Cons. Radiol. Lewisham Hosp. Lond.; Sen. Regist. (Radiol.) St. Geo. Hosp. Lond.; Clin. Research Fell. Mass. Gen. Hosp. Boston, USA.

BINGHAM, Martin Timothy Claremore, Augher BT77 0DJ — MB BCh BAO 1990 Belf.; MRCGP 1995; DFFP 1994; DRCOG 1993. (Belf.)

BINGHAM, Michelle Susan Limes Medical Centre, Limes Avenue, Alfreton DE55 7DW Tel: 01773 833133 Fax: 01773 836099 — MB ChB 1989 Glas. GP.

BINGHAM, Moira Ann 57 Brook Lane, Warsash, Southampton SO31 9FF — MB ChB 1973 Bristol; DRCOG 1977. Clin. Med. Off. (Child Guid.) E.leigh Hants.; Clin. Med. Off. (Family Plann.) St. Mary's Hosp. Portsmouth.

BINGHAM, Nigel Aaron 17 Springfield Court, Corbets Tey Rd, Upminster RM14 2AG — MB BCh BAO 1997 Belf.

BINGHAM, Paul 6 Forest Close, Newport PO30 5SF — MB BS 1980 Lond.; FRCS Ed. 1988; MRCOG 1989; MFPHM 1991. (Royal Free) Cons. (Pub. Health Med. & Communicable Dis. Control) Isle of Wight Health Auth.

BINGHAM, Robert Miles Great Ormond Street Hospital, London WC1N 3JH Tel: 020 7829 8865 Fax: 020 7829 8866 Email: rmbingham@compuserve.com — MB BS 1976 Lond.; MRCS Eng. LRCP Lond. 1976; FRCA 1980. (Char. Cross) Cons. Paediat. Anaesth. Hosp. for Sick Childr. Lond.

BINGHAM, Sarah Jane Rheumatology Department, Leeds General Infirmary, Great George St., Leeds LS1 3EX — MB BChir 1994 Camb.; MRCP 1997 Lond.; MA Camb. 1995, BA 1991. (Cambridge) Specialist Regist. (Rheum.) Yorks. Region. Socs: Brit. Soc. Rheum. Prev: SHO Rotat. (Med.) Addenbrooke's Hosp. Camb.

BINGHAM, Stuart James 20 Old Moutague Street, London E1 5PB Tel: 020 7247 7070 — MB BS 1982 Lond. Prev: SHO (Paediat.) Lond. Hosp.; SHO (Cas.) Lond. Hosp.; Clin. Med. Off. Tower Hamlets HA.

BINGHAM, William, Surg. Lt.-Cdr. RN (retired) Woodgarth, 2 Parkhouse Manor, Holywood BT18 0BQ Tel: 02890421897 — MB BCh BAO 1941 Belf.; MD Belf. 1951; FRCA. 1992; FFA RCSI 1960; FFA RCS Eng. 1953; DA RCPSI 1947. Prev: Cons. Anaesth. Ulster Hosp., Roy. Vict. Hosp. Belf. & Roy. Matern. Hosp. Belf.

BINGLE, John Pugh (retired) Gatescarth, 2 Allerton Drive, Upper Poppleton, York YO26 6JH Tel: 01904 794666 Fax: 01904 794666 Email: jpb@peakbp.force9.co.uk — MA (Hons. Physiol.) Oxf. 1947, DM 1964, BM BCh 1950; FRCP Lond. 1974, M 1955; DObst RCOG 1952. Prev: Cons. Med. Off. Gen. Accid. Life Assur. Co. York.

***BINGLE, Katherine Charlotte** 37 Harefield Avenue, Sutton SM2 7ND; 37 Harefield Aveue, Sutton SM2 7ND — MB ChB 1997 Birm.

BINGLEY, Penelope Juliet Diabetes & Metabolism, Medical School Unit, Southmead Hospital, Bristol BS10 7QR Tel: 0117 959 5337 Fax: 0117 959 5336 — MB BS 1981 Lond.; MD Lond. 1994; MRCP (UK) 1984; FRCP 1999. (Univ. Coll. Hosp.) Reader (Diabetic Med.) Univ. Bristol; Hon. Cons. Phys. S.mead Hosp. & United Bristol Hosps. Trust. Prev: Sen. Lect. (Diabetic Med.) Univ. Bristol; Sen. Lect. (Diabetes & Med.) St. Bart. Hosp. Lond.; Lect. (Med.) St. Bart. Hosp. Lond.

BINGOLD, Mr Alfred Charles 152 Harley Street, London W1N 1HH Tel: 020 7935 1858; 7 Ripley Close, Bickley, Bromley BR1 2TZ Tel: 020 8467 7018 — MB BS Lond. 1940; PhD Surrey 1972; FRCS Eng. 1947; MRCS Eng. LRCP Lond. 1939. (Lond. Hosp.) Hon. Cons. Orthop. Surg. Qu. Mary's Hosp. Sidcup. Socs: Fell. BOA. Prev: Cons. Orthop. Surg. Lambeth, S.wark & Lewisham AHA (T) & Greenwich & Bexley HA.

BINKS, Alfred Paul (retired) Abbattsfield, Ibstone, High Wycombe HP14 3XZ — BM BCh 1942 Oxf.; MA Oxf. 1961, BM BCh 1942; MRCGP 1959.

BINKS, Mr Anthony Stuart (retired) Trader Lodge, Trader Bank, Sibbey, Boston PE22 0UJ Tel: 01205 751076 — MB BS 1965 Newc.; FRCOG 1991, M 1972. Prev: Cons. O & G S. Lincs. (Boston) Health Dist.

BINKS, Christine The Surgery, Pound Close, Oldbury, Warley B68 8LZ; 70A Dog Kennel Lane, Oldbury, Oldbury B68 9LZ Tel: 0121 544 4341 — MB ChB 1975 Birm. Clin. Asst. Dept. A & E Birm. Gen. Hosp.

BINKS, Frank Allen Oakleigh, Mildred Avenue, Borehamwood WD6 2DH Tel: 020 8953 3280 — MRCS Eng. LRCP Lond. 1941; MD Lond. 1949, MB BS 1941; FRCP Lond. 1974, M 1949. (King's Coll. Hosp.) Cons. Phys. Gen. Med. Prev: Cons. Phys. Gen. Med. Edgware Gen. Hosp.; Sen. Regist. Edgware Gen. Hosp., Middlx. Hosp. & Whittington Hosp.; Lond.

BINKS, Michael Harvey 15A Gladys Road, London NW6 2PU — MB BS 1986 Lond.

BINKS, Simon Ellis 33 Manor Leas Close, Lincoln LN6 8DE — BM BS 1996 Nottm.

BINLESS, John Terence The Residence, The Surgery, Town St., Marple Bridge, Stockport SK6 5AA Tel: 0161 426 0270 Fax: 0161 427 3772; Chapel House, Staveley in Cartmel, Ulverston LA12 8NH Tel: 015395 31706 Fax: 0161 427 3772 — MB ChB Manch. 1954; MRCGP 1965; DCH Eng. 1958; DObst RCOG 1957. Self Employer Practitioner Stockport Lancaster; Medico-Legal (Expert Witness); Vasectomy; Erectile DysFunc. Clinic. Socs: RCGP; BMA; Manch. Med. Soc. Prev: Sen. Partner Gen. Med. Pract. Marple Bridge Stockport.

BINMORE, Timothy Keith Walker Medical Group, Church Walk, Newcastle upon Tyne NE6 3BS — MB ChB 1989 Aberd.; MRCGP 1993.

BINNEY, Lucy Elliot 96 Holywell Street, Oxford OX1 3SE — BM BCh 1991 Oxf.

BINNIE, Alastair Stewart Garven (retired) — MB ChB 1941 Liverp. Prev: RAMC 1942-46.

BINNIE, Arthur Stewart, MC (retired) 19A Grosvenor Road, Birkdale, Southport PR8 2JG Tel: 01704 563053 — MB ChB Liverp. 1952. War Pens. & Indust. Injuries Bd.ing Off. DHSS.

BINNIE, Bertram (retired) 5 Rysland Crescent, Newton Mearns, Glasgow G77 6EB — MB ChB 1932 Glas.; DO Eng. 1963. Prev: SHMO Ophth. Gartnavel Gen. Hosp. Glas.

BINNIE, Professor Colin David EEG Department, Ruskin Wing, King's College Hospital, Denmark Hill, London SE5 9RS Tel: 020 7346 4342 Fax: 020 7346 3725 Email: colin.binnie@kcl.ac.uk — FRCP Glasgow; FRCP Lond.; MD MA Bchir Cantab. (Guy's) Prof. Clin. Neurophysiol. Guy's, King's & St Thomas Sch. of Med. Lond.; Hon. Cons. Clin. (Neurophysiol.) Univ. Coll. Lond. Hosp. Maudsley Hosp. Lond. King's Coll. Hosp. Lond. Socs: Brit. Soc. Clin Neurophysiol. - past Pres..; Assoc. of Brit. Clin. Neurophysiol.; Roy. Soc. of Med. - past Counc. Mem. Prev: Cons. Clin. (Neurophysiol.) Bethlem Roy. & Maudsley Hosps. Lond.; Head of Clin. Neurophysiol., Instituut voor Epilepsiebestrijding, Aumertide, Netherlands; Phys. i/c, Dept. of Clin. Neurophysiol. St Bart's Hosp. Lond.

BINNIE, David Stewart Lagmhor Surgery, Little Dunkeld, Dunkeld PH8 0AD Tel: 01350 727269 Fax: 01350 727772 — MB ChB 1979 Dundee; MRCGP 1983; DRCOG 1982.

BINNIE, Denise Joy Friargate Surgery, Agard Street, Derby DE1 1DZ Tel: 01332 294040; 10 Kershope Drive, Oakwood, Derby DE21 2TQ Tel: 01332 678528 — MB ChB 1987 Leeds; MRCGP 1992; DRCOG 1990; Cert. Family Plann. JCC 1990. (Univ. Leeds) Prev: Course Organiser Derby VTS.

BINNIE, Francis James Fraser The Arthur Medical Centre, Four Lane Ends, Horsley Woodhouse, Ilkeston DE7 6AX Tel: 01332 880249; 20 Harvest Way, Oakwood, Derby DE21 2XB Tel: 01332 672079 Email: 100547.1076@compuserve.com — MB ChB 1975 Aberd.; MRCGP 1980. Trainer Derby VTS; Chairm. S. Amber Valley PCG. Prev: Course Organiser Derby VTS.

BINNIE, George Alan Christie (retired) Ladykirk, Norham, Berwick-upon-Tweed TD15 1XL Tel: 01289 382201 — LRCP LRCS Ed. LRFPS Glas. 1952; MRCGP 1961; DObst RCOG 1956. Prev: Ho. Surg. Memor Hosp. Darlington.

BINNIE, Jacquelyn Ann Helen Langlands Lodge, 48 Eskbank Road, Dalkeith EH22 3BX — MB ChB 1996 Ed. (Edinburgh) SHO (Geriat. Med.) Liberton Hosp. Edin. Prev: SHO (A & E) Edin. Roy.

Infirm.; Jun. Ho. Off. (Med.) W.ern Gen. Edin.; Jun. Ho. Off. (Surg.) Edin. Roy. Infirm.

BINNIE, James Alastair 5 Breary Lane, Bramhope, Leeds LS16 9AD Tel: 0113 284 2902 — MB ChB 1955 Birm.; MA 1999 Leeds; MRCGP 1986; DCH Eng. 1973. Hosp. Pract. (Paediat.) Wharfedale Hosp. Otley. Socs: W Riding M-C Soc. Prev: Ho. Surg. & Ho. Phys. Qu. Eliz. Hosp. Birm.; Surg. Lt. RN; Ho. Phys. St. Jas. Hosp. Leeds.

BINNIE, Mark Coleman (retired) 8 Fairway Close, Churston Ferrers, Brixham TQ5 0LG Tel: 01803 845573 — MB ChB 1941 Birm.; MRCP Lond. 1948. Cons. Geriat. Torbay Health Dist. Prev: Regist. (Med.) Selly Oak Hosp. Birm.

BINNIE, Mr Norman Rodger University Department of Surgery, Polworth Building, Aberdeen Royal Infirmary, Foresterhill, Aberdeen AB25 2ZN Tel: 01224 681818 Email: n.r.binnie@abdn.ac.uk; 22 Coldstone Avenue, Kingswells, Aberdeen AB15 8TT Tel: 01224 740481 — MB ChB 1979 Ed.; MD Ed. 1990, BSc (Med. Sci.) 1976; FRCS Ed. 1984. (Ed.) Cons. Surg. Aberd. Roy. Infirm; Hon. Sen. Lect. (Surg.) Univ. Aberd. Socs: BMA; Surgic. Research Soc.; Brit. Pelvic Research Gp. Prev: Sen. Lect. (Surg.) Univ. Aberd.; Sen. Regist. (Gen. Surg.) Roy. Infirm. Edin.; Reseach Fell. (Surg. & Urol.) Spinal Unit Edenhall & W.. Gen. Hosp. Edin.

BINNING, Alexander Robert 4 Donaldfield Road, Bridge of Weir PA11 3JJ — MB ChB 1987 Ed.; FRCA 1992. Sen. Regist. (Anaesth.) Ninewells Hosp. Dundee.

BINNING, Susanna Claire 12 Kemerton Road, Beckenham BR3 6NJ — MB ChB 1985 Bristol.

BINNINGTON, Ena (Jean) Slorach (retired) c/o Mrs MacDonald, 18 Hermitage Drive, Edinburgh EH10 6BZ — MB ChB 1938 St. And.

BINNS, Cathleen Alison Eskbridge Medical Centre, 8A Bridge Street, Musselburgh EH21 6AG Tel: 0131 665 6821 Fax: 0131 665 5488; 17 Dreghorn Park, Edinburgh EH13 9PH Tel: 0131 441 6394 — MB ChB 1991 Glas.; MRCGP 1996; DCCH RCP Ed. 1995; DRCOG 1994. (Glas.) p/t Gen. Practitioner Musselburgh E.bridge Med. Centre.

BINNS, Corinne Elizabeth 17 Hill Grove, Henleaze, Bristol BS9 4RL — MB ChB 1995 Manch.

BINNS, David Taylor (retired) 3 Church Meadow, High Bickington, Umberleigh EX37 9DT Tel: 01769 560945 — MB ChB Liverp. 1945; FRCGP 1976; DObst 1947. Prev: GP BridgN..

BINNS, Gillian Berkeley House, 93 High Road, Rayleigh SS6 7SJ — MB BS 1993 Lond.

BINNS, Helen Alexandra Medway House, Gads Hill, Trimmingham, Halifax HX2 7PX — MB ChB 1992 Liverp.

BINNS, Hilary 11 Crabtree Gardens, Headley, Bordon GU35 8LN — MB BS 1993 Newc.

BINNS, John Clive London Road Practice, 84-86 London Road, Bedford MK42 0NT Tel: 01234 266851 Fax: 01234 363998; 79 Grange Lane, Bromham, Bedford MK43 8PA Tel: 01234 822772 — BM 1978 Soton.; MRCGP 1982; DRCOG 1981. Prev: Dist. Med. Off. Grenfell Regional Health Serv. Flowers Cove Newfld., Canada.

BINNS, John Kenneth (retired) 83 Newton Grove, Newton Mearns, Glasgow G77 5QJ Tel: 0141 616 2592 — MB ChB 1951 Ed.; FRCP Ed. 1970, M 1960; FRCPsych 1977, M 1971; DPM Eng. 1958. Prev: Phys. Supt. & Cons. Psychiat. Leverndale Hosp. Glas.

BINNS, Mr Malcolm Stewart Department of Orthopaedics, Pontefract General Infirmary, Pontefract WF8 1PC Tel: 01977 606734 Fax: 01977 606723 — MB ChB 1972 Manch.; MChOrth Liverp. 1986; FRCS (Orthop.) Ed. 1984; FRCS Ed. 1979; MRCGP 1982; DCH Eng. 1975; DObst RCOG 1975. Cons. Orthop. Surg. Pontefract Gen. Infirm. Prev: Vis. Fell. Univ. Dept. Orthop. Hong Kong & Singapore.

BINNS, Theodore Barker 15 The Causeway, Horsham RH12 1HE Tel: 01403 261623 — FRCP Ed. 1965, M 1948; FRCP Lond. 1970, M 1949; FRCP Glas. 1972, M 1970; LRCP LRCS Ed. LRFPS Glas. 1940; FFPM RCP (UK) 1989; DCH Eng. 1950. (Roy. Colls. Ed.) Hon. Sen. Lect. (Pharmacol. & Therap.) Lond. Hosp. Med. Coll. Socs: Fell. Roy. Soc. Med.; Brit. Pharm. Soc.; Hon. Mem. Brit. Assn. Pharmaceut. Phys. Prev: Med. Dir. Ciba Laborat. Horsham; Regist. (Med.) Roy. Infirm. Edin.; Squadron Ldr. RAF.

BINSTED, Elizabeth Ann 'Pebbles', 55 Marine Drive, West Wittering, Chichester PO20 8HQ Tel: 01243 673271 — MB BS 1963 Lond.; MRCS Eng. LRCP Lond. 1963; FFA RCS Eng. 1967; DA Eng. 1965. (St. Thos.) Clin. Asst. (Anaesth.) Brookwood Hosp. Knaphill. Prev: Anaesth. Regist. Lord Mayor Treloar Hosp. Alton; Anaesth. Regist. St. Thos. Hosp. Lond.

BINT, Adrian John Dept. of Clinical Microbiology, Royal Victoria Infirmary, Queen Victoria Road, Newcastle upon Tyne NE1 4LP Tel: 0191 227 5120 Fax: 0191 201 0156; 2 Ashdale, Ponteland, Newcastle upon Tyne NE20 9DR — MB ChB 1971 Birm.; FRCPath 1989, M 1977. Cons. Microbiologist Roy. Vict. Infirm. Newc.; Lect. Univ. of Newc. upon Tyne. Socs: Assn. Med. Microbiol. (Chairm. Clin. Servs. Comm.); Roy. Coll. Of Pathologists. Chairm. Microbiol. CATT; Roy. Coll. Of Pathologists Chairm., N.. & Yorks. Regional Counc. Prev: Edr. Jl. Antimicrobial Chemother.

BINT, Alastair Halford 2 Ashdale, Ponteland, Newcastle upon Tyne NE20 9DR — MB ChB 1998 Ed.; MB ChB Ed 1998.

BINTCLIFFE, Brian John Manor View Practice, Bushey Health Centre, London Road, Bushey, Watford WD23 2NN Tel: 01923 225224 Fax: 01923 213270; Parson's Cottage, 5 Little Common, Stanmore HA7 3BZ — MB BS 1978 Lond.; MRCGP 1983; DRCOG 1982. (St. Bart.) Prev: Ho. Surg. St. Bart. Hosp. Lond.

BINTCLIFFE, Cyril John (retired) 42 Heath Drive, Gidea Park, Romford RM2 5QJ Tel: 01708 749188 — MRCS Eng. LRCP Lond. 1939. Admiralty Surg. & Agent. Prev: Ho. Surg. St. Bart. Hosp.

BINTCLIFFE, David John Lewis Gervis Road Surgery, 14 Gervis Road, Bournemouth BH1 3EG Tel: 01202 293418 Fax: 01202 317866; 44 Sandecotes Road, Pakestone, Bournemouth BH14 8PA — MB BS 1977 Lond.; BSc Soton. 1969; MRCS Eng. LRCP Lond. 1976. (St. Thos.) Socs: Old Carthusian Med. Soc. Prev: Ho. Surg. (Cardiothoracic Unit) St. Thos. Hosp. Lond.

BINTCLIFFE, Mr Ian William Lewis Royal Sussex County Hospital, Eastern Road, Brighton BN2 5BE Tel: 01273 696955 Ext: 7849 Fax: 01273 027061; Oaklea, Plumpton Green, Lewes BN8 4EA Tel: 01444 471267 — BSc Lond. 1967; MB BS Lond. 1970; FRCS (Orthop.) Ed. 1983; FRCS Eng. 1975; MRCS Eng. LRCP Lond. 1970. (St. Bart.) Cons. Orthop. Surg. Brighton Health Care NHS Trust. Socs: Fell. Roy. Soc. Med.; Fell. BOA; Brit. Trauma Soc. Prev: Sen. Regist. (Orthop.) Guy's & St. Thos. Hosps. Train. Scheme; Regist. (Orthop.) Char. Cross. Hosp. Lond.; Regist. Rotat. (Gen. Surg.) St. Bart. Hosp. Lond.

BINTLEY, Timothy Nigel 36 St Gluvias Street, Penryn TR10 8BJ — MB ChB 1997 Liverp.

BINYON, Sharon Elizabeth The Medical Centre, 4/6 Manor Court Avenue, Nuneaton CV11 5HX Tel: 01203 326111 — BM BS 1984 Nottm.; MSc Warwick 1993; BMedSci 1982; MRCPsych 1989. Cons. Psychiat. Med. Centre Nuneaton. Prev: Sen. Regist. (Psychiat.) W. Midl.; Regist. (Psychiat.) All Birm. Psychiat. Rotat.; SHO (Psychiat.) Highcroft Hosp.

BINYSH, Harry (retired) 26 Fernleigh Road, Winchmore Hill, London N21 3AL — LRCP LRCS 1944 Ed.; MD (Hyg.) Lond. 1949, MB BS 1944; LRCP LRCS Ed. LRFPS Glas. 1944; FFCM 1972; DPH Lond. 1949; DTM & H Eng. 1950. Prev: Area Med. Off. Lambeth, S.wark & Lewisham AHA.

BINYSH, Jean Katherine 28 Melbury Road, London W14 8AE — MB BS 1980 Lond.; MFPHM 1989; MFCM 1989; DCH RCP Lond. 1984.

BINZENHOFER, Joerg 5 Caroline Place, Lansdown Road, Bath BA1 5HU — State Exam Med 1990 Berlin.

BION, Julian Fleetwood Department of Anaesthetics & Intensive Care, University of Birmingham, Queen Elizabeth Hospital, Birmingham B15 2TH Tel: 0121 627 2060 Fax: 0121 627 2062 — MB BS 1975 Lond.; MD Lond. 1990; MRCP (UK) 1980; FFA RCS Eng. 1982; FRCP 1996. (Char. Cross) Reader (Intens. Care Med.) Birm. Univ.; Hon. Cons. IC Med. Qu. Eliz. Hosp. Birm. Socs: Counc. Intens. Care Soc.; BMA; Counc. Europ. Soc. Intens. Care Med. Prev: Regist. (Cardiol.) N.ampton Gen. Hosp.; Anaesth. N.wick Pk. Hosp. Harrow & Radcliffe Infirm. Oxf.; Research Fell. Clin. Shock Study Gp. Glas.

BIRAM, Richard William Stuart 56 Desborough Road, Hartford, Huntingdon PE29 1SW — MB BS 1997 Lond.

BIRAN, Leonard Arie Craven Road Medical Centre, 60 Craven Road, Leeds LS6 2RX Tel: 0113 295 3530 Fax: 0113 245 3532 Email: len.biran@tesco.net — MB ChB 1977 Dundee; DPhil Oxf. 1962; BSc Birm. 1958; FRCGP 1993, M 1982. p/t Gen. Practitioner, Princip. Prev: Lect. (Educat. Psychol.) Univ. Birm.; Assoc. Prof.

(Educat. Technol.) Internat. Centre for Advance Technical & Vocat. Train. Turin, Italy; Lect. (Med. Educat.) Univ. Dundee.

BIRAN, Renison Karamchand Gayton Road Health and Surgical Centre, Gayton Road, King's Lynn PE30 4DY Tel: 01553 762726 Fax: 01553 696819; 1 Hemington Close, King's Lynn PE30 3YB Tel: 01553 670075 — MB BS 1983 West Indies; BSc, MC Master Univ. Canada 1974. GP Princip. King's Lynn.

BIRBECK, Kevin Frank 37 Fanshaw Road, Eckington, Sheffield S21 4BW — MB ChB 1992 Sheff.

BIRCH, Alan Wych Cottage, Allithwaite, Grange-over-Sands LA11 7RA Tel: 015395 32634 — MB BS 1966 Lond.; MRCS Eng. LRCP Lond. 1963. (St. Bart.)

BIRCH, Alan David Old Hall Surgery, 26 Stanney Lane, Ellesmere Port, South Wirral CH65 9AD Tel: 0151 355 1191 Fax: 0151 356 2683; Gwern-y-Gwyddau, Nant, Pentre Halkyn, Holywell CH8 8BD — MB BCh 1975 Wales; MRCGP 1979; DCH Eng. 1978; Cert. Family Plann. 1979. GP Chesh. FPC. Socs: Ellesmere Port GP Comm.

BIRCH, Alison Gina Green Cottage, Foxcombe Road, Boars Hill, Oxford OX1 5DQ — MB BS 1994 Lond.

BIRCH, Anthony David James Department of Haematology, Falkirk & District Royal Infirmary, Major's Loan, Falkirk FK1 5QE Tel: 01324 624000 Fax: 01324 616034; The Brae, Dargai Terrace, Dunblane FK15 0AU Tel: 01786 823749 — BM BCh 1971 Oxf.; MRCP (UK) 1974; FRCPath 1989, M 1977; FRCP Glas. 1996. (St. Thos.) Cons. Haemat. Forth Valley Acute Hosps. NHS Trust. Prev: Sen. Regist. (Haemat.) King's Coll. Hosp. Lond.; SHO (Path.) St. Bart. Hosp. Lond.; Regist. (Haemat.) Hammersmith Hosp. Lond.

BIRCH, Mr Brian Robert Peter Department of Urology, Southampton University Hospital Trust, Tremona Road, Southampton SO16 6YD Tel: 02380 777222 Fax: 02380 283252 Email: brian.birch@ndirect.co.uk; Mapledean, Pikes Hill Avenue, Lyndhurst, Lyndhurst SO43 7AX Tel: 02380 283252 Fax: 01703 283252 Email: brian.birch@ndirect.co.uk — MB BChir 1980 Camb.; MA Camb. 1980; MD Camb. 1995; FRCS Eng. 1985. (St. Catharine's Camb. & King's Coll. Hosp. Lond.) Cons. Urol. Soton. Univ. Hosp. Socs: Fell. Roy. Soc. Med.; BMA; Brit. Assn. Urol. Surgs. Prev: Sen. Regist. (Urol.) Soton. Univ. Hosp.; Roche Lect. (Urol.) Inst. Urol.; Regist. (Urol.) E.bourne Gen. Hosp.

BIRCH, Christopher Robert Grantham and District Hospital, Manthorpe Road, Grantham NG31 8DG Tel: 01476 565232 Fax: 01476 590441 Email: chris.birch@ulh.nhs.uk — MB ChB 1968 Manch.; FRCP Lond. 1989; MRCP (U.K.) 1972. Cons. Phys. Grantham and Dist. Hosp. Socs: Nottm. M-C Soc; Lincoln Med. Soc. Prev: Sen. Regist. (Med.) Manch. Roy. Infirm.; Sen. Regist. (Med.) Univ. Hosp. S. Manch.; Regist. (Cardiol.) Manch. Roy. Infirm.

BIRCH, Mr David John Dept. Surgery, University Hospital, Lewisham, London SE13 6LH — MB BS 1987 Newc.; FRCS Eng. 1992. Regist. (Surg.) John Radcliffe Hosp. Oxf.; Cons. Gen. and Colorectal Surg., Univ. Hosp. Lewisham. Socs: Fell. Roy. Soc. Med.; Assn. of Surg.s; Assn. of Colopoctology. Prev: Spr (Surg.), Roy. Free Hosp., Lond..; Spr (Surg.), Chase Farm Hosp. Lond.; Spr (Surg.), Univ. Coll. Hosps., Lond.

BIRCH, Diana Mary Laura 13 Crescent Road, Beckenham BR3 6NF Tel: 020 8650 6296 Email: drdbirch@youthsupport.org; 30 Crystal Palace Park Road, London SE26 6UG Tel: 020 8659 7931 Fax: 020 8659 3309 Email: dianabirch@youthsupport.org.co.uk — MB BS Lond. 1970; MSc (Psychother.) Lond. 1989, MD 1986; MRCP (UK) 1977; FRCP 1998; MRCS Eng. LRCP Lond. 1970; FRCPCH 1997; DCH Eng. 1972. (Roy. Free) Dir. Youth Support; Edr. Jl. Adolesc. Health & Welf. Socs: Fell. Soc. Pub. Health; Fac. Community Health; Fell. Soc. Adolesc. Med. Prev: PMO Dept. Community Health Kings Coll. Hosp. Lond. & Dir. Youth Support; Sen. Community Health Med. Off. King's & Roehampton Health Dists.

BIRCH, Eugene William Gordon, DFM 76 Station Road, Waddington, Lincoln LN5 9QW — MB BS 1952 Lond.; MRCS Eng. LRCP Lond. 1952; MFCM 1973; DPH Leeds 1957. (Guy's) MOH & Princip. Sch. Med. Off. Lincs. (Parts of Kesteven) CC. Socs: Fell. Soc. MOH; Lincoln Med. Soc. Prev: Dep. Co. MOH Lindsey CC; Dep. MOH Watford Boro.; Ho. Phys. & Ho. Surg. Roy. Infirm. Bradford.

BIRCH, Frances 214 Bellenden Road, London SE15 4BY Tel: 020 7358 0811 — MA, MB BChir Camb. 1970; MA (Distinc.) Med. Ethics & Law Lond. 1988; BA Camb. 1966; MRCS Eng. LRCP Lond. 1969; DPMSA 1988. Private Pract. Psychodynamic Counsellor / Psychotherapist; Hon. Clin. Attchment Psychother. Dept. Maudsley Hosp. Lond. Prev: SHO Bethlem Roy. & Maudsley Hosp. Lond.; Cons. Palliat. Med. St. Raphael's Hospice N. Cheam Surrey; Med. Dir. & Cons. Hospice Unit Hosp. St. John & St. Eliz. Lond.

BIRCH, Geoffrey (retired) Woodside, Dipton, Stanley DH9 9EL Tel: 01207 570305 — MB BS 1951 Lond.; MRCS Eng. LRCP Lond. 1951; MRCGP 1958. Prev: Ho. Surg. Luton & Dunstable Hosp.

BIRCH, Harold Erskine Wardlaw Penylan Cottage, Brick Lane, Thorneyhill, Christchurch BH23 8DU Tel: 01425 672084 Fax: 01425 672084 Email: hew_birch@msn.com — MB ChB 1965 Glas.; BSc (Physiol., Hons.) Glas. 1963; MCOphth 1989; DO Eng. 1969; DObst RCOG 1967. (Glas.) Prev: Regist. (Ophth.) Oxf. Eye Hosp., Glas. Eye Infirm. & Bournemouth Eye Hosp.

BIRCH, Hilary Anne Flat 5, 29 Cambridge Park, Twickenham TW1 2JL Tel: 020 8892 9356 — MB BS 1988 Lond.; Dip RCPath. 1997; MRCPath. 1998. (King's Coll.) Specialist Regist. (Histopath.) Roy Marsden Hosp. Lond. Prev: Specialist Regist. (Histopath.) Char. Cross Hosp. Lond.; SHO (Surg.) St. Geo. Hosp. Lond.; Ho. Surg. King's Coll. Hosp. Lond.

BIRCH, Ian Douglass 27 Ashenground Road, Haywards Heath RH16 4PR — MB ChB 1990 Bristol.

BIRCH, Jacqueline Susan 69A Station Road, Marple, Stockport SK6 6AJ — MB ChB 1995 Bristol.

BIRCH, Jennifer Louise Flat 3 The Beeches, 13 Montgomery Road S7 1LN — MB ChB 1997 Leeds.

BIRCH, Mr Jeremy Farnham 3 East Avenue, Leicester LE2 1TE — MB ChB 1993 Bristol; BSc Hons. (Pharm) Bristol 1989; FRCS Eng. 1995. SHO (Surg.) Bath Roy. United Hosp.

BIRCH, John Charles Mather Avenue Practice, 584 Mather Avenue, Liverpool L19 4UG — MB ChB 1977 Bristol; DRCOG Lond. 1981. (Bristol) Princip. GP.

BIRCH, John Julian Bridge Street Surgery, Bridge Street, Louth LN11 0DR Tel: 01507 603121 Fax: 01507 605916; Willow Farm, Stewton, Louth LN11 8SD Tel: 01507 327356 — MB BChir 1972 Camb.; MA, MB Camb. 1972, BChir 1971; MRCGP 1980; DA Eng. 1974; DObst 1978. Prev: Med. Off. & Anaesth. Peebles Hosp. Brit. Virgin Is.s; Ho. Phys. Roy. S. Hants. Hosp. Soton.; Ho. Surg. Nottm. Gen. Hosp.

BIRCH, John Scrivener (retired) 101 Humberston Avenue, Humberston, Grimsby DN36 4ST Tel: 01472 812315 — MB ChB 1952 Liverp.; MRCGP 1968; DObst RCOG 1956. Prev: Ho. Off. (O & G) BRd.green Hosp. Liverp.

BIRCH, Jonathan Keith Woodlands Surgery, Tilgate Way, Tilgate, Crawley RH10 5BS Tel: 01293 525204 Fax: 01293 514778; Grove Lodge, Copthorne Common Road, Copthorne RH10 3LA Tel: 01342 718048 — MB BS 1987 Lond.; DRCOG 1991.

BIRCH, Julie-Anne, Squadron Ldr. RAF Med. Br. 6 Tedder Drive, Waddington, Lincoln LN5 9NG — MB ChB 1985 Leeds; MRCGP 1989; T(GP) 1992. Trainee GP RAF; SHO (Obst. & Gyn.) Ninewells Hosp. Dundee.

BIRCH, Katie Elizabeth 27 School Cl, High Wycombe HP11 1PH — MB BS 1997 Lond.

BIRCH, Kristina 5 Chestermaster Close, Almondsbury, Bristol BS32 4EH — BM 1994 Soton.; BSc (1st cl. Hons.) Bio. Med. Sci. Soton. 1993.

BIRCH, Lucia Jayne University Hospital, Birmingham NHS Trust, Selly Oak, Birmingham; 44 Woodleigh Avenue, Harborne, Birmingham B17 0NJ — MB BS 1997 Lond.; MA Camb. 1998. SHO Rotat. (Med.).

BIRCH, Marion (retired) Grey Road Surgery, 46-48 Grey Road, Liverpool L9 1AY Tel: 0151 525 3533 Fax: 0151 523 4958 — MB BS 1953 Durh. Prev: Sessional Med. Off. (Rheum. & A & E) Fazakerley Hosp. Liverp.

BIRCH, Maureen Clare MRC-HNR, Elsie Widdowson Lab, Fulbourn Road, Cambridge CB1 9LR Tel: 01223 426356 — MB BS 1983 Lond.; MRCGP 1987; DCH RCP Lond. 1985; DRCOG 1985. (St. Mary's) p/t Survey Doctor to Nation. Diet & Nutrit. Survey, MRC-HNR, Camb. Prev: GP St. Ives., Cambs.

BIRCH, Mr Michael Kevin Claremont Eye Wing, Royal Victoria Infirmary, Queen Victoria Road, Newcastle upon Tyne NE1 4LP Tel: 0191 232 5131 — BM BS 1986 Nottm.; BMedSci Nottm. 1984; FRCS Ed. 1991; FCOphth 1991; DO RCS Eng. 1990. (Nottm.) Cons. (Ophth.) Roy. Vict. Infirm.,Newc. Prev: Sen. Regist. (Ophth.) St.

Paul's Eye Unit Liverp.; Research Assoc. Unit of Ophth. Univ. Liverp.; Regist. (Ophth.) Mersey RHA.

BIRCH, Mr Nicholas Charles Longden Northampton General hospital, Cliftonville, Northampton NN1 5BD Tel: 01604 545625 — MB BS 1985 Lond.; BA (Hons.) Camb. 1982; FRCS (Orth.) 1996; FRCS Eng. 1989. (Gonville & Caius Coll. Camb. & King's Coll. Hosp. Lond.) Cons. Orthop. Surg. N.ampton Gen. Hosp. Socs: Fell. BOA; Hosp. Cons. & Spec. Assn.; Brit. Assn. of Spinal Surg.s. Prev: Sen. Regist. Rotat. (Orthop. Surg.) Roy. Free. Hosp. & Roy. Nat. Orthop. Hosp. Lond.

BIRCH, Paul Cadman Cronehills Health Centre, Cronehills Linkway, West Bromwich B70 8TJ Tel: 0121 553 0287 Fax: 0121 580 1821 Email: aucotbirch@aol.com; 9 Norman Close, Long Meadow, Worcester WR4 0HS Tel: 01905 745552 Fax: 01905 745553 Email: aucotbirch@aol.com — MB 1980 Camb.; BChir 1979; DRCOG 1983. (Cambridge & Charing Cross) Gen. Practitioner Sandwell (Wednesburg and W. Bromwich PCG); Hon. Lect. Birm. Univ. Med. Sch. Socs: BMA; CMF. Prev: Sen. Phys. Leprosy Mission Internat.; GP Humberside; Ho. Surg. (Gen. Surg., Urol. & ENT) Char. Cross Hosp. Lond.

BIRCH, Paul David Department of Radiology, Ysbyty Gwynedd, Penrhosgarnedd, Bangor BT20 Tel: 01248 384285 — MB BCh 1980 Wales; FRCR 1986. Cons. Radiol. N. W. Wales NHS Trust, Bangor; Clin. Dir., diagnostic & Clin. Support Serv.s; Dir., N. W. Wales NHS Trust, Bangor; Hon. Sen. Lect, Univ. of Wales, Bangor.

BIRCH, Peggy Marjorie 76 Station Road, Waddington, Lincoln LN5 9QW — MB BS 1949 Lond.; MRCS Eng. LRCP Lond. 1949. (Roy. Free) Socs: Lincoln Med. Soc. Prev: Ho. Off. (Cas. & Orthop.) Roy. Infirm. Bradford; Sen. Ho. Off. (Cas.) St. Luke's Hosp. Bradford.

BIRCH, Mr Peter Charles 4 Elm Bank Drive, Mapperley Park, Nottingham NG3 5AL — MB BS 1989 Newc.; FRCS Eng. 1994. Research Assoc. Sheff. Univ.

BIRCH, Peter Jonathan Northumbria Healthcare NHS Trust, Department of Histopathology, North Tyneside General Hospital, North Shields NE29 8NH Tel: 0191 293 2714 Fax: 0191 293 2796; 3 The Glebe, Stannington, Morpeth NE61 6HW — MB ChB 1984 Aberd.; MRCPath 1993. Cons. Histopath. & Cytopath. N. Tyneside Gen. Hosp. N. Shields. Prev: Sen. Regist. (Histopath) N.ern Regional HA; Regist. (Histopath) Portsmouth & SE Hants HA; SHO (Histopath.) Liverp. HA.

BIRCH, Philip Alexander Department of Radiology, Gloucestershire Royal Hospital, Great Western Road, Gloucester GL1 3NN Tel: 01452 395550 Fax: 01452 394535; Flock Mill, Far End, Sheepscombe, Stroud GL6 7RL Email: p.birch@virgin.net — MB BS 1973 Lond.; FRCR 1980. Cons. Radiol. Glos. Roy. Hosp. Prev: Staff (Radiol.) Roy. Perth Hosp. W.. Australia; Regist. & Sen. Regist. (Radiol.) John Radcliffe Hosp. Oxf.

BIRCH, Philippa Stephanie Jane Abbey Medical Practice, 95 Munks Rd, Lincoln LN2 5HR Tel: 01522 530334 Fax: 01522 569442; 19 Broadway, Lincoln LN2 1SQ — MB BS 1973 Lond.; MRCS Eng. LRCP Lond. 1973; DCH Eng. 1975. (Guy's) p/t Gen. Practitioner; Appeals Serv. - Med. Mem. Prev: SHO (Paediat.) St. Geo. Hosp. Lincoln; Ho. Surg. (ENT) Guy's Hosp. Lond.; Ho. Phys. (Gen. Med. & Infec. Dis.) Hither Green Hosp. Lond.

BIRCH, Rachel 9 Sorrel Close, Isham, Kettering NN14 1HX — BM 1994 Soton. SHO (Anaesth.) Winchester.

BIRCH, Raymond George Greenside, Stockers Hill, Rodmersham Green, Sittingbourne ME9 0PH Tel: 01795 473023 — MRCS Eng. LRCP Lond. 1940. (St. Bart.) Med. Off. Brit. Red Cross Soc.; Hon. Surg. Brit. Fire Serv. Assn. Socs: Roy. Coll. Gen. Pract.; Liveryman Worshipful Soc. of Apoth.

BIRCH, Richard John Tyclai, Llangors, Brecon LD3 7TR — BM BS 1995 Nottm.

BIRCH, Mr Rolfe Peripheral Nerve Injury Unit, Royal National Orthopaedic Hospital, Stanmore HA7 4LP Tel: 020 8954 2300 Fax: 020 8420 6582 — MChir Camb. 1989, MB 1970, BChir 1969; FRCS Ed. 1973; FRCS Glas. 1973. Orthop. Surg. Roy. Nat. Orthop. Hosp. Lond.; Hon. Orthop. Surg. Roy. Postgrad. Med. Sch. Hammersmith, Hosp. for; Sick Childr. Gt. Ormond St. & WellHo. Trust Lond.; Hon. Orthop. Surg. Nat. Hosp. Qu. Sq. Lond.; Hon. Civil Cons. RN.; Hon. Vis. Prof. Dept. of Neurol. Roy. Lond. Hosp.; Hon. Vis. Prof. Univ. of Shanghai. Prev: Head Orthop. Dept. St. Mary's Hosp. Lond.

BIRCH, Simon Flat 2, 22 Landguard Road, Southampton SO15 5DJ — BM 1993 Soton.

BIRCH, Stephen James Larks Lees, Coxhill, Boldre, Lymington SO41 8PS — MRCS Eng. LRCP Lond. 1974; BSc (Hons.) Lond. 1971, MB BS 1975; FRCR 1980; DMRD Eng. 1979. (St. Mary's) Cons. Radiol. Soton. & S.W. Hants. DHA. Prev: Radiol. Fell. Univ. Toronto, Canada; Ho. Surg. St. Mary's Hosp. Lond.; Ho. Phys. Addenbrookes Hosp. Camb.

BIRCH, Stephen Mark 30 Spring Walk, Whitstable CT5 4PP — MB ChB 1993 Dundee.

BIRCH, Susan Joy The Surgery, 2 Church Lane, Lyndhurst SO43 7EW Tel: 01703 282689; 13 Princes Crescent, Lyndhurst SO43 7BS Tel: 01703 282852 Fax: 01703 283252 Email: brianbirch@aol.com — MB BS 1986 Lond.; DRCOG 1991. (King's Coll. Hosp.) Socs: (Chairm.) New Forest Med. Soc. Prev: SHO (A & E) Bromley Hosp.; SHO (Anaesth.) Qu. Eliz. Milit. Hosp. Woolwich; SHO (Anaesth.) Camb. Milit. Hosp. Aldershot.

BIRCH, William David Arnold (retired) Caprice, High Street, Islip, Kidlington OX5 2RX Tel: 01865 377535 Fax: 01865 377535 Email: wdabirch@netscapeonline.co.uk — MB ChB 1950 Ed.; MA Oxf. 1979. Prev: GP Adviser Oxf. FHSA.

***BIRCH-VON RICHTER, Nadja Florence Ingeborg** 29 Redcliffe Road, Nottingham NG3 5BW Tel: 0115 960 4607 — MB ChB 1997 Manch.

BIRCHALL, Alan David The Surgery, 292 Derby Road, Lenton, Nottingham NG7 1QG Tel: 0115 947 4002 Fax: 0115 924 0783; Red Lion Cottage, 228 High Road, Chilwell, Nottingham NG9 5DB Tel: 0115 917 8591 — BM BS 1977 Nottm.; FRCGP 1993, M 1983.

BIRCHALL, Clare Elizabeth The Market Place Surgery, Cattle Market, Sandwich CT13 9ET Tel: 01304 613436/612589 Fax: 01304 613877; Fordwich House, Moat Lane, Fordwich, Canterbury CT2 0DP Tel: 01227 712591 — MB BS 1982 Lond.; DRCOG 1985.

BIRCHALL, Daniel 27 The Avenue, Rainford, St Helens WA11 8DT — MB BChir 1989 Camb.; MA Camb. 1990, BA (Hons.) 1986, MB BChir 1989; MRCP (UK) 1992; FRCR 1997. (Univ. Camb) Sen. Regist. (Radiol.) Hope Hosp. Salford. Prev: Regist. (Med.) Gold Coast Hosp., Austral.

BIRCHALL, Eric Wilfred Ferndale Unit, Fazakerley Hospital, Liverpool L9 7AE Tel: 0151 529 3556 Fax: 0151 529 3063; 16 College Road N., Blundellsands, Liverpool L23 8UT Tel: 0151 924 2824 Email: eric.birchall@virgin.net — MB ChB 1963 Liverp.; FRCP Ed. 1985; MRCP (UK) 1970; FRCPsych 1997; DPM Eng. 1967. (Liverp.) Cons. Psychiat. Fazakerley Hosp. Liverp.; Clin. Lect. (Psychiat.) Liverp. Univ. 1978. Socs: Liverp. Psychiat. Soc.; Liverp. Med. Inst.; BMA. Prev: Sen. Regist. (Psychiat.) Rainhill Hosp. Liverp.; Regist. (Med.) & Regist. (Psychiat.) St. Catherine's Hosp.; Birkenhead.

BIRCHALL, Geoffrey (retired) Bracken Hill, Trough Rd, Scorton, Preston PR3 1BP Tel: 01995 640722 — MB ChB Ed. 1957; FRCPath 1978, M 1967; DObst RCOG 1960. Prev: Cons. Path. BMH Rinteln, BFPO 31.

BIRCHALL, Helen Mary Brandon Mental Health Unit, Leicester General Hospital, Gwendolen Road, Leicester LE5 4PW Tel: 0116 225 6246 Email: helenbirchall@hotmail.com — MB ChB 1986 Leic.; MRCPsych 1993. Cons. Psychiat. (Eating Disorders).

BIRCHALL, Janet Elaine 1 Combe Cottages, Bourton Combe, Flax Bourton, Bristol BS48 3QL — MB ChB 1983 Leeds.

BIRCHALL, Professor John Philip Department of Otolaryngology & Head & Neck Surgery, Queens Medical Centre, Nottingham NG7 2UH Tel: 0115 942 1421 Fax: 0115 970 9196 — MD 1982 Newc.; MB BS 1972; FRCS Eng. 1982. Prof. Otorhinolaryng. Univ. Nottm.; Hon. Cons. Qu. Med. Centre Nottm. Prev: Sen. Lect. (Otolaryng.) Univ. Newc.

BIRCHALL, Lucia Ann Holly House, 17A Birches Lane, Kenilworth CV8 2AB Tel: 01926 55019 — MB ChB 1967 Leeds; FRCR 1977; DMRT Eng. 1973. Trust Grade Clin. Oncol. (Radiother.) Walsgrave Hosps. NHS Trust Coventry. Prev: Med. Dir. Myton Hamlets Hospice Warwick; Cons. Radiother. & Oncol. Coventry & Warks. Hosp. Coventry; Regist. (Radiother.) Christie Hosp. & Holt Radium Inst. Manch.

BIRCHALL, Martin Anthony University Department of ENT, c/o Southmead Hospital, Bristol BS10 5NB Tel: 0117 959 5158 Fax: 0117 959 5168 Email: martinbirchall@compuserve.com; The

Stables, 1A Sundays Hill, Lower Almondsbury, Bristol BS32 4DS Tel: 01454 613265 — MB BChir 1985 Camb.; MA Camb. 1986, MD 1994; FRCS Otol. 1994; FRCS (Otol.) Eng. 1989; FRCS Eng. 1988; MD 1994. Sen. Lect. (ENT Surg.) Bristol Univ. & Hon. Cons. ENT Surg. S.mead Hosp. Bristol. Socs: Counc. Mem. Otorhinolaryngol. Research Soc.; Anat. Soc.; Counc. Mem. Brit. Assn. Head Neck Oncologists. Prev: Sen. Regist. (ENT Surg.) Roy. Nat. Throat, Nose & Ear Hosp. Lond.; Sen. Regist. (ENT) Roy. Berks. Hosp. Reading; Research Fell. Hammersmith Hosp. Lond.

BIRCHALL, Wayne 83 New Moss Road, Cadishead, Manchester M44 5JW — MB BChir 1984 Camb.; BA Camb. 1980, MA, MB 1984, BChir 1983; MRCGP 1987; DRCOG 1987. Prev: Trainee GP Plymouth VTS; Ho. Surg. MusGr. Pk. Hosp. Taunton; Ho. Phys. Co. Hosp. Hereford.

BIRCHENOUGH, Sarah Jane 4 Church Road, Ickford, Aylesbury HP18 9HZ Tel: 01844 339410; York District Hospital, Wigginton Road, York YO31 8HE Tel: 01904 631313 — MB ChB 1995 Leeds; BA (Hons.) Oxf. 1990; MRCP (UK) 1998. (Leeds) SHO (Gen. Med.) York Dist. Hosp. Prev: SHO (c/o Elderly) York Dist. Hosp.; Ho. Off. (Gen. Surg. & Orthop.) York Dist. Hosp.; Ho. Off. (Gen. Med.) St. Jas. Univ. Hosp. Leeds.

BIRCHER, Joanna 85 Beech Road, Stockport SK3 8HE Tel: 0161 429 7046 — MB ChB 1993 Manch.; MA Camb. 1994; DRCOG 1995; DFFP 1996; MRCGP, 1998. GP Regist. Stockport. Prev: Ho. Off. (Surgic. & Med.) Stepping Hill Hosp.; SHO Stepping Hill Hosp.

BIRCHER, Mr Martin Derek St Georges Hospital, Blackshaw Road, Tooting, London SW17 0QT Tel: 020 8725 3241; Fairways, The Warren, Ashtead KT21 2SE Tel: 01372 275414 Fax: 01372 271647 — MB BS 1977 Lond.; FRCS Ed. 1982; FRCS Eng. 1982. Cons. Orthop. St. Geo. Hosp. Lond. Prev: Cons. Orthop. Epsom Dist. Hosp.

BIRCHER, Richard 85 Beech Road, Stockport SK3 8HE Tel: 0161 429 7046 — MB ChB 1993 Manch.; MA Camb. 1994; MRCGP, 1997. GP Princip., Stalybridge. Prev: Ho. Off. (Med. & Surg.) Stepping Hill Hosp. Stockport.

BIRCHETT, Sidney Harold 26 Tarvin Road, Chester CH3 5DH Tel: 01244 48844 — MB BS 1949 Lond.; DCH Eng. 1951. (King's Coll. Hosp.) Socs: Chester & N. Wales Med. Soc. Prev: Med. Regist. Chester Roy. Infirm. & City Hosp. Chester; Paediat. Jun. Regist. Booth Hall Hosp. Manch.; Ho. Surg. King's Coll. Hosp.

BIRCHLEY, David William 39 Wye Court, Thornhill, Cwmbran NP44 5UL — MB BS 1996 Lond.

BIRCHWOOD, Edna Lindsay (retired) 11 Royston Court, Lichfield Road, Kew, Richmond TW9 3EH Tel: 020 8948 4742 — MB ChB 1932 Liverp.; DPH 1936. Prev: PMO Lond. Boro. Harrow.

BIRD, Professor Alan Charles Institute of Ophthalmology, Moorfields Eye Hospital, City Road, London EC1V 2PD Tel: 020 7253 3411 Fax: 020 7251 9350 Email: alan.bird@ucl.ac.uk — MB BS 1961 Lond.; MD Lond. 1974; FRCS Eng. 1967; MRCS Eng. LRCP Lond. 1961; DO Eng. 1964. (Guy's) Prof. Clin. Ophth. Inst. Ophth. Lond.; Hon. Cons. Moorfields Eye Hosp. Socs: BMA. Prev: SHO (Neurosurg.) Guy's-Maudsley Neurosurg. Unit; Resid. Surg. Moorfields Eye Hosp. Lond.; Clin. Fell. Bascom Eye Inst. Miami, USA.

BIRD, Angus Robson (retired) Crabtreebeck, Loweswater, Cockermouth CA13 0RU Tel: 0190 085255 — MB BS 1952 Durh.; MB BS (Hnrs.) Durh. 1952; FRCP Lond. 1978 M 1956. Prev: Cons. (Geriat. Med.) W. Cumbld. Hosp.

BIRD, Anne Park Parade Surgery, 27-28 Park Parade, Harrogate HG1 5AG Tel: 01423 502776 Fax: 01423 568036; 28 Rutland Drive, Harrogate HG1 2NS Tel: 01423 568394 — MB BS 1971 Lond.; MRCS Eng. LRCP Lond. 1971; DObst RCOG 1973; DCH Eng. 1974; MRCGP 1976. (King's Coll. Hosp.)

BIRD, Anne Stuart Department Psychiatry, Royal Free Hospital, Pond St., London NW3 2QG Tel: 0207 941 1601 Email: ann.bird@rfh.nthames.nhs.uk — MB BS 1973 Lond.; FRCPsych 2001; MRCS Eng. LRCP Lond. 1973; MRCPsych 1979. (Westm.) Cons. & Hon. Sen. Lect. Community Psychiat. Roy. Free Hosp. Lond. Prev: Clin. Researcher & Hon. Sen. Regist. Roy. Free Hosp. Lond.; Sen. Regist. Roy. Free Hosp. Lond.

BIRD, Anthony Peter 43 Edward Road, Birmingham B12 9JP Tel: 0121 446 2500 — MA Oxf. 1957; MB ChB Birm. 1970. GP Birm.; Hon. Tutor Dept. of Theology Univ. of Birm.

BIRD, Caroline Roseanne Gumley Lodge, Gumley, Market Harborough LE16 7RS — MB BS 1996 Lond. p/t GP Regist. Kettering VTS.

BIRD, Charles Frank Department of Anatomy, Guys Hospital, St Thomas St., London SE1 9RT; 39 Kenilworth Avenue, London SW10 7LP — MB BS 1991 Lond.

BIRD, Charles William Edzell, Watling St., Dordon, Tamworth B78 1TE Tel: 01827 892893 — MB ChB 1947 Birm. (Birm.) Prev: Ho. Surg. Qu. Eliz. Hosp. Birm.

BIRD, Charles William Handley Sonning Common Health Centre, Wood Lane, Sonning Common, Reading RG4 9SW Tel: 01734 722188; East Manor Farm Cottage, Peppard Common, Henley-on-Thames RG9 5LA Tel: 01491 628138 — MB BS 1985 Lond.; MRCGP 1989; DRCOG 1991; Cert. Family Plann. JCC 1989. (The Royal London Hospital) Hon. Fell. Dept. of Primary Health Care Univ. of Oxf. Prev: Trainee GP Frimley Pk. Hosp. VTS; Clin. Med. Off. W. Surrey N.E. Hants. HA; Med. Off. Kapsuwar Hosp. Kenya.

BIRD, Charlotte Marie The Croft, Wrekenton, Gateshead NE9 Tel: 0191 487 6129; 28 Elmfield Road, Gosforth, Newcastle upon Tyne NE3 4BA — MB BS 1984 Lond.; DRCOG 1988; DGM RCP Lond. 1986.

BIRD, Professor Colin Carmichael Dean Faculty of Medicine, University of Edinburgh Medical School, Teviot Place, Edinburgh EH8 9AG Tel: 0131 650 3181 Fax: 0131 650 6525 Email: colinc.bird@ed.ac.uk — MB ChB 1961 Glas.; FRSE 1992; PhD Glas. 1967, MB ChB 1961; FRCS Ed. 1995; FRCP Ed. 1989; FRCPath 1980, M 1968; F Med Sci 1998. Dean Fac. Med. & Provost Fac. Med. & Veterin. Med. Univ. Ed. Prev: Prof. & Head Dept. Path. Univ. Edin.; Prof. Path. Univ. Leeds.

BIRD, David Francis French Weir Health Centre, French Weir Avenue, Taunton TA1 1NW Tel: 01823 331381 Fax: 01823 323689; 12 Stoneleigh Close, Staplegrove, Taunton TA2 6ET — MRCS Eng. LRCP Lond. 1972; BSc Lond. 1969, MB BS 1972; MRCP (UK) 1975; AKC. (King's Coll. Hosp.)

BIRD, David Ian Holmlea, Southwell Road, Kirklington, Newark NG22 8NF — MB ChB 1984 Leeds; T(GP) 1991.

BIRD, Derek Oliver Davenport House Surgery, Bowers Way, Harpenden AL5 4HX Tel: 01582 767821 Fax: 01582 769285; Maplecroft, 18 Moreton End Lane, Harpenden AL5 2HB Tel: 01582 760661 — MB BS 1962 Lond.; MRCS Eng. LRCP Lond. 1962. (St. Geo.) Prev: Ho. Surg. St. Geo. Hosp. Lond. & Luton & Dunstable Hosp.; Ho. Phys. Barnet Gen. Hosp.

BIRD, Donald William Kemp (retired) Pott's Ghyll, Nether Row, Hesket Newmarket, Wigton CA7 8LB Tel: 016974 78322 — MB BChir 1952 Camb.; MA Camb. 1952; FRCPsych. 1983, M 1971; DPM Eng. 1966. Prev: Cons. Psychiat. Adolesc. Dept. Tavistock Clinic.

BIRD, Elizabeth Ena 2 Newgate, Highgate Park, Fulwood, Preston PR2 8LR — MB BCh BAO 1948 Dub. (T.C. Dub.) Clin. Med. Off. Chorley & S. Ribble Dist. Auth. Prev: Med. Off. Mill RD. Outpat. Clinic Liverp.; Ho. Phys. Olive Mt. Childr. Hosp. Liverp. & David Lewis N..; Hosp. Liverp.

BIRD, Mr George Graham 24/26 George Lane, Notton, Wakefield WF4 2NL Tel: 01226 722083 — MB ChB 1959 Leeds; FRCS Eng. 1966; FRCS Ed. 1965. (Leeds) Cons. Surg. Wakefield Health Dist.

BIRD, George Lawrence Arthur Maidstone Hospital, Hermitage Lane, Maidstone ME16 9QQ Tel: 01622 729000 Fax: 01622 723014 Email: georgebird@lineone.net — MB BS 1982 Lond.; MA Camb. 1986, BA 1979; MD Lond. 1990; FRCP; Cert in Teaching 1999. Cons. Gen. Med. & Gastroenterol. Maidstone Hosp. Kent. Socs: Brit. Soc. Gastroenterol.; Amer. Assn. Study Liver Dis.; Liveryman Soc. Apoth. Lond. Prev: Sen. Regist. (Gastroenterol. & Genera Med.) Gartnavel Gen. Hosp. & W.ern Infirm. Glas.; Clin. Research Fell. Inst. Liver Studies King's Coll. Hosp. Lond.; Ho. Phys. Roy. Lond. Hosp.

BIRD, Helen Claire 26 Greasby Road, Greasby, Wirral CH49 3NE — MB ChB 1996 Liverp.

BIRD, Professor Howard Anthony Clinical Pharmacology Unit, Chapel Allerton Hospital, Leeds LS7 4SA Tel: 0113 392 4721 Fax: 0113 392 4723; 28 Rutland Drive, Harrogate HG1 2NS Tel: 01423 568394 — MB BChir 1971 Camb.; MA Camb. 1971, MD 1980; FRCP Lond. 1985; MRCP (UK) 1973. Prof. Pharmacol. Rheum. Univ. Leeds; Cons. Rheum. Leeds Gen. Infirm. Chapel Allerton Hosp.

Leeds. Prev: Reader ((Rheum.) Univ. Leeds; Sen. Lect. Univ. Leeds; Regist. Roy. Nat. Hosp. Rheum. Dis. Bath.

BIRD, Hugh Claud Handley (retired) The Slate Barn, Seamark Road, Brooksend, Birchington CT7 0JL Tel: 01843 846619 Email: hugh.bird@which.net — MB BChir Camb. 1948; MA Camb. 1948; FRCGP 1982, M 1968; DCH Eng. 1953; DObst RCOG 1952. Prev: GP Maidstone.

BIRD, Jean Mary 13 Hawth Crescent, Seaford BN25 2RR — MB BS 1960 Lond.; MRCS Eng. LRCP Lond. 1960; MCOphth 1991; DO Eng. 1965. (Roy. Free) Ophth. Med. Pract. (Ophth.) Med. Eye Centre Burgess Hill. Prev: Clin. Asst. (Ophth.) Roy. Surrey Co. Hosp. Guildford.

BIRD, Jennifer Mary Avon Haematology Unit, Bristol Oncology Centre, Horfield Road, Bristol BS2 8ED; 8 Richmond Park Road, Bristol B58 3AP Tel: 0117 946 6396 — MB BS 1983 Lond.; MRCP (UK) 1986; MD 1998; MRCPath 1999. (Westminster)

BIRD, Jeremy Farm House, Farm Lane, Orchard Hill, Queen Mary's Avenue, Carshalton SM5 4NR Tel: 020 8770 8039 — MB ChB 1984 Ed.; BSc (Hons.) Biochem. Lond. 1979; MRCPsych. 1989. Cons. Psychiat. Merton & Sutton Comminuty NHS Trust; Hon. Sen. Lect. (Psychiat. of Disabil.) St. Geo. Med. Sch. Prev: Sen. Regist. Rotat. (Psychiat.) SW Thames Train. Scheme; Regist. Rotat. (Psychiat.) Roy. Free & Friern Hosps. Train. Scheme.

BIRD, Jillian Edmiston 71 Wilderness Road, Reading RG6 7RF Tel: 01734 669894 — MB BS 1974 Lond.; BSc Lond. 1971; MRCGP 1979; T(GP) 1991; DO Eng. 1978; DRCOG 1977; DCH Eng. 1976. (St. Thos.) Asst. GP Reading. Prev: Course Organiser & Trainer (Gen. Pract.) Reading VTS.

BIRD, John Richard 17 Macclesfield Road, Wilmslow SK9 2AA Tel: 01625 523292 — MB BS 1967 Lond.; MRCS Eng. LRCP Lond. 1967; FRCPsych 1990, M 1974; DPM Eng. 1973. (Univ. Coll. Hosp.) Indep. Psychiat. Chesh. Socs: Fell. Manch. Med. Soc.; Assn. Analyt. Psychother. in NHS. Prev: Cons. Psychother. Cheadle Roy. Hosp.; Cons. Psychiat. & Psychother. Tutor Qu. Eliz. Milit. Hosp. Woolwich.

***BIRD, Jonathan Houston,** Capt. RAMC Flat 1, 33 St Stephen's Gardens, East Twickenham, Twickenham TW1 Email: 101717.2233@compuserve.com — MB BS 1997 Lond.; BSc Lond. 1994.

BIRD, Jonathan Michael Burden Centre, Freuchay Hospital, Bristol BS10 1JB Tel: 0117 918 0713 Fax: 0117 918 6721 Email: jmbird@compuserve.com; Heath House Priory Hospital, Bell Hill, Bristol BS16 1EQ Tel: 0117 952 5255 — MB ChB 1974 Bristol; BSc Bristol 1971; FRCPsych 1991, M 1978. (Bristol) Cons. Neuropsychiat. Burden Neurol. Hosp. Bristol; Clin. Sen. Lect. (Ment. Health) Univ. Bristol; Apoth. Lect. (Hist. of Med.) Univ. Bristol. Socs: (Hon. Sec.) Brit. Neuropsychiat. Assn.; Bristol M-C Soc. Past pres; (Hon. Sec.) Bristol Medico Historical Soc. Prev: Med. Dir. (Community Psychiat.) Serv. Hamilton, Canada; Sen. Regist. (Psychiat.) Maudsley Hosp. Lond.; Regist. (Psychiat.) Bristol Health Dist. (T).

BIRD, Julian Department of Psychological Medicine, King's College Hospital, Denmark Hill, London SE5 9RS Tel: 020 7848 0796 Fax: 020 7848 5129 — MB BChir 1966 Camb.; 1966 MB BChir Camb.; 1965 MA Camb.; 1998 FRCPsych; 1974 MRCPsych; FRCP 1998; MRCP 1972. Cons. Psychiat. Ravensbourne NHS Trust; Hon. Cons. & Sen. Lect. King's Coll. Sch. Med. & Dent. Lond. Univ.; Chairm. Med. Interview Teach. Assn. Socs: Fell. Roy. Soc. Med.; USA Acad. On Phys. Pat. Chairm. Med. Interview Teading Assn.; BMA. Prev: Vis. Prof. of Liaison Psychiat. Univ. of Alabama, USA; Sen. Regist. Maudsley Hosp.; Ho. Off. St. Geo. Hosp. Lond.

BIRD, Katherine Lucy Hazel Cottage, 9 Underhill Lane, Farnham GU10 3NF — MB BS 1996 Lond. (St. Bartholomews)

BIRD, Kathleen Jane 'Martins', 22 Lincoln Hatch Lane, Burnham, Slough SL1 7HD — MB ChB 1976 Birm.; FFA RCS Eng. 1981; DA Eng. 1978.

BIRD, Kathleen Salome (retired) Crabtreebeck, Loweswater, Cockermouth CA13 0RU Tel: 0190 085255 — MB BS 1949 Durh. Prev: Clin. Med. Off. W. Cumbria Health Dist.

BIRD, Michelle C C (retired) 3 Kempsfield, Devizes SN10 5AX Tel: 01380 728033 — MB ChB 1960 Birm.; MRCPsych 1971; DPM Eng. 1967. Prev: Cons. Psychiat. Roundway Hosp. Devizes.

BIRD, Monica Mary St Merryn, Shores Road, Woking GU21 4HJ Tel: 01483 760703 — MB BS 1940 Lond.; DCH Eng. 1943. (Lond. Sch. Med. Wom.)

BIRD, Nigel The Surgery, 138 Beaconsfield Villas, Brighton BN1 6HQ Tel: 01273 552212 Fax: 01273 271148 Email: nigel.bird@gp-981042.nhs.uk — MB BS 1987 Lond.; MRCP (UK) 1991; DFFP 1995; DRCOG 1994; DCH RCP Lond. 1993. (St. Bart. Hosp.)

BIRD, Nigel John Park Avenue Medical Centre, 166-168 Park Avenue North, Northampton NN3 2HZ Tel: 01604 716500 Fax: 01604 721685; 16 Atterbury Way, Great Houghton, Northampton NN4 7AU Tel: 01604 762541 — BM BCh 1970 Oxf.; MA Oxf. 1970; MRCGP 1975; DObst RCOG 1972. (Oxf.) Clin. Asst. (Palliat. Med.) Cynthia Spencer Hse. N.ampton; Clin. Asst. (Dermat.) N.ampton Gen. Hosp. Prev: Trainee GP N.ampton VTS; Ho. Phys & Ho. Surg. Radcliffe Infirm. Oxf.

BIRD, Oliver John, Squadron Ldr. RAF Med. Br. South West Lodge, Rede Road, Whepstead, Bury St Edmunds IP29 4ST — MB ChB 1988 Sheff.; MRCGP 1995; DRCOG 1996. Prev: Sen. Med. Off. UK Support Unit Ramstein Air Base, BFPO 109.

BIRD, Philip Arthur (retired) 204 Cop Lane, Penwortham, Preston PR1 9AB Tel: 01772 743221 Email: p.bird@yahoo.co.uk — MB ChB 1962 Liverp. Prev: Ho. Off. (Meds., Surg. & O & G) Ormskirk & Dist. Gen. Hosp.

BIRD, Rachel Jane 12 Stoneleigh Close, Staplegrove, Taunton TA2 6ET Tel: 01823 282062 — BM BS 1998 Nottm.; BM BS Nottm 1998; B.Med.Sci (Hons), 1995. SHO (Vasc.), W. Cumbld. Hosp., Whitehaven, Cumbria.

BIRD, Richard Ashton 16 Front Street, Morton, Gainsborough DN21 3AA — MB ChB 1962 Sheff.; DObst RCOG 1965. (Sheff.)

BIRD, Mr Richard le Roy Department of Surgery, Barnet General Hospital, Wellhouse Lane, Barnet EN5 3DJ Tel: 020 8216 4000 Fax: 020 8216 5447 — MB BS 1979 Lond.; BSc Lond. 1976, MS Lond. 1992; FRCS Eng. 1983. (Univ. Coll. Hosp.) Cons. Surg. (Gen. & Vasc. Surg.) Barnet Gen. Hosp. Socs: Vasc. Surg. Soc. of GB and Irel.; Assn. Surg.; BMA. Prev: Sen. Regist. Roy. Free Hosp. Lond.; Clin. Research Fell. Univ. Dept. Surg. Roy. Free Hosp. Lond.; Sen. Regist. (Gen. Surg.) Chase Farm Hosp.

BIRD, Roy Leonard (retired) 18 Centurion Gate, Caerleon, Newport NP18 1NS Tel: 01633 430017 — MB BS 1951 Lond.; FRCP Ed. 1994; MRCP Ed. 1962; FRCPsych 1992, M 1972; DPM Eng. 1960. Prev: Cons. Psychiat. St. Cadoc's Hosp. Caerleon.

BIRD, Ruby 263 Wake Green Road, Birmingham B13 9XH — MB BS 1940 Madras; DGO 1942. (Madras Med. Coll.) Asst. Med. Off. City of Birm. Pub. Health Dept. Socs: BMA. Prev: Asst. Med. Off. O & G B.J. Med. Coll. Poona.

BIRD, Rupert Harold 7 The Friary, Lichfield WS13 6QG — MB BCh 1987 Wales.

BIRD, Sarah Anne Alice Elmside Cottage, The Avenue, Sneyd Park, Bristol BS9 1PB Email: saabird@yahoo.com — MB BCh 1994 Wales. GP Regist., Portishead Health Centre. Socs: BMA; MPS. Prev: SHO (c/o Elderly), Bristol Gen. Hosp.; SHO (Paediat.), S.mead Hosp., Bristol; SHO. (A&E) Frenchay Hosp. Bristol.

BIRD, Scott 81 Fairwater Drive, Woodley, Reading RG5 3JG — MB ChB 1998 Birm.; ChB Birm. 1998.

BIRD, Seònaid Iseabail Deirdre 213 Derbyshire Lane, Sheffield S8 8SA Tel: 0114 255 0972 — MB ChB 1958 Sheff.

BIRD, Simon Charles The Surgery, 162 Long St., Dordon, Tamworth B78 1QH — MB ChB 1978 Birm.

BIRD, Stella Frances Links Medical Practice, 27 Brook Lane, Bromley BR1 4PX Tel: 020 8857 0011 — MB ChB 1987 Manch.; MRCGP 1993.

BIRD, Stephen Peter Glover Abbey Health Centre, East Abbey Street, Arbroath DD11 1EN Tel: 01241 870311 Fax: 01241 875411; Littleton of Airlie, Kirriemuir DD8 5NS Tel: 01575 530353 Fax: 01575 530353 — MB ChB 1984 Manch.; BSc (Med. Sci.) St. And. 1981. Lt.-Cdr. RN Reserve.

BIRD, Susan Marie 10 Huddington Glade, Yateley GU46 6FG Tel: 01252 890480 — BM Soton 1988; MRCGP 1994; DFFP 1994; DCH RCP Lond. 1992. Prev: Trainee GP Reading VTS.

BIRD, Thomas (retired) The Place, Loweswater, Cockermouth CA13 0SU Tel: 01946 861463 — MD Durh. 1953, MB BS 1942; FRCPath 1969, M 1963.

BIRD, Thomas Michael Department of Anaesthesia, Royal Lancaster Infirmary, Ashton Road, Lancaster LA1 4RP Tel: 01524 583517 Fax: 01524 583519 Email: mike.bird@l.bay-tr.n.west.nhs.uk; 151 Eden Park, Lancaster LA1 4SJ Tel: 01524

63459 Email: mchlbird@aol.com — MB BChir 1975 Camb.; MA Camb. 1976; FFA RCS 1980. (Cambridge University & St. Bartholomew's Hosp, London) Cons. Anaesth. & Intens. Care Morecambe Bay Hosp.s NHS Trust; Clin. Director, Critical Care; Morecambe Bay Hosp.s Trust. Socs: Manch. Med. Soc.; Intens. Care Soc.; Assn. of Anaesth.s. Prev: Sen. Regist. & Regist. (Anaesth.) Sheff.; Lect. (Anaesth.) Univ. Calgary, Canada.

BIRDI, Azmy Vispi The Medical Centre, Lower Road, Cookham Rise SL6 9HX Tel: 01628 524646 Fax: 01628 810201 — MBBS 1988; MD (Obst. & Gyn.) Bombay 19881; MRCOG (Roy. Coll. Obst. & Gyn.) 1997; MRCGP (Roy. Coll. Gen. Pract.) London 2001. (Grant Medical College, Bombay, India) GP Princip. Socs: Brit. Menopause Soc.; Roy. Coll. of Obstretrics & Gynaecologists, Lond.; Roy. Coll. of Gen. Practitioners, Lond. Prev: Specialist Regist. Gen. Pract., Claremont Surg., Miadenhead 1999-2001; Specialist Regist. (Obst. & Gyn.) John Radcliffe Hosp., Oxf. 1998-1999; Specialist Regist. (Obst. & Gyn.) Wexham Pk. Hosp., Slough 1997-1998.

BIRDI, Mr Inderpaul Department of Cardiac Surgery, Papworth Hospital, Papworth Everard, Cambridge CB3 8QD — BM BS 1989 Nottm.; FRCS Eng. 1993.

BIRDI, Jasminder Singh The Elms Medical Centre, Tilley Close, Main Road, Hoo, Rochester ME3 9AE Tel: 01634 250142; Emrick Lodge, Old Watling St, Rochester ME2 3UG — MB BS 1986 Newc.; DGM RCP Lond. 1990.

BIRDI, Prem Kumar Staff House No 1, Nevill Hall Hospital, Brecon Road, Abergavenny NP7 7EG — MB BS 1982 Guru Nanak Dev India.

BIRDI, Satwant Singh 241 Bath Road, Hounslow TW3 3DA — MB BS 1982 Newc.

BIRDSALL, Mary Ann John Radcliffe Hospital, Headley Way, Headington, Oxford OX3 9DU — MB ChB 1986 Auckland.

BIRDSALL, Mr Paul David Torbay Hospital, Lawes Bridge, Torquay TQ2 7AA — MB ChB 1989 Leeds; FRCS Eng. 1993; FRCS (Orth) 1999. Cons. Ortho Surg., Torbay Hosp., Torquay. Prev: SHO (Orthop.) Manch. Roy. Infirm. & N. Manch. Gen. Hosp.; Demonst. (Anat.) Univ. Birm.; Specialist Regist. (Orthop. Surg.) N. Deanery S. Tyneside Healthcare Trust.

BIRDWOOD, George Fortune Brodrick Westmeon, Langley Hill, Kings Langley WD4 9HE Tel: 01923 263996 Fax: 01923 270507 Email: georgebirdwood@compuserve.com — MB BChir 1954 Camb.; MA Camb. 1965. (Camb. & St. Bart.) Socs: Fell. Roy. Soc. Med.; Fell. Med. Soc. Lond.; Liveryman Soc. Apoth. Prev: Freelance Med. Jl.ist & Translator; Mem. Parole Bd. for Eng. & Wales; Med. Edr. Ciba-Geigy Scientif. Pub.ats.

BIRINDER, Kaur Thandi Worsbrough Health Centre, Oakdale, Worsbrough, Barnsley S70 5EG Tel: 01226 204090 Fax: 01226 771966 — MB BS 1986 Madras; MRCOG 1990.

BIRING, Manmohan Singh 1 Rodney Way, Colnbrook, Slough SL3 0PN — MB BS 1989 Lond.; BSc (Hons.) Lond. 1986, MB BS 1989.

BIRKBY, Edward Anthony The Health Care Surgery, 63 Palgrave Road, Sheffield S5 8GS Tel: 0114 234 1200 Fax: 0114 231 4591 — MB ChB 1975 Sheff.; BMedSci St. And. 1972; MRCGP 1979; DRCOG 1983.

BIRKET, Ian James Ambleside Health Centre, Rydal Road, Ambleside LA22 9BP Tel: 015394 32693 Fax: 015394 32520 — MB ChB 1972 Manch.; MRCGP 1981; DObst RCOG 1975. Prev: SHO (Paediat., O & G Geriat.) Withington Hosp. Manch.

BIRKETT, Christopher Ian 1 Burnside, Giggleswick, Settle BD24 0BJ — MB ChB 1998 Liverp.; MB ChB Liverp 1998.

BIRKETT, Eleanor Sylvia 33 Nile Grove, Edinburgh EH10 4RE — MB ChB 1996 Aberd.

BIRKETT, Jennifer Anne The Surgery, 2 Mark Street, Rochdale OL12 9BE Tel: 01706 43183 Fax: 01706 526640; Amon-RA, 1 Broadhalgh Road, Bamford, Rochdale OL11 5NJ — MB ChB 1974 Birm.; DCH Eng. 1980; DObst RCOG 1976. (Birm.) Prev: GP (Civil.) attached to RAMC Germany; Trainee GP Worcester Roy. Infirm.

BIRKETT, John Francis Tudor Lodge Health Centre, 3 Nithsdale Road, Weston Super Mare BS23 4JP Tel: 01934 622665 Fax: 01934 644332 — MB BS 1983 Lond.; MA Camb. 1983; MRCGP 1989. Prev: Trainee GP Leek, Staffs & Abbey Hulton.

BIRKETT, John Raymond (retired) The Gouldings, Old Church Road, Colwall, Malvern WR13 6ET Tel: 01684 540105 — MB ChB 1954 St. And.; DObst RCOG 1956. Prev: Ho. Surg. (O & G) Dundee Roy. Infirm.

BIRKETT, Neville Lawn, CStJ (retired) Beardwood, Carter Road, Grange-over-Sands LA11 7AG Tel: 015395 32286 — MB BChir 1942 Camb.; MA Camb. 1943. JP. Prev: Co. Surg. Cumbld. & W.mld. St. John Ambul. Brig.

BIRKETT, Paul Brian Lawrie Barrow Hospital, Barrow Gurney, Bristol BS48 3SG Tel: 0117 928 6600 Fax: 0117 928 6650 Email: paul.birkett@bristol.ac.uk — MB BS 1983 Lond.; MRCPsych 1988. (Middlesex Hospital Medical School) Cons. Gen. Adult Psychiat. Avon & W.ern Wilts. Ment. Healthcare NHS Trust. Prev: Sen. Regist. Maudsley & Bethlem Roy. Hosps. Lond. & Nat. Hosp. Neurol. & Neurosurg. Lond.

BIRKETT, Robert Michael The Admin Unit, Eversfield Hospital, West Hill Road, St Leonards-on-Sea TN38 0NG Tel: 01424 445026 Ext: 276 Fax: 01424 426858 — MB ChB 1976 Liverp.; MRCPsych 1981. Cons. Adult Psychiat. Hastings & Rother NHS Trust. Prev: Regist. Rotat. Liverp. Hosps.; SHO (Psychiat.) & Ho. Off. Sefton Gen. Hosp. Liverp.

BIRKHEAD, John Scrivener Stowe Hill House, Weedon, Northampton NN7 4SF Tel: 01327 340288 — MB BChir 1969 Camb.; MB Camb. 1969, BChir 1968; FRCP Lond. 1983; MRCP (UK) 1971. (St. Thos.) Cons. Phys. N.ampton Gen. Hosp. Prev: Sen. Regist. Radcliffe Infirm. Oxf.; Regist. Hammersmith Hosp. & Postgrad. Med. Sch.; Resid. Med. Off. Nat. Heart Hosp.

BIRKILL, Rosemary Jane 58 Newport Road, Balsall Health, Birmingham B12 8QD — MB BChir Camb. 1964; MRCPsych 1976; DPM Eng. 1968; DObst RCOG 1966. (Camb. & St. Bart.) Sen. Doctor Birm. Brook Advis. Centres; Sen. Clinic Med. Off. (Family Plann.) BromsGr./Redditch Health Dist. & Sandwell Dist. HA. Prev: Clin. Asst. (Psychiat.) Avalon Day Hosp. Redditch.

BIRKIN, Angela Elizabeth Burley Park Doctors, Burley Park Medical Centre, 273 Burley Road, Leeds LS4 2EL Tel: 0113 230 4111; Micklefield Grange, Micklefield Lane, Rawdon, Leeds LS19 6BA — MB BChir 1982 Camb.; MA Camb. 1983; MRCGP 1986; DRCOG 1986. (Univ. Camb. Sch. Clin. Med.)

BIRKIN, Nigel John c/o Nobles Isle of Man Hospital, Westmoreland Road, Douglas IM1 4QA — MB ChB 1969 St. And.; FRCP Lond. 1994; MRCP (UK) 1981; DObst RCOG 1971. (St. And.) Cons. Paediat. Noble's Is. of Man Hosp. Prev: Lect. (Paediat.) Char. Cross Hosp. Med. Sch. Lond.; Regist. (Paediat.) P. of Wales Childr. Hosp. Randwick, Austral.

BIRKIN, Philippa Jane Fron Ganol, Pentre Celyn, Ruthin LL15 2HR — MB ChB 1998 Birm.

BIRKINSHAW, Kathryn Louise The Orchard, Stanedge Road, Bakewell DE45 1DG — MB ChB 1987 Manch.

BIRKINSHAW, Keith James Queen Margaret Hospital NHS Trust, Whitefield Road, Dunfermline KY12 0SU Tel: 01383 624656 Fax: 01383 621668; Falside Smiddy, Boarhills, St Andrews KY16 8PT Tel: 01383 880479 Email: birk@falside.freeserve.co.uk — MB BS Lond. 1964; FRCA. 1968. (Middlx.) p/t Cons. Anaesth. Qu. Margt. Hosp. Dunfermline; Anat. Demonst., St Andrews Univ. Socs: Pain Soc. & Europ. Soc. Regional Analgesia; Hosp. Cons. & Spec. Assn. & Assn. Anaesth. Prev: Cons. Anaesth. Bronglais Gen. Hosp. Aberystwyth; Sen. Regist. (Anaesth.) Mulago Hosp. Kampala, Uganda; SHO (Anaesth.) United Oxf. Hosps.

BIRKINSHAW, Robert Ian 37 Broadway, Barnsley S70 6QL — MB ChB 1990 Leeds; MRCP (UK) 1994.

BIRKINSHAW, Stephen Edward Poynton The Almshouse Surgery, Trinity Medical Centre, Thornhill Street, Wakefield WF1 1PG Tel: 01924 327150 Fax: 01924 327165 — MB ChB 1971 Leeds; DAGP (Dip. in Adv. Gen. Prac.) Newc. 1998; MRCGP 1979; DCH Eng. 1974; DObst RCOG 1973. (Leeds University) Prev: SHO (Obst.) Leeds Matern. Hosp.; Ho. Phys. (Paediat.) & Ho. Surg. (ENT) Leeds Gen. Infirm.

BIRKMYRE, Alison Cameron Rutherglen Health Centre, 130 Stonelaw Road, Rutherglen, Glasgow G73 2PQ Tel: 0141 531 6020 Fax: 0141 531 4130; 24 Cadzow Drive, Glasgow G72 8ND — MB ChB 1979 Glas.; MRCGP 1983; DRCOG 1982.

BIRKS, Deirdre Mary Patricia 7 Stumperlowe Hall Road, Fulwood, Sheffield S10 3QR Tel: 0114 230 6974 — MB ChB 1973 Sheff. GP Chesterfield. Prev: SHO (Obst.) N.. Gen. Hosp. Sheff.; SHO (Ophth.) & Ho. Phys. & Ho. Surg. Roy. Hosp. Sheff.

BIRKS, Miss Doreen Ann Frensham Cottage, Berwick, Polegate BN26 6SP Tel: 01323 870361 — MB BS Lond. 1949; FRCS Eng. (Ophth.) 1962; FRCS Ed. (Ophth.) 1961; FRCOphth. 1988 Eng.; DO Eng. 1953. (Roy. Free) Hon. Cons. Ophth. St. Thos. Hosp. Lond.; Emerit. Cons. Ophth. Sutton & W. Merton Dist. Eye Unit Sutton Hosp.; Hon. Ophth. Surg. Roy. Sch. for the Blind, Leatherhead. Socs: Fell. Roy. Soc. Med.; Liveryman Worshipful Soc. of Apoth. Prev: Sen. Regist. & Ho. Surg. Roy. Eye Hosp. Lond.; Regist. (Ophth.) St. Jas. Hosp. Balham.

BIRKS, Dorothy Vaughan Barnsley Health Authority, Hillder House, Gawber Road, Barnsley S75 2PY Tel: 01226 777010 Fax: 01226 773978; 10 Haugh Lane, Sheffield S11 9SA — MB ChB 1971 Aberd.; FFPHM RCP (UK) 1995; MFCM RCP (UK) 1983; DPH Eng. 1977. Dir. (Pub. Health) Barnsley HA. Prev: Cons. Pub. Health Med. Sheff. HA.

BIRKS, Eleanor Irene Evelyn Hospital, 4 Trumpington Road, Cambridge CB2 2AF Tel: 01223 370919 Fax: 01223 353223; Stable Cottage, Home Farm, High St., Babraham, Cambridge CB2 4AG Tel: 01223 835280 Fax: 01223 353223 — MB ChB 1966 Manch.; MPhil Camb. 1989; BSc Manch. 1963; MRCP Lond. 1969. Med. Dir. Screening Cambs. Prev: GP Camb.; Regist. (Cardiol.) Papworth Hosp. Papworth Everard; Ho. Phys. Manch. Roy. Infirm.

BIRKS, Emma Jane Westfield House, 3 Bodenham Road, Folkestone CT20 2NU Tel: 01303 850602 Fax: 01303 226453 — MB BS 1992 Lond.; BSc (Hons.) Immunopath. Lond. 1989. SHO (Renal) Guy's Hosp. Lond. Prev: SHO (Cardiol.) Hammersmith Hosp. Lond. & Harefield Hosp. Middlx.; SHO (Repirat. Med.) Lond. Chest Hosp.

BIRKS, Katherine Alison 258 Hills Road, Cambridge CB2 2QE — BM BCh 1998 Oxf.; BM BCh Oxf 1998.

BIRKS, Margaret Ellen 51 Holybrook Road, Reading RG1 6DG — MB BS 1996 Lond.

BIRKS, Richard John Scriven Department of Anaesthetics, C Floor, Royal Hallamshire Hospital, Sheffield S10 2JF — MB ChB 1973 Sheff.; FFA RCS Eng. 1978. Cons. Anaesth. Sheff. Teachg. Hosp.s Trust. Socs: Obst. Anaesth. Assn.; Coun. Mem. Assoc of Anaesth. Brit. & Irel.; Reg. Adv.RCAnaesth. N. Trent. Prev: Cons. Anaesth. Chesterfield Trent RHA; Sen. Regist. (Anaesth.) Sheff. AHA (T); Specialist (Anaesth.) Acad. Ziekenhuis Groningen, Netherlands.

BIRKS, Sarah Frances 8 Bramleys, Kingston, Lewes BN7 3LF — MB BS 1981 Lond.; MA Camb. 1984, BA (Hons.) 1978; MRCP (UK) 1986. (Guy's)

BIRLEY, David Anthony Haydon Priory Road Surgery, Priory Road, Park South, Swindon SN3 2EZ Tel: 01793 521154 Fax: 01793 512562; Marsh Cottage, Lower Wanborough, Swindon SN4 0AR Tel: 01793 790438 Fax: 01793 790438 — MB BChir 1975 Camb.; MA Camb. 1975; MRCGP 1982; DCH Eng. 1981; DRCOG 1981. (St. Thos. Hosp. Lond.) Clin. Asst. (Dermat.) P.ss Margt. Hosp. Swindon. Socs: BMA. Prev: GP Trainee Halifax; SHO (Med.) W. Cornw. Hosp. Penzance; SHO (Cas. & Orthop.) P.ss Margt. Hosp. Swindon.

BIRLEY, Doreen Mary (retired) 16 Upper Shirley Road, Croydon CR0 5EA — MB ChB 1956 St. And.; FFA RCS Eng. 1962; DA Eng. 1959. Prev: Cons. Anaesth. Moorfields Eye Hosp. Lond. & N. Middlx. Hosp. Lond.

BIRLEY, Humphrey David Leatham Fairleigh, Osbert Road, Liverpool L23 6UP — MB BS 1982 Lond.; MRCP (UK) 1988; DTM & H RCP Lond. 1991; DCH RCP Lond. 1984.

BIRLEY, James Leatham Tennant, CBE Upper Bryn, Longtown, Hereford HR2 0NA — BM BCh 1952 Oxf.; FRCP 1976, M 1958; FRCPsych 1976, M 1971; DPM Lond. 1962. (St. Thos.) Emerit. Cons. Psychiat. Bethlem Roy. & Maudsley Hosps. Lond. Socs: (Ex-Pres.) BMA. Prev: Ex-Pres. Roy. Coll. Psychiat.; Dean Inst. Psychiat.; Dean Roy. Coll. Psychiat.

BIRLY, Ajay — BM BS 1989 Nottm.; MRCGP 1993; DCH 1993; Cert. Family Plann 1992; BMedSci Nottm. 1989. GP; Forens. Med. Examr. (Police Surg.) Metrop. Police Lond.

BIRMAN, Pascal Servier Research & Development, Fulmer Hall, Windmill Road, Slough SL3 6HH — MD 1989 Paris.

BIRMINGHAM, Anthony Terence (retired) Medical School, Queens Medical Centre, Clifton Blvd, Nottingham NG7 2UH Tel: 0115 970 9480 Fax: 0115 970 9259 — MB BS 1955 Lond.; BSc (Hons.) Lond. 1952; MRCS Eng. LRCP Lond. 1955. Prev: Prof. Pharmacol. Univ. Nottm. Med. Sch.

BIRMINGHAM, Joanna Susan 43 Clarence Road, Harborne, Birmingham B17 9LA — MB BS 1990 Newc.

BIRMINGHAM, Luke Stephen Reaside Clinic, Birmingham Great Park, Bristol Road S., Birmingham B45 9BE Tel: 0121 453 6161 — MB BS 1988 Newc.; MRCP 1991; MRCPsych 1995; MD 1999. Clin. Lect. (Forens. Psych.).

BIRMINGHAM-MCDONOGH, Stephanie Myra Louise Carisbrooke House Surgery, 1A Pope Road, Bromley BR2 9SS Tel: 020 8460 4611 Fax: 020 8460 9450; Tel: 020 8776 0452 — MB BCh BAO 1981 NUI; MRCPI 1985; MRCGP 1987; DCH NUI 1983. (Univ. Coll. Dub.) Princip. GP Carisbrooke Ho. Bromley. Prev: GP The Burnham Surg., Burnham-on-Crouch, Essex.

BIRN-JEFFERY, Joanna Baddow Road Surgery, 115 Baddow Road, Chelmsford CM2 7PY Tel: 01245 351351 Fax: 01245 494192 — MRCS Eng. LRCP Lond. 1988; MRCS Eng LRCP Lond. 1988.

BIRNEY, Sharon Marie 17 Martin Court, Hamilton ML3 6ND — MB ChB 1994 Glas.

BIRNIE, Mr Alexander John Milne 8 Grange Terrace, Sunderland SR2 7DF Tel: 0191 510 0555 Fax: 0191 565 5998; Eshwood House, Acton Road, Esh Winning, Durham DH7 9PL Tel: 0191 373 4457 Fax: 0191 373 4457 Email: birnie@eshwoodhouse.freeserve.co.uk — MB ChB 1954 Aberd.; FRCS Ed. 1968. Indep. Pract. Durh. & Sunderland Orthop.; Med. Off. to the Brit. Judo Assoc. Socs: Fell. BOA. Prev: Cons. Orthop. Surg. Dryburn Hosp. Durh. Gen. Hosp. Sunderland; Ho. Surg. Roy. Infirm. Aberd.; SHO Birm. Accid. Hosp. & Mt. Vernon Centre For Plastic Surg. & Jaw Injury N.wood.

BIRNIE, Gordon Bell Riverbank Surgery, Riverbank, Janet Street, Thurso KW14 7AR Tel: 01847 892027/892009 Fax: 01847 892690 — MB ChB 1978 Aberd.; MRCGP 1982; DRCOG 1981.

BIRNIE, Trevor The Surgery, Denmark St., Darlington DL3 0PD — MB BCh BAO 1972 Belf.; MRCGP 1976; DObst RCOG 1975.

***BIRNS, Jonathan Michael** 35 Stanway Gardens, Edgware HA8 9LN Tel: 020 8905 4810 — MB BS 1998 Lond.; MB BS Lond 1998; BSc, 1994.

BIRNSTINGL, Mr Martin Avigdor (retired) 60 Fitzjohns Avenue, London NW3 5LT Tel: 020 7435 5362 Fax: 020 7435 5362 — MB BS 1946 Lond.; MS Lond. 1958; FRCS Eng. 1952. Sen. Examr. Surg. Univ. Lond. Prev: Sen. Cons. Surg. St. Bart. Hosp. Lond.

BIRRELL, Alison Lennox Nethergate Medical Centre, 2 Tay Square, Dundee DD1 1PB Tel: 01382 21527 Fax: 01382 26772; Ashwood, 81 Dundee Road, West Ferry, Dundee DD5 1LZ Tel: 01382 739583 — MB ChB 1967 St. And. (St. And.) Prev: SHO (Anaesth.) Dundee Roy. Infirm.

BIRRELL, Ann Christine 3 Moor Park, Ruskington, Sleaford NG34 9AJ — MB ChB 1963 St. And. Prev: Ho. Surg. Dunfermline & W. Fife Hosp.; Ho. Phys. Cameron Bridge Hosp. Fife; Civil. Med. Pract. Brit. Milit. Hosp. Hong Kong.

BIRRELL, David Hamilton Nethergate Medical Centre, 2 Tay Square, Dundee DD1 1PB Tel: 01382 21527 Fax: 01382 26772; Ashwood, 81 Dundee Road, West Ferry, Dundee DD5 1LZ Tel: 01382 739583 — MB ChB 1967 St. And.; BSc St. And. 1964, MB ChB 1967. (St. And.) Prev: SHO (A & E) Dundee Roy. Infirm.; Demonst. (Anat.) Univ. Dundee; Regist. Rotat. (Surg.) E.. RHB (Scotl.).

BIRRELL, Fraser Nicolson ARC Epidemology Unit, Stopford Building, Oxford Road, University of Manchester, Manchester M13 9PT Tel: 0161 275 5038 Fax: 0161 275 5043 Email: fraser.birrell@man.ac.uk — MB BChir 1992 Camb.; MA Camb. 1993, BA 1989; MRCP (UK) 1994. Clin. Res. Fell. ARC Epidemiol. Unit Manch.; Hon. Specialist Regist. Manch. Roy. Infirm. Socs: Brit. Soc. Rheum.; BMA. Prev: Regist. Rotat. (Rheum.) Cannock, OsW.ry & Stoke.

BIRRELL, Keith Graham 2 Auton Court, Bearpark, Durham DH7 7AW Tel: 0191 384 5755 Email: v.l.birrell@ncl.ac.uk; Herrington Medical Centre, Philadelphia Lane, Houghton-le-Spring DH4 4LE Tel: 0191 584 2632 Fax: 0191 584 3786 — BM BS 1989 Nottm.; BMedSci Nottm. 1987, BM BS 1989; MRCGP 1993; DRCOG 1994; DFFP 1994; DTM & H 1997. (Nottm.) GP Princip. Prev: VSO - Advisor to Dist. Med. Off. Zanzibar Tanzania; Trainee GP N.d. VTS.

BIRRELL, Lisa Norma GKN plc, PO Box 55, Redditch B98 0TL Tel: 01527 517715 Fax: 01527 517700; 9 Barwell Close, Dorridge, Solihull B93 8TH Tel: 01564 778316 Fax: 01564 771633 Email: lnbirrell@aol.com — BM BS 1987 Nottm.; BMedSci Nottm. 1985; MRCGP 1992; DCCH RCGP 1993; AFOM RCP 1998. Occupat. Phys. Worcs. Prev: Clin. Lect. (Occupat. Med.) Inst. Occupat. Health Univ. Birm.

BIRRELL, Virginia Louise 2 Auton Court, Bearpark, Durham DH7 7AW Email: v.l.birell@ncl.ac.uk — MB BS 1990 Newc.; MRCPCH 1999; MRCP (UK) 1993. (Newc.) p/t Specialist Regist. in Paediat. N.ern Regional HA. Prev: VSO - Advisor to Dist. Med. Off. Zanzibar, Tanzania.

BIRRELL, William Litster 148 Forest Road, Walthamstow, London E17 6JQ — MB ChB 1951 Glas. (Glas.) Dep. Div. Surg. 'J' Div. Metrop. Police. Prev: Ho. Surg. Vict. Infirm. Glas.; Squadron Ldr. RAF Med. Br.

BIRRING, Ranjit Kaur 28 Tachbrook Road, Southall UB2 5JA — MB ChB 1996 Manch. SHO Anaesth.QMC & Notts. City.Hosp. Prev: Ho. Off. (Med.) Withington Hosp. Manch.; Ho. Off. (Surg.) Hope Hosp. Salford; SHO (Med.) Bedford Gen. Hosp.

BIRRING, Surinderpal Singh Department of Respiratory Medicine, Kettering General Hospital, Rothwell Road, Kettering NN16 8UZ — MB ChB 1995 Manch. Specialist Regist., Respirat. Med., Kettering Gen. Hosp..

BIRSCHEL, Philip Room 10, Cripps Centre, Northampton General Hospital, Northampton NN1 5BD Tel: 01604 34700; 6 Kinniside Avenue, Mirehouse, Whitehaven CA28 9SY Tel: 01946 62127 — MB ChB 1993 Sheff. SHO (Paediat.) N.ampton Gen. Hosp. Prev: SHO (A & E) Roy. Hallamsh. Hosp. Sheff.; SHO (Med.) Nether Edge Hosp. Sheff.

BIRT, Alison Jayne Little Marsh, Little Marsh Lane, Field Dalling, Holt NR25 7LL — MB BS 1984 Lond. (St. Geo.)

BIRT, Carlton Henry The Thatched Cottage, North Weirs, Brockenhurst SO42 7QA — MRCS Eng. LRCP Lond. 1928; DPH Birm. 1937. (Birm.) Surg. Capt. RN (Ret.).

BIRT, Christopher Alan Birmingham University Health Services Management Centre, Park House, 40 Edgbaston Park Road, Birmingham B15 2RT Tel: 0121 414 7050 Fax: 0121 414 7051 Email: c.a.birt@bham.ac.uk; spa Cottage, The Square, Strathpeffer IV14 9DE Tel: 01997 420013 Fax: 01997 420013 — MB BChir Camb. 1966; MSc Manch. 1977; MA Camb. 1967; FRCP Ed. 1986, M 1973; FFPHM 1982, M 1977; T (PHM) 1991; DObst RCOG 1969. (Camb. & St. Thos.) Cons. Pub. Health Med. Wolverhampton Health Exec. & Sen. Lect. (Pub. Health) Birm. Univ. Health Servs. Managem. Centre; Hon. Clin. Sen. Lect. (Pub. Health) Glas. Univ. Med. Sch.; Sen. Lect. (Pub. Health) HSMC Univ. Birm.; Dir. Univ. Birm. Collaboration Pub. Health Europe; Hon. Cons. (Pub. Health Med.) DoH Exec. W. Midl.; Hon. Cons. (Pub. Health Med.) Wolverhampton HA; Mem. Edit. Bd. Cardiovasc. Risk Factors. Socs: Fell. Manch. Med. Soc.; Soc. Social Med.; Vice-Pres. Europ. Pub. Health Alliance. Prev: Cons. Pub. Health Med. Highland HB; Chief Admin. Med. Off. W.. Isles HB; Area Med. Off. Stockport AHA.

BIRT, Raymond Colin The Old World's End, Church End, Paglesham, Rochford SS4 2DN — MB BS 1960 Lond.; FFA RCS Eng. 1964. (St. Bart.)

BIRT, Mr St John Michael Clive, OBE (retired) Pilot House, Gorey, Grouville JE3 6DU Tel: 01534 851137 — MB BS 1939 Lond.; FRCS Eng. 1947; MRCS Eng. LRCP Lond. 1939. Prev: Surg. Regist. & Tutor St. Thos. Hosp.

BIRTCHNELL, John Anthony Institute of Psychiatry, De Crespigny Park, London SE5 8AF Fax: 0207 703 5796; 16 Ardbeg Road, London SE24 9JL Tel: 0207 274 8484 Email: john.bir@virginnet.co.uk — MB ChB 1959 Ed.; MD Ed. 1966; FRCPsych 1981 M 1971; Dip. Psychother. Aberd. 1967; DPM Eng. 1963; FBPsS 1996. (Ed.) Hon. Sen. Lect. Inst. Psychiat. Lond.; Hon. Cons. Psychiat. Maudsley Hosp. Lond. Socs: Soc. Psychother. Research; Assn. Family Ther.; Hon. Mem. BAAT. Prev: Mem. Scientif. Staff MRC Social Psychiat. Unit; MRC Clin. Research Fell. (Ment. Health) Univ. Aberd.; Sen. Regist. St. John's Hosp. Stone.

BIRTCHNELL, Sandra Anne Chichester Priority Care, Grayling Well Hospital, Chichester PO19 4FX Tel: 01243 787970 Fax: 01243 815141 — MB BS 1971 Lond.; MSc Clin. Psychother. Lond. 1985, MB BS 1971; MRCPsych 1982. Cons. Psychiat. Chichester Priority Care. Prev: Cons. Psychiat. Greenwich Dist. Hosp.; Sen. Regist. St. Geo. Hosp. Lond.; Regist. Graylingwell Hosp. Chichester.

BIRTHISTLE, Karl Anthony Joseph 917B Garratt Lane, Tooting, London SW17 0LT — MB BCh BAO 1988 NUI; MSc NUI 1992; LRCPSI 1988; MRCPI 1991; Dip. GU Med. Soc. Apoth. Lond. 1994; DRCPath 1994. Sen. Regist. (Virol.) St. Geo. Hosp. Lond.

BIRTLE, Alison Jane Top Flat, 114 St Dunstan's Road, London W6 8RA Email: abil@skveg.demon.co.uk — MB BS 1992 Lond.; FRCR (Clinical Oncol), 1999; MRCP (UK) 1996; BSc Lond. 1987. (Char. Cross & Westm.) Regist. (Clin. Oncol.) Mt. Vernon Hosp., N.wood, Middlx. Socs: RSM. Prev: Regist. (Clin. Oncol.) Middlx. Hosp. Lond.; Regist. (Clin. Oncol.) Roy. Free Hosp., Lond.

BIRTLE, Janice South Birmingham Mental Health Trust, Main House, 201 Hollywood Way, Birmingham B31 5HE Tel: 0121 678 3636 Fax: 0121 678 3635 — MB ChB 1979 Birm.; MSc (Psychother.) 1989; MRCPsych 1983. Cons. Psychother.; Dir. Therap. Comm. Serv.; Sen. Clin. Lect. Birm. Univ. Socs: UK Counc. Psychother.; W Midl. Instit. Psychotherap.; Assn. Psychoanal. & Psychotherap. Prev: Lect. (Psychiat.) & Hon. Sen. Regist. (Psychother.) Uffculme Clinic Birm.

BIRTLES, Peter Charles Tel: 08192 652266 Fax: 01892 668607; 28 Newton Willows, Groombridge, Tunbridge Wells TN3 9RF — MB BS 1980 Lond.; BSc Lond. 1976; MRCGP 1985; DRCOG 1984. (Guy's)

BIRTLES, Thomas David, MBE 23 Levens Close, Poulton-le-Flyde, Blackpool Tel: 01253 899835 — MB ChB 1959 Liverp.; DAvMed Eng. 1975. (Liverp.) Med. Off. DHSS. Socs: Fac. Occupat. Med. RCP Lond. Prev: Wing. Cdr. RAF Med. Br.

BIRTLEY, Eleanor Jane Far Horizon, West Ashling Road, Hambrook, Chichester PO18 8UF — BM 1993 Soton.

BIRTS, Robin John Mann Cottage, Moreton-in-Marsh GL56 0LA; The Dower House, Todenham, Moreton-in-Marsh GL56 9PE — MB BS 1967 Lond.; MRCS Eng. LRCP Lond. 1966; DObst RCOG 1970. (Guy's) Clin. Asst. Moreton Dist. Hosp. Socs: BMA. Prev: SHO (O & G & Paediat.) St. Luke's Hosp. Guildford.

BIRTWELL, Anthony John Department of Medicine for the Elderly, Derby City General Hospital, Uttoxeter Road, Derby DE22 3NE; 7 Canal Bank, Shardlow, Derby DE72 2GL — MB BS 1975 Lond.; BSc Lond. 1972; FRCP Lond. 1995; MRCP (UK) 1979. (Middlx. Hosp. Med. Sch.) Cons. Phys. Med. Elderly Derby City Hosp. Prev: Sen. Regist. NW RHA; Lect. (Med.) Leeds Gen. Infirm.

BIRTWHISTLE, Mary Bernadette 16 Canterbury Avenue, Fulwood, Sheffield S10 3RT Tel: 0114 230 8374 — MB ChB 1982 Ed. Clin. Research Asst. Dept. of Clin.Oncol.W.on Pk. Hosp. Sheff..

BIRTWHISTLE, Timothy John Charles Central Surgery, King Street, Barton-upon-Humber DN18 5ER Tel: 01652 635435 Fax: 01652 636122; Westacre, 23 Westfield Road, Barton-upon-Humber DN18 5AA Tel: 01652 633051 Email: timbir@bmshomes.com — MB ChB 1974 Liverp.; MBA Durh. 1997; MRCGP 1986; DObst RCOG 1976. (Liverp.) Prev: Ho. Off. BRd. Green Hosp.; Ho. Off. (Obst.) Mill Rd. Matern. Hosp. Liverp.

BIRTWISTLE, Ian Harry (Surgery), 152/154 Derbyshire Lane, Stretford, Manchester M32 8DU Fax: 0161 0865 4990; 225 Barton Road, Stretford, Manchester M32 9RB Tel: 0161 865 2880 Fax: 0161 865 4990 — MB ChB 1963 Manch.; AFOM 1982; MRCGP 1974; DIH Soc. Apoth. Lond. 1970; DObst RCOG 1965. (Manch.) Socs: Soc. Occupat. Health. Prev: Hosp. Occupat. Health Pract. Trafford Gp. Hosps.; Clin. Asst. (Occupat. Health) Pk. Hosp. Davyhulme; Ho. Surg. Manch. Roy. Infirm.

BIRTWISTLE, Margaret Law Molebridge Practice, 3 Cannon Side, Fetcham, Leatherhead KT22 9LE Tel: 01372 379941 Fax: 01372 361178 — MB BS 1960 Lond.; MRCS Eng. LRCP Lond. 1960; DA Eng. 1963. (Roy. Free) Prev: Cas. Off. & Jun. Anaesth., & Sen. Res. Anaesth. Roy. Free Hosp.; Ho. Surg. Luton & Dunstable Hosp.

BIRTWISTLE, Susan Mary Oakley Surgery, Sainfoin Lane, Oakley, Basingstoke RG23 7HZ Tel: 01256 780338 — MB BS Lond. 1969; MRCS Eng. LRCP Lond. 1968. (Roy. Free) Prev: SHO (Obst.) St. Thos. Hosp. Lond.; Ho. Phys. Wycombe Gen. Hosp. High Wycombe; Ho. Surg. Roy. Free Hosp. Lond.

BIRTWISTLE, Sybil (retired) 66 Station Road, Fulbourn, Cambridge CB1 5ES Tel: 01223 880777 — MB ChB Liverp. 1957; MRCS Eng. LRCP Lond. 1957; DCH Eng. 1961; DObst RCOG 1960. Indep. Specialist. (Allergy & Environm. Med.) Camb. Prev: SHO Alder Hey Childr. Hosp.

BIRZGALIS, Mr Andrew Raimond Department of ENT, Wythenshawe Hospital, Southmoor Road, Wythenshawe, Manchester M23 9LT — MB ChB 1982 Manch.; BSc (Hons.) Manch. 1979; FRCS (Otol.) Eng. 1989; FRCS Eng. 1988; FRCS Ed. 1987. Cons. Otolaryngol. Manch. Roy. Infirm. & Christie Hosp. Manch. Prev: Sen. Regist. N. W.. RHA.

BISARYA, Anand Kumar Sandy Lane Health Centre, Sandy Lane, Skelmersdale WN8 8LA Tel: 01695_ 727772 Fax: 01695 727771 — MB BS 1962 Vikram; MS (Surg.) Vikram Univ. Ujjain 1981; DObst RCOG 1973. (Gajra Raja Med. Coll. Gwalior) JP. Prev: Regist. (Accid. & Orthop.) Greenock Roy. Infirm.; SHO (Surg.) Roy. Hosp. Sick Childr. Glas.; SHO (Gyn. Surg.) Roy. Infirm. Glas.

BISARYA, Asha Sandy Lane Health Centre, Sandy Lane, Skelmersdale WN8 8LA Tel: 01695_ 727772 Fax: 01695 727771 — MB BS 1971 Vikram; DRCOG 1977. (Gandhi Med. Coll. Bhopal) Prev: SHO (Gyn.) Vict. Hosp. Kirkcaldy.

BISATT, John Frazer 40 North Park Road, Bramhall, Stockport SK7 3JS — MB BS 1993 Lond.

BISCHOFF, Ronald Edmond Howell 46 Wimpole Street, London W1M 1DG Tel: 020 7224 4174 Fax: 020 7224 4171; 4/69 Earls Court Square, London SW5 9DG Tel: 020 7370 5218 Fax: 020 7373 3046 Email: docbillybischoff@msn.com — MB ChB 1976 Cape Town; DA (UK) 1982. Indep. GP Lond.; Med. Dir. (Health Screening) BMI Health Servs.

BISCOE, Charles Alan (retired) The Doctor's House, Stithians, Truro TR3 7AY Tel: 44129 861035 Email: biscoe@stithinas.fsbusiness.co.uk — MB BS Lond. 1949; MRCS Eng. LRCP Lond. 1949.

BISCOE, Timothy John Provost's Office, University College, Gower St., London WC1E 6BT Tel: 020 7380 7022 Fax: 020 7813 2812; 21A Highpoint, North Hill, London N6 4BA — MB BS 1957 Lond.; BSc Lond. 1953, DSc 1992; FRCP Lond. 1983. (Lond. Hosp.) Pro-Provost Univ. Coll. Lond. Socs: Physiol. Soc.; Pharmacol. Soc. Prev: Jodrell Prof. Physiol. Univ. Coll. Lond.; Ho. Surg. Thoracic Unit & Ho. Phys. Lond. Hosp.

BISHAI, Ingi Anwar Helmi Department Anaesthetics, Eastbourne General Hospital, Kings Drive, Eastbourne BN21 2UD Tel: 01323 417400; The Old Mill House, 85 Willingdon Road, Eastbourne BN21 1TZ Tel: 01323 735814 — MB BCh 1980 Cairo; MD Cairo 1986; DA (UK) 1990. Staff Grade (Anaesth.) E.bourne Gen. Hosp. Prev: Staff Grade (Anaesth.) Leicester Roy. Infirm.; SHO (Anaesth.) Walsgrave Hosp. Coventry; Lect. (Anaesth.) Cairo Univ. Hosp., Egypt.

BISHAI, Kamal Ragheb Tewfik Chigwell Medical Centre, 300 Fencepiece Road, Hainault, Ilford IG6 2TA Tel: 020 8500 0066 Fax: 020 8559 8670; 12 Felstead Road, London E11 2QJ — MB BCh 1977 Ain Shams; Cert of Adv Studies in Health Managem, Imperial Coll. 1999; FCOphth 1989; MRCGP 1989; FRCS Ed. 1984. Clin. Asst. (Ophth.) Roy. Lond. Hosp.; Epping Forest PCG Bd. Mem.

BISHAI, Wadie (retired) Ash House, 33 Park Lane, Knebworth SG3 6PH Tel: 01438 235329 — MB BCh Cairo 1947; LMSSA Lond. 1965; DGO Dub. 1952. Prev: Princip. GP Herts FHSA.

BISHARA, Samir A Gilfach Road Medical Centre, 10 Gilfach Road, Tonyrefail, Porth CF39 8HE Tel: 01443 671068 Fax: 01443 674396.

BISHAY, Mr Ehab Shafik Seif 25 Regent Road, Birmingham B17 9JU Tel: 0121 426 4140 Email: chab.bishay@btinternet.com — MB BS 1992 Lond.; FRCS 1996 Eng. (St Bartholomew's Medical College) Specialist Regist. Cardiolthoracic Surg., W. Midl.s Rotat. Prev: Research Fell., The Cleveland Clinic Foundat., USA, 1998-2000; Sen. Ho. Off., St. Thomas' Hosp., Lond., 1996-1997 (Cardiothoracic Surg.); Jun. Regist., St Bart. Hosp., Lond., 1995-1996, (Cardiothoracic Surg.).

BISHAY, Mr Michel Sobhy Khalil Royal United Hospital, Combe Park, Bath BA1 3NG Tel: 01225 428331; Drumway, Marksbury, Bath BA2 9HS — MB ChB 1982 Cairo; FRCS (Orth.) 1995; FRCS Glas. 1988. Cons. Orthop. Roy. United Hosp. Bath. Socs: BMA & Brit. Trauma Soc.; Fell. BOA. Prev: Sen. Regist. & Research Regist. (Orthop.) Roy. United Hosp. Bath; Regist. (Orthop. Surg.) Morriston Hosp. Swansea.

BISHAY, Shafik Seif 84 Station Avenue, West Ewell, Epsom KT19 9UG — MRCS Eng. LRCP Lond. 1979.

BISHIERI, Samy Youssef Garas Royal Cornwall Hospitals, Treliske Hospital, Truro TR1 3LJ — MB BCh 1979 Ain Shams; MRCOG 1994; MSc Cairo 1985. (Ain Shams, Egypt) Staff Gyn. & Obst. RCH (Treliske) Truro, Cornw. Socs: BSCCP.

BISHOP, Alastair 39 Ripon Drive, Glasgow G12 0DU — MB ChB 1994 Glas.

BISHOP, Andrew John North Hampshire Hospital, Basingstoke RG24 9NA Tel: 01256 313633; 150 Plover Way, London SE16 7TZ Tel: 0207 231 2891 — MB BChir 1988 Camb.; MA 1987 Cantab.; MD Camb. 1996; MRCP (UK) 1990. Cons. Cardiol., N. Hants. Hosp., Basingstoke. Prev: Research Fell. & Hon. Regist. Roy. Brompton Hosp. Lond.; Regist. (Cardiol.) Roy. Brompton Hosp. Lond.; Sen. Regist. (Cardiol.) St. Thos. Hosp. Lond.

BISHOP, Angela Phyllis The Surgery, Gladstone Road, Chesham HP5 3AD Tel: 01494 782884 Fax: 01494 786106; 30 Church Street, Chesham HP5 1HU Tel: 01494 786749 — MB BS 1976 Lond.; MRCS Eng. LRCP Lond. 1976. (Roy. Free)

BISHOP, Cecil (retired) The Glen, Playford Road, Little Bealings, Woodbridge IP13 6ND — MB BS 1953 Lond.; MRCS Eng. LRCP Lond. 1953; FFA RCS Eng. 1960; DA Eng. 1955. p/t Cons. Anaesth. Ipswich Health Dist. Prev: Sen. Regist. Dept. Anaesth., Ho. Phys. & Ho. Surg. Guy's Hosp. Lond.

BISHOP, Mr Christopher Charles Rigby University College London Hospitals, Mortimer St., London W1G 6DE Tel: 020 7380 9409 Fax: 020 7380 9312; 149 Harley Street, London W1N 2DE Tel: 020 7235 6086 Fax: 020 7730 2840 — MB BChir 1978 Camb.; MA Camb. 1978, BA 1974, MChir 1987, MB 1978, BChir 1977; FRCS (Eng.) 1981. (Camb. & St. Thos.) Cons. Gen. Surg. Univ. Coll. Lond. Hosp.; Hunt. Prof. RCS. Prev: Lect. (Surg.) St. Thos. Hosp. Lond.; Regist. (Surg.) St. Thos. Hosp. Lond. & Soton. Gen. Hosp.

BISHOP, Clifford William The Hamilton Practice, Keats House, Bush Fair, Harlow CM18 6LY Tel: 01279 692700 Fax: 01279 692719; Newports, 84 High Wych Road, Sawbridgeworth CM21 0HQ Tel: 01279 722610 — MB BS 1972 Lond.; MRCS Eng. LRCP Lond. 1972. Exec. Chair, Harlow PCT.

BISHOP, Mr Colin 79 Harley Street, London W1G 8PZ Tel: 020 7486 1104 Fax: 020 7935 9850 — MB BS 1971 Lond.; FRCS 1979 Lond.; MRCS Eng. LRCP Lond. 1971. (Char. Cross) Cons. Plastic Surg. Lond. Socs: Fell. Med. Soc. Lond.; Fell. Roy. Soc. Med.; BMA. Prev: Regist. (Plastic Surg.) Hammersmith Hosp. Lond.; Regist. (Gen. Surg.) St. Margt.s Hosp. Epping; Resid. Med. Off. Lond. Clinic.

BISHOP, David Anthony Occupational Health Department, Room 5/135, Ford Motor Company, Dagenham RM9 6SA Tel: 020 8526 5233; 7 Oaklea Avenue, Chelmsford CM2 6BY Tel: 01245 352681 — MB BS Lond. 1967; MRCS Eng. LRCP Lond. 1967; FFOM RCP Lond. 1994, MFOM 1985, AFOM 1982; GAM Cert. Inst. Aviat. Med. Farnborough; DIH Eng. 1982; DA Eng. 1974; DTM & H Liverp. 1973; DObst RCOG 1969. (King's Coll. Hosp.) Sen. Med. Off. Ford Motor Company Dagenham. Socs: Assn. Aviat. Med. Examr.; Soc. Occupat. Med. & Chelmsford Med. Soc. Prev: Ho. Surg. Dulwich Hosp.; Resid. Med. Off. P.ss Margt. Hosp. Childr. Perth, Austral.; Med. Off. i/c Serowe Hosp., Botswana.

BISHOP, David George Martin (retired) 42 The Green, Hurworth-on-Tees, Darlington DL2 2AA Tel: 01325 720895 — MRCS Eng. LRCP Lond. 1968; FFA RCS Eng. 1972. Cons. Anaesth. Darlington & N.allerton Hosp. Gp.

BISHOP, David Gordon 20 Bratch Lane, Wombourne, Wolverhampton WV5 9AD — MB ChB 1991 Leic.; DCH RCPS Glas. 1997. SHO (Community Child Health) 1st Community Health NHS Trust Stafford; Clin. Asst. (child & Adolesc. Psychiat.); Staff Grade in Community Paediat.; Trainee Family Therapist. Socs: MSS & Med. Protec. Soc.

BISHOP, David Selwyn Church Street Surgery, 15 Church Street, Calne SN11 0HY Tel: 01249 821831 Fax: 01249 816020; The Paddock, Cherhill, Calne SN11 8XX Tel: 01249 812986 — MB BChir 1973 Camb.; MA Camb. 1972; MRCP (UK) 1974; DRCOG 1979. Prev: Sen. Regist. (Med.) Ahmadu Bello Univ. Teach Hosp. Zaria, Nigeria; Regional Med. Off. N.. Region of Malawi; Ho. Phys. St. Thos. Hosp. Lond.

BISHOP, Diana 12 Willis Close, Great Bedwyn, Marlborough SN8 3NP — MB BS 1963 Lond.; MRCS Eng. LRCP Lond. 1963. (Roy. Free)

BISHOP, Eirean Sarah c/o 21 Loughrigg Park, Ambleside LA22 0DY — MB ChB 1991 Glas.; DGM RCPS Glas. 1994; MRCGP 1997; DFFP 1997. (Glas.)

BISHOP, Eveline Annie Little Byletts House, Pembridge, Leominster HR6 9HY Tel: 01544 388587 — MB BS 1937 Lond.; MRCS Eng. LRCP Lond. 1936; DCH Eng. 1944. (Univ. Coll. Hosp.) Prev: Caroline Harrold Research Schol. Childr. Hosp. Birm.; Cas. Surg. W. Bromwich Dist. Hosp.; Ho. Surg. King Edwd. VII Hosp. Windsor.

BISHOP, Fiona Royal Victoria Infirmary, Victoria Road, Newcastle upon Tyne NE1 4LP Tel: 0191 232 5131; 19 Clifford Road, Boston Spa, Wetherby LS23 6BQ — MB ChB 1993 Manch.; MA Oxf. 1995. SHO (Ophth.) Roy. Vict. Infirm. Newc. Prev: SHO (Ophth.) Newc. Gen. Hosp. & N. Riding Infirm. Middlesbrough.

BISHOP, Fiona Mary Market Harborough Medical Centre, 67 Coventry Road, Market Harborough LE16 9BX Tel: 01858 464242 Fax: 01858 462929; Spring Barn, Main St, Tur Langton, Leicester LE8 0PJ — MB ChB 1987 Leic.; MRCGP 1992; DRCOG 1991. (Leicester) GP Princip. Socs: BMA; RCG.

BISHOP, Helen Pembroke House Surgery, 1 Fortescue Road, Preston, Paignton TQ3 2DA Tel: 01803 553558 Fax: 01803 663180; 3 Dartside, Totnes TQ9 5HL Tel: 01803 867768 — BM BS 1992 Nottm.; MRCGP 1996; DCH RCP Lond. 1996; BMedSci (Hons) Nottm. 1990; DFFP 1998. (Nottingham) G.P Princip.

BISHOP, Helen Elizabeth 116 Hangingwater Road, Sheffield S11 7ES — MB ChB 1992 Sheff.

BISHOP, Mr Hugh Macnair Royal Bolton Hospital, Minerva Road, Farnworth, Bolton BL4 0JR Tel: 01204 390326 Fax: 01204 390326; Hurst Bank, 497 Corley New Road, Bolton BL1 5DQ Tel: 01204 494525 Fax: 01204 494785 — MB BS 1970 Lond.; DM Nottm. 1983; FRCS Eng. 1976; FRCS Ed. 1976; MRCS Eng. LRCP Lond. 1970. (Middlx.) Cons. Surg. The Roy. Bolton Hosp, Bolton. Socs: Brit. Assn. Surg. Oncol.; Chair Brit. Assn. Surg. Oncol. BrE. Audit Gp. Prev: Sen. Regist. (Surg.) Oxf. RHA; Tenovus Surgic. Research Fell. Univ. Nottm.; Regist. (Surg.) Derby Roy. Infirm.

BISHOP, Hugh Samuel 174 Crown Street, Aberdeen AB11 6JD — MB ChB 1996 Aberd.

BISHOP, Ian Stuart Doctors Mess, Royal Cornwall Hospital (Treliske), Truro TR1 3LJ — MB ChB 1989 Birm. SHO (Gen. Med.) Treliske Hosp. Truro.

BISHOP, Jacqueline Fiona 18 Palfrey Close, St Albans AL3 5RE — MB BS 1994 Lond.

BISHOP, Jennifer Mary 142 Totley Brook Road, Dore, Sheffield S17 3QU — MB ChB 1971 Birm.

BISHOP, Jill Mercia North wales Cancer Treatment Centre Project Office, Glan Clwyd Hospital, Rhuddlan Road, Bodelwyddan, Denbigh LL16 5UJ — MB ChB 1990 Sheff.; MRCP (UK) 1994; FRCR, 1997. Cons. Clin. Oncol., N. Wales Cancer Treatm. Centre. Prev: Regist. (Clin. Oncol.) Cookridge Hosp. Leeds.

BISHOP, Joan Margaret Ticehurst House Hospital, Ticehurst, Wadhurst TN5 7HU Tel: 01580 200391; The Barn, Knights in the Hole, Jarvis Lane, Goudhurst, Cranbrook TN17 1L Tel: 01580 211081 — MB BS Lond. 1952; MRCS Eng. LRCP Lond. 1952. (Roy. Free) Sen. Med. Off. (Psychiat.) Ticehurst Hse. Hosp. Ticehurst E. Sussex. Socs: Affil. Mem. Roy. Coll. Psychiats. Prev: Clin. Asst. (Psychiat.) Kent & Sussex Hosp. Tunbridge Wells.

BISHOP, John Michael 78 Bridge End, Warwick CV34 6PD Tel: 01926 495957 — MRCS Eng. LRCP Lond. 1948; DSc Birm. 1966, MD (Hnrs.) 1956, MB ChB 1948; FRCP Lond. 1965, M 1953. (Birm.) Socs: Assn. Phys. & Brit. Thoracic Soc. Prev: Prof. Med. Univ. Birm.; Phys. United Birm. Hosps. & Birm. RHB; Rockefeller Trav. Fell. (Med.) 1956-57.

BISHOP, John Paul Ladylaw, Rosalee Brae, Hawick TD9 7HH — MB ChB 1997 Ed.

BISHOP, Leslie Anne 128 Minster Court, Liverpool L7 3QE — MB BS 1984 West Indies.

BISHOP, Lucy Jane 6 Walnut Grove, Radcliffe on Trent, Nottingham NG12 2AD Tel: 0115 933 3147 — MB ChB 1995 Birm.; ChB Birm. 1995; MRCP (UK) June 1998. SHO Rotat. (Med.) St. Richards Hosp. Chichester. Socs: BMA; MPS. Prev: SHO (A & E) Chase Farm Hosp.; Ho. Off. (Med.) Walsall Manor Hosp.; Ho. Off. (Surg.) Warwick Gen. Hosp.

BISHOP, Lyndsey Dorothy 35a Union Street, Lossiemouth IV31 6BG — MB ChB 1998 Ed.; MB ChB Ed 1998. (Edinburgh)

BISHOP, Malcolm Clive Thorpe Road Surgery, 64 Thorpe Road, Peterborough PE3 6AP Tel: 01733 310070 Fax: 01733 554834; 9 Fallowfield, Orton Wistow, Peterborough PE2 6UR Tel: 01733 234449 Fax: 01733 892356 Email: malc@bisho.demon.co.uk — MB BS 1979 Lond.; D.Occ.Med. RCP Lond. 1995. (Kings Coll. Hosp.) Prev: Trainee GP St. Cross Hosp. Rugby VTS; SHO Rotat. (Trauma) Addenbrooke's Hosp. Camb.; Ho. Phys. Liver Unit King's Coll. Hosp. Lond.

BISHOP, Margaret The Surgery, Turnberry, Greens Lane, Golding Lane Mannings Heath, Horsham RH13 6JW Tel: 01403 252276 Fax: 01403 252276 — MB BS Durh. 1959. (Durh.)

BISHOP, Michael Arthur Northcroft Surgery, Northcroft Lane, Newbury RG14 1BU Tel: 01635 31575 Fax: 01635 551857 — MB BS 1967 Lond.; MRCGP 1974; DObst RCOG 1969. Prev: Ho. Surg. & Ho. Phys. St. Mary's Hosp. Lond. (Harrow Rd. Br.); Obst. Ho. Off. Camb. Matern. Hosp.

BISHOP, Mr Michael Charles 6 Walnut Grove, Radcliffe-on-Trent, Nottingham NG12 2AD Tel: 0160 733147 — MRCS Eng. LRCP Lond. 1967; MD Lond. 1976, MB BS 1967; FRCS Eng. 1975; MRCP (U.K.) 1970. (Univ. Coll. Hosp.)

BISHOP, Mildred Patterson (retired) 6 Tregarth Road, Chichester PO19 4QU Tel: 01243 527612 — LRCP LRCS 1936 Ed.; LRCP LRCS Ed. LRCPS Glas. 1936. Prev: Lect. Physiol Wom. Christian Med. Coll. Ludhiana, Punjab.

BISHOP, Nichola Jane 41 Hathaway Road, Sutton Coldfield B75 5HY — MB BS 1998 Newc.; MB BS Newc 1998.

BISHOP, Nicholas Shaftesbury Medical Centre, 480 Harehills Lane, Leeds LS9 6DE Tel: 0113 248 5631 Fax: 0113 235 0658; 22 Gledhow Wood Grove, Leeds LS8 1NZ — MD 1989 Camb.; MA Camb. 1980, MD 1989, MB 1979, BChir 1978; MRCP (UK) 1980. GP Leeds.

BISHOP, Nicholas Lloyd United Bristol Healthcare NHS Trust, Headquarters, Marlborough St., Bristol BS1 3NU Email: nicholas.bishop@ubht.swest.nhs.uk — MB BS 1973 Lond.; MRCS Eng. LRCP Lond. 1973; FRCR 1977; DMRD Eng. 1976. (Guy's) Med. Dir. U.B.H.T.; Cons. Clin. Radiol. U.B.H.T. Socs: (Bd. Mem.) Brit. Assn. Med. Managers; Brit. Soc. Interven. Radiol. Prev: Cons. Diagn. Radiol. Roy. Sussex Co. Hosp. Brighton; Sen. Regist. (Diagn. Radiol.) Addenbrooke's Hosp. Camb.; Regist. (Diagn. Radiol.) Guys Hosp. Lond.

BISHOP, Patricia Rosemary (retired) Lyndhurst, 11 Mount Road, Upton, Wirral CH49 6JA Tel: 0151 678 9199 — MB ChB Liverp. 1962; DObst RCOG 1964.

BISHOP, Paul Manley Culcheth Surgery, Thompson Avenue, Culcheth, Warrington WA3 4EB Tel: 01925 765101 Fax: 01925 765102; The Cottage, 78 Burford Lane, Lymm WA13 0SJ — MRCS Eng. LRCP Lond. 1966; DPM Eng. 1971. (King's Coll. Lond. & Liverp.) Prev: Chairm. & Hon. Med. Advisor Mainstream Drug Counselling Serv. Warrington; Vis. Psychiat. Risley Remand Centre; Clin. Asst. (Psychiat.) Halton Gen. Hosp. & NewCh. Hosp. Culcheth.

BISHOP, Mr Paul Nicholas The University of Manchester, Department of Ophthalmology, Manchester Royal Eye Hospital, Manchester M13 9WH — BM BS 1983 Nottm.; PhD Manch. 1993; FRCS Eng. 1989; FCOphth 1989; DO RCS Eng. 1988. Hon. Cons. (Ophth.) Manch. Roy. Eye Hosp.

BISHOP, Paul William Department of Histopathology, Wythenshawe Hospital, Southmoor Road, Manchester M23 9LT Tel: 0161 291 2159 Fax: 0161 291 2125; Tel: 0161 432 3035 Email: 100046.1102@compuserve.com — MB BCh 1981 Oxf.; BA Camb. 1978; MRCPath 1988; FRCPath. Cons. Histopath. S. Manch. HA. Prev: Lect. (Histopath.) Univ. Manch.; Sen. Regist. & Regist. (Histopath.) N. W.. RHA.

BISHOP, Rachel Anne 7B College Place, London E17 3QA; Kunde Hospital, PO Box 224, Kathmandu, Nepal Email: kunde@vishnu.ccsi.com.np — MB ChB 1991 Leeds; MRCGP 1995; DRCOG 1995. (Leeds) Phys. The Sir Edmund Hillary Foundat., Kunde Hosp., Nepal.

BISHOP, Richard Ian Department of Pathology, Leeds General Infirmary, Great George St., Leeds LS1 3EX — MB ChB 1993 Manch.; MRCPath 2000; MA Oxon. (Oxford Preclinical, Manchester Clinical)

BISHOP, Robert Yarr (retired) Lyndhurst, 11 Mount Road, Upton, Wirral CH49 6JA — MB ChB 1959 St. And.; DObst RCOG 1960. Med. Adviser Tulip Internat. Prev: Med. Adviser Tulip Internat.

BISHOP, Rodney Philip The Mead, Blackford, Yeovil BA22 7EF — MRCS Eng. LRCP Lond. 1960.

BISHOP, Susan Elizabeth InterAct Health Management, Port of Liverpool Building, Pier Head, Liverpool L3 1BZ Tel: 0151 224 1400; 6 Knowsley Road, Cressington Park, Liverpool L19 0PE — MB ChB 1975 Liverp.; AFOM RCP Lond. 1981; DIH Eng. 1979 (Liverp.) p/t Dep. Chief Occupat.al Phys., InterAct Health Managem., Liverp.; Liverp. Anglican Cathedral (pt) Occupat.al Health Phys. Socs: Soc. Occupat. Med.; Accredit. specialist (Occupat.al Med.) 1998. Prev: Occupat. Health Phys. Bristol Myers-Squibb Moreton, Liverp.; Med. Off. Pilkington Bros. Ltd. St. Helens & Dista Products, Speke Liverp.; Ho. Off. (Med.& Surg.) & SHO (Med.) Whiston Hosp.

BISHOP, Timothy Michael 159 Andover Road, Newbury RG14 6NB — MB BS 1994 Lond.

BISHOP, Yvonne Moira The Surgery, The Old Vicarage, The Green, Pirbright, Woking GU24 0JE Tel: 01483 474473; 3 Saddlers Close, Merrow, Guildford GU4 7DA Tel: 01483 452917 — MB ChB 1973 Liverp.; DObst RCOG 1976. (Liverpool) GP.

BISHOP-CORNET, Hugh Robert Lee Leyland House Surgery, 18 Derby Street, Ormskirk L39 2BY Tel: 01695 579501 Fax: 01695 571724; Hurlston Gate Farm, Southport Road, Scarisbrick, Ormskirk L40 8HF Tel: 01704 840140 — MRCS Eng. LRCP Lond. 1976; BSc Liverp. 1970, MB ChB 1976; DRCOG 1979.

BISHOP-MILLER, Jane Stirling Royal Infirmary, Livilands Gate, Stirling FK8 2AU Tel: 01786 471225 Fax: 01786 446925 — MB ChB 1989 Ed.; BSc Ed. 1987; MRCP (UK) 1992. Cons. Phys. (c/o Elderly), Stirling Roy. Infirm. Socs: Brit. Geriat. Soc. Prev: Sen. Regist. (Geriat.) Lothian HB; Regist. Rotat. (Geriat.) Lothian HB.; SHO (Neurol.) W.. Gen. Hosp. Edin.

BISHTON, Ian Michael King's Mill Centre for Healthcare Services, Mansfield Road, Sutton-in-Ashfield NG17 4JL Tel: 01623 622515; 9 Chatsworth Close, Ravenshead, Nottingham NG15 9JA — MB ChB 1983 Leeds; FRCA. 1990; DA (UK) 1987. Cons. (Anaesth.) King's Mill Centre, Sutton in Ashfield. Socs: Fell. Roy. Coll. Anaesth.; Obst. Anaesth. Assn. Prev: Sen. Regist. (Anaesth.) Newc. Gen. Hosp. & Freeman Hosp. Newc.; Regist. (Anaesth.) Mansfield & Nottm. Hosps.; SHO (Gen. Med.) Roy. Halifax Infirm. & Leeds Infirm.

BISHTON, Roger Benjamin Bowes Health Centre, Pier Road, Tywyn LL36 0AT Tel: 01654 710238 Fax: 01654 712143 — BA Camb., MB 1959, BChir 1958; DObst RCOG 1960. (Middlx.) Prev: Resid. (Anaesth.) Middlx. Hosp. Lond.; Ho. Off. (Gen. Med., Gen. Surg. & Obst.) Middlx. Hosp. Lond.

BISHTON, Ronald Leslie (retired) Hideaway House, Tapps Close, Milborne Port, Sherborne DT9 5AT Tel: 01963 251202 — MB ChB 1943 Birm.; MD Birm. 1953; FRCPath 1965. Prev: Cons. Path. Bath Clin. Area.

BISKE, Evelyn Mary (retired) 5 Kingsmead, Chester CH2 1EF Tel: 01244 380056 — MRCS Eng. LRCP Lond. 1932.

BISLEY, Mr Geoffrey Gibson, OBE, KStJ Corner Cottage, Shelley, Ipswich IP7 5QX Tel: 01473 823407 — MRCS Eng. LRCP Lond. 1940; FRCS Eng. 1981; FRCOphth. 1988; DTM & H Liverp. 1951; DO Eng. 1955. (King's Coll. Hosp.) Socs: Ophth. Soc. UK. Prev: Warden & Chief Surg. St. John Ophth. Hosp. Jerusalem; Sen. Ophth. Cons. Kenyatta Nat. Hosp. Nairobi & Adviser (Ophth.) to Govt. Kenya; Hon. Lect. & Examr. Ophth. Med. Sch. Univ. Nairobi & Univ. Makerere, Uganda.

BISPHAM, Alessandra Chelsea & Westminster Hospital, 369 Fulham Road, London SW10 9NH Tel: 020 8746 8000; 31 Grafton Way, West Molesey KT8 2NW Tel: 020 8783 1753 — MB ChB 1975 Sheff.; MRCPsych 1980; Cert. Family Plann. JCC 1985. SCMO (O & G) Chelsea & W.m. Hosp. Socs: Inst. Psychosexual Med.; Lond. Soc. Family Plann. Doctors.; Brit. Soc. Psychosomatic Obst. & Gyn.

BISS, Gerald Claverton 454 Lea Bridge Road, Leyton, London E10 7DY Tel: 020 8539 3246 — MB ChB 1952 Ed. (Ed.) Prev: Ho. Phys. Roy. Infirm. Edin. & Roy. Hosp. Sick Childr. Edin.; Obst. Ho. Surg. Roy. United Hosp. Bath.

BISS, Kenneth 44 Abbey Road, Medstead, Alton GU34 5PB — MB BS 1951 Lond.; MRCS Eng. LRCP Lond. 1951; MRCGP 1963; DA Eng. 1954. (St. Geo.) Socs: Fell. Roy. Soc. Med.; Fac. Anaesth. RCS Eng.

BISS, Tina Tracey 23 Churchill Crescent, South Molton EX36 4EL Tel: 01769 573731 Fax: 01769 573731 — BM BS 1997 Nottm.

BISSELL, Anne Eccles 9 Baron's Court, Dedemere Risa, Marlow SL7 1XX — MB ChB 1977 Glas.; MRCP (UK) 1981; MRCGP 1985; FRCPS Glas. 1991; DCH RCPS Glas. 1979.

BISSELL, Iain James Radcliffe Infirmary, Woodstock Road, Oxford OX2 6HE Tel: 01865 224646 Fax: 01865 224978; 4 Stoke Place, Old Headington, Oxford OX3 9BX Tel: 01865 764105 — MB BS 1994 Lond.; BSc Lond. 1991. (St. Bart. Hosp.) SHO (Neurosurg.) Radcliffe Infirm., Oxf. Prev: Demonst. (Anat. & Phys.) Univ. Sheff.; SHO (Trauma) John Radcliffe Hosp., Oxf.; SHO (Orthop.) Nuffield Orthop. Centre, Oxf.

BISSENDEN, Jeffrey George Dept. of Paediatrics, City Hospital NHS Trust, Dudley Road, Birmingham B18 7Q — BM BCh 1969 Oxf.; FRCP Lond. 1986, M 1972. Cons. Paediat. City Hosp. NHS Trust Birm.; Hon. Sen. Lect. (Child Health) Univ. Birm. Socs: (Finance Comm.) Brit. Paediat. Assn. Prev: Lect. (Child Health) E. Birm. Hosp.; Assistenzarzt, Kinderklinik, Medizinische Hochschule Hannover, W. Germany.

BISSESSAR, Elizabeth Ann Northampton General Hospital, Cliftonville NN4 0NE Tel: 01604 545724 Fax: 01604 545095 — MB BCh BAO 1980 NUI; MRCPI 1983. Cons. Clin. Neurophysiol. N.ampton Gen. Hosp.

BISSET, Alice Margaret Central FP Clinic, 13 Golden Square, Aberdeen AB10 1RH Tel: 01224 642711; 26 Brown Street, Woodside, Aberdeen AB24 4EZ Tel: 01224 483499 — MB ChB 1971 Aberd.; DObst RCOG 1973. SCMO (Community Med.) Grampian HB. Socs: Nat. Assn. Family Plann. Doctors; Soc. Contracep. Prev: Clin. Med. Off. (Community Med.) Grampian HB; SHO (O & G) Cresswell Hosp. Dumfries.

BISSET, Amanda Jayne 10 Riverside Road, Shoreham-by-Sea BN43 5RB — BChir 1992 Camb.

BISSET, Ann Fiona Lothian Heath, 148 The Pleasance, Edinburgh EH8 9RS Tel: 0131 537 9167 — MB ChB 1981 Dundee; MA Ed. 1972; MFPHM RCP (UK) 1994. (Dundee) Cons. (Pub. Health Med.) Lothian HB. Prev: Cas. Off. Roy. Infirm. Aberd.; Ho. Phys. Ninewells Hosp. Dundee; Ho. Surg. Stracathro Hosp. Angus.

BISSET, Catherine Margaret 6 Muirhouse Cottages, Stow by Galashiels, Galashiels TD1 2QL — MB ChB 1976 Aberd.; MSc Ecology 1992. (Aberd.) Staff Grade, Acute Adult Community Psychiat. Dingleton Hosp., Melrose Borders. Prev: EC Species & Habitats Directive, Scott. Natural Heritage; Staff Grade (HIV Counselling) City Hosp. Edin.; Regist. (Psychiat.) Dingleton Hosp. Melrose.

BISSET, David Lamont Department of Histopathology, Royal Bolton Hospital, Minerva Road, Farnworth, Bolton BL4 0JR Tel: 01204 390534 Fax: 01204 390946 Email: david.bisset@boltonh-tr.nwest.nhs.uk; Tel: 01204 853127 — MB ChB 1979 Manch.; BSc St. And. 1976; MRCPath 1986; FRCPath 1999. Cons. Histopath. Roy. Bolton Hosp. Prev: Sen. Regist. Univ. Hosp. S. Manch.; Regist. (Histopath.) Wythenshawe Hosp. Manch.; Ho. Surg. & Ho. Phys. Bolton Gen. Hosp.

BISSET, Professor Gordon Wood (retired) 16 Nascot Wood Road, Watford WD17 4SA Tel: 01923 221724 — MB BS 1952 Lond.; DPhil Oxf. 1955; MRCS Eng. LRCP Lond. 1952. Prev: Prof. of Pharmacol. St. Thos. Hosp. Lond.

BISSET, Janet Margaret (retired) 175 Tottington Road, Harwood, Bolton BL2 4DF Tel: 01204 307654 — MB ChB Ed. 1949; FRCGP 1976, M 1965; DCH Eng. 1952. Prev: GP. Bolton.

BISSET, Jennifer Anne Coles Lane Health Centre, Coles Lane, Linton, Cambridge CB1 6JS Tel: 01223 891456 Fax: 01223 890033 — MB BS 1987 Lond.; MA Camb. 1992, BA 1984; DFFP 1996. Prev: Staff Grade (Geriat.s) Addenbrookes Hosp.; Clin. Asst. (Palliat. Care) Arthur Rank Ho. Camb.; SHO (Palliat. Med.) Arthur Rank Hse. Camb.

BISSET, John Glen Villiers, CD 26 Ward Avenue, Cowes PO31 8AY Tel: 01983 292600 Fax: 01983 292600 — MB ChB Glas. 1951; FRCSC 1962; DABO 1964; DO Eng. 1962. (Glas.) Prev: Cons. Ophth. Brit. Milit. Hosp. Iserlohn, W. Germany; Lect. (Ophth.) Sunnybrook Hosp., Univ. Toronto; Cons. Ophth. Defence & Civil Inst. Environm. Med. Downsview Ontario.

BISSET, John Gothard (retired) Corner Cottage, Main St., Eccles, Kelso TD5 7QP Tel: 01890 840522 — MB ChB Glas. 1960, DPH 1965; FFCM 1981, M 1974. Prev: Cons. Pub. Health Med. Borders HB.

BISSET, Leslie George Moncrieff Leven Health Centre, Victoria Road, Leven KY8 4ET Tel: 01333 425656 Fax: 01333 422249 — MB ChB 1973 Aberd.; DRCOG 1977.

BISSET, Reid Fyfe (retired) Glover Street Medical Centre, 133 Glover Street, Perth PH2 0JB Tel: 01738 621844 Fax: 01738 636070 — MB ChB 1964 Aberd.; DObst RCOG 1967.

BISSET, Robert Angus Lamont Frogs Hollow, 89 Moor Lane, Wilmslow SK9 6BR Tel: 01625 527593 — MB BS 1979 Lond.; FRCR 1985. (St. Bart.) Cons. (Radiol.) N. Manch. Gen. Hosp. Socs: Fell. Roy. Coll. Radiol. Prev: Sen. Regist. (Radiol.) Booth Hall Childr. Hosp. Manch.; Regist. (Diag. Radiol.) Manch. Roy. Infirm.; SHO (Med.) Bolton Gen. Hosp.

BISSET, Mr William Hugh (retired) 102 Morningside Drive, Edinburgh EH10 5NS Tel: 0131 447 6315 — MB ChB Ed. 1954; FRCS Ed. 1960. Prev: Cons. Paediat. Surg. Roy. Hosp. Sick Childr. Edin. & Edin. N.. Hosp. Gp.

BISSET, William Michael Department of Medical Paediatrics, Royal Aberdeen Childrens Hospital, Cornhill Road, Aberdeen AB25 2ZG Tel: 01224 554715 Fax: 01224 550707 — MB ChB 1979 Ed.; MSc Lond. 1986; BSc Ed. 1976, MD 1988; FRCP Ed. 1994; MRCP (UK) 1982; FRCPCH 1997; DCH Eng. 1981. (Edinburgh) Cons. Paediat. & Paediat. Gastroenterol. Roy. Aberd. Childr. Hosp.; Hon. Sen. Lect. (Child Health) Univ. Aberd. Socs: ESPGHAN; BSPGHAN. Prev: Sen. Lect. (Child Health) Univ. Aberd.; Lect. (Paediat. Gastroenterol.) Inst. Child Health Lond.; Regist. (Med. Paediat.) Roy. Hosp. for Sick Childr. Edin.

BISSETT, David Christopher Bruce Glanrhyd Surgery, Riverside, Beaufort, Ebbw Vale NP23 5NU Tel: 01495 301210 Fax: 01633 350684; Meadow Lea Farm, Llanvetherine, Abergavenny NP7 8RG Tel: 01873 821340 — MB ChB 1972 Birm.; MRCGP 1980; DCH Eng. 1976; DObst RCOG 1974.

BISSETT, Elaine Margaret 20 Lennel Avenue, Edinburgh EH12 6DW Tel: 0131 346 4616 — MB ChB 1981 Aberd.; DRCOG 1984.

BISSETT, James The Robert Henry Surgery, 7A Newtownards Road, Comber, Newtownards BT23 5AU — MB BCh BAO 1988 Belf.; MRCGP 1993; DRCOG 1992; DCH RCPSI 1991; DMH Belf. 1990.

BISSETT, James Donald 30 Morven Road, Bearsden, Glasgow G61 3BY — MB ChB 1982 Manch.; BSc (Med. Sci.) St. And. 1979. SHO (Cardiothoracic Med.) Wythenshawe Hosp. Manch.

BISSETT, John Jamieson (retired) 6 Victoria Crescent Road, Glasgow G12 9DB Tel: 0141 334 2348 — MB ChB 1943 Glas. Prev: Ho. Surg. Vict. Infirm. Glas.

BISSETT, Sarah Mavis (retired) 6 Victoria Crescent Road, Glasgow G12 9DB — MB ChB 1945 Glas. Prev: Assoc. Specialist (Cytol.) Glas. Roy. Matern. Hosp. & Stobhill Gen. Hosp. Glas.

BISSON, Dina Louise Department of Obstetrics & Gynaecology, Southmead Hospital, Bristol BS10 5NB Tel: 0117 950 5050 Fax: 0117 959 5178; 21 Henleaze Gardens, Henleaze, Bristol BS9 4HH — MB ChB 1982 Manch.; 1982 MB ChB Manch.; 1992 MD Manch.; 1987 MRCOG; 1985 DCH RCP Lond.; 2000 FRCOG. Cons. O & G S.mead Hosp. Bristol. Prev: Sen. Reg. S.mead Hosp., Bristol; Research Regist. Roy. United Hosp. Bath; Lect. (O & G) Univ. Bristol.

BISSON, Jonathan Ian Monmouth house, University Hospital Of Wales, Heath Park, Cardiff CE14 4XW Tel: 02920 793940 Fax: 02920 743928 Email: bissonj@cardiff.ac.uk — DM 2000 Soton.; BM Soton. 1986; MRCPsych 1991; Dip. Clin. Psychother. Lond. 1993. (Southampton) Cons. Psychiat. (Liaison Psychiat.)Cardiff & Vale NHS Trust; Clin. Director, Gen. Ment. Health, C&V NHS Trust. Socs: Memeber of Exec. Bd. and Bull. Edr. Europ. Soc. of Traum. Stress Studies. Prev: Lect. & Hon. Sen. Regist. (Psychol. Med.) Univ. Wales Coll. Med.; Sen. Regist. (Psychiat.) St. Tydfil's Hosp. Merthyr Tydfil; Sen. Specialist (Psychiat.) Brit. Milit. Hosp. Iserlohn.

BISSON, Marcus Anthony Meadowmist, Rue Des Bergers, Castel GY5 7AP — BM BS 1995 Nottm.

BISSON, Margaret Joan Robur, Belvidere Road, off Lower Argyll Road, Exeter EX4 4RR Tel: 01392 52367 — MB ChB 1960 Bristol; AFOM RCP Lond. 1987. Indep. Occupat. & Homoeop. Phys. Exeter.

BISSON, Peter Geoffrey Robur, Belvidere Road, off Lower Argyll Road, Exeter EX4 4RR Tel: 01392 52367 — MB ChB Bristol 1960. Acupunc. Practioner (Private). Prev: Assoc. Specialist (Nephrol.) Wonford Hosp. Exeter.

BISSOONAUTH, Soorendra 46 Thrums Avenue, Bishopsbriggs, Glasgow G64 1ER — MB ChB 1970 Glas.

BISWAS, Aditi SMA Medical Centre, 693-695 High Road, Leyton, London E10 6AA Tel: 020 8539 2078 Fax: 020 8558 3833 — MB BS 1973 Calcutta; MB BS 1973 Calcutta.

BISWAS, Anita Claire Centre for Sports Medicine, C Floor West Block, University Hospital, Nottingham NG7 2UH Tel: 0115 924 9924 — BM BS 1993 Nottm.; MSc 1998. (Nottingham) Clin. Fell. in Sports Med.; Team. Doc. Brit. Mt.ain. Biking. Team.

BISWAS, Anup 12 Bruce Drive, Chestnut Manor, W. Bridgford, Nottingham NG2 7RJ Tel: 0704 475 0319 Email: anup.biswas@breathemail.net — MB BS 1987 Lond.; FRCA 1994. (Guys. Hosp.) Cons., Anaesth., Nottm. City Hosp. NHS Trust. Socs: Obst. Anaesth. Assn.; Age Anaesth.; AA.

BISWAS, Arijit 9 Windermere, Fazakerley Hospital, Longmoor Lane, Liverpool L9 7AL Tel: 0151 525 5980 — MB BS 1980 Calcutta; MRCOG 1989.

BISWAS, Ashoke 3 The Grange, Cottam, Preston PR4 0LR — MB BS 1988 Lond.

BISWAS, Mr Bashistha Kumar 29 Pelham Road, Gravesend DA11 0HU — MB BS 1976 Calcutta; FRCS Glas. 1986.

BISWAS, Mr Basudeb c/o Anaesthetics Secretary, Tameside General Hospital, Fountain St., Ashton-under-Lyne OL6 9RW — MB BS 1971 Calcutta; FRCSI 1985.

BISWAS, Chandrima 21 Cannonbury Avenue, Pinner HA5 1TW — MB BS 1992 Lond.

BISWAS, Chitra c/o Anaesthetic Secretary, Tameside General Hospital, Ashton-under-Lyne OL6 9RW — MB BS 1971 Calcutta; DA (UK) 1979.

BISWAS, Debashis 20 Lake Road, London SW19 7ER — MB BS 1997 Lond.

BISWAS, Debasis 160 Cavendish Road, London SW12 0DB Tel: 020 8673 3187 — MB BS 1982 Calcutta; MRCP (UK) 1990; DCH RCPS Glas. 1988.

BISWAS, Gautom 41 Eastwell House, Weston St., London SE1 4DH Tel: 020 7403 2579; 115 Chudleigh Road, London SE4 1HP — MB BS 1990 Lond. Prev: Ho. Phys. Orpington Hosp. Kent; Ho. Surg. Kent & Canterbury Hosp.

BISWAS, Haripada (retired) 4 Pavenham Drive, Edgbaston, Birmingham B5 7TW — MB BS 1952 Calcutta; MRCPI 1985; MRCPsych 1972; DPM Eng. 1972; DTM & H Calcutta 1962. Prev: Cons. Psychiat. Highcroft Hosp. Birm.

BISWAS, Krupavathi Rectory Road Surgery, 201 Rectory Road, Pitsea, Basildon SS13 1AQ Tel: 01268 727736 Fax: 01268 727045 — MB BS 1963 Madras; MRCOG 1972.

BISWAS, Minakshi Anaesthetic Department, Maidstone Hospital, Hermitage Lane, Maidstone ME16 9NN Tel: 01622 729000; Merrihill, Caring Lane, Maidstone ME17 1TJ — MB BS 1971 Calcutta; FFA RCS Eng. 1977; DA (UK) 1974. Cons. Anaesth. Maidstone Hosp. Socs: Assn. Anaesth.; Assn. Obst. Anaesth.

BISWAS, Mr Prasanta Kumar Glenroyd Medical Centre, 164 Whitegate Drive, Blackpool FY3 3LF Tel: 01253 762156 Fax: 01253 838428 — MB BS 1954 Calcutta; FRCS Eng 1967.

BISWAS, Mr Satya Prasad Department of Orthopaedic & Trauma, Kettering General Hospital NHS Trust, Rothwell Road, Kettering NN16 8UZ Tel: 01536 493795 Fax: 01536 493796; Little Acre, 6 Cross Lane, Aldwincle, Kettering NN14 3EG Tel: 01832 720018 — MB BS 1972 Calcutta; MSc (Ortho.) Lond. 1984; FRCS Eng. 1983. Cons. Orthop. & Trauma Kettering Gen. Hosp. NHS Trust. Socs: Brit. Orthop. Assn.; Brit. Elbow & Shoulder Soc.; Rheum. Surgic.. Soc.

BISWAS, Sharmila 4 Pavenham Drive, Edgbaston, Birmingham B5 7TW — MB ChB 1984 Sheff.; DCH RCP Lond. 1989. Med.Off. N. Qu.sland. Australia; Vis. Med. Off. Cairns Base Hosp. Socs: Cairns Div. of GP; Rep. Populat. Health Plann.. Prev: Trainee GP. Sheff. NW Lond. Birm.; GP. Birm.; GP. Cairns Australia.

BISWAS, Subhash Ranjan Naha Briercliffe Road Surgery, 357 Briercliffe Road, Burnley BB10 1TX Tel: 01282 424720 Fax: 01282 429055 — MB BS 1965 Gauhati; T(GP) 1991.

BISWAS, Sujoy Woodlands, Plough Lane, Lathom, Ormskirk L40 6JL Tel: 0151 734 2020 — MB ChB 1990 Liverp.

BISWAS, Mr Suman Department of Ophthalmology, Royal Preston Hospital, Sharoe Green Lane, Fulwood, Preston PR2 9HT — MB BS 1989 Madras; FRCS Ed. 1993.

BISWAS, Sumita 9 Raleigh Close, Sketty, Swansea SA2 8LE — MB BCh 1985 Wales.

BISWAS, Susanta Kumar Rectory Road Surgery, 201 Rectory Road, Pitsea, Basildon SS13 1AQ Tel: 01268 727736 Fax: 01268 727045 — MB BS 1964 Dacca; MRCP (UK) 1975.

BISWAS, Susmito 55 Priory Street, Bowdon, Altrincham WA14 3BQ — MB BS 1992 Lond.

BISWAS, Swethajit 61 Booths Farm Road, Great Barr, Birmingham B42 2NR — MB ChB 1996 Sheff.

BISWAS, Umapati The Surgery, 144 Grove Lane, London SE5 8BP Tel: 020 7274 3762 — MB BS 1969 Patna. (P. of Wales Med. Coll.) Prev: Trainee GP Monklands/Cumbernauld VTS; Regist. (Psychiat.) Hartwood Hosp. Shotts.

BITENSKY, Lucille 38 Sheen Park, Richmond TW9 1UW Tel: 020 8940 2422 Fax: 020 8940 2422 — MB BCh 1953 Witwatersrand; DSc Lond. 1972, PhD 1962; MRCP (UK) 1981; FRCPath 1974, M 1964. Hon. Sen. Research Fell. (Med. & Histopath.) Char. Cross & W.m. Med. Sch. Lond.; Dep. Head Unit of Cellular Pharmacol. & Toxicol. Robt.s Inst. Univ. Surrey Guildford. Socs: Roy. Soc. Med. (Ex-Vice Pres. Path. Sect.); (Ex. Treas.) Brit. Div. Internat. Acad. Path. Prev: Dep. Head Div. Celluar Biol. Kennedy Inst. Rheum. Lond.; Vis. Prof. Pharmacol. Roy. Free Hosp. Med. Sch.; Vis. Prof. Med. McGill Univ. Montreal.

BITNER-GLINDZICZ, Maria Aniela Katarzyna Department of Clinical & Molecular Genetics, Institute of Child Health, 30 Guilford St., London WC1N 1EH Tel: 020 7242 9789 Fax: 020 7813 8141 Email: mbitnerg@hgmp.mrc.ac.uk; 10 Briston Grove, London N8 9EX — MB BS 1987 Lond.; MB BS (Hons.) Lond. 1987; PhD Lond. 1996, BSc 1984; MRCP (UK) 1990; DCH RCP Lond. 1991. (Univ. Coll.) MRC Clin. Scientist Award Inst. Child Health Lond. Socs: Clin. Genetics Soc. Prev: MRC Train. Fell. Clin. Genetics Inst. Child Health Lond.; SHO Rotat. (Paediat.) Qu. Eliz. Hosp. Childr. Lond.; SHO Rotat. (Med.) Guy's Hosp. Lond.

BITTAR, Wafa 5 Dunadry Mews, Belfast Road, Antrim BT41 2HE — MD 1982 Aleppo.

BITTINER, Pauline Weasel Score, Fordrift Close, Gotham, Nottingham NG11 0JX — MB ChB 1958 Leeds.

BITTINER, Stephen Bruce Department of Dermatology, Doncaster Royal Infirmary, Armthorpe Road, Doncaster DN2 5LT Tel: 01302 366666 Email: bruce.bittiner@gwx400.drinah-tr.trent.nhs.uk; 22 Whin Hill Road, Bessacarr, Doncaster DN4 7AF Tel: 01302 371428 — MB ChB 1978 Sheff.; FRCP Lond. 1997; MRCP (UK) 1982; T(M) 1990. Cons. Dermat. Doncaster Roy. Infirm. & Bassetlaw Dist. Gen. Hosp. Socs: Brit. Assn. Dermatol. Prev: Lect. Univ. Sheff. 1987-1991.

BIVONA, David Flat 3, 38 Belsize Square, London NW3 4HL — State Exam Med 1988 Berlin.

BIWER, Julian Edward Yorkstones, 10 Elmete Avenue, Roundhay, Leeds LS8 2JX Tel: 0113 2655 692 Fax: 0113 216 1145 Email: julian@biwer.freeserve.co.uk — MB BS 1973 Lond.; BSc Lond. 1970, MB BS 1973; DRCOG 1977. (Middlesex) Regional Med. Off. Benefits Agency Med. Serv. Prev: GP Folkestone; Ho. Off. United Norwich Hosps. & Middlx. Hosp. Lond.

BIZBY, Lettice Jane Penwnshwn, Glanaman, Ammanford SA18 — MB BCh 1976 Wales.

BIZON, Mieczyslaw Jerzy Highbridge Medical Centre, Pepperall Road, Highbridge TA9 3YA Tel: 01278 783220 Fax: 01278 795486; The Gables, 148 Worston Road, Highbridge TA9 3JX Tel: 01278 783928 Fax: 01278 783928 Email: mike.bizon@virgin.net — MB ChB 1975 Bristol; MRCGP 1980. Police Surg. (Dep.) Avon & Som. Police. Prev: Clin. Asst. (ENT) Bristol Roy. Infirm.; Trainee GP Mid Devon VTS; SHO (Gyn.) Ham Green Hosp. Bristol.

BJARNASON, Ingvar Thor Department of Medicine, King's College School of Medicine, Bessemer Road, London SE5 9PJ Tel: 020 7737 4000 Fax: 020 7346 3313 Email: ingvar.bjarnson@kcl.ac.uk; 9 Cardiff Road, Hanwell, London W7 2BW Tel: 020 8567 9574 — Cand Med et Chir 1977 Reykjavik; MSc Biochem. Lond. 1983; MD Reykjavik 1986; MRCPath 1991; DSc 1997; FRCP 1999. Reader (Med. & Gastroenterol.) King's Coll. Sch. of Med. & Dent. Socs: Med. Res. Soc. & Brit. Soc. Gastroenterol.; Amer. Gastroenterol. Assn. Prev: Sen. Lect. (Clin. Biochem.) King's Coll. Lond.; Clin. Staff MRC Clin. Research Centre; Hon. Cons. & Hon. Sen. Regist. N.wick Pk. Hosp. Harrow.

BJORN, Janet Margaret Cobbers, Forest Row RH18 5JZ Tel: 01342 822009; Orchard House, Victoria Hospital, Lewes BN7 1PE Tel: 01273 402510 — MB ChB St. And. 1970; MRCPsych 1977. Cons.(Child Psychiat.) Vict. Hosp. Lewes. E Sussex.; Cons. (Child Psychiat.) Chailey NeuroDisabil. Serv. Chailey. E.Sussex. Socs: Med. Wom. Federat. (Sec. Sussex Div.). Prev: Cons. Child Psychiat. Paediat. Clinic, Thomson Med. Centre, Singapore; Research Asst. Cornell Neuropsychiat. Div. New York.

BJORNDAL, Birthe Elisabeth The Margaret Centre, Whipps Cross University Hospital, Leytonstone, London E11 1NR Tel: 020 8535 6604 Fax: 020 8535 6952 Email: bjorndal@doctors.org.uk; Email: bjorndal@doctors.org.uk — MB BCh 1990 Wales; MRCP (UK) 1995. (Wales) Cons., The Margt. Centre, Whipps Cross Univ. Hosp., Leytonstone, Lond. E11 1NR.

BLACH, Mr Rudolf Karl Lister House, 11-12 Wimpole St., London W1M 7AB Tel: 020 7636 3407 Fax: 020 7436 2870; Summers, Northfield Avenue, Lower Shiplake, Henley-on-Thames RG9 3PB Tel: 0118 940 4549 Fax: 0118 940 2848 — MB BChir 1956 Camb.; MA Camb. 1959, BA 1952, MD 1965; FRCS Eng. 1962; FRCOphth 1988. (Camb. & St. Thos.) Hon. Cons. Ophth. King's Coll. Hosp. Lond.; Cons. Ophth. St. Dunstan's. Socs: Fell. Roy. Soc. Med.; (Dep. Chairm.) Brit. Counc. Preven. of Blindness; (Ex-Dep. Master) Oxf. Ophth. Congr. Prev: Cons. Surg. Moorfields Eye Hosp.; Dean Inst. Ophth. Univ. Lond.; Cons. Ophth. Surg. St. Mary's Hosp. Lond.

BLACHFORD, Raymond Dudley (retired) 33 Grange Hill Road, King's Norton, Birmingham B38 8RE Tel: 0121 458 3116 — MB BS 1938 Lond.; MD Lond. 1947; FRCP Lond. 1969, M 1940; MRCS Eng. LRCP Lond. 1938.

BLACK, Alan Arnold (retired) 12 Wykeham Terrace, Brighton BN1 3FF — MB BS 1954 Lond.; DPM Lond. 1959; MD Lond. 1965; FRCPsych. 1981 M 1971. Prev: Med. Mem. Ment. Health Review Tribunal.

BLACK, Alan Gilchrist Path House Medical Practice, Path House, Nether Street, Kirkcaldy KY1 2PG Tel: 01592 644533 Fax: 01592 644550; 3 Blair Place, Hygrove Park, Kirkcaldy KY2 5SQ Tel: 01592 269534 Fax: 01592 269534 Email: a.black@dial.pipex.com — MB ChB 1971 Ed.; BSc (Med. Sci.) Ed. 1968, MB ChB 1971; DObst RCOG 1973. (Ed.) Managing Dir. Exeter Systems. Socs: PHCSG of BCS. Prev: Med. Off. Brit. Steel Corpn. Scotl.; Regist. (Gen. Med.) Milesmark Hosp. Dunfermline; SHO (Gen. Med.) Doncaster Roy. Infirm.

BLACK, Alan Johnston, TD Blackwell Associates, Ocean House, Edgewater Road, Belfast BT3 9JQ Tel: 01232 770288 Fax: 01232 773119 Email: blackwell.associates@btinternet.com; 7 Manselton Park, Bangor BT20 4LY — MB BCh BAO 1981 Belf.; MRCP (UK) 1984; MFOM RCP Lond. 1992, A 1990. (Queen's Belfast) Indep. Occupat. Cons. Socs: Soc. Occupat. Med. (Sec. N. Irel. Gp.). Prev: Med. Off. N. Irel. Electricity; Sen. Regist. (Occupat. Med.) EHSSB N. Irel.

BLACK, Alan Sinclair 8 Broughton Avenue, Richmond TW10 7TS — MB BS 1982 Lond.

BLACK, Alexander John (retired) 126 Newmarket Road, Norwich NR4 6SB Tel: 01603 452957 — MB 1960 Camb.; BChir 1959; MD Camb. 1969; FRCPath 1984, M 1970; DObst RCOG 1962. Prev: Cons. Haemat. Norf. & Norwich Hosp.

BLACK, Allan (retired) Red Roofs, 17 Galadale, Newtongrange, Dalkeith EH22 4RQ — MB ChB 1952 Ed.

BLACK, Andrew 24 Main Street, Barton under Needwood, Burton-on-Trent DE13 8AA — MB BS 1997 Lond.

BLACK, Mr Andrew James Merrington Milton Cottage, Milton Road, Wokingham RG11 1DE Tel: 01734 783399 — MB BS 1989 Lond.; FRCS Eng. 1993.

BLACK, Andrew Kilgour Out Patients Department, Rochford Hosptial, Union Lane, Rochford SS4 1 Tel: 01702 578183 Email: rbp26@dial.pipex.com; 150 Oakleigh Park Drive, Leigh-on-Sea SS9 1RU Email: drakb@globalnet.co.uk — MB ChB 1974 Ed.; MRCPsych. 1981. Cons. Psychiat. (Adult Ment. Illness) S.end Health Dist.; Clin. Tutor Examr. MRCPsych Pt I; Vis. Cons. Psychiat. Bullwood Hall Prison.

BLACK, Andrew McLaren Spiers Department of Anaesthesia, Bristol Royal Infirmary, Bristol BS2 8HW; Woodside, Hallen Lodge, Hallen, Bristol BS10 7RH — BM BCh 1970 Oxf.; DPhil, MA, BM BCh Oxf. 1970; FRCA 1988; FANZCA 1976. (Oxf.) Cons. Sen. Lect. Dept. Anaesth. Bristol Univ. Socs: Europ. Acad. Anaesthesiol.; Assn. Anaesth. Gt. Brit. & Irel.; BMA. Prev: Clin. Lect. Nuffield Dept. Anaesth. Radcliffe Infirm. Oxf.; Regist. (Anaesth.) St. Vincent's Hosp.

Sydney, Australia; Sen. Regist. Dept. Critical Care Auckland Hosp., N.Z.

BLACK, Angus David Fraser Solwayside, Port Carlisle, Carlisle CA7 5BU — MB ChB 1998 Liverp.; MB ChB Liverp 1998.

BLACK, Angus William, Group Capt. RAF Med. Br. Retd. Lowlands, Bath Road, Marlborough SN8 1NR Tel: 01672 53278 — MB ChB 1951 Ed.; FRCPsych 1980, M 1971; DPM Eng. 1962.

BLACK, Ann Dora Traumatic Stress Clinic, 73 Charlotte St., London W1T 4PL Tel: 020 7530 3666 Fax: 020 7530 3677 Email: dorablack@compuserve.com — MB ChB Birm. 1955; FRCPsych 1979, M 1971; DPM Eng. 1958; FRCPCH 1996. (Birm.) Hons. Cons. Child Psychiat. Traum. Stress Clinic Lond.; Hon. Cons. & Sen. Lect. Roy. Free Hosp.; Vis. Hon. Cons. Psychiat. Hosp. Sick Childr. Gt. Ormond St. Lond. Socs: CRUSE; BMA; Eur. Soc. Traum. Stress. Prev: Dir. & Cons. Traum. Stress Clinic; Cons. Child Psychiat. Edgware Gen. Hosp. & Roy. Free Hosp. Lond.; Regist. Bethlem Roy. & Maudsley Hosps.

BLACK, Ann Elizabeth Department of Anaesthetics, Great Ormond Street Hospital for Children, NHS Trust, London WC1N 3JH Tel: 020 7405 9200; 36 Ingersoll Road, London W12 7BD — MB BS 1977 Lond.; FRCA. 1986; DA (UK) 1985; DRCOG 1982. (Roy. Free) Cons. Anaesth. Hosp. Sick Childr. Gt. Ormond St. Lond. Prev: Sen. Regist. (Anaesth.) Guy's Hosp. Lond.; Fell. (Anaesth.) Childr.'s Hosp. of Philadelphia USA; Regist. (Anaesth.) Univ. Coll. Hosp.

BLACK, Brian Alan (retired) The Village Surgery, 5 Barrow Point Avenue, Pinner HA5 3HQ Tel: 020 8429 3777 Fax: 020 8429 4413 — MB BS 1956 Durh. Prev: Clin. Asst. (Med.) Watford Gen. Hosp.

BLACK, Professor Carol Mary, CBE Royal Free Hospital, Pond St., London NW3 2QG Tel: 020 7794 0432 Fax: 020 7435 0143 Email: c.black@rfcucl.ac.uk; Flat 3, 2 Ferncroft Avenue, Hampstead, London NW3 7PG Tel: 020 7794 0560 Fax: 020 433 3760 Email: black@mistral.co.uk — FRCP, 2001; MB ChB Bristol 1970; BA Bristol 1962, MD 1973; FRCP Lond. 1988; MRCP (UK) 1973. Prof. Rheum. Roy. Free Hosp. Lond. Socs: Brit. Soc. Rheum.& Amer. Coll. Rheum.; Assn. Phys. Prev: Cons. Rheum. W. Middlx. Hosp.

BLACK, Charles Neil Dunbar Medical Centre, Abbey Road, Dunbar EH42 1JP Tel: 01368 862327 Fax: 01368 865646; 4 Hallhill Steadings, Dunbar EH42 1RF Tel: 01368 862599 — MB ChB 1986 Manch.; MRCGP 1990; DRCOG 1990.

BLACK, Christine Janet Margaret 65 Mount Annan Dr, Glasgow G44 4RX — MB ChB 1997 Glas.

BLACK, Christopher Charles (retired) St Martins, 8 Hove Park Road, Hove BN3 6LA Tel: 01273 507900 Fax: 01273 507900 — BA Camb. 1958, MB 1962, BChir 1961.

BLACK, Claire Elizabeth 28 Kensington Drive, Belfast BT5 6NU — MB BCh BAO 1994 Belf.

BLACK, Corrinda 176 Ledard Road, Langside, Glasgow G42 9RG — MB ChB 1996 Glas.; MRCP 1999. SHO (Med.).

BLACK, Cyril Kenneth 19 Broomcroft Road, Newton Mearns, Glasgow G77 5ER — LRCP LRCS 1945 Ed.; LRCP LRCS Ed. LRFPS Glas. 1945.

BLACK, David Central Surgery, Corporation Street, Rugby CV21 3SP Tel: 01788 574335 Fax: 01788 547693 — MB ChB 1987 Manch.; MRCP (UK) 1990.

BLACK, David (retired) 3 Wood Stanway Drive, Bishops Cleeve, Cheltenham GL52 8TL Tel: 01242 676066 — MB BCh BAO Belf. 1937; DOMS Eng. 1947. Prev: Cons. Ophth. Walton Hosp. Liverp.

BLACK, David Alexander The Surgery, High St., South Milford, Leeds LS25 5A — MB BS 1965 Durh. (Newc.) Socs: BMA. Prev: Ho. Surg. Roy. Infirm. Sunderland; Demonst. Anat. Univ. Glas.; SHO (Surg.) St. Jas. Hosp. Leeds.

BLACK, David Allan Betts Avenue Medical Centre, 2 Betts Avenue, Benwell, Newcastle upon Tyne NE15 6TD Tel: 0191 274 2767/2842 Fax: 0191 274 0244; 2 Betts Avenue, Newcastle upon Tyne NE15 6TQ Tel: 0191 274 2767 Fax: 0191 274 0244 — MB BS 1981 Newc.; MRCGP 1985; DRCOG 1984. (Newc. u. Tyne)

BLACK, David Anderson 111 Elsdon Avenue, Seaton Delaval, Whitley Bay NE25 0JL Tel: 0191 237 0601 — MB BS 1955 Durh. Prev: Ho. Surg. & Ho. Phys. Shotley Bridge Gen. Hosps.; SHO Chester-le-St. Gen. Hosp.

BLACK, David Andrew Queen Mary's Hospital, Frognal Avenue, Sidcup DA14 6LT — MB BChir 1980 Camb.; MA Camb. 1981; FRCP Lond. 1994; MRCP (UK) 1983; MBA Hull 1997. (Camb. and St. Thos.) Cons. Phys. (Gen. & Geriat. Med.) Qu. Mary's Hosp. Sidcup; Med. Dir. Socs: Brit. Geriat. Soc.; Brit. Soc. Gastroenterol.; Brit. Assn. Med. Managers. Prev: Sen. Regist. (Gen. & Geriat. Med.) Guy's Hosp. Lond. & Hastings Hosp.; Regist. (Med.) St. Thos. Hosp. Lond.

BLACK, David Harrison Hamel House, 50 Western Way, Alverstoke, Gosport PO12 2NQ Tel: 01705 511793 — MB BS 1955 Lond.; MRCS Eng. LRCP Lond. 1955; DObst RCOG 1960. (St. Bart.) Examg. Med. Pract. DSS. Prev: Hosp. Pract. (O & G) St. Mary's Hosp. Portsmouth.

BLACK, David William Scarsdale, Newbold Road, Chesterfield S41 7PF — BM 1988 Soton.; MPH 1997; MFPHM 1999; MRCGP 1992; DObst RCOG 1990. (Southampton) Cons. in Pub. Health Med., Chesterfield PCT, Chesterfield. Prev: Regist. (Psychiat.) ChristCh., NZ; Trainee GP Portsmouth VTS; SHO (Med., Geriat. & Paediat.) St. Mary's Hosp. Portsmouth.

BLACK, Dawn Ingersley Building, Macclesfield District General Hospital, Victoria Road, Macclesfield SK10 3 Tel: 01625 421000; Tel: 0161 428 7370 — FRCP 2001; MSc Manch. 1988; BSc St. And. 1979; MD Manch. 1989, MB ChB 1982; MRCPsych 1986. Cons. Psych. Macclesfield Dist. Gen. Hosp. Macclesfield; Hon. Assoc. Lect. (Psychiat.) Manch. Univ.; Ment. Health Act Commbsioner; Medal Memeber of Ment. Health Review Tribunal. Prev: Cons. Psychia. Hope Hosp. Sal; Lect. (Psychiat.) Manch. Univ.; Clin. Research Fell. (Psychiat.) Manch. Univ.

BLACK, Diana Margaret Christian Brantwood, St James St., Dingwall IV15 9JA — MB ChB 1972 Ed. (Ed.) Prev: Regist. Craig Dunain Hosp. Inverness.

BLACK, Diana Margaret Susan 6 The Pightle, Burnham Thorpe, King's Lynn PE31 8HT — MB BS 1990 Lond.; MRCGP 1995.

BLACK, Donald Kerr (retired) 31 Areley Court, Stourport-on-Severn DY13 0AR Tel: 01299 822159 — MB ChB 1936 Ed.; MRCOG 1949; MRCGP 1953. Prev: Sen. Obst. Lucy Baldwin Matern Hosp. Stourport.

BLACK, Doris Jean (retired) 14 Windsor Road, Chorley PR7 1LN Tel: 01257 62414 — MB BCh BAO 1948 Dub.; BA Dub. 1946, MB BCh BAO 1948; FRCPsych. 1987, M 1972; DPM Eng. 1971. Prev: Cons. Child & Adolesc. Psychiat. Blackburn Dist.

BLACK, Dorothy (retired) 8 Tara Wood, Farmhill Road, Holywood BT18 0HS Tel: 01232 425162 — MB BCh BAO 1949 Belf.; DOMS RCPSI 1965; DPH Belf. 1954. Assoc. Specialist E. Health & Social Servs. Bd.

BLACK, Dorothy Florence Mary (retired) Victoria Mill House, Framlingham, Woodbridge IP13 9EG Tel: 01728 724131 — MB ChB MB ChB Liverp. 1951; DCH Eng. 1953; DPM Eng. 1968; FRCPsych 1985, M 1972. Prev: Sen. Med. Off. DoH.

BLACK, Sir Douglas A K The Old Forge, High St., Whitchurch-on-Thames, Reading RG8 7EN Tel: 0118 984 4693 — MB ChB (Commend.) St. And. 1936; FFOM 1983; FFPHM RCP (UK) 1983; FRCPsych 1982; FRCPath 1979; FACP 1978; Hon. FFOM RCP Lond. 1984; Hon. FRCOG 1983; BSc St. And. 1933, MD (Hons. & Rutherford Gold Medal) 1940; Hon. LLD Birm. 1984; Hon. MD Sheff. 1984; Hon. DSc St. And. 1972, Manch. 1978, Leic. 1980 & Camb. 1994; FRCP Lond. 1952, M 1939; FRCP Ed. 1979; FRCPI 1979 FRCP Glas. 1978; FRCGP 1983; MB ChB 1936 St. And. (St. And.) Emerit. Prof. Med. Univ. Manch.; Hon. Consg. Phys. Manch. Roy. Infirm. Socs: (Ex-Pres.) BMA (Ex-Chairm. Bd. Sci.); Assn. Phys.; Med. Res. Soc. Prev: Hon. Consg. Phys. Manch. Roy. Infirm.; Sir Arthur Sims Commonw. Trav. Prof. 1971; RCP Lond. Lecturesh.: Goulstonian 1953, Bradshaw 1965, Linacre 1970, 1970, Harv. Orator 1977, Lloyd Robt.s 1980.

BLACK, Douglas George Black and Partners, Sherwood Health Centre, Elmswood Gardens, Sherwood, Nottingham NG5 4AD Tel: 0115 960 7127 Fax: 0115 985 7899; 31 Richmond Drive, Mapperley Park, Nottingham NG3 5EL Tel: 0115 962 2046 Email: dgb6382@aol.com — BM BS 1980 Nottm.; BMedSci Nottm. 1978, BSc 1975; FRCGP 1994, M 1987; DRCOG 1987. (Nottingham) Lect. (Gen. Pract.) Univ. Nottm.; Chairm. Nottm. Commiss.ing GP. Socs: Hon. Sec. Nottm. Medico - Chirurgical Soc. Prev: Chairm. Nottm. Non-Fundholders Gp.; Chairm. Nottm. Dist. Med. Advis. Comm.

BLACK, Duncan Kerr Mather Brantwood, St James St., Dingwall IV15 9JA — MB ChB 1972 Ed.; MRCGP 1976.

BLACK, Eamon Thomas Joseph Health Centre, Great James Street, Londonderry BT48 7DH Tel: 028 7136 4016 — MB BCh

BAO 1984; MRCGP 1989; DCH RCP Lond. 1988; DGM RCP Lond. 1988; DRCOG 1987.

BLACK, Edward Alexander 15 The Pleasance, London SW15 5HF — MB BS 1992 Lond.

BLACK, Elizabeth Anne Department of Child Health, Ulster Hospital, Dundonald, Belfast BT16 1RH Tel: 01232 484511 Fax: 01232 561368 — MB BCh BAO 1981 Belf.; MRCP (UK) 1985; FRCPCH. (Queen's Univ. Belf.) Cons. Paediat. Ulster Hosp. Socs: BMA; RCP Edin.; Fell. Roy. Coll. Paediat. & Child Health. Prev: Cons. Paediat. Coleraine Hosp.; Sen. Regist. (Community Paediat. & Neonat.) Oxf. Radcliffe Hosps.; Sen. Regist. (Paediat.) Roy. Berks. Hosp. Reading & Gt. Ormond St. Hosp.

BLACK, Elspeth Alice 73 Russell Drive, Bearsden, Glasgow G61 3BB — MB ChB 1998 Aberd.; MB ChB Aberd 1998.

BLACK, Fiona Mary Flat 3F1, 3 Lonsdale Terrace, Edinburgh EH3 9HN — MB ChB 1998 Ed.; MB ChB Ed 1998. PRHO Gen. Med. Roy. InfirmEdin. Prev: PRHO Gen.Surg.Prthop.Vict. Hosp.Kirkcaldy.

BLACK, Fiona Mary Philomena 25 West Avenue, Gosforth, Newcastle upon Tyne NE3 4ES — MB BCh BAO 1987 Dub. Post-Doctural Research Fell. Dept. Cardiol. Baylor Coll. of Med.

BLACK, Fredrick Samuel (retired) 6 Bowers Close, Riseley, Bedford MK44 1DP Tel: 01234 708475 — MB BCh BAO Belf. 1947; DPH Bristol 1972. Prev: Wing Cdr.RAF Med. Br.

BLACK, George Harold Parkside Family Practice, Eastleigh Health Centre, Newtown Road, Eastleigh SO50 9AG Tel: 023 8061 2032 Fax: 023 8062 9623 — MB BCh BAO 1972 Dub.

BLACK, Gerald Wilson (retired) 8 Tarawood, Farmhill Road, Holywood BT18 0HS Tel: 02890 425162 — MB BCh 1949 Belf.; MB BCh BAO Belf. 1949; DA RCPSI 1952; FFA RCS Eng. 1955; PhD Belf. 1969, MD 1959; FRCPI 1974, M 1969; FFA RCSI 1961. Prev: Cons. Anaesth. Roy. Belf. Hosp. Sick Childr. & Roy. Vict. Hosp. Belf.

BLACK, Gillian — MB BCh BAO 1992 Belf.; MRCOG, 1998. Specialist Regist. James Cooke Univ. Hosp. Middlesbrough. Prev: SpR N. Tyneside Hosp.; SpR Roy. Vict. Infirm. Newc. Upon Tyne.

BLACK, Godfrey Greenwell (retired) Tree Tops, Church St., Wargrave, Reading RG10 8EP — MB BS 1937 Durh. Prev: Med. Regist. Roy. Vict. Infirm. Newc-upon-Tyne.

BLACK, Gordon 1F1, 60 Cowan Road, Edinburgh EH11 1RJ Tel: 0131 337 7003 — MB ChB 1991 Ed.; MRCGP 1996; DRCOG 1995; DCH RCP Lond. 1993. (Ed.) CPD Tutor.

BLACK, Graeme Charles Mackinlay 4 Moor Lane, Woodford, Stockport SK7 1PP — BM BCh 1987 Oxf.; DPhil Oxf. 1994; FRCOphth 1996. Sen. Regist. (Clin. Genetics) St. Mary's Hosp. Manch.; Lect. (Genetic Ophth.) Manch. Roy. Eye Hosp. Prev: Lect. (Genetics) St. Catherines Coll. Oxf.; SHO (Ophth.) Roy. Berks. Hosp. Reading.

BLACK, Graham Sydney 143 Kenton Lane, Newcastle upon Tyne NE3 3QB Tel: 0191 285 3919 — MB BS 1949 Durh.

BLACK, Gregory Campion 11 The Wick, Hertford SG14 3HN — MB ChB 1994 Leic.; DRCOG 1998. Socs: M.R.C.G.P.

BLACK, Heather Jane 24 Upper Hartwell, Stone, Aylesbury HP17 8NZ — MB ChB 1993 Sheff.; MRCP (UK) 1996.

BLACK, Helen Elizabeth Warren Bunbury Medical Practice, The Surgery, Bunbury, Tarporley CW6 9PJ Tel: 01829 260218 Fax: 01829 260411; Bunbury Medical Practice, Bunbury, Tarporley CW6 9PJ Tel: 01829 260218 — MB ChB 1990 Ed.; DRCOG 1993. (Edinburgh)

BLACK, Henry John (retired) 28 Longlands Road, Slaithwaite, Huddersfield HD7 5DN — MB BCh BAO 1956 Belf.; FRCPath 1979, M 1967. Cons. Microbiol. Huddersfield HA. Prev: Cons. Microbiol. Huddersfield HA.

BLACK, Horace (retired) 3 Sandmoor Close, Leeds LS17 7RP Tel: 01132 665123 — MB ChB Leeds 1948; MRCS Eng. LRCP Lond. 1973. Fact. Med. Off. Doncasters Monkbridge Forgers Leeds. Prev: GP Leeds.

BLACK, Iain Laidlaw Melbourne Healthcare Centre, Penn Lane, Melbourne, Derby DE73 1EF Tel: 01332 862124 Fax: 01332 865154; 1 Oak Road, Thulston, Derby DE72 3EW Tel: 01332 74314 — MB ChB 1973 Glas.; MRCP (UK) 1978; DCH Eng. 1976.

BLACK, Ian Ewart, SBStJ Rowan Lodge, Fildyke Close, Meppershall, Shefford SG17 5LF Tel: 01462 816022 Fax: 01462 851717 Email: ianblack1@cs.com — MB ChB 1963 Manch.; MFPM 1990. Cons. Pharm. Med. & Med. Law Rowan Lodge Cons. Beds. Socs: (Ex Treas.) Brit. Assn. Pharmaceut. Phys.; BMA. Prev: Med. Dir. AAH Meditel Ltd.

BLACK, Ian Herbert Cecil Antrim Hospital, 45 Bush Road, Antrim BT41 2RL Tel: 01849 424262 Fax: 01849 424249 Email: blackihc@aol.com; Tara, 141 Galgorm Road, Ballymena BT42 1DE Tel: 0282 565 6611 Email: ihcblack@aol.com — MB BCh BAO 1973 Dub.; DP Med. 2001; FFA RCSI 1978. (Trinity Coll. Dub.) Cons. Anaesth. Antrim Hosp. Prev: Sen. Regist. (Anaesth.) EHSS Bd.; Research Assoc. (Anaesth.) Qu. Univ. Belf.

BLACK, Ian Joseph (retired) 13 Forbes Place, St Andrews KY16 9UJ — MB ChB Ed. 1960; MRCGP 1976; DPM Eng. 1968; DObst RCOG 1964. Med. Adviser Nursing Home Registration & Inspection Unit Springfield Hse Fife HB Cupar, Fife; Med. Assessor Nestor Disabil. Anal. Med. Servs. Edin. Prev: Princip. GP Glenrothes Fife.

BLACK, Mr Ian Myles 'Lislea', 104 Galgorm Road, Ballymena BT42 1AE — MB BCh BAO 1993 Belf.; FRCS Otol, 1998.

BLACK, James Elder Inverurie Medical Group, Health Centre, 1 Constitution Street, Inverurie AB51 4SU Tel: 01467 621345 Fax: 01467 625374 — MB ChB 1968 Ed.

BLACK, James Paterson Wards Medical Practice, 25 Dundonald Road, Kilmarnock KA1 1RU Tel: 01563 526514 Fax: 01563 573558 — MB ChB 1972 Glas. (Glas.)

BLACK, Sir James Whyte 3 Ferrings, London SE21 7LU — MB ChB 1946 St. And.

BLACK, Jan Bank House Surgery, 84 High Street, Farnborough, Orpington BR6 7BA Tel: 01689 857691 Fax: 01689 850042 — MB BS 1968 Lond.; Cert Av Med MoD (Air) & CAA; Aviat. Auth. 1979. (Univ. Coll. Hosp.) Authorised Med. Examr. Civil Aviat. Auth. Socs: BMA & Aerospace Med. Assn.

BLACK, Jeanie Findlater (retired) Beechwood, Spinney Field, Moorgate, Rotherham S60 3BB Tel: 01709 364425 — MB BS 1948 Lond.; MRCS Eng. LRCP Lond. 1946; DCH Eng. 1949; Cert FPA 1963; Cert. Venereol. Liverp. 1951. Prev: SCMO Rotherham HA.

BLACK, Jennie Jadwiga Bootham Park Hospital, Bootham, York YO30 7BY; Hazel Cottage, South Back Lane, Stillington, Stockton-on-Tees, York YO61 1ND — MB ChB 1994 Leic. SHO (Psychiat.) Bootham Pk. Hosp. York.

BLACK, Jennifer Elaine Barrington Oswald Medical Practice, 4 Oswald Road, Chorlton, Manchester M21 9LH Tel: 0161 881 4744 Fax: 0161 861 7027 — MB ChB 1980 Manch.

BLACK, Jeremy John Andrew Llandaff North Medical Centre, 99-101 Station Rd, Llandaff North, Cardiff CF14 2FD Tel: 029 2056 7822 Fax: 029 2056 7814 — MB BS 1987 Lond.; DRCOG 1992; Dip Ther. 1999; BA Camb. 1984; MRCGP 1993. (Charing Cross & Westminster Medical School) Princip. In Gen. Pract. Prev: Maj.-RAMC; SHO (Med.) Camb. Milit. Hosp. Aldershot.; SHO A&E Lancaster Roy. Hosp.

BLACK, Joan Elizabeth Bridget Milton Cottage, 13 Milton Road, Wokingham RG40 1DE Tel: 01189 783399; Milton Cottage, 13 Milton Road, Wokingham RG40 1DE Tel: 01189 783399 — LRCPI & LM, LRSCI & LM 1960; LRCPI & LM, LRCSI & LM 1960. (RCSI) Socs: Fell. BMA; BAACH. Prev: Princip. Clin. Med. Off. W. Berks. HA; Ho. Phys. Meath Hosp. & Co. Dub. Infirm.; Ho. Surg. Mercer's Hosp. Dub.

BLACK, Joan Sylvia 11 Davies Close, Barton Park, Marlborough SN8 1TW — MB BCh BAO 1955 Belf.; DPH 1958.

BLACK, Joanne Henrietta 98 Morgans Hill Road, Cookstown BT80 8BW — MB BS 1993 Lond.

BLACK, Mr John 79 Graham Road, Great Malvern, Malvern WR14 2JW Tel: 01684 573901 — MD 1978 Birm.; MA, MD Birm. 1978; MB Camb. 1969, BChir 1968; FRCS Eng. 1973. (St. Thos.) Cons. Surg. Worcester Roy. Infirm. Socs: Fell. Assn. Surgs.; Assn. Endoscopic Surgs. Prev: Lect. (Surg.) Univ. Birm.; Sen. Regist. (Surg.) Birm. AHA (T); Regist.(Surg.) Wolverhampton Hosp. Gp.

BLACK, John Alexander (retired) Appletree Cottage, The Street, Petham, Canterbury CT4 5QY — MB ChB St. And. 1948; MFCM 1972; DPH Liverp. 1959. Prev: Area Specialist (Pub. Health.) E. Health & Social Serv. Bd. N. . Irel.

BLACK, John Angus (retired) Victoria Mill House, Victoria Mill Road, Framlingham, Woodbridge IP13 9EG Tel: 01728 724131 — MB BChir 1942 Camb.; MD Camb. 1951; FRCP Lond. 1965, M 1943. Hon. Cons. Paediat. King's Coll. Hosp. & Hosp. for Sick

Childr. Lond.; Mem. Optimum Populat. Trust. Prev: Cons. Paediat. Childr. Hosp. & Jessop Hosp. for Wom. Sheff.

BLACK, Mr John Balfour McKay (retired) The Beeches, Houghton, Carlisle CA3 0LL Tel: 01228 22670 — MB ChB Ed. 1957; FRCS Ed. 1965. Cons. Surg. ENT Depts. Cumbld. & NW Midl. Clin. Area. Prev: Ho. Phys. Peel Hosp. Galashiels.

BLACK, Mr John Edward (retired) North Tyneside General Hospital, Rake Lane, North Shields NE29 — MB BCh BAO 1960 Belf.; BSc (1st cl. Hons.) Belf. 1957, MB BCh BAO 1960; FRCS Ed. 1964; FRACS 1972. Cons. Gen. Surg. N. Tyneside HA. Prev: Specialist (Surg.) W. Coast Hosp. Bd., N.Z.

BLACK, Mr John Henry Artt Lislea, 104 Galgorm Road, Ballymena BT42 1AE Tel: 01266 652452 — MB BCh BAO 1959 Belf.; FRCS Ed. 1967; DObst RCOG 1961. (Qu. Univ. Belf.) Cons. ENT Surg. N. Area Bd. Socs: N.. Irel. Audiological Assn. & Ulster Med. Soc.; Irish Otolaryng. Assn. Prev: SHO ENT Surg. Roy. Vict. Hosp. Belf.; Sen. Regist. ENT Surg. United Bristol Hosps.; Ho. Surg. Belf. City Hosp.

BLACK, Mr John Joseph Merrington John Radcliffe Hospital, Headley Way, Oxford OX3 9DU Tel: 01865 221467 Fax: 01865 222094 Email: john.black@orh.nhs.uk; 8 Old Nursery View, Kennington, Oxford OX1 5NT Tel: 01865 327577 Fax: 01865 327577 Email: johnjmblack@email.msn.com — MB BS 1984 Lond.; FRCS Ed. 1989; FFAEM 1999. (Guy's) Cons. Regist. (A & E Med.) John Radclife Hosp. Oxf.; Coll. Lect. (Anat.) St. Edmund Hall Oxf. Socs: BMA; Brit. Assn. Accid. & Emerg. Med. Prev: Regist. Rotat. (Cardiothoracic) Guy's, Brook, St Thos. & King's Coll. Hosps. Lond.; Cardiac Surgic. Research Fell. Nat. Heart & Lung Inst. & Harefield Hosp. Lond.; A & E Sen. Reg., Oxf. Region.

BLACK, John Michael 3A Gayton Road, London NW3 1TX Tel: 020 7435 3592 — MB BS 1959 Lond.; MRCS Eng. LRCP Lond. 1958; FRCPsych 1981, M 1971; DPM Eng. 1964. (Lond. Hosp.) Socs: Fell. Roy. Soc. Med. Prev: Cons. Psych. & Med. Dir. Bedford Child & Family Psychiat. Serv.; Research Asst. Social Med. Unit Guy's Hosp. Lond.; Sen. Regist. & Regist. Child Guid. Train. Centre Lond.

BLACK, Kenneth Miller 8 Broughton Place, Hamilton ML3 9HJ — MB ChB 1987 Ed.

BLACK, Lucy Diana 4 Moor Lane, Woodford, Stockport SK7 1PP — BM BCh 1988 Oxf.

BLACK, Margaret Colette 195 Garron Road, Glenariffe, Ballymena BT44 0RA — MB BCh BAO 1987 Belf.

BLACK, Margaret Louise Cross Cottage, South Cerney, Cirencester GL7 5UG Tel: 01285 861993 Fax: 01285 861993 Email: mlblack@easynet.co.uk — MB ChB Birm. 1947; MD Birm. 1992; MRCS Eng. LRCP Lond. 1947; DCH Eng. 1949. (Birm.) Prev: Regist. (Med.) Childr. Hosp. Birm.; Clin. Asst. (Haemat.) Solihull Hosp.; Ho. Phys. Birm. Gen. Hosp.

BLACK, Margaret Mary (retired) Appletree Cottage, The Street, Petham, Canterbury CT4 5QY — MSc NUI 1951, MB BCh BAO 1950; FFA RCS Eng. 1955. Prev: Cons. Anaesth. Our Lady's Hosp. Sick Childr. Crumlin & Austin Hosp. Melb., Austral.

BLACK, Marguerite Jean Kiln House, Pump Lane North, Marlow SL7 3RD — MB BS 1964 Lond.; MRCS Eng. LRCP Lond. 1964. (St. Thos.) Assoc. Specialist (Thoracic Med.) Wycombe Gen. Hosp. Prev: Med. Asst. (Gen. Med.) Wycombe Gen. Hosp.; Cas. Off. St. Thos. Hosp. Lond.; SHO (Anaesth.) & Ho. Surg. Peace Memor. Hosp. Watford.

BLACK, Marilyn Moore Child Development Centre, Poole Hospital NHS Trust, Poole BH15 2JB — MB ChB 1975 Birm.; MRCP (UK) 1979. (Birm.) Cons. Paediat. Poole Gen. Hosp. Socs: Fell. Roy. Coll. Paediat. & Child Health; Brit. Paediatric Neurol. Assn.

BLACK, Marjorie Department of Forensic Medicine and Science, University of Glasgow, Glasgow G12 8QQ Tel: 0141 330 4574 Fax: 0141 330 4602 — MB ChB 1985 Glas.; FRCPath 2001; MRCPath 1992. (Glas.) Cons. Forens. Path. Univ. Glas. Prev: Sen. Regist. (Path.) W.. Infirm. Glas.; Regist. (Path.) Glas. Roy. Infirm.

BLACK, Marjorie Macadie (retired) 1 Shaftesbury Terrace, Dundee DD2 1HJ Tel: 01382 669607 — MB ChB 1944 Aberd.; DPH Aberd. 1949. Prev: SCMO Dundee Health Dist.

BLACK, Professor Martin Munro St John's Institute of Dermatology, St Thomas' Hospital, London SE1 7EH Tel: 020 7922 8232 Fax: 020 7620 0890 Email: martinblack@kcl.ac.uk; 21 Deans Way, Hampstead Garden Suburb, London N2 0NF Tel: 020 8883 7900 Fax: 020 8883 4687 — MB BS Durh. 1963; MD Newc. 1970; FRCP Lond. 1979, M 1967; FRCPath 1991. Prof. of DermatoPath. & Dermatological ImmunoPath., St. John's Dermat. Centre, St. Thos. Hosp. Lond. Inst. Dermat. Lond.; Hon. Cons. Dermat. to the Army; Pres. Europ. Acad. Dermat. Venereal. 2000 - 2002. Socs: Fell. (Counc. Mem.) Roy. Soc. Med.; (Pres.) Internat. Comm. Dermat. Path.; (Ex-Hon. Sec.) Brit. Assn. Dermat. Prev: Sen. Regist. (Dermat.) Inst. Dermat. Lond.; Regist. (Dermat.) Roy. Vict. Infirm. Newc.; Ho. Phys. & Ho. Surg. Roy. Vict. Infirm. Newc.

BLACK, Mary Ethna c/o Apple Tree Cottage, The Street, Petham, Canterbury CT4 5QY — MB BCh BAO 1982 NUI; FFPHM 1999; 1998 FAFPHM; BA NUI 1982; MPH Harvard Univ. Boston 1990; MRCP (UK) 1986; MFPHM 1993; DObst RCPI 1984; DCH NUI 1984; DTM & H Liverp. 1984. Head of Child Protec. Sect. UNICEF Bosnia & Herzegovina. Prev: Prof. of Pub. health univ of Qu.sland Australia; Technical Off. Coordination & Resource Mobilisation Unit WHO Regional Office.

BLACK, Mary Pelc (Cuthill) Tel: 0131 536 9400 Fax: 0131 536 9405; 8 Greenbank Terrace, Edinburgh EH10 6ER — MB ChB 1977 Dundee; MRCGP 1981; DRCOG 1979. Princip. GP Edin.

BLACK, Michael Portscatho Surgery, Gerrans Hill, Portscatho, Truro TR2 5EE Tel: 01872 580345 Fax: 01872 580788; Little Treluggan Manor, Ruan Highlanes, Truro TR2 5LP Tel: 01872 580348 — MB ChB 1976 Manch.; MRCGP 1985; DRCOG 1981. (Manch.)

BLACK, Michael Anthony Hunslet Health Centre, 24 Church St., Leeds LS10 2PE Tel: 0113 270 5194 Fax: 01332 702795 — MB ChB 1964 Leeds; BSc (Hons.) Anat. Leeds 1962. Prev: Clin. Asst. (ENT) St. Jas. Hosp. Univ. Leeds.

BLACK, Mr Michael John Munro 3 Greenacres, Ponteland, Newcastle upon Tyne NE20 9RT Tel: 01661 823338 — MB BS 1966 Durh.; FRCS Eng. 1970. Cons. Plastic Surg. Roy. Vict. Infirm. Newc. U. Tyne.

BLACK, Professor Nicholas Andrew Health Services Research Unit, Department of Public Health & Policy, LSHTM, Keppel St., London WC1E 7HT Tel: 020 7927 2228 Fax: 020 4363611 Email: nick.black@ishtm.ac.uk — MB ChB 1974 Birm.; MD Birm. 1983; FFPHM RCP (UK) 1990; MFCM RCP (UK) 1984; DCH Eng. 1976; DRCOG 1976. Prof. Health Servs. Research Lond. Sch. Hyg. & Trop. Med.

BLACK, Nicol Messer Imrie North of Tyne communicable Diseases Control Unit, Institute of Pathology, Newcastle General Hospital, Newcastle upon Tyne NE20 9PU Tel: 0191 273 3584 Fax: 0191 272 4139 Email: nmiblack@cdcu.demp.co.uk; 3 Riverside, Ponteland, Newcastle upon Tyne NE20 9PU — MB ChB 1972 St. And.; MFPHM RCM 1989 (UK); MFPHM RCP (UK) 1989; MRCGP 1977; FFPHM 2000 UK. Cons. Communicable Dis. Control Newc. & N. Tyneside HA. Prev: Regional Cons. Communicable Dis. Control & Environm. Health N.. RHA; Cons. Primary Care Riyadh Milit. Hosp., Saudi Arabia; Lect. (Med. Educat.) Univ. Dundee.

BLACK, Paula Dorothy (cons. rooms), 27a Queens Terrace, London NW8 6EA Tel: 020 7483 0099 Fax: 020 7483 3988; 36 Briavels Court, Ashley Road, Epsom KT18 5HP Tel: 01372 727264 — LMSSA 1951 Lond.; DObst RCOG 1960. (W. Lond.) Indep. Psychother. Lond. Socs: Affil. RCPsych; BMA. Prev: Assoc. Specialist (Psychiat.) Horton Hosp. Epsom; Asst. Dept. O & G E.bourne Hosp. Gp.; Regist. (O & G) St. Richard's & Roy. W. Sussex Hosps. Chichester.

BLACK, Mr Peter David 11 Poplar Avenue, Gorleston-on-Sea, Great Yarmouth NR31 7PW Tel: 01493 602854 Fax: 01493 602854 Email: black.eyes@virgin.net — MB BS Lond. 1967; BSc (Physiol., Hons.) Lond. 1964; FRCS Eng. 1975; MRCS Eng. LRCP Lond. 1967; FRCOphth 1988; DO Eng. 1972. (St. Geo.) Cons. Ophth. Surg. Jas. Paget Hosp. Gorleston. Socs: Fell. Amer. Acad. Ophth. Prev: Cons. Surg. (Ophth.) RAF Hosp. Ely; Hon. Cons. Surg. (Ophth.) Addenbrooke's Hosp. Camb.; Surg. St. John's Ophth. Hosp. Jerusalem, Israel.

BLACK, Peter John 20 Foxes Dale, Blackheath, London SE3 9BQ Tel: 020 8852 5854 — MB 1967 Camb.; MA; BChir 1966; MRCPath 1973. (Camb. & St. Thos.) Cons. Haemat. Qu. Eliz. Hosp., woolwich< Lond. Prev: Sen. Regist. (Haemat.) Guy's Hosp. Lond.; Ho. Surg. St. Thos. Hosp. Lond.; Regist. (Path.) Guy's Hosp. Lond.

BLACK, Mr Peter Ruthven Macgregor 74 Dunkeld Road, Ecclesall, Sheffield S11 9HP Tel: 0114 236 7293 Email: prmblack@netscape.net — MB BCh 1989 Wales; FRCS Ed. 1993;

ATLS RCS Eng. 1994; Dip. Clin. Gait Anal. Univ. Strathclyde 1997; FRCS Orth.1998. (Wales) Regist. Rotat. (Orthop.) Sheff. Socs: Brit. Orthop. Train. Assn.; Brit. Orthop. Assn.; Fell. Roy. Coll. Surg. Edin. Prev: SHO (Orthop.) N.. Gen. Hosp. Sheff.; SHO (Gen. Surg.) St. Jas. Hosp. & Seacroft Hosp. Leeds; SHO (Orthop.) Harrogate Dist. Hosp.

BLACK, Mr Randal John Carmarthenshire NHS Trust, West Wales General Hospital, Glangwili, Carmarthen Tel: 01267 227166 Fax: 01267 227983; Holcwm W., Ferryside SA17 5TY Tel: 01267 267876 Fax: 01267 267903 Email: holcwmwest@aol.com — LRCPSI 1975; FRCSI 1980. Cons. Traum. & Orthop. Surg. Carmarthenshire NHS Trust. Socs: Corr. Mem. Irish Orthop. Assoc.; BOA Counc. Mem. Prev: Sen. Regist. (Orthop.) Meath, Adelaide & Nat. Childr. Hosps. Dub.

BLACK, Rebecca Sian Dept of O+G, John Radcliffe Hospital, Headley Way, Oxford OX3 9DL; 8 Old Nursery View, Kennington, Oxford OX1 5NT — MB BChir 1993 Camb.; MRCOG 1999. Regist. (O + G) John Radcliffe Hosp. Prev: Research Fell. (Obst.) St. Geo. Hosp. Med. Sch. Lond.

BLACK, Robert Lester (retired) 33 Daylesford Road, Cheadle SK8 1LE Tel: 0141 428 2477 — LRCP LRCS Ed. LRFPS Glas. 1947; BA Open 1983; MRCGP 1954. Prev: Ho. Surg. Plastic & Maxillo-Facial Unit St. Jas. Hosp. Leeds.

BLACK, Robert Neil Henry 45 Swan Spring Avenue, Edinburgh EH10 6NA — MB ChB 1993 Manch.

BLACK, Roger Anthony Lester Whitevale Medical Group, 30 Whitevale Street, Glasgow G31 1QS Tel: 0141 554 2974 Fax: 0141 554 3979 — MB ChB 1981 Dundee; MPhil Glas. 1997; MRCGP 1985; DFFP 1993; DFM Glas. 1993; Cert. Family Plann. JCC 1985; DRCOG 1984. Hon. Sen. Lect. in Gen. Pract. Univ. of Glas. Prev: SHO (Med. & Paediat.) Stepping Hill Hosp. Stockport; Ho. Off. (Med. & Rheum.) Hope Hosp. Salford.

BLACK, Roland George 98 Morgans Hill Road, Cookstown BT80 8BW — MB ChB 1993 Ed.

BLACK, Ronald (retired) 49 Vicarage Lane, Northampton NN2 6QS Tel: 01609 713755 — MB ChB 1934 Glas. Prev: Asst. Cas. Surg. Glas. Roy. Infirm.

BLACK, Rosemary Joy Department of Dermatology, Craigavon Area Hospital, Craigavon BT63 5QQ; 19 Dorchester Park, Belfast BT9 6RH — MB BCh BAO 1981 Belf.; MB BCh BAO (Commend. Med. & Surg.) Belf. 1981; MRCPI 1991; MRCGP (Distinc.) 1986; DRCOG 1986; DCH RCPI 1985. (Queen's University Belfast) Assoc. Specialist (Dermat.) Craigavon Area Hosp. Socs: Fell. Ulster Med. Soc.; Brit. Assn. Dermat.

BLACK, Sarah Elizabeth Wonford House Hospital, Dryden Road, Exeter EX2 5AF Tel: 01392 487 8989 — MB BChir 1981 Camb.; MA Camb. 1982; MRCPsych 1986. Cons. Old Age Psychiat. Exeter. Prev: Cons. Psychogeriat. Gateshead HA; Regist. & Sen. Regist. Rotat. (Psychiat.) Newc. HA.

BLACK, Sarah Katharine 28 Longlands Road, Slaithwaite, Huddersfield HD7 5DN — MB ChB 1992 Ed.

BLACK, Sarah Marie 5 Gloucester Close, Tytherington, Macclesfield SK10 2JZ Tel: 01625 432843 Fax: 01625 613629 Email: drsblack@hotmail.com — BM BS 1996 Nottm.; BMedSci 1994. SHO (Med.) E. Gloucestershire NHS Trust Cheltenham. Prev: Resid. Med. Off. (A & E) Perth, W. Australia; Jun. Ho. Off. City Hosp. Nottm.; Jun. Ho. Off. MusGr. Pk. Hosp. Taunton.

BLACK, Sheila Mary (retired) Rivendell, Westwood Avenue, Stranraer DG9 8BT Tel: 01776 702920 — MB ChB Ed. 1950. Prev: Med. Off. (Child Health) Dumfries & Galloway Area Health Bd.

BLACK, Sheila McKenzie Occupational Health Department, Civic Centre, Barras Bridge, Newcastle upon Tyne NE1 8PB Tel: 0191 232 8520; 8 Birney Edge, Ponteland, Newcastle upon Tyne NE20 9JJ — MB ChB 1975 Dundee; DIH Eng. 1986. Occupat. Health Phys. Newc. CC. Prev: Med. Off. BBC; Med. Off. GLC.

BLACK, Stephen John Chapeloak Practice, 347 Oakwood Lane, Leeds LS8 3HA Tel: 0113 240 9999 Fax: 0113 235 9233; 347/349 Oakwood Lane, Leeds LS8 3HA Tel: 0113 240 9999 — MB ChB 1976 Leeds; DA Eng. 1979.

BLACK, Stephen Landale Park View Surgery, Haverflatts Lane, Milnthorpe LA7 7PS Tel: 015395 63327 Fax: 015395 64059; Ayrefield, Silverdale Road, Arnside, Carnforth LA5 0EH Tel: 01524 761823 — MB ChB 1971 Manch.; DObst RCOG 1973. (Leeds) Socs: BMA. Prev: Trainee GP Nottm. & Manch. VTS.

BLACK, Susan Margaret Coniston Medical Practice, The Parade, Coniston Road, Patchway, Bristol BS34 5TF Tel: 0117 969 2508 Fax: 0117 959 0456 — MA Oxf. 1970, BM BCh 1970; MRCGP 1990; DCH RCP Lond. 1989; DRCOG 1988. (Oxford) GP Princip. Socs: BMA; NHS Fed.; MEDACT.

BLACK, Teresa Jane Wolverhampton Healthcare NHS Trust, 10/12 Tettenhall Road, Wolverhampton WV1 4SA; Upper House, Buildwas Road, Ironbridge, Salop, Telford TF8 7DW — MB ChB 1979 Bristol; MRCPsych. 1984. Cons. Psychotherapist Wolverhampton Healthcare NHS Trust. Socs: Manch. Med. Soc. Prev: Cons. Psychother. Coventry Healthcare NHS Trust; Cons. Psychother. Ment. Health Servs. Salford; Sen. Regist. (Psychother.) Manch. Roy. Infirm.

BLACK, Thomas William 10 Crane Close, Stratford-upon-Avon CV37 9EE — MB ChB 1996 Birm.

BLACK, Timothy Reuben Ladbroke, CBE Gorsedene Mill House, Mill Lane, Lower Beeding, Horsham RH13 6PX Tel: 01403 891523 Fax: 01403 891599 — MB BS Lond. 1963; MRCP Lond. 1966; MRCS Eng. LRCP Lond. 1962; DTM & H Liverp. 1968; MPH N. Carolina 1970. (St. Geo.) Chief Exec. Marie Stopes Internat. Socs: Fell.Roy.soc.Med; Fell.Roy.soc.Trop.Med.Hyg.; Fell.Fac.Fam.Plann.MRCOGT. Prev: Cons. Phys. New Guinea Med. Serv.; Regist. Harefield Hosp.; Ho. Surg. & Ho. Phys. Harare Hosp. Salisbury, S. Rhodesia.

BLACK, Victoria Elizabeth Gilford Health Centre, Castleview, Gilford, Craigavon BT63 6JS Tel: 028 3883 1225; 67 Moygannon Road, Donaghcloney, Craigavon BT66 7PN Tel: 01762 323182 — MB BCh BAO 1984 Belf.; MRCGP 1989; DCH Dub. 1988. (Qu. Univ. Belf.) Socs: BMA; Assoc. Mem. Nat. Assn. Family Plann.; Roy. Coll. Gen. Pract. Prev: GP Dungannon; Trainee GP Stranraer Health Centre; SHO (Cas., Med., Paediat. & Gyn.) Craigavon Area Hosp.

BLACK, William The State Hospital, Carstairs, Lanark ML11 8RP Tel: 01555 840112 Fax: 01555 840024 Email: blackw@tsh.org.uk — MB ChB 1985 Aberd.; MRCPsych 1990. (Aberdeen) Cons. Forens. Psychiat. State Hosp. Carstairs.; Vis. Forens. Psychiat.; HMP Corntovale, Stirling. Prev: Sen. Regist. (Forens. Psychiat.) Rampton Hosp. Notts.; Regist. (Psychiat.) Roy. Edin. Hosp.

BLACK, William David (retired) 172 Craigcrook Road, Edinburgh EH4 3PP Tel: 0131 336 3309 — MB ChB 1951 Ed. Prev: GP I. of Bute, Liberton Edin. & Aberchirder.

BLACK, Mr William Pollok (retired) Dhumount, Hilton, Dornoch, Sunderland IV25 3PW — MB ChB Glas. 1950; MD Glas. 1964; FRCS Glas. 1969; FRCS Ed. 1959; FRCOG 1967, M 1957; DObst RCOG 1954. Prev: Cons. O & G Roy. Infirm. & Glas. Roy. Matern. Hosp.

BLACKADDER, Eric Sutton (retired) 14 East Shore, Pittenweem, Anstruther KY10 2NH Email: eric@ericb.demon.co.uk — MB ChB 1951 Ed.; DSM Ed. 1969; FRCP Ed. 1988, M 1985; FRCP Glas. 1983, M 1980; FFOM RCP Lond. 1984, MFOM 1978; MFPHM 1974; MRCGP 1961; DIH Soc. Apoth. Lond. 1968; DObst RCOG 1956. Prev: Governor & Gp. Med. Dir. BUPA.

BLACKALL, David Henry 84 Heol Las, North Cornelly, Pyle, Bridgend CF33 4DL Tel: 01656 579 — MB BCh 1956 Wales.

BLACKBOURN, Michael Standidge (retired) The Lodge, 26 Church Lane, Timberland, Lincoln LN4 3SB Tel: 01526 378235 — MB ChB Manch. 1962; MRCS Eng. LRCP Lond. 1962; Dph Manch. 1968; DCH RCPS Glas. 1965; DObst RCOG 1965.

BLACKBOURN, Robert James 26 Church Lane, Timberland, Lincoln LN4 3SB — MB BS 1993 Lond.

BLACKBURN, Alan Rodney The Oaks Surgery, Applegarth Avenue, Park Barn, Guildford GU2 8LZ Tel: 01483 563424 Fax: 01483 563789 — MB ChB 1967 Manch.; DObst RCOG 1970. (Manch.) Socs: Guildford Med. Soc.

BLACKBURN, Amanda Ranskill Mount, Blyth Road, Ranskill, Retford DN22 8LR — MB ChB 1982 Sheff.; FCAnaesth. 1989. Cons. Anaesth. Rotherham Gen. Hosps. Trust.

BLACKBURN, Andrew Michael Thomas Belmont Surgery, St. James Square, Wadhurst TN5 6BJ Tel: 01892 782121 Fax: 01892 783989; Old Beeches, Turners Green Road, Wadhurst TN5 6TR — BM BS 1986 Nottm.; BMedSci (Hons.) Nottm. 1984; DCH RCP Lond. 1992; DObst Auckland 1989.

BLACKBURN, Ann Marie, AE Dept of Healthcare of the Elderly, King's College Hospital, East Dulwich Grove, London SE22 8PT Tel: 020 8778 7957; Tel: 0208 464 8775 — MB BChir 1974 Camb.; BA (Hons. Pharmacol.) 1971; MD 1981; MA Camb. 1975; FRCP

Lond. 1994; MRCP (UK) 1976. (Cambridge University and King's College Hospital London) Cons. Phys. & Hon. Sen. Lect. Kings Coll. Sch. Med. & Dent. & King's Coll. Hosp. Lond.; Maj. RAMC (v) 1995-; Med. Adviser to S.E.Lond. Abbeyfield extra care Soc. Socs: Brit. Geriat. Soc. & Endocrine Soc. Prev: Lect. (Med.) Guy's Hosp. Med. Sch. Lond.; MRC Research Fell. Roy. Postgrad. Med. Sch. Hammersmith Hosp. Lond.; Squadron Ldr. Roy. Auxil. Air Force 1978 - 95.

BLACKBURN, Anna Louise 49 Padgate, Thorpe End, Norwich NR13 5DG Tel: 01603 702213 — MB ChB 1993 Manch.; MRCP (UK) 1997. (Manch.) GP Regist. & Staff Grade Anaesth. Med. Paget Hosp. Gorleston VTS. Prev: GP VTS.

BLACKBURN, Blandina Seraphina 61 Fairway Avenue, Tilehurst, Reading RG30 4QB — MRCS Eng. LRCP Lond. 1986; MD Bombay 1981, MB BS 1978.

BLACKBURN, Mr Christopher William Department Oral & Maxillofacial Surgery, Hull Royal Infirmary, Anlaby Road, Hull HU3 2JZ Tel: 01482 28541; Mires Farm House, The Mires, North Newbald, York YO43 4SE — MB ChB 1975 Dundee; MDS Sheff. 1988; BDS Ed. 1971; FRCS Ed. 1986; FDS RCS Ed. 1978. Cons. (Oral & Maxillofacial Surg.) Hull & E. Yorks. HA.; Hon. Clin. Tutor Univ. Sheff.; Clin. Dent. Tutor N. Humberside. Prev: Lect./Hon. Cons. Dept. Oral & Maxillofacial Surg. Univ. Manch.

BLACKBURN, Daniel James 29 Hartington Road, Toxteth, Liverpool L8 0SD — MB ChB 1998 Liverp.; MB ChB Liverp 1998.

BLACKBURN, Dean Anthony 64 Cedar Glade, Dunnington, York YO19 5PL — MB ChB 1992 Leic.

BLACKBURN, John Christopher 12 High Street, Chiseldon, Swindon SN4 0NG — MB ChB 1966 Ed.; MRCGP 1973.

BLACKBURN, John Roger (retired) 2 Roseway, Ashton-on-Ribble, Preston PR2 1HE Tel: 01772 729763 — MRCS Eng. LRCP Lond. 1961.

BLACKBURN, Joseph Robert Chan Staines Health Centre, Knowle Green, Staines TW18 8XD Tel: 01784 42456 619 — BM BCh 1981 Oxf.; MA Camb. 1982, BA 1978; MRCP (UK) 1984; MRCGP 1986; DCH RCP Lond. 1986; DRCOG 1985. Postgrad. Tutor (Gen. Pract.) Ashford Hosp. Middlx.; Clin. Gov. Surrey Thames PCG; Caldicott Guardian Surrey Thames PCG; GP Specialist in Diabetes, Surrey Thames PCG. Prev: Trainee GP Hammersmith Hosp. VTS; SHO (Gen. Med.) Freeman Hosp. Newc. u. Tyne; Chiarm. Surrey Thames PCG.

BLACKBURN, Kenneth Fleming (retired) 34 Anthony's Avenue, Poole BH14 8JH Tel: 01202 707684 — MRCS Eng. LRCP Lond. 1941. Prev: Cas. Off., Ho. Phys. & Anaesth. & Ho. Phys. Skin Dept. Croydon Gen.

BLACKBURN, Louise Mary 77 Crookes Road, Sheffield S10 5BD — MB ChB 1995 Sheff. Sen. SHO (Paediat.) Rotherham DGH.

BLACKBURN, Mark Richard William 8 Finsbury Avenue, Lytham St Annes FY8 1BP — MB BS 1994 Newc.

BLACKBURN, Michael Eric Chan 5 Pasture View, Underwood Park, Sherburn in Elmet, Leeds LS25 6LZ — MB ChB 1985 Leeds; BSc (Hons.) Leeds 1982, MB ChB 1985; MRCP (UK) 1988. Tutor & Hon. Regist. (Paediat.) Univ. Leeds. Prev: SHO (Paediat.) St. Jas. Univ. Hosp. Leeds; SHO (Paediat./Cardiol.) Killingbeck Hosp. Leeds; Regist. (Paediat.) Roy. Infirm. Huddersfield.

BLACKBURN, Mr Munindra Nigel Coach Cottage, 38 Hersham Road, Walton-on-Thames KT12 1JH Tel: 01932 21849 — MB BS 1972 Lond.; FRCS Eng. 1977; FRCS Ed. 1976. (King's Coll. Hosp.)

BLACKBURN, Muriel (retired) 6 Hilton Court, Brooks Rd, Sutton Coldfield B72 1HN — MB BS Lond. 1959; FRANZCP 1986, M 1973; DPM Leeds 1966.

BLACKBURN, Patricia Anna Community Mental Health Team, 7 Balcen Street, Hull HU2 8HP Tel: 01482 321590 Fax: 01482 371591; Mires Farm House, The Mires, North Newbald, York YO43 4SE — MB ChB 1972 Aberd.; MRCPsych 1991. Cons. Psychiat. Hull & E. Riding Community Health NHS Trust. Prev: Sen. Regist. (Psychiat.) Bootham Pk. Hosp. York; SCMO N. Manch. Gen. Hosp.; Regist. (Psychiat.) Sheff.

BLACKBURN, Peter John, Brigadier late RAMC Retd. President, Standing Medical Board, Delhi Barracks, Tidworth SP9 7AE Tel: 01980 841221; Kimpton Lodge, Kimpton, Andover SP11 8PH Tel: 01264 772133 — MB BCh BAO 1958 Dub.; MA Dub. 1960; FFOM 1987, M 1981; FFCM 1982, M 1973; DPH Bristol 1971; DTM & H Eng. 1967; DIH Soc. Apoth. Lond. 1962. (TC Dub.) Pres. Standing Med. Bd. Tidworth. Prev: Cdr. RAMC Train. Gp. Aldershot; Army Cons. Adviser Pub. Health Med.; Comanding Off. Camb. Milit. Hosp. Aldershot.

BLACKBURN, Roger Anthony (retired) The Old Pound, Queen St., Cubbington, Leamington Spa CV32 7NA Tel: 01926 426594 — MB BCh BAO 1962 Dub.; MA Dub. 1970.

BLACKBURN, Sally D Haworth Road Health Centre, Haworth Road, Bradford BD9 6LL Tel: 01274 541701 Fax: 01274 546533 — MB ChB 1960 Leeds; MMedSci Leeds 1986. (Leeds) Prev: Ho. Off. (Surg. & Paediat.) St. Luke's Hosp. Bradford.

BLACKBURN, Stella Catherine Frances 15 Little Comptons, Horsham RH13 5UW — MB BS 1983 Lond.; MA Camb. 1984; MSc 1993; Dip Pharm. Med.; Dip Lond Sch Hyg & Trop Med. Princip. Scientif. Admin., Europ. Med. Eval.s Soc.; Hon Lect. Lond. Sch. of Hyg. & Trop. Med.

BLACKBURN, Mr Thomas Philip David 61 Fairway Avenue, Tilehurst, Reading RG30 4QB — MB BS 1981 Lond.; FRCS Eng. 1986.

BLACKBURN, Timothy David Vernon 11A Birchington Road, London N8 8HR — MB BS 1994 Lond.; MA Camb. 1995. SHO (Anaesth.) Hillingdon Hosp., Uxbridge.

BLACKBURN, Timothy Keith 15 Herne Hill, London SE24 9NF — MB BS 1998 Lond.; MB BS Lond 1998.

BLACKBURN, Victoria Mary Margaret 66 Leighton Road, London NW5 2QE — MB BS 1994 Lond.

BLACKBURNE, Mr John Stephen 152 Harley Street, London W1N 1HH Tel: 020 8446 4573 — BM BCh 1966 Oxf.; MA, BM BCh Oxf. 1966; FRCS Eng. 1972. (Oxf. & St. Bart.) Cons. Surg. (Orthop.) Barnet Gen. Hosp. Lond. Socs: BMA; Brit. Orthop. Assn.

BLACKER, Mr Anthony James Robins Pinderfields Hospital, Aberford Road, Wakefield WF1 4DG; 18 Tenterden Way, Leeds LS15 8XJ Tel: 07818 073688 Email: tony@blacker.org — MB ChB 1992 Birm.; FRCS Irel. 1996. (Birmingham) Specialist Regist. (Urol.) Yorksh. Socs: BAUS; BMA.

BLACKER, Charles Vernon Russell The Priory Hospital, Bristol Bs16 1EQ Tel: 0117 952 5255 Fax: 0117 952 5552 — MB BS 1977 Lond.; MD Lond. 1989; FRCPsych 1994, M 1983. (Guy's Hosp.) Cons. Psychologist, The Priory Hosp. Gp.. Bristol; Hon. Sen. Lect. Dept of Ment. Health Exeter. Socs: Roy. Soc. Med.; Med. Defence Union. Prev: Cons. & Hon. Lect. (Psychiat.) St. Bart. Hosp. Lond.; Hon. Sen. Regist. St. Bart. Hosp. Lond.; Regist. (Psychiat.) Guy's Hosp. Lond.

BLACKER, Ian The Gables, 11 Nab Wood Drive, Shipley BD18 4HP — MB ChB 1966 Leeds; DObst RCOG 1968; FFA RCS Eng. 1973. (Leeds) Cons. Anaesth. Bradford AHA. Prev: Sen. Regist. (Anaesth.) Yorks. RHA; Regist. (Anaesth.) Gen. Infirm. Leeds.

BLACKER, John Patrick Drummond New Road Surgery, 46 New Road, Bromsgrove B60 2JS Tel: 01527 872027 Fax: 01527 574516; Newlands, 27 New Road, Bromsgrove B60 2JL Tel: 01527 72330 — MB ChB 1968 Manch.; FRCGP 1995, M 1974; DA Eng. 1970. (Manch.) Hon. Sen. Clin. Lect. Univ. Birm.; Chairm. Hereford & Worcs. MAAG. Prev: SHO (Anaesth.) Ipswich & E. Suff. Hosps.; Ho. Off. (O & G) Univ. Hosp. S. Manch.

BLACKER, Pauline Alice Child & Family Psychiatry, Rykneld, Bedford Close, Bedford St., Derby DE22 3PF Tel: 01332 347323 Fax: 01332 205310; 32 Havelock Street, Sheffield S10 2FP Tel: 0114 272 1814 — MB ChB 1976 Sheff. Child & Family Therapist Psychiat. S.. Derbysh. Ment. Health NHS Trust. Prev: Ho. Off. Sheff. Childr. Hosp. NHS Trust; Ho. Off. W.on Pk. Hosp. NHS Trust Sheff.

BLACKETT, Mr Richard Lees Pen-y-Dre, Pentwyn Lane, Govilon, Abergavenny NP7 9RW Fax: 01873 859168; Pen-y-Dre, Pentwyn Lane, Govilon, Abergavenny NP7 9RW Tel: 01873 831396 — MB ChB 1974 Leeds; MB ChB (Hons.) Leeds 1974; BSc (Hons.) Leeds 1971, ChM 1983; FRCS Eng. 1978. Cons. Gen. Surg. Nevill Hall Hosp. Abergavenny. Socs: Assn. Surg.; Vasc. Surgic. Soc.; BMA. Prev: Sen. Regist. (Gen. Surg.) Univ. Hosp. Wales Cardiff & Maelor Hosp. Wrexham; Research Fell. Univ. Dept. Surg. Leeds Gen. Infirm.

BLACKETT, William Logan (retired) Broadgait, Gullane EH31 2DH Tel: 01620 843159 — MB ChB 1946 Ed.; MRCGP 1979.

BLACKFORD, Mr Hubert Noel c/o Fitzwilliam Hospital, Milton Way, South Bretton, Peterborough PE3 9AQ Tel: 01733 261717; Wood Cottage, Laundry Road, Apethorpe, Peterborough PE8 5DQ Tel: 01780 470264 Fax: 01780 470264 — MB BChir 1971 Camb.; MSc Lond. 1980; MA, MB Camb. 1971, BChir 1970; FRCS Eng.

1975. (St Thomas' Hospital London) Cons. Urol. Edith Cavell Hosp. P'boro. Prev: Sen. Regist. (Urol.) Guy's Hosp. Lond.; Sen. Regist. (Gen. Surg.) St. Thos. Hosp. Lond.; Regist. (Surg.) St. Thos. Hosp. Lond.

BLACKFORD, Kirsten Elizabeth Molly 41 Arundel Way, Newquay TR7 3AG — MB ChB 1993 Birm.; ChB Birm. 1993.

BLACKFORD, Patrick 2 Edge Hill Road, Four Oaks, Sutton Coldfield B74 4NU Tel: 0121 353 1854 Fax: 0956 141692 — MB ChB 1977 Birm.; MRCGP 1987; T(GP) 1991; DAvMed 1988; DRCOG 1983.

BLACKFORD, Sharon Louise Walker Department of Dermatology, Singleton Hospital, Sketty, Swansea SA2 8QA Tel: 01792 205666 Fax: 01792 285324 — MB BCh 1984 Wales; MRCP (UK) 1988. Cons. Dermat. Singleton Hosp. Swansea.

BLACKHALL, Fiona Helen Flat 4, Ship Canal House, 21 Slate Wharf, Manchester M15 4SX — MB ChB 1992 Manch.; BSc (Hons.) St. And. 1989; MRCP (UK) 1995. Clin. Lect. (Med. Oncol.) Christie Hosp. Manch. Socs: (Sec.) Med. Wom. Federat. (Younger Co-opted Mem. of Exec. Comm.); BMA; Doctors for a Wom. Choice in Abortion Assn. Prev: SHO (Med. Oncol. & Endocrine) Christie Hosp. Manch.; SHO (Gen. Med.) Manch. Roy. Infirm.; SHO (Cardio Respirat. Med.) Wythenshawe Hosp.

BLACKHURST, Guthrie Flat 4, 26 Athole Gardens, Glasgow G12 9BB — MB ChB 1991 Glas.

BLACKHURST, Helen Ruth 20 Manor Way, Burbage, Hinckley LE10 2NN — MB ChB 1997 Manch.

BLACKIE, Dominic Mark Department of General Practice, Whelan Building, University Liverpool, Liverpool L69 — MB ChB 1984 Liverp.; LMCC 1993; MRCGP 1990. Sen. Clin. Lect. (Gen. Pract.) Dept. Primary Care Univ. Liverp. Socs: Liverp. MAAG.

BLACKIE, Philip John 64 Milton Court Road, London SE14 6JJ — MB BS 1997 Lond.

BLACKIE, Ronald Alasdair Stuart 43a Wimpole Street, London W1M 7AF Tel: 020 7486 5091 Email: rasblackie@aol.com; 28 Claremont Road, Teddington TW11 8DG — MB ChB 1976 Ed.; BSc (Med. Sci.) (Hons.) Ed. 1973, MB ChB 1976; FRCPath 1997; MRCPath 1983. (Edinburgh University) Indep. Priv. Histopath. & Cytologist. Socs: Soc. Apoth.; Med. Soc. of Lond.; Roy. Soc. Med. Prev: Cons. Pathol. Farrer-Brown Histopath.; Cons. Pathol. JS Path. PLC; Sen. Lect. (Pathol.) Char. Cross.

BLACKLAY, Anne Elizabeth Rock House, Priory Road, Warwick CV34 4NA — MB BS 1976 Lond. Staff Grade Paediat. Oncol. Birm. Childr.'s Hosp.

BLACKLAY, Harriet Catherine The Rowans Surgery, 1 Windermere Road, Streatham, London SW16 5HF Tel: 020 8764 0407 — MB BS 1975 Lond.; MRCGP 1990. Socs: Brit. Med. Acupunct. Soc.

BLACKLAY, Mr James Bryden (retired) Washington, Smeeth, Ashford TN25 6RD Tel: 0130 381 3210 — MB BS 1943 Lond.; FRCS Eng. 1948; DLO Eng. 1953. Prev: ENT Surg. Roy. Vict. Hosp. Folkestone & William Harvey Hosp.

BLACKLAY, Oliver Hugh, TD (retired) 19 Little Meadow, Loughton, Milton Keynes MK5 8EH Tel: 01908 605991 Email: hughblacllay@luneone.net — MB BS 1951 Lond.; MRCGP 1966. Prev: GP, Bolton.

BLACKLAY, Mr Peter Francis Warwickshire Private Hospital, The Chase, Old Milverton Lane, Leamington Spa CV32 6RW Tel: 01926 427971; Rock House, Priory Road, Warwick CV34 4NA Tel: 01926 490523 — MB BS 1976 Lond.; MS Lond. 1986; FRCS Eng. 1980. Cons. Gen. & Vasc. Surg. S. Warks Hosp.; Cons. Vasc. Surg., Walsgrave Hosp., Coventry. Prev: Sen. Regist. (Surg.) Lond. Hosp. Whitechapel; Lect. (Vasc. Surg.) Sydney Univ. NSW Austral.

BLACKLEDGE, George Roden Peter Medical Affairs Department, Zeneca Pharmaceuticals, Alderley Park, Macclesfield SK10 4TG Tel: 01625 512392 Fax: 01625 516904 — MB BChir 1972 Camb.; MB BChir Camb. 1973; PhD Manch. 1981; MD Camb. 1982; FRCP Lond. 1990; MRCP (UK) 1975. Head Oncol. Clin. Research Zeneca Pharmaceut. Prev: Hon. Cons. Med. Oncol. & Dir. W. Midl. Cancer Clin. Trials Unit; Sen. Lect. (Med. Oncol.) Dept. Med. Qu. Eliz. Hosp. & Dudley Rd. Hosp. Birm.

BLACKLEE, Mr Malcolm Ernest Pickering Surgery, Southgate, Pickering YO18 8BL Tel: 01751 472441 Fax: 01751 475400; Churchfield House, Newton-on-Rawcliffe, Pickering YO18 8QA Tel: 01751 472585 Fax: 01751 477842 — MB BS 1961 Lond.; FRCS Ed. 1971; MRCS Eng. LRCP Lond. 1961; DObst RCOG 1964. (Guy's) Hosp. Pract. (Gen. Surg.) Whitby Hosp. N. Yorks. Socs: York Med. Soc.

BLACKLIDGE, Robert David The Health Centre, Park Road, Frome BA11 1EZ Tel: 01373 464343 Fax: 01373 464343; Park Hill Grange, Bath Road, Frome BA11 2HL Tel: 01373 463436 — MB 1963 Camb.; BChir 1962; DObst RCOG 1965. (Guy's) Prev: Ho. Phys. & Ho. Surg. St. Martin's Hosp. Bath; Ho. Surg. (O & G) Ulster Hosp. Dundonald.

BLACKLIN, Jill Greasby Surgery, Greasby Health Centre, Greasby Road, Greasby, Wirral CH49 3NH Tel: 0151 678 3000 Fax: 0151 604 1813 — MB ChB 1975 Liverp.; MRCOG 1980.

BLACKLOCK, Mr Alexander Robert Eadie Davenport Consultants Ltd., 5 Davenport Road, Earlsdon, Coventry CV5 6QA Tel: 024 7667 7838 Fax: 02476713822; Sion House, High Street, Kenilworth CV8 1LY Email: rob-blacklock@hotmail.com — MB ChB Ed. 1968; FRCS Ed. 1974; FRCS Eng 1998. (Ed.) Cons. Urol. Walsgrave Hosp. Coventry W. Midl. RHA; Hon. Med. Off. Coventry Rugby Football Club; Hon. Med. Off. Kenilworth Rugby Football club; Assoc. Prof. of Surg., Director of Med. Educat., St Geo.s Univ. Sch. of Med., Grenada, W.Indies. Socs: Corr. Mem. - Amer. Urological; Fell. Roy. Soc. Med.; Brit. Assn. Urol. Surg. Prev: Sen. Regist. (Urol.) W. Midl. RHA.

BLACKLOCK, Andrew Philip 31 Clifton Dr, Sprotbrough, Doncaster DN5 7NL — MB ChB 1997 Leeds.

BLACKLOCK, Neil Stewart Park Medical Centre, Shavington Avenue, Newton Lane, Chester CH2 3RD Tel: 01244 324136 Fax: 01244 317257; The Manse, Moor Lane, Waverton, Chester CH3 7QW Fax: 01244 335840 — MB ChB 1984 Manch.; BSc (Med. Sci.) St. And. 1981; MRCGP 1991; DRCOG 1987. Socs: Brit. Assn. Sport & Med. Prev: SHO (Gen. Med.) Wythenshawe Hosp. Manch; SHO (Dermat.) Manch. Skin. Hosp.; SHO (O & G) Hope Hosp. Salford.

BLACKLOCK, Professor Norman James, KCVO, OBE 42 Western Way, Alverstoke, Gosport PO12 2NQ — MB ChB 1950 Glas.; MSc Manch. 1982; FRCS Eng. 1957. (Glas.) Prof. Emerit. Urol. Univ. Manch. Socs: Brit. Assn. Urol. Surgs.; Roy. Soc. Med. Prev: Med. Off. HM The Qu. on Visits AbRd.; Hon. Cons. Urol. Univ. Hosp. of S. Manch.; Surg. Capt. RN, Cons. Urol. RN Hosp. Haslar.

BLACKMAN, Alison Margaret The Surgery, Mill Road, Ballasalla IM9 2EA Tel: 01624 823243 Fax: 01624 822947; Clonaige, Douglas Road, Castletown IM9 1TH — MB ChB 1981 Manch.; MRCGP 1985; Cert. Family Plann. JCC 1986; DRCOG 1984. Hosp. Practitioner (Diabetes) Nobles Hosp. Douglas; Clin. Tutor (Gen. Pract.) I. of Man.

BLACKMAN, Anthony Joseph Eve Hill Medical Practice, 29-53 Himley Road, Dudley DY1 2QD Tel: 01384 254423 Fax: 01384 254424; 236 Hagley Road, Stourbridge DY8 2JS — MB BS 1975 Lond.; BDS Lond. 1970; MRCS Eng. LRCP Lond. 1975; MRCGP 1979; LDS RCS Eng. 1969. (Universiyt College London) GP.

BLACKMAN, Catherine Patricia 28 West St, Earls Banton NN2 6NZ; Capell House, 9 The Green, Flore, Northampton NN7 4LG Tel: 01327 341210 — MB BS 1985 Newc. GP Earls Banton. Socs: MDU; BMA; MWF. Prev: Asst. GP Weedon & Flore; Clin. Asst. (Rheum., Colposcopy & Geriat.) Dryburn Hosp. Durh.; Locum work.

BLACKMAN, Christopher Mark Kensington Group Practice, Kensington Road, Road, Douglas IM1 3PF Tel: 01624 676774 Fax: 01624 614668; 3 Woodside Terrace, Douglas IM2 3AH — MB ChB 1981 Manch.; MRCGP 1985; DRCOG 1984. GP Douglas, I. of Man.

BLACKMAN, Daniel James Department of Cardiology, University of Wales College of Medicine, Heath Park, Cardiff CF14 4XN Tel: 029 2074 3535 Fax: 029 2074 3500; 6 Pen-y-Wain Place, Roath Park, Cardiff CF24 4GA Tel: 029 2049 3730 — MB ChB 1992 Birm.; MB ChB (Hons.) Birm. 1992; MRCP (UK) 1995. Research Fell. (Cardiol.) Univ. of Wales Coll. of Med. Cardiff. Prev: SHO (ITV) Univ. Hosp. Wales, Cardiff; SHO (Geriat. & Rheum.) Addenbrooke's Hosp. Camb.; SHO (Cardiol.) Papworth Hosp. Camb.

BLACKMAN, Glen Malcolm 3 Shakespeare Road, London SE24 0LA — MB BS 1978 Lond.; BSc (Hons.) Lond. 1975, MB BS 1978. (Univ. Coll. Lond. & Westm.)

BLACKMAN, Jacques Andre Weybridge Medical UK Ltd., 5 Walpole Park, Caenshill Road, Weybridge KT13 0SB — MB ChB 1993 Pretoria.

BLACKMAN, Jennifer Margaret 3 Benslow Rise, Hitchin SG4 9QX Tel: 01462 451573 Email: jennyblackman@hotmail.com — MB ChB 1997 Bristol. A & E SHO, The Lister Hosp, Stevenage.

BLACKMAN, Mark Holdfast, Church Lane, Broxbourne EN10 7QF — MB BS 1994 Lond.

BLACKMAN, Melanie Jane 1 Lowther House, Foster St., Penrith CA11 7PA — MB ChB 1987 Birm.; ChB Birm. 1987.

BLACKMAN, Melinda Lucy Pontefract General Infirmary, Pontefract WF8 1PL Tel: 01977 600600 — MB ChB 1997 Leeds. SHO (Integrated Med.) Pontefract.

BLACKMAN, Rachel Helen Hartley Corner Surgery, 51 Frogmore Road, Blackwater, Camberley GU17 0DB Tel: 01252 872791 Fax: 01252 878910 — BM BS 1989 Nottm.; MRCGP 1993; DFFP 1993; DRCOG 1991. (Nottm. Univ. Med. Sch.) Prev: Trainee GP/SHO N.wick Pk. Hosp. VTS.

BLACKMAN, Saskia Elizabeth-Ann 1 Springfield, Western Rd, Crediton EX17 3NG — MB BS 1996 Lond.

BLACKMORE, Jane Elizabeth St James Surgery, 8-9 Northampton Buildings, Bath BA1 2SR Tel: 01225 422911 Fax: 01225 428398; The Willows, Homefield Road, Saltford, Bristol BS31 3EG — BM 1982 Soton.; MRCGP 1987; DRCOG 1986. GP Bath. Prev: SHO (Cas.) Roy. United Hosp. Bath; SHO (Geriat.) St. Martin's Hosp. Bath; SHO (O & G) S.mead Hosp. Bristol.

BLACKMORE, Jill Princess Royal Hospital NHS Trust, Telford, Apley Castle, Telford TF1 6TF Tel: 01952 641222; Spring Hill, Sheinton, Shrewsbury SY5 6DN Tel: 01952 510777 — BM 1985 Soton.; DRCOG 1987; DFFP 1998. Clin. Asst. (Colposcopy) P.ss Roy. Hosp. Telford; CMO Family Plann. Shrops.

BLACKMORE, John Michael Seaverns West Moors Group Practice, 175 Station Road, West Moors, Ferndown BH22 0HX Tel: 01202 872585 Fax: 01202 892155; Branch Surgery, Rushmoor House, 67-71 Church Road, Three Legged Cross, Wimborne BH21 6RQ Tel: 01202 813311 — MB BS 1970 Lond.; DObst RCOG 1972. (Univ. Coll. Hosp.) Socs: Bournem. & Poole Med. Soc. Prev: Resid. Toronto E. Gen. & Orthop. Hosp.; Clin. Asst. Varicose Vein Clinic Poole Gen. Hosp.

BLACKMORE, Mark James 52 Esher Road, Hersham, Walton-on-Thames KT12 4LG Tel: 01372 466680 — MB BChir 1990 Camb. Specialist Regist. (Anaesth.) S. W. Thames Region.

BLACKMORE, Michael Graydon 17 Conway Croft, Newport NP19 8JX — MB BCh 1978 Wales.

BLACKMORE, Stuart Charles Cedars Surgery, 8 Cookham Road, Maidenhead SL6 8AJ Tel: 01628 620458 Fax: 01628 633270 — MB ChB 1990 Cape Town; MB ChB 1990 Cape Town.

BLACKMORE, Susan Joanna 6 Blyton Close, Beaconsfield HP9 2LX — MB BS 1994 Lond. (Univ. Coll. Lond.) SHO Anaesth. Milton Keynes.Gen.Hosp. Prev: SHO (A & E) & Ho. Off. (Surg.) Wycombe Gen. Hosp.; Ho. Off. (Med.) Darlington Memor. Hosp.; SHO (Anaesth.) Wycombe Gen. Hosp. Bucks.

BLACKSHAW, Anthony John Department of Pathology, Bedford Hospital, Kempston Road, Bedford MK42 9DJ Tel: 01234 792149 Fax: 01234 792161 — MB BChir 1971 Camb.; MB BChir Camb. 1970; MA Camb. 1971; FRCPath 1988, M 1976. Cons. Histopath. Bedford Hosp. Socs: Brit. Soc. Gastroenterol. & Brit. Soc. Clin. Cytol. Prev: Cons. Histopath. St. Bart. Lond.; Cons. Histopath. & Cytopath. Hackney Hosp. Lond.; Sen. Regist. (Histopath.) St. Bart. & St. Mark's Hosps. Lond.

BLACKSHAW, Gareth Lee 33 Station Road, Mickleover, Derby DE3 5GH — MB ChB 1988 Otago; BA Vict. NZ 1982; Dip. Pract. Dermat. Wales 1996; Dip. Obst. Otago 1992. Dir. (Emerg.) Broken Hill Base Hosp.

BLACKSHAW, Mary Josephine 174 Kimbolton Road, Bedford MK41 8DN — MB BS 1971 Lond.

BLACKSHAW, Rachel Elizabeth The Old Vicarage, Broadhempston, Totnes TQ9 6AX — MB ChB 1998 Birm.

BLACKSTOCK, James Hillcrest Surgery, Wellow Lane, Peasedown St. John, Bath BA2 8JQ Tel: 01761 434469 Fax: 01761 432499; 1 Silver Street, Holcombe, Bath BA3 5EP Tel: 01761 233460 Email: james@blastock.demon.co.uk — MB BS 1975 Lond.; MRCP (UK) 1982; MRCGP 1984; Cert. Family Plann. JCC 1983. Assoc. Specialist (Gastroenterol.) Roy. United Hosp. Bath. Prev: Regist. (Med.) Mayday Hosp. Croydon.

BLACKSTONE, Howard Barrie, Surg. Capt. RN Retd. Serendip House, 38 Valletort Road, Stoke, Plymouth PL1 5PN — MRCS Eng. LRCP Lond. 1957; MRCGP 1974. (Leeds) p/t Clin. Asst., Community Drug Serv., Plymouth; Locum GP. Socs: Plymouth Med. Soc. Prev: Ho. Off. Obst., Gyn. & Ophth. & Ho. Phys. ScarBoro. Hosp.

BLACKSTONE, Victoria Heulwen 14 Ellington Road, London N10 3DG Tel: 020 8883 0983 — MB BS 1969 Lond.; MB BS Lond. 1968; MRCS Eng. LRCP Lond. 1969; MFHOM 1991; DObst RCOG 1974; Dip. Ven. Soc. Apoth. Lond. 1975. (Roy. Free) Homoeop. Phys. Lond. Prev: Phys. Univ. Coll. Lond.; Regist. (Genitourin. Med.) St. Mary's Hosp. Lond.

BLACKWALL, Madeline Clare Hermina Hollybrook Medical Centre, Hollybrook Way, Heatherton Village, Derby DE23 7TU Tel: 01332 523300; Blackwall, Kirk Ireton, Derby DE6 3JR Tel: 01335 370203 — MRCS Eng. LRCP Lond. 1976. (St. Bart.) Socs: Derby Med. Soc. & Derbysh. LMC.

BLACKWELL, Alistair Macleod (retired) Apartment 8, Cromer Court, 38 Wellington Terrace, Clevedon BS21 7EG Tel: 01275 872972 — MB ChB Aberd. 1950. Prev: Clin. Asst. (Psychiat.) Pastures Hosp. Mickleover.

BLACKWELL, Anona Lynne Singleton Hospital, Swansea NHS Trust, Sketty Lane, Swansea SA2 8QA Tel: 01792 285015 Fax: 01792 285014 Email: anona.blackwall@swansea-tr.wales.nhs.uk; Blossomfield, 1 Joiners Road, Three Crosses, Swansea SA4 3NY Tel: 01792 874088 — MRCS Eng. LRCP Lond. 1975; BSc (Hons.) Lond. 1970, MB BS 1975; Dip. Ven. Soc. Apoth. Lond. 1977; AKC; MRCP Lond. 1998. (Westm.) Cons. Genitourin. Singleton Hosp. Swansea. Prev: Lect. (Genitourin. Med.) St. Thos. Hosp. Med. Sch. Lond.

BLACKWELL, Bruce 94 Blenheim Road, Reading RG1 5NQ — MB BS 1997 Lond.

BLACKWELL, Craig Donald 8 Ventnor Place, Edinburgh EH9 2BP — MB ChB 1990 Manch.

BLACKWELL, David Howard 5 Miller Close, South Charford, Bromsgrove B60 3PG — MB ChB 1980 Birm.; DA (UK) 1986.

BLACKWELL, John Norman Gastroenterology Department, Stoke Mandeville Hospital, Mandeville Road, Aylesbury HP21 8AL Tel: 01296 316776 Fax: 01296 315202; Orchid House, Main Road, Lacey Green, Princes Risborough HP27 0PN Tel: 01844 275571 — MB ChB 1972 Dundee; FRCP Lond. 1996; FRCP Ed. 1989; MRCP (UK) 1975. Cons. Phys. & Gastroenterol. Stoke Mandeville Hosp. Aylesbury. Socs: Amer. Gastroenterol. Assn.; Brit. Soc. of Gastroenterol. Prev: Cons. Phys. & Gastroenterol. Whiteabbey Hosp. Newtownabbey; Lect. (Med.) Univ. Edin. & Roy. Infirm. Edin.; Regist. (Gen. Med. & Gastroenterol.) Roy. Infirm. Edin.

BLACKWELL, Lucy Katherine Flat 37,, East Quay Wapping Quay L3 4BU — MB ChB 1998 Liverp.; MB ChB Liverp 1998. SHO Rotat. Gladstone Hosp. Australia.

BLACKWELL, Mark Joseph Chiltern Wing, Sutton Hospital, Cotswold Road, Sutton SM2 5NF Tel: 020 8644 4343 — MB BS 1980 Lond.; MPhil Lond. 1996; MRCPsych 1987.

BLACKWELL, Martin Michael St Augustines Medical Practice, 4 Station Road, Keynsham, Bristol BS31 2BN Tel: 0117 986 2343 Fax: 0117 986 1176; High Meadow, Pensford Hill, Pensford, Bristol BS39 4JH Tel: 01761 490737 — MB ChB 1977 Bristol; BSc (Hons.) Bristol 1974; MRCP (UK) 1980; MRCGP 1984; DRCOG 1982.

BLACKWELL, Maurice 28 West Street, Selsey, Chichester PO20 9AB — MRCS Eng. LRCP Lond. 1945.

BLACKWELL, Monika Joanna (retired) 3 Broadoaks Cres, West Byfleet KT14 6RP Tel: 01932 342743 Email: dr.m.j.blackwell@which.net — MB BS 1990 Lond.; MRCGP 1996; DRCOG 1995; DFFP 1995. Occupat.al Health, Aldershot; Sports Injuries (various locations). Prev: Locum GP Shrivenham.

BLACKWELL, Verity Claire 2 Northgate Cottages, High St., Selsy, Chichester PO20 0QG — BM BS 1991 Nottm.

BLACKWELL-SMYTH, Peter Park Medical Centre, 19 Bridge Road, St Austell PL25 5HE Tel: 01726 73042 Fax: 01726 74349; Parc Gwyn, St. Stephen-in-Brannel, St Austell PL26 7RL Tel: 01726 822465 — MB BCh BAO 1973 Dub.; MDiv Gen. Theological Coll. New York 1967; MA Dub. 1972, MB BCh BAO 1973; DObst RCOG 1975. Dep. Coroner Mid Cornw. Prev: SHO (O & G) & SHO (Psychiat.) Roy. Cornw. Hosp. Truro; Intern Dr. Steevens' Hosp. Dub.

BLACKWOOD, Donald Lauder Govan Health Centre, 5 Drumoyne Road, Govan, Glasgow G51 4BJ Tel: 0141 531 8470 Fax: 0141 531 8471; 48 Monreith Road, Glasgow G43 2NZ — MB ChB 1975 Glas.; MRCGP 1979.

BLACKWOOD, Professor Douglas Rowland Department of Psychiatry, Royal Edinburgh Hospital, Morningside Park, Edinburgh EH10 5HF Tel: 0131 537 6000 Fax: 0131 537 6259 Email: dblackwood@ed.ac.uk; 7 Pitsligo Road, Edinburgh EH10 4RY Tel: 0131 447 9537 — MB ChB 1972 Ed.; PhD Ed. 1981; BSc St. And. 1967; FRCP Ed. 1994 M 1975; FRCPsych 1994, M 1982. (Edinburgh) Prof. (Psychiat.) Univ. Edin.

BLACKWOOD, Gilbert Wade The General Hospital, St Helier, Jersey Tel: 01534 59000; 3 Thornton Hall, Upper King's Cliff, St Helier, Jersey JE2 3GP Email: castle@itl.net — BM BCh 1973 Oxf.; MA Oxf. 1973; MRCS Eng. LRCP Lond. 1973; FRCPsych 1993, M 1977. Cons. Psychiat. Gen. Hosp. St. Helier. Prev: Cons. Psychiat. St. Jas. Univ. Hosp. Leeds; Sen. Clin. Lect. Univ. Leeds; Lect. (Ment. Health) Univ. Aberd.

BLACKWOOD, John Anderson (retired) Beechcroft, 23 Paisley Road, Renfrew PA4 8JH Tel: 0141 886 2455 — MB ChB 1944 Glas.

BLACKWOOD, Nigel James 86 Englefield Road, Islington, London N1 3LG — MB BChir 1991 Camb.; MA Camb. 1992. Regist. (Psychiat.) Maudsley Hosp. Lond. Prev: SHO (Renal) St. Thos. Hosp. Lond.; SHO (Neurol.) Char. Cross Hosp. Lond.; Ho. Off. (Med.) Univ. Coll. Med. Lond.

BLACKWOOD, Roger Arthur Cardiac Unit, Wexham Park Hospital, Slough Tel: 01753 525369; Waterside, 5 Hillhampton Place, Sunningdale, Windsor SL4 4TN Tel: 01344 876963 — BM BCh Oxf. 1970; MRCP (UK) 1973; FRCP Lond. 1988. Cons. Phys. & Cardiol. E. Berks. Dist.; Hon. Cons. Hammersmith Hosp. Lond.

BLADE, Patrick David (retired) 2 Chilton Ridge, Hatch Warren, Basingstoke RG22 4RG Tel: 01256 471545 Email: p.plade@btinternet.com — MB BS 1960 Lond.; DObst RCOG 1964. Prev: GP Basingstoke, Hants.

BLADEN, Carol Grove House Practice, St. Pauls Health Centre, High St, Runcorn WA7 1AB Tel: 01928 566561 Fax: 01928 590212; 18 Broadfield, Norton Fields, Runcorn WA7 6UE — MB ChB 1982 Liverp.; MRCP (UK) 1987; FRCR 1994. (Liverp.) GP Princip. Gr. Hse. Pract. Runcorn. Prev: Regist. (Clin. Oncol.) Clatterbridge Centre Oncol.; Research Regist. Adult Cardiothoracic Centre BRd.green Hosp. Liverp.; SHO (Med.) Dudley.

BLADES, Derek Stewart The Surgery, Bellingham, Hexham NE48 2HE; Wadge Head, Tarset, Hexham NE48 1PB — MB BS 1972 Newc.; FRCGP 1994, M 1977; MA (Educ.) Durham 1988. GP Trainer Newc. VTS; Course Organiser Newc. VTS. Prev: Trainee GP Newc. VTS; Demonst. (Anat.) Univ. Newc. Med. Sch.; Ho. Surg. (Gen. Surg.) Newc. Gen. Hosp.

BLADES, Horace Roy (retired) Flat 4, Melcombe Court, Dorset Square, Balcombe St., London NW1 6EP Tel: 020 7723 2947 — MRCS Eng. LRCP Lond. 1943; FRCA 1992; FFA RCS Eng. 1954; DA Eng. 1950. Hon. Cons. Anaesth. Hosp. Sick Childr. Gt. Ormond St. Lond. Prev: Cons. Anaesth. Qu. Eliz. Hosp. Childr. Lond.

BLADES, Rosemary Anne Department of Urology, Royal Preston Hospital, Sharue Green Lane N., Fulwood, Preston PR2 9HT Tel: 01772 710443 — MB BS 1987 Lond.; BSc Lond. 1984; MD Manch. 1995; FRCS Eng. 1991; FRCS (Urol.) 1997. (St. Geo. Hosp. Med. Sch.) Cons. Urol., Roy. Preston Hosp. Prev: Regist. (Urol.) Stepping Hill Hosp. Stockport; Regist. (Gen Surg.) Leicester Roy. Infirm.

BLADES, Stephen Michael Grove Medical Group, 1 The Grove, Gosforth, Newcastle upon Tyne NE3 1NU Tel: 0191 210 6680 Fax: 0191 210 6682; 1 The Grove, Newcastle upon Tyne NE3 1NU Tel: 0191 271 5503 — MB BS 1984 Newc.; BMedSc Newc. 1981, MB BS 1984; MRCP (UK) 1987; MRCGP 1989. Prev: SHO (Psychiat.) St. Geo. Hosp. Morpeth.; SHO (O & G) N. Tyneside Gen. Hosp.; SHO (Gen. Med.) Freeman Hosp. Newc.

BLADON, Cynthia Joyce (retired) Kerk Nurseries, Sicklebrook Lane, Coal Aston, Dronfield S18 3BE Tel: 01286 418286 — MB ChB 1950 Liverp.; DPH Liverp. 1958. Prev: Clin. Med. Off. Sheff. AHA (T).

BLADON, Yvonne Margaret East Midlands Electricity Health and Safety, Woodyard Lane, Off Lambourne Drive, Wollaton, Nottingham NG8 1GW Tel: 0115 901 8248 Fax: 0115 901 8216; 8 Creswell Drive, Ravenstone, Leicester LE67 2AG Tel: 01530 836245 Fax: 01530 836245 — MB ChB 1968 Aberd.; AFOM RCP Lond. 1989; DObst RCOG 1970. Company Med. Adviser E. Midl. Electricity Nottm. Socs: Soc. Occupat. Med.; BMA; Leic. Med. Soc. Prev: Med. Adviser BAMS; Company Med. Off. ABB Transportation Ltd Derby; Med. Off. (Occupat. Med.) Leics. Occupat. Health Serv.

BLAGDEN, Ann Karen Craig Dunain Hospital, Leachkin Road, Inverness IV3 8JU; Tornacara, Altnacardoch, Lentran, Inverness IV3 8RN Tel: 01667 462558 — MB ChB 1984 Aberd.; MB ChB Aberd. l984; MRCPsych. 1991; MRCGP 1988. Cons. Psychiat. Craig Dunain Hosp. Inverness. Prev: Trainee GP Aberd. VTS; Sen. Regist. (Health c/o Elderly, Psychiat.) Nottm.; SHO (Psychiat.) Craig Dunain Hosp. Inverness.

BLAGDEN, Mark David Avondale Surgery, 5 Avondale Road, Chesterfield S40 4TF Tel: 01246 232946 Fax: 01246 556246; Gooseberry Cottage, Holmesfield, Dronfield S18 7WB — MB ChB 1983 Leeds. Prev: Trainee GP Chesterfield VTS; Ho. Phys. Leeds Gen. Infirm.:; Ho. Surg. Pinderfields Gen. Hosp. Wakefield.

BLAGDEN, Sarah Patricia 3 Old Compton Lane, Farnham GU9 8BS — MB BS 1994 Lond.

BLAGDON, John (retired) — MB BS 1954 Lond.; MD Lond. 1973; MRCS Eng. LRCP Lond. 1954; DTM & H Eng. 1963. Prev: Cons. Blood Transfus. E. Anglia Regional Blood Transfus. Centre Camb.

BLAGG, Stuart Edward Cherry Trees, Satwell Close, Rotherfield Greys, Henley-on-Thames RG9 4QT — MB BS 1992 Lond.; BSc Lond. 1989, MB BS 1992.

BLAGGAN, Anoop Singh 50 Oakfield Road, Balsall Heath, Birmingham B12 9PL — MB BCh 1991 Wales.

BLAIKIE, Andrew John 16 Marshall Place, Perth PH2 8AG Tel: 01738 639207 Email: rachelbj@aol.com — MB ChB 1993 Ed.; BSc (Med. Sci.) Path. Ed. 1991. (Edin.) SHO (Ophth.) Himewells Hosp. Dundee.

BLAIKIE, Keith Johnson Sighthill Health Centre, 380 Calder Road, Edinburgh EH11 4AU Tel: 0131 453 5335; 33 Swanston Terrace, Edinburgh EH10 7DN — MB ChB 1986 Ed.; BSc (Hons.) Ed. 1984, MB ChB 1986; MRCGP 1990; DRCOG 1989. Prev: Trainee GP/SHO S. Lothian VTS.; Ho. Off. (Med.) W.. Gen. Hosp. Edin.; Ho. Off. (Surg.) E.. Gen. Hosp. Edin.

BLAIKLEY, Andrew Bruce Farmhouse Surgery, Christchurch Medical Centre, 1 Purewell Cross Road, Purewell, Christchurch BH23 3AF Tel: 01202 488487 Fax: 01202 486724; 38 Island View Avenue, Friars Cliff, Christchurch BH23 4DS — MB BS 1984 Lond.; DFFP 1998; DRCOG 1986. (Guy's) Prev: SHO (Paediat.) Poole Gen. Hosp.; SHO (O & G) Guy's Hosp. Lond.; SHO (A & E) Kent & Canterbury Hosp.

BLAIKLOCK, Mr Christopher Thomas Friarsfield House, Friarsfield Road, Cults, Aberdeen AB15 9LB Tel: 01224 867581 — MB BS 1961 Durh.; FRCS Eng. 1970; FRCP Lond. 1986, M 1966; DObst RCOG 1963. Cons. Neurosurg. Aberd. Roy. Infirm.

BLAIKLOCK, Judith Susan (retired) Friarsfield House, Friarsfield Road, Cults, Aberdeen AB15 9LB Tel: 01224 867581 — MB BS 1963 Lond.; MRCS Eng. LRCP Lond. 1963; FFA RCS Eng. 1969; DA Eng. 1966; DObst RCOG 1965. Prev: Cons. Anaesth. Aberd. Hosps.

BLAIKLOCK, Richard Alexander (retired) 5 Denwick View, West Acres, Alnwick NE66 2PZ Tel: 01665 602602 — MD Durh. 1936, MB BS 1933. Prev: Phys. & Anaesth. Alnwick Infirm.

BLAIN, Alastair Macleod (retired) Braco Lodge, 42 Mayne Road, Elgin IV30 1PB Tel: 01343 549090 — MB ChB Ed. 1961; MA Camb. 1962, BA 1958; MRCGP 1977; DObst RCOG 1964. Prev: Med. Off. Gordonstoun Sch. Elgin.

BLAIN, Camilla Rachel Victoria Garden Flat, 20 Henrietta St., Bath BA2 6LP — MB BS 1997 Lond.

BLAIN, Patricia Anne Eaglesfield, Elm Bank Road, Wylam NE41 8HS — MB ChB 1974 Glas.; MSc Newc. 1991; MFPHM RCP (UK) 1992; DObst RCOG 1976. Cons. Pub. Health Med. NHS N.. & Yorks. Regional Office. Prev: Sen. Regist. (Pub. Health Med.) N.. RHA.

BLAIN, Professor Peter George, CBE Department of Environmental and Occupational Medicine, Medical School, Newcastle upon Tyne NE2 4HH Tel: 0191 222 7254 Fax: 0191 222 6442 Email: p.g.blain@ncl.ac.uk — MB BS 1975 Newc.; PhD Newc. 1988 BMedSci (Hons.) 1972; FRCP Ed. 1991; FRCP Lond. 1990; MRCP (UK) 1978; MFOM RCP Lond. 1990; FFOM RCP Lond. 1997. Prof. Environm. Med. Univ. Newc. u. Tyne.; Cons. Phys., Newc. Hosp. NHS Trust. Prev: Head Biomed. Sci. & Human Toxicol. Centr. Toxicol. Laborat. ICI Plc.; Lect. (Clin. Pharmacol.) Univ. Newc.

BLAINE, Felix 17 Magrath Avenue, Chesterton Road, Cambridge CB1 — MB ChB 1996 Bristol.

BLAINEY, Andrew David 64 The Street, Little Waltham, Chelmsford CM3 3NT — MD 1987 Camb.; MB 1976, BChir 1975; FRCP Lond. 1994; MRCP (UK) 1978. Cons. Phys. Mid Essex HA. Prev: Sen. Regist St. Barts Hosp. Lond.

BLAIR, Adela Mavis 101 Atkins Road, London SW12 0AL Tel: 0208 674 7752 — MB BCh BAO 1951 Belf.; DCH Eng. 1955. (Qu. Univ. Belf.) p/t GP Princip. Socs: BMA. Prev: Ho. Off. O & G City & Co. Hosp. Lond.derry; Res. Med. Off. Nerv. Dis. Hosp. Belf. & Roy. Vict. Hosp. Belf.; Regist. Paediat. St. Mary's Hosp. Manch.

BLAIR, Agnes McRae Robertson (retired) Hillcrest, Bonar Crescent, Bridge of Weir PA11 3EH Tel: 01505 612296 — MB ChB 1957 Glas. Prev: Ho. Phys. & Ho. Surg. Roy. Alexandra Infirm. Paisley.

BLAIR, Alastair William Victoria Hospital, Kirkcaldy KY2 5AH Tel: 01592 261155 — MB ChB St. And. 1959; FRCP Ed. 1975, M 1965; DCH RCPS Glas. 1962. (St. And.) Cons. (Paediat.) Fife Area Health Bd. & Roy. Hosp. Sick Childr. Edin.; Clin. Sen. Lect. Child Health Univ. Aberd.; Hon. Sen. Lect. Fac. Med. Univ. Edin.; Postgrad. Tutor Vict. Hosp. Kirkcaldy; Hon. Sen. Lect. Biochem. Dept. St. And. Univ.; Hon. Sec. Scott. Paediat. Soc. Socs: Brit. Paediat. Assn.

BLAIR, Alexander Stuart Southern Medical Group, 322 Gilmerton Road, Edinburgh EH17 7PR Tel: 0131 664 2148; 12 Rose Park, Bonnyrigg EH19 3RL Tel: 0131 654 9717 — MB ChB 1988 Ed.; MRCGP 1992; T(GP) 1992.

BLAIR, Alexina MacLennan 11 Coronation Way, Bearsden, Glasgow G61 1DF Tel: 0141 942 4938 — B.Sc. Glas. 1936, M.B., Ch.B. (Distinc.) 1939. Prev: Ho. Surg. & Ho. Phys. Roy. Hosp. Sick Childr. Glas.

BLAIR, Alison Joyce Drymen Road Surgery, 96 Drymen Road, Bearsden, Glasgow G61 2SY Tel: 0141 942 9494 Fax: 0141 931 5496; 55 Dunellan Road, Milngavie, Glasgow G62 7RE — MB ChB 1987 Glas.; MRCGP 1991; DCH RCPS Glas. 1990; DRCOG 1990.

BLAIR, Alison May 1/R 52 Lawrence Street, Glasgow G11 5HD — MB ChB 1986 Ed.; MRCGP 1994.

BLAIR, Alistair Stewart 45 Cheviot View, Ponteland, Newcastle upon Tyne NE20 9BH — MB ChB 1993 Liverp.; DTM & H Liverp. 1996; DRCOG 1997; DCH 1998; MRCGP(Distinction) 1999.

BLAIR, Andrew David The Ashgrove Surgery, Morgan Street, Pontypridd CF37 2DR Tel: 01443 404444 Fax: 01443 480917; 28 Heol-y-Foel, Llantwit Fardre, Pontypridd CF38 2EQ Tel: 01443 208400 — MB ChB 1987 Manch.; MRCGP 1991; DRCOG 1991.

BLAIR, Andrew James 7 Lawrence Street, Glasgow G11 5HH — MB ChB 1993 Glas.

BLAIR, Andrew Lavery Trevor 28 Georgian Villas, Hospital Road, Omagh BT79 0AT — MB BCh BAO 1972 Belf.; DObst RCOG 1974; DCH RCPSI 1974; MRCP (UK) 1976; MD Belf. 1981; FRCP Ed. 1989; FRCP Lond. 1992; FRCPI 1997. Cons. Phys. Tyrone Co. Hosp. Omagh. Socs: Fell. Ulster Med. Soc.; Irish Endocrine Soc. & Irish Cardiac Soc.; Brit. Diabetic Assn. & Europ. Assn. Study Diabetes. Prev: Sen. Regist. (Endocrinol. & Diabetes) Roy. Vict. Hosp. Belf.

BLAIR, Angus Alastair Donald 9 Upper Wimpole Street, London W1M 7TD Tel: 020 7581 1110 & 071 323 4841 Fax: 020 7487 5256; 14 Basil Mansions, Basil St, London SW3 1AP Tel: 020 7584 1548 — MB 1963 Camb.; BChir 1962; MRCP Lond. 1967. (St. Thos.) Hon. Cons. Phys. St. Luke's Hosp. for Clergy Lond.; Med. Adviser Nigeria High Commiss. Socs: Fell. Roy. Soc. Med.; Med. Soc. Lond. Prev: Regist. (Med.) Middlx. Hosp. Lond.; Ho. Phys. Hammersmith & St. Thos. Hosp. Lond.

BLAIR, Mr Bryce Evans c/o Barclays Bank, Hayle TR27 4HR; South Lombard, Lanteglos-by-Fowey, Fowey PL23 1NA — MB BS 1936 Lond.; FRCS Eng. 1948; MRCS Eng. LRCP Lond. 1935; FRCOG 1959, M 1946. (St. Thos.) Socs: BMA & SW Gyn. Soc. Prev: Cons. Gyn. Roy. United Hosp. Bath.; Sen. Regist. Postgrad Med. Sch. Lond.; SHO (Obst.) St. Thos. Hosp.

BLAIR, Carol Susan 7 Charteris Park, Longniddry EH32 0NX — MB ChB 1991 Ed.; MRCP (UK) 1994. (Ed.) Spec. (Gastroenterol.), Edin. Roy. Infirm.

BLAIR, Cicely Pearl (retired) White Cottage, 41 Snaresbrook Road, London E11 1PQ Tel: 020 8989 9173 Fax: 020 8989 9173 — 1951 MRCS Eng. LRCP Lond. 1951; 1984 FRCP Lond. 1984; 1974 MRCP (UK) 1974. Cons. Dermat. Hartswood & Roding Hosps. Prev: Cons. Dermat. Barking & Havering & Brentwood DHA.

BLAIR, David Gourock Health Centre, 181 Shore Street, Gourock PA19 1AQ Tel: 01475 634617 — MB ChB 1974 Glasgow; MB ChB Glas. 1974. (Glasgow) GP Dumbarton.

BLAIR, David Alexander Streatham Park Surgery, 9 Mitcham Lane, London SW16 6LY Tel: 0208 769 0705 — MD 1960 Belf.; MB BCh BAO 1956. (Belf.) Prev: Lect. Qu. Univ. Belf.; Ho. Off. Ards. Hosp. Newtownards.

BLAIR, David Logan Anniesland Medical Practice, 778 Crow Road, Glasgow G13 1LU Tel: 0141 954 8860 Fax: 0141 954 0870; 37 Ballater Drive, Bearsden, Glasgow G61 1BZ Tel: 0141 942 4300 — MB ChB 1968 Glas.; FRCP Glas. 1988; MRCP (UK) 1971; FRCGP 1988; MRCGP 1976. Clin. Asst. Gartnavel Roy. Hosp. Glas.; GMC Performance Assessor. Socs: Roy. M-C Soc. Glas.; W Scotl. Fac. RCGP. Prev: Regist. (Gen. Med.), Resid. Ho. Off. W.. Infirm. Glas.; Regist. (Paediat.) Roy. Hosp. Sick Childr. Glas.

BLAIR, Mr David Wilson (retired) East Mount, 354 North Deeside Road, Cults, Aberdeen AB15 9SB — MB ChB 1954 St. And.; MD St. And. 1964, ChM (Commend.) 1959, MB ChB 1954; FRCS Ed. 1958. Cons. Surg. Aberd. Roy. Infirm. Prev: Sen. Lect. in Surg. Univ. Aberd.

BLAIR, Duncan Guy Sanderman, Surg. Lt.-Cdr. RN 17 Coate Drive, Worthy Down, Winchester SO21 2QZ — MB ChB 1991 Sheff. Hon. SHO (Ophth.) Soton. Eye Unit.

BLAIR, Edward McGregor 233 Glasgow Road, Dennyloanhead, Bonnybridge FK4 1QY; 44A Rectory Road, Oxford OX4 1BU Tel: 01865 798883 — MB ChB 1991 Dundee; BMSc (Hons) Dund 1988; MRCP (UK) 1995. (Dundee) Specialist Regist. (Clin. Genetics) Ch.ill Hosp. Oxf. Socs: Clin. Genetics Soc.; BMA. Prev: SHO (Med.) Bath, Roy. United Hosp. & Hull Roy. Infirm.

BLAIR, Edwina Elizabeth 27 Tormead Road, Guildford GU1 2JA Tel: 01483 68867 — MB ChB 1957 Birm.; DObst RCOG 1959. Sen. Clin. Med. Off. (Ment. Handicap) S.W. Surrey HA.

BLAIR, Elizabeth Joyce (retired) Sandbanks, South Bank, Hassocks BN6 8JP — MB BS Lond. 1952; Cert. Family Plann. JCC 1961. Prev: Clin. Asst. (Psychiat.) Kent AHA.

BLAIR, Professor Eric Lewis 113 Runnymede Road, Ponteland, Newcastle upon Tyne NE20 9HL Tel: 01661 822833 — MD 1964 Newc.; MD (Distinc.) Newc. 1964; MB BS Durh. 1948; FRCP Ed. 1971, M 1956. Socs: Hon. Mem. (Ex-Pres.) Brit. Soc. Gastroenterol. Prev: Prof. Physiol. & Acad. Sub-Dean Med. Sch. Univ. Newc.; Regist. (Med). Edin. Roy. Infirm.; Ho. Phys. & SHO (Med.) Roy. Vict. Infirm. Newc. u. Tyne.

BLAIR, Grant Fulham Clinic, 82 Lillie Road, London SW6 1TN Tel: 020 7386 9299 Fax: 020 7610 0635; 27 Loxley Road, Wandsworth, London SW18 3LL Email: grant-blair@msn.com — MB BS 1977 Lond.; MRCGP 1982; DCH RCP Lond. 1990. (St Georges Hospital Medical School) GP Tutor Char. Cross Hosp. Sch. Lond.; Teachg. Fell. Dept. Prim. Care & Gen. Prac. Imp. Coll. Sch. of Med.; Acad. Facilitator Imp. Coll. Sch. of Med. Socs: BMA.; BMA; ASME. Prev: Undergrad. GP Tutor Char. Cross Hosp. Med. Sch.

BLAIR, Iain Henderson The New Medical Centre, Crossley St., Wetherby LS22 6RT Tel: 01937 583081; Greenacres, 9 Spofforth Hill, Wetherby LS22 6SF Tel: 01937 582426 — MRCS Eng. LRCP Lond. 1960; MA Camb. 1959, MB 1965, BChir 1964; DObst RCOG 1964. (W. Lond.)

BLAIR, James Malcolm (cons. rooms), St David's House, 1 Uplands Terrace, Swansea SA2 0GU Tel: 01792 472922; 2 Old Kittle Road, Bishopston, Swansea SA3 3JU Tel: 01792 232672 Fax: 01792 232129 — MRCS Eng. LRCP Lond. 1961; FRCOG 1980, M 1966. Cons. O & G Swansea NHS Trust Singleton Hosp.

BLAIR, James Wilson Achbeag, Courthill Road, Rosemarkie, Fortrose IV10 8UE — MB ChB 1987 Ed.; FRCPS Glas. 1991.

BLAIR, Jean Anne Stewart 67 Highburgh Road, Glasgow G12 9EW Tel: 0141 339 0612 — MB ChB 1955 Glas. (Glas.) Med. Edr. Gtr. Glas. HB. Prev: Asst. Gen. Pract. Glas.; Res. Ho. Phys. Roy. Hosp. Sick Childr. Glas.; Res. Cas. Surg. Roy. Infirm. Stirling.

BLAIR, Jennifer Mary Royal Group of Hospitals, Grosvenor Road, Belfast BT8 6WT — MB BCh BAO 1992 Belf.; MB BCh Belf. 1992; FFARCSI Dub 1997. Specialist Regist. Roy. Gp. of Hosp.s, Belf. Socs: BMA; N. Irel. Soc. Anaesth.; Assn. Anaesth. Prev: Specialist Regist. (Anaesth.) Altnagelvin Hosp. Lond.derry; Specialist Regist. (Anaesth.) Antrim Area Hosp. Co. Antrim; SHO (Anaesth.) Roy. Vict. Hosp.

BLAIR, John Ferguson Blair and Kennedy, The Surgery, 4 South Liddle Street, Newcastleton TD9 0RN Tel: 013873 75202 Fax: 013873 75817 — MB ChB 1978 Ed. (Edinburgh)

BLAIR, John Norman 27A Bon Accord Road, Swanage BH19 2DW Tel: 01929 424881 — MB BCh BAO 1940 Belf. (Qu. Univ. Belf.)

BLAIR, John Samuel Greene, KStJ, OBE(Mil), TD (retired) The Brae, 143 Glasgow Road, Perth PH2 0LX Tel: 01738 623739 Fax: 01738 623739 Email: jgb143@aol.com — MB ChB 1951 St. And.; DObstRCOG 1952; BA Lond. 1955; FRCS Ed. 1958; ChM (High Commend.) St. And. 1961; FICS 1983; Hon. DLitt. St. And. 1991; FRCP Ed 1999. Reader (Hist. of Med.) (Hon.) Univ. St. And. Prev: Cons. Surg. Perth Roy. Infirm., Tayside HB.

BLAIR, Joseph Lindsay (retired) Trouville, School Lane, Warmingham, Sandbach CW11 3QL — MD 1947 Belf.; MB BCh BAO 1941; FRCP Ed. 1994, M 1954.

BLAIR, Judith Menzies 24 Queen Square, Glasgow G41 2AZ — MB ChB 1982 Glas.; MRCP (UK) 1991; MRCGP 1987; DRCOG 1987. Cons. Geriat. Med. S. Ayrsh. NHS Trust. Prev: Sen. Regist. (Gen. & Geriat. Med.) Leicester Hosps.

BLAIR, Margaret Mitchell Reid East Kerse Farm, Lochwinnoch PA12 4DU — MB ChB 1994 Glas.

BLAIR, Michael 76 Mount Charles Crescent, Alloway, Ayr KA7 4PA Tel: 01292 442016 — MB ChB 1970 Glas.; FRCP Glas. 1986; MRCP (UK) 1973. Cons. Paediat. Ayr Hosp. & CrossHo. Hosp. Kilmarnock. Prev: Sen. Regist. & Regist. Roy. Hosp. Sick Childr. Glas.; Regist. (Neonat. Paediat.) Roy. Matern. Hosp. Glas.

BLAIR, Mitchel Eliot Department of Paediatrics, Northwick Park Hospital, Watford Road, Harrow HA1 3UJ Tel: 020 8869 3330 Fax: 020 8426 6359 Email: m.blair@ic.ac.uk; 85 Evelyn Drive,, Pinner HA5 4RN — MB BS 1983 Lond.; MSc Lond. 1989, BSc (Hons.) 1980; FRCP (UK)1996; MRCP (UK) 1986; FRCPCH 1997. (Univ. Coll. Hosp.) Cons. Sen. Lect. in Paediat. & Child Health. Socs: Acad. Convenor Exec. Comm. Brit. Assn. Community Child Health; Soc. Pub. Health. Prev: Sen. Lect. (Child Health) Qu. Med. Centre Nottm.; Lect. (Community Paediat.) Qu. Med. Centre Nottm.; Regist. (Paediat.) Char. Cross Hosp. Lond.

BLAIR, Moira Ishbel Holmhead, Newcastleton TD9 0RA — MB ChB 1978 Ed.; MRCGP 1982. (Edinburgh)

BLAIR, Mr Paul Henry Beaumont 20 Shandon Park E., Bangor BT20 5HN — MB BCh BAO 1982 Belf.; FRCS Ed. 1986.

BLAIR, Robert Alan 27 Tormead Road, Guildford GU1 2JA — MB BS 1989 Lond. Trainee GP Hastings VTS. Prev: SHO (A & E) Roy. E. Sussex Hosp. Hastings; Ho. Off. (Med.) St. Helens Hosp. Hastings; Ho. Off. (Surg.) Kent & Canterbury Hosp.

BLAIR, Robert Edgar (retired) Gate House, Stoney Lane, Newport, Brough HU15 2RA Tel: 01430 441065 — MB ChB 1955 Liverp.; FRCGP 1982, M 1977.

BLAIR, Robert Gibb (retired) Achbeag, Courthill Road, Rosemarkie, Fortrose IV10 8UE Tel: 01381 620309 — LRCP LRCS Ed. LRFPS Glas. 1948; BA Open 1993; FRCOG 1971, M 1956, DObst 1953. Prev: Cons. O & G Lanark Co. Area.

BLAIR, Mr Robin Leitch Department of Otolaryngology, Ninewells Hospital & Medical School, Dundee DD1 9SY Tel: 01382 660111 Fax: 01382 632816 Email: robinlb@tuth.scot.nhs.uk — MB ChB Ed. 1968; FRCS Ed. 1973; FRCSC 1974; FACS 1975. (Edinburgh University) Cons. Otolaryngol. Dundee Teach. Hosps. NHS Trust; Head (Otolaryngol.) Univ. Dundee; Chairm. - SAC in OtoLaryngol. - Jt. Comm. in Higher Surgic. Train. Socs: Fell. Roy. Soc. Med.; Brit. Assn. Otol.; Brit. Assn. Ontologysists. Prev: Asst. Prof. Otolaryngol. Univ. Toronto.

BLAIR, Samuel James Alexander 35 Broom Gardens, Lenzie, Glasgow G66 4EH Tel: 0141 776 6581 — MB BCh BAO 1965 Belf.; MRCGP 1978; DObst RCOG 1968. (Belf.) Prev: Ho. Off. S. Tyrone Hosp. Dungannon; SHO (Surg.) Lagan Valley Hosp. Lisburn; Med. Supt. Ochadamu Med. Centre, Nigeria.

BLAIR, Stephen 55 Burnopfield Road, Rowlands Gill NE39 1QQ — MB ChB 1992 Ed.

BLAIR, Mr Stephen David Wirral Hospital Trust, Arrowe Park Hospital, Upton, Wirral CH49 5PE Tel: 0151 604 7054 — MRCS Eng. LRCP Lond. 1978; MS Lond. 1987, MB BS 1978; FRCS Eng. 1983; FRCS Ed. 1983. (St. Bart.) Cons. (Gen. & Vasc. Surg.) Wirral Hosp. Trust. Prev: Sen. Regist. Char. Cross Hosp.; Jun. Regist. St. Bart. Hosp. Lond.; SHO Lond. Hosp.

BLAIR, Stephen Eric The Village Green Surgery, The Green, Wallsend NE28 6BB Tel: 0191 295 8500 Fax: 0191 295 8519; 3 Park Villas, Gosforth, Newcastle upon Tyne NE3 4HU — MB BS 1976 Newc.; MRCP (UK) 1980. Dep. Chairm. LMC Newc. & N. Tyneside; Tutor (Gen. Pract.) N. Tyneside.

BLAIR, Susan Constance 50/a Coltbridge Avenue, Murrayfield, Edinburgh EH12 6AH — MB ChB 1989 Ed.; MRCGP 1994. (Ed.) Socs: Soc. Occupat. Med.

BLAIR, Thomas Trenham Stanhope Parade Health Centre, Gordon Street, South Shields NE33 4HX Tel: 0191 455 4621 Fax: 0191 427 3180 — MB BS 1970 Newc.

BLAIR, Zoe Anne Desborough Avenue Surgery, 65 Desborough Avenue, High Wycombe HP11 2SD Tel: 01494 526006 Fax: 01494 473569 — MB ChB 1987 Liverp.; MB ChB Livero. 1987; BSc Biochem. Liverp. 1982; MRCGP 1993; DRCOG 1991. Police Surg. Bucks.

BLAKE, Alison Ombersley Street, Droitwich WR9 8RD — MB ChB 1974 Sheff.

BLAKE, Alison Elizabeth Worcester Royal Infirmary, Rankswood, Worcester WR5 1HN Tel: 01905 760697 Fax: 01905760554; Lynton, Claines Lane, Claines, Worcester WR3 7RN Tel: 01905 452115 — MB ChB 1976 Birm.; MB ChB (Hons.) Birm. 1976; FRCP Lond. 1993; MRCP (UK) 1979. Cons. Clin. Neurophysiol. Hereford Co. Hosp., Worcester Roy. Infirm., Lea Castle Hosp. Kidderminster & Birm. Childr. Hosp.; Birm. Childr.s Hosp. Prev: Sen. Regist. (Clin. Neurophysiol.) Qu. Eliz. Hosp. Birm.; Regist. (Gen. Med.) Selly Oak Hosp. Birm.; SHO (Neurol.) Nat. Hosp. Qu. Sq. Lond.

BLAKE, Amanda Jane The Clapham Park Surgery, 72 Clarence Avenue, Clapham Park, London SW4 8JP Tel: 020 8674 0101; 112 Telford Avenue, Streatham Hill, London SW2 4XQ — MB BS 1985 Lond.; MRCP (UK) 1990; MRCGP 1996; DCH RCP Lond. 1991. (King's Coll. Sch. Med. & Dent.) Prev: Regist. (Paediat.) Mater Miser. Childr. Brisbane, Austral.; SHO (Paediat.) FarnBoro. Hosp.; SHO Rotat. (Med.) Stoke Mandeville Hosp. Aylesbury.

BLAKE, Ann Christine 35 Garth Drive, Chester CH2 2AF — MB ChB 1985 Liverp.; BPharm Bath 1978.

BLAKE, Mr Christopher Henry 21 Albert Road, Teddington TW11 0BD — MB BS 1994 Lond.; FRCS Eng 1999. SHO Urol. Alexander Hosp. Redditch. Prev: SHO Gen. Surg., Worcester Roy. Infirm.; SHO Paediat. Surg., Birm. Childr.s Hosp.; SHO Cardiothoracic Surg., Walsgrave Hosp., Coventry.

BLAKE, Clive Edward Manor Surgery, Forth Noweth, Chapel Street, Redruth TR15 1AU Tel: 01209 313313 Fax: 01209 313813; Vale House, Gilbert's Coombe, Redruth TR16 4QQ — MB BS 1973 Lond.; BSc (Hons.) Lond. 1970; MRCS Eng. LRCP Lond. 1973; FRCGP 1993, M 1984; MFFP 1993; DRCOG 1976. (St. Mary's)

BLAKE, David Charles Sedgwick, Wing Cdr. RAF Med. Br. Military District Hospital Unit, Eastlea, Peterborough District Hospital, Thorpe Road, Peterborough PE3 6DA Tel: 01733 874327 Email: david.blake@pbh-[r.anglox.nhs.uk]; 3 Pinewood Avenue, Wittering, Peterborough PE8 6BS — MB ChB Manch. 1979; BSc St. And. 1976; FFA RCS Eng. 1984. Cons. Anaesth. Milit. Dist. Hosp. Unit P'boro. Socs: Assn. Anaesth.; Tri-Serv. Anaesthatists Assn. Prev: Cons. Anaesth. TPMH Akrotiri; Sen. Specialist (Anaesth.) P.ss Alexandra's Hosp. Wroughton & Frenchay Hosp. Bristol; Unit Med. Off. RAF Valley.

BLAKE, David Hendry Flat 1, St Augustine's Court, Hagley Road, Edgbaston, Birmingham B16 9JU Tel: 0121 454 2300 — MB BS 1952 Durh.; MLCOM 1958. Indep. Cons. Manip. & Acupunc. Birm.

BLAKE, David Russell 2 Circus Place, Bath BA1 2PG — MB ChB 1974 Sheff.; FRCP (UK) 1988, M 1976. ARC Prof. Rheum. The Lond. Hosp. Med. Coll. Prev: Sen. Lect. (Rheum. Med.) Birm. Univ.; Sen. Regist. (Rheum.) Roy. Nat. Hosp. Rheum. Dis. Bath; Regist. (Med.) Newc. AHA (T).

BLAKE, Duncan Edward Priory Fields Surgery, Nursery Road, Huntingdon PE29 3RL Tel: 01480 52361 Fax: 01480 434640 — MA 1992 (Bchir) Camb.; MRCP (UK) 1996; DRCOG 1997; DFFP 1998; MRCGP 1998. (Camb.) Prev: SHO Rotat. (Med.) Ipswich Hosp.; SHO (Geriat.) W.morland Gen. Hosp. Kendal; VTS Hinchingbrooke Hosp.

BLAKE, Elizabeth Ruth Newbury Street Practice, Wantage Health Centre, Earston Lane, Wantage OX12 7AY — MB BS 1995 Lond.; BSc (Hons.) Lond. 1991. (Roy. Free) Partner - Gen. Pract.

BLAKE, Miss Gillian Mary Cheltenham General Hospital, Sandford Road, Cheltenham GL53 7AN Tel: 01242 222222; 1 Manse Gardens, Cheltenham GL51 3PG Tel: 01242 224546 — MB BS 1974 Lond.; FRCOphth 1994; DO Eng. 1982. (St. Mary's) Assoc. Specialist (Ophth.) E. Glos. NHS Trust.

BLAKE, Helena Mary 14 Peaks Hill, Purley CR8 3JE — MB BCh BAO 1976 NUI; FRCR 1982. Cons. Radiol. Mayday Hosp. Croydon. Prev: Sen. Regist. & Regist. (Radiol.) King's Coll. Hosp. Lond.

BLAKE, Henry Valentine (retired) 2 Houndean Rise, Lewes BN7 1EG Tel: 01273 480609 Email: blakes@hblake.demon.co.uk — MB BS 1956 Lond.; MRCGP 1965; DObst RCOG 1963. Prev: Gen. Practitioner.

BLAKE, Iain Campbell The Spinney, Everest Road, Atherton, Manchester Tel: 01942 885300, 02920 613173 Fax: 02920 613173 Email: jjandannette@onetel.net.uk — BM BS 1980 Nottm.; BMedSci Nottm. 1978; MRCPsych.1991; MRCGP 1984; DPM RCPSI 1989; DGM RCP Lond. 1987; DCH RCP Lond. 1983. Cons. Psychiat./Med. Director, The Spinney, Everest Rd., Atherton, Manch..

BLAKE, Ian David The Anchorage, Higher Stennack, Troon, Camborne TR14 9JS — MB BS 1996 Lond.

BLAKE, John (retired) 16 Yew Tree Avenue, Bradford BD8 0AD Tel: 01274 543812 — MB BS 1954 Lond.; BSc (Physiol.) Lond. 1951, MB BS 1954; FRCPsych 1986, M 1972; DPM Eng. 1963. Prev: Cons. Psychiat. W.wood Hosp. Bradford.

BLAKE, Mr John 14 Peaks Hill, Purley CR8 3JE Tel: 020 8660 9485 — MB BChir 1959 Camb.; MA Camb. 1959; FRCS Eng. 1964. (Camb. & Westm.) Emerit. Cons. Surg. Mayday Hosp., Shirley Oaks Hosp. Croydon & St. Anthony's Hosp. Cheam. Socs: Fell. Assn. Surgs. Prev: Sen. Regist. (Surg.) W.m. & Soton. Hosps.; Resid. Surg. Off. Woolwich Memor. Hosp.; Ho. Surg. St. Jas. Hosp. Balham.

BLAKE, John Gerard 3 Hall Gardens, Kildwick, Keighley BD20 9AF Tel: 01535 637480 — MB BCh BAO 1978 Dub.; FRCR 1987; DMRD Aberd. 1986; DCH NUI 1983. Cons. Radiol. Airedale Gen. Hosp. Keighley. Prev: Sen. Regist. (Diag. Radiol.) W. Midl. RHA; Regist. (Diag. Radiol.) Aberd. Roy. Infirm.; SHO (Orthop.) Regional Orthop. Unit Navan.

BLAKE, Mr John Richard Stares Department of Surgery, Kings Mill Hospital, Mansfield Road, Sutton-in-Ashfield NG17 4JL — MB BS 1966 Lond.; FRCS Eng. 1974; MRCS Eng. LRCP Lond. 1966. (Middlx.) Cons. Surg. King's Mill Centre for Health Care Servs. Sutton-in-Ashfield. Prev: Lect. (Surg.) Univ. Nottm.; Hon. Sen. Regist. (Surg.) Nottm. Hosps.

BLAKE, Jonathan George Portlethen Group Practice, Portlethen Health Centre, Bruntland Road, Portlethen, Aberdeen AB12 4QL Tel: 01224 780223 Fax: 01224 781317; 18 Macolms Mount W., Stonehaven AB39 2TF — MB ChB 1992 Aberd.; MRCGP 1996; DFFP 1996. (Aberd.) Partner, Portlethen Gp. Pract. Socs: BMA; MRCGP.

BLAKE, Julian Charles 78 Westbourne Park Road, London W2 5PL Tel: 020 7229 3232 — MB BS 1988 Lond.; BSc (Physiol.) Lond. 1983; MRCP (UK) 1994. (Roy. Free) SpR Clin. NeuroPhysiol., Nat. Hosp. For Neurol. & Neurosurg., Qu. Sq. Lond. Socs: Fell. Roy. Soc. Med. Prev: MRC Clin. Train. Fell. (Neurosci.) Roy. Free Hosp. Sch. Med. Lond.; Hon. Clin. Research Fell. Acad. Dept. Med. Roy. Free Hosp. Sch. Med.

BLAKE, Katharine Elizabeth (retired) 2 Houndean Rise, Lewes BN7 1EG Tel: 01273 480609 Email: blakes@hblake.demon.co.uk — MB BChir 1957 Camb.; MRCP Ed. 1962; DObst RCOG 1960. Prev: Gen. Practitioner.

BLAKE, Kathryn Helen 102 Oakwood drive, St Albans AL4 0XA Tel: 01727 861675 — MB BS 1988 Lond.; DRCOG 1991. p/t GP Herts.

BLAKE, Kathryn Ingram 43 Round-Barrow Close, Colerne, Chippenham SN14 8EF Tel: 01225 743021 — MB ChB 1982 Sheff.; BSc (Hons.) (Physiol.) Sheff. 1977, MB ChB 1982; MRCP (UK) 1987. Regist. (Paediat.) Sheff. Childr. Hosp. Prev: Regist. (Paediat.) MusGr. Pk. Hosp. Taunton.

BLAKE, Kean Motherwell Health Centre, 138-144 Windmill Street, Motherwell ML1 1TB Tel: 01698 263288 Fax: 01698 251267 — MB ChB 1982 Glas.; MRCGP 1987; DRCOG 1985.

BLAKE, Lian-Louise Woodpecker Cottage, Fairy Glen Road, Penmaenmawr LL34 6YU — MB BCh 1993 Wales.

BLAKE, Melanie Jane 76 Chaworth Road, West Bridgford, Nottingham NG2 7AD — BM BCh 1991 Oxf.

BLAKE, Paul Michael 36 Long Copse, Astley Park, Chorley PR7 1TH — MB ChB 1988 Liverp.; MRCGP 1992; DCH RCP Lond. 1992.

BLAKE, Peter Nicholas Irvinestown Health Centre, 20 Church Street, Irvinestown, Enniskillen BT94 1EH Tel: 028 6862 1212 Fax: 028 6862 8624 — MB BCh 1977 Belfast; MB BCh Belf. 1977. (Belfast) GP Enniskillen, Co. Fermanagh.

BLAKE, Peter Ronald Royal Marsden Hospital, Fulham Road, London SW3 6JJ Tel: 020 7808 2581 Fax: 020 78082258 Email: peter.blake@rmh.nthames.nhs.uk — MB BS 1976 Lond.; BSc Lond. 1973, MD 1988; FRCR 1982. Cons. Radiother. & Oncol. Roy. Marsden Hosp. Lond.; Hon. Sen. Lect. Inst. Cancer Research Univ. Lond. Socs: Brit. Gyn. Cancer Soc.; Roy. Coll. Radiologists; Brit. Inst. of Radiol. Prev: Sen. Regist. (Radiother.) Hammersmith Hosp. Lond.

BLAKE, Roger Andrew 1 Marshall Street, Cockenzie, Prestonpans EH32 0HT — MB ChB 1993 Ed.

BLAKE, Simon Richard 149-153 Chanterlands Avenue, Hull HU5 — MB ChB 1985 Leic. GP Hull. Prev: Trainee GP/SHO Bedford VTS; Ho. Off. (Med.) P'boro. HA; Ho. Off. (Urol. & Surg.) Leic. HA.

BLAKE, Stephen 62 Hilfield Lane, Aldenham, Watford WD25 8AJ — BM BCh 1984 Oxf.

BLAKE, Stephen Charles (retired) The Sycamores, Bawtry Road, Hatfield Woodhouse, Doncaster DN7 6PQ Tel: 01302 840197 — MB BCh BAO 1953 Dub.; LAH Dub. 1950; FFA RCS Eng. 1965. Prev: Cons. Anaesth. Roy. Infirm. Doncaster.

***BLAKE, Stephen McKenzie** 16 Balmoral Avenue, Beaumont Park, Huddersfield HD4 5LP — MB BS 1997 Lond.

BLAKE, Stuart John Southfield Medical Practice, 14 Southfield Loan, Edinburgh EH15 1QR Tel: 0131 669 0686 Fax: 0131 669 2929; 15 Glenfield Avenue, Galashiels TD1 2AP Tel: 01896 753697 — MB ChB 1992 Ed.; MRCGP 1996; DRCOG 1996; DCH 1997; DCCH 1998. (Ed.) Gen. Pract. Princip. Socs: Fell. Roy. Med. Soc. Edin.

BLAKE, Susan Mary St Johns Way Medical Centre, 96 St. Johns Way, London N19 3RN Tel: 020 7272 1585 Fax: 020 7561 1237; 83b Frognal, London NW3 6XX — MB ChB 1975 Manch.; MRCPsych 1980. Socs: Assoc. Mem. Brit. Assn. Psychother. Prev: Research Fell. & Hon. Sen. Regist. Inst. Psychiat. Lond.; Regist. (Psychiat.) Withington Hosp. Manch.

BLAKE, Thomas Michael Market Harborough Medical Centre, 67 Coventry Road, Market Harborough LE16 9BX Tel: 01858 464242 Fax: 01858 462929 — MB ChB 1987 Leic.; BSc (Hons.) Lond. 1982; MRCGP 1993; DFFP 1993; DRCOG 1991. (Leic.) Adviser Occupat. Health (H&SE). Prev: SHO (Psychiat.) Towers Hosp. Leicester; SHO Rotat. (Med. & O & G) Leicester Roy. Infirm.

BLAKE JAMES, Justin Wynne Seymour House Surgery, 154 Sheen Road, Richmond TW9 1UU Tel: 020 8940 2802 Fax: 020 8332 7877 — MB BS 1970 Lond.; MRCS Eng. LRCP Lond. 1970; MRCGP 1977; MFHom 2000. (St. Bart.) Prev: SHO St. John's Hosp. Dis. Skin Lond.; SHO (Oncol.) Roy. Marsden Hosp.; Ho. Off. St. Bart. Hosp. Lond.

BLAKE JAMES, Robert Benedict Wilberforce House Railway Street, Pocklington, York YO42 2QZ Tel: 01759 302519 Fax: 01759 305953 — MB BS 1963 Lond.; MRCP (UK) 1971; FRCP 1999. (St. Bart.)

BLAKEBOROUGH, Alison Jane Springwood Community Unit for The Elderly, Malton Hospital, Malton YO17 7NG — MB BS 1990 Newc. Staff Grade (Old Age Psychiat.) Springwood Malton.

BLAKEBOROUGH, Anthony Department of Radiology, C Floor, Royal Hallamshire Hospital, Sheffield S10 2JF Tel: 0114 271 3417 Fax: 0114 271 2606; 10 Fulwood Chase, Sheffield S10 3QZ — MB ChB 1988 Leeds; MRCP (UK) 1991; FRCR 1995. Cons. Radiol. Roy. Hallamshire Hosp. Sheff. Prev: research fell.sh. (MRI) SJUH Leeds; Regist. Rotat. (Diag. Radiol.) Leeds & Bradford VTS.; SHO Rotat. (Med.) Leeds Gen. Infirm.

BLAKEBOROUGH, John Leslie Earle Road Medical Centre, 131 Earle Road, Liverpool L7 6HD Tel: 0151 733 7172 — MB ChB 1970 Liverp.

BLAKEBOROUGH, Jonathan Bootham Park Hospital, Bootham, York YO30 7BY Tel: 01904 610777; 20 Arundel Grove, Woodthorpe, York YO24 2RZ — MB BS 1991 Newc.

BLAKEBROUGH, Ian Sedgwick Leighton Hospital, Crewe CW1 4QJ; Garden Green Farm, Higher Garden, Malpas SY14 7HR — MB ChB 1984 Liverp. Staff Paediat. Leighton Hosp. Crewe.

BLAKELEY, Alison Jane c/o 46 Webbs Close, Wolvercote, Oxford OX2 8PX — BM BCh 1998 Oxf.; BM BCh Oxf 1998.

BLAKELEY, Mr Christopher John Flat 6, Ormonde Court, 10-14 Belsize Grove, London NW3 4UP — MB BChir 1987 Camb.; MB Camb. 1987, BChir 1986; FRCS Eng. 1992; DSM 1997; FFAEM 1998. (Camb.) Cons. (A&E), E. Surrey Hosp., Redhill, Surrey. Socs: Fell. Roy. Coll. Accid. & Emerg. Med. Prev: Sen. Regist. Rotat. (A & E) St. Geo. Hosp. Lond.; Regist. Rotat. (A & E) Luton & Ealing; SHO Rotat. (Surg.) Norf. & Norwich.

BLAKELEY, Christopher Richard Pfizer Central Research, Sandwich CT13 9NJ Tel: 01304 616161; Forge Cottage, Upper St, Tilmanstone, Deal CT14 0JQ Tel: 01304 617468 — MB ChB 1977 Birm.; MD Birm. 1989; MRCP (UK) 1980; MFPM RCP (UK) 1995; FFA RCS Eng. 1985. Regional Manager Clin. Operat. Pfizer Centr. Research UK. Prev: Area Med. Dir. Pfizer Centr. Research, Spain; Clin. Project Manager Pfizer Centr. Research; MRC Train. Fell. Nuffield Dept. Anaesth. Oxf.

BLAKELEY, Sara Louise 109 Catherington Lane, Waterlooville PO8 9PD — BM 1993 Soton.; MRCP (UK) 1996. (Soton.)

BLAKELY, Arthur Philip Lewis (retired) The Brackens, 5 Elm Rd, Beckenham BR3 4JB Tel: 020 8658 2944 — MB ChB 1930 Manch.; MD Manch. (Commend.) 1933; MRCGP 1956. Prev: Ho. Phys. Lond. Chest Hosp. & Manch. Roy. Infirm.

BLAKELY, John James Andrew (retired) Darley House, Rowton Lane, Rowton, Chester CH3 6AT — MB BS Lond. 1943; MD Lond. 1947; MFOM 1982; DIH Eng. 1949; DPH Lond. 1947. Prev: Sen. Med. Off. Brit. Nuclear Fuels Ltd.

BLAKEMAN, John Mark 47 Cranberry Close, West Bridgford, Nottingham NG2 7TQ — MB ChB 1991 Leeds.

BLAKEMAN, Peter John 13B St Thomas Street, Newcastle upon Tyne NE1 4LE — MB BS 1988 Newc.

BLAKEMAN, Thomas Martin Langstrath, Greenfield Lane, Brampton CA8 1AU — MB BS 1993 Newc. SHO (A & E Med.) S. Tyneside Dist. Hosp. Prev: Ho. Off. (Med.) Cumbld. Infirm.; Ho. Off. (Surg.) Roy. Vict. Infirm. Newc. u. Tyne.

BLAKEMORE, Lynne Tracy Lofthouse Surgery, 2 Church Farm Close, Lofthouse, Wakefield WF3 3SA Tel: 01924 822273 Fax: 01924 825168; 7 Parkway, Crofton, Wakefield WF4 1SX Tel: 01924 864620 — MB BS 1988 Lond.; MRCGP 1993. Clin. Asst. (Cardiol.) Pinderfields Hosp. Wakefield.

BLAKEMORE, Mr Martin Eric Coventry & Warwickshire Hospital, Coventry CV1 4HT Email: martin@meblakemore.fsnet.co.uk — MB ChB 1970 Birm.; FRCS Ed. 1975. Cons. Trauma & Orthop. Surg. Coventry Hosps. Prev: Sen. Regist. Rotat. (Trauma & Orthop. Surg.) W. Midl.

BLAKEMORE, Richard Castlehead Medical Centre, Ambleside Road, Keswick CA12 4DB Tel: 017687 72025 Fax: 017687 73862 — MB BS 1993 Newc.

BLAKENEY, Irene Florence Agnes (retired) 92 Lansdowne Way, London SW8 2EP — MB BS Lond. 1950; BSc (1st cl. Hons.) Lond. 1935; MRCS Eng. LRCP Lond. 1950; MFCM 1973; DCH Eng. 1953; DPH Eng. 1956. Prev: Sen. Med. Off. DHSS.

BLAKENEY-EDWARDS, Nevill Piers (retired) Cheddar Medical Centre, Roynon Way, Cheddar BS27 3NZ Tel: 01934 742061 Fax: 01934 744374 — MB BS Lond. 1963; MRCS Eng. LRCP Lond. 1962; DObst RCOG 1966. Prev: SHO Paediat. Lister Hosp. Hitchin.

BLAKEWAY, Alison Clare Parkstone Health Centre, Mansfield Road, Parkstone, Poole BH14 0DJ; Sentosa, 36 Western Avenue, Branksome Park, Poole BH13 7AN — MB BS 1986 Lond.; DRCOG 1991. Trainee GP Poole VTS.

BLAKEWAY, Mr Charles Orthopaedic Department, Royal Bournemouth Hospital, Castle Lane East, Bournemouth BH7 7DW Tel: 01202 704927; Sentosa, 36 Western Ave, Branksome Park, Poole BH13 7AN Tel: 01202 701062 — MRCS Eng. LRCP Lond. 1979; BSc Lond. 1976, MB BS 1979; FRCS Eng. 1983. (St. Bart.) Cons. Orthop. Surg. E. Dorset HA. Socs: Fell. Brit. Orthop. Assoc.; Roy. Soc. Med. Prev: Sen. Regist. (Orthop.) St. Bart. Hosp. Train. Sch.; Fell. Brigham & Wom. Hosp., Harvard Med. Sch. Boston, USA; Regist. (Surg.) S.end Gen. Hosp.

BLAKEY, Andrew Faraday Department of Old Age Psychiatry, Withington Hospital, Manchester — MB ChB 1985 Liverp.; BSc (Hons.) Liverp. 1982; MRCP (UK) 1988; MRCPsych 1993. Clin. Research Fell. & Sen. Regist. (Psychiat.) Withington Hosp. Manch. Prev: Sen. Regist. (Gen. Adult Psychiat.) Manch. Roy. Infirm.; Regist. (Psychiat.) Mersey Regional Train. Scheme.

BLAKEY, Dennis Hugh Edensor House, Edensor, Bakewell DE45 1PH Tel: 01246 582434 — MB ChB 1943 Manch.; FRCOG 1965, M 1949. (Manch.) Emerit. Cons. O & G N. Derbysh. Dist. Socs: Sheff. M-C Soc.; (Ex-Pres.) N. Eng. Obst. & Gyn. Soc. Prev: Lect. (O & G) Univ. Sheff.; Sen. Regist. Jessop Hosp. Sheff.; Resid. (Obst. Surg.) St. Mary's Hosps. Manch.

BLAKEY, John Linthorpe Road Surgery, 378 Linthorpe Road, Middlesbrough TS5 6HA Tel: 01642 817166 Fax: 01642 824094 — MB BS 1973 Newc.; MRCGP 1978.

BLAKEY, Karen Glenwood, 134 Lightwood Road, Buxton SK17 6RW — BM BS 1998 Nottm.; BM BS Nottm 1998. (Nottingham) PRHO, Nottm. City Hosp. Prev: PRHO Derby City Hosp.

BLAKEY, Louisa Espaces, Jackmans Lane, Woking GU21 1QU — MB ChB 1992 Birm.; MRCGP 1996; DCH RCP Lond. 1995. (Birm.) p/t Retainer Gen. Pract.

BLAKEY, Ralph Eric (retired) 10 Corby Gate, Sunderland SR2 7JB — MB BS 1944 Durh. Prev: GP Sunderland.

BLAKEY, Richard Trevor Manor Oak Surgery, Horebeech Lane, Horam, Heathfield TN21 0DS Tel: 01435 812116 Fax: 01435 813737; 51 Springwood Road, Heathfield TN21 8JX Tel: 01435 864541 Fax: 01435 864541 — MB BS 1986 Lond. (Guy's Hosp. Lond.) Fundraising Co-ordinator SIMCAS Immediate Care Scheme; Basics Lect.; Dep. Chairm. Highweald PCG. Prev: Trainee GP Cornw.; SHO (Paediat. & O & G) Tunbridge Wells VTS.

BLAMEY, Professor Roger Wallas Nottinham International Breast Education Centre, Nottingham City Hospital, Nottingham NG5 1PB Tel: 0115 962 5707 Fax: 0115 962 7765; Westhorpe Home, Southwell NG25 0NG — MD 1970 Camb.; MA Camb. 1961, MD 1970, BChir 1960; FRCS Eng. 1966; FRACS (Hon); FRCS (Hon) Glas. (Middlx.) p/t Prof. Emerit. Nottm. City Hosp. Univ. of Nottm.; Cons. Surg. Nottm. City Hosp. Socs: Pres. Brit. Assoc. Surg. Oncol.'98-'00; Brit. Transpl. Soc. (Ex-Meetings Sec.).; Vice-Pres. Europ. Soc. Mastol. Prev: 2nd Asst. Dept. Surg. St. Vincent's Hosp. Univ. Melbourne, Austral.; Prof.Surg. Sci., Nott'm City Hosp, Univ. of Nott'm.

BLAMPIED, Alex Michael Cleveland Clinic, 12 Cleveland Road, St Helier, Jersey JE1 4HD Tel: 01534 722381/734121 — MB ChB 1985 Leic.; MRCGP 1990.

BLANCHARD, David Sydney Penkridge Medical Practice, St. Michael's Road, Penkridge, Stafford ST19 5AJ Tel: 01785 712300 Fax: 01785 713696 — MB ChB 1987 Aberd.; MRCGP 1991.

BLANCHARD, Gillian Frances Forest Glades Medical Centre, Bromsgrove Street, Kidderminster DY10 1PH Tel: 01562 822509 Fax: 01562 827046; Cartref, 12 Sweetpool Lane, Hagley, Stourbridge DY8 2XH — MB ChB 1985 Birm.; BSc (Hons.) Birm. 1982, MB ChB 1985; DRCOG 1990; DCH RCP 1989. Prev: Trainee GP Dudley VTS.

BLANCHARD, Hazel Claire 4 Barony Buildings, Nantwich CW5 5QQ — MB ChB 1997 Leeds.

BLANCHARD, Martin Roy 105 Harringay Road, London N15 3HP — MB BS 1982 Lond.; BSc Lond. 1979, MB BS 1982; MRCPsych 1988. Cons. & Hon. Sen. Lect. Old Age Psychiat. Roy. Free Hosp. Lond. Prev: Hons. Sen. Regist. Inst. Psychiat. Maudsley Hosp. Lond.; Regist. Rotat. Roy. Free Hosp.

BLANCHON, Bruno Jean Rene 115 Hampstead Way, London NW11 7JN — MB BS 1995 Lond.

BLANCO DAVILA, Rafael Kent & Canterbury Hospital, Ethelbert Road, Canterbury CT1 3NG — LMS 1992 Santiago de Compostela.

BLANCO RODRIGUEZ, Inmaculada Leighton Hospital, Leighton, Crewe CW1 4QJ — LMS 1990 Navarre.

BLANCO ROJO, Carlos Medway Hospital, Windmill Road, Gillingham ME7 5NY; 35 Denmead House, Highcliffe Drive, London SW15 4PS — LMS 1989 Cantabria.

BLAND, Anthony Kenmore Hoole Road Surgery, 71 Hoole Road, Chester CH2 3NJ Tel: 01244 325721 — MB ChB 1979 Manch.; BSc St. And. 1976; DA Eng. 1984.

BLAND, Caroline Jane 13 Park Road, Chandlers Ford, Eastleigh SO53 2EW — MB ChB 1997 Birm.

BLAND, Charles John Henry Department of Radiology, Royal Surrey County Hospital, Guildford GU2 5XU Tel: 01483 571122; 41 Loxley Road, London SW18 3LL Tel: 020 8874 6221 — MB BChir 1980 Camb.; MA Camb. 1980; FRCR 1987. Cons. Radiol. Roy.

Surrey Co. Hosp. Guildford. Prev: Regist. & Sen. Regist. (Radiol.) St. Geo. Hosp. Lond.

BLAND, David Glyn 16A Coplow Lane, Billesdon, Leicester LE7 9AD Tel: 0116 259 6452 Fax: 01162596452 — MB BCh 1984 Wales; MB BCh Wales l984; FRCA, 1993. Cons. (Anaeth), Leicester Gen. Hosp.

BLAND, Eileen Patricia (retired) Woodpecker Lodge, Romsey Road, Ower, Romsey SO51 6AE Tel: 01703 814822 Fax: 01703 814822 — MB ChB 1961 St. And.; FFA RCS Eng. 1969; DObst RCOG 1963. Prev: Dir. Anaesth. Pontefract Gen. Infirm.

BLAND, Elaine Susan 25 Elgin Avenue, Littleover, Derby DE23 7SE Tel: 01332 517132 — BM 1991 Soton. ResFel, Div. of Matern. Fetal Med., Ottawa Hsp, Canada. Socs: Roy. Coll. Gen. Pract. Prev: SHO (O & G) Macclesfield Dist. Gen. Hosp.; GP/Regist. Annan N. Surg. Dumfries; SHO (O & G) Addenbrooke's Hosp. Camb.

BLAND, Gareth John Hillsfield Health Centre, 1 Howard Street, Coventry CV1 4GH Tel: 024 7622 3446 Fax: 024 7622 5846 — BM BS 1981 Nottm.; BMedSci 1979; MRCP (UK) 1984; MRCGP 1987. GP Coventry; SHO (Med.) Walsgrave Hosp. Coventry. Prev: SHO (Paediat.) Leicester Roy. Infirm.; SHO (Med.) Walsgrave Hosp. Coventry; Regist. (Med.) Geo. Eliot Hosp. Nuneaton.

BLAND, Hubert Andries Copse Cottage, Church Lane, Brook, Godalming GU8 5UQ — MB ChB 1991 Cape Town.

BLAND, Jeremy Douglas Percy 3 The Green, Plough Lane, Upper Harbledown, Canterbury CT2 9BB Tel: 01227 764367 Fax: 01277 783048 Email: jbland@cix.compulink.co.uk — MB ChB 1981 Manch.; MRCP (UK) 1985. Cons. Clin. Neurophysiol. Kent & Canterbury Hosp. & Regional Neurosci. Centre King's Coll. Hosp. Lond. Prev: Sen. Regist. (Neurophysiol.) Qu. Eliz. Hosp. Birm.

BLAND, John William Spring Hill Medical Centre, Arley, Coventry CV7 8FD Tel: 01676 540863 Fax: 01676 540760; The Spinney, Spencers Lane, Berkswell, Coventry CV7 7BB Tel: 01676 533295 Fax: 01676 533295 — MB ChB Birm. 1959; MRCGP 1968; MFFP 1993; DObst RCOG 1961. (Birm.) Princip. in GP; Hosp. Pract. (A & E & Geriat.) Geo. Eliot Hosp. Nuneaton; Train. Doctor (Family Plann) N. Warks NHS Trust; Research Assoc. Inst. Populat. Studies Univ. Exeter; Chairm. N. Warks. PCG. Socs: BMA; W Midl. Assn. Family Plann. Doctors; RSM. Prev: Med. Advis. Warks HA.

BLAND, Joseph Mark The Crown Surgery, 23 High Street, Eccleshall, Stafford ST21 6BW Tel: 01785 850226 — BM BS 1980 Nottm.

BLAND, Julia Louise (Beck) Pathfinder Mental Health Services Trust, Department of Psychotherapy, Springfield Hospital, Harewood House, 61 Glenburnie Road, London SW17 7DJ Tel: 020 8682 6681 Fax: 020 8682 6476 — MB BS Lond.1982; MA Oxf. 1979; MRCPsych 1993. Sen. Regist. (Psychiat.) St. Geo. Hosp. Pathfinder NHS Trust Lond. Prev: Regist. (Psychiat.) St. Geo. Hosp. Lond.; SHO (A & E) St. Geo. Hosp. Lond.; Trainee GP Lond. SE1.

BLAND, Katherine Mary Eskdaill Medical Centre, Eskdaill Street, Kettering NN16 8RA Tel: 01536 513053 Fax: 01536 417572; Glebe Lodge, Church St, Woodford, Kettering NN14 4EX Tel: 01832 734266 — MB BS 1983 Lond.; MRCGP 1987; DRCOG 1987.

BLAND, Mr Kevin Godfrey 45 Wroxall Road, Solihull B91 1DR — MB ChB 1954 Birm.; FRCS Ed. 1965; FRCOG 1971. Sen. Specialist Lect. O & G Baragwanath Hosp. & Witwatersrand Univ. S. Africa.

BLAND, Laurance William 7 Falmouth Close, Eastbourne BN23 5RN — MB BS 1946 Lond. (Lond. Hosp.) Prev: Neurosurgic. Ho. Surg. Lond. Hosp. Annexe; Sen. Res. Pathol. St. Vincent's Hosp. New York; Path. Regist. W. Middlx. Hosp.

BLAND, Mr Nicholas Chandos 14 Bryony Road, Weoley Hill, Birmingham B29 4BU Tel: 0121 475 4754 — MB ChB 1956 Birm.; FRCS Eng. 1963; MRCS Eng. LRCP Lond. 1956; DCH Eng. 1959, DLO 1962. (Birm.) Cons. Otolaryngol. Birm. Childr. Hosp; Hon. Cons. Surg. City Hosp. Birm.; Aural Surg. Birm. Educat. Comm.; Alexander Wherner Piggott Fell.sh. (Jt.ly) 1967. Socs: Fell. Roy. Soc. Med.; (Ex-Chairm.) Brit. Soc. Audiol.; Brit. Assn. Otol. Prev: Sen. Regist. (Otorhinolaryng.), Ho. Surg. (ENT) & Ho. Phys. Med. United Birm. Hosps.

BLAND, Pauline Mary (retired) The Barn House, Burnett, Keynsham, Bristol BS31 2TF Tel: 0117 986 9437 Fax: 0117 986 9437 — MB ChB 1957 Bristol. Prev: Ho. Phys. & Ho. Surg. Bristol Roy. Infirm.

BLAND, Richard Mellins 82 The Headlands, Kettering NN15 6DQ Tel: 01536 512548 — MRCS Eng. LRCP Lond. 1950. (Middlx.) Authorised Med. Examr. (Civil Aviat.); Cremat. Ref.. Prev: Ho. Phys., Ho. Surg. & Cas. Off. Weymouth & Dist. Hosp.; Squadron Ldr. RAF.

BLAND, Roderick 66 Wonford Road, Exeter EX2 4LQ Tel: 01392 71045 — MB BS 1981 Lond. Regist. (Geriat. Med.) Soton HA.

BLAND, Ruth Margaret The Knowes, Auchans Road, Houston, Johnstone PA6 7EF — MB ChB 1988 Glas.; BSc (Hons.) St. And. 1984; MRCP (UK) 1993; DCH RCP Lond. 1992. (Glas.) Sen. Regist. (Paediat.) W. Scotl.; MRC, Mtubatuba S. Africa.

BLAND, Steven Aaron, Surg. Lt. RN 10 Ullswater Drive, Spondon, Derby DE21 7JY Email: 101707.2657@compuserve.com — MB ChB 1995 Manch.; BSc (Hons.) Biomed. Sci. Manch. 1992. (Manch.)

BLAND, Timothy Charles The Surgery, 58B Billet Lane, Hornchurch RM11 1XA Tel: 01708 442377 Fax: 01708 447362; 12 Beltinge Road, Haroldwood, Romford RM3 0UJ Tel: 01708 374141 — MB BS 1977 Lond.; DRCOG 1982. (Middlx.) Socs: BMA; Christ. Med. Fell.sh. Prev: Trainee GP Tamworth VTS; SHO (A & E & O & G) Leicester Roy. Infirm.; Ho. Phys. & Ho. Surg. Kettering Gen. Hosp.

BLANDFORD, Alan George (retired) Barren Down House, Leg Square, Shepton Mallet BA4 5LL — MB ChB Bristol 1960; DObst RCOG 1962. Prev: GP Shepton Mallet.

BLANDFORD, Anne Christine Blackhall & Peterlee Practice, Backhall Community Health Centre, Hesleden Rd TS27 4LQ Tel: 0191 586 4331, 0191 586 4844 — MB BChir 1989 Camb.; MA Camb. 1991; MRCGP 1996; DTM & H RCP Lond. 1994; DCH RCP Lond. 1993; DRCOG 1993. (Camb.) Gen. Pract. Princip. Prev: Doctor Woms. Christian Hosp. Multan, Pakistan; GP/Regist. Soton.; SHO (Paediat.) Heatherwood Hosp. Ascot.

BLANDFORD, Nicola Susan 25 Chedworth Street, Cambridge CB3 9JF Tel: 01223 356430 — MB BS Lond. 1970; MRCPsych 1981. (Middlx.) Cons. Psychother. Edith Cavell Hosp. P'boro. Socs: Assoc. Mem. Soc. Analyt. Psychol. Prev: Sen. Regist. (Psychother.) Addenbrooke's Hosp. Camb.; Regist. (Psychiat.) Fulbourn Hosp. Camb.; Clin. Asst. Exe Vale Hosp. Exeter.

BLANDFORD, Roger Llewellyn Cons. Physician, Bassetlaw DGH, Kilton Hill, Worksop S81 0BD Tel: 01224 638502, 01909 500990 Fax: 01909 502798 Email: louisemcevoy@yahoo.co.uk; Leaway, London Road, Retford DN22 7EB Tel: 01777 703575 Email: r.blanford@ntlworld.com — MB BCh 1971 Wales; MD Wales 1984; FRCP Lond. 1993; MRCP (UK) 1975. (Welsh Nat. Sch. Med.) Cons. Phys. (Gen. Med.) Bassetlaw HA. Socs: Brit. Diabetic Assn.; BMA; Assn. Brit. Cervical Diabologists. Prev: Sen. Regist. (Gen. Med.) Leicester Roy. Infirm.; Regist. (Gen. Med.) Liverp. Roy. Infirm.; Regist. (Cardiol. & Neurol.) Univ. Hosp. Wales Cardiff.

BLANDIN, Barbara Olive Sandown, La Rocque, Grouville JE3 9 Tel: 01534 544 — MB ChB 1961 Manch. Prev: Ho. Surg. & Ho. Phys. Manch. Roy. Infirm.

BLANDY, Professor John Peter, CBE (retired) 362 Shakespeare Tower, Barbican, London EC2Y 8NJ Email: john.blandy.net — BM BCh 1951 Oxf.; DM 1963 Manch., Oxf.; FRCS 1956; FRCS 1992 (hon). Prev: Cons. Urol., The Roy. Lond. Hosp.

BLANDY, Susan Elizabeth 39 Queens Road, Lyndhurst SO43 7BR Tel: 01703 282192 Fax: 01703 282177 Email: mike.h@mcmail; Central Health Clinic, East Park Terrace, Southampton SO14 0YL Tel: 01703 902518 Fax: 01703 902602 — MB BS 1978 Lond. Staff Grade Community Paediat. (Audiol.) Part Three. Socs: Assoc. mem. RCPCH. Prev: Clin. Med. Off. (Child Health) Hants. HA.; Clin. Asst. (Child Guid.) Soton; SHO (Paediat. Cardiol.) Soton W.. Hosp.

BLANE, David Bernard 145 Grosvenor Avenue, London N5 2NH — MB BS 1969 Lond.; MSc (Sociol.) Lond. 1972, MB BS 1969. (St. Thos.) Lect. (Med. Sociol.) Char. Cross Hosp. Med. Sch. Lond.

BLANEY, Charles Valentine (retired) 'Marie Ville', 19 Dromalane Road, Newry BT35 8AP Tel: 01693 62521 — MB BCh BAO 1947 NUI.

BLANEY, David Daniel Killin Medical Practice, Laggan Leigheas, Ballechroisk, Killin FK21 8TQ Tel: 01567 820213 Fax: 01567 820805 — MB ChB 1981 Ed.

BLANEY, John Aloysius (Surgery & resid.), 81 Church Road, Tranmere, Birkenhead CH42 5LE — LAH Dub. 1958. Princip. GP Tranmere. Prev: SHO Ormskirk Co. Hosp.; SHO Obst. Coombe Matern. Hosp. Dub.; SHO Sharoe Green Hosp. Preston.

BLANEY, Liam Patrick Four Elms Medical Centre, 103 Newport Rd, Roath, Cardiff CF24 0AF — MB BCh BAO 1987 NUI; FRCA 1993; DCH NUI 1989. (University College, Dublin) Cons. Pain Managem. & Anaesth., Univ. Hosp., Birm. NHS Trust, Birm. Socs: BMA; MDU; Internat. Assn. for Study of Pain (IASP).

BLANEY, Roger Woodburn House, Croft Road, Holywood BT18 0PB Tel: 01232 423753 Email: ruairi@doctor.com; Sruth na Coille, 9 Bóthar na Croite, Holywood BT18 0PB Tel: 01232 421922 Email: o.bleine@usa.net — MB BCh BAO 1957 Belf.; MD Belf. 1965, DPH 1961; FFCMI 1977; FFCM 1979 M 1972. (Belf.) Hon. Sen. Lect. Qu. Univ. Belf.; Hon. Cons. Community Med. Roy. Vict. Hosp. Belf. & E.. Health & Social Servs. Bd.; Vice-Dean Fac. Pub. Health Med. RCP of Irel. 1997. Socs: Soc. Social Med. & Internat. Epidemiol. Assn.; Fell. Ulster Med. Soc. Prev: Head Dept. Community Med. & Med. Statistics Qu. Univ. Belf.; Asst. Sen. Med. Off. N. Irel. Hosps. Auth.; Research Fell. in Enquiry Into Out-pat. Servs. At Guy's Hosp. (King Edwd. Hosp. Fund For Lond.).

BLANEY, Mr Sean Paul Alexander Linden, Noctorum Road, Birkenhead CH43 9UG — MB BS 1990 Lond.; PhD Lond. 1988, BSc 1985; FRCS Eng. 1995. Regist. Guy's & St Thomas' Hosp. Lond.; Specialist Regist. (Otolaryngol.) Gt. Ormond St. Hosp. Childr.; Specialist Regist. Guy's & St. Thos. Hosps. Lond.; Specialist Regist. Roy. Sussex. Co.. Hosp. Brighton. Prev: Regist. (Otolaryngol.) Lewisham Hosp.; SHO (Otolaryngol.) Roy. Nat. Throat, Nose & Ear Hosp. Lond.; SHO (Otolaryngol.) Addenbrooke's Hosp. Camb.

BLANK, Charles Eric (retired) 295 Ecclesall Road S., Sheffield S11 9PQ Tel: 0114 236 6528 — MB BCh 1955 Wales; PhD Lond. 1959. Prev: Reader (Med. Genetics) Univ. Sheff.

BLANK, Hilary Grace (retired) 28 Broadway, Cheadle SK8 1NQ Tel: 0161 428 5382 — MB ChB 1950 Liverp.; MRCS Eng. LRCP Lond. 1950; DCH Eng. 1953. Prev: Clin. Med. Asst. Centr. (Manch.) Health Dist. (T).

BLANK, Sarah Catrin Dr S.C. Blank, Hammersmith Hospital, Ducane Road, London W12 0NN Tel: 020 8383 3162 Email: cblank@cu.rpms.ac.uk; 5 Milton Road, London W3 6QA — MB BS 1990 Newc.; MRCP 1992. Research Fell., MRC Cyclotron Unit, Hammersmith Hosp., Lond. Prev: Clin. Stroke Fell., St Geo.s Hosp., Lond.; Specialist Regist. in Neurol., Newc.

BLANKERT, Marie Henriette Louise 17 Derby Square, Douglas IM1 3LS — MRCS Eng. LRCP Lond. 1967. (Roy. Free) Prev: Ho. Surg. Willesden Gen. Hosp. Lond.; Ho. Phys. Highlands Gen. Hosp. Lond.

BLANKFIELD, Colin Philip Limes Surgery, 8-14 Limes Court, Conduit Lane, Hoddesdon EN11 8EP Tel: 01992 464533 — MB BS 1980 Lond.; MRCGP 1984; DRCOG 1983. (Westm.) Prev: Trainee GP Lister Hosp. VTS Stevenage.

BLANKSON, John Michael Arosfa, 3 The Grove, Merthyr Tydfil CF47 8YR — LRCPI & LM, LRSCI & LM 1967; FRCPI 1982, M 1971; LRCPI & LM, LRCSI & LM 1967; DCH RCPSI 1969. (RCSI) Cons. Paediat. Mid Glam. HA. Prev: Hon. Sen. Regist. Guy's Hosp. Lond. & St. Laurence's Hosp. (Richmond) Dub.; Sen. Lect. (Child Health) Univ. Ghana Med. Sch. Accra, Ghana.

BLANKSON-BEECHAM, George 17A Kempshott Road, Streatham, London SW16 5LG — MB BCh BAO 1970 Dub.

BLANSHARD, Christine The Gastroenterology Unit, Middlesex Hospital, Mortimer St., London W1T 3AA Tel: 020 7636 8333 Fax: 020 7380 9162; 12 Albert Road, London N4 3RW Tel: 020 7281 4735 Fax: 020 7272 6019 — MB BChir 1986 Camb.; MB BChir Camb. 1987; MD Camb. 1996; MRCP (UK) 1990. Sen. Regist. (Gastroenterol.) Middlx. Hosp. Prev: Regist. (Hepatol.) Roy. Free Hosp.; Regist. (Gastroenterol. & Gen. Med.) N. Middlx. Hosp.; Research Fell. (Gastroenterol. & HIV) W.m. Hosp.

BLANSHARD, Christopher Gordon Danes Camp Surgery, Rowtree Road, East Hunsbury, Northampton NN4 0NY Tel: 01604 709426; 39 Bradden Road, Greens Norton, Towcester NN12 8BS — MB ChB 1979 Leeds; MRCGP 1986; Cert Family Plann. JCC 1983; DRCOG 1982.

BLANSHARD, Gerald Phoenix (retired) Alderbrook, Fulmer Lane, Fulmer, Slough SL3 6JA Tel: 01753 662270 — MA, MD Camb. 1955, MB BChir 1949; FRCP Lond. 1975, M 1955; LMCC 1958. Prev: Cons. Phys., hillingdon Hosp.

BLANSHARD, Hannah Jane Garden Flat, 39 Apsley Road, Bristol BS8 2SN Tel: 0117 973 9837 Email: rickyandhannah@dells53.freeserve.co.uk — MB BChir 1993 Camb.; FRCA 1997; MRCP 1998. SHO (Anaesth.) Frenchay Hosp. Bristol.

BLANSHARD, Mr Jonathan David ENT Department, North Hampshire Hospital, Aldermaston Road, Basingstoke RG24 9NA Tel: 01256 473202; The White House, Northington, Alresford SO24 9TH Tel: 01962 736199 — MB BS 1984 Lond.; FRCS (Orl.) 1993; FRCS Eng. 1990. (Univ. Lond., Middlx. Hosp.) Cons. ENT N. Hants. Hosp. Basingstoke. Socs: BAO - HNS; RSM; ORS. Prev: Sen. Regist. & Regist. Rotat. (ENT) Bristol, Bath & Plymouth HA; SHO (ENT) Roy. Nat. Throat, Nose & Ear Hosp. Lond.; SHO (Plastic Surg.) Qu. Mary's Hosp. Lond.

BLANSHARD, Keith Simpson Leicester General Hospital, Gwendolen Road, Leicester LE9 7TF Tel: 0116 249 0490 Email: keith.blanshard@eving.lgh-tr.trent.nhs.uk — MB BS 1981 Lond.; FRCR 1987. Cons. Radiol. Leics. Gen. Hosp. Prev: Cons. Radiol. St. Jas. Univ. Hosp. Leeds; Sen. Clin. Lect. Univ. of Leeds; Nycomed Research Fell. Roy. Vict. Infirm. Newc.

BLANSHARD, May Simpson Alderbrook, Fulmer Lane, Fulmer, Slough SL3 6JA Tel: 01753 662270 — MB ChB 1946 Aberd.; FFA RCS Eng. 1954; DA Eng. 1953. Prev: Cons. Anaesth. Harefield Hosp.; Cons. Anaesth. Qu. Mary's Hosp. Childr. Carshalton; Sen. Regist. Anaesth. Middlx. Hosp. Lond.

BLAQUIÈRE, Richard Murray Wessex Body Scanner Unit, Radiology Department, Southampton General Hospital, Southampton SO16 6YD Tel: 02380 796077 Fax: 02380 794281; Coombe Lee, The Crescent, Woodlands Road, Ashurst, Southampton SO40 7AQ Tel: 02380 292522 — MB ChB 1974 Manch.; BSc St. And. 1971; FRCR 1981. Cons. Radiol. Soton Univ. Hosps.; Cons. i/c Wessex Body Scanner Unit Soton Gen. Hosps. Socs: Brit. Inst. Radiol.; Roy. Soc. Med. Prev: Res. Fell. & Lect. Inst. Cancer Res. & Roy. Marsden Hosp.

BLASS, Doris Mina The Clock Tower Practice, 50-66 Park Road, Crouch End, London N8 8SU Tel: 020 8348 7711 — MB BS 1976 Melbourne.

BLASZCZYK, Andrew Adeline Road Surgery, 4 Adeline Road, Boscombe, Bournemouth BH5 1EF Tel: 01202 309421 Fax: 01202 304893 — BM 1987 Soton.; MRCGP 1992; DRCOG 1991.

BLATCH, James Rawson (retired) 31 Southleigh Road, Havant PO9 2QG — MB Camb. 1956, BChir 1955; DObst RCOG 1960; MLCOM 1983. Prev: Ho. Surg. (Obst.) & Ho. Phys. St. Mary's Hosp. Portsmouth.

BLATCH, Melanie Jane Lindisfarn, Penrose, Wadebridge PL27 7TB — MB BS 1987 Lond. Trainee GP Frimley Pk. Hosp. VTS.

BLATCH, Sheila Margaret Valentine (retired) 31 South Leigh Road, Havant PO9 2QG — MB BS (Hons. Obst. & Gyn.) Lond. 1958; MRCS Eng. LRCP Lond. 1958. Prev: Med. Off. (Family Plann.) Portsmouth.

BLATCHFORD, Howard Lister Old Fletton Surgery, Rectory Gardens, Old Fletton, Peterborough PE2 8AY Tel: 01733 343137 Fax: 01733 894739; 16 Riverside Gardens, Thorpe Meadows, Peterborough PE3 6GE Tel: 01733 555665 Fax: 01733 555665 Email: hblatchford@compuserve.com — MB ChB 1988 Leic.; BSc Leic. 1986.

BLATCHFORD, Mary Ellen Easterhouse Health Centre, 9 Auchinlea Road, Glasgow G34 9HQ Tel: 0141 531 8150 Fax: 0141 531 8110; 30 Partickhill Road, Glasgow G11 5BP Tel: 0141 334 4199 Fax: 0141 531 8158 — MB ChB 1985 Glas.; MRCGP 1990; DRCOG 1990; DCH RCPS Glas. 1989. Clin. Tutor (Gen. Pract.) Univ. Glas.; Hon Lect. (Pharmacy) Strathclyde Univ.

BLATCHFORD, Oliver Mark Walton Department of Public Health, Argyll & Clyde Health Board, Ross House, Paisley PA2 7BN Tel: 0141 842700 Fax: 0141 848 1414 Email: oliver.blatchford@achb.scot.nhs.uk; Email: o.blatchford@bigfoot.com — MB ChB 1983 Glas.; PhD 2000 Glas.; MPH Glas. 1995; B. Soc Sci Natal 1976; MFPHM RCP (UK) 1997; MRCGP 1989; DRCOG 1989. Cons. in Pub. Health, Argyll & Clyde Health Bd.; Hon. Clin. Sen. Lect. Pub. Health, Univ. of Glas. Socs: Soc. Social Med. Prev: Audit Research Fell., RCPS Glas.; Research Fell. (Pub. Health) Glas. Univ.; Princip. GP, Glas.

BLATCHLEY, Christopher Thorne, Friday St., Painswick, Stroud GL6 6QJ Tel: 01452 812476 — LMSSA 1979 Lond.; MB Camb. 1980, BChir 1979. (St. Thos.)

BLAU, Joseph Norman Out patient Dept, Hospital of St John & St Elizabeth, 60 Grove End Road, London NW8 9NH Tel: 0207 806

4060 Fax: 0207 266 2316; 5 Marlborough Hill, St. John's Wood, London NW8 0NN Tel: 020 7586 3804 Fax: 020 7586 3804 — MB BS 1952 Lond.; MD Lond. 1968; FRCP Lond. 1970, M 1955; FRCPath 1976, M 1968. (St. Bart.) Hon. Cons. Phys. Nat. Hosp. Qu. Sq. & Maida Vale Hosp.; Hon. Dir. City Lond. Migraine Clinic; Hon. Med. Adviser. Migraine. action. Assn; Cons. NeUrol. King Geo. Hosp., Ilford Essex; Cons. NeUrol., Hosp. St John and St. Eliz., Lond. NW8; Edr. Continued Professional Developm. Bull. (Neurol.). Socs: Fell. Roy. Soc. Med.; Med. Writers Gp. Soc. Authors; Assn. Brit. Neurols. Prev: Nuffield Med. Research Fell. Mass. Gen. Hosp., Boston, USA; Sen. Regist. (Neurol.) Lond. Hosp. & Maida Vale Hosp.; Capt. RAMC, Med. Off. Army Head Injuries Hosp. Wheatley.

BLAUTH-MUSZKOWSKI, Mr Christopher Iwo Anthony Cardiothoracic Unit, Guy's & St Thomas' NHS Trust, Lambeth Palace Road, lambeth palace Rd, London SE1 7EH Tel: 020 928 9292 Ext: 2909 Fax: 020 7922 8005 — MB BS 1979 Lond.; BSc (1st cl. Hons.) Lond. 1975; MS Lond. 1993; FRCS Eng. 1984; FRCS Ed. 1983; MRCS Eng. LRCP Lond. 1978. (St. Thos.) Cons. Cardiac Surg. Guy's & St. Thos. NHS Trust Lond.

BLAXILL, John Wallis (retired) 1 & 2 The Arms, Little Cressingham, Thetford IP25 6LZ Tel: 01953 882229 — MB Camb. 1955, MA, BChir 1954; DA Eng. 1971; DObst RCOG 1959; MRCGP 1964. Prev: Regist. Dept. Anaesth. Norf. & Norwich Hosp.

BLAXILL, Jonathan Mark 20 St Clare Road, Colchester CO3 3SZ — MB BS 1988 Lond.

BLAXLAND, Mr John William (retired) Foxleigh Grange, Ascot Road, Holyport, Maidenhead SL6 3LD Tel: 01628 629790 Fax: 01628 629790 — MB BS Lond. 1955; BSc (Physiol.) Lond. 1952; FRCS Eng. 1964; MRCS Eng. LRCP Lond. 1955. Prev: Cons. Gen. Surg. Windsor Hosp. Gp.

BLAXLAND, Norman Naylor 2 Welson Road, Folkestone CT20 2NW Tel: 01303 54818 — MB BS 1942 Lond.; MRCS Eng. LRCP Lond. 1942; DMRD Eng. 1950. (St. Mary's) Cons. Radiol. S.E. Metrop. Regional Hosp. Bd.

BLAXLAND, Stephen (retired) Parsonage Cottage, Saxtead, Woodbridge IP13 9QN Tel: 01728 685367 — BM BCh 1944 Oxf.; BA, BM BCh Oxf. 1944; DPM Eng. 1971; DObst RCOG 1950. Prev: Med. Asst. (Psychiat.) W. Suff. Hosp. Bury St. Edmunds.

BLAY, Eric Richard (retired) 86A Old Street, Hill Head, Fareham PO14 3HL Tel: 01329 662032 Email: eric@eblay.freeserve.co.uk — MB ChB 1951 Birm.; MRCGP 1961; DObst RCOG 1953. Prev: Med. Off. i/c Brit. Phosphate Commr. Christmas Is., Indian Ocean.

BLAYDES, Kathryn Elizabeth c/o The Mount, Killinghall, Harrogate HG3 2AY Tel: 01423 506500 — MB ChB 1986 Manch.; BSc (Med. Sci.) St. And. 1984; DRCOG 1993. Prev: Dep. Princip. Med. Off. HMS Cochrane Rosyth.; Trainee GP & Dep. Princip. Med. Off. HMS Warrior N.wood; SHO (O & G) Freedom Fields Hosp. Plymouth.

BLAYMIRES, Karin Leonie East Wing, Esk Medical Centre, Ladywell Way, Musselburgh EH21 6AA Tel: 0131 665 2267 Fax: 0131 653 2348 — MB ChB 1972 Otago. (Otago) GP Musselburgh, Midlothian.

BLAYNEY, Jill Elizabeth 6 Southwell Riverside, Bridgnorth WV16 4AS — MB ChB 1993 Birm.; ChB Birm. 1993. Prev: Trainee GP Sandwell HA.

BLAYNEY, Mr John David Michael 4 The Causeway, Llanblethian, Cowbridge CF71 7JE — MB BCh 1960 Wales; FRCS Eng. 1970. Cons. Orthop. Surg. P.ss of Wales Hosp. Bridgend. Socs: Fell. BOA. Prev: Sen. Regist. (Orthop.) Cardiff Roy. Infirm. & P. of Wales Hosp. Cardiff.

BLAYNEY, Michael Roger 88 Old Fallings Lane, Wolverhampton WV10 8BN — MB ChB 1991 Birm.; LDS RCS Eng. 1983; BDS Lond. 1983; ChB Birm. 1991.

BLAZEBY, Miss Jane Miranda Department of Surgery, Bristol Royal Infirmary, Bristol BS2 8HW Tel: 0117 928 2336 Fax: 0117 925 2736 Email: j.m.blazeby@bristol.ac.uk; Robinson House, 87 West Town Rd, Backvale BS48 3BH — MB ChB 1988 Bristol; BSc Bristol 1985; MD 1999; FRCS (Gen. Surg.)1999. (Bristol) MRC Clin. Scientist. Prev: Lect. in Surg.; Specialist Regist. Roy. Devon & Exeter Hosp.; Clin. Research Fell. (Surg.) Bristol Roy. Infirm.

BLAZEWICZ, Leszek Wladyslaw Botley Medical Centre, Elms Road, Botley, Oxford OX2 9JS Tel: 01865 248719 Fax: 01865 728116; Pantiles, Jarn Way, Boars Hill, Oxford OX1 5JF — BM BCh 1972 Oxf.; MA (1st Cl. Hons.) Camb. 1972; MRCP (UK) 1975; MRCS Eng. LRCP Lond. 1972; DObst. RCOG 1975; MRCGP 1982.

BLAZQUEZ ANGULO, Javier Andres Department of Gynaecology, Northwick Park Hospital, Watford Road, Harrow HA1 3UJ — LMS 1991 Complutense Madrid.

BLEACH, Mr Nigel Richard Department of ENT Surgery, Wexham Park Hospital, Wexham, Slough SL2 4HL; Addenbrookes, 98 Dropmere Road, Burnham, Slough SL1 8EL Tel: 01628 667368 Fax: 01628 667368 — MB ChB 1981 Birm.; FRCS Eng. 1987; FCSHK Coll. Surg. Hong Kong 1995. (Birmingham University) Cons. Otolaryngologist Wexham Pk. Hosp. Slough. Socs: Eur. Acad. Facial Plastic Surg.; Clin. Sec. Windsor & Dist. Med. Soc.; Brit. Assn. of Otorhinolaryngol.-Head & Neck Surg. Prev: Sen. Regist. (OtoLaryngol.) Char. Cross Hosp. Lond.

BLEAKLEY, Caroline Julie 37 Station Road, Sheffield S11 7AX — MB ChB 1990 Leeds.

BLEAKNEY, Robert Reginald 57 Main Street, Groomsport, Bangor BT19 6JR — MB BCh BAO 1993 Belf.

BLEASBY, Christine Jean Fairley Croftfoot Road Surgery, 44 Croftfoot Road, Glasgow G44 5JT Tel: 0141 634 6333 — MB ChB 1966 Glas.

BLEASDALE, Alison Mary Sinclair 5 Kelvin Road, Roath, Cardiff CF23 5ET — MB BCh 1995 Wales.

BLEASDALE, John Kenneth (retired) 1 Preston Cottages, Ermington, Ivybridge PL21 9NQ Tel: 01548 830509 — MB ChB 1953 Manch.; FRCGP 1982, M 1966. Prev: Sen. Ho. Off. P.ss Eliz. Orthop. Hosp. Exeter.

BLEASDALE, John Paul 23 Dalkeith Road, Sutton Coldfield B73 6PW Tel: 0121 355 7645 — MB ChB 1990 Leeds.

BLEASDALE, Robert Anthony 24 Moy Road, Roath, Cardiff CF24 4SG Tel: 029 2049 8388 — MB BCh 1994 Wales. (Univ. Wales Coll. Med.) SHO (Med.) Glan Hafren NHS Trust Gwent. Prev: SHO (Med.) Swansea NHS Trust.

BLEASE, David John Frederick Place Surgery, 11 Frederick Place, Weymouth DT4 8HQ Tel: 01305 774411 Fax: 01305 760417; 31 Melcombe Avenue, Weymouth DT4 7TF Tel: 01305 774411 — MB BS 1972 Lond.; MRCS Eng. LRCP Lond. 1972; MRCGP 1978; DObst RCOG 1974. (Roy. Free) Prev: SHO (O & G) Dorset Co. Hosp.; Ho. Phys. Hillingdon Hosp. Uxbridge; Ho. Surg. Roy. Free Hosp. Lond.

BLEASE, Simon Christopher Med-Tel Europe Ltd, Great Osbaston House, Osbaston, Monmouth NP25 5DL Tel: 01600 712642 Fax: 01600 712922 Email: simonblease@openmricentres.com; Great Osbaston House, Osbaston, Monmouth NP25 5DL — MB BCh 1982 Wales; FRCR 1988. (Cardiff) Dir. of Med. Servs.; Hon. Clin. Lect. Univ. Bristol; Vice-Pres. Magnetic Resonance Radiol. Assn. Socs: Magnetic Resonance Radiol. Assn.; Brit. Soc. Sport & Med.; Brit. Inst. Radiol. Prev: Cons. (Radiol.) Nevill Hall Hosp., Abergavenny; Cons. (Radiol.) P.ss Alexandra RAF Hosp., Swindon.

BLEBY, Michael John Arden Medical Centre, 1498 Warwick Road, Knowle, Solihull B93 9LE Tel: 01564 772010 Fax: 01564 771224; 146 Station Road, Knowle, Solihull B93 0EP — MB BChir 1980 Camb.; MA, MB BChir Camb. 1980; LMSSA 1980; MRCGP 1985; DRCOG 1985.

BLECHER, Theodore E (retired) 64 Parkside, Wollaton, Nottingham NG8 2NN Tel: 0115 925 5945 — MB BCh 1955 Witwatersrand; FRCP Ed. 1982, M 1962; FRCPath 1977 M 1965. Co-Dir. Nottm. Haemophilia Centre. Prev: Cons. (Haemat.) Nottm. HA.

BLECHYNDEN, John Christopher Southgate Surgery, 2 Forester Road, Southgate, Crawley RH10 6EQ Tel: 01293 522231 Fax: 01293 515655 — MB ChB 1978 Leeds; MRCGP 1982; DRCOG 1981.

BLEEHEN, Isobel Susan 28 Frithwood Avenue, Northwood HA6 3LU — MB BS 1988 Lond.

BLEEHEN, Professor Norman Montague, CBE St John's College, Cambridge CB2 1TP; 21 Bentley Road, Cambridge CB2 2AW Tel: 01223 354320 — BM BCh 1955 Oxf.; MA Oxf. 1955, BSc 1955; FRCP Lond. 1973, M 1957; FACR Hon. 1974; FRCR 1964; DMRT Eng. 1962. (Middlx.) Emerit. Prof. Clin. Oncol. & Head Dept. Univ. Camb. Socs: Fell. Roy. Soc. Med. Prev: Prof. Radiother. Middlx. Hosp. Med. Sch.; Lect. Dept. Regius Prof. Med. Oxf.; Jun. Specialist Med. RAMC.

BLEEHEN, Robert Edward 75 Colchester Avenue, Penylan, Cardiff CF23 9NY Email: bleehen@cardiff.ac.uk — MB BChir 1993 Camb.; MRCP 1996.

BLEEHEN, Professor Stanley Sholom 152 Harley Street, London W1N 1HH Tel: 020 7935 1858 Fax: 020 7224 2574; 3A Eastbury Avenue, Northwood HA6 3LB Tel: 01923 840889 — MB BChir 1959 Camb.; BA Camb. 1959; FRCP Lond. 1977, M 1964. (Camb. & Middlx.) Emerit. Prof. Dermat. Univ. Sheff.; Hon. Cons. Dermat. St. John's Inst. Dermat. St. Thos. Hosp. & Cons. Manor Hse. Hosp Lond. Socs: Fell. Roy. Soc. Med.; Fell. St. John's Hosp. Dermat. Soc.; BMA. Prev: Cons. Dermat. Sheff. HA; Research Fell. in Dermat. Harvard Med. Sch. Mass. Gen. Hosp. Boston, Mass., USA; Sen. Regist. (Dermat.) Univ. Coll. Hosp. Lond.

BLEETMAN, Anthony Birmingham Heartlands Hospital, Bordesley Green E., Birmingham B9 5SS Tel: 0121 424 2000 Fax: 0121 424 0260; Tel: 0121 733 2136 Fax: 0121 744 4389 Email: bleetman@enterprise.net — MD 1990 Tel Aviv; FRCS Ed. 1993; FFAEM 1997; Dip IMC RCS Ed. 1992. (Univ. Tel Aviv) Cons. A & E Heartlands Hosp. Birm.; Hon. Sen. Clin. Lect. (Surg.) Univ. of Birm. Socs: Founding Med. Fell. Fac. Pre-Hosp. Care RCS Ed.; Brit. Assn. Accid. & Emerg. Med.; BASICS. Prev: Sen. Regist. (A & E) W. Midl.; Regist. (A & E) Addenbrooke's Hosp. Camb.

BLEEZE, Kathryn Gail British Airways Health Services, Base Health Centre (G29), Gatwick Airport, PO Box 747, Gatwick RH6 0FH Tel: 01293 662344 — MB BS 1979 Lond.; DRCOG 1982. (Middlx.) Med. Off. Brit. Airways Health Serv. Prev: Trainee GP Windsor VTS; Squadron Ldr. RAF Med. Br.; Asst. Surg. P & O Lines.

BLEGAY, Mr Robert Nya 9 Croft Road, London SW19 2NF — MD 1983 Liberia; MD U. Liberia 1983; FRCS Ed. 1992.

BLEIKER, Philip Francois Morris, Harker, Bleiker and Partners, Ivybridge Health Centre, Station Road, Ivybridge PL21 0AJ Tel: 01752 690777 Fax: 01752 690252 — BM BS 1980 Nottm.; MSc. Exeter 1997; BMedSci Nottm. 1978; MFFP 1995; MRCGP 1987; DRCOG 1985. (Nottingham) Trainer (Gen. Pract.) Devon; Course Organiser Exeter. Prev: Trainee GP Glos. VTS; SHO Rotat. (Med.) Derby Roy. Infirm.

BLEIKER, Tanya Ownsworth Department Dermatology, Derbyshire Royal Infirmary, London Road, Derby DE1 2QY Tel: 01352 347141 Ext: 2835; The Threshing Barn, Main Street, Milton LE8 9DZ — BM BS 1992 Nottm.; BMedSci (Hons.) 1990; MRCP (UK) 1995. Cons. Dermat. Derbysh. Roy. Infirm. Prev: Regist. (Dermat.) Leicester Roy. Infirm.

BLEKSLEY, Michael Charles Pool Park, Eastcott, St Dominick, Saltash PL12 6TB — MB BChir 1981 Camb.; MA Camb. 1979, MB BChir 1981; MRCGP 1986. GP Gunnislake.

BLENCH, Pearl Irene (retired) Glanllyn, Felindre, Berriew, Welshpool SY21 8BE Tel: 01686 640637 — LRCP LRCS Ed. LRFPS Glas. 1947. Prev: Sen. Med. Off. Staffs. AHA.

***BLENCOWE, Hannah Jayne** 2 Westmorland Avenue, Weyton, Huntingdon PE28 2HS Tel: 01480 433391 Email: hbloencowe@hotmail.lcom — MB ChB 1998 Bristol.

BLEND, David Maurice 30 Etheldene Avenue, London N10 3QH Tel: 020 8883 1319 Fax: 020 8883 1319; 30 Etherdene Avenue, London N10 3QH Tel: 0208 883 1319 Fax: 0208 883 1319 — MB BS Lond. 1947; MRCPsych 1973; DPM Eng. 1968. (Lond. Hosp.) Socs: BMA. Prev: Cons. Psychiat. Hoddesdon Child & Family Psychiat. Clinics & Hailey Hall Sch.; Sen. Regist. (Psychiat.) Portman Clinic & W. Middlx. Hosp.; Sen. Regist. (Child Psychiat.) Qu. Eliz. Hosp. for Childr. & Hoxton Child. Guid. Unit.

BLENKARN, Robin Nigel 8 Kings Ride, Seaford BN25 2LN — MB BS 1988 Lond.

BLENKINSOPP, Errington Miles (retired) The Surgery, 31 High St., Brandon IP27 9JS Tel: 01842 810388 Fax: 01842 751242 — MRCS Eng. LRCP Lond. 1959; MA Camb. 1959; LMSSA Lond. 1958. Local Med. Off. Civil Serv. Thetford & Brandon. Prev: Med. Off. Dist. 1.

BLENKINSOPP, John Astra Zeneca, King's Court, Water Lane, Wilmslow SK9 5AZ Tel: 01625 535999; 1 Cardigan Road, Headingley, Leeds LS6 3AE Tel: 0113 278 6478 Fax: 0113 278 6478 — MB ChB 1988 Birm.; BPharm (Hons.) Bradford 1978; Grad. Dip. Managem. & Admin. Bradford Univ. 1979; Dip. Pharm. Med. RCP (UK) 1992. Med. Manager (Primary Care), Astra Zeneca; Hon. Vis. Lect. (Pharm. Practs.) Bradford Univ. Socs: Roy. Pharmaceut. Soc. Gt. Brit.; Brit. Assn. Pharm. Phys. Prev: Med. Adviser ICI Pharmaceuts. Chesh.; Clin. Research Phys. GHBA/Hazleton Clinic Leeds.

BLENKINSOPP, Pamela Frances 58A Dyne Road, London NW6 7DS — MB BS 1994 Lond.; DRCOG 1997; BSc Med. Microbiol. Lond. 1990; DFFP 1998. (Univ. Coll. Lond.) GP Regist. The Grange Med. Centre Seacroft Leeds. Prev: SHO (Paediat.) Pontefract Gen. Infirm.; GP/Regist. Garforth, Leeds; SHO (O & G) Leeds Gen. Infirm & Bradford Roy. Infirm.

BLENKINSOPP, Mr Peter Trafford Department of Maxillofacial Surgery, Queen Marys Hospital, Roehampton, London SW15 Tel: 020 8789 6611; Ashmount, Mount View Road, Claygate, Esher KT10 0UB Tel: 01372 464301 — MB BS 1974 Lond.; BDS Lond. 1968; FRCS Ed. 1986; FDS RCS Eng. 1975, LDS 1967. (King's Coll. Hosp. & Guy's Dent. Sch.) Cons. Oral & Maxillofacial Surg. Kingston Hosp. Surrey, Qu. Mary's Hosp. Roehampton & St. Heliers Hosp. Carshalton. Socs: Fell.Brit. Assoc. of Oral & Maxillofacial Surg.s; BMA; Eur. Assn. Cranio-Maxillo. Surg. Prev: Sen. Regist. Qu. Mary's Hosp. Roehampton & Univ. Coll. Hosp. Lond.; Sen. Asst. (Maxillofacial Surg.) Univ. Muenster, W. Germany.

BLENKINSOPP, William Keith (retired) 6 Parkfield Avenue, Amersham HP6 6BE — PhD Camb. 1971; MA Camb. 1963, MD 1967, MB 1961, BChir 1960; LMSSA Lond. 1960; FRCPath 1979, M 1967. Prev: Cons. Path. Watford Gen. Hosp.

BLENKIRON, Paul 23 Garth Terrace, Burton Stone Lane, York YO30 6DU — BM BCh 1988 Oxf.

BLESING, Claire Hilary The Radiotherapy Department, Chuchill Hospital, Old Road, Headington, Oxford OX3 7LJ Tel: 01865 225262 Fax: 01865 225264; Willow House, Mallins Lane, Longcot, Faringdon SN7 7TE — MB BChir 1987 Camb.; MSc (Oncol.) Glas. 1991; MA Camb. 1987; MRCP (UK) 1989; FRCR 1995. (Univ. Camb. & St. Thos. Hosp. Lond.) Cons. (Clin. Oncol.) The Ch.ill Hosp. Oxf. Socs: Fell. Roy. Coll. Radiols. Prev: Regist. (Clin. Oncol.) Qu. Eliz. Med. Centre Birm.; Asst. Doctor (Radiat. Oncol.) H.C.U.G. Geneva, Switz.; Regist. (Gen. Med.) W.. Infirm. Glas.

BLESING, Norbert Ernst Department of Haematology, Princess Margaret Hospital, Okus Road, Swindon SN1 4JU Tel: 01793 426051 Fax: 01793 426827 — State Exam Med 1981 Frankfurt; MSc (Oncol.) Glas. 1989; MD Frankfurt 1984; MRCP (UK) 1986; MRCPath 1995; FRCP (UK) 1997. (Johan-Wolfgang Goethe Univ., Frankfurt) Cons. Haemat. P.ss Margt. Hosp. Swindon, Wilts. Prev: Sen. Regist. (Haemat.) W. Midl.; Therap. Dir. (Immunol. & Oncol.) Serono Geneva, Switz.; Regist. (Haemat.) Glas. Roy. Infirm.

BLESOVSKY, Mr Ary (retired) Douglas Lodge, Brodick KA27 8AW — MB ChB Cape Town 1950; FRCS Eng. 1955; FRCS Ed. 1955. Prev: Cons. Cardio-Thoracic Surg. Newc. RHB & United Newc. Hosps.

BLESOVSKY, Lynda Teresa 15 Hopefield Avenue, London NW6 6LJ — MB BS 1984 Lond.; FCAnaesth. 1989. Regist. Roy. Free Hosp. Lond.

BLESSED, Garry 130 Runnymede Road, Ponteland, Newcastle upon Tyne NE20 9HN Tel: 01661 823018 — MB BS 1956 Durh.; MB BS (2nd cl. Hons.) Durh. 1956; FRCP Ed. 1972, M 1964; FRCPsych 1975, M 1971; DPM Eng. 1962. Hon. Clin. Sci. (Neurochem. Path.) Newc. Gen. Hosp. Prev: Cons. Psychogeriat. Newc. Gen. Hosp.; Cons. Psychiat. St. Nicholas Hosp. Gosforth; Sen. Research Assc. MRC Unit (Psychiat.) Newc.

BLESSING, Elaine 3 Claydown Way, Slip End, Luton LU1 4DU — MB BS 1996 Lond.

BLESSING, Karen The Old Manse, Kinellar, Aberdeen AB21 0SB — MB ChB 1982 Ed.; MD Aberd. 1992; MRCPath 1989.

BLETCHER, Michael Hurst 22 Louvain Road, Derby DE23 6BZ Tel: 01332 43371 — MB ChB 1956 Birm.; DMJ Soc. Apoth. Lond. 1971. (Birm.)

BLETHYN, Jane Old Cogan Hall, Sully Road, Penarth CF64 2TQ — MB ChB Leeds 1981; FRCR 1991. Cons. Radiol. Llandough Hosp. Cardiff. Prev: Sen. Regist. (Radiol.) Univ. Hosp. Wales Cardiff; Regist. (Radiol.) Roy. Hallamsh. Hosp. Sheff.

BLEVINS, Timothy Cameron Scott Eagle House Surgery, Eagle House, White Cliff Mill Street, Blandford Forum DT11 7DQ Tel: 01258 453171; The Tallet, Nutford, Blandford Forum DT11 0QJ Tel: 01258 459266 — MB BS 1984 Lond.; BSc Wales 1978; DRCOG 1987. (Westm.)

BLEWDEN, Wendy Elsie 3 Woodhall Avenue, Pinner HA5 3DY; 81 Field End Road, Eastcote, Pinner HA5 1TD — MB ChB 1982 Aberd.; MRCGP 1986; DCCH RCP Ed. 1987; DRCOG 1985.

BLEWETT, Andrew Earlston Wonford House Hospital, Dryden Road, Exeter EX2 5AF — MB ChB 1984 Glas.; MRCPsych 1990. (Glasgow) Cons. Gen. Adult Psychiat.Exeter.

BLEWETT, Kevin Amesbury North Lodge, Penshurst Place, Penshurst, Tonbridge TN11 8DH — MB BS 1985 Lond.

BLEWETT, Martina Louise Rachel Epsom General Hospital, Dorking Road, Epsom KT18 7EG Tel: 01372 735735; 30 Friars Avenue, Putney Vale, London SW15 3DU Tel: 020 8789 4424 — BM 1995 Soton.; DRCOG 1998. (Southampton) GP Regist. VTS Epsom Gen. Hosp. Surrey. Prev: SHO (Psychiat.) Surrey Heartlands Epsom; SHO (Paediat.) Epsom Gen. Hosp.; SHO (O & G) Epsom Gen. Hosp. Surrey.

BLEWITT, Linda Ann 31 Parkfield Road, Oldbury, Oldbury B68 8PS — BM BCh 1997 Oxf.

BLEWITT, Martin John 24 Suttons Avenue, Hornchurch RM12 4LF — MB BCh BAO 1957 NUI. (Galway) GP HornCh.; Clin. Asst. Vict. Hosp. Romford. Socs: BMA. Prev: Ho. Phys. S.. Hosp. Dartford; Ho. Surg. N. Kent Hosp. Gravesend; Ho. Surg. (Obst.) W. Hill Hosp. Dartford.

BLEWITT, Mr Neil Orthopaedic Department, Frenchay Hospital, Bristol BS16 1LE — MB ChB 1985 Leeds; FRCS (Orth.) 1995; FRCS Eng. 1989. Cons. Traum. & Orthop. Surg. Frenchay Hosp. Bristol; Sen. Clin. Lect. Univ. of Bristol. Socs: Brit. Orthop. Assn.; Brit. Orthop. Research Soc.; Brit. Elbow & Shoulder Soc. Prev: Sen. Regist. (Orthop. Surg.) N.. & Yorks. RHA; Lect. (Orthop. Surg.) Univ. Newc.; Regist. (Orthop.) N.. Region.

BLEWITT, Neville John The Bridges Practice, The Health Centre, Stepgates, Chertsey KT16 8HZ Tel: 01932 561199 — MB BS 1987 Lond.; MRCGP 1992; DRCOG 1990. (St. Thos. Hosp.) Clin. Asst. (Cardiol.) St. Peters Hosp. Chertsey. Prev: Trainee GP Chertsey; SHO (O & G) Wycombe Gen. Hosp.

BLEWITT, Robert William Knott House, High Knott Road, Arnside, Carnforth LA5 0AW — MB ChB 1972 Leeds; BSc Leeds 1969, MB ChB 1972; MRCPath 1978.

BLEWITT, Sandra Dawn Queen Mary's Hospital for Children, Epsom 2, St Helier Trust, Wrythe Lane, Carshalton SM5 1AA Tel: 020 8644 4343 — MB BS 1979 Madras; DCH RCP Lond. 1982; DRCOG 1989; MRCGP 1989; MRCP (UK) 1991; FRCPH,1997. Cons. Paediat. Qu. Mary's Hosp. for Childr. Carshalton.

BLICK, Ann Hedla (retired) 3 Fishermans Bank, Mudeford, Christchurch BH23 3NP Tel: 01202 486745 — MRCS Eng. LRCP Lond. 1951.

BLICK, Peter William Hammond Woodlands, Golden Hill, Ashley Lane, New Milton BH25 5AQ Tel: 01425 28337 — MB ChB 1974 Leeds.

BLIGH, Andrea Donna Mary Woodland Cottage, Sandy Lane, Whittington Heath, Lichfield WS14 9PB — MB ChB 1984 Bristol.

BLIGH, Professor John Gregory University Medical Education Unit, 3rd Floor, UCD Building, Royal Liverpool University Hospital, Prescot St., Liverpool L69 3BX Tel: 0151 706 4293 Fax: 0151 706 5876; 21 Abbots Park, Chester CH1 4AW — MB ChB 1978 Manch.; BSc St. And. 1975; MD Liverp. 1994; MMed Dundee 1989; FRCGP 1990, M 1982. (St. And.) Prof. Med. Educat. Univ. Liverp. Socs: Fell. RCGP. Prev: Prof. Primary Care Educat. Univ. Liverp.; Roy. Coll. Gen. Pract. Saudi Arabia Fell. 1991; Sen. Lect. (Med. Educat.) Univ. Liverp.

BLIGH, Mark David 76 Sutton Road, Waterlooville PO8 8QA — MB ChB 1993 Bristol. SHO (Med.) Derriford Hosp. Plymouth.

BLIGHT, Adrian Richard 47 Rectory Lane, Leybourne, Maidstone ME16 9N — MB BS 1990 Lond.; MRCP Lond. 1993.

BLIGHT, Andrew Philip Ashfield Surgery, 8 Walmley Road, Sutton Coldfield B76 1QN Tel: 0121 351 7955 Fax: 0121 313 2509 — MB BS 1982 Lond.; DRCOG 1985.

BLIGHT, Joy Shirley (retired) 5 Hewitt Close, Trowbridge BA14 7SG Tel: 01763 263343 — MB BS 1952 Lond.; MRCS Eng. LRCP Lond. 1952. Prev: Clin. Asst. (Cytol.) Dept. Pathol. Bristol Matern. Hosp.

BLIGHT, Kiri Joanne 1 Drakes Meadow, Cheriton Fitzpaine, Crediton EX17 4HU Tel: 01363 866305 Fax: 01363 866305 — MB ChB 1998 Ed.; MB ChB Ed 1998.

BLIGHT, Richard (retired) 5 Hewitt Close, Trowbridge BA14 7SG Tel: 01225 781497 — MB BS 1952 Lond.; MD Lond. 1968; DObst RCOG 1954. Prev: Cons. Sen. Lect. Dept. Path. Univ. Bristol.

BLIGHT, Simon Brymer, Trevingey Road, Redruth TR15 3DH — MB BS 1991 Lond.

BLINCOW, Allen Hodges Dalmarnock, 26 Silverwells Crescent, Bothwell, Glasgow G71 8DP — MB ChB 1972 Glas.

BLINDT, Daniel Mark 44 Church Street, Ringstead, Kettering NN14 4DH — BM BS 1989 Nottm.

BLINDT, Michael (retired) 26 Hill Turrets Close, Sheffield S11 9RE Tel: 0114 236 2289 Fax: 0114 236 2289 Email: compuserve@101370.2323 — MB ChB 1959 Sheff.; AFOM RCP Lond. 1980.

BLINSTON JONES, Michael Philip New Lyminge Surgery, Greenbanks, Lyminge, Folkestone CT18 8NS Tel: 01303 863160 Fax: 01303 863492; Prim Farm, Stelling Minnis, Canterbury CT4 6BD Tel: 01227 87854 — MRCS Eng. LRCP Lond. 1975; BSc. Lond. 1973, MB BS 1975; MRCP (UK) 1977.

BLISS, Alison Kay 56 Westaway Court, Savile St., St Helier, Jersey JE2 3XF — MB ChB 1990 Leeds; DA (UK) 1994. Regist. (Anaesth.) Jersey Gen. Hosp. St. Helier. Prev: SHO (Anaesth.) N. Manch. Gen. Hosp. & Roy. Oldham Hosp.

BLISS, Mr Brian Peter (retired) Barnwell, Wearde, Saltash PL12 4AX Tel: 01752 842482 Email: brian@pbliss.freeserve.co.uk — MB BS 1956 Lond.; MS Lond. 1969; FRCS Eng. 1961. Prev: Cons. Surg. Plymouth Gen. Hosp.

BLISS, Deborah Fortune Willowbrook Medical Practice, Brook Street, Sutton-in-Ashfield NG17 1ES Tel: 01623 440018; 38 Main Street, Woodborough, Nottingham NG14 6EA — BM BS Nottm. 1975, BMedSci 1973; MRCGP 1980; DRCOG 1979.

BLISS, Ghada Adel Saqf Tamarisk Cottage, South St., Steeple Aston, Bicester OX25 4RT — MB BCh 1972 Ain Shams, Egypt.

BLISS, Mr James Philip 216D Randolph Avenue, London W9 1PF — MB BS 1990 Lond.; MB BS (Distinc. Med.) Lond. 1990; BSc (Exp. Path.) Lond. 1988; FRCS Eng. 1995. Regist. Rotat. (Orthop. & Trauma) St. Mary's Hosp. Lond. Socs: Eur. Hip Soc.; Roy. Soc. Med. (Orthop. Sect.).

BLISS, Janet Louise 9 Olivedale Road, Liverpool L18 1DD — MB BS 1992 Lond. SHO (Gen. Med.) Aintree Hosps. Trust Liverp. Socs: BMA.

BLISS, Mary Rose Oaklea, Badgers Mount, Sevenoaks TN14 7AY Tel: 01959 534278 Fax: 020 8985 2007 Email: mary.bliss@virgin.net — MB BS 1958 Lond.; FRCP Lond. 1993; MRCP (UK) 1974. (Univ. Coll. Hosp.) Socs: Brit. Geriat. Soc. & Tissue Viability Soc.; Med. Res. Soc. Prev: Cons. Geriat. City & Hackney Community Servs. NHS Trust Lond.

BLISS, Peter Exeter Oncology Centre, Royal Devon & Exeter Healthcare NHS Trust, Barrack Road, Exeter EX2 5DW Tel: 01392 403921; 15 Howell Road, Exeter EX4 4LG — MB BS 1985 Lond.; BSc (Hons.) Lond. 1982; MRCP (UK) 1988; FRCR 1993. (Univ. Coll. Lond.) Cons. Oncol. Roy. Devon & Exeter Healthcare NHS Trust. Prev: Sen. Regist. (Clin. Oncol.) Roy. Marsden Hosp. Lond.; Regist. (Clin. Oncol.) W.. Gen. Hosp. Edin.; Lect. (Med. Oncol.) W.. Gen. Hosp. Edin.

BLISS, Mr Philip (cons. rooms) The Bath Clinic, Claverton Down Road, Combe Down, Bath BA2 7BR Tel: 01225 835555 Fax: 01225 835900; Tel: 01225 310564 Fax: 01225 311205 — MB BS 1954 Lond.; FRCS Eng. 1962. (St. Bart.) p/t Emerit. Cons. Surg. Orthop. Bath Health Dist. & Roy. Nat. Hosp. for Rheumat. Dis.; JP. Socs: Fell. BOA (Counc. Mem.); Assoc. Mem. Brit. Assn. Plastic Surgs.; (Pres.) Brit. Scoliosis Soc. Prev: Regist. Orthop & Accid. Servs. Radcliffe Infirm. & Nuffield Orthop. Centre. Oxf.; Res. Surg. Off. Plastic Unit & Jaw Injuries Centre, Qu. Vict. Hosp. E. Grinstead.

BLISS, Philip Weston 32 Priory Way, Harrow HA2 6DH — MB ChB 1991 Liverp.

BLISS, Mr Richard David 1 Whorlton Grange Cottage, Westerhope, Newcastle upon Tyne NE5 1ND — MB BChir 1987 Camb.; MA Camb. 1987, MB BChir 1987; FRCS Eng. 1991.

BLISS, Shelagh Mary Grehan Wingham Surgery, 67 High Street, Wingham, Canterbury CT3 1AA Tel: 01227 720205 — MB ChB Liverp. 1964.

BLISS, William Astley New Court Surgery, Borough Fields Shopping Centre, Wootton Bassett, Swindon SN4 7AX Tel: 01793

852302 Fax: 01793 851119 — MB BS 1967 Lond.; DObst RCOG 1972.

BLISS, Mr William Hamilton 49 Groombridge Road, London E9 7DP — MB BS 1993 Lond.; DTM & H Liverp. 1995; AFRCS Ed 1998; MRCS 1998. (St Barts Hosp) Specialist Regist. Orthop. N.. Deaney. Prev: Clin. and Research Fell. Orthop. Wamsbeck Gen. Hosp. Ashington; LAS Orthop. St. Mary's Hosp., Paddington; LAS Orthop. Char. Cross Hosp., Hammersmith.

BLISSETT, John Edward Park Lane Surgery, 2 Park Lane, Allestree, Derby DE22 2DS Tel: 01332 552461 Fax: 01332 541500 — MRCS Eng. LRCP Lond. 1972; BSc (1st cl. Hons. Anat.) Lond. 1969, MB BS 1972. (Char. Cross) Prev: SHO (Obst.) N.. Gen. Hosp. Sheff.; Ho. Surg. & Ho. Phys. Char. Cross Hosp. Lond.; SHO (Paediat.) Derbysh. Childr. Hosp. Derby.

BLISSITT, Lisa Claire Queen Elizabeth Psychiatric Hospital, Mindelsohn Way, Vincent Drive, Birmingham B15 Tel: 0121 627 2999; 218 Ridgacre Road, Quinton, Birmingham B32 1JR — MB ChB 1994 Birm.

BLIZZARD, John William Pitt Lodge, 94 Galleywood Road, Great Baddow, Chelmsford CM2 8DP Tel: 01245 475044 — MB BCh 1967 Wales; DA Eng. 1971; DObst RCOG 1969. Staff Anaesth. Qu. Vict. Hosp. E. Grinstead Sussex. Socs: Assn. Anaesth.; Burns & Plastic Surg. Anaesth.; Hist. Anaesth. Soc. Prev: Clin. Asst. (Anaesth.) Essex AHA; Regist. (Anaesth.) W. Glam. AHA.

BLOCH, Lauren Gabrielle 32 Woodlands, London NW11 9QL — MB ChB 1987 Sheff.

BLOCH, Thomas Peter Stephan Barn Close Surgery, 38-40 High Street, Broadway WR12 7DT Tel: 01386 853651 Fax: 01386 853982 — LRCP LRCS 1977 Ed.; MD Basle 1976; LRCP LRCS Ed. LRCPS Glas. 1977; MRCGP 1981; DRCOG 1980; Dip. Swiss Inst. Trop. Med. (Basle) Prev: SHO (Paediat.) Ch.ill Hosp. Oxf.; SHO (Obst.) John Radcliffe Hosp. Oxf.; SHO (Dermat.) Slade Hosp. Oxf..

BLOCH-ASHBRIDGE, Karen Margaret Springfield House, Broadway WR12 7BT — MB ChB 1975 Glas. Asst. Barn Cl. Surg. BRd.way. Prev: Asst. (Surg.) Gemeindespital Riehan Switz.; Asst. Med. Merian Iselin Spital, Basel, Switz.; Asst. (O & G) Kantonsspital Liestal Switz..

BLOCK, Mr Joseph (retired) 3 Invermark Terrace, Barnhill, Broughty Ferry, Dundee DD5 2QU Tel: 01382 76586 — MB ChB 1943 Cape Town; FRCS Eng. 1949; FRCS Ed. 1963. Prev: Cons. Neurosurg. Tayside Health Bd.

BLOCK, Rose 3 Invermark Terrace, Broughty Ferry, Dundee DD5 2QU — MB ChB 1985 Ed.; DRCOG 1987.

BLOCK, Ursula Manor Hospital, Moat Road, Walsall WS2 9PS — State Exam Med 1991 Aachen.

BLOCKEY, Graham John Leith Hill Practice, The Green, Ockley, Dorking RH5 5TR Tel: 01306 711182 Fax: 01306 712751 — MB BS 1979 Newc.; MRCGP 1993; DRCOG 1992.

BLOCKEY, Mr Noel Jackson (retired) Ibert Cottage, Ibert Road, Killearn, Glasgow G63 9PY Tel: 01360 50261 — MB ChB 1945 Manch.; MCh Orth (Director's Prize) Liverp. 1950; FRCS Eng. 1949; FRCS Glas. 1963; MRCS Eng. LRCP Lond. 1945. Orthop. Surg. Roy. Hosp. Sick Childr. Glas.; Orthop. Surg. W.. Infirm. Glas.; Barclay Lect. (Orthop. Surg.) Univ. Glas.

BLOCKEY, Pauline Belmont, Edale, Sheffield S33 7ZA Tel: 01433 244 — MB ChB 1942 Manch.; DPH 1954. (Manch.) Area Specialist (Child Health) Tameside AHA. Socs: BMA. Prev: SCMO Lancs. CC; Asst. MOH Co. Boro. Bolton; Ho. Surg. Roy. Infirm. Manch.

BLOFELD, Anthea (retired) 24 Elmwood, Welwyn Garden City AL8 6LE Tel: 01707 333694 Fax: 01707 333694 — MB BS 1954 Lond.; MRCPsych 1973; DPM Eng. 1969; DObst RCOG 1959. Prev: Cons. Child & Adolesc. Psychiat. St. Peter's Hosp. Chertsey & Medway Health Dist.

BLOGG, Colin Edward Nuffield Department of Anaesthetics, The Radcliffe Infirmary, Oxford OX2 6HE Tel: 01865 311188 Fax: 01865 794191 Email: colinblogg@nda.ox.ac.uk; 11 Park Town, Oxford OX2 6SN Tel: 01865 512111 Fax: 01865 515292 — MB BS 1966 Lond.; MRCS Eng. LRCP Lond. 1966; FFA RCS Eng. 1971; DObst RCOG 1968. (Lond. Hosp.) Cons. Anaesth. Radcliffe Infirm. Oxf.; Regional Adviser (Anaesth.) Oxf. Region; Sen. Clin. Lect. Univ. Oxf. Socs: Assn. Anaesth. GB & Irel.; Anaesth. Res. Soc.; Anaesth. Trav. Soc. Prev: Assoc. Prof. Univ. Texas S. W.. Med. Sch. Dallas, USA; Sen. Lect. & Cons. Lond. Hosp.; Attend. Anaesth. Baylor Univ. Med. Center Dallas, USA.

BLOM, Mr Ashley William Flat 13, Tuscany House, Durdham Park, Bristol BS6 6XA Email: blocat@msn.com — MB ChB 1991 Cape Town; FRCS Lond. 1997. Specialist Regist. Dept. Orthop. Surg. Bristol. Socs: BOA; BOTA. Prev: Oscor Lillie research fell., Univ. Bristol; Research Fell. Roy. Coll. Surgs. Univ. Bristol.

BLOM, Paul Stephen Ravenscroft Medical Centre, 166-168 Golders Green Road, London NW11 8BB Tel: 020 8455 2477 Fax: 020 8201 8298 — MB BS 1979 Lond.; DRCOG 1983; DCH RCP Lond. 1982. (Middlx. Hosp. Med. Sch.) Socs: BMA; LJMS.

BLOMFIELD, Ian Anthony Blomfield Practice, Nursery Lane Surgery, 150 Nursery Lane, Leeds LS17 7AQ Tel: 0113 293444 Fax: 0113 295 3440; Dinah's Cottage, Long Causeway, Adel, Leeds LS16 8DT Tel: 0113 267 3739 — MB ChB 1975 Leeds; MRCGP 1980; Cert. Family Plann. JCC 1980; DRCOG 1977. Clin. Asst. Younger Disabled Unit Leeds HA. Socs: BMA.

BLOMFIELD, Penelope Ingram 1 Canonbury, Shrewsbury SY3 7AG; Rosemount Cottage, KAnon Bury, Kingsland, Shrewsbury Tel: 01743 231979 — MB BS 1982 Lond.; MRCOG 1987. Sen. Regist. (O & G) N. Staffs. Med. Centre Stoke on Trent. Prev: Sen. Regist. Dudley Rd. Hosp. Birm.

BLOMFIELD, Robert George 7 Crossley Terrace, Hebden Bridge HX7 8AY Tel: 01422 844259 — MB ChB 1964 Ed.; DRCOG 1977. (Ed.) Homoeop. GP Todmorden & Hebden Bridge W. Yorks. Prev: Resid. in Surg., Med. & Dermat. Edin. Roy. Infirm.

BLOMFIELD, Stephen James William CAFTS, Spring House, 26 Market St., Buxton SK17 6LD Tel: 01298 72445 Fax: 01298 79238; 36 Redcar Road, Sheffield S10 1EX — MB ChB 1979 Sheff.; PhD Lond. 1971; BA Camb. 1965; MRCPsych 1984. Cons. Child & Family Psychiat.CHCS (N. Derbysh.) NHS Trust.

BLOMLEY, Alistair John 48 Princes Square, Stockton-on-Tees TS17 9HR — MB BS 1994 Newc.

BLOMLEY, David John (retired) Swallowfield Medical Practice, The Street, Swallowfield, Reading RG7 1QY Tel: 01734 883134 — MB 1956 Camb.; BChir 1955; DObst RCOG 1959. Prev: Ho. Phys. Dept. Cardiol. & Gen. Med. Centr. Middlx. Hosp.

BLOMLEY, Martin John Kjolsen Imperial College, Hammersmith Hospital, 150 du Cane Road, London W12 0HS Tel: 020 8383 1029 Fax: 020 8743 5409 Email: m.blomley@ic.ac.uk — MB BS 1986 Lond.; MD 2001; MA Camb. 1985; MRCP (UK) 1990; FRCR 1994. (Royal London) Sen. Lect. Hon. Cons. Imperial Coll. Lond. Socs: RSNA; BIR. Prev: Regist. (Diag. Radiol.) Hammersmith Hosp. Lond.; Cons. (Diag. Radiol.) Hammersmith Hosp. Lond.

BLONSTEIN, Laurence Henry (cons. rooms), 58 Parkside, Wimbledon Common, London SW19 5NL Tel: 020 8879 3292; 12 Burghley House, Somerset Road, London SW19 5JB Tel: 020 8947 4585 Fax: 020 8947 4585 — MB BChir 1954 Camb.; MB BChir Camb. 1955; MA Camb. 1954. (Middlx. Hosp.) Sect 12 (Ment. Health Act) Approved Doctor; Medico-Legal Expert in Med. Negligence, Personal Injury & Disabil.; Hon. Med. Off. Eng. & Lond. Amateur Boxing Assn. Prev: Clin. Asst. Community Team (Learning Disabil.) Wandsworth HA; Regist. (Psychiat.) St. Ebba's Hosp. Epsom; SHO (In-pat. Psychiat.) & Ho. Phys. Med. Unit Middlx. Hosp.

BLOOD, Anthony Michael Ogilvie (retired) Irstead House, Stratton, Bude EX23 9BP Tel: 01288 352267 — BM BCh 1949 Oxf.; BM BCh Oxon. 1949; FRCGP 1986, M 1966; DObst RCOG 1951. Prev: Nuffield Trav. Fell. 1967.

BLOODWORTH, Lionel Lindsay Orde Renal Unit, Ysbyty Gwynedd, Bangor LL57 2PW Tel: 01248 384328 Email: l.l.o.b@beinternet.com; 9 Maes Briallen, Llanrhos, Llandudno LL30 1JJ Tel: 01492 596063 — MB BCh 1975 Wales; FRCP Lond. 1993; MRCP (UK) 1978. (Cardiff) Cons. Phys. Ysbyty Gwynedd, Bangor. Socs: Renal Assn.; Soc. Phys. Wales.; EDTA. Prev: Cons. Phys. RAF Renal Unit RAF Hosp. Halton; Hon. Lect. Inst. Urol. Lond.; Sen. Specialist (Med.) RAF Renal Unit RAF Hosp. Halton.

BLOODWORTH, Simon Brigham 248 Blackness Road, Dundee DD2 1RR — MB ChB 1995 Dundee.

BLOOM, Caroline Anna The Surgery, 73 Holland Park, London W11 3SL Tel: 020 7221 4334 Fax: 020 7792 8517 — MB BS 1982 Lond.; MRCGP 1990; DRCOG 1987. (Middlx. Hosp.) GP (A & E) St. Mary's Hosp. Lond.

BLOOM, David Samuel 15 Oriel Drive, London SW13 8HF Tel: 020 8563 9854 Email: davbloom@msn.com — MB BCh 1971 Witwatersrand; PhD Witwatersrand 1975, BSc 1967, BDS 1965; MBA Kingston Univ. 1993; FFPM 1990, M 1989. Dir. Biouille Corp.

Socs: Fell. Roy. Soc. Med.; Physiol. Soc.; BRAPP. Prev: Dir. A. D. Little; Med. Dir. Beecham UK; Med. Dir. Schering Chem.s Ltd.

BLOOM, Howard Stanley, OStJ Room 211, Sutherland House, Brighton Road, Sutton SM2 5AN Tel: 020 8652 6028 Fax: 020 8652 6020; 3 Selbourne Close, Pound Hill, Crawley RH10 3SA Tel: 01293 885771 Fax: 01293 885771 Email: howiebloom@aol.com — MB BS 1976 Lond.; MRCGP 1981; DRCOG 1978; T (GP). (St. Bart.) Sen. Med. Off. DoH (on loan to BAMS); Co. Surg. St. John Ambul. Brig. Sussex; Police Surg. Sussex Constab.; Sen. Med. Off. S.. Co. ABA. Socs: BMA (Civil Servant Comm., Sec. & Ex-Chairm. Mid Downs Div. & ARM Rep.); Fac. Bd. SW Thames RCCP. Prev: GP Princip. & Trainer Crawley; Tutor (Gen. Pract.) St. Geo. Hosp. Med. Sch. Lond.; Ho. Surg. & Ho. Off. (Obst.) St. Bart. Hosp. Lond.

BLOOM, Ian Roger Braithwaite Church End Medical Centre, Church End, Old Leake, Boston PE22 9LE Tel: 01205 870666 Fax: 01205 870971; Trianthon House, Benington, Boston PE22 0DT Tel: 01205 760202 — MB BS 1970 Newc.; MRCGP 1974; DObst RCOG 1974. Prev: Trainee GP Newc. VTS; Ho. Surg. & Ho. Phys. Shotley Bridge Gen. Hosp.; Course Organiser (Gen. Pract.) Boston VTS.

BLOOM, Mr Ian Tobias Michael 4 Riverview Gardens, Twickenham TW1 4RT — MB ChB 1985 Leeds; MD Leeds 1994; FRCS Eng. 1990; FRCS Ed. 1989. Cons. Gen. Surg. Kingston Hosp. Kingston-upon-Thames. Prev: Sen. Regist. (Gen. Surg.) Chelsea & W.m. Hosp. Lond.

BLOOM, John Nicholas Alexander Clare House Practice, Clare House Surgery, Newport Street, Tiverton EX16 6NJ; 56 St. Peter Street, Tiverton EX16 6NR — MRCS Eng. LRCP Lond. 1976; BSc (Hons.) Lond. 1973; MRCGP 1980; DRCOG 1980. (Guy's) Trainee GP Exeter VTS. Prev: GP Schem Rotat. Exeter.

BLOOM, Margaret 7 New Square, Lincoln's Inn, London WC2A 3QS Tel: 020 7430 1660 Fax: 020 7430 1531; White Lodge, Coombe Hill Road, Kingston upon Thames KT2 7DU Tel: 020 8942 7090 Fax: 020 8942 7090 — BM BS 1975 Nottm.; BMedSci Nottm. 1973; MRCGP 1989. Asst. Dep. Coroner (Inner Lond. N.); Barrister Lincoln's Inn. Socs: Medico-Legal Soc.; Soc. HM Coroners Eng. & Wales; Soc. Doctors in Law. Prev: Princip. GP Kingston.

BLOOM, Philip Anthony Western Eye Hospital, Marylebone Road, London NW1 5YE Tel: 020 7886 3264 Fax: 020 7886 3259 — MB ChB 1984 Bristol; MB ChB Bristol l984; FRCS Ed. 1990; FRCOphth 1990. (Bristol University) Cons. Ophth. W.ern Eye Hosp. & Hillingdon Hosp.; Hon. Sen. Lext. Imperial Coll.; Roy. Coll. of Opthalmologists, CPD Co-Ordinator (N. Thames), Lond.; Roy. Coll. of Opthalmologists, Clin. Tutor In opthalmology, Hillingdon Hosp. Uxbridge. Socs: Hon. Treas. Roy. Soc. of Med., Sect. of Opthalmology.

BLOOM, Professor Stephen Robert Department of Metabolic Medicine, Hammersmith Hospital, Faculty of Medicine, Imperial College, Du Cane Road, London W12 0NN Tel: 020 8383 3242 Email: sbloom@ic.ac.uk; 49 Hollycroft Avenue, Hampstead, London NW3 7QJ Tel: 020 7435 0912 Fax: 020 7794 4624 — MB BChir 1967 Camb.; MA Camb. 1967, MD 1979; DSc Lond. 1982; FRCP Lond. 1978; FRCPath 1992; FMedSci 1997. (Univ. Coll. Lond. Med. Sch. Middlx. Hosp.) Prof. (Med.)Fac. of Med. Imperial Coll. Sch. Med. Lond.; Chairm. Metab. Med. Imperial Coll. Sch. Med. Lond.; Dir. of Path. Hammersmith Hosps. Trust Lond.; Hon. Cons. Hammersmith Hosps. Lond.; Head Divis. Investigative Sci. Imperial Coll. Socs: Med. Research Soc. (Ex Chairm.); Soc. for Endocrinol. (Chairm.); Diabetes UK (Ex Trustee and Ex Chairm. Research Comm.). Prev: Regist. (Med.) Profess. Unit Middlx. Hosp.; MRC Clin. Research Fell. Middlx. Hosp. Lond.

BLOOM, Stuart Lionel University College London Hospitals NHS Trust, Dept. Gastroenterlolgy, Middlesex Hospital, Mortimer St, London W1T 3AA Email: s.bloom@academic.ucch.nthames.nhs.uk; Lotmead Lock House, Croxley Hall, All Saints Lane, Croxley Green, Rickmansworth WD3 3BG Tel: 01923 897133 — MB BS 1984 Lond.; MA Oxf. 1981, DM 1994; MRCP (UK) 1989; FRCP 1999; CM (Oxford) 1994. (Univ. Lond. St. Thos.) Cons. Gastroenterol. Univ. Coll. Lond. Hosps. Socs: BMA; Brit. Soc. Gastroenterol. Prev: Lect. & Sen. Regist. Univ. Liverp.; Regist. (Gastroenterol.) John Radcliffe Hosp. Oxf.

BLOOM, Susan Janette 2/1, 57 West End Park Street, Glasgow G3 6LJ — MB ChB 1994 Glas.

BLOOM, Victor Roy Little Brook, Buckland in the Moor, Ashburton, Newton Abbot TQ13 7HN Tel: 01364 652664 Fax: 01364 652191 — BM BCh Oxf. 1957; MA Oxf. 1957; MRCP Lond. 1964; MFOM RCP Lond. 1982. (Univ. Coll. Hosp.) Socs: Fell. Roy. Soc. Med. Prev: Regist. Centr. Middlx. Hosp. Lond. & Hammersmith Hosp.; Ho. Phys. Univ. Coll. Hosp. Lond.

BLOOMBERG, Sylvia 5 The Mall, Swindon SN1 4JA — MD CM 1981 Canada; BSc McGill Univ. Canada 1977, MD CM 1981; MRCPsych 1987. Sen. Regist. (Psychiat.) Wilts.

BLOOMBERG, Terry John 5 Woodlands Park, Merrow, Guildford GU1 2TH Tel: 01483 566011 Fax: 01483 566011 — MB ChB Manch. 1970; MRCP (U.K.) 1974; FRCR 1977. (University of Manchester) Cons. (Radiol.) Roy. Surrey Co. Hosp. Guildford. Prev: Sen. Regist. (Radiol.) St. Geo. Hosp. Lond.; Sen. Regist. (Radiol.) Roy. Marsden Hosp. Lond.; Regist. (Radiol.) Roy. Nat. Orthop. Hosp. Lond.

BLOOMER, Anthony Cooper Sudell 11 Devonshire Place, London W1N 1PB Tel: 020 7935 2283 — MB BChir 1956 Camb.; MRCS Eng. LRCP Lond. 1956. (Camb. & St. Bart.) Med. Adviser Bowater Organisation; Med. Off. Roy. Acad. Music. Socs: Chelsea Clin. Soc. Prev: Ho. Surg. & Cas. Off. W. Middlx. Hosp.; Capt. RAMC.

BLOOMER, Helen Jane 24 Goddard End, Willowfield, Stevenage SG2 7ER — MB BS 1985 Lond.

BLOOMER, Jennifer Mary 46 Lankaster Gardens, London N2 9AJ — MB ChB 1978 Manch.; MRCGP 1983; DCH RCP Lond. 1983; DRCOG 1981.

BLOOMER, John The Surgery, 15 King Street, Paisley PA1 2PR Tel: 0141 889 3144 Fax: 0141 889 7134 — MB ChB 1978 Glasgow; MB ChB Glas. 1978. (Glasgow) GP Paisley, Renfrewsh.

BLOOMER, Monica Anne 89 Broadgate Lane, Horsforth, Leeds LS18 5DU Tel: 0113 258 4112 — MB ChB 1952 Birm. (Birm.) Prev: Ho. Phys. Bradford Childr. Hosp.; Ho. Phys. & Obst. Ho. Surg. St. Luke's Hosp. Bradford.

BLOOMER, Mr Peter George Appleyard (retired) 10 Woodthorpe Lane, Sandal, Wakefield WF2 6JH Tel: 01924 252678 — MB BChir 1956 Camb.; FRCS Eng. 1966; DLO Eng. 1958. Cons. ENT Surg. Pontefract & Wakefield Health Dists. Prev: Cons. ENT Surg. RAMC.

BLOOMER, Sheila Elizabeth 45 Bracknagh Road, Armagh BT60 4QA — MB ChB 1988 Dundee; MRCGP 1992.

BLOOMER, Timothy Norman 85 Ridings Fields, Brockholes, Huddersfield — MB BS 1988 Lond.; BSc (Hons.) Lond. 1985; MRCP (UK) 1992. Regist. (Cardiol.) Huddersfield Roy. Infirm.

BLOOMFIELD, Allan Eric Gate Cottage, Hadley Green Road, Barnet EN5 5PY — MB BS 1955 Lond.; MRCS Eng. LRCP Lond. 1955; MRCGP 1975; Cert FPA 1975; DObst RCOG 1959. (Univ. Coll. Hosp.) p/t Med.Tribunal Mem., The Appeals Serv. Prev: Clin. Tutor Acad. Dept. Gen. Pract. St. Bart. Hosp. Med. Coll. & Lond. Hosp. Med. Coll.; Vis. Prof. (Family Med.) McGill Univ. Montreal; Fell. Kellogg Centre For Advanced Studies In Primary Care Montreal Gen. Hosp.

BLOOMFIELD, David James Sussex Oncology Centre, Royal Sussex County Hospital, Eastern Rd, Brighton BN2 5BE Tel: 01273 696955 — MB BS 1987 Lond.; FRCR 1995; MRCP Lond. 1991. Cons. Clin. Oncologist Sussex Oncol. Centre Roy. Sussex Co. Hosp., Brighton; Cons. Clin. Oncologist, Worthing Gen. Hosp.; Cons. Clin. Oncologists, P.ss Roy. Hosp., Haylands Heath; Specialist Regist. Roy. Marsden Hosp.; Clin. Fell. Dept. of Med. Onocology, P.ss Margerat Hosp., Toronto; Specialist Regist. Middlx. & Mt Vernon Hosp. Socs: Roy. Coll. of Radiogist; Roy. Soc. of Med.; Brit. Oncol. Assocoation - Counc.

BLOOMFIELD, Michael Cupper North Cardiff Medical Centre, Excalibur Drive, Thornhill, Cardiff CF14 9BB Tel: 029 2075 0322 Fax: 029 2075 7705; 4 Balmoral Close, Lisvane, Cardiff CF14 0EX — MB BCh 1976 Wales; MRCGP 1980; DCH Eng. 1979; DRCOG 1978. p/t Specialist Pract. (Erectile DysFunc.) Old Surg. Clinic. Brotaf HA.

BLOOMFIELD, Peter Department of Cardiology, Royal Infirmary, Edinburgh EH3 9YW Tel: 0131 536 2008 Fax: 0131 536 2021 — MB ChB 1976 Ed.; MD Ed. 1989; FRCP Ed. 1992; MRCP (UK) 1978; FACC 1984. Cons. Cardiol. Roy. Infirm. Edin.; FACC; Mem. Amer. Bd. Internal Med. 1981; Mem. Amer. Bd. Internal Med. (Cardiol.) 1983. Socs: Brit. Cardiac Soc.; Brit. Med. Assn.; Amer. Coll. of Cardiol. Prev: Sen. Regist. W.. Gen. Hosp. Edin.; Regist.

(Cardiol.) Roy. Infirm. Edin.; Clin. Fell. Med. Harvard Med. Sch. (1980-3).

BLOOMFIELD, Susan Moira Department of Community Paediatrics, 10 Chalmers Crescent, Edinburgh Tel: 0131 536 0479; 8 Granby Road, Edinburgh EH16 5NL — MB ChB 1974 Ed.; MD Ed. 1992; FRCP Ed. 1997; MRCP Ed. 1978. (Ed.) Cons. Community Paediat. Prev: Mem. Amer. Bd. Pediatrics (Neonatol.) 1983; Instruc. (Pediat.) Univ. Mass. USA.

BLOOMFIELD, Mr Thomas Harvey 24 Ael Y Bryn, Tanerdy, Carmarthen SA31 2HB Tel: 01267 238285 Fax: 01267 221463 Email: thomas.bloomfield@btinternet.com — MB BS 1975 Lond.; BSc (Pharmacol.) Lond. 1972; MRCS Eng. LRCP Lond. 1975; FRCOG 1996, M 1983. (Lond. Hosp.) Cons. O & G W. Wales Gen. Hosp. Carmarthen & P. Philip Hosp. LLa.lli; Asst. Edr. Jl. Obst. & Gyn. Socs: Brit. Soc. Gyn. Endoscopy; Soc. Brit. Coloposcopy & Cervical Path.; Ordem dos Medicos Lisbon Portugal. Prev: Sen. Regist. (O & G) Hammersmith & N.wick Pk. Hosps.; Regist. (O & G) Guy's Hosp. Lond. & N.wick Pk. Hosp. Harrow.

BLOOR, Adrian John Clifton 35 First Avenue, Gillingham ME7 2LH — BChir 1994 Camb.; MB Camb 1995; MA 1995; MRCP 1997. Clin. Research. Fell. Haem.Univ. Cambs.

BLOOR, Anita Caroline The East Leicester Medical Practice, 131 Uppingham Road, Leicester LE5 4BP Tel: 0116 276 7145 Fax: 0116 246 1637 — BM BCh 1986 Oxf.; MA Oxf. 1987; MRCGP 1995; DRCOG 1990. (Oxford)

BLOOR, Graham Karl 23 Southfields Road, Eastbourne BN21 1BZ — MB BS 1983 Lond.; MRCP (UK) 1991; FRCA 1989; T(Anaes) 1995.

BLOOR, Imogen Ann Meriel The Surgery, 2 Mitchison Road, London N1 3NG Tel: 020 7226 6016; 8 Montpelier Road, London SE15 2HF — MB BS 1982 Lond.; BSc Lond. 1979; MRCOG 1988. (Univ. Coll. Hosp.) Prev: Trainee GP Kentish Town Health Centre Lond.; Regist. (O & G) W. Middlx. Hosp.; SHO Chelsea Hosp. for Wom. & Qu. Charlotte's Matern. Hosp.

BLOOR, John Michael Harnall Lane Medical Centre, Harnall Lane East, Coventry CV1 5AE Tel: 024 7622 4640 Fax: 024 7622 3859; 59 Maidavale Crescent, Styvechale, Coventry CV3 6GB Tel: 024 76 412211 — MB ChB Sheff. 1958. (Sheff.) Socs: BMA & Anglo-German Med. Soc. Prev: Ho. Phys. & Ho. Surg. City Gen. Hosp. Sheff.; Ho. Off. (Obst.) Lake Hosp. Ashton-under-Lyne.

BLOOR, Judith Alison Rangeways Road Surgery, 33 Rangeways Road, High Acres, Kingswinford DY6 8PN Tel: 01384 280111 Fax: 01384 401157; 49 Sandy Road, Norton, Stourbridge DY8 3AJ Tel: 01384 372013 Fax: 01384 441340 — MB ChB 1977 Liverp.; MRCGP 1981; DRCOG 1979. Clin. Asst. (Palliat. Care) Compton Hospice Wolverhampton.

BLOOR, Muriel (retired) 2 Ravenscroft, Wollaston Court, Stourbridge DY8 4SQ Tel: 01384 395908 — MB ChB 1950 Liverp. Prev: GP Kingswinford.

BLOOR, Roger Neil Edward Myers Unit, City General Hospital, Newcastle Road, Stoke-on-Trent ST4 6QG Tel: 01782 552316 — MRCS Eng. LRCP Lond. 1974; MD Liverp. 1995; MPsychMed Liverp. 1985; FRCPsych 1996, M 1979. (Liverp.) Cons. Psychiat. i/c Drugs & Alcohol City Gen. Hosp. Stoke-on-Trent; Sen. Clin. Lect. (Psychiat.) Univ. Keele.; Med. Dir. N. Staffs Combined Healthcare NHS Trust.

BLOORE, Carolyn Margaret The Petersgate Medical Centre, 99 Amersall Road, Scawthorpe, Doncaster DN5 9PQ Tel: 01302 390490; 41 Greenfield Gardens, Cantley, Doncaster DN4 6TF — MB ChB 1984 Sheff.; MB ChB Sheff. l984; MRCGP 1988.

BLOSS, Diana Elizabeth Brockway Medical Centre, 8 Brockway, Nailse, Bristol BS48 3PL Tel: 01483 850600 Fax: 01275 795601; Tylers Cottage, 42 Backwell Hill Road, Backwell, Bristol BS48 3PL Tel: 01275 463759 — MB ChB 1990 Liverp.; MRCGP 1996; DRCOG 1996. Clin. Asst.; Dmatology BRI.

BLOTT, Margaret Jennifer 73 Harley Street, London W1N 1DE Tel: 020 7935 5098 Fax: 020 7224 6853; 58 Walnut Tree Walk, London SE11 6DN Tel: 020 7793 0719 — MB BS Newc. 1982; MRCOG 1987. Cons. O & G King's Coll. Hosp. Lond.

BLOUNT, Angela Mary Atherley House Surgery, 143-145 Shirley Road, Shirley, Southampton SO15 3FH Tel: 023 8022 1964/0763 Fax: 023 8022 0763; 49 Pointout Road, Bassett, Southampton SO16 7DL Tel: 02380 787970 — BM 1985 Soton. Socs: BASICS.

BLOW, Carol Margaret Lower Road Surgery, 17 Lower Road, Fetcham, Leatherhead KT22 9EL Tel: 01372 378166 Fax: 01372 374734; Glenmore, Meadowside, Gt. Bookham, Leatherhead KT23 3LG Tel: 01372 459429 — MB BS 1980 Lond.; MRCP (UK) 1983; MRCGP 1986; DRCOG 1987. (Char. Cross Hosp. Med. Sch.)

BLOW, John David The Health Centre, Marmaduke Street, Hessle Road, Hull HU3 3BH Tel: 01482 323449 Fax: 01482 610920; 5 Walnut Close, Cottingham HU16 4PR — MB ChB 1978 Sheff.

BLOW, Roland John (retired) 13 Blagden Close, Southgate, London N14 6DE Tel: 020 8886 8764 Email: john@blow80.freeserve.co.uk — MB BChir 1954 Camb.; MA, MB Camb. 1954, BChir 1953; MRCS Eng. LRCP Lond. 1953; MFOM RCP Lond. 1978; DIH Soc. Apoth. Lond. 1969.

BLOWER, Aileen Grant 49A High Street, Lochwinnoch PA12 4AB — MB ChB 1987 Glas. SHO (Psychiat.) Leverndale Hosp. Glas.

BLOWER, Mr Alan Paske (retired) 6 Middle Street, Elton, Peterborough PE8 6RA Tel: 01832 280450 — MB BChir 1952 Camb.; MChir Camb. 1962; FRCS Eng. 1960; DMRD Eng. 1968. Prev: Wing Cdr. RAF Med. Br. (Radiol.).

BLOWER, Anthony Clement 32 Kelston Road, Cardiff CF14 2AJ; The Coach House, 19A Hafod Road, Hereford HR1 1SG — MB BS 1988 Lond.

BLOWER, Mr Anthony Leslie 30 Upper Dicconson Street, Wigan WN1 2AG — MB ChB 1979 Manch.; MD Manch. 1990; FRCS Eng. 1984; FRCS Glas. 1983. Cons. Surg. Gen. Surg. Roy. Albert Edwd. Infirm. Wigan. Prev: Sen. Regist. (Gen. Surg.) NW RHA.

BLOWER, Dorothy Eva (retired) 34 Church Avenue, Beckenham BR3 1DT Tel: 020 8650 4390 — MB BS 1923 Lond.

BLOWER, Peter Wingfield (retired) 48 Belmont Hill, London SE13 5DN Tel: 020 8852 3133 — MB BS 1955 Lond.; FRCP Lond. 1978, M 1962; MRCS Eng. LRCP Lond. 1954; DPhysMed. Eng. 1965. Prev: Cons. Phys. (Rheum.) Greenwich Dist. Hosp.

BLOWER, Samuel John Granville Road Surgery, 296 Granville Road, Sheffield S2 2RT Tel: 0114 272 3638; Milford House, 80 Norfolk Road, Sheffield S2 2SZ Tel: 0114 273 0559 — MB ChB Sheff. 1965; AFOM RCP Lond. 1988. (Sheffield) Phys. Occupat. Dormer Tools Ltd.; Occupat. Health Phys. Avesta Steels Sheff.; Occupat. Health Phys. Barnsley MBC. Socs: Soc. Occupat. Med. Prev: Ho. Surg. Doncaster Roy. Infirm.; Flight Lt. RAF Med. Br.; SHO (Cas.) Roy. Cornw. Hosp. Truro.

BLOWERS, David Alan David Blowers Associates Ltd, 4 Harrogate Road, Caversham, Reading RG4 7PN Tel: 01189 483282 Fax: 01189 962118 Mobile: 07778 287395 Email: david@davidblowers.co.uk — MB BS 1972 Lond.; BSc (Hons. Biochem.) Lond. 1969; FFPM RCP (UK) 1995; MFPM 1990; Dip. Pharm. Med. RCP (UK) 1982; DObst RCOG 1976. (Lond. Hosp.) Cons. Pharmaceut. Med. Reading; Chairm. BrAPP; Dir. CME/CPD Fac. of Pharm. Med. Socs: Fell. Roy. Soc. Med.; Fell. Fac. Pharmaceut. Phys.; Brit. Hypolipid. Assoc. Prev: Ho. Surg. & Ho. Phys. Lond. Hosp. & Regist. (Anaesth.) St. Mary's Hosp. Lond.; Research Regist. Whipps Cross Hosp. Lond.

BLOWERS, Helen Victoria 155 Longfellow Road, Worcester Park KT4 8BA Tel: 020 8287 0350 — BM 1997 Soton.

BLOWERS, John Frederick Arthur Square Medical Practice, High Street, Godalming GU7 1AZ Tel: 01483 415141 Fax: 01483 414881; Willowfield, New Road, Wormley, Godalming GU8 5SU Tel: 01428 684321 — MB BChir 1965 Camb.; MA Camb. 1965, BA (Hons.) 1961, MB 1966; Cert. Family Plann. JCC 1974; DObst RCOG 1970. (Camb. & St. Thos.) Prev: SHO (Neurosurg.) Addenbrooke's Hosp. Camb.; Cas. Off. St. Thos. Hosp. Lond.; Ho. Surg. (O & G) St. Stephen's Hosp. Lond.

BLOWERS, Robert (retired) 6 Moiser Close, Hartrigg Oaks, Haxby Road, New Earswick, York YO32 4DR Tel: 01642 700417 — MB BS Lond. 1946; MD Lond. 1950; FRCP Lond. 1970, M 1963; MRCS Eng. LRCP Lond. 1940; FRCPath 1963; Dip. Bact. Lond 1951. Prev: Head, Div. Hosp. Infec. & Microbiol. Clin. Research Centre N.wick Pk. Hosp. Harrow.

***BLOWFIELD, Philippa Clare Elizabeth** Wheathold Cottage, Wheathold, Ramsdell, Tadley RG26 5SA Tel: 01494 728495 Email: p.blowfield@doctors.org.uk — MB ChB 1997 Sheff.

BLOWS, Lucy Justine Helen 2 Loxwood Avenue, Worthing BN14 7QZ — BM 1995 Soton.

BLOWS, Michael 14 Bournbrook Road, Selly Oak, Birmingham B29 7BH — MB ChB 1984 Birm.

BLOXHAM, Clive Anthony 11 Thorneyholme Terrace, Blaydon-on-Tyne NE21 4PS — MB 1976 Camb.; BChir 1975; MRCP (UK) 1978.

BLOXHAM, Rebekah Elizabeth The Merrows, Todenham Road, Moreton-in-Marsh GL56 9NJ — MB BCh 1998 Wales.

BLOXHAM, Stanley Trevor Cradley Road Surgery, 62 Cradley Road, Cradley Heath, Warley B64 6AG Tel: 01382 569586 — MRCS Eng. LRCP Lond. 1966. (Birm.) Socs: BMA. Prev: SHO (O & G) Kettering Hosp.; SHO Psychiat. Centr. Hosp. Warwick.; Chairm. Dudley LMC.

BLOYE, Darran James Yorkshire Centre For Forensic psychiatry, Newton lodge, Wakefield WF1 3SP — BM 1992 Soton.; MRCPysch 1998.

BLUCK, Gillian Mary Devon House, Uffculme Psychotherapy Service, Mindelsohn Way, Edgbaston, Birmingham B15 2QR Tel: 0121 678 5800 — MB ChB 1989 Manch.; MRCPsych 1996. Specialist Regist. (Psychother.) Devon Ho., Birm. Socs: BMA; MDU; MRCPsych. Prev: Regist. (Psychiat.) All St.s Hosp.; Qu. Eliz. Psychiat. Hosp.; Uffculme Clinic.

BLUCK, Martin Mills (retired) 7 Ryles Close, Macclesfield SK11 8DA Tel: 01625 425800 Email: mmbluck.ryles.@tinyworld.co.uk — MB ChB 1960 Manch. Prev: Ho. Off. ENT Dept. Manch. Roy. Infirm.

BLUE, Alison Clair 26 Castle Walk, Penwortham, Preston PR1 0BP Tel: 01772 752336 — MB ChB 1983 Birm.

BLUETT, Desmond Gilliland, Surg. Cdr. RN Retd. (retired) Beech End, Sunning Avenue, Sunningdale, Ascot SL5 9PW Tel: 01344 624422 — 1952 MB BS Lond.; 1968 MD New York; 1951 MRCS Eng. LRCP Lond.; 1950 LMSSA Lond.; 1962 FRCOG 1982; 1972 FACS; 1969 FICS; 1953 DObst; 1962 MRCOG. Hon. Lect. Inst. O & G Hammersmith Hosp. Lond. Prev: Gyn. P.ss Margt. Hosp. Nassau, Bahamas.

BLUETT, Norman Howard North Devon District Hospital, Barnstaple EX31 4JB Tel: 01271 22577 — MB ChB 1966 Ed.; MRCP (U.K.) 1974; DCH RCPS Glas. 1972; DObst RCOG 1969. Cons. (Paediat.) N. Devon Dist. Hosp. Barnstaple. Prev: Sen. Regist. Evelina Childr. Dept. Guy's Hosp. Lond.

BLUETT, Patrick Joseph 74 St John's Road, Isleworth TW7 6NW Tel: 020 8560 2069 — MB BCh BAO 1955 NUI. (Galw.) Prev: Sen. Ho. Phys. Newton Abbot Hosp.

BLUGLASS, Jean Margaret Kerry The Woodbourne Priory Hospital, 21 Woodbourne Road, Edgbaston, Birmingham B17 8BY Tel: 0121 434 4343 Fax: 0121 434 3270 — MB ChB 1961 St. And.; FRCPsych 1986, M 1974; DPM Eng. 1973. Cons. Psychiat. Woodbourne Priory Hosp. Birm.; Sen. Clin. Lect. (Psychiat.) Univ. Birm. Socs: Vice-Pres. Brit. Assn. Counselling; Fell. Roy. Soc. Med. Prev: Sen. Research Fell. (Gen. Pract.) Teach. & Research Univ. Birm.; Dir. of Studies St. Christopher's Hospice Lond. & Hon. Sen. Lect. (Psychol. Med.) King's Coll. Med. Sch. & Inst. Psychiat.; Lect. (Psychiat.) Univ. Birm.

BLUGLASS, Professor Robert Saul, CBE c/o Reaside Clinic, Bristol Road S.Birmingham Great Park, Rubery, l, Birmingham B45 9BE Tel: 0121 678 3000 Fax: 02926640319 Email: rb@iatros.org.uk; Tel: 01926 640409 Fax: 01926 640319 Email: latros@compuserve.com — MB ChB 1957 St. And.; DPM Eng. 1961; MD St. And. 1967; FRCPsych 1976, M 1971; MRCP (UK) 1994; FRCP Lond.1997. (St. And.) Emerit. Prof. Forens. Psychiat. Univ. Birm.; Hon. Cons. Forens. Psychiat. Reaside Clinic, Birm.; Indep. Cons. Forens. Psychiat. Birm.; Hon. Cons. Adviser Psychiat. RAF. Socs: Fell. Roy. Soc. Med.; (Vice-Pres.) RAF Psychiat. Soc.; BMA. Prev: Prof. Forens. Psychiat. Univ. Birm.; Med. Dir. S. Birm. Ment. Health Trust; Cons. Forens. Psychiat. & Clin. Dir. Reaside Clinic Birm.

BLUMENTHAL, Ivan The Highfield Hospital, Manchester Road, Rochdale OL11 4LZ Tel: 01706 655121 Fax: 01706 646888; 38 Norford Way, Bamford, Rochdale OL11 5QS Tel: 01706 358954 Fax: 0161 627 8309 Email: ivan.blumenthal@norford.fsbusiness.co.uk — MB ChB Cape Town 1970; MRCP (UK) 1975; DCH Eng. 1974. (Cape Town) Cons. Paediat. Roy. Oldham Hosp.

BLUMFIELD, Abraham (retired) 166 Wythenshawe Road, Northenden, Manchester M23 0PF — MB ChB Liverp. 1930.

BLUMHARDT, Lance David Division of Clinical Neurology, University Hospital, Queen's Medical Centre, Nottingham NG7 2UH Tel: 0115 970 9456 Fax: 0115 970 9738 — MD 1980 Otago; BSc Vict. (Wellington) 1962; MB ChB 1967; FRACP 1977, M 1972. Prof. Clin. Neurol. Fac. Med. Univ. Hosp. Qu. Med. Centre Nottm. Prev: Reader (Clin. Neurol.) Univ. Liverp. Walton Hosp. Liverp.; Clin. Lect. Univ. Dept. Neurol. Oxf; MRC Research Fell. Inst. Neurol. Lond.

BLUMSOHN, Aubrey 27 Redcastle Crescent, Broughty Ferry, Dundee DD5 3NF — MB BCh 1985 Witwatersrand.

BLUNDELL, Adrian Geoffrey Nottingham City Hospital, Hucknall Road, Nottingham NG5 1PB; New House, Woodside, Poynton, Stockport SK12 1AQ Tel: 01625 878353 — BM BS 1997 Nottm. SHO (Med. Oncol.) Nottm. City Hosp.

BLUNDELL, Alison Clare Health Centre, Townley Close, Upwell, Wisbech — MB ChB 1992 Manch. p/t GP Princip. Upwell Health Centre Upwell.

***BLUNDELL, Alison Joanne** 68 Alton Road, Leicester LE2 8QA — MB BS 1998 Lond.; MB BS Lond 1998; BSc (Hons) 1st cl 1995, London.

BLUNDELL, Christopher Mark 44 Christchurch Road, Norwich NR2 3NE — MB ChB 1991 Sheff.

BLUNDELL, Evelyn Leslie Pathology Department, Cheltenham General Hospital, Sandford Road, Cheltenham GL53 7AN Tel: 01242 222222 Fax: 01242 272558 Email: eve.blundell@egnhst.org.uk; Springdale, Ludlow Green, Ruscombe, Stroud GL6 6DH Tel: 01453 750417 — MB ChB 1978 Liverp. 1978; MRCP 1987 UK; 1997 FRCPath. (M. 1987); FRCP 1999, Cons. Haemat. Cheltenham Gen. Hosp.

BLUNDELL, Fiona Jane Farnham Health Centre, Brightwells, Farnham GU9 7SA Tel: 01252 723122 Fax: 01252 728302; 31 Stephendale Road, Farnham GU9 9QP — MB ChB 1984 Bristol; DCH RCP Lond. 1991; DRCOG 1991.

BLUNDELL, Gillian (retired) 22/12 Kinellan Road, Edinburgh EH12 6ES — MB BS 1960 Lond.; PhD Belf. 1975; FRCPath 1985, M 1974; DObst RCOG 1962. Prev: Hon. Sen. Lect, Edin. Univ.

BLUNDELL, Mr James Knockdonagh, 19 Chapel Road, Bessbrook, Newry BT35 7AU Tel: 028 3083 0363 — MB BCh BAO 1949 Belf.; FRCSI (ad eund.) 1977; FRCS Ed. 1956. Hon. Cons. Gen. Surg. S.. HSSB; Chairm. Med. Advis. Comm. Norbrook Pharmaceut. Laborats.

BLUNDELL, Janine Merie Guestling Cottage, 149 High St., Lindfield, Haywards Heath RH16 2HT — MB ChB 1978 Leeds; MB ChB (Hons.) Leeds 1978.

BLUNDELL, Joan Wendy Peterborough Hospitals Trust, Thorpe Road, Peterborough PE3 6 Tel: 01733 874648; Lodge Farm, Aunby, Stamford PE9 4EE Tel: 01778 590280 — MB BS 1980 Lond.; BSc (1st cl. Hons.) Lond. 1977, MB BS 1980; MRCPath 1987; T(Path) 1991. Cons. Histol. & Cytopath. P'boro. Hosps. Trust.

BLUNDELL, Julie Anne Therese 43 Woodlane, Falmouth TR11 4RB — MB BS 1983 Lond.; BSc Lond. 1980; MRCP (UK) 1987; DRCPath 1996; MRCPath 1998. Regist. (Haemat.) Roy. Cornw. Hosp.

BLUNDELL, Michael David (retired) 21 Yallop Avenue, Gorleston, Great Yarmouth NR31 6HD — MB ChB 1967 St. And.; FFA RCS Eng. 1975; DA Eng. 1971. Cons. Anaesth. Jas. Paget Hosp. Gorleston Gt. Yarmouth. Prev: Cons. Anaesth. RAF Med. Br.

BLUNDELL, Michael David 16 Bedford Road, Nunthorpe, Middlesbrough TS7 0BZ — MB BS 1997 Newc.

BLUNDELL, Robert Evelyn 91 Wodeland Avenue, Guildford GU2 5LD Tel: 01483 65177; Lucea, Send Marsh Road, Ripley, Woking GU23 6JR Tel: 01483 224757 — MB BS 1962 Lond.; MRCS Eng. LRCP Lond. 1962; DObst RCOG 1964. (St. Geo.) Prev: Sen. Regist. (Paediat.) Univ. W. Indies; Regist. (Paediat.) Roy. Free Hosp. Lond.

BLUNDELL, Robert James North Ridge Medical Practice, North Ridge, Rye Road, Hawkhurst, Cranbrook TN18 4EX Tel: 01580 753935 Fax: 01580 754452; Diprose Farm Barn, Hinxden Lane, Benenden, Cranbrook TN17 4LE Tel: 01580 241884 Fax: 01580 754452 Email: robert.blundell@virgin.net — MB BS 1987 Lond.; DFFP 1996; DRCOG 1991; T(GP) 1991; Cert. Family Plann. JCC 1990. (St. Geo. Hosp. Med. Sch. Lond.) Bd. Mem. Kent Weald PCG. Prev: Trainee GP Portsmouth VTS; SHO (A & E) & Ho. Phys. St. Richard's Hosp. Chichester.

BLUNDELL, Susan Jayne Premier Health, Child Health, St Michaels Hospital, Trent Valley Road, Lichfield WS13 6EF Tel: 01543 414555; Keperra Lodge, 16B Wood Lane, Woodside, Morley, Derby DE7 6DH Tel: 01332 781141 — MB ChB 1984 Ed.; MRCGP 1988; DCCH RCP Ed. 1989; DRCOG 1987. (Ed.) Staff Grade (Community Paediat.) Premier Health NHS Trust. Prev: Trainee GP Lothian VTS.

BLUNDEN, Jane Department of Psychotherapy, Royal South Hants Hospital, Graham Road, Southampton SO14 0YG Tel: 02380 634288 Fax: 02380 825693 — MB BCh 1984 Wales; MB BCh Wales l984; MRCPsych 1989. Sen. Regist. (Psychother.) Roy. S. Hants. Hosp. Soton. Prev: Research Fell. (Psychiat.) Guy's Hosp. Lond. & Ticehurst Hse. Hosp.; Regist. (Psychiat.) St. Francis Hosp. Haywards Heath.

BLUNDSTONE, David Leonard (retired) Abberley House, Lime Tree Avenue, Bilton, Rugby CV22 7QT Tel: 01788 813273 — MB BS Lond. 1949.

***BLUNSUM, Emma Ann** 50 Downs Cote Drive, Bristol BS9 3TR — MB BCh 1997 Wales.

BLUNT, Alban John Cross Road Surgery, Cross Road, Rodwell, Weymouth DT4 9QX Tel: 01305 768844 Fax: 01305 760686 Email: alban.blunt@gp-j87075.nhs.uk; Tel: 01305 760205 — MB BS 1978 Lond.; MRCS Eng. LRCP Lond. 1978; MRCGP 1986. (St. Bart.)

BLUNT, Dinah Jane Lynden House, 27 Porthill Gardens, Shrewsbury SY3 8SB Tel: 01743 362537 Fax: 01743 362537; 23 Kintore Street, Annerley Qld 4103, Australia Tel: 00 61 07 38480208 Fax: 00 61 07 3843 0208 Email: crhastie@powerup.com.au — MB ChB 1988 Birm.; FFA RCSI 1995; DA (UK) 1991; FANZCA 1997. (Birm.) Specialist, Private Pract. (Anaesth.), Brisbane, Australia. Socs: Assn. Anaesth. GB & Irel.; Austral. Pain Soc.; Austral. Soc. Anaesth. Prev: Sen. Regist. (Anaesth.) Roy. Brisbane Hosp., Austral.; Regist. (Anaesth.) Bloomsbury & Islington HA; Sen. Med. Off. (Anaesth.) Ipswich Gen. Hosp., Austral.

BLUNT, Mark Charles 7 The Heath, Troston, Bury St Edmunds IP31 1EN — MB BS 1987 Lond.; BA (Hons.) Camb. 1984; FRCA 1994. Research Fell. (Anaesth.) Norf. & Norwich Hosp. Socs: Fell. Roy. Soc. Med.; Assn. Anaesth. GB & Irel.

BLUNT, Michael John (retired) 8 Marlborough Buildings, Bath BA1 2LX Tel: 01225 333468 — PhD Lond. 1956, MB BS 1945, LMSSA 1944; FRACS 1974; FRACO 1976. Prev: Challis Prof. Anat. Univ. Sydney.

BLUNT, Mr Richard John Glebe Barn, Stoke Pound Lane, Stoke Prior, Bromsgrove B60 4LE — MB ChB 1970 Birm.; MSc Birm. 1973, BSc 1970; FRCS Eng. 1975; FRCS Ed. 1975. Cons. Surg. Russells Hall Hosp. Dudley. Prev: Sen. Regist. (Surg.) Birm. HA (T); SHO Hammersmith Hosp.; Resid. Surg. Off. Worcester Roy. Infirm.

BLUNT, Stavia Brigitte Department of Neurology, Charing Cross Hospital, Fulham Palace Road, London W6 8RF; The Pines, 11 Putney Hill, London SW15 6BA — MB BS 1984 Lond.; PhD Lond. 1991; MA (1st cl. Hons. Physiol. Sci.) Oxf. 1981; MRCP (UK) 1987; FRCP 2000. p/t Sen. Lect. & Hon. Cons. (Neurol.) Imperial Coll. Sch. Mecdicine Char. Cross Campus; Cons. NeUrol. Pk.side Hosp. Lond. Socs: Fell. Roy. Soc. Med.; Soc. Neurosci.; Assn. Brit. NeUrol.s. Prev: Sen. Lect. (Neurol.) Hammersmith Hosp. Lond.; Lect. (Neurol.) Char. Cross Hosp. Lond.; Regist. (Neurol.) Nat. Hosp. Qu. Sq. & Char. Cross Hosp. Lond.

BLUNT, Susan Mary Birmingham Women's Hospital, Edgbaston, Birmingham B15 2TG Tel: 0121 472 1377 Fax: 0121 627 2602 — MB ChB 1976 Birm.; MD Birm. 1988; MRCOG 1982; FRCOG 2000. Cons. O & G Birm. Wom. Hosp. Prev: Cons. (O & G) Solihull Hosp.; Sen. Regist. (O & G) W. Midl. RHA; Research Regist. (Clin. Endocrinol.) Wom. Hosp. Birm.

BLUNT, Mr Victor Alan Walker (retired) Lynden House, 27 Port Hill Gardens, Shrewsbury SY3 8SB Tel: 01743 362537 — MB ChB 1956 Birm.; MB BS Queensld. 1972; BSc (Anat. & Physiol., Hons.) Birm. 1953; FRCS Ed. 1962; FRACS 1965; MRCS Eng. LRCP Lond. 1956; FRCOG 1979, M 1964; DCH Eng. 1960; DObst RCOG 1957. Prev: Cons. O & G Shrops. & Powys HA.

BLYTH, Allan Bruce East Wing, Esk Medical Centre, Ladywell Way, Musselburgh EH21 6AA Tel: 0131 665 2267 Fax: 0131 653 2348; The Steading, Harehope, Eddleston, Peebles EH45 88PR — MB ChB 1967 Ed.; DObst RCOG 1971. Socs: Roy. Soc. Med. & Soc. Investig. Elec. Phenomena in MS.

BLYTH, Angus Campbell Greenock Health Centre, 20 Duncan Street, Greenock PA15 4LY Tel: 01475 724477; 23 Balmoral Drive, Bishopton PA7 5HR — MB ChB 1970 Aberd.; DFM (Glas.) 1992. Police Cas. Surg.s, 'K' Div., Strathclyde Police Force. Prev: SHO (Psychiat.) & Regist. (Psychiat.) Roy. Cornhill Hosp. Aberd.; SHO (Anaesth.) S.end Gen. Hosp. W.cliff on Sea.

BLYTH, Ann Campbell Health Centre, Bank Street, Cupar KY15 4JN Tel: 01334 654945 Fax: 01334 657306; Southern Lodge, Abbotsford Place, St Andrews KY16 9HQ Tel: 01334 474132 — MB ChB 1984 Dundee; MRCGP 1988; DRCOG 1987.

BLYTH, Arthur Graham (retired) Shepherds Cottage, Little Ann, Andover SP11 7DW Tel: 01264 710369 — MB BS Lond. 1950; MRCS Eng. LRCP Lond. 1950; MRCGP 1964; DObst RCOG 1955. Prev: Med. Off. Farleigh Sch. Andover.

BLYTH, Christopher Paul James Royal Gwent Hospital, Newport NP20 2UB Tel: 01633 238442; Email: chris.blyth@linone.net — MB ChB 1988 Liverp.; BSc Liverp. 1985; FRCOphth 1993. Cons. Opthalmologist, Roy. Gwent Hosp., Newport; Cons. Opthalmologist - Universoty of Wales, Cardiff. Prev: Regist. (Ophth.) Cardiff Eye Unit; SHO (Ophth.) St. Paul's Eye Unit Roy. Liverp. Hosp.; Fell., Retinal Diagnostic Dept, Moorfields Eye Hosp., Lond.

BLYTH, Isabel Helen Mary (retired) 31 Oxford Road, Wakefield WF1 3LB — MB ChB Leeds 1943; DObst RCOG 1945.

BLYTH, Jennifer Ann Priscilla Bacon Lodge, The Colman Hospital, Unthank Road, Norwich NR2 2PJ Tel: 01603 288948 Fax: 01603 288988; 5 Town Close Road, Norwich NR2 2NB Tel: 01603 625458 — MB BS 1965 Lond.; FRCP Lond. 1994; MRCP Lond. 1969; MRCS Eng. LRCP Lond. 1965; T(M) 1991; DObst RCOG 1967. (Guy's) Cons. Phys. (Palliat. Care) & Med. Dir. Priscilla Bacon Lodge Norwich. Prev: Assoc. Specialist (Gen. Med.) Norwich Health Dist.

BLYTH, Joanna Marie Jessop Medical Practice, 24 Pennine Avenue, Riddings, Alfreton DE55 4AE Tel: 01773 602707 Fax: 01773 513502 — BM BS 1989 Nottm.; BMedSci Nottm. 1987; MRCGP 1994. (Nottm.) Prev: Trainee GP Derby VTS.

BLYTH, Mr Mark John Graham Dept. Trauma & Orthopaedics, Glasgow Royal Infirmary, 84 Castle Street, Glasgow G4 0SF Tel: 0141 211 4606 Fax: 0141 211 5929 — MB ChB 1990 Glas.; FRCS Glas. 1994; FRCS Ed. 1994; FRCS (Orth) 1999. (Glasgow) Cons. Orthopaedic Surg. Prev: Specialist Regist. (Orthop.) Glas. Roy. Infirm., W.. Infirm. Glas. & Ayr Hosp.; Regist. (Orthop.) Glas. Roy. Infirm.

BLYTH, Michael John, RD (retired) 119 Blackpool Old Road, Poulton-le-Fylde FY6 7RH Tel: FY6 7RH — MRCS Eng. LRCP Lond. 1965; MRCGP 1974. Prev: Civil. Med. Pract./Final Exam. Med. Off. MOD.

BLYTH, Moira 44 Greenholm Avenue, Clarkston, Glasgow G76 7AH — MB ChB 1998 Glas.; MB ChB Glas 1998.

BLYTH, Robert Allan (retired) 46 Thurstaston Road, Heswall, Wirral CH60 6RY Tel: 0151 342 6466 — MB ChB 1943 Liverp.; MRCS Eng. LRCP Lond. 1943; MFCM 1974. Prev: SCM (Social Servs.) Wirral AHA.

BLYTH, Robert Ian Kennedy (retired) 15 Rivermead Avenue, Exmouth EX8 3BH Tel: 01395 277774 — MRCS Eng. LRCP Lond. 1948. Prev: Cons. Psych. Ment. Handicap Langdon Hosp. Dawlish.

BLYTH, Thomas Hood 27 Glasgow Road, Denny FK6 5DW — MB ChB 1983 Glas.; MRCP (UK) 1989. Staff Grade (Rheum.) Falkirk & Dist. Roy. Infirm.; Research Asst. (Rheum.) Gartnavel Gen. Hosp. Glas. Prev: Regist. (Rheum. & Gen. Med.) Gartnavel Gen. Hosp.; Regist. (Rheum.) S. Cleveland Hosp. Middlesbrough; SHO (Rheum. & Med.) P.ss Alexandra Hosp. Harlow.

BLYTH, Thomas Peter 9 Dane Road, London W13 9AQ — MB BS 1996 Lond.; MRCP (London) 1999.

BLYTHE, Alex Ian 5 Prospect Place, Totley Rise, Sheffield S17 4HZ Tel: 0114 236 3309 Fax: 0114 236 3309 Email: alexb@doctors.net.uk — MB ChB 1997 Manch. (Manchester) SHO Sheff. Childr.'s Hosp.

BLYTHE, Andrew James Gaywood House Surgery, North St., Bedminster, Bristol BS3 3AZ Tel: 0117 966 1412 Fax: 0117 953 1250; Tel: 0117 968 3230 — BM BCh Oxf. 1990; BA Oxf. 1987; MRCGP 1995; DCH RCP Lond. 1994; DFFP 1994; DRCOG 1993. (Oxf.) Teachg. Assoc., Div. of Primary Health Care, Univ. of Bristol. Socs: MRCGP; Bd. Mem., Severn Fac. of Roy. Coll. of Gen. Practitioners. Prev: Partner with Dr. Chandler & Co.; Trainee GP Surbiton; SHO (Psychiat.) Barrow Hosp. Bristol.

BLYTON, Thomas Archer, TD (retired) Glenhaven, White Edge Drive, Baslow, Derby DE45 1SJ — BSc (Hons.) Wales 1931, MD 1948, MB BCh 1934. Prev: Mem. Brit. Turbec. Assn.

BOADEN, Ronald William Department Anaesthetics, Royal Devon & Exeter Hospital, Barrack Road, Exeter EX2 5DW Tel: 01392

402474 — MB BS 1977 Lond.; BSc (Hons.) Surrey 1971; FFA RCS Eng. 1981. Cons. Anaesth. Roy. Devon & Exeter Hosp. Exeter. Prev: Sen. Regist. (Anaesth.) Bristol Roy. Infirm.; Regist. & SHO (Anaesth.) King's Coll. Hosp. Lond.

BOAG, Andrew Goldie 10 Harley Street, London W1N 1AA Tel: 020 7935 0059; c/o International House, South St., Ipswich IP1 3NU Tel: 01473 212578 Fax: 01473 212578 — MB BS 1953 Lond. (Middlx.) Phys. Shrubland Hall Health Clinic Coddenham. Socs: Ex-Pres. Brit. Assn. Manip. Med.; Soc. Back Pain Research. Prev: Phys. Brit. Assn. Manip. Med. Clinic Italian Hosp. Lond.; Ho. Phys. Mt. Vernon Hosp. N.wood; Ho. Surg. N. Middlx. Hosp. Lond.

BOAG, David Eric Crosshouse Hospital, Kilmarnock KA2 0BE; 8 Libo Avenue, Uplawmoor, Glasgow G78 4AL — MB ChB 1977 Glas.; BSc (Hons.) Glas. 1974.

BOAG, David Sinclair Flat 2/2, 116 Novar Drive G12 9SX — MB ChB 1997 Ed.

BOAG, Fiona Caroline John Hunter Clinic, Chelsea & Westminster Hospital, 369 Fulham Road, London SW10 9TH Tel: 020 8746 5625 Fax: 020 8846 6198; 21 Gertrude Street, London SW10 0JN — MB BS 1980 Lond.; FRCP (UK) 1996; MRCP (UK) 1983. Cons. Phys. (Genitourin. Med.) Chelsea & W.m. Hosp. Lond. Socs: Soc. Study VD.; Fell. Roy. Coll. Phys. Prev: Sen. Regist. (Genitourin. Med.) St. Stephens Hosp. Lond.; Regist. (Genitourin. Med.) Univ. Coll. Hosp. Lond.; Regist. (Gen. Med.) Roy. Free Hosp. Lond.

BOAG, James William 123 Kilmarnock Road, Shawlands, Glasgow G41 3YT Tel: 0141 649 6231; 8 Ladeside Close, Newton Mearns, Glasgow G77 6TZ Tel: 0141 639 8892 — MB ChB 1982 Glas.

BOAG, Joan Carole The Consulting Rooms, 21 Neilston Road, Paisley PA2 6LW Tel: 0141 889 5277 Fax: 0141 848 5500; 4 Glen Lane, Uplawmoor, Glasgow G78 4DF — MB ChB 1977 Glas.; DRCOG 1981.

BOAK, Margaret Parkwood, East Park Drive, Blackpool FY3 8PW — MB ChB 1977 Bristol.

BOAKES, Anthony John Department of Genito-Urinary Medicine, Brookside, Station Way, Aylesbury HP20 2SQ Tel: 01296 488839 Fax: 01296 422024; Church Headland, Church Headland Lane, Whitchurch, Aylesbury HP22 4JX Tel: 01296 641219 — MB BS Lond. 1963; MSc (Biomechanics) Surrey 1968; FFA RCS Eng. 1969; Dip Ven Soc. Apoth. Lond. 1979; DA Eng. 1965. (Char. Cross) Cons. Genitourin. Med. Aylesbury Vale Healthcare NHS Trust; Civil Cons. Genitourin. Med. RAF. Socs: Med. Soc. Study VD; BMA; Assn. Genitourin. Med. Prev: Cons. Genitourin. Med. Univ. Coll. Hosp. Lond.; Cons. Clin. Pharmacol. Char. Cross Hosp. Lond.; Sen. Regist. (Genitourin. Med.) St. Thos. Hosp. Lond.

BOAKES, Janet Patterson 46 Village Way, Beckenham BR3 3NP Tel: 020 8650 9082 — MB BS 1964 Lond.; MRCS Eng. LRCP Lond. 1964; MRCPsych 1977. (Char. Cross) Cons. Psychother. St. Geo. Hosp. Lond. & Peper Harrow Foundat.; Mem. Inst. of Gp. Anal. Prev: Regist. (Psychiat.) Banstead Hosp.; Clin. Med. Off. Lambeth, S.wark & Lewisham AHA (T); Clin. Asst. (Developm. Paediat.) Lewisham Hosp. Lond.

BOAKYE, Laurence Kwasi Addei 60 Seacole Close, London W3 6TF — MB BS 1994 Lond.

BOARD, Arthur Paul Braehad, Woodlands Lane, Shorne, Gravesend DA12 3HH — MB BS 1976 Lond.

BOARD, Hedley Rex 17 Rectory Green, West Boldon, East Boldon NE36 0QD Tel: 0191 536 3276 — MB BS 1962 Durh.; FRCPsych 1987; DPM Eng. 1968. Cons. Psychiat. Cherry Knowle Hosp. Ryhope.; Med. Dir. Priority Healthcare Wearside NHS Trust.

BOARD, Joyce Olivia Mary (retired) 21 Park Road, Ipswich IP1 3SX Tel: 01473 256915 Fax: 01473 256915 — MB BS 1950 Lond.; BD Lond. 1982; FFPHM 1983, M 1972; DCH Eng. 1959. Prev: Cons. Pub. Health Med. E. Suff. HA.

BOARD, Peregrine Neil c/o Anaesthetic Department, Leighton Hospital, Middlewich Road, Crewe CW1 4QJ Tel: 01270 612162 — MB BS 1989 Lond.; BSc Lond. 1986; FRCA 1995. (Univ. Coll. Lond.) Cons. Anaes, Mid Chesh. Hsps NHS Trust; Specialist Regist. Rotat. (Anaesth.) Newc. Socs: BMA; Train. Mem. Assn. AnE.h. Prev: SHO Rotat. (Anaesth.) Newc. & Gateshead; SHO (Anaesth.) Roy. Liverp. Univ. Hosp.; Regist. Rotat. (Anaesth.) Newc. u. Tyne.

BOARD, Richard Hubert St. Michael's Hospice, Upper Maze Hill, St Leonards-on-Sea TN38 0LB Tel: 01424 456606 Fax: 01424 460473 Email: jlrb@lineone.net; 32 St Helens Down, Hastings TN34 2BQ Tel: 01424 432278 Fax: 0870 056 8250 Email: dick@theboards.demon.co.uk — MB BS 1972 Lond. Dep. Med. Director, St. Michael's Hospice; Course Organiser, Hastings GP Vocational Train. Scheme.

BOARD, Timothy Nicholas Ent Dept, Royal Bolton Hospital, Bolton BL4 0JR — MB ChB 1996 Manch.; BSc (Hons.) Manch. 1993.

BOARDLEY, Anna Claire The Angles, 31 Agates Lane, Ashtead KT21 2ND — BM 1998 Soton.

BOARDMAN, Alix Etta 17 Mansefield, Athelstaneford, North Berwick EH39 5BF — MB ChB 1994 Aberd.; DRCOG 1999. GP Reg. Hamilton.

BOARDMAN, Amanda Jane Norwood Medical Centre, 99 Abbey Road, Barrow-in-Furness LA14 5ES Tel: 01229 822024 Fax: 01229 823949 — MB ChB 1991 Manch.

BOARDMAN, Andrew David 165 St Annes Road E., Lytham St Annes FY8 3HP — MB ChB 1997 Manch.

BOARDMAN, Anthony Phillip Department of Psychiatry, Guy's, King's and St Thomas' Hospitals, Medical School, Guy's Hospital, London SE1 9RT Tel: 020 7231 4578 Fax: 020 7237 3526 Email: jedboard@atlas.co.uk; Flat 4, The Limes, 50 Croons Hill, London SE10 8HD — MB BS 1979 Lond.; PhD Lond. 1989; BSc Lond. 1976; MRCPsych 1984; FRCPsych 2000. Sen. Lect. & Cons. Psychiat. Social Psychiat. Guy's, King's & St Thomas' Hosps. Med. Sch., Guy's Hosp.

BOARDMAN, Christine Joy 5 Came View Close, Dorchester DT1 2AF — BM 1984 Soton.; BM Soton 1984; MRCPsych 1990; DCH RCP Lond. 1987. Sen. Regist. (Child & Adolesc. Psychiat.) W. Dorset Gen. Hosp. Dorchester. Socs: ACPP. Prev: Lect. (Psychiat.) Univ. Malawi; Regist. (Psychiat.) St. Geo. Hosp. Lond.; SHO (Paediat.) Poole Gen. Hosp.

BOARDMAN, David Richard 12 Cator Road, Carshalton SM5 3BX — MB BS 1997 Lond.

BOARDMAN, Diana (retired) Church Cottage, Charlton, Pershore WR10 3LQ Tel: 01386 861158 — MRCS Eng. LRCP Lond. 1958. Prev: GP Solihull.

BOARDMAN, Hugh Stanley 6 Stanton Road, Wimbledon, London SW20 8RL Tel: 020 8946 8882 Fax: 020 8944 0661 — MB BChir 1980 Camb.; MA Camb. 1981, BA 1977. (Camb. & St. Geo.)

BOARDMAN, Jacqueline 60 Smithybridge Road, Smithybridge, Littleborough OL15 0BQ Tel: 01706 371106 — MB ChB 1993 Liverp.; DCH RCP Lond. 1995. GP Regist. Castleton, Rochdale. Socs: BMA; Med. Protec. Soc. Prev: SHO (Paediat.) Blackburn, Hyndburn & Ribble Valley NHS Trust; SHO (Community Paediat.) Communicaire NHS Trust, Blackburn; SHO (Psychiat.) Tameside Gen. Hosp.

***BOARDMAN, James Peter** 65 Chalkwell Avenue, Westcliff on Sea SS0 8NL — MB BS 1996 Lond.

BOARDMAN, John Nuttall (retired) Fairmile, 181 Garstang Road E., Poulton-le-Fylde FY6 8JH Tel: 01253 882566 — MB ChB 1958 Liverp.; DObst RCOG 1965. Prev: SHO (Gen. Surg. & O & G) Vict. Hosp. Blackpool.

BOARDMAN, Julie 30 Westwood Road, Lytham St Annes FY8 5NX Tel: 01253 739866 — MB BS 1990 Newc.; MRCP (UK) 1993. GP Retainee, Sheff.

BOARDMAN, Keith Church Street Practice, 8 Church Street, Southport PR9 0QT Tel: 01704 533666 Fax: 01704 539239; 5 Westbourne Road, Southport PR8 2HZ — MB ChB 1982 Leeds; MRCGP 1990; DRCOG 1984. GP S.port Merseyside. Prev: GP Trainee Ormskirk & Dist. Gen. Hosp. VTS; Ho. Off. (Med. & Surg.) Ormskirk & Dist. Gen. Hosp.

BOARDMAN, Peter Laird (retired) Caldy, 3 Mayfield Park, Shrewsbury SY2 6PD Tel: 01743 232768 — MA Camb. 1959, MD 1966, MB 1960, BChir 1959; FRCP Lond. 1977, M 1961. Prev: Cons. Phys. Roy. Shrewsbury Hosp.

BOARDMAN, Philip 18 St Johns Court, Thorner, Leeds LS14 3AX; 18 St. John Court, Thorner, Leeds LS14 3AX — MB ChB 1986 Leeds; MRCP (UK) 1989.

BOASE, Mr David Louis The Eye Department, Queen Alexandra Hospital, Cosham, Portsmouth PO6 3LY Tel: 023 9228 6444 Fax: 023 9228 6440; Bittles Farm House, Hambledon, Waterlooville PO7 4QW Tel: 023 9263 2774 — MB BS Lond. 1968; FRCS Eng. 1975; MRCS Eng. LRCP Lond. 1968; FRCOphth 1988; DO Eng. 1973. (St. Thos. Hosp. Lond.) Cons. Ophth. Surg. Qu. Alexandra Hosp. Portsmouth Hosps. NHS Trust. Socs: Roy. Soc. Med. (Pres.

Elect Sect. Ophth.); UK & Irel. Soc. Cataract & Refractive Surgs.; Past Pres. S.. Ophth. Soc. Prev: Sen. Regist. Oxf. Eye Hosp.; Resid. Surg. Off. Moorfields Eye Hosp. Lond.

BOAST, Neil Roderick Redford Lodge Psychiatric Hospital, 15 Church St., London N9 9DY Tel: 020 8956 1234 Fax: 020 8956 1233 — MB ChB 1983 Birm.; MRCPsych 1989; Dip. Criminol. Lond . 1992. Cons. Forens. Psychiat Med. Director Redord Lodge, Partnership in Care; Hon. Sen. Lect. St. Bart. & Roy. Lond. Hosps. Med. Coll. Socs: Brit. Soc. Criminol.; Brit. Acad. of Forens. Sci.s. Prev: Cons. Forens. Psychiat. City & Hackney Community Servs. NHS Trust; Sen. Regist. (Forens. Psychiat.) NE Thames RHA; Regist. Rotat. (Psychiat.) Roy. Free Hosp. Lond. VTS.

BOAST, Peter William The Surgery, Gladstone Road, Chesham HP5 3AD Tel: 01494 782884 Fax: 01494 786106; 15 Gladstone Rise, High Wycombe HP13 7NW — MB BS 1981 Lond.

BOATENG, Kingsley Eric The Surgery, Stretton Avenue, Willenhall, Coventry CV3 3QA Tel: 024 7630 4330 Fax: 024 7669 7087; 8 Falcon Avenue, Binley, Coventry CV3 2ES — Vrach 1970 Kharkov; DPM Eng. 1977; Kharkov Med. Inst. USSR). Prev: Trainee GP Coventry VTS; SHO (Geriat. Med.) Whitley Hosp. Coventry; Regist. (Psychiat.) Walsgrave Hosp. Coventry.

BOBAK, Antony (retired) 7 Priory Close, Boxgrove Mews, Chichester PO18 0EA — MB ChB 1946 Polish Sch. of Med.

BOBAK, Stephen Alexander The Medical Centre, 13-15 Barmouth Road, Wandsworth, London SW18 2DT Tel: 020 8874 4984 Fax: 020 8877 0732 — BM BS 1986 Nottm.; BMedSci (Hons.) Nottm. 1984; DRCOG 1991; MRCGP 1992. (Nottm.) GP Lond.; SKY News Doctor; Freelance Med. Jl.ist & BRd.caster Lond. Socs: Med. Jl.ist's Assn.; Media Medics. Prev: Asst. Med. Edr. GP Newspaper.

BOBAT, Raziya Ahmed Flat 2A, Neville St., London SW7 3AR — MB ChB 1980 Natal.

BOBBA, Janardhana Rao Kent and Canterbury Hospital, Canterbury CT1 3NG; Hemel Hempstead General Hospital, Hillfield Road, Hemel Hempstead HP2 4AD Tel: 01442 3141 — MB BS 1972 Andhra; FFA RCSI 1987; DA Eng. 1978. (Rangaraya India) Assoc. Specialist (Anaesth.) Kent & Canterbury Hosp. Prev: Regist. (Anaesth.) Hemel Hempstead Hosp.; Regist. (Anaesth.) Kent & Canterbury Hosp.

BOBER, Margaret Jean West Cumberland Hospital, Whitehaven CA28 8JG — MB BS 1973 Lond.; MRCS Eng. LRCP Lond. 1973; MRCPsych 1978; FRCPsych 1998. (Roy. Free) Cons. Psychogeriat. W. Cumbld. Hosp. Whitehaven. Prev: Sen. Regist. (Psychiat.) Newc. Gen. Hosp.; Sen. Regist. Psychogeriat. Maudsley Hosp. Lond.; Regist. (Psychiat.) Middlewood Hosp. Sheff.

BOBER, Stephen Alexander West Cumberland Hospital, Hensingham, Whitehaven CA28 8JG Tel: 01946 693181 Fax: 01946 523507 — MRCS Eng. LRCP Lond. 1973; BSc Lond. 1970, MB BS 1973; MRCP (UK) 1977; FRCOG 1991, M 1979. (Roy. Free) Cons. (O & G) W. Cumbria HA. Prev: 1st Asst. (O & G) Univ. Newc.; Regist. (O & G) Newc. Gen. Hosp.; Regist. (O & G) St. Mary's Hosp. & Samarit. Hosp.

BOBET REYES, Rosa Maria 68B Gledhow Wood Road, Leeds LS8 4DH — LMS 1991 La Laguna.

BOBIC, Vladimir The Grosvenor Nuffield Hospital Knee Clinic, Wrexham Road, Chester CH4 7QP Tel: 01244 680444 Fax: 01244 680812; 14 Shotwick Park, Saughall, Chester CH1 6BJ Tel: 01244 881931 Fax: 01244 881931 Email: vladimir_bobic@msn.com — MD 1980 Belgrade; Spec. Orthop. Surg. Belgrade 1988. (Univ. Belgrade) Cons. Orthop. Knee Surg. Roy. Liverp. Univ. Hosps. BRd.green & Liverp. Socs: Internat. Arthoscopy Assn., Knee Surg. & Orthop. Sports Med.(ISAKOS) Mem. of Edu. Comm. and Commun. Comm.; Internat. Cartilage Repair Soc. (ICRS) Chairm. of Imaging Gp. Mem. of Edu. Comm.; Hon. Mem. Amer. Orthop. Soc. for Sports Med. (AOSSM). Prev: Specialist Orthop. Surg. P.ss Eliz. Orthop. Hosp. Exeter; Vis. Prof. Dept. of Radiol.; Stanford Univ. Med. Sch. Stanford Calif. USA.

BOBROW, Catherine Sue 6 Chandos Road, Bristol BS6 6PE — MB ChB 1993 Bristol.

BOBROW, Lynda Geraldine Department of Histopathology, Box 235, Addenbrooke's Hospital, Cambridge CB2 2QQ Tel: 01223 217163 Fax: 01223 216980 Email: lgb21@cam.ac.uk — MB BCh Witwatersrand 1963; FRCPath 1977. (Witwatersrand) Sen. Research Asst. Camb. Univ. Clin. Sch. Med.; Hon. Cons. Histopath Addenbrooke's Hosp. Camb. Prev: Sen. Lect. & Hon. Cons. Histopath. UMDS, Guy's Campus Lond.; Sen. Lect. & Hon. Cons. Path. Univ. Coll. Lond.

BOBROW, Professor Martin, CBE Department of Medical Genetics, Cambridge Inst. for Medical Research, Wellcome Building, Addenbrooke's Hospital NHS Trust, Hills Road, Cambridge CB2 2XY Tel: 01223 331154 Fax: 01223 331206 — MB BCh Witwatersrand 1963; DSc Witwatersrand 1980; FRCP Lond. 1986; FRCPath 1990; FRCPCH 1997. Prof. Med. Genetics Univ. Camb. Prev: P. Philip Prof. Paediat. Research United Med. & Dent. Schs. Lond.; Cons. Med. Genetics. Oxf. HA; Prof. Human Genetics Univ., Amsterdam.

BOCHSLER, James Alfred (retired) 173 A Woodcote Road, Wallington SM6 0QQ Tel: 020 8669 7971 Email: jbochsler@hotmail.com — LMSSA 1972 Lond.; Dip. Lond. Sch of Hygi. & Trop. Med 1999; ARC Kings, Lond 2001; Dip. Addic. Behaviour Lond. 1995; BA Open Univ. 1998; MSc Lond 1999. Prev: GP Princip., Lond.

BOCK, Peter Alwin 20 Westminster Road, Stoneygate, Leicester LE2 2EG — MB ChB 1993 Cape Town.

BOCKING, Lisa Jane Queens Medical Centre, 109 Queens Road, Richmond TW10 6HF — MB BS 1988 Lond.; DCH RCP Lond. 1992.

BOCTOR, Sherif Zakaria 60 Craven Gardens, Barkingside, Ilford IG6 1PF Tel: 020 8551 6223 — MB BCh 1972 Cairo; Dip. Ven. Apoth. 1979. Clin. Asst. (Genitourin. Med.) Newham Hosp. Lond., OldCh. Hosp. Romford, Roy. Lond. Hosp. Lond. & Barking Hosp. Socs: Amer. VD Assn.; Assn. Gernitourin. Med.; Soc. Study VD.

BODAGH, Ibrahim Yousif Oraha 7 Burnham Beeches, Chandlers Ford, Eastleigh SO53 4QS — MB ChB 1976 Mosul; MRCPI 1989.

BODALIA, Bhavesh Holbrook Lane Surgery, 268 Holbrook Lane, Coventry CV6 4DD Tel: 024 7668 8340 Fax: 024 7663 7526 — MB ChB 1987 Glas.; DRCOG 1992.

BODALIA, Rajesh Holbrook Lane Surgery, 268 Holbrook Lane, Coventry CV6 4DD Tel: 024 7668 8340 Fax: 024 7663 7526 — MB ChB 1990 Ed.

BODAMER, Olaf Alrich 8 Acacia Close, Stanmore HA7 3JR — State Exam Med 1989 Heidelberg.

BODANE, Arvind Kumar Psychiatry Department, Monkland Hospital, Monkscourt Avenue, Airdrie ML6 0JS; 4 Middlerise Road, Glasgow G68 9DP Tel: 01236 451450, 01473 737266 Fax: 01236 728372 Email: akbodane@doctors.org.uk — MB BS 1972 Indore; MRCPsych 1986. Cons. (Psychiat. Old Age) Monkland Dist. Gen. Hosp. Airdrie.

BODANI, Hitesh 8 Chasewood Park, Sudbury Hill, Harrow-on-the-Hill, Harrow HA1 3YP — MB BS 1987 Lond.

BODANI, Mayur 42 Herga Road, Harrow HA3 5AS — MB BS 1993 Lond.

BODANSKY, Harvey Jonathan Bedside Manor, 18 Sandmoor Lane, Alwoodley, Leeds LS17 7EA Tel: 0113 268 9282 Fax: 0113 268 9282 — MB ChB 1974 Liverp.; MD Liverp. 1983; FRCP Lond. 1995; MRCP (UK) 1978. Cons. Phys. (Gen. Med. Diabetes & Endocrinol.) Gen. Infirm. Leeds; Cons. Phys. BUPA Hosp. & Mid-Yorks. Nuffield Hosp. Leeds; Sen. Clin. Lect. (Med.) Univ. Leeds. Socs: Fell. Roy. Soc. Med.; Brit. Diabetic Assn. (Scientif. & Technical Sect.). Prev: Sen. Regist. (Gen. Med. & Diabetes) Leeds Gen. Infirm. & St. Jas. Univ. Hosp. Leeds; Research Fell. (Diabetes) & Hon. Sen. Regist. St. Bart. Hosp. Lond.; Regist. (Med.) Walton Hosp. Liverp.

BODARD, Sharon Jill Central Health Clinic, Tower Hill, Bristol BS2 0JD Tel: 0117 929 1010 Fax: 0117 927 2180 — MB ChB 1975 Birm.; MFFP, 1993. Dist. SCMO (Family Plann.) United Bristol Healthcare Trust.

BODASING, Neena 26 Craigs Avenue, Edinburgh EH12 8HS — MB ChB 1991 Ed.; MRCP (UK) 1995; DTM & H 1997. (Ed.) Specialist Regist. Communicable Dis. Monklands Dist. Gen. Hosp. Airdrie & Gartnavel Hosp. Glas.

BODDAM-WHETHAM, Andrew Hugh Cecil Prices Mill Surgery, Newmarket Road, Nailsworth, Stroud GL6 0DQ Tel: 01453 832424 Fax: 01453 833833 Email: ahctw@bizonline.co.uk; (branch Surgery), The Surgery, Middle Hill,, Chalford Hill, Stroud GL6 8BD Tel: 01453 883227 — MB BS 1971 Lond.; MB BS 1971 Lond; MRCS Eng LRCP Lond. 1971; DTM & H Liverp. 1978; DA Eng. 1974; DObst RCOG 1973. (King's Coll.) Occup. Health - Priv. Sector. Prev: Med. Off. Chogoria Kenya.

BODDEN, Erda Pamela The Elms, Elvendon Road, Goring-on-Thames, Reading RG8 0DT — LRCPI & LM, LRSCI & LM 1956;

LRCPI & LM, LRCSI & LM 1956; DPH Eng. 1960; LMCC 1958. (RCSI) Med. Off. Fair Mile Hosp. Wallingford. Prev: Asst. Co. Med. Off. & Sch. Med. Off. Bucks. CC & Dep. MOH Boro.; Slough; Sen. Intern. W.m. Hosp. Lond. Ontario, Canada; Intern. Toronto W.. Hosp. Canada.

BODDEN, Sarah Jane Bassetlaw District General Hospital, Worksop S81 0BD — MB ChB 1970 Bristol; MRCP (U.K.) 1974; DCH Eng. 1972. Prev: Sen. Regist. (Paediat.) Trent RHA; Clin. Research Fell. Birm. Univ.; Regist. (Paediat.) Oxf. RHA & Swindon HA.

BODDIE, Mr David Edward Department of Orthopaedic Surgery, Polwarth Building, Forester Hill, Aberdeen AB25 2ZD Tel: 01224 681818; TFR 61 Fonthill Road, Aberdeen AB11 6UQ Tel: 01224 583125 Email: dbabdn@61font.freeserve.co.uk — MB ChB 1991 Aberd.; FRCS Ed. 1995. (Aberd.) Specialist Regist. (Orthop. Surg.). Prev: Research Fell. (Surg.) Univ. Aberd. Med. Sch.; SHO (Basic Surg. Train.) Aberd. Roy. Infirm.; SHO (Cardiothoracic Surg. & Acccid. & Emerg.) Roy. Infirm. Edin.

BODDIE, Donald Frederick (retired) 23 Templar Way, Rothley, Leicester LE7 7RB Tel: 0116 237 6077 — MRCS Eng. LRCP Lond. 1962.

BODDIE, Hugh Grahame Department Neurology, North Staffordshire Royal Infirmary, Princes Road, Hartshill, Stoke-on-Trent ST4 7LN Tel: 01782 715444 — MB BS 1966 Lond.; FRCP Lond. 1985, M 1969; MRCS Eng. LRCP Lond. 1966. (Westm.) Cons. Neurol. N. Staffs. Roy. Infirm. Stoke. Prev: Sen. Regist. (Neurol.) Manch. Roy. Infirm.; MRC Clin. & Research Regist. (Neurol.) Newc. Gen. Hosp.; Regist. Neurol. N. Staffs. Hosp. Gp.

BODDINGTON, David Gamgee (retired) Down House, Bromyard HR7 4QH Tel: 01885 482495 — MB ChB 1956 Birm.; MSc Wales 1996; MRCS Eng. LRCP Lond. 1956; DObst RCOG 1957. Prev: Med. Off. St. Kilda, Hebrides.

BODDINGTON, Hilary Jane St Peters Surgery, 49-55 Portsmouth Road, Woolston, Southampton SO19 9RL Tel: 023 8043 4355 Fax: 023 8043 4195; 243 Manor Farm Road, Bitterne Park, Southampton SO18 1NZ Tel: 01703 559423 — MB BS 1984 Lond.; MA (Hons.) Camb. 1985; BSc (Hons.) Soton 1978; DRCOG 1986. (Lond. Hosp.) Trainee GP Soton VTS. Prev: SHO (A & E) Broomfield Hosp. Chelmsford; Ho. Surg. The Lond. Hosp.; Ho. Phys. Chelmsford & Essex Hosp. Chelmsford.

BODDINGTON, James Daniel Bethnal Green Health Centre, 60 Florida St., London E2 6LL Tel: 020 7739 6677 — MRCGP 2001 Sheff.; MB ChB Sheff. 1992; BMedSci Sheff. 1991; MSc Lond. 1997. GP Princip.

BODDY, Francis Andrew 26 Rowallan Gardens, Glasgow G11 7LJ Tel: 0141 339 4644 & profess. 041 339 3118 — MB ChB 1959 Ed.; FRCP Ed. 1981; MRCP (UK) 1975; FFCM 1976, F 1974; DPH Eng. 1968. Dir. Pub. Health & Obst. Research Unit Univ. Glas.; Hon. Pub. Health Specialist Gtr. Glas. Health Bd. Socs: Soc. Social Med.; Internat. Epidemiol. Assn. Prev: Sen. Lect.Dept. Community Med. Univ. Glas.; Lect. Dept. Social Med. Univ. Aberd.; Research Assoc. Med. & Health Research Assn. New York.

BODDY, Jane Letitia 73 Riefield Road, London SE9 2RB — MB BS 1998 Lond.; MB BS Lond 1998.

BODDY, Jean Elizabeth Britannia House, Britannia Road, Morley, Leeds LS27 0BQ Tel: 0113 392 7836; 32 Whiteley Croft Rise, Otley LS21 3NR — MB ChB 1973 Aberd.; BMedBiol (Hons.) Aberd. 1970; MRCPath 1985. Cons. Cytopath. Leeds Gen. Infirm.

BODDY, Kenneth 17 Crosswood Crescent, Balerno EH14 7LX Tel: 0131 449 5010 — MB BS 1964 Durh.; MRCOG 1971. (Newc.) Sen. Lect. (O & G) Univ. Edin.

BODDY, Nicola Yewtree Cottage, Wolferstan Drive, Bishopdown, Salisbury SP1 3XZ — MB ChB 1997 Aberd.

BODDY, Pascal James 50 Stonehill Road, Derby DE23 6TJ — MB BS 1993 Lond.

***BODDY, Rachael Sarah** 1 Woodhall Road, Wolverhampton WV4 4DL — MB ChB 1997 Birm.

BODDY, Miss Su-Anna Margaret Department of Paediatric Surgery, St George's Hospital, Blackshaw Road, London SW17 0QT Tel: 020 8725 2097 Fax: 020 8725 0711; 15 Bridgefield Road, Cheam, Sutton SM1 2DG Tel: 020 8661 7528 Email: madboddy@globalnet.co.uk — MB BS 1976 Lond.; MS Lond. 1992, MB BS 1976; FRCS Eng. 1983. (St. Bart.) Cons. Paediat. Surg. St. Geo. Hosp. Lond.; Flexible Train. Adviser to RCS Eng. Prev: Sen. Regist. (Paediat. Surg.) St. Geo. Hosp. Lond.; Sen. Regist. (Paediat. Surg.) St. Jas. Univ. Hosp. & Gen. Infirm. Leeds; Regist. (Paediat. Surg.) Birm. Childr. Hosp.

BODE, Dirk Walton Medical Centre, 2-4 Bedford Road, Liverpool L4 5PX Tel: 0151 525 6438 Fax: 0151 530 1748 — State Exam Med. Frankfurt 1991.

BODEN, Jacqueline Mary 104 New Road, Rubery, Birmingham B45 9HY Tel: 0121 453 3854 — MB BS 1987 Lond.; MRCGP 1993; Cert. Family Plann. JCC 1991; DFFP. (St. Thomas' Hospital Medical School) GP Princip.; Sen. Med. Off., Dudley and Sandwell Brook. Socs: BMS; DFFP. Prev: SHO (Psychiat.) Kidderminster Gen. Hosp.; Trainee GP Burwell, Cambs.

BODEN, Jane Louise 89 Roman Way, Birmingham B15 2SL — MB ChB 1991 Birm.

BODEN, Jeremy George c/o Station Medical Centre, RAF Bruggen BFPO 25 — MB ChB 1986 Manch.; MRCGP 1992; DAvMed FOM RCP Lond. 1995. Socs: BMA.

BODEN, Michael Geoffrey Chadderton Town Health Centre, Middleton Road, Chadderton, Oldham OL9 0LH Tel: 0161 628 4543 Fax: 0161 284 1658; 1 Tynwald Mount, Shaw Road, Royton, Oldham OL2 6HA Tel: 0161 633 4369 — MB BCh BAO Dub. 1966; MA Dub. 1992. Prev: Jun. Lect. (Anat.) TC Dub.

BODEN, Samantha Kate 77 High Ash Avenue, Leeds LS17 8RX Tel: 0113 268 8532 — MB BS 1991 Lond.; MRCP (UK) 1994.

BODENHAM, Andrew Robert Tel: 0113 392 6303 Fax: 0113 392 5682; 24 Main Street, Thorner, Leeds LS14 3DX — MB BS 1981 Lond.; FFA RCS Eng.1985. (St. Bart. Hosp. Lond.) Cons. Anaesth. & Dir. (Intens. Care) Leeds Gen. Infirm. Socs: Intens. Care Soc.; Coll. of Anaesth.s; Assoc. of Anaesth.s. Prev: Sen. Regist. (Anaesth. & Intens. Care) Leeds; Regist. Addenbrooke's Hosp. Camb.

BODENHAM, William Roy (retired) 82 Hulham Road, Exmouth EX8 3LA Tel: 01395 273461 — MB BS Lond. 1948; MRCS Eng. LRCP Lond. 1943; DObst RCOG 1947. Prev: Asst. Obst. Forest Gate Hosp.

BODENSTEIN, Maria Eva Homerton Hospital, Homerton Row, Hackney, London E9 6SR Tel: 020 8510 5544; 36 Tansley Close, Holloway, London N7 0HP Tel: 020 7700 8436 Email: 100626.3052@compuserve.come — MB ChB 1992 Stellenbosch; BA Pretoria 1982; Hons-B Journalism Stellenbosch 1984. Trainee GP/SHO Homerton Hosps. VTS. Socs: BMA. Prev: SHO (Paediat.) Qu. Eliz. Hosp. for Childr.; SHO (Psychiat.) Homerton Hosp.; SHO (A & E) Edgware Gen. Hosp.

BODEY, Sara Anne 56 Mauldeth Road W., Manchester M20 3FQ Tel: 0161 445 3200 — MB ChB 1993 Ed. SHO Rotat. (Med.) Nottm. City Hosp. Prev: SHO (A & E) Roy. Infirm. Edin.; SHO (Med. for Elderly) York Dist. Hosp.; Ho. Off. (Med.) Falkirk & Dist. Roy. Infirm.

BODEY, Mr William Norman Hillingdon Hospital, Uxbridge UB8 3NN Tel: 01895 238282 — MB BS 1969 Lond.; FRCS Eng. 1975. (Char. Cross) Cons. Orthop. Surg. Hillingdon & Mt. Vernon Hosps. Prev: Sen. Regist. (Orthop.) Bath DHA; Regist. Rotat. (Orthop.) Lord Mayor Treloar Hosp. Alton & Roy. Portsmouth Hosp.

BODGENER, Susan The Surgery, The Street, Wonersh, Guildford GU5 0PE Tel: 01483 898123 Fax: 01483 893104 — MB BS 1992 Lond.; BSc 1989, MRCGP 1997; DFFP 1997; DRCOG 1996. (Roy. Lond. Hosp. Whitechapel) GP Wonersh.

BODGER, David Henry (retired) 19 Oakhill, Claygate, Esher KT10 0TG Tel: 01372 466247 — MRCS Eng. LRCP Lond. 1943; MB BS Lond. 1943; DMRD Eng. 1949. Prev: Cons. Radiol. W. Middlx. & Teddington Hosps.

BODGER, John Nevin (retired) 30 Yorath Road, Whitchurch, Cardiff CF14 1QD Tel: 01222 624985 — MB Camb. 1955, BChir 1954; MRCS Eng. LRCP Lond. 1954; AFOM RCP Lond. 1981; DPH Wales 1960. Prev: Coll. Med. Off. Univ. Coll. Cardiff.

BODGER, Malcolm Alan Bramblehaies Surgery, College Road, Cullompton EX15 1TZ Tel: 01884 33536 Fax: 01884 35401 — MB BS 1981 Adelaide; MRCGP 1992.

BODGER, William Alfred Hugh Wychwood, Meadow Close, Bridge, Canterbury CT4 5AT — BM BCh 1966 Oxf.; MRCP (UK) 1976; FRCR 1981. Cons. Radiother. & Oncol. Kent & Canterbury Hosp.

BODGER, William Maddy 24 Brackendale, London N21 3DG — MRCS Eng. LRCP Lond. 1958.

BODHANI, Harish Devjibhai Dunstable Health Centre, Priory Gardens, Dunstable LU6 3SU Tel: 01582 699622 Fax: 01582 663431; The 'Midas', 312 Old Bedford Road, Luton LU2 7EJ Tel: 01582 416370 — MB BS 1973 Bombay. (Topiwala Nat. Med. Coll.) Princip. GP.

BODHE, Manjiri Mukul 7 Limes Way, Gawber, Barnsley S75 2NS — MB BCh 1997 Wales.

BODHINAYAKE, Buddhadasa 88 Nightingale Road, London N22 8PP — MB BS 1969 Ceylon; FRCPsych 1990, M 1978.

BODICOAT, Simon Peter Flat 2, 43 York St., Harborne, Birmingham B17 0HG — MB ChB 1987 Liverp.; MRCP (UK) 1993; FRCR 1997. (Liverp.) Specialist Regist. W. Midl. Radio. Rotat.

BODIN, Michael Alexander Belmont Health Centre, 516 Kenton Lane, Harrow HA3 7LT Tel: 020 8863 0911 Fax: 020 8863 9815; 11 Murray Road, Northwood HA6 2YP Tel: 01923 822541 — MB ChB 1960 Glas.; PhD Glas. 1970, BSc 1960; DObst RCOG 1962. Prev: Ho. Off. Roy. Infirm. & Matern Hosp. Glas.; Specialist Neuropsychol. Inst. Aviat. Med. FarnBoro.; Dep. Princip. Phys. Lond. Univ. Stud. Health Serv.

BODINGTON, Jocelyn Riviere (retired) St Annes, Links Road, Winchester SO22 5HP Tel: 01962 54876 — MB BChir 1936 Camb.; MA, MB BChir. Camb. 1936; MRCS Eng., LRCP Lond. 1934; FFA RCS Eng. 1954; DA Eng. 1947. Cons. Anaesth. N. Hants. Gp. Hosps.; Hon. Maj. late RAMC. Prev: Clin. Asst. Surg. Out-pats. Lond. Hosp.

BODIWALA, Dhaval 7 Blackthorn Lane, Oadby, Leicester LE2 4FA Tel: 0116 271 8899 — MB ChB 1997 Birm. (Birm.) SHO (Neurosurg.) N. Staffs NHS Trust; Gen. Surgic. SHO Rotat. Socs: BMA. Prev: SHO (A & E), N. Staffs NHS Trust; Ho. Off. (Med.) Heartlands Hosp. Birm.

BODIWALA, Gautam Govindlal, CBE, Deputy Lt. Accident & Emergency Department, The Leicester Royal Infirmary, Infirmary Square, Leicester LE2 4FA Tel: 0116 258 5274 Fax: 0116 258 6671; Lykkebo, 7 Blackthorn Lane, Oadby, Leicester LE2 4FA Tel: 0116 271 8899 Fax: 0116 271 8899 — Hon. DSc 2000; FIFEM 2000; MB BS Gujarat 1967; MS Gujarat 1969; FFAEM 1993; FICS 1983; FICA 1978; FRCS 2000; FRCP 1999. (B.J. Med. Coll. Ahmedabad) Cons. & Clin. Teach. A & E Leicester Roy. Infirm. & Med. Sch. Univ. Leicester; Hon. Treas. & Trustee Fac. A & E Med.; Chairm. JCHT A & E; JP. Socs: Roy. Soc. Med.; Amer. Coll. Emerg. Phys.; (Pres.) Leics. Medico-Legal Soc. Prev: Hon Treas. & Trustee Fac. A & E Med.; Hon. Treas. & Trustee Brit. Assn. A & E; Chairm. SAC in A & E Med.

BODKIN, Joan Rosemary 24 Eaton Place, Kemp Town, Brighton BN2 1EH Tel: 01273 686863 Fax: 01273 623402 — MB BCh BAO 1970 NUI; MICGP 1990. (Galway) GP Kemp Town Brighton.

BODKIN, Nicholas Liam Hove Medical Centre, West Way, Hove BN3 8LD Tel: 01273 430088 Fax: 01273 430172 — MB BCh BAO 1969 NUI. Socs: Irish Coll. Gen. Pract.

BODKIN, Simon Ernest Rohais Medical Centre, Rohais Road, St. Peter Port, Guernsey GY1 1FF Tel: 01481 723322 Fax: 01481 725200; Le Courtil Fontaine, Claire Mare Lane, St Peters, Guernsey GY7 9QA — BM 1980 Soton.; DRCOG 1986. Prev: Trainee GP Winchester VTS.

BODLE, Julia Frances 387 Studlands Park, Newmarket CB8 7AZ; Flat 23 Broad Lane Court, 160 Broad Lane, Sheffield S1 4BU Tel: 0114 266 9765 — MB ChB 1991 Leeds; DFFP 1997; Cert. Prescribed Equiv. Exp. JCPTGP 1997. (Leeds) Specialist Regist. (O & G)Yorks. Rotat.

BODLEY, Roger Nicholas Department of Radiology, Stoke Mandeville Hospital, Aylesbury HP21 8AL Tel: 01296 316915 Fax: 01296 316919; Conkers Farm, 178 Aylesbury Road, Bierton, Aylesbury HP22 5DT Tel: 01296 426204 — BM BCh 1973 Oxf.; 1973 MA; FRCR 1984; FRACGP 1980; DMR 1983; DObst RCOG 1977. (Oxford) Cons. Radiol. Stoke Mandeville Hosp. NHS Trust. Socs: Internat. Med. Soc. Paraplegia; Brit. Soc. Skeletal Radiol.; Brit. Soc. Interven. Radiol.

BODLEY SCOTT, Caroline Ann Medical Centre, Imphal Barracks BFPO 36 — BM 1980 Soton.; MFFP 1992; FRCGP 2001; MRCGP 1992; DRCOG l983. Civil. Med. Pract. (GP) Brit. Forces, Germany Health Serv.. Prev: Trainee GP I. of Wight VTS; Sen. Med. Off. Gen. Pract. Company Clinic Kitwe, Zambia; Clin. Asst. (Palliat. Med.) Earl Mt.batten Hse. Newport, I. of Wight.

BODLEY SCOTT, David Douglas The Wistaria Practice, 32 St. Thomas' Street, Lymington SO41 9NE Tel: 01590 672212 Fax: 01590 679930 — MB BS Lond. 1964; DObst RCOG 1966. (St. Bart.) Police Surg. Hosp. Practitioner (Geriats.); Fact. Doctor Civil Serv. M.O. Socs: Fell. Roy. Soc. Med. Prev: Ho. Phys. S.end Gen. Hosp.; Ho. Surg. & Obst. Ho. Surg. St. Helier Hosp. Carshalton.

BODLEY SCOTT, Jean (retired) Flat 4, Solent Mead, Church Lane, Lymington SO41 3RA — MA Ed. 1937, MB ChB 1941. Prev: Clin. Med. Off. W. Sussex AHA.

BODLEY SCOTT, Richard James House Doctors Surgery, Maryport Street, Usk NP15 1AB Tel: 01291 672633 Fax: 01291 672631 — MB ChB 1977 Bristol; MRCGP 1982; DCH Lond. 1980. (Bristol)

BODMAN, Arthur Paul (retired) 17 Forest Road, Fishponds, Bristol BS16 3XH Tel: 0117 965 1003 — MB ChB Bristol 1924. Prev: Ho. Phys. Roy. Devon & Exeter Hosp.

BODMER, Charles Walter Colchester General Hospital, Turner Road, Colchester CO4 5JL Tel: 01206 742514 Fax: 01206 832324 Email: charles.bodmer@essexrivers.nhs.uk — MB ChB 1985 Liverp.; MD Liverp. 1996; MRCP (UK) 1989; FRCP 2000. Cons. Phys. & Diabetol. Colchester Gen. Hosp. Prev: Sen. Regist. (Med.) Ipswich; Regist. (Med.) Clatterbridge Hosp. Wirral; Clin. Research Fell. (Med.) Univ. Liverp.

BODMER, Helen Clare Nuffield Department of Medicine, University of Oxford, John Radcliffe Hospital, Oxford OX3 9DU Tel: 01865 221350 — MB BS 1983 Lond.; DPhil. Oxf. 1989, MA, BA 1980; MRCP (UK) 1986. Wellcome Sen. Fell. (Clin. Sci.) John Radcliffe Hosp. Oxf. Prev: Wellcome Trav. research fell.sh. Strasbourg, France; MRC Train. Fell. Nat. Inst. Med. Research Lond.; SHO (Rheum. & Rehabil.) Nuffield Orthop. Centre Oxf.

BODNER, Alvin Castleton Health Centre, 2 Elizabeth Street, Castleton, Rochdale OL11 3HY Tel: 01706 658905 Fax: 01706 343990; 14 Fairhaven Avenue, Whitefield, Manchester M45 7QG Tel: 0161 796 0509 — MB ChB 1973 Manch.; MA Medical Ethics (Cancer & Palliative Care) 2001 Univ. Keele; FRCGP (Nominat) 1998; MRCGP 1978. (Manchester) Course Organiser Rochdale/Bury VTS; Clin. Governance Lead Rochdale PCG; Company Med. Off. Lancs.; GP Project Lead. Research & Developm. Bury/Rochdale HA. Prev: GP Clin. Tutor; Project Ldr. (Palliat. Care & Pract. Delevopm.) Quality Steering Gp. Direc. Springhill Hospice Rochdale.

BODSWORTH, Henry (retired) Grange Farm, Poulton, Chester CH4 9EE Tel: 01244 570483 — MB ChB 1956 Liverp.; DObst RCOG 1960. Prev: Surg. Lt. RN.

BODSWORTH, Sally Ann 91 Ebury Street, London SW1W 9QU Tel: 020 7730 4963 — MB BS 1986 Lond. (St. Thomas' Hosp. Med. Sch.)

BODY, Gillian Deborah 22 Sunlea Crescent, Stapleford, Nottingham NG9 7JP Tel: 0115 939 3873 — MB BS 1996 Lond.; BSc (Hons.) 1993. SHO Mid Trent Paediat. Rotat.

BOECKER, Henning MRC Clinical Sciences Centre, PET Neurosciences Gp., Royal Postgraduate Medical School, Hammersmith Hospital, Du Cane Road, London W12 0NN — State Exam Med 1991 Dusseldorf.

BOEING, Leonie 32 Bonnington Grove, Edinburgh EH6 4BL — MB ChB 1994 Aberd. (Aberd.) SHO (Ment. Health) S. E. Scotl.

BOEREE, Mr Nicholas Reginald Department of Orthopaedics, Southampton General Hospital, Tremona Road, Southampton SO16 6YD Tel: 02380 794492 Fax: 02380 794414; Penn House, Bramshaw, Lyndhurst SO43 7JL — MB BS 1982 Lond.; BSc Lond. 1979; FRCS (Orth.) 1995; FRCS Lond. 1988; FRCS Ed. 1987. Cons. Orthop. Surg. (Spinal Surg.) Soton. Gen. Hosp. Socs: Brit. Orthop. Assn.; Brit. Scoliosis Soc.; Soc. Back Pain Research. Prev: Sen. Regist. (Orthop.) Soton. Gen. Hosp.; Regist. (Orthop.) Bristol Roy. Infirm.; Research Fell. Stoke-on-Trent Spinal Serv.

BOERGER, Thomas-Odysseus 4 Wyndham Road, London W13 9TE — State Exam Med. Berlin 1990.

BOERSMA, Roelof (retired) The Old Vicarage, Brompton, Northallerton DL6 2QA Tel: 01609 773399 — MB ChB 1958 Ed.; LMCC 1961; DObst RCOG 1962. Prev: GP N.allerton.

BOESEN, Evelyn Anne Meta (retired) Honey Wood House, The Street, Brightwell, Cum Sotwell, Wallingford OX10 0RR Tel: 01491 834145 — MB BS Lond. 1953; MD Lond. 1973; MRCS Eng. LRCP Lond. 1953. Prev: Cons. Oncol. Roy. Free Hosp. Lond.

BOFFA, Judith Anne 6 Eastmount Road, York YO24 1BD Tel: 01904 646509 Fax: 01904 646743; Manor Farm, Rufforth, York YO2 3QF Tel: 01904 738143 — MB BS 1981 Lond.

BOFFA, Paul Salvino, SBStJ 3 The Red House, Limpsfield Chart, Oxted RH8 0QZ Tel: 01883 722238 — MD 1946 Malta. (Malta) Socs: Hon. Sec. Croydon Medico-Legal Soc.; (Ex-Pres.) Croydon Med. Soc. Prev: Clin. Asst. Warlingham Pk. Hosp.; Asst. Princip. Surg. Off. Croydon Gen. Hosp.; Res. Surg. Off. St. Leonard's Hosp.

BOFFA, Peter Benedict John Old Coulsdon Medical Practice, 2A Court Avenue, Old Coulsdon, Coulsdon CR5 1HF Tel: 01737 553393 Fax: 01737 550267; 20 Bencombe Road, Purley CR8 4DQ Tel: 020 8668 0255 Email: peter.boffa@boffa.demon.co.uk — MB BS 1976 Lond.; MRCP (UK) 1979; MRCGP 1987. (St. Georges Hospital Medical School) Socs: Croydon Medico-Legal Soc. Prev: Research Fell. E. Anglian RHA; Regist. (Thoracic Med.) Camb. HA; Regist. (Gen. Med.) Mayday Hosp. Croydon.

BOFFARD, Professor Kenneth David 49 Ovington Street, London SW3 2JA Tel: 020 7584 8181; 17 Pallinghurst Road, Parktown, Johannesburg 2193, South Africa Tel: 00 27 11 7264164 Fax: 00 27 11 7262985 Email: kdboffard@pixie.co.sa — MB BCh 1972 Witwatersrand; FACS 1998; FRCS Eng. 1979; FRCS Ed. 1978; BSc 1999. (Witwatersrand) Princip. Surg. & Head Trauma Unit Johannesburg Hosp.; Witwatersrand Univ. Med. Sch.; Prof. Dept. of Surg. Witwatersrand Univ. Med. Sch. Socs: Fell. Amer. Assn. Surg. of Trauma; Med. Soc. Lond.; S. Afr. Trauma Soc. Prev: Regist. (Surg.) Guy's Hosp. & Hosp. Sick Childr. Lond. & Birm. Accid. Hosp.

BOGAHALANDE, Senarath Foleshill Road Surgery, 949 Foleshill Road, Coventry CV2 5HW Tel: 024 7668 8482/8230 Fax: 024 7663 8273; 949 Foleshill Road, Coventry CV6 5HN Tel: 024 76 688482 — Vrach 1971 Moscow; Vrach Peoples' Friendship U 1971. (Peoples' Friendship U. Moscow) Socs: BMA & Overseas Doctors Assn. Prev: Regist. (Neurol. Surg.) Walsgrave Hosp. Coventry.

BOGAN, Joseph George 4 Rannoch Drive, Cumbernauld, Glasgow G67 4EP — MB ChB 1984 Glas.; MB ChB Glas. l984.

BOGDANOR, Judith Evelyn Jericho Health Centre, Walton Street, Oxford OX2 6NW Tel: 01865 311234 Fax: 01865 311087 — MB BS 1972 Lond.; MRCS Eng. LRCP Lond. 1972. (St. Bart.) Princip. GP Oxf.; Med. Off. Family Plann. Clinics Oxon. HA.

BOGDANOVIC, Marko Dusan 113 Okehampton Road, St Thomas, Exeter EX4 1EP — MB ChB 1991 Manch.

BOGER, Richard Frederick Coryndon (retired) Chantry House, Church St., Steyning BN44 3YB — MB BS Lond. 1970. Prev: GP Steyning, W. Sussex.

BOGGIANO, Peter 1 Beaconsfield Road, Widnes WA8 9LB Tel: 0151 424 3232 — MB ChB 1956 Liverp. Prev: Ho. Surg. (Gen. Surg. & Ophth.) & (O & G) & Ho. Phys. (Gen.; Med. & Dermat.) Clatterbridge Gen. Hosp. Bebington.

BOGGILD, Marian Elizabeth 56B Warron Drive, Wallasey CH45 0JT Tel: 0151 638 4113 Email: mazbogs@btinternet.com; 56B Warron Drive, Wallasey CH45 0JT — MB ChB 1990 Birm.; MRCGP, 1997; FPC, 1996; DRACOG 1993. GP.

BOGGILD, Michael Derek The Bolton Centre, Lower Lane, Liverpool L9 7LJ Tel: 0151 529 5719 Fax: 0151 529 5512 Email: boggild.m@wcnn-tr.nwest.nhs.uk — MB ChB 1986 Leic.; MD Leic. 1995; MRCP (UK) 1989. Cons. Neurolgist, The Walton Centre, Liverp. Socs: Assn. of Brit. NeUrol.s. Prev: Regist. (Neurol.) N. Staffs. Roy. Infirm.; Sheldon Research Fell. N. Staffs.; Regist. (Gen. Med.) N. Staffs. Roy. Infirm.

BOGGIS, Anthony Ronald John Newlands Medical Centre, Borough Road, Middlesbrough TS4 2EJ Tel: 01642 247029/247401 Fax: 01642 223803; Tel: 01740 631071 — MB BS 1981 Lond.; MRCGP 1985; DRCOG 1984. (St. Bart.) Trainer (Gen. Pract.) Middlesbrough; Clin. Asst. (Dermat.) & Clin. Med. Off. (Family Plann.) MiddlesBoro.; Chairm. Cleveland Med. Audit Advis. Gp.

BOGGIS, Caroline Rachel Macneill Nightingale Centre, Withington Hospital, Nell Lane, Manchester M30 9FS Tel: 0161 447 4060 — MB BS 1978 Lond.; FRCR 1985. Cons. Radiol. Manch. BrE. Screening & Withington Hosp.

BOGGON, David Graham Craigengar, Low Causeway, Culross, Dunfermline KY12 8HL — MB ChB 1986 Dundee; MRCGP 1991; MRCOphth 1989; DRCOG 1990; DO RCS Eng. 1988. Vis. Ophth. Downfield Surg. Dundee. Socs: BMA. Prev: Clin. Asst. (Ophth.) Dundee; Trainee GP Dundee; SHO (O & G & Geriat.) Perth Roy. Infirm.

BOGGON, Mr Richard Prothero (retired) 151 Writtle Road, Chelmsford CM1 3BP Tel: 01245 421722 Fax: 01245 421722 — MB BChir 1961 Camb.; MA, MChir Camb. 1972, MB 1961, BChir 1960; FRCS Eng. 1964. Prev: Retd. Gen. Surg. Chelmsford Gp. of Hosp.s.

BOGGS, Robert Ernest c/o Rev. & Mrs. R. E. Boggs, 18 Strangford Road, Downpatrick BT30 6SL — MB BCh BAO 1994 Belf.

BOGHOSSIAN-TIGHE, Seda Hambarsoom South London Blood Transfusion Centre, Cranmer Terrace, Tooting, London SW17 Tel: 020 8672 8501 Fax: 020 8767 4462; 52 Lindley Road, Walton-on-Thames KT12 3HA Tel: 020 8398 0796 — MB ChB 1974 Basrah; PhD Lond. 1984, MSc 1978; MRCPath 1985. Assoc. Specialist (Blood Transfus.) S. Lond. Blood Transfus. Centre. Prev: Regist. (Haemat.) St. Helier Hosp. Lond.; Regist. (Haemat.) St. Geo. Hosp. Lond.; SHO (Path.) W.m. Hosp. Lond.

BOGIE, William Hoechst House, Salisbury Road, Hounslow TW4 6JH Tel: 020 8754 3305 — MB ChB 1968 Birm.; MRCP (U.K.) 1971; Dip Pharm Med RCP (UK) 1976. Dir. Hoechst Pharmaceut. Hounslow; Non-Exec. Dir. A & H Cox & Remploy. Prev: Regist. (Med.) Qu. Eliz. Hosp. Birm.

BOGLE, Gillian Denise 35 Putnoe Heights, Putnoe, Bedford MK41 8EB — MB BS 1981 Lond.; MRCGP 1985.

BOGLE, Richard Gordon Common Wealth Building Department of Clinical Pharmacology, Hammersmith Hospital, Du Cane Road, London W12 0HS Tel: 020 83831000 Fax: 0208 9675007 Email: rgbogle@hotmail.com; 19 Barnfield Close, Earlsfield, London SW17 0AU Tel: 0208 9473102 Email: Rebogle@hotmail.com — MB BS 1996 Lond.; MRCP 1999; PhD Lond. 1992; BSc (Hons.) Lond. 1989. (St. Geo. Hosp. Med. Sch.) Regist. (Cardiol. and Clin. Pharmacol.) Hammersmith hosp. Socs: Brit. Pharm. Soc.; Lond. MicroCirc. Gp.; Brit. Hypertens. Soc. Prev: Regist. in toxicology, Nat. poisons Informat. Serv., Guys Hosp Lond.; SHO (Med.) Hammersmith Hosp. & nat. Hosp. for Neurol. & Neurosurg. Lond.

BOGOD, David George 4 Levens Close, West Bridgford, Nottingham NG2 6SN Tel: 0115 945 2170 Fax: 0115 962 7713 Email: david@bogod.freeserve.co.uk — MB BS 1980 Lond.; FRCA 1984. (Middlx.) Cons. Anaesth. City Hosp. Nottm.; Hon. Clin. Teach. Univ. Nottm. Socs: Assn. Anaesth. (Counc.); Obst. Anaesth. Assn. (Past Hon. Sec.). Prev: Sen. Regist. (Anaesth.) Univ. Hosp. Wales; Clin. Research Off. Univ. Wales Coll. Med.; Regist. (Anaesth.) Leics. Roy. Infirm.

BOGODA, Mrs Dayawathie Doctor's Residence, Southfield, Room No. 3, Stafford Road, Halifax HX3 0PA — MB BS 1972 Ceylon. (Colombo) Regist. (Anaesth.) Calderdale HA.

BOGUES, Bernard Ephrem Campbell Surgery, 10 Quarry Road, Dungannon BT70 1QR Tel: 028 8772 2751; 100 Earlswood Road, Belfast BT4 3EA Tel: 01232 671535 Email: ephrem@enterprise.net — MB BCh BAO 1980 Belf.; MRCGP 1989; DRCOG 1989; MMed Sci (Psychother.) Belf. 1996. (Qu. Univ. Belf.) GP Dungannon.; Psychodynamic Psychotherapist.

BOHANNAN, Philip John Creffield Road Surgery, 19 Creffield Road, Colchester CO3 3HZ Tel: 01206 570371 Fax: 01206 369908; 15 Wavell Avenue, Colchester CO2 7HR — MB ChB 1985 Aberd.

BOHEIMER, Klaus, TD Sheen Lane Health Centre, Sheen Lane, East Sheen, London SW14 8LP Tel: 020 8876 3901 Fax: 020 8878 9620 — MB BS 1949 Lond.; MRCS Eng. LRCP Lond. 1949. (St. Geo.) Clin. Asst. (Rheum.) Char. Cross. Hosp. Socs: Fell. Roy. Soc. Med. Prev: Ho. Surg., Cas. Off. & Resid. Asst. (Clin. Path.) St. Geo. Hosp.

BOHIN, Sandra Neonatal Unit, Leicester Royal Infirmary, Leicester LE1 5WW Tel: 01162 258 5522 Fax: 01162 258 5502 Email: sbohin@lri.org.uk; 8 The Willows, Burton-on-the-Wolds, Loughborough LE12 5AP — MB ChB 1985 Bristol; MRCP (UK) 1989; DCH RCP Lond. 1989; FRCPCH 1997. (Bristol) Cons. Neonatol. Leicester Roy. Infirm. Socs: Neonat. Soc.; Brit. Assn. Perinatal Med.; MRCPCH. Prev: Lect. (Child Health) Univ. Leicester; Research Fell. (Neonates) Leicester Roy. Infirm.; Regist. (Paediat.) City Hosp. Nottm.

BOHM, Yvonne Helen Overton Park Surgery, Overton Park Road, Cheltenham GL50 3BP Tel: 01242 580511; Home Farm, Foxcote, Andoversford, Cheltenham GL54 4LP Tel: 01242 820252 — MB ChB 1983 Bristol; MRCGP 1987; DRCOG 1986. Prev: Trainee GP

Cheltenham VTS; Ho. Phys. N. Devon. Dist. Hosp. Barnstaple; Ho. Surg. Cheltenham Gen. Hosp.

BOHN, Mr Gordon Leonard 10 Crawford Close, Earley, Reading RG6 7PE — MB BS 1935 Lond.; FRCS Eng. 1938. Prev: Surg. Reading Hosp. Gp.

BOHN, Patricia Mary Barton House Health Centre, 233 Albion Road, London N16 9JT Tel: 020 7249 5511 Fax: 020 7254 8985 — MB BS 1990 Lond. Trainee GP/SHO N. Middlx. Hosp. Haringey VTS. Prev: Ho. Off. (Med.) Guy's Hosp. Lond.; Ho. Off. (Surg.) Greenwich Hosp.

BOHRA, Chandra Gopal 45 Langley Drive, London E11 2LN — MB BS 1974 Rajasthan. (S.M.S. Med. Coll. Jaipur) Regist. Soton. Gen. Hosp.

BOHRA, Mr Prafull Kumar Halton General Hospital, Runcorn WA7 2DA Tel: 01928 714567 Fax: 01928 791021; Church View, Old Pewterspear Lane, Appleton, Warrington WA4 5QH Tel: 01925 861645 — MB BS 1974 Rajasthan; FRCS Ed. 1983. Gen. Surg. Halton Gen. Hosp. Runcorn. Socs: Assoc. Fell. Assn. of Surgs. GB; Assoc. Endoscopic Surg. GB & Irel. Prev: Cons. Surg. King Faisal Hosp. Taif, Saudi Arabia; Regist. (Gen. Surg. & Urol.) Geo. Eliot Hosp. Nuneaton.

BOHRA, Usha Anaesthetic Department, Halton General Hospital, Runcorn WA7 2DA Tel: 01928 719567 Fax: 01928 791021; Church View, Old Pewterspear Lane, Appleton, Warrington WA4 5QH Tel: 01925 861645 — MB BS 1981 Rajasthan; DA (UK) 1991. Staff Grade (Anaesth.) Halton Gen. Hosp. Runcorn. Prev: Regist. Rotat. (Anaesth.) Mersey; SHO (Anaesth.) Warrington Dist. Gen. Hosp.

BOINTON, Giles Basil Hardisty 8 Russell Street, Bath BA1 2QF — MB ChB 1974 Birm.

BOIRA SEGARRA, Maria Blanca 17 The Millars, Broomfield, Chelmsford CM1 7HJ — LMS 1983 Barcelona; LMS Autonoma Barcelona 1983.

BOISSARD, Joan Mary (retired) Kingsbury, Ditton Lane, Fen Ditton, Cambridge CB5 8SS — MRCS Eng. LRCP Lond. 1938. Prev: Cons. Bacteriol. Pub. Health Laborat. Serv.

BOISSIERE, Jane Anne BA Medical Services, Norcross, Thornton-Cleveleys FY5 3TA — MB ChB 1976 Dundee. Hosp. Pract. (Psychiat.) Shropsh. HA.

BOISSIERE, Philippe Francois Thomas BA Medical Services, Norcross, Thornton-Cleveleys FY5 3TA — MB ChB 1976 Dundee. Prev: Med. Off. DSS Lond.; GP Shrewsbury.

BOISSONADE, Julie Scarcewater House, Scarcewater Vean, St Clement, Truro TR1 1TA — MB ChB 1983 Manch.

BOISTON, Patricia Anne Pendre Surgery, Coleshill Street, Holywell CH8 7RS Tel: 01352 712029 Fax: 01352 712751; Llawenydd, Gwaenysgor, Rhyl LL18 6EW Tel: 01745 888588 — MB ChB 1986 Manch. Prev: SHO (Geriat.) H.M. Stanley Hosp. St. Asaph Clwyd VTS; SHO (Paediat. & Med.) Glan Clwyd Hosp. Bodelwyddan.

BOJANIC, Stana 24 Chancellors Road, London W6 9RS Tel: 020 8798 8556; 16 Hale Gardens, London W6 9SQ Tel: 020 8992 6796 — MB BS 1993 Lond.; BSc (Hons.) Lond. 1990; FRCS (I) 1995; FRCS Eng. 1997. (Char. Cross & Westm.) Research Regist. Dept. of Neurosurg. Frenchay Hosp. Prev: SHO (Plastic Surg.) Frenchay Hosp.; SHO (Gen. Surg.) Frenchay Hosp.; SHO (Neurosurg.) Frenchay Hosp.

BOKHARI, Asad Abbas 9 Cadshaw Close, Locking Stumps, Warrington WA3 7LR — MB ChB 1991 Manch.

BOKHARI, Khair — MB BS 1957 Madras; DCH 1960. (Madras Med. Coll.) Gen. Pract.

BOKHARI, Sikandhar Abbas 9 Cadshaw Close, Locking Stumps, Warrington WA3 7LR — MB BS 1959 Punjab; MRCPsych 1975; DPM Eng. 1974. (Nishtar Med. Coll.)

BOKHARI, Syed Ali Joo Queen Mary's Hospital, Frognal Avenue, Sidcup DA14 6LT Tel: 020 8302 2678 Ext: 4031 — MRCS Eng. LRCP Lond. 1986; MRCP (Paediat.) UK 1992; DCH RCP Lond. 1990; FRCPCH 1997. (The Middlesex Hospital Medical School) Cons. Paediat. Qu. Mary's Hosp. Sidcup. Socs: Med. Protec. Soc.; RCPCH; RCP. Prev: Sen. Regist. P'boro. Dist. Gen. Hosp. & Addenbrooke's Hosp. Camb.; Regist. (Paediat.) W. Middlx. Univ. Hosp. & W.m. Childr. Hosp. Lond.; SHO (Paediat. Nephrol. & Gen. Paediat.) Roy. Free Hosp. Lond.

BOLADE, Immanuel Oluwole Adesanya 25 Unity Close, London SE19 3NJ — MB BS 1981 Ibadan.

BOLADZ, Wlodzimierz Castle Bank, Ystradgynlais, Swansea Tel: 01639 3221 — Med. Dipl. Warsaw 1935. (Warsaw) Socs: BMA. Prev: Med. Off. No. 7 Polish Gen. Hosp.; Med. Off. i/c Polish Wing Att. Brit. Milit. Hosp. Lincoln; A.D.M.S. Polish Underground Army 1940-44.

BOLADZ, Wlodzimierz Paul Meddygfa Pengorof, Gorof Road, Ystradgynlais, Swansea SA9 1DS Tel: 01639 843221 Fax: 01639 843790; Manor Avon, Glanrhyd, Ystradgynlais, Swansea SA9 Tel: 01639 843452 — MRCS Eng. LRCP Lond. 1966. (St. Bart.) Prev: SHO Matern. Hosp. Middlesbrough; Ho. Phys. Sedgefield Gen. Hosp.; Ho. Surg. St. John's Hosp. Chelmsford.

BOLAJI, Mr Ibrahim Ismail Dept. of Obstetrics & Gynaecology, Diana, Princess of Wales Hospital, Scartho Road, Grimsby DN33 2BA Tel: 01472 874111 Fax: 01472 875452 Mobile: 07885 47001 Email: ibrahim.bolaji@nlg.nhs.uk; The White House, 99 Humberston Avenue, Humberston, Grimsby DN36 4ST Tel: 01472 812537 Fax: 01472 500492 Email: iibolajl@yahoo.com — MB BS 1979 Ibadan; FRCOG 2000; MRCPI 1996; MD NUI 1993; MRCOG 1987. Cons. (Obs & Gynae), Diana, P.ss of Wales Hosp., Grimsby; Cons. (Obs & Gynae), St Hugh's Hosp., Grimsby. Socs: BMA; Brit. Menopause Soc.; Europ. of Gynaecologists and Obst.s (EAGO). Prev: Sen. Regist. (Obst. & Gyn.) S. Cleveland Hosp. Middlesbough; Lect. Lond. Hosp. Med. Coll.; MRC Research Fell. (Endocrinol.) Galway.

BOLAM, Kenneth (retired) Harwin's, Boughton, King's Lynn PE33 9AG Tel: 01366 501047 — MB BS Durh. 1959. Prev: Adviser Brit. Sugar Corp.

BOLAM, Margaret Jennifer 166 Lewisham Way, London SE4 1UU Tel: 020 8 692 7365 — MB BS 1963 Lond.; MRCS Eng. LRCP Lond. 1963. (Roy. Free) Clin. Asst. (Genitourin. Med.) Greenwich, Mayday & Kings Healthcare Trusts. Prev: Clin. Asst. (Venerol.) Dreadnought Seaman's Hosp.; Ho. Phys. & Cas. Off. Dreadnought Seamen's Hosp. Greenwich; Ho. Surg. Miller Hosp. Greenwich.

BOLAM, Mr Reginald Frederick (retired) 12 The Ridgeway, Tonbridge TN10 4NQ Tel: 01732 354942 — MB BS 1952 Lond.; FRCS Eng. 1962. Prev: Cons. Gen. Surg. (Locum) NE & SW Thames RHA's.

BOLAM, Simon St George 7 Minton Mews, St Winifreds Road, Bournemouth BH2 6NZ — MB BS 1988 Lond.; BSc Lond. 1985; MRCP (UK) 1991.

BOLANCE RUIZ, Maria Inmaculada Huddersfield Royal Infirmary, Flat 17, Saville Court, Acre Street, Lindley, Huddersfield HD3 3EA — LMS 1993 Cordoba.

BOLAND, Gary Peter 17 Weaste Drive, Salford M5 2LU — MB ChB 1992 Manch.

BOLARUM, Sudha Rani 590 Derby Road, Nottingham NG7 2GZ — BM BS 1994 Nottm.

BOLAS, Roger 28 Woodlands Park Road, Axewell park, Blaydon-on-Tyne NE21 5AQ Tel: 0191 422 3188; 28 Woodlands Park Road, Axewell Park, Blaydon-on-Tyne NE21 5AQ Tel: 0191 422 3188 — MB ChB 1972 Ed.; Postgraduate Diploma in Business Administration, University of Leeds; BSc Ed. 1969; MRCGP 1976; DObst RCOG 1975. Chief Exec. Easington PCG. Prev: Sen. Med. Off. Health Care Directorate Primary Care Nat. Health Serv. Leeds; GP Blaydon; Lect. (Family Med.) Univ. Newc. u. Tyne.

BOLCINA, Alenka Lucia 279 Church Street, London N9 9JA — BM 1990 Soton.; FRCA 1996. (Univ. Soton.) Research Fell. (Pain Managem.) Char. Cross. Hosp. Lond. Prev: Specialist Regist. (Anaesth.) Nat. Hosp. Neurol. & Neurosurg. Lond.; Specialist Regist Char. Cross Hosp. Lond.; Regist. (Anaesth.) Roy. Surrey Co. Hosp. Guildford Surrey.

BOLD, Leslie (retired) Ingleside, Kemberton, Shifnal TF11 9LH Tel: 01952 581687 — MB ChB 1929 Manch.

BOLD, Thomas Alexander William Patrick 21 Milford Road, Duffield, Belper DE56 4EL — MB BS 1973 Lond.; MRCS Eng. LRCP Lond. 1973. (Roy. Free)

BOLDEN, Fiona Marion Wyndham House Surgery, Silverton, Exeter EX5 4HZ Tel: 01392 860034; 17 Church Street, Crediton EX17 2AQ Tel: 01363 777910 — MB ChB 1990 Bristol; MRCGP 1995. GP Princip. Prev: Trainee GP Haworth; SHO (Psychiat. & Paediat.) Airedale Hosp.

BOLDEN, Keith John (retired) The Chestnuts, Ebford, Exeter EX3 0QP Tel: 01392 874230 Fax: 01392 874230 — MA Camb., MB BChir 1963; FRCGP 1978, M 1969; DObst RCOG 1965. Sen. Lect. (Gen. Pract.) Univ. Exeter; Vis. Prof. RACGP. Prev: Regional Adviser (Gen. Pract.) Devon & Cornw.

BOLDUS, Margit (retired) 8 Minorca Close, Bamford, Rochdale OL11 5RP Tel: 01706 642885 — MB ChB Manch. 1961; BSc (Hons. Anat.) Manch. 1958. SCMO Pub. Health Dept. Rochdale.

BOLDY, David Andrew Renwick Pilgrim Hospital, Sibsey Road, Boston PE21 9QS Tel: 01205 364801 Fax: 01205 359257 — MB BChir 1978 Camb.; MA Camb. 1979, MD 1992; FRCP (UK) 1997. (Cam. & St. Mary's) Cons. Phys. Pilgrim Hosp. Prev: Sen. Regist. (Gen. & Thoracic Med.) E. Birm. Hosp.; Regist. (Gen. Med.) Dudley Rd. Hosp. Birm.; Regist. (Gen. Med.) Wycombe Gen. Hosp. High Wycombe.

BOLDY, Jean Alison Wadsley Bridge Medical Centre, 103 Halifax Road, Sheffield S6 1LA Tel: 0114 234 5025; Bentwood Lodge, Bent Hills, High Bradfield, Sheffield S6 6LJ — MB BS 1982 Lond.; MRCGP 1989; DRCOG 1986. (St. Mary's) Prev: Trainee GP Bradford VTS; Ho. Phys. St. Mary's Hosp. Lond.; Ho. Surg. York Dist. Hosp.

BOLDY, Jean Alison Renwick, MBE (retired) 31 Sollershott E., Letchworth SG6 3JN Tel: 01462 685057 — MB ChB 1948 Ed. Prev: Clin. Asst. Ortopaedics, Lister Hosp., Stevenage.

BOLEL, Selwyn Brian South Hill Crescent Surgery, 4 South Hill Crescent, Sunderland SR2 7PA Tel: 0191 567 5571 Fax: 0191 510 2810 — MB BCh 1973 Witwatersrand; MRCGP 1980.

BOLES, Peter Robert Swedish Log House, Burrswood, Groombridge, Tunbridge Wells TN3 9PU — MB BCh BAO 1989 Dub.

BOLGER, Aidan Patrick Dept. of Clinical Cardiology, National Heart & Lung Institute, London SW3 6LY — MB BS 1995 Lond.

BOLGER, Ciaran Mary The Laurals, 85 Church Road, Frampton Cotterell, Bristol BS36 2NE — MB BCh BAO 1987 Dub.; PhD Dub. 1995; BA Dub. 1984; FRCSI (SN) 1995; FRCSI 1991. Sen. Regist. & Lect. (Neurosurg.) Walton Hosp. Liverp. Socs: Brit. Neurol. Surg. Soc.

BOLGER, Mr John Paul BUPA Hospital, Ambrose Lane, Harpenden AL5 4BP Tel: 01582 763191 Email: eyelead@aol.com; 42 Firs Wood Close, Potters Bar EN6 4BY — MB BCh BAO 1976 NUI; FRCS Eng. 1982; DO Eng. 1980. (NUI Dublin) Indep. NHS Ophth. BUPA Hosp. Ambrose La. Harpenden; Surg., Ophthamology.1. 99 Harley St. Lond.; 2. Grayton Rd. Surgic. Centre, King's Lynn. Socs: Roy. Soc. Med.; Medico-Legal Soc. Prev: Cons. Ophth. Qu. Eliz. II Hosp. Welwyn Gdn. City; Sen. Regist. (Ophth.) Moorfields Eye Hosp. & Roy. Free Hosp. Lond.; Regist. (Ophth.) St. Thos. Hosp. Lond.

BOLGER, Oliver Henry (retired) 7 Hill Road, London NW8 9QE — LRCPI & LM, LRCSI & LM 1944.

BOLGER, Peter Gary PPP Healthcare, PPP House, Vale Road, Tunbridge Wells TN1 1BJ — MB ChB 1982 Leeds; MRCGP 1986; MFPHM 1991. Sen. Med. Adviser. Prev: Cons. Pub. Health Med. Berks HA Reading; Sen. Regist (Community Med.) S. W. RHA; Regist. Community Med. W. Midl. HA.

BOLIA, Ammanulla Abdul X-Ray Department, The Leicester Royal Infirmary, Infirmary Square, Leicester LE1 5WW; 7 St Andrews Drive, Oadby, Leicester LE2 2RG — MB ChB 1978 Glas.; FRCR 1984; DMRD Eng. 1983. Cons. Radiol. Leics. HA. Prev: Sen. Regist. (Radiol.) Trent RHA; Regist. (Radiol.) Sheff. AHA; SHO (Chest Med.) N.ampton AHA.

BOLIA, Rajendra Singh Abbey Surgery, 77 Woodhead Road, Abbey Hulton, Stoke-on-Trent ST2 8DH Tel: 01782 542671 Fax: 01782 544365 — MB BS 1963 Rajasthan.

BOLIA, Sandeep 6 Yew Tree Close, Light Oaks, Stoke-on-Trent ST2 7PR — BM BS 1998 Nottm.; BM BS Nottm 1998.

BOLIS, Giuseppe Ulisse Block B31, Pasteur Court, Queen's Medical Centre, Nottingham NG7 2UH — State Exam 1993 Milan.

BOLITHO-JONES, Ann The Consulting Rooms, Oxhey Drive, South Oxhey, Watford WD1 6RU Tel: 020 8428 2292; 22 Kingsfield Road, Oxhey, Watford WD19 4PS — MB ChB 1979 Sheff.; DCH RCP Lond. 1991.

BOLITHO-JONES, Philip Victor The Consulting Rooms, Oxhey Drive, South Oxhey, Watford WD1 6RU Tel: 020 8428 2292 — BMedSci (Hons.) Sheff. 1975, MB ChB 1978. GP Watford.

BOLL, Marilyn Dorothy Oakley Cowes Health Centre, 8 Consort Road, Cowes PO31 7SH; Tel: 01983 293934 — MB BS 1969 Lond.; MFFP RLOG 1993; MRCS Eng. LRCP Lond. 1969; MRCGP 1982. (St. Bart.) p/t Sen. Med. Off. (Family Plann.) I. of Wight HA; Clin. Asst. Foetal Ultrasound, Matern. Dept. st marys Hosp. Newport, Isle of Wight. Prev: Ho. Phys. St. Bart. Hosp. Lond.; Ho. Surg. Roy. S. Hants. Hosp. Soton.; SHO (A & E) Poole Gen. Hosp.

BOLL, Michael Davis Cowes Health Centre, 8 Consort Road, Cowes PO31 7SH Tel: 01983 295251 Fax: 01983 280461; 34 Newport Road, Cowes PO31 7PW — MB BS 1970 Lond.; MRCS Eng. LRCP Lond. 1970; MRCGP 1982; DObst RCOG 1974; DTM & H Liverp. 1974; DCH Eng. 1973. (Guy's) Prev: Trainee GP Wessex VTS; Ho. Phys. Edgware Gen. Hosp.; Med. Off. St. Luke's Hosp. Kaloleni, Kenya.

BOLL, Stephen Medical Health Centre, Sherburn, Durham DH6 1JE Tel: 0191 720 0441 Fax: 0191 372 1238; 10 Swinside Drive, Belmont, Durham DH1 1AD Tel: 0191 384 6615 Email: sboll@btinternet.com — MB BS 1976 Newc.; MRCGP 1981; DRCOG 1981. (Newcastle) GP Durh.; Hosp. Practitioner (Gastrointestinal Endoscopy).

BOLLAND, Emily 9 The Avenue, Alsager, Stoke-on-Trent ST7 2AN Tel: 01270 874107 — MB BS 1991 Lond.; MRCP (UK) 1996; DCH RCP Lond. 1994. (St. Mary's Lond.)

BOLLAND, Helen Elizabeth Craven Road Medical Centre, 60 Craven Road, Leeds LS6 2RX Tel: 0113 295 3530 Fax: 0113 295 3542 — MB ChB 1989 Leeds; MRCGP 1993.

BOLLAND, Helen Margaret King Cross Surgery, 199 King Cross Road, King Cross, Halifax HX1 3LE Tel: 01274 870744 Email: bolland@mornsvan.freeserve.co.uk — MB ChB 1994 Liverp.

BOLLAND, Jane Lucia Mary 7 Gardenfields, Little Shelford, Cambridge CB2 5HH — MB ChB 1985 Bristol; DRCOG 1988.

BOLLAND, John Alexander Woodview Medical Centre, 26 Holmecross Road, Thorplands, Northampton NN3 8AW Tel: 01604 670780 Fax: 01604 646208; Sunnyside, 22 The High St, Ravensthorpe, Northampton NN6 8EH Tel: 01604 771153 — MB ChB 1990 Liverp.; MRCGP 1994. (Liverp.)

BOLLAND, William Thomas 1 Albyn Place, Flat 3, West End, Edinburgh EH2 4NG — MB ChB 1996 Ed.

BOLLARD, Miss Ruth Caroline 3 Stoney Lane, Horsforth, Leeds LS18 4RA — MB ChB 1988 Liverp.; FRCS Glas. 1994. Regist. Rotat. (Surg.) N. & Yorks. Prev: SHO Rotat. (Surg.) Roy. Liverp. Hosp.; SHO (A & E) Roy. Liverp. Hosp.; Demonst. (Anat.) Liverp. Univ.

BOLLEDDULA, Krishna Prasad Flat 3A, Staff Residences, Lagan Valley Hospital, Hillsborough Road, Lisburn BT28 1JP — MB BS 1985 Sri Venkateswara.

BOLLEN, Mr Steven Robert Bradford Royal Infirmary, Duckworth Lane, Bradford BD9 6RJ Tel: 01274 364456 — MB ChB 1978 Birm.; FRCS Ed. (Orth.) 1990; FRCS Ed. 1985; FRCS Eng. 1985. Cons. Orthop. Surg. Bradford Hosps. Trust; Hon. Med. Adviser to Brit. Mt.aineering Counc.; Med. Commissuion Football Assoc.; Secretary Brit. Orthopaedic Sports Tramma Assoc. Socs: Acad. Sec. Brit. Orthop. Sports Trauma Assn.; Brit. Assn. for Surg. of Knee. Prev: Knee Surg. Fell. N. Sydney Orthop. & Sports Med. Centre; Arthritis & Rheum. Counc. Boots Research Fell. l987-l988.

BOLLON, Muriel Edith (retired) Uplands Way, North Stoke, Bath BA1 9AS Tel: 0117 932 5390 — MRCS Eng. LRCP Lond. 1940. Gen. Med. Practitioner (NHS), W.on-Super-Mare.

BOLODEOKU, Ebiere Oluwatimilehin 64 Redruth House, Grange Road, Sutton SM2 6RU — MB BS 1986 Lagos, Nigeria.

BOLS, Rebecca Marie-Christine 28 Sayer-Way, Knebworth SG3 6BN — MB ChB 1991 Aberd.

BOLSHER, Stephen John Stenhouse Medical Centre, Furlong Street, Arnold, Nottingham NG5 7BP Tel: 0115 967 3877 Fax: 0115 967 3838 — MB ChB 1975 Dundee; BSc (Hons.) St. And. 1972. GP Notts.; Lect. (Gen. Pract.) Univ. Nottm.

BOLSIN, Stephen Nicholas Cluley 42A Ravenswood Road, Bristol BS6 6BT — MB BS 1978 Lond.; BSc Lond. 1974; FFA RCS Eng. 1982.

BOLSON, Peter Frederick Russelgate, Roweltown, Carlisle CA6 6LX Tel: 016978 334 — MB 1967 Camb.; BChir 1966. (Camb. & St. Bart.)

BOLSOVER, Wilson John Maidstone &Tunbridge Wells NHS Trust, Pembury Hospital, Pembury, Tunbridge Wells TN2 4QJ Tel: 01892 823535 Fax: 01892 825246 Email: wilson.bolsover@mtw-tr.nhs.uk; 47 Sandown Park, Tunbridge Wells TN2 4RH — MB BS 1980 Lond.; MD Lond. 1993; MRCP (UK) 1985; FRCPCH (UK) 1997. (St. Thos.) Cons. Paediat. Pembury Hosp. Tunbridge Wells. Prev: Sen. Regist. & Regist. (Paediat.) St. Thos. Hosp. Lond.; SHO (Paediat.) Brompton Hosp. Lond.; SHO (Neonatol.) Hammersmith Hosp. Lond.

BOLSTER, Kevin Michael 375 Oxford Street, Sheffield S6 3FD — MB ChB 1998 Sheff.; MB ChB Sheff 1998.

BOLT, Christopher John (retired) 18 Frobisher Way, Greenhithe DA9 9JN Tel: 01322 370040 — MB BS Lond. 1961; MRCS Eng. LRCP Lond. 1961. Prev: Med. Policy Adviser, DSS, Lond.

BOLT, Clare Elizabeth Wreake View, 2 Brooksby Rd, Hoby, Melton Mowbray LE14 3EA — MB ChB 1997 Birm.

BOLT, Mr David Ernest, CBE (retired) Feniton House, Feniton, Honiton EX14 3BE Tel: 01404 850921 — MB ChB Bristol 1945; FRCS Eng. 1951. Prev: Cons. Surg. W. Middlx. Hosp. Isleworth & Lect. (Surg.) Univ. Lond.

BOLT, Geoffrey Leon, VRD (retired) 11 Nelson Street, King's Lynn PE30 5DY Tel: 01553 773819 — MB BS 1945 Lond.; FRCP Lond. 1975, M 1963. Prev: Cons. Phys. Qu. Eliz. Hosp. Kings Lynn.

BOLT, Helen Louise 40 Derwent Grove, Taunton TA1 2NJ — MB ChB 1989 Bristol. Trainee GP Taunton.

BOLT, James Michael Ashlers, 130 Upper Westwood, Bradford-on-Avon BA15 2DE — MB BCh 1998 Wales.

BOLT, Jean Mary Wilson 22 Lady Jane Gate, Bothwell, Glasgow G71 8BW — BSc Manch. 1949; MD Belf. 1978, MB BCh BAO 1955; FRCPsych 1983, M 1973; DPM RCPSI 1965; DPH Ed. 1958. Cons. Psychiat. Hartwood Hosp. Shotts. Prev: Cons. Psychiat. S. Warks.

BOLT, Jennifer Lennox Frome Valley Medical Centre, 2 Court Road, Frampton Cotterell, Bristol BS36 2DE Tel: 01454 772153 Fax: 01454 250078 — MB ChB 1974 Bristol; DRCOG 1976. GP Bristol.

BOLT, Joan Charlotte Dujardin 144 Chorley New Road, Bolton BL1 4NX Tel: 01204 43778 — MRCS Eng. LRCP Lond. 1933; MRCS Eng., LRCP Lond. 1933. (Lond. Sch. Med. Wom.)

BOLT, John Frederick (retired) Les Vielles Salines, Rue du Clos, L'Islet, St Sampsons, Guernsey GY2 4FN Tel: 01481 46155 Fax: 01481 49752 — MB BS 1956 Lond.; DA Eng. 1958. Mem. Staff P.ss Eliz. Hosp. Guernsey. Prev: Anaesth. RAF.

BOLT, Sally Helen 5 Belgrave Hill, Clifton, Bristol BS8 2UA — MB ChB 1996 Bristol.

BOLT, Sheelagh Brigid Westcotes Health Centre, Fosse Road South, Leicester LE3 0LP Tel: 0116 254 8568; Wreake View, Hoby, Melton Mowbray — MB BS 1967 Lond.; MRCS Eng. LRCP Lond. 1967. (Lond. Hosp.) Socs: BMA; Leic. Med. Soc. Prev: SHO (Med.) King Geo. Hosp. Ilford; SHO (Med.) Barking Hosp.

BOLT, Shirley Anne Hythe Medical Centre, (Forestside Medical Practice), Hythe, Southampton SO4 5ZB Tel: 02380 845955; Langley Close, West Common, Blackfield, Southampton SO45 1XJ Tel: 02380 891107 Fax: 01703 891107 — MB BChir 1958 Camb.; MRCGP 1980.

BOLTER, Pauline Jane Minster Health, 35 Monkgate, York YO31 8WE Tel: 01904 670949; 8 Sirocco Court, York YO31 8FE — MB BS 1985 Lond.; DTM & H 1996; DRCOG 1991. GP York. Prev: Med. Off. Shagarab Refugee Camp Sudan.; Staff Grade (A & E) York Dist. Hosp.; SHO (Paediat.) New Cross Hosp. Wolverhampton.

BOLTON, Amanda The Willow Surgery, Coronation Road, Downend, Bristol BS16 5DH Tel: 0117 970 9500 Fax: 0117 970 9501; 5 Brunel Close, Warmley, Bristol BS30 5BB — BM 1980 Soton.; MRCP (UK) 1984; DRCOG 1986. Clin. Asst., Bristol Dermat. Centre.

BOLTON, Andrew 1 Cranberry Close, Darwen BB3 2HR — MB ChB 1998 Sheff.; MB ChB Sheff 1998.

BOLTON, Andrew John Tinshill Lane Surgery, 8 Tinshill Lane, Leeds LS16 7AP Tel: 0113 267 3462 Fax: 0113 230 0402 — MB BS 1979 Newc.; MRCGP 1984.

BOLTON, Andrew Robert 54 St George's Road, North Shields NE30 3LA — MB BCh 1991 Witwatersrand. SHO (Paediat. Cardiol.) Freeman Hosp. Newc. u. Tyne. Prev: SHO (Paediat.) Shotley Bridge; SHO (Community Paediat. & Paediat.) Sunderland.

BOLTON, Anne 16 Rowan Road, London W6 7DU — MB BChir 1942 Camb.; FRCP Lond. 1972, M 1946; MRCS Eng. LRCP Lond. 1942; FRCPCH 1997; FRCPsych 1972; DPM Eng. 1950. (Univ. Coll. Hosp.) Hon. Cons. Childr. Psychiat. Middlx. Hosp. Lond. Socs: Fell. Roy. Soc. Med. Prev: Cons. Phys. in Psychol. Med. Eliz. G. Anderson Hosp.; Paediat. Psychiat. Belgrave Hosp. Childr.; Sen. Regist. Maudsley Hosp.

BOLTON, Anne Maris (retired) White House, Kirk Michael IM6 2HH Tel: 01624 878209 Fax: 01624 878848 — MB ChB 1961 Ed.; DObst RCOG 1964.

BOLTON, Barbara 20 Pinfold Lane, Romiley, Stockport SK6 4NP Tel: 0161 430 2480 — MB ChB 1948 Manch. (Manch.) Socs: Fell. Manch. Med. Soc.

BOLTON, Charlotte Emma Rebecca Langtoft, 12 Ashfield Drive, Upton, Macclesfield SK10 3DQ — BM BS 1995 Nottm. (Univ. Nottm.) SHO Rotat. (Med.) Torbay Hosp. Torquay.

BOLTON, Christopher Joseph 15 Glenpark Drive, Southport PR9 9FA — MB ChB 1996 Birm.

BOLTON, Claire (Kerrigan) The Surgery, Wolvery, Kidderminster DY11 5TH Tel: 01562 850800 Fax: 01562 852575 Email: claire.bolton@gp-m81608.nhs.uk — MB ChB 1992 Birm. (Birmingham) Gen. Practitioner.

BOLTON, Colin Farrar 6 Calverley Park Crescent, Tunbridge Wells TN1 2NB — BM 1951 Oxf.; BA, BM, BCh Oxf. 1951. (Oxf. & Guy's) CMO Reliance Mutual. Prev: Fell. Harvard Med. Sch. Boston, USA; Ho. Phys. Guy's Hosp. Lond.

BOLTON, David Taberer Carmel House, 180 Great North Road, Gosforth, Newcastle upon Tyne NE3 2DS — MB ChB 1970 Bristol; DObst 1972; FFA RCS Eng. 1975. Cons. Cardiothoracic Anaesth. Freeman Hosp. Newc. u. Tyne. Prev: Cons. Cardiothoracic Anaesth. Utrecht & Leiden, Netherlands.

BOLTON, Derek Samuel (retired) 4 Cloverhill Gardens, Belfast BT4 2LH — MB BCh BAO 1954 Belf. Prev: GP Belf.

BOLTON, Gordon Mackenzie Station View Medical Centre, 29A Escomb Road, Bishop Auckland DL14 6AB Tel: 01388 602050 Fax: 01388 601847 Email: gordon.bolton@gp-a83015.nhs.uk — MB ChB 1979 Ed.; MRCGP 1983. GP; Hosp. Practitioner, c/o Elderly, S. Durh. Health Care NHS Trust. Prev: Trainee GP N.d. VTS.; Ho. Off. (Gen. Surg.) Roy. Cornw. Hosp. Treliske; Ho. Off. (Gen. Med.) W.. Gen. Hosp. Edin.

BOLTON, Mr Harold (retired) Pinfold, 20 Pinfold Lane, Romiley, Stockport SK6 4NP Tel: 0161 430 2480 Email: sambolton@amserve.net — BSc Manch. 1939, ChM 1956, MB ChB (Distinc. Med. &; Surg.) 1942; FRCS Eng. 1948. Prev: Cons. Hand Surg. Stockport Gp. Hosps.

BOLTON, James Anthony Russell Cran, Gripper, Bolton and Evers, Health Centre, Chacewater, Truro TR4 8QS Tel: 01872 560346 Fax: 01872 561184; Trekensa, Old Tram Road, Devoran, Truro TR3 6NG Tel: 01872 864737 — MB BS 1982 Lond.; MFHom 1995; MRCGP 1989. (Westm.)

BOLTON, James Gerard Francis 38 Nelson Road, London SW19 1HT — MB BS 1990 Lond.; BSc (Hons.) Lond. 1987; MRCPsych 1995. (St. Geo. Hosp. Med. Sch. Lond.) Lect. (Psychiat.) St Geo.'s Hosp. Med. Sch.

BOLTON, Jennifer Ruth 3 Seascale Crescent, Wigan WN1 2HQ — MB ChB 1998 Bristol.

BOLTON, Jeremy Shaw Department of Liaison Psychiatry, Clare House, St Georges Hospital, Blackshaw Road, London SW17 0QT Tel: 020 8725 5517 Fax: 020 8725 5519 Email: jsbolton@sghms.ac.uk; 4 Brooklands Park, Blackheath, London SE3 9BL Email: jsbolton@ndirect.co.uk — MB BChir Camb. 1969; MA Camb. 1969; FRCPsych 1989, M 1975. (Camb. & Univ. Coll. Hosp.) p/t Cons. Psychiat. St. Geo. Hosp. & Springfield Hosp. Lond.; Assoc. Dean of Postgrad. Med. Kent, Surrey, Sussex Deanery; Hon. Sen. Lect. St. Geo. Hosp. Med. Sch. Lond. Socs: Fell. Roy. Soc. Med.; Harv. Soc.; Fell. Postrgad. Med. Counc. Mem. Prev: Sen. Regist. Bethlem Roy. & Maudsley Hosps.; Ho. Surg. & Ho. Phys. Univ. Coll. Hosp. Lond.; SHO (Med.) N.wick Pk. Hosp. Harrow.

BOLTON, John 3 Ridgeway Court, The Ridgeway, Westbury-on-Trym, Bristol BS10 7DG — MB BS 1998 Lond.; MB BS Lond 1998.

BOLTON, John Charles Victor (retired) The Cottage, Hinton St Mary, Sturminster Newton DT10 1NE Tel: 01258 472300 — MB BCh BAO 1947 NUI. Prev: Regist. Portsmouth Chest Servs.

BOLTON, Mr John Philip 9 Crescent E., Hadley Wood, Barnet EN4 0EL Tel: 020 8449 7352 — MB 1968 Camb.; MSc Brit. Columbia 1977; BChir 1967; FRCS Eng. 1971. (Middlx.) Cons. Surg. (Gen. Surg.), Barnet and Chase Farm Hosp.s, NHS Trust.; Jt. Med. Director, Barnet and Chase Farm Hosp.s, NHS Trust. Socs: Fell. Roy. Soc. Med. & Med. Soc. Lond.; ASGB & I.; AUGIS. Prev: Sen. Regist. (Gen. Surg.) Centr. Middlx. Hosp. Lond.; Regist. Cheltenham Gen. Hosp.; Research Fell. Dept. Surg. Univ. Brit. Columbia Vancouver, Canada.

BOLTON, John Philip Grimshaw Ministry of Defence, Gulf Veterans' Illnesses Unit, Room 6104, St. Christopher's House,

Southwark Street, London SE1 0TD Tel: 020 7305 3004 Email: smamod.uk@utinternet.com; 4 Court Close, Kidlington OX5 1NU Tel: 01865 374021 — MB ChB 1974 Bristol; MSc Community Med. Lond. 1990; MRCGP 1979; DRCOG 1978; MFPHM 2000. Med. Adviser, Gulf Veterans' Illnesses Unit. Socs: BMA; RSM. Prev: Regtl. Med. Off. 1st Bn. P. of Wales's Own Regt. Yorks.; Med. Off. 9 Signal Regt.; Chief Instruc. RAMC Train. Centre.

BOLTON, Jonathan Mark Howard Yew Tree Road Surgery, 8 Yew Tree Road, Tunbridge Wells TN4 0BA Tel: 01892 529601 Fax: 01892 527610 Email: jmhb@doctors.org.uk — MB BS 1981 Lond.; MA Camb. 1974. GP Tunbridge Wells.

BOLTON, Lesley Margaret Ysbyty Gwynedd, Penrhosgarnedd, Bangor LL57 2PW Tel: 01248 384975 Fax: 01248 384975; Wern Uchaf, Nr Half Way Bridge, Tal y Bont, Bangor LL57 3AX Tel: 01248 601418 — MB BS 1985 Newc.; MD Newc. 1995; MRCOG 1990. Cons. O & G.

BOLTON, Lorna Helen Castle Practice, Carrickfergus Health Centre, Taylors Avenue, Carrickfergus BT38 7HT Tel: 028 9336 4193 Fax: 028 9331 5947 — MB BCh BAO 1985 Belf.; MCOphth 1990; MRCGP 1989; DCH Dub. 1988; DRCOG 1988. Prev: SHO (Ophth.) Roy. Vict. Hosp. Belf.

BOLTON, Margaret Elizabeth The New Folly, Bell Mead, Ingatestone CM4 0FA Tel: 01277 352224 Fax: 01277 352868; The Cottage, Heronway, Hutton Mount, Brentwood CM13 2LG Tel: 01277 211010 — MRCS Eng. LRCP Lond. 1969; MFFP 1993; DObst RCOG 1972. (Roy. Free)

BOLTON, Michael War Pensions Agency, Norcross, Blackpool Tel: 01253 332969; 36 Hayhurst Road, Whalley, Clitheroe BB7 9RL Tel: 01254 824052 — MB ChB 1978 Manch.; BSc St. And. 1975. Benefits Agency Med. Servs. Med. Adviser War Pens. Agency Norcross Blackpool. Prev: GP Rishton Lancs. & Maidstone.

BOLTON, Monica Jane Manchester Royal Infirmary, Oxford Road, Manchester M13 9WL Tel: 0161 276 4810 Fax: 0161 276 4814; 67 Stamford Road, Longsight, Manchester M13 0SW — MB ChB (Hons.) Manch. 1978; MRCP (UK) 1982; MRCGP (Hons.) 1986; DRCOG 1985. Clin. Asst. (Clin. Haemat.) Manch. Roy. Infirm. Prev: GP Manch.

BOLTON, Patrick Farrar 18 Storeys Way, Cambridge CB3 0DT — MB BS 1979 Lond.

BOLTON, Peter John 163 High Road, North Weald, Epping CM16 6EB Tel: 01992 523685 Fax: 01992 523858 — MB BS 1969 Lond.; MRCS Eng. LRCP Lond. 1969; FRCOG 1988, M 1975. (Lond. Hosp.) Cons. O & G Harold Wood Hosp. Socs: Brit. Soc. Gyn. Endoscopy; Brit. Soc. Colpos. & Cerv. Path.; Fell. Roy. Soc. Med. Prev: Sen. Regist. (O & G) Hammersmith Hosp. Lond.; Regist. (O & G) Birm. Matern. & Wom's Hosp.

BOLTON, Philip William 4 Cloverhill Gardens, Belfast BT4 2LH — MB ChB 1991 Dundee.

BOLTON, Reginald, MBE (retired) Lealholm, Nyetimber Copse, West Chiltington, Pulborough RH20 2NE Tel: 01798 812548 — MRCS Eng. LRCP Lond. 1933; MB BS Lond. 1936; FRCP Lond. 1963, M 1938. Prev: Cons. Phys. Epsom Dist. Hosp.

BOLTON, Reuben (retired) 15 Orchard Drive, Whiterock, Killinchy, Newtownards BT23 6QT Tel: 01238 541610 — MB BCh BAO 1949 Belf.; MFOM RCP Lond. 1986, AFOM 1982; DIH Eng. 1982; CIH Dund 1981; DObst RCOG 1960. Med. Off. N. Irel. Dept. Health & Social Servs. Prev: Ho. Surg. Matern. Hosp. Hull & Roy. Vict. Hosp. Belf.

BOLTON, Robert Edward McKenzie Medical Centre, 20 West Richmond Street, Edinburgh EH8 9DX Tel: 0131 667 2955; 2FL, 60 Dundas St, Edinburgh EH3 6QS — MB ChB 1987 Ed.; MRCGP 1991; DCCH RCP Ed. 1992; DRCOG 1990. GP Princip. Prev: Trainee GP Airdrie VTS.

BOLTON, Robert Henry (retired) Half Acre, Boldre, Lymington SO41 8PD — BA; B.M., B.Ch. Oxf. 1932. Prev: Med. Off. Univ. Birm.

BOLTON, Robert Henry (retired) Drumkeen, Dunboyne Avenue, Larne BT40 1PS — MB BCh BAO 1949 Belf.; DObst RCOG 1951; FFA RCS Eng. 1957. Prev: Cons. Anaesth. E. Antrim Hosp. Gp.

BOLTON, Robin Paul Doncaster Royal Infirmary, Armthorpe Road, Doncaster DN2 5LT Tel: 01302 366666 Fax: 01302 553123 Email: Robin.Bolton@dbh.nhs.uk; Willow Bank, 5 Grange Close, Bessacarr, Doncaster DN4 6SE Tel: 01302 370202 Email: rbolton@leeds.force9.co.uk — BM BCh 1974 Oxf.; MD Bristol 1984; MA Camb. 1974; FRCP Lond. 1994; MRCP (UK) 1977. Cons. Phys. & Gastroenterol. Doncaster Roy. Infirm.; Clin. Dir.-Med. Socs: Brit. Soc. Gastroenterol. Prev: Lect. & Hon. Sen. Regist. (Med.) St. Jas. Hosp. Leeds.

BOLTON, Sheila Henrietta (retired) Drumkeen, Dunboyne Avenue, Larne BT40 1PS Tel: 01574 272923 — MB BCh BAO 1952 Belf.; DObst RCOG 1954. Prev: SHO (Obst.) Belf. City Hosp.

BOLTON, Simon Derek James 4 Cloverhill Gardens, Belfast BT4 2LH — MB ChB 1997 Glas.

BOLTON, Sonia Grace (retired) 10 Rose Tower, 62 Clarence Parade, Southsea PO5 2HX Tel: 01705 825899 — MB BS Lond. 1960; MRCS Eng. LRCP Lond. 1960; T(M) 1991; DObst RCOG 1962. Prev: SCMO (Child Health) City Portsmouth Community Health Care Servs.

BOLTON, Thomas Wilson 29 Bassett Road, Leighton Buzzard LU7 1AR Tel: 01525 373111 — MB BS 1956 Lond. (St. Bart.) Treasury Med. Off.; Police Surg. Socs: BMA.

BOLTON, Trevor Morrill Street Health Centre, Holderness Road, Hull HU9 2LJ Tel: 01482 320046; Mardon Cottage, Ferry Road, Wawne, Hull HU7 5XY Tel: 01482 824941 — MB ChB 1967 Manch.; MRCGP 1977. Socs: Hull Med. Soc.

BOLTON, Valerie Joy Upper Grosvenor Road Surgery, 150 Upper Grosvenor Road, Tunbridge Wells TN1 2ED Tel: 01892 515542 Fax: 01892 532247; Collingwood, 15 Wybourne Rise, Tunbridge Wells TN2 5JG Tel: 01892 538487 — MB BS 1978 Lond.; DRCOG 1982. (Guy's) GP Tunbridge Wells.

BOLTON, Victor Stewart 3 Llwyn Knottia Apartments, Cefn Road, Wrexham LL13 9TT — MB ChB 1966 Liverp.

BOLTON-MAGGS, Benjamin George 1 Heyes Mount, Rainhill, Prescot L35 0LU Tel: 0185 071 4171 Fax: 0151 430 7984 Email: bolton-maggs@compuserve.com — MB BChir 1975 Camb.; MA, MB Camb. 1975, BChir 1974; FRCS Eng. 1979. Cons. Orthop. Surg. St. Helens & Knowsley NHS Trust Hosps. Socs: Brit. Elbow & Shoulder Soc.; (Hon. Sec.) Brit. Elbow Shoulder Soc. Prev: Sen. Regist. (Orthop. & Traum. Surg.) The Lond. Hosp. Whitechapel.

BOLTON-MAGGS, Paula Helen Royal Liverpool Childrens NHS Trust, Alder Hey, Eaton Road, Liverpool L12 2AP Tel: 0151 228 4811 Fax: 0151 220 6070; 1 Heyes Mount, Rainhill, Prescot L35 0LU — BM BCh 1974 Oxf.; FRCP Lond. 1977; MRCP (UK) 1977; FRCPath 1997, M 1988; FRCPCH 1997. Cons. Paediat. Haemat. Roy. Liverp. Childr. NHS Trust. Prev: Sen. Regist. (Haemat.) Roy. Liverp. Hosp.

BOLWELL, Anthony Guy The White House, Sleepers Hill, Winchester SO22 4NA — MB BS 1969 Lond.; MB BS 1969 Lond.; MRCS Eng. LRCP Lond. 1968 MRCP (UK) 1977.

BOMANJI, Jamshed Institute of Nuclear Medicine, Middlesex Hospital, Mortimer St., London W1T 3AA Tel: 020 7380 9425 Fax: 020 7436 0603 Email: j.bomanji@nucmed.ucl.ac.uk — MB BS 1982 Punjab; PhD Lond. 1987; MSc Lond. 1984. Cons. Nuclear Med., Instit. of Nuclear Med., The Middx Hosp., Mortimer St., Lond. Socs: Brit. Nuclear Med. Soc.; Soc. Nuclear Med.; BMA. Prev: Cons. Nuclear Med. St. Barts. Hosp.; Sen. Research Fell. St. Barts. Hosp.; Cons. Nuclear Med. Pakistan.

BOMFORD, Adrian Bruce 32 Brockley View, Forest Hill, London SE23 1SL — MB BS Lond. 1969; MD Univ. Lond. 1982; BSc (Hons.) Lond. 1966; MRCP (UK) 1972. (Lond. Hosp. Med. Sch.) Reader (Med.) Inst. Liver Studies King's Coll. Sch. Med. & Dent. Lond.; Hon. Cons. Phys. King's Healthcare Trust. Prev: Lect. Med. (Liver Unit) Kings Coll. Sch. Med. & Dent.; Med. Regist. (Cardiac Dept.) Kings Coll. Hosp. Lond.

BOMFORD, Mr William Bruce Norris (retired) 9 Eden Mount, Carlisle CA3 9LY Tel: 01228 521184 — MB BS Lond. 1943; FRCS Eng. 1950; MFOM RCP Lond. 1978. Prev: Chief Med. Off. BP Plc.

BONAR, Judith Ann 4 Quicks Road, London SW19 1EZ — MB ChB 1994 Ed. SHO W.. Gen. Hosp. Edin. Socs: BMA. Prev: Ho. Off. (Surg. & Med.) Roy. Infirm. Edin.

BONAVIA, Alison Yarm Medical Centre, 1 Worsall Road, Yarm TS15 9DD Tel: 01642 786422 Fax: 01642 785617 — MB ChB 1988 Aberd.; MRCGP (Distinc.) 1994. Prev: Trainee GP Cleveland VTS.

BONAVIA, Iain Charles The Surgery, Tennant Street, Stockton-on-Tees TS18 2AT Tel: 01642 613331 — MB BS 1987 Newc.; MRCGP 1993; DCH RCP Lond. 1992. GP. Prev: Trainee GP Cleveland VTS.;

Tutor in Personal Professional Developm. at Univ. of Durh., Stockton Campus.

BOND, Alastair James 5 Rustic Cottages, Colinton Road, Edinburgh EH13 0LD — MB BS 1988 Newc.

BOND, Alison Mary 39A Westbourne Road, Southport PR8 2HY — MB ChB 1987 Leeds; MRCGP 1993.

BOND, Amanda Kirsty 15 Parsonage Close, Huish Episcopi, Langport TA10 9HN — MB BS 1996 Lond.

BOND, Mr Andrew Philip Swindon & Marlborough NHS Trust, Princess Margaret Hospital, Oaks Rd, Swindon SN1 4JU; Parsloes Farm House, Overtown, Wroughton, Swindon SN4 0SJ Tel: 01793 814889 Email: 007@clara.net — MB BCh 1975 Wales; FRCOG 1992, M 1980. (Welsh national school of Medicine) Cons. (Obst. & Gyn.) P.ss Margt. Hosp. Swindon. Prev: Lect. & Sen. Regist. (O & G) Univ. Liverp.; Regist. St. Catherine's Hosp. Birkenhead & Liverp. Matern. Hosp.; SHO Univ. Hosp. Wales.

BOND, Ann Robin 50 Streetly Lane, Four Oaks, Sutton Coldfield B74 4TX Tel: 0121 308 1019 — MB BS 1962 Lond.; MB BS Lond.1962. (Char. Cross)

BOND, Anthea Mary Birchwood Surgery, 232-240 Nevells Road, Letchworth SG6 4UB Tel: 01462 683456 — MB ChB 1988 Birm.; DRCOG 1991. Prev: Trainee GP/SHO Stoke-on-Trent HA VTS.

BOND, Anthony John 9 Queen Street, Whittlesey, Peterborough PE7 1AY Tel: 01733 204611 Fax: 01733 208926; Rose House, 2 Goodwin Walk, Werrington, Peterborough PE4 6GQ Tel: 01733 575070 Fax: 01733 575070 Email: ruthbond@compuserve.com — MB BS 1978 Lond.; MRCGP 1983; DRCOG 1982. (Lond. Hosp.) GP Whittlesey Cambs.

BOND, Carolyn Diane 17 Windermere Drive, Maghull, Liverpool L31 9BG — MB ChB 1978 Liverp.; DRCOG 1980.

BOND, Charles Alan 39 Annesdale, Ely CB7 4BN — BM BCh 1991 Oxf.

BOND, David William King's Mill Hospital, Mansfield Rd, Sutton in Ashfield NG17 4JL Tel: 01623 622515; Tel: 01773 874314 — MB ChB 1989 Bristol; MRCP (UK) 1996. (Bristol) Cons. Padiat. King's Mill Hosp. Mansfield. Prev: Regist. (Paediat.) Mansfield; SHO (Paediat.) Derbysh. Childr. Hosp.; Regist. (Paediat.) Qu. Med. Centre Nottm.

BOND, Egerton Brian 102 Circular Road, Belfast BT4 2GE — MD 1976 Belf.; MB BCh BAO 1968; FRCOG 1992, M 1973.

BOND, George Hugh (retired) — MB BChir Camb. 1950. Prev: Ho. Surg. ENT Dept. St. Thos. Hosp.

BOND, Glenys Mary (retired) 25A Chantry Road, Moseley, Birmingham B13 8DL — MRCS Eng. LRCP Lond. 1942. Prev: Sen. Med. Off. Family Plann. W. Midl. RHA & Solihull HA.

BOND, Graham Scott Road Medical Centre, Scott Road, Selby YO8 4BL Tel: 01757 700231 Fax: 01757 213647; Moat Cottage, Sherburn St, Caewood, Selby YO8 3SS — BM BS 1981 Nottm.; BMedSci Nottm. 1979; MRCGP 1987. (Nottm.) GP Princip. Prev: SHO (O & G) Manor Hosp. Walsall; Regist. (Med.) Hawkes Bay Hosp. Bd. NZ; SHO (Med.) St. Luke's Hosp. Bradford.

BOND, Helen Rosemary Hounslow and Spellthorne Community and Mental Health NHS TrustDepartment of Psychiatry, Ashford Hospital, London Road, Ashford TW15 3AA Tel: 01784 884200 Fax: 01784 884178 — MB BS Lond. 1968; MRCS Eng. LRCP Lond. 1968; MRCPsych 1979; T(Psychiat.) 1991. (Char. Cross) Cons. Psychiat. Ashford Hosp. Middlx. Prev: Sen. Regist. (Psychiat.) Char. Cross Hosp. Lond.

BOND, Hilary Elwyn Kingsmill 13 Alfred Terrace, Chipping Norton OX7 5HB Tel: 01608 641270; Masefield House, Boars Hill, Oxford OX1 5EY Tel: 01865 735373 — MB ChB 1988 Bristol. Clin. Asst. (A & E) Stoke Mandeville Hosp. Aylesbury. Prev: Clin. Asst. (A & E) Horton Gen. Hosp. NHS Trust Banbury; Clin. Asst. Oxf. Blood Transfus. Serv. John Radcliffe Hosp. Oxf.

BOND, Hugh Robertson Lester The Three Swans Surgery, Rollestone Street, Salisbury SP1 1DX Tel: 01722 333548 Fax: 01722 503626 — MB ChB 1989 Bristol; BSc (Hons.) Anat. Sci. Bristol; MRCGP 1994; DCH RCP Lond. 1993. (Bristol) Clin. Asst. (A & E) Salisbury Dist. Hosp.; Chairm. Wilcodoc (Out-of-Hours CoOperat.). Prev: Trainee GP/SHO (Geriat. Med.) Salisbury VTS; SHO (A & E & ENT) S.mead Hosp. Bristol.

BOND, Ian Douglas 3F3, 74 Leamington Terrace, Edinburgh EH10 4J — MB ChB 1989 Dundee.

BOND, Mr Kenneth Edgar c/o Coutts & Company (Adelaide Branch), 440 Strand, London WC2R 0QS; Castle Orchard House, Bungay NR35 1DD Tel: 01986 892246 — MRCS Eng. LRCP Lond. 1936; MB BChir Camb. 1938; MA Camb. 1938; FRCS Eng. 1941. (Camb. & St. Thos.) Cons. Surg. Europ. Hosp. Trust & Breach Candy Hosp. Bombay; Cons. Surg. Dis. of Colon & Rectum Bombay Hosp. & Masina Hosp. Bombay. Socs: Fell. Roy. Soc. Med.; FZS. Prev: Resid. Surgic. Off. St. Mark's Hosp. Dis. Rectum; Surg. Hampstead Gen. Hosp.; Sen. Regist. (Surg.) N. W.. Hosp. (Air Raid Surg.).

BOND, Lindsay Royston Tel: 01904 725854 Fax: 01904 453894 Email: lee.bond@excha.yhs-tr.northy.nhs.uk — MB BS 1979 Lond.; BSc (Hons.) Lond. 1976; FRCP Lond. 1996; MRCP (UK) 1983; MRCPath 1988; FRCPATH 1997. (St. Geo.) Cons. Haemat. York Dist. Hosp. Socs: Coun. Mem. York Med. Soc. Prev: Lect. & Hon. Sen. Regist. (Haemat.) St. Geo. Hosp. Med. Sch. Lond.; Regist. (Haemat.) King's Coll. Hosp. Lond.; SHO (Med.) Roy. Marsden Hosp. Surrey.

BOND, Margaret Eleanor 39 Osborne Avenue, Newcastle upon Tyne NE2 1JS; Woodburn, Benton Bank, Jesmad, Newcastle upon Tyne NE7 7BH Tel: 0191 265 5581 — MB BS 1990 Newc.; MRCGP 1996. (Newcastle upon Tyne) Staff Grade (Paediat. Immunol.) Newc. Gen. Hosp. Socs: BMA. Prev: Trainee GP/Regist. Wylam Surg. N.d.; SHO (Palliat. Med.) St. Oswalds Hospice Leeds; SHO (O & G) Dryburn Hosp. Durh.

BOND, Margaret Jean (retired) Glenside, 5 Bradda Glen Close, Porterin IM6 1HA Tel: 01624 832817 — MB ChB 1948 Liverp.; FFCM 1983, M 1974; DPH Liverp. 1972. Cons. Pub. Health Med. Wigan HA. Prev: Sen. Med. Off. (Clin.) Div. 10 Lancs. CC.

BOND, Mark David Inglis Ainsdale Village Surgery, 2 Leamington Road, Southport PR8 3LB Tel: 01704 577866 Fax: 01704 576644 — MB ChB 1985 Manch.; MRCGP 1991; DCH RCP Lond. 1990.

BOND, Michael Reaside Clinic, Rubery, Birmingham B45 9BE Tel: 0121 678 3000 Fax: 0121 678 3014 — MB ChB 1981 Birm.; MRCPsych 1985. Cons. Forens Psychiat. Reaside Clinic Birm.; Sen. Clin. Lect. (Psychiat.) Univ. Birm. Prev: Sen. Regist. (Forens. Psychiat.) W. Midl. VTS; Regist. (Psychiat.) Birm. Train. Scheme; SHO (Psychiat.) Hollymoor Hosp. Birm.

BOND, Professor Sir Michael Richard 2 The Square, University of Glasgow, University Avenue, Glasgow G12 8QQ Tel: 0141 330 3692 Fax: 0141 330 4605 Email: mrblw@salyut.mis.gla.ac.uk; 33 Ralston Road, Bearsden, Glasgow G61 3BA Tel: 0141 942 4391 — MB ChB 1961 Sheff.; PhD Sheff. 1971, MD 1965; FRCP Glas. 1981 M 1976; FRCS Ed. 1969; FRCPsych 1981 M 1971; DPM Eng. 1966; DSc (Hon. Leics) 1996; FRS (Ed.) 1998; FRCA (Hons) 1999. (Sheff.) Emerit. Prof. of Psychol. Med., Glas. Univ. Socs: (Pres.) Brit. Pain Soc.; (Pres-Elect) Internat. Assoc. for the Study of Pain. Prev: Prof. Psychol. Med. Univ. of Glas.; Asst. Lect. (Surg. & Psychiat.) Univ. of Sheff.; Lect. (Neurosurg.) Univ. of Glas.

BOND, Michelle Lorraine 7 Hall Close, Kislingbury, Northampton NN7 4BQ — MB ChB 1994 Bristol.

BOND, Paul Robert Reeth Surgery, Reeth, Richmond DL11 6ST Tel: 01748 884396 Fax: 01748 884250 — MB BS 1975 Lond.; MRCP (UK) 1978; MRCGP 1986. (King's Coll. Hosp. Lond.) Prev: Regist. (Med.) Hillingdon Hosp. Uxbridge.

BOND, Reginald The Surgery, Stonehouse, Winchcombe, Cheltenham GL54 5LL Tel: 01242 602307; Churchwell, Gretton, Cheltenham GL54 5EU Tel: 01242 602446 — MB ChB 1965 Ed.; DObst RCOG 1970; MRCGP 1971. (Ed.) Socs: BMA. Prev: SHO (Obst.) Ayrsh. Centr. Hosp. Irvine; Ho. Phys. & Cas. Off. Leith Hosp. Edin.

BOND, Richard Geoffrey 2 Horseshoes Place, Thame OX9 3LL Tel: 01844 214658 Email: blackhed@msn.com — MB BS 1990 Lond.; FRCS Lond. 1995. (Roy. Free Hospital School of Medicines) Specialist Regist. - Oxf.

BOND, Richard Ian Bridge Road Surgery, 1A Bridge Road, Oufton Broad, Lowestoft NR32 3LJ Tel: 01502 565936 Fax: 01502 531539; 8 Fern Avenue, Oulton Broad, Lowestoft NR32 3JF Tel: 01502 586196 — MB BS 1975 Lond. (Middlesex Hosp.)

BOND, Sarah Elizabeth Louise The Health Centre, North St., Kingsclere, Newbury RG20 5QX Tel: 01635 296000 Fax: 01635 299282 — BM 1983 Soton.; MRCGP 1992.

BOND, Shirley Angeline 54 Harbut Road, Battersea, London SW11 2RB — MB BS 1960 Lond.; MRCS Eng. LRCP Lond. 1960; FFA RCS Eng. 1967; DA Eng. 1963. (Lond. Hosp.) Socs: Roy. Soc.

Med. Prev: Sen. Regist. W.m. Hosp. & St. Thos. Hosp. Lond.; Regist. Roy. Marsden Hosp. Lond.

BOND, Mr Stanley Arthur 77 Hallam Street, London W1N 5LR — MB ChB 1937 Glas.; FRCS Eng. 1949; MRCOG 1941.

BOND, Stephen Edward 4 Heol-y-Graig, Porthcawl CF36 5PB — MB BS 1997 Lond.

BOND, Susan Adelaide Medical Centre, 36 Adelaide Road, Andover SP10 1HA Tel: 01264 351144 Fax: 01264 358639; Springvale, Clatford Lodge, Anna Valley, Andover SP11 7DL Tel: 01264 362440 — BM BS 1983 Nottm.; BMedSci (1st cl.) Nottm. 1981; DRCOG 1986; Cert. Family Plann. JCC 1986. (Nottingham) p/t Area Occupat. Health Phys. Marks & Spencer Andover. Socs: Mem. Soc. Occupat.al Med.; Mem. Soc. Occupat.al Med. Prev: Trainee GP Englefield Green VTS; SHO (Psychiat.) Ashford Hosp. Middlx.; SHO (O & G) St. Peters Hosp. Chertsey.

BOND, Susanne Jane The Valley Surgery, 81 Bramcote Lane, Chilwell, Nottingham NG9 4ET Tel: 0115 943 0530 Fax: 0115 943 1958 — MB ChB 1990 Sheff.; MRCGP 1994. Prev: Trainee GP Notts. VTS.

BOND, Sylvia Louise Western Road Medical Centre, 99 Western Road, Romford RM1 3LS Tel: 01708 746495 Fax: 01708 737936; 2 Ashlyn Grove, Hornchurch RM11 2EG Tel: 014024 43732 — MB ChB 1986 Bristol; MRCGP 1992; DCH RCP Lond. 1990; DRCOG 1989. Prev: Trainee GP Portsmouth VTS.

BOND, Timothy Peter Branley Bar, Old Hill, Flyford Flavell, Worcester WR7 4DA — MB ChB 1997 Leeds.

BOND, Winifrid Margaret (retired) The Cottage, Windmill Hill, Ashill, Ilminster TA19 9NT Tel: 01823 480362 — MB BS 1944 Lond.; MRCS Eng. LRCP Lond. 1940; MFCM 1973; DObst RCOG 1948; DCH Eng. 1950. Prev: Ho. Phys. EMS Horton Hosp. Epsom.

BONDE, Kristina Charleton, Colinsburgh, Leven KY9 1HG — Lakarexamen Stockholm 1978.

BONDS, Peter Richard The Surgery, Yeoman Lane, Bearsted, Maidstone ME14 4DS Tel: 01622 737326/738344 Fax: 01622 730745 — MB BS 1970 Lond.; MRCS Eng. LRCP Lond. 1970. (Westm.)

BONE, Adam David Watney Riverside House, Stoke Road, Clare, Sudbury — MB BS 1990 Lond.

BONE, Alan Richard Southwell House, Back Lane, Rochford SS4 1AY Tel: 01702 545241/2; 63 Lingfield Drive, Rochford SS4 1DZ Tel: 01702 544835 — MB BS 1957 Lond.; DObst RCOG 1959. (Middlx.) Socs: BMA. Prev: Ho. Phys. Middlx. Hosp. Lond.; Ho. Surg. & Ho. Off. (O & G) Centr. Middlx. Hosp.; Squadron Ldr. RAF Med. Br.

BONE, Andrea Mary The Atherstone Surgery, 1 Ratcliffe Road, Atherstone CV9 1EU Tel: 01827 713664 Fax: 01827 713666; 9 Moorcroft Close, Nuneaton CV11 6TB — MB ChB 1984 Leic.; MB ChB Leic. l984; DRCOG 1987. GP Atherstone Warks. Prev: SHO/Trainee GP Nuneaton Hosps. VTS.

BONE, Angela Department for International Development (DFID), 94 Victoria Street, London SW1E 5JL; Email: angie.bone@virgin.net — MB ChB 1991 Manch.; DTM & H 1995 Liverpool; MSc 2001 Pub Health in Dev Countries Lond.; MRCP Lond. 1994. (Manchester) Assoc. Professional Off. Health & Populat. Div., DFID.

BONE, Christine Elizabeth Killawarra, 3 Woodend, Forres IV36 0WZ — MB ChB 1979 Manch.

BONE, Mr Colin Douglas Macleod Hirondelle House, Flitcham, King's Lynn PE31 6BX Tel: 01485 600272 Fax: 01485 600583 Email: colinbone@flitcham.demon.co.uk — MB BChir Camb. 1969; MA Camb. 1974, BA 1966; FRCOG 1992, M 1976; DObst RCOG 1973; DA Eng. 1972. (Camb. & Lond. Hosp.) Cons. O & G Qu. Eliz. Hosp. King's Lynn & N. Cambs. Hosp. Wisbech. Socs: BMA & HCSA.; Brit. Soc. Gyn. Endoscopy. Prev: Sen. Regist. (O & G) St Geo. Hosp. Lond.; Regist. (O & G) Harold Wood Hosp. & St Mary's Hosp. Paddington.

BONE, David Department of Child & Family Psychiatry, Queen Elizabeth Hospital, Sheriff Hill, Gateshead NE9 6SX Tel: 0191 482 0000 Ext: 2396 — MB ChB 1979 Ed.; MRCPsych 1984.

BONE, David Harbord (retired) c/o Mrs. N.C.H. Crane, 8 Bromley College, London Road, Bromley BR1 1PE Tel: 020 846 4578 — MRCS Eng. LRCP Lond. 1942. Prev: Med. Asst. Leybourne Grange Hosp. W. Malling.

BONE, Francis James Area Department Bacteriology, Dumfries & Galloway Royal Infirmary, Bankend Road, Dumfries DG1 4AP Tel: 01387 246246 Fax: 01387 241367 Email: f.bone@dgri.scot.nhs.uk — MB BS Durh. 1966; FRCPath 1985, M 1973. (Newc.) Cons. Bacteriol. Area Dept. Bact. Dumfries & Galloway Roy. Infirm. Socs: Assn. Clin. Path.(Past Pres. 1994-97); Scott. Microbiol. Assn.; Brit. Infec. Soc. Prev: Sen. Regist. Centr. Microbiol. Laborats. W.. Gen. Hosp. Edin.; Regist. (Microbiol.) Roy. Vict. Infirm. Newc.; Demonst. (Microbiol.) Med. Sch. Univ. Newc.

BONE, Professor Ian Institute of Neurological Sciences, Sothern General Hospital, 1345 Govan Road, Glasgow G51 4TF Tel: 0141 201 2468 Fax: 0141 201 2993 Email: bone@dgib.epulse.net; Bardistane, 3 Ossian Road, Newlands, Glasgow G43 2JJ Tel: 0141 649 0721 Fax: 0141 569 7883 Email: ian_bone@yahoo.com — MB ChB 1970 St. And.; FRCP Lond. 1990; FRCP (Glas.) 1985; MRCP (UK) 1974; FRCP Ed 1996. Cons. Neurol. Inst. Neurol. Sci. S.. Gen. Hosp. Glas.; Hon. Clin. Prof. Univ. Glas. Socs: Fell. Assn. Phys. UK & Irel.; Fell. Assn. Brit. Neurologs.; Fell. Scot. Assn. Neurolog. Sci. Prev: Tutor (Neurol.) Univ. Leeds & Hon. Sen. Regist. (Neurol.) Leeds AHA (T); Regist. Inst. Neurol. Sci. S.. Gen. Hosp. Glas.; Regist. Stobhill Gen. Hosp. Glas.

BONE, James Charles Butler (retired) Greyladies, 42 The Street, Brooke, Norwich NR15 1JT Tel: 01603 558241 — MB BS Lond. 1936; MRCS Eng. LRCP Lond. 1936; MB BS 1936 Lond. Prev: GP Partner, Wolverhampton.

BONE, John Arthur St Pauls Medical Centre, St. Pauls Square, Carlisle CA1 1DG Tel: 01228 524354 Fax: 01228 616660; 2 The Orchard, Great Corby, Carlisle CA4 8LS — MB BS 1975 Newc.; BSc 1972 (Hons.) Newc.; MRCGP 1979. Gen. Practitioner, Carlisle; Police Surg., N. Cumbria; Occ. Health Adviser, Carnaud Metal Box; Occ. Health Adviser, Cumbrian Newspaper Gp.

BONE, John Michael Royal Liverpool Hospital, Prescott St., Liverpool L7 8XP Tel: 0151 709 0141 — MB ChB 1964 Ed.; FRCP London 1981; BSc Ed. 1961; FRCP Ed. 1979, M 1968. (Ed.) Cons. Nephrol. Liverp. AHA (T). Socs: Internat. Soc. Nephrol.; Renal Assn.; Europ. Dialysis & Transpl. Assn. Prev: Lect. Dept. Med. Univ. Edin.; Instruc. Washington Univ. Sch. Med. & Assoc. Phys. Jewish Hosp. St.; Louis, U.S.A.

BONE, John William Flitwick Surgery, The Highlands, Flitwick, Bedford MK45 1DZ Tel: 01525 712171 Fax: 01525 718756; Berrybrook, 27A Ampthill Road, Maulden, Bedford MK45 2DA Tel: 01525 405119 Fax: 01525 405119 Email: drbone@arsenalfc.net — MB ChB 1969 Liverp.; MRCGP 1975; DObst RCOG 1972; DCH Eng. 1971. Prev: SHO (Paediat. & O & G) Clatterbridge Hosp. Bebington.

BONE, Margaret Betts Avenue Medical Centre, 2 Betts Avenue, Benwell, Newcastle upon Tyne NE15 6TD Tel: 0191 274 2767/2842 Fax: 0191 274 0244; 2 Betts Avenue, Bentwell, Newcastle upon Tyne NE15 6TQ — MB ChB 1983 Manch.; BSc (Hons.) Physiol. Manch. 1980, MB ChB 1983; MRCGP 1987; DRCOG 1986. Prev: Trainee GP W. Wylam Health Centre N.ld.; Ho. Off. (Surg.) Qu. Eliz. Hosp. Gateshead; Ho. Off. (Med.) Dryburn Hosp. Durh.

BONE, Mark Paul 68 Musbury Street, London E1 0PL — MB ChB 1989 Leeds.

BONE, Michael Frederick South Tyneside District Hospital, Harton Lane, South Shields NE34 0PL Tel: 0191 454 8888 Fax: 0191 202 4180 — MB BS Lond. 1971; BSc (Biochem.) Lond. 1968; MRCP (UK) 1975; DCH Eng. 1974; FRCP 2000. (St. Geo.) Cons. (Phys.) S. Tyneside. Socs: BTS; BSACI; ERS. Prev: Cons. Phys. Gen. & Respirat. Med. Russells Hall Hosp. Dudley.; Sen. Regist. (Med. & Thoracic Med.) Birm.; Regist. (Med.) Univ. Hosp. Wales Cardiff.

BONE, Peter John Stanley (retired) 6 The Chowns, Harpenden AL5 2BN Tel: 0158 27 60354 — MB BS 1971 Lond.; DObst RCOG 1973. Prev: SHO (Paediat.) Watford Gen. Hosp.

BONE, Susannah Ruth 126 Stanley Road, Teddington TW11 8TX — MB ChB 1991 Otago.

BONG, Choon Looi 16/8 East Parkside, Edinburgh EH16 5XL — MB ChB 1997 Ed. SHO (Anaesth.).

BONG, Jan Jin 72 Beckhill Walk, Meanwood, Leeds LS7 2RW — MB ChB 1996 Leeds.

BONG, Jan Ling 68 Queenborough Gardens, Glasgow G12 9TU Tel: 0141 334 7973 Email: janlb1997@aol.com — MB ChB 1993 Dundee; MRCP (UK) 1997. SHO (Dermat.) Monklands Hosp. Prev: SHO (Med.) Stobhill Hosp.

BONGILLI, Joan Sunjuba Charters, Druidstone Road, St Mellons, Cardiff CF3 6XD — MB BS 1980 Lond.; MSc Wales 1997; DCH RCP Lond. 1986. Staff Grade (Community Paediat.) Cardiff; Staff

Grade (Paediat.) Univ. Hosp. Wales. Prev: Community Med. Off. (Child Health) Gwent HA; SHO (Neonat. Paediat.) S.mead Hosp. Bristol; SHO (Paediat.) Qu. Eliz. Hosp. Lond.

BONHAM, Dorothy Agnes Dykebar Hospital, Grahamston Road, Paisley PA2 7DE Tel: 0141 884 5122 Fax: 0141 884 7162 Email: dorothy.bonham@renver-pct.scot.nhs.uk — MB ChB 1980 Aberd.; BMedBiol Aberd. 1977; MRCPsych 1985. Cons. Psychiat. Renfrewsh. & Inverclyde Primary Care NHS Trust; Hon. Clin. Sen. Lect. Univ. Glas. Prev: Cons. Psychiat. Ayrsh. & Arran HB.

BONHAM, Trevor John Princess Medical Centre, Princess Street, Woodlands, Doncaster DN6 7LX Tel: 01302 723406 Fax: 01302 723433; Willowford Farm, Melton Mill Lane, High Melton, Doncaster DN5 7TE — MB ChB 1979 Liverp.; MSc Birm. 1969; BSc Liverp. 1963; DRCOG 1981. (Liverp.)

BONIFACE, Kathryn Jane 5 Ascot Road, Moseley, Birmingham B13 9EN — BM 1987 Soton.; MRCGP 1993; DCH RCP Lond. 1991. Prev: GP Woodstock.

BONIFACE, Simon John Department Clinical Neurophysiology, Addenbrooke's NHS Trust, Hills Road, Cambridge CB2 2QQ Tel: 01223 217136 Fax: 01223 336941; 42 Glisson Road, Cambridge CB1 2HF — MB BS 1983 Lond.; FRCP (UK) 1999; MA (Cambridge) 1998; MRCOphth 1989; BSc (Hons.) Lond. 1980, MD 1991. (Univ. Coll. Hosp.) Cons. Clin. Neurophysiol. Addenbrooke's NHS Trust Camb.; Assoc. Lect. Fac. of Clin. Med. Univ. of Camb. Socs: Brit. Soc. Clin. Neurophysiol.; Osler Club Lond.; Assn. Brit. Clin. Neurophysiol. Prev: Sen. Regist. (Clin. Neurophysiol.) Radcliffe Infirm. Oxf.; MRC Train. Fell. Univ. Dept. Clin. Neurol. Oxf. & William Carleton Gibson Jun. Research Fell. Green Coll. Oxf.; SHO (Neurol.) Nat. Hosp. Nerv. Dis. Lond.

BONIKOWSKI, Edmund Jan Medical Rehabilitation, Hounslow & Spelthorne, Community & Mental Health NHS Trust, West Middlesex University Hospital, Twickenham Road, Isleworth TW7 6AF Tel: 020 8565 5798; 211 Jersey Road, Osterley, Isleworth TW7 4RE Tel: 020 8847 0231 — MB BS 1987 Lond.; BSc (Hons.) Mech. Engin. Bristol 1979; C Eng MIMech E 1992; MRCS Eng. LRCP Lond. 1986. (Char. Cross & Westm. Med. Sch.) Cons. Rehabil. Med. Hounslow & Spelthorne Community & Ment. Health Trust; Hon. Cons. Rehabil. Med. W. Middlx. Univ. Hosp. NHS Trust. Prev: Sen. Lect. & Hon. Cons. Rehabil. Char. Cross & W.m. Med. Sch. Lond.; Lect. & Hon. Sen. Regist (Rehabil.) Char. Cross & W.m. Med. Sch. Lond.; SHO Rotat. (Gen. Med.) Wexham Pk. Hosp. Slough & King Edwd. VII Hosp. Windsor.

BONINGTON, Suzanne Claire 48 Cresswell Grove, West Didsbury, Manchester M20 2NH Tel: 0161 445 7315 Email: alec@creswell.demon.co.uk — MB BS 1993 Lond.; BSc Epidemiol. & Med. Statistics Lond. 1990; MRCP (UK) 1996. Specialist Regist. (Radiol.) Manch. Train. Scheme. Prev: SHO (Med.) N.wick Pk. Hosp. Harrow.

BONN, Gillian Lowry, Bonn and Desai, Cairn Valley Medical Practice, Kirkgate, Dunscore, Dumfries DG2 0UQ Tel: 01387 820266 Fax: 01387 820562; Hillhead Cottage, Auldgirth, Dumfries DG2 0TS — MB ChB 1982 Aberd.; MRCGP 1987; DCCH RCP Ed. 1988; DRCOG 1986. Prev: SCMO Dumfries & Galloway HB.

BONN, John Anthony 1 Spencer House, Somerset Road, Wimbledon, London SW19 5HX Tel: 020 8946 2132 — MRCS Eng. LRCP Lond. 1961; MB BS (Hnrs.) Lond. 1961, DPM 1967; MRCP Lond. 1964; FRCPsych 1981 M 1971. (St. Bart.) Cons. i/c Stress Unit St. Bart. Hosp. Lond.; Sen. Lect. & Cons. Psychiat. St. Bart. & Hackney Hosp. Lond. Socs: Soc. Psychosomatic Research & Soc. Clin. Psychiatrs. Prev: Lect. Physiol. & Psychiat. St. Bart. Hosp. Med. Coll. Lond.; Regist. (Psychiat.) & Sen. Regist. (Psychiat.) Maudsley Hosp. Lond.

BONN, Simon Michael Joseph Cleveland Clinic, 12 Cleveland Road, St Helier, Jersey JE1 4HD Tel: 01534 722381/734121; Hamlet Farm, Rue de la Hambie, Houge Bie, St Saviour, Jersey JE2 7UQ Tel: 01534 51355 — MB BS 1979 Lond.; MRCGP 1985; DRCOG 1982. (St. Bart.)

BONN, Wendy Ann Willow Brook Health Centre, Birch Grove, Llanmartin, Newport NP18 2JB Tel: 01633 413258; Nannygoat Cottage, Common-y-Coed, Magor, Newport NP26 3AX Tel: 01633 880519 Fax: 01633 882147 — MB BS 1987 Lond.; BSc Lond. 1984, MB BS 1987.

BONNAR, Angela Jane Bonnar and Partners, Sunnyside Surgery, Hawkins Road, Penzance TR18 4LT Tel: 01736 63340 Fax: 01736 332116; Downs Barn Farm, St. Buryan, Penzance TR19 6DG — MB BS 1977 Newc.; DRCOG 1980.

BONNAR, Brian Charles Mountsandel Surgery, 4 Mountsandel Road, Coleraine BT52 1JB Tel: 028 7034 2650 Fax: 028 7032 1000 — MB BCh BAO 1988 Belf.; DRCOG 1991; DCH Dub. 1990; MRCGP 1991. Course Organiser (Gen. Pract.). Socs: Christ. Med. Fell.sh.

BONNAR, Grainne Elizabeth Hillhead Family Practice, 33 Stewartstown Road, Belfast BT11 9FZ Tel: 028 9028 6800 Fax: 028 9060 2944; 60 Harberton Park, Belfast BT9 6TT Email: grainne.bonnar@tibus.com — MB BCh BAO 1987 Belf.; MMedSci in Med. Educ. (Distinct.) 1998; DCH Dub. 1992; MRCGP 1991; DRCOG 1991. (Qu. Univ. Belf.) Course Organiser for GP Antrim area N. Irel. GP VTS; Assoc. Lect. (Health Assessm. for Nurse Practioners) Belf. Prev: Assoc. Lect. (Health Assessm. for Nurse Practitioners) Belf.

BONNAR, Sally Elizabeth Centre for Child Health, 19 Dudhope Terrace, Dundee DD3 6HH; Craigie Lodge, 12 Queen St, Perth PH2 0EQ — MB ChB 1975 Glas.; MRCPsych 1985. Cons. Child & Adolesc. Psychiat. Dundee Healthcare NHS Trust.

BONNARD, Mavis Anne (retired) Moon House, Brookland, Romney Marsh TN29 9RW Tel: 01797 344233 — MB BS 1961 Lond.; MRCS Eng. LRCP Lond. 1961. Prev: Assoc. Specialist (A & E) William Harvey Hosp. Ashford.

BONNE, Wiebe Rob Southfield Surgery, 12-16 Southfield Loan, Edinburgh EH15 1QR Tel: 0131 669 0686 Fax: 0131 669 2929; 1 Park Avenue, Edinburgh EH15 1JT — MB ChB 1960 Ed.

BONNELAME, Mr Thomas Douglas St. Louis, Victoria, Mahe, Seychelles; 34 Hazel Avenue, Kirkcaldy KY2 5EB Tel: 01592 201832 — MB BS 1983 Tasmania; BMedSc 1980; FRCS Ed. Ophth. 1992; MCOphth 1988; DO Glas. 1988. SHO (Ophth.) Vict. Hosp. Kirkcaldy.

BONNER, Claire Veronica 84 Constantine Road, London NW3 2LX — MB ChB 1993 Ed.

BONNER, Frank Ernest (retired) Middleton Farm, Little Hereford, Ludlow SY8 4LQ — MB BS 1951 Lond.

BONNER, Kathleen Mary 116 Westwood Park, London SE23 3QH — MB BCh BAO 1981 Dub.; MB BCh Dub. 1981.

BONNER, Philippa Margaret 25 Rectory Close, Marsh Gibbon, Bicester OX27 0HT — MB ChB Ed. 1965; DObst RCOG 1967. (Edinburgh) Med. Off. Dept. O & G Aylesbury Vale Matern. Unit Stoke Mandeville Hosp.

BONNER, Sarah Elizabeth 25 Rectory Close, Marsh Gibbon, Bicester OX27 0HT — MB BS 1996 Lond.; BSc (Hons.) Lond. 1993. (London Hospital Medical College) SHO (Transpl. Surg.) Addenbrooke's Hosp. Camb., SHO (Orthop. &Trauma), Hinchinbrooke Hosp., Huntingdon, Cambs; Basic Surgic. Trainee Addenbrooke's Camb. Prev: SHO (Gen. Surg.), Hinchingbrooke Hosp., Huntingdon, Cambs; SHO (Transpl.ing), Addenbrookes Hosp., Camb.; SHO (A&E.), Furness Gen. Hosp., Barrow-in-Furness.

BONNER, Stephen Michael Cheriton House, Department of Anaesthesia, James Cook University Hospital, Marton Road, Middlesbrough TS4 3BW — MB BS 1987 Newc.; MRCP (UK) 1990; FRCA 1994. Cons.(Anaes.) James Cook Univ. Hosp.; Edr., CPD Anaesth.; Hon. Clin. Lect., Univ. of Durh. Socs: BMA; Intens. Care Soc. Prev: Sen. Regist. (Anaesth. & ITU) Roy. Vict. Infirm. Newc.; Regist. Rotat. (Anaesth. & ITU) N.. Region; Regist. (Anaesth. & ITU) S. Cleveland Hosp.

BONNER-MORGAN, Barbara Mary 117 High Street, Gorleston-on-Sea, Great Yarmouth NR31 9RE Tel: 01493 440436 — MRCS Eng. LRCP Lond. 1960; FRCOphth 1991; DO RCS Eng. 1966. (St. Bart. Hosp. Lond.) Indep. Pract (Ophth.). Socs: Fell. Roy. Soc. Med.; BMA; Oxf. Ophth. Congr. Prev: Cons. Ophth. Bd. of Health Guernsey & P.ss Eliz. Hosp. Guernsey; Cons. Ophth. Vict., Austral.

BONNER-MORGAN, Geoffrey Richard (retired) 2 The Glade, Stoneleigh, Epsom KT17 2HB — MB BS Lond. 1955; MRCS Eng. LRCP Lond. 1955; DObst RCOG 1959.

BONNER-MORGAN, Robin Peter 117 High Street, Gorleston-on-Sea, Great Yarmouth NR31 9RE Tel: 01493 440436; 10 Harley Street, London W1N Tel: 020 7224 1202 — MB BS 1959 Lond.; MRCS Eng. LRCP Lond. 1959; FRCOphth 1992; FRACS (Ophth.) 1971; DO RCS Eng. 1965. (St. Bart. Lond.) Indep Pract. (Ophth.). Socs: Oxf. Ophth. Soc. Prev: Cons. Ophth. E. Dyfed HA, Bronglais Gen. Hosp. Aberystwyth; Cons. Ophth. Bd. of Health Guernsey, Channel Is.; Ophth. Vict., Austral.

BONNES, Thomas Mark Murray Road Surgery, 50 The Murray Road, East Kilbride, Glasgow G75 0RT Tel: 01355 225374 Fax: 01355 239475; 3 Trent Place, Broad Meadows, East Kilbride, Glasgow G75 8RU — MB ChB 1986 Ed.

BONNET, Joel Marc Herts Health Authority, Tonman House, 63 - 77 Victoria Street, St Albans AL1 3ER — MB BS 1981 Lond.; MSc Lond. 1996; MRCGP 1985; DRCOG 1983; MFPHM 1998. (Guy's) Cons., Pub. Health Med., Herts Health Auth. Socs: BMA. Prev: Pub. Health med Train.,Nthames RNA; Clin. Asst. Endoscopy Unit Hillingdon Hosp.

BONNET, Michel S The Surgery, 233 Wells Road, Bristol BS4 2DF Tel: 0117 977 0018 Fax: 0117 972 3428 — MB ChB 1978 Glas.; BSc Beirut 1969; Cert. Family Plann. JCC 1983; Cert. Prescribed Equiv. Exp. JCPTGP 1983; DRCOG 1980. (Univ. Glas. Med. Sch.) Prev: Chairm. SW Br. of Fac. of Homoeop. GB.

BONNET, Stephan Joseph Station Road Practice, 66-68 Station Road, Ainsdale, Southport PR8 3HW — MB ChB 1969 Liverp.; FRCGP 1996; MRCGP 1977; DObst RCOG 1972. Course Organiser Mersey Region. Prev: SHO (Psychiat.) & Ho. Off. (Obst.) W. Chesh. Hosp. Chester; SHO (Paediat.) Clatterbridge Hosp. Bebington.

BONNEVIE, Jonna Elisabeth Monteagle Surgery, Tesimond Drive, Yateley GU46 6FE Tel: 01252 878992 Fax: 01252 860677; Hollywell, Copes Lane, Bramshill, Hook RG27 0RQ Tel: 01734 326575 — MD 1972 Copenhagen.

BONNEY, Mr George Louis William 6 Wooburn Grange, Grange Drive, Wooburn Green, High Wycombe HP10 0QU Tel: 01628 525598 — MB BS Lond. 1943; MS Lond. 1947; FRCS Eng. 1945; MRCS Eng. LRCP Lond. 1943. (St. Mary's) Socs: Sen. Fell. BOA; Hon. Fell. Med. Defence Union; Fell. Roy. Soc. Med. Prev: Cons. Orthop. Surg. S.end-on-Sea Hosp. Gp.; Cons. Orthop. Surg. St. Mary's Hosp. Lond.; Surg. Lt. RNVR.

BONNEY, Gillian Department Anaesthesia, Pontefract General Infirmary, Friarwood Lane, Pontefract WF8 1 Tel: 01977 600600 — MB ChB Leic. 1984; FRCA Lond. 1992; DA (UK) 1986. (Leicester) p/t Cons. Anaesth. Pontefract Gen. Infirm. Pontefract.

BONNICI, Mr Albert Victor District General Hospital, King's Drive, Eastbourne BN21 2UD Tel: 01323 413726; Mylor Cottage, Upper Dicker, Hailsham BN27 3QJ Tel: 01323 845312 — MRCS Eng. LRCP Lond. 1979; FRCS Ed. 1985. (Sheff.) Cons. Orthop. Dist. Gen. Hosp. E.bourne. Socs: Brit. Orthop. Assn.; Brit. Trauma Soc.; Brit. Elbow & Shoulder Soc. Prev: Sen. Regist. (Orthop.) SE Thames RHA; Shoulder & Upper Limb Fell. Toronto, Canada; Research Assoc. (Orthop.) Guys Hosp. Lond.

BONNICI, Walter, Lt.-Col. RAMC 2 Hazelhurst Close, Burpham, Guildford GU4 7SP Tel: 01483 69911; 2 Hazel Hurst Close, Burpham, Guildford GU4 7SP Tel: 01483 824135 Email: elaine@kabon.demon.co.uk — MRCS Eng. LRCP Lond. 1977 University of Malta Med School; MRCGP 1987; DCH 1980.

BONNIN, Benedicte Lisa Torbay Hospital, Lawes Bridge, Torquay TQ2 7AA — MB BCh BAO 1992 Dub.

BONNINGTON, Ruth Margaret 10 Bewick Road, Gateshead NE8 4DP Tel: 0191 377 1536; Email: ruth.bonnington@fish.co.uk — BM BS 1987 Nottm.; MRCGP; DRCOG; BMed. Sci. Nottm. 1985. Prev: GP Chilwell Nottm.; Trainee GP Nottm. VTS.

BONNINGTON, Simon Paul Andre Hambledon Cottage, Water Lane, Somerton TA11 6RG Tel: 01458 272876 — MB ChB 1990 Bristol.

BONNYMAN, Sheena Dutton The Bungalow, Fleming Hospital, Aberlour AB38 9PR Tel: 01340 882110 Fax: 01340 882113; Fae.Me.Well, Cothal, Fintray, Aberdeen AB21 0HU Tel: 01224 722500 Fax: 01224 722066 — MB ChB Aberd. 1965; MRCPsych 1977; DPM Eng. 1970. (Aberd.) p/t Locum Cons. Psychiat., Ols Age Psychiat. The Bungalow, Fleming Hosp., Aberlour. Prev: Dir. Geriat. Psychiat. Alberta Hosp. Edmonton, Canada.; Cons. Psychiat. Bellsdyke Hosp. Larbert.; Asst. Prof. (Psychiat. & Behavioural Sc.) Creighton Univ. Sch. Med. Omaha, USA.

BONSALL, Adrian Mark 13 Fyfield Way, Littleton, Winchester SO22 6PB — MB BS 1997 Lond.

BONSALL, John Lytton The Old Coach House, Foxhill, Petworth GU28 0HE Tel: 01798 343833 Fax: 01798 344312 Email: 100754.3337@compuserve.com — MB BS 1975 Lond.; MRCS Eng. LRCP Lond. 1975; FFOM RCP Lond. 1992, MFOM 1985, AFOM 1980; DIH Eng. 1980; Cert. Av. Med. 1994. (Roy. Free) Indep. Cons. (Occupat. Phys.) W. Sussex. Socs: Soc. Occupat. Med.; IAPOS & BOHS. Prev: Chief Med. Off. IBM (UK) Ltd; Manager Safety, Health & Environm. ICI AgroChem.s; Div. Med. Off. Schering Agrochem. Ltd. Camb.

BONSALL, Peter Alexander Cubbington Road Surgery, 115 Cubbington Road, Leamington Spa CV32 7AJ Tel: 01926 425131 Fax: 01926 427254 — MB ChB 1990 Birm.; MRCGP 1994. (Birmingham)

BONSELL, Eric Michael The Medical Centre, 25 South King Street, Blackpool FY1 4NF Tel: 01253 290315 Fax: 01253 290315; 20 Elizabeth Close, Staining, Blackpool FY3 0EF Fax: 01253 290315 — MB ChB 1987 Manch.; BSc 1984 St. And.; MRCGP 1991. Gen. Med. Practitioner; Clin. Asst., Palliat. Care, Trinity Hospice, Blackpool.

BONSER, Mr Robert Stuart Queen Elizabeth Hospital, Queen Elizabeth Medical Centre, Edgbaston, Birmingham B15 2TH Tel: 0121 472 1311, 0121 627 2543 Fax: 0121 627 2542 Email: robert.bonser@university-b.wmids.nhs.uk — MB BCh 1977 Wales; FRCP 2001; FRCS 1989 (C/T); FRCS Eng. 1982; MRCP (UK) 1979. Cons. Cardiothoracic Surg. Qu. Eliz. Hosp. Birm.

BONSEY, Madeleine Marie Francine Church Cottage, Church Lane, Sidlesham, Chichester PO20 7RH — MB BS 1981 Lond.; DRCOG 1984.

BONSHEK, Richard Edward Academic Department of Ophthalmology, Royal Eye Hospital, Oxford Road, Manchester M13 9WH Tel: 0161 276 5568 Fax: 0161 273 6354 Email: richard.bonshek@man.ac.uk — MD 1978 CM McGill Canada; MA Oxf. 1981, BA Oxf. 1972; LMCC 1979; FRCPath 1997. (McGill) Lect. (Path. Med.) Sch. Univ. Manch.; Hon. Cons. Ophth. Path. Cent. Manch. Childr. Univ. Hosp.s NHS Trust. Socs: Brit. Assn. for Ocular-Path., (Mem.); Brit. NeuroPath. Soc., (Mem.); Path. Soc. of Gt. Britain & Irel., (Mem.). Prev: Sen. Regist. (Neuropath.) Sch. Univ. Manch.; Clin. Lect. (Neuropath.) Inst. Psychiat. Lond.; Clin. Lect. Nuffield Dept. Path. John Radcliffe Hosp. Headington.

BONSOR, Graham Bridge House, Main St., Weeton, Leeds LS17 0AY — MB ChB 1968 Birm.; FRCR 1975; DA Eng. 1971; DMRD Eng. 1973. Cons. Radiol. Leeds Gen. Infirm. Socs: BMA. Prev: Regist. (Radiol.) Nottm. Univ. Gp. Hosps.; Regist. (Anaesth.) Coventry Gp. Hosps.

BONSU, Augustine Kwaku 14 Lytcott Drive, West Molesey KT8 2TJ Tel: 020 8941 7596 Fax: 020 8941 7596 Email: lydia.b@which.net — MB ChB 1973 Ghana; FFA RCS Eng. 1981. (Ghana and Liverpool) Cons. (Anaesth.). Socs: Soc. Paediatric Anaesth.

BONTHALA, Chandra Mohan St Crispin Hospital, Duston, Northampton NN5 4UN Tel: 01604 52323; 8 Teal Close, Ladybridge Drive, Northampton NN4 9XF Tel: 0604 701195 — MB BS 1973 Osmania; MRCPsych 1980; DPM Eng. 1979. (Gandhi Med. Coll. Hyderadad) Cons. Psychiat. (Psychogeriat.) St. Crispin Hosp. N.ampton. Socs: Fell. Roy. Soc. Med.; Brit. Assn. Psycho-Pharmacol.; IMSA New Delhi, India. Prev: Sen. Regist. (Psychiat.) St. Crispin Hosp. N.ampton & Warneford & John Radcliffe Hosps. Oxf.

BONTHRON, Professor David Terry Molecular Medicine Unit, University of Leeds, St. James's University Hospital, Leeds LS9 7TF — BM BCh 1983 Oxf.; FRCPath 2001; MA Camb. 1984; MRCP (UK) 1989; FRCP Ed. 1998. Prof. of Molecular Paediat., Univ. of Leeds; Hon. Cons. Clin. Genetics , Leeds Teachg. Hosp.s. Socs: Assoc. of Phys.s of GB & I. Prev: Prof. Med. Genetics Univ. Edin.; Leukaemia Research Fund Lect. Inst. Molecular Med. Oxf.; Fell. Paediat. Harvard Med. Sch.

BONWICK, Helen Elizabeth 60 Church Street, Milnthorpe LA7 7DZ — MB ChB 1988 Liverp.

BONWITT, Caroline The Foreland Medical Centre, 188 Walmer Road, London W11 4EP Tel: 020 7727 2604 Fax: 020 7792 1261 — MB BS 1972 London; MB BS 1972 London.

BOOBIS, Mr Leslie Harold 36 Osbaldeston Gardens, Newcastle upon Tyne NE3 4JE Tel: 0191 285 0190 Email: les.boobis@virgin.net — MB ChB 1973 Glas.; MD 1988; FRCS Eng. 1979; FRCS Ed. 1979. (Glasgow) Cons. Gen. Surg. Sunderland Roy. Hosp.; Sen. Lect. (Surg.) Univ. of Newc. Socs: Assn. Surg.; Vasc. Surg. Soc. Gt. Brit. & Irel.; Eur. Soc. Vasc. Surg. Prev: Sen. Regist. (Surg.) Leicester AHA; Regist. (Surg.) Leicester AHA; Clin. Research Fell. Univ. Leicester.

BOOBYER, Malcolm David 6 Rounds Hill, Kenilworth CV8 1DU Tel: 01926 53162 — MB ChB 1964 Birm.; FFA RCS Eng. 1970; DA

Eng. 1967; DObst RCOG 1966. (Birm.) Cons. Anaesth. Coventry DHA. Socs: Assn. Anaesths. & Midl. Soc. Anaesths. Prev: Sen. Regist. (Anaesth.) Midl. Area Train. Scheme; Regist. (Anaesth.) United Birm. Hosps.; Ho. Phys. & Ho. Surg. United Birm. Hosps.

BOOCOCK, Anne Margaret South London and Maudsley NHS Trust, 108 Landor Road, Stockwell, London SW9 9LT Tel: 020 7411 6100 — MB BS 1985 Lond.; MSc Lond. 1992; MRCPsych 1990. Clin. Director, Lambeth Adult Ment. Health; Cons. & Hon. Sen. Lect. S. Lond. Maudsley NHS Trust. Prev: Sen. Regist. (Psychiat.) Roy. Free Hosp. Lond.

BOOCOCK, Geraldine Rose Ormskirk District General Hospital, Wigan Road, Ormskirk L39 2AZ Tel: 01695 577111 Fax: 01695 583148; Hazelmere, 28 Winifred Lane, Aughton, Ormskirk L39 5DJ Tel: 01695 422732 Email: grb@aughton.u-net.com — MB ChB 1976 Manch.; FRCP Lond. 1995; FRCP Lond. 1994; MRCP (UK) 1980; DCH Eng. 1978. (Manch.) S.port & Ormskirk Hosp. NHS Trust. Prev: Sen. Regist. (Paediat.) Booth Hall, St. Mary's & Wythenshawe Hosps. Manch.; Cons. Paediat. Ormskirk Dist. Gen. Hosp. & S.port Dist. Gen. Hosp.

BOOCOCK, Olivia Kate 1 Gosford House, Tredegar Rd, London E3 2HG — MB BS 1997 Lond.

BOODHOO, Mata Gowri 4 Tangier Road, Guildford GU1 2DE Tel: 01483 68619 — MB BS 1967 Lond.; FRCS Ed. 1973; DO Eng. 1970. (Roy. Free) Socs: U.K.ISC.R.S. Prev: Sen. Regist. (Ophth.) Lambeth Hosp. Lond.; Cons. Ophth. St. Peter's Hosp. Chertsey.

BOODHUN, Roy 125 Dellfield, St Albans AL1 5HA — MB ChB 1996 Manch.

BOOG-SCOTT, Thomas James Tel: 01584 872939 Fax: 01584 876490; 2 The Barns, Pipe Aston, Ludlow SY8 2G Tel: 01584 831347 — MB BChir 1976 Camb.; MA Camb. 1973; MRCS Eng. LRCP Lond. 1975; MRCGP 1981; DRCOG 1981; DCH RCP Lond. 1981; Cert. Family Plann. JCC 1979. (Camb. & Char. Cross) Clin. Asst. (Geriat.) Ludlow Hosp. Prev: Sen. Resid. King Edwd. VII Memor. Hosp. Hamilton, Bermuda; SHO/Trainee GP Plymouth VTS.

BOOGERT, Theodorus Hendricus Wilhelmus Cornerways Practice, School Lane, Ringwood BH24 1LG — Artsexamen 1989 Nijmegen.

BOOHAN, Tara Louise 27 Talbot Road, London N6 4QS — MB BS 1994 Lond.

BOOHENE, Jeanette Anima 98 Ancrum Street, Spital Tongues, Newcastle upon Tyne NE2 4LR — MB BS 1996 Newc.; BSc Newc. 1991. SHO (Gen. Med.) Darlington Memor. Hosp. Prev: SHO (Elderly Care Med.) Darlington Memor. Hosp.

BOOKER, Dawn Agnes Avonmead Ward, Southmead Hospital, Westbury on Trym, Bristol BS10 5NB; 21 Dorcas Avenue, Stoke Gifford, Bristol BS34 8XG — MB BCh 1989 Wales; T(GP) 1993. Clin. Med. Off. (Psychiat. of Old Age) S.mead Hosp. Bristol. Prev: Trainee GP W. Glam. VTS.

BOOKER, Diane Florence Bryn-Tirion, Highfield Road, Osbaston, Monmouth NP25 3HR Tel: 01600 772918 — MB ChB 1969 Sheff.

BOOKER, Joseph Martin Crossley Practice, 16 Henley Road, Coventry CV2 1LP; 23 Lavenham Close, Slade View, Nuneaton CV11 6GP — MB ChB 1980 Birm.; T(GP) 1991; DRCOG 1984. (Birm.) Bd. Mem. Coventry E. PCG. Prev: Clin. Asst. (Ment. Handicap) Narberth Way Home Coventry; Trainee GP/SHO Hastings Dist. VTS; SHO (Accid & Orthop.) Burton Dist. Hosp. Centre.

BOOKER, Kathleen Mary Noëlle Gull Cottage, 27 Farrier St., Deal CT14 6JR — LRCPI & LM, LRSCI & LM 1953; LRCPI & LM, LRCSI & LM 1953; LAH Dub. 1952. (RCSI)

BOOKER, Mr Michael William Department of Obstetrics & Gynaecology, Mayday University Hospital, London Road, Croydon CR7 7YE Tel: 020 8401 3000 Fax: 020 8657 0755 Email: mbooker@uk-consultants.co.uk; 235 Banstead Road, Banstead SM7 1RB Tel: 020 8786 7855 Fax: 020 8657 0755 — MB ChB 1978 Liverp.; 1978 MB ChB Liverp.; 1984 MRCOG; 2000 FRCOG. (Liverpool) Cons. O & G Mayday Univ. Hosp. Croydon; Dist. Tutor RCOG. Socs: Amer. Fertil. Soc.; Roy. Soc. Med. & Mem. Brit. Fertil. Soc.; Eur. Soc. Human Reproduct. Prev: Cons. O & G Mayday Univ. Hosp. Croydon; Lect. & Hon. Sen. Regist. (O & G) King's Coll. Hosp. Lond.

BOOKER, Nigel Jeremy Dr N J Booker, Prices Mill Surgery, Newmarket Rd, Nailsworth, Stroud GL6 0DQ Tel: 01453 832424 Fax: 01453 833833; 6 The Hill, Merrywalks, Stroud GL5 4EP Tel: 01453 753375 — MB ChB 1974 Birm.; MRCGP 1978; DRCOG 1976.

BOOKER, Pamela Longfield Medical Centre, Princes Road, Maldon CM9 5DF Tel: 01621 856811 Fax: 01621 852627 — MB BS 1966 Lond.; MRCS Eng. LRCP Lond. 1966; MRCGP 1984; DA Eng. 1968. (Roy. Free) Prev: Ho. Surg. & Ho. Phys. St. Richard's Hosp. Chichester; SHO (Anaesth.) Roy. W. Sussex Hosp. Chichester.

BOOKER, Peter Driscoll Dept. Anaesthesia, RLCH, EAton Rd, Liverpool L12 2AP Tel: 0151 252 5460 Email: peterdb@liv.ac.uk — MB BS 1973 Lond.; FFA RCS Eng. 1977. (Lond. Hosp.) Sen. Lect. (Paediatric Anaesth.), Univ. of Liverp. Prev: Cons. Paediat. Anaesth. Roy. Liverp. Childr. Hosp.

BOOKER, Ruth Janet (retired) St Johns Health Centre, Oak Lane, Twickenham TW1 3PA Tel: 020 8891 0073 Fax: 020 8744 0060 — MB BS 1966 Lond.; MRCS Eng. LRCP Lond. 1966.

BOOKLESS, Alec Smeed, TD (retired) 9 Churchway, Sanderstead, South Croydon CR2 0JS Tel: 020 8657 2472 — MB BChir 1938 Camb.; MD Camb. 1940, MA, MB BChir 1938; MRCS Eng. LRCP Lond. 1935; FRCGP 1969. Hon. Lt.-Col. RAMC, TA. Prev: Med. Specialist RAMC.

BOOKLESS, David William (retired) 38 Parkland Crescent, Horning, Norwich NR12 8PJ Tel: 01692 630346 — MB ChB 1950 Ed.; DPH Eng. 1957; FFCM 1977, M 1972. Prev: Dist. Med. Off. Norwich HA.

BOOKLESS, Douglas John Throckley Surgery, Back Victoria Terrace, Throckley, Newcastle upon Tyne NE15 9AA Tel: 0191 267 4005 Fax: 0191 229 0646 Email: john.bookless@th9.nant-ha.northy.nhs.uk — MB BS 1974 Newc.; FRCGP; MRCGP 1978. GP Tutor, W. Locality, Newc. PCT/ Newc. Univ.; Chair W. Locality Newc. PCT; Teachg. Assoc. Dept. Primary Health Care, Newc. Univ.; GP Trainer, N.umbria V.T.S.

BOOLELL, Mitradev Charing Cross Hospital, Fulham Palace Road, London W6 8RF; Flat 8, Rosiers Court, St Dunstans St, Canterbury CT2 8DA — MB ChB 1981 Bristol; MRCP (UK) 1985. Research Fell. (Endocrinol. & Physiol.) Char. Cross Hosp. Lond. Prev: Regist. (Neurol.) Walton Hosp. Liverp.; Regist. (Med.) Roy. Liverp. Hosp.; SHO (Med. & Haemat.) N. Middlx. Hosp. Lond.

BOOLS, Christopher Nigel Child & Family Therapy Service, Chippenham Family Health Centre, Goldney Avenue, Chippenham SN15 1ND Tel: 01249 656321 Fax: 01249 461351 — MB ChB 1981 Manch.; MMedSc Leeds 1987; MRCPsych 1986. (Manchester) Cons. Child & Adolesc. Psychiat.Avon & Wilts. Ment. Health Care Trust. Prev: Sen. Regist. (Child Psychiat.) Yorks. HA; Regist. (Psychiat.) Leeds HA.

BOOM, Steven John 7 Dolphin Road, Pollokshields, Glasgow G41 4LE — MB BS 1984 Lond.

BOOMERS, Gystberta Wilhelmina Maria 123 Wilbury Road, Letchworth SG6 4JG — Artsexamen 1986 Groningen; MRCGP 1993.

BOOMERS, Oscar Wiro 123 Wilbury Road, Letchworth SG6 4JG — Artsexamen 1985 Groningen; FRCA 1993.

BOOMLA, Darius Fardoon, MBE (retired) 58 Rennets Wood Road, Elthamn, London SE9 2ND Tel: 020 8850 9943 — MB BS 1953 Lond.; MCOphth 1964.

BOOMLA, Kambiz Roointan Faridoon Chrisp Street Health Centre, 100 Chrisp Street, London E14 6PG Tel: 020 7515 4860 Fax: 020 7515 3055; 61 Chesterton Road, London E13 8BD Tel: 020 8552 0791 — MB BChir 1977 Camb.; MB Camb. 1977, BChir 1976; MRCP (UK) 1979; FRCGP 1996; DRCOG 1980. (Cambridge & St. Bartholomews)

BOOMLA, Roointon Faridoon 62 Parkhurst Road, Bexley DA5 1AS Tel: 01322 525510 — MB, BS Lond. 1941; DPhysMed. Eng. 1970. (St. Bart.) Socs: Hunt. & NW Kent M-C Socs.

BOOMLA, Soraya St Stephens Health Centre, Bow Community Hall, William Place, London E3 5ED Tel: 020 8980 1760 Fax: 020 8980 6619 — MB BS 1982 Lond.

BOON, Andrew Peter Department Histopathology, St James's University Hospital, Beckett St., Leeds LS9 7TF Tel: 0113 206f 4582 Fax: 0113 206 5943 Email: andrew.boon@leedsth.nh.uk — MB ChB 1981 Birm.; MD Birm. 1992; MRCPath (Histopath.) 1988; FRCPath 1997. (Birmingham) Cons. Path. St Jas. Univ. Hosp. Leeds; Sen. Clin. Lect. (Path.) Univ. Leeds; Div.al Med. Director, Leeds Teachg. Hosps. NHS Trust. Socs: Brit. Soc. Clin. Cytol.; Assn. Clin.

Path.; Brit. Soc. Dermatopath. Prev: Lect. (Path.) Univ. Birm.; Hon. Sen. Regist. W. Midl. RHA.

BOON, Andrew Webster Department of Paediatrics, Royal Berkshire Hospital, London Road, Reading RG1 5AN Tel: 0118 987 7525 Fax: 0118 987 8383 Email: andrew.boon@+bbh-tr.nhs.uk; Little Chesters, The Street, Eversley RG27 0PJ Fax: 0181 973 1567 — MB BS 1971 Lond.; MB BS (Hons.) Lond. 1971; BSc (Hons. Physiol.) Lond. 1968, MD 1981; FRCP Lond. 1992; MRCP (UK) 1974; MRCS Eng. LRCP Lond. 1971; FRCPCH 1997; DCH Eng. 1975. (St. Bart.) Cons. Paediat. Roy. Berks. Hosp. Reading. Socs: Reading Path. Soc. Prev: Sen. Lect. & Hon. Cons. Paediat. N.. Gen. Hosp. Sheff.; Sen. Regist. Hosp. Sick Childr. Gt. Ormond St. Lond.; Research Fell. (Paediat.) City Hosp. Nottm.

BOON, Catherine Sheila Whitley House Surgery, Moulsham Street, Chelmsford CM2 0JJ Tel: 01245 352194 Fax: 01245 344478 — BChir 1989 Camb.; MRCGP 1995; DCH RCP Lond. 1993; DRCOG 1992.

BOON, Mr Francis James 26 Greenacres, Fulwood, Preston PR2 7DA — MB BS 1971 Newc.; FRCS Ed. 1977. Cons. Rehabil. Med. Roy. Preston Hosp. Prev: Demonst. (Anat.) Univ. Newc.; Regist. (Thoracic Surg.) Seaham Hall Hosp. Seaham Harbour; Regist. (Orthop. Surg.) Roy. Vict. Infirm. Newc.

BOON, Frank Webster (retired) 8 Hillfort Close, Dorchester DT1 2QT Tel: 01305 262775 — MB BS Durh. 1935; MRCGP 1958. Prev: Treasury Med. Off.

BOON, Helen Mary Dow Surgery, William Street, Redditch B97 4AJ Tel: 01527 62285 Fax: 01527 596260; 49 Malvern Road, Bromsgrove, Bromsgrove B61 7HE Tel: 01527 835550 — MB BS 1985 Lond.; DRCOG 1992; DCH RCP Lond. 1990; MRCGP Lond. 1996. (St. Bartholomew's Hospital Medical School) GP Partner. Socs: BMA; RCGP.

BOON, Jean Evelyn Balmore Park Surgery, 59A Hemdean Road, Caversham, Reading RG4 7SS Tel: 0118 947 1455 Fax: 0118 946 1766 — BM BS 1978 Nottm.; BMedSci 1976.

BOON, Julia Elizabeth Guilsborough Surgery, High Street, Guilsborough, Northampton NN6 8PU Tel: 01604 740210/740142 Fax: 01604 740869 — MB BS 1987 Newc.; MRCGP 1991; DRCOG 1989. Clin. Assist. Rheum.; Sen. C.M.O. Family Plann. Socs: BMA. Prev: Trainee GP N.ampton VTS.

BOON, Mark Richard 17 Churchill Drive, Spalding PE11 2RL Tel: 01775 761815 — MB BS 1994 Lond. GP Regist. Riverside VTS, Fulham, Lond. Prev: SHO (Psychiat.) Riverside Ment. Health Unit Chelsea & W.minster Hosp.; SHO (A & E) Chelsea & W.minster Hosp., Fulham Rd.

BOON, Nicholas Antony Department of Cardiology, Royal Infirmary Edinburgh, Lauriston Place, Edinburgh EH3 9YW Tel: 0131 536 2004 Fax: 0131 536 2021; 7 Cobden Crescent, Edinburgh EH9 2BG Fax: 0131 622 0184 — MB BChir 1976 Camb.; FRCP 1987 (Ed.); MA Camb.1976,BA (1st cl.HONs.) 1972, MD 1984; MRCP (UK) 1977; FESC 1996. Cons. Cardiol. Roy. Infirm. Edin.; Chairm. Hosp. care and professional Train. Comm. of Brit. heart Foundat., Counc. and executor Comm. of Brit. heart Foundat. Socs: Fell. Europ. Soc. Cardiol.; (Counc.) Brit. Cardiac Soc. Prev: Lect. (Cardiovasc. Med.) John Radcliffe Hosp. Oxf.

BOON, Rachel Louise Teviot Medical Practice, Teviot Road, Hawick TD9 9DT Tel: 01450 370999 Fax: 01450 371025 — MB ChB 1991 Birm.; MmRCGP 1998. Prev: SHO (Paediat.) Bradford HA.

BOON, Robert Leo Joseph 37 Reservoir Road, Liverpool L25 6HR — MB BS 1992 Lond.

BOON, Sarah Jane 21 The Mount, Wakefield WF2 8QP — MB BS 1993 Newc.

BOONE, Doron Lavee St George Health Centre, Bellevue Road, St. George, Bristol BS5 7PH Tel: 0117 961 2161 Fax: 0117 961 8761; Hambrook Court, Hambrook, Bristol BS16 1RY — MRCS Eng. LRCP Lond. 1978; BSc (1st cl.) Lond. 1975, MB BS 1978; MRCGP 1983. (Guy's)

BOONHAM, Janet Clare 54 Guelder Road, High Heaton, Newcastle upon Tyne NE7 7PP Tel: 0191 266 7502 — MB BS 1993 Newc. Career Start GP, Fulwell Health Centre, Sunderland.

BOONIN, Adrian Simon Bellbrooke Surgery, 395-397 Harehills Lane, Leeds LS9 6AP Tel: 0113 249 4848 Fax: 0113 248 4993; 61 Sandhill Oval, Leeds LS17 8EF Tel: 0113 269 5802 Email: adrian@boonin.freeserve.co.uk — MB ChB 1982 Leeds; MRCGP 1986; DRCOG 1985; Cert Family Plann. JCC 1986. GP Princip.; Sen. Clin. Lect. Acad. Unit of GP Leeds Univ.

BOORER, Caroline Gail The Old Rectory, Northfield Road, Quarrington, Sleaford NG34 8RT Tel: 01529 414214 Fax: 01529 414214 — MB BS 1974 Lond. (King's Coll. Hosp.) Dr. Reprod. Health Care, Marie Stopes Internat. (p/t); Community Med. Off. (Community Health & Family Plann.) S. Lincs. HA.; CMO (Family Plann.) Centr. Notts. NHS Trust (p/t). Socs: Fac. Fam. Plann. & Reproduc. Health Care; Fell.Roy. Soc. Med. Prev: CMO (Family Plann.) N. W. Anglia NHS Trust (p/t).

BOORMAN, David Graham 7 Wood Lane, Harborne, Birmingham B17 9AY — MB ChB Birm. 1993.

BOORMAN, Mr John Gavin Queen Victoria Hospital, East Grinstead RH19 3DZ Tel: 01342 410210 Fax: 01342 315512 — MB ChB 1974 Ed.; BSc (Hons.) Ed. 1971; FRCS (Plast) 1986; FRCS Eng. 1978. Cons. Plastic Surg. Qu. Vict. Hosp. E. Grinstead. Prev: Cons. Plastic Surg. Cannisburn Hosp. Glas.

BOORMAN, Patricia Ann 20 Westhall Park, Warlingham CR6 9HS — MB BCh 1991 Wales; FRCS Eng. 1996. Specialist Regist. (Gen. Surg.) SE Thames Region.

BOORMAN, Steven Robert Concept 2000, 250 Farnborough Road, Farnborough GU14 7LU Tel: 01252 528576 Fax: 01252 528325; Yew Tree Cottage, 3 Queens Lane, Upper Hale, Farnham GU9 0LU — MB BS 1983 Lond.; MFOM RCP Lond. 1996, AFOM 1991; MRCGP 1988; T(GP) 1991. Chief Med. Off., Post Off.; Hon. Sen. Clin. Lect. Inst. Occupat. Med. Birm. Socs: Fell. Roy. Soc. Med. (Pres. Sect. Counc.); Soc. Occupat. Med. Prev: Med. Adviser to Sec. of State Transport.

BOOS, Christopher John, Capt. RAMC Medical Mess, Royal Hospital, Haslar Road, Haslar, Gosport PO12 2AA — MB BS 1994 Lond.; Dip. IMC RCS Ed. 1997. (St. Mary's Hosp. Med. Sch.) SHO (Med.) Roy. Hosp. Haslar Gosport, Hants.; RSN. Socs: MPS; Haywood Club; OMA. Prev: Trainee GP Bulford Gp. Pract.; SHO (A & E) Roy. Lond. Hosp.; Ho. Off. St. Mary's Hosp. Med. Sch.

BOOS, Kelvin Patrick 10 Osborne Road, Kingston upon Thames KT2 5HB — MB BCh BAO 1989 NUI.

BOOT, Mr Dalton Alexander Department Orthopaedic Surgery, Warrington Dist. Gen. Hospital, Lovely Lane, Warrington WA5 1QG Tel: 01925 662282 Fax: 01925 662211; Tel: 0161 929 0838 — MB BS 1976 Lond.; MCh Orth. 1986; FRCS Ed. 1980. Cons. Orthop. Warrington & Halton Hosps. Socs: Brit. Soc. Surg. Hand & Brit. Orthop. Assn. Prev: Lect. (Orthop.) Liverp. HA; Regist. (Orthop.) Lothian HB; SHO Redhill Gen. Hosp.

BOOTE, David John Portsmouth Oncology Centre, St Mary's Hospital, Milton Road, Portsmouth PO3 6AD Tel: 023 92 286000; Trundleside, West Stoke Road, West Broyle, Chichester PO19 3PL — MB BS 1983 Lond.; FRCR 1992; FRCP (UK) 1987; BSc (Hons.) Lond. 1980. (St. Mary's) Cons. Clin. Oncol. St. Mary's Hosp. Portsmouth. Socs: BMA; BOA; RVS. Prev: Hon. Sen. Regist. (Clin. Oncol.) Addenbrooke's Hosp. Camb.; Regist. (Radiother.) W.m. Hosp. Lond.; SHO (Med. Oncol.) Roy. Free Hosp. Lond.

BOOTE, Heidi Olga (retired) 43 White Gate Gardens, Harrow Weald, Harrow HA3 6BW Tel: 020 8954 1971 — MD Zurich 1947; LMSSA Lond. 1952.

BOOTES, Mr John Anthony Hart Shirley Oaks Hospital, Poppy Lane, Croydon CR9 8AB Tel: 020 8655 2255 Fax: 020 8656 2868; 10 Manor Way, Purley CR8 3BH Tel: 020 8660 1469 Fax: 020 8763 1788 — MB BS Lond. 1963; BSc (Hons. Physiol.) Lond. 1959; FRCS Eng. 1967; MRCS Eng. LRCP Lond. 1963; FRCOG 1984; MRCOG (Gold Medal) 1971. (St. Bart.) Hon. Lect. Univ. Lond. Socs: BMA & Brit. Fertil. Soc.; BMA. Prev: Cons. O & G Mayday Univ. Hosp. Croydon; Cons. & Lect. Univ. W. Indies, Jamaica; Resid. (Med.) Qu. Charlotte's Matern. Hosp. & Chelsea Hosp. Wom.

BOOTH, Adam John 11 George Road, Guildford GU1 4NP — BM 1994 Soton.

BOOTH, Alexandra Claire Frome Medical Practice, Health Centre, Park Road, Frome BA11 1EZ Tel: 01373 301300 Fax: 01373 301313; Lower Rudge Farm, Rudge, Frome BA11 2QE Tel: 01373 831150 Email: alexandra.hernag@virgin.net — MB BS 1980 Lond.; MRCGP 1985; D.Occ.Med. RCP Lond. 1995; DRCOG 1983; Cert. Family Plann. JCC 1983. (St. Mary's)

BOOTH, Amanda Frances 1 Woodhouse Lane, Sale M33 4JS — MB BS 1986 Newc. Ho. Phys. Hope Hosp. Salford. Socs: BMA.

BOOTH, Andrew Charles Girlington Road Surgery, 252 Girlington Road, Bradford BD8 9PB Tel: 01274 491448/9 Fax: 01274 483362; 11 Cropredy Close, Queensbury, Bradford BD13 1QY — MB BS 1987 Lond.

BOOTH, Andrew David 11 Upper Crescent Road, North Baddesley, Southampton SO52 9JQ — MB ChB 1980 Leeds; MRCOG 1988; MRCGP 1985.

BOOTH, Andrew Philip Cleadon, Ollerton Road, Edwinstowe, Mansfield NG21 9QE Email: andrew.booth@virgin.net — BM BS 1983 Nottm.; BMedSci Nottm. 1981; AFOM RCP (UK) 1992. Sen. Occupat. Phys. Business Healthcare Ltd. Notts. Socs: Soc. Occupat. Med.; Brit. Assn. Immed. Care Schemes; Fac. Pre Hosp Care. Prev: Occupat. Phys. Manch. Airport plc; Med. Off. Brit. Coal Corp. NE Gp.; SHO (Anaesth.) York HA.

BOOTH, Ann 1A Forest Close, Wendover, Aylesbury HP22 6BT — MB BChir 1981 Camb.; MRCP (UK) 1984; FRCR 1987. Cons. Radiol. Stoke Mandeville Hosp. Aylesbury. Prev: Sen. Regist. Hammersmith Hosp. Lond.; Regist. (Radiodiag.) Bristol Roy. Infirm.

BOOTH, Anne Mary (retired) 9 Hillside, Barnham Broom, Norwich NR9 4DF Tel: 01603 759409 — MRCS Eng. LRCP Lond. 1949. Prev: Med. Off. Nursing Staff Health Serv. St. Bart. Hosp. Lond.

BOOTH, Anthony Irwin, Col. late RAMC (retired) Taiping, 15 South Mead, Berg Regis, Wareham BH20 7HY Tel: 01929 472081 — LRCPI & LM, LRSCI & LM 1954; LRCPI & LM, LRCSI & LM 1954; DA Eng. 1959. Prev: Sen. Specialist Anaesth. Brit. Milit. Hosp. Hong Kong BFPO1.

BOOTH, Anthony John Hinchingbrooke Hospital, Huntingdon PE29 6NT Tel: 01480 456131 — MB ChB 1979 Manch.; MRCP (UK) 1983; FRCR 1987. Cons. Radiol. Hinchingbrooke Hosp. Huntingdon. Prev: Sen. Regist. (Radiol.) Sheff. Radiol. Serv.

BOOTH, Arthur Hamilton (retired) 91 Drayton Road, Irthlingborough, Wellingborough NN9 5TQ Tel: 01933 65934 — MB BS 1933 Madras; DTM & H Eng. 1937; DOMS Eng. 1938. Prev: Ho. Phys. Trop. Hosp. Lond.

BOOTH, Brian Patrick Camberley Health Centre, 159 Frimley Road, Camberley GU15 2QA Tel: 01276 20101 Fax: 01276 21661; 31 Parkway, Camberley GU15 2PD — MB BS 1973 Lond.; MRCGP 1983; DRCOG 1977; DA Eng. 1978. Course Organiser Frimley VTS.

BOOTH, Christopher Aubin (retired) Lower Manor, Frampton Mansell, Stroud GL6 8JG Tel: 01285 760212, 01283 703407 Fax: 01285 760885 Email: boothca@lineone.net — MB BS 1961 Lond.; MRCGP 1973; DObst RCOG 1966.

BOOTH, Christopher Charles Sutton Medical Group, Allenby's Chase, Spalding PE12 9SY Tel: 01406 362081; 3 Pudding Poke Lane, Lutton, Spalding PE12 9HZ — MB ChB 1985 Manch.; MRCGP 1990.

BOOTH, Sir Christopher Charles 9 Kent Terrace, London NW1 4RP Tel: 020 7724 3379 — MD 1958 St. And.; MB ChB St. And. 1951; LLD (Hon) Dundee 1982; MD (Gold Medal) St. And. 1958; FRCP Lond. 1964, M 1954; FRCP Ed. 1969. (St. And.) Harv. Librarian Roy. Coll. Phys. Lond. Socs: Assn. Phys. & Brit. Soc. Gastroenterol.; Foreign Mem. Amer. Philosoph. Soc. Prev: Dir. Clin. Research Centre N.wick Pk. Hosp. Harrow; Prof. Med. Postgrad. Med. Sch. Lond.; Regist. (Med.) & Tutor Postgrad. Med. Sch. Lond.

BOOTH, Christopher John 31 Stanford Way, Walton, Chesterfield S42 7NH — MB ChB 1983 Leeds.

BOOTH, Christopher John 66 Westwood Road, Tilehurst, Reading RG3 5DP Tel: 01734 427421; 67 Park Lane, Tilehurst, Reading RG31 5DP — MB BChir 1952 Camb.; MRCS Eng. LRCP Lond. 1952; DObst RCOG 1957. (St. Mary's) Prev: Ho. Phys. Ipswich Gen. Hosp.; Capt. RAMC; Asst. MOH Middlx. CC.

BOOTH, Mr Christopher Michael Great Tey Ward, Colchester general Hospital, Colchester CO4 5JL Tel: 01206 742450 Fax: 01206 742039 Email: m.taylor@erhc-tr.nthames.nhs.uk; Gatton House, East Bergholt, Sudbury CO7 6QT Email: chrisfiona.booth@btinternet.com — MB BS Lond. 1969; FRCS Eng. 1976; MRCS Eng. LRCP Lond. 1969. (St Bartholomews Hospital) Cons. Urol. Dist. Gen. Hosp. Colchester; Cons. Urol. Oaks Hosp. Colchester; Cons. Urol. Suff. Nuffield Hop. Ipswich. Socs: Brit. Assn. Urol. Surgs. & Colchester Med. Soc.; Irish. Soc. Of Urol. Prev: Sen. Regist. (Urol.) Dub.; Research Regist. (Urol.) Middlx. Hosp. Lond.; Regist. (Urol.) St. Pauls Hosp. Lond.

BOOTH, Christopher William Port View Surgery, Higher Port View, Saltash PL12 4BU — MB BS 1988 Lond.; DFFP 1995; DRCOG 1995. (St. Mary's London) Prev: Trainee GP/Regist. Kingsbridge Health Centre; Trainee GP HMS Tamar Hong Kong; SHO (O & G) Freedom Fields Hosp. Plymouth.

BOOTH, Cyril (retired) 47 Allesley Hall Drive, Coventry CV5 9NS Tel: 02476 711133 — MB ChB 1953 Manch.; FRCGP 1977, M 1965. Vice Chairm. Coventry & Warks. Postgrad. Centre. Prev: Chairm. Regional Med. Comm.

BOOTH, Mr David (retired) The Hawthorns, Parkgate Road, Newdigate, Dorking RH5 5AH Tel: 01306 631409 Fax: 01306 631409 — MB BS 1960 Lond.; FRCS Eng. 1967; MRCS Eng. LRCP Lond. 1960; FRCOG 1981 M 1968; DObst RCOG 1963. Med. Dir. Crawley & Horsham NHS Trust; Cons. O & G Crawley & Horsham Hosps. Prev: Sen. Regist. (O & G) Woolwich Gp. Hosps.

BOOTH, David 22 Grove Street, Barnsley S71 1EX — MB ChB 1996 Leeds.

BOOTH, David Francis Vicarage Road Medical Centre, Vicarage Road, Mickleover, Derby DE3 5EB Tel: 01332 513283 Fax: 01332 518569 — MB ChB 1979 Bristol; MRCGP 1984.

BOOTH, David John Wilton The Health Centre, St. Katherine's Court, Newburgh, Cupar KY14 6EB Tel: 01337 840462 Fax: 01337 840996; Burnside Cottage, Manse Road, Abernethy, Perth PH2 9JP Tel: 01738 850636 — MB ChB 1984 Bristol; MRCGP 1989. GP. Prev: Trainee GP Kirriemuir; SHO (A & E) Dundee Roy. Infirm.; SHO (O & G) P'boro. Dist. Gen. Hosp.

BOOTH, David Jonathan 7 Bracken Close, Lichfield WS14 9RU — MB BS 1998 Newc.; MB BS Newc 1998.

BOOTH, Dominic 2 Sycamore Barn, Reagill, Penrith CA10 3ER — MB BS 1991 Lond.

BOOTH, Dorothy Hyslop (retired) 3 Raasay Road, Inverness IV2 3LR — MB BS 1952 Durh. Prev: Clin. Asst. (Cytol.) Raigmore Hosp. Inverness.

BOOTH, Mr Dudley Bronson 12 Glen Road, Bridge of Allan, Stirling FK9 4PL — MB ChB 1971 Glas.; FRCS Glas. 1975.

BOOTH, Eileen Mary, Wing Cdr. RAF Med. Br. Retd. (retired) 19 Seaford Road, Cleethorpes DN35 0NB Tel: 01472 812414 — MB ChB Manch. 1957; MSc (Occupat. Med.) Lond. 1972; MFOM 1980; DIH Eng. 1972. Prev: RAF Med Off.

BOOTH, Fiona Jane Parkfield M.C, Sefton Road, New Ferry, Wirral CH62 5HS Tel: 0151 644 0055; 50 Covertside, West Larby, Wirral CH48 9UL Tel: 0151 625 2858 Email: r.dasgupk@btinternet.com — MB ChB 1992 Liverp.; BSc (Hons.) Liverp. 1989; DFFP 1996. GP Partner, Birkenhead,Wirral. Prev: Trainee GP Birkenhead, Wirral.

BOOTH, Frances Helen Marshes, Butt Lane, Snaith, Goole DN14 9DY Tel: 01405 860111 Fax: 01405 863901; 4 Beckwith Hall Drive, Riccall, York YO19 6SY Tel: 01757 249384 — MB BS 1991 Lond.; MRCGP 1996; DRCOG 1995. (The Royal London Hospital Medical College)

BOOTH, Frances Mary 4 Cradle Lane, Frith End, Bordon GU35 0QT; 4 Cradle Lane, Bordon GU35 0QT — BM BCh 1974 Oxf.; MA, BM BCh Oxf. 1974; MRCGP 1981; DRCOG 1980; DCH Eng. 1979. Asst. (Homeopath.) Guildford Surrey; Clin. Asst. (Psychother.) Connaught Hse. Roy. Hants. Hosp.; CMO Family Plann. Basingstoke & N. Hants HA. Prev: SHO (Psychiat.) Roy. S. Hants. Hosp. Soton.; Ho. Surg. St. Richards Hosp. Chichester; Ho. Phys. Lond. Hosp. Whitechapel.

BOOTH, Frank Department of Haematology, Alexandra Hospital, Redditch B98 7UB Tel: 01527 503 030 Fax: 01527 512 007 — MB BS 1976 Lond.; MRCP 1979 UK; MRCPath 1984; BSc 1973 Lond; FRCP 1998 Lond; MRCS Eng. LRCP Lond. 1976; FRCPath 1996. (St. Geo.) Cons. Haemat. Worcs. Acute Hosp.s NHS Trust. Socs: Brit. Soc. Haematol.; Assn. Clin. Path.; Am. Soc. Of Haemat. Prev: Cons. Haemat. Roy. Berks. Hosp. Reading; Sen. Regist. (Haemat.) John Radcliffe Hosp. Oxf.; Regist. (Gen. Med.) St. Geo. Hosp. Lond.

BOOTH, Helen Louise Department of Thoracic Medicine, UCL Hospitals, The Middlesex Hospital, Mortimer St., London W1T 3AA Tel: 0207 380 9005 — MB BS 1986 Newc.; FRCP 2001; BMedSc Newc. 1983; MRCP (UK) 1990. Cons. (Thoracic & Gen. Med.) Univ. Coll. Hosps. Lond. Prev: Sen. Regist. (Thoracic Med.) Univ. Coll. Hosps. Lond.; Sen. Regist. (Thoracic Med.) Whittington Hosp. Lond.; Sen. Regist. (Respirat. Med.) Newc. Gen. Hosp.

BOOTH, Humphrey Clarke 190 Ripple Road, Barking IG11 7PR — MB BS 1961 Lond.; MRCS Eng. LRCP Lond. 1960; MRCGP 1973. (Westm.) Socs: BMA & W. Norf. Clin. Soc. Prev: Ho. Surg.

Gordon Hosp.; Ho. Phys. Hosp. SS John & Eliz.; Obst. Off. W. Norf. & King's Lynn Hosp.

BOOTH, Professor Ian Westerby University of Birmingham, Institute of Child Health, Clinical Research Block, Whittall St., Birmingham B4 6NH Tel: 0121 333 8717 Fax: 0121 333 8701 Email: i.w.booth@bham.ac.uk; Wellingtonia House, Banbury Street, Kineton CV32 0JS Tel: 01926 640135 Fax: 01926 640135 Email: profib@aol.com — MB BS 1972 Lond.; MSc (Distinc.) Biochem. 1982, BSc (Hons.) Physiol. 1969, MD 1987, MB; BS 1972; FRCP Lond. 1991; MRCP (UK) 1977; FRCPCH 1997; DCH Eng. 1975; DObst RCOG 1974. (King's Coll. Hosp.) Leonard Parsons Prof. of Paediat. & Child Health, Inst. Child Health, Univ. Birm.; Ass. Dean , Univ. Birm. Med. Sch.; Head Acad. Dept. Paediat. & Child Health Birm.; Hon. Cons. Phys. Childr. Hosp. Birm.; Dir. Inst. Child Health Birm. Socs: Eur. Soc. Paediat. Gastroenterol. & Nutrit.; Brit. Soc. of Paediat. Gastroenterol. and Nutrit.; Brit. Soc. Gastroenterol. Prev: Prof. & Reader Paediat., Gastroenterol. & Nutrit. Inst. Child Health Univ. Birm.; Child Health Univ. Lond.; Roy. Coll. Phys. Eden Research Fell. (Child Health) Inst. Child Health Univ. Lond.

BOOTH, James Connon Donald (retired) 4 Craigdhu Avenue, Milngavie, Glasgow G62 6DX — MB ChB 1956 Aberd.; FRCP Ed. 1984, M 1969; FRCPsych 1988, M 1971; DPM Eng. 1962. Prev: Cons. Psychiat. Stobhill Hosp. Glas.

BOOTH, John Barton St. Bridget's Hospice, Kensington Rd, Douglas IM1 3PE Tel: 01624 626530 Fax: 01624 623846; 24 The Crofts, Castletown IM9 1LZ — MB BS 1963 Lond.; FRCS (Orl.) Eng 1968; MRCS Eng. LRCP Lond. 1963; MRAeS 1988; AKC. (King's Coll. Hosp.) Phys., St. Bridget's Hospice; Hon. Cons. St. Luke's Hosp. for the Clergy Lond.; Hunt. Prof. RCS Eng.; Hon. Civil Cons. (Otol.) RAF. Socs: Fell. Zool. Soc. Lond.; Hon. Mem. Amer. Otol. Soc.; Past Assoc. Mem. Amer. Neurotol. Soc. Prev: Edr. Jl. Laryng. & Otol. (Asst. Edr. 1979-87); Hon Cons. Otol. St Barts. Hosp. & The Roy. Lond. Hosp.; Cons. Surg. Roy. Nat. Throat, Nose & Ear Hosp. Lond. (1989-92).

BOOTH, John Edwin 9 Zion Street, Gawthorpe, Ossett WF5 9QT — MB ChB 1979 Leeds.

BOOTH, John Lister (retired) 55 Poll Hill Road, Heswall, Wirral CH60 7SW Tel: 0151 342 1944 — MRCS Eng. LRCP Lond. 1957; FRCR 1975; FFR 1966; DMRT Eng. 1963. Prev: Cons. Radiother. & Oncol. Clatterbridge Centre for Oncol.

BOOTH, John Samuel 117 Norton Road, Stourbridge DY8 2RP — MB ChB 1973 Dundee.

BOOTH, John Trygve Melbourne House Surgery, 12 Napier Court, Queensland Crescent, Chelmsford CM1 2ED Tel: 01245 354370 Fax: 01245 344476; Herons Way, Stump Lane, Springfield, Chelmsford CM1 7SJ Email: j.t.booth@talk21 — MB BS 1978 Lond.; DRCOG 1981. (Middlx. Hosp.) Drs Booth, Cass, Pitt & Sarjudsen, Melbourne Ho. Surg., Chelmsford; Cas. Off. Basildon Hosp. Essex; SHO (Obst.) Basildon Hosp. Essex.; Cas. Off. Basildon Hosp. Essex; St. John Ambul. Brig. Essex; Asst. Co. Med. Off.

BOOTH, John Vincent 4 Wells Close, Brampton, Huntingdon PE28 4UJ — MB ChB 1989 Glas.

BOOTH, Jonathan Charles Loughridge Department of Gastroenterology, The Royal Berkshire Hospital, Reading RG1 5AN Tel: 0118 987 7347 Fax: 0118 987 8738 Email: drbooth@excite.com; 35 St Andrews Road, Henley-on-Thames RG1 1HZ — MB BS 1987 Lond.; BSc Lond. 1987, MD. MRCP.; MRCP (UK) 1990. (St Marks Hospital, Raddington) Cons. Gastroenterol. The Roy. Berks. Hosp. Reading. Socs: GMC; MRCP; RSM. Prev: Sen. Regist. Gastroenterol. Chelsea W.m. Hosp.; Sen. Regist. Gastroenterol. & Ueratology, St Mary's Hosp., Paddington.

BOOTH, Joseph Patrick (retired) Blackwater House, Ashdon Road, Radwinter, Saffron Walden CB10 2UA Tel: 01799 599833 — MB BS 1955 Lond.; MRCS Eng. LRCP Lond. 1955; DObst RCOG 1957. Prev: Urol. & Orthop. Ho. Surg. King's Coll. Hosp.

BOOTH, Judith Ann Davis and Partners, 274 Manchester Road, Warrington WA1 4PS Tel: 01925 631132 Fax: 01925 630079 — MB ChB 1986 Manch.; MRCGP 1990.

BOOTH, Judith Anne Airedale General Hospital, Steeton, Keighley BD20 6DT Tel: 01535 652511; Yarnbury Cottage, Moor Lane, Grassington, Skipton BD23 5EQ Tel: 01756 752948 — MB ChB 1979 Leeds; DRCOG 1982. Med. Advisor Benefits Agency; Clin. Asst. (Cytotoxic Ther. & Obst.) Airedale Gen. Hosp. Keighley; Clin. Asst. BrE. Clinic Airedale Gen. Hosp.; Med. Adviser, Benefits Agency. Prev: GP Asst. Bingley; GP Grassington.

BOOTH, Kathryn 10A Ballylesson Road, Magheramorne, Larne BT40 3HL — MB BCh BAO 1980 Belf.

BOOTH, Kevin Richard 35 Welwyndale Road, Sutton Coldfield B72 1AW — MB ChB 1994 Manch.

BOOTH, Linda Vivien Public Health Medicine Department, North & Mid Hampshire Health Authority, Harness House, Aldermaston Road, Basingstoke RG24 9NB — MB BS 1979 Lond.; MFPHM 2002; FRCPath 1996, M 1985; Dip. Clin. Microbiol Lond. 1983. Cons. Communicable Dis. Control. N. & Mid Hants. HA.

BOOTH, Lionel James 5 Sylvan Drive, Coventry CV3 6AB Tel: 024 76 419843 — MB ChB 1964 Liverp.; FRCP Lond. 1982, M 1968; FRCP Canada 1973. Cons. Phys. Walsgrave Hosp. Coventry.

BOOTH, Malcolm Graham Royal Infirmary, Castle St., Glasgow G4 05F Tel: 0141 211 4620 Fax: 0141 211 4622 Email: mgb2j@udcf.gla.ac.uk; 18 Colquhoun Drive, Bearsden, Glasgow G61 4NQ Tel: 0141 943 0956 Email: malcolm.booth@lineone.net — MB ChB 1984 Ed.; MPhil Glas. 1995; FRCA 1991. Cons. Anaesth. & Intens. Care Glas. Roy. Infirm.

BOOTH, Mary Cathleen (retired) 7 Lodge Gardens, Harpenden AL5 4JE — MB BS Lond. 1957; BSc (Special Physiol. 1st cl. Hons.) Lond. 1955; DObst RCOG 1962.

BOOTH, Mr Michael Ian Havenhill, Roundwood Road, High Wycombe HP12 4HD Tel: 01494 520973; 1 Chapel Street, Downley, High Wycombe HP13 5XH Tel: 01494 520973 Email: mlandlb@1chapelst.freeserve.co.uk — BM BCh 1990 Oxf.; BA Phys. Sci. Oxf. 1987; FRCS Eng. 1994. (Oxf.) Specialist Regist. Rotat., Oxf. Prev: Regist. Rotat. (Gen. Surg.) Wycombe, Reading & Oxf.; SHO (Cardiothoracic Surg.) Harefield Hosp.; SHO (Gen. Surg.) Wycombe Gen. Hosp. High Wycombe & St Mary's Hosp. Lond.

BOOTH, Nicholas Steven 20 Springfield, Ovington, Prudhoe NE42 6EH Tel: 01661 835551 Fax: 01661 830316 Email: n.s.booth@ncl.ac.uk — MB BS 1978 Lond.; MA Camb. 1979; MRCGP 1983; DCH RCP Glas. 1982. (Camb. & King's Coll. Hosp.) Princip. Clin. Research Assoc. Sowerby Unit for Primary Care Informatics Univ. Newc. u. Tyne. Socs: Fell. RCGP N. Eng. (Fac. Computer); Chairm. Primary Health Care Specialist Gp. Brit. Computer Soc. Prev: GP Trainer Prudhoe; Trainee GP N.umbria VTS; SHO Rotat. (Paediat.) Newc. U. Tyne.

BOOTH, Nigel Paul The Kiltearn Medical Centre, Hospital St., Nantwich CW5 5RN Tel: 01270 610200; 1 The Poplars, Marsh Lane, Edleston, Nantwich CW5 8PA Tel: 01270 610454 — MB ChB 1991 Manch.; BSc (Hons.) Physiol. Manch. 1988; DRCOG. Trainee GP Nantwich. Prev: GP Gladstone Qu.sland, Austral.; SHO (Geriat.) Burton Dist. Gen. Hosp.; SHO (O & G) Roy. Lancaster Infirm.

BOOTH, Patricia Mary (retired) 6 The Brambles, Trumpington, Cambridge CB2 2LY — MB BS Lond. 1959; MRCS Eng. LRCP Lond. 1958. Prev: Family Plann. Sen. Med. Off. Camb.

BOOTH, Mr Patrick John (retired) Cliff Cottage, Siliwen Road, Bangor LL57 2SU Tel: 01248 362547 — MB BS 1955 Lond.; FRCS Eng. 1970; DLO Eng. 1960. Prev: Cons. ENT Surg. Gwynedd Hosp. Bangor.

BOOTH, Paul Jonathan Number 18 Surgery, 18 Upper Oldfield Park, Bath BA2 3JZ Tel: 01225 427402 Fax: 01225 484627; 77 Bloomfield Avenue, Bear Flat, Bath BA2 3AA — MB ChB 1978 Birm.; MRCGP 1983; DRCOG 1981. Prev: Tainee GP Shrewsbury VTS; Ho. Phys. & Ho. Surg. Roy. Shrewsbury Hosp.

BOOTH, Peter Alan Earnswood Medical Centre, 92 Victoria Street, Crewe CW1 2JR Tel: 01270 257255 Fax: 01270 501943; 96 Main Road, Wybundury, Nantwich CW5 7LS — MB ChB 1982 Leeds; MRCGP 1986; DRCOG 1985.

BOOTH, Philip, Wing Cdr. RAF Med. Br. Retd. Neonatal Unit, Aberdeen Maternity Hospital, Cornhill Road, Aberdeen AB25 2ZL Tel: 01224 681818 Fax: 01224 554604 Email: phil.booth@arh.grampian.scot.nhs.uk; 93 Beaconsfield Place, Aberdeen AB15 4AD Tel: 01224 647714 — MB ChB 1978 Ed.; MRCP (UK) 1984; FRCP Ed. 1995; DCH RCP Lond. 1982; FRCPCH 1997. (Ed.) Cons. & Clin. Sen. Lect. (Paediat.) Aberd. Matern. Hosp.; Clin. Dir. Obst., Gyn. & Neonatology. Socs: Assn. Perinatal Med.; Fell. Roy. Coll. Paediat. & Child Health; Paediat. Intens. Care Soc. Prev: Cons. Advisor (Paediat.) RAF; Cons. Paediat. RAF Hosp. Wegberg, Germany (Wing Cdr. RAF Med. Br.); Hon. Sen. Regist. (Paediat.) King's Coll. Hosp. & Guy's Hosp. Lond.

BOOTH, Philippa Jayne 7 Crescent St, Islington, London N1 1BT; 7 Crescent St, Islington, London N1 1BT — MB BS 1996 Lond.; MRCP Part 1, UK, Jan 98. (UMDS) SNO Gen. Med.; Guys Hosp.

BOOTH, Raymond Trygve (retired) Friars, 192 Brentwood Road, Herongate, Brentwood CM13 3PN Tel: 01277 810527 — MB BS 1953 Lond.; FRCOG 1974, M 1958. Prev: Cons. O & G Basildon & Thurrock HA.

BOOTH, Mr Robert Arnold Deverell National Westminster Bank Plc, 18 St Thomas Centre, Exeter EX4 1DB Email: robertbooth@btinternet.com — MB ChB Birm. 1962; MD Birm. 1975; FRCS Eng. 1967; FRCS Ed. 1966. (Birm.) Cons. Surg. Qu. Mary's Hosp. Roehampton & Putney Hosp. & Kingston Hosp., Kingston upon Thames Surrey; Cons. Surg. New Vict. Hosp.; Mem. Ct. Examrs. RCS Ed. Socs: Brit. Soc. Gastroenterol.; Brit. Soc. Coloproctol. Prev: Vis. Fell. Univ. Texas Med. Br. Galveston, Texas, USA; Sen. Lect. (Surg.) W.m. Hosp. Lond.

BOOTH, Rosemary Helen 4 Craigdhu Avenue, Milngavie, Glasgow G62 6DX Tel: 0141 956 3164 — MB ChB 1961 Ed.; Postgrad. Dip. Counc. 1996. (Ed.) Counsellor Marie Curie Centre Glas.; Pract. Counsellor (Gen. Pract.) Bearsden; Hon. Lect. Dept. Postgrad Med. Educat. Univ. Glas. (p/t); Facilitetas Dep. Med. Univ. Glas (p/t). Prev: Macmillan Research Fell. Dept. Postgrad. Med. Educat. Univ. Glas.; Clin. Asst. (Psychogeriat.) Gartnavel Roy. Hosp. Glas.

BOOTH, Ruth Wellspring Surgery, St. Anns Health Centre, St. Anns, Well Road, Nottingham NG3 3PX Tel: 0115 9505907/8 Fax: 0115 988 1582 — MB ChB 1978 Birm.; MRCGP 1987. (Birmingham)

BOOTH, Sara The Oncology Centre, Box 193, Addenbrooke's Hospital, Hills Road, Cambridge CB2 2QQ Tel: 01223 586703 Email: sara.booth@msexc.addenbrooke.anglox.nhs.uk; Blackwater, Ashdon Road, Radwinter, Saffron Walden CB10 2HA — MB BS 1983 Lond.; FFA RCSI 1988. (Roy. Free Hosp.) MacMillan (Palliat. Med.). Prev: Hon. Cons. Phys. Sir Michael Sobell Ho. Oxf.

BOOTH, Stella Highfield Cottage, Mimbridge, Chobham, Woking GU24 8HE — MRCS Eng. LRCP Lond. 1945; MPH Yale Univ. 1962. Mem. Clin. Br. Collaborative Research of Nat. Cancer Inst., Nat.; Insts. Health Bethesda, USA. Prev: Act. Chief Epidemiol. Field Studies Br. Div. Air Pollut. US Pub.; Health Serv. Washington, DC; Med. Off. Cancer Program NJ State Dept.; Health Trenton; Chief of Med. M.D. Anderson Hosp. Cancer Houston.

BOOTH, Mr Stephen Jeremy Accident & Emergency Department, Chelsea & Westminster Hospital, Fulham Road, London SW10 9NH Tel: 020 8746 8015 — MB BS 1979 Lond.; FRCS Ed. 1985. (Roy. Free) Cons. A & E & Clin. Dir. Emerg. Med. Chelsea & W.m. Hosp. Lond.; Vis. Lect. N. W.. Univ. Chicago, USA; Hon. Cons. A & E Med. Roy. Brompton Hosp. Lond. Socs: Fell. Roy. Soc. Med.; Brit. Assn. Accid. & Emerg. Phys.; Founder Fell. Fac. A & E Med. Prev: Sen. Regist. (A & E) W.m. Hosp. Lond.; Regist. (Paediat. Surg.) W.m. Childr. Hosp. & W.m. Hosp. Lond.; Demonst. (Anat.) Roy. Free Hosp. Sch. Med. Lond.

BOOTH, Stephen Nicholas 21 Blakebrook, Kidderminster DY11 6AP Tel: 01562 754700 — MB ChB 1968 Birm.; MD Birm. 1975; FRCP (UK) 1983, M 1971. Cons. Phys. Worcs. Acute NHS Trust; Kidderminster Hosp. Worchester Roy. Infirm. Prev: Sen. Regist. (Med.) Manch. AHA (T); Research Fell. Dept. Experim. Path. Univ. Birm.; Regist. (Med.) Plymouth Gen. Hosp.

BOOTH, Stuart Andrew 26 Hospital Road, Bury St Edmunds IP33 3JU Tel: 01284 764507; 162 Rolleston Road, Burton-on-Trent DE13 0LE Tel: 01283 568325 — MB ChB 1993 Birm. (Univ. Birm.) Specialist Regist. (Anaesth) Addenbrookes Hosps. NHS Trust, Camb. Socs: Soc. Occupat. Med.; Intens. Care Soc.; MRCAnaesth. Prev: SHO Derbys. Roy. Infirm.; SHO Stafford Dist. Gen. Hosp.; SHO (Anaesth.) W. Suff. NHS Trust Bury St. Edmunds.

BOOTH, Susan Angela (retired) 3 Potter Road, Hadfield, Glossop SK13 2RA — MB ChB 1981 Manch.; DRCOG 1984.

BOOTH, Susanne Jane Vine Farm, Sutton, Askern, Doncaster DN6 9LB — MB BS 1996 Lond.

BOOTH, Tamsin Ruth 94 Clarence Road, Wimbledon, London SW19 8QD Tel: 020 8543 4854; 94 Clarence Road, Wimbledon, London SW19 8QD Tel: 020 8543 4854 Email: tamsinbooth@yahoo.com — BM 1995 Soton.; BSc Soton. 1994; DCH 1998; DRCOG 1999. (Soton.) SHO (Paediat.) Chelsea & W.minster Hosp. Prev: SHO (HIV) Chelsea & W.minster Hosp.; SHO (c/o Elderly) W. Middlx. Hosp.; SHO (A & E) Qu. Mary's Hosp. Lond.

BOOTH, Timothy Franklyn 3 Smith's Wynd, Jedburgh TD8 6DH — MB ChB 1992 Ed. SHO (Psychiat.) Herdmanflat Hosp. Haddington.

BOOTHBY, Christopher Brooke (retired) St Nicholas, Hollow Road, Bury St Edmunds IP32 7AU Tel: 01284 754456 — MB BS Lond. 1962; FRCP Lond. 1982, M. 1968; MRCS Eng. LRCP Lond. 1962; FRCPCH 1997. Prev: Cons. Paediat. W. Suff. Gen. Hosp. Bury St. Edmunds.

BOOTHBY, Henry Alexander Stag Park Farm, Petworth GU28 9LZ — MB BCh BAO 1987 NUI; LRCPSI 1987.

BOOTHBY, Margaret Elizabeth St Nicholas, Hollow Rd, Bury St Edmunds IP32 7AU Tel: 01284 754436 Email: meg-boothby@hotmail.com — MB ChB 1997 Birm. (Birm) SHO O & G. City Hosp. Birm.

BOOTHMAN, Bernard Robert Department of Neurology, Royal Preston Hospital, Sharoe Green Lane N., Fulwood, Preston PR2 9HT; Sycamore House, Corner Bank Close, Great Plumpton, Preston PR4 3LT — MB ChB 1980 Birm.; FRCP 2000 u.k; MRCP (UK) 1983; DCH RCP Lond. 1985; DRCOG 1985. Cons. Neurol. Preston Acute Hosps. NHS Trust. Socs: Assn. of Brit. NeUrol.s. Prev: Med. Dir. Memory Assessm. Clinics. (UK) Ltd. Bradford; Regist. (Neurol.) Gen. Infirm. Leeds.

BOOTHMAN, John 5 Highgate Avenue, Fulwood, Preston PR2 8LL Tel: 01772 717261 — MB BS 1951 Lond.

BOOTHROYD, Anne Elisabeth Radiology Department, Alder Hey Children's Hospital, Eaton Road, Liverpool L12 Tel: 0151 228 4811; Austerson Old Hall, Alvanley, Helsby, Warrington WA6 9EH — MB ChB 1982 Liverp.; FRCR Eng. 1987.

BOOTHROYD, Clare Manda Ashton House, 15 George Street, Leamington Spa CV31 1ET Tel: 01926 428321 Fax: 01926 427232; Keeper's Cottage, Banbury Road, Oakley Wood, Leamington Spa CV33 9QJ Tel: 01926 651134 Email: iainc@ibm.net — BM BS 1982 Nottm.; MPhil. (Molec. Biol.) Nottm. 1980, BM BS 1982; MRCGP 1991. (Nottingham) GP Princip.

BOOTHROYD, Elizabeth Clare The Surgery, 83 Main Road, Broughton, Chester CH4 0NR Tel: 01244 520615; 7 Hunters Croft, Higher Kinnerton, Chester CH4 9PD Tel: 01244 661250 — MB ChB 1988 Sheff.; MB ChB (Hons.) Sheff. 1988; MA Camb. 1989; MRCGP 1992; DRCOG 1990. Socs: BMA. Prev: Trainee GP/SHO (O & G) Wrexham VTS; Ho. Off. (Gen. Med. & Gen. Surg.) Countess of Chester Hosp.

BOOTHROYD BROOKS, Bernard George Harroway Edge, Keppel Road, Dorking RH4 1NG Tel: 01306 882084 — MRCS Eng. LRCP Lond. 1963; BSc (Hons.) Lond. 1959, MB BS 1963; MRCPsych 1971; DPM Eng. 1966. (St. Bart.) Indep. Cons. Child Psychiat. Dorking. Prev: Cons. Child Psychiat. W.m. Hosp. Lond.; Assoc. Prof. Child Psychiat. Memor. Univ. Newfld.; Sen. Regist. Hosp. Sick Childr. Gt. Ormond St.

BOOTHROYD BROOKS, Eleanor Mary (retired) Harroway Edge, Keppel Road, Dorking RH4 1NG Tel: 01306 882084 Email: marybrookes2000@aol.com — MB ChB 1956 Manch.; MFCM 1972; DPH Eng. 1966; FFCM. Prev: Cons. Pub. Health Med. Camden & Islington HA.

BOOTLE, Stuart John Inverbeg, Reservoir Road, Whaley Bridge, High Peak SK23 7BW Tel: 01663 732174 Fax: 01663 732174 Email: stuboot@yahoo.com — MB ChB 1985 Manch.; BSc (Hons.) Manch. 1982; MRCGP 1989; DRCOG 1989. Prim. Care Diabetes Specialist, Health Care Continuum, Whaley Bridge. Prev: Trainee GP Stepping Hill Hosp. VTS.

BOOTON, Paul Department of General Practice & Primary Care, King's College School Medicine & Dentistry, Bessemer Road, Camberwell, London SE5 9PJ Tel: 020 7312 5653 Fax: 020 7312 5686 Email: p.booton@kcl.ac.uk; 118 Pepys Road, Telegraph Hill, London SE14 5SG Tel: 020 7652 1431 — MB BS 1979 Lond.; BSc (Hons.) Psychol. Lond. 1975; MRCP (UK) 1985; MRCGP 1988. Sen. Lect. (Med. Educat.) Kings Coll. Sch. Med. & Dent. Lond.; Undergrad. Sub-Dean King's Coll. Sch. Med. & Dent. Lond. Prev: Lect. (Gen. Pract.) UMDS Lond.; Regist. (Med.) OldCh. Hosp. Romford; Med. Off. Kai Tak & Sham Shui Po Refugee Camps, Hong Kong.

BOOTON, Richard Northwest Lung Centre, Wythenshawe Hospital, Southmoor Rd, Manchester M23 9LT Tel: 0161 946 2603 Email: booty2yt@aol.com — MB ChB 1992 Leeds; MRCP 1998.

BOOTS, Margaret Ann Department of Haematology, District General Hospital, Turner Road, Colchester CO4 5JL Tel: 01206 747474 Fax: 01206 742400 Email: maggieboots@essexrivers.nhs.uk; Timberlea, Coles Oak Lane, Dedham, Colchester CO7 6DN Tel: 01206 322209 — MB BS 1972 Lond.; MRCS Eng. LRCP Lond. 1972; FRCPath 1990, M 1978. (Char. Cross) Cons. Haemat. Dist. Gen. Hosp. Colchester.

BOOTY, Jane 30 Crossgate Mews, Harwood Road, Stockport SK4 3AP — MB ChB 1989 Manch.; BSc (Hons.) Manch. 1983, MB ChB 1989.

BOOY, Professor Robert Dept of Child Health, Royal London Hosp, Whitechapel, London E1 1BB Tel: 020 7377 7245 Fax: 020 7377 7091 Email: r.booy@mds.qmw.ac.uk; 103 Marlborough Road, Grandpont, Oxford OX1 4LX Tel: 01865 726436 — MB BS 1984 (Hons.) Queensland; 1992 FRACP; 1998 MSc; 1997 MRCPCH; 2000 FRCPCH; MD 2000. Cons. Paediat., Prof of Child Health, RLH.

BOOYA, Nisreen Hanna Department of Psychiatry, Dewsbury District Hospital, Halifax Road, Dewsbury WF13 4HS Tel: 01484 512000 Fax: 01484 517317 Email: nhbooya@aol.com — MB ChB 1974 Baghdad; MSc (Human Genetics) Ed. 1981; MRCPsych 1980; DPM Eng. 1979. Cons. Psychiat. Bath HA.; Cons. Psychiat. Dewsbury NHS Trust; Sen. Clin. Lect. Leeds Univ.; Tutor & Clin. Coordinator.

BOPEARACHCHI, Terrence Jayantha Perera 27 Kingsley Crescent, High Wycombe HP11 2NL Tel: 01494 532546 — MB BS 1978 Sri Lanka; MRCS Eng. LRCP Lond. 1988; DLO RCS Eng. 1989. SHO (Otolaryngol.) Wycombe Gen. Hosp. High Wycombe. Prev: SHO (ENT) Kingston Hosp. Kingston upon Thames; SHO (ENT) N. Riding Infirm. Middlesbrough.

BOR, Simon (retired) 95 Harley Street, London W1N 1DF Tel: 020 7935 6930 Fax: 020 7224 1967 — MB ChB 1952 Cape Town; FRCP Lond. 1989; FRCP Glas. 1972. Prev: Cons. Dermat. Essex Nuffield Hosp. Brentwood, Essex.

BORA, Ashraf Uddin Coronation Street Surgery, 6A Coronation Street, South Shields NE33 1BA Tel: 0191 456 2856 Fax: 0191 427 0630 — MB BS 1968 Dibrugarh. (Dibrugarh) GP S. Shields.

BORA, Dayananda The Surgery, 35 Warwick Road, Sparkhill, Birmingham B11 4RA Tel: 0121 772 0352; 77 Church Road, Molesey, Birmingham B13 9EB Tel: 0121 449 6927 Fax: 0121 449 3737 Email: dayabora@hotmail.com — MB BS 1965 Gauhati. (Assam Med. Coll. Dibrugarh) Prev: SHO (Cas.) Roy. Salop Infirm. Shrewsbury.

BORA, Mr Jadu Moni Scartho Road Hospital, Grimsby DN33 2BA — MB BS 1966 Gauhati; FRCS Eng. 1979.

BORA, Ronita 2 Whitestone Close, Lostock, Bolton BL6 4RN — MB BS 1998 Lond.; MB BS Lond 1998.

BORAL, Sumant Shobhan (retired) Shantiniketan, 2 Woodview, Grays RM17 5TF Tel: 01375 76043 — MB BS Calcutta 1959. Clin. Asst. ENT Orsett Hosp.; Div. Surg. St. John Ambul. Brig. Prev: ENT Ho. Surg. R. G. Kar Med. Coll. Hosps. Calcutta.

BORALESSA, Harischandra 33 Priests Lane, Brentwood CM15 8BU Tel: 01277 210221 — MB BS 1967 Ceylon; MRCP (UK) 1975; MRCPath 1980. Dept. Dir. NE Thames Transfus. Centre Brentwood.; Hon. Cons. Haemat. Univ. Coll. & Middlx. Hosp. Lond. Prev: Sen. Regist. (Haemat.) Middlx. Hosp. Lond. & Edgware Gen. Hosp.

BORALESSA, Harsha Havering Hospitals NHS Trust, Oldchurch Rd, Romford RM7 Tel: 01708 708443 Fax: 01708 708192; 33 Priests Lane, Brentwood CM15 8BU Tel: 01277 210221 Email: harshibora@compuserve.com — MB BS 1967 Ceylon; FFA RCS Eng. 1978. (University of Sri Lanka, Faculty of Medicine, Kandy) Cons. (Anaesth.) OldCh. Hosp. Romford. Socs: Intens. Care Soc.; Roy. Coll. of Anaesth.; Assn. of Anaesth. Prev: Regist. (Anaesth.) Univ. Coll. Hosp. Lond.; Sen. Regist. (Anaesth) Hammersmith Hosp. Lond.

BORALESSA, Ramasiri 462 Russell Court, Woburn Place, London WC1H 0NL — MB BS 1979 Colombo.

BORASTERO, Euripides William The High House, High House Lane, Tardebigge, Bromsgrove B60 3AQ — LRCPI & LM, LRSCI & LM 1972; LRCPI & LM, LRCSI & LM 1972; MRCGP 1977; DCH RCPS Glas. 1976; DObst RCOG 1975.

BORCHARDT, Felix Jacques Abbotswood Medical Centre, Defford Road, Pershore WR10 1HZ Tel: 01386 552424; Ivy House, Fladbury, Pershore WR10 2QA — MB BChir 1969 Camb.; MA, MB Camb. 1969, BChir, 1968; DObst RCOG 1970. (Camb. & St. Thos.) Hosp. Pract. (Paediat.) Worcester Roy. Infirm. Prev: Ho. Surg. St. Thos. Hosp. Lond.; Ho. Phys. St. Peter's Hosp. Chertsey; Resid. Med. Off. (Med. & Paediat.) Univ. Alberta Edmonton, Canada.

BORDAT, Serge Paul Edme 26 Donne Place, London SW3 2NH — MD 1953 Bordeaux.

BORDER, David John Department of Medicine, York District General Hospital, York; 7 Hilltop, Portishead, Bristol BS20 8RH — MB ChB 1998 Leeds.

BORDIN, Paolo 258b Kilburn Lane, London W10 4BA — State Exam 1989 Trieste.

BORE, Jacqueline Claire Lakeside Health Centre, Tavy Bridge, Thamesmead, London SE2 9UQ Tel: 020 8301 3281; The Lodge, Markington, Harrogate HG3 3PH — MB BS 1983 Lond.; MA Oxon 1980. Lect. Dept. Gen. Pract. United Med. & Dent. Schs. Of Guys & St. Thos Hosps. Prev: Trainee GP Greenwich/Brook VTS.

BORE, Joanne Teresa Mill Farm, Milland Lane, Liphook GU30 7JP — MB BS 1985 Lond.

BOREHAM, Jonathan James Campbell The Surgery, 18 Thurloe Street, London SW7 2ST Tel: 020 7225 2424 Fax: 020 7225 1874 Email: jonathanboreham@gp-e87071.nhs.uk; Tel: 020 7731 5512 — MRCS Eng. LRCP Lond. 1977; DRCOG 1982. p/t GP Lond.; Med. Off., Quantas Airlines; Med. Off. HH Saudi Research. Socs: Fell. Roy. Soc. Med. Prev: Bd. Mem. S. Kensington Chelsea & W.minster PCG; RMO 21 SAS(V).

BOREHAM, Mr Peter Francis, OBE (retired) The Old Coach House, Landsdown Crescent, Cheltenham GL50 2JX Tel: 01242 522627 — MB BChir 1945 Camb.; MChir Camb. 1955, MA, MB BChir 1945; FRCS Eng. 1949. Prev: Cons. Surg. & Urol. Cheltenham Gen. Hosp.

BOREHAM, Philip Anthony Cardiology Department, Ward 14, Frenchay Hospital, Bristol BS16 1LE Tel: 0117 918 6652 Fax: 0117 975 3848 — MB BS 1985 Lond.; MRCP (UK) 1989. (The London Hosp. Medical Coll. Univ. of London) Cons. Cardiol. Frenchay Hosp, Bristol. Prev: Sen. Regist. (Cardiol.) Bristol Roy. Infirm.

BOREK, Barbara Teresa Department of Forensic Medicine, United Medical & Dental Schools, Guy's & St Thomas's Hospitals, St Thomas St., London SE1 9RT — BM 1985 Soton.

BORELAND, Griffith John Dundonald House, Upper Newtownards Road, c/o Medical & Allied DHSS, Belfast BT4 3SF — MB BCh BAO 1977 Belf.; BSc Belf. 1969; MRCGP 1986. Sen. Med. Off. DHSS Belf.

BORER, Elizabeth Frances 31 Harlestones Road, Cottenham, Cambridge CB4 8TR — MB BS 1982 Lond.

BORET, Frank Anthony Dep. Of Obstetrics & Gynaecology, Watford General Hospital, Vicarage Road, Watford WD18 0HB Tel: 0151 625 0774, 01923 244366 Fax: 01923 217939; 11 Mereworth, Wirral CH48 1QT Fax: 01923 217939 — Vrach 1987 Rostov Med Inst USSR; MRCOG; Advanced Certificate in Obstetric Ultrasound. (Rostov State Medical Institute) Cons. (O & G) Watford Gen. Hosp., Watford, Herts. Socs: Brit. Matern. & Fetal Med. Soc. Prev: Specialist Regist. (O & G) Hillingdon Hosp. Uxbridge; Spec.t Regist. (O & G) St. Mary's Hosp. Paddington; Spec. Regist. (O & G) Chelsea & W.minster Hosp. Lond.

BORG, Andrew Gwent Healthcare NHS Trust, Department of Rheumatology, Nevill Hall Hospital, Abergavenny NP7 7EG Tel: 01873 732369 Fax: 01873 732370 Email: andrew.borg@geoent.wales.nhs.ok — MD 1986 Malta; MD 1993 Manch.; DMedRehab RCP 1994 Lond.; MRCP 1990 (UK); FACR 1995; MD Manch. 1993; MRCP (UK) 1990; FACR 1995; DMedRehab RCP Lond. 1994; FRCP 2000 Edin; FRCP 2000 Lond. (Univ. Malta) Cons. Rheum. Gwent Rheum. Serv. Nevill Hall Hosp. Abergavenny; Cons. (Rheum.) Roy. Nat. Hosp. for Rheumatic Dis. Bath. Socs: BMA; Internat. Fell. Amer. Coll. Rheum.; Brit. Soc. Rheum. Prev: Sen. Regist. (Rheum.) Freeman Hosp. Newc.; Research Fell. (Rheum.) Staffs. Rheum. Centre; Regist. (Gen. Med.) Shotley Bridge Gen. Hosp. Durh.

BORG, Charles (retired) High Birch Cottage, Gawsworth, Macclesfield SK11 8UG Tel: 01625 434897 — MD 1934 Malta; BSc Malta 1930; FRCP Glas 1971, M 1962; FRFPS Glas. 1942;

MRCPsych 1971; DPM Lond. 1951. Hon. Cons. Psychiat. Leighton Hosp. Crewe. Prev: Cons. Psychiat. Leighton Hosp. Crewe.

BORG-BARTOLO, Peter Paul Millennium Medical Centre, 121 Weoley Castle Road, Weoley Castle, Birmingham B29 5QD Tel: 0121 427 5201 Fax: 0121 427 5052; Tel: 0121 477 2783 — MRCS Eng. LRCP Lond. 1979. (Roy. Univ. Malta Med. Sch. & Westm. Hosp. Med. Sch.) Sen. partner, Millennium Med. Centre, Birm.; Clin. Asst. (A & E) S. Birm. Trauma Unit Selly Oak Hosp.; Mem. Birm. LMC; Final year Med. Stud. tutor, Dept. Gen. Pract., Univ. Birm. Socs: Fell. RSM. Prev: Chairm. Nourthfield PCG; Chairm. Weoley Castle Commiss.ing Gp.

BORG COSTANZI, Joseph M Monton Medical Centre, Canal Side, Monton Green, Eccles, Manchester M30 8AR.

BORG GRECH, Victor Meadowbank Health Centre, 3 Salmon Inn Road, Falkirk FK2 0XF Tel: 01324 715446 Fax: 01324 717986 — MD 1958 Malta. (Malta) GP Falkirk.

BORGSTEIN, Bernadette Mary Elizabeth Clare House, St Georges Hospital, Blackshaw Road, London SW17 0QT Tel: 020 8725 3728; Doddington Clinic, 311 Battersea Pk Road, London SW11 4LU Tel: 020 7441 0900 — MB BS 1981 Lond.; MRCP (UK) 1988; DCH RCP Lond. 1986; MSc Lond. 1997. (Roy. Free Hosp. Sch. Of Medicine) SCMO (Audiol.) Wandsworth HA. Prev: SCMO (Community Child Health) Wandsworth HA.

BORGSTEIN, Rudolf North Middlesex Hospital, Sterling Way, London N18 1QX — Artsexamen 1980 Groningen; FRCR 1988; DTM Roy. Trop. Inst. Amsterdam 1982; DMRD (RCR) 1987. Cons. Radiol. N. Middlx. Hosp. Prev: Sen. Regist. (Radiol.) Lond. Hosp. Whitechapel; Regist. (Radiol.) Qu. Mary's Hosp. Roehampton.

BORHANZAHI, Khodabakhsh 10 Dover Place, Clifton, Bristol BS8 1AL — MB ChB 1991 Bristol.

BORKETT-JONES, Mr Howard John Accident & Emergency Department, Watford General Hospital, Vicarage Road, Watford WD18 0HB Tel: 01923 217507 — MB BS 1979 Lond.; FRCS Eng. 1984. (Char. Cross) Cons. A & E Watford Gen. Hosp.; Med. Dir. Mt. Vernon & Watford Hosps. NHS Trust. Prev: Rotat. Sen. Regist. (A & E) St. Richards Hosp. Chichester & Char. Cross Hosp. Fulham; Regist. (A & E) King's Coll. Hosp. Lond.; Regist. (Gen. Surg.) St. Helier Hosp. Carshalton.

BORKETT-JONES, Sheila Elizabeth (cons. rooms) Attenborough Surgery, Bushey Health Centre, London Road, Bushey, Watford WD23 2NN Tel: 01923 224267 Fax: 01923 818594 Email: borkettjones@compuserve.com — MB BS 1979 Lond.; BSc (1st cl. Chem. Hons.) Nottm. 1972; MRCP (UK) 1983; MRCS Eng. LRCP Lond. 1979. (Char. Cross) Bd. Mem. PCG; LMC Mem. Prev: Regist. (Gen. & Thoracic Med.) Roy. Surrey Co. Hosp. Guildford; Regist. (Gen. Med. & Cardiol.) Ashford Hosp. Middlx.

BORLAND, Colin David Ross Hinchingbrooke Hospital, Huntingdon PE29 6NT Tel: 01480 416005 Fax: 01480 416561 Email: colin.borland@hbhc.tr-anglox.uk; 13 Hawkes End, Brampton, Huntingdon PE28 4TW Tel: 01480 453978 Fax: 01480 416561 Email: colin.borland@tail21.com — MD 1988 (Medal) Camb.; MB 1977, BChir 1976; FRCP Lond. 1994; MRCP (UK) 1979. (St. Geo.) Cons. Gen. & Geriat. Med. Hinchingbrooke Hosp. Huntingdon. Prev: Sen. Regist. (Gen. & Geriat. Med.) W. Suff. Hosp. Bury St. Edmunds; Regist. (Med.) & Research Fell. Addenbrooke's Hosp. Camb.; SHO Lond. Chest. Hosp.

BORLAND, Colin William Department of Anaesthetics, Balfour Hospital, Newscapa Road, Kirkwall KW15 1BH Tel: 01856 885400 Fax: 01856 885413 Email: cb_gas@doctor.org.uk; Bea House, Back Road, Stromness KW16 3AW Tel: 01856 851043 Fax: 01856 851043 Email: colin.borland1@virgin.net — MB ChB 1974 Glas.; BSc (Hons.) Physiol. Glas. 1969; FRCA 1979; Dip. Palliat. Med. Wales 1994. (Glas.) Cons. Anaesth. Balfour Hosp. Kirkwall; Mem. Orkney Area Med. Comm. Socs: BMA; Assn. Anaesth. GB & Irel.; N. Brit. Pain Assn. Prev: Princip. GP Orkney & Highland HB; Trainee GP Raigmore Hosp. Inverness VTS; Med. Off. (Anaesth.) Camb. Milit. Hosp. Aldershot & BMH Dharan, Nepal.

BORLAND, David Stuart Alloa Health Centre, Marshill, Alloa FK10 1AQ Tel: 01259 216701 — MB ChB 1981 Dundee. GP Alloa, Clackmannansh.

BORLAND, Eve Margaret Benachie, Fossoway, Kinross KY13 0UW Tel: 01577 840082 Email: emborland@eggconnect.net — MB ChB 1954 Glas.; FFA RCS Eng. 1969; T(Anaes) 1991; DA Eng. 1960; Dip. Med. Acup. 1995. (Glas.) Private practitioner of complementary Med.; Med. Ref., Crematorium, Dunfermline. Socs: (Ex-Pres.) Edin. & E. Scotl. Soc. Anaesth.; Brit. Soc. Med. & Dent. Hypn.; Brit. Med. Acup. Soc. Prev: Cons. Anaesth. W. Fife Health Dist. (Dunfermline); SHO (Anaesth.) Bristol Roy. Infirm.; Ho. Off. (Anaesth.) N. Glos. Area.

BORLAND, Gordon Alexander Wotherspoon (retired) Flat 3, 7 Holmwood Grove, Netherlee Place, Cathcart, Glasgow G44 3YL Tel: 0141 637 8650 — MB ChB 1957 Glas.; DObst RCOG 1959. Clin. Asst. Mearnskirk Hosp. Newtonmearns Glas. Prev: Ho. Phys. & Ho. Surg. Vict. Infirm. Glas.

BORLAND, Pauline Margaret Janet (retired) Allt Darach, Strachur, Cairndow PA27 8BZ Tel: 01369 860317 — MB ChB St. And. 1943. Prev: Asst. MOH Roxburghsh.

BORLEY, Mr Neil Roderick Nuffield Department of Surgery, John Radcliffe Hospital, Headington, Oxford OX3 9DU Fax: 01865 768876 Email: neil.borley@nds.ox.ac.uk; Laburnum Cottage, West End, Launton, Bicester OX26 5DG — MB BS 1990 Lond.; 9994 FRCS Eng. 1994; 1994 FRCS Ed. 1994; FRCS 2000 (Sen Surg). (Guy's) Hon. Sen. Regist. (Gen. Surg.) John Radcliffe Hosp. Oxf.; Clin. Lect. (Gen. Surg.) Nuffield Dept Surg. John Radcliffe Hosp. Oxf. Socs: Assn. Coloproctol.; ASGBI. Prev: Regist., John Radcliffe Hosp. Oxf.; SHO (Gen. Surg.) Kent & Canterbury Hosp.; SHO (Cardiothoracic Surg.) Papworth Hosp.

BORLEY, Mr Nigel Cochran 61 The Drive, Tonbridge TN9 2LS; 24 Maple Mews, London SW16 2AL Email: nigel@borleywhite.demon.co.uk — BM 1994 Soton.; MRCS 1998.

BORLEY, Stephen Robert Clyde Street Medical Centre, 1A Clyde Street, Leicester LE1 2BG Tel: 0116 262 8368; Willowbrook Medical Centre, 195 Thurncourt Rd, Leicester LE5 2NL Tel: 0116 241 1700 — MB ChB Leeds 1979; MRCGP 1983; DRCOG 1982.

BORMAN, Colette Anne 28 Postbridge Road, Coventry CV3 5AH — MB BCh 1992 Wales. Trainee GP Bridgend.

BORMAN, Edwin Miles Anaesthetics Department, Walsgrave Hospitals NHS Trust, Clifford Bridge Road, Coventry CV2 2DX — MB ChB 1984 Cape Town; FRCA 1994; FFA RCSI 1993. (Univ. Cape Town, S. Afr.) Cons. Anaesth. Walsgrave Hosp. Coventry. Socs: (Counc.) BMA (Centr. Cons. & Specialists Comm.; (Counc.) GMC; Jnr. Doctors Comm. Past chair. Prev: Sen. Regist. Rotat. (Anaesth.) W. Midl. Train. Scheme, Walsgrave Hosp. Coventry; Regist. Rotat. (Anaesth.) S. Midl. Train. Scheme; SHO & Regist. (Anaesth.) Plymouth.

BORN, Anthony James The Forge, Dorsley Barns, Old Plymouth Road, Totnes TQ9 6DN Tel: 01803 863892 — MB BS 1986 Lond.; MRCP (UK) 1989; DCH RCP Lond. 1993; DA (UK) 1991.

BORN, Faith Elizabeth (retired) Flat 5 Walden Lodge, 48 Wood Lane, London N6 5UU — MB BS 1956 Lond.; MRCS Eng. LRCP Lond. 1956; Dip Bact . Lond. 1961. Prev: on Staff Pub. Health Laborat. Serv.

BORN, Professor Gustav Victor Rudolf Pathopharmacology Unit, William Harvey Research InStreet, St Bartholomew's & The Royal London School of Medicine & Dentistry, Charterhouse Square, London EC1M 6BQ Tel: 020 7982 6070 Fax: 020 7982 6071 — MB ChB 1943 Ed.; Hon. MD Providence 1986; FRCP Lond. 1976; Hon DSc Loyola Chicago 1994; FRS 1972; DPhil Oxf. 1951, MA 1956; DSc Paris 1987; Hon. Bordeaux 1979; MD (Hon.) Munich 1989; Hon. MD Leuven 1979; Hon. MD Münster 1980; Hon. MD Edinb. 1982. Emerit. Prof. Pharmacol. Univ. Lond. (King's Coll.). Socs: Physiol. Soc. & Brit. Pharmacol. Soc.; Brit. Soc. Thrombosis & Haemostasis. Prev: Vandervell Prof. Pharmacol. RCS Eng. & Univ. Lond.; Hon. Dir. MRC Thrombosis Research Gp.; Sheild Prof. Pharmacol. Univ. Camb.

BORN, Matthew Stephen 45 Woodford Avenue, Gants Hill, Ilford IG2 6UH — MB BS 1990 Lond.

BORON, Ida 60 Caiystane Gardens, Edinburgh EH10 6SY — MB BS 1977 Lond.; BSc Lond. 1973, MB BS 1977. (King's Coll. Hosp.) Clin. Asst. P.ss Alexandra Eye Pavil. Edin.

BOROOAH, Pabitra Ram Apurba House Surgery, 154a Shooters Hill Road, Blackheath, London SE3 8RP Tel: 020 8856 4990 Fax: 020 8856 1056 — MB BS 1970 Gauhati; MB BS 1970 Gauhati.

BOROWSKY, Mr Keith Adrian Medway Hospital, Windmill Road, Gillingham ME7 75NY — MB ChB 1982 Witwatersrand; M. Med (Ortho) (urts) 1993; FCS (SA) (Ortho) 1991. Cons. (Orthop.) Medway Hosp.; Cons. BUPA Alexandrea, Imptan La., Walderslade.

Socs: BMA; BOA. Prev: Cons. Private Pract., MilPk. Hosp., Johannesburg.

BORRELLI, Paul Brierley Howgrave-Graham and Partners, The Surgery, Moot Lane, Downton, Salisbury SP5 3QD Tel: 01725 510296 Fax: 01725 513119; Kyte Croft, Slab Lane, Woodfalls, Salisbury SP5 2NE Tel: 01725 510541 — MB BS 1981 Lond.; MRCGP 1985; DRCOG 1986.

BORRILL, Jonathan Kingsley 11 Springdale Gardens, Didsbury, Manchester M20 2QY — BM BS 1990 Nottm.; B.Med.Sci. (Hons.) Nottm. 1988; FRCS (Eng.) 1994. N. W. Orthop. HST Train. Scheme.

BORRILL, Leslie Stuart 33 Dartford Road, Aylestone, Leicester LE2 7PQ — MB ChB 1996 Leic.

BORRILL, Margaret Anne South Arholme Group Practice, High Street, Epworth, Doncaster DN9 1EP Tel: 01427 872232; Email: pk.nik@virgin.net — MB BS 1991 Newc. p/t GP Epworth S. Yorks.

***BORRILL, Zoe Louise** 11 Springdale Gardens, Didsbury, Manchester M20 2QY — MB ChB 1995 Manch.

BORROWMAN, Edwin Haig 34 McNabb Street, Dollar FK14 7DL — MB ChB 1995 Manch.

BORROWMAN, James (retired) Boulevard House, 80 Grange Road, Alloa FK10 1LU Tel: 01259 2688 — MB ChB 1939 Ed.; MFCM 1972; DPH Ed. 1947.

BORROWS, Richard John 100 Cotton Avenue, London W3 6YF — MB BChir 1994 Camb.

BORSADA, Mr Stanley Chhotalal Shakespeare Street Surgery, 1 Shakespeare Street, Loughborough LE11 1QQ Tel: 01509 268060 Fax: 01509 216146; 1 Strachan Close, Leicester Road, Mountsorrel, Loughborough LE12 7FJ — MB BS 1954 Gujarat; FRCS Ed. 1966. (B.J. Med. Coll. Ahmedabad) Surg. GP Mt.sorrel & LoughBoro.. Socs: Fell. Roy. Coll. Surgs. Edin. Prev: Surg. GP Killingworth Health Centre; Surg. GP Cowan Heron Hosp. Dromore; Surg. Banbridge Hosp.

BORTHWICK, Ailsa Square Medical Practice, High Street, Godalming GU7 1AZ Tel: 01483 415141 Fax: 01483 414881; Rally Wood, Hascombe Road, Godalming GU8 4AA Tel: 01483 414999 Fax: 01483 423232 Email: ailsa_dooley@hotmail.com — MB BChir 1983 Camb.; MA, MB Camb. 1983, BChir 1982; DA Eng. 1984. (Cambridge) Partner at GP, The Sq., Godalming; Med. Off. CharterHo. Godalming. Socs: BMA; BASM; MOSA Pres. Prev: SHO (Anaesth.) Frimley Pk. Hosp.; Trainee GP FarnBoro. VTS; SHO (Paediat.) Frimley Pk. Hosp.

BORTHWICK, James Malcolm St Ronans, 17 Dargarvel Avenue, Dumbreck, Glasgow G41 5LU — MB ChB 1979 Ed.; BSc Ed. 1976, MB ChB 1979; FRCA 1984. (University of Edinburgh) Cons. Neuroanaesth. Inst. Neurol. Sci. S.. Gen. Hosp. Glas. Prev: Cons. Anaesth. W.. Infirm. Glas.

BORTHWICK, John Bishop, MBE (retired) 12 Scott Crescent, Galashiels TD1 3JS Tel: 01896 752221 — MD Ed. 1949, MB ChB 1935; FRCP Ed. 1941.

BORTHWICK, Leslie John Lister Hospital, Corey's Mill Lane, Stevenage SG1 4AB — MB ChB 1969 Aberd.; FRCP Lond. 1992; MRCP (U.K.) 1973. Cons. Phys. i/c Diabetes & Endocrinol. Lister Hosp. Stevenage.

BORTHWICK, Margaret June Quarry Street Surgery, 24 Quarry Street, Johnstone PA5 8ED Tel: 01505 321733 Fax: 01505 322181; Holmcroft, Ladysmith Avenue, Kilbarchan, Johnstone PA10 2AS Tel: 01505 705474 Fax: 01505 346251 Email: pborthwick@kilbarchan.demon.co.uk — MB ChB 1971 Ed.; DCH RCPS Glas. 1974; DObst RCOG 1974. (Edinburgh)

BORTHWICK, Max Harvey Beverley (retired) 6 Beacon Down Avenue, Plymouth PL2 2RU Tel: 01752 772985 — MRCS Eng. LRCP Lond. 1951. Prev: Clin. Med. Off. Plymouth HA.

BORTHWICK, Michael Alan Osborne Road Surgery, 200 Osborne Road, Jesmond, Newcastle upon Tyne NE2 3LD Tel: 0191 281 4777 Fax: 0191 281 4309 — MB BS 1972 Newc.; MRCGP 1976; DObst RCOG 1975. Med. Off. Roy. Grammar Sch. Newc. Prev: Trainee GP Newc. VTS.

BORTHWICK, Robin Mathieson Theale Medical Centre, Englefield Road, Theale, Reading RG7 5AS Tel: 0118 930 2513 Fax: 0118 930 4419; Weywood, Ashampstead Road, Bradfield, Reading RG7 6BH Tel: 01734 744799 — MB ChB 1970 Glas.; DObst. RCOG 1972.

BORTHWICK, Susan Doris The Tod Practice, 12 Durham Road, Raynes Park, London SW20 0TW Tel: 020 8946 0069 Fax: 020 8944 2927; 7 Burghley Road, London SW19 5BG Tel: 020 8672 1651 — MB ChB 1982 Glas.; DRCOG 1985.

BORTHWICK-CLARKE, Andrew Department of Radiology, General Hospital, St Helier, Jersey Tel: 01534 59000; Wyvern, Pontorson Lane, Clement, Jersey — MB BS 1974 Lond.; FRCR 1984. Cons. Radiol. Gen. Hosp. St. Helier, Jersey. Prev: Cons. Radiol. Camb. Milit. Hosp. Aldershot; Sen. Regist. (Radiol.) Kings Coll. Hosp. Lond.

BORTON, Chloe Ground Floor Flat, 145 Saltram Crescent, London W9 3JT — MB BS 1998 Lond.; MB BS Lond 1998.

BORUCH, Lisa Ann 239 Harrow Road, London E11 3QA — MB BS 1991 Lond.

BORYSIEWICZ, Professor Leszek Krzysztof Department of Medicine, University of Wales College of Medicine, Heath Park, Cardiff CF14 4XN Tel: 029 2074 2307 Fax: 029 2074 4091 Email: borys@borys.demon.co.uk; 6 The Avenue, Llandaff, Cardiff CF5 2LQ — MB BCh 1975 Wales; MB BCh (Hons.) Wales 1975; PhD Lond. 1986; BSc (Hons.) Wales 1972; FRCP Lond. 1989, M 1977. (Univ. Wales Coll. Med.) Prof. Med. & Hon. Cons. Univ. Hosp. Wales Cardiff. Socs: Fell. of Acad. of Med. Scis. Prev: Lect. (Med. & Infec. Dis.) & Hon. Phys. Addenbrooke's Hosp. Camb.; Wellcome Trust Sen. Lect. (Infec. Dis.) Addenbrooke's Hosp. Camb.; Lister Inst. Research Fell., Sen. Lect. (Med.) Roy. Postgrad. Med. Sch. & Hon. Cons. Phys. Hammersmith Hosp. Lond.

BORZYSKOWSKI, Matgorzata Newcomen Centre, Guy's Hospital, St Thomas St., London SE1 9RT Tel: 020 7955 4636 Fax: 020 7955 4950 Email: margaret.borzykowski@gstt.sthames.nhs.uk — MB BS 1971 Newc.; MB BS (Hons.) Newc. 1971; FRCP Lond. 1993; MRCP (UK) 1973; FCPCH 1997. p/t Cons.NeuroDevelopm.al Paed. Guy's Hosp. Lond. Socs: Roy. Coll. Paediat. and Child Health; Med. Advis. Comm. & Assoc. Spina Bifida & Hydrocephalus; Exec. Comm. of Soc. for Research into Spina Bifida & Hydrocephalus. Prev: Hon. Sen. Regist. (Paediat.) Guy's Hosp. Lond.; Regist. (Paediat.) Guy's Hosp. Lond. & Roy. Alexandra Hosp. Brighton; SHO (Paediat.) Hosp. Sick Childr. Gt. Ormond St. Lond.

BOS, Ewoud Gerard Rikend, Mont Pellier, Gloucester GL1 1LY Tel: 01452 891 023 Email: ewoud.bos@severn_tr.swest.nhs.uk; 2 Darcey Lode, Didcot OX11 7UB Tel: 01235 812 459 Email: ewoud.bos@doctors.org.uk — Artsexamen 1987 Free U Amsterdam; DCH 1991 RCP Lond; MRCP 1992 UK. (Amsterdam Free Univ.) Locum Cons. Paediat., (Community). Prev: Sen. Regist. in Community Paediat. at Hugh Ellis Paediatric Assesment Centre, Ch.hill Hosp., Oxf.; Sen. Regist. (Paediat.) Roy. Berks. Hosp. Reading; Specialist (Paediat.) Amer. Miss. Hosp., Bahrain.

BOSANQUET, Camilla 34E Upper Montagu Street, London W1H 1RP Tel: 020 7262 3899; Wyndside, Church Road, Ryarsh, West Malling ME19 5LB Tel: 01732 842351 — MB BChir Camb. 1948; MRCS Eng. LRCP Lond. 1945; FRCPsych 1976, M 1971; DPM 1961; DCH Eng. 1948. (Camb. & Univ. Coll. Hosp.) p/t Jungian Analyst & Psychotherapist Lond. & W. Malling, Kent. Socs: Profess. Mem. Soc. Anal. Psychol. (Train. Analyst); Founder Mem. Guild Psychother.; BMA. Prev: Cons. Psychiat. & Advis. Lond. Sch. Economics; Clin. Asst. (Psychol. Med.) Univ. Coll. Hosp. Lond.; Psychiat. Adviser to King's Coll. Lond.

BOSANQUET, Henry Gustavus 22 Stanhope Road, Darlington DL3 7AR — MB ChB 1976 Birm.; BA Camb. 1971; MRCPsych 1983.

BOSANQUET, Mr Robert Campbell 7 Graham Park Road, Gosforth, Newcastle upon Tyne NE3 4BH — MB BChir 1969 Camb.; FRCS Eng. 1976; FRCOphth. 1989; DO Eng. 1974. (Univ. Coll. Hosp.) Cons. Ophth. Roy. Vict. Infirm. Newc. u. Tyne. Prev: Ophth. Internat. Grenfell Assn. St. Anthony Newfld.; Sen. Regist. Manch. Roy. Eye Hosp.; Med. Off. Mendi Hosp. S.. Highlands, Papua.

BOSCH, Gideon 19 Dale Gardens, Woodford Green IG8 0PB — MB ChB 1981 Orange Free State.

BOSCOE, Michael Jennings Harefield Hospital, Harefield, Uxbridge UB9 6JH — MB BS 1974 Lond.; MRCS Eng. LRCP Lond. 1974; FFA RCS Eng. 1979. (Lond. Hosp.) Cons. Anaesth. Harefield Hosp. Middlx. Socs: Assn. Anaesth.; Assn. Cardiothoracic Anaesth. Prev: Sen. Regist. (Anaesth.) Guy's Hosp. Lond., Greenwich Dist. Hosp.; Lond. & Brook Gen. Hosp. Lond.; Sen. Regist. (Anaesth.) Univ. Hosp. Leiden, Holland.

BOSE, Mr Alfred Ashok Kumar Ryhope Health Centre, Black Road, Sunderland SR2 0RY Tel: 0191 521 0210 Fax: 0191 521 4235 — MB BS 1964 Calcutta; FRCS Eng. 1970; FRCS Ed. 1970.

BOSE, Amal Krishna Harefield hospital, Hill End Rd, Harefield, Uxbridge UB9 6JH Tel: 01895 823737 Email: a.bose@talk21.com; 30 Tooting Bec Road, London SW17 8BD — MB BS 1994 Lond.; 1994 MB BS Lond.; 1991 BSc (Hons.) Lond.; MRCS 1999 Lond. (St. George's Hospital Medical School) Regist. Cardiothoracic Surg., Roy. Brompton & Harefield NHS Trust. Socs: Fell.of the Roy. Soc. of Med. Prev: Sen. Ho. Off., Cardiothoracic Surg., Blackpool Vict. Hosp.

BOSE, Mr Aniruddha Plastic Surgery Unit, Frenchay Healthcare NHS Trust, Bristol Road, Bristol BS16 1LE Tel: 0117 970 1212; 17 Bampton Court, Gamston Village, Nottingham NG2 6PA Tel: 0115 945 5910 — MB BS 1981 Calcutta; FRCS Glas. 1986. Sen. Regist. (Plastic Surg.) Frenchay Healthcare NHS Trust Bristol. Socs: Fell. Internat. Coll. Surgs.; Fell. Roy. Soc. Med.; Fell. Internat. Soc. Burn Injuries. Prev: Fell. Hand. Surg. Pulvertaft Hand Centre Derbysh. Roy. Infirm.; Regist. (Plastic Surg.) City Hosp. Trust Nottm. & Char. Cross Hosp. Lond.; SHO Rotat. (Surg.) Medway Gp. Hosps.

BOSE, Anjan The Surgery, 49 Bridge Road, Grays RM17 6BZ Tel: 01375 390575 — MB BS 1971 Indore; MD (Pharmcol.) Lond. 1975; DA (UK) 1981.

BOSE, Jagadish Chandra 4 Lindrick Gardens, Chesterfield S40 3JJ Tel: 01246 239206 — MB BS 1964 Calcutta; MD Calcutta 1974; MRCPI 1986. Staff Phys. Chesterfield. Socs: Amer. Coll. Chest Phys.

BOSE, Kalyan 54 Abbotts Park Road, London E10 6HX — MD 1979 Gauhati; MB BS 1976; MRCP (UK) 1981.

BOSE, Keya 22 Newbury Walk, Kirkheaton, Huddersfield HD5 0LQ — MB ChB 1992 Leeds; DRCOG 1996.

BOSE, Milan Kumar North Street Central Surgery, North Street, Newport NP20 1HX Tel: 01633 251228 Fax: 01633 221228 — MB BS 1970 Utkal; MD (Radiother.) Delhi 1973.

BOSE, Monica 90 Chasefield Road, London SW17 8LN — MB BS 1992 Lond.; BSc (Hons) Lond. 1991; MRCP 1995. (St. Geo. Hosp. Med. Sch.) Specialist Regist. Med/Gastroent. S. W. Thames region.

BOSE, Nirmal Kumar 13 Brookland Close, London NW11 6DJ — MB BS 1965 Calcutta; BSc Calcutta 1959, MB BS 1965; DTM & H Liverp. 1970; DVD Liverp. 1970; DCH RCPSI 1975.

BOSE, Mr Pabitra Paul Kumar Larches, 2 Crispin Way, High Wycombe HP11 1PP Tel: 01494 22626 — MB BS 1957 Calcutta; FRCS Ed. 1963; DLO Eng. 1964. Cons. ENT Surg. Gen. Hosp. Scunthorpe, S. Humberside & Goole Dist. Hosp. Socs: Brit. Assn. Otolaryng.; Fell. Roy. Soc. Med. Prev: Cons. ENT Surg. P.ss Mary's RAF Hosp. Halton; Sen. Specialist (ENT) Ahmadi Hosp. Kuwait; Sen. Regist. (ENT) Bradford Roy. Infirm. & Leeds Gen. Infirm.

BOSE, Mr Pradeep 35 St Helens Road, Cardiff CF14 4AR — MB BS 1985 Delhi; FRCS Ed. 1992.

BOSE, Ranjit Kumar 81 Linden Lea, Compton, Wolverhampton WV3 8BQ Tel: 01902 20754 — MB BS 1958 Calcutta; MRCP (UK).

BOSE, Roger Chandra Flat 37C, Block 2, Hallam Close, West Bromwich B71 4HU Tel: 0121 553 1831; 16 Bosvean Gardens, Truro TR1 3NQ Tel: 01872 78758 — MB ChB 1994 Bristol. SHO Rotat. (Surg.) Sandwell Gen. Hosp. W. Bromwich.

BOSE, Subhas Chandra (retired) 9 Aran Close, Hale, Liverpool L24 5SB Tel: 0151 425 3306 — MB BS Lond. 1957; BSc Calcutta 1949; MFFP 1993. Prev: SCMO (Family Plann.) Liverp. AHA (T).

BOSE, Utpaul 73 Wilmers Court, Stracey Road, London NW10 8XN; 9 foxwood Road, Blackheath, London SE3 9HT Tel: 020 8852 7890 Email: vg16@pipex.dial.com — MB BS 1992 Lond.; BSc Anthropology 1989; MSc Mental health 1996; MRC Psych 1997. (Roy.Free) Clin. Research Fell. Forens. Psychiat. Bracton Centre Bexley. Prev: Reg.Intens..Care Bexley; Reg.Brighton; Reg.Research.Lewisham.

BOSHIER, Andrew John 51 Ashwood Circle, Bridge of Don, Aberdeen AB22 8XU — MB ChB 1992 Aberd.

BOSLEY, Alan Robert John Oxleigh House, Ashford, Barnstaple EX31 4BW Tel: 01271 322397 Fax: 01271 377101; North Devon District Hospital, Raleigh Park, Barnstaple EX31 4JB Tel: 01271 378980 Fax: 01271 378980 Email: arbosley@argonet.co.uk — MB BS 1971 Lond.; FRCP Lond. 1993; MRCP (UK) 1975; MRCS Eng. LRCP Lond. 1971; DCH Eng. 1974. (St. Mary's) Cons. Paediat. N.ern Devon Healthcare Trust. Prev: Sen. Regist. Univ. Hosp. Wales; Regist. Llandough & St. Davids Hosps. Cardiff.

BOSLEY, Catherine Mary Guy's Hospital, Department of Psychiatry, St Thomas St., London SE1 9RT — MB BS 1985 Lond.; MRCPsych 1990. Research Assoc. UMDS Guy's Hosp. Lond.

BOSLEY, Peter Vaughan Kirkham Medical Practice, St Albans Road, Babbacombe, Torquay TQ1 3SL Tel: 01803 323541 Fax: 01803 313411; Eldon, 113 Ilsham Road, Wellswood, Torquay TQ1 2HY Tel: 01803 211957 — MB BS 1971 Lond.; MRCS Eng. LRCP Lond. 1971; DA Eng. 1974. (St. Mary's)

BOSMA, Jark 23 Woodleigh Close, Liverpool L31 4LB — MD 1990 Ghent.

BOSMAN, Daniel Hendrik (retired) Royal College of Surgeons of England, Lincoln's Inn Fields, London WC2A 3PE — MB ChB 1948 Cape Town; MSc Stellenbosch 1969; FDS RCS Eng. 1986. Sen. Lect. Anat. RCS Eng. Prev: Surg. Regist. Coventry & Warks. Hosp.

BOSMAN, Deborah Ruth 37 Westpoint, 9 Shortlands Grove, Bromley BR2 0ND Email: deborah.bosnen@ukgateway.net — MB BS 1992 Lond.; BSc Lond. 1989; MRCP (UK). (King's Coll. Lond.) Research Fell. (Diabetes) Kings Coll. Hosp. Socs: BMA; BDA. Prev: Specialist Regist. Poole Gen. Hosp.

BOSMAN, Dennis Lionel 4 Heathfield Farm, Greenside, Ryton NE40 4JA — MB ChB 1982 Cape Town.

BOSMAN, Derek Albert Cavelia House, East Harlsey, Northallerton DL6 2BL — MB ChB 1985 Pretoria.

BOSMAN, Jacques Johann 8 Chatworth House, 7 Westridge Road, Southampton SO17 2HD; 37 Westpoint, 9 Shortlands Grove, Bromley BR2 0ND Email: deborah.bosman@ukgateway.net — MB ChB 1992 Stellenbosch; DRCOG 1997. GP Kent. Prev: GP/Regist. Hythe; SHO Soton. Gen. Hosp.

BOSMANS, Luc Plastic Surgery Unit, Mount Vernon Hospital, Rickmansworth Road, Northwood HA6 2RN — MD 1990 Louvain.

BOSS, Derek Peter Hollies Medical Practice, Tamworth Health Centre, Upper Gungate, Tamworth B79 7EA Tel: 01827 68511 Fax: 01827 51163 — MB ChB 1972 Sheff.; BSc (Hons. Biochem.) Sheff. 1968; MRCGP 1976; DCH Eng. 1975; DObst RCOG 1974. Prev: Trainee GP Coventry VTS.

BOSS, Gisela 3 Princes Rise, Lewisham, London SE13 7PP; 3 Princes Rise, London SE13 7PP Tel: 020 8852 3895 Email: gibossi@aol.com — MB BS 1952 Lond.; MRCS Eng. LRCP Lond. 1952; DCH Eng. 1957. (King's Coll. Hosp.) Socs: Thoracic Soc. Prev: Chest. Phys. Lewisham & Guy's Health Dists. (T); SHO (Paediat.) Lewisham Hosp. Lond.; Ho. Off. Qu. Eliz. Hosp. Childr. Hackney Rd.

BOSS, Jeffrey Mark Newman (retired) Castle Coach House, Castle Pitch, Stroud GL5 2HP Tel: 01453 759231 Fax: 01453 759231 Email: doresh@pop3.poptel.org.uk — MB BS 1948 Lond.; PhD Camb. 1953; BSc Lond. 1949; MRCS Eng. LRCP Lond. 1948. Prev: Sen. Lect. (Physiol.) Univ. Bristol.

BOSS, John Michael North Devon District Hospital, Barnstaple EX31 4JB Tel: 01271 22577; Hewish Barton, Muddiford, Barnstaple EX31 4HH Tel: 01271 850221 — MB ChB 1972 Birm.; FRCP Lond. 1994; MRCP (UK) 1975. Cons. Dermat. Glos. Roy. Hosp. NHS Trust.

BOSS, Vivienne Christine The Aldergate Medical Practice, The Mount, Salters Lane, Tamworth B79 8BH Tel: 01827 54775 Fax: 01827 62835; Yew Tree House, Haunton Road, Harlaston, Tamworth B79 9HS — MB ChB 1972 Sheff.; BSc (Hons. Biochem.) Sheff. 1968; MRCGP 1976; DObst RCOG 1975.

BOSSANO, David Joseph Rusholme Health Centre Tel: 0161 225 6699 Email: david.bossano@gp.p84072.nhs.uk — MB BS 1994 Lond.; DRCOG 1996; MRCGP 1998; BSc Lond. 1990. p/t GP Princip. Rusholme Health Centre. Manch. Prev: SHO (A & E) Roy. Lancaster Infirm.; SHO (O & G & Paediat.) King's Coll. Hosp. Lond.; Ho. Surg. Vale of Leven Hosp. Alexandria.

BOSSLEY, Cara Jayne 48 St Leonards Road, Hertford SG14 3JW — MB ChB 1998 Manch.; MB ChB Manch 1998.

BOSSON, Sara Mancunian Community Heallth NHS Trust, Lungsight HC., 526-528 Stockport Rd, Manchester M13 0RR Tel: 0161 225 9274 Fax: 0161 248 1238; 34 St Johns Road, Old Trafford, Manchester M16 7GX Email: sbasson@doctors.net — MB ChB 1990 Liverp.; BSc (Hons.) Liverp. 1987; DFFP 1994; MMED Sci(Child Health) Leeds 1999. (Liverpool) Staff Grade (Paediat.) Mancunian Community NHS Trust. Socs: Brit. Paediat. Assn.; RCPCH; BACCH. Prev: SHO (Paediat.) & Clin. Med. Off. (Community Paediat.) St. Helens & Knowsley NHS Trust; SHO Rotat. (Urol.) Newc. HA; SHO (A & E) Bolton HA.

BOSSOWSKA, Izabella Joanna 51 Craven Gardens, Wimbledon, London SW19 8LU — MB ChB 1979 Wales; MSc Wales 1976, MB ChB 1979; Cert. Family Plann JCC 1984; DRCOG 1981.

BOSTAN, Amar Mahmood 1 Park Grove, Keighley BD21 3LL — MB ChB 1995 Leic.

BOSTOCK, Anthony Denys (retired) 10 Brinkley Way, Felixstowe IP11 9TX Tel: 01394 275997 — MB ChB 1952 Manch.; FFCM 1983, M 1972; DPH Manch. 1958. Prev: SCM (Environm. Health) W. Suff. HA & Leeds E. HA.

BOSTOCK, David Brinnington Health Centre, Brinnington Road, Stockport SK5 8BS Tel: 0161 430 4002 Fax: 0161 430 2918; 14 Davenport Park Road, Stockport SK2 6JS Tel: 0161 456 9121 — MB 1971 Camb.; BChir 1970; DObst RCOG 1976; DA Eng. 1975.

BOSTOCK, Elizabeth Ann Ghyll Croft, 12 Brook St., Hebden, Skipton BD23 5DQ — MB ChB 1959 Leeds.

BOSTOCK, Frank (retired) Daisy Bank, Littlebeck, Whitby YO22 5HA Tel: 01947 810752 Email: frank.bostock@btinternet.com — MB ChB Leeds 1960; MRCS Eng. LRCP Lond. 1960; FFA RCS Eng. 1965. Prev: Cons. in Anaesth. Leeds (St. Jas.) Univ. Hosp.

BOSTOCK, John Ferrier (retired) Rosetree Cottage, Shiprod's Drive, Wheatsheaf Road, Henfield BN5 9AR Tel: (01273) 493327 — MB BS Lond. 1966; FRCOG 1987, M 1971. Indep. Cons. Gyn. Surg. Hove.

BOSTOCK, John Francis Wickham Surgery, Station Road, Wickham, Fareham PO17 5JL Tel: 01329 833121 Fax: 01329 832443; Seasons, Clubhouse Lane, Waltham Chase, Southampton SO32 2NN — MB BS 1968 Lond.; MRCP (UK) 1972; MRCS Eng. LRCP Lond. 1968; DObst RCOG 1970. (St. Bart.) Socs: BMA. Prev: Hosp. Pract. (Diabetes) Soton. Gen. Hosp.; Regist. (Med.) Soton. Gen. Hosp.; Ho. Surg. St. Bart. Hosp. Lond.

BOSTOCK, Thomas Stephen Vladimir Belsize Lane Surgery, 37 Belsize Lane, Hampstead, London NW3 5AS Tel: 020 7794 5787 — MB BS 1978 Lond.; LLB Lond. 1969; Cert. Family Plann. JCC 1981; Cert. Prescribed Exp Gen. Pract. (JCPTGP) 1981. (St. Bart) Med. Assessor Social Security Appeal Tribunals; Med. Mem. Disabil. Appeal Tribunals. Socs: Med.-Legal Soc.; BMA. Prev: Cas. Off. Roy. Lond. Hosp.; Clin. Asst. Health Care Elderly P.ss Louise Hosp. Kensington; Ho. Surg. (ENT & Surg.) St. Bart's Hosp. Lond.

BOSTON, Barbara Karen Whiteabbey Health Centre, Doagh Road, Whiteabbey, Newtownabbey BT37 9QN Tel: 01232 864341 — MB ChB 1986 Aberd.; MRCGP 1990; DCH RCPSI 1991; Cert. Family Plann. JCC 1990; DRCOG 1989.

BOSTON, Mr Derek Atwell Wellesley Hospital, Eastern Avenue, Southend-on-Sea SS2 4XH Tel: 01702 462944 Fax: 01702 600160 — MB BS 1972 Lond.; FRCS Eng. 1977. (Middlx.) Cons. Orthop. Surg. S.end & Wellesley Hosps. Socs: Fell. BOA & Roy. Soc. Med. Prev: Lect. (Orthop. Surg.) Soton. Univ.; Hon. Sen. Regist. Soton. Gen. Hosp. & Lord Mayor Treloar Hosp. Alton; Regist. (Orthop. Surg.) St. Thos. Hosp. Lond.

BOSTON, Francis Kenneth (retired) Tar Wood House II, 14 Stockerston Road, Uppingham, Oakham LE15 9UD Tel: 01572 821486 — MB BChir 1933 Camb.; MA Oxf. 1963; MA Camb. 1933; MRCS Eng. LRCP Lond. 1930; FFA RCS Eng. 1951; DA Eng. 1939. Prev: Cons. Anaesth. United Oxf. Hosps.

BOSTON, Paul Francis Michael Carlisle Centre, Nether Edge Hospital, 75 Osborne Road, Sheffield S11 9BF Tel: 0114 271 6630 Fax: 0114 271 6019 Email: p.boston@shef.ac.uk — MB ChB 1976 Sheff.; PhD Camb. 1982, MA 1977, BA 1973; MRCPsych 1994; Dip. Pharm. Med. RCP (UK) 1984. Cons. (Old Age Psychiat.) Nether Edge Hosp. Sheff.; Hon. Sen. Clin. Lect. Univ. of Sheff. Socs: Fell. Roy. Statistical Soc.; BMA; Brit. Assn. of PsychoPharmacol. Prev: Lect. (Psychiat.) Univ. Leicester & Hon Sen. Regist. Leicester Gen. Hosp.; Regist. Rotat. (Psychiat.) Notts. Train. Scheme; Clin. Research Manager Boots Company plc Nottm.

BOSTON, Mr Victor Ernest 69A Thornyhill Road, Killinchy, Newtownards BT23 6SG Tel: 01238 541872 — MD 1980 Belf.; MB BCh BAO 1968; FRCS Ed. 1972. Cons. Surg. (Paediat.) Roy. Belf. Hosp. Sick Childr.

BOSWELL, Anne Margaret 3 St Peter's Road, Aldeburgh IP15 5BG — MB BS 1991 Lond.

BOSWELL, Christine Margaret 16 College Close, Rowlands Castle PO9 6AJ — MB ChB 1978 Manch.; DRCOG 1984.

BOSWELL, Graham Victor Bronglais General Hospital, Aberystwyth SY23 1ER Tel: 01970 623131 Fax: 01970 635923 Email: graham.boswell@ceredigion-tr.wales.nhs.uk; Sunny Hill, Llanbadarn Road, Aberystwyth SY23 1EY Email: gvboswell@hotmail.com — MB BS 1979 Lond.; FRCP Lond. 1994; MRCP (UK) 1983. Cons. Phys. (Geriat. Med.) Bronglais Hosp. Aberystwyth. Prev: Sen. Regist. (Geriat. Med.) S. Glam. & E. Dyfed HA; Regist. (Med.) N. Staffs. Med. Centre Stoke-on-Trent.

BOSWELL, Jack, DFC (retired) 5 Guthrie Street, Carnoustie DD7 6EL Tel: 01241 52465 — MB ChB 1952 St. And. Prev: Asst. Dir. E. Scotl. Blood Transfus. Serv. Ninewells Hosp. Dundee.

BOSWELL, Paul Andrew Microbiology Department, The North Hampshire Hospital, Aldermaston Road, Basingstoke RG24 9NA Tel: 01256 313310 Fax: 01256 314904; Hobbes, Dorchester Way, Greywell, Hook RG29 1BX Tel: 01256 703633 — MB ChB 1966 Bristol; FRCPath 1984, M 1972. Cons. Med. Microbiol. The N. Hants. Hosp. Basingstoke; Hon. Clin. Sen. Lect. Soton. Univ. Med. Sch. Socs: Assn. Med. Microbiol. Prev: Sen. Lect. & Hon. Cons. Microbiol. Kings Coll. Hosp. Lond.; Sen. Regist. (Bacteriol.) St. Bart. Hosp. Lond.; Lect. (Bacteriol.) Middlx. Hosp. Med. Sch.

BOSWELL, Timothy Charles John Department of Microbiology and Infectious Diseases, Nottingham City Hospital, Hucknall Road, Nottingham NG5 1PB Tel: 0115 969 1169 Ext: 45572 Fax: 0115 962 7766 Email: tboswell@ncht.brent.nhs.uk — MB BS 1989 Lond.; BSc Lond. 1986; MRCPath 1997; MD Lond. 1997. Cons. Med. Microbiol. Pub. Health Laborat. Nottm. Prev: Sen. Regist. (Med. Microbiol.) Pub. Health Laborat. Birm.

BOSWOOD, Sarah Bridget South Hay, Kingsley, Bordon GU35 9NR Tel: 01420 474376 — BM BCh 1972 Oxf.

BOSWORTH, Michael Robert 713 Yardleywood Road, Billesley, Birmingham B13 0PT; 10 Hazel Drive, Hollywood, Birmingham B47 5RJ — MB ChB 1985 Birm.; DRCOG 1988. Forens. Med. Examr. Prev: Clin. Asst.

BOSWORTH, Philip The Surgery, White Cliff Mill St., Blandford Forum DT11 7BH Tel: 01258 452501 Fax: 01258 455675 Email: pbos@litwilv.demon.co.uk; Little Wilverley, 9 Shaston Road, Stourpaine, Blandford Forum DT11 8TA Tel: 01258 454428 Email: 100711.3160@compuserve.com — MB ChB 1976 Bristol; BSc (Hons. Chem.) Lond. 1971; FRCS Eng. 1981; MRCGP 1984. Med. Off. Bryanston Sch.

BOTELHO DE GUSMAO DE MORAES, Maria Francisca Rheumatology Unit, Hammersmith Hospital, Du Cane Road, London W12 0NN — MB BCh 1985 Witwatersrand.

BOTELL, Elizabeth Jane — MB ChB 1970 Sheff.; DFPP 1999; (Mem. Inst. Psychosexual Med.) DFPP 1994. (Sheff. 1970) p/t SCMO (Sexual Health) I. of Wight; Chairm. Inst. Psychosexual Med.; SCMO (Psychosex. Med.) S.amp. City PCT; SCMO (Psychosex. Med.) I of Wight. Socs: Brit. Menopause Soc.; Inst. Psychosexual Med. (Chairm. Counc.); Fac. Fam. Plann. & Reproductive Healthcare. Prev: Med. Off. Bury St. Edmunds Health Dist.; Asst. Med. Off. Sheff. Co. Boro.

BOTELL, Laurie Thomas Sandown Medical Centre, Melville Street, Sandown PO36 8LD Tel: 01983 402464 Fax: 01983 405781; 47 The Fairway, Lake, Sandown PO36 9EG Tel: 01983 402864 — MB ChB 1971 Sheff.; BSc (Hons.) Sheff. 1968, MB ChB 1971; DObst RCOG 1976. GP Tutor Isle of Wight. Prev: Trainee GP W. Suff. VTS; Demonst. (Anat. & Physiol.) Univ. Sheff.

BOTELL, Rachel Elizabeth 47 The Fairway, Lake, Sandown PO36 9EG — MB BS 1998 Lond.; MB BS Lond 1998.

BOTFIELD, Claire Hilda Bcomley Hospitals NHS Trust Email: clairebotfield@doctors.org.uk — MB BS 1990 Lond.; FRCA 1994. (The Lords Hosp. Med. Sch.) Cons. Anaesth. & Intens. Care Med. Socs: Brit. Med. Assn.; Roy. Coll. Of Anaesth.s; Intens. Care Soc.

BOTHA, Mr Abraham Jacobus Whipps Cross Hospital, Leytonstone, London E11 1NR; 77 Monkhams Drive, Woodford Green IG8 0LD — MB ChB 1983 Stellenbosch; MD Lond. 1995; FRCS (Gen.) 1996; FRCS Eng. 1990. Cons. Surg. Socs: Assn. Upper G.I. Surg.; Surg. Research Soc.; Assn. Endoscopic Surg.

BOTHA, Marie Elizabeth 70 Bradbourne Road, Sevenoaks TN13 3QA Tel: 01732 455903 — MB ChB 1969 Pretoria; MFHom 1984; DA Eng. 1972. Dip. Inst. Psychother. & Counselling 1989.

BOTHA, Roger André Department of Anaesthetics, City Hospital Trust, Dudley Road, Birmingham B18 7QH Tel: 0121 507 4343 — MB BS 1974 Lond.; MRCS Eng. LRCP Lond. 1974; FFA RCS Eng. 1979. (Guy's) Cons. Anaesth. Dudley Rd. Hosp. Birm. Prev: Sen.

Regist. (Anaesth.) Birm. HA; Regist. (Anaesth.) Nott. City & Gen. Hosps.

BOTHAM, James Russell Waddington 52 Maybrick Road, Bath BA2 3PX — MB BS 1994 Lond.

BOTHAM, Lorraine Health Centre, Beech Avenue, Rhosllanerchrugog, Wrexham LL14 1AA Tel: 01978 845955 Fax: 01978 846757 — MRCS Eng. LRCP Lond. 1985; DRCOG 1988. Trainee GP Hope.

BOTHAM, Stephen Anthony The Health Centre, Padeswood Road, Buckley CH7 3HZ; Hafod Owen, Lower Mountain Road, Hope, Wrexham LL12 9RW — MB BS 1984 Lond.; MA Camb. 1981; MRCGP 1989; DRCOG 1987. Trainee GP Woking VTS.

BOTHAMLEY, Graham Henry Department of Respiratory Medicine, The Homerton Hospital, Homerton Row, London E9 6SR Tel: 020 8510 7814 Fax: 020 8510 7687 — BM BCh 1980 Oxf.; PhD Lond. 1990; MA Oxf. 1981, BA (Hons.) Physiol. Sc. 1977; MRCP (UK) 1985. Cons. Gen. & Respirat. Med. Homerton Hosp. Lond.; Hon. Sen. Lect. St. Bart., Roy. Lond. & Qu. Mary Med. Coll. Lond. Socs: Brit. Thorac. Soc.; Brit. Soc. Immunol.; Amer. Thoracic Soc. Prev: Sen. Regist. Univ. Coll. Hosps. & Lond. Chest Hosp.; Clin. Scientist MRC TB & Related Infecs. Unit Hammersmith Hosp. Lond.

BOTHEROYD, Eric Martin Unicorn House, Bainbridge, Leyburn DL8 3EH — MB ChB Birm. 1967; BSc Birm. 1964; MFOM 1988; DIH (Soc. Apoth.) 1981. (Birm.) Prev: Sen. Employm. Med. Adv. Health & Safety Exec. Aberd.

BOTHERWAY, Andrew Harry 14 Amherst Road, Kenilworth CV8 1AH — MB ChB 1996 Leeds.

BOTHERWAY, Gwyneth Joyce Doreen (retired) Galeed, Farnham Lane, Farnham Royal, Slough SL2 3RY Tel: 01753 642820 — MB BS 1954 Lond.; MRCS Eng. LRCP Lond. 1954; MFFP 1993. Health Screening P.ss Margt. Hosp. Windsor. Prev: Med. Off. Family Plann. Assn. (Retd.).

BOTHRA, Jugnu Psychiatry for Elderly, Daisy Hill House, Lynfield Mount Hospital, Bradford BD9 6DP Tel: 01274 613937 — MB BS 1970 Rajasthan. (SMS Med. Coll. Jaipur, India) Clin. Med. Off. (Psychiat. for Elderly) Bradford; Inceptor Roy. Coll. Psychiat. Prev: Clin. Med. Off. High Royds Hosp. Leeds.

BOTHWELL, Janet Elizabeth Department of Dermatology, Barnsley District General Hospital, Gawber St., Barnsley S75 2EP Tel: 01226 777773 Fax: 01226 774971; The Old School House, Holmfield, Clayton W., Huddersfield HD8 9LZ Tel: 01484 865717 Fax: 01484 865717 — MB BCh 1983 Witwatersrand; Mmed (SA); FFDerm (S Afr). Cons. Dermat. Barnsley Gen. Hosp. Prev: Research Regist. (Dermat.) Liverp.; Cons. Dermat. Johannesburg & Hillbrow Hosps. S. Afr.

BOTHWELL, Janice Elizabeth St Angelo House, Ballinamallard, Enniskillen BT94 — MB BCh BAO 1992 Belf.

BOTHWELL, Peter William 114 Shipston Road, Stratford-upon-Avon CV37 7LR Tel: 01789 204363 — MD Aberd. 1961, MB ChB 1946; DPH Aberd. 1950. (Aberd.) Managing Dir. Caliber Design Ltd. (Automotive Safety Design); Bidford-on-Avon. Socs: Soc. Social Med & Roy. Aeronaut. Soc. Prev: Epidemiol. & Lect. Preven. Med. Univ. Bristol & Bristol Pub. Health; Dept.; Head, Motor Cycle Research Unit Univ. Birm.; Head, Bioeng. BSA/Triumph Research Estab.

BOTHWELL, Robert Alexander c/o Dr Janet Bothwell, Department of Dermatology, Barnsley District General, Gawber Road, Barnsley S75 2EP — MB BCh 1982 Witwatersrand.

BOTMA, Anna Magritha c/o PRN, 42 Theobalds Road, London WC1X 8NW — MB ChB 1991 Stellenbosch.

BOTMAN, Antonia Geertruida Maria Flat 9A, Llys Ceirios, Ysbyty Gwynedd Hospital, Penrhosgarnedd, Bangor LL57 2PW — Artsexamen 1994 Amsterdam.

BOTROS, Ashraf Maxwell St George's Medical Centre, 276 Lady Margaret Road, Southall UB1 2RX Tel: 020 8578 2421 — MB BCh 1987 Assiut; MB BCh Assiut Egypt 1987; MRCOG 1994. GP Ealing, Lond. Socs: Med. Protec. Soc. Prev: GP/Regist. Bournemouth; SHO (Paediat.) P.ss Alexandra Hosp. Harlow Essex; Staff Grade (O & G) Darlington.

BOTROS, Fayez Nazeer 134 Harley Street, London W1G 7JY Tel: 020 7935 2737 Fax: 020 7487 3071; 27 Southwood Lawn, Highgate, London N6 5SD — MB BCh 1955 Cairo; LMSSA Lond. 1965. (Ein-Shams) Socs: Soc. Apoth. Lond.; BMA; Hunt. Soc. Prev: GP Lond.; Regist. (Path.) Roy. Berks. Hosp. Reading.

BOTROS, Hoda Staunton Group Practice, 3-5 Bounds Green Road, Wood Green, London N22 8HE Tel: 020 8889 4311 Fax: 020 8826 9100 — MB BS 1992 Lond.; BSc Lond. 1989; DRCOG 1995; MRCGP 1997; RCGP Lond. (St. Bart.) Prev: GP/Regist. Morris Hse. Surg. Lond.

BOTT, Edward Charles Arden, CBE (retired) The Chesteine, High St, Taunton TA4 1LW — MB BChir 1949 Camb.; FRCP Lond. 1982, M 1951. Prev: Chief Med. Off. Metrop. Police.

BOTT, Michael Colchester Uplands Clinic, 28 Wilbury Road, Hove BN3 3JP Tel: 01273 773838 Fax: 01273 820754 Email: drmikebott@talk21.com; Tel: 01323 832283 Fax: 01323 832283 — MB BS Lond. 1958; MRCS Eng. LRCP Lond. 1958; MRCPsych 1971; DPM Eng. 1965. (Char. Cross Hosp. Med. Sch.) Cons. Psychiat. Uplands Clinic Hove. Socs: E.bourne Med. Soc.; Brighton & Hove Med. Soc. Prev: Cons. Psychiat. Godden Green Clinic Sevenoaks; Cons. Psychiat. Hailsham & Hastings Hosp. Gps.; Sen. Regist. York Clinic Guy's Hosp. Lond.

BOTT, Michael Harris 8 Allenhall Way, Kirkella, Hull HU10 7QU Tel: 01482 654247 Email: michael-bott@lineone.net; 8 Allanhall Way, Kirkella, Hull HU10 7QU Tel: 01482 654247 — MB ChB 1955 Sheff. Assoc. Fac. Homoeop.; Tribunal Med. Mem. Appeals Serv., Leeds. Prev: Clin. Asst. Birm. Accid. Hosp.; Obst. Ho. Surg. City Hosp. Nottm.; Ho. Phys. Rotherham Hosp.

BOTT, Mr Simon Roger John Rake Court, Station Lane, Milford, Godalming GU8 5AD — MB BS 1994 Lond.; FRCS 1998.

BOTTERILL, Ian David 8 Albert Road E., Hale, Altrincham WA15 9AL — MB ChB 1991 Manch.

BOTTGER, Sabine St James's University Hospital, Beckett St., Leeds LS9 7TF; 35 Wetherby Road, Leeds LS8 2JU — State Exam Med 1991 Heidelberg.

BOTTING, Janice Ruth 3 Twyn Court, Usk NP15 1BH — MB BS 1997 Lond.

BOTTING, Jonathan Paul The Surgery, 1 Glebe Road, Barnes, London SW13 0DR Tel: 020 8748 1065 — MB BS 1982 Lond.; MSOM 1993 (Mem. Soc. of Orthop. Med.); MRCGP 1989; DRCOG 1988. (Middlesex) GP Barnes Lond. Prev: SHO (Oncol.) Roy. Marsden Hosp. Sutton; SHO (Thoracic Med.) St. Thos. Hosp. Lond.; SHO (Cardiol.) Nat. Heart. Hosp. Lond.

BOTTING, Mr Terence David John (retired) 273 Warwick Road, Olton, Solihull B92 7AB Tel: 0121 707 4757 Fax: 0121 707 7907 Email: botti@supanet.com — MB ChB 1957 Birm.; FRCS Eng. 1963. Cons. Orthop. & Traum. Surg. Selly Oak & Accid. Hosps. Birm. Prev: Sen. Regist. Orthop. Surg. Roy. Orthop. & Accid. Hosps. Birm.

BOTTO, Marina Rheumatology Unit, Hammersmith Hospital, Du Cane Road, London W12 0NN Tel: 020 8743 2030 Fax: 020 8743 3109 — State DMS 1990 Verona.

BOTTOM, Sarah Frances Evelyn Jorvik Medical Practice, 6 Peckitt Street, York YO1 9WF Tel: 01904 639171 Fax: 01904 633881; The Rosary, The Roseary, Low St, Thornton Le Clay, York YO60 7TG Tel: 01653 618715 Email: howlbeck@aol.com — MB ChB 1972 St. And. (St. Andrews) Princip. Gen. Pract.; Clin. Governance Lead for Selby & York PCT. Prev: GP Trainer.

BOTTOMLEY, Ann Margaret Hope Family Medical Centre, Hawarden Road, Hope LL12 9NL Tel: 01978 760468; Silverburn Lodge, Bowling Bank, Wrexham LL13 9RL — MB ChB 1986 Manch.; BSc St. And. 1983. Prev: Trainee GP/SHO (O & G & Paediat.) Wrexham VTS; SHO (A & E) & Ho. Off. (Gen. Med. & Gen. Surg.) Wrexham Maelor Hosp.

BOTTOMLEY, Cecilia Peggy Evelyn Horestone 24 Walcot Square, London SE11 4TZ — MB BChir 1995 Camb.; DFFP 1997. (University of Cambridge and UMDS) SHO (O & G) Kings Coll. Hosp. Lond. Prev: Clin. Research Fell. (Genitourin. Med.) Kings Coll. Hosp. Lond.; SHO (O & G) Univ. Coll. Hosp.

BOTTOMLEY, David Martin King Cookridge Hospital, Leeds LS16 6QB Tel: 0113 392 4206 Fax: 0113 392 4072 Email: david.bottomley@leedsth.nhs.uk — MB BS 1985 Lond.; MRCP (UK) 1988; FRCR 1992. (Westminister Hosp.) Cons. (Clin. Oncol.) Cookridge Hosp. Leeds. Socs: BMA; MPS. Prev: Research Regist. Char. Cross & W.m. Med. Sch.; Regist. (Radiother. & Oncol.) W.m. Hosp. Lond. & Mt. Vernon Hosp. N.wood Middlx.; Sen. Regist. (Radiother. & Oncol.) Cookridge Hosp. Leeds.

BOTTOMLEY, David Reginald William Park Health Centre, 190 Duke Street, Sheffield S2 5QQ Tel: 0114 272 7768 — MB ChB 1983 Sheff.

BOTTOMLEY, Derek Hart (retired) Hawsteads, 29 Linden Avenue, Darlington DL3 8PS Tel: 01325 489924 — MRCS Eng. LRCP Lond. 1951. Police Surg. Prev: Squadron Ldr. RAF Med. Br.

BOTTOMLEY, Emma Louise The Annex, Highfield House, Goggs Lane, Salisbury SP5 2NY — MB BS 1993 Newc.

BOTTOMLEY, John Gordon Hart College Street Health Centre, Leigh WN7 2RF Tel: 01942 674431 Fax: 01924 609061 — MB ChB 1980 Leeds; BSc (Hons.) Leeds 1976; MRCPCH; DCCH RCP Ed. 1987. (Leeds) SCMO (Community Child Health) Wigan & Leigh NHS Trust. Socs: BACCH.

BOTTOMLEY, John Michael 21 Carr Lane, Sandal, Wakefield WF2 6HJ — MB ChB 1993 Liverp.

BOTTOMLEY, Mr John Philip The Department of Radiology, The Royal Infirmary, Huddersfield HD3 7EH; The Barn House, 29 Walshaw Mill Road, Meltham, Holmfirth HD9 4EA Tel: 01484 554630 — MB ChB 1964 Liverp.; MB ChB 1964 Liverp.; FRCS 1969; FRCS 1970 Eng.; FRCR 1975; DMRD 1973 Liverp. Cons. Radiol. Huddersfield Roy. Infirm.

BOTTOMLEY, Malcolm Brooke Brunswick Cottage, 42 Combe Road, Combe Down, Bath BA2 5HY Tel: 01225 833757 Fax: 01225 833757 — MB ChB Sheff. 1958; DObst RCOG 1962. (Sheff.) Indep. Sports Phys. Bath; Med. Dir. Univ. Bath Distance Learn. Course (Sports Med.) for Doctors; Sports Rehabil. St. Mary's Coll. Univ. Surrey. Socs: Brit. Assn. Sport & Med.; Clin. Soc. Bath. Prev: GP Ellesmere; Med. Off. Bath Univ.; Olympic Med. Off. 1988.

BOTTOMLEY, Nicola 6 St Martins Close, Epsom KT17 4DR Tel: 01372 748340 — MB ChB 1994 Sheff.; DCH RCP Lond. 1996; MRCGP Lond 1998. (Sheff.) GP. Prev: GP Regist. VTS, Epsom Gen. Hosp.; Ho. Off. (Surg. & Med.) Barnsley Dist. Gen. Hosp.

BOTTOMLEY, Sarah Elizabeth 7 Grosvenor Road, Batley WF17 0LX — MB ChB 1990 Bristol.

BOTTOMLEY, Walter 42 Lache Lane, Chester CH4 7LR — MB BCh BAO 1954 Dub.; BA, MB BCh BAO Dub. 1954; LDS Durh. 1961. (T.C. Dub.) Prev: Ho. Off. Banbridge Hosp. Co. Down; RAMC.

BOTTOMLEY, Walter William Dept Dermatology, Devonshire Road Hospital, Devonshire Road FY3 8AZ; Email: bjorndal@doctors.org.uk — MB ChB 1984 Liverp.; FRCP 2001. Cons. Dermat. Devonsh. Rd. Hosp. Blackpool. Prev: Lect. (Dermat.) Leeds Gen. Infirm.; Regist. (Dermat.) Hull Roy. Infirm.; Regist. (Respirat. Med.) Walsgrave Hosp. Coventry.

BOTTONE, Nicholas Peter Yew Tree Cottage, Hutton, Berwick-upon-Tweed TD15 1TS — MB BS 1987 Lond.; MSc (Econ-HPF) Lond. 1993. (St. Thos. Hosp. Med. Sch.) Policy Adviser Glaxo-Wellcome. Prev: Primary Care Adviser NHS Scotl. Scott. Off.; Lect. (Pub. Health Med.) UMDS St. Thomas Hosp. Lond.

BOTTRILL, Dennis The Hermitage, Rakehead, Ulverston LA12 Tel: 01229 52000 — MRCS Eng. LRCP Lond. 1942. (Birm.)

BOTTRILL, Mr Ian David ENT Dept, Eadcliffe Infirmary, Woodstock Rd, Oxford OX2 Tel: 01865 228586 — BM 1986 Soton.; FRCS (Otol.) Eng. 1991; FRCS (ORL) 1996. (Southampton) ENT Cons. Radcliffe Infirm. Oxf. & Stoke Mandeville Hosp. Aylesbury. Prev: Sen. Regist. (ENT) Addenbrooke's Hosp. Camb., Roy. Nat. Throat, Nose & Ear Hosp.; Research Fell. (Otol.) New Eng. Med. Center Boston, USA; Regist. (ENT) Profess. Unit Roy. Nat. Throat, Nose & Ear Hosp. Lond.

BOTWOOD, Nicholas Allan John Flat 1, 7 Brownlow Mews, London WC1N 2LD — MB BS 1992 Lond.

BOUCH, Charles Joseph Kennedy Gartnavel Royal Hospital, 1055 Great Western Road, Glasgow G12 0XH Tel: 0141 211 3600; 9 Varna Road, Jordanhill, Glasgow G14 9NE Tel: 0141 576 9833 — MB ChB 1982 Glas.; MRCPsych 1986. Cons. Psychiat. Gartnavel Roy. Hosp. Glas. Socs: Director of Continuing Professional Developm., Roy. Coll. of Psychiat.s. Prev: Sen. Regist. (Psychiat.) Gtr. Glas. HB; Regist. (Psychiat.) Stobhill Hosp. Glas.

BOUCH, David Christopher 21 Ashfield Road, Stoneygate, Leicester LE2 1LB — MB ChB 1996 Leeds.

BOUCH, Dennis Clive Department of Pathology, Leicester Royal Infirmary, Leicester LE1 5WW Tel: 0116 258 6587 Fax: 0116 270 4499 — MB ChB 1965 Ed.; BSc Ed. 1962; FRCPath 1985, M 1973. (Ed.) Cons. Pathol. Leicester Roy. Infirm.; Home Office Path. Socs: Path. Soc. & Assn. Clin. Path.; Brit. Assn. Forens. Med. & Brit. Acad. Forens. Sci. Prev: Lect. (Pathol.) Univ. Edin.; Ho. Surg. & Ho. Phys. Roy. Infirm. Edin.

BOUCH, Kay Bridge Road Surgery, 1A Bridge Road, Oufton Broad, Lowestoft NR32 3LJ Tel: 01502 565936 Fax: 01502 531539; 141 Yarmouth Road, Lowestoft NR32 4AF — MB BS 1980 Lond.; MRCGP 1984; DRCOG 1982.

BOUCHER, Audrey Mary Grace Whitchurch Surgery, Bell Street, Whitchurch RG28 7AE Tel: 01256 892113 Fax: 01256 895610; 14 Cadnam Close, Oakley, Basingstoke RG23 7AF Tel: 01256 780011 — MB BS 1974 Lond.; DRCOG 1976. (Roy. Free)

BOUCHER, Barbara Joan (retired) The Royal London Hospital, London E1 1BB Tel: 020 7377 7293 Fax: 020 7377 7636 Email: bboucher@doctors.org.uk — MB BS Lond. 1957; BSc (Hons.) Lond. 1954, MD 1969; FRCP Lond. 1974, M 1961. Hon. Cons. Sen. Lect. St Bart's & The Roy. Lond. Med. and Dent. Sch., QM& W Coll. Prev: Sen. Regist. (Med.) Lond. Hosp.

BOUCHER, Charles Maxwell (retired) 4 Glenavon, Arnewood Park, New Milton BH25 6TU Tel: 01425 616074 — MB BCh BAO 1940 Belf.; MD Belf. 1963; MRCGP 1956. JP. Prev: Sen. Med. Off. DHSS.

BOUCHER, Jeremy 3 Cowleaze Road, Broadmayne, Dorchester DT2 8EW — MB BS 1966 Lond.; MRCS Eng. LRCP Lond. 1966; MRCGP 1986.

BOUCHER, Karen Joy Young People's Service, 3 North Parade Buildings, Bath BA1 1NS Tel: 01225 448373; 51 Devonshire Buildings, Bath BA2 4SU — MB ChB 1980 Bristol; MRCPsych 1984. Cons. Adolesc. Psychiat. Young People's Serv. Bath. Prev: Sen. Regist. (Child & Adolesc. Psychiat.) Bath.

BOUCHER, Louis Basil 1 Kestrel Drive, Sundorne Grove, Shrewsbury SY1 4TT — MB ChB 1992 Stellenbosch.

BOUCHER, Mr Nigel Robert Chesterfield & North Derbyshire Hospital, Calow, Chesterfield S44 5BL Tel: 01246 277271 Ext: 3768 Fax: 01246 552659 — MB ChB 1987 Birm.; FRCS Eng. 1991; FRCS (Urol.) 1997. (Birmingham) Cons. Urol. Surg. Chesterfield & N. Derbysh. Hosp. Socs: BAUS. Prev: Regist. (Urol.) Roy. Hallamsh. Hosp. Sheff.

BOUCHER, Susan Louise Everest House Surgery, Everest Way, Hemel Hempstead HP2 4HY Tel: 01442 240422 Fax: 01442 235045 — MB BS 1986 Lond.; BSc Lond. 1983; MRCGP 1990; DRCOG 1990. (University College London) Prev: Trainee GP Laindon Health Centre VTS; SHO (Cas.) Basildon Hosp.; SHO (Obst. & Gyn) Orsett Hosp.

BOUCHERAT, Anne Family Consultancy Service, Barnstaple Health Centre, Vicarage St., Barnstaple EX32 7BH Tel: 01271 71761 Fax: 01271 328157 — MB BS 1981 Lond.; MRCPsych 1986. Cons. Child & Adolesc. Psychiat. & Cons Psychiat. (Adult Learning Disabil.) N..Derm Healthcare Trust,Barnstable.

BOUCHERAT, Rosemary (retired) 69 Church Street, Bawtry, Doncaster DN10 6HR — MB BS Lond. 1959; MRCPsych 1974; DObst. RCOG 1961; DA Eng. 1963, DCH 1965; DPM Eng. 1969. Prev: Cons. (Child Psychiat.) Doncaster AHA.

BOUCHET, Veronique Anne 62 Brighton Road, London N16 8EG — MB BS 1983 Lond.; BSc Lond. 1980, MB BS 1983; DRCOG 1988.

BOUCHIER, Professor Ian Arthur Dennis, CBE (retired) 8A Merchiston Park, Edinburgh EH10 4PN Tel: 0131 228 1457 — MB ChB 1954 Cape Town; FRS Ed. 1985; MD Cape Town 1960; FRCP Ed. 1973; FRCP Lond. 1970, M 1961; FFPHM RCP (UK) 1993; Hon. FCP (SA) 1992; FIBiol 1988; F.Med.Sci 1993. Chief Scientist Scott. Office. Prev: Prof. Med. Univ. Dundee & Univ. Edin.

BOUGHDADY, Mr Ilhamy Saad Iskander 3 Meadow Close, Hale, Altrincham WA15 8JR Tel: 0161 980 4689 — MB BCh 1981 Ain Shams; MB BCh Ain Shams, Egypt 1981; MD Ain Shams, Egypt 1991; FRCS Eng. 1990; FRCS Ed. 1989.

BOUGHEY, Olwen Mary Simpson Barnie Garth, 39 Linden Way, Boston PE21 9DS Tel: 01205 364491 — MB BS 1959 Lond.; DObst RCOG 1962; DA Eng. 1963. (Middlx.)

BOUGHEY, Mr William Neil Fenton (retired) Barnie Garth, 39 Linden Way, Boston PE21 9DS Tel: 01205 364491 — MB BS 1954 Lond.; FRCS Eng. 1967; FRCS Ed. 1967. Prev: Sen. Regist. (Orthop.) Leicester Hosp. Gps. & Harlow Wood Orthop.

BOUGHTON, Brian Alleyne 14 Crosslands, Thurlestone, Kingsbridge TQ7 3TF Tel: 01548 560403 — MB ChB 1959 Birm.

(Birm.) Prev: Ho. Phys. & Ho. Surg. (Obst.) Dorset Co. Hosp. Dorchester; Ho. Surg. Portwey Hosp. Weymouth.

BOUGHTON, Brian John 63 Fitzroy Avenue, Harborne, Birmingham B17 8RH — MD 1979 Birm.; MB ChB 1967; MRCP (UK) 1973; FRCPath 1987, M 1974. (Birm.) Sen. Lect. (Haemat.) Univ. Birm.; Hon. Cons. Qu. Eliz. Hosp. Birm.; Brit. Soc. Thrombosis & Haemostasis. Socs: Brit. Soc. Haemat. Prev: Clin. Lect. (Univ. Oxf.) Radcliffe Infirm. Oxf.; John Alexander Stewart Fell. Qu. Univ. Kingston, Ontario; Sen. Regist. Soton. Univ. Gp. Hosps.

BOUGHTON, Paul Richard 65 Montrouge Crescent, Epsom Downs, Epsom KT17 3PB — MB BS 1983 Lond.

BOUHAIMED, Manal Mansoor 27 Bedford Road, Plymstock, Plymouth PL9 7DE — MB ChB 1992 Glas.

BOUKALIS, Athanasios Lawn Cottage, Lawn Road, Hampstead, London NW3 2XS — MB BS 1998 Lond.

BOUKI, Konstantina 14C Silverknowes View, 1F, Edinburgh EH4 5PY — Ptychio Iatrikes 1988 Thessalonika.

BOULD, Emma-Jane 14 Downlands Way, South Wonston, Winchester SO21 3HS — MB BS 1997 Lond.

BOULD, Matthew Dylan 1 Sidmouth Avenue, Newcastle ST5 0QN — MB ChB 1997 Leeds.

BOULD, Mr Michael 24 Woodland Road, Merry Hill, Wolverhampton WV3 8AR — MB BChir 1990 Camb.; MA Camb. 1990; FRCS Eng. 1995. Specialist Regist. Rotat. (Orthop.) Bristol. Prev: SHO Rotat. (Surgic.) Bristol Roy. Infirm.; SHO Rotat. (Trauma) Addenbrooke's Hosp. Camb.

***BOULIND, Clare Emma** West Dairy Cottage, Hanby Lane, Welton-le-Marsh, Spilsby PE23 5TA Tel: 01754 890515 Fax: 01754 890515 — MB ChB 1996 Sheff.

BOULIND, Peter Rodney Beacon Medical Practice, 40 Algitha Road, Skegness PE25 2AJ Tel: 01754 897000 Fax: 01754 761024.

BOULIS, Mr Zoser Fouad Farnborough Hospital, Farnborough Common, Orpington BR6 8ND Tel: 01689 814140; 24 Hayes Road, Bromley BR2 9AA Tel: 020 8464 8856 — MRCS Eng. LRCP Lond. 1975; MB BS Khartoum 1965; FRCS Glas. 1975; FRCS Eng. 1973; FRCS Ed. 1973; FRCR 1982; DMRD Eng. 1980; ECFMG Cert 1974. (Khartoum) Cons. Radiol. Bromley Hosp. Nat. Health Serv. Trust. Socs: BMA; Brit. Med. Ultrasound Soc. Prev: Sen. Regist. (Diag. Radiol.) Roy. Free Hosp. Lond.; SHO (Gen. Surg.) Roy. Marsden Hosp. Lond.; Regist. (Gen. Surg.) Barking Hosp.

BOULIS-WASSIF, Saad 13 Montagu Gardens, Wallington SM6 8EP — LMSSA 1961 Lond.; FRCR Lond. 1975; FFR Lond. 1967. Head of Oncol. Dept. Milit. Hosp. Riyadh, Saudi Arabia. Socs: BMA. Prev: Sen. Cons. Rotterdam Radiother. Inst., Holland; Head of Radiother. Dept. Tripoli Guard Hosp., Libya; Sen. Regist. (Radiother.) Velindre Hosp., Cardiff.

BOULLIN, Julian Paul 15 Pine Walk, Surbiton KT5 8NJ — MB BS 1997 Lond.

BOULOS, George Bushra Tilehurst Surgery, Tylers Place, Pottery Road, Tilehurst, Reading RG30 6BW Tel: 0118 942 7528 Fax: 0118 945 2405; Marisuzy, 7 Copse Close, Tilehurst, Reading RG31 6RH Tel: 01734 421716 Email: gboulos@netcomule.co.uk — MB BS 1976 Lond.; MRCS Eng. LRCP Lond. 1977; MRCGP 1983; Cert Family Plann. & Contracep. JCC 1981. (St. Mary's) Assoc. Teach. (Gen. Pract.) St. Mary's Hosp. Med. Sch. Lond.; GP Trainer Oxf. Region. Prev: Regist. (Gen. Med.) St. Chas.' Hosp. Lond.; SHO (A & E) St. Mary's Hosp. Lond. (Harrow Rd. Br.); SHO (Neurol., Dermat. & Venereol.) St. Mary's Hosp. Lond.

BOULOS, Professor Paul Bernard Department of Surgery, Royal Free and University College Medical School, 2nd Floor, 67-73 Riding House St., London W1W 7EJ Tel: 020 7679 9317 Fax: 020 76799317 Email: e.collins@ucl.ac.uk; St. Anne, 15 Richmond Road, New Barnet, Barnet EN5 1SA Tel: 020 8449 6552 — MB BS Khartoum 1966; MS Lond. 1980; FRCS Eng. 1972; FRCS Ed. 1971; FCS HK(Hon) 2000. (Khartoum) Prof. (Surg.) Univ. Coll. Med. Sch. Lond.; Cons. Surg. Univ. Coll. & The Middlx. Hosps. Lond. Socs: Fell. Assn. Surgs. & Assoc. Coloproctol. GB & Irel.; Fell. Roy. Soc. Med. (Mem. Counc. Coloproctol. Sect.); Brit. Soc. Gastroenterol. & Surg. Research Soc. Prev: Sen. Regist. (Surg.) Univ. Coll. Hosp. & St. Mark's Hosp. Lond.; Research Fell. the Middlx. Hosp. Lond.

BOULOUX, Pierre-Marc Gilles Centre for Neuroendocrinology, Royal Free Hospital, Pond St., London NW3 2QG Tel: 020 7830 2128 Fax: 020 7431 6435 Email: pmgb@rfhsm.ac.uk; 18 Lordship Park, Stoke Newington, London N16 5UD Tel: 020 7503 4021 — MRCS Eng. LRCP Lond. 1977; BSc (1st cl. Hons. Physiol.) Lond. 1974, MD 1987; MB BS (Hons., Distinc. Surg. & Applied Pharmacol. & Therap.) Lond. 1977; MRCP (UK) 1979; FRCP Lond. 1992. (St. Bart.) Reader (Endocrinol.) & Hon. Cons. Phys. Roy. Free Hosp. Lond. Socs: Fell. Roy. Soc. Med.; Brit. Hypertens. Soc.; Soc. Endocrinol. Prev: Lect. (Med.) St. Bart. Hosp. Lond.; MRC Train. Fell. (Endocrinol.) St. Bart. Hosp. Lond.; Ho. Phys. Med. Profess. Unit St. Bart. Hosp. Lond.

BOULSTRIDGE, Lisa Jayne Hillcrest Lodge, Watling St., Grendon, Atherstone CV9 2PW — BM BS 1994 Nottm. (Nottingham) SHO (Oncol.) Leics. Roy. Infirm.

BOULTBEE, Dorothy Rosa Rachel (retired) Library Cottage, Barrow Crt., Barrow Gurney, Bristol BS48 3RW Tel: 01275 464268 — MB BCh BAO 1932 Dub.

BOULTBEE, Joseph Edwin 15 Daylesford Avenue, London SW15 5QR — MB BCh BAO 1964 Dub.; FRCR 1975; DMRD Eng. 1972 DObst RCOG 1972. (TC Dub.) Cons. Radiol. Char. Cross Hosp. Prev: Sen. Regist. (Radiol.) Lond. Hosp.; Regist. (Radiol.) Guy's Hosp. Lond.

BOULTER, Ann Rachel University Medical Practice, Elms Road, Off Pritchatts Road, Edgbaston, Birmingham B15 2SE Tel: 0121 414 5111 Fax: 0121 414 5108 — MB ChB 1984 Birm.; T(GP) 1991. Prev: SHO (Paediat. & O & G) Good Hope Gen. Hosp. Birm.; SHO (Psychiat.) Highcroft Hosp. Birm.

BOULTER, Mark Jeremy Michael Richards and Partners, Llanfair Surgery, Llanfair Road, Llandovery SA20 0HY Tel: 01550 720648 Fax: 01550 721428; Nant Ddu, Rhandirmwyn, Llandovery SA20 0NG Tel: 01550 20159 Email: mark.boulter1@virgin.net — MB BS 1983 Lond.; MA Camb. 1980; MRCP (UK) 1986; MRCGP (Distinc.) 1991. Prev: GP Llandysul; Clin. Asst. (Gen. Pract.) Llandysul; SHO (O & G) W. Wales Gen. Hosp.

BOULTER, Professor Patrick Stewart Quarry Cottage, Salkeld Dykes, Penrith CA11 9LL Tel: 01768 898822 Fax: 01768 898822 Email: psboulter@aol.com; Quarry Cottage, Salkeld Dykes, Penrith CA!1 9LL Tel: 01768 898822 Fax: 01768 898822 Email: psboulter@aol.com — MB BS 1955 Lond.; 1955; 1996 Hon. FFAEM; 1992 Hon. FCS (SA); 1992 Hon. FCS (Sri Lanka); 1984 Hon. FRACS 1984; 1997 FRCP Lond.; 1993 FRCS Glas.; 1993 FRCP Ed.; 1958 FRCS Eng.; 1958 FRCS Ed.; 1993 Hon. FRCSI; 1955 MRCS Eng. LRCP Lond.; 1992 Hon. FCS Hong Kong; 1996 D.Univ, Surrey. (Guy's) Emerit. Cons. Oncol. & Gen. Surg. Roy. Surrey Co. & St. Lukes Hosp. & Regional Radiother. Centre Guildford; Examr. FRCS Edin. & Glas.; Penrose-May Teach. RCS Eng.; Hon. Tutor (Surg.) Guy's Hosp. Med. Sch. Lond.; Trustee and Mem. , Health and Welf. Comm., Thalidomide Trust, 1995 -; Prof. Surg. Sci. Univ. Surrey; Cons. Surg. Jarvis BrE. Screening Centre Guildford (Former); Vis. Surg. Cranleigh Village Hosp. & Cobham & Dist. Cottage Hosp. (Former); Chairm. Scott. Conf. Roy. Coll. & Facilities (Former); Examr. Univs. Lond., Edin., Singapore & Malaya. Socs: Fell. Assn. Surgs. (Ex-Chairm. Educat. Advis. Comm.); Hon. Mem. Assn. Surg. India 1992; Hon. Fell. Coll. Surg. Sri Lanks. Prev: Regent RCS Ed. 1995; Sen. Regist. (Surg). Guy's Hosp. & Dumfries & Galloway Roy. Infirm.; Pres. RCS Ed.

BOULTON, Professor Andrew James Michael Department of Medicine, Manchester Royal Infirmary, Oxford Road, Manchester M13 9WL Tel: 0161 276 4452 Fax: 0161 274 4740 Email: ajmb@fs1.cmht.nwest.nhs.uk; The Old Police House, 4 Buxton Road W., Disley, Stockport SK12 2JA Tel: 01663 766209 — MB BS 1976 Newc.; MD Newc. 1985; FRCP Lond. 1992; MRCP (UK) 1979. Prof. Med. Univ. Manch.; Hon. Cons. Phys. Manch. Roy. Infirm.; Chairm. Postgrad. Educat. Europ. Diabetes Assn. Socs: Eur. Diabetic Assn.; Brit. Diabetic Assn.; Amer. Diabetes Assn. Prev: Vis. Asst. Prof. Med. Univ. Miami; Regist. Profess. Med. Unit & Diabetic Research Regist. Roy. Hallamshire Hosp. Sheff.

BOULTON, David John Bounden Hill Farm, Banbury Road, Charwelton, Daventry NN11 3YY Tel: 01327 262303 Fax: 01327 262303 Email: david@cherwell.force9.co.uk — MRCS Eng. LRCP Lond. 1966; LMSSA Lond. 1963; MFFP 1993; Dip Ven Soc. Apoth. Lond. 1978; DObst RCOG 1966. (Guy's) Med. Off. Dept. Genitourin. Med. N.ampton Gen. Hosp. Prev: Sen. Partner Danetre Med. Pract. Daventry; SCMO N.ampton HA.

BOULTON, Frank Ernest NBS Southampton Centre, Coxford Road, Southampton SO16 5AF Tel: 02380 296700 Fax: 02380 296760 Email: frankboulton@msmail.nbs.nhs.uk — MD Lond. 1975, BSc,

MB BS 1965; FRCPath 1985, M 1972; FRCP Ed 1997. (St. Thos.) Lead Phys. NBS Soton. Centre. Socs: Brit. Soc. Haematol. & Brit. Blood Transfus. Soc.; Brit. Soc. Haemostasis & Thrombosis.; Coun. Mem. Brit. Blood Transfus. Soc. 1995 - 2000. Prev: Cons. & Dep. Dir. Edin. Regional Blood Transfus. Serv. Roy. Infirm. Edin.; Cons. Haemat. Liverp. Roy. Infirm.; Sen. Lect. (Haemat.) Liverp. Univ., Lond. Hosp. Med. Coll. & Sen. Regist. Lond. Hosp.

BOULTON, Janet Mary Newham General Hospital, Glen Road, London E13 8SL Tel: 020 7476 4000 Fax: 020 7363 8364; 58A Redington Road, London NW3 7RS Tel: 020 7435 5886 — MB BS 1963 Lond.; MRCS Eng. LRCP Lond. 1963; FRCOG 1986, M 1969. (Roy. Free) Cons. O & G Newham Healthcare NHS Trust.

BOULTON, John Dept of Medicine, Northern General Hospital, Sheffield S5 7AU; 138 Hangingwater Road, Sheffield S11 7ES — MB ChB 1998 Sheff.; MB ChB Sheff 1998.

BOULTON, John Victor William Dalton House Surgery, 66 Edgcumbe Avenue, Newquay TR7 2NN Tel: 01637 873209 — MB BS 1975 Lond.; MRCS Eng. LRCP Lond. 1974; MRCGP 1980; DRCOG 1978.

BOULTON, Jonathan Edward St Thomas' Hospital, Lambeth Palace Road, London SE1 7EH Tel: 020 7928 9292; 50D Clapham Common Southside, London SW4 9BX Tel: 020 7978 1793 — MB BChir 1989 Camb.; MRCP (UK) 1992. SHO (Ophth.) St. Thos. Hosp. Lond.

BOULTON, Maxwell (retired) Kingsway, St John's Avenue, Thorner, Leeds LS14 3BZ Tel: 0113 289 2371 — MB ChB 1953 Leeds. Prev: GP Leeds.

BOULTON, Thomas Babington, OBE, TD, ERD (retired) Townsend Farm, Streatley-on-Thames, Reading RG8 9JX Tel: 01491 872756 Fax: 01491 872562 — MB BChir 1949 Camb.; 1949 MB BChir Camb.; 1981 MA Oxf.; 1950 MA Camb.; 1992 FRCA 1992; 1985 FDS RCS Eng; 1954 FFA RCS Eng.; 1953 DA Eng; 1999 MD Camb. Hon. Cons. Anaesth. Oxf. & Reading. Prev: Cons. Anaesth. & Clin. Lect. Nuffield Dept. Anaesth. Oxf. & Roy. Berks. Hosp. Reading.

BOULTON-JONES, John Michael 5 Glassford Street, Milngavie, Glasgow G62 8DS Tel: 0141 956 5353 — MB 1967 Camb.; BChir 1966; FRCP Glas. 1984; FRCP Lond. 1982, M 1969. (Guy's) Cons. Phys. & Nephrol. Glas. Roy. Infirm. Prev: Sen. Regist. Hammersmith Hosp.; Med. Regist. Guy's Hosp. Lond.; Ho. Surg. Orpington Hosp.

BOULTON-JONES, John Robert Flat 3, 160 Great Western Road, Glasgow G4 9AE — MB ChB 1992 Ed.

BOULTON-JONES, Rachel Victoria 5 Glassford Street, Milngavie, Glasgow G62 8DS — MB ChB 1993 Ed.

BOUND, Denise Sonia Mill View Hospital, Nevill Ave, Hove BN3 7HZ Tel: 01273 696011 — MB BS 1972 Lond.; MRCS Eng. LRCP Lond. 1972; MRCPsych 1977; DObst RCOG 1974. (King's Coll. Hosp. Med. Sch.) Staff Grade Psychiat. Mill View Hosp., Nevill Ave, Hove, BN3 7HZ. Prev: Clin. Asst. Gen. Psychiat. New Sussex Hosp. Brighton.

BOUND, John Pascoe (retired) 48 St Annes Road E., St Annes, Lytham St Annes FY8 1UR Tel: 01253 724686 — MB BS 1943 Lond.; MD Lond. 1950; FRCP Lond. 1971, M 1950; MRCS Eng. LRCP Lond. 1943; DCH Eng. 1943. Hon. Cons. Paediat. Blackpool & Fylde Gp. Hosps. Prev: 1st Asst. Childr. Dept. Univ. Coll. Hosp.

BOUNDS, Mr Graham Arthur Department of Oral & Maxillofacial Surgery, Mount Vernon & Watford Hospitals NHS Trust, Northwood, Harrow HA2 6RN Tel: 01923 844436 Fax: 01923 844321; 24 Kingsway, Gerrards Cross SL9 8NT — MB BCh 1982 Wales; FRCS Ed. 1987; BDS Newc. 1973; FDS RCS Eng. 1977. Cons. Maxillofacial Surg. Mt. Vernon & Watford Hosps. NHS Trust; Hon. Clin. Tutor Welsh Nat. Sch. Med. (Dent. Sch). Socs: Brit. Assn. Oral & Maxillofacial Surg. Prev: Sen. Regist. (Oral & Maxillofacial Surg.) St. Richard's Hosp. Chichester, St. Thos. Hosp. & St. Geo. Hosp. Lond.

BOUNDS, Rosalind Joy Lydney Health Centre, Lydney GL15 5NQ Tel: 01594 842167; Ross Farm, Woodside, Woolaston, Lydney GL15 6PB — MB BCh 1985 Wales; MRCGP 1989; DCH RCP Lond. 1988; DRCOG 1987. Princip.

BOURAS, Nicandros York Clinic, Guy's Hospital, London SE1 3RR Tel: 020 7955 4792 Fax: 020 7020 7955 4232 Email: n.bouras@umds.ac.uk — Ptchion Iatrikes Athens 1968; PhD Lond. 1979; Med. Dip. Athens 1968; FRCPsych 1993. (Med. Sch. Athens Univ.) Prof. of Psychiat., Guys-Kings-St Thomas, Med. Sch.; Hon. Sen. Lect. (Psychiat.) Guy's Hosp. UMDS; Hon. Cons. Pschiatrist, S. Lond. and Maudsley, NHS Trust. Prev: Hon. Sen. Regist. (Psychiat.) Guy's Hosp. Med. Sch. & Lewisham Psychiat. Research Unit; Cons. Psychiat. Lewisham & Guy's Ment. Health Trust.

BOURDILLON, Peter John Hammersmith Hospital, Du Cane Road, London W12 0HS Tel: 020 8383 3951 Fax: 020 8383 3952 Email: pbourdillon@msn.com; 13 Grove Terrace, London NW5 1PH Tel: 020 7485 6839 — MB BS 1965 Lond.; FRCP Lond. 1983, M 1968. (Middlx.) Cons. (Clin. Physiol.) Hammersmith Hosp.; Sen. Princip. Med. Off. DoH; Hon. Sen. Lect. Univ. Lond. Socs: Brit. Cardiac Soc. & Sect. Measurem. Med. Roy. Soc. Med. Prev: Sen. Regist. Hammersmith Hosp. Lond.; Regist. (Med.) & Ho. Phys. Middlx. Hosp. Lond.

BOURDILLON, Ralph Edmund Moose Lodge, Clay Head, Baldrine, Douglas IM4 6DP; 36 Woodbourne Road, Douglas IM1 3AN Tel: 01624 415 — MB ChB 1959 Liverp.; BDS 1954; FRCP Lond. 1975, M 1963. (Liverp.) Cons. Phys. I. of Man Health Servs. Bd.; Mem. Liverp. Med. Inst. & I. of Man Med. Soc. Prev: Med. Regist. Sefton Gen. Hosp. Liverp.; Sen. Med. Regist. Walton Hosp. Liverp. Sen. Med. Regist. Roy. S..; Hosp. Liverp.

BOURHILL, Biddy Davidson (retired) 74 St Jame's Oaks, Trafalgar Road, Gravesend DA11 0QU — MB ChB 1954 Ed.; DPM Eng. 1972; DTM & H Liverp. 1957. Prev: Clin. Asst. (p/t) Psychiat. Stone Ho. Hosp. Dartford.

BOURKE, Brian Eamonn 152 Harley Street, London W1N 1HH Tel: 020 7935 2477 Fax: 020 7224 2574; 70 Rivermead Court, Ranelagh Gardens, London SW6 3RZ Tel: 020 7731 0275 Fax: 020 7731 0275 — MB BS 1971 Lond.; FRCP LOND. 1989; MRCP (UK) 1974; T(M) 1991. (King's Coll. Hosp.) Cons. Phys. (Gen. Med. & Rheum.) St. Geo. Hosp. Lond.; Hon. Sen. Lect. St. Geo. Hosp. Med. Sch. Lond. Socs: (Hon.-Sec.) Brit. Soc. Rheum.; Roy. Soc. Med. (Pres. Rheum. Sect.); Brit. Soc. Immunol. Prev: Sen. Regist. & Regist. (Gen. Med. Rheum.) Char. Cross Hosp. Lond.; Regist. St. Stephen's Hosp. Lond.; SHO (Gen. Med.) Lond. Hosp.

BOURKE, Bridget Elizabeth Kings Road Surgery, 27b Kings Road, Sandy SG19 1EJ Tel: 01767 682277 Fax: 01767 691436 — MB BCh BAO 1984 NUI; DCH RCPSI 1989; DObst. RCPI 1988. (University College Galway, Ireland) GP.

BOURKE, James Bernard General Surgery Directorate, University Hospital, Queen's Medical Centre, Nottingham NG7 2UH Tel: 0115 970 9251 Fax: 0115 919 4451; 20 Victoria Crescent, Sherwood, Nottingham NG5 4DA Tel: 0115 9624 966 Fax: 0115 9624 966 — MB BChir 1965 Camb.; MA, MB Camb. 1965, BChir 1964; FRCS Eng. 1969; FRCS Ed. 1967; MRCS Eng. LRCP Lond. 1964. (Camb. & Lond. Hosp.) Cons. Surg. Gen.. Univ. Hosp. NHS Trust. Socs: Surg. Research Soc. & Brit. Soc. Gastroenterol.; Soc. Study of Human Biol.; Assoc. for the Study of Med. Educat. Prev: Med. Dir., Nottm. Univ. Hosp., NHS Trust; Sen. Lect. (Surg.) Univ. Nottm.; Lect. (Surg.) Lond. Hosp. Med. Coll.

BOURKE, John Joseph (retired) Sunny Meed Surgery, 15-17 Heathside Road, Woking GU22 7EY Tel: 01483 772760 — MB BCh BAO 1943 NUI; MB BCh. BAO (2nd Cl. Hnrs.) NUI 1943. Prev: Ho. Phys. Mater Miser. Hosp. Dub.

BOURKE, John Pius University Department of Cardiology, Freeman Hospital, Freeman Road, Newcastle upon Tyne NE7 7DN Tel: 0191 284 3111 Fax: 0191 213 0498 Email: j.p.bourke@ncl.ac.uk — MB BCh BAO 1979 NUI; MRCPI 1982; DCH NUI 1981; FRCPI 1996; MD NUI 1997; FRCP Lond. 1997. (UCD Irel.) Sen. Lect. (Cardiol.) Univ. Newc. u. Tyne; Hon. Cons. (Cardiol.) Freeman Gp. Hosps. NHS Trust Newc.; Hon. Cons. (Cardiol.), Gt. Ormond St. Hosp. Lond. Prev: Regist. (Med.) St. Vincent's Hosp. Dub.; Brit. Heart Foundat. Anglo-Austral. Research Fell. W.mead Hosp. Sydney. Austral.

BOURKE, Katherine Anne 19 West Kensington Court, Edith Villas, London W14 9AA — MB ChB 1992 Otago.

BOURKE, Michael Joseph Sunny-Meed Surgery, 15-17 Heathside Road, Woking GU22 7EY Tel: 01483 772760 Fax: 01483 730354; 2 Dorset Drive, Woking GU22 7DX — MB BCh BAO 1983 NUI; BSc 1977; LRCPI & LM, LRCSI & LM 1983; DObst. NUI 1985; DCH NUI 1985. Prev: SHO (Obst.) Rotunda Dub.; SHO (Paediat.) Temple St. Hosp. Dub.; SHO (Respirat. Med.) QEMH Perth W.. Australia.

BOURKE, Michael Patrick The Coach House, Peter St., Shepton Mallet BA4 5LW Tel: 01749 342739; 59 Balcombe Street, London NW1 6HD Tel: 020 7723 7511 — MB ChB 1943 Bristol; MRCS Eng. LRCP Lond. 1943; DCH Eng. 1947. (Bristol) Socs: BMA. Prev:

Indust. Med. Off. C & J Clarks Showerings & Avalon Chem. Co. Ltd.; Ho. Phys. & Cas. Off. Bristol Roy. Infirm.; Maj. RAMC.

BOURKE, Paul Joseph 97 Gilmerton Dykes Avenue, Edinburgh EH17 8LR — MB ChB 1998 Aberd.; MB ChB Aberd 1998.

BOURKE, Serena Katherine 57 Eccles Road, Battersea Road, London SW11 1LZ — MB BS 1997 Lond.

BOURKE, Stephen Christopher 28 Elmfield Gardens, Gosforth, Newcastle upon Tyne NE3 4XB — MB BCh BAO 1991 Belf. (Belf.) Regist. (Gen. & Respirat. Med.) Newc. u. Tyne. Socs: RCP.

BOURKE, Stephen Joseph Department of Respiratory Medicine, Royal Victoria Infirmary, Newcastle upon Tyne NE1 4LP Tel: 0191 282 0141 Fax: 0191 227 5224; Tel: 0191 236 8207 — MB BCh BAO 1981 NUI; MD NUI 1991; FRCPI 1996; MRCPI 1984; FCCP 1993; T(M) 1992; DCH NUI 1983; FRCP Lond. 1998. (Univ. Coll. Dub.) Cons. Phys. Roy. Vict. Infirm. & Sen. Lect. Univ. Newc. u. Tyne. Socs: Brit. Thorac. Soc. & Europ. Respirat. Soc.

BOURKE, Susan Louise 20 Victoria Crescent, Nottingham NG5 4DA — BM 1990 Soton.

BOURNE, Andrew John Hingham Rectory, Hingham, Norwich — MB ChB 1986 Birm.; ChB Birm. 1986.

BOURNE, Andrew Julian GP Registrar, Penryn Surgery, Saracen Way, Penryn — MB BS 1996 Lond.; MB BS Lond 1996.

BOURNE, Catherine Mair 25 Old Gate Road, Thrussington, Leicester LE7 4TL — BM BS 1988 Nottm.; MRCGP 1992.

BOURNE, David Ronald Manchester Royal Infirmary, Oxford Rd, Manchester M1 — MB ChB 1991 Manch.

BOURNE, Mr Gordon Lionel (retired) Oldways, 31 The Bishop's Avenue, London N2 0BN Tel: 020 8458 4788 Fax: 020 8458 4788 — MRCS Eng. LRCP Lond. 1945; FRCS Eng. 1952; FRCOG 1964, M 1956. Hon. O & G St. Bart. Hosp. Lond.; Hon. Gyn. Roy. Masonic Hosp. Lond.; Examr. Obst. & Gyn. Univ. Lond., Oxf. & Manch., RCOG, Soc. Apoth. Lond. & Centr. Midw. Bd. Prev: Sen. Regist. (O & G) St. Bart. & N. Middlx. Hosps.

BOURNE, Helen Carol 170 Biddulph Road, Chell Green, Stoke-on-Trent ST6 6TB — MB ChB 1995 Manch.

BOURNE, John Andrew Department of Anaesthetics, Stepping Hill Hospital, Stockport SK2 7JE — MB ChB Manch. 1969; FFA RCS Eng. 1974. Cons. Anaesth. Stockport Acute Servs. Trust. Socs: Fell. Manch. Med. Soc.; Obst. Anaesth. Assn.

BOURNE, John Tamblyn Medical Department Chesterfield and North Derbyshire, Royal Hospital, Chesterfield S44 5BL Tel: 01246 277271; Westmoor, 1 Linden Avenue, Chesterfield S40 3LF Tel: 01246 566489 — MB ChB 1974 (Hons) Bristol; BSc (Hons.) Bristol 1971; MD Bristol 1981; FRCP Lond. 1993. Cons. Phys. Chesterfield & N. Derbysh. Roy. Hosp. Chesterfield. Socs: BMA; Brit. Soc. Rheum. Prev: Sen. Regist. (Gen. Med. & Rheum.) St. Bart. Hosp. Lond.; Regist. (Gen. Med.) Bristol Roy. Infirm.; Research Fell. Rush-Presbyt.-St. Luke's Med. Center Chicago, USA.

BOURNE, Joyce (retired) The Bungalow, 62 Edilom Road, Manchester M8 4HZ Tel: 0161 740 4528 Fax: 0161 720 7171 — MB ChB 1958 Manch.; DA Eng. 1960. Prev: GP Salford.

BOURNE, Julie Pamela Anaesthetic Department, Queen Alexandra Hospital, Southwick Hill Road, Cosham, Portsmouth PO6 3LY — MB ChB 1985 Dundee; FRCA 1993; DA (UK) 1988.

BOURNE, Malcolm Jonathan Bickerstaffe House, 53 Garstang Road, Preston PR1 1LB Tel: 01772 562547 Fax: 01772 885517 Email: malcolm.bourne@virgin.net; 51 Newton Drive, Greenmount, Bury BL8 4DH Tel: 01204 880607 Email: malcolm.bourne@virgin.net — MB BS 1987 Lond.; MSc Manch. 1995; BA (Hons.) Oxf. 1983; MRCPsych 1991. Cons. Child & Adolesc. Psychiat. Preston (Blackpool, Wyre & Fylde Community NHS Trust); Freelance Expert Witness, Child Psychiat. Socs: Assn. Child Psychiat. & Psychol.; BMA. Prev: Sen. Regist. Rotat. (Child & Adolesc. Psychiat.) Manch.; Regist. (Child Psychiat.) Manch. Train. Scheme; SHO Rotat. (Gen. Psychiat.) N. Manch. Train. Scheme.

BOURNE, Martin Stanley (retired) Baguley Brow Farm, Heywood Old Road, Middleton, Manchester M24 4QR Tel: 0161 643 2806 Fax: 0161 655 3895 — Hon. MSc Salford 1973; MB ChB Manch. 1954; MRCGP 1968. Prev: Sen. Med. Off. Stud. Health Serv. Manch. Univ.

BOURNE, Michael William 11 Rushton Drive, Upton-by-Chester, Chester CH2 1RE Tel: 01244 371378 — MB BS 1981 Lond. Lect. (Radiodiag.) Univ. Liverp. Socs: FRCR.

BOURNE, Mr Roger Higher Ashford Cottage, Ashford, Barnstaple EX31 4BY — MB BS 1970 Lond.; FRCS Eng. 1975; MRCS Eng. LRCP Lond. 1970. (St. Mary's) Cons. Surg. N. Devon Dist. Hosp. Prev: Sen. Regist. W.m. Hosp. Lond.; Lect. in Surg. Char. Cross Hosp. Lond.; Surg. Regist. Qu. Mary's Hosp. Roehampton & Putney Hosp. Lond.

BOURNE, Rupert Richard Alexander Riversleigh Farm, Charles Hill, Tilford, Farnham GU10 2AU — MB BS 1994 Lond.; BSc Univ. Lond 1991. (Lond. Hosp. Med. Coll.) SHO Ophth. Roy. Berks. Hosp. Reading & Radcliffe Infirm. Oxf.

BOURNE, Sally Ann Fiona St Luke's Hospital, Blackmoorfoot Road, Huddersfield HD4 5RQ — MB ChB 1991 Leeds.

BOURNE, Sarah Jane Winfield, Commonside, Bookham, Leatherhead KT23 3LA — MB BS 1997 Lond.

BOURNE, Sarah Joanne 24 Heol Cae Copyn, Loughor, Swansea SA4 6SF — MB ChB 1997 Manch.

BOURNE, Stanford 14 Fitzjohns Avenue, London NW3 5NA Tel: 020 7794 7188; 9 Bigwood Road, London NW11 7BB Tel: 020 8455 7869 Fax: 020 8455 7869 Email: drbourne@dialstart.net — MB BS 1952 Lond.; MRCP Lond. 1957; MRCS Eng. LRCP Lond. 1952; FRCPsych 1975, M 1971; DPM Eng. 1958. (Univ. Coll. Hosp.) Socs: Brit. Psychoanal. Soc. Prev: Cons. Psychother. Tavistock Clinic; Sen. Regist. Tavistock Clinic Lond.; Regist. Maudsley Hosp. Lond.

BOURNE, Mr Thomas Holland Gynaecological Ultrasound & Minimal Access Surgery Unit, Department Obstetrics & Gynaecology, St Georges Hospital Medical School, Cranmer Terrace, London SW17 0RE Tel: 020 8725 0050/1908 Fax: 020 8725 0094 Email: tbourne@gynae-scanning.com — MB BS 1984 Lond.; MRCOG 1990; PhD Göteborg 1995. (Middlx. Hosp. Med. Sch. Lond.) Cons. & Hon. Sen. Lect. (O & G) St. Geo. Hosp. Lond.; Med. Adviser to the Ectopic Pregn. Trust. Socs: Chairm. Europ. Soc. Endosonogr. Gyn. & Obst.; Internat. Gyn. Cancer Soc.; Founder Mem. Internat. Soc. Ultrasound Obst. & Gyn. Prev: Research Fell. Centre for Surgic. Technol. Catholic Univ. of Leuven, Belgium; Lect., Hon. Sen. Regist. & Sen. Research Fell. (O & G) King's Coll. Hosp. Lond.

BOURNE, Timothy Mark Anaesthetic Department, Leicester Royal Infirmary, Leicester LE1 5WW — MB BS 1988 Lond.; FRCA 1994. Cons. (Anaesth.), Leicester Roy. Infirm.

BOUSFIELD, John David Yew Tree House, Upper Broughton, Melton Mowbray LE14 3BG Tel: 01664 823298 — MB BS 1963 Lond.; FFA RCS Eng. 1970; DA Eng. 1966. (St. Bart.) Cons. (Neuroanaesth.) Qu. Med. Centre Nottm. Prev: Cons. (Neuroanaesth.) Derbysh. Roy. Infirm.; Sen. Regist. (Anaesth.) Hosp. Sick Childr. Gt. Ormond St. & St. Thos.; Hosp. Lond.; Regist. (Anaesth.) St. Bart. Hosp. Lond.

BOUSFIELD, Peter Fredrick Deeholme, Gayton Road, Heswall Lower Village, Wirral CH60 8QF — MB ChB 1972 Liverp.; FRCOG 1989, M 1977. Cons. (O & G) Walton & Fazakerley Hosps.; Dir. Fazakerley Assisted Conception Unit. Prev: Sen. Regist. (O & G) Univ. Hosp. S. Manch.

BOUSFIELD, Susan Kay Heswall Medical Centre, Telegraph Road, Heswall, Wirral CH60 7SG Tel: 0151 342 2230 — MB ChB 1973 Liverp.

BOUSKILL, John c/o Medical Department, Shell Chemicals UK Ltd., Carrington, Manchester M31 4AJ Tel: 0161 776 3124 — MB ChB 1974 Manch.; MFOM RCP Lond. 1983. (Manch.) Med. Off. Shell Chem.s UK Ltd.

BOUSKILL, Keith Carruthers Fieldside House, High Toynton, Horncastle LN9 6NP — MB BS 1967 Lond.; FRCPath 1987, M 1975. (Middlx.) Cons. Histopath. Lincoln. Co. Hosp. Socs: BMA & Assn. Clin. Paths.; Internat. Acad. Path. Prev: Cons. Histopath. Centr. Hosp. Abu Dhabi; Cons. Histopath. King Khalid Nat. Guard Hosp. Jeddah; Cons. Histopath. Pilgrim Hosp. Boston.

BOUSQUET, Miss Pauline Mayda (retired) 37 Nether Close, London N3 1AA — MB BS 1951 Lond.; MRCS Eng. LRCP Lond. 1951; MRCOG 1960. Prev: Cons. (O & G) Hackney Gp. Hosps.

BOUTON, Marie Jean Flat 4, Lathom Court, 690 Liverpool Road, Southport PR8 3NQ — MB BS 1950 Lond.; MD Lond. 1958; FRCPath 1980, M 1963. (St. Bart.) Hon. Lect. (Path.) Liverp. Univ.; Cons. Path. Alder. Hey Childr. Hosp. Liverp. Socs: Liverp. Med. Inst. & Liverp. Paediat. Club. Prev: Sen. Regist. Guy's & Lewisham Gp. Laborat.; Ho. Phys. Childr. Dept. St. Bart. Hosp.; Histopath. & Radiobiol. Dept. Roy. Cancer Hosp.

BOUTROS, Naim Wakim Meseha 22 Beltinge Road, Harold Wood, Romford RM3 0UJ — MB BCh 1972 Alexandria; MRCS Eng. LRCP Lond. 1981.

BOUTWOOD, Miss Audrey Anne (retired) 1 Wilton Square, Islington, London N1 3DL Tel: 020 7359 2802 Fax: 020 7354 9690 — MB BS 1951 Lond.; FRCOG 1974, M 1959, DObst 1953. Prev: Cons. Gyn. United Eliz. G. Anderson Hosp. & Hosp. for Wom. Soho Lond.

BOUWER, Johannes Cornelius Flat 2, Block 1, Royal Shrewsbury Hospital North, Mytton Oak Road, Shrewsbury SY3 8XF Tel: 01743 261000 — MB ChB 1992 Stellenbosch.

BOUZYK, Peter Christopher Alexander Montpellier Health Care, Montpellier House, 47 Rodney Road, Cheltenham GL50 1HX Tel: 01242 221685 Fax: 01242 261854 Email: peterb@montpellier-health.com; Treetops, Oakridge Lynch, Stroud GL6 7NY Tel: 01285 760274 Fax: 01285 760274 — MB BS 1986 Lond.; BSc Lond. 1981. (Char. Cross & Westm.) Med. Dir. Montpellier Health Care Cheltenham. Prev: Primary Health Care Adviser Montpellier Healthcare Cheltenham; Indep. GP Stroud.

BOVETT, Edwin John (retired) Glenover House, Maury's Lane, West Wellow, Romsey SO51 6DB Tel: 01794 323291 — BM BCh 1954 Oxf.; MRCGP 1966.

BOVILL, Begona Anne 40 Combe Park, Bath BA1 3NR Tel: 01225 824963 — MB BS 1987 Lond.; MSc Clin. Microbiol. Lond. 1993; MRCP (UK) 1990; DTM & H RCP Lond. 1998. (Royal Free) Sen. Regist. Hosp. for Trop. Dis.s Lond. Prev: Regist. Rotat. (Infec. Dis. & Gen. Med.) Coppetts Wood Unit Roy. Free Hosp. Lond.; Lect. (Med. Microbiol.) Lond. Hosp. Med. Coll.; SHO Rotat. (Med.) Whipps Cross Hosp. Lond.

BOVILL, Inaki Philip 24 Bartholomew Close, London SW18 1JQ — MB BS 1993 Lond.

BOWATER, George Beech (retired) 1 Greening Drive, Birmingham B15 2XA Tel: 0121 454 3071 — MB ChB 1940 Birm.; MRCS Eng. LRCP Lond. 1940. Prev: Lt. Col. IMS.

BOWATER, Rachel Louise 113 Yarborough Crescent, Lincoln LN1 3NE — MB ChB 1995 Leic.

BOWBEER, John Tams Brig Surgery, 107 New Road, Ayr KA8 8DD Tel: 01292 262697 Fax: 01292 265926 — MB ChB 1984 Aberd.; MB ChB Aberd. l984; MRCGP 1988.

BOWBRICK, Miss Virginia Anne 24 Amsterdam Road, Isle of Dogs, London E14 3JB — MB BS 1989 Lond.; FRCS (Eng) 1996. Specialist Regist. (Gen. Surg.), SE Thames; Research Fell., St Mary's Hosp.

BOWCOCK, Leslie White Gable, Sunny Hollow, The Brampton, Newcastle ST5 0RW Tel: 01782 615566 — MB ChB 1950 Birm.; MFOM RCP Lond. 1989. (Birm.) Cons. Occ. Phys. N. Staffs.; Med. Adviser Roy. Crown Derby, Roy. Doulton Plc. Socs: Soc. Occupat. Med.; Hon. Fell. N. Staffs. Med. Inst.; Fell. Inst. Material. Prev: Regist. Orthop. Hosp. Hartshill; Hosp. Asst. Res. Surg. Off. N. Staffs. Roy. Infirm.; Director Med. Illustration N. Staffs H. A.

BOWCOCK, Stella Jane Haematology Department, Queen Mary's Hospital, Sidcup DA14 6LT Tel: 020 8308 3023 Fax: 020 8308 3153 Email: stella.bowcock@qms-tr.sthames.nhs.uk — MB BS 1980 Lond.; MA Oxf. 1981; MRCP (UK) 1983; MRCPath (Haemat.) 1987. Cons. Haemat. Qu. Mary's Hosp. Sidcup; Lead Clinician Cancer Serv. Qu. Mary's Hosp. Sidcup. Socs: Brit. Soc. Haematol. Prev: Sen. Regist. (Haemat.) W. Middlx. & Hammersmith Hosps. Lond.; Regist. (Haemat.) Middlx. & Univ. Coll. Hosp. Lond.

BOWDEN, Alison Stella St Andrews Medical Centre, St. Andrews Court, Pinewood Gardens, Southborough, Tunbridge Wells TN4 0LZ Tel: 01892 515455 Fax: 01892 514019 — MB BS 1978 Lond. GP Tunbridge Wells.

BOWDEN, Andrew Noel The Walton Centre, Liverpool L9 7LJ — MRCS Eng. LRCP Lond. 1963; BSc (Hons.) Lond. 1961, MB BS 1964; FRCP Lond. 1980, M 1967. (Guy's) Cons. Neurol. The Walton Centre for Neurol. & Neurosurg.; Liverp. & Countess of Chester Hosp.; Lect. Dept. of Med. Univ. Liverp. & Roy. Liverp. Univ. Hosp. Socs: Assn. Brit. Neurol. & Liverp. Med. Inst. Prev: Sen. Regist. Nat. Hosp. Qu. Sq. Lond. & King's Coll. Hosp. Lond.

BOWDEN, Andrew Philip Dept. of Rheumatology, Healey Bldngs., Rochdale Healthcare NHS Trust, Rochdale BB4 6RP Tel: 01706 754691 Fax: 01706 754693 — MB ChB 1988 Birm.; MRCP (UK) 1993; MSc Manc. 1998. (Birmingham) Cons. Rhuem. Birch Hill. Hosp. Rochdale + Rochdale Infirm.; Cons. Rheum. Bury Gen. Hosp.. Bury & Fairfield Hosp., Bury. Socs: Brit. Soc. Rheum.; BMA; Manch. Med. Soc. Prev: Clin. Lect. (Rheum.) Manch. Univ.; Sen. Regist. (Rheum.) Manch. Roy. Infirm.; Sen. Regist. (Rheum.) Hope Hosp. Salford.

BOWDEN, Ann Dames MV Courage, Brent Way, Brentford TW8 8ES Tel: 020 8758 9887 — MB ChB Manch. 1963; MFOM RCP Lond. 1996; DCH Eng. 1966. (Manch.) Hosp. Pract. (Homoeop.) Roy. Lond. Homoeop. Hosp. Prev: GP Twickenham; Ho. Phys. (Neurol.) & Ho. Surg. Manch. Roy. Infirm.; Ho. Phys. Evelina Childr. Hosp. of Guy's Hosp.

BOWDEN, Barry Graham Old Station Surgery, 39 Brecon Road, Abergavenny NP7 5UH Tel: 01873 859000 Fax: 01873 850163; 1 Windsor Road, Abergavenny NP7 7BB Tel: 01873 855841 — MB ChB 1968 Bristol; MRCGP 1990; DRCOG 1971.

BOWDEN, David Edgar (retired) Nobroyd, 8 Wakefield Road, Ackworth, Pontefract WF7 7DE Tel: 01977 611537 Email: dbowden@doctors.net.uk — MB ChB 1957 Bristol; MRCGP 1966. Prev: Sen. Med. Off. Benefits Agency Med. Serv. S. Leeds.

BOWDEN, Mr David Frank 9 Stad Plas Hen, Llawddaniel, Gaerwen LL60 6HW Tel: 01248 421092 — MB ChB 1982 Birm.; FRCS Ed. 1987. Regist. (Surg.) Dudley HA.

BOWDEN, David Frederick Field House Surgery, 18 Victoria Road, Bridlington YO15 2AT Tel: 01262 673362; Woodford House, Iliham, Driffield YO25 4RL Tel: 01262 420420 — BM BCh 1972 Oxf.; MA Camb. 1972; DObst RCOG 1974.

BOWDEN, Gareth Medical Services, Five Ways House, Edgbaston, Birmingham B15 1ST Tel: 0121 626 3194 Fax: 0121 626 3210; 27 Greenhill Road, Moseley, Birmingham B13 9SS Tel: 0121 689 2618 — MB ChB 1973 Birm. Med. Adviser, Med. Servs., Birm. Prev: GP Birm.

BOWDEN, Helen Finch 14 Northgate, Cottingham HU16 4HH — MB ChB 1984 Bristol. Trainee GP Croydon. Prev: SHO (Gyn.) Mayday Univ. Hosp. Lond.; SHO (Gen. Med.) Roy. Devon & Exeter (Wonford) Hosp.

BOWDEN, Jane Elizabeth Post Office Stores, West Harptree, Bristol BS18 6EA — MB BS 1992 Lond.

BOWDEN, John Brian Finaghy Health Centre, 13-25 Finaghy Road S., Belfast BT10 0BW Tel: 028 628211; 130 Great Victoria Street, Belfast BT2 7BG Tel: 02890 325679 — MB BCh BAO 1950 Belf.; MRCGP 1965. (Qu. Univ. Belf.) Med. Off. (p/t) Down Dist. Counc. Socs: Fell. Ulster Med. Soc.

BOWDEN, Lydia Suzanne Neonatal Unit, South Manchester University Hospital Trust, Southmoor Road, Wythenshawe, Manchester M23 Tel: 0161 291 2807 Email: lydia.bowden@smuht.nhs.nwest.nhs.uk; 1 Lyme Grove, Altrincham WA14 2AD Tel: 0161 928 6009 Email: lydia.bowden@zoom.co.uk — MB ChB 1988 Dundee; MRCP (UK) 1993. (Dundee) Cons. (Neonatology & Paediat.) S. Manch. Univ. Hosp. Trust. Socs: BMA; MRCPCH; Brit. Assoc. of Perinatal Med. Prev: Sen. Regist. Rotat. (Paediat.) Mersey; Regist. Rotat. (Paediat.) Mersey; SHO (Paediat.) City Gen. Hosp. Stoke on Trent & Roy. Manch. Childr. Hosp.

BOWDEN, Lynette Jane Blake House Surgery, Black Torrington, Beaworthy EX21 5QE Tel: 01409 23340; 2 Providence Place, Hartland, Bideford EX39 6BG Tel: 01237 441775 — MB BS 1978 Newc.; MFHom 1988; DRCOG 1981. Socs: Fac. Homoeop.; Brit. Soc. Med. & Dent. Hypn. Prev: GP Hartland.

BOWDEN, Melanie Frances Fairmile Hospital, Reading Rd, Chasey, Oxford OX10 9HH Tel: 01491 651281 — MB BS 1986 Newc.; MRCPsych 1995. Regist. (Psychiat.) Oxf. Prev: Regist. (Psychiat.) Newc.

BOWDEN, Michael Ian 10 Ascot Road, Moseley, Birmingham B13 9EL Tel: 0121 449 3420 Email: tomtenasc@breathe.uk — MB ChB 1984 Birm.; FCAnaesth. 1990. (Birmingham) Cons. Anaesth. Univ. Hosp. Birm. Prev: Regist. (Anaesth.) Centr. Birm. HA; Research Fell. (Anaesth.) Univ. of Birm.; Lect. (Anaesth.) Univ. of Birm.

BOWDEN, Michael William Protodigm Ltd., 6th Floor, Hamilton House, 111 Marlowes, Hemel Hempstead HP1 1BB Tel: 01442 212594 Fax: 01442 214261; 61 Merlin Way, Bicester OX26 6YG Tel: 01869 369496 Email: 101363.1542@compuserve.com — MB ChB 1985 Liverp.; MFPM RCP (UK) 1992; DFFP 1992; Dip. Pharm. Med. RCP (UK) 1990. Dir. (Clin. Developm.) Protodigm Ltd. Hemel Hempstead. Socs: Brit. Assn. Pharmaceut. Phys. Prev: Sen. Med. Adviser Wyeth Laborat. Maidenhead; Sen. Med. Adviser SmithKline

Beecham Pharmaceut. Welwyn Gdn. City; Sen. Med. Adviser & Manager of Med. Affairs Cilag Ltd. High Wycombe.

BOWDEN, Paul Charles St Andrews Medical Centre, St. Andrews Court, Pinewood Gardens, Southborough, Tunbridge Wells TN4 0LZ Tel: 01892 515455 Fax: 01892 514019; Badgers Wood, Furzefield Avenue, Speldhurst, Tunbridge Wells TN3 0LD — MB BS 1977 Lond.; BSc (Hons.) Pharmacol. 1974; MRCGP (Distinc.) 1988. GP Trainer Kent. Prev: GP Tutor Tunbridge Wells.

BOWDEN, Paul Michael Anthony Maudsley Hospital, Denmark Hill, London SE5 8AZ Tel: 020 7703 6333 Fax: 020 7919 3573 — MPhil Lond. 1973; MRCP (UK) 1969; MRCS Eng. LRCP Lond. 1965; FRCPsych 1983, M 1973; FRCP (UK) 1998. (Guy's) Cons. Forens. Psychiat. Bethlem Roy. & Maudsley Hosp. Lond. & Home Office; Edr. Jl. Forens Psychiat. Socs: Acad. Forens. Sci. Prev: Cons. Forens. Psychiat. SW Thames RHA; Sen. Lect. (Psychiat.) St. Geo. Hosp. Lond.; Sen. Regist. (Psychol. Med.) Hammersmith Hosp.

BOWDEN, Philip William Medical Centre, The Green, Brailsford, Derby DE6 3BX — MB BS 1949 Lond.; MRCGP 1962. (Univ. Coll. Hosp.) Clin. Asst. Pastures Hosp. Mickleover. Prev: Cas. Off. Miller Gen. Hosp.; Ho. Surg. N. Middlx. Hosp.; RAMC (Nat. Serv.).

BOWDEN, Reed Norman London Deanery (GP Dept), 20 Guilford Road, London WC1N 1DZ Tel: 020 7692 3203 Fax: 020 7692 3262; 75 Old Road, Harlow CM17 0HF Tel: 01279 410326 Fax: 01279 442590 Email: rbowden75@aol.com — MB BChir 1966 Camb.; MRCP (UK) 1972; FRCGP 1991, M 1974; DObst RCOG 1972. (Cambridge/St. Geo.) p/t Assoc. Dean (Gen. Prac.) Lond. Deanery. Socs: Harlow Med. Soc. Prev: Princip. GP; Examr. MRCGP; Clin. Asst. (Med.) P.ss Alexandra Hosp. Harlow.

BOWDEN, Professor Ruth Elizabeth Mary, OBE 6 Hartham Close, Hartham Road, London N7 9JH Tel: 020 7607 3464 Fax: 020 7607 3464 — MB BS 1940 Lond.; MB BS (Hons.) Lond. 1940; DSc Lond. 1957; FRCS Eng. 1973; MRCS Eng. LRCP Lond. 1940. (Lond. (RFH) Sch. of Med. for Women) Emerit. Prof. Anat. Univ. Lond.; Hon. Research Fell. Inst. Neurol Lond. Socs: Fell. Roy. Soc. Med. & BOA; Life-Mem. (Ex-Pres.) Anat. Soc. GB & Irel.; Med. Wom.'s Federat. (Ex. Pres). Prev: Univ. Prof. Anat. Roy. Free Hosp. Sch. Med. Lond.; Sir William Collins Prof. Human & Comparative Anat. Roy. Coll. Surg. Eng. 1984-9; WHO Cons. Anat. Univ. Khartoum.

BOWDEN, William Martin (retired) 47 Hylton Road, Hartlepool TS26 0AG Tel: 01429 272795 — MB ChB Ed. 1960; FRCS Ed. 1967; Dip Sports Med. Ed. 1997 RCS Ed; FFAEM 1993. Prev: Cons. Surg. i/c (A & E) Hartlepool Hosp. Gp.

BOWDITCH, Mr Mark Graham Ipswich Hospital, Heath Rd, Ipswich — MB ChB 1989 Manch.; FRCS (Tr. & Orth.) 1998; BSc (Hons.) Physiol. Manch. 1986; FRCS Eng. 1993; FRCS Ed. 1993. (Manchester) Orthop./ Trauma Cons. Ipswich. Socs: Brit. Orthop. Assn.; Brit. Assn. Sport & Med.; Brit. Assn. Knee Surg. Prev: SHO Rotat. Sheff.; Fell. Knee & Shoulder Surg., Adelaide. Australia; Specialist Regist. Rotat. (Orthop.) Camb.

BOWDITCH, William Barrett Royal Crescent and Preston Road Practice, 25 Crescent Street, Weymouth DT4 7BY Tel: 01305 774466 Fax: 01305 760538; Cobbleston, Friar Waddon Road, Upwey, Weymouth DT3 4EN — MB BS 1981 Lond.; BSc Lond. 1978, MB BS 1981; MRCGP 1988; DRCOG 1984.

BOWDLER, Mr David Anthony Tel: 020 8333 3191 Fax: 020 8333 3188 Email: david.bowlder@uk-consultants.co.uk; Hillfarrance, 11 Holbrook Lane, Chislehurst BR7 6PE Tel: 020 8295 4802 — MB BS Lond. 1976; FRCS (ENT & Otolaryngol.) Eng. 1982; FRCS Eng. 1980; T(S) 1991. (Westm. Med. Sch.) Cons. Otorhinolaryng. Univ. hosp.Lewisham,Qu. Eliz. Hosp. Lond.

BOWDLER, Gareth Richard RM 522 TB2, Withington Hospital, Nell Lane, West Didsbury, Manchester M20 8LR — MB ChB 1998 Manch.; MB ChB Manch 1998.

BOWDLER, Stuart Ross Redcote, Lower Wood, All Stretton, Church Stretton SY6 6LF Tel: 01694 751307 — MB ChB 1992 Dundee; FRCA 2000. Specialist Regist. Birm. Sch. of Anaesth. Socs: Assn. Anaesth.; Intens. Care Soc.; Pain Soc. Prev: SHO (Anaesth.) Univ. Hosp. Birm.

BOWEN, Andrew 28 Parry Road, Morriston, Swansea SA6 7DS — MB ChB 1993 Sheff.; BSc (Hons. Physics) Bristol 1984.

BOWEN, Angela Louise St George's Hospital, Blackshaw Road, London SW17 0QT; 56 Tantallon Road, London SW12 8DG — MB BS 1990 Lond.; MRCP (UK) 1993. Regist. Rotat. (Haemat.) SW Thames HA. Prev: Regist. (Haemat.) St. Lukes Hosp. Guildford.

BOWEN, Anne Carolyn Dyfed Road Health Centre, Dyfed Road, Neath SA11 3AP Tel: 01639 635331 — MB BCh 1989 Wales; MRCGP 1993; DRCOG 1991. (Univ. Wales Coll. Med.) Clin. Asst. (ENT) Neath Gen. Hosp.

BOWEN, Anthony Harries Southbourne Sports Medicine & Acupuncture - Private Clinic, Thornham Farm House, Shore Road, Prinsted, Emsworth PO10 8HS Tel: 01243 374398 Fax: 01243 377155 — MB BCh Wales 1965; Dip. Med. AC 1997; DObst RCOG 1969. Med. Examr. BUPA Med. Centre Havant; Doctor i/c S.bourne Sports Med. Clinic. Socs: Brit. Med. Acupunct. Soc.; Brit. Assn. Sport & Med.; Brit. Inst. Musculoskeletal Med. Prev: Ho. Surg. (Urol. & Obst.) Cardiff Roy. Infirm.

BOWEN, Barbara Mary 30 Temple Street, Brill, Aylesbury HP18 9SX — MB ChB Ed. 1968. S.C.M.O. Community Child Health Horton Gen. Hosp. Banbury.

BOWEN, Catherine Rhian 1 Plasdraw Road, Aberdare CF44 0NR — MB BCh 1995 Wales.

BOWEN, David Aubrey Llewellyn Trefan, 19 Letchmore Road, Radlett WD7 8HU Tel: 01923 856936 Fax: 01923 856936 — MB BChir 1947 Camb.; MA Camb. 1947; FRCP Ed. 1971, M 1954; FRCP Lond. 1982, M 1978; FRCPath 1975, M 1964; DPath Eng. 1955; DMJ Soc. Apoth. Lond. 1962. (Middlx.) Emerit. Prof. Forens. Med. Univ. Lond. Socs: Brit. Assn. of Forens. Med., Pres. 1927 - 1939. Prev: Prof. & Reader (Forens. Med.) Char. Cross Hosp. Med. Sch. Lond.; Lect. Forens. Med. St. Geo. Hosp. Med. Sch.; Lect. Forens. Med. Univ. Oxf.

BOWEN, David John The New Surgery, Longford Road, Holyhead LL65 1TR Tel: 01407 762341 Fax: 01407 763996; Iroko, Trearddur Road, Trearddur Bay, Holyhead LL65 2UE Tel: 01407 860150 — MB BCh 1972 Wales.

BOWEN, David John (retired) — MB BS 1957 Lond.; MRCS Eng. LRCP Lond. 1956; FFA RCS Eng. 1963; DA Eng. 1960. Cons. Anaesth. Roy. Hants. Co. Hosp. Winchester. Prev: Sen. Regist. (Anaesth.) Cardiff Roy. Infirm.

BOWEN, David Roderick Vivian 47 Vernon Road, Leigh-on-Sea SS9 2NG — MB BS 1987 Lond.

BOWEN, David Roland (retired) High Mead, 23 Heol Derlwyn, Rhiwbina, Cardiff CF14 6JU Tel: 01222 624296 — MB BCh 1947 Wales; BSc, MB BCh Wales 1947. Asst. Chest Phys. Thoracic Outpats. Dept. Llandough Hosp. Penarth. Prev: Regist. (Thoracic Med.) Harefield Hosp.

BOWEN, David Timothy Department of Haematology, Dundee Teaching Hospitals NHS Trust, Ninewells Hospital, Dundee DD1 9SY Tel: 01382 660111 Fax: 01382 645731 Email: d.t.bowen@dundee.ac.uk; 8 Middlebank Crescent, Dundee DD2 1HY — MB BChir 1982 Camb.; MA (Camb.) 1979; MRCP (UK) 1986; MRCPath 1993; MD (Camb.) 1991. (Cambridge and Middlesex Hospital) Sen. Lect. & Hons. Cons. (Haemat.) Ninewells Hosp. Dundee.

BOWEN, Elisabeth Sarah 16 The Causeway, Horsham RH12 1HE; Cefn Coed Uchaf, Llanfaglan, Caernarfon LL54 5RF Tel: 01268 672773 Fax: 01268 672773 Email: ocean.discovery@btinternet.com — MB BCh 1992 Wales. GPR YSBYTY Gwynedd Scheme. Prev: SHO (A & E) Addenbrooke's Hosp. Camb.

BOWEN, Elizabeth (retired) 44 Nunnery Fields, Canterbury CT1 3JT Tel: 01227 472036 — MB ChB 1949 Bristol; MRCS Eng. LRCP Lond. 1948; DCH Eng. 1950.

BOWEN, Elizabeth Frances Flat 1, 6 Ardbeg Road, London SE24 9JL — MB BS 1990 Lond.; PhD Lond. 1997; BSc Lond. 1987, MB BS 1990; MRCP (UK) 1993. (Roy. Free Hosp.) Sen. Regist. (Respirat./Gen. Med.) St Geo. Hosp. Tooting Lond. Prev: Research Regist. (HIV/AIDS) Roy. Free Hosp. Sch. Med. Lond.; SHO (Med.) Hammersmith & Brompton Hosps.

BOWEN, Elizabeth Mary 5 Percival Avenue, Hampstead, London NW3 4PY Tel: 020 7435 2373 — MB BS Lond. 1964; MRCS Eng. LRCP Lond. 1964; DA Eng. 1967.

BOWEN, Esther Jane 31 Flemish Cl, St Florence, Tenby SA70 8LT — MB BCh 1997 Wales.

BOWEN, Fiona Elizabeth 36 Sunningdale Road, Bromsgrove B61 7NN Tel: 01527 574045 — MB ChB 1975 Ed.; MFPHM RCP (UK) 1990; DA Eng. 1978. GP Regist. Prev: Sen. Ho. Off. Dudley VTS; Sen. Ho. Off. QEPH; Cons. in Pub. Health Med. Birm. DHA.

BOWEN, Gareth James The Health Centre, Westfield Walk, Leominster HR6 8HD Tel: 01568 612084 Fax: 01568 610340; Rowley Grange, Hamnish, Leominster HR6 0QN Tel: 01568 760670 — MB BS 1972 Lond.; MFHom 1996; DObst RCOG 1975. (St. Geo.)

BOWEN, Geoffrey William 1 The Cottages, Skelwith Fold, Ambleside LA22 0HT Tel: 015394 32693 Fax: 015394 32433 — MB ChB 1961 Manch. (Manch.) Med. Off. Langdale-Ambleside Mt.ain Rescue Team. Prev: SHO (O & G) Preston Roy. Infirm.; SHO Booth Hall Childr. Hosp. Manch.; Ho. Surg. Manch. Roy. Infirm.

BOWEN, Hannah Patricia The Surgery, North St., Lostwithiel PL22 0EF Tel: 01208 87589 Fax: 01208 873710; Rivendell, Couchsmill, Lostwithiel PL22 0RX — MB BS 1974 Lond.; DA Eng. 1976; AKC. (King's Coll. Hosp. Lond.) Asst. Bowen & Howe Lostwithiel; Clin. Med. Off. (Family Plann.) Cornw. Socs: Assoc. Mem. Brit. Med. Acupunc. Soc.; Diplomate Fac. Family Plann. and Repro. Health Care. Prev: SHO (Anaesth.), Ho. Phys. & Ho. Surg. Plymouth Gen. Hosp.

BOWEN, Howard Grawys The Health Centre, Caebricks Road, Cwmbwria, Swansea SA5 8NS — MB BCh 1954 Wales; BSc MB BCh Wales 1954. (Cardiff) Prev: Ho. Surg. Ophth. & ENT Cardiff Roy. Infirm.; Ho. Phys. Dept. Child Health Llandough Hosp.

BOWEN, Howard John Clydach Health Centre, Sybil Street, Clydach, Swansea SA6 5EU Tel: 01792 843831 Fax: 01792 844902 — MB BCh 1971 Wales; DObst RCOG 1973.

BOWEN, Iestyn Rhys Lostwithiel Medical Practice, North Street, Lostwithiel PL22 0EF Tel: 01208 872589 Fax: 01208 873710; Rivendell, Couchsmill, Lostwithiel PL22 0RX Tel: 01208 872589 — MB BS 1971 Lond.; MRCS Eng. LRCP Lond. 1971; DA Eng. 1973. GP Lostwithiel. Prev: SHO (Anaesth.) & Ho. Phys & Ho. Surg. Kings Coll. Hosp.; SHO (Med.) Plymouth Gen. Hosp.

BOWEN, Inez 74 Wimmerfield Avenue, Swansea SA2 7DA Tel: 01792 24209 — MB BCh 1955 Wales; BSc, MB BCh Wales 1955. (Cardiff) SCMO Swansea Health Dist.

BOWEN, Ingrid Eie 58 Highmead Avenue, Newton, Swansea SA3 4TY Tel: 01792 361600 — Cand Med Oslo 1979; DFFP 1995; DRCOG 1997. Clin. Med. Off. Family Plann. Dept. Clan-y-Mor NHS Trust Swansea; Clin. Asst. (geritoUrin. Med.) Clan-y-Mor NHS Trust. Prev: SHO (O & G) Singleton Hosp. Swansea.

BOWEN, Joanna Marian Rudge Farm, Lustleigh, Newton Abbot TQ13 9SL — MB BS 1993 Lond.

BOWEN, Joanna Talbot 6 Pembroke Vale, Bristol BS8 3DN — MB BS 1985 Lond.; MRCPsych 1990. Socs: Soc. Study Addic.; Brit. Med. Acupunct. Soc.; Med. Counc. Alcoholism. Prev: Sen. Regist. & Regist. Rotat. (Psychiat.) Char. Cross Hosp. Lond.; Sen. Regis. The Maudsley Hosp. Lond.

BOWEN, Joanne Claire 114 Vale Street, Upper Gornal, Dudley DY3 3XF — MB ChB 1998 Birm.

BOWEN, John Antony Poland (retired) 67 Church Road, London SW19 5DQ — MRCS Eng. LRCP Lond. 1944; MRCGP 1966. Prev: Ho. Surg. W.m. Hosp.

BOWEN, John Charles 8 Sedgefield Road, Manchester M26 1YE — MB ChB 1986 Leeds.

BOWEN, Mr John Edgar 30 Harley Street, London W1G 9PW Tel: 020 7636 0955 Fax: 020 7636 3497; The Priors, Cowden, Edenbridge TN8 7JD Tel: 01342 850452 — MB 1962 Camb.; MA Camb. 1963, BChir 1961; FRCS Eng. 1965. (Camb. & St. Thos.) Hon. Cons. Plastic Surg. Qu. Vict. Hosp. E. Grinstead. Socs: Brit. Assn. Plastic Surg.; Brit. Assn. Aesthetic Plastic Surgs. Prev: Cons. Plastic Surg. Guy's Hosp. Lond. & St. Bart. Hosp. Rochester; Sen. Regist. (Plastic Surg.) Qu. Vict. Hosp. E. Grinstead; SHO (Plastic & Orthop. Surg.) Hosp. Sick Childr. Gt. Ormond St. Lond.

BOWEN, John Montgomery Seacroft, 10 Giltar Way, Penally, Tenby SA70 7QR Tel: 01834 843403 — MB BCh 1939 Wales; BSc Wales 1936; FRCOG 1961, M 1948. (Cardiff) Cons. O & G Newport & E. Mon., N. Mon. & Rhymney & Shirmowy Hosp. Managem. Comms. Socs: Fell. Roy. Soc. Med. Prev: Sen. Regist. & Ho. Surg. (O & G) Cardiff Roy. Infirm.; Squadron Ldr. RAF Med. Serv. 1940-6.

BOWEN, John Richard Christopher Princess Margaret Hospital, Wroughton, Swindon SN4 0QJ — MB BCh 1986 Wales; MRCP (UK) 1992.

BOWEN, John Robert Tenby Surgery, The Norton, Tenby SA70 8AB Tel: 01834 844161 Fax: 01834 844227 — MB BS 1970 Lond.; MRCS Eng. LRCP Lond. 1970.

BOWEN, Judith Sian 25 The Hermitage, Richmond TW10 6SH — MB BS 1991 Lond.

BOWEN, Kathleen Anne Clark (retired) Shelsley Beauchamp, Worcester WR6 6RH Tel: 01886 812261 — MB BChir 1945 Camb.; MRCS Eng. LRCP Lond. 1944; DObst RCOG 1947. Prev: Ho. Accouch. King's Coll. Hosp.

BOWEN, Lawrence William (retired) Bradby W., Gonalston, Nottingham NG14 7JA Tel: 0115 966 3763 — MB BS 1946 Lond.; MRCS Eng. LRCP Lond. 1946; DPM Bristol 1953.

BOWEN, Lesley Mary McLaren (retired) Alkborough, Scunthorpe DN15 9EY Tel: 01724 720070 — MB BS Lond. 1945; MRCS Eng. LRCP Lond. 1945. Prev: Ho. Phys. Univ. Coll. Hosp.

BOWEN, Marjorie (retired) Rhyd House, Woodlands Avenue, Rustington, Littlehampton BN16 3ER — MB BS Lond. 1956. Prev: GP.

BOWEN, Marjorie Ethel Merrymeet, Glasllwch Lane, Newport NP20 3PR Tel: 01633 65712 — MB BCh 1939 Wales; BSc, MB BCh Wales 1939. (Cardiff) Prev: Ho. Phys. Med. Unit Welsh Nat. Sch. Med.

BOWEN, Marjorie Lettice (retired) 18 Blenheim Way, Horspath, Oxford OX33 1SB Tel: 01865 872569 — MB BCh BAO 1954 Dub.; MRCGP 1975; DCH Eng. 1958. Prev: GP Cowley.

BOWEN, Mary Elizabeth Valerie (retired) Cilborth, Lewis Terrace, New Quay SA45 9PG Tel: 01545 560304 — MB BCh 1951 Wales.

BOWEN, Mr Michael Leslie 10 Harley Street, London W1N 1AA Tel: 0131 447 5263, 0207 467 8471 Fax: 0207 467 8312 Email: mikebowen@quista.net; Box Tree House, 3 St Andrews Rd, Old Headington, Oxford OX3 9DL Tel: 01865 432680 Fax: 01865 463432 Email: mikebowen@quista.net — MB ChB 1986 Dundee; FRCS Ed. 1991; MRCP 1997 Ire; MRCOG 1996. (Dundee University) Cons. Obst. & Gynaecologist; Mediacl Adviser, Dept. of Health, Area 651C, Skipton Ho., 80 Lond. Rd, Lond., SE1 6LH. Socs: Mem. Of Brit. Gyn. Cancer Soc.; Mem. Of Oxf. Med. Soc.; Mem. Of Coelia Shauta Club. Prev: Specialist Regist. (O & G) John Radcliffe Oxf.; Regist. (O & G) John Radcliffe Oxf.

BOWEN, Philippa Louise Roehampton Surgery, 191 Roehampton Lane, London SW15 4HN Tel: 020 8788 1188 Fax: 020 8789 9914; 181 Roehampton Lane, London SW15 4HP Tel: 020 8789 1556 — MB BCh 1976 Wales. (Welsh Nat. Sch. Med.)

BOWEN, Rebecca Louise 9 Kingsmill, Bristol BS9 1BZ — BM BS 1998 Nottm.; BM BS Nottm 1998.

BOWEN, Richard Gwilym Penylan Surgery, 74 Penylan Road, Cardiff CF23 5SY Tel: 029 2049 8181 Fax: 029 2049 1507 — MB BCh 1969 Wales; MRCGP 1980; Dip. Pract. Dermat. Wales 1990. (Cardiff) Hon. Clin. Tutor Welsh Coll. Med. Socs: (Treas.) Cardiff Med. Soc.; BMA. Prev: Pres. Cardiff Med. Soc.

BOWEN, Robert Llewellyn Aylesford Medical Centre, Admiral Moore Drive, Royal British Legion Village, Aylesford ME20 7SE Tel: 01622 717389 Fax: 01622 790436 — MB BS 1977 Lond.; MRCS Eng. LRCP Lond. 1977; MRCGP 1983; Dip. Palliat. Med. Wales 1991; DRCOG 1981. (Char. Cross) Prev: Trainee GP Gt. Yarmouth & LoW.oft VTS; Ho. Off. Char. Cross Hosp. & Frimley Pk. Hosp.

BOWEN, Roderick William St Thomas Surgery, Rifleman Lane, St Thomas Green, Haverfordwest SA61 1QX Tel: 01437 763100 — MB BS 1951 Lond.; DObst RCOG 1957. (St. Thos.)

BOWEN, Ronald Alwyne (retired) 64 Southway, London NW11 6SA Tel: 020 8455 7317 — MB BS Lond. 1941; MRCS Eng. LRCP Lond. 1940; FFA RCS Eng. 1953; DA Eng. 1946. Prev: Anaesth. i/c St. Bart. Hosp. Lond.

BOWEN, Susan Patricia Hackwood Partnership, Essex House, Worting Road, Basingstoke RG21 8SU Tel: 01256 470464 Fax: 01256 357289 — MB ChB 1983 Auckland; MB ChB 1983 Auckland.

BOWEN, Yvonne Mary Hollies Medical Practice, Tamworth Health Centre, Upper Gungate, Tamworth B79 7EA Tel: 01827 68511 Fax: 01827 51163; Forest Lodge, Clifton Campville, Tamworth B79 0BH — BM BS Nottm. 1984, BMedSci 1982; MRCGP 1989; DRCOG 1988; DCH RCP Lond. 1987.

BOWEN-DAVIES, Peter Edward Pfizer Ltd., Ramsgate Road, Sandwich CT13 9NJ Tel: 01306 643973 Fax: 01306 655564 Email: bowenp@pfizer.com; Milk Wood, The Plantation, Storrington, Pulborough RH20 4JG — MB BChir 1979 Camb.; BA Camb. 1975, MA; FRCS Ed. 1983; MRCGP 1985; Dip. Pharm Med. RCP (UK) 1991; DRCOG 1984; MFPM 1992. (St. Bart.) Assoc. Med. Dir. Pfizer

Ltd. Socs: Fell. Roy. Soc. Med.; BMA. Prev: Head Clin. Developm. Unit. II Shering Health Care Ltd.; Med. Advisor Ciba-Geigy Horsham; GP Plymouth.

BOWEN-JONES, Ann Maesyrhedydd, Tregarth, Bangor LL57 4AE — MB BS 1971 Lond.; MRCS Eng. LRCP Lond. 1972; DObst RCOG 1974. (St. Mary's) Socs: BMA. Prev: Ho. Phys. St. Chas. Hosp. Lond.; Ho. Surg. Harold Wood Hosp. Romford; Obst. Off. Prof. Unit St. Mary's Hosp. Lond.

BOWEN-PERKINS, Hywel Henry (Surgery), Shadbolt House, Shadbolt Park, Worcester Park KT4 7BX Tel: 020 8337 3966 Fax: 020 8330 1928; Hazelby House, Furze Hill, Kingswood, Tadworth KT20 6HB — MB BS 1975 Lond.; MRCS Eng. LRCP Lond. 1975; LMSSA Lond. 1975. (Guy's) Hon. Clin. Tutor (Gen. Pract.) St. Geo. Hosp. Med. Sch.; Med. Adviser Medico-Legal Reporting; Prescribing Load, Mid Surrey PCG; Appt. Dr. (Health and Safety Exec.) Asbestos Regs. Socs: Soc. Occupat. Med.; Liveryman & Freeman Worshipful Soc. Apoth. City of Lond.; Brit. Med. Ultrasound Soc. Prev: Occupat. Health Phys. Marks & Spencer; Clin. Asst. (Genitourin. Surg.) Epsom Dist. Hosp.; Chairm. Mid Surrey PCG.

BOWEN-SIMPKINS, Emma Jane 73 Pennard Road, Southgate, Swansea SA3 2AJ — MB BCh 1993 Wales.

BOWEN-SIMPKINS, Peter (cons. rooms), Sancta Maria Hospital, Ffynone Road, Swansea SA1 6DF Tel: 01792 479050 Fax: 01792 641452 Email: pbs.boscos@virgin.net; Cysgod-y-Bryn, 6 Brynview Close, Reynoldston, Swansea SA3 1AG Fax: 01792 390458 — MB BChir 1967 Camb.; MA Camb. 1967; MRCS Eng. LRCP Lond. 1966; MFFP 1993; FRCOG 1985, M 1973. (Camb. & Guy's) Cons. O & G Singleton Hosp. Swansea; Mem. (Counc.) RCOG; Hon. Treas. RCOG; Clin. Dir., Cromwell IVF & Fertil. Centre, Swansea. Socs: Brit. Fertil. Soc.; Brit. Menopause Soc.; BMA. Prev: Resid. Med. Off. (Gyn.) Samarit. Hosp. Wom. Lond.; Resid. Med. Off. (Obst.) Qu. Charlotte's Matern. Hosp. Lond.; Sen. Regist. Middlx. Hosp. & Hosp. for Wom. Lond.

BOWEN-WRIGHT, Hazel Equa 20 Bingham Road, Croydon CR0 7EB — MB BS 1992 Lond.

***BOWER, Christopher Peter Roy** Department of Dermatology, Bristol Royal Infirmary, Marlborough St., Bristol BS2 8HW Tel: 0117 923 0000; 180 St Michaels Hill, Kingsdown, Bristol BS2 8DE Tel: 0117 923 9403 — MB ChB 1992 Ed.; BSc (Hons.) Ed. 1990; MRCP (UK) 1995.

BOWER, Edward Lee 118 Queens Road, Bury St Edmunds IP33 3ES — MB BS 1994 Lond.

BOWER, Helen Davies Midstreams, Station Road, Bosham, Chichester PO18 8NG Tel: 01243 573037 — MB BS Lond. 1959; MRCS Eng. LRCP Lond. 1958; DObst RCOG 1961. (Roy. Free) Med. Off. (Elderly Health) Qu. Alexandra Hosp., Cosham, Portsmouth. Socs: BMA.

BOWER, Ian Park Road New Surgery, Park Road, Barnoldswick, Colne BB18 5BG Tel: 01282 812244 Fax: 01282 850220; Carr Beck, Barnoldswick, Colne BB18 5XD Tel: 01282 812087 — MB ChB 1957 Leeds; DA Eng. 1965. (Leeds) Med. Off. Carlson Filtration Ltd. Barnoldswick. Prev: Squadron Ldr. RAF Med. Br.; SHO (Anaesth.) Bradford Hosp. Gps.; Cas. Off. Bradford Roy. Infirm.

BOWER, Katherine Laura 47 Lady Byron Lane, Knowle, Solihull B93 9AX — MB ChB 1998 Manch.; MB ChB Manch 1998.

BOWER, Mark David Medical Day Unit, Chelsea and Westminster Hospital, 369 Fulham Road, London SW10 9NH Tel: 020 8237 5054 Fax: 020 8746 8836 Email: m.bower@cxwms.ac.uk — MB BChir 1985 Camb.; PhD Camb. 1993, MA (Zool.) 1986, MB BChir 1985; MRCP (UK) 1989. Sen. Lect. (Oncol.) Chelsea & W.minster Hosp. Prev: Sen. Regist. (Oncol.) Hammersmith Hosp. Lond.; Sen. Regist. (Oncol.) Char. Cross Hosp. Lond.; Clin. Research Fell. (Oncol.) St. Bart. Hosp. Lond.

BOWER, Noreen Pearl (retired) 27 Ingham Road, South Croydon CR2 8LT Tel: 020 8657 7713 — MB BS Madras 1944.

BOWER, Pamela Mary Christine (retired) 373 Woodstock Road, Oxford OX2 8AA Tel: 01865 515209 — MB ChB 1944 Birm.; DObst RCOG 1946. Prev: Med. Off. Occupat. Health Oxf. AHA (T).

BOWER, Patrick Jonathan Balham Park Surgery, 92 Balham Park Road, London SW12 8EA Tel: 020 8767 8828 Fax: 020 8682 1736 — MB BS 1977 Lond.; MA Camb. 1978, BA 1974; MRCGP 1981; DRCOG 1979. (Univ. Coll. Hosp.) Prev: Trainee GP Lond. (Char. Cross) VTS.

BOWER, Philip Simon Cromwell Place Surgery, Cromwell Place, St. Ives, Huntingdon PE27 5JD Tel: 01480 462206 Fax: 01480 465313; Email: phil.bower@virgin.net — MB BS 1984 Lond.; MRCGP 1989; Cert. Family Plann. JCC 1989.

BOWER, Rachel Charlotte 63 Tudor Road, London E9 7SN — MB BChir 1992 Camb.

BOWER, Rachel Louise 2 Oakdale Crescent, Lindly, Huddersfield HD3 3WE; 16 Market Place, Castle Donnington, Derby DE74 2JB — BM BS 1996 Nottm.; MRCP.

BOWER, Ronald James 22 Lightwood Close, Knowle, Solihull B93 9LS — MRCS Eng. LRCP Lond. 1942; BA Camb. 1940. (St. Bart.) Prev: Temp. Maj. RAMC; Cas. Off. Roy. Surrey Co. Hosp. Guildford; Ho. Phys. Maidstone Gen. Hosp.

BOWER, Sarah Jane 4 Malvern Road, London E6 1LT — MB BS 1983 Lond.; MRCOG 1989. Research Fell. Kings. Coll. Hosp. Lond.

BOWER, Stephen John The Surgery, High St., South Milford, Leeds LS25 5AA Tel: 01977 682202; Larchfield House, Church St, Barkston Ash, Tadcaster LS24 9PJ Tel: 01937 557514 — MB ChB 1976 Liverp.

BOWER, Susan Mary The Surgery, 1 Crawley Lane, Pound Hill, Crawley RH10 7DX Tel: 01293 549916 Fax: 01293 615382; 4 Grange Road, Crawley Down, Crawley RH10 4JT Tel: 01342 714896 Email: ian.dennis@virgin.net — MB ChB 1976 Birm.; MRCGP 1980; DRCOG 1979.

BOWER, Susanne 24 Hawthorn Way, Darras Hall, Ponteland, Newcastle upon Tyne NE20 9RU Tel: 01661 824984 Fax: 0191 222 8988 Email: susanne.bower@ncl.ac.uk — MB ChB 1971 Sheff.; PhD Newc. 1980; Dip. Musculoskel Med. Lond. 1997. Lect. Univ. Newc. Socs: Trustee & Vice-Chairm. of the Comp., Accred. and Educ. Bd. of the Brit. Med. Acupunc. Soc.; Brit. Inst. Musculoskel. Med.; N. Region Pain Gp. Prev: Research Off. Newc. Univ. Med. Sch.

BOWERING, Anthony Richard Crosstree Close Surgery, 1 Crosstree Close, Broadmayne, Dorchester DT2 8EN Tel: 01305 852231 Fax: 01305 853658 — MB BS 1976 Lond.

BOWERING, Katherine 70 Northwold Avenue, West Bridgford, Nottingham NG2 7JD — MB BS 1997 Newc.

BOWERING, Roderick John Bertram Worle Health Centre, 125 High St, Worle, Weston Super Mare BS22 6HB Tel: 01934 510510 Fax: 01934 522088 — MB BS 1976 Lond.; MRCS Eng. LRCP Lond. 1974. (Guy's)

BOWERMAN, Mr John Ernest Princess Grace Hospital, 42-52 Nottingham Place, London W1U 5NY Tel: 0207 486 1234 Fax: 0207 908 2168 Email: info@princessgrace.hcahealthcare.co.uk; Pond Cottage, Whitmore Vale, Grayshott, Hindhead GU26 6JB Tel: 01428 713314 Fax: 01428 713314 Email: johnbowerman.maxfac@btinternet.co — MB ChB 1965 Bristol; BDS (Hons.) Bristol 1953; FRCS Ed. 1985; FDS RCS Eng. 1965, LDS 1954. (Bristol) Indep. Cons. Oral & Maxillofacial Surg. Lond. Socs: Fell. Brit. Assn. Oral & Maxillofacial Surg. (Ex-Mem. Counc.); Eur. Assn. Cranio-Maxillo. Surg. (Ex-Mem. Counc.). Prev: Recogn. Teach. Univ. Lond. & Examr. Roy. Coll. Surgs. Eng.; Cons. Oral & Maxillofacial Surg. W.m. Hosp., Qu. Mary's Hosp. Roehampton, Epsom Dist. Hosp. & Roy. Dent. Hosp. Lond.; Sen. Regist. W.m. Hosp. Teach. Gp. & Univ. Coll. Hosp. Dent. Sch.

BOWERMAN, Roderick Dougal Forest End, Waterlooville PO7 7AH; 142 West Street, Havant PO9 1LP — BM BCh 1984 Oxf.; MA Oxf. 1986; MRCGP 1987; DRCOG 1993. Chairm., HDOCS GP Co-op. Prev: GP Tasmania; Trainee GP I. of Wight VTS.

BOWERS, Eric Francis (retired) Wayside, County Lane, Iverley, Stourbridge DY8 2SB Tel: 01562 882101 — MB BS 1949 Lond.; BSc (Physiol.) Lond. 1946; FRCPath 1972, M 1964; DCP Lond 1958; DPath Eng. 1956. Cons. Path. Dudley HA. Prev: Sen. Regist. & Asst. Bacteriol. Univ. Coll. Hosp. Lond.

BOWERS, Julia Caroline Beighton Health Centre, Queens Road, Beighton, Sheffield S20 1BJ Tel: 0114 269 5061; 16 Ashfurlang Park, Sheffield S17 3LD — MB ChB 1983 Sheff.; MRCGP 1989. GP Partner. Sheff.

BOWERS, Keith Edward James, Capt. RAMC Retd. (retired) 4 Alder Dale, Wolverhampton WV3 9JF Tel: 01902 422631 — MRCS Eng. LRCP Lond. 1951. Prev: Ho. Surg. (Cas. & Orthop.) Luton & Dunstable Hosp.

BOWERS, Margaret Joanne Dept. of Haematology, Belfast City Hosp., Lisborn Road, Belfast BT9 &ab Email:

magbag3@hotmail.com — MB ChB 1993 Ed.; 2001 Dip.RCPATH; BSc (Hons) 1991; MRCP Ed. 1996. (Edinburgh) Specialist Regist. (Haemat.), Belf. Prev: Regist. (Haemat.) Locum Appointment for Train.

BOWERS, Peter John Staveleigh Clinic, Tameside & Glossp Community & Priority Services NHS Trust, Stamford St., Stalybridge SK15 1JT Tel: 0161 303 8121 Fax: 0161 331 5270 Email: peterbowers@exchange.tgcps.tri.nwestnhs.uk; 6 Clifton Avenue, Fallowfield, Manchester M14 6UB Tel: 0161 224 9508 Email: peterjohnbowers@hotmail.com — MB ChB 1973 Manch.; BSc Lond. 1967; MSc (Psychiat.) Manch. 1980; FRCPsych 1996, M 1978; AKC. (Manch.) Cons. Child & Adolesc. Psychiat. & Med. Dir. Tameside & Glossop Community Priority Servs. NHS Trust. Socs: Fell. Manch. Med. Soc.; Assn. Child Psychol. & Child Psychiat.; Assn. of Family Therapists. Prev: Tutor (Child & Adolesc. Psychiat.) Univ. Manch. & Roy. Manch. Childr. Hosp.; Sen. Regist. (Child & Adolesc. Psychiat.) Manch. Rotat. Scheme; Regist. (Psychiat.) Withington Hosp. Manch.

BOWERS, Peter William Dermatology Department, Royal Cornwall Hospitals Trust, Treliske, Truro TR1 3LJ Tel: 01872 253253 Fax: 01872 252657 Email: lisa.duckham@rcht.swest.nhs.uk; 14 Treseder's Gardens, Truro TR1 1TR Tel: 01872 24070 Fax: 0870 063 3629 Email: lois.bowers@virgin.net — BM BCh 1971 Oxf.; MA Oxf. 1971; FRCP Lond. 1994; MRCP (UK) 1981; FRACP 1981; MRCGP 1975. (St. Thos. & University College Oxford) Cons. Dermat. Cornw. Socs: Brit. Assn. Dermat.; Pres. Brit. Soc. Dermat. Surg. Prev: Sen. Regist. (Dermat.) Notts. HA; Regist. Univ. Otago Med. Sch. Dunedin. NZ.

BOWERS, Simon Geoffrey 34 Brookdale Road, Liverpool L15 3JE — MB ChB 1998 Liverp.; MB ChB Liverp 1998.

BOWERS, Stephen Laurence Blackford House Medical Centre, 137 Croft Lane, Hollins, Bury BL9 8QA Tel: 0161 766 6622 Fax: 0161 796 2748; 3 St. Georges Road, Unsworth, Bury BL9 8JG Tel: 0161 767 9155 — MB ChB 1981 Manch.; BSc (Med. Sci.) St. And. 1978; MRCGP 1985; Cert. Prescribed Exp. JCPTGP 1986; DRCOG 1983; Cert. Family Plann. JCC 1983. (Manch. & St. And.) Socs: BMA. Prev: Ho. Surg. Withington Hosp. Manch.; Ho. Phys. Manch. Roy. Infirm.

BOWES, Charles Henry Gordon Ryehill House, Brass Castle Lane, Nunthorpe, Middlesbrough TS8 9ED Tel: 01642 316192 — MB BS 1942 Durh. (Durh.) Socs: BMA.

BOWES, John Butlin (retired) Cottle's Farm, Publow, Pensford, Bristol BS39 4JA Tel: 01761 490285 — MB BS 1955 Lond.; FFA RCS Eng. 1962. Cons. Anaesth. United Bristol Hosps. & Cossham-Frenchay Hosp. Gp. Prev: Lect. Dept. Anaesth. Univ. Bristol.

BOWES, Penelope Jane 16 Home Park Road, Saltash PL12 6BH — MB BCh 1985 Wales.

BOWES, Robert Jenkins Ianford, Old Hay Lane, Dore, Sheffield S17 3GN — MB ChB 1975 Liverp.; MRCP (UK) 1982; FRCP Lond. 1998. Cons. Cardiol. Regional Cardiac Centre N. Gen. Hosp. Sheff. Socs: Brit. Pacing & Electrophysiol. Gp.; Brit. Cardiac Interven. Soc. Prev: Sen. Regist. (Cardiol.) N.. Gen. Hosp. Sheff.; Research Fell. (Cardiol.) Wythenshawe Hosp. Manch.

BOWES, Robert John The Surgery, Kingswood Road, Tunbridge Wells TN2 4UJ Tel: 01892 511833 Fax: 01892 517597; 9 The Glebe, Pembury, Tunbridge Wells TN2 4EN — MB BS 1982 Lond.; BSc Lond. 1979, MB BS 1982; MRCGP 1989; DRCOG 1986; DCH RCP Lond. 1987. Prev: Trainee GP Tunbridge Wells VTS.

BOWEY, Olga Tolworth Hospital, Red Lion Road, Tolworth, Surbiton KT6 7QU Tel: 020 8390 0102 — MUDr 1970 Czechoslovakia. (Komensky Univ.) Assoc. Specialist Psychiat. Kingston Dist. Community NHS Trust.

BOWHAY, Alyson Ann Old Forge, Albaston, Gunnislake PL18 9AL — MB BS 1982 Lond.; BSc Lond. 1977, MB BS 1982; MRCGP 1986; DRCOG 1986.

BOWHAY, Andrew Richard The Jackson Rees Department of Paediatric Anaesthsia, Royal Liverpool Childrens Hospital, Alder Hey, Eaton Road, Liverpool L12 2AP Tel: 0151 228 4811 Fax: 0151 252 5460 Email: andrew.bowhay@rlch-tr.nwest.nhs.uk — MB BS 1979 Lond.; FRCA Eng. 1984. (Char. Cross) Cons. Paediat. Anaesth. Roy. Liverp. Childr. Hosp. Alder Hey. Prev: Sen. Regist. (Anaesth.) Addenbrooke's Hosp. Cambs.; Sen. Regist. (Anaesth.) Godfrey Huggins Sch. Med. Zimbabwe; Regist. (Anaesth.) Hosp. for Sick Childr. Gt. Ormond St. Lond.

BOWIE, Alan Niven, Surg. Lt.-Cdr. RN Hillside, Sand Lane, Calstock PL18 9QX Email: abowie@cwcom.net — MB ChB 1992 Dundee. (Dundee) Roy.Naval. Med.Off. Socs: BMA.

BOWIE, Cameron The Old Farmhouse, Clayhanger, Chard TA20 3BD Tel: 01460 66488 Fax: 01460 66534 Email: 100637.163@compuserve.com — MB BS 1968 Lond.; MRCP (UK) 1974; FFPHM RCP (UK) 1989; DCH Eng. 1973. (St. Thos.) Pub. Health Research & Consultancy Som. Prev: Dir. of Pub. Health Som.

BOWIE, Mr Harold Ian Cameron (retired) 99 Birchy Close, Solihull B90 1QL Tel: 01564 824519 — MB ChB 1942 Aberd. Prev: Cons. Orthop. Surg. Corbett Hosp. Stourbridge & Guest Hosp. Dudley.

BOWIE, Ian Macleod Elizabeth Street Medical Centre, 9 Elizabeth Street, Corby NN17 1SJ Tel: 01536 202507 Fax: 01536 206099 — MB ChB 1990 Leic. Prev: VTS Kettering.

BOWIE, James Cameron (retired) 6 Bruce Crescent, Lerwick ZE1 0PB Tel: 01595 693774 Fax: 01595 693774 — MB ChB 1940 Aberd. Prev: Phys. Univ. Health Serv. Birm.

BOWIE, Joseph Sim Ingersley Building, Macclesfield District General Hospital, Victoria Road, Macclesfield SK10 3BL — MB ChB 1985 Aberd.; MRCPsych 1990. Cons. Psychiat. E. Chesh. NHS Trust. Prev: Cons. (Psychiat.) Trafford NHS Trust; Sen. Regist. (Psychiat.) NW RHA; Regist. (Psychiat.) Grampian HB.

BOWIE, Juliet Eve Morley Street Health Centre, Morley Street, Brighton BN2 2RA Tel: 01273 696011 Ext: 3839 Fax: 01273 692229 — MB BCh 1985 Wales; MRCGP 1990; DRCOG 1989. Sen. Clin. Med. Off., Sexual Health Serv.s, S. Downs Health, Brighton; GP Asst., Mid Sussex Healthcare, Hurstpierpoint, W. Sussex.

BOWIE, Margaret Jean (retired) 167 Bishop Road, Bishopston, Bristol BS7 8NA Tel: 0117 942 4332 — MB ChB 1948 Bristol; DFFP 1992. Prev: Dist. SCMO Bristol & W.on HA.

BOWIE, Peter Charles Walter Bramley Clinic, 255 Town St., Leeds LS13 3EJ Tel: 0113 295166 Email: medpcwb@leeds.ac.uk — MB ChB 1980 Leeds; MD Leeds 1995; MMedSci Leeds 1984; MRCPsych 1984.

BOWIE, Richard Alexander (retired) Department of Anaesthesia, Victoria Hospital, Hayfield Road, Kirkcaldy KY2 5AH Tel: 01592 643355 Fax: 01592 647090 — MB ChB Ed. 1959; FFA RCS Eng. 1965; DObst RCOG 1961. Cons. Anaesth. Fife Acute Hosps. NHS Trust. Prev: Sen. Regist. (Anaesth.) Roy. Infirm. Edin.

BOWIE, Robert Alexander 51 Park Mount Drive, Macclesfield SK11 8NT — BM BS 1992 Nottm.

BOWIE, Susan Jacqueline West Ayre Surgery, West Ayre, Hillswick, Shetland ZE2 9RW Tel: 01806 503277 — MB ChB 1979 Glas.; MRCGP 1983.

BOWKER, Anthony Michael Benson Department of Radiology, York District Hospital, Wigginton Road, York YO31 8HE Tel: 01904 631313 Email: anthony.m.bowker@excha.yhs-tr.northy.nhs.uk — MB ChB 1979 Leeds; FRCR 1986; MA York 2000. Cons. Radiol. York Dist. Hosp.; Clin. Director, Radiol. and Path. Prev: Cons. Radiologist, Huddersfield Roy. Infirm.; Cons. Radiologist, ScarBoro. Gen. Hosp.

BOWKER, Carey Hadden 44 St Thomas's Street, Portsmouth PO1 2EZ Tel: 02392 431410 Fax: 02392 431411 Email: carey@chbowker.demon.co.uk — MB BChir Camb. 1969; MA Camb. 1969; FFPM 1998. (Camb. & St. Bart.) Prev: Med. Dir. Servier Laborats. UK; Med. Adviser Wellcome Foundat. Ltd.; Med. Adviser G.D. Searle & Company.

BOWKER, Colene Margaret Paediatric Pathology, Women's Centre, John Radliffe Hospital, Oxford OX3 9DU Tel: 01865 221246; 36 Stanway Close, Witney OX28 5GA — MB ChB 1984 Sheff.; MRCPath 1994. Cons. Paediat. Path. John Radcliffe Hosp. Oxf. Prev: Sen. Regist. (Histopath.) John Radcliffe Hosp. Oxf.

BOWKER, David Malcolm John Elliott Unit, Samuel Falk Centre, Birch Hill Hospital, Rochdale OL12 9QB Tel: 01706 377777 Fax: 01706 754325 — BM 1977 Soton.; 1963 BSc (Hons.) Ed.; 1966 PhD Wales; 1982 MRCPsych.; 1998 FRCPsych. ((Soton.)) Cons. Psychiat. Birch Hill Hosp. Rochdale. Prev: Sen. Regist. (Psychiat.) Univ. Hosp. S. Manch.; Regist. (Psychiat.) John Radcliffe Hosp. Oxf.; Ho. Off. (Med.) Soton. Gen. Hosp.

BOWKER, John Richard (retired) Summerfield, Boroughbridge Road, Bishop Monkton, Harrogate HG3 3QN Tel: 01765 677545 — MSc (Health Physics) Salford 1973; MB ChB Leeds 1948; MFOM

RCP Lond. 1978; MRCGP 1955; DIH Eng. 1956; DObst RCOG 1950. Prev: Sen. Occupat. Phys. S. E. Elect. Bd.

BOWKER, Lesley Kenyon 10 James Wolfe Road, Oxford OX4 2PY — BM 1990 Soton.; MRCP (UK) 1993.

BOWKER, Michael Henry Wye Valley Surgery, 2 Desborough Avenue, High Wycombe HP11 2RN Tel: 01494 521044 Fax: 01494 472770; 35 Trees Road, Hughenden Valley, High Wycombe HP14 4PN — MB BChir 1967 Camb.; BChir 1966; DCH Eng. 1969; DObst RCOG 1968. (St. Bart.) Prev: Med. Off. Save the Childr. Fund Nutrit. Unit Mbale, Uganda; SHO (Paediat.) St. Bart. Hosp. Lond.

BOWKER, Richard Philip 17 Charnwood Grove, West Bridgford, Nottingham — MB BS 1997 Lond.

BOWKER, Sylvia Grace Preston Road Surgery, 5 Preston Road, Leyland, Preston PR25 4NT Tel: 01772 622505; 38 Church Road, Leyland, Preston PR25 3AA Tel: 01772 432522 — MB ChB 1964 Sheff.; MB ChB Manch. 1971.

BOWKER, Timothy John 23 Priory Grove, London SW8 2PD — MB BChir 1978 Camb.; MSc McGill Univ. 1989; MA Camb. 1979, MD (Raymond Horton-Smith Prize) Camb. 1992; MRCP (UK) 1980. (Westm.) Cons. (Cardiol.) St. Mary's Hosp. & Centr. Middlx. Hosp. Lond.; Hon. Sen. Lect. (Cardiac Med.) Nat. Heart & Lung Inst. Socs: Brit. Med. Laser Assn.; Brit. Cardiac Soc. Prev: Regist. (Med.) Nat. Heart Hosp. Lond.; SHO (Med.) Nat. Hosp. Nerv. Dis. Lond.; SHO (Med.) Hammersmith Hosp. Lond.

BOWLER, Clare St Francis Unit, City Hospital, Nottingham NG5 1PB Tel: 0115 962 8011 Fax: 0115 962 8071; 4 Skiddaw Close, Gamston, Nottingham NG2 6RS — MB BS 1986 Lond.; MPhil Leic. 1996; MRCPsych 1991. Cons. Psychiat. Nottm. Health Care. Prev: Lect. (Psychiat.) Univ. Leic.

BOWLER, Eric Richard (retired) The Larches, Holme Lane, Holme, Scunthorpe DN16 3RB Tel: 01652 653729 — MB ChB Sheff. 1950; Cert. Av Med. MoD (Air) & CAA. 1974. Prev: GP Brigg.

BOWLER, Geoffrey Michael Ralph, TD Department of Anaesthetics, Royal Infirmary Edinburgh, Lauriston Place, Edinburgh EH3 5YW Tel: 0131 536 3651 Fax: 0131 536 3672; 24 Laverleith gardens, Edinburgh EH3 5PS — MB ChB 1975 Ed.; FFA RCS Eng. 1981. (Ed.) Cons. Anaesth.,Lothian Univ. Hosp.s NHS Trust; Clin. Teach. Univ. of Edin. Socs: BMA & Assn. Anaesth.; Ed. & E. Scot. Soc. Anaesth.; Resusc. Counc. Prev: Sen. Specialist Qu. Eliz. Milit. Hosp. Lond.; Research Fell. (Anaesth.) Roy. Infirm. Edin.; Sen. Regist. (Anaesth.) Roy. Infirm. Edin.

BOWLER, Helen Louise 8 Thornfield Way, Hinckley LE10 1BE — BM BS 1998 Nottm.; BM BS Nottm 1998.

BOWLER, Ian Department of Anaesthetics, Llandough Hospital, Penlan Rd, Penarth CF64 2XX; 12 Cae Garw Bach, St Fagans, Cardiff CF5 6HH — MB BCh 1990 Wales; FRCA 1996. (Univ. Wales Coll. Med.) Cons. Anaesth. Cardiff & Vale NHS Trust. Socs: Assn. Anaesth.; BMA; BASICS. Prev: Clin. Lect. UWCM; SPR Anaesth. UHW; SHO (Anaesth.) Univ. Hosp. Wales NHS Trust.

BOWLER, Ian Colin John Walker Department of Microbiology, Level 7, The John Radcliffe, Oxford Radcliffe Hospital NHS Trust, Oxford OX3 9DU Fax: 01865 220890 Email: ian.bowler@ndm.ox.ac.uk — MB ChB 1982 Bristol; MB ChB (Hons.) 1982; BSc Bristol 1979; MRCP (UK) 1987; MRCPath 1991; FRCP (UK) 1998; FRCPath 2000. (Bristol) Microbiol. Oxf. Radcliffe Hosp. NHS Trust; Hon. Cons. Clin. Lect. Univ. Oxf. Prev: Cons. Microbiologist Pub. Health Laborat. Serv.; Sen. Regist. (Bacteriol.) Oxf. RHA; Regist. (Med.) Frenchay Hosp. Bristol.

BOWLER, Ian Michael (retired) Department of Child Health, Royal Gwent Hospital, Newport NP20 2UB Tel: 01633 234613 Fax: 01633 656309 — MB ChB 1982 Sheff.; MRCP (UK) 1987; FRCPCH 1997; DRCOG 1985. Cons. Paediat. Roy. Gwent Hosp. Newport; Vis. Cons. Respirat. Paediat., Univ. Hosp. Of Wales, Heath Pk. Prev: Sen. Regist. (Paediat.) Soton. Gen. Hosp.

BOWLER, John Vaughan Department of Neurology, Royal Free Hospital, Pond St., London NW3 2QG Tel: 020 7830 2387, 020 7931 1577 Email: j.bowler@rfc.cicl.ac.uk — MB BS 1984 Lond.; BSc Lond. 1981; MRCP (UK) 1987; MD Lond. 1993. (St. Thomas's Hospital Medical School) Cons. Neurol. Roy. Free & N. Middlx. Hosps. Lond. Socs: Fell.of the Roy. Soc. of Med.; Corr. Assoc. Mem. of the Amer. Acad. of Neurol.; Fell. of the Roy. Coll. of Phys.s. Prev: Lect. (Neurol.) Imperial Coll. Sch. of Med.

BOWLER, Patrick James The Courthouse Clinic, New Road, Brentwood CM14 4GD Tel: 01277 203000 Fax: 01277 220505 Email: info@courthouseclinic.com; Nunns, Coxtie Green Road, Brentwood CM14 5RP — MB BS 1974 Lond.; MRCS Eng. LRCP Lond. 1974; DRCOG 1977. (London Hospital) Med. Dir. Cosmetic Dermat. Clinic, Ct. Ho. Clinic, Brentwood; Med. Director, Cosmetic Dermat. Clinic, 95 Harley St, Lond. Socs: Chairm. Brit. Assocaition of Cosmetic Doctors; Europ. Soc. of Cosmetic & Aesthetic Dermat.

BOWLER, Stephanie Kristina Milford House, Old Warleigh La, Tamerton Foliot, Plymouth PL5 4ND — MB BCh 1997 Wales.

BOWLER, Victoria Anne 6 Rownham Hill, Leigh Woods, Bristol BS8 3PU — MB BS 1988 Lond.

BOWLES, Anne 29 Manor Road, Great Bowden, Market Harborough LE16 7HE Tel: 01858 463082 — MB BS 1956 Lond.; DObst RCOG 1958. (Lond. Hosp.) Sen. Clin. Off. Leics. HA.

BOWLES, Brenda Joyce Muriel Intensive Care Unit, Hope Hospital, Stott Lane, Salford M6 8HD Tel: 0161 789 7373 — MB BS 1976 Lond.; MRCS Eng. LRCP Lond. 1976; FFA RCS Eng. 1982. (Guy's) Cons. Anaesth. & Intens. Care Hope Hosp. Salford.

BOWLES, Cecilia Jane Anne 9 Maritime Street, London E3 4QQ — MB BS 1991 Lond.; MRCP (UK) 1994. (The London Hospital Medical College) Specialist Regist. (Gastroenterol. & Gen. Med.) N. E. Thames; Research Regist. Brit. Soc. Gastroenterol. Roy. Free Hosp. Prev: Regist. (Gastroenterol.) Roy. Lond. Hosp.; Regist. (Gastroenterol.) Homerton Hosp. Lond.; Regist. (Gastroenterol.) S.end Hosp.

BOWLES, Elizabeth Mary (retired) Soller, Manor Lea Road, Milford, Godalming GU8 5EF Tel: 01483 417599 — MB BS 1936 Lond. Prev: Asst. Med. Off. Surrey AHA.

BOWLES, Ian Michael Framfield House Surgery, 42 St. Johns Street, Woodbridge IP12 1ED Tel: 01394 382157 — BM BCh 1967 Oxf.; FRCP 1999 Lond; MRCP (UK) 1972; DCH Eng. 1970; DObst RCOG 1970. (Oxf. & Univ. Coll. Hosp.) GP Princip.; Med. Off. Woodbridge & Abbey Schs. Prev: SHO (Paediat.) All St.s' Hosp. Chatham; Ho. Phys. Univ. Coll. Hosp.; Accred. Phys. Maple Ridge Hosp., Canada BC.

BOWLES, John Newman X-Ray Department, Southend Hospital, Prittlewell Chase, Westcliff on Sea SS0 0RY — MB BS 1976 Lond.; BSc (1st cl. Hons.) Sussex 1969; MRCP (UK) 1980; FRCR 1986. Cons. (Radiol.) S.end Hosp. Prev: Sen. Regist. (Radiol.) St. Thos. Hosp. Lond.

BOWLES, Kenneth Rex Gloster Green, Norwood Lane, Iver SL0 0EW — LMSSA 1959 Lond.; MB Camb. 1960, BChir. 1959; DObst RCOG 1961. (St. Bart.)

BOWLES, Margaret Honora (retired) 31 Mark Road, Headington, Oxford OX3 8PB Tel: 01865 760825 — 1938 MB ChB Bristol 1938; 1994 BA (OU).

BOWLES, Mr Matthew John Liver Transplant Unit, King's college Hospital, Denmark Hill, London SE5 9RS Tel: 01273 696955 Fax: 020 7346 3575 Email: matthew.bowles@btinternet.com; Flat 3, 80 Queen's Drive, London N4 2HW Tel: 020 76990 4066 — MB BS 1986 Lond.; BSc Lond. 1983; FRCS Ed. 1990; FRCS Eng. 1991; FRCS (Gen) 1997; MS Lond 1999. (Med. Coll. St. Bart. Hosp. Lond.) Sen. Regist. (Gen. Surg.) Roy. Sussex Co. Hosp. Brighton; Sen. registra, Liver Transpl. Surg., King's Coll. Hosp., Lond.

BOWLES, Robert Martin Lafayette Upper Knapps, Shire Lane, Lyme Regis DT7 3ET Tel: 01297 442100 Fax: 01297 445192 Email: bob.bowles@which.net — MRCS Eng. LRCP Lond. 1956. (St. Mary's) Adviser GP Pract. Managem. Finance & Computing. Socs: (Comm.) Primary Health Care Gp.; Brit. Computer Soc. (Chairm. Financial s/i Gp. Primary Health & Care). Prev: GP Lyme Regis; Edit. Adviser Pulse & Edit. Adviser Doctor; Ho. Surg. & Ho. Phys. Weymouth & Dist. Hosp.

BOWLES, Shirley Ann Countess of Chester Hospital, Health Park, Liverpool Road, Chester CH2 1UL Tel: 01244 365652 Fax: 01244 365386 Email: shirley.bowles@coch-tr.nwest.nhs.uk — MB ChB 1981 Manch.; MRCPath 1996. Cons. Chem. Path. Countess Chester NHS Trust; Postgrad. Clin. Tutor Countess of Chesh. Hosp.

BOWLEY, Carole Anne Upper Chorlton Road Surgery, 171 Upper Chorlton Road, Manchester M16 9RT Tel: 0161 881 4293 Fax: 0161 860 5265 — MB ChB 1987 Sheff.; MRCGP 1993.

BOWLEY, Christopher John Department of Anaesthesia, City Hospital, Hucknall Road, Nottingham NG5 1PB Tel: 0115 969 1169 Fax: 0115 962 7713 Email: cbowley@ncht.org.uk; Plumtree House, Walk Close, South St, Draycott, Derby DE72 3PN Tel: 01332 873985 Fax: 01332 873985 Email: j.bowley@virgin.net — MB BS

1972 Lond.; MRCS Eng. LRCP Lond. 1972; ECFMG Cert 1978; FFA RCS Eng. 1976. (St. Mary's) Cons. Anaesth. Qu.s Med. Centre Nottm. & Nottm. City Hosp. Socs: Linkman Assn. Anaesth. Prev: Instruc. Anesthesiology Univ. Michigan Hosp. Ann Arbor, USA.

BOWLEY, Clare Louise c/o Mr & Mrs D. Hodge, Brocas Lands, Mortimer, Reading RG7 2HB Tel: 01189 332327 Fax: 01189 332327 Email: dericcb@global.co.za; PO Box 130675, Bryanston 2021, South Africa Tel: 00 27 011 463 3187 Fax: 00 27 011 392 7569 — MB ChB 1996 Cape Town. (University of Cape Town) Med. Off. (O & G) Baragwanath Hosp. Soweto. Prev: Intern Baragwanath Hosp. Soweto.

BOWLEY, Mr Douglas Malcolm George 7 Barneshall Avenue, Worcester WR5 3EU — MB BS 1990 Lond.; FRCS Eng. 1996. (St Thos.)

BOWLEY, Emma Caroline Havant Health Centre Suite B, PO Box 41, Civic Centre Road, Havant PO9 2AQ Tel: 023 9248 2124 Fax: 023 9247 5515 — MB BS 1991 Lond.

BOWLEY, Judith Ann Southport & Formby DGH, Town Lang Kew, Southport PR8 6NJ Tel: 01704 547471, 01704 704468 Email: judith.bowley@mail.soh-tr.nwest.nhs.uk; 8 Red Cat Lane, Burscough L40 0RE — MB BCh 1977 Wales; FRCPath 1997; Dip. Bact. Manch. 1986. Cons. Microbiol. S.port & Ormskirk NHS Trust.

BOWLEY, Nicolas Bryan X-Ray Department, Queen Victoria Hospital, Holtye Road, East Grinstead RH19 3DZ — MB BS 1972 Newc.; FRCR 1977; DMRD Eng. 1976. Cons. Radiodiag. Qu. Vict. Hosp. Maxillofacial Injuries & Burns Unit E. Grinstead. Prev: Cons. Hammersmith Hosp. Lond.; Sen. Lect. (Radiodiag.) Roy. Postgrad. Med. Sch.; Sen. Regist. & Regist. (Radiodiag.) Hammersmith Hosp. Lond.

BOWLEY, Richard Neil The Surgery, Well Lane, Stow-on-the-Wold, Cheltenham GL54 1EQ Tel: 01451 830625 — MB ChB 1993 Bristol; LF Hom. Glagow 1998; MRCGP 1997; DFFP 1996; DRCOG 1996.

BOWLING, Bradley Stephen 8 Harebell Place, Abbeymead, Gloucester GL4 4AH — MB ChB 1990 Liverp.

BOWLING, Jonathan Christopher Richard 5 The Woodfines, Hornchurch RM11 3HR — MB ChB 1993 Bristol; MRCP (Lond.) 1997. (Bristol) Research Regist. Dermat., Qu.s Med. Center, Nottm. NG7 2UM. Prev: SHO (IC) Fenchay Hosp. Bristol; Med. SHO Frenchay Hosp. Bristol.

BOWLING, Pamela Iris Violet Sunnyhill, 7 Hardwick Lane, Bury St Edmunds IP33 2QF Tel: 01284 768250 — MB ChB 1965 Birm.; MRCPsych 1977; DPM Eng. 1974. (Birm.) Cons. (Psychiat.) Kneesworth Hse. Hosp. Royston. Prev: Cons. (Psychiat.) W. Suff. Hosp. Bury St. Edmonds; Sen. Regist. W. Suff. Hosp. Bury St. Edmunds; SHO Addenbrooke's Hosp. Camb.

BOWLING, Timothy Edmund North Staffordshire Hospital NHS Trust, Department of Gastroenterology, City General Hospital, Stoke-on-Trent ST4 6QG Tel: 01782 552382 Fax: 01782 712052; Riverside House, 23 Park Drive, Trentham, Stoke-on-Trent ST4 8AB — MB BS 1986 Lond.; MD Lond. 1994; MRCP (UK) 1989; FRCP 2000. Cons. Gastroenterol. & Gen. Med. N. Staffs. Hosp. Stoke-on-Trent. Prev: Sen. Regist. (Gastroenterol.) Univ. Coll. Lond. Hosps. & Whittington Hosp. Lond.; Research Fell. (Gastroenterol.) Centr. Middlx. Hosp. Lond.; Regist. (Gen. Med. & Gastroenterol.) St. Mary's Hosp. & Centr. Middlx. Hosp. Lond.

BOWMAN, Adam 8 Westmoreland Gardens, Gateshead NE9 6HP — MB ChB 1992 Glas.

BOWMAN, Alexander Dennis Orchards, 24 The Green, West Drayton UB7 7PQ Tel: 01895 446477 — MB BS Durh. 1948. Clin. Complaints Adviser Med. Defence Union; Sec. Middlx. LMC. Socs: Windsor Med. Soc. Prev: Course Organiser Hillingdon VTS; Chairm. Hillingdon LMC; Sec. Middlx. LMC.

BOWMAN, Alison Health Centre, Pipeland Road, St Andrews Tel: 01334 473441; Woodlands, Blebo Craigs, Cupar KY15 5UQ Tel: 01334 850302 — MB ChB 1986 Ed.; BSc (Hons.) Pharm. Ed. 1979; Dip. Ther. Wales 1995. (St Andrews/ Edinburgh) GP Princip. Prev: Regist. (Med.) Ninewells Hosp. Dundee.

BOWMAN, Allison Marie Clackmannan Health Centre, Clackmannan FK10 Tel: 01259 723725 Fax: 01259 724791; 11 Ladywood, Clackmannan FK10 4SX — MB ChB 1980 Glas.; MRCGP 19884; DA (UK) 1987; DRCOG 1982.

BOWMAN, Andrew Harold 9 Kentmere Close, Gatley, Cheadle SK8 4RD — MB ChB 1982 Manch.; MRCGP 1986.

BOWMAN, Angela 2FL, 47 Colinton Road, Edinburgh EH10 5EN — MB ChB 1980 Ed.

BOWMAN, Ann Forrester, Bowman and Rowlandson, Berry Lane Medical Centre, Berry Lane, Longridge, Preston PR3 3JJ Tel: 01772 783021 Fax: 01772 785809; Jesson House, Alston Lane, Alston, Preston PR3 3BN Tel: 01772 784306 — MB ChB 1982 Manch.; MRCGP 1986; DCH RCP Lond. 1984; DRCOG 1984. Prev: Trainee GP Roy. Preston Hosp. VTS.

BOWMAN, Christine Anne Department of Genitourinary Medicine, Nottingham City Hospital NHS Trust, Hucknall Road, Nottingham NG5 1PB Tel: 0115 962 7746 — BM BCh 1982 Oxf.; MA Oxf. 1983, BA 1979; MA Oxf 1983; MRCP (UK) 1985; FRCP Lond. 1995. (Oxf.) Cons. Phys. (Genitourin. Med.) City Hosp. Nottm.; Dir. of Postgrad. Educat.; Dep. Med. Director. Socs: Med. Soc. Study VD; Assoc. of Genitourin. Med.; Brit.Assoc.ofMed Manag. Prev: Sen. Regist. (Genitourin.) Gen. Infirm. Leeds; Regist. (Genitourin. Med.) Roy. Hallamsh. Hosp. Sheff.; Regist. (Med.) City Hosp. Nottm.

BOWMAN, Christopher Mark The Tonbridge Clinic, 339 Shipbourne Road, Tonbridge TN10 3EU Tel: 01732 350255 Fax: 01732 362343 — MB BChir 1976 Camb.; MLCOM 1992; FRACGP 1984; DMS Med. Soc. Apoth. Lond. 1994. (Camb.) Specialist i/c, Maidstone and Malling PCT Back Pain Serv.; Mem. Brit. Inst. Musculoskeletal Med. Socs: Regist. Osteop. Prev: Specialist Phys. (Musculo-skeletal Med.) Kent & Sussex Weald NHS Trust.

BOWMAN, Christopher Richard Chulmleigh Health Centre, Three Crossways, Chulmleigh EX18 7AA — MB ChB 1978 Bristol; BSc (Hons.) Bristol 1975; DRCOG 1983. N. Devon PCT Exec. Comm. Mem.

BOWMAN, Clare Marie Flat 2(L), 5 Carillon Road, Glasgow G51 1QL — MB ChB 1985 Glas.

BOWMAN, Clive Edward BUPA Care Service, Bridge House, Outwood Lane, Horsforth, Leeds LS18 4UP Tel: 01934 636363; Burrough House, Barrows Croft, Cheddar BS27 3BH Tel: 01934 742027 Fax: 01934 742027 Email: drbowman@mcmail.com — MB ChB 1978 Bristol; BSc (Hons.) Bristol 1975; FRCP Lond. 1995; FRCP Ed. 1994; MRCP (UK) 1982; MRCS Eng. LRCP Lond. 1978. Med. Dir. BUPA care Serv.s; Cons. Med. Adviser BUPA Care Servs.; Sen. Clin. Lect. Univ. Bristol; Assoc. Dir. Internat. Instit. on Health & Ageing Univ. of Bristol; Cons. Phys. (Geratol.) W.on Gen. Hosp. Avon. Socs: (Sec.) Bristol M-C Soc.; Brit. Geriat. Soc. Prev: Sen. Regist. Roy. Cornw. Hosp. Truro; Regist. (Med.) Torbay Hosp. Torquay & Bristol Roy. Infirm.

BOWMAN, David Miller Hillfields Health Centre, 1 Howard St., Coventry CV1 4GH Tel: 024 76 220661; Aberlemno, 19 Stivichall Croft, Coventry CV3 6GP Tel: 024 7641 4531 — MB ChB 1961 St. And.; AFOM RCP Lond. 1981; DObst RCOG 1964. Med. Dir. (Occupat. Health Serv.) City of Coventry; Med. Ref. Coventry Crematorium. Socs: ALAMA Soc. Occupat. Med. Prev: Asst, Med. Off. Chrysler UK Ltd.; Clin. Asst. Coventry & Warks. Hosp.

BOWMAN, Duncan Edward New Health Centre, Stephenson Terrace, Felling, Gateshead Tel: 0191 469 2311; 4 Carlton Terrace, Low Fell, Gateshead NE9 6DE Tel: 0191 482 0759 — MB BS 1979 Newc.

BOWMAN, Frank Michael Bolton General Hospital, Minerva Road, Farnworth, Bolton BL4 0JR Tel: 01204 390666 Fax: 01204 390660; Jesson House, Alston Lane, Longridge, Preston PR3 3BN Tel: 01772 784306 Email: frankbowman@compuserve. com — MB ChB 1984 Manch.; MSc Manch. 1990; MRCPsych. 1988. Cons. Child Psychiat. Bolton Gen. Hosp. Socs: MRCPsych MRCBych; Manch. Med. Soc.; Bolton and Dist. Med. Soc. Prev: Sen. Regist. (Child & Adolesc.) Psychiat. Univ. Manch.

BOWMAN, Greta Olivia 32 Beaconsfield Villas, Brighton BN1 6HD Tel: 01273 554681 — MB BS 1969 W. Indies.

BOWMAN, Iris Margaret Lempriere (retired) Far Well, Millside, Witherslack, Grange-over-Sands LA11 6SG Tel: 015395 52423 — MB ChB 1947 Ed. Prev: Clin. Asst. (Anaesth.) Nottm. HA (T).

BOWMAN, Julia Mary 19 Rosslyn Terrace, Glasgow G12 9NA — MB ChB 1995 Glas.

BOWMAN, Margaret Philip (retired) 15 Woodburn Avenue, Fenham, Newcastle upon Tyne NE4 9EL Tel: 01632 744382 — MB ChB 1922 Aberd.

BOWMAN, Michael John Edward House, 7 Lisson Grove, London NW1 6SH Tel: 020 7535 7901 Fax: 020 7724 8115 — MB ChB

1965 Ed.; BSc (Hons.) Ed. 1962; FRCPsych 1994, M 1972; DPM Eng. 1970. (Ed.) p/t Vis. Cons. Psychiat. The Florence Nightingale Hosp., Lond.; Vis. Cons. Psychiat. The Cromwell Hosp., Lond., SW7. Prev: Cons. Gen. Adult Psychiat. Enfield Community Care NHS Trust; Sen. Regist. (Psychol. Med.) Univ. Coll. Hosp. Lond.; Regist. & Hon. Sen. Regist. Maudsley Hosp. Lond.

BOWMAN, Pearl Bowman and Khan, Craven Park Health Centre, Shakespeare Crescent, London NW10 8XW Tel: 020 8965 0151 Fax: 020 8965 4921; 4 Carlton Close, West Heath Road, London NW3 7UA Tel: 020 8458 8090 Fax: 020 8458 0340 — MB BS 1959 Lond.; MRCGP 1969. (Middlx.) Prev: Ho. Surg. Bolingbroke Hosp.; Ho. Phys. Canad. Red Cross Memor. Hosp. Taplow.

BOWMAN, Richard Anthony Avondale, 4 Chesham Place, Bowdon, Altrincham WA14 2JL — MB 1971 Camb.; BChir 1970; FFA RCS Eng. 1975. (Westm.) Socs: IC Soc.

BOWMAN, Richard James 5 Ilkeston Ct, Scunthorpe DN15 7UB — MB ChB 1997 Leic.

BOWMAN, Richard John Craig Clinic 3, Addenbrooke's Hospital, Cambridge CB2 2QQ — MB BChir 1990 Camb.; MA Camb. 1987. SHO (Ophth.) Addenbrooke's Hosp. Camb.

BOWMAN, Roger William Ty Brith, Minera, Wrexham LL11 3DW Tel: 01978 757747 Fax: 0151 350 2579 Email: roger.bowman@vauxhall.co.uk — MB BCh Wales 1962; MFOM RCP Lond. 1978; DObst RCOG 1967. Med. Off. Vauxhall Motors Ellesmere Port. Socs: Soc. Occupat. Med. Prev: RAMC.

BOWMAN, Ruth Margaret 3 Fryth Mead, St Albans AL3 4TN — MB ChB 1996 Birm.

BOWMAN, Sheila Jane Health Centre, Newcastle Road, Chester-le-Street DH2 1DE Tel: 0191 388 7771; 4 Carlton Terrace, Low Fell, Gateshead NE9 6DE — MB BS 1979 Newc.; MRCGP 1983; DRCOG 1981.

BOWMAN, Simon Jonathan Rheumatology Department, The Medical School, University of Birmingham, Birmingham B15 2TT Tel: 0121 414 6778 Fax: 0121 414 6794; 195 Russell Road, Moseley, Birmingham B13 8RR — MB BS 1986 Lond.; FRCP 1999 UK; PhD Lond. 1995; BSc Lond. 1983; MRCP (UK) 1989. Hons. Cons. & Sen. Lect. Univ. Birm. Socs: Brit. Soc. Rheum.; Amer. Coll. Rheum.; Brit. Soc. Immunol. Prev: MRC Clin. Scientist Fell.sh.; Sen. Regist. Oxf. Hosps.; MRC Train. Fell.sh. UMDS Guy's Hosp.

BOWMAN, Steven Nigel Tree Tops, Peckforton Hall Lane, Spurstow, Tarporley CW6 9TF — MB ChB 1988 Manch.; DRCOG 1991. Prev: Trainee GP/SHO Countess of Chester Hosp.

BOWMAN, Susan Jane 37 Kenwood Park Road, Nether Edge, Sheffield S7 1NE Tel: 0114 258 0914 — MB BS 1989 Newc.; DCH RCPS Glas. 1996. Trainee GP Sheff.

BOWMER, Roger George Benefits Agency Medical Services, Arden House, Regent Centre, Gosforth, Newcastle upon Tyne NE3 3JN Tel: 0191 223 3065; 32 Wreigh Burn Fields, Thropton, Morpeth NE65 7LP Tel: 01669 620011 — MB BS Lond. 1970; MRCGP 1974. (St. Geo.) Med. Adviser Benefits Agency Newc. u. Tyne. Prev: GP Bedlington; Occupat. Health Phys. N.d. HA; Trainer GP N.umbria VTS.

BOWN, Matthew James 67 Westhall Road, Warlingham CR6 9HG — MB BCh 1997 Wales.

BOWN, Naomi Joan (retired) Abbots Leight Nursing Home, The Manor House, Manor Road, Abbots Leigh, Bristol BS8 3RP Tel: 01275 374669 — MB ChB 1924 Bristol. Prev: GP, Bristol.

BOWN, Paul Jeffries 45 Leith Towers, Grange Vale, Sutton SM2 5BY — MB BS 1992 Lond.

BOWN, Robert Leslie Frimley Park Hospital, Frimley, Camberley GU16 7UJ Tel: 01276 604080 Fax: 01276 604148; 21 Old Acre, Streets Heath, West End, Woking GU24 9JT Tel: 01276 857917 — MB BS 1964 Lond.; FRCP 1981, M 1967; MRCS Eng. LRCP Lond. 1964. (St. Bart.) Cons. Phys. & Gastroenterol. Frimley Pk. Hosp.; Hon. Sen. Lect. Med. Colls. of Roy. Hosps. Lond. Socs: Brit. Soc. Gastroenterol. Prev: Sen. Regist. (Med.) & Hon. Lect. (Med. Gastroenterol.) St. Bart. Hosp. Lond.; Regist. (Med.) Doncaster Roy. Infirm.

BOWN, Stephanie Dora Mulberry House, Abberton Road, Fingringhoe, Colchester CO5 7BN — MB BS 1982 Lond.; MB BS (Hons. Obst. & Gyn.) Lond. 1982; MRCP (UK) 1987. Prev: Regist. (Med.) Ipswich Hosp.; SHO (Med.) Centr. Middlx. Hosp.; Ho. Off. Roy. Free Hosp. Lond.

BOWN, Professor Stephen Glendening National Medical Laser Centre, Department of Surgery, Charles Bell House, 67-73 Riding House St., London W1P 7LD Tel: 020 7679 9090 Fax: 020 7813 2828 Email: s.bown@ucl.ac.uk; 10 Watling Street, St Albans AL1 2PX Tel: 01727 833701 — MB BChir 1972 Camb.; MB BChir Camb. 1971; AM Harvard 1966; MD Camb. 1984, MA 1969; FRCP Lond. 1991; MRCP (UK) 1974; LMSSA Lond. 1971. (Camb. & Univ. Coll. Hosp.) Prof. Laser Med. & Surg. Univ. Coll. Lond.; Dir. Nat. Med. Laser Centre Lond.; Hon. Cons. Phys. UCL Hosp. NHS Trust. Socs: Internat. Photodynamic Assn. (Bd. of Directors); (Ex-Pres.) Brit. Med. Laser Assn.; Brit. Soc. Gastroenterol. Prev: Sen. Clin. Lect. Univ. Coll. Lond. Med. Sch.; Sen. Regist. (Gastroenterol.) Univ. Coll. Hosp. Lond.; Lect. (Med.) Univ. Singapore.

BOWNES, Ian Thomas 38 Moira Drive, Bangor BT20 4RW — MB BCh BAO 1980 Belf.

BOWNESS, Paul 43 Hill View Road, Oxford OX2 0DA — BChir 1986 Camb.; MRCP (UK) 1989. MRC Train. Fell. Molecular Immunol. Gp. Inst. Molecular Med. John Radcliffe Hosp. Oxf.

BOWNS, Christopher Mark 50 Cliffefield Road, Sheffield S8 9DL — MB ChB 1986 Sheff.; BA (Phil) Sheff. 1992.

BOWRA, Gordon Trevor (retired) — MB BS 1961 Lond.; MRCS Eng. LRCP Lond. 1960; MFOM RCP Lond. 1978; DIH Eng. 1974. Prev: Sen. Employm. Med. Off. H.S.E.

BOWREY, David James Ash House, 3 Ash Park, Ystradowen, Cowbridge CF71 7SR Email: bowrey@cf.ac.uk — MB BCh 1992 Wales; FRCS Eng. 1996. (Univ. Wales Coll. Med.) Specialist Regist. Surg. Univ. Hosp. Wales Cardiff. Socs: Assn. of Surg.; Assn Surg. in Train.; Assn. of Upper GI Surgs. Prev: RCS Research Fell.

BOWRING, Alison 28 Forest Road, Aberdeen AB15 4BS Tel: 01224 324833 — MB ChB 1989 Dundee. SHO (Neonat.) Aberd. Matern. Hosp.

BOWRING, Anthony Robert Warrell Queensway Surgery, 75 Queensway, Southend-on-Sea SS1 2AB Tel: 01702 463333 Fax: 01702 603026 Email: tbowring@cs.com — BM BCh 1976 Oxf.; MRCS Eng. LRCP Lond. 1975. (Oxford, Barts) GP Princip. S.end.

BOWRING, Neil Arthur Cameron Haworth Road Health Centre, Haworth Road, Bradford BD9 6LL Tel: 01274 541701 Fax: 01274 546533 — MB ChB 1969 St. And.

BOWRING, Sharon Astrid Cameron 3 North Dean Park Avenue, Bothwell, Glasgow G71 8HH — BM BCh 1994 Oxf.

BOWRON, Paul Bishopgate Medical Centre, 178 Newgate Street, Bishop Auckland DL14 7EJ Tel: 01388 603983 Fax: 01388 607782; 37 Dene Hall Drive, Bishop Auckland DL14 6UF Tel: 01388 601658 — MB BS 1983 Newc.; MRCGP 1988. (Newc. u. Tyne)

BOWRY, Akhilesh 618 Manchester Road, Sheffield S10 5PT — MB BS 1988 Lond.

BOWRY, Jane Old Bridge Cottage, The Bridges, Ringwood BH24 1EA — MB BS 1989 Lond.; BSc Lond. 1983. (St Georges London) Socs: BMA; Med. Protec. Soc.

BOWRY, Richard Flat 4, 67 Enys Road, Eastbourne BN21 2DN — MB BS 1994 Lond.

BOWRY, Sheilini 6 Brambling Way, Oadby, Leicester LE2 5PA — MB ChB 1983 Leeds.

BOWRY, Victoria Ann 618 Manchester Road, Sheffield S10 5PT — MB BS 1990 Lond.

BOWSER, Jayne 51 Hansell Drive, Dorridge, Solihull B93 8RG — MB ChB 1978 Birm. Prev: Trainee GP Solihull VTS.

BOWSHER, David Richard Pain Research Institute, University Hospital, Aintree, Liverpool L9 7AL Tel: 0151 529 5820 Fax: 0151 529 5821 Email: pri@liv.ac.uk; 51 Hillview Gardens, Liverpool L25 7XE Tel: 0151 428 5737 Email: bowsher@liv.ac.uk — MB BChir 1950 Camb.; 1961 PhD Liverp.; 1947 BA (2nd Cl. Hons.) Camb.; 1994 FRCP Ed.; 1987 MRCP Ed; 1991 FRCPath; 1960 MD; 2000 ScD Camb.; 1950 MA; 1981 MRCPath. (Camb. & Univ. Coll. Hosp.) p/t Emerit. Cons. Neurol. STET (Pain Relief); Hon. Sen. Fell. (Neurol. Sci.) Univ. Liverp. Socs: Internat. Assn. Study Pain (Ex-Pres. Brit. & Irish Div.); (Ex-Pres.) N. Eng. Neurol. Assn.; Physiol. Soc. Prev: Reader & Hon. Cons. Neurol. (Neurol. Sci.) Univ. Liverp.; Research Fell. Harvard Univ.; Prof. Assoc. Fac. des Sci.s de Paris.

BOWSHER, Francine Marjorie East Lynne Medical Centre, 3-5 Wellesley Road, Clacton-on-Sea CO15 3PP Tel: 01255 220010 Fax: 01255 476350 — MB BS 1977 Lond.; DRCOG 1979. (Roy. Lond.) Gen. Practitoner.

BOWSHER, Mr Winsor Graham St Joseph's Hospital, Harding Avenue, Malpas, Newport NP20 6ZE Tel: 01633 234989 Fax: 01633 238595; Plas Newydd Cottage, Porthcarne St, Usk NP15 1RZ Tel: 01291 672574 Fax: 01291 671127 Email: winsor.bowsher@virgin.net — MB BS 1981 Lond.; MA Camb. 1982, MChir 1991; FRCS (Urol.) Lond. 1990; FRCS Lond. 1986; FRCS Ed. 1986; FEBU 1993. Cons. Urol. Surg. Roy. Gwent Hosp.; Hon. Cons. Urol. Surg. Velindre Hosp. Cardiff. Socs: Fell. Roy. Soc. Med.; Brit. Assn. Urol. Surgs.; SIU. Prev: Research Regist. St. Barts. Hosp. Lond.; Sen. Regist. The Roy. Lond. Hosp.; Vis. Fell. & Staff Cons. St. Vincent's Hosp. Melbourne, Austral.

BOWSKILL, Paul Anthony Fairhill Medical Practice, 81 Kingston Hill, Kingston upon Thames KT2 7PX Tel: 020 8546 1407 Fax: 020 8547 0075; 48 Lower Ham Road, Kingston upon Thames KT2 5AJ Tel: 020 8549 6595 — MB BS 1975 Lond.; Dip. Occ. Med. 1997. (St Georges)

BOWSKILL, Richard James 8 Sudeley Place, Brighton BN2 1HF — MB BChir 1989 Camb.; MRCP (UK) 1991; MRCPsych 1994. Cons. Psychiat. Prev: Lect. (Biological Psychiat.) UMDS.

BOWSKILL, Suzanne Jane 48 Lower Ham Road, Kingston upon Thames KT2 5AJ Tel: 020 8549 6595 Fax: 020 8549 6595 — MB BS 1982 Lond.; DRCOG 1984. (Char. Cross) GP Kingston. Prev: GP Surbiton Surrey; SHO (Obst.) St. Thos. Hosp. Lond.; SHO (Geriat.) Qu. Mary's Hosp. Roehampton.

BOWTHORPE, John Court Barton, Creech St Michael, Taunton TA3 5PW Tel: 01823 443436 — MB BS Lond. 1969; DObst. RCOG 1971.

BOWTON, Patricia Ann The William Fisher Medical Centre, High Street, Southminster CM0 7AY Tel: 01621 772360 Fax: 01621 773880 — MB BS Lond. 1988.

BOWYER, Frances Marian X-Ray Department, Princess of Wales Hospital, Coity Road, Bridgend CF31 1RQ — MB BCh 1978 Wales; FRCR 1983. Cons. (Diag. Radiol.) P.ss of Wales Hosp. Bridgend.

BOWYER, Mr Gavin William, Maj. RAMC Department of Orthopaedics, Southampton General Hospital, Southampton SO16 6YD Tel: 01705 796140 Fax: 01705 796141 Email: gwbowyer@aol.com; 8 Crabthorne Farm Lane, Hill Head, Fareham PO14 3HH Tel: 01329 664591 — BM BCh 1985 Oxf.; FRCS (Orth.) 1995; FRCS Eng. 1989; MChir Camb. 1998. Sen. Lect. (Orthop. & Trauma) Soton. Gen. Hosp.; Cons. (Orthops. & Trauma) Roy. Hosp. Haslar; DMCC Apoth. 1994. Socs: Fell. Brit. Orthop. Trauma Assn.; Brit. Orthop. Assn. Prev: Sen. Regist. (Orthop. & Trauma) Soton Gen. Hosp.; Fell. (Orthop. Trauma) Shock Trauma Center, Baltimore, USA.

BOWYER, Jean Josephine The Childrens Unit, St Peters Hospital, Guildford Road, Chertsey KT16 0PZ Tel: 01932 692762 Fax: 01932 875171; 32 Albany Park Road, Kingston upon Thames KT2 5SW Tel: 020 8546 2989 Fax: 020 8240 4025 — DM Oxf. 1984; BA Animal Physiol. Oxf. 1966, BM BCh 1969; MRCP (UK) 1973; FRCP 1994; FRCPCH 1996. (St. Thos.) Cons. Paediat. St. Peter's Hosp. Chertsey.; Regional Adviser Paediat. S. Thames. Prev: Sen. Regist. (Paediat.) Kingston Hosp. Surrey S.W. Thames AHA; Hon. Sen. Regist. (Paediat.) & Research Fell. Brompton Hosp. Lond.; Cons. Paediat. Min. of Defence Aviat. Hosp. Jedda.

BOWYER, Jeremy Duncan Sandstone Cottage, 86 High St., Tarvin, Chester CH3 8JB — BM 1990 Soton.; FRCOphth 1996. Specialist Regist. (OPTH) St Paul's Eye Unit, Roy, Liverp. Hosp., Liverp. Socs: MDU & BMA. Prev: SHO (Ophth.) Qu. Alexandra Hosp. Portsmouth; SHO (Neurosurg.) Roy. Hallamsh. Hosp. Sheff.; SHO (Opth) Qu.Med. Centre. Nottm.

BOWYER, Justin David Great Ormond Street Childrens Hospital, Great Ormond St., London WC1N 3JH; Flat 4, 61 Chiswick High Road, London W4 2LT — MB BS 1994 Lond.

BOWYER, Katherine Mary 47 Glenside, Appley Bridge, Wigan WN6 9EG — MB BS 1993 Lond.

BOWYER, Mary Stevenson (retired) 3 Westbank Terrace, Stonehaven AB39 2EA Tel: 01569 63686 — MB ChB 1940 Glas.; BSc Glas. 1937, MB ChB 1940.

BOWYER, Philip Keith X-Ray Department, Victoria Hospital, Blackpool FY3 8NR Tel: 01253 303663; 6 St Leonard's Road West, St. Annes, Blackpool FY8 2PF Tel: X Directory — MB ChB 1973 Manch.; FRCR 1982; DMRD Eng. 1979. Cons. Radiol. Blackpool Vict. Hosp. Prev: Sen. Regist. & Regist. Manch. Radiol. Rotat. Scheme.

BOWYER, Mr Richard Charles St Richard's Hospital, Spitalfield Lane, Chichester PO19 4SE Tel: 01243 788122 Fax: 01243 831501; 24 West Street, Chichester PO19 1QP Tel: 01243 789630 Fax: 01243 536591 Email: r.bowyer@dial.pipex.com — MB BS 1983 Lond.; BSc Lond. 1980, MS 1993; FRCS (Gen.) 1995; FRCS Eng. 1988; CCSt (General Surg) 1997 STA; Accreditation Gen Surgery ICHST 1996. (St. Geo. Hosp. Med. Sch.) Cons. Gen. Surg. St Richard's Hosp. Chichester. Socs: Assn. Surg.; BASO BrE. Gp.; Internal Hepato Pancreatobiliary Assn. Prev: Sen. Regist. Rotat. S. Thames (W.).

BOWYER, Rosemary Linda 15 Cavendish Road, Oxford OX2 7TN — MB BS 1984 Lond.; BSc Lond. 1981, MB BS 1984. (Westm.) Prev: SHO St. Woolos Hosp. Newport, Gwent; SHO Morriston Hosp. Swansea; SHO Radiother. Centre Bristol.

BOX, Benjamin Granary House, Milton, Appleby-in-Westmorland CA16 6LX — BM BCh 1997 Oxf.

BOX, Christopher John, Col. late RAMC Old School House, Lower Road, Charlton All Saints, Salisbury SP5 4HQ — MB BS 1973 Lond.; MSc (Occupat. Med.) Lond. 1985, MB BS 1973; MFOM RCP Lond. 1985, AFOM 1981; T(GP) 1991; T(OM) 1991; DAvMed. (Eng.) 1981; DRCOG 1977; FFOM 1998. (St Georges Hospital) Cons. Occupat. Med. RAMC. Socs: Soc. Occupat. Med. Prev: Cons. Aviat. Med. RAMC.

BOX, David Edward O'Connell Fulwood Green Medical Centre, Fulwood Green Medical Centre, Jericho Lane, Liverpool L17 4AR Tel: 0151 727 2440 Fax: 0151 726 1936; 21 Ranelagh Drive N., Liverpool L19 9DS — MB ChB 1974 Liverp.; MRCP Glas. 1982. (Liverpool) Clin. Asst. (Psychiat.).

BOX, Deborah Clare Parkside 5 Tors Road, Okehampton EX20 1EF — MB ChB 1997 Dundee.

BOX, Joan Estelle Medical Research Council, 20 Park Crescent, London W1B 1AL Tel: 020 7636 5422 Fax: 020 7436 5229 Email: joan.box@headoffice.mrc.ac.uk; 61 Wood Vale, London N10 3DL Tel: 020 8883 5300 Email: joan@aol.com — MB BS Lond. 1968; FRCP Lond. 1997; MRCP (UK) 1971. (St. Thos.) Clin. Research Liaison Manager, Med. Research Counc. Prev: Asst. Dir. Clin. Research Centre (MRC) N.wick Pk. Hosp.; Lect. (Physiol.) Guy's Hosp. Med. Sch. Lond.; SHO (Neurol.) Roy. Surrey Co. Hosp. Guildford.

BOX, Kerstin Margaret Laurencekirk Medical Group, Blackiemuir Avenue, Laurencekirk AB30 1DX Tel: 01561 377258 Fax: 01561 378270 — MB ChB 1987 Ed.; BSc Ed. 1984; MRCP (UK) 1990; MRCGP 1992; DCCH RCP Ed. 1993.

BOX, Margaret Patricia Homefield, St Mary's Road, Portishead, Bristol BS20 6QW Tel: 0117 842148 — MB ChB 1944 Bristol. (Bristol) Clin. Med. Off. Bristol & W.on HA. Prev: Ho. Surg. Roy. Infirm. Bristol; RAMC 1944-47; Supernum. Clin. Pathol. Roy. Infirm. Bristol.

BOX, Mark Jolyon Priory Medical Centre Partnership, Cape Road, Warwick CV34 4JP; Keepers Cottage, Church Road, Snitterfield, Stratford-upon-Avon CV37 0LF Tel: 01789 730261 — MB BS 1982 Lond.

BOX, Owen Matthew Pasadena, Hazel Lane, Rudgeway, Bristol BS35 3QW Tel: 01454 414529 — MB ChB 1991 Liverp.; MRCPsych 1995. Specialist Regist. United Med. & Dent. Sch. Lond. Prev: Regist. (Psychiat.) UMDS; SHO (Psychiat.) E. Sussex.

BOX, Stewart Anthony 12 Strathalmond Road, Edinburgh EH4 8AF — MB ChB 1989 Ed.; MRCP (UK) 1994. (Ed.)

BOX, William David The Willows, 70 Hardwick Road, Wellingborough NN8 5AG Tel: 01933 678161 — MB ChB 1962 Birm. p/t Clin. Med. Off. (Family Plann.) N.ants.; GP Locum. Socs: Kettering & N.ants. Med. Socs. Prev: Ho. Phys. Ronkswood Hosp. Worcester; Ho. Surg. (O & G) Gulson Hosp. Coventry; Ho. Phys. (Paediat.) City Hosp. Chester.

BOX, Mr William John Oldfield (retired) 23 St Mary's Road, Stratford-upon-Avon CV37 6XG — MB ChB 1946 Ed.; FRCS Ed. 1961; FRCS Eng. 1962; DMRD Eng. 1966; FFR 1968. Prev: Cons. Radiol. S. Warks. Hosp. Gp.

BOXALL, Mark Colin 69 Southwood, Coulby, Newham, Middlesbrough TS8 0UF — MB ChB 1996 Glas.

BOXALL, Mr Terence Alyn (retired) Calumet, Beaconfields, Sevenoaks TN13 Tel: 01732 457067 — MB BS 1955 Lond.; MS Lond. 1967; MRCS Eng. LRCP Lond. 1955; FRCS Eng. 1962; DObst

RCOG 1959. Prev: Cons. Gen. Surg. Bromley, Orpington & Sevenoaks Hosps.

BOXER, Candida Mary 4 West Meads, Onslow Village, Guildford GU2 7SS — MB BS 1978 Lond.; MRCP (UK) 1992.

BOXER, Daniel Ithamar X-Ray Department, Watford General Hospital, Vicarage Road, Watford WD18 0HB Tel: 01923 217645 Fax: 01923 217674; 5 Acorn Close, Stanmore HA7 2QS Email: dboxer@compuserve.com — MB BS 1981 Lond.; BSc (Hons.) Lond. 1978; MRCP (UK) 1985; FRCR 1989. (St. Bartholomew's) Cons. Radiol. Watford Gen. Hosp. Prev: Sen. Regist. (Radiol.) St. Mary's & Centr. Middlx. Hosps. Lond.; Regist. (Radiol.) W.m. Hosp. Lond.

BOXER, Josephine Celia Canbury Medical Centre, 1 Elm Road, Kingston upon Thames KT2 6HR Tel: 020 8549 8818 Fax: 020 8547 0058; 14 Albany Park Road, Kingston upon Thames KT2 5SW Tel: 020 8549 8818 — MB BS Lond. 1968; MRCS Eng. LRCP Lond. 1968; DObst RCOG 1970. (Roy. Free) Prev: SHO (Paediat.) Roy. Liverp. Childr. Hosp.; Ho. Surg. (Obst.) Edgware Gen. Hosp.; Ho. Surg. Roy. Free Hosp. Lond.

BOXER, Mark Everard Histopathology Department, Conquest Hospital, The Ridge, St Leonards-on-Sea TN37 7RD Tel: 01424 758023 — MB BChir 1977 Camb.; MB Camb. 1977, BChir 1976; MA Camb. 1977; MRCPath 1982. (Univ. Camb. & St. Thos. Hosp.) Cons. Histopath. Conquest Hosp. St. Leonards-on-Sea. Prev: Cons. Histopath. Worcester Roy. Infirm.; Sen. Regist. (Histopath.) Poole & Soton Gen. Hosps.; Lect. (Path.) Univ. Sheff.

BOXX, Pamela Jean, Group Capt. RAF Med. Br. (retired) Alderdale, Carr Bridge PH23 3AU Tel: 01479 841545 — MB ChB St. And. 1963; FRCOG 1985, M 1973; Lic Med 1980 BAAR; BAC 1984 BAAR. Indep. Pract. Traditional Chinese Med., Carr-Bridge & Inverness. Prev: Cons. O & G RAF Med. Br. (1977-1990).

BOYARS, Leonard 29 Calder Grange, Liverpool L18 3LW — MB ChB 1937 Liverp.; DObst RCOG 1947. (Liverp.) Prev: Asst. Resid. Med. Off. Clatterbridge Gen. Hosp. Bebington & Alder Hey Hosp. Liverp.; Resid. Med. Off. Sefton Gen. Hosp. Liverp.

BOYCE, Alexandra Henley Medical Centre, Prince Harry Road, Henley in Arden, Solihull B95 5DD Tel: 01564 793333 — MB ChB 1986 Ed.; MRCGP 1991; DRCOG 1991. (Ed.)

BOYCE, Anna Catherine Louise Low House Barn, Ayside, Grange-over-Sands LA11 6HY — MB BS 1992 Lond.

BOYCE, Claire Anne Medical Group Surgery, Linenhall Street, Banbridge BT32 3EG Tel: 028 4062 3303 — MB BCh BAO 1994 Belf.; DRCOG 1998 Roy. Coll. of Obstetricians & Gynaecologists; MRCGP 1999 Roy. Coll. of Gen. Practitioners; DFFP 2000 Fac. of Family Plann. & Reproductive Healthcare of the RCOG; DCH RCPSI 1998. p/t Gen. Practitioner, Med. Gp. Surg., Banbridge; Staff Grade, Community Child Health, Armagh and Dungannon H&SST, Vict. Ho., Tower Hill, Armagh. Socs: Roy. Coll. of Gen. Practitioners; Ulster Med. Soc.; Brit. Assn. of Community Child Health.

BOYCE, Clive Trevor Hodge Road Surgery, 2 Hodge Road, Worsley, Manchester M28 3AT Tel: 0161 790 3615 Fax: 0161 703 7638; 12 Chatsworth Road, Ellesmere Park, Eccles, Manchester M30 9DY — MB ChB 1974 Manch.; MFFP Faculty of Family Planning, Royal College of Obstetrics and Gynaecology; MRCGP 1980. (Manchester) GP Princip.; Instruc. Med. Off. (Family Plann.) Bury HA. Socs: Fac. Fam. Plan.

BOYCE, Craig John Village Farm Cottage, Llowes, Hereford HR3 5JD Tel: 01497 847870 — MB BCh 1969 Wales. (Welsh Nat. Sch. Med. Cardiff) Surg. Chief Off. Roy. Fleet Auxil. Prev: SHO (Cas.) Cardiff Roy. Infirm.; SHO (Surg.) Rookwood Hosp. Cardiff; GP Sunderland.

BOYCE, Mr Dean Edward Dept. of Plastic Surgery, University Hospital, Birmingham, Caddlebarn Rd, Birmingham Tel: 0121 627 1627; 14 Sandhilis Road, Barnt Green, Birmingham B45 8NR Email: deanboyce@compresive.com — MB BCh 1990 Wales; MD 1999 Wales; FRCS Ed. 1995; FRCS Eng. 1995. (University of Wales College of Medicine) Specialist Regist. (Plastic & Reconstruc. Surg.) W. Midl. Rotat.al Train. Scheme. Prev: Surgic. Research Regist. Univ. of Wales Coll. of Med.

BOYCE, Douglas John Fir Glen, Higher Chillington, Ilminster TA19 0PT — MB ChB Birm. 1968. (Birm.) Prev: GP Crewkerne; Ho. Surg. & Ho. Phys. E. Birm. Hosp.; Ho. Surg. (Obst.) Sorrento Matern. Hosp. Birm.

BOYCE, John Maurice Howard (retired) 'Pengwern', 22 Island Farm Close, Bridgend CF31 3LY — MB BS 1961 Lond.; FRCPath 1981, M 1969. Prev: Cons. Bacteriol. E. Glam. Gen. Hosp. Pontypridd.

BOYCE, Joseph 23 Polar Avenue, Bishopton PA7 5AD — MB ChB 1986 Glas.

BOYCE, Katie Emily 15 Lockside View, Rugeley WS15 1NJ Tel: 01889 801574 Fax: 01889 801352 Email: katie@doctors.org.uk — MB ChB 1996 Birm.; ChB Birm. 1996. (Birm.) SHO Rotat. (Surg.) Birm. Heartlands Hosp. Prev: Ho. Off. (Med.) Qu. Eliz. Hosp. Birm.; Ho. Off. (Surg.) Birm. Heartlands Hosp.

BOYCE, Malcolm James Hammersmith Medicines Research, Central Middlesex Hospital, Park Royal, London NW10 7NS Tel: 020 8961 8344 Fax: 020 8961 8665 Email: mboyce@hmr-pharmacology.co.uk; 143 Holland Road, London W14 8AS Tel: 020 7602 3119 — BSc (Physiol.) Bristol 1966; MB ChB Bristol 1969; MRCP (UK) 1972; FFPM 1990; FRCP Lond. 1999. Managing & Clin. Dir. Hammersmith Med. Research Centr. Middlx. Hosp. Lond.; Research Fell. (Clin. Pharmacol.) St. Bart. Hosp. Lond.; Mem. N. Thames Multicentre Research Ethics Comm. (MREC). Socs: Brit. Pharm. Soc. (Clin. Sect.); Brit. Soc. of Allergy & Clin. Immunol.; Assn. Human Pharmalogists in the Pharmaceut. Industry.

BOYCE, Mr Robert Charles Leslie Depatment of Ophthalmology, Claremont Wing, Royal Victoria Infirmary, Newcastle upon Tyne NE1 4LP — BM BS 1993 Nottm.; BSc (1st cl. Hons.) Electronics Salford 1984; BMedSci (1st cl. Hons.) 1991; FRCS Ophth. (Notts) Specialist Regist. Roy. Vict.. Infirm. Newc.

BOYCE, Robert Patrick Grassendale Medical Practice, 23 Darby Road, Liverpool L19 9BP Tel: 0151 427 1214 Fax: 0151 427 0611 — MB BCh BAO 1984 NUI.

BOYCE, Stephen Alexander 2 Glenagherty Drive, Ballymena BT42 1AG — MB BS 1998 Newc.; MB BS Newc 1998.

BOYCE, Mr Stephen Henry 176 Troon Avenue, Greenhills, E. Kilbride, Glasgow G75 8TJ Tel: 0141 242213 — MB ChB 1991 Glas.; MSc Glas. 1997; FRCS Ed. 1995; Dip. IMC RCS Ed. 1993. Staff Grade (A & E) CrossHo. Hosp. Kilmarnock. Socs: Fac. Pre-Hosp. Care. Prev: SHO (A & E) CrossHo. Hosp. Kilmarnock.

BOYCE, Susanne 'Rowandale', 17 Dunvegan Avenue, Kirkcaldy KY2 5SG Tel: 01592 202737 — MB ChB 1967 Ed.; DA Eng. 1972.

BOYCE, Tamsin Heather 50 Valley Road, Welwyn Garden City AL8 7DN — MB BCh 1998 Wales.

BOYCE, William Jonathan 20 Raveley Street, London NW5 2HU Tel: 020 7267 4761 — BM BCh 1976 Oxf.; MSc Lond. 1980; MA Oxf. 1976, DM 1988; MRCP (UK) 1979; FFCM 1993. Dir. of Health Studies Audit Commiss. for Eng. & Wales. Prev: Acting Dist. Med. Off. N.ampton HA; Sen. Regist. (Community Med.) Oxf. RHA; Field Dir. (E.. Sudan) for Oxfam.

BOYCOTT, Antony 14 Walton Rise, Westbury on Trym, Bristol BS9 3EW — MB ChB 1975 Bristol. Med. Off. Mendip Cave Rescue Organisation.

BOYD, Aelwen (retired) Lynwood, 146 Oulton Road, Stone ST15 8DR — MRCS Eng. LRCP Lond. 1948. Prev: Clin. Asst. ENT Dept. Mid Staffs. HA.

BOYD, Alan Keith Longmynd, 16 Torkington Road, Wilmslow SK9 2AE Email: alan.boyd@alderley.zeneca.com — MB ChB 1980 Birm.; BSc. (Hons.) Birm. 1977; FFPM RCP (UK); Dip. Pharm. Med. RCP (UK) 1987. Head of Med. Research Zeneca Pharmaceut. Macclesfield. Prev: Med. Dir. ICI Pharmaceut., Canada; Sen. Med. Adviser ICI Pharmaceut. Macclesfield; Research Phys. Human Pharmacol. Dept. Glaxo Research Ltd. Greenford.

BOYD, Alan Laurie Murray Road Surgery, 50 The Murray Road, East Kilbride, Glasgow G75 0RT Tel: 01355 225374 Fax: 01355 239475; 99 East Kilbride Road, Busby, Glasgow G76 8JE Tel: 0141 644 1772 — MB ChB 1979 Glas.; MRCGP 1983. Stud. Tutor Glas. Univ.

BOYD, Mr Alan Thomas Victoria Hospital, Hayfield Road, Kirkcaldy KY2 5AH; 2 Alexander III Street, Kinghorn, Burntisland KY3 9SD — MB ChB 1980 Ed.; BSc Ed. 1977, MD 1993; FRCS Ed. 1985. Cons. Surg. Vict. Hosp. Kirkcaldy. Prev: Sen. Regist. (Gen. Surg.) Yorks. Region.

BOYD, Alastair Hugh 126 Ennisdale Drive, West Kirby, Wirral CH48 9UB — MB ChB 1981 Liverp.; FRCA. 1989; FFA RCSI 1988.

BOYD, Alastair Stewart Dumbarton Health Centre, Station Road, Dumbarton G82 1PW Tel: 01389 602633 Fax: 10289 602623 — MB ChB 1978 Glas.; BSc (Hons.) Glas. 1975, MB ChB 1978; MRCP,

Glasgow, 1983; DCH 1986; Dip Occ. Med. 1997; AFOM 1998. Socs: Soc. Occupat. Med.; BMA; Brisigh Soc. Study Infec.

BOYD, Alastair Stuart Basement Flat, 79 Camberwell Grove, London SE5 8JE — MB ChB 1986 Aberd. SHO Auckland Hosp. Bd., NZ. Prev: Ho. Surg. Inverclyde Roy. Hosp.; Ho. Phys. Glas. Roy. Infirm.

BOYD, Andrew Hopkin (retired) 23 Ayr Road, Prestwick KA9 1SY Tel: 01292 476992 — MB ChB 1949 Glas. Prev: GP Prestwick.

BOYD, Andrew Peter MacBryde Twin Oaks Medical Centre, Ringwood Road, Bransgore, Christchurch BH23 8AD Tel: 01425 672741 Fax: 01425 674333 — MB BS 1973 Lond.; MRCGP 1980; DRCOG 1980; DA Eng. 1979. (St. George's)

***BOYD, Angela Clare** Flat 1, 20 Lady Lawson, Edinburgh EH3 9DS — MB ChB 1998 Ed.; MB ChB Ed 1998.

BOYD, Angus Archibald William (retired) 151 New Hall Lane, Bolton BL1 5HP Tel: 01204 843541 — MB ChB Aberd. 1949.

BOYD, Cameron Edward The Scott Clinic, Rainhill Road, St Helens WA9 5BD Tel: 0151 430 6300 Fax: 0151 430 8147; Forensic Psychiatry Service, 36 Rodney St, Liverpool L1 9AA Tel: 0151 709 7010 Fax: 0151 709 8476 — 1977 DPM Eng.; FRCP 1995 (Psych); MRCP 1977 (Psych). Cons. Forens. Psychiat. to NW RHA & The Mersey area. Socs: BMA.

BOYD, Carolyn 532 Clarkston Road, Netherlee, Glasgow G44 3RT — MB ChB 1985 Glas.; DCCH RCP Ed. 1994. Staff Grade Doctor (Community Child Health) W. Lothian NHS Trust. Prev: SHO (Community Paediat.) Gtr. Glas. HB.

BOYD, Catherine Mary Department of Histopathology, Poole Hospital NHS Trust, Longfleet Road, Poole BH15 2JB Tel: 01202 442211 Fax: 01202 448452 — MB ChB 1976 Bristol; FRCPath M 1987. Cons. Cytopath. & Histopath. E. Dorset.

BOYD, Cecil Hugh (retired) Eastwood, Old Ashford Road, Lenham, Maidstone ME17 2PX Tel: 01622 858285 — MB ChB 1939 Leeds; LRCP LRCS Ed. LRFPS Glas. 1939; FFA RCS Eng. 1975; DA Eng. 1947. Prev: Cons. Anaesth. Maidstone Health Dist.

BOYD, Charles Adam Richard 23 Blenheim Drive, Oxford OX2 8DJ Tel: 01865 515085 Fax: 01865 272420 — BM BCh 1970 Oxf.; BA Oxf. 1966, BSc 1968, MA 1970; DPhil Oxf. 1976. Lect. (Anat.) Univ. Oxf.; Tutorial Fell. Brasenose Coll. Oxf. Socs: Physiol. Soc. Comm. Sec. and Chairm.; Chairm. Edit. Bd. J.Physiol. Prev: Lect. (Physiol.) Univ. Dundee Med. Sch.; Research Fell. (Biochem.) Univ. Oxf.; Ho. Phys. Univ. Coll. Hosp. Lond.

BOYD, Christopher Sydney 9 Muskett Heights, Carryduff, Belfast BT8 8SP — MB BCh BAO 1992 Belf.

BOYD, Colin Baxter 30 Crichton Road, Rothesay, Rothesay PA20 9JR — MB ChB 1973 Ed.; MRCGP 1977; DObst RCOG 1975.

BOYD, David Carson Wyke Regis Health Centre, Portland Road, Weymouth DT4 9BE Tel: 01305 782226 Fax: 01305 760549 — MB ChB 1983 Bristol; MRCGP 1993; DGM RCP Lond. 1987; Cert. Family Plann. JCC 1985. (Bristol) Prev: Trainee GP Lydney Glos.

BOYD, David Hugh Aird (retired) 25 Cherry Tree Park, Balerno EH14 5AQ Tel: 0131 538 5720 — MB ChB 1949 Edin.; MD Edin. 1963; FRCP Edin. 1965, M 1956. Prev: Hon. Sen. Lect. Dept. Med. Univ. Edin.

BOYD, David William (retired) Brendon Lea, Parsonage Lane, Kingston-st-Mary, Taunton TA2 8HL Tel: 01823 451794 — BM BCh 1957 Oxf.; BA Oxf. 1950, BM BCh 1957; FRCP Lond. 1975, M 1964; MRCS Eng. LRCP Lond. 1956. Prev: Cons. Phys. N. Devon Health Dist.

BOYD, Doreen Dorothy Kerrsland Surgery, 169 Upper Newtownards Road, Belfast BT4 3HZ Tel: 028 9029 6600 Fax: 028 9047 1942 — MB BCh BAO 1978 Belf.; MRCGP 1983; DRCOG 1981. (Queen's University Belfast)

BOYD, Elizabeth Margaret Anne 25 Castle Gardens, Belfast BT15 4GA Tel: 02890 778783 — MB BCh BAO 1973 Belf. (Belf.)

BOYD, Eric John Somerville 1 Montquhir Farm Cottages, Carmyllie, Arbroath DD11 2QS — MB ChB 1975 Liverp.; MRCP (UK) 1977.

BOYD, Fiona Elspeth 8 Muirfield Road, Inverness IV2 4AY Tel: 01463 231014 — MB ChB 1980 Glas.; MFFP 1994.

BOYD, Fiona Frances 9 Northbank Road, Kirkintilloch, Glasgow G66 1EZ — MB ChB 1991 Dundee.

BOYD, Francis (retired) 51 Benvarden Road, Ballymoney BT53 6NN Tel: 0126 57 41393 — MB BCh BAO 1936 Belf. Prev: Asst. Med. Off. St. Mary Islington Hosp. (L.C.C.).

BOYD, Gavin Ferniehill Road Surgery, 8 Ferniehill Road, Edinburgh EH17 7AD Tel: 0131 664 2166 Fax: 0131 666 1075 — MB ChB 1981 Ed.; BSc (Med. Sci.) Ed. 1978; MRCGP 1986. (Edin.) Gen. Practitioner, Edin.; Clin. Asst., Dept. of Diabetes and Endocrinol., W.. Gen. Hosp., Edin.

BOYD, Gavin 9 Northbank Road, Kirkintilloch, Glasgow G66 1EZ — MB ChB 1964 Glas.; BSc (Hons.) Glas. 1961, MD (Hons.) 1975; FRCP Ed. 1982, M 1968; FRCP Glas. 1979, M 1968. (Glas.) Cons. Phys. Stobhill Hosp. & Glas. Roy. Infirm.; Hon. Clin. Sen. Lect. (Med.) Uviv. Glas. Prev: Sen. Regist. (Med.) Glas. Roy. Infirm.; Ure Schol. Glas. Univ.; Ho. Phys. & Ho. Surg. Glas. Roy. Infirm.

BOYD, H Kathryn 9 Downing Park, Portstewart BT55 7JE — MB BS 1982 Newc.

BOYD, Hamish William (retired) — MB ChB 1947 Glas.; FRCP Glas. 1977, M 1962; FRFPS Glas. 1953; FFHom. 1957, M 1952; DCH Eng. 1951. Prev: Cons. Phys. Glas. Homoeop. Hosp.

BOYD, Hilary Georgina Mary Young Peoples Centre, 10 College Gardens, Belfast BT7 Tel: 01574 841616 — MB ChB 1990 Liverp.; DCH 1999; MRC Psych. 1997. p/t SpR Child & Adolesc. Psychiat., Young Peoples Centre, Belf. Socs: BMA; Roy. Coll. Psychiat. Prev: SHO (Psychiat.) Gransha Hosp. Lond.derry; Child & Family Clinic Roy. Belf. Hosp. for Sick Childr.

BOYD, Mr Iain Edward Princess Anne Hospital, Coxford Road, Southampton SO16 5YA Tel: 02380 796042; 7 The White House, Westover Road, Milford on Sea, Lymington SO41 0PW Tel: 02380 292324 — MB ChB 1960 Glas.; FRCOG 1982; M 1969; FRCS 1968 Ed.; FRCS Ed. 1968; FRCOG 1982, M 1969. Cons. Gyn. Univ. Soton. Teachg. Hosp. Socs: Bristol Gyn. Cancer Soc.; Brit. Soc. of Colposcopy and Cervical Path.; Gyn. Vis. Soc. of United Kingdom and Irel.

BOYD, Isobel Margaret Royal Liverpool Childrens Hospital, Alder Hey, Eaton Road, Liverpool L12 2AP Tel: 0151 228 4811 Fax: 0151 228 0328; 11 Kenway, Rainford, St Helens WA11 8AX — MB BS 1972 Lond.; BSc (Hons.) Lond. 1969; MRCS Eng. LRCP Lond. 1972; FFA RCS Eng. 1978; DCH Eng. 1975. Cons. Anaesth. Roy. Liverp. Childr. Hosp. & Hon. Lect. Univ. Liverp. Socs: Assn. Paediat. Anaesth. Gt. Brit. & N. Irel.; Paediat. IC Soc.

BOYD, Jack 3 Russell Crescent, Brighton BN1 3TH — MB BS 1958 Lond.; MRCP Lond. 1965.

BOYD, James 42 Acorn Crescent, Larbert FK5 3LT — MB ChB 1985 Glas.

BOYD, James Ferguson (retired) 44 Woodend Drive, Glasgow G13 1TQ Tel: 0141 959 2708 — MB ChB Glas. 1948; MD (Commend.) Glas. 1960; FRCP Glas. 1975, MR 1972; FRCP Ed. 1966, MR 1957; FRCPath 1973, M 1963. Prev: Sen. Lect. (Path. Infec. Dis.) Glas. Univ.

BOYD, James Patrick 101 Clare Avenue, Chester CH2 3HR — MB BCh BAO 1989 Dub.; MB BCh Dub. 1989.

BOYD, James Rogers (retired) 10 Easter Livilands, Stirling FK7 0BQ — MB ChB 1940 Aberd. Prev: Vis. Phys. Bannockburn Infec. Dis. Hosp.

BOYD, Jennifer 65 Trowell Road, Nottingham NG8 2EJ Tel: 0115 928 8744 — MB ChB 1953 Birm.; DObst RCOG 1954. (Birm.) Socs: Brit. Geriat. Soc. Prev: Assoc. Specialist Dept. Health Care Elderly Nottm.; GP King's Norton; Regist. (Geriat.) Sherwood Hosp. Nottm.

BOYD, Jennifer Mary 20 Strathview Place, Methven, Perth PH1 3PP — MB ChB 1988 Glas. Clin. Asst. (Colposcopy) Stobhill Hosp. Glas.

BOYD, Joan (retired) 18 Williamson Road, Ashley Hill, Bristol BS7 9BH Tel: 0117 924 7700 — MB ChB Bristol 1940.

BOYD, John 3 Chelston Drive, Cheadle SK8 3PH — LRCP LRCS 1951 Ed.; LRCP LRCS Ed. LRFPS Glas. 1951.

BOYD, John Ainslie Royal Cornhill Hospital, Aberdeen AB25 2ZH Tel: 01224 404043 Fax: 01224 840976 Email: j.boyd@abdn.ac.uk — MB ChB 1988 Aberd.; BMed Biol. (Hons.) Aberd. 1987; MRCPsych 1992. (Aberd.) Cons. Forens. Psychiat.; Clin. Sen. Lect., Univ. of Aberd. Prev: Sen. Regist. (Forens. Psychiat.) Murray Roy. Hosp.

BOYD, John Cameron Health Centre, 14 Market Place, Carluke ML8 4BP Tel: 01555 752150; 27 Hillhouse Farm Gate, Lanark

ML11 9HT — MB ChB 1985 Glas. Prev: Trainee GP Dumbarton; SHO (Obst.) Ayrsh. Centr. Hosp. Irvine; SHO (A & E) Roy. Alexandra Hosp. Paisley.

BOYD, John Denis Erne Health Centre, Cornagrade Road, Enniskillen BT74 6AY Tel: 028 6632 2707; Ardnaree, 11 Cooper Crescent, Enniskillen BT74 6DQ Tel: 01365 322707 — MB BCh BAO 1967 Belf.; MRCGP 1978. Clin. Asst. (Geriat.) Co. Hosp. Enniskillen; GP Adviser Omagh & Fermanagh Unit of Managem. Socs: Chairm. Fermanagh GP Assn. & W.. Area LMC. Prev: Asst. Surg. P. & O. Lines Ltd.; Med. Off. U.K.A.E.A.

BOYD, Mr John Gordon Abbott Laboratories Limited, Norden Road, Maidenhead SL6 4XE Tel: 01628 644180 Fax: 01628 644325; Rowanlea, Old Acres Lane, Charvil, Reading RG10 9QL — MB ChB 1979 Glas.; FRCS Glas. 1984. Head (Clin. Developm.) Abbott Laborats. Ltd. Maidenhead.

BOYD, John Stephen Cadogan Park Surgery, 34 Cadogan Park, Belfast BT9 6HH; 15 Broomhill Park, Belfast BT9 5JB — MB BCh BAO 1982 Belf.; MRCP (UK) 1985; MRCGP 1987; DCH RCPI 1986; DRCOG 1986.

BOYD, Mr John Stewart, OBE (retired) 15 Castle Park, Ardglass, Downpatrick BT30 7UD — MB BCh BAO 1941 Belf.; FRCS Ed. 1948. Cons. Surg. (Gen. Surg.) Downpatrick Hosp. Gp. Prev: Flight Lt. RAFVR 1942-6.

BOYD, John Truesdale (retired) 27 Kingsburgh Road, Edinburgh EH12 6DZ Tel: 0131 337 5197 — MB BCh BAO 1945 Belf.; DPH 1949; FFCM 1973; SM Harvard 1952. Prev: Sen. Med. Off. Scott. Home & Health Dept.

BOYD, Juliet Dorothy 2 Vineyard Hill Road, Wimbledon, London SW19 7JH Tel: 020 8946 2514 Fax: 020 8946 8069 — MB BS 1964 Lond.; MRCS Eng. LRCP Lond. 1964; FFA RCS Eng. 1969; DA Eng. 1967. (Guy's) Cons. Anaesth. St. Geo. Hosp. Lond. Prev: Asst. Med. Dir. St. Raphaels Hosp. Cheam; Cons. Anaesth. S. Lond. Hosp.; Sen. Regist. (Anaesth.) Middlx. Hosp. Lond. & Qu. Mary's Hosp. Childr.Carshalton.

BOYD, Karen Lesley Assisted Conception Unit, C Floor, Clarendon Wing, Leeds Infirmary, Belmon Grove, Leeds Tel: 0113 243 2799 Fax: 0113 392 6662 Email: ivfuser@ulth.northy.nhs.uk; Glenholme, 4 Eaton Road, Ilkley LS29 9PU Tel: 01943 601637 — MB ChB 1987 Leeds; MRCOG 1993. (Leeds) Clin. Fell. (Reproductive Med.) The Gen. Infirm. at Leeds. Prev: Regist. (O & G) Leeds Trust.; Specialist Regist. (O & G) Bradford Trust; Specialist Regist. (O & G) Halifax.

BOYD, Karen Lesley 22 Culramoney Road, Ballymoney BT53 8HP — MB ChB 1989 Manch.; MRCGP 1993.

BOYD, Katherine 35 Collinbridge Park, Newtownabbey BT36 7SY — MB ChB 1996 Glas.

BOYD, Kathleen Elizabeth Stokes Medical Centre, Braydon Avenue, Little Stoke, Bristol BS34 6BQ Tel: 01454 616767 Fax: 01454 616189 — MB BCh BAO 1982 Belf.; MB BCh Belf. 1982; DCH Dub 1985; DRCOG 1986.

BOYD, Kathryn 238 Stanton Road, Fenham, Newcastle upon Tyne NE4 5LJ — MB BS 1979 Newc.

BOYD, Kevin David Priors Roses, Debach, Woodbridge IP13 6BZ — MB BS 1998 Lond.; MB BS Lond 1998.

BOYD, Kevin Thomas 51 Clovelly Avenue, Grainger Park, Newcastle upon Tyne NE4 8SE Tel: 0191 272 0889 — MB BS 1990 Newc.; Dip. Sports Med. Scotl. 1993. PeriFell.ship Rotat. (Surg.) Newc. u Tyne.

BOYD, Kirsty Jean Fairmile Marie Curie Centre, Frogston Road W., Edinburgh EH10 7DR Tel: 0131 445 2141 Fax: 0131 445 5845 Email: med2@mcccfairmile.u-net.com; 51 Craiglockhart Road, Edinburgh EH14 1HH Tel: 0131 443 4252 — MB ChB 1983 Glas.; MB ChB (Hons.) Glas. 1983; FRCP (E) 1997; MRCP (UK) 1986; MRCGP 1988; DRCOG 1988. (Glasgow) Cons. Fairmile Marie Curie Centre & Roy. Infirm. Edin. Socs: BMA; Assn. for Palliat. Med. Prev: Cons. Wheatfields Hospice & Cookridge Hosp. Leeds; Sen. Regist. & Regist. St. Christopher Hospice Lond.; Regist. St. Joseph's Hospice Lond.

BOYD, Linda Elizabeth Clarendon Medical, 35 Northland Avenue, Londonderry BT48 7JW Tel: 028 7126 5391 Fax: 028 7126 5932 — MB BCh BAO 1978 Belf.; DRCOG 1980; DCH 1981.

BOYD, Lorraine Marie Millfield Surgery, Millfield Lane, Easingwold, York YO61 3JR Tel: 01347 821557 — MB ChB 1983 Ed.; MRCGP 1987.

BOYD, Malcolm James Cardiac Department, Frimley Park Hospital, Portsmouth Road, Frimley, Camberley GU16 7UJ Tel: 01276 604250 Fax: 01276 604188; Kingsbury, 51 Ridgway Road, Farnham GU9 8NR Tel: 01252 716785 — MB BS Lond. 1969; FRCP Lond. 1991; MRCP (UK) 1972. (St. Geo. Hosp. Med. Sch. Lond.) Cons. Cardiol. Frimley Pk. Hosp. NHS Trust. Socs: Brit. Cardiac. Soc. Prev: Lect. & Sen. Regist. (Med.) St. Geo. Hosp. Lond.; Regist. (Med.) St. Geo. Hosp. Lond.; Resid. Med. Off. Nat. Heart Hosp. Lond.

BOYD, Margaret Joyce Willis (retired) 4 Upper Glenburn Road, Bearsden, Glasgow G61 4BW Tel: 0141 942 0399 — MB ChB Glas. 1951. Prev: Med. Off. Scott. Nat. Blood Transfus. Serv.

BOYD, Marion Stewart (retired) 3 Glen Gardens, Falkirk FK1 5LQ — MB ChB Glas. 1952; MRCGP 1964.

BOYD, Mary Ann Murray Road Surgery, 50 The Murray Road, East Kilbride, Glasgow G75 0RT Tel: 01355 225374 Fax: 01355 239475; 99 East Kilbride Road, Busby, Glasgow G76 8JE — MB ChB 1978 Glas.; MRCGP 1982.

BOYD, Mary Dickeson Allan (retired) 26 Parkhead Road, Sheffield S11 9RB — MB ChB 1922 Glas.

BOYD, Mary Mackay Macdonald 25 West Street, Seaford BN25 1EE — MB ChB 1946 Ed.; MB ChB (Hons.) Ed. 1946; FRCP Ed. 1994; MRCP (UK) 1951; MFCM RCP (UK) 1974; DPH Eng. 1958; DCH RCP Lond. 1950; DObst RCOG 1948. (Ed.) Sen. Med. Off. (Child Health) E. Sussex HA. Prev: Regist. (Paediat.) Roy. Hosp. Sick Childr. Bristol; Ho. Surg. W.. Gen. Hosp. Edin.; Buchanan Schol. in Midw. & Gyn. 1946.

BOYD, Matthew Walter John Fir Lodge, 124 Bryansford Road, Newcastle BT33 0PP Tel: 028 437 26463 — MB BCh BAO 1943 Belf.; MD Belf. 1948; FRCP Ed. 1968; MRCP (UK) 1952; FRCPI 1980, M 1978. Hon. Cons. Rheum. Belf. City & Musgrave Pk. Hosps. Socs: Hon. Mem. Brit. Soc. Rheum.; Emerit. Mem. Amer. Coll. Rheum.; Hon. Mem.Dish soc. For Rheumatol. Prev: Cons. Phys. & Phys. i/c Dept. Rheum. Dis. Belf. City Hosp. & Musgrave Pk. Hosp. Belf.

BOYD, Michael Ian 6 Delaine Road, Withington, Manchester M20 4QP — MB ChB 1985 Manch.; FRCA 1992.

BOYD, Morna Nance 56 Laxdale Drive, Head of Muir, Denny FK6 5PR Tel: 01324 814919 — MB ChB 1988 Glas. (Univ. Glas.) GP Retainer Scheme.

BOYD, Nicholas Robert Hawker 109 Culford Road, London N1 4HT — MB 1962 Camb.; BChir 1961; DObst RCOG 1965. (Camb. & Univ. Coll. Hosp.)

BOYD, Nicholas Watt The Old Rectory, Armitage, Rugeley WS15 4AL — MB ChB 1987 Liverp.

BOYD, Noeleen Ann Mary 306 Saintfield Road, Belfast BT8 6PE; 200 Killinchy Road, Lisbane, Comber, Newtownards BT23 5NE Tel: 01238 541477 Fax: 01238 541396 — MB BCh BAO 1983 Belf.; Dip. RCPR 1994; MRCPR (Immunol.) 1998. Sen. Regist. (Immunol.) Roy. Vict. Hosp. Belf. Socs: MRCPath.; BMA.

BOYD, Mr Norman Adrian, OBE (retired) Tenth House, New Road, Wootton Bridge, Ryde PO33 4HY Tel: 01983 882232 Email: yachtnina@cs.com — MRCS Eng. LRCP Lond. 1958; MS Lond. 1972, MB BS 1958; FRCS Eng. 1965; FRCS Ed. 1963; DTM & H Eng. 1961. Cons. Orthop. Surg. Orchard Hosp., Newport, Isle of Wight. Prev: Cons. Orthop. Surg. Camb. Milit. Hosp. Aldershot.

BOYD, Owen Francis Intensive Care Unit, Royal Sussex Hospital, Eastern Road, Brighton BN2 5BE Tel: 01273 474987 — MB ChB 1985 Leic.; MRCP (UK) 1988; FRCA 1995. Cons. IC Med.; Cons. Anaesth. Socs: Europ. Soc. Intens. Care Med. Prev: Research Regist. (Intens. Care) St. Geo. Hosp. Lond.

BOYD, Patricia Anne Oxford Prenatal Diagnosis Service, Women's Centre, Oxford Radcliffe Hospital, Headington, Oxford OX3 9DU Tel: 01865 221716 Fax: 01865 221164; 23 Blenheim Drive, Oxford OX2 8DJ Tel: 01865 515085 — MB BS 1971 Lond.; MD Lond. 1984; MRCS Eng. LRCP Lond. 1971. (Univ. Coll.) Clin. Co-ordinator Prenatal Diagn. Oxf. HA. Prev: Sen. Regist. (Clin. Cytogenetics) Ch.ill Hosp. Oxf.; Regist. (Path.) John Radcliffe Hosp. Oxf.

BOYD, Mr Patrick John Ramsay St Heler Hospital, Wrythe Lane, Carshalton SM5 1AA Tel: 020 8296 2809 Fax: 020 8296 2809; 2 Vineyard Hill Road, Wimbledon, London SW19 7JH Tel: 020 8946 2514 Fax: 020 8946 8069 — MB BS 1967 Lond.; 1967 MB BS Lond.; 1972 FRCS Eng.; 1965 MRCS Eng. LRCP Lond.; 1992 FEBU. (Guy's) Cons. Urol. Epson and St. Helier NHS Trust; Clin. Sub-Dean, st. Geo.'s Hosp. Med. Sch. Socs: BMA; RSM. Prev: Lect. (Urol.) Char. Cross & Roy. Marsden Hosps. Lond.; Research Fell. & Regist. (Surg.) St. Thos. Hosp. Lond.

BOYD, Robert Cameron (retired) Malvern, 6 Grantham Avenue, Lowerwalton, Warrington WA4 6PF Tel: 01925 61278 — MB BCh BAO 1951 Belf. Prev: Ho. Off. Roy. Vict. Hosp. Belf.

BOYD, Professor Robert David Hugh Principal's Office, St George's Hospital Medical School, Cranmer Terrace, London SW17 0RE Tel: 020 8725 5008 Fax: 020 8672 6940 Email: rboyd@sghms.ac.uk; The Stone House, Adlington, Macclesfield SK10 4NU Tel: 01625 872400 Fax: 01625 872400 — MB BChir 1963 Camb.; MSc (Hon.) Manch. 1985; FRCP Lond. 1977, M 1965; FFPHM; FRCPCH; F.Med Sci. (Univ. Coll. Hosp.) Princip St. Geo. Hosp. Med. Sch. Lond.; Hon. Cons. St. Geo. Healthcare NHS Trust (St. Geo. Hosp.). Prev: Prof. Paediat. Univ. Manch.; Dean Fac. Med. Univ. Manch.; Sen. Lect. Univ. Coll. Hosp. Med. Sch. Lond.

BOYD, Robert John Inglis (retired) Cranleigh, 10 The Holm, Cumnock KA18 1AW Tel: 01290 421643 — MB ChB 1950 Glas. Prev: Resid. Surg. Off. Clackmannan Co. Hosp.

BOYD, Robin Jordan 98 Turnpike Lane, London N8 0PH Tel: 020 8889 6770 Fax: 020 8889 3131 — MB BS 1970 Lond.; MA Oxf. 1974; MRCS Eng. LRCP Lond. 1970; AFOM RCP Lond. 1983; DCH Eng. 1973. (St. Thos.)

BOYD, Roy Victor (retired) 65 Trowell Road, Nottingham NG8 2EJ Tel: 0115 928 8744 Email: rayjane.boyd@virgin.net — MB BS 1957 Lond.; FRCP Ed. 1982, M 1963; FRCP Lond. 1979, M 1962; DCH Eng. 1959. Prev: Regional Postgrad. Dean Trent RHA.

BOYD, Russell 20 Stonechat Close, Ellenbrook, Worsley, Manchester M28 7XQ — MB ChB 1989 Ed.; BMedSci Ed. 1987; MRCP (UK) 1994; Dip IMC RCS Ed. 1996. (Ed.)

BOYD, Stephen Andrew Samuel 91 Maryville Park, Belfast BT9 6LQ — MB BCh BAO 1994 Belf.

BOYD, Stewart Gregor Department of Clinical Neurophysiology, Great Ormond Street Children's NHS Trust, Great Ormond St., London WC1N 3JH Tel: 020 7405 9200 Fax: 020 7829 8627 Email: s.boyd@compuserve.com — MB ChB 1971 Aberd.; MD Aberd. 1987. Cons. Clin. Neurophysiol. Hosp. Sick Childr. Lond.

BOYD, Terence Henry The Ulster Hospital, Dundonald, Belfast BT16 1RH Tel: 01232 484511 — MB BCh BAO 1984 Belf.; MB BCh BAO Belf. l984; FFARCSI 1988. Cons. Anaesth. Ulster Hosp.

BOYD, Thomas Ian (retired) 29 The Glebe, Lavenham, Sudbury CO10 9SN — MB ChB 1952 Glas.

BOYD, Thomas Jan Manor View Practice, Bushey Health Centre, London Road, Bushey, Watford WD23 2NN Tel: 01923 225224 Fax: 01923 213270; 5 King George Avenue, Bushey, Watford WD23 4NT Tel: 020 8950 4519 Fax: 020 8386 0496 — MB BChir 1976 Camb.; MA Camb. 1977; FRCGP 1995, M 1983; DRCOG 1979. Mem. Panel Examrs. RCGP. Prev: Assoc. Dean Postgrad. Gen. Pract.; Course Organiser Watford VTS.

BOYD, Timothy Hendry 8 Hilton Road, Disley, Stockport SK12 2JU — BM BCh 1996 Oxf.

BOYD, Una Barrie The Health Centre, Testwood Lane, Totton, Southampton SO40 3ZN Tel: 023 8086 5051 Fax: 023 8086 5050; Forest Edge, The Crescent, Woodlands Road, Ashurst, Southampton — MB ChB 1965 Glas.

BOYD, Vanda 120 High Storrs Road, Sheffield S11 7LF Tel: 0114 266 5767 — MB ChB 1971 Bristol; ECFMG Cert. 1971; FFA RCS Eng. 1977; DA Eng. 1974; DObst RCOG 1973. Cons. Anaesth. Rotherham Dist. Gen. Hosp. Prev: Sen. Regist. (Anaesth.) Sheff. AHA (T); Sen. Regist. (Anaesth.) A.B.U. Hosp. Kaduna, Nigeria; Regist. (Anaesth.) United Bristol Hosp.

BOYD, Walter Henry 5 Kell Road, Clogher BT76 0HY — MB BCh BAO 1986 Belf.; MB BCh Belf. 1986; MRCGP 1991; T(GP) 1991; DCH Dub. 1990; DRCOG 1988. SHO (A & E) Belf. City Hosp. Prev: Trainee GP/SHO Ulster Hosp. Dundonald VTS.

BOYD, Mr Walter Nugent (retired) Lynwood, 146 Oulton Road, Stone ST15 8DR — MB ChB 1940 Glas.; FRCS Ed. 1948; DMRD Ed. 1954. Prev: Cons. Radiol. N. Staffs. Roy. Infirm. & Haywood Hosp. Burslem.

BOYD, William Dalziel (retired) 49/12 Belford Road, Edinburgh EH4 3BR Tel: 0131 226 5465 — MB ChB 1954 Ed.; FRCP Ed. 1971, M 1960; FRCPsych 1973, M 1971; DPM Eng. 1960. Prev: Cons. Psychiat. Lothian HB.

BOYD, William Proctor Old Mill Surgery, 100 Old Mill Road, Uddingston, Glasgow G71 7JB Tel: 01698 817219 — MB ChB 1979 Glas.; BSc (Hons.) Strathclyde 1974.

***BOYDE, Adam Marcus** 7 Walcott Avenue, Christchurch BH23 2NQ Tel: 01202 461358 Email: amboyde@yahoo.co.uk — MB BS 1998 Lond.; MB BS Lond 1998; BSc 1995.

BOYDE, Professor Tom Robin Caine Flat D, 21 Devonshire Place, London W1G 6HZ Tel: 020 7487 2926 Fax: 07079 007058 Email: tboyde@medical.demon.co.uk — MB BS Lond. 1955; MD Lond. 1967; FRCPath. (Univ. Coll. Hosp.) Emerit. Prof. Univ. Hong Kong; Fell. Hong Kong Coll. Path. Socs: Roy. Soc. Med.; BMA; Fell. Roy. Coll. of Path. Prev: Prof. Biochem. Univ. Hong Kong & Makerere Univ. Kampala, Uganda.

BOYDELL, Jeanette Sheila 138 Grove Road, Wallasey CH45 0JF — MB ChB 1949 Manch. (Manch.) Prev: Ho. Surg. Oldham & Stockport Infirms.; Rotat. Intern. Hosp. St. Barnabas New York, USA.

BOYDELL, John Herbert (retired) Old Timbers, Well Road, Crondall, Farnham GU10 5PW Tel: 01252 850417 — MRCS Eng. LRCP Lond. 1945; MB BS Lond. 1948; DCH Eng. 1949. Prev: Gen. Practitioner, Leeds.

BOYDELL, Leslie Rosevear Legaterriff House, Lough Road, Ballinderry Upper, Lisburn BT28 2HA — MB BCh BAO 1977 Dub.; MSc (Nutrit.) Lond. 1979; MFCM 1989; MRCGP 1983; DRCOG 1981.

BOYDEN, Jane Elizabeth 73 Moscow, Thornton, Bradford BD13 3SQ — MB ChB 1991 Dundee.

***BOYDEN, Julia Frances Alice** 5 Chestnut Avenue, Radley College, Abingdon OX14 2HS Tel: 01235 543095 — MB ChB 1994 Leic.

BOYE, Gilbert Lantey Department of Clinical Pharmacology, The Royal Infirmary, Lauriston Place, Edinburgh EH3 9YW — MB BCh BAO 1966 NUI.

BOYER, Mary Gwendolin May (retired) Chadwich Manor, Redhill Lane, Bromsgrove B61 0QF Tel: 0121 453 2323 Fax: 0121 453 2323 Email: mgbdykes@aol.com — MB ChB 1955 Birm. Prev: Assoc. Specialist (Head Injury Rehabil.) Childr. Hosp. Trust Birm.

BOYES, Brian Eliel Tameside General Hospital, Ashton-under-Lyne OL6 9RW Tel: 0161 331 6366; Cow Hey Farm House, Cow Hey Farm, Glossop Road, Marple Bridge, Stockport SK6 5NX Tel: 0161 427 1396 — MB ChB 1964 Ed.; FRCP Glas. 1980, M 1968; FRCP Lond. 1986, M 1968. (Ed.) Cons. Phys. Tameside Gen. Hosp. Ashton-under-Lyne. Prev: Lect. (Med.) Univ. Manch.; Research Fell. (Med.) Univ. Glas.; Hon. Regist. Univ. Dept. Med. W.. Infirm. Glas.

BOYES, George Michael Pearson (retired) 5 Alston Road, Hemel Hempstead HP1 1QT Tel: 01442 235843 — MB BChir 1952 Camb.; MA, MB BChir Camb. 1952; FRCGP 1978, M 1972; DIH Soc. Apoth. Lond. 1959; DA Eng. 1955; DObst RCOG 1954.

BOYES, Rebecca Elizabeth — MB BS 1992 Lond.; MRCGP 1999. p/t GP Princip., Granville Ho. Med. Centre, Adlington; Clin. Med. Off. Family Plann., Chorley. Prev: GP Regist. Tarleton Health Centre Preston.

BOYES, Simon Ashley 8 Basset Mews, 6 Ardnave Crescent, Bassett, Southampton SO16 7NW — BM 1993 Soton.

BOYES, William Roslyn, Albion Terrace, Saltburn-by-the-Sea TS12 1LT Tel: 01287 62401 — MB ChB Leeds 1944. (Leeds) Socs: Newman Assn.; Assn. Med. Internat. de N.-D. de Lourdes. Prev: Cas. Off. Harrogate Gen Hosp.; Ho. Surg. & Ho. Phys. Middlesbrough Gen. Hosp.; Res. Med. Off. W. La. Hosp. Middlesbrough.

BOYHAN, Carmel Rose North Road West Medical Centre, 167 North Road West, Plymouth PL1 5BZ Tel: 01752 662780 Fax: 01752 254541; Brook House, Labert Road, Tamerton Foliot, Plymouth PL5 4NB Tel: 01752 766462 — MB BCh BAO 1988 NUI; MRCGP 1993.

BOYLAN, Bernard Paul North Berwick Health Centre, 54 St Baldred's Road, North Berwick EH39 4PU — MB BCh BAO 1988 NUI.

BOYLAN, Brendan Gerard 529 Price Street, Birkenhead CH41 8DU — MB BS 1985 Lond.

BOYLAN, Colm Edmund Flat 118, Tower Block 2, Withington Hospital, Nell Lane, Manchester M20 2LR — MB BCh BAO 1992 NUI.

BOYLAN, James John Bernard 11 Milbourne Court, Sedgefield, Stockton-on-Tees TS21 2JD — MB BS 1982 Lond.; BSc Lond. 1980, MB BS 1982.

BOYLAN, Mary Dolores Kingshill, East St., Rochford SS4 1DB — MB BCh BAO 1976 NUI.

BOYLAN, Terence Moore c/o Toronto Dominion Bank, 62 Cornhill, London EC3V 3PL — MB BCh BAO 1958 NUI; FRCP(C) 1973; MRCPsych 1972; DPM 1963.

BOYLE, Adrian Alexander Beacon Hill House, Langbar, Ilkley LS29 0EU — BM 1994 Soton.

BOYLE, Alan Stevenson The Medical Specialist Group, PO Box 113, Alexandra House, Les Frieteaux, St Martin's, Guernsey GY1 3EX Tel: 01481 38565 Fax: 01481 37782; Elounda, Clos De La Grande Marche, Kings Road, St. Peter Port, Guernsey GY1 1QD Tel: 01481 723085 Fax: 01481 728543 — MB ChB 1973 Glas.; FFA RCS Eng. 1978; DObst RCOG 1975. Cons. Anaesth. P.ss Eliz. Hosp. Guernsey.

BOYLE, Mr Alasdair Hugh Wilson North Devon District Hospital, Raleigh Park, Barnstaple EX31 4JB — MB BS 1970 Lond.; FRCS Ed. 1980; FRCOG 1990, M 1978. (St. Thos.) Cons. (O & G) S. W. RHA. Prev: Sen. Regist. (O & G) Yorks. RHA; Regist. (O & G) Qu. Eliz. Matern. Centre Edgbaston.

BOYLE, Allison Mary Redwood, Wey Road, Weybridge KT13 8HW — MB BS 1993 Lond.

BOYLE, Anne Gray 59 Hauteville, St Peter Port, Guernsey GY1 1DQ Tel: 01481 724288 — MB ChB 1964 Ed.; DA Eng. 1968. (Univ. Ed.) Prev: Clin. Asst. (Anaesth.) Kirklees AHA; Anaesth. Regist. Edin. Centr. Hosp. Gp.

BOYLE, Anne Mary Elizabeth The Surgery, Mill Street, Puddletown, Dorchester DT2 8SH Tel: 01305 848333 Fax: 01305 848061; Email: annemeboyle@compuserve.com — DCN 1982; MRCGP 1984; DTM & H 1980; MB ChB 1979 Manchester; DRCOG 1983. (Manchester) Gen. Practitioner, Puddletown, Dorset.

BOYLE, Brendan Eugene Warbrick-Smith and Partners, The Moat House Surgery, Beech Close, Warboys, Huntingdon PE28 2RQ Tel: 01487 822230 Fax: 01487 823721; Moat House Surgery, Beech Close, Warboss, Huntingdon PE28 2RQ Tel: 01481 822230 — MB ChB 1976 Ed.; BSc (Hons.) Ed. 1974; MRCP (UK) 1979. (Ed.)

BOYLE, Catriona Elizabeth Largent Flatt Walks Health Centre, 3 Castle Meadows, Catherine Street, Whitehaven CA28 7QE Tel: 01946 692173 Fax: 01946 590406; Howgarth, Pardshaw, Cockermouth CA13 0SP Tel: 01900 825532 Email: catriona@howgarth.demon.co.uk — MB ChB 1988 Dundee; BMSc (Hons.) Dund 1985; MRCGP 1994; DFFP 1994. Clin. Asst. (Cardiol.) W. Cumbria Health Care NHS Trust; Regional Med. Off. Brit. Athletic Federat. Socs: Amer. Coll. Phys. Prev: Trainee GP W. Cumbria VTS; Hon. Team Doctor Scott. Comonwealth Games team for Kuala Lumpur 1998.

BOYLE, Charles Brendan Health Centre, Kinawley, Enniskillen BT92 4BW Tel: 028 6774 8691 Fax: 028 6774 8949 — MB ChB 1967 Glas.

BOYLE, David Dorrington Royal Maternity Hospital, Grosvenor Road, Belfast BT12 6BB Tel: 01232 894633 Fax: 01232 235256 Email: david.bayle1@royalhospitals.n-i.nhs.uk; The Grey House, 3 Deramore Park S., Belfast BT9 5JY Tel: 01232 665169 Email: ddboyle@dnd.co.uk — MB ChB 1968 Ed.; FRCOG 1986, M 1973; DObst RCOG 1971. (Ed.) Cons. O & G Roy. Vict. & Roy. Matern. Hosps. Belf.; Hon. Lec. Qu.s. Univ.Belf. Prev: Lect. & Cons. O & G (Univ. Natal) King Edwd. VIII Hosp. Durban, S. Afr.

BOYLE, Deborah Claire Maria 58A Goldhurst Terrace, London NW6 3HT — MB ChB 1991 Sheff.; DFFP 1996. Specialist Regist. (O & G), N. W. Thames Region.

BOYLE, Dennis McCord 46 Malone View Road, Belfast BT9 5PH Tel: 01232 611056 Fax: 01232 611056 Email: drdennis99@aol.com — MD 1960 Belf.; MB BCh BAO Belf. 1957; FRCPI 1991; FRCP Lond. 1976, M 1962; FCCP 1990; FESC 1988. Socs: Brit. Assn. Phys.; Brit. & Irish Cardiac Soc.; Irish Hyperlipidaemia Assn. Prev: Cons. Cardiol. Roy. Gp. Hosp. Belf. & Ulster & N. Down Hosp. Trust.

BOYLE, Dikshita The Turret Medical Centre, Catherine Street, Kirkintilloch, Glasgow G66 1JB Tel: 0141 211 8260 Fax: 0141 211 8264 — MB ChB 1987 Dundee; MRACGP 1994; MRCGP 1994.

BOYLE, Douglas Sealy Cromwell Cottage, Pitt, Winchester SO22 5QW — MRCS Eng. LRCP Lond. 1941.

BOYLE, Douglas Stuart Lehman and Partners, Hightown Surgery, Hightown Gardens, Banbury OX16 9DB Tel: 01295 270722 Fax: 01295 263000; Dolphin House, Market Place, Deddington, Banbury OX15 0SE Tel: 01869 338340 — MB BS 1981 Lond.; BA (Eng. Lit.) Oxf. 1970; MRCGP 1991. (St. Bart.) Bd. Mem. & Clin. Governance Head PCG.

BOYLE, Hilary Christine Stanmore House Surgery, Linden Avenue, Kidderminster DY10 3AA Tel: 01562 822647 Fax: 01562 827255; 30 Blakebrook, Kidderminster DY11 6RG Tel: 01562 68535 — MB ChB 1973 Birm. Prev: Clin. Med. Off. Kidderminster DHA.

BOYLE, Irene Forbes Dunn (retired) 29 Canterbury Road, Herne Bay CT6 5DQ — MB ChB 1961 Glas. Prev: Ho. Phys. & Ho. Surg. Hairmyres Hosp. E. Kilbride.

BOYLE, James Gerald 16 Yeavering Close, Gosforth, Newcastle upon Tyne NE3 4YU; 6 Coronation Park, Aughnacloy BT69 6AW — MB BCh BAO 1988 Belf.; BSc Belf. 1984; MRCGP 1992; DFFP 1993; DMH Belf. 1993; DRCOG 1991; DCH RCPI 1991. Regist. (Radiol.) N. & Yorks. RHA. Prev: SHO Daisy Hill Hosp. Newry.

BOYLE, James Patrick (retired) 26 Kinmount Avenue, Glasgow G44 4RR Tel: 0141 632 8909 — MB ChB. Glas. 1950; DCH RCPS Glas. 1964.

BOYLE, Jennifer Ann Warbrick-Smith and Partners, The Moat House Surgery, Beech Close, Warboys, Huntingdon PE28 2RQ Tel: 01487 822230 Fax: 01487 823721; Croft House, High St, Warboys, Huntingdon PE17 2TA Tel: 01487 823316 — MB ChB 1976 Ed.; BSc (Hons.) Ed. 1974; MRCP (UK) 1979; DRCOG 1980; DCH Eng. 1979; LFHom 1998. (Ed.) Socs: Nat. Assn. Family Plann. Doctors; Licensed Mem. Fac. Homeop.

BOYLE, John Anthony X-Ray Department, Scarborough Hospital, Scarborough YO12 6QL — MB BS 1977 Lond.; MRCS Eng. LRCP Lond. 1977; FRCR 1985.

BOYLE, John Joseph Patrick 43 Studholme Crescent, Penwortham, Preston PR1 9NE — MB ChB 1987 Manch.

BOYLE, John Patrick 29 Old Coach Avenue, Belfast BT9 5PY — MB BCh BAO 1992 Dub.; MB BCh Dub. 1992.

BOYLE, Mr Jonathan Robert Dept. of Vascular Surgery, E Level, Southampton General Hospital, Tremona Rd, Southampton SO16 6YD — MB ChB 1991 Leic.; FRCS 2001; MD 1991 Leic.; FRCS Ed. 1996. Specialist Regist., (Gen. Surg.) Wessex, Vasc. Surg., Soton. Gen. Hosp.; Sen. Regsitrar in Vasc. Surg., Roy. Adelaide Hosp., Adelaide, S. Australia, 6000 Jan 2002-3. Socs: Surg. Research Soc.; Eur. Soc. Vasc. & Endovasc. Surg.; Vasc. Surg. Soc. Of Gt. Britain & Irel. Prev: Clin. Research Fell. (Surg.) Univ. of Leicester; SHO (Surg.) Leics. HA.

BOYLE, Joseph Staplegrove Manor, Taunton TA2 6EG — MB ChB 1977 Glas.; MRCGP 1994; DRCOG 1992. (University of Glasgow)

BOYLE, Joseph James Department of Medicine, Addenbrooke's Hospital, Cambridge CB2 2QQ Email: jjbl@mole.biol.cam.ac.uk — MB ChB 1991 Glas.; BSc Glas. 1988. MRC Clin. Train. Fell. (Med.) Univ. Camb. Socs: BMA; Path. Soc. Prev: SHO (Histopath.) Glas.

BOYLE, Kathleen Christine 46 Campsie Drive, Bearsden, Glasgow G61 3HX — MB ChB 1994 Glas.

BOYLE, Kathleen Renee 57 Polwarth Road, Brunton Park, Gosforth, Newcastle upon Tyne NE3 5NE Tel: 0191 236 5552 — MB BCh BAO 1979 NUI; DCH NUI 1981. (NUI) Clin. Asst. Newc. u. Tyne.

BOYLE, Kevin 4 Prospecthill Place, Glasgow G42 0JS — MB ChB 1981 Glas.

BOYLE, Margaret Mary Isobel 30 Croft Hill, Cairnshill Road, Belfast BT8 6GX Tel: 01232 790781 — MB BCh BAO 1981 Belf.; MSc Ed. 1986; MFPHM 1990; FFA RCSI 1985. Sen. Med. Off. DHSS N. Irel. Prev: Sen. Regist. (Pub. Health Med.) EHSSB Belf.

BOYLE, Mr Mark Andrew 16 Kingsford Avenue, Muirend, Glasgow G44 3EU — MB ChB 1991 Glas.; BDS 1983; FDS RCPS Glas.1987; FRCS Glas. 1994.

BOYLE, Michael Andrew 19 Beaufort Drive, Kirkintilloch, Glasgow G66 1AX Tel: 0141 776 1638; 295 Crow Road, Glasgow G11 7BQ — MB ChB 1989 Glas. GP Regist. Balfron Nr Glas.

BOYLE, Michael Daniel The New Surgery, Victoria Road, Wargrave, Reading RG10 8BP Tel: 0118 940 3939 Fax: 0118 940 1357; The Surgery, Victoria Road, Wargrave, Reading RG10 8BP — MB BCh 1984 Wales; MRCGP 1988; DRCOG 1990; DCH RCP Lond. 1989. Prev: SHO (Psychiat.) Moorhaven Hosp., Ivybridge, Devon.

BOYLE, Michael Francis Linlithgow Health Centre, 288 High Street, Linlithgow EH49 7ER Tel: 01506 670027; 6 Burgess Hill, Linlithgow EH49 6BX — MB ChB 1981 Dundee; DRCOG 1985.

BOYLE, Michael James, OBE, OStJ, Surg. Capt. RN Retd. (retired) 30 Thornhill Road, Mannamead, Plymouth PL3 5NE — MB BChir 1952 Camb.; MA Camb. 1952, BA (Nat. Sc. Trip.) 1948, MB BChir 1952; AFOM RCP Lond. 1983; DLO Eng. 1960. Prev: Ho. Surg. St. Mary's Hosp. Portsmouth & St. Helier Hosp. Carshalton.

BOYLE, Michael Simon Birley Health Centre, 120 Birley Lane, Sheffield S12 3BP Tel: 0114 239 2541 Fax: 0114 264 5814; 120 Birley Lane, Birley, Sheffield S12 3BP Tel: 0114 239 2541 — MB ChB 1989 Sheff.; MRCGP 1993. Dip. Family Plann. JCPT. Prev: Trainee GP Doncaster VTS.

BOYLE, Natalie Jane 79 Priory Road, Linlithgow EH49 6BP Email: natboyle@hotmail.com — MB ChB 1994 Ed. SHO (Ophth.) Roy. Vict. Infirm. Newc.

BOYLE, Neil Alexander (retired) Brigstone House, Lothersdale, Keighley BD20 8HX Tel: 01535 630759 Fax: 01535 630759 — MB ChB Ed. 1963; FRCP Lond. 1997; FRCP Ed. 1983, M 1971; FRCPCH 1997. Prev: Community Paediat. Guernsey.

BOYLE, Nicholas Hamilton 24 Cornwall Gardens, London SW7 4AW — BM 1987 Soton.

BOYLE, Noel Brian Joseph Waterside Health Centre, Glendermott Road, Londonderry BT47 6AU Tel: 028 7132 0100 Fax: 028 7132 0117; 42 Bayswater, Londonderry BT47 6JL Tel: 01504 345710 — MB BCh BAO 1985 Belf.; MRCGP 1990; DRCOG 1993. (Queen's Belfast)

BOYLE, Patrick Granby Place Surgery, Granby Place, 1 High Street, Northfleet, Gravesend DA11 9EY Tel: 01474 352447/362252 — MB BCh BAO 1969 NUI.

BOYLE, Patrick, Wing Cdr. RAF Med. Br. Retd. RGIT Ltd, 338 King St., Aberdeen AB24 5BQ Tel: 01224 619619; Ahlan, Aulton Road, Cruden Bay, Peterhead AB42 0NJ Tel: 01779 812958 — MB ChB 1974 Ed.; MRCGP 1983. (Ed.) Phys. Coordinator (Occupat. Health). Socs: Assoc. Fac. Occupat. Med; Assoc. Mem. Soc. Occupat. Med. Prev: Princip. Med. Off. Roy. Airforce of Oman; SMO RAF Leuchars.

BOYLE, Patrick Douglas Stakes Lodge Surgery, 3A Lavender Road, Waterlooville PO7 8NS Tel: 023 9225 4581 Fax: 023 9235 8867; 37 Tilmore Gardens, Petersfield GU32 2JE Tel: 01730 266004 — MB BS 1972 Lond.; BSc Lond. 1969. (St. Thos.)

BOYLE, Peter Harry 130 Northwood Lane, Clayton, Newcastle ST5 4BN — MB ChB Birm. 1956; MRCS Eng. LRCP Lond. 1956.

BOYLE, Philip Terence (retired) 11 High Croft, Collingham, Wetherby LS22 5AH — MB BChir 1941 Camb.; MRCP Lond. 1949; MRCS Eng. LRCP Lond. 1940. Prev: Regist. Pathol. Harrogate Gen. Hosp.

BOYLE, Robert John Fairstead Hall, Terling, Chelmsford CM3 3AT — MB ChB 1995 Bristol.

BOYLE, Roger Michael The Paddocks House, Copmanthorpe, York YO2 3SU Tel: 01904 706701 Fax: 01904 631121 — MB BS 1972 Lond.; FRCP Lond. 1991; MRCP (UK) 1976. Cons. Phys. York Dist. Hosp.; Edit. Comm. Brit. Heart Jl. Socs: Brit. Cardiac Soc. Prev: Lect. Dept. Cardiovasc. Studies Univ. Leeds; Research Regist. Regional Cardiac Centre Wythenshawe Manch.; SHO (Med.) Lond. Hosp.

BOYLE, Ronald Thomson (retired) The Holt, Carr Lane, Eastlound, Doncaster DN9 2LT Tel: 01302 365200 Email: ronboyle@btinternet.com — MB ChB 1952 Glas.; DObst RCOG 1957. Med. Examr. Life Assur. Socs. & DSS. Prev: GP Doncaster.

BOYLE, Simon 15 Peachtree Close, Fulwood, Preston PR2 9NR — MB ChB 1996 Sheff.

BOYLE, Simon Paul Redlish House, Redlish Lane, Padside, Harrogate HG3 4AL — MB ChB 1997 Leeds. Orthop. Prev: A & E.

BOYLE, Stephen Basil (retired) Pyke House, Chapel-en-le-Frith, High Peak SK23 9RT — MRCS Eng. LRCP Lond. 1953.

BOYLE, Susan Department of Cellular Pathology, Northwick Park Hospital, Watford Road, Harrow HA1 3UJ Tel: 020 8869 3306 — MB BS 1976 Lond.; BSc Lond. 1973; MRCPath 1984. Cons. Histopath. N.wick Pk. & St Mark's NHS Trust Harrow.

BOYLE, Suzanne Christine 19 Beaufort Drive, Kirkintilloch, Glasgow G66 1AX — MB ChB 1995 Manch.

BOYLE, Mr William James 28 Rodney Street, Liverpool L1 2TQ Tel: 0151 709 8160; Bronte, 5 Elmsley Road, Mossley Hill, Liverpool L18 8AY Tel: 0151 724 2734 — MB ChB 1960 Liverp.; MChOrth Liverp. 1968; FRCS Ed. 1966; MRCS Eng. LRCP Lond. 1960. Cons. Orthop. Surg. N. Chesh. Hosp. Socs: Fell. BOA; Medico-legal.Soc.Merseyside; Liverp. Inst. Med. Prev: Cons. Orthop. Surg. Warrington NHS Trust; Sen. Lect. (Orthop. Surg.) Univ. Liverp.

BOYLES, Andrew Fraser Yatton Family Practice, 155 Mendip Road, Yatton, Bristol BS49 4ER Tel: 01934 832277 Fax: 01934 876085; Merryn Cottage, West Hay Road, Wrington, Bristol BS40 5NR Fax: 01934 863179 — MB ChB 1967 Bristol.

BOYLES, Derek John Lower House, East St., Pembridge, Leominster HR6 9HA — MB ChB 1954 Birm.; FFA RCS Eng. 1964. Cons. Anaesth. I. of Man Hosps. Socs: BMA & I. of Man Med. Soc. Prev: Cons. Anaesth. Birm. (Dudley Rd.) Hosp. Gp.; Sen. Regist. (Anaesth.) United Birm. Hosps.; Regist. Anaesth. Warwick Hosp.

BOYLSTON, Professor Arthur William Molecular Medicine Unit, Clinical Sciences Building, St James's Hospital, Leeds LS9 7TF Tel: 0113 206 5681 Fax: 0113 244 4475 Email: msjawb@stjames.leeds.ac.uk — MD 1969 Harvard; BA Yale 1964; FRCPath 1988; MRCPath 1976. (Harvard) Prof. Path. & Moc. Med., Dept. Path. Univ. Leeds. Prev: Reader St Mary's Hosp., Med. Sch., Lond.

BOYNE, Ines Christina 14 Garrioch Drive, Glasgow G20 8RS Tel: 0141 946 8096 Email: iboyne@yahoo.com — State Exam Med 1990 Hamburg; FRCA 1995; DA (UK) 1992. Specialist Regist. (Anaesth.) Vict. Infirm. NHS Trust Glas. Socs: BMA; Train. Mem. Assn. AnE.h.; Obst. Anaesth. Assn. Prev: SHO (Anaesth.) W. Glas. NHS Trust.

BOYNS, Arthur Richard Y Ganolfan Iechyd, Wynne Road, Blaenau Ffestiniog LL41 3DW Tel: 01766 830205 Fax: 01766 831121; Trwyn-y-Garnedd, Tan-y-Bwlch, Blaenau Ffestiniog LL41 3YY Tel: 01766 590381 — MB BCh 1960 Wales; PhD Birm. 1966, BSc 1963; D.Occ.Med. RCP Lond. 1995. (Cardiff)

BOYNS, David Robert (retired) 1 Stryd y Bailey, Cydweli/Kidwelly SA17 5AZ Tel: 01554 890921 Email: davidboyns@doctors.net.uk — MB BCh 1951 Wales; BSc Wales 1948; MRCP Lond. 1961; DCH Eng. 1955. Prev: Course Organiser Carmarthen GPVTS.

BOYS, Deirdre Heather The Cottage Hall Farm, Warboys Road, Bury PE26 2NU Tel: 01487 814179 — MB BS 1991 Lond.; MRCP 1998. (Roy. Free Hosp.) Specialist Regist. PeterBoro. Dist. Hosp. Prev: SHO (Paediat. & O & G) Luton & Dunstable NHS Trust; SHO Roy. Free Hosp. NHS Trust; SHO Milton Keynes Gen. Hosp.

BOYS, John Edwin Department of Anaesthesia, West Suffolk Hospital, Bury St Edmunds IP33 2QZ Tel: 01284 713000 — MB BS 1967 Lond.; BSc (Special) Lond. 1964; FFA RCS Eng. 1972. (Univ. Coll. Hosp.) Cons. Anaesth. W. Suff. Hosp. Bury St. Edmunds. Prev: Sen. Regist. (Anaesth.) Bristol Roy. Infirm., Plymouth Hosp. Gp. & Frenchay Hosp. Bristol.

BOYTON, Rosemary Jane 18 Cyprus Avenue, Church End, London N3 1ST — MB BS 1990 Lond.; BSc Lond. 1987; MRCP (UK) 1993, PhD 2000.

BOZEK, Tomas 4 Kensington Court, London W8 5DL — BM BCh 1976 Oxf.; MRCP (UK) 1979. Cons. Phys. Palliat. Med. Guy's & Lewisham NHS Trust Guy's & St. Thos. Hosp. Lond. Prev: Cons. Phys. & Med. Oncol. Laurentian Hosp. Ontario, Canada; Hon. Sen. Regist. Roy. Marsden Hosp. Lond.; Regist. Univ. Coll. Hosp. & Roy. Marsden Hosp. Lond.

BOZMAN, Mr Edward Harvey High Street Surgery, 25 High Street, Tollesbury, Maldon CM9 8RG Tel: 01621 869204 Fax: 01621 869023; Prentice Hall, Prentice Hall Lane, Tollesbury, Maldon CM9 8RN Tel: 01621 860230 — MRCS Eng. LRCP Lond. 1964; BSc Lond. 1961, MB BS 1964; FRCS Eng. 1970. (King's Coll. Hosp.) Prev: Ho. Phys., Ho. Surg. & SHO King's Coll. Hosp. Lond.

BOZZINO, Joseph Manuel 53 Rokeby Drive, Kenton, Newcastle upon Tyne NE3 4JY Tel: 01632 857239 — MD 1969 Malta; MRCP (UK) 1975; FRCR 1977. (Malta) Cons. (Radiother. & Oncol.) Regional Radiother. Centre Newc. Gen.

BRABBINS, Clare Jane Rathbone Hospital, Mill Lane, Old Swab, Liverpool L13 4AW — MB ChB 1987 Manch.

BRABEN, Peter Stanley 4 Oriel Road, Ashton-in-Makerfield, Wigan WN4 9RQ — MB ChB 1992 Leeds.

BRABIN, Professor Bernard John Child and Reproductive Health Group, Liverpool School of Tropical Medicine, Pembroke Place, Liverpool L3 5QA Tel: 0151 708 9393 Fax: 0151 708 8733 Email: l.j.taylor@liverpool.ac.uk; 1 Whinmoor Close, Noctorum, Birkenhead CH43 7XR — MB ChB 1972 Manch.; PhD Lond. 1984, MSc Human Nutrit. 1975; FRCP (C) 1978; Amer. Bd. Certified Paediat. 1979.

(Univ.manch) Prof. of Troopical Paediatricans Univ. Liverp.; Prof. of Trop. Child Health, Acad. Med. Centre, Amsterdam. Socs: Fell. RCP Surg. Canada; Stand. Comm. Internat. Soc. Trop.Paediat.; Liverp.Paediat.Club. Prev: Staff Mem. Inst. Med. Research Papua New Guinea; Sen. Resid. Hosp. Sick Childr. Toronto; Staff. Mem. Roy. Trop. Inst. Amsterdam.

BRABINER, David 14 Church Street, Kilburn, Belper DE56 0LU — MB ChB 1991 Sheff.

BRACCHI, Alfred Louis Christopher Anthony Marius Tudor Gate Surgery, Tudor St., Abergavenny NP7 5DL Tel: 01873 855991; Maisemore, 11 Albany Road, Abergavenny NP7 7BD Tel: 01873 852284 — MB BS 1951 Lond.; MRCS Eng. LRCP Lond. 1951; LMSSA Lond. 1951. (Univ. Coll. Hosp.)

BRACCHI, Robert Christopher Guy Tudor Gate Surgery, Tudor Street, Abergavenny NP7 5DL Tel: 01873 855991 Fax: 01873 850162; 2 Belgrave Close, Abergavenny NP7 7AP — MB BCh 1981 Wales; BSc (Hons.) Biochem. Wales 1976; MRCGP 1985; Dip. Ther. Wales 1995; Dip. Pract. Dermat. Wales 1993. Course Organiser (Pharmacol. Therap. & Toxicol.) Univ. Wales Coll. Med. Llandough Hosp. NHS Trust Cardiff. Prev: SHO (Gen. Med.) Caerphilly & Dist. Miners Hosp; SHO (O & G) St. David's Hosp. Cardiff; SHO (Paediat.) Cardiff Roy. Infirm.

BRACE, Rev. Alistair Andrew 55 Sprout Lane, Benthall TF12 5QY Tel: 01952 884031 — MB BS 1976 Newc.; DRCOG 1978. Locum G.P.

BRACE, Candia Helen 6 South Terrace, High St., Farningham, Dartford DA4 0DF — MB BS 1991 Lond.; BSc Lond. 1988; MRCP (UK) 1994. Trainee GP Maidstone VTS.

BRACE, Christine Ann Devaney Medical Centre, 40 Balls Road, Oxton, Prenton CH43 5RE Tel: 0151 652 4281 Fax: 0151 670 0445; Westwards, 42 Mount Road, Higher Bebington, Wirral CH63 5PL Tel: 0151 608 4538 Fax: 0151 608 3193 Email: chris_brace@lineone.net — MB ChB 1968 Liverp.; MB ChB (Hons.) Liverp. 1968; DA Eng. 1971. (Liverp.) Socs: (Ex-Hon. Sec.) Birkenhead Med. Soc.; Liverp. Med. Inst. Prev: Locality Facilitator (Birkenhead N.) FHSA; SHO (Anaesth.) Roy. Gwent Hosp. Newport; Ho. Phys. & Ho. Surg. St. Catherine's Hosp. Birkenhead.

BRACE, Joanne Victoria 42 Mount Road, Bebington, Wirral CH63 5PL Tel: 0151 608 4538 — MB ChB 1994 Birm.; MB ChB (Hons.) Birm. 1994; MFFP 1997. SHO (O & G) Birm. Wom. Hosp. Prev: SHO (O & G) City Hosp. NHS Trust Birm.

BRACE, William Devereux Burmans Farmhouse, Cottage Lane, Shottery, Stratford-upon-Avon CV37 9HH Email: wbrace@compuserve.com — MB BS 1981 Lond.; BA (Cantab) 1978; MRCP (UK) 1985; MRCPath 1992; DTM & H 1997.

BRACE, William Lloyd (retired) High Knowle Cottage, 6 Dark Lane, Budleigh Salterton EX9 6QR Tel: 01395 446435 — MRCS Eng. LRCP Lond. 1941; MB BS Lond. 1947. Prev: Ho. Off. (Surg., ENT & Cas.) St. Mary's Hosp. Lond.

BRACEBRIDGE, Michael Charles The Surgery, Staunton-on-Wye, Hereford HR4 7LT Tel: 01981 500227 Fax: 01981 500603; The Old Barn, Mansel Lacy, Hereford HR4 7HQ — MB BS Lond. 1969. (St. Mary's) Princip. GP. Prev: Squadron Ldr. RAF Med. Br.

BRACEBRIDGE, Samantha Patricia 62 Stanstrete Field, Black Notley, Braintree CM7 8WP — MB BS 1992 Lond.; DFFP 1997; DRCOG 1996; MRCGP, 1998. (Lond.)

BRACEGIRDLE, Andrew Paul Durnford Medical Centre, 113 Long Street, Middleton, Manchester M24 6DL Tel: 0161 643 2011 Fax: 0161 653 6570; 2 Brooksbottom Close, Ramsbottom, Bury BL0 9YP Tel: 01706 821181 Fax: 01706 821181 Email: andy@bracegirdlea.freeserve.co.uk — MB ChB 1988 Manch.; MRCGP 1995; T(GP) 1995; DRCOG 1994. (Univ. Manch.) Prev: GP/Regist. Rossendale.

BRACEGIRDLE, Mr John Pontesbury, Church Road, Bury St Edmunds IP29 5QH — MB BS Lond. 1962; FRCS Eng. 1970; MRCS Eng. LRCP Lond. 1962. (Lond. Hosp.) Cons. Orthop. Surg. W. Suff. Hosp. Bury St. Edmunds. Socs: Fell. Brit. Orthop. Assn. Prev: Sen. Regist. (Orthop.) Middlx. Hosp. & Roy. Nat. Orthop. Hosp. Lond.; Regist. Roy. Nat. Orthop. Hosp. Lond.; Resid. Surg. Off. Roy. W. Sussex Hosp. Chichester.

BRACEWELL, Mr Alan (retired) Merle Cottage, 30 Ravine Road, Canford Cliffs, Poole BH13 7HY Tel: 01202 708746 — MB BChir 1954 Camb.; BA Camb. 1951; FRCS Eng. 1961. Prev: Cons. ENT Surg. E. Dorset Hosp. Gp.

BRACEWELL, Andrew Charles Edward 17/5 Lauriston Gardens, Edinburgh EH3 9HH — MB ChB 1998 Ed.; MB ChB Ed 1998.

BRACEWELL, Brian Frederick Clarence House, Russel Road, Rhyl LL18 3BY Tel: 01745 350980 — MB ChB 1956 Liverp.

BRACEWELL, Melanie Ann 42 Stumperlowe Park Road, Fulwood, Sheffield S10 3QP — BM BS 1995 Nottm.

BRACEWELL, Melissa Anne Child Development Centre, Orchard House, Graylingwell Hospital, Chichester; 2 Exmouth Gardens, Horton Heath, Southampton SO50 7LL — MB BS 1987 Lond.; MA; FRCPCH; MRCP; DCH. Cons. Community (Paediat.) Chichester.

BRACEWELL, Robert Martyn University of Birmingham Medical School, Queen Elizabeth Neuroscience Centre, Queen Elizabeth Hospital, Edgbaston, Birmingham B15 2TH Tel: 0121 472 1311 Fax: 0121 627 2105 Email: r.m.bracewell@bham.ac.uk; Hertford College, Oxford OX1 3BW Tel: 01865 279400 Email: robert.bracewell@university-b.wmids.nhs.uk — BM BCh 1994 Oxf.; PhD Mass. Inst. Technol. 1991; MA Oxf. 1992; MRCP (UK) 1997. (Oxf.) Clin. Lect. (Neurol.) Med. Sch. Univ. Birm.; Lect. (Med.) Hertford Coll. Oxf.; Lect. (Neurophysiol.) Exeter Coll. Oxf. Socs: Soc. Neurosci.; Brit. Neurosci. Assn.; Assoc. Brit. NeUrol.s. Prev: SHO (Neurol.) Radcliffe Infirm. Oxf.; SHO (Neurol.) Nat. Hosp. Qu. Sq. Lond.; SHO Rotat. (Gen. Med.) Nuffield Dept. Clin. Med. Oxf. Radliffe Hosp.

BRACEY, Alexander Paul Netherley Health Centre, Middlemass Hey, Liverpool L27 7AF Tel: 0151 498 4054 Fax: 0151 487 5767 — MB ChB 1966 Liverp.; MFFP 1993; MRCGP 1972; DObst RCOG 1970. GP Neighbourhood Represen. for Locality Purchasing Liverp. HA; Doctor BAMS; Sen. Clin. Med. Off. (Family Plann.) & Clin. Med. Off. (Child Health) Liverp HA; Mem. Bd. S. Liverp.PCG. Socs: BMA & Brit. Soc. Med. & Dent. Hypn.; Expert Witness Inst. 1997; Liverp. Med. Inst. Prev: Ho. Surg. & Ho. Phys. Vict. Centr. Hosp. Wallasey; Ho. Surg. (Obst.) Sefton Gen. Hosp. Liverp.

BRACEY, Brendan James Ealing General Hospital, Uxbridge Road, Southall UB1 3HW Tel: 020 8967 5328 Fax: 020 8967 5797 Email: bracey@ealingas.demon.co.uk; 69 Hartham Road, London N7 9JJ — MB BS 1979 Lond.; MRCP (UK) 1984; MRCS Eng. LRCP Lond. 1979; FFA RCS Eng. 1986. (St. Bart.) Cons. (Anaesth.) Ealing Gen. Hosp. Socs: Intens. Care Soc. Prev: Sen. Regist. (Anaesth.) Roy. Free Hosp. Lond., Hosp. for Sick Childr., Gt. Ormond St.; + Hosp. for Nerv. Dis.s Qu. Sq., Harefield Hosp. Middlx.

BRACEY, Mr David John Treliske Hospital, Truro TR1 3LJ; Carnon Yard, Trolver Croft, Feock, Truro TR3 6RT Tel: 01872 865217 Fax: 01872 870090 Email: david.bracey@btinternet.com — MB ChB Birm. 1969; FRCS Eng. 1974; DA Eng. 1971. (Birm.) Cons. Orthop. Surg. Roy. Cornw. Hosp. Truro. Socs: Fell. BOA; Brit. Assn. Surg. Knee; Brit. Scoliosis Soc. Prev: Clin. Fell. Sunnybrook Med. Centre, Toronto; Sen. Regist. Robt. Jones & Agnes Hunt Orthop. Hosp. OsW.ry; Regist. (Surg.) Roy. Perth Hosp., W.. Austral.

***BRACEY, Emma Elizabeth Catherine Lewis** 3 London Road, Harrow HA1 3JJ — MB BS 1994 Lond.; BSc (Hons.) Lond. 1991, MB BS 1994.

BRACHE, Julie Anne Ruevinto, Les Jenemies, St Saviour, Jersey — MB BS 1993 Lond.

BRACHER, David Health & Safety Executive, Kiln House, Pottergate, Norwich NR2 1DA — MB ChB 1974 Sheff.; LMCC 1979; MFOM RCP Lond. 1987, AFOM 1985; MRCGP 1983; Dip IMC RCS Ed. 1991; DRCOG 1982. Med. Insp. EMAS, Health and Safety Exec. Prev: Med. Manager BP Exploration Europe Aberd.; Regional Med. Off. Midl. Zone BT Birm.; Med. Off. BNFL Sellafield.

BRACK, Michael John Tel: 01253 306966 Fax: 01253 655518; 6 Beach Avenue, Ansdell, Lytham St Annes FY3 9BD Email: brack7and 6@aol.com — MB ChB 1984 Sheff.; MD Leics. 1995; MRCP (UK) 1988; FRCP 1999. Cons. Phys. (Cardiol.) Blackpool; Clin. director Med.; Hon. Sen Lec. Socs: BCIS.

BRACKA, Mr Aivar Department of Plastic Surgery, Wordsley Hospital, Stourbridge DY8 5QX Tel: 01384 244451 Fax: 01384 244436 Email: liz.warby@dudleygoh-tr.wmids.nhs.uk; 173 Balmoral Road, Wordsley, Stourbridge DY8 5JY — MB ChB 1972 Sheff.; FRCS Eng. 1978. Cons. Plastic Surg. Wordsley Hosp. Stourbridge. Prev: Sen. Regist. (Plastic Surg.) Wordsley Hosp. Stourbridge; Regist. (Surg.) Sefton Gen. Hosp. Liverp.; Regist. (Burns & Plastic) Whiston Hosp. Prescot.

BRACKEN, Heron Anthony 27 Clifton Rise, London SE14 Tel: 020 8692 1387; 9 Hyndewood, Bampton Road, Forest Hill, London

SE23 2BJ Tel: 020 8699 9911 — MB BS 1948 Madras. (Madras) Socs: BMA.

BRACKEN, Patrick John Department of Applied Social Studies, University of Bradford, Bradford — MB BCh BAO 1982 NUI; MA NUI 1992, MD 1994; MRCPsych 1986; DPM RCPI 1986. Cons. Psychiat. Bradford Home Treatm. Serv.; Sen. Research Fell. (Applied Social Studies) Univ. Bradford. Prev: Cons. Psychiat. Astom CMHI Birm.; Staff Psychiat. Med. Foundat., Uganda.

BRACKENBURY, Mr Edward Thomas Tel: 0131 536 3693 Fax: 0131 229 0659 Email: edward.brackenbury@luht.scot.nhs; Email: edward.brackebur@luht.scot.nhs — MB ChB 1984 Manch.; BSc (Hons.) 1st Class Anat. Manch. 1981; ChM Manch. 1994; FRCS Ed. 1990; FRCS (CTh) 1998. (Univ. Manch.) Cons. (Cardiothoracic Surg.), The Roy. Infirm. of Edin. Socs: Mem., Brit. Med. Assn.; Assoc. Mem. Soc. Perfusionists; Soc. Cardiothoracic Surgs. GB & Irel. Prev: Specialist Regist. (Cardiothoracic Surg.) Trent RHA; Regist. (Cardiothoracic Surg.) King's Coll. Hosp. Lond.; Research Fell. (Oncol. & Urol.) W.. Gen. Hosp.

BRACKENRIDGE, John Denys, CBE (retired) 14 Burton Close, Boston PE21 9QW Tel: 01205 361158 — MB ChB 1948 Leeds; DObst RCOG 1952; FRCGP 1976, M 1962.

BRACKENRIDGE, Paula Hexham General Hospital, Hexham NE46 1QJ Tel: 01434 606161 Fax: 01434 607920 — MB BS 1969 Lond.; MBA Durh. 1996. Assoc. Specialist N. Region Spinal Injuries Unit Hexham.

BRACKENRIDGE, Robert David Campbell 175 Andrewes House, Barbican, London EC2Y 8BA Tel: 020 7638 5926 Fax: +44 (20) 814 3013 Email: dr_brackenridge@swissre.com; 175 Andrews House, Barbican, London EC2Y 8BA Tel: 020 7638 5926 — MB ChB 1941 Glas.; MD Glas. 1950; FRCP Glas. 1973, M 1962; FRFPS Glas. 1948. (Glas.) Consg. Med. Off. Swiss Re Life & Health. Socs: Hon. Mem. Amer. Acad. Insur. Med.; Fell. Assn. Med. Soc. Prev: Sen. Regist. (Med.) Co. Hosp. Whiston; Ho. Surg. W.. Infirm. Glas.; Squadron Ldr. RAFVR.

BRACKENRIDGE, Robert Glen (retired) 45 Leazes Park, Hexham NE46 3AX — MB ChB 1951 Ed.; FRCP Lond. 1977, M 1964; FRCP Ed. 1971, M 1956. Prev: Cons. Phys. Hexham Gen. Hosp., Roy. Vict. Infirm. Newc. Trust.

BRACKLEY, Karen Jane 50 Wolsey Road, Sunbury-on-Thames TW16 7TY Tel: 01923 780083; 12 Court Oak Road, Harborne, Birmingham B17 9TJ Tel: 0121 682 6350 — BM BS 1987 Nottm.; BMedSci Nottm. 1985; MRCOG 1992; DM Nottm. 1997. (Nottm.) Lect. (Fetal Med.) Birm. Wom. Hosp. Socs: BMA (POWAR Represen.); Brit. Matern. & Fetal Med. Soc. Prev: Research Fell. (O & G & Therap.) Nottm. Univ.; Regist. & SHO Rotat. (O & G) Trent HA.

BRACKLEY, Philip Thurman Henry 40 The Oval, Stafford ST17 4LQ — BM BS 1997 Nottm.

BRAD, Lawrence Duncan Ashley Westbourne Medical Centre, Milburn Road, Bournemouth BH4 9HJ Tel: 01202 752550 — MB BCh 1989 Wales; MRCGP 1994; DCH RCP Lond. 1993. (Univ. Wales Coll. Med.)

BRADA, Michael The Royal Marsden NHS Trust, Downs Road, Sutton SM2 5PT Tel: 020 8661 3272 Fax: 020 8661 3127 Email: mbrada@icr.ac.uk; 91 Kenilworth Avenue, Wimbledon, London SW19 7LP Tel: 020 8879 7439 Fax: 020 8286 1194 — MB ChB 1975 Bristol; 1975 MB ChB Bristol; 1972 BSc (Biochem.) Bristol; 1997 FRCP Lond.; 1978 MRCP (UK); 1984 FRCR; 1997 FRCP. Sen. Lect. & Cons. Clin. Oncol. Inst. Cancer Research & Roy. Marsden Hosp. Lond.; Hon. Cons. Nat. Hosp. for Neurol. & Neurosurg. Lond., St. Geo's & Atkinson Morley's Hosps. Lond. Socs: Pres. Europ. Assn. Neuro-oncol.; Chairm. UKCCCR Brain Tumours Gp. Prev: Lect. (Radiother. & Oncol.) Roy. Marsden Hosp. Lond.; Regist. (Haemat.) Roy. Liverp. Hosp.; Regist. (Radiother. & Oncol.) Roy. Marsden Hosp. Lond.

BRADBEER, Caroline Sarah St Thomas' Hospital, London SE1 7EH Tel: 020 7928 9292 Fax: 020 7922 8291 Email: caroline.bradbeer@gstt.sthames.nhs.uk; 37 Pagoda Avenue, Kew, Richmond TW9 2HQ Tel: 020 8948 6929 Fax: 020 8948 6929 — MB BS 1979 Lond.; FRCP Lond. 1995; MRCP (UK) 1984. (St. Thos.) Cons. Genitourin. Med. Guys & St. Thomas Hosp. Trust Lond.; Clin.Dir. (Specialist Med.) Guys & St. Thomas'. Socs: (Ex-Exec.) Brit. Soc. for Colposcopy & Cervical Path.; (Ex-Coun). Mem. Med. Soc. for Study of VD; S.E Thomas Represen. Assn. for Genito-verinary Med. (AGUM). Prev: Gp. Clin. Dir. (Clin. Servs.) Guys & St. Thos. Hosp. Trust Lond.

BRADBEER, Elizabeth Gay Stagshaw High House, Sandhoe, Hexham NE46 4NE — MB BS 1967 Newc.; DA Eng. 1969.

BRADBEER, Peter James 1 West Bucks, Bucks Cross, Bideford EX39 5DT — MB ChB 1997 Bristol.

BRADBEER, Mr Thomas Linthorn (retired) Old Vicarage, Dunsford, Exeter EX6 7AA — MB BS 1950 Lond.; FRCS Eng. 1956; DLO Eng. 1952; MRCS Eng.LRCP Lond 1949. Prev: Cons. Otolaryngol. Exeter DHA.

BRADBEER, Timothy Meirion 85 Court Lane, London SE21 7EF — BM 1992 Soton.; MRCPsych. 1997. (Southampton) Specialist Regist. (Psychiat.).

BRADBERRY, Sally Marie West Midlands Poisons Unit, City Hospital NHS Trust, Dudley Road, Birmingham B18 7QH Tel: 0121 507 5539 Fax: 0121 507 5620 — MB ChB 1990 Birm.; MB ChB (HOns.) 1990; BSc (Hons.) Birm. 1987; MRCPI 1994. Sen. Med. Off. Nat. Poisons Informat. Serv. Birm. Centre. Socs: Fell. Roy. Soc. Med.; Eur. Assn. Poisons Control Centres & Clin. Toxicol.; Amer. Acad. Clin. Toxicol.

BRADBERRY, Stanley William (retired) Pinewood Lodge, Kanes Hill, Southampton SO19 6AJ Tel: 02380 402925 — MB ChB 1962 Liverp.; DObst RCOG 1965. Med. Adviser S.ampton & S.W.Hants. HA.

BRADBROOK, Mr Richard Anthony (cons. rooms), Mount Stuart Hospital, St Vincents Road, Torquay TQ1 4UP Tel: 01803 313881; 1 Poplar Terrace, Fore St., Ipplepen, Newton Abbot TQ12 5RW Tel: 01803 813603 — MB BS 1965 Lond.; FRCS Eng. 1969; MRCS Eng. LRCP Lond. 1965. (St. Mary's) Cons. Urol.S.Devon Health Care Trust. Torbay Hosp. Torquay, Devon. Socs: Fell. Roy. Soc. Med. (Mem. Sect. Urol.); Brit. Assn. Urol Surg. Prev: Sen. Regist. (Surg.) United Bristol Hosps.; Research Fell. Welsh Nat. Sch. Med. Cardiff; Regist. Rotat. (Surg.) Sheff. Roy. Infirm.

BRADBROOKE, Jeremy Guy (retired) 1 Sunnybank, Hilperton Road, Trowbridge BA14 7JE Tel: 01225 752825 Fax: 01225 752825 Email: bradbr.isun.trow@faxvia.net — MB BS Lond. 1960; DObst RCOG 1963; MRCGP 1974; DA Eng. 1973; DCH Eng. 1968; LMCC 1971. Prev: Ho. Surg. Lond. Hosp.

BRADBROOKE, Shirley Anne X-Ray Department, Princess Grace Hospital, 42-52 Nottingham Place, London W1U 5NY Tel: 020 7908 2030 Fax: 020 7908 2275 Email: sabradbrooke@hotmail.com; 13 Thornton Place, London W1H 1FL Tel: 020 7935 7471 Fax: 020 7935 7471 — MB BS 1972 Lond.; FRCR 1977; DObst RCOG 1974. (St. Geo.) Cons. Radiol. BrE. Unit. P.ss Grace Hosp.; Cons. Radiol. Lond. Clinic, Cromwell Hosp., Harley St. Prev: Cons. Radiol. St Bart. Hosp. Lond.; Sen. Regist. (Radiol.) & Ho. Phys. St. Geo. Hosp. Lond.

BRADBURN, Brian Gregory The Old Sweet Shop, The Street, Ickham, Canterbury CT3 1QN — MB ChB 1972 Glas.; FFA RCS Eng. 1977. Cons. (Anaesth.) Kent & Canterbury Hosp. Socs: BMA; Assn. Anaesth. Gt. Brit. & Irel. Prev: Sen. Regist. Guy's Hosp.; Regist. W.. Infirm. Glas..

BRADBURN, Mr David Michael Wansbeck District General Hospital, Woodhorn Lane, Ashington NE63 9JJ — MB ChB 1984 Manch.; BSc (Hons.) Manch. 1981; MD Newc. 1993; FRCS Eng. 1988. Cons. Surg. Wansbeck Dist. Gen. Hosp. Ashington.

BRADBURN, Helen Silsden Boats, Canal Wharfe, Elliott St., Silsden, Keighley BD20 0DE — MB ChB 1998 Leeds.

BRADBURN, Jennifer Winifred 16 Ryecroft Lane, Worsley, Manchester M28 2PN — MRCS Eng. LRCP Lond. 1967. (Manch.) Regist. (Anaesth.) Univ. Hosp. W. Indies Mona, Jamaica.

BRADBURN, Joanne Claire 46 Woodhey Road, Ramsbottom, Bury BL0 9RB — BM BS 1994 Nottm.; BMedSci Nottm. 1992; MRCP (UK) 1998. (Nottingham) SHO (Med.) Qu. Med. Centre Nottm.

BRADBURN, Valerie Mary Taunton & West Somerset Trust, Family Planning & Child Health Community Services, East Reach Centre, Taunton TA1 3HQ Tel: 01823 332659 & 331121; Broom House, Pedwell Lane, Ashcott, Bridgwater TA7 9BE Tel: 01458 210622 — MB BS Lond. 1961; MFFP 1993; DObst RCOG 1963. (Roy. Free) SCMO Family Plann. & Community Child Health Taunton & Som. NHS Trust. Socs: Fac. Fam. Plann. & Reproduc. Health Care; Assoc. Mem. Inst. Psycho-Sexual Med. Prev: Clin. Med. Off. (Family Plann.) Lewisham Health Dist.; Clin. Med. Off. (Family Plann.) Bromley AHA; Surg. Lt. RN.

BRADBURY, Andrew John Paediatric Department, Wythenshawe Hospital, Southmoor Road, Manchester M23 9LT Tel: 0161 291 2268 Fax: 0161 291 5037 — MB BS 1974 Lond.; 1971 BSc Lond.; 1978 MRCP (UK); 1974 MRCS Eng. LRCP Lond.; 1976 DCH Eng.; 1998 FRCPCH. (St. Mary's) Cons. Paediat. S. Manch. Univ. Hosp. NHS Trust.

BRADBURY, Professor Andrew Walter University Department of Vascular Surgery, Lincoln House (Research Institute), Birmingham Heartlands Hospital, Bordesley Green East, Birmingham B9 555 Tel: 0121 424 1633 Fax: 0121 424 1633 Email: bradbua@heartsol.wmids.nhs.uk — MB ChB 1985 Edinburgh; BSc Ed. 1983, MD 1992, MB ChB 1985; FRCS Ed. 1992. (Edinburgh) Prof. of Vasc. Surg. Univ. of Birm.; Cons. Vasc. Surg. Birm. Heartlands Hosp. Socs: Vasc. Surgic. Soc. of Gt. Britain & Irel.; Europ. Vasc. Surgic. Soc.; Assn. of Surg.s of Gt. Britain & Irel. Prev: Sen. Lect. Univ. of Edin.; Cons. Vasc. Surg. Edin. Roy. Infirm.; Sen. Regist. (Surg.) Roy. Infirm. Edin.

BRADBURY, Anthony Newhaven Health Centre, Chapel Street, Newhaven BN9 9PW Tel: 01273 517000 Fax: 01273 515845 — MB BS 1968 Lond. (King's Coll. Hosp.)

BRADBURY, Antonia Gladys 154 Albion Road, London N16 9JS; 8 Rugby Road, Catthorpe, Lutterworth LE17 6DA — MB BS 1987 Lond.

BRADBURY, Carol Elizabeth Dept. of Genito Urinary Medicine, Royal Hallamshire Hospital, Glossop Road, Sheffield S10 2JF; 12 Chester Street, Norwich NR2 2AY Tel: 01603 617101 — MB ChB 1988 Sheff.; Dip. GU Med., Soc. Of Apothecaries, Lond. 1999; JCPTGP Aug. 1995. p/t Staff Grade Genito Urin. Med., Roy. Hallamshire Hosp., Sheff.; Locum in Gen. Pract., Sheff. Prev: SHO (Genitourin. Med. & A & E) Roy. Hallamsh. Hosp. Sheff.; SHO (Gen. Med.) Barnsley Dist. Gen. Hosp.; SHO (Oncol.) W.. Pk. Hosp. Sheff.

BRADBURY, Catherine Mary 1 Top Locks, Wheat Lane, Ormskirk L40 4BX — MB ChB 1983 Leeds.

BRADBURY, Edward Malcolm Dig Street Surgery, Dig Street, Hartington, Buxton SK17 0AQ Tel: 01298 84315 Fax: 01298 84899; Whytecote, Church St, Youlgreave, Bakewell DE45 1WL Tel: 01629 636359 — MB BS 1967 Lond.; MRCS Eng. LRCP Lond. 1967; DTM & H Liverp. 1974. (King's Coll. Hosp.) Prev: Med. Off. Save the Childr. Fund Sudan; SHO (Paediat.) St. Stephen's Hosp. Chelsea; Ho. Surg. & Ho. Phys. King's Coll. Hosp. Lond.

BRADBURY, Emma Louise 181 Beamhill Road, Burton-on-Trent DE13 9QN — MB ChB 1998 Liverp.; MB ChB Liverp 1998.

BRADBURY, Gillian Anne 45 South Grove, Sale, Manchester M33 3AT — MB ChB 1996 Birm.

BRADBURY, Mr John Anthony The Yorkshire Clinic, Bradford Road, Bingley BD16 1TW Tel: 01274 560311 Fax: 01274 551247; Lindley House, Cinder Lane, Lindley, Otley LS21 2QP Tel: 0113 284 3239 Fax: 0113 284 3239 — MB ChB 1981 Leeds; FRCS Glas. 1985; FCOphth. 1989. Cons. Ophth. Bradford Roy. Infirm.

BRADBURY, Katherine Margaret 131 Adel Lane, Leeds LS16 8BW — BM BS 1998 Nottm.; BM BS Nottm 1998.

BRADBURY, Mark Gerard 22 Bracewell Road, North Kensington, London W10 6AE — MB BS 1985 Lond.

BRADBURY, Martin Daniel 19/7 Damside, Dean Village, Edinburgh EH4 3BB — MB ChB 1995 Ed.

BRADBURY, Professor Michael William Blackburn 103 North End Road, London NW11 7TA Tel: 020 8458 5788 Email: mw.bradbury@virgin.net — BM BCh 1956 Oxf.; DM Oxf. 1962. Socs: Fell. Med. Soc. Lond.; Fell. Roy. Soc. Med.; Physiol. Soc. Prev: Prof. King's Coll. Lond.; Sen. Lect. St. Thos. Hosp. Lond.; Asst. Prof. Physiol. Univ. Calif., USA.

BRADBURY, Myles James Edward 69 Victoria Road, Harborne, Birmingham B17 0AQ — MB ChB 1996 Birm.

BRADBURY, Mr Neil 40 Conway Street, Long Eaton, Nottingham NG10 2AE — MB ChB 1985 Sheff.; FRCS Eng. 1991.

BRADBURY, Nigel James Lester Dental Surgery, Thorley Neighbourhood Centre, Villiers-Sur-Marne, Thorley, Bishop's Stortford CM23 4LG Tel: 01279 507695 Fax: 01371 870191 Email: bradburys@dial.pipex.com; 18 James Street, Oxford St, London W1H 5HN Tel: 020 7629 2164 Fax: 020 7491 8790 — MB BS 1981 Lond.; BDS Lond. 1974; LDS RCS Eng. 1975. (Lond. Hosp.) Lect. Oral Surg.; Princip. (Oral & Gen. Dent. Surg.) E. Herts. HA; Oral & Gen. Dent. Surg. Kensington & Chelsea HA & N.E Thames RHA. Prev: Lect. & SHO Oral Maxillo-Facial Surg. Lond. Hosp.

BRADBURY, Penelope Ann 6 Baytree Close, Chichester PO19 4UF — MB BCh 1994 Wales.

BRADBURY, Penelope Anne Stonecroft Medical Centre, 871 Gleadless Road, Sheffield S12 2LJ Tel: 0114 398575 Fax: 0114 265 0001 — MB ChB 1983 Dundee; DRCOG 1987.

BRADBURY, Peter Gavin Broomfield Hospital, Chelmsford CM1 7ET Tel: 01245 514099 Fax: 01245 514494; Royal London Hospital, Whitechapel, London E1 1BB Tel: 020 7377 7000 Ext: 3382 Fax: 020 7377 7008 — BM BCh Oxf. 1973; MA Oxf. 1973; FRCP Lond. 1994; MRCP (UK) 1976; MRCS Eng. LRCP Lond. 1972. Cons. Neurol. Broomfield Hosp. Chelmsford & Roy. Hosps. Lond.; Cons. NeUrol., Harley St. Neurol. Clinic, Harley St., Lond. W1G 6AU Tel: 020 7486 3760, Fax: 020 7486 4601.

BRADBURY, Philippa 5 Nelson Street, Edinburgh EH3 6LF — MB ChB 1997 Ed.

BRADBURY, Rosemary Ann Commonside Farm, North Lane, Cawthorne, Barnsley S75 4AQ Tel: 01226 765796 — MB BS 1969 Newc. Med. Off. Family Plann. Barnsley HA. Socs: Inst. Psycho-Sexual Med. Prev: Med. Off. Family Plann. Assn.; Ho. Phys. & Ho. Surg. Kettering Gen. Hosp.

BRADBURY, Samantha Lara 5 Thornham Close, Bury BL8 1HH — BM BS 1996 Nottm.

BRADBURY, Susan Elizabeth Garbutt's Lane, Hutton Rudby, Yarm TS15 0DN — MB ChB 1980 Dundee.

BRADBURY, Susan Mary Orchard Surgery, Knypersley Road, Norton-in-the-Moors, Stoke-on-Trent ST6 8HY Tel: 01782 534241 Fax: 01782 541068; 2 Oakville Avenue, Burslem, Stoke-on-Trent ST6 7DY Tel: 01782 818541 — MB ChB 1980 Liverp.; DRCOG 1983.

BRADBURY, Victor Douglas The Surgery, 8 Shenfield Road, Brentwood CM15 8AB Tel: 01277 218393 Fax: 01277 201017 — MRCS Eng. LRCP Lond. 1966. (St. Mary's) Med. Off. Brentwood Sch. Prev: Med. Off. P.ss Margt. Hosp. Nassau, Bahamas.

BRADBY, Geoffrey Vernon Hugh 91 Knightlow Road, Harborne, Birmingham B17 8PX — MB BS 1971 Lond.; FRCP Lond. 1989; MRCP (UK) 1974; MRCS Eng. LRCP Lond. 1971. (Westm.) Cons. Phys. Sandwell Healthcare NHS Trust. Socs: Brit. Soc. Gastroenterol. Prev: Sen. Regist. (Med.) Qu. Eliz. Hosp. Birm.; Research Fell. Dept. Experim. Path. Univ. Birm.

BRADDING, Peter Department of Respiratory Medicine, Glenfield Hospital, Groby Road, Leicester LE3 9QP Tel: 0116 287 1471; 4 Grebe Close, Barrow upon Soar, Loughborough LE12 8YB — BM 1985 Soton.; DM Soton. 1995; MRCP (UK) 1988.

BRADDOCK, Alan 9 Wallhill Cottages, Dobcross, Oldham OL3 5BN Tel: 01457 875322 — MB ChB 1948 Manch. (Manch.) Socs: Life Fell. Manch. Med. Soc.; Oldham Med. Soc. Prev: Occpat. Health Phys. Oldham HA; Ho. Surg. Manch. Roy. Infirm. & Salford Roy. Hosp.; Demonst. (Anat.) Dept. Univ. Manch.

BRADDOCK, Lesley 8 Coppice Drive, Oswestry SY11 1EZ — MB BCh 1998 Belf.; MB BCh Belf 1998.

BRADE, David Alexander The Health Centre, Withnell, Chorley PR6 0DB Tel: 01254 830311 — MRCS Eng. LRCP Lond. 1964. (Manch.) Prev: Clin. Asst. (Dermat.) Chorley & Dist. Hosp.; Ho. Surg. Preston Roy. Infirm.; Ho. Phys. Sharoe Green Hosp. Fulwood.

BRADEY, Nicholas 12 Broadmeadows, Darlington DL3 8SP — MB BS 1980 Lond.; BSc. Lond. (Pharmacol.) 1977; MRCP (UK) 1983; FRCR 1987. (Univ. Coll. Hosp.) Cons. Neuroradiol. Middlesbrough Gen. Hosp. Socs: Roy. Coll. Radiol.; Assoc. Mem. Brit. Soc. Neuroradiol. Prev: Sen. Regist. (Neuroradiol.) Leeds Gen. Infirm.; Sen. Regist. & Regist. (Diag. Radiol.) Manch. Roy. Infirm.; SHO (Gen. Med.) Hope Hosp. Manch.

BRADFIELD, Alfred Maxwell (retired) Treacle Cottage, Barwick, Yeovil BA22 9TB Tel: 01935 429534 — MB ChB N.Z. 1948; MRCP Lond. 1956; FRCPsych. 1982, M 1973; DPM Eng. 1957. Prev: Cons. Psychiat. Yeovil Dist. Hosp. & Tone Vale Hosp. Taunton.

BRADFIELD, Professor John Walter Bradfield (retired) Department of Pathology, Bristol Royal Infirmary, Marlborough St., Bristol BS2 8HW Tel: 0117 928 2586 Fax: 0117 929 2440 Email: john.bradfield@bristol.ac.uk — BM BCh Oxf. 1963; PhD Lond. 1971; FRCPath 1987, M 1975. Prev: Prof. Histopath. Univ. Bristol & Hon. Cons. Histopath. United Bristol Healthcare NHS Trust.

BRADFIELD, Paula Caroline 39 Lower Redland Road, Bristol BS6 6TB Tel: 0117 973 8837 Fax: 0117 973 8837 — MB BS Lond. 1964. (St. Mary's)

BRADFIELD, Richard Maitland 111 Wirksworth Road, Duffield, Derby DE56 4GY — MRCS Eng. LRCP Lond. 1959.

BRADFIELD, Mr William John Dickson, OBE, MC, TD (retired) Barn Cottage, Fisherton De La Mere, Warminster BA12 0PZ Tel: 01985 248232 — MB BS 1950 Lond.; MB BS (Hons.) Lond. 1950; FRCS Eng. 1953. Med. Adviser Brit. Commonw. Ex-Serv. League; Med Adviser Med. Foundat. for the c/o the Victims of Torture; Trustee Brit. Red Cross. Prev: Res. Asst. Surg., Sen. Regist. (Surg.) & Sen. Cas. Off. St. Thos. Hosp. Lond.

BRADFIELD STOWELL, Philip 16 Milner Street, London SW3 2PU Tel: 020 7584 2108; 5 Cornish Place, Aspley Qld. 4034, Australia Tel: 00 61 73 8631446 Fax: 00 61 73 3563255 Email: pbdoc@compuserve.com — MB BS 1977 Lond. (St. Thos.) Socs: Fell. Austral. Coll. Nutrit. & Environm. Med. Prev: Ho. Off. (Surg.) Derby City Hosp.; Ho. Phys. St. Luke's Hosp. Guildford; Med. Off. Breakspear Hosp. Abbotts Langley.

BRADFORD, Adam Timothy 49 Lyonsdown Avenue, New Barnet, Barnet EN5 1DX — MB BS 1984 Lond.; MRCGP 1989; DRCOG 1989. GP Walworth. Prev: Trainee GP Hampstead; SHO (Paediat.) Mayday Hosp. Croydon.; SHO (O & G) Whittington Hosp. Lond.

BRADFORD, Alfred Norman Beattie (retired) Holt House, Winchester Road, Chilworth, Southampton SO16 7LH Tel: 02380 769848 — MB BCh BAO 1949 Belf. Med. Off. English Golf Union. Prev: GP Soton.

BRADFORD, Andrew Peter James 126 Northfield Road, Kingsnorton, Birmingham B30 1DX — MB ChB 1994 Dundee.

BRADFORD, Ann Newall (retired) Cedarwood, 105 Highgate Lane, Lepton, Huddersfield HD8 0HQ Tel: 01484 605179 — MB BS 1953 Lond.; FRCGP 1982, M 1963; LMSSA Lond. 1952. Med. Mem. Appeal Serv. Panel; Med. Assessor Appeals Serv. Panel. Prev: Med. Off. Bd.ing Panel DHSS.

BRADFORD, Christine Anne 21 Polson Drive, Johnstone PA5 8RU — MB ChB 1989 Glas.

BRADFORD, Claire Rosalind 72 Fern Avenue, Jesmond, Newcastle upon Tyne NE2 2QY — BM BS 1984 Nottm.; BM BS Nottm. l984.

BRADFORD, David Cordley (retired) 211 Barnwood Road, Gloucester GL4 3HS Tel: 01452 617297 — MB BChir Camb. 1947; MRCS Eng. LRCP Lond. 1947.

BRADFORD, David Edward (retired) 40 Bolton Avenue, Richmond DL10 4BA — MB ChB 1957 Sheff.; MSc (Health Admin.) Hull 1983; FRCP Ed. 1976, M 1965; DTM & H Eng. 1960.

BRADFORD, Elizabeth Mary Whitehead (retired) 84 Crawford Road, Milngavie, Glasgow G62 7LF Tel: 0141 956 2308 Fax: 0141 956 2308 Email: bettybradford@beeb.net — MB ChB 1959 Ed.; FFA RCS Eng. 1966; DA Eng. 1963; DObst RCOG 1961. Prev: Cons. Anaesth. Roy. Infirm. Glas.

BRADFORD, Henry William Shrublands, Fornham All Saints, Bury St Edmunds IP28 6LE Tel: 01284 754690 — MRCS Eng. LRCP Lond. 1938; DCH Eng. 1941. (Middlx.) Police Surg. W. Suff. Constab. Socs: Diabetic Assn. & Police Surgs. Assn. Gt. Brit. Prev: Med. Regist. Addenbrooke's Hosp. Camb.; Res. Med. Off. Belgrave Hosp. Childr.; Med. Off. RAFVR.

BRADFORD, Hugh Russell Caen Health Centre, Braunton EX33 1LR Tel: 01271 812005 Fax: 01271 814768; Sharlands House, Sharlands Lane, Braunton EX33 1AY Tel: 01271 815797 — MB BS 1987 Lond.; DA (UK) 1991. (Lond. Hosp. Med. Coll.) Prev: Clin. Asst. (A & E) N. Devon Dist. Hosp. Barnstaple; Trainee GP/SHO N. Devon Dist. Hosp. Barnstaple; SHO (Anaesth.) Roy. Sussex Co. Hosp. Brighton.

BRADFORD, James Alistair 3 Aldene Court, Chilwell, Beeston, Nottingham NG9 5BS — LMSSA 1955 Lond. (Oxf. & Roy. Free) Exam. Off. DHSS. Prev: Clin. Asst. ENT Surg. Scunthorpe Gen. Hosp.; Div. Surg. St. John Ambul. Brig; SHO Gen. Surg. W. Hill Hosp. Dartford.

BRADFORD, Jane Marie 9 Bradshaw Hall Drive, Bradshaw, Bolton BL2 4NY — MB ChB 1993 Liverp.

BRADFORD, Paul (retired) 12 Ashwood Grove, Horbury, Wakefield WF4 5HY Tel: 01924 372596 — MB ChB Leeds 1952.

BRADFORD, Phoebe (retired) Orchard House, Castleton, Whitby YO21 2HA Tel: 01287 660380 — MRCS Eng. LRCP Lond. 1938; DCH RCP Lond. 1949; DPH Eng. 1946. Prev: Ho. Phys. Qu. Hosp. Childr. Hackney.

BRADFORD, Mr Robert The Royal Free Hospital, Pond St., Hampstead, London NW3; 47 Grand Avenue, London N10 3BS — MB BS 1979 Lond.; BSc Lond. 1976, MD 1988; FRCS Eng. 1985. (Univ. Coll. Hosp.) Cons. Neurosurg. & Sen. Lect. Roy. Free Hampstead Trust; Hon. Cons. Nat. Hosp. Neurol. & Neurosurg. & Roy. Nat. Throat, Nose & Ear Hosp.; Hon. Cons. Neuosurg. Roy. Nat. Orthop. Hosp. Trust Stanmore; Advanced Trauma Life Support Instruc. RCS; Mem. MRC Brain Tumor Working Party; Mem. Brit. Spinal Injuries Comm. Socs: Fell. Roy. Soc. Med. (Counc. Mem. Sect. Neurol.). Prev: Sen. Regist. Nat. Hosp. Neurol. & Neurosurg. Lond.; Regist. (Surg.) Univ. Coll. Hosp. Lond.

BRADFORD, Susan Lesley Gleadless Medical Centre, 636 Gleadless Road, Sheffield S14 1PQ Tel: 0114 239 6475 Fax: 0114 264 2277; 36 Moorside, Blackbrook Road, Fulwood, Sheffield S10 LLN Tel: 0114 230 4201 — MB ChB 1978 Sheff.; MRCGP 1982; MRCP (UK) 1984.; DRCOG 1981. GP Princip.; GP Trainer; GPCA Migraine Clinic Roy. Hallamshire Hosp. Sheff. Socs: BMA; RCGP; Migraine in Primary Care Assn. (Spokesperson). Prev: Regist. (Geriat./Gen. Med.) Nether Edge Hosp. Sheff.

BRADFORD, William Paterson (retired) St Merryn, Higher Park Road, Braunton EX33 2LG Tel: 01271 813805 Fax: 01271 812097 Email: willieb2784@breathmail.net — MB ChB 1963 Ed.; FRCOG 1983, M 1970, DObst 1966. Prev: Cons. O & G N. Devon Dist. Hosp. Barnstaple.

BRADGATE, Mark Geoffrey Department of Pathology, Birch Hill Hospital, Rochdale OL12 9QB Tel: 01706 517300 Ext: 5830 Fax: 01706 517295 — MB BS 1977 Lond.; BSc (Hons.) Physiol. Lond. 1973; FRCPath 1996, M 1986. (St. Thos.) Cons. Histopath. Rochdale Healthcare NHS Trust. Socs: Fell. Roy. Soc. Med.; Assn. Clin. Path.; Internat. Acad. Path. (Brit. Div.). Prev: Sen. Regist. & Regist. (Histopath.) W. Midl. RHA; SHO (Path.) Leicester AHA.

BRADING, Louise Sarah Alma Road Surgery, 68 Alma Road, Portswood, Southampton SO14 6UX Tel: 023 8067 2666 Fax: 023 8055 0972 — MB ChB 1988 Liverp.

BRADING, Lynn Carol Crossroads Surgery, 478 Cricklade Road, Swindon SN2 7BG Tel: 01793 725113 Fax: 01793 701205; 3 School Row, Haydon Wick, Swindon SN25 1JQ Tel: 01793 729155 — MB BS 1985 Lond.; BSc Leeds 1980; MRCGP 1989; DCH RCP Lond. 1987; DRCOG 1987. (Char. Cross) Paediat. Clin. Asst. P.ss Margt. Hosp. Swindon. Prev: SHO (Obst., Paediat., Geriat. & Psych.) Swindon HA.

BRADISH, Mr Christopher Frederick Royal Orthopaedic Hospital, Northfield, Birmingham B31 2AP Tel: 0121 685 4000 Fax: 0121 454 1594; 22 Westfield Road, Edgbaston, Birmingham B15 3QG Tel: 0121 456 1696 Fax: 0121 454 1594 Email: bradish@dircon.co.uk — MB BS 1977 Lond.; MA Oxf. 1977; FRCS Eng. 1981; MRCS Eng. LRCP Lond. 1977. (King's Coll. Hosp.) Cons. Orthop. Surg. Roy. Orthop. Hosp. & Childr. Hosp. Birm. Socs: Brit. Orthop. Assn.; Eur. Paediat. Orthop. Soc.; Pres. Brit. Limb Reconstruction Soc. Prev: Sen. Regist. Rotat. (Orthop.) St. Bart. Hosp. Lond.

BRADLAW, Sir Robert Vivian, CBE The Manse, Stoke Goldington, Newport Pagnell MK16 Tel: 01903 58281 — MRCS Eng. LRCP Lond. 1928; DDSc Melbourne 1950; Hon. Doctorate Univ. Meshed 1970 & Montreal 1952; FACD 1968; FRACD 1970; MDS Durh. 1948; FRCS Eng. 1949; FDS RCS Eng. 1947, Ed. 1949 & Irel. 1965, RCPS; Glas. 1967; DCL Newc. 1965; LLD Belf. 1965, Birm. 1979; DSc Malta 1965, Boston 1969, Leeds 1979. (Guy's) Chev. de la Sante Publique (France); Hon. Prof. Oral Path. RCS; Emerit. Prof. Oral Med. Univ. Lond. Socs: Hon. Fell. Roy. Soc. Med.

BRADLEY, Alastair Russell Tramways Medical Centre, 54 Holme Lane, Sheffield S6 4JQ Tel: 0114 234 3418 Fax: 0114 285 5958 — MB ChB 1990 Sheff.

BRADLEY, Alison Elizabeth The Surgery, 54 Thorne Road, Doncaster DN1 2JP Tel: 01302 361222 — BM BS 1985 Nottm.; BMedSci 1983; MRCGP 1989; DRCOG 1988. GP Doncaster.

BRADLEY, Alison Jane Radiology Department, Wythenshave Hospital, Southmoor Rd, Manchester M23 9LT Tel: 0161 291 6224 Fax: 0161 291 6201; 14 Kentmere Close, Gatley, Cheadle SK8 4RD — MB ChB Sheff. 1988; MRCP (UK) 1991; FRCR 1995. Cons. Radiol. Wythenshave Hosp., S.moor Rd. Wythenshave Manch. Prev: Sen. Regist. Rotat. (Radiol.) Manch.; Regist. Rotat. (Radiol.) Manch.; SHO (Gen. Med. & Diabetes) Roy. Hallamsh. Hosp. Sheff.

BRADLEY, Annette Stafford Place Surgery, 4 Stafford Place, Weston Super Mare BS23 2QZ Tel: 01934 415212 Fax: 01934 612463 — MB ChB 1974 Sheff.

BRADLEY, Anthony Michael Castelstead, Pinetree Avenue, Boston Spa, Wetherby LS23 6HA Tel: 01937 845708 — MRCS Eng. LRCP Lond. 1969. Med. Off. DSS Leeds. Prev: Sen. Med. Off. HM Prison Wakefield.

BRADLEY, Antonia Christianne Ty-Cwm, Nant-Y-Groes, Aberdar Road, Aberdare CF44 0NL — MB BCh 1996 Wales.

BRADLEY, Professor Benjamin Arthur de Burgh University Bristol Department Transplant Sciences, Southmead Health Services,, Westbury on Trym, Bristol BS10 5NB Tel: 0117 959 5340 Fax: 0117 0117 9506277 Email: ben.bradley@bris.ac.uk; East Barn, The Pound, Lower Almondsbury, Bristol BS32 4EF Tel: 01454 201077 Fax: 01454 201077 Email: ben.bradley@bris.ac.uk — MB ChB 1965 Birm.; PhD Birm. 1970, MSc 1967; FRCPath 1987, M 1974; MA Camb. 1974; FRCP 1999. (Birm.) Dir. Univ. Bristol Dept. Transpl. Sci.; Prof. Univ. Bristol Fac. Med.; Chairm. Edit. Bd. Europ. Jl. Immogenetics. Socs: Transpl. Soc.; (Ex-Pres.) Euro. Foundn. For Immunogenetics.; (Ex-Pres.) Brit. Soc. Histocompatability & Immunogenetics. Prev: Dir. UK Transpl. Serv.; Sen. Lect. (Immunohaematol.) Univ. Leiden, Netherlands; Asst. Dir. of Research Camb. Univ.

BRADLEY, Bernard Leo 35 Hayling Road, Sale M33 6GN — MB BCh BAO 1980 Dub.; MD Dub. 1994; MRCPI 1983. (T.C. Dublin) Cons. Phys. (Gen. & Respirat. Med.) Roy. Bolton NHS Trust. Prev: Sen. Regist. (Thoracic & Gen. Med.) Wythenshawe Hosp. & N. Manch. Gen.Hosp.; Clin. Research Fell. Nat. Heart & Lung Inst. Lond.; Regist. Respirat. Med. Serv. W. Edin.

BRADLEY, Caroline Louise — MB BS 1985 Lond.; MRCP (UK) 1988; MRCPsych 1994; Dip. Forensic.Psychiatry. 1998. Cons. Forens. Psychiat., Avon & Wilts. Ment. Health Partnership NHS Trust. Prev: Research.Train.Fell.Wellcome.Health.Servs.Oxf.Uni.; Cons. Forens. Psychiat. Ravenswood Ho. Wickham.

BRADLEY, Catherine Margaret The Surgery, Brig Royd, Ripponden, Sowerby Bridge HX6 4AN Tel: 01422 822209; Longley Farm, Longley Lane, Norland, Sowerby Bridge HX6 3SA — MB ChB 1981 Dundee; MRCGP 1988; DA RCS Eng. 1983. Princip. GP Halifax.

BRADLEY, Christine Jane The Surgery, 221 Whaddon Way, Bletchley, Milton Keynes MK3 7EA Tel: 01908 373058 Fax: 01908 630076; 18 Hamilton Lane, Bletchley, Milton Keynes MK3 5LU — BM Soton. 1983; MRCGP 1987; DRCOG 1986. Prev: Trainee GP I. of Wight VTS; Ho. Phys. Roy. United Hosp. Bath; Ho. Surg. St. Mary's Hosp. Portsmouth.

BRADLEY, Christopher Sunnybank House Medical Centre, 506 Huddersfield Road, Towngate, Wyke, Bradford BD12 9NG Tel: 01274 424111 Fax: 01274 691256; Norton House, Sheriff Lane, Bingley BD16 3EN — MB ChB 1982 Glas.; Election to FRCP 1999; MSc Glas. 1989, MD 1992; MRCP (UK) 1985; BSc. Glas. 1979. Cons. Med. Oncol. Bradford Roy. Infirm.; Hon. Sen. Lect. Univ. Bradford. Prev: Clin. Research Fell. (Med. Oncol.) Univ. Glas.; Sen. Regist. (Med. Oncol.) St. Jas. Univ. Hosp. Leeds.

BRADLEY, Professor David John Ross Institute of Tropical Hygiene, London School of Hygiene & Tropical Medicine, Keppel St., London WC1E 7HT Tel: 020 7927 2216 Fax: 020 7580 9075 Email: dbradley@lshtm.ac.uk — MB BChir 1961 Camb.; Hon. FCI WEM 1981; MA Oxf. 1970, DM 1972; MA Camb. 1961; FRCP Lond. 1985; FFPHM RCP (UK) 1979, M 1976; FRCPath 1981, M 1972; FIBiol. (Univ. Coll. Hosp.) Prof. Trop. Hyg. Univ. Lond. & Dir. Ross Inst.; Edr. Trop. Med. & Internat. Health; Hon. Cons. Phys. Bloomsbury HA; Hon. Specialist Community Med. N. Thames RHA, Kensington & Chelsea HA; Research Adviser Lond. Sch. Hyg. & Trop. Med.; Co-Dir. Malaria Refer. Lab. PHLS; Mem. WHO Expert Comm.; Chairm. Ext. Review Comm. Swiss Trop. Inst. etc. Socs: Fell Roy. Soc. Trop. Med. & Hyg. Prev: Trop. Research Fell. The Roy. Soc. & Exeter Coll. Oxf.; Sen. Lect. (Preven. Med.) Makerere Med. Sch. Kampala, Uganda; Med. Research Off. Ross Inst. Trop. Hyg. Bilharzia Unit Mwanza, Tanzania.

BRADLEY, Debra Susan Department of Child Psychiatry, Royal Manchester Children's Hospital, Pendlebury, Manchester M27 4HA Tel: 0161 727 2409 — MB BS 1984 Lond.; MRCPsych 1997; DCH 1988.

BRADLEY, Edith Joan (retired) St Peter's Cottage, Lower Rowe, Holt, Wimborne BH21 7DZ Tel: 01202 882025 — MB BS 1958 Lond.; DObst RCOG 1964. Prev: Resid. in Internal Med. Duval Med. Center, Jacksonville, U.S.A.

BRADLEY, Elizabeth Crieff Health Centre, King Street, Crieff PH7 3SA Tel: 01764 652456 Fax: 01764 655756; Willoughby House, Gordon Road, Crieff PH7 4BL Tel: 01764 652035 — MB ChB 1974 Glas.; MFHom 1989. Hon. Med. Off. Crieff Dist. Hosp. & Glenalmond Coll.

BRADLEY, Elizabeth Ann 99 Reyarts Park Road, London NW1 8UR Tel: 0207 722 0038 Fax: 0207 586 4395 — MB BS 1988 Lond.; MRCOG 1994. Regist. (O & G) St. Thoms. Hosp. Lond.; GP Partner. Prev: Ho. Off. (Med.) Roy. United Hosp. Bath; Ho. Off. (Surg.) Countess of Chester Hosp.; SHO O & G, Barts Hosp.

BRADLEY, Elizabeth Frances Stanfield House, 86 Hampstead High St., London NW3 1RE — MB BS 1969 Lond.; MRCS Eng. LRCP Lond. 1969; MSc 1972 Lond.; FRCPsych 1976; DIH Eng. 1972. Cons. Child Psychiat. Tavistock Clinic. Socs: Brit. Psychoanal Soc. Prev: Cons. Child Psychiat. Croydon Child Guid. Clinic.

BRADLEY, Elizabeth Margaret Terrington Surgery, Church Lane, Terrington, York YO60 6PS Tel: 01653 648260 Fax: 01653 648267 Email: terrinton.surg@gp-b82619.nhs.uk — MB ChB 1976 Dundee; Pre Hospital Emergency Care.

BRADLEY, Gillian Elmwood Health Centre, Huddersfield Road, Holmfirth, Huddersfield HD9 3TR Tel: 01484 681777 Fax: 01484 689603; The Stables, Marble Hall, Lamma Wells Road, Holmfrith, Huddersfield HD9 2SN Tel: 01484 682499 — MB ChB 1984 Leeds; MRCGP 1988; DRCOG 1987.

BRADLEY, Gillian Clare 10 Chalfont Close, Appleton, Warrington WA4 5JT — MB ChB 1996 Manch.

BRADLEY, Graham William William Harvey Hospital, Ashford TN24 0L2 Tel: 01233 616266; Brook House, The Street, Brook, Ashford TN25 5PF Email: gwb@grahambradley.supanet.com — MB ChB 1967 Manchester; MB ChB 1967; BSc 1964; PhD 1971 Bristol; MRCP (UK) 1973; FRCP Lond. 1989. Socs: Thorasic Soc. Prev: Sen. Regist. Soton. & Portsmouth Rotat.; Med. Research Fell. (MRC) Midhurst Med. Research Inst.; Research Fell. (Wellcome) Nobel Inst. for Neurophysiol. Karalinska Inst. Stockholm.

BRADLEY, Helen Patricia Stenton Farm, High St., Laughton on le Morthen, Sheffield S25 1YF — MB ChB 1982 Liverp.; MRCGP 1986; DRCOG 1985.

BRADLEY, Henry John (retired) Lyndon, Liverpool Road, Buckley CH7 3LH Tel: 01244 549621 — MRCS Eng. LRCP Lond. 1955.

BRADLEY, Ian Cuthbert Teule Hospital, Private Bag, Muheza, Tanga, Tanzania; Hill Farm House, Pontesford, Shrewsbury SY5 0UH Tel: 01743 790244 — MB BS 1960 Durh. (Newc.) Med. Off. Primary Health Care, Muheza Dist. Tanzania. Prev: GP Pontesbury, Shrews; Med. Off. African Manganese Co. Ghana; Med. Off. Unilever Nigeria & Cameroon.

BRADLEY, James Anthony Gerard 10 Duncoole Park, North Circular Road, Belfast BT15 — MB BCh BAO 1976 NUI; BSc (Econ) Belf. 1966. (Cork) GP Antrim Health Centre; Med. Off. Med. Ref. Serv. Royston Hse. Belf. Prev: SHO (Obst. & Gyn, Surg. & Cas.) Route Hosp. Ballymoney; SHO (Med.) White Abbey Hosp. Newton Abbey.

BRADLEY, Jane Clare Barnet Hospital, Wellhouse Lane, Barnet EN5 3JD Fax: 020 8732 6825 — MB ChB 1968 Birm.; BSc Open 1995; FRCP Lond. 1988; MRCP (UK) 1973; T(M) 1991. Cons. Phys. Respiration Med., Barnes & Chase Farms Hosp. NHS Trust. Prev: Sen. Regist. St. Mary's Hosp. Lond.; Regist. (Med.) St. Thos. Hosp. Lond.; Resid. Med. Off. Nat. Heart Hosp. Lond.

BRADLEY, Jean Johnstone 85 Sefton Gardens, Aughton, Ormskirk L39 6RY Tel: 01695 422286 — MB ChB 1961 Liverp.; DObst RCOG 1963. (Liverp.)

BRADLEY, Jean Margaret (retired) East Coker, Hook Lane, Aldingbourne, Chichester PO20 6SR Tel: 01243 543965 Email: brad.saff@virgin.net — MB BS 1955 Lond.; FRCPath 1979, M 1967. Prev: Sen. Lect. (Microbiol.) Roy. Free. Hosp. Sch. Lond.

BRADLEY, Jeremy Albrighton Medical Practice, Shaw Lane, Albrighton, Wolverhampton WV7 3DT; Holly Tree Cottage, Tong, Shifnal TF11 8PW Tel: 01902 375179 — MB ChB 1988 Birm.; MRCGP 1993; DRCOG 1993. Prev: Trainee GP Alexandra Hosp. Redditch VTS; SHO (Dermat.) Birm. Skin Hosp.

BRADLEY, Jeremy Mark Bradley Shaw Health Centre, Crookesbroom Lane, Hatfield, Doncaster DN7 6JN Tel: 01302 841373; Doubloon, Top Lane, Kirk Bramwith, Doncaster DN7 5SW — MB ChB 1985 Birm.; MRCGP 1989.

BRADLEY, Professor John Andrew Box 202, Level E9, Department Surgery, Addenbrookes NHS Trust, Hills Road, Cambridge CB2 2QQ Tel: 01223 762001 Fax: 01223 762523 Email: jab52@cam.ac.uk — MB ChB 1975 Leeds; PhD Glas. 1982; FRCS Glas. 1979. Prof. Surg., Univ. Camb.; Hon. Cons. Addenbrooke's Hosp. Camb. Socs: Fell.of the Acad. of Med Sci.s; Brit. Transpl. Soc. (Pres. 1999-2002). Prev: Prof. Surg. & Immunol. W.. Infirm. Glas.; Cons. Surg. & Hon. Prof. Surg. W.. Infirm. Glas.; Lect. (Surg.) W.. Infirm. Glas.

BRADLEY, Mr John Anthony Colchester District General Hospital, Turner Road, Colchester CO4 5JL; The Olde House, Mersea Road, Peldon, Colchester CO5 7QE — MB ChB 1977 Bristol; FRCS Eng. 1982. Cons. Orthop. Surg. Colchester Dist. Gen. Hosp. Socs: Fell. Roy. Coll. Surg.s of Eng.; Fell. of the Brit. Orthopaedic Assn.; Fell. of the Roy. Soc. of Med.

BRADLEY, Mr John Graham The Manse, Scalby, Scarborough YO13 0QS Tel: 01723 375726 Fax: 01723 375903 — MB ChB 1964 Ed.; FRCS Ed. 1968; FRCS 1998 Lond. Cons. Orthop. Surg. ScarBoro. & NE Health Care Trust. Socs: Fell. BOA; BMA; Brit. Hip Soc. Prev: Sen. Regist. (Orthop.) Sheff. AHA (T); Regist. (Orthop.) W.. Infirm. Glas.; Demonst. (Anat.) Univ. Edin.

BRADLEY, John Jennery 3 Park House, 56 Hendon Lane, London N3 1TT Tel: 020 8349 2458 — MB BS 1953 Lond.; FRCP Lond. 1973, M 1959; MRCS Eng. LRCP Lond. 1953; FRCPsych 1973, M 1972; DPM Eng. 1957. (Middlx.) Emerit. Cons. Psychiat. Camden & Islington Community Health Servs. NHS Trust; Hon. Sen. Lect. UCL. Prev: Assoc. Dir. Psychiat. Bergen Pines Hosp. Paramus, USA; Sen. Regist. (Psychol. Med.) St. Thos. Hosp. Lond.; Ho. Phys. Profess. Med. Unit Middlx. Hosp.

BRADLEY, John Patrick 13 Ingle Head, Fulwood, Preston PR2 3NS Tel: 01772 774550 — MB BCh BAO Belf. 1956, DPH 1961; DMRD Eng. 1971; DCH RCPS Glas. 1964. (Belf.) Cons. (Radiodiagn.) Preston Health Dist. Prev: Sen. Regist. (Radiodiag.) Manch. Roy. Infirm.; Regist. (Radiodiagn.) United Bristol Hosps.

BRADLEY, John Richard Department of Medicine, Addenbrooke's Hospital, Cambridge CB2 2QQ Tel: 01223 217828 — BM BS 1981 Nottm.; DM Nottm. 1990, BMedSci 1979, BM BS 1981; MRCP (UK) 1984; FRCP 1997; MA (Cantab) 2000. Cons. Phys. and Nephrologist. Prev: Lect. & Sen. Regist. (Gen. & Renal Med.) Addenbrooke's Hosp. Camb.; Vis. Research Assoc. Harvard Med. Sch.; Research Schol. Molecular Cardiobiol. Prog. Yale Univ.

BRADLEY, Mr John William Paulton (retired) 32 Radnor Mews, London W2 2SA Tel: 020 7706 9491 Fax: 020 7706 2193 — BM BCh Oxf. 1952; FRCS Eng. 1960. Prev: Cons. Surg. Hillingdon, Mt. Vernon Hosp. & Harefield Hosps.

BRADLEY, Joseph Nicholas Caer Ffynnon Surgery, Caer Ffynnon, Springfield Street, Dolgellau LL40 1LY Tel: 01341 422431 Fax: 01341 423717 — MB ChB 1978 Liverp.; MRCGP 1982; DRCOG 1981.

BRADLEY, Julian Andre The Surgery, 37 Park Road, Teddington TW11 0AU Tel: 020 8977 5481 Fax: 020 8977 7882; 4 Sudbrook Gardens, Petersham, Richmond TW10 7DD Tel: 020 8940 9377 — MB BS 1973 Lond.; FRCP 2001; MRCP (UK) 1977; MRCS Eng. LRCP Lond. 1973; MRCGP 1980; DRCOG 1978. (Westm.) GP Course Organiser W. Middlx.; Med. Director & Clin. Governance, LEAD Teddington, Twickenham, Hampton PCT. Prev: Regist. (Med.) W. Middlx. Hosp.; SHO (Obst.) W. Middlx. Hosp. Lond.; Ho. Phys. & Ho. Surg. W.m. Hosp. Lond.

BRADLEY, Julian Henry The Stonedean Practice, Stony Stratford Health Centre, Milton Keynes MK11 1YA Tel: 01908 261155; Caladan, 4 Tudor Gardens, Stony Stratford, Milton Keynes MK11 1HX Tel: 01908 261626 — MB ChB 1979 Bristol; FRCGP 1993, M 1983; DRCOG 1982. Tutor (Gen. Pract.) Milton Keynes; GP Tutor RAF. Socs: Fell. Roy. Soc. Med. Prev: Trainee GP Som. VTS; Ho. Phys. Bristol Roy. Infirm.; Ho. Surg. S.mead Hosp. Bristol.

BRADLEY, Karen Elizabeth 53 Sandygate Park, Sheffield S10 5TZ — MB ChB 1990 Sheff.

BRADLEY, Karen Jane The Pine House, Goodley Stock, Crockham Hill, Edenbridge TN8 6TA — MB BS 1996 Lond.; BSc 1993. (Char. Cross & Westm.) SHO (Gen. Med.), Oxf. Radcliffe NHS Trust. Prev: SHO (Gen. Med.) Kingston & Dist. NHS Trust; (A & E Med.) St Mary's Hosp. Lond.; Ho. Off. Posts.

BRADLEY, Katharine Farquharson (retired) Crantock, Church Lane, Wexham, Slough SL3 6LE Tel: 01753 524216 — MB ChB St. And. 1948; T(Psychiat.) 1990; DPM Eng. 1973. Prev: Cons. Psychiat. Windsor.

BRADLEY, Kevin Martin 40 Castle Road, Tipton DY4 8DZ — BM BCh 1990 Oxf.; MRCP (UK) 1993.

BRADLEY, Lesley Anne Florence Road Surgery, 26 Florence Road, Ealing, London W5 3TX Tel: 020 8567 2111; 1 Florence Road, Ealing, London W5 3TU Tel: 020 8567 2111 — MB BS 1982 Lond.; DRCOG 1986.

BRADLEY, Lisa Jayne 19 Windermere Road, London SW15 3QP — MB BS 1992 Lond.; DRCOG 1996; DFFP 1996. (Charing Cross and Westminster)

BRADLEY, Lloyd John Flat 14, College Green Court, 55-57 Barrington Road, London SW9 7JG — MB BS 1997 Lond.

BRADLEY, Lyn 138 Windsor Drive, Chelsfield, Orpington BR6 6HQ — MB ChB 1980 Bristol.

BRADLEY, Marcus David 59 Mooreland Road, Bromley BR1 3RD — MB BS 1996 Lond. (St Mary's Hospital Medical School) Clin. Research Fell. (NeuroBiol.). Prev: SHO, Neurol.; SHO, IC; SHO, Gen. Med., Rheum., Endocrinol.

BRADLEY, Marie Louise 22 Cronstown Road, Newtownards BT23 8QS — MB ChB 1997 Dundee.

BRADLEY, Marilyn Gwynneth Royal Liverpool University Hospital, Liverpool L7 8XP Tel: 0151 706 2621; 21 Alresford Road, Liverpool L19 3QZ Tel: 0151 494 0384 — MB ChB 1976 Liverp.; MRCP (UK) 1986; Dip. Ven. Liverp. 1979. Sen. Regist. (Genitourin. Med.) Roy. Liverp. Hosp. Prev: Regist. (Venereol.) Roy. Liverp. Hosp.

BRADLEY, Mark Charles 65 Baildon Road, Baildon, Shipley BD17 6PX — MB ChB 1987 Leeds.

BRADLEY, Martin Andrew Newbold Surgery, 3 Windermere Road, Chesterfield S41 8DU Tel: 01246 277381 Fax: 01246 239828; Lismoor, 15 Ryehill Avenue, Brookside, Chesterfield S40 3PD Tel: 01246 569139 Email: martin@mabradley.demon.co.uk — MB ChB 1982 Sheff.; MRCGP 1987. GP Princip.; Chairm. Chesterfield PCG.

BRADLEY, Mary C S Minfor Surgery, Park Road, Barmouth LL42 1PL Tel: 01341 280521 Fax: 01341 280912 — MB ChB 1978 Manchester; MB BCh 1978 Manchester.

BRADLEY, Mary Katharine H.M. Prison (Exeter), New North Road, Exeter EX4 4EX Tel: 01392 278321 Fax: 01392 422647 — MB 1979 Camb.; BChir 1978; MRCGP 1982. Med. Off. HM Prison Exeter.

BRADLEY, Mercia Joan (retired) 12 Mildmay Court, Odiham, Hook RG29 1AX Tel: 01256 704897 — MB ChB Bristol 1943. Prev: Clin. Med. Off. W. Surrey & N.E. Hants. Health Dist.

BRADLEY, Michael Jameson Stenton Farm, High St., Laughton en le Morthen, Sheffield S25 1YF — MB ChB 1982 Liverp.; FRCR 1987; DMRD Liverp. 1986. Cons. Radiol. Rotherham Dist. Gen. Hosp. Prev: Sen. Regist. (Radiol.) Liverp.; Lect. Chinese Univ. Hong Kong; Regist. (Radiol.) Liverp.

BRADLEY, Neville Alan Earlston Road Surgery, 1 Earston Road, Wallasey CH44 5UX Tel: 0151 639 2635 Fax: 0151 638 7008 — MB ChB 1972 Liverp.; Cert. MHS Open 1995. (Liverpool) Clin. Governance Lead Wallasey PCG. Prev: Clin. Asst. (Cas.) Liverp. Roy. Infirm.; SHO (Cas.) Liverp. Roy. Infirm.; SHO (Cas. & Surg.) Balfour Hosp. Kirkwall & Dunoon & Dist. Gen. Hosp.

BRADLEY, Nicholas Cadbury Albert Ide Lane Surgery, Ide Lane, Alphinton, Exeter EX2 8UP Tel: 01392 439868 Fax: 01392 493513 — MB BChir 1978 Camb.; MA, MB BChir Camb. 1978; MRCGP 1982. GP Exeter; Research Fell. Inst. Gen. Pract. Univ. Exeter.

BRADLEY, Mr Norman Luton & Dunstable Hospital Tel: 01227 766877 Fax: 01277 783191; George House, Bridge St., Wye, Ashford TN25 5ED Tel: 01233 812035 — MB BS 1975 Lond.; BDS Lond. 1968; FRCS Eng. 1980; LDS RCS Eng. 1969; FFD, RCSI 1982. (St. Bart. & Roy. Dent. Hosp.) Cons. Oral & Maxillofacial Surg. Kent & Canterbury Hosp. Socs: BMA; Fell. Brit. Assn. Oral & Maxillofacial Surg. Prev: Cons. Oral & Maxillofacial Surg. William Harvey Hosp. Ashford; Sen. Regist. (Oral & Maxillofacial Surg.) Guys, W.m. & Univ. Coll. Hosps. Lond.

BRADLEY, Orlagh Patricia 48 Stratfield Road, Oxford OX2 7BQ — MB BCh BAO 1982 Belf.; MRCGP 1986.

BRADLEY, Pamela Skegoneill Health Centre, 195 Skegoneill Avenue, Belfast BT15 3LL Tel: 028 9077 2471 Fax: 028 9077 2449; 617 Doagh Road, Ballyearl, Newtownabbey BT36 5RZ — MB BCh BAO 1981 Belf.; MPhil (Med. Ethics & Law) Belf. 1994; MRCGP 1985; DObst RCOG 1984; DCH RCPSI 1984. (Queen's Belfast) GP Princip.; Hosp. Practitioner (Dermat.) Belf. City Hosp.

BRADLEY, Patricia Anne 63 Pinewood Road, Uplands, Swansea SA2 0LS Tel: 01792 202548 — MB BCh BAO 1964 Belf.; MFCM 1978; DTM & H Liverp. 1974; DCH RCPS Glas. 1971; DObst RCOG 1966. Sessional Med. Off. (Family Plann.) NHS Trust; Clin. Asst. (Subst. Misuse) PSALT Project. Prev: GP Upper Swansea Valley.

BRADLEY, Mr Patrick James The Nottingham Nuffield Hospital, 748 Mansfield Road, Woodthorpe, Nottingham NG5 3FZ Tel: 0115 993 2008 Fax: 0115 993 2036; 37 Lucknow Drive, Mapperley Park, Nottingham NG3 5EU Tel: 0115 960 7031 Fax: 0115 960 7031 — MB BCh BAO 1973 NUI; FRCS Ed. 1979; FRCSI 1977; DCH NUI 1975; FRCS 1998 Lond. (Univ. Coll. Dub.) Cons. Otolaryngol. Head & Neck Oncolgist Univ. Hosp. Nottm. Socs: Pres. Sect. Laryngol./Rhinol. RSM; Brit. Assn. Surg. Oncol. (Coun. Mem.); Chairm., Brit. Assn. of Otolaryngol., Head and Surg. , Educ. & Train. Comm. Prev: Sen. Regist. (ENT) Roy. Liverp. Hosp.; Regist. (ENT) Liverp. ENT Infirm; SHO St. Vincents Hosp. Dub.

BRADLEY, Paul Clinical Skills Resource Centre, 2nd Floor, E Block, The Old Infirmary, University of Liverpool, Liverpool L69 3BX Tel: 0151 794 8236 Fax: 0151 794 8237 Email: pbradley@liv.ac.uk; 11 Northway, Curzon Park, Chester CH4 8BB — MB ChB 1978 Leeds; MB ChB Leeds. 1978; FRCGP 1993. Sen. Lect. (Healthcare Educat.) Univ. Liverp.

BRADLEY, Paul Brendan Omagh Health Centre, Mountjoy Road, Omagh BT79 7BA Tel: 028 8224 3521; 12 Gleannan Park, Killyclogher, Omagh BT79 7XZ Tel: 01662 249026 — MB BCh BAO 1989 Belf.; MB BCh BAO NUI Belf. 1989; MRCGP 1993; DRCOG 1992; DGM RCPS Glas. 1991.

BRADLEY, Professor Paul Frank Department of Oral & Maxillofacial Surgery, London Hospital Medical & Dental College, Turner St., London E1 2AD Tel: 020 7377 7050 Fax: 020 7377 7121 — MRCS Eng. LRCP Lond. 1966; MD Lond. 1989, MB BS 1966; BDS Birm. 1959; FRCS Ed. 1988; FDS RCS Ed. 1985; FDS RCS Eng. 1967, LDS 1959. (Lond. Hosp.) Prof. Oral & Maxillofacial Surg. Univ. Lond., Lond. Hosp. Med. Coll.; Hon. Cons. Roy. Lond. Hosp. Prev: Prof. Oral & Maxillofacial Surg. Univ. Edin. & Hon. Cons. Lothian HB; Cons. Oral & Maxillofacial Surg. Clwyd HA & Research Assoc. to Univ. Liverp.; Sen. Lect. (Oral Surg.) Univ. Liverp. & Hon. Cons. BRd.green Hosp., Regional Maxillofacial Unit & United Liverp. Hosps.

BRADLEY, Mr Peter Anthony Accident & Emergency Departmnet, Bradford Royal Infirmary, Duckworth Lane, Bradford BD9 6RJ Tel: 01274 542200 — MB ChB 1980 Liverp.; FRCS Ed. 1988. Cons. Accid. & Emerg. Med. Prev: Regist. (Orthop.) Bradford Roy. Infirm.

BRADLEY, Peter Garth 1 Cottingvale, Morpeth NE61 1DW — MB ChB 1968 Manch. Socs: Assn. Anaesth. Gt. Brit. & N. Irel. Prev: Sen. Regist. P'boro. Dist. Hosp.; Regist. Lond. Hosp.

BRADLEY, Peter Michael Northamptonshire Health Authority, Highfield, Cliftonville Road, Northampton NN1 5DN Tel: 01604 615251 Fax: 01604 615146 Email: pbradley@greenor.demon.co.uk; 37 Cliftonville Court, Cliftonville, Northampton NN1 5BZ Tel: 01604 545204 Email: p.bradley@greenor.demon.co.uk — MB BS 1988 Newc.; MA (Health Care Ethics) Leeds 1995; MPH Birm. 1997; MRCGP 1992; DCCH RCP Ed. 1993; MFPHM RCP (UK) 1997. Specialist Regist. (Pub. Health Med.) Anglia & Oxf. NHS Exec. Prev: Clin. Med. Off. (Child Health) Leeds HA; Trainee GP Norwich & Wakefield.

BRADLEY, Rachel Jane De Burgh The East Barn, The Pound, Almondsbury, Bristol BS32 4EF — MB ChB 1994 Birm. SHO (A & E) Bristol.

BRADLEY, Robert Colin Phillips (retired) The Cardinal Clinic, Oakley Green, Windsor SL4 5UL Tel: 01753 869755 Fax: 01773 869755 — MB BCh BAO Dub. 1952; MA, Dub. 1959, BA 1950; FRCPsych 1987, M 1971; T(Psychiat.) 1991; DPM Eng. 1961; Europ Spec Qualif Gen Med Counc 1996. Prev: Cons. Psychiat. Windsor.

BRADLEY, Robert John Royal Sussex County Hospital, Department of Obstetrics & Gynaecology, Eastern Road, Brighton BN2 5BE Tel: 01273 696955; The Hove Nuffield Hospital, 55 New Church Road, Hove BN3 4BG Tel: 01273 779471 Fax: 01273 220919 — MB BS 1979 Lond.; MD Lond. 1991; MRCGP 1983; MRCOG 1985; DCH RCP Lond. 1983; DRCOG 1982. Cons. O & G Roy. Sussex Co. Hosp. Brighton. Prev: Sen. Regist. & Regist. (O & G) King's Coll. Hosp. Lond.; SHO (Obst.) Qu. Charlotte's Matern. Hosp. Lond.

BRADLEY, Robert Keith Angel Hill Surgery, 1 Angel Hill, Bury St Edmunds IP33 1LU Tel: 01284 753008 Fax: 01284 724744; Nowton House, Breckey Ley, Nowton, Bury St Edmunds IP29 5LT — MB 1980 Camb.; MB 1980; BChir 1979; MA 1980 Camb.; MRCP (UK) 1985; MRCGP 1988; DCH RCP Lond. 1987; DRCOG 1986. GP Princip.; Clin. Asst. (Diabetes) W. Suff. Hosp. Prev: Med. Off. RN.

BRADLEY, Roisin Sarah Denise 1065 Manchester Road, Castleton, Rochdale OL11 2XJ — MB ChB 1995 Glas.

BRADLEY, Professor Ronald Duncan Toys Hill Farm House, Toys Hill, Westerham TN16 1QE Tel: 01732 750217 — MB BS 1955 Lond.; BSc, MB BS Lond. 1955; FRCP Lond. 1984, M 1978. Emerit. Prof. Intens. Ther. Med. St. Thos. Hosp. Lond.

BRADLEY, Rosalind (retired) Old Hastings House, High St., Hastings TN34 3ET — MB BS 1922 Lond. Prev: Med. Off. Infant. Welf. Clinics LCC.

BRADLEY, Sally Anne Department of Radiology, Selly Oak Hospital, Sellyoak, Birmingham B29 6JD; 86 Reddings Road, Moseley, Birmingham B13 8LR Tel: 0121 449 2955 — MB ChB 1982 Birm.; FRCR 1988. Cons. Radiol. Univ. Hosp. Birm. NHS Trust. Prev: Sen. Regist. & Regist. (Radiol.) W. Midl. RHA.

BRADLEY, Sally Margaret Anne 33 Churchwood Road, Didsbury, Manchester M20 6TZ — MB ChB 1986 Manch.; MSc Manch. 1991; MRCGP 1995; MFPHM RCP (UK) 1992; DRCOG 1988. (Manch.) Cons. (Pub. Health) Salford & Trafford Health Auth. Prev: Med. Dir. Community Healthcare Bolton; Cons. Pub. Health Med. W. Yorks. HA; Regist. (Pub. Health) NW RHA.

BRADLEY, Sarah Jane 56 Sketty Road, Swansea SA2 0LG — MB BCh 1972 Wales.

BRADLEY, Sheena Josephine 37 Lucknow Drive, Mapperley Park, Nottingham NG3 5EU Tel: 0115 960 7031 — MB BCh BAO 1973 NUI; FRCR 1986; DMRD Liverp. 1983. Cons. Radiol. (RHA) Grantham & Kesteven Gen. Hosp. Lincs.

BRADLEY, Shirley Carrickfergus Health Centre, Taylors Avenue, Carrickfergus BT38 7HT; 617 Doagh Road, Ballyearl, Newtownabbey BT36 5RZ — MB BCh BAO 1981 Belf.; MPhil (Med. Ethics & Law) Belf. 1994; MRCP (UK) 1984; MRCGP 1986; DCH RCPSI 1985; DRCOG 1985. (Qu. Univ. Belf.)

BRADLEY, Simon Nicholas Grange Road Surgery, Grange Road, Bishopsworth, Bristol BS13 8LD Tel: 0117 964 4343 Fax: 0117 935 8422; 48 Coronation Road, Bedminster, Bristol BS3 1AR Tel: 0117 966 1645 — MB BS 1980 Lond.; MRCGP 1984; DCH RCP Lond. 1983. (Univ. Coll. Hosp.) Dir. Informat. Technol. Demonst. for Primary Care. Prev: Trainee GP N.wick Pk. Hosp. VTS.

BRADLEY, Stephen David Derwent, 4 Malvern Meadow, River, Dover CT16 3AH — MRCS Eng. LRCP Lond. 1950; BA Camb. 1946, MB BChir 1951. (Camb. & King's Coll. Hosp.) Prev: Ho. Surg. ENT Dept. King's Coll. Hosp.

BRADLEY, Mr Stephen Meredith Osman 18 Bracknell Gardens, London NW3 7EB Tel: 020 7435 8790 Fax: 020 7433 3803 — MB BChir 1975 Camb.; MB Camb. 1975, BChir 1974; MA Camb. 1975; FRCS Eng. 1981. (St. Bart.) Med. Off. Gesa Asst. Lond. Socs: BMA & BAMPA. Prev: Sen. Regist. (Cardiac Surg.) St. Anthony's Hosp. Cheam; Regist. (Cardiothoracic Surg.) St. Bart. Hosp. Lond.; SHO (Med.) Whittington Hosp. Lond.

BRADLEY, Susan Gillian Ditton Lodge, 86 Slough Road, Datchet, Slough SL3 9AG Tel: 01753 542891 — MB BS 1970 Lond.; MRCS Eng. LRCP Lond. 1970. (Roy. Free)

BRADLEY, Suzan Margaret Stanley Villa Farm, Weeton, Kirkham, Preston PR4 3HN — MB ChB 1981 Liverp.; MRCGP 1987.

BRADLEY, Terence Stewartstown Health Centre, 212 Stewartstown Road, Dunmurry, Belfast BT17 0FB Tel: 028 9060 2931 Fax: 028 9060 5728; 28 Mount Eden Park, Belfast BT9 6RB — MB BCh BAO 1974 Belf.; MRCGP 1978.

BRADLEY, Una Patricia Upper Flat, 107 West Hill Road, London SW18 5HR — MB BS 1992 Lond.

BRADLEY, Vincent Paul Promenade Medical Centre, 46 Loch Promenade, Douglas IM1 2RX Fax: 01624 661833; The Willows, 9 Oakdale, Governors Hill, Douglas IM2 — MB ChB 1976 Glas. (Univ. Glas.) Police Surg. Isle of Man Constab.; Manx Organisation

Motorsport Med. Offs. Socs: Assn. Police Surg.; BMA. Prev: Staff Grade Cas. Off. Nobles Hosp. Isle of Man.

BRADLEY, William Andrew Health Centre, 118 Ravenhill Road, Fforestfach, Swansea SA5 5AA Tel: 01792 581666; 11 William Bowen Close, Gowerton, Swansea SA4 3HE — MB BCh 1984 Wales; BSc (Hons.) Wales 1979, MB BCh 1984; MRCGP 1989; DRCOG 1987. Prev: SHO Morriston Hosp. Swansea VTS; Ho. Off. Univ. Hosp. Wales, Cardiff & Morriston Hosp. Swansea.

BRADLEY, William Joseph (retired) 40 Castle Road, Tipton DY4 8DZ Tel: 0121 557 4299 — MB BCh BAO NUI 1949; LM Nat. Matern. Hosp. Dub. 1952.

BRADLEY, William Neil Upper Flat, 107 West Hill Road, London SW18 5HR — MB BS 1992 Lond.

BRADLEY, William Pierre Litherland 1 Hawthorn Rise, Prestbury, Macclesfield SK10 4AJ — MB ChB 1994 Dund.

BRADLEY-MOORE, Deborah Margaret (retired) 3A Bath Road, Thatcham, Newbury RG18 3AG — MB ChB 1929 Ed.; FRCS Ed. 1932.

BRADLEY-SMITH, Guy Charles St Thomas Health Centre, Cowick Street, St. Thomas, Exeter EX4 1HJ Tel: 01392 676677 Fax: 01392 676677; Clopton Down, Clapham, Exeter EX2 9UW Tel: 01392 833283 — BM BCh 1980 Oxf.; BA (Camb.) 1977; MRCGP 1984; DRCOG 1984; DCH RCP Lond. 1983.

BRADLEY-STEVENSON, Clare Louise 13 Cherry Tree Avenue, Scarborough YO12 5DX; 35 Sanderson Close, Whetstone, Leicester LE8 6ER — MB ChB 1996 Leeds. SHO (Paediat.) ScarBoro. Gen. Hosp.

BRADLOW, Anthony Battle Hospital, Reading RG30 1AG Tel: 0118 963 6375 Fax: 0118 963 6744 — LLM 1977 (Cardiff Law School); MD Cape Town 1985, MB ChB 1972; FRCP Lond. 1993; MRCP (UK) 1977; DCH RCP Lond. 1975. Cons. Rheum. And Phys., Roy. Berks. and Battle Hosps., Reading, RG30 1AG. Socs: Brit. Soc. Rheum. Prev: Sen. Regist. Nuffield Orthop. Centre Oxf.; Regist. (Med.) Hope Hosp. Salford; SHO Radcliffe Infirm. Oxf.

BRADMORE, Rosemary (retired) 11 Carmarthen Avenue, Cosham, Portsmouth PO6 2AG Tel: 01705 321869 — MB ChB 1942 Ed.; DCH Eng. 1947, CPH 1946. Prev: Asst. Med. Off. (Sch. & Infant Welf.) Hants. CC.

BRADNOCK, Mr Brian Robert Denis Peter Huntsmoor, Stoney Lane, Hemel Hempstead HP3 0DP — MB ChB 1982 Ed.; FRCS Ed. 1988. Regist. (Orthop.) Roy. Infirm. Edin. Prev: Basic Surg. Rotat. Roy. Infirm. Edin.; Ho. Off. (Surg.) E.. Gen. Hosp. Edin.; Ho. Off. (Med.) Leith Hosp. Edin.

BRADNOCK, Jennifer Phyllis Wellington Medical Centre, Bulford, Wellington TA21 8PW Tel: 01823 337442 Fax: 01823 663551; Headmasters House, Queens College, Trull Rd, Taunton TA1 4QT Tel: 01823 337442 — MB BS 1965 Lond.; MRCS Eng. LRCP Lond. 1965; DCH Eng. 1968; DObst RCOG 1967. (Guy's) Ass GP. Wellington. Prev: GP Harrogate; Clin. Asst. (O & G) Lewisham Hosp.; SHO Chest Clinic St. Luke's Hosp. Bradford.

BRADNOCK, Katherine Mary Fair Winds, Jordans, Beaconsfield HP9 2TG Tel: 01494 875218 — MB BS 1977 Lond.; MA Camb. 1973; MRCS Eng. LRCP Lond. 1977; MRCGP 1991; DRCOG 1990. (Roy. Free) Clin. Asst. (Cardiol.) Wexham Pk. Hosp.; GP Asst.

BRADPIECE, Mr Howard Austin 3 Thrift Cottages, Brickendon Lane, Brickendon, Hertford SG13 8NR — MB BCh 1977 Witwatersrand; FRCS Eng. 1982.

BRADSHAW, Alison Jane The Surgery, Balmuir Gardens, London SW15 6NG Tel: 020 8788 0818/659 2272 — MB BS 1983 Lond.; BA (Hons.) Oxf. 1978; MRCGP 1987. (St. Bart.) Prev: Trainee GP Char. Cross Hosp. VTS.

BRADSHAW, Charles Robert 51 Mayow Road, London SE23 2XH Tel: 020 8699 5579 — MB BS 1965 Lond.; FRCR 1975; FFR 1974. (King's Coll. Hosp.) Radiol. Lewisham Hosp. Socs: Brit. Inst. Radiol.; Fell. Roy. Soc. Med. Prev: Radiol. Qu. Eliz. Milit. Hosp. Lond.; Cons. Adviser Radiol. to Army.

BRADSHAW, Christine Jane 19 Pine Ridge Road, Burghfield Common, Reading RG7 3NB — MB BS 1993 Lond.; BSc (Hons.) Ed. 1980; MB BS (Hons.) Lond. 1993; MRCP (UK) 1996. Med. Regist., Roy. Cornw. Hosp., Treliske, Truro. Prev: Research Regist. ITU St. Geo.s Hosp. Lond.; SHO Nat. Hosp. for Neurol. & Neurosurg. Lond.

BRADSHAW, Colin Marsden Road Surgery, The Health Centre, Marsden Road, South Shields NE34 6RE Tel: 0191 454 0457 Fax: 0191 427 1793; 9 Tynemouth Place, North Shields NE30 4BJ Tel: 0191 257 2389 Fax: 0191 427 1793 Email: colin.bradshaw@dial.pipex.com — MB ChB 1977 Sheff.; FRCP Lond. 1996; MRCP (UK) 1979; FRCGP 1991, M 1982. Hon. Sen. Clin. Research Assoc. Centre for Health Servs. Research Newc.; Chairm. S. Tyneside MAAG. Socs: BMA. Prev: GP Trainer N.d. VTS; GP Tutor S. Tyneside PGMC; Vis Staff Phys. N.. Med. Unit Univ., Manitoba, Canada.

BRADSHAW, David James 5 Sandy Lane, Boughton, Chester CH3 5UL Tel: 01244 318633 — MB ChB 1990 Liverp.

BRADSHAW, David Martin 126 Belgrave Road, Gorseinon, Swansea SA4 6RB — MB ChB 1984 Manc.; MB ChB Manc. l984. SHO (Anaesth.) Trafford HA Manch. Prev: Ho. Surg. Vict. Hosp. Blackpool; Ho. Phys. Birch Hill Hosp. Rochdale.

BRADSHAW, Derrick (retired) 11 Old Garden Court, Mount Pleasant, St Albans AL3 4RQ Tel: 01727 55500 — MB BS 1955 Lond.

BRADSHAW, Elizabeth Gertrude Ealing HospitalNHS Trust, Uxbridge Road, Southall UB1 3HW Tel: 0208 967 5328 Fax: 0208 967 5797 Email: bradshaw@ealingas.demon.co.uk — MRCS Eng. LRCP Lond. 1964; MD Lond. 1979, MB BS 1964; DA Eng. 1966; FRCA 1968 (Roy. Free) Cons. (Anaesth.) Ealing Hosp. S.all.

BRADSHAW, Elsa Mary (retired) The Penthouse, 40 Riverside House, Williamson Close, Ripon HG4 1AZ Tel: 01765 609181 — MB ChB Manch. 1951.

BRADSHAW, Faye Louise 22 Carlisle Avenue, Penwortham, Preston PR1 0QP — MB ChB 1997 Liverp.

BRADSHAW, Fiona Margaret (retired) 13 Alderbank Terrace, Edinburgh EH11 1SX — MB ChB 1986 Ed.; MRCGP 1991. Trainee GP Craigshill Livingstone VTS.

BRADSHAW, Frances Rose Selbourne House, 1 Union St., Hyde SK14 1NG Tel: 0161 368 4464 Fax: 0161 367 8837 — MB ChB 1986 Manch.; MRCGP 1991; DRCOG 1990; DCH RCP Lond. 1988; M.Med. Sci . Sheff 1997; Dip Therapeutics 1998 Liverp. Primary Care Med. Adviser. Prev: GP Worsley; Trainee GP Cheadle Hulme Stockport VTS; SHO (Paediat., Obst. & Geriat.) Stepping Hill Hosp. Stockport.

BRADSHAW, Helen Dorothy The Coombs, 28 South Road, Grassendale Park, Liverpool L19 0LT — MB ChB 1995 Sheff.

BRADSHAW, Henry Justin Broghas Cottage, Quay Road, St Agnes TR5 0RS; Dunkirk Mill, Rosemary Lane, Freshford, Bath BA2 7UD — MB ChB 1987 Bristol; DA (UK) 1994; DCH RCP Lond. 1991; DObst Auckland 1990. Trainee GP Redruth, Cornw. Prev: SHO (Anaesth.) Roy. Cornw. Hosp. (Treliske) Truro; SHO (Psychiat.) St. Lawrence Hosp. Bodmin; SHO (ENT) Roy. Cornw. Hosp. (City) Truro.

BRADSHAW, James 18 Abbey Road, Darlington DL3 8LR Tel: 01325 380034 — BM BCh 1953 Oxf.; MA (Hon. Physiol.) Oxf. 1953; FRCOG 1981, M 1970. Prev: Cons. O & G Duchess of Kent's Milit. Hosp. Catterick Garrison.

BRADSHAW, James David (retired) The Penthouse, 40 Riverside House, Williamson Close, Ripon HG4 1AZ Tel: 01765 609181 — MB ChB Manch. 1951; FRCR 1975; FFR 1961; DMRT Eng. 1959. Prev: Hon. Cons. Radiother. & Oncol. Sheff. HA & Trent RHA.

BRADSHAW, James Henry Eastgate Surgery, 31B York Place, Knaresborough HG5 0AD Tel: 01423 867451 Fax: 01423 860446 Email: eastgate_31b_docs@msn.com; Cobble Barn, Westfield Lane, Arkendale, Knaresborough HG5 0QS Tel: 01423 340750 Fax: 01423 340017 Email: james_h_bradshaw@msn.com — MB BS 1982 Lond.; MRCGP 1986; DCH RCP Lond. 1986; DRCOG 1984. (Char. Cross) Socs: BMA; Harrogate Med. Soc. Prev: Trainee GP Derby VTS.

***BRADSHAW, Joanne Helen** 26 Walter Scott Avenue, Wigan WN1 2RH — MB ChB 1997 Leeds.

BRADSHAW, John, MBE (retired) Abney House, 11 Hexton Road, Glastonbury BA6 8HL Tel: 01458 31779 — MB ChB 1963 Sheff.

BRADSHAW, John Dennis (retired) Meadow View, Townend Road, Walkington, Beverley HU17 8SY — MB ChB Manch. 1954.

BRADSHAW, John Peter Pery (retired) 14 Stumperlowe View, Sheffield S10 3QU Tel: 0114 2302 371 — MRCS Eng. LRCP Lond. 1947; MD (Med.) Lond. 1950, MB BS 1947; FRCP Lond. 1970, M 1949. Prev: Cons. Neurol. United Sheff. Hosps.

BRADSHAW, John Richard Department of Neuroradiology, Frenchay Hospital, Frenchay Park Road, Bristol BS16 1LE — MB BCh BAO 1967 Dub.; FRCP Canada 1974; FRCR 1973; DMRD Eng.

1971. Cons. Neuroradiol. SW RHA. Prev: Asst. Prof. Radiol. Memor. Univ. St. John's Newfld.; Cons. Radiol. St. John's Gen. Hosp. Newfld.

BRADSHAW, Karen Agnes Birmingham Childrens Hospital, Steelhouse Lane, Birmingham B4 6NH Tel: 0121 333 9999 Fax: 0121 333 9998 — MB ChB 1990 Glas.; MRCP Glas. 1993; FRCR Lond. 1997. Cons. Paediat. Radiol. Socs: Collegiate Mem. Roy. Coll. Phys.; Assoc. Mem. Roy. Coll. Radiol.; Fell. Roy. Coll. of Radiologists. Prev: Sen. Regist. Rotat. (Radiol.) W. Midl. HA; Regist. Rotat. (Radiol.) W. Midl. HA; SHO (Med.) Telford Hosp. Shrops. HA.

BRADSHAW, Margaret Jane Department of Medicine for the Elderly, Brighton General Hospital, Brighton BN2 3EW Tel: 01273 696955; 9 The Avenue, Lewes BN7 1QS — MB ChB 1975 Bristol; FRCP Lond 1996; MRCP (UIK) 1978. (Bristol) Cons. Phys. Geriat. Med. Brighton Healthcare Trust. Prev: Cons. Phys. Geriat. Med. Nevill Hall Hosp. Abergavenny; Lect. (Geriat. Med.) Univ. Hosp. Wales Cardiff; Research Fell. (Gastroenterol.) Frenchay Hosp. Bristol.

BRADSHAW, Michael Francis (retired) 14 Woodbridge Road E., Ipswich IP4 5PA Tel: 01473 726836 — MB BS 1962 Lond.; MRCS Eng. LRCP Lond. 1962; DObst RCOG 1964. GP Ipswich. Prev: Orthop. Ho. Surg. Guy's Hosp.

BRADSHAW, Muriel Kathleen Vailima, 78 Westcliff Park Drive, Dawlish EX7 9ER Tel: 01626 865286 — BM BCh 1950 Oxf.; BA (Hons.) Animal Physiol. Oxf. 1950, MA, BM BCh 1953. (Oxf.) Clin. Med. Off. Community Health (Family Plann.) Exeter HA. Prev: Clin. Med. Off. Community Health (Family Plann.) Birm. & Solihull HAs; Ho. Surg. N. Staffs. Roy. Infirm. Stoke-on-Trent; W.. Samoan Governm. Health Assessor for W. Samoans entering N. Zealand.

BRADSHAW, Nicholas John Martin Flat 2, 4 Linden Park Road, Tunbridge Wells TN2 5QL — MB BS 1993 Lond.

BRADSHAW, Mr Roger Bailey (retired) Heather Cottage, Welsh Saint Donats, Cowbridge CF71 7SS — MB ChB 1957 Sheff.; FRCS Eng. 1966. Prev: Cons. ENT Surg. Univ. Hosp. of Wales Cardiff.

BRADSHAW, Stephen James Department of Psychiatry, Stockport Healthcare Trust, Stepping Hill Hospital, Stockport SK2 2JE Tel: 0161 419 5724 Fax: 0161 419 5786 — MB ChB 1984 Manch.; MSc Manch. 1993; BSc St And. 1981; MRCPsych 1991. Cons. Old Age Psychiat. Stepping Hill Hosp. Stockport.

BRADSHAW, Thomas Crawford (retired) Cobblers, Brook Lane, Fovant, Salisbury SP3 5JB Tel: 01722 714697 — BM BCh 1943 Oxf.

BRADSHAW, Timothy 28 Showell Road, Droitwitch Spa, Droitwich WR9 8UY — BM BS 1995 Nottm.

BRADSHAW, Tracey Anne 26 Mosshill Road, Bellshill ML4 1NQ — MB ChB 1994 Aberd.

BRADSHAW, Wayne William 13 Kelmscott Road, London SW11 6QX — MB BS 1965 Western Australia.

BRADSHAW, William Herron Adrain, DFC (retired) 259 Birkby Road, Birkby, Huddersfield HD2 2DW Tel: 01484 530096 — MB BCh BAO 1954 Belf. Prev: Clin. Asst. (Obst.) Roy. Infirm. Huddersfield.

BRADSHAW-SMITH, Jeremy Houlton (retired) 4 Salston Barton, Strawberry Lane, Ottery St Mary EX11 1RG Tel: 01404 812681 Email: b-sthetis@eclipse.co — MB BS 1958 Lond.; DTM & H Eng. 1960; DObst RCOG 1964. Prev: Ho. Phys. St. Peter's Hosp. Chertsey.

BRADSTOCK-SMITH, Matthew Roy Bersted Green Surgery, Durlston Drive, North Bersted, Bognor Regis PO22 9TD — MB BS 1988 Lond.; DRCOG 1992.

BRADSTREET, Catherine Margaret Patricia (retired) 15 Lantern Close, London SW15 5QS Tel: 020 8392 1601 — MB BS 1946 Lond.; FRCPath 1970; Dip. Bact. Lond. 1952. Prev: Dir. Standards Laborat. For Serol. Reagents, Centr. Pub. Health Laborat. Lond.

BRADWELL, Professor Arthur Randell Department of Immunology, Medical School, Birmingham University, Birmingham B15 2TJ — MB ChB Birm. 1968; FRCP Lond. 1983; MRCP (UK) 1971; MRCPath 1982.

BRADWELL, Mr Robert Alexander 6 Rutland Road, Harrogate HG1 2PY Tel: 01423 502897 — MB ChB 1963 St. And.; FRCS Ed. 1966; FRCS Eng. 1970. (St. And.) Cons. Otolaryngol. Harrogate Health Dist. Socs: N. Eng. ENT Soc. & Scott. ENT Soc. Prev: Cons. Otolaryngol. Lothian Health Bd.; Hon. Sen. Lect. Edin. Univ.; Sen. Regist. Bristol United Hosps.

BRADY, Adrian James Brendan Department of Medical Cardiology, Glasgow Royal Infirmary, Glasgow G31 2ER Tel: 0141 211 4727 Fax: 0141 211 1171 Email: a.j.brady@clinmed.gla.ac.uk — MB ChB 1985 Ed.; BSc (1st cl. Hons.) Physiol. Ed. 1983, MD 1993; FRCP Ed. 1997; MRCP (UK) 1988. Cons. Cardiol. Glas. Roy. Infirm.; Mem. (Ex-Chairm.) Brit. Hypertens. Research Gp. Socs: Brit. Cardiac Soc.; Comm. Mem. of Brit. Soc. for Cardiovasc. Research; Fell. RCP Edin. Prev: Sen. Regist. (Cardiol.) Qu. Eliz. Hosp. Birm.; Regist. (Cardiol.) Nat. Heart & Lung Inst.; Regist. (Clin. Pharmacol. & Cardiol.) Hammersmith Hosp. Lond.

BRADY, Angela Frances Kennedy Galton Centre, Northwick Park Hospital, Watford Road, Harrow HA1 3UJ Tel: 020 88692795 Fax: 020 8869 3106 Email: a.brady@ic.ac.uk — MB ChB 1990 Dundee; BMSc (Med. Genetics) Dund 1987; MRCP (UK) 1993; PhD (Genetics) Lond. 1998. p/t Cons. Clin. Genetics Kennedy-Galton Centre N.wick Pk. Hosp. Socs: Brit. Soc. Human Genetics; Skeletal Opplaine Gp.

BRADY, Angela Joy 15 Ashville Avenue, Eaglecliffe, Stockton-on-Tees TS16 9AU — BM BS 1983 Nottm.; BMedSci Nottm. 1981; MRCGP 1989. Specialist Regist. (Palliat. Med.) Butterwick Hospice Stockton-on-Tees. Prev: Clin. Asst. (BrE. Assessm. Unit) Newc. Gen. Hosp. Newc.

BRADY, Brian Michael 83 Whitburn Road, Bathgate EH48 2RN — MB ChB 1996 Ed.

BRADY, Clive Timothy Malcolm Manor Drive Surgery, 3 The Manor Drive, Worcester Park KT4 7LG Tel: 0208 337 0545 Fax: 020 8335 3281 — MB BS 1975 Lond.; DRCOG 1982. (Lond. Hosp. Med. Coll.) GP; Mem. Kingston & Richmond LMC. Socs: Fell. Roy. Soc. Med.; BMA (Hons. Treas. Mid Surrey,Kingston & Esher Div). Prev: SHO (Accid. Serv.) Luton & Dunstable Hosp.; SHO Rotat. (Surgic.) Norf. & Norwich Hosp.; SHO (O & G) Beckenham & Bromley Hosps.

BRADY, Darren William John 53 London Road, Stretton, Warrington WA4 5PH; 61 Alexandra Road, Reading RG1 5PG — BM 1996 Soton. SHO (A & E) Roy. Berks Hosp. Reading. Prev: Ho. Off. (Surg.) Portsmouth NHS Trust; Ho. Off (Med.) Swindon/MarlBoro. NHS Trust.

BRADY, Dennis William George 94 Crewe Road, Nantwich CW5 6JD Tel: 01270 623076 — MB ChB 1959 Sheff.; MFOM RCP Lond. 1983; DPH Lond. 1966. (Sheff.) Regional Med. Off. LMR Br. Prev: Dep. MOH Glos. Co. Boro.; SHO (Clin. Pathol.) Sheff. Roy. Infirm.; Ho. Phys. Sheff. Childr. Hosp.

BRADY, Desmond Barngables, Pennington, Ulverston LA12 7NY Email: desbrady@netcentre.net — MB ChB 1973 Leeds; DObst RCOG 1976; Dip. Psych 1998. (Leeds Univ.)

BRADY, Jonathan Lewis 18 Broadway, Cheadle SK8 1NQ Tel: 0161 428 8808 Email: jonathanbrady@mcmail.com — MB BS 1987 Lond.; MD Lond. 1994; MRCOG 1995. (St George's Hospital) Specialist Regist. (O & G) Sharoe Green Hosp. Preston.

BRADY, Jullien Alexander 4 Darmonds Green Av, Liverpool L6 0DP — MB BS 1997 Lond.

BRADY, Martin Hebburn Health Centre, Campbell Park Road, Hebburn NE31 2SP Tel: 0191 451 6234 — MB BS 1978 Newc. Acupunc., Mt.batton Surg. (Tel:0191 451 6264). Socs: MDDUS.

BRADY, Mary Catherine Imelda Corraclare House, Kinawlay, Enniskillen — LRCPI & LM, LRSCI & LM 1956; LRCPI & LM, LRCSI & LM 1956; MFCM 1973; DCH NUI 1960, DPH 1962; LM Rotunda 1958.

BRADY, Michael Colin Springfield House Medical Centre, 275 Huddersfield Road, Oldham OL4 2RJ Tel: 0161 633 2333 Fax: 0161 628 6682 — MB ChB 1973 Manch.; DObst RCOG 1976; Cert Contracep. & Family Plann. RCOG, RCGP &; Cert FPA 1976. (Manch.)

BRADY, Michael David Spa Surgery, 205 High Street, Boston Spa, Wetherby LS23 6PY Tel: 01937 842842 Fax: 01937 841095; Old School House, Station Road, Tadcaster LS24 9JG — MB ChB 1982 Leeds; MRCGP 1987. Med. Dir. Martin Hse. Childr. Hospice.

BRADY, Michele Margaret Mary 15 Windsor Park, Belfast BT9 6FQ — MB BCh BAO 1976 Dub.; FFA RCSI 1981.

BRADY, Owen Howard Gerard Alder Hey Childrens Hospital, Eaton Road, Liverpool L12 2AP — MB BCh BAO 1985 NUI; LRCPSI 1985.

BRADY, Peter Anthony 31 Stepping Stones Road, Coundon, Coventry CV5 8JT — MB ChB 1987 Liverp.; MRCP (UK) 1990.

BRADY, Philip Joseph Ros Erne, 8 Darling St., Enniskillen BT74 7EP — MB BCh BAO 1940 NUI.

BRADY, Robert Archway Medical Centre, 652 Holloway Road, London N19 3NX — MB BS 1982 Lond.

BRADY, Seamus Thomas 151 Templegrove, Buncrana Road, Londonderry BT48 0RF Tel: 02871 266230; 151 Templegrove, Brncrana Road, Londonderry BT48 0RF Tel: 02871 266230 — MB BCh BAO 1974 Belf.; FFR RCSI 1984. Cons. Radiol. Antrim Hosp. Prev: Clin. Dir. (Radiol.) United Hosp. Gp.

BRADY, Sharon c/o Brady, 23 Sandfield Rd, Headington, Oxford OX3 7RN — MB BS 1996 Lond.

BRADY, Stephen David 18 Clemshaw Close, Heywood OL10 3HG — MB ChB 1985 Manch.

BRADY, Suzanne 50 Canford Cliffs Road, Lower Parkstone, Poole BH13 7AA — MB BCh 1991 Wales; MSc (Sports Med.) Nottm. 1997; FRCS Ed. (A&E) 1997; Dip/MC RCS Ed 1998. Specialist Regist. (A&E) Soton. Gen. Hosp. Prev: Resid. Med. Off. (A & E) St. Mary Hosp. Lond.

BRADY, Tracey Louise (Gaunt) The Gowerton Medical Centre, Mill Street, Gowerton, Swansea SA4 3ED Tel: 01792 872404 Fax: 01792 875170 — MB BS 1993 Lond.; MA Camb. 1994; DRCOG 1995; DFFP 1996; MRCGP 1997. (Char. Cross & Westm.) GP Princip., Gowerton Med. Centre, Swansea.

BRADY, Vincent Patrick Joseph 4 Hillary Drive, Audlem, Crewe CW3 0HJ — MB BCh BAO 1980 Dub.

BRADY-HENRY, Mrs Mary Bridget Quisisana, Lisnaskea, Enniskillen — MB BCh BAO 1935 NUI; DPH 1937.

BRAEMAN, Christine 3 Lower Terrace, The Dardy, Llangattock, Crickhowell NP8 1PR — MB BCh 1992 Wales.

BRAET, Veronique The Cottage, 69 Station Way, Cheam, Sutton SM3 8SD — MD 1989 Louvain.

BRAFIELD, Allan John Edmund (retired) 38 Byron Avenue, South Woodford, London E18 2HQ Tel: 020 8989 0457 — MB BS Madras 1942; FRCPath 1971; Dip. Path. Eng. 1954; DCP Lond 1951. Hon. Cons. Haemat. Whipps Cross Hosp. Lond. Prev: Cons. Haemat. Whipps Cross Hosp. Lond.

BRAFMAN, Abrahao Henrique 20 Hollycroft Avenue, London NW3 7QL Tel: 020 7435 4057 Fax: 020 7435 4057 Email: abrafman@excite.com — MD 1954 Brazil; LAH Dub. 1967; MRCPsych 1972; DPM Eng. 1968. Hon. Sen. Lect. Psych.& Behavioural Sci. Roy. Free & Univ. Coll. Sch. of Medicin. Socs: Assoc. Mem. Brit. Psychoanal. Soc. Prev: Consult. Roehampton Child Guid. Unit; Cons. Child Psychiat. Qu. Mary's Hosp. Roehampton, Lond.

BRAGA, Anna Angela (retired) The Old Post Office, Suckley, Worcester WR6 5EE Tel: 01886 884458 — MB BS 1949 Lond.; MRCS Eng. LRCP Lond. 1949; DPM Eng. 1970. Assoc. Specialist (Psychiat.) Worcs. Developm. Project (p/t) W. Midl. RHA. Prev: Princip. GP Putney.

BRAGANZA, Denise Marie Rohini 19 Kings Road, Sale M33 6QB Email: dmbraganza@aol.com — MB ChB 1994 Bristol; BSc Biochemistry, 1992. Cardiol. Specialist Regist.

BRAGANZA, Joan Marie Department of Gastroenterology, Royal Infirmary, Oxford Road, Manchester M13 9WL Tel: 0161 276 4884 Fax: 0161 276 4168; 19 King's Road, Sale M33 6QB — MB BS 1967 Bombay; MSc Manch. 1974; DSc Manch. 1995; FRCP Lond. 1981 M 1968; FRCPath 1995. (Grant Med. Coll.) Reader (Gastroenterol.) & Hon. Cons. Manch. Roy. Infirm. Socs: Fell. Manch. Med. Soc.; Brit. Soc. Gastroenterol.; Assn. Phys. Prev: Lect. (Gastroenterol.) Manch. Roy. Infirm.; SHO (Med.) & Regist. (Med. Research) Manch. Roy. Infirm.; Ho. Phys. Oldham Roy. Infirm.

BRAGANZA, Mervyn Aloysious Hulme House Group Practice Centre, 175 Royce Road, Hulme, Manchester M15 5TJ Tel: 0161 226 3854 Fax: 0161 227 8454; 12 Wincham Road, Sale M33 4PL Tel: 0161 973 1941 — MB BS 1958 Vikram; DCH RCPS Glas. 1966.

BRAGG, Anthony Joseph Damian 4 Albany Close, Reigate RH2 9PP — MB ChB 1976 Sheff.; MBA Univ. Surrey 1995; Dip. Pharm. Med. RCP (UK) 1985. Med. Dir. Novo Nordisk Pharmaceut. Crawley. Socs: Fac. Pharmaceut. Phys. (UK) 1993.

BRAGG, Elizabeth Anne 16 Watson Road, Llandaff North, Cardiff CF14 2JA — MB ChB 1993 Liverp. Staff Grade Caerphilly Dist. Miners Hosp. Caerphilly. Prev: SHO (Paediat.) E. Glam. Gen. Hosp. Pontypridd.

BRAGG, James Michael Stoke Gifford Medical Centre, Ratcliffe Drive, Stoke Gifford, Bristol BS34 8UE Tel: 0117 979 9430 Fax: 0117 940 6999; 20 Brent Road, Horfield, Bristol BS7 9QZ — MB ChB 1988 Bristol; DFFP 1994.

BRAGG, Patricia Mary Oldwell Surgery, 10 Front Street, Winlaton, Newcastle upon Tyne NE21 4CD Tel: 0191 414 2339 Fax: 0191 414 6779 — MB BS 1980 Newc.; MRCGP 1985; DCCH 1984. Princip. GP.

BRAGMAN, Susan Geraldine Lorraine Department of Pathology, Queen Elizabeth Hospital, Stadium Road, Woolwich, London SE18 4QH Tel: 020 8836 6000 — MB BS 1977 Lond.; MSc (Clin. Microbiol.) 1985; MRCS Eng. LRCP Lond. 1977; MRCPath 1985. (Roy. Free) Cons. Microbiol. Qu. Eliz. Hosp. NHS Trust.

BRAGONIER, Reginald 44 Sommerville Road, St Andrews, Bristol BS7 9AB Tel: 0117 924 5643 — MB ChB 1987 Birm.; MRCP (UK) 1991; DTM & H Liverp. 1992; DCH RCP Lond. 1991. (Birm.) Health Adviser, Health Net Internat., E. Timor. Socs: BMA; Ord. Mem. RCPCH. Prev: Clin. Fell. Hon. Regist. Bristol Childr. Hosp.; Regist. Birm. Childr. Hosp.; Med. Off. Wete Dist. Hosp. Pemba, Tanzania.

BRAHAM, Annette Nicole 28 Bancroft Avenue, East Finchley, London N2 0AS — MB BS 1981 Lond.; BSc Lond. 1978.

BRAHAM, Deborah Laureen 18 The Rise, Edgware HA8 8NR — BM 1997 Soton.

BRAHIM, Kerryn Azlan 41 Ellen Wilkinson Crescent, Manchester M12 4JU — MB BS 1995 W. Indies.

BRAHMA, Arun Kevin 45 Moor Allerton Crescent, Leeds LS17 6SH — MB ChB 1988 Manch.

BRAHMA, Arun Vishvanath (retired) 3 Ravensworth Gardens, Ellington, Morpeth NE61 5HP Tel: 01670 860372 — MB BS 1960 Nagpur; DCH Eng. 1962. Prev: GP. Morpeth 1967-1996.

BRAHMA, Prabir Kumar Ash Grove Surgery, Cow Lane, Knottingley WF11 9BZ Tel: 01977 673141 Fax: 01977 677054 — MB BS 1965 Gauhati.

BRAHMACHARI, Amal Krishna The Hawthorns, Priorslee Village, Telford TF2 9NW — MB BS 1955 Calcutta; MRCGP 1972; DPH Liverp. 1968. GP Telford. Prev: Regist. (Med.) Derby Gps. Hosp.; Sen. Asst. Port Med. Off. Hull & Goole; Med. Off. Calcutta Port Trust Hosps.

BRAHMBHATT, Mr Ghamshyam Ambalal Court Yard Surgery, John Evans House, 28 Court Yard, London SE9 5QA Tel: 020 8850 1300 Fax: 020 8294 2378 — MRCS Eng. LRCP Lond. 1975; FRCS Ed. 1974.

BRAID, Donald Pirret (retired) ortona, 41 Charlotte St, Helensburgh G84 7SE Tel: 01436 674523 — MB ChB 1956 Ed.; FFA RCS Eng. 1963. Prev: Cons. Anesth. W.. Infirm. Glas.

BRAID, Janet Foster House, Middleton St Gerorge, Darlington DL2 1TQ — MB ChB 1943 Ed. (Edin.) Prev: Res. Ho. Surg. Roy. Hosp. Sick Childr. Edin.; Res. Med. Off. Ruchill Hosp. Glas.

BRAID, Neil William Pen y Maes Health Centre, Beech Street, Summerhill, Wrexham LL11 4UF Tel: 01978 756370 Fax: 01978 751870 — MB BS 1979 Lond.; MRCGP 1984; DRCOG 1982.

BRAIDEN, James John — MBBS 1982 London; DCH 1986 London; MRCGP 1986 London. Clin. Asst., Chest Med.

BRAIDLEY, Mr Peter Charles Chestermian Wing, Northern General Hospital, Herries Road, Sheffield S57AU Tel: 0114 226 6777 Email: pbraidley@hotmail.com — MB BS 1988 Lond.; FRCS 1992 Eng; FRCS 1998 ((CTh)) Eng. (Roy. Free Hosp. Lond.) Cons. Cardiothoracic Surg. Sheff. Teachg. Hosp.s Trust, Sheff.. Socs: Soc. Cardiothoraic Surgs. of GB & Irel.; Roy. Soc. Med.; Int. Soc. Heart. Lung Transpl.ation. Prev: Research Regist. Papworth & Addenbrooke's Hosps.; Specialist Regist. Rotat. (Cardiothoracic Surg.) Anglia & Oxf.; Hunt. Prof. RCS Eng.

BRAIDWOOD, Mr Andrew Shaw 60 Wellshot Drive, Cambuslang, Glasgow G72 8BN Tel: 0141 642 1330 — MB ChB 1962 Glas.; FRCS Glas. 1972; DCH RCPS Glas. 1966; DObst RCOG 1964. (Glas.) Cons. Orthop. Surg. Monklands Dist. Gen. Hosp. Airdrie; Orthop. Regist. Vict. Infirm. Glas. Socs: BMA; Fell. Brit. Orthop. Assn. Prev: Sen. Orthop. Regist. Vict. Infirm. Glas.; Regist. Regional Plastic Surg. Unit Glas.; Ho. Off. Vict. Infirm. Glas. & Roy. Infirm. Glas.

BRAIDWOOD, Elizabeth Anne Irthington, Kirkton Road, Dumbarton G82 4AS — MB ChB 1974 Glas.; BSc (Hons. Biochem.) Glas. 1970, MB ChB 1974; MRCP (UK) 1976; MRCGP 1980.

BRAIDWOOD, Janet Mary Borders General Hospital, Melrose TD6 9BS — MB ChB 1978 Glas.; FFA RCS Eng. 1984. (Univ. Glas.) Cons. Anaesth. Borders Gen. Hosp. Melrose.

BRAILSFORD, Jennifer Ann Denise X-Ray Department, Poole NHS Trust, Longfleet Road, Poole BH15 2JB — MB 1983 Camb.; MB BChir Camb. 1983; MA Camb. 1984; MRCP (UK) 1986; FRCR 1990. Cons. Radiol. Poole Hosp. NHS Trust.

BRAILSFORD, Mairead McKenzie Ardwork, Ardlarach Road, Ardfern, Lochgilphead PA31 8QN — MB ChB 1976 Glas.

BRAIMBRIDGE, Mr Mark Viney (retired) 22 Upper Park Road, London NW3 2UP Tel: 0207 722 5218 Fax: 020 730 89 1076 Email: rangbox@msn.com — MA, MB BChir Camb. 1951; FRCS Eng. 1954. Cons. Surg. St. Thos. Hosp. Prev: Sen. Lect. St. Thos. Hosp. Med. Sch.

BRAIN, Mr Albert Jeffrey Li 19 Woodhall Lane, Balsham, Cambridge CB1 6DT — MB BS 1971 Lond.; MS Lond. 1984; FRCS Eng. 1977; MRCS Eng. LRCP Lond. 1971; Specialist Accredit. Paediat. Surg. RCS Eng. 1989; Specialist Accredit. Gen. Surg. RCS Eng. 1983. (Guy's) Cons. Paediat. Surg. Addenbrooke's Hosp. Camb. Prev: Cons. Paediat. Surg. Norf. & Norwich Hosp.; Sen. Regist. (Gen. Surg.) Middlx. Hosp. Lond.; Sen. Regist. (Paediat. Surg.) Hosp. Sick Childr. Gt. Ormond St. Lond.

BRAIN, Andree Georgia Christina Star House, Cooksmill Green, Chelmsford CM1 3SH Tel: 01245 248217 — MB BS 1967 Lond.; MRCS Eng. LRCP Lond. 1967. (Lond. Hosp.) Clin. Asst. (Anaesth.) Broomfield Hosp. Chelmsford. Socs: Assn. Anaesth. Prev: Clin. Asst. (Anaesth.) OldCh. Hosp. Romford; SHO (Anaesth.) Lond. Hosp.; Ho. Surg. & Ho. Phys. Chelmsford & Essex Hosp.

BRAIN, Andrew John Seaward Havering Hospitals NHS Trust, Gubbins Lane, Romford RM3 0BE Tel: 01708 708214 Fax: 01708 708099 Email: andrewbrian@haveringh-thnthames.nhs.uk; 28 Gablefields, Sandon, Chelmsford CM2 7SP — MB BS 1968 Lond.; BSc (Special) Physiol. Lond. 1965; FRCP Lond. 1991; MRCP (UK) 1971; MRCS Eng. LRCP Lond. 1968. (Lond. Hosp.) Cons. Phys. OldCh. Hosp. Romford. Socs: Renal Assn.; Med. Res. Soc. Prev: Sen. Regist. Div. Med. Lond. Hosp.; Fell. (Nephrol.) Univ. Michigan Med. Sch. Ann Arbor, USA; Lect. (Med.) Lond. Hosp.

BRAIN, Mrs Anne Cottage Farm, Lower Tasburgh, Norwich NR15 1LT — MB BS 1973 Lond.; FRCS Eng. 1979; MRCS Eng. LRCP Lond. 1973. (Roy. Free)

BRAIN, Anthony Robert Drs Brian, Pearson, Aung, West, Ridsdillsmith and McColl, Heath Road, Woolpit, Bury St Edmunds IP30 9QU Tel: 01359 240298 Fax: 01359 241975 Email: tony.brain@gp-d83055.nhs.uk; The Old Mill House, School Lane, Rattlesden, Bury St Edmunds IP30 0SE Tel: 01449 736483 — MB ChB 1972 Manch. (Manchester) Gen. Pract. Woolpit, Bury St Edmunds. Prev: Ho. Surg. Oldham & Dist. Gen. Hosp.; Ho. Phys. W. Suff. Gen. Hosp.; SHO (Paediat.) Bedford Gen. Hosp.

BRAIN, Archibald Ian Jeremy Department of Anaesthetics, Royal Berkshire Hospital, London Road, Reading RG1 5AN; Sandford House, Fan Court Gardens, Longcross Road, Chertsey KT16 0DJ Tel: 01932 875370 — LMSSA Lond. 1970; MA Oxf. 1987; FFA RCSI 1977. (St. Bart.) Hon. Cons. Anaesth. Roy. Berks. Hosp. Reading; Hon. Research Fell. Inst. Laryngol. Lond. Socs: Assn. Anaesth.; Anaesth. Res. Soc.; Hon. Mem. Soc. Airway Managem. (USA). Prev: Hon. Cons. Anaesth. N.wick Pk. Hosp. Harrow; Cons. Anaesth. Newham Gen. Hosp. Lond.; Lect. (Anaesth.) The Lond. Hosp. Whitechapel.

BRAIN, Caroline Elizabeth London Centre for Paediatric Endochnology, Middlesex Hospital, 3rd Floor Dorville House, Mortimer Street, London W1N 8AA Fax: 020 7636 2144; 54 Gore Road, Victoria Park, London E9 7HN Fax: 0208 9857451 Email: cbrain@easynet.co.uk — MB BS Lond. 1979; MD Lond. 1993; MRCP (UK) 1983. (Roy. Lond. Hosp. Med. Sch.) Cons. Paediatric Endocrinologist, Gt. Ormond St. & The Middlx. Hosp.s. Prev: Hon. Cons. Paediat. (Endocrinol.) Roy. Marsden Hosp. Sutton; Cons. Paediat. (Endocrinol.) St. Geo. Hosp. Lond.

BRAIN, Mr David John 30 Wellington Road, Edgbaston, Birmingham B15 2ES Tel: 0121 440 1105 — MB ChB 1949 Bristol; FRCS Eng. 1955; DLO Eng. 1951. (Bristol) Hon. Cons. ENT Surg. Qu. Eliz. Hosp. Birm.; Clin. Teach. in Otolaryng. Univ. Birm. Socs: Pres. Europ. Rhinol. Soc.; Fell Roy. Soc. Med.; Brit. Assn. Otolaryngols. Prev: Sen. Regist. ENT Dept. Roy. Infirm. Edin.; ENT Regist. Univ. Coll. Hosp. Lond.; Regist. Roy. Nat. Throat, Nose & Ear Hosp. Lond.

BRAIN, Gillian Anne New Southgate Surgery, Buxton Place, off Leeds Road, Wakefield WF1 3JQ Tel: 01924 334400 Fax: 01924 334439 — MB ChB 1989 Leeds; DRCOG 1991. Clin. Asst. (Paediat.) Pinderfields Gen. Hosp. Wakefield.

BRAIN, Gordon Robert Henry Bramblys Grange Health Centre, Bramblys Drive, Basingstoke RG21 8UW Tel: 01256 467778 Fax: 01256 814190 — MB BS 1976 Lond.; MRCS Eng. LRCP Lond. 1976.

BRAIN, Henrietta Philippa Seaward Star House, Cooksmill Green, Chelmsford CM1 3SH — MB BS 1994 Lond.

BRAIN, Mrs Marjorie (retired) 43 Walton Road, Ware SG12 9PF Tel: 01920 462785 Email: almabrain@btopenworld.com — MB BCh BAO 1954 Dub. 1954. Prev: Gen. Med. Practioner, Herts.

BRAIN, Monica Mary (retired) 7 Connaught Road, Rowditch, Derby DE22 3LU Tel: 01332 371198 — MB BChir Camb. 1955; DObst RCOG 1958. Prev: GP Derby.

BRAIN, Nicola Dorothy Walsgrave Hospitals NHS Trust, Clifford Bridge Road, Walsgrave, Coventry CV2 2DX Tel: 024 76 602020 Fax: 024 76 535166 Email: nicola.brain@wh-tr.wmids.nhs.uk — MB ChB 1979 Ed.; MRCP (UK) 1985. (Edinburgh University) Cons. Rehabil. Med. Univ. Hosp.s, Coventry & Warks. NHS Trust; Princip. Lect. Univ. Coventry. Socs: FRCP (Lond.). Prev: Sen. Regist. Derbysh. Roy. Infirm.; Research Fell. Christie Hosp. Manch.; Tutor (Rheum.) Univ. Manch.

BRAIN, Paul Darren 24A Gauden Road, London SW4 6LT — MB BS 1994 Lond.

BRAIN, Robert Neville (retired) — LRCP LRCS Ed. LRFPS Glas. 1958 Ed.; LMSSA Lond. 1958. Clin. Asst. (Med.) Manor Hosp. Nuneaton; Indust. Med. Off. 3M's Atherstone. Prev: Sen. Ho. Phys. Manor Hosp. Nuneaton.

BRAIN, Stephen Paul 16 Fifth Avenue, Northville, Bristol BS7 0LP — MB ChB 1988 Manch.; T(GP) 1993.

BRAINE, Karl Flat 9, Alpine Court, 8-10 Palatine Road, Manchester M20 3JA — MB ChB 1993 Manch.

BRAITHWAITE, Mr Bruce Donald Queens Medical Centre, Clifton Bouceuard, Nottingham NG7 2DN Tel: 0709 2139047 Fax: 0709 2139047 Email: surgeon@BDB.org.uk — MB BChir 1988 Camb.; LMSSA Lond 1988; FRCS (Gen Surg) 1999; Mchir 1996; FRCS (Eng) 1992; BA 1985; MA 1988. (Cambridge University) Socs: Vasular Surgic. Soc. (Counc. Mem); Assn Surg. of Gt. Britain & Irel.

BRAITHWAITE, Catherine Pryde Oak Lodge Surgery, 32 Miller Street, Hamilton ML3 7EN Tel: 01698 282350 Fax: 01698 282502; 9 Manse Brae, Dalserf, Larkhall ML9 3BN Tel: 01698 881004 — MB ChB 1968 Aberd.

BRAITHWAITE, Derek Willis, OBE (retired) 9 Hazel Drive, Ripley, Woking GU23 6LQ Tel: 01483 222920 — MB BS Durh. 1952. Prev: Provin. Med. Off. RePub. of Zambia.

BRAITHWAITE, Mr Ian Jonathan Countess of Chester Hospital, Liverpool Road, Chester CH2 1UL Tel: 01244 300021 — MD 1994 Liverp.; MA Camb. 1985; BM BCh Oxf. 1985; FRCS Ed. 1989; FRCS (Orth.) 1994; MChOrth (Liverp.) 1994; FRCS (Eng.) 1997. Cons. Orthop. Surg. Chester. Prev: Fell. (Spinal Surg.) Roy. Nat. Orthop. Hosp. Lond.; Sen. Regist. Mersey.

BRAITHWAITE, Jane Eleanor Gay The Thatch, Chapel Lane, Norwich NR7 0EX Tel: 01603 533543 — MB BChir 1976 Camb.; FRCPath 1997; FRCP (Ed) 1995; BA Camb. 1973, MA 1974; FRCP Lond. 1996; MRCP (UK) 1982; MRCPath 1989. Cons. Haemat. Calderdale & Huddersfield NHS Trust. Socs: Brit. Soc. Haematol. Prev: Sen. Regist. (Haemat.) St. Geo. Hosp. Lond.; Regist. Haematol. St. Geo. Hosp. Lond.; SHO (Gen. Med.) St. Geo. Hosp. Lond.

BRAITHWAITE, Jeffrey Mark 13 Oast House Crescent, Farnham GU9 0NP — MB BCh 1988 Wales.

BRAITHWAITE, Malcolm George, OBE, Col. L/RAMC Long Barn, Hindon Road, Monkton Deverill, Warminster BA12 7EZ — MB ChB 1975 Birm.; MFOM RCP Lond. 1989, AFOM 1987; DIH Lond. 1987; DAvMed FOM RCP Lond. 1984; DObst 1980; 1999 FFOM RCP Lond. Cons. Aviat. Med. Warminster; Research Med. Off. DRA Centre for Human Sci. FarnBoro.. Prev: Sen. Specialist (Aviat. Med.) RAMC.

BRAITHWAITE, Michael X-Ray Department, North Staffs Royal Infirmary, Hartshill, Stoke-on-Trent ST4 7LN; Hilldene, Audlem Road, Woore, Crewe CW3 9RL Tel: 01630 647819 — MB ChB 1972 Ed.;

MRCP (UK) 1975; FRCR 1978. Cons. Radiol. N. Staffs. Roy. Infirm. Stoke-on-Trent.

BRAITHWAITE, Mr Peter Allen 27 Heol Wen, Rhiwbina, Cardiff CF14 6EG Tel: 029 2062 7729 — MB BS 1971 Tasmania; MA Wales 1989; FRCS Eng. 1976. Cons. Surg. P. Chas. Hosp. Merthyr Tydfil. Prev: Sen. Lect. (Surg.) Univ. Hosp. Wales; Lect. Surg. Univ. Hosps. Melbourne & Tasmania.

BRAITHWAITE, Philip Anaesthetic Department, Pinderfields Hospital, Aberford Road, Wakefield WF1 Tel: 01924 212348 — MB ChB 1980 Dundee; FFA RCSI 1989. Cons. Anaesth. Pinderfields Hosp. Wakefield. Socs: Assn. Anaesth. Prev: Cons. Anaesth. Gen. Infirm. Leeds.

***BRAITHWAITE, Richard** St Mary's Hospital, Parkhurst Road, Newport PO30 5TD Tel: 01983 524081 — BM 1997 Soton.

BRAITHWAITE, Sally Ann 24 Rheidol Terrace, London N1 8NS — MB ChB 1993 Bristol.

BRAKE, Robert Clive 9 Wentworth Road, Four Oaks, Sutton Coldfield B74 2SD — MB BCh 1970 Wales; MRCGP 1975. (Cardiff)

BRAM, George 14E Cadogan Square, London SW1X 0JU Tel: 020 7235 5985 — MD 1934 Naples; FRCPsych 1972. Socs: BMA. Prev: Cons. Psychiat. & Phys. Supt. Mabledon Hosp. Dartford; Med. Off. Neuropsychiat. Dept. Univ. Turin; Head of Neuropsychiat. Div. Dept. Health of Polish Govt.

BRAMBLE, Bozena Pathology Department, Ashford Hospital, London Road, Ashford TW15 3AA Tel: 01784 884513 or 884052; 122 Brodrick Road, Hampden Park, Eastbourne BN22 9NY Tel: 07932 362829 — MUDr 1970 Palacky Univ. Czech.; FRC Path; MRCPath 1987. Cons. Histocytopath. Ashford Middlx. Socs: Roy. Coll. of Path.; Assn. of Clin. Pathologists; MDU MUF Assn. of Forens.e Pathologists.

BRAMBLE, David John Pear Tree Cottage, Chapel Lane, Harmston, Lincoln LN5 9TB — MB ChB 1982 Leic.

BRAMBLE, Mr Frank James 5 Roslin Road, Bournemouth BH3 7JA Tel: 01202 529680 — MRCS Eng. LRCP Lond. 1966; MS Lond. 1975, MB BS 1966; FRCS Eng. 1971. (Middlx.) Cons. Urol. Roy. Vict. Hosp. Bournemouth. Prev: Sen. Regist. Urol. Leeds Gen. Infirm.; Ho. Surg. & Cas. Surg. Off. Middlx. Hosp.; Ho. Phys. Roy. N.. Hosp. Lond.

BRAMBLE, Professor Michael Graham Endoscopy Centre, South Cleveland Hospital, Marton Road, Middlesbrough TS4 3BW Tel: 01642 854846 Fax: 01642 854765 Email: m.g.bramble@durham.ac.uk; 666 Yarm Road, Eaglescliffe, Stockton-on-Tees TS16 0DP Tel: 01642 780761 Fax: 01642 648575 — MB ChB 1973 Sheff.; MD Sheff. 1983; FRCP Lond. 1995; FRCP Ed. 1986; MRCP (UK) 1975. Cons. Phys. S. Tees Acute Hosps. NHS Trust; Prof. Centre for Health Studies Univ. of Durh. Socs: Fell. RCP; Brit. Soc. Gastroenterol.; N. Eng. Gastroenterol. Soc. Prev: Sen. Regist. Roy. Vict. Infirm. Newc.; Regist. (Med.) N. Tees Gen. Hosp.

BRAMBLE, Nicholas Paul 19 Tichborne Street, Leicester LE2 0NQ — MB ChB 1988 Leic.

BRAMBLEBY, Peter Jonathan St. Andrews House, Norwich NR7 0HT Tel: 01603 307206 Fax: 01603 307104 Email: peter.brambleby@norfolk.nhs.uk; 21 Glenalmond, Norwich NR4 6AG Tel: 01603 505332 — MB BS 1980 Lond.; FRCP Ed. 1995; MRCP (UK) 1986; MFPHM RCP (UK) 1989; DCH RCP Lond. 1984; FFPHM 1998. (Roy. Free Hosp.) Cons. Pub. Health Norf. HA; Hon. Sen. Lect. Univ. E. Anglia; Exec. Comm., Norwich Primary Care Trust. Prev: Cons. Pub. Health E. Sussex HA; Sen. Regist. (Pub. Health Med.) SE Thames RHA; Regist. (Paediat.) Roy. Aberd. Childr. Hosp.

BRAME, Mr Kevin George Scarborough District, Woodlands Drive, Scarborough YO12 6QL Tel: 01723 342475; The Old Vicarage, 29 Main St, Seamer, Scarborough YO12 4PS Tel: 01723 864755 — MB BS 1976 Lond.; BSc Lond. 1973; MS Lond. 1988; FRCS Eng. 1980; MRCS Eng. LRCP Lond. 1976. (Guy's) Cons. Surg. & Urol. ScarBoro. & E. Yorks. Dist. HA. Socs: Brit. Assn. Urol. Surg.; E.A.U. Prev: Sen. Regist. (Urol.) St. Paul's & Guy's Hosps. Lond.; Sen. Regist. (Gen. Surg.) Lewisham Hosp. Lond.

BRAMHALL, Mr Simon Roderick The Liver Unit, Queen Elizabeth Hospital, Edgbaston, Birmingham B15 2TH Tel: 0121 697 8492 Fax: 0121 414 1833 Email: s.r.bramhall@bham.ac.uk; Tel: 01527 592905 — MB ChB 1988 Birm.; FRCS (Gen. Surg.) 1997; FRCS Ed. 1993; MD Birm. 1998. (Univ. of Birm.) Hon. Cons. (Surg.) Q.E. Hosp.; Clin. Lect. (Surg) Univ. Birm. Prev: Clin. Lect. (Surg.) Univ. Birm.; Clin. Research Fell. Dudley Rd. Hosp. Birm.; Regist. Profess Unit Qu. Eliz. Hosp.

BRAMLEY, Angela Margaret Tel: 0113 243 6436 — MB BS 1976 Newc.; MRCGP 1980; LLB (Hons) 1998. Medico Legal Advisor. Prev: GP.

BRAMLEY, Caron Holmcroft Surgery, Holmcroft Road, Stafford ST16 1JG Tel: 01785 242172; Hollybank Farm, Garshall Green, Milwich, Stone ST18 0EP — MB ChB 1988 Birm.; DRCOG 1992. GP. Prev: Trainee GP Mid. Staffs. HA VTS; Ho. Phys. New Cross Hosp. Wolverhampton; Ho. Surg. Sandwell Dist. Gen. Hosp.

BRAMLEY, Lady Hazel Morag (retired) Greenhills, Back Lane, Hathersage, Hope Valley, Sheffield S32 1AR Tel: 01433 650502 — MB ChB 1951 Glas.; MA Glas. 1945. Indep. Psychosexual Med. Sheff.; Lect. Malaysian Coll. GPs 1995; Seminar Train. Doctor Inst. Psychosexual Med. Prev: Specialist (Psychosexual Med.) Barnsley Family Plann. Cl.

BRAMLEY, Mr John Ewart Dawson (retired) 20 anson Drive, Stafford ST17 0LT Tel: 01785 660186 — MB ChB Sheff. 1959; BDS Birm. 1951; FRCS Eng. 1970; FRCS Ed. 1968. Prev: Cons. Orthop. Surg. Mid-Staffs. Hosp. Gp.

BRAMLEY, Keith William Forest Gate Surgery, Hazel Farm Road, Totton, Southampton SO40 8WU Tel: 02380 663839 Fax: 02380 667090; 10 Whartons Close, Colbury, Ashurst, Southampton SO40 7EE Tel: 02380 292148 — MB ChB 1957 Birm. (Birm.) Prev: Ho. Surg. (O & G), Ho. Phys. (Gen. Med.) & SHO (Gen. Surg.) Hallam Hosp. W. Bromwich; Flight Lt. RAF Med. Serv.

BRAMLEY, Maria Dawn 1 Keats Drive, Hucknall, Nottingham NG15 6TE; 4 Westmorland Drive, Didsbury, Manchester M20 2TA Tel: 0161 445 7034 — MB ChB 1991 Sheff.; FRCS Eng. 1995. p/t SpR. Gen. Surg., N.W. Region. Prev: Clin. Research Fell., S. Manc. Uni. Hosp., NHS Trust.; SHO. Gen. Surg. N. Gen. Hosp. Sheff..

BRAMLEY, Michael John Holly House, Watling St., Potterspury, Towcester NN12; The Health Centre, Stony Stratford, Milton Keynes MK7 7PB Tel: 01908 565555 — MB BS 1970 Newc.; MRCP (UK) 1973; DPM Eng. 1975. GP Stony Stratford.

BRAMLEY, Professor Sir Paul Anthony Greenhills, Back Lane, Hathersage, Hope Valley, Sheffield S32 1AR Tel: 01433 650502 — 1952 MB ChB Birm. 1952; 1945 BDS Birm. 1945; 1994 Hon. MD Sheff.; 1989 Hon. DDSC Prince of Songkla; 1987 Hon. DDS Birm.; 1984 FRCS Eng.; 1952 MRCS Eng. LRCP Lond.; 1953 FDS RCS Eng. 1953; 1982 FRACDS; 1944 LDS. (Birm.) Emerit. Prof. Dent. Surg. Univ. Sheff.; Emerit. Cons. Oral Surg. Trent RHA; Emerit. Civil. Cons. Roy. Navy. Socs: BMA & BDA; BAOMS. Prev: Dean Fac. Dent. Surg. & Mem. Counc. RCS Eng.; Dean Sch. Clin. Dent. Univ. Sheff.; Mem. Roy. Commiss. NHS.

BRAMLEY, Peter Nigel Stirling Royal Infirmary, Livilands, Stirling FK8 2AU; Newton Cottage, St. Margaret's Drive, Dunblane FK15 0DP — MB ChB 1984 Leeds; BSc (Hons.) Leeds 1981; MRCP (UK) 1987. Cons. Gastroenterol. & Gen. Phys. Stirling Roy. Infirm.

BRAMLEY, Rhidian The Firs, Broad Lane, Tanworth-in-Arden, Solihull B94 5DP — MB ChB 1991 Manch.; BSc Hons. (Path.) Manch. 1989; MRCP (UK) 1995. Specialist Regist. (Radiol.) NW RHA. Prev: SHO (Gen. Med.) Manch. Roy. Infirm.; SHO (Gen. Med.) Blackburn & Ribble Valley HA; SHO (A & E) S. Manch. HA.

BRAMLEY, Rhonwen Helen The Firs, Broad Lane, Wood End, Tanworth-in-Arden, Solihull B94 5DP — BM BCh 1996 Oxf.

BRAMLEY, Roger John The Seaton & Colyton Medical Practice, 148 Harlepath Road, Seaton EX12 2DU Tel: 01297 20877 — BM BS 1988 Nottm.; BMedSci. Nottm. 1985; MRCGP 1994; DRCOG 1994; T(GP) 1994.

BRAMLEY, Sian The Firs, Broad Lane, Wood End, Tanworth in Arden, Solihull B94 5DP Tel: 01564 742274 Fax: 01564 742959 — MB BCh 1967 Wales. (Cardiff) Socs: BMA.

BRAMMAH, Alison Lindsay Doctor's Mess, Cumberland Infirmary, Newton Road, Carlisle CA2 7HY Tel: 01228 23444; Glebe House, Upper Chute, Andover SP11 9EG Tel: 01264 730684 — MB BS 1992 Lond.

BRAMMAH, Therese Bernadette Rheumatology Department, Tameside Acute Trust, Fountain St., Ashton-under-Lyne OL6 9RW Tel: 0161 331 6724; 10 Cabot Close, Warrington WA5 9QQ — MB ChB 1986 Liverp.; MRCP (UK) 1990. (Liverpool) Cons. (Rheumatol.) Tameside Hosp. Ashton Under Lyne; Hon. Arc Research Fell. Arc Epidemiol. Research Unit Manch. Socs: Brit. Soc. Rheum.; BMA. Prev: Sen. Regist. (Rheumatol.) Hope Hosp. Manch.; Clin.

Lect./Regist. (Rheumatol.) Univ. Manch. & Hope Hosp.; Regist. (Gen. Med.) Walton Hosp. Liverp. & Countess of Chester Hosp.

BRAMMAR, David Keith 14 Storth Avenue, Sheffield S10 3HL — MB ChB 1961 Sheff.; DO Eng. 1968.

BRAMMAR, Mr Timothy James 65 Abbots Road, Leicester LE5 1DD — MB BS 1993 Lond.; MB BS (Hons. Distinc. in Surg.) Lond. 1993; BA (Hons.) Liverp. 1987; FRCS Eng. 1997. Specialist Regist. E. Anglian (Camb.) Rotat. Orthop. Prev: SHO Rotat. (Surg.) United Bristol Health Trusts; Demonst. (Anat.) Char. Cross Hosp. Lond.; Ho. Off. (Surg.) & SHO Ipswich NHS Trust.

BRAMMER, Christopher George Bury Helath Care NHS Trust, Fairfield General Hospital, Rochdale Old Road, Bury BL9 7TD Tel: 0161 705 3210 Fax: 0161 705 3410 Email: alunella@hotmail.com — MB ChB 1991 Ed.; MRCPath 2000; MRCP (UK) 1994. (Edinburgh) Cons. Haematologist, Bury Health Care NHS Trust; Cons. Haematologist, Rochdale Health Care NHS Trust. Prev: SHO (Neurol.) Walton Centre for Neurol Liverp.; SHO (Med. for Elderly & Cardiol.) BRd.green Hosp. Liverp.; Specialist Regist. (Haemat.) Roy. Liverp. & BRd.green Univ. Hosps. Liverp.

BRAMMER, Muriel Ann Community Health Services NHS Trust, Southern Derbyshire, Ilkeston Health Centre, South St., Ilkeston DE7 5PZ Tel: 0115 930 5599 Fax: 0115 944 5955 — MB ChB Sheff. 1964; DCH Eng. 1967. (Sheff.) Clin. Med. Off. S. Derbysh. HA. Socs: MRCPCH; BACCH. Prev: Dept. Med. Off. Derbysh. AHA; Clin. Asst. & Ho. Phys. Derbysh. Childr. Hosp.; Ho. Phys. City Gen. Hosp. Sheff.

BRAMMER, Philip Anthony 169 Albion Way, Verwood BH31 7LT — MB ChB 1992 Birm.; MRCP 1996.

BRAMMER, Roger David 139 Tiverton Road, Selly Oak, Birmingham B29 6BS Tel: 0121 472 3950 — MB ChB 1994 Birm. SHO (Surg.) Sandwell Dist. Gen. Hosp. Lyndon, W. Bromwich. Prev: Lect. (Anat.) Univ. Birm. Med. Sch.

BRAMPTON, William John Department Anaesthetics, Cheltenham General Hospital, Cheltenham GL53 7AN Tel: 01242 222222 Fax: 01242 273405 Email: william.brampton@egnhst.org.uk — MB BChir 1981 Camb.; MA Camb. 1982, MB BChir 1981; FRCA 1986. Cons. Anaesth. E. Gloucestershire NHS Trust. Socs: Assn. Anaesth. & Intens. Care Soc. Prev: Sen. Regist. Rotat. (Anaesth.) Oxf.shire RHA; Asst. Prof. Anaesth. Univ. Maryland, USA; Regist. Rotat. (Anaesth.) Bristol & W.on & Bath Health Authorities.

BRAMWELL, Eleanor Ruth 2 St Ian's Croft, Addingham, Ilkley LS29 0RS — MB ChB 1990 Leeds.

BRAMWELL, Ewen Crighton, MBE (retired) Mill Cottage, Holmwood, Dorking RH5 4NT Tel: 01306 889232 Fax: 01306 889232 — MB BChir Camb. 1955; MA Camb. 1956; DObst RCOG 1961. Chairm. Cameron Fund; Med. Mem. NHS Tribunal. Prev: GP Surrey.

BRAMWELL, Frances Elizabeth 6 Hilary Close, Polegate BN26 5JH — LMSSA 1949 Lond. (Roy. Free) Prev: Ho. Phys. & Ho. Surg. Roy. Hosp. Richmond; Jun. Cas. Off. Qu. Mary's Hosp. For E. End.

BRAMWELL, John Crighton Sevenposts Surgery, 326A Prestbury Road, Prestbury, Cheltenham GL52 3DD Tel: 01242 244103 Fax: 01242 253571; Fax: 01242 674261 — MB BS 1984 Lond.; DRCOG 1989; DCH RCP Lond. 1989. Prev: Trainee GP Malvern; SHO (O & G) P.ss Alexandra Hosp. Harlow; SHO (Paediat.) Epsom Dist. Hosp.

BRAMWELL, Reginald Warwick 11 Palmers Avenue, Grays RM17 5TX — MRCS Eng. LRCP Lond. 1958.

BRAMWELL, Roderick Guy Byrom The Grange, Barnoldby Le Beck, Grimsby DN37 0AS — MB BS 1973 Lond.; BSc Lond. 1970, MB BS 1973; FRCA 1979; DA Eng. 1976. Cons. Anaesth. N. E. Lincs. NHS Trust. Prev: Sen. Regist. (Anaesth.) Middlx. Hosp. Lond.

BRAMWELL, Stephen Oliver, MBE, Col. late RAMC Retd. (retired) 95 Lower Park Road, Hastings TN34 2LE Tel: 01424 427466 — MB ChB Ed. 1937; FRCA 1992; FFA RCS Eng. 1953; DA Eng. 1950. Prev: Cons. Anaesth. RAMC & Adviser (Anaesth.) To War Office.

BRAMWELL, Mr Stephen Paul Department of Urology, Raigmore Hospital NHS Trust, Inverness IV3 3UJ Tel: 01463 704000; 18 Chanonry Crescent, Fortrose IV10 8RH Tel: 01381 621647 — MB ChB 1978 Ed.; BSc (Hons.) Physiol. Ed. 1975; FRCS Glas. 1982; FRCS Edin. 2000. Cons. Urol. Raigmore Hosp. NHS Trust, Inverness. Socs: BMA; Brit. Assn. Urol. Surg.; Sec. Scott. Urol. Soc. Prev: Hon. Sen. Lect. Aberd. Univ.

BRANAGAN, Graham William 2 Silversmiths Way, Woking GU21 3HG — MB BS 1994 Lond.

BRANAGAN, John Paul Allergan Ltd., Coronation Road, High Wycombe HP12 3SH; 1 Mount Pleasant Road, Ealing, London W5 1SG Tel: 020 8991 2862 — MB BCh BAO 1978 Dub.; BA Dub. 1978; FRCPI 1991, M 1982; MFPM 1993. (Trinity Coll. Dub.) Gp. Clin. Research Dir. Verum Internat. Guildford; Mem. Amer. Coll. Clin. Pharmacol. Socs: Irish Cardiac Soc.; Amer. Soc. Clin. Pharmacol. & Therap. Prev: Dep. Managing Dir./Med. Dir., Eisai Europe Ltd. Lond.; Med. Dir. Inst. Clin. Pharmacol. Irel. & USA; Regist. (Cardiol.) St. Jas. Hosp. Dub.

BRANCH, Kingsley George James Paget Hospital, Lowestoft Road, Gorleston, Great Yarmouth NR31 6LA Tel: 01493 452452; 29 Bernard Road, Gorleston-on-Sea, Great Yarmouth NR31 6EG Tel: 01493 653485 — MB ChB 1956 Birm.; DA Eng. 1965; FFA RCS Eng. 1969. Cons. Anaesth. Gt. Yarmouth & Waveney Health Dist. Socs: Assn. Anaesth. Gt. Brit. & Irel. Prev: Cons. in Anaesth. RAF; Cons. Anaesth. St. Vincentius Ziekenauis Groenlo Holland.

***BRANCHFIELD, Patrick Joseph John** Flat 1/2, 12 Rutland Court, Kinning Park, Glasgow G51 1JZ Tel: 0141 429 0828 — MB ChB 1998 Glas.; MB ChB Glas 1998.

BRAND, Alexander James Orchar 48 Deanhill Court, Upper Richmond Road W., East Sheen, London SW14 7DL Tel: 020 8878 2327 — MB BS 1991 Lond.; MRCP (UK) 1995. (St. Thos. Hosp.) Specialist Regist. (Rheum. & Gen. Med.) Chelsea & W.m. Hosp.

BRAND, Andrea Dagmar 8 Hemdean Road, Caversham, Reading RG4 7SX Tel: 0118 948 2277 — MB ChB 1988 Manch.; MRCGP 1995. DFFP. Socs: BMA; RGCP. Prev: Trainee GP Cambs.; Resid. - Family Med. UMASS, MA, USA; Resid. - Internal Med. UMASS, MA, USA.

BRAND, Anna Jane 57 Barley Road, Great Chishill, Royston SG8 8SD — MB BS 1997 Lond.

BRAND, Anne Elizabeth 27 Ranby Road, Sheffield S11 7AJ — MB ChB 1989 Sheff.; FRCA 1996. Regist. (Anaesth.) Centr. Sheff. Univ. Hosps.

BRAND, Christopher Stephen 27 Ranby Road, Sheffield S11 7AJ — MB ChB 1989 Sheff.; FRCOphth 1995.

BRAND, David Sutherland Rohais Medical Centre, Rohais, St Peter Port, Guernsey GY1 1FF Tel: 01481 23322; Rockmount, Pleinmont Road, Torteval, Guernsey Tel: 01481 65436 — MB ChB 1974 Glas.

BRAND, Felicity Jane 14 Pelham Road, Clavering, Saffron Walden, Saffron Walden CB11 4PQ — MB ChB 1997 Sheff.; MB ChB (Hons) Sheff. 1997. Prev: SHO (A & E), Brighton; PRHO (Surg.), Brighton; PRHO (Med.), Brighton.

BRAND, Ian Russell Hillside, Burley Woodhead, Ilkley LS29 7AS — MB BCh 1981 Wales; MRCP (UK) 1984; FRCR 1989. Cons. Radiol. Airedale Gen. Hosp. Prev: Sen. Regist. (Diag. Radiol.) Leeds Gen. Infirm. & St. Jas. Univ. Hosp.; SHO Rotat. (Med. & Paediat.) Dudley Rd. Hosp. Birm.; Trainee GP Egton & Danby.

BRAND, James Stuart Gordon 2 The Link, Risinghurs, Oxford OX3 8DU Tel: 01865 741313 — MB BS 1985 Lond.; BSc Lond. 1982; MRCGP 1990; Cert. Family Plann. JCC 1989; DGM RCP Lond. 1988. (Char. Cross & Westm.) Prev: Trainee GP Aylesbury & Crawley; Trainee GP/SHO Harold Wood Hosp.

BRAND, Jane Vivienne Beech Grove Surgery, Mall Road, Brading, Sandown PO36 0DE Tel: 01983 407775 Fax: 01983 406277 — MB ChB 1971 Birm.; DA Eng. 1974. Prev: Clin. Asst. Diabetic Unit St. Mary's Hosp. Newport.

BRAND, Joseph John, Surg. Lt.-Cdr. RN Retd. 31 The Avenue, Alverstoke, Gosport PO12 2JS Tel: 01705 587218 — MB BS Lond. 1957; MD Lond. 1968; MRCS Eng. LRCP Lond. 1956. (King's Coll. Hosp.) Clin. Asst. (Occupat. Health) Portsmouth Hosps. NHS Trust. Socs: BMA; Soc. Occup. Med. Prev: GP Gosport Hants.; Med. Off. (Research) RAF Inst. Aviat. Med.; Clin. Research Asst. (Pharmacol.) Edin. Univ.

BRAND, Mary Ann Jeffrey Torrance (retired) 62 Edenbank Road, Cupar KY15 4UA — MB ChB 1944 Ed.; MD Ed. 1950; FRCR 1952; DMRT 1948. Prev: Cons. Radiother. W.. Gen. Hosp. Edin.

BRAND, Nicholas Robin Edward 52 Foulden Road, London N16 7UR — MB BS 1991 Lond. (St. Bartholomews)

BRAND, Peter Beech Grove Surgery, Mall Road, Brading, Sandown PO36 0DE Tel: 01983 407775 Fax: 01983 406277 — MRCS Eng. LRCP Lond. 1971; MRCGP 1979; DObst RCOG 1973. (Birmingham Univ.) GP. Prev: GP, Poole.

BRANDER, Elizabeth Anne Spieker Red Hill Surgery, 11 Redhill, Chislehurst BR7 6DB Tel: 020 8467 7419 Fax: 020 8295 1270 — MB BS 1990 Lond.; BSc Lond. 1987; DFFP 1994; MRCGP 1995; DRCOG 1994; DGUM 1998. (King's College London) p/t GP Princip. Redhill Surg.

BRANDES, Emile Alexander Victoria Road Health Centre, Victoria Road, Washington NE37 2PU Tel: 0191 416 2578 Fax: 0191 415 7382 — MB BCh 1976 Withwatersrand; MB BCh Witwatersrand 1976. (Withwatersrand) GP Washington Tyne & Wear.

BRANDMAN, Stuart The Conifers, 171 High Road, Chigwell IG7 6PS Tel: 020 8500 2924 — MB BS 1979 Lond.; DRCOG 1982.

BRANDNER, Brigitta 123 Kyverdale Road, London N16 6PS — State Exam Med 1987 Berlin; FRCA 1993.

BRANDON, Anne-Marie 14 Uddingston Road, Bothwell, Glasgow G71 8PH Tel: 0141 853024 — MB ChB 1990 Dundee; MRCGP 1995.

BRANDON, Daniel Joseph 8 Brierie Hill Grove, Crossle, Johnstone PA6 7BW — MB ChB 1985 Glas.

BRANDON, Emma Louise Anaesthetic Department, Milton Keynes General Hospital NHS Trust, Standing Way, Eaglestone, Milton Keynes MK6 5LD; 42 Hollow Wood, Olney MK46 5LZ — MB ChB 1994 Ed.; BSc (Hons.) Biochem. Ed. 1991. SHO (Anaesth.) Milton Keynes NHS Trust. Prev: SHO (Anaesth.) Roy. Infirm. Edin.; SHO (A & E) Milton Keynes NHS Trust.

BRANDON, Helene Anne Newcastle General Hospital, Westgate Road, Newcastle upon Tyne NE4 6BE Tel: 0191 273 8811; 33 Reid Park Road, Newcastle upon Tyne NE2 2ER — MB ChB 1989 Manch.; MA Manch. 1983, BA 1979, MB ChB 1989. SHO (O & G) Newc. Gen. Hosp. Prev: SHO (O & G) St. Mary's Hosp. Manch.; SHO (Surg.) Withington Hosp. Manch.

***BRANDON, Sophie Eleanor Grace** First Floor Flat, 136 Antill Road, London E3 5BN Tel: 020 8981 8724; First Floor Flat, 136 Antill Road, London E3 5BN Tel: 020 8981 8724 — MB BS 1998 Lond.; MB BS Lond 1998.

BRANDON, Professor Sydney 19 Holmfield Road, Leicester LE2 1SD Tel: 0116 210 9534 Fax: 0116 210 9533 Email: sbrandon1@compuserve.com — MB BS 1954 Durh.; MD Durh. 1960; FRCPsych 1973, M 1971; FRCP Lond. 1985, M 1980; DPM Durham. 1961; DCH Eng. 1956. (Newc.) Emerit. Prof. of Psychiat. & Postgrad. Dean Univ. Leicester; Hon. Civil. Cons. (Psychiat.) RAF. Socs: Fell. Roy. Soc. Med. (Pres. Psychiat. Sect.).; (Ex-Chairm.) Assn. Univ. Teach. Psychiat. Prev: Reader (Psychiat.) Univ. Manch.; Nuffield Foundat. Fell. Univ. Newc.; Vis. Fell. (Psychiat.) Columbia Univ., NY.

BRANDRETH, Ashton Roland (retired) Ash Tree Cottage, Brook Bottom, Manchester Road, Tideswell, Buxton SK17 8LL Tel: 01298 871876 — MB BS Lond. 1943; MRCS Eng. LRCP Lond. 1943.

BRANDRETH, Thomas Keith (retired) 15 High Street, Heckington, Sleaford NG34 9RA Tel: 01529 960397 — MB BS Lond. 1949. Prev: Ho. Phys. Chase Farm Hosp. Enfield & City Hosp. Derby.

BRANDRICK, Mr John Thomas ENT Department, Fairfield General Hospital, Bury BL9 7TD Tel: 0161 764 3989 Fax: 0161 705 3671; Hawthorns, 45 Bury New Road, Ramsbottom, Bury BL0 0AR Tel: 01706 822473 — MB ChB 1978 Birm.; BDS Birm. 1968; FRCS Eng. 1983; FDS RCS Eng. 1979. (Univ. Birm.) Cons. ENT Surg. Bury & Rochdale Health Dist. Socs: BMA; Brit. Assn. Otol.; Roy. Soc. Med. Prev: Sen. Regist. (ENT Surg.) W. Midl. HA; Regist. (ENT) Qu. Eliz. Hosp. Birm.; Regist. (Oral & Maxillofacial Surg.) Greenbank Hosp. Plymouth.

BRANDTS, Hans Harald 4 Swift Street, Ashton-under-Lyne OL6 8HA Tel: 0161 343 4216 — State Exam Med. Bonn 1990.

BRANFOOT, Mr Jonathan Toby Carre Leeds General Infirmary, Great Greorge St., Leeds LS1 3EX; 1 Kingsland Avenue, Stoke-on-Trent ST4 5LA Tel: 01782 749254 Email: toby.branfoot@almac.co.uk — MB BS 1989 Lond.; FRCS Ed. 1995; Dip. IMC RCS Ed. 1994; DA (UK) 1994. (St. Bart.) Specialist Regist. Rotat. (Orthop.) Leeds. Socs: Fell. Fac. Pre-Hosp. Care; BOTA. Prev: SHO (Orthop.) N. Staffs. Hosp.; SHO (Surg.) Wrexham Maellor Hosp.; SHO (Anaesth.) Roy. Shrewsbury Hosp.

BRANFOOT, Kerensa Jane Temple House Surgery, Temple St., Keynsham, Bristol BS31 1EJ — MB BS 1992 Lond.; BSc (Hons.) Wales 1986; MRCGP 1996; DFFP 1995; DRCOG 1994; Dip. Therapeut 1998. (Lond.) GP Princip.

BRANFORD, Margaret Rushden Hospital, Wymington Road, Rushden NN10 9JS Tel: 01536 494313 Fax: 01933 410754 — MB ChB 1973 Ed.; BSc (Med. Sci.) Hons. 1970; MRCPsych 1989. (Univ. Ed.) Cons. Psychiat. of Old Age N.amptonshire Healthcare NHS Trust. Prev: Sen. Regist. Oxf. Regional Train. Scheme; Psychiatric SHO/Regist. N.ants. Train. Scheme; SHO Geriat. Vict. Hosp. Kirkcaldy.

BRANFORD, Olivier Alexander 2 St Katherines Road, Caterham CR3 6ST — MB BS 1998 Lond.; MB BS Lond 1998.

BRANFORD, William Andrew Kettering General Hospital, Rothwell Road, Kettering NN16 8UZ Tel: 01536 492185 — MB ChB 1973 Ed.; FRCP Lond. 1994; FRCP Ed. 1990; MRCP (UK) 1975. p/t Cons. Dermat. Kettering Dist. Socs: Fell. Roy. Med. Soc. Edin.; Fell. Roy. Soc. Med. (Mem. Sect. Dermat.). Prev: Sen. Regist. (Dermat.) Coventry AHA; Ho. Surg. Roy. Infirm. Edin.; Ho. Phys. City Hosp. Edin.

BRANKER, Magda Delicia 19 Cornwallis Court, Lansdowne Way, London SW8 2NU — MB BS 1998 Lond.; MB BS Lond 1998.

BRANKIN, Eamonn Church Street, 7 Church Street, Coatbridge ML5 3EE Tel: 01236 422678 Fax: 01236 431411; 3 Barrachavie Grove, Garrowhill, Glasgow G69 6SS — MB ChB 1986 Glas.; MSc 2000 (Med Sci) Glas.; MRCP (UK) 1995; MRCGP 1990; DFM Glas. 1995; Dip. IMC RCS Ed. 1990. (Glasgow) Princip. in Gen. Pract.; Assoc. Adviser in Gen. Med. Pract. Scot. Counc. for Postgrad. Med. & Dent. Educ., & Hon. Clin. Sen. Lect. Dept of Postgrad. Med. Univ. of Glas; Sen./Co-ordinating Med. Off., Dept of Maj. Event Med., Gt.er Glas. Health Bd., Galsgow.; Hosp. Practitioner in Diabetic Med. Roy. Alexandra Hosp. NHS Trust, Paisley. Socs: M-C Soc. Glas.; Brit. Assn. Immed. Care Schemes; Brit. Assn. Sport & Med. Prev: Research Fell. Glas. Roy. Infirm.

BRANLEY, Howard Matthew 86 Redbridge Lane W., London E11 2LA Email: hbranley@aol.com — MB ChB 1992 Liverp.; Cert Av Med, 1997; MRCP(UK), 1996. Specialist Regist. in Respitory Med., Imperial Coll. Sch. of Med., The Hammersmith Hosp., Lond.; Hon. Research Fell., Dept of Allergy & Clin. Immunity, Nat. heart & Lung Inst., Imperial Coll. Sch. of Med., Lond. Socs: Brit. Thoracic Soc. Prev: Specialist Regist. Resp Med, St. Mary's Hosp. Lond.; Specialist Regist. Resp Med, St Albans & Hemel Hempstead Hosp.; SHO Med., Ealing Hosp., Lond.

BRANN, Leslie Robert Towson and Partners, Juniper Road, Boreham, Chelmsford CM3 3DX Tel: 01245 467364 Fax: 01245 465584; The Keep, Nounsley Road, Hatfield Peverel, Chelmsford CM3 2NQ — MB BS 1979 Lond.; BSc CNAA 1972; M Med. Sci. Univ. Sheff. 1997; MRCS Eng. LRCP Lond. 1979; MRCGP 1983; Dip. Clin. Hyp. Univ. Sheff. 1991; DRCOG 1981. (Guy's) Chairm. Chelmsford PCG. Socs: (Vice-Pres.) BSECH; Accred. Mem. Brit. Soc. Med. & Dent. Hypn. Prev: Trainee GP Chelmsford VTS.

BRANNAM, Helen Rachel Brooklyn Cottage, Ash Thomas, Tiverton EX16 4NS — MB ChB 1997 Birm.

BRANNAN, Mr Martin Antony (retired) Princess Elizabeth Hospital, Le Vauquiedor, St Martin's, Guernsey GY4 6UU Tel: 01481 725241 Fax: 01481 35905 — MB BS 1965 Newc.; FRCOG 1984, M 1971; DObst 1968. Prev: Cons. O & G P.ss Eliz. Hosp.

BRANNEN, Ian Cameron (retired) 51 Grove Road, Norwich NR1 3RQ Tel: 01603 631501 — MB ChB 1947 Aberd.; 1987 BA (Hons.) Univ. E. Anglia; 1947 MB ChB Aberd.; 1954 MRCP Ed.; 1972 MFCM; 1957 DPH Ed.; FRCP 1994 Ed. Prev: Dist. Community Phys. Norwich.

BRANNIGAN, Mary (retired) Mill Cottage, Lemmington Hall, Alnwick NE66 2BH — LRCP LRCS 1949 Ed.; LRCP LRCS Ed. LRFPS Glas. 1949.

BRANNIGAN, Ronan 4 Kylemore Gardens, Omagh BT79 7LL — MB ChB 1996 Dundee.

BRANSBURY, Anthea Jane Stoke Mandeville Hospital, Aylesbury HP21 8AL Tel: 01296 315551; Chaundy's Farm, Westfield Road, Long Crendon, Aylesbury HP18 9EG Tel: 01844 201379 Email: chaundys@aol.com — MB BS 1971 Lond.; MRCP (UK) 1975; Cert. Family Plann JCC 1982. (St. Thos.) Staff Grade (Dermat) Stoke Mandeville Hosp. Aylesbury& Amersham; BPAs- 2 evening sessions;

Brook Adivsory Clinic- session per week, family Plann., Milton Keynes. Socs: NAFPAD; BAD; Eur. Contact Dermat. Research Gp.

BRANSBY-ZACHARY, Mr Marc Adrian Peter Southern General Hospital, 1345 Govan Road, Glasgow G51 4TF Tel: 0141 201 1473; 6 Turnberry Avenue, Glasgow G11 5AQ Email: bz.glasgow@cableol.co.uk — MB BS 1979 Lond.; FRCS Ed. 1985. (St. Thos.) Cons. Orthop. Surg. S.. Gen. Hosp. Glas. Prev: Sen. Regist. (Orthop.) Addenbrooke's Hosp. Camb.

BRANSCOMBE, Fionnuala Maeve 286 Dunchurch Road, Rugby CV22 6HX Tel: 01788 817394 — MB BCh BAO 1968 Dub.

BRANSFIELD, John Joseph Flat 24, Victoria Mill, Belmont Wharf, Skipton BD23 1RL Tel: 01756 792309 — MB BCh BAO NUI 1946. (Univ. Coll. Dub.)

BRANSON, Anthony Nigel North cottage, East Warehouse, Newcastle upon Tyne NE18 0LL — MB 1977 Camb.; BChir 1976; MRCP (UK) 1980; FRCR 1984; FRCP 1999. Cons. Clin. Oncol. Regional Radiother. Centre Newc. u. Tyne.

BRANSON, Elizabeth Oaklea, Corpusty, Norwich NR11 6XA — MB ChB 1980 Leic.; MRCGP 1985. (Leic.)

BRANSON, Helen Irene Coombe Flat, Oakford House, Shaldon Road, Combeinteignhead, Newton Abbot TQ12 4RR — MB BS 1992 Lond.

BRANSON, Katharine 8 Lord Street, Bollington, Macclesfield SK10 5BN — BChir 1995 Camb.

BRANSON, Katharine Mildred Harold (retired) 5/24 Oswald Road, Edinburgh EH9 2HE Tel: 0131 667 3553 — MRCS Eng. LRCP Lond. 1937; MS Lond. 1946, MB BS 1938; FRCS Eng. 1941; FRCS Ed. 1956. Prev: Surg. Bruntsfield & Longmore Hosps. Edin.

BRANSON, Ruben Roy 1 Burnside Gardens, Kirkcudbright DG6 4JY — MB ChB 1995 Glas.

BRANT, Professor Herbert Arnold 10 Broadland Lodge, 18 Broadlands Rd, London N6 4AW Tel: 020 8348 4505 Fax: 020 8340 4833; 10 Broadlands Lodge, 18 Broadlands Road, London N6 4AW Tel: 020 8348 4505 Fax: 020 8340 4833 — MB ChB 1951 NZ; MD Lond. 1975; FRCP Ed. 1977, M 1964; FRCS Ed. 1963; FRCOG 1974, M 1963. (University of Otago, NZ) Emerit. Prof. O & G Univ. Coll. Med. Sch. Lond.; Emerit. Cons. Univ. Coll. Hosps. Lond. Socs: BMA; RSM. Prev: Prof.clin.Obst.Gyn.Univ.coll.Lond; Hon. Cons. Univ. Coll. Hosp.

BRANT, Jonathan Martin Papworth Hospital, Papworth Everard, Cambridge CB3 8RE; 2 Oakhurst Road, Highfield, Southampton SO17 1PP — MB BChir 1989 Camb.; FRCR 1998; MA Camb. 1989; MRCP (UK) 1992. Cardiothoracic Fell. (Radiol) Papworth Hosp. Prev: SHO (Med.) Canterbury & Thanet HA.

BRANT, Stephen Edward Glenlyn Medical Centre, 115 Molesey Park Road, East Molesey KT8 0JX Tel: 020 8979 3253 Fax: 020 8941 7914 — FRCP (Lond) 2001; MB BS Lond. 1977; MSc Lond. 1989; MRCP (UK) 1980; MRCGP 1984; DCH RCP Lond. 1984; DRCOG 1983. (St. Geo.) Prev: Regist. (Gen. Med.) St. Geo. Hosp. Tooting; SHO (O & G) St. Heliers Hosp. Sutton; SHO (Gen. Med.) Roy. Marsden Hosp. Sutton.

BRANTIGAN, Pamela Dawn Mulbarton Surgery, The Common, Mulbarton, Norwich NR14 8JG Tel: 01508 570212 Fax: 01508 570042 — MB ChB 1983 Leic.

BRANTINGHAM, Philip, SBStJ (retired) Saville Medical Group, 7 Saville Place, Newcastle upon Tyne NE1 8DQ Tel: 0191 232 4274 Fax: 0191 233 1050 — MB BS 1961 Durh.; DObst RCOG 1962. Hosp. Pract. St. Nicholas' Hosp. Gosforth; Exec. Mem. LMC. Prev: Ho. Surg. Roy. Vict. Infirm. Newc.

BRANTON, Donald William 5 Penleonard Close, Exeter EX2 4NY Tel: 01392 54207 — MRCS Eng. LRCP Lond. 1967; DObst RCOG 1970. (St. Mary's) Prev: Ho. Phys. & Ho. Surg. King Edwd. Memor. Hosp. Ealing.

BRANTON, John Frederick The Old Fire Station, Albert Terrace, Beverley HU17 8JW Tel: 01482 862236; 25 Northgate, Walkington, Beverley HU17 8ST — MB BS 1958 Lond.; MRCS Eng. LRCP Lond. 1958; FRCGP 1988, M 1968; DGM RCP Lond. 1986; DCH Eng. 1967; DObst RCOG 1966. (Univ. Coll. Hosp.) Socs: BMA.

BRANTON, Timothy 23 Mallaby Close, Shirley, Solihull B90 2PW — BM BS 1989 Nottm.

BRANWOOD, Arthur Whitley 48B High Street, Haddington EH41 3EE Tel: 01620 825525 — MD Ed. 1947, MB ChB 1942; FRCP Lond. 1974, M 1948; FRCP Ed. 1948, M 1945; FRCPath 1969; FACP 1968. Socs: Fell. Fac. Med. Edin. Univ. Prev: Prof. Path. Cornell Univ. New York; Prof. Path. Columbia Univ. New York.

BRAR, Mr Avtar Singh 72 Whirlow Court Road, Sheffield S11 9NT — MB BS 1985 Lond.; MSc Lond. 1995; FRCS Ed. 1992. Specialist Regist. Rotat. Sheff. Prev: Research Fell. Roy. Free Hosp. Sch. Med. Lond.; Regist. Hillingdon Hosp. Uxbridge; Regist. (Trauma & Intens. Care) Groote Schuur Hosp., Cape Town.

BRAR, Helen Baljit Kaur — BM BS 1990 Nottm.; BMedSci (Hons.) Nottm. 1988; FRCA 1997. (Nottm. Univ. Med. Sch.) Specialist Regist. (Anaesth.) Newc. u. Tyne.

BRAR, Salina 4 Marfleet Cl, Lower Earley, Reading RG6 3XL — MB BCh 1997 Wales.

BRAR, Surendar Singh Golders Green Road Surgery, 188 Golders Green Road, London NW11 9AY Tel: 020 8455 1907 — MB ChB 1988 Glas. SHO (A & E) P.ss Alexandra Hosp. Harlow GP VTS.

BRARA, Mr Narindarsingh 31 Balvernie Grove, Southfields, London SW18 5RR Tel: 020 8874 2526 — MB BS 1943 Punjab; MS Agra 1953; BSc Punjab 1938, MB BS 1943; FRCS Glas. 1962; FRFPS Glas. 1957; FRCS Ed. 1957. (King Edwd. Med. Coll. Lahore) Prev: Brigadier Indian AMS, Cons. Orthop. Surg.

BRAS, Paul Johannes King's College Hospital, Denmark Hill, London SE5 9RS Tel: 020 7737 4000; 51 Courtney Road, Colliers Wood, London SW19 2EE — MB BS 1980 Lond.; FRCA 1984. Cons. Anaesth. King's Coll. Hosp. Lond. Prev: Cas. Off. Lond. Hosp. Whitechapel.

BRASH, Charles John Hamilton Greig York Road Surgery, 127 York Road, Hartlepool TS26 9DN Tel: 01429 234646 Fax: 01429 861559 — MB ChB 1978 Glas.

BRASH, Mr John Harry Dalemorr, Woodville Road, Keighley BD20 6JA — MB ChB 1970 Ed.; BSc (Hons.) Ed. 1968, MB ChB 1970; FRCS Ed. 1976; FRCOG 1988, M 1975. Cons. (O & G) Airedale Gen. Hosp. Keighley. Socs: Fell. Edin. Obst. Soc. Prev: Lect. & Sen. Regist. (O & G) St. Jas. Univ. Hosp. Leeds; SHO (O & G) Simpson Memor. Matern. Pavil. & Roy. Infirm. Edin.; Regist. (O & G) W.. Gen. Hosp. Edin.

BRASS, Helen Una (retired) Flat 11, Shrewsbury House, Cheyne Walk, Chelsea, London SW3 5LN — MB BCh BAO Dub. 1942. Prev: Sen. Med. Off. Lancs. HA.

BRASS, Paul Roland Shalva, 27 Angmering Lane, Willowhayne Estate, East Preston, Littlehampton BN16 2TA Tel: 01903 784532 Fax: 01903 786568 — MB BS Lond. 1958; MRCS Eng. LRCP Lond. 1958. (King's Coll. Hosp.) Chief Med. Off. Sterling Insur. Company. Prev: Chief Med. Off. Consolidated Insur. Company.

BRASSETT, Cecilia 105 Victoria Road, Cambridge CB4 3BS Tel: 01223 60288 — MB 1987 Camb.; BChir 1986; FRCS Eng. 1991. Research Regist. Addenbrooke's Hosp. Camb.; Anat. Supervisor Univ. Camb. Prev: Regist. (Gen. Surg.) Maidstone Hosp. Kent; SHO (Gen. Surg.) W. Suff. Hosp. Bury St. Edmunds; Med. Off. (Gen. Surg.) United Christian Hosp., Hong Kong.

BRASSILL, John William Manchester Road Surgery, 280 Manchester Road, Warrington WA1 3RB Tel: 01925 230022 Fax: 01925 575069 — MB BCh BAO 1985 Dub.

BRATBY, Mark John 24 Mark Mansions, Westville Road, London W12 9PS — MB BS 1998 Lond.; MB BS Lond 1998.

BRATCH, Jatinder Singh 46 Montagu Avenue, Newcastle upon Tyne NE3 4JN — MB ChB 1993 Sheff.

BRATT, Andrew 577 Halliwell Road, Bolton BL1 8BZ Tel: 01204 41154 — MB ChB St. And. 1970; DA Eng. 1974; DCH RCPS Glas. 1973; DObst RCOG 1973. (St. And.) Prev: SHO (Anaesth.) Vict. Hosp. Blackpool; Ho. Off. (O & G) Oldham & Dist. Gen. Hosp.; Ho. Phys. Maryfield Hosp. Dundee.

BRATT, Christine Ashley (retired) Rose Cottage, Horsham Road, Handcross, Haywards Heath RH17 6DF Tel: 01444 400318 — MB BS 1950 Lond.; MRCS Eng. LRCP Lond. 1949; DObst RCOG 1953; AFOM RCP Lond. 1981. Prev: Med. Off. BP plc Aden.

BRATT, Clive Cavell (retired) 18 Alexander Close, Bognor Regis PO21 4PR — MB BS Lond. 1953. Prev: GP Bognor Regis.

BRATT, Helen Jane 62 Rosewood Drive, Winsford CW7 2UW — MB BCh 1997 Wales.

BRATT, Kevin Graham The Surgery, 178 Musters Road, West Bridgford, Nottingham NG2 7AA Tel: 0115 981 4472, 0115 982 1836 Fax: 0115 981 2812 — BM BS 1982 Nottm.; BMedSci 1980 Nottm.; Cert. Family Plann. 1985. (Nottm.) GP Nottm. Socs: Assoc. Mem. Roy. Coll. Gen. Pract.; BMA. Prev: Trainee GP Mansfield VTS;

SHO (A & E), Ho. Off. (Surg. & Med.) Mansfield Gen. Hosp.; SHO (O & G & Paediat.) King's Mill. Hosp. Sutton-in-Ashfield.

BRATTEN, Morag Crawford Kilmartin Farm House, Balnain, Glenurquhart, Inverness IV63 6TJ Tel: 01456 476257 — MB ChB 1958 Glas.

BRATTEN, Mr Neil Turner (retired) Kilmartin Farm House, Balnain, Glenurquhart, Inverness IV63 6TJ Tel: 01456 476257 — MB ChB 1960 Glas.; FRCS Ed. 1966. Prev: Clin. Lect., OtoLaryngol., Univ. of Glas.

BRATTON, Mary Louise 58 Pen-y-Peel Road, Canton, Cardiff CF5 1QY — MB BS 1982 Adelaide.

BRATTY, Catherine Ann Cranleigh Health Centre, 18 High Street, Cranleigh GU6 8AE Tel: 01483 273951 Fax: 01483 275755; Alderley Cottage, The Common, Cranleigh GU6 8NS Tel: 01483 272891 — MB BCh BAO 1981 Belf.; MRCGP 1985; DRCOG 1984. (Queen's University Belfast)

BRATTY, John Raymond Ferndale, Hillside Road, Radcliffe on Trent, Nottingham NG12 2GZ — MB BCh BAO 1983 Belf.; BSc (Hons.) 1980; Dip. Pharm. Med. RCP (UK) 1988; DA (UK) 1986.

BRAUDE, Professor Peter Riven GKT Department of Obstetrics & Gynaecology, 10th Floor North Wing:, St Thomas' Hospital, London SE1 7EH Tel: 020 7922 8105 Fax: 020 7620 1227 Email: peter.braude@kcl.ac.uk — MB BCh 1972 Witwatersrand; PhD Camb. 1981, MA 1975; BSc Witwatersrand 1968; FRCOG 1993, M 1982; DPMSA 1983. Prof. O & G & Head Div. Wom. & Childr. Health Guy's, King's & St. Thos. Hosps. Sch. of Med.; Mem. HFEA. Prev: Lect. (Obst.) Univ. Camb.; Hon. Cons. O & G Addenbrooke's Hosp. Camb.; Exec. Sec. Assn. of Profs. O & G.

BRAUDE, Walter 24 Agamemnon Road, London NW6 1DY Tel: 020 7794 8073 — MB ChB 1967 Cape Town; BA Cape Town 1961, MB ChB 1967. (Cape Town) Prev: SHO Dept. Anaesth. Univ. Coll. Hosp. Lond.; Ho. Off. & SHO Groote Schuur Hosp. Cape Town, S. Africa.

BRAUER, Ernst (retired) 14 Rivington Avenue, Woodford Green IG8 8LS Tel: 020 8551 0252 — LRCP LRCS Ed. LRFPS Glas. 1936; MD Breslau 1934. Prev: Ho. Surg. Eye, Ear, Nose & Throat Dept. Roy. Infirm. Preston.

BRAUER, Susan Eileen Braeside, Church Farm, Old Blidworth Village, Mansfield NG21 0QH — MB BS 1974 Lond.; MRCS Eng. LRCP Lond. 1974; FRCR 1984. Cons. Radiol. King's Mill Hosp. Sutton-in-Ashfield. Prev: Cons. Radiol. Mansfield Dist. Gen. Hosp.

BRAUN, Michael Stuart Hyfrydle, Llanasa Road, Gronant, Prestatyn LL19 9TF — MB ChB 1998 Manch.; MB ChB Manch 1998. (University of Manchester) PRHO Vasc. & Urol. Surg., Manch. Roy. Infirm. Prev: PRHO Gen. Med./Gastroencerology, Manch. Roy. Infirm.

BRAUNOLD, Gillian Anne Kilburn Park Medical Centre, 12 Cambridge Gardens, London NW6 5AY Tel: 020 7624 2414 Fax: 020 7624 2489; Brookside, The Rise, Edgware HA8 8NR Tel: 020 8958 3304 Fax: 020 8958 3304 Email: gilian@kilburn.demon.co.uk — MB BS 1979 Lond.; MRCGP 1996; Cert. Family Plann. JCC 1981. (Char. Cross Hosp. Med. Sch.) Chairm. Brent & Harrow LMC.

BRAVE, Isaac Harold Grosvenor House, 11 Grosvenor Road, Colwyn Bay LL29 7YF — LRCPI & LM, LRSCI & LM 1947; LRCPI & LM, LRCSI & LM 1947.

BRAWN, Carolyn Mary 86 Park Hill, Moseley, Birmingham B13 8DS Tel: 0121 449 3227 — MB BS 1970 Lond. GP Birm. Prev: Clin. Med. Off. (Community Med. Child Health) Centr. Birm. HA; GP Soton.; GP Melbourne, Austral.

BRAWN, Lyndsey Ann 7 Highcliffe Place, Highstorrs, Sheffield S11 7LW — MB ChB 1980 Leic.; MRCP (UK) 1983. Research Regist. Roy. Hallamsh. Hosp. Sheff.

BRAWN, Mr William James 86 Park Hill, Moseley, Birmingham B13 8DS Tel: 0121 449 3227 — MB BS 1970 Lond.; FRCS Eng. 1975; FRACS 1981. Cons. Paediat. Cardiac Surg. Childr. Hosp. Birm.; Sen. Clin. Lect. Birm. Univ. Prev: Cons. Paediat. Cardiac Surg. Roy. Childr. Hosp. Melbourne, Australia.

BRAY, Alan James SWIMS Ltd, 24 Kenilworth Road, Knowle, Solihull B93 0JA Tel: 01564 778865 Fax: 01564 771198 Email: dr@abray.fsbusiness.co.uk; Blackhorse Gardens, Clyst-Honiton, Exeter EX5 2AB Tel: 01392 367519, 01392 445159 — MB ChB 1972 Glas.; DA Eng. 1979; AFOM RCP Lond. 1990; MFOM 2000. Cons. (occ med), S. W. InDepend. Med. Serv.s Ltd; Occupat.al Phys. acute Worceste NHS Trust.

BRAY, Alan Philip Royal National Hospital Trust, Brockley Hill, Stanmore HA7 4LP; 1 Main Street, Kirkby Lonsdale, Carnforth LA6 2AQ Tel: 015242 71380 — MB BS 1961 Lond.; MRCS Eng. LRCP Lond. 1961; FFA RCS Eng. 1966; DA Eng. 1964. (Middlx.) Cons. Anaesth. Roy. Nat. Orthop. Hosp Trust. Socs: BMA; Assn. Anaesth.; Liveryman Soc. Apoth. Prev: Sen. Regist. & Regist. (Anaesth.) St. Geo. Hosp. Lond.; SHO (Anaesth.) Lond. Hosp.; Jun. Res. Asst. Anaesth. Middlx. Hosp. Lond.

BRAY, Anthony John (retired) 5 The Paddock, Killams Lane, Taunton TA1 3YA Tel: 01823 274184 — MB ChB 1953 Birm.; DObst RCOG 1957. Prev: Mem. Staff Ilfracombe & Dist. Tyrrell Hosp.

BRAY, Barbara Margaret East Surrey Hospital, Redhill RH1 5RH; Wynchmore, 41 Oast Road, Oxted RH8 9DU — MB BS 1980 Lond.; FFA RCS Eng. 1984. Cons. Anaesth. E. Surrey Hosp.

BRAY, Barry Vivian Henry Normandy Lodge, Halland, Lewes BN8 6PS — MB BS 1964 Lond.; MRCS Eng. LRCP Lond. 1963; MRCP (UK) 1972; MRCGP 1974.

BRAY, Colin Lionel 2 Longmeade Gardens, Wilmslow SK9 1DA Tel: 01625 520423 — BSc Lond. 1957, MB BS 1960; FRCP Lond. 1976, M 1963. (Lond. Hosp.) Cons. Cardiol., Alexandra Hosp.Mill La. Cheadle. Socs: Brit. Cardiac Soc. Prev: Cons. Cardiol. Regional Cardiac Centre, Univ. Hosps. Of S.Manch. & Univ. Dept. Med. Manch.; Sen. Regist. Clin. Cardiol. Unit Hammersmith Hosp.; Ho. Phys. Cardiac Dept. & Research Fell. Cardiac Dept. Lond. Hosp.

BRAY, Edward Charles Chiltern House Medical Centre, 45-47 Temple End, High Wycombe HP13 5DN Tel: 01494 445701 Fax: 01494 530483; 52 Fair Ridge, High Wycombe H11 1PL Tel: 01494 445701 Email: ed.bray@virgin.net — MB BS 1976 Lond.; MRCS Eng. LRCP Lond. 1975; MRCGP Lond. 1980; DRCOG 1977. (Guy's) Princip. in Gen. Pract.; Bd. Mem. and prescribing lead Wycombe area PCG; Chairm. Wycombe Prescribing Comm.; Vice Chairm. Bucks, Theraputics Comm. Socs: Hon. Sec. Childern Med. Golfing Soc.

BRAY, Eleanor Lucy Cannington Health Centre, Mill Lane, Cannington, Bridgwater TA5 2HB Tel: 01278 652335 Fax: 01278 652453; The Spinney, Charlynch Lane, Spaxton, Bridgwater TA5 1BJ — BSc Lond. 1979, MB BS 1982; DRCOG 1987; DCH RCP Lond. 1985.

BRAY, Gary Pengilley Department of Gastroenterology, Southend Hospital, Westcliff on Sea SS0 0RY Tel: 01702 221158 Fax: 01702 221379; 87 Tyrone Road, Thorpe Bay, Southend-on-Sea SS1 3HD Tel: 01702 589502 Email: bizebub@msn.com — MB BS 1983 Lond.; FRCP (UK) 1999; BSc (Hons.) Lond. 1980, MD 1993; MRCP (UK) 1986. (Lond. Hosp.) Cons. Phys. & Gastroenterol. S.end Hosp. Socs: Brit. Soc. Gastroenterol. Prev: Sen. Regist. (Gen. Med. & Gastroenterol.) Chelsea & W.m. Hosp. Lond.; Clin. Research Fell. Inst. Liver Studies King's Coll. Hosp. Lond.; SHO (Gen. Med. & Endocrinol.) Hammersmith Hosp. Lond.

BRAY, George Panfu 36 Leith Road, Darlington DL3 8BG Tel: 01325 484848 — MB ChB 1972 Ed.; BSc (Med. Sci.) Ed. 1969, MB ChB 1972; MRCPsych 1976; DPM Eng. 1976. (Ed.) Cons. (Adult Ment. Illness) S.W. Durh. Health Dist. Prev: SHO (Psychiat.) Kingsway Hosp. Derby.

BRAY, Geraldine Marjorie Evergreen Oak Surgery, 43 Commercial Road, Parkstone, Poole BH14 0HU Tel: 01202 747496 Fax: 01202 743624 Email: gbray@gp-j81086.nhs.uk — MB BS 1980 Lond.; MSc McGill 1971; BA York 1969; MRCGP 1985; DRCOG 1983. (Charing Cross)

BRAY, Ian Luther Clifford (retired) Merifield House, Church Barns, The Street, Stratfield, Mortimer, Reading RG7 3NU — MB BS 1957 Lond.; DObst RCOG 1962. Prev: Ho. Surg. (Gyn. & Obst.) Canad. Red. Cross Memor. Hosp. Taplow.

BRAY, Jeremy Keith Hungerford Surgery, The Croft, Hungerford RG17 0HY Tel: 01488 682507 Fax: 01488 681018; 27 The Croft, Hungerford RG17 0HY Tel: 01488 684350 — MB BS 1972 Lond.; MRCGP 1978.

BRAY, Jessica Dawn The Spinney Surgery, Ramsey Rd,, St Ives, Huntingdon PE28 2 — MB ChB 1987 Sheff.

BRAY, Joanne Hilary The Health Centre, Thornton Dam Lane, Gilberdyke, Brough HU15 2UL Tel: 01430 440225 Fax: 01430 440646; 8 Belgrave Drive, North Cave, Brough HU15 2NN Tel: 01430 424422 — MB ChB 1986 Leeds.

BRAY, Jocelyn Alan Birtley Medical Group Practice, Birtley Medical Group, Durham Road, Birtley, Chester-le-Street DH3 2QT Tel: 0191 410 3421 Fax: 0191 410 9672; 1 Ruskin Road, Chester-le-Street DH3 1AD Email: jossbray@aol.com — MB BS 1987 Newc.; MRCGP 1993; MRCPsych 1992; T(GP) 1993. Prev: Regist. Rotat. (Psychiat.) N.. RHA.

BRAY, John Edward Clifford Merrifield House, Church Farm Barns, The Street, Mortimer, Reading RG7 3NU — MB BS 1990 Lond.

BRAY, Joseph Columba 40 Grieve Street, Dunfermline KY12 8DN Tel: 01383 621856 — MB BCh BAO 1981 NUI; MRCPsych 1989. Cons. Psychiat. Qu. Margt. Hosp. Dunfermline. Prev: Lect. (Clin. Psychiat.) Univ. Leicester.

BRAY, Mr Lindsay Charles Royal Eye Infirmary, Dorset County Hospital, Dorchester DT1 2JY Tel: 01305 251150 — MB BS 1984 Lond.; FRCS Eng. 1989; FRCOphth 1989. p/t Cons. Ophth. Dorset Co. Hosp. Dorchester; Cons. Ophth., Yeovil Dist. Hosp., Yeovil, Som. Prev: Sen. Regist. (Ophth.) Sunderland Eye Infirm.; Regist. (Ophth.) Newc. Gen. Hosp.; SHO (Ophth.) St. Paul's Eye Hosp. Liverp.

BRAY, Lorna Mary Ursula Kipling Unit, Conquest Hospital, The Ridge, Hastings TN34 2 Tel: 01424 755255; Little Holton, School Lane, Burwash, Etchingham TN19 7DU Tel: 01435 882400 Fax: 01435 882400 — MB BS 1968 Lond.; FRCP 2001; MRCP (UK) 1974; MCRS Eng. LRCP Lond. 1968; DCH RCP Lond. 1970; FRCPCH. (Middlesex) Cons. Paediat. (With spec. int. in comm. Paediats) Conquest Hosp. Hastings; Clin. Dir. Childr.s Serv.s. Socs: Brit. Assn. of Comm. Doctors in Audiol.; Roy. Coll. Paediat. & Child Health (Fell.); Brit. Med. Acupunc. Soc. (Mem.). Prev: Cons. Paediat. E.bourne Dist. Gen. Hosp.

BRAY, Margaret Grange Cottage, Bampton OX18 2JW Tel: 01993 850223 — MB ChB 1961 Birm.; MRCS Eng. LRCP Lond. 1961. Clin. Asst. (Anaesth.), Swindon HA.

BRAY, Michelle Kimberley Dr Moss and Partners, 28-38 Kings Road, Harrogate HG1 5JP Tel: 01423 560261 Fax: 01423 501099; 14 Low Mills Court, Shaw Mills, Harrogate HG3 3HJ — MB ChB 1984 Liverp.; MRCGP 1988; T(GP) 1991; DRCOG 1986. (Liverp.)

BRAY, Nicholas John Mill Street Surgery, Mill Street, North Petherton, Bridgwater TA6 6LX Tel: 01278 662223 Fax: 01278 663727; Laburnum House, Queen St, North Petherton, Bridgwater TA6 6RQ Tel: 01278 662110 Email: nick.bray@lineone.net — MB ChB 1984 Birm.; MA Camb. 1984; MRCGP 1988; DRCOG 1987. (Birmingham) Mem. of Som. Coast PCG Bd. Prev: Med. Off. Whangaroa Health Servs., NZ; Trainee GP Som. VTS; Ho. Phys. Qu. Eliz. Hosp. Birm.

BRAY, Rachel Lavinia Springfield Surgery, Elstead, Godalming GU8 6EG Tel: 01252 703122 Fax: 01252 703215; Speedwell, Seale Road, Elstead, Godalming GU8 6LF — MB BS 1972 Lond.; MRCS Eng. LRCP Lond. 1972; MRCGP 1979; DCH Eng. 1976; DObst RCOG 1975. Prev: SHO (Anaesth.) Kings Coll. Hosp. Lond.; Ho. Surg. (O & G) King's Coll. Hosp. Lond.; SHO (Paediat.) Sydenham Childr. Hosp.

BRAY, Robin Joseph Department of Anaesthesia, Royal Victoria Infirmary, Queen Victoria Road, Newcastle upon Tyne NE1 4LP Tel: 0191 232 5131; 5 Moor Place, Gosforth, Newcastle upon Tyne NE3 4AL — MB BS 1969 Lond.; BA Open 1987; FRCA 1974; DA Eng. 1972; DObst RCOG 1971. (Univ. Coll. Hosp.) Cons. Anaesth. Roy. Vict. Infirm. Newc. Socs: Paediat. Intens. Care Soc.; Assn. Anaesth. & Assn. Paediat. Anaesth. Prev: Sen. Regist. (Anaesth.) Newc. AHA (T); Regist. (Anaesth.) Roy. Infirm. Edin.; SHO (Anaesth.) Radcliffe Infirm. Oxf.

BRAY, Sheila Joan Calcot Medical Centre, Hampden Road, Chalfont St. Peter, Gerrards Cross SL9 9SA Tel: 01753 887311 — MB BS 1979 Lond.; MRCGP 1993; DRCOG 1991; DCH RCP Lond. 1990. (Char. Cross Hosp. Med. Sch. Lond.)

BRAYBON, Edith Clee (retired) St Cleer, 80 Priory Avenue, Hastings TN34 1UL — MB BS 1957 Lond.

BRAYBON, Keith Wilfrid (retired) St Cleer, 80 Priory Avenue, Hastings TN34 1UL Tel: 01424 427527 — MB BS Lond. 1956; DObst RCOG 1959.

BRAYBROOKE, Jason Roy 20 West Avenue,, Clarendon Park,, Leicester — MB ChB 1994 Leic.

BRAYBROOKE, Jeremy Paul ICRF Medical Oncology, The Churchill Hospital, Headington, Oxford OX3 7LJ Tel: 01865 741841 Fax: 01865 226179 Email: braybroo@icrf.icnet.uk; 3 The Croft, Marsh Baldon, Oxford OX44 9LN — BM 1991 Soton.; BSc Soton. 1990; MRCP (UK) 1994; DTM & H Liverp. 1995. (Soton.) Clin. Research Fell. Oxf. Prev: Regist. (ICRF Med. Oncol.) Oxf.; SHO (Gen. Med.) Roy. Devon & Exeter Hosp.; SHO (Oncol.) Portsmouth.

BRAYBROOKE, Jill 3 Town Green Street, Leicester LE7 7NU Tel: 0116 237 4727 — BM 1976 Soton.; MRCGP 1984. GP. Prev: Trainee GP Plympton VTS.; SHO (Gen. Med.) Plymouth Gen. Hosp.

BRAYBROOKS, Luz Stella Dryland Surgery, 1 Field Street, Kettering NN16 8JZ Tel: 01536 518951 Fax: 01536 486200; 41 Ridgway Road, Kettering NN15 5AQ — D Med y Cir Colombia 1973. GP. Prev: Specialist (Internal Med.) Nat. Univ. Colombia.

BRAYDEN, Patricia Catherine Flat 18, Thackeray Manor, 22 Manor Park Road, Sutton SM1 4AH — MB BChir 1991 Camb.; MA Camb. 1992, BA 1988; MRCP (UK) 1993. Regist. (Gen. & Geriat. Med.) John Radcliffe Hosp. & Radcliffe Infirm. Oxf. Socs: Brit. Geriat. Soc. Prev: Regist. (Gen. & Geriat. Med.) Stoke Mandeville Hosp. Aylesbury; SHO Rotat. (Med.) N.. Gen. Hosp. Sheff.; SHO (Geriat. Med.) W. Suff. Hosp. Bury St. Edmunds.

BRAYLEY, Michaela 8 Backford Close, Birkenhead CH43 2NB — MB ChB 1989 Ed.

BRAYLEY, Mr Nigel Frederick, Surg. Lt.-Cdr. RN Retd. Emergency Department, Colchester District General Hospital, Colchester CO4 5JL Tel: 01206 747474 Fax: 01206 742395 — MB BS 1973 Lond.; FRCS Eng. 1980; MRCS Eng. LRCP Lond. 1973; FFAEM 1994. (Roy. Free) Cons. Emerg. Colchester Dist. Gen. Hosp.; Lead Clin. A & E NHS Info. Auth.; Fell. Fac. Mem. HSSI, ESSEX Univ.; REgional ALS Rep for UK Resus Counc. Socs: Fell. Fac. Accid. & Emerg. Med.; Brit. Assn. Accid. & Emerg. Med. Prev: Sen. Regist. (A & E) Oxf. HA; Regist. (Accid & Emerg.) Gloucester Roy. Hosp.; Regist. (Orthop.) Roy. Free Hosp. Lond. Windsor Gp. Hosps.

***BRAYLEY, Sharon Lorna** 23 Inglis Road, Colchester CO3 3HU Tel: 01206 563627 Email: sbrayley@hotmail.com; 23 Inglis Road, Colchester CO3 3HU Tel: 01206 563627 — MB BS 1998 Lond.; MB BS Lond 1998; History of medicine BSc(Hons) Lond. 1996; AIS Course Colchester 1998.

BRAYNE, Carol Elspeth Goodeve Department Community Medicine, Institute of Public Health, Forvie Site, Robinson Way, Cambridge CB2 2SR Tel: 01223 330334 Fax: 01223 330330 Email: carol.brayne@medschl.cam.ac.uk; Pound Farm, Weston Green, Weston Colville, Cambridge CB1 5NX — MB BS 1981 Lond.; MSc (Epidemiol.) Lond. 1985, MD 1991; MRCP (UK) 1984; MFPHM RCP (UK) 1992; FFPHM (UK) 1998. (Roy. Free) Lect. (Epidemiol.) Univ. Camb.; Hon. Cons. Pub. Health Med. Camb. Prev: MRC Fell. Epidemiol.; Vis. Prof. Indianapolis, 1996; Vis. Prof. Austral. Nat. Univ. 1997.

BRAYSHAW, Jan Maryon 80 Churchfields Drive, Bovey Tracey, Newton Abbot TQ13 9QZ Tel: 01626 832867 — MB ChB 1996 Bristol. (University of Bristol) SHO (Paediat.), Torbay Hosp., Torquay. Prev: SHO (Paeds) Derriford Hosp., Plymouth; SHO (A & E) Derriford Hosp. Plymouth; PRHO (Gen. Med. & c/o Elderly) S.mead Hosp. Bristol.

BRAYSHAW, Maira Samantha Barts and The London NHS Trust, Whitechapel, London — MB ChB 1993 Manch.; FRCA. (St. Andrews and Manchester) p/t Specialist Regist. N. Thames. Socs: Assn. Anaesth.; BMA.

BRAYSHAW, Sarah Anne Moorcroft, Moorside, Cleckheaton BD19 6JT — MB ChB 1973 Manch.; FFA RCSI 1978. Cons. Anaesth. Dewsbury Dist. Hosp. W. Yorks.

BRAYSHAY, Muriel Jane (retired) Brocklehurst Nursing Home, Cavendish Road, Withington, Manchester M20 1JG — MB ChB 1936 Manch.

BRAZENDALE, Inga Frances Blackberry Hall, Blackberry Lane, Trimingham, Norwich NR11 8HS — MB BS Lond. 1968; LLB 1987; FFA RCS Eng. 1987. (Roy. Free Lond.)

BRAZENOR, Evelyn Louis Ferris 19 Queens Court, The Brampton, Newcastle ST5 1ST — MB BS 1954 Lond.

BRAZIER, Mr David John 8 Upper Wimpole Street, London W1M 7TD Tel: 020 7935 5038 Fax: 020 7487 2968 — MB BS 1976 Lond.; FRCS Eng. 1983; FRCOphth 1988; DO Eng. 1982. (St. Thos.) Cons. Ophth. Univ. Coll. Lond. Hosps.; Hon. Cons. Ophth. Roy. Free. Hosp. Lond. & Cataract Centre Chase Farm Hosp. Enfield. Prev: Sen. Regist. (Ophth.) Nat. Hosp. Neurol. & Neurosurg. & St. Thos. Hosp. Lond.; Resid. Surg. Off. Moorfields Eye Hosp. Lond.

BRAZIER, David Terence Church Street Surgery, 11 Church Street, Littleborough OL15 8AA — MB ChB 1988 Manch.; DCCH RCP Ed. 1992. Trainee GP Rochdale. Prev: Trainee GP/SHO Rotat. Roy. Oldham Hosp. VTS; SHO (A & E) Bolton Roy. Infirm.; Ho. Off. (Med. & Surg.) Davyhulme Pk. Hosp.

BRAZIER, Elisabeth Ann 19 Haddon Court, Shakespeare Road, Harpenden AL5 5NB Tel: 01582 763669; 5 Gaveston Drive, Berkhamsted HP4 1JE — MB BS 1990 Lond.; MRCGP 1995; DRCOG 1994; DFFP 1994; DCH RCP Lond. 1993. (Roy. Free Hosp. Lond.)

BRAZIER, Jonathan Charles The Surgery, Parkwood Drive, Warners End, Hemel Hempstead HP1 2LD Tel: 01442 250117 Fax: 01442 256185; 5 Gaveston Drive, Berkhamsted HP4 1JE — MB BS 1990 Lond.; MRCGP 1996; DFFP 1995; DCH RCP Lond. 1995; DRCOG 1994. (Roy. Free Hosp.) Prev: Trainee GP St Albans.

BRAZIER, Lilias Hillcoat (retired) 9 Mill Street, Ludlow SY8 1AZ Tel: 01584 873089 Fax: 01584 872403 — MB ChB Glas. 1948; DObst RCOG 1950. Prev: Ho. Surg. Roy. Infirm., Roy. Matern. Hosp. & Roy. Samarit. Hosp. Glas.

BRAZIER, Melinda Doiran — MB BS 1991 Lond.; FRCA 1998.

BRAZIL, Mr Edward Vincent Accident & Emergency Department, Leicester Royal Infirmary, Infirmary Square, Leicester LE1 5WW; Flat 4, 16 Alexandra Road, Leicester LE2 2BB — MB BCh BAO 1990 NUI; FRCSI 1994.

BRAZIL, Lucy Caroline Alexandra Royal Marsden Hospital, Fulham Road, London SW3 6JJ; 5 Prima Road, London SW9 0NA Tel: 020 7582 9797 — MB BS 1988 Lond.; BSc (Hons.) Lond. 1985; MRCP (UK) 1993. Specialist Regist. (Clin. Oncol.) Roy. Marsden Hosp. Sutton; Clin. Research Fell. Inst. Cancer Research & Neuro-oncol. Unit. Roy. Marsden Hosp Sutton. Socs: BMA; Assn. Palliat. Med.; Roy. Coll. Radiol. Prev: Sen. Regist. (Palliat. Med. & Oncol.) Hammersmith Hosp. Lond.

BREACH, Charlotte Suzannah 88A Hackford Road, London SW9 0RG Tel: 020 7587 1382 — MB BS 1997 Lond.; BSc (Hons) Lond. 1994. (St Marys Medical School, Imperial College, London) A & E Sen. Ho. Off., Chelsea & W.minster Hosp., Lond. Prev: Gen. Surg. SHO, St. Mary's Hosp., Lond.

BREACH, James Francis 189 Albert Bridge Road, Belfast BT5 4PW Tel: 028 457109; 1 Massey Park, Belfast BT4 2JX — MD 1952 Belf.; MB BCh BAO 1942; DPhysMed. Eng. 1964. (Belf.) Socs: Ulster Med. Soc. Prev: Res. Med. Off. EMS; on Gp Staff Dept. Physical Med. Roy. Vict. Hosp. Belf.

BREACH, Martin James Wallace 47 Kings Road, Belfast BT5 6JH — MB ChB 1987 Birm.; MRCGP 1991.

BREACH, Mr Nicholas Mackenzie The Consulting Suite, 82 Portland Place, London W1N 3DH Tel: 020 7636 1298 Fax: 020 7436 2954; 9 Devonshire Close, London W1G 7BA Tel: 020 7580 4925 Email: 106625.417@compuserve.com — MB BS Lond. 1970; FRCS Eng. 1973; BDS Lond. 1963; MRCS Eng. LRCP Lond. 1970; FDS RCS Eng. 1968, L 1963. (St. Thos. & Roy. Dent. Hosp.) Regional Plastic Surg. Centre Mt. Vernoy Hosp N.wood. Socs: Fell. Roy. Soc. Med.; Brit. Assn. Plastic Surg. Prev: Cons. Reconstruc. Surg. Head & Neck Unit Roy. Marsden Hosp. Lond.; Cons. Plastic Surg. Qu. Vict. Hosp. E. Grinstead & Brighton HA; Dir. McIndoe Burns Centre Qu. Vict. Hosp. E. Grinstead.

BREADY, Kevin Aloysius Springfield Road Surgery, 66-70 Springfield Road, Belfast BT12 7AH Tel: 028 9032 3571 Fax: 028 9020 7707 — MB BCh BAO 1970 Belf.

BREADY, William Dominic Dublin Road Surgery, 4 Dublin Road, Castlewellan, Newcastle BT31 9AG Tel: 028 4372 3221 Fax: 028 4372 3162 — MB BCh BAO 1972 Belf.

BREAKELL, Andrew 9 Alton Close, Liverpool L38 9GE — MB ChB 1987 Liverp.

BREAKEY, Francis William Bryan, MBE The Bungalow, Westfield, Gosforth, Newcastle upon Tyne NE3 4YE — MB BS 1949 Durh.; MRCGP 1960. (Newc.)

BREAKEY, Robina Middlemass The Bungalow, Westfield, Gosforth, Newcastle upon Tyne NE3 4YE — MB BS 1949 Durh. (Newc.)

BREAKWELL, John Berwyn House Surgery, 13 Shrubbery Avenue, Worcester WR2 Tel: 01905 22888; 5 Springfield Close, Worcester WR5 3BQ — MB ChB 1970 Birm.; DObst RCOG 1973. Vis. Lect. Oxf. Brookes Univ. Socs: Nat. Chairm. Childr. Chronic Arthritis Assn.; BMA & McCarrison Soc. Prev: Cons. GP Computer Systems Aah-Meditel BromsGr.; GP Princip. Worcester; SHO (Paediat.) Worcester Roy. Infirm. (Ronkswood Br.).

BREAKWELL, Lee Mark 128 Crookes Road, Sheffield S10 5BE — MB ChB 1994 Sheff.

BREALEY, David Andrew Haydens Cottage, The Pound, Cookham, Maidenhead SL6 9QE — MB BS 1994 Lond.

BREALEY, Sharareh 72 Lansdowne Road, Stanmore HA7 2SA — MB BS 1994 Lond.

BREAR, Sarah Elizabeth York Bridge Surgery, 5 James Street, Morecambe LA4 5TE Tel: 01524 831111 Fax: 01524 832493 — MB BS 1979 Lond.; BSc Lond. 1976, MB BS 1979; FFA RCS Eng. 1984.

BREAR, Steven Gary Intensive Care Unit, Wythenshawe Hospital, Wythenshawe, Manchester M23 9LT Tel: 0161 998 7070 Fax: 0161 291 2582; The Toll House, 1 Fog Lane, Didsbury, Manchester M20 6AT — MB BS 1976 Lond.; FRCP Lond. 1996; MRCP (UK) 1978; MRCS Eng. LRCP Lond. 1976. Dir. (Intens. Care) & Cons. Phys. Wythenshawe Hosp. Manch. Socs: Intens. Care Soc.; Brit. Thorac. Soc. Prev: Cons. Phys. (Critical Care) N. Manch. Gen. Hosp.

BREAREY, Stephen Paul 65 Gaddesby Road, Kings Heath, Birmingham B14 7EX — MB ChB 1998 Birm.

BREARLEY, Brian Fenton (retired) 3 Willow Tree Avenue, Barton, Preston PR3 5DH Tel: 01772 864659 — MB BChir Camb. 1942; MA Camb. 1943, BA (1st cl. Hons. Nat. Sc. Trip; Pt. I) 1939, MD 1951; FRCP Lond. 1970, M 1948; MRCS Eng. LRCP Lond. 1942. Prev: Cons. Phys. Roy. Infirm. Preston, Sharoe Green Hosp. Preston & Chorley & Dist. Hosp.

BREARLEY, Frederick Roland (retired) 1 The Paddock, Broom Hall Avenue, Wrenthorpe, Wakefield WF1 2BX — MRCS Eng. LRCP Lond. 1950.

BREARLEY, John Mansfield Roslea Surgery, 51 Station Road, Bamber Bridge, Preston PR5 6PE Tel: 01772 335128 Fax: 01772 492248; Congham House, Moss Lane E., Leyland, Preston PR25 4SE Tel: 01772 621015 — MB BChir 1975 Camb.; MB BChir Camb. 1974; MA Camb. 1975; MRCGP 1979; DRCOG 1979.

BREARLEY, Jonathan Daniel Mark 113 Newark Street, London E1 2ET — MB BS 1997 Lond.

BREARLEY, Marjorie Mary (retired) St Cuthbert's Cottage, Ackworth, Pontefract WF7 7EJ Tel: 01977 704944 — MB ChB Leeds 1943. Prev: Sen. Med. Off. (Admin.) Pontefract HA.

BREARLEY, Robert Larter Wessex Blood Transfusion Centre, Coxford Road, Southampton SO16 5AF Tel: 02380 296736 Fax: 02380 296760 — MB BS 1969 Lond.; MD Lond. 1980; MRCP (UK) 1972; MRCS Eng. LRCP Lond. 1969; FRCPath 1992, M 1980. Cons. Haemat. Wessex Regional Transfus. Centre. Socs: Fell. Roy. Soc. Med.; Brit. Blood Transfus. Soc. Prev: Sen. Regist. St. Bart. Hosp. Lond.; Cons. Haemat. Roy. Brisbane Hosp, Austral.; Sen. Lect. Chinese Univ. Hong Kong.

BREARLEY, Mr Roger (retired) 33 Queens' Drive, Mossley Hill, Liverpool L18 2DT Tel: 0151 722 7088 — MB ChB 1945 Liverp.; ChM Liverp. 1959, MB ChB 1945; FRCS Eng. 1949. Prev: Cons. Surg. Whiston Hosp. Prescot & St. Helens Hosp.

BREARLEY, Mr Stephen Whipps Cross Hospital, Whipps Cross Road, Leytonstone, London E11 1NR Tel: 020 8535 6670 Fax: 020 8535 6606; The White House, 29 Pages Lane, London N10 1PU Tel: 0370 981609 Fax: 020 8365 3768 Email: vacusurg@aol.com — MB BChir 1978 Camb.; MChir Camb. 1990, MA 1978; FRCS Eng. 1981. Cons. Gen. & Vasc. Surg. Whipps Cross Hosp.; Elected Mem. & Chairm. Registration Comm. Gen. Med. Counc. Socs: Vasc. Surg. Soc.; Assn. Surg.; Roy. Soc. Med. Prev: Sen. Regist. Qu. Eliz. Hosp. Birm.; Chairm. Hosp. Jun. Staffs Comm. BMA.

BREARLEY, Thomas (retired) St Cuthbert's Cottage, Ackworth, Pontefract WF7 7EJ Tel: 01977 704944 — LMSSA Lond. 1948. Prev: Ho. Surg. Pontefract Gen. Infirm.

BREARS, Oliver Broadgate, OBE Scawby House, 31 High St., Kirton-in-Lindsey, Gainsborough DN21 3JX Tel: 01652 648393 — MRCS Eng. LRCP Lond. 1939; LDS RCS Eng. 1936; MRCGP 1953. (Guy's) Civil. Med. Pract. Min. of Defence (Army). Socs: Fell. Roy. Soc. Med. Prev: Maj. IMS OC No. 2 Indian Maxillo-Facial Surg. Unit; Civil Surg. Hanthawaddy Dist, Burma; Chief Med. Off. Burmah Oil Co. Ltd.

BREATHNACH, Professor Aodan Seosamh 4 Pelhams Close, Pelhams Walk, Esher KT10 8QB Tel: 01372 466459 — MB BCh BAO 1947 NUI; MSc NUI 1945, BSc 1943, MD 1957, MB BCh BAO

(1st; c. Hons.) 1947. (Univ. Coll. Dub.) Emerit. Prof. Anat. St. Mary's Hosp. Med. Sch. Lond.; Hon. Sen. Research Fell. Div. Phys. & Inst. Dermat. United Med. Dent Sch. St. Thos. Hosp. Lond. Socs: BMA & BAD. Prev: Asst. Lect. (Anat.) Univ. Coll. Dub.; Sen. Ho. Phys. Mater Miser. Hosp. Dub.; Ho. Phys. St. Luke's Hosp. Guildford.

BREATHNACH, Aodhan Sean Department of Microbiology, St Thomas's Hospital, London SE1 7EH Tel: 020 7928 9292; 59 Bournemouth Road, Merton Park, London SW19 3AR — MB BCh BAO 1987 Dub. Prev: Lect. (Microbiol.) St. Thos. Hosp. Lond.

BREATHNACH, Stephen Michael St John's Institute of Dermatology, St Thomas's Hospital, Lambeth Palace Road, London SE1 7EH Tel: 020 7620 0370 Fax: 020 7620 0369; 14 Larpent Avenue, Putney, London SW15 6UP Tel: 020 8789 6564 — MB BChir 1975 Camb.; MA Camb. 1975, PhD 1987, MD 1983; FRCP Lond. 1991; MRCP (UK) 1976; T(M) 1991. (St. Thos.) p/t Cons. Dermat. & Sen. Lect. St. John's Inst. Dermat. St. Thos. Hosp. Lond.; Cons. Dermat. Epsom & St. Helier NHS Trust, Epsom, Surrey. Socs: Brit. Assn. Dermat.; Roy. Soc. Med. (Fell. Dermat. Sect.); St John's Hosp. Dermatol. Soc. Prev: Hon. Cons. Dermat. & Reader (Med. Dermat.) Char. Cross & W.m. Med. Sch. Lond.; Vis. Assoc. Dermat. Br. Nat. Cancer Inst. NIH Bethesda, USA; Sen. Regist. St. John's Hosp. for Dis. of Skin Lond.

BREBNER, Cecilia May (retired) 9 Lochend Drive, Bearsden, Glasgow G61 1ED Tel: 0141 943 2377 — MB ChB 1944 Manch.; BSc Manch. 1942, MB ChB 1944; DCH Eng. 1947. Prev: Assoc. Specialist Psychiat. Roy. Hosp. Sick Childr. Glas.

BREBNER, Hugh (retired) 9 Lochend Drive, Bearsden, Glasgow G61 1ED Tel: 0141 943 2377 — MD Aberd 1954, MB ChB 1943; FRCP Lond. 1972, M 1949; FRCP Glas. 1968, M 1964. Prev: Sen. Regist. Roy. Infirm. Manch. & Kingston Hosp.

BRECHIN, Susan Flat 1, 29 Regent Moray St., Glasgow G3 8AL — MB ChB 1992 Aberd.

BRECKENRIDGE, Professor Alasdair Muir, CBE Department of Pharmacology & Therapeutics, University of Liverpool, Ashton St., Liverpool L69 3BX Tel: 0151 794 5542 Fax: 0151 794 5540 Email: ambreck@liverpool.uk; Cree Cottage, Feather Lane, Heswall, Wirral CH60 4RL Tel: 0151 342 1096 Fax: 0151 342 1096 — MB ChB 1961 St. And.; MB ChB (Hons.) St. And. 1961; MSc (Commend.) Lond. 1969; BSc St. And. 1961; MD (Hons.) Dundee 1973; FRCP Ed. 1989; FRCP Lond. 1974, M 1964. (St. And.) Prof. Clin. Pharmacol. Univ. Liverp. Socs: Med. Res. Soc. Brit. Pharmcol. Soc. Prev: Asst. Dept. Med. Qu. Coll. Dundee; Sen. Lect. (Clin. Pharmacol.) Roy. Postgrad. Med. Sch.; Cons. Phys. Hammersmith Hosp. Lond.

BRECKENRIDGE, Mr Iain Mackay (retired) 3 The Parade, Whitchurch, Cardiff CF14 2EE Tel: 02920 215447 Fax: 02920 215776 — MB ChB 1957 St. And.; Chm (Commend.) Dund 1970; MB ChB (Hons.) St. And. 1957; FRCP Ed. 1975, M 1961; FRCS Ed. 1964; FRCS Eng. 1964. Prev: Cons. Cardiothoracic Surg. Univ. Hosp. Wales Cardiff.

BRECKENRIDGE, Jean Lightbody Grantham & District Hospital, 101 Manthorpe Road, Grantham NG31 6DG Tel: 01476 565232 Fax: 01476 590441; 15 Rowanwood Drive, Gonerby Hill Foot, Grantham NG31 8GT Email: jbreck1103@aol.com — MB ChB 1974 Ed.; FFA RCS Eng. 1979. Cons. Anaesth. Grantham Dist. Hosp. Prev: Sen. Regist. (Anaesth.) Leics. AHA (T); Regist. (Anaesth.) W.. Infirm. Glas. & Law Hosp. Carluke.

BRECKENRIDGE, Ross Alexander Cree Cottage, Feather Lane, Wirral CH60 4RL — BM BCh 1994 Oxf.

BRECKER, Naomi Aviva 34 Collingwood Avenue, London N10 3ED — MB BS 1985 Lond.; MA (Distinc.) Lond. 1990, BSc (Hons.) 1982; MFPHM 1996. (St. Bart. Hosp. Med. Coll.) Sen. Regist. (Pub. Health Med.) N. Thames RHA. Prev: Regist. (Pub. Health Med.) NE Thames RHA; SHO (Gyn.) Samarit. Hosp. for Wom. Lond.; SHO (Obst.) St. Mary's Hosp. Lond.

BRECKER, Stephen Jon David St George's Hospital, Blackshaw Road, London SW17 0QT Tel: 020 8725 1390 Fax: 020 8725 0211 Email: sbrecker@sghms.ac.uk — MB BS 1984 Lond.; 1999 FESC; 2000 FRCP; MB BS (Dinstinc.) Lond. 1984; FACC 1999; BSc (Hons.) Lond. 1981, MD 1993; MRCP (UK) 1987. (St. Thos.) Cons. Cardiol. St. Geo. Hosp. Lond.; Sen. Lect. St Geo. Hosp. Med. Sch. Univ. Lond. Socs: Fell. Roy. Soc. Med. Prev: Sen. Regist. (Cardiol.) Lond. Chest Hosp. & Roy. Brompton Hosp.; Brit. Heart Foundat. Jun. Research Fell. Roy. Brompton Nat. Heart & Lung Hosp.; Regist. (Cardiol.) Lond. Chest Hosp. & Nat. Heart & Chest Hosp.

BRECKNELL, John Edward 146 Sturton Street, Cambridge CB1 2QF; Addenbrooke's Hospital, Hills Road, Cambridge CB2 2QQ — BChir 1996 Camb.; MA Cantal. 1997; PLD Cantal. 1996; MB Cantal. 1996. Basic Surg. Trainee Addenbrooke's Hosp. Camb.

BRECKON, Kathryn Elizabeth 193 Scotforth Road, Lancaster LA1 4PR Tel: 01524 60262 — MB ChB 1985 Birm.; MRCP (UK) 1989; MRCGP 1993; T(GP) 1993; DRCOG 1991. GP Lancaster Retainer Scheme.

BREDDY, Paul Norman 39 Thornhill Road, Plymouth PL3 5NF Tel: 01752 667041 — MB ChB 1964 Bristol; BSc Bristol 1961, MB ChB 1964; DA Eng. 1971. (Bristol) Assoc. Specialist (Anaesth.) Plymouth Dist. Gen. Hosp. Prev: GP Plymouth; Surg. Lt. RN (1965-70).

BREDELL, Peter Martin c/o Dr Grays Hospital, Ward 2, Elgin IV30 1SN — MB ChB 1995 Pretoria.

BREDEMEYER, Aisha 7 Sunningdale Road, Saltash PL12 4BN — MB BS 1996 Lond.

BREDOW, Maria-Teresa Department for Community Child Health, 4th Floor, King Square House, King Square, Bristol BS2 8EF Tel: 0117 900 2350 Fax: 0117 900 2370 Email: marin.bredow@ubht.swest.nhs.uk — MB ChB Bristol 1981; MRCP (UK) 1986; DRCOG 1983. Cons. Paediat. (Comm. Child Health).

BREE, Cyril Gustave 36 Birchdale Road, Applelim, Warrington WA4 5AR — MRCS Eng. LRCP Lond. 1933; DTM & H Eng. 1946. (Univ. Coll. Hosp.) Prev: Cas. Off. & Ho. Phys. Willesden Gen. Hosp.; Asst. Med. Off. Co. Sanat. & Isolat. Hosp. Leicester.

BREE, Margaret Mary Flat 6/3, 79 Candleriggs, Glasgow G1 1NP Tel: 0141 552 3670 — MB ChB 1996 Glas. (Univ. Glas.) SHO (Paediat.) Roy. Hosp. for Sick Childr. Glasg. Prev: Ho. Off. (Gen. Surg.) Glas. Roy. Infirm.; Ho. Off. (Gen. Med.) Cartnavel Gen. Hosp.

BREE, Stephen Edward, Surg. Lt.-Cdr. RN 9 Ralston Place, West Ferry, Dundee DD5 1NP — MB ChB 1987 Ed.

BREED, John Hutley (retired) Lambrigg, Underbarrow, Kendal LA8 8BL — MB BS 1952 Lond.; FFA RCS Eng. 1961; DA Eng, 1957. Surg. Lt. RNR. Prev: Cons. Anaesth. Univ. Hosps. S. Manch.

BREEDEN, Jan Stephanie 42 Farnworth Street, Widnes WA8 9LH — MB ChB 1994 Ed.

BREEN, Cormac Patrick MacCormick Department of Renal Medicine, King's College Hospital, East Dulwich Grove, London SE22 8PT Tel: 020 7346 6234 Fax: 020 7346 6442 Email: srkru@globalnet.co.uk; 63 Taylor's Lane, Sydenham, London SE26 6QL — MB BS 1991 Lond.; BSc (Hons.) Lond. 1988; MRCP (UK) 1994. (UCL Medical School) Research Regist. (Nephrol.) Dept. of Renal Med. King's Coll. Hosp. Lond. Prev: Specialist Regist. (Nephrol.) King's Coll. Hosp. Lond.; Regist. (Med.) Greenwich Dist. Hosp. Lond.

BREEN, David Anthony Department of Public Health Medicine, Dumfries and Galloway Health Board, Grierson House, The Crichton, Bankend Road, Dumfries DG1 4ZG Tel: 01387 272724 Fax: 01387 272759 Email: dbreen@dghb.scot.nhs.uk; 3 Hillview Avenue, Georgetown, Dumfries DG1 4DX Tel: 01387 263068 Fax: 01387 272759 Email: docdavebreen@hotmail.com — MB BCh BAO 1977 NUI; MFPHM 1991; DObst 1981 RCPI; DCH 1979 NUI; FFPHM 1996; MICGP 1984; MRCGP 1983; MSc 1985 (Community Health) Dub. (Univ. Coll. Dubl.) Cons. Pub. Health Med. Dumfries & Galloway HB; Hon. Clin. Sen. Lect. Univ. Glas. Prev: Assoc. Med. Off. Health Simcoe Co. Barrie, Ontario, Canada; GP Co. Kerry Rep. of Irel.

BREEN, David John Department of Radiology, Southampton University Hospitals NHS Trust, Southampton General Hospital, Tremona Rd, Southampton SO16 — MB BS 1986 Lond.; MRCP (UK) 1989; FRCR 1994. Cons. Abdom. Radiol. Hull Roy. Infirm. Socs: Radiol. Soc. of N. Amer.; Brit. Soc. of Internat. Radiol.; Europ. Soc. of GI and Abdom. Radiol. Prev: Sen. Regist. (Radiol.) John Radcliffe Hosp. Oxf.; Regist. (Radiol.) St. Geo. Hosp. Lond.; SHO (Renal Unit) St. Thos. Hosp. Lond.

BREEN, Desmond Paul 16 Whiteley Wood Road, Whiteley Woods, Sheffield S11 7FE Tel: 0114 230 8631 — BM BS 1983 Nottm.; BMedSci Nottm. 1981, BM BS 1983; FRCA 1989. (Nott.) Cons. Anaesth. & Intens. Care Roy. Hallamsh. Hosp. Sheff. Socs: BMA; Anaesth. Assn.; Intens. Care Soc. Prev: Sen. Regist. (Anaesth.) Roy. Hallamsh. Hosp. Sheff.; Research Fell. Intens. Care Unit & Hon.

Research Asst. (Anaesth.) Roy.Hallamsh. Hosp. Sheff.; Regist. & SHO (Anaesth.) Sheff. HA.

BREEN, Donal Sean Treacy (retired) 24 Poplar Road, Smethwick, Smethwick B66 4AW — LRCPI & LM, LRSCI & LM 1956; LRCPI & LM, LRCSI & LM 1956.

BREEN, Elizabeth Mary Josephine 34 Fleetcroft Road, Wirral CH49 5LZ — MB BCh BAO 1986 NUI; MRCPI 1995. (University College Cork, Ireland) Sen. Regist. (Paediat.) Alder Hey Hosp. Liverp. Socs: BMA. Prev: Regist. (Paediat.) Alder Hey Hosp. Liverp.; SHO (Paediat.) Blackburn & Leighton Hosp. Crewe; SHO (Paediat. Oncol.) Christie Hosp. Manch.

BREEN, Emer Patricia 2 Duneira Park, Larne BT40 1PF — MB BCh BAO 1994 Belf.

BREEN, Helen Alexandra The Health Centre, Mountjoy Road, Omagh BT79 7BA Tel: 01662 243521; 20 Glenhordial Road, Omagh BT79 7JT Tel: 01662 249593 — MB ChB 1984 Ed.; MRCGP 1989; DRCOG 1987. Staff Grade (Community Paediat.) Sperrin Lakeland Health & Social Serv. Trust Omagh, Co. Tyrone.

BREEN, John Thomas 147 Wickham Way, Beckenham BR3 3AP Tel: 020 8650 4038 — MB ChB Glas. 1960; MRCGP 1970; DFFP 1993; Cert Family Plann. JCC 1974; DObst RCOG 1961. (Glas. Roy. Infirm.) Med. Tibunal Mem., Appeals Serv. Socs: Fell. Roy. Soc. Med.; BMA (Ex-Chairm. Bromley Div.). Prev: Examr. RCGP; SHO Roy. Matern. Hosp. Glas.; Ho. Phys. & Ho. Surg. Roy. Infirm. Glas.

BREEN, Nicholas John 15 Findon Road, London W12 9PZ — MB BCh BAO 1987 NUI.

BREENE, Emma Rebecca 2 Osborne Gardens, Belfast BT9 6LE — MB ChB 1997 Aberd.

BREESE, Cecilia Wendy Piggots, Church End, Bledlow, Princes Risborough HP27 9PD — MB BS 1981 Lond.; MRCGP 1988.

BREESE, Donald William (retired) Cove House, Lamorna Cove, Penzance TR19 6XQ Tel: 01736 731476 — MB BS 1953 Lond.

BREESE, Elizabeth Olive The Downham Clinic, 24 Churchdown, Downham, Bromley BR1 5PT Tel: 020 8695 6575 Fax: 020 8695 0586; 11 Meriden Close, Bromley BR1 2UF Tel: 020 8464 1354 — MB BS 1977 Lond.; 1998 DCS (Dip. Med Studies), Kings Coll. London; MRCS Eng. LRCP Lond. 1977; DFFP 1997; DRCOG Eng. 1980; DCH Eng. 1979. (Guy's Hosp.) p/t Tutor (Gen. Pract.) & GP Princip., King's Coll. Med. Sch. Lond. Socs: Assoc. Mem. BPA. Prev: Hosp. Pract. (Paediat.) Qu. Mary's Hosp. Sidcup; Tutor (Gen. Pract.) Guys/St. Thomas's Hosp.

BREESE, Harry Timothy Richard Willow Street Medical Centre, 81-83 Willow Street, Oswestry SY11 1AJ Tel: 01691 653143 Fax: 01691 679130 — MB BCh 1986 Wales; MRCGP 1991; DRCOG 1988. Prev: SHO (Geriat. & ENT) Croydon HA; SHO (Gen. Surg. & ENT) Mayday Hosp. Croydon.

BREESE, Sarah Jane 2 Castle Court, Shrawardine, Shrewsbury SY4 1AH Tel: 01743 790325 — MB BS 1991 Lond. GP Retainer; The Surg., Hinton La., Pontesbury, Shrewsbury. Socs: BMA. Prev: SHO (A & E) Stafford Dist. Gen. Hosp.; Ho. Off. (Med.) Stafford Gen. Infirm.; Ho. Off. (Surg.) Cheltenham Gen. Hosp.

BREESE, Silvanus Christopher The Surgery, 15 High Street, Overton on Dee, Wrexham LL13 0ED Tel: 01978 710666 — MB ChB 1988 Bristol; MRCGP 1994. GP Princip.

BREESE, Victoria Lynne 41 Bryn Marl Road, Mochdre, Colwyn Bay LL28 5EA — BM BS 1998 Nottm.; BM BS Nottm 1998.

BREESON, Mr Anthony John Women's & Children's Department Division, Lincoln County Hospital, Greetwell Road, Lincoln LN2 5QY Email: breeson@enterprise.net — MB BS 1970 Lond.; MRCS Eng. LRCP Lond. 1970; FRCOG 1990, M 1976. (St.Bartholomews London) Cons. (O & G)United Lincs. Hosp. Trust; Hon. Lect. Nottm. Univ. Qu. Med. Centre. Socs: Brit. Menopause Soc; Examr. for part II MRCOG; RCOG OSCE (Mem. Sub Comm.). Prev: Sen. Regist. & Regist. (O & G) St. Thos. Hosp. Lond.; Sen. Regist. (O & G) Poole Gen. Hosp.

BREEZE, Charles Department of Anaesthesia, Whiston Hospital, Prescot — MB BS 1972 Lond.; FFA RCS Eng. 1983; DObst. RCOG 1975. Cons. Anaesth. Whiston Hosp. Prescot.

BREEZE, Richard William Barnet General Hospital, Wellhouse Lane, Barnet EN5 3DJ; Fairways, 90 Valley Road, Welwyn Garden City AL8 7DP — MB ChB 1973 Manch.; BSc (Hons.) (Physiol.) Manch. 1970, MB ChB 1973; MRCP (UK) 1977; Dip Pharm Med RCP (Uk) 1979. Cons. Phys. (Geriat. Med.) Barnet HA. Socs: Brit. Geriat. Soc. & BMA. Prev: Sen. Regist. (Geriat. Med.) Trent RHA; Hon. Clin. Asst. Roy. Hallamshire Hosp. Sheff.; Med. Specialist RAF Hosp. Cosford.

BREEZE-STRINGFELLOW, Barrie (retired) The Cygnets, Westmere, Hanley Swan, Worcester WR8 0DG — MB ChB 1957 Leeds; DObst RCOG 1960.

BREIMER, Lars Holger Clincal Research Division, Sanofi Winthrop Ltd., One Onslow St., Guildford GU1 4YS Tel: 01483 554401 Fax: 01483 554827 Email: lars.breimer@gb-guild-pharma.guild/.elfsanofi.fr — BM BCh 1978 Oxf.; PhD Gothenburg 1985; MA Oxf. 1979, BA (1st cl. Hons.) 1975; MRCPath 1994. Clin. Research Phys. Sanofi Winthrop Ltd. Guildford; Hon. Sen. Lect. Combined Health Care Sci. Fac of St Geo Hosp Med Sch Univ Lond & Kingston Univ 1997; Hon. Clin. Fell. Mt. Vernon Hosp. Cancer Treatm. Centre, N.wood 1996; Lect. Diploma in Pharmaceutical Med. Univ. Wales Sch. of Pharmacy Cardiff 1997. Socs: Fell. Linnean Soc. Lond.; Soc. Endocrinol. & Soc. Free Radical Research; Eur. Atherosclerosis Soc. Prev: Clin. Lect. & Hon. Sen. Regist. (Chem. Path. & Human Metab.) Roy. Free Hosp. Sch. Med. Lond.; Research Fell. Inst. Cancer Research Chester Beatty Laborats. Lond.; Beit Memor. Research Fell. & Hon. Regist. Roy. Postgrad. Med. Sch. Hammersmith Hosp. Lond.

BRELEN, Hanna Margareta Flat G4 Ziggurat, Saffron Hill, London EC1N 8QX — MB BS 1998 Lond.; MB BS Lond 1998.

BRELSFORD, Kathryn Jane 12 Walshaw Lane, Burnley BB10 2DL — MB ChB 1993 Liverp.

BREMER, Conrad (retired) c/o Mrs Hazel Rush, Mill House Studio, The Common, New Buckenham, Norwich NR16 2BH — MD 1942 Leeds; MB ChB 1940; FRCP Lond. 1968, M 1943. Prev: Cons. Phys. Roy. Infirm. Sunderland.

BREMNER, Alan Almington House, Market Drayton TF9 2QR Tel: 01630 653272 Fax: 01630 653272 — MB ChB 1960 Aberd.; MRCGP 1968; DObst RCOG 1963. (Aberdeen) Socs: N. Staffs. Med. Inst. Prev: GP Market Drayton; Lect. (Gen. Pract.) Univ. Edin.; Ho. Surg. Raigmore Hosp. Inverness.

BREMNER, Alan Ronald Fiddes 1 (3F3) Spittlefield Crescent, Newington, Edinburgh EH8 9QZ — MB ChB 1996 Ed.

BREMNER, Alastair Eric Castle Hill Surgery, Castle Hill Gardens, Torrington EX38 8EU Tel: 01805 623222 Fax: 01805 625069 — MB BS 1989 Lond.; MRCGP 1997; BSc (Psychol.) Lond. 1985. Prev: Trainee GP Painswick Glos.

BREMNER, Archibald Douglas, TD Rutherglen Health Centre, 130 Stonelaw Road, Rutherglen, Glasgow G73 2PQ Tel: 0141 531 6025 Fax: 0141 613 3450 — MB ChB 1964 Glas.; DObst RCOG 1966; DCH RCPS Glas. 1966. (Glasgow) Sen. Partner in Gen. Pract. Socs: BMA. Prev: Hon. Surg. to HM The Qu.; Sen. Regist. (Path.) Vict. Infirm. Glas.; Lect. Univ. Coll. Nairobi.

BREMNER, Billie-Jean 70 Main Street, Glenluce, Newton Stewart DG8 0PS; Flat 9, 69 Crystal Palace Pk Road, Crystal Palace, London SE26 6UT — MB ChB 1994 Glas. SHO (Paediat.) Greenwich Dist. Gen. Hosp. Prev: SHO (O & G) Greenwich Dist. Gen. Hosp.

BREMNER, Donald Cockenzie & Port Seton Health Centre, Avenue Road, Prestonpans EH32 0JL Tel: 01875 812998 Fax: 01875 814421 — MB ChB 1985 Ed.; MRCGP 1989; DCCH RCP Ed. 1990. Trainee GP & Trainee (Community Paediat.) Edin.

BREMNER, Mr Fion Domnall Department of Neuro-ophthalmology, National Hospital for Neurology & Neurosurgery, Queen Square, London WC1N 3BG Tel: 020 7837 3611 Fax: 0207 207 0751 Email: fdbremner@doctors.org.uk — MB BS 1991 Lond.; PhD (Neurophysiol.) Lond. 1988, BSc (1st cl. Hons. Physiol.) 1985; FRCOphth 1996. (United Med. & Dent. Sch. of Guy's & St. Thos. Hosp. Lond.) Clin. Fell. Dept. of Neuro-Ophth. Nat. Hosp. For Neurol. Lond. Socs: Physiol. Soc. Mem.; Roy. Coll. Of Ophth.s, Fell.; Roy. Soc. of Med. Fell. Prev: Specialist Regist. (Ophth.) St. Bart. Hosp. Lond.; Specialist Regist. (Ophth.) Moortiesse Eye Hosp. Lond.; Specialist Regist. (Ophth.) QE II Hosp. Welwyn Gch. City.

BREMNER, Harold Alan Lodgehill Road Clinic, Lodgehill Road, Nairn IV12 4RF Tel: 01667 452096 Fax: 01667 456785; Langley, 11 Thurlow Road, Nairn IV12 4EZ — MB ChB 1964 Aberd.; DObst RCOG 1969. Prev: O & G Regist. Raigmore Hosp. Inverness; Ho. Off. Perth Roy. Infirm. & Aberd. Matern. Hosp.

BREMNER, Ian Sherwood Bishopgate Medical Centre, 178 Newgate Street, Bishop Auckland DL14 7EJ Tel: 01388 603983 Fax: 01388 607782 — MB BS 1988 Newc.; MRCGP 1992; DCCH RCP Ed. 1991.

BREMNER, John Archibald Gordon Sheffield Virology Services, Royal Hallamshire Hospital, Glossop Road, Sheffield S10 2JF Tel: 0114 271 2276 Fax: 0114 278 9376 Email: johnbremner@msn.com — MB BS 1988 Lond.; MB BS (Hons.) Path. Lond. 1988; MSc Virol. 1991; MRCPath 1997. Cons. Virol. Roy. Hallamshire Hosp. Sheff. Socs: Amer. Soc. Microbiol.; Soc. Gen. Microbiol.; Eur. Clin. Virol. Gp. Prev: Sen. Regist. Regional Virus Laborat. Glas.; Regist. Virus Ref. Div. Centr. Pub. Health Laborat. Lond.

BREMNER, Margaret Hamilton 16 Christie Grange, Newhills, Aberdeen AB21 9SE Tel: 012240 713868 — MB ChB 1985 Aberd.; MRCPsych 1990.

BREMNER, Penelope Ann 12 Lambourne Drive, Bagshot GU19 5BY — MB BCh 1990 Wales.

BREMNER, Shirley Cross Houses, Shrewsbury SY5 6JN Tel: 01743 761242; 7 Hexham Way, Shrewsbury SY2 6QX — MB ChB Aberd. 1960; Dip. Community Paediat. Warwick 1982. (Aberd.) Sen. Community Paediat. Shrops. HA. Socs: Fac. Comm. Health. Prev: SHO (Ophth.) Woodend Hosp. Aberd.; SHO (Cas.) Roy. N.. Infirm. Inverness.

BREMNER-SMITH, Miss Alice Teresa Orthopaedics Department, Bristol Royal Infirmary, Bristol BS2 8HW; Top Flat, 2 Chantry Road, Clifton, Bristol BS8 2QD — MB BCh 1990 Wales; BSc Wales 1987; FRCS (Eng.) 1996; FRCS (Ed.) 1996. Specialist Regist. (Orthop.) Bristol Roy. Infirm. Socs: Fell. Roy. Coll. Surgs. Eng. & Edin. Prev: Specialist Regist. W.on Gen. Hosp. W.on & MusGr. Pk. Hosp. Taunton.

BRENCHLEY, Jane 38 Finkle Hill, Sherburn in Elmet, Leeds LS25 6EA — MB ChB 1990 Leeds.

BRENCHLEY, Simon Andrew Churchview Cottage, 51 High St.,Chapeltown, Turton, Bolton BL7 0EW — MB ChB 1987 Manch.; BSc (Med. Sci.) St. And. 1984. SHO (Med.) S. Manch. HA.

BRENDEL, Sabine Christiane 28 Devonshire Mews W., London W1G 6QF — State Exam Med 1990 Frankfurt.

BRENER, Neil David The Priory Hospital North London, Grovelands House, The Bourne, Southgate,, London N14 6RA Tel: 020 8882 8191 Fax: 020 8447 8138 — MB BS 1984 Lond.; MRCPsych. 1988. Med. Dir. & Cons. Psychiat.Priory Hosp. N. Lond. Prev: Cons. Psychiat. Qu. Mary's Univ. Hosp. Roehampton.; Sen. Regist. & Regist. Rotat. (Psychiat.) Char. Cross Hosp. Lond.

BRENMAN, Eric 7 Regents Park Terrace, London NW1 7EE — MRCS Eng. LRCP Lond. 1943; MB BS Lond. 1944, DPM 1949; MRCPsych 1973. (St. Bart.) Pres. Inst. Psychoanal. Prev: Scientif. Chairm. Brit. Psychol. Soc.

BRENNAN, Albert Francis 8 Buchanan Drive, Newton Mearns, Glasgow G77 6HT — MB ChB 1989 Glas.

BRENNAN, Alexandra Mary 18 Wood Leason Avenue, Lyppard Hanford, Worcester WR4 0EU — MB BS 1996 Lond.; BSc (Hons.) 1995; DRCOG 1999. (Roy. Free Hosp. Sch. Med.) Prev: HO(surg) Chase Farm Hosp., Enfield; HO(Med.), Roy. Free Hosp. Lond.; SHO (A&E, ITU) Roy. Free Hosp. Lond.

BRENNAN, Amanda Lesley 14 Orchard Drive, Little Leigh, Northwich CW8 4RW — BM BS 1995 Nottm.

BRENNAN, Andrew Philip Good Hope Hospital, Rectory Road, Sutton Coldfield B75 7RR Tel: 0121 378 2211 — MB ChB 1993 Birm.

BRENNAN, Bernadette Marie Dympna 14 Halstead Avenue, Manchester M21 9FT — MB ChB 1987 Manch.; BSc St. And. 1984. Regist. (Paediat.) Booth Hall Childr. Hosp. Manch. Prev: Regist. (Paediat.) Qu. Pk. Hosp. Blackburn; SHO Roy. Manch. Childr. Hosp.

BRENNAN, Bernard Patrick Michael Green Street Clinic, 118-122 Green Street, Eastbourne BN21 1RT Tel: 01323 722908 Fax: 01323 723136; 17 Rochester Close, Eastbourne BN20 7TW Tel: 01323 738168 — MB ChB 1981 Birm.; DA Eng. 1984. Clin. Asst. (Dermat.) E.bourne.

BRENNAN, Catherine Kerigan and Partners, The Surgery, 4 Captain French Lane, Kendal LA9 4HR Tel: 01539 720241 Fax: 01539 725048; 5 Kirkbil Green, Kendal LA9 7AJ — MB BS 1983 Lond.; MRCGP 1988; DRCOG 1986. (Middlx. Hosp.) p/t Princip. GP Kendal.; Clin. Asst., Med. for the Elderly, W.morland Gen. Hosp., Kendal. Prev: Trainee GP VTS Kettering Gen. Hosp.; Ho. Surg. & Ho. Phys. Kettering Gen. Hosp.

BRENNAN, Cecilia Agnes Mary Brennan and Neylan, The GP Centre, 322 Malden Road, North Cheam, Sutton SM3 8EP Tel: 020 8644 0224; 26A West Place, Wimbledon Common, London SW19 4UH Tel: 020 8946 9989 — MB BS 1977 Lond.; DRCOG 1982; DFFP 1996. (Barts.) Socs: BMA; BMAS. Prev: Trainee GP Univ. Coll. Hosp. Lond.; Ho. Surg. St. Stephens Hosp. Lond.; Ho. Phys. Nuffield Dept. of Med. Radcliffe Infirm. Oxf.

BRENNAN, Clare Louise 5 Prospect Place, Horsforth, Leeds LS18 4BW — MB ChB 1987 Birm.; MRCGP 1992; DRCOG 1991; MRCPsych 1997. (Birmingham) Regist. (Psychiat.) Machar Ho. Day Hosp. Leeds. Socs: BMA; MRCPsych.

BRENNAN, David Raymond Morfa Lane Surgery, 2 Morfa Lane, Carmarthen SA31 3AX Tel: 01267 234774 Fax: 01267 230628 — MB BCh BAO 1980 NUI.

BRENNAN, Dennis John Joseph The Hospital of St John & St Elizabeth, 60 Grove End Road, London NW8 9NH Tel: 020 7286 5126 — MB BS 1968 Lond.; MRCS Eng. LRCP Lond. 1968; DMRT Eng. 1973. Gp. Med. Adviser J. Sainsbury plc; Phys. Internat. Xerox, J. Rothschild Holdgs., Nat. Counc. YMCA, Advertising Standards Auth, Hosp of St John & St Eliz. Socs: Fell. Roy. Soc.; Med. Soc. Lond. Prev: Sen. Regist. Mt. Vernon Hosp. Lond.; Regist. (Radiother.) St. Bart. Hosp. Lond.; Ho. Surg. Surgic. Unit. Univ. Coll. Hosp. Lond.

BRENNAN, Donnacad Joseph Mary 114 Melbreck, Ashurst, Skelmersdale WN8 6SZ Tel: 01695 32803 — MB BCh BAO 1978 NUI; DAO 1987; MRCGP 1989; DCH RCPSI 1987. Med. Dir. Maharishi Ayureda Health Centre Skelmersdale.

BRENNAN, Edna (retired) Robin Hill, 10 The Bryn, Sketty Green, Swansea SA2 8DD Tel: 01792 201400 — MB BCh 1952 Wales; BSc Wales 1949, MB BCh 1952. Prev: GP Swansea.

BRENNAN, Francis Joseph 44 Elgin Mansions, Elgin Avenue, Maida Vale, London W9 1JQ Tel: 020 7289 7140; 48 Summerville, Clontarf, Dublin 3, Republic of Ireland Tel: 00 353 1 8531034 Fax: 00 353 1 8531034 Email: fbrennan@iol.ie — MB BCh BAO 1988 Dub.; MA Dub. 1992; MSc (Sports Med.) Lond. 1995; MRCGP 1992; DRCOG 1992; DCH RCP Lond. 1992. (Univ. Dub.) Ship Phys. Orient Lines (MV Marco Polo). Prev: Ship Phys. Carnival Cruise Lines Gulf of Mexico; Regist. (Med.) Hillsbrow Hosp. Johannesburg, S. Afr.; Princip. Ho. Off. (A & E & Psychiat.) Nambour Gen. Hosp. Qu.sland, Austral.

BRENNAN, John Mammography Department, Royal Devon & Exeter Hospital (Wonford), Barrack Road, Exeter EX2 5DW; Heath House, Heath Lane, Whitestone, Exeter EX4 2HJ Tel: 01647 61393 — MB BS 1978 Lond.; MRCS Eng. LRCP Lond. 1977; FRCR 1985. (Guy's) Cons. Radiol. Exeter HA. Prev: Cons. Radiol. Cornw. & I. of Scilly HA.; Sen. Regist. (Radiol.) W.m. Hosp. Lond.; Regist. (Radiol.) Notts. AHA.

BRENNAN, Mr John Aquinas Regional Vascular, 8C Link, Royal Liverpool University Hospital NHS Trust, Liverpool L7 8XP Tel: 0151 706 3419 Fax: 0151 706 5827; 33 Cheltenham Avenue, Liverpool L17 2AR Tel: 0151 733 5272 — MB ChB 1985 Birm.; MD Leic. 1993; FRCS (Gen.) 1996. (Birm.) Cons. Vasc. Surg. Roy. Liverp. Univ. Hosp. NHS Trust. Socs: Eur. Soc. Vasc. Surg.

BRENNAN, John Lester (retired) 16 Butterfield Road, Wheathampstead, St Albans AL4 8PU Tel: 0158 283 2230 — MB BS 1944 Lond.; LLM Keele 1986; MD Lond. 1953; MRCP Lond. 1951; LMSSA Lond. 1944; FRCPath 1977, M 1965. Barrister-at-Law Middle Temple. Prev: Cons. Path. Robt. Jones & Agnes Hunt Orthop. Hosp. OsW.ry & Shrops. HA.

BRENNAN, John William Crofton Surgery, 109A Crofton Road, Orpington BR6 8HU Tel: 01689 822266 Fax: 01689 891790 — MB BS 1980 Lond.; MRCP (UK) 1983; AFOM RCP Lond. 1994; MRCGP 1985; DMJ(Clin) Soc. Apoth. Lond. 1992; DRCOG 1984; DCH RCP Lond. 1984; Cert. FPA 1984. (King's Coll. Hosp.)

BRENNAN, Joyce Hilda (retired) 16 Butterfield Road, Wheathampstead, St Albans AL4 8PU Tel: 0158 283 2230 — MB BS 1947 Punjab; DObst RCOG 1951. Prev: Clin. Asst. Shelton Hosp. Shrewsbury.

BRENNAN, Kevin Saint Vincent Medical Centre, 77 Thorne Road, Doncaster DN1 2ET Tel: 01302 361318; The Old Rectory, Littleworth Lane, Old Rossington, Doncaster DN11 0HB Tel: 01302 865139 Email: southviewbren@email.msn.co.uk — MB BS 1981 Newc.; DCH RCP Lond. 1986; DRCOG 1986. Hosp. Practitioner Anaesth. Doncaster Roy. Infirm.

BRENNAN, Liam Department of Anaesthesia, Box 93, Addenbrooke's Hospital NHS Trust, Hills Road, Cambridge CB2 2QQ Tel: 01223 217434 Fax: 01223 217223; 1 Queen's Close, Balsham,

Cambridge CB1 6HL — MB BS 1983 Lond.; BSc Lond. 1980; FRCA 1990; DA (UK) 1987. (King's Coll. Hosp. Med. Sch.) Cons. Paediat. Anaesth. & Dir. Paediat. Day Surg. Addenbrooke's Hosp. Camb.; Mem. Resusc. Counc. (UK); Tutor Roy. Coll. Anaesth. Socs: Assn. Paediat. Anaesth.; Assn. Anaesth. GB & Irel. Prev: Sen. Regist. Rotat. (Anaesth.) St. Thos. Hosp. Lond.; Regist. (Anaesth.) Hosp. for Sick Childr. Gt. Ormond St. Lond.; Regist. Rotat. (Anaesth.) Univ. Coll. & Middlx. Hosps. Lond.

BRENNAN, Maria Elizabeth Brewster (retired) Flat 6, 13 Duke Street, 60 Duke St., Grosvenor Square, London W1M 5DS Tel: 020 7629 0720 — MRCS Eng. LRCP Lond. 1949.

BRENNAN, Mark Wilmslow Health Centre, Chapel Lane, Wilmslow SK9 5HX Tel: 01625 548555 Fax: 01625 548287 — MB ChB 1989 Manch.; MA Camb. 1982, BA (Hons.) 1979; MRCGP 1995; DFFP 1993. (Manch.) GP Wilmslow; Private GP. Socs: BMA; Fell.RSM. Prev: Assoc. Med. Dir. BUPA; GP Cheadle; Hosp. Practitioner.

BRENNAN, Mary Estelle 107 Bridgeman Road, Coventry CV6 1NS Tel: 024 76 23876 — MD Leeds 1975, MB ChB 1962; DCH Eng. 1966; DPH Lond. 1968. (Leeds) Lect. Social Med. Birm. Univ. Med. Sch.

BRENNAN, Mary Rose 33 Caw Park, Waterside, Londonderry BT47 6LZ — MB BCh BAO 1950 NUI.

BRENNAN, Mary Teresa 11 Caddington Road, Cricklewood, London NW2 1RP — MB BS 1980 Lond.

BRENNAN, Michelle Louise 6 Codling Close, London E1W 2UX — MB BS 1997 Lond.

BRENNAN, Neil Raymond Abbey Medical Practice, Abbey Street BT48 9DN Tel: 028 7136 4016 — MB BCh BAO 1978 Belf.; MRCGP 1982.

BRENNAN, Mr Nigel Queens Medical Centre, 6/7 Queen Street, Barnstaple EX32 8HY Tel: 01271 372672 Fax: 01271 341902 — MB BS 1977 Lond.; FRCS Ed. (A&E Med. & Surg.) 1984; MRCS Eng. LRCP Lond. 1977; MRCGP 1986. (Char. Cross) Prev: Regist. (Med.) N. Devon. HA; Hon. Sec. N. Devon Homoeop. Soc.

BRENNAN, Patricia Olivia Biddulph A&E Department, Childrens Hospital, Western Bank, Sheffield S10 2TH Tel: 0114 271 7000 Fax: 0114 271 7531 — MB ChB Sheff. 1970; FRCP Lond. 1994; MRCP (UK) 1980; FRCPCH 1997; FFAEM 1994; DCH Eng. 1973. (Univ. Sheff.) Cons. Paediat. (A & E) Childr. Hosp. Sheff.; Hon. Lect. Socs: BAEM; BASPCAN; BMA. Prev: Sen. Regist. Childr. Hosp. Sheff.

BRENNAN, Paul Nottingham City Hospital, Hucknall Road, Nottingham NG5 1PB Tel: 0115 969 1169; 50 Wood Lane, Hucknall, Nottingham NG15 6LR — MB BS 1992 Newc.; BMedSc (Hons.) Newc. 1989; MRCP (UK) 1995. (Newc. u. Tyne) Specialist Regist. (Clin. Genetics) Nottm. City Hosp. Socs: Clin. Genetics Soc.

BRENNAN, Peter Andrew 11 Oxlease Close, Romsey SO51 7HA Email: brennandocs@btinternet.com; 11 Oxlease Close, Romsey SO51 7HA — MB BS 1994 Lond.; FDS RCS Eng. 1992; BDS Lond. 1986; FRCS Eng. 1997; FRCSI 1997. (King's Coll. Hosp.) Specialist Regist. (Oral & Maxillofacial Surg.) S. Coast Train. Progr. Prev: SHO (Gen. Surg.) Addenbrooke's Hosp. Camb.; Ho. Off. (Surg.) Maidstone; Ho. Off. (Med.) King's Coll. Hosp. Lond.

BRENNAN, Raymond Michael William 21 Grange Crescent, Bangor BT20 3QJ — MB BCh BAO 1976 NUI.

BRENNAN, Robert Joseph 10 Dunhugh Park, Londonderry BT47 2NL — MB BCh BAO 1991 Belf. SHO (Anaesth.) Leicester Roy. Infirm.

BRENNAN, Stephen 5 Lindley Farm, Cinder Lane, Lindley, Otley LS21 2QN — MB ChB 1982 Glas.

BRENNAN, Stephen Robert Winhill House, Thornhill, Bamford, Hope Valley S33 0BR Tel: 01433 651423 Fax: 0114 271 4363 — MB BS 1969 Lond.; FRCP Lond. 1985; MRCP (UK) 1972; MRCS Eng. LRCP Lond. 1969. (St. Bart.) Cons. Gen. Med. & Respirat. Dis. N. Gen. Hosp. Sheff.; Med. Mem., Appeals Serv., Leeds; Chairm., N. Sheff. Local Research Ethics Comm. Socs: BMA; BTS; (Br. Sec.) Catholic Doctors Guild. Prev: Sen. Regist. Roy. Hosp. Sheff.

BRENNAN, Susan Anne Hazelhurst, 32 Thornhill Road, Edgerton, Huddersfield HD3 3DD — MB ChB 1987 Leeds.

BRENNAN, Susan Mary Azurdia and Partners, Civic Medical Centre, Civic Way, Bebington, Wirral CH63 7RX Tel: 0151 645 6936 Fax: 0151 643 1698 — MB ChB 1977 Birm.; MRCGP 1981; DRCOG 1981. (Birm.) Clin. Asst, Diabetic Clin. Wirral Hosp. NHS Trust. Prev: Clin. Med. Off. (Child Health) Gtr. Glas. HB; Princip. GP Newc.

BRENNAN, Thomas (retired) 387 Beverley Road, Anlaby, Hull HU10 7BQ Tel: 01482 653703 — LRCP LRCS 1951 Ed.; LRCP LRCS Ed. LRFPS Glas. 1951; MFOM RCP Lond. 1978. Prev: Med. Off. Shipp. Federat.

BRENNAN, Mr Thomas Gabriel Rounday Hall, BUPA Hospital Leeds, Jackson Avenue, Roundhay, Leeds LS8 1NT Tel: 0113 269 3939; Fairfield, Rigton Green, Bardsey, Leeds LS17 9AR — MB BCh BAO 1962 NUI; BSc (Anat.) (Hons.) NUI 1964; FRCS Eng. 1968; FRCS Ed. 1968; FRCSI 1968. (Univ. Coll. Dub.) Cons. Gen. Surg. St. Jas. Univ. Teach. Hosp. Leeds. Prev: Rotating Sen. Regist. (Gen. Surg.) Leeds RHB.

BRENNAN, Vincent John Shantallow Health Centre, Racecourse Road, Londonderry BT48 8NL Tel: 028 7135 1323 — MB BCh BAO 1976 Dub.; BA Dub., MB BCh BAO 1976; DObst RCPI 1981.

BRENNAN-BENSON, Paul 86 Chichester Road, Bognor Regis PO21 2AD Email: drpbbenson@aol.com — MB BS 1997 Lond.; PhD 1992; BSc 1987. (University College, London) SHO (Med. Rotat.), Roy. Lond. & St. Bartholomews. Prev: Sen. research Fell., Cancer research campaign; SHO, Middlx. Hosp., Dept. of Genito-Urin. Med.

BRENNAND, Duncan James Flat 2B, Lauderdale Mansions, Lauderdale Road, London W9 1NE — MB BS 1996 Lond.

BRENNAND, Elizabeth Janet (retired) 1 Brompton Terrace, Perth PH2 7DH Tel: 01738 623257 — MB BS 1961 Lond.; MRCS Eng. LRCP Lond. 1961; MRCOphth 1988; DO Eng. 1963. Prev: Assoc. Specialist (Ophth.) Perth Roy. Infirm. & Ninewells Hosp. Dundee.

BRENNAND, Janet Elizabeth The Queen Mothers Hospital, York Hill, Glasgow G3 8SJ — MB ChB 1988 Ed.; MRCOG 1995; MD 1999. (Edinburgh University) Specialist Regist. & Fell. in Fetal Med., The Qu. Mothers Hosp. Glas. Prev: Regist. (O & G) Glas. Roy. Matern. Hosp. & Glas. Roy. Infirm.

BRENNAND, Mr John Kinder (retired) 1 Brompton Terrace, Perth PH2 7DH Tel: 01738 623257 — MB BS 1959 Lond.; FRCS Eng. 1966; MRCS Eng. LRCP Lond. 1959; AKC. Prev: Cons. ENT Surg. Co. & City of Perth & Ninewells Hosp. Dundee.

BRENNAND-ROPER, David Andrew Cardiothoracic Department, 6th Floor East Wing, St Thomas' Hospital, London SE1 7EH Tel: 020 7928 9292 Fax: 020 7378 7881; Suite 201, Emblem House, London Bridge Hospital, 27 Tooley St, London SE1 2PR Tel: 020 7357 8467 Fax: 020 7357 8467 — BM BCh 1971 Oxf.; MA Oxf. 1971; FRCP Lond. (Oxf. & Guy's) Cons. Cardiol. Guy's & St. Thos. Trust; Cons. Cardiol. Joyce Green Hosp. Dartford; Hon. Lect. Brit. Heart Foundat. Socs: Eur. Cardiac Soc.; Brit. Cardiac Soc.; BMA. Prev: Sir Thos. Oppenheimer Research Fell. Guy's Hosp. Lond.; Hon. Sen. Regist. & Regist. (Cardiol.) Guy's Hosp. Lond.

BRENNAND ROPER, Stephen Michael L'Aumone and St Sampson's Practice, Grandes Maisons Road, St. Sampson, Guernsey GY2 4JS Tel: 01481 245915 Fax: 01481 243179; Osborne Lodge, Rue Des Fauconnaires, St Andrews, Guernsey GY6 8UF Tel: 01481 723357 Fax: 01481 723357 — MB BS 1975 Lond.; MA Oxf. 1975. Med. Adviser St John's Ambul. & Rescue Serv. Guernsey. Socs: BMA; Primary Care Rheum. Soc. Prev: Regist. (Intens. Care & Toxicol.) Guy's Hosp. Lond.; Regist. (Med.) Guy's Hosp. Lond.

BRENNEN, Mr Michael David Plastic Surgery Unit, The Ulster Hospital, Dundonald, Belfast BT9 5JR Tel: 02890 669150; 40 Deramore Road, Belfast BT9 5JR — MB BCh BAO 1968 Belf.; FRCS Ed. 1972. Cons. Plastic & hand Surg., The Ulster Hosp., Dundonald. Socs: Brit. Assn. Plastic Surg.; Brit. Soc. Surg. Hand; Internat. Soc. Reconstruc. MicroSurg.

BRENNEN, Robert Gibson 62 The Ridgeway, Tonbridge TN10 4NL Tel: 01732 353979 — MB BCh BAO 1940 Belf.; MFCM 1972; DPH Bristol 1948.

BRENNER, Bernard Nathan 12 Constable Close, London NW11 6TY — MB BCh 1972 Witwatersrand; MRCOG 1978.

BRENNER, Eithne Rose 40 Gloxinia Walk, Hampton TW12 3RF — MB BCh BAO 1989 NUI; DCH RCP Lond. 1992; DRCOG 1992. Trainee GP Cleveland VTS.

BRENNER, Robert Elliot Department of Neurology, Royal Free Hospital, Pond St., London NW3 Tel: 020 7830 2868 Fax: 020 7431 1577; 32 Harman Drive, South Hampstead, London NW2 2ED Tel: 020 8452 1611 — MB BS 1983 Lond.; MRCP (UK) 1988. Cons. Neurol. Roy. Free Hosp. Lond. & St. Albans & Hemel Hempstead Hosp. Prev: Research Fell. NMR Research Gp. Inst. Neurol. Lond.

BRENT, Keith Alan 8 The Paddocks, Wembley Park, Wembley HA9 9HE Email: kbrent@hotmail.com — MB BChir 1990 Camb.; BA Camb. 1987; MRCP (UK) 1995. Regist. (Paediat.) Univ. Coll. Hosp. Lewisham, Lond. Prev: Regist. (Paediat.) Sydney Childr. Hosp.
BRENT, Peter George Law Medical Group, 124-128 Harrow Road, Wembley HA9 6QQ Tel: 0208 903 4848 Fax: 0208 903 3680; 8 The Paddocks, Wembley HA9 9HE Tel: 0208 904 1909 — MB BS Lond. 1961; PhD Lond. 1959, BSc 1956; MRCS Eng. LRCP Lond. 1961; MRCGP 1992; FRCGP 1998. (Westm.) Gen. Practitioner; Clin. Asst. Dermat. N.wick Pk. Hosp., harrow; Vis. Phys., BUPA Med. Centre, Lond. Socs: Med. Soc. Lond. Prev: Regist. St. Bart. Hosp.; SHO St. Stephen's Hosp. Lond.; Ho. Phys. W.m. Hosp.
BRENT, Walter Manfred 74 Overton Drive, London E11 2NW Tel: 020 8989 8287 — MRCS Eng. LRCP Lond. 1948; MD Leipzig 1933. (Leipzig, Vienna, Freiburg) Socs: BMA. Prev: Asst. Surg. EMS Pk.side Emerg. Hosp. Macclesfield; Vis. Surg. Baguley Emerg. Hosp.
BRENTNALL, Ann Lucy Philippa Albemarle Surgery, 27 Albemarle Crescent, Scarborough YO11 1XX Tel: 01723 360098 Fax: 01723 501546 — MB BS 1984 Lond.; MRCGP 1989; DRCOG 1988.
BRENTNALL, Christopher John Appletree Medical Practice, 47a Town Street, Duffield, Belper DE56 4GG Tel: 01332 841219 — MB ChB 1973 Birm.; DA Eng. 1975.
BRENTNALL, George Creswell (retired) Slinfold, The Street, Walberswick, Southwold IP18 6UH Tel: 01502 722090 — MRCS Eng. LRCP Lond. 1936; MD (Obst. & Gyn.) Lond. 1945, MB BS 1937; FRCOG 1961, M 1949. Prev: Cas. Ho. Surg. St. Bart. Hosp.
BRENTON, David Percy The Postgraduate Office, The Middlesex Hospital, Mortimer St., London W1T 3AA — MD Camb. 1974, BA, MB 1961, BChir 1960; FRCP Lond 1978, M 1963. (Camb. & Univ. Coll. Hosp.) Reader in Inherited Metab. Dis.s. Dept. Med. Sch. of Med. Univ. Coll. Lond.; Dir. of Med. Educat. UCL Hosps. Trust.
BRENTON, Jane Elizabeth 12 Hazelwood Crescent, Elburton, Plymouth PL9 8BL — BM 1998 Soton.
BRERETON, Andrew George Mowbray House, 277 North End, Northallerton DL7 8DP Tel: 01609 775281 Fax: 01609 778029 — MB BS 1968 Lond.; MRCS Eng. LRCP Lond. 1968; DObst RCOG 1974. (King's Coll. Hosp)
BRERETON, Michael Joseph The Queens Road Medical Practice, The Grange, St Peter Port, Guernsey GY1 1RH — MB BCh BAO 1984 Belf.; MRCP (UK) 1988; MRCGP 1990; DRCOG 1989.
BRERETON, William John The Dale House, Boraston, Tenbury Wells WR15 8LH — MB ChB 1998 Birm.
BRERETON-SMITH, Gillian Court Cottage, The Street, Shimpling, Bury St Edmunds IP29 4HS — MB ChB 1979 Ed.; MRCGP 1985; Dip. Palliat. Med. Wales 1997; DRCOG 1984. Assoc. Specialist St. Nicholas Hospice Bury St. Edmunds.
BRESLAND, Michael Keith 21 Randal Park, Portrush BT56 8JJ — MB ChB 1989 Manch.; FFARCSI 1995. (Manchester)
BRESLIN, Louise 13 Whitelea Crescent, Balerno, Edinburgh EH14 7HF — MB ChB 1996 Aberd.
BRESLIN, Thomas Joseph 7 Rivers Close, WateringburySmiths Hill House, Maidstone ME18 5RP; Room 303, Rowan House, Royal Liverpool University Hospital, Prescot St., Liverpool L7 8XP — MB BCh BAO 1989 NUI.
BRESNEN, Darren 48 Hexham Avenue, Seaham SR7 8NB — MB ChB 1998 Manch.; MB ChB Manch 1998.
BRET DAY, Robin Carew 84 Harley Street, London W1G 7HW Tel: 020 7486 2109; Oakwood, 12 North Park, Iver SL0 9DJ Tel: 01753 653226 — MRCS Eng. LRCP Lond. 1958; FDS RCS Eng. 1954, LDS 1951. (Guy's) Cons. Dent. Surg. Guy's Hosp. Lond. Socs: Fell. Roy. Soc. Med.; BMA. Prev: Cons. Dent. Surg. Edgware Gen. Hosp.; Sen. Regist. Oral Surg. Dept. E.man Dent. Hosp. Lond.; Asst. to Vis. Dent. Surgs. Guy's Hosp. Dent. Sch.
BRETHERICK, Anne (retired) 3 Waterloo Place, Duncombe St, Kingsbridge TQ7 1LX Tel: 01548 852979 Fax: 01548 852979 — MB ChB 1960 Leeds.
BRETHERICK, Paul John (retired) 3 Waterloo Place, Duncombe St., Kingsbridge TQ7 1LX Tel: 01548 852979 Fax: 01548 852979 — MB ChB Leeds 1961.
BRETHERTON, Karen Fiona Westcotes House, Westcotes Drive, Leicester LE3 0QU; 8 Grenfell Road, Stoneygate, Leicester LE2 2PA — MB ChB 1988 Liverp.; MRCPsych 1993. Cons. Psychiat. Childr. with learning disbilities. Prev: Sen. Regist. (Psychiat. of Learning Disabil.) N.. & Yorks. Region.; Regist. Rotat. (Psychiat.) SE Thames RHA Train. Scheme & Mersey RHA Train. Scheme.
BRETLAND, Cleone Barbara St Michael's Hospital, Trent Valley Road, Lichfield WS13 6EF Tel: 01543 414555; 18 Risborrow Close, Etwall, Derby DE65 6HY — MB ChB 1984 Leic.; DCCH Warwick 1995; DRCOG 1987. (Leicester) Staff Grade (Child Health & Family Plann.) Premier Health St. Michael's Hosp. Staffs.; Community Med. Off. (Family Plann.) S. Derbysh. HA; Sen. Community Med. Off. Socs: Assoc. Mem. BPA. Prev: GP Birm.; Clin. Asst. Bloomsbury Terminal Care Support Team; SHO St. Mary's Hospice Birm.
BRETLAND, Michael John 11 Lansdowne Road, Colwyn Bay LL29 7YD — MB BCh 1996 Wales. (Univ. Wales Coll. Med.) SHO Rotat. (Med.) Nevill Hall Hosp., Abergavenny, Gwent. Prev: Ho. Off. (Med.) Nevill Hall, Abergavenny; Ho. Off. (Surg.) E. Glam. Gen. Hosp.
BRETLAND, Peter Maynard (retired) 3 Bramalea Close, North Hill, Highgate, London N6 4QD Tel: 020 8340 2092 — MB ChB 1945 Liverp.; MSc Nuclear Med. Lond. 1985; MD Liverp. 1968; FRCR 1975; FFR 1961; DMRD Eng. 1958. Hon. Sen. Lect. (Radiol.) UCH Med. Sch. Lond. Prev: Cons. Radiol. Whittington & Roy N.ern Hosps. Lond.
BRETMAN, Mandy Deborah Tel: 01522 575306 Fax: 01522 515364 Email: mandy.bretman@lincs-ha.nhs.uk — MB ChB 1982 Glas.; FFPHM 2001 (RCPUK); MFPHM RCP (UK) 1990. Direct. of Pub. Health. Socs: Glas. M-C Soc. Prev: Cons. (Pub. Health Med.) Lincs HA; Sen. Regist. (Pub. Health Med.) Trent RHA; Regist. (Community Med.) Trent RHA.
BRETT, Adam Dallas c/o Crossways, Kellaton, Kingsbridge TQ7 2ES — MB BS 1990 Lond.
BRETT, Andrew Scott 27 Gorsefield, Freshfield, Liverpool L37 7HE — MB BS 1989 Lond.
BRETT, Bernard Thomas 25 Heathville Road, Crouch End, London N19 3AL — MB BS 1991 Lond.; BSc Lond. 1988, MB BS 1991; MRCP (UK) 1994. Research Fell. Roy. Free Hosp. Prev: Regist. (Gastroenterol. & Gen. Med.) Edgware Gen. Hosp. Lond.; SHO Rotat. (Med.) N.wick Pk. Hosp.; Regist. Roy. Free Hosp.
BRETT, Charles John Scott Torrington Park Health Centre, 16 Torrington Park, North Finchley, London N12 9SS Tel: 020 8445 7622/4127 — MB BS 1967 London; MB BS 1967 London.
BRETT, Charles Timothy Francis 207 Clarendon Park Road, Clarendon Park, Leicester LE2 3AN — MB ChB 1990 Leic.
BRETT, Daniel Dallas 48 Matthews Green Road, Wokingham RG41 1JU — MB BS 1992 Lond.
BRETT, Edward Morgan Paul (retired) 97 South End Road, London NW3 2RJ Tel: 020 7435 0383 — BM BCh 1952 Oxf.; DM Oxf. 1967, MA 1952; FRCP Lond. 1974, M 1959; FRCPCH Hon 1996. Cons. Paediat. Neurol. Hosp. Sick Childr. Gt. Ormond St. & Nat. Hosps. Nerv. Dis. Lond. Prev: Sen. Regist. (Neurol.) Hosp. Sick Childr. Gt. Ormond St.
BRETT, Ian 1 Ward Lane, Diggle, Oldham OL3 5JT — MB ChB 1976 Dundee; FRCR 1987. Cons. Radiol. Tameside Dist. Gen. Hosp.
BRETT, Jeanne Margaret Norbury Health Centre, 2B Pollards Hill N., Norbury, London SW16 4NL Tel: 020 8679 1700; 27 Fitzjames Avenue, Croydon CR0 5DL Tel: 020 8654 8677 — MB ChB 1960 Manch. (Manch.) Prev: Civil. Med. Pract. Army Berlin; SHO (Med.) Mayday Hosp. Thornton Heath.
BRETT, Judith Vivienne 20 Gower Street, London WC1 Tel: 020 7636 7628 — MB BS 1968 Lond.; MRCS Eng. LRCP Lond. 1968; DObst RCOG 1970. (Roy. Free) Phys. i/c Univ. Lond. Centr. Inst. Health Serv. Prev: SHO Acad. Unit. Psychiat. Middlx. Hosp. Lond.; SHO St. John's Hosp. Dis. Skin Lond.
BRETT, June Elizabeth (retired) 92 Court Road, Eltham, London SE9 5NS Tel: 020 8850 3084 Email: juneli.brett@virgin.net — 1952 MB BChir Camb.; 1952 MA Camb.; 1952 MRCS Eng. LRCP Lond.; 1957 FRCA; 1954 DA Eng. Prev: Cons. Anaesth. Brook Gen. Hosp. & Greenwich Dist. Hosp. Lond.
BRETT, Mr Martin Clive Ashton Warrington Hospital NHS Trust, Lovely Lane, Warrington WA5 1QL Tel: 01925 635911 — MB BS 1983 Lond.; MA Oxf. 1985; ChM Liverp. 1994; FRCS Eng. 1987. Cons. Gen. Surg. Warrington Hosp. Trust. Socs: Assn. Surg.; Brit. Assn. Surgic. Oncol. Prev: Sen. Regist. (Gen. Surg.) Mersey RHA; Career Regist. Mersey RHA.
BRETT, Mr Martin Stuart (retired) Yondover House, Stratford Tony, Salisbury SP5 4AT Tel: 0172 271 8223 — MB BS (Hnrs.)

Lond. 1945; FRCS Eng. 1948. Prev: Cons. Orthop. Surg. Salisbury Gen. Infirm. & Odstock Hosp.

BRETT, Mary Therese Department Cellular Pathology, Southmead Hospital, Westbury-on-Trym, Bristol BS10 5NB Tel: 0117 959 5641 Fax: 0117 959 0087 — BM 1978 Soton.; BM (Hons.) Soton. 1978; FRCPC (Gen. Path.) 1985; FRCPath 1997, M 1988. Cons. Cytol. & Histopath. S.mead Hosp. Bristol. Prev: Cons. Histopath. & Cytol. St. Helier Hosp. Carshalton; Sen. Regist. (Histopath.) St. Geo. Hosp. Lond.; Resid. (Path.) Kingston Gen. Hosp. Ontario, Canada.

BRETT, Matthew 31 Newmarket Road, Cambridge CB5 8EG — MB BChir 1990 Camb.; MRCP (UK) 1994. SHO (Neurol.) Nat. Hosp. Neurol. & Neurosurg. Qu. Sq. Lond.

BRETT, Michael John Edwin Riversdale Surgery, 59 Bridge Street, Belper DE56 1AY Tel: 01773 822386; Laund Farm, 1 Laund Farm Mews, Far Laund, Belper DE56 1FP Email: mike.brett@btinternet.com — BM BS 1986 Nottm.; MRCGP, 1991; DRCOG, 1991. Socs: MPS.

BRETT, Sarah Louise 2 Church Farm Barn, Church St., Weybourne, Holt NR25 7SX — MB BCh 1992 Wales.

BRETT, Thomas Justin Edward 22 The Precincts, Canterbury CT1 2EP Tel: 01227 459757 — MB BS 1992 Lond. SHO Auckland Hosp., NZ.

BRETTELL, Andrew Mid-Cheshire Homeopathic Group, 2 Watling Street, Northwich CW9 5EX Tel: 01606 42445 — MB ChB 1975 Liverp.

BRETTELL, Francesca Rose 13 William Street, South Gosforth, Newcastle upon Tyne NE3 1SA — MB BS 1994 Newc.; BA (Hons.) Oxf. 1991.

BRETTELL, Paul Brian Varney The Surgery, Central Clinic, Hall Street, Dudley DY2 7BX Tel: 01384 253616 Fax: 01384 253332 — MB ChB 1965 Birm.

BRETTINGHAM, Lisa Clare 11 Hovendens, Sissinghurst, Cranbrook TN17 2LA — MB BS 1987 Lond.

BRETTLE, Raymond Patrick Infectious Diseases Unit, Western General Hospital, Crewe Road, Edinburgh EH4 2XU Tel: 0131 537 2841 Fax: 0131 537 2878 Email: ray.brettle@ed.ac.uk — MB ChB 1974 Ed.; MD Ed. 1995; FRCP Ed. 1986; MRCP (UK) 1976. (Ed.) Cons. Phys. Infec. Dis. Unit W.ern Gen. Hosp. Edin.; Mem. Edit. Bd. Internat. J. STD AIDS & Genitourin. Med.; Pat. Serv. Director, Lothian Univ. NHS Trust, Edin.; Reader (Med.) Univ. Edin. Socs: Brit. Infec. Soc.; Assn. Phys.; Brit. HIV Assn. Prev: Fell.sh. (Infec. Dis.) Med. Sch. N. Carolina, USA; Sen. Regist. (Med. & Communicable Dis.) Edin.; Regist. (Med.) Roy. Postgrad. Med. Sch. Hammersmith Hosp. Lond.

BREUER, Judith London Hospital Medical College, 37 Ashfield St., London E1 1BB; 6 Creighton Road, London NW6 6ED Tel: 020 8968 4087 — MB BS 1981 Lond.; MD Lond. 1995; MRCPath 1990. Sen. Lect. (Virol.) Roy. Lond. Hosp. Prev: MRC Research Fell. Nat. Inst. for Med. Research Lond.; Sen. Regist. (Virol.) St. Mary's Hosp Lond.; Regist. (Microbiol.) Kings Coll. Hosp. Lond.

BREUNING, Stefan Gerhard Ernst 12 West Eaton Place, London SW1X 8LS — MB BCh 1989 Witwatersrand.

BREW, Christopher John 1 Queensway, Irlam, Manchester M44 6ND — MB ChB 1995 Manch.

BREW, David St John 42 Bury Meadows, Rickmansworth WD3 1DR — MB BS 1949 Lond.; MRCPath 1965. (Middlx.) Asst. Pathol. Bland-Sutton Inst. Path. Middlx. Hosp. Sen. Lect. in; Path. Bland-Sutton Inst. Path. Middlx. Hosp. Lect. Dept. Path. Univ. Ibadan, Nigeria.

BREW, Elinor Francesca Maddock Wordsworth Surgery, 97 Newport Road, Cardiff CF24 0AG Tel: 029 2049 8000 Fax: 029 2045 5494 — MB ChB 1981 Birm.

BREW, Iain Falconer Lerwick Doctors Group, The Health Centre, South Road, Lerwick ZE1 0RZ Tel: 01595 693201 Fax: 01595 697113; Sunshine Cottage, Easter Quarff, Shetland ZE2 9EX Tel: 01950 477426 Email: brew.family@zetnet.co.uk — MB ChB 1991 Sheff.; MRCGP 1995; DFFP 1994; DRCOG 1993. (Sheff.) GP Princip. Lerwick; Mem. LMC; GP Mem. of Shetland Health Bd. Purchasing Team; Vice-Chairm. Shetland Research Ethics Comm. Prev: SHO Lincoln Co. Hosp. VTS.

BREW, John Raymond The Health Centre, Saunder Bank, Burnley BB11 2EM Tel: 01282 831249 — MB ChB 1959 Liverp.; DObst RCOG 1961. (Lond.) Mem. Med. Bd.ing Panel DHSS. Socs: BMA. Prev: Ho. Surg. (Orthop)., Ho. Phys. (Gen. Med.) & Ho. Surg. (O & G); Vict. Hosp. Blackpool.

BREW, Michael Donald Alexandra Villa, 19 Marine Parade, Sheerness ME12 2PQ Tel: 01795 585058 Fax: 01795 585158 — MB ChB 1971 Liverp.; MRCGP 1975.

BREW, Mrs Pamela Francesca Mary 7 Malvern Close, South Wootton, King's Lynn PE30 3UJ Tel: 01553 675862 — BM BCh 1945 Oxf.; MA Oxf. 1948. (Oxf.) Prev: Clin. Med. Off. Ealing & Kensington AHAs; Ho. Surg. Burns Unit & Regist. Cas. Dept. Accid. Hosp. Birm.; Ho. Phys. Radcliffe Infirm. Oxf.

BREW, Shona 144 Parkville Road, Didsbury, Manchester M20 4TY Tel: 0161 445 0947; 144 Parkville Road, Didsbury, Manchester M20 4TY Tel: 0161 445 0947 — MB ChB 1995 Manch.; DRCOG 1997; Dip Family Plann 1999. GP Regist., heald Green Health Centre, Finney La., heald Green, Stockport; Stockport GP VTS.

BREW, Stewart Henry 82 High Street, Hinderwell, Saltburn-by-the-Sea TS13 5ES — MB ChB 1963 Liverp.

BREW-GRAVES, Emmeline Harriet The Surgery, 1 Richmond House, East Street, London SE17 2DU Tel: 020 7703 7393 Fax: 020 7708 3077; 12 Neville Court, 35 Weir Road, Balham, London SW12 0NU — MB BS 1987 Lond.; MSc (public health), Lond. Sch. Hyg.& Trop. Med. Univ. Lond. 1998; MRCGP 1992; DRCOG 1991.

BREWER, Andrew Kinson Road Surgery, 440 Kinson Road, Bournemouth BH10 5EY Tel: 01202 574604 Fax: 01202 590029; 30 Twemlow Avenue, Parkstone, Poole BH14 8AN Tel: 01202 749563 — MB BS 1983 Lond.; BSc (Hons.) Anat. Lond. 1980, MB BS 1983. (St. Thomas' Hospital Medical School)

BREWER, Angus Edwin (retired) Millfield, Caddington, Luton LU1 4AR Tel: 01582 840542 Fax: 01582 842630 — MRCS Eng. LRCP Lond. 1939; FRCPath 1963. Prev: Cons. Path. Hampstead Gen. Hosp., Vict. Hosp. Barnet & St. Geo. Hosp. Lond.

BREWER, Mr Arthur Clifford, TD (retired) Stable Cottage, West Lodge, Hundred Acres Road, Wickham, Fareham PO17 6JD Tel: 01329 834008 — MB ChB 1935 Liverp.; FRCS Eng. 1938; MRCS Eng. LRCP Lond. 1935; FICS 1956. Prev: Hon. Surg. Roy. Infirm. Liverp., Hahnemann Hosp. & St. Helens Hosp. Lancs.

BREWER, Belinda Mary — MB BS 1992 Lond.; MRCGP; MRCP. (Charing Cross & Westminster) p/t GP; Clin. Asst. Cardiol.; Hosp.L Practitioner Cardiol. Prev: SpR Med.; Sito Palliat. Care; Spr A& E.

BREWER, Colin Leslie The Stapleford Centre, 25A Eccleston St., London SW1W 9NP Tel: 020 7823 6840 Fax: 020 7730 3409 Email: cb@stap-cen.demon.co.uk — MB BS 1963 Lond.; MRCS Eng. LRCP Lond. 1963; MRCPsych 1972; DPM Eng. 1968. (St. Bart.) Med. Dir. Stapleford Addic. Centres Lond. & Stapleford Tawney Essex; Hon. Research Fell. Dept. Psychiat. Univ. Birm. Socs: Fell. Roy. Soc. Med.; Foundat./Bd. Mem., Internat. Soc. Of Addic. Med. Prev: Dir. Community Alcoholism Treatm. Serv. W.m. Hosp. Lond.; Specialist (Psychiat.) Repat. Gen. Hosp. Adelaide, Austral.; Asst. Surg. P. & O. Orient Lines.

BREWER, Desmond John (retired) Woodstock, Ballard Close, Lytchett Matravers, Poole BH16 6EW Tel: 01202 622752 — MB BS Lond. 1947; FRCP Ed. 1982, M 1959; MRCS Eng. LRCP Lond. 1947. Prev: Cons. Chest Phys. Brierton Hosp. Hartlepool & N. Tees Hosp. Stockton-on-Tees.

BREWER, Douglas Bertram (retired) 50 St Agnes Road, Moseley, Birmingham B13 9PN Tel: 0121 449 0127 Email: dbrew885@netscapeonline.co.uk — MRCS Eng. LRCP Lond. 1943; MD (Path.) Lond. 1948, MB BS 1943; FRCPath 1965. Prev: Prof. Morbid Anat. Univ. Birm.

BREWER, Irene Louisa Sunnybank, 6 Overbeck Drive, Barrow-in-Furness LA13 0HD — MB ChB 1980 Manch. CMO Psychosexual Counselling Barrow-in-Furness; Clin. Med. Off. (Family Plann. & Psychosex. Counselling) Cumbria HA.

BREWER, Jeremy Spencer (retired) — MB BS 1960 Lond.; MRCS Eng. LRCP Lond. 1960; FRCGP 1989, M 1968; DCH Eng. 1965; DObst RCOG 1962. Med. Adviser to Operat. Mobiliattion Ships. Prev: Ho. Off. (Paediat.) P.ss Louise Hosp. Childr. Kensington.

BREWER, Nicholas Jason 22 Ainsley Street, London E2 0DL — MB BS 1997 Lond.

BREWER, Peter James (retired) 24-26 Northam Road, Hedge End, Southampton SO30 4FL Tel: 0148 96 423 — MB BS 1961 Lond.; MRCS Eng. LRCP Lond. 1961. Prev: Sen. Ho. Off. Roy. Devon & Exeter Hosp. Exeter.

BREWER, Peter John Jeaffreson Looe Health Centre, Looe PL13 1HA — MB BCh 1970 Wales; DObst RCOG 1973; DA Eng. 1973; Cert. JCC Lond. 1979. (Cardiff) Socs: BMA; Brit. Med. Acupunct. Soc. Prev: GP Anaesth. W.. Memor. Hosp. Corner Brook, Canada; Regist. (Anaesth.) Roy. Gwent Hosp. Newport.

BREWER, Philip Arnewood Practice, Milton Medical Centre, Avenue Road, New Milton BH25 5JP Tel: 01425 620393 Fax: 01425 624219; 41 Acacia Road, Hordle, Lymington SO41 0YG Tel: 01425 615442 — MB BS 1987 Lond.; MRCGP 1991.

BREWER, Sarah Helen Email: drsarah@compuserve.com — MB BChir 1983 Camb.; MA Camb. 1983. Freelance Med. Jl.ist; Clin. Asst. (Genitourin. Med.) Qu. Eliz. Hosp. King's Lynn. Socs: Soc. Authors (Med.); Med. Jl.ists Assn.; Guild Health Writers. Prev: GP Plymouth; Trainee GP Addenbrooke's Hosp. Camb. VTS; Head Med. Developm. Haymarket Publishing Gp.

BREWERTON, Derrick Arthur 173 Ashley Gardens, Emery Hill St., Westminster, London SW1P 1PD Tel: 020 7828 0985 Fax: 020 7931 7635 — MD 1947 CM McGill; BSc CM McGill 1947; LMS Nova Scotia Med. Bd. 1948; FRCP Lond. 1969, M 1952. (McGill) Emerit. Prof. Rheum. Univ. Lond. Prev: Prof. Rheum. Univ. Lond.; Cons. Phys. (Rheum.) W.m. Hosp. & Roy. Nat. Orthop. Hosp. Lond.

BREWERTON, Jonathan Michael Devonshire Lodge Practice, Eastcote Health Centre, Abbotsbury Gardens, Eastcote, Pinner, Ruislip HA5 1TG Tel: 020 8866 0200 Fax: 020 8429 3087; 95 Copse Wood Way, Northwood HA6 2TU Tel: 01923 820575 Fax: 01923 840010 Email: jonbrewerton@lineone.net — MB BS 1976 Lond.; MRCS Eng. LRCP Lond. 1976; MRCGP 1983; DRCOG 1982. (St. Bart.) Prev: SHO Rotat. (Gen. Med.) Mt. Vernon Hosp. N.wood & Harefield Hosp.; SHO (O & G) Canad. Red Cross Memor. Hosp. Taplow; GP Stoke Poges VTS.

BREWERTON, Sally Ann 30 Middle Way, Oxford OX2 7LG — MB BS 1987 Lond.; MRCGP 1994.

BREWIN, David Michael Clifford Health Centre, Shaftesbury SP7 8DH Tel: 01747 52371; Old Bozley Farm House, Long Lane, Cann, Shaftesbury SP7 0BJ Tel: 01747 53785 — MRCS Eng. LRCP Lond. 1967; DObst RCOG 1969. (St. Thos.) Prev: Ho. Off. Dorset Co. Hosp.; SHO (Obst.) Poole Gen. Hosp.; Squadron Ldr. RAF Med. Br.

BREWIN, Mr Ernest Garside (retired) 58 Farrar Lane, Adel, Leeds LS16 7AF Tel: 0113 267 7036 — MB ChB 1945 Leeds; ChM Leeds 1955; FRCS Eng. 1957. Prev: Cons. Thoracic & Cardiovasc. Surg. Stoke-on-Trent.

BREWIN, John Stedman Department of Psychiatry, South Block B Floor, Queens Medical Centre, University Hospital NE7 2UH Tel: 0115 924 9924 — BM BS 1986 Nottm.; MRCPsych 1991. Acad. Cons. Psychiat. Univ. Hosp. Nottm. Prev: Lect. & Hon. Sen. Regist. (Psychiat.) Univ. Nottm.

BREWIN, Julia Elaine The Jessoop Medical Practice, 24 Pennine Avenue, Riddings, Derby DE5 54AE Tel: 01773 602707; Tel: 02920 498942 — BM BS 1986 Nottm.; BMedSci Nottm. 1984; MRCGP 1991; DCH RCP Lond. 1990. Prev: Trainee GP Ripley Derbysh.; SHO (Gen. Med.) Derby Roy. Infirm.

BREWIN, Michael Douglas 16 Greenland Road, Selly Oak, Birmingham B29 7PP — MB ChB 1974 Bristol; FFA RCS Lond. 1981. Cons. Anaesth. Centr. Birm. HA.

BREWIN, Peter Hooper (retired) 3 Selstone Crescent, Sleights, Whitby YO22 5DJ — MB ChB 1952 Leeds; DPH 1961.

BREWIS, Alford William (retired) Garda, Elmbank Road, Wylam NE41 8HS Tel: 01661 853126 — MB ChB 1960 Ed. Med. Off., Blood Transfus. Donor Sessions, p/t. Prev: Gen. Pract., Blaydon.

BREWIS, Mr Clive 25 Barrow Road, Burton-on-the-Wolds, Loughborough LE12 5TB — MB BChir 1993 Camb.; BA (Hons.) Camb. 1991; FRCS Eng. 1997; FRCS (Gen Surg.) Eng. 1997; FRCS Eng. 1998. (Cambridge)

BREWIS, Gillian Margaret Health Centre, Constitution St, Inverurie AB51 4SU Tel: 0146 762 1345 Email: gillian.brewis@inverurie.grampian.scot.nhs.uk — MB ChB 1984 Ed.; MRCGP 1990; DRCOG 1988; DA (UK) 1987. Gen. Practitioner (Partner), Inverurie. Prev: Asst. GP Inverurie; Trainee GP Inverurie VTS.

BREWIS, John Edward 3 Mount Drive, Bebington, Wirral CH63 5NX — MB ChB 1974 Liverp.

BREWIS, Mary (retired) High Barn, High Side, Bassenthwaite, Keswick CA12 4QG Tel: 0176 8776 485 — MB BS 1960 Durh.; MD Newc. 1964. Prev: Assoc. Specialist Radiother. Newc. Gen. Hosp.

BREWIS, Robert Alistair Livingston (retired) High Barn, High Side, Bassentwaite, Keswick CA12 4QG Tel: 0176 877 6485 Email: ralb@ralbrewis.demon.co.uk — MB BS Durh. 1960; MD Newc. 1966; FRCP Lond. 1974, M 1962; MRCP Ed. 1963. Prev: Cons. Phys. & Med. Dir. Roy. Vict. Infirm. NHS Trust.

BREWIS, Robert Paul Peartree Lane Surgery, 110 Peartree Lane, Welwyn Garden City AL7 3XW Tel: 01707 329292; 135 Parkway, Welwyn Garden City AL8 6JB — MB BS 1972 Lond.

BREWIS, Veronica Thelma Arbory Street Surgery, Arbory Street, Castletown IM9 1LN — MB ChB 1974 Liverpool. (Liverpool) GP Castletown, Isle of Man.

BREWOOD, Mr Anthony Frank Morgan Bury General Hospital, Walmersley Road, Bury BL9 6PG Tel: 0161 764 6081 Fax: 0161 705 3435; 9 Linnet Hill, Half Acre, Rochdale OL11 4DA — MB ChB 1974 Manch.; FRCS Eng. 1997; FRCS Ed. 1981. Cons. Orthop. Surg. Bury HA. Socs: Fell. BOA.

BREWS, Andrew John Marshes, Butt Lane, Snaith, Goole DN14 9DY Tel: 01405 860111 Fax: 01405 863901 — MB ChB 1986 Leeds.

BREWSTER, Aileen Mary The Medical Centre, Queens Road, Dunbar EH42 1EE Tel: 01368 863226 Fax: 01368 865646; Abbeyview, 33 Dunbar Road, Haddington EH41 3PJ Tel: 01620 823629 Email: clanbrewster@btinternet.com — MB ChB 1981 Dundee; MRCGP 1985; DRCOG 1983. Socs: BMA. Prev: Trainee GP Perth VTS; Ho. Phys. Perth Roy. Infirm.; Ho. Surg. Ayr Co. Hosp.

BREWSTER, Alison Elizabeth Velindre Hospital, Whitchurch, Cardiff CF14 2TL; 17 The Walk, Roath, Cardiff CF24 3AF — MB BCh 1982 Wales; BSc Wales 1979, MD 1991; FRCR 1988. Cons. Clin. Oncol. Velindre Hosp. Cardiff. Socs: BMA; Assoc. Mem. Brit. Med. Acunpunc. Soc. Prev: Cons. Clin. Oncol. Bristol; Sen. Regist. (Radiother. & Oncol.) Manch.

BREWSTER, Andrew Lee 2 Tedder Road, Southampton SO18 4SH — BM 1994 Soton.

BREWSTER, Barry Steven, MBE, TD (retired) The Little House, Church St., Settle BD24 9JE Tel: 01729 823454 — MB BCh BAO Dub. 1959; MA (Mod. Nat. Scs.) Dub. 1954; MRCGP 1974; DObst RCOG 1962; LM Rotunda. Prev: Ho. Surg. (Orthop.) Adelaide Hosp. Dub.

BREWSTER, David Heron Scottish Cancer Intelligence Unit, Trinity Park House, South Trinity Road, Edinburgh EH5 3SQ; Abbeyview, 33 Dunbar Road, Haddington EH41 3PJ — MB ChB 1981 Bristol; MSc (Distinc.) Ed. 1991; FFPHM RCP (UK) 1999; MRCGP 1985; DCH RCP Lond. 1985; DRCOG 1983. Director, Scott. Cancer Registry; Hon. Clin. Sen. Lect., Dept. of Community Health Sci.s, Fac. of Med., Univ. of Edin.. Socs: BMA; Soc. for Social Med.; Internat. Epidemiol. Assn. Prev: Sen. Regist. (Pub. Health Med.) Common Servs. Agency Edin.; GP Haddington; Trainee GP Perth VTS.

BREWSTER, Howard (retired) Linsfort, 4 Golf Hill Drive, Moffat DG10 9ST — MB BCh BAO 1949 Belf.; MD Belf. 1949, MB BCh, BAO 1938, DPH 1947; MFCM 1972. Prev: Flight Lt. R.A.F.V.R. Med. Br. 1941-46.

BREWSTER, Hugh Arthur Dumfries & Galloway Royal Infirmary, Bankend Road, Dumfries DG1 4AP Tel: 01387 246246; Wallaroo, 3 Robertson Avenue, Dumfries DG1 4EY Tel: 01387 263186 Fax: 01387 241639 — MB BCh BAO 1969 Dub.; MA Dub. 1967; FFA RCS Eng. 1975; DA Eng. 1972; DObst RCOG 1971. (Trinity Coll. Dub.) Cons. Anaesth. Dumfries & Galloway HB; Hon. Clin. Sen. Lect. Univ. Glas. Socs: Assn. Anaesth. GB & Irel.; Obst. Anaesth. Assn.; Scott. Soc. Anaesth. Prev: Sen. Regist. (Anaesth.) Univ. Coll. Hosp. Lond.; SHO (Surg.) Mildmay Miss. Hosp. Lond.; Ho. Off. Altnagelvin Hosp. Lond.derry.

BREWSTER, Jennifer Ann 9 Cheldon Road, West Derby, Liverpool L12 0RN — MB ChB 1994 Liverp. (Liverp.) Specialist Regist. (O & G), Yorks. Deanery. Prev: SHO (O & G) Liverp. Wom. Hosp.; Ho. Off. (O & G) Liverp. Wom. Hosp.

BREWSTER, John Howard Stanley Surgery, 1 East Brougham Street, Stanley, Perth PH1 4NJ Tel: 01738 828294 Fax: 01738 827770; Luncarty & Bankfoot Surgery, Perth PH1 3HE — MB ChB 1976 Ed.; MICGP 1986; MRCGP 1980; ECFMG Cert. 1976; Cert. Family Plann. JCC 1980; DRCOG 1980. (Ed.) Socs: BMA. Prev: Trainee Gp Doncaster VTS; Ho. Surg. Deaconess Hosp. Edin.; Ho. Phys. Seddon Memor. Hosp., Gore, NZ.

BREWSTER, Martin Forrest (retired) Dunure, Station Rd, Wigtown, Newton Stewart DG8 9DZ Tel: 01988 402273 — MB ChB Glas. 1956; DObst RCOG 1961. Prev: GP Wigtown Wigtownsh.

BREWSTER, Nigel Palmer Community Hospital, Wear St., Jarrow NE32 3UX Tel: 0191 451 6030 Fax: 0191 451 6001; 14 Halterburn Close, Kingsmere, Gosforth, Newcastle upon Tyne NE3 4YT Tel: 0191 285 1023 — MB 1979 Camb.; MA Camb. 1979, MB 1979, BChir 1978; MRCP (UK) 1984. Cons. Paediat. (Community Child Health). Socs: MRCPCH. Prev: Sen. Regist. (Community Child Health) N. Tyneside HA; Clin. Med. Off. St. Helens & Knowsley HA; Regist. (Paediat.) Roy. Hosp. Sick Childr.Glas.

BREWSTER, Mr Nigel Trevor Princess Margaret Rose Orthopaedic Hospital, Frogston Road W., Edinburgh Tel: 0131 536 4600; 29 Park Road, Dalkeith EH22 3DH Tel: 0131 663 1875 — MB ChB 1986 Ed.; FRCS Ed. 1992; FRCS (Orth.) Ed. 1996. (Edinburgh) Sen. Lect. & Hon. Cons. Orthop. Surg. Univ. of Edin. Roy. Infirm. of Edin., Roy. Hosp. for Sick Childr. Edin. Socs: BMA; BOA. Prev: Sen. Regist. (Orthop.) Edin. Roy. Infirm.; Career Regist. (Orthop.) Aberd. Roy. Infirm.; Regist. (Orthop.) Raigmore Hosp. Inverness.

BREWSTER, Mr Simon Frederick Department of Urology, Churchill Hospital, Oxford OX3 7LJ Tel: 01865 225717 Fax: 01865 226086 — MD 1994 Bristol; MB BS (Hons.) Lond. 1986; BSc Lond. 1983; FRCS (Urol.) 1997. (Char. Cross & Westm. Med. Sch.) Cons. (Urol.) Ch.ill Hosp. Oxf. Socs: Full Mem. Brit. Assn. Urol. Surgs.; Brit. Prostate Gp.; Eur. Assn. Urol. Prev: Sen. Regist. (Urol.) S. W. Rotat.

BREX, Peter Anthony Department of Neurology, King's College Hospital, London SE5 9RS Tel: 020 737 4000 Email: p.brex@ion.ucl.ac.uk — MB BS 1992 Lond.; MD 2001 Lond.; MRCP (UK) 1996; MRCP (UK) 1996. (King's College London) Specialist Regist. in Neurol., King's Coll. Hosp., Lond. Socs: Assn. of Brit. NeUrol.s (Assoc. Mem.). Prev: Research Fell. NMR Research Gp. Inst. of Neurol. Lond.

BREYTENBACH, Willem Jacobus Janse Flat 3, Eaton House, 41 St Peters Road, Margate CT9 1TJ — MB ChB 1991 Stellenbosch.

BRIAN, Christopher John St Annes Group Practice, 161 Station Road, Herne Bay CT6 5NF Tel: 01227 742226 Fax: 01227 741439 — MB BS 1977 Lond.; BSc (Hons.) Lond. 1974; MRCGP 1983; DRCOG 1982; Dip. Med. Acupunc. 1997. (St. Thos.) Socs: Brit. Med. Acupunct. Soc.

BRIAN, Jill Child Health Department, Loddon NHS Trust, North Hampshire Hospital, Aldermaston Road, Basingstoke RG24 9NA Tel: 01256 313083 — MB ChB Birm. 1970. Staff Grade Paediat. (child health) NHS Trust Basingstoke.

BRIANT, Bertha Alice (retired) 22 Copperfield Court, Rectory Road, Broadstairs CT10 1HE — MB BS 1929 Lond.; MRCS Eng. LRCP Lond. 1929. Prev: RAF (Wom. Med. Serv.).

BRIANT, Mr Ernest Raymond, Col. late RAMC (retired) 30 Chobham Road, Frimley, Camberley GU16 8PF — MB BS Lond. 1953; FRCS Eng. 1960. Prev: Consult. in Surg. & Orthop. RAMC.

BRIANT, Janet Lesley, OBE (retired) 1 Bromsgrove Road, Romsley, Halesowen B62 0ET — MB ChB 1947 Birm.; MRCS Eng. LRCP Lond. 1947. Prev: Sen. Partner Gen. Pract. Warley.

BRICE, Cynthia Helen Inverarnold, Avery Lane, Leeds, Maidstone ME17 1TE — MB ChB 1971 Liverp.

BRICE, David Doyle Royal Liverpool & Broadgreen University Hospitals NHS Trust, Prescot St., Liverpool L7 8XP Tel: 0151 706 2000 Fax: 01517065646; 39 Menlove Gardens W., Liverpool L18 2DL Tel: 0151 722 4182 Fax: 0151 722 4182 — MB BS 1964 Lond.; MRCS Eng. LRCP Lond. 1964; FFA RCS Eng. 1969. (St. Geo.) Cons. Anaesth. Roy. Liverp. & BRd.green Univ. Hosps. NHS Trust & Univ.Hosp.Aintree Liverp. Socs: Liverp. Soc. Anaesth.; Difficult Airway Soc.; Assn. Dent. Anaesth. Prev: Sen. Regist. Liverp. AHA (T).

BRICE, James Henry 50 Hulatt Road, Cambridge CB1 8TH — MB BChir 1981 Camb.; BA Camb. 1978.

BRICE, Mr Jason Giles (retired) BUPA Chalybeate Hospital, Tremona Road, Southampton SO9 6UY Tel: 023 8076 4334 Fax: 023 8076 4361 — MB BS 1949 Lond.; FRCS Eng. 1953. Cons. Neurosurg. BUPA Chalybeate Hosp. Soton. Prev: Cons. Neurosurg. Wessex RHA.

BRICE, John Anthony Rammell Ulverston Health Centre, Victoria Road, Ulverston LA12 0EW Tel: 01229 583732; 3 Lightburn Avenue, Ulverston LA12 0DJ Tel: 01229 584468 — BM BS 1976 Nottm.; BMedSci Nottm. 1974, BM BS 1976; BA Camb. 1964. Prev: SHO (Geriat.) Sherwood Hosp. Nottm.; SHO (Dermat.) City Hosp. Nottm.; SHO (Obst.) Firs Matern. Hosp. Nottm.

BRICE, John Edward Hatton Fernleigh, Forton, Montford Bridge, Shrewsbury SY4 1ET Tel: 01743 850103; Royal Shrewsbury Hospital, Mytton Oak Road, Shrewsbury SY3 8XQ Tel: 01743 261073 Fax: 01743 261444 — MB ChB 1971 St. And.; MD Dundee 1981; FRCP Lond. 1995; FRCPCH 1997; DObst RCOG 1973. Cons. Paediat. Roy. Shrewsbury Hosp.

BRICE-SMITH, John (retired) Fursham Down Farm, Spreyton, Crediton EX17 5EE Tel: 01647 231346 — MRCS Eng. LRCP Lond. 1958; MFOM RCP Lond. 1979; DIH Eng. 1964; DPH Lond. 1963. Med. Adviser, Devon C.C.; Occ. Health Visitor, ST. Geo., Exeter. Prev: Chief Med. Off. S.W. Gas Keynsham.

BRICK, Susan Jennifer University Medical Centre, University College, Swansea SA2 8PX Tel: 01792 295321; 443 Gower Road, Killay, Swansea SA2 7AN Tel: 01792 299274 — MB BCh 1982 Wales; DRCOG 1984.

BRICK, Thomas Dermot 99 Anglesea Road, Ipswich IP1 3PJ Tel: 01473 53748 — MB BCh BAO 1945 Dub.; DMRD Eng. 1950. (TC Dub.) Socs: BMA. Prev: on Staff St. Paul's Hosp. Vancouver, Canada; Cons. Radiol. Colon. Med. Serv., Malaya & Hong Kong Govt.

BRICKA, Chantal Cromwell Hospital, Cromwell Road, London SW5 0TU Tel: 020 7460 2000 — MD 1975 Marseilles.

BRICKER, Simon Richard Wilson Red Latches, Kings Drive, Caldy, Wirral CH48 2JE Tel: 0151 625 8199 Email: bricker@globalnet.co.uk — MB ChB 1981 Birm.; MA Camb. 1976; FFA RCS Eng. 1985; T(Anaesth.) 1991. Cons. Anaesth. Countess of Chester Hosp.; Examr. Final FRCA; Regional Adviser (Anaesths.) Mersey. Prev: Sen. Regist. Rotat. (Anaesth.) Mersey Regional Train. Scheme; Regist. (Paediat. Anaesth.) Alder Hey Childr. Hosp.; Regist. (Anaesth.) Leicester Hosps.

BRICKNELL, Martin Charles Marshal, Maj. RAMC Craven Cottage, 53 Albany Road, Fleet GU51 3PU — BM 1987 Soton.; MRCGP 1994; DRCOG 1994; DFFP 1993; MFOM RCP Lond. 1997. (Southampton) Socs: BMA; Soc. Occup. Med.

BRIDGE, Adrian Read Church Street Surgery, Church Street, Martock TA12 6JL Tel: 01935 822541 Fax: 01935 826116 — MB BS 1992 Lond.; DRCOG 1996; MRCGP 1998. GP. Prev: Trainee GP/SHO Yeovil VTS.; SHO (Histopath.) St. Mary's Hosp. Lond.

BRIDGE, Anne-Louise Sycamore House, 4 Lismore Road, Buxton SK17 9AN — MB BS 1997 Lond.

BRIDGE, Arthur James The Whinny, South Charlton, Alnwick NE66 2LY — MRCS Eng. LRCP Lond. 1951; FDS RCS Eng. 1956, LDS 1945. (Guy's) Socs: Fell. Brit. Assn. Oral Surgs. Prev: Cons. Dent. Surg. Guy's Hosp. & Evelina Childr. Hosp.; Asst. to Vis. Dent. Surgs. & Sen. Regist. (Prosth.s) Guy's Hosp. Lond.

BRIDGE, Gerald William Kershaw Harrogate Clinic, 23 Ribon Road, Harrogate HG1 2JL Tel: 01423 500599 Fax: 01423 531074; 14 St. George's Place, Mount Vale, York YO24 1DR Fax: 01904 637823 — MB ChB 1965 Otago; MRCPsych 1972; T(Psych) 1991; DPM Eng. 1972. p/t Vis. Cons. Psychiat. Harrogate Clinic, Harrogate. Socs: Fell.Roy. Soc. of Med.; York Med. Soc. Prev: Cons. Psychiat. The Retreat, York.

BRIDGE, John Robert Upper Manor Road Surgery, 95 Upper Manor Road, Paignton TQ3 2TQ Tel: 01803 558034 Fax: 01803 523339; 21 Winsu Avenue, Paignton TQ3 1QG Tel: 01803 558034 — MB ChB 1972 Dundee; MRCGP 1976; DCH Eng. 1975; DObst RCOG 1974. Prev: Trainee GP Walsall VTS; Ho. Phys. Torbay Hosp. Torquay; Ho. Surg. Treliske Hosp. Truro.

BRIDGE, Marie-Louise Tidmarsh 33 Manor Road, Ashbourne DE6 1EH — BM BS 1998 Nottm.; BM BS Nottm 1998.

BRIDGEMAN, Kay Brookside Surgery, Stretton-on-Dunsmore, Rugby CV23 9NH Tel: 024 7654 2525 Fax: 024 7654 5617 — MB ChB 1991 Birm.; MRCGP 1996. (Birmingham)

BRIDGENS, Joshua Paul 66 High Street, Marshfield, Chippenham SN14 8LP — MB BS 1998 Lond.; MB BS Lond 1998.

BRIDGER, Andrew David Northlands Wood Surgery, 7 Walnut Park, Haywards Heath RH16 3TG Tel: 01444 458022 Fax: 01444 415960; 33 Millvale Meadows, Milland, Liphook GU30 7LZ Tel: 0142 876470 — MB BS 1988 Lond.; BSc Lond. 1984, MB BS 1988; MRCGP 1993; Cert. Family Plann. JCC 1991; DRCOG 1991.

Prev: Trainee GP P.ss Roy. Hosp. VTS; SHO (Geriat.) Epsom Dist. Hosp.; Ho. Off. (Med.) St. Richard's Hosp. Chichester.

BRIDGER, Christopher Alan Park Grove Surgery, 94 Park Grove, Barnsley S70 1QE Tel: 01226 282345 — MB ChB 1980 Sheff. GP VTS Dewsbury HA.

BRIDGER, Colin, Group Capt. RAF Med. Br. Retd. Orchard House, Field Road, Rodborough, Stroud GL5 3SR Tel: 01453 752188 — MB BS 1963 Lond.; FRCP Lond. 1985; MRCP (UK) 1972. (St. Bart.) Prev: Cons. Med. RAF Hosp. Wegberg & P.ss Mary RAF Hosp. Halton; Sen. Regist. (Med.) Frenchay Hosp. Bristol; Cons. Med. Brit. Forces Health Complex Wegberg BFPO 40.

BRIDGER, Daniel Henry The Surgery, 11 Thorpe Road, Staines TW18 3EA Tel: 01784 454965 Fax: 01784 441244 — MB ChB 1979 Leeds; MRCGP 1983.

BRIDGER, Elizabeth Mary (retired) Glebe Cottage, Churchgate, Hallaton, Market Harborough LE16 8TY — MB BS 1953 Lond.; MRCS Eng. LRCP Lond. 1953.

BRIDGER, Mr John Edward (retired) 131 High Street, Melbourn, Royston SG8 6AP Tel: 01763 250611 — MB BS 1950 Lond.; FRCS Ed. 1961; FRCS Eng. 1961; MRCS Eng. LRCP Lond. 1950. Demonst. Anat. Dept., Univ. of Camb. Prev: Surgic. 1st Asst., Ho. Phys. & Ho. Surg. Lond. Hosp.

BRIDGER, Michael Grover (retired) Marsh Cottage, Graffham, Petworth GU28 0NY Tel: 01798 867335 — MB BS Lond. 1954; MRCGP 1978; DObst RCOG 1957. Prev: Cas. Off. Roy. S. Hants. Hosp. Soton.

BRIDGER, Mr Michael William Marshall Department of ENT, Level 7, Derriford Hospital, Plymouth PL6 8DH Tel: 01752 763183 Fax: 01752 763185 Email: mike.bridger@phat.swest.nhs.uk; Brook House, Shaugh Prior, Plymton, Plymouth PL7 5ES Tel: 01752 839656 — MB BS 1968 Lond.; FRCS (Orl.) Ed. 1976; FRCS Eng. 1973; MRCS Eng. LRCP Lond. 1968. (Guy's Hosp.) Cons. ENT Surg. Plymouth Hosps. NHS Trust; Vis. Lect. - Coll. of St Mark & St John, Plymouth. Socs: Head & Neck Oncol. Soc.; Brit. Assn. of Otolaryngologists, Head & Neck Surg.s; Brit. Performing Arts Med. Trust. Prev: Sen. Regist. (ENT) Middlx. Hosp. Lond.; Research Fell. (Otolaryngol.) Univ. Toronto, Canada; Sen. Regist. Roy. Nat. Throat Nose & Ear Hosp. Lond.

BRIDGER, Penelope Claire East Sussex, Brighton and Hove Health Authority, 36-38 Friars Walk, Lewes BN7 2PB Tel: 01273 403594 Fax: 01273 403600 Email: pennyb@esbhhealth.cix.co.uk; 19 Cornford Park, High St, Pembury, Tunbridge Wells TN2 4PW Tel: 01892 825450 Fax: 01892 825450 Email: p.bridger@lineone.net — MB BS 1979 Lond.; MFPHM RCP (UK) 1994; FFPHM 2000. (St. Thos.) Cons. Pub. Health E. Sussex, Brighton & Hove HA. Prev: Cons. Pub. Health Med. Bromley Health; Sen. Regist. (Pub. Health Med.) SE Inst. Pub. Health & Bromley Health.

BRIDGER, Stephen 2 Monterey Court, Varndean Drive, Brighton BN1 6TE Tel: 01273 561493 — MB BS 1988 Lond.; BSc Lond. 1985; MRCP (UK) 1991. Regist. (Med.) King's Coll. Hosp. Prev: Regist. (Med.) Heatherwood Hosp. Ascot & Roy. Sussex Co. Hosp.

BRIDGER, Victoria Jane Tregony Road Surgery, Tregony Road, Probus, Truro TR2 4JZ — MB BS 1982 Lond.; DCH RCP Lond. 1986; DRCOG 1986. (St. Thomas' Hospital)

BRIDGES, Allan Barron 6 Strachan Crescent, Dollar FK14 7HL — MB ChB Dundee 1982; MD Dundee 1994; MRCP (UK) 1987; FACA 1992. Cons. Phys. (Cardiol.) Stirling Roy. Infirm. Prev: Sen. Regist. (Cardiol.) Stobhill Hosp. Glas.; Research Regist. (Med.) Univ. Dundee.

BRIDGES, Ian Howard Church Street Surgery, St Mary's Courtyard, Church Street, Ware SG12 9EF Tel: 01920 468941 Fax: 01920 465531 Email: churchstware@gp-e82102.nhs.uk — MB BS 1972 Lond. (Lond. Hosp.) Socs: Assur. Med. Soc. Prev: SHO (O & G) Whipps Cross Hosp. Lond.; SHO (A & E) King Geo. V Hosp. Ilford; Ho. Off. King Geo. V Hosp. Ilford.

BRIDGES, Jane Elizabeth Chelsea & Westminster Hospital, 369 Fulham Road, London SW10 9NH Tel: 020 8746 8000 — MB ChB 1981 Leic.; FRCOG 2001; MRCOG 1986. Cons. Gyn. Chelsea & W.m. Hosp. Lond.; Cons. Gyn. Omologist, Roy. Marsden Hosp., Fulham Rd., Lond. Prev: Research Fell. The Lond. Hosp.; Sen. Regist. Soton.

BRIDGES, Jennifer Grace Moorhead 41 Wheatfield Heights, Ballygally, Larne BT40 2RT — MB BCh BAO 1984 Belf.; MB BCh BAO Belf. I984; DCH RCPI 1987; DRCOG 1987. Trainee GP Lurgan VTS. Prev: SHO (A & E Paediat., Gen. Med. & O & G) Craigavon Area Hosp.

BRIDGES, John Moore, CBE (retired) 9 Shrewsbury Drive, Belfast BT9 6PL Tel: 01232 669049 — MB BCh BAO Belf. 1954; MD Belf. 1958; FRCP Glas. 1988; FRCP Ed. 1970, M 1961; FRCPath 1979. Prev: Prof. Haemat. Qu. Univ. Belf.

BRIDGES, Justina 30 Chapel Street, Ibstock LE67 6HE — MB ChB 1998 Manch.; MB ChB Manch 1998.

BRIDGES, Leslie Roy Department of Pathology, University of Leeds, Leeds LS2 9JT Tel: 0113 233 3360 Fax: 0113 233 3404 Email: l.r.bridges@leeds.ac.uk; 8 Wigton Park Close, Leeds LS17 8UH Tel: 0113 266 9238 — MB BS 1981 Lond.; BSc Physiology 1978; MRCPath 1989. (The London Hosp.) Sen. Lect./Hon. Cons. Neuropath., Leeds Gen. Inf. Univ. Leeds. Socs: Brit. Neuropath. Soc.

BRIDGES, Margaret Lauretta Mabel (retired) 14 Cedar Crescent, St Mary's Bay, Romney Marsh TN29 0XQ Tel: 01303 874526 — MB BS 1948 Lond.; MRCS Eng. LRCP Lond. 1947; FFA RCS Eng. 1955; DA Eng. 1951. Prev: Assoc. Specialist Nat. Blood Transfus. Serv. SW Thames RHA.

BRIDGES, Matthew James c/o Cripps Postgraduate Medical Centre, Northampton General Hospital, Northampton NN1 5BD — MB ChB 1994 Leic.

BRIDGES, Nicola Anne Chelsea and Westminster Hospital, 369 Fulham Road, London SW10 9NH Tel: 020 8746 8000 Fax: 020 8746 8644 Email: n.bridges@ic.ac.uk; 372 Queensbridge Road, London E8 3AR Tel: 020 7241 1028 Fax: 020 7241 1032 — BM 1982 Soton.; DM Soton. 1995; MRCP (UK) 1985; DCH RCP Lond. 1985. (Southampton) Cons. (Paediat. Endocrinol. & diabetes) Chelsea & W.minster Hosp. Lond.; Hon. Cons. Paediat. Endocrinol., St Mary's Hosp. Praed St. Lond.; Hon. Sr. Lect. Imperial Coll. Med. Sch. Socs: Eur. Soc. Paediat. Endocrinol.; The Endocrine Soc. Prev: Sen. Regist. (Paediat.) Chelsea & W.minster Hosp. Lond.; Lect. (Paediat. Endocrinol.) Middlx. Hosp. Lond.; Research Regist. (Paediat.) Middlx. Hosp. Lond.

BRIDGES, Victoria Jane 57 Pydar Street, Truro TR1 2DN Tel: 01872 356000 Email: vickybridges@tinyonline.co.uk — MB ChB 1991 Ed.; MB ChB; MRC Psych. (Ed.) Cons. In Old Age Psychiat., Cornw. Healthcare Trust, Truro. Prev: Specialist Regist. (Old Age Psychiat.).

BRIDGES, Walter Gilbert (retired) 61 Aysgarth Road, Yarnton, Kidlington OX5 1ND — MB ChB 1939 St. And.; MD St. And. 1942.

BRIDGETT, Christopher Kenneth Sth Ken. & Chelsea Mental Health Centre, Number 1, Nightingale Place, London SW10 9NG Tel: 020 8846 6053 Fax: 020 8846 6119; Fax: 020 8846 6119 — BM BCh 1969 Oxf.; MA Oxf. 1969; FRCPsych 1989, M 1976. (St. Bart) Cons. Psychiat. Chelsea & W.minster Hosp. Lond.; Cons. Psychiat. Roy. Brompton Hosp. Socs: Fell. Roy. Soc. Med.; BMA. Prev: Cons. Psychiat. St. Mary Abbots Hosp. Lond.; Sen. Regist. (Psychiat.) Oxon. AHA (T); SHO Addenbrooke's Hosp. Camb.

BRIDGEWATER, Ann Lewis The Valley Surgery, 81 Bramcote Lane, Chilwell, Nottingham NG9 4ET Tel: 0115 943 0530 Fax: 0115 943 1958 Email: ann@whitfield37.fsnet.co.uk — MB BS 1967 Lond.; FRCGP 2000; MRCS Eng. LRCP Lond. 1967; MRCGP 1993. (Roy. Free) Partner in Gen. Pract., Valley Surg., Chilwell, Nottm.; Lect. (Gen. Pract.) Univ. Nottm.

BRIDGEWATER, Benjamin James Martin Wythenshawe Hospital, South Moor Road, Manchester M23 9LT Tel: 0161 998 7070; 18 Kingston Road, Didsbury, Manchester M20 2RZ Tel: 0161 445 2345 — MB BS 1986 Lond.; FRCS (CTh) UK 1997; PhD Lond. 1993. (St. Mary's) Cons. Cardiothoracic Surg. Wythenshawe Hosp. Manch.; Hon. Cons. Surg., Trafford Gen. Hosp.. Manch. and Leighton Hosp., Crewe. Socs: The Soc. Of Cardiothoracic Surg.s of GB and Irel.; Brit. Cardiac Soc. Guidelines and Med. Pract. Comm.

BRIDGEWATER, Caroline Helen 165 Heavygate Road, Sheffield S10 1PG — MB ChB 1994 Sheff. SHO (Med.) Chesterfield & N. Derbysh. Roy. NHS Trust. Prev: Ho. Off. (ENT, Surg. & Neurol.) Roy. Hallamsh. Hosp. Sheff.; SHO Rotat. (Med.) Roy. Hallamsh. Hosp. & N.ern Gen. Hosp. Sheff.; SHO (Oncol.) W.on Pk. Hosp. Sheff..

BRIDGEWATER, John Allen 68 Savernake Road, London NW3 2JR Tel: 020 7267 5714 Email: jabridgewater@yahoo.com — MB BS 1986 Lond.; PhD Lond. 1997; MA Oxf. 1983; MRCP (UK) 1989. (Oxf. & Middlx.) Sen. Lect. & Hon. Cons., Univ. Coll. Med. Sch., Lond. & N. Middlx. Hosp. Socs: Assoc. Cancer Phys.s.

BRIDGEWATER, Ruth Abigail Mary 9 Hawthorn Gardens, Whitley Bay NE26 3PQ — MB BS 1989 Newc.

BRIDGMAN, Gail Cameron Community Child Health, Unit 12, Maldon and S. Chelmsford PCT, Atlantic Square, Witham CM9 Tel: 01376 302612 Fax: 01376 302649 Email: sue.stock@mecmht.nhs.uk — MB BS Lond. 1965; FRCP Lond. 1991, M 1969; MRCS Eng. LRCP Lond. 1965; FRCPCH 1997; DCH Eng. 1967. (Middlx.) Cons. Paed. Community Child Health, Maldon and S. Chelmsford PCT, Middlx.; Cons. Paediat. St. John's Hosp. Chelmsford. Socs: BMA; Fell. Roy. Soc. Med. Prev: Sen. Regist. (Paediat.) Qu. Eliz. Hosp. Childr. Hackney; Regist. (Paediat.) Gen. Infirm. Leeds; SHO (Paediat.) Middlx. Hosp. Lond.

BRIDGMAN, John Cameron Houghtons, 26 Church St., Great Baddow, Chelmsford CM2 7HY — MB ChB 1995 Leeds.

BRIDGMAN, John Francis Houghtons, 26 Church St., Great Baddow, Chelmsford CM2 7HY Tel: 01245 71294 — MB BS 1965 Lond.; FRCP Lond. 1982, M 1968; MRCS Eng. LRCP Lond. 1965; DObst RCOG 1967. (Middlx.) Cons. Phys. Basildon & Orsett Hosp. Socs: Brit. Diabetic Assn. Prev: Ho. Phys. Hammersmith Hosp.; Sen. Med. Regist. Gen. Infirm. Leeds; Ho. Surg. Middlx. Hosp. Lond.

BRIDGMAN, Keith Malcolm (retired) Burwood, One Tree Hill Road, Guildford GU4 8PL Tel: 01483 569039 — MB BS Lond. 1959; DObst RCOG 1963. Indep. Med. Adviser Pharmaceut. Med. Surrey. Prev: Med. Dir. Knoll (UK) Burgess Hill Sussex.

BRIDGMAN, Kevin Arthur Lundbeck Ltd., Sunningdale House, Caldecotte Lake Business Park, Caldecotte, Milton Keynes MK7 8LF Tel: 01908 649966 Fax: 01908 647888 — MB ChB 1987 Leeds; MRCGP 1992. (Univ. Leeds) Med. Adviser (Pharmaceut. Phys.) Lundbeck Ltd. Milton Keynes. Prev: GP Milton Keynes.

BRIDGMAN, Nadia Mary James Fisher Medical Centre, 4 Tolpuddle Gardens, Bournemouth BH9 3LQ Tel: 01202 522622 Fax: 01202 548480 — MB BS 1988 Lond.

BRIDGMAN, Stephanie Jane The Old Forge, Langford Budville, Wellington TA21 0RW — MB BS 1988 Lond.; MRCGP 1996; DCH RCP Lond. 1995. Prev: GP/Regist. Hants.

BRIDGMAN, Mr Stephen Adrian North Staffordshire Health Authority, Heron House, Grove Road, Stoke-on-Trent ST4 4LX Tel: 01782 298124 Fax: 01782 298135 — MB ChB 1980 Aberd.; MD Aberd. 1987; FRCS Ed. 1988; FRCS Glas. 1988; MFPHM RCP (UK) 1994; MPH Liverp. 1992. (Aberd.) Cons. Pub. Health Med. N. Staffs. HA; Sen. Lect. (Surgic. Trials & Epidemiol.) Univ. Keele; Sen. Lect. Centre Health Plann. & Managem. Univ. Keele. Socs: Brit. Orthopaedic Assn.

BRIDGMAN, William Mark Old Lake, 26 Wood Lane, Bearwood, Bournemouth BH11 9NG — MB ChB 1988 Otago; BSc Otago 1983, MB ChB 1988; MRCP Lond. 1994; DRCOG 1995; MRCGP 1996. (Otago, NZ)

BRIDGWATER, Frederick Arthur James (retired) 32 Silhill Hall Road, Solihull B91 1JU — MB ChB 1947 Birm.; FRCPath 1977, M 1965; Dip. Bact. Lond 1958. Prev: Cons. Bacteriol. E. Birm. Hosp. & Hon. Sen. Clin. Lect. Fac. Med. Univ. Birm.

BRIDGWOOD, Peter Simon 38 Monument Lane, Tittensor, Stoke-on-Trent ST12 9JH — MB ChB 1989 Leic.

BRIDGWOOD, William Graham Health Division, Shell Centre, London SE1 7NA Tel: 020 7934 3720 Fax: 020 7934 7046; 4 Hawkesley Close, Strawberry Hill, Twickenham TW1 4TR Tel: 020 8892 7682 — MB BS 1966 Lond.; MSc Lond. 1984; MRCS Eng. LRCP Lond. 1966; FRCP Lond. 1984, M 1968; FFOM RCP Lond. 1990, MFOM 1984. Chief Health Adviser Shell Internat. Petroleum Co. Ltd. Lond. Socs: Fell. Roy. Soc. Med.; Soc. Occupat. Med.

BRIDLE, Mr Simon Haydn 53 Parkside, Wimbledon, London SW17 5NX Tel: 020 8947 9524 Fax: 020 8947 0490 Email: simon.bridle@btinternet.com; 7 First Avenue, London SW14 8SP Tel: 020 8878 3114 — MB BS 1981 Lond.; FRCS (Orth.) 1992; FRCS Eng. 1986. Cons. Orthop. Surg. St. Geo. Hosp. Lond.

BRIDSON, Christopher Michael Wells Health Centre, Glastonbury Road, Wells BA5 1XJ Tel: 01749 672137 Fax: 01749 679833; Yew Tree House, West Horrington, Wells BA5 3ED Tel: 01749 676173 — MB BS 1983 Lond.; MRCGP 1988; D.Occ.Med. RCP Lond. 1995. (Westminster) p/t Sch. Med. Off. Wells Cathedral Sch. Som.; Company Doctor Thales, Cubic Systems, Invelesic. Socs: Med. Off. Sch. Assn.

BRIDSON, John Marshall (retired) 7 Albany Close, Wombwell, Barnsley S73 8ER Tel: 01226 210154 Fax: 01226 210164 Email: john.bridson@doctors.org.uk — MB BS Lond. 1966; FRCP Lond. 1993; MRCS Eng. LRCP Lond. 1965; FRCPCH 1998. Clin. Dir. Child Health CMT; Chairm. Child Advocacy Internat. Prev: Cons. Paediat. Barnsley Dist. Gen. Hosp.

BRIEGER, Johanna Elsbeth Gertrude 29 Ventress Farm Court, Cherry Hinton Road, Cambridge CB1 8HD Tel: 01223 213639 — MRCS Eng. LRCP Lond. 1944; MA Camb. 1977, MB BChir 1946; MFHom 1959. Indep. Analyt. Pyscother. Camb. Socs: Brit. Assn. Psychother.; Soc. Analyt. Psychol. Prev: Ho. Phys. Eliz. G. Anderson Hosp.; Regist. Med. High Wood Hosp. Childr. Brentwood; Phys. Roy. Lond. Homoep. Hosp.

BRIEL, Ruth Cordelia Garnet Woodburn, 3 Batt House Road, Stocksfield NE43 7QZ Tel: 01661 843601 — MB BS 1988 Newc.; MRCPsych 1995. Specialist Regist. (Old Age Psychiat.) Brighton Clinic Newc. u. Tyne. Prev: Regist. (Psychiat.) Univ. Newc. u Tyne; SHO (c/o Elderly) Newc. Gen. Hosp.; SHO (Psychiat.) Shotley Bridge Gen. Hosp.

BRIEN, Patricia Frances 6 Maple Lodge, Roe Green Avenue, Roe Green, Worsley, Manchester M28 2SA — MB ChB Ed. 1970; DObst RCOG 1973.

BRIERLEY, Angela Jean 2 Heatherlea Road, Fence, Burnley BB12 9EJ — MB ChB 1969 Manch. Anaesth. (Dent. Clinics) Lancs. AHA. Prev: Regist. (Anaesth.) Burnley Gen. Hosp.

BRIERLEY, Anthony Frederick Michael 10 St Augustine's Road, Edgbaston, Birmingham B16 9JU — MB ChB 1974 Birm.; Dip GU Med 1977; 1980 Dip Family Planning; MA Oxf. 1965; MFPHM 1986. Clin. Asst. Whittall St. Clinic, Birm. Prev: Cons. Pub. Health Med. Warks. HA.

BRIERLEY, Denys Spalding Neilans (retired) Castle Lodge, Longtown, Hereford HR2 0LD Tel: 01873 860241 — MB BS 1948 Lond.; MRCS Eng. LRCP Lond. 1946; DObst RCOG 1954; DCH Eng. 1952. Prev: Ho. Phys. & Jun. Regist. Childr. Dept. St. Bart. Hosp. Lond.

BRIERLEY, Duncan Mills (retired) 9 The Green, Thriplow, Royston SG8 7QX — MB ChB 1942 Manch.; MB ChB (Hons.) Manch. 1942; DCH Eng. 1947. Prev: GP Worcester.

BRIERLEY, Elizabeth Jane St. Lukes Hospital, Little Hornton Lane, Bradford BD5 0NA — MB BS 1986 Newc.; PhD 2000 Newc.; MRCP (UK) 1990; DGM RCP Lond. 1988. p/t Cons. (c/o the Elderly) St. Lukes Hosp. Bradford. Prev: Specialist Regist. (Geriat. Med.) Roy. Vict. Infirm. Newc.; Cons. & Sen. Lect. Geriat. Med., Roy. Vict. Infirm., Newc.-upon-Tyne.

BRIERLEY, Emma-Jane 23 Bicknor Road, Orpington BR6 0TS — MB ChB 1998 Bristol.

BRIERLEY, Janet Kathryn 6 Chapter Drive, Kimberley, Nottingham NG16 2QD — MB BS 1979 Newc.; FFA RCS Eng. 1984. Sen. Regist. (Anaesth.) Nottm. E. Midl. HA. Prev: Regist.(Anaesth.) Newc. HA.; Research Assoc. Neurol. Univ. Newc. u. Tyne; SHO (Gen. Med.) Dryburn Hosp. Durh.

BRIERLEY, Joseph 36 Tracy Drive, Newton-le-Willows WA12 8PX — MB ChB 1993 Leeds.

BRIERLEY, Lorna Markham (retired) 6 Prince's Buildings, Clifton, Bristol BS8 4LB Tel: 0117 973 9790 — MB ChB 1945 Bristol; MRC Psych 1971; BA Hons (OU) 1959. Prev: Med. Off. DHSS.

BRIERLEY, Richard Paul 6 Park Wood Close, Broadstairs CT10 2XN — MB BS 1997 Lond.

BRIERLEY, Shirley Anne Bradford Health Authority, New Mill, Victoria Roiad, Saltaire, Bradford BD18 3LD; 3 Altar Drive, Heaton, Bradford BD9 5QB Tel: 01274 499588 — MB ChB 1981 Leeds; MPH 2001; MMed. Sci. 1999; MRCGP 1986. p/t Specialist Regist. in Pub. Health. Prev: Paediat. Chimolo Hosp. Mozambique.

BRIERLY, Emma Katherine 4 Ipswich Road, Woodbridge IP12 4BU Tel: 01394 382616 — MB BS 1992 Lond.; MRCGP 1999; DA (UK) 1996; DRCOG 1998. (St. Geo. Lond.) p/t Gen. Practitioner Brighton.

BRIERLY, Mary Carol (retired) 152 Penistone Road, Shelley, Huddersfield HD8 8JQ — MB ChB 1949 Leeds. Prev: Cons. Dermat. Huddersfield Health Dist. & Calderdale AHA.

BRIERLY, Robert David 8 Coombe Gardens, West Wimbledon, London SW20 0QU Tel: 020 8946 3300 — MB BS 1993 Lond.; FRCS Eng. 1997. (St Bart. Hosp.) Research.Fell. Urol. Roy.Sussex. Co..Hosp.Brighton. Prev: Demonst. (Anat.) Qu. Mary & W.field Coll. Univ. Lond.; SHO Rotat. (Surg.) Roy. Sussex Co. Hosp.

BRIERS, Peter John X-Ray Department, Cheltenham General Hospital, Cheltenham — BSc (Physiol., Hons.) Lond. 1959, MB BS 1962; MRCP Lond. 1967; FFR 1972; DMRD Eng. 1969. (Lond. Hosp.) Cons. Radiol. Cheltenham Gen. Hosp.; Dir. Glos. BrE. Screening Serv.; QA Radiol. S. W. Regions. Prev: Sen. Regist. Radiodiag. Dept. United Bristol Hosps.; Radiol. Mulago Hosp. Kampala, Uganda; Regist. (Radiodiag.) United Cardiff Hosps.

BRIESS, David Andrew Otto Bethlem & Maudsley NHS Trust, Denmark Hill, London SE5 8AZ Tel: 020 7703 6333; 81 Stamford Court, Goldhawk Road, Hammersmith, London W6 0XE Tel: 020 8846 9708 Fax: 020 8846 9708 — MB BS 1994 Lond.; BSc Lond. 1991. (Char. Cross & Westm. Hosps.)

BRIFFA, Antonia Clare 16 Donaldson Road, London NW6 6NB — MB BS 1989 Lond.

BRIFFA, Dorothy Mary Carmel 19 Walford Road, Stoke Newington, London N16 8EF Tel: 020 7254 2733 Fax: 020 7288 6495 Email: mtc@ccweb.co.uk — MB BS 1984 Lond.; MRCP (UK) 1990; Dip. FMSA 1998. (St. Mary's Hosp. Med. Sch. Lond.) Solicitor Dawson & Co Lincolns Inn Lond. Prev: Regist. (Med.) Mayday Hosp. Croydon; SHO (Radiother.) St. Bart. Hosp. Lond.; SHO (Gen. Med.) Chase Farm Hosp. Enfield & Ashford Hosp. Middlx.

BRIFFA, Joanna Maria 10 St Elmo Road, Shepherds Bush, London W12 9EA Tel: 020 8743 1834 — MB BS 1982 Lond.; MRCGP 1988; DCH RCP Lond. 1986; DA (UK) 1985.

BRIFFA, John Peter James Woolaston House, 25 Southwood Lane, Highgate, London N6 5ED Tel: 020 8341 3422 Fax: 020 8340 1376 Email: woolastonhouse@btinternet.com; 9 Grove Avenue, Muswell Hill, London NW5 1EH Tel: 020 8365 3829 Fax: 020 8365 3829 Email: drjbriffa@aol.com — MB BS 1990 Lond. Private-Practising Nutrit.al Phys.; Health Jl.ist.

BRIFFA, Joseph Edward Observatory W., Church Road, Crowborough TN6 1BN Tel: 01892 652444 — MD 1949 Malta; BSc Malta 1946, MD 1949; DA Eng. 1954; FFA RCS Eng. 1959. (Malta) Cons. Anaesth. Tunbridge Wells Hosp. Gp. Socs: Fell. Assn. Anaesths. Gt. Brit. & Irel. Prev: Asst. Anaesth. Bridge of Earn Hosp. Perthsh.; Anaesth. Regist. Mt. Vernon Hosp. N.wood.

BRIFFA, Joseph Victor, KStJ (retired) 14 Dellwood Gardens, Clayhall, Ilford IG5 0EH Tel: 020 8550 0738 — MD Malta 1956; LM Nat. Matern. Hosp. Dub. 1958; BPharm 1953. Prev: SCMO (Child Health) Thameside Community Healthcare NHS Trust.

BRIFFA, Mr Norman Paul 121 Sellywood Road, Bournville, Birmingham B30 1XA — MB ChB 1983 Sheff.; FRCS (Eng.) 1988. Sen. Transpl. Fell. Papworth Hosp. Camb. Prev: Regist. (Cardiothoracic Surg.) W. Midl.; Regist. (Surg.) Manch. Roy. Infirm.; SHO (Gen. Surg.) Derby City Hosp.

BRIFFA, Rebecca Mathilda St Bartholemews Hospital, West Smithfield, London EC1A 7BE Tel: 020 7377 7000; 212 Kempton Court, 2 Durward St, London E1 5BB — MB ChB 1996 Ed.; MB ChB Ed. 1996 & Hons.; MA Cantab.; MRCP. SHO, Infec. Immunity.

BRIFFA, Mr Vincent 34 Sterne Street, London W12 8AD Tel: 020 8743 7578 — MD 1949 Malta; FRCS Eng. 1978; DLO Eng. 1956. (Malta) Vis. Colleague Roy. Postgrad. Med. Sch. Lond.; Hon. Med. Adviser Malta High Commiss. Lond.; Hon. Laryngol. Roy. N. Coll. Music Manch. Prev: Assoc. Specialist (ENT) Dept. Surg. Hammermsith Hosp. Lond.; Vis. ENT Surg. HMP Wormwood Scrubs; Hon. Vis. Surg. St. Mary's Hosp. Lond.

BRIFFA BOOTHMAN, Joseph (retired) 2 Egglestone Square, Boston Spa, Wetherby LS23 6RX Tel: 01937 843561 — MD 1955 Malta; MFPHM 1973; DPH Leeds 1963. Prev: SCMO York HA.

BRIGDEN, Charles Edward 30 Cambridge Mansions, Cambridge Road, London SW11 4RU — MB BS 1994 Lond. SHO Rotat. (Surg.) Chelsea & W.minster Hosp. & S.end Gen Hosp.

BRIGDEN, Geoffrey Swinton East Somerset NHS Trust, Yeovil District Hospital, Higher Kingston, Yeovil BA21 4AT Tel: 01935 707556 Fax: 01935 411974; The Old Rectory, Church St, West Coker, Yeovil BA22 9BD — MB BS 1979 Lond.; MD Lond. 1991; FRCP 1989; MRCP (UK) 1983. (Lond. Hosp.) Cons. Cardiol. Yeovil Dist. Hosp. Som.; Cons. Cardiol. (Hon.) MusGr. Pk. Hosp. Taunton Som.; Cons. Cardiol. (Hon.) Roy. Bournemouth Hosp. Dorset. Socs: Brit. Cardiac Interven. Soc. Prev: Sen. Regist. (Cardiol.) N.wick Pk. Hosp. Harrow & Lect. (Cardiovasc. Med.) St. Mary's Hosp. Med. Sch. Lond.; Regist. (Cardiol.) Walsgrave Hosp. Coventry; Research Fell. (Cardiol.) N.wick Pk. Hosp. Harrow.

BRIGDEN, Wallace David Levanter, Harbour Way, Bosham, Chichester PO18 8QH Tel: 01243 573121 Fax: 01243 574842 Email: derigden@levanter.u-net.com — MB BS 1967 Lond.; FRCP Lond. 1985; MRCP (UK) 1973; FFPM RCP UK 1993. (Univ. Coll. Hosp.) Indep. Cons. Pharmaceut. Med. W. Sussex. Prev: Med. Dir.(Europe) Cephalon Inc.; Asst. Dir.(Clin. Research), Wellcome Research Laboraory Beckenham.

BRIGDEN, Wallace William (retired) Willow House, 38 Totteridge Common, London N20 8NE Tel: 020 8959 6616 — MB BChir 1941 Camb.; MD Camb. 1951, MA 1941; FRCP Lond. 1950, M 1941. Hon. Cons. Phys. & Phys. Cardiol. Dept. Lond. Hosp.; Hon. Cons. Phys. Nat. Heart Hosp.; Hon. Cons. Cardiol. RN; Cons. Phys. Munich Re-Insur. Company. Prev: Dean & Dir. Inst. Cardiol.

BRIGG, David John Department of Radiology, Fairfield General Hospital, Rochdale Old Road, Bury BL9 7TD — MB ChB 1977 Manch.; BSc (Hons.) Manch. 1974; FRCR 1982; DMRD 1981; DCH Eng. 1979. Cons. Radiol. Bury Healthcare NHS Trust.

BRIGG, Mr John Kenneth Conder Bank, Kit Brow Lane, Ellel, Nr. Galgate, Lancaster LA2 0QG Tel: 01524 751402 — MB 1969 Camb.; MA Camb. 1968, MB 1969, BChir 1968; FRCS Eng. 1972. (Camb. & St. Thos.) Cons. Gen. Surg. Roy. Lancaster Infirm. Socs: BMA. Prev: Sen. Regist. Manch. Roy. Infirm. Regist. Manch. Roy. Infirm.; SHO & Ho. Surg. St. Thos. Hosp. Lond.

BRIGG, Joyce Margaret Flemming (retired) Links Lodge, Sands Lane, Mirfield WF14 8H Tel: 01924 492664 — MB ChB 1944 Leeds.

BRIGG, Michael James The Surgery, 148 Forton Road, Gosport PO12 3HH Tel: 023 9258 3333 Fax: 023 9260 1107; 37 Western Way, Alverstoke, Gosport PO12 2NF Tel: 023 9252 1646 — MB BChir 1983 Camb.; BChir 1982; BA Oxf. 1979; DRCOG 1993; Cert. Family Plann. JCC 1992; DCH RCP Lond. 1989. (New Addenbrooke's Hospital Cambridge) Princip. GP. Prev: Trainee GP Handforth VTS; Regist. (Paediat.) Redhill Gen. & Crawley Hosps.; Regist. & Community Med. Off. (Paediat.) Newham Gen. Hosp.

BRIGG, Peter Donald Southlea Surgery, 276 Lower Farnham, Aldershot GU11 3RB Tel: 01252 344868 Fax: 01252 342596; 6 Lodge Hill Road, Lower Bourne, Farnham GU10 3QN Tel: 01252 735014 — MB BS 1980 Lond.; FRCS Eng. 1985. (Lond. Hosp.) Police Surg./FME - Surrey Police.

BRIGG, Wendy Margaret Marriner The Medical Centre, Plas Penrhyn, Bae Penrhyn Bay, Llandudno LL30 3EU Tel: 01492 549368 Fax: 01492 548103; White Gables, Gannock Park, Deganwy, Conwy LL31 9PJ Tel: 01492 584346 — MB ChB 1974 Manch. Prev: GP Conwy.

BRIGGS, Andrew Charles Palmerston Road Surgery, 18 Palmerston Road, Buckhurst Hill IG9 5LT Tel: 020 8504 1552 Fax: 020 8559 2517; 45 Tycehurst Hill, Loughton IG10 1BZ Tel: 020 8508 8463 — MB BChir 1982 Camb.; MA 1982 Camb. Prev: Clin. Asst. (Dermat.) St. Margts. Hosp. Epping.; Mem. W. Essex GP Med. Advis. Comm.

BRIGGS, Andrew Clive Stamford Resource Centre, St George's Avenue, Stamford PE9 1UN Tel: 01780 757142 Fax: 01780 757193 Email: andrew.briggs@lht.nhs.uk — MB ChB 1980 Leic.; LLM 2001 Newcaslte; MRCPsych 1985. (Leicester) Cons. (Psychiat.) Lincs. Healthcare NHS Trust. Prev: Lect. Dept. Psychiat. Univ. Leicester; Regist. Towers Hosp. Leicester; Ho. Phys. Groby Rd. Hosp. Leicester.

BRIGGS, Anthony Pattison The Health Centre, Bath Road, Buxton SK17 6HL Tel: 01298 24105 Fax: 01298 73227 — MB ChB 1963 Manch.; MRCS Eng. LRCP Lond. 1963; MRCOG 1970. (Manch.)

BRIGGS, Bettina Anne The Bourne Galletly Practice, The Surgery, 40 North Road, Bourne PE10 9BT Tel: 01778 562200 — MB ChB 1981 Leic.; MRCGP 1985; DRCOG 1984. Prev: Trainee GP Leicester VTS.

BRIGGS, Brian Henry John Lane End Medical Group, 25 Edgwarebury Lane, Edgware HA8 8LJ Tel: 020 8958 4233 Fax: 020 8905 4657 — MB BChir Camb. 1969; MA Camb. 1970. (Camb.) Prev: Clin. Asst. (Surg.) Edgware Gen. Hosp.; Vis. Med. Off. Merrivale Old Peoples Home Edgware; SHO (Cas. & Anaesth.) Whittington Hosp. Lond.

BRIGGS, Catherine Helen Flat 6, 13 Vincent Avenue, Chorlton-cum-Hardy, Manchester M21 9GR — MB ChB 1996 Manch.

BRIGGS, Clare 2/4 Kirklee Terrace, Glasgow G12 0TQ — MB ChB 1993 Aberd.

BRIGGS, David Maurice 7 Royd Lane, Deepcar, Sheffield S36 2RZ — MB ChB 1996 Leic.

BRIGGS, Edward Dickon Avignon, Ranelagh Drive, Bracknell RG12 9DA — MB ChB 1995 Manch. SHO (Anaesth.), Kettering Gen. Hosp.

BRIGGS, Edward William Wright 59 Dorrator Road, Camelon, Falkirk FK1 4BN — MB ChB 1971 Ed.

BRIGGS, Eleanor Mary 48 Kingsborough Gardens, Glasgow G12 9NL Tel: 0141 334 9744 — MB ChB 1961 Glas. SCMO (Family Plann.) Gtr. Glas. Health Bd.

BRIGGS, Elizabeth Jennifer Saltcoats Health Centre, 17-19 Raise Street, Saltcoats KA21 5LX Tel: 01294 466150 Fax: 01294 462828; Weirston, 27 Bowfield Road, West Kilbride KA23 9LD Tel: 01294 823992 — MB BCh BAO 1965 Belf. (Belf.) Socs: BMA.

BRIGGS, Elizabeth Mary Guild (retired) 57 Stratherrick Road, Inverness IV2 4LL Tel: 01463 230481 — MB ChB St. And. 1954. Prev: Med. Asst. (Haemat.) Raigmore Hosp. Inverness.

BRIGGS, Frances Anne Medical Centre, Wisbech Road, Thorney, Peterborough PE6 0SD Tel: 01732 270219; 10 West End, Yaxley, Peterborough PE7 3LJ Tel: 01733 243295 — MB ChB 1986 Manch.; MRCGP 1990; DGM RCP Lond. 1989. Socs: BMA.

BRIGGS, Gavin Mark 36 Greer Park Drive, Newtownards, Belfast BT8 7YQ — MB BCh BAO 1992 Belf.; MB BCh Belf. 1992.

BRIGGS, Geoffrey Herbert (retired) The Cedars, 58 Middleton Road, Pickering YO18 8NH Tel: 01751 472106 — MB ChB Leeds 1944; MRCGP 1954. Prev: Resid. Med. Off. City Fev. Hosp. Bradford.

BRIGGS, Geoffrey Oswald Atyeo (retired) The Kennels, Thoresby Park, Ollerton, Newark NG22 9EH Tel: 01623 822150 — MB BCh 1935 Camb.; MA Camb. 1935, BA (1st cl. Nat. Sc. Trip. Pt.1, 2nd cl. Pt. 2) 1930; MRCP Lond. 1936; MRCS Eng. LRCP Lond. 1933; DPH Eng. 1939. Prev: Cons. Chest Phys. Ransom Hosp. Rainworth.

BRIGGS, Geraint Dyfed 3 Parc-yr-Onnen, Llwyn Meredith, Carmarthen SA31 1ED — MB ChB 1995 Manch.

BRIGGS, Godfrey John Frank, VRD Fairoaks, 74 London Road S., Poynton, Stockport SK12 1LG Tel: 0161 872504 — MB BS 1944 Durh.; DPM Eng. 1969. Socs: Founder Mem. Oxf. Inst. Psychiat.; Fell. Brit. Soc. Med. & Dent. Hypn. Prev: Cons. Psychiat. Winwick Hosp.; Past Pres. Brit. Soc. Med. & Dent. Hypn.; Surg. Regist. Stockport & Buxton, & Macclesfield Hosp. Gps.

BRIGGS, Jacqueline Ann 8 Darwell Drive, Stone Cross, Pevensey BN24 5PG — MB BS 1993 Lond.

BRIGGS, James Charles 194 Stoke Lane, Westbury-on-Trym, Bristol BS9 3RU Tel: 0117 968 1415 Fax: 0117 968 1415 Email: james@briggs13.fsnet.co.uk — MB BS Lond. 1958; FRCPath 1977, M 1965; DPath Eng. 1963. (St. Thos.) p/t Ref. City of Bristol. Socs: Fell. Hosp. Cons. & Specialists Assn.; (Ex-Pres.) Cossham Med. Soc. Prev: Surg. (Path.) Frenchay Hosp. Bristol; Clin Teach. (Path.) Univ. Bristol.

BRIGGS, James Douglas (retired) 48 Kingsborough Gardens, Glasgow G12 9NL Tel: 0141 334 9744 Email: douglas.briggs@ukgateway.net — MB ChB 1961 Glas.; MB ChB Glas 1961; FRCP Lond. 1979, M 1964; FRCP Ed. 1975, M 1964; FRCP Glas. 1972, M 1965. p/t Med. adviser to UK Transpl., Bristol. Prev: Cons. Phys. (Renal Dis.) W.. Infirm. Glas.

BRIGGS, James Richard Paediat. Department, District General Hospital, Lovely Lane, Warrington WA5 1QG Tel: 01925 635911 — MB ChB 1973 Dundee; FRCP 1996; MRCP (UK) 1980; FRCPCH 1997; DCH RCPS Glas. 1976. Cons. Paediat. Dist. Gen. Hosp. Warrington. Socs: Brit. Soc. Allergy & Clin. Immunol.; Brit. Aerobiol. Federat.; Eur. Acad. Allergol. & Clin. Immunol. Prev: Regist. Roy. Hosp. Sick Childr. Edin.; Sen. Regist. N.wick Pk. Hosp. Harrow; Sen. Regist. St. Mary's Hosp. Paddington.

BRIGGS, Jocelyn Elizabeth Royal Shrewsbury Hospital NHS Trust, Mytton Oak Road, Shrewsbury SY3 8XQ; 25 The Crescent, Town Walls, Shrewsbury SY1 1TH Tel: 01743 247097 — MB BS 1980 Lond.; BSc (Psych.) Lond. 1977; MRCP (UK) 1984; FRCP 1994. (Lond. Hosp.) Cons. Phys. with interest in Geriat. Med. Roy. Shrewsbury Hosp. Prev: Sen. Regist. Rotat. (Geriat. & Gen. Med.) W. Midl. RHA.

BRIGGS, John Columbanus Newbury Park Health Centre, Perrymans Farm Road, Ilford IG2 7LE Tel: 020 8554 1094 — LRCPI & LM, LRSCI & LM 1956; LRCPI & LM, LRCSI & LM 1956. (RCSI) Socs: Ilford Med. Soc.

BRIGGS, John Stephen Hulton West Kirby Health Centre, Grange Road, Wirral CH48 4HZ Tel: 0151 625 9171 Fax: 0151 625 9171 — MB ChB 1985 Liverp. Clin. Asst. (Psychiat.) Wirral. Prev: Trainee GP Sutton Chesh.; SHO (O & G & Paediat.) Arrowe Pk. Hosp. Wirral.

BRIGGS, Jonathan Andrew Whitchurch Health Centre, Armada Road, Bristol BS14 0SU Tel: 01275 835625 Fax: 01275 540035; 7 Clifton Vale, Clifton, Bristol BS8 4PT Tel: 0117 929 1289 — MB BS 1984 Lond.; MRCGP 1988; DRCOG 1989; DFFP 1998. (The London Hospital Medical College) Bd. Mem. S. E. Bristol PCG.

BRIGGS, Joseph Hodgson (retired) 148 Harley Street, London W1N 1AH Tel: 020 7637 4177 Fax: 020 7224 1528 — MB BS 1951 Lond.; MRCP Lond. 1958. Prev: Cons. Phys. Brit. Telecom.

BRIGGS, Lorraine Mary Lothian Health, Deaconness House, 148 Pleasance, Edinburgh EH8 6RS Tel: 0131 536 9072 Fax: 0131 536 9287 Email: briggs1@lothian.hb.scot.nhs.uk; 1 Learmonth Terrace, Edinburgh EH4 1PQ Tel: 0131 332 1596 — MB ChB 1974 Aberd.; MRCGP 1979; DRCOG 1979. (Aberdeen University) Head of Nursing Home Regulat. & Inspection Unit Lothian HB.

BRIGGS, Martin Joseph 30 The Drive, Hove BN3 3JD Email: dr@mjpbr.ggs.freeserve.co.uk; 11 Upper Wish Hill, Willingdon, Eastbourne BN20 9HB Email: dr@mjpbr.ggs.freeserve.co.uk — MB BS 1985 Lond.; 1999 DFPHM. (Middlesex Hospital) Private Med. Practioner, Occupat.al Health Hove; Private Med. Practitioner, Occupat. Health,. Socs: Brit. Med. Acupunc. Soc., Mem.; Brit. Med. Informat. Soc., Mem. Prev: Sen. Regist. (Pub. Health Med.), E. Sussex Brighton and Hove HA.

BRIGGS, Martin William 54 Merriefield Avenue, Broadstone BH18 8DE — MB BS 1981 Lond.; DRCOG 1985.

BRIGGS, Mr Michael The Haven, Newland St., Eynsham, Oxford OX8 Tel: 01865 881298; Dornford Cottage, Lower Dornford, Wootton, Woodstock OX20 1ES Tel: 01993 811237 — MSc Oxf. 1974; MB BS Lond. 1963; FRCS Eng. 1969; MRCS Eng. LRCP Lond. 1963. (St. Thos.) Prev: Cons. Neurosurg. Radcliffe Infirm. Oxf.; Cons. Neurosurg. SE Metrop. Neurosurg. Unit Brook Gen. Hosp. Lond.; Research Fell. (Neurosurg.) Radcliffe Infirm. Oxf.

BRIGGS, Michael Andrew Brunswick House Medical Group, 1 Brunswick Street, Carlisle CA1 1ED Tel: 01228 515808 Fax: 01228 593048; Brunstock Cottage, Brunstock, Carlisle CA6 4QG — MB ChB 1971 St. And.; MRCGP 1975; Dip. Palliat. Med. Wales 1997; DObst RCOG 1974; Cert FPA 1975. Med. Dir. Eden Valley Hospice Carlisle; Med. Off. Pirelli (UK). Prev: Trainee GP Univ. Newc. VTS; Ho. Surg. & Ho. Phys. Torbay Hosp. Torquay.

BRIGGS, Mr Michael Clarke St Paul's Eye Unit, Royal Liverpool University Hospital, Prescot St., Liverpool L7 8XP Tel: 0151 706 2000 Email: mcbriggs@aol.com; Truro, Crescent Road, Crosby, Liverpool L23 6US Tel: 0151 924 2375 — MB ChB 1986 Glas.; FRCS Ed. 1992. Specialist Regist. (Ophth.) St Paul's Eye Unit, Liverp.

BRIGGS, Mr Patrick Colm 27 Devonshire Place, London W1N 1PD Tel: (20) 7224 4333 Email: patrick.briggs@dial.pipex.com — MB BCh BAO 1978 NUI; LRCPI & LM, LRCSI & LM 1977; FRCS (Plast Surg.) Eng. 1991; FRCS Eng. 1981; FRCSI 1981; FICS 1990; T(S) 1992. Indep. Pract. (Plastic Surg.) Lond.; Hon. Cons. Plastic Surg. St Mary's Hosp. Paddington. Socs: Brit. Assn. Plastic Surg.; Plastic Surg. Research Counc. N. Amer.; Fell. Roy. Soc. Med. Prev: Sen. Regist. (Plastic Surg.) Regional Hosp. Wilton, Cork; Director Plastic Surg. Research Laborat. Allegheny Singer Research Inst. Pittsburgh, USA; Regist. (Plastic Surg.) NW Thames Regional Plastic Surg. Unit.

BRIGGS, Paula Elizabeth Truro, Crescent Road, Blindellsands, Liverpool L23 6US Tel: 0151 924 2375 Fax: 0151 928 2008 — MB ChB 1987 Glas.; MFFP 1994; MRCGP 1991.

BRIGGS, Pauline 98 Burnmill Road, Market Harborough LE16 7JG Tel: 01858 431362 — MB ChB 1982 Leic. Sessional Clin. Med. Off. Leicester HA. Prev: Ho. Off. Leicester Gen. Hosp.

BRIGGS, Mr Peter Joseph Department of Orthopaedics, Freeman Hospital, Newcastle upon Tyne NE7 7DN Tel: 0191 284 3111; 34 Chollerford Close, Newcastle upon Tyne NE3 4RN Tel: 0191 284 7035 — MB ChB Manch. 1981; BSc Manch. 1978, MD 1994; FRCS Eng. 1987. (Manch.) Cons. Orthop. Newc. Gen. Hosp. & Freeman Hosp. Newc. u. Tyne. Socs: Brit. Orthop. Assn.; Brit. Orthop. Foot Surg. Soc.; Amer. Orthop. Foot & Ankle Soc. Prev: Cons. Orthop. Cheviot & Wansbeck NHS Trust Ashington; Sen. Regist. & Regist. (Orthop.) N.. RHA; Regist. (Surg.) Newc. u. Tyne.

BRIGGS, Peter Wilson 45E Odhams Walk, Covent Gdn., London WC2H 9SB Tel: 020 7836 3234 Fax: 020 7240 8807 — MRCS Eng. LRCP Lond. 1967; FFPHM 1997, M 1990. (Guy's) Chairm. Health Audit Internat. Specialist Health Consultancy Lond. Socs: Conserv. Med. Soc.; InDepend. Doctors Forum. Prev: Dir. (Pub. Health) Ealing DHA; Specialist (Community Med.) Cleveland AHA; Med. Off. DoH.

BRIGGS, Mr Raymond David The Royal Infirmary, Livilands Gate, Stirling FK8 2AU Tel: 01786 434063 Fax: 01786 434432; Tipperty, 12 Strachan Crescent, Dollar FK14 7HL Tel: 01259 742702 — MB ChB 1973 Aberd.; FRCS Ed. 1978; FRCS Glas. 1998. (University of Aberdeen) Cons. Orthop. & Musculoskeletal Trauma Stirling Roy. Infirm. Prev: Sen. Regist. (Orthop. Surg.) Grampian HB.

BRIGGS, Richard Alban Summertown Group Practice, 160 Banbury Road, Oxford OX2 7BS Tel: 01865 515552 Fax: 01865 311237; 4 Meadow Way, Yarnton, Kidlington OX5 1TA Tel: 01865 377189 Email: richardabriggs@btinternet.com — BM BCh 1984 Oxf.; MA Oxf. 1986, BM BCh 1984; MRCGP 1988; DRCOG 1986. (Oxf.) Tutor (Gen. Pract.) Univ. of Oxf. Prev: Trainee GP Bath VTS; SHO (Paediat.) Roy. United Hosp. Bath.

BRIGGS, Robert David The David Briggs Practice, Hythe Medical Centre, Beaulieu Road, Hythe SO45 4ZB Tel: 023 8084 5955 Fax: 023 8084 1869; Lowcroft, Sway Road, Brockenhurst SO42 7SG Tel: 01590 622172 — MB ChB 1962 Liverp.; MRCGP; DObst RCOG 1964; Cert FPA 1974. (Liverp.) Socs: BMA. Prev: Regist. (Med.) Walton Hosp. & Alder Hey Child. Hosp. Liverp.

BRIGGS, Professor Roger Selwyn James Centre Block, Level E, Southampton General Hospital, Southampton SO16 6YD Tel: 02380 796134 Fax: 02380 796134 Email: rsb1@soton.ac.uk; 75 Northlands Road, Southampton SO15 2LP Tel: 02380 634072 — MB BS Lond. 1972; MSc Lond. 1979; FRCP Lond. 1988; MRCP (UK) 1977; MRCS Eng. LRCP Lond. 1972. (King's Coll. Hosp.) Prof. Geriat. & Dean, Fac of Med. Health & Biological Siences Univ. Soton.; Hon. Cons. (Geriat. Med.) Soton. Gen. Hosp. Socs: Fell. Roy. Soc. Med.; Brit. Geriat. Soc. Prev: Sen. Regist. (Geriat. Med.) Leicester Gen. Hosp.; Wellcome Research Schol. Insts. Psychiat. & Neurol. Lond.; Regist. (Gen. Med. & Neurol.) Leicester Roy. Infirm.

BRIGGS, Roger Simon Romiley Health Centre, Chichester Road, Romiley, Stockport SK6 4QR Tel: 0161 494 1234 Fax: 0161 406 8932; 3 Whiteoak Close, Marple, Stockport SK6 6NT — MB ChB 1984 Manch.

BRIGGS, Sally Ruth Royal Bolton Hospital, Bolton BL4 0JR; 72 Mallard Crescent, Poynton, Stockport SK12 1HT — MB ChB 1997 Birm. Med. SHO Roy. Bolton Hosp. Bolton. Prev: Ho. Off. (Surg.) Heartlands Hosp.; PRHO (Med.) Sandwell.

BRIGGS, Sharon Joyce Carnegie Family Planning Clinic, Inglis St., Dunfermline KY12 7AX Tel: 01383 722911; 9 Wyckliffe, Dunfermline KY12 9BA Tel: 01383 720154 — MB ChB 1981 Glas. Care Gp. Manager Woms. Health Serv. Fife Healthcare NHS Trust; GP Trainee; Police Surg. Fife. Socs: BMA; Foundat. Mem. Fac. Family Plann. & Reproduc. Health Care; Assn. Police Surg. Prev: SHO (O & G) Dunfermline Unit; Trainee GP Dunfermline; SHO (Anaesth.) Law Hosp. Carluke.

BRIGGS, Stewart William Philip Chirk Lodge, Winchester Hill, Romsey SO51 7NF Tel: 01794 515960 Fax: 01794 515960 Email: drspike@drspike.demon.co.uk — BM 1994 Soton.; BSc (Hons.) Surrey 1984. (Southampton) SHO (Anaesth.) Soton. Gen. Hosp. Socs: Inst. Marine Engineers; BMA; MDU. Prev: Ho. Off. Roy. S. Hants. Hosp. Soton.; Ho. Off. (Med.) Soton. Gen. Hosp.; SHO (IC) Qu. Alexandra Hosp. Portsmouth.

BRIGGS, Mr Timothy Paul Department of Urology, Barnet General Hosp, Well House Lane, Barnet EN5 3DS Tel: 020 8440 5111 Fax: 020 7431 5245; Department of Urology, Barnet General Hospital, Well House Lane, Barnet EN5 3DJ Tel: 020 8440 5111 — MB BS 1984 Lond.; BSc Lond. 1981, MS 1994; FRCS (Urol.) 1996; FRCS Ed. 1989; FRCS (Eng.) 1989. (St. Bart.) Cons. (Urol.) Barnet and Chorse farm NHS Trust. Socs: Fell. Roy. Soc. Med.; Brit. Assn. Urol. Surgs. Prev: Sen. Regist. (Urol.) The Concord Repatrutical Hosp, Sydney, Australia; Sen. Regist. Middlx. Hosp. & Inst. Urol. Lond.; Higher Trainee (Urol.) St. Peter's Hosp. (Middlx. Hosp.) Lond.

BRIGGS, Mr Timothy William Roy The Royal National Orthopaedic Hospital Trust, Brockley Hill, Stanmore HA7 4LP Tel: 020 8954 2300; Lane Farm, Chapel Lane, Totternhoe, Dunstable LU6 2BZ — MB BS 1982 Lond.; MCh (Orth.) Liverp. 1991; FRCS Eng. 1987; FRCS Ed. 1987. (The Royal London) Cons. Orthop. & Traum. Surg. Roy. Nat. Orthop. Hosp. Trust, Stanmore; Med. Director RNOHT; Surgic. Tutor RCS (Eng). Socs: Fell. Roy. Soc. Med.; Fell. BOA; Europ. Musculoskeletal Oncol. Soc. Prev: Sen. Regist. (Orthop.) Roy. Nat. Orthop. Hosp. Stanmore; Regist. (Orthop.) Roy. Lond. Hosp.

BRIGHAM, John David Villette Surgery, Suffolk Street, Hendon, Sunderland SR2 8AX Tel: 0191 567 9361 Fax: 0191 514 7476; 12 Roker Park Terrace, Roker, Sunderland SR6 9LY Tel: 0191 564 0704 Email: john.brigham@virgin.net — MB ChB 1982 Dundee. Bd. Mem. Sunderland N. PCG.

BRIGHAM, Sara Anne 3 Weardale Road, Liverpool L15 5AU — MB ChB 1994 Liverp. Ho. Off. Rotat. (O & G) Liverp. Wom. Hosp. Socs: Med. Sickness Soc. Prev: Ho. Off. Warrington Hosp. NHS Trust.

BRIGHOUSE, Diana Helen Shackleton Department Anaesthesia, Level E, Centre Block, Southampton General Hospital, Southampton SO16 6YD Tel: 02380 777222; The Anchorage, Lands End Road, Old Burlesdon, Southampton SO31 8DN Tel: 02380 402385 — BM 1978 Soton.; FFA RCS Eng. 1983. Cons. Anaesth. Shackleton Dept. Anaesth. Soton. Socs: Assn. Anaesth.; Obst. Anaesth. Assn. Prev: Sen. Regist. Nuffield Dept. Anaesth. Oxf.; Regist. (Obst. & Anaesth.) Qu. Charlottes Matern. Hosp. Lond.

BRIGHOUSE, Walter Alan (retired) — MB BChir 1958 Camb.; MB Camb. 1958. Med. Off. RAF Fylingdales. Prev: Chiar. Egton Fund Holding Consortium.

BRIGHT, Catherine Margaret 48 Redbridge Lane W., Wanstead, London E11 2JU — MB BCh 1994 Wales; BSc. Hons 1986; PhD.(Edinborough) 1989. (University of Wales College of Medicine) Specialist Regist. Psychiat. Socs: MRCPsych.

BRIGHT, Edgar Bulmer, AFC (retired) Copper Beech, Lower Seagry, Chippenham SN15 5EP — MB ChB 1937 Aberd.; DTM & H Eng. 1953. Prev: Hon. Phys. to HM the Qu.

BRIGHT, Elizabeth Anne 4 Brookside, Exning, Newmarket CB8 7HP — MB ChB 1992 Bristol; DCH RCP Lond. 1997; FRCA 1998. (Bristol) Specialist Regist. Anaesth. Wessex Region. Prev: SHO.Neonat..IC.Soton; SHO paediat.IC.Cardiac.Bristol .Childr.s.Hosp; SHO Anaesth. Oxf. Rotat.

BRIGHT, Helen 10 Harley Street, London W1N 1AA Tel: 020 7467 8406 Fax: 020 7467 8312 Email: drhelenbright@aol.com — MB BS 1983 Lond.; BSc (Hons.) Lond. 1980; MRCPsych 1988. (Royal Free Hosp London) Indep. Cons. (Psychiat.) Lond. PTSD; Director www.businessstressline.com. Socs: Fell. Roy. Soc. Med. Prev: Cons. St. Clements Hosp. Ipswich; Lect. (Psychiat.) Roy. Lond. Hosp.

BRIGHT, Jane Accident & Emergency Department, Royal Shrewsbury Hospital North, Mytton Oak Road, Shrewsbury SY3 8XQ; Baschurch House, Abbey Foregate, Shrewsbury SY2 6BL — MB ChB 1977 Sheff. (Sheff. Med. Sch.) GP Regist. & SHO (A & E) Roy. Shrewsbury Hosp. Socs: Med. Defence Union. Prev: GP/Regist. Shrewsbury; Regist. (Psychiat. of Elderly Ment. Ill) Shelton Hosp. Shrewsbury; Regist. (Child & Adolesc. Psychiat.) Child & Family Serve. Bourne Hse. Shrewsbury.

BRIGHT, Jeremy John Lower Street Health Centre, Lower Street, Tettenhall, Wolverhampton WV6 9LL Tel: 01902 444551 — MB ChB 1979 Liverp.; DRCOG 1983.

BRIGHT, John Christopher 80 Allt-Yr-Yn Road, Newport NP20 5EF — BM 1994 Soton.

BRIGHT, Keith John Wheatfield Surgery, 60 Wheatfield Road, Lewsey Farm, Luton LU4 0TR Tel: 01582 601116 Fax: 01582 666421 — MB BS 1972 Lond.; MRCS Eng. LRCP Lond. 1972; MRCGP 1976; DObst RCOG 1975.

BRIGHT, Malcolm St Davids Clinic, Bellevue Terrace, Newport NP20 2LB Tel: 01633 251133 Fax: 01633 221096 — BM BCh 1965 Oxf.; MA, BM BCh Oxf. 1965; MRCGP 1977; DObst RCOG 1972. (Oxf. & Lond. Hosp.) Socs: BMA & Mem. Gwent Med. Soc. Prev: Ho. Surg. Lond. Hosp.; Regist. (Med.) Mile End Hosp.; SHO (O & G) Roy. Gwent Hosp. Newport.

BRIGHT, Mr Michael Valentine (retired) 4 Brookside, Exning, Newmarket CB8 7HP Tel: 01638 577449 Fax: 01638 577449 Email: caradoc4@cs.com — MB BChir Camb. 1962; MA Camb. 1962; FRCS Ed. 1969; MRCS Eng. LRCP Lond. 1962; FRCOG 1982, M 1969. Prev: Cons. O & G, Addenbrooke's Hosp., Camb.

BRIGHT, Peter Hayne (retired) Longtree, 3 Dr Brown's Road, Minchinhampton, Stroud GL6 9DQ — MA, MB BChir Camb. 1948; DObst RCOG 1951. Prev: Hosp. Pract. (Surg.) Stroud Gen. Hosp.
BRIGHT, Philip 2 Comsey Road, Great Barr, Birmingham B43 7RG — MB ChB 1987 Birm.; ChB Birm. 1987.
BRIGHT, Philippa Ellen 15 Admirals Walk, Greenhithe DA9 9QP — MB BS 1998 Lond.; MB BS Lond 1998.
BRIGHT, Stephen Thomas 42 Queens Road, Blackhill, Consett DH8 0BW — MB ChB 1988 Birm.; MSc (Hons.) Computer Sci. Birm. 1984, BSc (Hons.) Anat. 1983; MRCGP 1992; T(GP) 1992; DRCOG 1992. Ships Doctor. Prev: Trainee GP Middlesbrough VTS; Ships Doctor P & O Cruises.
BRIGHT-THOMAS, Rachel Marie 87 Hamstead Road, Handsworth, Birmingham B20 2BP — BM BCh 1993 Oxf.; BA Hons. Camb. 1990. (Univ. Oxf. Med. Sch.) SHO (Gen. Surg.) Broomfield Hosp. Chelmsford. Socs: BMA; MDU. Prev: SHO (Orthop.) Broomfield Hosp. Chelmsford; SHO (Cas.) Univ. Coll. Hosp. Lond.
BRIGHT-THOMAS, Rowland John 87 Hampstead Road, Handsworth, Birmingham B20 2BP — MB ChB 1994 Manch.
BRIGHTEN, Karina Ann Community Paediatrics Department, Cheshire Community Healthcare Trust, Barony Headquarters, Nantwich CW5 5QU Tel: 01270 610000; Meadow View, 3 The Old Orchard, Cuddington, Northwich CW8 2GZ Tel: 01606 301247 — MB ChB 1979 Manch. Staff Grade Community Paediat. Chesh. Community Healthcare Trust Nantwich.
BRIGHTEN, Patrick William (retired) The Glove Factory, Newquay St, Appledore, Bideford EX39 1LU Tel: 01237 478219 Email: patrick@brighten.freeserve.co.uk — MB BS 1965 Lond.; FFA RCS Eng. 1973; DA Eng. 1972. Prev: Cons. Anaesth. N. Devon Infirm. Barnstaple.
BRIGHTLEY, Kathleen Margaret Department of Child and Family Psychiatry, Downend Clinic, Buckingham Gardens, Downend, Bristol BS16 Tel: 0117 956 6025 — MB ChB 1980 Glas.; MRCPsych 1985. Cons. Child & Adolesc. Psychiat. Frenchay Health Trust. Prev: Cons. Highland Health Bd.; Sen. Regist. (Child & Adolesc. Psychiat.) Bristol & W.on HA; Regist. (Psychiat.) Bristol & W.on HA.
BRIGHTLING, Christopher Edward Department of Respiratory Medicine, Glenfield Hospital, Groby Road, Leicester LE3 9QP — MB BS 1993 Lond. Specialist Regist., Repiratory Med., Glenfield Hosp., Leicester.
BRIGHTMAN, Christopher Anthony John The Public Health Laboratory, The County Hospital, St Annes's Road, Lincoln LN2 5RF — MB BChir 1972 Camb.; MA Camb. 1973; MSc. (Parasitol.) Lond. 1977; MRCPath 1986; Cert. Prescribed Equiv. Exp. 1982. Cons. Bacteriol. Pub. Health Laborat. Lincoln. Socs: The Museums' Consultation Soc. Prev: Sen. Regist. (Bacteriol.) St. Lukes Hosp. Guildford; Sen. Regist. (Bacteriol.) St. Geo. Hosp. Lond.; SHO (Path.) Char. Cross Hosp. Lond.
BRIGHTMAN, David Christopher Fax: 01924 870052 — MB ChB 1987 Leeds. Socs: MPS. Prev: SHO (Psychiat.) Stanley Royd Hosp. Wakefield; SHO (Paediat.) Pinderfields Hosp. Wakefield; SHO (O & G) Huddersfield Roy. Infirm.
BRIGHTMORE, Mr Terence Gerald James (retired) 12 Westminster Avenue, Chester CH4 8JB Tel: 01244 680342 — MB BS 1961 Lond.; MRCS Eng. LRCP Lond. 1961; MS Lond. 1983; FRCS Eng. 1966. Prev: Cons. Surg. Chester Health Dist.
BRIGHTWELL, Mr Andrew Philip St Alban, 8 Lyndhurst Road, Exeter EX2 4PA Tel: 01392 430300 Fax: 01392 421889 Email: apb@saint-alsan.com; Newcombes, Newton St. Cyres, Exeter EX5 5AW Tel: 01392 851235 Fax: 01392 851234 — MB BS 1978 Lond.; FRCS (Otol.) Eng. 1983. (St. Thos.) Cons. Otolaryngol. Roy. Devon & Exeter Hosp. Prev: Sen. Regist. (ENT Surg.) Soton. Gen. Hosp.; Hon. Lect. Audiol. Inst. Sound & Vibration Research Univ. Soton.; Regist. (ENT Surg.) Roy. Ear Hosp. Univ. Coll. Hosp. Lond.
BRIGHTWELL, Cherry Glesni The Surgery, 218 Ifield Drive, Ifield, Crawley RH11 0EP Tel: 01293 547846 — MB BS 1982 Lond.; DCH RCP Lond. 1987; DRCOG 1985; DA (UK) 1984.
BRIGHTWELL, Philip 40 Orchard Avenue, Shirley, Croydon CR0 7NA — MB BS 1944 Lond. (Guy's) Socs: Croydon Med. Soc. Prev: Res. Surg. Off. Roy. Hants. Co. Hosp. Winchester & St. John's Hosp.; Lewisham; Clin. Asst. Genito-Urin. Dept. Croydon Gen. Hosp.
BRIGLMEN, Charles John 14 Moray Place, Edinburgh EH3 6DT Tel: 0131 225 8025 Fax: 0131 225 6749; Tel: 0131 339 4345 Fax: 0131 225 6749 — MB ChB 1955 Ed.; DObst RCOG 1960. Cons. Hypnother. & Orthop. Med. Moray Pl. & Murrayfield Hosp. Edin. Socs: Fell. Brit. Soc. Med. & Dent. Hypn.; Brit. Assn. Manip. Med.; Inst. Orthop. Med. & Internat. Soc. Hypn. Prev: Flight Lt. RAF Med. Br.; Ho. Phys. & Ho. Surg. Edin. Roy. Infirm.; Ho. Surg. (Obst.) Raigmore Hosp. Inverness.
BRIGNALL, Miss Carol Gillian Cumberland Infirmary, Carlisle CA2 7HY Tel: 01228 23444 Email: cg.brignall@ncumbria-acute.nhs.uk — MB BS 1980 Newc.; FRCS Ed. 1985. Cons. Orthop. Surg. Cumbld. Infirm. Carlisle. Socs: Fell. BOA. Prev: Sen. Regist. (Orthop.) N.. RHA; Regist. (Orthop.) Newc. HA.
BRIGNALL, Katherine Anne 19 Vine Av, Sevenoaks TN13 3AH — MB ChB 1997 Bristol.
BRIGSTOCKE, Sarah-Jane Croft Cottage, Bakers Lane, Knowle, Solihull B93 8PR — BM 1998 Soton.
BRIGSTOCKE, Timothy William Owen Ringwood Health Centre, The Close, Ringwood BH24 1JY Tel: 01425 478901 Fax: 01425 478239 — MB BS 1975 Lond.; MRCS Eng. LRCP Lond. 1975.
BRIJ, Seema Onnetta Top Left, 17 Clarence Drive, Glasgow G12 9QN — BM BS 1994 Nottm.
BRILEY, Mary Department of Radiology, Southampton General Hospital, Southampton SO16 6YD — BM BCh 1986 Oxf.; FRCR 1993. Cons. Radiol. Roy. S. Hants. Hosp. Soton. Prev: Sen. Regist. (Radiol.) John Radcliffe Hosp. Oxf.
BRILL, Albert Maurice (retired) 32 Sandhill Oval, Alwoodley, Leeds LS17 8EA Tel: 0113 268 1355 — MRCS Eng. LRCP Lond. 1953. Prev: Ho. Phys. ScarBoro. Hosp.
BRILL, Gordon 5 Hobart Court, 14 Sunset Avenue, Woodford Green IG8 0TQ Tel: 020 8505 6424 — LRCP LRCS Ed. LRFPS Glas. 1946; DObst RCOG 1956. (Anderson Coll. Glas.) Socs: N. Eng. O & G Soc. & Glas. O & G Soc. Prev: Ho. Surg. Glas. Roy. Infirm.; Sen. Ho. Off. Gyn. Cancer Unit, Qu. Eliz. Hosp. Gateshead; Jun. Regist. (Obst.) Ayrsh. Centr. Hosp.
BRILL, Guy Christopher (retired) 23 Rosebery Road, Alresford SO24 9HQ — MB BChir 1959 Camb.; MA, MB Camb. 1959, BChir 1958; FRCGP 1975, M 1965. Prev: GP Alresford.
BRILL, Samuel Emanuel 6 Mornington Road, Woodford Green IG8 0TS Tel: 020 8504 7144 — MB ChB 1955 Glas.; FRCP Lond. 1986; FFOM RCP Lond. 1982, M 1978; DIH Soc. Apoth. Lond. 1968. (Glas.) Socs: Fell. Roy. Soc. Med. (Ex-Pres. Sect. Occupat. Med.); (Ex-Pres.) Soc. Occupat. Med. Prev: Chief Med. Off. Ford Motor Co.; Hon. Cons Occupat. Med. the Army; Chairm. SAC Occupat. Med.
BRIM, Victor Donald 97 Ringley Road, Whitefield, Manchester M45 7HU — MB ChB Manch. 1960; FFA RCS Eng. 1968; DA Eng. 1965; DObst RCOG 1964. Cons. Anaesth. Tameside Acute Trust. Socs: Fell. Manch. Med. Soc. Prev: Sen. Regist. Manch. Roy. Infirm.; Ho. Surg. (Surg. & Orthop.) Ancoats Hosp. Manch.; Ho. Phys. (Med.) & Ho. Surg. (O & G) Crumpsall Hosp. Manch.
BRIMACOMBE, Lawrence (retired) 23 Abbey Lane, Sheffield S8 0BJ Tel: 0114 274 5360 — MB ChB Sheff. 1954; MRCGP 1965. Prev: Hosp. Pract. (Cas.) Roy. Hallamsh. Hosp. Sheff.
BRIMACOMBE, Moira Catherine Abbey Lane Surgery, 23 Abbey Lane, Sheffield S8 0BJ Tel: 0114 274 5360 Fax: 0114 274 9580; 10 Broad Elms Lane, Sheffield S11 9RQ Tel: 0114 236 5106 Email: brimacombe@btinternet.com — MB ChB Sheff. 1967; MRCPsych 1973; DPM Eng. 1972. (Univ. Sheff.) Socs: BMA; GPWA. Prev: Clin. Asst. (Child Psychiat.) Sheff. Childr. Hosp.; Regist. (Psychiat.) Maudsley Hosp. Lond.; Regist. (Psychol. Med.) Middlx. Hosp. Lond.
BRIMBLECOMBE, Pauline Ruth Newnham Walk Surgery, Wordsworth Grove, Cambridge CB3 9HS Tel: 01223 366811 Fax: 01223 302706; Tel: 01233 846906 — MB BChir 1978 Camb.; MSc 2001; MRCGP 1983; DRCOG 1982; DCH RCP Lond. 1982. Socs: Med. Wom.s Federat.Vice Pres. 2001-2002.
BRIMELOW, Andrew Edward Calrow Fold, Calrofold Lane, Rainow, Macclesfield — MB ChB 1983 Ed.
BRIMS, Fraser John Hall 25 Knights Bank Road, Fareham PO14 3JY — MB ChB 1997 Leic.
BRINCKENHOFF, Wiktor-Olaf (retired) 52 Malvern Drive, Woodford Green IG8 0JP Tel: 020 8504 8030 — LRCPI & LM, LRSCI & LM 1956; LRCPI & LM, LRCSI & LM 1956; MRCGP 1966. Prev: Clin. Asst. (O & G) Roy. Lond. Hosp. (Mile End).
BRIND, Alison Mary North Staffordshire Hospital, City General, Newcastle Road, Stoke-on-Trent ST4 6QG Tel: 01782 552390 Fax:

01782 712052 Email: alisonbrind@virgin.net; 1 Granville Terrace, Stone ST15 8DF Tel: 01785 816695 — MB BS 1984 Newc.; MD (Commend.) Newc. 1991, BMedSci (Hons.) 1981; MRCP (UK) 1987. Cons. Gastroenterol. N. Staffs. Hosp. NHS Trust. Socs: Brit. Assn. Study Liver; Eur. Assn. Study Liver; Brit. Soc. of Gastroenterol. Prev: Sen. Regist. Liver Unit Freeman Hosp. Newc.; MRC Trav. Fell. Paris; Regist. Inst. Liver Studies King's Coll. Lond.

BRINDLE, John Malcolm (retired) Leebeer, Hoo Meavy, Yelverton PL20 6JB Tel: 01822 852611 — MA, BM BCh Oxf. 1956; FRCR 1975; FFR 1962; DMRT Eng. 1959.

BRINDLE, Michael John Radiology Department, The Queen Elizabeth Hospital, Gayton Road, King's Lynn PE30 4ET Tel: 01553 766266 Fax: 01553 613838; The Orchard, Hall Lane, South Wootton, King's Lynn PE30 3LQ Tel: 01553 672825 Fax: 01553 674727 — MB ChB 1958 Liverp.; MD Liverp. 1967; FRCP Canada (Diag. Radiol.) 1972; FRCR 1989; MRad Liverp. 1971; DMRD Liverp. 1964. (Liverp.) Cons. Diag. Radiol. King's Lynn Dist. Gen. Hosp. Socs: (Pres.) Roy. Coll. Radiol.

BRINDLE, Miles Jonathan Appleton Village Surgery, 2-6 Appleton Village, Widnes WA8 6DZ Tel: 0151 423 2990 Fax: 0151 424 1032 — MB ChB 1988 Liverp.

BRINDLE, Nicholas Smith Flat B, 3 Ashleigh Road, Leeds LS16 5AX — MB ChB 1990 Manch.

BRINDLE, Peter Malcolm Air Balloon Surgery, Kenn Road, St George, Bristol BS5 7PD Tel: 0117 906 6614 Email: pbrindle@airballoon.uk.co.uk; 39 St. Albans Road, Bristol BS6 7SF Tel: 0117 904 4466 Email: peterbrindle@lineone.net — MB ChB 1994 Bristol; BSc MB ChB Bristol 1994. G.P Regist., Air Balloon Surg., Bristol. Prev: Sen. Med. Off. Hlabisa Hosp. Kwazulud-Natal, S. Afr.

BRINDLE, Richard John Public Health Laboratory, Portsmouth Hospitals, Portsmouth PO3 6AQ Tel: 02392 866204 Fax: 02392 824652; The Hollow, 50 Southwick Road, North Boarhunt, Fareham PO17 6DJ — BM 1978 Soton.; MSc Lond. 1987; DM Soton. 1993; MRCP (UK) 1985; MRCPath 1993; DTM & H RCP Lond. 1980. Cons. Microbiol. Portsmouth PHL; Infec. Control Doctor., Portsmouth Hosp.s. Prev: Sen. Regist. (Microbiol.) Oxf. PHL; Dist. Med. Off. Vanuatu, S. Pacific; Hon. Lect. (Microbiol.) Univ. Nairobi.

BRINDLE, Thomas Wynne (retired) 2 Coppice Close, Woodley, Stockport SK6 1JH — MB ChB 1933 Manch.; FFCM 1981 M 1972; DPH Liverp. 1947. Prev: Area Med. Off. Chesh. AHA.

BRINDLEY, Andrew John 8 Woolfall Heath Avenue, Liverpool L36 3TN — MB ChB 1993 Sheff.; e.

BRINDLEY, Edward (Surgery) 129 Marple Road, Offerton, Stockport SK2 5EP Tel: 0161 483 4986; Offerton Health Centre, Offerton Lane, Stockport SK2 5AR Tel: 0161 480 0326 — MB ChB 1962 Sheff.; DObst RCOG 1964. (Sheff.) Prev: SHO Obst. & Gyn. N.. Gen. Hosp. Sheff.; Ho. Phys. Childr. Hosp. Sheff.; Ho. Surg. Roy. Hosp. Sheff.

BRINDLEY, Mr Giles Skey (retired) 102 Ferndene Road, London SE24 0AA Tel: 020 7274 2598 Email: gsbrindley@rcsed.ac.uk — MB BChir 1951 Camb.; FRS; MD Camb. 1956; FRCP Lond. 1973, M 1969; Hon. FRCS Eng. 1988; MRCS Eng. LRCP Lond. 1950. Prev: Hon. Dir. MRC Neurol. Prostheses Unit.

BRINDLEY, Leslie John Park House Medical Centre, 6 Aspinall Street, Prescot L34 5QU Tel: 0151 426 5253 Fax: 0151 431 0652; 531 Burrows Lane, Eccleston, St Helens WA10 5AN — MB ChB 1980 Liverp.; DRCOG 1987. (Liverpool) Mem. St Helens & Knowsley LMC; Mem. Centr. & S. Knowsley PCG. Prev: SHO (Orthop. & A & E) Walton Hosp. Liverp.; SHO (O & G) Liverp. Matern. Hosp. & Woms. Hosp. Liverp.

BRINDLEY, Ronald Joseph Whittington Road Surgery, 9 Whittington Road, Norton, Stourbridge DY8 3DB Tel: 01384 393120 Fax: 01384 353636 — MB ChB 1984 Birm.

BRINDLEY, Sandra Mary Tel: 01384 277377 Fax: 01384 402329 — MB ChB 1983 Birm.; MRCGP 1988; DRCOG 1987; DCH RCP Lond. 1986. GP Kingswinford. Prev: Clin. Asst. (Neonatol.) Wordsley Hosp.; Trainee GP Dudley VTS; Jun. Ho. Off. Qu. Eliz. Hosp. Birm. & E. Birm. Hosp.

BRINK, Anne Katherine 34 Minster Road, Oxford OX4 1LY Tel: 01865 246127; PO Box 10346, Kampala, Uganda Tel: +256 75 719127 Email: gtzuwa@swiftusaanda.com — MB BS 1984 Lond.; BA Oxon. 1981; DTM & H Liverp. 1990.

BRINKLEY, Alexandra Mary Elizabeth Norfolk Park Health Centre, Tower Drive, Sheffield S2 3RE Tel: 0114 276 9661 Fax: 0114 276 9471; Parkside, 14 Oakbrook Road, Ranmoor, Sheffield S11 7EA Tel: 0114 230 4286 — MB BCh 1984 Wales; MRCGP 1992; DCP (Distinc.) Sheff. 1990; DCH RCP Lond. 1989. GP Trainer Sheff.

BRINKLEY, David Christopher Page Hall Medical Centre, 101 Owler Lane, Sheffield S4 8GB Tel: 0114 261 7245 Fax: 0114 261 1643; 14 Oakbrook Road, Sheffield S11 7EA — MB BS 1985 Lond.; MRCGP 1992; DCH RCP Lond. 1990. Prev: SHO (Paediat.) Doncaster Roy. Infirm.

BRINKLEY, Diana Mary (retired) 51 Hollywood Road, Dulwich, London SW10 9HX Tel: 020 7352 7909 — MB BS 1945 Lond.; 1945 MB BS Lond.; 1958 MA Camb.; 1977 FRCR; 1950 DMRT Eng. Prev: Cons. Radiother. Cromwell Hosp. Lond. & Sloane Hosp. Beckenham.

BRINKLEY, Mark Alan Shrewsbury Road, Shifnal TF11 8AJ Tel: 01952 460414 Fax: 01952 463192 Email: mark.brinkley@gp-m82038.nhs.uk — MB ChB 1983 Birm.; MRCGP 1992; DRCOG 1990. Princip. Gen. Pract., Shifnal & Priorilee Med. Pract., Shrops. Prev: Clin. Asst. (Gen. Surg. & ENT) Wolverhampton Hosps.

BRINKLOW, Katharine Ann 7 Cherrydale Road, Camberley GU15 1SR — MB BS 1998 Lond.; MB BS Lond 1998.

BRINKMANN, Dirk Alexander 5 Ranmere Street, London SW12 9QQ — MB ChB 1991 Cape Town.

BRINKSMAN, Hilary Janice Wingate Medical Centre, 79 Bigdale Drive, Northwood, Liverpool L33 6YJ Tel: 0151 546 2958 Fax: 0151 546 2914; 9 Tudor Close, Rainford, St Helens WA11 8SD Tel: 01744 886059 — MB ChB 1986 Liverp.

BRINKSMAN, Stephen Ridgacre House Surgery, 83 Ridgacre Road, Quinton, Birmingham B32 2TJ Tel: 0121 422 3111 — MB ChB 1986 Liverp. GP Prescriber Mary St., Birm.

BRINSDEN, Mark Dudley Manor Farm, High Street, Yelling, St Neots, Huntingdon PE19 6SD — MB BS 1993 Lond.

BRINSDEN, Peter Robert, Surg. Cdr. RN Retd. Bourn Hall Clinic, Bourn, Cambridge CB3 7TR Tel: 01954 719111 Fax: 01954 718826 Email: peter.brinsden@seromo.com; Manor Farm, Yelling, St. Neots, Huntingdon PE19 6SD Tel: 01480 880272 Fax: 01480 880272 Email: brinsdemp@aol.com — MB BS Lond. 1966; MRCS Eng. LRCP Lond. 1966; FRCOG 1989, M 1976; DObst RCOG 1971. (St. Geo.) Cons. Gyn. & Med. Dir. Bourn Hall Clinic Camb.; Affilated Lect. Univ. Camb. Clin. Sch. Socs: Fell. Roy. Soc. Med.; BMA; Brit. Fertil. Soc. Prev: Cons. O & G King Fahad Hosp. Saudi Arabian Nat. Guard, Saudi Arabia; Cons. O & G Wellington Hosp. Lond. & RN Hosp. Plymouth.

BRISCOE, Catherine Ruth Richards and Partners, Llanfair Surgery, Llanfair Road, Llandovery SA20 0HY Tel: 01550 720648 Fax: 01550 721428; Nant Ddu, Rhandirmwyn, Llandovery SA20 0NG Tel: 01550 720159 — BChir 1984 Camb.; MA Camb. 1985. (Cambridge and St. Marys) Prev: GP Llandysul.

BRISCOE, Charles Edward (retired) Dudwick Cottage, Buxton, Norwich NR10 5HX Tel: 01603 279249 Fax: 01603 279024 Email: c.briscoe@faston.co.uk — MB 1963 Camb.; BChir 1962; FFA RCS Eng. 1968; DA Eng. 1966; DObst RCOG 1965. Prev: Asst. Specialist (Anaesth.) Norf. & Norwich Hosp.

BRISCOE, James Jonathan Daly Patrick House, 5 Maney Corner, Birmingham Road, Sutton Coldfield B72 1QL Tel: 0121 685 6685 Fax: 0121 321 2695; 1 Maney Hill Road, Sutton Coldfield B72 1JJ — MB ChB Birm. 1988; MRCPsych 1994. (Birmingham) Cons. Community Psychiat. N.ern Birm. Ment. Health (NHS) Trust; Liveryman Soc. Apoth. Lond. Prev: Sen. Regist. Rotat. (Psychiat.) W. Midl. Train. Scheme.

BRISCOE, John Hubert Daly, LVO (retired) Wistaria House, 54/56 Kings Road, Windsor SL4 2AH Tel: 01753 855321 Fax: 01753 851869 Email: jhdb@ukonline.co.uk — MA Camb. 1963, MB 1958, BChir 1957; MRCGP 1968; DObst RCOG 1959. Prev: Apoth. HM Ho.hold at Windsor & HM The Qu. Mother's Ho.hold at Roy. Lodge.

BRISCOE, Martin Hugh Wonford House Hospital, Dryden Road, Wonford, Exeter EX2 5AF Tel: 01392 403459 — MB BCh 1978 Wales; MRCPsych. 1982. Cons. Adult Psychiat. Exeter City. Prev: Wellcome Research Fell. 1982; Lect. Psychol. Med. Univ. Hosp. Wales.

BRISCOE, Maura 1 Sandhurst Drive, Stranmills, Belfast BT9 5AY — MB BCh BAO 1978 NUI; LRCPI & LM, LRCSI & LM 1978; MRCGP 1983; DCH Dub. 1982; DObst. RCPI 1981. Med. Off. DHSS. Prev: GP Armagh.

BRISCOE, Oliver Villiers Gainsborough Clinic, 80 Lambeth Road, London SE1 7PW Tel: 020 7928 5633 Fax: 020 7928 1702; Woodlands, Nethern Court Road, Woldingham, Caterham CR3 7EF Tel: 01883 653426 Fax: 01883 653427 — MB BS Lond. 1953; FRCP Lond. 1979; MRCP (UK) 1957; FRCPsych 1976, M 1971; DPM Lond. 1962. (Roy. Lond. Hosp.) Cons. Psychiat. Socs: Fell. Roy. Soc. Med.; Expert Witness Inst.; Assn. for Child Psychol. & Psychiat. Prev: Cons. Phys. Bethlem Roy. & Maudsley Hosps. Lond.; Hon. Sen. Lect. Roy. Postgrad. Med. Sch. Lond.; Sen. Lect. (Forens. Psychiat.) Sydney Univ.

BRISCOE, Rosemary Anne Brae Health Centre, Brae, Shetland ZE2 9QJ Tel: 01806 522543 — MB BS 1981 Lond.; MRCGP 1990; DCH RCP Lond. 1984; DRCOG 1984. (St. Bart.)

BRISLEY, Glyn David Taverham Surgery, Sandy Lane, Taverham, Norwich NR8 6JR Tel: 01603 867481 Fax: 01603 740670 — MB ChB 1965 Leeds. (Leeds) Prev: SHO (Med.) St. Luke's Hosp. Bradford; Regist. (Path.) St. Luke's Hosp. Guildford; Regist. St. Thos. Hosp. Lond.

BRISTOL, Mr James Bernard Cheltenham General Hospital, Sandford Road, Cheltenham GL53 7AN Tel: 01242 273177 Fax: 01242 273663 Email: james.bristol@egnhst.org.uk; 4 Greenhills Road, Cheltenham GL53 9ED Tel: 01242 250304 — MB ChB 1971 Birm.; MD Birm. 1990; FRCS Eng. 1977. p/t Cons. Surg. E. Glos. NHS Trust; Lead Clinician, BrE. Cancer, Three Counties Cancer Centre (Glos., Hereford & Worcs); Exec. Comm. Mem. BASO BrE. Specialty Gp. Socs: Fell. Roy. Soc. Med. (Mem. Sect. Surg. & Coloproctol.); Brit. Assn. Surgic. Oncol. Prev: Lect. (Surg.) Univ. Bristol; Regist. (Surg.) Roy. United Hosp. Bath; Ship's Surg. RMS Edin. Castle.

BRISTOL, Katherine Elizabeth 71 Lansddowne Avenue, Grimsby DN32 0BX; 12 Symes Park, Weston, Bath BA1 4PA Tel: 01225 329443 — BM BCh 1993 Oxf.; DCH 1996; DRCOG 1997. GP Non Princip. Socs: BMA. Prev: GP Trainee; SHO (O & G); SHO (ENT).

BRISTOL, Michael Paul Factory Lane West, Halstead CO9 1EX; 39 Coggeshall Road, Earls Colne, Colchester CO6 2JR Tel: 01787 222669 Fax: 01787 222669 — MB BChir 1973 Camb.; MA, MB Camb. 1973, BChir 1972; MRCGP 1976; DObst RCOG 1974. Prev: Trainee GP Ipswich VTS.

BRISTOW, Andrew Ian Little Harwood Health Centre, Plane Tree Road, Blackburn BB1 6PH Tel: 01254 580931 Fax: 01254 695794 — MB ChB 1985 Manch.

BRISTOW, Anne Hilary The Faulds, 17 Borough Park, Torpoint PL11 2PY Tel: 01752 814105 — MB BCh BAO 1955 Dub.; FFA RCS Eng. 1968; DA Eng. 1958.

BRISTOW, Aubrey Stretton Edward 17 Wimpole Street, London W1M 7AD — MB BS 1978 Lond.; MRCS Eng. LRCP Lond. 1978; FFA RCS Eng. 1982.

BRISTOW, Michael Francis Sutton Hospital (St Helier Trust), Cotswold Road, Sutton SM2 5NF; Department of Community Psychiatry, St Georges Hospital, Blackshaw Road, London SW17 0QT — MB BS 1980 Lond.; MRCPsych 1987. Cons. Psychiat. Sutton Hosp. Surrey; Sen. Lect. St. Geo. Hosp. Lond.

BRISTOW, Susan Elizabeth — MB BS 1988 Lond.; MRCOG 1994. p/t Cons. (O & G) Hexham Gen. Hosp. Hexham. Prev: Clin. Research Assoc. (Urol.) Univ. Newc.; Regist. (O & G) S.mead Hosp. Bristol.; Regist. (O & G) Roy. Devon & Exeter Hosp. (Heavitree).

BRITCHFORD, Robert Eric River House, Goose Green, Lambourn, Newbury RG17 8YB — MRCS Eng. LRCP Lond. 1973; MRCPsych 1979. GP Child Psychiat. MarlBoro. Coll. Prev: Sen. Specialist (Neuropsychiat.) P.ss Alexandr's Hosp. Wroughton; SHO (Psychiat.) Exe Vale Hosp. Exeter.

BRITLAND, Alison Ann Paediatric Department, Airedale General Hospital, Steeton, Keighley BD20 6TD Tel: 01535 652511; Tel: 01535 652410 — MB ChB 1987 Aberd.; MRCP (UK) 1996; FRCPCH 1997. (Aberd.) Cons. Paediat. Airedale Gen. Hosp. Keighley. Prev: Staff Grade (Paediat.) Neonat. Unit Ayrsh. Centr. Hosp.

BRITO-BABAPULLE, Finella Marie Chrystalene Royal Berkshire Hospital, London Road, Reading RG1 5AN Tel: 01189 877757 Fax: 01189 877755 Email: mlayton@btinteernet.com; 9 Luckmore Drive, Earley, Reading RG6 7RP Tel: 0118 987 7757 Fax: 0118 987 7755 — MRCS Eng. LRCP Lond. 1978; 1978 MRCS Eng. LRCP Lond.; 1981 MRCP (UK); 1984 MRCPath; 1999 FRCPath. (University of Columbo, Ceylon) Cons. Haemat. Roy. Berks. Hosp.; Hon Lect. Univ. Reading. Socs: BMA; MPS.

BRITO RAMOS, Jose Miguel 23 Mornington Road, Norwich NR2 3NA — LMS 1987 La Laguna.

BRITT, Christopher Paul Health Centre, Handsworth Avenue, Highams Park, London E4 9PD Tel: 020 8527 0913 Fax: 020 8527 6597; 66 Wellington Road, London E11 2AU — MB BS 1987 Lond.

BRITT, Jonathan Richard Woodgate, Latchmoor Grove, Gerrards Cross SL9 8LN — MB BS 1990 Lond.

BRITT, Roger Graham 42 Victoria Street, Newark NG24 4UT — MRCS Eng. LRCP Lond. 1945; DMRD Eng. 1948; FFR 1955. (Birm.) Emerit. Radiol. Leics. HA; Begley Anat. Stud. RCS Eng. 1945. Prev: Cons. Radiol. Leicester Roy. Infirm.; Sen. Regist. X-Ray Dept. P'boro. Memor. Hosp.; Lect. (Radiol. Anat.) Univ. Birm.

BRITTAIN, Alan Harvey 11 Haddon Crescent, Attenborough Lane, Chilwell, Nottingham NG9 5JU Tel: 0115 925 4053 — MB ChB 1955 Birm.; DObst RCOG 1960. (Birm.)

BRITTAIN, Christopher Neil Sargent Cancer Care for Children, 158 South St., St Andrews KY16 9EG Tel: 01334 470044 Fax: 01334 470144; The White House, Smithy Brae, Kilrenny, Anstruther KY10 3JN Tel: 01333 310191 — MB ChB 1974 Dundee; MRCGP 1979; Dip. IMC RCS Ed. 1989; DRCOG 1978; MBA Herriot Watt 1997. (Dundee) Dir. Sargent Cancer Care for Childr. (Scotl.). Socs: (Past Chairm.) Brit. Assn. for Immediate Care; Resusc. Counc.; Fell. Roy. Soc. Med. Prev: Sen. Partner Anstruther Med. Pract.

BRITTAIN, David Richard 52 Colney Lane, Cringleford, Norwich NR4 7RF — MB BS 1973 Lond.; DRCOG 1976.

BRITTAIN, Mr Geoffrey Paul Henry Sussex Eye Hospital, Eastern Road, Brighton BN2 5BF Tel: 01273 606126 Fax: 01273 693674; 51 Withdean Road, Brighton BN1 5JB Tel: 01273 509814 Email: pandmbrittain@compuser.com — MB BCh BAO 1981 NUI; BSc Birm. 1973; FRCS Eng. 1986; FCOphth 1989; LRCPI & LM, LRCSI & LM 1981; DO Dub. 1985. (Royal College of Surgeons in Ireland) Cons. Ophth. Sussex Eye Hosp. Brighton & P.ss Roy. Hosp. Haywards Heath. Socs: BMA; S.ern Ophth. Soc.; Eur. Soc. Ophth. Plastic & Reconstruc. Surg. Prev: Fell. Oculoplastic Surg. Moorfields Eye Hosp. Lond.; Sen. Regist. Wolverhampton & Midl. Co. Eye Infirm.; Regist. (Ophth.) The Leicester Roy. Infirm.

BRITTAIN, George John Cecil (retired) Ballaqueeny, Farrant Park, Castletown IM9 1NG Tel: 01625 823660 — MB ChB Liverp. 1940; MD Liverp. 1944; FFA RCS Eng. 1953; FFA RCSI 1960; DA RCPSI 1945. Prev: Cons. Anaesth. Wigan & Leigh Gp. Hosps. & Regional Centre Hip Surg. Wrightington Hosp.

BRITTAIN, John Tel: 01883 348981 Fax: 01883 652409; Valley Lodge, Butlers Dene Road, Woldingham, Caterham CR3 7HH Tel: 01883 653030 Fax: 01883 652409 Email: 100526.3624@compuserve.com — DIP Inst. Biol. Toxicol. 1995; MB BS Lond. 1952; MD Kansas 1977; MRCS Eng. LRCP Lond. 1959; AFOM RCP Lond. 1988; DIH Soc. Apoth. Lond. 1987. (St. Mary's) p/t Occupat. Phys. Laporte Fluorides Rotherham, Fred Olsen Shipping Ipswich; Med. Adviser Comm. Technique Europ. Du Fluor GEFIC, Brussels. Socs: Soc. Occupat. Med.; Brit. Toxicol. Soc.; Med. Soc. Lond. Prev: Clin. Asst. (Med. Outpats.) St. Mary's Hosp. Lond.; Ho. Surg. W. Lond. Hosp.; Attend. Phys. Susan Allen Memor. Hosp. El Dorado, Kansas, USA.

BRITTAIN, Phoebina (retired) 1 Farrants Park, Castletown IM9 1NG Tel: 01624 823660 — MB BCh BAO Dub. 1940; BA Dub. 1940. Prev: Clin. Asst. (Ophth.) Roy. Infirm. Wigan & Roy. Infirm. Derby.

BRITTAIN, Richard Vincent Newbold Verdon Medical Practice, 14 Arnolds Crescent, Newbold Verdon, Leicester LE9 9PZ Tel: 01445 822171 Fax: 01445 824968; Southgate, 24 Sutton Lane, Market Bosworth, Nuneaton CV13 0LB Tel: 01455 290587 — MB ChB Liverp. 1967; MRCGP 1974. (Liverp.) Prev: Rotat. Intern Roy. S.. Hosp. Liverp.; SHO Roy. Liverp. Childr. Hosp.; Ho. Surg. (Obst.) Sefton Gen. Hosp. Liverp.

BRITTAIN, Roger Dean The Old Rectory, Brinklow, Rugby CV23 0NE Tel: 01788 832660 Fax: 01788 833220 Email: dr.roger.brittain@msn.co.uk — MD 1970 Univ. Pennsylvania; MA Camb. 1968; LMSSA Lond. 1975; MRCS Eng. LRCP Lond. 1975; MFCMI 1979; MPH Yale 1974. (Camb. & Univ. Penna.) Dir. Nihon

Shika & Anglo-Amer. Dent. Gp. Prev: Dist. Community Phys. N. Manch. Health Dist. & Dist. Med. Off. Warks. HA; Specialist Community Med. (Informat. & Research) E. Anglian RHA.

BRITTEN, Charles Stewart Child & Family Consultation Service, St Peter's Hospital, Spital Road, Maldon CM9 6EG Tel: 01621 722900 Fax: 01621 722919; The Rows, Church Road, Layer de la Haye, Colchester CO2 0EU Tel: 01206 738299 Email: stewartbritten@cs.com — MB BS 1965 Lond.; FRCPsych 1996, M 1972; DPM Ed. & Glas. 1968. (St. Bart.) Cons. Child & Adolesc. Psychiat. NE Essex Ment. Health Trust. Socs: Assn. Child Psychother. Prev: Regist. Cassel Hosp. Richmond; Ho. Off. Lusaka Centr. Hosp.

BRITTEN, Clive Mark Parkside Clinic, 63 - 65 Lancaster Rd, London W11 1QG Tel: 020 7221 4656 Fax: 020 7243 0276 — MB BS 1981 Lond.; MA Oxf. 1990, BA 1977; MRCPsych 1986. (Middlx. Hosp.) Cons. Child Psychiat. Pk.side Clinic, Lond.; Cons. (Child Psychiat.) Pk.side Clinic Lond. Prev: Cons. (Child Psychiat.) Barnet; Sen. Regist. (Child Psychiat.) Hosp. for Sick Childr. Gt. Ormond St. Lond.

BRITTEN, Lindsey Denise The Scott Practice, 1 Greenfield Lane, Balby, Doncaster DN4 0TG Tel: 01302 850546 Fax: 01302 855338 — BM BS 1991 Nottm.

BRITTEN, Mr Simon Bristol Royal Infirmary, Marlborough St., Bristol BS2 8HW Tel: 0117 923 0000 Email: traumawarrior@hotmail.com; Top Floor Flat, 1 Lansdown Rd, Clifton Village, Bristol BS8 3AA Tel: 0117 973 0228 — BM 1990 Soton.; FRCS 2001 (Tr & Orth); FRCS Eng. 1994. (Soton.) Specialist Regist. (Trauma & Orthop.) Bristol Higher Surg. Train. Scheme. Socs: BMA; Assoc. Mem. BOA; Brit. Trauma Soc. Prev: Hon. Research Fell. Postgrad. Med. Sch. Univ. Bath; Regist. (Orthop.) Roy. United Hosp. Bath; SHO Rotat. (Surg.) Roy. United Hosp. Bath.

BRITTEN, Mr Simon Robert Easedale House, Church Lane, Backwell, Bristol BS48 3JJ; 15 Verlands, Congresbury, Bristol BS49 5BL — MB 1974 Camb.; BChir 1973; FRCS Eng. 1978; MRCPsych. 1982. Cons. Psychiat. & Clin. Dir. (Med.) W.on Area Health Trust.

BRITTENDEN, John c/o Dr Julie Brittenden, 22 Warrender Park Road, Edinburgh EH9 1JG — MB ChB 1994 Bristol.

BRITTENDEN, Julie 1FR, 22 Warrender Park Road, Edinburgh EH9 1JG; Flat 2, 48 Skene Terrace, Aberdeen AB10 1RP — MB ChB 1988 Aberd.

BRITTLEBANK, Andrew David 1B St George Terrace, Jesmond, Newcastle upon Tyne NE2 2SU — MB BS 1983 Newc.

BRITTLIFF, Jocelyn Yorkhill NHS Trust, Glasgow G3 8SJ Tel: 0141 201 0000; 16 Coach Road, Warton, Carnforth LA5 9PR — MB ChB 1993 Leic. (Leic.) SHO (Paediat. A & E) Yorkhill NHS Trust Glas. Prev: SHO (Intens. Care) Walsgrave Hosp. Coventry; SHO (Spinal Injuries) Qu. Eliz. Nat. Spinal Injuries Unit S.. Gen. Hosp. Glas.; SHO (Trauma & Orthop.) S. Birm. Trauma Unit & Roy. Orthop. Hosp.

BRITTO, Darryl John Joseph St Luke's Hospital, Blackmoorfoot Road, Halifax HD4 5RQ Tel: 01484 343586 — MB BS 1983 Poona; MRCPsych 1991. (B.J.Medical College Poona India) Cons. Psychiat. St. Luke's Hosp. Huddersfield. Prev: Cons. Psychiat. Calderdale Healthcare NHS Trust; Cons. Pschiat. Shrops. Ment. Health NHS Trust; Sen. Regist. (Gen. Adult Psychiat.) W. Mid. RHA.

BRITTO, Mr Jonathan Anthony 15 Malmans Way, Beckenham BR3 6SA Fax: 020 8658 6819 — MB BS 1990 Lond.; BSc (1st cl. Hons.) Lond. 1987; FRCS Ed. 1994. Craniofacial Fell. Gt. Ormond St. Hosp. for Childr. Lond. Prev: Clin. Fell. (Surg.) Harvard Med. Sch. Beth Israel Hosp. Boston, Mass., USA.

BRITTO, Joseph Frederick Department of Paediatrics, St Mary's Hospital, South Wharf Road, London W2 1BL — MB BS 1986 Bombay.

BRITTON, Amanda Elizabeth Mary Hackwood Partnership, Essex House, Worting Road, Basingstoke RG21 8SU Tel: 01256 470464 Fax: 01256 357289; The Old Rectory, Sherfield-on-Loddon, Basingstoke RG27 0EX Tel: 01256 880237 Fax: 01256 883799 Email: britton@sherfield.demon.co.uk — MB ChB 1981 Birm.; MRCGP 1985; DCH RCP Lond. 1984; DRCOG 1983; MFFP. (Birmingham) Gen. Practitioner.

BRITTON, Amanda Louise The Surgery, 56 Blairderry Road, Streatham, London SW2 4SB Tel: 020 8671 3340 Fax: 020 8671 9281; 5 Prescott Close, London SW16 5LD Tel: 020 8764 3028 — BSc (Hons.) Path. Lond. 1980, MB BS 1983; DCH RCP Lond. 1989; DRCOG 1986; Cert. Family Plann. JCC 1985. (Guy's) Instruc. Doctor Family Plann. 1989. Prev: SCMO (Family Plann.) & Clin. Med. Off. (Child Health) W. Lambeth; Trainee GP Poole VTS.

BRITTON, Mr Berry Julian 23 Banbury Road, Oxford OX2 6NN Tel: 01865 515404 Fax: 01865 220659 Email: bj@britton50.fsnet.co.uk; 89 Lonsdale Road, Oxford OX2 7ET Tel: 01865 515404 Fax: 01865 220659 Email: bj@britton50.fsnet.co.uk — MB BS 1965 Lond.; MA Oxf. 1979; MS Lond. 1975; FRCS Eng. 1970. (St. Bart.) Cons. Surg. Oxf. Radcliffe Hosp. Oxf.; Sen. Clin. Lect. (Surg.) Univ. Oxf.; Fell. Green Coll. Oxf. Socs: BMA; Int. Hepato-Biliary and Pancreatic Assn.; Assn. Upper G.I. Surg. Prev: Dir. (Clin. Studies) Univ. Oxf.; Clin. Reader (Surg.) Univ. Oxf.; Sen. Regist. (Surg.) Roy. Gwent Hosp. Newport.

BRITTON, Cheryl Ann Ribblesdale House Medical Centre, Market Street, Bury BL9 0BU Tel: 0161 764 7241 Fax: 0161 763 3557; 5 Lower Cribden Avenue, Rawtenstall, Rossendale BB4 6SW — MB ChB 1982 Birm.; DRCOG 1986.

BRITTON, Mr David Clayton 32 Cleveland Walk, Bath BA2 6JU Tel: 01225 317296 Email: david.britton@ruh-swest.nhs.uk — MB BS 1965 Durh.; MS Newc. 1976; FRCS Eng. 1970. Cons. Surg. Roy. United Hosp. Bath; Mem., Ct. of Examr.s, Roy. Coll. of Surg.s of Eng. Socs: Fell. Roy. Soc. Med. (Mem. Sect. Proctol.); Brit. Soc. Gastroenterol. Prev: Sen. Regist. (Surg.) St. Mark's Hosp. Lond. & Roy. Vict. Infirm.; Newc.

BRITTON, David Edward Roger The Surgeries, Lombard Street, Newark NG24 1XG Tel: 01636 702363 Fax: 01636 613037; 31 Valley Prospect, Newark NG24 4QH Tel: 01636 702172 — MRCS Eng. LRCP Lond. 1971; MB BS Lond. 1971, BDS 1962; DObst RCOG 1973; LDS RCS Eng. 1962. (St. Bart's & Lond. Hosp.) Chairm. N. Notts. Primary Care Clin. Audit Gp.; Chairm. Newark Constituency Local Med. Comm.

BRITTON, Gillian Vaughan Woodham House, 92 Ashley Road, Walton-on-Thames KT12 1HP Tel: 01932 225472 Fax: 01932 244127 — MB BS Lond. 1971; MRCS Eng. LRCP Lond. 1970; AFOM RCP Lond. 1980. (St. Bart.) SCMO (Occupat. Health) St. Peter's Hosp. NHS Trust. Socs: Soc. Occupat. Med. Prev: Med. Off. Centr. Electr. Generat. Bd. & Marks & Spencer Ltd.; Ho. Phys. (Paediat.) St. Bart. Hosp. Lond.; Ho. Surg. Whipps Cross Hosp. Lond.

BRITTON, Ingrid 62 The Fairway, Saltburn-by-the-Sea TS12 1NG — MB BCh 1989 Wales. Regist. (Radiol.) Glas. Roy. Infirm.

BRITTON, Mr John Matthew The Old Rectory, Sherfield-on-Loddon, Basingstoke RG27 0EX — BM BCh 1979 Oxf.; BA Camb. 1976; FRCS Eng. 1983. Cons. Orthop. Surg. Basingstoke Dist. Hosp. & Lord Mayor Treloar Hosp.Alton Hants. Prev: Sen. Regist. (Orthop. Surg.) Roy. United Hosps. Bath.

BRITTON, John Newton Britton and Partners, 10 Spencer Street, Carlisle CA1 1BP Tel: 01228 29171; (Surgery), 10 Spencer St, Carlisle CA1 1BP — MB ChB 1969 Ed.; MRCP (UK) 1973; DObst RCOG 1971. (Ed.)

BRITTON, Mr John Philip St Richard's Hospital, Spitalfields Lane, Chichester PO19 4SE — MD 1990 Bristol; BSc Bristol 1977, MD 1990, MB ChB 1980; FRCS Eng. 1985. Cons. Urol. Surg. St. Richard's Hosp. Chichester. Prev: Sen. Regist. (Urol.) Guy's Hosp. Lond.; Tutor (Urol.) St. Jas. Univ. Hosp. Leeds.

BRITTON, Professor John Richard Division of Respiratory Medicine, University of Nottingham, City Hospital, Nottingham NG5 1PB Tel: 0115 840 4765 Fax: 0115 840 4771 Email: john.britton@nottingham.ac.uk — MB BS 1978 Lond.; MSc (Epidemiol.) Lond. 1988, BSc (Pharmacol.) 1975, MD 1987; FRCP Lond. 1994; MRCP (UK) 1981; MRCS Eng. LRCP Lond. 1978. Prof. (Respirat. Med.) Unit City Hosp. Nottm.

BRITTON, Juliet Anne Atkinson Morley's Hospital, Copse Hill, Wimbledon, London SW20 0NE Tel: 020 8946 7711; Great Brockhamhurst, Brockhamhurst Road, Betchworth RH3 7AP — MB BS 1976 Lond.; MRCP (UK) 1980; FRCR 1983; DMRD 1982; FRCP 2000 Edin. (St. Bart.) Cons. Neuroradiol. Atkinson Morley's Hosp. Lond.; Hon. Cons. Neuroradiol. Roy. Marsden Hosp. Sutton & Frimley Pk. Hosp. Epsom Gen. Hosp. Surrey. Prev: Sen. Regist. Nat. Hosp. & Lond. Hosp. Sick. Childr. Lond.; Sen. Regist. (Radiol.) Guy's Hosp. Lond.; Regist. (Med.) King Edwd. VII Hosp. Windsor.

BRITTON, Professor Keith Eric Department of Nuclear Medicine, St Bartholomews Hospital, West Smithfield, London EC1A 7BE Tel: 020 7601 7144 Fax: 020 7601 7149 — MB BChir Camb. 1963; MSc Lond. 1971; MD Camb. 1971, MA 1963; FRCP Lond. 1979, M

1965; MRCS Eng. LRCP Lond. 1963; FRCR 1993. (Middlx.) Prof. Nuclear Med. St. Barts & Roy. Lond. Sch. Med. & Dent. Qu. Mary W.field Univ. Lond.; Cons. Phys. & Phys. i/c Nuclear Med. St. Bart. Hosp. Lond.; Hon. Dir. CRUK Nuclear Med. Gp.; Hon. Cons. Nuclear Med. St. Marks Hosp.; Technical Asst. Expert Internat. Atomic Energy Agency; Sen. Edr. World J. Nuclear Med.; Ex-Chairm. CoOperat. Sc. & Tech. COST B2 Europ. Community; Ex- Vis. Prof. Univ. Naples. Socs: (Ex-Pres.) Soc. Nuclear Med. Europe; (Ex-Pres.) Brit. Nuclear Med. Soc.; (Ex-Chairperson Europe Comm.) Europ. Assn. Nuclear Med. Prev: Sen Lect. Hon. Cons. Nuclear Med., Middlx. Hosp., Lond. 1973-1976.

BRITTON, Mark Gordon The Mews, Runnymede Hospital, Chertsey KT16 0RQ Tel: 01932 877824 Fax: 01932 877825; Woodham House, 92 Ashley Road, Walton-on-Thames KT12 1HP Tel: 01932 225472 Fax: 01932 244127 Email: markbritt@aol.com — MB BS Lond. 1970; MSc Lond. 1981, MD Lond. 1982; FRCP Lond. 1990; MRCP (UK) 1974; MRCS Eng. LRCP Lond. 1970; DIH Lond. 1981. (St. Bart.) Cons. Phys. St. Peter's Hosp. Chertsey (Respirat. Med.); Chairm. Brit. Lung Foundat.; Hon. Cons. King Edwd. VII Hosp. Offs. Lond.; Hon. Cons. & Sen. Lect. St. Geo. Hosp. Lond. Socs: Coun. Brit. Thoracic Soc.; Eur. Respirat. Soc.; Amer. Thoracic Soc. Prev: Med. Dir. St Peters Hosp. NHS Trust; Sen. Regist. (Gen. & Thoracic Med.) & Wellcome Research Fell. Roy. Lond. Hosp.; Resid. Med. Off. King Edwd. VII Hosp. Offs. Lond.

BRITTON, Mary Elizabeth Academic Unit Diabetes & Endocrinology, Whittington Hospital, London N8; 7 Glasslyn Road, Crouch End, London N8 8RJ — MB ChB 1981 Glas.; BSc (Hons.) Glas. 1978; MRCP (UK) 1986. Research Regist. (Diabetes) Whittington Hosp. Lond.

BRITTON, Michael John Headlands Surgery, 20 Headlands, Kettering NN15 7HP Tel: 01536 518886 Fax: 01536 415385; 35 West Furlong, Kettering NN15 7LF Tel: 01536 2746 — MB BS 1967 Lond.; MRCS Eng. LRCP Lond. 1967; DObst RCOG 1969. (Lond. Hosp.) Clin. Asst. Skin Dept. Kettering Gen. Hosp. Socs: BMA. Prev: SHO (Obst.) St. Margt.'s Hosp. Epping; SHO (Paediat.) P.ss Alexandra Hosp. Harlow.

BRITTON, Nancy Ramsay 139 Brampton Road, Carlisle CA3 9AX — MB ChB 1969 Ed.; DObst RCOG 1972; DA Eng. 1971.

BRITTON, Mr Peter Damian Department of Radiology, Addenbrookes Hospital, Hills Road, Cambridge CB2 2QQ Tel: 01223 245151 Fax: 01223 217866 Email: peter.britten@msexc.addenbrookes.anglox.nhs.uk — MB BS 1980 Lond.; FRCS Glas. 1985; FRCR 1988. Cons. Radiol. Addenbrooke's Hosp. Camb.; Dir. of Camb. & Huntingdon BrE. Screening Serv. Socs: Brit. Inst. Radiol.; Fell. Roy. Coll. Radiologists; Roy. Coll. Radiol. BrE. Gp. Prev: Sen. Regist. & Regist. (Radiol.) Addenbrooke's Hosp. Camb.; Regist. (Surg.) St. Bart. Hosp. Lond.

BRITTON, Priscilla Surrey Hampshire Borders NHS Trust, The Jarvis Centre, Stoughton Road, Guildford GU1 1QT Tel: 01483 782000; 3 The Crossways, Onslow Village, Guildford GU2 7QG Tel: 01483 568027 Fax: 01483 568027 Email: 101603.21@compuserve.com — BM 1981 Soton.; BM (Hons.) Soton. 1981; DCH RCP Lond. 1984. Staff Grade Paediat. Surrey Hants. Borders NHS Trust. Socs: Assoc. Mem. Roy. Coll. Paediat. & Child Health; Brit. Assn. Community Child Health.

BRITTON, Rachel Jane 78a Lyth Hill Road, Bayston Hill, Shrewsbury SY3 0EX — BM BCh 1996 Oxf.

BRITTON, Ronald Skirrow 24 Hillfield Road, London NW6 1PZ — MB BS 1956 Lond.; FRCPsych 1979, M 1971; DTM & H Eng. 1961, DPM 1963. (Univ. Coll. Hosp.) Train. Analyst Brit. Psychoanalyt. Soc. Lond. Prev: Chairm. Dept. Childr. & Parents Tavistock Clinic; Vis. Prof. (Child Psychiat.) Letterman Gen. Hosp., San Francisco, USA.

BRITTON, Sian Elen The Glenlyn Medical Centre, 115 Molesey Park Road, East Molesey KT8 0JX — MB BS 1988 Lond.; BA Oxf. 1985; MRCGP 1992; T(GP) 1992; DRCOG 1991; DCH RCP Lond. 1990. (Char. Cross & Westm.) GP. Prev: Trainee GP Kingston VTS.

BRITTON, Susan Alison Monkgate Health Centre, 31 Monkgate, York YO3 7PB Tel: 01904 630352; 4 North Parade, York YO30 7AB — MB ChB 1973 Birm.; DRCOG 1978. Clin. Med. Off. (Community Health) York; Clin. Asst. (Genitourin. Med.) Leeds & Bradford. Prev: Princip. GP Morley W. Yorks.; Regist. (Microbiol.) Gen. Infirm. Leeds; SHO (O & G) St. Lukes Hosp. Bradford.

BRITTON, Thomas Cornelius 23 Madrid Road, London SW13 9PF — MB 1983 Camb.; BChir 1982.

BRITZ, Maurice Crockham Cottage, Vanners Lane, Enborne, Newbury RG20 0LB Tel: 01635 45994 Fax: 01635 45994 — MB BS 1964 Lond.; MRCS Eng. LRCP Lond. 1962; DA Eng. 1966. (St. Bart.)

BROAD, Anna Jean 9 Davenport Drive, Brunton Park, Newcastle upon Tyne NE3 5AE — MB BS 1988 Newc.; MRCGP 1992. GP Locum; Occupat.al Med.

BROAD, Mr Charles Peter (retired) Bournemouth Nuffield Consulting Rooms, 65 Lansdown Road, Bournemouth BH1 1RN Tel: 01202 292234 Fax: 01202 294612 — MB BS Lond. 1956; FRCS Eng. 1965. Prev: Cons. Orthop. & Accid. Surg. Bournemouth & E. Dorset Hosp. Gp.

BROAD, Eileen Anna Lamboll (retired) 78 Old Dover Road, Canterbury CT1 3AY Tel: 01227 463544 — MB BS 1929 Lond.

BROAD, Gareth James The Topsham Surgery, The White House, Holman Way, Topsham, Exeter EX3 0EN Tel: 01392 874646 Fax: 01392 875261 — MB ChB 1991 Bristol.

BROAD, Gillian Avalon 13 Higher Port View, Saltash PL12 4BU — MB BS 1958 Lond.; MRCS Eng. LRCP Lond. 1958; DA Eng. 1960. (Roy. Free) Assoc. Specialist (Anaesth.) Plymouth Gen. Hosp.

BROAD, Martyn Victor John Brook Street Surgery, 7 Brook Street, Woodsetton, Dudley DY3 1AD Tel: 01902 883346 Fax: 01902 673757; 43 Sytch Lane, Wombourne, Wolverhampton WV5 0JP — MRCS Eng. LRCP Lond. 1972.

BROADBELT, Robert Peter 15 Sandy Lane, West Kirby, Wirral CH48 3HY; Central Park Medical Centre, 132-134 Liscaro Road, Wallasey — MB ChB Liverp. 1986.

BROADBENT, Alan Rex (retired) — MRCS Eng. LRCP Lond. 1956; MFPHM RCP (UK) 1986; MFOM RCP Lond. 1978; MFCM RCP (UK) 1972; DIH Eng. 1965; DPH Eng. 1964. Prev: Cons. Occupat. Phys. Worcester.

BROADBENT, Carolyn Ruth 172 Green Ridges, Headington, Oxford OX3 8LZ — MB ChB 1989 Leeds; FRCA 1995. Speicalist Regist. (Anaesths.) John Radcliffe Hosp. Oxf. Prev: Specialist Regist. (Anaesth.) Milton Keynes Hosp.; Regist. (Anaesth.) Wexham Pk. Hosp. Slough; SHO (Anaesth.) Bradford Roy. Infirm.

BROADBENT, Colin 42 Linden Avenue, Darlington DL3 8PP Tel: 01325 67546 — MB ChB St. And. 1961. (Dundee) Socs: BMA. Prev: Ho. Surg. Law Hosp. Carluke; Ho. Phys. City & Co. Hosps. York; SHO Surg. Roy. Infirm. Lancaster.

BROADBENT, Deborah Mary St Paul's Eye Unit, Royal Liverpool University Hospital, Prescot St., Liverpool L7 8XP Tel: 0151 706 2419 Fax: 0151 706 2419 Email: dbroadbent@rlbuh-tr.nwest.nhs.uk; The Studio, 25 Newburns Lane, Oxton, Prenton CH43 5SX Tel: 0151 651 1913 Fax: 0151 651 1913 — MB ChB 1976 Liverp.; DO Lond. 1981; DRCOG Lond. 1978. (Liverpool) Dir. Diabetic Retinopathy Screening Serv. Directorate of Ophth. Roy. Liverp. Univ. Hosp. Socs: MRCOphth.

BROADBENT, Jane Victoria South Bromley Hospiscare, Orpington Hospital, Sevenoaks Road, Orpington BR6 9JU Tel: 01689 605300 Fax: 01689 605303; 9 Orchard Road, Bromley BR1 2PR Tel: 020 8460 1844 — MB BS 1983 Lond. (University College London) Clin. Med. Off. S. Bromley Hospiscare.

BROADBENT, John Arthur Mark 67 Grafton Way, London W1T 6JB — MB BS 1983 Lond.; BSc (Hons.) Lond. 1980, MB BS 1983; MRCOG 1990. Lect. (O & G) & Hon. Sen. Regist. Univ. Coll. Hosp. Lond.

BROADBENT, Mark Richard Flat 3, 191 Canongate, Edinburgh EH8 8BN — MB ChB 1998 Ed.; MB ChB Ed 1998.

BROADBENT, Patricia Anne 2 Wigwam Close, Poynton, Stockport SK12 1XF — MB ChB 1987 Sheff.; MRCGP 1993; DRCOG 1992.

BROADBENT, Peter John Middlewich Road Surgery, 6 Middlewich Road, Sandbach CW11 1DL Tel: 01270 767411 Fax: 01270 759305 — MB BS 1972 Lond.

BROADBENT, Valerie Ann (retired) 32 Barton Road, Cambridge CB3 9LF Tel: 01223 62291 — MB BS 1963 Lond.; MRCP (UK) 1969; MRCS Eng. LRCP Lond. 1963; DCH Eng. 1966. Prev: Cons. Paediat. Oncol. Addenbrooke's Hosp. Camb.

BROADBENT, William Babington (retired) 6 Earlsmead, Letchworth SG6 3UE Tel: 01462 682767 — MB ChB 1967 Ed.; DObst RCOG 1970. Prev: Ho. Off. Roy. Infirm. Edin.

BROADBRIDGE, Anthony Turner (retired) Cedar Tree House, West Clandon, Guildford GU4 7UR Tel: 01483 222467 — MRCS Eng. LRCP Lond. 1948; FRCR 1986; DMRD Lond 1952. Prev: Cons. Radiol. Roy. Surrey Co. & St. Luke's Hosps. Guildford.

BROADBRIDGE, Carl Timothy John 73 University Road, Aberdeen AB24 3DR — MB ChB 1996 Aberd.

BROADBRIDGE, Richard John Martin, Wing Cdr. RAF Centre of Aviation Medicine, RAF Henlow, Henlow SG16 6DN Tel: 01462 8515 1515 Ext: 6181 Fax: 01760 814167; 44 Chestnut Avenue, Henlow SG16 6ER — MB BS 1982 Lond.; MRCGP 1990; DFFP 1994; DAvMed FOM RCP Lond. 1991; DRCOG 1987. (Middlesex hospital med school) Off. commanding Aviat. Med. Train. wing RAF centre of Aviat. Med. Socs: Roy. Aeronaut. Soc. Prev: Sen. Med. Off. RAF Coltishall.; RAF command flight Med. Off.; Sen. Med. Off. RAF Marham.

BROADER, Mr John Harvey The Surgery, Wharf Road, Gnosall, Stafford ST20 0D Tel: 01785 822220; The Surgery, Wharf Road, Gnosall, Stafford ST20 0D — MB 1964 Camb.; BChir 1963; FRCS Eng. 1970. Socs: BMA.

BROADFIELD, Emma-Jane Cully 21 Meadows Road, Sale M33 7BG — MB ChB 1995 Manch. SHO (Gen. Med.) N. Manch. Gen. Hosp. Manch.

BROADFIELD, John Brian 22 Hayne Road, Beckenham BR3 4JA Tel: 020 8650 5253 & profess. 071 274 6222 — MB BS 1967 Lond.; MRCS Eng. LRCP Lond. 1967; FFA RCS Eng. 1972; DObst RCOG 1970. (Middlx.) Cons. (Anaesth.) Kings Coll. Hosp. Lond. Prev: Beckwith-Smith Res. Fell. Dept. Anaesth. Kings Coll. Hosp. Lond.; Sen. Regist. (Anaesth.) Kings Coll. Hosp. Lond.; Hon. Cons. Toronto Gen. Hosp.

BROADHEAD, Alistair David Saltash Health Centre, Callington Road, Saltash PL12 6DL Tel: 01752 842281 Fax: 01752 844651; East Beira, Pillaton, Saltash PL12 6QS — MB BS 1982 Lond.; MRCGP 1988. (Char. Cross) GP Saltash. Prev: SHO (O & G) Plymouth HA & Freedom Fields Hosp. Plymouth; Trainee GP Plymouth VTS; SHO (Med. Rotat.) Gwynedd HA.

BROADHEAD, Jeremy Charles The Priory Hospital Hayes Grove, Prestons Rd, Hayes, Bromley BR2 7AS Tel: 0208 462 7722 Fax: 0208 462 5028 Email: jeremybroadhead@compuserve.com — MB BS 1983 Lond.; MPhil. Lond. 1990; MA Oxf. 1980; MRCPsych 1988. (Univ. Oxf. & Middlx. Hosp. Lond.) Staff Cons. Psychiat. The Priory Hosp. Hayes Gr.; Hon. Sen. Lect. Inst. Psychiat. Lond. Prev: Serv. Clin. Director, Waitermata Ment. Health Servs.; New Zealand Cons. Psychiat. Bethlem & Maudsley NHS Trust; Lond. Sen. Regist. (Psychiat.) Maudsley Hosp. Lond.

BROADHEAD, Michael William 59A Tollington Park, London N4 3QW — MB BS 1992 Lond.

BROADHEAD, Robert Lumb The Secret Gardens, Marsh Green, Edenbridge TN8 5PP — MB BS 1970 Lond.; FRCP Lond. 1988; MRCP (UK) 1974; MRCS Eng. LRCP Lond. 1970; DTM & H Liverp. 1972; DCH Glas. 1972; DRCOG 1973. (Middlx.) Sen. Lect. (Paediat.) Univ. Liverp.; Sen. Lect. (Trop. Paediat.) Liverp. Sch. Trop. Med.; Hon. Cons. Alder Hey Childr. Hosp. Liverp.

BROADHEAD, Timothy John 17 Kingsbridge Way, Beeston, Nottingham NG9 3LW Tel: 0115 922 0937 — MB ChB 1989 Leeds; MRCOG 1995. Specialist Regist. (O & G), Qu.s Med. Centre, Nottm.

BROADHURST, Alan Desmond Vicarage Grove, Great Barton, Bury St Edmunds IP31 2SU Tel: 01284 787288 — MB ChB 1955 Sheff.; MRCS Eng. LRCP Lond. 1955; FRCPsych 1984, M 1971; DPM Eng. 1963; M.I.Biol. 1983; F.I.Biol. 1998. (Sheff.) Clin. Teach. (Psychopharmacol.) Univ. Camb. Socs: Fell. Roy. Soc. Med.; Brit. Assn. for Psychopharmacol.; BMA. Prev: Cons. Psychiat. W. Suff. Hosp. Bury St. Edmunds; Cons. Phys. Chest Clinic Addenbrooke's Hosp. Camb.; Sen. Regist. Addenbrooke's & Fulbourn Hosps. Camb.

BROADHURST, Mr Bernard Wade (retired) Cedar House, Collingwood Road, Witham CM8 2DY Tel: 01376 512105 — MB BChir 1952 Camb.; FRCS Eng. 1960. Cons. Orthop. Surg. S.end Health Dist. Prev: Sen. Regist. (Orthop.) St. Thos. Hosp. Lond.

BROADHURST, Caroline 32 Eighth Avenue, Bridlington YO15 2NA Tel: 01262 602184 — MB ChB 1980 Leeds; MRCGP 1992; DCH RCP Lond. 1984; MRCPsych 1997. (Leeds) CMO (Psychiat.) E. Yorks. Community Nat. Health Serv. Trust. Socs: BMA & MPS; Roy. Coll. Psychiat. Prev: SHO Rotat. (Psychiat.) N. Yorks. Train. Scheme.

BROADHURST, Colette 174 Prospect Road, Scarborough YO12 7LB Tel: 01723 360178 Fax: 01723 561807; Email: benosullivan@doctors.org.uk — MB ChB 1992 Ed.; Dip Palliat Med 1998; BSc 1989; MRCGP 1996; DRCOG 1995. Gen. Practitioner, Prospect Rd. Surg., ScarBoro.

BROADHURST, Edward Ralph 77 Hornsey Lane Gardens, Highgate, London N6 5PA Tel: 020 8347 8213 Fax: 020 8341 1452 Email: ed-broadhurst@compuserve.com — BM BCh 1980 Oxf.; MA Oxf. 1984, BA 1977, BM BCh 1980; FRCP 1997; MRCP (UK) 1983; FRCPCH 1997. Cons. Paediat. Whittington Hosp. Lond.; Hon. Sen. Lect. (Paediat.) UCL. Socs: Brit. Assn. Perinatal Med. Prev: Sen. Regist. (Paediat.) Addenbrooke's Hosp. Camb.; Sen. Regist. (Paediat.) Norf. & Norwich Hosp.; Research Regist. Respirat. Unit Hosp. Sick Childr. Gt. Ormond St. Lond.

***BROADHURST, Mark Alan Charles Zingrich** 79 Spooner Road, Sheffield S10 5BL Tel: 01142 686194 Email: mark.b@dial.pipex.com — MB ChB 1997 Sheff.; BSc (Hons.) Pharmacol. & Toxicol. Lond. 1992.

BROADHURST, Paul Anthony Borders General Hospital, Melrose TD6 9BS Tel: 01896 826648 Fax: 01896 836636 Email: paul.broadhurst@borders.scot.nhs.uk — MB ChB 1983 Dundee; MD Dundee 1992; MRCP (UK) 1986; 2000 FESC; FRCP 1999. (Dundee) Cons. (Cardiol.) Bordens Gen. Hosp. Melrose & Roy. Infirm. Ed.; Cons. (Cardiol.) Murrayfield Hosp, Edin. Socs: Brit. Pacing and Electrophysiol. Gp.; Brit. Cardiac Soc. Prev: Sen. Regist. (Clin. Cardiol.) St. Bart. Hosp. Lond.

BROADHURST, Richard Joseph Douglas Daisy Villa, St Margaret's Hope, Orkney KW17 2SN Tel: 01856 831206 Fax: 01856 831663; Cools, South Ronaldsay, Orkney KW17 2AJ Tel: 01856 831429 — MB BS 1966 Lond.; MRCS Eng. LRCP Lond. 1966.

BROADHURST, Vernon (retired) Polwithen, 5 Lowenac Gardens, Camborne TR14 7EX Tel: 01209 712023 — MB ChB Manch. 1948. Prev: Regional Med. Off. DHSS.

BROADLEY, Andrew John McKenzie Magnolia Cottage, Church St., Modbury, Ivybridge PL21 0QP Tel: 01548 830504 — MB ChB 1992 Dundee; BMSc (Hons.) Dund 1989. SHO (Med.) Derriford Hosp. Plymouth.

BROADLEY, Claire Evelyn Strebor House, Birchwood Grove Road, Burgess Hill RH15 0DL — BM 1998 Soton.

BROADLEY, John Nettleton Gorsley House, Pett Bottom, Bishopsbourne, Canterbury CT4 6EH — MB BS 1966 Lond.; MRCS Eng. LRCP Lond. 1966; FFA RCS Eng. 1971. Cons. Kent & Canterbury Hosp. Prev: Sen. Regist. St. Geo. & Nat. Heart Hosps. Lond.; Regist. St. Geo. Hosp. Lond.

BROADLEY, Karen Elizabeth Royal Marsden Hospital NHS Trust, Fulham Road, London SW3 6JJ Tel: 020 7352 8171 Fax: 020 7376 5064 Email: karen.broadley@rmh.nthames.nhs.uk; 19 Scott Close, Windmill Green, Wandsworth Common, London SW18 2TG Tel: 0208 871 1055 — MB BS 1987 Lond.; FRCP (uk) 2000. (St Mary's) Cons. Palliat. Med. & Hon. Sen. Lect. Roy. Marsden Hosp. NHS Trust Lond.; Edr.ial Bd. CME Pallitive Med. Socs: Exec. Mem. Assn. Palliat. Med.; Roy. Soc. Med. Prev: Sen. Regist. (Palliat. Med.) St. Bart. Hosp. & Roy. Free Hosp. Lond.; Research Regist. (Palliat. Med.) Hammersmith Hosp. & Pembridge Unit; Regist. (Clin. Oncol.) Hammersmith Hosp.

BROADLEY, Penelope Sue Radiology Department, Sheffield Childrens Hospital, Western Bank, Sheffield S10 2TH Tel: 0114 271 7166 Fax: 0114 271 7514 — MB ChB 1986 Bristol; MRCP (UK) 1989; FRCR (UK) 1993. Cons. (Radiol. Paediat.), Sheff. Childr.'s Hosp. Prev: SHO (Gen. Med.) Torbay Hosp.

BROADLEY, Roger Malcolm Medical Centre, Church Road, Thornton-Cleveleys FY5 2TZ Tel: 01253 827231 Fax: 01253 863478; 60 Tarn Road, Thornton-Cleveleys FY5 5AX — MB ChB 1967 Liverp.; MRCGP 1973; DCH Eng. 1974; DObst RCOG 1969. (Liverp.) Prev: SHO (O & G & Paediat.) City Gen. Hosp. Stoke-on-Trent; Ho. Off. Vict. Centr. Hosp. Wallasey.

BROADLEY, Simon Andrew Neurology Department, Addenbrooke's Hospital, Hills Road, Cambridge CB2 2QQ Tel: 01223 217842 Email: sab49@medschl.cam.ac.uk; 10 Boundary Court, Rathmore Road, Cambridge CB1 7BB Tel: 01223 247770 Fax: 01223 336942 — MB ChB 1989 Manch.; BSc (Hons.) Experim. Immunol. & Oncol. Manch 1986; MRCP (UK) 1993. Clin.

Research Fell. Univ. Camb.; Specialist Regist. (Neurol.) SW Region. Prev: Regist. (Gen. Med.) Lancaster Acute Hosp. NHS Trust.

BROADWAY, James William Deptartment of Anaesthetics, Ipswich Hospital, Heath Road, Ipswich IP4 5PD Tel: 01473 702016 Fax: 01473 702643; Threefields, The St, Holbrook, Ipswich IP9 2PX Tel: 01473 327673 — MB BS 1981 Lond.; BSc (Hons.) Lond. 1979; FRCA 1989. (St. Thos.) Cons. Anaesth. Ipswich Hosp. Socs: Christ. Med. Fell.sh.; Obst. Anaesth. Assn. Prev: Sen. Regist. (Anaesth.) St. Thos. Hosp. Lond.; Med. Off. Brit. Antarctic Survey; Gen. Profess. Train. Scheme (Anaesth.) Bloomsbury HA.

BROADWAY, Peter James, Wing Cdr. RAF Med. Br. Retd. Dept Anaesthesia, North Tees General Hospital, Hardwick, Stockton-on-Tees TS16 9BG — MB BS 1979 Lond.; FFA RCS Eng. 1985. (St. Mary's Hosp. Lond.) Cons. Anaesth. N. Tees Gen. Hosp. Stockton-on-Tees. Prev: Cons. Anaesth. RAF.

BROADWAY, Shelagh Marjorie (retired) 4 Anchor Way, Pill, Bristol BS20 0JY — MRCS Eng. LRCP Lond. 1959; DCH Eng. 1965; DObst RCOG 1962.

BROADWITH, Elizabeth Anne West Herts Community Health NHS Trust, St Peters House, Bricket Road, St Albans AL1 3WZ Tel: 01727 829407; 22 Holborn Close, St Albans AL4 9YG Tel: 01727 836088 — MB ChB 1973 Liverp.; MFFP 1993; DCH Eng. 1981; DObst RCOG 1975. Head of Family Plann. Serv. (Family Plann.) W. Herts. Community NHS Trust.; Clin. Asst. (Genitourin. Med.) Mt. Vernon & Watford Hosps. NHS Trust; Clin. Med. Off. Harrow Family Plann. Serv. Prev: Clin. Med. Off. NW Herts. HA.

BROBBEL, Nicola Jane 5 East Lane Cottages, East La, Shipton by Beningbrough, York YO30 1AJ — MB ChB 1997 Sheff.

BROBERG, Gareth The Flat, 51 High Street, Princes Risborough HP27 0HE — MB ChB 1997 Stellenbosch.

BROCH, Jason Ian 16 The Fairway, Leeds LS17 7QJ — MB ChB 1997 Manch.

BROCHWICZ-LEWINSKI, Maryna Jadwiga 170 Bramhall Lane S., Bramhall, Stockport SK7 2JE — BM BCh 1992 Oxf.

BROCK, Mr Bevis Henry (retired) Willow Cottage, Burcombe, Salisbury SP2 0EJ — MB BChir 1946 Camb.; FRCS Eng. 1954; MRCS Eng. LRCP Lond. 1945. Hon. Cons. Orthop. Surg. Salisbury Hosp. Gp. Prev: Sen. Regist. (Orthop.) Guy's Hosp.

BROCK, Cathryn Susan 14 Lichfield Road, London E3 5AT — MB BS 1988 Lond.; MRCP (UK) 1992. Regist. (Gen. Med. & Med. Oncol.) Lister Hosp. Stevenage. Prev: SHO (Gen. Med.) St. Margt. Hosp. Epping; SHO (Med. Oncol.) Roy. Lond. Hosp.; SHO (Gen. Med.) Newham Gen. Hosp. Plaistow.

BROCK, Doreen Muriel The Chantry, 70 Priests Lane, Shenfield, Brentwood CM15 8BZ Tel: 01277 212388 — MB BS Lond. 1958; MRCS Eng. LRCP Lond. 1959. (Lond. Hosp.) Prev: Assoc. Specialist (Geriat.) Harold Wood Hosp.; Regist. Roy. Masonic Hosp. Lond. & King Edwd. VII Hosp. Midhurst; Med. Regist. Lond. Hosp.

BROCK, Jill Elizabeth Sebert Pine Ridge, Stanley Avenue, Bebington, Wirral CH63 5QF Tel: 0151 608 2330 — BM BCh 1962 Oxf.; MA Oxf. 1963, BM BCh 1962; FFR 1970; DMRD Eng. 1972; DMRT Eng. 1967. (Oxf. & Middlx.) Cons. Radiother. Clatterbridge Hosp. Wirral. Prev: Sen. Regist. Dept. Radiother. Clatterbridge Hosp. Wirral; Hon. Sen. Regist. Dept. Diag. Radiol. Ch.ill Hosp. Oxf.; Regist. Dept. Radiother. Ch.ill Hosp. Oxf.

BROCK, Josephine South Durham Health Care NHS Trust, Archer Street Clinic, Archer St., Darlington DL3 6LS Tel: 01325 465218 — MB BS 1963 Durh.; DCH Eng. 1966. SCMO S. Durh. Healthcare NHS Trust. Socs: Fac. Comm. Health.

BROCK, Juliet Aimee 11 Forsyth Road, Newcastle upon Tyne NE2 3DB — MB BS 1997 Newc.

BROCK, Juliet Elizabeth Claire 5 Vardens Road, London SW11 1RQ — BM BCh 1996 Oxf.

BROCK, Nicola Jane Parkside Family Practice, Green Road Surgery, 224 Wokingham Road, Reading RG6 1JT — MB ChB 1982 Sheff.; DRCOG 1984.

BROCK, Patrick John Murray (retired) 23 Luckmore Drive, Earley, Reading RG6 7RP — MB BCh 1966 Wales; FFA RCS Eng. 1972; DObst RCOG 1969. Cons. (Anaesth. Dept.) Roy. Berks. Hosp. Reading; Mem. S. W.. Anaesth. Assn. Sen. Regist. Anaesth. Dept. United Bristol Hosps; Fell. (Anaesth.) Univ. Virginia, U.S.A.

BROCK, Pauline Anne Claire 4 Stonegarth, Greystoke, Penrith CA11 0TX Tel: 017684 83303 — MB BCh 1986 Wales; MRCGP 1992; DCCH RCP Ed. 1992; MSc Newc. 1995; DFFP Ed. 1997. (Cardiff) Staff Grade (Family Plann. & Reprod. Health Care) N. Lakeland Health Care; GP Retainee Scheme Penrith. Prev: Sen. Regist. Pub. Health N. Cumbria HA; Clin. Med. Off. N. Lincs.; Trainee Paediat. Edin.

BROCK, Peter Geoffrey Wyeth Ledederle, Huntercombe Lane S., Taplow, Maidenhead SL6 0PH Tel: 01628 544951 Fax: 01628 540022; 94 St. Johns Road, Locks Heath, Southampton SO31 6NF — MB BS 1969 Lond.; BSc Lond. 1966; MRCS Eng. LRCP Lond. 1969; FFPM RCP (UK) 1989. Med. Dir. Wyeth Ledederle Taplow. Prev: Prof. Nephrol. Univ. Iowa, USA; Sen. Lect. (Primary Care) Soton.

BROCK, Raymond Sidney (retired) 17 Lawson Road, Wrexham LL12 7BA — MD 1935 Liverp.; MA Liverp. 1958, MD 1935, MB ChB 1924. Prev: Ho. Phys. David Lewis N.. Hosp. Liverp.

BROCK, Samuel Henry (retired) 40 Bramley Lane, Lightcliffe, Halifax HX3 8NS — MB ChB 1959 Ed.; FFPHM RCP (UK) 1991; MFCM 1973; DPH Lond. 1964. Prev: Dir. Pub. Health Calderdale HA.

BROCK, Susannah Joy Oncology Department, Royal South Hampshire Hospital, Southampton — BM BCh 1993 Oxf.; MRCP 1996. Specialist Regist. Clin. Oncol.

BROCK, Mr Terence Philip (retired) The Chantry, 70 Priests Lane, Shenfield, Brentwood CM15 8BZ Tel: 01277 212388 Fax: 01277 201496 — MB BS 1962 Lond.; FRCS Eng. 1969; FRCS Ed. 1968. Prev: Cons. Surg. Harold Wood Hosp. Essex.

BROCKBANK, Eleanor Clare 16 Danemere Street, Putney, London SW15 1LT Tel: 020 8788 5553 — MB ChB 1994 Manch. SHO (Genitourin. Med.), St. Thomas's Hosp., Lond. Prev: Clin. research fell. (Obst.), Roy. Free Hosp., Lond.; Med. Off. (O & G), Negelezana Hosp., S. Africa.

BROCKBANK, James The Surgery, 37 Park Road, Teddington TW11 0AU Tel: 020 8977 5481 Fax: 020 8977 7882; 15 School Road, Hampton Hill, Hampton TW12 1QL Tel: 020 8979 6184 — MB BS 1984 Lond.; BDS Lond. 1972, MB BS 1984; MRCGP 1989; FDS RCS Eng. 1976. Trainers Workshop W. Middlx. Hosp. VTS. Socs: (Exec. Comm.) Continuing Care at Home. Prev: Regist. (Faciomaxillary Surg.) N. Wales Hosps.; Trainee GP W. Middlx. Hosp. VTS Isleworth.

BROCKBANK, John Edward Thornbury Lodge, Fulwood Road, Sheffield S10 3BN — MB ChB 1991 Leic.

BROCKBANK, John Keith Priory Manor, Rayrigg Road, Windermere LA23 1EX — MRCS Eng. LRCP Lond. 1967; BA Oxf. 1964, BM BCh 1968; MRCPsych 1972; DPM Eng. 1971. (Oxf. & St. Thos.) Cons. Psychiat. Littlemore Hosp. Oxf. & Radcliffe Infirm. Oxf. Prev: Ho. Surg. Worthing Hosp.

BROCKBANK, Marie Hilda Camden & Islington Community Trust, Crowndale Health Centre, 59 Crowndale Road, London NW1 1TN Tel: 020 7530 3000 Fax: 020 7530 3044; 24 Highgate West Hill, First Floor Flat, Highgate, London N6 6NP Tel: 020 8341 3293 — MB ChB Edin. 1963; DPH Lond. 1966. (Ed.) SCMO (Community Paediat.). Socs: BMA; RCPCH; Soc. Pub. Health.

BROCKBANK, Mr Michael Jonathan Salisbury District Hospital, Odstock Road, Salisbury SP2 8BJ Tel: 01722 336262; Woodgrange Cottage, 92 Bouverie Avenue, Salisbury SP2 8DX Tel: 01722 336262 — MB BS 1980 Lond.; BSc (Biochem.) Lond. 1977, MB BS 1980; FRCS Ed. 1986; FRCS Lond. 1986. Cons. Otolaryngol. Salisbury HA. Prev: Sen. Regist. Roy. Nat. Throat, Nose & Ear Hosp., St. Geo. Hosp. & Gt. Ormond St. Hosp. Lond.; Lect. Univ. Hong Kong.

BROCKELSBY, Jeremy Charles Flat 4, 19 Lenton Road, Nottingham NG7 1DQ; Flat 19, Cavell Court, Block C21, Queens Medical Centre, Nottingham NG4 — MB BS 1994 Lond.; BSc Lond. 1989. SHO (O & G) Qu. Med. Centre Nottm.

BROCKI, Jane Louise Hope Farm Medical Centre, Hope Farm Road, Great Sutton, South Wirral CH66 2WW Tel: 0151 357 3777 Fax: 0151 357 1444; Hope Farm Medical Centre, Hope Farm Road, Great Sutton, South Wirral CH66 2WW Tel: 0151 357 3777 — MB ChB 1987 Liverp.; Cert. Family Plann. JCC 1990. Med. Off. (Palliat. Care) Chester FHSA; Med. Off. (Family Plann.) Wirral NHS Trust. Socs: NW Soc. Family Plann. and Sexual Health.

BROCKINGTON, Alice Rose 3F1/3 Cambridge Street, Edinburgh EH1 2DY — MB ChB 1997 Ed.

BROCKINGTON, Colin Fraser 44 Silverburn, Ballasalla Tel: 01624 823465 — MA (Hons.) Camb. 1928, MD 1932, BChir 1930, DPH;

(Distinc.) 1928; MRCP Lond. 1957; MRCS Eng. LRCP Lond. 1927; Hon. MSc Manch. 1955. (Guy's & Camb.) Barrister-at-Law Middle Temple; Prof. Emerit. Social & Preven. Med. Univ. Manch. Socs: Fell. Soc. Community Med. Prev: Co. MOH Warks.; Co. Med. Off. W. Riding.

BROCKINGTON, Ian Fraser Lower Brockington Farm, Bredenbury, Bromyard HR7 4TE — MB BChir 1961 Camb.; MRCP Lond. 1964.

BROCKINGTON, Jennifer Mary Highfield Day Hospital, Newcastle Road, Chester-le-Street DH3 3UD Tel: 0191 333 3762 Fax: 0191 333 3761 — MB BS 1968 Lond.; MRCS Eng. LRCP Lond. 1967; MRCPsych 1984. (Roy. Free) Cons. Psychiat. of Old Age Community Health Care N. Durh. NHS Trust. Prev: GP Gateshead FPC; Clin. Asst. (Geriat. Med.) Newc. HA (T); Regist. (Psychiat.) Newc. HA.

BROCKINGTON, Joyce Margaret (retired) 44 Silverburn Estate, Ballasalla IM9 2DT Tel: 01624 3465 — MRCS Eng. LRCP Lond. 1934; DPH Lond. 1937.

BROCKLEBANK, Anna-Marie Nicholson Heroncroft, Southdown Road, Woldingham, Caterham CR3 7DP — BM 1977 Soton.

BROCKLEBANK, David Mark 8 Birchwood Road, Malvern WR14 1LD Tel: 01886 832647 — MB ChB 1992 Liverp.; MRCP (UK) 1995. Regist. The Hillingdon Hosp. Middlx. Prev: SHO S.port & Formby NHS Trust; SHO Kidderminster NHS Trust; Ho. Off. S.port & Formby NHS Trust.

BROCKLEBANK, John Trevor St James University Hospital, Leeds LS9 7TF Tel: 0113 243 3144; 5 Woodbourne, Pk Avenue, Leeds LS8 2JW Tel: 0113 265 3592 — MB BS 1962 Durh.; FRCP Ed. 1984; FRCP Lond. 1982; MRCP (UK) 1972. Sen. Lect. & Cons. Paediat. Leeds Univ.

BROCKLEBANK, Maureen Cecilia Silecroft, Princess Road, Lostock, Bolton BL6 4DS — MB BS 1963 Lond.; DObst RCOG 1965. (St. Thos.) SCMO (Family Plann.) Rochdale. Socs: Fac. Community Health; Fac. Family Plann.; Inst. Psychosexual Med.

BROCKLEHURST, Mr Gordon Neurosurgical Service, Royal Infirmary, Hull HU3 2JZ Tel: 01482 28541 Ext: 4359 — MB BChir 1956 Camb.; MD Camb. 1981, M Chir 1968 MB BChir 1956; FRCS Eng. 1962. (Guy's) Cons. Neurosurg. Humberside AHA. Prev: Asst. Prof. Neurosurg. Univ. Kentucky Kentucky Lexington, U.S.A.; Sen. Regist. (Neurosurg.) Lond. Hosp.; Elmore Research Stud. Camb. Univ.

BROCKLEHURST, Ian Christopher 4 Higher Lydgate Park, Grasscroft, Oldham OL4 4EF — BM BS 1985 Nottm.; B Med. Sci. (Hons.) 1983; FRCA 1993. Cons. Anaesth. Oldham NHS Trust. Socs: BMA; Assn. Anaesth.; Obst. Anaesth. Assn. Prev: Sen. Regist. (Anaesth.) N. W.. RHA; Regist. (Anaesth.) N. W.. RHA; SHO (Anaesth.) Roy. Preston Hosp.

BROCKLEHURST, Professor John Charles, CBE (retired) 59 Stanneylands Road, Wilmslow SK9 4EX — MB ChB Glas. 1947; MSc Manch. 1974; MD (Hons. & Bellahouston Gold Medal) Glas. 1950; FRCP Lond. 1984; FRCP Glas. 1972, M 1962; FRCP Ed. 1970, M 1961; FRFPS 1960. Prev: Assoc. Dir. Research Unit Roy. Coll. Phys. Lond.

BROCKLEHURST, John Richard Liquorpond Street Surgery, 10 Liquorpond Street, Boston PE21 8UE Tel: 01205 362763 Fax: 01205 358918; 10 Liquor Pond Street, Boston PE21 8UE Tel: 01205 62763 — MB BS 1972 Lond.; DCH Lond. 1974. GP Boston Lincs. Prev: SHO Roy. Manch. Childr. Hosp.; Regist. (Paediat.) P. of Wales Hosp. Sydney, Australia; Regist. (Paediat.) Darwin Hosp. N.T., Australia.

BROCKLEHURST, Mary Yvonne 15 Fairway Drive, Rowany, Port Erin IM9 6LR Tel: 01624 835341 — MB ChB 1974 Glas.

BROCKLEHURST, Peter National Perinatal Epidemiology Unit, Institute of Health Sciences, Old Road, Oxford OX3 7LF Tel: 01865 227000 Fax: 01865 227002 Email: peter.brocklehurst@perinat.ox.ac.uk — MB ChB 1985 Dundee; MSc (Epidemiol.) Lond. 1994; MRCOG 1991. Cons. Clin. Epidemiol. (Perinatal Epidemiol.) Nat. Perinatal Epidemiol. Inst. Of Health Sci.s.

BROCKLESBY, Katherine Jane The Old Station, 18 Station Road, East Leake, Loughborough LE12 6LQ — MB BS 1996 Lond.

BROCKLESBY, Sonia Jane 47 Woodberry Crescent, London N10 1PJ — MB BS 1991 Lond.

BROCKLESS, Julian Brian Paul Slough Child and Adolescent Mental Health Service, Fir Tree House, Upton Hospital, Albert St., Slough SL1 2BJ Tel: 01753 635645; Paediatric Department, Wexham Park Hospital, Slough Tel: 01753 633000 — MB ChB 1977 Bristol; BSc Bristol 1974; MRCPsych 1981. Cons. Child & Adolesc. Psychiat. Wexham Pk. Hosp. Slough & Slough Child & Family Guid. Clinic.; Vis. Psychiat. Roy. Holloway Coll. Prev: Sen. Regist. (Child & Adolesc. Psychiat.) St. Thos. & Guy's Hosps.; Regist. (Psychiat.) St. Bart. Hosp. Lond.

BROCKMAN, Barbara Joyce Fair Oak Service, St James Hospital, Locksway Road, Portsmouth Tel: 023 92 822444 Fax: 023 92 829980 — MB ChB 1977 Bristol; FRCPsych 1998; MMedSc (Ethics) Birm. 1997; MRCPsych. 1983; DCH Eng. 1979. (Bristol) Cons. Forens. Psychiat. St James Hosp. Prev: Cons. Forens. Psychiat. Reaside Clinic.

BROCKSMITH, Debra MRC Unit, Hodgkin Building, University of Leicester, Leicester LE1 9HN — MB ChB 1992 Leic.; BSc Leic. 1990, MB ChB 1992. MRC Research Fell. Toxicol. Unit. Leicester Univ.

BROCKSOM, Lindsey Alison Sunneydene, High St., Milverton, Taunton TA4 1LL — BM BS 1992 Nottm.

BROCKWAY, Benedict Derek James 21 Springvale Road, Kings Worthy, Winchester SO23 7LT Tel: 01962 881749 — MB BS 1996 Lond.; BSc (Hons.) Lond. 1995. (Royal Free Hospital School of Medicine) SHO (Gen. Med.); Clin. Asst. (A & E). Prev: SHO (A & E).

BROCKWAY, Claire Marie Farthings, Firbank Drive, St Johns, Woking GU21 1QT — MB BS 1991 Lond.; MRCP (UK) 1997. (King's Coll. Hosp.)

BROCKWAY, Michael Stanley Culag, Edinburgh Road, Linlithgow EH49 6AA — MB ChB 1983 Aberd.

BROD, Jan Leonard 94 Northumberland Road, Leamington Spa CV32 6HG — MB ChB 1991 Birm.; ChB Birm. 1991.

BRODBELT, Mr Andrew Robert Walton Centre for Neurology & Neurosurgery, Rice Lane, Walton, Liverpool L9 1AE Tel: 0151 525 3611 Fax: 0151 529 4772 Email: brodbe-a@wcnn.co.uk — MB ChB 1991 Liverp.; BSc (Hons.) Liverp. 1988; FRCS Ed. 1996. Specialist Regist. (Neurosurg.) Walton Centre for Neurol. & Neurosurg. Liverp. Prev: SHO (Neurosurg.) Walton Centre for Neurol. & Neurosurg. Liverp.

BRODBIN, Cornelius Commonfield Road Surgery, 156 Commonfield Road, Woodchurch, Birkenhead CH49 7LP Tel: 0151 677 0016; 156 Commonfield Road, Woodchurch, Wirral CH49 7LP — MB ChB 1980 Liverp.; DRCOG 1982.

BRODERICK, Mary Martina (Moira) Alfreton Clinic, Grange St., Alfreton DE55 7JA Tel: 01773 833219; 22 Goodsmoor Road, Littleover, Derby DE23 7NH — MB BCh BAO 1979 NUI; DCH RCP Lond. 1992. Assoc. Specialist Child Health (Physical Disabil.) S. Derbysh. HA. Prev: Clin. Med. Off. (Comm. Child Health) Derby; SHO (Paediat.) Good Hope Hosp. Sutton Coldfield; SHO (Anaesth.) Derbysh. Roy. Infirm.

BRODERICK, Nigel John Department of Radiology, Nottingham City Hospital, Hucknall Road, Nottingham NG5 1PB Tel: 0115 969 1169 Fax: 0115 962 7776; 66 Hallfields, Edwalton, Nottingham NG12 4AA — BM BS 1979 Nottm.; BMedSci Nottm. 1977; MRCP (UK) 1982; FRCR 1985. Cons. Paediatric Radiologist Nottm. City Hosp. and Qu.s Med. Centre Nottm. Prev: Fell. (paediat. Radiol.) Indiana Univ. USA; Sen. Regist. (Radiol.) Univ. Hosp. Wales Cardiff.; SHO (Gen. Med.) Univ. Hosp. Wales Cardiff.

BRODIE, Adam Freeman The Pines, 48 Southburn Rd, Blanefield, Glasgow G63 9DB — MB ChB 1997 Glas.

BRODIE, Carol Agnes The Old Rectory, Scaleby, Carlisle CA6 4LJ — MB ChB 1986 Ed.

BRODIE, Catriona Jenner Health Centre, 201 Stanstead Road, London SE23 1HU Tel: 020 8690 2231 — MB ChB 1983 Glas. GP VTS St. Thos. Hosp. Lond.

BRODIE, Dallas John Carswell House, 5 Oakley Terrace, Glasgow G31 2HX Tel: 0141 554 6267 Fax: 0141 556 6967 — MB ChB 1979 Glas.; MRCPsych 1984. Cons. Psychiat. Pk.head. Hosp. Glas.

BRODIE, David Anthony Nuffield Road Medical Centre, Nuffield Road, Chesterton, Cambridge CB4 1GL Tel: 01223 423424 Fax: 01223 566450 — MB ChB 1964 Otago; MRCGP 1988.

BRODIE, David Byron 17 Rivelin Park Crescent, Sheffield S6 5GF — MB ChB 1994 Leeds.

BRODIE, David George Market Street Medical Centre, 112-114 Market Street, Hindley, Wigan WN2 3AZ Tel: 01942 256221 Fax: 01942 522479 — MB ChB 1984 Manch.

BRODIE, David Paul 48 Orchard Road, Seer Green, Beaconsfield HP9 2XU — MB BS 1974 Lond.; MRCS Eng. LRCP Lond. 1974; DRCOG 1976.

BRODIE, Gabrielle Diana 29 High Street, Chesterton, Cambridge CB4 1NQ — MB ChB 1996 Sheff.

BRODIE, Graham Thornbrook Surgery, Thornbrook Road, Chapel-en-le-Frith, Stockport SK23 0RH Tel: 01298 812725 Fax: 01298 816221; 3 Rowton Grange Road, Chapel-en-le-Frith, High Peak SK23 0LA — MB BS 1973 Newc.; MRCGP 1978; DRCOG 1976. Prev: Trainee GP E. Cumbria VTS; Med. Off. Zambian Flying Doctor Serv.; SHO (O & G) Hexham Gen. Hosp.

BRODIE, Jack Edward (retired) 83 Clifton Avenue, Hartlepool TS26 9QP Tel: 01429 273776 — MB ChB Glas. 1944. Prev: Ho. Phys. S.. Gen. Hosp. Glas.

BRODIE, Jo-Anne Beth 34 Manor Road, South Hinksey OX1 5AS — MB ChB 1997 Liverp.

BRODIE, Joan Elizabeth Tillicoultry Health Centre, Park Street, Tillicoultry FK13 6AG Tel: 01259 750531 Fax: 01259 752818 — MB ChB 1986 Aberd.

BRODIE, Kanthini Willow, St Georges Hospital, 117 Suttons Lane, Hornchurch RM12 6RS; 13 The Dell, Great Warley, Brentwood CM13 3AL — MB BS 1986 Colombo; MRCP (UK) 1991; FRCPCH 1997; DCH RCPS Glas. 1991. Cons. Community Paediat. Barking, Havering & Brentwood Community Care NHS Trust. Prev: Sen. Regist. (Paediat.) Haringey Health Care NHS Trust Tottenham.

BRODIE, Katharine McEwen (retired) Tigh-na-Lochan, Beith KA15 2HX Tel: 01505 502992 — MB ChB Aberd. 1949. Prev: GP Beith.

BRODIE, Professor Martin Jeffrey Epilepsy Unit, University Department of Medicine & Therapeutics, Western Infirmary, Glasgow G11 6NT Tel: 0141 211 2572 Fax: 0141 334 9329 Email: martin.j.brodie@clinmed.gla.ac.uk; 48 Southburn Road, Blanefield, Glasgow G63 9DB Tel: 01360 770747 Fax: 01360 770747 Email: mbrodieeu@aol.com — MB ChB 1971 Glas.; MD Glas. 1977; FRCP Ed. 1991; FRCP Glas. 1985; MRCP (UK) 1973. (Univ. Glas.) Cons. Clin. Pharmacol. Univ Med. Dept. W.. Infirm. Glas.; Dir. Epilepsy Epilepsy Unit & Hon. Prof. Med. & Clin. Pharmacol. Univ. Glas.; Chairm. Gtr. Glas. Drug & Therap. Comm.; Chairm. W. Scotl. Epilepsy Research Gp. Socs: Assn. Phys.; Internat. League against Epilepsy; Amer. Epilepsy Soc. Prev: Lect. (Clin. Pharm.) Roy. Postgrad. Med. Sch. Lond.; Lect. (Mat. Med.) Univ. Glas.

BRODIE, Norman Harry, RD (retired) Great Maytham Hall, Rolvenden, Cranbrook TN17 4NE Tel: 01580 240830 — MB ChB 1952 Liverp. Prev: Surg. Cdr. RNR, Sen. Med. Off. Sussex Div. RNR.

BRODIE, Robert Health Centre, Thornhill DG3 5AA Tel: 01848 330208 Fax: 01848 330223; Kilchattan, Corstorphine Road, Thornhill DG3 5NB — MB ChB 1973 Glas.; DObst RCOG 1975. (Glasgow) GP Princip.

BRODIE, Mr Stuart Watson Pinewood, Picton Avenue, Bridgend CF31 3HD Tel: 01656 652010 — MB ChB 1970 Glas.; FRCS Glas. 1975. Cons. Otolaryngol. BRD Morganning NHS Trust Bridgend. Prev: Cons. Otolaryng. Highland HB.

BRODIE, Timothy Robert Colin 57 Riverside Gardens, Romsey SO51 8HN — MB BChir 1957 Camb.; MRCS Eng. LRCP Lond. 1957.

BRODIE, Valerie Anne Community HQ, Retford Hospital, North Road, Retford DN22 7XF Tel: 01777 705261; The Old Barn, Top St, Askham, Newark NG22 0RP Tel: 01777 838881 — MB ChB Ed. 1969; BSc (Med. Sci.) Ed. 1966; DFFP 1993; Dip. Community Paediat. Sheff. 1990. (Ed.) Clin. Med. Off. (Family Plann. & Child Health) Bassetlaw Trust. Socs: BMA.

BRODIE, Mr William (retired) Sherstone, West St., Fontmell Magna, Shaftesbury SP7 0PF Tel: 01747 811292 — MB ChB Glas. 1946; FRCS Glas. 1962; FRFPS Glas. 1956. Prev: Sen. Orthop. Cons. Saudi Arabia Nat. Guard Hosp., Jeddah.

BRODIE-FRASER, Fiona 5 The Maltings, West Felton, Oswestry SY11 4EL — MB BS 1990 Lond.; MRCGP 1996; DCH RCP Lond. 1994. (Roy. Free Hosp. Sch. Med.)

BRODISON, Adrian Mervyn 17 Agharan Road, Dungannon BT71 4HF — MB ChB 1990 Manch.; MRCP (UK) 1993.

BRODRIBB, Mr Arthur John Masterman Devriford Hospital, Devriford Road, Plymouth PL6 8DH Tel: 01752 700200 — MRCS Eng. LRCP Lond. 1966; BSc Lond. 1963, MS 1978, MB BS 1966; FRCS Eng. 1972. (St. Bart.) Cons. Gen. Surg. Plymouth Gen. Hosp. Prev: Sen. Regist. Gen. Surg. Radcliffe Infirm. Oxf.; Ho. Surg. St. Bart. Hosp. Lond.

BRODRIBB, John Harry George (retired) 3 Sutton Avenue, Seaford BN25 4LA Tel: 01323 891037 — MB ChB 1940 Leeds; FRCP Ed. 1971, M 1961; FRCR 1975; FFR 1958; DMRD Eng. 1955. Prev: Lt.-Col. RAMC.

BRODRIBB, Peter Francis The Abbey Practice, The Family Health Centre, Stepgates, Chertsey KT16 8HZ Tel: 01932 561199 Fax: 01932 571842; 14 Fletcher Close, Ottershaw, Chertsey KT16 0JT — MB BS 1970 Lond.; MRCP (UK) 1975; MRCS Eng. LRCP Lond. 1970; DCH Eng. 1973; DObst RCOG 1972. (St. Bart.) Prev: Regist. (Paediat.) St. Helier Hosp. Carshalton; Ho. Surg. (Obst.) Redhill Gen. Hosp.; SHO (Paediat.) Qu. Eliz. Hosp. Sick Childr. Lond.

BRODRICK, Peter Matthew Mount Vernon Hospital, Rickmansworth Road, Northwood HA6 2RN Tel: 01923 826111 Fax: 01923 844626; Rowan House, Manor Rd, Penn, High Wycombe HP10 8HY Tel: 01494 816171 Email: peter@mbrodrick.freeserve.co.uk — MB BS 1980 Lond.; MRCS Eng. LRCP Lond. 1979; FFA RCS Eng. 1983. (Char. Cross) Cons. Anaesth. Mt. Vernon Hosp. Lond.; Hon. Cons. Paul Strickland Scanner Centre. Socs: Assn. Anaesth.; BMA; Plastic Surg. & Burns Anaesth. Assn. Prev: Sen. Regist. (Anaesth.) Middlx. Hosp. Lond.; Research Fell. (Anaesth.) Nat. Hosp. for Nerv. Dis. Lond.; Regist. (Anaesth.) Roy. Surrey Co. Hosp. Guildford.

BRODRICK-WEBB, Catherine Ann Little Orchard, Lakewood Close, Chandler's Ford, Eastleigh SO53 1EY — BM BS 1993 Nottm.

BROGAN, Catherine Mary O'Connell Director of Public Health and Health Policy, Brent and Harrow Health Authority, Grace House, Harrovian Business Village, Bessborough Road, Harrow HA1 3EX Tel: 020 8966 1045 Fax: 020 8426 8646 Email: catherine.brogan@hbv.bah-ha.nthames.nhs.uk; Westlington Farm, Dinton, Aylesbury HP17 8UL Tel: 01296 748069 Fax: 01296 748069 — MB BS 1974 Lond.; MSc (Pub. Health Med.) Lond. 1992; MFPHM RCP (UK) 1994; FFAEM FFPHM RCP (UK) 2000. (The London Hospital Medical School) Director of Pub. Health and Health Policy Brent and Harrow Health Auth. Socs: Action for Safe Motherhood (UK). Prev: Cons. Pub. Health Med. NHS Exec Anglia & Oxf.; Sen. Regist. (Pub. Health Med.) Bucks. HA; Dir. Mother & Child Health Progr. Sultanate of Oman.

BROGAN, Denis Paul Queens Road, Earls Colne, Colchester CO6 2RR Tel: 01787 222022; The Cottage, Goulds Road, Alphamstone, Bures CO8 5HP Tel: 01787 269636 — MB BS 1972 Lond.; BSc Lond. 1969; DObst RCOG 1975. (Lond. Hosp.) Socs: Colchester Med. Soc. & BMA. Prev: Ho. Phys. & Ho. Surg. Lond. Hosp.; Trainee GP Colchester VTS.

BROGAN, Edward Brogan and Partners, The O'Connel Street Medical Centre, 6 O'Connell Street, Hawick TD9 9HU Tel: 01450 372276 Fax: 01450 371564; Blinkbonny, Hawick TD9 7HS Tel: 01450 78029 — MB ChB 1966 Ed.; DObst RCOG 1970. (Ed.) Clin. Lect. (Gen. Pract.) Univ. Edin. Socs: Ed. Obst. Soc. & BMA.

BROGAN, Kevin Bosco Mary 18 Thorville Park, Omagh BT78 5HQ — MB BCh BAO 1978 Belf.

BROGAN, Paul Anthony 24A South Villas, London NW1 9BT — MB ChB 1993 Manch.

BROGAN, Robert Timmons Greater Glasgow Health Board, Dalian House, PO Box 15327, 350 St Vincent St., Glasgow G3 8YU Tel: 0141 201 4952 Fax: 0141 201 4949 — MB ChB 1984 Ed.; MRCPsych 2000; MFPHM 1993 RCP (UK); MPH Glas. 1991; MRCGP 1990; DA (UK) 1986. SPR General Psychiatry; Hon. Senior Lecturer Public Health Glasgow University. Socs: BMA; MDDUS.

BROGAN, Thomas Daniel (retired) Moor Head, 34 Park Road, Disley, Stockport SK12 2LX Tel: 01663 762417 Fax: 01663 762417 Email: tbrogan1@compuserve.com — MB BS 1959 Lond.; PhD Lond. 1953, BSc 1945, MD 1966; FRCPath 1977. Prev: Cons. Path. (Microbiol.) Stockport HA.

BROGAN, Vincent Mary 6 Woodmansterne Road, Coulsdon CR5 2DD Tel: 020 8680 0350 Fax: 020 8680 0350; 22 Fernhurst Road, Croydon CR0 7DG — MB BCh BAO 1980 NUI; MRCOphth 1991; DCH RCSI 1989; DO RCSI 1989. Indep. GP Croydon.

BROGDEN, Paul Richard Burton Croft Surgery, 5 Burton Crescent, Leeds LS6 4DN Tel: 0113 274 4777 Fax: 0113 230 4219 — MB ChB 1988 Leeds.

BROHAN, Elizabeth 82 Lickhill Road N., Stourport-on-Severn DY13 8RU — MB ChB 1997 Liverp.

BROHI, Abdul Qayoom The Surgery, 60 Leytonstone Road, London E15 1SQ Tel: 020 8534 1533 Fax: 020 8534 4283 — MB BS 1963 Sind; MB BS 1963 Sind.

BROHI, Ali Hassan Karimbux The Broadway Surgery, 3 Broadway Gardens, Monkhams Avenue, Woodford Green IG8 0HF Tel: 020 8491 3344 Fax: 020 8491 0116; Little Ferns, 26 Linden Crescent, Woodford Green IG8 0DG Tel: 020 8504 2234 — MB BS 1954 Karachi; LRCP LRCS Ed. LRFPS Glas. 1959. (Dow Med. Coll. Karachi)

BROHI, Karim Hassan Trauma Unit, Royal London Hospital, Whitechapel, London E1 1BB Tel: 020 7247 6722 Email: karim@trauma.org; 72 Ladbroke Grove, Notting Hill, London W11 2HF Tel: 020 7727 1597 — MB BS 1991 Lond.; BSc (1st cl. Hons.) Computer Science 1988; FRCS 1996; FRCA 1996. Hon. Lect. (Trauma & Critical Care) Roy. Lond. Hosp. Socs: Roy. Soc. Med.; Amer. Aerospace Med. Assoc.; Eur. Assn. Trauma & Emerg. Surg. Prev: Sen. Regist. (Trauma) Groote Scowur Hosp. Cape Town S. Africa.

BROKATE, Anja Southmead Hospital, Westbury-on-Trym, Bristol BS10 5NB — State Exam Med. Berlin 1991.

BROLLY, Thomas Brian 5A Rathcoole Close, Newtownabbey BT37 9AP — MB BCh BAO 1970 Belf.

BROMAGE, Mr James David Kettering General Hospital, Rothwell Road, Kettering NN16 8UZ; Frithsden House, 5 Station Road, Gretton, Corby NN17 3BU — MB BS 1973 Lond.; FRCS Eng. 1979; FRCS Ed. 1979. (St. Mary's) Cons. (Orthop.) Kettering Gen. Hosp. Prev: Lect. (Anat.) Univ. Lond.; Sen. Regist. (Orthop.) Char. Cross Hosp. Lond.; Regist. (Orthop.) St. Mary's Hosp. Lond.

BROMAGE, Mary-Clare Catherine 32 Wilton Square, Islington, London N1 3DW Tel: 020 7226 0395; 101 West 81st Street, New York NY 10024, USA Tel: 212 724 3307 — MB ChB 1986 Bristol. Prev: Hon. Paediat. Fell. Cornell Med. Centre New York Hosp., USA; SHO (Paediat.) W.m. Childr. Hosp. & King's Coll. Hosp. Lond.; Clin. Med. Off. (Paediat.) Bloomsbury & Islington HA.

BROMAN, Sidney Merton (retired) 2 Oakfield, Prestwich, Manchester M25 0DP Tel: 0161 740 2772 — MB ChB 1950 Manch. Prev: Capt. RAMC.

BROMBACHER, Jochen Hans-Peter Department of Anaesthesia, Leicester Royal Infirmary, Infirmary Square, Leicester LE1 5WW — State Exam Med 1993 Berlin.

BROMHAM, Belinda 7 Westbury Park, Durdham Down, Bristol BS6 7JB Tel: 0117 973 4180 — MB BS 1957 Lond.; DObst RCOG 1961. (Middlx.) Sen. Clin. Med. Off. United Bristol Healthcare Trust. Prev: SCMO Brook Advis. Centre Bristol; Med. Off. Family Plann. Assn. High Wycombe; Asst. Sch. Med. Off. Berks. CC.

BROMHAM, Beryl Mary (retired) Haigh End, Alne Cross, York YO61 1SD Tel: 0134 73 312 — MB BCh BAO 1953 Belf.; MRCPsych 1972; DPM Leeds 1967; DObst RCOG 1955. Mem. Brit. Jl. Psychiat. Prev: Cons. Gen. & Geriat. Psychiat. Clifton Hosp. York.

BROMHAM, Catherine Elizabeth Flat 2, 31-32 Ford Square, London E1 2HS — MB BS 1997 Lond.

BROMHAM, Jennifer Anne 9 Rockhill Drive, Mountsorrel, Loughborough LE12 7DS — MB BS 1988 Lond.

BROMHEAD, Helen Jane 45 Rockstone Lane, Southampton SO14 6HZ — BM BS 1990 Nottm.; FRCA 1998. Specialist Regist. (Anaesth.) Wessex Rotat.

BROMIGE, Robert Michael Compass House Medical Centres, King Street, Brixham TQ5 9TF Tel: 01803 855897 Fax: 01803 855613 — MB BS 1986 Lond.; MRCP (UK) 1990; MRCGP 1994; DA (UK) 1991. (Char. Cross Hosp. Med. Sch.) GP Princip. Prev: Trainee GP Totnes, Devon; Regist. (Med.) Freemantle Hosp., W.. Austral.; SHO (O & G) S.lands Hosp. Shoreham-by-Sea.

BROMILOW, Andrew 11 Marine Terrace, Liverpool L22 5PR — MB ChB 1977 Liverp.

BROMILOW, James Edward 60 St Andrews Road, Henley-on-Thames RG9 1JD — BM 1996 Soton.

BROMLEY, A B Whittaker Lane Medical Centre, Whittaker lane, Prestwich, Manchester M25 5EX Tel: 0161 773 1580.

BROMLEY, Bernard John The Health Centre, 35 Monkgate, York YO3 7PB Tel: 01904 626234 Fax: 01904 671699; 29 Chestnut Avenue, York YO31 1BR Tel: 01904 626234 — MB BS Lond. 1969; MRCS Eng. LRCP Lond. 1969; DObst RCOG 1972. (Lond. Hosp.)

BROMLEY, Carolyn Louise The Glen, Victoria Hill Road, Fleet GU13 8LG — MB ChB 1996 Cape Town.

BROMLEY, Mr Christopher Leonard Gordon 34 Croeswylan Crescent, Oswestry SY10 9PP — MB ChB 1970 Glas.; FRCS Eng. 1978; FRCS Ed. 1976.

BROMLEY, Elizabeth Juliet Teresa 2 Glastonbury Avenue, Hale, Altrincham WA15 8QB — MB BS 1994 Lond.

BROMLEY, Joanna Siobhan 91 The Avenue, Stoke-on-Trent ST4 6BY — BM BS 1994 Nottm.

BROMLEY, Jonathan 16 Montrose Avenue, Bristol BS6 6EQ — MB ChB 1998 Bristol.

BROMLEY, Mr Lance Lee 26 Molyneux Street, London W1H 5HW — MB BChir 1944 Camb.; FRCS Eng. 1946; MRCS Eng. LRCP Lond. 1944. (Camb. & St. Mary's) Hon. Cons. Cardiothoracic Surg. St. Mary's Lond. Socs: Soc. Thoracic Surgs. Gt. Brit. & Irel.. Prev: Dir. Med. & Health Serv. Gibraltar; Sen. Regist. Hammersmith Hosp. & Postgrad. Med. Sch.; Research Fell. in Surg. Harvard Med. Sch.

BROMLEY, Lesley Muriel 86 Grafton Road, Selsey, Chichester PO20 0JA — MB BS 1980 Lond.

BROMLEY, Paul Arnold 8 Guildhill Road, Bournemouth BH6 3EY — MB BCh BAO 1970 Belf. (Belf.) Sen. Regist. (Community Med.) Roy. Vict. Hosp. Boscombe. Prev: Regist. (Community Med.) N.ants. AHA; Med. Off. Murchison Miss. Hosp. Port Shepstone, S. Africa; Sen. Med. Off. (Research) Dept. Pharmacol. Univ. Orange Free State.

BROMLEY, Paul Thomas Readesmoor Medical Group Practice, 29-29A West Street, Congleton CW12 1JP Tel: 01260 276161 Fax: 01260 297340; High Oaks, 19 Leek Road, Congleton CW12 3HU Tel: 01260 278191 Fax: 01260 297340 — MB ChB 1976 Manch.

BROMLEY, Peter Noel Anaesthetic Department, Birmingham Children's Hospital, Steelhouse Lane, Birmingham B4 6NH Tel: 0121 333 9622 Email: peter.bromley@bhamchildrens.wmids.nhs.uk; 4 Fairmead Rise, Birmingham B38 8BS — MB BS 1987 Lond.; FRCA 1992. Cons. Anaesth. Birm. Childr.'s Hosp.; Cons. Anaesth. Qu. Eliz. Hosp. Birm. Socs: Assn. Anaesth.; Assn. Paed. Anaesth.; Internat. Liver Transpl.ation Soc. Prev: Sen. Regist. (Anaesth.) St. Thos. Hosp. Lond.; Research Fell. (Anaesth.) Liver Transpl. Kings Coll. Hosp. Lond.; Regist. (Helicopter Emerg. Med. Serv.) Roy. Lond. Hosp.

BROMLEY, Sarah Elizabeth Ashcroft Surgery, 22 Sherwood Place, Bradford BD2 3AG Tel: 01274 637076 Fax: 01274 626979; 470 Street Lane, Moortown, Leeds LS17 6HA Tel: 0113 266 2246 — MB ChB 1990 Leeds.

BROMLY, Adrienne Clare Well Close Square Surgery, Well Close Square, Berwick-upon-Tweed TD15 1LL Tel: 01289 356920 Fax: 01289 356939 — MB BS 1987 Newc.; MRCGP 1991; DRCOG 1991; Dip Ther. (Newc. u. Tyne) Clin. Asst. (Cas. & Optholmology) Berwick Infirm.; Clin. Direct. Berwick Infirm. Operat.al Managem. Bd. Prev: Trainee GP Berwick upon Tweed; SHO (Psychiat.) Roy. Edin. Hosp.; SHO (O & G) Falkirk & Dist. Roy. Infirm.

BROMLY, Julian Christopher Saville Medical Group, 7 Saville Place, Newcastle upon Tyne NE1 8DQ Tel: 0191 232 4274 Fax: 0191 233 1050 — MB BS 1982 Newc.; MRCGP 1986; DRCOG 1986. Sen. Research Assoc. Univ. Newc. u Tyne Med. Sch.; Sec. Geordie Young Pract. Gp. Prev: Trainee GP N.umbria VTS.

BROMWICH, Emma Jane Woodpecker Cottage, Dale Abbey, Ilkeston DE7 4PJ — MB ChB 1996 Bristol.

BROMWICH, Helen Lucy 156 Purlewent Drive, Weston, Bath BA1 4BE — MB ChB 1995 Bristol. GP Regist., Hope Ho. Surg., Radstock, Bath.

BROMWICH, Peter David Midland Fertility Services, Third Floor, Centre House, Court Parade, Aldridge, Walsall WS9 8LT Tel: 01922 455911 Fax: 01922459026 — MB ChB 1972 Birm.; MRCOG 1980. (Univ. Coll. Zimbabwe) Med. Dir. Midl. Fertil. Servs.; Med. Off. Family Plann. Clinics Oxon. Prev: Clin. Lect. Nuffield Dept. O & G Univ. Oxf.; Lect. (O & G) Birm. Matern. Hosp.; Regist. (O & G) Roy. Sussex Co. Hosp. Brighton.

BRON, Professor Anthony John Nuffield Laboratory/Ophthalmology, Walton St., Oxford OX2 6AW Tel: 01865 248996 Fax: 01865 794508 Email: anthony.bron@eye.ox.ac.uk; 10 Warnborough Road, Oxford OX2 6HZ Tel: 01865 57982 Fax: 01865 794508 — MRCS Eng. LRCP Lond. 1960; BSc Lond. 1957, MB BS 1961; FRCS Eng. 1968; FCOphth 1989; DO Eng. 1964; F Acad .Med. Sci. (Guy's) Clin. Prof. Ophth. Univ. Oxf.; Hon. Cons. Oxf. Eye Hosp. & Moorfields Eye Hosp. Lond. Socs: Fell.Roy. Soc. of Med.

(Ex-Pres. of Ophth. Sect.); Counc. Oxf. Ophth. Congr.; Soc. Fells. John Hopkins Univ. Prev: Sen. Lect. (Ophth.) & Research Asst. Inst. Ophth. Lond. & Moorfields Eye Hosp. Lond.; Alex P. Wernher Memor. Trust Fell. Wilmer Inst. Johns Hopkins Hosp. Baltimore, USA.

BRONKS, Ian Gervaise (cons. Rooms), 64 Broadway, Duffield DE56 4BU Tel: 01332 841438 Fax: 01332 843660; (cons. rooms), 10 Harley St, London W1N 1AA — MB ChB Sheff. 1959; MRCP Ed. 1962; FRCP Ed 1998; MRCS Eng. LRCP Lond. 1959; FRCPsych 1981, M 1971; DPM Eng. 1965. (Sheff.) Cons. Psychiat. Emerit. Kingsway Hosp. Derby; Mem. Parole Bd. Prev: Sen. Regist. (Psychiat.) United Sheff. Hosps. & Sheff. RHB; Ho. Phys. (Neurol.) Hammersmith Hosp.; Cons. Psychiat. & Mem. Parole Bd. Kingsway Hosp. Derby.

BRONNERT, Nicholas Henry Northgate Medical Centre, 10 Upper Northgate Street, Chester CH1 4EE; 47A Daleside, Upton, Chester CH2 1EN — MB BS 1975 Lond.; MSC (Ethics of Health Care) Liverp. 1998; MRCGP 1979; MRCS Eng. LRCP Lond. 1975. (St. Mary's) Mem. of Local Research Ethics Comm.

BRONSDON, Carole Eve The Surgery, 5 Kensington Place, London W8 7PT Tel: 020 7229 7111 Fax: 020 7221 3069; 64 Lawrence Road, Richmond TW10 7LR Tel: 020 8332 2908 — MB ChB 1984 Dundee; MRCGP 1989; DRCOG 1988. (Dund.) GP Princip. Prev: SHO (A & E) Char. Cross Hosp. Lond.; SHO (Psychiat.) Char. Cross Hosp. Lond.; SHO (Med.) Ninewells Hosp. Dundee.

BRONSDON, Christopher John Norman 17 Warwick Street, Sheffield S10 1LX — MB ChB 1993 Sheff.

BRONSTEIN, Adolfo Miguel MRC Human Movement & Balance Unit, Institute of Neurology, National Hospital for Neurology & Neurosurgery, Queen Square, London WC1N 3BG Tel: 020 7837 3611 Fax: 020 7837 7281 Email: dizzymrc@ion.ucl.ac.uk — Medico 1975 Buenos Aires; MRCP Hon.) 1999; PhD (Med.) Lond. 1990. Clin. Scientist MRC Human Movement & Balance Unit, & Hon. Sen. Lect. Inst. Neurol. Lond.; Hon. Cons. (Neurol.) Nat. Hosps. Lond. Socs: Barany Soc.; Assn. Brit. Neurol. Prev: Hon. Regist. & Sen. Regist. (Neurol.) Nat. Hosps. Lond.; Resid. & Sen. Resid. (Neurol.) Hosp. Ramos Mejia, Buenos Aires.

BRONTE, Julie Elizabeth Wynne Hill Surgery, 51 Hill Street, Lurgan, Craigavon BT66 6BW — MB BCh BAO 1991 Belf.; MRCGP 1994; DCH RCPS Glas. 1994; DRCOG 1994. Prev: GP/Regist. Lurgan Co. Armagh.

BRONTE-STEWART, Carola Mary Baronscourt Surgery, 89 Northfield Broadway, Edinburgh EH8 7RX Tel: 0131 657 5444 Fax: 0131 669 8116 — MB ChB 1979 Ed.; DRCOG 1983.

BRONTE-STEWART, Joan Mary (retired) 17 Turnberry Road, Glasgow G11 5AG — MB ChB 1948 Cape Town; DO Eng. 1953. Prev: Assoc. Specialist (Ophth.) W.. Infirm. Glas.

BROOK, Alan Charles Longroyde Surgery, 38 Castle Avenue, Rastrick, Brighouse HD6 3HT Tel: 01484 721102; Mason's Cottage, 105 Lower Edge Road, Elland HX5 9PL Tel: 01422 376603 Email: alan@robodoc.force9.co.uk — MB BS 1982 Newc.; BMedSc (1st. cl. Hons.) Newc. 1979, MB BS 1982; MRCGP 1986; DRCOG 1986. (Newcastle upon Tyne) Chairm. Calderdale PCG; Sec. Calderdale PCG.

BROOK, Alexis 3 Eton College Road, London NW3 2BS Tel: 020 7586 5340; 3 Eton College Road, London NW3 2BS — MB BChir Camb. 1948; MA Camb. 1943; MRCS Eng. LRCP Lond. 1943; FRCPsych 1974, M 1971; DPM Eng. 1953. (Middlx.) Hon. Cons. Psychother. Tavistock Clinic Lond.; Emerit. Cons. N.wick Pk. & St. Mark's NHS Trust. Socs: Fell. Roy. Soc. Med.; Assn. Psychoanal. Psychother. in NHS; Hon. Affil. Br. Psycho-Anal. Soc. Prev: Cons. Psychiat. Cassel Hosp. Ham Common; Sen. Regist. Napsbury Hosp.; Regist. Maudsley & Bethlem Roy. Hosp.

BROOK, Audrey Mary Florence (retired) 48 Sheffield Road, Killamarsh, Sheffield S21 2EA Tel: 0114 247 7622 Fax: 0114 247 7601 Email: drbrook@gemsoft.co.uk — MB ChB Sheff. 1953. Prev: GP Sheff.

BROOK, Brian John (retired) 15A Chelveston Road, Raunds, Wellingborough NN9 6DA — MB BS 1953 Lond.; MRCGP 1974. Prev: Gen. Pract.

BROOK, Professor Charles Groves Darville (retired) The Middlesex Hospital, Mortimer St., London W1T 3AA Tel: 020 8521 0553 Fax: 020 8521 0553 Email: c.brook@ucl.ac.uk — MB BChir Camb. 1964; MA Camb. 1964, MD 1972; FRCP Lond. 1979, M 1967; FRCPCH 1997; DCH Eng. 1968. Prof. Emer. Paediat. Endocrinol. UCL; Cons. Paediat. UCL Hosps. & Gt. Ormond St. Childr. Hosp. Prev: Dir. Lond. Centre of Paediat., Endocrinol.

BROOK, Charles Peter Beynon (retired) 55 Maids Causeway, Cambridge CB5 8DE — MB BS 1952 Lond.; MD Lond. 1974; MA Camb. 1980; LMSSA Lond. 1952; FRCPsych 1971; DPM Eng. 1959. Life. Fell. Hughes Hall Camb. Prev: Cons. Psychogeriat. Camb. HA.

BROOK, Cynthia Mary West Calder Medical Practice, Dickson Street, West Calder EH55 8HB Tel: 01506 871403; 1 Saxe Coburg Terrace, Edinburgh EH3 5BU — MB BS 1976 Newc.; BSc (Hons.) Sheff. 1969; FRCGP 1996, M 1980. GP Trainer W. Calder.; Clin. Director Primary Care Directorate W. Lothian Healthcare (NHS) Trust. Prev: Assoc. Adviser (Gen. Pract.) SW Lothian; GP Advis. Panel MDD US; Regist. (Child & Adolesc. Psychiat.) W. Lothian.

BROOK, Denys Wynn (retired) c/o Midland Bank Plc, 354 Mare St., London E8 1HU — MRCS Eng. LRCP Lond. 1957; DIH Lond. 1976; DPH Lond. 1969. Prev: Adviser Family Med. Saudi MoD & Aviat. Dahran.

BROOK, Doreen Rachael 5 Grasmere Road, Beeston, Nottingham NG9 3AQ Tel: 0115 925 5553 — MB ChB 1956 Sheff. PMO (Child Health) Nottm. DHA.

BROOK, Fiona Mary Alice X-Ray Department, Royal Gwent Hospital, Cardiff Road, Newport NP20 2UB Tel: 01633 234339 Fax: 01633 234324 — MB ChB 1981 Ed.; BSc (Med. Sci.) Ed. 1978; FRCR 1987; DMRD Aberd. 1985. (Edinburgh) Cons. Radiol. Roy. Gwent Hosp. Newport. Prev: Sen. Regist. (Diag. Radiol.) Nottm. Hosps. & Regist. (Diagn. Radiol.) Aberd. Roy. Infirm.

BROOK, Frances Barbara Histopathology Department, Sandwell Healthcare NHS Trust, Lyndon, West Bromwich B71 4HJ Tel: 0121 607 3428 — MB ChB Birm. 1981; MRCPath 1989; FRCPath 1996. Cons. Histopath. Sandwell Gen. Hosp., W. Bromwich.

BROOK, Gerald Keith Barton Surgery, Barton Terrace, Dawlish EX7 9QH Tel: 01626 888877 Fax: 01626 888360 — MB ChB 1974 Leeds; MRCGP 1978; DRCOG 1978.

BROOK, Henrietta Diana Darville 34 Cheriton Square, London SW17 8AE — MB BChir 1992 Camb.; MA Camb. 1993; MRCP (UK) 1996; MRCGP 1998. (King's Coll. Hosp. Lond.) GP Lond. Socs: Med. Defence Union; BMA. Prev: GP/Regist. Lond. VTS; SHO Rotat. (Med.) St. Mary's Univ. Hosp. Lond.

BROOK, Jacqueline Department of Anaesthetics, Dewsbury & District Hospital, Halifax Road, Dewsbury WF13 4HS Tel: 01924 512000 — MB BS 1981 Newc.; 1991 FRCA Lond. Cons. Anaesth. Dewsbury & Dist. Hosp. W. Yorks.

BROOK, Jane Frances 16 Cold Knap Way, Barry CF62 6SQ — BM BS 1979 Nottm.

BROOK, John Hugh Robert 23 Oakhill Avenue, London NW3 7RD Tel: 020 7435 0211 Fax: 020 7431 5450 — MB BS 1971 Lond.; BSc Lond. 1968; MRCS Eng. LRCP Lond. 1971; MRCGP 1976; DObst RCOG 1975; DCH Eng. 1975. (Lond. Hosp.) Med. Off. Lex Serv. Plc. Socs: Fell. Roy. Soc. Med.; Brit. Med. & Dent. Hypn. Soc. Prev: Trainee GP Lond. (N. Middlx. Hosp.) VTS; SHO (ENT Dept.) Lond. Hosp.; Ho. Surg. & Ho. Phys. Lond. Hosp.

BROOK, John Michael, CB, QHS, Air Vice-Marshal RAF Med. Br. Medical Centre, RAF Brampton, Huntingdon PE28 2EA Tel: 01480 52151; 2 Vicarage Fields, Hemingford Grey, Huntingdon PE28 9BY Tel: 01480 493575 — MB ChB 1957 Leeds; FRCGP 1992, M 1972; MFOM RCP Lond. 1980, AFOM 1979; DAvMed Eng. 1974. Civil. Med. Practitioner, RAF Brampton, Huntingdon, Camb., Wyton Pract. Socs: BMA. Prev: Dir. Gen. RAF Med. Servs.; Dep. Princip. Med. Off. RAF Strike Command; Commandant RAF Centr. Med. Estabmt. Off. Commanding Defence Serv. Med. Rehabil. Unit.

BROOK, Lynda Ann Dept. Of Paediatric Oncology, RLCH Alder Hey, Eaton Rd, Liverpool L12 2AP Tel: 01256 356081, 0151 228 4811 Email: andi.clay@lineone.net; 9 Hoyle Road, Hoylake, Wirral CH47 3AG Tel: 0151 632 0177 Email: warburton@btinternet.com — MB ChB 1989 Leic.; MSc 2001 Manc.; MRCP (UK) 1993. (Leicester) p/t Sen. Regist. (Paediatric Oncol. & Palliat. Care) Alder Hey Childr. Hosp. Liverp.; Director, Claire Ho. Childr.'s Hospice, Wirral. Socs: Roy. Coll. Paediat. and Child Health; Assn. of Palliat. Med.; Assn. Childr. With Life Threatening or Life Limiting Illness. Prev: Regist. Rotat. (Gen. Paediat. & Paediat. Cardiol.) Alder Hey Childr. Hosp. Liverp.; Regist. Rotat. (Neonat.) Fazakerley Dist. Gen. Hosp. Liverp.; Regist. Rotat. (Gen. Paediat.) Arrowe Pk. Hosp. Wirral.

BROOK, Malcolm George (retired) Links Cottage, 25 Stonegate, Wye, Ashford TN25 5DD — MRCS Eng. LRCP Lond. 1960. Prev: Ho. Surg. W. Lond. Hosp.

BROOK, Margaret Eleanor (retired) 21 Calf Croft Place, Lytham St Annes FY8 4PU Tel: Ex Directory — MB BCh BAO Dub. 1945; BA Dub. 1943. Prev: Asst. Co. Med. Off. Chesh. CC.

BROOK, Mary Elizabeth Meltham Road Surgery, 9 Meltham Road, Lockwood, Huddersfield HD1 3UP Tel: 01484 432940 Fax: 01484 451423 — MB BS 1986 Newc.; MRCGP 1992. Prev: SHO (Gen. Med.) Bishop Auckland Gen. Hosp.; SHO (Neonat.) Sheff. HA; SHO (O & G) Newc. HA.

BROOK, Matthew Ian Portland Group Practice, The Health Centre, Park Estate Road, Easton, Portland DT5 2BJ Tel: 01305 820422 Fax: 01305 824143; 40 Chamberlaine Road, Wyke Regis, Weymouth DT4 9EY Tel: 01305 777937 — BM 1987 Soton.; 1999 DCM Beijing. (Soton.) Med. Acupunc. Prospect Ho., 13 Carlton Rd S, Weymouth, Dorset. Socs: Chinese Med. Inst. & Register (Accredit. Mem.); Brit. Med. Acupunct. Soc. (Mem.). Prev: Med. Off. Mangango Mission Hosp. W.. Province, Zambia.

BROOK, Matthew Tobin Dan yr Helyg Isaf, Newcastle Emlyn SA38 9RG — BM 1996 Soton.

BROOK, Michael Gary Central Middlesex Hospital, Acton Lane, London NW10 7NS Tel: 020 8453 2221 Fax: 020 8453 2224 Email: gary.brook@cmh-tr.nthames.nhs.uk; 103 Northaw Road W., Northaw, Potters Bar EN6 4NS — MB BS 1978 Lond.; BSc Lond. 1975, MD 1990; MRCP (UK) 1985; Dip. GU Med. Soc. Apoth. Lond. 1995; DRCOG 1981; DTM & H RCP Lond. 1981; DCH RCP Lond. 1981; FRCP 2000. (King's Coll. Hosp.) Cons. Genitourin. Med. & HIV Med. Centr. Middlx. Hosp. Lond.; Hon. Sen. Lect. Acad. Dept. STDs, UCL 1997. Socs: Med. Soc. Study VD; Clin. Infec. Soc.; Assn. Genitourin Med. Prev: Sen. Regist. (Genitourin. & HIV Med.) Whittington & Middlx. Hosps. Lond.; Sen. Regist. (Gen. Med., Infec. Dis. & Trop. Med.) Roy. Free, Coppetts Wood & Hosp. for Trop. Dis. Lond.; Regist. (Gen. Med. & Infec. Dis.) Hither Green Hosp. Lond.

BROOK, Nancy Mary Hermitage Farm, Hermitage Green Lane, Winwick, Warrington WA2 8SL — MB ChB 1962 Manch.; DPH 1966; MRCPsych 1980. p/t Cons. (Psychiat.) Winwick Hosp. Warrington. (Alcohol Treatm. Serv.). Prev: Sen. Regist. (Psychiat.) Clatterbridge Hosp. Wirral.

BROOK, Nicholas Edward 3 Balfour Place, Putney, London SW15 6XR Tel: 020 8789 7259; 3 Balfour Place, Putney, London SW15 6XR Tel: 020 8789 7259 — MB BS 1993 Lond. (Charing Cross and Westminster) Specialist Regist. (O & G).

BROOK, Peter Nigel 2 The Lawns, Sheffield S11 9FL — MB BS 1990 Lond.

BROOK, Rachel c/o M. G. Newman, 3 Bretaneby, High St., Seal, Sevenoaks TN15 0AJ — MB ChB 1994 Auckland.

BROOK, Richard Helsby Health Centre, Lower Robin Hood Lane, Helsby, Warrington WA6 0BW Tel: 01928 723676 Fax: 01928 725677 — MB ChB 1972 Liverp.; FRCGP 1995; MRCGP 1977; DObst RCOG 1974.

BROOK, Rosemary Eydom House, Cheddon Reoad, Taunton — MB ChB 1987 Manch.; MSc (Med.) Manch. 1996; MRCPsych 1993. Sen. Regist. (Gen. Psychiat.) Roy. Preston Hosp.Cons. Psychitrist, Taunton.

BROOK, Sarah Jane The Surgery, 148 Forton Road, Gosport PO12 3HH Tel: 023 9258 3333 Fax: 023 9260 1107; 3 Clayhall Road, Gosport PO12 2BB Email: brookie_gosport@yahoo.co.uk — MB BS 1990 Lond.; MRCGP 1994; DRCOG 1993.

BROOK, Sarah Madeleine 1 Manners Close, Uffington, Stamford PE9 4UB — MB ChB 1979 Manch.

BROOK, Simon Stanley Brooklands Avenue Medical Centre, 7 Brooklands Avenue, Cambridge CB2 2BB Tel: 01223 356715 Fax: 01223 357789; 215 Hills Road, Cambridge CB2 2RN Tel: 01223 564416 — MB BS 1961 Lond.; MRCS Eng. LRCP Lond. 1961; MRCGP 1972; DObst RCOG 1964. (Guy's) Clin. Teach. (Gen. Pract.) Univ. Camb. Clin. Med. Sch. Socs: Fell. Roy. Soc. Med.; BMA. Prev: SHO (Cas.), Ho. Phys. & Ho. Surg. Lewisham Hosp.; Ho. Surg. (Obst.) Redhill Gen. Hosp.

BROOK, Valerie Dickens Place Surgery, Dickens Place, Chelmsford CM1 4UU Tel: 01245 442628 Fax: 01245 443647 Email: valerie.brook@gp-f81024.nhs.uk; 42 Roxwell Road, Chelmsford CM1 2NB Tel: 01245 355648 — MB BS 1965 Lond.; MRCS Eng. LRCP Lond. 1965; DObst RCOG 1967. (St. Mary's) Socs: BMA & LMC; RSM; Chairm. N. Essex. LMC, Retd. Prev: Hosp. Pract. Young Chronic Sick Unit St. John's Hosp. Chelmsford, Retd.

BROOK, William Alexander Darville Cherry Orchard Cottage, Broad Campden, Chipping Campden GL55 6UU — MB ChB 1990 Ed.

BROOKBANKS, Colin Francis Gordon The Health Centre, Ash Meadow, High Street, Much Hadham SG10 6DE Tel: 01279 842242 Fax: 01279 843973 — MB BS 1971 Lond.; MRCS Eng. LRCP Lond. 1971; MRCGP 1977. (St. Bart.) Prev: Ho. Surg. Dept. Orthop. Surg. St. Bart. Hosp. Lond.; Ho. Phys. Gen. Med. Metrop. Hosp. Lond.

BROOKE, Adrian Mark 44 Clarendon Park Road, Leicester LE2 3AD — MB ChB 1988 Leic.; BSc (Med. Sci.) Leic. 1985; MRCP (UK) 1992. Lect. (Community Child Health) Univ. Leic. & Hon. Sen. Regist. Fosse Health Trust Leics. Socs: Roy. Coll. Paediat. & Child Health; Brit. Assn. Community Child Health. Prev: Regist. Rotat. Birm. Childr. Hosp. NHS Trust; Clin. Research Fell. (Child Health) Univ. Leic.

BROOKE, Andrew Edward Pavilion Family Doctors, 153A Stroud Road, Gloucester GL1 5JJ Tel: 01452 385555 Fax: 01452 387905 — MB ChB 1981 Leic.; MRCGP 1985; DRCOG 1985.

BROOKE, Angus James St Nicholas Medical Centre, Stevenage; 64 Grenville Way, Stevenage SG2 8XZ — MB ChB 1996 Sheff. (Sheffield) VTS Trainee (GP Regist.) Gen. Pract., Welwyn Garden City.

BROOKE, Antonia Stubham Lodge, Clifford Road, Ilkley LS29 0AX — MB BS 1997 Lond.

BROOKE, Barbara Mary Beilby House, Wetherby LS22 5DX Tel: 01937 62391 — MB ChB 1950 Leeds. (Leeds)

BROOKE, Clare Margaret Windhill Green Medical Centre, 2 Thackley Old Road, Shipley BD18 1QB Tel: 01274 584223 Fax: 01274 530182; Stubham Lodge, Clifford Road, Ilkley LS29 0AX — MB BS 1964 Lond.; MRCS Eng. LRCP Lond. 1964; DObst RCOG 1966. (Middlx.) Clin. Asst. Bradford Roy. Infirm.

BROOKE, Deborah Belle Mary Bracton Centre, Bracton Lane, Dartford DA2 7AF Tel: 01322 294300 Fax: 01322 293595 — MB BS 1981 Lond.; MD Lond. 2001; MPhil Lond. 1995; MRCPsych 1988; MRCGP 1986; DCH RCP Lond. 1985; DRCOG 1985. (Guy's Hosp. Med. Sch.) Cons. Forens. Psychiat. Oxleas NHS Trust, Bexley Hosp.; Sen. Lect. (Forens. Psychiat.) UMDS Guy's Hosp. Lond.

BROOKE, Diana Jane 3 Hockley Mill, Church Lane, Twyford, Winchester SO21 1NT Tel: 01962 711652 Fax: 01962 711653 Email: brookensr@aol.com — MB BS 1984 Lond.; DCH RCP Lond. 1993; DA (UK) 1990. Staff Grade (Community Child Health) Soton. Community Serv. Health Care Trust. Prev: Staff Grade (Community Child Health) Greenwich Health Care Trust; Staff Grade (Paediat.) John Radcliffe Hosp. Oxf.

BROOKE, Duncan Nigel 65 Poplar Road, London SE24 0BL Tel: 020 7326 1909 Email: dbrooke@dbrooke.abel.co.uk — MB BS 1988 Lond. Prev: SHO (ITU) Middlx. Hosp. Lond.; SHO (A & E) Qu. Eliz. Hosp. Childr. Lond.; SHO (Surg.) Hammersmith Hosp. Lond.

BROOKE, Edward Martin Iona, Rock, Wadebridge PL27 6LS — MB BS 1977 Lond.; MRCS Eng. LRCP Lond. 1977; MRCGP 1984; DRCOG 1978.

BROOKE, Jane Patricia Pocklington Group Practice, The Surgery, 7 Barmby Road, Pocklington, York YO42 2DL Tel: 01759 302500 Fax: 01759 305123; Sykes Farm, Burnby, York YO4 2RS — MB ChB 1981 Leeds.

BROOKE, John Vivian Elwick Bank Surgery, Elwick Bank, Shapinsay, Orkney KW17 2EA Tel: 01856 711284 Fax: 01856 711348; 19 Rue Berlioz, 06000 Nice, France Tel: 0493162572 Fax: 0493162572 Email: john.brooke.wanrdoo.fr — MB ChB 1967 Ed.; BSc (Hons. Pharmacol.) Ed. 1965; MRCGP 1975; Dip. IMC RCS Ed. 1995; DCH Eng. 1970; DObst RCOG 1969. (Ed.) Mem. Fac. Pre-Hosp. Care RCS Edin. Socs: BMA; BASICS. Prev: SHO (Paediat. & O & G) Kent & Canterbury Hosp.; Ho. Phys. & Ho. Surg. Roy. Infirm. Edin.

BROOKE, Judith Ann Barnwood Road Surgery, 51 Barnwood Road, Gloucester GL2 0SE — MB ChB 1981 Leic.; MRCGP 1985; DCH RCP Lond. 1984; DRCOG 1984. GP Trainer, Gloucester. Prev: Trainee GP Burton on Trent VTS.

BROOKE, Mark Darren Leylands Medical Centre, 81 Leylands Lane, Bradford BD9 5PZ Tel: 01274 770771 Fax: 01274 771088 — MB ChB 1983 Leeds; MSc (Sports Med.) Lond. 1995; MRCGP 1987; DRCOG 1986; Cert. Family Plann. JCC 1986. (Leeds) Team Phys.

Bradford Bull RLFC & BALASA; Med. Off. Disabil. Sport UK Athletics; GP Trainer, Bradford VTS. Prev: Trainee GP Bradford VTS; Ho. Off. (Gen. Surg. & Urol.) Leeds Gen. Infirm.; Ho. Off. (Gen. Med. & Cardiol.) Bradford Roy. Infirm.

BROOKE, Michael John Atherley House Surgery, 143-145 Shirley Road, Shirley, Southampton SO15 3FH Tel: 023 8022 1964/0763 Fax: 023 8022 0763 — BM 1984 Soton.

BROOKE, Patrick Nicholas Russell Briar Cottage, Upper Bucklebury, Reading RG7 6SD — MB BS 1991 Lond.

BROOKE, Rebecca C. C. Salford Royal Hospital, NHS Trust, Department Of Dermatology, Stott Lane, Salford M6 8MD — MB ChB 1989 Manch.; MRCP (UK) 1995.

BROOKE, Sara Diane Department of Psychiatry, Leicester General Hospital, Gwendolen Road, Leicester LE5 4PW Tel: 0116 258 4597; 151 Knighton Road, Leicester LE2 3TS — MB ChB 1989 Leics.; MRCPsych. 1995; MPhil. Leics. 1997.

BROOKE, Sarah Judith Russell 80 Pinewood Green, Iver SL0 0QH Tel: 01753 651456 — MB BS 1986 Lond.; DRCOG 1988. (Westm.)

BROOKE, Stephen Richard Mark 168 Victoria Road, Swindon SN1 3BU Tel: 01793 535584; 5 Roche Close, Swindon SN3 6JQ — MB BS 1982 Lond.; MA Camb. 1982; DA Eng. 1984; DCH RCP Lond. 1986; DRCOG 1985. (Lond. Hosp. Med. Coll.) Socs: Christian Med. Fell.sh. Prev: Clin. Med. Off. (Paediat.) Broxbourne; SHO (Obst.) Wycombe Gen. Hosp.; SHO (Anaesth.) Welwyn Garden City.

BROOKE, William Edward The Hollies, Hawley Lane, Hale, Altrincham WA15 0DR Tel: 0161 980 7066 — MB BS 1954 Lond.; MFOM RCP Lond. 1983; MRCGP 1966; DIH Soc. Apoth. Lond. 1967. (Lond. Hosp.) Sen. Occupat. Phys. Univ. Manch. Inst. Sci. & Technol. Prev: GP Altrincham; Med. Adviser Clayton Aniline Co. Ltd.; Occupat. Phys. S. Manch. HA.

BROOKE BARNETT, John William Flat 18, 65 Courtfield Gardens, London SW5 0NQ — MB BS 1952 Lond. (St. Mary's) Chairm. Roy. Med. Benevolent Fund; Chairm. Brit. Med. & Dent. Studs. Trust; Med. Adviser Scand.n Benevolent Soc. Prev: Sec. Med. Defence Union; Ho. Surg. (Gyn. & Obst.) St. Mary's Hosp.; Resid. Surg. Off. Roy. Marsden Hosp.

BROOKER, Arthur Edward William 36 Charleston Court, West Cliff Road, Broadstairs CT10 1RY Tel: 01843 600380 — MB BS Lond. 1939; MD Lond. 1963; MRCS Eng. LRCP Lond. 1937; FRCGP 1970. (St. Bart.) Socs: Brit. Soc. Rheum. Prev: Clin. Asst. Med. Profess. Unit, Roy. Hosp. Sheff.; Sen. Regist. (Med.) Roy. Postgrad. Med. Sch. Lond.; Extern.-Intern St. Bart. Hosp. Lond.

BROOKER, Bertram Keir 54 Top Road, Kingsley, Warrington Tel: 01928 788516 Fax: 01928 788516 — MB ChB Liverp. 1955; MRCPsych 1971; DPM Eng. 1963. Prev: Cons. Psychiat. Winwick Hosp. Warrington.

BROOKER, Catherine Belinda 321-B Upper Street, London N1 2XQ — MB BS 1991 Western Australia.

BROOKER, Mr David Shammuah Otolaryngology Dept, Royal Victoria Hospital, Grosvenor Rd, Belfast BT12 6BA; 90 Circular Road, Belfast BT4 2GE Tel: 02890 761224 — MB BCh BAO 1976 Belf.; FRCS 1982 (Ed.); FRCS 1986 (Otol). Cons. Otolaryngologist, Roy. Gp. of Hosp.s, Belf.

BROOKER, Georgia Eveline Maria Willow Ridge Top Road, Kingsley, Warrington WA6 8DB Tel: 01928 788516 Email: georgia brooker@hotmail.com — MB ChB 1997 Bristol. (Bristol)

BROOKER, Iain Parkinson Macduff Medical Practice, 100 Duff Street, Macduff AB44 1PR Tel: 01261 833777 Fax: 01261 835100 Email: iain-brooker@macduff.grampian.swt.nhs.uk — MB ChB 1982 Aberd.; MRCGP 1994; Dip. Practical Dermatol. 1998. (University of Aberdeen) Princip. GP, Macduff Med. Pract., Macduff, Aberd.shire. Prev: Med. Dir. Chalmers Hosp. Banff, Aberd.shire, AB45 1JA.

BROOKER, Ian Mackintosh, Squadron Ldr. RAF Med. Br. (retired) Heughead, Cothal Dyce, Aberdeen AB21 0HT Tel: 01224 722240 — MB ChB 1950 Aberd.; MRCGP 1961. Aviat. Med. Examr.

BROOKER, James Christopher Wolfson Unit, St Marks Hospital, Watford Road, Harrow HA1 3UJ Email: jimbrooker@compuserve.com — MB BS 1991 Lond.; BSc (Hons.) Lond. 1988; MRCP (UK) 1994. Clin. Research Fell. St Mark's Hosp. Prev: Specialist Regist. (Gastroenterol.) Roy. Free Hosp.; Specialist Regist. (Gastroenterol.) N. Middlx. Hosp.; Specialist Regist. (Gastroenterol.) Basildon Hosp.

BROOKER, Richard John — MB BCh 1983 Wales; FRCPCH 1999; MRCP (UK) 1991; DCH RCP Lond. 1989. Cons. Paediat., Roy. Aberd. Childr.s Hosp. Prev: Lect. in Child Health, Univ. of Aberd.; Clin. Fell., Brit. Columbia Childr. Hosp.; Regist., Roy. Childr.s Hosp.

BROOKES, Beata Irena 24 Formosa Street, London W9 2QA Tel: 020 7289 9006 — MB BS 1987 Lond.; FRCS Glas. 1992; FRCS Eng. 1992.

BROOKES, Carl Ivan Oliver 39 Gillespie Road, London N5 1LH Tel: 020 7704 0899; 48 Daver Court, Chelsea Manor St, London SW3 3TS Tel: 020 7376 8534 — MB BS 1988 Lond.; BA Oxf. 1985; MRCP (UK) 1991. Specialist Regist. (Cardiol.) Roy. Brompton Hosp. Lond. Socs: Cardiac Club; BCIS.

BROOKES, Catherine Emma 8 Low Moorlands, Dalston, Carlisle CA5 7NX — BM BS 1995 Nottm.

BROOKES, Cheryl Elizabeth 1 Dene Cottage, Milley Road, Waltham St Lawrence, Reading RG10 0JU — MB ChB 1971 Sheff.

BROOKES, Christine Margaret (retired) 143 Westhall Road, Warlingham, Croydon CR6 9HJ Tel: 01883 623193 — MB BS 1954 Lond.; MRCS Eng. LRCP Lond. 1953; FFA RCS Eng. 1973; DA Eng. 1969. Prev: Cons. Anaesth. Croydon AHA.

BROOKES, Christopher Edward 24 Marl Road, Radcliffe-on-Trent, Nottingham NG12 2GY — MB ChB 1996 Leeds.

BROOKES, Christopher Noel 40 Ravenswood, Bolton BL1 5TL — MB ChB 1992 Liverp.

BROOKES, David Brian Abbey Park Hospital, Dalton Lane, Barrow-in-Furness LA14 4TP Tel: 01229 813388 Fax: 01229 81336; Grievegate, Leasgill, Milnthorpe LA7 7EY Tel: 01539 563964 Fax: 01539 563964 — MB ChB Manch. 1958; FRCP Lond. 1983; FRCP Ed. 1982. (Manchester) p/t Vis. Dermatol. Noble's Hosp. I. of Man. Socs: Fell. Roy. Soc. Med.; Brit. Assn. Dermat.; N. Eng. Dermat. Soc. Prev: Cons. Dermat. Furness & W.morland NHS Trusts; Sen. Regist. (Dermat.) Roy. Free Hosp. Lond.; Resid. Med. Off. Manch. Roy. Infirm.

BROOKES, Emma Jane 8 Norwich Drive, Harborne, Birmingham B17 8TB — MB ChB 1991 Sheff.; MRCGP 1999; DFFP 1998; DRCOG 1998. Socs: MRCGP.

BROOKES, Ewa Maria (retired) 14 Collingwood Crescent, Broughty Ferry, Dundee DD5 2SX — MB BS Lond. 1962; FRCP Ed. 1996; MRCS Eng. LRCP Lond. 1962; FRCPath 1985, M 1973. Prev: Director, E. Scotl. Blood Transfus. Serv., Ninewells Hosp., Dundee.

BROOKES, Mr Gerald Barry (cons. rooms), 106 Harley St., London W1N 1AF Tel: 020 7224 4560 Fax: 020 7935 7701; The Pent House, 34 King St., Covent Garden, London WC2E 8JD Tel: 020 7836 1181 — MB ChB 1974 Sheff.; FRCS (Orl.) Eng. 1979. Cons. ENT & Neuro-otol. Surg. Nat. Hosps. Neurol. & Neurosurg. Qu. Sq. & Roy. Nat. Throat, Nose & Ear Hosp. Lond.; Hon. Sen. Lect. (Otolaryngol.) Univ. Lond., Inst. Laryngol. & Otol. & Inst. Neurol. Socs: Fell. Amer. Neurotol. Soc.; Roy. Soc. Med. (Fell. Sects. Otol. & Laryngol.); Brit. Assn. Otol. Prev: TWJ Clin. & Research Fell. (Otol. & Neurol-otol.) Univ. Michigan, USA; Sen. Regist. (ENT) Lond. Hosp.; Regist. (ENT) King's Coll. Hosp. Lond.

BROOKES, Guy Sheldon 54 Folly Lane, Cheddleton, Leek ST13 7DA — MB ChB 1993 Liverp.

BROOKES, Jean-Pierre Christopher Midol, OSJ, TD, Col. late RAMC Retd. Buckton, Llangorwen, Aberystwyth SY23 3DP — BA Camb. 1955; LMSSA Lond. 1958; FFA RCS Eng. 1969. (Camb. & St. Mary's)

BROOKES, Jocelyn Asher Simon The Middlesex Hospital UCLH London, Mortimer Street, London W1T 3AA Tel: 020 7380 9015 Ext: 9286 Fax: 020 7380 9068 Email: jocelyn.brookes@vclh.org; Flat 6, Palm Court, 11-13 Fellows Road, London NW3 3LT Tel: 020 7483 3534 Email: joebrookes@msn.com — MB BS 1986 Lond.; MRCP (UK) 1991; FRCR 1996. (Univ. Coll. Lond. Med. Sch.) Cons. Interven.al Radiologist Vasc. Unit.

BROOKES, Mr John Desmond Millmead, Billingshurst Road, Broadbridge Heath, Horsham RH12 3LR — MB BChir 1979 Camb.; FRCS Eng. 1986; T(S) 1991. Cons. Otolaryngol. Crawley Hosp. Prev: Sen. Regist. (Otolaryng.) Kent & Sussex Hosp. Tunbridge Wells.

BROOKES, Mr John Leslie Flat 2, 23 Brondesbury Park, London NW6 7BS Tel: 020 8459 5114; 9 Larch Close, Darfield, Barnsley S73 9NS — MB BS 1993 Lond.; BSc (Hons.) Lond. 1992; FRCOphth Lond. 1998. (St. Mary's) Wellcome Found. Clin. Research Fell. (Molecular Genetics) Imperial Coll. of Sci. Technol. & Med. Lond.

Prev: SHO (Ophth.) W.ern Eye Hosp. Lond.; SHO (Ophth.) Kingston Hosp. Lond.; SHO (Neurosurg.) Brook Gen. Hosp.

BROOKES, Joseph Maxime Gerard Midol 44 Parkside, Grammar School Walk, Huntingdon PE29 3LF — MRCS Eng. LRCP Lond. 1955; MB Camb. 1956, BChir 1955; FRCOG 1980, M 1963.

BROOKES, Julia Lesley Whinfield Surgery, Whinbush Way, Darlington DL1 3RT Tel: 01325 481321 Fax: 01325 380116; Linden, 74A Darlington Road, Hartburn, Stockton-on-Tees TS18 5ET Tel: 01642 570085 — MB BS 1981 Newc.; MRCGP 1985; DA Eng. 1983.

BROOKES, Kenneth Roderick 53 Strathmore Road, Moordown, Bournemouth BH9 3NT — LMSSA 1946 Lond. Prev: Regist. (Anaesth.) W. Dorset Hosp.

BROOKES, Lionel Douglas c/o Barclays Bank Ltd., 2 High St., Sheffield S1 1QE — BM BCh 1954 Oxf. (Oxf. & St. Bart.) Prev: Mem. Scientif. Staff Nat. Inst. Med. Research (Hampstead Laborats,); Sen. Research Off. Med. Research Counc. of NZ.

BROOKES, Marie Therese Iona, 18 Burnside Road, High Burnside, Rutherglen, Glasgow G73 4RS Tel: 0141 634 4218 — MB ChB 1958 Liverp.; DFM 1988. (Liverp.) Cons. A & E Monklands Dist. Gen. Hosp. Airdrie. Prev: Cons. A & E Clwyd AHA.

BROOKES, Mark Richard Long Lane Surgery, 15 Long Lane, Liverpool L19 6PE Tel: 0151 494 1445 — MB ChB 1982 Liverp. SHO (Psychiat.) Winwick Hosp. Warrington.

BROOKES, Mary Theresa Ixworth Surgery, Peddars Close, Ixworth, Bury St Edmunds IP31 2HD Tel: 01359 230252 Fax: 01359 232586; The Poplars, The St, Hepworth, Diss IP22 2PX Tel: 01359 252241 Fax: 01359 252241 — MB BS 1983 Lond.; DRCOG 1988. Prev: GP Mildenhall; SHO (O & G) W. Suff. Hosp. Bury St. Edmunds; Trainee GP Camb. VTS.

BROOKES, Matthew James 18 The Croft, Badsworth, Pontefract WF9 1AS — MB ChB 1996 Bristol.

BROOKES, Merton (retired) 21 Park Lane Court, Bury New Road, Salford M7 4LP Tel: 0161 792 0344 — MB ChB Manch. 1945. Prev: Demonst. (Anat.) Univ. Manch.

BROOKES, Nigel Richard De Parys Medical Centre, 23 De Parys Avenue, Bedford MK40 2TX Tel: 01234 350022 Fax: 01234 213402; 38 Waterloo Road, Bedford MK40 3PG Tel: 01234 341663 — MB BChir 1980 Camb.; MRCGP 1984; DRCOG 1983.

BROOKES, Philip Hedley Proctor and Partners, Doctors Surgery, 42 Heaton Road, Heaton, Newcastle upon Tyne NE6 1SE Tel: 0191 265 5911 Fax: 0191 265 6974; 32 Balmoral Terrace, South Gosforth, Newcastle upon Tyne NE3 1YH Tel: 0191 285 4960 — MB BS 1979 Newc.; MRCGP 1983; DTM & H Liverp. 1986; DRCOG 1982. Prev: Med. Off. Govt. St. Helena.; Dir. Shining Hosp. Community Health Project Pokhara, Nepal.

BROOKES, Philip Thomas Heathfield, Bell Lane, Lower Broadheath, Worcester WR2 6RP — MB ChB 1992 Birm.; FRCS (Eng) 1997. (Birm.) Specialist Regist. Gen. Surg. W. Mids. Rotat.

BROOKES, Robert Charles (retired) Felbrigg, 143 Westhall Road, Warlingham CR6 9HJ — MB BS 1953 Lond.; MRCS Eng. LRCP Lond. 1953; FFA RCS Eng. 1959; DA Eng. 1955; DObst RCOG 1954. Sen. Lect. (Anaesth.) Inst. Dent. Surg. Prev: Cons. Anaesth. Croydon Hosp. Gp. & E.man Dent. Hosp.

BROOKES, Robert Henry Lowgate Surgery, 19 Lowgate, Gosberton, Spalding PE11 4NL Tel: 01775 840204 Fax: 01775 841108; Shropshire House, Westhorpe Road, Gosberton, Spalding PE11 4EN — MB ChB 1978 Sheff.

BROOKES, Mr Roger Whitehead Iona, 18 Burnside Road, Rutherglen, Glasgow G73 4RS — MB ChB 1964 Manch.; FRCS Eng. 1974; FRCS Ed. 1970. (Manch.) Cons. (Gen. & Vasc. Surg.) Monklands Dist. Gen. Hosp. Airdrie; Hon. Clin. Lect. Surg. Univ. Glas. Socs: Vasc. Soc. Gt. Brit. & Irel. Prev: Sen. Surg. Regist. Roy. Liverp. Hosp. & Chester Roy. Infirm.; Regist. (Surg.) Walton Hosp. Liverp.

BROOKES, Rowan Upton Village Surgery, Wealstone Lane, Upton, Chester CH2 1HD Tel: 01244 382238 Fax: 01244 381576 — MB ChB 1987 Manch.

BROOKES, Samuel Victor (retired) 27 Calvin Road, Winton, Bournemouth BH9 1LN — MRCS Eng. LRCP Lond. 1941.

BROOKES, Simon David 59 Langtons Wharf, The Calls, Leeds LS2 7EF — MB ChB 1998 Leeds.

BROOKES, Sophie Kate 8 Norwich Drive, Birmingham B17 8TB — MB ChB 1993 Leic.; MRCGP 1998.

BROOKES, Mr Victor Stanley (retired) 9 Hintlesham Avenue, Edgbaston, Birmingham B15 2PH Tel: 0121 454 1468 — MB ChB (Hons.) Birm. 1943; FRCS Eng. 1949; MRCS Eng. LRCP Lond. 1943. Hon. Cons. Surg. Gen. Hosp., Qu. Eliz. Hosp. & Childr. Hosp. Birm.; Sen. Fell. Assn. Surgs. GB. Prev: Cons. Surg. W. Midl. Police.

BROOKES-WHITE, Philippa Jane Sarah 9 Hintlesham Avenue, Birmingham B15 2PH — MB BCh 1992 Wales.

BROOKFIELD, Charles David Roger The Medical Centre, J.C. Bamford Excavators Ltd., Rocester, Uttoxeter ST14 5JP Tel: 01889 590323 Fax: 01889 593186; The Croft, Hurstons Lane, Alton, Stoke-on-Trent ST10 4AP Tel: 01538 702570 — MB BChir 1970 Camb.; MB Camb. 1970, BChir 1969; MA Camb. 1970. (Oxf.) Company Med. Adviser JC Bamford Excavators Ltd. Rocester Staffs. Socs: New York Acad. Sci.; Roy. Soc. Med.; Soc. Of Occup. Med. Prev: GP Cheadle; Ho. Off. (Surg.) N. Staffs. Roy. Infirm.; Ho. Phys. Radcliffe Infirm. Oxf.

BROOKFIELD, David Samuel Kirkaldy North Staffordshire Maternity Hospital, Hilton Road, Stoke-on-Trent ST4 6SD Tel: 01782 552445 Fax: 01782 552481; 855 Lightwood Road, Rough Close, Stoke-on-Trent ST3 7HA Tel: 01782 312090 Fax: 01782 312090 Email: brookfielddavid@hotmail.com — MB ChB 1968 Liverp.; 1987 FRCP (UK); 1974 DCH Eng.; 1996 FRCPCH. Cons. Paediat. N. Staffs. Matern. Hosp. Harpfields; Asst. Off. for Higher Specialist Train., RCPCH; Vice Chairm. of Paediatric Comm. of W. Midl.s Postgrad. Med. and Dent. Educat. Socs: Pres. of Midl. Regional Paediatric Soc. Prev: Lect. (Child Health) Univ. Soton.; Lect. (Child Health) Univ. Dar-es-Salaam; Regist. (Paediat.) Alder Hey Hosp. Liverp.

BROOKINGS, Christopher Henry Central Surgery, Sussex Road, Gorleston NR31 6QB Tel: 01493 414141 Fax: 01493 656253; 48 High Road, Gorleston, Gorleston NR31 0PE — MB BS 1970 Lond.; MRCP (UK) 1972; Assoc. Fac. Occupat. Med. RCP Lond. 1980. (St. Geo.) Sen. Partner Centr. Surg., Gorleston; Phys. i/c - N. Sea Med. Centr. BrE. Screening Clinic, Gorleston. Prev: Regist. St. Geo. Hosp. Lond.

BROOKLYN, Trevor Norman North Hampshire Hospital, Aldermaston Road, Basingstoke RG24 9NA Tel: 01256 473202 — MB ChB 1991 Cape Town; MRCP (UK) 1996. Specialist Regist. (Gastroenterol.) N. Hants. Basingstoke. Socs: Med. Protec. Soc. Prev: SHO (Gastroenterol.) Barnet Gen. Hosp.; SHO (Gen. Med.) Edgware Gen. Hosp.; SHO (Gen. Med.) Edendale Hosp., S. Afr.

BROOKMAN, Caroline Anne Department of Anaesthetics, Western General Hospital, Crewe Road South, Edinburgh EH4 2XU Tel: 0131 537 1000 — MB ChB 1990 Ed.; FRCA 1995. (Edinburgh) Cons. Anaesth., W.ern Gen. Hosp., Edin. Prev: SHO Rotat. (Anaesth.) SE Scotl. Train. Scheme, Roy. Infirm. Edin. & St. Johns Livingston; SPR Rotat., Anaesthetics, SE Scotl. Train. Scheme.

BROOKS, Adam John 192 Cobden View Road, Crookes, Sheffield S10 1HT — MB ChB 1992 Sheff.

BROOKS, Alan Arnold 44 Varna Road, Hampton TW12 2BQ Tel: 020 8979 0226 — MB BS 1983 Lond.; BSc Lond. 1980; MD Lond. 1996; MFFP 1995; MRCOG 1991; DCH RCP Glas. 1987. (Univ. Coll. Hosp.) Lect. & Sen. Regist. (O & G) Char. Cross & W.m. Med. Sch. Lond. Socs: Brit. Fertil. Soc. Prev: Regist. (O & G) Qu. Mary's Hosp. Sidcup.

BROOKS, Alan Paxton 24 Boundary Street, London E2 7JE Tel: 020 7613 2868 — MB BS 1978 Lond.; BSc Lond. 1975; FRCR 1985; DMRD 1983. (King's Coll. Hosp.) Sen. Lect. & Hon. Cons. (Diag. Radiol.) St. Bart. Hosp., Roy. Lond. Hosp. & Lond. Chest Hosp. Lond. Prev: Vis. Asst. Prof. Diagn. Radiol. UCSD Med. Centre San Diego, Calif. USA; Sen. Regist. (Diag. Radiol.) & Regist. St. Bart. Hosp. Lond.

BROOKS, Alan Stanley Bowman 11 Kings End, Bicester, Bicester OX26 6DR — MRCS Eng. LRCP Lond. 1968; BA Camb. 1965; DO Eng. 1975. Ophth. Med. Pract. Oxon.; Clin. Asst. (Ophth.), Oxf. Eye Hosp. & Horton Gen. Hosp., Banbury.

BROOKS, Alison Clare 175 Godstow Road, Wolvercote, Oxford OX2 8PG Tel: 01865 513854 — MB BS 1989 Lond.; BSc (Hons.) Lond. 1986; MRCP (UK) 1994.

BROOKS, Alison Clare Tel: 01263 712461 Fax: 01263 713211; The Old Post Office, Edgefield, Melton Constable NR24 2AL Tel: 01263 587236 — MB BS 1983 Newc.; MRCGP 1987; DCH RCP Lond. 1985; DRCOG 1985. (Newc.) p/t GP Princip. Prev: Trainee GP

Norf. FPC; SHO (A & E & Paediat.) Norf. & Norwich Hosp.; SHO (Obst.) Rosie Matern. Hosp. Camb.

BROOKS, Alison Graham Princes Street Surgery, 69 Princes Street, Thurso KW14 7DH Tel: 01847 893154; The Grange, 1 Clarence Street, Thurso KW14 7HE Tel: 01847 894685 — MB ChB 1984 Ed.; MRCGP 1988; DRCOG 1987; DFFP 1996. (Ed.) GP Thurso.; Police Surg. of N.ern Constab.; CMO Family Plann. Prev: SHO (O & G) E. Gen. Hosp; Ho. Off. Med. Unit E.. Gen. Hosp.; Ho. Off. Gastrointestinal Unit W.. Gen. Hosp.

BROOKS, Alistair 24 Garstang Road W., Poulton-le-Fylde, Blackpool — MB ChB 1968 St. And. (St. And.) Med. Off. Dept. Health Social Security. Prev: Ho. Off. (Surg.) Clackmannan Co. Hosp. Alloa; Ho. Off. (Med.) Ballochmyle Hosp. Mauchline; SHO (Med.) Cumbld. Infirm. Carlisle.

BROOKS, Andrew James Lister House Surgery, Lister House, 53 Harrington Street, Pear Tree, Derby DE23 8PF Tel: 01332 271212 Fax: 01332 271939 — BM BS 1990 Nottm.; BMedSci Nottm. 1988; MRCGP 1994. Prev: Trainee GP Derby VTS.

BROOKS, Andrew Philip Royal Hampshire County Hospital, Winchester SO22 5DG Tel: 01962 863535 Fax: 01962 824378 — MB ChB 1971 Sheff.; MSc Ed. 1976; MD Sheff. 1979; FRCP Lond. 1992; FRCP Ed. 1986; MRCP (UK) 1974. (Sheff.) Socs: Fell. Roy. Soc. Med.; Diabetes UK. (Med. & Scientif. & Educat. Sect.); Europ. Assn. Study Diabetes & diabetes Educat. study Gp. Prev: Sen. Regist. E Anglia RHA Ipswich Hosp. & Addenbrooke's Hosp. Camb.; Train. Fell. Med. Research Counc. Dept. Human Genetics Univ. Edin.; Lect. (Med.) Univ. Edin.

BROOKS, Andrew Richard 70 Seabridge Road, Newcastle ST5 2HT — MB BS 1996 Lond.

BROOKS, Annabel Yule Ramblers, Church Place, Pulborough RH20 1AF — MB ChB 1992 Manch.; BSc St. And. 1989. SHO (O & G) All St.s Hosp. Chatham. Prev: Medic Raleigh Internat. Zimbabwe.

BROOKS, Anthony Michael James Henry Department of Anaesthetics, Hinchingbrooke Hospital, Huntingdon PE29 6NT Tel: 01480 416416 Fax: 01480 416561; 30 Church Road, Great Stukeley, Huntingdon PE28 4AL Tel: 01480 455621 — MB BS 1978 Lond.; BSc Lond. 1975; FRCA Eng. 1983. (Lond. Hosp.) Cons. Anaesth. Hinchingbrooke Hosp. Socs: Assn. Anaesth.; Intens. Care Soc. Prev: Sen. Regist. (Anaesth.) Univ. Hosp. Wales.

BROOKS, Ashley Scott 194 Brickhill Dr, Bedford MK41 7NX Tel: 01234 266361 — MB ChB 1997 Leeds. (Leeds) SHO A&E Barnsley DGH. Socs: MPS.

BROOKS, Bernard James (retired) The Cedar Cone, Scholards Lane, Ramsbury, Marlborough SN8 2PL Tel: 01672 520135 — MB BS 1955 Lond.; MRCS Eng. LRCP Lond. 1955; FRCGP 1980, M 1968; DObst RCOG 1956. Prev: GP Princip. 1960-87.

BROOKS, Bethan Victoria 7 Linden Drive, Lostock Hall, Preston PR5 5AS — MB BCh 1990 Wales.

BROOKS, Carol Ann 65 Royal Lodge Road, Belfast BT8 7UL Tel: 01232 793931 — MB BCh BAO 1992 Belf.; MRCGP 1996; DCH Dub. 1995; DFFP 1996; DRCOG Lond. 1997.

BROOKS, Carole Anne Birchwood Surgery, 232-240 Nevells Road, Letchworth SG6 4UB Tel: 01462 683456; 33 Cloisters Road, Letchworth SG6 3JR Tel: 01462 480827 — MB ChB 1984 Liverp.; DRCOG 1989. Prev: SHO (Med.) Walton Hosp. Liverp.; SHO (O & G) Lister Hosp. Stevenage.

BROOKS, Claire Elizabeth Southlea Surgery, 276 Lower Farnham Road, Aldershot GU11 3RB Tel: 01252 344868 Fax: 01252 342596; Runfold Farm Cottage, St. Georges Road, Runfold, Farnham GU10 1PL Tel: 01252 783682 Email: claire@alveyc.freeserve.co.uk — MB ChB 1984 Bristol; MRCGP 1989. Prev: Trainee GP Aldershot; SHO (O & G) Wexham Pk. Hosp. Slough; SHO (Paediat.) Heatherwood Hosp. Ascot.

BROOKS, David Peterloo Medical Centre, 133 Manchester Old Road, Middleton, Manchester M24 4DZ Tel: 0161 643 5005 Fax: 0161 643 7264; The Barn, Tonacliffe Road, Whitworth, Rochdale OL12 8SJ Tel: 01706 521166 Fax: 0161 654 7264 — MB ChB Manch. 1963; MD Manch. 1971; FRCGP 1978, M 1968; DObst RCOG 1965. Assoc. Dir. GP Educat. Dept. Postgrad. Med. & Dent. Univ. Manch; Chairm. GP Writers Assn. Prev: Provost NW Fac. Roy. Coll. Gen. Practs.; Ho. Phys. & Ho. Surg. Manch. Roy. Infirm.; Ho. Surg. (Obst.) Withington Hosp. Manch.

BROOKS, David Arthur Lincoln Deepdale Road Healthcare Centre, Deepdale Road, Preston PR1 5AF Tel: 01772 655533 Fax: 01772 653414 — MB BCh 1987 Wales.

BROOKS, Professor David James Imperial College School of Medicine, Hammersmith Hospital, London W12 0NN Tel: 020 8383 3172 Fax: 020 8383 2029 Email: dbrooks@esc.mrc.ac.uk; 24 Sutton Road, Heston, Hounslow TW5 0PF Tel: 020 8572 0672 Fax: 020 8572 0672 — MB BS 1979 Lond.; BA (Hons.) Oxf. 1972; MD Lond. 1986; FRCP Lond. 1993; MRCP (UK) 1982; Dsc Med Lond 1998. (Univ. Coll. Lond.) Hartnett Prof. of Neurol. Hammersmith Hosp. & Nat. Hosp. for Neurol. & Neurosurg. Lond.; Head Neurosci. MRC. Cyclotion Unit Hammersmith Hosp. Socs: UK Pk.inson's Dis. Soc. Med. Advis. Panel; EU Assn. of Cell Transpl. (NECTAR); Assn. Brit. Neurols. Prev: Reader & Hon. Cons. Neurol. Lond.; Sen. Lect. & Hon. Cons. (Neurol.) Hammersmith, Ealing & Nat. Hosp. Neurol.

BROOKS, David John Chesterfield and North Derbyshire Royal Hospital NHS Trust, Calow, Chesterfield S44 5BL Tel: 01246 552670 Fax: 01246 552713 Email: david.brooks@cndrh-tr.trent.nhs.uk; 544 Chatsworth Road, Chesterfield S40 3AY Tel: 01246 568510 — MB ChB 1987 Liverp.; MRCGP 1992; T(GP) 1991; DRCOG 1990. Macmillan Cons. in Palliat. Med.; Hon. Lect. in Palliat. Med., Univ. of Sheff. Socs: Assn. for Palliat. Med.; Brit. Sleep Soc.; Briktish Soc. for Med. and Dent. Hypn. Prev: CRC Lect. (Palliat. Med.) Univ. Sheff.; SHO (Palliat. Med.) Hayward Hse. Nottm.; GP Chesterfield.

BROOKS, David Kilroy (retired) The Granary, Lordington, Chichester PO18 9DB Tel: 01243 378900 — MB BS 1954 Lond.; PhD Lond. 1967, MD 1963; FACP 1970; FACC 1970; FCCP 1978; FRCPath 1979, M 1967. Prev: Hon. Cons. Phys. St. Mary's Hosp. Lond.

BROOKS, Edward Francis (retired) Swaywood Cottage, Mead End Road, Sway, Lymington SO41 6EE Tel: 01590 682303 — MB BS 1953 Lond.; DA Eng. 1958. Prev: GP Highcliffe.

BROOKS, Eileen Mary Teresa (retired) 73 Havant Road, Emsworth PO10 7LE Tel: 01243 379446 — MB BCh BAO NUI 1942. Prev: Surg. Lt. RNVR.

BROOKS, Evelyn Ruth (retired) 69 Barton Road, Cambridge CB3 9LG Tel: 01223 350207 — LMSSA 1954 Lond. Liveryman Soc. Apoth.

BROOKS, Geoffrey Moneymoon, Preston Road, Ribchester, Preston PR3 3YD — MB ChB 1957 Manch. Company Med. Off. James Hall (S.port) Ltd. Preston; Mem. Med. Bd.ing Panel DSS. Adjudicating Med. Auth. Prev: GP Preston.

BROOKS, Gordon John 27 Monckton Road, Alverstoke, Gosport PO12 2BG Tel: 01705 584616 Fax: 01705 502568 Email: gordon.brooks@btinternet.com — MB ChB 1980 Dundee; PhD Lond. 1993. Systems Designer EMIS Med. Informat. Systems Ltd. Leeds. Prev: Surg. Lt-Cdr. RN.

BROOKS, Helen Dept. of Anaesthesia, Leicester Royal Infirmary, Leicester LE1 5WW — BM 1989 Soton.; MRCP (UK) 1992; FRCA 1995. (Southampton) p/t (Anaesth.) Leicester Roy. Infirm.

BROOKS, Helen Ruth Fernbank, King St., London N2 8EA — MB BS 1989 Lond.

BROOKS, Jack William (retired) Quaranta, 40 Brackley Avenue, Colwyn Bay LL29 7UU Tel: 01492 530843 Fax: 01492 530843 — MRCS Eng. LRCP Lond. 1954; FFA RCS Eng. 1969; DA Eng. 1963. Hon. Clin. Teach. Univ. Wales & Univ. Manch. Prev: Cons. Anaesth. Clwyd N. Hosp. Gp.

BROOKS, Jacqueline 67a Frien Barnet Road, London N11 3EH — MB BCh 1991 Witwatersrand.

BROOKS, Jan Elizabeth Birnam Bank, Birnam Glen, Birnam, Dunkeld PH8 0BW — MB ChB 1979 Dundee; MRCGP 1983; DCH RCP Lond. 1983; DRCOG 1982.

BROOKS, Jason Whitworth Polstrong Cottage, Polstrong, Camborne TR14 0QA — MB BS 1994 Lond.

BROOKS, Joanne Rose 29 New Cheltenham Road, Kingswood, Bristol BS15 1TL Email: jobrooksearle@hotmail.com — MB BS 1990 Lond.; DCH; MRCP; MRCPCH. (Royal London) Specialist Regist. (Paediat.), Dept of Community Child Health, Bath.

BROOKS, John Bradley Standish Brooks, 9 West Street, Congleton CW12 1JN Tel: 01260 277716 Fax: 01260 297947; Astbury View, Church Lane, North Rode, Congleton CW12 2PE Tel: 01260 223486 Fax: 01260 297947 — MB BS 1971 Lond.; MRCGP 1977; DObst RCOG 1976; DCH Eng. 1974. (St. Bart.) Clin. Med.

Off. Macclesfield HA. Socs: Roy. Soc. Med. Prev: Trainee GP Brighton & Lewes VTS; SHO (Paediat.) Roy. Alexandra Hosp. Sick Childr. Brighton.

BROOKS, John Michael Hall (retired) 11 Elmodesham House, High St., Amersham HP7 0EN Tel: 01494 722992 — BM BCh 1952 Oxf.; BM BCh Oxon. 1952.

BROOKS, Mr Jonathan Henry The Portland Hospital, 214 Great Portland Street, London W1W 5QN Tel: 0207 3875566 Fax: 0207 3875599 Email: jhbrooks@obgynae.co.uk — MB BChir 1974 Camb.; MB Camb. 1974, BChir 1973; FRCS Ed. 1983; MRCS Eng. LRCP Lond. 1973; FRCOG 1995, M 1980; DRCOG 1977; DCH RCPS Glas. 1977. Indep. Specialist in Obs. & Gyn., Isle of Man; Cons., The Portland Hosp.; Hon. Cons., St. Lukes Hosp. Prev: Sen. Regist. (O & G) W. Midl. RHA. & Hon. Lect. Univ. Birm.; Lect. (O & G) Bristol Univ.; Cons. Gyn. Hinchingbrooke Hosp. Huntingdon.

BROOKS, Judith Denise The Beckington Family Practice, St Luke's Surgery, St Luke's Road, Beckington, Bath BA11 6SE Tel: 01373 830316 Fax: 01373 831261 Email: stlukes@globalnet.com; 8 Goose Street, Beckington, Bath BA11 6SS — MB ChB 1981 Bristol; MRCGP 1989; DRCOG 1987; DCH RCP Lond. 1985. (Bristol)

BROOKS, Kathleen Mary Beaver Lodge, Greet, Winchcombe, Cheltenham — MB BS 1961 Lond.; MRCS Eng. LRCP Lond. 1961; DCH Eng. 1964; DRCOG 1963.

BROOKS, Kathryn Jane Surgery, Judges Close, East Grinstead RH19 3AE Tel: 01342 324628 Fax: 01342 318055; Pickeridge, Chapel Lane, Forest Row, East Grinstead RH19 5BU Tel: 01342 822294 — MB ChB 1980 Bristol; MRCGP 1986; DRCOG 1986. Prev: Trainee GP Torbay VTS.

BROOKS, Mr Marcus John 62 Biddulph Mansions, Elgin Avenue, Maida Vale, London W9 1HT Tel: 020 7266 5870 Email: marcus.brooks@btinternet.com — MB BChir 1993 Camb.; MA Camb. 1995, BA (Med. Sci) 1991; FRCS Eng. 1998. Clin. Research Fell.(Vascula) St Mary's Hosp., Paddington, Lond. Prev: SHO (Paediat. Surg.) Gt. Ormond St. Hosp. SHO (Vasc. Surg.) St. Mary's Hosp. Paddington; SHO (Orthop.) Centr. Middlx. Hosp.; SHO (Vasc. Surg.) Ashford Hosp. Middlx.

BROOKS, Margaret Elizabeth Department of Radiology, Aberdeen Royal Infirmary, Foresterhill, Aberdeen AB25 2ZN Tel: 01224 681818 Email: margaret.brooks@arh.grampian.scot.nhs.uk; Forester's Croft, Stonehaven AB39 3QA — MB ChB 1985 Glas.; FRCR 1993; DMRD Aberd. 1992; FRCP Edin 2000. Cons. Radiol. Aberd. Roy. Infirm. Prev: Cons. Radiol. The Ayr Hosp.; Sen. Regist. (Radiol.) Roy. Infirm. Edin.; Regist. (Radiol.) Aberd. Roy. Infirm.

BROOKS, Marie Elizabeth Sandywell House, Three Ashes La, Newent GL18 1DF — MB ChB 1997 Bristol.

BROOKS, Maurice Ronald West Street Surgery, 16 West Street, Newport PO30 1PR Tel: 01983 522198 Fax: 01983 524258; 6 Cypress Road, Newport PO30 1EY — MB ChB 1974 Birm.; BSc (Hons. Anat. Sci.) Birm. 1971, MB ChB 1974; MRCP (UK) 1977. (Birmingham) Prev: SHO (Med.) Birm. Gen. Hosp.; SHO Midl. Centre Neurosurg. & Neurol.; Ho. Surg. Birm. Accid. Hosp.

BROOKS, Michael Grange Road Practice, Bermandsey Health Centre, 108 Grange Road, London SE1 3BW Tel: 020 7237 1078 — MB BS 1981 Lond.; BSc Lond. 1978, MB BS 1981; FRCS Ed. 1986. (King's Coll.) GP Lond. Prev: Regist. (Cardiothoracic Surg.) King's Coll. Hosp. Lond.; Regist. (Surg.) John Radcliffe & Ch.ill Hosps. Oxf.

BROOKS, Mr Michael Damien 42 Underhill Road, London SE22 0QT — MB BS 1981 Lond.; FRCS (Gen.) 1996; FRCS Eng. 1986. (St. Thos. Hosp.)

BROOKS, Neil Charles Leighton Hospital, Middlewich Rd, Crewe CW1 4QJ — MB ChB 1988 Liverp.; FRCA 1994. Cons. Anaesth., Leighton Hosp., Crewe.

BROOKS, Nicholas Hugh Cardiac Department, South Manchester University Hospitals NHS Trust, Wythenshawe Hospital, Manchester M23 9LT Tel: 0161 291 2387 Fax: 01612912389 Email: nickh.brooks@smuht.nwest.nhs.uk — MB BS 1970 Lond.; MB BS (Hons.) Lond. 1970; MD Lond. 1979; FRCP Lond. 1990; MRCP (UK) 1973. (St. Bart. Hosp.) Cons. Cardiol, S. Manch. Univ. Hosp.s NHS Trust Wythenshawe Hosp. Manch. Socs: Chairm.: Specialist Advisery Comm. in Cardiol. 2000; Brit. Cardiac Soc. (Hon. Sec 1996-98); Fell. Europ. Soc. Cardiol. Prev: Clin. Lect. (Cardiol.) Cardiothoracic Inst.; Hon. Sen. Regist. (Cardiol.) Lond. Chest Hosp. & Lond. Hosp.; Research Fell. Brit. Heart Foundat., St. Geo. Hosp. Lond.

BROOKS, Norman Charles (retired) Sedgley, Eagle Brow, Lymm WA13 0NA Tel: 0192 575 4877 — MB BS Lond. 1953. Prev: Ho. Surg., Out-pat. Off. & Asst. Ho. Phys. Guy's Hosp. Lond.

BROOKS, Patricia Jean 51 Gunnersbury Court, Bollo Lane, Acton, London W3 8JN — MB BCh 1961 Witwatersrand; DObst RCOG 1970; MRCGP 1969. (Witwatersrand) Socs: BMA. Prev: Regist. (Psychiat.) St. Bernards Hosp. S.all; Ho. Off. (Med. & Surg.) Baragwanath Hosp.; Ho. Off. (O & G) Gulson Rd. Hosp. Coventry.

BROOKS, Patrick William (retired) 11 Thirlestane Road, Edinburgh EH9 1AL Tel: 0131 447 7634 Fax: 0131 447 7634 — MB ChB Ed. 1963; BSc Ed. 1960; FRCPsych 1996, M 1971; DPM Ed. 1968. Prev: Sen. Med. Off. Scott. Office Dept. of Health.

BROOKS, Mr Peter Lewis (retired) 25 Le Brun Road, Eastbourne BN21 2HY Tel: 01323 33802 — MB BS 1959 Lond.; FRCS Eng. 1964; MRCS Eng. LRCP Lond. 1959. Prev: Cons. Surg. E.bourne Dist. Gen. Hosp.

BROOKS, Peter Ronald Knowle House Surgery, 4 Meavy Way, Crownhill, Plymouth PL5 3JB Tel: 01752 771895 — MB BS 1980 Lond.

BROOKS, Peter Thomas Radiology Department, Lister Hospital, Coreys Mill Lane, Stevenage SG1 4AB Tel: 01438 781028 Fax: 01438 781176 Email: peterbrookes@breathemail.net; 33 Cloisters Road, Letchworth SG6 3JR Email: brooks@33cloisters.freeserve.co.uk — MB ChB 1979 Liverp.; FRCR 1986; DMRD Liverp. 1984. Cons. Radiol. Lister Hosp. Stevenage.

BROOKS, Peter Timothy Eglwysbach Surgery, Berw Road, Pontypridd CF37 2AA Tel: 01443 406811 Fax: 01443 405457 — MB BS 1983 Lond.; BSc (Hons.) Physiol. Lond. 1980; MRCP (UK) 1986; MRCGP 1989; DRCOG 1989. (St. Mary's) GP; Hosp. Practitioner (Neurol.), Univ. Hosp. of Wales, Cardiff. Prev: Regist. (Neurol.) Univ. Hosp. Wales Cardiff; Regist. (Med.) Roy. Gwent Hosp. Newport; Ho. Surg. & Ho. Phys. St. Mary's Hosp. Lond.

BROOKS, Philip Edward Victoria House, Eign St., Hereford HR4 0AN Tel: 01432 272012 — MB ChB 1971 Sheff.; MSc Manch. 1979; FFCM 1987, M 1981. (Univ. Sheff.) Dir. Pub. Health Herefordsh. HA. Socs: Assn. Directors of Pub. Health; Soc. Community Med. Prev: SCM (Social Servs.) Glos. AHA; Sen. Regist. (Community Med.) N. W.. RHA; Regist. (Psychiat.) Univ. Hosp. S. Manch.

BROOKS, Rachel Mary Riverside Health Centre, Cowbridge Road E., Cardiff CF11 9SH Tel: 029 2037 1221; 40 Tydraw Road, Roath Park, Cardiff CF23 5HB — MB ChB 1984 Liverp.; MB ChB Liverp. l984; MSc (Commnity Child Health) Wales 1997; DCH RCP Lond. 1995. Staff Grade Doctor Child & Adolesc. Health Directorate Cardiff; Lect. Dept. of Child Health 1998.

BROOKS, Richard Little Plumstead Hospital, Norwich NR13 5EW Tel: 01603 711277 — BM BS 1980 Nottm.; BMedSci Nottm. 1978; MRCGP 1985. (Nottm.) Staff Grade (Learning Disabilities), Norwich Community Health Partnership, Norwich. Prev: Staff Grade Pract. (Psychiat. Old Age) Norf. Ment. Health Care NHS Trust Norwich; Clin. Med. Off. (Psychiat. Old Age) Norf. Ment. Health Care NHS Trust Norwich.

***BROOKS, Richard David** 819 Wilmslow Road, Didsbury, Manchester M20 2SN Tel: 0161 445 5561 — MB ChB 1996 Manch.

BROOKS, Robert Vincent Lister House Surgery, The Common, Hatfield AL10 0NL Tel: 01707 268822 Fax: 01707 263990; Tel: 01707 268822 — MB BS 1976 Lond. (St. Bart.) GP Princip. Prev: Squadron Ldr. RAF Med. Br.; Ho. Phys. N. Middlx. Hosp. Lond.; Ho. Surg. Metrop. Hosp. Lond.

BROOKS, Roderick John (retired) The Elms, Dundee Rd, Meigle, Blairgowrie PH12 8SD Tel: 01828 640827 — MB BS Lond. 1973; BSc (Hons.) Lond. 1970; MRCS Eng. LRCP Lond. 1973. Prev: GP Brighton, E Sussex.

BROOKS, Roderick William Somerville 33 Gorway Road, Highgate, Walsall WS1 3BE Tel: 01922 39338 — MB ChB 1976 Bristol; MRCP (UK) 1982; LMSSA Lond. 1976. Cons. Phys. (Geriat. Med.) Walsall HA. Prev: Sen. Regist. Rotat. (Gen. & Geriat. Med.) W. Midl. HA; Regist. (Geriat. Med.) Dudley Rd. Hosp. Birm.; Regist. (Geriat. Med. & Gen. Med.) Pilgrim Hosp. Boston.

BROOKS, Roger John Anaesthetics Department, Royal Infirmary,, Huddersfield HD3 3EA — BM BS 1975 Nottm.; PhD Nottm. 1971, BPharm 1967, BM BS 1975; FFA RCS 1981.

BROOKS, Ronald Frank Woodlands, 10 Coburg Road, Dorchester DT1 2HW Tel: 01305 263651 — MB ChB Bristol 1942; MRCP Ed. 1950; FRCP Ed. 1998. (Bristol) JP Dorset; Dep. Med. Off. HM Prison Dorchester; Local Civil Serv. Med. Off. Dorchester. Socs: Fell. Roy. Soc. Med.; BMA. Prev: Ho. Phys. Canad. Red Cross Memor. Hosp. Taplow; Regist. (Med.) Gen. Hosp. Soton.; Sen. Regist. (Med.) Barnet Gen. Hosp.

BROOKS, Sarah Jane 130 Victor Road, Penge, London SE20 7JT — MB BS 1994 Lond.; MA Camb. 1994; MRCP 1998. SHO (A & E) Hastings; SHO Haemophilia Centre Oxf. Radcliffe; SHO (Med.) Bournemouth; SHO (Histopathol.) Char. Cross Hosp.; SHO (Community Psychiat.) GP VTS Univ. Hosp. Lewisham Trust. Socs: MDU; BMA; Roy. Coll. Phys.

BROOKS, Scott Galt 19 Springfield Road, Bishopbriggs G64 1PG Tel: 0141 772 4744; 40 Kirkintilloch Road, Lenzie G66 4RL Tel: 0141 772 4744 — MB ChB 1950 Glas. (Glas.)

BROOKS, Sheila 11 Church Road, Helen's Bay, Bangor BT19 1TP Tel: 01247 853213 — MB BCh BAO 1953 Belf. (Belf.) SCMO E. Health & Soc. Serv. Bd. N. Irel. Prev: Train. Med. Off. Federat. of Family Plann. Assns. Malaysia.

BROOKS, Simon John 3 Steeds Ter, Oakhill, Bath BA3 5HB — MB BS 1997 Lond.

BROOKS, Mr Stephen Gerard Fairfax House, Bilbrough, York YO23 3PH — BM BCh 1981 Oxf.; MA Oxf. 1982; ChM Leeds 1992; FRCS Eng. 1986. (Oxf.) Cons. Gen. Surg. York Dist. Hosp.; Hon. Serv. Lect. in Surg., The Univ. of Leeds. Socs: Surgic. Research Soc.; Assn. Surg.; Vasc. Surgic. Soc. GB. Prev: Sen. Regist. Yorks. Health; Regist. (Gen. Surg.) St. Jas. Univ. Hosp. Leeds.

BROOKS, Stephen John David 20 Lodge Gardens, Alverstoke, Gosport PO12 3PY — MB BCh BAO 1962 Dub.; MD Dub. 1977; MRCP (UK) 1971; DCH Eng. 1972. (Dub.) Socs: BMA; Amer. Soc. Microbiol.

BROOKS, Mr Stuart The Paddocks, Lapworth St, Lapworth, Solihull B94 5QS Tel: 01564 783305 Fax: 01564 785396 Email: orthobrooks@compuserve.com — MB BS 1976 Lond.; BSc Lond. 1973; FRCS Eng. 1980. Cons. Orthop. & Trauma Surg. Heartlands & Solihull Hosp. NHS Trust. Prev: Sen. Regist. (Orthop.) Roy. Orthop. Hosp. Birm.; Regist. (Orthop.) Roy. Orthop. Hosp. Birm.; Regist. Rotat. (Surg.) St. Jas. Hosp. Leeds.

BROOKS, Susan Catherine A & E Dept, Yeovil District Hospital, Higher Kingston, Yeovil B21 4BT Tel: 01935 475122 — MB ChB 1973 Manch.; MRCGP 1979; DA Eng. 1978. Cons. (A & E Med.) Yeovil Dist. Hosp.

BROOKS, Thomas Arnold Victor 87 Wyatt Park Road, London SW2 3TW Tel: 020 8674 0509 — MB ChB 1953 Bristol. (Bristol) Prev: Ho. Surg. (Midw. & Gyn.) Taunton & E. Som. Hosp.; Ho. Surg. (Cas. & Orthop.) Bristol Roy. Infirm.

BROOKS, Timothy John Gilby Babbling, Bourne Gardens, Porton, Salisbury SP4 0NU Tel: 01980 612032 Email: tim.brooks@mcmail.com — LMSSA 1980 Lond.; MA Camb. 1981, MB BChir 1980; BSc Lond. 1992; MRCPath 1993. cons. Microbiol. Army Med. Servs.

BROOKS, William Cross Cottage, Credenhill, Hereford HR4 7DJ Tel: 01432 761875 — MB BS 1950 Lond.; MRCS Eng. LRCP Lond. 1950; FFA RCS Eng. 1955. (Univ. Coll. Hosp.) Cons. Anaesth. Hereford Hosp. Gp. Socs: Fell. Roy. Soc. Med. Prev: Sen. Regist. Anaesth. Univ. Coll. Hosp.; Vis. Fell. Anaesth. Strong Memor. Hosp. Univ. Rochester, U.S.A.; RAF.

BROOKS, William Vincent 69 Ingrebourne Garden, Upminster RM14 1BN — MB BS Lond. 1950. (St. Bart.)

BROOKSBANK, Mr Andrew James 17 Briggland Court, Wilsden, Bradford BD15 0HL — MB ChB 1993 Aberd.; FRCS Ed 1997.

BROOKSBANK, Helen Ann Shepherds Barn, Fockbury Mill Lane, Dodford, Bromsgrove B61 9BA — MB ChB 1993 Birm.; ChB Birm. 1993.

BROOKSBANK, Kenneth Linn 8 Kendal Road, East Kilbride, Glasgow G75 8QT — MB ChB 1995 Glas.

BROOKSBY, Iain Alasdair Burns Hill House Consulting Rooms, Bupa Hospital, Old Watton Road, Colney, Norwich NR4 7SZ Tel: 01603 454196; Swainsthorpe Hall, Swainsthorpe, Norwich NR14 8QA Tel: 01508 470398 Fax: 01508 471538 — MB Camb. 1970, BChir 1969; FRCP Lond. 1985; MRCP (UK) 1972. (St. Thos.) Cons. Phys. (Cardiol.) Norf. & Norwich Univ. Hosp. NHS Trust; Med. Dir., Norf. & Norwich Univ. Hosp. NHS Trust. Prev: Sen. Regist. (Med.), Cardiac Regist. & Brit. Heart Foundat. Research; Fell. St. Thos. Hosp. Lond.

BROOKSBY, William Paul Pontefract General Infirmary, Friarwood Lane, Pontefract WF8 1PL Tel: 01977 606713 Fax: 01977 606317 Email: paul.brooksby@panp-tr.northy.nhs.uk — BM BS 1985 Nottm.; DM 1994. (Nottingham) Cons. Cardiol. Socs: RCP; Brit. Cardiac Soc.; Brit. Soc. Echocardiogr. Prev: Sen. Regist. (Cardiol.) Univ. Hosp. Nottm.

BROOKSHAW, Joan Doreen The Willows, Somerswey, Shalford, Guildford GU4 8EQ — MB BS 1962 Lond.; MRCS Eng. LRCP Lond. 1962; FRCR 1975; FFR 1974; DMRT Eng. 1966. (Middlx.) Prev: Sen. Regist. (Radiother.) Guy's Hosp. Lond.

BROOM, Andrew Michael 13 Durham Avenue, Bromley BR2 0QE — MB ChB 1984 Leeds; MB ChB Leeds l984.

BROOM, Carolyn Sunfield Medical Centre, Sunfield Place, Stanningley, Leeds — MB ChB 1976 Leeds; MRCGP 1983; DRCOG 1980. GP Pudsey.

BROOM, Ian Geoffrey 21-23 Maurice Avenue, Mallacoota Vic. 3892, Australia Tel: 0151 580777 Fax: 0151 580668; 8 Crossway, Bramhall, Stockport SK7 1LB — MB BCh 1984 Wales; BSc (Hons.) St. And. 1981; MB BCh Wales l984; MRCGP 1989; DA (UK) 1990. Prev: Rural Regist. (Gen. Pract.) NSW, Austral.; SRMO (Obst. & Gyn.) Geelong Hosp. Vict., Austral.; SHO (Anaesth.) Stepping Hill Hosp. Stockport.

BROOM, John Department of Clinical Biochemisty, Medical School Buildings, Foresterhill, Aberdeen AB25 2ZN Tel: 01224 681818; Bracken Lea, Rhu-Na-Haven Road, Aboyne AB34 5JB — MB ChB 1975 Glas.; BSc (Hons.) Aberd. 1971; MRCP (UK) 1993; MRCPath 1987. Cons. Clin. Biochem. Aberd. Roy. Hosps. NHS Trust; Sen. Lect. (Clin. Biochem.) Univ. Aberd. Socs: Assn. Clin. Biochem. (Sec. Scott. Region.). Prev: Lect. & Sen. Regist. (Surg.) & Clin. Biochem. Univ. Aberd.; Wellcome Research Fell. (Path.) Glas. W.. Infirm.

BROOM, Terasa 20 Cygnet Road, Chatham ME5 8SB — MB ChB 1998 Leeds.

BROOMAN, Ian Charles The Oaks, Nightingale Way, Swanley BR8 7UP Tel: 01322 668775 Fax: 01322 668010; Foxhole, Calfstock Lane, Farningham, Dartford DA4 9JH Tel: 01322 863240 — MRCS Eng. LRCP Lond. 1973; FRCGP 1993, M 1984. (King's Coll. Hosp.)

BROOMAN, Mr Peter John Cole 10 Red Lane, Disley, Stockport SK12 2NP; (rooms), Ryley Mount, 432 Buxton Road, Stockport SK2 7JQ — MB ChB 1972 Sheff.; FRCS Eng. 1977. Cons. Urol. Surg. Stepping Hill Hosp. Stockport.

BROOMBY, Rupert Charles William Oak Croft, West Heath Lane, Sevenoaks TN13 1TA — MB ChB 1996 Manch.

BROOME, Catherine Jane 9 Croft Manor, Glossop SK13 8PP — MB ChB 1987 Birm.

BROOME, Ian James Department of Anaesthesia, Falkirk and District Royal Infirmary, Major's Loan, Falkirk FK1 5QE — MB ChB 1984 Manch.

BROOME, Jonathan David 9 Croft Manor, Glossop SK13 8PP — MB ChB 1989 Birm.

BROOME, Jonathan Richard, Surg. Cdr. RN Institute of Naval Medicine, Crescent Road, Alverstoke, Gosport PO12 2DL Tel: 01705 768031 Fax: 01705 504823; c/o 17 Front Street, Shotley Bridge, Consett DH8 0HH Tel: 01207 581020 — MB BS 1980 Lond.; MRCP (UK) 1985; MFOM RCP Lond. 1992, A 1988; DIH Eng. 1988. (King's Coll. Hosp.) Head Undersea Med. & Cons. Adviser Diving Med. Inst. Naval Med. Alverstoke; Med. Dir. (Hyperbaric Med.) Roy. Hosp. Haslar Gosport Hants.; Defence Adviser (Diving Med.). Socs: Undersea & Hyperbaric Med. Soc.; Soc. Occupat. Med. Prev: Exchange Med. Off. US Naval Med. Research Inst., Bethesda, MD; Dep. Princip. Med. Off. HM Naval Base Portsmouth; Occupat. Health Med. Off. Clyde Submarine Base FasLa.

***BROOME, Matthew Richard** 5 Carter Gr, Hereford HR1 1NT Tel: 01432 278033 Email: m.broome@iop.kcl.ac.uk — MB ChB 1997 Birm.; MBChB (Hons.) Birm. 1997; BSc (Hons.) Birm. 1994.

BROOME, Muriel (retired) 30 Warren Road, Woodley, Reading RG5 3AR Tel: 0118 969 3528 — MB BS Lond. 1955; MFFP 1994; DObst RCOG 1956. Dir. Family Plann. Serv. W. Berks. HA.

BROOME, Paul Christopher 125 Valley Road, Chorleywood, Rickmansworth WD3 4BN Tel: 01923 711224 Fax: 01923 711225 — MB ChB 1975 Sheff.; FFPM RCP (UK) 1994. Vice-Pres. & Med.

Dir. Clin. Trials & Regulat. Affairs Aphton Corp. Calif., USA. Prev: Med. Dir. BIOS (Consultancy & Contract Research) Bagshot.

BROOMFIELD, Alexander Allen Flat 5, 32 Sutherland St., London SW1V 4JZ — MB BS 1996 Lond.

BROOMFIELD, Dorothy May (retired) 48 Shakespeare Road, Luton LU4 0HS Tel: 01582 573195 — MB BCh BAO Dub. 1955. Prev: Clin. Med. Off. S. Beds. Community Health Care Trust.

BROOMFIELD, Dylan James 180 Walton Road, Sale M33 4FG — MB BS 1996 Lond.

BROOMFIELD, Rebecca Jane Downside East, 26 Quarry Road, Winchester SO23 0JG — MB ChB 1998 Birm.

BROOMHALL, John Torbay Hospital, Lawes Bridge, Torquay TQ2 7AA Tel: 01803 614567 Email: john.broomhall@sdevonhe-tr.swest.nhs.uk; Kings Aish House, Luscombe Lane, Paignton TQ3 3ZW Tel: 01803 557908 Email: broomhall@btinternet.com — MB BS 1975 Lond.; BSc Lond. 1972; FRCP Lond. 1994; MRCP (UK) 1980; FRCPCH 1997. (Roy. Lond. Hosp. Med. Coll.) Cons. Paediat. Torbay Hosp. Torquay. Socs: Regional Advisor (S.W.) RCPCH. Prev: Cons. Neonat. Roy. Devon & Exeter Hosp.; Lect. (Paediat.) Char. Cross Hosp. Lond.

BROOMHEAD, Charles Robert Matthew Hawthorns Surgery, 331 Birmingham Road, Sutton Coldfield B72 1DL Tel: 0121 373 2211 Fax: 0121 382 1274; 18 Greenhill Road, Sutton Coldfield B72 1DS Tel: 0121 350 8668 Fax: 0121 382 1274 Email: charles.broomhead@lineone.net — MB ChB 1974 Birm.; MRCGP 1981; DRCOG 1978; DA Eng. 1976. (Birmingham) Hon. Clin. Lect. Univ. of Birm.

BROOMHEAD, Christopher John 37 Park Avenue S., London N8 8LU — MB BS 1986 Lond.; BSc Lond. 1983, MB BS 1986; FRCA. 1992.

BROOMHEAD, Mr Ivor William (retired) 7 Saxon Place, Lower Buckland Road, Lymington SO41 9EZ Tel: 01590 671975 — MB BChir 1948 Camb.; BA Camb. 1945, MA 1949, MChir 1958; FRCS Eng. 1954. Prev: Cons. Plastic. Surg. Roy. Masonic Hosp., Hosp.for Sick Childr. & Guy's Hosp. Lond.

BROOMHEAD, Leslie Robert Flat 2, Hamilton Gate, 53 Hamilton Road, London W5 2EE — MB ChB 1993 Leeds.

BROOMHEAD, Maureen Elizabeth The Surgery, 2 Schoolacre Road, Shard End, Birmingham B34 6RB Tel: 0121 747 2911 Fax: 0121 730 3006; 18 Greenhill Road, Sutton Coldfield B72 1DS Tel: 0121 350 8668 — MB ChB 1975 Birm. (Birmingham)

BROPHY, Christopher Stephen The Lakeside Practice, The Health Centre, Spa Pool Rd, Askern, Doncaster DN6 0JB Tel: 01302 700212 Fax: 01302 707870 — BM BS 1978 Nottm.; BMedSci (Hons.) 1976. (Nottm.)

BROPHY, Conor Jane 55 Westella Road, Kirkella, Hull HU10 7QL — MB BS 1978 Adelaide; MRCP (UK) 1982.

BROPHY, Joseph Vincent Wells Road, Strood, Rochester ME2 2PW Tel: 01634 719692 Fax: 01634 717855 — BM BCh 1974 Oxf.; MRCGP 1991; DTM & H Liverp. 1983; DRCOG 1977.

BROSCH, James Anthony Hathaway Surgery, 32 New Road, Chippenham SN15 1HR Tel: 01249 447766 Fax: 01249 443948 — MB BChir 1986 Camb.; MA Camb. 1985; MRCGP 1991; DRCOG 1990. Prev: SHO (A & E) Roy. Gwent Hosp. Newport; SHO (Paediat.) Nevill Hall Hosp. Abergavenny Gwent; Resid. Med. Off. Kempsey Dist. Hosp. NSW, Austral.

BROSENS, Jan Flat B, 126 Talbot Road, London W11 1JA — MD 1990 Louvain.

BROSH, Suzanne Jane 2 Beechfield Grove, Commbe Dingle, Bristol BS9 2RZ — MB BS 1975 Lond.; FFA RCS Eng. 1979.

BROSNAHAN, Donal Michael 36 Wilson Road, Sheffield S11 8RN — MB BCh BAO 1981 NUI.

BROSNAN, Catherine Margaret 77 Pentney Road, Balham, London SW12 0PA — MB BS 1989 Lond.; FRCA 1994. Specialist Regist. (Anaesth.) Lond.

BROSNAN, R D Birches Medical Centre, Polefield Road, Prestwich, Manchester M25 2GU Tel: 0161 773 3037 Fax: 0161 773 3640.

BROSNAN, Stephen Gerard Dept. of Anaesthetics, Luton & Dunstable Hospital, Lewsey Rd, Luton LU4 0DZ — MB BS 1989 Lond.; FRCA 1994. Cons. Anaesth. Luton & Dunstable NHS Trust.

BROSTER, Gillian Margaret 75 South Lodge Drive, Southgate, London N14 4XG — MB ChB 1975 Ed.; MRCPsych 1985; MFHom 1980; MRCGP 1980; DCH Eng. 1980; DRCOG 1979. Cons. Child & Family Psychiat. Enfield Community Care Trust. Prev: Sen. Regist. (Child & Family Psychiat.) Tavistock Clinic Lond.

BROSTOFF, Professor Jonathan Centre for Allergy Research, Department of Immunology, University College London Medical School, Middlesex Hospital, London W1N 8AA Tel: 020 7504 9351 Fax: 020 7504 9357 Email: j.brostoff@ucl.ac.uk; 34 Fitzjohns Avenue, London NW3 5NB Tel: 020 7435 1563 Fax: 020 7435 7648 — BM BCh Oxf. 1960; MA Oxf. 1960, BA (Hons. Physiol.) Oxf. 1956; DSc Lond. 1987; DM Oxf. 1980; FRCP Lond. 1980, M 1966; FRCPath 1982, M 1974. (St. Mary's) Prof. Allergy & Environm. Health Univ Coll. Lond. Med. Sch.; Phys. i/c Allergy Clin. Middlx. Hosp.; Hon. Cons. Phys. Middlx. Hosp. Lond.; Dir. Diagn. Immunol. Laborat. UCL Hosps. Socs: Fell. Roy. Soc. Med. (Ex-Pres. Sect. Clin. Immunol. & Allergy); (Ex-Sec.) Brit. Soc. Allergy & Clin. Immunol. Prev: Leverhulme Research Schol.; Erasmus Wilson Demonst. RCS; Regist. (Allergy) St. Mary's Hosp. Lond.

BROTHERIDGE, Sean Paul Harrogate District Hospital, Lancaster Park Road, Harrogate HG2 7SX Tel: 01423 555305 Email: sean.brotheridge@hhc tr.northy.nhs.uk — MB ChB 1990 Leeds; MRCP (UK) 1993. Cons.Phys. & Geriat. Socs: Brit. Geriat. Soc.; Brit. Assn. Stroke Phys. Prev: Regist. (Gen. & Geriat. Med.) Leeds & Bradford Hosp.; Sen. Regist. (Gen. & Geriat. Med.) Leeds & Bradford Hosp.

BROTHERSTON, Jenny 71 Front Street, Lockington, Driffield YO25 9SH — MB ChB 1991 Dundee.

BROTHERSTON, Kenneth George Scottish Executive Health Department, St Andrew's House, Regent Road, Edinburgh EH1 3JG Tel: 0131 244 2275 Fax: 0131 244 2069 Email: ken.brotherston@scotland.gov.uk; 17 Station Road, South Queensferry EH30 9HY Tel: 0131 331 2329 — MB ChB 1976 Ed.; MSc Ed. 1981; MFCM 1986; FFPHM 1998. Med. Systems Dir. Common Serv. Agency Edin. Prev: Sen. Regist. (Community Med.) Common Serv. Agency Edin.

BROTHERSTON, Mr Tor Michael 6 Ravenhill Park Gardens, Belfast BT6 0DH — MB ChB 1979 Belf.; FRCS Ed. 1984; FRCSI 1984.

BROTHERTON, Mr Brian James (retired) Pear Tree Cottage, Bonby Lane, Skipwith, Selby YO8 5SW — MB ChB 1965 Ed.; FRCS Ed. 1970. Prev: Cons. Orthop. Surg. York Health Dist.

BROTHERTON, Michelle Joanne 134 Chestnut Drive, Sale M33 4HR — MB ChB 1998 Liverp.; MB ChB Liverp 1998.

BROTHERWOOD, Andrew Peter Albany House Surgery, Albany Terrace, Barbourne, Worcester WR1 3DU Tel: 01905 26086 Fax: 01905 26888 — MB ChB 1988 Birm.; MRCGP 1993; DRCOG 1991. (Univ. Birm.) Prev: Trainee GP Dudley VTS; Ho. Surg. E. Birm. Hosp.; Ho. Phys. Russells Hall Hosp. Dudley.

BROTHERWOOD, Raymond William, OStJ (retired) 1A Kingswood Road, Tadworth KT20 5EE Tel: 0173 781 3678 — MB BS 1952 Lond.; MRCS Eng. LRCP Lond. 1952; DObst RCOG 1953. Prev: Dept. Sec. Counc. for Postgrad. Med. Educat. Eng. & Wales.

BROTHWELL, Judith Ann c/o Briary Unit, Harrogate District Hospital, Harrogate HG2 7SX Tel: 01423 885959 — BM BS 1980 Nottm.; MRCPsych 1986. Cons. Old Age Psychiat. Harrogate Healthcare NHS Trust. Prev: Sen. Regist. (Psychiat.) Yorks. HA.

BROUCKAERT, Sophia Mary 80 Eccleston Square, London SW1V 1PP — MB BCh 1992 Witwatersrand.

BROUGH, Ann Kirkton (retired) Holeyn Hall, Wylam NE41 8BQ Tel: 01661 852535 — MB BS 1952 Durh.; FRCOG 1989; MRCOG 1976. Prev: Assoc. Specialist (Gyn. & Oncol.) Qu. Eliz. Hosp. Gateshead.

BROUGH, Mr Barry Joseph The Fryern Surgery, Oakmount Road, Chandlers Ford, Eastleigh SO53 2LH Tel: 023 8025 2122/2082; 32 Velmore Road, Chandlers Ford, Eastleigh SO53 3HE Tel: 01703 252579 — MB BChir 1963 Camb.; MA, MB Camb. 1964, BChir 1963; FRCS Eng. 1969. (Camb. & St. Mary's) Med. Off. Brit. Jun. Rowing Team. Prev: Research Fell. Monash Univ. Melb., Austral.; Sen. Regist. Alfred Hosp. Melb., Austral.; Regist. Roy. Masonic Hosp. Lond.

BROUGH, Colin (retired) The Saughs, Gullane EH31 2AL Tel: 01620 842179 — MB ChB 1956 Ed.; FRCP Ed 1982, M 1981; FFCM 1978, M 1972; DIH Eng. 1965; DPH 1965. Prev: Chief Admin. Med. Off. Lothian HB Edin. Hon. Sen. Lect. (Community Med.) Univ. Edin.

BROUGH, David William (retired) 'Coppice Lodge', 8 Heathfield Close, Congleton CW12 4ND Tel: 01260 275355 — MB ChB 1973 Manch.; MIBiol 1968.

BROUGH, Douglas Ivor (retired) Ground Floor Flat, 53 Chelsham Road, London SW4 6NN Tel: 020 7978 1379 — MB BS Lond. 1957; FRCPsych 1977, M 1972; DPM Eng. 1963. Prev: Cons. Psychiat. Bexley & Lewisham Gps. Hosps.

BROUGH, Frank Trevor 45 Kirkgate, Cockermouth CA13 9PJ Tel: 01900 823117 — MRCS Eng. LRCP Lond. 1958; BA 1955, MB BChir Camb. 1958; FRCOG 1980, M 1967. (Camb. & Guy's) Socs: Fell. N. Eng. Obst. & Gyn. Soc. Prev: Cons. Obstetr. & Gynaecol. W. Cumbld. Hosp. Whitehaven; Regist. (O & G) Gloucester Roy. Hosp; Regist. Profess. Unit O & G Qu. Eliz. Hosp. Birm.

BROUGH, Geraldine Moira 6 Stormont Road, London N6 4NL Tel: 020 8348 3349 — MB ChB 1971 Birm.; MRCP (UK) 1975. (Birm.) Clin. Asst. (Rheum.) Roy. Free Hosp. Lond. Prev: Regist. (Rheum.) Middlx. Hosp. Lond.

BROUGH, Graeme David 30 Lauchope Street, Chapel Hall, Motherwell Tel: 01236 762144; 30 Biggar Road, Newarthill, Motherwell ML1 5SS Tel: 01698 861264 — MB ChB 1985 Dundee; MRCGP 1989; DRCOG 1989.

BROUGH, Michael David Leven Medical Practice, Tollcross Health Centre, Ponton Street, Edinburgh EH3 9QQ Tel: 0131 536 9700 — MB ChB 1979 Ed.; MRCGP 1985; DRCOG 1984.

BROUGH, Mr Michael David The Consulting Suite, 82 Portland Place, London W1N 3DH Tel: 020 7935 8910 Fax: 020 7436 2954; 6 Stormont Road, London N6 4NL Tel: 020 8348 3349 Fax: 020 8347 6247 — MB BChir 1968 Camb.; MA Camb. 1969; FRCS Eng. 1974; MRCS Eng. LRCP Lond. 1968. (Middlx.) Cons. Plastic Surg. & Hon. Sen. Lect. Univ. Coll. Hosp. Lond.; Cons. Plastic Surg. Roy. Free Hosp., Whittington Hosp. & King Edwd. VII Hosp. For Offs Lond; Hon. Cons. Plastic Surg. St. Luke's Hosp. for Clergy. Socs: Fell. Roy. Soc. Med. (Ex-Pres. Plastic Surg. Sect.).; Brit. Assn. Plastic Surg.(Pres. 2002). Prev: Cons. Plastic Surg. NE Thames Regional Plastic Surg. Centre St. And. Hosp. Billericay; Cons. Plastic Surg. Qu. Eliz. Hosp. Childr. Lond. & Whipps Cross Hosp. Lond.

BROUGH, Peter Robert Woodland Practice, Holmwood Health Centre, Franklin Avenue, Tadley RG26 4ER Tel: 0118 981 4166 Fax: 0118 981 1432 — MB BS 1975 Lond.; MRCGP 1987; DRCOG 1979. GP Tadley.; Trainer in Gen. Pract.; Trainer Convenor; GP Scheme Organiser. Prev: Ho. Off. Dulwich Hosp. Lond.; Ho. Off. Basingstoke Dist. Hosp.; Trainee GP Basingstoke VTS.

BROUGH, Philipa Jane 155 Burton Road, Manchester M20 1LD — MB ChB 1987 Manch.; DRCOG 1992.

BROUGH, Richard Andrew 2 Ivy Bank Close, Bolton BL1 7EF — MB ChB 1993 Liverp.

BROUGH, Mr Richard James 155 Burton Road, West Didsbury, Manchester M20 1LD Tel: 0161 434 7080 — MB ChB 1987 Manch.; FRCS Eng. 1992. Regist. (Urol.) Manch. Roy. Infirm.

BROUGH, Mr Stephen James Simon The Michael Heal Department of Urology, Leighton Hospital, Middlewich Road, Crewe CW1 4QJ Tel: 01270 612010 Fax: 01270 250168; 'The Tythe Barn', Haughton, Tarporley CW6 9RN Tel: 01829 260175 Fax: 01829 261475 Email: stevebrough@hotmail.com — MB ChB 1983 Birm.; MSc Birm. 1990; FRCS (Urol.) 1995; FRCS Eng. 1989. (Birmingham University) Cons. Urol. Leighton Hosp. Crewe. Socs: Brit. Assn. Urol. Surgs.; BMA. Prev: Sen. Regist. Rotat. (Urol.) Cardiff & Swansea; Regist. (Urol.) P.ss Alexandra Hosp., Brisbane; Regist. & Tutor (Urol.) St. Jas. Univ. Hosp. Leeds.

BROUGH, William Holeyn Hall, Wylam NE41 8BQ Tel: 01661 852535 — MB BS Durh. 1952; FRCPsych 1977, M 1971; DPM Eng. 1968. (Durh.) Cons. Psychother. Woodlands Rd. Clinic Middlesbbrough; Hon. Cons. Psychotherapist. Roy. Vict. Infirm. Newc. Socs: Assoc. Mem. Brit. Psychoanal. Soc. Prev: Cons. Psychiat. Psychother. S. Grampian Health Dist.; Sen. Regist. Tavistock Clinic; 1st Asst. Internal Med. Mayo Clin., USA.

BROUGH, Mr William Andrew Ryley Mount, 432 Buxton Road, Stockport SK2 7JQ Tel: 0161 483 9333 Fax: 0161 419 9913; 138 Gill Bent Road, Cheadle Hulme, Cheadle SK8 6NJ — MRCS Eng. LRCP Lond. 1976; BSc (Hons.) Lond. 1973, MB BS 1976; FRCS Eng. 1980. (St. Geo.) Cons. Gen. Surg. Stepping Hill Hosp. Stockport. Prev: Lect. (Surg.) Hope Hosp. Manch.; Regist. (Surg.) Addenbrooke's Hosp. Camb.; Ho. Phys. St. Geo. Hosp. Lond.

BROUGHAM, Carol Anne Cruddas Park Surgery, 178 Westmorland Road, Cruddas Park, Newcastle upon Tyne NE4 7JT — MB BS 1988 Newc.

BROUGHAM, Penelope Anne Waldegrave Clinic, 82 Waldegrave Road, Teddington TW11 8NY Tel: 020 8943 2424 Fax: 020 8977 6626; 173 Woodford Road, Woodford, Stockport SK7 1QE — MB ChB 1976 Liverp.; 1995 Dip. Med. Acupuncture; MSc UCL (Applied Hypnosis) Nov. 1998; Dip. Clin. Hypnosis (UCL) 1997. Specialist in Acupunc., Hypn. and Complementary Med.; Lect. Brit. Med. Acupunc. Soc.; Dip. Ac (Beijing) Coll. Traditional Chinese Med. Socs: Brit. Med. Acupunct. Soc.; Brit. Soc. Med. & Dent. Hypn.; Brit. Soc. Experim. & Clin. Hypn.

BROUGHTON, Sir Alfred Davies Devonsher (retired) Stockwell Shay Farm, Batley Tel: 01924 474321 — MRCS Eng. LRCP Lond. 1929; MA, MB BChir Camb. 1937; DPM Leeds 1936, DPH 1937. DL; MP; Squadron Ldr. RAFVR. Prev: Receiv. Room Off. Lond. Hosp.

BROUGHTON, Alison Jean Plot 6, Abbey Cross, 136 Dudley Road W., Tividale, Warley — MB ChB 1994 Birm.; ChB Birm. 1994.

BROUGHTON, Mr Andrew Cooper Mannington, Southgate, Pontefract WF8 1QT Tel: 01977 606473; Rose Lea House, Hillam, Leeds LS25 5HE Tel: 01977 682446 — MB BS 1966 Lond.; FRCS Eng. 1973; MRCS Eng. LRCP Lond. 1967. (St. Mary's) Cons. Gen. Surg. Pontefract Gen. Infirm. Prev: Med. Off. Brit. Transafrican Expedition; Sen. Regist. (Surg.) Leeds Univ. Hosp.; Research Fell. Med. & Surg. Research Inst. Univ. Alberta, Canada.

BROUGHTON, Andrew Nicholas 4 Carter Avenue, Elms Park, Ruddington, Nottingham NG11 6NP — MB BChir 1985 Camb.; MA Camb. 1986, BA (Hons.) 1982, MB 1985, BChir 1984; DA (UK) 1987. Regist. (Anaesth. & ITU) Roy. Infirm. Huddersfield. Prev: SHO (Anaesth. & ITU) Ipswich Hosp. Suff.; Ho. Phys. (Cardiol.) Addenbrookes Hosp. Camb.; Ho. Surg. (Gen. Surg.) Hinchingbrooke Hosp. Huntingdon.

BROUGHTON, David Lance Department Medicine for Elderly, James Cook University Hospital, Marton Road, Middlesbrough TS4 3BW Tel: 01642 850850 — MB BS 1980 Newc.; MD Newc. 1992; MRCP (UK) 1983. Cons. Phys. Elderly James Cook Univ. Hosp. Socs: Brit. Geriat. Soc.

BROUGHTON, David Michael 4 Finchley Way, Morley, Leeds LS27 0RF Tel: 0113 253 7762; 93 Bradford Road, Shipley BD18 3BX — MRCS Eng. LRCP Lond. 1959. (Leeds) Socs: Fell. Roy. Soc. Health.

BROUGHTON, Jean Loveday 154 Church Road, Urmston, Manchester M41 9DL Tel: 0161 748 5665; 62 Harboro Road, Sale M33 Tel: 0161 969 1116 — MRCS Eng. LRCP Lond. 1941. (Roy. Free) Socs: Fell. Manch. Med. Soc. Prev: Ho. Surg. & Ho. Phys. E. Surrey Hosp.; Res. Med. Off. Childr. Hosp. Shadwell; Hon. Capt. RAMC, Graded Anaesth.

BROUGHTON, Jean Margaret Birchfield Health Centre, Birchfield, 4 Church Road, Whitchurch, Cardiff CF14 2DZ Tel: 029 2052 2455/2355 Fax: 029 2052 2686 — MB BCh 1965 Wales. (Cardiff) GP Cardiff.

BROUGHTON, Liam John Cliff Villages Medical Practice, Mere Road, Waddington, Lincoln LN5 9NX Tel: 01522 720277 Fax: 01522 729174; 122 Station Road, Waddington, Lincoln LN5 9QS Tel: 01522 823579 Fax: 01522 823579 Email: g&lbroughton@btinternet.com uk — MB BS 1983 Lond.; BSc (Hons.) Lond. 1980; DRCOG 1988; DCH RCPS Glas. 1986; MRCGP 1987. Prev: Trainee GP Torbay VTS.

BROUGHTON, Louise Ann Mill House, Wick, Cowbridge CF71 7QU — MB BS 1976 Lond.; MRCS Eng. LRCP Lond. 1976; DRCOG 1978. Clin. Med. Off. Comm. Health Serv. S. Glam. HA.

BROUGHTON, Michael David The Surgery, Roman Way, Billingshurst RH14 9QZ Tel: 01403 782931 Fax: 01403 785505 — MB BS 1979 Lond.; MRCGP 1994; DRCOG 1982. Prev: GP Trainee Portsmouth; Ho. Off. Qu. Alexandra Hosp. Portsmouth; Ho. Off. Lewisham Hosp. Lond.

BROUGHTON, Nicholas Burt 5 Lunardi Court, Puckeridge, Ware SG11 1UT — BM BS 1989 Nottm.

BROUGHTON, Nicholas Irwin 11 Brocklehurst Drive, Prestbury, Macclesfield SK10 4JD — MB BChir 1993 Camb.

BROUGHTON, Robert Bruce Knight BMA Welsh House, 1 Cleeve House, Cardiff Business Park, Llanishen, Cardiff CF4 5GJ Tel: 029 2076 6277; Birchfield, 4 Church Road, Whitchurch, Cardiff CF14 2DZ Tel: 029 2062 5092 — MB BCh 1966 Wales; DMRD

Eng. 1972. Welsh Sec. BMA. Socs: The John Snow Soc. Prev: Cons. Radiol. E. Glam. Gen. Hosp.; Unit Gen. Manager Taff Ely Health Unit; Co-Ordinator & Adviser Med. Audit (Wales).

BROUGHTON, Ronald Burgess (retired) 10 Park Road, Salford M6 8HN Tel: 0161 788 0663 — MB ChB 1945 Manch.; MRCS Eng. LRCP Lond. 1945.

BROUGHTON, Sarah Frances 7 Hailey Court, Llandaff North, Cardiff CF4 2FA — MB BCh 1998 Wales.

BROUGHTON, Simon John Flat 1, 24 Tritton Road, West Dulwich, London SE21 8DE — BM 1994 Soton.; MRCP Lond. 1998. (Southampton) SHO (Paediat.) Roy. Brompton Hosp. Lond.; Specialist Regist. Rotat. (Paediat.) St. Peters Chertsey. Prev: SHO (Paediat.) Chelsea & W.m. Hosp. Lond.

BROUGHTON, William Edward, OStJ (retired) 23 Seaway Court, Seaway Lane, Torquay TQ2 6RJ Tel: 01803 200365 Email: broughton@seaway.ndo.co.uk — MB ChB (Hons.) Manch. 1942; MRCP Lond. 1972; MFOM RCP Lond. 1978; DIH Eng. 1947. Prev: Chief Med. Adviser Shell Internat. Petrol Co.

BROW, Mr Timothy David 42 Glendale Drive, Wimbledon, London SW19 7BG Tel: 020 8241 7727 Fax: 020 8241 3347 Email: brow@bigfoot.com — MB BS 1984 Lond.; BSc (Hons.) Lond. 1981; FRCS Eng. 1993. (Char. Cross) Regist. (Gen. Surg.), Roy. Sussex. Socs: BMA; RCS. Prev: Regist. (Vasc. Surg.) Roy. Brompton Hosp. Lond.; Regist. (Gen. Surg.) Greenwich Dist. Hosp.; SHO (Cardiothoracic Surg.) St Thos. Hosp. Lond.

BROWELL, Mr David Andrew Queen Elizabeth Hospital, Gateshead NE9 6SX Tel: 0191 487 8989; 139 Edge Hill, Darras Hall, Ponteland, Newcastle upon Tyne NE20 9JT — MB BS 1985 Newc.; BSc (Hons.) Liverp. 1980; FRCS Eng. 1989. (Newc. u. Tyne) Cons. Surg. Qu. Eliz. Hosp. Gateshead, Tyne & Wear.

BROWELL, Janet Alexandra Osborne Road Surgery, 200 Osborne Road, Jesmond, Newcastle upon Tyne NE2 3LD Tel: 0191 281 4777 Fax: 0191 281 4309; 139 Edgehill, Darras Hall, Ponteland, Newcastle upon Tyne NE20 9JT Tel: 01661 860298 — MB ChB 1983 Aberd.; MRCGP 1988.

BROWETT, Mr John Peter (cons. rooms), 95 Harley St., London W1G 6AF Tel: 020 7486 9323 Fax: 01707 876218; New Park House, Newgate St. Vill., Hertford SG13 8RD Tel: 01707 875729 Fax: 01707 876218 — MB BS 1969 Lond.; FRCS Eng. 1974; MRCS Eng. LRCP Lond. 1969. (St. Bart.) Cons. Orthapaedic Surg. Socs: Fell. BOA; BMA; ISAKOS, Internat. Soc. of Arthroscopy. Prev: Cons. Orthop. Surg. St. Bart. Hosp. Lond.; Sen. Regist. Rotat. (Orthop.) St. Bart. Hosp. Lond.; Ho. Surg. St. Bart. Hosp. Lond.

BROWN, Adam Lingard 15 Lime Tree Av, Retford DN22 7BB — MB BS 1997 Lond.

BROWN, Adrian Flat 4, 46 Sale Hill, Sheffield S10 5BX — MB ChB 1994 Sheff.

BROWN, Adrian Christopher Treetops, 15 Southway, Manor Park, Burley in Wharfedale, Ilkley LS29 7HJ — MB BS 1994 Newc.

BROWN, Adrian Michael 66 North Place, Teddington TW11 0HN Email: abrown@sghms.ac.uk — MB ChB 1988 Manch. Socs: Roy. Coll. Gen. Pract.

BROWN, Agnes Anderson Morton (retired) West Mount, 20 Menzieshill Road, Dundee DD2 1PW Tel: 01382 566444 Email: ossie.agnes@obrown.fsnet.co.uk — MB ChB Glas. 1947. Prev: Ho. Off. Midw. (Gyn.) & Ho. Surg. Stobhill Hosp. Glas.

BROWN, Aileen Elizabeth Levenwick Medical Practice, Gord, Levenwick, Shetland ZE2 9HX Tel: 01950 422240 Fax: 01950 422201 — MB ChB 1979 Aberd.

BROWN, Alan David Gillespie Simpson Memorial Maternity Pavillion, Royal Infirmary, Lauriston Place, Edinburgh EH3 9YW Tel: 0131 536 1000 Fax: 0131 536 3493 Email: dradgbrown@hotmail.com; 37 Heriot Row, Edinburgh EH3 6ES Tel: 0131 225 8197 Fax: 0131 225 6749 Email: dradgbrown@hotmail.com — MB ChB 1963 Ed.; FRCS 1990 Ed; FRCOG 1981, M 1968; Cert FPA 1973. Cons. O & G Roy. Infirm., Edin.. & Hon. Clin. Sen. Lect. Univ. Edin.; Cons. Gynaecologist & Vice Chair, Caledonia Youth. Socs: Counc. & Cases Comm. Med. Protec. Soc. (Past); Surgic. Travellers. & Gyn. Club of Gt. Brit.; Clouston Club, Edin. Prev: Sen. Lect. & Hon. Cons. Dept. O & G Univ. Hosp. S. Manch.; Sen. Regist. Dept. O & G W.. Gen. Hosp. Edin.; MRC Clin. Research Fell. Urodynamic Clinic Middlx. Hosp. Lond.

BROWN, Alan Geoffrey 2 Woodstock Drive, Worsley, Manchester M28 2WW Tel: 0161 728 2769 Email: dr.agb@nt/world.com — MB ChB 1960 Manch.; MRCGP 1971; DObst RCOG 1963. (Manch.) Part Time EMP -Benefits Agency. Prev: GP Manch.; Ho. Surg. & Ho. Phys. W. Manch. Hosp. Gp.; Ship's Surg. Booth SS Co.

BROWN, Alan George 11 Pitbauchlie Bank, Dunfermline KY11 8DP — MB ChB 1983 Ed.

BROWN, Alan John Posterngate Surgery, Portholme Road, 4 Park St., Selby YO8 4QH Tel: 01757 702561 Fax: 01757 213295 — MB ChB Bristol 1968; DObst RCOG 1971.

BROWN, Alastair Nisbet (retired) 203 Queens Road, Aberdeen AB15 8DB Tel: 01224 208987 — MB ChB 1961 Aberd.; DObst RCOG 1963. Mem. The Appeals Serv. Prev: GP Aberd.

BROWN, Alastair Peter 30 Grange Road, Bangor BT20 3QQ — MB BCh BAO 1994 Belf.

BROWN, Alexander Campbell Department of Mental Health, University of Bristol, 41 St Michael's Hill, Bristol BS2 8DZ Tel: 0117 928 7771 — MB BChir 1956 Camb.; MA Camb. 1957, MD 1965; FRCPsych 1978, M 1971; DPM Lond. 1961. (Camb. & Middlx.) Hon. Research Fell. Ment. Health Univ. Bristol. Socs: Fell. Roy. Soc. Med. Prev: Cons. & Sen. Lect. (Ment. Health) Univ. Bristol; Sen. Lect. (Psychol. Med.) Welsh Nat. Sch. Med. Cardiff; Sen. Regist. Bethlem Roy. & Maudsley Hosps. Lond.

BROWN, Alexander Laird (retired) 30 Darley Avenue, West Didsbury, Manchester M20 2YD Tel: 0161 283 7669 Email: xelarose@tinyworld.co.uk — MB BS 1954 Durh.; MSc Manch. 1983; FRCGP 1990, M 1974. Prev: Sen. Lect. (Gen. Pract.) Manch. Univ.

BROWN, Alexander Laird (retired) 29 Geraldine Road, Malvern WR14 3NT — MB ChB 1938 Birm. Div. Surg. St. John Ambul. Brig. Prev: Cas. Ho. Surg. Gen. Hosp. Birm.

BROWN, Alfred Macdonell (retired) 3 Bath Road, Norton St Phillip, Bath BA2 7LB Tel: 0137 387542 — MRCS Eng. LRCP Lond. 1952.

BROWN, Alice Anne Flat 303, Smithfield Buildings, 44 Tib St., Manchester M4 1LA Email: alice.b@oxroad.zen.co.uk — MB ChB 1994 Manch.; DTM & H Liverp. 1995. GP Regist. Robins La. Surg. Bramhall Stockport. Prev: SHO (Neonat. Med.) St Mary's Hosp. Manch.; SHO (O & G) Dunedin Hosp., New Zealand.

BROWN, Alicia Mary Elizabeth Royal Devon And Exeter Hospital, Barrack Rd, Exeter EX2 5DW Tel: 01392 403705 — MB ChB 1977 Auckland; BSc (Human Biol.) Auckland 1974; FRACP 1983; Dip Obst Auckland 1979. p/t Cons. Rheum. RD+E Hosp. Exeter. Socs: Brit. Soc. Rheum.; Roy. Devon and Exeter Med. Soc. Prev: Specialist Regist. (Rheum.) Derriford Hosp. Plymouth; Clin. Asst. (Rheum.) Roy. Devon & Exeter Hosp.; Sen. Regist. (Rheum.) Guy's & St. Mary's Hosps. Lond.

BROWN, Alison Joanna The Medical Centre, Hospital Road, Stratton, Bude EX23 9BP Tel: 01288 352133; Southern House, Maiden Road, Stratton, Bude EX23 9DQ Tel: 01288 355638 — MRCS Eng. LRCP Lond. 1974; DObst RCOG 1976.

BROWN, Alison Luford Ward 4, Freeman Hospital, Newcastle upon Tyne NE7 7DN Tel: 0191 284 3111 Email: alison.brown@tfh.nuth.northy.nhs.uk; 27 The Grove, Gosforth, Newcastle upon Tyne NE3 1NE — MB BChir 1979 Camb.; MD Camb. 1989, MA 1981; MRCP (UK) 1982; FRCP Ed. 1998; FRCP Lond. 1998. (Univ. Camb.) Cons. Nephrol. Freeman Gp. Hosp. Trust Newc. u. Tyne.

***BROWN, Alistair Ernest** Lyndhurst, Burnthouse Lane, Toft Monks, Beccles NR34 0ES Tel: 01502 677458 — BM BS 1996 Nottm.

BROWN, Mr Alistair John 11 Threave Place, Newton Mearns, Glasgow G77 6YD — MB ChB 1991 Glas.; FRCS Glas. 1995. (Glas.) Specialist Regist. (Gen. Surg.), Gartnavel Gen. Hosp. Prev: Spr Hairmyers Hosp.; Spr Law Hosp.; Research Fell., Glas. Roy. Infirm.

BROWN, Alistair Martin Davidson Pallion Health Centre, Hylton Road, Sunderland SR4 7XF Tel: 0191 567 4673; 9 Lodgeside Meadow, Sunderland SR3 2PN — MB ChB Dundee 1976; MRCGP 1980; DRCOG 1978.

BROWN, Allan Scrimgeour (retired) 1 Comiston Rise, Edinburgh EH10 6HQ Tel: 0131 445 1031 — MB ChB Ed. 1941; FFA RCS Eng. 1953; DA Eng. 1948; FRCA Eng. Prev: Cons. Anaesth. (Surg. Neurol.) Roy. Infirm. Edin. & W.. Gen. Hosp. Edin.

BROWN, Allen Keith Clairmont, off Haverbreaks Road, Haverbreaks, Lancaster LA1 5XD Tel: 01524 65721 — MB ChB 1959 Manch.; FRCP Lond. 1977, M 1964. Hon. Cons. Phys. Lancs. & Cumbria AHAs. Socs: Fell. Manch. Med. Soc.; Brit. Cardiac Soc. Prev: Sen. Regist. (Cardiol.) Sefton Gen. Hosp. Liverp.; Regist. (Med.) Ancoats Hosp. Manch. & Pk. Hosp. Davyhulme.

BROWN, Alva Ian Oberlin House, Greenacres, Oldham OL4 3HS Tel: 0161 633 1135 — MRCS Eng. LRCP Lond. 1964. Socs: BMA. Prev: Ho. Surg. Vict. Hosp. Keighley; Ho. Phys. Noble's I. of Man Hosp. Douglas; Ho. Surg. (Obst.) Chester City Hosp.

BROWN, Amanda Jane Little Chalfont Surgery, 200 White Lion Road, Little Chalfont, Amersham HP7 9NU Tel: 01494 762323 Fax: 01494 765973; Whichert Lodge, Penn Road, Knotty Green, Beaconsfield HP9 2TN — MB BS 1979 Lond.; BSc Lond. 1976, MB BS 1979; DRCOG 1983; Cert. Family Plann. RCOG & RCGP 1983.

BROWN, Andrea Karen Keymer Residence, Brighton General Hospital, Elm Grove, Brighton BN2 3EW Tel: 01273 696011 — MB ChB 1990 Leeds. SHO (Gen. Surg.) Roy. Sussex Co. Hosp. Brighton. Prev: Ho. Off. (Gen. Med.) St. Jas. Hosp. Leeds; Ho. Off. (Gen. Surg.) Leeds Gen. Infirm.

BROWN, Andrea Lee Radiology Department, Royal Berkshire Hospital, London Road, Reading RG1 5AN Tel: 0118 987 7929 Fax: 0118 987 8087 — MB BS 1989 Lond.; MRCP (UK) 1992; FRCR 1995. Cons. (Radiol.) Roy. Berks. Hosp., Reading. Socs: Roy. Coll. Radiol.; RCR BrE. Gp.; RSNA. Prev: Sen. Regist. (Radiol.) St. Geo.'s Hosp. Lond.; Clin. Fell., McMaster Hosp., Hamilton, Canada; Regist. (Radiol.) N.wick Pk. Hosp. Harrow HA.

BROWN, Andrew Barclay Levenshulme Health Centre, Dunstable St., Manchester M19 3BX Tel: 0161 225 4033 — MB ChB 1960 Manch.; DObst RCOG 1962. (Manch.)

BROWN, Andrew Bruce 71 Crown Road, West Derby, Liverpool L12 8RS — MB ChB 1985 Liverp.

BROWN, Andrew David 3 Arbuthnott Loan, Broughty Ferry, Dundee DD5 3TN — MB ChB 1990 Glas.

BROWN, Mr Andrew Edwin Queen Victoria Hospital, Holtye Road, East Grinstead RH19 3DZ Tel: 0132 410210 Ext: 305 Fax: 0132 328339 Email: andrew.brown@qvh-tr.sthames.nhs.uk — MB BS 1973 Lond.; BDS (Hons.) Lond. 1969; FRCS Ed. 1986; MRCS Eng. LRCP Lond. 1973; FDS RCPS Glas. 1975; FDS RCS Eng. 1975, LDS 1968. (Guy's) Cons. Surg. (Oral & Maxillofacial) Qu. Vict. Hosp. E. Grinstead; Hon. Civil. Cons., RAF; Cons. Surg., (Oral & Maxillofacial), Kent & Sussex Hosp. Tunbridge Wells; Cons. Surg., (Oral & Maxillofacial), Conquest Hosp., Hastings. Socs: Fell. Brit. Assn. Oral & Maxillofacial Surg.; Brit. Assn. Head & Neck Oncol.; Fell., Internat. Assn. Of Oral & Maxillofacial Surg.s. Prev: Sen. Regist. (Oral & Maxillofacial Surg.) Qu. Vict. Hosp. E. Grinstead; Regist. (Oral Surg.) E.man Dent. Hosp. Lond.; Ho. Surg. ENT Guy's Hosp. Lond.

BROWN, Andrew George 99 Carsington Crescent, Allestree, Derby DE22 2QT — MB ChB 1987 Ed.; MRCGP 1995; DCH 1991; DRCOG 1998. (Edinburgh) Private GP Medicentre Solihull. Prev: GP Princip. Medicentre Solihull.

BROWN, Andrew Greig (retired) 36 Lindisfarne Gardens, Tweedmouth, Berwick-upon-Tweed TD15 2YA — MB ChB 1938 Ed.

BROWN, Andrew James 4 Woodlands Close, Milton-under-Wychwood, Oxford OX7 6LS — MB BS 1973 Lond.; MRCP (UK) 1976.

BROWN, Andrew John 19 Kingsway W., Westlands, Newcastle ST5 3PT — MB ChB 1987 Bristol.

BROWN, Andrew Keith Acreswood Surgery, 5 Acreswood Close, Coppull, Chorley PR7 5EJ Tel: 01257 793578 Fax: 01257 794005 — MB ChB 1979 Liverp. Socs: Primary Care Gastroenterol. Soc.; Brit. Menopause Soc.

BROWN, Andrew Kristian 6 Cragg Terrace, Rawdon, Leeds LS19 6LF Tel: 0113 250 4266 — MB ChB 1995 Leeds; MRCP (UK), 1999. SHO (Med.), Seacroft Hosp., Leeds.

BROWN, Andrew Malcolm Slaidburn Health Centre, Shay Lane, Slaidburn, Clitheroe BB7 3EP Tel: 01200 446229 — MB ChB 1983 Liverp.

BROWN, Mr Andrew Mark Sean Maxillofacial Centre, Selly Oak Hospital, Raddlebarn Road, Birmingham B29 6JD Tel: 0121 627 8332 Fax: 0121 627 8893 Email: oralongcol@aol.com; Rowans, 25A Wellington Road, Edgbaston, Birmingham B15 2ES Tel: 0121 440 3195 Fax: 0121 440 8084 Email: brownams@aol.com — MB BS 1981 Lond.; BDS Lond. 1974; FRCS Ed. 1988; FDS RCS Eng. 1984, LDS 1974. Cons. Maxillofacial Surg. Selly Oak Hosp. Birm.; Hon. Sen. Clin. Lect. Univ. Birm. Socs: Fell. Brit. Assn. Oral & Maxillofacial Surg.; Brit. Assn. Head & Neck Oncol.

BROWN, Andrew Patrick (retired) Dragon House, Shirburn Road, Watlington, Watlington OX9 5BZ Tel: 01491 613251 — MA Camb.; LMSSA Lond. 1954.

BROWN, Andrew Paul Burney Street Practice, 48 Burney Street, London SE10 8EX Tel: 020 8858 0631 Fax: 020 8293 9616 — MB BS 1982 Lond.; BSc 1979 Lond.; MRCP (UK) 1985; DCH RCP Lond. 1988. (St. Geo.) GP Lond.

BROWN, Andrew Playdon Templeton 76 Kingsway Park, Davyhulme, Manchester M41 7FH — MB BS 1977 Newc.

BROWN, Mr Andrew Raymond Leicester Royal Informary, Infirmary Square, Leicester LE1 5WW Tel: 0116 254 1414 — BM 1989 Soton.; FRCS 1999 (Ed. Tr. & Orth.); FRCS Ed. 1993. Specialist Regist. (Orthop.), Leicester. Socs: BOA. Assoc.; BOTA. Prev: Allograft Fell. (Orthop.), Perth, W.. Australia; Research SHO (Orthop.) Glenfield Gen. Hosp. Leicester; SHO Rotat. (Surg.) E. Birm. Hosp.

BROWN, Andrew Smithson Flat 7, 50 Northumberland Road, Newcastle upon Tyne NE1 8SG — MB BS 1987 Newc.

BROWN, Angela Sylvia Theresa Department of Cardiology, Kings College Hospital, enmark Hill, London SE5 9RS Tel: 020 7737 4000 Email: rcha253@kcl.ac.uk; 108 Derinton Road, Tooting, London SW17 8HY — MB 1987 Camb.; BChir 1986; MRCP (UK) 1990. (Camb.) Research Fell., Hon. Regist. & Lect. (Cardiol.) King's Coll. Hosp. Lond. Prev: Regist. (Cardiol.) King's Coll. Hosp. Lond.

BROWN, Ann Elizabeth (retired) The Red House, Church Lane, Nunthorpe, Middlesbrough TS7 0PD Tel: 01642 318066 — MB BS Durh. 1963; FFA RCS Eng. 1967. Hon. Clin. Lect. (Anaesth.) Univ. Newc. Prev: Cons. Anaesth. S. Cleveland Hosp.

BROWN, Ann Mary (retired) 12 Lindisfarne Road, Newcastle upon Tyne NE2 2HE Tel: 0191 281 4141 — MB BS Durh. 1959.

BROWN, Anne Margaret Sandford Surgery, 4-6 Tyneham Close, Sandford, Wareham BH20 7BQ Tel: 01929 554493 Fax: 01929 550661; 77 High Street, Lytchett, Matravers, Poole BH16 6BJ Tel: 01202 632249 — MB BS 1978 Lond.; DRCOG 1982; Cert. Family Plann. JCC 1982. (Charing Cross Hospital Medical School) GP Princip.; Community Med. Off. Dorset.; PCG Bd. Mem. Prev: Clin. Asst. Diabetes Poole Gen. Hosp.

BROWN, Annemarie Suzanne Whiston Hospital, St Helens and Knowsley Hospital Trust, Prescot L35 5DR Tel: 0151 426 1600; Sarnia, 20 Buckingham Road W., Heaton Moor, Stockport SK4 4BA Tel: 0161 432 1129 — MB ChB 1996 Liverp. SHO Merseyside Regional Surgic. Rotat. Prev: SHO (A & E) Whiston Hosp.; SHO (Gen. Surg.) Whiston Hosp.; PR Ho. Off. Whiston Hosp.

BROWN, Anthony Albert Fernbank, Cumwhitton, Carlisle CA8 9EX — MB ChB 1965 Ed.; MRCOG 1971. Cons. O & G City Matern. & City Gen. Hosps. Carlisle. Socs: Edin. Obst. Soc. Prev: Sen. Regist. O & G Roy. Vict. Infirm. & P.ss Mary Matern.; Hosp. Newc. upon Tyne; Lect. Dept. O & G Univ. Liverp. Mill Rd. Matern. Hosp. Liverp.

BROWN, Anthony Robert 18 Plough Close, Rothwell, Kettering NN14 6YF — MB BS 1981 Lond. (Westm.)

BROWN, Archibald Stephen Canon House, 6 Canon ST, Shirley, Southampton SO15 5PQ; Bunker's Hill, Romsey Rd, Whiteparish, Salisbury SP5 2SA — BM BS 1981 Nottm.; MRCPsych 1990. Cons. (Psychiat.) Soton NHS Comm. Trust. Prev: Regist. (Psychiat.) Nottm.; Sen. Regist. (Psychiat.) Soton. NHS Community Trust; Regis (Psychiat.) John Oxley Mem. Hosp. Qu.sland, Australia.

BROWN, Arthur Geoffrey (retired) 7 Rannoch House, 10 Lindisfarne Road, Newcastle upon Tyne NE2 2HE — MB BS 1954 Durh. Prev: Ho. Surg. P.ss Mary Matern. Hosp. Newc.

BROWN, Mr Arthur Hedley (retired) The Red House, Church Lane, Old Nunthorpe, Middlesbrough TS7 0PD Tel: 01642 318066 — MB BS 1957 Durh.; MS Newc. 1971; FRCS Eng. 1963; FRACS 1978. Cons. Cardiothoracic Surg. & Chief of Serv. S. CLeveland Hosp.; Hon. Lect. Univ. Newc. Prev: Cons. Cardiothoracic Surg. St. Thos. Hosp. Lond. & Freeman Hosp Newc.

BROWN, Arthur Ivor Parry (retired) Long Thatch, Church Lane, Balsham, Cambridge CB1 6DS Tel: 01223 893012 — MB BS Lond. 1933; MRCS Eng. LRCP Lond. 1931; FFA RCS Eng. 1951; DA Eng. 1935. Prev: Anaesth. Lond. Hosp.

BROWN, Mr Ashley Allen Rawreth Hall, Rawreth Lane, Wickford SS11 8SS — MB BS 1967 Lond.; MD Lond. 1973; FRCS Ed. 1971; FRCS Eng. 1971. (St. Bart.) Roy. Soc. Med. Prize for Surg. Regist. 1972; Clin. Tutor (Gen. Surg.) S.end Hosp.; Hon. Teach. (Surg.) Univ. Lond.; Examr. Univ. Lond. Prev: Sen. Regist. (Surg.) St. Bart. Hosp. Lond.; Research Regist. St. Bart. Hosp.; SHO (Neurosurg.) Frenchay Hosp. Bristol.

BROWN, Ashley Johnstone The Knoll, 47A Colquhoun St., Helensburgh G84 9LQ — MB ChB 1994 Glas.

BROWN, Ashley St John Mark Institute of Hepatology, University College London, 69-75 Chenies Mews, London WC1E 6HX Tel: 0207 7679 6514 Email: ashley.brown@uci.ac.uk; Broadoak, 17 Hagsdell Road, Hertford SG13 8BG Tel: 01992 584594 — MB ChB 1988 Liverp.; BSc Liverp. 1985; MRCP (UK) 1992. Vis. Res. Fell., Inst. Hepat., Univ. Coll. Lond. Socs: Brit. Assn. for the Study of Liver. Prev: SHO Rotat. (Med.) Roy. Vict. Infirm., Newc. Gen. Hosp. & Freeman Hosp. Newc.

BROWN, Audrey Helen 9 Montagu Terrace, Edinburgh EH3 5QX — MB ChB 1990 Glas.

BROWN, Avril Gwendolen 118 Greasby Road, Greasby, Wirral CH49 3NG — MB ChB 1960 Liverp.; DObst RCOG 1962. (Liverp.)

BROWN, Barbara (retired) 7 Rannoch House, 10 Lindisfarne Road, Newcastle upon Tyne NE2 2HE — MB BS 1957 Durh.; BSc Durham. 1952. Prev: Ho. Off. Roy. Vict. Infirm. Newc.

BROWN, Barbara Anne 273 Maltby Drive, Hoe Green Vill., Enfield EN1 4ES — MB BCh BAO 1986 NUI; LRCPI & LM, LRCSI & LM 1986.

BROWN, Barbara Anne Chulmleigh Health Centre, Three Crossways, Chulmleigh EX18 7AA Tel: 01769 580269 Fax: 01769 581131; Cowlas, Burrington, Umberleigh EX37 9NA Tel: 01769 60240 — MB ChB 1978 Bristol; MB ChB (Hons.) Bristol 1978; MRCGP 1987; DCH RCP Lond. 1980.

BROWN, Barbara Joan Brownhill Farm, Birkenshaw, Bradford BD11 2JL Tel: 01274 681385 — MB ChB Leeds 1959. (Leeds) Med. Off. Nat. Blood Transfus. Serv. Prev: Sen. Ho. Off. Anaesth. St. Jas. Hosp. Leeds.

BROWN, Barclay Conoco(Uk) Limited, Rubs Lane House, Anderson Drive, Aberdeen AB15 6FZ Tel: 01224 205933 — MB ChB 1968 Aberd.; MFOM RCP Lond. 1991; DObst RCOG 1973. Eropean Regional Med. Director Conoco(UK) Ltd.; Performance Assessor GMC. Socs: Soc. Occupat. Med.; Aberd. M-C Soc. Prev: Sen. Med. Off. BP Exploration Aberd.; Company Med. Advisor Britoil plc; Med. Off. RAF.

BROWN, Beata 33 Southgate Road, Potters Bar EN6 5EA — LMSSA 1993 Lond.

BROWN, Beatrice Elizabeth 29 Uphill Grove, Mill Hill, London NW7 4NH Tel: 020 8959 3031 — MRCS Eng. LRCP Lond. 1945.

BROWN, Benjamin David The Croft, Adale Road, Smalley, Ilkeston DE7 6DZ — MB ChB 1998 Leeds.

BROWN, Betsy (retired) 25 Cheviot Drive, Newton Mearns, Glasgow G77 5AT Tel: 0141 639 2892 — MB ChB Glas. 1945; FRCS Eng. 1955; DLO Eng. 1950; DPH Glas. 1948. Prev: Cons. ENT Surg. Bradford Roy. Infirm.

***BROWN, Campbell Norman** 85 Locksley Park, Finaghy, Belfast BT10 0AT Tel: 01232 288942 — MB BCh 1998 Belf.; MB BCh Belf 1998.

BROWN, Carol Ann Kingsmills Medical Practice, 18 Southside Road, Inverness IV2 3BG Tel: 01463 235245 Fax: 01463 01443 714400; 80 Cradlehall Park, Inverness IV2 5DA Tel: 01463 791308 — MB ChB 1975 Aberd.; DA Eng. 1980; DRCOG 1977. Prev: Trainee GP Inverness VTS; Asst. GP Gundagai NSW Australia; Regist. (Anaesth.) Palmerston N. Hosp., NZ.

BROWN, Carole Anne The Manor Surgery, Middle St., Beeston, Nottingham NG9 1GA Tel: 0115 9256127 & 258181 — MB ChB 1965 Glas. (Glas.) Socs: Nottm. M-C Soc., & BMA. Prev: Jun. Ho. Off. (Med.) Roy. Infirm. & Roy. Hosp. Sick Childr. Glas.; Jun. Ho. Off. (Obst.) E.. Dist. Hosp. Glas.

BROWN, Carole Susan (Surgery), Saxon Way, Dersingham, King's Lynn PE31 6LY Tel: 01485 540463 Fax: 01485 543944; 22 Station Road, Dersingham, King's Lynn PE31 6PR — MB BS 1971 Lond.; MRCS Eng. LRCP Lond. 1971; MFFP 1993; FRCGP 1993, M 1975; Cert. Contracep. & Family Plann. RCOG & RCGP 1975; DObst RCOG 1974. (Roy. Free) Hosp. Pract. (Psychosexual Med.) Norf. Prev: Trainee GP King's Lynn VTS; Ho. Phys. & Ho. Surg. Rush Green Hosp. Romford.

BROWN, Caroline Jane Chestnuts Surgery, 70 East Street, Sittingbourne ME10 4RU Tel: 01795 423197 Fax: 01795 430179 — MB BS 1983 Lond.; BSc Lond. 1980; Cert. Family Plann. JCC 1989; DCCH RCP Ed. 1987.

BROWN, Caroline Jane Tam's Brig Surgery, 107 New Road, Ayr KA8 8DD Tel: 01292 262697 Fax: 01292 265926; The Willows', 5 Langmuir Avenue, Perceton, Irvine KA11 2DR Tel: 01294 222255 Email: cjbpooh@tinyworld.co.uk — MB ChB 1992 Glas.; MRCGP 1996; DRCOG 1995. Socs: BMA.

BROWN, Caroline Lindsey 3 Pinewood Drive, Mansfield NG18 4PG — MB ChB 1998 Leeds.

BROWN, Caroline McMillan 7A Lace Street, Nottingham NG7 2JT — BM BS 1991 Nottm.; DRCOG 1995.

BROWN, Catherine Borough Lane Surgery, 2 Borough Lane, Saffron Walden CB11 4AF Tel: 01799 524224 Fax: 01799 524830; 8 The Willows, Great Chesterford, Saffron Walden CB10 1QL Tel: 01799 530987 Fax: 01799 531218 — MB BS 1978 Newc.; FFA RCS Eng. 1984. Med. Off. Bell Internat. Coll. Socs: BASICS.

BROWN, Catherine Frances Preston Park Surgery, 2a Florence Road, Brighton BN1 6DJ Tel: 01273 559601/566033 Fax: 01273 507746 — MB BS 1988 Lond.; MRCGP 1992; DRCOG 1992.

BROWN, Catherine Louise High Place, Lewes Road, Blackboys, Uckfield TN22 5LF; 3 Laurence Court, Rosendale Road, Stoneleigh, Epsom KT17 2JQ — MB BS 1997 Lond. SHO (Pschiat), Epsom Gen. Hosp.

BROWN, Catherine Margaret Department of Radiology, Peterborough District Hospital, Thorpe Road, Peterborough PE3 6DA — MB ChB 1979 Ed.; FRCR 1985. Cons. Radiol. P'boro. Dist. Hosp.

BROWN, Catherine Mary 13 The Meadows, Templemore Road, Londonderry BT48 8RJ — MB BCh 1998 Belf.; MB BCh Belf 1998.

BROWN, Catherine Mary Lendrum 45 Orchard Drive, Chorleywood, Rickmansworth WD3 5QN — MB BS 1962 Lond.; MRCS Eng. LRCP Lond. 1960. (Roy. Free) Socs: BMA. Prev: Ho. Surg. (Gyn.) Roy. Free Hosp.; Ho. Phys. Eliz. G. Anderson Hosp.

BROWN, Mr Charles Alexander (retired) Combe House, Winters Lane, Redhill, Bristol BS40 5SH Tel: 01934 862426 — MB ChB Aberd. 1939; MA Aberd. 1935, MD 1946; FRCS Eng. (Ophth.) 1948; DOMS Eng. 1943. Prev: Cons. Ophth. Surg. Bristol Eye Hosp. & S.W. RHB.

BROWN, Charles Alexander Russell Brown and McKelvie, Medical Centre, Feorlin Way, Garelochhead, Helensburgh G84 0DG Tel: 01436 810370; Woodlands, Dunavard Road, Garelochhead, Helensburgh G84 0AB — MB ChB 1977 Manch.; BSc St. And. 1974.

BROWN, Charles Norman Emral House, Halls Lane, Waltham St Lawrence, Reading RG10 0JB Tel: 0118 934 3431 — MRCS Eng. LRCP Lond. 1938. (Guy's) Prev: Cas. Off. Guest Hosp. Dudley; Med. Resid. United Hosp. Port Chester, U.S.A.; Maj. RAMC.

BROWN, Charles Palmer (retired) 33 School Lane, Newton with Scales, Preston PR4 3RT Tel: 01772 683996 — MB ChB 1943 Manch.; LMSSA Lond. 1943; FFA RCS Eng. 1954; DA Eng. 1930. Hon. Cons. Blackpool Health Dist. Prev: Cons. Anaesth. Ormskirk & S.port Hosp. Gps.

BROWN, Charlotte Kate 7 Princes Close, Balsham, Cambridge CB1 6EE — MB ChB 1990 Leeds.

BROWN, Christine Saltash Health Centre, Callington Road, Saltash PL12 6DL Tel: 01752 842281 Fax: 01752 844651; 8 Venn Gardens, Hartley, Plymouth PL3 5PW Tel: 01752 771114 Fax: 01752 705596 Email: marrone@btinternet.com — MB BS 1976 Lond.; MRCS Eng. LRCP Lond. 1976. GP Saltash.

BROWN, Christine Ann 23 Nuthatch Close, Creekmoor, Poole BH17 7XR — BM 1993 Soton.; DA (UK) 1996. SHO O & G Roy. Bournemouth Hosp. Prev: SHO Orthop. Poole & Bourne. Gen. Hosp.; SHO A&E Soton. Gen. Hosp.; SHO Med. Lymington Hosp.

BROWN, Christine Aylmer Pantiles, Chapel Lane, Swallow, Lincoln LN7 6DE Tel: 01472 371582; 33 Laceby Road, Grimsby DN34 5BH Tel: 01472 79529 — MB BS 1965 Lond.; MRCS Eng. LRCP Lond. 1965; DCH Eng. 1967. (Roy. Free) Prev: SHO (Anaesth.) & (Paediat.) York Co. Hosp.

BROWN, Christine Mary (retired) Oberlin House, Greenacres, Oldham OL4 3HS Tel: 0161 633 1135 — MB ChB 1962 Leeds; DObst RCOG 1964. Prev: GP Oldham.

BROWN, Christine Sandra 9 Chyngton Way, Seaford BN25 4JA — MB BS 1992 Lond.

BROWN, Christopher Collinson Springfield, Forthvean Road, Porthtowan, Truro TR4 8AY — MB ChB 1978 Birm.

BROWN, Christopher Dennis Dr Davison and Partners, Parkgate Health Centre, Park Place, Darlington DL1 5LW — MB ChB 1991 Leic.; DCH RCP Lond. 1997; DGM RCP Lond 1997; MRCGP 1998. Gp Princip. Prev: Salaried GP Cleveland Career Start, Worth Ormesby health Centre, Middlesbrough; GP/Regist. Cleveland VTS; SHO (O & G) Blackpool Vict. Hosp.

BROWN, Christopher Ian Watson Shawbirch Medical Centre, 5 Acorn Way, Shawbirch, Telford TF5 0LW Tel: 01952 641555 Fax: 01952 260913; 181 Holyhead Road, Wellington, Telford TF1 2DP Tel: 01952 252498 — MB ChB 1981 Liverp.; MRCGP 1986; DRCOG 1985.

BROWN, Christopher John Richardson Watson Wyatt Worldwide, 21 Tothill St., London SW1H 9LL Tel: 020 7227 2270 Fax: 020 7227 2233; 8 Melcombe Court, Dorset Square, London NW1 6EP Tel: 020 7723 5758 — MB ChB 1985 Manch.; MBA Cranfield Sch. Managem. 1991. Princip. Socs: BMA. Prev: Sen. Cons. Deloitie & Touche Consg. Gp.; Business Manager Norwich Union Healthcare; Trainee GP Lymington.

BROWN, Christopher Latham 7 Wolsey Close, Kingston upon Thames KT2 7ER Tel: 020 8942 5077 — MB BS 1957 Lond.; FRCPath 1979, M 1967; DObst RCOG 1961. (Lond. Hosp.) Sen. Lect. (Path.) Inst. Path. Lond. Hosp. Socs: BMA; Brit. Soc. Clin. Cytol. Prev: SHO Clin. Laborats. & SHO (Venereol.) Lond. Hosp.; Ho. Surg. (Obst.) Kingston Hosp. Kingston-on-Thames.

BROWN, Christopher Mark Danton Ivry Street Medical Practice, 5 Ivry Street, Ipswich IP1 3QW Tel: 01473 254718 Fax: 01473 287790 — MB 1972 Camb.; BChir 1971. Course Organiser Ipswich VTS. Prev: Ho. Surg. St. Mary's Hosp. Paddington; Ho. Phys. Addenbrooke's Hosp. Camb.; SHO (Paediat.) Paddington Green Childr. Hosp. Lond.

BROWN, Christopher Paul Treves (retired) 30 Gills Hill, Radlett WD7 8BZ Tel: 01923 857444 Fax: 01923 857444 Email: cptrevesb@aol — MB BS Lond. 1962; LLB Lond. 1992; FRCPsych 1996, M 1972; DPM Eng. 1968; DA Eng. 1964. Prev: Cons. Psychiat. Luton & Dunstable Hosp.

BROWN, Christopher Robin, TD (retired) Mel Valley, Oxford Lodge, Stowe, Buckingham MK18 5DA Tel: 01280 814222 — MB BS Lond. 1958; DObst RCOG 1962; DA Eng. 1960. Hon. Med. Off. Buckingham Hosp. Prev: SHO (Anaesth.) & Ho. Phys. (Paediat.) Stoke Mandeville Hosp.

BROWN, Christopher Tibbits North Mill, Wareham BH20 4QW Tel: 01929 552055 — MB ChB 1951 Bristol; MRCGP 1961; DObst RCOG 1953. (Bristol) Socs: BMA. Prev: Med. Off. Brit. Antarctic Survey Base, Halley Bay (1962-3); Ho. Phys. Frenchay Hosp. Bristol; Obst. Ho. Surg. S.mead Hosp. Bristol.

BROWN, Claire Joyce Fulwell Medical Centre, Ebdon Lane, off Dene Lane, Sunderland SR6 8DZ Tel: 0191 548 3635 — MB BS 1984 Newc. GP Sunderland.

BROWN, Claudine Mary Rosalind (retired) Redwing, South Park, Sevenoaks TN13 1EL Tel: 01732 454918 — MRCS Eng. LRCP Lond. 1950; DCH Eng. 1954. Clin. Asst. (Child Guid.) Maidstone. Prev: Sen. Regist. (Dermat.) Roy. Free Hosp.

BROWN, Clement Hamill, TD 17 Madingley Road, Cambridge CB3 0EG Tel: 01223 360065 Fax: 01223 360065 — MB ChB 1963 Birm.; FRCP Lond. 1995; MRCP Lond. 1966; FRCR 1975. p/t Med. Direct. E. Anglian Cancer Registry. Prev: Cons. Radiother. & Oncol. Addenbrooke's Hosp. Camb.

BROWN, Mr Colin Nuffield Hospital, Derriford, Plymouth PL6 8BG Tel: 01752 761835 Fax: 01752 768969; Little Haslemere, Golf Links Road, Yelverton PL20 6BN Tel: 01822 852740 — MS Lond. 1977, MB BS 1965; FRCS Eng. 1970; MRCS Eng. LRCP Lond. 1965. (Char. Cross) Cons. Surg. Plymouth Gen. Hosp. Prev: Sen. Surg. Regist. St Geo. Hosp. Lond. & St Jas. Hosp. Lond.; Research Fell. TuLa. Univ. New Orleans, USA.

BROWN, Colin 8 East London Street, Edinburgh EH7 4BH — MB ChB 1991 Ed.; DRCOG 1995. GP Regist. St. Ronans Health Centre Innerleithen. Prev: Trainee GP Borders Gen. Hosp. Melrose VTS; SHO (Gen. Med.) S. Tyneside HA; Cas. Off. Dunfermline & W. Fife Hosp.

BROWN, Colin Bertram Sheffield Kidney Institute, Northern General Hospital, Herries Road, Sheffield University Medical School, Sheffield S5 7AU Tel: 0114 271 5309 Fax: 0114 261 7397 Email: cbbrown1@compuserve.com; Platts Farm, Ughill, Bradfield, Sheffield S6 6HU Tel: 0114 285 1334 Fax: 0114 285 1094 — MB BS 1968 Lond.; BSc (Hons.) Lond. 1965; FRCP Lond. 1985, M 1971; MRCS Eng. LRCP Lond. 1968. (Guy's) Cons. Renal Phys. Sheff. Kidney Inst. N. Gen. Hosp. Socs: Internat. Soc. Nephrol.; Internat. Soc. Peritoneal Dialysis (Chairm. Pub. Comm.); Renal Assn. (Sec. Registry Comm.). Prev: Sen. Regist. (Renal Med.) Guy's Hosp. Lond.; Research Fell. Harvard Univ. Med. Sch.; Ho. Phys. Guy's Hosp. Lond.

BROWN, Colin Mark 11 Heazle Place, Stroud GL5 1UW — MB ChB 1985 Liverp.; MD Liverp. 1994; MRCP (UK) 1988. Socs: Roy. Coll. Phys.; BMA; Brit. Soc. Gastroenterol. Prev: Research Fell. Hope Hosp. Salford Univ. Manch. Sch. Med.; Clin. Regist. (Gastroenterol.) & SHO (Geriat. Med.) Hope Hosp. Salford; SHO (Med.) Whiston & St. Helens Hosps.

BROWN, Colin Richard, Air Commodore RAF Med. Br. Bondgate Surgery, Infirmary Close, Alnwick NE66 2NL; Aldersyde, Alnmouth Road, Alnwick NE66 2PS — MB ChB 1969 Ed.; Adv. Cert. Aviation Medicine; BSc (Med. Sci.) Ed. 1966; MRCGP 1996. Gen. practitioner Alnwick, N.d.; Mem. N.d. LMC. Socs: BMA. Prev: Ho. Surg. Peel Hosp. Galashiels; Ho. Phys. E.. Gen. Hosp. Edin.

BROWN, Colin Wilson Worgan Downlands, Hackwood Lane, Cliddesden, Basingstoke RG25 2NH Tel: 01256 465925 — MRCS Eng. LRCP Lond. 1953; DO Eng. 1963. (St. Thos.) Med. Pract. (Ophth.) Reading. Prev: Hons. Cons. & Clin. Asst. (Ophth.) St. Thos. Hosp. Lond.; Regist. (Ophth.) St. Peter's Hosp. Chertsey; Ho. Surg. (Ophth.) St. Thos. Hosp. Lond.

BROWN, Colin Wylie Glenburn Health Centre, Fairway Ave, Paisley PA2 8DX Tel: 0141 884 7788 Fax: 0141 561 1090 Email: colin.brown@renver-pct.scot.nhs.uk; Drumlins, Hillside Rd, Barrhead G78 1ES Tel: 0141 881 4122 Email: colinbrown@bigfoot.com — MB BChir 1977 Camb.; LMSSA Lond. 1976; MRCGP 1981; DRCOG 1979. (King's Coll. Lond.) Gen. Med. Practitioner. Prev: Trainee GP W.. Infirm. VTS.

BROWN, Craig Arbuthnott Aralia, 4 St Cuthberts Avenue, Dumfries DG2 7NZ; St. Ronans Health Centre, Buchan Place, Innerleithen EH44 6QE Tel: 01896 830203 Fax: 01896 831202 — MB ChB 1979 Aberd.; MRCGP 1983; DRCOG 1981; DCH Glas. 1982.

BROWN, Craig Kerr Westcourt, 12 The Street, Rustington, Littlehampton BN16 3NX Tel: 01903 784311 Fax: 01903 850907 — MB ChB 1972 Glas.; MRCGP 1976; DObst RCOG 1975. (Glas.) Prev: Med. Off. Montebello Miss. Hosp., S. Afr.

BROWN, Daniel John 17 New Street, Carnforth LA5 9BX — MB ChB 1992 Manch.; FRCS Eng. 1997. Specialist Regist. Rotat. (Orthop.) Mersey Region.

BROWN, David Lower Bourne Surgery, 41 Frensham Road, Lower Bourne, Farnham GU10 3PZ — BM BCh 1991 Oxf.

BROWN, David Allan 35 Sheepburn Road, Uddingston, Glasgow G71 7DT — MB ChB 1969 Glas.

BROWN, David Campbell, OStJ, Surg. Cdr. RN Institute of Naval Medicine, Alverstoke, Gosport PO12 2DL Tel: 02392 768026 Email: ye30@dial.pipox.com; Fordes, Church St, Ropley, Alresford SO24 0DR Tel: 01926 773221 Email: david.brown28@virgin.net — MB ChB 1979 Sheff.; MSc Occupat. Med. Lond. 1984; MRCS Eng. LRCP Lond. 1979; MFOM RCP Lond. 1988; 1998 FFOM Lond; 1992 MSc London. Head of Submarine and Radiat. Med. Inst. of Naval Med.; Cons. Occupat. Med. RN.; Prof. of Naval Occupat.al Med.; Cons. Adviser in Submarine and Radiat.; Med. to Med. Director Gen. (Navy); Defence Adviser in Radiat. Med. Socs: Mem. Soc. Radiat. Protec.; Fell., Roy. Soc. of Med.; Mem., Soc. Occup. Med. Prev: Ho. Off. (Gen. Med.) Rotherham Dist. Gen. Hosp.; Ho. Off. (Surg. & Orthop.) R.N. Hosp. Haslar; Squadron Med. Off. Second Submarine Squadron.

BROWN, David Charles 18 Bailey Road, Oxford OX4 3HY — MB BCh BAO 1982 Belf.; BSc Belf. 1979, MD 1989. Clin. Lect. Univ. Oxf.

BROWN, David Charles Falt 12, Nampara Court, Grannys Lane, Perranporth TR6 0HS — MB ChB 1996 Birm.

BROWN, David Edward 327 Uppingham Road, Leicester LE5 4DN Tel: 0116 276 8388 — MB BS 1950 Lond.; MRCS Eng. LRCP Lond. 1949; FFA RCS Eng. 1956; DA Eng. 1953, DCH 1951. (Middlx.)

Cons. Anaesth. Leicester Roy. Infirm.; Cons. to Pain Relief Servs. Leicester Area. Socs: Founder Fell. Internat. Assn. Study of Pain; Intractable Pain Soc. Prev: Sen. Regist. (Anaesth.) Middlx. Hosp. & Lond. Chest Hosp.; Regist. Middlx. Hosp.; Jun. Regist. Lond. Hosp.

BROWN, David George Pearson, Wing Cdr. RAF Med. Br. Retd. (retired) 88 Main Street, Leuchars, St Andrews KY16 0HF Tel: 01334 838437 — MB ChB St. And. 1952. Prev: GP Leuchars.

BROWN, David Graeme The Health Centre, Preston Road, Prestonpans EH32 9QS Tel: 01875 810736; 136 Milton Road W., Edinburgh EH15 1RQ Tel: 0131 669 1404 — LRCP LRCS Ed. LRFPS Glas. 1949. (Roy. Colls. Ed.) Prev: Anaesth. Caithness Hosp. Gp.; Police Surg. Caithness Constab.

BROWN, David Hume Arndale Resource Centre, 80-90 Kinfauns Drive, Drumchapel, Glasgow G15 7TS — MB ChB 1984 Glas.; FRCP Ed 1999; MRCPSych 1990; MRCP (UK) 1988; BSc (Hons. Physiol.) Glas. 1981. (Glasgow) Cons. Psychiat. Gartnavel Roy. Hosp.; Hon. Clin. Sen. Lect. Univ. of Glas. Prev: Sen. Regist. (Psychiat.) Roy. Dundee Liff Hosp.; Regist. (Psychiat.) Gartnavel Roy. Hosp. Glas; SHO & Regist. (Gen. Med.) Stobhill Hosp. Glas.

BROWN, David James Gordon Flat 2/1, 66 Overnewton St., Glasgow G3 8RZ — MB ChB 1994 Glas.

BROWN, David John The Surgery, Field Road, Stainforth, Doncaster DN7 5AF Tel: 01302 841202 — MB BS 1976 Newc.; MRCGP 1980; DA (UK) 1980. Prev: SHO (Anaesth.) Roy. Vict. Infirm. Newc.; Ho. Surg. & Ho. Phys. Roy. Vict. Infirm. Newc.

BROWN, David Leslie (retired) Walford Mill Medical Centre, Knobcrook Road, Wimborne BH21 1NL — MB ChB 1963 Sheff.; DObst RCOG 1965. Prev: Ho. Phys. City Gen. Hosp. Sheff.

BROWN, David Leslie 6 Churchfield Court, Girton, Cambridge CB3 0XA; Box 109, Clinical Immunology, Addenbrooke's Hospital, Hills Road, Cambridge CB2 2QQ — MB BChir Camb. 1965; MA Camb. 1992, MD (Raymond Horton-Smith Prize) 1972; FRCPath 1985, M 1971. (Camb.) Cons. Clin. Immunol. Addenbrooke's Hosp. Camb.; Dir. Research & Developm. & Asst. Med. Dir. Addenbrooke's Hosp. Camb.; Assoc. Lect. Univ. Camb. Prev: Assessor Regius Prof. Physic Univ. Camb.; Dir. (Path.) Addenbrooke's Hosp. Camb.; Lect. & Hon. Cons. Roy. Postgrad. Med. Sch. Lond.

BROWN, David Michael Gellatly Netherfield House, Station Road, Seghill, Cramlington NE23 7EF Tel: 0191 237 0643 Fax: 0191 237 1091; 3 Roseworth Close, Gosforth, Newcastle upon Tyne NE3 1SW Tel: 0191 284 7391 — MB BS 1979 Newc.; MRCGP 1983; DRCOG 1982. GP; Clin. Governance Lead Blyth Valley PCG.

BROWN, David Percy Stockton Hall Psychiatric Hospital, The Village, Stockton-on-the-Forest, York YO3 9UN Tel: 01904 400500 — MB ChB 1973 Ghana; MRCPsych 1981; FRCPsych 2000. (Univ. Ghana Med. Sch.) Cons. Psychiat. Stockton Hall Hosp.; Med Dir. Stockton Hall Hosp. Prev: Cons. Psychiat. Forens. Rampton Hosp.; Cons. Psychiat. Woodlands Hosp. Cults, Aberd.; Hon. Clin. Sen. Lect. Dept. Ment. Health Aberd. Univ.

BROWN, David Robertson Brown and Partners, 35 Saughton Crescent, Edinburgh EH12 5SS Tel: 0131 337 2166 Fax: 0131 313 5059 — MB ChB 1974 Ed.; MRCGP 1980.

BROWN, David Rowatt Oak Lodge Surgery, 32 Miller Street, Almada Lane, Hamilton ML3 7EN Tel: 01698 282350 Fax: 01698 282502; 16 McIntosh Way, Motherwell ML1 3BB — MB ChB 1974 Glas.; Cert. JCC Lond. 1980. GP Hamilton.

BROWN, David Taylor 18 Winton Grove, Edinburgh EH10 7AS — MB ChB 1972 St. And.; FFA RCS Eng. 1977. Cons. Anaesth. Roy. Infirm. Edin. Prev: Lect. (Anaesth.) Univ. Edin. Sen. Regist. (Anaesth.) Roy. Infirm.; Edin.; Regist. Dept. Anaesth. Roy. Infirm. Edin.

BROWN, David William 90 Manygates Lane, Wakefield WF2 7DW — MB ChB 1980 Leeds.

BROWN, David William Graham 23 Sydney Road, Muswell Hill, London N10 2LR — MB BS 1976 Lond.; MSc Lond. (Med. Microbiol.) 1980, MB BS 1976; MRCPath (Virol.) 1983. Cons. Virol. Virus Refer. Laborat. Centr. Pub. Health Laborat. Colindale Lond.

BROWN, Deborah 654 George Street, Aberdeen AB25 3XN — MB ChB 1994 Aberd.

BROWN, Denise Ann Bartholomew House, Boothferry Road, Goole DN14 7AL Tel: 01405 720820 — MB BS 1982 Lond. Clin. Asst. (Psychiat.) Bartholomew Hse. Goole Scunthorpe Community NHS Trust. Prev: SHO & Regist. (Psychiat.) Guy's Hosp. Lond.

BROWN, Dennis Geoffrey Group Analytic Practice, 88 Montagu Mansions, London W1U 6LF Tel: 020 7935 3103 Fax: 020 7935 1397 Email: dgb@gapractice.org.uk — MB ChB 1951 Leeds; MD Leeds 1970; FRCP Ed. 1982, M 1961; FRCPsych 1978, M 1971; DPM Leeds 1959. (Leeds) Socs: Assoc. Mem. Brit. Psychoanal. Soc.; (Ex-Pres.) Gp. Analyt. Soc. Lond.; Roy. Soc. Med. Prev: Cons. Psychotherapist St. Geo. & St. Mary's Hosps. Lond.; Research Asst. Acad. Dept. Psychiat. Middlx. Hosp. Lond.; Lect. (Psychiat.) Univ. Leeds.

BROWN, Derek Peter (retired) Meadow Court, Alcester Road, Wooton Wawen, Solihull B95 6BQ Tel: 01564 792768 Email: derek.p.brown@btinternet.co.uk — MB BS 1954 Lond.; BSc Lond. 1951; MRCGP 1973; DIH 1969; DMJ (Clin.) Soc. Apoth. Lond. 1967. GP Asst. to Dr MP Buckley, Studley, Warwks. Prev: GP Princip., Eccleshall, Stafford.

BROWN, Derek Robin Pritchard 108 Hill Street, Glasgow G3 6UA — MB BS 1985 Lond.; MRCPsych 1990. Sen. Regist. (Old Age Psychiat.) Glas.

BROWN, Desmond Alexander Paediatric Department, Altnagelvin Hospital, Altnagelvin, Londonderry BT47 6SB Tel: 02871 345171 Fax: 02871 611292 Email: desmond.brown@virgin.net — MB BCh BAO Belf. 1976; MRCP (UK) 1979; FRCPS Glas. 1991. (Qu. Univ. Belf.) Cons. Paediat. Altnagelvin Area Hosp. Lond.derry. Prev: Neonatologist Mt. Sinai Hosp. Toronto.

BROWN, Domenyk William Hay 7 Bracken Brae, Broughty Ferry, Dundee DD5 1RX — MB ChB 1997 Aberd.

BROWN, Dominic Harold 3 Hyde Cottages, Handcross, Haywards Heath RH17 6EZ — MB ChB 1995 Birm.

BROWN, Mr Donald Buchanan, TD (retired) 13 Chalmers Crescent, Edinburgh EH9 1TS Tel: 0131 667 2442 — MB ChB Glas. 1934; FRCS Eng. 1947; FRFPS Glas. 1947; FRCS Glas. 1962. Prev: Surg. i/c Wards, W.. Infirm. Glas.

BROWN, Donald Craig Royal Hospital for Sick Children, Edinburgh EH9 1LF Tel: 0131 536 0000 Fax: 0131 536 0001 Email: donald.brown@luht.scot.nhs.uk — MB BCh BAO 1983 Belf.; FRCP Ed 1999; FRCPH 1999; MD Belf. 1993; DCCH RCP Ed. 1989; DCH RCPI 1986. (Queen's Belfast) Cons. Roy. Hosp. Sick Childr. Edin.; Hon. Sen. Lect., Univ. of Edin. Socs: Scott. Paediat. Soc.; Fell. Roy. Coll. of Phys. Edin.; Fell. Roy. Coll. of Paediat. & Child Health. Prev: Sen. Regist. Roy. Hosp. Sick Childr. Edin.; Clin. Fell. Roy. Childr. Hosp. Melbourne, Austral.; Clin. Research Fell. MRC Edin.

BROWN, Donald Farquhar Elgin Medical Centre, 10 Victoria Crescent, Elgin IV30 1RQ Tel: 01343 547512 Fax: 01343 546781; Buinach Lodge, Kellas, Elgin IV30 8TS Tel: 01343 890209 Fax: 01343 890296 — MB ChB 1971 Glas. Ltd. Specialist (Path.) Grampian HB. Prev: Path. W. Grampian Health Dist.; Regist. (Haemat. & Gen. Med.) Glas. Roy. Infirm.

BROWN, Donald MacGregor (retired) 2 South Road, Busby, Clarkston, Glasgow G76 8JB Tel: 0141 644 1148 — MB ChB 1961 Glas.; FFA RCS Eng. 1969; DObst RCOG 1966. Cons. Anaesth. Roy. Infirm. Glas. Prev: Ho. Off. (Obst.) Robroyston Hosp. Glas.

BROWN, Dorothy Anne (retired) 27 Church Way, Sanderstead, South Croydon CR2 0JT Tel: 020 8657 7492 Fax: 020 8657 7492 — MB BS Lond. 1959; FRCP Lond. 1993; MRCP (UK) 1978; DObst RCOG 1961. Cons. Phys. (Geriat. Med.) Mayday Hosp. Croydon. Prev: Sen. Regist. (Geriat. Med.) St. Geo. Hosp. Tooting.

BROWN, Mr Douglas Charles Flat 2, Wester Drumlins, 49 Partickhill Road, Glasgow G11 5AB Tel: 0141 357 4149 — MB ChB 1985 Glas.; FRCS Glas. 1989; FRCS Ed. 1989.

BROWN, Duncan Richard 12 Clifestone Drive, East Morton, Keighley BD20 5RR — MB ChB 1994 Aberd.

BROWN, Edward James (retired) The Old Owls Barn, Sudbrook, Ancaster, Grantham NG32 3QS — MB BS 1961 Lond.; MRCS Eng. LRCP Lond. 1961.

BROWN, Edward Leslie St Neots Surgery, 47 Wolseley Road, Plymouth PL2 3BJ Tel: 01752 561305 Fax: 01752 605565 — MB ChB 1975 Birmingham; MB ChB 1975 Birmingham.

BROWN, Edwin Louis Rees (retired) 21 Greenhill Place, Edinburgh EH10 4BR Tel: 0131 447 6560 — LRCP LRCS Ed. LRFPS Glas. 1949.

BROWN, Edwina Anne Charing Cross Hospital, Fulham Palace Road, London W6 8RF Tel: 020 8846 1234 Fax: 020 8846 7589; 1 Abbotsbury Close, London W14 8EG Tel: 020 7460 2402 — BM BCh 1973 Oxf.; DM Oxf. 1983, BA 1970; MRCP (UK) 1975; FRCP

1993. (Oxf. & Univ. Coll. Hosp.) Cons. Nephrol. Char. Cross Hosp. Lond. Socs: Renal Assn.; Internat. Soc. Nephrol.; Internat. Soc. Peritoneal Dialysis. Prev: Sen. Regist. (Nephrol.) Char. Cross Hosp. Lond.; Fell. (Nephrol.) Yale Med. Sch. New Haven, USA; Regist. (Med.) Univ. Coll. Hosp. Lond.

BROWN, Eileen Margaret Child Services, Northampton General Hospital, Cliftonville, Northampton NN1 5BD Tel: 01604 634700; 6 Naomi Close, Northampton NN3 3PG Tel: 01604 407205 — MB ChB Cape Town 1966; DCCH Warwick 1996. (Cape Town) Staff Grade Med. Off. (Community Child Health). Socs: Soc. Pub. Health; Fac. Fam. Plann.; MRCPCH. Prev: SCMO (Family Plann.) N.ampton HA.

BROWN, Eleanor Down Lisburn HSS Trust, 81 Market St., Downpatrick BT30 6LZ Tel: 01396 613511; Westgate, 15 The Strand, Portaferry, Newtownards BT22 1PF Tel: 012477 28309 — MB BCh BAO 1986 Belf.; BSc (Biochem.) Belf. 1983; MRCGP 1993; DRCOG 1992; DMH Belf. 1991; DCH RCPS Glas. 1990. Clin. Med. Off. (Community Child Health) Down Lisburn Trust Downpatrick. Socs: BMA & MWF; BACCH. Prev: SHO (Paediat.) Roy. Belf. Hosp. for Sick Childr.

BROWN, Eleanor Sian 117 Black Oak Road, Cyncoed, Cardiff CF23 6QW Tel: 029 2075 8689 Email: 113637.1272@compuserve.com; 350 Cyncoed Road, Cyncoed, Cardiff CF2 6RZ Tel: 029 2076 2514 Fax: 01222 764262 — MB ChB Manch. 1977; DRCOG 1979.

BROWN, Elisha Francis Oakleigh, 21 Harmony Hill, Lisburn BT27 4EP — MB BCh BAO 1960 Dub.; BA, MB BCh BAO Dub. 1960. Cas. Off. Lagan Valley Hosp. Lisburn.

BROWN, Elizabeth Meadowbank Health Centre, 3 Salmon Inn Road, Polmont, Falkirk FK2 0XF Tel: 01324 715540 Fax: 01324 716723; Garden House, 13 Gartcows Road, Falkirk FK1 5EF Tel: 01324 613481 — MB ChB 1971 Glas.

BROWN, Elizabeth 14 Knebworth Road, Bexhill-on-Sea TN39 4JH — MB ChB 1994 Leic.

BROWN, Elizabeth Anne 90 Fore Street, Chudleigh, Newton Abbot TQ13 0HT — MB BS 1983 Lond.; MRCGP 1987; DRCOG 1986. (St. Mary's)

BROWN, Elizabeth Anne The Surgery, 1 Troy Close, Tadworth Farm, Tadworth KT20 5JE Tel: 01737 362327 Fax: 01737 373469 — MB ChB 1987 Birm.; DRCOG 1990.

BROWN, Elizabeth Fleur 22 Montpellier House, Suffolk Square, Cheltenham GL50 2DY Tel: 01242 572535 — MB BS 1983 Lond.; BSc Lond. 1980, MB BS 1983; MRCP (UK) 1986; FRCR 1989. Cons. Radiol. Gloucester Roy. Hosp. Prev: Sen. Regist. (Radiol.) S. W.. HA; Regist. (Med.) Orsett Dist. Gen. Hosp.; SHO The Lond. Hosp.

BROWN, Elizabeth Hicks 1 Deepdale Place, Broughty Ferry, Dundee DD5 3DD — MB ChB 1952 St. And.

BROWN, Elizabeth Joyce (retired) China Close, Highweek, Newton Abbot TQ12 1PY Tel: 01626 352774 — MB BS Lond. 1946. Prev: Ho. Phys. Roy. Free Hosp.

BROWN, Elizabeth Louise 142 Ribchester Road, Clayton-Le-Dale, Blackburn BB1 9EE — MB ChB 1998 Leeds.

BROWN, Elliot Graham Rowan House, 7 Woodfall avenue, Barnet EN5 2EZ Tel: 020 8449 8788 Email: eb@ebconsulting.co.uk; 7 Woodfall Avenue, Barnet EN5 2EZ Tel: 020 8441 9906 — MB ChB 1973 Sheff.; BMedSci (Hons.) Sheff. 1970; MRCGP 1978; FFPM RCP (UK) 1989; Dip. Pharm. Med. 1986. (Sheff.) Managing Dir., EBC Ltd, EBT Ltd; Assoc. Edr., Int. Jl. Pharmaceut. Med; Mem. Bd. Exam. Fac. of Pharmaceut. Med. RCP; Hon Sen. Lect. Lond.; Hon. Cons. WHO, UMC. Socs: Fell.Roy.soc.med; Drug Informat. Assn.; Internat. Soc. Pharmademiol. Prev: Sen. Med. Assessor, Med.s Control Agency, UK; Dir. Euro Pharmacovigilance, Lilly Research Centre; Med. Dir. Marion Merrell Dow Ltd. Uxbridge.

BROWN, Elspeth Morag Department of Paediatric Cardiology, Wessex Cardiothoracic Centre, Southampton General Hospital, Tremona Road, Southampton SO16 6YD Tel: 02380 777222 — MB ChB 1986 Leic.; MRCP (UK) Glas. 1990.

BROWN, Emily 16 Cecil Street, Leeds LS12 2AL — MB ChB 1997 Leeds.

BROWN, Enid Muriel 6 Keble House, Manor Fields, Putney Hill, London SW15 3LS — MB BS 1959 Lond.; BA (Hons.) Lond. 1951, MB BS 1959; MFOM RCP Lond. 1978; DIH Eng. 1974; DA Eng. 1962. (St. Bart.)

BROWN, Eric 39 Oak Place, Kilmarnock KA1 2EU — MB ChB 1989 GLAS.

BROWN, Eric William John Willands, Queens Avenue, Maidstone ME16 0EN Tel: 01622 752217 Fax: 01622 752217 Email: e.brown@clara.net.co.uk — MB BS (Hons.) Lond. 1956; DObst RCOG 1959. (St. Thos.) Prev: Cas. Off. & Ho. Phys. St. Thos. Hosp. Lond.; Ho. Surg. (Obst.) Lambeth Hosp.

BROWN, Ernest Arthur (retired) 4 Hangleton Manor Close, Hove BN3 8AJ Tel: 01273 413229 — MB BS 1949 Lond.; MRCP Lond. 1967; FRCPsych 1986, M 1972; LMSSA Lond. 1948; DPM Eng. 1965. Prev: Cons. (Psychother.) St. Francis Hosp. Haywards Heath & Lady Chichester Hosp. Hove.

BROWN, Erwin Martin Department of Medical Microbiology, Frenchay Hospital, Bristol BS16 1LE Tel: 0117 970 1212 Fax: 0117 957 1866 Email: erwin.brown@north-bristol.sweet.nhs.uk; 31 Park Crescent, Frenchay, Bristol BS16 1NZ Tel: 0117 956 6090 — MB BCh 1979 Wales; MSc Univ. Toronto 1972, BSc 1968; FRCPath 1996, M 1986; Dip. Bact. Univ. Toronto 1969. Cons. Med. Microbiol. Frenchay Hosp. Bristol; Sen. Clin. Lect. (Microbiol.) Univ. Bristol. Prev: Sen. Regist. (Med. Microbiol.) Univ. Hosp. Wales Cardiff; Regist. Pub. Health Laborat. Univ. Hosp. Wales Cardiff.

***BROWN, Ewan Russell Stewart** 4 Bennochy Avenue, Kirkcaldy KY2 5QE Tel: 01592 204261 — MB ChB 1998 Ed.; MB ChB Ed 1998.

BROWN, Fiona Lamont Audiology Unit, 4B Auchingramont Road, Hamilton ML3 6JP Tel: 01698 281500; 187 Silvertonhill Avenue, Hamilton ML3 7PG — MB ChB 1978 Glas.; DCCH RCP Ed.; DRCOG 1980; Mem of Roy. Pa. Child Health 1998. SCMO (Audiol.) Lanarksh. HB. Socs: Fell. Coll Med.; Dip. Fac. Family Plann. & Reproduc. Health Care.

BROWN, Francis Oughterson (retired) 3 Cherrylea, Castleton Park, Auchterarder PH3 1QG — MB ChB 1945 Glas.; MA Camb. 1947; FRCP Glas. 1980, M 1962; FRFPS Glas. 1949; FRCR 1975; DMRD Eng. 1957. Prev: Cons. Radiol. Forth Valley HB.

BROWN, Francis Robert Bell (retired) 10 Moira Drive, Bangor BT20 4RN — MB BCh BAO 1954 Belf.; FRCPI 1986, M 1967; MRCPsych 1972; DPM RCSI 1961. Prev: Cons. Psychiat. Purdysburn Hosp. Belf.

BROWN, Freda Jane Pilgrim Health Trust, Pilgrim Hospital, Sibsey Road, Boston PE21 9Q; 12 Harrowby Lane, Grantham NG31 9HX — MB ChB 1969 Aberd. Assoc. Specialist (Community Paediat.), Pilgrim Health Trust, Boston. Socs: Brit. Paediat. Assn.; BACCH; FRIPHH.

BROWN, Freda Mary 128 Church Street, Great Burstead, Billericay CM11 2TR Tel: 01277 623891 — MB ChB 1958 Manch.; DA Eng. 1962.

BROWN, Gareth George Court Road Surgery, 29 Court Road, Barry CF63 4YD Tel: 01446 733181 Fax: 01446 420004 — MB BCh 1977 Wales. Prev: Trainee Gen. Pract. Bridgend VTS; SHO (O & G) Roy. Gwent Hosp. Newport; SHO (Paediat.) Merthyr & Cynon Valley Health Dist.

BROWN, Gareth James 45 Drumpellier Av, Cumbernauld, Glasgow G67 4NP — MB ChB 1997 Dundee.

BROWN, Gareth MacGillivray 6 Parc Close, Llangybi, Usk NP15 1PN — MB BCh 1995 Wales.

BROWN, Garry Kenneth Department of Biochemistry, Genetics Unit, University of Oxford, South Parks Road, Oxford OX1 3QU Tel: 01865 275214 Fax: 01865 275318 Email: gkb@bioch.ox.ac.uk — MB BS 1972 Sydney; PhD Sydney 1976, BSc (Med.) 1969; FRCP Lond. 1997. Lect. (Biochem.) Univ. Oxf.; Hon. Cons. Med. Genetics Ch.ill Hosp. Oxf. Prev: Sen. Lect. (Paediat.) Univ. Melbourne, Austral.

BROWN, Gary Winston Conquista, Mill Road, Chopwell, Newcastle upon Tyne NE17 7HA — MB BS 1982 Newc.

BROWN, Gavin Albert Flat B, 315 North Woodside Road, Glasgow G20 6LA — MB ChB 1998 Glas.; MB ChB Glas 1998.

BROWN, Geoffrey Neil 83 Belsize Lane, London NW3 5AU — MB ChB 1967 Manch.; MRCPsych 1980.

BROWN, Geoffrey Newall, TD, OStJ Flat 3, Beechwood Court, Holm Road, Didsbury, Manchester M20 2UA Tel: 0161 434 6041 — MB ChB 1966 Manch.; MRCS Eng. LRCP Lond. 1966; FFOM RCP Lond. 1987, MFOM 1980; DIH Soc. Apoth. Lond. 1971. Socs: (Ex-Hon. Sec.) Soc. Occupat. Med.; Brit. Med. Pilots Assn. Prev: Sen.

Med. Off. DoH; Sen. Med. Off. MoD (PE); Hon. Col. 220 (1st Home counties) Field Ambul. RAMC (V).

BROWN, George Laing (retired) 115 Eaves Lane, Bucknall, Stoke-on-Trent ST2 8LE — MD Glas. 1942, MB ChB 1936, DPH 1939. Prev: Cons. Phys. Infec. Dis. Bucknall Hosp.

BROWN, George Laird (retired) 3 Washington Road, Barnes, London SW13 9BG Tel: 020 8748 2522 — MB BS 1952 Lond.; MRCS Eng. LRCP Lond. 1952; DObst RCOG 1953. Prev: Med. Off. St. Paul's Sch. Lond.

BROWN, George Morris Wilsden Medical Practice, Health Centre, Townfield, Wilsden, Bradford BD15 0HT Tel: 01535 273227 Fax: 01535 274860; Cliffestones, 12 Cliffestone Drive, E. Morton, Keighley BD20 5RR Tel: 01274 565742 — MB ChB 1969 St. And.

BROWN, George Rennie (retired) 29 Dovecot Park, Aberdour, Burntisland KY3 0TE — MB ChB 1950 Glas.; FRCOG 1973, M 1960. Prev: Cons. O & G Dunfermline.

BROWN, George Russell (retired) 79 Berkeley Court, Glentworth St, London NW1 5ND Tel: 020 7487 5207 — MRCS Eng. LRCP Lond. 1954; LDS RCS Eng. 1959. Prev: Ho. Surg. S.lands Hosp. Shoreham-by-Sea.

BROWN, George Watson Doctors Surgery, Half Moon Lane, Wigton CA7 9NQ Tel: 016973 42254 Fax: 016973 45464; Criffel View, 11 spittal Farm, Wigton CA7 0EP Tel: 0169 734 2743 Email: george_uk@msn.com — MB ChB St. And. 1969; DCH RCPS Glas. 1972. Fact. Med. Off. UCB Sidac Ltd. Wigton.

BROWN, George William Wood Cottage, Wood Grove, Skipton BD23 1UJ; 24 Brookdene Avenue, Oxhey, Watford WD19 4LF Tel: 01923 29024 — LRCP LRCS 1951 Ed.; LRCP LRCS Ed. LRFPS Glas. 1951; DPH Leeds 1965. (Ed.) Socs: Fell. Soc. Community Med.; Leeds Med.-Leg. Soc. Prev: Ho. Surg. Tynemouth Infirm.; GP Anaesth. & Cas. Off. Hartlepools Hosp. Gp.; Dep. Med. Off. Health Huddersfield Co. Boro.

BROWN, Georgina Louise Ground Left, 101 Armadale St., Glasgow G31 2PY — MB ChB 1995 Dundee. SHO Elderley Care, Law Hosp. Carluke; SHO Acid. & Emerg. Monklands Hosp. Airdrie. Socs: BMA; MPS; MSS. Prev: SHO Spinal Unit S.. Gen. Hosp. Glas.

BROWN, Geraint Ceri Stewart Intensive Care Unit, North Manchester General Hospital, Crumpsall, Manchester M8 5RB Tel: 0161 795 4567 — MB ChB 1980 Manch.; 1986 FFA RCS Eng.; MPhil 1999 Lancaster. (Manchester) Cons. Intens. Care N. Manch. Healthcare NHS Trust. Prev: Cons. Anaesth. Tameside & Glossop Acute Servs. NHS Trust.

BROWN, Gerrard Joseph 5 Irwell Road, Warrington WA4 6AX — MB ChB 1992 Sheff.

BROWN, Gervase Beverley (retired) 204 Wallasey Road, Wallasey CH44 2AG Tel: 0151 638 2216 — MB ChB 1947 Liverp.; MRCS Eng. LRCP Lond. 1947.

BROWN, Gillian Louise 36 Glenkeen Avenue, Newtownabbey BT37 0PH — MB BCh BAO 1989 Belf.; MB BCh Belf. 1989.

BROWN, Gina Radiology Dept, Royal marsden Hospital, Fulham Road, London SW3 6JJ Tel: 020 7808 2571 Fax: 020 7352 0726 Email: g.brown@virgin.net — MB BS 1988 Lond.; MRCP (UK) 1991; FRCR 1994. (Kings Coll.Hosp.Med.Sch.London) Cons.Radiol.Roy.marsden.Lond. Prev: Research Fell.Univ.Wales.; Sen.Reg.Wales Radioltrain.Cardiff; Sen.Reg.St Geo.s Hosp.Lond.

BROWN, Gladys May (retired) Welcome House, North Bank, Belford NE70 7LY Tel: 01668 213758 — MB ChB 1961 Manch.; FRCOG 1983, M 1968. Prev: Assoc. Specialist (O & G) N. Manch. Dist. Gen. Hosp.

BROWN, Glyn Thomas 372 Hagley Road, Edgbaston, Birmingham B17 8BJ Tel: 0121 429 2466 — MB ChB 1955 Birm.; BDS 1963. (Birm.)

BROWN, Gordon 1 The Gables, The Plain, Epping CM16 6TW; Badger House, Wing Close, Epping Rd, North Weald, Epping CM16 6DX Email: goggie@free4all.co.uk — MB ChB 1983 Dundee. (Dundee)

BROWN, Gordon Edward Kings Park Community Hospital, Gloucester Road, Bournemouth BH7 6JF — MRCS Eng. LRCP Lond. 1974; BSc Lond. 1971, MB BS 1974; MRCPsych. 1982. (St. Mary's) Cons. Psychiat. St Anns Hosp. Canford Cliffs Poole. Prev: Sen. Regist. (Psychiat.) Wessex RHA; Regist. (Psychiat.) Roy. S. Hants. Hosp. Soton.

BROWN, Graeme Christopher The Surgery, 10 Bolton Road, Eastbourne BN21 3JY Tel: 01323 730537 Fax: 01323 412759 — MB BS 1988 Lond.; BSc Lond. 1985; MRCGP 1992; DRCOG 1990. (St. Bart. Hosp. Lond.)

BROWN, Graham Moreland Victoria Road Surgery, 129A Victoria Road, Kirkcaldy KY1 1DH Tel: 01592 263332 Fax: 01592 644288 — MB ChB 1976 Ed.; MRCGP 1980; DRCOG 1978. GP Kirkcaldy.

BROWN, Grahame John Royal Orthopaedic Hospital NHS Trust, Northfield, Birmingham B31 2AP Tel: 0121 685 4061 — MB ChB 1979 Bristol; BSc Bristol 1976; AFOM RCP (UK) 1994; MRCGP 1985; Dip. Sports Med. Scotl. 1992. Cons. Phys. (Orthop. & Sports Med.) Roy. Orthop. Hosp. Birm. Socs: Brit. Assn. Sports Med. & Soc. Occupat. Health.; Brit. Inst. Musculo Skeletal Med. Prev: GP Birm. Univ. Pract.; GP Hellesdon Norwich; Med. Off. RAF.

BROWN, Gwendolen Mary London Road Practice, 84-86 London Road, Bedford MK42 0NT Tel: 01234 266851 Fax: 01234 363998; The Manse, 2 Higham Drive, Wigmore, Luton LU2 9SP Tel: 01582 414633 Email: docgeorgie@aol.com — MB ChB Bristol 1963; FRCGP 1988, M 1977; DObst RCOG 1965. (Bristol) Mentor (Gen. Pract.) Bedford. Socs: BMA. Prev: Clin. Tutor (Gen. Pract.) Bedford HA; Clin. Asst. (Paediat.) Lister Hosp. Hitchin; Asst. Resid. Med. Off. Roy. Hosp. Sick Childr. Bristol.

BROWN, Gwyneth Mipaka, Crossfield Avenue, Porthcawl CF36 3LA — LRCP LRCS 1948 Ed.; LRCP LRCS Ed., LRFPS Glas. 1948; CPH Wales 1950. (Roy. Coll. Ed.) Departm. Med. Off. (Sessional) Glam. CC. Prev: Ho. Phys. W. Wales Gen. Hosp. Carmarthen & Childr. Hosp. Derby; Asst. MOH Co. Boro. Swansea.

BROWN, Harold James (retired) Parkfield, 538 Wellingborough Road, Weston Favell, Northampton NN3 3HZ Tel: 01604 401163 — MB 1941 Calcutta. Prev: Clin. Asst. Eye Dept. N.ampton Gen. Hosp.

BROWN, Harry The Medical Centre, 143 Rookwood Avenue, Leeds LS9 0NL Tel: 0113 249 3011 Fax: 0113 240 1958 — MB ChB 1983 Glas.; MRCGP 1987; Cert. Family Plann. JCC 1987; DRCOG 1986. Prev: Trainee GP Vict. Infirm. Glas. VTS; Ho. Off. (Med.) Roy. Alex. Infirm; Ho. Off. (Surg.) Stobhill Hosp. Glas.

BROWN, Harry Birrell 25 Castle Bay Court, Largs KA30 8DS Tel: 01475 673541 — MB ChB 1943 Glas.; FFCM 1981 M 1972; DPH Glas. 1948. (Univ. Glas.) Specialist (Community Med.) Dumfries & Galloway HB; Flight Lt. RAFVR. Socs: Fell. Soc. MOH. Prev: MOH Dumfries Co. & Burgh; MOH Wigtownsh.; Asst. Sch. Med. Off. Blackpool.

BROWN, Harry Morrow Highfield House, Highfield Gardens, Derby DE22 1HT Tel: 01332 331500 Fax: 01332 361748 Email: harry@morrow.brown.freeserve.co.uk — MB ChB Ed. 1939; MD (Commend. For Thesis) Ed. 1950; FRCP Ed. 1965; MRCP (UK) 1949. (Ed.) Emerit. Cons. Allergist Derby; Mem. Europ. Acad. Allergol. & Clin. Immunol.; Mem. Amer. Acad. & Amer. Coll. Allergy & Clin. Immunol. Socs: Brit. Soc. Allergy & Clin. Immunol.; Eur. Acad. Allergol. & Clin. Immunol.; Amer. Acad. & Amer. Coll. Allergy & Clin. Immunol. Prev: Cons. & Research Dir. Asthma & Allergy Treatm. & Research Centre Derby; Emerit. Cons. Phys. & Allergist Derwent Hosp. Derby, Derby Childr. Hosp. & Derby Chest Clinic; Sen. Regist. Chest Clinic Dundee.

BROWN, Hazel Anne Glentworth Surgery, Dalton Terrace, York YO24 4DB Tel: 01904 658542 Fax: 01904 671979; 80 Knavesmire Crescent, York YO23 1ET — BM 1980 Soton.; DRCOG 1985.

BROWN, Heather Jane 17 Styles Place, Yelvertoft, Northampton NN6 6LR — MB BS 1998 Lond.; MB BS Lond 1998.

BROWN, Heidi 3 Scowcroft Drive, Morecambe LA4 6SG — MB ChB 1993 Dundee.

BROWN, Helen (retired) Levesley House, City Road, Stathern, Melton Mowbray LE14 4HE — MB BS 1950 Lond.; MRCS Eng. LRCP Lond. 1949.

BROWN, Helen Clow (retired) 21 St Catherine's Place, Edinburgh EH9 1NU Tel: 0131 667 8040 — MB ChB Aberd. 1954; MRCGP 1966.

BROWN, Helen Margaret Holywood Arches Health Centre, Westminster Avenue, Belfast BT4 1NS Tel: 028 9056 3354 Fax: 028 9065 3846; 47 Belsize Road, Lisburn BT27 4BS Tel: 01846 674655 — MB BCh BAO 1986 Belf.; MRCGP 1990; DRCOG 1990. (Qu. Univ. Belf.)

BROWN, Helen Marguerite 8 Talygarn Street, Gabalfa, Cardiff CF14 3PT — MB BS 1993 Lond.; MRCGP 1997; DFFP 1996; DRCOG 1995.

BROWN, Helga Anne University Hospital of North Durham DH1 5TW Tel: 0191 333 2333; 4 Greta Place, Lanchester, Durham DH7 0EZ — MB BS 1988 Lond.; MRCP (UK) 1992; DGM RCP Lond. 1994. (Univ. Coll. & Middlx. Sch. Med.) Cons. Phys. with interest in Med. For elderly, Univ. of N. Durh., N. Durh. Healthcare NHS Trust. Prev: Sen. Regist. (Med. for Elderly), Bedford Hosp. NHS Trust.; Sen. Regist. (Med. for Elderly) Addenbrooke's Hosp. Camb.; Sen. Regist. (Gen. Med.) Hinchingbroke Hosp. Huntingdon.

BROWN, Henry Barry 2A High Ash Drive, Leeds LS17 8QY Tel: 0113 268 6158 — MB ChB 1950 Leeds; MRCS Eng. LRCP Lond. 1950. (Leeds) Socs: Brit. Soc. Med. & Dent. Hypn. Prev: Ho. Phys. Staincliffe Gen. Hosp. Dewsbury; Flight Lt. RAF.

BROWN, Henry Campbell (retired) Windward, Kilmington, Axminster EX13 7RG Tel: 01297 32015 — MB BS 1947 Durh.; MRCS Eng. LRCP Lond. 1948. Prev: Surg. Lt. RN.

BROWN, Henry Colin Salisbury Medical Centre, 474 Antrim Road, Belfast BT15 5GF Tel: 028 9077 7905 — MB BCh BAO 1970 Belf.; MRCP (U.K.) 1973.

***BROWN, Hereward** 20 St Johns Road, Old Trafford, Manchester M16 7GX — MB ChB Manch. 1996.

BROWN, Howard Gordon 23 Trinity Gardens, Thornton-Cleveleys FY5 2UA — MB ChB 1987 Birm.

BROWN, Howard Greig Meadowbank Health Centre, 3 Salmon Inn Road, Polmont, Falkirk FK2 0XF Tel: 01324 715540 Fax: 01324 716723; Garden House, 13 Gartcows Road, Falkirk FK1 5EF Tel: 01324 613481 — MB ChB 1971 Glas.

BROWN, Hugh Coulter The Health Centre, 33main Street, Dalmellington, Ayr KA6 7QL Tel: 01292 550238 Fax: 01292 551342 Email: hugh.brown@aapct.scot.nhs.uk; Lochview, Bellsbank Road, Dalmellington, Ayr KA6 7PR Tel: 01292 551427 Email: hugh.brown@virgin.net — MB ChB 1988 Glas.; MRCGP 1992. (University of Glasgow) Vice chair. Carnich & Down ValleyLHCC, AYR. Prev: Trainee GP StoneHo. Hosp. VTS.

BROWN, Mr Hugh Goundry, TD (retired) Heatherlea, 12 Lindisfarne Road, Jesmond, Newcastle upon Tyne NE2 2HE — MB BS 1949 Durh.; FRCS Eng. 1958. Prev: Consult. Plastic Surg. Unit Roy. Vict. Infirm. Newc. upon Tyne.

BROWN, Iain Donald Macgregor 2 South Road, Clarkston, Glasgow G76 8JB — MB ChB 1997 Glas.

BROWN, Iain Grant Springburn Health Centre, 200 Springburn Way, Glasgow G21 1TR Tel: 0141 531 9681 Fax: 0141 531 6705 — MB ChB 1984 Glas.

BROWN, Iain Michael 8 Circular Road, Prestwich, Manchester M25 9WF Tel: 0161 773 2136 — MB ChB 1994 Manch.; MB ChB (Hons.) Manch. 1994; BSc St. And. 1991. SHO Rotat. (Surg.) MRI Manch. Prev: SHO (Paediat. Surg.) St. Jas. Hosp. Leeds; Demonst. (Anat.) Univ. Leeds; Ho. Off. (Gen. Surg.) N. Manch. Gen. Hosp.

BROWN, Ian Sidney Sussex College, Cambridge University, Cambridge CB2 3HU Tel: 01223 61501; The Research Laboratories, Cambridge University School of Clinical Medicine, The Radiotherapeutic Centre, Addenbrooke's Hospital, Cambridge CB2 2QQ — MB BChir 1980 Camb.; MA Camb. 1980, PhD 1973, MD 1986, MB 1980, BChir 1979; BSc Birm. 1969; BA Uppsala 1977; FRSC 1986, M 1982; Chem. 1982. Stanley Elmore Sen. Fell. Med. Scis., Dir. Clin. Med.; Praelector Sidney Sussex Coll. Camb.; Hon. Regist. Radiother. & Clin. Oncol. Addenbrooke's Hosp. & Camb. & P'boro. Dist. Hosp.; Asst. Dir. Research Camb. Univ. Sch. Clin. Med. Socs: Fell. Camb. Philosophical Soc.; Anglo-German Med. Soc. & Radiat. Research Soc. Prev: Hon. Regist. Gen. Surg. Newmarket Hosp.; Vis. Fell. Radiat. Oncol. Univ. Texas 1975-76.

BROWN, Ian Southampton University Hospitals NHS Trust, Dept Occupational Health, Southampton General Hospital, Tremona Road, Southampton SO16 6YD Tel: 02380 794156 Fax: 02380 794324; Garstane House, The Mulberries, East Hanney, Wantage OX12 0JS Tel: 01235 868055 Fax: 01235 868390 — MB BS 1977 Newc.; DDAM FOM, RCP Lond.; BSc Newc. 1972; FFOM RCP Lond. 1994, MFOM 1989, AFOM 1985; FRCP Lond. 1998. (University of Newcastle-upon-Tyne) Cons. Phys. (Occupat. Health & Toxicol.) Soton.Univ.Hosp; Hon. Sen. Lect. Inst. Occupat. Health Univ. Birm.; Registered Toxicol. Brit. Toxicol. Soc.; Ref. Brit. Jl. Indust. & Environm. Med.; Chairm. of Pesticides Residues Comm. Socs: Occupat. Med.; Brit. Thorac. Soc.; Brit. Toxicology Soc.(mem). Prev: Europ. Med. Dir. Dow Elanco Ltd.; Clin. Tutor (Family Med.) Newc. Univ.; Dep. Area Med. Off. Nat. Coal Bd.

BROWN, Mr Ian Andrew Robert (retired) The Old Rectory, Smethcott, Church Stretton SY6 6NX Tel: 01694 751214 — MB ChB 1957 Ed.; FRCS Ed. 1965; FRCS Eng. 1965; FRCOphth 1993; DO Eng. 1963. Prev: Sen. Regist. Birm. & Midl. Eye Hosp.

BROWN, Ian Dempster Bonnyrigg Health Centre, High Street, Bonnyrigg EH19 2DA; Gowanbrae, 17 Newbattle Road, Dalkeith EH22 3DD Tel: 0131 663 3946 — MB ChB 1974 Aberd.; MRCGP 1978; Cert JCC Lond. 1978. Clin. Asst. St. Joseph's Hosp. Rosewell.

BROWN, Ian Graham Carnegie (retired) North House Surgery, North St., Ripon HG4 1HL Tel: 01765 690666 Fax: 01765 690285 — MRCS Eng. LRCP Lond. 1958; MB Camb. 1959, BChir 1958; MRCGP 1968; DObst RCOG 1960. Prev: Local Treasury Med. Off.

BROWN, Ian Hugh 13 Queens Park Road, Burnley BB10 3LB — MB BS 1972 Lond.; MRCP (UK) 1977; DCH Eng. 1975. Cons. Paediat. Burnley Gen. Hosp. Prev: Sen. Regist. (Developm. Med. & Paediat. Neurol.) Bristol Childr. Hosp.

BROWN, Ian Lamont 4 Park Road, Chryston, Glasgow G69 9DS Tel: 0141 779 2140 Email: ibrown2931@aol.com; University Department of Pathology, Western Infirmary, Glasgow G11 6NT Tel: 0141 211 2209 Email: ilb1j@clinmed.gla.ac.uk — MB ChB 1974 Glas.; MRCPath 1982; FRCPath 1994. Sen. Lect. (Path.); Hon. Cons. Path. W.. Infirm. Glas.

BROWN, Ian MacDiarmid (retired) 30 Lawns Avenue, Eastbourne BN21 1PJ Tel: 01323 736072 — MB ChB 1942 Aberd. Hon. Cons. Geriat. E.bourne Health Dist. Prev: Maj. RAMC.

BROWN, Ian Macpherson Health Centre, Thornhill DG3 5AA Tel: 01848 330208 Fax: 01848 330223; Merrick, Corstorphine Road, Thornhill DG3 5NB Tel: 01848 330630 — MB ChB Glas. 1969. Med. Off. Thornhill Hosp. & Thornhill Day Hosp. Prev: Ho. Off. (Med. & Surg.) & SHO (O & G) Stirling Roy. Infirm.

BROWN, Ian McLachlan Department of Obstetrics & Gynaecology, Bristol Maternity Hospital, Southwell St., Bristol BS2 8EG — MB BS 1967 Lond.; FRCOG 1983, M 1972.

BROWN, Ian Michael Campbell The Penryn Surgery, Saracen Way, Penryn TR10 8HX Tel: 01326 372502 Fax: 01326 378126 — MB BS 1986 Lond.; MA Oxf. 1985; DRCOG 1991; DCH RCP Lond. 1990; DGM RCP Lond. 1988. (Guy's)

BROWN, Irene (retired) Parade House, The Parade, Monmouth NP25 3PA Tel: 01600 716762 — MB BS 1928 Lond.; MRCS Eng. LRCP Lond. 1926; DPM. Eng. 1931. Prev: Ho. Phys. Char. Cross Hosp.

BROWN, Iris Elizabeth c/o Mrs A Ropel, 10 Springfield Meadows, Weybridge KT13 8AJ Tel: 01932 36080 — MB BCh BAO 1951 Dub.; BA. (T.C. Dub.) Princip. Gen. Pract. Cleveland Dist. Health Area. Socs: BMA. Prev: Ho. Phys. & Ho. Surg. Moyle Hosp. Larne; Obst. Ho. Surg. PeterBoro. Memor. Hosp.; Asst. MOH Durh. CC.

BROWN, Isobel Clare Timperley Health Centre, Grove Lane, Timperley, Altrincham WA15 6PH; 21 Sylvan Avenue, Sale M33 3NP — MB ChB 1984 Bristol; MRCGP 1990; DCH RCPS Glas. 1988; DRCOG 1986. Asst. GP Altrincham. Prev: Trainee GP Manch.

BROWN, Isobel Margaret (retired) 2A Windsor Avenue, Radyr, Cardiff CF15 8BW — MB BCh 1951 Wales. Prev: GP Cardiff.

BROWN, Isobel McKenzie Department of Medicine for Elderly, Woodend Hospital, Aberdeen AB15 6XS Tel: 01224 683131; 10 Forestside Road, Banchory AB31 5ZH Tel: 01330 824353 Email: home@iainisobel.freeserve.co.uk — MB ChB Ed. 1961. Clin. Asst. (Med. for Elderly) Woodend Hosp. Aberd. Prev: Ho. Phys. & Ho. Surg. Perth Roy. Infirm.; Ho. Off. Murray Roy. Hosp.

BROWN, James Andrew 175 Mussenden Road, Castlerock, Coleraine BT51 4TX — MB BCh BAO 1976 Belf.

BROWN, James David Kingsley 10 Stonemead Avenue, Hale Barns, Altrincham WA15 0BQ Tel: 0161 980 4965 — MB ChB 1966 Aberd.; FRCR 1975; DMRD Eng. 1973. Cons. Radiol. Hope Hosp. Manch.

BROWN, Mr James Douglas, OBE (retired) 4 Inverkar Road, Ayr KA7 2JT Tel: 01292 263153 Fax: 01292 263153 — MB ChB 1955 Ed.; FRCS Ed. 1966. Prev: Chairm. S. Ayrsh. Hosp. NHS Trust.

BROWN, James George Beckdale House, White Hart Lane, Wood Street Village, Guildford GU3 3EA — MB BS 1998 Newc.; MB BS Newc 1998.

BROWN, James Gordon The White rose Surgery, Exchange Street, South Elmsall WF9 2RD Tel: 01977 642412 Fax: 0870 1219362 Email: james@sportsinjurymanager.co.uk; Tel: 0113 2614590 Email: james@sportsinjurymanager.co.uk — MB ChB 1994 Manch.; BSc

(Hons.) St. And. 1991; MSc Sports Med. Nottm. 1997. (St. And.) p/t Primary Care Cons., Musculoskeletal and Sports Med., S. Elmsall; CEO Medesol Ltd E-athlete records Cons. Boots PLC; Team Phys. Eng. U21 Rugby Union. Socs: UKADIS -Co founder Head of IT; BIMM- Mem.; RLMA- Mem. Prev: Lect. (Anat.) Univ. Leeds; SHO (Rheum.), Pontefract Gen. Infirm.; GP Regist., P.s St. Surg., Normanton.

BROWN, James Hamilton Murray Flat 5, Williamson House, North Devon District Hospital, Raleigh Park, Barnstaple EX31 4JD — MB ChB 1996 Bristol; BEng. (Hons.) CNAA 1988. SHO Surgic. Rotat. N. Devon Dist. Hosp.

BROWN, James Michael, MBE (retired) Barncote, 6 Hall Drive, Bramhope, Leeds LS16 9JE Tel: 0113 284 2504 Email: jmb2504@hotmail.com — BChir 1958 Camb.; MB 1959 Camb.; MRCGP 1970; DA Eng. 1964; DObst. RCOG 1959. Prev: GP Leeds RAF Med. Br.

BROWN, James Richard Issard 46 Chatham Street, London SE17 1NY — MB BS 1996 Lond.

BROWN, James Robert 12 Cleveland Road, St Helier, Jersey JE2 4PB Tel: 01534 22381; South Point, 3 Clos De La Motte, St. Clement, Jersey JE2 6LW Tel: 01534 855422 — MB ChB St. And. 1959; LMCC 1960. (St. And.)

BROWN, James Robert Flat 3, 156 Palatine Road, Manchester M20 2QH — MB BS 1989 Lond.

BROWN, James Scott Mountsandel Surgery, 4 Mountsandel Road, Coleraine BT52 1JB Tel: 028 7034 2650 Fax: 028 7032 1000 — MB BCh BAO 1979 Belf.; MD Belf. 1994; FRCGP 1995, M 1983; DRCOG 1983; DCH RCPSI 1982. Vice Chairm. RCGP Counc.; Chairm. Servs. Network RCGP & Publishing Managing Gp. RCGP; GP Clin. Tutor; Chairm. of GP Studies (Prof.) Instit. of Postgrad. Med. & Health Scis. Univ. of Ulster. Socs: BMA.

BROWN, Mr James Stephen Maxillofacial Surgery, University Hospital Aintree, Aintree Hospitals Trust, Longmoor Lane, Liverpool L9 7AL Tel: 0151 529 5283 Fax: 0151 529 5288 Email: brownjs@globalnet.co.uk; 30 New Road, Lymm WA13 9DY Tel: 01925 758067 — MRCS Eng. LRCP Lond. 1985; BDS Ed. 1979; FRCS Ed. 1988; FDS RCS Eng. 1987; MD Birm. 1994. (Westminster) Cons. Oral & Maxillofacial Surg. Univ. Hosp. Aintree Liverp.; Hon. Sen. Lect. (Oral Surg.) Liverp. Dent. Sch. Socs: BMA; Brit. Assn. Oral & Maxillofacial Surg.; Brit. Assn. Head & Neck Oncol. Prev: Sen. Regist. (Oral & Maxillofacial Surg.) Qu. Eliz. Hosp. Birm.

BROWN, James Stewart (retired) 3 Glentye Gardens, Falkirk FK1 5NT Tel: 01324 625350 — MB BCh BAO 1958 Dub.; MA, MB BCh BAO Dub. 1958; DMRD Eng. 1964. Prev: Cons. Radiol. Falkirk Roy. Infirm.

BROWN, Mr James Tulloch (retired) Morven, High St., Lochmaben, Lockerbie DG11 1NH Tel: 01387 811883 — MB ChB 1938 Glas.; FRCS Ed. 1946. Prev: Cons. Orthop. Surg. W.. Infirm. & Gartnavel Gen. Hosp. Glas.

BROWN, Jane Harriet 38 Downs Side, South Cheam, Sutton SM2 7EQ — MB BS 1998 Lond.; MB BS Lond 1998.

BROWN, Jane Louise Gloucestershire Royal Hospital, Great Western Road, Gloucester GL1 3NN Tel: 01452 528555; Wold House, The Highlands, Painswick, Stroud GL6 6SL Tel: 01452 812300 — MB ChB 1973 Dundee; FFA RCS Eng. 1978. (Dundee) Cons. Anaesth. Glos. Roy. NHS Trust. Socs: Brit. Assn. Day Surg.

BROWN, Janet Dorothy (retired) 46 St Andrews Road, Sheffield S11 9AL Tel: 0114 255 3850 — MRCS Eng. LRCP Lond. 1965. Clin. Asst. (Haemat.) N. Gen. Hosp. Sheff. Prev: Asst. Sch. Med. Off. Liverp.

BROWN, Janet Elizabeth 44 Albermale Avenue, Newcastle upon Tyne NE2 3NQ — MB BS 1993 Newc.

BROWN, Janette Johnston (retired) Broadoak, 25 Warwick Road, Hale, Altrincham WA15 9NP Tel: 0161 941 1442 — MB ChB Glas. 1959; FFA RCS Eng. 1975; DA Eng. 1961. Prev: Cons. Anaesth. Salford HA (T).

BROWN, Jean Cameron Beechenhurst, Culver St., Newent GL18 1JA Tel: 01531 820040 — MB ChB 1951 Aberd.

BROWN, Jean Margaret Coleridge Medical Centre, Canaan Way, Ottery St Mary EX11 1EQ Tel: 01404 814447 — MB 1974 Camb.; BA Camb. 1970, MB 1974, BChir 1973; MRCGP 1980.

BROWN, Jeffrey Ryan 29 Pine Valley, Rostrevor, Newry BT34 3DE Tel: 016937 38617 — MB BCh BAO 1995 Belf.

BROWN, Jehoiada John (retired) Loretto, Clydeview, Dumbarton G82 4AG Tel: 01389 762933 — MB BS 1952 Lond.; MB BS (Hons.) Med. Lond. 1952; FRSE; BSc (1st cl. Hons.) Lond. 1948; FRCP Lond. 1970, M 1957; MRCS Eng. LRCP Lond. 1952. Prev: Phys. Med. Research Counc. Blood Pressure Unit, W.ern Infirm., Glas.

BROWN, Jennifer The Craig W., Homefield Road, Saltford, Bristol BS31 3EQ — MB ChB 1989 Ed.; MRCPsych 1995. Trainee GP Bath. Prev: Regist. (Psychiat.) Bath; SHO (O & G) Falkirk; SHO (Paediat.) Stirling.

BROWN, Jennifer Ann Scott Lendrum (retired) — MB BS 1962 Lond.; MRCS Eng. LRCP Lond. 1962. Prev: Ho. Phys. Hampstead Gen. Hosp.

BROWN, Jennifer Wanda Ifton Hill House, Portskewett, Newport NP26 5TT — MB ChB 1978 Bristol.

BROWN, Jeremy Martin 16 Flora Grove, St Albans AL1 5ET — MB BS 1985 Lond.

BROWN, Mr Jeremy Nicholas Northern General Hospital NHS Trust, Herries Road, Sheffield S5 7AU Tel: 0114 243 4343; Whitegates, Riddings Lane, Hope Valley S32 3YS Tel: 01433 639195 Fax: 01433 639195 Email: jezbrown@doctors.org.uk — MB ChB 1987 Sheff.; FRCS (Orth) 1997; FRCS Ed. 1992. Cons. In Knee Surg. & Sports Trauma.

BROWN, Jeremy Rea Duncan Langton Medical Group, St. Chads Health Centre, Dimbles Lane, Lichfield WS13 7HT Tel: 01543 258983 Fax: 01543 414776; Easter Hill, Christchurch Lane, Lichfield WS13 8AL Tel: 01543 419194 Fax: 01543 419194 Email: jrdbdoc@aol.com — MB ChB 1968 Ed.; BSc (Hons.) Ed. 1965; FRCP Ed. 1995; MRCP (UK) 1972; FRCGP 1991, M 1974; MICGP 1987; DObst RCOG 1973; DCH Eng. 1973. (Ed.)

BROWN, Jill Bonner (retired) 254 Park Road, Peterborough PE1 2UR Tel: 01733 568425 — MA, MB Camb. 1962, BChir 1961; MRCS Eng. LRCP Lond. 1961. Prev: SCMO (Child Health) PeterBoro. Health.

BROWN, Jillian Anne 16 St Ann's Drive, Giffnock, Glasgow G46 6JP Email: browns@giffnock10.freeserve.co.uk — MB ChB 1993 Glas.; MRCP (UK) 1998. (Univ. Glas.) Prev: SHO, Ill Glas. Roy. Infirm.

BROWN, Joan Derby Medical Centre, 8 The Derby Square, Epsom KT19 8AG Tel: 01372 726361 — MB ChB 1968 Birm. (Birm.) Socs: BMA. Prev: Ho. Phys. & Ho. Surg. E. Birm. Hosp.

BROWN, Joan Cuthbert Rutherford 77 Kirk Brae, Liberton, Edinburgh EH16 6JN Tel: 0131 664 4592 — LRCP LRCS 1947 Ed.; LRCP LRCS Ed. LRFPS Glas. 1947. (Edinburgh) Clin. Med. Off. Lothian Health Bd. Prev: Jun. Hosp. Med. Off. (Anaesth.) Peel Hosp. Galashiels; Ho. Surg. Stobhill Hosp. Glas.; Ho. Phys. Deaconess Hosp. Edin.

BROWN, Joan Margaret 11 Thornlea, Hepscott, Morpeth NE61 6NY Tel: 01670 517735 — MB BS Durh. 1948. (Newc.)

BROWN, Joan Margaret Queen Victoria Hospital, East Grinstead RH19 3DZ Tel: 01342 410210 Fax: 01342 323420; 14 The Old Convent, Moat Road, East Grinstead RH19 3RS Tel: 01342 313796 — MB ChB 1959 Birm.; FFA RCS Eng. 1968; DObst RCOG 1961. (Birm.) Cons. Anaesth. Qu. Vict. Hosp. E. Grinstead. Socs: Brit. Burns Assn.; Intens. Care Soc.; Plastic Surg. & Burns Anaesth. Assn. Prev: Sen. Regist. (Anaesth.) Nat. Heart Hosp. Lond.; Regist. (Anaesth.) Brompton Hosp. Lond.; Clin. Fell. (Anesth.) Mass. Gen. Hosp. Boston, USA.

BROWN, Joanna Victoria 7 Springfield Close, Rhiwderin, Newport NP10 8RZ Tel: 01633 893057 — MB BS 1993 Lond.; BSc Lond. 1990. SHO (Anaesth.) N. Devon Healthcare Trust Barnstaple. Prev: RMO Sir Chas. Gardner Hosp. Perth WA; SHO (A & E) Roy. Free Hosp. Lond.; SHO (Med.) King Geo. Hosp. Ilford.

BROWN, Johanna Kate 14 Laburnum Grove, New Malden KT3 3LQ — BM BS 1993 Nottm.

BROWN, John — MB BChir 1981 Camb.; MA Camb.; MD 1998 Camb.; MRCP (UK) 1983. (Cambridge) Vice Pres. and Head of Experim. Med. (Europe/Internat.), GlaxosmithKline; Hon. Cons. Phys. Addenbrooke's Hosp. Camb. Prev: Lect. (Clin. Pharmacol.) Roy. Postgrad. Med. Sch. Univ. Lond.; Regist. (Clin. Pharmacol.) Hammersmith Hosp. Lond.; Univ. Lect. (Physiol.) Univ. Camb.

BROWN, John Alexander Hunter, Lt.-Col. (retired) Delgany, Old Cambus, Cockburnspath TD13 5YS Tel: 01368 830322 Email: johnbrowni@ntlworl.com@mcmail.com — MB BS Lond. 1944; MD

Lond. 1949; FRCPath 1964; DTM & H Eng. 1951. Private practitioner in Forens. Med., Berwicksh., Scotl. Prev: Cons. Path. N. Staffs. Hosp. Gp. & Home Off. Path.

BROWN, Mr John Andrew Carron (retired) 16 Christchurch Road, Norwich NR2 2AE Tel: 01603 53094 — MB BS 1949 Lond.; FRCS Eng. 1955; FRCOG 1975, M 1959, DObst 1951. Cons. O & G Norf. & Norwich Hosp. Gp.; Exam. RCOG. Prev: Sen. Regist. Dept. O & G Addenbrooke's Hosp. Camb.

BROWN, Mr John Gordon Musgrave Park Hospital, Stockman's Lane, Belfast BT9 7JB; Mullindrern, 23 Newforge Lane, Belfast BT9 5NU Tel: 02890 661461 Fax: 02890 664283 — MD 1991 Belf.; MB BCh BAO 1979; FRCS Ed. 1983; 1991 MD BRCF. (Queens University, Belfast) Cons. Orthop. Surg. Green Pk. Trust Ulster Hosp. Prev: Cons. & Sen. Lect. QUB.

BROWN, John Hallam 60 Braefoot Avenue, Milngavie, Glasgow G62 6JT — MB ChB 1973 Glas.; BSc (Hons.) Glas. 1971, MB ChB 1973; FFA RCS Eng. 1978; FFA RCSI 1977. Cons. Anaesth. W.. Infirm. Glas..

BROWN, Mr John Hamish Good Hope Hospital, Rectory Road, Sutton Coldfield B75 7RR; 32 Bedford Place, Sutton Coldfield B75 6AB — MB ChB 1978 Sheff.; FRCS Ed. 1984.

BROWN, John Henry Renal Unit, Antrim Area Hospital, Bush Road, Antrim BT41 2QB Tel: 01849 424000 Fax: 01849 424293 Email: henrybrown@uh.n-i.nhs.uk; 25 Burandell Manor, Lisburn BT28 3AX — MB BCh BAO 1981 Belf.; FRCP 1999; MD Belf. 1988; MRCP (UK) 1984. (Queen's University Belf.) Cons. Nephrol. Antrim Area Hosp.; Hon. Cons. Nephrol. Belf. City Hosp. Socs: Renal Assn.; Eur. Dialysis & Transpl. Assn.; Brit. Transpl. Soc. Prev: Sen. Regist. (Nephrol.) Belf. City Hosp. & Manch. Roy. Infirm.

BROWN, John Keith 28 Vert Court, Haldane Avenue, Haddington EH41 3PX — MB ChB 1961 Manch.; FRCP Ed. 1975, M 1966; DCH Eng. 1966. (Manch.) Cons. Paediat. Neurol. Roy. Hosp. Sick Childr. & Simpson Memor.; Matern. Pavil. Edin. Socs: UK Gp. Paediat. Neurol.; Soc. Study Inborn Errors Metab. Prev: Sen. Regist. Roy. Hosp. Sick Childr. & Simpson Memor. Matern. Pavil. Edin.; Regist. Stepping Hill Hosp. Stockport.

BROWN, John Kerr (retired) Gilridge Lodge, Cowden, Edenbridge TN8 7HH Tel: 01342 850679 — MB ChB 1942 Glas.; BSc Glas. 1939; MFCM 1973; DPH Glas. 1947. Area Med. Off. Greenwich & Bexley AHA. Prev: MOH & Princip. Sch. Med. Off. Lond. Boro. Greenwich.

BROWN, John Morrison Western Health and Social Services Board, 15 Gransha Park, Londonderry BT47 6FN Tel: 01504 860086 Fax: 01504 860311; Appenzell, 37 Strabane Road, Castlederg BT81 7HZ Tel: 0166 26 71525 — MB BCh BAO 1966 Belf.; FRCGP 1984, M 1971; DObst RCOG 1968. (Belf.) Med. Adviser Family Pract. Serv. Unit. W.. Area Bd. Prev: Ho. Off. Lurgan Hosp.; SHO (Med.) Lurgan Hosp.; Princip. in Gen. Pract.

BROWN, John Neville The Park Surgery, 116 Kings Road, Herne Bay CT6 5RE Tel: 01227 742233 Fax: 01227 742277 — BM BCh 1968 Oxf.; FRCP 2001; Cert Contracep. & Family Plann. RCOG & RCGP 1974. Socs: BMA. Prev: Regist. (Med.) St Mary's Hosp. Portsmouth; SHO Qu. Alexandra Hosp. Portsmouth; Ho. Phys. St. Geo. Hosp. Lond.

BROWN, John Ronald, Brigadier late RAMC — MB BCh BAO 1966 Dub.; MA Dub. 1991; MSc Occupat. Med. Lond. 1982; BA Dub. 1964; FFOM RCP Lond. 1993, MFOM 1985, AFOM 1983; DCH Eng. 1973. Chief Exec. Defence Med. Train. org. Socs: Fell. Roy. Soc. Med.; Soc. Occupat. Med.; Internat. Assn. Phys. of Overseas Servs. Prev: comd.def.med.svces Train. centre; Dir. Med. Operat.s MOD; Force Chief Med. Off. UNPR.

BROWN, John Stuart, OStJ, MBE (retired) Thornhills Medical Group, 732 London Road, Larkfield, Aylesford ME20 6BQ Tel: 01732 843900 Fax: 01732 872633 — MB BS 1959 Lond.; MB BS (Hons.) Lond. 1959; MRCS Eng. LRCP Lond. 1959; FRCGP 1989, M 1972; DCH Eng. 1973; DObst RCOG 1961; AKC 1959. Prev: Ho. Surg. & Ho. Phys. King's Coll. Hosp. Lond.

BROWN, John Wallace 48 Argarmeols Road, Freshfield, Liverpool L37 7BZ Tel: 0170 48 79138 — MB ChB 1952 Liverp.; MRCS Eng. LRCP Lond. 1952; DObst RCOG 1955. (Liverp.) Prev: Ho. Surg. (Obst.) Heathfield Rd. Matern. Hosp. Birm.; Ho. Surg. (Orthop.) David Lewis N.. Hosp. Liverp.; Ho. Phys. BRd.green Hosp. Liverp.

BROWN, Jonathan Charles Myers Ash Tree House, Church Street, Kirkham, Preston PR4 2SE Tel: 01772 686688 Fax: 01772 672054; 9 Grange Lane, Newton-with-Scales, Preston PR4 3RS Fax: 01179 672054 — MB ChB 1984 Manch.; MB ChB Manch. l984; MRCGP 1988.

BROWN, Jonathan Laird 91 Yeldham Road, London W6 8JQ Tel: 020 8748 0045 — MB BS 1981 Lond.; MSc Clin. Microbiol. Lond. 1989; MA Camb. 1982, MD 1994; MRCP (UK) 1984; MRCS Eng. LRCP Lond. 1981; DTM & H RCP Lond. 1993. Sen. Regist. (Med.) St. Mary's Hosp. Lond. Socs: Fell. Roy. Soc. Trop. Med. & Hyg.; Brit. Soc. Study of Infec.; Brit. Soc. Gastroenterol. Prev: Sen. Regist. (Infec. Dis.) N.wick Pk. Hosp.; Lect. (Microbiol.) Lond. Hosp.; Regist. (Infec. Dis. Unit.) Rush Green Hosp. Essex.

BROWN, Joseph Thomas (retired) 14 Cresthill Avenue, Grays RM17 5UJ Tel: 01375 371665 — MB ChB 1933 Glas.; DPA . Lond. 1946; DPH Glas. 1937. Prev: Cons. Phys. (Dis. Chest) NE Met. RHB.

BROWN, Josephine Anna 12 Hilton Avenue, Scunthorpe DN15 8BD — MB ChB 1991 Leeds; DRCOG 1994; MRCGP 1995.

BROWN, Josephine Louise Department of Anaesthesia, Leeds General Infirmary, Great George Street, Leeds LS1 3EX Tel: 0113 392 6672 Email: jobrown@ulth.northy.nhs.uk — MB BS 1985 Newc.; FRCA. 1991. onsultant Anaesth., The Gen. Infirm. at Leeds. Prev: Sen. Regist. (Anaesth.) Yorks. RHA.; Regist. Gt. Ormond St. Hosp. for Sick Childr.; Regist. Leeds Gen. Infirm.

BROWN, Joyce Winifred (retired) 16 Heron Road, Kelvedon, Colchester CO5 9NE Tel: 01376 570450 — MB ChB 1941 Bristol; MFCM 1974; DPH Bristol 1947. Prev: SCMO (Community Med.) Mid Essex HA.

BROWN, Judith 11 Cavendish Place, Troon KA10 6JG — MB ChB 1998 Ed.; MB ChB Ed 1998.

BROWN, Judith Anne Drs Lothian, Mahon Daly, Brown and Wright, 122 Shrub End Road, Colchester CO3 4RY Tel: 01206 573605 Fax: 01206 500219; 10 Fitzwalter Road, Colchester CO3 3SS Tel: 01206 577906 Fax: 01206 768393 Email: alanjab@hotmail.com — MB BS 1969 Lond.; DRCOG 1991. (Lond Hosp.) Prev: SHO (A & E) Colchester Gen. Hosp.; Ho. Surg., Ho. Phys. & SHO (Obst.) St. John's Hosp. Chelmsford; SHO Obst. And Gynae., Colchester Gen. Hosp., 1990.

BROWN, Judith Catherine Robert Frew Medical Centre, Silva Isdland Way, Wickford SS12 9NR Tel: 01268 578800 Fax: 01268 578825 — BM BS 1982 Nottm.; BMedSci Nottm. 1980; DRCOG 1985. (Nottingham)

BROWN, Judy Ann 26 Glenmillan Pa, Belfast BT4 2JE — MB BCh 1998 Belf.; MB BCh Belf 1998.

BROWN, Julia Felicity Dunhampstead House, Dunhampstead, Droitwich WR9 7JX Tel: 01905 773313 — MB ChB 1977 Manch. GP.

BROWN, Julia Mary Leyburn Medical Practice, The Nurseries, Leyburn DL8 5AU Tel: 01969 622391 Fax: 01969 624446 — MB BS 1992 Newc.

BROWN, Julia Mary Community House, Fountain Frive, Carshalton SM5 4NR Tel: 020 8770 8325 Fax: 020 8770 8335; 63B Seddon Road, Morden SM4 6ED Tel: 020 8640 3859 — MB BCh 1969 Wales; DTCH Liverp. 1979; DCH 1972; DObst. RCOG 1970. Assoc. Specialist Merton & Sutton HA; Assoc. Specialist St. Helier Hosp. Carshalton. Socs: Assoc. Mem. Brit. Paediat. Assn. Prev: Doctor, Manorom Christian Hosp. Thailand; Clin. Med. Off. Glam. Co. Counc..

BROWN, Julian David Frambury Lane Surgery, Frambury Lane, Newport, Saffron Walden CB11 3PY Tel: 01799 540570 Fax: 01799 542126 — MB BS 1994 Lond.

BROWN, Julian Martin 21 Pembroke Road, Clifton, Bristol BS8 3BA — MB ChB 1992 Birm.

BROWN, Juliet Georgia 31 Barrington Road, London N8 8QT — MB ChB 1990 Manch.

BROWN, June Beatrice 32 Moorcroft Road, Moseley, Birmingham B13 8LX Tel: 0121 449 1433 — M.B., Ch.B. Birm. 1948.

BROWN, June Muriel (retired) North Mill, Wareham BH20 4QW Tel: 01929 552055 — MD 1967 Bristol; MB ChB 1952, DPH 1968. Prev: Clin. Asst. Accid. Dept. Poole Gen. Hosp.

BROWN, Justin John Spencer Melbury Close, Chislehurst BR7 5ET — MB ChB 1990 Leic.

BROWN, Karen 17 Bemersyde Drive, Jesmond, Newcastle upon Tyne NE2 2HL — MB BS 1987 Newc.; MRCOG 1992; Dip Med. Sci. 1995. Sen. Regist. (O & G) Univ. Newc. u. Tyne.

BROWN, Karen Amanda Tower House Surgery, Newton Abbot TQ13 0HL; Nightingale House, The Poplars, Chudleigh Knighton, Newton Abbot — MB BS 1977 Lond.; MRCS Eng. LRCP Lond. 1977. (Guy's).

BROWN, Karen Macmillan 29 Culzean Crescent, Newton Mearns, Glasgow G77 5SW — BM 1994 Soton.; BSc Strathclyde 1987.

BROWN, Katherine Louise 220 Sheen Lane, London SW14 8LB — MB BChir 1993 Camb.

BROWN, Kathryn Elizabeth Firth Park Road Surgery, 400 Firth Park Road, Sheffield S5 6HH Tel: 0114 242 6406 — MB ChB 1990 Sheff.; MRCGP 1995.

BROWN, Kathryn Jane King Street Surgery, 39 King Street, Bathgate EH48 1AZ Tel: 01506 53134 Fax: 01506 683134; Lochend, 56 St. Ninians Road, Linlithgow EH49 7BN — MB ChB 1985 Ed. (Edinburgh) GP.

BROWN, Kathryn Jean North Tees General Hospital, Hardwick, Stockton-on-Tees TS19 8PE Tel: 01642 617617; Taiaroa, 2 Garforth Close, Norton, Stockton-on-Tees TS20 1TU — MB BS 1987 Lond.; BSc Soton. 1982; MRCP (UK) 1991. (St. Geo. Hosp.) Sen. Regist. (Paediat.) N. Tees Gen. Hosp. Stockton on Tees. Prev: Regist. (Paediat.) Roy. Childr. Hosp. Melbourne, Vict., Austral.; Regist. (Paediat.) Luton & Dunstable Hosp.

BROWN, Kathryn-Louise Poole General Hospital, Longfleet Road, Poole BH15 2JB — MB BS 1990 West. Austral.

BROWN, Kenneth Alan Campbell (retired) 15 Seymour Road, East Molesey KT8 0PB Tel: 020 8979 3253 — MB ChB 1956 Glas.; MRCGP 1963; DCH Eng. 1960; DObst RCOG 1960. Prev: GP E. Molesey.

BROWN, Kenneth Frederick Collingwood (retired) The Green, Anstey, Leicester LE7 7FT Tel: 0116 236 3207 — MB BChir Camb. 1941; BA Camb. 1938; FRCGP 1975, M 1953. Hon. Librarian Leicester Med. Soc. Prev: Clin. Teach. Univ. Leicester Med. Sch.

BROWN, Kenneth George Edmund Diabetes Centre, Farnborough Hospital, Orpington BR6 8ND Tel: 01689 814160 Fax: 01689 814169 Email: kbrown@bromley.town.co.uk; Lock Skinners Farm House, Chiddingstone, Edenbridge TN8 7NA — MB BChir. Camb. 1967; BA Camb. 1964, MA; FRCP Lond. 1988; MRCP (UK) 1970. (Guy's) Cons. Phys. with s/i in Diabetes Bromley HA; Med. Director, Bromley Hosp.s Trust. Socs: Brit. Diabetic Assn. (Jt. Sec. Educat. Sec.).; Fell. Roy. Coll. Phys.s. Prev: Clin. Tutor Bromley NHS Trust; Assoc. Dean S. Thames Postgrad. Med. & Dent. Educat. Dept.; Dir. Resource Managem. Bromley NHS Trust.

BROWN, Kenneth Guthrie — MB BS 1972 Lond.; MRCGP 1976; DObst RCOG 1976. (Lond. Hosp.) Prev: Trainee GP Airedale VTS; Ho. Phys. & Ho. Surg. Lond. Hosp.

BROWN, Kenneth James Anderson, TD Bruntsfield Medical Practice, 11 Forbes Road, Edinburgh EH10 4EY Tel: 0131 228 6081 Fax: 0131 229 4330; 50 Spylaw Bank Road, Edinburgh EH13 0JG Tel: 0131 441 2132 — MB ChB 1969 Glas.; MRCGP 1975; AFOM RCP Lond. 1988; CIH Dund 1985. GP. Prev: Med. Off. Armed Forces.

BROWN, Kenneth John The Surgery, 143 Park Road, Camberley GU15 2NN Tel: 01276 26171 — MB BCh BAO 1970 Belf.; MRCGP 1977; DObst RCOG 1976.

BROWN, Kenneth McKenzie Radiology Department, Dr. Gray's Hospital, Elgin IV30 1SN Tel: 01343 543131 — MB ChB 1980 Glas.; FRCR 1989. Cons. Radiol. Dr. Gray's Hosp. Elgin Grampian HB. Prev: Sen. Regist. Rotat. (Radiol.) W.. Infirm. & S. Gen. Hosp. Glas.; Regist. (Radiol.) Stobhill Gen. Hosp. Glas.; SHO (Surg.) Hull HA.

BROWN, Kenneth Paul Hudson Family Medical Centre, 171 Carlton Road, Nottingham NG3 2FW Tel: 0115 504068 Fax: 0115 950 9844 — BMedSci Nottm. 1982, BM BS l984; MRCGP 1988; DRCOG 1988; DCH RCP Lond. 1987; DGM RCP Lond. 1986. (Nottingham) Lect. (Gen. Pract.) Med. Sch. Qu. Med. Centre Nottm. Prev: Trainee GP Nottm. VTS; Ho. Off. (Med.) Derbysh. Roy. Infirm.; Ho. Off. (Surg.) Dryburn Hosp. Durh.

BROWN, Kenyon Carnarvon (retired) The Grey House, Brasted, Westerham TN16 1JA Tel: 01959 563250 — MB BS 1938 Lond.; MRCS Eng. LRCP Lond. 1937; DA Eng. 1940. Prev: Cons. Anaesth. Sevenoaks Hosp.

BROWN, Kevin Peter Bideford Medical Centre, Abbotsham Road, Bideford EX39 3AF Tel: 01237 476363 Fax: 01237 423351; Downderry, Chope Road, Northam, Bideford EX39 3QE — MB ChB 1975 Bristol; FRCGP 1996, M 1981; DRCOG 1979. Course Organiser Barnstaple N. Devon VTS.

BROWN, Kirsteen Elizabeth Flat 4, 2 East Suffolk Road, Edinburgh EH16 5PH — MB ChB 1992 Ed.; FRCA 1997. (Edinburgh) Specialist Regist. (Anaesth.) Roy. Infirm. Edin. Prev: Clin. Fell. (ITU), Roy. Infirm.; SHO (Anaesth.), Roy. Infirm.; SHO (Cardiac Surg.), Roy. Infirm.

BROWN, Kirsten Rachel Margaret Ladymeade, 1 Higher Warborough Road, Galmpton, Brixham TQ5 0PF — MB ChB 1997 Glas.

BROWN, Laurence Jeffrey Ross The White House, Main St., Ullesthorpe, Lutterworth LE17 5BT — MB BS 1978 Lond.; MRCS Eng. LRCP Lond. 1978; MRCPath 1985. Cons. Histopath. Leicester Roy. Infirm.

BROWN, Leyland Shirley 80 Gravelly Bank, Lightwood, Stoke-on-Trent ST3 7EF — MB ChB 1950 Ed.; MF Hom. 1982.

***BROWN, Linda** 89 Merryton Tower, Motherwell ML1 2LX Tel: 01698 258250 — MB ChB 1998 Glas.; MB ChB Glas 1998.

BROWN, Linda Gail Hoole Road Surgery, 71 Hoole Road, Chester CH2 3NJ Tel: 01244 325721; 47 Bluebell Close, Huntington, Chester CH3 6RP — MB ChB 1988 Liverp.; MRCGP 1993; T(GP) 1993; DRCOG 1992; DGM RCP Lond. 1991; DFFP 1994. (Liverp.) Clin. Med. Off. (Family Plann.) Chester & Halton Community NHS Trust. Prev: Asst. GP to Dr. A.K. Bland, Chester; Asst. GP to Dr. S. Fordham, Halewood, Liverp.; Trainee GP Chester VTS.

BROWN, Linda Margaret Longfield Medical Centre, Princes Road, Maldon CM9 5DF Tel: 01621 856811 Fax: 01621 852627; School House, Conduit Lane, Woodham Mortimer, Maldon CM9 6SZ — MB ChB 1984 Manch.

BROWN, Linda Mary Bootham Park Hospital, York YO30 7BY Tel: 01904 610777 — MB ChB 1976 Leeds; MRCPsych 1980. Cons. (Psychiat. of Old) York HA.

BROWN, Linda Vera Brown 1 Westside Gardens, 6 Partickhill Road, Glasgow G11 5B Email: ribrow@globalnet.co.uk — MRCS Eng. LRCP Lond. 1966; MRCGP 1982.

BROWN, Lois Mairi MacLeod Ladymeade, 1 Higher Warborough Road, Galmpton, Brixham TQ5 0PF — MB ChB 1998 Bristol.

BROWN, Louisa Margaret 38 Nether Craigour, Edinburgh EH17 7SB Tel: 0131 666240 — MB ChB 1990 Ed.; MRCGP 1994; DFFP 1995. (Edinburgh)

BROWN, Louise Ann Alexandra NHS Healthcare Trust, Woodrow Drive, Redditch B98 7UB Tel: 01527 503030 Ext 4979 — MB BS 1977 Lond.; MRCS Eng. LRCP Lond. 1977; MRCPath 1989. (Char. Cross) Cons. Histopath. Alexandra NHS Healthcare Trust Redditch. Prev: Histopath. Sen. Regist., Leicester Roy. Infirm. Leicester Histopath., Sen. Regist., Leeds Gen. Infirm. Leeds.

BROWN, Louise Margaret Haresfield House Surgery, 6-10 Bath Road, Worcester WR5 3EJ Tel: 01563 523593 Fax: 01563 573552 — MB ChB 1992 Glas.; DRCOG 1995; DCH RCPS Glas. 1995; DFFP 1995. (Univ. Glas.)

BROWN, Lynda Ann Sunnyside, High St, Hemingford Abbots, Huntingdon PE28 9AH Tel: 01480 493804 Email: lynda.brown@dial.pipesc.com — MB BS 1982 Newc.; DRCOG 1995; MRCGP 1998. GP. Prev: GP Regist. Huntingdon.

BROWN, Lynn Margaret Patrick and Partners, Rise Park Surgery, Revelstoke Way, Nottingham NG5 5EB Tel: 0115 927 2525; 32 Benington Drive, Wollaton, Nottingham NG8 2TF Tel: 0115 928 4493 — MB BS 1977 Lond.; MMedSci (Primary Health Care) Nottm. 1996; MRCS Eng. LRCP Lond. 1977; MRCGP 1981; DRCOG 1981. (Guy's Hosp.) p/t Princip. GP; Tutor (Gen. Pract.) Nottm. Univ. Med. Sch.

BROWN, Lynn Marie 2F1 79 Fountainbridge, Edinburgh EH3 9PU — MB ChB 1998 Ed.; MB ChB Ed 1998.

BROWN, Madeline (retired) 37 Argyle Place, Aberdeen AB25 2HU Tel: 01224 633996 — MB ChB 1962 Aberd.; MRCPsych 1976; Dip. Psych. Aberd. 1981. Prev: Sen. Regist. (Child & Family Psychiat.) Roy. Aberd. Hosp. Sick Childr.

BROWN, Malcolm Morecambe Health Centre, Hanover St., Morecambe LA4 5LY Tel: 01524 418418 — MB ChB 1945 Ed.; MRCGP 1955; DObst RCOG 1950. (Ed.) Prev: Ho. Surg., Ho. Phys. & O & G Ho. Surg. St. Luke's Hosp.; Bradford.

BROWN, Malcolm Cameron Unsworth Group Practice, Peter House, Captain Lees Road, Westhoughton, Bolton BL5 3UB Tel: 01942 812525 Fax: 01942 813431; 6 Holly Dene Drive, Lostock,

Bolton BL6 4NP — MB ChB 1981 Manch.; FRCGP 1985; Dip. Palliat. Med. Cardiff 1993; DRCOG 1984. (Manchester) Clin. Asst. (Endoscopy) Bolton Gen. Hosp. Socs: Pres. Bolton Med. Soc. 1998-99. Prev: Trainee GP Bolton Gen. Hosp. VTS.

BROWN, Mr Malcolm Geoffrey Causeway Hospital, 4 Newbridge Rd, Coleraine BT52 1HS Tel: 02870 346147 Email: malcolm.brown@chsst.n-i.nhs.uk; Macleary Lodge, 9 Macleary Road, Coleraine BT51 3QX Tel: 02870 320976 Fax: 02870 320027 Email: maclearysurgery@aol.com — MB BCh BAO 1981 Belf.; MD Belf. 1992; FRCS Ed. 1985. Cons. Gen. & Vasc. Surg. Causeway Hosp. Socs: Fell. Assn. Surgs.; Ulster Med. Soc.; Viking Surg. Club. Prev: Sen. Regist. (Gen. & Vasc. Surg.) Roy. N. Shore Hosp. Sydney, Austral.; Sen. Regist. (Vasc. Surg.) Roy. Vict. Hosp. Belf.; Sen. Regist. (Gen. Vasc. Surg.) Belf. City Hosp.

BROWN, Malcolm Roy Pollokshaws Doctors Centre, 26 Wellgreen, Glasgow G43 1RR Tel: 0141 649 2836 Fax: 0141 649 5238; 8 Bruce Road, Pollokshields, Glasgow G41 5EJ Tel: 0141 429 0174 — MB ChB 1973 Glas.

BROWN, Mr Marcus John Keith Macgillivray 6 Parc Close, Llangybi, Usk NP15 1PN — MB ChB 1967 Ed.; FRCS Ed. 1971. Cons. Surg. (ENT) Roy. Gwent Hosp. Newport. Prev: Sen. Regist. Univ. Hosp. Wales Heath, Cardiff; Chief Resid. Toronto Gen. Hosp. Canada; Ho. Off. Hosp. Sick Childr. Gt. Ormond St., Lond.

BROWN, Margaret Anita Southport and Ormskirk Hospitals, Southport & Formby District General Hospital, Town Lane, Southport PR8 6PN Tel: 01704 864309; 44 Green Lane, Formby, Liverpool L37 7BH — MB BS 1980 Lond.; FRCR 1986. (Girton Coll. Camb., King's Coll. Hosp. Lond.) p/t Cons. Radiol. S.port & Ormskrk NHS Trust. Prev: Sen. Regist. (Radiol.) Mersey RHA.

BROWN, Margaret Patricia 178 Singlewell Road, Gravesend DA11 7RB — MB BS 1985 Lond.; LMSSA 1984.

BROWN, Margaret Valmai West Walk Surgery, 21 West Walk, Yate, Bristol BS37 4AX Tel: 01454 272200; Myrtle Cottage, Old Sodbury, Bristol BS37 6NE — MB ChB 1954 Bristol; DPH Lond. 1963. Prev: Obst. Ho. Surg. S.mead Hosp. Bristol.

BROWN, Mario John Carlo 12A Carew Road, Northwood HA6 3NL — MB BS 1973 Lond.

BROWN, Marion Jane The Health Centre, Marmaduke Street, Hessle Road, Hull HU3 3BH Tel: 01482 323449 Fax: 01482 610920 — MB ChB 1986 Aberd.

BROWN, Marita Ruth Kingston Hospital, Wolverton Avenue, Kingston upon Thames KT2 7QB Tel: 020 8546 7711; 7 Wolsey Close, Kingston upon Thames KT2 7ER Tel: 020 8942 5077 — MB BS 1957 Lond.; FRCP Lond. 1986, M 1966; MRCS Eng. LRCP Lond. 1957; DCH Eng. 1959. (Lond. Hosp.) Cons. Rheum. New Vict. Hosp. Kingston; Med. Mem. of the Med. Appeals Tribunal. Socs: Fell. Roy. Soc. Med.; Brit. Soc. Rheum.; Brit. Med. Assn. Prev: Regist. Physical Med. King's Coll. Hosp.; Med. Regist. Kingston Hosp.; SHO (Paediat.) St. Thos. Hosp. Lond.

BROWN, Mark Andrew Tinshill Lane Surgery, 8 Tinshill Lane, Leeds LS16 7AP Tel: 0113 267 3462 Fax: 0113 230 0402; Over Lane Hall, Over Lane, Rawdon, Leeds LS19 6DN Tel: 0113 250 5549 — MB ChB 1984 Leeds; MB ChB Leeds l984; MRCGP 1988; MRCOphth 1991; DRCOG 1987. Clin. Asst. (Ophth.) Harrogate Dist. Hosp. Prev: GP Mt. Haven, Papua New Guinea; Trainee GP Otley VTS; SHO (Ophth.) Leeds Gen. Infirm.

BROWN, Mark Anthony Eglwysbach Surgery, Berw Road, Pontypridd CF37 2AA Tel: 01443 406811 Fax: 01443 405457; 4 Park Road, Radyr, Cardiff CF4 8DG — MB BCh 1987 Wales; MRCGP 1992; DRCOG 1992; Cert. Family Plann. JCC 1991; DCH RCP Lond. 1990. GP; Clin. Assist. Dermatol. Roy. Glam. Hosp., Llantrisant.; GP Trainer.

BROWN, Mr Mark Fillingham 31 Quarry Avenue, Hartshill, Stoke-on-Trent ST4 7EW Tel: 01782 411517 Fax: 01782 411995 Email: fillingham@aol.com; The Hill, Station Road, Barlaston, Stoke-on-Trent ST12 9DQ Tel: 01782 373 2000 Fax: 01782 373765 — MB BChir 1985 Camb.; PhD CNAA 1984; MA Camb. 1984, MB BChir 1985; FRCS Ed. 1990; FRCS (Orth.) 1995. (Cambridge) Cons. Orthop. & Spinal Surg. N. Staffs. Hosp. Stoke-on-Trent. Socs: Brit. Orthop. Assn.; Brit. Orthop. Research Soc.; Brit. Cervical Spine Soc. Prev: Regist. (Orthop.) Hammersmith Hosp. Lond.; Spinal Fell. Roy. Adelaide Hosp.; Spinal Fell. RNOH Stanmore.

BROWN, Mark Melvin 3 Shirley Road, Nottingham NG3 5DA — BM BS 1987 Nottm.

BROWN, Mark Talbot 9 The Windmills, Broomfield, Chelmsford CM1 7HL; Mid Essex Health Authority, Broomfield Hospital, Chelmsford CM1 7ET — MB ChB 1995 Cape Town.

BROWN, Professor Martin Meredith Institute of Neurology, Box 6, The National Hospital for Neurology and Neurosurgery, Queen Square, London WC1N 3BG Tel: 020 7837 3611 Fax: 020 7833 8613 — MB BChir 1976 Camb.; MA Camb. 1984, BA 1972, MD 1984; FRCP Lond. 1994; MRCP (UK) 1978. (Camb. & Middlx.) Prof. of Stroke Med., Inst. of Neurol., Univ. Coll. Lond.; Cons. (Neurol.) The Nat. Hosp. for Neurol. & Neurosurg., Lond. Socs: Pres. Brit. Assn. Stroke Phys.s ('01-'02). Prev: Reader in Neurol., St Geo.'s Hosp. Med. Sch., Lond.; Regist., Nat. Hosp. for Nerve Disorders, Lond.; Sen. Regist., The Lond. Hosp.

BROWN, Martin Russell c/o Doctors' Mess, Torbay District General Hospital, Lawes Bridge, Torquay TQ2 7AA — MB BS 1994 Lond. (Kings College School of Medicine and Dentistry London) Med. SHO Torbay Hosp. Torquay Devon. Prev: Med. Resid. Roy. Perth Hosp. Perth, W.ern Australia.

BROWN, Mary Elizabeth McNulty and Partners, Torkard Hill Medical Centre, Farleys Lane, Shieldfield, Nottingham NG15 6DY Tel: 0115 963 3676 Fax: 0115 968 1957; 34 Doverbeck Drive, Woodborough, Nottingham NG14 6ER Tel: 0115 965 4502 — BM 1981 Soton.; MRCGP 1987; DRCOG 1986.

BROWN, Mary Margaret Corriecravie House, Carriecravie, Sliddery, Brodick KA27 8PD Email: belhaventce@geocities.com; 5 Belhaven Terrace, First Floor, Glasgow G12 0TF — MB ChB 1993 Glas.; FRCS Glas. 1997. Specialist Regist. in Urol., W. Scotl.

BROWN, Mary McEwan Auchtermuchty Health Centre, 12 Carswell Wynd, Auchtermuchty, Cupar KY14 7AW Tel: 01337 828262 Fax: 01337 828986; 47 Main Street, Dunshalt, Cupar KY14 7EX — MB ChB 1987 Dundee; MRCGP 1991.

BROWN, Mary Mussen (retired) 7 Chequers Quay, Queen St., Emsworth PO10 7AD Tel: 01243 372478 — MB BCh BAO (Hons.) Belf. 1949. Prev: Med. Off. Portsmouth Family Plann. Serv.

BROWN, Matthew Arthur Metabolic Bone Unit, Nuffield Orthopaedic Centre, Windmill Road, Headington, Oxford OX3 7DL Tel: 01865 227621 Fax: 01865 287501 Email: mbrown@well.ox.ac.uk — MB BS 1987 Sydney; FRACP 1993; MD 1997. Cons. Rheumatologist, Nuffield Orthopaedic centre & John Radcliffe Hosp. Oxf.; Sen. Research Fell. Wellcome Trust centre for human genetics, Oxf. Socs: Austral. Rheum. Assn.; Brit. Rheum. Assn. Prev: Sen. Regist. (Rheum.) Roy. N. Shore Hosp. Sydney, Austral.; Sen. Regist. (Rheum.) P. Henry & P. of Wales Hosp. Sydney, Austral.

BROWN, Mrs Meenu Fairway Surgery, 475 Bordesley Green East, Yardley, Birmingham B33 8PP Tel: 0121 783 2125 Fax: 0121 785 0416; 25 Englestede Close, Handsworth Wood, Birmingham B20 1BJ — MB ChB 1976 Birm.; 2000 Oxf. (Birm.) GP Birm.; Clin. Asst. (Ophth.) Dudley HA. Prev: SHO (Ophth.) Wolverhampton HA; SHO Rotat. (Med. & O & G) Dudley Rd. Hosp. Birm.

BROWN, Melanie Jane 5 West Lawn, Ashbrooke, Sunderland SR2 7HW — MB BS 1994 Newc.

BROWN, Melvyn Trevor Worcester Royal Infirmary, Worcester WR5 1HN — MB ChB 1972 Bristol; MRCS Eng. LRCP Lond. 1972; DObst RCOG 1976; FRCR 1983; DMRD Eng. 1981. Cons. Radiol. Worcester Roy. Infirm.

BROWN, Michael Lond. Sch. of Hyg. & Trop. Med., Keppel Street, London Email: michael.brown@ishtm.ac.uk; 29 Wolseley Road, London N8 8RS Tel: 020 8348 5188 — BM BCh 1994 Oxf.; BA Oxf. 1991; MRCP Lond. 1997. (Oxf.) Specialist Regist. (Infec. Dis.s & Gen Med.), Univ. N. Thames; Wellcome Trust Research Train. Fell. In Clin. Trop. Med. at Lond. Sch. of Hyg. & Trop. Med. + Uganda Virus Research Inst., Uganda. Prev: SHO Med. Rotat. St. Geo.s Hosp. NHS Trust.

BROWN, Michael Alan Irvine Jary, Yates and Brown, Well Street Medical Centre, Well Street, Cheadle, Stoke-on-Trent ST10 1EY Tel: 01538 753114 Fax: 01538 751485; The Barn, Oakamoor Road, Cheadle, Stoke-on-Trent ST10 4QR Tel: 01538 751485 — MB ChB 1979 Birm.; MRCGP 1983; DRCOG 1982.

BROWN, Michael Charles 114 Staunton Road, Headington, Oxford OX3 7TN — BM BCh 1962 Oxf.; DM Oxf. 1974, MA, BSc, BM BCh 1962. (Middlx.) Lect. (Physiol.) Univ. Oxf.; Fell. & Physiol. Tutor Trinity Coll. Oxf. Socs: Physiol. Soc. Prev: Ho. Phys. Middlx. Hosp. Lond.; Ho. Surg. Centr. Middlx. Hosp. Lond.

BROWN, Michael James (retired) 46 St Andrew's Road, Sheffield S11 9AL Tel: 0114 255 3850 — MB ChB 1964 Liverp.; FRCPath. 1982, M 1970. Prev: Cons. Haemat. Sheff. AHA (T).

BROWN, Mr Michael Meredith, RD Bushmans, Ramsnest, Chiddingfold, Godalming GU8 4ST Tel: 01428 644421 — MB BChir 1942 Camb.; FRCS Eng. 1944; MRCS Eng. LRCP Lond. 1943. (Camb. & St. Thos.) Socs: Brit. Thorac. Soc. & Soc. Thoracic Surgs. Prev: Emerit. Cons. Thoracic Surg. Roy. Surrey Co. Hosp.; Guildford & K. Edwd. VII Hosp. Midhurst; Hon. Cons. Thoracic Surg. St. Geo. Hosp. Lond.

BROWN, Minnie Watson (retired) Brora, Culdoach Rd, Tongland, Kirkcudbright DG6 4LU Tel: 01557 330522 — MB ChB Ed. 1959; DA Eng. 1964. Prev: Med. Asst. (Anaesth.) Ashington Gen. Hosp.

BROWN, Miriam Beatrice Darnall Road Surgery, 246 Darnall Road, Darnall, Sheffield S9 5AN; 33 Gatefield Road, Sheffield S7 1RD — MB ChB 1986 Sheff.; DGM RCP Lond. 1990. Prev: SHO (Geriat. & Gen. Med.) Nether Edge Hosp. Sheff.; SHO (A & E) Childr. Hosp. Sheff. & Doncaster Roy. Infirm.

BROWN, Mollie Astill (retired) Cedar Croft, 25 Gaia Lane, Lichfield WS13 7LW Tel: 01543 263735 — MB BChir Camb. 1946; MRCGP 1953; DCH Eng. 1956; DObst RCOG 1948. Prev: Sen. Resid. Childr. Hosp. Halifax, N.S.

BROWN, Morag Isobel The Hollies, Ellwyn Crescent, Galashiels TD1 2AZ — MB ChB 1968 Glas.; BA Open Univ. 1980; MRCPath 1983; DA Eng. 1970. (Glas.) Cons. Microbiol. Borders Gen. Hosp. Melrose.

BROWN, Professor Morris Jonathan Clinical Pharmacology Unit, Level 6, ACCI, Addenbrooke's Hospital, Box 110, Cambridge CB2 2QQ Tel: 01223 336743 Fax: 01223 762576 Email: mjb14@medsch1.cam.ac.uk; 104 Grange Road, Cambridge CB3 9AA Fax: 01223 510944 — MB BChir 1975 Camb.; MB (Distinc. Physic) Camb. 1975, BChir 1974; MSc Lond. 1980; MA Camb. 1984, BA 1971, MD 1984; FRCP Lond. 1986; MRCP (UK) 1976. (Camb. & Univ. Coll. Hosp.) Prof. Clin. Pharmacol. Camb. Univ.; Cons. Phys. Addenbrooke's Hosp. Camb.; Fell. & Dir. Clin. Studies Gonville & Caius Coll. Prev: MRC Sen. Fell.sh. 1982; Raymond Horton-Smith Prize Camb. 1984; Sen. Lect. (Clin. Pharmacol.) Roy. Postgrad. Med. Sch. Lond.

BROWN, Neil Campbell 12 Bishop Court, Colyton EX24 6RQ Tel: 01297 553557 — MB ChB 1949 Manch. (Manch.) Prev: Maj. RAMC; Ho. Phys. Manch. Roy. Infirm.; Ho. Surg. Ancoats Hosp. Manch.

BROWN, Neil Maclean (retired) An Ataireachd, 18 Ainslie Road, Girvan KA26 0AZ — MB ChB (Commend.) Glas. 1956; FRCGP 1986, M 1963; DObst RCOG 1958.

BROWN, Neil Peter Yardley Green Medical Centre, 73 Yardley Green Road, Bordesley Green, Birmingham B9 5PU Tel: 0121 773 3838 Fax: 0121 506 2005; Five Oaks, Coleshill Heath Road, Marston Green, Birmingham B37 7HY — MB ChB 1972 Birm. Gen. Med. Pract. Birm.; Birm. Family Pract. Comm.

BROWN, Neville Peter Richard Riverside Surgery, Le Molay Littry Way, Bovey Tacey, Newton Abbot TQ13 9QP Tel: 01626 832666; The Old Vicarage, Chudleigh Knighton, Newton Abbot TQ13 0ET — MB BS 1977 Lond.

BROWN, Nicholas Alan 106 Kernan Gardens, Portadown, Craigavon BT63 5RA — MB ChB 1998 Glas.; MB ChB Glas 1998.

BROWN, Nicholas Hugh Rowden Surgery, Rowden Hill, Chippenham SN15 2SB Tel: 01249 444343 Fax: 01249 446797; Nocketts, Derry Hill, Calne SN11 9PJ Tel: 01249 445650 — BM BCh 1985 Oxf.; MA Camb. 1985; MRCGP 1990; DA (UK) 1991; DRCOG 1988. Prev: Princip. Med. Off. Emmaus Hosp. Natal, S. Afr.; Trainee GP Exeter VTS.

BROWN, Nicholas Jan Winthrop West Cumberland Hospital, Whitehaven CA28 8JG — MB ChB 1985 Leic.; MRCP (UK) 1989; DTM & H Liverp. 1993. Cons. Paediat. W. Cumbria. Prev: Sen. Regist. (Paediat.) Aberd.; Lect. (Paediat.) Univ. Papua New Guinea; Regist. (Paediat.) Glas. Hosps.

BROWN, Nicholas John Sheepcot Medical Centre, 80 Sheepcot Lane, Garston, Watford WD25 0EA Tel: 01923 672451 Fax: 01923 681404; 10 Highclere Drive, Hemel Hempstead HP3 8BT Tel: 01442 244248 Email: nick.brown1@which.net — MB BS 1979 Lond. (Middlesex Hospital) Principle in Gen. Pract., Sheepcot Med. Centre, Watford; Police Surg., Herts. Constab.; Mem. Prorecsion Exec. Comm.. Watford. Socs: Roy. Soc. Med.; Assn. of Police Surg.s.

BROWN, Nicholas Matthew Clinical Microbiology, Box 236, Addenbrooke's Hospital, Cambridge CB2 22W Tel: 01787 370011; 19 Beechwood Avenue, Bottisham, Cambridge CB5 9BE — MB ChB 1985 Bristol; MD Bristol 1996; MRCP (UK) 1990; MRCPath 1993. Cons. Med. Microbiol. Addenbrooke's Hosp. Camb. Prev: Sen. Regist. (Microbiol.) Bristol Roy. Infirm. & S.mead Hosp. Bristol.

BROWN, Nicholas Stephen Lyndon Resource Centre, Hobs Meadow, Olton, Solihull B92 8PW Tel: 0121 743 7626 — MB ChB 1979 Birm.; MRCPsych 1983; FRCPsych 1999.

BROWN, Nicola King George Hospital, Barley Lane, Goodmayes, Ilford IG3 8YB; 17 Oxford Road, London N4 3HA Tel: 020 8211 0110 — MB BS 1984 Lond. Assoc. Specialist (A & E) King Geo. Hosp. Goodmayes; Assoc. Fell. Fac. A & E Med. Socs: Brit. Assn. Accid. & Emerg. Med.

BROWN, Nicola Kathryn Cathays Surgery, 137 Cathays Terrace, Cardiff CF24 4HU Tel: 029 2022 0878 Fax: 029 2038 8771 — MB BCh 1978 Wales; DRCOG 1980.

BROWN, Nigel 26 Yew Tree Drive, Oswaldtwistle, Accrington BB5 3AX; 23 Belfry Way, Edwalton, Nottingham NG12 4FA Tel: 0115 945 2156 — MB ChB 1989 Aberd.; MRCP (UK) 1992. Specialist Regist. (Cardiol.) Qu. Med. Centre, Nottm.; Research Fell. (Cardiol) Qu. Med. Centre, Nottm.; Regist. (Cardiol) City Hosp., Nottm..; Regist. (Men & Cardiol) Qu. Med. Centre, Nottm. Prev: SHO (Med.) Glenfield Hosp. Leicester.

BROWN, Nigel James 33 Maes-y-Sarn, Pentyrch, Cardiff CF15 9QQ — MB BCh 1996 Wales.

BROWN, Mr Norman Ernest 2 Vicarage Road, Leamington Spa CV32 7RH Tel: 01926 425290 — MB BS 1958 Lond.; FRCS Eng. 1970. (St. Geo.) Cons. Ophth. S. Warks. Health Dist.

BROWN, Oliver James 11 West Newington Place, Edinburgh EH9 1QT — MB ChB 1995 Manch.

BROWN, Oswald Taylor, OBE (retired) West Mount, 20 Menzieshill Road, Dundee DD2 1PW — MB ChB Glas. 1939; FRCP Ed. 1969, M 1962; FRCP Glas. 1964, M 1962; FRFPS Glas. 1947. Hon. Cons. Phys. Tayside HB. Prev: Cons. Phys. i/c Geriat. Serv. Roy. Vict. Hosp. Dundee.

BROWN, Pamela Milne Ross Fleishman-Hillard, 25 Wellington St., London WC2E 7DA Tel: 020 7306 9000 Fax: 020 7497 0096 Email: brownp@fleisman.com; 138 Overland Road, Mumbles, Swansea SA3 4EU Tel: 01792 367532 Fax: 01792 362171 — MB ChB 1980 Ed.; DFFP 1996; DRCOG 1983. (Ed.) Dir. Healthcare, Fleishman-Hillard Lond.; GP Swansea. Socs: (Sec.) Primary Care Rheum. Soc.; (Counc. Managem.) Nat. Osteoporosis Soc. Prev: GP Mumbles; GP Swansea; SHO (A & E, Paediat. & O & G) Neath Gen. Hosp.

BROWN, Patricia Margaret Fell Lane Farm, Holylandswaine, Sheffield S30 6JA — MB 1975 Camb.; BChir 1974.

BROWN, Patricia Margaret Gaskell (retired) 23 Carrick Court, Kennington Park Road, London SE11 4EE Tel: 020 7582 9618 — MB BS Lond. 1964; MRCS Eng. LRCP Lond. 1964; DFFP 1993; DCCH RCP Ed. 1993. Prev: Sen. Clin. Med. (Child Health) S. Kent Community Healthcare Trust.

BROWN, Paul (retired) — BM 1982 Soton.

BROWN, Paul Charles Caskgate Street Surgery, 3 Caskgate Street, Gainsborough DN21 2DJ Tel: 01427 612501 Fax: 01427 615459 — MB ChB 1979 Sheff.

BROWN, Paul Philip (retired) 7 Baytree Court, High St, Prestbury, Cheltenham GL52 3AU Tel: 01242 524042 — MA Camb. 1941; MRCS Eng. LRCP Lond. 1939. Prev: Squadron Ldr. RAFVR.

BROWN, Paula Alison 26 Highview, Mulgrave Way, Knaphill, Woking GU21 2BX — MB BS 1998 Lond.; MB BS Lond 1998.

BROWN, Mr Peffers Watson (retired) Svinget, Dundas Terrace, Melrose TD6 9QU Tel: 01896 822299 — MB ChB 1957 Ed.; FRCS Ed. 1964; DObst RCOG 1962. Prev: Cons. Surg. Borders Gen. Hosp. Melrose.

BROWN, Percy Edgar 178 Singlewell Road, Gravesend DA11 7RB Tel: 01474 355331 — MB BS Lond. 1946; MRCP Lond. 1949; MRCGP 1971; Dip. Addic. Behaviour Lond. 1992. (Guy's) Clin. Asst. Bracton Clinic Bexley Hosp. Socs: Inst. Psychosexual Med.; BMA. Prev: Sen. Med. Off. HM Prison Serv.; Sch. Med. Off. Kent AHA; Flight Lt. RAF Med. Br.

BROWN, Peter National Hospital for Neurology & Neurosurgery, London WC1N 3BG Tel: 020 7837 3611 Fax: 020 7278 9836 — MB BChir 1985 Camb.; FRCP (UK) 1999; MA Camb. 1985, MD

1993; MRCP (UK) 1987. Cons. Neurol. Nat. Hosp. Neurol. & Neurosurg. Lond. & Middlx. Hosp.

BROWN, Peter St Davids Clinic, Bellevue Terrace, Newport NP20 2LB Tel: 01633 251133 Fax: 01633 221096; 7 Springfield Close, Rhiwderin, Newport NP10 8RZ — MB BS 1967 Lond.; MRCGP 1979; DObst RCOG 1969. (Char. Cross) Prev: SHO (O & G) W. Middlx. Hosp. Isleworth; Ho. Surg. & Ho. Phys. Char. Cross Hosp.

BROWN, Peter Corrie Cadney (retired) 13 Ramsdale Road, Bramhall, Stockport SK7 2PZ Tel: 0161 440 0960 — MB ChB 1961 Manch.; DObst RCOG 1964. p/t Med. Mem. "The Appeals Serv." (Advisery only), Anchorage Quay, Salford, Lancs.

BROWN, Peter Esmond (retired) Catfield House, School Road, Catfield, Great Yarmouth NR29 5DA — MB ChB 1937 Ed.; FRCP Ed. 1964, M 1947; DPH Ed. 1953. Prev: Sen. Lect. Community Med. Univ. Sheff.

BROWN, Peter Finlay Wold House, The Highlands, Painswick, Stroud GL6 6SL Tel: 01452 812300 — MB ChB 1973 St. And.; BMSc Dund 1970; FRCR 1979. Cons. Radiol. Cheltenham Gen. Hosp.

BROWN, Peter Grover Buchanan Road Surgery, 72 Buchanan Road, Sheffield S5 7AL Tel: 0114 245 6679; 1 Blackbrook Drive, Lodge Moor, Sheffield S10 4LS Tel: 0114 230 4130 — MB ChB 1974 Sheff.; MB ChB (Hons.) Sheff. 1974.

BROWN, Peter Howell Royal Infirmary, Perth PH1 1NX Tel: 01738 623311 — MB ChB 1982 Aberd.; MD Aberd. 1994; MRCP (UK) 1985. Cons. Phys. (Gen. & Respirat. Med.) Roy. Infirm. Perth. Socs: Brit. Thorac. Soc.; Scott. Thoracic Soc. Prev: Sen. Regist. (Respirat. Med.) Aberd. Hosps.; Clin. Fell. (Cystic Fibrosis) W.. Gen. Hosp. Edin.; Research Fell. & Regist. (Respirat. Med.) N.. Gen. Hosp. Edin.

BROWN, Peter Inglis 43 Magdalen Yard Road, Roseangle, Dundee DD1 4NE Tel: 01382 346500 Fax: 01382 345515; 3 Newmill Gardens, St Andrews KY16 8RY Tel: 01334 475239 — MB ChB Glas. 1952; MRCGP 1965. Fee Pain Doctor/Examg. Med. Practitioner - N. D. A. (Nestor Disabil. Anal.) Dundee. Prev: Med. Adviser B.A.M.S. Dundee; Reg. Med. Off. SHMD Dundee; Prin. Gen. Pract. Alexandria Dunbaronsh.

BROWN, Peter James Ellon Group Practice, Health Centre, Schoolhill, Ellon AB41 9AH Tel: 01358 720333 Fax: 01358 721578 — MB ChB 1988 Aberd.

BROWN, Mr Peter Maurice Milton Keynes General NHS Trust, Standing Way, Eaglestone, Milton Keynes MK6 5LD Tel: 01908 243140 Fax: 01908 608112 Email: susanbrown@uk-consultants.co.uk; The Old Stable Yard, Upper Weald, Calverton, Milton Keynes MK19 6EL Tel: 01908 561771 Fax: 01908 561771 Email: peterandsue@uk-home.co.uk — MB BCh BAO Belf. 1969; FRCS Ed. 1977; FRCS Eng. 1974. (Queens University. Belfast) Cons. ENT Surg. & Clin. Dir. Head & Neck Directorate Milton Keynes Gen NHS Trust. Socs: Brit. Assn. Otol.; Roy. Soc. Med.; Europ. Acad. of facial plastic Surg. Prev: Sen. Regist. (ENT) Bristol HA; Regist. (ENT) Gen. Hosp. Nottm.; Regist. (Plastic Surg.) Regional Centre Plastic Surg. Billericay.

BROWN, Peter Morgan Brynarthur, 2 Maes y Dderwen, Monument Hill, Carmarthen SA31 3LX Tel: 01267 236103 — MB BCh 1960 Wales; FFOM RCP Lond. 1985, MFOM 1978; DIH Soc. Apoth. Lond. 1970; DPH Wales 1964. (Cardiff) Cons. Occupat. Med. Socs: Soc. Occupat. Med.; Assn. Local Auth. Med. Advisers; Brit. Acad. Forens. Sci. Prev: Dep. Chief Med. Adviser Civil Serv. Occupat. Health Serv.; Sen. Employm. Med. Adviser Health & Safety Exec.; Regional Med. Off. Nat. Dock Labour Bd.

BROWN, Peter Philip (retired) 5 Cromwell Quay, Shore St, Dunbar EH42 1FN Tel: 01368 863355 — MB BS 1951 Lond.; MD Lond. 1968; MRCS Eng. LRCP Lond. 1951; FRCPath 1975, M 1963; Dip. Bact. 1961. Prev: Lect. (Bact.) Univ. Edin.

BROWN, Peter Robert (retired) Craig House, Pitcairngreen, Perth PH1 3LX Tel: 0173 884 0268 — MB BCh BAO 1957 Belf.; FFA RCS Eng. 1965; DA Eng. 1960; DTM & H Eng. 1961; FRCA. Prev: Cons. Anaesth. Perth Roy. Infirm. & Huddersfield Roy. Infirm.

BROWN, Peter Thomas Kirkwood Shankill Health Centre, 135 Shankill Parade, Belfast BT13 1SD Tel: 028 9024 7181 — MB BCh BAO 1979 Belf.; MRCGP 1983; Cert. Family Plann. JCC 1983; DRCOG 1982.

BROWN, Peter William 'Culmore', 12 Stoneleigh Road, Coventry CV4 7AD Tel: 024 76 419135 — MB ChB 1954 Birm. (Birm.) Occupat. Health Phys. Walsgrave Hosp. Coventry. Prev: Surg. Lt. RN.

BROWN, Peter William Gordon Department of Diagnostic Imaging, Northern General Hospital NHS Trust, Herries Road, Sheffield S5 7AU Tel: 0114 243 4343 — MB ChB 1984 Birm.; BSc (Hons.) Birm. 1981; FRCS Ed. 1988; FRCR 1992. Cons. Radiol. N. Gen. NHS Trust Sheff. Socs: Assoc. Mem. Europ. Soc. Uroradiol.; Brit. Soc. Interven. Radiol. Prev: Sen. Regist. (Diagn. Radiol.) Sheff. HA.

BROWN, Philip David The Linden Centre, Woodlands Way, Broomfield, Chelmsford CM1 7LS — MB BS 1998 Lond.; MB BS Lond 1998.

BROWN, Philip Dudley 4 St Oswald's Close, Wern Road, Sebastopol, Pontypool NP4 5DS Tel: 01495 764424; Willowdene, 15 Willow Walk, Englefield Green, Egham TW20 0DQ Tel: 01784 432742 — MB ChB 1982 Leic.; PhD Lond. 1976, BSc 1972; DTM & H Liverp. 1992.

BROWN, Philip Martin Scarborough Hospital, Scarborough YO12 6QT Tel: 01723 342036; Folkton Manor, Folkton, Scarborough YO11 3UQ Tel: 01723 890323 — MB BS 1971 Lond.; MD Lond. 1985, BSc (Pharm.) 1968, MB BS 1971; FRCP (UK) 1974. (King's Coll. Hosp.) Cons. Phys. ScarBoro. Hosp. Socs: BMA Med. Assn. (Br. Sec.); Brit. Diabetic Assn. Prev: Lect. Med. St. Thos. Hosp. Lond.; Research Fell. & Regist. (Metab. Med.) St. Thos. Hosp. Lond.; Regist. (Gen. Med.) Brighton Gen. Hosp.

BROWN, Philip Michael Highfield, Haworth Road, Wilsden, Bradford BD15 0JX — MB ChB 1971 Leeds; FFA RCS Eng. 1978; DObst RCOG 1973; DA Eng. 1975.

BROWN, Philip Morrison Guild Community Healthcare NHS Trust, Department of Psychotherapy, 1 Albert Road, Fulwood, Preston PR2 8PJ Tel: 01772 401370 Fax: 01772 787344 — MB ChB 1986 Aberd.; MRCPsych 1992; Dip. Psychother. 1998. Cons. Psychotherapist, Guild Community Healthcare NHS Trust. Socs: Roy. Coll. Psychiat.; N. W. Inst. Dynamic Psychother.; Soc. Psychother. Research.

BROWN, Philip Scott (retired) 65 Northover Road, Westbury-on-Trym, Bristol BS9 3LQ — BM BCh 1946 Oxf.; MRCP Lond. 1952. Prev: Reader in Pharmacol. Univ. Bristol.

BROWN, Phillip Michael The Hutton Centre, St Lukes Hospital, Marton Road, Middlesbrough TS4 3AF Tel: 01642 283380 Fax: 01642 283345 — MB BS 1986 Lond.; MRCPsych 1992. (Guy's) Cons. (Forens. Psychiat.) Tees & N. E. Yorks NHS Trust. Prev: Research Fell. (Psychiat.) UMDS Guy's Hosp. Lond.

BROWN, Phillipa Latham Flat 4, Gable End House, 16 Cleveland Way, London E1 4TU — MB BS 1998 Lond.; MB BS Lond 1998.

BROWN, Rachel Anne Montpelier Health Centre, Bath Buildings, Bristol BS6 5PT Tel: 0117 942 6811 Fax: 0117 944 4182 — BM BS 1992 Nottm.; MRCGP 1996; DFFP 1995; DRCOG 1995. (Nottm.) Prev: GP/Regist. Bristol.

BROWN, Rachel Catherine 340 Kelvindale Road, Glasgow G12 0QS — MB ChB 1996 Glas.

BROWN, Rachel Emma 12 Castle Street, Ryde PO33 2EG — MB ChB 1997 Bristol.

BROWN, Mr Raymond David Department of Ophthalmology, Central Outpatients, Hartshill Road, Stoke-on-Trent ST4 7PA Tel: 01782 715444; School Farm, Onneley, Crewe CW3 9QJ Tel: 01782 750913 — MB 1980 Camb.; BA 1977 Camb.; BChir 1979 Camb.; MA 1981 Camb.; BSc Leic. 1967; FRCS Ed. 1984; FRCOphth 1988; DO RCS Eng. 1983. Cons. Ophth. Surg. N. Staffs. Roy. Infirm. Stoke-on-Trent; Sen. Clin. Tutor Univ. Keele. Prev: Sen. Regist. & Regist. Ophth. Birm. & Midl. Eye Hosp.; SHO (Ophth.) Addenbrookes Hosp. Camb.

BROWN, Mr Raymond Henry Leighton (retired) The Noup, 5 Ridge Avenue, Marple, Stockport SK6 7HJ Tel: 0161 427 4435 — MB ChB 1951 Manch.; FRCS Eng. 1964. Prev: Cons. Orthop. & Traum. Surg. Stockport AHA (T).

BROWN, Raymond Peter Maritia Barrow Hospital, Barrow Gurney, Bristol BS48 3SG Tel: 01275 392811 — BM BCh 1977 Oxf.; MA Oxf. 1991; MRCPsych 1984. (Oxford and St. Thomas' (London)) Cons. Psychother. United Bristol Hosp.; Mem. Severnside Inst. Psycho Ther.; Sen. Clin. Lect. Univ. of Bristol. Socs: Assn. Psychoanal. Psychother. NHS; Gp. Analyt. Soc.; Brit. Assn. of Gp.

Psychotherapists. Prev: Cons. Psychother. Psychother. Unit. Newport I. of Wight; Sen. Regist. (Psychother.) Portman Clinic Lond.

BROWN, Raymond Solomon Paediatric Department, Stoke Mandeville Hospital, Aylesbury HP21 8AL Tel: 01296 315000 Fax: 01296 315163 Email: raymond.brown@smh.nhs.uk; Old Farm, 20 South Hills, Brill, Aylesbury HP18 9TQ Tel: 01844 238232 Fax: 01844 239338 Email: brown.brill@ukgateway.net — MB BCh 1966 Witwatersrand; FRCP Lond. 1983; MRCP (UK) 1972; FRCPCH 1997; FCP(SA) 1971. (Witwatersrand) Cons. Paediat. Stoke Mandeville Hosp. Aylesbury. Socs: Fell. Roy. Soc. Med. Prev: Sen. Regist. Radcliffe Infirm. Oxf.; Regist. (Neonat.) Hammersmith Hosp. Inst. Child Health Lond. & Transvaal Memor Hosp., Johannesburg.

BROWN, Rebecca Ellen 48 Brampton Drive, Liverpool L8 7SU — MB ChB 1997 Liverp.

BROWN, Richard Hinchingbrooke Hospital, Huntingdon PE29 6NT Tel: 0114 276 1111 Fax: 0114 275 4847; Flat 3, 183 Belsize Road, London NW6 4AB — MB BS 1993 Lond.; MA Camb. 1993; FRCS Eng. 1997. (Univ. Camb. & King's Coll. Hosp.) Socs: Fell. Roy. Soc. Trop. Med.; Brit. Orthop. Train. Assn. Prev: SHO Rotat. (Paediat. Med., Orthop. & A & E) Sheff.

BROWN, Richard Charles Alan Aldersyde, Alnmouth Road, Alnwick NE66 2PS — MB BCh 1997 Wales.

BROWN, Richard Clive 276 Ringwood Road, Ferndown, Wimborne BH21 6 — BM 1986 Soton.; DTM & H RCP Lond. 1993. SHO (Anaesth.) Qu. Alexandra Hosp. Portsmouth.

BROWN, Richard Collingwood Argyll and Clyde Acute Hospitals trust, Trust Offices, Royal Alexendra Hospital, Corxbar Rd, Paisley PA2 9PN Tel: 0141 580 4959 Fax: 0141 580 4127 Email: richard.brown@rah.scot.nhs.uk — MB BChir 1967 Camb.; MB 1968 Camb.; MA; FRCP Lond. 1994; FRCP Glas. 1986; MRCP (UK) 1970. (Middlx. Hosp. Med. Sch.) Med. Dir. Argyll & Clyde acute Hosp.s NHS Trust.

BROWN, Richard Lawrence Grosvenor Street Surgery, 4 Grosvenor Street, St Helier, Jersey JE1 4HB Tel: 01534 30541 Fax: 01534 887948 — MB BS 1975 Lond. (Univ. Coll. Hosp.) Prev: Trainee GP Ipswich VTS.

BROWN, Richard Lingard Tall Trees Surgery, Rectory Road, Retford DN22 7AY Tel: 01777 701637 Fax: 01777 710619; 15 Lime Tree Avenue, Retford DN22 7BB Tel: 01777 702264 — MB ChB Sheff. 1966. (Sheff.) Fact. Dr. N. Rubber Co. Retford.; Partner in Gen. Pract. Socs: BMA. Prev: Clin. Asst. Doncaster Roy. Infirm.; SHO (Phys.) Roy. Infirms. Sheff. & Doncaster; Ho. Phys. Sheff. Childr. Hosp.

BROWN, Richard Mark 4 Glen Luss Gardens, Craigmarloch, Cumbernauld, Glasgow G68 0DJ Tel: 0141 736249 Email: rmbrown@telinco.co.uk — MB ChB 1995 Dundee. (Dundee) SHO (Urol) Stobhill Hosp. Glasg. Socs: BMA. Prev: SHO (A & E) S.. Gen. Hosp. Glas.

BROWN, Richard Michael Wilton Health Centre Partnership, Wilton Health Centre, Market Place, Wilton, Salisbury SP2 0HT Tel: 01722 742404 Fax: 01722 744116 Email: drrbrown@gpiag-asthma.org; Highlands, 76 Shaftesbury Road, Wilton, Salisbury SP2 0DS Tel: 01722 741366 Fax: 01722 741366 — MB BS 1978 Lond.; BSc (Hons.) Lond. 1975, MB BS 1978; MRCGP 1984; DRCOG 1983; DFFP 1997. (Univ. Coll. Hosp.)

BROWN, Richard Nicholas Farnborough Hospital, Bromley Hospitals NHS Trust, Orpington BR6 8ND Tel: 01689 814000 — MB BS 1989 Lond.; 1997 (Dip. Advanced Obstetric Ultrasound) RCOG RCR; 2000 (Fetal Med. Foundation) Diploma in fetal medicine; MRCOG 1994; DFFP 1994. Cons, (O&G and Foetal Med.) FarnBoro. Hosp., Orpington; Ed. GynaecoPathol. Socs: Brit. Med. Ultrasound Soc.; Brit. Gyn. Endoscopy Soc.; Internat. Soc. Ultrasound in Obst. & Gyn. Prev: Regist. Rotat. (O & G) King's Coll. Hosp. Lond.; SHO (O & G) St. Thos. Hosp. & St. Bart. Hosp. Lond.; Demonst. (Human Morphol.) & Resid. Med. Off. Univ. Soton.

BROWN, Mrs Rita (retired) Windrush, South Row, Chilton, Didcot OX11 0RT Tel: 01235 834282 — MB ChB 1961; FRCP Lond. 1996; MRCP (UK) 1974. Prev: Cons. Allergy & Clin. Immunol. Roy. Berks. Hosp. Reading.

BROWN, Robert (retired) 14 Friarside Cose, Yarm TS15 9JG Tel: 01642 780848 — MD 1972 Manch.; MB ChB 1963; FRCOG 1981, M 1968, DObst 1966. Prev: Cons. O & G N. Tees Hosp. Gp.

BROWN, Robert Rathbone Hospital, Mill Lane, Liverpool L13 4AW — MB ChB 1979 Manch.; MRCPsych 1987; MRCGP 1984; DRCOG 1981.

BROWN, Robert (retired) 29 Glasgow Road, Paisley PA1 3PB Tel: 0141 889 3356 — MB ChB 1961 Glas.; MRCGP 1976.

BROWN, Robert (retired) Essex Nuffield Hospital, Brentwood CM15 8EH Tel: 01277 263263 — MB ChB 1956 Manch.; BSc Manch. 1953; FRCP Lond. 1974, M 1961. Cons. Phys. Basildon Hosp., St. And. Billericay & Orsett Hosp.; Hon. Clin. Teach. Middlx. & UCH Lond. Prev: Sen. Regist. (Med.) Roy. Vict. Infirm. Newc.

BROWN, Mr Robert Fraser Old Court House, Back St., Aldborough, Boroughbridge, York YO51 9EX — MB BS 1963 Sydney; FRCS Ed. 1968. (Sydney) Prev: Cons. Orthop. Surg. St. Jas. Hosp. Leeds.

BROWN, Robert Heron Burnbank Medical Centre, 18 Burnbank Road, Hamilton ML3 0NQ Tel: 01698 286555 Fax: 01698 286686; Parkside, Silverwells, Bothwell, Glasgow G71 8AZ — MB ChB Glas. 1966; DObst RCOG 1968. (Glas.)

BROWN, Mr Robert James Daisy Hill Hospital, 5 Hospital Road, Newry BT35 8DR Tel: 028 3083 5000; 4 Dublin Road, Loughbrickland, Banbridge BT32 3NW Tel: 028 4066 9083 — MB BCh BAO 1979 Belf.; FRCSI 1999; MD Belf. 1989; FRCS Ed. 1983. (Qu. Univ. Belf.) Cons. Gen. Surg. Daisy Hill Hosp. Newry, Co. Down.

BROWN, Robert MacArthur 36 Wick Crescent, Bristol BS4 4HG Tel: 0117 977 6751 Fax: 0117 971 0505 Email: brown5@which.net — MB ChB Birm. 1953; DObst RCOG 1961. (Birm.) Med. Off. BRd.way Lodge Treatm. Centre Chem. Dependency, W.on Super Made. Prev: Med. Off. HM Prison Bristol; GP Bristol; Clin. Asst. Avon Drug Probl. Team.

BROWN, Mr Robert Mervyn 17B Deanfield, Londonderry BT47 6HY Tel: 01504 47231 — MB BCh BAO 1963 Belf.; FRCS Eng. 1972; DO Eng. 1967. (Belf.) Cons. (Ophth.) Altnagelvin Area Hosp. Lond.derry. Prev: Res. Surg. Off. Moorfields Eye Hosp. Lond.

BROWN, Robert Morris 25 Bolton Street, Brixham TQ5 9BZ — MB ChB 1969 Aberd.

BROWN, Robert William Department of Anaesthetics, St George's Hospital, Blackshaw Road, Tooting, London SW17 0QT; 57 Ellerton Road, Wandsworth, London SW18 3NQ — MB BS 1984 Lond.; MRCP (UK) 1987; FRCA 1990. Cons. Cardiothoracic Anaesth. St. Geo. Hosp. Lond. Prev: Sen. Regist. (Anaesth.) St. Geo. Hosp. Lond.; Clin. Fell. (Cardiothoracic Anaesth.) Harefield Hosp.

BROWN, Roderick John Kilner (retired) 9 The Pippins, Wilton, Ross-on-Wye HR9 6BQ Tel: 01989 566422 — MB BChir 1942 Camb.; FRCP Lond. 1967, M 1948; MRCS Eng. LRCP Lond. 1942; FRCPCH 1997; DCH Eng. 1951. Prev: Cons. Paediat. Middlx. Hosp. Lond.

BROWN, Mr Roger Dunhampstead House, Dunhampstead, Droitwich WR9 7JX Tel: 01905 773313 — MB ChB 1973 Liverp.; BSc (Hons.) Liverp. 1970, ChM 1984, MB ChB 1973; FRCS Eng. 1977. (Liverpool) Cons. Surg. Alexandra Hosp. Redditch Worcs. Prev: Sen. Regist. (Surg.) Univ. Hosp. Wales.

BROWN, Roger Thomas Kos Clinic, 4 Roydlands Street, Hipperholme, Halifax HX3 8AF Tel: 01422 205154 Fax: 01422 201443; 4 Landemere Syke, Northowram, Halifax HX3 7SJ Tel: 01422 206261 — MB BS 1981 Lond.; MRCGP 1988. (St Bartholomews) Gen. Practitioner, Hipperholme, Halifax; Club Doctor, Halifax Blue Sox RIFC; Club Doctor, Halifax Town AFC. Prev: Regist. (Anaesth.) Bradford Roy. Infirm.; SHO (O & G) St. Luke's Hosp. Bradford; SHO (Paediat.) St. Luke's Hosp. Bradford.

BROWN, Roger William Molecular Medicine Centre, Department of Medicine, Western General Hospital, Edinburgh EH4 2XU; 10 Moira Drive, Bangor BT20 4RN — BM BCh 1988 Oxf.; MRCP 1991 UK; PhD 1996 Edin.; BA Camb. 1985. Clin. Sen Lec,. Hon. Cons., W.. Gen. Hosp. Edin. Prev: Hon. Sen. Regist.

BROWN, Roisin Cecelia Mary 230 Grange Road, London E13 0HB — MB BS 1991 Lond.

BROWN, Mr Ronald Frank, Air Commodore RAF Med. Retd. (retired) Bridle House, East Pallant, Chichester PO19 1TZ Tel: 01243 776564 — MA, BM BCh Oxon. 1950; FRCS Eng. 1956. Prev: Cons. Plastic Surg. RAF.

BROWN, Ronald James Hamilton Park Terrace Surgery, 7A Park Terrace, Stirling FK8 2JT — MB ChB 1976 Glas.; FRCGP 1995, M 1980. (Glas.) Clin. Asst. (Diabetes) Stirling Roy. Infirm.

BROWN, Ronald Michael Department of Anaesthesia, Leighton Hospital, Middlewich Road, Crewe CW1 4QJ Tel: 01270 255141 Fax: 01270 587696; Hawthorn Cottage, Seven Sisters Lane, Ollerton, Knutsford WA16 8RL Email: spike_molecule@compuseve.com — MRCS Eng. LRCP Lond. 1984; FRCA 1991; DA (UK) 1987. (Sheff.) Cons. Anaesth. Leighton Hosp. Crewe. Socs: Obst. Anaesth. Assn. & Soc. Computing and Technol. Anaesth.; Obst. Anaesth. Assn.& Brit. Assoc. Day Surg. Prev: Sen. Regist. NW RHA; Research Fell. (Clin. Pharmacol.) Vanderbilt Univ. Med. Center, Nashville, Tennessee, USA; Regist. Rotat. (Anaesth.) Mersey RHA VTS.

BROWN, Rosemary Brenda Friarwood Surgery, Carleton Glen, Pontefract WF8 1SU Tel: 01977 703235 Fax: 01977 600527; 6 Rutland Avenue, Pontefract WF8 3RD — MB ChB Leeds 1982. GP Pontefract, W. Yorks.

BROWN, Russell David Manor Park Medical Centre, High Street, Polegate BN26 5DJ Tel: 01323 482301 Fax: 01323 484848; Email: russell@freeola.net — MB ChB 1993 Leic. GP. Manor Pk. Med. Centre, Polegate; Clin. Asst. (Gen. Med.) E.borne Hosps. NHS Trust, E.borne.

BROWN, Ruth Alicia Bakker, Brown, Jacobs and Wormell, Lisson Grove Health Centre, Gateforth Street, London NW8 8EF Tel: 020 7723 2213 — MB BS 1986 Lond.; BSc Lond. 1975; MRCGP 1990; DCH RCP Lond. 1989.

BROWN, Ruth Marcia 20 Odell Place, Priory Road, Edgbaston, Birmingham B5 7RQ — MB ChB 1978 Birm.; FRCPath 1997, M 1988.

BROWN, Ruth Mary Accident & Emergency Department, King's College Hospital, Denmark Hill, London SE5 9RS Tel: 020 7346 3330 Email: ruth.m.brown@kcl.ac.uk — MB BS 1983 Lond.; FRCS 1994; FRCS Ed. 1988; FRCS Eng. 1988; FFAEM 1997. Cons. A & E King's Coll. Hosp. Lond. Prev: Sen. Regist. (A & E) SW Thames RHA.; Regist. (A & E) King's Coll. Hosp. Lond.

BROWN, S E The Groves Medical Centre, 72 Coombe Road, New Malden KT3 4QS Tel: 020 8336 2222 Fax: 020 8336 0297.

BROWN, Sally Ann 72 Beaconsfield Road, Canterbury CT2 7LH — MB ChB 1997 Sheff.

BROWN, Sally Jane The Whitfield Practice, Hunslet Health Centre, 24 Church Street, Leeds LS10 2PE Tel: 0113 270 5194 Fax: 0113 270 2795; 5 Avenue Lawns, Leeds LS17 7HP Tel: 0113 225 1197 — MB ChB 1981 Leic.; MRCGP 1986. Prev: Trainee GP Hallwood Health Centre; SHO (O & G & Paediat.) Whiston Hosp.; SHO (Paediat.) St. Helen's & Knowsley HA.

***BROWN, Samantha Jane** 26 Box Hill, Scarborough YO12 5NG Tel: 01723 372677 — MB BS 1997 Lond.

BROWN, Sandra Milne Ross Kilsyth Medical Partnership, Kilsyth Health Centre, Burngreen Park, Kilsyth, Glasgow G65 0HU Tel: 01236 822081 Fax: 01236 826231 — MB ChB 1983 Ed.

BROWN, Sara Judith 4 Pond Cottages, Greenside, Ryton NE40 4AF — MB ChB 1996 Ed.; BSc (Hons.). (Edinburgh) SHO (Med.) Newc.

BROWN, Sheila Elizabeth St Patricks Centre for Community Health, Frank St, Highgate, Birmingham B12 Tel: 0121 440 2422 — MB ChB 1979 Birm.; DRCOG 1983. SCMO (Family Plann.) St Patricks Centre for Community Health, Birm.; Clin. Asst. GU Med.

BROWN, Sheila Veronica 14 River Crescent, Ninewells, Dundee DD2 1UJ Tel: 01382 642458 — MB ChB 1965 St. And. (St. And.) Med. Research Asst. Med. Eval. & Monitoring Gp. Dept. Clin. Pharmacol. Univ. Dundee.

BROWN, Shelagh Frances West End Surgery, 19 Chilwell Road, Beeston, Nottingham NG9 1EH Tel: 0115 925 4443 Fax: 0115 922 1255; Croft Cottage, 1 South St, Draycott, Derby DE72 3PP — MB ChB 1984 Liverp.; MB ChB Liverp. l984. Prev: Trainee GP Wirral VTS.

BROWN, Shirley Ann (retired) 9 Kingsley Meade, Trencreek, Newquay TR8 4PY Tel: 01637 871445, 01603 286286 Fax: 01603 288261 — MB ChB 1975 Leeds; MRCGP 1981. Retainer GP. Prev: SHO (Gyn.) Redruth Hosp. Cornw.

BROWN, Simon Albert 29 Dovecote Gardens, London SW14 8PN — MB BS 1988 Lond.

BROWN, Simon James 8 East Mount, Newtownards BT23 8SE — MB ChB 1998 Ed.; MB ChB Ed 1998.

BROWN, Simon Jeremy Mews Close Health Centre, Mews Close, Ramsey, Huntingdon PE26 1BP Tel: 01487 812611 Fax: 01487 711801 — MB ChB 1989 Bristol; MRCGP 1993; DA (UK) 1994; DRCOG 1992. GP Princip. Ramsey Health Centre; VTS Course Organiser, Addenbrookes Camb. Prev: Trainee GP/SHO (Anaesth.) Hinchingbrooke Hosp. Huntingdon VTS; Ho. Phys. W.on Gen. Hosp. Taunton; Clin. Asst. (Anaesth.) Hinchingbroke Hosp. Huntingdon.

BROWN, Simon Nicholas Sandhurst Group Practice, 72 Yorktown Road, Sandhurst GU47 9BT Tel: 01252 872455 Fax: 01252 872456; Redford House, 94 Scotland Hill, Sandhurst GU47 8JZ — MB BS 1982 Lond.; DRCOG 1988; DCH RCP Lond. 1987; Dip. IMC Ed. 1997. Co-Ordinator Berks., Hants. & Surrey Immediate Care Scheme. Prev: Trainee GP Owlsmoor VTS.

BROWN, Simon Robert 6 Raven Close, Sandbach CW11 1SF Tel: 01270 766247 Fax: 01270 766247 — MB ChB 1982 Birm.; MB ChB. Birm. 1982; DAvMed FOM RCP Lond. 1997. Monarch Airlines Ltd, Lond. Luton Airport; Aviat. Med. Specialist Centre for Human Scis. DERA FarnBoro. Hants; Aviat. Med. Soc. AvMed Ltd, Sandbach Chesh. Prev: CAA Authorised Med. Examr. Riyadh.

BROWN, Mr Stephen 12 Malone Beeches, Belfast BT9 6UB — MB BCh BAO 1967 Belf.; FRCS Ed. 1971. (Belf.) Cons. Paediat. Surg. Roy. Belf. Hosp. Sick Childr. Prev: Resid. Asst. Surg. Hosp. Sick Childr. Gt. Ormond St.

BROWN, Stephen 16 Parkstone Avenue, Carleton, Poulton-le-Fylde, Blackpool — MB ChB 1982 Manch.

BROWN, Stephen Albert 8 Valley Road, Dewsbury WF12 0JY Tel: 01924 489859 — MB ChB 1975 Leeds.

BROWN, Mr Stephen Charles William Department of Urology, Stepping Hill Hospital, Stockport SK2 7JE Tel: 0161 419 4989 Fax: 0161 419 5699 Email: scwbrown@shurology.demon.co.uk; 20 Woodfield Road, Cheadle Hulme, Cheadle SK8 7JS Email: stephenbrown@uromus.demon.co.uk — MB BS 1981 Lond.; MA Camb. 1982; MD Lond. 1992; FRCS (Urol.) 1994; FRCS Eng. 1985. Cons. Urol. Stepping Hill Hosp. Stockport.

BROWN, Stephen Gerald Edward Brookside Group Practice, Brookside Close, Earley, Reading RG6 7HG Tel: 0118 966 9222; 49 Brighton Road, Reading RG6 1PS — MB BS 1971 Lond.; MA Reading 1990; DTM & H Liverp. 1979; DCH RCP Lond. 1979; DObst RCOG 1973. (Roy. Free Hosp. Lond.)

BROWN, Stephen Paul Millbarn Medical Centre, 34 London End, Beaconsfield HP9 2JH Tel: 01494 675303 Fax: 01494 680214; 30 Woodside Close, Amersham HP6 5EF — MB ChB 1986 Birm.; MRCGP 1993; DRCOG 1991; DCH RCP Lond. 1988.

BROWN, Stephen Thomas Coleman Health Centre, Park Drive, Stenhousemuir, Larbert FK5 3BB Tel: 01324 554136 Fax: 01324 553622 — MB ChB 1986 Aberd.

BROWN, Stephen William Little Plumstead Hospital, Norwich NR13 5EW Tel: 01603 711343 Fax: 01603 711508 Email: stephen.brown@msmail.nchp-trust.anglox.nhs.uk — MB BChir 1977 Camb.; MA Camb. 1977; MA Nottm. 1974; MRCPsych. 1981; FRCPsych. 1998. (King's College Hospital London) Clin. Dir., Learning Disabils. Serv. Norwich Community Health Partnership NHS Trust; Sen. Lect. Sch. Health Univ. E. Anglia. Socs: Fell. Roy. Soc. Med. Prev: Cons. i/c Med. Servs. David Lewis Centre for Epilepsy Chesh.; Sen. Clin. Lect. (Psychiat.) Univ. Keele; Hon. Cons. Neuropsychiat. Hope Hosp. Salford.

BROWN, Steven Leonard The Surgery, Barr Lane, Brinklow, Rugby CV23 0LN Tel: 01788 832994 Fax: 01788 833021 Email: steve@brown.blsc0.warwick-ha.wmids.nhs.uk; Pailton Court, Coventry Road, Pailton, Rugby CV23 0QA Tel: 01788 833119 Email: steve@maincl.demon.co.uk — MB ChB 1980 Birm.; MA Camb. 1980; MRCGP 1984; DRCOG 1984; DCH RCP Lond. 1983. Assoc. Research Fell. Univ. Warwick; Chairm. Warks. Med. Audit Advis. Gp. Socs: Brit. Inst. Musculoskel. Med.

BROWN, Mr Steven Ross 11 StumperloweAve., Sheffield S10 3QN Tel: 0114 230 9520 Email: steve.brown@freeseve.co.uk — MB ChB 1990 Sheff.; BMedSci 1987; FRCS Eng. 1994. Specialist Regist. Gen. Surg. Sheff.

BROWN, Steven Russell 19 Rhosfryn EStreet, Penrhosgarnedd, Bangor LL57 — MB BS 1983 Lond. (St. Thos.)

BROWN, Stuart Andrew 7 Blackwood Avenue, Newton Mearns, Glasgow G77 5JY — MB ChB 1994 Glas.

BROWN, Susan 25 Polstead Road, Oxford OX2 6TW — MB BCh 1975 Wales; MSc Lond. 1982; MRCOG 1980; DCH Eng. 1978; MRCGP 1981.

BROWN, Susan 49 Craigs Road, Edinburgh EH12 8EW — MB ChB 1977 Sheff.

BROWN, Susan Elizabeth 45 Drumpellier Avenue, Cumbernauld, Glasgow G67 4NP — MB ChB 1990 Dundee.

BROWN, Susan Elizabeth Barbicon Health, Austin Friars House, 2-6 Austin Friars, London EC2 2HE Tel: 020 7638 4988; Whitecroft, 1 Godolphin Road, Seer Green, Beaconsfield HP9 2XQ Tel: 01494 680822 — MB ChB 1968 Sheff.; MRCGP 1978; Dip. Occ. Med. RCP Lond. 1997; DObst RCOG 1970; FFA RCS Eng. 1974. (Sheff.) Occupat. Health Phys. Barbican Health Lond. Prev: Princip. GP Amersham; Sen. Regist. (Anaesth.) Radcliffe Infirm. Oxf.

BROWN, Susan Jean 4 Hollymount, Bearsden, Glasgow G61 1DQ — MB ChB 1987 Glas.; MRCPsych 1994; MRCGP 1991. Sen. Regist. Gartnavel Roy. Hosp. Glas.

BROWN, Susan Jean Castle Surgery, 5 Darwin Street, Castle, Northwich CW8 1BU Tel: 01606 74863 Fax: 01606 784847; 72 Willow Lane, Appleton Park, Warrington WA4 5EA — MB ChB 1982 Manch.; MRCGP 1986; DCH RCP Lond. 1987; DRCOG 1984. Prev: Trainee GP Sandbach VTS; CMO Chester; CMO Shrewsbury.

BROWN, Susan Margaret Park Medical Centre, 434 Altrincham Road, Manchester M23 9AB Tel: 0161 998 5538 Fax: 0161 945 8026 — MB ChB Manch. 1974.

BROWN, Susan Mary Mount Farm Surgery, Lawson Place, Bury St Edmunds IP32 7EW Tel: 01284 769643 Fax: 01284 700833; 7 Burrells Orchard, Bury St Edmunds IP33 3TH — MB BS 1982 Lond.; MRCGP 1986; DRCOG 1985.

BROWN, Susan Mary Longlands Child Development Centre, Westbourne Drive, Lancaster LA1 5EE Tel: 01524 34331; 6 The Cotton Shed, Low Mill, Lancaster Road, Caton, Lancaster LA2 9HX Tel: 01524 771559 — MB BChir 1972 Camb.; MB BChir Camb 1972; MA Camb. 1972; FRCP Lond. 1974; DCH Eng. 1973; MScWarwick 1997. (Cambridge & Guys) Cons. Community Paediat. Longlands Child Developm. Centre Lancaster. Prev: Cons. Paediat. Walsgrave Hosp. Coventry; Sen. Regist. (Paediat.) Coventry & Birm.; Regist. (Paediat.) City Hosp. Nottm.

BROWN, Sylvia Mary (retired) Paxmead, Blebo Craigs, Cupar KY15 5UG Tel: 01334 850320 — MRCS Eng. LRCP Lond. 1949.

BROWN, Mr Terence Damian 23 Swaledale Avenue, Rainhill, Prescot L35 4NT Tel: 0151 426 2982 — MB ChB 1985 Liverp.; FRCS Ed. 1991; FFAEM 1996; DA (UK) 1993. Cons. A & E & Intens. Care Whiston Hosp. Merseyside.

BROWN, Terence Reginald Wells Mead, Sweethay Lane, Staplehay, Taunton TA3 7HD — MB BS 1965 Lond.; MRCP Lond. 1968; FRCR 1975; FFR 1973; DMRD Eng. 1971. (St. Geo.) Cons. Radiol. MusGr. Pk. Hosp. Taunton.

BROWN, Thomas (retired) 5 Bowling Green Road, Mount Vernon, Glasgow G32 0SR Tel: 0141 778 3404 — MB ChB 1949 Glas.; DObst RCOG 1954. Prev: SHO (Obst.) St. Helen Hosp. Barnsley.

BROWN, Thomas Albert (retired) Donorrton, 91 Belfast Road, Newtownards BT23 4TS Tel: 01247 812001 — MB BCh BAO 1946 Belf.; MD Belf. 1961; FFA RCSI 1962; DA RCPSI 1952. Prev: Cons. Anaesth. N. Down Hosp. Gp. & S. Armagh Hosp. Gp.

BROWN, Thomas Arthur Scott 11 Thornlea, Hepscott, Morpeth NE61 6NY Tel: 01670 517735 — MB BS 1939 Durh. (Durh.)

BROWN, Mr Thomas Ian Spowart 44A Loughborough Road, Kirkcaldy KY1 3DA — MB ChB 1968 Aberd.; FRCS Ed. 1973; DObst RCOG 1970. Cons. (Orthop. Surg.) Fife Health Bd.

BROWN, Thomas Mathieson St Johns Hospital at Howden, Livingston EH54 6PP Tel: 01506 419666; Tel: 01506 848265 — MB ChB 1979 Ed.; MPhil Ed. 1988, BSc 1976; MRCP (UK) 1983; MRCPsych 1985; FRCP (E) 1998; FRCPsych 1999. (Edinburgh) Cons. (Psychiat.) St. John's Hosp. at Howden Livingston. Prev: Sen. Regist. (Psychiat.) & Trainee (Psychiat.) Rotat. Roy. Edin. Hosp.; Regist. (Med.) Inverclyde Roy. Hosp.

BROWN, Thomas Walton, Col. late RAMC Retd. (retired) 20 Convent Road, Broadstairs CT10 3BE Tel: 01843 862975 — MB ChB 1949 Birm.; MRCS Eng. LRCP Lond. 1949; FRCOG 1980, M 1967, DObst 1950; DTM & H Eng. 1959. Prev: Cons. (O & G) Brit. Milit. Hosp. Münster W. Germany.

BROWN, Tierna Mary The Surgery, Bellyeoman Road, Dunfermline KY12 0AE Tel: 01383 721266 Fax: 01383 625068 — MB BCh BAO 1987 NUI; LRCPSI 1987; MRCGP 1992.

BROWN, Mr Timothy Hudson Morriston Hospital, Swansea SA6 6NL Tel: 01792 703221 Fax: 01792 703224 Email: tim.brown@swansea_tr.wales.nhs.uk; Email: brown320@aol.com — MB 1978 (chb) leeds; MD Leeds 1992; FRCS Eng. 1983. (leeds university) Cons. Gen. Surg. & Gastrointestinal Surg. Morriston Hosp. Swansea; Vis. Cons. Surg., Neath Hosp., Neath. Socs: Brit. Soc. Gastroenterol.; Assn. Surg.; Assn. Upper G.I. Surg. Prev: Sen. Regist. Rotat. (Surg.) N. W.. RHA; Lect. (Surg.) Univ. Louisville, USA; Regist. (Surg.) N. Manch. Gen. Hosp. & Stepping Hill Hosp. Stockport.

BROWN, Timothy Peter La Hausse Hillcrest, Wiullow Brook, Stanton-on-the-Wolds, Nottingham NG12 5BB — BChir 1990 Camb.

BROWN, Timothy Simon University Health Service, University of Edinburgh, Richard Verney Health Centre, 6 Bristo Square, Edinburgh EH8 9AL Tel: 0131 650 2777 Fax: 0131 662 1813 — MB ChB 1978 Manch.; BSc St. And. 1975; MRCGP 1982; AFOM RCP Lond. 1992; DRCOG 1981. GP Edin. Prev: Med. Off. i/c Maprik Hosp. Papua New Guinea.

BROWN, Timothy Stewart Sandford Surgery, 4-6 Tyneham Close, Sandford, Wareham BH20 7BQ Tel: 01929 554493 Fax: 01929 550661; Hopmans Farm House, Lytchett Matravers, Poole BH16 6BJ Tel: 01202 632249 — MRCS Eng. LRCP Lond. 1977; MB BS Lond. 1980; Cert. Family Plann. JCC 1982; DA Eng. 1980. (Roy. Free) GP Princip.; Clin. Asst. (Anaesth.) Roy. Bournemouth Gen. Hosp. Prev: Regist. (Anaesth.) Soton. Gen. Hosp.; Asst. Police Surg.

BROWN, Trevor 5 Laurelvale, Belfast BT4 2EP Tel: 028 9065 4428 — MB BCh BAO 1971 Belf.; DCH RCPS Glas. 1973; DObst RCOG 1974; MRCGP 1976; MRCP 1977; FRCPCH 1997. (Queen's Belfast) Cons. Paediat. Ulster Hosp. Belf. N. Irel.

BROWN, Trevor Shaun Wadsworth House, Wadsworth, Oxenhope, Keighley BD22 9ND Tel: 01535 642261 — MB BS 1966 Lond.; MRCP (UK) 1971; MRCS Eng. LRCP Lond. 1966; FRCR 1976; DMRD Eng. 1975. (Guy's) Cons. Radiol. & Clin. Dir. Directorate of Diag. Imaging Bradford Hosp. Trust; Hon. Lect. (Radiol.) Univ. Leeds. Prev: Sen. Regist. (Med. Radiodiag.) Univ. Hosp. Wales; Regist. (Gen. Med.) ScarBoro. Hosp.; Regist. (Gen. Med.) Maryfield Hosp. & Chest Serv. Dundee.

BROWN, Miss Valerie Anne (rooms), Thornbury Hospital, 312 Fulwood Road, Sheffield S10 3BR Tel: 0114 266 1133; 16 Belgrave Road, Sheffield S10 3LN — MB ChB Liverp. 1970; MD Sheff. 1983; FRCOG 1989, M 1976; DObst 1972; MD 1983 Sheff. (Liverpool) Cons. (O & G) Jessop Wing, Centr. Sheff. Univ.

BROWN, Verity Jane Derby Road Practice, 52 Derby Road, Ipswich IP3 8DN Tel: 01473 728121 Fax: 01473 718810; High Trees, Shaw Valley Road, Marltesham, Woodbridge IP12 4SH Tel: 01394 386510 — MB BS 1978 Lond.; MRCGP 1984; DRCOG 1980.

BROWN, Victoria Alison 8 Jewsbury Way, Thorpe Astley, Leicester LE3 3RR — MB ChB 1998 Leic.; MB ChB Leic 1998.

BROWN, Wallace Francis St Briac, 69 Broad Lane, Coventry CV5 7AH Tel: 024 76 73341 — MB BCh BAO 1959 Belf.; DObst RCOG 1961.

BROWN, Wendy Helen 86 Heavygate Road, Sheffield S10 1PF — MB ChB 1998 Sheff.; MB ChB Sheff 1998.

BROWN, Wilfred Stuart (retired) 50 Rosebarn Lane, Exeter EX4 5DP Tel: 01392 435988 — MRCS Eng. LRCP Lond. 1948.

BROWN, William Aldershot Health Centre, Wellington Avenue, Aldershot GU11 1PA Tel: 01252 24577 Fax: 01252 24577; The Stables, 1 Warrington Mews, St. Peter's Park, Aldershot GU11 3BP Tel: 01252 25192 — MB BS 1960 Lond.

BROWN, William Albert (retired) 2 Parklands Court, Castle Eden, Hartlepool TS27 4TQ Tel: 01429 837295 — MD 1952 Durh.; MB BS 1942; FRCGP 1973, M 1953. Prev: Chairm. N. Eng. Fac. RCGP.

BROWN, William Alexander (retired) 65 Pentland View, Edinburgh EH10 6PY Tel: 0131 445 2966 — MB ChB 1966 Ed.; FFA RCSI 1974; FFA RCS Eng. 1974. Prev: Cons. Anaesth. St John's Hosp. Howden, Livingston.

BROWN, Mr William Christian (retired) 100 Southbrae Drive, Glasgow G13 1UA Tel: 0141 959 4635 — MB ChB 1950 Glas.; FRFPS Glas. 1961; FRCS Glas. 1962. Prev: Cons. ENT Surg. Roy. Hosp. Sick Childr. & Gartnavel Gen. Hosp. Glas.

BROWN, William Glyn (retired) 41 Gorse Bank Road, Hale Barns, Altrincham WA15 0BB Tel: 0161 980 2226 — MB BCh 1953 Wales; BSc Wales 1948; FRCPath 1978, M 1966. Prev: Cons. Path. Ancoats Hosp. Manch. & N. Manch. Gen. Hosp.

BROWN, William Mackenzie Russell The Surgery, Spa Road E., Llandrindod Wells LD1 5ES Tel: 01597 824291 — MB ChB 1988 Manch.; BSc St. And. 1985; MFHom 1996; MRCGP 1992; DGM RCPS Glas. 1992; DRCOG 1991. Prev: Trainee/SHO Dumfries VTS.

BROWN, William Mark 37 Upper Malvern Park, Cairnshill Road, Belfast BT8 6TE — MB BCh BAO 1996 Belf.

BROWN, William Rhind (retired) Flat 1, 11 Whistlefield Court, Canniesburn Rd, Bearsden, Glasgow G61 1PX Tel: 0141 942 2709 — LRCP LRCS Ed. LRFPS Glas. 1946; MFOM RCP Lond. 1980; DIH Eng. 1954; DIH Soc. Apoth. Lond. 1953; DPH Ed. 1953. Prev: Mem. Indep. Tribunal Serv.

BROWN, William Roger Harron Medical Centre, 12 East King Street, Helensburgh G84 7QL Tel: 01436 673366 Fax: 01436 679715; Invergair, 6 Upper Sutherland Crescent, Helensburgh G84 9PQ Tel: 01436 675115 Fax: 01436 671146 Email: rbrown4981@aol.com — MB BCh BAO 1988 Belf.; MRCGP 1993. GP Princip. Helensburgh; Audit Facilitator Argyll & Clyde Dumbarton Dist.; PGEA Postgrad. Course Organiser. Socs: Clin. Audit Assn. Prev: Trainee GP Glas. VTS; Trainee GP Ulster Hosp. Dundonald VTS.

BROWN, Zoe 25 Gosling Close, Hatton, Warrington WA4 5PB — BM BS 1996 Nottm.

BROWN-DOBLHOFF-DIER, Dorothea Kirkgate Surgery, 215 Kirkgate, Wakefield WF1 1JJ Tel: 01924 371331 Fax: 01924 378121; 23 Eastmoor Road, Wakefield WF1 3RZ Tel: 01924 366233 — MD 1985 Vienna; T(GP) 1989.

BROWNBILL, Clare Louise Derwent, Middletown, Welshpool SY21 8DA — MB ChB 1997 Liverp.

BROWNE, Alexander Stephenson, SBStJ 68 Widney Manor Road, Solihull B91 3JQ — MB ChB 1942 Glas.; MFOM RCP Lond. 1978. Prev: Capt. RAMC.

BROWNE, Ann Margaret 6 Cornwall Gardens, Brighton BN1 6RJ Tel: 01273 500725 Email: annjackburron@compuserve.com — MB BS 1957 Lond. (Middlx.) Indep. GP Brighton; Appeals Trib. Socs: BMA. Prev: GP Brighton; BrE. Phys. Roy. Sussex Co. Hosp.; Cas. Off. & Ho. Phys. S. Lond. Hosp. Wom. & Childr. Clapham.

BROWNE, Mr Anthony Omer John 30 Upper Dicconson Street, Wigan WN1 2AG Tel: 01942 42366; Fairhurst Hall, Chorley Road, Parbold, Wigan WN8 7AN Tel: 01257 462312 — MCh NUI 1988; FRCSI 1980; LRCPI 1975LRCSI 1975; DObst RCPI 1977; DCH NUI 1977. Cons. Orthop. Surg. Roy. Albert Edwd. Infirm. Wigan, Leigh Infirm. & The Hip Centre Wrightington Hosp. Prev: Fell. Shoulder & Elbow Surg. Columbia New York, USA; Fell. Mayo Clinic Rochester MN, USA.

BROWNE, Mr Benjamin Harding Glasgow Royal Infirmary, 16 Alexandra Parade, Glasgow G31 2ER Tel: 0141 211 5542 Fax: 0141 211 1220; 23 James Watt Road, Milngavie, Glasgow G62 7JX — MB ChB 1980 Sheff.; PhD Lond. 1971, BSc 1968; FRCS Eng. 1984; FCOphth 1989; DO RCS Eng. 1984. Cons. Ophth. Glas. Roy. Infirm. Prev: Cons. Lanarksh. HB; Sen. Regist. Tennent Inst. Ophth. Glas.; Regist. Oxf. Eye Hosp.

BROWNE, Bernard Dominic Patrick Tranwell Unit, Queen Elizabeth Hospital, Gateshead NE10 9RW Tel: 0191 403 6312 Fax: 0191 403 6221 — MB BCh BAO 1973 Dub.; FRCPI 1995, M 1982; FRCPsych 1994, M 1981; DPM RCPSI 1980; DObst RCPI 1977; DCH NUI 1974. (Dublin) Cons. Psychiat. Qu. Eliz. Hosp. Gateshead; Hon. Clin. Lect. (Psychiat.) Univ. Newc. Socs: Fell. Roy. Soc. Med.; BMA. Prev: Sen. Regist. (Psychiat.) Roy. Vict. Infirm. Newc.

BROWNE, Bradley Lorrimer Department of Anaesthesia, Musgrove Park Hospital, Taunton TA1 5DA Tel: 01823 333444 Fax: 01823 342526 — MB BCh 1982 Witwatersrand; 1991 FRCA Royal College of Anaesthetics; 1979 BSc Witwatersrand. (Univ. Witwatersrand, SA) Cons. (Anaesth. & IC), MusGr. Pk. Hosp., Taunton. Socs: Anaesth. Res. Soc.; Assn. Anaesth.; Intens. Care Soc. Prev: Lect., Univ. of Newc.; Research Regist., Univ. Bristol; Sen. Regist., Univ. Bristol.

BROWNE, Christopher Harold The Avenue Surgery, 14 The Avenue, Warminster BA12 9AA Tel: 01985 846224 Fax: 01985 847059; 47 The Downlands, Warminster BA12 0BD Tel: 01985 215534 — MB BS Lond. 1970; MRCS Eng. LRCP Lond. 1970; MRCP (UK) 1974; DRCOG 1977; AKC. (King's Coll. Hosp.) GP Warminster; Sen. Med. Off. Wincanten Racecourse. Prev: Lect. (Thoracic Med.) Cardiothoracic Inst. Lond.; Regist. (Med.) Whipp's Cross Hosp.; Ho. Phys. King's Coll. Hosp. Lond.

BROWNE, Colin John The Black Country Family Practice, Health Centre, Queens Road, Tipton DY4 8PH Tel: 0121 557 6397 — MB ChB 1967 Glas.

BROWNE, David John 6 Longhill Road, Ovingdean, Brighton BN2 7BE — MB ChB 1940 Liverp.; MRCS Eng. LRCP Lond. 1940; MRCGP 1966. (Liverp.) Socs: BMA. Prev: Clin. Asst. Roy. Infirm. & Eye Infirm. Liverp.; Med. Off. Mill Rd. Infirm. Liverp.

BROWNE, Derek Stanley Browne, Smith, Baynes and Orton, The Surgery, Highwood Road, Brockenhurst SO42 7RY Tel: 01590 622272 Fax: 01590 624009; Merrival Lodge, Rhinefield Road, Brockenhurst SO42 7SW Tel: 01590 622272 Fax: 01590 624009 — MB BS 1967 Lond.; MRCP (UK) 1970; MRCS Eng. LRCP Lond. 1967; FRCGP 1997, M 1977; DObst RCOG 1975; DTM & H Liverp. 1969; FRIPPH 1998. (St. Bart.) Med. Adviser Health Educat. Dept. Soton. & SW Hants. HA (T); Mem. Fac. Community Health 1989. Socs: Fell. Hunt. Soc. & Roy. Soc. Trop. Med. & Hyg.; Wessex Health Promotion Steering Gp.; Nat. Advis. Gp. Age Well. Prev: Sen. Regist. (Med.) Ahmadu Bello Univ. Teachg. Hosp. Zaria, Nigeria; Regist. Med. Profess. Unit St. Bart. Hosp.; SHO (Cardiol.) Brompton Hosp. Lond.

BROWNE, Diane Gustavia Fairfield Centre, Fairfield Grove, Charlton, London SE7 8TX Tel: 020 8858 5738 Fax: 020 305 3005 — MB BS 1985 Newc.; MRCGP 1994; DFFP 1995; DRCOG 1992. GP Charlton. Socs: Med. Defence Union; BMA.

BROWNE, Doreen Rosemary Gladys 7 Crown Reach, 145 Grosvenor Road, London SW1V 3JU Tel: 020 7828 1405 Fax: 020 7828 1405 — MB BS 1959 Lond.; MSc Soc. Anthropol. Lond. 1983; MRCS Eng. LRCP Lond. 1959; FFA RCS Eng. 1966; DObst RCOG 1962; DA (UK) 1962; DCH Eng. 1961. (Roy. Free) Socs: Fell. Roy. Soc. Med.; Intens. Care Soc.; Brit. Med. Acupunct. Soc. Prev: Cons. Anaesth. & Dir. of Intens. Care Unit Roy. Free Hosp. Trust Lond.; Counc. Mem. Roy. Coll. Anaesth.; Sen. Lect. Univ. Benin Teach. Hosp., Nigeria.

BROWNE, Duncan Lindsay Rushleys, Station Road, Aldeby, Beccles NR34 0BY Tel: 01502 677375 Fax: 01502 678273 — MB BS 1994 Lond.; BSc (Hons) Lond. 1991; MRCP 1998. (University College London)

BROWNE, Elizabeth Foster 15 Bisham Gardens, Highgate Village, London N6 6DJ Tel: 0208 340 3838 — BM BCh 1949 Oxf.; MRCPsych 1971; DPM Eng. 1959. (Oxf.) Socs: Profess. Mem. Soc. Analyt. Psychol.; Assoc. Mem. Brit. Psychoanal. Soc. Prev: Cons. Child Psychiat. Child & Family Clinic Watford.

BROWNE, Frederick William Arthur c/o Avoca Unit, Knockbracken Healthcare Park, Saintfield Road, Belfast BT8 8BH Tel: 028 9056 5803 Fax: 028 9056 5480 — MB BCh BAO 1979 Belf.; BSc (Anat.) Belf. 1976; MRCPsych 1984. Cons. Forens. Psychiat. Knockbracken Healthcare Pk. Belf. Prev: Cons. Forens. Psychiat. Purdysburn Hosp. Belf.

BROWNE, Gabriel Patrick Richard 7 Heidegger Crescent, London SW13 8HH — MB BCh BAO 1979 NUI; FFA RCS Eng. 1985; DA (UK) 1983. Cons. Anaesth. Roy. Marsden Hosps. Lond. Prev: Cons. Anaesth. Qu. Mary's Univ. Hosp. Lond.

BROWNE, Gemma Mary 80 Roseburn Street, Downs, Edinburgh EH12 5PL — MB BCh BAO 1988 NUI.

BROWNE, Gerald Robert 67 Burges Road, Southend-on-Sea SS1 3HT — MB ChB 1992 Birm.

BROWNE, Gerard Anthony 24 Sharman Park, Belfast BT9 5HJ — MB BCh BAO 1979 NUI.

BROWNE, Gillian Lorna (retired) Wychbold, Church Road, Tattingstone, Ipswich IP9 2NA Tel: 01473 328543 — MB BCh BAO 1955 Dub.; BA, MB BCh BAO Dub. 1955; FRCOG 1989; MRCOG 1961, DObst 1959. Prev: Clin. Med. Off. Community Health Family Plann. Clinics W. Suff. HA & Allington N+HS Trust Ipswich.

BROWNE, Gordon Robin Walker Glenlyn Medical Centre, 115 Molesey Park Road, East Molesey KT8 0JX Tel: 020 8979 3253 Fax: 020 8941 7914 — MB BS 1966 Lond.; MRCP (UK) 1971. (St. Bart.) Prev: Regist. (Haemat.) St. Bart. Hosp. Lond.; Ho. Phys. (Med.) N. Middlx. Hosp. Lond.; Ho. Phys. & Ho. Surg. Whipps Cross Hosp. Lond.

BROWNE, Joanna Sophie St Bartholomew's Medical Centre, Manzil Way, Cowley Road, Cowley, Oxford OX4 1XB Tel: 01865 242334 Fax: 01865 204018 — BSc Bristol 1972; DPhil Oxf. 1975,

BM BCh 1979; MRCGP 1984; DCH RCP Lond. 1983; DRCOG 1983; Dip. Occ. Med 1996. GP St. Bart. Med. Centre Oxf. Prev: Clin. Asst. (Obst.) John Radcliffe Hosp. Oxf.; Occupat. Health Off. Oxf. Brookes Univ.

BROWNE, John Anthony Priestwell Close, 53 Jenkin Road, Horbury, Wakefield WF4 6DP Tel: 01924 272188 Fax: 01132 381262 — MB ChB 1986 Leeds; MRCGP 1991; DRCOG 1990. Gen. Practitioner, Windsor Ho. Surg., Leeds. Prev: Trainee GP Seascale Cumbria.

BROWNE, John Michael 98 The Drive, Alwoodley, Leeds LS17 7QQ — MB BCh BAO 1979 NUI; LRCPI & LM, LRCSI & LM 1979.

BROWNE, Jonathan Norman Carryduff Surgery, Hillsborough Road, Carryduff, Belfast BT8 8HR Tel: 028 9081 2211 Fax: 028 9081 4785; 177 Belfast Road, Ballynahinch BT24 8UR — MB BCh BAO 1973 Belf.

BROWNE, Keith William National Westminster Bank, 19 Miller Road, Ayr KA7 2AX — MB ChB 1967 Bristol.

BROWNE, Kevin Woodthorpe (retired) Leicester House, North Creake, Fakenham NR21 9JP Tel: 01328 738129 Fax: 01328 730227 Email: kevinbrowne@easynet.co.uk — MB BS 1956 Lond.; MA Oxf. 1946; MSc Lond. 1981; MRCS Eng. LRCP Lond. 1956; MFOM RCP Lond. 1985; MRCGP 1963; DIH Eng. 1980; DObst RCOG 1958; DCH Eng. 1958.

BROWNE, Linda Esther Freemen's Common Health Centre, 161 Welford Road, Leicester LE2 6BF Tel: 0116 255 4776 Fax: 0116 254 9518 — MB ChB 1990 Leic.; Dip Occ Med. Fac. of Occupat. Med. 1998; DFFP 1994. (Univ. Leicester Med. Sch.) GP Partn.

BROWNE, Mark Nicholas Killin Osmaston Road Medical Centre, 212 Osmaston Road, Derby DE23 8JX Tel: 01332 346433 Fax: 01332 345854 — MB ChB 1985 Manch.; MRCGP 1989. Socs: Derby Med. Soc. Prev: Trainee GP Clitheroe; SHO (Paediat.) St. Mary's Hosp. Manch.; SHO (Gen. Med.) Leighton Hosp. Crewe.

BROWNE, Mr Matthew Kennedy, OBE (retired) Nuffield Hospital, Beaconsfield Road, Glasgow G12 0PJ Tel: 0141 334 9441 — MB ChB 1954 Glas.; BSc (Hons.) Glas. 1951. MD (Commend.) 1959; FRCS Glas. 1979; FRCS Ed. 1961. Med. Dir. Monklands & Bellshill Hosps. NHS Trust Airdrie; Cons. Surg. Monklands Dist. Hosp. Airdrie; Clin. Sub-Dean Fac. Med. Univ. Glas. Prev: Cons. Surg. Glas. Roy. Infirm.

BROWNE, Michael James The Health Centre, Bildeston, Ipswich IP7 7EX Tel: 01449 740254; Copt Hall, Bildeston, Ipswich IP7 7BH Tel: 01449 741003 — MB BCh 1975 Wales; MRCGP 1980; DCH Eng. 1978; DRCOG 1977. Prev: Trainee GP Bury St. Edmunds VTS; GP Tutor W. Suff.; Med. Asst. St. Nicholas Hospice Bury St. Edmunds.

BROWNE, Michael John Manor Hospital, Walsall WS2 9PS — MB BS 1976 Lond.; MRCS Eng. LRCP Lond. 1976; FRCOG 1996, M 1982. (Guy's Hosp.) p/t Cons. O & G Manor Hosp. Walsall; Hon. Sen. Lect. (Obst. & Gyn.) Birm. Univ.; Med. Director Walsall Manor Hosp. Trust; Chairm. Regional Obst. & Gynae. Servs. Comm. Socs: Fell. Birm. & Midl. Obst. & Gyn. Soc.; Midl. Fertil. Soc. Prev: Sen. Regist. Leicester Roy. Infirm.; Lect. Char. Cross Hosp. Lond.; Regist. S.meads Hosp. Bristol.

BROWNE, Nicholas Barnaby 159 Green Lanes, Islington, London N16 9DB — MB BS 1996 Lond.; BSc (Hons.) 1993. (University College London) SHO (Gen. Med.) Blackburn Hosp. Prev: Ho. Off. (Surg.) Roy. Bolton Hosp.; SHO (Gen. Med.) Roy. Bolton Hosp.; Ho. Off. (Gen. Med.) Ipswich Hosp.

BROWNE, Nicholas Charles Abbey Medical Centre, 63 Central Avenue, Beeston, Nottingham NG9 2QP Tel: 0115 9255323/9250862 Fax: 0115 922 0522 — BM BS 1985 Nottm.; BMedSci Nottm. 1983; MRCGP 1989; DRCOG 1989. (Nottingham) Clin. Tutor (Gen. Pract.) Univ. Nottm.

BROWNE, Nicholas Derwent Foster 17 Stockwell Park Crescent, London SW9 0DQ Tel: 020 7274 6347 — MB BS 1955 Lond.; MRCPsych 1972; DPM Eng. 1961. (Middlx.) Socs: Brit. Psycho-Analyt. Soc. Prev: Regist. Child Guid. Clinic King's Coll. Hosp.; Ho. Surg. Neurosurg. Unit & Depts. Thoracic & Plastic Surg. Middlx.; Hosp.

BROWNE, Norman Power (retired) Doghouse Farm, Stone St., Petham, Canterbury CT4 5PU — MB BCh BAO 1948 Dub.; MA Dub. 1950, BA 1948. Prev: Surg.-Lt. Med. RN.

BROWNE, Peter Harold (retired) 64 Widmore Road, Bromley BR1 3BD Tel: 0208 460 7022 — MB BS Lond. 1954; DObst RCOG 1956. Prev: GP Bromley, Kent.

BROWNE, Peter Percival Maxwell, Surg. Cdr. RN Retd. 40 Castle Road, Cowes PO31 7QZ — MRCS Eng. LRCP Lond. 1948; MFCM 1973; DPH Lond. 1953. (Middlx.) Med. Off. Home Office Lond. Socs: BA. Prev: Ho. Phys. Profess. Med. Unit Middlx. Hosp. Isleworth; Med. Off. RAF; Med. Off. RN.

BROWNE, Richard John 16 Moylena Road, Antrim BT41 4PA — MB BCh BAO 1994 Belf.

BROWNE, Mr Richard John Stewart The Hampshire Clinic, Basingstoke RG24 7AL Tel: 01256 57111 Fax: 01256 840758; The Lynches, Kingsclere, Newbury RG20 5PS Tel: 01635 298406 — MB BS 1967 Lond.; FRCS Eng. 1973; FRCS Ed. 1973; MRCS Eng. LRCP Lond. 1967. (Univ. Coll. Hosp.) Cons. Orthop. Surg. Basingstoke Dist. Hosp. & Lord Mayor Treloar Hosp. Alton; Hon. Cons. Orthop. Surg. Lord Mayor Treloar Coll. & Haemophilia Centre Alton; Med. Director, N. Hants. Hosp., NHS Trust. Prev: Sen. Regist. (Orthop.) Univ. Coll. Hosp. Lond. & W.m. Hosp. Lond.; Regist. Roy. Nat. Orthop. Hosp. Lond.

BROWNE, Rita Elizabeth Chelsea and Westminster Hospital, 369 Fulham Road, Chelsea, London SW10 9NH; 45 Woodlands Road, Edmonton, London N9 8RP — MB BS 1994 Newc.; MRCP (UK) 1998. Specialist Regist. (Genitourin. And HIV Med.). Socs: MPS; MSSVD; BHIVA. Prev: SHO (Med.) Sunderland Gen. Hosp.; Specialist Regist. (Gen. Med. & COTE) Sunderland Roy. Hosp.

BROWNE, Robert David The Health Centre, Campfield Road, Shoeburyness, Southend-on-Sea SS3 9BX Tel: 01702 577701 Fax: 01702 577726; 67 Burges Road, Thorpe Bay, Southend-on-Sea SS1 3HT Tel: 01702 585811 — MB BCh BAO 1967 Dub.; MA Dub. 1965; Cert. Family Plann. JCC 1992. Socs: BMA.

BROWNE, Robert Emmet 5 Ennerdale Close, Oadby, Leicester LE2 4TN — MB ChB 1993 Leic.

BROWNE, Ronald Vincent 46 Priory Avenue, Blackrock, County Dublin, Republic of Ireland; Glencoe, Camp De Moulins, St Martins, Guernsey GY4 6DZ — LRCPI & LM, LRSCI & LM 1976; LRCPI & LM, LRCSI & LM 1976; MRCPsych 1984; MICGP 1984; DCH RCPSI Lond. 1980; Cert. Family Plann. 1980; DObst RCPI 1979. Cons. Psychiat. Castel Hosp. Guernsey. Prev: Cons. Psychiat. Bryn-y-Neuadd Hosp. Llanfairfechan & Coed Du Hosp. Clwyd.

BROWNE, Samuel Ernest Dartford East Health Centre, Pilgrims Way, Dartford DA1 1QY Tel: 01322 74211; 17 The Close, Wilmington, Dartford DA2 7ES Tel: 01322 225302 — MB BCh BAO 1946 Belf. (Belf.)

BROWNE, Sarah Elizabeth Meredith Royal Gwent Hospital, Cardiff Road, Newport NP9 4SZ Tel: 01633 238323 — MB BS 1978 Lond.; MRCP (UK) 1982. (St. Bart.) Cons. Phys. Gwent Healthcare NHS Trust.

BROWNE, Stephen Denis The Surgery, 1536 Pershore Road, Stirchley, Birmingham B30 2NW Tel: 0121 458 1031 Fax: 0121 459 1182; 178 Pineapple Road, Stirchley, Birmingham B30 2TY Tel: 0121 444 4820 — MB ChB 1971 Birm.; MB ChB Birm. 1974; BSc (Hons., Med. Biochem.) Birm. 1971; MRCGP 1980; DRCOG 1976. (Birm.) Socs: BMA. Prev: Trainee GP E. Birm. VTS; Ho. Phys. Worcester Roy. Infirm. (Ronkswood Br.); Ho. Surg. Selly Oak Hosp. Birm.

BROWNE, Stephen Robert Southernhay House Surgery, 30 Barnfield Road, Exeter EX1 1RX — MB ChB 1981 Birm.; T(GP) 1991. GP Exeter.

BROWNE, Thomas Derek, AE 73 Dukes Wood Drive, Gerrards Cross SL9 7LQ Tel: 01753 882572 Email: doctderek@aol.com — MB BCh BAO Belf. 1950; FFOM RCP Lond. 1986, MFOM 1978; FFOM RCPI 1983, MFOM 1978; T(OM) 1991; Specialist Accredit. Occupat. Med. JCHMT 1978; DIH Eng. 1961; DPH Lond. 1960. (Qu. Univ. Belf.) Cons. Occupat. Phys. Bucks.; JP. Socs: Fell. Roy. Soc. Med.; Brit. Toxicol. Soc. Prev: Div. Med. Off. ICI Paints Div.; Squadron Ldr. RAF Med. Br.; Tutor (Med.) Qu. Univ. Belf.

BROWNE, Mr Thomas Francis 1 Clos George Morgan, Morriston, Swansea SA6 6LZ — MB BCh BAO 1982 NUI; FRCS Eng. 1989; LRCPI & LM LRCSI & LM 1982.

BROWNELL, Alison Isabel Department of Haematology, Old Church Hospital, Romford RM7 0BE; 6 Elrington Road, London E8 3BJ — MB ChB 1976 Aberd.; FRCP Lond. 1996; FRCPath 1996, M 1986. Cons. Haemat. OldCh. Hosp. Romford.

BROWNELL, Lisa Wendy 14 Barleycroft, Hadfield, Glossop SK13 2EX Email: lisa.brownell@virgin.net — MB ChB 1994 Birm.; BSc (Hons.) Pharmacol. Birm. 1991; MRCPsych 1998. (University of Birmingham) Specialist Regist. (Psychiat.), W. Midl., Rotat. Prev: SHO Rotat. (Psychiat.) Birm. Train. Scheme; Ho. Off. (Surg.) N. Staffs. Roy. Infirm.; Ho. Off. (Med./Cardiol.) Univ. Hosp. Birm.

BROWNFIELD, Mark Owen Newton The New Surgery, The Nap, Kings Langley WD4 8ET Tel: 01923 261035 Fax: 01923 269629; 123 Horsecroft Road, Hemel Hempstead HP1 1PX Tel: 01442 399588 — MB BS 1988 Lond.; MRCGP 1992; DRCOG 1993. (Char. Cross & Westm. Med. Sch.) Bd. Mem. Dacorum Prim. Care Gp.; Clin. Asst. (A & E) Watford Gen. Hosp. Socs: Med. Protec. Soc.; BMA; RCGP. Prev: SHO (Psychiat.) Wycombe Gen. Hosp.; SHO (Paediat.) Amersham Gen. Hosp.; SHO (O & G & A & E) Wycombe Gen. Hosp.

BROWNFIELD, Richard Newton (retired) Chichester Occupational Health Service, St. Richard's Hospital, Spitalfield Lane, Chichester PO19 4SE Tel: (01243) 788122 Fax: (01243) 533994 — MB BS Lond. 1961; MFOM RCP Lond. 1992, A 1986; MRCGP 1970; DObst RCOG 1963. Cons. Occupat. Phys. Portsmouth Hosps. NHS Trust, Roy. W. Sussex NHS Trust. Prev: GP Portsmouth.

BROWNHILL, Adam James 311 Oxford Road, Macclesfield SK11 8JZ — MB BS 1998 Lond.; MB BS Lond 1998.

BROWNHILL, Jennifer Edna Skene Medical Group, Westhill Drive, Westhill AB32 6FY Tel: 01224 742213 Fax: 01224 744664; 28 Westhill Heights, Westhill AB32 6RY — MB ChB 1985 Aberd.; MRCGP 1989; DRCOG 1988.

BROWNIE, Elaine Campbell 5 Mains Circle, Westhill, Westhill AB32 6HD — MB ChB 1981 Aberd.; MRCGP 1987; DRCOG 1985.

BROWNING, Andrew Corbett 30 Fontwell Gardens, Horton Heath, Eastleigh SO50 7NL Tel: 01703 695582 — BM 1994 Soton.; BM (Hons.) Soton. 1994; BSc (Hons.) Soton. 1993; FRCophth 1998. (Med. Sch. Soton.) Specialist Regist. (Ophth.) Qu.s Med. Centre, Nottm. Socs: Fell. Inst. Biomed. Sci. Prev: SHO (Ophth.) Soton. Eye Unit; SHO (Neurosurg.) Soton. Gen. Hosp.

BROWNING, Andrew James Francis New Cross Hospital, Wolverhampton WV10 0QP Tel: 01902 307999 Fax: 01902 643030; The Old House, Ash Hill, Compton, Wolverhampton WV3 9DR Tel: 01902 420000 Fax: 01902 772943 Email: mr.browing@rwh-Tr.hns.uk — MB ChB 1972 Birm.; BSc (Hons.) (Physiol.) Birm. 1969, MD 1986; FRCOG 1991, M 1979; DObst RCOG 1976; DCH Eng. 1974. (Birm.) Cons. O & G New Cross Hosp. Wolverhampton. Socs: Fell. Roy. Soc. Med.; BMA. Prev: Sen. Regist. (Obst. & Gyn) W. Midl. RHA; Research Regist. Dept. Clin. Endocrinol. Birm. & Midl. Hosp. Wom.

BROWNING, Benjamin Sacheverel 13 Springfield, Clifford, Wetherby LS23 6HQ — BM BS 1992 Nottm.

BROWNING, Carol Angela Carlton Gardens Surgery, 27 Carlton Gardens, Leeds LS7 1JL Tel: 0113 295 2678 Fax: 0113 295 2679; 3a Stainbeck Lane, Leeds LS7 3SL Tel: 01132 952666 Fax: 01132 952667 — MB ChB 1966 St. And. (St. And.)

BROWNING, Christopher John Addenbrookes Hospital, Cambridge CB2 2QQ Tel: 01223 245151; 37 Hills Avenue, Cambridge CB1 7UY Tel: 01223512900 Email: cjb23@cam.ac.uk — MB BChir 1990 Camb.; MA Oxf. 1988. Regist. (Clin. Oncol.) Addenbrooke's Hosp. Camb. Socs: BMA (Nat. Jun. Doctors Comm.).

BROWNING, David John Christopher 60 Heath Farm Road, Stourbridge DY8 3BY — MB ChB 1983 Birm.; FFA RCS Eng. 1988; DA (UK) 1986. Regist. (Anaesth.) Qu. Eliz. Hosp. Birm. Prev: SHO (A & E) Selly Oak Hosp. Birm.; SHO (Anaesth.) Russells Hall Hosp. Dudley; Ho. Off. (Surg.) Gen. Hosp. Birm.

BROWNING, Mr Frank Sacheverel Chips The Leeds Nuffield Hospital, 2 Leighton Street, Leeds LS1 3BR Tel: 0113 3882000; Low Farm, High St, Clifford, Wetherby LS23 6HJ Tel: 01937 845729 Fax: 01937 845271 Email: chipmol@totalise.co.uk — MB ChB St. And. 1966; FRCS Eng. 1971. (St. And.) Socs: Brit. Assn. Plastic Surg.; Brit. Assn. Aesthetic Plastic Surgs.; Med. Equestrian Assn. Prev: Sen. Regist. (Plastic Surg.) St. Jas. Hosp. Leeds & St. Luke's Hosp. Bradford; Research Fell. (Microsurg.) St. Vincent's Hosp. Melbourne.; Cons. Plastic Surg., St. Jas. Hosp. & Gen. Infirm., 1980-1999.

BROWNING, Mr Gavin George Paterson 23 Braehead Avenue, Edinburgh EH4 6QN Tel: 0131 339 6514 — MB ChB 1971 St. And.; FRCS Ed. 1976. Socs: Fell. Roy. Soc. Med. (Mem. Sect. Coloproctol.); St. Mark's Assn. Prev: Lect. (Hon. Sen. Regist.) Univ. Coll. Lond.; Research Fell. St. Mark's Hosp. Lond.; Hosps.; Regist. (Surg.) Edin. Teach. Hosp. Off. St. Mark's Hosp. Lond.

BROWNING, Professor George Gordon Department of Otolaryngology & Head and Neck Surgery, Glasgow Royal Infirmary, University NHS Trust, Glasgow G31 2ER Tel: 0141 211 4000 Fax: 0141 211 4896; 19 Kew Terrace, Glasgow G12 0TE Tel: 0141 334 6205 — MB ChB 1964 Glas.; MD Glas. 1974; FRCS Ed. 1970; FRCS Glas. 1976. Prof. Otorhinolaryng. Univ. Glas.; Cons. Otol. Scott. Sect., MRC Instit. Hearing Research Glas. Roy. Infirm. Univ NHS Trust; Sen. Clin. Adviser MRC Instit. Hearing Research Nottm.; Hon. Cons. Otolaryngol. Dept. Otolaryngol. & Head & Neck Surg., Glas. Roy. Infirm. Socs: Brit. Soc. Acad.s Pres.; Otorhinolaryngol. Research Soc. (Ex-Pres.); Roy. Soc. Med. Sect. Otol. Pres. Prev: Sen. Regist. (Otorhinolaryng.) Gtr. Glas. HB; Regist. (Otorhinolaryng.) Roy. Infirm. Glas.; Regist. (Gen. Surg.) W.. Infirm. Glas.

BROWNING, Huw 125 Clasemont Road, Morriston, Swansea SA6 6AH — MB BCh 1985 Wales.

BROWNING, Mr James Jonathan 6.05 Kelvin Campus, West of Scotland Science Park, Glasgow G20 0SP Tel: 0141 945 4653 Email: jamesbrowning@gyneideas.com; 12 Sherbrooke Gardens, Glasgow G41 4HU Tel: 0141 427 1450 — MB ChB 1980 Manch.; MD Bristol 1993; FRCS Ed. 1984; MFFP 1995; T(OG) 1992; FRCOG 2000. Managing Director, Gyne Ideas Ltd. Prev: Dir. Research & Developm. Ethicon Ltd.; Cons. & Sen. Lect. (O & G) St. Michael's Hosp. Bristol.; Dir. New Businesses Ethicon Ltd.

BROWNING, James Weir (retired) Sunnyside, Aveley, Purfleet, Grays Tel: 01708 864880 — MB ChB 1952 Glas.; DObst RCOG 1954. Assoc. Fac. Occupat. Med. RCP Lond. Prev: Ho. Off. Hairmyres Hosp. E. Kilbride, & Lennox Castle Matern. Hosp. Lennoxtown.

BROWNING, Janet Paton Parkhead Health Centre, 101 Salamanca Street, Glasgow G31 5BA Tel: 0141 531 9070 Fax: 0141 531 9020 — MB ChB 1960 Glas.; BSc (Hons.) Glas. 1957. (Glas.) GP Pk.head Health Centre Glas. Prev: Regist. Stobhill Hosp. Glas. & Asst. Lect. in Mat. Med. Univ. Glas.; Jun. Ho. Off. Stobhill Hosp. Glas. & S. Gen. Hosp. Glas.

BROWNING, Jennifer Gordon 19 Kew Terrace, Glasgow G12 0TE Tel: 0141 334 6205 Email: jenbrowning@hotmail.com — MB ChB 1997 Ed. (Edinburgh)

BROWNING, John Davidson Lanarkshire Acute Hospitals NHS Trust, Trust Office, Bellshill Maternity Hospital, North Road, Bellshill ML4 3JN Tel: 01698 747292; Chapelgill Cottage, Broughton, Biggar ML12 6JA — MB ChB 1971 Glas.; FRCP Glas. 1989; MRCP (UK) 1974; FRCPath 1989, M 1977. Med. Dir., Lanarksh. Acute Hosps. NHS Trust.

BROWNING, June Anne Chapelgill Cottage, Broughton, Biggar ML12 6JA Tel: 0189 94 361 — MB ChB 1971 Glas.; DCCH RCP Ed. 1988.

BROWNING, Louise Elizabeth 61 Warner Road, London SE5 9NE — MB BS 1997 Lond.

BROWNING, Margaret Elisabeth 34 Thirsk Road, Northallerton DL6 1PH Tel: 01609 776025 & profess. 779911 — MB ChB 1971 Glas.; DObst RCOG 1973. SCMO N.allerton Health Dist. N. Yorks. Prev: Med. Off. Ayrsh. & Arran HB.

BROWNING, Mary Rossiter Cardiff Royal Infirmary, Newport Road, Cardiff CF24 0SZ; Email: mary.browning@virgin.net — MB BS 1983 Lond.; BSc Lond. 1981; DFFP 1994; Dip. GU Med. Soc. Apoth Lond. 1994; DRCOG 1990; DCH Otago 1987; MRCP Ireland 1997. (Royal Free Hospital School of Medicine) Specialist Regist. (Genitourin. Med.) Cardiff Roy. Infirm. Socs: BMA; Soc. Study VD; AGUM. Prev: SHO (Gen. Med.) P.ss of Wales Bridgend; Regist. (Genitourin. Med.) Cardiff Roy. Infirm.; Regist. (Gen. Pract.) Cardiff.

BROWNING, Michael 32 Eric Street, London E3 4TQ — MB BS 1997 Lond.

BROWNING, Michael James 33 Chester Road, London E11 2JR — MB BS 1988 Lond.; FRCA 1995.

BROWNING, Michael John University of Leicester, Department of Microbiology & Immunology, PO Box 138, Medical Sciences Building, University Road, Leicester LE1 9HN; Department of Immunology, Leicester Royal Infirmary, Leicester LE1 5WW — BM BCh 1981 Oxf.; PhD Glas. 1987, BSc 1978; MRCPath 1994. (Glasgow/Oxford) Sen. Lect. (Immunol.) Univ. Leicester; Hon. Cons. Immunol. Leicester Roy. Infirm. Trust. Socs: MRCPath.; Brit. Soc. Immunol.; Brit. Soc. Histocompatibility & Immunogen.

BROWNING, Neil McAulay 34 Thirsk Road, Northallerton DL6 1PH Tel: 01609 776025 & profess 0609 779911 — MB ChB 1971 Glas.; FRCP Glas. 1988; MRCP (UK) 1974; MRCPath 1979. (Glas.) Cons. Haemat. Friarage Hosp. N.allerton. Prev: Sen. Regist. (Haemat.) W.. Infirm. Glas.; Regist. (Haemat.) Ballochmyle Hosp. Mauchline; Regist. Med. Unit Kilmarnock Infirm.

BROWNING, Richard Charles Pfizer Ltd., Ramsgate Road, Sandwich CT13 9NJ Tel: 01304 645191 Fax: 01304 653806 Email: brownr2@pfizer.com; Hatchetts, Nonington, Dover CT15 4JU Tel: 01304 842527 — MB BS 1974 Newc.; FFPM RCP (UK) 1993, M 1989; DPharm Med (UK) 1981; DRCOG 1978. (Newcastle upon Tyne) Dir. Strategic Plann. Pfizer Ltd.; Vice-Pres. Fac. Pharmaceut. Med. Socs: Fell. Roy. Soc. Med.; BMA; Amer. Soc. Clin. Pharmcol. Prev: Gen. Manager Pfizer Middle E. & Centr. Afr.; Dir. Business Developm. Pfizer, New York; Vice Pres. Med. Dir. Pfizer Afr./Mid. E.

BROWNING, Robert (retired) 20 Haggswood Avenue, Glasgow G41 4RE Tel: 0141 427 3334 — MB ChB Glas. 1937.

BROWNING, Sally Martin Erith Centre, Park Crescent, Erith DA8 3GE — MB ChB 1977 Glas.; MRCPsych. 1982. Cons. Psychiat. Oxleans NHS Trust; Hon. Lect. United Med. & Dent. Schs. Guy's & St. Thos. Lond. Prev: Lect. (Ment. Health) Univ. Bristol.

BROWNING, Samantha Jane 13 Springfield, Clifford, Wetherby LS23 6HQ — BM BS 1993 Nottm.

BROWNING, Mr Simon Thomas Department of ENT, Singleton Hospital, Swansea SA1 8QA Tel: 01792 205666 Ext: 5567 Email: roro@dircon.co.uk — MB BCh 1987 Wales; FRCS Ed. 1994; M.Phil 1997; FRCS 1998. (univ.Wales) Cons. Otoaryngologist; Sen. Clin. Tutor, Swansea Clin. Sch. Socs: Mem. Brit. Assn. Otolaryngol.; BMA; Clin. Anatomists. Prev: SHO (A & E) Bristol Roy. Infirm.; SHO (ENT) S.mead Hosp. Bristol; Demonst. (Anat.) Bristol Univ.

BROWNJOHN, Aleck Michael The General Infirmary, Great George St., Leeds LS1 3EX Tel: 0113 392 2541 Fax: 0113 392 5074 Email: aleckb@ulth.northg.nhs.uk; The Beeches, Weetwood Park Drive, Leeds LS16 5AD Tel: 0113 275 6219 — MB BS 1970 Lond.; MB BS (Hons.) Lond. 1970; FRCP Lond. 1986; MRCP (UK) 1972; MRCS Eng. LRCP Lond. 1970. (Middlx.) Cons. Phys. Gen. Infirm Leeds; Sen. Lect. (Med.) Univ. Leeds. Socs: Renal Assn. & Med. Research Soc. Prev: Sen. Regist. Lond. Hosp.; Lect. (Med.) Univ. Lond. Hosp. Med. Coll.

BROWNLEADER, Simon Mark 69 Salmon Street, London NW9 8PR — MB BS 1992 Lond.

BROWNLEE, Keith Graham 1 West End Close, Horsforth, Leeds LS18 5JN — MB ChB 1984 Leeds; MB ChB Leeds l984; MRCP (UK) 1988.

BROWNLEE, Mandy Jane 17 Whinchat Tail, Guisborough TS14 8PW — MB ChB 1989 Leeds; BSc (Hons.) Anat. Leeds 1986.

BROWNLEE, Michael Raymond John Mackay Clinic, Bolton General Hospital, Minerva Road, Bolton BL4 0JR Tel: 01204 390390 — MB ChB 1982 Manch.; MRCPsych 1987. Cons. Psychiat. Bolton HA. Prev: Sen. Regist. (Psychiat.) Manch. Roy. Infirm.; Regist. (Psychiat.) Prestwich Hosp. Salford.

BROWNLEE, Neil Hutton 6 Dundas Street West, Saltburn-by-the-Sea TS12 1BL Tel: 01287 622207; 17 Whinchat Tail, Guisborough TS14 8PW — MB ChB 1989 Leeds; MRCGP 1993; DRCOG 1992.

BROWNLEE, Mr Thomas James (retired) Claremont, Manor House Lane, Higher Heath, Whitchurch SY13 2HN — MB ChB 1937 Ed.; FRCS Ed. 1939. Prev: Off. i/c Surgic. Div. RAMC.

BROWNLEE, William Cochrane King Edward VII Hospital, Midhurst GU29 0BL Tel: 01730 812341 Fax: 01730 811154; The Wheel House, Chichester Road, Midhurst GU29 9QE Tel: 01730 814223 Email: 100662.255@compuserve.com — MB BChir 1973 Camb.; MSc Camb. 1973; MRCP (UK) 1974; FRCP 1997. Cons. Cardiol. & Phys. King Edwd. VII Hosp. Midhurst. Prev: Sen. Regist. (Med.) Manch. Roy. Infirm.; Regist. (Med.) Bristol Roy. Hosp. & Roy. Devon. & Exeter Hosp. Wonford.

BROWNLEES, William (retired) 60 Alder Park, Antrim BT41 1JU Tel: 01849 466973 — MB BCh BAO 1953 Dub. Prev: Assoc. Specialist Braid Valley Hosp. Ballymena.

BROWNLIE, Graham St John Department of Anaesthetics, Derriford Hospital, Plymouth PL6 8DH Tel: 01752 792692; Overleat, Lake Lane, Dousland, Yelverton PL20 6LZ — MB ChB 1981 Brist.; FFA RCS Lond. 1986. Cons. Anaesth. Plymouth HA. Prev: Sen. Regist. (Anaesth.) SW Region.

BROWNLIE, Hilary Anne Denmead Health Centre, Hambledon Road, Denmead, Waterlooville PO7 6NR Tel: 023 9225 7112 Fax: 023 9225 7113 — MB BS 1986 Lond.; MRCGP 1990; DRCOG 1988. (Guy's Hosp. Med. Sch.) p/t GP Denmead Health Centre Denmead. Prev: Trainee GP Portsmouth & S. E. HA.

BROWNLIE, Mary Forbes (retired) 77 Bassett Green Close, Southampton SO16 3QX Tel: 01703 769609 — MB ChB Glas. 1937; DPH Liverp. 1947. Prev: Cons. Chest Phys. Soton. Centr. Chest Clinic.

BROWNLIE, Robert Valleyfield Health Centre, Chapel Street, High Valleyfield, Dunfermline KY12 8SJ Tel: 01383 880511 Fax: 01383 881848; Pebble Cottage, 12 Main St, Newmills, Dunfermline KY12 8SS — MB ChB 1979 Ed. Adj. Med. Off. Benefits Agency Med. Servs; Mem. Med. Disabil. Appeal Tribunal.

BROWNLIE, Sheila Margaret McNicol 40 Westwood Road, Lytham St Annes FY8 5NX Tel: 01253 734453 — MB ChB 1955 Glas.; DObst RCOG 1957; FFA RCS Eng. 1962; DA Eng. 1958.

BROWNLOW, Andrew Howard 10 Boscombe Cliff Road, Bournemouth BH5 1JL — MB BS 1991 Lond.

BROWNLOW, Henry Colin 54 Stratford Street, Iffley Fields, Oxford OX4 1SW — MB ChB 1990 Manch.; BSc (Hons.) Manch. 1987; FRCS Eng. 1995. Clin. Lect. (Orthop.) Oxf.

BROWNRIDGE, Charles Edward (retired) 42A Goucester Road, Almondsbury, Bristol BS32 4HA Tel: 01454 617550 Email: cebrownridge@aol.com — MRCS Eng. LRCP Lond. 1939. Prev: Surg. Lt.-Cdr. RNVR.

BROWNRIDGE, David Stanley Ombersley Medical Centre, Hastings House, Kidderminster Road, Ombersley, Droitwich WR9 0EL Tel: 01905 620202 Fax: 01905 621188; Vern House, Worcester Road, Hartlebury, Kidderminster DY11 7XQ — MB BS 1969 Lond.; MRCS Eng. LRCP Lond. 1969; DObst RCOG 1973; DCH Eng. 1971. (Char. Cross) Socs: BMA (Hon. Sec. Worcs. Div.). Prev: SHO (Paediat.) Good Hope Hosp. Sutton Coldfield; Ho. Phys. Manor Hosp. Walsall; Ho. Surg. W. Lond. Hosp.

BROWNRIGG, Edward Kingsmill (retired) Church Cottage, Ellisfield, Basingstoke RG25 2QR Tel: 01256 381221 — MB BS 1946 Lond.; MRCS Eng. LRCP Lond. 1937; FFA RCS Eng. 1954; DA Eng. 1947. Prev: Cons. Anaesth. Basingstoke & Dist., & Lord Mayor Treloar Orthop. Hosp.

BROWNRIGG, Melita Rose The Health Centre, Melbourn Street, Royston SG8 7BS Tel: 01763 242981 Fax: 01763 249197; Shingay Hill, Croydon, Royston SG8 0DN — MSc Sussex 1973; BA Manch. 1972; MB Camb. 1983, BChir 1982; MRCGP 1990; DRCOG 1989; DCH RCP Lond. 1987. GP Princip. Royston Health Centre; GP Trainer. Prev: Trainee GP St. Ives Camb. VTS; SHO Rotat. (Med.) Addenbrooke's Hosp. Camb.

BROWNRIGG-GLEESON, Joseph Abraham James Nuffield Health Centre, Witney, Oxford OX28 6JQ Tel: 01865 3641; Orchard House, Minster Lovell, Oxford Tel: 0199 387254 — LRCPI & LM, LRSCI & LM 1947; LRCPI & LM, LRCSI & LM 1947. (RCSI)

BROWNSDON, Christopher Edward The Surgery, 13 Camberwell Green, London SE5 7AF Tel: 020 7703 3788 — MRCS Eng. LRCP Lond. 1971; MA, BM BCh Oxf. 1971; DObst RCOG 1973. Police Surg. No. 1 Dist. Metrop. Police; Liveryman, Worshipful Soc. Apoth. Lond.

BROWNSDON, Diana Jane Nobles Hospital, Westmoreland Road, Douglas IM1 4QA Tel: 01624 642642; Hebron, Grove Mount, Ramsey IM8 3HE Tel: 01624 813997 — MB ChB 1972 Liverp.; Cert. FPA 1974. Clin. Asst. (Gyn.) Noble's Hosp. Douglas I of Man. Socs: BMA (Overseas Div.); MSSVD; BSCPP. Prev: SHO (Venereol.) Liverp. Roy. Infirm.

BROWNSDON, John Kirkpatrick Ramsey Group Practice Centre, Grove Mount South, Ramsey IM8 3EY Tel: 01624 813881 Fax: 01624 811921; Hebron, Grove Mount, Ramsey IM8 Tel: 01624 813997 — MB ChB 1969 Liverp.; DObst RCOG 1974. Med. Off. RNLI Ramsey; Chairm. Exec. Comm. I.of Man Med. Soc. Socs: I. of Man Med. Soc. Prev: SHO (Orthop.) Warrington Infirm. & Roy. S.. Hosp. Liverp.; Ho. Off. (O & G) BRd.green Hosp. Liverp.

BROWNSETT, Paula Marie 'Bethany', 38 Burway Meadow, Alrewas, Burton-on-Trent DE13 7EB — MB BS 1991 Lond.; MRC Psych 1998. (Lond. Hosp. Med. Coll.) Specialist Regist. (Psychiat) W. Midl. Rotat. Prev: Regist. Rotat. (Psychiat.) St. Mary's Hosp. Lond.; SHO Rotat. (Psychiat.) St. Mary's Hosp. Lond.

BROWNSON, Anthony Jonathan The Surgery, Marsh Lane, Misterton, Doncaster DN10 4DL Tel: 01427 890206 Fax: 01427 891311 — MB ChB 1984 Sheff.; MRCGP 1989.

BROWNSON, Gemma Maria The Pump House, Soss Lane, Misterton, Doncaster DN10 4DQ — MB ChB 1984 Sheff.; MRCGP 1988.

BROWNSON, Mr Peter Department of Trauma & Orthopaedics, University Hospital Aintree, Liverpool L9 7AL Tel: 0151 529 3349 Fax: 0151 529 2549; Tel: 0151 327 4248 Email: brownsonp@aol.com — MB ChB 1986 Liverp.; DM Nottm. 1994; FRCS Ed. 1991; FRCS (Orth.) Ed. 1997. Cons. Orthop. Surg. Univ. Hosp. Aintree. Socs: B.O.R.S.; B.E.S.S.

BROWNSON, Sara Elizabeth 8 Redvers Road, Warlingham CR6 9HN — MB BS 1983 Lond.

BROWSE, Mr Dominic James Email: dominic.browse@goodhot.wmids.nhs.uk; 3 Holly Lane, Sutton Coldfield B75 5AT Tel: 0121 323 3499 — MB BS 1985 Lond.; MS Lond. 1995; FRCS Eng. 1989; FRCS (Gen Surg) 1998. (St. Barts, London) Cons. Surg, GI/Laporoscopic Surg., Good Hope Hosp.; Sen. Regist. (Surg.) King's Coll. Hosp. Lond. Prev: Sen. Reg. S.E. Thames.

BROWSE, Professor Sir Norman Leslie Corbet House, Butes Lane, Alderney GY9 3UW Tel: 01481 823716 Fax: 01481 824677 Email: norman.browse@virgin.net — MB BS Lond. 1955; Hon. FCM (SA) 1993; Hon. F.Amer.Coll.Surg. 1995; MD Bristol 1961; FRCP Lond. 1993; FRCS Eng. 1959; Hon. FRCS Ed. 1995; Hon. FACS 1995; Hon. FRCSI 1994; Hon. FRCP & S 1994; Hon. FRACS 1993. (St. Bart.) Prof.Surg. Emerit. UMDS Guy's & St. Thos. Hosp.; Hon. Cons. Surg. St. Thos. Hosp. Lond. Socs: (Ex-Pres.) RCS Eng.; (Ex-Pres.) Europ. Soc. Cardiovasc. Surg.; (Ex-Pres.) Soc. Vasc. Surg. UK & Irel. Prev: Asst. Dir. Dept. Surg., Prof. Vasc. Surg. St. Thos. Hosp. Lond.; Lect. (Surg.) W.m. Hosp. Lond.; Harkness Fell. & Research Asst. Mayo Clinic Rochester, Minn., USA.

BROWSE, Sheila Carol 49 Sunnybank Close, Aldridge, Walsall WS9 0YR — MB BS 1988 Lond.; MRCGP 1992; DRCOG 1993; DCH RCP Lond. 1990.

BROX, Georg Alexander HB-Path Unlimited, 39 Bywater House, Harlinger Street, London SE18 5SP Email: jangeorg@yahoo.com — State Exam Med 1976 Mainz. (Univ. Mainz) Cons. Histopath. & Laborat. Dir.-Manager Indep. Sector Histopath. Laborat. Socs: Path. Soc.; Assn. Clin. Paths.; Brit. Soc. Clin. Cytol. Prev: Cons. Path. Sch. Med. Frankfurt Univ.

BROXTON, Jacqueline Solveig St Andrews Medical Centre, 30 Russell Street, Eccles, Manchester M30 0NU Tel: 0161 707 5500; 241 Heywood Old Road, Rhodes, Middleton, Manchester M24 4QR — MB BS 1966 Durh.

BRUCE, Alex (retired) The Sycamores, Strang Road, Union Mills, Douglas IM4 4NP Tel: 01624 852107 — MB ChB Aberd. 1961; FFA RCS Eng. 1965. Prev: Cons. Anaesth.Dr Grays Hosp. Elgin Moray.

BRUCE, Alexander Taylor (retired) Fishergate House, The Quay, Sandwich CT13 9EN — MB ChB 1951 Ed.

BRUCE, Allan Wales Ardrigh, West Auchlea, Kingswells, Aberdeen AB15 8ST — MB ChB 1974 Aberd.; MPhil Glas. 1994.

BRUCE, Andrew Stephen Walter 312 School Road, Sheffield S10 1GR Tel: 0114 266 6783 Email: aswborth@aol.com — MB ChB 1993 Sheff.; FRCS (Eng.) 1997. SHO (Orthop. Surg.) N.ern Gen. Hosp. Sheff. Prev: SHO (Vasc. Surg.) N.ern Gen. Hosp. Sheff.; SHO (Plastic Surg.) N.ern Gen. Hosp. Sheff.; SHO (Orthop. Surg.) N.ern Gen. Hosp. Sheff.

BRUCE, Ann Elizabeth 54 Uffington Road, London SE27 0ND Tel: 020 8670 3783 — MB BS 1973 Lond.; BSc (Psychol.) Lond. 1972; MRCS Eng. LRCP Lond. 1973. (St. Thos.) Indep. Jungian Anal. Lond. Socs: Assoc. Profess. Mem. Soc. Anal. Psychol.; UK Counc. Psychother.; Brit. Assn. Psychoanalytic & Psychodynamic Supervision. Prev: Sen. Med. Off. (Adoption & Fostering) Wandsworth HA; Princip. Phys. (Child Health) Battersea Wandsworth HA.

BRUCE, Arnold Moreton Lodge, Holly Walk, Hampstead, London NW3 6RA Tel: 020 7435 4233 Fax: 020 8459 7809 — MRCS Eng. LRCP Lond. 1944.

BRUCE, Bryana Isabel Mary Potter Health Centre, Gregory Boulevard, Hyson Green, Nottingham NG7 5HY Tel: 0115 942 0330; 15 Oundle Drive, Wollaton Park, Nottingham NG8 1BN Tel: 0115 970 2603 Fax: 0115 970 2603 — MRCS Eng. LRCP Lond. 1962; BA Dub. 1961, MB BCh BAO 1962; DObst RCOG 1964. (T.C. Dub. & St. Mary's) Socs: BMA; Med. Chir. Soc. Prev: Ho. Surg. Centr. Middlx. Hosp.; Ho. Phys. King Edwd. Memor. Hosp. Ealing; Obst. Ho. Surg. City Lond. Matern. Hosp.

BRUCE, Carolynn Louise McDonald Bridgeton Health Centre, 201 Abercromby Street, Glasgow G40 2DA Tel: 0141 531 6600 — MB ChB 1984 Glas.; MRCGP 1989; DCH RCPS Glas. 1987. (Univ. Glas.) Socs: BMA. Prev: Trainee GP Glas.

BRUCE, Cathy Elizabeth Joy Hamilton Place, Beacon Rd W., Crowborough TN6 1QL — MB BS 1997 Lond.

BRUCE, Christine Elsie Holm Farm, King Edward, Banff AB45 3NB Tel: 01261 821247 — MB ChB 1982 Aberd.; DRCOG 1986. Clin. Med. Off. (Community Child Health) Grampian Healthcare NHS Trust.

BRUCE, Mr Colin Ernest Alder Hey Children's Hospital, Eaton Road, Liverpool L12 2AP Tel: 0151 228 4811 — MB ChB 1985 Liverp.; FRCS (Orth.) 1996; FRCS Eng. 1989. (Liverp.) Cons. Orthop. & Trauma Surg. Alder Hey Childr.'s Hosp. Liverp. Socs: Fell. Roy. Coll. Surg. Eng.; Fell. BOA; Brit. Soc. Childr. Orthop. Surg.

BRUCE, David Anderson Princes Street Surgery, 155 Princes Street, Dundee DD4 6DG Tel: 01382 461090 Fax: 01382 461091; 15 Hillcrest Road, Dundee DD2 1JJ — MB ChB 1981 Dundee; MRCGP 1985; DCH RCP Lond. 1985; DRCOG 1983.

BRUCE, David Ian Radiology Department, Leicester General Hospital NHS Trust, Gwendolen Road, Leicester LE5 4PW Tel: 0116 249 0490; 8 Grassholme Drive, Loughborough LE11 4NS — MB ChB 1980 Bristol; FRCR 1986. Cons. Diag. Radiol. Leicester Gen. Hosp. Socs: Brit. Inst. Radiol. Prev: Cons. Diag. Radiol. Glenfield Gen. Hosp. Leicester; Sen. Regist. (Diag. Radiol.) Leic. Roy. Infirm.; Regist. (Diag. Radiol.) Roy. Hallamsh. Hosp. Sheff.

BRUCE, David Wilson Department of Medicine & Elderly Care, Hartlepool General Hospital, Holdforth Road, Hartlepool TS24 9AH Tel: 01429 522208 Fax: 01429 869852; Millbrooke House, The Tudors, Hart Village, Hartlepool TS27 3BS Tel: 01429 233518 — MB ChB 1982 Glas.; MRCP (UK) 1986; FRCP 1999. Cons. Phys. Hartlepool Gen. Hosp.; Clin. Tut. Hartlepool Gen. Hosp.; Director of Med. Educat., N. Tees & Hartleypool Trust. Prev: Sen. Regist. (Geriat. Med.) City Hosp. Edin.; Regist. (Med.) Stirling Roy. Infirm.; Regist. (Geriat. Med.) Gartnavel Gen. Hosp.

BRUCE, Diane Lesley Department of Cardiorespiratory Medicine, Poole General Hospital, Longfleet Road, Poole BH15 2JB — MB BS 1988 Lond.; BSc (Hons.) Newc. 1979; MB BS (Hons. Path.) Lond. 1988; MRCP (UK) 1992. Socs: BMA & Roy. Soc Med.

BRUCE, Douglas John Rutherglen Health Centre, 130 Stonelaw Road, Rutherglen, Glasgow G73 2PQ Tel: 0141 531 6065 — MB ChB 1985 Glas.; DRCOG 1988.

BRUCE, Mr Duff Morrison Top Flat, 121 Hamilton Place, Aberdeen AB15 5BD — MB ChB 1986 Aberd.; FRCS Ed. 1992.

BRUCE, Elizabeth 6 Bedwell Road, Belvedere DA17 5LF — BM 1998 Soton.

BRUCE, Elizabeth Margaret Moorend Farm, Dockray, Matterdale, Penrith CA11 0LE — MB BS 1951 Durh.; MRCPsych 1976; DPM Eng. 1958.

BRUCE, Ellen Jean Meadowpark Street Surgery, 214 Meadowpark Street, Glasgow G31 2TE Tel: 0141 554 0464; 45 Buchanan Drive, Rutherglen, Glasgow G73 3PF — MB ChB 1965 Glas. (Glas.) Prev: SHO (O & G) Maryfield Hosp. Dundee.

BRUCE, Gillian Anne Macdonald Great Western Road Medical Group, 327 Great Western Road, Aberdeen AB10 6LT Tel: 01224 571318 Fax: 01224 573865 — MB ChB 1974 Aberd.; MRCGP 1978; DRCOG 1976. (Aberd.) Socs: M-C Soc.

BRUCE, Gordon McKay (retired) Coire Beag, Corry Road, Muir of Ord IV6 7TL Tel: 01463 870060 — MB ChB 1960 Aberd.; DObst RCOG 1963. Prev: Ho. Phys. & Ho. Surg. Roy. Infirm. Aberd.

BRUCE, Grahame James Crosbie The Aldergate Medical Practice, The Mount, Salters Lane, Tamworth B79 8BH Tel: 01827 54775 Fax: 01827 62835 — MB ChB 1981 Aberd. Socs: Tamworth Area Med. Emerg. Serv.

BRUCE, Gregor Matheson Riverdale House, 11 Station Terrace, Peterhead AB42 4UE Tel: 01779 821123 — MB ChB 1985 Ed.; MRCGP 1990; DRCOG 1988.

BRUCE, Helen Caroline — BM 1989 Soton.; MRCGP 1993. p/t GP Retainer.

BRUCE, Henry Thomson (retired) Springburn Health Centre, 200 Springburn Way, Glasgow G21 1TR Tel: 0141 531 9611 Fax: 0141

531 6706 — MB ChB 1967 Aberd. Prev: Regist. (Laborat. Med.) W.. Infirm. Glas.

BRUCE, Ian Alexander 24 Abbot Meadow, Penwortham, Preston PR1 9JX — MB ChB 1997 Manch.

BRUCE, Ian Norman 135 Circular Road, Belfast BT4 2GF — MB BCh BAO 1988 Belf.; MRCP (UK) 1991.

BRUCE, Mr Ivan 97 Dene Road, Didsbury, Manchester M20 2TB — MB ChB 1943 Leeds; FRCS Ed. 1948; MRCGP 1968. (Leeds) Socs: Bolton & Dist. Med. Soc. Prev: Sen. Regist. (Surg.) Warrington Infirm.; Regist. (Surg.) Blackburn Roy. Infirm.; Sen. Receiv. Room Off. Leeds Gen. Infirm.

BRUCE, James (retired) 2 Queensferry Terrace, Edinburgh EH4 3ES Tel: 0131 343 2469 — MB ChB 1954 Aberd. Prev: GP Edin.

BRUCE, James (retired) Abbeville, 13 Southside Place, Inverness IV2 3JE Tel: 01463 233907 — MB ChB Glas. 1940; BSc (Hons.) Glas. 1934, MD (Commend.) 1954; FRCPath 1963. Prev: Cons. Biochem. Highland HB.

BRUCE, Mr James Department of Surgery, Royal Manchester Childrens Hospital, Pendlebury, Manchester M30 4HA; 28 Netherha Road, Buckie AB56 1EP — MB ChB 1978 Aberd.; FRACS (Paed Surg); FRCS Ed. Cons. Surg. Manch. Childr.'s Hosp.; Cons. Surg., Roy. Mancheste Childr.'s Hosp., Boch Hall Childr.'s Hosp., St Mary's Hosp. Manch. Socs: Coun. mem. Manch. Med. Soc. Sect. of Surg. Prev: Assn Prof. of Surg., State Univ. of New York,child Hosp. of Buffalo; Sen. Registra, Roy. Childr.'s Hosp., life source; Sen. Registra, Manch. Childr.'s Hosp.

BRUCE, James Henry, OBE (retired) North Lodge, 29 Kilmore Road, Lurgan, Craigavon BT67 9BP Tel: 01762 322611 — MD (Commend.) Belf. 1949, MB BCh BAO (2nd Cl; Hnrs.) 1945; FRCP Lond. 1973, M 1951; FRCP Ed. 1969, M 1951. Prev: Cons. Phys. Craigavon Area Hosp.

BRUCE, James Henry Ian (retired) 972 Holderness Road, Hull HU9 4AB Tel: 01482 374455 — MB ChB 1948 Glas.; MRCGP 1960.

BRUCE, Jane Tait Hawkhill Medical Centre, Hawkhill, Dundee DD1 5LA Tel: 01382 669589 Fax: 01382 645526; Woodcroft, Old Whisky Road, Auchternoone, Dundee DD3 0RD Tel: 01382 320369 — MB ChB 1981 Dundee; MRCGP 2001; DRCOG 1983. UnderGrad. Tutor - Univ. of Dundee.

BRUCE, Janet Marjorie Brandon Mental Health Unit, Leicester General Hospital, Gwendolen Road, Leicester LE5 4PW Tel: 01162 256200 Fax: 01162 256228 — MB ChB 1982 Sheff.; MRCPsych 1987. Cons. Psychiat. Gen. Adult Psychiat. Brandon Ment. Health Unit Leicester Gen. Hosp. Prev: Cons. Psychiat. Gen. Adult Psychiat. Derby City Gen. Hosp. Acute Ment. Health Unit.

BRUCE, Joan Tugwell (retired) 34 Southwood Park, Highgate, London N6 5SG — MRCS Eng. LRCP Lond. 1953; MB BS Lond. 1953; Acad. DPM (Lond.) 1960; FRCP Lond. 1986, M 1957; FRCPsych 1979, M 1971. Prev: Cons. Psychiat. Friern Hosp. & Roy. Nat. Orthop. Hosp. Lond.

BRUCE, Joanna Mary Flat 5, 81 Mount Ephraim, Tunbridge Wells TN4 8BS — MB BS 1996 Lond.

BRUCE, John (retired) 14 Park View, Crowle, Scunthorpe DN17 4JA Tel: 01724 710942 — MB ChB Aberd. 1941. Prev: Med. Off. Stracathro Hosp. Brechin.

BRUCE, John David Polventon, Fletcher's Bridge, Bodmin PL30 4AN Tel: 01208 72535 Fax: 01208 77552 — MB BS 1952 Lond.; FRCGP 1978, M 1970; DObst RCOG 1953. (St. Bart.) HM Coroner E. Cornw. Dist. Prev: Princip. GP Bodmin; Course Organizer Cornw. VTS; Mem. Panel of Examrs. RCGP.

BRUCE, Mr John Edwin Forde 15 Oundle Drive, Wollaton Park, Nottingham NG8 1BN Tel: 0115 970 2603 Fax: 0115 970 2603; 2 Regent Street, Nottingham NG1 5BQ Tel: 0115 947 4755 — MB BS 1962 Lond.; FRCS Eng. 1967; MRCS Eng. LRCP Lond. 1962; FRCOG 1983, M 1970. (St. Mary's) Cons. Obst & Gyn. City Hosp. Nottm. Socs: BMA; Nottm. Med. Chirurgical Soc. Prev: Sen. Regist. (O & G) King's Coll. Hosp. & SE. Metrop. RHB; Regist. (O & G) St. Mary's Hosp. Lond.; Resid. Med. Off. Qu. Charlotte's Matern. Hosp. Lond.

BRUCE, John Gavin Edward (retired) Beech House, Garmancarr Lane, Wistow, Selby YO8 3UW Tel: 01757 268371 Email: j_bruce@talk21.com — MB ChB 1960 Leeds. Prev: GP Selby.

BRUCE, Katherine Mary 7 Valletta Close, Chelmsford CM1 2PT — BM 1994 Soton.

BRUCE, Kenneth Ian (retired) 41 Hull Road, York YO10 3JP Tel: 01904 413842 — MB ChB 1937 Ed. Prev: Res. Med. Off. W. La. Hosp. Middlesbrough.

BRUCE, Laetitia Mary (retired) 5 Ruthven Court, Adderstone Crescent, Newcastle upon Tyne NE2 2HH — MB ChB St. And. 1946. Prev: Regist. (Paediat.) P.ss Mary Matern. Hosp. Newc. u. Tyne.

BRUCE, Leslie Barton 3 Childwall Park Avenue, Liverpool L16 0JE Tel: 0151 722 7664 — MB ChB Liverp. 1948. (Liverp.) Capt. RAMC. Socs: Brit. Soc. Med. Hypnotists. Prev: Ho. Surg. St. Helens Hosp.

BRUCE, Linda Elspeth 116 Kinghorne Road, Dundee DD3 6LD — MB ChB 1986 Dundee. Trainee GP. VTS Dundee.

BRUCE, Linda Margaret Brogan and Partners, The O'Connel Street Medical Centre, 6 O'Connell Street, Hawick TD9 9HU Tel: 01450 372276 Fax: 01450 371564; Calaburn, Hawick TD9 7NU Tel: 01450 372540 — MB ChB 1982 Glas.; MRCGP 1986; DRCOG 1986. Prev: GP/Regist. (Med.) CrossHo. Hosp. Kilmarnock; SHO (Geriat.) CrossHo. Hosp. Kilmarnock; Trainee GP W. Kilbride.

BRUCE, Malcolm Scott Community Drug Problem Service, Royal Edinburgh Hospital, Morningside Place, Edinburgh EH10 5HP Tel: 0131 537 8345 — MB ChB 1980 Aberd.; PhD Lond. 1989; MRCPsych 1984. Cons. Psychiat. (Addic.) Roy. Edin. Hosp. Prev: Sen. Regist. Oxf. RHA; Researcher Hon. Lect. Inst. Psychiat. Lond.; Sen. Regist. Rotat. (Psychiat.) St. Thos. Hosp. Lond.

BRUCE, Margaret Patricia Beauparcq, Route de la Trinitié, Trinity, Jersey JE3 5JP Tel: 01534 861223 — LRCP LRCS Ed. LRFPS Glas. 1953; FFA RCSI 1972; DA RCPSI 1961; DA Eng. 1960. Hon. Cons. Jersey. Socs: Fell. Roy. Soc. Med.; Assn. Anaesths.; Mell. BMA 1999. Prev: Cons. Anaesth. Jersey Gen. Hosp.

BRUCE, Margaret Pauline Croydon Health Authority, Knollys House, 17 Addiscombe Road, Croydon CR0 6SR — BM BS 1978 Nottm.; MSC (Public Health) 2000; BMedSci Nottm. 1976; DCH RCP Lond. 1992; DRCOG 1981. (Univ. Nottm.) p/t Specialist Regist. (Pub. Health Med.) Croydon Health Auth. Prev: Clin. Med. Off. (Child Health) Mid Sussex NHS Trust.; SpR Pub. Health Med. E. Sussex Brighton & Hove HA.

BRUCE, Nigel Graeme Department of Public Health, PO Box 147, Liverpool University, Liverpool L69 3BX Tel: 0151 794 5582 Fax: 0151 794 5588 Email: ngb@liv.ac.uk; Red Walls, School Lane, Bunbury, Tarporley CW6 9NR Tel: 01829 261305 Fax: 01829 260421 Email: nigel.bruce1@virgin.net — MB BS 1980 Lond.; PhD (Epidemiol.) Lond. 1991, MSc (Distinc.) Epidemiol. 1985; FFPHM 1997; MFPHM 1990; MRCGP 1984; BA Camb. 1977. (Lond. Hosp.) Sen. Lect. (Pub. Health) Univ. Liverp.

BRUCE, Robert Charles Hedderwick 48 Kilner House, Clayton St., London SE11 5SE — MB BS 1993 Lond.

BRUCE, Stanley Parker Carisbrooke, Innellan, Dunoon PA23 7SR — MB ChB 1946 Ed.

BRUCE, Stephen Neville 2 Chandlers Ford, Houghton-le-Spring DH4 7SB — BM BS 1989 Nottm.; MRCP (UK) 1993.

BRUCE, Stirling James Shettleston Health Centre, 420 Old Shettleston Road, Glasgow G32 7JZ Tel: 0141 531 6220 Fax: 0141 531 6206; 25 Williamwood Park W., Netherlee, Glasgow G44 3TE Tel: 0141 637 3417 — MB ChB 1984 Glas.; MRCGP 1988; DRCOG 1987. Trainee GP Glas. Socs: BMA & RCGP.

BRUCE, Stuart Alexander Department of Medicine for the Elderly, Conquest Hospital, The Ridge, St Leonards-on-Sea TN37 7RD Tel: 01424 755255 — MB BS 1974 Lond.; MD Lond. 1994, BSc 1970; FRCP Lond. 1993; MRCP (UK) 1979; MRCS Eng. LRCP Lond. 1974. (UCHMS) Cons. Phys. Dept. Med. for Elderly Conquest Hosp. St Leonards-on-Sea; Hon. Sen. Clin. Lect. Inst. Human Performance UCL; Chairm. (Gastroenterol. & Nutrit.) s/i Gp. BGS. Socs: BSG; BGS.

BRUCE, Terence John Robert Department of Psychological Med., St Bartholomew's Hospital, West Smithfield, London EC1A 7BE Tel: 020 7601 7946 Fax: 020 7601 7969 — MB Camb. 1966, BChir 1965; MA Camb. 1966; MRCS Eng. LRCP Lond. 1965; FRCPsych 1985, M 1972; DPM Eng. 1969. (Camb. & Guy's) Hon. Cons. St. Bart. Hosp. Lond. Socs: Fell. Roy. Soc. Med.; Assoc. Mem. Brit. Psychoanalyt. Soc. Prev: Cons. Young People's Unit Roy. Edin. Hosp.

BRUCE, Victor Robert (retired) Eastwood, Altass, Rosehall, Lairg IV27 4EU Tel: 01549 441285 — MB BS 1956 Lond.; DObst RCOG 1958. Prev: Ho. Surg. Lond. Hosp.

BRUCE, Vivian Richard (retired) 25A George Douglas Drive, Ryedale, Dumfries DG2 7ES Tel: 01387 250134 — MB BS 1942 Lond.; MRCS Eng. LRCP Lond. 1942; FRCGP 1979, M 1953; DObst RCOG 1952. Prev: Assoc. Adviser (Gen. Pract.) Univ. Bristol.

BRUCE, William Riddoch (retired) The Eaves Surgery, St. Nicholas Street, Bodmin PL31 1AG Tel: 01208 72161. Clin. Asst. (Orthop.) Cornw. & Is. of Scilly HA.

BRUCE-CHWATT, Robert Michael York Lodge, 1 York Road, Richmond TW10 6DR Tel: 020 8940 9781 Fax: 020 8940 9781 — MB BS 1975 Lond.; Cert. Family Plann. JCC 1984; Cert. Av. Med. 1982; DFFP 1993. (Roy. Free) Forens. Med. Examr. (Metrop. Police); Marine Med. Examr. to Roy. Norwegian Embassy. Socs: Internat. Assn. Phys. in Overseas Serv. Prev: Sen. Surg. P&O S.N. Co Ltd Soton.; SHO (Plastic Surg. & Ophth.) Hosp. Sick Childr. Lond.; Ho. Phys. (Gen. Med. & Cardiol.) Roy. Free Lond.

BRUCE JA JA, Mr Dadson Fawari 62 Gellatly Road, New Cross, London SE14 5TT — MB BChir 1974 Camb.; FRCS RCPS Glas. 1997. (King's College London) Clin. Asst. (Orthop. & Trauma) Old Ch. Hosp. Romford Essex. Prev: Regist. (Orthop.) Old Ch. Hosp. Romford Essex.

BRUCE-JONES, Peter Nigel Ewart Elderly Care Unit, Dorset County Hospital, Williams Avenue, Dorchester DT1 1JY Tel: 01305 255261 — MB ChB 1985 Bristol; MRCP (UK) 1990. Cons. In elderly care, W. Dorset Gen. Hosp.s NHS Trust. Socs: Brit. Geriat. Soc. Prev: Sen. Regist. (Med. for Elderly & Gen. Med.) Soton. Gen. Hosp.

BRUCE-JONES, William Dennis Alexander Miles House, Bathwick Hill, Bath BA2 6HF Tel: 01225 324212 Fax: 01225 330689 — MB BS 1984 Lond.; MPhil Lond. 1994; MRCPsych 1990. (Medical college of ST Bartholomews) Cons. Psychiat.Avon & Wilts. Partnership Ment. healthcare Trust. Prev: Lect. & Hon. Sen. Regist. St. Bart. Hosp. Lond.; Sen. Regist. (Psychiat.) Bethlem Roy. & Maudsley Hosp. Lond.; Sen. Regist. Nat. Hosp. for Neurol. & Neurosurg. Lond.

BRUCE-LOMBA, Elizabeth Angela 109 Trent Road, Beeston, Nottingham NG9 1LP — MB ChB 1992 Leicester.

BRUCE-SMITH, James (retired) 17 Gartcows Road, Falkirk FK1 5EF Tel: 01324 637300 — MB ChB 1948 Ed.; FRCP Ed. 1987; MRCP (UK) 1983; DObst RCOG 1951. Prev: Vice-Chairm. Centr. Birm. HA.

BRUCK, Peter Eric Red Roofs Practitioners, 31 Coton Road, Nuneaton CV11 5TW Tel: 024 7635 7100 Fax: 024 7664 2036; 6 Klevedon Close, Nuneaton CV11 6PS — MB BS 1982 Lond.; MRCGP 2001; BSc Lond. 1979; MRCP (UK) 1988. (St. Geo.) Princip. in Gen. Pract. Prev: Regist. & SHO Rotat. (Med.) King's Coll. Hosp. Lond.; SHO (Med. & Cardiol.) Mayday Hosp. Croydon; SHO (O & G) St. Geo. Hosp. Lond.

BRUCKNER, Felix Ernest (cons. rooms), Parkside Hospital, 53 Parkside, Wimbledon, London SW19 5NX Tel: 020 8971 8000 — MB BS Lond. 1960; FRCP Lond. 1978, M 1965; MRCS Eng. LRCP Lond. 1960; DCH Eng. 1962. (Lond. Hosp.) Cons. Phys. Rheum. & Rehabil. St. Geo. Hosp. Lond. Socs: Fell. Roy. Soc. Med. (Pres. Sect. Rheum. & Rehabil.); Brit. Soc. Rheum.

BRUDENELL, Mr John Michael (retired) The Barn, Station Road, Hever, Edenbridge TN8 7ER Tel: 01732 863086 Fax: 01732 863086 Email: brudenell@ukonline.co.uk — MB BS 1949 Lond.; 1956 FRCS Eng.; 1973 FRCOG; 1993 MFFP (RCOG); 1958 MRCOG. Prev: Cons. Gyn. King Edwd. VII Hosp. Lond.

BRUDENELL, Mr Marcus John Rothwell The Barn, Station Road, Hever, Edenbridge TN8 7ER — MB BS 1990 Lond.; FRCS Eng. 1995.

BRUDNEY, Charles Scott 32 Painswick Road, Cheltenham GL50 2HA — MB BCh 1990 Wales. SHO Rotat. (Anaesth.) Roy. Lond. Hosp. Prev: SHO Rotat. (Med.) Stoke Mandeville Hosp. Aylesbury; SHO (Haemat.) Roy. Berks. Hosp.; SHO (A & E) St. Bart. Hosp. Lond.

BRUDNEY, Jonathan Keith South Meadow Surgery, 3 Church Close, Eton, Windsor SL4 6AP Tel: 01753 833777 Fax: 01753 833689; Tel: 01753 859091 Email: jbrudney@onetel.net.uk — MRCS Eng. LRCP Lond. 1986; MRCGP 1992; DRCOG 1992. (Char. Cross & Westm.) GP S.meadow Surg. Eton; Sch. Doctor Eton Coll. Prev: Trainee GP/SHO Colchester Gen. Hosp. VTS.

BRUEGEL, Josephine (retired) 19 Charlton Lodge, Temple Fortune Lane, London NW11 7TY Tel: 020 8458 3535 — MD 1942 Czechoslovakia. Prev: JHMO Whittington Hosp. Lond.

BRUEGGEMANN, Peter Michael Acorn Lodge, Macks Loke, Reepham Road, Briston, Melton Constable NR24 2JL Tel: 01263 860828 Email: pbrueggemann@compuserve.com — State Exam Med. Essen 1991; FRCS Pt I Glas. 1997; FRCS Pt I Lond. 1997; FRCS Pt II Ed. 1998. (Univ. Essen, Germany) SHO (O & G), Norf. & Norwich Hosp. Prev: SHO (Gen. Surg.) Norf. & Norwich Hosp.; Train. Fell. (Orthop. surg.) Norf. & Norwich Hosp.

BRUETON, Louise Anne Clinical Genetics Unit, Birmingham Womens Healthcare NHS Trust, Methmley Park Rd, Birmingham B15 2TG Tel: 0121 627 2630 — MB BS 1984 Lond.; FRCP; MD Lond. 1996; MRCP (UK) 1987. (Royal Free) p/t Cons. Clin. Genetics Birm. Wom.s Healthcare NHS Trust Birm. Socs: FRCP; Brit. Soc. of Human Genetics. Prev: Cons. Clin. Genetics Kennedy Galton Centre, Norhtwick Pk. Hosp. Harrow.

BRUETON, Martin John 40 Furze Lane, Purley CR8 3EG Tel: 020 8660 1503 Email: m.brueton@ic.ac.uk; Chelsea & Westminster Hospital, Dept. Of Paediatric Gastroenterology, 369 Fulham Road, London SW10 9NH Tel: 020 8746 8628 Fax: 020 8746 8770 — MB BS Lond. 1967; MSc Birm. 1977; MD Lond. 1978; FRCP Lond. 1986; MRCP (UK) 1971; DCH Eng. 1971; FRCPCH 1997. (St. Bart.) Cons. Paediat., Chelsea and W.minster Hosp.; Hon. Reader (Child Health) Imperial Coll., Fac. of Med., Lond.; Hon. Cons. Paediat. St Marys Hosp., & Roy. Brompton Hosp Lond. Socs: Brit. Soc. Gastroenterol.; Eur. Soc. Paediat. Gastroenterol, Hepat. & Nutrit.; Brit. Soc. Paediat. Gastroenterol., Hepat. & Nutrit. Prev: Lect. (Paediat.) Inst. Child Health Birm. Childr. Hosp.; Sen. Regist. (Paediat.) Ahmadu Bello Univ. Hosp. Zaria, Nigeria; Regist. (Paediat.) St. Bart. Hosp. Lond.

BRUETON, Nancy Rushton (retired) 76 Mellstock Avenue, Dorchester DT1 2BQ Tel: 01305 264678 — MB ChB Bristol 1942.

BRUETON, Mr Richard Neville 45 Grosvenor Road, London N10 2DR — MRCS Eng. LRCP Lond. 1971; MD Lond. 1988, MB BS 1971; FRCS Eng. 1976.

BRUFORD, Mary Kelland Elgin, Dauntsey Lane, Weyhill, Andover SP11 8EB — MB BS 1977 Lond.; BSc Lond. 1974; MRCS Eng. LRCP Lond. 1977. Socs: B.S.R.

BRUGGEN, Clarence Peter Leem (retired) 21 Mackeson Road, London NW3 2LU Tel: 0207 485 6771 Fax: 0207 419 9077 Email: pbruggen@cableinet.co.uk — MB ChB 1957 Ed.; FRCPsych 1979, M 1971; DPM Eng. 1963; DCH Eng. 1960; DObst RCOG 1959. Hon. Lect., Dept. of Psychiat. (Sect. of Psychother.) King's Coll. Prev: Cons. Psychiat. Hill End Adolesc. Unit Hill End Hosp. St. Albans.

BRUGGINK, Elisabeth Maria Alberta Whinfield Surgery, Whinbush Way, Darlington DL1 3RT Tel: 01325 481321 Fax: 01325 380116 — Artsexamen 1988 Free Univ. Amsterdam; Artsexamen Free Univ Amsterdam 1988. (Free Univ. Amsterdam) GP Darlington, Co. Durh.

BRUGHA, Traolach Sean Department of Psychiatry, University of Leicester, Brandon Mental Health Unit, Leicester General Hospital, Gwendolen Road, Leicester LE5 4PW Tel: 0116 225 6295 Fax: 0116 225 6235 Email: psychiatry@le.ac.uk; Inwoods House, Hall Wood, Hallaton, Market Harborough LE16 8UH — MB BCh BAO 1977 NUI; MD NUI 1987; MRCPsych 1981. Sen. Lect. (Psychiat.) Univ. Leicester; Hon. Cons. (Psychiat.) Leics. Ment. Health Servs. NHS Trust. Prev: Mem. Clin. Sc. Staff MRC Soc. Psychiat. Unit, Inst. Psychiat. Lond.; Hon. Lect. (Psychiat.) Inst. Psychiat. Univ. Lond.; Regist. & Hon. Sen. Regist. (Psychiat.) Bethlem Roy. & Maudsley Hosp. Lond.

BRUGMAN, Martinus Jacobus Johannes 28 Bowershott, Letchworth SG6 2ET — Artsexamen 1989 Leiden.

BRUIJLANTS, Bruno Flat E, 41 Outram Road, Croydon CR0 6XG — MD 1990 Louvain.

BRULL, David Joseph 13 Woodside Avenue, London N12 8AN — MB BS 1992 Lond.; MB BS (Hons.) Lond. 1992; BSc (Gen. Path.) Lond. 1989; MRCP (UK) 1995. SHO (Intens. Care) Lewisham Hosp.

BRUMBY, John Francis 54 Ernesettle Green, Ernesettle, Plymouth PL5 32SX Tel: 01752 361374; 552 Budshead Road, Whitleigh, Plymouth PL5 4DG Tel: 01752 773352 — MB BCh 1968 Wales; MRCGP 1974; Dip. IMC RCS Ed. 1992; Cert. Family Plann. JCC 1978.

BRUMBY, Peter Longrigg Medical Centre, Leam Lane Estate, Felling, Gateshead NE10 8PH Tel: 0191 469 2173 Fax: 0191 495 0893 — MB BS 1978 Ncle. GP Gateshead, Tyne & Wear.

BRUMFITT, William Department of Medical Microbiology, Royal Free Hospital, Pond St., Hampstead, London NW3 2QG Tel: 020 7794 0500 Fax: 020 7435 9694; 9 Boreham Holt, Allum Lane, Elstree, Borehamwood WD6 3QF Tel: 020 8953 1218 — MB BS 1951 Lond.; PhD Lond. 1961, MD 1959; FRCP Lond. 1973, M 1953; FRCPath 1969, M 1964. (St. Mary's) Prof. Med. Microbiol. Roy. Free Sch. Med.; Cons. Med. Microbiol. & Urin. Infect. Clinic Roy. Free Hosp.; Examr. (Extern.) Univ. Lond.; Apptd. Teach. (Med. Microbiol.) Univ. Lond. Socs: Founder Chairm. Brit. Soc. Antimicrobial Chemother.; Roy. Soc. Med. Prev: Foundat. Prof. Pathol. Soton. Univ. Med. Sch.; Consult. & Sen. Lect. (Bacteriol.) St. Mary's Hosp. Med. Sch. Lond.; MRC Schol. Wright Fleming Inst. Microbiol. St. Mary's Hosp. Lond.

BRUML, Sarah Kate 107 Stockwell Road, London SW9 9TJ; 4 Landsdowne Gardens, London SW8 2EG Tel: 020 7622 3883 — MB ChB 1981 Bristol; MRCGP 1985; DRCOG 1984.

BRUMMITT, John Michael Tel: 01666 825825 Email: mbrum66865@aol.com; Yewtree Cottage, Charlton, Malmesbury SN16 9DL Tel: 01666 822591 — MRCS Eng. LRCP Lond. 1966; MB BS Lond. 1967, BDS 1961; LDS RCS Eng. 1961; DA Eng. 1969. (Guy's) p/t Clin. Asst., Dermat. Dept., P.ss Margt. Hosp., Swindon. Prev: Ho. Phys. (Paediat.) Guy's Hosp. Lond.; Ho. Off. Roy. Sussex. Hosp. Brighton; Ho. Surg. (O & G) Brighton Gen. Hosp.

BRUMMITT, Peter Ian Lancing Health Centre, Penstone Park, Lancing BN15 9AG Tel: 01903 843300 — MRCS Eng. LRCP Lond. 1973; BSc Lond. 1979, MB BS 1973; DObst RCOG 1975. (King's Coll. Hosp.)

BRUMMITT, Peter James The Wooda Surgery, Clarence Wharf, Barnstaple Street, Bideford EX39 4AU Tel: 01237 471071 Fax: 01237 471059; Marshford House, Churchill Way, Northam, Bideford EX39 1NR Tel: 01237 477206 — MB ChB 1968 Liverp.; MRCP (UK) 1973. (Liverp.) Gen. Practioner Wooda Surg., Bideford N.am EX39 4AU.

BRUMWELL, Philip Howard Crookes Valley Medical Centre, 1 Barber Rd, Sheffield S10 1EA Tel: 0114 266 0703, 02920 747747 Fax: 0114 267 8354; 44 Pant y Dderwen, Pontyclun CF72 8LY — MB ChB 1991 Sheff.; BMedSci. 1991; MRCGP 1995; DRCOG 1994. (Sheffield University) SpR: Histopath., Cardiff. Prev: GP Princip., Cardiff.

BRUMWELL, Susan Elaine Flat 2, 31 Wilbury Road, Hove BN3 3PB — MB ChB 1987 Manch.; MRCGP Manch. 1996; DRCOG 1994; DFFP 1995. (Manch.)

BRUN, Mr Claude (retired) Peregrines, Northcote Road, Langho, Blackburn BB6 8BG — MB BS 1941 Lond.; MS Lond. 1953; FRCS Eng. 1943; MRCS Eng. LRCP Lond. 1941. Prev: Cons. Surg. Blackburn Health Dist.

BRUNDELL, Mr Simeon Mark 63 Columbine Road, West Hamilton, Leicester LE5 1UG — BM BS 1992 Nottm.; FRCS Eng. 1997.

BRUNELL, Carol Lesley Upper Crisbrook Mill, Hayle Mill Road, Maidstone ME15 6XR — MB BCh 1974 Wales; MRCP (UK) 1978; FRCR 1983; DMRD 1981.

BRUNET, Martin Dominic Binscombe Medical Centre, 106 Binscombe, Godalming GU7 3PR Tel: 01483 415115 — MB ChB 1992 Manch.; MRCGP 2000; MA (Cantab.) 1993; MRCP (UK) 1995. (Manchester) Gen. Practitioner Princip. Prev: Regist. (Med.) Ashford; SHO (Med.) Manch. Roy. Infirm.; Regist. (Med.) Kingston Dist. Gen. Hosp.

BRUNING, Timothy John 1/4 Regent Gardens, Grimsby DN34 5AT — MB 1986 Camb.; BChir 1985; MRCGP 1991.

BRUNJES, Henry Otto London Bridge Hospital, 27 Tooley St., London SE1 2PR Tel: 020 7403 4884 Fax: 020 7407 3162; Blendon, 8 The Cliff, Roedean, Brighton BN2 5RE Tel: 01273 697806 Fax: 01273 621306 — MB BS 1980 Lond.; BSc Lond. 1977; DRCOG 1983. (Guy's Hosp.) Company Doctor Bevan Funnell, Newhaven; Med. Dir. Brighton Sports Injury Clin.; Med. Dir. Premier Med. Socs: (Counc.) Brighton & Sussex M-C Soc.; Roy. Soc. Med. Prev: GP Brighton; Police Surg. E. Sussex.

BRUNNER, Hilary Edgcumbe Department of Anaesthetics, Royal Shrewsbury Hospital Trust, Mytton Oak Road, Shrewsbury SY3 8XQ; Lower Farm, Habberley, Pontesbury, Shrewsbury SY5 0TP — MB BChir 1982 Camb.; BA Camb. 1979; FCAnaesth. 1992; FFA RCSI 1991. Cons. Anaesth. Roy. Shrewsbury Hosp. Trust.

BRUNNER, Imogen Charlotte 53 Oxford Gardens, London W10 5UJ — MB BS 1993 Lond.

BRUNNER, Michael David 17 Holden Road, London N12 8HP — MB BS 1986 Lond.; FCAnaesth. 1991; DA (UK) 1989. (St. Bart.) Cons. Anaesth. N.wick Pk. Hosp. Prev: Sen. Regist. (Anaesth.) Roy. Free Hosp. Lond.; Regist. (Anaesth.) Kings Coll. Lond.; SHO (Anaesth.) Barnet Gen. Hosp.

BRUNNER, Peter Constantin 1 Oxford Drive, Ruislip HA4 9EY Tel: 020 8866 6589; Veritas, 36 Dene Road, Northwood HA6 2DA Tel: 01923 823322 Fax: 01923 827168 — MB BS 1962 Lond.; MRCS Eng. LRCP Lond. 1962. (St. Bart.) Med. Off. N.wood & Pinner Cott. Hosp. Socs: Brit. Acad. Foren. Sc. & BMA. Prev: Ho. Surg. Redhill Hosp.; Ho. Phys. Harefield Hosp.

BRUNNING, John Seaforth, Fort Road, Gosport PO12 2DT — MD 1965 Bristol; MB ChB 1958; FRCPsych 1982, M 1971; DPM Eng. 1962. Prev: Cons. Psychiat. St. Jas. Hosp. Portsmouth.

BRUNSDON, David Frederick Valentine (retired) April Cottage, Littlehempston, Totnes TQ9 6LW Tel: 01803 862336 Fax: 01803 862336 — MB BS 1946 Lond.

BRUNSKILL, Janice 43 Stonesby Avenue, Leicester LE2 6TX — MB ChB 1995 Leic.

BRUNSKILL, Jonathan Mark Edwin Antelope Annex, West End, Northleach, Cheltenham GL54 3HG — MB BS 1991 Lond.

BRUNSKILL, Nigel John 16 Oakay, Frisby on the Wreake, Melton Mowbray LE14 2NF — MB ChB 1984 Leic.; MB ChB Leic. l984; MRCP (UK) 1987. Fell. Nephrol. Renal Div. Washington Univ. St. Louis Missouri, USA. Prev: Regist. (Nephrol.) Roy. Hallamsh. Hosp. Sheff.

BRUNSKILL, Mr Peter John Airedale General Hospital, Skipton Road, Steeton, Keighley BD20 6TD Tel: 01535 625211 Fax: 01535 651078 Email: peter.brunskill@anhst.nhs.net; Ingle Nook, Ferncliffe Drive, Utley, Keighley BD20 6HN Tel: 01535 665282 Fax: 01535 609831 Email: peter@brunskill.org — MB ChB 1980 Manch.; BSc (Med. Sci.) St. And 1977; T(OG) 1991; MRCOG 1986, FRCOG 1998; T(GP) 1986. (St Andrews/Manchester) Cons. O & G Airedale HA; Cons. Obst. & Gyn. Yorks. Clinic Bingley, W. Yorks.; Cons. Obst. & Gyn. Gisburne Pk. Hosp. Gisburne, Lancs. Socs: N. Eng. Obst. & Gyn. Soc.; Christ. Med. Fell.sh.; Brit. Soc. Gyn. Endoscopy. Prev: Sen. Regist. (O & G) Wessex RHA & Hon. Lect. Univ. Soton.; Regist. (O & G) Birm. Matern. Hosp. & Birm. & Midl. Hosp. for Wom.; SHO (O & G) St. Mary's Hosp. Manch.

BRUNT, Adrian Murray Staffordshire Oncology Centre, North Staffordshire Royal Infirmary, Princes Road, Hartshill, Stoke-on-Trent ST4 7LN Tel: 01782 554588 Fax: 01782 554649 Email: murraybrunt@yahoo.com — MB BS 1983 Lond.; MRCP (UK) 1986; FRCR 1990; T(R) (CO) 1991. (Westm.) Cons. Clin. Oncol. N. Staffs Hosp. Stoke-on-Trent.

BRUNT, Colin Vaughan 3 Beechfield, Norden Road, Bamford, Rochdale OL11 5PA — MB ChB 1995 Sheff.

BRUNT, Elizabeth Louise 59 Denmark Avenue, Woodley, Reading RG5 4RS — BM BS 1997 Nottm.

BRUNT, Karen Elizabeth Stannally Farm, Stoney Royd Lane, Todmorden OL14 8EP — MB ChB 1995 Leics.

BRUNT, Marina Evelyn Anne 17 Kingshill Road, Aberdeen AB15 5JY — MB ChB 1957 Liverp.; DObst RCOG 1959; B.Th 1989 (Aberdeen). Med. Off. Diabetic Clinic Aberd. Prev: SHO (Obst.) Liverp. Matern. Hosp.; Ho. Surg. Liverp. Roy. Infirm.

BRUNT, Nicola Jane 41 Wilby Street, Northampton NN1 5JX — MB ChB 1987 Manch.

BRUNT, Professor Peter William, OBE (retired) 17 Kingshill Road, Aberdeen AB15 5JY Tel: 01224 314204 Fax: 01224 316899 — MB ChB 1959 Liverp; MD Liverp. 1967; MFRCP Lond 1964; FRCP Lond. 1976; FRCP Ed 1981. Hon. Clin. Prof. Med. Univ. Aberd.; Phys. to HM the Qu. in Scotl.; Mem. (Vice-Chairm.) Med. Counc. Alcoholism. Prev: Hon. Lect. (Med.) Roy. Free Hosp. Lond.

BRUNTON, Carol Jock's Lodge, Balmonth Farm, Carnbee, Anstruther KY10 2RU — MB ChB 1987 Aberd.; MRCP (UK) 1990. Research Regist. (Nephrol.) Roy. Free Hosp. Lond.

BRUNTON, Dodson Patrick (retired) 13 Hamilton Place, Perth PH1 1BB Tel: 01738 627512 — MB ChB 1951 Glas.; DPH 1955; MFCM 1972. Prev: SCMO Grampian Health Bd.

BRUNTON, Frederick James (retired) Heathland Roman Road, Dibden Purlieu, Southampton SO45 4QJ Tel: 02380 843134 — MB BS 1950 Lond.; FRCP Lond. 1976, M 1956; FFR 1963; DMRD Eng. 1958. Prev: Cons. Radiol. Soton. Hosp. Gp.

BRUNTON, Joan Nicola 32 Mersey Avenue, Maghull, Liverpool L31 9PL — MB BS 1994 Lond.; BSc (Hons.) Psychol. Lond. 1991. (UMDS Guy's & St. Thos. Hosps.) SHO (Gen. Psychiat. & Rehabil.) Epsom Gen. Hosp.

BRUNTON, John Menzies (retired) 7 Transy Grove, Dunfermline KY12 7QP Tel: 01383 721800 — MB ChB St. And. 1943; DMRD Ed. 1953.

BRUNTON, John Norman Department of Radiology, Aberdeen Royal Infirmary, Aberdeen AB25 2ZN; 58 Broomhill Road, Aberdeen AB10 6HT — MB ChB 1985 Aberd.; MRCP (UK) 1990. Regist. (Radiol.) Aberd. Roy. Infirm. Prev: Regist. (Med.) Aberd. Roy. Infirm.; Regist. (Microbiol.) Roy. Infirm. Glas.; SHO (Med.) Monklands Dist. Gen. Hosp. Airdrie.

BRUNTON, Katherine Sarah Knightsbridge Medical Centre, 71-75 Pavilion Road, Knightsbridge, London SW1X 0ET Tel: 020 8237 2600 Fax: 020 8237 2626; 24 Friars Place Lane, Acton, London W3 7AP Tel: 020 8740 7808 — MB BS 1988 Lond.; MRCGP 1992; DRCOG 1991. GP Princip.; Cement Teach./Tutor for UnderGrad. Med. Stud.s Imperial Coll. Med. Sch.

BRUNYATE, Peter Hilliard Marshfield, Wick, Pucklechurch and Colerne Surgeries, 2 Back Lane, Marshfield, Chippenham SN14 8NQ Tel: 01225 891265 Fax: 01225 892149 — MB BChir 1970 Camb.; MA, MB Camb. 1970, BChir 1969; DObst RCOG 1972. (Camb. & St. Thos.) Prev: SHO (Paediat.) Roy. Devon & Exeter Hosp.; SHO (Accid & Emerg.) Roy. Devon & Exeter Hosp.; Ho. Off. (O & G) Lambeth Hosp.

BRUSH, John Philip 35 (2F2) Barony Street, Edinburgh EH3 6NX Email: basil@cableinet.co.uk — MB ChB 1989 Ed.; MRCP (UK) 1992; DMRD Ed. 1995; FRCR 1996. Regist. (Clin. Radiol.) Roy. Infirm. Edin. Socs: Collegiate Mem. RCP. Prev: SHO (Med.) S. Tyneside.

BRUTON, Dudley Malcolm (retired) Wildwood, 24 Rotherfield, Henley-on-Thames RG9 1NN Tel: 01491 575143 — MB BS 1956 Lond.; MSc Lond. 1974; FFOM RCP Lond. 1980, MFOM 1978; DIH Soc. Apoth. Lond. 1965. Prev: Dir. of Med. Servs. Rothmans of Pall Mall (Internat.) Ltd.

BRUTON, John Anthony Market Cross Surgery, 7 Market Place, Mildenhall, Bury St Edmunds IP28 7EG Tel: 01638 713109 Fax: 01638 718615 — MB BS 1985 Lond.; MRCGP 1989; DRCOG 1988.

BRUTON, Louie Ann Northfield Health Centre, St Helier's Road, Northfield, Birmingham B31 Tel: 0121 475 1534; 26 Chantry Road, Moseley, Birmingham B13 8DH — MB BS 1966 Lond.; MRCP (UK) 1972; MRCS Eng. LRCP Lond. 1965; DCH Eng. 1967. (St. Bart.) Prev: Research Fell. Inst. Child Health Birm. Univ.

BRUUNS, Jörg The White House, 97 South Street, Eastbourne BN21 4LR Tel: 01323 720606 Fax: 01323 412331 — State Exam Hannover 1991.

BRUZAUD, Joseph Donne (retired) Old Walls, 5 Wirksworth Road, Duffield, Belper DE56 4GH Tel: 01332 841003 — MRCS Eng. LRCP Lond. 1941. Prev: RAMC, TA, Regtl. Med. Off. Att. Derbysh. Yeo.

BRYAN, Mr Alan James Department of Cardiac Surgery, Bristol Royal Infirmary, Bristol BS2 8HW Tel: 0117 928 2821 Fax: 0117 928 3871; Whinstone House, Downside Road, Backwell, Bristol BS48 3DQ Tel: 01275 472710 — BM BS 1982 Nottm.; DM Nottm. 1995; BMedSci Nottm. 1980; FRCS (Cth) 1992; FRCS Eng. 1986. (Nottm.) Cons. & Hon. Sen. Lect. (Cardiac Surg.) Bristol Roy. Infirm. & Univ. Bristol. Socs: Soc. Cardiothoracic Surgs. GB & Irel.; Brit. Cardiac Soc. Prev: Fell. Cardiac Surg. Washington Univ. Med. Centre St. Louis, USA; Sen. Regist. (Cardiothoracic Surg.) Univ. Hosp. Wales; Regist. (Cardiothoracic Surg.) Papworth Hosp. Camb.

BRYAN, Amanda Jane — MB BS 1993 Lond.; MRCP (UK) 1998. (King's College, Lond.) Specialist Regist. Gen./Geriat. Med., S. W. Thames. Socs: Brit. Geriat. Soc.

BRYAN, Anthony Gary 13 Wellington Street, Stapleford, Nottingham NG9 7BE — BM BS 1983 Nottm.; BMedSci (Hons.), BM BS Nottm. 1983.

BRYAN, Bettina Alexandra 45 Brighton Terrace, Sheffield S10 1NT Tel: 0114 268 0566 Email: n.p.bryan@sheffield.ac.uk — State Exam Med 1988 Heidelberg; State Exam Med. Heidelberg 1988; PhD (Hist. & Philosophy Sci.) Lond. 1997; MSc (Hist. & Philosophy Sci.) Lond. 1992. (Heidelberg, Germany) Indep. Med. Adviser Benefit Agency; Research Asst. Dept. of Philosophy Univ. of Durh.. Socs: BMA; MDU; Roy. Soc. Med.

BRYAN, Elizabeth Mary The Multiple Births Foundation, Queen Charlotte's & Chelsea Hospital, Du Cane Rd, London W12 0SH Tel: 020 8383 3519 Fax: 020 8383 3041; Quercwm, Vowchurch, Hereford HR2 0RL Tel: 01981 550521 Fax: 01981 550521 Email: ebyan@higgins7.co.uk — MB BS Lond. 1966; MD Lond. 1976; FRCP Lond. 1989; MRCP (UK) 1970; MRCS Eng. LRCP Lond. 1966; FRCPCH 1997; DCH RCPS Glas. 1968. (St. Thos.) p/t Med. Dir. Multiple Births Foundat.; Hon. Cons. Paediat. Qu. Charlotte's & Chelsea Hosp. Socs: Fell. Roy. Soc. Soc. of Med.; Mem. of the Neonat. Soc.; Honarary Mem. of Brit. Assn. of Perinatal Med. Prev: Reader (Paediat.) Imperial Coll. Sch. of Med., Lond.; Director of the Multiple Births Foundat.

BRYAN, Isobel Rosemary Jane 29 Rydens Road, Walton-on-Thames KT12 3AB Tel: 01932 227673 Fax: 01932 246711 — MB ChB 1993 Ed.; BSc (Hons.) Ed. 1991.

BRYAN, Linda Helen The Surgery, High Street, Wombourne, Wolverhampton WV5 9DP Tel: 01902 892209 Fax: 01902 892441; Brackendale, Greensforge Lane, Stourton, Stourbridge DY7 5BB Tel: 01384 878084 — MB ChB 1983 Birm.

BRYAN, Mr Nicolas Paul 45 Brighton Terrace Road, Sheffield S10 1NT Tel: 0114 268 0566 Email: n.p.bryan@sheffield.ac.uk — MB BS 1991 Lond.; FRCS Eng. 1996. (St. Thos. Med. Sch. Lond.) Specialist Regist. (Urol), St James Hosp., Leeds. Socs: Med. Defence Union; BMA. Prev: SHO (Gen. Surg.) Roy. Marsden Hosp. Lond. & Barnsley Gen. Hosp.; SHO (Orthop.) Luton & Dunstable Hosp.; SHO (Gen. Surg.) Hammersmith Hosp.

BRYAN, Paul Lancelot Dominic Church Street Practice, Wantage Health Centre, Oxford Tel: 0123 573245; 22 Ormond Road, Wantage OX12 8EG Tel: 01235 764133 Email: paul.bryan@ntlworld.com — BM BCh 1978 Oxf.; BA Oxf. 1975; MRCGP 1991.

BRYAN, Richard Trevor 6 Clarenden Place, St Mary's Road, Harborne, Birmingham B17 0DZ — MB ChB 1995 Birm. Basic Surg. Trainee, Univ. Hosps., Birm. NHS Trust. Socs: BMA; MDU.

BRYAN, Sean Anthony 9 Lynn Drive, Eaglesham, Glasgow G76 0JJ — MB ChB 1979 Manch.

BRYAN, Stephen James Cullen 29 Lloyd Square, London WC1X 9AD — BM BCh 1980 Oxf.

BRYAN, Stuart Richard 1 Browfoot Close, Carnforth LA5 9XT — MB BS 1996 Newc.

BRYAN, Tamsin Ann 37 The Avenue, Andover SP10 3EP — MB BS 1993 Lond.

BRYAN-BROWN, Aubrey Bernard Edgar 4 The Ridgway, Sutton SM2 5JY — LRCPI & LM, LRSCI & LM 1957; LRCPI & LM, LRCSI & LM 1957; DObst. RCOG 1959.

BRYAN-JONES, Julie Catriona 29A Dunster Road, Stirling FK9 5HX — MB ChB 1994 Ed.

BRYANS, Richard Ashley Medical Centre, 140 Groomsport Road, Bangor BT20 5PE Tel: 028 9146 4444 Fax: 028 9127 2229; Tel: 0289 147 0102 — MB BCh BAO 1972 Belf.; DRCOG 1978.

BRYANS, Stephen Arthur (retired) 176 Cambridge Street, London SW1V 4QE Tel: 020 7821 9439 — MB BS 1956 Lond.; BSc Lond. 1953; DCH Eng. 1959. Prev: GP Lond.

BRYANT, Anna Jane Coach House, Southill Rd, Chislehurst BR7 5EE — MB BS 1996 Lond.

BRYANT, Bernard Simon (retired) 296 Didsbury Road, Heaton Mersey, Stockport SK4 3JH Tel: 0161 432 7595 Fax: 0161 432 7595 — MB ChB Manch. 1961. Prev: Gen. Pract. at Heaton Mersey. Stockport.

BRYANT, Catherine Anne 2B Oak Avenue, Enfield EN2 8LB — MB 1991 Camb.; BChir 1990; MRCP (UK) 1993.

BRYANT, Catherine Maria Portslade County Clinic, Old Shoreham Road, Portslade, Brighton BN41 1XR Fax: 01273 412078 — MB BS 1989 Lond.; DRCOG 1998; MRCGP 1995; DGM RCP Lond. 1991. (Roy. Free Hosp. Sch. Med.) GP Portslade.

BRYANT, Christopher John The Triangle Bungalow, Watergore, South Petherton TA13 5JQ — MB BS 1986 Queensland.

BRYANT, Gareth Lovemead Group Practice, Roundstone Surgery, Polebarn Circus, Trowbridge BA14 7EH Tel: 01225 752752 Fax: 01225 776388; Kingston House, 6 Greater Lane, Edington,

Westbury BA13 4QP — MB BS 1987 Lond.; MRCGP 1993; DCH RCP Lond. 1991. Prev: Trainee GP Bath VTS; SHO (Gen. Med.) Roy. Devon & Exeter Hosp.

BRYANT, Mr Geoffrey David Richard Royal Sussex County Hospital, Eastern Road, Brighton BN2 5BE Tel: 01273 696955 Fax: 01273 680627 Email: geoff.bryant@brighton-healthcare.com; 76 Overhill Drive, Brighton BN1 8WJ Tel: 01273 550648 Email: bryantg@pavilion.co.uk — MB BS 1981 Lond.; BSc (Hons.) Lond. 1977; FRCS Eng. 1985; FRCS Ed. 1984; MRCS Eng. LRCP Lond. 1980; DA (UK) 1989. (Lond. Hosp.) Cons. A & E Roy. Sussex Co. Hosp. Brighton. Socs: Fell. Fac. A & E Med.; Brit. Assn. Accid. & Emerg. Med. Prev: Sen. Regist. (A & E) Roy. Sussex Co. Hosp. Brighton; Regist. (A & E) St. Peter's Hosp. Chertsey; Regist. (Gen. Surg.) Brook Gen. Hosp. Woolwich.

BRYANT, Gerardine Maria Claire Leicestershire Health, Gwendolen Road, Leicester LE5 4QF Tel: 0116 273 1173 Fax: 0116 258569; Nether Ashe, Sutton Lane, Etwall, Derby DE65 6LQ Tel: 01283 732451 Email: gbryant@globalnet.co.uk — MB ChB 1983 Birm.; MRCGP 1988; DFFP 1993; DRCOG 1987; DCH RCP Lond. 1986. (Birmingham) Specialist Regist. (Pub. Health Med.) Leics. Health. Socs: Derby Med. Soc.; Sands Cox Soc. Prev: GP Princip.; GP Med. Advisor.

BRYANT, Jacqueline Elizabeth Marcham Health Centre, Marcham Road, Abingdon OX14 1BT Tel: 01235 522602 — MB ChB 1986 Birm.; MB ChB (Hons.) Birm. 1986; BSc (Hons.) Birm. 1983; MRCGP 1990; T(GP) 1991; DRCOG 1988; DCH RCP Lond. 1988.

BRYANT, Josephine Gail Orchard Surgery, Baldock Road, Buntingford SG9 9DL Tel: 01763 272410 Fax: 01763 273023 — MB BS 1970 Lond.; MRCS Eng. LRCP Lond. 1970.

BRYANT, Kathryn Muriel Eskdaill Medical Centre, Eskdaill Street, Kettering NN16 8RA Tel: 01536 513053 Email: kay.bryant@gp-k83013.nhs.uk; The Coach House, Glendon Hall, Kettering NN14 1QE — BM BS 1981 Nottm.; BMedSci Nottm. 1979; MRCGP 1986; DRCOG 1984. GP Princip.; GP Trainer, Kettering V.T.S.

BRYANT, Mr Kenneth Marrable (retired) 18 Claremont Road, Ealing, London W13 0DQ Tel: 020 8997 3671 — MB BS 1950 Lond.; FRCS Eng. 1958; MRCS Eng. LRCP Lond. 1950. Hon. Cons. Orthop. Surg. St. Geo. Hosp., & Bolingbroke Hosp. Lond. Prev: Sen. Regist. (Orthop.) & Regist. (Surg.) Char. Cross Hosp. Lond.

BRYANT, Mark George Hamlyn The Tynings, Church Lane, Stoulton, Worcester WR7 4RE — BM 1998 Soton.

BRYANT, Martin Thornton Tanner Hemel Hempstead General Hospital, Hillfield Road, Hemel Hempstead HP2 4AD Tel: 01582 763199; Felden Close, Sheethanger Lane, Felden, Hemel Hempstead HP3 0BG Tel: 01442 212319 Fax: 0870 0568 745 Email: mttb@hemelh.demon.co.uk — MB BChir 1961 Camb.; BA Camb. 1956; DObst RCOG 1962; FFA RCS Eng. 1974; T(Anaesth.) 1991. (Camb. & Lond. Hosp.) Cons. Anaesth. BUPA Hosp. Herts.; Dir. Pain Relief Serv. St Albans & Hemel Hempstead NHS Trust. Prev: Cons. Anaesth. & Clin. Tutor St Albans & Hemel Hempstead NHS Trust; Cons. Anaesth. Qu. Eliz. Hosp. Kings Lynn; Sen. Regist. W.m. & Bournemouth Hosps.

BRYANT, Mr Martyn John Department of Orthopaedics, Royal Hospital, Chesterfield Tel: 01246 277271 Ext: 3119 Fax: 01246 552660 — MB BS 1981 Lond.; MD Belf. 1991; FRCS (Orthop.) 1993; FRCS Eng. 1985. Cons. Orthop. Roy. Hosp. Coll. Socs: Fell. of the Brit. Orthop. Assoc.; Brit. Hip Soc.

BRYANT, Mr Paul Anthony 24 Westville Road, Barnsley S75 2TR Tel: 01226 203413 — MB BS 1972 Lond.; FRCS Eng. 1979. Cons. (Orthop.) Barnsley Dist. Gen. Hosp.

BRYANT, Pauline Anne Department of Primary Care and Population Sciences, Royal Free Hospital Medical School, Pond St., London NW3 Tel: 020 7794 0500; Flat B, 53 Englands Lane, Belsize Park, London NW3 4YD Tel: 020 7722 0178 — MB BS 1991 Lond.; DCH RCP Lond. 1996; DRCOG 1995; DGM RCP Lond. 1993. (Middlx. & Univ. Coll.) GP Regist. Hapmstead Gp. Pract. Lond.; Lect. (Community Based Teachg.) Roy. Free Univ. Med. Sch. Lond. Prev: Lond. Acad. Train. Scheme Regist.; GP Regist. Hampstead Gp. Pract.

BRYANT, Richard Charles 194 Blair Athol Road, Sheffield S11 7GE — MB BS 1996 Lond.

***BRYANT, Richard John** 26 Sackville Road, Crookes, Sheffield S10 1GT — MB ChB 1998 Sheff.; MB ChB Sheff 1998.

BRYANT, Richard Neil Devon Square Surgery, Devon Square Surgery, Newton Abbot TQ12 2HH Tel: 01626 332182 — MB BS 1983 Lond.; BA Camb. 1980; MRCGP 1987; T (GP) 1991; DCH RCP Lond. 1986; DRCOG 1985. (Kings) GP Occupat. Med. Centrax Ltd. Socs: Exeter Medico-Legal Soc.

BRYANT, Ruth Mary Tel: 01788 544264 Fax: 01788 575783; 216 Dunchurch Road, Rugby CV22 6HR Tel: 01788 816341 — MB ChB 1971 Bristol; FFA RCSI 1977; DA Eng. 1975; DObst RCOG 1973. Med. Off. Rugby Sch.; PCG Bd. Mem. Socs: BMA; MOSA. Prev: Trainee GP Lond. VTS; Regist. (Anaesth.) Middlx. Hosp. Lond.

BRYANT, Victoria Musgrave 24 Westville Road, Barnsley S75 2TR Tel: 01226 203413 — BM BCh 1971 Oxf.; DO Eng. 1974. Clin. Asst. (Ophth.) Barnsley Dist. Gen. Hosp.

BRYARS, Mr John Howard 'Long Ridge', 58 Harmony Hill, Lisburn BT27 4ET — MB BCh BAO (2nd cl. Hons.) Belf. 1969; MD (Hons.) Belf. 1977; FRCS Ed. (Ophth.) 1974; DO RCPSI 1972. Cons. Ophth. Roy. Vict. Hosp. Belf. Socs: FFCOphth; Assoc. Mem. Ulster Med. Soc.

BRYARS, Norah Elizabeth Long Ridge, 58 Harmony Hill, Lisburn BT27 4ET — MB BCh BAO Belf. 1969; DCH RCPSI 1971. Clin. Med. Off. Lisburn Health Centre; Assoc. Mem. Ulster Med. Soc. Socs: Assoc. Mem. Ulster Med. Soc.; Assoc. Mem. Brit. Assoc. Comm. Doctors in Audiol.

BRYCE, David Kirk Lakenham Surgery, 24 Ninham Street, Norwich NR1 3JJ Tel: 01603 765559 Fax: 01603 766790 — MRCS Eng. LRCP Lond. 1968.

BRYCE, Fiona Christine Dept OBS &Gynaecol, Friardale Hospital, Northallerton DL6 1JG Tel: 01609 777 1444 — MB ChB 1979 Leeds; MRCOG 1984; FRCOG 1997. (Leeds) Cons. O & G Friarage Hosp. N.allerton. Prev: Sen. Regist. (O & G) Leeds.

BRYCE, Gillian Mary Musgrove Park Hospital, Taunton TA1 5DA Tel: 01823 333444 Fax: 01823 344517 — MB ChB 1980 Glas.; FRCS Ed. 1984; FFAEM 1993. Cons. A & E Med. Taunton & Som. Trust; Med. Dir. W. Country Ambul. Trust. Socs: Roy. Soc. of Med.; Brit. Ambul. Serv.s Med. Advisers Gp.

BRYCE, Iain Gardner 23 Thornhill Gardens, Newton Mearns, Glasgow G77 5FU — MB ChB 1984 Glas.; FRCOphth 1991. (Glasgow) Cons. Ophth. Surg. S.ern Gen. Hosp./ Vict. Inf. Glas.; Cons. Ophtalmic Surg.; Ross Hall Hosp., Glas.; HCI Med. Centre, Glas.

BRYCE, James Craig (retired) 6 Glen Gardens, Falkirk FK1 5LQ Tel: 01324 622285 — MB ChB Glas. 1950; MRCGP 1958. Prev: Assoc. Specialist Roy. Scott. Nat. Hosp. Larbert.

BRYCE, James Graham 24 Adelaide Place, Dundee DD3 6LF — MB ChB 1977 Glas.; MRCPsych 1982; DRCOG 1979.

BRYCE, Joycelyn Ada Community Paediatric Department, Borders General Hospital NHS Trust, Borders General Hospital, Melrose TD6 6BS Tel: 01896 754333 Fax: 01896 822887; East Fordel, High Cross Avenue, Melrose TD6 9SQ Tel: 0189 682 2354 — MB ChB Glas. 1970. (Glas.) SCMO Borders Child Health Unit.

BRYCE, Kathryn Anne 2 Talbot Road, London SE22 8EH — MB BS 1991 Lond.; MRCP (UK) 1995.

BRYCE, Richard Paul Scotia Pharmaceuticals Ltd., Scotia House, Castle Business Park, Stirling FK9 4TZ Tel: 01786 895100 Fax: 01786 895450; Drumside, Clathy, Gask, Crieff PH7 3PH — MB ChB 1981 Ed.; MRCGP 1987; Dip. Pharm. Med. RCP (UK) 1996; DFFP 1993; DCH RCP Lond. 1990; DRCOG 1988; AFPM 1996. (Ed. Univ.) Med. Dir. Scotia Pharmaceut. Socs: BMA. Prev: Head. Med. Dept. Servier Laborats. Ltd. Slough; Med. Off. (HQ) Brit. Gas. plc Lond.; Surg. Lt. Cdr RN.

BRYCE-SMITH, Roger (retired) W White Roses, Cabin, Bishops Castle SY9 5JG Tel: 01588 638746 — BM BCh 1942 Oxf.; MA Oxf. 1943, DM 1955, BM BCh 1942; FFA RCS Eng. 1953; DA Eng. 1947. Prev: Cons. Anaesth. Oxf. AHA.

BRYCESON, William Tycho The Bull's House, 3 Rousham Road, Tackley, Kidlington OX5 3AJ — MB BS 1996 Newc.

BRYDEN, Alyson Muir Ninewells Hospital, Dundee DD1 9SY — MB ChB 1992 Glas.

BRYDEN, Mr Archibald Alastair Gordon Academic Urology Unit, 1 Floor, Royal Hallamshire Hospital S10 2JF Tel: 0114 2713757 Fax: 0114 2712268 Email: gbryden@hotmail.com — MB ChB 1990 Manch.; FRCS (Urol) 2000; MD Manch. 2000; BSc (Med. Sci.) St. And. 1987; FRCS Eng. 1994. (St. Andrews/ Manch) Sen. Lect. & Hons. Cons. Urological Surg.. Univ. Sheff./ Roy. Hallamshire

Hosp. Socs: Brit. Assn. Urol. Surgs. Prev: Clin. Lect. in Urol., N. W. region, higher Urol. Train. scheme.

BRYDEN, Daniele Clare 1 St Aidan's Close, Outwood, Radcliffe, Manchester M26 1YJ Tel: 0161 724 5424 — MB ChB 1990 Manch.; FRCA 1995. Cons. Anaesth. Salford Rpy. Hosp. NHS Trust.

BRYDEN, Fiona Marion 11 Cleveden Gardens, Glasgow G12 0PU — MB ChB 1984 Ed.; BSc (Hons.) Ed. 1982; FRCR 1989. Cons. Radiol. Stobhill Hosp. Glas. Prev: Sen. Regist. (Radiol.) Glas. Roy. Infirm. Glas.; Regist. (Radiol.) S.. Gen. Hosp. Glas.

BRYDEN, George Towers (retired) Myreton, 6 Thistle Avenue, Grangemouth FK3 8YH Tel: 01324 483735 — MB ChB 1950 Glas.

BRYDEN, Helen Stephens 19 Fairfax Avenue, Glasgow G44 5AL — MB BCh 1982 Wales; MRCGP 1986; DFFP 1994; T(GP) 1991; DRCOG 1984. Med. Advisor Benefits Agency Med. Servs. Glas. Prev: Princip GP Glas.; GP & Occupat. Phys. Hong Kong.

BRYDEN, John Stephens Bryden Consulting Ltd., 34 Sherbrooke Drive, Glasgow G41 5AA Tel: 0141 427 2959 Fax: 0141 427 2959 — MB ChB 1956 Glas.; MSc Strathclyde 1971; MRCP Glas. 1993; FFPHM 1977, M 1974; Dip. Soc. Med. Ed. 1968. Indep. Cons. Pub. Health Glas.; Hon. Sen. Clin. Lect. Glas. Univ. Prev: Cons. Pub. Health Gtr. Glas. HB; Chief Admin. Med. Off. Argyll & Clyde HB.

BRYDEN, Peter James The Surgery, 174 Lower Glen Road, St Leonards-on-Sea TN37 7AR Tel: 01424 721616/852270 Fax: 01424 854812 — MRCS Eng. LRCP Lond. 1976; BSc Lond. 1971, MB BS 1976; MRCGP 1981; DGM RCP Lond. 1989. (Roy. Free) Socs: Chairm. E. Sussex MAAG.

BRYDIE, Alan David 14 Elizabeth Street, Stirling FK8 2HL — MB ChB 1994 Glas.

BRYDIE, David Hardie 3 Broomley Drive, Giffnock, Glasgow G46 6PD — MB ChB 1991 Glas.

BRYDIE, Sarah Elizabeth Flat 2/3, 16 Plantation Park Gardens, Glasgow G51 1NW — MB ChB 1992 Glas.

BRYDON, Catherine Watson Dept. of Anaesthesia, Western Infirmary, Glasgow G11 6NT Tel: 0141 211 2069 Email: cath.brydon@dial.pipex.com; Tel: 0141 339 9643 — MB ChB 1986 Aberd.; FRCA 1991. Cons. Anaesth. W. Glas. Hosp. Univ. NHS Trust.

BRYDON, Roger Allan 4 Thomson Road, Currie, Edinburgh EH14 5HP — MB ChB 1996 Aberd.

BRYDON, Stewart Michael Health Centre, Springfield Road, Stornoway HS1 2PS Tel: 01851 704888 Fax: 01851 703005 — MB ChB 1982 Ed.; BSc 1979 Edinburgh. (Ed.) Prev: GP I. of Benbecula W.. Isles; SHO (Psychiat.) Sunnyside Roy. Hosp. Montrose; SHO (Paediat. Surg.) Roy. Hosp. Sick Childr. Glas.

BRYDONE, Gavin Foster Crerar Milton Surgery, 132 Mountcastle Drive South, Edinburgh EH15 3LL; Gordon Bank, Broomieknowe, Lasswade EH18 1LN Tel: 0131 663 2488 — MB ChB 1969 Ed.; BSc Ed. 1966. (Univ. Ed.)

BRYER, Anthony George (retired) Cae Parc, Trallong, Brecon LD3 8HP Tel: 01874 638848 Fax: 01874 638848 Email: anthbryer@excite.co.uk — MB BS 1956 Lond.; MRCS Eng. LRCP Lond. 1956; DObst RCOG 1959. Prev: Hosp. Pract. (Orthop.) Hemel Hempstead Gen. Hosp.

BRYETT, Anne Gordon Binscombe Medical Centre, 106 Binscombe, Farncombe, Godalming GU7 3QL Tel: 01483 415115; 72 Busbridge Lane, Godalming GU7 1QQ — MB BS 1977 Lond.; MRCS Eng. LRCP Lond. 1977. Prev: GP Edgeware.

BRYETT, Kevin Alan c/o Pasteur Merieux MSD, Clivemont House, Clivemont Road, Maidenhead SL6 7BU Tel: 01628 785291 Fax: 01628 71722; The Dressmakers House, Alma Road, Windsor SL4 3HN Tel: 01753 840310 Fax: 01753 842770 — MB BS 1976 Lond.; MRCS Eng. LRCP Lond. 1976; MFPM 1989; DRCOG 1978. (St. Geo.) Managing Dir. - German Region Pasteur Merieux MSD; Dir. of New Business Developm. - PMMSD Gp. Europe. Prev: Managing Dir. Pasteur Merieux MSD (UK & Irel.); Area Med. Dir. (Europe) Inst. Merieux Gp. Lyon France; Med. Dir. Merieux UK.

BRYLEWSKI, Jane Eugenie The Slade House, Headington, Oxford OX3 7JH Tel: 01865 228101 Fax: 01865 228182 Email: jane.b@btinternet.co.uk; The Willows, Signet, Burford OX18 4JQ Tel: 01993 822479 Fax: 01993 824749 Email: jane.b@btinternet.co.uk — MB BS 1974 Lond.; BSc (Hons.) Lond. 1974; MRCPsych 1981. (St. Geo. Hosp. Med. Sch.) Cons. Psychiat. (Learning Disabil.) Slade Hse. Oxf. Prev: Sen. Regist. (Learning Disabil.) Slade Hosp. Oxf.

BRYLEWSKI, Stephen, Principal Nuffield Health Centre, Welch Way, Witney OX28 6JQ Tel: 01993 703641; The Willows, Singnet Farm North, Burford OX18 4JQ — MB BS Lond. 1973; DRCOG 1976.

BRYNBERG, Michael (retired) 78 Marlborough Mansions, Cannon Hill, London NW6 1JT Tel: 020 7435 1946 — Med. Dip. Vilno 1933. Prev: Mem. BMA.

BRYNES, Gillian Dawn 13 Hollybank Cr, Banchory AB31 5TX — MB ChB 1997 Ed.

BRYNES, Russell Mark The Surgery, 1 Kimberworth Road, Rotherham S61 1AH Tel: 01709 561442/562319 Fax: 01709 740690 — MB ChB 1982 Manch.; MRCGP 1986; DA (UK) 1984.

BRYSON, Adam West Glasgow Hospitals University NHS Trust, Western Infirmary, Dumbarton Road, Glasgow G11 6NT Tel: 0141 211 2333 Fax: 0141 211 1920; Minerva Lodge, 4 Seven Sisters, Lenzie, Kirkintilloch, Glasgow G66 3AW Tel: 0141 776 7875 Email: adam.bryson@aol.com — MB ChB 1969 Glas.; FFPHM 1995; MRCP Glas. 1996; MRCGP 1978; MPH Glas. 1983; FRCP Glas. 1998. (Glas.) Cons. Pub. Health Med. & Med. Dir. W. Glas. Hosps. Univ. NHS Trust. Socs: BMA; Glas. Roy. Med-Chir. Soc. Prev: Unit Med. Off. W.. Infirm. Glas./Gartnavel Hosp. Unit; Cons. (Primary Care) Armed Forces Hosp. Riyadh, Saudi Arabia; GP Kirkintilloch.

BRYSON, Mr Arthur Frank, OBE (retired) 4 Lewes Crescent, Brighton BN2 1FH Tel: 01273 699330 — MA Camb., MB 1937, BChir 1936; FRCS Eng. 1937; MRCS Eng. LRCP Lond. 1935. Prev: Cons. Orthop. Surg. Ilford Hosp. Gp.

BRYSON, Caroline Anna 17 Edenderry Cottages, Shaws Bridge, Belfast BT8 8RY Tel: 01232 644882 Email: c.a.bryson@tack21.com — MB BCh BAO 1993 Belf.; MRCOG, 1998. Specialist Regist. (O & G) Craigavon Area Hosp., Portadown. Socs: BMA; Ulster Obs. & Gyn. Soc. Prev: SHO (O & G) Belf. City Hosp.; SHO (O & G) Roy. Matern.; Specialist Regist. (O & G) Lagan Valley Hosp. Lisburn.

BRYSON, David Drysdale 4 Middleton Road, Hutton Rudby, Yarm TS15 0JT Tel: 01642 700634 — MB ChB 1953 Glas.; DPH 1956; FFOM RCP Lond. 1986, MFOM 1978; DIH St. And. 1963. (Glas.) Occupat. Health Cons. Cleveland; Cleveland Occupt. Health Assoc. Exec.; Clin. Tutor (Occupat. Health) Univ. Newc.; Med. Adviser MTM plc Rudby Hall. Prev: Chief Med. ICI Chem. & Polymers Ltd. Wilton; Dep. Chief Med. Off. Imperial Chem. Industries PLC. Wilton; Sen. Med. Off. Organics Div. I.C.I. Stevenson.

BRYSON, Elizabeth Alice Kelburn Street Medical Practice, 10 Kelburn Street, Millport KA28 0DT Tel: 01475 530329 Fax: 01475 530338; Clifton, 47 Marine Parade, Millport KA28 0EF Tel: 01475 530338 — MB ChB 1976 Aberd.; DRCOG 1978.

BRYSON, Gareth William 4 Seven Sisters, Kirkintilloch, Glasgow G66 3AW — MB ChB 1998 Glas.; MB ChB Glas 1998.

BRYSON, Isabella Alma Bank, 15 Lovers Walk, Dumfries DG1 1LR Tel: 01387 255288 — MB ChB Ed. 1946; DLO Eng. 1950. (Univ. Ed.) Prev: Asst. ENT Surg. Dumfries & Galloway Roy. Infirm.

BRYSON, James Athol Mackenzie Kelburn Street Medical Practice, 10 Kelburn Street, Millport KA28 0DT Tel: 01475 530329 Fax: 01475 530338 — MB ChB 1976 Glas. GP Princip. Millport.

BRYSON, Joan Margaret Fell Cottage, 123 Kells Lane, Low Fell, Gateshead NE9 5XY Tel: 0191 487 2656 Fax: 0191 491 0473; 33 Earlswood Ave, Low Fell, Gateshead NE9 6AH — MB ChB 1981 Ed.; MRCGP 1986; DCCH RCP Ed. 1985.

BRYSON, Joanna Mary 14 Whiteside, Newtownards BT23 4UP — MB BS 1997 Lond.

BRYSON, John Millard (retired) 2- 5 Claremont Buildings, Claremont Bank, Shrewsbury SY1 1RJ Tel: 01743 362090 — MB BCh BAO 1936 Dub.; MA, MB BCh BAO Dub. 1936; MRCGP 1953. Prev: Med. Off. H.M. Prison Shrewsbury.

BRYSON, Mr John Richard 6 Marine Terrace, Waterloo, Liverpool L22 5PR; 31 Rodney Street, Liverpool L1 9EH Tel: 0151 709 8522 — MB BS 1966 Lond.; FRCS Eng. 1974; MRCS Eng. LRCP Lond. 1966; DObst RCOG 1968. (Lond. Hosp.) Cons. Plastic & Burns Surg. Whiston & Alder Hey Hosps.; Clin. Lect. Univ. Liverp. Prev: Sen. Regist. (Plastic Surg.) Bangour Gen. Hosp. & Roy. Hosp. Sick Childr. Edin.; Regist. (Plastic Surg.) St. Lawrence Hosp. Chepstow.

BRYSON, John Rowan (retired) The Health Centre, Market St., Colne BB8 0LJ Tel: 01282 862451 Fax: 01282 871698 — MB ChB 1948 Glas. Chairm. Lancs. LMC. Prev: Ho. Surg. Glas. Roy. Infirm.

BRYSON, Jonathan Learmont School Lane Surgery, School Lane, Thetford IP24 2AG Tel: 01842 753115; 19 Little London Lane,

Northwold, Thetford IP26 5NH — MB BS 1985 Lond.; MRCGP 1990. Prev: Community Med. Off. Frimley Childr. Centre; SHO Frimley Pk. Hosp. VTS; SHO (A & E) Roy. Surrey Co. Hosp. Guildford.

BRYSON, Lawrence George South Tyneside District Hospital, Harton Lane, South Shields NE34 0FL Tel: 0191 454 8888 Fax: 0191 202 4180; 3 Littledene, Gateshead NE9 5AF Tel: 0191 482 3721 — MB BS 1968 Newc.; FRCP Edin. 1999; FRCP Lond. 1985. Cons. Phys. S. Tyneside Dist. Hosp. Socs: Roy. Soc. of Med. (Fell.). Prev: Regist. (Cardiol.) St. Thos. Hosp. Lond.; Ho. Phys. & Sen. Regist. (Gen. Med.) Roy. Vict. Infirm. Newc.

BRYSON, Mary Catherine 15 Tullyheran Road, Maghera BT46 5JQ Tel: 01648 45403 Fax: 01648 45780 Email: glenshegga@aol.com; Casa de los Estudios, Las Cruces, La Libertao, Peten, Guatemala Email: tikalnet@guate.net — MB BCh BAO 1993 Belf.; Dip. Child Health Roy. Coll. Phys. Irel. & Roy. Coll. Surg. Irel. 1996. Co-ordinator Wom.'s Health Integrated Community Health Project Peten Guatemala. Socs: BMA.

BRYSON, Michael Robert Department of Anaesthesia, Royal Victoria Infirmary, Newcastle upon Tyne Tel: 0191 232 5131; 18 Highbury, Jesmond, Newcastle upon Tyne NE2 3DX Tel: 0191 281 4858 Email: michael@bryson78.freeserve.co.uk — MB BS 1965 Durh.; FFA RCS Eng. 1972. (Durh.) Cons. Anaesth. Newc. Roy. Vict. Infirm.; Hon. Lect. Med. Sch. Newc.; Regional Assessor, (Anaesth.), confidential enquiry into Matern. deaths. Socs: Assn. Anaesths.; (Comm.) Obst. Anaesth. Assn.; Eur. Soc. Regional Anaesth. Prev: Pres. N. Eng. Soc. Anaesth.; Chairm. Working Party Anaesth. Asst. Obst. Units (N. Region); Chairm. Regional Working Party Implications on Changes to Obtaining Consent. (N. Region).

BRYSON, Michelle Sarah Flat 21R, 94 Deanston Drive, Glasgow G41 3LH — MB ChB 1995 Leics.

BRYSON, Neil Henry Learmont Bletchingdon Road Surgery, Bletchingdon Road, Islip, Kidlington OX5 2TQ Tel: 01865 371666 Fax: 01865 842475 — BM BCh 1983 Oxf.; BA Oxf. 1980, BM BCh 1983; MRCGP 1987; DRCOG 1987. Prev: Trainee GP Boston Lincs. VTS; Ho. Surg. Roy. United Hosp. Bath; Ho. Phys. John Radcliffe Hosp. Oxf.

BRYSON, Patrick Harold Ross The Karis Medical Centre, Waterworks Road, Edgbaston, Birmingham B16 9AL Tel: 0121 454 0661 Fax: 0121 454 9104; 29 Wentworth Road, Birmingham B17 9SN — MB ChB 1980 Birm.; MRCGP 1984; DRCOG 1985; DCH RCP Lond. 1983.

BRYSON, Patrick Niall Duke Medical Centre, 28 Talbot Road, Sheffield S2 2TD Tel: 0114 272 0689 Fax: 0114 275 1916; Chantrey House, 67 Brookhouse Hill, Fulwood, Sheffield S10 3TB — MB BCh BAO 1969 NUI; DRCOG 1977.

BRYSON, Philip John Villiers The Diving Diseases Research Centre, The South West Hyperbaric Medical Centre, Tamar Science Park, Derriford, Plymouth PL6 8BQ Tel: 01752 209999 Fax: 01752 209115; Foxworthy, Lutton, Ivybridge PL21 9SS Tel: 01752 837852 — MB ChB 1983 Bristol; MRCGP 1988; DCH 1986; DRCOG 1987. (Univ. Bristol Med. Sch.) Phys. Diving Dis. Research Centre; Med. Adv. Sub Aqua Assn. Plymouth; Dir. - Phase 1 Clin. Trials Unit Ltd.; Mem. Plymouth Tissue Viability Advis. Panel; Mem. Brit. Facial & Audiological Implant Gp.; Mem. Brit. Diving Med. Advis. Comm. Socs: Undersea & Hyperbaric Med. Soc.; S. Pacific Undersea Med. Soc.; BMA. Prev: Manager Clin. Physiol./Pharmacol. Lab Phase 1, Plymouth.

BRYSON, Philippa Robin Claire 102A Kynance, Treliske Hospital, Truro TR1 3LJ; Chantrey House, 67 Brookhouse Hill, Fulwood, Sheffield S10 3TB — MB ChB 1996 Liverp.

BRYSON, Thomas Henry Learmont, TD 10 South Drive, Upton, Wirral CH49 6LA Tel: 0151 677 3324 — MB ChB 1953 Glas.; FFA RCS Eng. 1959; DA Eng. 1958. (Glas.) Cons. Anaesth. Liverp. Matern. Hosp. & Roy. Liverp. Univ. Hosp.; Lt. Col. RAMC TA. Socs: (Ex-Pres.) Obst. Anaesth. Assn.; Assn. Anaesth. Prev: Hon. Surg. to H.M. the Qu.; Lect. (Anaesth.) Univ. Liverp.; Cons. Anaesth. Govt. of Uganda.

BRZECHWA-AJDUKIEWICZ, Andrew Adam 36 St Gabriel's Road, London NW2 4SA — MB ChB 1961 Bristol; MRCP (UK) 1968.

BRZESKI, Maciej Stefan Rheumatology Unit, Falkirk & District Royal Infirmary, Major's Loan, Falkirk FK1 5QE Tel: 01324 616021 — MB ChB 1983 Manch.; BSc (Hons.) St. And. 1980; MRCP (UK) 1988; FRCP (Glas.) 1987. Cons. Rheum. Falkirk & Dist. Roy. Infirm. & Stirling Roy. Infirm. Prev: Sen. Regist. (Rheum. & Gen. Med.) Stoke Mandeville Hosp. & Wexham Pk. Hosp.; Regist. (Rheum.) Glas. Roy. Infirm.

BRZEZICKI, Anthony John Tel: 020 8651 1141 Fax: 020 8651 5011; Twelve Trees, 33 Kingswood Way, South Croydon CR2 8QL — MB BS 1979 Lond.; MRCGP 1984; DRCOG 1984; Cert. Family Plann. JCC 1984. (Middlesex) Course Organiser E. Surrey VTS; Chair Centr. Croydon PCG.

BSAT, Raif Abdul-Ghani 18 Albany Gardens, Hampton Lane, Solihull B91 2PT — MB BCh 1975 Cairo.

BU'LOCK, Frances Ann Dept of Paediatric Cardiol, Glenfield Hosp, Groby St, Leicester LE3 9QP Tel: 0116 287 1471 Fax: 0116 250 2422; Brantwood, 200 Station Rd, Glenfield, Leicester LE3 8GT Tel: 0116 232 2248 Fax: 0116 250 2422 Email: malcolm.mcgregor@virgin.net — BM BCh 1985 Oxf.; MA Camb. 1986, BA (Hons.) 1982; MD Camb. 1995; MRCP (UK) 1988. Cons. (Paediat Cardiol.) Glenfield Hosp Leicester. Socs: Brit. Cardiac Soc.; BMA; BPCA. Prev: Sen. Regist. (Paediat. Cardiol.) Alder Hey Childr. Hosp.; Regist. (Paediat. Cardiol.) Birm. Childr. Hosp.; Research Fell. (Paediat. Cardiol.) Roy. Hosp. Sick Childr. Bristol.

BUBB, Anthony Roger Beccles Medical Centre, 7-9 St. Marys Road, St. Marys Road, Beccles NR34 9NQ Tel: 01502 712662 Fax: 01502 712906; Greenacres, Barsham, Beccles NR34 8HN Tel: 01502 713314 — MB BChir 1968 Camb.; MA Camb. 1968; FRCS Eng. 1973. (Camb. & St. Geo.) Socs: BMA. Prev: Regist. (Gen. Surg.) St. Margt.'s Hosp. Epping; SHO (Surg. Rotat.) United Norwich Gp. Hosps.; Cas. Off. & Ho. Phys. St. Geo. Hosp. Lond.

BUBB, Samantha Clare 64 Windsor Terrace, South Gosforth, Newcastle upon Tyne NE3 1YL — MB BS 1998 Newc.; MB BS Newc 1998.

BUBNA-KASTELIZ, Bruno St Martin's Hospital, Midford Road, Bath BA2 5RP Tel: 01225 832383 — MB BS 1965 Lond.; FRCP Lond 1987, M 1974; MRCS Eng. LRCP Lond. 1965. (St. Bart.) Cons. Geriat. Bath & W. NHS Trust; Co-Dir. Inst. for Refugee Health Care Studies (Sch. of Postgrad. Med. Univ.Bath); Clin. Tutor Bath & W. NHS Trust. Socs: Brit. Geriat. Soc. Prev: Sen. Regist. Char. Cross Hosp. Lond.; Regist. Harefield Hosp.; Ho. Off. Mt. Vernon Hosp. N.wood.

BUCH, Ashesh Narendra 44 Lonsdale Road, Walsall WS5 3HJ — MB ChB 1992 Birm.

BUCH, Keyur Anilkant Department of Orthopaedics, Louth County Hospital, High Holme Road, Louth LN11 0EU — MB BS 1987 Gujarat; MB BS Gujarat, India 1987.

BUCH, Mamta Heena 44 Lonsdale Road, Walsall WS5 3HJ — MB ChB 1995 Birm.

BUCH, Maya Hema 44 Lonsdale Road, Walsall WS5 3HJ — MB ChB 1995 Birm.

BUCHALTER, Ian Mark Tregenna Group Practice, Portway, Woodhouse Park, Manchester M22 0EP Tel: 0161 499 3777, 020 8919 5657 Fax: 0161 493 9119, 020 8985 0278 — MB BCh BAO 1984 NUI; LRCPI & LM, LRCSI & LM 1984; DObst RCPI 1986. GP Manch.

BUCHALTER, Maurice Brian 11 Lower Cwrt-y-Vil, Penarth CF64 3HQ — MB BCh BAO 1980 Dub.; MRCPI 1982.

BUCHAN, Professor Alan Robson March House, The Common, Windermere LA23 1JQ Tel: 01539 488882; 5 Glebe Road, Oadby, Leicester LE2 2LD Tel: 0116 270 4345 Email: arb@arbuchan.fsnet.co.uk — MB BS 1953 Durh.; MD Newc. 1966; DPH 1960; FFPHM 1976, M 1972. Emerit. Prof. Dir. Pub. Health & Dist. Med. Off. Leics. HA. Socs: Leic. Med. Soc.; Leic. Medico Legal Soc. Prev: Hon. Prof. Community Med. Leicester Univ.; Hon. Clin. Teach. Fac. Med. Leicester Med. Sch.; Area Med. Off. Leics. AHA (T).

BUCHAN, Professor Alastair Mitchell Department of Clinical Neuroscience, Alberta Stroke Program, 1162, 1403-29 Street North West, Calgary AB T2N 2T9, Canada Tel: 403 670 1582 Fax: 403 670 1602 Email: buchan@acs.ucalgary.ca; 5 Giebe Road, Oadby, Leicester LE2 2LD Tel: 01162 704345 — BM BCh 1980 Oxf.; MA Camb. 1981; MRCP (UK) 1983; FRCP Ed 1997; LMCC 1986; FRCPC (Neurol.) 1986. Prof. (Stroke Research) Univ. Calgary; Cons. (Neurol.) Foothills Med. Centre; Scientist Alberta Heritage Med. Research Foundat.; Dir. Alberta Stroke Progr. Socs: Fell. Stroke Co. Amer. Heart Assoc.; Amer. Acad. Neurol.; Soc. Neurosci. Prev: MRC

Centennial Fell. Neurol. Cornell Univ. Med. Sch. New York; SHO (Med. & Neurol.) Radcliffe Infirm. Oxf.; SHO (Med. & Cardiol.) Hammersmith Hosp. Roy. Postgrad. Med. Sch.

BUCHAN, Alexander Healthcall Services PLC, Massey Road, Thornaby, Stockton-on-Tees TS17 4EY Tel: 01642 631000 Fax: 01642 631002; Oaklea, 7 William St, Cairnbulg, Fraserburgh AB43 8WS Tel: 01346 582613 Fax: 01346 582613 Email: alexbuchan@doctors.org.uk — MB ChB 1983 Aberd. Locum Gen. Practitioner, Healthcall Serv.s PLC, Thornaby; Gen. Practitioner, Princip. Thorntree Surg., MiddlesBoro.

BUCHAN, Mr Alexander Campbell (retired) Glenora, 11 Marine Parade, North Berwick EH39 4LD Tel: 01620 893531 — LRCP LRCS Ed. LRFPS Glas. 1940; FRCS Ed. 1943; FDS RCS Ed. 1970, L 1939. Prev: Cons. Plastic Surg. Bangour Gen. Hosp.

BUCHAN, Alexander Stewart 21 Chalmers Crescent, Edinburgh EH9 1TS Tel: 0131 667 1127 — MB ChB 1966 Ed.; FFA RCS Eng. 1970. (Ed.) Cons. (Anaesth.) Roy. Infirm. Edin. Socs: Scott. Soc. of Anaesth.; Obst. Anaesth. Assn.; Assn. Anaesths. Gt. Britain & Irel.

BUCHAN, Andrew Bruce Wallace Town Health Centre, Green Wing, Lyon Street, Dundee DD4 6RB Tel: 01382 459519 Fax: 01382 453110 — MB ChB 1974 Dundee; BSc (Med. Sci.) St. And. 1971; DFMSc 2001; DRCOG 1977. (St. And. & Dundee) Prev: Res. Med. Off. Roy. Brisbane Hosp., Australia; SHO (O & G) Bangour Gen. Hosp. Broxburn; SHO (Psychiat.) Roy. Dundee Liff Hosp.

BUCHAN, Catriona Corrine Kirkhouse, Beeswing, Dumfries DG2 8JF — MB ChB 1989 Glas.; MRCGP 1993.

BUCHAN, David Allan 134 Ochiltree, Dunblane FK15 0PB — MB ChB 1985 Glas. Prev: Regist. Rotat. (Psychiat.) Murray Roy. Hosp. Perth.

BUCHAN, David Reginald (retired) 3 Walton Mews, Hanley Road, Malvern Wells, Malvern WR14 4PH — MRCS Eng. LRCP Lond. 1929. Prev: Capt. RAMC.

BUCHAN, Gwynneth Isabel 10 Binny Park, Ecclesmachan, Broxburn EH52 6NP — MB ChB 1967 Birm. (Birm.) Staff Grade (Community Paediat.) St. John's Hosp. W. Lothian. Prev: Med. Off. Dept. Comm. Med. Lothians HB.

BUCHAN, Hazel (retired) High Cross House, 37 High Cross Avenue, Melrose TD6 9SQ Tel: 01896 822254 — MB ChB Glas. 1967. Prev: Clin. Asst. Staff Health Centre Leeds Gen. Infirm.

BUCHAN, Iain Edward Medical Informatics Unit, University of Cambridge, Institute of Public Health, Cambridge CB2 2SR Tel: 01223 330306 Fax: 01223 330330 Email: ieb21@cam.ac.uk; Wolfson College, Cambridge CB3 9BB — MB ChB 1991 Liverp.; BSc Liverp. 1989; DPH, 1998. Specialist Regist. (Pub. Health Med.) Anglia Deanery; Sen. Research Fell. Wolfson Coll. Camb. Socs: Fell. Roy. Statistical Soc.; Fell. Brit. Med. Informatics Soc.; Fell. Inst. Anal. & Progr.rs.

BUCHAN, Ian Carpenter Howden Health Centre, Howden West, Livingston EH54 6TP Tel: 01506 423800 Fax: 01506 460757; 10 Binny Park, Ecclesmachan, Broxburn EH52 6NP Tel: 01506 853230 — FRCGP 1998; MB ChB Birm. 1964; MD Aberd. 1972; MRCPsych 1976; MRCGP 1974; DPM Eng. 1973; DObst RCOG 1970. Prev: Research Fell. Dept. Gen. Pract. Univ. Aberd.; SHO Midl. Nerve Hosp. Birm.

BUCHAN, Ian Charles Ewell Court House, Ewell Court Avenue, Ewell, Epsom KT19 0DZ — MB ChB 1980 Aberd.; MRCPsych 1989.

BUCHAN, John Llandrindod Wells Hospital, Temple Street, Llandrindod Wells LD1 5HF Tel: 01597 822951; Upper Mill, Cwmdauddwr, Rhayader LD6 5EY — MB ChB 1977 Aberd.; FRCGP 2001; MRCGP 1981; DFFP 1993; Dip. Pract. Dermat. Wales 1990; DRCOG 1981. Staff Grade Phys. Age Care/EMI Llandrindod Wells Hosp.; Clin. Asst. in Dermat. Llandrindod Wells Hosp. Socs: Founder Mem. Primary Care Dermat. Soc. Prev: SHO (Psych.) Kingseat Hosp. Newmachar; SHO Aberd. Matern. Hosp.; Princip. in Pract. Rhayader Ponys.

BUCHAN, John Cameron St James University teaching Hsp, Leeds LS9 7TF; 37 High Cross Avenue, Melrose TD6 9SQ — MB BS 1996 Newc.

BUCHAN, Jon Geramount Surgery, Geramount, Stronsay, Orkney KW17 2AE Tel: 01857 616321 Fax: 01857 616294 — BM BCh 1964 Oxf.; MRCGP 1995; DObst RCOG 1967. (Oxf. & Westm.) Prev: Med. Adviser Benefits Agency Sutton; Sen. Med. Off. Benefits Agency Lond.

BUCHAN, Judith Alison Ferniehill Road Surgery, 8 Ferniehill Road, Edinburgh EH17 7AD Tel: 0131 664 2166 Fax: 0131 666 1075 — MB ChB 1991 Manch.; BSc Med.Sci St. And. 1988. GP Edin.

BUCHAN, Mr Keith Gunn Department of Cardiothoracic Surgery, University Hospital of Wales, Heath, Cardiff CF14 4XW Tel: 029 2074 3284; 3 Crystal Rise, Heath, Cardiff CF14 4HP Tel: 029 2025 0996 — MB ChB 1986 Glas.; BSc St. And. 1983; FRCS Ed. 1992; MRCP (UK) 1989. Specialist Regist. (Cardiothoracic Surg.) Univ. Hosp. Wales Cardiff. Socs: Soc. Cardiothoracic Surg. GB and Irel. Prev: Regist. (Surg.) K. Edwd. VIII Hosp. Durban, S. Afr.; Regist. (Med.) W.. Infirm. Glas.; SHO (Cardiothoracic Surg.) W.. Infirm. Glas.

BUCHAN, Kevin Milne 15D St Swithin Street, Aberdeen AB10 6XB — MB ChB 1995 Aberd.

BUCHAN, Mr Martin Campbell Flat 14, Offers Court, Winery Lane, Kingston upon Thames KT1 3GQ Tel: 020 8547 0662 Email: mbuchan@hotmail.com — MB ChB 1990 Glas.; FRCS Ed. 1994. Specialist Regist. (Trauma & Orthop.) Rotat., Hammersmith. Prev: Specialist Regist., Mayday Univ. Hosp., Croydon; Specialist Regist., Jersey Gen. Hosp., Jersey; Specialist Regist., W. Middlx. Univ. Hosp., Middlx.

BUCHAN, Mary Florence Mameulah, Newmachar, Aberdeen AB21 0QD — MB BCh BAO 1972 Belf.; DObst. RCOG 1975.

BUCHAN, Peter Cameron Tel: 01896 822254 Fax: 01896 823893 Email: petercbuchan@compuserve.com; High Cross House, 37 High Cross Avenue, Melrose TD6 9SQ Tel: 01896 822254 — MB ChB 1967 (Commend) Glas.; M.Th 1999 Ed.; BSc (Hons.) Glas. 1964, MD 1980; FRCOG 1986, M 1974; MRCGP 1974; T(OG) 1991; DObst 1969. Cons. O&G. Medico-Legal and risk Managem. consultancy. Socs: Fell. Roy. Soc. Med.; BMA; Ed. Obst. Soc. Prev: Cons. O&G, Borders Gen. Hosp.; Med. Dir. Borders Gen. Hosp. Trust; Sen. Clin. Lect. (O & G) Univ. Leeds.

BUCHAN, Robert Douglas Kennedy (retired) Simedro, 18 Lower St., Salhouse, Norwich NR13 6RW Tel: 01603 720565 — MB ChB 1955 Glas.

BUCHAN, Roderick Neil May 31 Church Hill, Camberley GU15 2HA — MB ChB 1996 Bristol.

BUCHANAN, Alec William Department of Forensic Psychiatry, Institute of Psychiatry, De Crespigny Park, London SE5 8AF Tel: 020 7701 0123 — MB ChB 1981 Ed.; PhD Camb. 1996; MPhil Camb. 1993; MPhil Lond. 1991; MD Ed. 1996; MRCPsych 1989. (Ed.) Clin. Sen. Lect. (Forens. Psychiat.) Inst. of Psychiat. Lond.; Hon. Cons. (Forens. Psychiat.) Maudsley Hosp. Lond. Prev: Sen. Regist. Maudsley Hosp. Lond.; Sen. Regist. BRd.moor Hosp.; Train. Fell. Inst. Psychiat. Lond.

BUCHANAN, Alexander Angus (retired) Longacre, 67 Putnoe Lane, Bedford MK41 9AE Tel: 01234 353718 — MRCS Eng. LRCP Lond. 1955; BSc (1st cl. Hons.) Lond. 1952, MB BS 1955; FRCP Lond. 1976, M 1960. Hon. Cons. Phys. Bedford Gen. Hosp. Prev: Chief Med. Off. City of W.m. Assur. Co. Ltd.

BUCHANAN, Alison Jane Camden Road Surgery, 142 Camden Road, London NW1 9HR Tel: 020 7284 0384 Fax: 020 7428 0493; 28 Fordington Road, Highgate, London N6 4TJ — MB BS 1983 Lond.; BSc Lond. 1989, MB BS 1983; MRCGP 1989; DRCOG 1987; DA (UK) 1985.

BUCHANAN, Andrew The Consulting Rooms, 21 Neilston Road, Paisley PA2 6LW Tel: 0141 889 5277 Fax: 0141 848 5500 — MB ChB 1973 Glas.; FRCP Glas. 1993; MRCP (UK) 1978; DObst RCOG 1975.

BUCHANAN, Carol Elizabeth 119 Spital, Aberdeen AB24 3HX Tel: 01224 583081; 31 Cranford Road, Aberdeen AB10 7NJ Tel: 01224 325873 Email: carol@ceddie.freeserve.co.uk — MB BCh BAO 1987 Belf.; MRCGP 1993; DRCOG 1993; DCH Dub. 1992. (Qu. Univ. Belf.) p/t GP Princip. Socs: BMA. Prev: SP Retainee, N.field, Aberd.; Trainee GP Cumnock Ayrsh. VTS.

BUCHANAN, Charles Rutherford Department of Child Health, King's College Hospital, Denmark Hill, London SE5 9RS Tel: 020 7346 3431 Fax: 020 7346 3643; Hale Place, 29 Hale St, East Peckham, Tonbridge TN12 5HL Tel: 01622 871816 Fax: 01622 872158 — MB ChB 1979 (Hons.) Manch.; BSc (1st cl. Hons.) Manch. 1976; MRCP (UK) 1982; FRCPCH 1997. Cons. Paediat. Endocrinol. King's Coll. Hosp. Lond. Socs: Chairm. of Brit. Soc. Paediatric Endocrinol. & Diabetes (BSPED) - 2001. Prev: Endrocrinol.

& Research Fell. Roy. Childr. Hosp. Melbourne Vict., Austral.; Lect. Inst. of Child Health Lond.

BUCHANAN, Deryck Watson King (retired) 25 Longmeadow Road, Saltash PL12 6DP Tel: 01752 217467 — MB ChB 1946 St. And.; MRCGP 1958. Prev: Scott. Sec. BMA.

BUCHANAN, Diana Rust c/oRespiratory Unit Office, Southamptin General Hospital, Southampton SO16 6YD Tel: 02380 794626 — MB ChB 1973 Aberd.; MSc Lond. 1993, MD 1989; MRCP (UK) 1978; CCST 1999. Sen. Regist. Soton. Hosps. NHS Trust. Prev: Regist. King's Coll. Hosp. Lond.; Research Fell. Roy. Nat. Heart & Lung Inst. Brompton Hosp. Lond.; Regist. Brompton Hosp. Lond.

BUCHANAN, Mr Donald Darwin 117 Leopold Avenue, Birmingham B20 1EX — MB BS West Indies 1981; FRCS Ed. 1989.

BUCHANAN, Douglas James The British Council, Bridgewater House, 58 Whitworth St., Manchester M1 6BB Tel: 0161 957 7471 Fax: 0161 957 7029 Email: douglas.buchanan@britishcouncil.org; 10 Rosemoor Gardens, Appleton, Warrington WA4 5RG Tel: 01925 261206 Fax: 01925 261206 Email: dj.gkbuchanan@ntlworld.com — MB ChB Ed. 1966; FRCS Eng. 1975; FRCS Ed. 1974. (Edinburgh) Dir. Health Brit. Counc.; Non-Exec. Dir. Clatterbridge Centre for Oncol. NHS Trust. Socs: BMA. Prev: Surg. & Med. Adviser Zambia Consolidated Copper Mines.

BUCHANAN, Duncan Alastair (retired) Coille, Hawick TD9 8RS Tel: 01450 73557 — MB ChB 1956 Ed. Prev: Ho. Surg. Simpson Matern. Pavil. Roy. Infirm. Edin.

BUCHANAN, Elizabeth Christina Craigmhor, Gruinart, Isle of Islay PA44 7PP — MB ChB 1977 Glas.

BUCHANAN, Elizabeth Horlock (retired) Davenal House Surgery, 28 Birmingham Road, Bromsgrove B61 0DD Tel: 01527 872008 — MB ChB 1951 Birm.; MB ChB (2nd cl. Hons.) Birm. 1951; MRCP Lond. 1954. Prev: Ho. Surg. & Ho. Phys. Qu. Eliz. Hosp. Birm.

BUCHANAN, Elizabeth Margaret (retired) Coille, Hawick TD9 8RS Tel: 01450 73557 — MB ChB 1957 Ed.; LRCP LRCS Ed. LRFPS Glas. 1957; DObst RCOG 1959. Prev: Med. Off. Family Plann. (Borders AHB).

BUCHANAN, Elizabeth Urquhart (retired) Landalla Cottage, Glenisla, Blairgowrie PH11 8PH Tel: 01575 582318 Fax: 01575 582318 — MB ChB 1953 Manch.; DCH Eng. 1955; BSc (Household & Soc. Sci.) Lond. 1946.

BUCHANAN, Geneve Krikor Whiston Hospital, Prescot L35 5DR Tel: 0151 426 1600 Fax: 0151 430 1901; 10 Rosemoor Gardens, Appleton, Warrington WA4 5RG Tel: 01925 261206 Fax: 01925 261206 — LMSSA Lond. 1969; FRCS Ed. 1968. Assoc. Specialist (O & G) Whiston Hosp. Merseyside. Socs: Brit. Med. Ultrasound Soc.; Brit. Fertil. Soc. Prev: Cons. Obst. Zambia Consolidated Copper Mines Kalulushi, Zambia.

BUCHANAN, Mr George BUPA Wellesley Hospital, Eastern Avenue, Southend-on-Sea SS2 4XH Tel: 01702 462944 Fax: 01702 600160 Email: georgebuchanan@btinternet.com; 55 The Broadway, Thorpe Bay, Southend-on-Sea SS1 3HG Tel: 01702 588257 Email: georgebuchanan@btinternet.com — MB ChB Glas. 1957; FRCS Ed. 1965; FRCS Glas. 1963; FRCS Eng. 1998. (Glas.) p/t Cons. ENT Surg. BUPA Wellesley Hosp. S.end on Sea; Hon. Cons. ENT Surg. S.end Hosp. Socs: Fell. Roy. Soc. Med.; BMA; Brit. Assn. Otorhindlaryngol. Head & Neck Surg.s. Prev: Sen. Lect. (Laryngol. & Otol. & Sub-Dean Inst. Laryngol. & Otol.) Univ. Lond.; Sen. Regist (ENT) Edin. Roy. Infirm.

BUCHANAN, Gillian Erica Bramleys, The Common, Winchmore Hill, Amersham HP7 0PN — MB ChB 1978 Aberd.

BUCHANAN, Mr Gordon Neil 22 St Olafs Road, London SW6 7DL Tel: 020 7381 3757 Email: gorden-buchanan@hotmail.com — MB BS 1993 Lond.; MSc 2001 Lond.; FRCS Eng 1997. (St. Thos.) Specialist Regist. (Gen Surg) E.bourne Dist. Gen. Hosp.; Research Fell., St Mark's Hosp. Socs: BMA. Prev: Specialist Regist. (Gen. Surg. Kent & Sussex Hosp., Roy Tunbridge Wells; SHO (Gen. Surg.) Qu. Eliz. Qu. Mother Hosp. Margate; SHO (Orthop. & Urol.) Kent & Canterbury Hosp.

BUCHANAN, Hilary Kathryn Shankill Health Centre, 135 Shankill Parade, Belfast BT13 1SD Tel: 028 9024 7181; 36 Dub Lane, Belfast BT9 5NB Tel: 028 906 11075 — MB ChB BAO 1973 Belf.; MRCGP 1981; DObst RCOG 1976. (Belf.) Prev: SHO (Gen. Med.) Coleraine Hosp.; Med. Off. Popondetta Hosp., Papua New Guinea.

BUCHANAN, Ian North Devon District Hospital, Raleigh Park, Barnstaple EX31 4JB Tel: 01271 22577 Fax: 01271 311541; 1 Masefield Avenue, Pilton, Barnstaple EX31 1QJ Tel: 01271 76771 — MB ChB 1975 Glas.; BDS Glas. 1964; FDS Glas. 1970. Cons. Oral & Maxillofacial Surg. N. Devon Healthcare Trust. Socs: Fell. Brit. Assn. Oral & Maxillofacial Surg.; Brit. Dent. Assn. Prev: Sen. Regist. (Oral & Maxillofacial Surg.) Leeds.

BUCHANAN, Ian Ross London Road Medical Practice, 12 London Road, Kilmarnock KA3 7AD Tel: 01563 523593 Fax: 01563 573552; 12 London Road, Kilmarnock KA3 7AE — MB ChB 1977 Glas.; MRCGP 1986.

BUCHANAN, Ian Samuel 14 Meadowbank, Jordanstown, Newtownabbey BT37 0UP Tel: 0196 03 64193 — MB BCh BAO 1981 Belf.; MRCGP 1986; DRCOG 1984.

BUCHANAN, Ian Scoular (retired) 60 Woodbourne, Augustus Road, Birmingham B15 3PJ Tel: 0121 454 1082 — MB BS 1936 Lond.; MD Lond. 1939; FRCP Lond. 1970, M 1938; MRCS Eng. LRCP Lond. 1936. Prev: Cons. Phys. Dudley Rd. Hosp. Birm.

BUCHANAN, Ian Yule The Croft Surgery, Eastergate, Chichester PO20 6RP Tel: 01243 543240 Fax: 01243 544867; Ndirande, Fontwell Avenue, Eastergate, Chichester PO20 6RU Tel: 01243 542951 — MB BS 1981 Lond.; MRCGP 1986; DCH RCP Lond. 1985; DRCOG 1984. Prev: Trainee GP Chichester VTS.

BUCHANAN, Isabel Joyce 1 Lammermuir Place, Kirkcaldy KY2 5RD — MB ChB 1952 Ed.; DPH Ed. 1958. Clin. Med. Off. Fife Health Bd. Prev: Clin. Med. Off. Herts. AHA.

BUCHANAN, Ivan Francis Mackinnon (retired) The Gables, Histon, Cambridge CB4 9JD Tel: 01223 232678 — MA Camb., MB BChir 1958; MRCS Eng. LRCP Lond. 1956; DObst RCOG 1959. Prev: Ho. Surg. & Ho. Phys. Bristol Roy. Infirm.

BUCHANAN, James 10 Fairfield House Gardens, Saxmundham IP17 1DL Tel: 01728 604492 — MB ChB Glas. 1949; MD Glas. 1966; FRCP Ed. 1972, M 1957; FRCP Glas. 1970, M 1962; FRFPS Glas. 1954. (Glas.) Prev: Cons. Phys. Law Hosp. Carluke; Sen. Regist. (Med.) Vict. Infirm. Glas.; Regist. (Med.) W.. Infirm. Glas.

BUCHANAN, Mr James Andrew Fownes The Conquest Hospital, The Ridge, St Leonards-on-Sea TN37 7RD Tel: 01424 755255 Fax: 01424 758040; Beech House, Church Hill, Sedlescombe, Battle TN33 0QP Tel: 01424 870399 Fax: 01424 870399 — MB BS 1986 Lond.; FRCS (Orth.) 1995; FRCS Eng. 1991; FRCPS Glas. 1991. (St. Mary's Hospital London) Cons. Orthop. Surg. The Conquest Hosp. Hastings. Prev: Sen. Regist. Roy. Nat. Orthop. Hosps.tanmore.

BUCHANAN, James Glen Stewart (retired) Landalla Cottage, Glenisla, Blairgowrie PH11 8PH Tel: 01575 82318 — MB ChB 1947 Ed.; FRCGP 1987, M 1964; DObst. RCOG 1959; DCH Eng. 1952.

BUCHANAN, Mr James Meredith 13 Westfield Avenue, Gosforth, Newcastle upon Tyne NE3 4YH Tel: 0191 285 3232 — MB BS 1967 Lond.; FRCS Eng. 1972; MRCS Eng. LRCP Lond. 1967. (St. Geo.) Cons. Orthop. Surg. Sunderland Dist. Gen. Hosp.; Hon. Clin. Lect. Univ. Newc. Socs: Fell. Brit. Orthop. Assoc. Prev: Sen. Regist. (Orthop.) St. Geo. Hosp. Lond. & SW Thames Regional Orthop. Train. Scheme.

BUCHANAN, Jane (retired) c/o Midland Bank, 72 Park Lane, London W1Y 4ER — MRCS Eng. LRCP Lond. 1953; DObst RCOG 1955. Prev: ENT Ho. Surg. St. Thos. Hosp.

BUCHANAN, Jean (retired) 'Greenways', Upper Cumberland Walk, Tunbridge Wells TN2 5EH — MB ChB 1947 Ed.; DPH Eng. 1961. Prev: GP Princip.

BUCHANAN, Jessie Reid Gray Bossinney, Foxhill Crescent, Leeds LS16 5PD Tel: 0113 278 6853 — MB ChB Ed. 1943. (Univ. Ed.) Prev: Asst. Venereol. Gen. Infirm. Leeds; Clin. Asst. VD Dept. Simpson Matern. Pavilion, Roy. Infirm. Edin.; Ho. Surg. VD Dept. Roy. Infirm. Edin.

BUCHANAN, John Donald Michael Darmady Lab., Queen Alexander Hospital, Cosham, Portsmouth Hants PO6 3LY Tel: 023 9228 5259; Gosport PO12 2JY — MB BChir 1969 Camb.; DCP 1974 Lond.; FRCPath 1989; M 1977; MA 1969 Camb.; MA Camb. 1969; FRCPath 1989, M 1977; DCP Lond 1974. (St. Thos.) Cons. Histopath. Portsmouth NHS Trust. Socs: Assn. Clin. Path.; Path. Soc. Prev: Cons. Adviser in Path. to MDG (N); Sen. Regist. St. Mary's Hosp. Portsmouth; Ho. Surg. Kingston Hosp.

BUCHANAN, Mr John McKenzie (retired) Rowan House, Whitmon Heath, Newcastle ST5 5HS — MB ChB 1951 Glas.; FRCS Ed. 1959. Prev: Cons. Surg. N. Staffs. Hosp. Centre Stoke-on-Trent.

BUCHANAN, Josephine Mary Wostenholm Road Surgery, 1 Wostenholm Road, Sheffield S7 1LB Tel: 0114 255 1124 Fax: 0114 258 7682; 462 Redmires Road, Sheffield S10 4LG — MB ChB 1976 Aberd.; MRCP (UK) 1983; MFHom 1996; MRCGP 1985; DCH Eng. 1980.

BUCHANAN, Judith 13 Westfield Avenue, Gosforth, Newcastle upon Tyne NE3 4YH Tel: 01632 853232 — MB BS 1970 Newc. Prev: Sen. Regist. (Histopath.) Freeman Hosp. Newc.; Regist. (Histopath.) St. Jas. Hosp. Balham; Regist. St. Mary's Gen. Hosp. Portsmouth.

BUCHANAN, Karen Jane Marine Avenue Medical Centre, 64 Marine Avenue, Whitley Bay NE26 1NQ; 7 Letchwell Villas, Forest Hall, Newcastle upon Tyne NE12 7AA — MB BS 1989 Newc.; MRCGP 1994; DRCOG 1994. p/t Gen. Pract. Princip.

BUCHANAN, Professor Keith Deans Email: k.buchanan@qub.ac.uk; The Lomond, 30 North Circular Road, Lisburn BT28 3AH Tel: 028 9260 1207 Fax: 028 9262 7971 Email: kd@kbuchanan.fsbusiness.co.uk — MB ChB Glas. 1958; PhD Belf. 1973; MD (Commend.) Glas. 1969; FRCPI 1986, M 1985; FRCP Lond. 1977, M 1964; FRCP Ed. 1973, M 1961; FRCP Glas. 1970, M 1963; F.Med.Sci 1999. (Glas.) p/t Prof. Emerit. Med. Qu. Univ. Belf. & Hon. Cons. Phys. Roy. Vict. Hosp. Belf.; Prof. Gen. Med. Endocrinol. & Diabetes 1976. Socs: Med. Res. Soc.; Eur. Soc. Clin. Investig.; Brit. Diabetic Assn. Prev: Sen. Regist. (Med.) Glas. Roy. Infirm.; Instruc. (Med.) & Sen. Research Fell. (Endocrinol.) Univ. Washington, USA.

BUCHANAN, Kenneth Alexander (retired) 14 Napier Road, Heaton Moor, Stockport SK4 4HG Tel: 0161 432 1414 — MB ChB St. And. 1948. Prev: Gen. Practioner.

BUCHANAN, Linda Alison The Surgery, High Street, Thorpe-le-Soken, Clacton-on-Sea CO16 0DY Tel: 01255 861850 Fax: 01255 860330; The Limes, High St, Thorpe-Le-Soken, Clacton-on-Sea CO16 0EA Tel: 01255 861850 — MB ChB 1976 Aberd.

BUCHANAN, Linda Moon Falkirk & District Royal Infirmary, Majors Loan, Falkirk FK1 5QE; 134 Ochiltree, Dunblane FK15 0PB — MB ChB 1985 Glas.; MRCP (UK) 1988. (Glas. Univ.) Cons. Phys. (Diabetes & Endocrinol.), Falkirk & Dist. Roy. Infirm. Prev: Regist. (Endocrinol. & Gen. Med.) Glas. Roy. Infirm.; Sen. Regist. in Diabetes & Endocrinol. Roy. Infirm. Glas.

***BUCHANAN, Malcolm Alexander** 4 The Brambles, Balsham, Cambridge CB1 6ED; 4 Aitchison's Close, 58 West Port, Edinburgh EH1 2LB — MB ChB 1998 Ed.; MB ChB Ed 1998; BSc (Hons) Ed 1995.

BUCHANAN, Marion Elizabeth Bolton Union Street Surgery, 12 Union Street, Kirkintilloch, Glasgow G71 7AP Tel: 0141 776 2468 Fax: 0141 775 3341 — MB ChB 1979 Glas.

BUCHANAN, Maris Elizabeth The Pines Medical Centre, Archerale, Archeracle PH36 4JU Tel: 01967 431231 Fax: 01967 431396 Email: administrator@gp55662.liglIendhb.scot.nhs.uk; Carnlia, Salen, Acharacle PH36 4JN Tel: 01967 431464 Ext: 205 — MB ChB 1982 Dundee; PhD U.N.E. 1974; MA St. And. 1969; DRCOG 1985. GP Princip. Socs: BMA; BASICS; Lochaber Med. Soc.

BUCHANAN, Marjory Mann (retired) 15 Clydeneuk Drive, Uddingston, Glasgow G71 7SZ Tel: 01698 814942 — MB ChB 1951 Glas.; MFCM 1972; DPH Glas. 1961; DObst RCOG 1954.

BUCHANAN, Mark James 72 Bolton Road West, Ramsbottom, Bury BL0 9ND — BM BS 1996 Nottm.

BUCHANAN, Mary Womens Nationwide Cancer Control Campaign, Suna House, 128-130 Curtain Road, London EC2A 3AR Tel: 020 7729 4688 Fax: 020 7613 0771; Little Glebe, 5 Pitfield Drive, Meopham, Gravesend DA13 0AY Tel: 01474 812085 Fax: 01474 815036 — MRCS Eng. LRCP Lond. 1955; DFFP 1993. (Manch.) Chairm. Wom. Nat. Cancer Control Campaign; Med. Off. (Family Plann.) Dartford & Gravesham HA.; Med. Off. Marks & Spencer plc. Socs: Fell. Roy. Soc. Med.; BMA. Prev: GP Gravesend; Ho. Off. (Med.) Blood Transfus. Serv. (SW Metrop. Region).

BUCHANAN, Mrs Mary Douglas (retired) 55 Ormonde Avenue, Glasgow G44 3QY — MB ChB 1947 Glas.; DCH Eng. 1951. SCMO Renfrew Health Dist. Prev: Asst. Med. Off. Renfrew CC.

BUCHANAN, Michael Frederic Gray (retired) Bosinney, 30 Foxhill Crescent, Leeds LS16 5PD Tel: 0113 278 6853 Email: mikebuchanan@lineone.net — MB ChB Ed. 1944; FRCP Ed. 1959, M 1950; DCH Eng. 1948. Prev: Sen. Lect. Paediat & Child Health, Univ. Leeds.

BUCHANAN, Neil Milne Mackie Royal Hampshire County Hospital, Winchester SO22 5DG Tel: 01962 824919; Royal National Hospital for Rheumatic Diseases, Upper Borough Walls, Bath BA1 1RL — MB ChB 1979 Glas.; FRCP 2001 LONDON; FRCP Ed. 1994; FRCP Glas. 1992; MRCP (UK) 1982. Cons. Rheum. Roy. Hants. Co. Hosp. Winchester & Roy. Nat. Hosp. Rheum. Dis. Bath; Hon. Cons. Phys. St. Thos. Hosp. Lond.; Hon. Sen. Lect. (Med.) Univ. of Bath 1997.

BUCHANAN, Paul Laurence Camberley Health Centre, 159 Frimley Road, Camberley GU15 2QA Tel: 01276 20101 Fax: 01276 21661; Arcall, 34 Upper Pk Road, Camberley GU15 2EF Tel: 01276 22698 — MB BS 1966 Lond.; DCH Eng. 1968; DObst RCOG 1968. (Lond. Hosp.) Socs: BMA. Prev: Med. Off. Child Med. Care Unit Enugu, Nigeria; Surg. P. & O. Lines Ltd.

BUCHANAN, Philip Mushroom Cottage, Hamptworth Lane, Redlynch, Salisbury SP5 2PB — BM 1983 Soton.

BUCHANAN, Rachel Wideopan Medical Centre, Great North Road, Newcastle upon Tyne NE13 6LN; Muddle House, Slaley, Hexham NE47 0AA — MB BCh BAO 1979 Belf.; DRCOG 1982.

BUCHANAN, Robert Archibald Undercliffe, Lamlash, Brodick KA27 8LZ Tel: 0177 06 202 — MB ChB 1948 Glas. (Univ. Glas.) Prev: Ho. Surg. Falkirk & Dist. Roy. Infirm. & Matern. Sect. Ayrsh. Centr.; Hosp. Irvine; Capt. RAMC.

BUCHANAN, Mr Robert Christie 1 Lammermuir Place, Kirkcaldy KY2 5RD — MB ChB 1951 Ed.; FRCS Ed. 1958; FRCS Eng. 1967. (Ed.) Cons. (Gen. Surg.) Vict. Hosp. Kirkcaldy. Prev: Cons. (Surg.) St. Leonard's & Mildmay Miss. Hosps. Lond.; Sen. Surg. Specialist Govt. Malawi; Sen. Regist. Plastic Surg. Maxillo-Facial Unit Bangour Gen. Hosp.

BUCHANAN, Robin Bruce 24 Cowan Road, Shandon, Edinburgh EH11 1RH — MB ChB 1986 Aberd. Regist. Gen. (Psychiat.) Lanarksh.

BUCHANAN, Roger Brade Royal S Hants Hospital, Southampton SO14 0YG Tel: 023 8082 5380 Fax: 023 8082 5653; 23 Grovsvenor Road, Chandlers ford, Eastleigh SO53 5BU Tel: 02380 252963 — MB BS 1967 Lond.; FRCP Lond. 1986; MRCP (UK) 1972; FRCR 1975; FFR 1973; DMRT Eng. 1972. (Middlx.) Cons. Radiother. Wessex Regional Radiother. Centre Roy. S. Hants. Hosp. Soton.; Civil. Cons. to RN; Hon. Clin. Sen. Lect. Fac. Med. Univ. Soton.; Dean, Fac. Clin. Onocol. Roy. Coll. Radiol. Prev: Regist. Fac. Clin. Onocol. Roy. Coll. Radiol; Clin. Tutor Soton. Gen. Hosp.; Clin. Sub-Dean Fac. Med. Univ. Soton.

BUCHANAN, Ronald Mills Greenfield Surgery, 1 Claremont Avenue, Woking GU22 75F Tel: 01483 771171; Beechlawn, St. Johns Hill Road, Woking GU21 1RQ Tel: 01483 773377 — MB ChB 1962 Glas. (Glas.) p/t Asst. GP Surrey. Prev: GP Woking; Med. Off. Govt. of St. Lucia & S. Pacific Health Serv. Fiji.

BUCHANAN, Rose (retired) Hill Farm House, Droxford Road, Swanmore, Southampton SO32 2PY — MB BS 1961 Lond.; FRCPath 1984, M 1973. Prev: Cons. Histopath.

BUCHANAN, Sarah Hermione Jill Lanercost, Lynx Hill, East Horsley, Leatherhead KT24 5AX — MB BS 1958 Durh.; Cert. FPA 1972; DObst RCOG 1959. (Durh.) Indep. Pract. Psychother.; Assoc. Inst. Psychosexual Med. Prev: Ho. Off. (Phys.) Roy. Vict. Infirm. Newc.; Resid. Med. Off. W.m. Hosp. Brit. Columbia, Canada; Resid. Med. Off. King Edwd. VII Hosp. Bermuda.

BUCHANAN, Sheena Mary (retired) Aros, North Connel, Oban PA37 1RA — MB ChB 1950 Ed.; DObst RCOG 1953; DPH Glas. 1967.

BUCHANAN, Stuart 19 Helensview Cr, Newtownards BT23 4QN — MB BCh BAO 1997 Belf.

BUCHANAN, Stuart Bruce 31 Knockagh Road, Newtownabbey BT36 5BW — MB BCh 1997 Belf.

BUCHANAN, Mr Trevor Arthur Stanley 30 Hawthornden Road, Belfast BT4 3JW Tel: 01232 657697 — MB BCh 1972 Belf.; BSc Belf. 1969, MB BCh BAO Belf. 1972; FRCS Ed. 1978; FRCOphth. Lond. 1988. (Queens University Belfast) Cons. Ophth. Roy. Vict. Hosp. Belf.; Cons. Ophth. Ards & Bangor Hosps.

BUCHANAN, William Edmund Alexander, VRD (retired) Beech Lea, Meikleour, Perth PH2 6DZ Tel: 01738 883285 — MB ChB 1943 St. And. Prev: Med. Asst. Dept. Anaesth. St. And. Univ. & Dundee Roy. Infirm.

BUCHANAN, William Mackie (retired) 55 Ormonde Avenue, Muirend, Glasgow G44 3QY — MD 1968 Glas.; MB ChB 1952, DPH 1959; FRCPath 1977, M 1967.

BUCHANAN-BARROW, Sheena Jill 58 Dancer Road, Kew, Richmond TW9 4LB; 51 Winchester Road, St. Margarets, Twickenham TW1 1LE — MB BS 1977 Lond.

BUCHDAHL, Roger Martin Hillingdon Hospital, Hillingdon, Uxbridge UB8 3NN; 5 Aldebert Terrace, London SW8 1BH Tel: 020 7582 1030 — MB BChir 1978 Camb.; MRCP (UK) 1981; FRCP; FRCPCH. (Guy's Hosp., Lond.) Cons. Paediat. Hillingdon Hosp. Middlx.; Cons. (Paediat.), Roy. Brompton & Harefield NHS Trust. Prev: Sen. Regist. (Paediat.) King's Coll. Hosp. Lond.; Lect. (Paediat. Nephrol.) Guy's Hosp. Lond.; Regist. (Paediat.) Brompton Hosp. Lond. & Hillingdon Hosp. Uxbridge.

BUCHER, Janet 3 Craven Road, Reading RG1 5LF; 104 Grove Road, Bladon, Oxford OX20 1RA — MB BS 1975 Lond.; BSc 1975; MRCPsych 1979. Cons. Child Psychiat. W. Berks. HA.

BUCHER, Air Commodore Thomas Joseph Paschal (retired) 26 Witchford Road, Ely CB6 3DP Tel: 01353 662755 — MB BS 1957 Lond.; FRCS Ed. 1969. Prev: Cons. Advisor Orthop. Surg. RAF Med. Br.

BUCHIN, Eva Maria (Private) Stamford Hill Practice, 2 Egerton Road, London N16 6UA — State Exam Med 1982 Heidelberg.

BUCHTHAL, Anna Barbara 31 Wolseley Road, Crouch End, London N8 8RS — MRCS Eng. LRCP Lond. 1971; MA, BM BCh Oxf. 1971; FFA RCS Eng. 1977; DIC Engin. in Med. Lond. 1970.

BUCK, Alice Emily 7 Pembridge Place, London W2 4XB — LMSSA 1944 Lond.; MD (Psych. Med.) Leeds 1950, MB ChB 1945; MRCS Eng., LRCP Lond. 1944. (Leeds) Pres. Buck Inst. Psychodynamic Studies Ltd. Socs: Fell. Roy. Soc. Med.; Brit. Psychiat. Soc. Prev: Asst. Psychiat. Phys. Cassel Hosp.; Asst. Dept. Psychiat. Maida Vale Hosp. Nerv. Dis.; Fulbright Schol.

BUCK, Andrew Charles (retired) The Old Chapel, Muckleford, Dorchester DT2 9SW — MRCS Eng. LRCP Lond. 1961; BSc (Physiol) Lond. 1958, MB BS 1961; Dip. Bact. Lond 1967; MCPath 1968. Prev: Sen. Regist. (Bact.) St. Bart. Hosp.

BUCK, Brenda Mary (retired) 5 De Vere Gardens, off Melbury Road, Woodthorpe, Nottingham NG5 4PH Tel: 0115 926 3172 — MRCS Eng. LRCP Lond. 1946; MD Lond. 1951, MB BS 1946; MRCP Lond. 1951. Prev: Clin. Asst. in Dermat. Nottm. Univ. Hosp.

BUCK, Diana Catherine Kingsthorpe Medical Centre, Eastern Avenue South, Northampton NN2 7JN Tel: 01604 713823 Fax: 01604 721996; Northfield House, Topend, Pytchley, Kettering NN14 1EX — MRCS Eng. LRCP Lond. 1974; BSc (Hons.) Lond. 1971, MB BS 1974; MRCGP 1978; DObst RCOG 1976. (Roy. Free) Clin. Asst. Dept. Dermat. Kettering Gen. Hosp. Socs: Fell. St. John's Dermat. Soc. Prev: Clin. Asst. Dermat. Bedford Gen. Hosp.; Regist. (Dermat. & Gen. Med.) Roy. Free Hosp. Lond.

BUCK, Hubert Anthony 263 Nottingham Road, Mansfield NG18 4SE Tel: 01623 22893 — MRCS Eng. LRCP Lond. 1942; FFA RCS Eng. 1954; DA Eng. 1944; BDS (Hons.) Lond. 1947; LDS RCS Eng. 1947. (Guy's) Cons. Anaesth. Mansfield Area. Socs: Assn. Anaesths. Gt. Brit.

BUCK, Jacqueline Janet Rawlinson's End, The Street, Brandeston IP13 7AD — BM BS 1989 Nottm.; BMedSci. Nottm. 1987; MRCP (UK) 1993; DCH RCP Lond. 1993; MSc Clinical Paed 1998. Specialist Regist. (Paediat.) Norf. & Norwich; Regist. (Paediat.) Ipswich. & Camb. Socs: BMA; Roy. Coll. Paediat. and Child Health.

BUCK, James William 31 Westlecot Road, Swindon SN1 4EZ — BM 1998 Soton.

BUCK, Mr John Edward (retired) 20 Madison Crescent, Bexleyheath DA7 5SZ Tel: 020 8303 5034 — MB ChB Ed. 1937; FRCS Eng. 1949; FRCS Ed. 1946. Prev: Cons. Orthop. Surg. Greenwich & Bexley AHA.

BUCK, Julia Catherine Westholme, Gorse Lane, Grantham NG31 7UE — MB BS 1998 Lond.; MB BS Lond 1998.

BUCK, Katharine Susan Department of Nephrology, Leicester General Hospital, Gwendolen Road, Leicester LE5 4PW Tel: 0116 249 0490; 122 Hartopp Road, Leicester LE2 1WF Tel: 0116 270 0614 — MB BS 1991 Lond.; MRCP (UK) 1994. (King's Coll. Hosp. Lond.) Regist. (Nephrol.) Leicester Gen. Hosp. Prev: Regist. (Diabetes) Leicester Gen. Hosp.; SHO (Renal Med.) Guy's Hosp. Lond.; SHO (Intens. Care Med.) Nottm. City Hosp.

BUCK, Lucie Mary Brownlee House, Mauldslie Road, Carluke ML8 5HW Tel: 01555 773459; Kirwan Women's Hospital, 187 Thuringowa Drive, Townsville N. Qld, Australia Tel: 00 61 747 730 222 — MB BS 1994 Lond. Regist. (O & G) Kirwan Wom.'s Hosp. Townsville Qu.sland, Australia. Prev: Clin. Research Fell. (O & G) Centre for Reproductive Biol. Univ. of Edin.; SHO (Obst.) Glas. Roy. Matern. Hosp.; SHO (Gyn.) Glas. Roy. Infirm. NHS Trust.

BUCK, Margot Elizabeth Sway Road Surgery, 65 Sway Road, Morriston, Swansea SA6 6JA Tel: 01792 773150 / 771392 Fax: 01792 790880; Rookwood House, Cimla Road, Neath SA11 3TL Tel: 01639 642736 — MB BS 1976 Lond.; MRCS Eng. LRCP Lond. 1976; FRCGP 1995, MR 1984; MRCOG 1981 D 1978. (St. Mary's) GP Morriston, Swansea. Prev: Regist. (Gyn. & Obst.) Middlx. Hosp. Lond.; Regist. (Gyn. & Obst.) Roy. Sussex Co. Hosp. Brighton.

BUCK, Mavis (retired) 34 Heronsforde, Ealing, London W13 8JE Tel: 020 8997 1219 — MB BS 1952 Lond.; FFA RCS Eng. 1961; DA Eng. 1954. Prev: Cons. Anaesth. W. Middlx. Hosp. Isleworth.

BUCK, Pamela 48 Carlton Road, Hale, Altrincham WA15 8RL Tel: 0161 980 2692 — MB BS 1970 Newc.; FRCOG 1989, M 1975. Sen. Lect. (O & G) Manch. Univ. Prev: Lect. O & G Sheff. Univ.; Regist. (O & G) Roy. Vict. Infirm. Newc.; Demonst. Anat. Univ. Newc.

BUCK, Peter Kenneth Bushloe End Surgery, 48 Bushloe End, Wigston LE18 2BA; Laurel Cottage, Hambleton, Oakham LE15 8TL Tel: 01572 756717 — MB BS 1972 Lond.; MRCS Eng. LRCP Lond. 1972; DObst RCOG 1974. (St. Mary's) Socs: BMA. Prev: SHO (Obst.) Leicester Roy. Infirm.; Ho. Surg. & Ho. Phys. Nottm. Gen. Hosp.

BUCK, Robert Graham Old Elms Surgery, 72A Lutterworth Road, Aylestone, Leicester LE2 8PG Tel: 0116 244 0010 Fax: 0116 224 0110 — MB BS 1972 Lond.; MRCS Eng. LRCP Lond. 1972. (St Marys Medical School London) Socs: LMC Mem.

BUCK, Sandra Meadows Health Centre, 1 Bridgeway Centre, The Meadows, Nottingham NG2 2JG; 48 Holme Road, West Bridgford, Nottingham NG2 5AD — MB ChB 1968 Liverp.; DCH RCP Lond. 1989. (Liverp.) SCMO (Child Health & Psychosexual Counselling) Nottm. Community Health NHS Trust. Socs: MRCPCH; Inst. Psychosexual Med. Prev: Clin. Med. Off. Nottm. FPA; Med. Off. Family Plann. Assn. Perth, Austral.; SHO (Paediat.) Roy. Belf. Hosp. Sick Childr.

BUCK, Susan Margaret 1 Beaufort Road, Edinburgh EH9 1AG; Tel: 0131 667 1249 — MB BS 1984 Lond.; MRCGP 1994; DRCOG 1991. (Charing Cross Hospital Medical School University of London) Prev: Trainee GP Som.

BUCK, Timothy James Flat 1, 80 Fonthill Road, Hove BN3 6HD Tel: 01273 204052 Email: drtim buck@aol.com — MB BS 1992 Lond.; DRCOG 1996; DFFP 1997; MRCGP Lond. 1997. (St. Thos. Hosp. Med. Sch. Lond.) Clin. Asst. (Psychiat.) Hove. Prev: Clin. Med. Off. Martlets Hospice Hove.

BUCK-BARRETT, Mr Ronald 45 The Cloisters, Tarleton, Preston PR4 6UL Tel: 01772 812790 — MB BS 1960 Lond.; FRCS Eng. 1971; MRCS Eng. LRCP Lond. 1959. (Lond. Hosp.) Cons. Surg. (ENT) Fairfield Indep. Hosp. Crank & Renacres Hall Indep. Hosp. Halsall. Prev: Cons. Surg. (ENT) Ormskirk & Dist. Gen. Hosp. & ENT Scarboro. Hosp. Gp.; Sen. Regist. Nottm. Gen. Hosp.

BUCKELL, Helen Monamy Bayldon (retired) 73 The Cloisters, Pegasus Grange, Whitehouse, Oxford OX1 4QQ Tel: 01865 791890 — PhD (Biochem.) Lond. 1951, BSc (Hnrs. Chem.) 1943; MB BS Lond. 1955; FRCPath 1978, M 1966. Prev: Cons. Chem. Path. St. Helier Hosp. Carshalton; Cons. Chem. Path.

BUCKELL, Nicholas Adrian 107 Denison Street, Beeston, Nottingham NG9 1DQ Tel: 0115 925 3777 — MB BS 1970 Lond.; MRCP (UK) 1973; MRCGP 1981; DCH RCP Lond. 1980. (Univ. Coll. Hosp.) Prev: Hon. Lect. Lond. Hosp. Whitechapel; Hon. Regist. St. Marks Hosp. Lond.

BUCKELS, Mr John Anthony Charles 87 Reddings Road, Moseley, Birmingham B13 8LP — MD 1986 Birm.; MB ChB 1972; FRCS Eng. 1977. Cons. Surg. (Transpl.) Qu. Eliz. Hosp. Birm. Prev: Sen. Regist. (Surg.) W. Midl. RHA; Research Fell. Harbor UCLA Med. Centre Calif., USA; Lect. in Anat. Med. Sch. Birm.

BUCKENHAM, Mary Gerardine New Hayesbank Surgery, Cemetery Lane, Kennington, Ashford TN24 9JZ Tel: 01233 624642 Fax: 01233 637304; Glendene, The Ridgeway, Smeeth, Ashford TN25 6SD — MB BCh BAO 1979 NUI.

BUCKENHAM, Timothy Michael Department of Diagnostic Radiology, St George's Hospital, Blackshaw Road, London SW17 0QT Tel: 020 8725 3298 Fax: 020 8725 3296 — MB ChB 1982 Otago; FRACR 1990; FRCR 1997. Cons. Vasc. Radiol. St. Geo. Hosp. Lond.

BUCKETT, William Michael Moel Llys, Mill Road, Meole Brace, Shrewsbury SY3 9JT; Reproductive Center, McGill University, Royal Victoria Hospital, 687 Av Des Pins Ouest, Montreal QC H4C 1H8, Canada Email: wbuckett@rvh062.ian.mcgill.ca — MB ChB 1988 Birm.; MRCOG 1994. (Birmingham) Clin. Fell. & Lect McGill Univ. Canada. Prev: Specialist Regist. Merseyside Rotat.; Research Fell. Liverp. Wom.'s Hosp.; Regist. W. Midl. Rotat.

BUCKINGHAM, Christopher John Brookmead Cottage, 40 Harlington Road, Sharpenhoe, Bedford MK45 4SG — MB BS 1952 Lond.; MRCS Eng. LRCP Lond. 1952; DObst RCOG 1956. (St. Geo.) Hon. Med. Cons. Brit. Racing Drivers Club Silverstone; Local Med. Advis. to The Civil Serv. Socs: Fell. Roy. Soc. Med.; Soc. Occupat. Med. Prev: Med. Cons. Camford Engin. Gp.; SCMO (Occupat. Health) S. Beds. HA & S. Beds. Dist. Counc.; Ho. Surg. & Resid. Obst. Asst. St. Geo. Hosp.

BUCKINGHAM, Jack Elwood, Perth Road, Birnam, Dunkeld PH8 0BH — MB ChB 1957 Sheff.; MFCM 1974; DPH Leeds 1968.

BUCKINGHAM, Karen Lisa 10 Coombe Road, Crookes, Sheffield S10 1FF Tel: 0114 267 0720 — MB ChB 1994 Auckland.

BUCKINGHAM, Michael Simm Smoke Acre, Crossway, Shawford, Winchester SO21 2BZ Tel: 01962 712227 Fax: 01962 712227 Email: mike.buckinham@virgin.net — MB BS 1968 Lond.; DM Soton. 1980; MRCS Eng. LRCP Lond. 1968; FRCOG 1987, M 1974, DObst 1970. Cons. O & G Roy. Hants. Co. Hosp. Winchester. Socs: BMA. Prev: Lect. & Sen. Regist. (Human Reproduc. & Obst.) Soton. Univ.; SHO (O & G) W.m. Hosp. Lond.

BUCKINGHAM, Paul Vinton Elizabeth Street Medical Centre, 9 Elizabeth Street, Corby NN17 1SJ Tel: 01536 202507 Fax: 01536 206099 Email: paul.buckingham@gp-k83016.nhs.uk; 4 Water Lane, Weldon, Corby NN17 3HJ Tel: 01536 266274 Email: paul@paulbuck.force9.co.uk — MB BS 1971 Lond.; MRCS Eng. LRCP Lond. 1971. (St. Mary's) Clin. Governance Lead Corby PCG. Prev: Trainee GP Kettering VTS; SHO (Anaesth.) Edgware Gen. Hosp.; Ho. Surg. St. Mary's Hosp. (Harrow Rd. Br.) Lond.

BUCKINGHAM, Mrs Rachel Anne 5 Fallodon Way, Henleaze, Bristol BS9 4HR Tel: 0117 949 6973 Fax: 0117 909 5187 — MB ChB 1991 Bristol; FRCS Eng. 1995. Specialist Regist. (Orthop.) Bristol. Socs: Assoc. Mem. BOA; BOTA.

BUCKINGHAM, Susan Jane Little Wadstray, Blackawton, Totnes TQ9 7DD — MB ChB 1993 Bristol.

BUCKLAND, Anthony Graham The Lonsdale Medical Centre, 1, Clanricarde Gardens, Tunbridge Wells TN1 1PE Tel: 01892 530329/517155 Fax: 01892 536583 Email: anthony.buckland@gp-g82768.nhs.uk; 35 Birling Road, Tunbridge Wells TN2 5LY Tel: 01892 528085 Email: tonybuckland@hotmail.com — MB BS 1976 Lond.; DRCOG 1979; Cert JCC Lond. 1979. (St. Thos.) Socs: BMA. Prev: CMO for Tunbridge Wells Equitable Life Assur. Comp.; Occupat. Med. Off. for Brit. Boxing Bd. of Control; Chief Med. Off. for Tunbridge Wells Equitable Life Assur. Co.

BUCKLAND, Charlotte-Sue 67 Southampton Road, Northampton NN4 8DZ — MB ChB 1991 Leeds.

BUCKLAND, Harry Mitchell (retired) The Surgery, 18 Augusta Close, Grimsby DN34 4TQ Tel: 01472 357897 — MB 1954 Camb.; BChir 1953; MRCGP 1963; DObst RCOG 1957.

BUCKLAND, Mr Jonathan Richard 18 Downside Road, Winchester SO22 5LU — MB ChB 1994 Birm.; ChB Birm. 1994; FRCS (Eng) 1998.

BUCKLAND, Matthew Scott Kings College Hospital, Kings Healthcare NHS Trust, Denmark Hill, London SE5 9RS Tel: 020 7737 4000; 5-16 Northwood Hall, Hornsey Lane, Highgate, London N6 5PL Tel: 020 8341 6958 — MB BS 1996 Lond.; BSc (Hons) 1993. (UCL Medical School) SHO (A & E) Lond.

BUCKLAND, Robert William St Hugh's Mead, Downside Road, Winchester SO22 5LU — MB ChB 1966 Ed.; FFA RCS Eng. 1970. Cons. Anaesth. Roy. Hants. Co. Hosp. Winchester.

BUCKLAND, Mr Robin Harold Northam Surgery, Bayview Road, Northam, Bideford EX39 1AZ Tel: 01237 474994; Speenholme, Primrose Lane, Marshfield, Northam, Bideford EX39 1NR — MB BS 1978 Lond.; FRCS Lond. 1983; MRCGP 1989. Prev: Regist. (Surg. & Orthop.) Wolverhampton.

BUCKLE, David John 106 Crockhamwell Road, Woodley, Newbury RG13 — MB BS 1980 Lond.; MRCGP 1984; DRCOG 1982. Clin. Gov. Lead, Wokingham PCG.

BUCKLE, Isabella Miller (retired) 6 Lillington Close, Leamington Spa CV32 7RN Tel: 01926 424875 — MB ChB Ed. 1944. Prev: Ho. Surg. Elsie Inglis Matern. Hosp. & Bruntsfield Hosp. Wom. Edin.

BUCKLE, James Richard Quarry House, North St., South Petherton TA13 5DA — MB ChB 1981 Bristol; MRCGP 1985; DRCOG 1985. GP Martock. Prev: Trainee GP Som. VTS.

BUCKLE, Richard James The Surgery, 25 St Mary's Road, Tickhill, Doncaster DN11 9NA Tel: 01302 742503 — MB ChB 1970 Ed.; MRCGP 1982.

BUCKLE, Richard Martin (retired) Brook Lodge, 29 Abbotts Way, Highfield, Southampton SO17 1NW Tel: (023)80 554673 — MB 1956 Camb.; BChir 1955; MD Camb. 1961; FRCP Lond. 1972, M 1958; MRCS Eng. LRCP Lond. 1955. Prev: Sen. Regist. & Lect. (Med.) St. Bart. Hosp. Lond.

BUCKLE, Susan Marie 370 Acklam Road, Acklam, Middlesbrough TS5 8AZ — MB ChB 1985 Sheff. Trainee GP Swindon. Prev: SHO (O & G) Doncaster Roy. Infirm.; SHO (Radiother. & Oncol.) W.on Pk. Hosp. Sheff.; SHO (Rheum.) St. Jas. Hosp. Leeds.

BUCKLER, David George Warwick Abington Health Complex, Doctors Surgery, 51A Beech Avenue, Northampton NN3 2JG Fax: 01604 450155; Cherry Orchard Cottage, 84 High St., Hardingstone, Northampton NN4 6OD — MB ChB 1983 Sheff.; MSc (Distinction Sports Individual); MRCP (UK) 1985; MRCGP 1990. Gen. Practitioner; Med. Director Aborgton Sports; Med. Clinic; Med. Off. N.arts Country Cricket Club. Socs: Brit. Assn. of Sports Med. Prev: VSO Nat. Hosp. Apia, W.. Samoa; SHO (Gen. Hosp.) N.ampton HA; Ho. Off. (Profess. Med. & Surg. Units) Hallamsh. Hosp. Sheff.

BUCKLER, Emma Charlotte 1 Hall Lane, Donisthorpe, Swadlincote DE12 7PL — MB ChB 1995 Leeds.

BUCKLER, Frederick Ridsdale (retired) Merrymead, 16charlton Rd, Shepton Mallet BA4 5NY Tel: 01749 3162 — MRCS Eng. LRCP Lond. 1939; DCH Eng. 1946. Prev: Squadron Ldr. RAFVR 1940-46 (twice mentioned in despatches).

BUCKLER, Helen Margaret Department of Endocrinology, Salford Royal Hospitals Trust, Hope Hospital, Salford M6 8HD Tel: 0161 787 5146 Fax: 0161 787 5989 Email: hbuckler@fs1.ho.man.ac.uk; Laurelbank, 23 Arthog Rd, Hale, Altrincham WA15 0LY Tel: 0161 980 0021 Fax: Docs@Bowdon.u net .com Email: ghelen @arthog.u-net.com — BM BS 1981 Nottm.; DM Nottm. 1992, BMedSci 1979; MRCP (UK) 1984; FRCP 1998. Cons. Phys. (Med., Endocrinol. & Diabetes) Hope Hosp. Salford. Prev: Lect. & Hon. Sen. Regist. Univ. Manch. Hope Hosp.; Research Fell.sh. P. Henry's Hosp. Monash Univ. Melbourne, Austral.; SHO (Gen. Med.) Hope Hosp. Manch.

BUCKLER, Jennifer Anne 2 Sedbergh Drive, Kendal LA9 6BJ — MB ChB 1979 Manch.

BUCKLER, John Michael Heslington (retired) Department of Paediatrics, Grosvenor Road, Clarendon Wing, Leeds LS2 9NS Tel: 0113 292 3905 — BM BCh Oxf. 1959; DSc Oxf. 1992, DM 1970; FRCP Lond. 1977, M 1965; DCH Eng. 1962. Hon. Sen. Lect. (Paediat.) Dept. Paediat. & Child Health Univ. Leeds. Prev: Cons. Paediat. Leeds AHA (T) & Yorks. RHA.

BUCKLER, Mr Keith Granville (retired) 3 Woodland Vale, Lakeside, Ulverston LA12 8DR Tel: 015395 30359 Fax: 015395 30359 Email: keith_buckler@hotmail.com — MB ChB Birm. 1955; FRCS Eng. 1962; DObst RCOG 1957. Prev: Cons. Surg. Bury & Burnley Gp. Hosps.

BUCKLER, Margaret Brandwood 3 Clumber Crescent S., The Park, Nottingham NG7 1EH Tel: 0115 941 8161 — MB ChB 1949 Sheff.; DObst RCOG 1950. (Sheff.) SCMO (Family Plann.) Nottm.; Clin. Asst. (Genitourin.) City Hosp. Nottm.; Hon. Med. Adviser Family Care Adoption Soc. Nottm. Prev: Ho. Phys. (Paediat.) Pk. Hosp. Davyhulme; Ho. Surg. (O & G) N.. Gen. Hosp. Sheff.

BUCKLER, Mary Elisabeth Lees 292 Victoria Park Road, Leicester LE2 1XE Tel: 0116 270 8641 Fax: 0116 270 8641 — MB ChB 1984 Leic.; MRCGP 1990; MFFP 1994; DCCH RCP Ed. 1989; DRCOG 1988. (Leic.) Clin. Med. Off. (Family Plann.) Fosse Health Trust Wom. & Childr. Servs.; Clin. Asst. (Genitourin. Med.) Leic. Roy. Infirm. Trust; GP Represen. Leic. LMC.

BUCKLER, Philip Wilkinson The James Cochrane Practice, Maude Street, Kendal LA9 4QE Tel: 01539 722124 Fax: 01539 734995 — MB BS 1976 Lond.; MRCP (UK) 1979; MRCGP 1984.

BUCKLEY, Alison The Archways Surgery, 86 Stockport Road, Romiley, Stockport SK6 3AA Tel: 0161 494 5337 Fax: 0161 406 7884; 67 Longhurst Lane, Marple Bridge, Stockport SK6 5AH Tel: 0161 449 7987 — MB ChB 1979 Sheff.; MB ChB Sheff. 1979 (Hons); MRCP (UK) 1982; MRCGP 1986; DCH RCP Lond. 1985; DRCOG 1984. (Sheffield) GP Princip. Stockport; Clin. Asst. in Dermat. Stepping Hill Hosp. Stockport.

BUCKLEY, Ann Marie 108 Greenfield Road, Harborne, Birmingham B17 0EF — MB BCh BAO 1989 NUI. SHO (Psychiat.) Nottm. VTS; SHO (Geriat. Adult Psychiat.) QMC. Prev: Ho. Off. Regional Hosp. Cork Irel.

BUCKLEY, Anthony Raymond, MBE (retired) Doelen House, Back Lane, Blakeney, Holt NR25 7NR Tel: 01263 740193 — MB BChir Camb. 1945; MRCP Lond. 1952; FFOM RCP Lond. 1985, MFOM 1978. Prev: Chief Med. Adviser Brit. Gas Corp.

BUCKLEY, Barbara Elizabeth West Hertfordshire Community Trust, 99 Waverley Road, St Albans AL3 5TL Tel: 01707 811888 Fax: 01707 857900; 49 Crescent W., Hadley Wood, Barnet EN4 0EQ Tel: 020 8440 4774 — MB BS 1984 Lond.; MRCP (UK) 1987; FRCPCH 1997. (St. Bart. Lond.) Cons. Child Health W. Herts. Community NHS Trust. Prev: Cons. Child Health. E. Herts. NHS Trust.; Sen. Regist. & Lect. (Paediat.) Roy. Free Hosp. Lond.

BUCKLEY, Cathryn Hilary 7 Linden Road, Didsbury, Manchester M20 2QJ — MB ChB Manch. 1962; MD Manch. 1980; FRCPath 1988, M 1976. Hon. Cons. Centr. Manch. NHS Trust. Prev: Sen. Lect. & Lect. (Path.) Univ. Manch.; Reader (Path.) Univ. Manch.

BUCKLEY, Charles Ian Wharton The Surgery, Whitminster Lane, Frampton on Severn, Gloucester GL2 7HU Tel: 01452 740213/741664 Fax: 01452 740989; Russell House, The Green, Frampton-on-Severn, Gloucester GL2 7EP Tel: 01452 740808 Email: charles.buckley@which.net — MB BS 1979 Lond.; MRCP (UK) 1982. (St. Mary's London)

BUCKLEY, Christopher Dominic 12 St Leonards Road, Headington, Oxford OX3 8AA — MB BS 1990 Lond.; MA Oxf. 1991.

BUCKLEY, Christopher John 67 Longhurst Lane, Mellor, Stockport SK6 5AH — MB ChB 1980 Sheff.; BMedSci. Sheff. 1978, MB ChB 1980; FFA RCS Eng. 1984. Med. Adviser, Astra Zeneca. Prev: Cons. (Anaesth.).

BUCKLEY, Colin Christopher 12 Old Bincombe Lane, Sutton Poytnz, Weymouth DT3 6NB — MB BCh BAO 1983 NUI; MRCPI 1987; MRCP (UK) 1987; LRCPI & LM, LRCSI & LM 1983. Cons. Dermat. Dorset Co. Hosp.

BUCKLEY, Cynthia Vivien Carolyne Cottage, Lawrence Lane, North Gorley, Fordingbridge SP6 2PG Tel: 01425 653164 — BSc (Hons.) Lond. 1979, MB BS 1982; MRCGP 1988; DRCOG 1988; DA (UK) 1987; DCH RCP Lond. 1986. (Guy's) Indep. Aeromed. Pract. Ringwood. Prev: Trainee GP Ringwood; SHO (Anaesth.) E. Dorset HA; SHO (O & G & Paediat.) Frimley Pk. Hosp.

BUCKLEY, David Martin George 8 Raysmith Close, Southwell NG25 0BG Tel: 01636 816764 — MB BS 1990 Lond.; BSc (Hons.) Lond. 1987, MB BS 1990; MRCP (UK) 1993. Regist. (Radiol.) Nottm. City Hosp. & Qu. Med. Centre Nottm.

BUCKLEY, David Michael The Surgery, Chestnut Walk, Stratford-upon-Avon CV37 6HQ Tel: 01789 292895 Fax: 01789 414721 Email: david.buckley@stratford.gp.org.uk; Wimpstone Farm, Wimpstone, Stratford-upon-Avon CV37 8NS Tel: 01789 450439 Email: david@wimpstone-farm.co.uk — MB BS 1984 Lond.; MRCGP 1988; DRCOG 1988. (Roy. Free Hosp.) GP Princip.; Clin. Asst. (Gastroenterol.) Warks.; Tutor (Gen. Pract.) S. Warks. Socs: Primary Care Soc. Gastroenterol.; GP Tutors Assn. Prev: SHO (Gen. Med.) Basildon; SHO (O & G) John Radcliffe Hosp. Oxf.

BUCKLEY, Mr Denis Dominic 34 Forest Grove, Eccleston Park, Prescot L34 2RZ — MB BCh BAO 1973 NUI; FRCSI 1978; MRCGP 1983; MICGP 1987; DO RCPI 1980.

BUCKLEY, Edward Ian James St Marys Health Centre, Cop Lane, Penwortham, Preston PR1 0SR Tel: 01772 744404 Fax: 01772 752967; 15 Uplands Chase, Fulwood, Preston PR2 7AW — MB ChB 1986 Manch.; DRCOG 1990; MRCGP 1994. (Manch.) Prev: SHO (Psychiat.) Whittingham Hosp. Preston GP VTS; SHO (O & G) Sharoe Green Hosp. Fulwood; SHO (Med. for Elderly) Chorley & Dist. Hosp.

BUCKLEY, Ernest Graham Scottish Council for Postgraduate Medical, & Dental Education, Hobart House, 4th Floor, 80 Hanover St., Edinburgh EH2 1EL Tel: 0131 225 4365 Fax: 0131 225 5891 Email: gb.scpmde@dial.pipex.com; Bankhead, 12 Laverockbank Road, Edinburgh EH5 3DA Tel: 0131 552 2712 — MB ChB Ed. 1970; BSc Ed. 1967; MD Ed. 1989; FRCP Ed. 1984; MRCP (UK) 1972; FRCGP 1982, M 1974; DObst RCOG 1974; FRCS Ed. 1999. (Edin.) Exec. Dir. Scott. Counc. Postgrad. Med. & Dent. Educat. Edin.; Co-Edr. Med. Educat. Socs: Hon. Sec. Assn. for Study of Med. Educ. Prev: Edr. Brit. Jl. Gen. Pract.; GP Livingston; Regional Adviser (Gen. Pract.) SE Scotl.

BUCKLEY, Franklin Barry (retired) The Barn, High Scalesceugh, Carleton, Carlisle CA4 0BT Tel: 016974 73749 — BSc (Hons. Physiol.) Birm. 1946, MB ChB (Hons.) 1949; FFA RCSI 1970; DA RCPSI 1968; DObst RCOG 1966. Prev: Cons. Anaesth. E. Cumbria Health Dist.

BUCKLEY, Hannah Kate Southampton General Hospital, Tremona Rd, Southampton SO16 6YD Tel: 023 8077 7222 — MB BS 1989 Lond.; MRCP (UK) 1993; DCH RCP Lond. 1992. (St. Geo. Hosp. Med. Sch.) p/t Specialist Regist. (Paediat.) Wessex Region. Socs: Roy. Coll. Paediat. & Child Health. Prev: Specialist Regist. St Marys Hosp. Portsmouth; Regist. Hosp. fo Sick Childr. Edin.

BUCKLEY, James Francis 6 Ravensworth Court, 570 Fulham Road, London SW6 5NN — MB BS 1998 Lond.; MB BS Lond 1998.

BUCKLEY, Mr James Richard Strachathro Hospital, Brechin DD9 Tel: 01356 665037 Fax: 01356 650247; Wellford House, Fern, Forfar DD8 3QT Tel: 01356 650247 Fax: 01356 650247 — MB BS 1977 Lond.; FRCS Ed. 1983. Cons. Orthop. Surg. Tayside HB; Hon. Sen. Lect. (Orthop. & Trauma Surg.) Univ. Dundee. Prev: Sen. Regist. (Orthop.) Tayside HB (Bridge of Earn & Dundee); Regist. (Orthop. Surg.) Dundee Roy. Infirm. & Derby Roy. Infirm.; SHO (Plastic Surg.) Nottm. City Hosp.

BUCKLEY, John Brocklebank Brae Cottage, Riverview Road, Pangbourne, Reading RG8 7AU Tel: 0118 984 2261 — MB ChB 1954 Manch.; BDS Liverp. 1961; LDS RCS Eng. 1960. (Manch. & Liverp.)

BUCKLEY, John Fennell The Health Centre, Rikenel, The Park, Gloucester GL1 1XR Tel: 01452 891110 Fax: 01452 891111 — MB ChB 1968 Ed.; DObst RCOG 1970. (Ed.) Socs: BMA. Prev: Ho. Phys. Bangour Gen. Hosp.; Ho. Surg. Dunfermline & W. Fife Hosp. & Forth Pk. Matern. Hosp.; Kirkaldy.

BUCKLEY, Mr John Graham Head & Neck Surgery, Leeds General Hospital, Leeds LS1 3EX Tel: 0113 392 8031 Email: jgrahambuckley@compuserve.com — MB ChB 1982 Birm.; MSc Birm. 1986; FRCS Eng. 1989. Cons. Head & Neck Surg., Leeds Gen. Infirm.; Clinician head and neck Oncol.; chair regional head and neck Clin. network; OtoLaryngol. Represen. on ncepod. Socs: BAOHNS; RSM; BMA.

BUCKLEY, John Harold McLellan 9 Seldon Close, Westcliff on Sea SS0 0AD Tel: 01702 342300 Fax: 01702 342300 — MB BS 1949 Lond.; MRCGP 1966. (Guy's) Socs: Fell. Roy. Soc. Med. Prev: Res. Obst. Off. Cheltenham Matern. Hosp.; Capt. RAMC, Jun. Specialist in Surg.; Regist. Paddington Gen. Hosp.

BUCKLEY, Kathleen Grace Hopwood House, The Vineyard, Lees Road, Oldham OL4 1JN Tel: 0161 628 3628 Fax: 0161 628 4970; 29 Kensington Road, Coppice, Oldham OL8 4BZ Tel: 0161 633 1191 Fax: 0161 628 4970 — MB ChB 1969 Manch.; DObst RCOG 1971. Family Plann. Clinic Doctor, Oldham NHS Trust. Socs: Oldham Med. Soc. & Brit. Soc. of Med. Dent. Hypn.. Prev: SHO (Med.) Baguley Hosp. Wythenshawe.

BUCKLEY, Keith British Aerospace Medical Centre, Tabuk, Saudi Arabia; 9 Bramcote Close, Aylesbury HP20 1QE Tel: 01296 395507 — MB BS 1974 Lond.; DRCOG 1977.

BUCKLEY, Mairin 8 Carrwood Avenue, Bramhall, Stockport SK7 2PX Tel: 0161 439 1350 — MB BCh BAO 1945 NUI; LM Rotunda 1945. (Univ. Coll. Dub.) Clin. Med. Off. Stockport AHA.

BUCKLEY, Margaret Patricia Studley Health Centre, 40 High Street, Studley B80 7HJ Tel: 01527 853311 Fax: 01527 854520 — MB ChB 1969. (Birmingham)

BUCKLEY, Margaret Ruth Newtownards Health Centre, Frederick Street, Newtownards BT23 4LS Tel: 028 9181 7239; 3 Knockdene

Park N., Knock, Belfast BT5 7AA — MB BCh BAO 1978 Belf.; MRCGP 1983; DCH Dub. 1979.

BUCKLEY, Maurice Peter Atlanta Surgery, 12 Walsall Road, Darlaston, Wednesbury WS10 9JL Tel: 01831 692814 — MB BCh BAO 1949 NUI. (Cork.) Apptd. Fact. Doctor Under Lead, Asbestos & Compressed Air Regulats.; Occupat. Phys. Nat. Home Care Wednesbury, Bradley & Foster Darlaston; Mid Foam Ltd. Smethwick, Newman Tonks Door Cl.rs Ltd. Walsall, MCR; Ltd. Coventry & Leamington Spa & Whelan Environm. Servs. Ltd. Birm. Socs: Soc. Occupat. Med. & Roy. Soc. Med. Prev: Ho. Phys. Warneford Hosp. Leamington Spa; Ho. Surg. Manor Hosp. Walsall; Jun. Specialist (ENT) Brit. Milit. Hosp. Wheatley.

BUCKLEY, Miriam Roberta Elizabeth 67 Sandhurst Gardens, Stranmillis Road, Belfast BT9 5AX Tel: 01232 666007 — MB BCh BAO 1994 Belf. Regist. (Radiol.) Roy. Vict. Hosp. Belf. Prev: SHO Roy. Vict. Hosp. Belf.; Ho. Off. Roy. Vict. Hosp. Belf.

BUCKLEY, Nicholas Godfrey Edmund St Georges Surgery, 46A Preston New Road, Blackburn BB2 6AH Tel: 01254 53791 Fax: 01254 697221; Redroofs, Spring Lane, Samlesbury, Preston PR5 0UX Tel: 01772 877643 — MB ChB 1982 Leic.; Cert Family Plann. JCC 1988. Prev: SHO Pilgrim Hosp. Boston.

BUCKLEY, Olive May Scotch Quarter Practice, Carrickfergus Health Centre, Carrickfergus BT38 7HT Tel: 028 9331 5800 Fax: 028 9331 5911; 54 Liberty Road, Carrickfergus BT38 9DJ — MB ChB 1986 Sheff.; MRCGP 1990; DRCOG 1991.

BUCKLEY, Patrick 236 Washway Road, Sale M33 4RB Tel: 0161 973 2595 — MB BCh BAO 1938 NUI.

BUCKLEY, Paul Andrew Frome Valley Medical Centre, 2 Court Road, Frampton Cotterell, Bristol BS36 2DE Tel: 01454 772153 Fax: 01454 250078 — MB ChB 1987 Bristol; MRCGP 1995; Dip. Paediat. Auckland 1993. Prev: Trainee GP Cardiff VTS; Regist. (Paediat.) Starship Childr. Hosp. Auckland, NZ; SHO (Urol. & Cas.) Cardiff Roy. Infirm.

BUCKLEY, Paul Michael Scarborough & North East Yorkshire Healthcare, Scarborough Hospital, Woodlands Drive, Scarborough YO12 6QL Tel: 01723 368111 — MB ChB 1977 Leeds; FFA RCS Eng. 1982. Cons. Anaesth. ScarBoro. & N.E. Yorks. Healthcare.

BUCKLEY, Philip Warren Annerley, Marbury Rd, Comberbach, Northwich CW9 6AU — MB ChB 1997 Birm.

BUCKLEY, Rachel White Rose Surgery, Exchange St., South Elmsall, Pontefract WF9 2RD — MB ChB 1990 Manch.; MRCGP 1995; DRCOG 1992. (Manch.) Prev: Community Med. Off. (Community Paediat.) Leicester; Trainee GP Bridge Hse. Med. Centre; SHO (O & G) N. Manch. Gen. Hosp.

BUCKLEY, Robert Guy Watledge Surgery, Barton Road, Tewkesbury GL20 5QQ Tel: 01684 293278; Fieldgate, Cheltenham Road, Bredon, Tewkesbury GL20 7NA — MB BS 1978 Lond.

BUCKLEY, Robert Milton 8 Platten Close, Needham Market, Ipswich IP6 8XE Tel: 01449 722518 Email: 104474.260@compuserve.com — MB ChB Cape Town 1954; FRCOG 1987, M 1970; DTM & H RCP Lond. 1962. Examg. Med. Pract. Benefit Agency Med. Serv. Prev: Med. Dir. Maluti Hosp. Lesotho, S.. Afr.

BUCKLEY, Professor Roger John Moorfields Eye Hospital, City Road, London EC1V 2PD Tel: 020 7253 3411 Fax: 020 7253 4696; 57A Wimpole Street, London W1M 7DF Tel: 020 7486 8959 Fax: 020 7935 5429 Email: rjbcity@aol.com — BM BCh Oxf. 1969; MA Oxf. 1969; FRCS Eng. 1979; FRCOphth 1993. (St. Thos.) Cons. Ophth. Moorfields Eye Hosp. Lond.; Prof. of Ocular Med. City Univ. Lond. Socs: Fell. Roy. Soc. Med.; (Ex-Pres.) Med. Contact Lens & occular surface Assn.; (Former Vice-Pres.) Internat. Soc. Contact Lens Research. Prev: Hon. Lect. Inst. Ophth. Lond.; Sen. Regist. (Ophth.) W.m. Hosp. Lond.; Resid. Surg. Off. Moorfields Eye Hosp. (City Rd.) Lond.

***BUCKLEY, Roisin Ann** 2A Mill Road, Burnham-on-Crouch CM0 8PZ — MB BS 1997 Lond.

BUCKLEY, Rosaleen Mary 34 Forest Grove, Eccleston Park, Prescot L34 2RZ — MB BCh BAO 1977 NUI.

BUCKLEY, Ruth Marjorie 120 Southend, Garsington, Oxford OX44 9DL Tel: 01865 361787; 120 Southend, Garsington, Oxford OX44 9DL Tel: 01865 361787 — MB ChB 1979 Bristol; MRCGP 1983; DRCOG 1982; DCCH RCP Ed. 1994. (Bristol) Prev: SCMO (Community Paediat.) Ipswich; GP Bedford; Clin. Asst. (Obst.) Bedford Gen. Hosp.

BUCKLEY, Sally Ann Elizabeth Dawlington Memorial Hospital, Hollyhurst Road, Darlington DL3 6HX — MB BS 1986 Lond.; BSc Lond. 1983; FCOphth 1990; DO RCS Eng. 1989. Cons. Ophth. Darlington Memor. Hosp. Prev: Regist. (Ophth.) Reading, Oxf. & Stoke Mandeville Hosp.; SHO (Ophth.) Roy. Eye Hosp. Manch. & Roy. Berks. Hosp.

BUCKLEY, Mr Simon Christopher 6 Hudson View, Tadcaster LS24 8JE Tel: 01937 531673 Email: scbuckle@globalnet.co.uk — MB BS 1990 Lond.; FRCS (Eng.) 1994. (St George's) Specialist Regist. (Orthop.) Yorks. Rotat. Socs: Sec. BOTA.

BUCKLEY, Stephen John Swan Surgery, Swan Street, Petersfield GU32 3AB Tel: 01730 264011 Fax: 01730 231093 — BM BS 1988 Nottm.; MRCGP 1992.

BUCKLEY, William Ernest Guy 139 St Georges Road, Cheltenham GL50 3EQ Tel: 01242 580644 — MB BChir 1951 Camb.; MRCS Eng. LRCP Lond. 1951. (Lond. Hosp.) Prev: Ho. Phys. & Ho. Surg. Orthop. & Accid. Dept. Lond. Hosp.

BUCKLEY-EVANS, John Dover Powerham Castle, Lanlivery, Bodmin PL30 5BU Tel: 01208 872277 — MB BCh 1958 Wales; LDS RCS Eng. 1964. (Cardiff) Med. Off. H.M. Dockyard Devonport; Surg. Lt.-Cdr. RNR. Prev: Med. Off. HMS Drake Devonport; Ho. Surg. St. David's Hosp. Accid. Unit Cardiff; Jt. Servs. Final Exam. Med. Off. Plymouth.

BUCKLEY-SHARP, Marcus David Chemical Pathology, Windeyer Building, Cleveland St., London W1T 4JF Tel: 020 7679 9238 Fax: 020 7679 9496 Email: mark.buckley-sharp@ucch.org — MB BS Lond. 1969, Dip. Biochem. 1966; FRCPath 1988, M 1976. (Middlx.) Cons. Chem. Path. Univ. Coll. Lond. Hosps.; Hon. Sen. Lect. (Chem. Path.) UCL Med. Sch. Socs: Fell. Roy. Soc. Med.; Fell. Brit. Computer Soc.

BUCKMAN, Atossa Elder and Partners, Paddington Green Health Centre, 4 Princess Louise Lane, London W2 1LQ Tel: 020 7887 1600 Fax: 020 7887 1635 — MB BS 1991 Lond.; BSc Lond. 1988; DRCOG 1996; DCH 1996. (Univ. Coll. Med. Sch.) GP Princip. Prev: SHO (c/o Elderly, St. Mary's Lond.; SHO (Obstet. & Gyn.) St. Mary's Lond.; SHO (Psychiat.) St. Mary's Lond.

BUCKMAN, Laurence Temple Fortune Health Centre, 23 Temple Fortune Lane, London NW11 7TE Tel: 020 8458 4431 Fax: 020 8731 8257; 21 Southover, Woodside Park, London N12 7JG Tel: 020 8446 4667 — MB BS 1977 Lond.; FRCGP 2001; MRCS Eng. LRCP Lond. 1977; MRCGP 1984. (Univ. Coll. Hosp.) Tutor (Gen. Pract.) Roy. Free Hosp. Med. Sch. Lond. Prev: Regist. (Med.) Mt. Vernon Hosp. Middlx.; SHO (Oncol.) Roy. Marsden Hosp. Lond.; Ho. Phys. Univ. Coll. Hosp. Lond.

BUCKMASTER, John Douglas Lilliput Surgery, Elms Avenue, Lindisfarne, Poole BH14 8EE Tel: 01202 741310 Fax: 01202 739122; Beechwood, 42 Sandecotes Road, Parkstone, Poole BH14 8PA Tel: 01202 746571 Email: buckmaster@bournemath-net.co.uk — MB Camb. 1978, MA, BChir 1977; DRCOG 1982. (St. Geo.) Prev: Trainee GP Bournemouth & Poole VTS; Ho. Phys. (Med.) St. Geo. Hosp. Lond.; Ho. Surg. Roy. E. Sussex Hosp. Hastings.

BUCKNALL, Christine Elisabeth Department of Respiratory Medicine, Stobhill Hospital, Batornock Road, Glasgow G21 3UW; High Blochairn Farm, Baldernock, Milngavie, Glasgow G62 6HE — MB ChB 1979; MD Ed. 1989; MRCP (UK) 1982; FRCP Glas. 1993; MRCGP 1989. Cons. Respirat. Phys. Socs: Scott. & Brit. Thoracic Soc. Prev: Trainee GP Glas. VTS; Audit Co-Ordinator, GGHB; Specialist Regist. Gen. & Respirat. Med. Glas.

BUCKNALL, Clifford Adrian Suite 302, Emblem House, London Bridge Hospital, 27 Tooley St., London SE1 2PR Tel: 020 7407 0292 Fax: 020 7357 0994 — MB BS 1979 Lond.; MD Lond. 1987; FRCP Lond. 1994; MRCS Eng. LRCP Lond. 1979; MRCP (UK) 1982. (Westm.) Cons. Cardiol. Guy's & St. Thos. Hosp. Lond.; Adviser in Cardiol. to Metropol. Police Serv. Socs: Fell. Roy. Soc. Med.; Brit. Cardiac Soc.; Brit. Cardiac Interven. Soc. Prev: Chief Med. Off Roy & Sun Alliance; Dir. Cardiac Servs. Gp.s & St. Thomas Hosp. Lond.; Cons. Cardiol. King's Coll. Hosp. Lond.

BUCKNALL, Jacqueline Lesley Department of Paediatrics and Child Health, Homerton Hospital, Homerton Row, London E9 6SR Tel: 020 8510 7762 Fax: 020 8510 7171 Email: jackie.bucknall@hamerton-hospital.nhs.uk; 13 St James Court, 71 Aldersbrook Road, Wanstead, London E12 5DL — MB BS 1988 Lond.; MRCP (UK) 1993; FRCPCH 1997. (St. Geo. Hosp. Med. Sch. Lond.) Cons. Paediatr. Barts & The Lond. NHS Trust, Lond.; Mem.

RCPCH A&E Grp.; Mem. RCPCH Gen. Paed. Grp. Socs: Internat. Coll. Paediat. & Child Care; Memb. Roy. Coll. Phys. (Lond.); Fell. Roy. Coll. Paediatr. & Child Health. Prev: Sen. Regist. (Paediat.) St. Mary's Hosp. Lond. & N.wick Pk. Hosp. Lond.; Regist. Rotat. (Paediat.) Burnley Gen. Hosp., Fairfield Gen. Hosp. & Roy. Manch. Childr. Hosp.; SHO Rotat. (Paediat.) Qu. Eliz. Hosp. for Childr. Lond., Homerton & Tadworth Ct. Childr. Hosp.

BUCKNALL, Roger Christopher Link 7C, Royal Liverpool Hospital, Prescot St., Liverpool L7 8XP Tel: 0151 706 3461 Fax: 0151 706 5834 Email: rbucknall@rcbuk_tv.nwestnhs.uk — MB BS Lond. 1969; FRCP Lond. 1983; MRCP (U.K.) 1971. Cons. Phys. Roy. Liverp. Hosp. & BRd.green Hosp. Liverp. Socs: Brit. Soc. Immunol. & Brit. Soc. Rheum. Prev: Sen. Regist. (Med.) Univ. Bristol & Roy. Nat. Hosp. Rheum. Dis. Bath; SHO (Med.) Roy. Sussex Co. Hosp. Brighton; Ho. Phys. (Paediat.) Guy's Hosp. Lond.

BUCKNALL, Mr Timothy Eric 1 Tutbury Road, Burton-on-Trent DE13 0NU Tel: 01283 566333; Westmorland Cottage, Old Hall Grounds, Rolleston-on-Dove, Burton-on-Trent DE13 9BS Tel: 01283 813336 — MRCS Eng. LRCP Lond. 1974; MS Lond. 1981, MB BS 1974; FRCS Eng. 1979. (Westm.) Cons. Gen. Surg. Burton-upon-Trent Dist. Gen. Hosp. Socs: Fell. Roy. Soc. Med. & Assn. Surgs.; Brit. Assn. Surg. Oncol. (Nat. Comm.). Prev: Sen. Regist. (Surg.) W.m. Hosp. Lond.; Regist. (Surg.) Warwick (S. Warks.) Health Dist.; Lect. (Surg.) W.m. Hosp. Med. Sch.

BUCKNELL, Sarah Jane 9 Riversleigh Avenue, Lytham St Annes FY8 5QZ Email: sarahtrout@hotmail.com — MB BS 1993 Newc.; FRCS Eng. 1997. Regist. Gen. Surg., St. Vincents Hosp. Melbourne, Australia (Accredit. Train. Scheme). Prev: Regist. (Cardiothoracic Surg.) Geelong Hosp. Vict. Austral.

BUCKNER, James Isaac Park House, Avonmouth, Bristol BS11 9EU — MB BCh BAO 1943 NUI.

BUCKNEY, Malcolm Norman MacDonald St. Peter Street, Dundee DD1 4JH; Ross Mill, Mains of Fowlis, By Invergowrie, Dundee DD2 5LQ Tel: 01382 360644 — MB ChB 1977 Dundee; MRCGP 1983; DCH RCP Glas. 1983. Prev: Regist. (Paediat.) Tayside Health Bd.

BUCKNILL, Andrew Thomas Abbotsford, Oxhey Drive S., Northwood HA6 3ET Tel: 01923 826220 — MB BS 1996 Lond.; BSc Lond. 1993. (Char. Cross & Westm.) SHO (Plastic Surg.) Char. Cross Hosp. Hammersmith Lond. Prev: Ho. Phys. St. Peter's Hosp. Chertsey; SHO (A & E) Char. Cross Hosp. Hammersmith Lond.; SHO (Neurosurg.) Roy. Lond. Hosp.

BUCKNILL, Mr Thomas Michael, RD 134 Harley Street, London W1N 1AH Tel: 020 7486 2622 Fax: 020 7224 1481; Abbotsford, Oxhey Drive, Northwood HA6 3ET Tel: 0192 74 24220 — MB BS Lond. 1964; FRCS Eng. 1970. (St. Bart.) Cons. Surg. (Orthop.) St. Bart. Hosp. Lond. & King Edwd. VII Hosp.; Surg. Cdr. RNR. Socs: Fell. RSM; BASK; Fell. Brit. Orthop. Assn. Prev: Orthop. Clin. Research Fell. Harvard Med. Sch. Boston, U.S.A.; Sen. Regist. Roy. Nat. Orthop. Hosp. Stanmore; Asst. Lect. Anat. St. Bart. Hosp. Med. Coll. Lond.

BUCKTON, Christine Cringleford Surgery, Cantley Lane, Norwich NR4 6TA Tel: 01603 54678 Fax: 01603 58287 — MB BS; MRCS Eng. LRCP 1967 London; MRCS Eng. LRCP 1967 London.

BUCZEK, Leon Antoni (retired) Wynchwood, Gypsy Crescent, Llanfoist, Abergavenny NP7 9LT Tel: 01873 2599 — MB ChB 1949 Polish Sch. of Med.

BUDD, Alan Keith, MBE 2 Barrington Close, Earley, Reading RG6 1ET — MB ChB Bristol 1968; BSc (Hons.) (Zool.) Wales 1962; MRCGP 1975; DObst RCOG 1970. (Bristol) p/t Bupa Screening Examnr. Reading; Co. Surg. Berks St Johns Ambul.; Locum Gen. Pract. Socs: BMA; RCGP; BASICS. Prev: Princ. Gen. Pract. Reading; SHO (O & G) Yeovil Gen. Hosp.; Ho. Phys. & Ho. Surg. S.mead Hosp. Bristol.

BUDD, Alison Jane 68 Abercrombie Street, London SW11 2JD Fax: 020 7207 0029 Email: alison@alibud.demon.co.uk — MB BS 1979 Lond.; FFA RCS Eng. 1983. (UCHMS) Cons. Anaesth. Moorfields Eye Hosp. Lond. Prev: Cons. Anaesth. Milton Keynes Hosp.; Sen. Regist. Rotat. Yorks. RHA.

BUDD, Barbara May Osborne House, High St., Deddington, Banbury OX15 0SL Tel: 01869 38011 — MB ChB Birm. 1962; DA Eng. 1964. (Birm.) S.C.M.O. Dent. Anaesth. Oxon. RHA; Med. Off. (Genitourin. Med.) Radcliffe Infirm. Oxf.; C.M.O. Family Plann. Oxf. Prev: Regist. (Anaesth.) Edgware Gen. Hosp.; Ho. Phys. Roy. Hosp. Wolverhampton.

BUDD, Christine Anne Elaine 84B Highbury Park, London N5 2XE Tel: 020 7704 8347 Email: cbudd@cinergy.co.uk — MB BS 1993 Lond.; DCH RCP Lond. 1996; DRCOG Lond. 1996. (St. Geo. Hosp. Lond.) GP Locum/ Islington. Prev: Trainee GP/SHO UCH Lond. VTS.

BUDD, Mr David William Guilford Walnut Tree Barn, Camp Lane, Warmington, Banbury OX17 1DH — FRCS Eng. 1967; LMSSA Lond. 1962. (Birm.) Cons. Surg. Horton Gen. Hosp. Banbury.

BUDD, Elizabeth Olwen Llanbryn, 2B Church St., Histon, Cambridge CB4 9JG — MB ChB 1995 Leics.

BUDD, Jeremy David East Quay Medical Centre, East Quay, Bridgwater TA6 5YB Tel: 01278 444666 Fax: 01278 445448 — MB 1981 Camb.; MA Camb. 1983, MB 1981, BChir 1980; MRCGP (distinc.) 1984; DRCOG 1984. Prev: Ho. Off. (Surg. & Med.) St. Mary's Hosp. Lond.; SHO (Psychiat.) Tone Vale Hosp. Taunton.

BUDD, Joanna Mary Woodside Farm House, Blake's Lane, Guarlford, Malvern WR13 6NZ — MB BS 1984 Lond.

BUDD, Mr John Steven Royal United Hospital, Combe Park, Bath BA1 3NG Tel: 01225 825491 Email: j.s.budd@bath.ac.uk; 152a Wellsway, Bath BA2 4SE — MD 1991 Leic.; BSc Lond. 1979, MB BS 1982; FRCS Eng. 1986. (St. Bartholomew's Medical School) Sen. Lect. & Hon. Cons. Surg. Roy. United Hosp. Bath. Socs: Vasc. Surg. Soc. Gt. Brit. & Irel.; Assn. Surg.; Eur. Soc. Vasc. Surg. Prev: Lect. (Surg.) Univ. of Leicester & Leicester Roy. Infirm.; Regist. (Gen. Surg.) P.ss Margt. Hosp. Swindon.

BUDD, Keith (retired) Newlands, Chevin Avenue, The Homestead, Menston, Ilkley LS29 6PE Tel: 01943 876331 Fax: 01943 870456 — MB ChB 1962 Leeds; FRCA 1968. Clin. Lect. (Anaesth.) Univ. Leeds; Lect. Schs. Studies Pharmacol. & Pharmacy Univ. Bradford. Prev: Cons. (Pain Managem.) Bradford Hosp. Trust.

BUDD, Michael (retired) Darras, 13 Eastfield Road, Ross-on-Wye HR9 5JY Tel: 01989 562751 — MB BS 1958 Lond.; LMSSA Lond. 1958; DObst RCOG 1961. Prev: GP Hereford.

BUDD, Pauline Phyllis 25 Upper Rose Hill, Dorking RH4 2EB Tel: 01306 888073 — MRCS Eng. LRCP Lond. 1947.

BUDD, Simon Timothy Lynfield Mount Hospital, Heights Lane, Bradford BD9 6DP — MB ChB 1988 Leic. SHO (Psychiat.) Lynfield Mt. Hosp. Bradford. Prev: SHO Rotat. (Med.) Bradford Roy. Infirm.; SHO Rotat. (Trauma) Addenbrooke's Hosp. Camb.

BUDD, Susan Kathleen Craigavon Area Hospital, 68 Lurgan Road, Craigavon BT63 5QQ Tel: 01762 334444; 44 Old Mill Heights, Hillsborough BT26 6RF Tel: 01846 689904 — MB BCh BAO 1992 Belf. Staff Grade Doctor (A & E) Craigavon Area Hosp. Craigavon.

BUDD, William Eric Robert Greycott, Pendoggett, Port Isaac PL29 3SX Tel: 01208 880239 — MRCS Eng. LRCP Lond. 1940. (Guy's) Prev: Cons. Geriat. Phys. Dartford & Gravesham Health Dist.; Dep. Med. Supt. S.. Hosp. Dartford; Surg. Lt. RNVR.

BUDDEN, Geoffrey Charles Cygnet Wing, Bedford Hospital, South Wing, Kempston Road, Bedford MK42 9DJ — MB BS 1971 Lond.; FRCOG 1991; MRCOG 1979, DObst 1975. (Middlx.) Cons. (O & G) Bedford Gen. Hosp. Prev: Sen. Regist. (O & G) Hammersmith Hosp. Lond.; Ho. Surg. Kettering Gen. Hosp.; Ho. Phys. Centr. Middlx. Hosp. Lond.

BUDDEN, Janine Maree The Belgravia Surgery, 26 Eccleston St., London SW1W 9PY Tel: 020 7590 8000 Fax: 020 7590 8010; 19 Minera Mews, London SW1W 9JD Tel: 020 7823 4920 Email: rubyb1234@aol.com — MB ChB 1992 Auckland; Dip Obst Auckland 1995; MRCGP 1998. GP Asst., Belgravia, Lond.

BUDDEN, Margaret Lovelace S.O.H.C., lake Street, Oxford OX1 4RP Tel: 01865 244428 — MB 1976 Camb.; BA Camb. 1972, MB 1976, BChir 1975; MRCP (UK) 1980; MRCGP 1981. (Lond. Hosp.) GP Oxf.. Prev: GP Trainee Lancaster; SHO (Med.) Newc. AHA (T); SHO (Paediat.) Newc. AHA (T).

BUDDEN, Michael Gareth Tel: 01494 26840; Chiltern Rise, 123 Totteridge Lane, High Wycombe HP13 7PH — MB BS 1950 Lond.; MRCGP 1968; DObst RCOG 1952. (Middlx.) Hosp. Pract. Dept. Dermat. Wycombe Gen. Hosp. Socs: BMA & Chiltern Med. Soc. Prev: Ho. Off. Dept. O & G Ho. Surg. Middlx. Hosp.; Squad. Ldr. RAF Med. Br.

BUDDEN, Peter Duncan St Andrews Medical Centre, 30 Russell Street, Eccles, Manchester M30 0NU Tel: 0161 707 5500; 7

Oldbrook Fold, Wood Lane, Timperley, Altrincham WA15 7PA Tel: 0161 904 9642 — MB ChB 1987 Manch.; BSc St. And. 1984; MRCGP 1991; DRCOG 1990. Prev: Trainee GP Manch. VTS; Trainee GP/SHO (O & G) Hope Hosp. Salford VTS.

BUDE, Anda 22 Stirling Road, Shortstown, Bedford MK42 0TX — MB BS Lond. 1983. (St. Bartholomews) SHO Psychiat. Bedford Hosp. Bedford. Prev: PRHO Surg.; PRHO Med.

BUDEWIG, Karen 75 Victoria Road, London NW6 6TB — State Exam Med 1990 Frankfurt.

BUDGE, Allison 15 Highfield Drive, Wembury, Plymouth PL9 0EX — BM 1991 Soton.

BUDGE, Catherine Christina (retired) 10 Ordiquish Road, Fochabers IV32 7HB Tel: 01343 820892 — MB ChB 1948 Aberd.; DPH Glas. 1966. Prev: Asst. Med. Off. Matern. & Child Welf. Glas. Corp.

BUDGE, Christopher James 15 Highfield Drive, Wembury, Plymouth PL9 0EX — BM 1991 Soton.

BUDGE, Elizabeth Mary Queens Park Medical Centre, Farrer Street, Stockton-on-Tees TS18 2AW Tel: 01642 679681 Fax: 01642 677124; 24 Richmond Road, Stockton-on-Tees TS18 4DT — MB BChir 1979 Camb.; MA, MB Camb. 1979, BChir 1978; MRCGP 1982; DCH RCP Lond. 1982.

BUDGE, Helen Jane Department of Child Health, University Hospital, Nottingham NG7 2UH — BM BCh 1991 Oxf.; BA Oxf. 1988; MRCP (UK) 1996; MRCPCH. (Oxf. Univ. Med. Sch.) Lect. in Child Health Univ. of Nottm.; Specialist Regist. (Paediat.) Oxf. Prev: SHO (Paediat.) Nottm.; Regist. (Paediat.) Oxf.

BUDGE, Timothy Simon Department of Anaesthetics, Northampton General Hospital, Northampton NN1 5DB — BChir 1995 Camb.

BUDGEN, John Patrick Boyce Osmaston Road Medical Centre, 212 Osmaston Road, Derby DE23 8JX Tel: 01332 346433 Fax: 01332 345854 — MB BS 1960 Lond.; MRCS Eng. LRCP Lond. 1960; DObst RCOG 1962; DCH Eng. 1962. (Guy's) Clin. Tutor (Fac. of Med.) Nottm. Univ. Prev: SHO (O & G & Paediat.) & Ho. Phys. St. Luke's Hosp. Guildford.

BUDGEN, Simon Adam Boyce Rose Cottage, 13 Cragg Terrace, Rawdon, Leeds LS19 6LF Tel: 0113 250 0403 Fax: 0113 250 0403 Email: abudgen@estancin.demon.co.uk — MB BS 1990 Lond.; BSc (Experim. Path.) Lond. 1987; FRCS Eng. 1995. Specialist Regist. (Orthop.) Leeds Gen. Infirm. Socs: Brit. Orthop. Assn. Prev: SHO (Orthop.) St. Jas. Hosp. Leeds & Ealing; SHO (Neurosurg.) Atkinson Morley Hosp. Wimbledon; SHO (Gen. Surg. & Orthop.) Mayday Hosp.

BUDGETT, Richard Gordon McBride British Olympic Medical Centre, Northwick Park Hospital, Watford Road, Harrow HA1 3UJ Tel: 020 8864 0609 Fax: 020 8864 8738; Crown Street Surgery, Crown St, London W3 8AS Tel: 020 8992 1963 — MB BS 1983 Lond.; BA Camb. 1980; MRCGP 1988; Dip. Sports Med. Lond. 1989; DRCOG 1987; DCH RCP Lond. 1986. (Cambridge University and Middlesex Hospital) Private Pract.: Sports Clinic Wementine Ch.ill Hosp., Sudbury Hill, Harrow, Middlx.; Chief Med. Off. Brit. Olympic Med. Centre N.wick Pk. Hosp.; Chief Med. Off. Med. Servs. for Brit. Olympic Assn.; Principle in Gen. Pract. Socs: BASM; Roy. Soc. Med. (Sports Med. Sect.); BMA.

BUDH-RAJA, Ved Prakash Green Lane Surgery, 67 Green Lane, Castle Bromwich, Birmingham B36 0AY Tel: 0121 747 6467 Fax: 0121 749 3613; 67 Green Lane, Castle Bromwich, Birmingham B36 0AY Tel: 0121 747 6467 Fax: 0121 749 3613 — MB BS 1964 Lucknow; MRCS Eng. LRCP Lond. 1971. (King Geo. Med. Coll.) Prev: Regist. (Chest Med.) Ham Green Hosp. Bristol.

BUDHANI, Shirazali Jafferali Remthulla Kidderminster Health Care Trust, Kidderminster General Hospital, Bewdley Road, Kidderminster DY11 6RJ Tel: 01562 823424; 27 Severnside Mill, Bewdley DY12 1AY — Vrach 1972 Leningrad. Assoc. Specialist (A & E & Trauma & Orthop.) Kidderminster Gen. Hosp. Prev: SHO (Orthop. & A & E) Hosp. St. Cross Rugby & Coventry & Warks. Hosp.

BUDHDEO, Shashikant Mawjibhai 3 Ivanhoe House, 130 Grove Road, London E3 5TW Tel: 020 8980 1767 Fax: 020 8980 1793 — MB BS 1959 Bombay; DRCOG 1971; DTM & H RCP Lond. 1968; DCH RCP Lond. 1967. GP Princip.

BUDHOO, Mr Misra Rai 4 Stock Grove, Milnrow, Rochdale OL16 3XB — MB ChB 1986 Manch.; MD Manch. 1995; FRCS Ed. 1990; FRCS Eng. 1990. Regist. N. Manch. Gen. Hosp. Prev: Regist. (Surg.) Birch Hill Hosp. Rochdale.

BUDIHAL, Shivabasappa Shivalingappa 53 Sylvan Drive, Newport PO30 5FL — MB BS 1974 Karnatak; MRCPI 1983. Clin. Research Phys. Interphase Research Unit St. Mary's Hosp. I. of Wight. Prev: Regist. (Gen. Med.) E. Glam. Gen. Hosp. Pontypridd; Regist. (Gen. Med.) Dartford Gp. of Hosps. Kent; Regist. (Geriat. Med.) Plymouth Gp. of Hosps. Devon.

BUDLEIGH, Mary Elizabeth (retired) 10 Winterbourne Mews, Lewes BN7 1HG — 1954 MB BChir Camb.; 1957 DObst RCOG; Approbation 1951 BA Camb. Prev: GP Sittingbourne.

BUDNY, Mr Peter George Tel: 01296 315113 Fax: 01296 315183; The Cruck Barn, Meadle, Aylesbury HP17 9UD Tel: 01844 347688 Fax: 01844 347688 — MB BS 1984 Lond.; BSc (Hons.) Anat. Lond. 1981; MSc Oxf. 1994; FRCS (Plast) 1997; FRCS Eng. 1988. (Lond. Hosp.) Cons. (Plastic, Reconstruc. & Burns Surg.) Stoke Mandeville Hosp. Aylesbury.; Cons. Plastic,Reconstruc. & burns Surg., Milton Keynes Gen. Hosp. Trust; Cons. S. Bucks Trust, Amersham & High Wycombe. Prev: Sen. Regist. (Plastic, Reconstruc. & Craniofacial Surg.) Radcliffe Infirm.; Regist. (Plastic & Burns Surg.) Stoke Mandeville Hosp.; Research Fell. (Craniofacial & Plastic Surg.) Radcliffe Infirm. Oxf.

BUENO CASQUERO, Gregorio 37A Chapel Street, Hemel Hempstead HP2 5AA — LMS 1987 Salamanca.

BUFFETT, Gareth John Gibson Carregwen Surgery, Church Road, Blaenavon NP4 9AF Tel: 01495 790264 Fax: 01495 790334; Broadhurst, The Park, Blaenavon NP4 9AQ Tel: 01495 791454 — MB ChB Ed. 1973; BSc Ed. 1970; FRCGP 1995, M 1977. VTS Course Organiser N. Gwent. Socs: RCGP (Treas. Welsh. Counc.).

BUFFEY, Andrew David 23 Queens Avenue, London N10 3PE — MB BS 1993 Lond.

BUFFIN, Mr John Terence Thornbury Hospital, 312 Fulwood Road, Sheffield S10 3BR Tel: 0114 266 1133; Holmbury, Thorncliffe Drive, Cheltenham GL51 6PY Tel: 01242 526313 — BM BCh 1955 Oxf.; FRCS Eng. 1965; DLO Eng. 1958. Prev: Cons. Med. Audiol. & ENT Surg. Sheff. DHA.

BUFTON, Hannah Jean Sarita 15 Llantrisant Street, Cathays, Cardiff CF24 4JB — MB BCh 1996 Wales.

BUFTON, Katherine Elizabeth The John Farman ICU, Box 17, Adenbrookes NHS Trust, Hills Rd, Cambridge CB2 2QQ Tel: 01223 217474; 25 Blenheim Drive, Wattisham Airfield, Ipswich IP7 7RS Tel: 01449 740276 Fax: 01449 740276 Email: drkate@globalnet.co.uk — MB ChB 1996 Birm.; ChB Birm. 1996; BSc (Hons) Pharmacology 1993. SHO IC, Adenbrookes Hsp, Camb.

BUGAIGHIS, Annette Elizabeth Overton Park Surgery, Overton Park Road, Cheltenham GL50 3BP Tel: 01242 580511 — MB BCh 1973 Wales; DRCOG 1976. GP Princip.

BUGG, George 16 Old Towns Close, Tottington, Bury BL8 3LH Email: gbugg95912@aol.com — MB ChB 1990 Manch.; DTM & H Liverp 1992; MRCOG 1997. Specialist Regist. O & G N. W. Region.

BUGLASS, Helen 11 Dunrobin Place, Stockbridge, Edinburgh EH3 5HZ Tel: 0131 343662 — MB ChB 1993 Aberd.; DRCOG 1995. SHO Rotat. (Anaesth.) S. E. of Scotl. Socs: MRCAnaesth.

BUGLER, Hilary The Practice Of Health, 31 Barry Road, Barry CF63 1BA Tel: 01446 700350 Fax: 01446 420795; Argae Farm, St. Andrews Major, Dinas Powys CF64 4HD — MB BS 1983 Newc.

BUGLER, John Anthony 12 Redroofs Close, The Avenue, Beckenham BR3 5YR — MB BCh BAO 1966 NUI. Regist. St. Thos. Hosp. Lond. Prev: Phys. Midl. Health Area & Gen. Hosp. Tullamore; Med. Tutor St. Vincent's Hosp. & Univ. Coll. Dub.

BUGLER, Robert Arthur (retired) Bridewell, Hawkchurch, Axminster EX13 5XL — MB BS 1955 Lond.; FRCPsych. 1983, M 1971; MRCGP 1964; DPM Eng. 1968.

BUHAMRAH, Eman Khaled Saleh c/o Mr. K. Buhamrah, Chairman & Managing Director, Petrochemical Industries Company, PO Box 1084, Safat 13011, Kuwait Tel: 00 965 2423426 Fax: 00 965 2445886; 12 Baliol Street, Flat 2/1, Glasgow G3 6UU — MB ChB 1995 Glas. SHO (Paediat.) Al-Adan Hosp., Kuwait. Prev: Ho. Off. (Surg.) W.. Infirm. Glas.; Ho. Off. (Med.) Hairmyers Hosp. E. Kilbride.

BUHRS, Ernst Gerardus Johannes 13 Rannoch Road, Bristol BS7 0SA — Artsexamen 1991 Free U Amsterdam; Artsexamen Free Univ Amsterdam 1991.

BUI, Thu Anh 10 Barncroft Drive, Hempstead, Gillingham ME7 3TJ — MB BS 1991 Lond.

BUICK, Mr Raymond George 68 Westfield Road, Edgbaston, Birmingham B15 3QQ Tel: 0121 454 1907 Email: r.g.buick@btinternet.com — MB BCh BAO 1972 Belf.; MB BCh 1972 Belf; FRCS Ed. 1976; FRCS Eng. (The Queens University of Belfast) Cons. Paediat. Surg. The Childr. Hosp. Birm.; Hon. Sen. Lect. Birm. Univ. Socs: (Exec. Com. Mem.) Brit. Assn. Paediat. Surg. Prev: Resid. Asst. Surg. Hosp. Sick Childr. Gt. Ormond St. Lond.; Surgic. Regist. The Fleming Memor. Hosp. Sick Childr. Newc.; Sen. Surgic. Regist. Our Lady's Hosp. Sick Childr. Dub.

BUIS, Christel University Department of Psychiatry, Mental Health Group, Royal South Hants. Hospital, 1 Brintons Terrace, Southampton SO14 0YG Tel: 02380 825544 Fax: 02380 234243 — Artsexamen 1990 Nijmegen; MD 1990. Regist. (Psychiat.).

BUISSON, Mr John Savile (retired) Savannah, Corberry Park, Dumfries DG2 7NG Tel: 01387 52370 — MB ChB 1961 Leeds; FRCS Ed. Orthop. 1984; FRCS Ed. 1968. Prev: Cons. Orthop. Surg. Dumfries & Galloway Roy. Infirm. Dumfries.

BUIST, Miss Laura Jane Renal Unit, University Hospital Birmingham NHS Trust, Queen Elizabeth Hospital, Edgbaston, Birmingham B15 2TH Tel: 0121 627 2427 Fax: 0121 627 2527 — MB ChB 1979 Glas.; FRCS (Eng.) 1999; MD Glas. 1991; FRCS Glas. 1983. Cons. Surg. (Transpl. & Gen. Surg.) Univ. Hosp. Birm. NHS Trust. Socs: Brit. Transpl. Soc.; Assn. Surg. Prev: Sen. Regist. (Transpl. & Gen. Surg.) W. Midl. HA.

BUIST, Michelle Manor View Practice, Bushey Health Centre, London Road, Bushey, Watford WD23 2NN Tel: 01923 225224 Fax: 01923 213270; 12 Coniston Road, Kings Langley WD4 8BU — MB BS 1989 Lond.; DFFP 1998; MRCGP 1993; DCH RCP Lond. 1992; DRCOG 1992. (Roy. Free Hosp. Sch. Med.) Socs: W Herts. & Watford Med. Soc. Prev: Trainee GP/SHO Watford VTS; Ho. Surg. (Gen. Surg. & Orthop.) Lister Hosp. Stevenage; Ho. Phys. Amersham Gen. Hosp.

BUIST, Robert Gerard 6 Rye View, High Wycombe HP13 6HL — MB ChB 1988 Auckland.

BUIST, Robert John Department of Anaesthesia, Medway Maritime Hospital, Windmill Road, Gillingham ME7 5NY Tel: 01634 830000 Fax: 01634 833856 — MB BS 1979 Lond.; FRCA; BA Oxf. 1976. Cons. Anaesth. & Pain Managem. Medway Hosp. Gillingham. Prev: Sen. Regist. (Anaesth.) St. Thos. Hosp. Lond.; Regist. (Anaesth.) St. Geo. Hosp. Lond.

BUIST, William Eric Seaton La Route Du Fort Surgery, 2 La Route Du Fort, St Helier, Jersey JE2 4PA Tel: 01534 31421 Fax: 01534 280776; La Chalet, Pontac, St Clement, Jersey JE2 6FQ Tel: 01534 856077 Fax: 01534 280776 — MB ChB 1981 Ed.; MRCGP 1988; DCH RCP Lond. 1984; DRCOG 1983. (Ed.) GP Jersey. Prev: Trainee GP Norwich VTS; SHO (Paediat.) Norf. & Norwich Hosp.; SHO (O & G) Simpsons Memor. Matern. Pavilion & Roy. Infirm. Edin.

BUKHARI, Naweed Ali Shah 27 Hunters Way, Enfield EN2 8NL — MB ChB 1993 Manch.

BUKHARI, Sayed Subhanalla Sandringham Building, Floor 5, Leicester Royal Infirmary, Leicester LE1 5WW Tel: 0116 258 6542 Fax: 0116 255 1949 Email: sayed.bukhari@public.path.msmail.lsi.tr-trent.nhs.uk — MB BS 1982 Peshawar; MSc London 1998; MRCPath 1997; Dip. GU Med. Soc. Apoth. Lond. 1993. Cons. Microbiol. Leicester Roy. Infirm. NHS Trust. Socs: Hosp. Infec. Soc.; BMA; Brit. Infec. Soc. Prev: Sen. Regist. (Microbiol.) Roy. Utd. Hosp. NHS Trust Bath; Sen. Regist. (Med. Microbiol.) Soton. Univ. Hosp. NHS Trust.

BUKHT, Mirza David Gething Wexham Park Hospital, Wexham Street, Slough SL2 4HL Tel: 01753 633185; Trematon Barton, NR Saltash, Saltash PL12 4RT Tel: 01753 633185 — MB BS 1975 Lond.; FFA RCS Eng. 1980. (Univ. Coll. Hosp.) Cons. (Anaesth.) Heatherwood and Wexham Pk. Hosps. Trust, Slough. Socs: Assn. of Anaesth.s, Gt. Britain and Irel.; Obstetric Anaesth.s Assn. Prev: Sen. Regist. (Anaesth.) St. Bart. Hosp. Lond.; Lect. (Anaesth.) Univ. Calgary, Canada.

BUKSH, Khoda 7 Reuther Avenue, Rutherglen, Glasgow G73 2SY — MB BS 1970 Dacca.

BUKUNOLA, Babatunde 30 Astral Avenue, Halifax HX3 8NN — MB ChB 1985 Manch. SHO (Anaesth.) Arrowe Pk. Hosp. Wirral. Prev: Ho. Off. (Med. & Surg.) Bury Gen. Hosp.

BUKY, Andrew 25 Lucknow Drive, Mapperley Pk, Nottingham NG3 5EU — MB BCh 1982 Wales.

BULCHAND, Rukmani Arrow Lodge Medical Centre, Kinwarton Road, Alcester B49 6PX Tel: 01789 763293 Fax: 01789 764380; Arrow Lodge, Henley St, Alcester B49 5QY Tel: 01789 763293 Fax: 01789 764380 — MS 1998 (Child Health) Warwick; DCP 1996 (Paediat.) Warwick; MBBS 1966. (P. of Wales Med. Sch., Patna)

BULCRAIG, Alastair Raymond Stanley Surgery, 1 East Brougham Street, Stanley, Perth PH1 4NJ Tel: 01738 828294 Fax: 01738 827770 — MB ChB 1971 St. And.; DObst RCOG 1973; MRCGP 1975.

BULCRAIG, Moira Elsie Vera Dalnagrian, Tayview, Luncarty, Perth PH1 3HE Tel: 01738 828141 — MB ChB 1971 Dundee; DObst RCOG 1973. Clin.Asst. Pyschiatry Learn.disabil.

BULEY, Ian David John Radcliffe Hospital, Oxford OX3 9DU — BM BCh 1983 Oxf.; MA Camb. 1983; MRCPath 1989. Cons. Histopath. John Radcliffe Hosp. Oxf. Prev: Sen. Regist. (Histopath.) John Radcliffe Hosp. Oxf.

BULGEN, Dianne Yvonne Countess of Chester Hospital, Liverpool Rd, Chester CH2 1UL Tel: 01244 365000 Fax: 01244 366455; Windrush, 26 Linksway, Upton-By-Chester, Chester CH2 1EA Email: d.bulgen@doctors.org.uk — MB BS 1968 Lond.; FRCP Lond. 1989, MRCP (UK) 1971; MRCS Eng. LRCP Lond. 1968. Cons. Rheum. Countess of Chester Hosp.

BULGER, Gerard Vincent Mathias Archway Surgery PMS, 52 High Street, Bovingdon, Hemel Hempstead HP3 0HJ Tel: 01442 833380 Fax: 01442 832093 Email: gerard.bulger@archway.nhs.uk; 12 Kings Road, Berkhamsted HP4 3BD Tel: 01442 864272 Fax: 01442 877191 — MB BS Lond.; MB BS Lond. 1976; BSc (Hons. Biochem.) Lond. 1972; MRCGP 1985; DCH Eng. 1979. (St. Bart. Hosp. Lond.) Princip. G.P. Archway Surg. PMS; Dir. Archway Develop.& Consult. Ltd. Lond. Socs: Fell. Roy. Soc. Med.; Roy. Coll. Gen. Practitioners; BMA. Prev: Regist. Whipps Cross Hosp. Lond.; Research Fell. Whittington Hosp. Lond.; Ho. Phys. St. Bart. Hosp. Lond.

BULGER, Jacqueline Mary 40 Seeleys Road, Beaconsfield HP9 1TB — MB ChB 1987 Leic.; MRCGP 1992.

BULKELEY, James Douglas Lyn Beauchamp House Surgery, 37 Baddow Road, Chelmsford CM2 0DB; The White House, 69 Sandford Mill Road, Chelmsford CM2 6SA Tel: 01245 469237 — MB BS 1973 Lond.; DTM Antwerp 1977; DObst 1976. Prev: Trainee GP W. Cumbld. Hosp. VTS; Med. Dir. Yakusu Hosp. & Rural Health Zone, Zaire; SHO (Anaesth.) W. Suff. Hosp. Bury St. Edmunds.

BULL, Adrian Richard PPP Healthcare, PPP House, Vale Road, Tunbridge Wells TN1 1BJ; 19 Ashburnham Gardens, Eastbourne BN21 2NA — MB ChB 1981 Ed.; DM Soton. 1993; MFCM RCP (UK) 1989; MRCGP 1986. Med. Dir. Prev: Cons. (Pub. Health Med.) E. Sussex HA, Yorks. HA.

BULL, Andrew David Department Histopathology, North Devon District Hospital, Raleigh Park, Barnstaple EX31 4JB Tel: 01271 322577 — MB ChB 1986 Sheff.; MRCPath 1993. (Univ. Sheff.) Cons. Histopath. N. Devon Dist. Hosp. Barnstaple. Prev: Sen. Regist. (Histopath.) Univ. Hosp. Wales Cardiff; Regist. Rotat. (Histopath.) Sheff. Train. Scheme; SHO (Histopath.) N.ern Gen. Hosp. Sheff..

BULL, Barbara Irene 11 Lakeside Drive, Esher KT10 9EZ — MB BS 1993 Lond.

BULL, Catherine Hospital for Sick Children, Great Ormond St., London WC1N 3JH Tel: 020 7405 9200 Email: kate.bull@gosh-tr.nthames.nhs.uk — MB BChir 1976 Camb.; FRCP Lond. 1994. (University of Cambridge) Sen. Lect. Inst. Child Health & Hon. Cons. Cardiol. Hosp. Sick Childr. Lond.

BULL, Charles Stuart Church End Medical Centre, Church End, Old Leake, Boston PE22 9LE Tel: 01205 870666 Fax: 01205 870971; Eastgate House, Wainfleet Road, Fishtoft, Boston PE21 9RZ Tel: 01205 355158 — MB BChir 1978 Camb.; MRCGP 1985; DRCOG 1981. (Camb. & Guy's) Course Organiser, Boston Vocational Train. Scheme. Prev: Trainee GP Cheltenham & Gloucester VTS; Ho. Phys. Lewisham Hosp. Lond.; Ho. Surg. Guy's Hosp. Lond.

BULL, Christopher Coulson (retired) 8 Welholme Road, Grimsby DN32 0DU Tel: 01472 354604 — MRCS Eng. LRCP Lond. 1952; LDS RCS Eng. 1945.

BULL, David (retired) Heathers, 14 Beverley Road, Leamington Spa CV32 6PJ Tel: 01926 427430 — LRCP LRCS Ed. LRFPS Glas. 1948. Prev: Regist. (Radiol.) Roy. Hosp. Wolverhampton.

BULL, David Michael Kensington Group Practice, Kensington Road, Road, Douglas IM1 3PF Tel: 01624 676774 Fax: 01624 614668; Rookwood, Quarterbridge Road, Douglas IM2 3RH Tel: 01624 672922 — MB ChB 1977 Liverp.; MRCGP 1984; DCH RCP Lond. 1984; DRCOG 1983.

BULL, David Richard 35 Saltram Crescent, Maida Vale, London W9 3JR Tel: 020 8964 9553 Fax: 020 8960 4685 Email: drdavebull@aol.com — MB BS 1993 Lond.; BSc Basic Med. Scs. & Hist. Med. (1st cl. Hons.) Lond. 1992. Med. Jl.ist, BRd.caster & Television Presenter Lond. Socs: Osler Club Lond.; BMA.

BULL, Derek William Park Slope Surgery, Blisworth, Northampton NN7 3BT Tel: 01604 858237; Candlebridge, Little Lane, Blisworth, Northampton NN7 3BS — MB BS 1949 Lond.; MRCS Eng. LRCP Lond. 1949; DCH Eng. 1954; DObst RCOG 1952. (St. Mary's)

BULL, Henry John McKenzie 7 Westbrooke, Worthing BN11 1RE Tel: 01903 201181 — MB BS 1972 Lond.; MB BS (Hons.) Lond. 1972; FRCP 1989; MRCS Eng. LRCP Lond. 1972. Cons. Phys. Worthing Hosp.

BULL, John Courtney (retired) Bowling Green Cottage, Hurst Road, Horsham RH12 2DW Tel: 01403 263510 — MB BS 1959 Lond.; FRCS Eng. 1963; MRCS Eng. LRCP Lond. 1959. Prev: Cons. Surg. Crawley Hosp., Horsham Hosp. & Qu. Vict. Hosp. E. Grinstead.

BULL, John Prince, CBE (retired) 73 Reddings Road, Moseley, Birmingham B13 8LP — MRCS Eng. LRCP 1941 Lond; MB BChir Camb. 1946; BA Camb. (Part II Nat. Sci. Trip. 1st Cl) 1938; MA Camb. 1945, MD 1951; FRCP Lond. 1969, M 1964. Prev: Dir., MRC Indust. Injuries & Burns Unit Birm. Accid. Hosp.

BULL, Judith Joan 7 Westbrooke, Worthing BN11 1RE Tel: 01903 201181 — MB 1971 Camb.; BChir 1970.

BULL, Mrs Lesley Ann Pall Mall Surgery, Pall Mall, Leigh-on-Sea SS9 1RB; 87 Tyrone Road, Thorpe Bay, Southend-on-Sea SS1 3HD Tel: 01702 589502 — MB BS 1982 Lond.; Cert. Family Plann. JCC 1986; DRCOG 1986. (Lond. Hosp.) Community Med. Off. Guildford. Prev: SHO (O & G) N. Middlx. Hosp. Lond.; SHO (Psychiat.) Claybury Hosp. Lond.; Ho. Off. (Gen. Med. & Gastroenterol.) St. Peter's Hosp. Chertsey.

BULL, Linda Nunwell Surgery, 10 Pump Street, Bromyard HR7 4BZ Tel: 01885 483412 Fax: 01885 488739; Park Cottage, Ashperton, Ledbury HR8 2SE Tel: 01531 670510 — MB ChB 1974 Birm.; MRCP (UK) 1979; DCH Eng. 1977.

BULL, Marie Doreen (retired) Heathers, 14 Beverley Road, Leamington Spa CV32 6PJ Tel: 01926 427430 — MB BS 1948 MB BS Lond. 1948; MRCS Eng. LRCP Lond. 1948; DTM & H Eng. 1950.

BULL, Martin William Lothian Health, Deaconess House, 148 Pleasance, Edinburgh EH8 9RS Tel: 0131 536 9000 Fax: 0131 536 9195; Flat 1F1, 7 Marchmont St, Edinburgh EH9 1EL Tel: 0131 229 5631 — MB BS 1990 Lond.; MSc (Community Health) Dub. 1995; BSc (Hons.) Immunol. Lond. 1987. Regist. (Pub. Health Med.) Lothian Health. Socs: BMA; Med. Protec. Soc.

BULL, Mary Eileen 5 Ellerton Road, London SW18 3NG Tel: 020 8870 3936 — MB ChB 1988 Sheff.; MRCGP 1994; T(GP) 1994; DFFP 1994.

BULL, Matthew James Diagnostic Imaging, Northern General Hospital, Herries Road, Sheffield S5 7AU Tel: 0114 271 5374; 263 Dobcroft Road, Ecclesall, Sheffield S11 9LG Tel: 0114 262 0206 — MB ChB 1980 Sheff.; FRCR 1987. Cons. Radiol. N. Gen. Hosp. Sheff.; Cons. Radiologist, Claremont Hosp. Sheff.; Cons. Radiologist, Thornbury Hosp. Sheff. Socs: Fell. Roy. Coll. Radiol.; Radiological Soc. of N. America. Prev: Sen. Regist. & Regist. (Radiol.) Sheff. HA; SHO (Gen. Med.) Walsgrave Hosp. Coventry; Ho. Surg. & Ho. Phys. N.. Gen. Hosp. Sheff..

BULL, Matthew James 22 The Horseshoe, Leverstock Green, Hemel Hempstead HP3 8QT Tel: 01442 213347 Email: drmattbull@hotmail.com — MB ChB 1996 Manch. SHO, GP VTS Scheme, Tunbridge Wells.

BULL, Mervyn Robert (retired) 12 Rhosnesni Lane, Wrexham LL12 7LY Tel: 01978 265384 — MRCS Eng. LRCP Lond. 1939. Prev: Capt. Serving in India.

BULL, Michael James Vendy (retired) 7 Lewis Close, Headington, Oxford OX3 8JD Tel: 01865 765333 Fax: 01865 740257 — BM BCh Oxf. 1950; MA Oxf. 1950; FRCGP 1978, M 1966; DObst RCOG 1956. Prev: Hosp. Pract. (Obst.) John Radcliffe Hosp. Oxf.

BULL, Mr Peter Denis Tower Cottage, Ranmoor Hill, Hathersage, Sheffield S32 1BQ Tel: 01433 650233 Fax: 01433 659376 Email: peter.bull@sheffield.ac.uk — MB BCh Wales 1967; FRCS Eng. 1975. Cons. ENT Surg. Centr. Sheff. Univ. Hosps. Trust; Cons ENT Surg. Childrs. Hosp. Sheff. Socs: (Ex-Pres.) Assn. Paediat.; Roy. Soc. Med. (Ex-Vice Pres. Sect. Laryngol.); Examr, Intercollegiate FRCS in OtoLaryngol. Prev: Sen. Regist. Avon AHA (T).

BULL, Peter Maxwell The Surgery, Cheriton Fitzpaine, Crediton EX17 4JB Tel: 01363 866322 Fax: 01363 866642; Ashley Court Cottage, Ashley, Tiverton EX16 5PD Tel: 01884 252325 Fax: 01884 252325 Email: drpbull@so1.co.uk — MB BChir 1974 Camb.; MA Camb. 1976; DTM & H Liverp. 1980; DObst. RCOG 1975. (Cambridge and Westminster)

BULL, Peter Townley Anaesthetic Department, Kings Mill Hospital, Sutton-in-Ashfield NG17 4JL Tel: 01623 622515 Fax: 01623 676027; Kota Tinggi, Mansfield Road, Farnsfield, Newark NG22 8HH Tel: 01623 882016 — MB ChB Liverp. 1967; FRCA Eng. 1976; FFA RCSI 1975; DA Eng. 1973. Cons. Anaesth. Kings Mill Health Care Trust. Socs: Assn. Anaesth.; BMA; Obst. Anaesth. Assn. Prev: Surg. Cdr. RN; Sen. Anaesth. Hosp. Ship Uganda 1982.

BULL, Philip William William Harvey Hospital, Kennington Road, Willesborough, Ashford TN24 0LZ Tel: 01233 633331 Fax: 01233 616044; Foxhole, Sandling Road, Sandling, Hythe CT21 4HG Tel: 01303 261608 Fax: 01303 260343 — MB BS 1979 Lond.; FRCP Lond. 1996; MRCP (UK) 1983; DA (UK) 1985. (St. Thos.) Cons. Rheum. William Harvey Hosp. Ashford. Prev: Sen. Regist. (Gen. Med. & Rheum.) Char. Cross & W.m. Hosp. Lond.; SHO (Thoracic Med.) Brompton Hosp. Lond.; SHO St. Thos. Hosp. Renal Unit.

BULL, Richard Edward Drs Turner and Bull, Dronfield H. C., High St., Dronfield S18 1PY; 4 Vale Close, Dronfield S18 1SF Tel: 01246 411298 — MB ChB 1983 Leeds; MB ChB (Hons.) Leeds 1983; DCH RCP Lond. 1987; MRCGP (Distinc.) 1988; DRCOG 1986; Cert. Family Plann. JCC 1986. Acad. Train. Fell., Scharr.

BULL, Richard Hillson Homerton Hospital, Homerton Row, London E9 6SR Tel: 020 8919 7690 — BM BCh 1982 Oxf.; MRCP (UK) 1985. Cons. Dermat. Homerton NHS Trust & Roy. Hosps. Trust Lond.

BULL, Russell Keith 34 Greystoke Gardens, Enfield EN2 7NX Email: russell.bull@btintermet.com — BChir 1990 Camb.; MB. Camb. 1991; MRCP (UK) 1994. (Cambridge) Specialist Regist., Addenbrookes Hosp., Camb.

BULL, Thomas Michael (retired) Woodcroft House, Comeytrowe Road, Trull, Taunton TA3 7NF Tel: 01823 282447 — MB BS 1957 Lond.; MRCS Eng. LRCP Lond. 1957; FFA RCS Eng. 1965; DA Eng. 1962. Cons. Anaesth. W. Som. Health Dist. Prev: Jt. Sen. Regist. (Anaesth.) St. Geo. Hosp. Lond. & Soton.

BULL, Mr Timothy Michael Trauma & Orthopaedic Dept, Chases Farm Hospital, The Ridgeway, Enfield EN2 8JL Tel: 020 8366 6600 Ext: 5991 Fax: 01223 777269 Email: tim.buk@virgin.net — MB BS 1986 Lond.; FRCS Eng. 1991; FRCS (Orth.) 1996. (Westminster) Cons. Orthop. & Spinal Surg. Chase Farm Hosp. Eng. Prev: Sen. Spine Fell. Qu.'s Med. Centre Nottm.; Sen. Regist. (Orthop.) Addenbrooke's Hosp. Camb.; Regist. (Orthop.) Roy. Nat. Orthop. Hosp. Stanmore.

BULL, Mr Tony Raymond 107 Harley Street, London W1 1DG Tel: 020 7935 3171 — MB BS 1958 Lond.; FRCS Eng. 1962; MRCS Eng. LRCP Lond. 1958. (Lond. Hosp.) Cons. Surg. Roy. Nat. Throat, Nose & Ear Hosp. Lond. & King Edwd. VII Hosp. for Offs.; Cons. Surg. Char. Cross Hosp. Lond.; Yearsley Lect. Roy. Soc. Med. 1982. Socs: Fell. Med. Soc. Lond.; Fell. Roy. Soc. Med. (Pres. Otol. Sect.). Prev: Sen. Fell. (Otol.) Memphis Foundat. USA; Ho. Surg. Lond. Hosp.

BULLARD, Henrietta the Oxford Clinic, Littlemore Mental health Centre, Oxford OX4 4XN Tel: 01865 223123 Fax: 01865 223465 Email: henrietta.bullard@oxmhc-tr.anglox.nhs.uk — MB BS Lond. 1962; MRCS Eng. LRCP Lond. 1962; FRCPsych 1997; DPM Eng. 1975; MRC Pysch 1976. (Lond. Hosp.) Cons. Forens. Psychiat. Oxon.Ment. health NHS Trust; Vis. Cons. Forens. Psychiat. HMP Bullingdon (Home Off.). Socs: Fell. Roy. Soc. Med.; Brit. Acad. Forens. Sci. Prev: Vis. Cons. Psychiat. HMP Grendon (Home Off.); Cons. Forens. Psych. W. Midl. RHA.

BULLAS, Brian Hamilton Brinklands, 8 Cavendish Road, Brincliffe, Sheffield S11 9BH Tel: 0114 255 0037 Fax: 0114 250 9992 — MB BS 1966 Lond.; MRCS Eng. LRCP Lond. 1966; DA Eng. 1969; FRS 2000. (St. Geo.) Vis. Anaesth. Methley Pk. Hosp. Wakefield; Med. Dir. Tapton Cliffe Clinic; Vis. Anaesth. Methley Pk. Hosp. Leeds. Prev: Med. Directer Beechwood Private Clinic Sheff.; Cons. Doncaster Roy. Infirm.; Sen. Resid. Univ. Manitoba, Canada.

BULLEID, John Allen (retired) Austrey Wood, Upper Toothills Road, Rownhams, Southampton SO16 8AL — MB BChir 1946 Camb. Prev: Res. Obstetr. & Ho. Surg. Guy's Hosp.

BULLEN, Alice Woodman George Eliot Hospital, College St., Nuneaton CV10 7DJ Tel: 02476 351351 — MB ChB 1970 Leeds; MD 1983 Leeds; FRCP 1986 UK; MRCP 1973 UK. (Leeds) Cons. Phys. Geo. Eliot Hosp. Nuneaton. Prev: Lect. Med. St. James Univ. Hosp. Leeds.

BULLEN, Mr Barry Richard George Eliot Hospital, College St., Nuneaton CV10 7DJ Tel: 024 7686 5111 Fax: 024 7686 5395; Email: b.r.bullen@btinternet.com — MB ChB (Hons.) Leeds 1970; FRCS Eng. 1974. (Leeds University) Cons. Surg. Geo. Eliot Hosp. Nuneaton; Clin. Teach. Fac. Med. Univ. Leics.; Hon Cons. Surg. Walsgrave Hosp. Coventry. Prev: Cons. Surg. Walsgrave Hosp. Coventry; Sen. Regist. Leeds (T) & Bradford HA.

BULLEN, Catherine 32 Fife Road, East Sheen, London SW14 7EL Tel: 020 8876 0025 — MB ChB 1974 Liverp.; FFA RCS Eng. 1978. UCLH Hosp. Lond.

BULLEN, Elizabeth Katrina 27 Tower Road W., St Leonards-on-Sea TN38 0RJ Tel: 01424 717793; 48 Mulgrave Road, Sutton SM2 6LX Tel: 020 8642 2050 — MB BS 1983 Lond.; Cert. Family Plann. JCC 1988; DRCOG 1987. GP St. Leonards-on-Sea Retainer Scheme.

BULLEN, Heather Alison Flat 5, Thorngrove Place, Aberdeen AB15 7FJ Tel: 01224 321885 — MB ChB 1992 Aberd. SHO (Gen. Adult Psychiat.) Roy. Cornhill Hosp., Aberd.

BULLEN, James Gerard Old Farm Surgery, 67 Foxhole Road, Paignton TQ3 3TB — MB ChB 1983 Birm.; MRCGP 1988; DCH RCP Lond. 1988; DRCOG 1988. Prev: Trainee GP Torbay Hosp. Torquay.

BULLEN, John Anthony Box Surgery, London Road, Box, Corsham SN13 8NA Tel: 01225 742361 — MB BCh BAO 1972 NUI; MRCP (UK) 1976.

BULLEN, Kevin Robert 21 Lowfield Drive, Thornhill, Cardiff CF14 9HT — MB BCh 1994 Wales.

BULLEN, Philip James 71 Speldhurst Road, Chiswick, London W4 1BY — MB ChB 1987 Manch.; MRCOG 1993.

BULLEN, Sarah Anne 17 Newton Mansions, Queen's Club Gardens, London W14 9RR — MB ChB 1988 Otago.

BULLEN, Sharonn 12 River Avenue, Thames Ditton KT7 0RS Tel: 020 8339 0038 Fax: 020 8339 0026 Email: sbullen@ndirect.co.uk — MB ChB 1974 Liverp.; Cert. Family Plann. JCC 1981; Cert. Prescribed Equiv. Exp. JCPTGP 1981. Clin. Asst. (Diabetes) Qu. Mary's Hosp. Lond.; Community Med. Off. Richmond, Twickenham & Roehampton HA.; Med. Off. St. Paul's Girls' Sch., Lond. Prev: Community Med. Off. Riverside HA.

BULLEN, Timothy Francis Meadowcroft Barn, Bury Road, Turton, Bolton BL7 0BS — MB ChB 1998 Liverp.; MB ChB Liverp 1998.

BULLER, Alexander John Cairnmore House, Port Ellen, Isle of Islay PA42 7AT — MB ChB 1995 Sheff.

BULLER, Professor Arthur John, ERD Lockhall Cottage, Cow Lane, Steeple Aston, Bicester OX25 4SG Tel: 01869 347502 Fax: 01869 340690 Email: ajbuller@f2c.co.uk — BSc, PhD, MB BS Lond. 1945; BA 1996; FRCP Lond. 1976, M 1969; FIBiol. 1978. (St. Thos.) Emerit. Prof. Physiol. Univ. Bristol. Socs: Physiol. Soc. & Med. Research Soc. Prev: Research Developm. Dir. Muscular Dystrophy Gp.; Chief Scientist DHSS; Mem. Med. Research Counc. (Ex-Chairm. Ment. Health & Neurobiol. Bd.).

BULLER, Christopher Huw Professorial Department, High Royds Hospital, Menston, Ilkley LS29 6AQ — MB BCh 1990 Wales.

BULLER, Nigel Pearson Department of Cardiology, Queen Elizabeth Hospital, Edgbaston, Birmingham B15 2TH Tel: 0121 627 2538 Fax: 0121 697 8304 Email: nigel.buller@university-b.wmids.nhs.uk; 115 Selly Park Road, Birmingham B29 7HY Tel: 0121 471 5247 Fax: 0121 472 7945 — MB BS 1980 Lond.; BSc 1977 Lond.; MRCP 1983 (UK); FRCP 1996 Lond.; BSc Lond. 1977; FRCP Lond. 1996; MRCP (UK) 1983. (St. Thos. Lond.) Cons. Cardiol. Qu. Eliz. Hosp. Birm.; Hon. Sen. Lect. Univ. Birm. Socs: (Counc.) Brit. Cardiovasc. Interven. Soc.; Brit. Cardiac Soc. Prev: Sen. Lect. & Cons. Cardiol. Roy. Brompton Hosp. Lond.; Sen. Regist. (Cardiol.) Harefield Hosp.; Lect. (Cardiol.) Cardiothoracic Inst. Lond.

BULLEY, Roger John Bulley and Partners, Hamdon Medical Centre, Matts Lane, Stoke-sub-Hamdon TA14 6QE Tel: 01935 822236 Fax: 01935 826565; Stoneleigh, Skillgate Lane, Chiselborough, Stoke-sub-Hamdon TA14 6TP Tel: 01935 881528 — MB BS 1976 Lond.; MRCS Eng. LRCP Lond. 1976; DRCOG 1981; DA Eng. 1979. (St. Bart.) GP Clin. Tutor Yeovil Postgrad. Centre; Clin. Asst. (Orthop.) S. Petherton; DHSS Med. Off.; Mem. Som. LMC (Chairm. Communication). Socs: BMA (S. W.. Elected Represen. GMSC); (Exec.) Nat. Assn. GP Tutors; Assoc. Mem. Roy. Coll. Gen. Pract. Prev: Trainee GP Cornw. VTS; SHO (Anaesth. & Med.) Roy. Cornw. Hosp. Truro; Ho. Phys. St. Leonard's Hosp. Lond.

BULLIMORE, David William Wallace Barnsley DGH Trust, Gawber Rd, Barnsley S75 2EP Tel: 01226 777879; Cloverley Villa, Daw Lane, Horbury, Wakefield WF4 5DS Tel: 01924 274271 Email: dwwbullimore@compuserve.com — MB ChB 1972 Bristol; BSc Bristol 1969, MD 1978; MRCP (UK) 1976. Cons. (Phys.) Barnsley DGH Trust. Socs: Assn. Study Med. Educat.; BMA; Brit. Soc. of Gastroenterol. (Ordinary). Prev: Sen. Lect. (Med.) St. Jas. Hosp. Leeds; Lect. (Med.) St. Jas. Hosp. Leeds.

BULLIMORE, Jill Annette (retired) Horsecombe House, Shepherds Walk, Bath BA2 5QU Tel: 01225 833510 Email: pizey@which.net — MB BS 1960 Lond.; MRCS Eng. LRCP Lond. 1960; FRCR 1968; DMRT Eng. 1966; MRCP 1997. Cons. Clin. Oncol. Bristol Oncol. Centre. Prev: Vice-Pres. Roy. Coll. Radiol.

BULLIMORE, Shelagh Patricia The Paddock Surgery, Chapel Lane, Thornhill, Dewsbury WF12 0DH Tel: 01924 465343 — MB ChB 1972 Bristol; MRCGP 1986; Cert. Med. Educat. Dundee 1995; DCH Eng. 1975; DA Eng. 1974. (Bristol) Course Organiser, W. Riding GPEC; Trainer (Gen. Pract.) Dewsbury. Socs: Med. Defence Union; Brit. Med. Assn. Prev: Clin. Asst. (Paediat. Oncol.) Bristol Childr. Hosp.

BULLMORE, Professor Edward Thomas Dept of Psychiatry, University of Cambridge, Addenbrookes Hospital, Cambridge CB2 2QQ Tel: 01223 336583 Fax: 01223 336581 Email: etb23@cam.ac.uk — MB BS 1985 Lond.; PhD Lond. 1997; BA Oxf. 1981; MRCP (UK) 1989; MRCPsych 1992. Prof of Psychiat. Prev: Wellcome Trust Advanced Clin. Research Train. Fell.; Sen. Lect. Inst. Psychiat. & Hon. Cons. Maudsley Hosp. Lond.; Wellcome Trust Clin. Research Train. Fell.

BULLMORE, George Hilary Lanyon (retired) 12 Portsmouth Road, Kingston upon Thames KT1 2LU Tel: 020 8546 9262 — BM BCh Oxf. 1938; MA Oxf. 1984, BA 1933; LMSSA Lond. 1938; DPM Eng. 1949. Prev: Dep. Phys. Supt. St. Ebba's Hosp. Epsom.

BULLOCH, Colin 11 The Avenue, Taunton TA1 1EA Tel: 01823 331042 — MB BS 1963 Lond.; LMCC 1967; DObst RCOG 1966; DMRD (Eng.) 1980. (Char. Cross) Prev: HM Coroner Ontario, Canada.

BULLOCK, Antony Ernest 20 Valkyrie Road, Westcliff on Sea SS0 8BX — MB BS 1959 Lond.; MRCS Eng. LRCP Lond. 1959; MRCGP 1976; DObst RCOG 1961.

BULLOCK, David Balfour Manor Surgery, Osler Road, Headington, Oxford OX3 9BP Tel: 01865 762535; Church Farm, Church Lane, Old marston, Oxford OX3 0PT Tel: 01865 722926 — MB BS 1974 Lond.; MSc Lond. 1968, MB BS 1974; MRCGP 1980; DCH Eng. 1976. (St. Thos.) Prev: SHO (Chest & Gen. Med.) Kingston Hosp.; SHO Paediat. W. Middlx. Hosp. Isleworth.

BULLOCK, David Wayne 181 Darby Street, Cooks Hill, Newcastle NSW 2300, Australia Tel: 0149 265233; 108 King George V Drive, Heath Park, Cardiff CF14 4EH — MB ChB 1978 Bristol; MRCGP 1983; DA Eng. 1982. GP Newc., Australia; Resid. Waikato Hosp. Hamilton, New Zealand. Socs: S. Pacific Underwater Med. Soc. Prev: GP Trainee Bristol; SHO (Anaesth.) S.mead Hosp. Bristol; SHO (Paediat.) N.ampton Gen. Hosp.

BULLOCK, David William Department of Microbiology, Derbyshire Royal Infirmary, Derby DE1 2QY Tel: 01332 347141 Fax: 01332 341513 — MB BS 1973 Lond.; FRCPath 1991. (Guy's) Cons. Clin. Microbiol. Derby Hosps. Socs: Path. Soc. & Assn. Clin. Path.; Brit. Soc. Antimicrob. Chemother. & Hosp. Infec. Soc. Prev: Sen. Regist. (Clin. Microbiol.) Roy. Infirm. Bristol; Regist. (Clin. Path.) Roy. Infirm. Sheff.

BULLOCK, Diana Louise Empain The Hawthorns, 1 Oxford Road, Redhill RH1 1DT Tel: 01737 762902 Fax: 01737 762902 — MB ChB 1981 Bristol; BA Oxf. 1976; MRCGP 1985; DCH RCP Lond. 1985; DRCOG 1984.

BULLOCK, Ernest Edgar (retired) 32 Devonshire Place, London W1G 6JL Tel: 020 7935 6409 — LMSSA 1938 Lond.; MA Camb. 1937; DPhysMed. Eng. 1953. Prev: Asst. Phys. in Physical Med. Edgware Gen. Hosp.

BULLOCK, James 2 Brackendale Way, Stourbridge, Dudley DY9 7HF — MB ChB 1994 Birm.

BULLOCK, Mr John (retired) 44 Somersall Lane, Chesterfield S40 3LA — MB ChB 1955 Sheff.; FRCS Glas. 1966; DLO Eng. 1963. Prev: ENT Surg. Roy. Hosp. Chesterfield.

BULLOCK, John (retired) 29 The Boulevard, Wylde Green, Sutton Coldfield B73 5JB — MB ChB Birm. 1954. Prev: GP Birm.

BULLOCK, Jonathan POBox 238, Chesterfield S40 3YQ — MB BS 1991 Lond. Prev: SHO (Neurosurg.) W.. Gen. Hsop. Edin.; Ho. Surg. Roy. Lond. Hosp.

BULLOCK, Mr Keith Nigel Department of Urology, Addenbrooke's NHS Trust, Hills Road, Cambridge CB2 2QQ Tel: 01223 216574 Fax: 01223 216069; 34 Newton Road, Cambridge CB2 2AL Tel: 01223 311877 Fax: 01223 311877 Email: knb.urol@dial.pipex.com — MB BChir 1975 Camb.; MA Camb. 1974, MD 1984; FRCS Eng. 1979. (Camb. & Guy's Hosp.) Cons. Urol. Addenbrooke's Hosp. Camb.; Hon. Lect. Univ. Camb. 1985.

BULLOCK, Mr Malcolm Robert Ross Department Neurosurgery, Institute of Neurological Sciences, Southern General Hospital, 1345 Govan Road, Glasgow G51 4TF — MB ChB 1975 Birm.; PhD Natal. 1987; FRCS Ed. (SN) 1983; FRCS Ed. 1980; FRCS Glas. 1980. Assoc. Prof. Neurosurg. Med. Coll. Virginia Commonw. Univ., USA; Mem. Edit. Bd. Internat. Soc. Cerebral Blood Flow & Metab. Prev: Sen. Lect. (Neurosurg.) Univ. Glas.; Sen. Lect. (Neurosurg.) Univ. Natal, S. Afr.; Regist. (Neurosurg.) Wentworth Hosp. Durban S. Africa.

BULLOCK, Mr Peter Robert Neurosurgical Department, Maudsley Hospital, De Crespigny Park, London SE5 8AZ Tel: 020 7703 6333 Fax: 020 7708 0159; 115 Burbage Road, London SE21 7AF — MB ChB 1977 Manch.; FRCS Eng. 1983; MRCP (UK) 1980. Cons. Neurosurg. Guy's, Maudsley & King's Coll Hosps. Lond. Prev: Sen. Regist. (Neurosurg.) Qu. Med. Centre Nottm.

BULLOCK, Rachel Elizabeth 7 Brooklands Avenue, Chapel-en-le-Frith, High Peak SK23 0PR — MB BS 1998 Lond.; MB BS Lond 1998.

BULLOCK, Robert Dean Health Centre, Old Street, Clevedon BS21 6DG Tel: 01275 871454 — MB BS 1964 Lond.; MRCS Eng. LRCP Lond. 1964; DObst RCOG 1966. (Lond. Hosp.) Prev: Ho. Surg. Lond. Hosp.; Ho. Phys. & Ho. Surg. (Obst.) St. John's Hosp. Chelmsford.

BULLOCK, Robert Edward Department of Anaesthesia, Newcastle General Hospital, Westgate Road, Newcastle upon Tyne NE4 6BE Tel: 0191 256 3198 Fax: 0191 256 3154 Email: robert.bullock@trvi.nuth.northy.nhs.uk — BM BCh 1974 Oxf.; MA Oxf. 1974; FRCP Lond. 1992; MRCP (UK) 1980; FRCA 1979. Cons. Anaesth. & Intens. Care Newc. Gen. Hosp.; Hon. Clin. Teach. Univ. Newc. Prev: Sen. Regist. (Anaesth.) Newc.; Research Fell. Cardiol. Roy. Vict. Infirm. Newc.; Regist. (Med.) Hexham Hosp.

BULLOCK, Rodney Gavin (retired) Riversmead, London Road, King's Worthy, Winchester SO23 7QL Tel: 01962 885923 Email: gavin.bullock@dial.pipex.com — MB BS 1967 Lond.; DObst RCOG 1974. Prev: Gen. Practioner, Riverside Pract,, Winchester.

BULLOCK, Roger Alan Victoria Hospital, Okus Road, Swindon SN1 4HZ Tel: 01793 481182 — MB BS 1981 Lond.; BA (Physiol. Sc.) Oxf. 1978; MRCPsych 1990. (St. Bart.) Cons. Old Age Psychiat. Vict. Hosp. Swindon. Socs: Fell. Roy. Soc. Med.; Internat. Psychogeriat. Assn. Prev: Sen. Regist. (Psychiat. Old Age) Chelsea & W.m. Hosp. Lond.; Sen. Regist. (Old Age Psychiat.) Char. Cross. Hosp. Lond.

BULLOCK, Timothy John Conolly Wing, Ealing Hammersmith and Fulham NHS Trust, Uxbridge Road, Southall UB1 3EU Tel: 020 8967 5015 Fax: 020 8967 5015 — MB BS 1984 Lond.; BSc Lond. 1981; MRCPsych 1990. Cons. Psychiat. Ealing Hosp. Prev: Lect. (Psychiat.) St Mary's Hosp. Med. Sch.

BULLON BARRERA, Francisco Jose Flat 10C South Residence, 167 Barley Lane, Ilford IG3 8YA — LMS 1990 Seville.

BULLOUGH, Alexandra Sian The Garth, Windmill Lane, Christleton, Chester CH3 7BS — MB ChB 1993 Liverp.

BULLOUGH, Colin Howard Watson Aberdeen Maternity Hospital, Dugald Baird Centre for Research on Womens Health, University of Aberdeen, Cornhill Road, Aberdeen AB25 2ZL Email: c.bullough@abdn.ac.uk; The Old Station, Glassel, Torphins, Banchory AB31 4DE — MB ChB 1963 Glas.; 1963 MB ChB Glas.; 1995 MSc Wales; 1980 MD Glas.; 1984 FRCOG; 1966 DCH RCPS Glas.; 1991 T(OG); 1972 MRCOG. (University of Glasgow) p/t Sen. Research Fell., Dugeld Baird Centre for Research on Wom.'s Health; Sen. Research Fell. Dept. of Obstetvies Gyn., Univ. Aberd. Prev: O & G Kamuzu Centr. Hosp. Lilongwe, Malawi.; Cons. O & G S. Tyneside HA; Project Manager Further Improvement of Med. Coll.s Bangladesh, The Brit. Counc.

BULLOUGH, John 78 Defoe House, Barbican, London EC2Y 8DN Tel: 020 7638 5334 — MB BS 1947 Lond.; MRCS Eng. LRCP Lond. 1944; FFA RCS Eng. 1954; DA Eng. 1948. (St. Bart.) Socs: Fell. Roy. Soc. Med.; Soc. Apoth. Lond. (Personal Mem. Fac. Hist. & Philosoph. Med. & Pharm.). Prev: Cons. Anaesth. Dartford Gp. Hosps.; Vis. Anaesth. S.port Gen. Infirm. & Ormskirk Gen. Hosp.; Regist. (Med.) Essex Co. Hosp. Colchester.

BULLOUGH, Robert 10 Chorley Road, Westhoughton, Bolton BL5 3PR Tel: 01942 813282 — MB ChB 1968 Manch.; MSc (Pub. Health) Manch. 1974, MB ChB 1968; MFCM 1981; DObst RCOG 1971. (Manch.) Dist. Specialist Community Med. (Informat. & Social Servs.); Rochdale Health Auth. Rochdale AHA.

BULMAN, Andrew Stephen Department of Radiotherapy and Oncology, Norfolk & Norwich Hospital, Norwich NR1 3SR Tel: 01603 287989 Fax: 01603 287463 Email: abulmanl@hotmail.com; Low Farm House, Low Road, Keswick, Norwich NR4 6TX Tel: 01603 454805 — MB BS 1972 Lond.; MS Lond. 1982, BSc (Anat. 1st Cl.) 1969; FRCS Eng. 1977; FRCR 1989. Cons. Radiother. & Oncol. Norf. & Norwich Hosp. Prev: Sen. Med. Off. DoH Lond.

BULMAN, Mr Charles Hunter Norfolk House, 46 Tithebarn Hill, Glasson Dock, Lancaster LA2 0DJ Tel: 01524 751494 — MB BS 1968 Lond.; FRCS Eng. 1973. (St. Thos.) Cons. ENT Surg. Roy. Lancaster Infirm.

BULMAN, Mr Geoffrey Michael Boone (retired) Kenwyn House, Kenwyn Road, Truro TR1 3SG Tel: 01872 273442 — MA, MB BChir Camb. 1952; FRCS Eng. 1961; MRCS Eng. LRCP Lond. 1952. Prev: Cons. Orthop. Surg. Cornw. & I. of Scilly HA.

BULMAN, Jennifer Nancy (retired) Clinical Assistant Oncology, Worcester Royal Infirmary, Castle St., Worcester WR1 3AS — MB ChB 1967 Birm. Med. Off. Leics. Hospice. Prev: Clin. Asst. (O & G) S. Worcs. Hosp. Gp.

BULMAN, Jonathan Michael Rowling End, Millbeck, Keswick CA12 4PS — MB ChB 1992 Ed.

BULMAN, Wendy Kathryn Queens Road Surgery, 27 Queens Road, Wimbledon, London SW19 8NW Tel: 020 8944 5916 Fax: 020 8947 8677 — MB 1980 Camb.; BChir 1979; MA Camb. 1980. GP Retainer Scheme Lond.

BULMAN, William Henry Suthergrey House Surgery, 37A St. Johns Road, Watford WD17 1LS Tel: 01923 224424 Fax: 01923 243710 — MB BS 1973 Lond.

BULMER, Mr John Holt (retired) Number 4, Cross Rd, Albrighton, Wolverhampton WV7 3RA Tel: 01902 372291 — MB BS (Hnrs.) Lond. 1953; FRCS Eng. 1961. Cons. Orthop. Surg. Wolverhampton Hosp. Gp. Prev: Sen. Regist. Robt. Jones & Agnes Hunt Orthop. Hosp. OsW.ry.

BULMER, John Nelson Kestrels, The Avenue, Kingsdown, Deal CT14 8DU Email: jnbulmer@yahoo.co.uk — MB BChir 1977 Camb.; MA, MB Camb. 1977, BChir 1976; FFA RCS Eng. 1980. (Camb. & St. Thos.) Cons. Anaesth. S. Kent Hosps. Trust.

BULMER, Nicholas John Field Farm, Main St., Kinoulton, Nottingham NG12 3EN — MB ChB 1996 Liverp.

BULMER, Nicola Jane Red Hill Street Health Centre, Red Hill St., Wolverhampton WV1 1NR Tel: 01902 444325 Fax: 01902 444442; Sawmill Cottage, Badger, Burnhill Green, Wolverhampton WV6 7JP Tel: 01746 783591 Fax: 01746 783591 — MB ChB 1982 Birm. SCMO (Audiol. & Child Health) Wolverhampton Healthcare; GP Clin. Asst. (Developm. Paediat. & Paediat. Audiol.) Roy. Wolverhampton Hosp. Trust. Socs: Brit. Assn. Community Drs in Audiol.; Roy. Coll. Paediat. & Child Health; Brit. Assn. for Community Child Health.

Prev: Trainee GP Telford VTS & E. Birm. Hosp. VTS; Ho. Phys. Qu. Eliz. Hosp. Birm.

BULMER, Paul John 235 Woodlands Road, Aylesford, Maidstone ME20 7QF — MB BS 1990 Lond.; MRCOG 1996. Clin. Research Fell. (UroGyn.), Bristol Urol. Inst.

BULMER, Richard Bertram Old Court, Brobury, Hereford HR3 6DX — BM BCh 1976 Oxf.; DO Lond. 1981; DRCOG 1979.

BULMER-VAN VLIET, Jacoba 8 Buster Walk, Petersfield — Artsexamen 1975 Free U Amsterdam; Artsexamen Free Univ Amsterdam 1975.

BULOW, Eileen Margaret (retired) Whiston House, Clifton, Shefford SG17 5ET Tel: 01462 812466 — MRCS Eng. LRCP Lond. 1943.

BULPITT, Professor Christopher John Imperial College School of Medicine, Care of the Elderly Section, Hammersmith Hospital, Du Cane Road, London W12 0HS Tel: 020 8743 2030 Fax: 020 8743 0798 Email: cbulpitt@rpms.ac.uk; 51 Mount Park Road, Ealing, London W5 2RS Tel: 020 8997 2535 — MSc (Med. Statistics) Lond. 1972, MD 1975, MB BS 1963; FRCP Lond. 1982, M 1967; MRCS Eng. LRCP Lond. 1963; FFPM RCP (UK) 1989. (Lond. Hosp.) Prof. Geriat. Med. Imperial Coll.; Hon. Cons. Med. Hammersmith Hosp. & Head c/o Elderly Sect., ICSM. Socs: BMA, ISH, BHS, IEA, RSM, MRS, BGS. Prev: Reader (Epidemiol.) Roy. Postgrad. Med. Sch. Lond.; Reader (Epidemiol.) Lond. Sch. Hyg. & Trop. Med.

BULPITT, David Charles Henry Aveley Medical Centre, 22 High St., Aveley, South Ockendon RM15 4AD Tel: 01708 865640 Fax: 01708 891658 Email: dbulpitt@cix.compulink.co.uk; 14 Henham Close, Billericay CM11 2NF Tel: 01277 651218 Email: david@pcranha.cix.co.uk — MB BS 1983 Lond.; MRCGP 1988; AFOM RCP Lond. 1995. (Westm.) GP S. Essex HA; Med. Advis. Harlow Occupat. Health Serv.; Occupat. Health Med. Adviser Merck Sharpe & Dohme. Socs: Soc. Occupat. Med.

BULSO, Vincent 49 Cadleigh Gardens, Birmingham B17 0QB — MD 1991 Lyon.

BULSTRODE, Professor Christopher John Kent Nuffield Department of Orthopaedic Surgery, Level 1, John Radcliffe Hospital, Oxford OX3 9DU Tel: 01865 220233 Fax: 01865 221766 Email: christopher.bulstrode@ndos.ox.ac.uk; 388 London Road, Headington, Oxford OX3 8DW Tel: 01865 459899, 01865 750922 Fax: 01865 872447 — BM BCh 1976 Oxf.; MA (Nat. Sc.) Camb. 1973; MA (Zool.) Oxf. 1971, MCh 1987, BM BCh 1976; FRCS (Orth.) 1992; FRCS Eng. 1982; FRCS Ed. 1982. (Oxf.) Hon. Cons. Orthop. Surg. Oxf.; Prof. (Orthop.) Univ. Oxf.; Director Of Educat. Roy. Coll. of Surg.s Edin. Socs: ASME; Brit. Orthopaedic Assn.; Brit. Med. Assn. Prev: Lect. (Surg.) Lond. Hosp. Whitechapel; Sen. Regist. (Orthop.) Lond. Hosp. Whitechapel; Med. Off. E.. Sudan Refugee Progr.

BULSTRODE, Neil Willem 3 Redgate Terrace, London SW15 2ES — MB BS 1993 Lond.

***BULTITUDE, Matthew Frank** 19 Carson Road, London SE21 8HT Tel: 070500 94859 Email: mfbultitude@hotmail.com — MB BS 1997 Lond.

BULTITUDE, Mr Michael Ian 134 Harley Street, London W1N 1AH Tel: 020 7487 4593 Fax: 020 7486 1042; 21 Carson Road, London SE21 8HT Tel: 020 8761 7537 — MB BChir Camb. 1965; FRCS Eng. 1970; FRCS Ed. 1969; LMSSA Lond. 1963. (Camb. & St. Thos.) Cons. Urol. Surg. Guy's & St. Thos. Hosp. Trust. Socs: Brit. Assn. Urol. Surgs.

BULTO CHIRIVELLA, Maria Del Montesanto Bethel Child & Family Centre, Mary Chapman House, Hotblack Road, Norwich NR2 4HH Tel: 01603 421950; 51 Eaton Road, Norwich NR4 6PR — LMS 1985 Valencia. Staff Grade (Child & Adolesc. Psychiat.) Bethel Child & Family Centre Norwich. Socs: BMA; Assn. Child Psychol. & Psychiat. Prev: Regist. (Psychiat.) Norwich Rotat.; Regist. (Psychiat.) St Mary's Hosp. Rotat. Lond.

BULUGAHAPITIYA, Digoarachchi Tilekawardhana Dayananda Rotherham District General Hospital, Moorgate Road, Oakwood, Rotherham S60 2UD — MB BS 1957 Ceylon; FRCP Lond. 1982, M 1968; FRCP Glas. 1985, M 1968. Cons. Paediat. Rotherham HA. Prev: Sen. Resid. Amer. Univ. Hosp. Beriut Lebanon; Paediat. Colombo S. Hosp. Sri Lanka.

BULUGAHAPITIYA, Digoarachi Sudantha 17 Mortain Road, Rotherham S60 3BY — MB ChB 1990 Leeds.

BUMBRA, Jasbir Singh Well Park, 39 Pittenweem Road, Anstruther KY10 3DT — MB ChB 1986 Dundee; Cert. Family Plann. JCC 1990. Mem. LMC.

BUMBRA, Laura Anne The Skerth Health Centre, Crail Road, Cellardyke KY10 3DJ Tel: 01333 310352 Fax: 01333 312525; Tel: 01333 312583 — MB ChB 1986 Dundee. p/t Gen. Practitioner.

BUMBY, Alyson Frances Central Middlesex Hospital, London NW10 7NS Tel: 020 8453 2630 — MB BS 1980 Lond.; BSc Lond. 1977, MSc (Audiol. Med.) 1991; FRCS (Otol.) Eng. 1987. Cons. Audiol. Phys. Centr. Middlx. Hosp. Prev: Sen. Regist. (Audiol. Med.) Roy. Surrey Hosp. Guildford.; Regist. (Audiol.) Roy. Nat. Throat Nose & Ear Hosp. Lond.

BUMRAH, Ravdip Singh 187 Victoria Road, London N9 9AU — MB BS 1994 Lond.

BUMSTEAD, Helen (retired) Hole Farm, Bickington, Newton Abbot TQ12 6PE Tel: 0162 682298 — MRCS Eng. LRCP Lond. 1923; DPH Eng. 1929. Prev: Res. Med. Off. FarnBoro. Hosp.

BUNBURY, Doris Elizabeth (retired) Cranhill Nursing, Home, Weston Rd, Bath BA1 2YA Tel: 01225 335645 — MB BS Lond. 1927; FRCPsych. 1971; MRCP Lond. 1935; DPM Eng. 1933. Prev: Sen. Investig. Indust. Health Research Bd. Med. Research Counc.

BUNCE, Mr Colin John Dept Urology, Barnet General Hospital, Wellhouse Lane, Barnet EN5 3DJ — MB BS 1983 Lond.; BSc Lond. 1980; FRCS (Urol.) 1995; FRCS Ed. 1988; FRCS Eng. 1988; FEBU 1997. (Middlx.) Cons. Urol. Barnet Hosp. Socs: Brit. Assn. Urol.; Roy. Soc. Mem. Roy. Soc. Med.; Europ. Assoc. Urol. Prev: Sen. Regist. (Urol.) Walsgrave Hosp. Coventry & Qu. Eliz. Hosp. Birm.; Regist. (Urol.) St. Mary's Hosp. Lond.

BUNCE, Nicholas Harry 123 Rhydypenau Road, Cycoed, Cardiff CF23 6PZ — MB BS 1991 Lond.; BSc Pharmacol. Lond. 1988; MRCP (UK) 1994. (London) Regist. (Cardiol.) St. Geo.'s Hosp. Lond. Prev: Regist. (Cardiol.) E. Surrey Hosp. Redhill; Regist. (Gen. Med.) St. Geo. Hosp. Lond.

BUNCH, Christopher Oxford Radcliffe Hospitals, The John Radcliffe, Headington, Oxford OX3 9DU Tel: 01865 221343 Fax: 01865 220069 Email: chris.bunch@ndm.ox.ac.uk; Bayswater Farm House, Bayswater Farm Road, Headington, Oxford OX3 8BY — MB ChB 1969 Birm.; MA Oxf. 1981; FRCP Ed. 1988; FRCP Lond. 1984; MRCP (UK) 1974. (Birm.) Cons. Phys. Oxf. Radcliffe Hosp. NHS Trust; Fell. of Wolfson Coll. Oxf. Socs: Fell.and Counc.lor, Roy. Coll. Phys. Lond.; Chairm.Brit. Assn. of Med. Managers.; Wellcome Trust Research Fell. Nuffield Dept. Clin. Med. Univ. Oxf.

BUNCH, Mr Geoffrey Alan (retired) Petwood, Cedar Avenue, Edgerton, Huddersfield HD1 5QH Tel: 01484 535505 Fax: 01484 535505 Email: gbunch@petwood.freeserve.co.uk — MB ChB Leeds 1961; ChM Leeds 1975; FRCS Ed. 1967; FRCS Eng. 1967. Cons. Surg. Huddersfield Roy. Infirm.; Subsidiary Assoc. Postgrad. Dean Univ. Leeds. Prev: Sen. Regist. (Surg.) Gen. Infirm. Leeds.

BUNDI, Ratankumari Sushila (retired) 8 Regents Gate, Bothwell Castle Park, Bothwell, Glasgow G71 8QU Tel: 01698 815219 — MB BS 1955 Delhi; DTD 1959; DMRT Eng. 1969.

BUNDLE, Annabelle Community Paediatrics, Unit 1 Winnington Hall, Winnington, Northwich CW8 4DU Tel: 01606 781055; Omega House, Sandfield Lane, Acton Bridge, Northwich CW8 2RH Tel: 01606 853150 — MB ChB 1972 Birm.; Cert. JCC Lond. 1979. (Birm.) Assoc. Specialist (Community Paediat.) Chesh. Community Healthcare Trust; Clin. Asst. Community Alcohol Team Mid. Chesh. Hosps. Socs: BMA; Founder Mem. Roy. Coll. Paediat. & Child Health; BACCH. Prev: Clin. Med. Off. Lancs. HA; Gen. Duties Med. Off. Nkana Hosp. Kitwe Zambia.

BUNDOCK, Andrew David Dyneley House Surgery, Newmarket Street, Skipton BD23 2HZ Tel: 01756 799311 Fax: 01756 707203; Windrush, 11 Stirtonber, Skipton BD23 1NH Tel: 01756 799445 Email: andy@dales.demon.co.uk — MB BS 1977 Lond.; MRCS Eng. LRCP Lond. 1977; MRCGP 1981; DRCOG 1980. (Guy's) Dep. Police Surg. N. Yorks. Prev: Trainee GP VTS Mayday Hosp. Croydon; Ho. Surg. Edgware Gen. Hosp.; Ho. Phys. Hither Green Hosp. Lond.

BUNDRED, Margaret Anne Albion House Suegery, Albion Street, Brierley Hill DY5 3EE Tel: 01384 70220 Fax: 01384 78284; Millbrook House, 76 Hyde Lane, Kinver, Stourbridge DY7 6AF Tel: 01384 877287 Email: james.anne.bundred@lineone.net — MB BCh BAO 1974 Belf.; MRCGP 1978; DRCOG 1977; DCH RCPSI 1976. (Queens University Belfast) Socs: BMA; Fac. Fam. Plann. & Reproduc. Health Care.

BUNDRED, Mr Nigel James University Hospital South Manchester, Nell Lane, West Aldbury, Manchester M20 2WL Tel: 0161 291 3842 Fax: 0161 291 3846; Tel: 0161 291 3842 Fax: 0161 291 3846 Email: bundredn@fs1.with.man.ac.uk — MB BS 1980 Newc.; MD Newc. 1990; FRCS Eng. 1986; FRCS Ed. 1985. (Manch.) Cons. Surg. Univ. Hosp. S. Manch. & Christie Hosp. Manch.; Reader (Surgic. Oncol.) Manch.; Cons. BrE. and Endocrine Surg.; Scientif. Advisery Bd. Mem. BrE. Cancer Campaign; Europ. Edr. Surg. Oncol. Jl. Socs: Brit. Assn. Surg. Oncol. (Mem. Nat. Comm.); Brit. Assn. Endocrin. Surg.; (Comm.) Surgic. Research Soc. Prev: Lect. (Surg.) Qu. Eliz. Hosp. Birm.; Post-Fell.sh. Regist. Profess. Surg. Unit Univ. Hosp. Wales Cardiff; Cruden Research Fell. & Lect. (Clin. Surg.) Univ. Edin.

BUNDRED, Peter Edward 7 Brickwall Green, Sefton, Liverpool L29 9AF Tel: 0151 794 5597 Email: peterb@lw.ac.uk — MRCS Eng. LRCP Lond. 1969; MD Lond. 1986, MB BS 1969. Sen. Lect. (Gen. Pract.) Univ. Liverp.; Fell. Liverp. Sch. Trop. Med. Prev: Prof. Family Med. Univ. Witwatersrand Johannesburg.

BUNDRED, Sara Michelle 20 Woodside, Stockport SK4 2DW — MB ChB 1992 Manch.

BUNDY, Allan Graeme Pencester Surgery, Dover CT16 1BW Tel: 01304 240553; Chilton Farm Cottage, Alkham, Dover CT15 7DR Tel: 01304 825481 — MB BS 1958 Lond.; CIH Dund 1969; DObst RCOG 1967; DTM & H Liverp. 1962. (St. Geo.) Police Surg. Dover. Socs: Fell. Roy. Soc. Trop. Med. & Hyg.; Fell. Roy. Soc. Med. Prev: SHO (O & G) Bedford Gen. Hosp.; Ho. Phys. St. Geo Hosp. Lond.

BUNDY, Jonathan Charles 87 Ranby Road, Sheffield S11 7AN — MB ChB 1991 Sheff.

BUNDY, Michael John Cranleigh Health Centre, 18 High Street, Cranleigh GU6 8AE Tel: 01483 273951 Fax: 01483 275755; Brown Eaves, 26 Horsham Road, Cranleigh GU6 8DW Tel: 01483 277758 Fax: 01438 277758 — MB BS 1984 Lond.; Dip. Sports Medicine 1999; MRCGP 1989; DRCOG 1988; DCH RCP Lond. 1987. (Guys Hospital, London) Gen. Practitioner, Cranleigh, Surrey. Socs: MPS, BASEM, UKADIS, BMA.

BUNGAY, Anton William 45 Whin Common Road, Downham Market PE38 0DX — BChir 1996 Camb.

BUNGAY, Claire Janine Canterbury Road Surgery, 186 Canterbury Road, Davyhulme, Manchester M41 0GR Tel: 0161 748 5559 Fax: 0161 747 1997; 26 Brogden Grove, Sale M33 7UG — MB BS 1993 Newc.; Dip. Obs. & Gyn. Roy. Coll. Obs. & Gyn. 1996; MRCGP 1998. (Newcastle) GP Principle. Socs: BMA; MSS; MDU. Prev: GP Regist. Handforth Health Centre; SHO Psychiat. Tameside Gen. Hosp. Ashton-u.-Lyne; SHO Dermatol./COTE, Hope Hosp. Salford.

BUNGAY, Diane Marie Frome Medical Practice, The Health Centre, Park Road, Frome BA11 1EZ Tel: 01373 301300 — MB ChB 1983 Bristol; DRCOG 1996; DFFP 1996; MRCGP 1998.

BUNGAY, Elisabeth Kate Beccles Medical Centre, 7-9 St. Marys Road, St. Marys Road, Beccles NR34 9NQ Tel: 01502 712662 Fax: 01502 712906; Ravensmere House, Old Market, Beccles NR34 9DZ — MB BS 1980 Lond.; DA (UK) 1986.

BUNGAY, Peter Mark 26 Brogden Grove, Sale M33 7UG Tel: 01625 529421 — MB ChB 1992 Manch.; MA (Cantab) 1993; FRCP 1997; MRCP (UK) 1995. Specialist Regist. Radiol. Manch.

BUNJE, Henry William 73 Temple Sheen Road, E. Sheen, London SW14 7RS Tel: 020 8876 5070 — MB BS 1944 Lond.; MD Lond. 1949; FRCP Lond. 1969, M 1946. (St. Bart.) Socs: Fell. Med. Soc. Lond. Prev: PMO HQ Staff. Med. Research Counc.; Med. Chief Asst. St. Bart. Hosp. Lond.; Lect. Med. Univ. Coll. W. Indies Jamaica.

BUNKALL, Sally Clare The Whipton Surgery, 378 Pinhoe Road, Whipton, Exeter EX4 8EG Tel: 01392 462770 Fax: 01392 466220; 13 Station Road, Exeter EX3 0DS Tel: 01392 873930 — MB ChB 1984 Manch.; BSc (Hons.) Manch. 1981; MRCGP 1989; DCH RCP Lond. 1988; Cert. Family Plann. JCC 1988.

BUNKER, Christopher Barry Department of Dermatology, Chelsea & Westminster Hospital, 369 Fulham Road, London SW10 9NH Tel: 020 8746 8169 Fax: 020 8746 8578; 3 Rudall Crescent, London NW3 1RR Tel: 020 7794 5943 Email: cbb@hamderm.demon.co.uk — MB BS 1981 Lond.; MA 1982, MD Camb. 1992; FRCP Lond. 1996; MRCP (UK) 1985; MRCS Eng. LRCP Lond. 1981. (St. Catharine's Coll. Camb. & Westm. Med. Sch.) Cons. Dermat. Chelsea & W.m. Hosp., Char. Cross Hosp., Roy. Marrden Hosp. & King Edwd. VII Hosp. Socs: Roy. Soc. Med.; Brit. Assn. Dermat.; Liveryman Worshipful Soc. of Apoth. Prev: Sen. Regist. (Dermat.) Univ. Coll. & Middlx. Sch. Med.; Sir Jules Thorn Research Fell. Univ. Coll. & Middlx. Sch. Med.; Regist. (Dermat., Med. & Psychiat.) Middlx. Hosp. Lond.

BUNKER, Jean Rachel 55d Lady Margaret Road, Kentish Town, London NW5 2NJ — MB BS 1986 Lond.

BUNKER, Mr Timothy David Swallow Thatch, Kenn, Exeter EX6 7XJ — MB BS 1976 Lond.; BSc Lond. 1973; MChOrth Liverp. 1987; MRCS Eng. LRCP Lond. 1976; FRCS Eng. 1981; FRCS Ed. 1981. Cons. Orthop. Surg. Exeter. Socs: Brit. Elbow & Shoulder Soc.; Eur. Shoulder & Elbow Soc.; Corr. Fell. Amer. Shoulder and Elbow Surg.s. Prev: Sen. Regist. (Orthop.) Exeter & Nottm.; Regist. (Orthop.) Bristol Roy. Infirm.

BUNN, Alex William 1 Hocroft Ave, London NW2 2EJ Tel: 020 7435 1196 — BM BCh 1996 Oxf.; DTM & H 1997. SHO (A & E) High Wycombe Gen. Hosp. Prev: Ho. Off. (Surg.) Stoke Mandeville Aylesbury; Ho. Off. (Med.) ROL Newc. U. Tyne.

BUNN, David Thomas Inglewood Surgery, 676 Blackburn Road, Bolton BL1 7AD Tel: 01204 301161 — MB ChB 1967 St. And. Prev: Regist. Gen. Med. & Chest Serv. E. RHB (Dundee).; GP. Todmorden Gp. Pract.

BUNN, Derek Ivor Gunton (retired) 145 Cricklewood Lane, London NW2 1HS Tel: 020 8450 5454 — MB BS 1959 Lond.; BSc Lond. 1955, MB BS 1959; DObst RCOG 1962. Med. Off. Univ. Coll. Sch. Hampstead. Prev: Sen. Lect. (Gen. Pract.) & Med. Off. (Stud. Health) Roy. Free Hosp. Med. Sch. Lond.

BUNN, Hazel Jean Department of Child Health, University of Leicester, Robert Kilpatrick Clinical Sciences Building, Leicester Royal Infirmary, Leicester LE2 7LX Tel: 0116 252 5805 Email: hjb@le.ac.uk; Flat 15, Stoneleigh Manor, Stoneygate Road, Leicester LE2 2AD — MB BCh 1993 Wales; MRCP (UK) 1996. (Cardiff) Specialist Regist. (Paediat.) Mersey Rotat., Aldersley Hosp.; Research fell., Dept Respirat. Paediat., Univ. of Leicester.

BUNN, James Edward Gunton School of Tropical Medicine and Hygeine, Benton, Liverpool; 16 Adelaide Terrace, Waterloo, Liverpool L22 8QD Tel: 0151 286 9953 — MB BS 1985 Lond.; MSc (Dist.) Lond. 1988; MRCP (UK) 1991; DCH RCP Lond. 1990; DTM & H Liverp. 1988. Lect. In Trop. Paediat., Liverp. Sch. of Trop. Med. Socs: Brit. Paediat. Assn. Prev: MRC Train. Fell. Dunn Nutrit. Unit Camb. & Keneba, The Gambia; Regist. (Paediat.) Yorks. RHA; MO Nixon Memor. Hosp. Segbwema, Sierra Leone.

BUNN, Mary Ruth 10 Queens Gardens, Benton, Newcastle upon Tyne NE12 9PL Tel: 0191 292 1313; 16 Adelaide Terrace, Waterloo, Liverpool L22 8QD Tel: 0151 286 9953 — MB BChir 1991 Camb.; DTM & H Lond. 1993; MRCGP 1998. (Cambs) Socs: MRCGP; CMF. Prev: Clin. Med. Off. to the MRC Keneba, The Gambia.

BUNN, Michael Neal Old Cottage Hospital Surgery, Alexandra Road, Epsom KT17 4BL Tel: 01372 724434 Fax: 01372 748171; 10 Burgh Wood, Banstead SM7 1EP — MB ChB 1987 Liverp.; MRCGP 1993. Full Time GP Principle, The Integrated Care Partnership, Old Cottage Hosp., Alexandra Rd., Epsom, Surrey. Prev: Trainee GP Tunbridge Wells VTS.

BUNN, Richard Trevor Nicholas 28 Richmond Ct, Lisburn BT27 4QU — MB BCh BAO 1997 Belf.

BUNN, Robert Graham (retired) 5 Finch's Close, Stapleford, Cambridge CB2 5BL — MRCS Eng. LRCP Lond. 1950. Prev: SHO Vict. Hosp. Deal.

BUNN, Robert Jonathon 6 Carsons Mews, Magherascouse Road, Ballygowan, Newtownards BT23 5RS — MB BCh BAO 1995 Belf.

BUNNAGE, Stephen John West End Surgery, 19 Chilwell Road, Beeston, Nottingham NG9 1EH Tel: 0115 925 4443 Fax: 0115 922 1255; 84 Church Lane, Cossall, Nottingham NG16 2RW — BM BS 1981 Nottm.; BMedSci 1979; MRCGP 1986. GP Beeston, Notts.

BUNNEY, Julie Ann 4 The Saltings, Hadleigh, Benfleet SS7 2BD — BM 1988 Soton.

BUNNEY, Mary Howarth (retired) 3 Upper Coltbridge Terrace, Edinburgh EH12 6AD Tel: 0131 337 6494 Fax: 0131 337 6494 — MB BS 1943 Lond.; FRCP Ed. 1987; MRCS Eng. LRCP Lond. 1942. Prev: Assoc. Dermatol. (Dermat.) Roy. Infirm. & Bruntsfield Hosp. Edin.

BUNNEY, Robert George Brannams Medical Centre, Brannams Square, Kiln Lane, Barnstaple EX32 8AP Tel: 01271 329004 Fax: 01271 346785; Merle's Croft, Rumsam Road, Barnstaple EX32 9EW

Tel: 01271 342649 Fax: 01271 46785 Email: rbunney@etnerprise.net — BSc Psychol. Lond. 1979, MB BS 1982; MRCP (UK) 1985; MRCGP 1988; DRCOG 1988. (Char. Cross) Prev: SHO (Gen. Med.) Good Hope Hosp. Sutton Coldfield; Regist. (Gen. Med.) Stobhill Hosp. Glas.; Regist. (Gen. Med.) Gold Coast Hosp. Qu.sland, Austral.

BUNOLA CERDA, Jose Amador 9 Lanark Street, Hull HU5 3NN — LMS 1989 U Autonoma Barcelona.

BUNSELL, Richard Philip Pfizer Euroclin, Ramsgate Road, Sandwich CT13 — MB ChB 1974 Birm.

BUNSTON, Matthew John 104 Ynysddu, Pontyclun CF72 9UE — MB BCh 1997 Wales.

BUNT, Robert James River Place Group Practice, River Place, Essex Road, London N1 2DE — MB BS 1988 Lond.; BSc (Psychol.) Lond. 1985; MRCGP 1992. Prev: Trainee GP Greenwich VTS.

BUNTING, Andrew 6 Rands EStreet, Preston — MB BS 1985 Lond.

BUNTING, Bronagh Mary 3 Sloan's Avenue, Carryduff, Belfast BT8 8DG — MB BCh BAO 1978 Belf.

BUNTING, Christopher 13 Victoria Street, Castlefields, Shrewsbury SY1 2HS Tel: 01743 249916 Fax: 01743 761601 Email: 100547.1002@compuserve.com — MB ChB 1967 Liverp.; MSc (Audiol. Med.) Manch. 1995; BA Open 1992; MRCPCH; DObst RCOG 1973. SCMO (Audiol.) Shrops. Community NHS Trust. Prev: Surg. Lt.-Cdr. RN; SHO (Paediat.) Alder Hey Childr. Hosp. Liverp.; Ho. Phys. & Ho. Surg. Walton Hosp. Liverp.

BUNTING, Derek Harold (retired) — MB ChB 1955 Manch. Prev: Asst. Res. Surg. Off. Ancoats Hosp. Manch.

BUNTING, Helen Elizabeth Department of Anaesthetics, Craigavon Area Hospital Group Trust, 68 Lurgan Road, Portadown, Craigavon BT63 5QQ Tel: 01762 334444 Fax: 01762 612 746d — MB BCh BAO 1987 Belf.; FFA RCSI 1991. Cons. Anaesth. Craigavon Area Hosp. Gp. Trust Portadown. Socs: Assn. Anaesth.; BMA; Intens. Care Soc.

BUNTING, John St James Medical Centre, Burnley Rd, Rawtenstall, Rossendale BB4 8HH Tel: 01706 213060 Fax: 01706 242127 — MB ChB 1975 Manch.

BUNTING, John Stanton (retired) 2 Holmdeane, 104 Evesham Road, Cheltenham GL52 2AL Tel: 01242 261372 — MB BS 1953 Lond.; LMSSA Lond. 1952; FRCR 1975; FFR 1961; DMRT Eng. 1958. Hon. Cons. Sue Ryder Foundat. Prev: Cons. Clin. Oncologist Oxf. RHA.

BUNTING, Laura 73 Craigadoo Road, Moorfields, Ballymena BT42 4RD — MB BCh BAO 1993 Belf.

BUNTING, Nicholas William 73 City Road, Nottingham NG7 2JL — BM BS 1993 Nottm.

BUNTING, Nigel George The Red House Surgery, 241 Queensway, Bletchley, Milton Keynes MK2 2EH Tel: 01908 375111 — MB BS 1990 Lond.

BUNTING, Peter Dunluce, 13 Eton Park, Fulwood, Preston PR2 9NL Tel: 01772 651736 Fax: 01772 791684 Email: peter@docbun.demon.co.uk — MB ChB 1981 Manch.; FFA RCS Eng. 1985. Cons. Anaesth. & Intens. Care Roy. Preston Hosp. Socs: Manch. Med. Soc.; Assn. Anaesth. GB & Irel.; Intens. Care Soc. Prev: Sen. Regist. (Anaesth.) Wythenshawe Hosp. Manch.; Lect. (Anaesth.) Manch. Roy. Infirm.; Regist. Rotat. (Anaesth.) Salford & Oldham HAs.

BUNTING, Reginald Arthur Avon & Somerset Constabulary, Occupational Health Department, Napier Miles Road, Kingsweston, Bristol BS11 0UT Tel: 0117 982 0108; Boskenna, The Green, Shirehampton, Bristol BS11 0HS Tel: 0117 982 2796 — MB ChB 1958 Bristol; DMJ(Path) Soc. Apoth. Lond. 1982; DObst RCOG 1960. Force Med. Off. & Princip. Police Surg. Avon & Som. Constab. Socs: BMA; (Pres.) Assn. Police Surgs.

BUNTING, Richard William The Surgery, 107 New Road, Ayr KA8 8DD Tel: 01292 262697; 10 Balminnoch Park, Doonbank, Ayr KA7 4EQ Tel: 01292 289869 — MB ChB 1982 Aberd. Prev: Trainee GP Ayr; SHO (Cas./Orthop.) Ayr Co. Hosp.; SHO (O & G) Ayrsh. Centr. Hosp. Irvine.

BUNTING, Roland Mark 9 Cowper Road, London SW19 1AA — MB BS 1998 Lond.; MB BS Lond 1998.

BUNTING, Samantha 5 Shingle Bay, Edgewater, Donaghadee BT21 0EF — MB BS 1998 Lond.; MB BS Lond 1998.

***BUNTING, Sarah Elizabeth** Rock Farm, Low La, Draughton, Skipton BD23 6EE Email: sarahcallin@hotmail.com; 2 Netherwitton Mill, Netherwitton, Morpeth NE61 4NU Tel: 01670 772450 — MB BS 1997 Newc.

BUNTING, Susan Louise Argyle Street Surgery, 141 Argyle Street, Heywood OL10 3SD Tel: 01706 366135 Fax: 01706 627706 — MB ChB 1983 Manch.; MRCGP 1988; DRCOG 1985. Prev: Trainee GP Birch Hill Hosp. Rochdale VTS.

BUNTING, Mr William (retired) Somerset Nuffield Hospital, Staplegrove Elm, Taunton TA2 6AN Tel: 01823 286991 — MB BS 1961 Lond.; FRCS Eng. 1967; MRCS Eng. LRCP Lond. 1961. Cons. Orthop. & Traum. Surg.Taunton. Prev: Sen. Regist. (Orthop.) P.ss Eliz. Orthop. Hosp. Exeter.

BUNTWAL, Neena Elizabeth Beresford Project, 36-42 Hare St, Woolwich, London SE18 6LZ Tel: 020 8854 9518 — MB BS 1990 Lond.; MA Oxf. 1991; MRCPsych. Cons. Psychiat. In Subst. misuse, S. Lond. & Maudsley NHS Trust. Prev: Sen. Regist. (Psychiat.) Bethlem & Maudsley NHS Trust.

BUNTWAL, Vivek St Thomas Surgery, Rifleman Lane, St. Thomas Green, Haverfordwest SA61 1QX Tel: 01437 762162 Fax: 01437 776811; Beg-Meil, Park Corner Road, Haverfordwest SA61 2XA Tel: 01473 760408 — MB BCh 1986 Wales; MRCGP 1990. GP Princip.; Young Fell. Roy. Soc. Med. Prev: Trainee GP Pembrokesh. VTS.

BUNYAN, Agnes Louise Laurel Cottage, Main St., St Boswells, Melrose TD6 0AZ — MB ChB 1998 Aberd.; MB ChB Aberd 1998.

BUNYAN, Paul Anthony 16 Kingshill Avenue, St Albans AL4 9QD — MB ChB 1998 Birm.

BUNYON, Sarah Jane 25 Kingsway, Taunton TA1 3YD — MB BS 1993 Newc.

BUONACCORSI, Eugenio Candido 18 Torrisdale Street, Coatbridge ML5 1ND — MB ChB 1960 Glas.

BURACK, Richard Jonathan North Street Medical Centre, 274 North Street, Romford RM1 4QJ Tel: 01708 764477 Fax: 01708 757656; 26 Temport Mead, North Weald, Epping OM16 6DY Tel: 01992 525158 Fax: 01992 525159 Email: burack1800@aol.com — MB BS 1988 Lond.; MRCGP 1992. (Lond. Hosp. Med. Sch.) Research Assoc. & Lect. for QMW Acad. Dept. of GP Mile End Lond. Socs: Med. Soc. for the Study of VD. Prev: GP Tutor Barking & Havering.

BURAS, Mr Juliusz Jan 42 Ainsdale Road, Leicester LE3 0UA — MB ChB 1983 Sheff.; FRCS Eng. 1990; FRCS Ed. 1990.

BURBIDGE, Alison Amelia 30 Fontwell Gardens, Horton Heath, Eastleigh SO50 7NL — BM 1994 Soton.; BSc (Hons.) Soton. 1993; MRCP 1998. (Soton.) SHO (Dermat.) Soton. Gen. Hosp. Prev: SHO (Cardiol.) Soton. Gen. Hosp.; SHO (Oncol.) Roy. S. Hants. Hosp. Soton.; SHO (Rheum. & Care Elderly)) Soton. Gen. Hosp.

BURBIDGE, Elizabeth (retired) Wild Goose Leys, Abbots Ripton, Huntingdon PE28 2LB — MRCS Eng. LRCP Lond. 1945. Prev: Clin. Med. Off. (Community Health) Cambs. HA (T).

BURBIDGE, Henry Charles (retired) 29 Mill Street, Kidlington OX5 2EE Tel: 01865 373337 — MRCS Eng. LRCP Lond. 1940; FFA RCS Eng. 1954; DA Eng. 1947. Prev: Cons. Anaesth. Nuffield Hosp. Gp. Oxf.

BURBIDGE, Michael John 29 Tonsley Place, Wandsworth, London SW18 1BH — MB BS 1968 Lond.; MRCS Eng. LRCP Lond. 1968; FFA RCS Eng. 1979; DA Eng. 1971. (Middlx. Hosp.) Sen. Regist. (Anaesth.) St. Thos. Hosp. Lond.

BURBIDGE, Nicola Vivien Wellesley Road Surgery, 7 Wellesley Road, Chiswick, London W4 4BJ Tel: 020 8995 4396 Fax: 020 8994 4314 — MB BS 1978 Lond.; MRCGP 1995; DRCOG 1984.

BURBRIDGE, Barbara Jill Applecross, Dark Lane, Kinver, Stourbridge DY7 6JA — MB ChB 1957 Manch.; FFA RCSI 1971; DA Eng. 1960.

BURBRIDGE, Denis Henry Dryburgh, OBE, OStJ (retired) 5 Ashton Court, Pembroke Close, Galmington, Taunton TA1 4LX Tel: 01823 322780 — MRCS Eng. LRCP Lond. 1936; DPH Lond. 1951; FFPHM 1989; FFCM 1974. Prev: Hon. Phys. to H.M. the Qu.

BURBRIDGE-JAMES, William Leonard 81 Charles Dickens House, Mansford St., London E2 6LU — MB BS 1984 Lond. (The London Hospital Medical College) N. Lond. Teach. Hosp. Rotat.al Train. Scheme in Psychiat.

BURBY, Nicholas Gerard Department of Orthopaedics, Queen Alexandra Hospital, Cosham, Portsmouth PO6 3LY — MB BS 1984 Bangalore; DOrth Trivandrum 1987; MSOrtho Trivandrum 1988;

MChOrtho Liverp. 1996. (St Johns Medical College Bangalore, India) Staff Orthop. Surg. Socs: BMA; MDU. Prev: Lect. (Orthop. Surg.) India; SHO (Orthop. Surg.) UK; Regist. (Orthop. Surg.) UK.

BURCH, Adrian John Rushden Medical Centre, Parklands, Wymington Road, Rushden NN10 9EB Tel: 01933 396000 Fax: 01933 396001 Email: ajburch@doctors.org.uk; Tel: 01933 623059 — MB BS 1970 Lond.; MRCS Eng. LRCP Lond. 1970; Dip. Biochem. Lond 1967. (Lond. Hosp.) Mem. N.ants. LMC.

BURCH, Anthony Martin Staverton Surgery, 51 Staverton Road, London NW2 5HA Tel: 020 8459 6865 Fax: 020 8451 6897 — MB BS 1980 Lond.; MB BS Lond. 1981; BA Oxf. 1976; MRCGP 1986. (Middlx.) Lect. (Gen. Pract.) St. Mary's Hosp. Med. Sch.

BURCH, David James Department of Obstetrics & Gynaecology, Royal Lancaster Infirmary, Ashton Road, Lancaster LA1 4RP Tel: 01524 65944 Fax: 01524 583585 Email: david.burch@l.bay-tr.nwest.nhs.uk — MB ChB 1983 Manch.; BSc St. And. 1980; MRCOG 1989; DRCOG 1985. Cons. O & G Roy. Lancaster Infirm. Prev: Sen. Regist. (O & G) Ipswich Hosp.; Regist. (O & G) P.ss Anne Hosp. Soton. & Addenbrooke's Hosp. Camb.

BURCH, Isobel Mary Carleton House, Back Lane, Langwathby, Penrith CA10 1NB Tel: 01768 881210; Carleton House, Back Lane, Langwathby, Penrith CA10 1NB Tel: 01768 881210 — MB BChir 1971 Camb.

BURCH, James Edward Philip 10 Drewetts Close, Rustington, Littlehampton BN16 3TL — MB BS 1991 Lond.

BURCH, Kenneth William Thame Health Centre, East Street, Thame OX9 3JZ Tel: 01844 261066 — MB BS 1974 Lond.; BSc (1st cl. Hons.) Lond. 1971, MB BS 1974; FRCGP 1993, M (Distinc.) 1979. (Univ. Coll. Lond. & St. Geo.) Prev: Trainee GP Oxf. VTS; Ho. Phys. St. Geo. Hosp. Lond.; Ho. Surg. N.wick Pk. Hosp. & Clin. Research Centre Harrow.

BURCH, Kirsty Lindsay Department of Microbiology, Blackburn Royal Infirmary, Bolton Road, Blackburn BB2 3LR — MB ChB 1985 Manch.; MSc Lond. 1992; BSc St. And. 1982; MRCPath 1994. Cons. Microbiologist, BRI (Locum), Blackburn. Prev: Sen. Regist. (Microbiol.) PHLS Ipswich Hosp., Soton. Gen. Hosp. & Luton & Dunstable Hosp.; Sen. Regist. (Microbiol.) PHLS Preston Hosp.

BURCH, Michael John Radcliffe Hospital, Oxford OX3 9DU; 24A Quarry High Street, Headington, Oxford OX3 8JX — MD 1993 Leeds; MB ChB 1982; MRCP (UK) 1985. Cons. Paediat. Cardiol. John Radcliffe Hosp. Oxf. Prev: Sen. Regist. (Paediat. Cardiol.) Hosp. Sick Childr. Gt. Ormond St. Lond.

BURCH, Polly 19 Vicarage Road, Alton GU34 1NZ — MB BS 1997 Lond. Psychiat. Trainee, E. Wilts. Healthcare Trust, Swindon. Socs: BMA; MDU. Prev: Ho. Off. Surg., Mayday Hosp., Thornton Heath, Surrey; Ho. Off. Med., Crawley Hosp., W.Sussex.

BURCH, Rosemary Jane Department of Obstetrics & Gynaecology, Queen Elizabeth Hospital NHS Trust, Stadium Road, Woolwich, London SE18 4QH Tel: 020 8836 4500 — MB BS 1990 Lond.; MRCP (UK) 1993; MRCOG (UK) 1997. (UCMSM) Cons. in Obst. and Gyn., Qu. Eliz. Hosp.

BURCHARDT, Andrew George 15 Grantham Road, London SW9 9DP — MB BS 1982 Lond.

BURCHETT, Kenneth Rodney 2 Norton Hill, Snettisham, King's Lynn PE31 7LZ Email: kenburchett@publiconline.co.uk — MB ChB 1978 Bristol; FFA RCS Eng. 1983. Cons. Anaesth. Qu. Eliz. Hosp. King's Lynn.

BURCOMBE, Douglas Raymond Trevalsa, 18 Pigeonhouse Lane, Rustington, Littlehampton BN16 2AZ Tel: 01903 783073 — MB BS 1956 Lond.; MRCS Eng. LRCP Lond. 1956; DObst RCOG 1961. (Guy's) Prev: Ho. Surg. & Ho. Phys. Orpington Hosp.; Flight Lt. RAF Med. Br.; Nuffield Pract. Soton.

BURCOMBE, Russell John Mount Vernon Hospital, Rickmansworth Road, Northwood HA6 2RN Tel: 01923 826111 Fax: 01923 844167; 3 Ingleby Gardens, Chigwell Row, Chigwell IG7 6EH Tel: 020 8500 7868 Fax: 020 8500 7868 Email: burcombe@cwcom.net — MB BS 1991 Lond.; BSc Biochem. (1st cl. Hons.) Lond. 1988; MRCP (UK) 1994; FRCR (I) 1999. (London Hospital Medical College) Clin. Research. Fell. the Marie Curie Research Wing Oncol.Mt. Vernon Hosp. N.wood Middx. Prev: SHO Rotat. (Med.) Colchester Gen. Hosp.; Ho. Off. (Surg.) Broomfield Hosp. Chelmsford; Ho. Off. (Med.) Roy. Lond. Hosp.

BURCOMBE, Sarah Anne — MB BS 1985 Lond.; DRCOG 1988. (Guy's) GP Asst. Stopsley Gp. Pract. Luton. Prev: Trainee GP Greenwich & Brook VTS.

BURD, David Andrew Ross Department of Plastic Surgery, Frenchay Hospital, Bristol BS16 1LE Tel: 0117 975399 Fax: 0117 975 3768 — MB ChB 1976 Aberd.; MD Aberd. 1995; FRCS Ed. 1982. Cons. Plastic Surg. Frenchay Healthcare NHS Trust. Prev: Sen. Regist. (Plastic Surg.) Withington Hosp. Manch.; Research Fell. (Path.) Harvard Med. Sch. & Mass. Gen. Hosp. & Shriners Burns Inst.

BURD, Doreen 6 Normanhurst Park, Matlock DE4 3BQ — MB ChB 1957 Liverp. (Liverp.) Prev: Med. Off. Family Plann. Assn.; Clin. Med. Off. E. Surrey AHA; GP Surrey.

BURD, Elizabeth (retired) Old Garden House, Honey Hall Lane, Congresbury, Bristol BS49 5JX Tel: 01934 852230 — MB ChB 1980 Bristol; FRCS Ed. 1987. Prev: Sen. Regist. (Histopath.) S.mead Hosp. Bristol.

BURD, Robert Mackinnon Dept. Of Dermatology, Leicester Royal Infirmary, Leicester LE1 5WW Tel: 0116 258 5162 Fax: 0116 258 6792; Tel: 01983 293934 — MB ChB 1990 Leic.; BSc Leic. 1987; MRCP (UK) 1994. (Leicester) Cons. Dermatol., Leicester Roy. Infirm..; Acting Med. Director, Leicester Laser Care Clin. Socs: Brit. Assn. Dermat.; Brit. Soc. Dermat. Surg. Prev: Specialist Regist. (Dermat.) Leeds Gen. Infirm.; Specialist Regist. (Dermat.) Leicester Roy. Infirm.; Cons. Dermatol., Hosp. Of St. Cross, Rugby.

BURDEN, Andrew Charles Diabetes Care, Leicester General Hospital, Leicester LE5 4PN Tel: 0116 258 4438 Fax: 0116 273 3067; 17 Westminster Road, Leicester LE2 2EH Tel: 0116 270 7897 Email: acfelix.burden@btinternet.com — MB ChB Bristol 1970; MD Leic. 1981; FRCP Lond. 1988; MRCP (UK) 1972. Cons. Phys. Leicester Gen. Hosp.; Hon. Sen. Lect. Univ. Leicester. Socs: Brit. Diabetic Assn.; Epidemiol. Study Gp. of EASD. Prev: Sen. Regist. (Gen. Med.) Leicester Roy. Infirm.; Regist. (Gen. Med.) N.. Gen. Hosp. Sheff.; SHO (Gen. Med.) Bath United Hosps.

BURDEN, Arthur David Department of Dermatology, Western Infirmary, Glasgow G11 6NT — MB ChB 1987 Manch.; MD Manch. 1997, BSc (Hons.) 1985, MB ChB 1987; MRCP (UK) 1990; DTM & H RCP Lond. 1991. Cons. Dermatol., Glas. W.ern Infirm. & Glas. Roy. Hosp. for Sick Childr. Prev: Regist. (Dermat.) W.. Infirm. Glas. & Skin Hosp. Manch.

BURDEN, Graham John Trelawney Avenue Surgery, 425 Trelawney Avenue, Langley, Slough SL3 7TT Tel: 01753 775545 Fax: 01753 775545 — MB BS 1972 Lond.

BURDEN, Michael Fabian 4 Victoria Avenue, Barrow-in-Furness LA14 5LA — MB ChB 1995 Leeds.

BURDEN, Pamela Louise Ethel Street Surgery, 88-90 Ethel St., Benwell, Newcastle upon Tyne NE4 8QA — MB BS 1990 Newc.; MRCGP 1994; DRCOG 1993.

BURDEN, Patricia Royal Berkshire Hospital, London Road, Reading RG1 5AN Tel: 0118 987 7716 Fax: 0118 987 8780; 27 Melrose Avenue, Reading RG6 7BN Tel: 0118 926 2962 — MB BS Lond. 1970; MRCPath 1978. (Char. Cross) Cons. Med. Microbiol. Pub. Health Laborat. Reading. Prev: Dir. Pub. Health Laborat. Dorchester.

BURDEN, Richard Paul Nottingham City Hospital, Hucknall Road, Nottingham NG5 1PB Tel: 0115 969 1169 Fax: 0115 962 7678 Email: rburden@ncht.org.uk — MB BS Lond. 1966; FRCP 1984, M 1971; MRCS Eng. LRCP Lond. 1966. (Lond. Hosp.) Cons. Phys. Nottm. City Hosp. Socs: Renal Assn. Prev: Sen. Regist. (Gen. Med. & Nephrol.) Soton. Univ. & Portsmouth; Hosps.; Renal Research Fell. N. Staffs. Hosp. Centre Stoke-on-Trent.

BURDEN, Robert John Department of Anaesthesia, Queen Alexandra Hospital, Cosham, Portsmouth PO6 3LY; 2 The Grange, Woodmancote, Emsworth PO10 8UX Tel: 01243 376525 — MB BS 1986 Lond.; MRCP (UK) 1990; FRCA 1993. (St Marys Hospital London) Cons. Anaesth. Qu. Alexandra Hosp. Portsmouth. Prev: Specialist Regist. (Anaesth.) Soton. & Portsmouth.

BURDETT, Mrs Audry Gillian (retired) 49 Friary Park, Ballabeg, Castletown IM9 4EN Tel: 01624 822692 — LRCP LRCS Ed. LRFPS Glas. 1947. Med. Off. Ronaldsway I. of Man Airport; Med. Off. Buchan Sch. Castletown. Prev: Med. Off. Family Plann. Assn. I. of Man.

BURDETT, Helen Julia Pine Cottage, Sheffield Road, Anston, Sheffield S25 5DS — MB ChB 1992 Bristol.

BURDETT, Nicholas George Armada Surgery, 28 Oxford Place, Plymouth PL1 5AJ — MB BS 1993 Lond.; DRCOG 1999. GP Princip. Plymouth; Staff Grade, Psychiat. Plymouth Primary Care Trust. Prev: Med. Off. Highpoint Prison Stradishall Suff.

BURDETT, Stewart James — MB ChB 1996 Liverp.; MRCGP 2000. (Liverpool) GP Princip.. Hedon. E. Yorks. Socs: Bd. Mem. RCGP (Huberside Fac.). Prev: GP Regist. (Med.).

BURDETT-SMITH, Cyril Barry The Health Centre, Meadway, Sale M33 4PS Tel: 0161 905 2850 — MB BS 1946 Lond.; MRCGP 1964; DObst RCOG 1951. (Char. Cross) Socs: BMA. Prev: Res. Surg. Off. St. Luke's Hosp. Anua; Ho. Off. York Matern. Hosp.; Ho. Phys. Char. Cross Hosp.

BURDETT-SMITH, Mr Peter Accident & Emergency Department, Royal Liverpool University Hospital, Precot Road, Liverpool L7 8XP Tel: 0151 706 2000 Fax: 0151 706 5899 Email: pbsmith@rlboh-tr.nwest.nhs.uk — MB BS 1983 Lond.; FRCS Ed. 1987; DA (UK) 1990; FFAEM 1994. (Charing Cross Hospital) Cons. A & E Med. Roy. Liverp. Univ. Hosp.; Hon. Clin. Lect. Anaesth. & ITU Univ. of Liverp. Socs: Brit. Assn. Accid. & Emerg. Med. (Treas. 1999). Prev: Sen. Regist. (A & E) Leeds; Regist. (A & E) Roy. Vict. Infirm. Newc. u. Tyne.

BURDGE, Anthony Howell Department of Histopathology, Maelor Hospital, Wrexham Tel: 01978 353153 — MB BS 1973 Lond.; MRCS Eng. LRCP Lond. 1973; MRCPath 1984. (Char. Cross) Cons. Histopath. Maelor Hosp. Wrexham. Prev: Lect. (Histopath.) Char. Cross Hosp. Lond.; Regist. (Path.) Roy. P. Alfred Hosp. Sydney Australia.

BURDIS, Barry Donovan 9 Broadmeadows, Darlington DL3 8SP — MB BS 1969 Newc.

BURDITT, Anne Fotherby Mount Pleasant Farm, Farmborough, Bath BA2 0BN Tel: 01761 70376 — MB BS 1962 Lond.; MRCS Eng. LRCP Lond. 1962; DMRD Eng. 1970. (Roy. Free) Clin. Asst. (Radiol.) Roy. United Hosp. Bath. Prev: Regist. & SHO Nuffield Dept. Med. Radcliffe Infirm. Oxf.; SHO Med. Unit Roy. Free Hosp. Lond.

BURDON, Andrew Christopher John The Avenues Medical Group, 27-29 Roseworth Avenue, Gosforth, Newcastle upon Tyne NE3 1NB Tel: 0191 285 8035; 2 Swarland Avenue, Longbenton, Newcastle upon Tyne NE7 7NH Tel: 0191 266 1558 — MB BS 1984 Lond.; MRCGP 1988; DRCOG 1987.

BURDON, Andrew Thompson (retired) 20 Woodlands, Gosforth, Newcastle upon Tyne NE3 4YL Tel: 0191 285 0538 — MB BS 1952 Durh. Prev: Hosp. Pract. St. Nicholas Hosp. Gosforth.

BURDON, Anthony William 1 Vicarage Road, King's Heath, Birmingham B14 7QA — MB ChB 1958 Birm.; DTM & H Eng. 1961.

BURDON, Douglas William (retired) 186 Rosemary Hill Road, Sutton Coldfield B74 4HP Tel: 0121 353 9314 — MB BS Lond. 1962; MRCS Eng. LRCP Lond. 1962; FRCPath 1983, M 1970. Prev: Cons. Microbiol. Univ. Hosp. Birm. NHS Trust.

BURDON, Mr Michael Anthony Department of Opthalmology, Selly Oak Hospital, Raddlebarn Road, Sally Oak, Birmingham B29 6JD Tel: 0121 627 1627 Ext: 53722 — MB BS 1985 Lond.; BSc Lond. 1982; MRCP (UK) 1989; FRCOphth 1992. (St Thomas' Hosp. Med. School, Univ. of Lond.) Cons. (Ophth.) Univ. Hosp. Birm. NHS Trust. Socs: Sec. Brit. Isles Neuro-Ophth. Club.

BURDON, Michael Shaun Chard Road Surgery, Chard Road, St. Budeaux, Plymouth PL5 2UE Tel: 01752 363111 Fax: 01752 363611; 24 Belair Road, Plymouth PL2 3QH — MB BS 1994 Lond.; DFFP 1998; MNCGP 1998. GP Princip.

BURDON, Peter John (retired) 6 Highfield Mews, Highfield Court, Brackley NN13 7HE Tel: 01280 700867 — MRCS Eng. LRCP Lond. 1946. Prev: Gen. Practioner at Freshwell Pract.,Finchingfield, Essex.

BURDSALL, Jake Eastout, Henfield BN5 9RU — MB ChB 1996 Bristol.

BURFITT, Elaine Mary 32 Hawthorn Road, Barry CF62 6LE — MB ChB 1987 Birm.; MRCP (UK) 1990; DCH RCP Lond. 1994.

BURFOOT, Christine Department Haemat., Wexham Park Hospital, Slough Tel: 01753 63300; 43 Picton Way, Caversham, Reading RG4 8NJ Tel: 01189 482454 — MB ChB Aberd. 1970; MRCPath 1986; FRCPath 1997. (Aberd.) Assoc. Specialist (Haemat.) Wexham Pk. Hosp. Slough. Prev: Cons. Haemat. RAF Halton; Sen. Regist. St. Geo. Hosp. Lond.

BURFORD, Nigel Ronald (retired) 75 Westhaven Crescent, Aughton, Ormskirk L39 5BN Tel: 01695 422641 — MB ChB 1967 Liverp.; DObst RCOG 1972.

BURFORD, Philip Anthony 75 Westhaven Crescent, Aughton, Ormskirk L39 5BN; 15 St Marys Close, Hessle, Hull HU13 0HJ — MB BS 1994 Lond.; FRCA 2000. Specialist Regist. Anaesth. Hull Roy. Infirm.

BURFORD, Roger (retired) Mundesley Medical Centre, Munhaven Close, Mundesley, Norwich NR11 8AR Tel: 01263 724500 Fax: 01263 720165 — MB ChB 1967 Birm.; BSc Birm. 1964; DObst RCOG 1970; DCH Eng. 1969.

BURFORD, Sarah Ann Jack Green Cottage, Brindle, Chorley PR6 8NS Tel: 01254 852944; Cormiston House, Milverton, Taunton TA4 1PQ Tel: 01823 401231 — MB BS 1990 Lond.; MRCGP; DCH RCP Lond. 1994; DRCOG 1993; MRLGP 1996. (St. Thomas' Hosp, Leeds) GP Taunton.

BURFORD, Timothy Michael Harts Hill Farm, Flaunden Lane, Bovingdon, Hemel Hempstead HP3 0PD — MB BS 1986 Lond.; BA Oxf. 1983.

BURGE, Mr Alan Jeremy Stuart, Lt.-Col. RAMC Retd. ENT Dept, Derriford Hospital, Plymouth Tel: 01752 777111 Fax: 01590 688050 Email: alan@palamos.co.uk; Viney Lodge, Viney Rd, Lymington SO41 8FF Tel: 01590 610217 — BM BCh Oxf. 1964; FRCS (Otolaryng.) RCS Eng. 1971; DLO RCS Eng. 1970. (Oxf.) Cons. ENT Surg., Derriford Hosp.

BURGE, Mrs Anne University Hospital Birmingham, Occupational health safety, Woodlands Nurses Home, Selly Oak Hospital, Birmingham B29 6JF Tel: 0121 627 1627 Ext: 5435 Fax: 0121 627 8312; 5 Leamington Court, Wells Road, Malvern WR14 4HF Tel: 01684 569225 — MB BS 1969 Lond.; MRCP (UK) 1972; MRCS Eng. LRCP Lond. 1969; AFOM RCP Lond. 1988; DObst RCOG 1971; MFOM RCP Lond. 1998. (Roy. Free) Assoc. Specialist Occupat. Health, Univ. Hosp. Birm. NHS Trust (p/t). Prev: Sen. Regist. (Infec. Dis.s) St. Ann's Lond.; Regist. (Infec. Dis.s) Roy. Free Hosp. Lond.

BURGE, Anne Jillian (retired) Berehul, Wingfield, Leighton Buzzard LU7 9QJ Tel: 01525 874111 — MB BS 1955 Lond.; DPH Lond. 1964; DCH Eng. 1958.

BURGE, Charles Kincaid Springfield Hospital, 61 Glenburnie Road, Tooting, London SW17 7DJ — MB BS 1988 Lond. Regist. (Psychiat.) Springfield Hosp. Lond.

BURGE, Mr David Michael Peartree Cottage, Canada Road, West Wellow, Romsey SO51 6DD — MB BCh 1973 Oxf.; FRCP Lond. 1995; MRCP (UK) 1983; FRCS Eng. 1978; FRACS (Paediat. Surg.) 1981; FRCPCH 1998. Cons. Paediat. Surg. Wessex Regional Centre Paediat. Surg. Soton Gen. Hosp. Socs: Hon. Sec. and Treas. Brit. Assn. Paediat. Surgs. Prev: Paediat. Surg. Soton Gen. Hosp.; Sen. Regist. Wessex Regional Centre; Regist. (Surg.) Alexandra Hosp. Childr. Sydney, Austral.

BURGE, Francesca Nancy 10 Linicro, Kilmuir, Portree IV51 9YN Tel: 01470 542227 Fax: 020 7681 1277 — MB BS 1982 Lond. (Univ. Coll.)

BURGE, Nicole Heidy Woodcroft, Burghead Road, Forres IV36 3UA Tel: 01309 691161 Email: asburge@aol.com — MB ChB 1991 Liverp.

BURGE, Mr Peter Denis Upper Green, Brill Road, Horton cum Studley, Oxford OX33 1BU — BM BCh 1971 Oxf.; MA Oxf. 1971; FRCS Eng. 1976. Cons. Hand Surg. Nuffield Orthop. Centre Oxf.; Clin. Lect. (Orthop. Surg.) Univ. Oxf. Prev: Clin. Reader (Orthop. Surg.) Univ. Oxf.; Fell. Hand Surg. Duke Univ. Durh. N. Carolina, USA.

BURGE, Peter Sherwood Birmingham Heartlands Hospital, Bordesley Green E., Birmingham B9 5SS Tel: 0121 424 0734 Fax: 0121 772 0292 Email: hayespa@heartsol.wmids.nhs.uk; Tel: 0121 424 0734 — MB BS Lond. 1969; MD Lond. 1985, MSc (Occupat. Med.) (Distinc.) 1978; FRCP Lond. 1985; MRCP (UK) 1972; MRCS Eng. LRCP Lond. 1969; FFOM RCP Lond. 1991, MFOM (Distinc.) 1984; DIH Eng. 1978. (Roy. Free) Cons. Chest Phys. Birm. Heartlands Hosp.; Hon. Sen. Lect. Inst. Occupat. Health Univ. Birm.; Edr. Adviser Thorax; Ed Eur Respirat. J. Socs: Eur. Respirat. Soc.; (Edit. Bd.) Indoor Air Internat.; Acad. Indoor Air Sci. Prev: Lect. (Clin. Immunol.) Cardiothoracic Inst. Univ. Lond.; Regist. (Med.) Whittington Hosp. & Univ. Coll. Hosp. Lond.

BURGE, Susan Mary Department of Dermatology, The Churchill, Oxford Radcliffe Hospital, Old Road, Headington, Oxford OX3 7LJ

Tel: 01865 228232 Fax: 01865 228260 Email: sue.burge@ndm.ox.ac.uk; Upper Green, Brill Road, Horton cum Studley, Oxford OX33 1BU Tel: 01865 351310 Email: sue.burge@ndm.ox.ac.uk — BM BCh 1975 Oxf.; DM Oxf. 1993; BSc Bristol 1972; FRCP Lond. 1994. (Bristol and Oxford) Cons. Dermatol. Oxf. Radcliff NHS Trust; Hon. Sen. Clin. Lect. Nuffield Dept. Med. Univ. Oxf.; Assoc. Director of Clin. Studies, The Med. Sch., Univ Oxf. Socs: Fell. Roy. Soc. Med.; Brit. Assn. Dermatol. Prev: Sen. Regist. (Dermat.) The Slade Hosp. Oxf.; Cons. Dermat. Stoke Mandeville Hosp. Aylesbury.

BURGE, Mr Timothy Stuart, Lt.-Col. RAMC Royal Hospital Haslar, Gosport PO12 2AA Tel: 02392 762481 Fax: 02392 762481 Email: plastics@haslib.demon.co.uk; 1 The Terrace, Royal Hospital Haslar, Gosport PO12 2AA Tel: 02392 528472 Fax: 02392 528472 Email: tburge@aol.com — MB ChB 1981 Bristol; FRCS Eng. 1988; FRCS (Plast) 1996. (Bristol) Cons. (Plastic Surg.), Roy. Hosp.Haslar, Gosport, Hants; Hon. Cons. (Plastic Surg.) Portsmouth Hosps. Trust, Portsmouth, Hants. Socs: BAPS; BAAPS; BBA. Prev: Hon. Sen. Regist. (Plastic Surg.) Qu. Mary's Univ. Hosp.; Trainee (Surg.) RAMC.; Hon. Sen. Regist. (Plastic Surg.), Qu. Marys Univ. Hosp.

BURGEN, Sir Arnold Stanley Vincent Department of Pharmacology, University of Cambridge, Tennis Court Road, Cambridge CB2 1QJ Tel: 01223 334060 Fax: 01233 334040 Email: asvb@hermes.cam.ac.uk; 8A Hills Avenue, Cambridge CB1 7XA Tel: 01223 415381 Fax: 01223 740144 — MB BS (Univ. Medal Distinc. Path., Med. Therap., Surg. & Obst.) 1945; FRS; MD Lond. 1959; FRCP Lond. 1969, M 1946; MRCS Eng. LRCP Lond. 1945; F Acad Med Sci 1998. (Middlx.) Pres. Academia Europaea Foreign Assoc. Nat. Acad. Sci. USA.; Master, Darwin Coll. Camb. Prev: Pres. Academia Europaea Foreign Assoc. Nat. Acad. Sci. USA.; Master, Darwin Coll. Camb.; Prof. (Pharmacol.) Univ. Camb.

BURGER, June Mary 668 Finchley Road, London NW11 7NP Tel: 020 8458 4303 — MRCS Eng. LRCP Lond. 1951; MFHom 1973; DCH Eng. 1954. (Liverp.) Indep. Homoeop. Med. Lond. Socs: BMA & Fac. Homoeopath. Prev: Paediat. Roy. Lond. Homeop. Hosp.; Sen. Med. Off. Altrincham Family Plann. Clinic; Ho. Phys. (Paediat.) Bolton & Dist. Gen. Hosp.

BURGERT, Sabine 54 Old Bath Road, Speen, Newbury RG14 1QL — State Exam Med 1987 Ulm.

BURGES, Clive Richard Occupational Health, Churchfield House II, Southend Hospital, Southend-on-Sea Tel: 01702 348911; Ballitore, Elton Park, Hadleigh Road, Ipswich IP2 0DE Tel: 01473 255909 — MB BS 1978 Lond. Sen. Occupat. Health Phys. S.end HA; Med. Off. (Occupat. Health) John Player & Sons Ltd. Ipswich.; Aviat. Med. Examr.

BURGES, Denys Charles L'Estrange Quinton Family Practice, 406 Quinton Road West, Birmingham B32 1QG Tel: 0121 421 6011; Claremont, 11 Somerset Road, Edgbaston, Birmingham B15 2QB — MB BChir 1954 Lond.; MA, MB Camb. 1955, BChir 1954; MRCS Eng. LRCP Lond. 1954; MFOM RCP Lond. 1978; MRCGP 1967; DIH Eng. 1966; CIH Dund 1965; DObst RCOG 1956; Specialist Accredit. (Occupat. Health) RCP Lond. 1978. (Camb. & Birm.) Med. Off. Boc. Ltd., W. Canning Ltd., Truflo Ltd., Tucker Fasteners & other Cos.; Local Treasury Med. Off.; Exam. Med. Pract. DHSS. Socs: BMA (Mem. Birm. Exec. Comm.); Soc. Occupat. Med. Prev: Capt. RAMC; Ho. Surg. (Obst.) Marston Green Matern. Hosp.; Ho. Phys. & Ho. Surg. Gen. Hosp. Birm.

BURGESS, Andrew James, Surg. Cdr. RN Derriford RN DHU, District General Hospital, Plymouth PL6 8DH Tel: 01752 763396, 01752 777111 Fax: 01752 763287 Email: andrew.burgess@phnt.swest.nhs.uk — MB ChB 1983 Sheff.; BSc (Human Biol. & Anat.) Sheff. 1979; FRCA 1994; FFA RCSI 1993; DA (UK) 1988. (Sheffield University) Cons. Anaesth. Derriford Hosp. Plymouth; Clin. Director Theatres Anaesth. RN. Socs: RN Med. Club; Assn. Anaesth. GB & Irel.; SASWR- Comm. Mem. Prev: Sen. Regist. Bristol Roy. Infirm.; Sen. Regist. & Regist. RNH Plymouth; PMO HMS Ark Roy.

BURGESS, Anthony Stuart The Surgery, Station Road, Great Massingham, King's Lynn PE32 2JQ Tel: 01485 518336 Fax: 01485 518725; 19 Lynn Road, Bircham, King's Lynn PE31 6RJ Tel: 01485 23618 — MB BS 1984 Lond.; MRCGP 1988; DCH RCP Lond. 1990. Clin. Asst. (Paediat.) Qu. Eliz. Hosp. King's Lynn. Prev: Sen. Med. Off. RAF Abingdon Oxf. & RAF Belize.; Hon. SHO (Paediat.) P'boro.

BURGESS, Benedict Martin 8 Tynemouth Place, Tynemouth, North Shields NE30 4BJ Email: benburgess@freeserve.co.uk — MB BChir 1996 Camb.; MA (Hons) Cantab. 1994; MB Bchir Cantab. 1996. (Cambridge) SHO (Surgic. Train., Rotat.), Hammersmith & Char. Cross Hosps., Lond. Prev: SHO (Otolaryncology), N.wick Pk. Hosp., Harrow; Anat. Demonst., Univ. of Camb.; SHO (A&E), St. Jame's Hosp., Leeds.

BURGESS, Mr Brian John Ty Reduit, 2 Two Stones Crescent, Kenfig Hill, Bridgend CF33 6DZ Tel: 01656 741395 — MB BS 1992 Lond.; BSc (Hons.) Lond. 1988. (St. Bart. Med. Coll.) Specialist Regist. (A & E) Roy. Gwent Hosp. Newport. Socs: Fell. Roy. Coll. Surg.s. Prev: Clin. Asst. (A & E) Singleton Hosp. Swansea; SHO (Otolaryngol.) Singleton Hosp. Swansea; SHO (Orthop.) Morriston Hosp. Swansea.

BURGESS, Caroline Margaret 10 Douglas Road, Nottingham NG7 1NW Tel: 0115 941 0858 — MB ChB 1994 Sheff.; MB ChB (Hons.) Sheff. 1994; BPharm (Hons.) Bath 1986; Dip. Clin. Pharm. Nottm. 1989. (Sheff.) Specialist Regist. (Anaesth.) Nottm.

BURGESS, Catherine Susan Malvern Cottage, Pembley Green, Copthorne Common, Copthorne, Crawley RH10 3LF — MB BS 1989 Lond.

BURGESS, Charles Smith Health Centre, Ellon Tel: 01358 20333 — MB ChB 1964 Aberd.; MRCGP 1975. Socs: BMA.

BURGESS, Mr Charles Terence Anthony, MBE, TD (retired) 20 Bankfield Lane, Southport PR9 7NJ Tel: 01704 25361 — MRCS Eng. LRCP Lond. 1937; MA, MB, BChir Camb. 1937; FRCS Eng. 1948. Prev: Cons. Gen. Surg. S.port & Dist. & Ormskirk & Dist. Hosp. Gps.

BURGESS, Colin Charles The Portland Practice, St Paul's Medical Centre, 121 Swindon Road, Cheltenham GL50 4DP Tel: 01242 707792 — MB ChB 1979 Bristol; MRCGP 1986; DRCOG 1982. Course Organiser Glos. GP VTS.

BURGESS, David Kenneth 60 Budmouth Avenue, Preston, Weymouth DT3 6QJ — MB BCh 1963 Wales; MRCGP 1977; DA Eng. 1966. (Cardiff) Socs: BMA. Prev: Ho. Phys., Ho. Surg. & SHO (Anaesth.) United Cardiff Hosps.

BURGESS, David Martin (retired) The Coastal Clinic, 4 Park Road, Gorleston, Great Yarmouth NR31 6EJ Tel: 01493 601770 Fax: 01493 442430 Email: dmburgess@friska.fsnet.co.uk — MB BS 1954 Lond.; FRCS Eng. 1960; FRACS 1964. Prev: Cons. Orthop. & Trauma Surg. Gt. Yarmouth & Waveney Health Dist.

BURGESS, Mr Donald Everett The Orchard, Holmcroft, Deans Lane, Walton on the Hill, Tadworth KT20 7TR Tel: 0173 781 4688 — MB BS 1946 Lond.; FRCS Ed. 1960; FRCOG 1968, M 1954. (Univ. Coll. Hosp.) Cons. O & G St. Helier Hosp. Carshalton & Nelson Hosp. Wimbledon; Hon. Sen. Lect. St. Geo. Hosp. Tooting. Socs: RSM. Prev: Sen. Regist. (O & G) Middlx. Hosp. Lond.; Regist. (O & G) Radcliffe Infirm. Oxf.; Regist (O & G) Postgrad. Med. Sch. Lond.

BURGESS, Dorothy, DStJ (retired) 14 Dellwood Gardens, Clayhall, Ilford IG5 0EH Tel: 020 8550 0738 — MD 1958 Malta; BPharm. 1955. Prev: Clin. Med. Off. (Child Health) Barking, Havering & Brentwood Community Healthcare.

BURGESS, Douglas Anderson Jamieson, Thorpe and Burgess, Moulton Medical Centre, High St, Moulton, Spalding PE12 6QB Tel: 01406 370265 Fax: 01406 373219; Hallgate House, 69 Hallgate, Holbeach, Spalding PE12 7HX Tel: 01406 423137 — MB ChB 1987 Aberd.; MRCGP 1993. Prev: Trainee GP/SHO Boston VTS; SHO (Cardiorespirat. Med. & Rheum.) Pilgrim Hosp. Boston; Ho. Off. (Med.) Stoke Mandeville Hosp.

BURGESS, Edward Herbert 68 Hurlingham Court, Ranelagh Gardens, London SW6 3UR Tel: 020 7736 4544 — MRCS Eng. LRCP Lond. 1955; MD Lond. 1967, MB BS 1955; MRCGP 1966. (St. Bart.) Med. Lect. Pre-retirem. Assn. Socs: Fell. Roy. Soc. Med.; Assoc. Fac. Occupat. Med. Roy. Coll. Phys. Prev: Med. Off. Bd. Inland Revenue; Sen. Div. Med. Off. (Med.) Civil Serv. Occupat. Health Serv.

BURGESS, Edward John Department of Chemical Pathology, The North Hampshire Hospital, Aldermaston Road, Basingstoke RG24 9NA Tel: 01256 313285 Fax: 01256 484905; 25/34 Liley Street, Cairns Qld 4870, Australia — MB BS 1981 Lond.; PhD Lond. 1979, BSc 1974, MB BS 1981; MRCPath 1991; CChem. 1992. (Westm.) Cons. Chem. Path. The N. Hants. Hosp. Socs: Fell. Roy. Soc. Med.; Nutrit. Soc. Prev: Sen. Regist. (Chem. Path.) Char.

Cross Hosp. Lond. & Roy. Berks. Hosp.Reading; Regist. (Chem. Path.) & SHO (Path.) Leicester Roy. Infirm.; SHO (Gen., Renal & Research Med.) Roy. Sussex Co. Hosp. Brighton.

BURGESS, Geoffrey Group Practice Surgery, Chester Road, Ellesmere Port, South Wirral CH65 6TG Tel: 0151 355 6151; 1 Woodland Bank, Mickle Trafford, Chester CH2 4QL — MB ChB 1975 Leeds; DRCOG 1979; DMJ (Clin.) 1981.

BURGESS, Geoffrey William Syme (retired) Croft Hill, Moresby, Whitehaven CA28 8UP Tel: 01946 692050 Fax: 01946 599409 Email: geoff.burgess@btinternet.com — MB BChir Camb. 1967; MA Camb. 1967; MRCS Eng. LRCP Lond. 1967; FRCGP 1993, M 1975. Appeals Serv. - Sessional. Prev: GP Distington, Workington.

BURGESS, Gerald Lynch (retired) Mount Pleasant, Corfe, Taunton TA3 7BU Tel: 01823 421322 — MB BS 1946 Lond.; MRCS Eng. LRCP Lond. 1937. Prev: Ho. Phys. Roy. Waterloo Hosp. Childr. & Wom.

BURGESS, Helen Ladybarn Group Practice, 177 Mauldeth Road, Fallowfield, Manchester M14 6SG Tel: 0161 224 2873 Fax: 0161 225 3276; 14 Marton Avenue, Didsbury, Manchester M20 5LN Tel: 0161 445 2512 — MB ChB 1984 Dundee; MRCGP 1991; DRCOG 1987. Bd Mem. S. Manch.PCG. Socs: Manch. Med. Soc.

BURGESS, Helen Katherine 10 Curzon Road, Weybridge KT13 8UW — BM 1998 Soton.

BURGESS, Henry Gwyn (retired) 10 Cambridge Road, Langland, Swansea SA3 4PE Tel: 01792 360336 — MB BCh Wales 1952.

BURGESS, Henry Jacques Leslie (retired) Craiglea Cottage, Glenisla, Blairgowrie PH11 8PS Tel: 01575 582218 — MSc Harvard 1972; MB ChB St. And. 1956; MFPHM RCP (UK) 1974; DPH Lond. 1962; DTM & H Liverp. 1958. Prev: Exec. Sec. UN Subcomm. Nutrit.

BURGESS, Isabel Catherine 5 Wesley Close, Sapcote, Leicester LE9 4HY — MB ChB 1993 Sheff.

BURGESS, Joanna Louise 1 Edward Drive, Helensburgh G84 9QP — MB ChB 1997 Manch.

BURGESS, John George Lane, Stanton, Bury St Edmunds IP31 2UB — MB BS 1949 Lond.; DObst RCOG 1956. (King's Coll. Hosp.)

BURGESS, John Edward, Col. L/RAMC Oaklawn House, Star Hill Drive, Churt GU10 2HP Tel: 01428 712203 Email: johnburgess@doctors.org.uk; 10 Tarragon Close, Farnborough GU14 9XF Tel: 01428 712203 — MB BS 1978 Lond.; Dip. Occ. Med. 1997; FRCGP 2001; MRCS Eng. LRCP Lond. 1978; MRCGP 1985; DRCOG 1984. (St. Bart.) Army GP Trainer Course Organiser.

BURGESS, John Edward 9 Belgrave Avenue, Hunstanton PE36 6DQ Tel: 01485 532152 Fax: 01485 535603 Email: docburgess@aol.com — MB ChB Birm. 1963; MSc (Distinc.) Lond. 1976; FFOM RCP Lond. 1982, M 1979; DIH Eng. 1976; DObst RCOG 1965. (Birm.) Cons. Occupat. Phys. Hunstanton; Med. Adviser, Norf. C.C.; A.H. Marks & Co; Cavell & Lind. Socs: Fell. Roy. Soc. Med.; Soc. Occupat. Med. Prev: Extern. Lect. Univ. Manch. Dept. Occupat. Health; GP Med. Adviser Bayer plc; Europ. Med. Adviser Ethyl Corp.

BURGESS, Judith Mary Haleacre Unit, Amersham General Hospital, Whielden St., Amersham HP7 0JD Tel: 01494 734523 — MB ChB 1975 Dundee; FRCPSych 1999; MRCPSych 1983; BSc (Med. Sci.) St And. 1972. Cons. Psychiat. S. Bucks. NHS Trust.

BURGESS, Lynne Margaret Flat 3, Prestbury Manor, Southam Road, Cheltenham GL52 3NQ — MB ChB 1996 Bristol.

BURGESS, Malcolm Battersby Sunnymead, 53 Birkenhead Road, Meols, Wirral CH47 5AF Tel: 0151 632 6660 Fax: 0151 632 5073; 11 Newton Park Road, West Kirby, Wirral CH48 9XE Email: macbatty@yahoo.com — MB ChB 1974 Aberd. Clin. Asst. Hoylake Cottage Hosp.; Asst. Med. Off. Hoylake Lifeboat.

BURGESS, Malcolm Ian Northwest Regional Cardiology Centre, South Manchester University Hospitals NHS Trust, Southmoor Road, Wythenshawe, Manchester M23 9LT Tel: 0161 998 7070; 10 Daisy Bank Mill Close, Culcheth, Warrington WA3 4JH Tel: 01925 766345 — MB ChB 1993 Dundee; MRCP (UK) 1996. Research Fell. (Cardiol.) Wythenshawe Hosp. Manch. Socs: Brit. Soc. Echocardiogr.; Brit. Soc. Heart Failure. Prev: SHO (Gen. Med. & Coronary Care) Wythenshawe Hosp. Manch.; SHO (Gen. Med.) Warrington Hosp. NHS Trust.

BURGESS, Mr Neil Alan Norfolk & Norwich Hospital, Brunswick Road, Norwich NR1 3SR Tel: 01603 507038 — MB BCh 1985 Wales; MCh Wales 1992; FRCS (Urol.) 1994; FRCS Ed. 1989. Cons. Urol. Norwich. Socs: Brit. Assn. Urol. Surg. Prev: Sen. Regist. (Urol.) Camb. & Norwich; Regist. (Urol.) Roy. Gwent Hosp. & Univ. Hosp. Wales; Regist. (Surg.) E. Glam. Hosp.

BURGESS, Nigel David Scott Green Meadows Surgery, Winkfield Road, Ascot SL5 7LS Tel: 01344 21627; Mahala, Devenish Lane, Sunningdale, Ascot SL5 9QU Tel: 01344 21362 — MB BS 1968 Lond.; DA Eng. 1972. (Middlx.) Prev: Med. Off. Nchanga Consolidated Copper Mines Ltd. Kitwe, Zambia.

BURGESS, Patricia Ann Bellair Clinic, Alverton St., Penzance TR18 4TA Tel: 01736 575501 — MB BCh 1973 Wales; DCH Eng. 1975. Assoc. Specialist. (Child Health) Roy. Cornw. Hosps. Trust.

BURGESS, Patricia Leonie (retired) Parrotts Frm., Parrots Lane, Cholesbury, Tring HP23 6NE — MB ChB 1970 Bristol; MRCGP 1980.

BURGESS, Paul Adrian Cellular Pathology, Hull Royal Infirmary, Anlaby Rd, Hull HU3 2JZ; 25 Woodlands, Beverley HU17 8BT — MB ChB 1971 Liverp.; FRCPath 1990, M 1978. Cons. (Histopath. & Cytol.) Hull & E. Yorks. Hosp.s NHS Trust. Prev: Sen. Regist. (Histopath.) Leics. AHA (T).

BURGESS, Paul Anthony The Surgery, 1 Cudworth House, Stewarts Road, London SW8 4UT Tel: 020 7498 9067; 28 Openview, Earlsfield, London SW18 3PE Tel: 020 8870 3238 — MB BS 1985 Lond.; DCH RCP Lond. 1987. Prev: Ho. Surg. & Ho. Phys. Medway Hosp.; Trainee GP Soton.

BURGESS, Penelope Charlotte Station Road Farm, Rippingdale, Bourne PE10 0TA — MB ChB 1996 Ed.

BURGESS, Mr Peter (retired) 5 Huntly Chase, Wilmslow SK9 2AU Tel: 01625 522959 Email: drpeterburgess@talk21.com — MB ChB 1950 Manch.; FRCS Ed. 1958; MRCGP 1962. Prev: Resid. Surg. Off. Wythenshawe Gen. Hosp. Manch.

BURGESS, Peter John The Medical Centre, 3A Whitby Drive, York YO31 1EX Tel: 01904 416541 Fax: 01904 416541 — MB ChB 1979 Manch.; MRCGP 1983; DRCOG 1982. GP Heworth York. Prev: Trainee GP VTS St. Asaph.; Ho. Phys. Roy. Alexandra Hosp. Rhyl; Ho. Surg. York Dist. Hosp.

BURGESS, Mr Phillip Department of Surgery, Swindon & Marlborough NHS Trust, Princess Margaret Hospital, Okus Road, Swindon SN1 4JU Tel: 01793 536231 Fax: 01793 426949 — MB ChB 1979 Birm.; BSc (Hons.) Hatfield 1975; MD Newc. 1988; FRCS Eng. 1983; FRCS Ed. 1983; T(S) 1991. (Birmingham) Cons. Surg. & Surg. Gastroenterol. Swindon & MarlBoro. Hosps. Wessex RHA; Trauma Fell. & Lect. (Surg.) Univ. Louisville Kentucky, USA; Mem. Ct. Examrs. RCS Engl.; Vis. Lect. Instit. of Med. Scis. Cranfield Univ. Socs: Surg. Research Soc., Injury Research Gp.; Brit. Assn. Surgic. Oncol. Prev: Sen. Regist. (Surg.) Univ. Newc. u Tyne; Regist. Rotat. (Surg.) Salford; Ho. Surg. Birm. Accid. Hosp.

BURGESS, Ronald Craig Alexander 1 Edward Drive, Helensburgh G84 9QP Tel: 01436 674845 — MB ChB 1990 Manch.; BSc (Med. Sci.) St. And. 1987; MRCGP 1995; DCH RCP Lond. 1995; DRACOG 1994; DTM & H Liverp. 1992; Dip. Family Plann.1998. Missions Medecins Sans Frontieres. Prev: Trainee GP Lancaster; RMO (O & G & Paediat.) John Hunter Hosp. Newc., NSW Austral.; SHO (Cas.) Macclesfield.

BURGESS, Sally Annette 13 Cherry Street, Stratton Audley, Bicester OX27 9AA — MB BCh 1988 Wales.

BURGESS, Sarah Elizabeth Priscilla Delafield, Little Haseley, Oxford OX44 7LH — MB ChB 1976 Leeds; FRCS Eng. 1982; DO Eng. 1980. Cons. Ophth. Swindon & Marlboro. Trust. Prev: Lect. (Ophth.) Univ. Oxf.; Research Fell. Cornell Univ. Med. Coll. New York.

BURGESS, Stephen Peter 1 St Josephs Court, Forest View, Chingford, London E4 7UA — MB BCh 1977 Wales; MRCOG 1983; MObst & Gyn Liverp. 1984; DCH RCP Lond. 1981. Cons. O & G Barking & Ilford HA. Prev: Sen. Regist. (O & G) Cardiff & Bangor; Regist. (O & G) Mill Rd. Hosp. Liverp.; Regist. (O & G) W. Chesh. Hosp. Chester.

BURGESS, Suzanne Email: suzanne.burgess@bt.internet.com — MB BS 1982 Lond.; MFFP 1995; MRCGP 1986; DRCOG 1984. p/t GP; Family Plann. Train. Doctor, Croydon and Surrey Downs NHS Trust, Croydon. Socs: Assur. Med. Soc.

BURGESS, Vivien Margaret The Doctors House, Victoria Road, Marlow SL7 1DN Tel: 01628 484666 Fax: 01628 891206; 23 Institute Road, Marlow SL7 1BJ — MB ChB 1967 Bristol.

BURGESS, Winifred (retired) Tawton House, Bishop's Tawton, Barnstaple EX32 0DB Tel: 01271 43441 — MB BS 1952 Lond.;

FRCP Lond. 1985, M 1955; MRCS Eng. LRCP Lond. 1952; DCH Eng. 1954. Prev: Cons. Paediat. Mbeya Gov. Hosp. Tanzania (ODA).

BURGESS, Yvonne Mary 1 Bracken Way, Newport TF10 7RL — MB ChB 1993 Bristol.

BURGIN, Mark Innes Rotherham Road Medical Centre, 100 Rotherham Road, Barnsley S71 1UT Tel: 01226 282587 Fax: 01226 291900 — BM BCh 1987 Oxf.; MRCGP 1994; DCH RCP Lond. 1993.

BURGNER, David Paul 7 Oatlands Road, Oxford OX2 0EU — MB ChB 1989 Bristol; BSc (Hons.) Bristol. 1986. MB ChB 1989; MRCP (UK) 1993; DTM & H Liverp. 1991. SHO (Paediat.) Roy. Hosp. for Sick Childr. Glas. Socs: MDU. Prev: SHO (Neonates.) S.mead Hosp. Bristol; SHO (Paediat.) Roy. United Hosp. Bath; SHO (A & E) Frenchay Hosp. Bristol.

BURGOYNE, John 2 Buckstone View, Edinburgh EH10 6PE Tel: 0131 445 2098 — MB ChB 1946 Glas.; FFA RCS Eng. 1954; DA Eng. 1953. (Univ. Glas.) Cons. Anaesth. Edin. Centr. Hosp. Gp. Socs: Assn. Anaesths.

BURGOYNE, Margaret Department of Pathology, Southern General Hospital NHS Trust, Glasgow — MB ChB 1981 Glas.; MRCPath 1988. Cons. Pathol. S.. Gen. Hosp. NHS Trust Glas.

BURGOYNE, Mr Philip William 8A Kingsley Road, Kilburn, London NW6 7RJ Tel: 020 7328 6605 — MB BS 1990 Lond.; FRCS Eng. 1995. Spinal Fell. Roy. Nat. Orthop. Hosp. Stanmore.

BURGOYNE, Sandra 10 Glanmor Crescent, Newport NP19 8AX — MB ChB 1973 Sheff.

BURGUL, Rajesh 36 Grosvenor Place, Aberdeen AB25 2RE Email: r.burgul@abdn.ac.uk — MB ChB 1990 Aberd. Regist. (Diag. Radiol.) Aberd. Roy. Hosps. NHS Trust.

BURGUL, Sharada Devi c/o Drive P.D. Burgul, 11 Craig Road, Workington CA14 3JU; Prakala, 11 Coulton Croft Road, Sacoed, Wakefield WF2 6DA Tel: 01924 240692 — MB BS 1971 Osmania. (Osmania Med. Coll. Hyderabad) SCMO Barnsley AHA.

BURK, Alexander 4 Highland Drive, North Nibley, Dursley GL11 6DX — MB BS 1987 Monash.

BURKART, Catherine Bridgett Memorial Hospital, Hollyhurst Road, Darlington DL3 6HX — MB BCh BAO 1985 NUI; LRCPI 1986.

BURKE, Adrian Gavin 1/75 Canning Street, Toxteth, Liverpool L8 7NW — MB ChB 1998 Liverp.; MB ChB Liverp 1998.

BURKE, Aggrey Washington Department Psychiatry, St George's Hospital Medical School, London SW17 0QT Tel: 020 8672 9944 — MB ChB 1968 Birm.; BSc (Hons.) Birm. 1966, MB ChB 1968; MRCPsych 1972; DPM Eng. 1971.

BURKE, Anne Marie 16 Meadow Hill, Newton Mearns, Glasgow G77 6SX — MB ChB 1968 Glas.; FFA RCSI 1975. Cons. Neuroanaesth. Inst. Neurol. Sc. S.. Gen. Hosp.

BURKE, Barbara Mary The Rock Surgery, 50 High Street, Frodsham, Warrington WA6 7HG Tel: 01928 732110 Fax: 01928 739273; Greenacre, Howey Lane, Frodsham, Warrington WA6 6DL Tel: 01928 732000 — MB ChB 1967 Liverp.; MRCGP 1976. (Liverp.) Hosp. Pract. (Dermat.) Halton Gen. Hosp.

BURKE, Barbara Mary Bellbrooke Surgery, 395-397 Harehills Lane, Leeds LS9 6AP Tel: 0113 249 4848 Fax: 0113 248 4993 — MB ChB 1967 Liverpool; MB ChB Liverp. 1967. (Liverpool) GP Leeds.

BURKE, Beverley John Barnet General Hospital, Wellhouse Lane, Barnet EN5 3DJ Tel: 0208 216 5479 Fax: 0208 8216 5480 — MRCS Eng. LRCP Lond. 1967; MB ChB Bristol 1967; MD Bristol 1980; FRCP Lond. 1990; MRCP (UK) 1971. (Bristol) p/t Cons. Phys. & Endocrinol. Barnet Gen. Hosp. Herts.; Hon. Sen. Lect. (Med.) Middlx. & UCH Sch. Med. Lond.; Cons Endocrinol., N. W. Lond. NHS Trust. Socs: Brit. Diabetic Assn. (Scientif. Sect.); Med. Res. Soc. Prev: Sen. Regist. (Med.) Bristol Roy. Infirm.; Sen. Regist. (Med.) Roy. Devon & Exeter Hosp.; Regist. (Research) Bristol Roy. Infirm.

BURKE, Bryan Edwin Bloomfield Avenue Surgery, 155 Bloomfield Avenue, Belfast BT5 5AB Tel: 028 9045 7677 — MB BCh BAO 1982 Belf.; MB BCh Belf. 1982; MRCGP 1987; DRCOG 1988; DGM RCP Lond. 1987; DCM Dub. 1986.

BURKE, Christopher William Department of Endocrinology, Radcliffe Infirmary, Oxford OX2 6HE Tel: 01865 224765 Fax: 01865 224617 — BM BCh 1960 Oxf.; DM Oxf. 1971, MA, BM BCh 1960; FRCP Lond. 1975, M 1964. (Oxf. & St. Bart.) Cons. Phys. Radcliffe Infirm. Oxf.; Clin. Lect. Univ. Oxf. Socs: Fell. Roy. Soc. Med.; Soc. Endocrin. Prev: Sen. Regist. & Tutor Endocrine Unit Dept. Med. Hammersmith Hosp. & Roy. Postgrad. Med. Sch.; Regist. (Gen. Med.) Hammersmith Hosp. Lond.; Regist. (Gen. Med.) St. And. Hosp. Bow.

BURKE, Daniel Fruitfield Cottage, Campmuir, Coupar Angus, Blairgowrie PH13 9JG; Slough Cottage, Fownhope, Hereford HR1 4PZ Tel: 01432 860959 — MB ChB 1989 Dundee; FRCA 1995. Specialist Regist. (Anaesth.) Ninewells Hosp. Dundee; Research Fell. (Anaesth.) Univ. Dundee. Socs: Scott. Soc. Anaesth.; ASRA; Soc. Scott. Anaesth.

BURKE, Daniel Mark Lea Farm, Sutton Wick, Bishop Sutton, Bristol BS39 5XR — MB BS 1994 Lond. SHO Rotat. (Surg.) Bath.

BURKE, Darah Kevin 17 Darnton Gardens, Ashton-under-Lyne OL6 6SG — MB ChB 1993 Manch.; DRCOG 1996; MRCGP, 1998. (Manch.) GP.

BURKE, Denis Anthony Department of Medicine, Cumberland Infirmary, Carlisle CA2 7NY Tel: 01228 523444 — MB BS 1980 Newc.; MD Newc. 1991; MRCP (UK) 1983; T(M) 1991; FRCP 1996. Cons. Phys. (Gen. Med. & Gastroenterol.) Cumbld. Infirm. Carlisle. Socs: Brit. Assn. Study Liver; Brit. Soc. Gastroenterol. Prev: Sen. Regist. & Regist. (Gastroenterol. & Gen. Med.) Leeds Gen. Infirm. & Roy. Vict. Infirm. Newc.; Research Regist. (Gastroenterol.) Leeds Gen. Infirm.

BURKE, Mr Derek Patrick Anthony 12 Colemeadow Road, Billesley, Birmingham B13 0JL — MB ChB 1983 Birm.; FRCS Ed. 1992.

BURKE, Derek Victor Driftway, Drive Road, Old Coulsdon, Croydon CR5 1BN Tel: 01737 551530 — MB BS Lond. 1955; MRCS Eng. LRCP Lond. 1954; LMSSA Lond. 1954. (Guy's) Ho. Off. (Obst.) All St.s' Hosp. Chatham; Ho. Phys. & Ho. Surg. Lewisham Hosp.

BURKE, Mr Dermot Dept. of Academic Surgery, Leeds General Infirmary, Room B40, Clarendon Wing, Great George St., Leeds LS1 3EX Tel: 0113 392 3465 Email: d.burke@leeds.ac.uk — MB ChB 1986 Manch.; FRCS Eng. 1990; PhD. Lond. 1999; FRCS (Gen. Surg) 1999. Sen. Lect. in Surg./Cons. Surg., Univ. of Leeds, Leeds. Socs: Brit. Assn. of Surgic. Oncol.; Brit. Oncol. Assn.; Assn. of ColoProctol. of Gt. Britain and Irel. Prev: RSO, St. Mark's Hosp., Harrow; Regist. (Spr), N. W. Thames; Britta-Dolan Research Fell., Chelsea & W.m. Hosp., Lond.

BURKE, Professor Francis Desmond Hazeldene, 24 Hazelwood Road, Duffield, Belper DE56 4DQ Tel: 01332 840579 Email: frank.burke@virgin.net; Tel: 01332 290480 Fax: 01332 291425 Email: frank.burke@virgin.net — MB BS 1967 Newc.; FRCS Eng. 1972; Specialist Accredit (Orthop.) RCS Eng. 1977. Cons. Hand Surg. S. Derbysh. HA; Vis. Prof. Hand Surg. Univ. Derby. Socs: (Ex-Pres.) Brit. Soc. Surg. Hand. Prev: Sen. Regist. Robt. Jones & Agnes Hunt Orthop. Hosp. OsW.ry; Fell. Hand Surg. Univ. Louisville, USA & Univ. Iowa, USA.

BURKE, Francis Edmund Brannel Surgery, 58 Rectory Road, St. Stephen, St Austell PL26 7RL Tel: 01726 822254 Fax: 01726 824450 — MB ChB 1967 Manch.; MSc Exon 1995. (Manch.)

***BURKE, Georgina** 43 Northway Road, Camberwell, London SE5 9AN Tel: 020 7738 7521 — MB BS 1997 Lond.; BSc Lond. 1994.

BURKE, Gladstone Austin Amos 71 Ormonds Drive, Bradley Stoke North, Bristol BS32 0DT — MB ChB 1991 Ed.

BURKE, Helen Boswell 20 Cleveland Square, Middlesbrough TS1 2NX Tel: 01642 242719, 246138 Fax: 01642 222291 — MB ChB 1990 Dundee; DRCOG 1996; MRCGP 1997. p/t GP Princip.; Asst. Police Surg. with Cleveland Police; Clin. Asst. (Cardiol.) The James Cook Univ. Hosp., Middlesbrough. Socs: BMA; Assn. of Police Surg.s.

BURKE, John Berry George 30 Millway, London NW7 3RB; 56 Millway, London NW7 3RA — MB BS 1950 Lond.

BURKE, John Edward Timothy Three Crossways, Chulmleigh EX18 7AA Tel: 01769 580269 Fax: 01769 581131 — BM 1981 Soton.; DA (UK) 1983. The Health Centre, Three Cross Ways, Chulmleigh, Devon. Prev: Family Phys./Anaesth. Med. Centre Ponoka, Canada.; 1993-1995 Family Phys./Anaesth., Olds, Alberta, Canada.

BURKE, John Gerard Andrew Mary Department of Psychiatry, University of Leicester, Clinical Sciences Building, Leicester Royal

Infirmary, PO Box 65, Leicester LE2 7LX — MB BCh BAO 1978 NUI.

BURKE, John Joseph 4 Monument Road, Wigan WN1 2LS — MB ChB 1954 Manch.

BURKE, Mr John Patrick Department of Ophthalmology, Royal Hallamshire Hospital, Sheffield S10 2JF Tel: 0114 271 2036 Fax: 0114 271 3747 — MB BCh BAO 1981 Dub.; BSc Dub. 1978, MA 1981; FRCS Glas. 1988; MRCPI 1985; FRCOphth. 1989; DO RCPSI 1986; FICS 1990. (Trinity Coll. Dub.) p/t Cons. Ophth. Centr. Sheff. Univ. Hosps. NHS Trust; Hon. Sen. Clin. Lect. Univ. Sheff. Socs: Amer. Assn. for Pediat. Ophth. & Strabismus; Eur. Strabismological Assn.; Internat. Strabismological Assn. Prev: Sen. Regist. (Ophth.) Roy. Hallamsh. Sheff.; Fell. (Paediat., Ophth. & Ocular Motility) Univ. Iowa Hosps. & Clinics, USA; Regist. Ninewells Hosp. & Med. Sch. Dundee.

BURKE, Joyce Beryl (retired) 1 Vicarage Road, Reading RG2 7AJ Tel: 0118 986 0623 — 1945 MB BS, Lond; 1951 MD Lond.; 1974 FRCP Lond.; 1945 MRCS Eng. LRCP Lond.; 1947 DObst RCOG; 1948 DCH Eng.; 1953 MRCP. Prev: Cons. Paediatr. Reading Area Dept. Paediat. Oxf. RHA.

BURKE, Laurence Jerome 1 Omdurman Road, Southampton SO17 1PH — MB BS 1993 Lond.

BURKE, Laurence John The Cross, Milborne Port, Sherborne DT9 5DH Tel: 01963 250334; Limerick House, North St, Milborne Port, Sherborne DT9 5EW — MB BS 1981 Lond.; MRCGP 1985; DRCOG 1984.

BURKE, Louise Patricia Pembroke House, Old Mill Lane, Oldbury, Bridgnorth WV16 5EY — MB BS 1986 Lond.

BURKE, Mrs Margaret Mary Saunton House, Callicroft Road, Patchway, Bristol BS12 Tel: 0117 969 1660 — MB BCh BAO 1950 NUI.

BURKE, Margaret Mary Penbury, Dane Grove, Mickle Trafford, Chester CH2 4DJ — BChir 1995 Camb.; BSc Hons 1993. Surgic. Trainee, Poole, Dorset.

BURKE, Margaret Mary Elizabeth Department of Pathology, Royal Brompton & Harefield NHS Trust, Harefield, Uxbridge UB9 6JH Tel: 01895 828929 Fax: 01895 828949 Email: mmburke@rbh.nthames.nhs.uk; Ash Tree Cottage, Hills Lane, Northwood HA6 2QL Tel: 01923 827944 — MB BCh BAO 1973 NUI; 1973 MB BCH BAO NUI; 1975 BSc NUI; 1995 FRCPath (M 1982); 1976 DCH NUI. (Univ. Coll. Dub.) Cons. Histopath. Roy. Brompton & Harefield NHS Trust, Harefield Middlx. Socs: Assn. Clin. Path; Internat. Acad. Path. (Brit. Div.); Soc. Internat. Heart & Lung Transpl. Prev: Cons. (Histopath.) Mt. Vernon & Harefield Hosps.; Cons. Histopath. St. Geo. Hosp. Med. Sch. Lond.; Clin. Lect. (Histopath.) Middlx. Hosp. Med. Sch. Lond.

BURKE, Michael Northwick Park Hosptial, Watford Road, Harrow HA1 3UJ Tel: 020 8869 2618 Fax: 020 8869 2577 Email: crooklets@msn.com; Crooklets, 39 Oxhey Road, Oxhey, Watford WD19 4QG Tel: 01923 253196 — MB BS 1971 Lond.; MS Lond. 1982; FRCS Eng. 1975; MRCS Eng. LRCP Lond. 1971. (Char. Cross) Cons. Surg. N.wick Pk. Hosp. Harrow; Hon. Sen. Lect. Imp. Coll. Med. Sch. Socs: Brit. Assn. Surgic. Oncol.; (Counc.) Assn. Surgs. Prev: MRC Clin. Scientif. Off. Clin. Research Centre Harrow; Sen. Regist. St. Mark's Hosp. & Roy. Free Hosp. Lond.

BURKE, Michael 36 Queen Street, Geddington, Kettering NN14 1AZ Tel: 01536 743192 — MB ChB 1983 Leic.

BURKE, Mr Michael Francis The Washington Hospital, Picktree Lane, Rickleton, Washington NE38 9JZ Tel: 0191 415 1272; Daisy Hill Cottages, Springwell Village, Gateshead NE9 7PQ Tel: 0191 417 7258 Fax: 0191 417 7258 — MB BS Durh. 1965; MD Newc. 1976; FRCS Eng. 1970; FRCOG 1989, M 1973. (Durh.) Cons. Gyn. & Specialist (Infertil. Microsurg.) Washington Hosp. Tyne & Wear. Socs: Ospreys Gyn. Soc.; Newc. Medico-Legal Soc.; N. of Engl. Obs. & Gyn. Soc. Prev: Ho. Surg., Ho. Phys. & Research Asst. Poisons Informat. Centre Roy. Vict. Infirm. Newc.; Lect. (O & G) Univ. Liverp.

BURKE, Michael Joseph Burnley General Hospital, Casterton Avenue, Burnley, Burnley BB10 2PQ Tel: 01282 474436 Fax: 01282 474434; Higher Small Hazels, Habergham Eaves, Burnley BB11 3RS Tel: 01282 438974 Fax: 01282 474434 Email: mikeburke_99@yahoo.co.uk — MB ChB 1970 Manch.; BA Open 1985; FRCP Lond. 1992; MRCP (UK) 1972. Cons. Rheum. Burnley Health Care Trust. Socs: Fell. Manch. Med. Soc.; Brit. Soc. Rheum.; BMA. Prev: Sen. Regist. (Rheum. & Rehabil.) Manch. Roy. Infirm.; William Hewitt Research Fell. Rheum. Research Unit Gen. Infirm. Leeds; Regist. (Med.) St. Geo. Hosp. Lond.

BURKE, Nicholas Joseph Shell UK Ltd., North West Occupational Health Centre, PO Box 3, Ellesmere Port, South Wirral CH65 4HB Tel: 0151 350 4358 Fax: 0151 350 4568 Email: njb.nwohc.demon.co.uk — MB BS 1978 Tasmania. (Tasmania) Socs: Fell. Austral. Fac. Occupat. Med.; Fell. Austral. Fac. Pub. Health Med.

BURKE, Nicola Jean 29 Kingfisher Close, Torquay TQ2 7TF — MB ChB 1996 Manch.

BURKE, Olivia Carmel Anne Child & Family Department, Tavistock Clinic, 120 Belsize Lane, Hampstead, London NW3 5BA Tel: 020 7435 7111 Fax: 020 7447 3733 — MB BCh BAO 1984 NUI; MRCPsych 1991; DObst RCPI 1987; DCH NUI 1986. (University College Dublin) Cons. in Child & Family Psychiat. Tavistock Clinic Lond. Prev: Sen. Regist. (Child & Family Psychiat.) Tavistock Clinic Lond.

BURKE, Patrick Joseph (retired) 300 Wilbraham Road, Manchester M21 0UU Tel: 0161 881 6437 — MB ChB 1936 Manch.; MRCS Eng. LRCP Lond. 1937.

BURKE, Paul Edwin (retired) 47 Knowsley Road, Wilpshire, Blackburn BB1 9PN — MB BS 1959 Lond.; MRCS Eng. LRCP Lond. 1959; FRCGP 1990, M 1976. Prev: GP Blackburn.

BURKE, Peter David St Bartholomew's Medical Centre, Manzil Way, Cowley Road, Cowley, Oxford OX4 1XB Tel: 01865 242334 Fax: 01865 204018; The Hollies, Marsh Baldon, Oxford OX44 9LL Tel: 01865 343356 Fax: 01865 343480 Email: pdb@ermine.ox.ar.uk — MB BCh BAO 1978 NUI; MB BCh BAO (Hons.) NUI 1978; FRCGP 1998; DFFP 1998; MA Oxf. 1993; MRCGP 1983; MRCPI 1982; Dobst RCPI 1981. (Univ. Coll. Dub.) GP Princip.; Tutor Princip. Med. Care Oxf. Univ.; Examr. Roy. Coll. Gen. Pract. Socs: ICGP; GP Writers Assn.; Assn. Univ. Depts. Gen. Pract. Prev: Sen. Lect. (Primary Med. Care) Univ. Soton.; SHO (Paediat.) Our Lady's Hosp. Dub.; SHO (Med.) Internat. Miss. Train. Hosp. Drogheda.

BURKE, Peter Leeson Greenacret., Howey Lane, Frodsham, Warrington WA6 6DL Tel: 01244 652031 Fax: 01244 652039 — MB ChB 1967 Liverp. (Liverp.)

BURKE, Ruth Alison 62 St Peters Road, Earley, Reading RG6 1PH — MB ChB 1988 Birm. GP Asst. Reading.

BURKE, Samantha Alison 13 Forge End, St Albans AL2 3EQ — MB ChB 1994 Bristol.

BURKE, Mr Samuel (retired) 21 The Fountains, 229 Ballards Lane, Finchley, London N3 1NL Tel: 020 8346 1406 — MRCS Eng. LRCP Lond. 1931; MB BS Lond. 1932; MD (Obst. & Gyn.) Lond. 1953; FRCS Ed. 1948; MRCOG 1953, DObst 1946. Prev: Regist. (O & G) Postgrad Med. Sch. Lond.

BURKE, Sean Christopher 8 Louie's Lane, Diss IP22 4LR — MB ChB 1993 Manch. SHO (Med.) Manch. Roy. Infirm. Prev: SHO (Med.) Burnley Gen. Hosp.; Ho. Off. Roy. Preston Hosp.

BURKE, Sharon Julia Oldchurch Hospital, Waterloo Road, Romford RM7 0BE Tel: 01708 708443; 9 Great Stony Park, High St, Ongar CM5 0TH — MB BS 1987 Lond.; FRCA 1993. Cons. (Anaesth.) OldCh. Hosp. Romford Essex. Socs: Assn. Anaesth. Prev: Clin. Fell. (Neuroanaesth.) The Toronto Hosp., Canada; Sen. Regist. (Anaesth.) St. Geo.s Hosp. Lond.; Regist. (Anaesth.) St. Geo. Hosp. & Qu. Mary's Univ. Hosp. Lond.

BURKE, Spencer Paul Bank House, Sheepway, Portbury, Bristol BS20 7TE — MB ChB 1987 Cape Town.

BURKE, Stephen John 39 Greenhill Road, Moseley, Birmingham B13 9SS Email: sburke@crystals.demon.co.uk — MB BCh BAO 1986 NUI; MRCP (UK) 1994. (UCD) Regist. Rotat. (Radiol.) W. Midl.

BURKE, Susan Lesley Bewsey Street Medical Centre, 40-42 Bewsey Street, Warrington WA2 7JE Tel: 01925 635837 Fax: 01925 630353; 305 London Road, Appleton, Warrington WA4 5JB — MB ChB 1982 Leic.; MRCGP 1988; DRCOG 1986.

BURKE, Ursula Bernadette 9 Hodder Road, Everton, Liverpool L5 0PZ — MB ChB 1986 Liverp.

BURKE, Walter Health Centre, Honiton Way, Penketh, Warrington WA5 2EY Tel: 0192 572 5644/7 Fax: 0192 572 791097 — MB BCh BAO 1954 NUI; MRCGP 1968. Socs: BMA. Prev: SHO (ENT) Hull Roy. Infirm; Ho. Phys. & Ho. Surg. Centr. Hosp. Galway.

BURKE, Winifred Marie Majella Crahamel House, 1-3 Duhamel Place, St Helier, Jersey JE2 4TP Tel: 01534 735742 Fax: 01534 735011 — MB BCh BAO 1986 NUI.

BURKE, Yvonne Louise 73 Kenilworth Road, Sale M33 5DA — MB ChB 1996 Bristol.

BURKE-WILLIAMS, Alice Irene (retired) Brentwood, Marylebone, Wigan WN1 2NT Tel: 01942 245539 — MB ChB 1943 Manch.; DPH Manch. 1947.

BURKETT, Janis Ann, Surg. Lt.-Cdr. RN Retd. HMP Winchester, Romsey Road, Winchester; St. Mary's Hospital, Ella Gordon Unit, Milton Road, Portsmouth PO3 6 — MB BCh BAO 1978 Belf.; MRCGP 1985; Cert. Family Plann. JCC 1983; DRCOG 1983. Med. Off. HMP Winchester; Clin. Asst. St. Mary's Hosp. Portsmouth. Prev: GP Fareham; Maj. RAMC; Surg. Lt.-Cdr RN.

BURKETT, Jennifer Dorothy East Gloucestershire NHS Trust, Child Health Services, County Offices, St.George's Road, Cheltenham GL50 3EW Tel: 01242 516235 Fax: 01242 234527; 22 Roman Way, Lechlade GL7 3BP Tel: 01367 252501 — MB BS Durh. 1960. (Newc. u. Tyne) Clin. Med. Off. E. Glos. NHS Trust. Socs: Brit. Paediat. Assn. Prev: Regist. (Psychiat.) St. Mary's Hosp. Stannington & St. Wulstans Hosp. Malvern; SHO (Path.) Cheltenham Gen. Hosp.

BURKHARDT, Albert (retired) 90 Ewell Park Way, Ewell, Epsom KT17 2NW Tel: 020 8393 6183 — MB BS 1932 Lond.; MRCS Eng. LRCP Lond. 1930. Prev: Clin. Asst. (Anaesth.) Epsom Gp. Hosps.

BURKHARDT, Antony John (retired) Salwood, Combe Wood Lane, Combe St Nicholas, Chard TA20 3NH Tel: 01460 65250 Email: burkhardanthony@ukf.net — MB ChB Manch. 1956; MRCGP 1969. Prev: GP Surrey.

BURKHARDT, Kurt Ivor The Parc Canol Group Practice, Parc Canol Surgery, Central Park, Church Village, Pontypridd CF38 1RJ Tel: 01443 203414 Fax: 01443 218218 — MB BCh 1984 Wales; Dip. Med. Tox. Wales 1999; MB BCh Wales l984; DPD 1999; MRCGP 1996; Dip. Ther. Wales 1995; DRCOG 1990. (Welsh Nat. Sch. Med.) Clin. Governance Lead for Rhondda, Cynon, Taff LHG. Socs: Rhondda Med. Soc.; BMA.

BURKILL, Andrew David Priory View Medical Centre, 2a Green Lane, Leeds LS12 1HU Tel: 0113 295 4260 Fax: 0113 295 4278; 42 Wentworth Avenue, Alwoodley, Leeds LS17 7TN — MB ChB 1986 Leeds.

BURKILL, Guy John Charles Department of Radiology, Chelsea & Westminster Hospital, 369 Fulham Road, London SW10 9NH Tel: 020 8746 8000; 87 Sugden Road, Battersea, London SW11 5ED Tel: 020 7228 2521 — MB BS Lond. 1993; BSc Lond. 1990; MRCP (UK) 1996. (Char. Cross & Westm. Med. Sch. Lond.) Specialist Regist. (Radiol.) Chelsea & W.m. Hosp. Lond. Prev: SHO Rotat. (Med.) Guy's Hosp. Lond.

BURKINSHAW, John Hugh (retired) Blue Seas, Porthcothan, Padstow PL28 8LR Tel: 01841 520191 — MB BChir 1939 Camb.; FRCP Lond. 1969, M 1947; MRCS Eng. LRCP Lond. 1937. Prev: Cons. Paediatr. St. Jas. Hosp. Lond. & Mayday Hosp. Croydon.

BURKINSHAW, Paul Raymond Standish Medical Practice, Rodenhurst, Church Street, Standish, Wigan WN6 0JP Tel: 01257 421909 Fax: 01257 424259; 120B Mossy Lea Road, Wrightington, Wigan WN6 9RD Tel: 01257 425330 — MB ChB 1983 Manch.; BSc Manch. 1980, MB ChB 1983; DRCOG 1986. (Manchester) Prev: Trainee GP W. Lancs. VTS; Ho. Surg. Hope Hosp. Salford; Ho. Off. (Med.) N. Manch. Gen. & Monsall Hosps.

BURKITT, Mr David Selwyn Tel: 0121 424 5558 Fax: 0121 706 1788 Email: dburkitt@aol.com; 28 St. Francis Avenue, Olton, Solihull B91 1EB Tel: 0121 706 1622 Fax: 0121 706 1788 — MB ChB 1977 Manch.; ChM Manch. 1989; FRCS Ed. 1983; T(S) 1993. Cons. Gen. Surg. Solihull & Heartlands Hosp. Birm. Prev: Sen. Regist. W. Midl.

BURKITT, Eric Aylmer (retired) Garden Flat, 5a Shaftesbury Avenue, Leeds LS8 1DR Tel: 0113 268 9641 — MRCS Eng. LRCP Lond. 1943; FRCPsych 1975, M 1971; DPM Eng. 1949. Prev: Sen. Cons. Psychiat. Darlington Memor. Hosp.

BURKITT, Mr Robert Townsend West Dippingwell, Farnham Common, Slough SL2 3PU Tel: 01753 643818 — BA (Sen. Mod.) Dub. 1934, MD 1945, MB BCh BAO; FRCS Eng. 1950; FRCSI 1946. (T.C. Dub.) Prev: Emerit. Cons. Surg. Ashford Hosp. Middlx.; Consg. Surg. Ashford Hosp. Middlx. & Hounslow Hosp.

BURKS, Christopher George 20 Granville Avenue, Boston PE21 7BY — MRCS Eng. LRCP Lond. 1964; DA Eng. 1967; DObst RCOG 1966. (Liverp.) Prev: Ho. Surg. & Ho. Phys., & Ho. Surg. (Obst.) Ipswich & E. Suff. Hosp.

BURLAND, John Geoffrey Hazlitt Pipers Corner, Old School Lane, Ryarsh, Maidstone — MB ChB 1973 Ed.

BURLEIGH, Alfred Ian (retired) 14 Barriedale Avenue, Hamilton ML3 9DB Tel: 01698421834 — BSc Glas. 1947, MB ChB 1952. Prev: Ho. Surg. S.. Gen. Hosp. Glas.

BURLEIGH, Alistair Rory Sutherland Horden Group Practice, The Surgery, Sunderland Road, Horden, Peterlee SR8 4QP Tel: 0191 586 4210 Fax: 0191 587 0700; 7 Lorimers Close, Peterlee SR8 2NH — MB ChB 1977 Manch.; MRCGP 1982.

BURLEIGH, Elizabeth Anne 36 Stamerland Avenue, Clarkston, Glasgow G76 8EZ Tel: 0141 644 1474 — MB ChB 1995 Glas. SHO (Geriat. Med.) Vict. Geriat. Unit, Vict. Infirm. NHS Trust Glas. Prev: Ho. Off. (Surg.) Roy. Alexandra Hosp. Paisley; Ho. Off. (Med.) Dumfries & Galloway Roy. Infirm.

BURLEIN, George Gosport Health Centre, Bury Rd, Gosport PO12 3PN Tel: 02392 583302; Moby House, 162 Priory Rd, Gosport PO12 4LQ Tel: 02392 524299 — 1987 3rd Hete Exam, W. Berlin; FRCS 1994. (Freie Universitaet W. Berlin) G.P.; Gen. Practitioner. Socs: Fell. Roy. Coll. of Surg.s, Edin.

BURLEY, David 27 Applehouse Terrace, Luddenfoot, Halifax HX2 6PU — MB ChB 1989 Leeds.

BURLEY, Delia Margaret Hambledon, 25 Burkes Road, Beaconsfield HP9 1PB — BM BCh 1973 Oxf.; MA Oxf. 1970, BM BCh 1973; DObst RCOG 1976. (Oxf. & King's Coll. Hosp.) Clin. Asst. Diabetic Retinopathy Screening Clin. Wycombe; Gen. Hosp. Prev: SHO (Psychiat.) & SHO (Paediat.) Univ. Coll. Hosp. Lond.; Trainee Gen. Pract. Lond. (Univ. Coll. Hosp.) Vocational Train.; Scheme.

BURLEY, Elizabeth Ruth 56 Barkers Lane, Sale M33 6SD — MB ChB 1994 Manch. (Bristol & Manch.) Trainee GP Stock VTS. Socs: BMA; MDU.

BURLEY, Jeremy Arthur 10 Knockroon Lane, Auchinleck, Cumnock KA18 2AJ — MB ChB 1986 Glas.

BURLEY, Lindsay Elizabeth Borders Health, Newstead, Melrose TD6 9DB Tel: 01896 825515 — MB ChB 1973 Ed.; FRCP Ed. 1985; MRCP (UK) 1976; FRCGP 1995, M 1977. Gen. Manager Borders Health; Hon. Sen. Lect. (Pub. Health Sci.) Edin. Univ. Prev: Dir. Plann. & Developm. Lothian HB; Unit Gen. Manager Lothian HB; Cons. Phys. E. Lothian.

BURLEY, Neil Michael James The Caludon Centre, Clifford Bridge Road, Walsgrave, Coventry CV2 2TE — MB ChB 1995 Leics.

BURLEY, Robert Matthew William 56 Barkers Lane, Sale M33 6SD — MB ChB 1994 Manch.; BSc (Hons.) St And. 1991. (St. And. Manch.) Basic Surgic. Trainee Bolton Hosps. NHS Trust. Socs: BMA; Med. & Dent. Defence Union Scotl.

BURLEY, Terence Kenneth Minster Medical Practice, 87-89 Princes Street, Peterborough PE1 2QP Tel: 01733 554478 Fax: 01733 556230; Airlie House, 1 Harewood Gardens, Longthorpe, Peterborough PE3 9NF Tel: 01733 264617 Fax: 01733 556230 — MB BS 1973 Lond. (St. Bart. Hosp.) Princip. Police Surg. Cambs. Constab.; Dep. Chief Med. Off., Pearl Assur. UK. Socs: BMA; Fell.of Roy. Soc. of Med. Prev: Squadron Ldr. (Surg.) RAF Hosp. Ely; Clin. Asst. (Colonoscopy) Edith Cavell Hosp. P'boro.; Med. Off. Perkins P'boro.

BURLING, Marian Barbara 40 Dunmore Road, London SW20 8TN Tel: 020 8879 1851; Email: s.finney@ic.ac.uk — MB BS 1978 Lond.; Dip Occ Med 2001; BSc Lond. 1975; MRCGP 1982; DRCOG 1982. (Roy. Free & Lond. Hosp.) Occupat.al Health Phys., Lond. Boro. of Hammersmith & Fulham. Socs: S.O.M. Prev: Med. Off. Marks & Spencer Plc; GP Lond.

BURLING, Philip Martin Ashlea, 1 Stanley Grove, Urmston, Manchester M41 9BR — MB ChB 1986 Manch.; Cert. Family Plann. JCC 1991.

BURLING, Sarah Anne 66A Parkhill Road, London NW3 2YT — MB BS 1997 Lond.

BURLING, Simon John Broad Oaks, Forest Glade, Epping CM16 6LD — MB BS 1990 Lond.

BURLINGHAM, Anthony Norton Norway House, Far End Lane, Sheepscombe, Stroud GL6 7RL — MB BS 1972 Lond.; FFA RCS Eng. 1980. (St. Thos.) Cons. (Anaesth.) Gloucester & Cheltenham Dist. Socs: Intens. Care Soc.; S. W.ern Soc. Anaesth. Prev: Sen.

Regist. (Anaesth.) Bristol Health Dist. (T); SHO (Anaesth.) St. Thos. Hosp. Lond.; Med. Off. (Anaesth.) Norway Ho. Hosp., Canada.

BURLINSON, Anthony Alfred Balance Street Practice, 36 Balance Street, Uttoxeter ST14 8JG Tel: 01889 562145 Fax: 01889 568164; Airdrie, Oldfields Road, Uttoxeter ST14 8DE Tel: 01889 562810 — MB BS 1980 Lond.; DRCOG 1984.

BURLINSON, Roderick Allan Flat 1, Ashton House, 58 Chilbolton Avenue, Winchester SO22 5HQ Tel: 01962 855535; c/o 4 Fairhaven, Main Road, Windermere LA23 1DX Tel: 01539 445950 — MRCS Eng. LRCP Lond. 1973.

BURLS, Amanda Jane Evaline Fdepartment of Public Health and Epidemiology, University of Birmingham, Edgebaston, Birmingham Tel: 0121 414 2582 Fax: 0121 414 7878 — MB BS 1990 Lond.; BA Oxf. 1978; MSc (Neurosci.) Lond. 1987, MB BS 1990; MSc (Public Health) London 1994. Sen. Clin. Lect. in Pub. health & epidmiology/ Honourary Cons. in Pub. Health Med. Socs: MFPHM; RSM.

BURLTON, David Aylmer Eagle House Surgery, Eagle House, White Cliff Mill Street, Blandford Forum DT11 7DQ Tel: 01258 453171 — MB BS 1973 Lond.; MRCS Eng. LRCP Lond. 1973; DRCOG 1978; Cert JCC Lond. 1977. (St. Bart.) GP Blandford Forum. Prev: Trainee Gen. Pract. Torbay Vocational Train. Scheme; Ho. Surg. Luton & Dunstable Hosp.; SHO (O & G) Poole Gen. Hosp.

BURMA WILSON, Olga Tel: 01484 343000 — MB ChB 1973 Leeds; MRCPsych 1979; DObst RCOG 1975. Cons. Psychiat. for Elderly St. Lukes Hosp. Huddersfield.

BURMAN, Ajit High Street Surgery, High Street, Astley Tyldesley, Manchester M29 8AL Tel: 01942 882950 Fax: 01942 886611 — MB BS 1971 Patna. (P. of Wales Med. Coll.)

BURMAN, Anthony Mark Flat 3, Burdett Mews, 1 Belsize Crescent, London NW3 5QX — MB BS 1998 Lond.; MB BS Lond 1998.

BURMAN, Anthony Stuart 22 Becksbourne Close, Maidstone ME14 2ED Tel: 01622 751322 Email: s.burman@btinternet.com — MB BS 1966 Lond.; MRCPsych 1972; DPM Eng. 1970; MSc Kent 1999. (Westm.) Cons. Psychiat. (Private Pract.). Prev: Hon. Cons. (Pyschiat.) Guy's Hosp. Lond.; Lect. (Physiol.) Guy's Hosp. Med. Sch. Lond.; Hon. Sen. Regist. & Research Fell. Acad. Dept. Psychol. Med. St. Bart. Hosp. Lond.

BURMAN, David (retired) 2 Chew Court Farm, Chew Magna, Bristol BS40 8SF Tel: 01275 332683 Fax: 01275 332683 Email: dburman@hemscott.net — BSc (Hons.) Lond. 1947, MD 1960, MB BS (Hons.) 1950; FRCP Lond. 1973, M 1956; MRCS Eng. LRCP Lond. 1950; DCH Eng. 1956; FRCPCH 1997. Prev: Cons. Paediat. United Bristol Hosps. & S. W.. RHB.

BURMAN, John Frank Royal Brompton Hospital, Sydney St., London SW3 6NP Tel: 020 7351 8400 Fax: 020 7351 8402 Email: j.burman@rbh.nthames.nhs.uk — MB BS Lond. 1970; MD Lond. 1982; FRCP Lond. 1994; MRCP (UK) 1973; MRCS Eng. LRCP Lond. 1970; FRCPath 1992, M 1982. Cons. Haemat. Roy. Brompton Hosp. Lond. Socs: Brit. Soc. Haematol.; ISTH; BSHT. Prev: Cons. Haemat. St. Bart. & Homerton Hosps. Lond.

BURMAN, Mr John Hesketh (retired) Kingfishers, Aqueduct Lane, Alvechurch, Birmingham B48 7BP Tel: 0121 445 1679 Fax: 0121 445 1679 Email: j.burman@virgin.net — MB ChB 1963 Birm.; FRCS Eng. 1970; FRCS Ed. 1967. Prev: Cons. Surg. BromsGr. & Redditch Dist. Hosps.

BURMAN, Lee The Old Vicarage, Spilsby Road, Horncastle LN9 6AL Tel: 01507 522477 Fax: 01507 522997; 39 Spilsby Road, Horncastle LN9 6AW Tel: 01507 525189 — BM BS 1993 Nottm.; BMedSci Nottm. 1991, BM BS 1993; DFFP 1998. (Nott.) Princip. in Gen. Pract. Horncastle Med. GP. Prev: Gen. Pract. Regist. Ch. Cl. Surg., Boston; Gen. Pract. Regist. Stickney Surg., Boston.

BURMAN, Rachel Elizabeth Mary 25 Chesterfield Road, Newbury RG14 7QB — MB BS 1988 Lond.

BURMAN, Richard Harold The Cassel Hospital, 1 Ham Common, Richmond TW10 7JF Tel: 020 8940 8181 Fax: 020 8940 2996; 9 Evelyn Road, Kew, Richmond TW9 2TF Tel: 020 8940 4600 — MB ChB 1960 Cape Town; MRCPsych 1971; DPM Cape Town 1967. Assoc. Specialist Riverside Ment. Health Trust NW Thames; Psychother. Cassel Hosp. Lond. Socs: Assoc. Mem. Brit. Assn. Psychother.; Assn. Psychoanalyt. Psychother. NHS. Prev: Specialist (Psychiat.) Groote Schuur Hosp. Univ. Cape Town.

BURMAN-ROY, Bijoy Gopal Quarry Street Surgery, 24 Quarry Street, Johnstone PA5 8ED Tel: 01505 321733 Fax: 01505 322181 — MB BS 1960 Calcutta; FRCGP 1993, M 1972. (R.G. Kar Med. Coll.) Prev: Regist. (Med.) Paisley Infec. Dis. Hosp. & W.. Infirm. Glas.; Asst. Chest Phys. Dunbartonsh. Area.

BURMAN ROY, Sheulee Anne Solent Road Practice, 9 Solent Road, London NW6 1TP Tel: 020 7530 2592 Fax: 020 7530 2591 — MB ChB 1988 Glas.; MRCGP 1995. GP The Solent Rd. Pract.

BURMANROY, Sumita 13 Ravensfield, Englefield Green, Egham TW20 0TW Tel: 01784 471421 — MB BS 1976 Ranchi; DCH RCP Lond. 1989.

BURMESTER, Hugh Basil Cyril 6 Eden Close, Wilmslow SK9 6BG Tel: 01625 529812 — MB 1962 Athens; LAH Dub. 1964; FRCPath 1982, M 1971. (Athens) Cons. Haemat. Wythenshawe Hosp. Manch. Socs: Brit. Soc. Haemat.

BURMESTER, Margarita Katharine Great Ormond Street Hospital for Children, Great Ormond Street, London WC1N 3JH — MB BS 1989 Lond.; MRCP (UK) 1994. (St Thomas's Hospital Medical School) Cons. Paediatric Intensivist, Gt. Ormond St. Hosp. Lond.

BURN, Ann Jane White House, The Frenches, Romsey SO51 6FE Tel: 01794 512164 — MB BS Lond. 1963; MRCS Eng. LRCP Lond. 1963. (Westm.) Prev: Ho. Phys. W. Middlx. Hosp. Isleworth; Ho. Surg. Qu. Mary's Hosp. Roehampton.

BURN, Audrey Julia (retired) 4 Clarence Crescent, Windsor SL4 5DT — MB BS Lond. 1956; MRCS Eng. LRCP Lond. 1956; DA Eng. 1958. Prev: GP Windsor.

BURN, David John Regional Neurosciences Centre, Newcastle General Hospital, Newcastle upon Tyne NE4 6BE Tel: 0191 273 8811 Fax: 0191 272 4823 Email: djburn@ncl.ac.uk — MB BS 1985 Newc.; MA Oxf. 1987; MD Newc. 1994; MRCP (UK) 1988; FRCP (UK) 1998. (Newcastle Upon Tyne) Cons. & Sen. Lect. (Neurol.) Roy. Vict. Infirm. Newc. u. Tyne. Prev: Sen. Regist. (Neurol.) Roy. Vict. Infirm. & Gen. Hosp. Newc.; Regist. (Neurol.) Hammersmith Hosp. Lond.; SHO (Neurol.) Nat. Hosp. Nerv. Dis. Qu. Sq. Lond.

BURN, George Parkinson (retired) 9 Skelda Rise, Ilkley LS29 9JE — BM BCh 1950 Oxf.; MA Oxf. 1953, BM BCh 1950. Prev: Lect. Dept. Clin. Biochem. Oxf. Univ.

BURN, Professor John Northern Genetics Service, 19 Claremont Place, Newcastle upon Tyne NE2 4AA Tel: 0191 222 7386 Fax: 0191 222 7143 Email: john.burn@ncl.ac.uk; 18 Sanderson Road, Jesmond, Newcastle upon Tyne NE2 2DS Tel: 01910281 2987 — MB BS 1976 Newc.; MD (Distinc.) Newc. 1991, MB BS 1976, BMedSc (Hons.) 1973; FRCP Lond. 1989; MRCP (UK) 1979; FRCPCH 1997. (Newc.) Prof. Clin. Genetics Univ. Newc. u. Tyne; Dir. N.. Genetics Serv.; Hon. Cons. Clin. Geneticist. Socs: Brit. Soc. Human Genetics; Bd. mem. Europ. Soc. of Human Genetics; Brit. Paediat. Assn. Prev: Cons. Clin. Geneticist Roy. Vict. Infirm. Newc.; Hon. Sen. Regist. (Clin. Genetics) Hosp. Sick Childr. Gt. Ormond St.; SHO Rotat. (Med.) & Regist. Rotat. (Paediat.) Roy. Vict. Infirm. Newc.

BURN, John Callander, MBE (retired) Brampton Medical Practice, The Surgery, Brampton CA8 1NL Tel: 0169 772551 — MB ChB Ed. 1959; DObst RCOG 1961. Mem. Cumbria LMC; Vice Chairm. Eden Valley Commiss.ing Gp. Prev: Non-Exec. Mem. E. Cumbria HA.

BURN, Mr John Ian Byworth Bend, Byworth, Petworth GU28 0HN Tel: 01798 343010 — BA (Man. Univ.) 2001; MB BS Lond. 1950; FRCS Eng. 1956. (St. Bart.) Emerit. Cons. Surg. King Edwd. VII Hosp. Midhurst; Hon. Cons. Surg. Char. Cross Hosp. Fulham. Socs: Fell. Assn. Surgs.; Fell. (Ex Vice-Pres.) Roy. Soc. Med.; Hon. Mem. Finnish Surg. Soc. Prev: Med. Dir. & Cons. Surg. King Edwd. VII Hosp. Midhurst; Cons. Surg. Hammersmith Hosp. & Asst. Dir. Surg. Studies Roy. Postgrad. Med. Sch.; Pres. Brit. Assn. Surgic. Oncol. Europ. Soc. Surg. Oncol. & World Federat. Surg. Oncol. Soc.

BURN, John Lancelot The Child Health Directorate, Royal Bolton Hospital, Minerva Road, Fanworth BL4 0JR Tel: 01204 390537, 0208 894 3742 Fax: 01204 390657, 0208 894 3768; The Paddock, Dunscar Fold, Egerton, Bolton BL7 9EH Tel: 01204 301999 Fax: 01204 301999 Email: burn@thepaddock/freeserve.co.uk — MB ChB 1963 Manch.; FRCP Lond. 1980, M 1968; FRCPCH 1997; DCCH RCP Ed. 1986; DCH RCPS Glas. 1965. (Manch.) Cons. Paediat. Bolton Hosp. NHS Trust; Sch. Med. Off., Manch. Grammar Sch. Socs: Bolton and Dist. Med. Soc.; Manch. Med. Soc. Hon. Treas.; Manch. & Dist. Medico Legal

Soc. Prev: Res. Med. Off. Childr. Hosp. Birm.; Lect. (Paediat. & Child Health) Univ. Manch.; Ho. Phys. & Ho. Surg. Manch. Roy. Infirm.

BURN, John Philip Southerden Poole Hospital, Longfleet Road, Poole BH15 2JB Tel: 01202 448070 — BM 1980 Oxf.; BA Camb. 1977; DM Oxf. 1993; MRCP (UK) 1983; FRCP Lond. 1998. Cons. (Rehabil. & Brain Injury) Poole Hosp. NHS Trust. Socs: Brit. Soc. Rehabil. Med.; Soc. Research in Rehabil. Prev: Sen. Regist. (Rehabil. Med.) Wessex RHA; Regist. (Health c/o Elderly) Nottm.; Research Regist. Univ. Dept. Clin. Neurol. Oxf.

BURN, Katherine Elizabeth Preston New Road Surgery, 293-295 Preston New Road, Blackburn BB2 6PL Tel: 01254 687672 Fax: 01254 696928 Email: katherine.burns@gp-p81214.nhs.uk — MB BS 1987 Lond.; BA (Hons.) Oxf. 1984; MRCGP 1993; DCH RCP Lond. 1991; DRCOG 1990. (Oxf. & The Lond. Hosp.) Coronary Heart Dis. Lead for Blackburn with Darwen Primary Care Trust. Prev: Trainee GP Lewisham & W. S.wark HA; Partnership with Belshaw & Gebbie.

BURN, Loic Fairhill Medical Practice, 81 Kingston Hill, Kingston upon Thames KT2 7PX Tel: 020 8 546 1771 Fax: 020 8 547 0075 — MRCS Eng. LRCP 1961 Lond.; BA Oxf. 1957; MRCS Eng. LRCP & Lond. 1961; DPhysMed Eng. 1972. Med. Off. Kingston Polytechnic. Socs: Ex-Pres. Brit. Assn. Manip. Med.; Pres. Internat. Federat. Manual Med.; Counc. Brit. League Against Rheum.

BURN, Mary Catherine Mill Lane House, Heugh, Stamfordham, Newcastle upon Tyne NE18 0NH — MB ChB 1965 Manch.; FFA RCS Eng. 1970. (Manch.) Cons. Anaesth. Freeman Rd. Hosp. Newc. u Tyne. Prev: Sen. Regist. Newc. RHB; Regist. United Newc. Hosps.

BURN, Matthew John Lambton 3 Derwent House, Elm Bank Estate, Wellhouse Lane, Barnet EN5 3DJ — MB BS 1996 Lond.

BURN, Patience Catherine (retired) 9 Skelda Rise, Ilkley LS29 9JE — MB BS 1946 Lond.; DCH Eng. 1949. Prev: Sen. Med. Off. (Community Med.) Oxf. AHA (T).

BURN, Paul Richard White House, The Frenches, East Wellow, Romsey SO51 6FE Tel: 01794 512164 — MB BChir 1989 Camb.; MA Cantab. 1991, MB BChir 1989; MRCP (UK) 1992; DA (UK) 1994; FRCR (UK) 1997. Regist. (Radiol.) Chelsea & W.m. Hosp. Lond.

BURN, Peter William Woodbridge Road Surgery, 165-167 Woodbridge Road, Ipswich IP4 2PE Tel: 01473 256251; The School House, Tuddenham, Ipswich IP6 9BT Tel: 01373 785622 — MB BS 1985 Lond.; MRCGP 1991; DCH RCP Lond. 1988. Socs: BMA.

BURN, Mr Robert Richard (retired) 116 Mount Cameron Drive S., St Leonards, East Kilbride, Glasgow G74 2LN — MB BS 1943 Lond.; FRCS Eng. 1950; MRCS Eng. LRCP Lond. 1943. Prev: Cons. Thoracic Surg. Hairmyres Hosp. E. Kilbride, Brook Gen. Hosp. Woolwich & Preston Hall Hosp.

BURN, Rowland Jameson (retired) White Medical Group, Health Centre, Ponteland, Newcastle upon Tyne NE16 4PD Tel: 01661 822222 — MB ChB 1965 Manch.; BSc (Hons. Chem.) Newc. 1971; MRCGP 1977.

BURN, Sasha Clare Frenchay Hospital, Bristol BS16 1 Tel: 0117 970 1212; 15 Westminster Court, Frogmore, London SW18 1HH — MB ChB 1996 Bristol; MRCS 1998. (Bristol) SHO (A & E) Roy. Lond. & Homerton Hosps. Prev: Demonst. (Anat.) Univ. of Bristol; Ho. Off. (Surg.) Frenchay Hosp.; Med. Ho. Off. S.mead Hosp.

BURN, Steven Dept. of Cardiology, Derbyshire Royal Infirmary, London Road, Derby DE1 2QY Tel: 01332 347141 — MB ChB 1986 Liverp.; MD 2000; MRCP (UK) 1990. (Univ. Liverp.) Cons. Cardiol., Derbysh. Roy. Infirm. Socs: Brit. Cardiac. Soc.; Brit. Soc. Echocardiogr.; Brit. Nuclear Cardiol. Soc. Prev: Regist. (Cardiol.) Hull Roy. Infirm.; Research Fell. (Cardiol.) Hull Roy. Infirm.; Regist. (Cardiothoracic Med.) Hope Hosp. Manch.

BURN, Wendy Katherine Newsam Centre, Seacroft Hospital, York Road, Leeds LS14 6UH Tel: 0113 206 2006 Fax: 0113 206 2007 — BM 1982 Soton.; MRCPsych 1987. Cons. Psychiat. for Elderly Leeds Community & Ment. Health Unit. Prev: Sen. Regist. (Psychiat.) Yorks. RHA.

BURNA ASEFI, Mohammad Sadiq 52 Haslemere Avenue, London W13 9UL — MD 1960 Kabul, Afghanistan.

BURNAND, Professor Kevin Guiver Department of Surgery, St Thomas' Hospital, Lambeth Palace Road, London SE1 7EH Tel: 020 7928 9292 Fax: 020 7928 8742 Email: k.burnand@umds.ac.uk; 10 Colinbrook Street, London SE1 6EZ Tel: 020 7401 3560 — MB BS Lond. 1967; MS Lond. 1980; FRCS Eng. 1972. (St. Thos.) Prof. Vasc. Surg. UMDS St. Thos. Hosp. Lond.; Hunt. Prof. RCS Eng.; Edr. Cardiovasc. Surg. Socs: Vasc. Surg. Soc. GB & Irel.; Soc. Vasc. Surgs. (USA); Surgic. Research Soc. Prev: Reader (Asst. Dir.) Dept. Surg. St. Thos. Hosp. Lond.; Sen. Regist. St. Thos. Hosp. Lond.

BURNAND, Norman John (retired) 1 Montpelier Court, Montpelier Road, London W5 2QN Tel: 020 8997 8418 — MRCS Eng. LRCP Lond. 1937. Squadron Ldr. RAFVR. Prev: Ho. Surg., Ho. Phys. & Res. Obstetr. Guy's Hosp.

BURNDRED, Ernest Featherstone (retired) Grove House, Ventnor PO38 1TH Tel: 01983 853818 — MB ChB 1940 Manch.

BURNE, Brian Henry, OStJ Amersham Health Centre, Chiltern Avenue, Amersham HP6 5AJ Tel: 01494 722111; Eden House, Clifton Lawns, Chesham Bois, Amersham HP6 5PT Tel: 01494 726721 Fax: 01494 572249 — MRCS Eng. LRCP Lond. 1950; MFCM RCP 1974; T(M) (Paed) 1991; DCH RCP Lond. 1990; DPH Eng. 1956. (St. Geo.) Comm. Phys. & Dist. Sen. Med. Off. Wycombe HA; Med. Cons. Chiltern Hundreds Housing Assn. plc; Med. Off. (Environm. Health) Chiltern DC; Founder, Hon. Treas. & Tutor Trustee Assn. Research Inf. & Child Developm; Pres. Soc. Pub. Health. Socs: BMA (Regional Represen. (Oxon.) Centr. Comm. Community Med.). Prev: Squadron Ldr. RAF Med. Br.; Ho. Surg. St. Geo. Hosp. Lond. & Gr. Hosp. Tooting & Vict. Hosp. Childr.; MoH Chiltern Div. Bucks CC.

BURNE, John Christopher 11 Christchurch Road, Dartford DA1 3DH Tel: 01322 26024 — MB BChir 1949 Camb.; MA, MD Camb. 1954, MB BChir 1949; MRCS Eng. LRCP Lond. 1943; FRCPath 1967, M 1963. (Westm.) Hon. Archiv. Joyce Green Hosp. Dartford. Prev: Cons. Pathol. Dartford Gp. Hosps.; Lect. (Path.) Univ. Manch.; Capt. RAMC.

BURNE, Julia Mary 20 Field Road, Thorne, Doncaster DN8 4AF — MB BS 1977 Ncle; MB BS 1977 Ncle.

BURNE, Sambrooke Roger St Bartholomew's Medical Centre, Manzil Way, Cowley Road, Cowley, Oxford OX4 1XB Tel: 01865 242334 Fax: 01865 204018 — MB BS 1970 Lond.; MRCGP 1974; DObst RCOG 1972. (Westm.) Med. Dir. Helen Ho. Hospice for Childr. Oxf.

BURNEL, Adam James 11 Strathearn Place, Edinburgh EH9 2AL — MB ChB 1990 Glas.

BURNELL, Fodla Brigid Kildare (retired) Hill Farm, Downham, Wymondham NR18 0SD — MB BCh BAO 1952 Dub.; MA Dub. 1952; DA Eng. 1954.

BURNELL, Hubert Cedric (retired) 130 Streetly Lane, Streetly, Sutton Coldfield B74 4TD Tel: 0121 353 7198 — MB ChB Birm. 1941; MRCS Eng. LRCP Lond. 1941; DObst RCOG 1947. Prev: Gen. Practitioner.

BURNELL, Simon Hugh 167 London Road, Holyhead LL65 2RA — MB BCh 1996 Wales.

BURNELL-NUGENT, Henrietta Mary Sheepham Mill, Modbury, Ivybridge PL21 0LX — MB 1977 Camb.; BChir 1976.

BURNESS, John Henry 5 Montague Road, Saltford, Bristol BS31 3LA Tel: 01225 872864 — MB ChB 1974 Aberd.; MRCP (UK) 1976; MRCGP 1991; DRCOG 1978. Med. Off. i/c Chavuma Mission Hosp. Prev: Med. Regist. Aberd. Teach. Hosps.

BURNET, Jill c/o Captain Burnet, RHQ, 21 Engineer Regiment BFPO 48 — MB BS 1987 Newc.; BSc (1st. cl. Hons.) Sheff. 1982. SHO (O & G) Qu. Mary Hosp. Roehampton. Prev: SHO (c/o Elderly/A & E) W. Middlx. Univ. Hosp.; SHO Rotat. (Med.) Roy. Free Hosp.

BURNET, Neil Gunn Department of Oncology, Addenbrooke's Hospital, Hills Road, Cambridge CB2 2QQ Tel: 01223 586705 Fax: 01223 217094 — MB BChir 1980 Camb.; MA Camb. 1981, MD 1993; FRCS Eng. 1985; FRCR 1990. (Cambridge and Westminster Medical School) Univ. Lect. & Hon. Cons. Oncol. Addenbrooke's Hosp. Camb. Prev: Cons. Clin. Oncol. Velindre Hosp. Cardiff; Sen. Regist. (Clin. Oncol.) Middlx. & Mt. Vernon Hosps. Lond.; Clin. Research Fell. & Hon. Sen. Regist. Inst. Cancer Research & Roy. Marsden Hosp.

BURNETT, Professor Alan Kenneth Department of Haematology, University of Wales College of Medicine, Heath Park, Cardiff CF14 4XN Tel: 029 2074 2375 — MD 1988 Glas.; MD (Hons) Glas. 1988, MB ChB Glas. 1970; FRCP Ed. 1991; FRCP Glas. 1984; MRCP (UK) 1973; FRCPath 1976, M 1976. Prof. Haemat. Univ. Wales Coll. Med. Cardiff. Prev: Cons. Haemat. Glas. Roy. Infirm.

BURNETT, Andrew Cameron Barnet Primary Care Trust, Hyde House, The Hyde, Edgware Road, London NW9 6AA Tel: 020 8201

4780; Ashwell, Marsh Road, Hamstreet, Ashford TN26 2JD Tel: 01233 732960 — MB BS 1978 Lond.; MRCS Eng. LRCP Lond. 1978; MFPHM RCP (UK) 1995; MRCGP 1983. (Roy. Free) Director of Health Improvement, Barnet Primary Care Trust. Prev: Sen. Med. Off. (Pub. Health Developm. Unit) DoH; Dir. (Primary Care Developm.) & Med. Adviser Kent FHSA; Princip. GP Kent.

BURNETT, Angela Claire Bromley-by-Bow Health Centre, St Leonards Street, London E3 3BT; 52 Riversdale Road, Highbury, London N5 2JT Tel: 020 7354 4732 Fax: 020 7702 7024 Email: a.c.burnett@qmw.ac.uk — MB BS 1985 Lond.; BSc (Physiol.) Lond. 1982; MRCGP 1989; DRCOG 1987; MSc 1996. (Lond. Hosp.) GP Partner; Examg. doctor Med. Foundat. for the c/o victims of torture; Spokesperson Assn. Gen. Pract. in Urban Deprived Areas. Prev: SHO (O & G) Simpson Memor. Matern. Pavil. & Roy. Infirm. Edin.; Ho. Phys. Lond. Hosp.; Ho. Surg. Whipps Cross Hosp. Lond.

***BURNETT, Claire** 134 Brownside Road, Cambuslang, Glasgow G72 8AH Tel: 0141 641 3036 — MB ChB 1998 Manch.; MB ChB Manch 1998; BSc 1995.

BURNETT, Elisabeth Beresford 19 Athole Gardens, Glasgow G12 9BA — MB ChB 1992 Glas.

BURNETT, Elizabeth Mary Rosemount, 56 Pipeland Road, St Andrews KY16 8JN Tel: 01334 474158 — MB ChB 1939 Glas. (Glas.) Prev: Med. Off. Ch. of Scotl. Hosp. Sulenkama, S. Afr.; Resid. Surg. Off. Oldham Roy. Infirm.

BURNETT, Frances Elizabeth Albany Lodge, Church Crescent, St Albans AL3 5JF Tel: 01727 834330 Fax: 01727 834182 — MB ChB 1984 Manch.; MRCPsych 1991; MRCGP 1988; DRCOG 1987; M.D. London 1999. Cons. Psychiat. W. Herts. Community Health NHS Trust. Prev: Sen. Regist. (Psychiat.) St. Bart. Hosp. Lond. & Glas.

BURNETT, Gavin Ramsay MacPherson Princes Street Surgery, 69 Princes Street, Thurso KW14 7DJ Tel: 01847 895986 Fax: 01847 892113 — MB ChB Aberd. 1981. GP Thurso, Caithness.

BURNETT, George Andrew Miller The Health Centre, Wood Lane, Sonning Common, Reading RG4 9SW Tel: 0118 972 2188 Fax: 0118 972 4633; Longcroft, Stoke Row Road, Peppard Common, Henley-on-Thames RG9 5JD Tel: 01491 628388 Fax: 01491 628388 — MB ChB 1981 Dundee; MRCGP 1985; DRCOG 1983. Prev: Trainee GP/SHO Dundee VTS; Ho. Off. Norf. & Norwich Hosp. & W. Norwich Hosp.; Ho. Off. Cumbld. Infirm. Carlisle.

BURNETT, Gordon Bernard St Andrew's Hospital, Northampton NN1 5DG Tel: 01604 29696 — MB ChB 1964 Aberd.; MD Aberd. 1976; FRCPsych 1987, M 1972; DPM Ed.1968. Cons. Psychiat. St. And. Hosp. N.ampton. Socs: Fell. Roy. Coll. Psychiat.; Amer. Psychiat. Assn. Prev: Prof. Psychiat. Univ. N. Carolina, USA. Fell. Austral. Nat. Univ. Canberra, Australia.

BURNETT, Helen Louise Cross House Farm, Sandyforth La, Lightfoot Green, Preston PR4 0AL — MB ChB 1997 Manch.

BURNETT, Henry Mercer (Harry) Craiglockhart Surgery, 161 Colinton Road, Edinburgh EH14 1BE Tel: 0131 455 8494 Fax: 0131 444 0161; Bealach Na. Ba., 3 Pentland Crescent, Edinburgh EH10 6NS Tel: 0131 447 6541 — MB ChB 1974 Ed.; BSc (Med. Sci.) Ed. 1971; Dip. Sports Med. 1998. Med. Dir. Care for Sport Ltd (Sports Med. Centre) Edin.; Med. Adviser Heriot Watt Univ. Sports Med. Centre; Hon. Adviser Scott. Common Wealth Games Counc. Socs: Comm. Mem.: BASEM (Scotl.).

BURNETT, Hugh Cairns Department of Radiology, Hope Hospital, Manchester; 2 Westmorland Road, Didsbury, Manchester M20 2TA — MB ChB 1991 Ed.; BSc (Hons.) Ed. 1989; MRCP (UK) 1994; FRCR 1997. Clin. Fell. (Interven.al GI Radiol.). Prev: Specialist Regist. (Radiol.) St. Bart. & The Roy. Lond. Hosp.

BURNETT, Isobel Ann 3 Dorchester Road, Fixby, Huddersfield HD2 2JZ Tel: 01484 423828 Fax: 01484 423828 — MB ChB 1983 Sheff.; FRC Path 2000; MB ChB (Hons.) Sheff. 1983; BA (Hons.) Lond. 1972; MRCPath 1992. p/t Cons. Microbiol. Calderdale & Huddersfield NHS Trust. Socs: Hosp. Infec. Soc.; Path. Soc. Prev: Sen. Regist. (Med. Microbiol.) Roy. Hallamsh. Hosp. Sheff.

BURNETT, James Brodie Crawford (retired) 19 Kingswood Avenue, Kingswells, Aberdeen AB15 8AE — MB ChB 1961 Aberd.; MRCGP 1975; DObst RCOG 1963; DA Eng. 1963.

BURNETT, Jane Margaret Pudsey Green Close, Kirkby Lonsdale, Carnforth LA6 2BS Tel: 01468 71336 — MB BS 1971 Lond. GP Bentham N. Yorks.; Clin. Asst. (Paediat.) W.morland Co. Hosp. Cumbria. Prev: Ho. Phys. & Ho. Surg. Kettering Gen. Hosp.

BURNETT, Joan Catherine Duncan 6 Kirkton Gardens, Westhill, Westhill AB32 6LE Tel: 01224 742570 Fax: 01224 742570 — MB ChB 1980 Aberd.; DFFP 1994. Med. Off. (Diabetes) Diabetic Clinic Woolmanhill Hosp. Aberd.; Clin. Med. Off. (Family Plann.) Cent. Family Plann. Clinic Aberd.; Med. Off. Travel Clinic.

BURNETT, John Alexander (retired) 3 Berrington Mews, Tenbury Wells WR15 8EY Tel: 01584 811419 — MRCS Eng. LRCP Lond. 1938; DA Eng. 1954.

BURNETT, John Patrick 6 Mare Park, Muirton, Auchterarder PH3 1LW — MB ChB 1992 Manch.

BURNETT, Jonathan Alexander Burnett and Burnett, The Health Centre, Tavanagh Avenue, Portadown, Craigavon BT62 3BU Tel: 028 3835 1393 — MB ChB 1989 Dundee.

BURNETT, Kenneth Joseph (retired) 414 Burton Road, Derby DE23 6AJ Tel: 01332 49642 — MB ChB 1945 Leeds. Prev: Orthop Ho. Surg. Leeds Gen. Infirm.

BURNETT, Leonard David Rosebank Cottage, Lovers Lane, Scone, Perth PH2 6RG Tel: 01738 627117 — MB ChB 1990 Manch.; BSc St And. 1987; DCH RCP Lond. 1995; DRCOG 1992; MRCGP 1997. (St. And. Manch.) GP Princip. The Perth & Scone Med. Gp. Perth. Prev: GP/Regist. Perth; Regist. (Med.) S.land Hosp., NZ; Med. Off., SA.

BURNETT, Lesley Joan Brydon 241 Lonsdale Road, London SW13 9QN — MB ChB 1974 Dundee.

BURNETT, Maureen Patricia Leicestershire & Rutland Healthcare NHS Trust, Children's Services, Bride Park Plaza, Thurmaston, Leicester LE1 7RG Tel: 0116 255 2525 Fax: 0116 255 3850 — MB ChB 1979 Leeds; FRCPCH (Founding); MRCGP 1983; DCH RCP Lond. 1983; DRCOG 1982; Cert. JCC Lond. 1982. (Leeds) Cons. Community Paediat. (Educat. Med.) Leics. & Rutland Healthcare NHS Trust. Socs: Brit. Assn. Community Child Health; MRCPCH. Prev: SCMO Leics. & Rutland NHS Trust.

BURNETT, Michael George Red Roofs, 31 Coton Road, Nuneaton CV11 5TW Tel: 024 7635 7100 Fax: 024 7664 2036 — MB BS 1985 Lond.; MA Camb. 1985; MRCGP 1989; T(GP) 1991; DTM & H Liverp. 1990; DRCOG 1988. Prev: Trainee GP Bewdley VTS.; Sen. Lect. Sch. of Health, Afr. Sch. of Mission, White River, S. Afr.; Med. Off. (Community Health), Themba Health Ward, Kangwane, S. Afr.

BURNETT, Norman Trevor Thornfield, Wigan Road, Ashton-in-Makerfield, Wigan WN4 9SZ Tel: 01942 727269 — MD 1961 Liverp.; MB ChB 1954. (Liverp.) Vis. Phys. Newton-Le-Willows Community Hosp. Socs: Liverp. Med. Inst.; Wigan & Leigh Med. Inst. Prev: Clin. Asst. (Ophth.) Wigan Infirm.; Clin. Asst. (Gen. Med.) Salford Roy. Hosp.; Vice-Chairm. Wigan LMC.

BURNETT, Peter John 3 Edgewood, Ponteland, Newcastle upon Tyne NE20 9RY Tel: 01661 24553 Fax: 01661 860755 — MB BS Durh. 1954; DObst RCOG 1959. (Durh.) Tutor (Family & Community Med.) Univ. Newc. Socs: Assoc. RCGP; BMA. Prev: Ho. Surg. & Ho. Phys. Roy. Vict. Infirm. Newc u. Tyne; Ho. Surg. P.ss Mary Matern. Hosp. Newc. u. Tyne; RAMC.

BURNETT, Peter Richard The Surgery, Southfields Road, Strensall, York YO32 5UA Tel: 01904 490532 — MB BS 1973 Lond. (St. Bart)

BURNETT, Philip Trescobeas Surgery, Trescobeas Road, Falmouth TR11 2UN Tel: 01326 434888 Fax: 01326 434899 — MB BS 1979 Lond.

BURNETT, Mr Richard Princess Margaret Rose Hospital, 41/43 Frogston Road W., Edinburgh EH10 7ED Tel: 0131 536 4600 Fax: 0131 536 4601 — MB ChB 1983 Aberd.; FRCS (Orth.) Ed. 1994; FRCS Ed. 1988. (Univ. Aberd.) B.U.P.A. Murrayfield Ho. Edin.; Hon. Sen. Lect. Edinb. Univ.; B.U.P.A. Murrayfield Ho. Edin.; Cons. Orthop. Surg. St. John's Hosp. Livingstone & P.ss Margt. Rose Hosp. Edin. Prev: Sen. Regist. (Orthop.) Roy. Infirm. Edin.; Clin. Lect. & Sen. Regist. (Orthop.) Qu. Eliz. Hosp. Adelaide; Regist. (Orthop.) Wexham & N.wick Pk. Hosps.

BURNETT, Robin Ross Eglinton Medical Practice, 16 Eglinton Street, Irvine KA12 8AS Tel: 01294 279178 Fax: 01294 313095; 79 Bank Street, Irvine KA12 0LL Tel: 01294 279750 Email: robinrburnett@cs.com — MB ChB 1961 Ed. (Ed.) Socs: BMA & Primary Health Care Specialist Gp.; Scottisch Heart and Arterial Dis. risk Preven. Soc. (S.H.A.R.P). Prev: Med. Supt. Nessie Kt. Hosp. Transkei, S. Afr.

BURNETT, Rodney Alister Dept. of Pathology, Western Infirmary, Glasgow G11 6NT Tel: 0141 211 Ext: 2473 Email:

rodney_burnett@hotmail.com — MB ChB 1970 St. And.; FRIPHH; FRCP 1996 Glas.; FRCPath 1976. Cons. Path. W.. Infirm. Glas. Socs: Assn. Of Clin. Pathologists - Vice Pres. Prev: Cons. Admin. Charge, Dept. Path. Stobhill Hosp. Glas.

BURNETT, Ronald Alexander Burnett and Burnett, The Health Centre, Tavanagh Avenue, Portadown, Craigavon BT62 3BU; 67 Mullahead Road, Tandragee BT62 2GA Tel: 02838 840528 — MB BCh BAO 1965 Belf. (Belf.) GP Portdown.

BURNETT, Ronald Charles St Clair Glencaird, Station Loan, Balero, Edinburgh EH14 7AW Tel: 0131 449 3055 — MB ChB 1961 Ed.; DPH 1964; MFCM 1974. (Ed.) Community Med. Specialist Common Servs. Agency Edin. Prev: Dist. Med. Off. W. Lothian Health Dist.; Community Med. Specialist N. Lothian Health Dist.; Asst. Sen. Med. Off. S.E. (Scotl.) RHB.

BURNETT, Roy James The Old School Surgery, The Old School, The Square, Tarves, Ellon AB41 7GX Tel: 01651 851777 Fax: 01651 852090; The Steading, Nether Tillymaud, Udny, Ellon AB41 6GF Tel: 01651 842081 — MB ChB 1981 Aberd.; DRCOG 1989. (Aberdeen) GP Princip. Socs: Ythan Med. Soc.; Ellon Med. Gp. Prev: Regist. (ENT) Aberd. Roy. Infirm.; SHO (Obst.) Aberd. Matern. Hosp.; SHO (Cas.) Roy. Aberd. Child. Hosp.

BURNETT, Sarah Jane Dimitra Cecil Fleming Building - VCLH, Grafton Way, London W1 Fax: 020 7228 1864 Email: info@sarahburnett.com; Fax: 020 7228 1864 Email: sarah@sarahburnett.com — MB BS 1985 Lond.; MB BS (Distinc. Path., Therap., Med. & Surg.) Lond. 1985; MBA Open Univ. 1995; MRCP (UK) 1988; FRCR 1992. (Westm.) Cons. Radiologist, VCLH Med. Director, Health Assess; Admissions Tutor Imperial Coll. Sch. of Med.; Vis. Fell. Imperial Sch. Managem. Lond. Socs: Brit. Soc. Skeletal Radiol.; Eur. Soc. Skeletal Radiol. Prev: Cons. Radiol. Roy. Nat. Orthop. Hosp.; Sen. Regist. (Radiol.) St. Bart. Hosp. Lond.; Research Fell. St. Marks Hosp. Lond.

BURNETT, Timothy Michael Green Close Surgery, Green Close, Kirkby Lonsdale, Carnforth LA6 2BS Tel: 015242 71210 Fax: 015242 72713 — MB BS 1971 Lond.; MA Oxf. 1967. (Middlesex Hospital) Prev: Ho. Phys. Middlx. Hosp.; Ho. Surg. Kettering Gen. Hosp.

BURNETT, Walter 27A Taylor Street, Forfar DD8 3JQ Tel: 01307 463643 — MB ChB 1941 Glas.; DPH Glas. 1947; MFCM 1973. (Univ. Glas.) Prev: MOH Co. Angus.

BURNETT, William Halliday 64 Murrayfield Gardens, Edinburgh EH12 6DQ Tel: 0131 346 0985 — MB ChB 1942 Ed. (Univ. Ed.)

BURNETT-HALL, Christabel Flora 2B Haldane Terrace, Jesmond, Newcastle upon Tyne NE2 3AN — MB BS 1998 Newc.; MB BS Newc 1998.

BURNEY, Abida Sultana 16 Beaufort Gardens, Hendon, London NW4 3QP Tel: 020 8202 0234 Fax: 020 8202 1663 — MB BS 1961 Punjab; FRCP Lond. 1988, M 1967; FRCP Ed. 1986, M 1966. (FJ Medical College, Lahore, Pakistan) Cons. Phys. Med. & Diabetes Burton Gen. Hosp.; Asst. Prof. Med. F. J. Med. Coll. Lahore, Pakistan; Vice-Pres. Pakistan Soc. Phys. Prev: Regist. (Gen. Med.) S. Lond. Hosp. for Wom.; SHO (Endocrinol.) New End Hosp. Lond.

BURNEY, Professor Peter Gordon James Department of Public HealthSciences, Kings College, Capital House, 42 Weston St., London SE1 3QD Tel: 020 7848 6609 Fax: 020 7848 6605 — MB BS 1977 Lond.; MD Lond. 1993; FFPHM RCP (UK) 1989, M 1983. Prof. Pub. Health Med. GKT Sch. of Med. King's Coll. Lond. Prev: Sen. Lect. (Community Med.) UMDS Guy's & St. Thos. Hosps. Lond.; Ho. Phys. Middlx. Hosp.

BURNEY, Peter John Thornbury Health Centre, Eastland Road, Thornbury, Bristol BS35 1DP Tel: 01454 412599 Fax: 01454 41911; West Shen, 28 Gloucester Road, Thornbury, Bristol BS35 1DG — MB ChB 1977 Manch.; MRCGP 1981; DRCOG 1979.

BURNEY, Mr Syed Rashid Muzaffar 14 Woodleigh Avenue, Friern Barnet, London N12 0LL — MB BS 1983 Aligarh; MB BS Aligarh Muslim, India 1983; FRCSI 1992. Staff Grade (A & E) Glan Clwyd Hosp. Rhyl Wales.

BURNFIELD, Alexander John Terstan Consultancy, Longstock, Stockbridge SO20 6DW Tel: 01264 810675 Fax: 07092 098104 Email: sandy.burnfield@andover.co.uk; Terstan Consultancy, Longstock, Stockbridge SO20 6DW Tel: 01264 810675 Fax: 07092 098104 Email: sandy.burnfield@andover.co.uk — MB BS 1968 Lond.; FRCPsych 1993, M 1972; DPM Eng. 1971. (Lond. Hosp.) p/t Dir. Corn Loft Studio & Consultancy Stockbridge, Hants.; Trustee, The Multiple Sclerosis Trust (UK). Socs: Pres. Andover & Winchester Br.es, MS Soc. Prev: Cons. Child & Adolesc. Psychiat. Andover NHS Trust; Chairm. Conf. Comm., Internat. Federat. of MS Socs.

BURNFORD, Alfred Myer, MBE (retired) Lynchetts, Barley, Royston SG8 8HT Tel: 01763 848265 — MB BS 1952 Lond.; MRCS Eng. LRCP Lond. 1951; DCH Eng. 1954; DObst RCOG 1954. Prev: Dep. Med. Supt. Roy. Perth Hosp.

BURNFORD, Richard Peter 51 Roseford Road, Cambridge CB4 2HA — MB BS 1985 Lond.

BURNHAM, Christopher Rowan 3 Gilpin Hill, Sway, Lymington SO41 6DT — MB BS 1998 Lond.; MB BS Lond 1998.

BURNHAM, Donna Annabelle 45 Kiln Road, Emmer Green, Reading RG4 8UE — MB ChB 1981 Leeds; FRCS Ed. 1994; MRCOG 1991.

BURNHAM, John Stuart Newtownards Health Centre, Frederick Street, Newtownards BT23 4LS Tel: 028 9181 6880; 2 Aspen, Donaghadee BT21 0QN Tel: 01247 888650 — MB BCh BAO 1973 Dub.; BA Dub. 1973.

BURNHAM, Paul Henry Tel: 01434 320077 Fax: 01434 320674; Moorfield, Sheild Hill, Haltwhistle NE49 9NN — MB BS 1973 Lond.; MRCGP 1978. GP Haltwhistle, N.d.

BURNHAM, Peter Richard 22 Booker Avenue, Liverpool L18 4RD — MB ChB 1991 Manch.

BURNHAM, Mr William Harvey Thornbury Health Centre, Eastland Road, Thornbury, Bristol BS35 1DP Tel: 01454 412599 Fax: 01454 41911 — MB BS 1968 Lond.; FRCS Eng. 1974. Prev: Sen. Med. Off. St. Helena Govt.

BURNHAM, William Rodney Department of Gastroenterology, Havering Hospitals NHS Trust, Oldchurch Hospital, Romford RM7 0BE Tel: 01708 46090 Fax: 01708 738227 — Fellow of European Board of Gastroenterology; MB BCh BAO Dub. 1969; MA Dub. 1980, MD 1980; FRCP Lond. 1988, M 1972. Cons. Phys. (Gastroenterol.) Havering Hosps. Romford; Hon. Cons. Gastroenterol. Roy. Lond. Hosp. Whitechapel. Socs: Brit. Soc. Gatroenterol.; Director of Med. Workforce Unit, Roy. Coll. Phys. Lond.; Reg. Train. Dir./Speciality Adv., Gastroenterol, N. Thames (E.). Prev: Regist. (Gen. Med. & Gastroenterol.) Addenbrooke's Hosp. Camb.; Regist. (Med.) St Mark's Hosp. Lond.; Lect. (Therap.) City Hosp. & Univ. Nottm.

BURNHAM-SLIPPER, Charles Nelson, TD (retired) 100 Waverley Road, Southsea PO5 2PS Tel: 01705 828166 — MRCS Eng. LRCP Lond. 1938; FRCGP 1979, M 1953. Prev: Maj. RAMC.

BURNIE, James Peter Department of Medical Microbiology, 2nd Floor, Clinical Sciences Building, Manchester Royal Infirmary, Oxford Road, Manchester M13 9WL Tel: 0161 276 4280 Fax: 0161 276 8826 — MB BChir 1981 Camb.; PhD Lond. 1991; MSc (Distinc.) Lond. 1984; MD Camb. 1986, MA 1981; MRCS Eng. LRCP Lond. 1980; MRCP (UK) 1982; FRCPath 1997, M 1986; DSc 1998. (Cambs/St Thomas hosp) Prof. Med. Microbiol. Univ. Manch; Hon. Cons. Manch. Roy. Infirm. & St. Mary's Hosp. Manch. & Dent. Sch. Prev: Sen. Lect. & Hon. Cons. Med. Microbiol. St. Bart. Hosp. Lond.

BURNIE, Malcolm Liddle 15 Glencourse Drive, Fulwood, Preston PR2 6AF — MB ChB 1989 Manch.

BURNIE, Sheila Gwendolen Stapleton (retired) 10 Beoley Close, Wylde Green, Sutton Coldfield B72 1EU Tel: 0121 355 1863 — MB ChB 1949 Birm.; MB ChB (Hons.) Birm. 1949; MRCS Eng. LRCP Lond. 1949; DObst RCOG 1952. Clin. Asst. Matern. Dept. Good Hope Hosp. Sutton Coldfield. Prev: Med. Off. Taylor Memor. Home Birm.

***BURNILL, Rebecca Jane** Flat 4, 73-75 Wellington Road, Fallowfield, Manchester M14 6BN — MB ChB 1994 Liverp.

BURNLEY, Steven Richard 1 Bramley Close, Cox Green, Maidenhead SL6 3HQ — MB ChB 1978 Bristol.

BURNS, Adrienne Mary Elizabeth Crow Clump, Yaffle Road, St George's Hill, Weybridge KT13 0QF Tel: 01932 843077 — MB ChB 1972 Glas.

BURNS, Professor Alistair Stanyer Department of Psychiatry, Withington Hospital, West Didsbury, Manchester M20 2LR; 9 Pheasant Rise, Bowdon, Altrincham WA14 3HL — MB ChB 1980 Glas.; MPhil Lond. 1987; MD (Hons.) Glas. 1991; FRCP Glas. 1993; MRCP (UK) 1983; FRCPsych 1996, M 1985; T(Psych) 1991; DHMSA 1984. (Glas.) Prof. Old Age Psychiat. Univ. Manch.; Edr. Internat. Jl. Geriat. Psychiat. Prev: Sen. Lect. (Psychiat.) Inst. Psychiat. Lond.;

Sen. Regist. & Regist. (Psychiat.) Maudsley Hosp. Lond.; Regist. (Med.) S.. Gen. Hosp. Glas.

BURNS, Alys Margaret West Suffolk Hospital, Hardwick Lane, Bury St Edmunds IP33 2QZ — BM 1983 Soton.; BM (Hons.) Soton. 1983; MRCP (UK) 1986; FRCA 1988. Cons. Anaesth. & Intens. Care W. Suff. Hosp. Bury St. Edmunds. Socs: Full Mem. Intens. Care Soc.; Asoc. of Anesth. Prev: Sen. Regist. (Anaesth.) E. Anglia RHA; Research Regist. (Intens. Care) Camb. HA; Regist. (Anaesth.) Camb. HA.

BURNS, Andrew 44 Stanlake Road, London W12 7HL — MB BS 1996 Lond.

BURNS, Mr Andrew Christopher Robert 39 Clayhill Close, Waltham Chase, Southampton SO32 2TT — BM 1990 Soton.; MA Oxf. 1989, BA (Chem.) 1985; FRCS Ed. 1994. Clin. Research Fell. (Surg.) Soton. Gen. Hosp. Prev: SHO (Cardiothoracic Surg.) Soton. Gen. Hosp.; SHO (Gen. Surg. & Urol.) Soton. Gen. Hosp. & Yeovil Dist. Hosp.; Ho. Surg. & Phys. Profess. Med. Unit Soton. Gen. Hosp.

BURNS, Ann 29 Hale Gardens, London W3 9SG — MB BCh BAO 1983 NUI; MRCPI 1986. Research Fell. Roy. Postgrad. Med. Sch. Hammersmith Hosp. Lond.

BURNS, Archibald Stirling (retired) 7 Park Terrace, Pitlochry PH16 5AY — B.Sc. Glas. 1938, M.B., Ch.B. 1940.

BURNS, Bernard Vincent 76 Mossfield Road, Birmingham B14 7JB — MB ChB 1992 Manch.; FRCS (Oto) Ed 1999.

BURNS, Brian Joseph 57 Rosedale Gardens, Sheffield S11 8QB — MB ChB 1998 Sheff.; MB ChB Sheff 1998.

***BURNS, Briony Jane** 57 Chalkwell Esplanade, Westcliff on Sea SS0 8JH; The Toll House, 35 Fishbourne Road, Chichester PO19 3HS — MB BChir 1992 Camb.; MA Camb. 1991, MB BChir 1992; MRCP (UK) 1994.

BURNS, David Anthony Leicester Royal Infirmary, Leicester LE1 5WW Tel: 0116 254 1414; 177 Mere Road, Wigston, Leicester LE18 3RN — MB BS 1969 Lond.; MRCP (UK) 1975. Emerit. Cons. Dermatol., Leicester Roya Infirm. Prev: Cons. Dermat. & Hon. Sen. Lect. Leicester Roy. Infirm.; Regist. & Sen. Regist. (Dermat.) The Roy. Free Hosp. Lond.

BURNS, Deborah Anne 59 Linton Street, London N1 7AN — MB BS 1986 Lond.; MRCP CH(UK) 1991; DCH RCP Lond. 1990. (Middlesex hospital medical school) Sen. Regist. (Paediat.) Flexible Train. Lond.

BURNS, Diana Mary 7 Downshire Crescent, Hillsborough BT26 6DD — MB BCh BAO 1977 Belf.; MRCGP 1981; DRCOG 1980.

BURNS, Duncan 8 Granville Road Road, Oxted RH8 0DA — BM 1991 Soton.; MRCGP 1995; DRCOG 1993. Prev: Trainee GP/SHO P.ss Roy. Hosp. Haywards Heath VTS.

BURNS, E Claire Community Paediatric Department, Ounsted Clinic, Churchill Hospital, Oxford OX3 7LJ Tel: 01865 225040; 25 Chalfont Road, Oxford OX2 6TL — MB BCh BAO 1971 Dub.; MD Dub. 1983; MRCP (UK) 1978; DCH Eng. 1975. Cons. Community Paediat. Ch.ill Hosp. Oxf. Prev: Cons. Community Paediat. Char. Cross Hosp. Lond.

BURNS, Eileen Leeds General Infirmary, Great George St., Leeds LS1 3EX Tel: 0113 243 2799 Fax: 0113 231 6557 — MB ChB 1991 Leeds 1991; MD Sheff. 1991; MB ChB Leeds 1981; MRCP (UK) 1984; FRCP 1998. (Leeds) Cons. Phys. Med. for Elderly Leeds Gen. Infirm.

BURNS, Fergal John 83 Orritor Road, Cookstown BT80 8BH — MB BCh BAO 1995 Belf.

BURNS, Fiona Margaret Flat 4/42, Durand Gardens, London SW9 0PP — MB ChB 1992 Otago; BMedSci 1989. (Otago Medical School, New Zealand) Specialist Regist. GVM/HIV.

BURNS, Frances Watt Ian Charles Cottage Hospital, The Health Centre, Castle Road East, Grantown-on-Spey PH26 3HR Tel: 01479 872484 Fax: 01479 873503; Woodberry, Speybridge, Grantown-on-Spey PH26 3NQ Tel: 01479 872297 — MB ChB 1966 Glas.; MRCGP 1976; DObst RCOG 1970. (Glas.) Socs: BMA.

BURNS, Gearoid Eugene Duncairn Gardens Surgery, 165 Duncairn Gardens, Belfast BT15 2GE Tel: 028 9074 3416 Fax: 028 9074 3416 — MB BCh BAO 1982 Belf.; MB BCh Belf. 1982; MRCGP 1985; DRCOG 1984.

BURNS, George Waddell Breconside, 3 Park Place, Lanark ML11 9HH — MB ChB 1940 Glas. (Glas.) JP. Prev: Ho. Phys. & Ho. Surg. Roy. Alexandra Infirm. Paisley; Ho. Surg. Thornhill Matern. Hosp.

BURNS, Graham Paul 28 Brandling Park, Newcastle upon Tyne NE2 4RR — MB BS 1992 Newc.; Dip Med Sci, 1996; MRCP, 1995; BSc Mathematics Nottm. 1984. Specialist Regist. in Respirat. & Gen. Med, N.ern Region. Socs: Spr Rep Spec. Adv. Comm. for Respirat. Med; SpR Rep. Brit. Thoracic Soc., Manpower & Train. Comm.; RCP ASSDG Tutor. Prev: MRC Clin. Train. Fell.

BURNS, Heather 130 Gilford Road, Lurgan, Craigavon BT66 7AH — MB BCh BAO 1989 Belf.; DRCOG 1991. Socs: Roy. Coll. Gen. Pract.; Roy. NZ Coll. Gen. Pract.

BURNS, Helen The Penryn Surgery, Saracen Way, Penryn TR10 8HX Tel: 01326 372502 Fax: 01326 378126; Lower Calamansack, Constantine, Falmouth TR11 5RN — MB BS 1982 Lond.

BURNS, Helen Joyce 64 Strines Road, Marple, Stockport SK6 7DU Tel: 0161 427 3813 — MB ChB 1981 Manch.; MRCGP 1988. (Manch.)

BURNS, Henry James Gerard Wellbrae, Gateside Road, Barrhead, Glasgow G78 1EP — MB ChB 1974 Glas.

BURNS, Ian James 9 Whitehouse Park, Wick KW1 4NX — MB ChB 1955 Glas. Co. Anaesth. Caithness. Socs: Scott. Soc. Anaesths. & Highland Med. Soc. Prev: Ho. Surg. W. Infirm. Glas.; Jun. Ho. Off. (Anaesth.) & Regist. (Anaesth.) Edin. Roy. Infirm.

BURNS, James Number 5, Sinclair Drive, Liverpool L18 0HN Tel: 0151 722 6266 — MB ChB 1961 Liverp.; MD Liverp. 1973; FRCPath 1981, M 1969. (Liverp.) p/t Home Office Path. Socs: (Pres.) Brit. Assn. Forens. Med.; Assn .Clin. Paths.; Path. Soc. Prev: Cons. Histopath. Selly Oak Hosp. Birm.; Cons. Histopath. St. John Gen. Hosp. New Brunswick, Canada; Lect. (Forens. Path.) Univ. Liverp.

BURNS, Jane Altrincham Medical Practice, Normans Place, Altrincham WA14 2AB Tel: 0161 928 2424 — MB ChB 1990 Manch.

BURNS, Jane Wilson 15A Field Road, Clarkston, Glasgow G76 8SE — MB ChB 1981 Glas.; FFA RCS Eng. 1987.

BURNS, Janet Elizabeth Royal Hospital for Sick Children, Sciennes Road, Edinburgh EH9 1LF — MB ChB 1973 Ed.; FRCP Ed. 1986; MRCP (UK) 1976; FRCPC 1982. Cons. (Paediat. Cardiol.) Roy. Hosp. Sick Childr. Edin.; Hon. Sen. Lect., health, Univ. fo Edin. Prev: Asst. Prof. (Paediat. Cardiol.) Univ. Maryland Hosp. Baltimore.

BURNS, Jennifer Mary Anne 14 Alexandra Park, Glasgow G66 5BH — MB ChB 1983 Glas.; MRCP (UK) 1986.

BURNS, Jessie Agnes Sheila Dallachy Park View, Lower Eaton, Eaton Bishop, Hereford HR2 9QE — MRCS Eng. LRCP Lond. 1953.

BURNS, Joanna Tishburn, Laneside Farm, Sawley, Clitheroe BB7 4LF — MB BS 1998 Newc.; MB BS Newc 1998.

BURNS, John Desmond Addy (retired) 11 Yare Court, 22A Yarmouth Road, Norwich NR7 0EF — MB BCh BAO Belf. 1949; MFCM RCPI 1974; FPHM 1990; DPH 1958. Prev: Cons. Communicable Dis. Control Norwich HA.

BURNS, John Moffatt Rose Cottage, Drygrange, Melrose TD6 9DJ Tel: 01896 849626 — MB BCh BAO 1973 Belf.; MRCGP 1978; DObst RCOG 1975. Freelance Occupat. Health Phys. Prev: GP Princ. Earlstone Berwicksh.; Dir. Occupat. Health & Sessional Med. Off. (Occupat. Health Serv.) Borders HB.

BURNS, John Murdie Accident and Emergency Department, Law Hospital NHS Trust, Carluke ML8 5ER Tel: 01698 361100; 55 Stewartan Drive, Cambuslang, Glasgow G72 8DQ — MB ChB 1985 Glas.

BURNS, Joseph Patrick John, MC The Grange, St Annes Hill, Chertsey KT16 9EP — MB BCh BAO 1941 Belf.; DPH 1948. (Belf.) Socs: BMA. Prev: Dep. MOH & Dep. Med. Ref. Islington Metrop. Boro.; Dep. MOH Willesden Boro. Counc. & Sen. Asst. Med. Off. Middlx. CC; Dep. MOH & Dep. Port Med. Off. Co. Boro. Gt. Yarmouth.

BURNS, Julie Amanda Ballyoan House, 106 Rossdowney Road, Londonderry BT47 5SU — MB BCh BAO 1992 Belf. Trainee GP Alexandria. Prev: SHO (Paediat., O & G & A & E) Altnagelvin Hosp. Lond.derry.

BURNS, Kathleen Mary Brenkley Avenue Health Centre, Brenkley Avenue, Shiremoor, Newcastle upon Tyne NE27 0PR Tel: 0191 251 6151 — MB ChB 1978 Glas.; MRCGP 1985; DCH RCP Lond. 1981; DRCOG 1980.

BURNS, Laurence John The Surgery, Upper Warrengate, Wakefield WF1 4PR; 1 The Mount, Thornes, Wakefield WF2 8QW Tel: 01924 371555 — MRCS Eng. LRCP Lond. 1952. (Liverp.)

BURNS, Lucy Sarah Forest Edge, 16 Larkhill Lane, Formby, Liverpool L37 1LX — MB ChB 1997 Bristol.

BURNS, Margaret Ferguson 28 Helensburgh Drive, Jordanhill, Glasgow G13 1RS — MB ChB 1968 Glas.

BURNS, Mark Simon Princes Park Health Centre, Bentley Road, Liverpool L8 0SY Tel: 0151 728 8313 Fax: 0151 728 8417; 7 Sydenham Avenue, Liverpool L17 3AU Tel: 0151 734 2894 — MB ChB 1983 Sheff.; DRCOG 1986. Prev: GP Birm.; Trainee GP Birm. VTS.

BURNS, Martin Mountbatten Medical Centre, 12 Victoria Road West, Hebburn NE31 1LD Tel: 0191 541 6266 Fax: 0191 451 6256 — MB ChB 1977 Manch.

BURNS, Pagan St Marys Surgery, Applethwaite, Windermere LA23 1BA Tel: 01539 488484 Fax: 01539 442838; The Cottage, Starnthwaite Ghyll, Crosthwaite, Kendal LA8 8HZ — MB ChB 1981 Manch.; BSc (Hons.) (Physiol.) Manch. 1978; FRCGP 1996, M 1985; DCH RCP Lond. 1984; DRCOG 1983. Course Organiser S. Cumbria VTS.

BURNS, Paul Robert Stuart Branston Surgery, Station Road, Branston, Lincoln LN4 1LH Tel: 01522 793081 Fax: 01522 793562; Balff Cottage, Barff Road, Potterhanworth, Lincoln LN4 2DU Tel: 01522 794352 Fax: 01522 793562 — MB ChB 1976 Dundee; Dip. Pract. Dermat. Wales 1996. Clin. Asst. (Dermat.) Lincoln Co. Hosp.

BURNS, Phoebe Stanton (retired) 12 Wardlaw Road, Bearsden, Glasgow G61 1AL — MB BCh BAO 1932 Belf.; DPH 1935. Prev: Sen. Med. Off. E. Health & Social Serv. Bd. N. W. Belf. Dist.

BURNS, Richard (retired) 30 Northumberland Road, New Barnet, Barnet EN5 1ED Tel: 020 8440 6190 — LRCP LRCS Ed. LRFPS Glas. 1945. Prev: Med. Off. Dept. Health & Social Security.

BURNS, Richard William Lodge Health, 20 Lodge Manor, Coleraine BT52 1JX Tel: 028 7034 4494 Fax: 028 7032 1759 — MB ChB 1975 Birm.; DRCOG 1977.

BURNS, Robert 14 Royal Crescent, Brighton BN2 1AL Tel: 01273 607711 — MB ChB Glas. 1994; BSc Glas. 1994. (Univ. Glas.) Socs: BMA (Mem. Brighton Div.); Sussex M-C Soc.; Brit. Inst. Musculoskel. Med. Prev: Clin. Asst. Rheum. Clinic. Roy. Sussex Co. Hosp.; Local Civil Serv. Med. Off.; Hon. Sec. & Treas. Brit. Assn. Manip. Med.

BURNS, Robert Andrew 6 Postboys Walk, Ballymoney BT53 6DA — MB BCh BAO 1978 Belf.; MRCGP 1983; DRCOG 1981.

BURNS, Roger Anthony 40 Charles Avenue, Lenton Abbey, Beeston, Nottingham NG9 2SH — MB BCh BAO 1984 NUI.

BURNS, Roger William St Thomas Surgery, Rifleman Lane, St. Thomas Green, Haverfordwest SA61 1QX Tel: 01437 762162 Fax: 01437 776811; The Old St. Mary's Vicarage, 27 Hill Lane, Haverfordwest SA61 1PR Tel: 01437 767102 — MB BS 1974 Lond.; MRCS Eng. LRCP Lond. 1974; MRCGP 1979; DRCOG 1978. (Guy's) GP Trainer Withybush Hosp. VTS; Course Organiser Pembrokesh. VTS. Socs: BMA. Prev: Tutor RCGP.

BURNS, Sara Hoghton Station Road Practice, 66-68 Station Road, Ainsdale, Southport PR8 3HW Tel: 01704 574137 Fax: 01704 573875 — MB ChB 1988 Liverp.; BSc Liverp. 1985; MRCGP 1992; DGM RCP Lond. 1991; DRCOG 1991.

BURNS, Sean George 3 Arthur Terrace, Stockport SK5 6AT — MB ChB 1989 Liverp.

BURNS, Sharon Maria 3 Lowlands Drive, Keyworth, Nottingham NG12 5HG — MB BS 1992 Lond.; MRCP (UK) 1996. Research Regist. in Cardiol. Papworth Hosp. Camb.

BURNS, Sheila Marie Regional Clinical Virology Laboratory, City Hospital, Greenbank Drive, Edinburgh EH10 5SB Tel: 0131 536 6330 Fax: 0131 536 6153 Email: sm.burns@scot.nhs.uk; Tel: 01875 833357 — MB ChB 1975 Ed.; BSc (Med. Sci.) 1972; FRCPath 1997. Cons. Virol. & Head of Diagnostic Virol. Regional Virus Laborat. City Hosp. Edin.; Hon. Sen. Lect. (Med. Microbiol.) Univ. Edin. Socs: Fell. Soc. Trop. Med. & Hyg.; Brit. Soc. Study of Infec.

BURNS, Shirley Joyce 41 Whitby Road, Runcorn WA7 5PS — MB ChB 1989 Manch.

BURNS, Sinead Clair Emily Mon Abri, Mucklestone Road, Loggerheads, Market Drayton TF9 4DA — MB BS 1998 Lond.; MB BS Lond 1998.

BURNS, Stephen Brian Stag Medical Centre, 162 Wickersley Road, Rotherham S60 4JW Tel: 01709 379285; 5 Stafford Drive, Moorgate, Rotherham S60 3DQ Tel: 01709 360972 Email: steveburns4@compuserve.com — MB ChB 1978 Sheff. GP Princip. & GP Tutor (Rotherham); Hon. Lect. Sheff. Univ.; Clin. Asst., Rotherham Hospice; Med. Off., Rotherham United Football Club. Socs: Hon. Sec. Rotherham Div. of Brit. Med. Assoc.

BURNS, Stewart Andrew The Health Centre, HMP/YOI Norwich, 9 Knox Road, Norwich NR1 4LU Tel: 01603 437531 Fax: 01603 702825 Email: drsaburns@aol.com — MB ChB 1975 Liverp. Sen. Med. Off. Norwich. Socs: Internat. Prison Med. Servs.; Coll. Prison Doctors; BMA.

BURNS, Suzanne Clare St Stephens Health Centre, Bow Community Hall, William Place, London E3 5ED Tel: 020 8980 1760 Fax: 020 8980 6619 — MB BS 1992 Lond.; BSc (Hons.) Lond. 1990; DRCOG 1996. (Univ. Coll. & Middlx.) GP Regist. Lond. Prev: SHO (Paediat.) St. Mary's Hosp. Portsmouth; SHO (Med.) Crawley; SHO (A & E) Ryde Hosp. Sydney, Austral.

BURNS, Professor Thomas Patrick Section of Community Psychiatry, Jenner Wing, St George's Hospital Medical School, Cranmer Terrace, London SW17 0RE Tel: 020 8725 5542 Fax: 020 8725 3538 — MB 1972 Camb.; MB BChir 1972; MD Camb. 1984; FRCPsych 1992, M 1975. Prof. Community Psychiat. St. Geo. Hosp. Med. Sch. Lond.; Clin. Dir. Adult Servs. Pathfinder Ment. Health NHS Trust. Prev: Cons. Psychiat. Uppsala Univ. Hosp., Sweden.

BURNS-BROWN, Ian Laurance St Leonard's Medical Centre, 145 Pleasance, Edinburgh EH8 9RU Tel: 0131 668 4547 Fax: 0131 667 5092; 76 Liberton Brae, Edinburgh EH16 6LB — MB ChB 1980 Aberd.

BURNS-BROWN, John (retired) Tamar, 3 Blackbarony Road, Edinburgh EH16 5QP Tel: 0131 667 5714 — MB ChB 1941 Ed.; DOMS Eng. 1950; DPH Ed. 1943. Prev: Med. Off. Sch. Eye Serv. E. Fife.

BURNS-COX, Christopher John Department of Medicine, Frenchay Hospital, Bristol BS16 1LE Tel: 0117 970 1212 Fax: 0117 957 3075; Southend Farm, Wotton-under-Edge GL12 7PB Tel: 01453 842243 Email: chris.burns-cox@virgin.net — MB BS 1960 Lond.; MD Lond. 1972; FRCP Lond. 1977, M 1963. (Middlx.) p/t Hon. Cons. Phys. Frenchay Hosp. Bristol; Locum Cons. Phys., Chegenham Gen. Hosp.; THET Lect., Tamave, Ghana; THET Adviser, Lond. Socs: Phys. Human Rights; (Exec. Comm.) NHS Cons. Assn.; Assn. Brit. Clin. Diaretol. Prev: Regist. (Med.) Univ. Coll. Hosp. Lond.; Lect. (Med.) Univ. Malaya; WHO Cons. Smallpox Eradication.

BURNS-COX, Nicholas Southend Farm, Wotton-under-Edge GL12 7PB — MB ChB 1990 Bristol; MD 2000 Bristol; FRCS (Eng.) 1994. Specialist Regist. in Urol. Socs: Fell. Roy. Coll. Surg.s of Eng.; Mem. Brit. Assn. of Urol.s. Prev: Research Fell. Bristol Urol. Inst.; SHO Surg. Rotat. Roy. Devon & Exeter Hosp.

BURNSIDE, Philip 73 Galgorm Road, Ballymena BT42 1AA — MB BCh BAO 1974 Belf.; MRCPath Lond. 1981.

BURR, Colin Richard Bourne Galletly Practice Team, 40 North Road, Bourne PE10 9BT Tel: 01778 562200 Fax: 01778 562207 — MB ChB 1983 Leic.; MRCGP 1987; DRCOG 1986.

BURR, Jennifer Margaret Clarendon Wing, Eye Department, Leeds General Infirmary, Leeds LS2 9NS Tel: 0113 292 2750; 32 Castle View, Wakefield WF2 7HZ Tel: 01924 252403 — MB ChB 1978 Birm.; MRCOphth 1993; DO RCS Eng. 1986. Ophth. Leeds Gen. Infirm.

BURR, Michael Leslie Centre for Applied Public Health Medicine, Temple of Peace And Health, Cathays Park, Cardiff CF10 3NW Tel: 029 2040 2463 Fax: 029 2040 2503 Email: michael.burr@bro-taf-ha.wales.nhs.uk; 18 Chartwell Drive, Lisvane, Cardiff CF14 0EZ Tel: 029 2075 8397 — DSc Lond. 2001; MB BS Lond. 1960; MD Lond. 1976; FFPHM RCP (UK) 1992; MFCM 1973; DPH Lond. 1967; DObst RCOG 1962. (Univ. Coll. Hosp.) Sen. Lect. Univ. Wales Coll. Med. Cardiff; Hon. Cons. Bro Taf HA. Socs: Eur. Soc. Cardiol. & Brit. Thoracic Soc.; Internat. Epidemiol. Assn. Prev: Epidemiol. MRC Epidemiol. Unit; MoH Stone UD & RD.

BURR, Robin Henry King Street Surgery, 38 King Street, Lancaster LA1 1RE Tel: 01524 32294 Fax: 01524 848412; SunnyBank, Whitbarrow Grove, Levens, Kendal LA8 8LT Email: robinburr@freeuk.com — MB BS 1967 Newc.; Dip. Health Mgt. Keele 1995; DObst RCOG 1972; DA Eng. 1971; Dip. Occ. Med. 1996. GP & Sen. Med. Off. Univ. Lancaster; Chair Lancaster PCT.

Socs: Fac. Anaesth. RCS Eng. Prev: SHO (O & G) Preston Hosp. N. Shields.; Ho. Off. & SHO (Anaesth.) Roy. Vict. Infirm. Newc. u. Tyne.

BURR, Robin Wilson 51 Landmere Gardens, Wells Road, Nottingham NG3 3BG — MB ChB 1987 Manch.

BURR, Stephen Andrew Henry 43 Hayclose Crescent, Kendal LA9 7NT — MB ChB 1989 Manch.; DCH RCP Lond. 1994. Staff Grade (Paediat.) Roy. Lancaster Infirm. Socs: Aerospace Med. Assn. Prev: SHO (Paediat.) Roy. Lancaster Infirm.; Ho. Off. (Surg. & Med.) Furness Gen. Hosp. Barrow-in-Furness; Staff Grade (Paedist.), Roy. Lancaster Infirm.

BURR, William Arthur Pinderfields Hospital NHS Trust, Aberford Road, Wakefield WF1 4DG Tel: 01924 814841 Fax: 01924 814977; 23 St. John's Square, Wakefield WF1 2RA Tel: 01924 376056 — MB ChB Birm. 1970; BSc Birm. 1967, MD 1980; FRCP Lond. 1986; MRCP (UK) 1973. (Birm.) Postgrad. Dean and Director of Postgrad. Med. and Dent. Educat., Yorks., Deanery. Socs: Brit. Thyroid Assn.; Soc. Endocrinol.; Diabetes UK. Prev: Cons. Phys. (Endocrinol., Diabetes & Gen. Med.) Pinderfields Hosp. Wakefield; Lect. (Med.) Qu. Eliz. Hosp. Birm.; SHO Hammersmith Hosp. Lond. & Nat. Hosp. Nerv. Dis. Lond.

BURRA, Fiona Frances Rose The Surgery, Hazeldene House, Great Haywood, Stafford ST18 0SU Tel: 01889 881206 Fax: 01889 883083 — MB ChB 1984 Birm.; DRCOG 1989.

BURRA, Venkata Suryanarayana Murthy Royal Liverpool University Hospital, Prescot St., Liverpool L7 8XP Tel: 0151 706 3202 Fax: 0151 706 5646 — MB BS 1985 Nagarjuna; 1985 MB BS Nagarjuna; 1995 MMed Sci. (Anaesth.) Belf.; 1989 MD (Anaesth.) Banaras Hindu Univ., Varanasi,; 1994 FFA RCSI. (Guntur Med. Coll. India) Cons. (Anaesth.) Roy. Liverp. & BRd.green Univ. Hosp.; Hon Lect. (Anaesth.) Univ. Liverp.; Asst. Edr., Brit. Jl. of Anaesth. Socs: Assn. Anaesth. GB & Irel.; Indian Soc. Anaesth.; Intens. Care Soc. Prev: Locum Sen. Regist. - Roy. Coll. Univ. Hosp.; Regist. (Anaesth.) Roy. Liverp. Univ. Hosp., BRd. Green Hosp. Liverp.& Belf. City Hosp. & Roy. Liverpo. Childr. Hosp. Alderhey.

BURRAGE, Maureen Valerie (retired) 2 Honey Lane, Burley, Ringwood BH24 4EN — MB BS 1956 Lond.; DCH Eng. 1959; DObst RCOG 1961. Prev: Area Specialist (Child Health) I. of Wight HA.

BURRELL, Catherine Craig Flat 1, Cathedral Court, Cathedral Green, Llandaff, Cardiff CF5 2EB — MB BCh 1995 Wales.

BURRELL, Christopher John Desmond (retired) 42 Bexton Road, Knutsford WA16 0DS Tel: 01565 2616 — MB BS 1957 Lond. Prev: Ho. Surg. & Ho. Phys. St. Mary's Hosp. Portsmouth.

BURRELL, Christopher Julian South West Cardiothoracic Centre, Derriford Hospital, Plymouth PL6 1DH Tel: 01752 792113 Fax: 01752 763078; Elmsleigh, Lodge Lane, Brixton, Plymouth PL8 2AU — MB BS 1979 Lond.; FRCP Lond. 1995; MRCP (UK) 1982; T(M) 1991. (Kings Coll. Hosp.) Cons. Cardiol. S. W. Cardiothoracic Centre Derriford Hosp. Plymouth; Hon. Cons. Cardiol. Roy. Hosps. Trust; Hon. Lect. Plymouth Postgrad. Med. Sch. Socs: BMA; Brit. Cardiac Soc.; Brit. Cardiovasc. Interven. Soc. Prev: Brit. Heart Foundat. Intermediate Research Fell.; Hon. Sen. Regist. Lond. Hosp.; Regist. St. Thos. Hosp. Lond.

BURRELL, Claire Margaret 7 Kingston Court, Whitley Bay NE26 1JP — MB BS 1991 Newc.

BURRELL, Clare Gillian Bannold Road Surgery, Rosalind Franklin House, Bannold Road, Waterbeach, Cambridge CB5 9LQ Tel: 01223 860387 Fax: 01223 576259 — MB BS 1984 Lond.; 2001 Dip. OCC Med; DRCOG 1988; Cert. Family Plann. JCC 1988. Socs: Assoc. Mem. Soc. of Occupat.al Med.

BURRELL, Craig Donald (retired) Flat 1, Cathedral Court, Cathedral Green, Llandaff, Cardiff CF5 2EB — MB ChB New Zealand 1951.

BURRELL, Helen Catherine Nottingham International Breast Education Centre, Nottingham City Hospital NHS Trust, Hucknall Rd, Nottingham NG5 1PB Tel: 0115 969 1689; Lynby, Wellow Rd, Eakring, Nottingham NG22 0DF Tel: 01623 870388 — MB BS 1986 Lond.; MRCP (UK) 1990; FRCR 1993. Cons. Radiol. (BrE. Imaging) Nottm. City Hosp. NHS Trust. Prev: Sen. Regist. (Radiol.) Nottm., Derby & Mansfield Train. Scheme.

BURRELL, Helen Elizabeth (retired) 57 Wellshot Dr, Cambuslane, Glasgow G72 8BN Tel: 013552 39111 — MB ChB 1981 Leeds; MB ChB Leeds. 1981. Prev: Regist. (Histopath.) Leeds Gen. Infirm.

BURRELL, Joan Mary (retired) 40 Victoria Street, Aberdeen AB10 1XA Tel: 01224 642860 — MB ChB 1945 Aberd.; MD (Commend.) Aberd. 1953; DObst RCOG 1948; DCH Eng. 1955. Prev: Asst. (Child Health) Univ. Aberd. & Hon. Clin. Asst. Roy. Hosp. Sick Childr. Aberd.

BURRELL, John Timothy Penn Manor Medical Centre, Manor Road, Penn, Wolverhampton WV4 5PY Tel: 01902 331166 Fax: 01902 575078 — MB ChB 1988 Birm. Prev: Trainee GP Birm.; SHO Wolverhampton HA VTS; SHO (Psychiat.) Kidderminster.

BURRELL, Mark Andrew Tilford, Preston and Burrell, Health Centre, Lawson Road, Norwich NR3 4LE Tel: 01603 427096 Fax: 01603 403074 Email: mark.burnell@gp-d82076.nhs.uk — BM BS 1984 Nottm.; MRCGP 1989; DObst RCPI 1987. (Nottingham)

BURRELL, Noel Leslie Ilchester Surgery, 17 Church Street, Ilchester, Yeovil BA22 8LN Tel: 01935 840207 Fax: 01935 840002 — MB 1956 Camb.; BChir 1955. Prev: Med. Regist. W. Cumbld. Hosp; Clin. Asst. (Med.) Workington Infirm.

BURRELL, Paul Gerard Blackhall and Peterlee Group Practice, Morven, Hesleden Road, Blackhall, Hartlepool TS24 4LQ Tel: 0191 586 4331 Fax: 0191 586 4844; Anneth Lowen, 18 Lumley Drive, Oakerside Park, Peterlee SR8 1NL Tel: 0191 586 3156 Email: ravdocsr8@compuserve.com — MB BS 1977 Newc.

BURRELL, Peter Stanley Richard (retired) 21 Liverton Whin, Saltburn-by-the-Sea TS12 1PQ Tel: 01287 622650 — MB ChB 1945 Leeds; DPH Leeds 1949; MFCM 1972. Prev: Dist. Med. Off. N. Tees Health Dist.

BURRELL, Simon James Porch Surgery, Beechfield Road, Corsham SN13 9DL — MB ChB 1979 Bristol; MRCGP 1985; MRCOG 1984. (Bristol) Princip. GP Corsham; Clin. lead for N. Wilts & Devises PCG. Prev: Dir. Of Commiss.ing Wilts. HA 1997-2000.

BURRELL, Stephen John Luton & Dunstable Hospital, Lewson Rd, Luton LU4 0DZ Tel: 01582 497205 Fax: 01582 497362 Email: stephen.burrell@ldh-tr.anglex.nhs.uk; 5 Churchover Close, Wylde Green, Sutton, Sutton Coldfield B76 1WG — MB BS 1987 Lond.; Diploma Obstetric Ultrasound (RCR/RCOG) 2000; MFFP 1995; BSc Lond. 1984; MRCP (UK) 1992; MRCOG 1994. (University College London) Cons. Obst. & Gyn. Luton & Dunstable Hosp. Luton. Prev: Subspeciality Trainee Fetal Med. Univ. Coll. Lond.

BURRIDGE, Alice Department of Radiology, Royal Victoria Infirmary, Newcastle upon Tyne Tel: 0191 232 5131; 80 Sunniside Road, Sunniside, Newcastle upon Tyne NE16 5NF Tel: 0191 488 9356 — MB ChB 1967 Sheff.; FFR 1974; DMRD Eng. 1973. Cons. Radiol. Roy. Vict. Infirm. Newc.

BURRIDGE, Duncan Neil The Medical Centre, Station Avenue, Bridlington YO16 4LZ Tel: 01262 670686 Fax: 01262 401685; 6 St James Road, Bridlington YO15 3PF Tel: 01262 401833 Email: dunburr@msn.com — MB ChB Manch. 1986; MRCGP 1990; DRCOG 1988. Prev: Trainee GP N.d. VTS.

BURRIDGE, Janine Mair Aylmer Lodge Surgery, Broomfield Road, Kidderminster DY11 5PA Tel: 01562 822015 Fax: 01562 827137 — MB BS 1981 Lond.; DRCOG 1984.

BURRIDGE, Jeffrey William New Mount Surgery, Margam Road, Port Talbot SA13 2BN Tel: 01639 884111 — MB BS 1984 Lond.

BURRIDGE, Matthew Guy 69 Dunstone View, Plymouth PL9 8TW — MB BS 1997 Lond.; BSc Lond. (University College London, Medical School)

BURRIN, Elizabeth Mary 19 Maywater Close, South Croydon CR2 0RS — MB BS 1997 Lond.; BSc Psychol with Basic Med Scis. SHO Psychiat. Handsley Hosp., Lond. Socs: Med. Defence Union. Prev: A & E Cas. Off., St. Geo.'s Hosp.; Surg. HO, P.ss Roy.; Med. HO, St. Helier NHS Trust, Carshalton.

BURROUGH, Mr Simon Jerome (retired) Mixbury Hall, Mixbury, Brackley NN13 5RL — BM BCh 1964 Oxf.; BA Oxf. 1964; FRCS Ed. 1971. Cons. Traum. & Orthop. Surg. Horton Gen. Hosp. Banbury. Prev: Lect. (Orthop. Surg.) Univ. Edin.

BURROUGHES, Ann Maria Bronglais General Hospital, Aberystwyth SY23 1ER Tel: 01970 623131; 34 Brynglas Road, Llanbadarn, Aberystwyth SY23 3QR Tel: 01970 624780 — MB ChB 1967 Manch.; MRCOG 1987; DObst RCOG 1970; FRCOG 1999. (Manch.) Staff Doctor (O & G) Bronglais Gen. Hosp. Aberystwyth. Prev: Regist. (O & G) Univ. Hosp. Wales Cardiff; Clin. Asst. (O & G) Bronglais Gen. Hosp. Aberystwyth.

BURROUGHS, Andrew Kenneth Hepato-Biliary and Liver Transplantation Unit, Royal Free Hospital, Pond Street, Hampstead,

London NW3 3QG Tel: 020 7472 6229 Fax: 020 7472 6226 Email: andrew.burroughs@talk21.com — MB ChB 1976 (Hons) Liverp.; MRCP (UK) 1978; FRCP Lond. 1991; T(M) 1991. (Univ. Liverp. Sch. Med.) Cons. Phys. & Hepatol. Roy. Free, Hampstead, NHS Trust; Hon. Sen. Lect. Roy. Free Hosp. Sch. Med.; Vis. Prof. Univ. of Florence 1995-present. Socs: Brit. Assn. Study Liver; Brit. Soc. Gastroenterol.; Eur. Assn. Study Liver (Sec. Scientif. Comm.) 1997-1999. Prev: Sen. Lect. & Hon. Cons. Med. Roy. Free Hosp. Sch. Med. Lond.

BURROUGHS, Elizabeth Ann Bawtry Health Centre, Station Road, Bawtry, Doncaster DN10 6RQ Tel: 01302 710326 Fax: 01302 719884 — MB BChir Camb. 1970; MA Camb. 1970, MD 1977. (Camb. & Guy's) Gen. Med. Practitioner; Med. Adviser Doncaster Health; Clin. Asst. St. John's Hospice Doncaster. Socs: BMA. Prev: John Stokes Research Fell. (Psychiat.) Univ. Sheff.; Ho. Phys. Guy's Hosp. Lond.; Ho. Surg. Birm. Accid. Hosp.

BURROUGHS, Susan Helen Tel: 01722 429108 Email: dr.s.burroughs@shc-tr.swest.nhs.uk — BM 1992 Soton.; BSc (Hons.) Soton. 1991. Cons. Histopath. and Cytopathologist, Salisbury Healthcare NHS Trust, Salisbury. Prev: SHO (Histopath.) Salisbury Dist. Hosp. & Soton. Gen. Hosp.; Specialist Regist. (Histopath.) Univ. Hosp. of Wales, Cardiff.

BURROW, Charles Thomas Department of Pathology, University Hospital, Aintree, Liverpool — MB ChB Liverp. 1969; MRCPath 1976; FRCPath 1987, M 1976. (Liverpool) Cons. Path. Univ. Hosp. Aintree, Liverp. (Aintree Hosps. Trust). Prev: Lect. (Path.) Univ. Liverp.; Sen. Regist. (Morbid Anat.) BRd.green Hosp. Liverp.

BURROW, Dorinda Elizabeth Maude Copthorne, The Undercliffe, Sandgate, Folkestone CT20 3AT Tel: 01303 48524 — MB ChB 1947 Ed. (Ed.) Med. Off. (Family Plann.) S.E. Kent Health Dist.

BURROW, Geoffrey Robert France 111 Queens Court, Ramsey IM8 1LQ Tel: 01624 814888 — MB ChB 1953 Leeds. (Leeds) Prev: Ho. Surg. Dewsbury Gen. Hosp.; Ho. Phys. Huddersfield Roy. Infirm.; Res. Med. Off. St. Luke's Hosp. Huddersfield.

BURROW, Janice Elizabeth 24 Cooper Road, Westbury on Trym, Bristol BS9 3RA — MB ChB 1976 Bristol; DRCOG 1979. Clin. Asst. (Neurol.) Frenchay Healthcare Trust Bristol; Clin. Asst. (Gastroenterol.) S.mead Hosp. Bristol. Prev: GP Bradley Stoke; GP Henleaze, Bristol Retainer Scheme; SHO (c/o Elderly) Bristol Gen. Hosp.

BURROW, Mary Anne Lockhart Kintail, 27 North Erskine Park, Bearsden, Glasgow G61 4LY Tel: 0141 942 0495 — MB ChB 1976 Glas.; DCH RCPS Glas. 1979; DRCOG 1978. Socs: Wom. Doctors Retainer Scheme & Roy. M-C Soc. Glas.; BMA. Prev: Regist. (Med.) Chalmers & P.ss Margt. Rose Orthop. Hosps. & Roy. Infirm. Edin.; SHO (Infec. Dis.) Ruchill Hosp. Glas.; SHO (Med. Paediat.) Roy. Hosp. Sick Childr. Glas.

BURROW, Sianed 10 Glynderwen Close, Sketty, Swansea SA2 8EQ — MB BS 1994 Lond.

BURROWES, Desmond Edward St John (retired) Uplands Cottage, Wellington Heath, Ledbury HR8 1NF Tel: 01531 632800 — MB BS 1945 Lond.; MD Lond. 1952; MRCP Lond. 1949; MRCS Eng. LRCP Lond. 1945. Prev: Regist. (Med.) & Ho. Phys. St. Thos. Hosp.

BURROWES, Horace Phillip (retired) 2 Barfield Drive, Yeadon, Leeds LS19 7SJ Tel: 0113 250 8026 — MB BS 1951 Lond.; DPM RCPSI 1964; DPH Liverp. 1956. Prev: Cons. Psychiat., Yorks. Regional HA.

BURROWES, Peter William Northgate Medical Practice, 1 Northgate, Canterbury CT1 1WL Tel: 01227 463570 Fax: 01227 786147; 4 Clock Tower Parade, Blean, Canterbury CT2 9HP — MB BS 1975 Lond.; MRCS Eng. LRCP Lond. 1975; DRCOG 1979.

BURROWES, William Lewson, SBStJ (retired) Cotsdale, Corsham SN13 9HT Tel: 01249 713353 — MD 1948 Belf.; MB BCh BAO 1943; FRCPI 1989; MRCPI 1949. Prev: Ho. Phys. & Ho. Surg. Roy. Vict. Hosp. Belf.

BURROWS, Alison Claire 15 Clear View, Kingswinford DY6 9XQ — BM BS 1990 Nottm.

BURROWS, Alison Jayne 13 Arthingworth Close, Binley, Coventry CV3 2HQ Tel: 024 76 453750 — MB ChB 1993 Leeds. Trainee GP Airedale Gen. Hosp.

BURROWS, Anderson Maria (retired) 25 Wynnstay Gardens, Allen St., London W8 6UR Tel: 020 7937 2017 — MB BS Lond. 1945; Roy. Free Hosp. Prev: Cons. (A & E) Ashford Hosp. Middlx.

BURROWS, Anthony Wayne 5 Buckden Road, Edgerton, Huddersfield HD3 3AX — BM BCh 1969 Oxf.; MSc Oxf. 1967, MA, DM 1982; FRCP Lond. 1992, M 1973. (St. Thos.) Cons. Phys. Huddersfield Roy. Infirm.; Hon. Sen. Lect. Universoity of Leeds. Prev: Sen. Regist. (Med.) Yorks. RHA; Med. Regist. & Hon. Sen. Regist. Radcliffe Infirm. Oxf.; Ho. Phys. St. Thos. Hosp. Lond.

BURROWS, Brian Denis 17 Shrewsbury Gardens, Belfast BT9 6PJ Tel: 028 668395; 17 Shrewsbury Gardens, Belfast BT9 6PJ — MB BCh BAO 1960 Belf.; DMRT Eng. 1965; FRCR 1975; FFR 1968. (Qu. Univ. Belf.) Prev: Cons. Radiotherap. & Oncol. N. Irel. Radiother. Centre Belf.

BURROWS, Cameron 59 Earnsdale Avenue, Darwen BB3 1JR; 1 Wheelwright Court, Walkhampton, Yelverton PL20 6LA Tel: 01822 854392 — MB ChB 1992 Aberd. SHO, Surg. Rotat., Perryford Hosp. Plymouth. Prev: A & E/Anat. Demonst. Liverp. Roy. Infirm.

BURROWS, Caroline Dorothy Margaret Cinderford Health Centre, Dockham Road, Cinderford GL14 2AN Tel: 01594 598020 — MB BS 1981 Lond.; DCH RCP Lond. 1984.

BURROWS, Cerys Jane Department of Histopathology, Macclesfield Hospital, Victoria Road, Macclesfield SK10 3BL Tel: 01625 661825; 69 Middlewich Road, Holmes Chapel, Crewe CW4 7ER — MB BS 1990 Lond.; MSc Lond. 1985; MRCPath 1998. (Char. Cross & Westm.) Cons. Macclesfield Hosp., Macclesfield.

BURROWS, Charles John Fasnagreanach, Malcolm Road, Peterculter AB14 0NX — LMSSA 1947 Lond. (St. Bart.) Asst. (Accid. Surg.) Roy. Infirm. Aberd.; Hon. Clin. Lect. in Surg. (Traum. & Orth.) Univ. Aberd. Prev: Ho. Surg. Harrow Hosp.

BURROWS, Christopher James Maurys Mount, Slab Lane, West Wellow, Romsey SO51 6BY — BM 1992 Soton. SHO (Anaesth.) Portsmouth Hosps. Trust.

BURROWS, David (Desmond) 11 Broomhill Park, Belfast BT9 5JB Tel: 02890 381699 Fax: 02890 664901 Email: abu21177@aol.com — MD 1957 Belf.; MB BCh BAO 1953; FRCP Lond. 1986; FRCPI 1981; FRCP Ed. 1969, M 1960. (Belf.) Socs: (Ex-Pres.) Brit. Assn. Dermat.; Hon. Mem. Amer. Dermat. Assn. & Spanish Dermat. Soc.; Hon. Corr. Mem. Finnish & Swedish Norwegians Dermat. Socs. Prev: Cons. Dermat. Roy. Vict. Hosp. Belf.; Prof. Clin. Med. Sch. Qu. Univ. Belf.

BURROWS, David Jonathan 14 Llanwnarth View, Govilon, Abergavenny NP7 9PL — MB BS 1996 Lond.

BURROWS, Deborah Ann 3 James Avenue, Roundhay, Leeds LS8 1LH Tel: 0113 266 2240 — MB BS 1990 Newc.; BSc (Hons.) Univ. of West. Ontario 1985; MRCP (UK) 1994. Regist. (Neurol.) Yorks. RHA.

BURROWS, Edmund Hartford Brackendale, Hadrian Way, chilworth, Southampton SO16 7HX Tel: 02380 767816 Fax: 02380 767816 — MB ChB 1951 Cape Town; MRad Liverp. 1963; FRCR 1977; DMRD Liverp. 1958; DMRD Eng. 1958. Emerit. Cons. Neuroradiol. Soton. Univ. Hosps.; Hon. Civil. Cons. RN Hosp. Haslar.; Emerit. Cons. Radiol. King Edwd. VII Hosp. Midhurst. Prev: Cons. Neuroradiol. Soton & S.W. Hants. HA (T) & Wessex Neurol. Centre Soton; Vis. Fell. (Radiol.) Univ. Rochester, NY; Sen. Regist. (Lysholm X-Ray) Nat. Hosp. Qu. Sq.

BURROWS, Frank David Charles Riverside Practice, Friarsgate Medical Centre, Winchester SO23 8EF Tel: 01962 853599 Fax: 01962 849982; Orchard House, 75 Stockbridge Road, Winchester SO22 6RP Tel: 01962 866531 — MB BS 1974 Lond.; MRCS Eng. LRCP Lond. 1974; DRCOG 1977. (Roy. Free)

BURROWS, Frederick George Osborne (retired) 17 Hayfield Road, Birmingham B13 9LG — MB BCh BAO 1949 Dub.; FRCS Eng. 1954; FFR 1965; DMRD Eng. 1962. Hon. Cons. Radiol. Birm. Centr. Health Dist. (T). Prev: Cons. i/c Diag. Radiol. Dept. Qu. Eliz. Hosp. Birm.

BURROWS, Geoffrey Edward (retired) Grasshopper Lodge, Field Broughton, Grange-over-Sands LA11 6HW Tel: 015395 36441 — MB ChB 1951 Liverp.; MD Liverp. 1976; MFOM RCP Lond. 1979. Prev: Med. Off. (Occupat. Health Serv.) Univ. Manch.

BURROWS, Gillian Carol Biochemistry Department, Stepping Hill Hospital, Poplar Grove, Stockport SK2 7JE Tel: 0161 419 5621 Fax: 0161 419 5668 Email: gillian.burrows@stockport-tr.nwest.nhs.uk; Styperson House, Brookledge Lane, Adlington, Chorley SK10 4JX Tel: 01606 891 3314 — MB ChB 1985 Leeds; MRCPath 1998. Cons. (Chem. Path.) Stepping Hill Hosp.

BURROWS, John Rimmer Half Year House, Calves Well Lane, West Runton, Cromer NR27 9LU — MB ChB 1955 Liverp.; MA Camb. 1957; DPhysMed. Eng. 1959. (Camb. & Liverp.) Med. Dir. Mundesley Hosp. Socs: Fell. Roy. Soc. Med.; Brit. Assn. Physical Med. Prev: Med. Off. Farnham Pk. Rehabil. Centre; Clin. Asst. (Physical Med.) Lond. Hosp.; Med. Off. RAF MRU Headley Ct., Surrey.

BURROWS, Joselyn Riverside Paractice, Friarsgate Medical Centre, Friarsgate, Winchester SO23 8EF Tel: 01962 853599; Holly Hill, 109 Andover Road, Winchester SO22 6AX Tel: 01962 882344 — BM 1984 Soton.; DRCOG 1990. SHO (Paediat.) Roy. Hants. Co. Hosp. Winchester. Prev: SHO (A & E Geriat. & O & G) Roy. Hants. Co. Hosp. Winchester.

BURROWS, Leonie Morgan 68 Plantation Road, Hextable, Swanley BR8 7SB — MB BS 1979 Lond.; BSc Lond. 1976, MB BS 1979; DRCOG 1982. GP Dartford. Prev: Trainee GP W. Kingsdown VTS; SHO (Neonat.) Lond. Hosp.; Dr. i/c Kilunge Hosp. Zanzibar, Tanzania (VSO).

BURROWS, Lorna Jule Dermatology Department, Salisbury Tel: 01722 336262 Fax: 01722 415071; Kents Cottage, Ihgh St, Broughton, Stockbridge SO20 8AD — MB BCh 1982 Witwatersrand; BSc Cape Town 1974, BSc (Hons.) Biochem. 1975. Assoc. Specialist (Dermat.) Salisbury Dist. Hosp. Socs: Brit. Assn. Dermat.; BSDS; ISDS. Prev: Research Regist. (Dermat.) Soton. Univ. Hosps.

BURROWS, Maurice McConnell (retired) 2 The Westwoods, Noctorum Road, Birkenhead CH43 9UQ Tel: 0151 652 2804 — MB BCh BAO 1949 Belf.; FFA RCS Eng. 1954; DA RCPSI 1952; DA Eng. 1952. Prev: Cons. Anaesth. Mersey RHA.

BURROWS, Mr Nigel Colin Salisbury District Hospital, Salisbury SP2 8BJ Tel: 01722 336262 Fax: 01722 331529; Orchard, Ringwood Road, Three Legged Cross, Wimborne BH21 6RB — BM 1981 Soton.; FRCS Ed. 1987; FFAEM 1995. (Southampton) Cons. A & E Salisbury Dist. Hosp. Prev: Sen. Regist. Rotat. (A & E) Luton & Dunstable & W.m. Hosps.; Regist. (A & E) Poole Gen. Hosp.

BURROWS, Nigel Peter Dermatology Department, Addenbrooke's Hospital, Hills Road, Cambridge CB2 2QQ Tel: 01223 216501 Fax: 01223 216863 Email: nigelburrows@msexc.addenbrookes.anglox.nhs.uk — MB BS 1985 Lond.; MD (Lond.) 1998; MRCP (UK) 1988. (St. Thomas' Hospital) Cons. Dermat. Addenbrooke's Hosp. Camb.; Cons. Derm. Hinchingbrooke Hosp., Huntingdon. Prev: Sen. Regist. (Dermat.) Addenbrooke's Hosp. Camb.; Regist. (Dermat.) Roy. Post Grad. Med. Sch., Hammersmith Hosp. & Ealing Hosp.; Regist. (Med.) Ham Green Hosp. Bristol.

BURROWS, Norman Ferguson Elliott 37 Fairacres Road, Oxford OX4 1TH Tel: 01865 246718 — BM BCh 1939 Oxf.; BA Oxf. 1936, MA, BM BCh 1939; MRCS Eng. LRCP Lond. 1939; DCH Eng. 1946. Socs: Fell. (Ex-Pres.) Hunt. Soc.; Fell. Roy. Soc. Med.; Brit. Paediat. Assn. Prev: Cons. Paediat. Nat. Adoption Soc.; Hon. Lect. (Paediat.) Univ. Coll. Hosp. Lond.; Sen. Regist. (Med. & Path.) Hosp. Sick Childr. Gt. Ormond St. Lond.

BURROWS, Pamela Susan The Health Centre, Trenchard Avenue, Thornaby, Stockton-on-Tees TS17 0DD Tel: 01642 762636 Fax: 01642 766464; Redwalls, 15 Thornton Road, Thornton, Middlesbrough TS8 9BS — MB BS 1981 Newc.; MRCGP 1985; DRCOG 1985. (Newcastle-upon-Tyne)

BURROWS, Peter (retired) 21 Greenhill Road, Liverpool L18 6JJ Tel: 0151 724 2571 — MB ChB 1949 Liverp.; MRCS Eng. LRCP Lond. 1950; MRCGP 1958. Prev: Vis. Med. Off. Marie Curie Foundat. Nursing Home Liverp.

BURROWS, Peter James Abbey Mead Surgery, Abbey Mead, Romsey SO51 8EN Tel: 01794 512218 Fax: 01794 514224; Maurys Mount, Slab Lane, West Wellow, Romsey SO51 6BY Tel: 01794 322077 Email: pjburrows@interalpha.co.uk — BM BCh Oxf. 1966; MRCP (UK) 1971; FRCGP 1984, M 1974; DObst RCOG 1972. (St. Thos.) Prev: Regist (Med.) Soton. Gen. Hosp.; SHO (Med.) Plymouth Gen. Hosp.; Ho. Off. (Paediat. & Neurol.) Radcliffe Infirm. Oxf.

BURROWS, Peter John Thorpe Wood Surgery, 140 Woodside Road, Norwich NR7 9QL; 24 Paston Way, Thorpe St Andrew, Norwich NR7 9LT Fax: 01244 378337 Email: mavis.evans@virgin.net, p.burrows@dial.pipex.com — MB ChB 1990 Sheff.; MRCGP 1995; DRCOG 1994. (Univ. Sheff.) p/t GP Norwich; Jt. Clin. Governance lead, BRd.land PCG, Norwich. Prev: Trainee GP Gt. Yarmouth & Waveney VTS; Ho. Off. (Med.) James Paget Hosp. Gt. Yarmouth; Ho. Off. (Orthop.) Roy. Hallamsh. Hosp. Sheff.

BURROWS, Roy 8 Park Lane, Richmond TW9 2RA Tel: 020 8948 4251 — MB ChB 1967 Liverp.; DPH Liverp. 1970; DPM Eng. 1976. (Liverp.) Sen. Med. Off. Head of Med. Servs. HMP Wandsworth. Prev: Clin. Med. Off. (Community Med.) Liverp. AHA.

BURROWS, Sally 61 Allen Road, Hedge End, Southampton SO30 4EU — MB BS 1988 Lond.; DCH RCP Lond. 1993; DRCOG 1992.

BURROWS, Sophie Kathryn Rowcroft Surgery, Merry Walks, Stroud Tel: 01453 764471; The Laurels, Jacks Green, Sheepscombe, Stroud GL6 7RA — MB BS 1984 Lond.; MRCGP (UK) 1989; DRCOG 1988; DA (UK) 1987; LLM 1999. GP Cheltenham; WM Dep. Coroner, Cheltenham. Socs: BMA; MRCGP. Prev: Trainee GP Glos. VTS.

BURROWS, William John Chipping Surgery, 1 Symn Lane, Wotton-under-Edge GL12 7BD Tel: 01453 842214 — MB ChB 1972 Bristol; DCH Eng. 1975.

BURSCOUGH, John Francis Riverside Surgery, Barnard Avenue, Brigg DN20 8AS Tel: 01652 650131 Fax: 01652 651551; Woodland View, Melton Road, Wrawby, Brigg DN20 8SS Tel: 01652 652624 — MB ChB 1981 Manch.

BURSEY, Roger Geoffrey Parkgate, Drigg Road, Seascale CA20 1NX Tel: 01946 727175 — MB ChB 1974 Sheff.; MFOM 1991, AFOM 1982. Indep. Occupat. Phys. Prev: Med. off. Brit. Nuclear Fuels; Regional Med. Adviser N. Lond. Post Off.; Cons. Occupat. Health Phys. W. Cumbld. Hosp. Whitehaven.

BURSLEM, Richard Waywell (retired) Lone Oak, Mereside Road, Mere, Knutsford WA16 6QR Tel: 01565 830100 Fax: 01565 830790 Email: barograph@aol.com — MB ChB 1944 Manch.; MB ChB (Hons.) Manch. 1944; MD Manch. 1947; FRCOG 1962, M 1948. Hon. Cons. Obst. & Gyn. UHSM & Withington Hosp. Manch.; Examr. RCOG. Prev: Lect. & Examr. (O & G) Univ. Manch.

BURSTEIN, Nathaniel (retired) 2 Gray's Inn Square, Gray's Inn, London WC1R 5AA Tel: 020 7242 6725 — BA, MB BCh BAO Dub. 1929.

BURSTON, Dallas John Ashbourne Pharmaceuticals, Victors Barns, Hill Farm, Brixworth, Northampton NN6 9DQ Tel: 01604 882190 Fax: 01604 880957; The Old Rectory, Arthingworth, Market Harborough LE16 8JT — MB BS 1975 Lond.; MRCS Eng. LRCP Lond. 1975. (St. Bart.) Chairm. & Chief Exec. Off. Dallas Burston Healthcase; Nat. Comm. Mem. Dispensing Doctors Assn. Prev: Trainee GP N.ampton VTS; SHO (Paediat., A & E & O & G) & Ho. Surg. N.ampton Gen. Hosp.

BURSTON, Geoffrey Robert (retired) 4 St. Hilary Close, Stoke Bishop, Bristol BS9 1DA — MB ChB 1962 Bristol; FRCP Ed. 1981 M 1968. Hon. Cons. Frenchay Healthcare Trust Bristol; Clin. Lect. (Geriat.) Dept. Med. Univ. Bristol. Prev: Cons. Phys. (Geriat. Med.) S.mead Health Serv. Trust Bristol.

BURSTON, Jennifer Irene 4 St Hilary Close, Stoke Bishop, Bristol BS9 1DA — MB ChB 1962 Bristol. Clin. Asst. Dept. Geriat. Med. S.mead HA.

BURSTON, John Tanyards, Rowsells Lane, Totnes TQ9 5AG Tel: 01803 868006 — MB BS 1951 Lond.; BSc (Special, Physiol.) Lond. 1948, MD 1959; MRCS Eng. LRCP Lond. 1951; FRCPath 1973, M 1961. (St. Thos.) Socs: Soc. Path. & Bact.; (Ex-Pres.) Assn. Clin. Path. Prev: Cons. Path. Portsmouth & I. of Wight Area Path. Serv. & Clin. Teach. Soton. Univ. Med. Sch.; Lect. Clin. (Path.) St. Thos. Hosp. Med. Sch. Lond.; Cons. Path. Stepney Gp. Laborat. Mile End Hosp.

BURSTOW, Angela Clare Staffa Health Centre, 3 Waverley Street, Tibshelf, Alfreton DE55 5NU Tel: 01773 872252 Fax: 01773 591712 — MB ChB 1992 Sheff.; DRCOG 1996; DCH RCP Lond. 1995; DFFP 1996; MRCGP 1996. (Sheffield) p/t GP Princip.; Family Plann. Doctor.

BURT, Alan John 3 Relugas Road, Edinburgh EH9 2NE — MB ChB 1970 Ed.; MD Ed. 1984; FRCP Ed. 1987; FRCPCH 1997. Cons. Paediat. St. John's Hosp. Livingston & Roy. Hosp. Sick Childr. Edin.; Hon. Sen. Lect. (Child Life & Health) Univ. Edin. Prev: Lect. (Child Life & Health) Univ. Edin.

BURT, Professor Alastair David University Department of Pathology, Royal Victoria Infirmary, Newcastle upon Tyne NE1 4LP Tel: 0191 232 5131 Fax: 0191 222 8100 Email: a.d.burt@ncl.ac.uk;

The Gables, Fairmoor, Morpeth NE61 3JL Tel: 01670 510518 — MB ChB 1981 Glas.; MB ChB (Commend.) Glas. 1981; BSc (Hons.) Glas. 1979, MD (Hons.) 1991; FRCPath 1997; FIBiol 1997. Head of Acad. Path., Prof. Path. & Hon. Cons. Path. Univ. Newc. u. Tyne Roy., Vict. Infirm. & Freeman Hosp.; Speciality Adviser Histopathol. Roy. Coll. of Path.; Edr.-in-Chief Liver. Socs: & Comm. Mem. Path. Soc. GB; Internat. Assn. Study Liver; Amer. Assn. Study Liver Dis. Prev: Peel Trav. Research Fell. Laborat. for Cell Biol. & Histol. Free Univ. Brussels (VUB) Belgium; CL Oakley Lect. 1993; Prof. Newc. uponTyne 1995-1998.

BURT, Bridget May Skellern and Partners, Bridport Medical Centre, North Allington, Bridport DT6 5DU Tel: 01308 421109 Fax: 01308 420869; Winford Farm, Halstock Leigh, Yeovil BA22 9QX Email: john.dearlove@virgin.net — MB ChB 1988 Manch.; DFFP 1994.

BURT, Miss Caroline Grace 5 bearfield Buildings, Bradford-on-Avon BA15 1RP Tel: 01225 866586 Email: caroline.burt@easynet.co.uk — MB BS 1993 Lond.; FRCS Lond. 1997; BSc Lond. 1990. Specialist Regist. in Gen. Surg., W. Midl. Rotat. Socs: ASIT; WIST. Prev: Specialist Regist. Vasc. Surg., heartland NHS trust; SHO Gen. Surg., Norf. & Norwich NHS Trust.

BURT, David Edward Robertson 93 Cranley Gardens, London N10 3AD — MB ChB 1973 Bristol; MSc Lond. 1993; FFA RCS Eng. 1979. Cons. Anaesth. St. Thos. Hosp. Lond.; Hon. Cons. Anaesth. Newham Health Dist. Socs: Fell. Roy. Soc. Med.; Assn. Anaesth. Gt. Brit. & Irel. & Anaesth. Res. Soc. Prev: Sen. Lect. (Anaesth.) Lond. Hosp. Med. Coll.; Regist. (Anaesth.) Roy. Nat. Throat, Nose & Ear Hosp. Lond.; Regist. (Anaesth.) Sheff. AHA (T).

BURT, Douglas Peebles Group Practice Surgery, Green Street, Forfar DD8 3AR Tel: 01307 462316 Fax: 01307 463623; Kinloch, 19 Glamis Road, Kirriemuir DD8 5BN Tel: 01575 575078 Email: kinloch@mcmail.com — MB ChB 1978 Glas.; MRCGP 1982. Prison Med. Off. Noranside Prison. Prev: Regist. (Med.) Stirling Roy. Infirm.

BURT, Eric Henry Walter (retired) 6 Trews Gardens, Kelvedon, Colchester CO5 9AQ Tel: 01376 570258 — MB BChir 1946 Camb.; MRCS Eng. LRCP Lond. 1945. Prev: Clin. Asst. (Radiother.) Essex Co. Hosp. Colchester.

BURT, Graham Oxford Anaesthetic Partnership, Felstead House, 23 Banbury Road, Oxford OX2 6NN Tel: 01865 559157 Fax: 01865 513089; 17 Burgess Mead, Oxford OX2 6XP Tel: 01865 554595 Fax: 01865 510518 Email: drgburt@cs.com — BM BCh 1972 Oxf.; MA Oxf. 1972; MRCGP 1983; FRCA 1977. (Oxford) Cons. Anaesth. Oxf. Radcliffe Trust, Oxf.; InDepend. Medico-legal Adviser. Socs: BMA; Assn. Anaesth.; Pain Soc. Prev: Manager Med. Defence Union; GP S.port; Gen. Profess. Trainee & Clin. Lect. (Anaesth.) Oxf.

BURT, Graham Forrest Hospital Hill Surgery, 7 Izatt Avenue, Dunfermline KY11 3BA Tel: 01383 731721 Fax: 01383 623352; 12 Maree Place, Crossford, Dunfermline KY12 8XU — MB ChB 1981 Dundee.

BURT, Gwendolyn Anne (retired) 12 Millwood, Lisvane, Cardiff CF14 0TL Tel: 02920 766156 — MB BCh 1954 Wales; BSc Wales 1951; DCH Eng. 1960; DObst RCOG 1958. Prev: GP Cardiff.

BURT, James Hendrie Stonewood, 17 Greenmount Drive, Greenmount, Bury BL8 4HA Tel: 0120 488 2440 — MB ChB 1946 St. And. (Dundee)

BURT, Joan Pauline 3 Relugas Road, Edinburgh EH9 2NE — MB ChB 1970 Ed.

BURT, John Richardson Southwood, Dunfermline KY11 4SS Tel: 01383 21423 — MB ChB 1951 St. And.

BURT, John Robert Fyffe Oliver and Partners, Millhill Surgery, 87 Woodmill Street, Dunfermline KY11 4JW Tel: 01383 621222 Fax: 01383 622862; Ailie Craig, Veere Park, Culross, Dunfermline KY12 8NE — MB ChB 1983 Aberd.; DFFP 1995. Prev: SHO (Infec. Dis.) Cameron Hosp. Fife; SHO (Paediat.) Vict. Hosp. Kirkcaldy; SHO (O & G) Dunfermline Matern. Hosp.

BURT, Leslie Gordon 5 Ravenscourt Avenue, London W6 0SL Tel: 020 8748 4023 — MB BS 1962 Lond.; MRCS Eng. LRCP Lond. 1963; BDS Sydney 1950; Hon. FRACDS 1966. (Char. Cross) Socs: BMA. & Assn. Anaesths. Gt. Brit. & Irel. Prev: Ho. Off. W. Lond. Hosp. & Centr. Middlx. Hosp.

BURT, Lindsay Mayfield Surgery, 246 Roehampton Lane, London SW15 4AA Tel: 020 8780 5770/5650 Fax: 020 8780 5649; 3 Sion Road, Twickenham TW1 3DR Tel: 020 8892 9326 — MB BS Lond. 1970; DObst RCOG 1972. (Charing Cross.) Assoc. Mem. Soc. Occupat. Med.

BURT, Paul Alexander Christie Hospital & Holt Radium Institute, Wilmslow Road, Withington, Manchester M20 4BX Tel: 0161 446 3000 Fax: 0161 446 3330; Willow House, 75 The Crescent, Davenport, Stockport SK3 8SL — MB ChB 1980 Birm.; MRCP (UK) 1983; FRCR 1988; FRCP 1998. Cons. Clin. Oncol. Christie Hosp. & Holt Radium Inst. Manch.; Vis. Clin. Oncol. Leighton Hosp. Crewe; Hon. Clin. Lect. (Oncol.) Inst. Cancer Studies Univ. of Manch. Prev: Regist. (Radiat. Oncol.) W.mead Hosp. Sydney, Austral.; SHO (Gen. Med. & Clin. Haemat.) E. Birm. Hosp.; SHO (Gen. Med.) Selly Oak Hosp. Birm.

BURT, Roy William Portslade Health Centre, Church Road, Portslade, Brighton BN41 1LX Tel: 01273 422525/418445 Fax: 01273 413510; Southwick, Brighton BN42 4HH Tel: 01273 418945 — MRCS Eng. LRCP Lond. 1958. (Leeds)

BURT, Ruth Margaret 19 Briarwood Drive, Cyncoed, Cardiff CF23 6SR Tel: 029 2075 9173 — MB ChB Sheff. 1966; DObst RCOG 1968. (Sheff.) Staff Grade Cardiff Community Healthcare; Clin. Asst. Univ. Hosps. of Wales. Prev: Med. Off. S. Glam. AHA (T).

BURT, Sarah Jane 91 The Lloyd, Hales, Market Drayton TF9 2PS — MB ChB 1993 Birm.

BURT, Victoria Ann 48 Middle Road, Kingswood, Bristol BS15 4XH Tel: 0117 957 2349 — MB ChB 1996 Leeds. SHO (Psychiat.), Barrow Hosp. Bristol. Prev: Gen. Pract. Regist. The Surg. St Mary St. Thornbury; SHO (c/o Elderly) Chapel Allerton/Wharfedale Hosp. Leeds.

BURTENSHAW, Andrew John 4 Emerald Close, Waterlooville PO7 8NZ — MB ChB 1998 Birm.

BURTENSHAW, Fergus George Rose Blackbird Leys Health Centre, 63 Blackbird Leys Road, Oxford OX4 6HL Tel: 01865 778244 — MB BS 1974 Lond.; DRCOG 1978.

BURTENSHAW, Hazel Mary (retired) 1 Bridge Street Road, Lavenham, Sudbury CO10 9SH Tel: 01787 247682 — MB BS Lond. 1959; MRCS Eng. LRCP Lond. 1959; FFA RCS Eng. 1968; DA Eng. 1963; DCH Eng. 1963; DObst RCOG 1961. Prev: Cons. Anaesth. Huddersfield Roy. Infirm.

BURTHEM, John 7 Coronation Drive, Penketh, Warrington WA5 2DD — MB ChB 1986 Liverp.; BSc (Hons.) Liverp. 1983, MB ChB (Hons.) 1986; MRCP (UK) 1989.

BURTLES, Richard (retired) 8 Ventnor Terrace, Edinburgh EH9 2BL Tel: 0131 667 6178 Email: dick.burtles@onet.co.uk — MB BS 1949 Lond.; FFA RCS Eng. 1956. Prev: Cons. Anaesth., Roy. Hosp. for Sick Childr., Edin.

BURTON, Albert Edward Woodside Health Centre, Barr Street, Glasgow G20 7LR Tel: 0141 531 9530 Fax: 0141 331 9545 — MB ChB 1969 Glas.; MB ChB (Commend.) Glas. 1969; MRCGP 1975.

BURTON, Alec Leslie 5 Moor Park Avenue, Preston PR1 6AS Tel: 01772 556989 Fax: 01772 616312; Higher Wham Farm, Long Moss Lane, Whitestake, Preston PR4 4XQ Tel: 01772 613781 Fax: 01772 616312 — MB BS Lond. 1966; FRCP Lond. 1989; MRCP (UK) 1972; MRCS Eng. LRCP Lond. 1966; DObst RCOG 1968. (King's Coll. Hosp.) Cons. Phys. (Gen. & Thoracic Med.) Preston Acute Hosps. NHS Trust. Prev: Cons. Phys. (Gen. & Thoracic Med.) Preston & Chorley Health Dist.; Sen. Regist. (Chest Unit & Med.) King's Coll. Hosp. Lond.

BURTON, Alison Jane Eveswell Surgery, 254 Chepstow Road, Newport NP19 8NL — MB BCh 1989 Wales.

BURTON, Andrew James Carrington House Surgery, 19 Priory Road, High Wycombe HP13 6SL Tel: 01494 526029; Orchard Cottage, Primrose Hill, Widmer End, High Wycombe HP15 6NU — MB BS 1980 Newc.; MRCGP 1984; DRCOG 1983; DCH RCP Lond. 1983. Hosp. Pract. (Cardiol.) S. Bucks. NHS Trust.

BURTON, Anthony Carver Carcroft Health Centre, Chestnut Avenue, Carcroft, Doncaster DN6 8AG Tel: 01302 723510; The Old Smithy, High St, Campsall, Doncaster DN6 9AF Tel: 01302 702794 & profess. 0302 723510 — MB ChB 1972 Sheff.; MRCOG 1978; FRCOG 1997. assoc. Special. Colposcopy. Rotherham. DGH. Prev: Regist. (O & G) St. Mary's Hosp. Lond.

BURTON, Anthony John Matthew 1 Throstle Nest View, Horsforth, Leeds LS18 4LR — BChir 1990 Camb.

BURTON, Benjamin John Lloyd 53B Englands Lane, London NW3 4YD — MB BS 1993 Lond.

BURTON, Carole Angela River View, 96 The Hythe End Road, Wraysbury, Staines TW19 5AP — MB BChir 1991 Camb. Partner in GP. Prev: Ho. Off. (Med.) Barnstaple Hosp.

BURTON, Carolyn Helen Fenham Hall Surgery, Fenham Hall Drive, Fenham, Newcastle upon Tyne NE4 9XD; 40 Mitchell Avenue, Jesmond, Newcastle upon Tyne NE2 3LA Tel: 0191 281 3857 — MB BS 1978 Newc.; MRCGP 1982; DRCOG 1980.

BURTON, Catherine Anne Lucy The New Surgery, 31-35 Linom Road, London SW4 7PB Tel: 020 7274 4220 Fax: 020 7737 0205; 53 Winterbrook Road, London SE24 9HZ — MB BChir 1979 Camb.; MB Camb. 1979, BChir 1978; DCH 1981; DRCOG 1980.

BURTON, Catherine Helen 10 Highcliffe Crescent, Ashingdon, Rochford SS4 3HN; 5 Ventress Farm Court, Cambridge CB1 8HD — BChir 1996 Camb.; MB Camb. 1996; MA Camb. 1998. (Cambridge) SHO (Med.) Hinchingbrooke Hosp. Huntingdon Camb. Prev: Ho. Off. (Surg.) PeterBoro.; Ho. Off. (Med.) Norwich.

BURTON, Christine Celia 19 Wentworth Road, Four Oaks, Sutton Coldfield B74 2SD Tel: 0121 308 0300 — MB ChB Birm. 1960. (Birm.) SCMO Birm. AHA (T); Paediat. Multiple Birth Foundat. (Twins Clinic) Lond. & Birm.; Med. Off. Family Plann. Assn. Nbc Birm. Prev: Ho. Phys. Birm. Gen. Hosp.; Ho. Surg. & Jun. Cas. Off. Birm. Childr. Hosp.

BURTON, Christopher David Sanquhar Health Centre, Station Road, Sanquhar DG4 6BT Tel: 01659 50221 Fax: 01659 58116; Broomfield Farm House, Sanquhar DG4 6JN Tel: 01659 50794 — MB ChB 1982 Ed.; MRCGP 1986. Prev: Trainee GP Restalrig Med. Pract. Edin.; SHO (Paediat. & O & G) Lothian HB.

BURTON, Christopher John Richard Bright Renal Unit, Southmead Hospital, Westbury-on-Trym, Bristol BS10 5NB Email: burton_c@southmead.swest.nhs.uk — MB BS 1987 Newc.; PhD Leicester 1996; MA Camb. 1988; MRCP (UK) 1990. (Newc.) Sen. Regist. (Renal Med.) Bristol; Cons. in renal Med., S.mead Hosp., Bristol. Socs: Renal Assn. Prev: Sen. Regist. renal Med., S.mead Hosp., Bristol; Research Regist. (Nephrol.) Leicester Gen. Hosp.

BURTON, Christopher Malcolm 1 Carlton House, Wolfed Crescent, London SE16 1SH — MB BS 1998 Lond.; MB BS Lond 1998.

BURTON, David James 5 Granville Road, Clacton-on-Sea CO15 6BX — MB ChB 1998 Bristol.

BURTON, Mr David James Corbett The Barn, Edale Road, Hope Valley S33 6ZF Tel: 01433 621567; 242 Low Lane, Horsforth, Leeds LS18 5QL Tel: 01132 589741 — MB ChB 1995 Leeds; MRCS(Eng) 1998. (Leeds University) SHO (Plastic Surg.) St James' Univ. Hosp. Prev: SHO Profess. Surgic. Unit, Leeds Gen. Infirm.; SHO (Cardiothoracic Surg.), Killingbeck Hosp. Leeds; SHO (A & E) Leeds Gen. Infirm.

BURTON, Dennis Frederick Tel: 01327 260230 Fax: 01327 262243 — MRCS Eng. LRCP Lond. 1979; DRCOG 1980.

BURTON, Dianne Mary Nora (retired) Morar, Seddon Road, Hale, Altrincham WA14 2UH Tel: 0161 928 5730 Email: diburton3@btinternet.com — MB ChB 1965 Bristol; MRCPsych 1972; DPM Eng. 1969. Prev: Cons. Adolesc. & Child Psychiat. Mersey RHA.

BURTON, Donald Arthur Paul (retired) Old Post Office, Gunthorpe, Melton Constable NR24 2NS Tel: 01263 860810 — MB BChir 1952 Camb.; MA Camb. 1953, MB BChir 1952; MRCGP 1969. Prev: GP Suff.

BURTON, Edith Jackson (retired) 76 Church Street, Brierley, Barnsley S72 9JG Tel: 01226 711389 — MB ChB 1946 Glas.; DObst RCOG 1948. Prev: SCMO Barnsley HA.

BURTON, Edward Alan University Department of Clinical Neuroloy, The Radcliffe Infirmary, Oxford OX2 6HE Email: ed.burton@clinical-neurology.ox.ac.uk — MB ChB 1991 Birm.; BSc (Hons.) Birm. 1988; MRCP (UK) 1994. Clin. Lect. (Neurol.) Radcliffe Infirm, Oxf.; Tutor in Neurosci. Keble Coll, Oxf.

BURTON, Elizabeth Carol Barnes Close Surgery, Barnes Close, Sturminster Newton DT10 1BN Tel: 01258 474500 Fax: 01258 471547 — MB ChB 1979 Liverp.

BURTON, Eunice Ruth (retired) 9 Clune Court, 120 Hutton Road, Shenfield, Brentwood CM15 8NQ Tel: 01277 223375 — MB BS Lond. 1957; FRCS Eng. 1964; FRCOG 1977, M 1961; DObst 1958; Postgrad. Dip. (Healthcare Ethics) KCL, 1996. Prev: Cons. O & G Harold Wood Hosp. Essex.

BURTON, Geoffrey The Riverside Surgery, Waterside, Evesham WR11 6JP Tel: 01386 40121 Fax: 01386 442615; 3 Manor Gardens, Aldington, Evesham WR11 5UB Tel: 01386 830153 — MB BS 1962 Durh.; DObst RCOG 1964.

BURTON, Geoffrey Winspear (retired) 28 Cote Park, Stoke Bishop, Bristol BS9 2AD Tel: 0117 968 5769 — MB ChB 1950 Leeds; BSc (Hons. Physiol.) Leeds 1947; FFA RCS Eng. 1957; DA Eng. 1956; DObst RCOG 1951. Prev: Cons. Anaesth. United Bristol Hosps.

BURTON, Gillian Ann Radford H. Centre, Ilkeston Road, Nottingham NG7 3GW Tel: 01159 420360 Email: gillian@burton1971.freeserve.co.uk; 18 Russell Road, Nottingham NG7 6HB Tel: 01159 787473 — MB ChB Bristol 1970; MRCPCH 1997; MSc Nottingham 1995; DRCOG Lond. 1972. Staff Grade (Community Paediat.) Nottm. Community Health Trust. Socs: MRCPCH.

BURTON, Gordon Ernest Whitehead, Squadron Ldr. RAF Med. Br. 19 Esplanade, Ryde PO33 2EH Tel: 01983 565225; Delphi, Yaverland Road, Sandown PO36 8QP Tel: 01983 406150 Email: gb@mtendele.demon.co.uk — MRCS Eng. LRCP Lond. 1984; MSc Lond. 1992; BSc Rhodesia 1975. Princip. GP; Med. Adviser Siemens, Cowes I. of Wight. Prev: Sen. Med. Off. (Radiat. Med.); Radiobiol. RAF Inst. Naval Med. Gosport; Sen. Med. Off. RAF Waddington.

BURTON, Graham James Department of Anatomy, Downing St., Cambridge CB2 3DY Tel: 01223 333771 Fax: 01223 333786; Primrose Farm Barn, Primrose Farm Road, Little Wilbraham, Cambridge CB1 5JZ Tel: 01223 811637 Email: gjb2@cam.ac.uk — MD 1984 Camb.; BM BCh Oxf. 1977. Reader in Human ReProduc. in the Dept. of Anotomy, Univ. of Camb. Socs: Fell. St. John's Coll. Camb.

BURTON, Helen Lyn Lyngford Park Surgery, Fletcher Close, Taunton TA2 8SQ Tel: 01823 333355 Fax: 01823 257022; 9 Woodbarton, Milverton, Taunton TA4 1LU Tel: 01823 400129 — MB BS 1981 Lond.; DCH RCP Lond. 1986; DRCOG 1984. Prev: SCMO (Community Child Health) Som.

BURTON, Hilary Vivien The Surgery, Park St., Ripon HG4 2BE Tel: 01765 692366; Trinity Hill, Ripon HG4 2EU — MB BS 1979 Lond.

BURTON, Ian Donald Barlow Medical Centre, 8 Barlow Moor Road, Didsbury, Manchester M20 6TR Tel: 0161 445 2101 Fax: 0161 445 9560; 7 Moorfield Road, West Didsbury, Manchester M20 2UZ Tel: 0161 434 3530 — MB ChB 1975 Manch.

BURTON, Ian Eric Department of Haematology, Wythenshawe Hospital, Manchester M23 9LT Tel: 0161 291 2114 Fax: 0161 292 2500 Email: ian.burto3@btinternet.com; Morar, Seddon Road, Hale, Altrincham WA14 2UH Tel: 0161 928 5730 — MB ChB 1965 Bristol; FRCP Lond. 1989; MRCP (UK) 1970; FRCPath 1987, M 1975. (Bristol) Cons. (Haemat.) Wythenshawe. Hosp. Manch. Socs: Brit. Soc. Haemat. & BMA.; BMA Brit Soc Haem. Prev: Sen. Regist. (Haemat.) Leeds Gen. Infirm.; Med. Regist. Leeds Univ. Hosp. (St. Jas.).

BURTON, Jacqueline (Hibberd) 19 Browning Road, Wadsley Bridge, Sheffield S6 1DA; Green Hallow, 60 Carrwood Road, Wilmslow SK9 5DN Tel: 01625 523928 — MB ChB 1990 Manch.

BURTON, James, OBE Warren Cottage, Hewshott Lane, Liphook GU30 7SU Tel: 01428 724706 — MB ChB 1946 Ed.; DTM Antwerp 1948. (Ed.) Socs: Fell. Roy. Soc. Trop. Med. & Hyg.; (Pres.) Med. Miss. Soc. Prev: Med. Dir. Jt. Mission Hosp. Equipm. Bd.; Med. Dir. Baptist Miss. Soc.; Med. Supt. Tremont Hosp. Tondo, Zaire.

BURTON, James Alan, OStJ The Barn, Edale Road, Hope, Hope Valley S33 6ZF Tel: 01433 621567 Fax: 01433 621567 Email: ja_burton@doctors.org.uk — MB ChB 1967 Sheff.; FRCP Lond. 1997; MRCP (UK) 1975; AFOM RCP Lond. 1979; MRCGP 1972. (Sheff.) Private GP; Occupat. Health Phys. Health & Safety Labs, Sheff. Socs: (Treas. & Ex-Pres.) Sheff. M-C Soc.; BMA. Prev: Late Dir. Univ. Health Serv. Univ. Sheff.; Area Surg. St. John Ambul. Brig.; Ho. Surg., Ho. Phys. & SHO Roy. Hosp. Sheff.

BURTON, Jennifer Diana (retired) Rusty Stack, Bulkington Road, Wolvey, Hinckley LE10 3LA Tel: 01455 220452 — MB ChB 1963 Birm.; FFA RCS Eng. 1969; DA Eng. 1965. Cons. Anaesth. N. Warks. HA. Prev: Regist. (Anaesth.) N.ampton Gen. Hosp. & United Bristol Hosps.

BURTON, Jennifer Susan 14 Distons Lane, Chipping Norton OX7 5NY Tel: 01608 641842 — MB ChB 1987 Liverp.; MRCP (UK) 1991. p/t Gen. Pactice Retainer, The Wychwood Surg., Milton under Wychwood, Oxon.

BURTON, John 12 Byefields, Kempsey, Worcester WR5 3NN — MRCS Eng. LRCP Lond. 1938. (Guy's) Prev: Med. Off. Worcester Coll. for Blind; Capt. RAMC; Ho. Surg. & Ho. Phys. Cossham Hosp. Bristol.

BURTON, John Andrew (retired) 14 Drummond Road, Inverness IV2 4NB Tel: 01463 230720 — MB ChB 1967 Glas.; BDS 1963; FRCP Glas. 1982; MRCP (UK) 1970. Cons. Phys. Raigmore Hosp. Inverness.

BURTON, John David Keith, CBE 7 Orchard Rise, Richmond TW10 5BX — MB BS 1952 Lond.; MRCS Eng. LRCP Lond. 1952; FFA RCS Eng. 1958; DA Eng. 1954. (Univ. Coll. Hosp.) HM Coroner Gtr. Lond. W. Dist.; Barrister Middle Temple 1964; Atkinson Morley Schl. For Surg. 1953; Coroner HM Ho.hold. Socs: (Ex-Pres.) Coroners Soc. Eng. & Wales; (Ex.Pres.) Medico-Legal Soc. Prev: Lect. (Anaesths.) St. Thos. Hosp. Med. Sch. Lond.; Regist. (Anaesth.) Roy. Marsden Hosp. Lond.; Cas. Off. (Surg.) Univ. Coll. Lond.

BURTON, John Howard William Station Road Surgeries, Station Road, Haworth, Keighley BD22 8NL Tel: 01535 642255/6 Fax: 01535 645380; Delf Hill Farm, Blackmoor Road, Oxenhope, Keighley BD22 9SS — MB BChir 1975 Camb.; MB Camb. 1975, MA, BChir 1974.

BURTON, Professor John Lloyd (retired) Norland House, 33 Canynge Rd, Clifton, Bristol BS8 3LD Tel: 0117 973 3933 — MB ChB 1964 Manch.; BSc (Hons. Physiol.) Manch. 1961, MD 1971; FRCP Lond. 1978, M 1967. Medico-legal Cons. in Dermat.. Prev: Prof. Dermat. Bristol Univ.

BURTON, John Thomas 44 Glandore Avenue, Belfast BT15 3FD — MB BCh BAO 1973 Belf.

BURTON, Mr John Withers Dumfries & Galloway Royal Infirmary, Dumfries DG1 4AP Tel: 01387 241041 Fax: 01387 241365 — MB BS 1980 Lond.; FRCS Eng. 1985. (St. Mary's) Cons. A & E Dumfries & Galloway Roy. Infirm. Prev: Dir. Emerg. Dept. Goulbourn Valley Base Hosp. Vict., Austral.; Surg. N.. Dist. Hosp. Vanuatu; Regist. (Gen. Surg.) P'boro Dist. Hosp.

BURTON, Jonathan Hugh ThE Elizabeth Courtauld Surgery, Factory Lane West, Halstead CO9 1EX Tel: 01787 475944 Fax: 01787 474506; Corner House, Straw Lane, Sudbury CO10 2AT Tel: 01787 371191 — MB ChB 1970 Bristol; MA Camb. 1966; MRCGP 1993; DCH RCPS Glas. 1972. (Bristol)

BURTON, Jonathan Paul 16 Manor Road, Lancing BN15 0EY — MB ChB 1997 Bristol.

BURTON, Julian Lindsay Low Mill Hall, Millner Lane, Scotton, Knaresborough HG5 9DH — MB ChB 1994 Sheff.

BURTON, Julie 8 Burlesdon Heights, Burlesdon, Southampton SO31 8DB — MB ChB 1993 Aberd.

BURTON, Katherine Linden Queensway Medical Centre, Olympic Way, Wellingborough NN8 3EP Tel: 01933 678767; 29 Harmans Way, Weedon, Northampton NN7 4PB — BM 1989 Soton.; DFFP 1993; DRCOG 1992.

BURTON, Kathleen Margaret Room M009, North Staff Hospitals, Newcastle Rd, Stoke-on-Trent ST4 6QG Tel: 01782 710791 Fax: 01782 425914; Church View Cottage, Pott Shrigley, Macclesfield SK10 5SA Tel: 01625 574983 Email: duncanmatheson@churchriewps.co.freeserve — MB ChB Birm. 1980; DRCOG 1983; DCH Eng. 1982. (Birm.) SCMO (Child Health) N. Staffs Hosp. (NHS Trust). Socs: Brit. Assn. Community Child Health; RCPCH; BAAF. Prev: Clin. Med. Off. (Child Health) N. Staffs. HA; SHO (O & G & Paediat.) City Gen. Hosp. Stoke.

BURTON, Kevin Anthony 34 Borland Road, Bearsden, Glasgow G61 2ND — MB ChB 1995 Glas.

BURTON, Lee Trumpington House, 56 High Street, Dulverton TA22 9DW Tel: 01398 323333 Fax: 01398 324030 — BSc (Hons.) Lond. 1979, MB BS 1982; MRCGP 1987; DRCOG 1987; DCH RCP Lond. 1985. Mem. Med. Equestrian Assn. (Steering Comm.). Prev: SHO (Paediat.) N.wick Pk. Hosp. & Clin. Research Centre Harrow; Res. Med. Off. Qu. Eliz. Hosp. Childr. Lond.; Res. Med. Off. Dept. Paediat. Oncol. St. Bart. Hosp. Lond.

BURTON, Leslie Lawrence Pierremont Unit, Memorial Hospital, Hollyhurst Road, Darlington DL3 6HX Tel: 01325 743568 Fax: 01325 743588; Email: leslie.burton@lineone.net — MB BS 1978 Newc.; BMedSc Newc. 1975; FRCPsych 1996, M 1982. Cons. Psychiat. Darlington Memor. Hosp. Prev: Cons. Psychiat. St. Lukes Hosp. Middlesbrough; Sen. Regist. (Forens. Psychiat.) David W.bury Centre Winterton Hosp.; Sen. Regist. (Psychiat.) Darlington Memor. Hosp.

BURTON, Lindsay John (retired) 57 Montrose Avenue, Luton LU3 1HP Tel: 01582 724371 — MB BS Lond. 1958; MRCS Eng. LRCP Lond. 1958; DObst RCOG 1960. Hosp. Pract. Ophth. Dept. Luton & Dunstable Hosp. Prev: Hosp. Pract. Ophth. Dept. Luton & Dunstable Hosp.

BURTON, Lorraine Jane Mowbray House, 277 North End, Northallerton DL7 8DP Tel: 01609 775281 Fax: 01609 778029; Brook House, Ingramgate, Thirsk YO7 1DD — MB BS 1988 Lond. GP.

BURTON, Margaret (retired) 11 Merthyr Terrace, Barnes, London SW13 8DL Tel: (0181) 748 4352 — MB ChB Ed. 1952. Prev: GP Lond.

BURTON, Margaret Allen Finlayson (retired) New Selma Cottage, Ledaig, Oban PA37 1QP Tel: 01631 720209 — MB ChB 1938 Glas.; BSc Glas. 1935.

BURTON, Margaret Hilary Cambridge & Huntingdon Health Commission, Ferndale, Fulbourn Hospital (366), Cambridge CB1 5EF Tel: 01223 218764 Fax: 01223 415643; Primrose Farm Barn, Little Wilbraham, Cambridge CB1 5JZ Tel: 01223 811637 — BM BCh 1977 Oxf.; MA Oxf. 1981, BM BCh 1977; MFPHM RCP (UK) 1993. Cons. Pub. Health Med. Camb. & Huntingdon Health Commiss.. Prev: Sen. Regist. (Pub. Health Med.) E. Anglian RHA.

BURTON, Margaret Muriel (retired) Coed Craig, Tanybryn Road, Colwyn Bay LL28 4AD Tel: 01492 547839 — MB BS 1938 Lond.; MRCS Eng. LRCP Lond. 1937; MRCOG 1941. Prev: 3rd Asst. O & G Unit, Ho. Surg. & In-pat. Obst. Asst. Roy. Free Hosp.

BURTON, Mr Martin James Department of Otolaryngology - Head & Neck Surgery, The Radcliffe Infirmary, Oxford OX2 6HE Tel: 01865 228587 Fax: 01865 228587; Felstead House, 23 Banbury Road, Oxford OX2 6NX Tel: 01865 404104 Fax: 01865 404116 — BM BCh 1983 Oxf.; MA Camb. 1984; DM Oxf. 1995; FRCS (Orl.) 1993; FRCS Eng. 1989. (Camb. & Oxf.) Cons. Otolaryngol. Radcliffe Infirm. Oxf.; Hon. Sen. Clin. Lect. Univ. of Oxf.; Co-ordinating Edr., Cochrane E.N.T. Distorders Gp. Socs: Fell. Roy. Soc. Med.; Brit. Assn. Otorhinol. Head & Neck Surg.; Otorhinolaryngog. Research Soc. (Treas.). Prev: Fell. (Otol. & Neurotol. & Skull Base Surg.) John Hopkins Hosp. Baltimore, Maryland, USA; Lect. (Otolaryngol.) Univ. Melbourne, Austral.; Fulbright Schol. Kresge Hearing Research Inst. Univ. Michigan, USA.

BURTON, Matthew John The Radcliffe Infirmary, Oxford OX2 Tel: 01865 311188; 84 Great Clarendon Street, Oxford OX2 6AU Email: matthewburton@compuserve.com — MB BChir 1994 Camb.; MA Camb. 1996, BA 1992; MRCP (Lond.) 1997. (Cambridge) SHO (Ophth.) Oxf. Ophth. Rotat. Prev: Ho. Off. (Gen. Med.) Addenbrooke's Hosp. Camb.; Ho. Off. (Gen. Surg.) Norf. & Norwich Hosp.; SHO (Gen. Med.) Hammersmith Hosp. Lond. & John Radcliffe Hosp. Oxf.

BURTON, Michael Francis Digby (retired) Overdale Croft, The Bailey, Skipton BD23 1AS Tel: 01756 700270 — MB BS Lond. 1955; MRCGP 1971; DObst RCOG 1957. Prev: Paediat. Ho. Off. Hillingdon Hosp. Uxbridge.

BURTON, Patricia Anne (retired) Norland House, 33 Canynge Road, Clifton, Bristol BS8 3LD Tel: 0117 973 3933 Email: pa.burton@virgin.net — MB ChB 1961 Manch.; FRCPath 1982, M 1971; DObst RCOG 1963. Prev: Hon. Sen. Lect. Univ. Bristol.

BURTON, Penelope Jane NHS Information Authority (Casemix Programme), Highcroft, Romsey Road, Winchester SO22 5EY Tel: 01962 844588 Fax: 01962 844711 Email: penny.burton@casemix.org.uk; 6 South End Close, Hursley, Winchester SO21 2LJ — MB ChB 1973 Aberd.; MSc (Community Health Developing Countries) Lond. 1985; MRCGP 1977; DTM & H Liverp. 1982; DRCOG 1977. Clin. Researcher NHS Informat. Auth. (Casemix Prog.) Winchester. Prev: Family Pract. Doctor McCulloch's Clinic Abu Dhabi, UAE; Cons. Progr. for Control Diarrh.l Dis. WHO, Geneva; Cons. Phys. (Primary Care) Riyadh Milit. Hosp., Saudi Arabia.

BURTON, Peter John Charles (retired) 36 King George Gardens, Chichester PO19 4LB — MRCS Eng. LRCP Lond. 1942; FFA RCS

Eng. 1954, FRCA; DA Eng. 1949. Prev: Cons. Anaesth. Worthing Dist. HA.

BURTON, Peter William Hawthorns Surgery, 331 Birmingham Road, Sutton Coldfield B72 1DL Tel: 0121 373 2211 Fax: 0121 382 1274; 19 Wentworth Road, Four Oaks Park, Sutton Coldfield B74 2SD Tel: 0121 308 0300 — MB ChB 1958 Birm. Asst. Socs: Birm. Med. Inst.; BMA. Prev: Ho. Surg. (O & G) & Ho. Phys. Selly Oak Hosp. Birm.; Ho. Surg. Gen. Hosp. Birm.

BURTON, Ralph Haight Integrated Care Partnership, Fitznells Manor Surgery, 2 Chessington Road, Ewell, Epsom KT17 1TF Tel: 020 8394 2365 Fax: 020 8393 9753; 7 Links Road, Epsom KT17 3PP Tel: 01372 721018 Fax: 01372 749153 — MB BS (Hons. Path.) Lond. 1966; MRCS Eng. LRCP Lond. 1966; FRCGP 1995, M 1975. (King's Coll. Hosp.) Sen. Lect. (Gen. Pract.) St. Geo. Hosp. Med. Sch. Socs: Croydon MAAG. Prev: Regional Audit Adviser BPMF (SW Thames); Sen. Tutor (Gen. Pract.) St. Geo. Hosp. Med. Sch.; Clin. Standards Adviser to BPMF SW Thames.

BURTON, Mr Richard Michael, CStJ, TD (retired) Briar Close, 16 Latchmoor Avenue, Gerrards Cross SL9 8LJ Tel: 01753 886979 — MB ChB Sheff. 1954; MD (USA) 1955; MFFP 1995; MRCS Eng. LRCP Lond. 1954; BSc Lond. 1958; MMSA Lond. 1960; MA Camb. 1962; M 1963; FRCS Eng. 1967; FRCOG 1978 FRCS Ed. 1964. Col. late RAMC (V) Cons. In Surg.; Med. Off. Brit. Red. Cross Soc. Prev: Cons. O & G Hillingdon & Ealing Hosps.

BURTON, Mr Robert Lewis Sunderland Eye Infirmary, Queen Alexandra Road, Sunderland SR2 9HP; The Barn, Old Durham, Off Benthouse Lane, Durham DH1 2RY — MB BS 1983 Lond.; FRCS Eng. 1987. Cons. Ophth. Sunderland Eye Infirm.

BURTON, Roger Christopher Balance Street Practice, 36 Balance Street, Uttoxeter ST14 8JG Tel: 01889 562145 Fax: 01889 568164; St. John's House, 28 Bromyard Road, St. John's, Worcester WR2 5BU — MB ChB 1985 Birm.; DRCOG 1989. Trainee GP Worcs. Socs: BMA; Assoc. Mem. RCGP. Prev: SHO (Obst.) Birm. Matern. Hosp.; SHO (Paediat.) Nevill Hall Hosp. Abergavenny Gwent; SHO (Ophth.) Worcester Eye Hosp.

BURTON, Rosemary Carol 16 Kilravock Street, London W10 4HX — MB BS 1992 Lond.; PhD Lond. 1988; BSc Univ. Sussex 1981. (Roy. Free Hosp.)

BURTON, Sarah Louise 53 Upper Hale Road, Farnham GU9 0NX — BM BS 1995 Nottm.

BURTON, Stephen James The Surgery, 91 Dodworth Road, Barnsley S70 6ED Tel: 01226 282535 — MB ChB 1980 Sheff.; MRCGP 1984.

BURTON, Sybil Dora (retired) Skansen, Kippford, Dalbeattie DG5 4LJ Tel: 01556 620251 — MB ChB 1943 Leeds. Prev: GP Partner, Burton.

BURTON, Thomas Pearson (retired) Skansen, Kippford, Dalbeattie DG5 4LJ Tel: 01550 620251 — MB ChB 1943 Leeds. Prev: GP Partner, Ripon.

BURTON, Tom, Squadron Ldr. RAF Med. Br. 16 Tom Lane, Fulwood, Sheffield S10 3PB Tel: 0114 229 5067 Email: tomandjackie@doctors.org.uk — MB BS 1991 Lond.; BSc Lond. 1990; MRCGP 1996; DCH RCP Lond. 1995; Dip. IMC RCS Ed. 1994; DFFP 1997. (St. Mary's Hosp. Med. Sch. Lond.) Clin. Fell. in Accid. & Emerg., Leeds Gen. Infirm., Gt. Geo. St., leeds LS1 3EX. Prev: Unit. Med. Off. RAF Bruggen; SHO Orthop. Barnsley; SHO Paediatric Accid. & Emerg., Sheff. Childr.'s Hosp.

BURTON, Mr Victor William (retired) 3 Castle Hill, Lancaster LA1 1YS Tel: 01524 69924 — MB ChB 1961 Ed.; FRCS Ed. 1967. Cons. Orthop. Surg. Roy. Lancaster Infirm. & W.morland Co. Hosp.

BURTON-WEST, Kate Elizabeth 127 Harley Street, London W1N 1DJ Tel: 020 7935 8570 — MB BS 1964 Lond.; MTh Lond. 1980; BSc (Special, Hons.) Lond. 1960, MB BS 1964; MRCS Eng. LRCP Lond. 1964; DA Eng. 1966. (Roy. Free) Clin. Asst. (Pain Relief) Dept. of Anaesth. Roy. Free Hosp. Lond. Socs: Fell. Roy. Soc. Med.; BMA. Prev: SHO (Anaesth.) N. Middlx. Hosp. Lond.; SHO Dept. Anaesth. Middlx. Hosp.; Ho. Surg. Roy. Free Hosp. Gray's Inn Rd.

BURTT, Glyn Jonathan 2 The Avenue, Bedford MK40 1EF — MB BS 1996 Lond.

BURVILL-HOLMES, Phyllis (retired) 12 Finchcroft Court, Prestbury, Cheltenham GL52 5BD — MRCS Eng. LRCP Lond. 1939; DMR Lond 1943. Prev: Asst, Radiol. Regist., Ho. Phys. & 1st Asst. Deep X-Ray Dept. Univ.

BURVILLE, Linda Margaret 21 The Spinneys, Bromley BR1 2NT Tel: 020 8402 1115 — MB BS 1984 Lond.; DA (UK) 1986. (St Barts Lond) Back Pain Off. Homeop. Hosp. Tunbridge Wells; Clin. Asst. Anaesth. Qu. Marys Sidcup. Prev: Regist. (Anaesth.) Whittington Hosp. & W.m. Hosp. Lond.

BURWELL, David Rowell Department of Anaesthesia, University Hospital of Wales, Cardiff CF4 4XW Tel: 029 2074 3107; 47 Locks Road, Locks Heath, Southampton SO31 6NS Tel: 01489 573598 — MB BChir 1990 Camb.; BA Camb. 1987; FRCA 1996. (Univ. Camb. Sch. Clin. Med.) Specialist Regist. (Anaesth.) Univ. Hosp. Wales Cardiff Train. Scheme. Prev: Regist. (Anaesth.) Wrexham Maelor NHS Trust Wales; SHO (Anaesth.) Addenbrooke's Hosp. Camb.; SHO (Neonat.) Roy. Sussex Co. Hosp. Brighton.

BURWELL, John Rowell (retired) 47 Locks Road, Locks Heath, Southampton SO31 6NS Tel: 01489 573598 Fax: 01489 557884 Email: john.burwell@btinteernet.com — MA, MB Camb. 1955, BChir 1954; DObst RCOG 1960. Prev: GP Soton.

BURWELL, Mr Jonathan Matthew Richard 23 St George's Road, Kingston upon Thames KT2 6DL — MB BS 1988 Lond.; FRCS Eng. 1993; FRCS (Orth.) 1997. Regist. (Orthop.) NW Thames Higher Surgic. Train. Progr. Prev: Demonst. (Anat.) Char. Cross & W.m. Med. Sch. Lond.; SHO Rotat. (Surg.) Whipps Cross Hosp. Lond.; SHO (Neurosurg.) Char. Cross Hosp. Lond.

BURWELL, Professor Richard Geoffrey Lime Tree House, 34 Dovedale Road, West Bridgford, Nottingham NG2 6JA Tel: 0115 923 2745 Fax: 0115 923 2272 — MB ChB 1952 Leeds; MD Leeds 1955; FRCS Eng. 1955. Russell S. Hibbs Award (Jt.ly) Scoliosis Research Soc., Harding Award Action Research; Emerit. Prof. Human Morphol. & Experim. Orthop. Univ. Nottm. Prev: Ex-Pres. Brit. Scoliosis Soc.; Ex-Pres. Brit. Orthop. Research Soc.; Prof. Orthop. Univ. Lond.

BURWOOD, Duncan Frederick Strathdee Bedgrove Surgery, Brentwood Way, Aylesbury HP21 7TL Tel: 01296 330330 Fax: 01296 399179; 84 Wendover Road, Aylesbury HP21 9NJ Tel: 01296 580280 Email: dfsburwood@cwcom.net — MB ChB 1976 Bristol; MRCGP 1980; DRCOG 1978. (Bristol) Clin. Asst. (Palliat. Care) Florence Nightingale Hse. Aylesbury. Prev: Clin. Asst. (Ment. Subn.ity) Manor Hse. Hosp. Aylesbury.

BURWOOD, Richard John Sussex Diagnostic Centre, 13 New Church Road, Hove BN3 4AA Tel: 01273 770044 Fax: 01273 726931; Blandford, Pomper Lane, Hurstpierpoint, Hassocks BN6 9LJ — MB BCh BAO 1964 Dub.; MD Bristol 1970; MA Dub. 1970, BA 1963; FRCR 1975; FFR 1972; DMRD Eng. 1968. (T. C. Dub.) Cons. Radiol. Roy. Sussex Co. Hosp. Brighton & Chailey Heritage, Chailey. Socs: Brit. Nuclear Med. Soc.; Brit. Inst. Radiol.; Eur. Assn. Nuclear Med. Prev: Cons. Nuclear Med., Kings Coll. Hosp.; Lect. (Radiodiag.) Univ. Bristol & Ahmadu Bello Univ. Zaria, Nigeria; Asst. Radiol. Tromso Sentralsykehuset, Norway.

BURY, Jonathan Paul 2 The Crescent, West Hagley, Stourbridge DY8 2XB — MB ChB 1996 Sheff.

BURY, Judith Kathryn Spittal Street Centre, 22-24 Spittal St., Edinburgh EH3 9DU Tel: 0131 537 8373 Fax: 0131 537 8303; 14 Merchiston Av, Edinburgh EH10 4NY Tel: 0131 228 9392 Fax: 0131 228 9392 Email: burywill@globalnet.co.uk — MB BChir 1970 Camb.; MA Camb. 1971; DCH RCPS Glas. 1974; Cert. Family Plann. JCC 1973; DObst RCOG 1972. (Camb. & Middlx.) Primary Care Facilitator (HIV & Drugs) Lothian HB. Prev: Med. Off. Community Drug Problem Serv. Roy. Edin. Hosp.; GP Edin.; Co-ordinating Dr. Edin. Brook Advis. Centre.

BURY, Mr Richard Neil Dimond Street Surgery, Pembroke Dock, Pembroke Tel: 01646 682146; White Hall, Pembroke SA71 4QT — MB BS 1979 Newc.; FRCS Ed. 1985.

BURY, Robert Frederick Nuclear Medicine Department, Leeds General Infirmary, Great George St., Leeds LS1 3EX Tel: 0113 392 6471 Fax: 0113 392 2598 Email: robertb@ulth.northy.nhs.uk; 3 Elmete Avenue, Oakwood, Leeds LS8 2JX Tel: 0113 293 1769 Email: bob.bury@doctors.org.uk — MB BS 1973 Lond.; BSc Lond. 1970; FRCS Eng. 1978; FRCR 1983. Cons. Radiol. Leeds Gen. Infirm; Sen. Clin. Lect. (Radiol.) Univ. Leeds. Prev: Cons. Radiol. P.ss Mary's RAF Hosp. Halton.

BURY, Roger Walter Radiology Department, Victoria Hospital, Blackpool FY3 8NR Tel: 01253 303870 Fax: 01253 306960; Windy Nook, 16 Norfolk Road, Lytham St Annes FY8 4JG — MB ChB 1981 Manch.; BSc (Hons.) Physiol. Manch. 1978, MB ChB 1981;

FRCR 1989. (Manchester) Cons. Radiol. Vict. Hosp. Blackpool.; Director of Direct Med. Imaging Ltd Lytham St Anne. Socs: Manc. Med. Soc.; Cardiac Radiol. Grp; Brit. Soc. Of Interven.al Radiol. Prev: Trainee GP Stepping Hill Hosp. Stockport VTS; Ho. Off. (Surg.) Stepping Hill Hosp. Stockport; Ho. Off. (Med.) Manch. Roy. Infirm.

BURZA, Nazir Ahmad Liverpool Road Health Centre, Liverpool Road, Hindley, Wigan WN2 3HQ Tel: 01942 255189 Fax: 01942 526217 — MB BS 1968 Gujarat; MB BS 1968 Gujarat.

BUSAIDY, Fawzy Salim 76 Priory Road, Hornsey, London N8 7EY Tel: 020 8340 7567 — MB ChB 1964 East Africa; MB ChB E. Afr. 1964, LMS 1956; DO Eng. 1964. (Makerere Univ. Coll.) Asst. Ophth. Roy. N. Hosp. Lond.; Clin. Asst. (Ophth.) Barnet Gen. Hosp.; Sch. Oculist Islington Boro; Oculist Health Centre Hendon. Socs: BMA. Prev: Med. Off. Liverp. Eye Hosp. & Zanzibar Govt. Hosp.; Med. Off. i/c Wete Hosp; Surgic. Specialist Govt. Hosp. Zanzibar.

BUSBY, Charlotte Rosalind 3 Larch Grove, Bingley BD16 4SF — MB ChB 1992 Manch.

BUSBY, Eileen Rosemary (retired) 4 Woodend, Esher KT10 8DA Tel: 020 8398 3311 — MB BS 1955 Lond.; MB BS (Hons. Surg.) Lond. 1955; FRCS Eng. 1959; FRCR 1975; FFR 1972; DMRT Eng. 1966. Hon. Cons. Radio. Oncol. Kingston Hosp. Prev: 1st Asst. (Assoc. Specialist) Dept. Radiother. Roy. Marsden Hosp.

BUSBY, Gail Patricia Flat 12,, Beech House, The Beeches, Manchester M20 2AH — MB BS 1996 W. Indies.

BUSBY, Hugh Ian Llanyravon Way Surgery, Llanyravon Way, Llanyravon, Cwmbran NP44 8HW Tel: 01633 483255 Fax: 01633 484130; 9 Newport Road, New Inn, Pontypool NP4 0NT — MB BCh 1965 Wales. Socs: BMA.

BUSBY, John Charles (retired) 22 Penshurst, Park Hill, Old Harlow, Harlow CM17 0PB Tel: 01279 429030 — BA Camb. 1933; MRCS Eng. LRCP Lond. 1936; DTM & H Eng. 1937. Prev: Cdr. Field Ambul.

BUSBY, John Walter Castle Street Surgery, The Old Dispensary, 8 Castle St., Warwick CV34 4BP Tel: 01926 494137 Fax: 01926 410348 — MB ChB Liverp. 1962; Cert. Av Med. 1984. (Liverp.) Aviat. Med. Examr.; Works Med. Off. Potterton Internat. & Avana Meat Products Warwick; Med. Off. DHSS; Med. Off. Various Companies. Socs: Brit. Soc. Med. & Dent. Hypn.; Brit. Med. Pilots Assn. Prev: Ho. Phys., Gyn. Ho. Surg. & Ho. Surg. Liverp. Stanley Hosp.

BUSBY, Mark Ian 49 Main Street, E. Ardsley, Wakefield WF3 2AP — MB ChB 1989 Leeds; MRCP(UK) 1992.

BUSBY, Mary Frances Crannull Cottage, The Old Orchard, Mill Lane, Calcot, Reading RG31 7RS — MB BCh BAO 1972 Belf.; MRCGP 1976; DObst RCOG 1975. Staff Med. Off. BrE. Screen. Unit. Reading.

BUSBY, Robert Edgar Albert Street Health Centre, Albert Street, Belfast BT12 4JR Tel: 028 9032 0777 — MB BCh BAO 1981 Belf.

BUSBY, Susan Chantal 3 Monument Lane, Rednal, Birmingham B45 9QQ — MB ChB 1992 Bristol.

BUSCH, Thomas Andreas Heinrich Main Road Surgery, Main Road, Stickney, Boston PE22 8AA Tel: 01205 480237 Fax: 01205 480987 — State Exam Med 1988 Bonn; MD Bonn 1988. (Bonn, Germany) GP; Clin. Asst. (Paediat.) Pilgrim Hosp. Boston; PCG Bd. Mem.

BUSCOMBE, Jacqueline Ann Essex Lodge, 94 Greengate Street, Plaistow, London E13 0AS Tel: 020 8472 4888 Fax: 020 8472 5777; 16 Sherwood Avenue, South Woodford, London E18 1PB Tel: 020 8989 2461 — MB BS 1984 Lond.; DFFP 1994; DCH RCP Lond. 1987; DGM RCP Lond. 1986; Dip. Inst. Psychosexual Med. 1998. (Westminster) Prev: Trainee GP Waltham Forest VTS.; SHO (Paediat.) Newham Gen. Hosp. Lond.; SHO (Geriat.) St. Pancras Hosp. Lond.

BUSCOMBE, John Richard Nuclear Medicine, Royal Free Hospital, Pond St., London NW3 2QG Tel: 020 7794 0500 Fax: 020 7830 2946 Email: buscombe@rthsm.ac.uk — MB BS 1984 Lond.; MSc Nuclear Med. Lond. 1990, MD 1994; MRCP (UK) 1988; FRCP Ed. 1998. (Lond. Hosp.) Cons. Nuclear Med. Roy. Free Hosp. Lond. Socs: Sec. Internat. Soc. Radiolabelled Blood Elements; Advisery Counc.; Euro. Assn. Nuclear Med. Prev: Clin. Lect. (Nuclear Med.) Univ. Coll. & Middlx. Sch. Med.; Regist. (Nuclear Med.) Middlx. Hosp. Lond.; Ho. Phys. Rochford Hosp.

BUSCOMBE, Paul Narrowcliff Surgery, Narrowcliff, Newquay TR7 2QF Tel: 01637 873363 Fax: 01637 850735 — MB ChB 1967 Liverp. Prev: GP Kettering.

BUSE, Peter Bousfield Health Centre, Westminster Road, Liverpool L4 4PP Tel: 0151 207 0813 — MB ChB 1973 Liverp.

BUSFIELD, Alison 40 Clobells, South Brent TQ10 9JW Tel: 01364 73220 Fax: 01364 73220 Email: 113076.1171@compuserve.com — MB BS 1982 Newc.; MRCGP 1986; DRCOG 1986; DCCH 1998. Staff Grade Roy. Devon & Exeter Hosp. Exeter.

BUSFIELD, Graham David Swallowfield Medical Practice, Swallowfield, Reading RG7 1QY Tel: 0118 988 3134 Fax: 0118 988 5759; Millworth House, Millworth Lane, Shinfield, Reading RG2 9EN Tel: 01189 884901 — MB BS 1976 Lond.; MRCS Eng. LRCP Lond. 1976; MRCGP 1982. (St. Mary's) Socs: BMA. Prev: SHO (Juvenile Rheum.) Canad. Red Cross Memor. Hosp. Taplow; SHO (Psychiat.) Pk. Prewett; SHO (O & G) Basingstoke Dist. Hosp.

BUSFIELD, Mr Hugh Malcolm Bristow East Midlands Nuffield Hospital, Rykneld Road, Littleover, Derby DE23 7SN Tel: 01332 517891 Fax: 01332 512481; South Willow, 20 Church Lane, Barrow Upon Trent, Derby DE73 1HB Tel: 01332 702081 — BM BCh 1960 Oxf.; MA Oxf. 1960; FRCOG 1981, M 1966. (St. Bart.) Cons. O & G Derby City Gen. Hosp.; Clin. Lect. Nottm. Univ.; Surg. Coalville Vasectomy Clinic Leics. AHA (T). Socs: Blair Bell Res. Soc.; Nuffield Vis. Soc. Prev: Sen. Regist. (O & G) United Oxf. Hosps.; Regist. (Gyn.) Liverp. Roy. Infirm.; SHO (Obst.) Mill Rd. Matern. Hosp. Camb.

BUSFIELD, James Duncan (retired) 2 Chapel Mews, Abbey Lane, Preston, Hull HU12 8TA — MB ChB 1954 Leeds. Prev: GP Patrington Hull.

BUSH, Alison Mary (retired) Pantile Cottage, 58 Firs Chase, West Mersea, Colchester CO5 8NN Tel: 01206 382978 — MB BS 1952 Lond.; DCH Eng. 1955; Dip. FPA. 1959. Prev: GP Colchester.

BUSH, Alison Pamela 64 Highland Road, Norwich NR2 3NW — MB ChB 1987 Leeds. SHO (Gen. Med.) Solihill Hosp. W. Midl. Prev: SHO (A & E) Russell's Hall Hosp. Dudley; Trainee GP/SHO E. Birm. Hosp. & Solihull Gen. Hosp. VTS.; SHO (Geriat.) Bassetlaw Dist. Gen. Hosp. Worksop.

BUSH, Andrew Royal Brompton Hospital, Sydney St., London SW3 6NP Tel: 020 7352 8121 Fax: 020 7351 8763 Email: a.bush@rbh.nthames.nhs.uk; 27 Haycroft Gardens, London NW10 3BJ Tel: 020 8965 3723 — MB BS 1978 Lond.; MA Camb. 1979, BA 1975, MD 1987; FRCP Lond. 1996; MRCP (UK) 1980; MRCPCH 1996; FRCPCH 1997. (Cambridge University and University College Hospital) Reader (Paediat. Respirat. Med.) Imperial Coll. Sch. Med. at Nat. Heart & Lung Inst.; Hon. Cons. Paediat. Roy. Brompton Hosp. Socs: Paediat. Intens. Care Soc.; Brit. Thorac. Soc.; Amer. Thoracic Soc. Prev: Sen. Regist. (Paediat.) Roy. Postgrad. Med. Sch. Hammersmith Hosp. Lond.; Regist. (Paediat.) Hillingdon & Brompton Hosps.; Brit. Heart Foundat. Research Fell. (Clin. Physiol. & Paediat. Cardiol.) & Hon. Regist. Brompton Hosp. Lond.

BUSH, Anne Christine Govanhill Health Centre, 233 Calder Street, Glasgow G42 7DR Tel: 0141 531 8361 Fax: 0141 531 8375 — MB ChB 1974 Leeds; MRCP (UK) 1977; MRCGP 1983; DCH RCP Eng. 1977. Prev: Princip. GP Kings Norton Birm.; Regist. (Paediat.) Hillingdon Hosp. Uxbridge; Regist. (Paediat.) Hammersmith Hosp. Lond.

BUSH, Cathryn Joanna Duyland The Burnhams Surgery, Churchwalk, Burnham Market PE31 8DH; Furze Tor, Clay Lane, Warningcamp, Arundel BN18 9QN Tel: 01903 882974 — MB BS 1993 Lond.; BSc 1993 Lond.; DFFP 1993 Lond. (Royal Free Hospital Medical School) GP Princip. The Burnhams Surg., Ch. Walk, Burnham Market, Norf..

BUSH, David MacKenzie Penn Surgery, 2a Coalway Road, Penn, Wolverhampton WV3 7LR Tel: 01902 333408 Fax: 01902 621540; Tel: 01902 897798 Email: drdmbush@aol.com — MB ChB 1986 Birm.; D.Occ.Med. RCP Lond. 1996; DFFP 1994; DRCOG 1991; DCH RCP Lond. 1990.

BUSH, Dudley James St James's University Hospital, Leeds LS9 7TF Tel: 0113 243 3144 — MB BS 1985 Newc.; FCAnaesth. 1990; DA (UK) 1987. Cons. Anaesth. St Jas. Univ. Hosp. Leeds. Prev: Sen. Regist. Rotat. (Anaesth.) Yorks. Region; Vis. Instruc. Univ. Michigan, USA; SHO & Regist. (Anaesth.) St. Jas. Univ. Hosp. Leeds.

BUSH, Gordon Henry (retired) Glendor, 26 Mount Road, Upton, Wirral CH49 6JB Tel: 0151 677 2986 — BM BCh 1953 Oxf.; FFA

RCS Eng. 1960; DA Eng. 1956; DM 1962 Oxf. Prev: Cons. Anaesth. Alder Hey Childr. Hosp. Liverp.

BUSH, Harriet Mary 3 Ashton House, 58 Chilbolton Avenue, Winchester SO22 5HQ — MB ChB 1992 Bristol; MRCP (UK) 1995. Specialist Regist., Palliat. Med. Socs: Assn. of Palliat. Med.; BMA; Brit. Med. Acupunc. Soc. Prev: SHO Rotat. (Gen. Med.) Brighton.

BUSH, James Aran 1 Ruskin Road, Derby DE1 3EU — MB ChB 1998 Manch.; MB ChB Manch 1998.

BUSH, John Kendall Gale Farm Surgery, 109-119 Front Street, Acomb, York YO24 3BU Tel: 01904 798329 Fax: 01904 798329; 32 Beckfield Lane, Acomb, York YO26 5RJ Tel: 01904 791883 — MB ChB 1979 Leeds; MRCGP 1982; DRCOG 1982; Cert. Family Plann. JCC 1982. Prev: SHO (A & E) Leeds AHA; SHO (O & G) Leeds AHA; SHO (Infec. Dis.) Leeds AHA.

BUSH, John Lancelot 90 Cowley Road, London SW14 8QB — MB ChB 1990 Otago.

BUSH, John Templeton The Medical Centre, 24-28 Lower Northam Road, Hedge End, Southampton SO30 4FQ Tel: 01489 785722 Fax: 01489 799414; Woodview, Kitnocks Hill, Curdridge, Southampton SO32 2HJ Tel: 01489 782526 — MB BS 1980 Lond.; MRCP 1983; MRCGP (Distinc.) 1986; DRCOG 1985. (Middlx.) Princip. - Gen. Pract.; Clin. Tutor. Prev: SHO & Regist. (Med.) Walsgrave Hosp. Coventry; SHO (O & G) N.ampton Gen. Hosp.; SHO (Paediat.) Shoreham-by-Sea Hosp.

BUSH, John Templeton (retired) The Bothey, High St., Shirehampton, Bristol BS11 0DG Tel: 0117 982 2976 — MB ChB 1954 Bristol; MFHom 1966. Prev: Cas. & Orthop. Ho. Surg. Bristol Roy. Infirm.

BUSH, Judith Mary 6 Ryegate Road, Sheffield S10 5FA — MB ChB 1991 Sheff.

BUSH, Karalie Jane Plymyard Avenue Surgery, 170 Plymyard Avenue, Eastham, Wirral CH62 8EH Tel: 0151 327 1391; Long Acre, Heaty Lane, Willaston, South Wirral CH64 1TP — MB ChB 1984 Leic.; MRCGP 1988; DGM 1988. (Leicester)

BUSH, Keith 6 Harley Street, London W1G 9PD Tel: 0207 636 1928 Fax: 0207 580 8782 — MB BS 1978 Lond.; MD Lond. 1992. (Roy. Free Hosp.) Orthop. Phys. Socs: Counc. Brit. Inst. Musculoskeletal Med.; Internat. Soc. Study Lumbar Spine; (Progr. Comm.) Europ. Spine Soc. Prev: Hon. Cons. Orthop. Surg. Roy. Nat. Orthop. Hosp. Lond.; Chairm. Soc. Orthop. Med.; Clin. Asst. (Rheum.) Roy. Free Hosp. Lond.

BUSH, Michael Francis Howard (retired) Cherry Place, Raydon, Ipswich IP7 5LH Tel: 01473 310554 — MB BS Lond. 1958; MRCS Eng. LRCP Lond. 1958; FFPHM 1976, M 1972; DPH (Distinc.) Lond. 1965; DCH Eng. 1961. Prev: Med. Dir. Allington NHS Trust.

BUSH, Peter Andrew The Surgery, 29 Chesterfield Drive, Ipswich IP1 6DW Tel: 01473 741349; 29 Chesterfield Drive, Ipswich IP1 6DW Tel: 01473 741349 — MB BS 1984 Lond.; MRCGP 1988; DRCOG 1986; DCH RCP Lond. 1986. (Guy's) Prev: SHO VTS Swindon; Ho. Phys. Orpington Hosp.; Ho. Surg. Lewisham Hosp.

BUSH, Peter Kennedy Duyland Willow Green Surgery, Station Road, East Preston, Littlehampton BN16 3AH Tel: 01903 758152 Fax: 01903 859986; Furzetor, Clay Lane, Warningcamp, Arundel BN18 9QN Tel: 01903 882974 — MRCS Eng. LRCP Lond. 1964. (Guy's) Prev: SHO (Obst.) Zachary Merton Matern. Hosp. Rustington; Ho. Surg. & Ho. Phys. Guy's Hosp. Lond.; Surg. Lt. RN.

BUSH, Raymond Aubrey (retired) 1 South Stone Court, South Road, Hythe CT21 6AS Tel: 01303 267148 — MB BS 1947 Lond.; LMSSA Lond. 1943; DObst RCOG 1948. Prev: Resid. Med. Off. Hove Gen. Hosp.

BUSH, Robert John (retired) East Wickham Farm, Welling DA16 3DA Tel: 020 8854 9171 — MB BS. Lond. 1943; MRCS Eng. LRCP Lond. 1943.

BUSH, Mr Stephen Accident and Emergency, St. James's University Hospital, Leeds LS9 7TF Tel: 0113 206 4997; 25 Belvedere Road, Leeds LS17 8BU Tel: 0113 268 4646 Email: steve.bush@cwcam.net — MB BS 1992 Lond.; FFAEM 2001; MA Oxf. 1995, BA 1989; FRCS (Eng.) 1996. Specialist Regist., Accid. & Emerg., St. Jas. Univ. Hosp., Leeds. Socs: BAEM; Amer. Coll. of Emerg. Phys.s; Intens. Care Soc.

BUSHBY, Alaistair Julian Russell 25 Marlborough Road, Chiswick, London W4 4EU — BChir 1990 Camb.

BUSHBY, Alan Fennell (retired) 120 Belper Road, Derby DE1 3EQ Tel: 01332 340819 Email: abushby@totalise.co.uk — LRCP LRCS Ed. LRFPS Glas. 1950; FRCOG 1972, M 1958; DObst RCOG 1952. Cons. O & G City Hosp. Derby. Prev: Sen. Regist. & Clin. Tutor (O & G) Jessop. Hosp. Wom. Sheff.

BUSHBY, Anthea Mary (retired) East Cottage, Allendale Road, Hexham NE46 2NB Tel: 01434 603724 — MB ChB 1949 Liverp.; MRCS Eng. LRCP Lond. 1948; DA Eng. 1954. Prev: Instruc. (Anaesth.) Johns Hopkins Hosp. Baltimore.

BUSHBY, David Robert Pearson, TD, OStJ Coach House, Campfield, Comrie, Crieff PH6 2HB Tel: 01764 670594 Fax: 01764 670918 Email: xpa94@dial.pipex.com — MB ChB 1962 St. And.; DObst RCOG 1964. Lt. Col. RAMC T & AVR. Prev: Paediat. Brit. Milit. Hosp. Munster; Resid. Med. Off. & Resid. Surg. Off. Maryfield Hosp. Dundee; Commanding Off. 225 (Highland) Field Ambul. RAMC (V).

BUSHBY, Professor Katharine Mary Dympna institue for Human Genetics, International Centre for Life, Central Parkway, Newcastle upon Tyne NE1 3DZ Tel: 0191 241 8737 Fax: 0191 241 8799 Email: kate.bushby@ncl.ac.uk; 16 Oaklands, Newcastle upon Tyne NE3 4YQ Tel: 0191 284 5381 — MB ChB 1986 Dundee; MSc (Med. Genetics) Newc. 1990; FRCP 1999; MRCP (UK) 1989. p/t Prof. (Neuromuscular Genetics) Univ. Newc. Prev: MRC Clin. Sci. Univ. Newc.; Clin. Research Assc. (Muscular Dystrophy) Univ. Dept. Neurosci. Newc. u Tyne; Regist. (Med. Paediat.) Roy. Hosp. For Sick Childr. Glas.

BUSHBY, Margaret 19 Burlington Road, Sheffield S17 3NQ — MB ChB 1983 Bristol; MRCGP 1988; DRCOG 1987.

BUSHE, Christopher John Flat 3, Silvermere, The Esplanade, Ventnor PO38 — MB BS 1981 Lond. Med. Dir. & Financial Dir. Stow Clinics. Prev: Med. Dir. Stow Ltd. & Schwarz Pharmaceut. Chesham; Med. Adviser Boehringer Ingelheim.

BUSHELL, Ann Christina (retired) Llwyn-yr-Ysgaw, Scleddau, Dwrbach, Fishguard SA65 9QT Tel: 01348 873048 — MB ChB 1977 Birm.; MRCPath 1983; FRCPath 1998. Prev: Cons. (Microbiol.) Withybush Gen. Hosp. HaverfordW..

BUSHELL, Mr Basil Wyvern Michael (retired) 11 Albany Close, Esher KT10 9JR Tel: 01372 464509 Fax: 01372 462536 — MB ChB 1949 Birm.; FRCS Eng. 1957; DLO Eng. 1952. Prev: Cons. ENT Surg. W. Middx. Univ. Hosp. Isleworth, Kingston Hosp. & Qu. Mary Hosp. Childr. Carshalton.

BUSHELL, Kathryn Elizabeth Garden Lane Medical Centre, 19 Garden Lane, Chester CH1 4EN Tel: 01244 346677; 4 Auden Close, St David's Park, Hawarden, Deeside CH5 3TJ — MB ChB 1989 Manch.; DRCOG 1992.

BUSHELL, Timothy Ewart Christopher Copper Beech, Church Lane, Birdham, Chichester PO20 7AT Tel: 01243 512159 Fax: 01243 512159 — MB BChir 1971 Camb.; FRCP Lond. 1995; MRCP (UK) 1974; MRCS Eng. LRCP Lond. 1969. (Guy's) Med. Adviser to the Assn. of Visitors to Immigr.s Detainees. Socs: Med. Soc. Study VD Prev: Cons. Genitourin. Med. St. Richard's Hosp. Chichester; Cons., Sen. Regist. & Regist. (Genitourin. Med.) Bristol Roy. Infirm.

BUSHER, Eleanor Head Tel: 01905 681781 — MB ChB 1981 Birm.; MRCGP 1986; DRCOG 1985.

BUSHER, Guy Louis Malvern Health Centre, Victoria Park Road, Malvern Link, Malvern WR14 2JY Tel: 01684 612703 Fax: 01684 612779 — BM 1981 Soton.; MRCGP 1987; DRCOG 1986.

BUSHMAN, John Andrew (retired) 33 Canonbury Square, Islington, London N1 2AN Tel: 020 7226 5064 Fax: 020 7226 5064 — LMSSA 1959 Lond.; FFA RCS Eng. 1967. Hon. Cons. St. And. & Newham Hosps. Lond. Prev: Acting Dir. Dept. Anaesth. RCS Eng.

BUSHNELL, Mark Gaius 82 Sloane Street, London SW1X 9PA Tel: 020 7245 9333 Fax: 020 7245 9232; 1A Ormonde Terrace, Regents Park, London NW8 7LP Tel: 020 7722 9795 — MB BS 1984 Lond. (St. Thos.)

BUSHNELL, Timothy Guy William Harvey Hospital, Kennington Road, Ashford TN24 0LZ Tel: 01233 616691; 9 Millfield, Ashford TN23 4GW Tel: 01233 642539 Fax: 01233 642539 Email: tim@tbushnell.freeserve.co.uk — MB BS 1984 Lond.; FRCA 1991. (Middlx. Hosp. Med. Sch.) Cons. Pain Managem. & Anaesth. S. Kent Hosps. NHS Trust; Cons., Palliat. ~Care, pilgrims Hospice, Ashford, Kent. Socs: Pain Soc.; IASP. Prev: Sen. Regist. St. Thos. Hosp. Lond.

BUSK, Charles Martin Anthony The Surgery, Front Road, Woodchurch, Ashford TN26 3SF Tel: 01233 860236 Fax: 01233 861373 — MB BS 1977 Lond.

BUSK, Stephen Hans (retired) 11 Westrow Road, Southampton SO15 2NA Tel: 01703 336937 — BA Camb. 1946; MRCS Eng. LRCP Lond. 1950. Prev: Ho. Surg. Roy. Hants. Co. Hosp. Winchester.

BUSS, Ronald John Austen (retired) 17 Dane John, Canterbury CT1 2QU Email: johnbuss@doctors.org.uk — MB BS 1963 Lond.; MRCS Eng. LRCP Lond. 1963; DObst RCOG 1965. Prev: Univ. Med. Off. Univ. Kent.

BUSSEY, Alan Laurence (retired) France Cottage, Higher Ashton, Exeter EX6 7QS Tel: 01647 252042 Fax: 01647 252042 — MB BS 1956 Lond.; FRCP Lond. 1991; MRCS Eng. LRCP Lond. 1956; FFPHM 1989; FFCM 1978, M 1974; MRCGP 1966; DObst RCOG 1958. Prev: Regist. Fac. Pub. Health Med.

BUSSEY, Tracey Jane Dermatology Dept., Clatterbridge Hospital, Bebington, Wirral CH63 4JY Tel: 0151 334 4000 — BM BS 1993 Nottm.; BMedSci Nottm. 1991. Staff Grade in Dermat., Wirral NHS Trust. Prev: GP Locum; SHO (Dermat.) Clatterbridge Wirral NHS Trust; GP Regist. & SHO (Med.) Countess of Chester Hosp.

BUSSIN, Jacqueline Lana 14 Castle Hill Road, Prestwich, Manchester M25 0FR Email: jacqui@freeserve.co.uk — MB ChB 1990 Leeds; MRCP (UK) 1994.

BUSSON, Mervyn The Old Forge, Main St., Shelton, Newark NG23 5JQ — MB ChB 1958 Bristol; MRCGP 1974; FFPM 1989; DA (UK) 1967; DObst RCOG 1961. Cons. Boots Healthcare Internat. & Dir. Europ. Research Schachtel Assocs. Inc. Prev: Med. Dir. Boots Co. PLC. Nottm.

BUSTAM, Anita Zarina 42 St Isan Road, Cardiff CF4 7LX — MB BCh 1992 Wales.

BUSTAMANTE SAINZ, Sara 17 Forge Drive, Claygate, Esher KT10 0HR — LMS 1991 Seville; FRCA 1997; ATLS 1996; PALS 1996; DA (UK) 1995. (Seville (Spain)) Specialist Regist. Rotat. SW Thames (St. Geo. Hosp.). Socs: BMA; Assn. Anaesth. GB & Irel.; MDU. Prev: Specialist Regist. St Helier Hosp.; SHO (Neonat..) Chelsea & W.m. Hosp.; SHO (Anaesth.) Frinmley Pk. Hosp. & Wolverhampton.

***BUSTANI, Porus Cyrus** 3 Shore Court, Shore Lane, Sheffield S10 3BW — MB BS 1991 Lond.

BUSTON, Margaret Helen (retired) 19 Over Lane, Almondsbury, Bristol BS32 4BL — MB ChB Bristol 1950; FRCP Lond. 1974, M 1956; DCH Eng. 1955. Prev: Cons. Paediat. Rochdale & Dist. Hosp. Gp.

BUSUTTIL, Professor Anthony, OBE Forensic Medicine Unit, University of Edinburgh, Teviot Place, Edinburgh EH8 9AG Tel: 0131 650 3281 Fax: 0131 651 1345 Email: professor.busuttil@ed.ac.uk; 78 Hillpark Avenue, Edinburgh EH4 7AL Tel: 0131 336 3241 Fax: 0131 336 3823 — MD 1967 Malta; FRCP Glas. 1993; FRCP Ed. 1989; FRCPath 1986, M 1973; MRCP Glas. 1990; DMJ Soc. Apoth. Lond. 1982. (Malta) Regius Prof. Forens. Med. Univ. Edin.; Sen. Police Surg. Ed.; Hon. Cons. Path. Socs: Chairm. Europ. Counc. Legal Med.; Fell. Brit. Assoc. Forens. Med.; Forens. Sci. Soc. & Roy. Soc. Med. Prev: Cons. Path. W.. Gen. Hosp. Edin.; Sen. Lect. Univ. Edin.; Regist. (Laborat. Med.) Univ. Dept. Path. & Lect. & Hon. Sen. Regist. Univ. Glas. W.. Infirm. Glas.

BUSUTTIL, Walter Priory Ticehurst House, Ticehurst, Wadhurst TN5 7HU Tel: 01580 200391 — MB ChB 1983 Manch.; MPhil Lond. 1995; MRCPsych 1992; MRCGP 1988. Cons. Psychiat.; Dir. (Post Traum. Stress Disorder Serv.) Post Traum. Stress Disorder Unit. Socs: UK Trauma Gp. (Middlx. Hosp.); Internat. Soc. Traum. Stress Studies. Prev: Sen. Regist. (Psychiat.) RAF Psychiat. Serv.; Sen. Regist. (Post Traum. Stress Disorder) RAF Psychiat. Serv.; Cons. (Psychiats.) Head Dept. of RAF Community Psychiat. E. Anglia.

BUSWELL, Christopher Kenneth The Surgery, 4 Londesborough Road, Market Weighton, York YO43 3AY Tel: 01430 873433; West Grange, Shude Hill, Goodmanham, York YO43 3HX — MB ChB 1985 Leeds. Socs: Med. Protec. Soc.; BMA; Med. & Dent. Defence Union of Scotl.

BUSWELL, Wendy Ann c/o 41 Simonside Road, Sunderland SR3 4EW — MB ChB 1973 Liverp.; FRCS Eng. 1979. Cons. A & E Med. Pontefract; Cons. Surg. Arran War Memor. Hosp.

BUSZEWICZ, Marta Joanna Department of Primary Care, Polulation Sciences, UCL & Royal Free Hospital School of Medicine, Archway Wing, Whittington Hospital, London N19 Tel: 020 7288 3468 Email: m.buszewicz@ucl.ac.uk; 84 Downs Park Road, Hackney, London E8 2HZ Tel: 020 7249 0778 — MB BS 1978 Lond.; BA (Physiol. Scs.) Oxf. 1975; MRCPsych 1994; MRCGP 1990; DCH RCP Lond. 1984; DRCOG 1981. Sen. Lect. (Community Based Teachg. & Research) & GP Asst. N. Lond. Prev: Research Worker Inst. Psychiat. Lond.; Regist. Rotat. (Psychiat.) Maudsley Hosp. Lond.; GP Lond.

BUTCHART, Mr Eric Gordon Department of Cardiac Surgery, University Hospital, Cardiff CF14 4XW Tel: 029 2074 3284; Ty Fry'N-Y-Coed, Pendoylan, Cowbridge CF71 7UF Tel: 01446 781533 Fax: 01446 781316 — MB BS 1965 Durh.; FRCS Eng. 1970. (Newc.) Cons. (Cardio-Thoracic Surg.) Univ. Hosp. Wales, Cardiff; Edr. Jl. Heart Valve Dis. Socs: Soc. Thoracic & Cardiovasc. Surgs.; Brit. Cardiac Soc. Prev: Sen. Regist. (Cardio-Thoracic Surg.) Freeman Hosp. Newc.; Research Fell. (Surg.) Harvard Univ. Boston, U.S.A.; Regist. (Cardio-Thoracic Surg.) Shotley Bridge Hosp.

BUTCHART, Graham David Butchart, The Surgery, King Street, Burton-on-Trent DE14 3BX Tel: 01283 741177 Fax: 01283 565657; 143 Newton Road, Winshill, Burton-on-Trent DE15 0TR Tel: 01283 741177 — MB ChB 1980 Dundee. Socs: Med. & Dent Defence Union Scotl.

BUTCHART, John Fraser (retired) Renart, 15 Uphill Road S., Uphill, Weston Super Mare BS23 4SG — MB ChB 1947 St. And. Prev: GP W.on-Super-Mare.

BUTCHER, Adrian Bruce Eardley and Partners, Biddulph Medical Centre, Well Street, Biddulph, Stoke-on-Trent ST8 6HD Tel: 01782 512822 Fax: 01782 510331; Poolfield House, 61 Grange Road, Biddulph, Stoke-on-Trent ST8 7RY — MRCS Eng. LRCP Lond. 1973. (Leeds) Princip. (Gen. Pract.); Clin. Asst. (Subst. Abuse Psychiat.) Edwd. Myers Unit, City Gen. Hosp. Stoke on Trent.

BUTCHER, Amanda Jane 41 Wentworth Park Avenue, Harborne, Birmingham B17 9QU — MB ChB 1990 Birm.; ChB Birm. 1990; FRCOphth 1996. (Birm.) Trust Grade (Ophth.) Dudley Gp. Hosps. NHS Trust.

BUTCHER, Anne Grove Cottage, 47 High St., Bourn, Cambridge CB3 7TR Tel: 01954 719232 — MB BS 1986 Lond.; DGM RCP Lond. 1988. Clin. Med. Off. Camb. Prev: Trainee GP Lister Hosp. Stevenage; Ho. Surg. Char. Cross Hosp. Lond.; Ho. Phys. Jas. Paget Hosp. Gt. Yarmouth.

BUTCHER, Anthony Sidney Fairbank Westmorland House, 55 Burkes Road, Beaconsfield HP9 1PW Tel: 01494 671195 — MB BChir 1951 Camb.; MA Camb. 1951; FRCOG 1971, M 1958. (Camb. & Guy's) Hon. Cons. S. Bucks. NHS Trust. Socs: BMA; Chiltern Med. Soc. Prev: Cons. O & G Wycombe DHA.; Sen. Regist. (O & G) Guy's Hosp. Lond.; Capt. RAMC.

BUTCHER, Christine (retired) Elmfield House, Petersfinger, Salisbury SP5 3BZ Tel: 01722 324150 — MB BS 1963 Lond.; FRCR 1972; DMRD Eng. 1970. Prev: Cons. Radiol. Salisbury Gen. & Roy. S. Hants. Hosps. Soton.

BUTCHER, Mr Christopher Charles 35A Walton Crescent, Oxford OX1 2JQ — MB BS 1989 Lond.; FRCS Eng. 1994.

BUTCHER, Mr Clifford Keith 6 Eaton Road N., West Derby, Liverpool L12 7JW Email: cliffbut@aol.com — MB ChB 1989 Liverp.; FRCS Ed. 1994.

BUTCHER, Clive Barry Clarence House, Clarence Crescent, Windsor SL4 1BU Tel: 01753 869999 Fax: 01753 869999; Voramar del Viñyet 'A' 1°-2a, Paseo Maritimo 6, 08870 Sitges, Barcelona, Spain Tel: 00 3493 894 8311 — MB ChB 1964 Liverp. (Liverp.) Cons. Sexual Med., Erectile DysFunc., Fertil. & Artific. Inseminat. Windsor; Gen. Med. Pract. Windsor; Liveryman The Worshipful Soc. of Apoth. of Lond.; Hon. Med. Off. Brit. Red Cross Soc. Windsor Div. Socs: World Assn. Sexol.; Brit. Erectile Disorder Soc. Prev: Ho. Surg. Poole Gen. Hosp. Dorset; Ho. Phys. King Edwd. VII Hosp. Windsor Berks.

BUTCHER, Clive Charles Anthony 44 Wychwood Road, Bingham, Nottingham NG13 8SB — MB BS 1978 Lond.; BSc (Anat.) Lond. 1975, MB BS 1978; MRCP (UK) 1982. (Char. Cross) Regist. (Radiol.) Nottm. Univ. Hosp.

BUTCHER, Graham Paul Southport District General Hospital, Town Lane, Kew, Southport PR8 6PN Tel: 01704 547471 — MB ChB 1984 Liverp.; MD Liverp. 1993; MRCP (UK) 1987. Cons. Phys. & Gastroenterol. S.port & Formby NHS Trust. Prev: Sen. Regist. (Med. & Gastroenterol.) St. Geo. Hosp. Lond.; Regist. (Gastroenterol.) Hammersmith Hosp. Lond.; Research Fell. (Med.) Roy. Liverp. Hosp.

BUTCHER, Herbert George Humphrey (retired) 4 Pottergate, Lincoln LN2 1PH Tel: 01522 527874 — MRCS Eng. LRCP Lond. 1931; MA Camb. 1931; DPH Lond. 1933. Prev: HM Coroner Lincoln & Dist.

BUTCHER, Jason Lewis Ivy House, Tram Road, Upper Cwnbran, Cwmbran NP44 5AD — MB BCh 1995 Wales.

BUTCHER, Jeremy Maxwell Countess of Chester Hospital, Liverpool Rd, Chester CH2 1UL — MB BS 1985 Lond.; FRCOphth. 1992. Cons. (Ophth.) Countess of Chester Hosp. Chester. Prev: Fell. (Ophth.) Gt. Ormond St. Hosp. for Childr.; Sen. Regist. Manch. Rotat. Eye Hosp.; Regist. Rotat. (Ophth.) NW Region.

BUTCHER, Joanna Lydia St Budeaux Health Centre, Stirling Road, St. Budeaux, Plymouth PL5 1PL Tel: 01752 361010 Fax: 01752 350675; Three Corner Meadow, Cargreen, Saltash PL12 6PA Tel: 01752 844302 — MB BS 1970 Lond.; MRCGP 1976; DA Eng. 1974; DObst RCOG 1972. (St. Geo.) Prev: Med. Off. (Fam. Plann. & Child Health) Plymouth Health Dist.; SHO (O & G) Plymouth Gen. Hosp. (Freedom Fields Br.); Ho. Phys. St. Geo. Hosp. Lond.

BUTCHER, Joanne Helen Cedar Lodge, Blackmore Road, Hookend, Brentwood CM15 0DS — MB BS 1998 Lond.; MB BS Lond 1998.

BUTCHER, Josephine Nantwich Health Centre, Beam Street, Nantwich CW5 5NX Tel: 01270 610181 Fax: 01270 610511; 3 Lomax Road, Willaston, Nantwich CW5 6RN Tel: 01270 663733 — MB ChB 1977 Manch.; BSc (Med. Sci.) St. And. 1974. Hosp. Pract. (Psychosexual Med.) W. Chesh. NHS Trust, Chester & Ment. Health Unit Leighton Hosp Mid,Chesh Trust & Withington Hosp Manch; Hon. Clin. Lect. Manch. Socs: Accred. Mem. Brit. Assn. Sexual & Marital Ther.; UK Counc. for Psychother. Prev: Ho. Phys. & Ho. Surg. Sharoe Green Hosp. Preston.

BUTCHER, Lynne Hazel Health Centre Practice, Bromsgrove Street, Kidderminster DY10 1PG Tel: 01562 822077 Fax: 01562 823733; Manderley, Quarry Bank, Hartlebury, Kidderminster DY11 7TE — MB ChB 1983 Leeds; MRCGP 1987; DRCOG 1987.

BUTCHER, Nicholas Bissell 200 Newpark Road, Shrewsbury SY1 2SP Tel: 01743 361509; 11 Hafren Road, Shrewsbury SY3 8NG Tel: 01743 358298 — MB BS 1990 Lond.; DRCOG 1996; DFFP 1998; MRCOG 1998. (St. Geo. Hosp. Med. Sch. Lond.)

BUTCHER, Pamela Mary (retired) 20 Broadmark Beach, Rustington, Littlehampton BN16 2JF Tel: 01903 776633 — MB BS 1953 Lond.; MRCS Eng. LRCP Lond. 1953. Prev: Ho. Phys. & Ho. Surg. P.ss Alice Hosp. E.bourne.

BUTCHER, Peter James Albert, VRD 33 Devonshire Place, London W1G 6JN Tel: 020 7935 1022 — MB BS 1949 Lond.; MRCP Lond. 1958; MRCS Eng. LRCP Lond. 1948. (St. Bart.) Phys. & Med. Adviser to Various Multinat. Cos. Insur. Gps. & Banks. Prev: Med. Regist. Roy. Free Hosp.; Research Asst. & Regist. Med. Profess. Unit, & Sen. Regist. & Demonst. Dept. Path. St. Bart. Hosp.

BUTCHER, Richard Michael 4 Toronto Drive, Smallfield, Horley RH6 9RB Tel: 01342 843969 — MB BChir 1953 Camb.; BA Camb. 1950. (Camb. & St. Mary's)

BUTCHER, Robert Anthony 24 Powers Close, Sandy SG19 1JS Tel: 01767 680105; Ivel Medical Centre, 35-39 The Baulk, Biggleswade SG18 0PX Tel: 01767 312441 — MB BS 1976 Lond.; FRCGP 1997. (St. Bart.)

BUTCHER, Simon James Calcot Medical Centre, Hampden Road, Chalfont St. Peter, Gerrards Cross SL9 9SA Tel: 01753 887311 Fax: 01753 890639 — MB BS 1975 Lond.; MRCGP 1984; DRCOG 1979. (St. Geo.) Prev: Ho. Phys. St. Geo. Hosp. Tooting.

BUTE, Kilian Jennifer Chessel Surgery - Bitterne Branch, 4 Chessel Avenue, Bitterne, Southampton SO19 4AA Tel: 023 8044 7777 Fax: 023 8042 5429; The Otters, Cranford Way, Highfield, Southampton SO17 1RN Tel: 023 805 54249 Fax: 023 8055 4390 Email: bute@compuserve.com — MB BS 1968 Lond.; MRCGP 1984; Cert. Family Plann. JCC 1984; DObst RCOG 1970. (St. Bart.) Managing Partner of Pract.; Hon. Clin. Teach. (Primary Med. Care) Univ. Soton. Prev: Med. Off. Mseleni Hosp., Zululand; SHO (Paediat.) St. David's Hosp. Bangor.

BUTLAND, Hazel Judith Whitchurch Surgery, 49 Oving Road, Whitchurch, Aylesbury HP22 4JFG Tel: 01296 641203; 24 Coppidwell Drive, Aylesbury HP21 9QF Tel: 01296 433672 — MB ChB 1979 Sheff.; MRCGP 1984; DFFP 1993. p/t Princip. GP, WhitCh.; Police Surg. Thames Valley Police, Aylesbury; Clin. Asst. Palliat. Care for Vale of Aylesbury PCT. Socs: RSM (Provinced Fell.). Prev: Princip. GP Aylesbury; Asst. GP Maidstone.

BUTLAND, Richard John Ashley The Winfield Hospital, Tewkesbury Road, Longford, Gloucester GL2 9WH Tel: 01452 331111 Fax: 01452 331200 — MB BChir 1976 Camb.; MD 1984 Camb.; MA 1976 Camb.; MRCP (UK) 1978; MRCS Eng. LRCP Lond. 1975. (Cambridge University M.S.) Cons. Gen. & Thoracic Med. Gloucester Roy. & Standish Hosps. Gloucester. Socs: Brit. Thorac. Soc.; Standards of Care Comm. Prev: Sen. Regist. Papworth Hosp.; Tutor (Thoracic Med.) Brompton Hosp. Lond.; Regist. Guy's & St. Geo. Hosps. Lond.

BUTLER, Alexandra Elizabeth Department of Medicine, Western General Hospital, Edinburgh EH4 2XU — MB BS 1984 Newc. Path. Resid. Mayo Clinic Rochester, USA. Prev: Jun. Trainee Microbiol. Newc. Gen. Hosp.

BUTLER, Alexis Helene Picket Post, Bray, Maidenhead SL6 2BD Tel: 01628 20620 — MB BS 1984 Lond. (St. Geo.)

BUTLER, Allison Jane 10 Welsby Close, Fearnhead, Warrington WA2 0DW — BM BS 1995 Nottm.

BUTLER, Andrew Charles 21 Royal Crescent, Edinburgh EH3 6QA — MB ChB 1990 Ed.

BUTLER, Andrew Charles Oxford Street Surgery, 20 Oxford Street, Workington CA14 2AL Tel: 01900 603302 Fax: 01900 871604 Email: acbwton@aol.com; Millbanks, Bridgefoot, Workington CA14 1YQ — MB BS 1977 Newc.; BSc (Hons. Physiol.) Newc. 1972; Dip. IMC RCS Ed. 1992; DRCOG 1980. Med. Adviser Cumbria Fire Serv.; Med. Adviser Iggesund PaperBd. (Workington) Ltd.; Police Surg.; Immediate Care Practitioner; Med. Adviser Speedway Control Bd.; Med. Off. Worthington Speedway; Mem. of ACU Med. Panel. Socs: Soc. Occupat. Med.; Brit. Assn. Immed. Care Schemes; Assn. Local Auth. Med. Advisers (Asst. Fire Bridge Rep.).

BUTLER, Andrew James The Brook, 138 High St., Sawston, Cambridge CB2 4HJ — BChir 1990 Camb.

BUTLER, Angela Susan Rose Bank, Penny Bridge, Ulverston LA12 7RQ — MB BS 1971 Lond. Clin. Asst. (Anaesth.) Furness Gen. Hosp. Barrow.

BUTLER, Ann Christine Ridge Hill MHU, Brierley Hill Road, Stourbridge DY8 5ST Tel: 01384 457373; Forest Lodge, The Compa, Kinver, Stourbridge DY7 6HS Tel: 01384 872322 — MB BS 1961 Durh.; DPM Eng. 1967; DCH Eng. 1964. Cons. Psychiat. (Learning Disabil.) Dudley Priority Health NHS Trust. Socs: Affil. RCPsych; BMA. Prev: Sen. Regist. (Child Psychiat.) Birm. AHA (T); Regist. (Psychiat.) Birm. RHA.

BUTLER, Anne Josephine Picket Post, Bray, Maidenhead SL6 2BD Tel: 01628 20620 — MB BCh BAO 1954 Dub.; BA, MB BCh BAO Dub. 1954. (T.C. Dub.)

BUTLER, Anthony Simon Ashton Road Surgery, 58 Ashton Road, Droylsden, Manchester M43 7BW Tel: 0161 370 1610 Fax: 0161 371 1258; 28 Ley Lane, Marple Bridge, Stockport SK6 5DD Tel: 0161 449 8532 — MB BCh BAO 1971 Dub.

BUTLER, Anthony Vivian John Student Health Service, 25 Belgrave Road, Bristol BS8 2AA Tel: 0117 973 7716 Fax: 0117 970 6804 — MB ChB 1968 Bristol. Director, Stud. Health Serv. Univ. Bristol. Socs: Brit. Assn. Health Servs. in Higher Ed. Prev: Hon. Research Fell. Anat. Univ. Birm.; Lect. (Anat.) Univ. Birm.

BUTLER, Bernadette Department of Obstetrics & Gynaecology, St Peter's NHS Trust, Chertsey KT16 0PZ Tel: 01932 872000; Overmead, 26 Mayfield Road, Weybridge KT13 8XB Tel: 01932 829647 Fax: 01932 829648 — MB BS 1978 Lond.; MRCS Eng. LRCP Lond. 1978; DRCOG 1987. (St. Thos. Hosp. Lond.) Clin. Asst. (O & G) St. Peter's Hosp. Chertsey. Prev: Regist. St. Geo. Hosp. Lond. & St. Peter's Hosp. Chertsey; Resid. Med. Off. Qu. Charlotte's Hosp. Lond.

BUTLER, Caroline Alice Scott Tel: 01273 271150; Tel: 01273 207248 — MB BS 1989 Lond.; Dip Occ Med 2001; MRCGP 1995; DRCOG 1993. Gen. Practioner - Partner Brighton.

BUTLER, Christine Margaret (retired) 52 Madeley Road, London W5 2LU Tel: 020 8998 8292 — MB BS 1959 Lond.; MRCS Eng. LRCP Lond. 1958; MRCOG 1964, DObst 1960. Prev: Med. Asst. Counc. Investig. of Fertil. Control.

BUTLER, Christopher Collett Llanedeyrn Health Centre, Maelfa, Llanedeyrn, Cardiff CF23 9PN Tel: 029 2073 1671 Fax: 029 2054 0129 — MB ChB 1986 Cape Town; MRCGP 1993.

BUTLER, Mr Christopher Michael Medway Hospital, Windmill Road, Gillingham ME7 5NY Tel: 01634 838984 Fax: 01634 833771; Colindean, Dunn Street Road, Bredhurst, Gillingham ME7 3LX — MB BS 1976 Lond.; MS Lond. 1985; FRCS Eng. 1980; MRCS Eng. LRCP Lond. 1976. (Westm.) Cons. Surg. Medway NHS Trust. Socs: Fell. Roy. Soc. Med.; Fell. Assn. Surg.; Vasc. Surg. Soc. Prev: Sen. Regist. (Surg.) St. Geo. Hosp. Lond. & Roy. Marsden Hosp. Lond.; Research Regist. (Vasc. & Surg.) Kings Coll. Hosp. Med. Sch. Lond.

BUTLER, Christopher Rance High Cedars, Theobalds, Hawkhurst, Cranbrook TN18 4AJ — MB ChB 1997 Ed.

BUTLER, Clarice Elise (retired) 10 Silver Birch Drive, Kinver, Stourbridge DY7 6AW Tel: 01384 877936 — MB ChB 1945 Birm. Prev: Asst. Co. Med. Off. & Sch. Med. Off. Worcs. & Hants. CC.

BUTLER, David Arthur Countess Mountbatten House, Moorgreen Hospital, Botley Road, West End, Southampton SO30 3JB Tel: 02380 477414 Fax: 02380 473501 Email: davidbutler@suht.swub.nhs.uk; 15 Oakmount Avenue, Southampton SO17 1ED — MB BS 1978 Lond.; MA Camb. 1979; MRCGP 1982; Dip. Palliat. Med. Wales 1992; DRCOG 1982. Cons. Palliat. Med. Soton. Univ. Hosp. NHS Trust & Winchester & E.leigh Healthcare NHS Trust. Prev: Cons. Palliat. Med. Aylesbury Vale Community Healthcare NHS Trust; Med. Dir. Florence Nightingale Hse. Stoke Mandeville Hosp. Aylesbury; GP Wendover.

BUTLER, The Hon. Mrs Diana Rosamund Eryl Mount Juliet, Old Mill Lane, Wester Culcabock, Inverness IV2 3XP Tel: 01463 237842 — MB ChB 1955 Ed.; DPM Eng. 1960; MRCPsych 1971. Socs: Assoc. Mem. Brit. Psycho-Anal. Soc. Prev: Sen. Regist. Leavesden Hosp.; Cons. Psychiat. Raigmore Hosp. Inverness; Cons. Psychiat. BoroCt. Hosp.

BUTLER, Eleanor Patricia Manor Brook Medical Centre, 117 Brook Lane, London SE3 0EN Tel: 020 8856 5678 Fax: 020 8856 8632; St. Margaret's Rectory, Brandram Road, London SE13 5EA Tel: 020 8852 0633 Fax: 020 8297 2877 — MB BS 1963 Lond.; MRCS Eng. LRCP Lond. 1963. (Roy. Free) Socs: W Kent M-C Soc. & BMA. Prev: Ho. Surg. Roy. Free Hosp.; Ho. Phys. (Paediat.) & Clin. Asst. (Rheum.) Dudley Rd. Hosp. Birm.

BUTLER, Elizabeth Blanche (retired) 6E Grosvenor Hill, Wimbledon Village, London SW19 4RU Tel: 020 8946 2375 Fax: 020 8946 2880 Email: xot33@dial.pipex.com — MD 1967 Wales; MB BCh 1947; FRCOG 1969, M 1954; MRCPath 1979; DObst 1949. Prev: Reader (Cytopathol.) Univ. Manch.

BUTLER, Elizabeth Vaughan Family Planning Service, Health Centre, St John Street, Mansfield NG18 1RH Tel: 01297 489226, 01623 784319 Email: liz.butler@stjohn.cnhc_tr.trent.nhs.uk — MB ChB 1967 Liverp.; MFFP 1993; Cert. Family Plann. JCC 1977. Cons. Family Plann. & Reproduc. Health, Centr. Mansfield Dist. Primary Care Trust. Prev: SCMO (Family Plann.) Centr. Notts. Healthcare NHS Trust.; Ho. Off. N.ampton Gen. Hosp.

BUTLER, Fiona Ogilvie The Surgery, 10 Redcliffe Street, London W10 Tel: 020 7460 2222; 34 Royal Crescent, London W11 4SN Tel: 020 7603 5828 Fax: 020 7603 2593 Email: fionabutler@zoo.co.uk — MB ChB 1988 Bristol; MRCGP 1994. (Bristol) Primary Care Tutor, London Deanery; professional Executive Committee, Kensington & Chelsea PCT.

BUTLER, Gary Dykes Hall Medical Centre, 156 Dykes Hall Road, Sheffield S6 4GQ Tel: 0114 232 3236 — MB ChB 1989 Sheff.; MRCGP 1993; DRCOG 1992. Lect. Inst. of Gen. Pract. & Primary Care Univ. of Sheff. Prev: SHO (Paediat.) Rotherham Dist. Gen. Hosp. VTS; SHO (O & G) Rotherham Dist. Gen. Hosp. VTS; Ho. Off. (Chest Med.) N.. Gen. Hosp.

BUTLER, Gary Everton Department of Paediatric and Adolescent Endocrinology, Clarendon Wing, Leeds General Infirmary, Belmont Grove, Leeds LS2 9NS Tel: 0113 392 3700 Fax: 0113 392 3225 — MB BS 1981 Lond.; MD Lond. 1993; FRCP (UK) 1997; MRCP (UK) (Paediat.) 1984; FRCPCH 1997. Cons. Paediat. Endocrinol. Leeds Gen. Infirm. Socs: Brit. Soc. Paediat. Endocrinol.; Eur. Soc. Paediat. Endocrinol.; Soc. for Endocrinol. Prev: Lect. (Paediat. Endocrinol.) Univ. Hosp. Cardiff; Clin. Scientist (Paediat.) MRC Human Genetics Unit W.. Gen. Hosp. Edin.

BUTLER, Gregory 65 Willson Road, Littleover, Derby DE23 7BY — MB BS 1989 Lond.; DRCOG 1994; DA (UK) 1992. Trainee GP Burton upon Trent. Prev: SHO Burton Dist. Hosp. VTS.

BUTLER, Hazel Jane Orchard End Surgery, Dorothy Avenue, Cranbrook TN17 3AY Tel: 01580 713622 Fax: 01580 715537 Email: hazelbutler@aol.com; High Cedars, Theobalds, Hawkhurst, Cranbrook TN18 4AJ Tel: 01580 752366 — MB ChB 1968 Bristol. (Bristol)

BUTLER, Helen Rosalind C/O Anaesthetic Department, Hillwgdon Hospital, Pield Heath Road, Uxbridge UB8 3NN — MB ChB 1983 Manch.; FRCA 1992. Staff Grade Anaesth. Rotherham Trust Hosp.

BUTLER, Henry Victor Spencer 226 Belenden Road, London SE15 4BY — MB BS 1988 Lond. (Char. Cross)

BUTLER, I G Belle Vale Health Centre, Hedgefield Road, Liverpool L25 2XE Tel: 0151 487 0514 Fax: 0151 488 6601.

BUTLER, Ian (retired) Riverside Medical Centre, Saville Road, Castleford WF10 1DP Tel: 01977 554831 — MRCS Eng. LRCP Lond. 1945. Apptd. Fact. Doctor Anson Cast Products Castleford. Prev: Resid. Med. Off. Pontefract Gen. Infirm.

BUTLER, Ian Andrew 10 Brookfield Road, London E9 5AH — MB BS 1992 Lond.

BUTLER, James Robert Honicknowle Green Medical Centre, Guy Miles Way, Honicknowle Green, Plymouth PL5 3PY — MB BS 1982 Lond.; MRCGP 1990. (Lond. Hosp.)

BUTLER, Jamie Dominic 7 Garner Close, Bowdon, Altrincham WA14 2JH — MB ChB 1993 Liverp.

BUTLER, Janet Ann University Mental Health Group, Royal South Hants Hospital, Southampton SO14 0YG — MB BS 1993 Lond.; BA Oxf. 1990; MRCP (UK) 1996; MRCPsych, 1998. MRC Clin. Train. Fello (Psychiat.). Prev: SHO Rotat. (Psychiat.) Maudsley Hosp. Lond.; SHO (Med.) Hammersmith Hosp. Lond.

BUTLER, John Antony (Surgery) 5 Woodlands Road, Redhill RH1 6EY Tel: 01737 761343; Little Pendell, Pendell Road, Bletchingley, Redhill RH1 4QH Tel: 01883 742862 — MB BChir 1954 Camb.; BA Camb. 1951. Prev: Ho. Surg. Ashford Hosp. Middlx.; Ho. Phys. W.m. Hosp. Lond.; Ho. Surg. (O & G) Roy. Hants. Co. Hosp.

BUTLER, Mr John Gerard Department of Cardiothoracic Surgery, Western Infirmary, Glasgow G11 6NT Tel: 0141 211 2194 — MB BCh BAO 1983 NUI; FRCSI 1988. Cons. (Cardiothoracic Surg.) W.. Infirm. Glas. Prev: Regist. W. of Scotl.

BUTLER, John Lynn, TD Hill House, 90 Station Road, Llanishen, Cardiff CF14 5UX Tel: 029 2075 2584 — MRCS Eng. LRCP Lond. 1949. (Cardiff)

BUTLER, Mr John Michael, Specialist Registrar Mellieha, Hill Fold, South Elmsall, Pontefract WF9 2BZ Tel: 01977 643689; Flat 27, Willow Park, Willow Bank, Fallowfield, Manchester M14 6XT Tel: 0161 225 4015 Email: jmb2@jmb2.freeserve.co.uk — BM BS 1992 Nottm. (Nottm.) Specialist Regist. (Emerg. Med.) N. W. Region. Socs: BASICS; Fell. Roy. Coll. Surgs. (Edin.). Prev: SHO (A & E) N. Manch. Gen. Hosp.

BUTLER, Julia Ann Mary 285 Brook Lane, Birmingham B13 0TL — MB BCh BAO 1990 NUI.

BUTLER, Julia Mary c/o 12 Whitworth Road, Sheffield S10 3HD — MB BS 1981 Lond.; MRCGP 1985; DTM & H Liverp. 1987; DRCOG 1984. (King's Coll. Hosp.) Prev: GP UMN Nepal.

BUTLER, Julie 17 Osprey Close, Worcester WR2 4BX — MB ChB 1998 Leeds.

BUTLER, Karen 64 Woodrow Dr, Wokingham RG40 1RT — MB ChB 1997 Manch.

BUTLER, Katherine Jane 38 Keydell Avenue, Waterlooville PO8 9TD — MB BS 1998 Lond.; MB BS Lond 1998.

BUTLER, Louise Marie 292 Wolverhampton Road W., Bentley, Walsall WS2 0DS Tel: 01902 418244 — MB ChB 1996 Dundee. (Dundee) GPVTS Walsall Manor Hosp. Prev: SHO Paediat. Manor Hosp.; Ho. (Surg.) New Cross, Wolverhampton; Ho. (Med.) Manor Hosp. Walsall.

BUTLER, Lucilla, SSStJ Birmingham & Midland Eye Centre, City Hospital NHS Trust, Dudley Road, Birmingham B18 7QH Tel: 0121 554 3801 Fax: 0121 507 6791 — MB BS 1980 Lond.; MA Oxf. 1981, BA 1977; FRCS Ed. 1986; FRCOphth 1987. Cons. Ophth. Birm. & Midl. Eye Centre. Prev: Cons. Ophth. Coventry & Warwick Hosp. & St. Cross Hosp.

BUTLER, Margaret Nurses Cottage, Old Palace Road, Weybridge KT13 8PH — MB BS 1984 Lond. SHO (Anaesth.) Guy's Hosp. Lond.

BUTLER, Mark Oliver Polson, The Street, Didmarton, Badminton GL9 1DT — MB BS 1985 Lond.; BSc (Hons.) Lond. 1982, MB BS 1985; MRCP (UK) 1989. Regist. (Haemat.) Roy. Free Hosp. Lond.; Mem. Med. Defence Union. Prev: SHO (Med.) Canterbury & Thanet HA.

BUTLER, Matthew John 29 Chester Crescent, Newcastle ST5 3RT — MB BS 1994 Lond.

BUTLER, Michael 5 The Stray, Longnewton, Stockton-on-Tees TS21 1DN — MB BS 1996 Lond.

BUTLER, Michael Andrew 275 Ashby Road, Scunthorpe DN16 2AB — MB ChB 1982 Leeds; MRCGP 1986; DRCOG 1984.

BUTLER, Michael Frank (retired) 3 South Cliff Parade, Broadstairs CT10 1TJ Tel: 01843 860011 — MB BS 1945 Lond.; FRCS Eng. 1949. Hon. Cons. Surg. I. of Thanet Dist. Hosp. Prev: Sen. Regist. (Surg.) W.m. Hosp.

BUTLER, Michael Liam 18 Pownall Avenue, Bramhall, Stockport SK7 2HE — MB ChB 1991 Manch.

BUTLER, Neil Guy Peter (retired) Old Orchard, Shillingford Abbot, Exeter EX2 9QF Tel: 01392 833313 — MB BS Lond. 1947; MRCS Eng. LRCP Lond. 1947; FFA RCS Eng. 1954; DA Eng. 1951. Prev: Cons. Anaesth. Exeter HA.

BUTLER, Professor Neville Roy International Centre for Child Studies, 86 Cumberland Road, Hotwells, Bristol BS1 6UG Tel: 0117 925 0835 Fax: 01179 093739 Email: mrbutler@aol.com; 86 Cumberland Road, Hotwells, Bristol BS1 6UG — MB BS 1943 Lond.; MD Lond. 1949; FRCP Lond. 1965, M 1946; FRCOG 1979; DCH Eng. 1949; FRCP 1996. (Char. Cross) Dir. of Internat. Centre for Child Studies; Vis. Prof. City Univ. Lond.; Dir. Youthscan UK (1970 Birth Cohort); Co-Dir. Nat. Child Developm. Study at 7 & 11 Years (1958 Cohort); Dir. Perinatal Mortality Survey Nat. Birthday Trust Fund. Prev: Emerit. Prof. Child Health Univ. Bristol; Phys. Hosp. Sick Childr. Gt. Ormond St. Lond.; Sen. Lect. Inst. Child Health Univ. Lond.

BUTLER, Nigel Stephen The Surgery, Outings Lane, Doddinghurst, Brentwood CM15 0LS Tel: 01277 821699 Fax: 01277 821226; The Old School House, 20 St. James Avenue, Ongar CM5 9EL Tel: 01277 821699 — MB BS 1979 Lond.; MRCS Eng. LRCP Lond. 1979; MRCGP 1983; DCH RCP Lond.1983; DRCOG 1982. (Westm.) Socs: Roy. Coll. Gen. Pract. (Essex Fac. Bd.); BMA. Prev: SHO (Gen. Pract.) Qu. Alexandra Hosp. Portsmouth VTS; Ho. Surg. Battle Hosp. Reading; Ho. Phys. Peace Memor. Hosp. Watford.

BUTLER, Patrick James Department of Anaesthesia, Southampton General Hospital, Tremona Road, Southampton SO16 6YD — MB ChB 1984 Birm.; FRCA 1989.

BUTLER, Paul Department of Neuroradiology, The Royal London Hospital, London E1 1BB Tel: 020 7377 7165 Fax: 020 7377 7165 Email: paulbutler@neurorad.demon.co.uk — MRCS Eng. LRCP Lond. 1976; BSc Lond. 1973, MB BS 1976; MRCP (UK) 1979; FRCR 1983; T(R) (CR) 1991; DMRD Eng. 1983. (Westm.) Cons. Neuroradiol. Barts and the Lond. NHS Trust; Hon. Cons. Essex Regional Centre for Neurol. & Neurosurg. OldCh., Romford. Socs: Brit. Soc. Neuroradiol.; Eur. Soc. Neuroradiol. Prev: Sen. Regist. (Neuroradiol.) Manch. Roy. Infirm.; Trainee Regist. (Radiol.) N. W.. RHA(T); Regist. Rotat. (Gen. Med.) Leics. AHA (T).

BUTLER, Peter Arnot Woodsend Road Surgery, 14 Woodsend Road, Flixton, Manchester M41 8QT Tel: 0161 747 4975 Fax: 0161 747 5321 — MB ChB 1970 Manch.; DObst RCOG 1972.

BUTLER, Peter Robin (retired) Downe Cottage, Chapel Hill, Dunsfold, Godalming GU8 4NZ Tel: 01483 200345 Fax: 01483 200345 — MB BS Lond. 1955; MRCS Eng. LRCP Lond. 1955; DObst RCOG 1960.

BUTLER, Robert 22 Independence Drive, Pinchbeck, Spalding PE11 3TR — MB ChB 1991 Manch.

BUTLER, Robert Edward Imperial College School of Medicine, Department of Academic Psychiatry, St Charles Hospital, London W10 6DZ Tel: 020 8962 4106 Email: r.e.butler@ic.ac.uk; Flat 5, 1 St George's Square, London SW1V 2HU — MB BS 1987 Lond.; MRCPsych 1993. (St. Geo. Hosp. Med. Sch. Lond.) Lect. & Hon. Sen. Regist. (Psychiat. of Old Age) St. Mary's Hosp. Med. Sch. Lond. Prev: Regist. (Psychiat.) Waikato, NZ; Regist. & SHO Rotat. (Psychiat.) N. Lond.

BUTLER, Robert Spencer (retired) 90 Hambalt Road, London SW4 9EJ — MB ChB 1962 Ed.; DObst RCOG 1966. Prev: SHO (Obst.) St. Thos. Hosp. Lond.

BUTLER, Robin Clive Robert Jones & Agnes Hunt Orthopaedic Hospital, Oswestry SY10 7AG Tel: 01691 404384; Glasfryn, Mount Drive, Oswestry SY10 7AG — MB BS 1972 Lond.; MD Lond. 1986; FRCP Lond. 1991; MRCP (UK) 1974; MRCS Eng. LRCP Lond. 1972. (Char. Cross) Cons. Rheum. Robt. Jones & Agnes Hunt Orthop. Hosp. OsW.ry & Roy. Shrewsbury Hosp. Socs: Brit. Soc. Rheum. Prev: Sen. Regist. (Rheum. & Med.) W.m. Hosp. Lond.; Lect. (Experim. Path.) Char. Cross Hosp. Med. Sch. Lond.

BUTLER, Mr Robin Ervin Hoebridge, Crofton Avenue, Lee-on-the-Solent PO13 9NJ Tel: 01329 662166 — MB ChB 1966 Bristol; FRCS Eng. 1974; FRCOphth 1988; DO Eng. 1968. (Bristol) Cons. Ophth. Surg. Qu. Alexandra Hosp. Portsmouth. Socs: Fell. Roy. Soc. Med. Prev: Regist. Bristol Eye Hosp. & Manch. Roy. Eye Hosp.; Sen. Regist. Soton. Eye Hosp.

BUTLER, Roderick Maynard (retired) 18 Beechcourt, Tower St., Taunton TA1 4BH — MB ChB Birm. 1949; DPH Lond. 1956. Prev: Med. Asst. Holywell Hosp. Antrim.

BUTLER, Sally Anne c/o St James' Hospital, Locksway Road, Milton, Portsmouth PO4 8LD Tel: 023 92 894324 Fax: 023 92 829980; 8 Skylark Way, The Pines, Saintbridge, Gloucester GL4 4QY Tel: 01452 422441 — MB BS 1990 Lond.; BSc Lond. 1987, MB BS 1990. (St Mary's) Staff Grade (Psychiat.) Challenging Behaviour Unit St James' Hosp. Portsmouth. Prev: Regist. (Psychiat.) Wessex Rotat.; SHO (Cas.) Canterbury.

BUTLER, Sandra Julia The Royal Hospital for Sick Children, Dalnair Street, Yorkhill, Glasgow G3 8SJ Tel: 0141 201 0096 — MB ChB 1990 Glas.; FRCR (UK) 2000; MRCP (Paediat.) 1993; FRCR Part I 1997. (Glas.) Specialist Regist. (Radiol.) W. Glas. Hosps. Univ. NHS Trust. Prev: Paediat. Regist. Roy. Aberd. Childr. Hosp.

BUTLER, Sean Vincent 139 Burnley Road, Blackburn BB1 3HN — BM 1995 Soton.

BUTLER, Simon James Cawood Western Road Surgery, 41 Western Road, Billericay CM12 9DX Tel: 01277 658117 Fax: 01277 658119 — MB BS 1983 Lond.; BSc Lond. 1980; DA (UK) 1985. Exec. Chairm., Billericay, Brentwood and Wickford PCT.

***BUTLER, Simon Peter** 22 Kinnaird Avenue, London W4 3SH — MB ChB 1997 Birm.

BUTLER, Susan Elizabeth 5 Lancaster Close, Pontefract WF8 3PH — MB ChB 1976 Leeds; MRCGP 1981.

BUTLER, Mr Thomas Kenneth Heinz 94 Mona Road, West Bridgford, Nottingham NG2 5BT Email: tom.butler2@virgin.net — MB ChB 1994 Leeds; FRCOphth 1999. (Uni of Leeds) SHO (Ophth.)Qu.s Med Centre, Univ. Hosp. Nottm. Socs: Fell.ship RSM. Prev: SHO (Neurol. & Neurosurg.) Pinderfields Gen. Hosp. Wakefield.

BUTLER, Timothy John (Surgery), 30 Longdale Avenue, Ravenshead, Nottingham NG15 9EA Tel: 01623 794222; Lin Cottage, Kirklington, Newark NG22 8ND Tel: 01636 813347 — MB ChB 1967 Liverp.; DObst RCOG 1971. Prev: SHO (Obst.) Odstock Hosp. Salisbury; Ho. Off. N.ampton Gen. Hosp.; Squadron Ldr. RAF Med. Br.

BUTLER, Ursula Georgina 47 St Andrews Road, Sheffield S11 9AL — MB BS 1970 Lond.; MRCP (UK) 1974. (Char. Cross) SCMO (Community Child Health) Community Health Sheff. Prev: Regist. (Paediat.) Notts. AHA (T); Regist. (Neonat. Paediat.) Hammersmith Hosp. Lond.

BUTLER, William Hope Glebe Cottage, Big Common Lane, Bletchingley, Redhill RH1 4QE Tel: 01883 743289 Fax: 01883 744355 — MB BS 1959 Lond.; MRCS Eng. LRCP Lond. 1959; FRCPath 1978, M 1970. (Univ. Coll. Hosp.)

BUTLER-GALLIE, Sara Pamela Charing Surgery, Charing, Ashford TN27 0HZ Tel: 01233 714141 Fax: 01233 713782 — MB ChB 1988 Sheff.; MRCGP 1993.

BUTLER-MANUEL, Mr Peter Adrian Conquest Hospital, The Ridge, St Leonards-on-Sea TN37 7RD Tel: 01424 755255; Tinkers Bar, The St, Sedlescombe, Battle TN33 0QJ — MB BS 1981 Lond.; FRCS (Orth.) 1992; FRCS Eng. 1986. (St. Thos.) Cons. Orthop. Surg. Conquest Hosp. Hastings. Socs: BOA; BASK. Prev: Sen. Regist. (Orthop. Surg.) St. Thos. Hosp. Lond., Roy. E. Sussex Hosp. Hastings & Roy. Sussex Co. Hosp. Brighton; Regist. (Orthop. Surg.) P.ss Margt. Hosp. Swindon & St. Thos. Hosp. Lond.

BUTLER-MANUEL, Mr Simon Alastair 9 Arundel Close, Wandsworth Common, London SW11 1HR — MB BS 1988 Lond.; FRCS Eng. 1992.

BUTLIN, Janet Ann Goldington Road Surgery, 2 Goldington Road, Bedford MK40 3NG Tel: 01234 351341; 67 Stonely, Huntingdon PE18 0EP — MB BS 1983 Lond.; MRCGP 1987; DRCOG 1986. Prev: GP Trainee Shefford Beds.; SHO (Psychiat.) Yare Clin. Norwich; SHO (O & G) Newmarket.

BUTLIN, Sarah Jane (retired) Ashtree Farm, Main Street, Thorganby, York YO19 6DB — MB ChB 1988 Liverp.; MRCGP 1995; DGM RCP Lond. 1992; DCH RCP Lond. 1992; DRCOG 1990; Cert Family Plann Full 1990. Indep. Sch. Med. Off. York. Prev: SHO (O & G) Fazakerley Hosp. Liverp.

BUTROUS, Ghazwan Saleem Pfizer Central Research, Ramsgate Road, Sandwich CT13 9NJ Tel: 01304 648591 Fax: 01304 655537 Email: ghazwan_butrous@sandwich.pfizer.com — MB ChB 1976 Baghdad; PhD (Cardiol.) Lond. 1989. Sen. Clin. Project Manager Pfizer Centr. Research; Hon. Sen. Lect. (Cardiol.) St. Geo. Hosp. Med. Sch. Lond. Socs: Fell. Europ. Soc. Cardiol.; Brit. Cardiac Soc.; N. Amer. Soc. Cardiac Pacing & Electrophysiol. Prev: Lect. (Clin. Cardiac Electrophysiol.) & Dir. Electrophysiol. Lab. St. Geo. Hosp. Med. Sch. Lond.; Lect. (Cardiol.) St. Bart. Hosp. Med. Sch. Lond.

BUTT, Alexander 45 Lavender Grove, Mitcham CR4 3HW — MB BS 1994 Lond. (St. Geo.)

BUTT, Alice 16 Granville Avenue, Oadby, Leicester LE2 5FL — MB BS 1969 Madras; DMRD Eng. 1982. (Christian Med. Coll. Vellore)

BUTT, Ambreen Masud Flat 1/3, 16 Dudley Drive, Glasgow G12 9SB — MB ChB 1989 Glas. Glas. NHS Trust.

BUTT, Andrew Jonathan Morton 94 Main Street, Davidson Mains, Edinburgh EH4 5AB Tel: 0131 467 1268 Email: jobutt@pigsty.fsbusiness.co.uk — MB ChB 1967 Ed.; BA Camb. 1961; FRCP Ed. 1987; FRCGP 1996, M 1977; DObst RCOG 1969. Clin.Asst. Monklands Hosp. Prev: Mem. Panel of Examrs. RCGP; Lect. (Gen. Pract.) Univ. Edin.; Sen. Regist. (Med.) Ahmadu Bello Univ. Zaria, Nigeria.

***BUTT, Asha** 16 Granville Avenue, Oadby, Leicester LE2 5FL — MB BS 1995 Lond.; BSc (Hons.) Lond. 1991.

BUTT, Assad Mehmood 2 Strathearn Avenue, Twickenham TW2 6JU Tel: 020 8894 4949 Email: assadbutt@hotmail.com; Tel: 020 8894 4949 Email: assadbutt@hotmail.com — MB BS 1987 Lond.; MRCP (UK) 1995; DCH RCP Lond. 1994. (Char. Cross & Westm., Univ. of Lond.) p/t Locum Cons., Dept. Paediat., Ashford & St. Peter's Hosp.s. Socs: Roy. Coll. of Paediat. & Child Health (Founder Mem.); Brit. Soc. of Paediatric Gastroenterol., Hepat. & Nutrit. (Full Mem.). Prev: Clin. & Research Fell., Div. of Paediatric Gastroenterol./Nutrit., The Hosp. for Sick Childr., Toronto, Ontario, Canada, Sept. 1998-June 2001; Clin./Research Fell., Dept. of Peadiatric Gastroenterol., Roy. Free Hosp., Hamstead.

BUTT, Khalid Shafiq 40 Stockton Drive, Woolfold, Bury BL8 1UQ — MB ChB 1986 Leic. SHO (Geriat.) Roy. Preston Hosp.

BUTT, Mr Mahmud 150 Crosland Road, Lindley, Huddersfield HD3 3SU — MB BS 1955 Punjab; FRCS Eng. 1977.

BUTT, Mariam Wiena 22 Stuart Road, London SW19 8DH — MB BS 1993 Lond.

BUTT, Mark Stephen Andaman Surgery, 303 Long Road, Lowestoft NR33 9DF Tel: 01502 517346 Fax: 01502 531450; White House Barn, Uggeshall, Beccles NR34 8BJ Tel: 01502 578519 — MB ChB 1981 Birm.; MRCGP 1985.

BUTT, Masood Ahmad 19 Kiltongue Cottage, Staff Residences, Monkscourt Avenue, Airdrie ML6 0JS — MB BS 1980 Punjab; LRCP LRCS Ed. LRCPS Glas. 1982.

BUTT, Muhammad Sohail Mahmood Orthopaedic Department, Russells Hall Hospital, Pensnett Road, Dudley DY1 2HQ — MB BS 1984 Karachi; FRCS Ed. 1990.

BUTT, Nauman Masud Flat 2/Left, 58 Wilton St., Glasgow G20 6RU — MB ChB 1994 Glas.

BUTT, Reginald Peter (retired) Cumbria, 39 Coastal Road, E. Preston, Littlehampton BN16 1SN Tel: 01903 773335 — MB BS 1950 Lond.; MRCS Eng. LRCP Lond. 1950. Prev: Med. Regist. St. Mary Abbot's Hosp. Lond.

BUTT, Rehana Falcon Road Surgery, 47 Falcon Road, Battersea, London SW11 2PH Tel: 020 7228 1619/3399 Fax: 020 7924 3375 — BM 1982 Soton.

BUTT, Sally Joanne Unthank Road Surgery, 38 Unthank Road, Norwich NR2 2RD Tel: 01603 624715; 3 Mill Hill Road, Norwich NR2 3DP Tel: 01603 612412 — MB BS 1986 Lond.; MRCP (UK) 1989. Prev: Trainee GP/SHO Rotat. (Med.) St. Bart. Hosp. Lond.

BUTT, Sarah Ann York Road Surgery, York Road, Southwold IP18 6AN Tel: 01502 722326 Fax: 01502 724708; White House Barn, Uggeshall, Beccles NR34 8BJ — MB ChB 1983 Birm.; MRCGP 1987.

BUTT, Sohail Studholme Medical Centre, 50 Church Road, Ashford TW15 2TU Tel: 01784 420700 Fax: 01784 424503 — BSc Lond. 1983, MB BS 1985; DCH RCP Lond. 1989.

BUTT, Tahira Yasmin 7 Tithe Close, Maidenhead SL6 2YT — MB BS 1997 Lond.

BUTT, William Paul Wingfield House, 22 Street Lane, Leeds LS8 2ET Tel: 0113 237 0321 Fax: 0113 237 0336 — MD 1959 Toronto; L Nova Scotia Prov Med 1963; FRCPC 1966; FRCR 1975.

BUTT, Zahida Afzal Ophthalmic Departnemt, Queen Elizabeth Hospital, Gayton Road, King's Lynn PE30 4EB Email: bzahida@aol.com — MB ChB 1985 Aberd.; FRCS Ed. 1990; FCOphth 1990; DO Glas. 1988; MD Aberdeen 1998. (Aberdeen Uni) Cons. Ophth., Qu. Elizabeh Hosp, Kings Lynn.Subspeciality: Ocular Plastics, Glaucoma. Socs: BMA; Amer. Acad. of Ophth. Prev: Regist. (Ophth.) P.ss Alexandra Eye Pavil. Roy. Infirm. Edin.; SHO (Ophth.) Stirling Roy. Infirm. & P.ss Alexandra Eye Pavil. Roy. Infirm. Edin.; Sen. Regist. (Ophth.) P.ss Alexandra Eye Pavil. Roy. Infirm. Edin.

BUTT, Mr Zulfiqar Ali 15 Sandringham Road, Northolt UB5 5HN — MB BS 1983 Peshawar; FRCS Ed. 1989.

BUTTAR, Pritpal Singh 43 Manor Road, Keynsham, Bristol BS31 1RB — MB BS 1986 Lond.

BUTTER, Keith Charles Tasburgh Lodge, Victoria Avenue, Woodhall Spa LN10 6TX Tel: 01526 352466 Fax: 01526 354462; Ash Cottage, Waddington, Lincoln LN5 9RT Tel: 01522 722693 Fax: 01522 723693 — MB BS 1978 Lond.; BSc (1st cl.) Lond. 1975; MRCP (UK) 1982. (Westm.) Prev: Lect. Renal Unit Lond Hosp. Whitechapel; Regist. Div. Med. Lond. Hosp.; Regist. (Med.) S.end & Rochford Hosps.

BUTTERELL, Helen Christine Department of Anaesthetics, 12th Floor, Royal Liverpool University Hospital, Prescot Street, Liverpool L7 8XP — MB ChB 1993 Liverp.

BUTTERFIELD, Mr Albert Roy (retired) Maisonette Flat, 15 Morgans Quay, The Strand, Teignmouth TQ14 8XP Tel: 01626 770091 — MB BChir Camb. 1952; MA Camb. 1952; FRCS Eng. 1956; MRCS Eng. LRCP Lond. 1952.

BUTTERFIELD, Frederick Edward 14 Haines Hill, Taunton TA1 4HW Tel: 01823 282140 — MB BS Durh. 1939.

BUTTERFIELD, John Kenneth, TD (retired) The Tawny House, 24 South Cliff, Bexhill-on-Sea TN39 3EJ Tel: 01424 212462 — LMSSA 1952 Lond.; MFCM 1972; DPH Eng. 1960. Prev: Community Phys. (Environm. Health) Hastings DHA.

BUTTERFIELD, John Stephen 23 Churchill Avenue, Southport PR9 9PS — MB ChB 1987 Liverp.; MRCP (UK) 1993; FRCR 1998. Specialist Regist. (Radiol.) Manch.

BUTTERFIELD, Joyce Kathleen The Health Centre, Little Lane, South Elmsall, Pontefract WF9 2NJ Tel: 01977 642733 Fax: 01977 645778; 3 Oxford Road, St. John's, Wakefield WF1 3LB Tel: 01924 370905 — MB ChB 1981 Leeds.

BUTTERFIELD, Neil Philip, Surg. Cdr. RN Royal Naval Hospital BFPO 52 Tel: 00 350 5245 Fax: 00 350 5270; 23 Old Naval Hospital BFPO 52 Tel: 00 350 47608 Fax: 00 350 47608 — MB BS 1979 Lond.; DA Eng. 1984; DAvMed. FOM RCP Lond. 1984. (St. Mary's Hosp. Lond.) Command Med. Off. Roy. Navy Gibraltar. Prev: Princip. Med. Off. Commando Train. Centre Roy. Marines Exmouth; Flotilla Med. Off. Roy. Brunei Navy; Princip. Med. Off. RNAS Yeovilton.

BUTTERFILL, Andrew Michael County Hospital, Hereford HR1 2ER Tel: 01432 355444 Fax: 01432 364036; 25 Barrs Court Road, Hereford HR1 1EQ Tel: 01432 269163 Email: butfil@globalnet.co.uk — MB ChB 1972 Sheff.; FRCP Lond. 1993; MRCP (UK) 1975; DCH Eng. 1974. (Sheff.) Cons. Paediat. Hereford Co. Hosp. Socs: BPNA; Neonat. Soc. Prev: Sen. Regist. (Paediat.) St. Thos. Hosp. Lond. & Wolfson Centre Lond.

BUTTERFILL, Jill Beatrice Child Health Department, Herefordshire Community Health Trust, Belmont Abbey, Hereford HR2 9RP Tel: 01432 344344; 25 Barrs Court Road, Hereford HR1 1EQ Tel: 01432 269163 — MB ChB 1971 Sheff.; MSc (Community Child Health) Warwick 1996; Dip. Community Paediat. Warwick 1991. SCMO

(Child Health) Herefordsh. Community Health Trust. Prev: Clin. Med. Off. (Child Health) Herefordsh. HA.

BUTTERISS, Michael Leighton Road Surgery, 1 Leighton Road, Linslade, Leighton Buzzard LU7 1LB Tel: 01525 372571 Fax: 01525 850414; Knoll House, Leighton Road, Wingrave, Aylesbury HP22 4PA Tel: 01296 681604 — MB BChir 1971 Camb.; MA, MB Camb. 1971, BChir 1970; MRCS Eng. LRCP Lond. 1970; MRCGP 1977; DAvMed Eng. 1979; DObst RCOG 1976. (St. Bart.) Prev: Sen. Med. Off. RAF; Commanding Off. Med. Wing P.ss Margt. RAF Hosp. Halton; Squadron Ldr. RAF Med. Br.

BUTTERS, Jane 6 Station Road, Hampton TW12 2BX Tel: 020 8979 0454 — MB BS 1985 Newc.; BMedSc Newc. 1982; FRCS Eng. 1994. Clin. Asst. (ENT Surg.) WellHo. Trust Lond. Prev: Regist. Rotat. (ENT) Roy. Nat. Throat, Nose & Ear Hosp., Middlx. Hosp., Qu. Eliz. Hosp. & Gt. Ormond St. Hosp. Childr. Lond.; SHO Rotat. (Surg.) N.wick Pk. Hosp. Harrow; SHO (Gen. & Paediat. Surg.) Hammersmith Hosp. Lond.

BUTTERS, Peter Bruce The Marlborough Medical Practice, George Lane, Marlborough SN8 4BY; High Kingsbury, Marlborough SN8 1HZ — MB BS 1983 Lond.; MRCP (UK) 1987; MRCGP 1990; T(GP) 1991; DRCOG 1989. (St. Bart.) Prev: Med. Off. Stratford Hosp., NZ; SHO (Med.) Worcester Roy. Infirm. & St. Helier Hosp. Carshalton; Trainee GP Norwich VTS.

BUTTERWORTH, David Ian Lea Cottage, 18 Low Lea Road, Marple Bridge, Stockport SK6 5AB Tel: 0161 427 7469 — MB ChB 1970 Ed.; BSc Ed. 1967, MB ChB 1970; MRCGP 1977. (Ed.)

BUTTERWORTH, David John 24 Coniston Drive, Darwen BB3 3BJ — MB ChB 1995 Manch.

BUTTERWORTH, David Michael Department of Histopathology, North Manchester General Hospital, Delauneys Road, Crmpsall, Manchester M8 5RB Tel: 0161 720 2377 — MB ChB 1984 Liverp.; FRCPath 1999; MRCPath 1991. Cons. Histopath. N. Manch. Gen. Hosp. Prev: Sen. Regist. Rotat. (Path.) N. W.. RHA; SHO & Regist. (Path.) Soton Gen. Hosp.; SHO (Path.) Fazakerley Hosp. Liverp.

BUTTERWORTH, Mr Edward Alexander Church End Cottage, Barton-in-the Clay, Bedford MK45 4LA — MB BS 1930 Lond.; FRCS Eng. 1933; MRCS Eng. LRCP Lond. 1929; DOMS Eng. 1945. (St. Mary's) Barrister-at-Law of The Middle Temple. Socs: BMA & Ophth. Soc. Prev: Chief Asst. Roy. Lond. Ophth. Hosp.; Research Asst. in Bact., &c. St. Mary's Hosp.

BUTTERWORTH, Hannah Elizabeth Shore Musgrove Park Hsp, Taunton TA1 5DA Tel: 01823 342845; 4 Chestnut Avenue, Radley College, Abingdon OX14 2HS — MB ChB 1998 Bristol. PRHO MusGr. Pk. Hsp, Taunton (Surg). Prev: PRHO Bristol Ryl Inf. (Med).

BUTTERWORTH, Janet 1 Forty Acre Close, Loggerheads, Market Drayton TF9 4RQ Tel: 01630 673202 — MB BCh 1985 Wales; MSc (Community Paediat.) Wales 1997; MRCGP 1990; DCH RCP Lond. 1990. Staff Grade Community (Paediat.) Mid Staffs. Prev: Staff Grade Taff, Ely & Rhondda M. Glam.; Trainee GP Bridgend VTS; SHO (Paediat.) Llandough Hosp. Cardiff.

BUTTERWORTH, Jeffrey Richard 1 Forty Acre Close, Loggerheads, Market Drayton TF9 4RQ — MB BCh 1992 Wales; MRCP (UK) 1996. Specialist Regist. Rotat. (Gen. Med. & Gastroenterol.) W. Midl. Socs: Sec. MERCIA Regist.s in Train. Prev: SHO (Gen. Med.) P.ss of Wales Hosp. M. Glam.; SHO (Cardiol.) Univ. Hosp. Wales Cardiff; SHO (Chest Med.) Llandough Hosp. Cardiff.

BUTTERWORTH, Joanne Louise 17 Coles Lane, Linton, Cambridge CB1 6JS — BM BCh 1996 Oxf.

BUTTERWORTH, Katrina 54 Turker Lane, Northallerton DL6 1QA — MB BS 1991 Newc.; DCH RCP Lond. 1993; MRCGP Lond. 1995; DTM & H Liverp. 1996. Probationary Med. Miss. to Nepal.

BUTTERWORTH, Kenneth Roy (retired) 12 Holmwood Road, Cheam, Sutton SM2 7JR Tel: 020 8393 5180 — MB BS Lond. 1968; PhD Lond. 1955, BPharm 1953; MRCS Eng. LRCP Lond. 1968; FRCPath 1983; FRPharmS 1953. Sen. Cons. Teachg. Bibra Toxicol. Internat. Carshalton; Vis. Prof. Toxicol. King's Coll. Lond. Prev: Sen. Cons. Teachg. Bibra Toxicol. Internat. Carshalton.

BUTTERWORTH, Mr Mark Stanley 8 Rona Road, London NW3 2JA — MB ChB 1987 Ed.; FRCS Glas. 1994.

BUTTERWORTH, Mildred Jean (retired) 1 Furnbrook Gardens, Kirkheaton, Huddersfield HD5 0DY — MB ChB 1965 Leeds; FRCOG 1984, M 1970, DObst 1967.

BUTTERWORTH, Patricia Margaret 38 Homewood Road, St Albans AL1 4BQ — MB BS 1963 Lond.; MRCS Eng. LRCP Lond. 1963; LMCC Toronto 1973; DObst RCOG 1965; DCCH RCP Ed. 1985. Socs: Brit. Paediat. Assn.; Amer. & Internat. Soc. Clin. Hypn.

BUTTERWORTH, Mr Paul Charles 2 The Lane, Weston-by-Welland, Market Harborough LE16 8HU — BM BS 1990 Nottm.; FRCS Ed. 1994. (Nottm.) Clin. Research Fell. (Surg.) Leicester Gen. Hosp.

BUTTERWORTH, Richard James Department of Neurology, Milton Keynes General Hospital, Standing Way, Eaglestone, Milton Keynes MK6 5LD; Church House, School Hill, Buckingham MK18 3PE — MB ChB 1990 Leeds; MRCP (UK) 1993; MD Leeds 1997. Cons. NeUrol. Milton Keynes Gen. Hosp. and Radcliffe Infirm. Oxf. Prev: Stroke Assn. Clin. Research Fell. King's Coll. Sch. Med. & Dent. Lond.; Specialist Regist. (Neurol.) Nat. Hosp. Neurol. & Neurosurg. Lond.

BUTTERWORTH, Stephen Edward Staff Residences, Walnut Street, Leicester Royal Infirmary, Infirmary Square, Leicester LE1 5WW — MB ChB 1993 Leic.

BUTTERY, Philip Christians Department of Clinical Neurology, Cambridge University, Addenbrooke's Hospital, Cambridge Tel: 01223 245151; 38 Blinco Dricve, Cambridge CB1 7TS Tel: 01223 501770 — BM BCh 1990 Oxf.; MRCP (UK) 1993. Hon. Regist. (Neurol.) Addenbrooke's Hosp. Camb.; Specialist Regist. (Neurol.) Norf. & Norwich Hosp. Norwich.

BUTTERY, Robert Christians 5 Spylaw Bank Road, Edinburgh EH13 0JW Tel: 0131 441 5000 — BM BCh 1992 Oxf.; MRCP (UK) 1995. (Oxf.) Specialist Regist. (Gen. & Respirat. Med.) W.. Gen. Hosp. Edin.

BUTTON, Calvin 9 Viewforth Road, Ryhope, Sunderland SR2 0NG — MB ChB 1996 Dundee.

BUTTON, Michael Robert 121 Billing Road, Northampton NN1 5RR — MB BS 1997 Lond.; MA. 1998. SHO. (Med.) N.ampton Gen Hosp.

BUTTON, Philip Donald Department of Anaesthetics, North Hampshire Hospital, Basingstoke RG24 9NA Tel: 01256 473202 Fax: 01256 354224; White House, 5 Yardley Road, Hedge End, Southampton SO30 0HP Tel: 01489 782674 Fax: 01256 354224 Email: pbutton@netcomuk.co.uk — BM 1980 Soton.; DRCOG 1987; DA (UK) 1986. (Southampton) Assoc. Specialist (Anaesth.) N. Hants. Hosp. Socs: Fac. Anaesth.; Assn. Anaesth. of GB & Irel. Prev: Staff Grade (Anaesth.) N. Hants. Hosp.

BUTTON, Phyllis Muriel (retired) Church Cottage, Cider Mill Lane, Chipping Campden GL55 — MRCS Eng. LRCP Lond. 1936; DPH Eng. 1943.

BUTTON, Robert Ian Hampshire LMCs, 12 Southgate St., Winchester SO23 9EF Tel: 01962 867793 Fax: 01962 841867; White Ladies, 46 Winston Rise, Four Marks, Alton GU34 5HP — MB BS 1965 Lond.; MRCS Eng. LRCP Lond. 1965; T(GP) 1991; DObst RCOG 1970. (Univ. Coll. Hosp.) Sec. & Treas. Hants. LMCs. Socs: Fell. BMA. Prev: Ho. Surg. & Ho. Phys. Cirencester Memor. Hosp; Ho. Off. (Obst.) BMH Hannover.

BUTTOO, Sindy Newlands Medical Centre, 315 Chorley New Road, Bolton BL1 5BP; 98 North Promenade, St Annes, Lytham St Annes FY8 2QP — MB BS 1982 Lond. Med. Dir. Newlands Med. Servs. Bolton.

BUTTRISS, Carol Joy 1 Thornton Dene, Beckenham BR3 3ND — MB BS 1987 Lond.; BSc (Hons. Physiol.) Lond. 1984. (St. Thos. Med. Sch.) Clin. Asst. (Haemat.) Mayday Hosp. Thornton Heath. Surrey. Socs: BMA. Prev: SHO (Paediat.) Sydenham Childr. Hosp.; SHO (Med.) St. Bart. Hosp. Rochester Kent; SHO (Med.) Medway Hosp. Gillingham Kent.

BUTTS, Doreen June 36 Hollingsworth Road, Croydon CR0 5RP — MB ChB 1954 Sheff.; MRCS Eng. LRCP Lond. 1954; DCH Eng. 1957.

BUTTS, Sarah Louise 2 Argyle Park, Dunblane FK15 9DZ — MB ChB 1997 Dundee.

BUX, Zuber Mohammed Brookhouse Medical Centre, Whalley Range, Blackburn BB1 6EA Tel: 01254 673887 Fax: 01254 697770 — MB ChB 1994 Liverp. Trainee GP Blackburn, Hyndburn & Ribble Valley Trust.

BUXTON, Ann Vivien (retired) 68 Granary Lane, Budleigh Salterton EX9 6ER Tel: 01395 444152 — MB ChB 1969 Bristol;

MSc Exeter 1988; MRCGP 1976; DObst RCOG 1973. Prev: Clin. Asst. (Dermat.) Roy. Devon & Exeter Hosp.

BUXTON, Clive St John Couny Durham Health Authority, Appleton House, Lanchester Road, Durham DH1 5XZ Tel: 0191 333 3232 Fax: 0191 333 3384 Email: cstjb@durpin.demon.co.uk; Rowans, The Paddock, Melmerby, Ripon HG4 5HW — MRCS Eng. LRCP Lond. 1976; MSc (Community Med.) Lond. 1982; MFPHM 1987; MBA Durh. 1996. Cons. Pub. Health Med. Co. Durh. & Darlington, HA; Med. Ref. Centr. Durh. Crematorium. Prev: Dir. Pub. Health N. Durh. HA; Specialist Community Med. Brent HA; Sen. Regist. (Community Med.) NE Thames RHA.

BUXTON, Edward John Swindon Lodge, Swindon Lane, Kirkby Overblow, Harrogate HG3 1HR — MB ChB 1980 Birm.

BUXTON, Fiona Anne Merelyth White Thorns, 3 Wynsham Way, Windlesham GU20 6JX — MB BS 1979 Lond.; MRCGP 1987. Asst. GP Sunninghill, Berks.

BUXTON, John Dominic (retired) The Wheel House, 14 Astra Court, Hythe Marina Vill., Hythe, Southampton SO45 6DZ Tel: 01703 847568 Fax: 01703 847568 — MRCS Eng. LRCP Lond. 1943; FFA RCS Eng. 1953; DA Eng. 1945. Prev: Cons. Anaesth. Guy's Hosp. Gp.

BUXTON, Katherine Mary 9 The Windings, Lichfield WS13 7EX — MB ChB 1995 Manch.

BUXTON, Mr Kenneth Leonard (retired) The Old Rectory, Moulsford, Wallingford OX10 9JB — MB BChir Camb. 1933; FRCS Eng. 1935; MRCS Eng. LRCP Lond. 1933; DTM & H Eng. 1937. Prev: Cons. (Surg. & Trop. Med.) Mildmay Miss. Hosp. Lond.

BUXTON, Neil Dept of Neurosurgery, University Hospital, Nottingham NG8 2UM Tel: 0115 924 9924 — MB ChB 1989 Leeds; FRCS Ed. 1994. Specialist Regist. Univ. Hosp. Nottm.

BUXTON, Nicholas David Orchard Health Centre, The Orchard, Gunnislake PL18 9JZ Tel: 01822 836241 Fax: 01822 833757 — MB ChB 1983 Bristol; MRCGP 1990; DRCOG 1989; DA (UK) 1987. Socs: Roy. Coll. Gen. Pract.

BUXTON, Nicola Jane Department of Paediatrics, Guy's Hospital, St Thomas St., London SE1 9RT Tel: 020 795 5500; 5 Vardens Road, Battersea, London SW11 1RQ Tel: 020 7585 1393 — MB ChB 1996 Bristol; BSc (Hons) Psychol. Bristol 1993. (Univ. Bristol) SHO (Paediat.) Guy's Hosp. Lond. Prev: SHO (A & E) St. Geo.'s Hosp. Lond.; Ho. Off. (Surg.) Demford Hosp. Plymouth; Ho. Off. (Med.) Bristol Roy. Infirm.

BUXTON, Paul Kenneth Murrayfield Hospital, 122 Corstorphine Road, Edinburgh EH12 6UD Tel: 0131 334 0363 Fax: 0131 334 7338; Old Inzievar House, Dunfermline KY12 8HA Tel: 01383 852424 Fax: 01383 852424 — MB BChir 1962 Camb.; MA Camb. 1965; FRCP (Ed.) 1985; MRCS Eng. LRCP Lond. 1962; MRCP (UK) 1970; FRCPC 1974. (Camb. & St. Thos.) Cons. Dermat. Roy. Infirm. Edin.; Clin. Teach. Univ. Edin. Socs: Fell. Roy. Soc. Med.; BMA; Brit. Assn. of Dermatol.s. Prev: Head of Dermat. Roy. Jubilee Hosp. Vict., Canada.

BUXTON, Pauline Amanda Flat 45, Gilbert Court, Green Vale, London W5 3AX — MB BS 1998 Lond.; MB BS Lond 1998.

BUXTON, Peter John, Surg. Cdr. RN Department of Radiology, Royal Hospital Haslar, Gosport PO12 2AA Tel: 01705 762508 Fax: 01705 762400 Email: 101660.1310@compuserve.com — BM BCh 1984 Oxf.; MA Oxf. 1986; FRCR 1992. (Oxf. Med. Sch.) Cons. Radiol. Roy. Hosp. Haslar Gosport. Prev: Sen. Regist. (Radiol.) RN Hosp. Haslar, Gosport & Soton. Gen. Hosp.

BUXTON, Mr Richard Anthony Victoria Hospital, Hayfield Road, Kirkcaldy KY2 5AH Tel: 01592 643355 Fax: 01592 648044; Bankton Cottage, 21 Bankton Park, Kingskettle, Cupar KY15 7PY Tel: 01337 830990 — MB BS Lond. 1969; FRCS Ed. (Orth.) 1982; FRCS Eng. 1975. (St. Geo.) Cons. Orthop. Surg. Fife HB. Socs: Fell. BOA; Brit. Orthop. Research Soc. Prev: Sen. Regist. (Orthop.) Edin. Roy. Infirm. & P.ss Margt. Rose Orthop. Hosp. Edin.; Regist. (Orthop.) Nuffield Orthop. Hosp. Oxf.; Ho. Phys. St. Geo. Hosp. Lond.

BUXTON, Richard Lees The Health Centre, Fieldhead, Shepley, Huddersfield HD8 8DR Tel: 01484 602001 Fax: 01484 608125; Clifton House, 168 Penistone Road, Shelley, Huddersfield HD8 8JB Tel: 01484 604774 — MB BS Dunelm 1968; BSc Newc. 1965; MRCP (UK) 1971. (Newcastle)

BUXTON, Roger St John, KStJ (retired) Borrowdale, Arundel Road, Norton, Chichester PO18 0JX Tel: 01243 543930 — MB BS 1948 Lond.; PhD Lond. 1958; MRCS Eng. LRCP Lond. 1948; MFPHM RCP (UK) 1982; DCH Eng. 1950. Prev: Dep. Chief Med. Off. St. John Ambul. Assn. & Co. Dir. Sussex.

BUXTON, Sarah Helena Hawthornden Surgery, Wharf Lane, Bourne End SL8 5RX Tel: 01628 522864 Fax: 01628 533226; 24 Oxford Crescent, Didcot OX11 7AY Tel: 01235 814252 — BA (Physiol. Sci.) Oxf. 1988, BM BCh 1988; MRCGP 1992; DCH RCP Lond. 1990; DRCOG 1990.

BUXTON, Mr Timothy Simon Department of Neurosurgery, Morriston Hospital, Swansea SA6 6NL Tel: 01792 703172 Fax: 01792 703455 Email: tsbuxton@hotmail.com — MB ChB 1983 Birm.; FRCS (SN) 1994; FRCS Ed. 1988. (Birm.) Cons. Neurosurg. Morriston Hosp. Swansea.

BUXTON-THOMAS, Muriel Simisola Kings College Hospital, Denmark Hill, London SE5 9RS Tel: 020 7346 3153 Fax: 020 7346 3516; The White House, Tyland Lane, Sandling, Maidstone ME14 3BH — MB BS 1971 Newc.; MSc Lond. 1978; FRCP Lond. 1989; MRCP (UK) 1974. Cons. Phys. Nuclear Med. King's Coll. Hosp. Lond.; Recognised Teach. Lond. Univ.; Vice-Chairm. SE Thames Nuclear Med. Specialty Advis. Comm.; Vice-Chairm. Clin. Audit King's Healthcare. Socs: Fell. Roy. Soc. Med.; Brit. Nuclear Med. Soc. (Counc. Mem.). Prev: Sen. Regist. Addenbrooke's Hosp. Camb.; Sen. Research Fell. St. Thos. Hosp. Lond.; Regist. (Med.) St. Thos. Hosp. Lond.

BUYSSE, Sophie Staff Residences, James Paget Hospital, Lowestoft Road, Gorleston, Great Yarmouth NR31 6LA — MD 1993 Louvain.

BWALYA, Godfrey Mulwale 139 Scartho Road, Grimsby DN33 2AN Tel: 01472 874111 — BSc Zambia 1978.

BYAM, James Edward Countess of Chester Hospital, Directorate of Surgery, Liverpool Road, Chester CH2 1BQ Tel: 01244 365000; 8 Shepsides Close, Great Sutton, South Wirral CH66 2HZ Tel: 0151 348 1330 — MB BS 1988 West Indies. SHO (Gen. Surg.) Countess of Chester Hosp.

BYARS, Gordon Keir The Park Surgery, St. Flora's Road, Littlehampton BN17 6BF Tel: 01903 717154 Fax: 01903 732908 — MB ChB 1978 Manch.; BSc St. And. 1975; DRCOG 1982.

BYATT, Christopher Muir Department of Medicine for Elderly, Queen Elizabeth Hospital, Gayton Road, King's Lynn PE30 4ET Tel: 01553 613628 Fax: 01553 613900 Email: christopher.byatt@klshosp.anglox.nhs.uk; Westgate House, Chapel Lane, Ringstead, Hunstanton PE36 5JX — MB BS 1979 Lond.; FRCP Lond. 1995; MRCP (UK) 1983. (Char. Cross) Cons. Phys. Qu. Eliz. Hosp. King's Lynn Norf. Socs: BMA & W. Norf. Clin. Soc. Prev: Sen. Regist. St. Geo. Hosp. Lond.; Regist. Guy's Hosp. Lond.; SHO (Med.) & Ho. Phys. Char. Cross Hosp. Lond.

BYCROFT, John Andrew 9 Buttercup Close, Spalding PE11 1YS — MB BS 1996 Lond.

BYDDER, Megan 15 Devonshire Road, Heaton, Bolton BL1 4PG — MB ChB 1995 Manch.

BYE, Ian Michael Locking Hill Surgery, Locking Hill, Stroud GL5 1UY Tel: 01453 764222 Fax: 01453 756278; The Old Pack Horse Inn, Ampney Saint Peter, Cirencester GL7 5SH Tel: 01285 851605 — MB ChB 1985 Bristol; DRCOG 1988. GP Stroud. Prev: Trainee GP Stroud VTS; Regist. (Med.) Rockhampton Base Hosp. Austral.; SHO (O & G) St. Pauls Hosp. Cheltenham.

BYE, Patrick Gilbert Tirrell (retired) Keeper's Cottage, Piltdown, Uckfield TN22 3XT Tel: 0182 572 3216 — MRCS Eng. LRCP Lond. 1954; MB Camb. 1955, BChir 1954; Dip. Pharm. Med. RCP (UK) 1976; DCH Eng. 1957. Prev: Sen. Med. Adviser Schering Health Care Ltd. Burgess Hill.

BYER, Lionel David Welford Road Health Centre, 693 Welford Road, Leicester LE2 6FQ Tel: 0116 288 4450 Fax: 0116 288 4436; 19 Toller Road, Leicester LE2 3HP — MB BS Lond. 1967; MRCS Eng. LRCP Lond. 1966; DObst RCOG 1970. (Guy's) Prev: Ho. Phys., Resid. Obst. & Cas. Off. Guy's Hosp. Lond.

BYERS, Alan Howard Elliott Hall Medical Centre, 165-167 Uxbridge Road, Hatch End, Pinner HA5 4EA Tel: 020 8428 4019 — MB BS 1971 Lond.; MRCS Eng. LRCP Lond. 1971; MRCGP 1993; DLO Eng. 1979; DObst RCOG 1973. (Char. Cross) GP Trainer Pinner. Prev: Hosp. Pract (ENT) Mt. Vernon Hosp. N.wood; Clin. Asst. (ENT) W.m. Hosp.; Resid. (ENT) Tel Hashomer Hosp., Israel.

BYERS, David Laing Greencroft Medical Centre (South), Greencroft Wynd, Annan DG12 6GS Tel: 01461 202244 Fax: 01461 205401 — MB ChB 1986 Aberd.; MRCGP 1990; DTM & H Liverp.

1995; DRCOG 1989. Prev: Stud. Liverp. Sch. Trop. Med.; GP & Dist. Med. Off. Papua New Guinea; Trainee GP Aberd. VTS.

BYERS, Elizabeth Anne Dingli, 5 Pinewood Close, Ashton Road, Lancaster LA2 0AD Tel: 01524 68338 — MB BS 1967 Newc. (Newc.)

BYERS, Gordon Fraser Department of Anaesthesia, Aberdeen Royal Infirmary, Aberdeen AB25 2ZN; 1 Cairnaquheen Gardens, Aberdeen AB15 5HJ — MB ChB 1983 Aberd.; FFA RCSI 1987. Cons. Anaesth. Aberd. Roy. Infirm. Prev: Sen. Regist. & Regist. (Anaesth.) Aberd. Roy. Infirm.

BYERS, Mark Brampton Medical Practice, 4 Market Place, Brampton CA8 1NL Tel: 016977 2551 Fax: 016977 41944 — MB BS 1986 Newc.; MRCGP 1991; DRCOG 1993; DFFP 1993; DA (UK) 1990; Dip. IMC RCS Ed. 1990.

BYERS, Paul Duncan 18 Wimpole Street, London W1M 7AD Tel: 020 7580 5206 Email: p.byers@ucl.ac.uk — MD 1945 CM Canada; PhD Lond. 1960; BSc McGill 1943; FRCPath 1977, M 1965; Lic. Newfld. Med. Bd. 1959. (McGill) Reader Emerit. (Morbid Anat.) Univ. Lond.; Hon. Sen. Lect. (Morbid Anat.) Roy. Postgrad. Med. Sch. Lond. Socs: Fell. Roy. Soc. Med.; Path. Soc. Prev: Reader (Morbid Anat.) & Head of Dept. Inst. Orthop. Lond.; Dean Inst. Orthop. Lond.; Regist. (Morbid Anat.) Postgrad. Med. Sch. Lond.

BYERS, Richard John Department of Pathological Sciences, University of Manchester, Stopford Building, Oxford Road, Manchester M13 9PT Tel: 0161 275 5300 Fax: 0161 275 5268 Email: r.byers@man.ac.uk; 102 Claude Road, Chorlton Ville, Manchester M21 8DF — MB ChB 1990 Manch.; MSc Manch. 1988, BSc (Hons.) 1985; MRCPath 1997; DRCPath 1995. MRC Clin. Train. Fell. Manch.; Lect. (Path.) Manch.; Hon. Cons. (Haemat. Path.) Manch. Prev: Clin. Lect. (Histopath.) & Hon. Sen. Regist. Univ. Manch.; Regist. (Histopath.) NW RHA; SHO (Path.) Manch. Roy. Infirm.

BYFIELD, David Michael 23 New Cross, Longburton, Sherborne DT9 6EJ — MB ChB 1982 Bristol; MRCPath 1989.

BYFORD, David Malcolm Maryhill Health Centre, 41 Shawpark Street, Glasgow G20 9DR Tel: 0141 531 8811 Fax: 0141 531 8808; 20 Dunellan Road, Roslinn, Milngavie, Glasgow G62 7RE — MB ChB 1982 Glas.; MRCGP 1986; DRCOG 1984. Syntex Award Winner Glas. W.. VTS 1986.

BYFORD, Simone 78 Taunton Road, London SE12 8PB — MB BS 1994 Newc.

BYLES, Daniel Beuzeville Oxford Eye Hospital, Radcliffe Infirmary, Woodstock Road, Oxford OX2 6HE Tel: 01865 311188 Fax: 01865 224013; Church Cottage, Combe, Oxford OX29 8NA Tel: 01993 891628 — MB ChB 1990 Bristol; FRCOphth 1995. Higher Specialist Trainee (Ophth.) Oxf. Socs: Fell. Roy. Soc. Med. Prev: SHO (Ophth.) Radcliffe Infirm. Oxf.; SHO (Ophth.) Roy. Berks. Hosp. Reading; SHO (Neurosurg.) Frenchay Hosp. Bristol.

BYLES, Lynne Elizabeth Gordon and Partners, The Redwell Medical Centre, 1 Turner Road, Wellingborough NN8 4UT Tel: 01933 400777 Fax: 01933 671959; Lorne House, 58 Hatton Pk Road, Wellingborough NN8 5AQ Tel: 01933 223197 — MB BS 1980 Lond. (Roy. Free Lond.)

BYLES, Naomi Susan 108 Elm Walk, London SW20 9EG Tel: 020 8540 3494 — MB BS Lond. 1966; MRCS Eng. LRCP Lond. 1966; FFARCS 1974.

BYLES, Peter Beuzeville Warren House, Wotton-under-Edge GL12 7HY Tel: 01453 844627 — MB 1964 Camb.; BChir 1963; DA Eng. 1966; DObst RCOG 1967. (Camb. & St. Bart.) Prev: GP Cheltenham; SHO (Anaesth.) & Ho. Off. (O & G) Gloucester, Stroud & Forest; Hosp. Gp.; Med. Off. Brit. Solomon Is.s Proctec.

BYLES, Peter Henry (retired) The Coach House, Hinton-in-the-Hedges, Brackley NN13 5NF — MB BS Lond. 1955; MRCPS Eng. LRCP Lond. 1995.

BYLINA, Edward Peter Bankfield Surgery, 15 Huddersfield Road, Elland HX5 9BA Tel: 01422 375537 Fax: 01422 370776 — MB ChB 1981 Dundee; BSc (Hons.) Aston 1977; MRCGP 1986; DCH RCP Lond. 1985. (Dundee) GP; Hosp. Pract. (Endoscopy) Halifax Gen. Hosp.; GP Trainer Yorks. Pennine VTS; Bd. Mem. Calderdale PCG.

BYNEVELT, Michael Department of Neuroradiology, Atkinson Morley Hospital, 31 Copse Hill, London SW20 0NE — MB ChB 1989 Auckland.

BYNG, Richard Norman The Rushey Green Group Practice, Central Lewisham Clinic, 410 Lewisham High Street, London SE13 6LJ Tel: 020 8314 5440 Fax: 020 771 4404; 2A Eliot Park, Lewisham, London SE13 7EG — BChir 1988 Camb.; MRCGP 1993. Hon. Lect. (Gen. Pract.) Lond. Socs: BMA; Med. Protec. Soc.

BYNG-HALL, John Julian Tavistock Clinic, 120 Belsize Lane, London NW3 5BA Tel: 020 7435 7111 Fax: 020 7431 7057; 24 Shirlock Road, London NW3 2HS Tel: 020 7485 6602 Fax: 020 7485 6602 Email: jbynghall@mistral.co.uk — MB BChir Camb. 1963; BA Camb. 1963; FRCPsych 1980 M 1972; DPM Eng. 1967; DSc (Hon.) 1997. (Univ. Coll. Hosp.) p/t Hon. Cons. Child & Family Psychiat. Tavistock Clinic Lond.; Hon. Sen. Lect. (Child Psychiat.) Roy. Free Hosp. Lond.; Hon. Assoc. Prof. Univ. Toronto. Socs: (Ex-Chairm.) Inst. Family Ther. Lond.; Assn. Family Ther. Prev: Sen. Regist. Tavistock Clinic Lond.; Regist. Fulbourn Hosp. Camb. & Maudsley Hosp. Lond.

BYNOE, Adrienne Geraldine Department of Haematology, Harrogate District Hospital, Lancaster Park Road, Harrogate HG2 7SX Tel: 01423 885959 Fax: 01423 555836 Email: geraldine.bynoe@hhc-tr.northy.nhs.uk.demon.co.uk — MB BS 1977 Lond.; MA Oxf. 1977; FRCPath 1996, M 1985. (St. Mary's) Cons. Haemat. Harrogate Healthcare Trust & United Leeds Teachg. Hosp. Trust; Hon. Vis. Fell. DoH Studies Univ. York 1996; Dip. Health Serv. Managem. York 1993. Prev: Policy Adviser Wom. in Med. NHS Exec.; Cons. Haemat. Leeds HA; Sen. Regist. (Haemat.) Leeds.

BYNOE, Jonathan Kellman Medical Centre, Beech Grove, Sherburn-in-Elmet, Leeds LS25 6ED Tel: 01977 682208 Fax: 01977 681665 Email: 101677.1240@compuserve.com — BM BCh 1975 Oxf.; MA Oxf. 1975; MRCGP 1979; DRCOG 1978. Prev: Trainee GP High Wycombe VTS; Ho. Phys. & Ho. Surg. Brook Gen. Hosp. Lond.

BYRAMJI, Niloufer Kobaad 5 Ashcombe Avenue, Surbiton KT6 6PX — MB BS 1986 Lond.; MRCGP 1991.

BYRD, Louise Marie 58 Fleetwood Road, Poulton-Le-Fylde, Blackpool — MB ChB 1992 Manch.

BYREN, Ivor De Villiers Genitourinary Medicine Department, Radcliffe Infirmary, Woodstock Road, Oxford OX2 6HE Tel: 01865 31118 Fax: 01865 224378 — MB ChB 1981 Cape Town; MRCP (UK) 1991; FRCP. Cons. Phys. Genitourin. Med. Radcliffe Infirm. NHS Trust. Oxf.; Hon Cons. (Infect. Dis.) John Radcliffe Hosp. Oxf.

BYREN, Joanna Clare Mellow End, Littleworth Cross, Seale, Farnham GU10 1JN — MB BS 1981 Lond.; MRCGP 1986; DRCOG 1986.

BYRNE, Aidan John Morriston Hospital, Morriston, Swansea SA6 6NL Tel: 01792 702222; 18 Derwen Fawr Road, Sketty, Swansea SA2 8AA Tel: 01792 702222 — MB BCh 1987 Wales; MRCP (UK) 1991; FRCA 1995. Cons. Morriston Hosp. Swansea. Socs: Soc. Computing and Technol. in Anaesth.; Anaesth. Res. Soc.; Soc. Europ. Simulators Applied to Med. (SESAM). Prev: Specialist Regist. E. Anglian Deanery; Regist. (Gen. Med.) Morriston Hosp. & Singleton Hosp. Swansea; SHO (Anaesth.) Morriston Hosp. & Singleton Hosp. Swansea.

BYRNE, Alexander James Suilven, Back Road, Alva FK12 5LH — MB ChB 1963 Glas.; FRCR 1975; FFR 1970; DMRD Eng. 1968. Cons. Radiol. Falkirk & Dist. Roy. Infirm. Prev: Sen. Regist. (Radiodiag.) Roy. Infirm. Edin.

BYRNE, Allen James 1 Hawthorn Place, Woodbridge IP12 4JZ — MB BCh BAO 1972 NUI; MRCPsych 1976. Cons. (Psychiat.) St. Clement's Hosp. Ipswich. Prev: Sen. Regist. St. Jas. Univ. Hosp. Leeds; Regist. St. Loman's Hosp. Dub.; Intern. Regional Hosp. Galway.

BYRNE, Andrew Jolyon Blue Haze, Forest Road, Oxton, Southwell NG25 0TD Tel: 0115 965 3759 Fax: 0115 965 2272 Email: ajb_deg@compuserve.com — MB ChB 1971 Sheff.; FRCA 1976; FFA RCSI 1975. Cons. Anaesth. Qu. Med. Centre Univ. Hosp. NHS Trust.

BYRNE, Ann 21 Linden Road, Westbury Park, Bristol BS6 7RJ — MB BS 1990 Lond. SHO (O & G) St. Michael's Hosp. Bristol.

BYRNE, Anne Elisabeth 4 Warren Road, Hoylake, Wirral CH47 2AR — MB ChB 1998 Ed.; MB ChB Ed 1998.

BYRNE, Anthony William 95 Overhill Gardens, Bridge of Don, Aberdeen AB22 8QR — MB ChB 1994 Aberd.

***BYRNE, Aoife Siobhan** 24 Upton Park, Belfast BT10 0LZ Tel: 01232 615828 — MB BCh BAO Belf. 1997.

BYRNE, Brendan Cecil 10 The Thatchers, Maidstone ME16 0XA — MB BCh 1990 Witwatersrand.

BYRNE, Brian 18 Bramwell Close, Sunbury-on-Thames TW16 5PU — MB ChB 1995 Manch.

BYRNE, Catherine Medical Centre, Rooley Lane, Bradford BD4 7SS Tel: 01274 223118 — MB ChB 1979 Manch.; MRCGP 1984; DCH RCP Lond. 1983.

BYRNE, Catherine — MB BS 1993 Newc.; MRCP(UK). (Newcastle Upon Tyne) Specialist Regist. Rotat. Nephrol. & Gen. Med. - N. Trent, Sheff. Prev: SHO Rotat. (Med.) S. Tees Trust Middlesbrough; Ho. (Gen. Surg.) N. Tyneside Dist. Gen. Hosp.; Ho. Off. (Gen. Med.) Roy. Vict. Infirm. Newc.

BYRNE, Christine Valerie The Loddon Vale Practice, Hurricane Way, Woodley, Reading RG5 4UX Tel: 0118 969 0160 Fax: 0118 969 9103; 8 Melody Close, Winnersh, Wokingham RG41 5LJ Tel: 01189 785700 — MB BS Lond. 1968; MRCS Eng. LRCP Lond. 1968; DRCOG 1982. (Roy. Free) Prev: Clin. Asst. (Genitourin.) Roy. Berksh. Hosp. Reading.

BYRNE, Professor Christopher David Thomas University of Southampton, Department of Medicine, South Academic Block, Level D, Southampton General Hospital, Southampton SO16 6YD Tel: 02380 798818 Email: cdtb@soton.ac.uk — MB BCh 1983 Wales; FRCP (UK) 1999; PhD Camb. 1992; MRCP (UK) 1986. (University of Wales College of Medicine) Prof. of Endocrinol. & Metab.; Direct. Wellcome Clin. Research Facility; Hon. Cons. Phys. Soton. Gen. Hosp. Socs: Comm. Mem. Brit. Hyperlipidaemia Assn.; Brit. Diabetic Assn. Prev: MRC Clinician Scientist & Hon. Cons. Phys. Addenbrooke's Hosp. Camb.; Post-Doctoral Trav. Fell. (Cardiovasc. Med.) Falk Cardiovasc. Research Center Stanford Univ. Sch. Med. Calif. USA; MRC Train. Fell. & Hon. Sen. Regist. (Med.) Addenbrooke's Hosp. Camb.

BYRNE, Mr Dominique Sean 24 Huntly Avenue, Giffnock, Glasgow G46 6LW — MB ChB 1984 Glas.; 1984 MB ChB Glas.; 1994 MD Glas.; 1995 FRCS (Gen.); 1989 FRCS Glas.; 1988 FRCS Ed. (Univ. Glas.) Cons. Gen. Surg. Gartnavel Gen. Hosp. Glas. Prev: Sen. Regist. (Gen. Surg.) S.. Gen. Hosp. Glas.

BYRNE, Edward James Henry 15 Old Rectory Close, Broughton Astley, Leicester LE9 6PP Tel: 01455 284120 — MB BCh BAO 1946 Belf.

BYRNE, Eileen Jane c/o Postgraduate Institute Medicine & Dentistry, 10-12 Framlington Place, Newcastle upon Tyne NE2 4AB Tel: 0191 222 8908 Email: eileenbyrne8@hotmail.com; 1 St Marys Drive, Sherburn Village, Durham DH6 1RL — MB BS 1990 Lond.; Cert. Med. Ed. 2000; MRCPI 1997. (St. Mary's London) Specialist Regist. (Paediat.) N.ern Region.

BYRNE, Eileen Patricia 4 Glenavie Park, Newtownabbey BT37 0QW — MB BCh BAO 1974 Belf.; MRCP (UK) 1979.

BYRNE, Eleanor Jane University of Manchester, Withington Hospital, Department Old Age Psychiatry, West Didsbury, Manchester M20 2LR Tel: 0161 291 3309 Fax: 0161 291 3316 Email: a-day@fs1-with-man-ac-uk — MB ChB 1973 Manch.; MRCPsych 1977; FRCPsych 1997. Sen. Lect. (Psychiat. Old Age) & Hon. Cons. Univ. Manch. Prev: Lect. Health c/o Elderly (Psychiat.) Univ. Nottm.; Staff Specialist (Neuropsychiat.) P. Henry Hosp., NSW, Austral.

BYRNE, Fergus Johnston Dumbarton Health Centre, Station Road, Dumbarton G82 1PW Tel: 01389 602644 Fax: 01389 602624; 33 Dumbuck Crescent, Dumbarton G82 1EJ — MB ChB 1961 Glas. (Univ. Glas.)

BYRNE, Francis Bank House, Saltor St., Stafford ST16 2JX Tel: 01785 58348; 239 Eccleshall Road, Stafford ST16 1PE Tel: 01785 42136 — MB BCh BAO 1957 Dub.; MA Dub. 1957, BSc 1953, MB BCh BAO 1957; LAH Dub. 1956. (T.C. Dub.) Med. Off. Lotus Shoe Co. Stafford. Prev: Regtl. Med. Off. 1st Bn. The E. Surrey Regt.; Ho. Phys. & Ho. Surg. Meath Hosp. Dub.; Sen. Ho. Off. (ENT) N. Staffs. Roy. Infirm.

BYRNE, Gabriel Paul East Tilbury Surgery, Princess Margaret Road, East Tilbury, Grays RM18 8YS Tel: 01375 843217 Fax: 01375 840423 — MB BCh BAO 1975 NUI; DRCOG 1978. (University College Dublin) GP. Prev: Dep. Doctor GP Relief Enterprise Ho. Lond.

BYRNE, Gerard Anthony Feeny Medical Centre, Main Street, Feeny, Londonderry BT47 4TD Tel: 028 7778 1501 Fax: 028 7778 1925 — MB BCh BAO 1978 NUI; MRCGP 1982; DCH RCPSI 1982; DRCOG 1981. (Univ. Coll. Dub.) SHO (O & G) Tyrone Co. Hosp. Omagh. Prev: SHO & Ho. Off. (Gen. Med.) Tyrone Co. Hosp. Omagh; Ho. Off. (Surg.) Co. Hosp. Wexford.

BYRNE, Mr Gerard John Research and Teaching, 2nd Floor, Withington Hospital, Nell Lane, Manchester M20 1LR Tel: 0161 291 3842, 0161 291 3846 Email: gedbyrne@compuserve.com; 1 Poplar Farm Close, Saughall Massie, Wirral CH46 1NZ Tel: 0151 605 0712 — MB ChB 1989 Manch.; FRCS 1999 Gensurg; FRCS Ed. 1993. Sen. Lect. in Surgic. Oncol. Univ. of Manch.; Cons. Surgon S. Manch. Univ. and Chrigtie Hosps. Socs: Mem. ASGBI; Mem. BASO; Past Pres. Assn. of Surg.s in Train. Prev: SHO Rotat. (Gen. Surg.) Dudley Rd. Hosp. Birm.; SpR (GenSurg) W. Midl.s.

BYRNE, Gerardine Carmel Shawpark Resource Centre, 41 Shawpark St., Maryhill, Glasgow G20 9DR Tel: 0141 531 8770 Fax: 0141 531 8778 — MB BCh BAO 1979 NUI; MRCGP 1986; MRCPsych 1989. (Univ. Coll. Dub.) Cons. Psychiat. (Community Psychiat.) Glas.

BYRNE, Hilary Anne 13 Meadow Rise, Shaw, Oldham OL2 7QG — MB ChB 1993 Manch.

BYRNE, Irene May 5 South Road, Grassendale Park, Liverpool L19 0LS; 24 High Street, Woolton, Liverpool L25 7TE — MB BCh BAO 1946 Belf. (Belf.) Prev: Ho. Surg. City Hosp. Belf.; Anaesth. Regist. Whiston; Sen. Anaesth. Regist. Sefton Gen. Hosp. Liverp.

BYRNE, James Elds Gorse, Willough Bridge, Market Drayton TF9 4EU Tel: 01630 647502 — MB BCh BAO 1971 Dub.; MA Dub. 1972; FRCP Lond. 1995; MRCP (UK) 1973; FRCPI 1985, M 1973. Cons. Dermat. N. Staffs. Hosp. Trust. Socs: Brit. Assn. Dermat. & N. Eng. & Midl. Dermat. Soc. Prev: Sen. Regist. (Dermat.) King's Coll. Hosp. Lond.; Hon. Clin. Asst. St. John's Hosp. Dis. of the Skin; Ho. Phys. & Surg. Meath Hosp. Dub.

BYRNE, Mr James Patrick 3 Handley Road, Bramhall, Stockport SK7 3EX — MB ChB 1989 Manch.; FRCS Ed. 1994; MD 1998. Socs: ASGBI; AUGIS; SRS.

BYRNE, Mr James Vincent Radcliffe Infirmary, Woodstock Road, Oxford OX2 6HE Tel: 01865 224316 Fax: 01865 224315 Email: jame.byrne@radiology.ox.ac.uk — MB BS 1974 Lond.; MD Lond. 1991; FRCS Eng. 1979; FRCR 1986. Cons. Neuroradiol. Radcliffe Infirm. Oxf. Socs: Brit. Soc. Neuroradiol. & Europ. Soc. Neuroradiol. Prev: Cons. Neuroradiol. Atkinson Morley's Hosp. Wimbledon; Sen. Regist. (Diag. Radiol.) Univ. Hosp. Wales Cardiff; Sen. Regist. (Neuroradiol.) Nat. Hosp. Nerv. Dis. Lond.

BYRNE, James Wenger 19 Lake Close, London SW19 7EG — MRCS Eng. LRCP Lond. 1935; MA, MB BChir Camb. 1937. (Camb., St. Thos. & Char. Cross)

BYRNE, Jennifer Louise Department of Haematology, City Hospital, Hucknall Road, Nottingham NG5 1PB Tel: 0115 969 1169 Fax: 0115 962 7742; 1 Pelham Crescent, The Park, Nottingham NG7 1AR Tel: 0115 947 0440 Email: p_j_byrne@msn.com — MB ChB 1986 Bristol; MB ChB (Hons.) Bristol 1986; PhD Lond. 1996; MRCP (UK) 1989; MRCPath 1997. (Bristol) Lect. & Hon. Sen. Regist. (Haemat.) City Hosp. Nottm. & Univ. Nottm. Socs: Brit. Soc. Haematol.; Eur. Gp. Blood & Marrow Transpl. Prev: Research Regist. (MRC Train. Fell.) Inst. Caner Research Chester Beatty Laborat. Lond.; Regist. (Haemat.) N. Middlx. Hosp.; Regist. & SHO (Haemat.) Roy. Free Hosp. Lond.

BYRNE, John Carmel 33 Antonine Road, Bearsden, Glasgow G61 4DP Tel: 0141 942 5343 — MB ChB 1988 Manch.; MRCP (UK) 1992. Regist. (Cardiol.) W.. Infirm. Glas. Socs: BMA; Brit. Soc. Echocardiogr. Prev: SHO (Med.) Blackburn Roy. Infirm.; SHO (Med.) Wythenshawe Hosp. Manch.

BYRNE, John Walter, Maj. RAMC Retd. (retired) Mistley, North Road, Bathwick, Bath BA2 6HE Tel: 01225 466151 — MB BCh BAO 1939 NUI.

BYRNE, John William 30 Marlborough Road, Sheffield S10 1DB — MB ChB 1990 Sheff.

BYRNE, Jonathan Alban 45A St Andrews Crescent, Dumbarton G82 3ES — MB ChB 1995 Bristol.

BYRNE, Judith Lavinia 2 Wellesbourne Farm, Wellesbourne, Warwick CV35 9SL — MB BCh 1971 Wales; DObst RCOG 1973.

BYRNE, Katharine Evelyn Paediatric Department, Royal Alexandra Hospital, Corsebar Road, Paisley PA2 9P Tel: 0141 887 9111; Croftdene, Hazelmere Road, Kilmacolm PA13 4JW — MB ChB Ed. 1966; FRCP Glas. 1992; MRCP (UK) 1975; DCH RCPS Glas. 1971;

FRCPCH. (Ed.) Cons. Paediat. Roy. Alexandra Hosp. Trust Paisley. Socs: Scott. Paediat. Soc.

BYRNE, Liam Geoffrey Rowe Avenue Surgery, Police Station Car Park, 264 South Coast Road, Peacehaven BN7 7PD Tel: 01273 579500/579505 Fax: 01273 579501 — MB BS 1986 Lond.; MRCGP 1991; DGM RCP Lond. 1991; DRCOG 1991.

BYRNE, Liam Joseph Patrick (retired) 14 Fruithill Park, Belfast BT11 8GD — MB BCh BAO 1949 Belf.

BYRNE, Margaret Mary The Health Centre, Granby St., Littleport, Ely CB6 1NE; 31 Merlin Drive, Ely CB6 3EE — MB BCh 1987 Wales; MRCGP 1992; T(GP) 1992. (Univ. Wales Coll. Med.) Prev: GP Neath, W. Glam.; Trainee GP Neath Gen. Hosp.

BYRNE, Maria Bernadette St Philips, LSE, Houghton St., London WC2A 2AE — MB ChB 1989 Leeds; MRCGP (Distinc.) 1994; DRCOG 1993; DFFP 1993.

BYRNE, Maureen Anne 33 Dumbuck Crescent, Dumbarton G82 1EJ — MB ChB 1995 Glas.; MB ChB Glas. 1995 BSc (Hons) 1992.

BYRNE, Michael Francis Sheskin, Honeys Green Lane, Liverpool L12 9EW Tel: 0151 254 1096 Email: mfbyrne@iol.ioe — MB ChB 1992 Liverp.; MA Camb. 1989; MRCP (UK) 1995. (Cambridge University and Liverpool University) Lect./Regist. (Gastroenterlogy & Pharmacol.) Beaumont Hosp. & Roy. Coll. of Surgs. in Irel., Dub. Socs: Train. Mem. Irish Soc. Gastroenterol. Prev: Regist. (A & E) Roy. N. Shore Hosp. Sydney, Austral.; SHO (Med.) Qu. Med. Centre Nottm.

BYRNE, Michael Patrick Links Medical Centre, Restalrig Park Medical Centre, 40 Alemoor Crescent, Edinburgh EH7 6UJ Tel: 0131 554 2141 Fax: 0131 554 5363 — MB BCh BAO 1986 NUI. GP Edin.

BYRNE, Micheline Anne Stephanie The Jefferiss Wing, St Mary's Hospital, Praed St., Paddington, London W1 2NY Tel: 020 7886 1621; 12 Cumberland Park, London W3 6SX — MB BCh BAO 1973 NUI; DObst RCPI 1976; MRCOG 1982. Cons. Phys. (Genitourin. Med.) St. Mary's Hosp. Lond.; Hon. Sen. Lect. Imperial Coll. Sch. of Med. Socs: BSCCP; (Counc.) BSSVD; Med. Soc. Study VD. Prev: Hon Sen. Regist. & Clin. Scientif. Off. Clin. Research Centre N.wick Pk. Harrow & St. Mary's Hosp. Lond.

BYRNE, Neville John British Airways Health Services, Waterside (HMAG), Harmondsworth, West Drayton UB7 0GB Tel: 020 8738 7706 Fax: 020 8738 9754 Email: neville.j.byrne@british-airways.com — MB BS 1974 Monash. Cons. Occupat. Phys. Overseas & Passenger Med. Servs. Lond. Prev: Head of Overseas & Passenger Med. Serv. Brit. Airways Health Servs. Lond.; Med. Off. Qantas Airways Sydney, Austral.

BYRNE, Patrick Henry Birchfield, 66 Highfield Road, Derby DE22 1GZ — MB BCh BAO 1941 NUI.

BYRNE, Patrick John Lennard Lodge, 3 Lennard Road, Croydon CR0 2UL Tel: 020 8700 8800 Fax: 020 8700 8809 — MB BS 1974 Lond.; MMedSci Nottm. 1979; MRCPsych. 1982. Cons. (Adolesc. Psychiat.). Socs: Assn. Child Psychol. & Psychiat.; Assn. Family Ther. Prev: Clin. Dir. Croydon Child & Adolesc. Ment. Health Serv.

BYRNE, Patrick Kevin Brook Medical Centre, Ecton Brook Road, Northampton NN3 5EN Tel: 01604 401185 Fax: 01604 403268; 80 Allard Close, Rectory Farm, Northampton NN3 5LZ Email: pkb@atallard.demon.co.uk — MB BCh BAO 1982 Dub.; MRCGP 1989. (Univ. Dub. Trinity Coll.) Prev: Trainee GP Leic. VTS; SHO (O & G) Wordsley Hosp. Stourbridge; Ho. Off. Mercers Hosp. Dub.

BYRNE, Paul Adrian Charles Rheumatology Department, Gainsborough Wing, Essex Rivers Healthcare NHS Trust, Colchester District Hospital, Turner Road, Colchester CO4 5JL — BChir 1987 Camb.; 1987 BChir Camb.; 1990 MA Camb.; 1992 MRCP Lond; 1991 DRCOG. (Univ. Camb.) Cons. Rheum. Colchester, Essex.

BYRNE, Paul Dominic St. Helier Hospital, Wrythe Lane, Carshalton SM5 1AA; 87 The Drive, Wallington SM6 9ND — MB BS 1976 Lond.; 1976 MB BS Lond.; 1973 BSc (Biochem. & Physiol.) Lond.; 1979 MRCP (UK); 1976 MRCS Eng. LRCP Lond.; 1983 FRCR. (Westm.) Cons. Radiol. St. Helier Hosp. Carshalton.

BYRNE, Paul Gerard 85 Dallas Road, London NW4 3JD — MB BS 1992 Lond.

BYRNE, Mr Paul Oliver Department of Neurosurgery, Queen's Medical Centre, University Hospital NHS Trust, Nottingham NG7 2UH; 1 Pelham Crescent, The Park, Nottingham NG7 1AR Email: p-j-byrne@msn.com — MB ChB 1984 Birm.; FRCS (SN) 1994; FRCS Eng. 1988; FRCS Ed. 1988. (Birm.) Cons. Neurosurg. Univ. Hosp. NHS Trust Nottm. Prev: Sen. Regist. (Neurosurg.) Birm.; Regist. (Neurosurg.) Lond.

BYRNE, Peter Glynn 10 Denby Croft, Monkspath, Solihull B90 4SQ — MB ChB 1995 Leic.

BYRNE, Peter Roy 102 Tyrwhitt Road, London SE4 1QB — MB BS 1993 Lond.

BYRNE, Robert Antony X-Ray Department, Glan Clwyd Hospital, Bodelwyddan, Rhyl LL18 5UJ Tel: 01745 583910 — MB ChB 1976 Liverp.; FRCR 1984; DMRD Liverp. 1981. Cons. Radiol. Glan Clwyd Hosp. Prev: Sen. Regist. (Radiol.) Liverp. Teach. Hosps.

BYRNE, Robert James Fitzgerald Barnwood Road Surgery, 51 Barnwood Road, Gloucester GL2 0SE Tel: 01452 523362 Fax: 01452 387931; 78 Cheltenham Road, Gloucester GL2 0LX Tel: 01452 500778 Fax: 01452 387931 Email: rbyrne3450@aol.com — MB BS 1972 Lond.; MRCS Eng. LRCP Lond. 1972. (Westm.) Clin. Asst. (Geriat.) Glos. Roy. Hosp. Prev: Trainee GP Gloucester VTS.

BYRNE, Ruth Louise 5 Stanley Road, Stockport SK4 4HL — BM BS 1989 Nottm.; FRCS Eng. 1993. Specialist Regist. (Urol.) Newc. u. Tyne.

BYRNE, Steven Department of Paediatrics, Blackpool Victoria Hospital, Whinney Heys Road, Blackpool FY3 8NR Tel: 01253 300000; Rosetree Cottage, High St, Elswick, Preston PR4 3ZB Tel: 01995 670666 — MB ChB 1984 Manch.; PhD Manch. 1994; BSc (Hons. Physiol.) Manch. 1981; MRCP (UK) 1989. Cons. Paediat. Blackpool Vict. Hosp. Socs: Neonat. Soc.; Paediat. Research Soc.; Brit. Paediat. Assn. Prev: Sen. Regist. Neonat. Med. Unit. St. Mary's Hosp. Manch.; Research Fell. Cystic Fibrosis Trust NW RHA; Regist. (Paediat.) Leicester Roy. Infirm.

BYRNE, Timothy Paul 24 Greenan Road, Newry BT34 2PJ — MB BCh BAO 1984 NUI; MRCPsych 1990.

BYRNE, William 2 Oakdale Road, Waterloo, Liverpool L22 9QS — MB ChB 1987 Manch.

BYRNE, William Henry Thomas Byrne, Langham, Apps, Finnie and McIlhinney, 186 Neasham Road, Darlington DL1 4YL Tel: 01325 461128 Fax: 01325 469123; 47 Clare Avenue, Darlington DL3 8SJ Tel: 01325 466376 Fax: 01325 469123 — MB BCh BAO 1977 Dub.; Dip. Pract. Dermat. Wales 1993.

BYRNE, Winifred Felicity 1 Hawthorn Place, Woodbridge IP12 4JZ — MB BCh BAO 1972 NUI; FFA RCSI 1976. Cons. Anaesth. Ipswich Hosp.

BYRNES, Colman Kevin Columba 1 Shrewsbury Park, Belfast BT9 6PN — MB BCh BAO 1993 Belf.

BYRNES, Mr Dermot Patrick Department of Neurosurgery, Royal Victoria Hospital, Grosvenor Rd,, Belfast BT12 6BA Tel: 028 9089 4972 Fax: 028 9023 7733; 1 Shrewsbury Park, Belfast BT9 6PN Tel: 028 9066 6603 — MB BCh BAO 1963 NUI; FRCSI 1969; FRCS Ed. 1967. Cons. Neurosurg. Roy. Vict. Hosp. Belf. Socs: BMA; Soc. Brit. Neurol. Surgs.; Irish Neurol. Assn. Prev: Tutor (Surg.) RCSI; Sen. Regist. (Neurosurg.) Roy. Vict. Hosp. Belf.; Asst. Prof. (Neurosurg.) Univ. Maryland Baltimore, USA.

BYRNES, Maria Ewa Stanislawa (retired) 45 Kirby Road, North End, Portsmouth PO2 0PF Tel: 01705 664150 — MB BS 1961 Durh.; MRCPsych 1971; DPM Eng. 1967. Prev: Cons. Child & Family Psychiat. Child & Family Ther. Servs. Portsmouth.

BYRNES, Rosemarie The High House, High House Lane, Tardebigge, Bromsgrove B60 3AQ — LRCPI & LM, LRSCI & LM 1974; LRCPI & LM, LRCSI & LM 1974.

BYRNES, Sheena Mary Antoinette 1 Shrewsbury Park, Belfast BT9 6PN — MB ChB 1991 Bristol.

BYRNES, Tiernan James Dermot 1 Shrewsbury Park, Belfast BT9 6PN — MB ChB 1997 Ed.

BYROM, Helen Jane 34 Knighthead Point, The Quarterdeck, London E14 8SR — MB BS 1991 Lond.

BYROM, Henry Cossington House Surgery, 51 Cossington Road, Canterbury CT1 3HX Tel: 01227 763377 — MB BS 1963 Lond.; BSc Lond. 1960, MB BS 1963. (Lond. Hosp.) Prev: Jun. Lect. in Surg. Lond. Hosp.

BYROM, Katharine 65 Cromwell Road, Canterbury CT1 3LE — MB BS 1996 Lond.

BYROM, Nigel Paul The Princess Elizabeth Hospital, Le Vauquiedor, St Martin's, Guernsey GY4 6UU Tel: 01481 725241; La Maison D'Aval, Route de la Bellee, Torteval, Guernsey GY8 0NB Tel: 01481 65346 — MB BS 1973 Lond.; MRCS Eng. LRCP Lond. 1973;

FRCP Lond. 1996; MRCP (UK) 1978. (Guy's Hosp. Med. Sch.) Phys. P.ss Eliz. Hosp. Guernsey. Socs: Renal Assn.; EDTA. Prev: Sen. Regist (Gen. Med. & Nephrol.) Nottm. City Hosp.; Research Fell. & Hon. Regist. (Nephrol.) Nottm. City Hosp.; Regist. & SHO (Gen. Med. & Nephrol.) Leicester Gen. & Groby Rd. Hosps.

BYROM, Richard Glazebrook 65 Cromwell Road, Canterbury CT1 3LE Tel: 01227 470466 — MB BS 1993 Lond. SHO (Surg.) ScarBoro. Gen. Hosp.

BYRON, Alan John 6 Madeira Road, Ventnor PO38 1QP Tel: 01983 855020 Email: alanbyron@bigfoot.com — MB ChB Sheff. 1964; MRCGP 1984; DPM Eng. 1968. (Sheff.) Prev: GP Sheff.; Asst. GP Barnsley; Hosp. Pract. Brit. Milit. Hosp. Münster BFPO 17.

BYRON, Margaret Ann Rheumatology Unit, Bristol Royal Infirmary, Bristol BS2 8HW Tel: 0117 928 2910 Fax: 0117 928 3841 Email: margaretbyron@bristol.ac.uk; 40 Durdham Park, Bristol BS6 6XE Tel: 0119 973 1775 — MB ChB 1974 Leeds; MB ChB (Hons.) Leeds 1974; BSc Physiol. (Hons.) 1971; MD Leeds 1990; FRCP Lond. 1994; MRCP (UK) 1977. Cons. (Rheum.) Bristol Roy. Infirm. & W.on-Super-Mare; Hon. Univ. Appointment; Sen. Clin. Lect. Socs: Brit. Soc. Rheum. & Brit. Soc. Rehabil. Med. Prev: Cons. Rheum. & Rehabil. Stoke Mandeville Hosp. Aylesbury; Hon. Sen. Regist. Fibrinol Research Gp. John Radcliffe Hosp. Oxf.; Sen. Regist. Juvenile Rheum. Unit Taplow & Roy. Postgrad. Sch. Med.

BYRON, Mark Geoffrey 35 St Benedict Crescent, Heath, Cardiff CF14 4DP — MB BCh 1984 Wales.

BYTHELL, Valerie Elizabeth Department of Anaesthesia, Royal Victoria Infirmary, Queen Victoria Road, Newcastle upon Tyne NE1 4LP — MB BS 1981 Lond.; BSc Lond. 1978, MB BS 1981; FFA RCS Eng. 1985. Cons. Anaesth. Roy. Vict. Infirm. Newc. u. Tyne. Prev: Cons. & Sen. Regist. (Anaesth.) St. Mary's Hosp. Lond. W2.

BYWATER, Andrew John KnightwickSurgery, Worcester WR6 5PH Tel: 01886 821279; Tel: 01886 880007 — MB BChir 1983 Camb.; MA Camb. 1982; LMSSA Lond. 1982; DA (UK) 1988. p/t Gen. Practitioner, Kt.wick Surg., Worcs; Clin. Asst. (Dermat. & Gastroenterol.) Worcester Roy. Infirm. Prev: Regist. (Med.) S.land Hosp. Invercargill, NZ; SHO (Anaesth.) Worcester Roy. Infirm.; Ho. Surg. W.m. Hosp. Lond.

BYWATER, Barry Churchfields Surgery, Recreation Road, Bromsgrove B61 8DT Tel: 01527 872163; Halfway House, Upper Gambolds Lane, Stoke Prior, Bromsgrove B60 3HB Tel: 01527 831709 — MB ChB 1968 Liverp.; FRCGP 1992, M 1977; DObst RCOG 1970. Project Team Mem. BromsGr. Total Purchasing Project. Socs: BromsGr. Gen. Pract. Assn.; BromsGr. & Redditch Med. Soc. Prev: Course Organiser (Gen. Pract.) Alexandra Hosp. Redditch; SHO (A & E) Walton Hosp. Liverp.; SHO (O & G) BRd.green Hosp. Liverp.

BYWATER, Henry Christopher Illingworth (retired) Wintersell Corner, Dwelly Lane, Edenbridge TN8 6QD Tel: 01732 866164 — MRCS Eng. LRCP Lond. 1955; MB BChir Camb. 1956; MA Camb. 1955; DObst RCOG 1960. Yeoman Worshipful Soc. Apoth. Lond. Prev: Ho. Surg. (ENT & Ophth.) W.m. Hosp. Lond.

BYWATER, James Rawdon Theale Medical Centre, Englefield Road, Theale, Reading RG7 5AS Tel: 0118 930 2513 Fax: 0118 930 4419 Email: james.bywater@gp-k81077.nhs.uk; Ryders, The Avenue, Bucklebury, Reading RG7 6NH Tel: 0118 974 4124 Fax: 0118 974 4124 — MB BChir 1980 Camb.; MA Camb. 1981; MRCGP 1984; DCH RCP Lond. 1983; DRCOG 1982. (Westm.) Gen. Practitioner; Exec. Comm. Chair. Reading Pct Reading. Prev: Trainee GP St. Peter's Hosp. Chertsey VTS; SHO (A & E) Roehampton; Ho. Phys. & Ho. Surg. Qu. Mary's Hosp. Roehampton.

BYWATER, Jane Elizabeth Duchess of Kent House, Dellwood Hospital, Lieben Road, Reading RG7 6NH Tel: 01189 550488 Fax: 01189 550496; Ryders, The Avenue, Bucklebury, Reading RG7 6NH — MB BS 1984 Lond.; MRCGP 1990; Dip. Palliat. Med. Wales 1993; DRCOG 1987. p/t Cons. Palliat. Med. Duchess of Kent Ho. Reading. Socs: Assn. of Palliat. Med. Prev: Med. Dir. Sue Ryder Home Oxon.

BYWATER, John Walter The Home Cottage, Lincomb, Stourport-on-Severn DY13 9RB Tel: 01299 250746 — MB BChir 1963 Camb.; MA, MB Camb. 1963, BChir 1962; DObst RCOG 1965. (St. Thos.)

BYWATER, Keith Haward 6 Old Road, Ruddington, Nottingham NG11 6NF Tel: 0115 921 1538 — MRCS Eng. LRCP Lond. 1944. (Middlx.) Regional Med. Off. DHSS.

BYWATER, Nikola Susann 14 Highmoor Park, Clitheroe BB7 1JB Tel: 01200 424091 Fax: 01200 424091 Email: nikkiby@aol.com — MB ChB 1994 Bristol; DRCOG 1997; MRCGP 1998. (Bristol)

BYWATER, Nuala Joan Hereford County Hospital, Hereford Tel: 01432 355444 — MB ChB 1982 Aberd.; FRCA 1994; PALS 1997; ALS 1997. (Specialist Regist. West Midlands School of Anaesthesia) Cons. Anaesth. Socs: Intens. Care Soc.; Obst. Anaesth. Assn. Prev: Specialist Regist. Birm. Hosps.; Med. Regist. Dunedin Hosp. New Zealand.

BYWATERS, Professor Eric George Lapthorne, CBE Long Acre, 53 Burkes Road, Beaconsfield HP9 1PW — MB BS 1933 Lond.; MB BS (Hons. Path.) Lond. 1933; Hon. MD Liege; FRCP Lond. 1950 M. 1937; Hon. FACP, FRCP Canada; MRCS Eng. LRCP Lond. 1933. (Middlx.) Emerit. Prof. Rheum. Roy. Postgrad. Med. Sch. Univ. Lond.; Hon. Cons. Windsor Gp. Socs: Hon. Fell. Roy Soc. Med. & RPG Med. Sch.; Hon. Mem. (Ex-Pres. & Librarian) Heberden Soc.; Hon. Mem. (Ex-Pres.) Europ. League against Rheum. Prev: Dir. Rheum. Unit (Med. Research Counc.) & Hon. Cons. Phys. Canad.; Red Cross Memor. Hosp. Taplow; Asst. Clin. Pathol. Bland-Sutton Inst. Middlx. Hosp.

BYWATERS, Jennifer Lesley Dept. of Health, Mental Health Branch, Room 5W08, Quarry Hse, Quarry Hill, Leeds LS2 7UE Tel: 0113 254 6279 Fax: 0113 254 5251 Email: jenny.bywaters@dott.gsi.gov.uk; 33 Swarthmore Road, Selly Oak, Birmingham B29 4NQ Tel: 0121 477 6418 Email: jlbywaters@aol.com — BM BCh 1973 Oxf.; MA Oxf. 1973; Cert. Family Plann. JCC 1987; FFPHM RCP (UK) 1997, M 1989. (Oxf.) Cons. Pub. Health Med. & Sen. Policy Manager, D of H, Leeds. Socs: Mem. Brit. Med. Assn. Prev: Cons. Pub. Health Med. Birm. HA; Sen. Regist. (Pub. Health Med.) E. Birm. HA; SCMO (Family Plann.) E. Birm. HA.

CABLE, Mr Hugh Richard 10 Sovereign Close, Kenilworth CV8 1SQ — MRCS Eng. LRCP Lond. 1967; FRCS Eng. 1975; DLO Eng. 1970. (Univ. Coll. Hosp.) Cons. ENT Surg. S Warks. Health Dist. Prev: Sen. Regist. Bristol Health Dist. (T).

CABOT, Kate Lucy Mill Hill Surgery, 111 Avenue Road, Acton, London W3 8QH Tel: 020 8992 9955 — MB ChB 1985 Bristol; MRCGP 1990; DRCOG 1989; DCH RCP Lond. 1988. Socs: BMA. Prev: SHO (Obst.& Gyn.) Hillingdon Hosp. GP VTS; SHO (Paediat.) Char. Cross Hosp. Lond.; Ho. Off. Bristol Hosps.

CABOT, Ricardo The Surgery, 1 Hicks Road, Markyate, St Albans AL3 8LJ — LMS 1985 Barcelona.

CABRERA ABREU, Jose Carlos Department of Clinical Chemistry, Birmingham Children's Hospital, Steelhouse Lane, Birmingham B4 6NH Tel: 0121 333 9911, 0121 333 9912 — LMS 1985 La Laguna; MSc (Clin. Biochem.) Surrey 1992; MRCPath 1998. Specialist Regist. (Paediatric Chem. Path.) Birminham Childr.'s Hosp. Socs: Assn. Clin. Biochem.s. Prev: Specialist Regist. (Chem. Path.) Univ. Coll. Lond. Hosp.

CABRERA CABRERA, Amelia Rose 25 Deva Lane, Chester CH2 1BW — LMS 1985 La Laguna.

CACCIATO, Angelo Mario Hartlepool General Hospital, Holdforth Road, Hartlepool TS24 9AH — State DMS 1993 Catania.

CACCIATORI, Matteo Princess Alexandra Eye Pavilion, Chalmers St., Edinburgh EH3 9HA — State Exam Pavia 1989.

CACHIA, Philip Greville Fernie House, Ladybank, Cupar KY15 7RU — MB ChB 1980 Ed.; MRCP (UK) 1983.

CACKET, Nicola Eve 19 Horse and Groom Lane, Chelmsford CM2 8PJ — MB BChir 1994 Camb.; MRCP.

CACKETTE, Colin George South Queensferry Group Practice, The Health Centre, Rosebery Avenue, South Queensferry EH30 9HA Tel: 0131 331 1396 Fax: 0131 331 5783; 50 Ravelston Dykes, Edinburgh EH4 3JB Tel: 0131 332 4494 — MB ChB 1977 Ed.; MRCGP 1981. Clin. Asst. (Diabetes) W.. Gen. Hosp. Edin.

CADAMY, Anthony Roger The Surgery, Scourie IV27 4SX — MB ChB 1970 Leeds; MRCGP 1977. G.P. Princip. S & KLB Health Care, Scourie. Prev: Med. Off. Ohmeda Keighley; Ho. Off. Airedale Gen. Hosp. E.burn.

CADAMY, Matthew Edward Galanthus, Hall Gardens, Kildwick, Keighley BD20 9AF — MB ChB 1997 Ed.

CADBURY, Anna-Louise 3rd Floor Flat, 13 Marlborough Buildings, Bath BA1 2LX Tel: 01225 480892 — BM BS 1997 Nottm. SHO GP VTS, Bath.

CADBURY, Naomi Louise 285 Lordswood Road, Birmingham B17 8PR — MB BCh 1998 Wales.

CADBURY, Rebecca Candia Meddygfa Rhiannon, Northfield Road, Narberth SA67 7AA Tel: 01834 860237 Fax: 01834 861625; Fron Haul, Login, Whitland SA34 0XB — MB BS 1981 Lond.; MRCP (UK) 1984; DRCOG 1986; DCH RCP Lond. 1985.

CADDELL, Ronald Forrester (retired) Baldowrie, 4 Annfield Road, Inverness IV2 3HP — LRCP LRCS Ed. LRFPS Glas. 1950; FRCPsych 1974, M 1971; DPM Eng. 1955. Prev: Dep. Phys. Supt. Craig Dunain Hosp.

CADDEN, Ian Samuel Hendry 23 Caw Park, Londonderry BT47 6LZ — MB BCh BAO 1997 Belf.

CADDICK, Angela Nicol Windrush Healt Centre, Welch Way, Witney Tel: 01983 702911 — MB BS 1991 Lond.; MRCGP 1995. (Middlx. Hosp. Med. Sch.)

CADDICK, Jennifer Frances Malthouse Barn, Barn Lane, Chelwood, Bristol BS39 4NN; 57 Ashleigh Grove, Jesmond, Newcastle upon Tyne NE2 3DJ Tel: 0191 281 4161 — MB BS 1996 Newc. (Newcastle upon Tyne) SHO (Gen. Surg.) N. Tyneside Dist. Gen. Hosp. Newc. Prev: SHO A & E N. Tees DGH Stockton upon Tees; Anat. Demonst. Univ. of Newc. Med. Sch.; Ho. Off. Med. Hexham Gen. Hosp. N.umberland.

CADDICK, Susan Lynne 242 Millhouses Lane, Sheffield S11 9JA — MB ChB 1987 Sheff.; BMedSci. (Hons.) 1987; MRCP (UK) 1991.

***CADDY, Alison Jane** 7 Roman Way, Thatcham RG18 3BP — MB BS 1998 Lond.; MB BS Lond 1998; BSc Lond 1995.

CADDY, Mr Christopher Michael Department of Plastic Surgery, Northern General Hospital, Herries Road, Sheffield S5 7AU Tel: 0114 271 5758 Fax: 0114 261 9651; 2 Tapton Park Mount, Ranmoor, Sheffield S10 3FH Tel: 0114 230 8327 Email: c.m.caddy@aol — MB ChB 1979 Ed.; BSc (Med. Sci.) Ed. 1976; FRCS (Plast Surg.) 1992; FRCS Ed. 1983; FCS(SA) Plast & Reconstruc. Surg. 1987. (Univ. Ed.) Cons. Plastic Surg. N. Gen. NHS Trust Hosp. Sheff.; Regional Specialty Adviser for Plastic Surg. Trent. Socs: Brit. Assn. Plastic Surg.; Brit. Soc. Surg. Hand; Brit. Assn. Aesth. Surgs. Prev: Fell. Hands & Microsurg. Indiana Hand Center Indianapolis, USA; Microsurg. Research Fell. Roy. Melbourne Hosp., Austral.; Regist. (Plastic Surg.) Groote Schuur Hosp. Cape Town.

CADDY, Grant Ryan 77 Victoria Road, Holywood BT18 9BG — MB ChB 1995 Bristol.

CADDY, Isabel Howson (retired) 4 Ashstead Lane, Godalming GU7 1SZ Tel: 01483 423207 — BM BCh 1947 Oxf.; BM BCh Oxon. 1947; DPH Eng. 1966. Prev: Sen. Med. Off. (Child Health) SW Surrey HA.

CADDY, Jennifer Mary Dept of Anaesthecia, Pontefract General Confirmacy, Pontefract WF8 1PL; Hikeb, 2 Orchard View, Estcourt Road, Darrington, Pontefract WF8 3AZ — MB ChB 1974 Bristol; FFA RCS Eng. 1980; DRCOG 1976. Cons. Anaesth. Pontefract Gen. Infirm. Prev: Cons. Anaesth. Milton Keynes Dist. Gen. Hosp.; Sen. Regist. (Anaesth.) Leeds Gen. Infirm.; Regist. (Anaesth.) Bristol. Roy. Infirm.

CADE, Alan Dept. of Paedatric & Child Health, Clarendon Wing,, Leeds General Infirmary, Belmont Grove, Leeds LS2 9NS Tel: 0113 243 2799 Fax: 0113 292 3902 Email: a.cade@leeds.ac.uk; 3 De Lacy Mount, Kirkstall, Leeds LS5 3JF Tel: 0113 226 6840 Email: alancade@yahoo.com — MB ChB 1988 Leeds; DCH RCP Lond. 1992; MRCP (UK) 1994. (Leeds) Lect. in Paediat., Leeds Gen. Infirm.; Hon. Specialist Regist. in Paediat. Socs: Brit. Paediat. Assn.; Paediat. Research Soc. Prev: Hon. Research Fell. (Paediat.) Gen. Infirm. Leeds; SHO (Paediat.) Derby Childr. Hosp., Qu. Med. Centre Nottm, Leeds Gen. Infirm. & Harrogate Dist. Hosp.

CADE, Arnold Nigel Blandford Hospital, Mill Down Road, Blandford Forum DT11 7DD Tel: 01305 361738 Fax: 01258 454894 Email: drancade@amsent.net — MB ChB 1972 Bristol; MRCPsych 1980; Cert. Occupat. Health Birm. 1988. (Bristol) Cons. Psychiat. Dorset Community Trust; Clin. Teach. (Old. Age Psychiat.) Bristol Univ.; Surg. Lt. Cdr. RNR (Ret'd.); Hon. Med. Off. BARC. Socs: BMA. Prev: Cons. Psychiat. of Old Age Plymouth CT; Cons. Psychiat. Old Age N. Devon Dist. Hosp. Barnstaple.; Sen. Regist. (Psychogeriat.) Exe Vale Hosp. Exeter.

CADE, Mr David Gorstage Bank, Weaverham Road, Sandiway, Northwich CW8 2SQ Tel: 01606 883759 — MB 1971 Camb.; MA Camb. 1970, MB 1971, BChir 1970; FRCS Eng. 1975. (Westm.) Cons. Surg. Leighton Hosp. Crewe. Prev: Sen. Surg. Regist. Manch. Hosp. Resid. Surg. Off. Salford Roy. Hosp.; & Regist. (Surg.) W.m. Hosp. Lond.

CADE, Heather Juliet 49 St Georges Wharf, 6 Shad Thames, London SE1 2YS — MB BS 1993 Lond.

CADE, Mr Mark Stuart 12 Lime Grove, Bury BL9 5ES — BM 1985 Soton.; FRCS Ed. 1989. Staff Grade (Urol.) Burnley Gen. Hosp. Socs: Assoc. Mem. BAUS. Prev: Regist. (Gen. Surg.) Burnley Gen. Hosp.

CADENHEAD, Alison Lesley 1/1, 1010 Crow Road, Anniesland, Glasgow G13 1JN — MB ChB 1994 Ed.

CADER, Muhammed Zameel 1 Star Hill, Birmingham B15 2LT — MB ChB 1997 Birm.

CADGE, Barbara Ann Royal National Throat Nose & Ear Hospital, Grays Inn Road, London WC1X 8EE Tel: 020 7837 8855 — MB ChB 1975 Bristol; MSc Manch. 1986; FRCP Lond. 1996. Cons. Audiological Med. Dept. Adult Audiolog. Rehabil. Roy. Nat. Throat, Nose & Ear Hosp. Lond.

CADIER, Mr Michael Alain Michel Department of Plastic Surgery, Salisbury District Hospital, Salisbury SP2 8BJ; The Old Farm House, Standlynch, Near Downton, Salisbury SP5 3QR — MB BS 1986 Lond.; MA Oxf. 1981, BA 1980; FRCS (Plast) 1996; FRCS Ed. 1990; ECFMG Cert. 1986; MS (Soton) 1998. (St.Thomas' Hospital, London) Cons. Plastic Surg. Salisbury Dist. Hosp. & Portsmouth Healthcare Trusts. Socs: Brit. Burns Assn.; BAPS; Hand Soc. Prev: Sen. Regist. (Plastic Surg.) Frenchay Hosp. Bristol; Regist. (Plastic Surg.) Odstock Hosp. Salisbury; Regist. (Surg.) Barnet Gen. Hosp.

CADIGAN, Denis Vincent 45 Moor Green Lane, Moseley, Birmingham B13 8NE — MB BCh BAO 1945 NUI. (Univ. Coll. Dub.)

CADIGAN, Patrick John 6 Chedworth Close, Bournville, Birmingham B29 4LS — LRCPI & LM, LRSCI & LM 1972; LRCPI & LM, LRCSI & LM 1972; MRCP (UK) 1974.

CADIGAN, Philip 53 The Green, West Cornforth, Ferryhill DL17 9JH — MB BCh BAO 1978 NUI; LRCPI & LM, LRCSI & LM 1978. Sen. Regist. (Radiol.) York Dist. Hosp.

CADLE, Derek Raymond (retired) Sunningdale, Ilsham Marine Drive, Torquay TQ1 2PN Tel: 01803 297514 — MB BS Lond. 1965; MRCS Eng. LRCP Lond. 1964; FFA RCS Eng. 1969; DObst RCOG 1966. Prev: Cons. Anaesth. & Intens. Care Med. Torbay Hosp. Torquay.

CADMAN, David Alec (retired) Beech House, 14 Deepwood Close, Earlswood, St Fagans, Cardiff CF5 4SJ Tel: 01222 595232 — MB BCh 1968 Wales. Prev: Clin. Research Asst. Roy. Gwent Hosp. Newport.

CADMAN, David Hugh Beechwood House, Rectory Road, Staple Grove, Taunton TA2 6EL — BM 1981 Soton.

CADMAN, Donald Spencer (retired) 42 Strathearn Avenue, Whitton, Twickenham TW2 6JX Tel: 020 8894 3133 — MB BChir Camb. 1941; FRCP Lond 1971, M 1943. Prev: Phys. Chest Dept. St. Thos. Hosp.

CADMAN, Dora Mahalah (retired) 5 Cranleigh Gardens, Kingston upon Thames KT2 5TX — MRCS Eng. LRCP Lond. 1925.

CADMAN, Jonathan Martin Flat 5, 62 Park Road, Southport PR9 9JB — MRCS Eng. LRCP Lond. 1978; MRCPsych 1985.

CADMAN, Marie 19 Chiltern Park, Thornbury, Bristol BS35 2HX — MB BCh 1998 Wales.

CADMAN, Philip John X-Ray Department, Wycombe Hospital, High Wycombe; 27 Laceys Drive, Hazlemere, High Wycombe HP15 7JY — BM 1979 Soton.; FRCR 1985; DRCOG 1981. Cons. Radiol. Wycombe HA.

CADMAN, Susan 31 Meadow Gardens, Beccles NR34 9PA Tel: 01502 714976 — MB ChB 1973 Liverp. Clin. Med. Off. (Family Plann.) James Paget Healthcare NHS Trust & Local Health Partnerships NHS Trust. Socs: Dip. Fac. Family Plann.

CADNESS-GRAVES, Bessie Helena Edith (retired) Arden House Nursing Home, 31 Upper Highway, Kings Langley WD4 8PP — MB ChB 1929 Manch.; MSc Manch. 1929; FRCPath 1965. Prev: Cons. Bacteriol. Roy. Boro. Kensington.

CADOGAN, Florence Roehampton House, Queens Mary's University Hospital, Roehampton Lane, London SW15 5PN; 113 East Sheen Avenue, London SW14 8AX Tel: 020 8876 8727 — MB BS 1954 Durh.; DPH 1958; MFCM 1973. Princip. Pub. Health Phys. Wandsworth, Richmond, Twickenham & Roehampton HA's. Socs: Fell. Roy. Soc. Med.; Soc. Occupat. Med.

CADOUX-HUDSON, Helen Sarah Pamela The Mill Cottage, Witney St., Burford, Oxford OX8 4DN — MB BS 1983 Lond.

CADOUX-HUDSON, Thomas Anthony Daniel Department of Neurosurgery, Radcliffe Infirmary, Woodstock Road, Oxford OX2 6HE Tel: 01865 224945 Fax: 01993 822141 Email: tadch@bioch.ox.ac.uk; Email: jim.cook1@virgin.net, t-cadouxhudson@lineone.net — MB BS 1982 Lond.; DPhil 1990; FRCS Eng. 1992; FRCS (Surgical Neorology) 1994. (St. Mary's Hospital Medical School, London & New College, Oxford) Cons. Neurosurg. Radcliffe Infirm. Oxf.; Sen. Clin. Scientist MRC Biochem & Clin. Magnetic Spectroscopy Unit John Radcliffe Hosp. Oxf. Socs: Brit. Soc. Neurol. Surgs. Prev: Sen. Regist. (Neurosurg.) Frenchay Hosp. Bristol.

CADSKY, Otakar c/o 13 Augustus Road, London SW19 6LW — MRCS Eng. LRCP Lond. 1976; BSc (Pharmacol.) Lond. 1972, MB BS 1976; MRCPsych 1981. Forens. Psychiat. Alberta Hosp. Edmonton Alberta Canada. Prev: Sen. Regist. (Foren. Psychiat.) BRd.moor Hosp. Crowthorne; Sen. Regist. (Child Psychiat.) Univ. Coll. Hosp. Lond. & (Child; Ment. Handicap) Harperbury Hosp. Radlett.

CADWGAN, Anthony Martin 57 Esslemont Avenue, Top Floor Left, Aberdeen AB25 1SS — MB ChB 1994 Aberd.

***CAESAR, Benjamin Colin** 45 Kyrle Road, London SW11 6BB — MB BS 1998 Lond.; MB BS Lond 1998; BSc (Hons) 1995.

***CAESAR, David Henry** 45 Kyrle Road, London SW11 6BB; Top Flat, 5 Nelson St., Edinburgh EH3 6UF Tel: 0131 557 6505 — MB ChB 1997 Ed.

CAESAR, Elizabeth Kerrfield, Heol Fargoed, Bargoed CF81 8PQ — MB BCh 1986 Wales.

CAESAR, Harvey Kerrfield, Heol Fargoed, Bargoed CF81 8PQ — BM 1992 Soton.

CAESAR, Mr Richard Henning Hollywood Cottage, Faringdon Road, Kingston Bagpuize, Abingdon OX13 5AF Email: riccaesar@hotmail.com — MB BChir 1993 Camb.; MA Camb 1992; FRCOphth 1996.

CAESAR, Susanne Ruth West View, School Lane, Bunbury, Tarporley CW6 9NR — MB ChB 1990 Ed.

CAFFERKEY, Michele 'Hillside', Courtfield Road, Plymouth PL3 5BB — MB ChB 1990 Sheff.; MRCP (UK) 1995. (Univ. Sheff.) Specialist Regist., Renal Med.

CAFFERTY, Maria do Amparo Nunes 1 Ashdene Close, Willerby, Hull HU10 6LW Tel: 01482 652256 Fax: 01482 659555 Email: jcaff16539@aol.com — Medico U. of Ceara, Brazil 1957.

CAFFERY, Imogen Louise 56 Clarkes Lane, Beeston, Nottingham NG9 5BL — MB ChB 1988 Manch.

CAFFREY, Elizabeth Anne 33 Alloa Road, London SE8 5AH — MA, MB Camb. 1975, BChir 1974; MRC Path 1982. Cons. Transfus. Med. E. Anglian Reg. Blood Transfus. Centre Camb. Prev: Clin. Path. Advisor AMI Med. Laborat. Servs. Lond.; Sen. Regist. (Haemat.) Guy's Hosp. Lond.; Regist. (Path.) St. Olave's Hosp. Lond.

CAGNEY, Bridget Michelle Marie 6 Derby Hills Farm Court, Melbourne, Derby DE73 1EE — MB BCh BAO 1988 NUI.

CAHALIN, Paul Andrew 93 Crundale Avenue, Kingsbury, London NW9 9PS — MB BS 1996 Lond.

CAHILL, Anne Barbara c/o 4 Wychwood Close, Seaview PO34 5JD — MB ChB 1993 Leeds; BA Exeter 1981.

CAHILL, Aubrey Cheadle Medical Practice, 1-5 Ashfield Crescent, Cheadle SK8 1BH Tel: 0161 428 7575 Fax: 0161 283 8884 — MB BCh BAO 1974 Belf.; MRCGP 1980.

CAHILL, Brendan Thomas Shaftesbury Medical Centre, 480 Harehills Lane, Leeds LS9 6DE Tel: 0113 248 5631 Fax: 0113 235 0658 — MB BS 1971 Newcastle; MB BS Newc. 1971. (Newcastle) GP Leeds.

CAHILL, Catherine 29 Gorse Avenue, Felpham, Bognor Regis PO22 6AY — MB ChB 1982 Glas. Regist. (Psychiat.) Graylingwell Hosp. Chichester. Prev: SHO (A & E) Roy. Sussex Co. Hosp. Brighton; SHO (Psychiat.) Graylingwell Hosp. Chichester; Jun. Ho. Off. (Surg.) Battle Hosp. Reading.

CAHILL, Mr Christopher John, Surg. Cdr. RN Retd. Queen Alexandra Hospital, Cosham, Portsmouth PO6 3LY Tel: 023 92 286000 Fax: 023 92 286937 Email: chris.cahill@porthosp.nhs.uk; 14 Linden Grove, Alverstoke, Gosport PO12 2EE Tel: 02392 522449 Fax: 02392 526364 — MB BS 1977 Lond.; FRCS Ed. 1986; FFAEM 1994. (Middl. Hosp.) Cons.(A & E Med.) & Clin. Dir, Div. of Med. Qu. Alexandra Hosp. Portsmouth; Med. Ref. and Adviser to Maritime and Coastguard Agency S.ampton. Prev: Cons. (A & E Med.) Roy. Hosp. Haslar, Gosport; Sen. Regist. (A & E Med.) Hope Hosp., Qu. Alexandra Hosp. Portsmouth & RNH Hosp. Gosport.

CAHILL, Mr Christopher Joseph Kingston Hospital, Galsworthy Road, Kingston upon Thames KT2 7QB Tel: 020 8934 2738 Fax: 020 8934 3268 Email: joe.cahill@kh.sthones.nhs.uk; The White House, Fairoak Lane, Oxshott, Leatherhead KT22 0TN Tel: 01372 842473 Fax: 01372 842473 Email: jcahill@compuserve.com — MB BChir 1977 Camb.; MChir Camb. 1986; FRCS Eng. 1980. Cons. Surg. Kingston Hosp. Kingston u. Thames. Socs: Fell. Roy. Soc. Med.; Hon.sec. Brit. Assn. Day Surg.; Internat. Surgic. Soc. Prev: Sen. Regist. (Surg.) W.m. Hosp. Lond.; Research Fell. & Regist. (Surg.) Roy. Surrey Co. Hosp. Guildford; Ho. Phys. & Ho. Surg. King's Coll. Hosp. Lond.

CAHILL, David John University of Bristol, St Michael's Hospital, Southwell St., Bristol BS2 8EG Tel: 0117 928 5704 Email: d.j.cahill@bris.ac.uk — MB BCh BAO 1981 NUI; MD Bristol 1995; MRCPI 1996; MRCOG 1986; DRCOG 1984. Cons. Sen. Lect. (Reproduc. Med.) Univ. Bristol, St. Michael's Hosp. Bristol; Assoc. Edr., Human ReProduc., Oxf.. Socs: Brit. Fertil. Soc.; Fell. Roy. Acad. Med. irel.; Inst. Obst. & Gyn. RCPI. Prev: Sen. Regist. (O & G) Roy. United Hosp. Bath; Clin. Research Fell. Univ. Dept. O & G Bristol Matern. Hosp.; Regist. Nat. Matern. Hosp. Dub.

CAHILL, Declan John 26 Arkwright Road, South Croydon CR2 0LL — MB BS 1993 Lond.

CAHILL, Donal Joseph 76 Harpenden Lane, Redbourn, St Albans AL3 7PB — MB ChB 1993 Manch.

CAHILL, John (retired) 10 Kettering Close, Calcot, Reading RG31 7DF — MB BCh BAO 1949 NUI; MRCGP 1972. Prev: Orthop. Regist. Mt. Gold Orthop. Hosp. Plymouth.

CAHILL, John Francis Bosco The Old Cross Keys, Princes Risborough, Aylesbury Tel: 01844 44488 Fax: 01844 274737; 3 Chinnor Road, Thame OX9 3LN Tel: 01844 213531 — MB BS 1980 Lond.; MA Oxf. 1981; MRCP (UK) 1983; MRCGP (Distinc.) 1985. (St. Thos.)

CAHILL, John Michael 58B Lambeth Road, London SE1 7PP — MB BCh BAO 1991 NUI.

CAHILL, John Patrick (retired) 10 Fairfield Meadows, Southwick, Trowbridge BA14 9RT — LRCPI & LM, LRCSI & LM 1950. Prev: Ho. Phys. Newmarket Gen. Hosp. & Fermanagh Co. Hosp. Enniskillen.

CAHILL, Mary Josephine 22 Union Road, Exeter EX4 6HZ — MB BS 1976 Mysore.

CAHILL, May Frances Anne The London Fields Medical Centres, 38-44 Broadway Market, London E8 4QJ Tel: 020 7254 2883 Fax: 020 7254 2066 — MB BCh BAO 1983 NUI; MRCGP 1989; DObst RCPI 1985. Core Tutor St. Bart. Med. Coll. Lond.; Exec. Mem. Core Gp. Hackney GP Forum. Prev: SHO (Gyn. & Urol.) Hammersmith Hosp. Lond.; SHO (O & G) Regional Hosp. Galway; SHO (Obst.) Hammersmith Hosp. Lond.

CAHILL, Patricia Helen Mary 20 Arkwright Road, Sanderstead, South Croydon CR2 0LD — MB BS 1987 Lond.

CAHILL, Thomas Edward Dolby Wlds, 22 Bath Road, Beckington, Bath BA11 6SW — MB BS 1988 Lond.

CAHIR, John Gerard Radiology Box 219, Addenbrookes NHS Trust, Long Rd, Cambridge CB3 0HR — MB ChB 1994 Manch.; MRCP 1997. SPR Radiol. Addenbrookes NHS Trust, Long Rd, Camb.

CAHN, Anthony Peter 76 Rokeby Road, Brockley, London SE4 1DF — MB BS 1986 Lond.

CAIACH, Siân Mair Department of Orthopaedics, Prince Philip Hospital, Bryngwyn Mawr, Dafen, Llanelli SA14 8QF; Parc Farm House, Trimsaranm Rd,, Llanelli SA15 4RD Email: siancaiach@hotmail.com — MB BS 1981 Lond.; FRCS Glas. 1987; MRCS Eng. LRCP Lond. 1981; Postgrad. Dip. (Forens. Med.) Glas. 1990. (Char. Cross) Cons. Orthop. Surg. P. Philip Hosp. LLa.lli. Prev: Sen. Regist. (Orthop. Surg.) Freeman Hosp. Newc.; Regist. (Orthop. Surg.) Dundee Roy. Infirm.; Demonst. (Anat.) Univ. Bristol.

CAIGER, Alice Catharine (retired) The Priory, Paternoster Row, Ottery St Mary EX11 1DP — MB ChB 1923 Sheff.

CAIGER, Bella Noel The Surgery, 262 Devonshire Avenue, Southsea PO4 9EH Tel: 023 9273 1358; Syme House, 33 Beach Road, Emsworth PO10 7HR Tel: 01243 370771 — MB BS 1983 Lond.; MRCGP 1988; DRCOG 1986. Prev: SHO (O & G & Paediat.) St. Mary's Hosp. Portsmouth; SHO (Psychiat.) St. Jas. Hosp. Portsmouth.

CAIGER, Michael The Surgery, 12 Victoria Road South, Southsea PO5 2BZ Tel: 023 9282 3857; Syme House, 33 Beach Road, Emsworth PO10 7HR — MB BS 1984 Lond.; BSc (Hons.) Lond. 1978, MB BS 1984; MRCGP 1989. Prev: Ho. Phys. Epsom Dist. Hosp.; Ho. Surg. RN Hosp. Haslar.

CAIN, Mr Angus John Woodhill Cottage, Barry, Carnoustie DD7 7SB Tel: 01382 532671 Email: angus@guscain.demon.co.uk — MB ChB 1991 Dundee; FRCS Ed. 1996.

CAIN, Anne Christine Mary 19 St Anthony's Crescent, Fulwood, Preston PR2 3GH — MB ChB 1984 Leeds; MB ChB Leeds l984.

CAIN, Arthur Richard Robyn (retired) 24 The Empire, Grand Parade, Bath BA2 4DF Tel: 01225 480665 — BM BCh 1956 Oxf.; MA Oxf. 1956; FRCP Lond. 1977, M 1963; FRCPCH 1997; DCH Eng. 1962; DObst RCOG 1958. Prev: Cons. Paediat. Bath. Health Dist.

CAIN, Mr David Lawrence Dorset County Hospital, William Avenue, Dorchester DT1 2UY — BM 1977 Soton.; BSc (Hons.) Wales 1972; FRCS Eng. 1981; FFAEM 1993. Cons. A & E Dorset Co. Hosp. Dorchester. Socs: Brit. Assn. Emerg. Med. Prev: Sen. Regist. (A & E) St. Richards Hosp. Chichester; Regist. (A & E) Poole Gen. Hosp.

CAIN, Juliet Evelyn Northgate Medical Centre, 10 Upper Northgate Street, Chester CH1 4EE Tel: 01244 379906 Fax: 01244 379703 — MB ChB 1987 Liverp.; DRCOG 1991. Socs: Chester & N. Wales Med. Soc. Prev: SHO (O & G) Liverp. Matern. Hosp.; SHO (Paediat.) Alder Hey childr. Hosp.; SHO (Radiother. & Oncol.) Clatterbridge Hosp. Wirral.

CAIN, Patricia Anne dept. Of Anaesthetics, Royal Oldham Hospital, Oldham OL1 2JH — MB ChB 1971 Manch.; FFA RCS Eng. 1976; DA Eng. 1973. Cons. Anaesth. Hull Roy. Infirm.

CAIN, Paul Andrew 33 West Hatch Manor, Ruislip HA4 8QU — MB ChB 1985 Bristol; AFOM RCP Lond. 1996; DAvMed FOM RCP Lond. 1993. Sen. Regist. (Occupat. Med.) Middlx. Socs: Soc. Occupat. Med.

CAIN, Paul Terence 19 Portland Place, Northampton NN1 4DH — MB BS 1994 Lond.

CAIN, Sharon 91 Mansfield Close, Birchwood, Warrington WA3 6RN — MRCS Eng. LRCP Lond. 1980; BSc Lond. 1977, MD 1993, MB BS 1980; MRCP (UK) 1986; FFA RCS Eng. 1984.

CAIN, Mr Terence John 82 Main Street, Skidby, Cottingham HU16 5TH — MB ChB 1969 Manch.; FRCS Ed. 1974. Cons. Orthop. Surg. Hull Roy. Infirm.

CAINE, David John The Court House, Dorstone, Hereford HR3 6AW — MB BS 1992 Lond.

CAINE, Jacqueline Louise 25 Avenue Terrace, York YO3 6AX — MB ChB 1996 Sheff.

CAINE, John Michael 9 Denton Drive, Wallasey CH45 7QS — MB ChB 1985 Aberd.

CAINE, Sarah Elizabeth 36 Queen Victoria Road, Westbury Park, Bristol BS6 7PE Tel: 0117 973 6743 Email: syncopal@msn.com; Bristol Royal Infirmary, Upper Maudlin St, Bristol BS1 Tel: 0117 923 0000 — MB BS 1991 Lond.; MRCP (UK) 1996. (Roy. Free Hosp.) Specialist Regist. (Geriats. & Gen. Med.) Bristol Roy. Infirm. Socs: Brit. Geriat. Soc. Prev: SHO Rotat. (Med.) United Bristol Healthcare NHS Trust; SHO (c/o the Elderly) St. Woolos Hosp. Newport; SHO (Orthop. & A & E) P.ss Margt. Hosp. Swindon.

CAIRA, Janet Christine Edith The Surgery, 39 Wood Lane, Elm Park, Hornchurch RM12 5HX Tel: 01708 450902 Fax: 01708 470875; 13 Ingleglen, Hornchurch RM11 3BB — MB BS 1967 Lond.; MRCS Eng. LRCP Lond. 1967.

CAIRD, Catherine Jane Boundary House Surgery, Boundary House, Mount Lane, Bracknell RG12 9PG Tel: 01344 483900 Fax: 01344 862203; 20 Goldsmith Way, Crowthorne RG45 7QP Tel: 01344 776243 — MB ChB 1983 Manch.; MRCGP 1987; DRCOG 1985. Prev: Trainee GP N.wick Pk. Hosp. Harrow VTS.

CAIRD, Francis Irvine (retired) 102 Victoria Road, Oxford OX2 7QE Tel: 01865 556426 Fax: 01865 556426 — BM BCh Oxf. 1953; DM Oxf. 1960; FRCP Glas. 1978, M 1975; FRCP Lond. 1973, M 1955. Prev: Prof. Geriat. Med. Univ. Glas.

CAIRD, George Robert Alexander House, 2 Salisbury Road, Farnborough GU14 7AW Tel: 01252 541155 — MSc 1999 London Univ.; MB BCh BAO Dub. 1968; MRCP (UK) 1972; MRCGP 1981, F 1993. (T.C. Dub.) Assoc. Dean (Gen. Pract.) K.S.S. Deanery; Internat. Developm. Adviser, RCGP. Socs: BMA & Assn. Course Organisers.; ex-Provost S. W. Thames Fac. RCGP. Prev: Assoc. Adviser (Gen. Pract.) SW Thames; Clin. Path. Bristol Roy. Infirm.; SHO Med. Soton. Univ. Hosp.

CAIRD, John Dudley Dreaper Lakefield Cottage, Shield Hill, Staley, Corbridge NE45 5LD — MB BCh BAO 1993 Dub.

CAIRD, Lucy Elizabeth Raigmost Hospital, Old Pertu Road, Inverness IV2 3UJ — MD 1993 Aberd.; MB ChB 1983; MRCOG 1988. Cons. in Obst. and Gyn., Raigmost Hosp., Inverness. Socs: Brit. Manopause Soc.; Brit. Fertil. Soc.

CAIRN, Abigail Marlene Clarence House, 3 Vicarage Lane, Rhuddlan, Rhyl LL18 2UE — MB BS 1997 Lond.

***CAIRN, Alexia Clementia Shaheen** Wychwood, Anchor Lane, Canewdon, Rochford SS4 3PA — MB BS 1994 Lond.; BSc Lond. 1993, MB BS 1994.

CAIRN, Julius Wasif Niaz Clairvoir 47 Thompson Way, Rickmansworth WD3 8GP Tel: 01923 333832 Email: jcairn@rbh.nthames.nhs.uk — MB BS 1991 Lond.; MRCP (UK) 1995. (Lond. Hosp. Med. Coll.) Specialist Regist. (Respirat. Med. & Gen. Med.); Research Regist. in Respirat. & Transpl. Med. Socs: Brit. Thorac. Soc.; Roy. Coll. Phys. Lond.; MDU. Prev: Regist. (Transpl. Med.) Harefield Hosp. Middlx.; Regist. (Respirat. Med.) Hillingdon Hosp. Middlx.; Regist. (Respirat. Med.) Centr. Middlx. Hosp. Lond.

CAIRNCROSS, Robert George Medical Education Unit, NHS Executive, Quarry House, Quarry Hill, Leeds LS2 7UE Tel: 01132 545856; 1 Moor Fields, Cawood Road, Wistow, Selby YO8 3YN Tel: 01757 268088 — MB ChB Aberd. 1968; FRCP Ed. 1987; MRCP (UK) 1974; FRCGP 1994, M 1976. Sen. Med. Off. DoH NHS Exec. Leeds. Prev: Dep. Sec. Scott. Counc. Postgrad. Med. Educat.

CAIRNS, Alastair John Derby Farm House, Treales Road, Treales, Preston PR4 3SR — MB ChB 1998 Dund.; MB ChB Dund 1998.

CAIRNS, Alison Department of Histopathology, Algernon Firth Institute of Pathology, Leeds General Infirmary, Leeds LS1 3EX — MB ChB 1992 Sheff.

CAIRNS, Andrew John The St Lawrence Surgery, 79 St. Lanewrence Avenue, Worthing BN14 7JL Tel: 01903 237346 — MB BS 1970 Lond.; MSc Univ. Lond. 1993; MRCGP 1976; Dip. Gen. Biochem. Lond. 1967. (Middlesex) Prev: Ho. Surg. Centr. Middlx. Hosp.; Ho. Phys. Harefield Hosp. Middlx.

CAIRNS, Andrew Paul Department of Rheumatology, Musgrave Park Hospital, Belfast BT9 7JB — MB BCh BAO 1995 Belf.; MD 2001 Queen's Univ. Belfast; MRCP (UK) 1998. (Qu. Univ. Belf.) Specialist Regist. Rheum., Musgrave Pk. Hosp. Belf. Socs: Irish Soc. For Rheumatol.; Ulster Soc. Of Internal Med.; Brit. Soc. For Rheum. Prev: Clin. Research Fell. Roy. Vict. Hosp. Belf.; LAT Regist. (Med.) Antrim Area Hosp.; LAT Regist. (Med.) Craigavon Area Hosp.

CAIRNS, Andrew William The Old Coach House, Hillbrow Road, Liss GU33 7PX — MB 1981 Camb.; MA Camb. 1980, MB 1981, BChir 1980.

CAIRNS, Carole Mary 18 Upper Grove, Dunmurry, Belfast BT17 0EL — MB BCh BAO 1983 Belf.; Cert. Family Plann. JCC 1987.

CAIRNS, Charles Stanley (retired) Cliffton, Torwoodhill, Rhu, Helensburgh G84 8LF Tel: 01436 820409 — MB ChB 1955 Ed.; FFA RCS Eng. 1964. Cons. Anaesth. W.. Infirm, Roy. Hosp. Sick Childr. & Qu. Mother's Hosp. Glas. Prev: Sen. Regist. (Anaesth.) Radcliffe Infirm. Oxf.

CAIRNS, Christopher John Stuart 8/7 Sienna Gardens, Edinburgh EH9 1PG — MB ChB 1993 Ed.

CAIRNS, David Haresfield House Surgery, 6-10 Bath Road, Worcester WR5 3EJ Tel: 01905 763161 Fax: 01905 767016; Perch Cottage, Post Office Lane, Kempsey, Worcester WR5 3NS — MB BCh BAO 1969 Belf.; DCH RCP Lond. 1973; DObst. RCOG 1971. (Belf.) Prev: Regist. (Anaesth.) Ronkswood Hosp. Worcs.

***CAIRNS, David Andrew** 6 Forrest Road, Edinburgh EH1 2QN Email: david.cairns@btinternet.com; 48 Chichester Park Centre, Ballymena BT42 4BE — MB ChB 1997 Ed.; BSc (Med. Sci.) 1995.

CAIRNS, David Archibald Orkney (retired) 28 Wilbury Road, Hove BN3 3JP Tel: 01273 207426 Fax: 01273 329751 — MB BS 1955 Lond.; MRCS Eng. LRCP Lond. 1955; DObst RCOG 1959; MRCGP 1969. Prev: SHO (Surg.) St. Bart. Hosp. Lond.

CAIRNS, Mr David William Linaver Farm, Lee Common, Great Missenden HP16 9JL — MB 1962 Camb.; BA Camb. 1958, MB 1962, BChir 1961; FRCS Ed. 1967; FRCS Eng. 1967. (Middlx.) Cons. (Gen. Surg.) High Wycombe Health Dist. Socs: Fell. Roy. Soc.

Med. Prev: Sen. Regist. (Vasc. Surg.) & Regist. (Urol.) Middlx. Hosp. Lond.; Resid. Surg. Off. St. Mark's Hosp. Lond.

CAIRNS, Denise Anne 1 Cramond Vale, Edinburgh EH4 6RB — MB BS 1967 Durh.

CAIRNS, Elizabeth Emma Dumbarton Health Centre, Station Road, Dumbarton G82 1PW Tel: 01389 602644 Fax: 01389 602624 — MB ChB 1966 Bristol. (Bristol) GP Dumbarton.

CAIRNS, Harold (retired) 114 Newport Road, Cardiff CF24 1DG — MRCS Eng. LRCP Lond. 1951; FRCGP 1976, M 1965. Med. Adviser Welsh Hosps. & Health Servs. Assn. Prev: Capt. RAMC.

CAIRNS, Hugh Stephen The Renal Unit, King's Healthcare, Denmark Hill, London SE5 9RS Tel: 020 7346 6236 Fax: 020 7346 6472 — MB BS 1979 Lond.; MD Lond. 1992; FRCP Lond. 1997; MRCP (UK) 1982; FRCP (UK) 1997. (Guy's Hosp.) Cons. Renal Phys. King's Coll. Hosp. Lond. Prev: Sen. Regist. (Nephrol.) UCL Med. Sch. Lond.

CAIRNS, Ivor Robert Lisburn Health Centre, Linenhall Street, Lisburn BT28 1LU Tel: 028 9260 3203 Fax: 028 9250 1311 — MB BCh BAO 1990 Belf.; MRCGP 1995; DRCOG 1995; DFFP 1994; DME RCPI 1993. (Qu. Univ. Belf.) Socs: Ulster Med. Soc.

CAIRNS, John Philip Greenfield, Northern Avenue, Much Hoole, Preston PR4 4GL — MB ChB 1997 Manch.

CAIRNS, Luth Margaret 224 Coombe Lane, London SW20 0QT — MB BS 1998 Lond.; MB BS Lond 1998.

CAIRNS, Mary 7 Ballinard Road, Broughty Ferry, Dundee DD5 3LG — MB ChB 1996 Dundee.

CAIRNS, Michael John 36 Connaught Place, Edinburgh EH6 4RQ — MB ChB 1998 Dund.; MB ChB Dund 1998; Msc Dund. 1993; Bsc Herlot-Watt 1991. GP Train. Scheme, Tayside.

CAIRNS, Neil James William Icknield Way Cottage, High St., Barney, Royston SG8 8JA — MB BS 1976 Newc.

CAIRNS, Pamela Anne St. Micheal's Hospital, Bristol BS2 8EG Tel: 0117 928 5824 Fax: 0117 928 5751 Email: pamela.cairns@ubht.swest.nhs.uk; Tel: 0117 973 1121 — MB BCh BAO 1987 Belf.; MD 1999 Queens Uni. Belf.; MRCP 1990 Glas.; DCH 1990 Glas.; 1998 MRCPCH Lond. Cons. Neonatologist Assoc. Director Neonat. Intens. Care Unit, UBHT, Bristol. Socs: Mem. of the Roy. Coll. of Paediat. and Child Health; Mem. of Brit. Assn. of Perinatal Med.

CAIRNS, Pamela Freda Park Grove Medical Centre, 22B Park Grove Terrace, Edinburgh EH4 7NX Tel: 0131 312 6600 Fax: 0131 312 7798; 20 Ravelston House Park, Edinburgh EH4 3LU Tel: 0131 332 7308 — MB ChB 1978 Ed.; MRCGP 1990.

CAIRNS, Peter Norman Edward 11 Farnham Park, Bangor BT20 3SR — MB ChB 1998 Ed.; MB ChB Ed 1998.

CAIRNS, Richard (retired) 165 Station Road, Cropston, Leicester LE7 7HH Tel: 0116 230 2154 — BChir 1933 Camb.; MB 1942.

CAIRNS, Richard James, MBE 11 Bilwell, Long Crendon, Aylesbury HP18 9AD Tel: 01844 201465 — MB ChB 1941 Glas. (Glas.) Prev: Capt. RAMC.

CAIRNS, Robert John (retired) Aspen House, Addington, West Malling ME19 5AX Tel: 01732 842250 — MB BS 1943 Lond.; FRCP Lond. 1968, M 1945; MRCS Eng. LRCP Lond. 1943. Prev: Cons. Dermat. St. Bart. Hosp. Rochester & Kent & Sussex Hosp. Tunbridge Wells.

CAIRNS, Stephen Andrew Derby Farm House, Treales Road, Treales, Kirkham, Preston PR4 3SR — MB BS 1971 Lond.; BSc (1st cl. Hons.) Lond. 1968, MD 1981; FRCP Lond. 1989; MRCP (UK) 1974. (Westm.) Cons. Phys. Roy. Preston Acute Hosps. NHS Trust. Prev: Sen. Regist. & Tutor Manch. Roy. Infirm. & Manch. Univ.; Regist. (Med.) Bristol Roy. Infirm.; SHO (Med.) Soton. Univ. Hosp. Gp.

CAIRNS, Stuart Robert Fulking Farmhouse, Fulking, Henfield BN5 9LX Tel: 01273 857549 — MB BS 1974 Lond.; MSc Lond. 1982, MD 1984; FRCP Lond. 1994. (King's Coll. Hosp.) Cons. Gen. Phys. & Gastroenterol. Roy. Sussex Co. Brighton. Socs: Brit. Soc. Gastroenterol.; Amer. Soc. Gastrointestinal Endoscopy. Prev: Sen. Regist. (Med. Gastroenterol.) The Middlx. Hosp. Lond.; Hon. Sen. Regist. (Med.) N.wick Pk. Hosp. & New Addenbrooke's Hosp. Camb.

CAIRNS, Stuart Ronald McDonald French Weir Health Centre, French Weir Avenue, Taunton TA1 1NW Tel: 01823 331381 Fax: 01823 323689; 10 Windmill Hill, North Curry, Taunton TA3 6LY Email: stuart.cairns@talk21.com — MB BS 1987 Lond.; MRCGP 1992; DRCOG 1991; DCH RCP Lond. 1990. (The London Hospital)

CAIRNS, Mr Terence Shawn c/o Transform, Lynwood, The Firs, Bowdon, Altrincham WA14 2TQ — MB BCh 1972 Witwatersrand; FRCS Ed. 1977.

CAIRNS, Thomas Shettleston Health Centre, 420 Old Shettleston Road, Glasgow G32 7JZ Tel: 0141 778 9191 Fax: 0141 778 9916; Melfort, 19 Peveril Avenue, Burnside, Rutherglen, Glasgow G73 4RD Tel: 0141 634 5544 — MB ChB 1952 Glas.

CAIRNS, Thomas David Hector Transplant Unit, 4th Floor, Clarence Wing, St Mary's Hospital, Praed St., London W2 1NY — MB BS 1984 Lond.

CAISLEY, John (retired) Priorsgate, Carrington Court, Birchy Close, Dickens Heath, Solihull B90 1QL Tel: 01564 824894 Fax: 01564 824894 — MRCS Eng. LRCP Lond. 1948; MD 1979. Prev: GP Macclesfield.

CAISLEY, Philip John 3 Ploverfield Close, Ashington NE63 8LX — MB BS 1988 Newc.

CAITHNESS, George Sinclair Landfall, 30 The Village, Thorp Arch, Wetherby LS23 7AG Tel: 01937 843316 — MB BCh BAO Dub. 1936. (T. C. Dub.) Socs: BMA. Prev: Med. Off. DHSS; Dep. Asst. Dir. Gen. AMD War Office; Lt.-Col. RAMC, Med. Specialist.

CAITHNESS, George Sutherland, MBE (retired) 16 Queen's Terrace, St Andrews KY16 9QF — MB ChB 1947 St. And.; MRCGP 1961; DObst RCOG 1948. Prev: Regist. (O & G) & Sen. Cas. Off. Roy. Infirm. Dundee.

CAITHNESS, Julian Sinclair Marblearch Terrace Surgery, 1 Marblearch Terrace, Florence Court Demesne, Enniskillen BT92 1EF Tel: 028 6634 8275 — MB BS 1972 Lond.; MRCP (UK) 1975; MRCGP 1978. GP FlorenceCt.. Prev: Cons. Primary Care Milit. Hosp. Riyadh, Saudi Arabia; SHO (O & G) N.ampton Gen. Hosp.; Trainee Gen. Pract. Camb.

CAKEBREAD, Stephen Robert The Health Centre, Iveldale Drive, Shefford SG17 5AD Tel: 01462 814899 Fax: 01462 815322; The Poplars, Clifton Road, Stanford, Biggleswade SG18 9JJ — BM 1978 Soton.; MRCGP 1983; DRCOG 1981. Prev: Trainee GP I. of Wight VTS.

CALAGHAN, Nigel Philip 51 Harland Road, Bridlington YO16 6RA — MB ChB 1988 Leeds; MRCGP 1996.

CALAMINICI, Mariarita Garden Flat 12, Goldhurst Terrace, London NW6 3HU — State Exam Reggio Calabria 1988; MD Reggio Calabria 1988; PhD Lond. 1996; MRC Path Lond.1998. Cons.(Histopathol.) St Barts Hosp. Lond. Socs: RCP; BNS.

CALAMVOKIS, John George Med. United, 591 Fulham Road, London SW6 5UA; 218 High Street, Burbage, Marlborough SN8 3AR Tel: 01672 810997 — Ptychio Iatrikes 1965 Athens. Med. Off. Med. United Lond. Prev: Regist. (Orthop.) Lister Hosp. Hitchin & S.end Gen. Hosp.; Sen. Orthop. Surg. Hygia Hosp., Athens.

CALATAYUD REVERT, Antonio 1St Floor Flat, 20 Denning Road, London NW3 1ST — LMS 1988 Valencia.

CALCOTT, Ronald Douglas Brackenhurst, 36 Beech Avenue, Worcester WR3 8PY — MB BS 1944 Lond.; MRCS Eng. LRCP Lond. 1944; DO Eng. 1952. (Westm.)

CALDAS, Carlos Manuel Simao da Silva 41 Hamble Street, London SW6 2RT — Lic Med 1984 Lisbon; Lic Med. Lisbon 1984.

CALDBECK, Carole Rosemary Caldbeck and Partners, Hurst Close, Gossops Green, Crawley RH11 8TY Tel: 01293 527138 Fax: 01293 522571; 31 Clitherow Gardens, East Park, Southgate, Crawley RH10 6TT Tel: 01293 535884 Fax: 01293 522571 — MB BCh BAO 1979 Belf.; DA RCPSI 1984. (Queens University Belfast) GP Crawley; Police Surg. Crawley. Socs: BMA & APS.

CALDER, Alexander Stuart Carmichael The Clifton Health Centre, Water Lane, Clifton, York YO30 6PS Tel: 01904 623259 — MB BS 1972 Lond.; Dobst RCOG 1976; MRCGP 1976.

CALDER, Alistair Duncan Brookside, Hampool Cottages, Bickleigh, Plymouth PL6 7AN — BM BCh 1997 Oxf.

CALDER, Professor Andrew Alexander Department of Obstetrics & Gynaecology, Centre for Reproductive Biology, 37 Chalmers St., Edinburgh EH3 9EW Tel: 0131 229 2575 Fax: 0131 229 2408; 21 Braid Avenue, Edinburgh EH10 4SR Tel: 0131 447 0490 — MB ChB 1968 Glas.; MD Glas. 1978; FRCS Ed. 1994; FRCP Ed. 1993; FRCP Glas. 1987, M 1985; FRCOG 1984, M 1972. (Glas.) Prof. O & G Univ. Edin. & Hon. Cons. Obst. Simpson Memor. Matern. Pavil.

Edin.; Hon. Cons. Gyn. Roy. Infirm. Edin. Socs: Blair Bell Res. Soc. & Soc. Study of Fertil.; Munro Kerr Soc. Study Reproductive Biol. (Ex-Sec., Ex-Chairm.). Prev: Research Fell. Nuffield Dept. O & G Univ. Oxf.; Sen. Lect. (O & G) Univ. Glas.; Cons. O & G Glas. Roy. Infirm. & Roy. Matern. Hosp. Glas.

CALDER, Brian Downie Medical Centre, 12 East King St., Helensburgh G84 7QL Tel: 01436 673366 Fax: 01436 679715 — MB ChB 1971 Glas.; MRCGP 1975; DObst RCOG 1974. (Glas.)

CALDER, Carolyn Brown Baillieston Health Centre, 20 Muirside Road, Baillieston, Glasgow G69 7AD Tel: 0141 531 8040 — MB ChB 1984 Glas.; MRCGP 1988.

CALDER, Carolyn Elizabeth 20 Fernville Road, Newcastle upon Tyne NE3 4HT — MB ChB 1997 Sheff.

CALDER, Mr David Andrew 4 Belvedere Place, Norwich NR4 7PP — MB BChir 1990 Camb.; FRCS Ed. 1994.

CALDER, Elizabeth 12 The Drive, Hartley, Plymouth PL3 5SU — MB BS 1965 Lond.; MRCS Eng. LRCP Lond. 1965; DA Eng. 1968. (St. Bart.) Med. Asst. Renal Unit Freedom Fields Hosp. Plymouth. Socs: Renal Assn. & Europ. Dialysis & Transpl. Assn. Prev: SHO (Anaesth.) Freedom Fields Hosp. Plymouth.

CALDER, Elizabeth Jane Margaret 29 Cessnock Road, Galston KA4 8LR — MB ChB 1981 Ed.; BSc Med Sci Ed. 1978; MRCPsych 1987.

CALDER, Francis Robert Flat 63, The Alders, Aldrington Road, London SW16 1TW — MB ChB 1992 Liverp.

CALDER, Gillian Ruth West End Surgery, 19 Chilwell Road, Beeston, Nottingham NG9 1EH Tel: 0115 925 4443 Fax: 0115 922 1255 — BM BS 1983 Nottm.; BMedSci Nottm. 1981; MRCGP 1988; DRCOG 1986. Prev: GP Welbeck Surg. Nottm.; SHO (Palliat. Med.) St. Gemma's Hospice, Leeds.

CALDER, Ian 28 Lydon Road, London SW4 0HW Tel: 020 7720 9279 — MB ChB 1971 Liverp.; FFA RCS Eng. 1976; DObst RCOG 1974. (Liverp.) Cons. Anaesth. Nat. Hosp. Nerv. Dis. Qu. Sq. Lond. & Roy. Free; Hosp. Lond. Prev: Sen. Regist. St. Thos. Hosp. Lond.; Ho. Off. Liverp. Roy. Infirm.

CALDER, Mr Ian Grant 5 Davenport Road, Coventry CV5 6QA — MB ChB 1977 Birm.; FRCS Eng. 1982. Cons. Ophth. Coventry HA.

CALDER, Ian Maddison, TD, OStJ, Col. L/RAMC Thorpe, Huntingdon Road, Girton, Cambridge CB3 0LG Tel: 01223 277220 Fax: 01223 276490 Email: calderpath@hotmail.com — MB ChB 1962 St. And.; DSc Dund 1992; MD Dundee 1976; MRCP (UK) 1996; MRCPath 1989; FRCPath 1995; FFOM RCP Lond. 1990, MFOM 1985; DMJ (Path.) Soc. Apoth. Lond. 1971. (St. And.) E. & N. Herts. NHS Trust, Lister Hosp., Stevenage Herts.; Staff Dept. Morbid Anat. Inst. Path. Lond. Hosp.; Research assoc. Fell., welcome Inst. of comparative Neurol., Univ. of Camb.. Madingley Rd., Camb. CB3 0EN. Socs: Fell. Roy. Soc. Med.; Assn. Clin. Patrol.; Brit. Assoc. Prev: Cas. Off. Norf. & Norwich Hosp.; Resid. Obst. Off. Ipswich & E. Suff. Hosp. (Heath Rd. Wing); Jun. Asst. Pathologist, Univ. of Camb.

CALDER, Mr James David Forbes 81 Sandycombe Road, Kew, Richmond TW9 2EP Tel: 0208 948 7736 Fax: 0208 948 7736 — MB BS 1991 Lond.; FRCS Lond. 1995. Specialist Regist. Rotat. (Orthop.) St. Mary's & Hammersmith Hosps. Lond.; Research Fell., RCS. Prev: SHO Rotat. St. Richard's Hosp. Chichester; SHO Roy. Brompton Hosp. Lond.; SHO Roy. Nat. Orthop. Hosp. Lond.

CALDER, James George Castlegait Surgery, 32 Castle Street, Montrose DD10 8AG Tel: 01674 672554 Fax: 01674 675025; 28 Dorward Road, Montrose DD10 8SB Tel: 01674 672554 — MB ChB 1974 Ed.; MRCGP 1978.

CALDER, Jan 4 Dagmar Gr, Nottingham NG3 4JE — MB ChB 1997 Ed.

CALDER, John (retired) 9 Pitbauchlie Bank, Dunfermline KY11 8DP — MB ChB Ed. 1946. Prev: Cons. Microbiol. Fife Area Laborat..

CALDER, John Forbes Department of Radiology, Victoria Infirmary, Glasgow G42 9TY Tel: 0141 201 6000 Fax: 0141 201 5497; 145 Clober Road, Milngavie, Glasgow G62 7LS Tel: 0141 956 3535 Fax: 0141 201 5497 Email: john.calder@gvic.scot.nhs.uk — MB ChB Glas. 1966; FRCP Glas. 1995; MRCP Glas. 1993; FRCR 1975; DMRD 1973; DObst RCOG 1968. Cons. Radiol. Vict. Infirm. Glas.; Hon. Clin. Sen. Lect. Glas. Univ. Socs: BMA; (Ex pres.) Scot. Radiol. Soc.; BMUS. Prev: Sen. Lect. (Radiol.) Univ. Aberd.; Govt. Med. Off. Malawi; Sen. Lect. (Radiol.) Univ. Nairobi, Kenya.

CALDER, Kathleen (retired) Ascelpion, Freuchie, Cupar KY15 7ET Tel: 01337 857323 — MB ChB 1959 Glas.; DCH RCPS Glas. 1962; DObst RCOG 1961. Prev: Clin. Med. Off. (Child Health) Fife HB.

***CALDER, Lynda** Glengate, Dornoch Road, Bonar Bridge, Ardgay IV24 3EB Tel: 01863 766532 — MB ChB Aberd. 1996; BSc (Med. Sci.) Hons. Path. Aberd. 1996.

CALDER, Malcolm William 7 College Road, Exeter EX1 1TE — MB BS 1962 Lond.; DObst RCOG 1966. (St. Mary's)

CALDER, Margaret Alexandra (retired) 43 Braid Road, Edinburgh EH10 6AW Tel: 0131 447 7767 — MD 1962 Ed.; MB ChB 1945. Prev: Cons. Microbiol. City Hosp. Edin.

CALDER, Margaret Helen Stewart (retired) 212 Saltshouse Road, Kingston upon Thames HU8 9HH — MB ChB Glas. 1947. Prev: Clin. Asst. (Gyn.) Gavin Brown Clin. P.ss Roy. Hosp. Hull.

CALDER, Morag Anne Clifton, 3 Hillside Crescent, Langholm DG13 0EE — MB ChB 1991 Ed.; DRCOG 1994; DCH RCP Lond. 1993; DTM & H Liverp. 1992. Med. Off. Opuwo Hosp. Opuwo Kunone, Namiba, S. Afr. Prev: SHO (O & G) E. Gen. Hosp. Edin.; SHO (A & E) Law Hosp. Carluke; SHO (Infec. Dis.) Seacroft Hosp. Leeds.

CALDER, Nicholas John 145 Clober Road, Milngavie, Glasgow G62 7LS — MB ChB 1997 Sheff. SHO (Surg., A&E), Sutherland Hosp., Sydney Australia.

CALDER, Peter Robert 62A Aberdeen Park, London N5 2BL — MB BS 1993 Lond.

CALDER, Sandra Catherine (retired) Ardnas, 29 Thorp Avenue, Morpeth NE61 1JR Tel: 01670 513937 Fax: 01670 513937 Email: calder@clara.net — MB ChB Ed. 1960. Prev: Clin. Med. Off. N.d. AHA.

CALDER, Serena Janet Holbrook Lane Surgery, 268 Holbrook Lane, Coventry CV6 4DD Tel: 024 7668 8340 Fax: 024 7663 7526; 12 Applecross Close, Westwood Heath, Coventry CV4 8JW Tel: 02476 421521 — MB ChB 1974 Glas. Socs: BMA. Prev: SHO (Obst.) William Smellie Hosp. Lanark.; Regist. (Geriat.) S. Gen. Hosp. Glas.; Regist. (Med.) Stobhill Hosp. Glas.

CALDER, Sheila Anne Block A, Clerkseat Building, Royal Cornhill Hospital, Cornhill Road, Aberdeen AB9 2XF Tel: 01224 663131 Fax: 01224 404466 Email: sheila.calder@apct.grampian.scot.nhs.uk; Tel: 01224 732878 Email: sheila.calder@ukgateway.net — MB ChB 1977 Aberd.; FRCPsych 2000; MRCPsych 1986. Cons. Psychiat. Roy. Cornhill Hosp. Aberd. & Hon. Sen. Lect. Dept. Ment. Health Univ. Aberd. Prev: Sen. Regist. (Psychiat.) Roy. Cornhill Hosp. Aberd.; Research Fell. (Ment. Health) Aberd.; Ho. Surg. & Ho. Off. Phys. Aberd. Teach. Hosps.

CALDER, Sigrid Karin 9/8 Ardmillan Place, Edinburgh EH11 2JU — MB ChB 1991 Ed.

CALDER, Mr Stuart James Dept. Orthopaedics, Leeds General Infirmary, Great George Street, Leeds LS1 3EX Tel: 0113 392 6767 — MB ChB 1986 Bristol; FRCS Eng. 1990; MD Leicester 1997; FRCS (Orth.) 1996. (Bristol University) Cons. Othopaedic Surg., Lees Gen. Infirm. Prev: Regist. Rotat. (Orthop.) Leeds.; Knee Fell., 1997-8 (Brisbane, Dr. Peter Myers.

CALDER, Valerie Helen 3 The Avenue, Corbridge NE45 5JB Tel: 01434 632784 — MB BS 1961 Durh. (Durh.) SCMO S. Tyneside HA.

CALDER, William Norman, MBE 9 Belvidere Street, Aberdeen AB25 2QS — MB ChB 1939 Aberd.

CALDERA, Saliya Rabindranath Marius Kapugama S 84 Woodville Drive, Portsmouth PO1 2TG — MB BS 1989 Lond.

CALDERBANK, Stephanie Jayne 312 Telegraph Road, Heswall, Wirral CH60 6SL; 101 Minster Court, Liverpool L7 3QD Tel: 0151 707 2174 — MB ChB 1996 Liverp.; BClinSci Liverp. 1994. SHO. Paediat. Whiston Hosp., Prescot. Socs: LMSS. Prev: SHO.Paediat., Wirral NHS Trust; SHO (Psychiat.) Wirral & W. Chesh. Community NHS Trust; SHO (A&E), Whiston.

CALDERHEAD, Richard John Earnswood Medical Centre, 92 Victoria Street, Crewe CW1 2JR Tel: 01270 257255 Fax: 01270 501943; Drake Cottage, Drake Lane, Acton, Nantwich CW5 8PD — MB ChB 1982 Ed.; BSc Ed. 1979, MB ChB 1982; DRCOG 1986.

CALDERON, Norman Vincent Stanley 20 Goodminns, Sedgeford, Hunstanton PE36 5NB Tel: 01485 70996 — MB BS 1953 Lond. (St. Geo.) Prev: Ho. Phys. Neurol. Dept. St. Geo. Hosp.; Ho. Surg. & Obst. Ho. Surg. Edgware Gen. Hosp.

CALDERON PELAYO, Ricardo 8 The Crescent, Basingstoke & District Hospital, Basingstoke RG24 9LX — LMS 1982 Oviedo.

CALDERWOOD, Catherine Jane 8 Broomhill Park, Belfast BT9 5JB — MB ChB 1993 Glas.

CALDERWOOD, David Kells O'Donel Tower Hill Medical Centre, 25 Tower Hill, Great Barr, Birmingham B42 1LG Tel: 0121 357 1077; Brownes Green House, 120 Handsworth Wood Road, Handsworth Wood, Birmingham B20 2PN Tel: 0121 554 1666 — MB ChB 1968 St. And.; DA Eng. 1971. (St. And.) Princip. Gen. Pract. Birm. Surg. Lt.-Cdr. RNR Tay Div. Prev: Regist. (Anaesth.) Dundee Roy. Infirm.

CALDERWOOD, Edith Mary (retired) 115A Abbots Road, Abbot's Langley, Watford WD5 0BJ — MB ChB Bristol 1966; DObst RCOG 1969; DA Eng. 1969. Prev: GP Bushey.

CALDERWOOD, Mr James William, OBE Musgrave Park Hospital, Stockmans Lane, Belfast BT9 7JB Tel: 01232 669501; 8 Broomhill Park, Belfast BT9 5JB Tel: 01232 666940 Fax: 01232 666940 — MB BCh BAO Belf. 1966; FRCS Ed. 1970. (The Queen's University of Belfast) Cons. Orthop. Surg. GreenPk. Healthcare Trust Belf.; Cons. Orthop. Surg. Roy. Vict. Hosp. Belf. Socs: Fell. BOA; Brit. Soc. Surg. Hand; Pres. Ulster Med. Soc. 1997-1998. Prev: Sen. Regist. N. Irel. Hosps. Auth.; SHO & Ho. Off. Roy. Vict. Hosp. Belf.

CALDERWOOD, Robin O'Donel Brownes Green House, 120 Handsworth Wood Road, Birmingham B20 2PN Tel: 07887 651167 — MB ChB 1998 Manch.; MB ChB Manch 1998; BSc (Hons) St. And 1995. Surgic. HO. to Mr D.J.Stewart; Surg. Roy. Preston Hosp. Prev: Orthop. Ho. Off. Roy. Preston Hosp.; Infec. Dis.s Ho. Ofiicer Roy. Preston Hosp.; Med. Ho. Off. N. Manch. Gen. Hosp.

CALDERWOOD, Vivien Sandra Tower Hill Medical Centre, 25 Tower Hill, Great Barr, Birmingham B42 1LG Tel: 0121 357 1077 — MB ChB 1969 St. And.

CALDICOTT, Lawrence Desmond 103 Birchwood Hill, Leeds LS17 8NT Tel: 0113 665856 — MB BS 1984 Lond.; FRCA. 1990; DA (UK) 1987. Sen. Regist. Rotat. (Anaesth.) Leeds. Prev: Post-Fell. Regist. (Cardiothoracic Anaesth.) N.: Gen. Hosp. Sheff.; Research Fell. (ICU & CCU) Roy. Hallamsh. Hosp. Sheff.

CALDICOTT, Mark Lawrence Bissoe Surgery, Bissoe Road, Carnon Downs, Truro TR3 6JD Tel: 01872 863221 Fax: 01872 864113; Cliff Cottage, Pill Creek, Feock, Truro TR3 6SE Tel: 01872 864201 — MB BS 1985 Lond.; MRCGP 1992; DFFP 1994; Dip. Palliat. Med. Wales 1997. (Westm.)

CALDON, Miss Lisa Jane Marie 43 Barkers Road, Nether Edge, Sheffield S7 1SD — MB ChB 1992 Leic.; FRCS Eng. 1998. SHO Rotat. (Gen. Surg.) N. Gen. Hosp. & Roy. Hallamshire Hosp. Sheff. Prev: SHO (Urol.) Roy. Hallamshire Hosp. Sheff.; SHO (Orthop.) N.ern Gen. Hosp.; SHO (Gen. Surg.) Roy. Hallamshire Hosp.

CALDWELL, Alasdhair James 56 C23 Cavell Court, Queens Medical Centre, Derby Road, Nottingham NG7 2UH — MB ChB 1992 Ed.

CALDWELL, Alison Jayne 66 Newsholme Close, Culcheth, Warrington WA3 5DE Tel: 01925 767994 — MB ChB 1994 Liverp.

CALDWELL, Andrea Jane 122 Invergarry Drive, Thornliebank, Glasgow G46 8UN Tel: 0141 638 9523 — MB ChB 1989 Glas. Trainee GP Glas. Prev: SHO (O & G & Geriat.) S.. Gen. Hosp. Glas. VTS.

CALDWELL, Arthur Stanley (retired) Fergusleigh, 10 West Fergus Place, Kirkcaldy KY1 1UR Tel: 01592 264071 — MB ChB 1943 Glas.; DPH 1951; MFCM 1972. Prev: SCM Fife Health Bd.

CALDWELL, Barry Martin Wellfield Surgery, 291 Oldham Road, Rochdale OL16 5HX Tel: 01706 355111; 27 Brookfield Drive, Littleborough OL15 8RH Tel: 01706 373153 — MB ChB 1978 Manch. Princip. GP Rochdale.

CALDWELL, Carole Jane Dept. of Histopathology, Kings College Hospital, Denmark Hill, London SE5 Tel: 020 7346 3557 Fax: 020 7346 3670; 10 Gairloch Road, Camberwell, London SE5 8NG — BM 1989 Soton.; BSc (Hons.) Soton 1988. BM (Hons.) 1989; MRC Path. 1997. (Southampton) Cons. Histopath., King's Coll., Lond.; Hon. Sen. Lect., King's Coll. Lond. Socs: BMA; Assn. Clin. Pathologies. Prev: Sen. Regist., St. Bart. Hosp.; Regist., St. Thomas' Hosp.

CALDWELL, David Cunningham (retired) Sylvan, Coupar Angus Road, Rosemount, Blairgowrie PH10 6LT — MB ChB 1938 Glas.; BSc (Hons. Path.) Glas. 1939, MB ChB 1938; FRCPath 1964. Prev: Dir. Path. S.end-on-Sea Hosp.

CALDWELL, David Laurie (retired) 2 Brinkburn Close, Totley Rise, Sheffield S17 3LS Tel: 0114 236 6894 — MB BChir 1939 Camb.; MA Camb. 1941. BA 1936; FRCP Lond. 1970, M 1941. Prev: Cons. Chest Phys. Wirral AHA.

CALDWELL, Gordon Worthing Hospital, Park Avenue, Worthing BN11 2DH Tel: 01903 205111 — MB BS 1980 Lond.; MA (Hons.) Oxf. 1977, DM 1992; MB BS (Hons.) Lond. 1980; MRCP (UK) 1983. Cons. Phys. Worthing Hosp. W. Sussex. Prev: Sen. Regist. (Diabetes) Newc. Hosps.; Research Regist. (Diabetic Retinopathy) Roy. Postgrad. Med. Sch. Lond.; Regist. (Endocrinol.) Roy. Infirm. Edin.

CALDWELL, Guy Cecil Forrester, DFC, DFM (retired) 39 Broad Street, Ludlow SY8 1NL Tel: 01584 873388 Fax: 01584 873388 — MB BS Lond. 1951; MRCS Eng. LRCP Lond. 1951. Prev: Cas. Off. W.m. Hosp.

CALDWELL, Helen Maclean (retired) East Lodges, 181 Clermiston Road, Edinburgh EH12 6UL — MB ChB 1952 Ed.; FRCGP 1985, M 1971; DObst RCOG 1956.

CALDWELL, Ian David Swan Lane Medical Centre, Swan Lane, Bolton BL3 6TL — MB BS 1976 Lond.

CALDWELL, Ian Wingate, Lt.-Col. RAMC Retd. (retired) Flat A4, Maison Victor Hugo, St Clement, Jersey JE2 6PW Tel: 01534 871561 — MB ChB 1939 Aberd.; MD Aberd. 1954; FRCP Lond. 1970. Prev: Cons. Dermat. Soton., N. Lincs. & Jersey Hosps.

CALDWELL, James (retired) Burnside, 66 Common Lane, Hemingford Abbots, Huntingdon PE28 9AW Tel: 01480 462080 — LRCP LRCS Ed. LRFPS Glas. 1946; MFCM 1975; DPH Glas. 1951. Prev: Community Phys. Cambs. AHA (T).

CALDWELL, James Allan (retired) The Sheiling, Badgeworth, Cheltenham GL51 4UW Tel: 01452 713000 — MB ChB 1956 Glas.; MRCGP 1984. Prev: GP Gloucester.

CALDWELL, James Douglas Riverside Cottage, Kinloch Rannoch, Pitlochry PH16 5PU Tel: 01882 632309 — MB ChB Ed. 1942. (Univ. Ed.)

CALDWELL, James Richard (retired) Silver Birches, Newick Hill, Newick, Lewes BN8 4QR — MB BS 1939 Lond.; MRCS Eng. LRCP Lond. 1939; FRCGP 1977, M 1953. Prev: Med. Off. Pouchlands Hosp.

CALDWELL, Jane Cochrane 2 Elm Avenue, Lenzie, Kirkintilloch, Glasgow G66 4HJ — MB ChB 1998 Glas.; MB ChB Glas 1998.

CALDWELL, Jennifer 3 Hall Bank S., Mobberley, Knutsford WA16 7JA — MB ChB 1982 Manch.; DO RCS Eng. 1986; DCH RCP Lond. 1985.

CALDWELL, John Gateacre Brow Surgery, 1 Gateacre Brow, Liverpool L25 3PA Tel: 0151 428 1851; 101 Walsingham Road, Childwall, Liverpool L16 3NS Email: john.caldwell@rapid.co.uk — MB ChB 1985 Manch.; BSc St. And. 1982. Clin. Asst. (Surg.) Sir Alfred Jones Memor. Hosp. Liverp.; Surg. Practitioner, BRd.green Hosp., Liverp. Socs: Primary Care Rheum. Soc.; GP Asthma Gp. Prev: SHO (O & G) Macclesfield Dist. Gen. Hosp.; SHO (Paediat.) Roy. Liverp. Childr. Hosp. Alder Hey; SHO (Geriat.) Newsham Gen. Hosp. Liverp.

CALDWELL, John Stewart (retired) Dunleigh, Aberlour AB38 9PR Tel: 01340 871458 Fax: 01340 871458 — MB ChB 1945 Aberd.; DObst RCOG 1949. Prev: Ho. Surg. Aberd. Roy. Infirm. & Matern. Unit. Newc. Gen. Hosp.

CALDWELL, Naomi Eliza 23 Woodford Street, Northampton NN1 5EN — BM BS 1996 Nottm.

CALDWELL, Paul James The Surgery, 21 North Bar Without, Beverley HU17 7AQ Tel: 01482 882546; 2 Church Farm Close, Lofthouse, Wakefield WF3 3SA Tel: 01924 822273 — MB BS 1981 Lond.; MRCGP 1990.

CALDWELL, Richard Anthony Glenalmond, 99 Park Road, Hale, Altrincham WA15 9JU Tel: 0161 980 1499 Email: rc@racdoc.freeserve.co.uk — MB ChB 1971 Manch.

CALDWELL, Mr Stuart Oast Barn, Dingle Road, Brockamin, Leigh, Worcester WR6 5JX — MB ChB 1989 Birm.; FRCS Ed. 1994. Specialist Regist. W. Midl. Higher Surg. Train. Scheme; Research Fell.

CALDWELL, Walter Farrant, MC (retired) 22 Leicester Avenue, Glasgow G12 0LU Tel: 0141 339 2166 — MB ChB 1941 Glas.; BSc Glas. 1938; FRCGP 1976.

CALDWELL, William Gordon Dickson (retired) 425 Heath Road S., Northfield, Birmingham B31 2BB Tel: 0121 475 5030 — MB BCh BAO Dub. 1941; MA Dub. 1943. BA 1940, MD 1943; FRCPI

1969, M 1950; FRCPath 1969, M 1964. Hon. Cons. Path. Dudley Rd. Hosp. Birm.; Hon. Sen. Clin. Lect. Univ. Birm. Prev: Cons. Path. Dudley Rd. Hosp. Birm.

CALE, Mr Alexander Ronald John Department of Cardrothoracic Surgery, Castle Hill Hospital, Castle Road, Cottingham HU16 5JQ — MB ChB 1985 Manch.; BSc St. And. 1982; FRCS Ed. 1989.

CALE, Catherine Mary Development Biology Unit, Institute of Child Health, 30 Guilford St., London WC1N 1EH Tel: 020 7242 9789 Email: ccale@ich.ucl.ac.uk — MB ChB 1989 Birm.; BSc (1st cl. Hons.) Birm. 1986; MRCP (UK) 1992. (Birm.) Clin. Research Fell. & Hon. Sen. Regist. Inst. Child Health Lond. Gt. Ormond St. Hosp.

CALEB, Jean Valentine 10 Albert Mansions, Crouch Hill, London N8 9RE — MB BCh BAO 1986 NUI; LRCPI & LM, LRCSI & LM 1986.

CALEY, George Leslie 291 Ashby Road, Scunthorpe DN16 2AB Tel: 01724 864426 — MB ChB 1958 Sheff.; DObst RCOG 1960. Prev: Ho. Surg. & Ho. Phys. City Gen. Hosp. Sheff.; O & G Ho. Surg. Memor. Hosp. PeterBoro..

CALEY, John Prestwidge Heath Lodge, Heath Avenue, Mansfield NG18 3EU — MB ChB 1949 Sheff.; FRCP Lond. 1973, M 1953. (Sheff.) Cons. Phys. Mansfield & Dist. Gen. Hosp., King's Mill Hosp.; Sutton-in-Ashfield & Harlow Wood Orthop. Hosp. Mansfield; Clin. Teach. & Clin. Tutor Univ. Nottm. Socs: E. Midl. Assn. Phys. & Nottm. M-C Soc. Prev: Sen. Med. Regist. United Sheff. Hosps.; Regist. (Med.) Manch. Roy. Infirm.; Ho. Phys. Profess. Med. Unit City Gen. Hosp. Sheff.

CALEY, Martin John Mill Road Surgery, 98A Mill Road, Ecclesfield, Sheffield S35 9XQ Tel: 0114 246 9419 — MB ChB 1975 Sheff.; MRCP (UK) 1978.

CALEY, Richard St Johns Medical Centre, 62 London Road, Grantham NG31 6HR Tel: 01476 590055 Fax: 01476 400042; 3 Dudley Road, Grantham NG31 9AA — MB BS 1972 Lond. (St. Geo.) Prev: Trainee GP I. of Wight VTS; Ho. Surg. Roy. Hants. Co. Hosp. Winchester; Ho. Phys. Chase Farm Hosp. Enfield.

CALHAEM, Malcolm Noel, RD Model Farm, Fradswell, Stafford ST18 0EX Tel: 01785 270297 — MB BS 1972 Newc.; BSc Wellington 1968; FFA RCS Eng. 1978; T(Anaesth.) 1991. Cons. Anaesth. Stafford Dist. Gen. Hosp. Socs: Assn. Anaesth. Gt. Brit. & Irel.; Assoc. Mem. Tri-Serv. Anaesth. Soc. Prev: Sen. Regist. (Anaesth.) Glas. Roy. Infirm.

CALIN, Andrei Royal National Hospital Rheumatic Disease, National Health Service Trust, Upper Borough Walls, Bath BA1 1RL Tel: 01225 465941 Fax: 01225 473437 Email: andrei.calin@virgin.net; Holmpatrick, Weston Road, Bath BA1 2XU Tel: 01225 421760 Fax: 01225 333341 — MB BChir Camb. 1968; MD Camb. 1977; FRCP Lond. 1986; MRCP (UK) 1970. Cons. Rheum. Roy. Nat. Hosp. Rheum. Dis. Bath; Assoc. Prof. Med. Stanford Univ. Med. Center Calif., USA. Socs: Brit. Soc. Rhem.; Amer. Coll. Rheum.; Amer. Coll. of Rheum. Prev: Assoc. Prof. Med. Stanford Univ. Sch. Med. Calif., USA; Chief (Rheum. Sect.) Veterans Admin. Hosp. Palo Alto, Calif.; Sen. Regist. Guy's Hosp. Lond.

CALIN, Hazel Jane (retired) Holmpatrick, Weston Road, Bath BA1 2XU Tel: 01225 421760 — MB 1972 Camb.; BChir. GP Bath; Research Assoc. Roy. Nat. Hosp. Rheum Dis. Bath. Prev: GP/Int Med. Palo Alto Med. Clinic, Palo Alto, Calif., USA.

CALLADINE, Clifford The Surgery, 19 High Street, Penistone, Sheffield S36 6BR Tel: 01226 762257 Fax: 01226 762984 — MB ChB 1979 Sheff.; BMedSci. Sheff. 1976, MB ChB 1979.

CALLADINE, Mary Ruth Howard The Queen Edith Medical Practice, 59 Queen Ediths Way, Cambridge CB1 8PJ Tel: 01223 247288 Fax: 01223 213459; 25 Almoners Avenue, Cambridge CB1 8NZ Tel: 01223 246742 — MB BChir Camb. 1959; MA Camb. 1959; MRCS Eng. LRCP Lond. 1959; MRCGP 1987. (Guy's) Princip. GP; Clin. Asst. (Gastroenterol.) Addenbrooke's NHS Trust Camb. Socs: BMA; Med. Wom. Federat. Prev: Research Asst. & Hon. Regist. (Paediat.) United Camb. Hosps.; Ho. Phys. & Asst. Ho. Surg. Guy's Hosp. Lond.

CALLAGHAN, Alfred William (retired) 17 Lavender Lane, Rowledge, Farnham GU10 4AX Tel: 0125 125 3245 — MB BCh BAO 1933 Dub.; MA Dub. 1945, MB BCh BAO 1933; LM Coombe 1946.

CALLAGHAN, Ann Llynwen 73 Llanishen Street, Heath, Cardiff CF14 3QD — MB BCh 1990 Wales.

CALLAGHAN, Beryl Mary Lesley Tan-y-Castll, Llanilar, Aberystwyth SY23 4PD Tel: 0197 47 213 — MB BS 1955 Lond.; MRCS Eng. LRCP Lond. 1955. (Roy. Free) GP Aberystwyth.

CALLAGHAN, Bridget Delia 43 Birley Road, London N20 0HB — MB ChB 1993 Birm.

CALLAGHAN, Ian Michael 1 Klea Avenue, London SW4 9HG — MB BS 1988 Newc.; BA Oxf. 1985. Socs: Med. Practs. Union; BMA. Prev: Med. Off. Donor Care Dept. S. Thames; Hon. Regist. (Genitourin. Med.) NW RHA; Tutor (Med. of AIDS) Manch. Univ.

CALLAGHAN, Judith Mary Long Lane Medical Centre, Long Lane, Liverpool L9 6DQ Tel: 0151 530 1009 — MB ChB 1992 Liverp.

CALLAGHAN, Kathryn Audrey 98 Highlands Road, Limavady BT49 9LY — MB BCh BAO 1994 Belf.

CALLAGHAN, Leanne Carol 39 Golf View, Ingol, Preston PR2 7EJ — MB ChB 1996 Sheff.

CALLAGHAN, Miss Maria c/o 22 Hatherley Avenue, Crosby, Liverpool L23 0SD Tel: 0151 928 2666; 108 Blantyre Road, Wavertree, Liverpool L15 3HT Tel: 0151 733 2461 — MB ChB 1990 Liverp.; FRCS Eng. 1996. (Liverp.) Prev: SHO (Orthop.) Chester; SHO (Renal Transpl. & Cardiothoracic) Liverp.

CALLAGHAN, Maria Josephine Dundonald Medical Centre, 1 St. Johns Wood Park, Dundonald, Belfast BT16 1RS Tel: 028 9048 3100 Fax: 028 9041 9252 — MB BCh BAO 1976 NUI; DCH RCPI 1980; DRCOG 1978.

CALLAGHAN, Marie 45 Muirhouse Drive, Motherwell ML1 2NJ — MB ChB 1984 Glas.

CALLAGHAN, Mary Winifred Yorkhill NHS Trust, Department of Medical Paediatrics, Yorkhill, Glasgow G3 8WD; Flat 4, West House, 42 Glasgow Road, Uddingston, Glasgow G71 7BA Tel: 01698 81573 — MB ChB 1984 Glas.; BSc (Hons.) Glas. 1981; MRCP (UK) 1996; MRCGP 1988; DCH RCPS Glas. 1987; DRCOG 1986. Specialist Regist. (Paediat.) Yorkhill NHS Trust Glas. Prev: SHO 3 (Paediat.) Roy. Alexandra Hosp. Paisley; SHO (Paediat.) Yorkhill NHS Trust Glas.; Clin. Med. Off. (Community Child Health) Lanarksh. HB.

CALLAGHAN, Michael Stuart David St Stephens Health Centre, Bow Community Hall, William Place, London E3 5ED Tel: 020 8980 1760 Fax: 020 8980 6619 — MB BS 1985 Lond.; MRCGP. GP Princip.

CALLAGHAN, Nigel John Tel: 0191 385 2512 — LMSSA 1986 Lond.; 2001 LLb (Hons); T (Gp) 1992; 2000 MCIArb; 2001 Dp.Pn.Med; 2000 Pg DL; 1990 FPCert. (Roy. Free Hosp. Sch. of Med.) Forens. Med. Examr.; Div.al Surg./Force Med. Off., Durh. Constab.; Med. Off. to HM Prison Serv.; Indep. Med. Adviser to Lord Chancellor (Appeals Serv.). Socs: Assoc. Of Police Surg.s; Brit. Acad. of Forens. Med. and Sci.; Forens. Sci. Soc. Prev: Principle in Gen. Pract.; Regtl. Med. Off., Durh. Light Infantry.

CALLAGHAN, Pamela Jean Haynes (retired) 2 The Boulevard, Worthing BN13 1LB Tel: 01903 246007 — MRCS Eng. LRCP Lond. 1957; DObst RCOG 1958. Community Med. Off. W. Sussex AHA.

CALLAGHAN, Peter (retired) Tan-y-Castell, Llanilar, Aberystwyth SY23 4PD Tel: 01974 241349 — MB BCh Wales 1951; FRCPath. 1976, M 1964. Prev: Cons. Pathol. Bronglais Hosp. Aberystwyth.

CALLAGHAN, Richard Philip (retired) 2 The Boulevard, Worthing BN13 1LB Tel: 01903 246007 — MB BS Lond. 1956; MRCS Eng. LRCP Lond. 1956; DObst RCOG 1969. Prev: Cas. Off. King's Coll. Hosp.

CALLAGHAN, Robert Raymond 14 Longspears Avenue, Gabalfa, Cardiff CF14 3NU Tel: 029 2031 6456 — MB BCh 1996 Wales; BSc (Hons) Pharm. Cardiff.

CALLAGHAN, Roger Timothy The Parklands Medical Practice, Park Road, Bradford BD5 0SG Tel: 01274 227575 Fax: 01274 693558; Parklands Medical Practice, 30 Buttershaw Lane, Bradford BD6 2DD Tel: 01274 678464 — MB ChB 1976 Leeds. Princip. Med. Off. Brit. Assn. Rally Doctors & BASICS. Socs: Assur. Med. Soc.

CALLAGHAN, Susan Mary Valkyrie Road Surgery, 20 Valkyrie Road, Westcliff on Sea SS0 8BX Tel: 01702 331255 Fax: 01702 437050; 87 Warren Road, Leigh-on-Sea SS9 3TT — MB BS 1983 Lond.; MRCGP 1988; DRCOG 1987; DCH RCP Lond. 1986.

CALLAGHAN, Therese Agnes National Blood Service, Mersey & N. Wales Centre, West Derby St., Liverpool L7 8TW Tel: 0151 551 8867 Fax: 0151 551 8895 Email: therese.callaghan@nbs.nhs.uk — MB ChB 1985 Glas.; BSc (Hons.) Glas. 1982; MRCP (UK) 1988; MRCPath 1996; Dip FM 1997. Cons. haematologist/ Lead clinician

Nat. Blood Serv. Mersey & N wales Centre. Prev: Sen. Regist. (Haemat. & Blood Transfus.) Transfus. Centre Glas. & W.; Regist. (Haemat.) Univ. Coll. Hosp. Lond.; Regist. (Gen. Med.) Hairmyres Hosp. E. Kilbride.

CALLAGHAN, Thomas Stanley The Mary Acre, Argyll St., Brechin DD9 6JL Tel: 01356 624725 — MD 1981 Belf.; MSc 1994 Dundee; MB BCh BAO (Hons.) 1972; FRCP Ed. 1992; MRCP (UK) 1976. Cons. Cardiol., Ninewells Hosp., Dundee. Socs: Fell. Ulster Med. Soc.; Scott. Soc. Phys.; Med. Research Soc.

CALLAHAN, Hilary Marie Old Fire Station Surgery, 68A Portsmouth Road, Woolston, Southampton SO19 9AN Tel: 023 8044 8558/8901 Fax: 023 8043 5569 — MB BS 1989 Lond.; MRCGP 1993.

CALLAM, Mr Michael John Bedford Hospital, Kempston Road, Bedford MK42 9DJ Tel: 01234 355122 Fax: 01234 792102 Email: mical@dial.pipex.com; 7 Rothsay Road, Bedford MK40 3PW Tel: 01234 325451 Fax: 01234 792102 Email: mical@dial.pipex.com — MB ChB 1974 Dundee; ChM Dund 1989,; FRCS Ed. 1979. Cons. Surg. Bedford Gen. Hosp.

CALLAN, Alyson Fleur 22 Pelham Road, London N15 4RN Tel: 020 8809 5228 — MB ChB 1987 Glas.; MSc Social Anthropol. Lond. 1993; MRCPsych 1991. (Univ. Glas.) Prev: Regist. (Psychiat.) Univ. Coll. Hosp. Lond.; Ho. Phys. Tameside Gen. Hosp. Lancs.; Sen. Regist. (Psychiat.) Guy's Hosp. Lond.

CALLAN, Margaret Fiona Clare 8 Mount Street, Oxford OX2 6DH — BM BCh 1987 Oxf.; BA Camb. 1984; MRCP (UK) 1990.

CALLANAN, Mr Keith William Richard c/o Postgraduate Institute for Medicine, Framlington Place, Newcastle upon Tyne NE2 4AB — MB BS 1989 Newc.; BMedSc Newc. 1986; FRCS Ed. 1994. Specialist Regist. (Gen. Surg.) Newc. u. Tyne. Prev: Clin. Research Assoc. Univ. Newc.; SHO (Gen. Surg.) Dryburn Hosp. Durh., Roy. Vict. Infirm. & Gen. Hosp. Newc.; Demonst. (Anat.) Univ. Newc. u. Tyne.

CALLANAN, Mr Vincent Patrick 19 Kingsford Park, Grange, Douglas, Republic of Ireland; 1 Woodyard Lane, Dulwich, London SE21 7BH — MB BCh BAO 1987 NUI; FRCS (Oto) 1994; FRCSI (ENT) 1993; FRCS (ORL-MNS) 1998. (Univ. Coll. Cork) Specialist Regist. (Otolaryngol., Head & Neck Surg.) Guy's & St. Thos. NHS Trust Lond. Socs: BMA; Brit. Assn. Otol. Head & Neck Surg.; Brit. Voice Assn.

CALLAND, Anthony Lawson The Surgery, Trellech, Monmouth NP5 4PE Tel: 01594 530334 Fax: 01594 530748; Sittingreen, Hudnalls Loop Road, St Briavels, Lydney GL15 6SG Tel: 01594 530373 Fax: 01594 530045 — MB ChB 1970 Liverp.; MRCGP 1977. Non. Exec. Dir. Gwent HA; Mem. (Chairm.) GMSC (Welsh & Fundholding Subcomm.). Prev: Demonst. (Anat.) Univ. Liverp.; Ho. Phys. & Ho. Surg. Liverp. Roy. Infirm.

CALLANDER, Christopher Campbell Anaesthetic Department, Royal Gwent Hosptial, Cardiff Road, Newport NP20 2UB — MB ChB 1979 Dundee; FRCA. 1984. Cons. Anaesth. Roy. Gwent Hosp. Newport.

CALLANDER, Gordon Walter Robert Cleveland Clinic, 12 Cleveland Road, St Helier, Jersey JE1 4HD Tel: 01534 722381/734121; La Maison de Douaire, La Hougue Farm, Route de Vinchelez, St Ouen, Jersey JE3 2DB Tel: 01534 483113 — MB ChB 1992 Ed.; MRCGP. (Edinburgh) GP Partner.

CALLANDER, Michael John Alliston Medical Centre, 28 Crofts Bank Road, Urmston, Manchester M41 0UH Tel: 0161 747 2411 Fax: 0161 747 8841; 21 Crossland Road, Chorlton Green, Manchester M21 9DU Tel: 0161 881 1752 Fax: 0161 283 8813 Email: mikecallander@lineone.net — MB ChB 1973 Manch.; DObst RCOG 1976. (Manchester) GP Princip.; Specialist Male Erectile DysFunc. Salford Community NHS Trust.

CALLANDER, Nanas 27 Arbor Lane, Winnersh, Wokingham RG41 5JE — MB ChB 1975 Glas.

CALLANDER, William Harte, Ex Capt. RAMC (retired) Great Horton Medical Centre, Paternoster Lane, Bradford BD7 3EE Tel: 01274 502905 Fax: 01274 522060 — MRCS Eng. LRCP Lond. 1950; DObst RCOG 1956. Prev: Ho. Surg. Orthop. Unit, Chase Farm Hosp. Enfield.

CALLAWAY, Elizabeth Jane 9 Toutie Street, Alyth, Blairgowrie PH11 8BP Tel: 01828 632405 — MB ChB 1987 Aberd. (Aberd.) Staff Psychiat. (Child & Adolesc. Psychiat.) Roy. Edin. Hosp. Prev: Sen. Regist. (Child & Adolesc. Psychiat.) Roy. Edin. Hosp.

CALLAWAY, Mark Paul Bristol Royal Infirmary, Marlborough St, Bristol BS2 8HW Tel: 0117 928 2672 Email: m.callaway@swesl.wbht.nhs.uk; 9 Ham Farm Lane, Emersons Green, Bristol BS16 7BW Tel: 0117 958 8827 Fax: 0117 958 8827 — BM 1989 Soton.; MRCP (UK) 1992; FRCR 1996. Sen. Regist. Univ. Bristol; Cons. Radiol.

CALLAWAY, Paul Lawrence Bognor Medical Practice, West Street, Bognor Regis PO21 1UT Tel: 01243 823864 Fax: 01243 623800; Churn Cottage, Cocking, Midhurst GU29 0HF — MB ChB 1978 Manch.; MRCP (UK) 1983. Prev: Trainee GP Soton.; Research Regist. (Diabetes) Roy. S. Hants. Hosp. Soton.; Regist. (Med.) Walton Hosp. Liverp.

CALLEAR, Andrew Blair Rustic Ridge, Dryton, Wroxeter, Shrewsbury SY5 6PR — MB BS 1988 Lond.; BSc (Anat.) Lond. 1985; FRCOphth 1992. (Char. Cross & Westm.) Cons. (Ophth) Roy. Strewsbury Hosp. NHS Trust.

CALLEBAUT, George Edward Henry (retired) 8 Lambourn Way, Chatham ME5 8PU Tel: 01634 660314 — MRCS Eng. LRCP Lond. 1950. Prev: Ho. Surg. Thoracic Unit & Sen. Ho. Off. VD Dept. Lond. Hosp.

CALLEJA, Jesus Macclesfield District General Hospital, Victoria Road, Macclesfield SK10 3BL — LMS 1993 Cantabria.

CALLEJA, Mario Anthony 30 Deerfold, Chorley PR7 1UH — MB ChB 1983 Liverp.

CALLEN, Nerys Rachel 172 Manor Way, Whitchurch, Cardiff CF14 1RN — MB BCh 1998 Wales.

CALLEN, Mr Peter John 8 Epworth Close, Truro TR1 1UP Tel: 01872 24220; Royal Cornwall Hospital Teliske, Truro TR1 3LJ Tel: 01872 252731 Fax: 01872 252933 — MB BS Lond. 1965; MB BS Lond. 1965; FRCS Eng. 1971; FRCS Eng. 1971; MRCS Eng. LRCP Lond. 1965; MRCS Eng. LRCP Lond. 1965; FRCOG 1991, M 1979; FRCOG 1991, M 1979. (King's Coll. Hosp.) Cons. (O & G) Cornw. & Scilly I. HA.; Sen. Clin. Lect. Obst. & Gyn. Univ. Bristol; Sen. Clin. Lect. Obst. & Gyn. Univ. Bristol 1997. Socs: BMA; BMA. Prev: Sen. Regist. (O & G) Qu. Charlottes Hosp. Lond.; Regist. (O & G) St. Thos. Hosp. Lond.

CALLENDER, Barbara Elizabeth Mount Oriel Surgery, 2 Mount Oriel, Belfast BT8 7HR Tel: 028 9070 1653 — MB BCh BAO 1974 Belf.; MRCGP 1982. Princip. GP Belf. Prev: Regist. (Haemat.) Roy. Vict. Hosp. Belf. & Roy. Belf. Hosp. Sick; Childr.

CALLENDER, John Simpson Royal Cornhill Hospital, Aberdeen AB25 2ZH Tel: 01224 663131 — MD Glas. 1991, MB ChB 1977; MRCPsych 1982; FRCPsych 1999. (Glasgow) Cons. Psychiat. Roy. Cornhill Hosp. Aberd.; Hon. Sen. Clin. Lect. Univ. Aberd.; Assoc. Med. Director,Grampian Primary care NHS Trust.

CALLENDER, Kay Hope Hospital, Stott Lane, Salford M6 8 — MB BCh 1976 Wales; MRCPsych. 1980. Cons. Psychiat. Hope Hosp. Salford; Hon. Lect. Univ. Manch.

CALLENDER, Michael Edwin 74 Osborne Park, Belfast BT9 6JP Tel: 028 660247 — MB BChir 1973 Camb.; MA Camb. 1974, MB BChir 1973; FRCP Lond. 1990; MRCP (UK) 1975. (Kings Coll. Hosp.) Cons. Phys. Roy. Vict. Hosp. Belf. Prev: Sen. Regist. (Gastroenterol. & Gen. Med.) Roy. Vict. Hosp. Belf.; Research Fell. (Liver Unit) King's Coll. Hosp. Lond.; SHO (Neurol.) Hammersmith Hosp. Lond.

CALLENDER, Patricia Anne 18 Cliff Park, Cults, Aberdeen AB15 9JT Tel: 01224 869643 — MB ChB 1974 Ed.; MRCGP 1979; DObst RCOG 1976. Asst. GP Cults, Aberd. Prev: SHO (Obst.) N.wick Pk. Hosp. Harrow; SHO (Paediat.) Lond Hosp.; SHO (Psychiat.) King's Coll. Hosp. Lond.

CALLENDER, Mr Roger, Squadron Ldr. RAF Med. Br. Retd. Dudley Group of hospital NHS Trust, Wordsley Hospital, Stourbridge DY8 5QX Tel: 01384 456111 Fax: 01384 244445 — MB BS 1971 Lond.; FRCOG 1992, M 1978. (University College Hospital) Cons. O & G Wordsley Hosp. Strourbridge. Prev: Cons. O & G Grenfell Regional Health Serv. Newfld., Canada.

CALLENDER, Sheila Theodora Elsie (retired) Rectory Farm, Horspath, Oxford OX33 1RJ — MB ChB 1938 St. And.; DSc Oxf. 1970; BSc, MB ChB St. And. 1938, MD 1944; FRCP Lond. 1962, M 1944. Prev: Clin. Reader Nuffield Dept. Clin. Med. Oxf.

CALLER, Hannah Angell 18 Pyrland Road, London N5 2JD Tel: 020 7359 1610 — MB BS 1992 Lond.

CALLER, Martin (retired) Hastoe Grove, Hastoe, Tring HP23 6LU — LMSSA 1948 Lond.; MA Camb. 1967.

CALLER, Pauline Judith 17 Brandling Park, Newcastle upon Tyne NE2 4RR — MB BS 1964 Durham.

CALLINAN, Liam Francis James Department of Psychiatry, Royal South Hampshire Hospital, Southampton SO9 4PE — MB ChB 1985 Glas.; MRCPsych 1992. Sen. Regist. (Psychiat.) S. Hants. Hosp. Soton. Prev: Regist. (Psychiat.) St. Clements Hosp. Ipswich.

CALLINGHAM, Robert Francis Haverthwaite Surgery, Backbarow, Ulverston LA12 8QF Tel: 015395 31619 Fax: 015395 31495 — MB ChB 1985 Manch.; BSc MedSci St. And. 1982. Clinic Asst. CDAT. Prev: Assoc. GP Tarbert, Argyll; Trainee GP Cumbria.

CALLISTER, Matthew Eric James 29 Eccles Road, Chapel-En-Le-Frith, High Peak SK23 9RR — BM BCh 1996 Oxf.

CALLOW, Christopher George, OBE, QHP, Maj.-Gen. late RAMC 13A Castle View Road, Weybridge KT13 9AB Email: ccallow@compuserve.com — MB ChB Ed. 1966; MSc (Community Med.) Lond. 1984; MFPHM RCP (UK) 1987; MFCM 1987; DPhysMed Eng. 1971; FFPHM 1996. (Ed.) CE Defence Med. Train. Organisation & CE Defence Secondary Care Agency; Dir. Gen. Med. Train. MoD. Socs: BMA. Prev: Commdr. Med. UKSL (G); Ace Med. Adviser Shape; Commdr. Med. HQ 1st Armoured Div.

CALLOW, Douglas Mark Gresford Medical Centre, Pilch Lane, Liverpool L14 0JE; 61 Park Road, Formby, Liverpool L37 6AB — MB ChB 1987 Liverp.; T(GP) 1994; DRCOG 1994. Prev: Trainee GP S.port; Trainee GP Wigan VTS.

CALLOW, Gillian The Surgery, 13 Fallodon Way, Henleaze, Bristol BS9 4HT Tel: 0117 962 0652 Fax: 0117 962 0839; 8 Rylestone Grove, Stoke Bishop, Bristol BS9 3UT Tel: 0117 962 9844 — MB BCh 1978 Wales; MRCGP 1984; DRCOG 1981. Prev: GP Clifton Bristol.

CALLOW, Nigel Wicket's End, Little Casterton, Stamford PE9 4BE Tel: 01780 762450 — MB BS 1972 Lond.; DObst RCOG 1975; DFFP 1997. (Middlx.)

CALLOW, Paul John Edward Street Surgery, 2 Edward Street, Oldham OL9 7QW Tel: 0161 627 0339 Fax: 0161 627 2437 — MB ChB 1977 Manch.

CALLOWAY, Stephen Paul Fulbourn Hospital, Cambridge CB1 5EF Tel: 01223 218892 Fax: 01223 219203 — MB BS 1972 Lond.; MA Camb. 1988; MD Lond. 1984; FRCP Lond. 1996; MRCP (UK) 1978; FRCPsych 1993, M 1979. (Roy. Free Hosp. Sch. of Healing, Lond.) Cons. Psychiat. Addenbrooke's NHS Trust Camb.; Assoc. Lect. Univ. Camb. Prev: Sen. Regist. (Psychiat.) Roy. Free Hosp. Lond.

CALLUM, David Michael, Lt.-Col. RAMC Retd. Mental Health Hospital, British Forces Health Complex BFPO 40 Tel: 0049 2161 908 2273 — MRCS Eng. LRCP Lond. 1961; MRCPsych 1980; DPM Eng. 1978; DObst RCOG 1963. (St. Mary's) Cons. Psychiat.Brit. Forces Germany Ment. Health Unit Wegberg, BFPO 40. Socs: BMA; Airborne Med. Soc. Prev: Cons. Psychiat. Cheadle Roy. Hosp.; GP Gosport Hants.; Ho. Phys. & Ho. Surg. (O & G) King Edwd. VII Hosp. Windsor.

CALLUM, Mr Kenneth Gordon East Midlands Nuffield Hospital, Rykneld Road, Derby DE23 7SN Tel: 01332 517891 Fax: 01332 523362; Whitehouse Farm, Main St, Egginton, Derby DE65 6HL Tel: 01283 732356 Fax: 01283 730466 Email: admin@bigfoot.com — MB BS Lond. 1962; MS Lond. 1977; FRCS Eng. 1970; FRCS Ed. 1969; MRCS Eng. LRCP Lond. 1962; DObst RCOG 1964; ATLS Instruct 1997. (St. Mary's) Cons. Surg. Derby Roy. Infirm. & Derby City Hosp.; Examr. RCS Eng.; Surgic. Coordinator for Nat. Confidential Enquiry into Peri-Operat. Deaths (NCEPOD). Socs: Fell. Roy. Soc. Med.; Fell. (Counc.) Assn. Surgs.; BMA. Prev: Regist. (Surg.) Harold Wood Hosp. & St. Thos. Hosp. Lond.; Ho. Surg. St. Mary's Hosp.

CALLUM, William David (retired) Whitelands, Dene Park, Tonbridge TN11 9NS Tel: 01732 355355 — MB BChir Camb. 1959; MRCS Eng. LRCP Lond. 1958; MA Camb. 1959; MRCGP 1977; DObst RCOG 1960. p/t Dermat.; HildonBoro. Med. Gp.; HildenBoro. Kent. Prev: GP Tonbridge.

CALMAN, Christopher Roy The Surgery, 73 Holland Park, London W11 3SL Tel: 020 7221 4334 Fax: 020 7792 8517 — BM BCh 1969 Oxf.; MA Oxf. 1969; MRCS Eng. LRCP Lond. 1969. Prev: Cas. Off. (Surg.) Middlx. Hosp. Lond.; SHO (Gen. Surg.) St. Anthony's Hosp. Cheam; SHO (Gyn.) St. Thos. Hosp. Lond.

CALMAN, Frances Mary Boughton Guy's & St Thomas' Cancer Centre, St. Thomas' Hospital, London SE1 7EH; 36 Lillieshall Road, London SW4 0LP Tel: 020 7720 8989 — MB BS 1969 Lond.; FRCP Lond. 1990; MRCP (UK) 1972; FRCR 1976; DMRT Eng. 1974; DCH Eng. 1971. (Roy. Free) Cons. Clin. Oncol. Guy's & St. Thos. Cancer Centre St. Thos. Hosp. Lond. Socs: Fell. Roy. Soc. Med.; Eur. Soc. Therap. Radiol.; Brit. Assn. of Head and neck oncologists. Prev: Cons. Radiother. Centre King's Coll. Hosp. Lond.; Lect. (Radiother.) Inst. Cancer Research & Roy. Marsden Hosp. Lond.; Ho. Phys. Med. Unit Roy. Free Hosp. Lond.

CALMAN, Sir Kenneth Charles, KCB Ainslea, 585 Anniesland Road, Glasgow G13 1UX Tel: 0141 954 9423 — MB ChB Glas. 1967; FRCPath 1992; FRCR 1990; FFPHM RCP (UK) 1989; FRCGP 1989; FRSE; PhD Glas. 1970, BSc 1964, MD (Hons.) 1973; FRCS Eng. 1995; FRCS Ed. 1991; FRCP Ed. 1989; FRCP Lond. 1985, M 1980; FRCS Glas. 1972; FRCOG 1996. Vice-Chancellor & Warden Univ. of Durh. Prev: Chief Med. Off. Eng. 1991-98; Chief Med. Off. Scott. Home & Health Dept. St. And. Hse. Edin.; Dean Postgrad. Med. & Prof. Postgrad. Med. Educat. Univ. Glas.

CALNAN, Professor Charles Dermod 80 Harley Street, London W1N 1AE Tel: 020 7935 3300 Fax: 020 7637 0242; West Claydon House, Lechlade GL7 3DS — MB BChir 1942 Camb.; MA Camb. 1942; FRCP Lond. 1962, M 1950. (Lond. Hosp. & Camb.) Hon. Cons. Dermat. Roy. Free Hosp. & St. John's Hosp. Dis. of Skin. Socs: Hon. Fell. Roy. Soc. Med.; Brit. Assn. Dermat. Prev: Research Assoc. (Dermat.) Hosp. of Univ. Pennsylvania, Philadelphia; Prof. Dermat. Inst. Dermat. Lond.

CALNAN, Professor James Stanislaus 23 King's Road, Berkhamsted HP4 3BH Tel: 01442 862320 — MRCS Eng. LRCP Lond. 1942; FRCS Ed. 1948; FRCP Ed. 1972, M 1948; MRCP Lond. 1948; DTM & H Eng. 1947; DA Eng. 1944; LDS RCS Lond. 1939. (Lond. Hosp.) Emerit. Prof. Plastic & Reconstruc. Surg. Roy. Postgrad. Med. Sch. Lond; Cons. Plastic Surg. Hammersmith Hosp. Lond. Socs: Fell. Roy. Soc. Med.; Fell. Coll. Speech Therap. (Hons.) 1962; Soc. of Authors (Chairm. Med. Writers Gp.). Prev: Hunt. Prof. RCS Eng. 1959; 1st Asst. Profess. Unit of Plastic Surg. Ch.ill Hosp. Oxf.; Co-ordinator of Research Comm. NW Thames RHA.

CALNE, Jane Anne Windmill Surgery, 30 Melton Road, Wymondham NR18 0DB Tel: 01953 607607 Fax: 01953 606482; Tel: 01953 607607 — MB BS 1982 Lond.; DRCOG 1986; DCH RCP Lond. 1985. GP. Prev: Trainee GP Norwich VTS.

CALNE, Sir Roy Yorke Department of Surgery, Addenbrooke's Hospital, Cambridge CB2 2QQ Tel: 01223 242708 Fax: 01223 410772; 22 Barrow Road, Cambridge CB2 2AS Tel: 01223 359831 — MB BS 1953 Lond.; MB BS (Hons. Distinc. Med.) Lond. 1953; FRCP Lond. 1989; FRCS Eng. 1958; MRCS Eng. LRCP Lond. 1953; FRS; MA Camb. 1965; MS Lond. 1961; MD (Hon.) Belf. 1994; MD (Hon.) Karachi 1994; MD (Hon. Causa) Hanover 1991; MD (Hon. Causa) Athens 1990; MD (Hon. Causa) Oslo 1986. (Guy's) Prof. Surg. Univ. Camb.; Hon. Fell. RCS Edin. 1993; Hon. Fell. UMDS 1995; Hunt. Prof. RCS Eng. 1963. Socs: Fell. Assn. Surgs.; Fell. Trinity Hall. Camb.; Hon. Fell. RCS Thailand 1992. Prev: Hon. Cons. & Sen. Lect. (Surg.) W.m. Hosp. Lond.; Lect. (Surg.) St. Mary's Hosp. Lond.; Harkness Research Fell. (Surg.) Harvard Med. Sch. & Asst. (Surg.) Peter Bent Brigham Hosp. Boston, Mass.

CALOGERAS, Antonia 3 Ranelagn Road, Winchester SO23 9TA — MB BS 1986 Newc.; BMedSc Newc. 1986, MB BS 1986; MRCP (UK) 1989. Regist. Rotat. (Gen. Med.) St. Thos. Hosp. Lond. Prev: SHO (Gen. Med.) Rotat. Newc.

CALOW, Christine Eichelsbacher Burnley Gen. Hosp., Casterton Avenue, Burnley BB10 2PQ — State Exam. Med. Erlangen 1986; DA (UK) 1992; MD Erlangen 1991; FRCA (UK) 1996. Cons. Anaesth. Burnley Gen. Hosp.

CALOW, Sarah Ann 4 Westbourne Avenue, Wirral CH48 4DP — BM 1994 Soton.

CALTHORPE, Mr Denis Arthur Doran Derbyshire Royal Infirmary, Derby DE1 2QY Tel: 01332 347141 Fax: 01332 254950 — MB BCh BAO 1979 NUI; MChOrth Liverp. 1990; FRCS Orth. 1994; FRCS Ed. 1984; FRCSI 1984; LRCPSI 1979. (Roy. Coll. Surgs. Irel.)

CALTHORPE, William Ross 1 Trevor Cl, Laceby, Grimsby DN37 7DH — MB ChB 1997 Birm.

CALVER, Alison Louise Wessex Cardiothoracic Centre, Southampton University, Tremona Road, Southampton SO16 6YD Tel: 023 8077 722 — MB BS 1986 Lond.; MA Camb. 1985; MD

Lond. 1993; MRCP (UK) 1989. (Uni. Coll. & Middlesex. Hosp.) Cons. Cardiol., Wessex Cardiothoracic Centre, S.ampton Univ. Hosp.; Cons. Cardiol., Roy. Hants. Co. Hosp, Winchester. Socs: BMA; Brit. Cardiac Soc.; Europ. Soc. of Cardiol. Prev: Regist. (Cardiol.) Lond. Chest Hosp. & St. Geo. Hosp. Lond.; Clin. Research Fell. (Pharmacol. & Clin. Pharmacol.) St. Geo. Hosp. Med. Sch. Lond.; Sen. Regist. (Cardiol) S.ampton Univ. Hosp..

CALVER, Mr David Michael Guy's Hospital, St Thomas St., London SE1 9RT Tel: 020 7955 5000 — MB BS 1969 Lond.; FRCS Ed. 1977; MRCS Eng. LRCP Lond. 1969; FRCOphth 1989; DO Eng. 1977. (King's Coll. Hosp.) Cons. Paediat. Ophth. Guy's Hosp. Lond. Prev: Resid. Surg. Off. Moorfields Eye Hosp. Lond.; Regist. (Ophth.) Sheff. United Hosps.; SHO (Ophth.) Kings Coll. Hosp. Lond.

CALVER, Gary Dennis Sandgate Road Surgery, 180 Sandgate Road, Folkestone CT20 2HN Tel: 01303 221133; 5 Dixwell Road, Folkestone CT20 2LG — MB BS 1980 Lond.; MRCGP 1989; DRCOG 1986; DGM RCP Lond. 1986. (Guy's) Chairm. E. Kent LMC; GPC Represen. Kent. Prev: SHO United Norwich Hosp.

CALVER, Rachel Kingswood, 368 Beccles Road, Carlton Colville, Lowestoft NR33 8HN Tel: 01502 518011 — BM BS 1997 Nottm. Med. SHO, Roy. Untied Hosp., Bath. Prev: SHO (A & E), Kingsmill Hosp., Mansfield; SHO (Surg.) Nottm. City Hosp.

CALVER, Mr Richard Frederick (retired) 5 Holm Hill, Wirral CH48 7JA Tel: 01404 814513 — MB ChB 1970 Liverp.; MChOrth 1977; FRCS Eng. 1975. Clin. Lect. (Orthop.) Liverp. Univ. Prev: Cons. Orthop. Surg. Walton & Fazakerley Hosp.

CALVERLEY, Edward Hilton (retired) Keldagarth, High Duddon, Broughton-in-Furness LA20 6ET Tel: 01229 716734 — MB ChB 1950 Leeds. Prev: Ho. Surg. ENT Dept. Gen. Infirm. Leeds.

CALVERLEY, Professor Peter Martin Anthony University Hospital Aintree, Longmoor Lane, Liverpool L9 7AL Tel: 0151 529 3687 Fax: 0151 529 3239; 17 Eshe Road N., Blundellsands, Liverpool L23 8UE Tel: 0151 924 3286 — MB ChB 1973 Ed.; FRCP Lond. 1990; FRCP Ed. 1990; MRCP (UK) 1976; FCCP 1990. Prof. of Med. (Chest & Rehabil.) Aintree Univ. Hosp.; Hon. Clin. Lect. Univ. Liverp.; Sen. Fell. Dept. Med. Roy. Liverp. Hosp. Socs: Brit. Thoracic Soc. & Amer. Thoracic Soc. Prev: Sen. Regist. (Gen. Med.) Dept. Med. Roy. Infirm. Edin.; MRC Trav. Fell. Meakins-Christie Laborats., McGill Univ. Montreal; Canada; MRC Clin. Research Fell. Dept. Med. Roy. Infirm. Edin.

CALVERT, Alan Hilary Cancer Research Unit, The Medical School, University of Newcastle upon Tyne, Framlington Place, Newcastle upon Tyne NE2 4HH Tel: 0191 222 8057 Fax: 0191 222 7556; Beech House, Burn Road, Blaydon-on-Tyne NE21 6JR — MD 1981 Camb.; MSc (Biochem.) Lond. 1977; MB 1973, BChir 1972; FRCP Lond. 1988; MRCP (UK) 1975. Prof. Clin. Oncol. & Dir. Cancer Research Unit Univ. Newc. u Tyne.; Hon. Cons. Newc. Gen. Hosp. Socs: Assn. Cancer Phys. Prev: Reader Instit. Cancer Research; Hon. Cons. Roy. Marsden Hosp. Lond.

CALVERT, Mr Charles Hazlett 20 Mountain Road, Newtownards BT23 4UL Tel: 01247 815996 — MD Belf.1976, BSc (Hons. Anat.) 1965, MB BCh BAO (Hons.) 1968; FRCS Eng. 1973; FRCS Ed. 1972. (Belf.) Cons. (Gen. Surg.) N. Downs & Ards Hosps. Socs: Assn. Surg.; Ulster Gastroenterol Soc.; Assoc. Mem. BAUS. Prev: Ho. Off. Roy. Vict. Hosp.; Sen. Regist. E.. HSSB; Jun. Cons. (Surg.) Univ. Cape Town.

CALVERT, Christopher Allan David Blackpool Victoria Hospital, Whinney Heys Road, Blackpool FY3 8NQ — MB BCh BAO 1971 Belf.; MRCPsych 1975. Cons. Psychiat. Blackpool, Wyre & Fylde Community NHS Trust.

CALVERT, Mr Denis George (retired) Old Weavers, Pitchcombe, Stroud GL6 6LW Tel: 01452 812580 — MB BS Lond. 1952; FRCS Eng. 1960; FRCS Ed. 1960. Prev: Cons. Surg. Gloucester Roy. Hosp.

CALVERT, Frank Raymond Whinthwaite Cottage, Brigsteer Road, Levens, Kendal LA8 8NU Tel: 0153 95 60691 — MB ChB Manch. 1949; DPH 1956. (Manch.)

CALVERT, George Johnston 1A Temple Road, Ballinderry Upper, Lisburn BT28 2PD — MB BCh BAO Belf. 1966; FRCPsych 1984, M 1972; DPM Eng. 1970; FRCPI 1997. (Belf.) Med. Dir. N.& W. Belf. Health & Social Serv. Trust; Cons. Psych. N. E. Health Bd., Irel.; Med. Adviser - Croft Comm. - NI. Socs: Past Chairm. - Irish Div. - The Roy. Coll. Of Psychiat.s. Prev: Cons. Psychiat. Muckamore Abbey Hosp. Antrim.; Med. Adviser - Beeches Missing Homes NI.

CALVERT, Graham Ernest Montalto Medical Centre, 2 Dromore Rd, Ballynahinch BT24 8AH Tel: 01622 741919; 11 Lancet Lane, Maidstone ME15 9RX — MB BS 1973 Lond.; MSc Univ. Lond. 1988; MRCP (UK) 1977; MRCGP 1982; FRCGP 1998. (The London Hospital) p/t Lect., Dept. of Gen. Pract., G.K.T. Med. Sch., King's Coll., Lond. Prev: Chief Med. Off. Chikankata Hosp., Zambia.

CALVERT, Hugh Telfer Royal Berkshire Hospital, Reading RG1 5AN; 11 Leicester Close, Henley-on-Thames RG9 2LD — MRCS Eng. LRCP Lond. 1940; BA Camb. 1937; MA 1941, MB BChir 1940; FRCP Lond. 1967, M 1948. (Camb. & St. Thos.) Dermatol. Reading & Dist. Hosp. Gp. Socs: Brit. Assn. Dermat.; Fell. Roy. Soc. Med. Prev: Ho. Surg. ENT Dept. & Regist. Skin Dept. St. Thos. Hosp.; Surg. Lt. RNVR.

CALVERT, Ian Malcolm Moor View, Hillary Terrance, Reeth, Richmond DL11 6TF Tel: 01748 884966 — MB BS 1972 Lond.

CALVERT, James Matthew 13 Drummond Place, Edinburgh EH3 6PJ Email: jcalvert@intercom.co.2a — BM BCh 1992 Oxf.; BSc (Hons.) St. And. 1989; MRCP (UK) 1996; MPH Harvard 1994; DTM & H RCP Lond. 1998. (Oxf.) Wellcome Trust Train. Fell. Clin. Trop. Epidemiol. Socs: Brit. Thorac. Soc. Prev: Fulbright Schol. Harvard Sch. Pub. Health.

CALVERT, Jane Erskine 12 South Inch Park, Perth PH2 8BU — MB ChB 1995 Dundee.

CALVERT, Jennifer Kathryn The John Redcliffe Hospital, Headley Way, Headington, Oxford OX3 9DU Tel: 01865 741166; Tel: 0131 557 0457 — BM BCh 1992 Oxf.; BA (Hons.) Oxf. 1989; MRCP (UK) 1995. (Oxf.) Specialist Regist. Rotat. (Paediat.) SE Scotl. Train. Scheme, Specialist Regstrar, Oxf. Deanery. Socs: Roy. Coll. Phys. Lond.; Scott. Paediat. Soc. Prev: Regist. Roy. Hosp. For Sick Childr., Edin.; SHO (Neonates) John Radcliffe Hosp. Oxf.; SHO (Paediat.) Nottm. City Hosp. & N.ants. Gen. Hosp.

CALVERT, John Anthony, KStJ Stranraer Health Centre, Edinburgh Road, Stranraer DG9 7HG Tel: 01776 706566; Hillhead of Craichmore, Stranraer DG9 0PN Tel: 01776 870219 — BSc (Hons.) Ed. 1960, MB ChB 1963; DObst RCOG 1966. (Ed.) Socs: Fell. (Ex-Pres.) Roy. Med. Soc. Edin. Prev: Edin. Univ. Postgrad. Research Schol. & Clin. Asst., & Ho. Phys. & Ho. Surg. Roy. Infirm. Edin.

CALVERT, Mr John Philip Singleton Hospital, Sketty Lane, Swansea SA2 8QA Tel: 01792 285259 Fax: 01792 285260; 641 Gower Road, Upper Killay, Swansea SA2 7EX Tel: 01792 203415 Fax: 01792 280521 — MB BChir 1973 Camb.; MB Camb. 1973, BChir 1972; MA Camb. 1973; FRCOG 1990, M 1978; DObst 1974. (St. Thos.) Cons. O & G Swansea NHS Trust; Assoc. Med. Director Swansea NHS Trust. Prev: Lect. & Hon. Sen. Regist. (O & G) Univ. Hosp. Wales Cardiff.

CALVERT, John Stuart Waterloo Road Surgery, 178 Waterloo Road, Blackpool FY4 3AD Tel: 01253 348619 Fax: 01253 404330 — MB ChB 1986 Manch.; MRCGP 1990; DRCOG 1991.

CALVERT, John William Orchard House Surgery, Fred Archer Way, Newmarket CB8 8NU Tel: 01638 663322 Fax: 01638 561921; Buck House, 21 The Avenue, Newmarket CB8 9AA Tel: 01638 663881 — MB BS 1968 Lond.; MRCS Eng. LRCP Lond. 1968; DObst RCOG 1970. (Westm.) Assoc. RCGP. Socs: BMA. Prev: SHO Psychiat. Unit W.m. Hosp. Lond.; Ho. Surg. Hillingdon Hosp. Uxbridge; SHO (Geriat.) Middlx. Hosp. Lond.

CALVERT, Julian Triscombe, Roslyn Road, Wellington, Telford TF1 3AX — MB ChB 1969 Birm.

CALVERT, Mr Matthew Hugo (retired) 34 Thorn Road, Bearsden, Glasgow G61 4BS Tel: 0141 942 2439 — BM BCh 1963 Oxf.; FRCS Eng. 1968; FRCS Ed. 1968. Prev: Cons.Gen. & Vasc Surg. Stobhill NHS Trust Glas.

CALVERT, Nigel Irving Rodney 17 Kirkstead Road, Carlisle CA2 7RD — MB ChB 1988 Leic.; MSc Newc. 1993; BSc Leic. 1985; MFPHM RCP (UK) 1995. (Leic.) Cons. Pub. Health Med. Dumfries & Galloway HB.

CALVERT, Mr Paul Thornton St. George's Hospital, Blackshaw Road, London SW17 0QT Tel: 020 8672 1255; 42 Sterndale Road, London W14 0HU Tel: 020 7603 8178 Fax: 020 7610 5407 — MB BChir 1974 Camb.; FRCS Eng. 1978. Cons. Orthop. Surg. St. Geo. Hosp. & Roy. Nat. Orthop. Hosp. Lond. Socs: Fell. BOA; Fell. Roy. Soc. Med.; Brit. Elbow & Shoulder Soc. Prev: Cons. Orthop. Surg. Hinchingbrooke Hosp. Huntingdon; Clin. Fell. (Paediat. Orthop.)

Childr. Hosp. Boston, USA; Sen. Regist. Roy. Nat. Orthop. Hosp. Lond.

CALVERT, Richard John Department of Histopathology, Bradford Royal Infirmary, Ducworth Lane, Bradford BD9 6RJ; 4 Park Copse, Hall Lane, Horsforth, Leeds LS18 5UN — MB ChB 1989 Leeds; BSc (Hons.) Leeds 1986, MB ChB 1989; M.R.C. Path 1997. (University of Leeds) Cons. (Histopath.), Bradford Roy. Infirm., Bradford. Socs: Brit. Div. Internat. Acad. Path.; Assn. Clin. Path. Prev: Sen. Regist. (Histopath.) Leeds Gen. Infirm.; Regist. (Histopath.) Leeds Gen. Infirm.; Ho. Off. (Gen. Med. & Gen. Surg.) Leeds Gen. Infirm.

CALVERT, Roger Martin Fairacre, 1 Main St., Smeeton Westerby, Leicester LE8 0QJ Tel: 0116 279 3456 Fax: 0116 279 3456 Email: rcalvert@ohservices.demon.co.uk — MB BS 1974 Newc.; MMedSc (Occupat. Health) Birm. 1991; MFOM RCP Lond. 1997; MRCGP 1978; DRCOG 1977. Occupat. Health Phys. (Self-employed).

CALVERT, Roger Martin Park Parade Surgery, 27-28 Park Parade, Harrogate HG1 5AG Tel: 01423 502776 Fax: 01423 568036; (Surgery), 27 & 28 Park Parade, Harrogate HG1 5AG — MB ChB 1970 Leeds; MB ChB (Distinc. Path.) Leeds 1970; DObst RCOG 1972.

CALVERT, Sandra Adamson Department Child Health, St George's Hospital, Blackshaw Road, London SW17 0QT Tel: 020 8725 3528 Fax: 020 8725 1933 Email: s.calvert@sghms.ae.uk; 12 Aynhoe Road, London W14 0QD Tel: 020 7602 2617 — MB BChir 1977 Camb.; MA Camb. 1977, MB BChir 1977; MRCP (UK) 1979; FRCP 1997. (Nevisham College Cambridge and the London Hospital) Cons. Neonat. St Geo. Hosp. Lond. Socs: Neonat. Soc.; MRCPCH. Prev: Neonat. Fell. Wom. & Infants Hosp. Providence USA; Neonat. Fell. Wom. Coll. Hosp. Toronto, Canada; Research Fell. (Paediat.) John Radcliffe Hosp. Oxf.

CALVERT, Shelagh Lynne Salisbury District Hospital, Odstock, Salisbury SP2 8BJ Tel: 01722 425050; Knoll Hill Cottage, Knoll Lane, Corfe Mullen, Wimborne BH21 3RF Tel: 01202 694534 — MB BS 1970 Lond.; MRCP (UK) 1974; MRCS Eng. LRCP Lond. 1970; FFA RCS Eng. 1976; DCH Eng. 1972. (St. Geo.) Cons. Anaesth. Salisbury Dist. Hosp. & Dorset Community NHS Trust Dorchester. Socs: Assn. Anaesth.; BMA; Brit. Assoc. of Day Surg. Prev: Cons. Anaesth. W.m. & St. Stephen's Hosps. Lond.; Sen. Resid. Respirat. Care Unit Toronto Gen. Hosp.; Ho. Phys. St. Geo. Hosp. Lond.

CALVERT, Simon Harland Spencer 5/6 South Clerk Street, Edinburgh EH8 9JD — MB ChB 1998 Ed.; MB ChB Ed 1998.

CALVERT, Stephen Felling Health Centre, Stephenson Terrace, Felling, Gateshead NE10 9QG Tel: 0191 469 2316 Fax: 0191 495 0059; 6 Charlcote Crescent, East Boldon NE36 0DT Tel: 0191 536 9723 — MB BChir 1974 Camb.; MA Camb. 1970; MRCGP 1978; DRCOG 1978. (King's Coll. Hosp.)

CALVERT, Susan Mair 4 Park Copse, Hall Lane, Horsforth, Leeds LS18 5UN — MB ChB 1989 Leeds; MRCOG 1995. (Leeds) Regist. Rotat. (O & G) Yorks. RHA.

CALVERT-WILSON, Ian Flat 2, Addington House, 3 Savile Park, Halifax HX1 3EA Tel: 01422 52159 — MB ChB Glas. 1937. (Glas.) Prev: Hon. Lt.-Col. RAMC (Mentioned in Despatches).

CALVEY, Thomas Andrew John 16 Mill Lane, Goostrey, Crewe CW4 8PN — MB ChB 1989 Leic. Trainee (Basic Surg.) Sheff.

CALVEY, Thomas Norman (retired) 16 Mill Lane, Goostrey, Crewe CW4 8PN Tel: 01477 533590 — PhD Liverp. 1962, BSc 1955, MD 1969, MB ChB 1958; FRCA 1993.

CALWELL, Amelia Margaret Isobel Whitehead Health Centre, 17B Edward Road, Whitehead, Carrickfergus BT38 9RU Tel: 028 9335 3454 Fax: 028 9337 2625 — MB BCh BAO 1969 Belf.; Cert. Family Plann. JCC 1977. (Belf.) p/t Approved Med. Off., Chamber of Shipping practicing at Whitehead. Socs: BMA & Med. Equest. Soc. Prev: SHO (Med) Moyle Hosp. Larne; SHO (O & G) Waveney Hosp. Ballymena.

CALWELL, Anna Isobel Jeannette Buena Vista, 6 Calwell Park, Ballycarry, Carrickfergus BT38 9HJ — MB BCh BAO 1957 Belf.

CALWELL, David Ernest 18 Downview Park, Belfast BT15 5HY Tel: 01232 779976 — MB BCh BAO Belf. 1953. Socs: MICGP & MRCGP; BMA.

CALWELL, Humphrey Barron Thames House, Marlow SL7 1QB Tel: 01628 482731 Fax: 01628 482731 — BM BCh 1951 Oxf.; MA, BM BCh Oxf. 1951. Med. Examr. Standard Life & Scott. Widows. Socs: Fell. Roy. Soc. Med.; Fell. & Hon. Mem. Assur. Med. Soc. Prev: Clin. Med. Off. Hambros Bank, Linklater & Paines etc.; Clin. Asst. (Gen. Med. & Neurol.) St. Mary's Hosp. Lond.; Ho. Phys. Middlx. Hosp. Profess. Unit.

CALWELL, Robert (retired) 3 Marlborough Drive, Carnalea, Bangor BT19 1HB Tel: 01247 472720 — MB BCh BAO 1942 Belf.; MRCGP 1968. Clin. Asst. (ENT) Bangor Hosp., Co. Down. Prev: Surg. Lt. RNVR.

CALWELL, William Perry Kirkwood 50 Fairacres, Roehampton Lane, London SW15 5LY Tel: 020 8878 3892 Fax: 020 8878 1746 — MB BS 1958 Lond.; MA Oxf. 1950; FRCPsych 1988, M 1971; DPM Eng. 1962. (Middlx.) Socs: Brit. Soc. Med. & Dent. Hypn. Prev: Med. Dir. Hounslow Child Guid. Clinic; Med. Dir. Hoxton Child Guid. Clinic; Sen. Regist. (Childr. & Parents) Tavistock Clinic.

CAM, John Francis (retired) 'Stonelea', High St., Purton, Swindon SN5 4AD Tel: 01793 770351 — MB BS Lond. 1958; MRCS Eng. LRCP Lond. 1958; FFA RCS Eng. 1963; DA Eng. 1960. Prev: Sen. Regist. Dept. Anaesth. King's Coll. Hosp. Lond.

CAMA, Elizabeth Frances 24 Hope Crescent, Larkhall ML9 2EL — MB BS 1968 Newc.; DObst RCOG 1971. SCMO (Child Health) Gtr. Glas. Health Bd. Prev: Clin. Med. Off. (Child Health) Lanarksh. Health Bd.; Ho. Off. W. Cumbld. Hosp. & Middlesbrough Gen. Hosp.

CAMA, Leonard Stanley Dunstan Swarthbeck Point, Howtown on Ullstwater, Penrith CA10 2ND Tel: 0185 36 420 — MB BS 1941 Durh. (Durh.) Asst. Anaesth. E. Cumbld. Hosp. Gp. Prev: Asst. Anaesth. Sedgefield Gen. Hosp.; Ho. Surg. Roy. Vict. Infirm. Newc.; Surg. Lt. RNVR 1942-46.

CAMAC, John Cramsie (retired) Deep Meadows, 80A Ashby Road E., Bretby, Burton-on-Trent DE15 0PT Tel: 01283 221651 — MB BS 1951 Lond.; MRCS Eng. LRCP Lond. 1950. Prev: Ho. Surg. & Ho. Phys. Pembury Hosp.

CAMARA, Bekai Secka 106 Old Farm Road, Strawberry Vale, E. Finchley, London N2 9RG — MB BS 1983 Lagos; MB BS Lagos, Nigeria 1983.

CAMARA XARDONE, Pedro Miguel 12 Talworth Road, Cardiff CF2 3EA — Lic Med 1989 Lisbon.

CAMBEEN, Leonardus Desire Alphonsus Franciscus Medacs, High Street House, Newmarket St., Skipton BD23 2HU — Artsexamen 1990 Nijmegen.

CAMBELL, Jane Fairlie (retired) Fieldside, Barnet Lane, Totteridge, London N20 8AS Tel: 020 8445 6507 — MB ChB 1945 Aberd.; DCH Eng. 1951. Prev: Asst. Med. Off. Lond. Boro. Enfield.

CAMBRIDGE, Gillian Charlotte Pemberley Surgery, 32 Pemberley Avenue, Bedford MK40 2LA — MB ChB 1983 Manch.; BSc Med. Sci. St. And. 1980; MRCP (UK) 1987; DCH RCP Lond. 1986; DRCOG 1986. Hosp. Pract. (Dermat.) Kettering Gen. Hosp.

CAMBRIDGE, Ian John Glyn Dulyn, Fron Crescent, Llanfairfechan LL33 0SF — MB BCh 1998 Wales.

CAMBRIDGE, Nicholas Anthony Greenside Surgery, 88 Greenside Road, Croydon CR0 3PN Tel: 020 8240 0072 Fax: 020 8240 0074; Acacia Lodge, 61 Bennetts Way, Shirley, Croydon CR0 8AF Tel: 020 8407 1972 Email: nacambridge@hotmail.com — MRCS Eng. LRCP Lond. 1977; Cert. Family Plann. JCC 1984. (Middlx. Hosp.) Primary Appoint. as GP; GP Tutor St. Geo. Hosp. Med. Sch. Lond. Socs: Fell.Med. Soc. of Lond.; (Ex-Hon.Sec.) Osler Club, Lond.; Fell. Roy. Soc. Med. (Ex-Pres. Hist. of Med. Sec.). Prev: Regist. (Radiol.) Middlx. Hosp. Lond.; SHO (A & E & Elderly Care) Middlx. Hosp. Lond.; Ho. Phys. Kettering Gen. Hosp.

CAMERON, Alan Dougal Queen Mothers Hospital, Glasgow G3 8SH Tel: 0141 201 0550 Fax: 0141 357 2785; 15 Greenock Avenue, Glasgow G44 5TS — MB ChB 1980 Glas.; MD Glas. 1991; MRCOG 1985; LMCC 1987. Cons. O & G Fetal Med. Qu. Mother's Hosp. Glas. Socs: Internat. Soc. Study Hypertens. in Pregn.; Fetal Med. & Surg. Soc.; Brit. Med. Ultrasound Soc. Prev: Lect. (O & G) Glas. Roy. Infirm.; Fell. (Matern. & Fetal Med.) Univ. Calgary Alberta, Canada.

CAMERON, Mr Alan Edmond Parsons 4 Parkside Avenue, Ipswich IP4 2UL Tel: 01473 253427 — BM BCh 1973 Oxf.; MA, MCh Oxf. 1983; FRCS Eng. 1978. Cons. Surg. Ipswich Hosp. Socs: Fell. Roy. Soc. Med.; BMA. Prev: Sen. Regist. King's Coll. Hosp. Lond.; Bernard Sunley Research Fell. RCS Eng.

CAMERON, Alasdair Henry Flat 1/1, 13 Mount Stuart Street, Glasgow G41 3YL — MB ChB 1998 Glas.; MB ChB Glas 1998.

CAMERON, Alastair Colville House, Station Road, March PE15 8NR — M.B., Ch.B. Glas. 1934.

CAMERON, Alastair Buchanan, MBE (retired) Achnacarry, 46 Townhead St., Lockerbie DG11 2AE Tel: 01576 202460 — MB ChB 1951 Glas.; FRCGP 1981, M 1973; Hon. FRCPCH 1997.

CAMERON, Alastair Ewen Vale of Leven District General Hospital, Alexandria G83 0UA Tel: 01389 54121 — MB ChB 1972 Glas.; FFA RCS Eng. 1976. Cons. (Anaesth.) Vale of Leven Dist. Gen. Hosp.

CAMERON, Mr Alexander (retired) The Old Rectory, Strumpshaw, Norwich Tel: 01603 712190 — MB ChB 1956 Ed.; ChM Ed. 1973, MB ChB 1956; FRCS Ed. 1961; FRCS Eng. 1962. Prev: Cons. Gen. Surg. Norwich Health Dist.

CAMERON, Alexander United Leeds Teaching Hospital, Leeds Infirmary, Leeds LS1 3EX Tel: 0113 392 2680 Fax: 0113 392 6557 Email: a.cameron@nltht.northy.nhs.uk; 6 Stonegate, Bingley BD16 4SA Fax: 01274 561600 — MB ChB 1972 St. And.; MRCP (UK) 1977; FRCP Lond. 1995; MBA Brunel 1997. (St. And.) Cons. Phys. (Geriat. Med.) Leeds Gen. Infirm. Socs: Fell. RCP; BGS; MDU.

CAMERON, Alexander John (retired) 20 Ardaluin Court, Newcastle BT33 0RT Tel: 028 437 23607 — LRCP LRCS Ed. LRFPS Glas. 1950; FRCP Ed. 1981 M, 1957; DTM & H Liverp. 1955. Prev: Cons. Phys. Downpatrick Gp. Hosps.

CAMERON, Alexandra Marie 39 Radbrook Road, Shrewsbury SY3 9BQ — MB BS 1997 Lond.

CAMERON, Alick (retired) Vinnicombes, Trusham, Newton Abbot TQ13 0NP Tel: 01626 853298 Email: alick@widgelum.demon.co.uk — MB ChB 1946 Ed.; MD 1952 Ed; DHMSA 1987; DO 1959 Eng; MRCGP 1959. Prev: Asst. Ophth. Hosp. Sick Childr. Gt. Ormond St. Lond.

CAMERON, Alistair Gordon The Rothbury Practice, 3 Market Place, Rothbury, Morpeth NE65 7UW Tel: 01669 620339 Fax: 01669 620583; Westhills House, Rothbury, Morpeth NE65 7YR Tel: 01669 621179 — MB BS 1977 Newc.; MB BS (Hons.) Newc. 1977; MRCP (UK) 1979; MRCGP 1982. Prev: SHO (Med.) Roy. Vict. Infirm. Newc.

CAMERON, Alistair Wood 279 Otley Road, Leeds LS16 5LN Tel: 0113 278 6132 — MB ChB 1975 Glas.; MRCGP 1982; MFCM RCP (UK) 1982; MPH Leeds 1980. (Glasg.) Clin. Asst. (A&E) Leeds Gen. Infirm. Prev: Sen. Med. Off. DoH; Med. Dir. Wakefield Family Health Serv. Auth.; GP Leeds.

CAMERON, Andrew Hamish Hackwood Partnership, Essex House, Worting Road, Basingstoke RG21 8SU Tel: 01256 470464 Fax: 01256 357289; 18 Pyotts Copse, Old Basing, Basingstoke RG24 8WE Tel: 01256 819909 — MB BCh BAO 1990 NUI; LRCPSI 1990; MRCGP 1995. GP.

CAMERON, Andrew James 23 Lane Side, Huddersfield HD5 0EP — MB ChB 1992 Leeds.

CAMERON, Andrew John Waterfield House Surgery, 186 Henwood Green Road, Pembury, Tunbridge Wells TN2 4LR Tel: 01892 825488 — MB BS 1985 Lond.

CAMERON, Angus Thomson Lorn Medical Centre, Soroba Road, Oban PA34 4HE Tel: 01631 563175 Fax: 01631 562708 — MB ChB 1972 Glas.

CAMERON, Anne Veronica Inchpark Surgery, 10 Marmion Crescent, Edinburgh EH16 5QU Tel: 0131 666 2121; 6B St. Margarets Road, Edinburgh EH9 1AZ — MB ChB 1979 Manch.; BSc St. And. 1976; DRCOG 1983.

CAMERON, Aziz Trelawn, Nackington Road, Canterbury CT4 7AX Tel: 01227 784944 Fax: 01227 784944 Email: drcameron@trelawncant.fsnet.co.uk — MD 1970 Tabriz; DPM Tehran 1978. Cons. Psychiat. William Harvey Hosp. Ashford Kent. Socs: BMA; Affil. Roy. Coll. Psychiat. Prev: Regist. (Psychiat.) Worcs. Roy. Infirm. & Seymour Clinic Swindon; SHO (Psychiat.) P.ss Alexandra Hosp. Harlow.

CAMERON, Barbara Ann Priory Fields Surgery, Nursery Road, Huntingdon PE29 3RL Tel: 01480 52361 Fax: 01480 434640; 6 Rosemary Road, Waterbeach, Cambridge CB5 9NB Tel: 01223 563295 — MB ChB 1991 Aberd.; DCH RCPS Glas. 1995; DRCOG - RCOG 1995; MRCGP - RCGP 1996; DFFP - FFPRHC 1996. (Aberdeen) GP. Prev: GP Regist. TayMt. Surg. Perth; SHO (O & G) Ninewells Hosp. Dundee; SHO (Paediat.) Stirling Roy. Infirm.

CAMERON, Bronislaw (retired) 2 Park Villas, The Green, Wallsend NE28 7NW Tel: 0191 262 4480 — Med. Dipl. Warsaw 1935. Prev: GP Med. Asst. (ENT) Preston Hosp. N. Sheilds.

CAMERON, Catherine 38 Lamberton Court, Pencaitland, Tranent EH34 5BL — MB ChB 1988 Ed.; MRCGP 1993. Trainee GP Livingston VTS. Prev: SHO (O & G, Psychiat. & Med.) Livingston.

CAMERON, Mr Charles Robert Department of Cardiothoracic Surgery, Guys Hospital, London SE1 9RT Tel: 020 7955 2535 Fax: 020 7955 4858; Tel: 01732 762424 — MB ChB Manch. 1970; FRCS Ed. 1976. Cons. Thoracic Surg. Guys Hosp. Lond. Socs: Soc. Cardiothoracic Surgs. GB & Irel.; Roy. Soc. Med.; BMA. Prev: Cons. Thoracic Surg. Brook Gen. Hosp. Lond.; Sen. Regist. (Cardiothoracic Surg.) Freeman Hosp. Newc.

CAMERON, Christopher Hayles (retired) Kingledores, 9 Kingscroft, Kelso TD5 7NU Tel: 01573 224218 Fax: 01573 224218 — MB ChB Ed. 1964; DObst RCOG 1967; MSc (by research) Eng Ed. 1999. Prev: GP Kelso.

CAMERON, Colin Flat 30, York House, Queen Alexandra Hospital, Southwick Hill Road, Cosham, Portsmouth PO6 3LY — MB ChB 1995 Glas.

CAMERON, David 18 Crosskeys Road, Ahoghill, Ballymena BT42 2QT — MB BCh BAO 1992 Belf.; MB BCh Belf. 1992.

CAMERON, David Allan Department of Clinical Oncology, Western General Hospital, Crewe Road S., Edinburgh EH4 2XU Tel: 0131 537 1000 Fax: 0131 537 1014 Email: david.cameron@ed.ac.uk — MB BS 1986 Lond.; MSc Ed. 1993; MA Camb. 1981; MRCP (UK) 1989; MD Ed. 1997. (London) Sen. Lect. (Med. Oncol.) Dept.Oncol.W.ern Gen. Hosp. Edin. Socs: Fell.Roy. Coll. Phys. Edin & ACP. Prev: Sen. Regist. (Med. Oncol.) W.. Gen. Hosp. Edin.; ICRF Clin. Research Fell. W.. Gen. Hosp. Edin.; Lect.(Med. Oncol). Edin. Univ. & W.. Gen. Hosp. Edin.

CAMERON, Diane Joan Smith 3 Grenville Court, Silverdale Road, Southampton SO15 2TD — BM 1995 Soton.

CAMERON, Donald (retired) 137 Horsham Road, Cranleigh GU6 8DZ — MB BChir 1957 Camb.; MA, MB Camb. 1957, BChir 1956. Prev: Obst. Ho. Surg. Mothers' Hosp. (Salvation Army) Lond.

CAMERON, Donald Findlater 124 Chaucer Drive, Aylesbury HP21 7LN — MB ChB 1955 Ed.

CAMERON, Donald John Craig (retired) 7 Duncan Avenue, Fochabers IV32 7HW Tel: 01343 820668 — MB ChB 1955 Glas.; FRCP Glas. 1985, M 1964; DObst RCOG 1957; DPH 1966; DCH Eng. 1960. Prev: Unit Med. Off. W. Unit Grampian HB & Dist. Med. Off. W. Dist. Grampian HB.

CAMERON, Donald William, MBE (retired) Tanlaw, Braid Road, Hawick TD9 9LZ Tel: 01450 74232 — LRCP LRCS 1951 Ed.; LRCP LRCS Ed. LRFPS Glas. 1951.

CAMERON, Douglas Drury House, 50 Leicester Road, Narborough, Leicester LE9 5DF Tel: 0116 286 3267 Fax: 0116 275 2840 — MB ChB 1969 Glas.; BSc (Hons. Physiol.) Glas. 1967, MD 1992; FRCPsych 1988, M 1974; DPM Eng. 1972. Sen. Lect. (Subst. Misuse) Univ. Leicester; Assoc. Edr. Addic. Research. Prev: Cons. Psychiat. Alcohol Problems Leics. HA (T); Regist. & Sen. Regist. Crichton Roy. Dumfries.

CAMERON, Duncan James Silver Springs Medical Practice, Beaufort Road, St Leonards-on-Sea TN37 6PP Tel: 01424 422300/426464 Fax: 01424 436400; 9 Baldslow Down, St Leonards-on-Sea TN37 7NH — MRCS Eng. LRCP Lond. 1968; DTM & H Liverp. 1971; DObst RCOG 1970. (St. Bart.) Prev: Med. Supt. Kabarole Hosp. Uganda; SHO (Anaesth.) Edgware Gen. Hosp.; Ho. Surg. Redhill Gen. Hosp.

CAMERON, Mr Duncan Stewart 52 Elmfield Road, Gosforth, Newcastle upon Tyne NE3 4BB Tel: 0191 285 1618 — MB BS 1964 Durh.; FRCS Ed. 1971. (Durh.) Cons. ENT Surg. Freeman Hosp. Newc. Socs: BMA & Scott. Otolaryng. Soc. Prev: Sen. Regist. ENT Dept. Roy. Infirm. Edin.; Regist. ENT Dept. Roy. Vict. Infirm. Newc.; Asst. Dept. Anat. Univ. Glas.

CAMERON, Edwin Arthur Balfour Lime Tree Surgery, Lime Tree Avenue, Findon Valley, Worthing BN14 0DL Tel: 01903 264101 Fax: 01903 695494 — MB BS 1972 Lond.; MRCS Eng. LRCP Lond. 1972; MRCGP 1977.

CAMERON, Eileen Marischal (retired) 2 Wildon Way, Radbrook, Shrewsbury SY3 9RD Tel: 01743 55738 — MB ChB 1942 Aberd.

CAMERON, Elaine Kingsway Medical Practice, 12Kingsway Court, Glasgow G14 9SS Tel: 0141 959 6000 Fax: 0141 954 6971 — MB ChB 1988 Glas.

CAMERON, Elizabeth Ann Mitchell and Partners, The Park Surgery, Old Tetbury Road, Cirencester GL7 1US Tel: 01285 654733 Fax: 01285 641408 — MB ChB 1982 Manch.; BSc (Hons.) Physiol. 1979; MRCGP 1987; DRCOG 1988. Prev: Trainee GP Swindon & Cirencester VTS; SHO (Obst.) St Paul's Hosp. Cheltenham; SHO (Orthop. & A & E) P.ss Margt. Hosp. Swindon.

CAMERON, Elizabeth Ann The Surgery, 41 Lyndhurst Road, Barnehurst, Bexleyheath DA7 6DL Tel: 01322 525000 Fax: 03122 523123 — MB BS 1984 Lond.; BSc Lond. 1981, MB BS 1984; MRCGP 1988; DRCOG 1988. Prev: GP Sidcup.

CAMERON, Elizabeth Anne Carlisle Road Surgery, 230 Carlisle Road, Queens Park, Bedford MK40 4HT Tel: 01234 351661 Fax: 01234 364884; 66 Tyne Crescent, Bedford MK41 7UL Tel: 01234 351777 — MB ChB 1977 Ed.

CAMERON, Emma Leslie (retired) Priorscroft, Hepburn Gardens, St Andrews KY16 9LS Tel: 01334 473996 — MB ChB 1951 Aberd.; MD Aberd. 1956; MRCPsych 1975; DPM Eng. 1970; DCH Eng. 1954. Prev: Assoc. Specialist (Psychiat.) Stratheden Hosp. Cupar.

CAMERON, Euan George Mackintosh The Surgery, The Old Vicarage, The Green, Pirbright, Woking GU24 0JE Tel: 01483 474473 — MRCS Eng. LRCP Lond. 1966; MB BS Lond. 1966, BPharm 1959; MRCGP 1975; DObst RCOG 1969; Dip. Pharm. Med. 1980. (Char. Cross) Prev: Ho. Phys. & Ho. Surg. W. Lond. Hosp.

CAMERON, Mr Evan (retired) Hazelbridge House, Chiddingfold, Godalming GU8 4TS Tel: 01428 683125 Fax: 01428 683125 — MA, BM BCh Oxf. 1954; FRCS Eng. 1966. Hon. Cons. Ophth. Surg. Roy. Surrey Co. Hosp. Guildford & Haslemere Hosp.; Examr. Brit. Orthoptic Bd. Prev: Ophth. 1st Asst. St. Geo. Hosp. Lond.

CAMERON, Mr Evan William John 2 Sciennes House Place, Edinburgh EH9 1NW Tel: 0131 668 1634 — MB ChB 1966 Ed.; BSc (Hons.) Ed. 1963, MB ChB 1966; FRCS Ed. 1973. (Ed.) Cardiothoracic Surg. Roy. Infirm. & City Hosp. Edin. Socs: Thoracic Soc. & Soc. Thoracic & Cardiovasc. Surg. Prev: Thoracic Surg. Wentworth & King Geo. V Hosps. Durban S. Africa.

CAMERON, Ewan Ferguson 50 Wallasey Village, Wallasey CH45 3NL Tel: 0151 691 2088; 43 Glen Park Road, Wallasey CH45 5JL Tel: 0151 639 1421 — MB ChB 1981 Manch.; MRCGP 1988; DRCOG 1984. GP Wallasey.

CAMERON, Ewen Alasdair Balfour 23 Harford Drive, Watford WD17 3DQ — BChir 1995 Camb.; MB Camb. 1995; BA Camb. 1993; MA Camb. 1997; MRCP (UK) 1998. Specialist Regist., Gastroenterol. & Gen. Med., Bedford Hosp.

CAMERON, Ewen Archibald (retired) Lowlyn, Stakeford Lane, Stakeford, Choppington NE62 5JB Tel: 01670 812070 — MB ChB St. And. 1952; FRCP Ed. 1971, M 1957. Hon. Cons. Phys. N.d. HA. Prev: Cons. Phys. N.ern Regional HA.

CAMERON, Ewen Wood 33 Grampian Avenue, Auchterarder PH3 1NY — MB ChB 1944 Glas.; BSc Glas. 1941, MB ChB 1944. (Univ. Glas.) Prev: Ho. Phys. Vict. Infirm. Glas.; Capt. RAMC.

CAMERON, Fergus John Department of Endocrinology, Great Ormond Street Hospital for Children NHS Trust, Great Ormond St., London WC1N 3JH — MB BS 1986 Melbourne; FRACGP 1994.

CAMERON, Fiona Margaret Lindsay Dept. of Anaesthesia, Ninewells Hospital, Dundee DD1 9SY — MB ChB 1989 Dundee; FRCA 1994. Socs: Obstetric Anaesth. Assn.

CAMERON, Fiona Sarah Peden Gill Cottage, Nr Elvanfoot, Biggar ML12 6TH Tel: 01864 505208 — MB ChB 1987 Aberd.; DCH RCPS Glas. 1992. Clin. Med. Off. (Paediat.) Motherwell.

CAMERON, Gordon Milton Surgery, 132 Mountcastle Drive South, Edinburgh EH15 3LL; 23 Knowesley Park, Haddington EH41 3TB Tel: 01620 826797 — MB ChB 1985 Ed.; DMS Med 1994 Lond.; 1972 Lond.; MRCGP 1989; DCH RCPS Glas. 1987. GP Princip. Edin. Socs: Fell. Soc. Orthop. Med. Prev: SHO (Med. & Neonat. Paediat.) Roy. Hosp. for Sick Childr. Glas.; SHO (O & G) Bangour Gen. Hosp.

CAMERON, Gordon Ian, TD, CStJ (retired) 2 Chestnut Avenue, Hessle HU13 0RJ Tel: 01482 648516 — MB ChB 1948 Glas.; FRCGP 1980, M 1963. DL. Prev: Col. late RAMC, TA, ADMS 50(N) Inf. Div. TA.

CAMERON, Hamish Alan Medical Affairs Department, Zeneca Pharmaceuticals, Alderly Park, Macclesfield SK10 4TG Tel: 01625 513764 — MB BS 1978 Lond.; MB BS (Hons.) Lond. 1978; BSc Lond. 1975; MRCP (UK) 1981; FFPM RCP (UK) 1994. (Univ. Coll. Hosp.) Manager Med. Affairs Dept. Zeneca Pharmaceuts. Prev: Med. Adviser Janssen Pharmaceuts.; Resid. Fell. (Therap.) Roy. Hallamsh. Hosp. Sheff.; Regist. (Med.) N. Staffs. Hosp. Centre Stoke-on-Trent.

CAMERON, Hamish Clark Surrey, Richmond TW10 5BL Tel: 0208 392 0660 Fax: 0208 876 5141; 2 King's Ride Gate, Richmond TW10 5BL Tel: 020 8392 0660 Fax: 020 8876 5141 — MB BChir 1960 Camb.; MA; FRCPsych 1981, M 1971; DPM Lond. 1968; MRCP (Lond.) 1964, FRCP 1968. (Camb. & Middlx.) Hon. Cons. & Hon. Sen. Lect. Child Psychiat. St. Geo. Hosp & Med. Sch. Lond.; Hon. Cons. Psychiat. Childlink Adopt. Soc.; Mem. Counc. Caldecott Found.; Mem. Screening Comm., Jt. Educat. Trust; Prof. Advr .Coram Family. (Formerly Thomas Coram Foundat.). Socs: Assoc. Mem. Brit. Psychoanal. Soc.; Assn. Child Psychol. & Psychiat.; BMA. Prev: Cons. Child Psychiat. Cassel Hosp. Richmond, Surrey; Sen. Regist. (Child Psychiat.) Bethlem Roy. & Maudsley Hosps.; Ho. Phys. Hosp. Sick Childr. Gt. Ormond St.

CAMERON, Heather Jean 23 Myrtle Av., Kirkintilloch, Glasgow G66 4HW — MB ChB 1986 Glas. Prev: Regist. (Psychiat.) S.. Gen. Hosp. Glas.; SHO (Psychiat.) Leverndale Hosp. Glas.

CAMERON, Heather Margaret 5 Murray Road, Scone, Perth PH2 6RQ — MB ChB 1987 Ed.; MRCGP 1991; DCCH RCP Ed. 1993. Clin. Research Fell. (Photobiol. & Dermat.) Ninewells Hosp. & Med. Sch. Dundee. Prev: Trainee GP Bangour Gen. Hosp., W. Lothian VTS.

CAMERON, Hector MacDonald, OBE (retired) 25 Gallowhill, Peebles EH45 9BG — MD 1945 Belf.; MD Belf. 1959. MB BCh BAO 1945; FRCPath 1968, M 1963. Prev: Sen. Lect. Path. Univ. Edin.

CAMERON, Helen Lee (retired) 44 Lauderdale Gardens, Hyndland, Glasgow G12 9QT Tel: 0141 339 4474 — MB BS 1954 Lond.; MRCS Eng. LRCP Lond. 1954. Prev: Cas. Off. & Ho. Phys. Roy. Free Hosp. Lond.

CAMERON, Helen Margaret Sunderland Royal Hospital, Kayll Road, Sunderland SR4 7TP Tel: 0191 565 6256 — MB BS 1979 Newc.; MB BS (Hons.) Newc. 1979; MRCOG 1984. Cons. O & G Sunderland HA. Prev: Sen. Regist. (O & G) N.. HA; Regist. (O & G) N.. RHA VTS.

CAMERON, Helen Stewart Medical Teaching Orgainisation, Medical Faculty Office, University of Edinburgh, Medical School, Teviot Place, Edinburgh EH8 9AG Tel: 0131 650 6829 / 6965 Email: helen.cameron@ed.ac.uk; 7B Kilgraston Road, Edinburgh EH9 2DR Tel: 0131 447 0060 Email: helen.cameron@ed.ac.uk — MB ChB 1980 Ed.; BSc (Med. Sci) Ed. 1977; MRCP (UK) 1986. (Ed.) Fell.Med.Edu. - Dep. Director of the Med. Teachg. Organisation. Prev: Regist. (Med.) N.ampton Gen. Hosp.; SHO (Radiother. & Oncol.) W.m. Hosp. Lond. & Cookridge Hosp. Leeds.

***CAMERON, Henry Alexander Charles** 20 Balfour Crescent, Wolverhampton WV6 0BJ Tel: 01902 751512 — MB BS 1998 Lond.; MB BS Lond 1998; BSc Lond (Hons.) 1995.

CAMERON, Hugh Alexander Allison and Partners, Maryhill Health Centre, 41 Shawpark Street, Glasgow G20 9DR Tel: 0141 531 8840 Fax: 0141 531 8848 — MB ChB 1987 Dundee.

CAMERON, Iain Alexander Nicolson 101 Greycraigs, Cairneyhill, Dunfermline KY12 8XW — MB ChB 1998 Glas.; MB ChB Glas 1998.

CAMERON, Iain Crawford 21 Newington Road, Hunters Bar, Sheffield S11 8RZ — MB ChB 1990 Sheff.

CAMERON, Professor Iain Thomas Department of Obstetrics & Gynaecology, University of Glasgow, The Queen Mother's Hospital, Yorkhill, Glasgow G3 8SJ Tel: 0141 201 0567 Fax: 0141 357 3610 Email: iain.t.cameron@clinmed.gla.ac.uk — MB ChB 1980 Ed.; BSc (Med. Sci.) Ed. 1977, MD 1988; MA Camb. 1992; MRACOG 1987; MRCOG 1986; T(OG) 1991. (Univ. Ed.) Regius Prof. O & G Univ. Glas. Prev: Univ. Lect., Cons. & Clin. Lect. (O & G) Univ. Camb.; Lect. (O & G) Univ. Edin.

CAMERON, Ian Alexander La Saline, Rue De La Saline, Grandes Rocques, Castel — MB ChB 1992 Sheff.

CAMERON, Ian Archer (retired) 37 Terregles Street, Dumfries DG2 9AA — MD 1962 Ed.; MB ChB 1949; FRCPsych 1979, M 1972; DPM Eng. 1955. Prev: Cons. Psychiat. Crichton Roy. Hosp. Dumfries.

CAMERON, Ian Hugh Department of Public Health Medicine, Leeds Health Authority, Blenhein House, Duncombe St, Leeds

LS1 4PL Tel: 0113 295 2038; 9 Staveley Road, Nabwood, Shipley BD18 4HD — MB ChB 1978 Liverp.; MA 1997 Leeds; FFPHM 1998; MFPHM 1990; MPH Leeds 1988.

CAMERON, Professor Ian Rennell University of Wales College of Medicine, Heath Park, Cardiff CF14 4XN Tel: 029 2074 2071 Fax: 029 2074 5306 — BM BCh Oxf. 1961; DM Oxf. 1969; FRCP Lond. 1976, M 1964. (St. Thos.) Vice-Chancellor Univ. Wales Coll. Med. Cardiff; Mem. CVCP; Mem. (Treas.) GMC; Mem. Commiss. for Health Improvement. Socs: Fell. Acad. Med. Soc.; Physiol. Soc.; Brit. Thorac. Soc. Prev: Prof. Med. & Princip. United Med. & Dent. Sch. Guy's & St. Thos. Hosps. Lond.; Dir. Research & Developm. SE Thames RHA; Sen. Lect. (Med.) St. Thos. Hosp. Med. Sch. Lond.

CAMERON, Innes Lorimer Cleveland Clinic, 12 Cleveland Road, St Helier, Jersey JE1 4HD; Montemare, Lasaline, St Ouen, Jersey JE3 2FG Tel: 01534 485458 — MB ChB 1983 Manch.; MRCGP 1987; DRCOG 1988; DCH RCP Lond. 1988. Prev: Trainee GP Jersey VTS; GP Nottm.; SHO (Psychiat.) Roy. S.. Hosp. Soton.

CAMERON, James Donald Hedley 23 Harford Drive, Watford WD17 3DQ — MRCS Eng. LRCP Lond. 1970; MB Camb. 1971, BChir 1970.

CAMERON, Professor James Malcolm 55 Coniston Road, Bromley BR1 4JG — MB ChB Glas. 1954; PhD Glas. 1966, MD (Commend.) 1959; FRCS Glas. 1983; FRCPath 1977, M 1965; DMJ(Path) Soc. Apoth. Lond. 1962. (Glas.) Emerit. Prof. Forens. Med. Univ. Lond. at Lond. Hosp. Med. Coll.; Consg. Edr. Med., Sc. & The Law. Socs: Amer. Acad. Forens. Sci. (Retd. Fell.). Prev: Prof. Forens. Med. Univ. Lond. Lond. Hosp. Med. Coll. & Hon. Cons. Lond. Hosp.; Ver Heyden de Lancey Reader (Forens. Med.) Counc. Legal Educat.; Hon. Cons. Forens. Med. to the Army at Home, RN & RAF.

CAMERON, Janet Bodelwy, Mount Road, St Asaph LL17 0DF — MB BS Lond. 1980; BSc Lond. 1977; DRCOG 1984. p/t GP Asst. Plas Meddyg. (Station Rd) Ruthin.

CAMERON, Janet Frances The Vestry, Tarbet, Loch Nevis, Mallaig PH41 4PP — MB ChB 1966 Glas.

CAMERON, Jenness Margaret Craiglockhart Surgery, 161 Colinton Road, Edinburgh EH14 1BE Tel: 0131 455 8494; 21 Morningside Gardens, Edinburgh EH10 5LE Tel: 0131 447 2348 Email: j.m.cameron@btinternet.com — MB ChB 1987 Ed.; MRCGP 1991; Cert. Family Plann. JCC 1991. (Ed.) GP Asst., Craiglockheart Surg., Edin. Socs: BMA; MRCGP. Prev: Staff Grade (HIV/Palliat. Care) Milestone Hse. Edin.; Trainee GP (Paediat.) Edin.; Trainee GP Craigshill Health Centre.

CAMERON, John Victoria Road Surgery, 21 Victoria Road, Acocks Green, Birmingham B27 7XZ Tel: 0121 706 1129 Fax: 0121 765 4927; 321 Warwick Road, Olton, Solihull B92 7AA Tel: 0121 706 7677 — MB ChB 1984 Ed.; MRCGP 1990; DRCOG 1989; DGM RCP Lond. 1987. Prev: Trainee GP Birm. VTS; SHO (O & G) Wom. Hosp. Birm.

CAMERON, John Angus Biggar Health Centre, South Croft Road, Biggar ML12 6BE Tel: 01899 220383 Fax: 01899 221583 — MB ChB 1978 Ed.; MRCGP 1982. GP Biggar; Non-Exec. Dir. Lanarksh. Health Bd. Hamilton.

CAMERON, Mr John Austen Percival, MBE (retired) Moonglow, Hill Road, Grayshott, Hindhead GU26 6HL Tel: 01428 604205 — MB ChB 1929 Ed.; MCh Orth. Liverp. 1946; FRCS Ed. 1935. Prev: Prof. Orthop. Surg. Univ. Malaya, Singapore.

CAMERON, John David Templepatrick Surgery, 80 Castleton, Templepatrick, Ballyclare BT39 0AZ Tel: 028 9443 2202 Fax: 028 9443 3707; 30 Lylehill Green, Templepatrick, Ballyclare BT39 0BF Tel: 01840 433144 — MB BCh BAO 1977 Belf.; MRCGP 1982; DRCOG 1981.

CAMERON, Mr John Hector (retired) Meadowland, 5 Southwood, Troon KA10 7EL — MB ChB 1946 Glas.; FRCS Glas. 1983; DO Eng. 1960. Prev: Cons. Ophth. Surg. Ayrsh. Gp. Hosps.

CAMERON, John Malcolm Weatherstone The Stables, Waughton Steading, East Linton EH40 3DY — MB ChB 1996 Glas.

CAMERON, Professor John Stewart, CBE Elm Bank, Melmerby, Penrith CA10 1HB Tel: 01768 881804 Fax: 01768 881105 Email: jstewart_cameron@email.msn.com — BSc (1st cl. Hons.) Lond. 1956, MD 1965, MB BS (Hons.) 1959; FRCP Lond. 1971, M 1960; MRCS Eng. LRCP Lond. 1958. (Guy's) Emerit. Prof. Renal Med. Guy's Hosp. King's Coll. Lond. Socs: Pres. Europ. Renal Assn. 1984-1987; Pres. Internat. Soc. Nephrol. 1993-1995.; Pres. Renal Assn. UK 1993-5. Prev: Research Fell. Cornell Med. Coll. New York; Ho. Off. Guy's Hosp. Lond.

CAMERON, Katharine Macphail (retired) 48/3 Coltbridge Avenue, Edinburgh EH12 6AH — MB ChB 1951 Ed.; BSc St. And. 1944; FRCPath 1974, M 1963. Prev: Sen. Lect. (Path.) Inst. Urol. Lond.

CAMERON, Kathryn Jane 37 Kilnford Court, Dundonald, Kilmarnock KA2 9DN — MB ChB 1994 Glas.

CAMERON, Kenneth Allan (retired) Blackford House, Haugh-of-Urr, Castle Douglas DG7 3LE — MB ChB Glas. 1951; MFCM 1974; Dip. Soc. Med. Ed. 1971. Prev: Princip. Med. Off. DSS.

CAMERON, Kenneth Sutherland (retired) 31 Barley Mill Road, Bridgehill, Consett DH8 8JS Tel: 01207 502189 — MB ChB Aberd. 1951; FCA RCSI 1964; DA Eng. 1957. Prev: Cons. Anaesth. Shotley Bridge Gen. Hosp.

CAMERON, Lewis (retired) Lawton Bank, 35 Ferry Road, Monifieth, Dundee DD5 4NS Tel: 01382 533833 — MB ChB 1959 Glas.; FFCM 1980, M 1974; Dip. Soc. Med. Ed. 1968. Prev: Chief Admin. Med. Off. & Dir. Pub. Health Tayside HB.

CAMERON, Lucy Anne 11 Tredegar Road, Caversham, Reading RG4 8QE — MB BS 1997 Lond.

CAMERON, Malcolm Gray (retired) 37 Chesterfield Avenue, Glasgow G12 0BN Tel: 0141 339 1330 — LRCP LRCS Ed. LRFPS Glas. 1953; AFOM RCP Lond. 1982. Prev: Sen. Partner, GP Gp. Pract., Springburn Health Centre, Glas.

CAMERON, Malcolm Gregor 26 George Road, Guildford GU1 4NP — MB BS 1996 Lond.; BDS Lond.1989; LDS RCS UK 1990; FDS RCS UK 1995. (St. Bartholomews Lond.) Surgic. SHO.Roy.Surrey.Co..Hosp.Guildford.

CAMERON, Mr Malcolm Maben Liley Beck, Clough Lane, Upper Hopton, Mirfield WF14 8EQ Tel: 01924 480588 Fax: 01924 480588 Email: mcameron@nigra.demon.co.uk — MB ChB 1966 Otago; BSc Vict. (Wellington) 1961; FRCS Ed. 1973. (Otago) Medico-Legal & Med. Negligence Cons. W. Yorks. Socs: Soc. Brit. Neurol. Surgs. Prev: Cons. Neurosurg. Pinderfields Hosp. Wakefield & St. Jas. Univ. Hosp. Leeds; Hon. Cons. (Neurosurg.) Gen. Infirm. Leeds; Sen. Regist. (Neurosurg.) Roy. Manch. Childr. Hosp. & Salford Roy. Hosp.

CAMERON, Margaret Ann Braemoray, 56 Hamilton Drive, Elgin IV30 4NJ Tel: 01343 542731 — MB ChB 1965 Aberd. (Aberd.) Prev: Med. Off. Grampian HB.

CAMERON, Margaret Dickson (retired) 21 Morston, Thornford, Sherborne DT9 6RB — MB ChB 1937 Aberd.; DPH Aberd. 1953; DMR Ed. 1946.

CAMERON, Margery Christine 97 Gladstone Way, Hawarden, Deeside CH5 3HE Tel: 01244 531629 — MB BCh BAO 1949 Belf. (Belf.)

CAMERON, Martin James 5 Anchorage Mews, Thornaby, Stockton-on-Tees TS17 6BG Tel: 01642 671886 — MB ChB 1994 Dundee; BMSc (Hons.) Dund 1992; DRCOG 1996. (Dund.) Specialist Regist. (O & G)Hartlepool Gen. Hosp. Hartlepool. Prev: SHO.W. Cumbria Health Care Trust Whitehaven.; SHO S. Cleveland Hosp. Middlesbrough.; SHO Sunderland City Hosp.

CAMERON, Mary Louise Highpoint House, Memorial Hospital, Shooters Hill, London SE18 3RZ — MB BS 1988 Adelaide; CCST 1997; MRCPsych 1992. Cons., Child & Adolesc. Psychiat. Socs: BMA & Med. Defence Union. Prev: Lect. (Child Psychiat.) SW Thames.

CAMERON, Maureen Elizabeth Lorn Medical Centre, Soroba Road, Oban PA34 4HE Tel: 01631 563175 Fax: 01631 562708 — MB ChB 1972 Glasgow; MB ChB Glas. 1972. (Glasgow) GP Oban, Argyll.

CAMERON, Michele-Yvette St Augustines Medical Practice, 4 Station Road, Keynsham, Bristol BS31 2BN Tel: 0117 986 2343 Fax: 0117 986 1176 — MB ChB 1986 Bristol; MRCGP 1990. (Bristol) Clin. Asst. (Geriat. Med.) Keynsham Hosp. Prev: SHO (Obst. & Paediat.) S.mead Hosp. Bristol; SHO (Geriat. Med.) Ham Green Hosp. Bristol; SHO (Gyn.) Bristol Gen. Hosp.

CAMERON, Niall MacLaine Govan Health Centre, 5 Drumoyne Road, Glasgow G51 4BJ Tel: 0141 531 8400 Fax: 0141 531 8404; 24 Churchill Drive, Broomhill, Glasgow G11 7LS — MB ChB 1982 Glas.; MRCGP 1986; DRCOG 1984.

CAMERON, Pauline Mary 2 Greenway Road, Timperley, Altrincham WA15 6BE Tel: 0161 969 2044 — MB ChB 1971

Manch.; DObst RCOG 1973. (Manch.) Clin. Asst. (Diag. Ultrasound) Stepping Hill Hosp. Stockport. Prev: SHO (Gyn. & Obst.) St. Mary's Hosp. Manch.; SHO (O & G) Stepping Hill Hosp. Stockport.

CAMERON, Peter Strang 358 Rowood Drive, Solihull B92 9LL — MB ChB 1972 Birm. (Birm.) SHO (Anaesth.) Sheff. AHA (T). Socs: BMA. Prev: Cas. Off. Sheff. AHA (T); Hosp. Med. Off. Mpilo Hosp. Bulawayo, Rhodesia.

CAMERON, Robert Iain 1 Balmoral Court, Lisburn Road, Belfast BT9 7GR — MB BCh BAO 1995 Belf.

CAMERON, Robert Thomas (retired) 1 Dalwhatswood Road, Newmilns KA16 9LT Tel: 01560 321114 — MB ChB Glas. 1953.

CAMERON, Roderick Charles Pearson Ninewells Hospital, Dundee DD1 9SY Tel: 01382 660111; Kirkhowe of Ruthven, Blairgowrie PH12 8RQ — MB ChB 1976 Ed.; BSc Ed. 1973; DMRD Ed. 1981. Cons. Radiol. Ninewells Hosp. & Med. Sch. Dundee.

CAMERON, Seonaid Catherine (retired) 1/21 Homeross House, Mount Grange, Strathearn Road, Edinburgh EH9 29X Tel: 0131 447 9103 — MB ChB 1949 St. And.; DPH Eng. 1957; DObst RCOG 1953.

CAMERON, Serena 51 Elms Avenue, Littleover, Derby DE23 6FB — MB ChB 1994 Sheff. (Sheff.) SHO (Med.) Derby City Gen. Hosp. Prev: SHO (A & E) Derbysh. Roy. Infirm.; SHO (Paediat.) Derbysh. Childr. Hosp.; Ho. Off. (Surg. & Med.) Rotherham Dist. Gen. Hosp.

CAMERON, Sharon Tracey Department of Obstetrics & Gynaecology, University of Edinburgh, Centre for Reproductive Biology, 37 Chalmers St., Edinburgh EH3 9EW Tel: 0131 229 2575 — MB ChB 1991 Ed.; MD 1996; MRCOG 1998. (Ed.) Specialist Regist. (O & G) Roy. Infirm. Edin.; Lect. in Obst. & Gyn. Socs: Soc. Study Fertil.; Brit. Fertil. Soc.; Soc. Endocrinol. Prev: Clin. Research Fell. (O & G) Centre for Reproduc. Biol. Edin.; SHO (O & G) Roy. Infirm. Edin.

CAMERON, Sheila Margaret Gordon House, 73 Banbury Road, Southam, Leamington Spa CV47 1HJ — MB BS 1956 Lond.

CAMERON, Stephen Jeremy (retired) Orchard Spring, Ripley Road, Knaresborough HG5 9BY — MB ChB 1963 Ed.; FRCP Ed. 1977, M 1967. Prev: Cons. Phys. Harrogate Health Dist.

CAMERON, Stephen John Dib Lane Practice, 112A Dib Lane, Leeds LS8 3AY; 18 Ilkeston Drive, Aspull, Wigan WN2 1QZ Tel: 01942 831869 — MB ChB 1993 Leeds. GP/Regist. Leeds. Prev: Demonst. (Anat.) Leeds Med. Sch.

CAMERON, Susan 23 Lane Side, Huddersfield HD5 0EP — MB ChB 1993 Liverp.

CAMERON, William James (retired) 17 Springwood Drive, Halifax HX3 0TQ Tel: 01422 363871 — MB ChB 1935 Aberd.

CAMERON, William Ross Teviot Medical Practice, Teviot Road, Hawick TD9 9DT Tel: 01450 370999 Fax: 01450 371025 — MB ChB Glas. 1979.

CAMERON, Zoe Ann Lebas Center, St. Saviours Road, St Helier, Jersey JE2 Tel: 01534 489933; Montemare, La Saline, St. Oven, Jersey JE3 2FG Tel: 01534 485458 — MB ChB 1983 Manch.; MRCGP 1989; DRCOG 1988; DCH RCPS Glas. 1987. Clin. Med. Off. Prev: GP St. Oven's village Surg., Jersey.

CAMERON-MOWAT, Colum (retired) 38 Courtland Drive, Chigwell IG7 6PW Tel: 020 8500 2880 — MB ChB Glas. 1944; BSc Glas. 1940; DIH Eng. 1964. Prev: Chairm. Redbridge & Waltham Forest FPC & LMC.

CAMERON-MOWAT, Gilbert Bruce Medical Centre, Bellshill ML4 1AX Tel: 01698 747666 — LRCP LRCS 1948 Ed.; LRCP LRCS Ed., LRFPS Glas. 1948. (Anderson Coll. Glas.)

CAMERON-MOWAT, Ian Colum Radiology Department, Orsett Hospital, Grays RM16 3EV — MB BS 1977 Lond.; BSc (Electronics) Nottm. 1970; FRCR 1986; DMRD 1982. Cons. Radiol. Orsett & Basildon Hosp. Essex. Prev: Sen. Regist. & Ho. Off. Lond. Hosp.; Regist. Guy's Hosp. Lond.

CAMERON-MOWAT, Rowena Jane Cameron-Mowat and Partners, Manford Way Health Centre, 40 Foremark Close, Hainault, Ilford IG6 3HS Tel: 020 8500 9938 Fax: 020 8559 9319; The Cottage, South Weald, Brentwood CM14 5QN — MB BS 1977 Lond.; MRCGP 1982; DRCOG 1979.

CAMERON-STREET, Rosemary Wendy (retired) 18 Broadacres, Broad Town, Swindon SN4 7RP — MRCS Eng. LRCP Lond. 1964; BSc Lond. 1961, MB BS 1964; MRCPsych 1973; DPM Eng. 1970. Prev: Cons. Psychiat. (Developm. Med.) P.ss Marina Hosp. Upton.

CAMERON-WOOD, Robert Andrew 24 Fawnbrake Avenue, London SE24 0BY — MB BS 1990 Lond.

CAMICI, Professor Paolo Guido MRC Cyclotron Unit, ICSM, Hammersmith Hospital, Du Cane Road, London W12 0NN Tel: 020 8383 3186 Fax: 020 8383 3742 Email: paolo@cu.rpms; Apt. 6, 18 Sloane Gardens, London SW1 Tel: (20) 7730 6647 — State MDS Pisa 1976.

CAMILLERI, Mr Andrew Edward Department of Otolaryngology, South Manchester University Hospital NHS Trust, Southmoor Road, Manchester M23 9LT Tel: 0161 291 2392 Fax: 0161 291 2392; Email: andrew.comilleri@smuht.nwest.nhs.uk — MB ChB 1983 Dundee; FRCS (Orl.) Eng. 1989; FRCS (Orl.) Ed. 1989; FRCS (Gen. Surg.) Ed. 1987; FRCS (ORL) Eng.1994. (Univ. Dundee) Cons. ENT Surg. S. Manch. Univ. Hosps. NHS Trust. Socs: Otorhinolaryng. Research Soc.; Brit. Assn. Otol.; Eur. Acad. Facial Plastic Surg. Prev: Sen. Regist. Rotat. (ENT Surg.) Manch.; Regist. (ENT Surg.) Glas. Roy. Infirm.; SHO (Plastic Surg.) Qu. Mary's Hosp. Roehampton.

CAMILLERI, Ivan George Canniesburn Hospiotal, Bearsden, Glasgow GG1 2AD Tel: 0141 211 5637 Fax: 0141 211 5632; 12 Boclain Road, Bearsden, Glasgow GG1 2AD Tel: 0141 943 2582 Fax: 0141 943 2583 — MD 1988 Malta; FRCS Ed. 1992; FRCS (Plast) 1997. Cons. (Plastic & Reconstruction Surg.)Canniesburn Hosp. Socs: Brit. Assn. of Plastic Surg.s; Brit. Assn. of Head and Neck Oncol. Prev: Pecialist Regist., Newc. -U-Tyne.

CAMILLERI, Jeremy Paul University Hospital of Wales, Heath Park, Cardiff CF14 4XW Tel: 029 2074 2627 Fax: 029 2074 5017; 7 East Rise, Llanishen, Cardiff CF14 0RJ Tel: 029 2075 1627 — MB BS 1985 Lond.; BSc (Biochem.) Lond. 1983; MRCP (UK) 1988. (Lond. Hosp. Med. Coll.) Cons. Rheum. Univ. Hosp. of Wales Cardiff. Socs: Brit. Soc. Rheum.; Brit. Paediat. Rheumatol. Gp. Prev: Cons. Rheum. Pontypridd & Dist. Hosp.

CAMILLERI-FERRANTE, Corinne Anglian Clinical Audit & Effectiveness Team, Institute of Public Health, University Forvie Site, Robinson Way, Cambridge CB2 2SR Tel: 01223 330362 Fax: 01223 330345; 1 Melbourne Place, Cambridge CB1 1EQ Tel: 01223 355632 Fax: 01223 512606 Email: corinne.camilleri@rdd-pheu.cam.ac.uk — MRCS Eng. LRCP Lond. 1980; BA Open 1989; FFPHM RCP (UK) 1995, M 1988. (Roy. Univ. Malta & Univ. Lond.) Dir. Anglian Clin. Audit & Effectiveness Team & CPHM. Prev: Cons. Pub. Health Med. E. Anglia RHA; Cons. Pub. Health Med. Croydon HA; Sen. Regist. (Community Med.) SW Thames RHA.

CAMM, Professor Alan John, CStJ, QHP St. George's Hospital Medical School, Department of Cardiological Sciences, Cranmer Terrace, London SW17 0RE Tel: 020 8725 3554 Fax: 020 8767 7141 Email: jcamm@sghms.ac.uk — MRCS Eng. LRCP Lond. 1971; BSc (Hons.) Lond. 1968, MD 1981, MB BS 1971; FRCP Lond. 1984; MRCP (UK) 1973; FACC 1981; FESC 1988. Chief, Dept. Cardiovasc. Sci., St. Geo.'s Hosp. Med. Sch.; Prof. Clin. Cardiol. Dept. Cardiovasc. Sci. St. Geo. Hosp. Med. Sch.Lond. Socs: Fell. Amer. Coll. Cardiol.; Brit. Cardiac Soc. (Pres. Elect); Fell. Europ. Soc. Cardiol. Prev: Chairm. Dept. Med. St. Geo. Hosp. Med. Sch. Lond.; Sir Ronald Bodley Scott Prof. Cardiovasc. Med. St. Bart. Hosp. Lond.; Wellcome Sen. Lect. (Cardiol.) St. Bart. Hosp. Lond.

CAMM, Charles Eric (retired) 2 Spernen Wyn Road, Falmouth TR11 4EH — MB BS Durh. 1953; DPH Durh. 1956; DIH Soc. Apoth. Lond. 1961; FFCM 1979, M 1972; AFOM RCP Lond. 1982. Prev: SCM, Common Servs. Agency Glas. (Scott. Health Serv.).

CAMM, Martin John Woodlands Surgery, 24 Woodlands, Meeting House Lane, Balsall Common, Coventry CV7 7FX Tel: 01676 532587 Fax: 01676 535154; The Cot, Woodyard, Off Maxstoke Close, Meriden, Coventry CV7 7NB — MB BS 1981 Lond.; MRCS Eng. LRCP Lond. 1980; DRCOG 1986; MRCGP 1997. (St. Bart.) Princip. GP Balsall Common. Prev: Trainee GP Solihull Hosp. VTS; SHO (Cas.) Lewisham Hosp.; Ho. Phys. & Ho. Surg. Plymouth Gen. Hosps.

CAMM, Peter Russell Dorset County Hospital, Williams Avenue, Dorchester DT1 1TS Tel: 01305 251150; Lester House, Linden Avenue, Dorchester DT1 1EJ Tel: 01305 251150 Fax: 01305 250250 — MB BS 1963 Lond.; MRCS Eng. LRCP Lond. 1963; FFR 1969; DMRD Eng. 1967. (Guy's) Cons. Radiol. W. Dorset Gen. Hosps. NHS Trust. Socs: Roy. Coll. Radiol.; Chairm. W. Dorset Med. Soc.; Brit. Inst. of Radiol. Prev: Med. Director W. Dorset Gen. Hosp.s NHS Trust.

CAMMACK, Adrian Edward Aberlour Health Centre, Queens Road, Aberlour AB38 9PR Tel: 01340 871210 Fax: 01340 871814; 38 High Street, Aberlour AB38 9QD Tel: 01340 871497 — MB ChB 1983 Ed.; BSc (Hons.) Ed. 1980; FRCS Ed. 1989; MRCGP 1994; DRCOG 1990. (Edinburgh University) Prev: Regist. W.. Gen. Hosp. Edin.; SHO E.. Gen. Hosp. Edin.; Ho. Off., SHO & Regist. Edin. Roy. Infirm.

CAMP, Anne Virginia York House, Isebrook Hospital, Wellingborough NN8 1LP Tel: 01536 493131 Fax: 01536 493242 Email: virginia.camp@rockhmtx.anglex.uk; 4 Elwes Way, Great Billing, Northampton NN3 9EA Tel: 01604 788831 Fax: 01604 413670 Email: avcamp@bigfoot.com — MB ChB 1965 Ed.; BSc (Path.) Ed. 1963; FRCP Lond. 1984, M 1970. (Ed.) Cons. Phys. (Rheum. & Rehabil.) Isebrook Hosp., WellingBoro.; Med. Dir. N.ants. Healthcare, NHS Trust. Socs: Brit. Soc. Rheum.; (Ex-Chairm.) Brit. Med. Acupunc. Soc.; Brit. Soc. Rehabil. Med. Prev: Cons. Phys. (Rheum. & Rehabil.) Amersham Gen. Hosp.; Sen. Regist. (Rheum. & Physical Med.) Battle Hosp. Reading & Nuffield Orthop. Centre Oxf.; Regist. Oxf. Regional Rheum. Dis. Research Centre, Stoke Mandeville.

CAMP, Brian John (retired) The Surgery, 2 Erith Road, Belvedere DA17 6EZ Tel: 01322 432315 Fax: 01322 440948 — MB BS Lond. 1960; DObst RCOG 1962. Med. Adviser BICC Ltd. Ferndale Foods; Approved Med. Examr. Seafarers Dept. Transport. Prev: Med. Adviser BICC Ltd. Ferndale Foods.

CAMP, Mr David Francis 18 Northfield Road, Worthing BN13 1QW — MB BS 1989 Lond.; MSc Surg. Sci. Lond. 1997; FRCS Eng. 1994. (St. Geo. Hosp. Med. Sch.) SHO (Plastic Surg.) List. Hosp. Stevenage.

CAMP, John James (retired) Rosewarne, Coleford GL16 8HL — MB BS 1955 Lond.; MRCS Eng. LRCP Lond. 1955; MRCGP 1962; DObst RCOG 1957. Prev: Ho. Surg. War Memor. Hosp. Woolwich.

CAMP, Professor Richard Doyle Reginal Division of Dermatology, University of Leicester Medical Sciences Building, University Road, Leicester LE1 9HN Tel: 0116 252 3061 Fax: 0116 252 5035; 14 Priory Road, Manton, Oakham LE15 8ST Tel: 01572 737729 — MB ChB Cape Town 1968; PhD Lond. 1979; FRCP Lond. 1989; MRCP (UK) 1975; FFDerm (S. Afr.) 1973. (Cape Town) Prof. Dermat. Univ. Leics.; Hon. Cons. Dermat. Leicester Roy. Infirm. Socs: (Ex. Chairm.) Brit. Soc. Investig. Dermat.; Brit. Pharm. Soc.; (Ex-Pres.) Europ. Soc. Dermat. Research. Prev: Prof. Experim. Dermat. St. John's Inst. Dermat. Lond.

CAMPBELL, Alan Compton Merrick, 11 Kemerton Road, Beckenham BR3 6NJ Tel: 020 8650 2104 — MRCS Eng. LRCP Lond. 1951; BDS Lond. 1944; FDS RCS Eng. 1955, LDS 1945; DOrth 1954. (Guy's) Emerit. Cons. Dent. Dept. for Childr. Guy's Hosp. Lond. Socs: Life Mem. (Ex-Pres., Ex-Libr. & Hon. Sec.) Brit. Soc. Study Orthodont. (Special Serv Award) 1986; Life Mem. Europ. Orthodontic Soc. Prev: Cons. Dent. Surg. & Cons. Orthodont. St. Mary's Hosp. Teach. Gp.; Cons. Orthodont. Hammersmith & W.. Middlx. Univ. Hosp.

CAMPBELL, Mr Alan John Ballards House, Ballards Lane, Limpsfield, Oxted RH8 0SN Tel: 01883 712915 — MB BS 1969 Lond.; FRCS Eng. 1974; FRCS Ed. 1973; MRCS Eng. LRCP Lond. 1969. (Westm.) Cons. Orthop. Surg. E. Surrey Hosp., Redhill & Crawley Hosp. Socs: Fell. BOA; BMA. Prev: Sen. Regist. (Orthop.) St. Geo. Hosp. Lond.; Research Fell. (Orthop.) Toronto Univ. Canada; Regist. (Orthop.) Kings Coll. Hosp. Lond.

CAMPBELL, Alasdair The Campbell Practice, Rutherglen Primary Care Centre, 130 Stonelaw Road, Rutherglen G73 2PQ Tel: 0141 531 6065 — MB ChB 1985 Glas.; BSc Pharmacol. Glas. 1982; MRCGP 1989. (Glasgow University) GP Rutherglen.

CAMPBELL, Alastair James Lettoch Farm Cottage, Killiecrankie, Pitlochry PH16 5LR — MB ChB 1969 Glas. (Glas.)

CAMPBELL, Alastair James High Stone Cottage, High St., Hampsthwaite, Harrogate HG3 2ET — MB ChB 1995 Bristol.

CAMPBELL, Alastair Nelson Department of Paediatrics, Royal Preston Hospital, Preston PR2 9HT Tel: 01772 710552 Fax: 01772 710 3551 Email: alastair.campbell@patr.nhs .uk; Byerworth Cottage, 3 Kinsacre, Churchtown, Preston PR3 0LQ Tel: 01995 603528 — MB BS 1974 Lond.; FRCP Lond. 1994; MRCP (UK) 1979; FRCPCH 1997. (Middlx.) Clin. Dir. (Paediat.) Roy. Preston Hosp.Cons. (Paediat) Roy.Preston Hosp.Preston.; Vis. Fell. Univ. Centr. Lancs. Socs: BMA; BAPM; RCPCH (Counc.). Prev: Sen. Regist. (Paediat.) N.. RHA; Fell. Hosp. Sick Childr. Toronto, Canada; Regist. (Paediat.) N.ampton Gen. Hosp.

CAMPBELL, Mr Alexander Craig Willem 48 Rose Street, Cumbernauld, Glasgow G67 4ER — MB ChB 1985 Glas.; FRCS Glas. 1990.

CAMPBELL, Professor Alexander George Macpherson 34 Woodburn Crescent, Aberdeen AB15 8JX Tel: 01224 312187 Fax: 01224 312187 — MB ChB 1955 Glas.; FRCP Ed. 1972, M 1961; Dip. Amer. Bd. Pediat. 1969, Neonat.-Perinat. Med. 1977; DCH RCPS Glas. 1959. (Glas.) Emerit. Prof. Child Health Univ. Aberd. Socs: Fell. Amer. Acad. Pediat.; Neonat. Soc. Prev: Regist. (Paediat.) Roy. Hosp. Sick Childr. Edin.; Assoc. Prof. Pediat. Yale Univ. Sch. Med. New Haven, USA; Prof. Child Health Univ. Aberd.

CAMPBELL, Alexander James St George's Surgery, St Pauls Medical Centre, 121 Swindon Road, Cheltenham GL50 4DP Tel: 01242 707755 Fax: 01242 707749 — MB BS 1978 Lond.; MRCP (UK) 1981; DRCOG 1982. (Middlx.) GP Cheltenham.

CAMPBELL, Alexander Thomson 2 Gadloch Avenue, Lenzie, Glasgow G66 5DB — MB ChB 1961 Ed.; MFCM 1974; DPH Glas. 1969.

CAMPBELL, Miss Alexandra Speir Royal College of Surgeons of Edinburgh, Nicolson St., Edinburgh EH8 9DW Tel: 0131 527 1600; 6 Saltcoats Gardens, Bellsquarry, Livingston EH54 9JD — MB ChB 1977 Glas.; FRCS Glas. 1981; FRCS Ed. 1981; DFM Glas. 1989. (University of Glasgow) Exec. Sec. RCS Edin. Prev: Sen. Med. Advisor. MDDUS; Cons. A & E Hartlepool Gen. Hosp.; Sen. Regist. (A & E) Sunderland Dist. Gen. Hosp.

CAMPBELL, Alison Elizabeth 57 Cherry Grove, Derwen Fawr, Swansea SA2 8AU — MB ChB 1990 Ed.; BSc (Hons.) Ed. 1988, MB ChB 1990; DTM & H RCP Lond. 1994; DA Lond. 1996; FRCA Lond. 1999. (Edinburgh) Specialist Regist. (Anaesth.), Wales.

CAMPBELL, Alison Jane Flat 22, 274 Dumbarton Road, Glasgow G11 6TU — MB ChB 1996 Glas.

CAMPBELL, Alison Margaret Aberdeen Royal Infirmary, Foresterhill, Aberdeen AB25 2ZN Tel: 01224 681818; 16 Kingshill Avenue, Aberdeen AB15 5HD Tel: 01224 314732 — MB ChB 1981 Aberd.; FFA RCS Eng. 1985. Cons. Anaesth. Aberd. Roy. Hosps. NHS Trust.

CAMPBELL, Mr Alistair Fraser Raigmore Hospital NHS Trust, Inverness IV2 3UJ Tel: 01463 704000 Fax: 01463 704596 — MB ChB St. And. 1968; FRCS Glas. 1993; FRCS Eng. 1974; FRCS Ed. 1974; T(S) 1991. (University of St Andrews) Cons. Orthop. Surg. Raigmore Hosp. NHS Trust Inverness.; Hon. Clin. Sen. Lect. Univ. of Aberd. Socs: Fell. BOA; Internat. Soc. Prosth. and Orthotics.

CAMPBELL, Alistair James Peter (retired) Brereton Park, Tattenhall, Chester CH3 9BY Tel: 01829 781432 — MB BChir 1959 Camb.; MA Camb. 1978; DA Eng. 1961. JP.; Civil. Med. Pract. Dale Barracks, Chester; Med. Off. Tarporley War Memor. Hosp.; Med. Off. 3rd Bn. Chesh. Regt. (TA). Prev: Resid. Ho. Surg. (Obst.) Matern. Hosp. Camb.

CAMPBELL, Allan Earll Reddick, Capt. RAMC Retd. 57 Weelsby Avenue, Grimsby DN32 0AU Tel: 01472 234597 Fax: 01472 234597 — LRCP LRCS Ed. LRFPS Glas. 1945; DMRD Eng. 1971; Cert. Av Med. MoD (Air) & CAA; Aviat Auth. 1978. Sen. Authorised Med. Examr. Civil Aviat. Auth. UK., Federal Aviat. Auth. USA & Canad. Aviat. Auth. Socs: Fell. Aviat. Auth. Amer. & Civil Aviat. Auth. Canada. Prev: Cons. Radiol. Grimsby HA; Sen. Regist. (Radiol.) Vict. Infirm. Glas.; SHMO (Geriat.) Mearnskirk Hosp. Glas.

CAMPBELL, Allan John Mackenzie (retired) 2 Dunlin Crescent, Craigend, Houston, Johnstone PA6 7JX Tel: 01505 613570 — MD 1956 Glas.; MB ChB 1945; FRFPS Glas. 1949; FRCP Glas. 1972, M 1962. Prev: Cons. Phys. Hairmyres Hosp. E. Kilbride.

CAMPBELL, Amanda Catherine 56 Newlands Road, Newlands, Glasgow G43 2JH — MB ChB 1988 Glas.

CAMPBELL, Amaryllis Jane New Pond Row Surgery, 35 South Street, Lancing BN15 8AN; Church Farm House E., 1 Church Close, Lancing BN15 0EZ — MB BS 1984 Lond.; BA Camb. 1978; DRCOG 1990.

CAMPBELL, Andrew (retired) Dairy Farm, Mansfield Road, Arnold, Nottingham NG5 8PN Tel: 01159 268600 — LRCPI & LM, LRSCI & LM 1941; LRCPI & LM, LRCSI & LM 1941. Prev: Intern Mercer's Hosp. Dub.

CAMPBELL, Andrew John 25 Bainton Road, Oxford OX2 7AF — MB BS 1998 Lond.; MB BS Lond 1998.

CAMPBELL, Angela Maria Mansionhouse Unit,Victoria Infirmary, South Glasgow University, Hospitals NHS Trust, Mansionhouse Road, Glasgow G41 3DX Tel: 0141 201 6126 Fax: 0141 201 6159; Flat 2, Cleveden House,, 5 Cleveden Road, Glasgow G12 0NT Tel: 0141 334 1868 — MB ChB 1986 Glas.; BSc (1st cl. Hons. Physiol.) Glas. 1983; MRCP (UK) 1991. (Glas. Univ.) Cons. Phys. (Med. for the Elderly) Vict. Infirm. S. Glas. Univ. Hosp.s NHS Trust, Glas..; Hon. Clin. Sen. Lect. Glas. Univ.. Socs: BMA; Brit. Geriat. Soc.; Scott. Soc. of Phys.s. Prev: Sen. Regist. & Hon. Clin. Lect. (Gen. & Geriat. Med.) Glas. Roy. Infirm.; Career Regist. (Gen. & Geriat. Med.) Stirling Roy. Infirm. & S.ern Gen. Hosp. Glas.; SHO3 (Geriat. Med.) Gartnavel Gen. Hosp. Glas.

CAMPBELL, Anita Merle Richmond Medical Centre, 462 Richmond Road, Sheffield S13 8NA Tel: 0114 239 9291 Fax: 0114 253 0737 — BM BCh 1979 Oxf.; MA, BM BCh Oxf. 1979; MRCGP 1986; Dip. Primary Care Rheumatol 1998 Bath. (Oxford) Gp Prinicipal; Trainer Sheff. VTS; GP Tutor Univ. of Sheff.; Chairm. S.E. Sheff. PCG. Socs: Primary Care Rheum. Soc. Prev: Trainee GP W. Wickham; Regist. (Med.) King's Coll. Hosp. Lond.; SHO (Gen. Med.) Newc. u Tyne AHA (T).

CAMPBELL, Ann Maris Craigshill Health Centre, The Mall, Craigshill EH54 5DY Tel: 01506 432621 Fax: 01506 430431; 33 B East Werberside, Fettees Village, Edinburgh EH4 1SU Tel: 0131 539 9995 Email: annmaris12@hotmail.com — MB ChB 1974 Glas.; MRCGP 1986; Dip. Forens. Med. Glas 1994. (Glas.) p/t G.P. Princip. Socs: BMA; Brit. Med. Acupunct. Soc.; Scott. Medico-Legal Soc. Prev: SHO (O & G) S.. Gen. Hosp. Glas.; SHO (Psychiat.) Bellsdyke Hosp. Larbert.; G.P. Princip., The Clinic, Buchananst St., Balfron.

CAMPBELL, Ann Pollock (retired) Redholm, 8 Newlands Place, East Kilbride, Glasgow G74 1AE Tel: 01355 223871 — MB ChB 1957 Glas.; DCH RFPS Glas. 1960. Prev: GP Glas.

CAMPBELL, Anne Margaret 19 King Edwards Gardens, London W3 9RE — MB ChB 1991 Ed. SHO (Anaesth. & ITU) St. John's Hosp. Livingston. Prev: SHO (Cardiothoracic Surg.) Roy. Infirm. Edin.; SHO (A & E) Falkirk & Dist. Roy. Infirm.

CAMPBELL, Anne Morrison West Calder Medical Practice, Dickson Street, West Calder EH55 8HB Tel: 01506 871403; 5 Elliot Gardens, Edinburgh EH14 1EH — MB ChB 1986 Ed.; DRCOG 1990. GP Edin.

CAMPBELL, Anne Patricia Department of .Cellular Pathology, Hull Royal Infirmary, Anlaby Road, Hull HU3 2JZ Tel: 01482 607713 Fax: 01482 607736 Email: anne.campbell@hey.nhs.uk; Croft Hill House, Arram, Beverley HU17 7NR Tel: 01964 550458 — MB ChB 1983 Sheff.; MD Sheff. 1994, BMedSci 1981; MRCPath 1989; FRCPath 1998. (Sheffield) Cons. Histopath. Hull & E. Yorks.. NHS Trust.

CAMPBELL, Anthony Charles Hilary 8 Oak Way, London N14 5NN Tel: 020 8368 3418 — LRCPI & LM, LRSCI & LM 1962; LRCPI & LM, LRCSI & LM 1962; MRCP (UK) 1973; FFHom 1976, M 1975. Socs: Brit. Med. Acupunc. Soc. Prev: Study Fell. Roy. Lond. Homoeop. Hosp.; Regist. Dept. Venereol. Roy. N.. Hosp.; Asst. Edr. Abstracts of World Med.

CAMPBELL, Archibald Angus Edenfield Centre, Prestwich Hospital, Prestwich, Manchester M25 3BL Tel: 0161 773 9121 Fax: 0161 798 7877 — BM BCh 1963 Oxf.; MPhil (Psychiat.) Lond. 1972; MA Oxf. 1961, BM BCh 1963; FRCP Lond. 1987, M 1968; FRCPsych 1983, M 1972; DPM Eng. 1970. (Oxf.) Cons. Forens. Psychiat. Home Office & N. W.. RHA; Hon. Assoc. Lect. Foren. Psychiat. Manch. Univ.; Cons. Psychiat. NSPCC Manch. & Rochdale Child Protec. Teams; Chairm. Forens. Sect. Roy. Coll. Psychiat. Socs: Fell. Roy. Soc. Med. & Manch. Med. Soc. (Ex. Pres. Psychiat. Sect.). Prev: Fulbright Schol. & Research Fell. Yale Univ., USA; Sen. Regist. Bethlem Roy & Maudsley Hosps. Lond.; Ho. Phys. Hammersmith Hosp. Lond.

CAMPBELL, Archibald Dunlop Littlebeck Hall, Gilstead, Bingley BD16 3LH Tel: 01274 566753 — MB ChB St. And. 1959; FFOM Lond 2000 A1979 M1983. p/t Med.Advis.Abbey Nat. PLC. Socs: Fell. Roy. Soc. Med. Prev: Med. Adviser The Nat. & Prov. Bldg. Soc.; Cas. Off. & Resid. Med. Off. Bradford Roy. Infirm.; Ho. Surg. (O & G) St. Luke's Hosp. Bradford.

CAMPBELL, Arthur James Gordon Sherwood House Medical Practice, 9 Sandon Road, Edgbaston, Birmingham B67 8DP Tel: 0121 420 0100 Fax: 0121 420 0107 — MB ChB 1958 Birm.; MRCS Eng. LRCP Lond. 1958. Prev: Ho. Surg. & Ho. Phys. Gen. Hosp. Birm.

CAMPBELL, Avril Rhona Johnstone Health Centre, 60 Quarry Street, Johnstone PA5 8EY Tel: 01505 324348 Fax: 01505 323710 — MB ChB 1977 Glasgow; MB ChB Glas. 1977. (Glasgow) GP Johnstone, Renfrewsh.

CAMPBELL, Beatrice Marigold Ty Carreg, North St., Totnes TQ9 5NZ Tel: 01803 865733 — MB ChB 1972 Bristol; BSc (Physiol.) Bristol 1969, MB ChB 1972; Cert. Family Plann. JCC 1974. (Bristol) SHO (Adult Psychiat.) Edith Morgan Centre Torbay Hosp. Torquay. Socs: Inst. Psychosexual Med.; Fac. Fam. Plann. & Reproduc. Health Care. Prev: SCMO (Counsellor in Psychosexual Med. & Family Plann.) Plymouth Community Servs. NHS Trust.

CAMPBELL, Brian Cameron 88 Kelvin Court, Glasgow G12 0AH Tel: 0141 339 0536 — MB ChB 1971 Glas.; MD Glas. 1977, MB ChB 1971; MRCP (UK) 1973. Cons. Phys., Roy. Infirm. of Edin.; Hon. Sen. Regist. Stobhill Gen. Hosp. Socs: Brit. Pharm. Soc. & Brit. Hypertens. Soc.; Roy. Soc. Med. Prev: Hon. Sen. Regist. Stobhill Gen. Hosp. Glas.; SHO Vict. Infirm. Glas.; Ho.Sen. Phys. Vict. Infirm. Glas.

CAMPBELL, Brian John Flat 3 The Grange, 114 Avenue Road, Acton, London W3 8QL Tel: 0802 446173 Fax: 020 8932 2471 — BM BCh 1986 Oxf.; BA Oxf. 1986; FRCA 1995. (Univ. Oxf.)

CAMPBELL, Cameron Robb Dixon Thorpe Health Centre, St. Williams Way, Thorpe, Norwich NR7 0AJ Tel: 01603 701010; 14 Broadland Drive, Thorpe End, Norwich NR13 5BT Tel: 01603 435952 — MB ChB Aberd. 1966; DA Eng. 1969. (Aberd.) Prev: Regist. & SHO (Anaesth.) Aberd. Roy. Infirm.; Ho. Off. Shotley Bridge Gen. Hosp.

CAMPBELL, Carl Victor 19A Causeway Road, Newcastle BT33 0DL Tel: 0208 437 23145 — MB BCh BAO 1972 Belf.; MLCOM 1987; MFHom 1985; LMCC 1977; Dip. Biomechanics Strathclyde 1996; DTM & H Liverp. 1986; DObst RCOG 1974; DM-S Med Apothecaries Hall 1999. (Belf.) Private Pract., Orthop. Musculoskeletal & Homeopathy; Sessional Med. Off. N.I. Civil Serv. Socs: Brit. Inst. Musculoskel. Med.; Brit. Assn. Sport & Exercise Med.. (B.A.S.E.M.); Soc. Occupat. Med.

CAMPBELL, Carol Margaret Ann (retired) Deerpark, 37 Ballyquin Road, Limavady BT49 9EY Tel: 028 7776 2321 Fax: 028 7161 1254 — MB BCh BAO Dub. 1974; BA Dub. 1971; MRCGP 1978; DRCOG 1978; DCH Eng. 1977. p/t Locum Clin. Med. Off., Community Paediat., Lond.derry. Prev: GP Limavady.

CAMPBELL, Carol Margaret Carmichael Strahaven Health Centre, The Ward, Strathaven ML10 6AS Tel: 01357 522993; 3 Marchmont Gardens, Strathaven ML10 6JD — MB ChB 1973 Glas.

CAMPBELL, Caroline Janet Furzetor, Sampford Spinney, Yelverton PL20 6LW Tel: 01822 853739 — MB ChB 1992 Ed.; BSc Ed. 1990; MRCP (UK) 1995; DTM & H RCP Lond. 1996; DA S. Afr 1998. (Ed.) Med.Off.Grey's Hosps. Africa. Socs: Roy. Med. Soc. Prev: Vocational Trainee McCord Hosp. Durban, S. Afr.; SHO Rotat. (Gen. Med.) Treliske Hosp. Cornw.

CAMPBELL, Carolyn Jane 1 Foxleigh Mansions, Claremont Road, Bristol BS7 8AJ — MB ChB 1998 Bristol.

CAMPBELL, Catherine Duncan 5 Cauldstream Place, Milngavie, Glasgow G62 7NL Tel: 0141 956 3190 — MB ChB St. And. 1960; DPH Dundee 1969; DObst RCOG 1961. (St. And.) Clin. Med. Off. N.E. Community Child Health Serv. Socs: Fell. Soc. Community Med. Prev: Med. Off. Lanarksh. CC; Ho. Surg. Glas. Roy. Matern. Hosp. & Roy. Hosp. Sick Childr. Glas.

CAMPBELL, Catherine Frances Louise The Old Vicarage, Hilderstone, Stone ST15 8SQ — MB BS 1977 Lond.; MSc (Gen. Psychiat.) Keele 1994; DRCOG 1980. Clin. Asst. (Psychiat.) Staffs. Prev: Princip. GP Edgware; SHO (Obst.) Whipps Cross Hosp. Lond.; SHO (Psychiat.) N. Staffs. Hosp.

CAMPBELL, Catherine Hamilton Pennine Medical Centre, 193 Manchester Road, Mossley, Ashton-under-Lyne OL5 9AJ; 1 Stead Way, Greenfield, Oldham OL3 7DY — MB ChB 1979 Manch.

CAMPBELL, Catherine Janet (retired) The Surgery, Strathpeffer IV14 9BA Tel: 01997 421455 — MB ChB 1969 Ed.; BSc (Med. Sci.) Ed. 1966, MB ChB 1969; FRCP Ed. 1984; MRCP (UK) 1973. Hosp. Pract. (Diabetes) Raigmore Hosp. Inverness. Prev: Regist. Diabetic Dept. Roy. Infirm. Edin.

CAMPBELL, Charlotte Elisabeth Ross Central Surgery, Bell Street, Sawbridgeworth CM21 9AQ Tel: 01279 723172 — MB BS 1988 Lond.; MRCGP 1994. Prev: GP St. Albans VTS; Ho. Phys. Roy. Free Hosp. Lond.; Ho. Surg. Orsett Hosp. Grays.

CAMPBELL, Charlotte Patricia 20 Church Road, Stoke Bishop, Bristol BS9 1QP — MB BS 1994 Lond.

CAMPBELL, Clare Margaret 2 Pumpherston Road, West Calder EH55 0AY; The Health Centre, Broxburn EH52 5JZ — MB BCh BAO 1978 Dub.; MRCGP 1983. (TC Dub.)

CAMPBELL, Clarke Ivan 27 Lough Road, Ballinderry Upper, Lisburn BT28 2JY — MB BCh BAO 1991 Belf.

CAMPBELL, Clive George Stewardship Department, Zeneca Agrochemicals, Fernhurst, Haslemere GU27 3JE Tel: 01428 655063 Fax: 01428 655758; 11 Tylston Meadow, Liphook GU30 7YB Tel: 01428 727165 — MB ChB 1982 Leeds; DRCOG 1987; AFOM RCP Lond. 1992; MFOM RCP London 1998; MIOSH.Instit.Occupatonal.Health.&.Saftey. (Leeds) Occupat. Phys. Zeneca Agrochem. Haslemere. Socs: Soc. Occupat. Med. Prev: Trainee Occupat. Phys. Midl. Occupat. Health Serv.

CAMPBELL, Coleen Mary 14 Westhill Road, Kingsnorton, Birmingham B38 8RX Tel: 0121 458 1297 — MB BCh 1989 Wales; DCH 1993; DRCOG 1994; MRCGP 1995.

CAMPBELL, Colin Department of Radiology, Southern General Hospital, 1345 Govan Road, Glasgow G51 4TF — MB ChB 1980 Glas.; FRCP Glas. 1993; MRCP (UK) 1983; FRCR 1988. (Glasgow University) Cons. Radiol. S.. Gen. Hosp. Glas.

CAMPBELL, Colin Alexander St. Michaels Hospital, St. Michaels Road, Warwick CV34 5QW Tel: 01926 406789 Fax: 01926 406702 — MB BCh BAO 1980 Belf.; MRCPsych 1985. Cons. Psychiat. St. Michaels Hosp. Warwick; Med. Dir. S. Warks. Combined Care Trust. Socs: Fell. Roy. Soc. Med.; BMA. Prev: Sen. Regist. (Psychiat.) Fulbourn Hosp. Camb.

CAMPBELL, Colin Andris North Staffordshire Hospital, Stoke-on-Trent ST4 6QG Email: cacampbell@doctors.org.uk — MB ChB 1972 Glas.; FRCP Lond. 1992; MRCP (UK) 1977; MRCGP 1976; DObst RCOG 1976; DCH Eng. 1975. (University of Glasgow) Prev: Sen Regist. (Paediat.) Hosp. Sick Childr. Lond.; Sen. Regist. (Paediat.) Lond. Hosp. Whitechapel; Research Fell. (Paediat. Gastroenterol.) Qu. Eliz. Hosp. Childr.

CAMPBELL, Mr Colin Anthony Eastwood Cottage, Rampside Road, Barrow-in-Furness LA13 0PT Tel: 01229 835798 Fax: 01229 835798 Email: colin.a.cambell@bizonline.com — MB BS Lond. 1966; FRCS Ed. 1975; MRCS Eng. LRCP Lond. 1965. (Char. Cross.) Cons. Orthop. Surg. Furness Gen. Hosp. Barrow-in-Furness. Socs: Fell. BOA; Brit. Trauma Soc. Prev: Cons. Orthop. Surg. P.ss Mary's RAF Hosp. Halton; Sen. Regist. (Orthop.) Harlow Wood Orthop. Hosp. Nottm.

CAMPBELL, Colin David Victoria Hospital, Whinney Heys Road, Blackpool FY3 8NR Tel: 01253 300000 — MB ChB 1986 Manch.; DGM RCP Lond. 1990. Regist. (Geriat. Med.) Vict. Hosp. Blackpool. Prev: SHO (Geriat. Med.) Vict. Hosp. Blackpool; SHO (Geriat. Med.) S.shore Hosp. Blackpool.

CAMPBELL, Colin Deas 8 Witchell, Wendover, Aylesbury HP22 6EG Tel: 01296 696492 — MB BS 1953 Lond.; FRCGP 1985, M 1960; DObst RCOG 1955. (St. Thos.) Socs: Fell. BMA. Prev: Ho. Surg. (Obst.) W. Middlx. Hosp. Isleworth; Ho. Phys. Peace Memor. Hosp. Watford.

CAMPBELL, Colin Donald 29 (TFR) Millar Cr, Edinburgh EH10 5HN — MB ChB 1997 Ed.

CAMPBELL, Colin John 2 Worden, Leyland, Preston PR25 3EL Tel: 01772 423555 Fax: 01772 623878; 2 Juniper Croft, Clayton Le Woods, Chorley PR6 7UF — MB ChB 1987 Manch.; DRCOG 1990. Prev: Trainee GP Weaverham Surg. Chesh.; SHO (Gen. Med.) Leighton Hosp. Crewe.

CAMPBELL, Mr Colin Scott Wythenshawe Hospital, Southmoor Road, Manchester M23 9LT Tel: 0161 291 2315 Email: rupertcb@aol.com; 136 Hale Road, Hale, Altrincham WA15 8RS — MB ChB Glas. 1970; FRCS Glas. 1977; FRCS Ed 1977; FRCSC Th Ed. 1984. Cons. Cardiothoracic Surg. Wythenshawe Hosp. Manch.

CAMPBELL, Colin Stewart Woodhall Spa New Surgery, The Broadway, Woodhall Spa LN10 6SQ Tel: 01526 353888 Fax: 01526 354445 — MB ChB 1977 Leeds; MRCGP 1982; DCH RCP Lond. 1981; DRCOG 1980. (Leeds) GP Woodhall Spa.; Course Organiser, Lincoln VTS for Gen. Pract.; GP Trainer. Prev: Ho. Phys. & Ho. Surg. Leeds Gen. Infirm.

CAMPBELL, Colin West 3 Eaglesham Road, Newton Mearns, Glasgow G77 5BE Tel: 0141 639 2753 — MB ChB 1979 Glas.; MRCGP 1986; DRCOG 1981.

CAMPBELL, Mr David Merlewood, 9 Church Lane, Upton, Chester CH2 1DJ Tel: 01244 383398 — MB BS 1967 Lond.; MRCS Eng. LRCP Lond. 1967; FRCS Ed. 1972; FRCS Eng. 1973. (Roy. Free) Cons. (Orthop. Surg.) Chester Roy. Infirm. & Countess of Chester. Socs: Brit. Orthop. Assn. & Chester & N. Wales Med. Soc. Prev: Sen. Orthop. Regist. Soton. Gen. Hosp. RSO Lord Mayor Treloar; Hosp. Alton.

CAMPBELL, David Arthur Foyle 21 Hillhead Street, Glasgow G12 8PX — MB ChB 1950 Glas.; MRCPsych 1972. Med. Dir. Davidson Clinic Glas. Prev: Regist. Roy. Edin. Hosp. Ment. Dis.; Res. Med. Off. Haslemere & Dist. Hosp.

CAMPBELL, David George Duncan Peterhead Group Practice, The Health Centre, Peterhead AB42 2XA Tel: 01774 474841 Fax: 01774 474848; Airlie Lodge, Longside, Peterhead AB42 4TE Tel: 01779 821394 Fax: 01779 474841 — MB ChB 1967 Ed.; MRCGP 1972; DObst RCOG 1970. (Edinburgh) Prev: Princip. GP Keith Health Centre & Lincoln Med. Centre, NZ.; Interne Rotat. Vancouver Gen. Hosp. Canada; Ho. Off. (O & G) E.. Gen. Hosp. Edin.

CAMPBELL, David George Robertson (retired) The Moorings, 17 Paget Road, Ipswich IP1 3RP Tel: 01473 251077 — BM BCh Oxf. 1949; MA Oxf. 1949. JP.

CAMPBELL, David George Stewart (retired) Redholm, 8 Newlands Place, East Kilbride, Glasgow G74 1AE Tel: 01355 223871 — MB ChB 1957 Glas.; DObst RCOG 1962. Prev: GP Glas.

CAMPBELL, David Ian 16 Winchmore Drive, Cambridge CB2 2LW — MB BS 1991 Lond.

CAMPBELL, David James Department of Obstetrics & Gynaecology, St. James University Hospital, Leeds LS9 7TF Tel: 0113 244 3144 Fax: 0113 242 6496; Croftinloan, 24 Wigton Chase, Alwoodley, Leeds LS17 8SG Tel: 0113 237 0537 — MB ChB 1983 Dundee; FRCOG 2001; MRCOG 1988. Cons. O & G St. Jas. Univ. Hosp. Leeds. Socs: BMA; FRCOG. Prev: Sen. Regist. St. Bart. Hosp. Lond.; Research Fell. King's Coll. Hosp. Lond.

CAMPBELL, David John 179 Tuffley Avenue, Gloucester GL1 5NR Tel: 01452 26262 — MB BS 1984 Lond. (Middlx.) Ho. Phys. Mt. Vernon Hosp. Lond. Prev: Ho. Surg. Mt. Vernon Hosp. Lond.

CAMPBELL, David Kondwani 23 Holland Gardens, Belfast BT5 6EG — MB BCh BAO 1994 Belf.

CAMPBELL, David Lister, TD (retired) The Caxton Surgery, Oswald Road, Oswestry SY11 1RD Tel: 01691 654646 Fax: 01691 670994 — MB ChB 1974 Ed.; BSc. (Med. Sci.) Ed. 1971, MB ChB 1974; MRCGP 1979; DRCOG 1979. Prev: Clin. Asst. (Dept. Spinal Disorders) Dame Agnes Hunt & Robt. Jones Hosp. OsW.ry.

CAMPBELL, David Malcolm Taylor Combs Ford Surgery, Combs Lane, Stowmarket IP14 2SY Tel: 01449 678333 Fax: 01449 614535 — MB BS 1984 Lond. (Roy. Free) Prev: SHO W. Suff. Hosp. Bury St. Edmunds.

CAMPBELL, David Neil Clark Department of Anaesthesia, Princess Margaret Hospital, Okus Road, Swindon SN1 4JU Tel: 01793 536231; Airedale House, King's Lane, Longcot, Faringdon SN7 7SS Tel: 01793 784125 — MB BS 1981 Lond.; FFA RCS Eng. 1987. Cons. Anaesth. P.ss Margt. Hosp. Swindon.

CAMPBELL, David Ronald 43 Logs Hill, Chislehurst BR7 5LN — MB BS 1983 Lond.

CAMPBELL, David William 89 Longstomps Avenue, Chelmsford CM2 9BZ — MB BS 1989 Lond.

CAMPBELL, Deborah Sabina 33 Antoine Road, Bearsden, Glasgow G61 4DP Tel: 0141 942 5343 — MB ChB 1988 Manch.; BSc Med. Sci. St. And. 1985; MRCGP 1996.

CAMPBELL, Deborah Susan c/o Douglas, 21 Bonnyton Drive, Eaglesham, Glasgow G76 0LT — MB ChB 1983 Ed.; MRCGP 1988.

CAMPBELL, Deirdre Elizabeth Dornoch Medical Practice, Shore Road, Dornoch IV25 3LS Tel: 01862 810213 Fax: 01862 811066; The Croft, 24 Skelbo Muir, Dornoch IV25 3QH — MB BCh BAO 1986 Belf.; MRCGP 1991; DCH RCPSI 1990; DRCOG 1992.

CAMPBELL, Derek Colin Flat 2, 9 Dogpole, Shrewsbury SY1 1EN — MB ChB 1982 Otago.

CAMPBELL, Deryck Warren (retired) 3 Orchard Street, Mickleover, Derby DE3 5DF Tel: 01332 513625 — MB ChB 1944 Birm. Prev: Ho. Surg. Qu. Eliz. Hosp. Birm.

CAMPBELL, Desmond Hugh Carrick Hill Medical Centre, 1 Carrick Hill, Belfast BT1 2JR Tel: 028 9043 973 — MB BCh BAO 1948 Belf.

CAMPBELL, Diane 5 Friar Place, Scotlandwell, Kinross KY13 9WN — MB ChB 1989 Glas.
CAMPBELL, Professor Sir Donald, CBE (retired) 27 Tannoch Drive, Milngavie, Glasgow G62 8AR Tel: 0141 956 1736 — MB ChB 1952 Glas.; FRCS Ed. 1993; FRCP Ed. 1993; FRCS Eng. 1985; FRCP Glas. 1982, M 1979; Hon. FRCSI 1994; FFA RCSI 1979; FFA RCS Eng. 1959; DA Eng. 1957. Prev: Chairm. W. Glas. Hosps. Univ. NHS Trust.
CAMPBELL, Mr Donald Eilean Donan, Caulfield Road, Inverness IV2 5BH — MB ChB 1993 Aberd.; FRCS Ed. 1998.
CAMPBELL, Donald (retired) 74 Newark Street, Greenock PA16 7TF Tel: 01425 21153 — MB ChB 1935 Glas.; DPH Liverp. 1940. Prev: Cons. Phys. Dis. of Chest Gateside Hosp. Greenock.
CAMPBELL, Mr Donald Angus Thainstone House, Hastings Road, Battle TN33 0TH Tel: 01424 773873 Fax: 01424 773873 Email: bellerophon@msn.com — MB ChB 1972 Ed.; BSc Ed. 1969; FRCS Eng. 1979; FRCS Ed. 1979. (Ed.) Indep. Surg. Lond. & Sussex Nuffield Hosp. Brighton; Med. Dir. Scand.n Med. Pract. Lond. Socs: Fell. Roy. Soc. Med.; BMA. Prev: Cons. Neurosurg. W. Midl. RHA; Sen. Regist. (Neurosurg.) Walton Hosp. Liverp.; Regist. (Neurosurg.) W.. Gen. Hosp. Edin.
CAMPBELL, Doreen Ann The Scottish Executive, Health Department, St Andrew's House, Edinburgh EH1 3DG Tel: 0131 244 2287; Tel: 01786 841918 Fax: 01786 841918 — MB ChB 1977 Glas.; MFPHM RCP (UK) 1993. (Univ. Glas.) Sen. Med. Off. Scott. Exec.. Edin. Prev: Cons. Pub. Health Med. Nottm. HA; Sen. Regist. (Pub. Health Med.) Nottm. HA; Regist. (Community Med.) Centr. Nottm. DHA.
CAMPBELL, Doris Margaret Department of Obstetrics & Gynaecology, University of Aberdeen, Foresterhill, Aberdeen AB25 2ZD Tel: 01224 681818 Fax: 01224 684880; 77 Blenheim Place, Aberdeen AB25 2DZ — MB ChB 1969 Aberd.; MD Aberd. 1973; FRCOG 1990, M 1975; DObst 1969. (Aberd.) Sen. Lect. (O & G Reproduc. Physiol.) Univ. Aberd.; Accredit. Nutrit.ist Inst. Biol. Socs: Founder Mem. Internat. Soc. Study of Hypertens. in Pregn.; Internat. Soc. Twin Studies; Nutrit. Soc. (Ex-Chairm. Scott. Gp.).
CAMPBELL, Dorothy Jean West End Surgery, Edward Road, Northolt UB5 6QN Tel: 020 8845 6363 Fax: 020 8841 8837; 77 Twyford Avenue, London W3 9QD — MB BS Lond. 1981; DRCOG 1984.
CAMPBELL, Douglas Townhill Surgery, Townhill District Centre, Southampton SO18 3RA Tel: 023 8047 2232 Fax: 023 8046 5107; 14 Megan Road, West End, Southampton SO30 3FR — MB BS 1988 Lond.; MRCGP 1992; DRCOG 1992; DFFP 1992. (Guy's Hosp.)
CAMPBELL, Mr Douglas Adam Department of Orthopaedic Surgery, St James' University Hospital, Beckett St., Leeds LS9 7TF Tel: 0113 243 3144 — MB ChB 1986 Dundee; ChM 2000; FRCS (Orth.) 1995; FRCS Ed. 1991. Cons. Hand Surg. St James Univ. Hosp. Leeds; Sen. Regist. (Orthop. Surg.) St James' Univ. Hosp. Leeds. Prev: Fell. (Hand Surg.) Nuffield Orthop. Centre Oxf.; Career Regist. (Orthop. Surg.) Yorks. RHA; Regist. Rotat. (Surg.) Dundee Hosps.
CAMPBELL, Douglas Robert Blackfield Health Centre, Blackfield, Southampton SO45 1XA Tel: 02380 899119 Fax: 02380 891217; Lime Cottage, Lime Walk, Dibden Purlieu, Southampton SO45 4RB Tel: 02380 844425 — MB BCh 1974 Wales; MSc 2000 (Med. Ed.) Cardiff; MRCGP 1978; DRCOG 1977. (Welsh National School of Medicine) GP Trainer Soton; Course Organiser Soton. VTS. Prev: Trainee GP Cardiff VTS; SHO (Geriat. & O & G) St. David's Hosp. Cardiff; Ho. Off. (Surg.) Univ. Hosp. Wales Cardiff.
CAMPBELL, Mr Duncan John 8 Victoria Avenue, Halesowen B62 9BL Tel: 0121 421 5951 — MB ChB 1967 Birm.; FRCS Ed. 1973; FRCS Eng. 1973. Cons. Surg. Selly Oak Hosp. Birm.
CAMPBELL, Edith Kathleen 14 West Hill Road, Kings Norton, Birmingham B38 8RX Tel: 0121 458 1297 — MB BCh BAO 1962 Belf. (Belf.) SCMO S. Birm. Health Auth. Socs: Fac. Comm. Health.
CAMPBELL, Elaine Barbara c/o R M Benson, Kenburn, 15 West Lennox Drive, Helensburgh G84 9AB — MB ChB 1987 Ed.; FRCA. 1992. Career Regist. (Anaesth.) Vict. Infirm. Glas. Socs: Assn. Anaesth. Gt. Brit. & Irel.; Glas. & W. Scot. Soc. Anaesth.
CAMPBELL, Elizabeth Dorothy 53 Sneyd Avenue, Newcastle ST5 2PZ Tel: 01782 616457 — MB ChB 1957 Birm. (Birm.) Prev: Ho. Phys. Childr. Hosp. Birm.; Ho. Surg. N. Staffs. Roy. Infirm.
CAMPBELL, Elizabeth Janet Langley Health Centre, Common Road, Slough SL3 8LE Tel: 01753 544288 Fax: 01753 592415; 40 Sutton Avenue, Langley, Slough SL3 7AW Tel: 01753 525643 — MB ChB 1972 Leeds; DObst RCOG 1975. Clin. Asst. (Dermat.) Mt. Vernon Hosp.
CAMPBELL, Elizabeth Mary (retired) 2 Sunningdale Square, Kilwinning KA13 6RH Tel: 01294 552615 — MB ChB 1951 Glas.; MRCOG 1964. Assoc. Specialist (O & G) Matern. Sect. Ayrsh. Centre. Hosp. Irvine. Prev: Resid. Ho. Surg. & Ho. Phys. Dumfries & Galloway Roy. Infirm.
CAMPBELL, Emma Jane Stennack Surgery, Old Stennack School, St Ives TR26 1RU Tel: 01736 793333 — MB ChB 1985 Bristol.
CAMPBELL, Ethel Margaret Joan (retired) Kintyre, Longniddry EH32 0NN Tel: 01875 853187 — MB ChB 1946 Ed.; BSc Ed. 1947; DOMS Eng. 1949.
CAMPBELL, Euan Cameron Ardmay, Clydeshore Road, Dumbarton G82 4AG Tel: 01389 2129 — MB ChB 1952 Glas.
CAMPBELL, Euan David Ross (retired) 4 St Edwards Close, London NW11 7NA Tel: 020 8455 5299 — BM BCh 1952 Oxf.; MA Oxf. 1952, BM BCh 1952; FRCP Lond. 1970, M 1954; DPhysMed. Eng. 1960. Rheum. Roy. Free Hosp. Lond. & Cell Barnes Hosp. St. Albans; Vice-Dean. Roy. Free Hosp. Sch. Med. Prev: Chief Asst. (Med.) St. Bart. Hosp.
CAMPBELL, Eugene 27 Eastbourne Avenue, London W3 6JR — MB ChB 1994 Manch.
CAMPBELL, Mr Ewen David Ogilvie, TD (retired) Dellifour, Kingussie PH21 1DQ — MB ChB 1935 St. And.; FRCS Ed. 1938; MRCGP 1952.
CAMPBELL, Felicity Agnes Dr MacBrayne and Partners, 19 Dinmont Road, Shawlands, Glasgow G41 3UJ Tel: 0141 632 8883 Fax: 0141 636 0654 — MB ChB 1980 Glas.; MRCP (UK) 1985; MRCGP 1984; DRCOG 1983; FRCP (Glas) 1998. (Glasgow) Hosp. Pract. Vict. Infirm. Glas.
CAMPBELL, Finlay Nicol 157 Claremont Road, Salford M6 8PA Tel: 0161 736 4288 — MB ChB 1957 Ed.; FFA RCS Eng. 1966; DA Eng. 1959. (Ed.) Cons. Anaesth. Oldham AHA. Socs: Assn. Anaesth.; Hosp. Consults. & Specialists. Assn. Prev: RAMC.
CAMPBELL, Fiona Department of Pathology, Royal Liverpool University Hospital, Duncan Building (5th Floor), Liverpool L69 3GA Tel: 0151 706 4483 Fax: 0151 706 5859 Email: f.campbell@liv.ac.uk — MB ChB 1988 Liverp.; BSc (Hons.) Liverp. 1985, MD 1995. Cons. Histopath. Roy. Liverp. Univ. Hosp. Prev: Sen. Regist., Regist. & SHO (Histopath.) S. Glam. HA Cardiff.
CAMPBELL, Fiona Anne 4 Oxgangs Terrace, Edinburgh EH13 9BY Tel: 0131 467 3574 — MB ChB 1991 Ed. SHO (Renal Med.) Roy. Infirm. Edin.
CAMPBELL, Fiona Anne Pain Management Centre, Queens Medical Centre Nottingham, Nottingham NG7 2UH Tel: 0115 970 9194 Email: finona.campbell@mail.qmcuh-tr.trent.nhs.uk — MD 1984 Canada; BSc Canada 1980; FRCA. 1990. Cons. Anaesth. & Pain Managem. Prev: Sen. Regist. (Anaesth.) Leicester Roy. Infirm.
CAMPBELL, Fiona Jane 25 Bainton Road, Oxford OX2 7AF — MB BS 1994 Lond.
CAMPBELL, Fiona Mary Department of Paediatrics, St. James University Hospital, Beckett St., Leeds LS9 7TF Tel: 0113 206 5924 Fax: 0113 206 5405; Croftinloan, 24 Wigton Chase, Alwoodley, Leeds LS17 8SG — MB ChB 1983 Dundee; MRCP (UK) 1986; DCH RCP Lond. 1985; FRCPCH 1997; MD 1998. (Univ. Dundee) Cons. Paediat. & Diabetologist St. Jas. Univ. Hosp. Leeds; Sen. Lect. (Child Health) Univ. of Leeds. Socs: Renal Assn.; MRCPCH; Brit. Assn. Paediat. Nephrol. Prev: Sen. Regist. (Paediat.) St. Jas. Univ. Hosp. Leeds; Research Fell. Inst. Child Health Lond.; Regist. (Paediat.) Hosp. for Sick Childr. Gt. Ormond St. Lond.
CAMPBELL, Frances Ethel 72 Hamilton Avenue, Harborne, Birmingham B17 8AR Tel: 0121 427 2589 — MB ChB 1958 Birm. (Birm.) Prev: Asst. Med. Off. Sandwell AHA; Ho. Surg. Gen. Hosp. Birm.; Ho. Phys. Qu. Eliz. Hosp. Birm.
CAMPBELL, Francis Dill (retired) 7 Riverside Road, Alnmouth, Alnwick NE66 2SD Tel: 01665 830812 — LRCP LRCS Ed. LRFPS Glas. 1938. Prev: Med. Off. DHSS N.. Region Newc.
CAMPBELL, Francis Stephen 30 Cloister Crofts, Leamington Spa CV32 6QQ — MB ChB 1981 Birm; MRCGP 1986; DRCOG 1986.
CAMPBELL, Fraser Pendyffryn Medical Group, Ffordd Pendyffryn, Prestatyn LL19 9DH Tel: 01745 886444 Fax: 01745 889831 — MB

ChB 1986 Liverp.; MBA Manch. 1992; MRCGP 1990; T(GP) 1991; DRCOG 1988. (Liverp.) GP Adviser NHS Exec. NW; Sessional Med. Off. NBS. Prev: Trainee GP Maghull & S. Sefton HA VTS; SHO Fazakerley & Walton Hosps. Liverp. & Roy. Liverp. Childr. Hosp. Alder Hey.

CAMPBELL, Professor Frederick Charles Department of Surgery, The Medical School, Framlington Place, Newcastle upon Tyne NE2 4 Tel: 0191 222 6000 Email: f.c.campbell@ncl.ac.uk; 11 Westfield Avenue, Gosforth, Newcastle upon Tyne NE3 4YH Tel: 0191 232 5131 Fax: 01382 641795 Email: f.c.campbell@nc1.ac.uk — MB ChB 1975 Glas.; MD (Hons.) Glas. 1983; FRCS Ed. 1988; FRCS Glas. 1980. Prof. Gastroenterol. Surg. & Cons. Surg. Univ. Newc. & Roy. Infirm. Newc. Socs: Brit. Soc. Gastroenterol.; Soc. Surg. of Alimentary Tract; Surgic. Research Soc. Prev: Reader, Hon. Cons., Sen. Lect. & Lect. (Surg.) Ninewells Hosp. Dundee.

CAMPBELL, Gary 67 Glenarm Road, Larne BT40 1DX — MB ChB 1998 Glas.; MB ChB Glas 1998.

CAMPBELL, Gayle 20 Coney Park, Stirling FK7 9LU — MB ChB 1995 Aberd. SHO (Plastic Surg.) Canniesburn Hosp., Glas. Socs: B.M.A; M.D.D.U.S.

CAMPBELL, George Bremner Buchanan Whitby Group Practice, Spring Vale Medical Centre, Whitby YO21 1SD Tel: 01947 820888 Fax: 01947 603194 — MB ChB 1983 Univ. Zimbabwe; MB ChB U Zimbabwe 1983; LRCP Ed. LRCS Ed. LRCPS Glas. 1983; DA (UK) 1988.

CAMPBELL, George David The Glenside Practice, 12B High St., Castle Bytham, Grantham NG33 4RZ Tel: 01780 410205 Fax: 01780 410817; Glen House, Glen Road, Castle Bytham, Grantham NG33 4RD Tel: 01780 410944 Fax: 01780 410817 Email: 101767.2505@compuserve.com — MB ChB 1975 Ed.; Dip. Pract. Dermat. Wales 1995; DA Eng. 1980; Dip. Travel Med. Glas. 1996. (Edinburgh) MD Witham Hall Sch. Prev: Late S/Ldr RAF Med. Br.

CAMPBELL, Georgina Claire 6 The Mount, Papcastle, Cockermouth CA13 0JY — MB ChB 1998 Glas.; MB ChB Glas 1998.

CAMPBELL, Gillian Lesley 27/28 Church Street, Whitehaven CA28 7EB Tel: 01946 693660; 60 Brigham Road, Cockermouth CA13 0BT — MB BS 1983 Lond.; MRCGP 1987. Prev: Med. Off. Panguma Hosp. E. Province, Sierra Leone.

CAMPBELL, Gillian Susan 11 Staverton Road, Oxford OX2 6XH Tel: 01865 513935 Fax: 01865 513935 Email: l.lustgarten@soton.ac.uk — MB BCh BAO 1968 Dub.; MA Dub 1969; MRCGP 1984. (TC Dub.) Adviser on Heroin Abuse; Reiki Therapist (Japanese Healing Ther.) Oxf.; Mem. Green Coll. Oxf. Socs: BMA.

CAMPBELL, Gordon Arnold Box 135, Department of Medicine for the Elderly, Addenbrooke's Hospital, Cambridge CB2 2QQ Tel: 01223 217786 Fax: 01223 217783; 5 Hedgerley Close, Cambridge CB3 0EW — MB BS 1974 Lond.; MA Camb. 1989; BSc (Hons.) Lond. 1971, MB BS 1974; FRCP Lond. 1994; MRCP (UK) 1979. (St. Thos.) Cons. Phys. Addenbrooke's Hosp. Camb.; Assoc. Lect. Univ. Camb. Socs: Brit. Geriat. Soc. & Bone & Tooth Soc. Prev: Sen. Regist. City Hosp. Nottm.; Research Fell. Qu. Med. Centre Nottm.

CAMPBELL, Gordon Forbes Gerrans Hill, Portscatho, Truro TR2 5EE — MB ChB 1976 Dundee; MRCGP 1981; DRCOG 1979. Socs: Pres. of Cornw. Clin. Soc. 1997; Chairm. of Cornw. Trainers Gp. 1995.

CAMPBELL, Gordon John Fulton Street Surgery, 94 Fulton Street, Glasgow G13 1JE Tel: 0141 959 3391 Fax: 0141 950 2692 — MB ChB 1993 Aberd.

CAMPBELL, Grace 14 Fairlie, Oakwood Park, Stewartfield, East Kilbride, Glasgow G74 4SE — MB ChB 1987 Aberd.; MRCGP 1991. GP Glas. VTS.

CAMPBELL, Grace Ann Margretta Bangor Health Centre, Newtownards Road, Bangor BT20 4LD Tel: 028 9146 9111; 1 Crawfordsburn Wood, Crawfordsburn, Bangor BT19 1XB Tel: 852434 — MB BCh BAO 1974; MRCGP 1978; DRCOG 1976; DCH Dub. 1977; Belf. GP Bangor. Prev: Trainee GP Scheme Bangor Health Centre; SHO (Obst.) Ulster Hosp. Dundonald; Woman's Retainer Scheme_ GP E.. HSS Bd. N. Irel.

CAMPBELL, Graham Cumming (retired) New Wood Lodge, Bridgnorth Road, Stourton, Stourbridge DY7 6RY — MRCS Eng. LRCP Lond. 1928.

CAMPBELL, Grant Alan 12 Blackwood Way, Pitreavie Castle, Dunfermline KY11 8TD — MB ChB 1994 Dundee; BMSc 1991 Dundee. GP (Regist.) Limekilns Surg. Fife. Prev: SHO, A+E, Falkirk Roy. Infermaty; SSHO Paediat., Ninewells Hosp., Dundee.

CAMPBELL, Gwen Anne Margaret 20 Ledcameroch Road, Bearsden, Glasgow G61 4AE — MB ChB 1983 Glas.

CAMPBELL, Hall Stewart Old School Surgery, 54 Station Road, Greenisland, Carrickfergus BT38 8TP Tel: 028 9086 4455 Fax: 028 9036 5367; 157 Upper Road, Greenisland, Carrickfergus BT38 8RT Tel: 01232 865433 — MB BCh BAO Belf. 1963; DObst RCOG 1965. (Belf.)

CAMPBELL, Harriet Rachel The Surgery, Godswell Lodge, Bloxham OX15 4ES Tel: 01296 720347; Email: pkeedwell@aol.com — MB BS 1993 Lond.; DRCOG 1996; DFFP 1997; MRCGP 1998. (Roy. Free Hosp. Med. Sch.) p/t GP Retainee - Bloxham. Socs: RCGP; RCOG. Prev: GP Regist. - Buckingham; GP Trainee Hosp. Tobs - Milton Meynes Hosp.

CAMPBELL, Harry Community Health Services, University of Edinburgh, Edinburgh EH8 9AG Tel: 0131 650 3118 Fax: 0131 650 6909 Email: harry.campbell@ed.ac.uk; Harvivestoun Home Farmhouse, Dollar FK14 7PX — MB ChB 1980 Ed.; BSc (Hons.) Pharmacol. Ed. 1977, MD 1993, MB ChB 1980; MSc Community Health in Developing Countries Lond. 1984; FRCP Ed. 1991; MRCP (UK) 1983; MFPHM RCP (UK) 1994; DCH RCPS Glas. 1982. Reader; Cons. Pub. Health Med. Lothian Univ. Hosp. NHS Trust; Sen.Lect. Prev: Cons. Pub. Health Med. Fife HB; Med. Off. ARI Progr. WHO Geneva, Switz.; Research Clin. Med. Research Counc. Gambia W. Africa.

CAMPBELL, Hazel Olive Cameron Highland Sexual Health - Family Planning, Royal Northern Infirmary, Ness Walk, Inverness IV3 5SF Tel: 01463 723209 Fax: 01463 714685; Drumashie Lodge, Dores, Inverness IV2 6TR — MB ChB 1968 St. And.; MFFP 1993; Cert. Family Plann. 1971. SCMO & Clin. Dir. (Family Plann.) Highland Communities NHS Trust; Regional Adviser (Family Plann.) Highlands; Clin. Asst. (Genitourin. Med.) Raigmore Hosp. NHS Trust Inverness. Socs: Scott. Family Plann. Med. Soc.; MSSVD.

CAMPBELL, Heather Gail Glendale Medical Centre, 155 High Street, Harlington, Hayes UB3 5DA Tel: 020 8897 8288 Fax: 020 8754 1539; Fairview, 22 Ottershaw Park, Ottershaw, Chertsey KT16 0QG Tel: 01932 872498 Fax: 01932 872498 — MB BS 1980 Lond.; BSc. Lond. 1977; MRCGP 1984; DRCOG 1984. (St. Bart.) Prev: Trainee GP Ealing Hosp. VTS Lond.; Ho. Surg. St. Bart. Hosp. Lond.; Ho. Phys. Whipps Cross Hosp.

CAMPBELL, Mr Hector Law Hospital, Carluke ML8 5ER Tel: 01698 361100 Fax: 01698 375868; Newhouse Farm, Ravenstruther, Lanark ML11 8NP — MB ChB 1974 Glas.; ChM Liverp. 1989; FRCS Glas. 1978. (Glas.) Cons. Surg. (Gen. Surg.) & Clin. Dir. (Surg.) Law Hosp. Carluke. Socs: Vasc. Surgic. Soc. GB & Irel.; Assn. Surg.; BMA.

CAMPBELL, Hector Crawford, MBE (retired) Cruachan, Killearn, Glasgow G63 9NP Tel: 01360 550959 — MB ChB 1939 Glas.; MRCGP 1968.

CAMPBELL, Helen 16 Cecil Street, Leeds LS12 2AL — MB ChB 1997 Leeds.

CAMPBELL, Helen Frances 104 Church Road, Sandford-on-Thames, Oxford OX4 4YB — MB BCh BAO 1989 Belf.; MB BCh BAO NUI Belf. 1989; MRCPsych 1994.

CAMPBELL, Helen Jane 25 Keyneston Road, Swindon SN3 3PS — MB ChB 1998 Sheff.; MB ChB Sheff 1998.

CAMPBELL, Helen Margaret 96 Queen Edith's Way, Cambridge CB1 8PP Tel: 01223 247578 — MB ChB 1946 Glas. (Univ. Glas.) Prev: Ho. Surg. Glas. Eye Infirm. & Lennoxcastle Matern. Hosp.; Ho. Phys. Larkfield Hosp. Greenock.

CAMPBELL, Henrietta 1A The Rookery, Killinchy, Newtownards BT23 6SY — MB BCh BAO 1973 Belf.; MFCM 1989. Chief Med. Off. DHSS N. Irel.

CAMPBELL, Hugh Ludovic 27 Finch Avenue, Sandal, Wakefield WF2 6SE — M.B., Ch.B. Glas. 1935. (Univ. Glas.)

CAMPBELL, Hugh Malcolm Freedom Health Centre, 78 Lipson Road, Plymouth PL4 8RH — MB BChir 1975 Camb.; MA Camb. 1976; MRCP (UK) 1979; MRCGP 1980; DRCOG 1980; Dip. Addict. Behaviour St George's Lond. 1997.

CAMPBELL, Iain Cameron Hunter Health Centre, Andrew Street, East Kilbride, Glasgow G74 1AD Tel: 01355 906676 Fax: 01355

906676; 82 Pitcairn Crescent, Hairmyres, East Kilbridge, Glasgow G75 8TD Tel: 01352 47809 — MB ChB 1978 Glas.; MRCGP 1985; DCH RCPS Glas. 1980; DRCOG 1980. (Glas.)

CAMPBELL, Iain Kerr Carronbank Medical Practice, Denny Health Centre, Carronbank House, Denny FK6 6GD Tel: 01324 822382 Fax: 01324 826675; 56 Laxdale Drive, Denny FK6 5PR Tel: 01324 826675 — MB ChB 1985 Glas.; MRCGP 1989.

CAMPBELL, Iain Murdoch Woodlands Farm, Newtown, Martley, Worcester WR6 6PR — MB ChB 1997 Liverp.

CAMPBELL, Professor Iain Taylor Deparment of Anaestaesia, Baguley House, Wythenshawe Hospital, Soutmoore Road, Manchester M23 9LT Tel: 0161 2915710 Fax: 0161 291 5714; 11 The Mews, Leigh Road, Worsley M28 2GT Tel: 0161 7906241 — MB BS Lond. 1968; MD Lond. 1975; MRCS Eng. LRCP Lond. 1968; FRCA Eng. 1975; DA Eng. 1973. (Guy's) Cons. Anaesth., S. Manch. Univ. Hosp.s NHS Trust; Prof. of Human Physiol., Liverp. John Moores Univ., Liverp.

CAMPBELL, Ian Path House Medical Practice, Path House, Nether Street, Kirkcaldy KY1 2PG Tel: 01592 644533 Fax: 01592 644550 — MB ChB 1975 Glas.; MRCGP 1991; Dip. Pract. Dermat. Univ. Wales 1994. GP Princip. Prev: Partner James St. Family Pract., Louth, Lincs.; Chief (Dept. of Family Med.) Oakville Trafalgar Hosp. Oakville Ontario Canada; Ho. Off. Stobhill Hosp. Glas..

CAMPBELL, Ian Alexander (retired) 23 Red Road, Borehamwood WD6 4SR Tel: 020 8953 1077 — MB BS 1955 Lond.; LMSSA Lond. 1952. Prev: Ho. Surg. Bolingbroke Hosp. Wandsworth.

CAMPBELL, Ian Allan Llandough Hospital, Penlan Road, Penarth CF64 2XX Tel: 01222 715417 Fax: 01222 350056; Glamorgan House, BUPA Hospital, Cardiff CF23 8XL Tel: 01222 736011 Fax: 01222 549930 — MB BS Lond. 1968; BSc Lond. 1965, MD 1978; FRCP Lond. 1987; FRCP Ed. 1982; MRCP (UK) 1971. (St. Geo.) Cons. Phys. (Thoracic Med.) Llandough Hosp. Cardiff. Socs: Internat. Union Against Tuberc. & Lung Dis.; Thoracic Soc. Wales; Brit. Thorac. Soc. Prev: Sen. Regist. (Gen. & Thoracic Med.) Bristol Roy. Infirm.; Brit. Thoracic Assn. Research Fell. Univ. Edin. Dept. Respirat. Dis. City Hosp. Edin.; Regist. Chest Unit Ch.ill Hosp. Oxf.

CAMPBELL, Ian Archibald (retired) Suilven, 34 The Holdings, Hatfield AL9 5HQ Tel: 01707 265888 — MB ChB 1948 St. And.

CAMPBELL, Ian Benson The Health Centre, 20 Duncan Street, Greenock PA15 4LY Tel: 01475 724477 Fax: 01475 727140; 16 Bedford Street, Greenock PA16 8PE — MB ChB 1968 Glas.; DObst RCOG 1970; AFOM RCP Lond. 1992. (Glas.) GP Greenock. Prev: Jun. Ho. Off. (Obst.) Stobhill Gen. Hosp. Glas.; Jun. Ho. Off. Glas. Roy. Infirm.

CAMPBELL, Ian Douglas The Salvation Army Headquarters, 101 Queen Victoria St., London EC4P 4EP Tel: 020 7236 5222 Fax: 0207489 1410 Email: ian_campbell@salvationarmy.org — MB BS 1977 Adelaide; MRCP (UK) 1980.

CAMPBELL, Ian Dugald, QHP (retired) 5 Succoth Park, Edinburgh EH12 6BX Tel: 0131 539 5965 — MB ChB 1939 Ed.; FRCP Ed. 1973, M 1970; FFCM 1974, M 1972. Prev: Chief Admin. Med. Off. Lothian HB.

CAMPBELL, Ian Keith Snettisham Surgery, Common Road, Snettisham, King's Lynn PE31 7PE Tel: 01485 541206 Fax: 01485 543259; Craven House, Lynn Road, Snettisham, King's Lynn PE31 7LW Tel: 01485 541179 — MB BS 1969 Lond.; BSc (Pharmacol., Hons.) Lond. 1966; FRCGP 1988, M 1976; DObst RCOG 1973. (St. Geo.) Prev: SHO (O & G) Qu. Eliz. Matern. Unit King's Lynn; Med. Resid. Vancouver Gen. Hosp., Canada; Ho. Phys. St. Geo. Hosp. Lond.

CAMPBELL, Mr Ian Ronald 22 Bramhall Close, West Kirby, Wirral CH48 8BP Tel: 0151 625 1449 — MB 1979 Camb.; BChir 1978; FRCS Eng. 1983; FRCR 1989; MD Camb. 1994; BSc 1994. Med. Statistician IC Statistical Servs.; Dir., Notify Med. Ltd. Prev: Sen. Regist. (Clin. Oncol.) Clatterbridge Hosp. Wirral.; Regist. (Radiother. & Oncol.) Clatterbridge Hosp. Wirral; Regist. (Surg.) Leics. HA.

CAMPBELL, Ian Wallace Willows Medical Centre, Church Street, Carlton, Nottingham NG4 1BJ Tel: 0115 940 4252 Fax: 0115 956 8876 — MB ChB 1982 Glas.; MRCGP 1988; DLO RCS Eng. 1987; DRCOG 1987.

CAMPBELL, Ian William Strathearn, 19 Victoria Road, Lundin Links, Leven KY8 6AY Tel: 01333 320533 — MB ChB 1969 Ed.; BSc (Med. Sci.) Ed. 1966; FRCP Glas. 1996; FRCP Ed. 1980; MRCP (UK) 1972. (Ed.) Cons. Phys. Vict. Hosp. Kirkcaldy; Hon. Sen. Lect. (Med.) Univ. Edin.; Hon. Prof. Biol. & Med. Sci. Univ. St. And. Prev: Sen. Regist. (Med.) & Regist. (Med. Diabetes & Metab.) Roy. Infirm. Edin.

CAMPBELL, Isobel Hamilton Dykebar Hospital, Paisley PA2 7DE Tel: 0141 884 5122 Fax: 0141 884 5425 — MB ChB 1977 Glas.; MPhil Ed. 1988; MRCPsych 1983. Cons. Psychiat. Dykebar Hosp. Paisley. Prev: Cons. Psychiat. Hartwood Hosp. Shotts; Cons. Psychiat. State Hosp. Carstairs.

CAMPBELL, Jacqueline Anne Lingwell Croft Surgery, Ring Road, Middleton, Leeds LS10 3LT Tel: 0113 270 4848 Fax: 0113 272 0030 — MB ChB 1984 Ed.

CAMPBELL, James, TD (retired) Tullich, 193 Queensferry Road, Rosyth, Dunfermline KY11 2JQ Tel: 01383 412044 — MB ChB 1947 Ed.

CAMPBELL, James Alexander 38 Tanera Avenue, Simshill, Glasgow G44 5BX — BChir 1978 Camb.

CAMPBELL, James Colin Plympton Health Centre, Plympton, Plymouth PL7 1AD Tel: 01752 341474 Fax: 01752 345757 — MB ChB 1971 Bristol; MRCS Eng. LRCP Lond. 1970; MRCGP 1978; DObst RCOG 1973; DCH Eng. 1973. (Bristol) Socs: BMA. Prev: SHO Bristol Roy Hosp. Sick Childr.; SHO Accid. & Emerg. Dept. Bristol Roy. Infirm.; Gen. Med. Off. (Volun. Serv. Overseas) Nixon Memor. Methodist Hosp.

CAMPBELL, James Dugald Stewart 60 Obsdale Park, Alness IV17 0TR Tel: 01349 882585 Email: jdscampbell_almess@yahoo.com — MB ChB 1966 Glas.; FRCGP 1995, M 1975; DPM Leeds 1974; DObst RCOG 1968. (Glas.) Socs: Full Mem. BALINT Soc.; Fell. RGCP. Prev: Partner Aalness Med. Ross-sh.. 1975-2000; Regist. (Psychiat.) Naburn Hosp. York; Med. Off. i/c Levuka Hosp., Fiji. 1970-1972.

CAMPBELL, James Hunter Grantham & Kesteven General Hospital, 101 Manthorpe Road, Grantham NG31 8DG Tel: 01476 65232 — MB ChB 1981 Manch.; MRCP (UK) 1984. Cons. Phys. Gen. & Respirat. Med. Grantham & Kesteven Gen. Hosp. Lincs.

CAMPBELL, Mr James Kininmonth, Surg. Cdr. RN Derriford Hospital, Plymouth PL6 8DH Tel: 01752 777111 Fax: 01752 763436 Email: james.campbell@phnt.swest.nhs.uk; 2 Berkeley Cottages, Collingwood Road, Stoke, Plymouth PL1 5GT Tel: 01752 560578 Fax: 01752 763436 Email: jamessonofdavid@hotmail.com — MB BS 1979 Lond.; FRCS Ed. 1986; MRCS Eng. LRCP Lond. 1979; FRCS Eng. 1998. (Westminster Hospital Medical School) Cons. Gen. Surg. Derriford Hosp. Plymouth. Upper GI Surg.. Demfed Hosp.. Head of upper SI cancer focus Gp.. Socs: Milit. Surg. Soc.; Assn. Surg.; Trav. Surg.s Soc. Prev: Sen. Regist. (Gen. Surg.) RN Hosp Haslar & RN Hosp. Plymouth; Hon. Sen. Regist. Bristol Roy. Infirm.

CAMPBELL, James Patrick McIntyre Princess Margaret Rose Orthopaedic Hospital, Fairmilehead, Edinburgh EH10 7ED Tel: 0131 536 4600 Fax: 0131 536 4601; Owl Hall, Burdiehouse Road, Edinburgh EH17 8SG Email: j-campbell@compuserve.com — MB ChB 1976 Ed.; MD Ed. 1985; MLCOM 1993; MRO 1993; MRCGP 1980; DRCOG 1980. Cons. Musculoskeletal Med. P.ss Margt. Rose Hosp. Edin. Socs: Internat. Assn. Study of Pain; Pain Soc.; Brit. Inst. Musculoskel. Med. Prev: GP Livingston; Hosp. Pract. (A & E) St. John's Hosp. Livingston; Research Fell. Univ. Edin.

CAMPBELL, James Ranald Carr Belmont House, Benniworth, Lincoln LN3 6SJ — MB BS 1973 Newc.; MRCGP 1977; DObst RCOG 1975.

CAMPBELL, James Somerville, OBE (retired) 1 Battery Place, Rothesay PA20 9DP Tel: 01700 502334 — MB ChB 1951 Glas.; FRCSC 1964. Prev: SCMO Health Control Unit Heathrow Airport.

CAMPBELL, Jane Love Anniesland Medical Practice, 778 Crow Road, Glasgow G13 1LU Tel: 0141 954 8860 Fax: 0141 954 0870 — MB ChB 1980 Glas.; MRCGP 1984; DRCOG 1982. (Glasgow)

CAMPBELL, Jane Marian Lattice Barn Surgery, 14 Woodbridge Road East, Ipswich IP4 5PA Tel: 01473 726836 Fax: 01473 273567 — MB BCh BAO 1978 NUI.

CAMPBELL, Jill Elizabeth Sydenham Green Health Centre, Holmshaw Close, London SE26 4TH Tel: 020 8676 8836 — MB BS 1982 Lond.; BA (Hons.) Oxf. 1979; MRCGP 1989; DRCOG 1988; DCH RCP Lond. 1987.

CAMPBELL, Mr John The Lourdes Hospital, Green Bank Road, Liverpool L18 1HQ Tel: 0151 733 7123; 14 Buffs Lane, Barnston, Wirral CH60 2SG Tel: 0151 342 9626 — MB ChB 1963 Liverp.;

MChOrth 1971; FRCS Ed. 1968; FRCS Eng. 1970. (Liverp.) Cons. Surg. (Orthop.) Liverp. AHA (T). Socs: Liverp. Med. Inst. & Brit. Orthop. Assn. Prev: Sen. Regist. (Orthop.) Liverp. RHB; Orthop. Regist. Roy. S.. Hosp. & Alder Hey Childrs. Hosp. Liverp.

CAMPBELL, John Alphonsus (retired) 8 Bushby's Park, Formby, Liverpool L37 2EF Tel: 01704874666 — BA, MB BCh BAO Dub. 1948; DCP Lond 1952; FRCPath 1971. Cons. Pathol. BRd.green Hosp. Liverp. Prev: Ho. Phys. Roy. City Dub. Hosp.

CAMPBELL, John Angus 160 (TFR) Bruntsfield Place, Edinburgh EH10 4ER — MB ChB 1990 Ed.

CAMPBELL, Mr John Angus, OBE (retired) 5 The Green, Cardrona Village, Peebles EH45 9LR Tel: 01896 830499 — MB ChB 1944 Ed.; ChM Ed. 1967, MB ChB 1944; FRCS Ed. 1948. Med. Adviser Brit. Aluminium Co. Ltd. Prev: Cons. Surg. Belford Hosp. Fort William.

CAMPBELL, Mr John Barry 44 Ashlawn Crescent, Solihull B91 1PS — MB ChB 1976 Birm.; MMSc Dundee 1979; FRCS Eng. 1983; FRCS Ed. 1982. Cons. Otolaryngol. E. Birm. & Solihull Hosps.

CAMPBELL, John Charles 1 Carrour Gardens, Bishopbriggs, Glasgow G64 3DG Tel: 0141 772 2103 — MB ChB 1964 Glas.; PhD Glas. 1973, MB ChB 1964; FRCPath 1988; MRCPath 1976. Cons. (Path.) Stobhill Gen. Hosp. Glas.

CAMPBELL, John Duthie (retired) Braeriach, 197 Old Bedford Road, Luton LU2 7EH Tel: 01582 731699 — MB ChB Aberd. 1951. Prev: JHMO St. Tydfil's Hosp. Merthyr Tydfil.

CAMPBELL, John Eamon Beaupré, 17 Dunlambert Avenue, Belfast BT15 3NH — MB BCh BAO 1987 Belf.; DRCOG 1991; DMH Belf. 1990.

CAMPBELL, John Gordon Beechfield, Calfmuir Road, Lenzie, Kirkintilloch, Glasgow G66 3UG — MB ChB 1963 Glas.; MRCPsych 1972; DPM Ed. & Glas. 1968. Cons. Psychiat. Woodilee Hosp. Lenzie. Socs: BMA. Prev: Sen. Regist. (Psychiat.) Middlx. Hosp. Lond. & Tavistock Centre Lond.; Regist. (Psychiat.) Roy. Edin. Hosp.

CAMPBELL, John Lennox Lambeth Walk Group Practice, 5 Lambeth Walk, London SE11 6SP Tel: 020 7735 4412 Fax: 020 7820 1888; 8 Nursery Place, Chipstead, Sevenoaks TN13 2RH Tel: 01732 455093 — MB ChB 1983 Ed.; BSc (Hons.) Ed. 1980; MRCGP 1987; T(GP) 1991; DRCOG 1986; DCH RCPS Glas. 1985; MD Edinbugh 1998. Sen. Lect. (Gen. Pract.) UMDS Guy's & St. Thos. Hosp. Lond. Socs: (Hon. Sec.) AUDGP. Prev: Lect. (Gen. Pract.) Univ. Edin.; SHO (Med. Paediat., O & G & A & E) Lothian HB.

CAMPBELL, John Mark Flat 3/3, 18 Oban Drive, Glasgow G20 6AF — MB ChB 1998 Glas.; MB ChB Glas 1998.

CAMPBELL, John Philip Russell (retired) Cherry Tree Cottage, Hockley Lane, Wingerworth, Chesterfield S42 6QQ Tel: 01246 279711 — MB BS 1955 Durh.; MRCGP 1967; DObst RCOG 1961.

CAMPBELL, Julian Roderick 73 West Cliffe Terrace, Harrogate HG2 0PU — MB BS 1984 Lond.; MA Camb. 1984; FRCA 1988. Sen. Regist. (Anaesth.) W. Midl. RHA.

CAMPBELL, Keith Alexander Adair (retired) Woodlands, The Stell, Kirkcudbright DG6 4SA Tel: 01557 330627 Fax: 01557 330627 — MB BS 1945 Lond.; DObst RCOG 1950. Prev: Ho. Phys. (Childr.) & Resid. Obst. Guy's Hosp.

CAMPBELL, Lachlan Breadalbane 10 Harley Street, London W1N 1AA Tel: 020 7362 0100 Fax: 079 73583065 020 7358 3065 Email: info@medexpert.co.cuk; 17 White Lodge, upper Norwood, London SE19 3HR Tel: 020 7362 0100 Fax: 079 7358 3065 — MB BS 1972 Adelaide; BMedSc (Hons.) Adelaide 1969; MRCPsych 1976; FRCP 2000 (psych). (Univ. Adelaide) Cons. Forens. Psychiat., Private Pract. Prev: Cons. Psychiat. Bethlem & Maudsley NHS Trust Lond.; Cons. Forens. Psychiat. Chadwick lodge, Milton keynes.

CAMPBELL, Lara Firtree Cottage, Duncryne Road, Gartocharn, Alexandria G83 8RY — MB ChB 1995 Glas.

CAMPBELL, Laura Mary 41 Norfolk Parade, Glen Road, Belfast BT11 8DA — MB ChB 1987 Aberd.

CAMPBELL, Lawrence Malcolm Southbank Road Surgery, 17-19 Southbank Road, Kirkintilloch, Glasgow G66 1NH Tel: 0141 776 2183 Fax: 0141 777 8321 — MB ChB Glas. 1971; FRCGP 1991, M 1982.

CAMPBELL, Lesley 8 York Road, Malton YO17 6AX — MB BS 1978 Lond.

CAMPBELL, Lesley Anne de Gay and Partners, The Surgery, 50 Barnaby Gate, Newark NG24 1QD Tel: 01636 704225 Fax: 01636 613044 — MB ChB 1981 Manch.; MB ChB (Hons.) Manch. 1981; MRCGP 1985; DRCOG 1983.

CAMPBELL, Leslie James Fitzgerald The Ivybrdige Health Centre, Station Road, Ivybridge PL21 0AJ Tel: 01752 690777 Fax: 01752 690252; Sunnyside, The Square, Ugborough, Ivybridge PL21 0NT — MB BChir Camb. 1991; MRCGP 1996; DRCOG 1994. Socs: S. Hams Med. Soc.Mem. S. Hams Med. Soc.

CAMPBELL, Linda Joyce Derriford Hospital, Plymouth PL6 8DH Tel: 01752 777111; 2 Berkeley Cottages, Plymouth PL1 5QT — MB BS 1979 Lond. Assoc. Specialist BrE. Clinican.

CAMPBELL, Louisa Anne 25 Bainton Road, Oxford OX2 7AF — MB BS 1991 Lond.

CAMPBELL, Lucy Helen The Old Rectory, Ford Lane, Northenden, Manchester M22 4NQ — MB ChB 1993 Manch.

CAMPBELL, Lyndsey Mary Jane 28 Crummock Gardens, Beith KA15 2HD — MB ChB 1995 Glas.

CAMPBELL, Lynne 74 Maule Street, Carnoustie DD7 6HB — MB ChB 1990 Ed.

CAMPBELL, Mabel 17 Regent Close, Lower Earley, Reading RG6 4EZ — LMS 1973 Navarra; DA Eng. 1977.

CAMPBELL, Malcolm Joseph Litfield House, 1 Litfield Place, Clifton, Bristol BS8 3LS Tel: 0117 973 1323 Fax: 0117 973 3303; 20 Church Road, Sneyd Park, Bristol BS9 1QP Tel: 0117 968 5566 — MB BS 1960 Lond.; FRCP Lond. 1978, M 1965; MRCS Eng. LRCP Lond. 1960. (St. Mary's) Cons. Neurol. Socs: BMA & Assn. Brit. Neurol.; Bristol Medico-Legal Soc. Prev: Resid. Med. Off. Nat. Hosp. Nerv. Dis. Lond.; Wellcome Sen. Research Fell. Dept. Neurol. Newc. Univ. Hosps.; Instruc. (Neurol.) Univ. Calif. Med. Center San Francisco, USA.

CAMPBELL, Mr Malcolm Sinclair (retired) 2 Allanson Drive, Cottingham HU16 4PF Tel: 01482 849516 — MB BS 1937 Lond.; MB BS (Hons.) Lond. 1937; FRCS Ed. 1941. Hon. Cons. Surg. Roy. Hull Hosps. Prev: Hon. Lt.-Col. RAMC.

CAMPBELL, Margaret Ann 58 Watson Street, Aberdeen AB25 2SU — MB ChB 1985 Aberd.; MRCGP 1989; DRCOG 1988. Community Med. Off. Grampian HB.

CAMPBELL, Margaret Anne Glenside Practice, Castle Bytham Surgery, 12b High Street, Castle Bytham, Grantham NG33 4RZ Tel: 01780 410205 Fax: 01780 410817; Glen House, Glen Road, Castle Bytham, Grantham NG33 4RD Tel: 01780 410944 Fax: 01780 410817 — MB ChB 1975 Ed.

CAMPBELL, Margaret Helen 52 Raby Drive, Raby Mere, Wirral CH63 0NL — MB ChB 1983 Leic.

CAMPBELL, Margaret Stewart 6 Poynt Chase, Worsley, Manchester M28 1FQ — MB ChB 1987 Manch.

CAMPBELL, Mary 85 Elmbridge, Harlow CM17 0JY — MB BS 1993 Lond.

CAMPBELL, Mary Annella (retired) The Firs, 44 Brand Hill, Woodhouse Eaves, Loughborough LE12 8SS Tel: 01509 890436 — MB ChB 1947 Aberd.; DObst RCOG 1949. Prev: Anaesth. Norf. & Norwich Hosp.

CAMPBELL, Mary Dorothy 64/6 Hall Road, St. John's Wood, London NW8 9PB Tel: 020 7286 9870 — LRCPI & LM, LRSCI & LM 1947; LRCPI & LM, LRCSI & LM 1947; FFA RCSI 1971; DA Eng. 1955. Asst. Anaesth. Hosp. St. John & Eliz. Lond.; Hon. Cons. Anaesth. Italian Hosp. Lond. Socs: Fell. Roy. Soc. Med.; Assn. Anaesths. Prev: Resid. Anaesth. Roy. Free. Hosp.

CAMPBELL, Mary Edith Upper Main Surgery, 20 Upper Main Street, Roslea, Enniskillen BT94 Tel: 028 6775 1496 — MB BCh BAO 1978 Belf.; MRCGP 1982; DRCOG 1982.

CAMPBELL, Mary Elizabeth Anne Lowerfield House, Easebourne St., Easebourne, Midhurst GU29 0AL — MB BS 1998 Lond.; MB BS Lond 1998.

CAMPBELL, Mary Graham (retired) Cuilfail, Drumchardine, Kirkhill, Inverness IV5 7PX — MB ChB 1943 Aberd.; MFCM 1974; DPH Aberd. 1954. Prev: SCMO Highland Health Bd.

CAMPBELL, Maureen 6 Ravenhill Park, Belfast BT6 0DE Tel: 01232 21009 — LRCPI & LM, LRSCI & LM 1952; LRCPI & LM, LRCSI & LM 1952.

CAMPBELL, Michael Fintan Stephen 35A Landseer Road, London N19 4JU — MB BCh BAO 1989 NUI.

CAMPBELL, Moira-Ann Department of Community Health, Udston Hospital, Farm Road, Hamilton ML3 9LA Tel: 01698 826770 Fax: 01698 713097; 16 Pitcairn Grove, E. Kilbride, Glasgow G75 8TN — MB ChB 1977 Glas.; DCCH RCP Ed. 1987. SCMO Dept. Community Health Udston Hosp. Hamilton.

CAMPBELL, Moira Baskerville (retired) Tirranmuir, Kippen, Stirling FK8 3HU Tel: 0178 687381 — MB ChB 1946 Ed. Prev: Cytol. Forth Valley HB.

CAMPBELL, Mona Mary Frances 82 Windmill Road, Minchinhampton Common, Stroud GL6 9EF — MB BCh BAO 1943 Dub.; BA, MB BCh BAO Dub. 1943. (TC Dub.)

CAMPBELL, Morag Elizabeth Schoolhouse, Castlebay HS9 5XD — MB ChB 1989 Ed.

CAMPBELL, Morag Shewan c/o Campbell, Byre Cottage, 8 Cathcart St., Ayr FK17 8HW Tel: 01877 330792 — MB ChB 1991 Aberd. Med. Off. (A & E) Dunedin Pub. Hosp. Dunedin, New Zealand. Prev: Med. SHO Roy. Alexandra Hosp. Corsebar Rd. Paisley, Scotl.

CAMPBELL, Neil Crawford 7 The Courtyard, Easter Beltie, Torphins, Banchory AB31 4AZ — MB BChir 1989 Camb.

CAMPBELL, Neil Malcolm 20 Truswell Avenue, Sheffield S10 1WJ — MB ChB 1991 Sheff.

CAMPBELL, Niall Gilmour Villiers House, Tolworth Hospital, Red Lion Road, Tolworth, Surbiton KT6 7QU Tel: 020 8296 1364 — MB BS 1984 Lond.; MRCPsych 1991. Cons. Psychiat. Kingston & Dist. NHS Trust Tolworth Hosp. Prev: SHO Rotat. (Psychiat.) Char. Cross & W.m. Hosps. Lond.; Sen. Regist. (Psychiat.) Char. Cross Hosp. Lond.; SHO (Paediat. & O & G) W. Glam. HA.

CAMPBELL, Niccola Mary Aurele Lorn & Islands District General Hospital, Glenshellagh Road, Oban PA34 5HH Tel: 01631 567500; Novar, Ardconnel Terrace, Oban PA34 5DJ — MB ChB 1987 Glas.; MRCGP 1993; DRCOG 1992. Staff Grade (Med. & c/o Elderly) Lorn & Is.s Dist. Gen. Hosp. Oban. Socs: BMA. Prev: SHO (Med.) Co. Hosp. Oban; SHO (Psychiat.) Argyll & Bute Hosp. Lochgilphead.

CAMPBELL, Nicola Jean 11 Raleigh Lane, Manchester M20 2BY — MB ChB 1994 Liverp.

CAMPBELL, Nigel Stewart Lisburn Health Centre, Linenhall Street, Lisburn BT28 1LU Tel: 028 9260 3090 Fax: 028 9250 1310 Email: nigel.capmbell@lisburncg.n-i.nhs.uk — MB BCh BAO 1988 Belf.; MRCGP 1992; DRCOG 1990; DCH Dub. 1990; Dip Occupat. Med. 1998. (Qu. Univ. Belf.) Gen. Practitioner, Lisburn Health centre, Lisburn; Chairm. Prescribing Task Gp. of Lisburn Commiss.ing Pilot. Socs: Ulster Med. Soc.; Lagan Valley GP Assoc.

CAMPBELL, Norah (retired) 44 Taunton Road, Sale M33 5DW Tel: 0161 969 8823 — BM BCh 1959 Oxf.; MA Oxf. 1960; FRCR 1984; MRCOG 1964, DObst 1961; DMRD Eng. 1983. Prev: Cons. Radiol. Trafford Gen. Hosp. Manch.

CAMPBELL, Norman MacDonald Shelley Surgery, 23 Shelley Road, Worthing BN11 4BS Tel: 01903 234844; 79 Manor Road, Worthing BN11 4SL Tel: 01903 233928 — MB BS 1954 Lond. Socs: Inst. Psychosexual Med.

CAMPBELL, Norman Stewart (retired) 10 Cedar Drive, Urmston, Manchester M41 9HY Tel: 0161 746 9109 — MB ChB 1962 Manch. Prev: GP Manch.

CAMPBELL, Nuala Nancy c/o Department of Anaesthetics, Torbay Hospital, Newton Road, Torquay TQ2 7AA — BM BS 1981 Nottm.; FFA RCS Eng. 1988. Cons. Anaesth. S. Devon Healthcare Trust. Socs: BMA; HCSA; RCA. Prev: Sen. Regist. (Anaesth.) SW RHA; Regist. (Anaesth.) Manch. Roy. Infirm.; SHO (Anaesth.) S.mead Hosp. Bristol.

CAMPBELL, Oonagh Craig Aitkenhead (retired) 11 College Street, St Andrews KY16 9AA — MB ChB 1961 Glas.

CAMPBELL, Patricia 57 Rosedale Gardens, Sheffield S11 8QB — MB ChB 1998 Sheff.; MB ChB Sheff 1998.

CAMPBELL, Patricia Janet Glenorchy, 118 Bramfield Road, Bulls Green, Knebworth SG3 6SA Tel: 01438 798472 Fax: 01438 798295 — MB ChB 1979 Aberd.; DFFP 1993. Med. Affairs Cons.

CAMPBELL, Patricia Marion The Medical Centre, 46-68 Bank Street, Alexandria Tel: 01389 752419; Braefoot Cottage, Croftame, Glasgow G63 0HG Tel: 01389 42222 — MB ChB 1980 Glas.; MRCGP 1984; DRCOG 1983. Retainee, The Med. Centre, 46-68 Bank St., Alexandria.

CAMPBELL, Patrick Leigh The Royal Shrewsbury Hospital, Shelton, Bicton Heath, Shrewsbury SY3 8DN Tel: 01743 261252 Fax: 01743 261279 — MB BS 1966 Lond.; MRCPsych 1972; DPM Eng. 1971. (Char. Cross) Cons. Psychiat. Shelton Hosp. Shrewsbury. Prev: Sen. Regist. (Psychiat.) Centr. Hosp. nr. Warwick; Regist. (Psychiat.) Hill End Hosp. St. Albans; Ho. Phys. Mt. Vernon Hosp. Middlx.

***CAMPBELL, Paul Charles** 94 Colonsay, St Leonards, East Kilbride, Glasgow G74 2HG Tel: 0141 239576 — MB ChB 1998 Glas.; MB ChB Glas 1998; BSC (hons.) Strathclyde 1992; MR Pharms. 1993.

CAMPBELL, Paul Jonathan New Milton Health Centre, Spencer Road, New Milton BH25 6EN Tel: 01425 621188 Fax: 01425 620646; 56 Sea Road, Barton-on-Sea, New Milton BH25 7NG Tel: 01425 613109 — MB ChB 1986 Bristol; MRCGP 1991; DCH RCP Lond. 1990. Prev: Trainee GP Bristol; SHO (Paediat.) S.mead Hosp. Bristol; SHO. (Paediat.) Roy. Hosp. for Sick Childr. Bristol.

CAMPBELL, Peter (retired) 1 Kidston Drive, Helensburgh G84 8QA — MB ChB 1951 Glas. Prev: GP Helensburgh.

CAMPBELL, Mr Peter York District Hospital, Wigginton Road, York YO31 8HE — MB BS 1985 Lond.; FRCS (Orth.) 1994; FRCS Ed. 1989. (King's Coll. Hosp. Lond.) Cons. Orthop. Surg. York. Dist. Hosp.

CAMPBELL, Peter Selsdon Park Medical Practice, 95 Addington Road, South Croydon CR2 8LG Tel: 020 8657 0067 Fax: 020 8657 0037 — MB BS 1987 Lond.; MA (Med. Sci.) Camb. 1988; MRCGP 1992; DRCOG 1991; DCH RCP Lond. 1989. (Pembroke Cambridge and Kings) GP Partner & Trainer. Prev: SHO (A & E) St. Mary's Hosp. Lond.; SHO & CMO (Paediat.) FarnBoro. Hosp.; SHO (O & G) FarnBoro. Hosp.

CAMPBELL, Peter Andrew Sowerby and Partners, The Health Centre, Park Road, Tarporley CW6 0BE Tel: 01829 733456 Fax: 01829 730124 — MB ChB 1990 Ed.; DRCOG 1993. (Ed.)

CAMPBELL, Peter Joseph 79 Manor Road, Worthing BN11 4SL — MB BS 1987 Lond.; DCH RCP Lond. 1991; DRCOG 1990.

CAMPBELL, Peter Lawrence (retired) Briarwood, Highfield Road, Sedbergh LA10 5DH Tel: 01539 620918 — MB BS 1953 Durh. Prev: Ho. Phys. Memor. Hosp. Darlington.

CAMPBELL, Peter Michael Fitzgerald Feathercombe, Hambledon, Godalming GU8 4DP; Flat 1, 16 Burlington Rd, Bristol BS6 6TL Tel: 0117 973 5151 — MB ChB 1996 Bristol. (Bristol) SHO.Med.Bristol.Roy.Infirm. Prev: SHO.Anaest.Som.; SHO.(A&E).

CAMPBELL, Peter Thomson Argyll Street Surgery, 246 Argyll Street, Dunoon PA23 7HW Tel: 01369 703279 Fax: 01369 704430; 66 John Street, Dunoon PA23 8BJ Tel: 01369 3279 — MB ChB 1979 Ed.; BSc (Med. Sci.) Ed. 1977. Clin. Asst. (Anaesth.) Dunoon Gen. Hosp. Prev: SHO (Anaesth.) Glas. Roy. Infirm.; SHO (Accid. & Orthop.) Ayr Co. Hosp.; Ho. Off. (Med.) W.. Gen. Hosp. Edin.

CAMPBELL, Philip Gerrard 25 Holland Road, Plymstock, Plymouth PL9 9BL — MB BCh 1992 Wales; MRCP (UK) 1997. (University of Wales College of Medicine) Research Fell. (Cardiol.) S. Cleveland Hosp. Middlesbrough. Prev: Regist. (Gen. Med. & Cardiol.) E. Glam. Hosp. Ch. Village Mid Glam.; SHO (Gen. Med.) Roy. Gwent Hosp. Newport.

CAMPBELL, Philip John 80 Burlow Road, Harpur Hill, Buxton SK17 9HX — MB ChB 1986 Sheff.

CAMPBELL, Phyllis Irene Court Yard Surgery, John Evans House, 28 Court Yard, London SE9 5QA Tel: 020 8850 5141 Fax: 020 8294 2380; Hucking Court Barn, Hucking, Maidstone ME17 1QT Tel: 01622 884120, 0208 473 6668 Fax: 01622 884120 — MB BCh BAO Belf. 1970; Dip. Occupational Health 1998. (Queens University Belfast) GP; Med. Adviser Occupat. Health; Trainer Family Plann. Socs: Soc. of Occupat. Med.

CAMPBELL, Richard Hubert Alexander Department of Child Health, Trafford General Hospital, Davyhulme, Manchester M41 5SL Tel: 0161 748 4022 Fax: 0161 746 2381; 189 Hale Road, Hale, Altrincham WA15 8DJ — MB ChB 1970 Ed.; FRCP Ed. 1982; MRCP (UK) 1974; FRCPCH 1997. Dir. of Child Health & Cons. Paediat. Trafford Gen.; Dep. Med. Dir., Trafford Healthcare NHS Trust. Socs: Paediat. Research Soc.; (Ex-Counc.) Brit. Paediat. Assn.; Internat. Soc. Paediat. Oncol. Prev: Cons. Paediat. Oncol. Manch.; Leukaemia Research Fell. & Hon. Sen. Regist. Hosp. Sick Childr. Gt. Ormond St.; Regist. Profess. Med. Unit Roy. Hosp. Sheff.

CAMPBELL, Mr Robert South Tyrone Hospital, Carland Road, Dungannon BT71 4AU — MB BCh BAO 1972 Belf.; BSc (Hons.) Belf. 1969, MB BCh BAO 1972; FRCS Ed. 1976; FRCSI 1976.

Demonst. Anat. Qu. Univ. Belf. Prev: Ho. Off. Belf. City & Musgrave Pk. Hosps.

CAMPBELL, Robert Charles Howard 60 South Clerk Street, Edinburgh EH8 9PS — MB ChB 1983 Ed.

CAMPBELL, Mr Robert Clark (retired) 4 Barrow Road, Cambridge CB2 2AS Tel: 01223 353366 Fax: 01223 353366 — MB ChB 1955 Aberd.; FRCS Eng. 1963; FRCS Ed. 1963. Prev: Cons. Plastic Surg. Addenbrooke's Hosp. Camb.

CAMPBELL, Robert Granger Lomond Medical Practice, Glenwood Health Centre, Glenrothes KY6 1HL — MB ChB 1980 Glas.; MPH 1998; MRCGP 1984; DRCOG 1982.

CAMPBELL, Robert Roderick Princess Royal Hospital, Apley Castle, Telford TF1 6TF Tel: 01952 641222 Fax: 01952 243405; 3 Hertford Close, Old College Fields, Wellington, Telford TF1 3PS — MB BS 1976 Lond.; MD Lond. 1988; FRCP Lond. 1994. Cons. Phys. (Med. & c/o the Elderly) P.ss Roy. Hosp. Telford. Prev: Lect. & Sen. Regist. (Gen. Med. & c/o Elderly) Univ. Bristol & Frenchay Hosp. Bristol.

CAMPBELL, Robert Stewart Douglas 31 Northumberland Gardens, Jesmond, Newcastle upon Tyne NE2 1HA — MB ChB 1985 Liverp.

CAMPBELL, Robyn Majella 12 Barnsley Close, Ash Vale, Aldershot GU12 5RH — BM BS 1984 Flinders.

CAMPBELL, Roderick 65 Warrender Park Road, Marchmont, Edinburgh EH9 1ES — MB ChB 1985 Aberd.; MRCOG; B Med Biol. Cons. O&G, Borders Hosp. Prev: SHO (Gen. Med.) Grampian Health Bd.

CAMPBELL, Mr Roderick John Keppoch Road Surgery, Keppoch Road, Culloden, Inverness IV2 7LL Tel: 01463 793400 Fax: 01463 793060 — MB ChB 1960 Ed.; FRCS Ed. 1964; MRCGP 1983. (Ed.)

CAMPBELL, Roderick John 6 Gemini Grove, Motherwell ML1 4SP — MB ChB 1998 Glas.; MB ChB Glas 1998.

CAMPBELL, Roderick Macrae, OBE 26 Bellfield Road, North Kessock, Inverness IV1 3XU Tel: 01463 731438 — MB ChB (Hons.) Aberd. 1933; MA Aberd. 1929; FFCM 1972; DPH Eng. 1937. (Aberd.) Socs: Hon. Life Fell. Soc. Pub. Health. Prev: Sen. Admin. Med. Off. N.. RHB (Scotl.); MOH Willenhall UD & Asst. Co. Med. Off. Staffs.; Maj. RAMC, Hyg. Specialist.

CAMPBELL, Rosalie Lilian 10 Riverdale Drive, Kilkeel, Newry BT34 4XR — MB BCh BAO 1987 Belf.

CAMPBELL, Rosalind Jane Deveron Medical Practice, or Banff health Centre, Clunie Street, Banff AB45 1HY Tel: 01261 812027; Tel: 01888 511506 — MB BS 1992 Lond.; DRCOG 1998. (Roy. Free Hosp.) GP Partner Deveron Med. Pract., Banff, Aberd.shire. Socs: Roy. Soc. of Med.; Med. Wom.s Federat. Comm. Mem.

CAMPBELL, Sandra Marion Dermatology Department, Royal Cornwall Hospital Trust, Truro; Lewis House, St Mawes, Truro TR2 5AY — MB ChB 1976 Dundee. Assoc. Specialist (Dermat.) Roy. Cornw. Hosp. Trust Truro.

CAMPBELL, Sarah 134 Broadoak Road, Langford, Bristol BS40 5HB — MB ChB 1996 Bristol. Socs: Brit. Geriat. Soc.

CAMPBELL, Sarah Helen Brereton Park, Tattenhall, Chester CH3 9BY — MB BS 1992 Lond.

CAMPBELL, Sarah Laverty (retired) — MB BCh BAO 1948 Belf.; MD Belf. 1952; FRCPI 1974, M 1952. Prev: Cons Paediat. Roy. Belf. Hosp Sick Childr.

CAMPBELL, Sarah Vivienne 9 Higher Lariggan, Penzance TR18 4NL — MB BCh 1993 Wales.

CAMPBELL, Sheila Anne 24 Burntbroom Gardens, Glasgow G69 7HX — MB ChB 1969 Glas.; MRCP (UK) 1977; DA Eng. 1972; DCH Eng. 1971.

CAMPBELL, Shirley Doris 11 Moorland Drive, Leeds LS17 6JP Tel: 0113 268 4220 — MB BCh BAO 1955 Dub.; BA Dub. 1954, MB BCh BAO 1955; DO Eng. 1961. Clin. Asst. Eye Dept. St. Jas. Hosp. Leeds. Prev: Res. Med. Off. Soton. Eye Hosp.; Regist. Bristol Eye Hosp.

CAMPBELL, Shona Helen Department of Radiology, The Glenfield Hospital, Groby Road, Leicester LE3 9QP Tel: 0116 287 1471 Fax: 0116 256 3349 Email: shonacampbell@uhl-tr.nhs.uk — MB ChB 1982 Aberd.; FRCR 1988. Cons. Radiol. The Glenfield Hosp. Leicester; Clin. Teach. Univ. Leicester. Socs: Brit. Soc. of Gastroentology; Brit. Madrid Ultrasound Soc.; Europ. Soc. of Gastrointestinal. Prev: Cons. Radiol. Aberd. Roy. Hosps. NHS Trust; Sen. Regist. & Regist. (Radiol.) Leicester Teachg. Hosp.

CAMPBELL, Simon Scott 192 Leicester Road, Loughborough LE11 2AH — MB ChB 1994 Birm.; ChB Birm. 1994.

CAMPBELL, Stephen Cardiology Department, Northern General Hospital, Sheffield Teaching Hospitals, NHS Trust, Sheffield S5 7AU; 36 Devonshire Road, Dore, Sheffield S17 3NT — MB BS 1977 Lond.; BSc (1st cl. Hons.) Lond. Physiol. 1974; MD Lond. 1989; FRCP Lond. 1993; MRCP (UK) 1980. (King's Coll. Hosp.) Cons. Cardiol. Sheff. Regional Cardiothoracic Unit N. Gen. Hosp. Sheff.; Hon. Sen. Lect. Sheff. Univ. Socs: Brit. Cardiac Soc.; Brit. Cardiovasc. Interven. Soc. Prev: Sen. Regist. (Cardiol.) John Radcliffe Hosp. Oxf.; Brit. Heart Foundat. Intermediate Research Fell. King's Coll Hosp. Lond.; Brit.-Amer. Research Fell. Harvard Med. Sch. Boston, USA.

CAMPBELL, Mr Stephen Henry Queen Elizabeth II Hospital, Welwyn Garden City AL7 4HQ Tel: 01707 365049 Fax: 01707 391334 — MB ChB 1983 Birm.; FRCS Ed. 1987; FRCOphth 1988. Cons. Ophth. E.& N. Herts. NHS Trust. Socs: BMA & Med. Defence Union. Prev: Sen. Regist. (Ophth.) King's Coll. Hosp. Lond.; Regist. (Ophth.) St. Pauls Eye Hosp. Liverp.; SHO (Ophth.) Birm. & Midl. Eye Hosp. Birm.

CAMPBELL, Stewart 12 Stonefield Crescent, Paisley PA2 7RU — MB ChB 1991 Glas.; MB ChB (Hons.) Glas. 1991; MRCP (UK) 1994. Specialist Regist. (Gastroenterol.) Stirling Roy. Infirm. Prev: Research Fell. Human Nutrit. Univ. Glas.; SHO Gastroenterol. Stobhill Hosp. Glas.; SHO (Cardiol.) Glas. Roy. Infirm.

CAMPBELL, Professor Stuart 34 Corfton Road, London W5 2HT Tel: 020 8997 8977 — MB ChB 1961 Glas.; FRCOG 1976, M 1965, DObst 1963. Prof. O & G King's Coll. Sch. Med. & Dent. Lond.; Hon. Fell. Amer. Inst. of Ultrasound in Med. & Brit. Med. Ultrasound Soc. Prev: Prof. Clin. O & G Inst. O & G, Qu. Charlotte's Hosp. & Chelsea Hosp. Wom.

CAMPBELL, Susan (retired) 4 St Edward's Close, London NW11 7NA Tel: 020 8455 5299 — MB BS 1957 Lond.; DCH Eng. 1960. Clin. Asst. Paediat Dept. Qu. Eliz. II Hosp. Welwyn Garden City; Sen. Clin. Med. Off. Family Plann. St. Albans. Prev: Ho. Phys. Childr. Dept. & Ho. Phys. & Ho. Surg. St. Bart. Hosp.

CAMPBELL, Susan Elaine Carolside Medical Centre, 1 Carolside Gardens, Clarkston, Glasgow G76 7BS Tel: 0141 644 3511 Fax: 0141 644 5525; 77 Nethervale Avenue, Netherlee, Glasgow G44 3XP — MB ChB 1983 Glas.; MRCGP 1987; DRCOG 1985. Clin. Asst. (Geriat.) Lanarksh. HB. Socs: BMA.

CAMPBELL, Thomas Murray 150 Crab Lane, Stafford ST16 1SP — MB ChB 1983 Glas.

CAMPBELL, Tiffany Jane 34 Corfton Road, London W5 2HT — MB ChB 1998 Ed.; MB ChB Ed 1998.

CAMPBELL, Walter Thomas Auchmillan Cottage Surgery, 1 Auchmillan Cottage, Mauchline KA5 6HD Tel: 01290 52565 — MB BCh BAO 1981 Belf.; MRCGP 1987. Med. Off. (Psychogeriat.) Ayrsh.

CAMPBELL, William Alexander Murrayfield Medical Practice, 8 Corstorphine Road, Edinburgh EH12 6HN Tel: 0131 337 6151 Fax: 0131 313 3450; 13 Gordon Road, Edinburgh EH12 6NB Tel: 0131 334 5196 Fax: 0131 270 1775 Email: w_a.campbell@which.net — MB ChB 1973 Ed.; FRCP Ed. 1994; MRCP (UK) 1976. (Edinburgh) Sen. Partner Murrayfield Med. Pract. Edin. Socs: Harveian Soc.; (Sen. Sec.) M-C Soc.; Clouston Club. Prev: Sen. Regist. MRC Clin. & Populat. Cytogenetics Unit Edin.; Regist. (Gen. Med.) Bangour Gen. Hosp.; SHO Peripheral Vasc. Clinic Roy. Infirm. Edin.

CAMPBELL, Mr William Bruce Royal Devon & Exeter Hospital, Barrack Road, Exeter EX2 5DW Tel: 01392 411611 — MB BS 1974 Lond.; MS Lond. 1984; FRCS Eng. 1979; FRCP Lond. 1996; MRCP (UK) 1979. (St. Bart.) Cons. Surg. Roy. Devon & Exeter Hosp. Exeter. Socs: Hon. Sec. Vasc. Surgic. Soc.; Assn. Surg.; Eur. Soc. Vasc. Surg. Prev: Clin. Lect. Nuffield Dept. Surg. Univ. Oxf.; Hon. Sen. Regist. Bristol Roy. Infirm.; Regist. Soton. Gen. Hosp.

CAMPBELL, William David Cheviot Way Health Centre, Cheviot Way, Bourtreehill South, Irvine KA11 1JU Tel: 01294 211993 Fax: 01294 218461 — MB ChB 1979 Dundee.

CAMPBELL, William Ian Ulster Hospital, Dundonald, Belfast BT16 1RH Tel: 02890 484511 Fax: 02890 561385 — MB ChB; 2001 DP Med. Dublin; MD Belf. 1989; FFA RCSI Dublin 1980; FRCA Lond. 1997; PhD Belf. 1997; MD 1989 Belf. (Queens University Belfast) Cons. Anaesth. With s/i in Pain Managem. Ulster Hosp. Dundonald; Examr. Primary FFA RCS of Irel.; Chairm. Med.

Staff Ulster Hosp. Dundonald; Hon. Treas., The Pain Soc. Lond. Socs: Assn. Anaesth.; Internat. Assn. Study of Pain; World Soc. Pain Clinicians.

CAMPBELL, William Jeffrey 14 Belmont Road, Lisburn BT28 3DB — MB BCh BAO 1984 Belf.; MB BCh Belf. I984.

CAMPBELL, William Meldrum Avondale Medical Practice, Strathaven Health Centre, The Ward, Strathaven ML10 6AS Tel: 01357 529595 Fax: 01357 529494 — MB ChB 1982 Glas.; BSc (Hons.) Glas. 1979, MB ChB 1982; MRCP (UK) 1985; MRCGP 1987.

CAMPBELL-BROWN, Mary Beatrice (retired) University Glasgow, Department Obst. & Gyn., Royal Infirmary Queen Elizabeth Building, 10 Alexandra Parade, Glasgow G31 2ER Tel: 0141 211 4547 Fax: 01334 652313 Email: gcl178@clinmed.gla.ac.uk — MB ChB St. And. 1958; DTM & H Eng. 1961; DObst RCOG 1960. p/t Hon. Sen. Research Fell. Glas. Prev: Clin. Asst. Roy. Infirm. Glas.

CAMPBELL-EDE, Susan Christine 8 Ettrick Road, Poole BH13 6LG — MB ChB 1977 Bristol; DA Eng. 1980.

CAMPBELL-HEWSON, Gregory Louis Accident & Emergency Department, Addenbrooke's Hospital, Cambridge, Cambridge CB2 2QQ Tel: 01223 586879; 6 South Green Road, Cambridge CB3 9JP — MB ChB 1985 Ed.; MRCP (UK) 1989; FFAEM 1999; FRCP 2000. Cons. (A&E).

CAMPBELL HEWSON, Quentin David 56 Lodore Road, Newcastle upon Tyne NE2 3NR — MB ChB 1988 Ed. Regist. (Paediat.) Roy. Vict. Infirm. Newc. u. Tyne. Socs: Roy. Coll. Phys. Edin. Prev: Regist. (Paediat.) Sunderland Dist. Gen. Hosp.

CAMPBELL-SMITH, Mr Timothy Alexander The Vicarage, Church Lane, Modbury, Ivybridge PL21 0QN Tel: 01548 820270 Email: timmuscs@aol.com — MB BS 1994 Lond.; BSc (Hons.) Lond. 1991; FRCS (Eng) 1998. (UMDS Guy's & St. Thos. Hosps.) SHO (Gen. Surg.) Roy. Sussex Co. Hosp. Brighton. Prev: SHO (IC & Gen. Surg.) Roy. Sussex Co. Hosp. Brighton; SHO (Orthop.) P.ss Roy. Hosp. Haywards Heath; SHO (ENT) Aberd. Roy. Infirm.

CAMPBELL-TAYLOR, Michelle Dennise 13 King Street, Aberman, Aberdare CF44 6UN — MB BS 1991 W. Indies.

CAMPHOR, Mr Ivan Ajay 75 Barnston Road, Heswall, Wirral CH60 1UE — MB BS 1984 Peshawar; FRCSI 1991.

CAMPHOR, Sarah 21 Malvern Drive, Gonerby Hill, Grantham NG31 8GA — MB BS 1985 Peshawar; FRCS Glas. 1991.

CAMPION, Alan Michael Flat 34, Vogans Mill Wharf, Mill St., London SE1 2BZ — MB BS 1989 Lond.

CAMPION, Geoffrey Richard Charles Church Street Surgery, 24 Church Street, Kidderminster DY10 2AW Tel: 01562 822051; The Beeches, 26 Blakebrook, Kidderminster DY11 6AP Tel: 01562 822252 — MRCS Eng. LRCP Lond. 1952; BA Camb. 1949; MB BChir 1952; MRCGP 1960; DObst RCOG 1956. (Lond. Hosp.) Prev: Thoracic Ho. Surg. & Receiv. Room Off. Lond. Hosp.; Surg. Lt. RNVR; Obst. Ho. Surg. Whittington Hosp. Lond.

CAMPION, Henry Mark Ross 1 Chiswick Staithe, Hartington Road, London W4 3TP — MB BS 1975 Lond.

CAMPION, Hugh Charles Ross Deaf Child & family Team, Hebdon Lodge, Springfield Hospital, 61 Glenburnie Road, London SW17 7DJ Email: rcampion@swlstg-tr.nhs.uk — MB BS 1983 Lond.; Diploma Behaviour Cognitive Psychotherapy, St Georges Medical School, U of L,2001; BSc Lond. 1979. (Roy. Free Hosp. Lond.) Staff Grade Psychiat., Deaf Child & Family Team (Nat. Deaf Serv.) S.W. Lond., St Geo.s, Ment. Health NHS Trust, Springfield Univ. Hosp., Lond. Prev: Regist. Alcohol & Drug Serv. Health Care Otago, Dunedin, NZ; Regist. Rotat. (Psychiat.)St.Geo. Hosp. Med. Sch. & Arun Valley.

***CAMPION, Jonathan Christopher** Upper Farm House, Penthorne Close, Grimscote, Towcester NN12 8LL — MB BS 1997 Lond.; BMedSci Lond. 1996.

CAMPION, Jonathan Edmund 39C Barton Road, West Kensington, London W14 9HB — MB BS 1991 Lond.

CAMPION, Kathryn Mary Elizabeth 14 Cardiff Road, Luton LU1 1PP Tel: 01582 444200; 11 Woodbank Avenue, Gerrards Cross SL9 7PY — MB BS 1983 Lond.; MFOM RCP Lond. 1994, AFOM 1991; DRCOG 1988. Employm. Med. Advis. Health & Safety Exec. Luton.

CAMPION, Peter David The Elms Medical Centre, 3 The Elms, Liverpool L8 3SS Tel: 0151 727 5555; Department of General Practice, University of Liverpool, PO Box 147, Liverpool L69 3BX Tel: 0151 794 5599 — BM BCh 1970 Oxf.; MRCP (U.K.) 1973; FRCGP 1990, M 1977; DCCH RCP Ed. 1985. (Lond. Hosp.) Sen. Lect. Gen. Pract. Univ. Liverp. Prev: Lect. (Gen. Pract.) Univ. Dundee; SHO (Paediat.) Qu. Eliz. Hosp. for Childr. Lond.; Lect. (Morbid Anat.) Lond. Hosp. Med. Coll.

CAMPION, Timothy Charles The Church Street Practice, David Corbet House, 2 Callows Lane, Kidderminster DY10 2JG Tel: 01562 822051 Fax: 01562 827251; "Overange", 3, Whitehill Road, Kidderminster DY11 6JH Tel: 01562 829058 Email: taincampion@ukonline.co.uk — MB BS 1984 Lond.; MRCGP 1988. (Lond. Hosp.) Prev: SHO (Geriat. Med.) Qu. Mary's & Barnes Hosps. Lond.; SHO (O & G) St. John's Hosp. Chelmsford; SHO (A & E) W. Middlx. Univ. Hosp. Isleworth.

CAMPION-SMITH, Charles Rollason Cornwall Road Surgery, 15 Cornwall Road, Dorchester DT1 1RU Tel: 01305 251128; 38 Prince of Wales Road, Dorchester DT1 1PW Tel: 01305 251755 — MB ChB 1975 Ed.; MRCGP 1986; DCH Eng. 1977. Assoc. Dir. GP Educat. Inst. Health & Community Serv. Bournemouth Univ. Socs: Assn. Palliat. Med.

CAMPKIN, Marie Ruth The Clock Tower Practice, 45 Middle Lane, Hornsey, London N8 8PH Tel: 020 8348 7711; 21 Myddelton Park, Whetstone, London N20 0JH Tel: 020 8445 1428 — MB BS 1956 Durh.; MRCGP 1974.

CAMPKIN, Nicholas Thomas Andrew Department of Anaesthetics, Queen Alexandra Hospital, Cosham, Portsmouth PO6 3LY Tel: 023 92 286279 Fax: 023 92 286681; 40 Portchester Road, Fareham PO16 8PT — MB ChB 1985 Bristol; FRCA 1991. (Bristol) Cons. Anaesth. Portsmouth Hosps. Socs: Assn. Anaesth.; Anaesth. Res. Soc.; Pain Soc. Prev: Sen. Regist. Soton. Hosps.; Regist. Magill (Anaesth.) W.m. Hosp.; Regist. (Anaesth.) MusGr. Pk. Hosp. Som.

CAMPKIN, Thomas Victor (retired) Thatched Cottage, Kew Lane, Old Bursledon, Southampton SO31 8DG Tel: 01703 402416 — MB BS Lond. 1950; FFA RCS Eng. 1957; DA Eng. 1955; MRCS Eng. LRCP Lond. 1949; FRCA 1994. Prev: Cons. Anaesth. Qu. Eliz. Hosp. Birm.

CAMPLING, Christine Chiltern House, 1 Beech Court, Aylesbury Road, Monks Risborough, Princes Risborough HP27 0UU — MB ChB 1979 Birm. Prev: Clin. Asst. (Dermat.) Chester Roy. Infirm.; SHO (O & G) & (Paediat.) Clatterbridge Hosp. Wirral; SHO (Dermat.) Newsham Gen. Hosp. Liverp.

CAMPLING, John Denys, OStJ (retired) Dairy Farmhouse, 1 Overstone Road, Moulton, Northampton NN3 7UG Tel: 01604 644280 Fax: 01604 642644 — BSc Hons. Physiol. Lond. 1950, MB BS 1953; MRCS Eng. LRCP Lond. 1953; FRCGP 1985; DObst RCOG 1956. Prev: Co. Surg. St. John Ambul. Brig. 1983-1994.

CAMPLING, Juliet Mary Barnfield Hill Surgery, 12 Barnfield Hill, Exeter EX1 1SR Tel: 01392 432761 Fax: 01392 422406; 72 Wonford Road, Exeter EX2 4LJ — MB ChB 1981 Bristol; MRCGP 1985; DRCOG 1986; DCH RCPS Glas. 1984.

CAMPLING, Penelope Marian Francis Dixon Lodge, Gypsy Lane, Leicester LE5 0TD — MB ChB 1982 Leic.; MRCPsych 1987. Cons. at Francis Dixon Lodge Therapeutic Community Leicester.

CAMPMAN, Guillermo Henrique The Forest Group Practice, The Surgery, Bury Road, Brandon IP27 0BU — Artsexamen 1987 Nijmegen. (Catholic University Nijmegen) GP Brandon Suff. Prev: Assoc. Specialist (A & E) Withybush Gen. Hosp. HaverfordW.; Trainee GP Dyfed.

CAMPOS COSTA, Durval Institute of Nuclear Medicine, UCLMS, Middlesex Hospital, Mortimer St., London W1T 3AA Tel: 020 7380 9425 Fax: 020 7436 0603 Email: d.costa@nucmed.ucl.ac.uk; 71 Holley Road, Wellington Court, London W3 7TR Tel: 020 8743 8453 Fax: 020 8743 8453 — Lic Med 1975 Oporto; Lic Med. Oporto 1975; PhD Lond. 1989, MSc 1985; FRCR 1997. Reader UCL Med. Sch. Lond.; Hon. Cons. Phys. UCL Hosps. NHS Trust. Socs: Brit. Nuclear Med. Soc.; Soc. Nuclear Med. (USA); Eur. Assn. Nuclear Med. Prev: Cons. Phys. (Nuclear Med.) Char. Cross Hosp. Lond.

CAMPRODON GAZULLA, Ricardo 78 Bucklers Mead Road, Yeovil BA21 5RB — LMS 1994 U Autonoma Barcelona.

CAMPTON, Jacob Luke 11 Larchwood, Portadown, Craigavon BT63 5UL — MB ChB 1997 Glas.

CAMRASS, Henry James (retired) 19 Herries Road, Glasgow G41 4DE Tel: 0141 423 2719 — LRCP LRCS 1945 Ed.; LRCP LRCS

Ed. LRFPS Glas. 1945. Prev: Res. Surg. Off. Gen. Hosp. Middlesbrough.

CAMSEY, Julie Mildred Bridge House, Lower St., West Chinnock, Crewkerne TA18 7PT; Gaywood House, North St, Bedminster, Bristol BS3 3 — MB ChB 1976 Bristol; MRCGP 1982.

CANAGARATNAM, Nirupa 36 Cranborne Avenue, Eastbourne BN20 7TT — MB BS 1998 Lond.; MB BS Lond 1998.

CANALE-PAROLA, Adrian Clifton Road Surgery, 26 Clifton Road, Rugby CV21 3QF Tel: 01788 543088 Fax: 01788 551496; 15 Longrood Road, Bilton, Rugby CV22 7RG Tel: 01788 817961 Email: aamac@discover.co.uk — MB BChir 1977 Camb.; MA, MB BChir Camb. 1977; DRCOG 1980. (Cambridge and King's College) Princip. GP; Clin. Asst. (Learning Disabil.). Socs: Rugby & Dist. Med. Soc.

CANAVAN, Anne Collette 27 Talbot Terrace, Lewes BN7 2DS Email: a.canavan@which.net — MB BCh BAO 1993 Belf.; FRCA Lond 1999. (The Queen's University of Belfast) Specialist Regist. (Anaesth.) Guy's Hosp. Lond. Socs: MRCAnaesth.; Anaesth. Assn.; Roy. Soc. Med.

CANAVAN, Desmond Adrian 89 Balmoral Avenue, Belfast BT9 6NZ Tel: 01232 660939 — MD 1966 Belf.; MB BCh BAO Belf. 1961; MD Belf 1966; FRCP Ed. 1996; FRCPI 1986, M 1964; FRCP Lond. 1979, M 1967. (Belf.) Cons. Phys. Roy. Vict. Hosp. Belf.; Lect. (Infec. Dis.) Qu. Univ. Belf. (1968). Prev: Sen. Tutor (Med.) Qu. Univ. Belf.; MRC Research Fell.; Regist. Mater Infirm. Hosp. Belf.

CANAVAN, Heber Rory Health Centre, Great James Street, Londonderry BT48 7DH Tel: 028 7137 8500 — MB BCh BAO 1978 NUI; MRCGP 1983.

CANAVAN, John Stephen Francis 7 Priestley Drive, Larkfield, Maidstone — MB ChB 1967 Manch.; MRCP (UK) 1971; FRCR 1980; DMRD Eng. 1978. Prev: Cons.Radiol., Maidstone HA & Guy's Hosp. Lond.

CANAVAN, Kevin Stephen 17 Richmond Terrace, Aberdeen AB25 2RQ — MB ChB 1990 Glas.

CANAVAN, Russell Ewart MacKenzie Well Cottage, Common Hill, Fownhope, Hereford HR1 4QA — MB BS 1998 Lond.; MB BS Lond 1998.

CANAVAN, Yvonne Mary (retired) Woodlands, 166 Shore Road, Whitehouse, Newtownabbey BT37 9TB — MD Belf. 1979, MB BCh BAO 1970; FRCS Ed. (Ophth.) 1975; DO RCPSI 1973; FRCOphth. Prev: Cons. (Ophth.) Roy. Vict. Hosp. Belf.

CANDAPPA, Nihal Joseph Camillus Upper Halliford Medical Centre, 270 Upper Halliford Road, Shepperton TW17 8SY Tel: 01932 785496 Fax: 01932 779277 — MUDr 1972 Charles Univ. Prague; MUDR Charles U Prague 1972; DObst RCPI 1977. (Charles Univ.) Prev: Regist. (O & G) Ayrsh. Centr. Hosp. Irvine & S.. Gen. Teach. Hosp. Glas.

CANDELIER, Claire Kathleen Caldy, 25A Kelso Place, London W8 5QG — MB ChB 1981 Sheff.

CANDISH, Charles Gerald Bristol Oncology Centre, Bristol B52 8ED — BChir 1994 Camb.; MB BChir Camb. 1994; MRCP 1998. (Cambridge)

CANDLER, Stella Christine (retired) 28 Bridgeland Street, Bideford EX39 2PZ Tel: 0123 723751 — MB ChB 1947 Bristol; MRCS Eng. LRCP Lond. 1947. Prev: SCMO Devon AHA.

CANDLER, Mr Thomas Oswald (retired) 28 Bridgeland Street, Bideford EX39 2PZ — MB BChir 1942 Camb.; FRCS Eng. 1949; MRCS Eng., LRCP Lond. 1942; FRCGP 1976, M 1965. Prev: GP Bideford.

CANDLIN, Mr Richard Eric, ERD 1 Hopping Lane, (Off St Mary's Grove), London N1 2NU Tel: 020 7226 8300 Fax: 020 7704 9312 Email: rcandlin@compuserve.com; 16 St. Mary's Grove, Canonbury, London N1 2NT Tel: 020 7226 3546 — MB ChB St. And. 1949; BSc St. And. 1946; FRCS Eng. 1953. Prev: Surg. (Orthop.) Manor Hse. Hosp. Lond.; Surg. (Traum. & Orthop.) St. Leonard's & Metrop. Hosps. Lond.

CANDLISH, William Department of Pathology, Royal Alexandra Hospital, Corsebar Road, Paisley PA2 9PN Tel: 0141 580 4164 Fax: 0141 580 4242 Email: william.candlish@rah.scot.nhs.uk — MB ChB 1981 Glas.; BSc (Hons.) Glas. 1978, MB ChB 1981; MRCPath 1991; FRCPath 1999. (University of Glasgow) Cons. Path. Roy. Alexandra Hosp., Paisley. Prev: Cons. Path. Dumfries & Galloway Roy. Infirm.; Sen. Regist. (Path.) Glas. Roy. Infirm.; Ho. Off. Glas. W.. Infirm.

CANDLISH, William 12 Osborne Avenue, Annbank Station, Ayr KA6 5DF — MB ChB 1981 Ed.

CANDY, David Charles Alexander St Richard's Hospital, Royal West Sussex Trusr, Chichester PO19 4SE Tel: 01243 831441 Fax: 01243 831431 Email: david.candy@rws-tr.nhs.uk; 66 Basin Road, Chichester PO19 2PU Email: d.candy@doctors.orguk — MB BS 1971 Adelaide; MSc Lond. 1979; MD Birm. 1986; FRCP Lond. 1989; MRCP (UK) 1975; MRCPCH 1996; FRCPCH 1997. (Univ. Adelaide, S. Austral.) Cons. Paediat. Gastroent. St Richards Hosp.; Vis. Sen. Lect. Dept of Child Health Univ. of S.ampton. Socs: Brit. Soc. Paediat. Gastroenterol. Hepat., Nutrit.; Brit. Soc. Gastroenterol. Mem. paediatric subcommitee; Eur. Soc. Paediat. Gastroenterol, Hepat., & Nutrit. Prev: Prof. Child Health King's Coll. Sch. Med. & Dent. Lond.; Hon. Cons. Paediat. (Communicable & Trop. Dis.) E. Birm. Hosp.; Wellcome Sen. Lect. (Paediat. & Child Health) Univ. Birm.

CANDY, Dorothy Ruth (retired) 11 Shamrock Way, Hythe Marina Village, Southampton SO45 6DY Tel: 01703 844149 — BM BCh 1961 Oxf.; MA, BM BCh Oxf. 1961; DCH Eng. 1965; DObst RCOG 1964.

CANDY, Edwina Patricia Yeovil District Hospital, Higher Kingston, Yeovil BA21 4AT Tel: 01935 75122; Tamarisk, 7 The Cross, Baltonsborough, Glastonbury BA6 8QW Tel: 01458 850179 Fax: 01458 850179 — MB ChB 1988 Bristol. SHO (A & E) Yeovil Dist. Hosp. Prev: Sen. Regist. & SHO (Psychiat.) Priory Pk. Hosp. Wells Som.; SHO (Surg.) Amersham Gen. Hosp.

CANDY, Jennifer Ruth 11 Shamrock Way, Southampton SO45 6DY — BM 1991 Soton.

CANDY, John Mark Glasgow Royal Infirmary, Anaesthetic Department, 84 Castle St., Glasgow G4 0SF Tel: 0141 211 4620; Top Right, 8 Caird Drive, Partickhill, Glasgow G11 5DS Tel: 0141 339 6524 — MB ChB 1989 Leeds; FFA CSI 1997. (Leeds) SHO (Anaesth.) Glas. Roy. Hosps. NHS Trust. Socs: MRCAnaesth.; Assn. Anaesth.; Scott. Intens. Care Soc. Prev: SHO (Anaesth.) Monklands Dist. Gen. Hosp. Airdrie.

CANDY, Josephine Joanna (retired) 9 St Margarets, Great Gaddesden, Hemel Hempstead HP1 3BZ Tel: 01442 843456 Fax: 01442 843456 — MB BCh Wales 1950; FFA RCS Eng. 1954. Prev: Cons. Anaesth. Hadi Hosp. Kuwait, Arabia.

CANDY, Julian (retired) 11 Shamrock Way, Hythe, Southampton SO45 6DY — MB BS 1963 Lond.; FRCP Lond. 1984, M 1967; FRCPsych 1981, M 1972; DPM Eng. 1968. Prev: Cons. Psychiat. St. John's Hosp. Aylesbury.

CANE, Clare Emma Riverside House, Turnoak Avenue, Woking GU22 0AJ — MB ChB 1997 Birm.

CANE, Cuthbert Skelding, VRD The Marsh House, Hungerford RG17 0SN Tel: 01488 684162 — MRCS Eng. LRCP Lond. 1937. (St. Bart.) Prev: Out-Pat. Asst. (Med.) St. Mary's Hosp. Padd.; Ho. Surg. (Cas.) St. Bart. Hosp.; Sen. Resid. Med. Off. St. And. Hosp. Dollis Hill.

CANE, Frederick Leslie (retired) 67 Church Street, Ossett WF5 9DS Tel: 01924 4055 — MB ChB 1933 Leeds. Prev: Res. Med. Off. Pub. Disp. & Hosp. Leeds.

CANE, John Martin (retired) New Close, Monk Sherborne, Tadley RG26 5HR Tel: 01256 850133 Fax: 01256 850133 — MB BS Lond. 1962; MRCS Eng. LRCP Lond. 1962. Prev: SHO (Obst.) City Hosp. Derby.

CANE, Paul Joseph 274 Tylehost, Guildford GU2 9XT — BM BS 1996 Nottm.

CANEPA-ANSON, Ann Caroline Mary 106 Burdon Lane, Cheam, Sutton SM2 7DA Tel: 020 8642 2063 — MB BS 1963 Lond.; MRCP Lond. 1969; MRCS Eng. LRCP Lond. 1963; DCH Eng. 1967.

CANEPA-ANSON, Rudolph Mayday University Hospital, London Road, Croydon CR7 7YE Tel: 020 8401 3624 Fax: 020 8665 0606; 106 Burdon Lane, Cheam, Sutton SM2 7DA Tel: 020 8770 7363 — MB BChir 1967 Camb.; FRCP 1995; MRCP (UK) 1970; FRCPC 1987. (Camb. & Middlx.) Cons. Cardiol. Mayday Univ. Hosp. Croydon & St. Geo. Hosp. Lond. Socs: Brit. Cardiac Soc.; Brit. CarioVasc. Interven. Soc.; Brit. Soc. Echocardiography. Prev: Cons. Cardiol. St. Michael's Hosp., Toronto & Asst. Prof. Med. Univ. Toronto, Ontario, Canada; Sen. Regist. Nat. Heart Hosp. Lond.

CANFIELD, Caroline Jane 8 Honister Grove, Beechwood, Runcorn WA7 2TY — MB BS 1991 Lond.; MRCP (UK) 1994; MRCGP 1996;

DCH RCP Lond. 1995. (St. Bart. Hosp. Med. Sch.) Socs: BMA. Prev: SHO (Psychiat.) BRd.oak Unit Liverp.

CANHAM, Natalie Louise Eiluned 27 Mill Farm Road, Harbourne, Birmingham B17 0QX — MB ChB 1995 Birm.; ChB Birm. 1995.

CANISIUS, Dona Sabina Dushanthi White City Health Centre, Australia Road, London W12 7PH; 7 Cardiff Way, Abbots Langley WD5 0TT Tel: 01923 681617 — MB BS 1980 Sri Lanka; MRCS Eng. LRCP Lond. 1988; MRCP (UK) 1986. Regist. (Med.) Epsom Gen. Hosp. Surrey. Prev: Regist. (c/o the Elderly) Char. Cross Hosp.; Regist. (Med.) Highlands Hosp. Lond.

CANN, Jorn 10 Rivermeadows, Water Lane, Exeter EX2 8BD Tel: 0132 496861 Email: tintin@canncer.freeserve.co.uk — BM 1992 Soton. Staff Grade (Haemat.), Roy. Devon & Exeter Hsp, Exeter. Prev: Ho. Off. (Med.) Toowoomba Base Hosp. Qu.sland, Australia.; Regist. (Med.) Bowoumba Base Hosp. Qu.sland, Australia; Ho. Off. (Med.) Rockhampton Base Hosp. Qu.sland, Australia.

CANN, Kathryn Jane Department of Medical Microbiology, Oxford Radcliffe Hospitals Trust, Headley Way, Oxford OX3 — MB BS 1981 Lond.; MSc Med. Microbiol. Lond. 1987, MB BS 1981; FRCPate 1990; MD Lond. 1991. (The London Hospital Medical School) Locum Cons. Med. MicroBiol. John Radcliffe Hosp. Oxf. Socs: BMA; RCPath.; Soc. for Gen. MicroBiol. Prev: Regist. (Microbiol.) W.m. Hosp. Lond.

CANN, Margaret Lesley Psychotherapy Department, Lynfield Mount Hospital, Bradford Community Health NHS Trust; Heights Lane, Bradford BD9 6DP Tel: 01274 363233 Fax: 01274 363145 Email: lesley.cann@bcht.northy.nhs.uk — MB BS 1971 Lond.; MRCS Eng. LRCP Lond. 1971; MRCPsych 1976; Dip. Psychother. Leeds 1987; DPM Lond. 1975. (Guys Hospital Medical School, London.) Cons. Psychother. Bradford Community Health NHS Trust. Socs: A.P.P. Assn. for Psychanalytic & Psychother. in the NHS; Soc. Psychother. Research; Yorks. Assn. Psychodynamic Psychoth.

CANN, Paul Adrian South Cleveland Hospital, Marton Road, Middlesbrough TS4 3BW Tel: 01642 854860 Fax: 01642 854765 Email: gitract@aol.com; Ingleby House, High St, Great Broughton, Middlesbrough TS9 7EG Tel: 01642 712176 — MD 1985 Leeds; MB ChB 1976; FRCP Lond. 1994; MRCP (UK) 1979. (Leeds) Cons. Phys. Gastroenterol. S. Cleveland Hosp. Middlesbrough. Socs: N. Eng. Gastroenterol. Soc. & Brit. Soc. Gastroenterol. Prev: Sen. Regist. (Med.) Roy. Hallamsh. Hosp. Sheff.; Research Fell. Clin. Research Unit Roy. Hallamsh. Hosp. Sheff.; Regist. (Med.) Dist. Hosp. York.

CANN, Phillip Caulton Fox Hill, Chester Road, Higher Walton, Warrington WA4 5LP — MB ChB 1960 Liverp.; MRCS Eng. LRCP Lond. 1960; DObst RCOG 1963.

CANNELL, Antonia Geraldine Susan Tel: 01522 560398 — MB BS 1990 Lond. p/t Gen. Practitioner, Lincoln; Gen. Practitioner, Alcohol & Subst. Misuse. Prev: Trainee GP Lincoln VTS; SHO (A & E) King Geo. Hosp. Ilford; Ho. Phys. St. Helens Hosp. Hastings.

CANNELL, Mr Hugh, RD, OStJ (cons. rooms), London Independent Hospital, Beaumont Square, London E1 4NL Tel: 020 7790 7544 Fax: 020 7790 7544 — MRCS Eng. LRCP Lond. 1965; MSc Wales 1971; MD Lond. 1977; FDS RCS Eng. 1969, LDS 1960; DPhilMed. Soc. Apoth. Lond. 1982. (Guy's) Hon.Cons. (Oral Surg.) Roy. Lond. Hosp. Trust & Coll.; Hon. Cons. Adviser Oral & Maxillofacial Surg. St. John's Med. Bd.; Hon. Cons. Adviser Oral & Maxiof., Dept. Social Security; Med. Mem., appeals Serv.. Socs: Fell. Brit. Assn. Oral & Maxillofacial Surg.; Founder Fell. Europ. Assn. Craniomaxillofacial Surg.; BMA. Prev: QHDS 1989-90; Regist. (Oral Surg.) Plymouth Gen. Hosp.; Ho. Phys. RN Hosp. Plymouth.

CANNELL, Lewis Bernard (retired) 391 Lauderdale Tower, Barbican, London EC2Y 8NA — MB BS 1958 Lond.; MA Oxf. 1972, BA 1951; LMSSA Lond. 1958; FRCR 1975; FFR 1974; DMRD Eng. 1970. Prev: Cons. Radiol. Aylesbury Health Dist.

CANNELL, Michael Charles Stewart Midway Surgery, 93 Watford Road, St Albans AL2 3JX Tel: 01727 832125 Fax: 01727 836384; 40 Gurney Court Road, St Albans AL1 4RL Tel: 01727 864160 — MB BS 1979 Lond.; MRCGP 1984; DRCOG 1982; MFHOM 1998. Clin. Asst. Roy. Lond. Homeopathic Hosp. Prev: SHO (O & G) Lond. Hosp.; SHO (Paediat.) Lond. Hosp.

CANNEY, James Crawford 62 Kitchen Lane, Ashmore Park Est., Wednesfield, Wolverhampton WV11 2JB Tel: 01902 732442 — MB ChB 1950 Manch. (Manch.) Prev: Ho. Surg. Warrington Infirm.

CANNEY, Rosalie Margaret Leigh Wood View, Wellington, Hereford HR4 8AT Tel: 0143 271428 — LRCP LRCS 1965 Ed.; MA Camb. 1940; LRCP LRCS Ed. LRCPS Glas. 1965. (Belf.) Socs: BMA & Nutrit. Soc. Prev: Ho. Off. (Med.) Tyrone Co. Hosp.; Ho. Off. (Surg.) Banbridge Hosp.; Ho. Off. (O & G) Hereford Co. Hosp.

CANNING, Bertha Sheila (retired) Chilcomb, Jubilee Hill, Pelynt, Looe PL13 2JZ — MB BS Lond. 1956; DObst 1957.

CANNING, Mr Christopher Randall Southampton Eye Unit, Southampton General Hospital, Tremona Road, Southampton SO16 6YD Tel: 02380 794758 Fax: 02380 794120; Boldre Grange, Southampton Road, Boldre, Lymington SO41 8PT Tel: 01590 672822 Fax: 01590 672822 Email: chris@boldre.demon.co.uk — MB BCh 1975 Witwatersrand; FRCS Eng. 1983; MRCP (UK) 1981; FCP(SA) 1980; FRCOphth 1989; DO RCS Eng. 1982. Cons. Ophth. Soton. Eye Hosp. Socs: Brit. Eye Study Gp. Prev: Sen. Regist. (Ophth.) Moorfields Eye Hosp. Lond.

CANNING, Clare Louise Medical Staffing, Hereford Hospitals N H S Trust, County Hospital, Hereford HR1 2ER — MB ChB 1997 Birm.

CANNING, Gerard John Thornliebank Health Centre, 20 Kennishead Road, Thornliebank, Glasgow G46 8NY Tel: 0141 531 6979 Fax: 0141 531 6910 — MB ChB 1987 Glas.; BSc (Physiol.) Glas. 1984, MB ChB 1987; FRCPS Glas. 1991.

CANNING, Gordon Patrick 21 Bulloch Avenue, Giffnock, Glasgow G46 6NF Tel: 0141 638 4564 — MB ChB 1980 Glas.; FRCP(UK)1995; MRCP (UK) 1984. (Glas.) Cons. Phys. Dept. Med. for the Elderly, Hairmyres Hosp., E. Kilbride. Socs: BMA; Brit. Geriat. Soc.; Glas. Med. Chir. Soc. Prev: Cons. Phys.(Geriat. Med.) Monklands Dist. Gen. Hosp. Airdrie.; Sen. Regist. (Geriat. & Gen. Med.) S.. Gen. Hosp. Glas.; Regist. (Geriat. Med.) Stobhill Hosp. Glas.

CANNING, James Joseph Dungorm, Stanley Road, Paisley PA2 6HJ — MB ChB 1978 Glas.

CANNING, James Michael (retired) 27 Victoria Road, Poulton-le-Fylde FY6 7JA — MB BCh BAO 1947 NUI. Prev: Med. Off. DHSS.

CANNING, John Timothy The Health Centre, PO Box 101(a), The Health Centre, 20 Cleveland Square, Middlesbrough TS1 2NX Tel: 01642 242192 Fax: 01642 231809; 80 The Grove, Marton-in-Cleveland, Middlesbrough TS7 8AP Tel: 01642 316493 — MB ChB 1979 Sheff.; MRCGP 1983. Mem. (Sec.) Cleveland LMC. Socs: GMSC. Prev: Trainee GP Cleveland VTS; Ho. Off. Barnsley Dist. Gen. Hosp.

CANNING, Julie Catherine 45 Arkleston Road, Paisley PA1 3TH — MB ChB 1989 Glas.

CANNING, Monica Flat 1/L, 37 Dudley Drive, Hyndland, Glasgow G12 9RP — MB ChB 1993 Glas.; MRCP (UK) 1997.

CANNING, Sheila Bertha (retired) Chilcomb, Jubilee Hill, Pelynt, Looe PL13 2JZ — MB BS 1956 Lond.; DObst RCOG 1957. Exam. Med. Off. DHSS. Prev: Ho. Surg. N. Middlx. Hosp. Lond.

CANNING, Tania Maria Garden Cottage, The Hill, Staunton, Gloucester GL19 3QQ — BChir 1990 Camb.

CANNING, Una Bernadette 74 Bessbrook Road, Mountnorris, Armagh BT60 2DB Tel: 01861 507254 — MB BCh BAO 1992 Belf.; DRCOG 1996; DCh. Dubl. 1996; MRCGP 1997. SHO (Med.) Waveney Hosp. Ballymena. Socs: Roy. Coll. Gen. Pract.

CANNING, William Carbis 71 Landor Road, Knowle, Solihull B93 9JA Tel: 0156 45 776200 — MRCS Eng. LRCP Lond. 1955; LLB 1988; MRANZCP 1977; MRCPsych 1972; DPM Eng. 1969; DObst RCOG 1957. (St. Bart.) Cons. Forens. Psychiat. Janet Shaw Clinic Chelmsey Hosp. Birm. Prev: Cons. Foren. Psychiat. All St.s Hosp. Birm.; Cons. Psychiat. Adolesc. Unit Hollymoor Hosp. Birm.; Dir. Forens. Psychiat. Serv. Ment. HA, Vict.

CANNING, William Geoffrey Acorn Cottage, 53 Bescar Lane, Scarisbrick, Ormskirk L40 9QR Tel: 01704 880558 — MB ChB 1943 Liverp. (Liverp.) Prev: Res. Med. Off. Smithdown Rd., Hosp. Liverp.; Maj. RAMC.

CANNINGS, Ian Richard 14 Leawood Croft, Holloway, Matlock DE4 5BD — MB ChB 1997 Leeds.

CANNIZZARO, Stefano Mayfield Medical Centre, 37 Totnes Road, Paignton TQ4 5LA Tel: 01803 558257 — MB ChB 1988 Leic.; MRCGP 1992; DCH RCP Lond. 1991. Prev: Trainee GP Torbay VTS; Ho. Phys. Pilgrim Hosp. Boston Lincs.; Ho. Surg. Leicester Gen. Hosp.

CANNON, Miss Andrea Margaret Derriford Hospital, Plymouth PL6 8DH Tel: 01752 777111 — MB ChB 1989 Sheff.; FRCS Ed.

1993. Specialist Regist (Urol), Derriford Hosp., Plymouth. Prev: Specialist Regist. (Urol.) Roy. Devon & Exeter Hosp.; Specialist Regist. (Urol.) MusGr. Pk. Hosp. Taunton; Research Fell. (Urol.) S.mead Hosp. Bristol.

CANNON, Anne Marie The Inverurie Medical Group, The Health Centre, Constitution St., Inverurie AB51 9SQ Tel: 01467 621345 Fax: 01467 625374 Email: anne.cannon@inverurie.grampian.scot.nhs.uk; Pennan, 143 North St, Inverurie AB51 4TL — MB BS 1975 Lond.; BSc (Hons.) Lond. 1972; FRCS Eng. 1980; MRCS Eng. LRCP Lond. 1975; MRCGP 1985; DRCOG 1985. (Lond. Hosp.)

CANNON, Charlotte Helen Princess Margaret Hospital, Okus Road, Swindon SN1 4JU Tel: 01672 536531; Forest Hill House, Marlborough SN8 3HN Tel: 01672 513363 — BChir 1979 Camb.; DGM RCP Lond. 1991. Assoc. Specialist (Med.) Swindon & MarlBoro. Healthcare Trust. Socs: Brit. Geriat. Soc. Prev: Clin. Asst. (Geriat. Med.) Savernake Hosp.; Trainee GP MarlBoro.; SHO (A & E) Salisbury Infirm.

CANNON, David Stanley Hinchcliff (retired) Coldbeck House, Ravenstonedale, Kirkby Stephen CA17 4LW Tel: 0153 96 23230 Fax: 0153 96 23230 Email: david.cannon@coldbeck.demon.co.uk — MRCS Eng. LRCP Lond. 1950; FRCGP 1975, M 1968; DObst RCOG 1952. Prev: Ho. Phys. (Paediat.) Lond. Hosp.

CANNON, Dianna Jane Taunton & Somerset Hospital, Musgrove Park, Taunton TA1 5DA — MB BS 1990 Tasmania.

CANNON, Helen Claire 30 Stanley Street, Southsea PO5 2DS Email: lesandhelen@stanleyst.freeserve.uk — MB BS 1991 Lond.; BSc (Hons.); DFFP; DRCOG; MRCGP. (Middlesex Hospital Medical School) GP Partner. Socs: BMA - Mem.; RCCP; RCOG.

CANNON, Helen Louise Kiln Cottage, Parrotts Lane, Buckland Common, Tring HP23 6NX — MB ChB 1998 Manch.; MB ChB Manch 1998.

CANNON, Joanna Sarah Upwell Street Surgery, 91 Upwell Street, Sheffield S4 8AN Tel: 0114 261 8608; 9 New Houses, Piccadilly, Chesterfield S41 0EJ — BM 1984 Soton.; BM Soton 1984; MRCGP 1988; DCH RCP Lond. 1988; DRCOG 1987. (soton.) GP. Prev: GP Chesterfield; Trainee GP/SHO St. Mary's Hosp. Lond. VTS; Dist. Health Off. Mchinji, Malawi (VSO).

CANNON, John Clayton Ixworth Surgery, Peddars Close, Ixworth, Bury St Edmunds IP31 2HD Tel: 01359 230252 Fax: 01359 232586; Cross House, Ixworth, Bury St Edmunds IP31 2JB — MB BS 1976 Lond.; BSc (Hons.) Lond. 1973; FRCGP 1997, M 1980; Dip. Ther. Lond. 1997; DFFP 1995; DRCOG 1980. (Guy's & King's Coll. Hosp.) Prev: Vis. Fell. Med. Mass. Gen. Hosp., Boston, USA.

CANNON, Mr John Drummond Law Hospital, Carluke ML8 5ER Tel: 01698 361100; The Cottage, Biggarshiels Road, Biggar ML12 6RE Tel: 01899 221078 Email: john@jcannon.freeserve.co.uk — MB ChB St. And. 1972; ChM Dund 1982; BMSc (Hons., Anat.) Dund 1969; FRCS Ed. 1977. (St. And.) Cons. Surg. Law Hosp. Carluke. Prev: Sen. Regist. (Surg.) Ninewells & Assoc. Hosps. Dundee; Regist. (Surg.) Inverness Hosps.; Regist. (Cardiothoracic Surg.) W.. Infirm. Glas.

CANNON, Mr Leslie Brian, Surg. Lt.-Cdr. RN 30 Stanley Street, Southsea PO5 2DS — MB BS 1991 Lond.; BSc (Hons.) Lond. 1988; FRCS 1997. (UCMSM) Regist. (Orthop.) Roy. Hosp. Haslar.

CANNON, Mary 52 Primrose Gardens, London NW3 4TP — MB BCh BAO 1988 NUI; MRCPsych 1993.

CANNON, Nicola 70/5 Craighouse Gardens, Edinburgh EH10 5UN — MB ChB 1991 Ed.

CANNON, Peter (retired) 1 Coombe Rise, Shenfield, Brentwood CM15 8JJ Tel: 01277 226146 — MB Camb. 1958, BChir 1957; MA Camb. 1958; FRCP Lond. 1977, M 1964; MRCS Eng. LRCP Lond. 1957. Prev: Cons. Phys. Haroldwood Hosp. Essex.

CANNON, Peter Douglas The Croft, 16 Stanwell Avenue, Birkby, Huddersfield HD2 2BY Tel: 01484 426945 Fax: 01484 426945 — MB ChB 1973 Leeds; MDS (Oral Surg) Sydney 1965, BDS 1964; FRACDS 1965; FDS RCS Eng. 1968. (Leeds) Cons. (Oral & Maxillo Facial Surg.) Huddersfield NHS Trust; Med. Adviser McAlpine Stadium Huddersfield; Divisonal Surg. St. John Ambul. Huddersfield. Socs: BMA; Fell. Brit. Assn. Oral & Maxillofacial Surg.; Brit. Dent. Assn. Prev: Sen. Regist. Dept. Oral & Maxillo-Facial Surg. Lond. Hosp.

CANNON, Peter Gordon (retired) 7 Beacon Grange Park, Sadberge, Darlington DL2 1TW — MB ChB 1949 St. And.; DPH 1953; FRCPsych 1984, M 1971; DIH Eng. 1958; DPM Durham. 1962. Prev: Cons. Psychiat. N. Tees Gen. Hosp. Stockton & Winterton Hosp. Sedgefield.

CANNON, Mr Peter Mark Bridge Street Medical Practice, 20 Bridge Street, Loughborough LE11 1NQ Tel: 01509 263018 Fax: 01509 211427 — BM BCh 1987 Oxf.; MA Camb. 1990; FRCS Lond. 1991; MRCGP 1995. (Oxf.) Prev: Research Regist. (Gen. Surg.) City Hosp. Nottm.

CANNON, Roger Nevile Westerlea, 35 Victoria Road, Lenzie, Glasgow G66 5AR — MB ChB 1960 Glas.; DObst RCOG 1962.

CANNON, Ronald 38 Eaton Mews S., London SW1W 9HR Tel: 020 7235 8971; Russet House, Kingston Gorse, Angmering, Littlehampton BN16 1SG Tel: 01903 783677 — MB BS 1944 Lond.; MRCS Eng. LRCP Lond. 1944. (Middlx.) Socs: BMA. Prev: Cas. Surg. Off. & Res. Med. Off. Acton Hosp.; Asst. Med. Off. W. Middlx. Co. Hosp.

CANNON, Stephen Robert Royal National Orthopaedic Hospital, Brockley Hill, Stanmore HA7 4LP Tel: 07923 828898; St Giles Lodge, Amersham Road, Chalfont St Giles HP8 4RZ Tel: 01494 872242 — MB BChir 1974 Camb.; MB BChir Camb. 1975; MCh Orth. Liverp. 1985; FRCS Eng. 1979; DObst RCOG 1976. (Middlx.) Cons. Orthop. Surg. Roy. Nat. Orthop. Hosp.; Mem. Edit. Bd. Brit. Jl. Bone & Jt. Surg.; Edit. Sec. Brit. Orthop. Assn. Socs: Fell. BOA; Eur. Musculoskeletal Oncol. Soc. & Internat. Limb Salvage Soc. Prev: Sen. Regist. (Orthop.) Middlx. Hosp. Lond.; Regist. (Orthop.) Stoke Mandeville Hosp. Aylesbury; Regist. Rotat. (Surg.) Middlx. Hosp. Lond.

CANNON, William James 139 Woolwich Road, Abbey Wood, London SE2 0DW; 385 Erith Road, Erith DA8 — MB BS 1957 Lond. (Westm.) Socs: BMA. Prev: Ho. Phys. & Obst. Ho. Surg. Redhill Co. Hosp.

CANOREA, Felisa 26 Broad Street, Syston, Leicester LE7 1GH — LMS 1991 U Autonoma Madrid.

CANSFIELD, Peter John Leicestershire Health Authority, Gwendolen Road, Leicester LE5 4QF Tel: 0116 258 8503 — BM BCh 1983 Oxf.; MPH 2000 Univ. of Nott'ham; MA Oxf. 1984; MRCGP 1987. (Oxford) SpR in Pub. Health. Prev: Clin. Asst. (Psychiat.) c/o Elderly Mapperley Hosp. Nottm.; Trainee GP Keighley & Skipton VTS; SHO (Med., O & G, Psychiat. & Cas.) Airedale Gen. Hosp. Keighley.

CANSICK, Janette Christine Green Shutters, Hillview Road, Claygate, Esher KT10 0TU — MB BChir 1994 Camb.; MA Camb. 1996, BA 1992; MRCP 1998. Specialist Regist. (Paediat.) Roy. Shrewsbury Hosp. Prev: SHO (Paediat.) N.ampton Gen. Hosp.; SHO (Peadiat.) John Radcliffe Hosp., Oxf.; SHO (Peadiat.) Roy. Brampton Hosp.

CANT, Andrew James Department of Paediatrics, Newcastle General Hospital, Westgate Road, Newcastle upon Tyne NE4 6BE Tel: 0191 273 8811 Fax: 0191 273 0183 Email: a.j.cant@ncl.ac.uk; 9 Woodside, Darras Hall, Ponteland, Newcastle upon Tyne NE20 9JA — MB BS 1978 Lond.; BSc Lond. 1975, MD 1986; FRCP Lond. 1994; MRCP (UK) 1981; FRCPCH 1997. (King's Coll. Lond. & St. Geo.) Cons. Paediat. Immunol. & Infec. Newc.; Sen. Lect. (Child Health) Univ. Newc. Prev: Sen. Regist. Hosp. for Sick Childr. Gt. Ormond St. Lond.; Regist. (Paediat.) Guy's Hosp. Lond.; AFRC/MRC Research Fell. Dept. Child Health St. Geo. Hosp. Med. Sch. Lond.

CANT, Bernadette University of East Anglia Health Centre, University of East Anglia, Earlham Road, Norwich NR4 7TJ Tel: 01603 592172; 4 Tuckswood Lane, Norwich NR4 6BD Tel: 01603 250003 — MB BS 1983 Lond.; DCH; DRCOG. GP Univ. E. Anglia Health Center.

CANT, Gillian Barbara (retired) 21 Oxford Road, Hampton Poyle, Kidlington OX5 2QD Tel: 01865 373630 Fax: 01865 373630 Email: gcant@compuserve.com — MB BChir Camb. 1945.

CANT, Isabel Mary (retired) 48 Harborne Road, Edgbaston, Birmingham B15 3HE Tel: 0121 454 2635 — MB ChB (Gold Medal Med. & Surg.) Birm. 1936. Prev: Med. Off. King Edwd.'s High Sch. For Girls. Birm.

CANT, Mr James Stanley (retired) 19 Beechlands Avenue, Netherlee, Glasgow G44 3YT Tel: 0141 637 2122 — MB ChB 1953 Glas.; FRCS Ed. 1963; FRCS Glas. 1962; FRCOphth 1987; DO Eng. 1960. Examr. RCS Edin.; Examr. RCPS Glas. Prev: Cons. Ophth. Surg. Vict. Infirm. & S.. Gen. Hosp. Glas.

CANT, Margaret Elizabeth (retired) Quoylobs, Holm, Orkney KW17 2RY Tel: 01856 78300 — MB ChB 1950 Ed.

CANT, Margaret Mary Kingsway Surgery, 655 Kingsway, Burnage, Manchester M19 1RD Tel: 0161 432 2725 Fax: 0161 947 9192 — MB ChB 1987 Manch.; BA (Hons.) York 1976; MRCGP 1992; DRCOG 1991.

CANT, Melanie Elizabeth, Principal Haslemere Health Centre, Church Lane, Haslemere GU27 2BQ Tel: 01483 783023 Fax: 01428 645065 — MB BS 1987 Lond.; MRCGP 1994; DRCOG 1992; Cert. Family Plann. JCC 1992; DCH RCP Lond. 1991. Socs: Haslemere Med. Soc. Prev: Trainee GP Godalming.

CANT, Ronald Fraser (retired) 32 Leicester Avenue, Cliftonville, Margate CT9 3BZ — MB ChB 1948 Aberd.; DMRD Ed. 1954. Prev: Cons. Radiol. Canterbury & Thanet Health Dist.

CANTARINI, Mireille Veronique 12 Templeton Crescent, Eastfield Park, Wedt Derby, Liverpool L12 5NE — MB ChB 1993 Bristol.

CANTER, Alan Keith Bridge Road Surgery, 66-88 Bridge Road, Litherland, Liverpool L21 6PH Tel: 0151 949 0249 Fax: 0151 928 2008 — MB 1970 Camb.; MA Camb. 1971, MB 1970, BChir 1969. (King's Coll. Hosp.)

CANTER, Mr Richard John Department ENT Surgery, Royal United Hospital, Combe Park, Bath BA1 3NG Tel: 01225 824556; Tel: 01225 469023 — MB BS 1976 Lond.; FRCS Eng. (ENT) 1982; FRCS Eng. 1980; Ph.D. 1998. Cons. Otolaryngol. Bath DHA; Hon. Sen. Lect. Postgrad. Sch. Med. Univ. Bath.

CANTI, Gordon (retired) Brook Farm House, Corfe, Taunton TA3 7BU Tel: 01823 421623 — MB BS 1950 Lond.; MRCS Eng. LRCP Lond. 1942; FRCPath 1976, M 1964. Prev: Cons. Path. Cytol. St. Bart. Hosp.

CANTILLON, Charles John Peter Mary Lambeth Walk Group Practice, 5 Lambeth Walk, London SE11 6SP Tel: 020 7735 4412 Fax: 020 7820 1888 — MB BCh BAO 1983 NUI; LRCPI & LM LRCSI & LM 1983.

CANTLAY, John Simon Forth House, Cross Green, Cockfield, Bury St Edmunds IP30 0LG — MB ChB 1969 Aberd.; DMRD 1974; FRCR 1977. Cons. Radiol. W. Suff. Hosp. Bury St. Edmunds.

CANTLEY, Patricia Marion Liberton Hospital, Lasswade Road, Edinburgh EH16 6UB Tel: 0131 536 7800 Fax: 0131 536 7896; 85 Malbet Park, Edinburgh EH16 6WB Tel: 0131 672 3331 Email: patricia.cantley@btinternet.com — MB ChB 1988 Ed.; BSc (Med. Sci.) Hons. Ed. 1986; MRCP (UK) 1991; FRCP Ed 1999. (Edinburgh) Cons. Phys. Geriat. Med. Liberton & Roy. Inf. Hosp. Edin. Socs: (Ex-Sen. Pres.) Roy. Med. Soc. Edin. Prev: Sen. Regist. (Gen. Med.) St. John's Hosp. Livingston; Regist. (Med. for Elderly) Borders Gen. Hosp. Melrose.

CANTLIE, James (retired) 16 Bridge Street, Christchurch BH23 1EB Tel: 01202 482717 — MB ChB Aberd. 1942.

CANTON, David Ebsworth Saundersfoot Medical Centre, Westfield Road, Saundersfoot SA69 9JW Tel: 01834 812407 Fax: 01834 811131; 4 Cooksyeat View, Sardis Lane, Kilgetty SA68 0UA — MB BS 1986 Lond.; BSc (1st cl. Hons.) Pharmacol. Lond. 1983; MRCGP 1993. Prev: Trainee GP Withybush Hosp. HaverfordW.; SHO Neath Gen. Hosp.; SHO Roy. Gwent & St. Woolos Hosps. Gwent.

CANTON, John Llewellyn, TD (retired) 30 Beaufort Avenue, Langland Bay, Swansea SA3 4PB Tel: 01792 369738 Email: johncanton@compuserve.com — MB BS 1957 Lond.; FFA RCS Eng. 1967; DA Eng. 1959. Lt.-Col. RAMC (V), Cons. Anaesth. Prev: Cons. Anaesth. Singleton Hosp. & W. Glam. AHA.

CANTON, Lucy Claire 7 Lynwood Road, Epsom KT17 4LF — MB ChB 1992 Birm. SHO (Paediat.) Roy. Manch. Childr.'s Hosp. Prev: SHO (Paediat.) Countess of Chester Hosp.

CANTONS, Catherine Ann Belsize Priory Health Centre, 208 Belsize Road, London NW6 4DX Tel: 020 7624 9466; 24 Burgess Hill, Hampstead, London NW2 2DA — MB BS 1975 Lond. GP Prinvipal. Socs: BMA.

CANTOPHER, Timothy George Alexander Priory Hospital Sturt, Sturts Lane, Walton on the Hill, Tadworth KT20 7RQ Tel: 0173 781 4488 — MB BS 1979 Lond.; BSc Lond. 1976; FRCPsych 1997, MR 1983. Cons. Psychiat. & Med. Director Priory Hosp. Sturt; Hon. Tutor & Sen. Research Fell. (Addic. Behaviour) St. Geo. Hosp. Med. Sch. Lond. Prev: Cons. Psychiat. Homewood NHS Trust.

CANTOR, Abraham Max (retired) 27 Cortworth Road, Sheffield S11 9LN Tel: 01142 368124 Email: marox@globalnet.co.uk — MB BCh BAO Dub. 1950; MD Dub. 1961; FRCPI 1970, M 1956. Prev: Cons. Phys. Rotherham Dist. Gen. Hosp.

CANTOR, Mr Daryl David Cromwell Hospital, London SW5 0UT Tel: 020 7460 5509 Fax: 020 7730 4686; 56 Acre Lane, London SW2 5SP Tel: 020 7733 9390 — MB BS Melbourne 1963; FRCS Ed. 1968; T(S) 1991. (Melbourne University) Socs: Fell. Roy. Soc. Med.

CANTOR, Frank Michael Chestnuts Surgery, 70 East Street, Sittingbourne ME10 4RU Tel: 01795 423197 Fax: 01795 430179 — MB ChB 1974 Bristol.

CANTOR, Jack (retired) Trevose, 34 Preston Lane, Faversham ME13 8LG Tel: 01795 532680 — MRCS Eng. LRCP Lond. 1949; MRCGP 1958; DObst RCOG 1952. Prev: Ho. Surg. (O & G) Kent & Canterbury Hosp.

CANTOR, Raphael 103 Newport Road, Cardiff CF24 0AF Tel: 029 2048 5526 Fax: 029 2048 2871; 6 Hollybush Road, Cyncoed, Cardiff CF23 6TA Tel: 029 2075 6217 — MB BChir 1965 Camb.; MA Camb. 1965; MRCS Eng. LRCP Lond. 1964; MRCGP 1974; DGM RCP Lond. 1986. (Camb. & Univ. Coll. Hosp.) Clin. Asst. (Psychiat. for Elderly) Lansdowne Hosp. & Roy. Hamadryad Hosp. Cardiff. Socs: BMA; Camb. Univ. Med. Grads. Soc. Prev: Ho. Surg. N. Middlx. Hosp.; Ho. Phys. Addenbrooke's Hosp. Camb.; Ho. Phys. (Paediat.) Univ. Coll. Hosp.

CANTOR, Timothy Jefferson Thornhills Medical Group, 732 London Road, Larkfield, Aylesford ME20 6BQ Tel: 01732 843900 Fax: 01732 872633; Charlton House, Birling Road, Ryarsh, West Malling ME19 5JS Tel: 01732 842790 — MB BS 1974 Lond.; MRCGP 1981; FRCOG 1995. (Middlx.) Gen. Practitioner Princip., Thornhills Med. Gp., Larkfield. Prev: SHO (Obst.) S.mead Hosp. Bristol; SHO (Obst. & Gyn) Nottm. City Hosp.; Ho. Surg. Middlx. Hosp. Lond.

CANTRELL, George Lyall (retired) 'Penwic', 5 Spicer Road, Exeter EX1 1SX Tel: 01392 275714 — MB ChB Manch. 1945; DO Eng. 1951. Prev: Cons. Ophth. Surg. W. of Eng. Eye Infirm. Exeter.

CANTRELL, Paul Joseph Flat 3, 24 Warrington Crescent, London W9 1EL — MB BCh BAO 1987 NUI; LRCPSI 1987.

CANTRELL, Philomena Warrington Hospital NHS Trust, Lovely Lane, Warrington WA5 1QG; 63 Field Lane, Appleton, Warrington WA4 5JR — MB BCh BAO 1983 NUI; LRCPI & LM, LRCSI & LM 1983; FRCR 1990; DMRD 1988. Cons. Radiol. Warrington Dist. Gen. Hosp. Trust. Socs: Fell. Roy. Coll. Radiol. Prev: Sen. Regist. (Radiol.) Liverp.; Regist. (Radiol.) Aberd. Roy. Infirm.; SHO (Respirat. Med. & Gastroenterol.) St. Laurences Hosp. Dub.

CANTRELL, Winifred Dorothy Jane Dept. of Anaesthesia, Whipps Cross University Hospital, Whipps Cross, London E11 1NR Tel: 01931 715323, 020 8535 6614 Fax: 01931 715087 — MB BS 1968 Lond.; MRCS Eng. LRCP Lond. 1968; FFA RCS Eng. 1973. p/t Cons. Anaesth. Whipps Cross Hosp. Lond.; Clin. Lead Clin. Governance, Critical Care Directorate. Socs: Roy. Soc. Of Med.; Brit. Med. Assn.; Harveian Soc.

CANTWELL, Bernadette John Radcliffe Hospital, Headington, Oxford OX3 9DU; Birchwood, Park Lane, Ystrad Mynach, Hengoed CF82 7BX Tel: 01443 813237 — MB BS 1996 Lond.; BSc (Psychol.) UCL 1993. SHO John Radcliffe Hosp. Oxf. Prev: Jun. Ho. Off. Guy's & Lewisham Hosps. Lond.

CANTWELL, Bernard Joseph — MB BCh BAO 1972 NUI; MD NUI 1985; FRCPI 1990, M 1989; MRCP (UK) 1976; FRCP 1999. Cons. Med. Oncol. Newc. Nuffield Hosp., Washington Hosp. Tyne & Wear & Cleveland Nuffield Hosp. Stockton on Tees; Vis. Cons. Roy. Vict. Infirm. Newc. u. Tyne. Socs: Brit. Assn. for Cancer Res.; Assn. Cancer Phys. Prev: Sen. Lect. (Clin. Oncol.) & Hon. Cons. Med. Oncol. Univ. Newc.

CANTWELL, Harold Frank (retired) Lodge Farm, Overton Road, Ibstock, Leicester LE67 6PD — MRCS Eng. LRCP Lond. 1948. Prev: Ho. Phys. & Res. Anaesth. St. Stephen's Hosp. Fulham.

CANTWELL, Roch 16 Portland Road, West Bridgford, Nottingham NG2 6DL — MB BCh BAO 1985 NUI.

CANTY, Mr Derrick Peter Conor (cons. rooms) Elm House, 2 Mauldeth Road, Withington, Manchester M20 4ND Tel: 0161 434 9715; 31 Bramhall Park Road, Bramhall, Stockport SK7 3DQ Tel: 0161 439 4902 — MB BCh BAO 1966 NUI; FRCS Eng. 1975; FRCS Ed. 1974. Cons. Otolaryngol. Manch. Roy. Infirm.; Hon. Clin. Lect. Dept. Audiol. & Educat. of the Deaf Manch. Univ. Prev: Sen. Regist. (Otolaryngol.) Manch. Roy. Infirm.

CANTY, Marie Christine The Bridges Practice, The Health Centre, Stepgates, Chertsey KT16 8HZ Tel: 01932 561199; 2 Dorset Drive, Shaftesbury Road, Woking GU22 7DX Tel: 01483 768205 — MB BCh BAO 1983 NUI; LRCPI & LM, LRCSI & LM 1983; MRCGP 1988; DObst NUI 1987; DCH NUI 1985. Prev: SHO (Paediat.) Our Ladys Hosp Crumlin Dub.; SHO (O & G) Coombe Hosp. Dub.; SHO (Med.) Blanchardstown Dub.

CANTY, Stephen John 31 Bramhall Park Road, Bramhall, Stockport SK7 3DQ — MB ChB 1996 Manch.

CANTY, Mr Stuart Hamilton The Horton Hospital, Oxford Road, Banbury OX16 9AL Tel: 01295 275500 Fax: 01295 229617; Oak House, Chalford Park, Old Chalford, Chipping Norton OX7 5QR — BM BCh 1977 Oxf.; BA (Hons.) Oxf. 1974, MA (Hons.) 1977; FRCS Eng. 1981; MRCS Eng. LRCP Lond. 1977; FRCOG 1997, M 1984. (Oxf. & King's Coll. Hosp.) Cons. O & G Oxf. Radcliffe Hosps. NHS Trust Horton Hosp. Banbury. Socs: Brit. Menopause Soc.; Blair Bell Res. Soc.; BSCCP. Prev: Lect. (Human Reproduc. & Obst.) Univ. Soton; Regist. (O & G) St. Thos. Hosp. Lond.; Resid. Med. Off. Qu. Charlotte's Matern. Hosp. Lond.

CAOLES, Una Francesca 27 Trevelyan Road, Tooting, London SW17 9LR Tel: 0208 672 5487 — MD 1991 Oregon; FRCS 2000 (Otolaryngology) Ed; BA 1987 (Hons) John Hopkins University; 1994 PLAB, GMC; 1992 Dip of Nat. Bd. Of Med. Examiners, USA; FRCS 1999 (Gen. Surg.) Ed; 1991 NY state licence to practice medicine & surgery; DRCOG 2001. GP registra. Socs: NY state Licence to Pract. Med. & Surg.; Young FRSM; FRCS Ed. Prev: SHO (O&G) Kings Col. Hosp. Lond.; Sen. SHO (ENT) Roy. Surrey Co. Hosp. Guildford.; SHO (ENT) St Geo.'s Lond.

CAPALDI, Agnes Dougan Medical Centre, 1 High Street, Neilston, Barrhead G78 3HJ Tel: 0141 880 6505 Fax: 0141 881 9266; Wellbrae, Gateside Road, Barrhead, Glasgow G78 1EP Tel: 0141 880 8838 Fax: 0141 880 8838 — MB ChB 1980 Glas.; MRCGP 1984; DRCOG 1982. (Glasgow University) GP; Clin. Asst. (BrE. Dis.) Roy. Alexandra Hosp. Paisley. Prev: Clin. Med. Off. Community Child Health Gtr. Glas. Health Bd.

CAPANNI, Paolo Damiano, Maj. RAMC Army Medical Directorate, Keogh Barracks, Ash Vale, Aldershot FU12 5RQ; 20 Kew Terrace, Glasgow G12 0TE Tel: 0141 357 1956 — MB ChB 1991 Glas.

CAPARROTTA, Luigi 48 Honeyman Close, Brondesbury Park, London NW6 7AZ Tel: 020 8451 3353 — MD 1975 Padua; MPhil Lond. 1992. (Italy) Assoc. Specialist. (Psychother.) Roy. Free Hosp. Lond. Socs: Brit. Psychoanal Soc. Prev: Clin. Asst. (Psychiat.) Felix Brown Day Hosp.; Regist. (Psychother.) Cassel Hosp. Richmond.

CAPE, Alison Marie Hillcrest, Woodside, Bedlington NE22 5NE — MB ChB 1998 Dund.; MB ChB Dund 1998.

CAPE, Mr John (retired) Oakfield, Gill Bank Road, Ilkley LS29 0AU Tel: 01943 600744 — MB BS 1958 Durh.; FRCS Ed. 1963; MChOrth Liverp. 1967. Prev: Cons. Orthop. Airedale Gen. Hosp.

CAPEHORN, David Mark William 26 Burlington Gardens, Banbury OX16 9NQ — MB ChB 1989 Bristol. Fell. (A & E) Bristol Childr. Hosp.

CAPEHORN, Matthew Stephen 92 Wadsworth Road, Bramley, Rotherham S66 1UD — MB ChB 1996 Sheff.; BMedSci Sheff. 1993. GP Regist. Greenside Greasbrough Rotherham. Prev: SHO (O & G) Rotherham; Ho. Off. (Med. & c/o Elderly) Rotherham; Ho. Off. (Surg.) Rotherham.

CAPEK, Michael Edward Yaron Wythenshawe Road Surgery, 216A Wythenshawe Road, Northern Moor, Manchester M23 0PH Tel: 0161 998 2503 Fax: 0161 945 0695 — MB ChB 1979 Leeds; MRCGP 1983; M.Sc. (Health Psychology) City University 1996; B.A. Open University 1998. (Leeds)

CAPEL, John Philip (retired) Hatters Cottage, 66 School Road, Frampton, Cotterell, Bristol BS36 2DA Tel: 01454 778396 Fax: 01454 775396 — LRCP LRCS Ed. LRFPS Glas. 1950. Prev: Cons. i/c Accid. Dept. Frenchay Hosp. Bristol.

***CAPEL, Margred Madeline** Ty Derw, 53 Chaldon Common Road, Caterham CR3 5DH — MB BS 1998 Lond.; MB BS Lond 1998; BSc (Hons) 1995 Lond.

CAPELL, Elizabeth Arthur (retired) 21 Manor Court, Swindon Village, Cheltenham GL51 9SD — MRCS Eng. LRCP Lond. 1955; LMSSA Lond. 1954.

CAPELL, Hilary Allison Centre for Rheumatic Diseases, Glasgow Royal Infirmary, Castle St., Glasgow G4 0SF Tel: 0141 211 4965 Fax: 0141 552 4862; 8 Gadloch Avenue, Lenzie, Kirkintilloch, Glasgow G66 5NP Tel: 0141 775 0449 — MD 1992 Glas.; MB BCh Witwatersrand 1972; BA Open 1992; FRCP Ed. 1997; FRCP Glas. 1985; MRCP (UK) 1975. (Witwatersrand) Cons. Phys. Centre Rheum. Dis. Roy. Infirm. Glas.; Hon. Sen. Lect. (Med.) Univ. Glas.

CAPES, David Edward Pickering Surgery, Southgate, Pickering YO18 8BL Tel: 01751 72441 Fax: 01751 75400 — MB BS 1976 Newc.; MRCGP 1980.

CAPES, Hilda Mary (retired) 28 Three Crowns House, South Quay, King's Lynn PE30 5DT — MB BS Lond. 1933; Founder FRCPsych 1971; DPM Eng. 1937. Prev: Cons. (Child & Adolesc. Psychiat.) Wessex RHB.

CAPEWELL, Ann Elizabeth York House, Whiston Hospital, Warrington Road, Prescot Tel: 0151 430 1224 Fax: 0131 537 5140 — MB BS 1978 Newc.; MRCP (UK) 1981; FRCP 1996 Edinburgh. (Newcastle) Cons. Phys. W. Histon Hosp. Merseyside. Socs: Brit. Geriat. Soc. & Internat. Continence Soc.; ACE Anaesth. Assn. Prev: Cons. Phys. (Geriat. Med.) Roy. Vict. Hosp., Edin.; Research Fell. Univ. Dept. Geriat. Med. Cardiff; Sen. Regist. (Geriat. & Gen. Med.) Edin. Hosps.

CAPEWELL, Professor Simon John Department of Public Health, University of Liverpool, Liverpool L69 3GB — MB BS 1977 Newc.; MSc Ed. 1993; MD Newc. 1988; MRCP (UK) 1981; MFPHM RCP (UK) 1995; FRCPE 1996. Chair (Clin. Epidemiol.) Liverp. Univ. Prev: Sen. Lect. (Pub. Health) Univ. Glas.; Sen. Med. Off. Scott. Office Edin.; Lect. (TB & Chest Dis.) Univ. of Wales.

CAPILDEO, Rudy Hill House, Blackmore Road, Fryerning, Ingatestone CM4 0NW Tel: 01277 353003 Fax: 01277 356966 Email: rcapildeo@uk-consultants.co.uk — MB BS 1968 Lond.; FRCP Lond. 1992; MRCP (UK) 1972. (St. Geo.) Cons. Neurol. Basildon & Thurrock Health Dist. Essex.; Hon. Sen. Lect., Univ. Coll. Lond.; Vis. Cons. Roy. Coll. Lond. Socs: Fell. Roy. Soc. Med.; Med. Soc. Lond. Prev: Cons. Neurol. Regional Centre for Neurol. & Neurosurg. Romford; Sen. Regist. (Neurol.) Char. Cross Hosp. Lond.; Assoc. Prof. Neuroepidemiol. NINCDS, NIH Bethesda, USA.

CAPLAN, Alfred 18 Cambridge Gardens, London NW6 5AY — MRCS Eng. LRCP Lond. 1938. (Univ. Coll. Hosp.) Prev: Med. Off. Hackney Hosp.; Squadron Ldr. R.A.F.V.R. 1939-43.

CAPLAN, Bernard Timperley Health Centre, 169 Grove Lane, Timperley, Altrincham WA15 6PH; The Coach House, Woodville Road, Altrincham WA14 2AN — MB ChB Liverp. 1965; AFOM 1980; MRCGP 1973; DIH Eng. 1978; DObst RCOG 1967; DFFP 1995; LFHOM 1996. (Liverp.) Med. Off. Shell UK. Prev: Ho. Phys. Wythenshawe Hosp. Manch.; Ho. Surg. (O & G) & Ho. Surg. Withington Hosp. Manch.

CAPLAN, Bridget Angela Nilgari, 14 Granville Road, Oxted RH8 0DA Tel: 01883 714620 — MB BS 1961 Lond. (St. Thos.) Regist. Childh. Cancer Research Gp. Oxf. Prev: Cas. Off. & Ho. Phys. St. Thos. Hosp. Lond.

CAPLAN, Gerald 57 Sergeants Lane, Old Hall Park, Whitefield, Manchester M45 7TR Tel: 0161 796 6825 — MB ChB 1955 Manch.; BSc (Hons.) Manch. 1952; FRCGP 1983; DObst RCOG 1957. (Manch.) Mem. Manch. HA. Prev: GP Manch.; Hosp. Pract. (ENT) Withington Hosp. Manch.; Ho. Phys. & Ho. Surg. (O & G) Crumpsall Hosp. Manch.

CAPLAN, Harold 1 The Close, Southgate, London N14 6DP Email: caplans@btinternet.com — MB BS Lond. 1949; MD Lond. 1961; MRCS Eng. LRCP Lond. 1946; FRCPath 1967; Barrister at Law Middle Temple 1981. (Lond. Hosp.) Socs: Fell. Roy. Soc. Med.; BMA. Prev: Mem. (Vice-Chairm.) Enfield HA; Dir. Path. Manor Ho. Hosp. Lond.; Cons. Path. Chase Farm & Highlands & Manor Hse. Hosps.

CAPLAN, Harold Leslie Private Patients Wing, University College Hospital, Grafton Way, London WC1E 6DB Tel: 020 7387 9300; Edward House, 7 Lisson Grove, London NW1 6SH Tel: 020 7723 1987 Fax: 020 7738 8384 Email: haroldcaplan@hotmail.com — MB BS 1960 Melbourne; MPhil Lond. 1970; BA Melbourne 1966, MB BS 1960; FRCPsych 1985, M 1971; FRACP 1973, M 1966. (Melb.) Socs: Brit. Psycho-Analyt. Soc. Prev: Cons. Child Psychiat. St. Geo. Hosp. Lond. & Wandsworth Child Guid.; Cons.Child.Adoles.Psychiat.UCL.Lond; Sen. Regist. Maudsley Hosp. Lond.

CAPLAN, Malcolm Denis (retired) Tall Timbers, 1 Malmesbury Road, St Leonards, Ringwood BH24 2QL Tel: 01202 872976 — MB

BS 1945 Lond.; MRCS Eng. LRCP Lond. 1944. Prev: Exam. Med. Off. DHSS.

CAPLAN, Mandy Oak Leigh Medical Centre, 58 Ash Tree Road, Crumpsall, Manchester M8 5SA Tel: 0161 740 1226 Fax: 0161 795 8611; 20 Wentworth Avenue, Whitefield, Manchester M45 7GQ Tel: 0161 796 1086 — BM BS 1985 Nottm.; BMedSci Nottm. 1983; MRCGP 1989; DRCOG 1987.

CAPLAN, Mark Paul Warrington Hospital NHS Trust, Lovely Lane, Warrington WA5 1QG Tel: 01925 635911; Rose Cottage, Duddon Common, Duddon, Tarporley CW6 0HG Tel: 01829 781314 — MB ChB 1984 Liverp.; FRCR Lond. 1992; DMRD Eng. 1992. Cons. Radiol. Warrington NHS Trust Warrington. Prev: Sen. Regist. (Radiol.) Liverp.; SHO (Geriat. Med.) Ormskirk Gen. Hosp.

CAPLAN, Richard Paul Southern General Hospital, 1345 Govan Road, Glasgow G51 4TF Tel: 0141 201 1948 — MB ChB 1978 Glas.; MRCPsych. 1982. Cons. Psychiat. S.. Gen. Hosp. Glas.; Hon. Sen. Lect. Univ. Glas. Prev: Cons. Psychiat. Lincoln Co. Hosp.; Sen. Regist. (Psychiat.) St. Geo. Hosp. Lond.; Regist. (Psychiat.) Guy's Hosp. Lond.

CAPLAN, Russell Simon Fernlea Surgery, 114 High Road, London N15 6JR Tel: 020 8809 6445 Fax: 020 8800 4224; 38 Athenaeum Road, Whetstone, London N20 9AH Tel: 020 8445 6701 — MB BS 1983 Lond.; MRCGP 1987. (Lond. Hosp. Whitechapel) Clin. Asst. (Diabetes) Whittington Hosp. Lond.; Clin. Asst. (Paediat.) Whipps Cross Hosp. Lond. Prev: Trainee GP Newham Gen. Hosp. VTS; Ho. Surg. OldCh. Hosp. Romford; Ho. Phys. Whipps Cross Hosp. Leytonstone.

CAPLIN, Benjamin Daniel 15 Spittal Street, Edinburgh EH3 9DY — MB ChB 1998 Ed.; MB ChB Ed 1998.

CAPLIN, George Ingol Health Centre, 87 Village Green Lane, Preston PR2 7DS Tel: 01772 787652 Fax: 01772 769733; 248 Garstang Road, Fulwood, Preston PR2 9QB Tel: 01772 718964 — LAH Dub. 1963. (RCSI) Clin. Asst. (Anaesth.) Roy. Preston Hosp. & Sharoe Green Hosp. Preston. Socs: BMA & Preston Medico-Ethical Soc. Prev: SHO (Anaesth.) & Ho. Off. (O & G) Preston Roy. Infirm.; Ho. Phys. Sharoe Green Hosp. Preston.

CAPLIN, Gerald Flat 45, Bath Hill Court, Bath Road, Bournemouth BH1 2HR Tel: 01202 292675 — MB BCh BAO 1950 Dub.; MRCGP 1966. SCMO (Occupat. Health) Roy. Vict. Hosp. Bournemouth. Prev: Ho. Phys. Roy. Sussex Co. Hosp. Brighton; Med. Sen. Ho. Off. Hope Hosp. Salford; Med. Regist. Roy. Vict. Hosp. Boscombe.

CAPLIN, Henry (retired) 41 Lodge Close, Canons Drive, Edgware HA8 7RL Tel: 020 8952 9286 — MRCS Eng. LRCP Lond. 1934; MD Lond. 1946, MB BS 1936; FCPath 1965. Pathol. Forest Hosp. Gp. Prev: RAMC 1939-45, Pathol.

CAPLIN, John Louis Department of Cardiology, Hull Royal Infirmary, Anlaby Road, Hull HU3 2JZ Tel: 01482 674902 Fax: 01482 321128 Email: johncaplin@yahoo.com — MB BS 1976 Lond.; BSc Lond. 1973, MD 1987; FRCP Lond. 1995; MRCP (UK) 1978. (Univ. Coll. Hosp.) Cons. Cardiol. Hull & E. Yorks, Cardiothoracic Centre. Socs: Brit. Cardiac Soc.; Paul Dudley White Soc.; Brit. Nuclear Cardiol. Soc. Prev: Sen. Regist. (Cardiol.) Soton. Gen. Hosp.; Clin. Research Fell. (Cardiol.) Mass. Gen. Hosp. Boston, USA; Regist. (Cardiol.) St. Bart. Hosp. Lond.

CAPLIN, Lewis Aaron 117 Shacklewell Lane, London E8 2EB — MB BS 1998 Lond.; MB BS Lond 1998.

CAPLIN, Martyn Evan Department of Medicine, Royal Free Hospital, Pond St., London NW3 2QG Tel: 0207 433 2863 Fax: 0207 433 2853 Email: m.caplin@rfc.uc/.ac.uk — BM 1987 Soton.; BSc (Hons.) Sheff. 1983; MRCP (UK) 1992. Cons. Physican & Gastroenterol., Roy. Free Hosp. NHS Trust. Socs: Chairm. UK Neuroendocrine tumour Gp.; Mem. Europ. Neuroendocrine Tumour Gp. Prev: Lect. & Sen. Regist. (Gastroenterol & Gen. Med.) Roy. Free Hosp. Lond.; Research Fell. Roy. Free Hosp.; Regist. (Gen. Med. & Gastroenterol) Roy Free Hosp. & Edgware Gen. Hosp.

CAPLIN, Maxwell, OBE (retired) 498 Finchley Road, London NW11 8DE Tel: 020 8455 3314 — MRCS Eng. LRCP Lond. 1940; FRCP Lond. 1977, M 1975. Prev: Cons. Phys. Lond. Chest Hosp. & Hon. Sen. Lect. Univ. Lond.

CAPLIN, Sally Ann Wellspring Surgery, St. Anns Health Centre, St. Anns, Well Road, Nottingham NG3 3PX Tel: 0115 9505907/8 Fax: 0115 988 1582 — BM BS 1991 Nottm.; MRCGP 1995. (Nottm.) GP Princip. Socs: BMA.

CAPLIN, Mr Scott 38 Wirksmoor Road, New Mills, High Peak SK22 3HU Email: scottcaplin@lineone.net — MB ChB 1988 Sheff.; FRCS Eng. 1993. (Sheffield) NW Region Higher Surgic. Train. Scheme.

CAPOCCIA, Giovanna 4 Westend Crogty, Burgh-by-Sands, Carlisle CA5 6BT — State Exam Siena 1984.

CAPONIGRO, Francesco CRC Department of Medical Oncology, Alexander Stone Building, Garscube Estate, Switchback Road, Bearsden, Glasgow G61 1BD — State Exam 1984 Naples.

CAPOOR, Ujvala — MB BS 1996 Lond. (UMDS (Guy's & St. Thomas')) SHO in Anaesthetics, Centr. Middlx. Hosp., Lond.

CAPOORE, Harbaksh Singh Penfield Farm, Perrywood, Selling, Faversham ME13 9RU Tel: 01227 752265 — MB ChB 1943 Leeds; BChD, LDS Leeds 1941, MD 1946; MRCS Eng. LRCP Lond. 1944; FRCPsych 1974, M 1971; DPM Eng. 1946. (Leeds) p/t Hon. Cons. (Psychiat.) Kent & Canterbury Hosp.; Hon. Cons. Psychiat. Bexley DHA Hosps. Socs: Fell. Roy. Coll. Psychiat.; New York Acad. Sci. Prev: Cons. Psychiat. Bexley Hosp. & Qu. Mary's Hosp. Sidcup; Cons. Psychiat. Dartford & Gravesham Health Dist.; Sen. Asst. Med. Off. W.R. Ment. Hosp. Burley-in-Wharfedale & St. And. Hosp. Norwich.

CAPP, Simon Peter 4 Spindle Warren, Havant PO9 2PU — BM 1983 Soton.; MRCGP 1987; DRCOG 1987.

CAPPER, Elizabeth (retired) Old Rose Cottage, Elton, Ludlow SY8 2HQ Tel: 0156 886234 — MB ChB 1944 Ed.; MFCM 1973; DPH 1948. Prev: Clin. Med. Off. Shrops. HA.

CAPPER, John Leonard Halford (retired) 49 Battlefield Road, St Albans AL1 4DB Tel: 01727 59475 — MB BS 1953 Lond.; MRCS Eng. LRCP Lond. 1953; DObst RCOG 1959.

CAPPER, Mr John William Ridley Chartley, The Common, Hyde Heath, Amersham HP6 5RW Tel: 01494 784043 — MB BS 1975 Lond.; FRCS Eng. 1980; MRCS Eng. LRCP Lond. 1975. (St. Bart.) Cons. ENT Surg. High Wycombe War Memor. Hosp. Prev: Sen. Regist. (ENT) Bristol & Bath HAs; Regist. & SHO (ENT) Roy. Nat. Throat, Nose & Ear Hosp. Lond.

CAPPER, Maureen Elizabeth Bountree, Glenfarg, Perth PH2 9NL — MB ChB 1963 Leeds; DObst RCOG 1965.

CAPPER, Nancy Dorothy (retired) Martlets, Harpford, Sidmouth EX10 0NQ Tel: 01395 568198 — BM BCh 1944 Oxf.; DCH Eng. 1945. Prev: Clin. Med. Off. Birm. AHA (T).

CAPPER, Rosamond Hilda Adora The Vicarage, Malpas, Newport NP20 6GQ Tel: 01633 852047 — MB BChir 1977 Camb. Prev: Clin. Med. Off. E. Dyfed HA; Ho. Phys. Roy. Gwent Hosp. Newport; Ho. Surg. St. Woolos Hosp. Newport.

CAPPER, Ruth The Bath Clinic, Claverton Down, Bath BA2 7BR — MB BCh BAO 1987 Belf.; FRCSI 1991.

CAPPER, Sarah Joan 4 Belgrave Av, Marple, Stockport SK6 6LY — MB ChB 1997 Sheff.

CAPPER, William Malcolm Margaret Street Surgery, Margaret Street, Ammanford SA18 2PJ Tel: 01269 592477 Fax: 01269 597326; Llwch-is-Awel, Betws, Ammanford SA18 2PF — MB BCh 1981 Wales; DRCOG 1983; DA (UK) 1988.

CAPPERAULD, Mr Ian (retired) Old Mill House, Dalkeith EH22 2AQ Tel: 0131 663 2469 Fax: 0131 663 6527 — MB ChB 1957 Glas.; FRCS Eng. 1989; FRCS Glas. 1980; FRCS Ed. 1962; DObst RCOG 1960. Prev: Exec. Dir. Research & Cons. Surg. Ethicon Ltd. Edin.

CAPPIN, Mr John Michael Leicester Clinic, Scraptoft Lane, Leicester LE5 1HY Tel: 0116 276 9401; 2 Stoughton Drive south, Oadby, Leicester LE2 2RH — MB BChir 1965 Camb.; FRCS Eng. 1971; FCOphth. 1989; DO Eng. 1968. (Camb. & Lond. Hosp.) Emerit. Cons. Ophth. Surg. Leicester Roy. Infirm. Socs: Fac. Ophth. & Ophth. Soc. U.K.; Midl. ophthalmological Soc.; Ukiscr. Prev: Jt. Sen. Regist. King's Coll. Hosp. & Moorfields Eye Hosp. Lond.; SHO (Ophth.) Univ. Coll. Hosp. Lond.; Demonst. Path. Dept. Sheff. Univ.

CAPPIN, Simon James 21 Stoughton Drive S., Leicester LE2 2RJ — MB BCh 1993 Wales.

CAPPLEMAN, Therese Ann Scarborough General Hospital, Scalby Road, Scarborough YO12 6QL Tel: 01723 368111; 1 Woods Close, Burniston, Scarborough YO13 0JB Tel: 01723 870415 — MB BS 1989 Lond. SHO (A & E) ScarBoro. Hosp.

CAPPS, Erica Grace Shand Princess Royal Hospital, NHS Trust, Apley Castle FP1 6TF Tel: 01952 641222 — MB ChB 1981 Glas.;

DRCOG 1984. p/t Asst. Phys. c/o the Elderly & Rehab., Paul Brown Unit, P.ss Roy. Hosp. Telford. Prev: GP Axminster.

CAPPS, Frederick Peter Anders, RD (retired) The Mount Cottage, 4 The Mount, Shrewsbury SY3 8PS Tel: 01743 354540 — MB BS 1956 Lond.; FRCP Lond. 1980, M 1964; DObst RCOG 1958. Prev: Cons. Paediat. Roy. Shrewsbury Hosp.

CAPPS, Nigel Eric Department of Clinical Biochemistry, Telford Hospital, Apley Castle, Telford TF1 6TF — MB ChB 1981 Glas.; BSc (Hons.) Glas. 1978; MRCPath 1989. Cons. Chem. Path. Shrops. Prev: Sen. Regist. (Chem. Path.) Roy. Devon & Exeter Hosps.; Regist. Biochem. Vict. Infirm. Glas.

CAPPS, Mr Stephen Nicholas Jackson Paediatric Surgery, St. Georges Hospital, Blackshaw Road, London SW17 0QT Tel: 020 8725 3322 Fax: 020 8725 0711 — MB BS 1975 Lond.; BSc (Hons.) Lond. 1972; FRCS Eng. 1980. Cons. (Paediat. Surg. & Paediat. Urol.) St. Geo.'s Hosp. Lond.; Sen. Lect. St. Geo. Hosp. Lond.; Cons. (Paediat. Surg. & Paediat. Urol.) St Helier Hosp. Lond. Socs: Mem. Brit. Assn. of Paediatric Surg.s. Prev: Sen. Regist. (Paediat. Surg.) Hosp. for Sick Childr. Gt. Ormond Sreet Lond.

CAPPUCCIO, Professor Francesco Paolo Department of General Practice & Primary Care, St. George's Hospital Medical School, Cranmer Terrace, London SW17 0RE — MB BS Naples 1981; State DMS 1981 Naples; MSc Lond. 1993; MD (Hons.) Naples 1984; MRCP Lond. 1996; DLSHTM Lond 1996; FRCP Lond 1999. Prof. & Hon. Cons. Phys. St. Geo. Hosp. Med. Sch. Lond.; Sen. Lect. (Epidemiol.) LSHTM Lond. Socs: Brit. Hypertens. Soc.; Eur. Soc. Hypertens.; Am. Heart Assoc. Prev: Clin. Research Fell. & Hon. Regist. St. Geo. Hosp., Char. Cross & W.m. Med. Sch. Lond.; Clin. Lect. Epidemiol. LSHTM Lond.; Reader & Cons. Phys. St Geo. Hosp. Med. Sch. Lond.

CAPRA, Margaret (retired) 90 Victoria Drive, London SW19 6HQ Tel: 020 8788 6672 — MRCS Eng. LRCP Lond. 1945; MFCM 1974; DPH Eng. 1956. Prev: PMO Hounslow, Hammersmith & Ealing HA.

CAPRA, Michael Libero Department of Child Health, Queen's Medical Centre, Nottingham NG7 2UH Tel: 020 7386 7304 — MB BCh 1987 Witwatersrand; MRCP (UK) 1995; Dip. Obst. S. Afr. 1991; DCH S. Afr. 1991. Lect. in Child Health Qu. Med. Centre Nottm.

CAPRIO, Leo Holly House, Meadow Close, Wilmslow SK9 6JN; Holly House, Meadow Close, Wilmslow SK9 6JN Tel: 01625 529506 — MB ChB 1957 Manch.; MRCGP 1972. (Manch.) GP Manch. Socs: Assur. Med. Soc. Prev: Sen. Ho. Off. (Med.) Bolton Gen. Hosp.; Obst. Ho. Off. Hope Hosp. Salford; Med. Off. RAF.

CAPSTICK, Ian (retired) Goose House, East Horrington, Wells BA5 3DP Tel: 01749 673494 Fax: 01749 673494 — MB BS 1959 Durh.; FRCGP 1975, M 1966; DObst RCOG 1962. Prev: Med. Dir. St. Peters Bristol.

CAPSTICK, Mary Eiluned Lloyd Pengarth, Radyr, Cardiff CF15 8EA Tel: 029 2084 2583 — MB BCh 1952 Wales; BSc Wales 1949; DObst RCOG 1954. (Cardiff) Prev: Ho. Surg. (Gen. Surg.), Ho. Surg. Dept. O & G & Regist. Dept.; Radiother. Roy. Infirm. Cardiff.

CAPSTICK, Norman Stanley (retired) 24 Aldsworth Avenue, Goring by Sea, Worthing BN12 4XQ Tel: 01903 503575 — MD Lond. 1961, MB BS 1950; FRCP Ed. 1982, M 1958; MRCS Eng. LRCP Lond. 1949; MRCPsych 1971; DPM Eng. 1956. Consult. i/c Worthing & Dist. Psychiat. Serv. Prev: Sen. Regist. St. Bart. Hosp.

CAPUANO, Anthony 7 Butterworth Way, Greenfield, Oldham OL3 7PS Tel: 01457 832590 Fax: 01457 836083 Email: anthony@capuano.demon.co.uk — BM BS 1989 Nottm.; DRCOG 1992; MRCGP 1993. (Nottingham)

CAPUTO, Massimo Department of Cardiac Surgery, Bristol Infirmary, Marlborough St., Bristol BS2 8HW — State Exam 1992 Modena; Styate Exam Modena 1992.

CARA, David Mills Dukeswood, Dartnell Avenue, West Byfleet, Weybridge — BM BCh 1991 Oxf.

CARABINE, Una Attracta Department of Anaesthetics, Royal Hospitals Trust, Grovenor Road, Belfast BT12 6BA — MB BCh BAO 1983 Belf.; MD Belf. 1989; FFA RCSI 1987. Cons. Anaesth. Roy. Gp. Hosps. Belf.

CARABOTT, Ferdinand Harold Wood Hospital, Gubbins Lane, Romford RM3 0BE Tel: 01708 708480; 62 Malvern Road, London E8 3LJ Email: ferdycarabott@compuserve.com — MRCS Eng. LRCP Lond. 1978; MD Malta 1989; MRCP (UK) 1983; FRCP 2000 FRCP (uk) 2000. Cons. Dermat. Havering Hosps. Socs: Fell. Roy. Soc. Med.; BMA; Brit. Assn. of Dermatol.s. Prev: Research Regist. St. John's Hosp. for Skin Dis. Lond.; SHO (Med.) St. Bart. & Whipps Cross Hosps. Lond.

CARACHI, Mr Robert 37 Dalkeith Avenue, Dumbreck, Glasgow G41 5LH — MD 1973 Malta; PhD Glas. 1983; FRCS Glas. 1977. (Malta) Sen. Lect. Univ. Glas.; Hon. Cons. Paediat. Surg. Roy. Hosp. Sick Childr. Glas.

CARAHER, Michelle Marie Flat 1, 15 Sale Place, London W2 1PX — MB BCh BAO 1988 NUI; LRCPS &I 1988.

CARAMELLO, Alessandra Jocelyn 1 The Stonebow, Thornton-Le-Beans, Northallerton DL6 3SR — MB ChB 1992 Aberd.; Dip.Child. Health 1993 Glasgow. (Aberdeen) GP Locum, Fife.

CARAMITSOS, Jean Theodore 49 Goldsboro Avenue, Blackpool FY3 9RJ Tel: 01253 61756 — MB BCh 1969 Ain Shams. (Ain Shams)

CARANCI, Giovanni Antony Bridge Surgery, 8 Evesham Road, Redditch B97 4LA — MB ChB 1986 Leic.; MRCGP 1990; DGM RCP Lond. 1989; DRCOG 1988. (Leic.) Ho. Phys. Geo. Eliot Hosp. Nuneaton; Trainee GP Shepshed Leics.

CARANZA, Roberto Augusto Home Farm, Fen La, East Keal, Spilsby PE23 4AY — Medico 1981 Buenos Aires; Medico Buenos Aires 19981.

CARAPETI, Mr Emin Assatour Department of surgery, St Mark's Hospital, Watford Road, Harrow HA1 3UJ Tel: 020 8 235 4000 Fax: 0181 235 4162; 49C Warwick Avenue, Maida Vale, London W9 2PR — MB BS 1989 Lond.; BSc Lond. 1986; FRCS Eng. 1993. (Guy's Hosp. Med. Sch.) Cons. Surg. St Marks's Hosp. Lond. Socs: Ass. ColoProctol. of GB & IRE (Ass.Memb); BMA; Roy. Soc. Med. Prev: SHO Rotat. (Surg.) N.wick Pk. Hosp.; Prosector (Anat.) Unit Med. & Dent. Schs. Guy's & St. Thos. Hosp. Lond.; Ho. Surg. Roy. Free Hosp. Lond.

CARAPIET, Arthur Minas (retired) 95 Harewood Road, Isleworth TW7 5HN — MB BS 1951 Calcutta.

CARAPIET, Denise Araxi 41 Burdell Avenue, Sandhills, Oxford OX3 8EE — MB BS 1988 Lond.; DA (UK) 1990. Regist. Rotat. (Anaesth.) Oxf. & Reading. Prev: SHO (Anaesth.) Yeovil Dist. Hosp.; SHO (Anaesth. & Paediat.) John Radcliffe Hosp. Oxf.

CARBARNS, Ian Russell Inglis Astrazeneca, Alderley Park, Macclesfield SK10 4TG Tel: 01625 513242 Fax: 01625 590086 Email: ian.carbarns@astrazeneca.com; 18 Villa Farm, Newcastle Road, Arclid, Sandbach CW11 2UQ Tel: 01477 500741 Fax: 01477 500741 Email: ian.carbarns@bigfoot.com — MB ChB 1985 Ed.; BSc (Med. Sci) (Hons. Biochem.) Ed. 1983; Dip. Pharm. Med. RCP (UK) 1992. (Ed.) Med. advisor, Astrazeneca, Macclesfield U.K. Socs: Fac. Pharmaceut. Med. RCP UK; Roy. Med. Soc. Prev: Sen. Med. Adviser, Novarts, Basel Switz.; Clin. Research Phys. Sanofi Winthrop Ltd. Guildford; SHO Rotat. (Med.) Edin.

CARBARNS, Neil James Burgess Department of Clinical Microbiology & Infection control, Gwent Healthcare NHS Trust, Nevill Hall Hospital, Brecon Road, Abergavenny NP7 7EG Tel: 01873 732817 Fax: 01873 732265 Email: dr.carbarns@gwent.wales.nhs.uk; Shewis, Llangattock, Crickhowell NP8 1LD Tel: 01873 811394 Fax: 01873 811394 Email: ncarbarns@hotmail.com — MB ChB 1983 Ed.; BSc (Med. Sci.) (Hons. Bacteriol.) Ed. 1980; MRCPath 1992; FRCPath 2000. (Ed.) Cons. Med. Micriobiol. Gwent Healthcare NHS Trust, Abergavenny; Cons. Med. Microbiologist JMJ Laboratories Ltd., Abergavenny. Socs: Brit. Infec. Soc..; Amer. Soc. Microbiol.; Brit. Soc. Antimicrob. Chem. Prev: Sen. Regist. (Clin. Bacteriol. & Med. Microbiol.) Univ. Hosp. Wales & Pub. Health Laborat. Cardiff; SHO (Profess. Cardiol. Unit & Respirat. Med.) Roy. Infirm. Edin.; Ho. Phys. Profess. Med. Unit & Ho. Surg. (Vasc. Surg.) Roy. Infirm. Edin.

CARBARNS, Sheila Ann Creich Surgery, Bonar Bridge IV24 3ER Tel: 01863 766379 Fax: 01863 766768 Email: sheila.carbans@doctors.org.uk — MB ChB 1990 Ed.; MRCGP 1995; DFFP 1995; DRCOG 1993. (Univ. Ed.) Assoc. GP Bonar Bridge, Sutherland; Clin. Assist. Care Elderly, Migdale Hosp. Bonar Bridge, Sutherland. Socs: Nat. Soc. of assoc. GPs - Sec. Prev: Assoc. GP Applecross, W.er Ross; Med. Off. Highland Brook Advis. Centre; Assoc. GP I. of Lewis.

CARBERRY, Paul James Riverlyn Medical Centre, Station Road, Bulwell, Nottingham NG6 9AA Tel: 0115 927 9214; 14 Albemarle Road, Woodthorpe, Nottingham NG5 4FE — MB BS 1968 Lond.; MRCS Eng. LRCP Lond. 1968; DObst RCOG 1971. (King's Coll.

Hosp.) Prev: Ho. Phys. Dulwich Hosp. Lond.; Ho. Surg. (Orthop. & Neurosurg.) King's Coll. Hosp. Lond.; SHO (Obst.) St. Mary's Hosp. Manch.

CARBONELL CASASUS, Jose Javier 20 The Crescent, Rauceby Hospital, Sleaford NG34 8PR — MB ChB 1983 Sheff. Ho. Off. (Med.) P.ss Alexandra's RAF Hosp. Wroughton. Prev: Ho. Off. (Surg.) Grantham & Kesteven Gen. Hosp. Lincs.

CARBONES CASANOVAS, Francesc Xavier 7 Alexandra Terrace, Dorchester DT1 1UE — LMS 1993 Barcelona; LMS Autonoma Barcelona 1993.

CARBY, Anna Elizabeth 14A Greyhound Road, London W6 8NX — MB BS 1994 Lond.

CARD, Isobel Rintoul (retired) Drumnoth, Brae of Scurdargue, Rhynie, Huntly AB54 4HG — MB ChB 1960 Ed.; FRCP Lond. 1987, M 1965; FRCPsych 1979, M 1972; DPM Leeds 1969. Prev: Med. Dir. Wheatfields Hospice Leeds.

CARD, Timothy Richard 15 Bicester Close, Whitchurch RG28 7HE — MB ChB 1992 Bristol.

CARDALE, John Dowglass (retired) 30 Grove Road, Lydney GL15 5JG Tel: 01594 42580 — MB ChB 1941 Bristol. Prev: Squadron Ldr. RAFVR Med. Br.

CARDASH, Tanya Kate 17 Burnham Court, Brent St., London NW4 2RE — MB BS 1998 Lond.; MB BS Lond 1998.

CARDELL, Brian Southwell (retired) Silver Birches, Warren Close, Cross-in-Hand, Heathfield TN21 0TD Tel: 01435 862904 — MD Lond. 1950, MB BS 1942; MRCS Eng. LRCP Lond. 1942; FRCPath 1965. Prev: Reader in Morbid Anat. King's Coll. Hosp. Med. Sch.

CARDEN, Mr David George 53 Trafalgar Road, Birkdale, Southport PR8 2NL — MB ChB 1971 Liverp.; MChOrth Liverp. 1983; FRCS Ed. 1977; FRCS Eng. 1977. Cons. Orthop. Surg. S.port & Formby HA.

CARDEN, Margaret (retired) 81 The Village, Haxby, York YO32 2JE Tel: 01904 750035 — MB ChB 1950 Leeds; MRCPsych 1975; DPM Eng. 1973. Prev: Clin. Asst. (Child Psychiat.) S.mead HA.

CARDER, Pauline Joanna Dept. Pathology, St.James University Hospital, Beckett St., Leeds LS10 7TF — MB ChB 1986 Ed.; FRCPath; BSc Ed. 1983, MB ChB 1986. Cons. Histopath. St. James'. Univ. Hosp. Leeds.

CARDEW, Martin Philip (retired) Rookley Manor, Niton Road, Rookley, Ventnor PO38 3NR Tel: 01983 721233 — LMSSA 1949 Lond.; DA Eng. 1956. Prev: Assoc. Specialist (Orthop./A & E) Roy. I. of Wight Co. Hosp. Ryde.

CARDEW, Peter Nairn (retired) Rushton Farm House, Rushton, Wareham BH20 6AL Email: petercardew@compuserve.com — MRCS Eng. LRCP Lond. 1942. Prev: Dir. (Audio Visual Communicat.) St. Mary's Hosp. Med. Sch. Lond.

CARDEW, Sarah Melora Earl Mountbatten Hospice, Halberry Lane, Newport PO30 2ER Tel: 01983 522106 Fax: 01983 521429; Rookley Manor, Rookley, Ventnor PO38 3NR Tel: 01983 522106 — MB BS 1975 Lond.; BSc Lond. 1972; DGM RCP Lond. 1986. (Guy's) Sen. Med. Off. (Palliat. Med.) Earl Mt.batten Hospice Newport, I. of Wight. Prev: GP Clin. Asst. (Geriat.) I. of Wight Community Health Care NHS Trust; SHO (A & E) Roy. I. of Wight Co. Hosp. Ryde; Ho. Surg. St. Mary's Hosp. Newport, I. of Wight.

CARDING, Katharine Anne Park Road Medical Practice, 93 Park Road, Wallsend, Newcastle upon Tyne — MB BS 1985 Newc.; MRCGP 1989; DCH RCP Lond. 1988; DRCOG 1988. Socs: MDU; BMA; RCGD.

CARDNO, Alastair George Divisions of Psychological Medicine and Medical Genetics, University of Wales College of Medicine, Heath Park, Cardiff CF14 4XN — MB ChB 1986 Dundee; MMedSc (Clin. Psychiat.) Leeds 1994; MRCPsych 1991.

CARDNO, George Watt Asclepion, Freuchie, Cupar KY15 7ET Tel: 01337 857323 — MB ChB 1951 Aberd.; Dobst RCOG 1953 Lond. (Aberd.) Socs: BMA. Prev: Resid. Med. Off. Childr. Hosp. Sunderland; Resid. Obst. Off. Brit. Hosp. Mothers & Babies Lond.; Ho. Surg. Dulwich Hosp.

CARDNO, Neil Asclepion, Freuchie, Cupar KY15 7ET — MB ChB 1992 Dundee. Specialist Regist. (Anaesth. & IC) Sunderland Roy. Hosp.

CARDOE, Neil (retired) Valley House, The Common, Shotesham All Saints, Norwich NR15 1YD — MB BS Durh. 1944; FRCP Lond. 1974, M 1954; DPhysMed Eng. 1959. Prev: Cons. Rheum. Norf. & Norwich Hosp., Qu. Eliz. Hosp., King's Lynn, & St. Michael's Hosp. Aylsham.

CARDOZO, Professor Linda Dolores 8 Devonshire Place, London W1N 1PB Tel: 020 7935 2357 Fax: 020 7224 2797 Email: lcardozo@compuserve.com; The Sloes, Potter Street Hill, Pinner HA5 3YH Tel: 020 8866 0291 Fax: 020 8866 0129 — MB ChB 1974 Liverp.; MD Liverp. 1979; FRCOG 1991, M 1980. Cons. Gyn. King's Coll. Hosp. Lond.; Prof. Urogyn. King's Coll. Lond.; Pres. Assoc. Chartered Physiotherapist Woms. Health; Edit. Bd. Brit. Jl. Urol.; Edit. Brit. Jl. Obst. & Gyn., Neurourol., Neurodynamcis & Internat. Urogyn. Jl. Socs: (Vice-Pres.) Internat. Urogyn. Assn.; Internat. Continence Soc.; Brit. Menopause. Soc. Counc.. Prev: Clin. Research Fell. (Urodynamics) St. Geo. Hosp. Lond.

CARDWELL, Mary Elizabeth 64 The Chase, Benfleet SS7 3BY Tel: 01268 792503 — MB ChB 1992 Manch. SHO (Anaesth.) Leicester Roy. Infirm. Socs: BMA; Assn. Anaesth. Prev: SHO (A & E) Vict. Hosp. Blackpool; Ho. Off. (Gen. Med.) Stepping Hill Hosp. Stockport; Ho. Off. (Gen. Surg.) Hope Hosp. Salford.

CARDWELL, Michael David 6 Dumpton Gap Road, Broadstairs CT10 1TA Tel: 01843 604169 — BM BS 1978 Nottm.; BA (Hons.) York 1973; BMedSci (Hons.) Nottm. 1976, BM BS 1978; MRCGP 1987. Prev: Regist. (Thoracic Med.) Morriston Hosp. Swansea; Regist. (Gen. Med.) Univ. Hosp. Wales, Cardiff; SHO (Paediat.) Morriston Hosp. Swansea.

CARDY, Gillian Claire (retired) Leaze Cottage, Watson's Court, Melksham SN12 6JX Tel: 01225 703859 — MB BS 1957 Lond.; MRCS Eng. LRCP Lond. 1957; FFFP 1993. Prev: SCMO United Bristol Health Care Trust.

CARE, Ailsa Elizabeth The Health Centre, Spaines Road, Fartown, Huddersfield HD2 2QA Tel: 01484 544318; 72 Huddersfield Road, Brighouse HD6 3RD Tel: 01484 710118 — MB ChB 1989 Leeds; MRCGP 1994.

CARE, Eleanor Ann Church House, Fort Road, Lavernock, Penarth CF64 5UL Tel: 029 2070 0039 — MB BCh 1964 Wales; DGM RCP Lond. 1987. (Cardiff)

CAREN, Christine Anne Woodland Practice, Holmwood Health Centre, Franklin Avenue, Tadley RG26 4ER Tel: 0118 981 4166 Fax: 0118 981 1432; The Stables, Kingsclere House, Kingsclere, Newbury RG20 5SL — BM Soton. 1982; MRCGP 19886; DRCOG 1988; DCH RCP Lond. 1986. GP Princip.; GP Trainer.

CAREW, Mr Robert Ian 34 Leigh Drive, Elsenham, Bishop's Stortford CM22 6BY — MB BS 1988 Lond.; BSc (Anat.) Lond. 1985; FRCS Eng. 1993. Regist. (Orthop.) OldCh. Hosp. Romford Essex. Prev: Regist. (Orthop.) Roy. Nat. Orthop. Hosp. Stanmore & Whipps Cross Hosp. Lond.; SHO Rotat. (Surg.) Whipps Cross Hosp. Lond.

CAREW-MCCOLL, Mr Michael Garford House, 2 Watling St. Road, Fulwood, Preston PR2 8DY — LRCPI & LM, LRSCI & LM 1969; LRCPI & LM, LRCSI & LM 1969; FRCSI 1974. Cons. A & E Roy. Preston Hosp. Socs: BMA. Prev: Sen. Regist. (A & E) Preston Roy. Infirm.; Clin. Asst. Corbett Hosp. Stourbridge; Regist. (Accid.) Kidderminster Gen. Hosp.

CAREY, Adam Henry 101 Honeybrook Row, London SW12 0DL Tel: 020 8675 4433 — BM BCh 1988 Oxf.; MA Camb. 1989, B 1985. Research Regist. (O & G) MRC Train. Fell. (Molecular Biol. & Biochem.) St. Mary's Hosp. Med. Sch. Lond. Prev: SHO (O & G) King's Coll. Hosp. Lond.

CAREY, Albert Stuart (retired) 30 Prestbury Avenue, Marus Bridge, Wigan WN3 6SG Tel: 01942 247750 — MB ChB Leeds 1945; DPH Leeds 1950; DPM Eng. 1965; FRCPsych. 1982, M 1971. Prev: Med. Admin. & Cons. Psychiat. NewCh. Hosp. Culcheth.

***CAREY, Anne-Marie Diane** 20 Bulwer Road, Leicester LE2 3BU — MB ChB 1995 Leic.

CAREY, Audrey (retired) Gooseberry Hall Cottage, Cherry Garden Lane, Nonington, Dover CT15 4HJ Tel: 01304 841623 — MRCS Eng. LRCP Lond. 1942; DPhysMed. Eng. 1955. Prev: Cons. Rheum. & Rehabil. Canterbury & Thanet & SE Kent Health Dists.

CAREY, Beverly Jane 26 Elms Crescent, London SW4 8RA; 101 Honeybrook Road, London SW12 0DL — BM BS 1991 Nottm.

CAREY, Brendan Michael Radiology Department, Cookridge Hospital, Leeds LS16 6QB Tel: 0113 392 4281 Fax: 0113 392 4014 — MB BCh BAO 1979 NUI; FRCR 1986. Cons. Radiol. Leeds Gen. Infirm. & Cookridge Hosp. Leeds.; Hon. Clin. Lect. Univ. Leeds. Prev: Sen. Regist. (Radiol.) Leeds Gen. Infirm. & St. Jas. Hosp. Leeds.

CAREY, Catherine Mary Ursula Heart & Lung Unit, Torbay Hospital, Torquay TQ2 7AA Tel: 01803 654822 Fax: 01803 655163 — MB BS 1979 Lond.; MRCP (UK) 1982; FRCP 1997. (St. Thos.) Cons. (Cardiol.).

CAREY, Daniel Thomas Whiteman's Surgery, Whitefriar's Street, Perth PH1 1PP Tel: 01738 627912 Fax: 01738 643969 — MB BCh 1988 N U Irel; MB BCh N U I 1988. (N U Irel) GP Perth.

CAREY, de Lisle 19 Creek End, Emsworth PO10 7EX — MRCS Eng. LRCP Lond. 1926. (St. Mary's) Prev: Lt. Col. Late IMS.

CAREY, Fiona Mary 8 Nutt's Corner Road, Crumlin BT29 4BW — MB BCh BAO 1990 Belf.; MB BCh Belf. 1990.

CAREY, Francis Anthony Department of Pathology, University Medical School, Teviot Place, Edinburgh EH8 9AG — MB BCh BAO 1985 NUI.

CAREY, Graham Robert 28 Princes Road, Newcastle upon Tyne NE3 5AL — MB ChB 1987 Ed.; MRCGP 1993; DCCH 1994; FRCA 1998. (Edinburgh) Specialsit Regist. Anaesth. Newc. Sch. Socs: Brit. Med. Acupunct. Soc.

CAREY, Gwyneth Ellis (retired) Hengoed Isa, Bontuchel, Ruthin LL15 2DD Tel: 01824 702913 — MB ChB 1948 Liverp.; MFCH/FFCH 1989; MFCM RCP (UK) 1984. Foundat. Mem. Fac. Community Health Soc. Pub. Health; Hon. Mem. Assn. Research Infant & Child Developm. Prev: Sen. Med. Off. Clwyd AHA.

CAREY, Mr John Anthony 19 Point Out Close, Southampton SO16 7LS — MB BCh BAO 1984 NUI; FRCSI 1988.

CAREY, John Malcolm (retired) Copperfields, Ashcombe Lane, Kingston, Lewes BN7 3JZ Tel: 01273 471383 Fax: 01273 471338 Email: johnmcarey@aol.com — MRCS Eng. LRCP Lond. 1961; FRCGP 1982, M 1975; DObst RCOG 1964. Prev: Med. Dir. St. Wilfrid's Hospice E.bourne.

CAREY, John Michael The Surgery, The Street, Holbrook, Ipswich IP9 2PZ Tel: 01473 328263 Fax: 01473 327185 — MB ChB 1978 Sheff.; MRCP (UK) 1983.

CAREY, Martyn Peter Department of Neuropathology, Queen Elizabeth Hospital, Edgbaston, Birmingham B15 2TH Tel: 0121 627 2102 Fax: 0121 627 2101 — MB BS 1978 Lond.; FRCPath 1997, M 1988. Cons. Neuropath. Qu. Eliz. Hosp. Birm.; Hon. Clin. Sen. Lect. Univ. Birm. Socs: Brit. Neuropath. Soc. Path. Soc. of GB and Irel. & Assn of Clin. Pa. Prev: Cons. Neuropath. Midl. Centre for Neurosurg. & Neurol.

CAREY, Michelle Louise 49 St Winifreds Road, Harrogate HG2 8LW — MB BS 1997 Newc.

CAREY, Nicola Frances Stour Surgery, 49 Barrack Road, Christchurch BH23 1PA Tel: 01202 464500 Fax: 01202 464529; Farne House, Armstrong Road, Brockenhurst SO42 7TA Tel: 01590 624043 — MB ChB 1980 Otago; MRCGP 1987; DCH Otago 1983; DFFP (UK) 1997. (Otago) p/t GP Partner. Prev: GP & Clin. Asst. Youth Clinic ToltonRetainer Scheme; GP Partner ChristCh., New Zealand.

CAREY, Mr Patrick Declan Vinrose, Boheravoroon, Thurles, County Tipperary, Republic of Ireland; 35 Highview Road, Ealing, London W13 0HA Tel: 020 8 997 4741 — MB BCh BAO 1982 NUI; MCh 1993; FRCSI 1987. Lect. & Sen. Regist. St. Mary's Hosp. Med. Sch. Lond. Prev: Vis. Lect. Chinese Univ. Hong Kong 1992-1993.

CAREY, Peter Andrew 55 Torbay Road, London NW6 7DU — MB BS 1989 Lond.; MRCP (UK) 1992. Specialist Regist. (Cardiol.), N. W. Thames Region. Prev: Regist. (Gen. Med. & Cardiol.) Milkton Keynes Dist. Gen. Hosp. & John Radcliffe Hosp.

CAREY, Peter Brian Royal Liverpool University Hospital, Prescott St., Liverpool L7 8XP Tel: 0151 706 2000 Fax: 0151 706 5806; 35 Greenbank Road, Liverpool L18 1HG Tel: 0151 733 5943 — MB ChB 1970 Liverp.; FRCP Lond. 1993; MRCP (UK) 1979. Cons. Genitourin. Med. Roy. Liverp. Univ. Hosp.

CAREY, Peter Edward 12 Ashgate Road, Broomhill, Sheffield S10 3BZ — MB ChB 1995 Sheff.

CAREY, Peter John Sunderland Royal Hospital, Kayll Road, Sunderland SR4 7TP Tel: 0191 565 6256 Fax: 0191 569 9007 Email: peter.carey@chs.northy.nhs.uk; 50 Fern Avenue, Jesmond, Newcastle upon Tyne NE2 2QX Tel: 0191 281 3283 — MB BS 1979 Newc.; FRCP Lond. 1995; MRCP (UK) 1982; MRCPath 1988; FRCPath 1997; FRCP Ed. 1998. Cons. Haemat. Sunderland Roy. Hosp. Prev: Lect. (Med. Haemat.) Univ. Newc.

CAREY, Richard John Hamleaze, Bristol Road, Keynsham, Bristol BS31 2AA Tel: 0117 986 2029 — MB ChB 1949 Bristol; MRCS Eng. LRCP Lond. 1948. (Bristol) Prev: Regist. Edgware Gen. Hosp.; JHMO Old Windsor Hosp.; Ho. Phys. Cheltenham Gen. Hosp.

CAREY, Siobhan Aileen 161 Gortgole Road, Portglenone, Ballymena BT44 8AU — MB BCh BAO 1992 Belf.; MB BCh Belf. 1992.

CAREY, Stephen James Crichton Royal Hospital, Dumfries DG1 4TG — MB BCh BAO 1983 Belf.; MRCGP 1994; DMH Belf. 1991; MRCPsych 1997. Specialist Regist. (Psychiat.) Gt.er Glas. Community & Med. Health NHS Trust.

CAREY, William Donald Higginson Coombe House, Bradford Peverell, Dorchester DT2 9SE Tel: 0130 5889 334 — MB BS 1988 Lond.; MA Oxf. 1986, BA 1979; PhD Imperial Coll. 1983. Regist. (Gen. Med.) Char. Cross Hosp. Lond. Prev: SHO (Gen. Med.) St. Marys Hosp. Lond.

CAREY SMITH, Richard Lovel 88C Walterton Road, London W9 3PQ — MB BS 1996 Lond.

CARGILL, Adam Francis 54 Quentin Road, London SE13 5DF; 1 Tidpr Lawns, Leeds LS8 2JR Tel: 0113 232 3588 — MB BS 1963 Lond.; MRCP (U.K.) 1970; FRCR 1980; DMRD Eng. 1977. (St. Thos.) Prev: Cons. Radiol. Dartford & Gravesham Health Dist.

CARGILL, Mr Alexander O'Rourke East Midland Nuffield Hospital, Rykneld Road, Derby DE23 7SN Tel: 01332 843150 — MB ChB Ed. 1965; FRCS Ed. 1970. Cons. Surg. (Orthop.) Derbysh. AHA. Socs: Brit. Orthop. Assn.; Brit. Assn. Surg. of the knee; Soc. of Expert Witnesses. Prev: Sen. Regist. (Orthop.) Harlow Wood Orthop. Hosp. Mansfield & Nottm.; Gen. Hosp.

CARGILL, Allan Frederick Liscard Group Practice, Croxteth Avenue, Liscard, Wallasey CH44 5UL Tel: 0151 638 4764 Fax: 0151637 0579; 17 Marlowe Road, Wallasey CH44 3BZ Tel: 0151 638 6174 — MB ChB 1966 Leeds.

CARGILL, Catherine Lucy Blackwater Medical Centre, Princes Road, Maldon CM9 7DS Tel: 01621 854204 Fax: 01621 850246; 6 Lodge Road, Maldon CM9 6HW Tel: 01621 840050 — MB ChB 1987 Bristol; MA Oxon. 1986; DRCOG 1991. (Bristol) Socs: Roy. Soc. Med.; BMA.

CARGILL, Jacqueline Silvia (retired) 22 St Germains, Bearsden, Glasgow G61 2RS Tel: 0141 942 2164 — MB ChB 1965 Glas.; FRCPath 1987, M 1974. Prev: Cons. Microbiol. Vict. Hosp. Blackpool.

CARGILL, Jane Makeney Lodge, Milford, Derby DE56 0RS — MB BS 1968 Lond.

CARGILL, Janice Munro Milltown Surgery, Milltown, Applecross, Strathcarron IV54 8LS Tel: 01520 744252/744235 Fax: 01520 744344; Carn-geal, Camusterrach, Applecross, Strathcarron IV54 8LU Tel: 01520 744227 — MB ChB 1973 Dundee; MRCP (UK) 1976.

CARGILL, Robert Iain Department of Cardiology, Aberdeen Royal Infirmary, Foresterhill, Aberdeen AB25 2ZN Tel: 01224 681818 Fax: 01224 840692 Email: r.i.cargill@abdn.ac.uk; Ballavane, Whitecairns, Aberdeen AB23 8XA Tel: 01651 862164 — MB ChB 1989 Dundee; MRCP (UK) 1992. Specialist Regist. (Cardiol.) Aberd. Roy. Infirm. Prev: Research Fell. (Clin. Pharmacol.) Univ. Dundee & Ninewells Hosp. & Med. Sch. Dundee.

CARGILL, Victoria Helen Tel: 01786 451375; 26 Beechwood, Linlithgow EH49 6SF Email: cargill@btinternet.com — MB ChB 1992 Birm.; DCH RCP Lond. 1995; DFFP 1995; DRCOG 1994; JCTGP Certificate 1998. (Birm.) GP Practitioner. Prev: GP Princip. (PT), Allan Pk., Stirling; GP Regist., W. Calder, W. Lothian.

CARGIN, James Anthony 1 Mourneview Park, Dromore BT25 1QL — MB BCh BAO 1985 Belf.

CARGO, Patricia Elizabeth Adam Avenue Medical Centre, 1 Adam Avenue, Airdrie ML6 6DN Tel: 01236 763581 Fax: 01236 750507; 14 Cleveden Gardens, Kelvinside, Glasgow G12 0PT — MB ChB 1982 Aberd.; Cert. Family Plann. JCC 1985; DRCOG 1985.

CARHART, Paul Adrian Seascale Health Centre, Gosforth Road, Seascale CA20 1PN Tel: 019467 28101 Fax: 019467 27895; Willow Bank, 7 Hunter Rise, Beckermet CA21 2YP — MB ChB 1989 Manch.; MRCGP 1994; DRCOG 1992. (Manch.)

CARL, Ian Lee 109 Clare Road, Waringstown, Craigavon BT66 7SB — MB BCh BAO 1997 Belf.

CARLAW, Nicolette Ann (retired) 2a Victoria St, Kirriemuir DD8 5DH Tel: 01575 573795 — MB ChB 1959 Glas.; MRCGP 1968. Prev: GP Renfrew.

CARLAW, William Greig Carlaw and Partners, The Health Centre, Mid Street, Bathgate EH48 2QS Tel: 01506 635837 Fax: 01506 636263; 30 Torphin Bank, Colinton, Edinburgh EH13 0PH Tel: 0131 441 6782 — MB ChB 1976 Glas.

CARLE, David Leslie (retired) 63 Keswick Road, Cringleford, Norwich NR4 6UQ Tel: 01603 456473 — MB BS 1964 Lond.; MRCS Eng. LRCP Lond. 1964; DObst RCOG 1966.

CARLE, Mr George Coll Medical Practice, Aringour, Isle of Coll PA78 65Y Tel: 01879 230326 Fax: 01879 230418; Doctor's House, Avinagour, Isle of Coll PA78 6SY Tel: 01879 230326 Fax: 01879 230418 — MB ChB 1976 Aberd.; FRCS Ed. 1981. (Aberd.) Princip. Coll. Med. Pract. Prev: Partner, Trentview Med. Pract.; Sen. Regist. (Psychiat.) St. Clements Hosp. Ipswich; Trainee GP Walton-on-The-Naze VTS.

CARLESS, Andrew Gordon Maxwell (retired) Stroud Lodge, New North Road, Exeter EX4 4AG Tel: 01392 78045 — LMSSA 1967 Lond.; MB Camb. 1968, BChir 1967; DObst RCOG 1970. JP.

CARLESS, Carol Anne Carless & Bartholomew, Libra House, Fore St., Sidmouth EX10 8AJ Tel: 01395 577337 Fax: 01395 577545; Stroud Lodge, New North Road, Exeter EX4 4AG Tel: 01392 78045 — MB ChB Sheff. 1968; DO RCS Eng. 1984. (Sheff.) Partner in Private Optical Pract.

CARLESS, Jeremy John Surgery House, Hughenden Valley, High Wycombe Tel: 0124 024 3275 — MB BS 1962 Lond.

CARLETON, Henry Cowburn Savage 3 Somerset Square, London W14 8EE — MB BS 1997 Lond.; BSc (Hons) UCL 1996. (St Bartholomews)

CARLETON, Peter Joseph Tel: 01482 441298 — BM BCh 1964 Oxf.; MA Oxf. 1964; FRCS Eng. 1970; FRCS Ed. 1969. (Lond. Hosp.) Locum Cons. Surg., ScarBoro. Hosp., N. Yorks. Socs: Assn. Surg.; Brit. Assn. Surgic. Oncol.; Yorks. BrE. Cancer Gp. Prev: Cons. Gen. Surg. Hull Roy. Infirm. & W.wood Hosp. Beverley; Sen. Regist. Leeds Gp. Hosp.; Surg. Regist. Lond. Hosp. & St. Jas. Hosp. Balham.

CARLETON, Rebecca Lucy 167 Forest Avenue, Skene AB5 4UU — MB ChB 1987 Glas.; DRCOG 1993. SHO Rotat. (Psychiat.) Woodilee & Stobhill Hosps. Glas. Prev: Trainee GP/SHO Alexandria; SHO Rotat. (Surg.) W.. Infirm. Glas.; Ho. Off. (Med. & Surg.) Gartnavel Gen. Hosp. Glas.

CARLEY, Joanne Mary Mental Health Unit, Chesterfield & North Derbys Royal Hospital, Calow, Chesterfield S44 5BL Tel: 01246 277271 — MB ChB 1979 Liverp.; MRCPsych. 1983; Dip. Psychother. Liverp. 1987. Cons. Psychiat. N. Derbysh. HA.

CARLEY, Richard Harry Department of Anaesthetics, The Princess Royal Hospital, Telford TF1 6TF — MB BS 1973 Lond.; MRCS Eng. LRCP Lond. 1973; FFA RCS Eng. 1983; DRCOG 1976. (Charing Cross Hospital) Cons. Anaesth. P.ss Roy. Hosp. Telford.

CARLEY, Simon David c/o Manchester Royal Infirmary, Oxford Road, Manchester M13 9WL Tel: 0161 276 1234; Flat 15, Exeter Court, 376 Wilmslow Road, Manchester M20 3NA Tel: 0161 448 0287 — MB ChB 1992 Manch. SHO Rotat. (Gen. Surg.) Manch. Prev: SHO (Orthop. & A & E) Manch. Roy. Infirm.; SHO (Anat.) Sheff. Univ.

CARLILE, Aileen Kennedy Whitley Road Health Centre, Whitley Road, Whitley Bay NE26 2ND Tel: 0191 253 1113 — MB ChB 1984 Glas.; MRCGP 1988; DRCOG 1987. Prev: GP SIdcup.

CARLILE, David 38 Littleton Street, Glasgow G23 5PA — MB ChB 1982 Glas.; DA (UK) 1985. Med. Serv. Off. Al Awda Project Hosp. Ahmadi, Kuwait. Prev: Regist. (Anaesth.) Good Hope Hosp. Sutton Coldfield.

CARLILE, Dorothy (retired) 17 Greenoak Drive, Sale M33 3QA Tel: 0161 962 5717 — MB ChB 1958 Sheff.; DPH Manch. 1962. Prev: Asst. MOH & Asst. Sch. Med. Off. Salford.

CARLILE, Elizabeth (retired) 120A Mount View Road, Sheffield S8 8PL — MB ChB 1945 Bristol. Prev: Clin. Asst. Dept. Rheum. & Rehabil. Leicester Roy. Infirm.

CARLILE, Jane Louisa The Croft, Hillside Road, Rothbury, Morpeth NE65 7YF Tel: 01669 621639 — MB BS 1991 Newc.; MRC.Psych. Jan. 1999. Clin. Asst. (Adult Psychiat.) The Grange Newc. u. Tyne; Staff grade (Subst. misuse); CSMT, Blyth.

CARLILE, Robert Mark Tynan Surgery, 15 Dartan Ree, Tynan, Armagh BT60 4QT Tel: 028 3756 8214 Fax: 028 3756 8837 — MB BCh BAO 1986 Belf.; MRCGP 1991.

CARLILE, William Wilson Pitsmoor Surgery, 151 Burngreave Road, Sheffield S3 9DL Tel: 0114 272 8228; 8 Woodvale Road, Sheffield S10 3EX — MB BS 1980 Lond.; MRCGP 1986; DRCOG 1987.

CARLIN, Daniel Donald The Medical Centre, 3 Edinburgh Road, Perth PH2 8AT — MB ChB 1985 Dundee.

CARLIN, Elizabeth Marie 185 West Street, Hoyland, Barnsley S74 9DX — MB ChB 1984 Sheff.

CARLIN, Geoffrey Francis Doctors Surgery, East High Street, Airdrie ML6 6LF Tel: 01236 764722 Fax: 01236 750444; 229 Nilston Road, Bannock, Bonnybridge FK4 1UF — MB ChB 1978 Dundee; Dip. Community Health Studies Glas. 1988; DRCOG 1983. GP.

CARLIN, Helen Whyte 14 Cranbrooks, Wheaton Aston, Stafford ST19 9PZ — LRCP LRCS 1944 Ed.; LRCP LRCS Ed. LRFPS Glas. 1944.

CARLIN, Jill 112 Greenleach Lane, Worsley, Manchester M28 2TY Tel: 0161 727 8795 Email: carlins@compuserve.com — MB ChB 1984 Manch.; MRCP (UK) 1988; FRCR 1997. Regist. (Radiol.) NW RHA. Prev: SHO (Med.) N. Manch. Gen. Hosp. & Blackburn Roy. Infirm.

CARLIN, Norma Elizabeth Furlong Medical Centre, Furlong Road, Tunstall, Stoke-on-Trent ST6 5UD Tel: 01782 577388 — MB BCh 1977 Wales; MRCGP 1981.

CARLIN, Paul Gerard Mary Portstewart Medical Centre, Mill Road, Portstewart BT55 7PQ Tel: 028 7083 2600 Fax: 028 7083 6871; 24 Swilly Road, Portstewart BT55 7DJ Tel: 0126583 4374 — MB BCh BAO 1982 Belf.; MB BCh Belf. 1982; MRCGP 1986; DCH Dub. 1985.

CARLIN, Mr William Vere North Staffs Royal Infirmary, Stoke-on-Trent — MB BCh 1977 Wales; FRCS Eng. 1982. Cons. ENT Surg. N. Staffs. Roy. Infirm.

CARLING, Alison Bisset Royal Gwent Hospital, Cardiff Road, Newport NP20 2UB Tel: 01633 234167 Fax: 01633 234168; Email: alison.carling@ntlworld.com — MB ChB 1977 Aberd.; FFA RCS 1982 Eng. Cons. Anaesth. Roy. Gwent Hosp. Newport, Gwent. Prev: Sen. Regist. (Anaesth.) Univ. Hosp. Wales, Cardiff.

CARLING, David 25 Throstle Walk, Slyne, Lancaster LA2 6LD — MB ChB 1956 Birm.; DTM & H Liverp. 1957. (Birm.) Prev: Chief Med. Off. Sudan United Miss.; Med. Supt. Vom Christian Hosp., Nigeria.

CARLING, John Russell (retired) 9 East Hill Close, Fareham PO16 8SE Tel: 01329 280123 — LMSSA 1958 Lond. Prev: SHO Grimsby Matern. Hosp.

CARLING, William Hugh (retired) 3 Coach Hill, Titchfield, Fareham PO14 4EE Tel: 01329 841745 — MB BChir 1954 Camb. Prev: Med. Dir. Fareham Cardiac Rehabil. Unit.

CARLISH, Sidney 8 Moor Green Lane, Moseley, Birmingham B13 8ND Tel: 0121 449 0544 — MB ChB 1957 Birm.; MRCPsych 1971; DPM Eng. 1963. Socs: Brit. Psychoanal Soc.; Roy. Coll. Psychiat.; BMA. Prev: Cons. Psychotherap. Uffculme Clinic Birm.; Med. Asst. Cassel Hosp. Richmond; Regist. Maudsley Hosp. Lond. & Univ. Coll. Hosp. Lond.

CARLISLE, Andrew John Botley Health Care Centre, Mortimer Road, Botley, Southampton SO32 2UG Tel: 01489 782021 Fax: 01489 780699 — MB BS 1985 Newc.; MRCGP 1989. GP Soton.

CARLISLE, Hazel Ruth 18 Oakfield Avenue, Firswood, Manchester M16 0HS — MB BS 1994 Newc.

CARLISLE, Heather Audrey Isobel 18 Grange Road, Ballymena BT42 2DS Tel: 01266 656314 Email: 101363.616@compuserve.com — MB BCh BAO 1989 Belf.; MRCGP 1996; DRCOG 1994; DCH Dub. 1995; DGM RCP Lond. 1993. Trainee GP Darvel, Ayrsh.

CARLISLE, John Bernard 1 Devizes Road, Upavon, Pewsey SN9 6ED — MB ChB 1992 Bristol.

CARLISLE, Joyce Mallalieu (Surgery), 32 Foxley Lane, Purley CR8 3EE Tel: 020 8660 1304 Fax: 020 8660 0721; Kilderkin, Coulsdon Lane, Chipstead, Coulsdon, Croydon CR5 3QH Tel: 01737 553557 — MB ChB Ed. 1964; DObst RCOG 1965. (Ed.)

CARLISLE, Raymond 23 Haven Green, Ealing Broadway, London W5 2UP Tel: 020 8566 7666; 30 Creffield Road, Ealing Common, London W5 3RP Tel: 020 8993 5399 — MB BChir 1957 Camb.;

MA Camb. 1967, BA (Nat. Sci.) 1950, MD 1967; FRCP Lond. 1975, M 1961; DTM & H RCP Lond. 1962. Med. Cons. Haven Green Clinic Ealing. Prev: Sen. Cardiol. Cons. Qatif Centr. Hosp., Saudi Arabia; Prof. Med. Univ. Zambia Sch. Med. Lusaka, Zambia; Hon. Cons. Cardiol. N.wick Pk. Hosp. Harrow.

CARLISLE, Robert Paul 126 Hillhall Road, Lisburn BT27 5JA — MB BCh BAO 1997 Belf.

CARLISLE, Robin Dawes Roundwood Surgery, Wood Street, Mansfield NG18 1QQ Tel: 01623 648880 Fax: 01623 631761; 3 Johnson Drive, Berry Hill Lane, Mansfield NG18 4BB Tel: 01623 659029 — BSc Lond. 1981, MB BS 1984; MRCGP 1988; DCH RCP Lond. 1988; DRCOG 1987.

CARLISLE, Robin James Thomas 65 Moss Road, Ballinmaskeagh, Banbridge BT32 3NZ — MB BCh BAO 1977 Belf.; FFA RCSI 1981. Cons. (Anaesth.) Daisy Hill Hosp. Newry.

CARLISLE, Sylvia Anne Tel: 0117 971 1211 — MB ChB 1972 Otago; DA Eng. 1979; Dip. Obst. Auckland 1974. (Otago) Prev: Regist. (Anaesth.) Bristol. Roy. Infirm.; SHO (Anaesth.) Weymouth & Dist. Hosp.

CARLISLE, Thomas Anthony The Surgery, 162 Long St., Dordon, Tamworth B78 1QA; Bridge Farm Cottage, Spon Lane, Grendon, Atherstone CV9 3DU Tel: 01827 715354 — MRCS Eng. LRCP Lond. 1954. (Manch.) Prev: Sen. Resid. Med. Off. Stockport Infirm.; Ho. Surg. Withington Hosp. Manch.; Ho. Off. (O & G) Hope Hosp. Salford.

CARLOS, Adrian Joseph 6 Golders Gardens, London NW11 9BT — MB ChB 1996 Manch.

CARLSON, Mr Gordon Lawrence 62 Polefield Road, Prestwich, Manchester M25 2QW; 42 Poppythorn Lane, Prestwich, Manchester M25 3BY — MD 1993 Manch.; BSc Manch. 1982, MD 1993, MB ChB 1985; FRCS Eng. 1989.

CARLSON, Jonathan Neil Rutherford Tothill Surgery, 10 Tothill Avenue, Plymouth PL4 8PH Tel: 01752 664424 — MB BS 1982 Lond.

CARLSON, Kevin Johan Vernon (retired) Path Cottage, Hickling, Norwich NR12 0YJ Tel: 01692 598360 — MB ChB 1938 Bristol; MRCGP 1960.

CARLSON, Norman Rutherford (retired) 92 Castle Drive, Pevensey Bay, Pevensey BN24 6LA Tel: 01323 765500 Email: norman.carlson@care4free.net — MB BS Lond. 1942; MRCS Eng. LRCP Lond. 1942.

CARLSON, Rudolf Gunnar Carl Gustav (retired) 7 English Road, Old Catton, Norwich NR6 7RL Tel: 01603 427458 — MB ChB 1932 Bristol; MB ChB (Gold Medal) Bristol 1932; DObst RCOG 1950; MMSA 1951. Prev: Obstetr. Drayton Hall Matern. Hosp.

***CARLSSON, Rachel Linda** Frenchay Hospital, Beckspool Rd, Bristol BS16 1LE Tel: 0117 970 1212; 11 Grange Road, Southbourne, Bournemouth BH6 3NY Tel: 01202 251127 — MB ChB 1998 Bristol.

CARLTON, Doreen Ruth 9 Palmer Close, Kingston Hill, Stafford ST16 3RQ — MB BS Lond. 1966; FRCP Lond. 1989; MRCP (UK) 1973; MRCS Eng. LRCP Lond. 1966; FRCPCH 1997; DCH Eng. 1969; DObst RCOG 1968. (Roy. Free) Cons. Paediat. Stafford . Gen. Hosp.

CARLTON, Elizabeth Ann 72 Moor Drive, Liverpool L23 2UR — MB BS 1994 Newc. GP Regist., Camberley Surrey. Prev: SHO Psychiat.; SHO O & G; SHO Paediat.

CARLTON, John Hope (retired) The Old Rectory, Clenchwarton, King's Lynn PE34 4AA Tel: 01553 828475 — MRCS Eng. LRCP Lond. 1964. Prev: Clin. Asst. (Dermatol.) Qu. Eliz. Hosp. King's Lynn.

CARLTON, Olivia Hazel London Transport Occupational Health, Griffith House, 280 Old Marylebone Road, London NW1 5RJ Tel: 020 7918 1790 Fax: 020 7918 1146; 11 Fielding Street, London SE17 3HE Tel: 020 7701 7043 — MB BS 1983 Lond.; MFOM RCP Lond. 1994, AFOM 1991; DRCOG 1986. Head of LT Occupat. Health; Sen. Med. Adviser, Occupat. Health Policy, Dept. of Health. Socs: Soc. Occupat. Med. Prev: Med. Off. LTMS; Trainee GP Rotat. Kingston Hosp. VTS.

CARLUKE, Ian 76 Deanburn, Penicuik EH26 0HY — MB ChB 1990 Aberd.

CARLYLE, Abdul Kareem 21 Abbotsgrange Road, Grangemouth FK3 9JD — MB ChB 1996 Glas.

CARLYLE, Alison Virginia 1R 9 Roxburgh Street, Hillhead, Glasgow G12 9BH — MB ChB 1996 Glas.

CARLYLE, Barbara Elaine Pitteuchar Health Centre, Glamis Centre, Glenrothes KY7 4RH — MB BS 1979 Newc.; MRCGP 1983; DRCOG 1982. p/t GP in Glenrothes, Fife. Prev: GP E.er Hse. Glas.

CARLYLE, David Leslie Pitteuchar Health Centre, Glamis Centre, Glenrothes KY7 4RH Tel: 01592 775162 Fax: 01592 630477; Shippen, Hillfoot Farm, Dollar FK14 7PL Tel: 01259 743895 — MB BS 1979 Newc.; MRCP (UK) 1981; MRCGP 1986; DRCOG 1986.

CARLYLE, David Newton Old Catton Surgery, 55 Lodge Lane, Norwich NR6 7HQ Tel: 01603 423341 Fax: 01603 486445; 33 Waverley Road, Norwich NR4 6SQ — MB ChB 1973 Glas.; MRCGP 1979; DRCOG 1975. Prev: SHO (Gen. Med.) Vict. Infirm Glas.

CARLYLE, Joseph Edward (retired) 49 Hawthorn Crescent, Garnieland, Erskine PA8 7BY Tel: 0141 812 3871 — MB ChB 1947 Glas.

CARLYLE, Roy Frederick Northcote House Surgery, Northcote House, 8 Broad Leas, Huntingdon PE27 5PT Tel: 01480 461873 Fax: 01480 460612 — MB BS 1971 Lond.; PhD (Pharmacol.) Lond. 1964, BSc (Physiol. 1st cl.; Hons) 1961, MB BS 1971. Socs: Brit. Pharmacol. Soc. & Physiol. Soc. Prev: Dep. Supt. Physiol. Laborat. (ANTE) Gosport; Lect. in Pharmacol. King's Coll. Lond.

CARLYON, Angela Mary Elizabeth Tamsin Woodbridge Hill Surgery, 1 Deerbarn Road, Guildford GU2 8YB Tel: 01483 562230 Fax: 01483 452442 — MB BS 1983 Lond.; MRCGP 1987; DRCOG 1989; DCH RCP Lond. 1986. (Roy. Free Hosp. Sch. Med.) Prev: CMO Community Child Health Sheff.; SHO (O & G) Rotherham Dist. Gen. Hosp.; Trainee GP Worksop.

CARLYON, Lester Ambrose Avenue Surgery, 76 Ambrose Avenue, Colchester CO3 4LN Tel: 01206 549444 Fax: 01206 369910; 4 Inglis Road, Colchester CO3 3HU Tel: 01206 577738 — MB BS 1965 Newc.

CARMALT, Martin Hugh Blanchard University Hospital Birmingham NHS Trust, Selly Oak Hospital, Birmingham B29 6JD Tel: 0121 627 1627 Fax: 0121 627 8292 — BChir 1962 Camb.; MB Camb. 1963; BA Camb. 1959, MA 1963; MD (Hons) Birm. 1970; FRCP Lond. 1980, M 1965. (Camb. & Birm.) Cons. Phys. Selly Oak Hosp. Univ. Hosp. Birm. NHS Trust; Sen. Clin. Lect. (Med.) Birm. Univ.; Cons. Phys., Roy. orthapaedic Trust NHS Birm. Prev: Sheldon Clin. Research Fell. & Sen. Regist. Dept. of Med. & Wolfson Research Laborat. Qu. Eliz. Hosp. Birm.; Resid. Med. Off. Warneford Hosp. Leamington Spa; Ho. Off. Birm. Gen. Hosp.

CARMAN, David Hugh The Surgery, Miller Way, Wainscott, Rochester ME2 4LP Tel: 01634 717450 — MB BS 1976 Lond.; MRCS Eng. LRCP Lond. 1976; MRCGP 1980; DRCOG 1980.

CARMAN, Suzannah Jill Woodlands, 46A Silchester Road, Pamber Heath, Basingstoke RG26 3EF — MB BS 1993 Lond.

CARMI, Michael Albert Murad Baruch White Lodge Medical Practice, 68 Silver Street, Enfield EN1 3EW Tel: 020 8363 4156 Fax: 020 8364 6295; 7 Compton Terrace, Hoppers Road, London N21 3NR Tel: 020 8882 0960 Email: mikecarmi@aol.com — MB ChB 1967 Manch.; FRCGP 1984, M 1975; DObst RCOG 1971. Assoc. Dean Postgrad. Med. in Gen. Pract. Med. & Dent. Educat. N. Thames E.; Vis. Prof. Primary Health Care; Hon. Sen. Lect. Roy. Free Univ. Coll. Prev: Course Organiser N. Middlx. & Chase Farm Hosps. VTS; Sen. Lect. (Gen. Pract.) Roy. Free Hosp. Sch. Med. Lond.

CARMICHAEL, Alastair Ross (retired) 96 Potters Lane, Send, Woking GU23 7AL — MRCS Eng. LRCP Lond. 1952. Prev: GP Woking.

CARMICHAEL, Andrew James The James Cook University Hospital, Marton Road, Middlesbrough TS4 3BW Tel: 01642 854721 Fax: 01642 854763 Email: andrew.carmichael@email.stahnhst.norythy.nhs.uk; Glenside, 76 High St, Great Broughton, Middlesbrough TS9 7EG — MB BS 1982 Newc.; MRCP (UK) 1986; FRCP (Lond.) 1998. Cons. Dermat. The James Cook Univ. Hosp. Middlesbrough. Socs: Ordinary Mem. N. Eng. Dermatol. Soc.; Ordinary Mem. Brit. Soc. Paedriatric Dermatol.; Ordinary Mem. Brit. Assn. Dermatol. Prev: Sen. Regist. (Dermat.) Univ. Hosp. Wales Cardiff; Regist. (Dermat.) Skin Hosp. Birm.

CARMICHAEL, Andrew James Department of Medicine (Level 5), Addenbrooke's Hospital, Cambridge CB2 2QQ Tel: 01223 336862; 2 Sycamore Close, Cambridge CB1 8PG — MB BS 1984 Lond.; PhD Camb. 1993; MA Oxf. 1985; MRCP (UK) 1987. MRC Train. Fell. & Clin. Scientist Dept. Med. Addenbrooke's Hosp. Camb.

CARMICHAEL, Catherine Mary The Old Rectory, Norton Road, Snitterby, Gainsborough DN21 4TZ — MB ChB 1983 Sheff.

CARMICHAEL, David John Scott Southend Hospital, Prittewell Chase, Westcliff on Sea SS0 0RY Tel: 01702 435555 Fax: 01702 221259; Email: cobbfamily@easynet.co.uk — MB BS 1973 Lond.; FRCP Lond. 1994; MRCP (UK) 1976. Cons. Phys. & Nephrol. S.end Hosp. Prev: Sen. Regist. St. Mary's Hosp. Lond.; Regist. Addenbrooke's Hosp. Camb.

CARMICHAEL, David Neil 10 Cabot Close, Old Hall, Warrington WA5 9QQ — MB ChB 1986 Liverp.; MRCPI 1991. Research Fell. (Diabetes) Dept. Postgrad. Med. Univ. Keele; Hon. Regist. N. Staffs. Roy. Infirm. Prev: Regist. (Gen. Med.) Halton Gen. Hosp. Runcorn; SHO Walton & Fazakerley Hosps. & BRd.green Cardiac Unit Liverp.

CARMICHAEL, Deborah Jane 2 Parklands Gate, Bramhope, Leeds LS16 9AG Tel: 0113 284 2663 — MB BS 1970 Lond.; MRCS Eng. LRCP Lond. 1970; MRCOphth 1989; DO Eng. 1982. (Guy's) Assoc. Specialist (Ophth.) Leeds Gen. Infirm.; Assoc. Specialist (Community Paediat. Ophth.) Leeds Community & Ment. Health Teching Trust. Prev: Clin. Asst. (Ophth.) Leeds Gen. Infirm.; Clin. Med. Off. (Ophth.) Leeds Community & Ment. Health Teachg. Trust; Asst. (Ophth.) Ch. Miss. Soc. Mvumi Hosp., Tanzania.

CARMICHAEL, Donald Stewart Ridgeway House, Ridgeway, Colyton EX24 6RP — MB 1956 Camb.; BChir 1955. (Guy's) Cons. Path. Haemat. Harlow Health Dist. Prev: Sen. Regist. (Clin. Path.) Lond. Hosp.; Regist. (Haemat.) Guy's Hosp. Lond.

CARMICHAEL, Eleanor Joan (retired) West Lea, Hillside W., Rothbury, Morpeth NE65 7YW Tel: 01669 620570 — MB BS Durh. 1949; FRCGP 1972. Prev: GP Newc.

CARMICHAEL, George Laurin Murray Pain Clinic, Department of Clinical Neurosciences, Western General Hospital, Crewe Road, Edinburgh EH4 2XU Tel: 0131 537 1659 Fax: 0131 537 2179; 38 Liberton Brae, Edinburgh EH16 6AF Tel: 0131 664 5265 Email: murray_carmichael@compuserve.com — MB ChB 1965 Ed.; FFA RCS Eng. 1974; DA Eng. 1970. (Ed.) Cons. Anaesth. (Clin. Neurosci.) W.. Gen. Hosp. Edin. Socs: Assn. Anaesths. & BMA; Pain Soc. Prev: Sen. Regist. (Anaesth.) Edin. Roy. Infirm.; Squadron Ldr. RAF Med. Br.; Anaesth. Brit. Red Cross Surg. Team Cambodia.

CARMICHAEL, Hugh Alisdair Vale of Leven Hospital, Alexandria G83 0UA Tel: 01389 754121; 20 Collylinn Road, Bearsden, Glasgow G61 4PN — MB ChB 1970 Glas.; FRCP Glas. 1988; MRCP (UK) 1973. (GlaSGOW) Cons. Phys. Vale of Leven Hosp. Alexandria. Prev: Regist. Glas. Roy. Infirm.; Sen. Regist. Glas. W.. Infirm. & Gartnavel Gen. Hosp. Glas.

CARMICHAEL, Iain Alexander Castle Douglas Medical Group, Castle Douglas Health Centre, Academy Sreett, Castle Douglas DG7 1EE Tel: 01556 503888 Fax: 01556 504302; Health Centre, Academy St, Castle Douglas DG7 1EE — MB ChB 1967 Glas.; MRCP (U.K.) 1973. (Glas.) Socs: BMA. Prev: SHO (Gen. Med.) Stobhill Hosp. Glas.; Regist. (Gen. Med.) & Regist. (Haemat.) Glas. Roy. Infirm.

CARMICHAEL, Ian McClelland, Col. late RAMC Retd. Lamberts, Wilsford, Pewsey SN9 6HB — MRCS Eng. LRCP Lond. 1944; DMRD Eng. 1954.

CARMICHAEL, Ian William Douglas 8 Lydgate Walk, Westbury Park, Newcastle ST5 4LT Tel: 01782 620835 — MB ChB 1987 Dundee; FRCS Ed. 1994. Specialist Regist. Rotat. (Orthop.) Birm.

CARMICHAEL, Professor James CRC Department of Clinical Oncology, City Hospital, Nottingham NG5 1PB Tel: 0115 962 7927 Fax: 0115 962 7923; 11 Cherrytree Lane, Edwalton, Nottingham NG12 4AL — MB ChB 1975 Ed.; MD Ed. 1987; MRCP (UK) 1979. CRC Prof. Clin. Oncol. & Hon. Cons. Nottm. City Hosp.; Prof. Univ. Nottm. Prev: ICRF Sen. Lect. & Hon. Cons. Clin. Oncol. Ch.ill Hosp. Oxf.; Lect. (Clin. Oncol.) Newc. Gen. Hosp.; Research Fell. Nat. Cancer Inst. Naval Med. Radiat. Oncol. Br. Bethesda Maryland, USA.

CARMICHAEL, James Charles Gordon (retired) 32 Stoops Road, Bessacarr, Doncaster DN4 7ER Tel: 01302 55815 — MRCS Eng. LRCP Lond. 1963; FFA RCS Eng. 1970; DA Eng. 1968; DTM & H Eng. 1965. Cons. Anaesth. Doncaster Roy. Infirm.

CARMICHAEL, James Horsfall Elliott (retired) 2 Woolton Hill Road, Liverpool L25 6HX Tel: 0151 428 3326 — MB ChB 1945 Liverp.; MD Liverp. 1953; FRCR 1975; DMRD Eng. 1951. Prev: Cons. Radiol. BRd.green Hosp. Liverp.

CARMICHAEL, James Richard Glebe Farm, Bracebridge Heath, Lincoln LN4 2HZ — BM BS 1997 Nottm.

CARMICHAEL, Jean 35 Wilson Gardens, Newcastle upon Tyne NE3 4JA Tel: 0191 285 4211 — MB BS 1950 Durh. (Newc.)

CARMICHAEL, Jean Ogilvie Ross (retired) 20 Woburn Court, Stanmore Road, Richmond TW9 2DD — MB ChB 1949 Liverp.; DPH Liverp. 1959.

CARMICHAEL, Jenny 2 Sycamore Close, Cambridge CB1 8PG — MB ChB 1994 Leic.; MRCP (UK) 1997. Action Research Train. Fell. Dept. Med. Genetics Camb.

CARMICHAEL, Jill 5 Chestnut Avenue, Killearn, Glasgow G63 9SJ — MB ChB 1985 Aberd.; MRCGP 1989; DCCH RCP Ed. 1990; DCH RCPS Lond. 1990; DRCOG 1988. Staff Grade Paediat. Yorkshill NHS Trust.

CARMICHAEL, Paul Department of Renal Medicine, Kent & Canterbuy Hospital, Ethelbert Road, Canterbury CT1 3NG Tel: 01227 766877 ext 4509 Fax: 01227 783073; 19 Water Meadows, Marlow Meadows, Fordwich, Canterbury CT2 0BF — MB ChB 1985 Ed.; PhD Lond. (Immunol.) 1995; BSc (Med. Sci.) Ed. 1984; MRCP (UK) 1989. Cons. (Nephrol.) Kent & Canterbury Hosp. Socs: Roy. Coll. Phys.; Amer. Soc. Nephrol.; Eur. Dialysis & Transpl. Assn. Prev: Sen. Regist. (Nephrol.) St. Jas. Hosp. Leeds; Regist. (Med. & Renal) Ealing & Hammersmith Hosp. Lond.; MRC Train. Fell. RPMS Hammersmith Hosp. Lond.

CARMICHAEL, Robert John, CBE, Surg. Capt. RN Retd. (retired) Netherton, 25 Catisfield Lane, Fareham PO15 5NW Tel: 01329 843528 Email: carmichaelbob@hotmail — MB BS 1956 Lond.; MSc (Radiat. Biol.) Lond. 1969, MB BS 1956; MFOM RCP Lond. 1980. Prev: Cons. Occupat. Med. (Radiat. & Submarine Med.) & Head of Defence Radiol. Protec. Serv. Inst. Naval Med. Alverstoke.

CARMICHAEL, Robin Donald Gordon Wakefield Hospice, Aberford Road, Wakefield WF1 4TS Tel: 01924 387260 Fax: 01924 362769; 2 Parklands Gate, Bramhope, Leeds LS16 9AG Tel: 0113 284 2663 — MB BS 1970 Lond.; MRCS Eng. LRCP Lond. 1970; MRCGP 1979; Dip. Palliat. Med. Wales 1995; DTM & H Liverp. 1974. (Guy's) Clin. Asst. (Palliat. Med.) Wakefield Hospice; Hon. Med. Adviser St. Geo. Crypt Leeds. Prev: GP Leeds; Med. Supt. (Ch. Miss. Soc.) Mvumi Hosp., Tanzania.

CARMICHAEL, Rosamund Mary 20 Collylinn Road, Bearsden, Glasgow G61 4PN — MB ChB 1968 Glas. (Glas.) Regist. (Ophth.) Glas. W.. Infirm. Prev: Regist. (Psychiat.) Gartnaval Roy. Infirm. Glas.; SHO (Ophth.) Ophth. Inst. Glas.; SHO (Ophth.) Glas. Eye Infirm.

CARMODY, Elizabeth Ann The Lodge, 1 Spen Lane, Leeds LS5 3EJ Tel: 0113 295 3590 Fax: 0113 295 3288 — MB ChB 1987; BSc (Hons.) Leeds 1984,; MMedSci (Clin. Psychiat.) Leeds 1993; MRCPsych. 1991. (Leeds) Cons. Psychiat. & Learning Disabil., Leeds CMH Trust. Socs: MRCPsych. Prev: Cons. Psychiat. Learning Disabil. Leeds CMH Trust; Sen. Regist. (Ment. Handicap) Meanwood Pk. Hosp. Leeds; Hon. Sen. Regist. (Ment. Handicap) St. Geo. Hosp. Med. Sch. Lond.

CARMODY, Moira Catherine Heaton Moor Medical Centre, 32 Heaton Moor Road, Stockport SK4 4NX Tel: 0161 432 0671 — MB ChB 1985 Leic.; BSc Leic. 1982; MFFP 1995; MRCGP 1990.

CARNACHAN, Gordon Alexander (retired) Upper Greenways, 27 Kentsford Road, Grange-over-Sands LA11 7AP — MB ChB Glas. 1946; DObst RCOG 1950.

CARNAGHAN, Lesley Edith 2 Sharman Park, Belfast BT9 5HJ — MB BCh BAO 1969 Belf. Asst. Med. Off. Qu. Univ. Belf.; Clin. Asst. Dermat.

CARNAGHAN, Marjorie Gertrude (retired) 15 Upper Churston Rise, Seaton EX12 2HD Tel: 01297 22216 — MB BS 1938 Lond.; BSc, MB BCh Wales 1937; MRCS Eng. LRCP Lond. 1937; MFCM 1974; DObst RCOG 1944; CPH Eng. 1946. Prev: SCM Wolverhampton AHA.

CARNAGHAN, Paul Albert Tel: 01776 706566 — MB BCh BAO 1983 Belf.; MRCGP 1989; DMH Belf. 1990; DCH RCPSI 1989; DRCOG 1987. (Belf.) GP Stranraer Health Centre. Prev: Med. Off. Ekwendeni CCAP Hosp. Malawi.

CARNALL, Douglas John BMJ, BMA House, Tavistock Square, London WC1H 9JR Tel: 020 7383 6044 Fax: 020 7383 6418 Email: douglas@carnall.demon.co.uk; 7 Navarine Grove, London E8 1AJ — MB ChB 1989 Sheff.; MRCGP 1994. Research Fell. Univ. Coll. Lond.; Freelance Edr. BMJ.

CARNE, Andrew Jeremy 91 Neasden Lane, London NW10 2UE; 11A Dingwall Road, Wandsworth, London SW18 3AZ Email: carnes@btinternet.com — MB BS 1996 Lond. (Charing Cross and Westminster)

CARNE, Christopher Alan Clinic 1A, Addenbrooke's Hospital, Hills Road, Cambridge CB2 2QQ Tel: 01223 217774 Fax: 01223 217807 Email: christopher .carne@mstxc.addenbrooks.anglox.nhs.uk — MB BS 1978 Lond.; MA Camb. 1991; MD Lond. 1989; FRCP Lond. 1994; MRCP (UK) 1981; T(M) 1991. (Middlx.) Cons. Genitourin. Med. Addenbrooke's Hosp. Camb.; Assoc. Lect. Fac. Clin. Med. Camb. Univ. Socs: Assn. Genitourin. Med.; Med. Soc. Study VD (Counc. Mem.). Prev: Lect. (Genitourin. Med.) Middlx. Hosp. Med. Sch. Lond.

CARNE, David Ronald Dunchurch Surgery, Dunsmore Heath, Dunchurch, Rugby CV22 6AP — MB BS 1975 Melborne.

CARNE, (H) James, MBE 7 Wood Lane, Highgate, London N6 5UE Tel: 020 8883 3366 Fax: 020 8883 6614 Email: drjamescarne@aol.com — MB BS Lond. 1952; FRCGP 1978, M 1966. (Lond. Hosp.) p/t Private GP; Med. Expert Witness. Socs: Hon Life Fell. Med. Soc. Lond.; Fell. Roy. Soc. Med.; Treas. Nat. Assoc. Primary Care. Prev: Sen. Lect. Qu. Mary & W.field Coll.; RAF Med. Off.; Ho. Surg. Lond. Hosp.

CARNE, John Richard Camin, Surg. Capt. RN Passfield Lodge, Passfield, Liphook GU30 7RU Tel: 01428 751594 Fax: 01428 751594 — MB BCh BAO Dub. 1971; BA Dub. 1971.

CARNE, Martin Stuart Parklane Surgery, Mill Street, Tonyrefail, Porth CF39 8AG Tel: 01443 670567 Fax: 01443 674437 — MB BCh 1977 Wales.

CARNE, Peter Rudiger 19 Fulshaw Avenue, Wilmslow SK9 5JA — MB ChB 1987 Manch.

CARNE, Stuart John, CBE 5 St Mary Abbots Court, Warwick Gardens, London W14 8RA Tel: 020 7602 1970 Fax: 020 7602 1970 Email: carne@ukgateway.net — MB BS 1950 Lond.; MRCS Eng. LRCP Lond. 1950; FRCGP 1970, M 1958; DCH Eng. 1956. (Middlx.) Gen. Practitioner; Hon. Civil. Cons. Gen. Pract. RAF; Pres. Roy. Coll. Gen. Practitioners. Socs: Fell. Roy. Soc. Med. (Ex-Pres. Sect. Gen. Pract.& Ex-Pres. Utd. Serv. Sec.). Prev: Sen. Tutor (Gen Pract.) Roy. Postgrad. Med. Sch. Lond. & Pres. Roy. Coll. Gen. Pract.; Chairm. Standing Med. Advis. Comm.; Pres. World Organisat. Nat. Colls. & Acads. Gen. Pract.

CARNE-ROSS, Ian Pattison Granby Place Surgery, Granby Place, 1 High Street, Northfleet, Gravesend DA11 9EY Tel: 01474 352447/362252; West View, Meopham Green, Gravesend DA13 0QB Tel: 01474 814822 Fax: 01474 320775 — MB BS 1971 Lond.; MRCS Eng. LRCP Lond. 1972. (King's Coll. Hosp.) Prev: SHO (Cas.) Kings Coll. Hosp. Lond.; Ho. Surg. Kings Coll. Hosp. Lond.; Ho. Phys. Staffs. Gen. Infirm. Stafford.

CARNEGIE, Alastair Moir The Market Place Surgery, Cattle Market, Sandwich CT13 9ET Tel: 01304 613436/612589 Fax: 01304 613877; Chestnut Farm House, Marshborough, Sandwich CT13 0PJ Tel: 01304 813120 — MB BS 1978 Lond. (Char. Cross) GP Sandwich; Clin. Asst. (Rheum. & Gen. Med.) Buckland Hosp. Dover; Clin. Asst. (Diabetes) Kent & Canterbury Hosps. Socs: Med. Off. Sch. Assn.; (Part Pres.) Becket Med. Soc., Canterbury; Worshipful Soc. Of Apothecians, Lond. Prev: Resid. (Paediat. Med.) Hosp. Sick Childr. Toronto, Canada; Ho. Surg. Char. Cross Hosp. Lond.; Ho. Phys. Roy. Sussex Co. Hosp. Brighton.

CARNEGIE, Christina Mary Dorothea 1 Mortlake Road, Kew, Richmond TW9 3JE Tel: 020 8948 5848 Fax: 020 8332 0183 — MB BS 1976 Lond.; MFPM RCP (UK) 1990; FFPM RCP (UK) 1994. (King's Coll. Hosp.) Med. Dir. Abbott Laborat. Ltd. Prev: Sen. Med. Adviser Abbott Laborat. Ltd.; Regist. (Anaesth.) St. Bart. Hosp. Lond.; SHO (Anaesth.) Guy's Hosp. Lond.

CARNEGIE, David Michael Long Range, Keyhaven, Lymington SO41 0TQ Tel: 01590 643386 — MB BS 1950 Lond.; LMSSA Lond. 1943; FFA RCS Eng. 1953; DA Eng. 1947. (Guy's) Socs: Fell. Assn. Anaesth. GB & Irel. & Roy. Soc. Med. Prev: Emerit. Cons. Anaesth. Guy's Hosp., Chelsea Hosp. Wom. & Evelina Childr. Hosp. Lond.; Cons. Anaesth. Guy's-Maudsley Neurosurg. Unit & Thoracic Units, SE Metrop. RHB; Chief Asst. (Anaesth.) Guy's Hosp.

CARNEGIE, Graham Francis Moir (retired) Melstock, Ashdown Road, Forest Row RH18 5BN — BM BCh 1948 Oxf.; BM BCh Oxon. 1948; MRCP Lond. 1954. Prev: Regist. (Med.), Sen. Med. Cas. Off. & Ho. Phys. St. Thos. Hosp.

CARNEGIE, Margaret Rosamond Chestnut Farmhouse, Marshborough, Sandwich CT13 0PJ — MB BS 1977 Lond.; MRCS Eng. LRCP Lond. 1977; DCH RCP Lond. 1980. Prev: GP Trainee HildenBoro. Kent; Resid. (Paediat.) Hosp. Sick Childr. Toronto; SHO (Paediat.) Roy. Alexandra Hosp. Brighton & Guys Hosp. Lond.

CARNEGIE-BROWN, Patricia Mary, Maj. RAMC Medical Centre, Princess Royal Barracks BFPO 47 — MB ChB 1987 Manch.; MRCGP 1994; DRCOG 1993; DFFP 1993. (Manch.) Med. Off. Catterick Garrison N. Yorks.; Med. Off. HM Forces.

CARNEGIE-SMITH, Kaetrin Foxglove Cottage, Carr Lane, Scalby, Scarborough YO13 0SB Tel: 01723 371350 — MB ChB 1966 Aberd.; MFCM RCP (UK) 1984. (Aberd.) Indep. Cons. Pub. Health Med. ScarBoro. Prev: Dir. Pub. Health ScarBoro. HA; Cons. Pub. Health Med. N.allerton HA.

CARNEGY, Angus Gillies and Overbridge Medical Partnership, Brighton Hill, Sullivan Road, Basingstoke RG22 4EH Tel: 01256 479747; Yeovil House, Rosebery Road, Alresford SO24 9HQ — MB BS 1989 Lond.; MRCGP 1993; DCH RCP Lond. 1994; DRCOG 1991. (King's Coll. Lond.) Prev: Trainee GP/SHO (Psychiat.) Pk. Prewett Hosp. Alresford.; SHO (A & E) W. Middlx. Hosp.; SHO (O & G) Hillingdon Hosp.

CARNELL, Dawn Michele The Marie Curie Research Wing, Mount Vernon Hospital, Northwood HA6 2RN Tel: 01923 844852 Fax: 01923 844167 Email: dawn.carnell@virgin.net; Greenway, Bagslate Moor Road, Rochdale OL11 5XT Tel: 01706 641914, 01707 872270 — MB BS 1991 Lond.; FRCR 2001; BSc (Hons.) Lond. 1988; MRCP (UK) 1996. (Roy. Free Hosp. Lond.) CRC Clin. Research Fell., Marie Curie Research Wing, Mt. Vernon Hosp., N.wood, Middx. Socs: Roy. Coll. Radiol.; Fell. Roy. Soc. Med. Prev: Specialist Regist./Clin. Oncol., The Middlx. Hosp. Lond.; Specialist Regist./Clin. Oncol., The Roy. Marsden Lond.

CARNEY, Charles John 13 Hillend Road, Arbroath DD11 2AR — MB BCh 1980 Witwatersrand.

CARNEY, Donald Philip (retired) 48 Madeira way, Eastbourne BN23 5UJ Tel: 01424 846501 — MB BCh BAO 1951 NUI. Prev: Vis. Med. Off. BRd.water Lodge Old People's Home Tottenham.

CARNEY, Gwyn Emyr 344B Woodstock Road, Oxford OX2 8BZ — MB BS 1998 Lond.; MB BS Lond 1998.

CARNEY, Louise Jane 58 The Culvert, Bradley Stoke, Bristol BS32 8AB — MB ChB 1997 Bristol.

CARNEY, Margaret Hill House, Mount Park Road, Harrow on the Hill, Harrow HA1 3JY — MB BS Durh. 1960, DPM 1963; MRCPsych 1976. Cons. Child & Adolesc. Psychiat., St Andrews at Harrow. Bowden Ho. Clinic, Lond. Rd Harrow HA1 3TL. Prev: Cons., Child & Adolesc Psychiat., S. Bucks. NHS Trust.

CARNEY, Mary Regina The Surgery, Chapel Street, Willington, Crook DL15 0EQ Tel: 01388 746342; White Rose Cottage, 11 Station Road, Witton-le-Wear, Bishop Auckland DL14 0AN Tel: 01388 488415 Fax: 01388 488415 — MB BCh BAO 1979 NUI; MRCGP 1984; DRCOG 1982; DCH RCP Lond. 1981. (Univ. Coll. Dub.) GP Princip. Prev: GP Career Start - Co. Durh.; Retainer Scheme - Co. Durh.; GP Bishop Auckland.

CARNEY, Michael William Patrick (retired) Hill House, Mount Park Road, Harrow HA1 3JY — MB BCh BAO 1954 NUI; MD NUI 1965; FRCPI 1971, M 1957; FRCPsych 1974, M 1971; T(Psychiat.) 1991; DPM Eng. 1958. Vis. Cons. Psychiat. Priory Hosp. Lond., Bowden Hse. Clinic Harrow & Roy. Masonic Hosp. Lond. Prev: Cons. Psychiat. N.wick Pk. & Shenley Hosps.

CARNEY, Pauline Strensall Medical Practice, The Surgery, Southfields Road, Strensall, York YO32 5YA Tel: 01904 490532 Fax: 01904 491927 — MB ChB 1973 Liverp.; MRCGP 1982; DObst RCOG 1976.

CARNEY, Philip Joseph Edward 9 Falcon House, Old Gloucester St., London WC1N 3AA — MB BS 1981 Lond.

CARNEY, Steven Alan National Deaf Pstchiatric Service, Old Church, Bedford Hill, London SW12 — MB ChB 1983 Liverp.; MRCPsych 1992; Dip. Prison Med. 1998. (Liverp.) Assoc. Specialist, Nat. Deaf Psychiat. Serv., Balham. Prev: Sen. Med. Off. HM Prison Durh.; Med. Off. HM Prison Hindley; Regist. Rotat. (Psychiat.) Salford Train. Scheme.

CARNEY, Stuart Michael 29 Lambton Court, High Rickleton, Washington NE38 9HE — MB ChB 1996 Ed.

CARNEY, Timothy Alan Burn Brae Surgery, Hencotes, Hexham NE46 2ED Tel: 01434 603627 Fax: 01434 606373 — MB BS 1969

Newc.; MD Newc. 1987; FRCGP 1993, M 1973; DObst RCOG 1973. Trainer GP Hexham. Prev: SHO St. Nicolas' Hosp. Gosforth; Ho. Surg. S. Shields Gen. Hosp.; Ho. Phys. Newc. Gen. Hosp.

CARNIE, John Charles Tollgate Cottage, Nuneaton Road, Over Whitacre, Coleshill, Birmingham B46 2NR — MB ChB 1974 Ed.; FFA RCS Eng. 1978. Cons. Anaesth. W.. Midl. RHA.

CARNIE, Philip William The Coach House, 15 West Coombe, Bristol BS9 2BA — MB ChB 1949 Manch.

CARNON, Andrew Grant Department of Public Health, University of Glasgow, 2 Lilybank Gardens, Glasgow G12 8RZ — MB ChB 1985 Birm.; BSc Ed. 1978; MFPHM RCP (UK) 1993; MPH Glas. 1991; DA (UK) 1989. MRC Research Fell. (Pub. Health) Univ. Glas. Prev: Lect. (Pub. Health) Univ. Glas.

CARNWATH, Thomas Christopher Mark Substance Misuse Services, Chapel Road, Sale, Manchester M33 7FD Tel: 0161 912 3170 Fax: 0161 912 3212 Email: thom@a34pom.demon.co.uk; Grafton House, Marlborough Road, Bowdon, Altrincham WA14 2RW Tel: 0161 929 1442 — MB 1975 Camb.; MA Camb. 1974, MB 1975, BChir 1974; MRCGP 1980; FRCPsych 1997, M 1980. Cons. Psychiat. Trafford Gen. Hosp. Davyhulme Manch.; Specialist in Addic. Psychiat. Prev: Cons. Psychiat. Tone Vale Hosp. Som.; Sen. Regist. (Psychiat.) Manch. AHA (T).

CARO, Adrian John (retired) Brick Kiln Cottages, Daffy Green, Bradenham, Thetford IP25 7QG Tel: 01362 820608 — MB BS 1970 Lond.; PhD (Genetics) Univ. E. Anglia 1978; MRCS Eng. LRCP Lond. 1970; FRCGP 1989, M 1976; DObst RCOG 1972. Prev: Sen. Partner Theatre Roy. Surg. Dereham, Norf.

CARO, Colin Gerald Imperial College, Centre for Biological & Medical Systems, London SW7 2BX Tel: 020 7594 5180 Fax: 020 7584 6897 Email: c.caro@ic.ac.uk — MB BCh Witwatersrand 1949; BSc (Hons.) Witwatersrand 1949, MD 1961; FRCP Lond. 1991; FRCP Ed. 1968, M 1954. (Witwatersrand) Emerit. Prof. Physiol. Mech. & Sen. Research Fell. Imperial Coll. Lond.; Foreign Fell. Amer. Inst. Med. & Biol. Engin. Socs: Physiol. Soc.; Corr. Mem. Amer. Physiol. Soc.; Med. Res. Soc. Prev: Dir., Centre for Biological & Med. Systems, Imperial Coll.; Lect. (Med.) St. Thos. Hosp. Lond.; Research Assoc. Grad. Sch. Med. Univ. Penna.

CAROE, John William (retired) 6 College Road, Eastbourne BN21 4HY Tel: 01323 735044 — MB BChir 1972 Camb.; MB (Distinc.) BChir Camb. 1972; MA Camb. 1972; MRCP (UK) 1977. Hosp. Pract. (Radiother. & Oncol.) E.bourne Dist. Gen. Prev: Regist. (Gen. Med.) Stoke Mandeville Hosp. Aylesbury.

CAROE, Mrs Mary Elizabeth Vann, Hambledon, Godalming GU8 4EF, 01428 683413 Fax: 01428 683413 Email: mary@carne.com — MB BS Lond. 1963; MFFP 1993; FRCS (Plast) 1997. (Westminster) Police Surg. Surrey Constab. (Guildford Div.).

CAROLAN, Bridget Agnes Lowenva, Forest Lane, Papplewick, Nottingham NG15 8FF — MB BCh BAO 1974 Belf.; MRCGP 1978.

CAROLAN, Clare Mary 24 Todhill Avenue, Kilmarnock KA3 2EG — MB ChB 1991 Dundee.

CAROLAN, Edward Gabriel Sandacre, 190 Harborne Road, Edgbaston, Birmingham B15 3JJ Tel: 0121 454 5700 — MB BCh BAO 1946 NUI.

CARP, Gerald Woolf (retired) 3 Florida Court, Westmoreland Road, Bromley BR2 0TR Tel: 020 8460 5802 — MB BS Lond. 1954; LMSSA Lond. 1954. Prev: Ho. Phys. & Ho. Surg. Epsom Dist. Hosp.

CARPENTER, Annie Pack Home Lodge, Horsmonden, Tonbridge TN12 8NE Tel: 0189 272 2545 — MB ChB 1945 Glas. (Glas.)

***CARPENTER, Eleanor Clare** 42 Bryn Siriol, Hengoed CF82 7TA Fax: 01443 875625 — MB BCh 1997 Wales; BSc Hons. Anat. Wales 1993.

CARPENTER, Elizabeth Hammond Thorncliffe, Denford Road, Longsdon, Stoke-on-Trent ST9 9QG — MB ChB 1971 Sheff.; FRIPHH. (Sheff.) SCMO (Rheum.) N. Staffs. Hosps. Socs: Fac. Community Health; Brit. Soc. Rheum.; Soc. Pub. Health. Prev: Clin. Med. Off. N. Staffs. Health Dist.; Clin. Med. Off. Centr. Health Dist. (T) (Sheff.); Cas. Off. Sheff. Roy. Infirm.

CARPENTER, George Iain Centre for Health Service Studies, George Allen Wing, The University, Canterbury CT2 7NF Tel: 01227 827760 Fax: 01227 827868; Glebe Cottage, St Stephens Green, Canterbury CT2 7JU Tel: 01227 471038 — MB ChB 1975 Ed.; BSc (Med. Sci.) Ed. 1972, MD 1991; FRCP Ed. 1994; FRCP Lond. 1993; MRCP (UK) 1978. Sen. Lect. (Health c/o Elderly) King's Coll. Sch. Med. & Dent. Prev: Cons. Phys. Geriat. & Rehabil. Med. Winchester; Sen. Regist. (Geriat.) St. Geo. Hosp. Tooting & Unit Brighton Hosp.

CARPENTER, Gordon Roy Moorland Medical Centre, Dyson House, Regent Street, Leek ST13 6AU Tel: 01538 399008 Fax: 01538 398228; Thorncliffe, Denford Road, Longsdon, Stoke-on-Trent ST9 9QG Tel: 01538 399678 — MB ChB 1971 Sheff.; Dip. Community Paediat. Warwick 1989. Examr. DCH Roy. Coll. of Phys. Prev: Regist. (Paediat.) Childr. Hosp. Sheff.; SHO (A & E) Sheff. Roy. Infirm.; SHO (Neonat. Paediat.) Jessop Hosp. Wom. Sheff.

CARPENTER, Helena Cicely Winifred (retired) 2 The Glen, Glen Path, Sunderland SR2 7TX Tel: 0191 567 9143 — MB BS Durh. 1947; DPH Newc. 1968.

CARPENTER, Jane Elizabeth Hope Hospital, Stott Lane, Manchester M6 8HD Tel: 0161 789 7373; 7 Manor Gardens, Wilmslow SK9 2DQ — MB ChB 1981 Bristol. SHO.(Microbiol.) Hop Hosp. Manch. Prev: SHO (Gen. Med.) Wythenshawe Hosp. Manch.

CARPENTER, Janice Lyall 3 Long Meadow, Bedgrove, Aylesbury HP21 7EJ — MB ChB 1980 Aberd.; DA RCS Eng. 1984. Prev: Clin. Asst & Regist. (Anaesth.) Stoke Mandeville Hosp. Aylesbury; SHO (Anaesth) Yeovil Dist. Hosp. Yeovil; SHO (Anaesth.) W.on Gen. Hosp. W.on Super Mare.

CARPENTER, John Paul The Royal West Sussex Trust, St. Richards Hospital, Spitalfield Lane, Chichester PO19 Tel: 01243 788122; 2 Sea Lane Close, East Preston, Littlehampton BN16 1NQ Tel: 01903 788122 Fax: 01903 783341 — MB BS 1996 Lond.; BSc Lond. 1993. (UMDS Guy's & St. Thos.) SHO (Med.) St Richard's Hosp. Chichester. Prev: SHO (A & E) St. Thos. Lond.; Ho. Off. Napier Hosp. Hawkes ay New Zealand; Ho. Off St. Richard's Hosp. Chichester & St. Thos. Hosp. Lond.

CARPENTER, Lindsay Jane 129 Treen Road, Tyldesley, Manchester M29 7HB — MB ChB 1996 Leic.

CARPENTER, Lisa Springfield Lodge, 52 Graham Road, Malvern WR14 2HU — MB ChB 1998 Sheff.; MB ChB Sheff 1998.

CARPENTER, Margaret Jennifer Murray Room 5E56, Department of Health, Policy Directorate, Quarry House, Quarry Hill, Leeds LS2 7UE Tel: 0113 254 5934 Fax: 0113 254 5936 Email: jennie.carpenter@doh.gsi.gov.uk; High Roans Farm House, Sheriff Hutton Road, Strensall, York YO32 5TS — MB BChir 1973 Camb.; MA Camb. 1972; FFPHM RCP (UK) 1993, M 1989; MFCM 1986. Head, Policy - Evidence, Policy Directorate; Dept. of Health; Vis. Sen. Lect., Nuffield Inst., Leeds. Prev: Dir. of Pub. Health N. Yorks. HA, York HA & E. Birm. HA.; Head Pub. Health Developm., Dept.s of Health.

CARPENTER, Mark Richard Moatfield House, Appleton Roebuck, York YO5 7EE — MB ChB 1991 Ed.

CARPENTER, Michael Crahamel Medical Practice, Crahamel House, 1-3 Duhamel Place, St Helier, Jersey JE2 4TP Tel: 01534 735419 Fax: 01534 735011; Lousarie, Les Routeurs, St. Peter's Valley, Jersey JE3 7DF Fax: 01534 735011 — MB ChB 1976 Bristol; MRCP (UK) 1980.

CARPENTER, Michael Anthony Pinderfields & Pontefract, Hospitals NHS Trust, Aberford Road, Wakefield WF1 4EE Tel: 01924 213358 Fax: 01924 814497; 69 Gledhow Wood Road, Gledhow, Leeds LS8 4DG Tel: 0113 294 1934 — MB ChB 1984 Leeds; MRCP (UK) 1989; FRCP 2000. Cons. Phys. (Elderly Med.) Pinderfields Hosps. Wakefield. Socs: Brit. Geriat. Soc. Prev: Sen. Regist. (Med. for Elderly) Yorks. Region; Regist. (Med. for Elderly) Leeds Gen. Infirm.

CARPENTER, Michael Elrick, Surg. Lt. RN Retd. (retired) Lynwood, 129 Church Lane E., Aldershot GU11 3ST Tel: 01252 24199 — BM BCh 1951 Oxf.; MA Oxf. 1951; MRCP Lond. 1966. Cert. Specialist Train. (EEC) in Gen. (Intern.) Med.; Med. Adviser NE Hants. Centre Catholic Marriage Care Ltd. Prev: Regist. (Med.) Univ. Coll. Hosp. & Fulham Hosp.

CARPENTER, Michelle 21 Murvagh Close, Cheltenham GL53 7QX — MB ChB 1992 Pretoria.

CARPENTER, Paul Graham Broadway Medical Centre, 65-67 Broadway, Fleetwood FY7 7DG Tel: 01253 874222 Fax: 01253 874448; Iffley House, 45 Station Road, Thornton-Cleveleys FY5 5HZ Tel: 01253 874222 Fax: 01253 874448 — MB ChB 1980 Manch.; MRCGP 1984; DRCOG 1984. Sch. Med. Off., Rossall Sch., Fleetwood, Lancs. Prev: Admiralty Surg. & Agent Fleetwood.

CARPENTER, Percival Benjamin 6 Sandra Close, Aldridge, Walsall WS9 8UW Tel: 0192253214 Email: pcsandra@globalnet.uk

— MB ChB 1957 Birm.; MRCS Eng. LRCP Lond. 1957; FRCR 1965; DMRD Eng. 1963. Prev: Sen. Regist. Dept. Radiol. United Birm. Hosps.

CARPENTER, Peter Kenneth Kingswood CLDT,, Hanham Road, Kingswood, Bristol BS15 8PG Tel: 0117 967 8900 Fax: 0117 967 1669 Email: peter.carpenter@bwc-tr.swot.nhs uk — MB ChB 1981 Leic.; BSc (Hons.) Med. Sci. Leic. 1979; MRCPsych 1986; FRCPsych 2000. Cons. Psychiat. Learning Disabil. Banes-PCT; R.M.O. The Hayes Unit, Pilning, S. Gloucestershire; Hon. Sen. Clin. Tutor Univ. Bristol. Socs: Fell. Roy. Soc. Med. Prev: Sen. Regist. (Ment. Handicap) Hortham Hosp. Bristol; Lect. (Psychiat.) Leicester Univ.; Regist. (Psychiat.) Leicester.

CARPENTER, Richard Morley Haxby and Wigginton H.C., The Village, Wigginton, York YO32 2LL Tel: 01904 760125; High Roans Farm House, Sheriff Hutton Road, Strensall, York YO32 5TS Tel: 01904 490316 — MB BS 1972 Lond.; BSc (Pharmacol.) Lond. 1969; MRCGP 1977; DRCOG 1976; Dip. Ther. Newc. 1999. (Univ. Coll. Hosp.) Prev: GP Tamworth.

CARPENTER, Mr Robert 116 Harley Street, London W1N 1HG Tel: 020 7935 7413 Fax: 020 7487 5829 Email: rob-car@email.msn.com; 181 Roehampton Lane, London SW15 4HP Tel: 020 8789 1556 — MB BS 1980 Lond.; MS Lond. 1988; BDS (Hons.) Wales 1974; FRCS Eng. 1984. (Middlx.) Cons. Surg. BrE. and Endocrine & and Assn. Director Cancer Serv.s Barts and The Lond. NHS Trust Lead Clinician BrE. Unit St. Bart. & Roy. Lond. Hosp.; Mem. Ct. of Examr.s , Chairm. BrE. Cancer Tumour Bd. Nethames cancer network.; Mem. Med. Advisery Planner.; Brit. BrE. Cancer Coalition.; BrE. cancer Care.; Wom.s Nationwide cvancer Control Campaign. Socs: Fell. Roy. Soc. Med.; Surgic. Research Soc.; Brit. BrE. Gp. Prev: Lect. (Surg.) Univ. Dept. Surg. Soton.; Regist. (Surg.) & Trustees Research Fell. (Surg.) Char. Cross Hosp. Lond.; Regist. (Surg.) W.m. Hosp. Lond.

CARPENTER, Ruth Frances South Durham Healthcare NHS Trust, Archer Street Health Clinic, Archer St., Darlington DL3 6LT Tel: 01325 465218 Fax: 01325 363306 Email: ruth.carpenter@smtp.sdhc-tr.northy.nhs.uk — MB ChB 1978 Manch.; FRCPCH 1996; DCCH RCP Ed. 1988; MMed.Sc. Leeds 1997. Cons. Community Paediat. S. Durh. Health Care NHS Trust.

CARPENTER, Sallie Elizabeth Lupset Health Centre, Off Horbury Road, Wakefield WF2 8RE Tel: 01924 376828 Fax: 01924 201649; 23 Swift Way, Sandal, Wakefield WF2 6SQ — MB ChB 1980 Leeds; MRCGP 1986; DRCOG 1984; DCH RCP Lond. 1983.

CARPENTER, Simon Forsyth The Surgery, 1 Troy Close, Tadworth Farm, Tadworth KT20 5JE Tel: 01737 362327 Fax: 01737 370954 Email: simoncarpenter@doctors.org.uk; 15 Greenways, Tadworth KT20 7QE Email: simoncarpenter@doctors.org.uk — MB ChB Sheff. 1968; MRCGP 1977. (Lond.) Socs: Brit. Soc. Experim. & Clin. Hypn.; Brit. Soc. Med. & Dent. Hypn.; Roy. Soc. of Med. Prev: SHO (Paediat.) W. Middlx. Hosp. Isleworth; SHO (O & G) Nether Edge Hosp. Sheff.; Asst. Cas. Off. Roy. Hosp. Sheff.

CARPENTER, Susan 3 Avonmore Avenue, Guildford GU1 1TW Tel: 01483 301086 — MB ChB 1971 Manch.; DObst RCOG 1973; DCH Eng. 1974.

***CARPENTER, Tyrone Thomas** 95 Princes George Avenue, London N14 4SN — MB BS 1994 Lond.; BSc Lond. 1991.

CARPENTER, Walter Francis Fairyhouse, Wellfarm Road, Warlingham CR6 9JL Tel: 01883 622820 — MB BCh BAO Dub. 1939; DA Eng. 1958. (TC Dub.)

CARR, Adrian William Rowland Beechwood Surgery, 371 Chepstow Road, Newport NP19 8HL Tel: 01633 277771 Fax: 01633 290631 — MB ChB 1977 Bristol; MRCGP 1982; DCCH RCP Ed. 1993; DGM RCP Lond. 1987; DCH RCP Lond. 1983; DRCOG 1980.

CARR, Alan Clive Meadowbrook Road Surgery, 4 Meadowbrook Road, Halesowen B63 1AB Tel: 0121 550 1034 Fax: 0121 550 4758 — MB ChB 1983 Manch. SHO (Med./Geriat.) Pk. Hosp. Davyhulme, Manch. Prev: SHO (A & E) & Ho. Off. (Med.) Pk. Hosp. Davyhulme Manch.; Ho. Off. (Surg.) Withington Hosp. Manch.

CARR, Alan Stephen Eskdaill Medical Centre, Eskdaill Street, Kettering NN16 8RA Tel: 01536 513053 Fax: 01536 417572; 24 Buckwell Close, Desborough, Kettering NN14 2PD Tel: 01536 761403 Email: kbo45@dial.pipex.com — MB BS 1974 Lond. Socs: Roy. Coll. Gen. Pract.

CARR, Alastair Craig — MB ChB 1991 Dundee; MSc 2000 Glasgow University; FRCA 1996; DA (UK) 1995. (Univ. Dundee) Lect. (Anaesth & Intens. Care), St Geo.s Hosp. Med. Sch.; Clin. Lect. (Anaesth.) Univ. of Glas.; Specialist Regist. St Geo.s Hosp., Lond. Socs: Assn. Anaesth. GB & Irel.; W Scotl. Intens. Care Gp.; Intens. Care Soc. Prev: Specialist Regist. Intens. Care Med., Lothan Hosps. Univ. NHS Trust; Specialist Regist.& Lect. (Anaesth.) Glasg. Roy. Infirm. Univ. NHS Trust; SHO (Anaesth.) W. Glas. Hosps. Univ. NHS Trust.

CARR, Alison Jane The Crookes Practice, 203 School Road, Sheffield S10 1GN Tel: 0114 266 0677; 145 Rustlings Road, Sheffield S11 7AB — MB BS 1984 Lond.; MRCGP 1989; DRCOG 1987. GP Sheff. Retainer Scheme. Prev: Trainee GP Whipps Cross Hosp. Lond. VTS.

CARR, Alison Mary West House, Butts Lane, Eaglescliffe, Stockton-on-Tees TS16 9BU — MB BS 1997 Lond. (Kings College School of Medicine and Dentistry London) Ho. Off. (Gen. Surg.). Prev: Ho. Off. (Gen. Med.).

CARR, Alison Sylvia Plymouth NHS Trust, Derriford Hospital, Derriford Road, Plymouth PL6 Tel: 01752 792691/2 Email: alison.carr@phnt.swest.nhs.uk; Uppaton House, Buckland Monachorum, Yelverton PL20 7LL Tel: 01822 855511 — MB BS 1985 Lond.; BSc (Hons.) Lond. 1987; FRCA 1992; DCH RCP Lond. 1990; DA (UK) 1987. (St. Bartholomews) Cons. (Paediat. Anaesth.) Plymouth NHS Trust. Socs: Fell. Roy. Coll. Anaesth. Prev: Clin. Research Fell. (Anaesth.) Hosp. Sick Childr. Toronto, Canada; Regist. Rotat. (Anaesth.) Trent; Sen. Regist. Rotat. (Anaesth.) S. W.

CARR, Mr Andrew Jonathon Nuffield Orthopaedic Centre, Windmill Road, Headington, Oxford OX3 7LD; The Barn House, Woodeaton, Oxford OX3 9TN — MB ChB 1982 Bristol; ChM Bristol 1989, MB ChB 1982; FRCS Eng. 1986. Cons. Orthop. Surg. Nuffield Orthop. Centre Oxf. Prev: Shoulder Fell. Seattle, USA; Research Fell. Melbourne, Austral.; Sen. Regist. (Orthop.) John Radcliffe Hosp. & Nuffield Orthop. Centre Oxf.

CARR, Ann Emily (retired) 2 Pine Tree Grove, Middleton St George, Darlington DL2 1AG Tel: 01325 333725 — MB ChB 1952 Bristol. Prev: Med. Off. Barnard Castle Family Plann. Clinic.

CARR, Caroline Anne Department of Anaesthesia, Moorfield Eye Hospital, City Road, London EC1V 2PD Tel: 020 7253 3411; 41 Battlefield Road, St Albans AL1 4DB Tel: 01727 833998 Fax: 01727 765234 Email: caroline.carr@cwcom.net — MB BS 1977 Lond.; BA Oxf. 1974, MA 1978; FFA RCS Eng. 1982. (St. Mary's) Cons. Anaesth. Moorfields Eye Hosp. Socs: Brit. Ophthal. Anaesth. Soc. (Exec. Comm.); Assn. Anaesth.; Roy. Soc. Med. Prev: Sen. Regist. (Anaesth.) Roy. Free Hosp. Lond.; Cons. Anaesth. E.man Dent. Hosp. Lond.

CARR, Christine Park Mews, Bilham Road, Clayton West, Huddersfield HD8 9PA — MB BS 1984 Lond.

CARR, Christine Mary (retired) Redwood Lodge, Spring Hill, Arley, Coventry CV7 8FE Tel: 01676 541158 Fax: 01676 541216 — MB ChB 1948 Sheff. Prev: Princip. GP Coventry.

CARR, Christopher Michael Edmund 17 Evesham Avenue, Whitley Bay NE26 1QR — MB BS 1979 Newc.

CARR, Claude Morris (retired) c/o 76 Tower Road W., St Leonards-on-Sea TN38 0RL Tel: 01424 425031 — MB BChir Camb. 1933; MA Camb. 1933. Prev: GP.

CARR, Miss Cornélia Sonia The Old Vicarage, 101 Aylesbury Road, Bierton, Aylesbury HP22 5BT — MB BS 1991 Lond.; BSc (Hons.) Lond. 1988; FRCS Eng. 1995; MS Lond. 1997. Specialist Regist. (Cardiothoracic) St. Thomas Hosp. Lond. Socs: Roy. Soc. Med. Prev: SHO III (Cardiothoracic) Papworth; SHO (Cardiothoracic Surg.) Guy's Hosp. Lond.; Research Fell. UCL Lond.

CARR, Darren Mark 32 Ashleigh Road, Tean, Stoke-on-Trent ST10 4DU — MB BS 1998 Lond.; MB BS Lond 1998.

CARR, David West House, Egglescliffe Hall, Egglescliffe, Stockton-on-Tees TS16 9BU — MB BChir 1969 Camb.; MA Camb. 1969; FRCP Ed. 1986; FRCP Lond. 1982; MRCP (UK) 1971. (Univ. Coll. Hosp.) Cons. Phys. N. Tees Gen. Hosp. Stockton-on-Tees. Prev: Sen. Regist. (Med.) Newc. Univ. Hosps.; Research Fell. (Phys.) Fac. of Med. Univ. Manitoba Winnipeg; Ho. Phys. Med. Unit. Univ. Coll. Hosp. Lond.

CARR, David Joseph O'Colmain and Partners, Fearnhead Cross Medical Centre, 25 Fearnhead Cross, Fearnhead, Warrington WA2 0HD Tel: 01925 847000 Fax: 01925 818650 — MB BCh

BAO 1985 Dub.; MRCGP 1992; DRCOG 1991. Socs: BMA; Diabetes Gp. (Mersey Region).

CARR, David Maxwell The Crown Surgery, 23 High Street, Eccleshall, Stafford ST21 6BW Tel: 01785 850226 — MB BS 1986 Lond.; DRCOG 1992. Med. Off. IMP & YOI Dake Hall. Prev: SHO (Surg. & Orthop.) Stafford; Cas. Off. Stafford.

CARR, David Wilfred Rowland Combe Down House, The Avenue, Combe Down, Bath BA2 5EG Tel: 01225 832226; Tamarisk, Stone House Lane, Combe Down, Bath BA2 5DW Tel: 01225 833430 — MB ChB 1961 Bristol. Prev: Ho. Surg. & Ho. Phys. Bristol Roy. Infirm.; SHO Bristol Matern. Hosp.; Med. Off. Prior Pk. Coll. Bath.

CARR, Denis Harvey Sandyhurst, Sandy Lane, Northwood HA6 3ES — MD 1983 Glas.; FRCP Glas. 1986; MRCP (UK) 1975; FRCR 1977; DMRD Eng. 1976; T(R) (CR) 1991. Cons. Radiol. Roy. Brompton Hosp. Lond. Prev: Cons. Radiol. W.. Infirm. Glas.; Sen. Lect. (Diag. Radiol.) Roy. Postgrad. Med. Sch. Hammersmith Hosp. Lond.; Sen. Regist. (Radiol.) Glas. Roy. Infirm.

CARR, Denise Annette 4 Heathfield, Chislehurst BR7 6AE — MB BS 1978 Lond.; MRCGP Lond. 1983. p/t Clin. Asst. (Dermatol.) Greenwich HA.

CARR, Eric Francis (retired) 116 Holly Lane E., Banstead SM7 2BE Tel: 01737 353675 — MRCS Eng. LRCP Lond. 1943; MA, MB BChir Camb. 1943; FRCP Lond. 1971, M 1948; FRCPsych 1972; DPM Lond. 1952. Prev: Cons. Psychiat. Epsom & W. Pk. Hosp. Gp. & Sen. PMO DHSS.

CARR, Frances Gertrude (retired) Carlton House, 22 Tankerville Terrace, Wooler NE71 6DJ — MB ChB 1943 Manch.

CARR, (Frances) Noel (retired) 91 Mudeford, Christchurch BH23 3NJ Tel: 01202 482509 — MRCS Eng. LRCP Lond. 1944; FRCGP 1978, M 1953.

CARR, Mr George Raymond (retired) 16 Briarlands Close, Bramhill, Stockport SK7 2RB — MB ChB 1945 Manch.; MD Mich. 1945; BSc Manch. 1942, ChM 1957; FRCS Eng. 1951. Prev: Cons. Surg. Stockport & Buxton Hosp. Centre.

CARR, Harold (retired) 4 Westfield, Gosforth, Newcastle upon Tyne NE3 4YE Tel: 0191 285 1674 — MB BS Durh. 1939; BSc Liverp. 1950. Prev: Asst. Orthop. Surg. Qu. Eliz. Hosp. Gateshead.

CARR, Helen Fiona — MB BS 1991 Lond.; DFFP 1995; DCCH RCGP 1994; DRCOG 1994; MRCGP 1996. (Charing Cross and Westminster) p/t GP Retainee, Riverside Surg., Horsham. Prev: Research Fell. Acad. Unit of Primary Care Univ. of Sussex.

CARR, Howard Martyn Harrison 4 Broomfield Road, Heaton Moor, Stockport SK4 4ND — MB ChB 1980 Manch.

CARR, James Michael Butterfield (retired) Mulberry Lodge, 27 The Avenue, Healing, Grimsby DN41 7NA Tel: 01472 882251 — MB ChB Ed. 1957; DPH Leeds 1963. Prev: GP Grimsby.

CARR, John Douglas Lytham House, Lower Wortley, Leeds LS12 Tel: 0113 263 8481 — MB ChB 1950 St. And.; MRCGP 1963; DA Eng. 1970.

CARR, John Malcolm High Street, Charlton on Otmoor, Kidlington OX5 2UQ — MB ChB 1954 Leeds; MFOM RCP Lond. 1979; Cert Av Med 1979; DObst RCOG 1957. Prev: Lt. RAMC; Ho. Surg. Hosp. Wom. Leeds; Ho. Phys. Leeds Matern. Hosp.

CARR, Mr John Vincent Law Womens Directorate, Queen Elizabeth NHS Trust, Stadium Rd, Woolwich SE8 4QH Tel: 0208 836 4378 Fax: 0208 836 4395 — MB BS 1974 Lond.; BSc (Hons.) Lond. 1971; FRCS Eng. 1981; FRCOG 1996, M 1983; T(OG) 1991. Cons. Obst. & Gynaecologist. Socs: Internat. Soc. Gyn. Endoscopy; Brit. Soc. Gyn. Endoscopy. Prev: Sen. Regist. King's Coll. Hosp. Lond.; Cons. O & G Greenwich Healthcare Trust.

CARR, Judith Frances Kingswinford Medical Practice, The Health Centre, Standhills Road, Kingswinford DY6 8DN Tel: 01384 271241 Fax: 01384 297530 — MB ChB 1980 Dundee; MRCGP 1984. Socs: Brit. Soc. Med. & Dent. Hypn.; Assn. Palliat. Med. Prev: Med. Off. Compton Hall Hospice Wolverhampton.; Head Med. Serv. Mary Stevens Hospice Stourbridge; Hon. Cons. Palliat. Med. Dudley Gp. Hosps.

CARR, Julian Barrington 122 Milton Grove, London N16 8QY; 3 Limelands, Greetwell Road, Lincoln LN2 4AR — MB BS 1988 Lond.

CARR, Karen Lesley London Road Medical Practice, 97 London Road, Gloucester GL1 3HH Tel: 01452 522079 Fax: 01452 387884 — MB ChB 1984 Manchester; MB ChB Manch. 1984. (Manchester) GP Gloucester.

CARR, Kathleen Zelie Therese (retired) 9 Anson Court, Atlantic Wharf, Cardiff CF10 4AL — MB BCh BAO 1968 Dub.; MRCP (UK) 1979; DObst RCOG 1973; DCH RCPSI 1971. Prev: Paediat. 546th Gen. Disp. US Forces Mannheim, W. Germany.

CARR, Kirsteen Camperdown, 32A Gosford Road, Longniddry EH32 0LF; 8A Bridge Street, Musselburgh EH21 6AG Tel: 0131 665 6821 — MB ChB 1978 Aberd.; MRCGP 1984; DCCH RCP Ed. 1984; DRCOG 1983.

CARR, Lucinda Jane Great Ormond Street For Children NHS Trust, Great Ormond Street, London Tel: 0207 405 9200; 8 St. Pauls Place, London N1 2QE — MB ChB 1984 Bristol; FRCPCH 1997; MD Bristol 1994; MRCP (UK) 1988; DCH RCP Lond. 1986. (Univ. Bristol) Cons. Paediat. Neurol. Gt. Ormond St. Hosp. Lond. Socs: Brit. Paediat. Neurol. Assn.; Eur. Acad. Childh. Disabil.; FRCPCH. Prev: Sen. Regist. (Neurol.) Gt. Ormond St. Hosp. Lond.

CARR, Mary Elizabeth The Oaks Medical Centre, 18-20 Villa Street, Beeston, Nottingham NG9 2NY Tel: 0115 925 4566 Fax: 0115 967 7470 — MB BS 1973 Lond.; MRCS Eng. LRCP Lond. 1973. (Roy. Free) Med. Off. Chetwynd Barracks Chilwell, Nottm.

CARR, Mary Matheson Department of Dermatology, University Hospital of North Durham, Durham DH1 5TW Tel: 0191 333 2329 Fax: 0191 333 2045 Email: m.carr@ndhcnt.nrthy.nhs.uk; The Rowans, Silver Garth, Barton, Richmond DL10 6NG Tel: 01325 377511 — MB BS 1975 Lond.; BSc (Pharmacol., Hons.) Lond. 1972, MD 1989; FRCP Lond. 1994; MRCP (UK) 1978. (Univ. Coll. Lond. & Univ. Coll. Hosp.) Cons. Dermat. N. Durh. Health Care Trust; Hon. Clin. Lect. (Dermat.) Univ. Newc. Socs: Fell. Roy. Soc. Med. (Mem. Dermat. Sect.); Brit. Assn. Dermat.; Brit. Soc. Paediat. Dermatol. Prev: Sen. Regist. (Dermat.) Dryburn Hosp. Durh. & Bishop Auckland Gen. Hosp.; Research Fell. & Hon. Sen. Regist. (Dermat.) Roy. Infirm. Edin.; Lect. (Dermat.) Manch. & Salford Hosp. Skin Dis.

CARR, Mr Michael Wansbeck General Hosp, Woodhorn Lane, Ashington NE63 9JJ Tel: 01670 529209 — MB BS 1985 Newc.; FRCS Ed. 1991. Cons. Surg. (Gen. Surg.) Wansbeck Gen. Hosp. Ashington N.d.; Cons. BrE. Surg. Roy. Vict. Infirm. Newc. Upon Tyne. Prev: Sen. Regist. (Gen. Surg.) Roy. Vict. Infirm. Newc.; Sen. Regist. (Gen. Surg.) N. Tees Hosp.; Sen. Research Assoc. Prof. Surg. Unit Univ. Newc.

CARR, Mr Michael Hugh Nab Lodge, 16 Nab Lane, Shipley BD18 4HJ Tel: 01274 581248 — MB ChB 1955 Leeds; BSc Leeds 1951, MB ChB 1955; FRCS Eng. 1962; FRCS Ed. 1960. (Leeds) Cons. Orthop. Surg. Bradford Roy. Infirm. Socs: Brit. Orthop. Assn. Prev: Tutor in Orthop. United Bristol Hosps.; Regist. Robt. Jones & Agnes Hunt Orthop. Hosp. OsW.ry; Res. Surg. Off. Gen. Infirm. Leeds.

CARR, Mr Michael Joseph Temple Longfield Medical Centre, Princes Road, Maldon CM9 5DF Tel: 01621 856811 Fax: 01621 852627; Trust Cottage, Kelvedon Road, Little Braxted, Witham CM8 3ES Tel: 01621 892929 — MB ChB St. And. 1971; FRCS Eng. 1977; FRCS Ed. 1976; DRCOG 1980.

CARR, Mr Nicholas David 33 Beaufort Avenue, Langland, Swansea SA3 4NU — MB ChB 1974 Bristol; MD 1985; FRCS Eng. 1979.

CARR, Norman (retired) Tor Hill House, Ipplepen Road, Marldon, Paignton TQ3 1SE Tel: 01803 553948 — MB ChB 1958 Leeds; DObst RCOG 1963. Prev: Gen. Pract., Torquay.

CARR, Norman John Department of Cellular Pathology, Mailpoint 2, Southampton General Hospital, Tremona Road, Southampton SO16 6YD Tel: 023 8079 6051 Fax: 023 8079 6869 Email: norman.carr@suht.swest.nhs.uk — MB BS 1983 Lond.; MRCPath 1991; T(Path) 1991. (St. Geo.) Cons. Histopath. S.ampton Univ. Hosps. NHS Trust; Hon. Research Fell. N.wick Pk. & St. Mark's NHS Trust. Socs: Assn. Clin. Path.; Brit. Soc. Gastroenterol.; Internat. Acad. Path. Prev: Speciality Adviser (Histopath). Defence Secondary Care Agency Cons. Histiopath. Roy. Hosp. Haslar.; Staff Path. Armed Forces Inst. Path. Washington, DC.

CARR, Patrick Worthing Hospital, Lyndhurst Road, Worthing BN11 2DH Tel: 01903 205111 Fax: 01903 285045 — MB BS 1984 Lond.; MRCP (UK) 1987; FRCP 1999. (Westm. Med. Sch.) Cons. Phys. (Intens. Care & Renal Med.) Worthing Hosp. Prev: Sen. Regist. (Renal & Gen. Med.) St. Thos. Hosp. Lond.

CARR, Patrick John High Street Surgery, 59 High Street, Kelvedon, Colchester CO5 9AE Tel: 01376 573666 Fax: 01376 573602 — MB BS 1984 Lond.

CARR, Peter Dening Balintraid House, Delny, Invergordon IV18 0LY — MB BS 1979 Lond.; MA Camb. (Cambridge and The London Hospital) Psychotherapist (private Pract.).

CARR, Peter Herbert Darlington Memorial Hospital, Holly Hurst Road, Darlington DL3 6HX Tel: 01325 380100; The Rowans, Siver Garth, Barton, Richmond DL10 6NG Tel: 01325 377511 — BM BS 1976 Nottm.; BMedSci 1974; BDS St. And. 1971; FRCP Lond. 1993; FRCP Ed. 1988; MRCP (UK) 1980. Cons. Geriat. (s/i in Gen. Med.) Darlington Memor. Hosp. Socs: BMA & Brit. Geriat. Soc. Prev: Sen. Regist. (Geriat. & Gen. Med.) Edin. Hosps.; MRC Research Fell. W.. Gen. Hosp. Edin.; Regist. (Gen. & Metab. Med.) Manch. Roy. Infirm.

CARR, Rachel Jane Fairview House, Park Row, Frampton, Cotterell, Bristol BS36 2BS — MB BS 1991 Lond.

CARR, Reginald Private Medical Clinic (Orthopaedics), 19 Carlton St., Blyth NE24 2DB Tel: 01670 363334 Fax: 01670 797045; 126 Bondicar Terrace, Blyth NE24 2JZ Tel: 01670 363334 — MB BS 1950 Durh.; FRCGP 1976, M 1958; DCH Eng. 1956; DObst RCOG 1953. Orthop. Phys./ Registered Osteopath. Socs: BMA; Newc. Obst. & Gyn. Soc.; Fell. of Roy. Soc. of Med. Prev: Cas. Off. Newc. Gen. Hosp.; Resid. Med. Off. Mona Taylor Matern. Hosp. Stannington; SHO (O & G) S. Shields Gen. Hosp.

CARR, Richard Allen Pathology Laboratory, South Warwickshire NHS Trust, Warwick CV34 5BJ Tel: 01926 495321 Fax: 01926 482600 Email: richard.carr@swarkhosp-tr.wmids.nhs.uk; 41 Remburn Gardens, Warwick CV34 5BH Tel: 01926 496240 Email: rac1@racarr.freeserve.co.uk — MB ChB 1991 Sheff.; BMedSci (Path.) Sheff. 1990; Dip RCPath 1996; MRCPath 1997. (Sheffield University) Cons. Histopath., S. Warks. Gen. Hosp. NHS Trus. Socs: BMA; Assn. Clin. Path.; Int. Assn. Path. Prev: Clin. Lect. & Hon. Sen. Regist. (Histopath.) Guy's & St. Thomas's Hosp.; Regist. Rotat. (Histopath.) Lewisham & Guy's & St. Thomas's Hosp. Lond. & Roy. Sussex Hosp. Brighton; SHO (Histopath.) Birm. Heartlands NHS Trust.

CARR, Mr Richard James Trafalgar, 2 The Square, High Pine Close, Weybridge KT13 9EA Tel: 01932 856740 — MB ChB 1977 Sheff.; BDS (Hons.) Lond. 1971; FRCS Ed. 1986; FFD, RCSI 1982; LDS RCS Eng. 1972. (Sheffield University) Cons. Oral & Maxillofacial Surg. Univ. W. Middlx.; Cons. Oral & Maxillofac SMRG, Cranofacial Surg. unit Chelsea & W.minster Hosp.. Prev: Sen. Regist./Lect. King's Coll. Sch. Med. & Dent. Lond.; Regist. W.m. Hosp. & Qu. Mary's Hosp. Roehampton.

CARR, Richard Martin Park Drive Health Centre, 2A Park Drive, Leicester Forest East, Leicester LE3 3FN Tel: 0116 289 8111; 29 Church Lane, Desford, Leicester LE9 9GD Tel: 01455 824326 — MB BS 1975 Lond.; MRCGP 1979. (King's Coll. Hosp.) GP Leicester.

CARR, Robert Department of Haematology, St. Thomas' Hospital, Lambeth Palace Road, London SE1 7EH Tel: 020 7928 9292 Fax: 020 7928 5698 — MB ChB 1977 Ed.; BSc (Bact., Hons.) Ed. 1974; FRCP Lond. 1996; FRCP Ed. 1996; MRCP (UK) 1980; FRCPath (Haemat.) 1996, M 1986. (Ed.) Sen. Lect. & Cons. (Haemat.) St. Thos. Hosp. Lond. Prev: Sen. Regist. (Haemat.) Roy. Liverp. Hosp.; Regist. (Haemat.) Roy. Infirm. Edin.

CARR, Robert James Shropshire Health Authority, William Farr House, Mytton Oak Road, Shrewsbury SY3 8XL Tel: 01743 261356; 18 West Hermitage, Shrewsbury SY3 7JP Tel: 01743 340248 — MB ChB 1985 Manch.; BSc (Hons.) Med. Biochem. Manch. 1982; MFPHM RCP (UK) 1994; MRCGP 1990. (Manch.) Cons. Pub. Health Med. Shrops. HA.

CARR, Robin Grainger Park Surgery, 25 The Park, Yeovil BA20 1DG Tel: 01935 474196 Fax: 01935 411429; Primrose Cottage, Chiselborough, Stoke-sub-Hamdon TA14 6TW — MB BS 1981 Lond.; MRCGP 1987; DGM RCP Lond. 1991; DRCOG 1988. Clin. Asst. (Chest Med.) E. Som. NHS Trust; Clin. Governance Lead GP (S. Som. PCG).

CARR, Sally Ann 81 Mercia Avenue, Charlton, Andover SP10 4EJ — MB ChB 1994 Birm.

CARR, Siobhan Bernice The Royal London Hospital, 2nd floor Fielden House, Whitechapel, London E1 1BB Tel: 020 7377 7000 Fax: 020 7337 7743 Email: sb-carr@hotmail.com; Tel: 020 7249 0619 — MB BS 1988 Lond.; MRCP (UK) 1993; MSc 1996; FRCPC 2000. (St. Bart.) Cons. Paediat. Barts and The Lond. NHS Trust. Prev: Lect. & Hon. Sen. Regist. (Gen. & Respirat. Paediat.) Roy. Free Hosp. Lond.

CARR, Stephen Philip 10 The Avenue, Hadfield, Glossop SK13 2AN Tel: 01457 853196 Email: spcarr@compuserve.com — MB ChB 1983 Manch. Prev: Regist. (Anaesth.) Manch. Roy. Infirm.; Trainee GP Tameside VTS.

CARR, Susan Jane, Brigadier late RAMC Leicester General Hospital, Gwendolen Road, Leicester LE5 4PW Tel: 0116 249 0490 — MB BS 1983 Newc.; MD Newc. 1990; FRCP. (Newcastle upon Tyne) Cons. Nephrol. Leicester Gen. Hosp. Prev: Lect. (Med., Hypertens. & Nephrol.) Univ. Leics.; Regist. (Gen. Med. & Nephrol.) Leics. Gen. Hosp.; Clin. Research Assoc. & Hon. Regist. (Nephrol.) Freeman Hosp. Newc.

CARR, Mr Thomas William Southend Hospital, Prittlewell Chase, Westcliff on Sea SS0 0RY Tel: 01702 435555 Fax: 01702 221209; Wellesley Hospital, Eastern Avenue, Southend-on-Sea SS2 4XH Tel: 01702 462944 Fax: 01702 589694 — MB BS 1979 Lond.; MS Lond. 1991; FRCS Eng. 1983; T(S) 1991. (Westm.) Cons. Urol. S.end Hosp. Socs: Brit. Assn. Urol. Surgs.; Brit. Prostate Gp.; RSM. Prev: Sen. Regist. (Urol.) New Cross Hosp. Wolverhampton, Qu. Eliz. Hosp. & Dudley Rd. Hosp. Birm.

CARR, Valentine Arthur 41 Remembrance Road, Friar Park, Wednesbury WS10 0TD — MB BS 1975 Lond.; FFA RCS Eng. 1981.

CARR, Wendy Marbeth The Avenues Medical Group, 5 Osborne Avenue, Jesmond, Newcastle upon Tyne NE2 1PQ Tel: 0191 281 0041 Fax: 0191 284 1417 Email: wendymcarr@docotrs.org.uk — MB ChB 1983 Aberd.; MRCGP 1987; DFFP 1993; DRCOG 1988. (Aberdeen) Hosp. Practitioner Metab. Bone Dis. Clinic, Freemantle Hosp., Newc. upon Tyne; Professional Exe. Commiettee Mem. Newc. PCT; GP Chair Newc. N. Locality. Socs: Brit. Menopause Soc.; Nat. Osteoporosis Soc. Prev: Clin. Med. Off. Gateshead HA; Asst. GP Chainbridge Med. Partnership. Gateshead; SHO (Fertil. Regulat.) Newc. Gen. Hosp.

CARR, William Duncan The Surgery, Anderson Drive, Leslie, Glenrothes KY6 3LQ Tel: 01592 620222 Fax: 01592 620553; The Old Manse, 2 Douglas Road, Leslie, Glenrothes KY6 3JZ Tel: 01592 742492 — MB ChB 1975 Dundee; Cert. Family Plann. JCC 1976. Network Ldr. (Scotl.) for PROFIAD. Socs: BMA & Lomond Med. Soc. Prev: Trainee GP Fife VTS; Ho. Off. (Surgic.) Vict. Hosp. Blackpool; Ho. Off. (Med.) Cameron Hosp. Fife.

***CARR, Zoe Eleanor** 10 Broadwell Close, Abbeymead, Gloucester GL4 4XX Tel: 01452 372882 — MB ChB 1997 Birm.

CARR-BAINS, Stephen The Oaks Surgery, Applegarth Avenue, Park Barn, Guildford GU2 8LZ Tel: 01483 563424 Fax: 01483 563789; Findon Lodge, Christmas Hill, Shalford, Guildford GU4 8HN Tel: 01483 562732 Fax: 01483 562732 — MB BChir Camb. 1978; MA Camb. 1979; DRCOG 1986. (St. Thos.) Med. Off. Surrey Univ.; Mem. LMC (W. Surrey). Socs: Guildford Med. Soc.

CARR-BRION, Justine Mary Helena 82B Belsize Park Gardens, London NW3 4NG — MB BS 1987 Lond.; MSc (Pharmacol.) Lond. 1996; MRCGP 1993; DRCOG 1990; DCH RCP Lond. 1989; DFFP 1996. (UCL)

CARR-HILL, Sylvaine Madeleine Marthe Swansea NHS Trust, Central Clinic, 21 Orchard St., Swansea SA1 5AT Tel: 01792 651501 Fax: 01792 517018 — MD 1974 Paris. Assoc. Specialist (Community Paediat.) Glan-y-Mor Trust Swansea. Socs: Fac. Community Health.

CARR-SAUNDERS, Edmund Morris (retired) Low Brow Nelson, Dalston, Carlisle CA5 7LE Tel: 01228 710394 — MB BS 1960 Lond.; MA Oxf. 1959; MRCP Lond. 1964; DCH Eng. 1965.

CARR-WHITE, Gerald Stopes 99 High View Road, Guildford GU2 7RY — MB BS 1993 Lond.

CARRACHER, Shirley Jane Garen Cottage, Achandunie, Alness — MB ChB 1981 Glas.

***CARRADICE, Duncan Peter** Heronslea, Horne Row, Danbury, Chelmsford CM3 4JN Tel: 01245 224877 — BM BS 1996 Nottm.

CARRADINE, Jane Suzannah Beech House Surgery, 29 York Place, Knaresborough HG5 0AD Tel: 01423 862220; The House on the Hill, Byards Park, Knaresborough HG5 9BB Tel: 01423 863395 — MB ChB 1979 Bristol; MRCGP 1985; DFFP 1994; DRCOG 1982.

CARRADINE, Stuart Harrogate District Hospital, Harrogate HG2 7SX Tel: 01423 885959 — MB ChB 1972 Bristol; MRCP (UK)

1975; FRCR 1979. Cons. Radiol Harrogate Healthcare NHS Trust; Cons. Radiol York Health Servs. NHS Trust. Prev: Regist. (Radiodiag.) United Hosp. Bristol; Sen. Ho. Phys. Roy. United Hosp. Bath; Sen. Regist. (Radiodiag.) United Hosp. Bristol.

CARRAGHER, Miss Angela Maureen Lagan Valley Hospital, Lisburn BT28 1JP Tel: 01846 665141; 27 Windsor Park, Belfast BT9 6FR — MB BCh BAO 1980 NUI; FRCS Ed. 1985. (NU 1 Galway) Cons. Gen. Surg. Lagan Valley Hosp. Lisburn; MD Anderson Assocs. Socs: Fell. Ulster Med. Soc. Prev: Internat. Fell. (Surgic. Oncol.) MD Anderson Cancer Center Houston, USA; Sen. Regist. & Regist. (Gen. Surg.) N. Irel.; SHO Rotat. (Surg.) Belf.

CARRAGHER, Lynn Margaret — MB ChB 1990 Glas.; FRCA 1999; BSc (Hons.) Glas. 1987; MRCP (UK) 1995. (Glas. Univ.) Specialist Regist. (Anaesth.) Glas. Roy. Infirm. Prev: SHO (Anaesth.) Glas. Roy. Infirm.; SHO (Anaesth.) Monklands Dist. Gen. Hosp. Airdrie; SHO (Med.) Perth Roy. Infirm.

CARRAGHER, Michael Shaun The Surgery, Marshall House, Bancroft Court, Hitchin SG5 1LH Tel: 01462 420740 — MB ChB 1985 Sheff.

CARRAGHER, Patrick James St. Serf's Medical Practice, Loch Leven Health Centre, Lathro, Kinross KY13 8SY Tel: 01577 862122 Fax: 01577 862515; The Orchard, St. Ronan's Drive, Kinross KY13 8AA — MB ChB 1982 Dundee; MRCGP 1987; DRCOG 1986. GP; Med. Officier, Rachel Ho. (Childr.'s Hospice) Avenue Rd., Kinross, Tayside. Socs: Assoc. of Childr.'s Hospices; Scott. Heart & Artery Risk Preven.

CARRASCO, Carolina Del Pilar 30 Silverthorn Way, Wildwood, Stafford ST17 4PZ — MB ChB 1997 Liverp.

CARRASCO, Maria Patrocinia 120 Beechcroft Road, London SW17 7DA — MB BS 1994 Lond.

CARRATT, Susan Lesley Glenridge Lodge, Callow Hill, Virginia Water GU25 4LQ — MB BS 1981 Lond. (St. Thos.) SHO (O & G) Canad. Red Cross Memor. Hosp. Taplow. Prev: SHO (Gen. Med.) Ashford Hosp. Middlx.

CARRDUS, Peter John (retired) 52 Blackpool Road N., St. Annes-on-Sea, Lytham St Annes FY8 3DF — MB BS 1954 Lond. Prev: Ho. Phys. & Ho. Surg. Pk. Hosp. Davyhulme.

CARRE, Elsa Ali Bethany Churchill Ward, Fullbrook Centre, Chuchill House, Headinton, Oxford OX3; 161 The Slade, Headington, Oxford OX3 7HW Tel: 01865 308043 Email: 9li@acume-freeserve.co.uk — MB ChB 1987 Glas. SHO Psychiat.

CARRÉ, Professor Ivo John Le Val Farm, Le Blicqs, St Andrews, Guernsey GY6 8YD Tel: 01481 236557 — MB BChir 1945 Camb.; MA Camb. 1954, BA 1942, MD 1957; FRCPI 1977; FRCP Lond. 1968, M 1951; MRCS Eng. LRCP Lond. 1944; DCH Eng. 1950; Hon FRCPCH 1996. (Camb. & St. Thos.) Emerit. Prof. Child Health Qu. Univ. Belf. Socs: Brit. Soc. Paediat. Gastroenterol. & Nutrit.; Emerit. Mem. Europ. Soc. Paediat. Gastroenterol. & Nutrit. Prev: Prof. & Lect. Child Health Qu. Univ. Belf.; Clin. Research Fell. Roy. Childr. Hosp. Melbourne, Austral.

CARRECK, Geoffrey Charles 290 Stoops Lane, Bessacarr, Doncaster DN4 7JB Tel: 01302 530558 — MB BChir 1970 Camb.; BA Camb. 1967; MFOM RCP Lond. 1985, FFOM 1994, AFOM 1980; DIH Soc. Apoth. Lond. 1980. Occupat. Health Medicinal Adviser, Doncaster Metropoilitan, Boro. Counc.; Cons. Occupat. Phys. Business Healthcare Ltd. Mansfield WoodHo. Socs: Soc. Occupat. Med. Prev: Princip. Med. Off. Brit. Coal Corp.

CARRELL, Professor Robin Wayne University Department of Haematology, CIMR, Hills Road, Cambridge CB2 2XY Tel: 01223 336788 Fax: 01223 336827; 19 Madingley Road, Cambridge CB3 0EG Tel: 01223 312970 — MB ChB 1959 Otago; PhD Camb. 1968, MA 1968; FRCP Lond. 1990; FRACP 1973; FRCPath 1986; FRS (NZ) 1980. Prof. Haemat. Addenbrooke's Hosp. & Univ. Camb.; Fell. (Prof. Haemat.) Trinity Coll. Univ. Camb.

CARRELL, Mr Thomas Wyatt George 19 Madingley Road, Cambridge CB3 0EG — MB BChir 1992 Camb.; FRCS (Eng) 1996.

CARRERAS, Joseph Christopher Bernard Edgar (retired) Inglewood, The Avenue, Bushey, Watford WD23 2LL Tel: 01923 229474 Fax: 01923 237954 — MB BS Lond. 1950; DHMSA Lond. 1979; DObst RCOG 1955. Authorised Med. Examr. Civil Aviat. Auth. Prev: Res. Med. Off. High Wycombe & Dist. War Memor. Hosp.

CARRERO CABO, Agar Candida Trafford General Hospital, Moorside Road, Davyhulme, Manchester M41 5SL — LMS 1992 Santiago de Compostela.

CARRI, John Peter (retired) Slievenamon, Leeswold, Mold CH7 4SA Tel: 01352 770453 — LRCPI & LM, LRSCI & LM 1944; LRCPI & LM, LRCSI & LM 1944; DCH RCPSI 1948. Prev: Ho. Phys. Meath Hosp. Dub. & Nat. Childr. Hosp. Dub.

CARRI, Mark Patrick South Parade Surgery, 7 South Parade, Llandudno LL30 2LN Tel: 01492 876907 Fax: 01492 871480; Bodafon Hall, Bodafon Road, Craigside, Llandudno LL30 3BB — MB ChB 1984 Manch.; MB ChB Manch. I984; MRCGP 1988; DCH RCP Lond. 1987. Prev: Trainee GP Oldham VTS.

CARRICK, Mr Dale Gordon 243 Milngavie Road, Bearsden, Glasgow G61 3DQ Tel: 0141 942 6344 — MB ChB 1977 Glas.; FRCS Eng. 1982. Cons. ENT Surg. W.. Infirm. Glas.; Hon. Clin. Lect. Univ. Glas. Socs: Fell. Roy. Soc. Med. Prev: Sen. Regist. (ENT) Univ. Hosp. Wales Cardiff; Regist. (ENT) Glas. Roy. Infirm.

CARRICK, Diana (retired) 14 Cairnhill Gardens, St Andrews KY16 8QX Tel: 01334 476530 — MB ChB St. And. 1947.

CARRICK, George Hamilton (retired) 5 Welton Old Road, Welton, Brough HU15 1NT Tel: 01482 665115 — MB BS 1946 Lond.; MRCS Eng. LRCP Lond. 1946. Prev: Cons. Phys. Younger Disabled Unit Castle Hill Hosp. Cottingham.

CARRICK, Heather Jane 12 Riverside Drive, Great Burdon, Darlington DL1 3JW — MB BS 1975 Lond. Med. Adviser Benefits Agency Med. Serv. Durh. Prev: GP Darlington.

CARRICK, Janet Celia Mental Health Unit, Chase Farm Hospital, The Ridgeway, Enfield EN2 8 Tel: 020 8366 6600 — MB BS 1982 Lond.; BSc Lond. 1979; MRCPsych 1986. Cons. Old Age Psychiat. Chase Farm Hosp. Enfield.

CARRICK, Lucy Ann 70 Glasgow Road, Blanefield, Glasgow G63 9HX — MB ChB 1997 Glas.

CARRICK, Pauline Anne Grianan, 1 The Sycamores, Bishop's Stortford CM23 5JR Tel: 01279 657149 — MB ChB 1973 Glas.

CARRIE, David Ian Bell (retired) 3 Rounall Avenue, Dalbeattie DG5 4TA Tel: 01556 612589 — MB ChB 1952 Ed. Prev: Med. Off. Scott. Prisons Med. Serv.

CARRIE, Donald Raymond Saint Hildas Surgery, 50 St Hildas Street, Sherburn, Malton YO17 8PH — MB ChB 1981 Sheff.; BSc Sheff. 1976; DRCOG 1985; DCH RCP Lond. 1984. Clin. Asst. (Ophth.) ScarBoro. Prev: Trainee GP Burton-on-Trent VTS; SHO (Paediat.) Sheff. HA.

CARRIE, Len Edwards Scrymgeour (retired) 104 Cumnor Hill, Oxford OX2 9HY Tel: 01865 862032 — MB ChB 1955 Ed.; FFA RCS Eng. 1963; DA Eng. 1960. Hon. Cons. Anaesth.; Oxf.shire Health Auth. Prev: Cons. Anaesth. Oxf. HA.

CARRIE, Lucy Anne Village Green Surgery, The Green, Wallsend NE28 6BB — MB BS 1989 Newc.; MRCP (UK) 1992; MRCGP 1995. Prev: Trainee GP Doncaster.

CARRIE, Margaret (retired) Flat 13, 8 Orchard Brae Ave, Edinburgh EH4 2HP Tel: 0131 332 8613 — MB ChB 1952 Ed.; DCH Eng. 1955. Prev: SCMO Lothian HB.

CARRIE, Marie, SSStJ (retired) The Lodge, Easthorpe, Malton YO17 6QX Tel: 01653 697598 — MB ChB St. And. 1950. Prev: GP Yorks.

CARRIE, Mr Sean Dept of Otocarynology, Freeman Hospital, Newcastle upon Tyne Tel: 0191 284 3111 Email: sean.carrie@acl.ac.uk — MB ChB 1988 Aberd.; FRCS Eng. 1993; FRCS Glas. 1992; FRCS (Orl.) Eng. 1997. Sen. Regist. (ENT) N. RHA. Prev: Regist. (ENT) Trent RHA; Sen. Regist.. (ENT) N.RHA.

CARRIERE, Giovanni c/o Drive A. Cerullo, 1 Stockbridge Cottages, Tilford Road, Farnham GU10 2DD — State Exam Pisa 1989.

CARRIGAN, Thomas Denis 1 Lytham Way, Lindley, Huddersfield HD3 3WG — MB BS 1990 Sydney.

CARRINGTON, Belinda Queen Elizabeth The Queen Mother, Hosp., St Peters Road, Margate CT9 4AN — MB BS 1998 Lond.; MB BS Lond 1998.

CARRINGTON, Bernadette Mary Christie Hospital NHS Trust, Wilmslow Road, Manchester M20 4BX Tel: 0161 446 3318 — MB ChB 1981 Liverp.; MRCP (UK) 1984; FRCR 1987.

CARRINGTON, David Public Health Laboratory, Myrtle Road, Bristol BS2 8EL Tel: 0117 929 1326 Fax: 0117 922 6611 Email: dr.d.carrington@btinternet.com; Langdale, London Road, Bracknell

RG12 2UL — MB BS 1976 Lond.; BSc Lond. 1972, MB BS 1976; MRCPath (Virol.) 1983; DTM & H Liverp. 1982; FRCPath (Virol) 1996. (Lond. Hosp.) Cons. Med. Virologist; Sen. Clin. Lect. Univ. of Bristol. Socs: Clin. Serv.s Comm., Assoc. of Med. Microbiologists; Panel Examr. Virol. Roy. Coll. Path. Prev: Sen. Lect. & Cons. Clin. Virol. St. Geo. Hosp. & Med. Sch. Lond.; Sen. Lect. Bact./Virol. Univ. Glas. Virus Laborat. Glas. Roy. Infirm.; Cons. Virol. Regional Virus Laborat. Ruchill Hosp. Glas.

CARRINGTON, Elizabeth Anne Sylvia (retired) Deepdene, 14 Crescent E., Hadley Wood, Barnet EN4 0EN Tel: 020 8449 8391 Fax: 020 8449 4791 — MB BS Lond. 1963; MRCS Eng. LRCP Lond. 1963.

CARRINGTON, Ingela Kaur — MB BS 1994 Lond.; BSc (Hons.) (Physiol.) Lond. 1991; DRCOG 1997; MRCGP. 1998. (Univ. Coll. Lond.) Full-time Princip. in Gen. Pract., Soton. Prev: Hse. Surg. Edgware Gen. Hosp.; Hse. Phys. Roy. Bournemouth Hosp.; GP Regist. Salisbury Wilts.

CARRINGTON, Ivan Martin The Surgery, Lower Quinton, Stratford-upon-Avon CV37 8SJ Tel: 01789 720820 Fax: 01789 720052 — MB BS 1968 Newc.; DObst RCOG 1974. Clin. Asst. (Radiother.) S. Warks. Gen. Hosps. NHS Trust.

CARRINGTON, Mark Edward Queen Elizabeth The Queen Mother, Hosp., St Peters Road, Margate CT9 4AN — MB BS 1998 Lond.; MB BS Lond 1998.

CARRINGTON, Minet Felbrigg, Heath Drive, Potters Bar EN6 1EJ — MB ChB 1988 Pretoria; FRCA Lond. 1997.

CARRINGTON, Nicholas Charles 20 Avondale Court, Leeds LS17 6DT — BM BS 1994 Nottm.

CARRINGTON, Patrick Anthony Department of Haematology, Hope Hospital, Stott Lane, Salford M6 8HD — MB ChB 1981 Liverp.; MRCP (UK) 1985; MRCPath 1990.

CARRINGTON, Peter Matthew 100 Sandringham Road, South Gosforth, Newcastle upon Tyne NE3 1PY — MB BS 1992 Newc.

CARRINGTON, Mr Richard William James 34 Grove Walk, Norwich NR1 2QH — MB BS 1989 Lond.; FRCS Ed. 1994.

CARRITT, Christian Agnes Kirkwood (retired) 137 Gloucester Road, London SW7 4TH Tel: 020 7370 5980 — BM BCh 1953; MA 1953. Prev: Med. Off. Macmillan Publishers, Mustard Catering, Artemis Fine Arts.

CARROL, Enitan Delphine Dept. Paediatric Infectious Diseases and Immunology, Newcastle General Hospital, Westgate Road, Newcastle upon Tyne NE4 6BE Tel: 0191 273 8811 — MB ChB 1989 Aberd. SHO (Paediat.) Roy. Manch. Childr. Hosp. Prev: SHO (Med.) P. Chas. Hosp. Merthyr Tydfil.

CARROLL, Aine Maria 6 Manse Road, Kilkeel, Newry BT34 4BN — MB BCh BAO 1992 Belf.; MB BCh Belf. 1992.

***CARROLL, Alan Patrick** 50 Ewell Park Way, Stoneleigh, Epsom KT17 2NW — MB ChB 1996 Leeds; BSc Psychol (Hons.).

CARROLL, Alison Lynne Roddinbrae, Hillhead of Newton, Camphill, Lumphanan, Banchory AB31 4RN Tel: 01224 492884 — MB ChB 1978 Aberd. Med. Advisor (Occupat. Med.) Aberd.

CARROLL, Alison Mary Wand Medical Centre, 279 Gooch Street, Highgate, Birmingham B5 7JE Tel: 0121 440 1561 Fax: 0121 440 0060; 66 Cambridge Road, Kings Heath, Birmingham B13 9UD Tel: 0121 444 3472 — MB ChB 1974 Birm; MRCGP 1978; DObst RCOG 1976. (Birmingham) Hon. Clin. Lect. Med. Sch. Univ. Birm.

CARROLL, Andrew Northern Hosp, 185 Cooper St, Epping Vic 3076, Australia Email: andrewcarroll100@hotmail.com; 132 Abbottshey Ave, Liverpool L18 7JT — BM BCh 1992 Oxf.; MA Camb. 1993; M.Med.Sci. Leeds 1998. (Oxf.) Cons. (Psychiat.) N.ern Hosp. Epping. Socs: Roy. Coll. Psychiat. Prev: Regist. Friarage Hosp. N.allerton; Regist. Harrogate Dist. Hosp.; Regist. (Psychiat.) Bootham Pk. Hosp. York.

CARROLL, Ann-Marie Outwood Surgery, 581A Leeds Road, Outwood, Wakefield WF1 2JL Tel: 01924 822626 Fax: 01924 870975 — MB ChB 1978 Leeds; DCH (London) 1982; MRCGP (London) 1987. (Leeds) GP Wakefield, W. Yorks.

CARROLL, Brendan Nicholas Windsor House Surgery, 2 Corporatiion St., Morley, Leeds LS27 9NB Tel: 0113 252 5223 Fax: 0113 238 1262; Fieldhead, 12 Grosvenor Road, Batley WF17 0LN Tel: 01924 442399 — MB ChB 1977 Leeds. Course Organiser Leeds W. VTS.

CARROLL, Camille Buchholz 9 Donovan Ct, Northampton NN3 3DD Email: cbc@valise.com — BM BCh 1997 Oxf. (Oxf.) Ho. Off. (Surg.) Bath Roy. United Hosp.; Ho. Off. (Med.) John Radcliffe Hosp. Oxf.

CARROLL, Carmen Buchholz The Tower Block, Hope Hospital, Eccles Old Road, Salford M6 8HD; 9 Donovan Court, Weston Favell, Northampton NN3 3DD — MB ChB 1994 Manch.; MB ChB (Hons.) Manch. 1994; BSc Anatom Sci. (1st cl. Hons.) Manch. 1991; MRCP (UK) 1997. (Univ. Manch.) Research Regist. Hope Hosp. Salford. Prev: SHO (Gen. Med.) City Gen. Hosp. Stoke-on-Trent.

CARROLL, Catherine Mary Ninewells Hospital, Dundee DD1 9SY; Bennoch Mhor, Fairview, Luncarty, Perth PH1 3HS Tel: 01738 828443 — MB ChB 1987 Dundee. SHO (O & G) Ninewells Hosp. Dundee. Socs: BMA. Prev: Trainee GP Perth VTS; SHO (Paediat.) Stirling; SHO (Cas.) Perth Roy. Infirm.

CARROLL, Craig David Charles Flat 4, 35 Brownsville Road, Heaton Moor, Stockport SK4 4PF Email: carigdc@caroll17.freeserve.co.uk; Yew Tree Flat, Meryfair Mansions, Mersy Road, Manchester M20 2PY — MB ChB 1993 Manch.; FRCA Prim. 1997; FRCA Final 1998. (Manchester) Specialist Regist. N.W. Region. Socs: Manch. Med. Soc.; Train. Mem. Assn. Anaesth. Prev: Specialist Regist. (Anaesth.) Blackpool Vict. Hosp.; SHO (Anaesth.) UMSM Wythenshawe; SHO (Anaesth.) Stepping Hill Hosp. Stockport.

CARROLL, David Sutherland The Surgery, Bellfield, Banchory AB31 5XS Tel: 013302 2121; Oakleigh House, Auchattie, Banchory AB31 6PT Tel: 013302 2766 — MB ChB 1975 Aberd.; MRCP (UK) 1979; MRCGP 1981; Dip. Palliat. Med. Wales 1996. (Aberdeen) GP Princip. Banchory; GP Facilitator (Palliat. Care) Grampian HB.

CARROLL, Derek Henry Donnybrook House Group Practice, Clarendon Street, Hyde SK14 2AH Tel: 0161 368 3838 Fax: 0161 368 2210 — MB ChB 1956 Manch.

CARROLL, Eileen (retired) 112 Newton Drive, Blackpool FY3 8JA — MB ChB Glas. 1947. Prev: Med. Off. DHSS.

CARROLL, Geoffrey Dermot Medical Director, North Essex Health Authority, Collingwood Road, Witham CM8 2TT Tel: 01376 516515 Fax: 01376 515598; London School of Hygiene & Tropical Medicine, Keppel St, London WC1E 7HT Tel: 020 7636 8636 — MB BCh BAO 1973 NUI; MSc (Soc. Med.) Lond. 1979; FFPHM 1989. Med. Dir. N. Essex HA; Hon. Sen. Lect. (Pub. Health & Policy) Lond. Sch. Hyg. & Trop. Med. Socs: BMA & Chelmsford Med. Soc. Prev: Regional SCM; UK Min. Defence K. Khalid Hosp. Jeddah, Saudi Arabia.

CARROLL, Geraldine Central Health Centre, North Carbrain Road, Cumbernauld, Glasgow G67 1BJ Tel: 01236 737214 Fax: 01236 781699 — MB ChB 1987 Glas.; MRCGP 1991.

CARROLL, Gillian Ann 3 Langford Mill, Mill Lane, Langford, Biggleswade SG18 9QB — MB BS 1975 Lond.

CARROLL, Ian Christopher Grange Farm, Biggin Hall Lane, Thurlaston, Rugby CV23 9LD — MB ChB 1998 Manch.; MB ChB Manch 1998.

CARROLL, James (retired) Windy Ridge, Pipewell, Kettering NN14 1QY Tel: 01536 760888 — MB BCh BAO 1946 NUI; DPH (Hnrs.) 1952, DCH 1953; LM Nat. Matern. Hosp. 1951. Prev: GP Corby.

CARROLL, Jason Paul Malachy 1F2 109 Broughton Road, Edinburgh EH7 4EQ Tel: 0131 447 8548 Email: jasoncarroll33@hotmail.com — MB ChB 1997 Ed.

CARROLL, Jennifer Mary Antonia Whipps Cross Hospital, Whipps Cross Road, Leytonstone, London E11 1NR; 9 North Road, London N6 4BD — MB BCh BAO 1984 NUI; MRCP (UK) 1991. Cons. Med. for Elderly Whipps Cross Hosp. Lond. Socs: Brit. Geriat. Soc. Prev: Sen. Regist. (Gen. Med. & c/o Elderly) Lister Hosp. & Chelsea & W.m. Hosp. Lond.; Regist. (Med.) W.m. Hosp. Lond.

CARROLL, John The Surgery, Main Street, Northiam, Rye TN31 6ND Tel: 01797 252244 Fax: 01797 252077 — MB BS 1975 Lond.; MRCS Eng. LRCP Lond. 1972; MRCGP 1978; DRCOG 1976; FRCGP 1999. (St. Bart.)

CARROLL, John (retired) Kilkeel Health Centre, Knockchree Avenue, Kilkeel, Newry BT34 4BS Tel: 028 4176 2601 Fax: 028 4176 5485 — MB BCh BAO 1952 Belf.; MICGP 1988.

CARROLL, John Desmond Portledge, The Drive, Wonersh, Guildford GU5 0QW Tel: 01483 892452 — 1998 K.S.G.; MD NUI 1955, MB BCh BAO 1950; FRCPI 1982; FRCP Ed. 1970, M 1965; FRCP Lond. 1977, M 1965. (Univ. Coll. Dub.) Cons. Neurol. S.-W. Metrop. RHB; Cons. Neurol. Regional Neurolog. Unit Roy. Surrey Co. Hosp. Guildford; Reader in Clin. Neurol. Univ. Surrey Guildford.

Socs: Assn. Brit. Neurols. Prev: Neurol Regist. Guy's Hosp.; Res. Med. Off. Nat. Hosp. Qu. Sq.; Sen. Regist. (Neurol.) King's Coll. Hosp.

CARROLL, Kevin Brendan Enville Mount, Enville Road, Bowdon, Altrincham WA14 2PF — MB ChB 1969 Manch.; BSc (Hons.) Manch. 1966, MB ChB 1969; MRCP (UK) 1972. Cons. Thoracic Phys. Wythenshawe Hosp. Manch. Socs: Brit. Thoracic Soc. & Brit. Soc. Clin. Immol. & Allergy. Prev: Lect. Brompton Hosp. Lond.

CARROLL, Kevin Patrick Charles Elm House Surgery, 29 Beckenham Road, Beckenham BR3 4PR — MB ChB 1982 Dundee; MRCGP 1986; DFFP 1994; DCH RCP Lond. 1985; DRCOG 1984. GP Beckenham.

CARROLL, Martin James, Wing Cdr. RAF Med. Br. Retd. Rose Cottage, Church Road, Grafham, Huntingdon PE28 0BB Tel: 01480 812917 — MB ChB 1976 Bristol; DAvMed. FOM RCP Lond. 1989. Seagoing Med. Off. Cunard Line Ltd. Soton.

CARROLL, Mary Patricia Ellesmere, Hunningham, Leamington Spa CV33 9DU — MB BS 1977 Lond.; MD Lond. 1987; MRCP (UK) 1979.

CARROLL, Mary Sheila Annie (retired) 44 Mead Road, Livermead, Torquay TQ2 6TF Tel: 01803 607283 — MB BCh BAO 1950 NUI; MFCM 1972; DPH Eng. 1962.

CARROLL, Nadine 12 Moreton Road, Wirral CH49 6LL — MRCS Eng. LRCP Lond. 1981; MD Liverp. 1989, MB ChB 1981; FRCP 1998.

CARROLL, Neill Sutherland The Elms Medical Centre, 3 The Elms, Liverpool L8 3SS Tel: 0151 727 5555; 6 St. Michael's Road, Blundellsands, Liverpool L23 8SB — MB BS 1994 Lond.; BSc Lond. 1991; MRCGP 1998. GP Assoc., The Elms Med. Centre. Prev: GP Regist., Liverp. VTS; Ho. Off. (Surg.) Watford Gen. Hosp.; Ho. Off. (Med.) W. Middlx. Univ. Hosp.

CARROLL, Nicholas Roger X-ray Department, Box 219, Addenbrookes Hospital, Hills Road, Cambridge CB2 2QQ Tel: 01223 216533 Email: nickcarroll61@hotmail.co.uk; The Gables, Carmel St, Great Chesterford, Saffron Walden CB10 1PH Tel: 01763 260465 — MB BChir 1990 Camb.; MRCP (UK) 1994; FRCR 1995. Cons. Radiol. Addenbrooke's Hosp. Camb.

CARROLL, Nicola Jean 4 Monteagle Close, Grange Park, Swindon SN5 6EF — MB ChB 1991 Aberd. SHO (Psychiat.) RAF Wroughton.

CARROLL, Paul Victor Joseph Flat 6 E2 Gassiot House, St Thomas's Hospital, London SE1 EC7 — MB BCh BAO 1991 Dub.

CARROLL, Rachel Louise Fiveways, The Green, Gressenhall, Dereham NR20 4DT Tel: 01362 860932 — MB BS 1991 Newc.; MRCGP 1995; DFFP 1995; DRCOG 1995; DCH 1994. (Newc. u. Tyne)

CARROLL, Mr Raymund Noel Patrick Clinical Consulting Rooms, Beeches Consulting Centre, Mill Lane, Cheadle SK8 2PY Tel: 0161 491 2698 Fax: 0161 428 1692; The Medico-Legal Practice, The Manchester Clinic at The Manchester Royal Infirmary, Oxford Road, Manchester M13 9WL Tel: 0161 445 2588 Fax: 0161 445 2623 — MB BCh BAO 1962 NUI; LLM 2001 (LAMP); BSc NUI 1964; FRCS Eng. 1970; FRCS Ed. 1968. (Univ. Coll. Dub.) Hon. Cons. Urol. Manch. Roy. Infirm., St. Mary's Hosp. Manch. & Hon. Lect. (Urol.) Univ. Manch. Socs: Brit. Assn. Urol. Surgs. & Internat. Soc. Urol. Prev: Regist. (Gen. Surg. & Urol.) Hammersmith Hosp. & Roy. Postgrad. Med. Sch. Lond.; Ho. Phys. & Ho. Surg. St. Vincent's Hosp. Dub.; Sen. Regist. (Urol.) Manch. RHA.

CARROLL, Richard 41 Lambshear Lane, Lydiate, Liverpool L31 2JU — MB ChB 1990 Sheff.; MRCP (UK) 1993. Hon. Sen. Regist. Clin. Research Fell. Prev: Regist. (Cardiol.) W. Midls. Rotat.

CARROLL, Robert Anthony 37 Killaire Park, Bangor BT19 1EG — MB BCh BAO 1994 Belf.

CARROLL, Simon Michael Elmham Surgery, Holt Road, Elmham, Dereham NR20 5JS Tel: 01362 668215 Fax: 01362 668625; Fiveways, The Green, Gressenhall, Dereham NR20 4DT Tel: 01362860932 — MB BS 1991 Newc.; BA Hons. (French) Soton. 1985; MRCGP 1995; DCH 1994; DFFP 1995; DRCOG 1995. (Newcastle upon Tyne)

CARROLL, Stephen Roger CPR Worldwide Ltd., Northburgh House, 10 Northburgh St., London EC1V 0AY Tel: 020 7282 1249 Fax: 020 7282 1222 Email: s.carroll@cprworldwide.com; Flat 9, 2, Millenium Square, 283, Tooley Street, London SE1 2PW Tel: 020 7378 9721 — MB BS 1980 Lond.; MRCS Eng. LRCP Lond. 1980. (King's Coll. Hosp.) Cons. Internat. Healthcare Pub. Relations Lond. Socs: Fell. Roy. Soc. Med.; BMA. Prev: Asst. Med. Off. THFC plc; GP Cheshunt.

CARRON, Daniel Benedict, MBE (retired) Treetops, Fairfield, Scartho, Grimsby DN33 3DY Tel: 01472 823449 — MB BCh BAO 1952 NUI; BSc (Hons.) NUI 1948, MB BCh BAO (Hons.) 1952; FRCP Lond. 1978, M 1967; FRCP Ed. 1971, M 1963. Prev: Sen. Regist. Dept. Med. Roy. Vict. Infirm. Newc.

CARRON, Rebecca Isabel The Gables, High St., Wanborough, Swindon SN4 0AE — MB BCh 1995 Wales.

CARRON-BROWN, Sarah Louise 16 Christchurch Road, Norwich NR2 2AE — MB BS 1998 Newc.; MB BS Newc 1998.

CARRUTH, Joanna Sarah 39 Afghan Road, London SW11 2QD — MB BS 1994 Lond.

CARRUTH, Mr John Arthur Shentall ENT Department, Royal South Hampshire Hospital, Southampton SO9 4PE Tel: 02380 825214; Glebe Cottage, Farley Chamberlayne, Romsey SO51 0QR — MB BChir 1963 Camb.; PhD Amsterdam 1992; MA Camb. 1962; FRCS Eng. 1966. (Camb. & Guy's) Cons. ENT Surg. Soton. Univ. Hosps.; Sen. Lect. (ENT Surg.) Soton. Univ.; Dir. Europ. Community Concerted Action Progr. for Med. Laser Developm. Socs: (Ex-Pres.) Europ. Laser Assn.; (Elec.) Counc. RCS Eng.; (Ex-Pres.) Internat. Photodynamic Assn. & Brit. Med. Laser Assn. Prev: Sen. Regist. (ENT) Char. Cross Hosp. Lond.; Regist. (ENT) Guy's Hosp. Lond.; Windsor Stud. Emmanuel Coll. Camb.

CARRUTHERS, Anne 9 Longridge Drive, Whitley Bay NE26 3EL Tel: 0191 252 6072 — MB BS 1962 Durh.; DPH Newc. 1968. Sen. Med. Off. Gateshead Healthcare NHS Trust.

CARRUTHERS, Benjamin (retired) Lindos, Walford Road, Ross-on-Wye HR9 5PQ Tel: 01989 765586 — MB ChB 1938 Liverp. Prev: Gyn. Ho. Surg., Ho. Phys. & Sen. Ho. Surg. Gen. Hosp. Birkenhead.

CARRUTHERS, David Bain (retired) 5 Douglas Road, Long Eaton, Nottingham NG10 4BH Tel: 0115 973 3155 — MB ChB 1946 Glas.

CARRUTHERS, David Bruce 21 Viewforth, Edinburgh EH10 4JD — MB ChB 1997 Ed.

CARRUTHERS, David Mark Dept Rheumatology, University of Birmingham, Edgbaston, Birmingham B15 2TT; 98 Bournbrook Road, Selly Oak, Birmingham B29 7BU Tel: 0121 472 7624 — MB BS 1987 Lond.; MRCP (UK) 1992; PHd. 1999. Clin. Lect. (Rheum.) Univ. of Birm. Prev: Research Regist. (Rheum.) Univ. Birm.; Regist. (Med.) Norf. & Norwich Hosp.

CARRUTHERS, David Michael Cape Cornwall Surgery, Market Street, St. Just-in-Penwith, Penzance TR19 7HX Tel: 01736 788306 — MB ChB 1988 Bristol; MRCGP 1994. (Bristol)

CARRUTHERS, Gemma Jane 1A Francis Avenue, St Albans AL3 6BL; 26 Upper Culver Road, St Albans AL1 4EE Tel: 01727 839819 — MB ChB 1992 Leeds; DRCOG 1996; DFFP 1997; MRCGP 1997.

CARRUTHERS, George Barry Wimpole Street Medical Centre, 55 Wimpole St., London W1G 8YL Tel: 020 7486 4646 Fax: 01323 730857; Southwood, 15 Ditton's Road, Eastbourne BN21 1DR Tel: 01323 730857 Fax: 01323 730857 — MB BS Lond. 1947; MD Lond. 1950. (Middlx.) Hon. Cons. Dept. Urol. St. Thos. Hosp. Lond.; Vis. Med. Off. Nat. Heart Hosp. Lond.; Med. Dir. Wimpole St. Med. Centre Lond.; Gen. Edr. Wolfe Med. Atlases. Socs: Fell. Roy. Soc. Med. Prev: Regist. Dept. Neurol & Ho. Phys. to Prof Med. Middlx. Hosp.; Ho. Phys. Brompton Hosp. Lond.; Clin. Med. Off. Thames Water Auth.

CARRUTHERS, Helen Jane Maylands Healthcare, 300 Upper Rainham Road, Hornchurch RM12 4EQ Tel: 01708 476411 Fax: 01708 620039; 30 St Andrews Place, Shenfield, Brentwood CM15 8HH — MB ChB 1985 Leeds; MRCGP 1991; DRCOG 1989.

CARRUTHERS, James Graham Wards Medical Practice, 25 Dundonald Road, Kilmarnock KA1 1RU Tel: 01563 526514 Fax: 01563 573558 — MB ChB 1965 Glas. (Glas.) GP Kilmarnock. Prev: Ho. Off. (Surg./Med.) Kilmarnock Infirm.

CARRUTHERS, Janet Rose (retired) 27 Ellington Road, Muswell Hill, London N10 3DD Tel: 020 8883 2924 — MB BS 1960 Lond.; MSc (Occupat. Med.) Lond. 1979; MRCS Eng. LRCP Lond. 1960; FFOM RCP Lond. 1991, MFOM 1983, AFOM 1980; DIH Eng. 1979. Prev: Co. Med. Off. STC Telecomm. Ltd. Lond.

CARRUTHERS, John William Clauchrie, Auldgirth, Dumfries DG2 0XN — MB ChB 1971 Glas.

CARRUTHERS, Louise Rosalind Brook 1 Hunters Gate, Tangmere Road, Tangmere, Chichester PO20 6GT Tel: 01243 539384 — MB ChB 1993 Manch.; DRCOG 1995. SHO (Psychiat.) Graylingwell Hosp. Chichester.

CARRUTHERS, Malcolm Euan Gold Cross Medical Services, 20/20 Harley St., London W1G 9PH Tel: 020 7636 8283 Fax: 020 7636 8292 Email: www.goldcrossmedical.com — MB BS 1960 Lond.; MD Lond. 1973; MRCS Eng. LRCP Lond. 1960; FRCPath 1985, M 1973; MRCGP 1966. (Middlx.) Cons. Androl. Gold Cross Med. Servs. Lond. Socs: Eur. Acad. Androl. Prev: Cons. Clin. Laborat. Servs. Bethlem Roy. & Maudsley Hosps. Lond.; Sen. Lect. (Chem. Path.) Inst. Ophth. Lond. & St. Mary's Hosp. Lond.; Pres. Soc. Psychosomatic Research.

CARRUTHERS, Mr Robert Keith (retired) The Old Vicarage, Nargate St, Littlebourne, Canterbury CT3 1UJ Tel: 01227 721548 — MB ChB St. And. 1961; ChM Dund 1972; FRCS Eng. 1967; FRCS Ed. 1966. Cons. Urol. Kent & Canterbury Hosp. & Thanet Dist.

CARRUTHERS, Simon Charles Old Fire Station, Albert Terrace, Beverley HU17 8JW Tel: 01482 862236 Fax: 01482 861863 — MB BS 1988 Lond.; BSc (Hons.) Lond. 1985; MRCGP 1994; DCH RCP Lond. 1993; DRCOG 1993; DA (UK) 1992. Prev: Trainee GP Otley; SHO (Palliat. Med.) St. Gemma's Hospice Leeds.

CARRUTHERS, Mr William Andrew Frederick Royal Cornwall Hospitals Trust, Treliske, Truro TR1 3LJ Tel: 01872 253905 Fax: 01872 253908; Ivycliff, 52 Trefusis Road, Flushing, Falmouth TR11 5UB Tel: 01326 374262 — MB BS Sydney 1967; FRCOphth 1989; FRACO 1975; MACO 1974; DO Sydney 1974; DTM & H Sydney 1968. (Univ. Sydney) Cons. Ophth. Surg. Roy. Cornw. Hosps. Trust. Socs: Fell. Roy. Soc. Trop. Med. & Hyg.; BMA; S. W.. Ophth. Soc. Prev: Sen. Regist., Chief Clin. Asst. & Outpat. Off. Moorfields Eye Hosp. Lond.; Regist. (Ophth.) Roy. P. Alfred Hosp. Sydney.

CARSER, Judith Elizabeth 10 Strangford Avenue, Belfast BT9 6PG — MB BCh 1998 Belf.; MB BCh Belf 1998.

CARSLEY, Hazel Anne Heath House Surgery, Free School Lane, Halifax HX1 2PS Tel: 01422 365533 Fax: 01422 345851 — MB ChB 1984 Leeds.

CARSON, Alan John Glenavon, 15 Station Road, South Queensferry EH30 9HY — MB ChB 1991 Ed.

CARSON, Andrew Albert George, TD Lushoto, 20 Craigweil Avenue, Radlett WD7 7EX — MB BCh BAO 1942 Belf.; MFCM 1973; DPH Lond. 1956. (Belf.) Prev: Med. Off. Oversea Civil Serv.; Resid. Surg. Off. Dist. Hosp. Banbridge.

CARSON, Andrew James Benner Whittington Hill House, Darnford Lane, Lichfield WS14 9JQ — MB ChB 1980 Birm.; BSc Birm. 1977, MB ChB 1980; FRCGP 1993, M 1985. Lect. (Gen. Pract.) Med. Sch. Birm.

CARSON, Brian Tel: 01926 425436 Fax: 01926 427257; 22 Canning Street, Liverpool L8 7NT — MB BCh BAO 1964 Belf.; MRCOG 1972; DRCOG 1967. Socs: BMA & Roy. Coll. Obst. & Gyn. Prev: Gen. Practitioner Princip.; Med. Supt. Kapsowar Hosp. Kenya; Cons. O & G Kabarnet Hosp. Keyna.

CARSON, Catherine Anne Queensfort House, 8 Annavale Avenue, Carryduff, Belfast BT8 8NZ Tel: 01232 814956 — MB BCh BAO 1987 Belf.; FRCR 1993. Cons. Radiol. Craigavon Area Hosp.

CARSON, David George 1 Lake Farm Cottages, Pendell Road, Bletchingley, Redhill RH1 4QH — MB ChB 1980 Dundee. Head Profess. Developm. E. Lond. & City HA.

CARSON, Dawn Patricia 65 Allan Park, Kirkliston EH29 9BP — MB ChB 1995 Aberd.

CARSON, Dennis John Department of Child Health, Institute of Clinical Science, Grosvenor Road, Belfast BT12 6BE Tel: 028 90 240503 Fax: 028 90 236455 — MB BCh BAO 1973 Belf.; FRCP Lond. 1989; MRCP (UK) 1976; FRCPch 1997. Sen. Lect. Qu. Univ. Belf.; Cons. Paediat. Roy. Belf. Hosp. for Sick Childr.

CARSON, Derek John Lockhart, OBE (retired) 27 Knockagh Road, Newtownabbey BT36 5BW Tel: 02890 8630581232 863058 — MD 1963 Belf.; MB BCh BAO Belf. 1957; BA Open 1981; MPhil Belf. 1996; MD (Hnrs.) Belf. 1963, MB BCh BAO 1957; FFPath RCPI 1982. Cons. Dep. State Pathol. N. Irel.

CARSON, Elizabeth Anne Castle Douglas Medical Group, Castle Douglas Health Centre, Academy Street, Castle Douglas DG7 1EE — MB ChB 1982 Glas.

CARSON, Elizabeth Jane 168 Baginton Road, Styvechale, Coventry CV3 6FT; Wescoe Villa, Crag Lane, Huby, Leeds LS17 0EJ — MB ChB 1985 Leeds. Staff Grade (Anaesth.) Pinderfields Hosp. Wakefield.

CARSON, Enid Grace (retired) Thiemodha, 35 Scarlett Road, Castletown IM9 1NS — MB BCh BAO 1953 Belf.; DCH Eng. 1958. Prev: Asst. Med. Off. Lond. Boro. Richmond upon Thames.

CARSON, Francis Damian Gerard The Ulster Hospital, Dundonald, Belfast BT16 1RH; 5 Croft Manor, Holywood BT18 0QD, Republic of Ireland — MB BCh BAO 1986 NUI; FRCA 1992. Cons. (Anaesth.) Ulster Hosp. Belf.

CARSON, Gilbert Frederick 166 Bridge Street, Portadown, Craigavon BT63 5AS — MB BCh BAO 1976 Belf.

CARSON, Hastings Elwin Axel (retired) 62 Cheyne Court, Chelsea, London SW3 5TT Tel: 020 7352 9026 — MB BS Lond. 1946; MSc (Hyg.) Harvard 1952; MD Lond. 1951, DPH (Distinc.) 1950; FFCM 1972. Prev: Dist. Med. Off. Richmond, Twickenham & Roehampton HA.

CARSON, Ian Wellington 20 Malone Hill Park, Belfast BT9 6RD — MD (Hons.) Belf. 1974, MB BCh BAO 1968; FFA RCSI 1972. Cons. Anaesth. Cardiac Surgic. Unit Roy. Vict. Hosp. Belf.; Med. Dir. Roy. Gp. Hosps. Trust Belf. Prev: Asst. Prof. Dept. Anaesth. Stanford Univ. Calif. U.S.A.; Research Regist. Dept. Anaesth. Qu. Univ. Belf.; Ho. Phys. & Ho. Surg. Roy. Vict. Hosp. Belf.

CARSON, James Gerard Antrim Area Laboratory, Antrim Hospital, 45 Bush Road, Antrim BT41 2RL Tel: 01849 424106 — MB BCh BAO 1979 Belf.; MRCPath 1985. Clin. Dir. Laborat. Serv. United Hosps. Gp.

CARSON, Colonel John, Col. late RAMC Retd. (retired) Royal Hospital Chelsea, London SW3 4SR — MB ChB 1957 Liverp.; FRCP Lond. 1980, M 1965; DTM & H Lond 1962. Phys. Surg. Roy. Hosp. Chelsea. Prev: Cons. Med. Camb. Milit. Hosp. Aldershot.

CARSON, Joseph Martin 42 Fort Street, Belfast BT12 7BH — MB BCh BAO 1983 Belf.

CARSON, Kevin George Stephen Flat 31, Downfield Lodge, Downfield Road, Bristol BS8 2TQ — MB ChB 1994 Bristol.

CARSON, Lesley Sian Link Building, Pathology Department, Medical School, Foresterhill, Aberdeen AB25 2ZD Tel: 01224 681818 Email: l.s.carson@abdn.ac.uk — MB ChB 1990 Aberd.; MRCGP 1994. (Aberdeen Univ.) p/t Specialist Regist. (Histopath.) Dept. Path. Univ. Aberd. Prev: SHO Cornhill Hosp. Aberd. Healthcare NHS Trust.

CARSON, Michael Benner (retired) Long Close, 8 Ramley Road, Pennington, Lymington SO41 8GQ Tel: 01590 672844 — MB BS 1944 Lond. Prev: Regist. (Surg.) Burns Unit (MRC) Birm. Accid. Hosp.

CARSON, Michael Perry Lisburn Health Centre, Linenhall Street, Lisburn BT28 1LU Tel: 02892 603333 Fax: 02892 501313 — MB BCh BAO 1983 Belf.; MRCGP Belf. 1987; DMH Belf. 1991; DRCOG Lond. 1988; DCH Dublin 1986. GP Partner; Hosp. Pract. (Forens. Psychiat.) Knockbracken Healthcare Pk. Hosp., Belf.; Prison Med. Off.; Civil Serv. Occupat. Health Scheme Doctor Lisburn.

CARSON, Nessan Patrick Sayce Walnut Tree Health Centre, Blackberry Crt, Milton Keynes MK7 7NR — MB BS 1984 Lond.; MRCGP 1989; DRCOG 1988. GP Milton Keynes. Prev: SHO (A & E) Mansfield & Dist. Gen. Hosp.; Ho. Phys. (Cardiol.) Char. Cross Hosp. Lond.; Ho. Surg. Milton Keynes Dist. Gen. Hosp.

CARSON, Patricia Elizabeth Rosemary McConnell, Carson and Mathews, The Health Centre, Tavanagh Avenue, Portadown, Craigavon BT62 3BU Tel: 028 3835 1145 Fax: 028 3839 2628; 47 Vicarage Road, Portadown, Craigavon BT62 4HF Tel: 028 3833 7742 — MB BCh BAO 1979 Belf.; MB BCh BAO 1979 (Hons.) Belf.; MRCGP 1983; DCH NUI 1982.

CARSON, Pauline Freda Joan 106 Hermitage Drive, Perth PH1 2SY — MB BCh BAO 1991 Belf.

CARSON, Peter Hugh Macaulay 540 Etruria Road, Newcastle ST5 0SX; 540 Etruria Road, Basford, Newcastle ST5 0SX Tel: 01782 614419 Fax: 01782 630270 — BM BCh 1955 Oxf.; FRCP Lond. 1975, M 1960; FACC 1968. (Westm.) Indep. Cons. Cardiol. Stoke-on-Trent & Newc. u. Lyme; Roy Scott Lect. 1966 W.. Reserve Univ. Cleveland Ohio at Metrop. Gen. Hosp.; Sen. Research Fell. Keele Univ. Socs: Brit. Cardiac Soc. & Airborne Med. Soc. Prev: Cons. Cardiol. City Gen. Hosp. Stoke-on-Trent; Asst. Prof. of Med. & Paediat. Case W.. Reserve Univ. Ohio; Dir. of Cardiac Catheterizat. Laborat. Metrop. Gen. Hosp. Cleveland, Ohio.

CARSON, Philip Cecil Stuart House, 34 Glyn Way, Hawarden, Deeside CH5 3NL Tel: 01244 531759 — MB BCh BAO 1987 Belf.; MRCGP 1991; DMH Belf. 1991; DRCOG 1990.

CARSON, Rory Louis, RD 79 Killane Road, Limavady BT49 0DL Tel: 0150 47 62729 — MB BCh BAO Belf. 1949, DPH 1954; FFOM RCPI 1983, M 1977; MRCGP 1975; MFCM 1972; MMSA Lond. 1963; DCH RFPS Glas. 1962; Specialist Accredit. (Occupat. Health) RCP Lond. 1989; DObst RCOG 1953; AFOM RCP Lond. 1983. (Belf.) PMO Du Pont (UK) Ltd. Maydown Works Lond.derry; Surg. Lt.-Cdr. RNR; Area Surg. St. John Ambul. Socs: Soc. Occupat. Med. (N. Irel. Gp. Chairm.); Internat. Commiss. Occupat. Health. Prev: MOH City & Co. Boro. Lond.derry; Hosp. Med. Off. Mid-Ulster Hosp. Magherafelt; SHO Off. Lissue Br. Roy. Belf. Hosp. Sick Childr.

CARSON, Ruth Eleanor 54 Beechfield Drive, Conlig, Bangor BT19 7ZW Tel: 01247 469157 — MB BCh BAO 1967 Belf.; DObst RCOG 1969.

CARSON, Ruth Georgina 1 Lake Farm Cottages, Pendell Road, Bletchingley, Redhill RH1 4QH Tel: 01883 742012 — MB ChB 1987 Dundee; DFFP 1994. Indep. Pract. Redhill.

CARSON, Sally Jane Grange Cottage, 53 London Road, Westerham TN16 1BB — MB BS 1987 Lond.

CARSON, William Gilston (retired) St. Martins, 12 Union Place, Montrose DD10 8QB — LRCP LRCS 1937 Ed.; LRCP LRCS Ed. LRFPS Glas. 1937; MRCGP 1962; LDS RCS Ed. 1936. Hon. Maj. RAMC. Prev: Dent. Off. Roy. Infirm. Edin.

CARSS, George Alexander Queen Alexandra Hospital, Portsmouth PO6 3LY Tel: 023 92 286000; Bell Cottage, Church Road, Newtown, Fareham PO17 6LL Tel: 01329 832267 — MB ChB 1972 Ed.; BSc Med. Sci. Ed. 1969; FRCS Eng. 1978; FFAEM 1993; DA Eng. 1975. Cons. A & E Qu. Alex. Hosp. Portsmouth.; Surg. Cdr. Roy. Naval Reserve. Prev: Sen. Regist. (A & E) Frenchay Hosp. Bristol.

CARSTAIRS, Jill Louise Windmill House, Hadley Green, Barnet EN5 — MB BS 1973 Lond.; DRCOG 1978.

CARSTENSEN, Olaf Tulloch Cottage, Rafford, Forres IV36 2SL — State Exam Med 1989 Lubeck.

CARSWELL, Adam Hislop Paterson (retired) 71 Clepington Road, Dundee DD4 7BQ Tel: 01382 456699 — MB ChB 1949 Glas.

CARSWELL, Anne Marie Stokes Medical Centre, Braydon Avenue, Little Stoke, Bristol BS34 6BQ Tel: 01454 616767 Fax: 01454 616189 — MB ChB 1965 Glas.; FFA RCS Eng. 1972. (Lond.)

***CARSWELL, Christine Margaret** 15 Broom Crescent, Barrhead, Glasgow G78 1PS Tel: 0141 880 6430 — MB ChB 1998 Glas.; MB ChB Glas 1998.

CARSWELL, Fleming Department of Child Health, Children's Hospital, St Michael's Hill, Bristol — MD 1986 Bristol; PhD Leeds 1969; BSc (Hons.) Glas. 1959; MB ChB Glas. 1962; FRCP Lond. 1981, M 1965. (Glas.) Reader Child Health Univ. Bristol. Socs: Brit. Paediat. Assn. & Brit. Soc. Immunol. Prev: Ho. Phys. Roy. Hosp. Sick Childr. Glas.; MRC Clin. Research Fell. Leeds; Lect. in Child Health Univ. Glas.

CARSWELL, Mr George Fisher (retired) Myrtlebank House, Industry St., Kirkintilloch, Glasgow G66 3AD Tel: 0141 776 3354 — MB BS Lond. 1962; FRCS Ed. 1969. Prev: Cons. Urol. Lancaster Roy. Infirm. Forness Gen. Hosp. W.morland Gen. Hosp.

CARSWELL, Mr John Wilson, OBE 52 Salter's Close, Rickmansworth WD3 1HH Tel: 01923 350444 — MB BS Lond. 1961; FRCS Eng. 1967; MRCS Eng. LRCP Lond. 1961. (Westm.)

CARSWELL, Margaret Jane (retired) 38 Park Avenue, Orpington BR6 9EH — MB BS Lond. 1962; MRCS Eng. LRCP Lond. 1962.

CARSWELL, Marrion Anne Whyte Flat 4, 151 High Street, Auchterarder PH3 1AD — MB ChB 1981 Dundee; DA Eng. 1984.

CARSWELL, Neil Stuart 9 Cliff Road Gdns, Leeds LS6 2EY — MB ChB 1997 Leeds.

CARSWELL, Theresa Mary 19 Longbank Road, Ayr KA7 4SA — MB ChB 1986 Aberd.; MRCGP 1990. Clin. Med. Off. (Child Health) Ayrsh. & Arran HB.

CARSWELL, William Lancaster House, 174 Chamber Road, Oldham OL8 4BU Tel: 01457 878724 — MB ChB 1961 Glas.; FRCOG 1984, M 1971. Cons. O & G Roy. Oldham Hosp. Prev: Sen. Regist. Glas. Roy. Infirm. & Glas. Roy. Matern. Hosp.

CARSWELL, William Allan Millway Medical Practice, Hartley Avenue, Mill Hill, London NW7 2HX Tel: 020 8959 0888 Fax: 020 8959 7050 — MB BS 1966 Lond.; MA Oxf. 1965; MRCS Eng. LRCP Lond. 1966; DObst RCOG 1972. (Westm.) Course Organiser Barnet VTS. Socs: Fell. Lond. Med. Soc. Prev: Regist. (Med.) Centr. Middlx. Hosp. Lond.; Ho. Phys. W.m. Hosp.

CARTER, Adam Christian 2 Horseshoe Walk, Bath BA2 6DE — MB BS 1990 Lond.

CARTER, Adrian Roger 28 Ethelbert Road, Canterbury CT1 3NF — MB BS 1966 Lond.; MRCP (U.K.) 1970; FRCR 1975; FFR 1973; DMRD Eng. 1971. (Lond. Hosp.) Cons. Radiol. Kent & Canterbury Hosps. NHS Trust. Prev: Sen. Regist. (Diag. Radiol.) Lond. Hosp.; Regist. (Diag. Radiol.) Guy's Hosp. Lond.; SHO (Infec. Dis.) St. Ann's Hosp. Lond.

CARTER, Alan Charles 2 Regent Bank, Wilmslow SK9 6LE Tel: 01625 526669 — MRCS Eng. LRCP Lond. 1957. (Liverp.) Asst. in Path. Nat. Blood Transfus. Serv. Manch. Socs: Fell. Manch. Med. Soc.; BMA. Prev: Sen. Regist. (Haemat.) Manch AHA (T); Regist. (Path.) Withington Hosp. Manch. & Manch. Roy. Infirm.

CARTER, Alexander Peter 26 Station Road, Okehampton EX20 1EA — MB ChB 1975 Liverp.; MRCP (UK) 1978; DRCOG 1980.

CARTER, Andrew John 19 Granby Cr, Spital Bebington, Wirral CH63 9NY — MB ChB 1997 Leeds.

CARTER, Ann Eileen Sutherland 107 Cheyne Walk, London SW10 0DJ Tel: 020 7352 0871 — MB BS 1972 Lond. (St. Thos.) Community Med. Off. Wandsworth HA; Treas. Lond. Soc. Family Plann. Doctors. Socs: Fac. Community Health.

CARTER, Annabel Jane Manor Farmhouse, Little Beside, St Day, Redruth TR16 5PX — MB ChB 1996 Bristol.

CARTER, Anthony Graham Aylmer Lodge Surgery, Broomfield Road, Kidderminster DY11 5PA Tel: 01562 822015 Fax: 01562 827137 — MB ChB 1988 Birm.; MRCGP 1993; DRCOG 1991. (Birmingham)

CARTER, Anthony John 21 Church Road, Alsager, Stoke-on-Trent ST7 2HB Tel: 01270 875009 — MB ChB 1966 Ed.; FFA RCS Eng. 1976; FFA RACS 1975; DA Eng. 1971; DObst RCOG 1969. Cons. Anaesth. N. Staffs. Hosp. Centre Stoke-on-Trent. Socs: BMA; Roy. Soc. Med.; Hist. Anaesth. Soc. Prev: Staff Anaesth. Roy. Wom. Hosp. Melb., Austral.; Sen. Regist. W.m. Hosp. Lond.

CARTER, Mr Archibald Edmund (retired) 39 York Avenue, London SW14 7LQ — MB BS 1945 Lond.; MB BS (Hons. Surg.) Lond. 1945; FRCS Eng. 1947. Prev: Cons. Surg. Ealing Hosp. Lond.

CARTER, Mr Charles James Manners Royal Bournemouth Hospital, Castle Lane E., Bournemouth BH7 7DW Tel: 01202 704149 Fax: 01202 704623; 9 Motcombe Road, Branksome Park, Poole BH13 6DJ Tel: 01202 764721 Fax: 01202 764579 Email: charliecarter@msn.com — MB ChB 1986 Liverp.; FRCS Eng. 1990; FRCS (Urol) 1997. Cons. Urol. Surg. Socs: Brit. Assoc. of Urological Surg.s (Full). Prev: Research Regist. (Gen. Surg.) Soton. Gen. Hosp.; Regist. Rotat. (Gen. Surg.) Liverp. HA; Wessex Higher Surgic. Train. Progr. Urol.

CARTER, Christina Barbara 143 Ellesmere Road, Shrewsbury SY1 2RA — MB ChB 1989 Sheff.

CARTER, Christopher Department of haematology, The Royal Infirmary, Acre St., Huddersfield HD3 3EA Tel: 01484 422191 Fax: 01484 342843 Email: chris.carter@huddersfield-tr.nenthy.nhs.uk — MB ChB 1977 Leeds; MRCP (UK) 1983; MRCPath 1987; FRCPath 1997; FRCP Ed. 1998. (Leeds) Cons. Haemat. Huddersfield Roy. Infirm. Socs: Brit. Soc. Haematol. Prev: Sen. Regist. Rotat. (Haemat.) Birm. Hosps.; Regist. (Haemat.) Roy. Hallamsh. Hosp. Sheff.; Regist. (Gen. Med.) Rotherham Dist. Gen. Hosp.

CARTER, Christopher Alan Upjohn Ltd., Fleming Way, Crawley RH10 2LZ Tel: 01293 582353; 4 Selwyn Close, Crawley RH10 3TQ — MB BS 1980 Lond.; FFA RCS Eng. 1986. Marketing Manager Upjohn Ltd. Prev: Sen. Regist. (Anaesth.) Sheff.; Regist. (Cardiothoracic Anaesth.) N.ern Gen. Hosp. Sheff.; Regist. (Anaesth.) Roy. Hallamsh. Hosp.

CARTER, Clare Marie Winifred Bernadatte C 7 St Nicholas Grove, Ingrave, Brentwood CM13 3RA — MB BS 1975 Lond.; BSc Lond. 1971. MB BS 1975; MRCS Eng. LRCP Lond. 1974.

CARTER, Dalton Yewdall 11 Marine Point, West Parade, Worthing BN11 5EE Tel: 01903 248444 — LRCP LRCS Ed. LRFPS Glas. 1934; MRCGP 1958. (Leeds) Socs: BMA. Prev: Clin. Asst. W. Riding Ment. Hosp.; Anaesth. St. Bart. Hosp. Rochester; Hon. Anaesth. Brighton & Hove Dent. Hosp.

CARTER, Mr David Arthur 47 Station Road, North Ferriby HU14 3DG Tel: 01482 632109 — MB ChB 1960 Leeds; FRCS Ed. 1968. (Leeds) Cons. (ENT) Roy. Infirm. Hull. Prev: Regist. ENT Dept. Gen. Infirm. Leeds; Demonst. Anat. Leeds Med. Sch.

CARTER, David James (retired) Alexandra Healthcare NHS Trust, Woodrow Drive, Redditch B98 7UB — MB BChir Camb. 1963; MA Camb. 1964, MD 1976; FRCP Lond. 1981, M 1969; DCH Eng. 1965. Cons. Phys. Alexandra Healthcare NHS Trust Redditch.

CARTER, Edith Caroline Christine (retired) 80 Harborne Road, Oldbury B68 9JH Tel: 0121 429 3325 — MB BS Lond. 1946. Prev: Ho. Phys. & Ho. Surg. Three Cos. Emerg. Hosp. (Roy. Free Hosp.

CARTER, Elaine Patricia The Childrens Hospital, Leicester Royal Infirmary, Leicester LE1 5WW Tel: 0116 254 1414; The Gables, Robert Hall Road, Arnesby, Leicester LE8 5UX Tel: 0116 247 8243 — MB ChB 1980 Sheff.; MA Camb. 1978, BA 1975; FRCP Lond. 1995; MRCP (UK) 1983; FRCPCH 1997. (Sheffield) Cons. Paediat. Leicester Roy. Infirm. Socs: Sec. Internat. Task Force Roy. Coll. Phys.s and Child Health; ICHG; BMA. Prev: Cons. (Paediat.) Whipps Cross Hosp.; Technical Manager Famine Relief Camp Ethiopia; Sen. Regist., Greayt Ormond St Hosp.

CARTER, Elaine Rae 51 Whitland Road, Liverpool L6 8NP — MB ChB 1993 Liverp.; DCH 1996.

CARTER, Elizabeth Ann Readesmoor Medical Group Practice, 29-29A West Street, Congleton CW12 1JP Tel: 01260 276161 Fax: 01260 297340; Warrendale, 100 Biddulph Road, Congleton CW12 3LY Tel: 01260 271094 — BM BS 1987 Nottm.; BMedSci Nottm. 1985; MRCGP (Distinc.) 1992. (Nottm.)

CARTER, Elizabeth Jane Hope 23 The Avenue, Lewes BN7 1QS Tel: 01273 483986 — MB BS 1977 Lond.; MRCS Eng. LRCP Lond. 1976; DMJ(Clin) Soc. Apoth. Lond. 1995; DCH Eng. 1980. (St. Thos.) Police Sur. Sussex Police; Clin. Asst. (Gynl.); Clin. Asst. (Psychiat.). Socs: Assn. Police Surg.; RSM.

CARTER, Elizabeth Joan Marsden, 10 Castle Road, Bayston Hill, Shrewsbury SY3 0NG — MB BS 1954 Durh.; Cert. FPA 1971. (Durh.) Clin. Med. Off. Shropsh. HA.

CARTER, Frances Clare 2 Desborough Avenue, High Wycombe HP11 2RN; 29 Ford Way, Downley, High Wycombe HP13 5XW — MB BS 1981 Lond.; DRCOG 1984. (St. Mary's, Paddington) p/t GP Princip. Prev: Trainee GP Wycombe Gen. Hosp. VTS.

CARTER, Frances Eleanor The Surgery, 6 Queens Walk, Ealing, London W5 1TP Tel: 020 8997 3041 Fax: 020 8566 9100; 36 Woodville Gardens, Ealing, London W5 2LQ Tel: 020 8997 2319 Fax: 020 8997 2319 Email: f.carter@ic.ac.uk — MB BS 1967 Lond.; BSc (Physiol) Lond. 1964; MRCP (UK) 1971; MRCGP 1996. (Middlx. Hosp. Med. Sch.) GP Partner; Sen. Teach. Fell. (Dept. Primary Care) Imperial Coll. Sch. Med. Prev: Regist. (Venereol.) Middlx. Hosp. Lond.; SHO St. Stephen's Hosp. Lond.; Ho. Phys. Brompton Hosp. Lond.

CARTER, Francis The Landscape Surgery, High Street, Garstang, Preston PR3 1FA Tel: 01995 603355 Fax: 01995 601810; Innisfree, 53 Croston Road, Garstang, Preston PR3 1HQ Tel: 01995 602106 — MRCS Eng. LRCP Lond. 1960; MRCGP 1968; DObst RCOG 1965. (Manch.) Local Med. Off. Civil Serv. Med. Serv. Socs: BMA. Prev: SHO (O & G) & Ho. Phys. Preston Roy. Infirm.; Ho. Surg. Sharoe Green Hosp. Preston.

CARTER, Francis George Temperley Hillgate, Crossways Road, Grayshott, Hindhead GU26 6HD Tel: 01428 606224 — MRCS Eng. LRCP Lond. 1950. (St. Bart.) Socs: BMA. Prev: Ho. Surg. & Ho. Phys. Gen. Hosp. N.ampton; Surg. Lt. RNVR.

CARTER, Francis James (retired) Jacaranda, Kilbride Road, Dunoon PA23 7LL Tel: 01369 702589 — LRCP LRCS Ed. LRFPS Glas. 1939.

CARTER, Frank Clifford Moorlands Surgery, 139 Willow Road, Darlington DL3 9JP Tel: 01325 469168; Baydale House, 317 Coniscliffe Road, Darlington DL3 8AH Tel: 01325 466125 — MB BS 1976 Newc.

CARTER, G Brian Bajac House, 2 The Avenue, Dunstable LU6 2AA Tel: 01582 606763 Fax: 01582 606763 Email: drbriancarter@compuserve.com — MB BS 1956 Lond.; DObst RCOG 1957. (Lond. Hosp.) Med. Translation from German (freelance). Socs: Comm. Mem. Anglo-German Med. Assn.; BMA; Med. Network, Inst. Translation & Interpreting. Prev: GP Luton; Ho. Off. (O & G) Hope Hosp. Salford; Ho. Surg. Salford Roy. Hosp.

CARTER, Gaynor Susan Selborne Road Medical Centre, 1 Selborne Road, Sheffield S10 5ND Tel: 0114 268 4422 Fax: 0114 266 9892; 73 Oldfield Road, Stannington, Sheffield S6 6DU Tel: 0114 234 0173 — MB ChB 1969 Sheff.; DObst RCOG 1972.

CARTER, Gillian Elizabeth 42 Anderson Drive, Burghmuir, Perth PH1 1JX — MB ChB 1996 Dundee.

CARTER, Gordon Huntly Health Centre, Jubilee Hospital, Bleachfield Street, Huntly AB54 8EX Tel: 01466 792116 Fax: 01466 794699; Ardgour, Lennox Terrace, Huntly AB54 8HG Tel: 01466 793264 — MB ChB 1986 Ed.; MRCGP 1990; DRCOG 1988. Prev: SHO (A & E) Raigmore Hosp. Inverness; Trainee GP Inverness VTS; Ho. Off. (Gen. Surg.) Raigmore Hosp. Inveness.

CARTER, Gregory John 50 Stockport Road, Marple SK6 6AB Tel: 0161 426 0299 — MB ChB 1987 Birm.; MRCGP 1992; DCH RCP Lond. 1990; DRCOG 1989. Prev: Trainee GP/SHO Macclesfield Dist. Gen. Hosp. VTS.

CARTER, Guy Stephen Edwards The Surgery, Walford House, Shrewsbury Street, Prees, Whitchurch SY13 2DH Tel: 01948 840206 Fax: 01948 840765 — MB BS 1978 Lond. (Middlx.) Bd. Mem. Shrops. Co. PCG Clin. Governance Lead. Socs: BASICS; SPA. Prev: Bd. Mem. N.E.Shrops. PCG Clin. Governance Lead.

***CARTER, Helen** 68 Rosslyn Dr, Wirral CH46 0SZ — MB ChB 1997 Birm.

CARTER, Howard Raymond St Peter's Medical Centre, 30-36 Oxford Street, Brighton BN1 4LA Tel: 01273 606006 Fax: 01273 623896; 18 Tongdean Avenue, Hove BN3 6TL Tel: 01273 553631 — MB BS 1969 Lond. (St. Mary's) Socs: Roy. Soc. Med. Prev: Ho. Phys. & Ho. Surg. Harold Wood Hosp.; SHO (Cas. & Orthop.) Battle Hosp. Reading; SHO (O & G) Qu. Eliz. II Hosp. Welwyn Garden City.

CARTER, Ian Spencer Newport Pagnell Medical Centre, Queens Avenue, Newport Pagnell MK16 8QT Tel: 01908 611767 Fax: 01908 615099 — MB BChir 1981 Camb.; MA Oxf. 1981; MRCGP 1986; Cert. Family Plann. JCC 1986; DCH RCP Lond. 1984. Prev: Trainee GP Oxf.; SHO (Paediat.) Wycombe Gen. Hosp.

CARTER, Irene Martha The Old Rectory, Saleby, Alford LN13 0HZ — MB ChB 1981 Dundee; BMSc Dund 1978, MB ChB 1981.

CARTER, James Henry Department of Anaesthesia, Sunderland Royal Hospital, Sunderland SR4 7TP Tel: 0191 565 6256 Fax: 0191 569 9217 — MB ChB 1985 Dundee; FRCA 1992; DA (UK) 1989. Cons. (Anaesth.) Sunderland Roy. Hosp. Socs: Soc. for Educat. in Anaesth. Prev: Sen. Regist. (Anaesth.) Newc. Hosp.; Fell. Anaesth. Woms. Coll. Hosp. Toronto; Cons. Anaesth. King Edwd. VII Hosp., Bermuda.

CARTER, Jamieson John Barnaby Seeps Barn, Calcot, Fossebridge, Cheltenham GL54 3JZ — MB BS 1998 Lond.; MB BS Lond 1998.

CARTER, Janet Elizabeth Flat 1, 25 Queensdown Road, London E5 8NN — MB BChir 1989 Camb.

CARTER, Jeremy Richard 16 Silverdale Road, Burgess Hill RH15 0EF — MB BS 1997 Lond.

CARTER, Joanne Kiveton Park Medical Practice, Kiveton Park Primary Care Centre, Chapel Way, Kiveton Park, Sheffield S26 6QU Tel: 01909 770213; 52 Oakfield Avenue, Chesterfield S40 3LE — MB ChB Leic. 1985.

CARTER, John Alasdair Fraser Pendleside Medical Practice, Clitheroe Health Centre, Railway View Road, Clitheroe BB7 2JG Tel: 01200 422674 Fax: 01200 443652; Oak House, Eastham St, Clitheroe BB7 2HY Tel: 01200 425904 Email: alascarter@aol.com — MB ChB 1975 Leeds; MB ChB (Hons.) Leeds 1975; MRCGP (Distinc.) 1979; DRCOG 1978; DFFP 1993; Dip. Med. Acupunc. 1995. (Leeds) Socs: Brit. Soc. Med. & Dent. Hypn.; GP Writers Assn.; Brit. Med. Acupunct. Soc. Prev: Trainee GP Gt. Yarmouth & Waveney VTS; Ho. Off. Huddersfield Roy. Infirm.

CARTER, John Ames St Lawrence Surgery, 4 Bocking End, Bocking, Braintree CM7 9AA Tel: 01376 552474; Bocking Lodge, Bocking End, Braintree CM7 9AE Tel: 01376 552460 — MB BS Lond. 1960; MRCS Eng. LRCP Lond. 1960; MRCGP 1971; DObst RCOG 1962. (St. Mary's) Prev: Ho. Surg. St. Mary's Hosp.; SHO (Obst.) & Ho. Phys. St. John's Hosp. Chelmsford.

CARTER, John Anthony Broomfield Hospital, Department Anaesthetics, Broomfield, Chelmsford CM1 7ET; 4 Snows Court, Great Waltham, Chelmsford CM3 1DE Tel: 01245 360145 — LMSSA 1979 Lond.; MA Camb. 1980, MB BChir 1979; FFA RCS Eng. 1984. Cons. Anaesth. Broomfield Hosp. Chelmsford.

CARTER, John Anthony Department of Anaesthesia, Frenchay Hospital, Bristol; Court Barton, Church Road, Doynton, Bristol BS30 5SU — MB BS 1973 Lond.; FFA RCS Eng. 1980. (St. Geo.) Regist. Prize Soc. Anaesth. S. W.. Region; Cons. Anaesth. Frenchay HA. Socs: IC Soc.; Assn. Anaesth. Gt. Brit. & Irel. Prev: Sen. Regist. (Anaesth.) S. W.. RHA; Sen. Regist. (Anaesth.) S. Austral. Anaesth. Train. Scheme; SHO (Anaesth.) P.ss Alexandra's Hosp. RAF Wroughton.

CARTER, John Braham 4 Dovecote Mews, Chorlton Green, Chorlton cum Hardy, Manchester M21 9HN — MB ChB 1991 Manch. Regist. (Radiol.) Manch. Roy. Infirm. Prev: SHO (A & E) Withington Hosp. Manch.; Ho. Off. (Surg.) Withington Hosp. Manch.; Ho. Off. (Med.) Robt. Barnes Unit Manch. Roy. Infirm.

CARTER, John Christopher Park Street Surgery, 33 Park Street, Leamington Spa CV32 4QN Tel: 01926 422580 Fax: 01926 410338 — MB ChB 1979 Birm.; BSc (Anat.) Birm. 1976, MB ChB 1979; MRCGP 1983; DRCOG 1981; Cert. Family Plann. JCC 1981; Cert. Av. Med. 1988. Med. Adviser Brit. Parachute Assn.

CARTER, John Clive Charles (retired) Old Orchard, New House Lane, Poslingford, Sudbury CO10 8QX Tel: 01787 277980 — MB BS 1962 Lond. Prev: Ho. Off. (O & G) St. And. Hosp. Billericay.

CARTER, John Henry Procter Lytham Road Surgery, 2 Lytham Road, Fulwood, Preston PR2 8JB Tel: 01772 716033 Fax: 01772 715445 — MB ChB 1984 Manch.; BSc St. And. 1981; MB ChB Manch. l984; MRCGP 1989; DRCOG 1988; DCH RCP Lond. 1987. Prev: Trainee GP Preston; SHO (Paediat. & Accid & Emerg.) Roy. Preston Hosp.; SHO (Paediat.) Alder Hey Childr. Hosp. Liverp.

CARTER, John Keith (retired) 1 Maplesden Close, Maidstone ME16 9JY Tel: 01622 726794 Email: kcarter@netcomuk.co.uk — MB BS Lond. 1949; MRCS Eng. LRCP Lond. 1948; FRCPath 1974, M 1964. Prev: Cons. Path. Maidstone Hosp.

CARTER, John Lister Bredin Department of Maxillofacial Surgery, The Royal London Hospital, Whitechapel, London E1 2AD Tel: 020 7377 7051 Fax: 020 7377 7095; Department of Oral & Maxillofacial Surgery, St. Margaret's Hospital, Epping Tel: 01279 827130 — MB BS 1978 Lond.; BDS Lond. 1973; FRCS Glas. 1984; MRCS Eng. LRCP Lond. 1978; FDS RCS Eng. 1983; T(S) 1991. Cons. Surg. Oral & Maxillofacial Surg. Roy. Lond. Hosp., St. Margt. Hosp. Epping & P.ss Alexandra Hosp. Harlow; Maxillofacial Unit Train. Dir. St. Barts & Roy. Lond. Hosps. Socs: Brit. Assn. Oral & Maxillofacial Surg.; Eur. Assn. Maxillo. Surg.; BMA. Prev: Sen. Regist. (Oral & Maxillofacial Surg.) Univ. Coll., W.m. & Qu. Mary's Hosps. Lond. & Munster Hosp.; Regist. (Oral & Maxillofacial Surg.) Lond. Hosp. Whitechapel; Profess. Ho. Surg. Maxillofacial Unit Lond. Hosp. Med. Coll.

CARTER, John Richard (retired) 90 Tranby Lane, Anlaby, Hull HU10 7EA Tel: 01482 657387 — MB BS 1946 Lond.; FRCP Lond. 1973, M 1948; MRCS Eng. LRCP Lond. 1942. Cons. Chest Phys. Hull & N. Humberside Health Dists. Prev: Med. Off. N.. Territory Australia.

CARTER, John Timothy Great Minster House, 76 Marsham Street, London SW1P 4LY Tel: 020 7944 2030 Fax: 020 7944 2029 Email: tim_carter@detr.gsi.gov.uk; 2 Thorngrove Avenue, Solihull B91 3XJ Email: tim.carter@virgin.net — MB BChir Camb. 1968; MSc (Occupat. Med.) Lond. 1973; FRCP Lond. 1987; FFOM RCP Lond. 1984, MFOM 1980; DHMSA 1978; DIH Eng. 1973. (Univ. Coll. Hosp.) Chief Med. Adviser (Transport Safety) D.E.T.R.; Hon. Sen. Clin. Lect. Inst. Occupat. Health, Univ. Birm.; Occupat. Health Cons. Solihull. Prev: Dir. Field Operats. & Med. Servs. Health & Safety Exec.; Sen. Med. Off. B.P. Chem.s; Lect. (Occupat Med.) Lond. Sch. Hyg. & Trop. Med.

CARTER, Mr John William, Col. late RAMC 9 Middle Avenue, Farnham GU9 8JL Tel: 01252 715129 — MB BS Lond. 1956; FRCS Eng. 1967; FRCS Ed. 1967; MRCS Eng. LRCP Lond. 1956; DTM & H Eng. 1965. (King's Coll. Hosp.)

CARTER, Jonathan James 6 Allesborough Road, Pershore WR10 1JH — MB BS 1998 Lond.; MB BS Lond 1998.

CARTER, Joseph Joachin 2 Baile Hill Ter, York YO1 6HF — MB ChB 1997 Sheff.

CARTER, Joyce Mary Liverpool Health Authority, Department of Public Health, Hamilton House, 24 Pall Mall, Liverpool L3 6AL Tel: 0151 285 2303 Fax: 0151 285 2007 Email: joyce.carter@liverpool-ha.nwest.nhs.uk — MB ChB 1977 Liverp.; MSc Manch. 1987; MFPHM 1989; MFCM 1987; DRCOG 1980. (Liverpool) Cons. Pub. Health Med. Liverp. HA.

CARTER, Judith Abbey Medical Centre, Norman Street, Leeds LS5 3JN Tel: 0113 295 1844 Fax: 0113 295 1845 — MB ChB 1973 Liverp.; Cert. Family Plann. JCC 1979; DObst RCOG 1975.

CARTER, Judy Ann Hatherley Cottage, Preston St Mary, Lavenham, Sudbury CO10 9NG — MB BS 1963 Lond.; MRCP (UK) 1974; MRCS Eng. LRCP Lond. 1963; DObst RCOG 1966; DCH Eng. 1965. Cons. Community Paediat. W. Suff. HA.

CARTER, Justin Marcus East House Farm, Trimdon Village, Trimdon Station TS29 6NH — MB ChB 1998 Bristol.

CARTER, Kim Marina 10 Allensbank Crescent, Cathays, Cardiff CF14 3PR — MB BCh 1993 Wales. SSHO O & G Llandough Hosp. Cardiff.

CARTER, Kim Teresa 321 Barkham Road, Wokingham RG41 4DG — MB BS 1997 Lond.

CARTER, Laurence David George Tisbury Surgery, Park Road, Tisbury, Salisbury SP3 6LF Tel: 01747 870204 Fax: 01747 871023 — MB ChB 1986 Manch.; MRCGP 1991; DCH RCP Lond. 1990; DRCOG 1988. Prev: Trainee GP Upavon Wilts.; SHO Blackburn Gp. VTS.

CARTER, Lesley The Beeches, Main Road, Huxley, Chester CH3 9BG Tel: 0182 924283 — MB ChB 1983 Liverp. Prev: SHO (Obst. Gyn. & Paediat.) Tarporley.

CARTER, Lisa Jane Ground Floor Flat, 5 Lovaine Row, North Shields NE30 4HF — MB ChB 1993 Ed.

CARTER, Lorna Joanne 1 The Mount, Ryton NE40 3NH — MB BS 1990 Newc.; MA Oxf. 1991, BA 1987; MRCGP 1994; DRCOG 1994; DCCH RCP Ed. 1993. GP Ryton. Prev: Trainee GP N.umbria; SHO (Psychiat.) Shotley Bridge Gen. Hosp.; SHO (O & G) Sunderland Dist. Gen. Hosp.

CARTER, Mark Paul 13 Maple Close, Kinver, Stourbridge DY7 6BT — MB ChB 1996 Leeds.

CARTER, Martyn James Gastroenterology & Liver Unit, Royal Hallamshire Hospital, Sheffield S10 2JF; 24 Walton Road, Botanical Gardens, Sheffield S11 8RE Tel: 0114 263 1286 Email: martyncarter@compuserve.com — BChir 1990 Camb.; MRCP (UK) 1994.

CARTER, Mary Yeo Bank, Congresbury, Bristol BS49 5JA — MRCS Eng. LRCP Lond. 1938; MRCPsych 1971; DPM Sydney 1945. (Univ. Coll. Hosp.) Emerit. Cons. Child Psychiat. & Subn. Bristol Health Dist. (T). Socs: BMA & Assn. for Child Psychol. & Psychiat. Prev: Hon. Asst. Cons. Psychiat. Roy. Alexandra Hosp. For Childr., Sydney, NSW.; Clin. Asst. (Child Psychiat.) SE RHB Scotl.; Sen. Regist. (Child Psychiat.) Aberd.

CARTER, Mary Elizabeth (cons. rooms), 138 Harley St., London W1N 1AH Tel: 020 7935 0554; 71 Marble House, Elgin Avenue, London W9 3PT Tel: 020 7289 5883 — MB BS 1954 Lond.; MD Lond. 1961; FRCP Ed. 1974, M 1965. (St. Mary's) Sen. Research Fell. (Clin.) Dept of Biol. & Med. Systems Imperial Coll. Lond.; Cons. Phys. & Hon. Clin. Sen. Lect. (Rheum. & Rehabil.) St. Mary's Hosp. Lond. Socs: Fell. Roy. Soc. Med.; Brit. Soc. Rheum.; Brit. Soc. Rehabil. Med. Prev: Sen. Regist. (Med.) & Ho. Phys. Med. Unit St. Mary's Hosp.; Regist. (Med.) Rheum. Research Unit. Canad. Red Cross Memor. Hosp. Taplow.

CARTER, Maxwell John 79 Harley Street, London W1N 1DE Tel: 020 7935 7403; 39 Gunnersbury Avenue, Ealing Common, London W5 3XD Tel: 020 8992 0394 — LRCP LRCS Ed. LRFPS Glas. 1959; BDS Sydney 1953; FACDS 1966. Med. Off. to Various Companys. Socs: Assur. Med. Soc.; Soc. Occupat. Med.

CARTER, Melanie Dawn Rowheath Farm, Rectory Road, Weeley Heath, Clacton-on-Sea CO16 9BL Tel: 01255 830330 Email: melaniecarter81@hotmail.com — MB BS 1997 Lond. (UCL Med.Sch.) SHO. Surg. Rotat. Ipswich. Hosp. Suff. Socs: WIST; ASIT; SCARS (SNO.Representive). Prev: Surg.HO.Whittington.Hosp.; Med.HO.Ipswich.Hosp.

CARTER, Michael Charles Nicholas Stanwell Road Surgery, 95 Stanwell Road, Ashford TW15 3EA Tel: 01784 253565 Fax: 01784 244145 — MB BS 1975 Lond.; DCH Eng. 1977.

CARTER, Michael Greenwood Stone Cottage, 14 Summerhill Rd, Prestbury, Macclesfield SK10 4AH Tel: 01625 820927 Fax: 01625 820471 — MB ChB Sheff. 1965; BPharm (Hons.) Lond. 1960; FRCP Ed. 1995; FFPM RCP (UK) 1989; Dip. Pharm. Med. RCP (UK) 1977. Dir. Zeneca Pharmaceut. Chesh.; Bd. Mem. Galen Plc; Bd. Mem.

Metris Therap; Bd. Mem. Radamacher; Bd. Mem. Phairson Med.; Bd. Mem. Kudos Pharmaceut.; Venture Partner, Schroder's Int. Life Scis. Socs: Fell. Roy. Pharmaceut. Soc.; Roy.Soc. Med. Prev: Mem. Med. Commiss.; Dir. Pharmaceut. Div. Roche Products Ltd. Welwyn Gdn. City; Internat. Med. & Marketing Dir. Zeneca Pharmaceut. Chesh.

CARTER, Michael Ivor 33 Wallace Drive, Eaton Bray, Dunstable LU6 2DF Tel: 01525 221187 Fax: 01525 221187 — MB BChir 1978 Camb.; MA Camb. 1977; FFA RCS Eng. 1982; DA Eng. 1979. Cons. Anaesth. Luton & Dunstable Hosp. Socs: BMA; Assoc. Mem. Assn. Anaesth. GB & Irel.; Obst. Anaesth. Assn. Prev: Sen. Regist. Rotat. (Anaesth.) Middlx. Hosp.

CARTER, Mr Michael Rust Wessex Neurological Centre, Southampton General Hospital, Tremona Road, Southampton SO16 6YD Tel: 02380 777222 Fax: 02380 794148; Tel: 01722 339658 — FRCS (Neurology) 2001; BM Soton. 1988; FRCS (Ed.) 1993; FRCS (Eng.) 1993. (Southampton University Medical School) Specialist Reg. Neurosurg., Wessex Neurol. Centre, Soton. Gen. Hosp.; Hon. Research Regist. Genetics, Wessex Regional Genetics Laborat., Salisbury Dist. Hosp. Prev: Regist. Gen. Surg. Soton.; Regist. Gen. Surg. Salisbury; Regist. Cardiothoracic Surg. Soton.

CARTER, Naomi Department of Forensic Pathology, University of Sheffield, The Medico-Legal Centre, Watery St., Sheffield S3 7ES Tel: 0114 273 8721 Fax: 0114 279 8942 Email: forensic.path.@sheffield.ac.uk — MB ChB 1988 Liverp.; BSc (Hons.) Liverp. 1985; MRCPath (Histopath.) 1994; DRCPath (Forens. Path.) 1995. (Univ. Liverp.) Sen. Lect. & Hon. Cons. (Forens. Path.) Univ. Sheff.; Cons. Path. Home Off. Socs: Path. Soc.; Assn. Clin. Path.; Brit. Assn. Forens. Med. Prev: Lect. & Hon. Sen. Regist. Sheff. Univ.; Regist. (Histopath.) Roy. Hallamsh. Childr. & N.. Gen. Hosps. Sheff.; SHO (Histopath.) Roy. Liverp. Hosp.

CARTER, Mr Neil John Thornton Road Surgery, 299 Thornton Road, Croydon CR0 3EW Tel: 020 8683 1255 Fax: 020 8251 0166; 38 Plough Lane, Purley CR8 3QA Tel: 020 8668 5180 Fax: 020 8407 0850 Email: 123456789@cableinet.co.uk — MB BS Calcutta 1958; FRCS Eng. 1965. (Calcutta) Med. Advisor Brit. Gas Trading, Staines, Middlx. Socs: Soc. Occupat. Med. & BMA. Prev: Regist. (Surg.) Hereford Gp. & Croydon Gen. Hosp.; Clin. Asst. Mayday Hosp. Dermat. & Rheum.

CARTER, Neill William Roy 25 Scotts Close, Churchstow, Kingsbridge TQ7 3RB — MB BS 1997 Lond.

CARTER, Nelson Paul Sandwell General Hospital, Department of Anaesthetics, Lyndon, West Bromwich B71 4HJ Tel: 0121 553 1831; 1 Moorland Road, Edgbaston, Birmingham B16 9JP Tel: 0121 455 0885 — MB BS 1978 Lond.; BSc (Biochem. Hons.) Lond. 1975, MB BS 1978; FFA RCS Eng. 1984. Cons. Anaesth. Sandwell Healthcare NHS Trust.

CARTER, Nicholas Charles, SHO — MBBS. (Imperial College School of Medicine) Basic Surgic. Trainee, 2 Year Rotat. Prev: Surgic. Ho. Off., Gen. Surg., Chelsea and W.m. Hosp.; Surgic. Ho. Off., Gen./ Resp. Med., Chelsea and W.m. Hosp.

CARTER, Nicola Jane Green Lane Medical Centre, 15 Green Lane, Stoneycroft, Liverpool L13 7DY Tel: 0151 228 9101 Fax: 0151 228 2472 — MB ChB 1984 Liverp.; MRCGP 1989; MFFP 1993.

CARTER, Patricia Edwina West Cumberland Hospital, Hensingham, Whitehaven CA28 8TG Tel: 01496 693181 — MB ChB 1975 Aberd.; MRCP (UK) 1979; FRACP 1984; DCH RCP Lond. 1977. Cons. Paediat. W. Cumbld. Hosp. Prev: Sen. Regist. (Paediat.) Roy. Aberd. Childr. Hosp.; Regist. (Paediat.) Roy. Edin. Childr. Hosp.; Regist. (Paediat.) Roy. Brisbane Childr. Hosp.

CARTER, Paul Brian 19 Granby Crescent, Wirral CH63 9NY — MB BS 1994 Newc.

CARTER, Paul Frederick Beale Department of Community Child Health, Sycamore House, 111 Birmingham Road, Walsall WS1 2NL Tel: 01922 858148 Fax: 01922 626971 Email: carterp@cht.walsallch-tr.wmids.nhs.uk; Bancroft House, Nethertown, Hamstall Ridware, Rugeley WS15 3QH Tel: 01889 504347 Email: pcarter@bancroftho.freeserve.co.uk — MB BS 1977 Lond.; MA Camb. 1977, BA (Engin.) 1971; MRCP (UK) 1981; DCH Eng. 1979; FRCPCH 1997. (Lond. Hosp.) Cons. Community Paediat. Walsall.; Hon. Vis. Lect. community paediatric dept, Univ. of Warwick.; Hon. Sen. Clin. Lect., Div. of reproductive and child hhealth, Univ. of Birm. Prev: SCMO Grampian HB; Clin. Med. Off. Sheff. HA; SHO Hosp. Sick Childr. Gt. Ormond St.

CARTER, Mr Paul Gareth Tel: 020 8672 1255 Fax: 020 8725 2030; 36 Ravenscoft Park, High Barnet, Enfield EN5 4NH Tel: 020 8449 3410 Email: paulgcarter@aol.com — MB BS 1983 Lond.; BSc (Hons.) Lond. 1980; FRCS Eng. 1988; MRCOG 1991; MD (Lond) 1998. (St. Bart.) Cons. St. Geo. Hosp. Lond.; Admitting rights to Pk.side Hosp., Wimbledon, the Portland Hosp., Lond. Bridge Hosp. Prev: Clin. Research Fell. (Gyn. Oncol.) St. Bart. & Roy. Marsden Hosps. Lond.; Regist. (O & G) Guy's Hosp. Lond.; SHO (O & G) Qu. Charlotte's & Chelsea Hosp. Lond.

CARTER, Paul Gerard St. Richard's Hospital, Chichester PO19 4SE Tel: 01243 788122 — MB ChB 1983 Liverp.; MD Bristol 1992; FRCS (Urol.) 1994; FRCS Ed. 1988. Cons. Urol. Surg. St. Richards Hosp., Chichester. Prev: Sen. Regist. (Urol.) S.E. Thames.

CARTER, Paul Sydney 56 Montacute Way, Wimborne BH21 1TZ — MB BS 1980 Lond.; MS Lond. 1995; FRCS (Gen.) 1997; FRCS Eng. 1987. Cons. (Gen.Surg), Roy. Liverp. Univ. Hosp. Socs: Roy. Soc. Med. (Colproctol. Sect.); Assn. Coloproctol. Prev: Sen. Reg (Gen.Surg), Soton. Gen. Hosp.; Sen. Regist. (Gen. Surg.) St Geo. Hosp.; ICRF Research Fell. Colorectal Cancer Unit St. Marks Hosp. Lond.

CARTER, Peter Allan The Surgery, 37 Warwick Avenue, Grimsby DN33 1EJ Tel: 01472 877876 Fax: 01472 752122; Willow Dene, Hawthorne Avenue, Scartho, Grimsby DN33 2NE Tel: 01472 823444 Fax: 01472 823444 — MB BS 1958 Lond.; MRCS Eng. LRCP Lond. 1958; DObst RCOG 1960. (St. Mary's) Marine Safety Agency Med. Off. Grimsby; Martin John Turner Schol.. 1955. Socs: BMA (Sec. Grimsby Div.). Prev: SHO Matern. Hosp. Camb.; Ho. Phys. Roy. Berks. Hosp. Reading & Paddington Green Childr. Hosp.

CARTER, Peter Andrew 36 Stubbs Wood, Amersham HP6 6EX — MB BS 1997 Lond.

CARTER, Peter Eric Graham, MBE (retired) Dalbarrach Cottage, Cullerlie, Westhill AB32 6UX Tel: 01224 743231 — MB ChB Aberd. 1968; MA Camb. 1958; DObst RCOG 1972. Prev: Asst. (Orthop. Surg.) & Phys. (Community Health) Grampian HB.

CARTER, Peter John 81 Tolmers Road, Cuffley, Potters Bar EN6 4JJ — MB BS 1947 Lond.

CARTER, Peter Martin 44 Capelands, New Ash Green, Longfield DA3 8LG Tel: 01474 873421 — MB ChB 1982 Bristol. Indep. GP Kent. Prev: GP Swanley; SHO (Paediat.) Liverp. HA; SHO (Med.) Bromley HA.

CARTER, Peter Sheldon 23 Shear Bank Road, Blackburn BB1 8AP Tel: 01254 57375 — MB ChB 1957 Liverp. (Liverp.)

CARTER, Philip Andrew West-Winds, Bradshaw Lane, Halifax HX2 9XB — MB ChB 1995 Dundee.

CARTER, Philip Paul (retired) 2 Highfield Crescent, Southampton SO17 1SF Tel: 023 8055 6264 Email: philip_p.carter@virgin.net — MB ChB 1957 Manch.; FRCGP 1979, M 1974.

CARTER, Ralph Trevor Jacobus 27 Jocelyn Road, Richmond TW9 2TJ — MB ChB 1985 Sheff.; MSc City 1991, MB ChB 1985. Med. Advisor, roche Products Ltd., Welwyn Garden City; Clin. Asst. (A & E), W.Middlx. Univ. Hosp. (pat-time). Socs: Brit. Assn. Med. Managers. Prev: Gen. Manager, St. Helier NHS Trust; MSc Studies Business Systems Anal. & Design City Univ. Lond.; SHO (O & G) Sheff.

CARTER, Richard (retired) Marsden, 10 Castle Road, Bayston Hill, Shrewsbury SY3 0NG — MB BS 1957 Durh.

CARTER, Richard Alan (retired) 1 Lindsworth Road, Kings Norton, Birmingham B30 3NH Tel: 0121 459 7205 — MA Camb. 1955, MB BChir 1954; FRCP Lond. 1981, M 1956; FRCPath 1975, M 1965. Prev: Cons. Path. Hollymoor & Marston Green Hosps.

CARTER, Richard Charles Tokewood Surgery, Fair Oak Road, Fair Oak, Eastleigh SO50 8AU Tel: 023 8069 2000 Fax: 023 8069 3891 — MB ChB 1975 Liverp.; DRCOG 1977; Cert Contracep. & Family Plann. RCOG, RCGP &; Cert FPA 1975. Prev: Ho. Off. (Gen. Med., O & G) Ormskirk & Dist. Gen. Hosp.

CARTER, Richard Charles The Gatehouse, Breinton, Hereford HR4 7PB — MB BS 1986 Lond.; DA (UK) 1990. Regist. (Anaesth.) St. Geo. Hosp. Lond.

CARTER, Professor Richard Lawrance, CBE (retired) Childrens Department, Royal Marsden Hospital, Sutton SM2 5PT Tel: 020 8643 8901 — BM BCh Oxf. 1960; DSc Lond. 1976; MA Oxf. 1960, DM 1966; FFPM RCP (UK) 1994; FRCPath 1978, M 1969. Cons. Path. Thames Cancer Registry. Prev: Vis.Prof.Sch.Biological Sci. Uni.Surrey.

CARTER, Robert Tel: 0183 369 0707 Fax: 0183 369 0840; The Old Vicarage, Laithkirk, Middleton in Teesdale, Barnard Castle DL12 0NS — MB ChB 1985 Manch.; MRCGP 1990. (Manchester) Prev: GP. Partner Middleton St. Geo.; Trainee GP Cleveland VTS; SHO (Gen. Med.) Bolton HA.

CARTER, Robert Lewis 7 The Paddock, Lisvane, Cardiff CF14 0AY — MB ChB 1997 Ed.

CARTER, Robert Nattress (retired) Leeholm, 44 Griffin Road, Braybrooke, Market Harborough LE16 8LH Email: robertn.carter@lineone.net — MB ChB 1958 Aberd.; DObst RCOG 1960; MRCGP 1969. Tutor Roy. Free Hosp. Med. Sch. Lond.; GP Trainer Newc. RHA. Prev: Lect. Univ. Edin. Gen. Pract. Teachg. Unit.

CARTER, Robin George Hollands and Partners, Bridport Medical Centre, North Allington, Bridport DT6 5DU Tel: 01308 421896 Fax: 01308 421109; 6 Bowhayes, Bothen Hampton, Bridport DT6 4EB — MB ChB 1972 Liverp.; MRCGP 1981; DA Eng. 1979; DObst RCOG 1974.

CARTER, Romilly Grace 9 Venturefair Avenue, Dunfermline KY12 0PF — MB BCh BAO 1974 Belf.; DRCOG 1976. GP Fife.

CARTER, Ronald Charles Willen Village Surgery, Beaufort Drive, Willen, Milton Keynes MK15 9ET Tel: 01908 230877 Fax: 01908 230885 — MB ChB 1975 Birm.

CARTER, Ronald Frank 149 Gledhow Valley Road, Leeds LS7 4JU Tel: 0113 262 4258 — MB ChB 1952 Leeds. Dir. IC Unit & Med. Asst. (Anaesth.) St. Jas. Hosp.; Leeds. Socs: Assoc. Mem. Yorks. Soc. Anaesths. Prev: SHO Anaesth. Roy. Gwent Hosp. Newport; Anaesth. Regist. & Anaesth. SHO Leeds Gen. Infirm.

CARTER, Ronald Frank (retired) 9 Cecil Close, Watlington, King's Lynn PE33 0JS Tel: 01553 810035 — MB BS 1969 Lond.; FFA RCS Eng. 1976. Prev: Cons. Anaesth. Freeman Hosp. Newc.

CARTER, Sara Elizabeth Lawrence Hill Health Centre, Hassell Drive, Bristol BS2 0AN Tel: 0117 955 5241 Fax: 0117 941 1162 — BM 1983 Soton.

CARTER, Sarah Joanne 5 Airlie Court, Glenagles Village, Auchterarder PH3 1SA — MB ChB 1995 Dundee; DRCOG 1998. SHO Paediat., Stirling Roy. Infirm. Prev: SHO A & E, Stirling Roy. Infirm.; SHO Dermat., Ninewells Hosp. Dundee; SHO O & G, Stirling Roy. Infirm.

CARTER, Sheila Handley Ger-y-Nant, Abergwili, Carmarthen SA31 2JL — MB ChB 1960 Glas. Assoc. Specialist Paediat. Dept. W. Wales Gen. Hosp. Carmarthen.

CARTER, Shelley Jane 6 De Redvers Road, Poole BH14 8TS — BM 1992 Soton.

CARTER, Sidney John, Group Capt. RAF Med. Br. Retd. (retired) Holme Crest, Mount Pleasant, Greenodd, Ulverston LA12 7RG Tel: 01229 861341 — MB BS 1955 Lond.; FFA RCS Eng. 1966; DA Eng. 1963. Prev: Cons. Anaesth. Furness Gen. Hosp. Barrow in Furness.

CARTER, Simon Richard The Surgery, 14 Leach Green Lane, Rubery, Birmingham B45 9BL Tel: 0121 453 3516; 4 The Stables, Old Birmingham Road, Alvechurch, Birmingham B48 7TQ — MB ChB 1988 Birm. (Univ. Birm.) Socs: BMA.

CARTER, Mr Simon Robert Royal Orthopaedic Hospital Oncology Service, Royal Orthopaedic Hospital, Birmingham B31 2AP Tel: 0121 685 4150 Fax: 0121 627 8644; Rambervillers, 11 Marlborough Avenue, Bromsgrove B60 2PG Tel: 01527 874866 — MB BS 1979 Lond.; FRCS Lond. & Glas. 1983. (St. Thos.) Cons. Bone Tumour Treatm. Serv. Roy. Orthop. Hosp. Birm. Socs: Brit. Orthop. Assn.; Internat. Soc. Limb Salvage Surg.; Brit. Orthop. Oncol. Soc. Prev: Sen. Regist. & Regist. Birm. Orthop. Train. Scheme; Regist. & SHO Rotat. (Surg.) N. Staffs. Roy. Infirm.; Cas. Off. St. Thos. Hosp. Lond.

CARTER, Mr Simon St Clair 147 Harley Street, London W1G 6BL Tel: 020 7487 4426 Fax: 020 7935 5608; 24 Milson Road, London W14 0LJ Tel: 020 7602 3270 Fax: 020 7371 2231 — MB BS 1976 Lond.; FRCS Eng. 1982; FRCS Ed. 1981; MRCS Eng. LRCP Lond. 1976. (Westm.) Cons. Urol. Hammersmith Hosps. Trust. Socs: Fell. Roy. Soc. Med. Hon. Sec.; Liveryman Worshipful Soc. Apoth. Prev: Cons. Urol. Centr. Middlx. Hosp.; Sen. Regist. St. Peters Hosp. Lond.; Lect. Inst. Urol. Lond.

CARTER, Sita Monica Station Road Surgery, 74 Station Road, West Wickham BR4 0PU Tel: 020 8777 8245; 148 Woodland Way, West Wickham BR4 9LU — MB ChB 1971 Bristol; DObst RCOG 1973. Prev: Ho. Surg. Dreadnought Seaman's Hosp. Greenwich; Ho. Phys. & Ho. Surg. (O & G) Qu. Mary's Hosp. Sidcup.

CARTER, Sophie Eleanor 23 Orchard Avenue, Woodham, Addlestone KT15 3EA — BM BCh 1998 Oxf.; BM BCh Oxf 1998.

CARTER, Stephen Merrick Flat 1, 8 Henleaze Road, Bristol BS9 4EX; Rowan Cottage, 17 Grange Close N., Henleaze, Bristol BS9 4BY Tel: 01179 622987 — MRCS Eng. LRCP Lond. 1971. Sessional Doctor S.mead Blood Transfus. Centre Bristol. Prev: Sessional Doctor S.mead Blood Transfus. Centre Bristol; Ho. Phys. Rochford Hosp.; Ho. Surg. Harold Wood Hosp.

CARTER, Steven The Old Rectory, Saleby, Alford LN13 0HZ — MB ChB 1981 Dundee.

CARTER, Susan Jane Gossops Green Medical Centre, Hurst Close, Mowbray Drive, Gossops Green, Crawley RH11 8LD; 33, Depot Road, Horsham RM13 5ME Tel: 01403 218785 — BM 1984 Soton.; MRCGP 1990; DRCOG 1988. p/t Asst. (Gen. Pract.) Retainer Scheme Gossops Green Med. Centre Crawley. Prev: Asst. GP Chesterfield; Clin. Med. Off. (Community Child Health) Gwent HA.

CARTER, Miss Susan Maureen Academic Department of Surgery, Royal Free Hospital, Pond St., London NW3 2QG — BM 1984 Soton.; FRCS Eng. 1993. Research Fell. (Acad. Surg.) Roy. Free Hosp. Lond. Prev: SHO (Vasc. & Gen. Surg.) St. Geo. Hosp. Lond.; SHO (Gen. Surg.) Chelsea & W.m. Hosp. Lond.; SHO (Urol.) St. Geo. Hosp. Lond.

CARTER, Teresa Annunziata Community House, 124 Middleton Road, Morden SM4 6RW Tel: 020 8685 9922; 6 Banks Way, Guildford GU4 7NL — MB BS 1983 Lond.; MRCP (UK) 1987; DCH RCP Lond. 1986. SCMO (Community Paediat.) Merton & Sutton HA. Socs: Community Paediat. Gp.; Brit. Paediat. Assn. Prev: Clin. Med. Off. (Community Paediat.) Wandsworth HA.

CARTER, Thomas Acheson Harden Lothian Health Board, Deaconess Hospital, 148 Pleasance, Edinburgh EH8 9RS Tel: 0131 536 9180 Fax: 0131 536 9164 Email: harden.carter@lhb.scot.nhs.uk; 9 Venturefair Avenue, Dunfermline KY12 0PF Tel: 01383 720560 — MB BCh BAO 1973 Belf.; MRCP (UK) 1977; MRCGP 1981; MFPHM 1985; FFPHM 1998; FRCP 1998. Cons. Pub. Health Med. Lothian Health Bd.; Cons. Pub. Health Priority Serv.s and child health. Prev: Cons.Pub.Health med. Forth Valley Health Bd.

CARTER, Thomas John, OBE (retired) 7 St Pauls Way, Finchley, London N3 2PP Tel: 020 8343 4005 Fax: 020 8343 4007 Email: john@carterj.freeserve.co.uk — MRCS Eng. LRCP Lond. 1957. Prev: Sen. Med. Dir. Healthcall Gp. Plc.

CARTER, Timothy James West Sussex Health Authority, 1 The Causeway, Durrington, Worthing BN12 6BT Tel: 01903 708444 Email: tim.carter@wsha.nhs.uk; 3 Uplands Avenue, Worthing BN13 3AA — MB BS 1973 Lond.; 1997 (Dth) Cardiff; MRCS Eng. LRCP Lond. 1973; DA Eng. 1978. (St. Thos.) Med. Adviser W. Sussex HA; Partner, The Surg., Burgess Hill. Prev: Partner St Andrews Surg. Lewes; SHO Yeovil Dist. Hosp.; Ho. Off. St. Thos. Hosp.

CARTER, Timothy John Moore Health Centre, Moore Health Centre, Moore Road, Bourton on the Water, Cheltenham GL54 2AZ — MB BChir 1972 Camb.; MA Camb. 1972; MRCGP 1979; DObst RCOG 1975. Clin. Asst. (Geriat. Med.) E. Glos. NHS Trust. Socs: Roy. Soc. Med.

CARTER, Timothy Ralph Garth (cons. rooms), 54 Burdon Lane, Cheam, Sutton SM2 7BY Tel: 020 8642 9391 Fax: 020 8770 1614 — MA Camb. 1964, MB BChir 1963. (Camb. & St. Bart.) Prev: Ho. Surg. St. Bart. Hosp.; Ho. Phys. S.end Gen. Hosp. Surg. Lt. RN.

CARTER, Tobias Edward 3 Glebe Road, Long Ashton, Bristol BS41 9LJ — MB ChB 1996 Aberd.

CARTER, Vivien Lesley Rectory Meadow Surgery, School Lane, Amersham HP7 0HG Tel: 01494 727711 Fax: 01494 431790; 44 Copperkins Lane, Amersham HP6 5QP — MB BS 1983 Lond.; MRCGP 1988; DRCOG 1987. Socs: Brit. Med. Acupunct. Soc.

CARTER, Vivienne 203 Conkwell, Bradford-on-Avon BA15 2JQ — MB BS 1971 Newc.

CARTER, Professor Yvonne Helen Medical Sciences Building, Queen Mary University of London, Mile End Road, London E1 4NS Tel: 020 7882 7906 Fax: 020 7882 7905 Email: y.h.carter@qmul.ac.uk; 25 Thames Crescent, Chiswick, London W4 2RU Tel: 020 8994 9797 Fax: 020 8994 9797 — MB BS 1983 Lond.; Fmed Sci 1998; BSc (Hons. cl. IIa Basic Med. Sc. Pharmacol.) Lond. 1980; MB BS (Distinc. Obst. & Gyn.) Lond. 1983; MD Lond. 1994; FRCGP 1994, M 1987; DCH RCP Lond. 1986; DRCOG 1985.

(St. Mary's) Prof. & Head Dept. Gen. Pract. & Primary Care St. Bart. & Roy. Lond. Sch. Med. & Dent., Barts and the Lond., Qu. Mary's Sch. of Med. and Dent.; GP Chrisp. St. Health Centre, Tower Hamlets. Socs: Fell.Acad. Med. Sci.s; Fell. RSM; Fell. RSA. Prev: Sen. Lect. (Gen. Pract.) Univ. Birm.; GP Liverp. & Newc. u. Lyme; Trainee GP/SHO S. Sefton HA VTS.

CARTHIGESAN, Skandhini 3 Tillingbourne Gardens, London N3 3JJ — MRCS Eng. LRCP Lond. 1988; MRCP (UK) Paediat. 1992; DCH RCP Lond. 1994. Cons. Paediat. Medway Maritime Hosp. Gillingham, Kent.

CARTLEDGE, Aidan Geoffrey Wildwood, Forest Road, East Horsley, Leatherhead KT24 5EY — MB BS 1996 Lond. (St Georges) SHO (Psychiat.) Ridgewood Centre Frimley Surrey.

CARTLEDGE, Jonathan David 24 Orchard Way, Studley B80 7NZ — MB ChB 1988 Bristol.

CARTLEDGE, Mr Jonathan James — MB BCh 1990 Wales; FRCS Ed. 1995. Specialist Regist. (Urol.) Leeds.

CARTLEDGE, Robert (retired) 89 Cyprus Road, Mapperley Park, Nottingham NG3 5ED Tel: 0115 960 5501 — MB ChB 1952 Sheff. Prev: Ho. Phys. & Asst. Cas. Off. Roy. Hosp. Sheff.

CARTLEDGE, William Simon 1 Stalls Cottage, Lugg Bridge Farm, Lugg Bridge, Hereford HR1 3NA — MB ChB 1994 Birm.; DRCOG 1996.

CARTLIDGE, Mr David Accident & Emergency Department, Glanclwyd DGH, Boddelwyddan, Rhyl LL18 5UJ Tel: 01745 534109 — MB ChB 1978 Manch.; FRCS Ed. 1989; FRCS Lond. 1983; FFAEM 1995; DA (UK) 1990. Cons. A & E Med. Glan Clwyd Dist. Gen. Hosp. NHS Trust. Prev: Sen. Regist. (A & E Med.) Yorks. RHA.

CARTLIDGE, Elaine Allison North Avenue Surgery, 18 North Avenue, Cambuslang, Glasgow G72 8AT Tel: 0141 641 3037 Fax: 0141 646 1905 — MB ChB 1976 Glas.; MRCP (UK) 1979.

CARTLIDGE, Mr Ian James 249 Fenwick Road, Giffnock, Glasgow G46 6JQ — MB ChB 1972 Ed.; FRCS Ed. 1976.

CARTLIDGE, Margaret Eleanor 1 Hawthorn Road W., Gosforth, Newcastle upon Tyne NE3 4DN Tel: 0191 285 3241 — MB ChB 1966 St. And. (St. And.) Gen. Pract.

CARTLIDGE, Niall Edward Foster 1 Hawthorn Road W., Gosforth, Newcastle upon Tyne NE3 4DN Tel: 0191 285 3241 Fax: 0191 285 3241 Email: nefcartlidge@ncl.ac.uk — MB BS 1966 Newc.; MB BS (1st cl. Hons.) Newc. 1966; FRCP Lond. 1980, M 1968. (Newc.) Cons. & Sen. Lect. (Neurol.) Roy. Vict. Infirm. Newc. Prev: Fell. Neurol. Mayo Clinic Rochester USA; 1st Asst. (Neurol.) Roy. Vict. Infirm. Newc.

CARTLIDGE, Patrick Hugh Thurstan Department of Child Health, University Hospital of Wales, Heath Park, Cardiff CF14 4XN Tel: 029 2074 3387 Fax: 029 2074 4302; 6 Meadowgate Close, Whitchurch, Cardiff CF14 7EX — MB ChB 1980 Sheff.; DM Nottm. 1988; FRCP Lond. 1994; MRCP (UK) 1983; FRCPCH 1997. Sen. Lect. (Child Health) Univ. Wales Coll. Med. Cardiff. Socs: Neonat. Soc. Paediat. Research Soc.; Brit. Assn. Perinatal Med. Prev: Sen. Regist. (Paediat.) S.mead Hosp. Bristol; Regist. (Paediat.) & MRC Research Fell. City Hosp. Nottm.

***CARTLIDGE-EIGHAN, Mrs Rachel Elizabeth** 5 Hallworth Avenue, Audenshaw, Manchester M34 5ST Tel: 0161 370 2305 — MB ChB 1996 Liverp.; BA (Med. Sci.) Cantab. 1993.

CARTMEL, Richard Michael Ailsworth Surgery, 32 Main Street, Ailsworth, Peterborough PE5 7AF Tel: 01733 380686 Fax: 01733 380400; 144 Mayors Walk, Peterborough PE3 6HA Tel: 01733 310110 Fax: 01733 894722 — BM BCh 1977 Oxf.; BA (Hons) Oxf. 1973. GP; NW Anglia LMC. Socs: Bd. Mem. Dispensing Doctors Assn. Prev: SHO (Neurol.) Spinal Injuries Pinderfields Hosp. Wakefield; SHO (Cardiol. & Chest) Papworth Hosp. Camb.

CARTMELL, Emma Louise 25 Netherland Road, Barnet EN5 1BW — MB BS 1995 Lond.; MRCP (Paediat.) Lond. 1998. Prev: SHO (Paediat. Oncol.) Middlx. Hopsital; SHO (Neonatology) Barnet Gen. Hosp.; SHO (Paediat.) Barnet Gen. Hosp.

CARTMELL, Mark Timothy North Devon District Hospital, Raleigh Park, Barnstaple EX31 4JB — MB BS 1994 Lond.

CARTMELL, Nigel Vincent 44 Woodley Avenue, Thornton-Cleveleys FY5 4EJ — MB BS 1994 Lond.

CARTMILL, Ann Dolores Sarehole Surgery, 60 Colebank Road, Hall Green, Birmingham B28 8EY Tel: 0121 777 1315 Fax: 0121 777 0865; Tel: 0121 705 0267 — MB BS 1990 Lond.; BSc (Hons.) Lond. 1987; MRCGP 1994; DFFP 1996; DRCOG 1996. (St Georges) GP Princip.; Clin. Asst. (Paediat. Dermat.) Birm. Childr. Hosp. Prev: Trainee GP/SHO Rotat. S. Birm. HA VTS.

CARTMILL, Dorothy Joan 29 Whitehouse Lane, Great Preston, Woodlesford, Leeds LS26 8BH — MB BCh BAO 1949 Dub. (T.C. Dub.)

CARTMILL, Jacqueline Louise 47 Legacorry Road, Richhill, Armagh BT61 9LF — MB BCh BAO 1994 Belf.

CARTMILL, Miss Maria 70 Selby Road, West Bridgford, Nottingham NG2 7BL — MB ChB 1990 Sheff.; FRCS Eng. 1994. (Sheff.) Specialist Regist. (Neurosurg.). Socs: Brit. Neuro-oncol. Gp.; Eur. Soc. Paediat. Neurosurg.; Soc. Brit. Neurolog. Surgs. (SBNS).

CARTMILL, Richard Samuel Victor Good Hope Hospital, Rectory Road, Sutton Coldfield B75 7RR Tel: 0121 378 2211 Fax: 0121 378 6029 Email: richard.cartmill@lineone.ney; 52 Station Road,, Sutton Coldfield B73 5JY Tel: 0121 355 0550 Email: richard.carthill@lineone.net — MB BCh BAO 1983 Belf.; MFFP 1995; MRCOG 1988, D 1985. (Qu. Univ. Belf.) Cons. Obstertrician & Gyn.; Coll. tutor, RCOG; Hosp. Tutor. Socs: Birm. & Midl Obst & Gyn. Soc; BSCC. Prev: Sen. Regist. (O & G) Jessops Hosp. for Wom. Sheff.; Regist. (O & G) St. Jas. Leeds; Ho. Surg. & Ho. Phys. Roy. Vict. Hosp. Belf.

CARTMILL, Thomas David Ivor Department of Microbiology, Birch Hill Hospital, Rochdale Healthcare NHS Trust, Rochdale OL12 9QB Tel: 01706 377777 Fax: 01706 755727; 7 Raynham Avenue, Didsbury, Manchester M20 6BW Tel: 0161 445 5570 — MB ChB 1982 Ed.; BSc (1st. cl. Hons.) (Bacteriol.) Ed. 1980; FRCPath 1998; Dip. Bact. (Distinc.) . Manch. 1990. (Edinburgh) Cons. Microbiol. Rochdale Healthcare NHS Trust. Socs: Brit. Soc. Antimicrob. Chemother.; Hosp. Infec. Soc. Prev: Sen. Regist. (Microbiol.) NW Region Train. Scheme; Regist. (Microbiol.) Newc. Gen. Hosp.; SHO (Path.) N. Manch. Gen. Hosp.

CARTNER, Rosalind 220 Gilesgate, Durham DH1 1QN Tel: 0191 384 4040 — MB BS 1960 Madras; FRCPath 1986, M 1974; DCP Madras 1966. (Christian Med. Coll. Vellore) Hon, Cons. Haemat. N. Durh. Healthcare; Clin. Lect. Med. (Haemat.) Univ. Newc. Socs: Fell., Roy. Soc. of Med. Prev: Sen. Regist. (Path.) Newc. Gen. Hosp.; Sen. Regist. (Haemat.) Sunderland AHA.

CARTON, Mr Andrew Thomas Mary Department of Maxillofacial Surgery, Crosshouse Hospital, Kilmarnock KA2 0BE Tel: 01563 577293 Fax: 01563 577300 Email: cartona@nayrshire.scot.nhs.uk; Moorfield House, St Quivox Road, Prestwick KA9 1JF Tel: 01292 678970 — MB BCh BAO 1990 Dub.; BDentSc BA 1981; MA Dub. 1990; MB BCh Dub. 1990; FRCS (Max. Fac.) 1995; FRCS Ed. 1993; FDS RCPS Glas. 1986; FFD RCSI 1985. (Sch. of Phys. Univ. of Dub. Trinity Coll.) Cons. Oral & Maxillofacial Surg. N. Ayrsh. & Arran NHS Trust CrossHo. Hosp. Kilmarnock; Hon. Sen. Lect. Univ. Glas. Socs: Fell. Brit. Assn. Oral & Maxillofacial Surg.; Brit. Assn. Head & Neck Oncol.; Roy. Soc. Med. Prev: Sen. Regist. (Maxillofacial Surg.) N.. Region.

CARTON, Patrick Finton 16 Hawthorn Manor, Carryduff, Belfast BT8 8SR — MB BCh BAO 1995 Belf.

CARTON, Richard Paul Lawrence (retired) 7 Peile Drive, Taunton TA2 7SZ Tel: 01823 352832 Fax: 01823 350692 — LRCPI & LM, LRSCI & LM 1943; LRCPI & LM, LRCSI & LM 1943; LM Rotunda 1944. Prev: Ho. Surg. & Res. Obst. Off. Vict. Hosp. Blackpool.

CARTON-KELLY, Peter Stanley (retired) Old Stone Cottage, Barrell Hill, How Caple, Hereford HR1 4TB Tel: 01989 740648 Fax: 01989 740648 Email: peterlegrand@tack21.com — MRCS Eng. LRCP Lond. 1948; LM Coombe 1952. Chairm. Indust. Injury Med. Bd.; Clin. Asst. (Med. & Psychiat.) St. Mary's Hosp. Hereford; Surg. Lt.-Cdr. RNVR. Prev: Clin. Clerk Coombe Hosp. Dub.

CARTWRIGHT, Anthony James, Flight Lt. RAF Med. Br. Brook Farm, Bowesgate Road, Bunbury, Tarporley CW6 9PP Email: anthony@kildare.freeserve.co.uk — MB ChB 1995 Sheff.

CARTWRIGHT, Brian Leslie Revoan, Main St., Urquhart, Elgin IV30 8LG — MB ChB 1970 St. And.; MRCP (U.K.) 1974. (St. And.) Cons. (Gen. & Geriat. Med.) Dr. Gray's Hosp. Elgin. Prev: Sen. Regist. (Geriat. Med. Unit) Dundee Health Dist.; Regist. (Gen. Med.) S. Grampian Health Dist. Regist. Raigmore Hosp.; Inverness.

CARTWRIGHT, David Ernest The Surgery, Bull Yard, Simson Street, Spilsby PE23 5JE Tel: 01790 752555 Fax: 01790 754457; Campion House, Willoughby Drive, Spilsby PE23 5EX Tel: 01790 54000 — MB ChB 1979 Sheff.

CARTWRIGHT, David James 2 Goldsmith Place, Longton, Stoke-on-Trent ST3 1SG — MB ChB 1998 Glas.; MB ChB Glas 1998.

CARTWRIGHT, David Paul Forge Cottage, Brook Lane, Sutton-on-the-Hill, Ashbourne, Derby DE6 5JA Tel: 01283 733619 Fax: 01283 733698 — MB ChB 1971 Manch.; FFA RCS Eng. 1975. Cons. Anaesth. Derby City Hosp. & Derbysh. Roy. Infirm. Derby; Clin. Teach. (Anaesth.) Univ. Nottm. Socs: Assn. Anaesth.; Derby Med. Soc.; Counc. Roy. Coll. of Anaesth.s. Prev: Sen. Regist. Avon HA (T); Regist. (Anaesth.) Wythenshawe Hosp. Manch. & NE Manch. Gp. Hosps.

CARTWRIGHT, Frederick Fox (retired) Flat 31, Swallowfield Park, Reading RG7 1TG Tel: 01734 885743 — MRCS Eng. LRCP Lond. 1934; FFA RCS Eng. 1948; DA Eng. 1935. Prev: Sen. Anaesth. & Dir. Dept. Anaesth. Kings Coll. Hosp.

CARTWRIGHT, Frederick Stewart West Dorset General Hospitals NHS Trust, West Dorset Hospital, Damers Road, Dorchester DT1 2JY — BM 1980 Soton.

CARTWRIGHT, Hannah Frances 9 De Burgh Park, Banstead SM7 2PP — BM 1998 Soton.

CARTWRIGHT, Jennifer Claire 10 Horton Crescent, Rugby CV22 5DJ — MB ChB 1992 Cape Town.

CARTWRIGHT, Joanna Louise 16 St Catherine's Close, The Park, Roby, Liverpool L36 5RX Tel: 0151 480 0618 Email: joannac1@hotmail.com — MB ChB 1994 Liverp.; DFFP 1996; LoC 1UT; MFFP Pt 1; Mrcog Pt 1. (Liverpool) O & G, Warrington DGH, Warrington, Chesh.; SCMO, Wirral Brook AC; CMO Warrington Community NHS Trust; CMO Liverp. Brook AC. Socs: MRTOG; JDC BMA. Prev: Clin. research fell., Clatterbridge Cancer Reseach Trust, Wirral; SHO (O & G), Liverp. Wom.'s Hosp.

CARTWRIGHT, Joanne Elizabeth Long Eaton Health Centre, Midland St., Long Eaton, Nottingham NG10 1NY Tel: 0115 973 2370; 5 Far Croft, Breaston, Derby DE72 3HL Tel: 01332 872663 — MB ChB 1988 Manch.; MRCGP 1992; DRCOG 1991; DCH RCP Lond. 1990.

CARTWRIGHT, John, Wing Cdr. Regional Occ Med Dept, RAF Lyneham, Chippenham SW15 4PZ — MB BS 1985 Lond.; MMedSc. Birmingham (Occ. Health) 1997; MFOM -RCP(Fom) 1998. RAF Cons. Occupat. Phys. Socs: Soc. Occup. Med.

CARTWRIGHT, Joseph John Springfield Bungalow, Birdlip, Gloucester GL4 8JH — MB ChB 1990 Leeds.

CARTWRIGHT, Judith Lynne Hedgerows, 27 Green Lane, Harby, Melton Mowbray LE14 4BQ Tel: 01252 684619 — MB ChB 1997 Bristol. (Bristol) SHO (O & G), N. Hants. Hosp. Basingstoke. Prev: SHO (A & E), Frimley Pk. Hosp., Frimley; Ho. Off. (Med.) Wexham Pk. Hosp. Slough; Ho. Surg. (Gen. Surg.) N. Devon Dist. Hosp. Barnstaple.

CARTWRIGHT, Julia 100 Stickley La, Dudley DY3 2JH — BM BCh 1997 Oxf.

CARTWRIGHT, Katharine Elizabeth 23 Teversal Av, Nottingham NG7 1PY — BM BS 1997 Nottm.

CARTWRIGHT, Mrs Kathleen Ina MacNicol (retired) 1 Silver Street, Deal CT14 6LB Tel: 01304 372034 — MB ChB 1967 Aberd.; BSc Aberd. 1964, MB ChB 1967; MRCPsych 1973; DPM Ed. & Glas. 1970. Prev: Locum Cons. Child & Family Psychiat. Lenworth Clinic Ashford.

CARTWRIGHT, Professor Keith Anthony Vincent Public Health Laboratory, Gloucester Royal Hospital, Great Western Road, Gloucester GL1 3NN Tel: 01452 305334 Fax: 01452 307213 Email: kcartwright@phls.org.uk — BM BCh 1971 Oxf.; MA Oxf. 1992, BA 1967; FRCPath 1988, M 1978. (Oxf. & Middlx.) Gp. Dir. PHLS S. W.; Hon. Cons. Microbiol. Glos. Roy. Hosp.; Personal Chair in Clin. MicroBiol., Univ. Bristol, Aug 1997; Med. Director, Meningitis Trust. Prev: Dir. Pub. Health Laborat. Gloucester; Cons. Microbiol. W.. Gen. Hosp. Edin.

CARTWRIGHT, Lionel Nelson Hadleigh House Medical Centre, 20 Kirkway, Broadstone BH18 8EE Tel: 01202 692268 Fax: 01202 658954; 8 Moor Road, Broadstone BH18 8BB Tel: 01202 693226 Email: lnc@btinternet.com — BM BCh 1980 Oxf.; MA Oxf. 1980; MRCGP 1984; DRCOG 1984. Hosp. Practitioner (Chest Med.) Poole Gen. Hosp.; PCG Bd. Mem. Poole Centr. & N.

CARTWRIGHT, Marc Andrew Sleaford Medical Group, Riverside Surgery, 47 Boston Road, Sleaford NG34 7HD Tel: 01529 303301 Fax: 01529 415401; Sleaford Medical Group, 47 Boston Road, Sleaford NG34 7HD Tel: 01529 497562 — MB ChB 1985 Manch.; T(GP) 1994; DFFP 1994; DA (UK) 1991. (Manch.) Prev: SHO Nottm. VTS; SHO (Anaesth.) Leic. Roy. Infirm.; SHO (Gen. Med.) Stafford Dist. Gen. Hosp.

CARTWRIGHT, Neil Hafod Las, Field Farm Lane, Buckley CH7 3PD — MB BS 1998 Lond.; MB BS Lond 1998.

CARTWRIGHT, Nigel Paul Whiteoaks, 8 Holgate, Clifton Village, Nottingham NG11 8NH — BSc (Hons.) Manch. 1981, MB ChB (Hons.) 1984; MRCGP 1988; DRCOG 1987; DCH RCP Lond. 1987. (Manchester) Prev: Trainee GP Roy. Preston Hosp. VTS.

CARTWRIGHT, Nina Valerie Wolvercote Surgery, 73 Godstow Road, Wolvercote, Oxford OX2 8PE Tel: 01865 556044 — MB BS 1966 Lond.; DObst RCOG 1969. (Univ. Coll. Lond. & Oxf.) Prev: Ho. Phys., Ho. Surg. & Obst. Ho. Off. United Oxf. Hosps.

CARTWRIGHT, Peter Hugh Queens Hospital, Belvedere Road, Burton-on-Trent DE13 0RB Tel: 01283 566333; 70A Lower Outwoods Road, Burton-on-Trent DE13 0QU — MB ChB 1979 Manch.; MRCP (UK) 1982. Cons. Dermat. Burton Hosps. NHS Trust. Prev: Cons. Dermat. S. Lincs. HA; Sen. Regist. (Dermat.) N. Staffs. Hosp. Centre Stoke-on-Trent; Regist. (Dermat.) Leeds Gen. Infirm.

CARTWRIGHT, Philip Donald Princess Royal Hospital, Apley Castle, Telford TF1 6TF Tel: 01952 641222 Fax: 01952 243405 Email: philipcartwright@doctors.org.uk; Bush Cottage, Longdon-on-Tern, Telford TF6 6LQ Email: philipcartwright@doctors.org.uk — MB ChB 1978 Birm.; FFA RCS Eng. 1983; DEAA 1987; MA Keele 1999. Cons. Anaesth. P.ss Roy. Hosp. Telford. Socs: Fell. Europ. Acad. Anaesthesiol.; Assn. Anaesths.; Internat. Assn. Study of Pain. Prev: Oeverlaekare Dept. Anaesth. Oskarshamns, Sjukhus, Sweden; Asst. Prof. Anaesth. McGill Univ. & Montreal Childr. Hosp.; Clin. Fell. (Anaesth.) McGill Univ. Montreal.

CARTWRIGHT, Professor Raymond Alfred Leukaemia Research Fund Centre, University of Leeds, 30 Hyde Terrace, Leeds LS2 9LN Tel: 0113 244 3517 Fax: 0113 242 6065 Email: p.a.pickles@leeds.ac.uk; Flat 2, 26 Park Avenue, Harrogate HG2 9BG — FRCP Edin 2000; MB BChir Camb. 1968; PhD Durh. 1973; MA Camb. 1969; FFOM RCP (UK) 1995; FFPHM RCP (UK) 1990; MFCM 1982. (St. Geo.) Dir. & Prof. Cancer Epidemiol. Leukaemia Research Fund Centr. Clin. Epidemiol. Univ. Leeds; Hon. Cons. Epidemiol. Leeds Teachg. Hosps.; Dir. Health Serv. Res. Centre Leeds Univ.; Non-Exec. Mem. Leeds, H.A. Prev: Cons. Epidemiol. York RHA Regional Cancer Organisat.; Ho. Off. (Med. & Surg.) Dryburn Hosp. Durh.; Lect. (Anthropol.) Univ. Durh.

CARTWRIGHT, Robin Steels Lane Health Centre, 384-388 Commercial Road, London E1 0LR Tel: 020 7265 8655 Fax: 020 7702 8023 — MB BS 1970 Lond.; MRCGP 1996; DRCOG 1971. (Univ. Coll. Lond.) G.P. Trainer; V.T.S. Course Organiser. Socs: BMA; Balint Soc.

CARTWRIGHT, Professor Rodney Yonwin (retired) Public Health Laboratory, St. Luke's Hospital, Guildford GU1 3NT Tel: 01483 66091 Fax: 01483 577571 — MB ChB 1963 Birm.; FRCPath 1984, M 1972. Cons. Microbiol. Dir. PHLS S. Thomas; Hon. Vis. Prof. Clin. Microbiol. Univ. Surrey. Prev: Ho. Phys. Qu. Eliz. Hosp. Birm.

CARTWRIGHT, Roma Heather 37 Ravenslea Road, London SW12 8SL — MB ChB 1987 Manch. Trainee GP/SHO (O & G) Univ. Coll. Hosp. Lond. Prev: SHO (Paediat.) Middlx. Hosp. & Booth Hall Hosp. Manch.; SHO (A & E) Univ. Hosp. S. Manch.

CARTWRIGHT, Sheila Christine (retired) Potterton Hall W., Potterton, Barwick-in-Elmet, Leeds LS15 4NN — MB BS 1969 Lond.; BSc Lond. 1966; MRCS Eng. LRCP Lond. 1969; FRCR 1975; FFR 1974; DMRT Eng. 1973. Prev: Cons. Radiother. & Oncol. Regional Centre for Cancer Treatm. Leeds.

CARTWRIGHT, Simon Richard Faringdon Health Centre, Coxwell Road, Faringdon SN7 7ED Tel: 01367 242388 Fax: 01367 243394; Rowan Cottage, Pound Lane, Clanfield, Bampton OX18 2RA — MB BS 1986 Lond.; MRCGP 1991; DCH RCP Lond. 1990; DRCOG 1988. (Westm.) Prev: Regist. (Paediat.) Waikato Hosp., NZ; Trainee GP Summertown Health Centre Oxf.

CARTWRIGHT, Stephen Terence Keelinge House Surgery, 176 Stourbridge Road, Dudley DY1 2ER Tel: 01384 77194 Fax: 01384 820210 — BM BS 1980 Nottm.; MRCGP 1986; Cert. Family Plann. JCC 1986; DRCOG 1986. Clin. Governance Lead, Beacon & Castle PCG, Dudley; GP Tutor.

CARTY, Austin Timothy Royal Liverpool Hospital, Prescot Street, Liverpool L7 8XP Tel: 0151 706 2000 Fax: 0151 706 5856; 6 Grosvenor Road, Cressington Park, Liverpool L19 0PL Tel: 0151 427

6727 Fax: 0151 494 9182 Email: cartyah@aigburth.u_net.com — MB BCh BAO NUI 1964; FRCPI 1981, M 1967; FRCR 1975; FFR RCSI 1972; FFR 1972; DMRD Eng. 1970. (Univ. Coll. Dub.) Cons. Radiol. CT Scanning Roy. Liverp. Hosp. Socs: Liverp. Med Inst.. (Ex-Hon Librarian); R.S.M. Prev: Med. Dir. Roy Liverp. Hosp. NHS Trust; Sen. Regist. (Radiol.) Univ. Coll. Hosp., St. Marks Hosp. & Hosp. Sick Childr. Gt. Ormond St. Lond.

CARTY, Caroline Anne 31 Monreith Road, Newlands, Glasgow G43 2NY Tel: 0141 632 1033 — MB ChB 1966 Glas.

CARTY, Elizabeth 34 Benson Quay, Garnet St., Wapping, London E1W 3TR Tel: 020 7488 2441 — BM BS 1991 Nottm.; BMedSci Nottm. 1988; MRCP (UK) 1994. Regist. (Gen. Med. & Gastroenterol.) Roy. Lond. Hosp.

CARTY, Professor Helen Marie Louise Alder Hey Childrens Hospital, Eaton Road, Liverpool L12 2AP Tel: 0151 252 5432 Fax: 0151 252 5533; 6 Grosvenor Road, Cressington Park, Liverpool L19 0PL Tel: 0151 427 6727 Fax: 0151 427 6727 — MB BCh BAO 1967 NUI; FRCP Lond. 1996; FRCPI 1981, M 1970; FRCR 1975; FFR 1974; DMRD Eng. 1972; FRCPCH 1997. (Univ. Coll. Dub.) Prof. Paediat. Radiol. Univ. Liverp. & Hon. Cons. Radiol. Alder Hey Childr. Hosp. Liverp. Socs: Fell. Roy. Soc. Med.; (Ex-Pres.) Liverp. Med. Inst.; (Counc.) Europ. Soc. Paediat. Radiol. Prev: Cons. Radiol. Alder Hey Childr. Hosp. Liverp. & Roy. Liverp. Childr. NHS Trust Hosp.; Regist. (Radiol.) St. Thos. Hosp. Lond; Tutor (Med.) Univ. Coll. & Mater Hosp. Dub.

CARTY, Jonathan 173 Cornhill Dr, Aberdeen AB16 5HN — MB ChB 1997 Aberd.

CARTY, Mr Matthew John 31 Monreith Road, Newlands, Glasgow G43 2NY Tel: 0141 632 1033 — MB ChB 1966 Glas.; FRCS Glas. 1985; FRCS Ed. 1971; FRCOG 1983, M 1970. Cons. O & G S.. Gen. Hosp. Glas. Prev: Lect. (Midw.) Qu. Mother's Hosp. Glas.

CARTY, Monica Helen 18 St Edwards Drive, Sudbrooke, Lincoln LN2 2QR — MB ChB 1970 Liverp.; DObst RCOG 1972. Clin. Asst. Med. Lincoln Hosps. Prev: Ho. Phys. Clatterbridge Hosp. Bebington; Ho. Surg. St. Jas. Hosp. Leeds; SHO (Obst.) St. Mary's Hosp. Leeds.

CARTY, Mr Nicholas James Salisbury District Hospital, Odstock, Salisbury SP2 8BJ Tel: 01722 336262; Little Woodfalls Farmhouse, The Ridge, Woodfalls, Salisbury SP5 2LW Tel: 01725 511500 — MB 1982 Camb.; MS 1990 Soton.; MB 1982, BChir 1981; FRCS Eng. 1986; FRCS Ed. 1986. Cons. Surg. Salisbury Dist. Hosp. Socs: BASO; Assn. Of Surg.s. Prev: Regist. (Surg.) Wessex HA.

CARTY, Paul Andrew Hampton Medical Centre, Lansdowne, 49a Priory Road, Hampton TW12 2PB Tel: 020 8979 5150 Fax: 020 8941 9068; 33A Halliford Road, Sunbury-on-Thames TW16 6DP — MB BS 1987 Lond.; MRCGP 1991. Prev: SHO (Psychiat.) W. Middlx. Univ. Hosp.; Trainee GP St. Peters Chertsey VTS.

CARTY, Sara Madelaine 18 St Edwards Dr, Sudbrooke, Lincoln LN2 2QR — MB BS 1997 Newc.

***CARTY, Suzanne Jacqueline** 7 Durrell Way, Shepperton TW17 8HR — MB BS 1997 Lond.

CARUANA, Anton 4 Northgate, Lincoln LN2 1QS — MRCS Eng. LRCP Lond. 1978.

CARUANA, Michael Paul Swanage Health Centre, Railway Station Approach, Station Road, Swanage BH19 1HB Tel: 01929 422231 — MB BS 1975 Lond.; MRCGP 1995; FRACP (NZ) 1981; DRCOG 1995; DCH RCP Lond. 1994. (Middlx.) Med. Advisor to Swanage Community Hosp. Socs: Cardiac Soc. Austral. & NZ. Prev: Hon. Lect. Auckland Med. Sch.; Cons. Cardiol. Middlemore Hosp. Auckland & Hon. Lect. Auckland Med. Sch.; Cons. Phys. & Cardiol. NW Gen. Hosp. Burnie, Tasmania.

CARUANA, Mr Peter Aberdeen Royal Hospitals NHS Trust, c/o Eye OPD, Aberdeen Royal Infirmary, Gorresterhill Road, Aberdeen Tel: 01224 681818 Ext: 53214 Fax: 01224 840746 Email: p.caruana@abdn.ac.uk; 28 Canmore Park, Stonehaven AB39 2WJ Tel: 01569 762633 — MD 1986 Malta; FRCS Ed. 1990; FCOphth 1991; MD Keele 1998. (Univ. Malta) Specialist Regist. (Ophth.) Aberd. Roy. Hosps. NHS Trust; Hon. Lect. Med. Sch. Aberd. Univ. Prev: Research Fell. (Neuro-Ophth.) Keele Univ. Sch. Postgrad. Med.

CARUCCI, Patrizia Hambleden Court, St Francis Road, London SE22 8DE — State Exam Turin 1991.

CARULLI, Maria Teresa Flat 2, 143 Abbey Road, London NW6 4SL — State Exam 1992 Modena.

CARUS, Anne Maria 29 Hamilton Road, Tiddington, Stratford-upon-Avon CV37 7DD — MB BS 1979 Lond.

CARVALHO, Aires Medical Centre, Southwood Village Centre, Links Way, Farnborough GU14 0NA Tel: 01252 371715; 44 The Crescent, Farnborough GU14 7AS Tel: 01252 376266 — MB BS 1954 Lucknow; MRCP Glas. 1964; DTM & H Ed. 1962. (King Geo. Med. Coll.) Locum-PRN. Socs: BMA. Prev: Cons. Phys. Govt. Hosp. Zanzibar; Cons. Phys. Daressalaam Gp. Occupat. Health Serv. Daressalaam, Tanzania.

CARVALHO, Richard Rome Nunes 51 Woodsome Road, London NW5 1SA — MB BS 1971 Lond.; MRCS Eng. LRCP Lond. 1971; FRCPsych 1996, M 1976. Private Analytic/Psychother. Pract.; Psychoanalyt. Psychother.; Analyt. Psychol; Train. Alalyst. Brit. Assn. Psychother. Socs: Tavistock Soc. Psychother.; Soc. Analyt. Psychol. Prev: Cons. Psychother. St. Mary's Hosp. Lond.; Sen. Regist. Tavistock Clinic.

CARVEL, David Robert Biggar Medical Practice, Biggar ML12 6BE Email: david.carvel@biggar.lanpct.scot.nhs.uk; Gillespie House, 2 Manse Dr, Biggar ML12 6BD — DFM 2001 (Diplom in Forensic Medicine); MB ChB Manch. 1991; BSc St. And. 1988; DRCOG 1996; MRCGP 1999. GP Princip. & Police Surg. (trainee), Biggar Med. Prac., Lanarksh. Socs: Scott. Medico-legal Soc.; Assn. of Police Surg.s. Prev: GP (Locum) Hokiange Health, Rawene, New Zealand; GP Regist. Paisley.

CARVEL, Mercedes Daisy (retired) 78 Alexander Drive, Cirencester GL7 1UJ — MB ChB 1945 Ed.; FFA RCS Eng. 1961; DA Eng. 1955. Prev: Cons. Anaesth. St. Jas. Hosp. Balham & St. Geo. Hosp. Lond.

CARVELL, Mr John Edward Salisbury District Hospital, Salisbury SP2 8BJ Tel: 01722 429393 Fax: 01722 320924 Email: tracey.johns@shc-tr.swest.nhs.uk; Newstead, 143 Bouverie Avenue S., Salisbury SP2 8EB Tel: 01722 330519 Fax: 01722 320924 — MB ChB St. And. 1970; MMSc Dundee 1974; FRCS Ed. 1977; FRCS Eng. 1997. (St. And.) Cons. Orthop. Surg. Salisbury Health Care Trust; Hon. Sec. Wessex CCSC; Chairm. Wessex RCSC; Mem. Orthop. Subcomm. of CCSC; Chairm. Wessex LNC Forum. Socs: Fell. Brit. Scoliosis Soc.; Fell. BOA; BMA. Prev: Sen. Regist Nuffield Orthop. Centre & Accid. Serv. John Radcliffe Hosp. Oxf.; Regist. (Orthop. & Traum.) Roy. United Hosp. & Roy. Nat. Hosp. Rheum.

CARVELL, Simon Paul 38 Severn Street, Bridgnorth WV15 6BB — MB ChB 1994 Birm.; ChB Birm. 1994.

CARVER, Christine Heather 8 Twixbears, Tewkesbury GL20 5BT — MB ChB 1996 Birm.

CARVER, Edmund David Department of Anaesthesia, Birmingham Children's Hospital, Steelhouse Lane, Birmingham B4 6NH Tel: 0121 333 9623 Email: ed.carver@bhamchildrens.wmids.nhs.uk — MB BS 1989 Newc.; MRCP (UK) 1992; FRCA 1996. Cons. Anaesth., Birm. Chidren's Hosp. Prev: Specialist Regist. (Anaesth.) Freeman Hosp. Newc.; Specialist Regist., Newc. Hosps. NHS Trust; Fell. in Paediaric Anaesth., Hosp. for Sick Childr., Toronto.

CARVER, Henry Charles (retired) The Firs, 7 St Edwins Close, High Coniscliffe, Darlington DL2 2NQ Tel: 01325 374630 — LRCP LRCS 1954 Ed.; LRCP LRCS Ed. LRFPS Glas. 1954. Prev: GP Darlington.

CARVER, Mr Nigel AGB House, 18 Avery Hill Rd, London SE9 2BD Tel: 020 8 850 1020 Fax: 020 8 859 0202 Email: ncplastic@aol.com — MB BS 1983 Lond.; BSc (Hons.) Lond. 1980, MS 1993, MB BS 1983; FRCS Eng. 1987; FRCS (Plast.) 1996. (St. Mary's) Cons. Plastic Surg., Roy. Lond. Hosp.

CARVER, Paul Henry Centre for Occupational Health, Martham House, Norfolk and Norwich Hospital, Brunswick Road, Norwich NR3 1SR Tel: 01603 287035; 20 Turnham Green, Norwich NR7 0TU Tel: 01603 700607 — MB BS 1964 Lond.; DObst RCOG 1969. (Roy. Free) Prev: Ho. Phys. Roy. Free Hosp. Lond.; Ho. Surg. Roy. N.. Hosp. Lond.

CARVER, Richard Anthony Department of Diagnostic Imaging, Farnborough Hospital, Orpington BR6 8ND Tel: 01689 814141; 48 Marlborough Crescent, Sevenoaks TN13 2HJ — MB BChir 1975 Camb.; FRCS Eng. 1981; FRCR 1986. Cons. Radiol. Bromley Hosps. NHS Trust; Cons. (Radiol.) Sloane Hosp. Socs: Brit. Inst. Radiol.; Brit. Med. Ultrasound Soc.; BMA. Prev: Sen. Regist. (Diagn. Radiol.) Sheff. United Hosp.; Regist. (Radiol.) Sheff.; Regist.(Surg.) Luton & Dunstable Hosp.

CARVER, Richard Tregarthen Cedar Practice, John Scott Health Centre, Green Lanes, London N4 2NU Tel: 020 7690 1151 Fax: 020 8809 6900 — MB ChB 1973 Liverp. Prev: Med. Off. W. Afr. Field Trip Assn.; Lect. (Health Care) All Nations for Christ Bible Inst. Benin City, Nigeria.

CARVILL, Joan Marie Phyllis Tuckwell Hospice, Waverley Lane, Farnham GU9 8BL Tel: 01252 729400; 75 Pullman Lane, Godalming GU7 1YB — LRCPI & LM, LRSCI & LM 1971; LRCPI & LM, LRCSI & LM 1971; DRCOG 1996; DCH Eng. 1974. (Royal College of Surgeons in Ireland) Staff Grade Phys. (Palliat. Med.) Phyllis Tuckwell Memor. Hospice Farnham.

CARVILL, Patricia Therese Rosebank Surgery, Ashton Road, Lancaster LA1 4JS Tel: 01524 842242 Fax: 01524 844839 — LRCP 1976 Ireland; MRCGP (DCH); L LM RCP Irel L LM RCS Irel 1976. (Ireland) GP Lancaster.

CARVILL, Susan Catherine Admirals Court, 37 Nelson Way, Bilton, Rugby CV22 7LW Tel: 01788 817586; 21A Cofton Church Lane, Cofton Hackett, Bromsgrove B45 8PS — MB BCh 1987 Wales; BSc (Hons.) Physiol. Wales 1982; MRCPsych 1994. (Univ. Wales Coll. Med.) p/t Sen. Regist. (Learning Disabil.) W. Midl. Socs: BMA. Prev: Regist. (Psychiat.) Birm.; SHO (Psychiat.) Warwick; SHO (Geriat.) Dudley Rd. Hosp. Birm.

CARY, Amanda Jill New Road Surgery, 166 New Rd, Croxley Green Tel: 01923 772877; 14 Fairview Drive, Watford WD17 4ST Tel: 01923 816262 — MB ChB 1979 Leeds; MRCGP 1984; DRCOG 1983; DCH RCP Lond. 1982; Cert. Prescribed Equiv. Exp. JCPTGP 1983. p/t GP Retainee; Examg. Med. Practitioner for N. D. A. Prev: Med. Adviser Benefits Agency, Wembley; GP Hemel Hempstead.

CARY, Maria Teresa Ann Ringwood Health Centre, The Close, Ringwood BH24 1JY Tel: 01425 478901 Fax: 01425 478239; 39 Kingswood Rise, Four Marks, Alton GU34 5BE Tel: 01420 562751 Fax: 01420 562751 — MB ChB 1985 Bristol; DFFP 2000; DRCOG 1990; DCH RCP Lond. 1989. p/t GP Princip. Ringwood Health Centre The Cl. Ringwood Hants BH24 1JY. Prev: Gen. Pract. Rotat. Frimley Pk. Hosp.; Clin. Med. Off. Frimley Clin. Centre.

CARY, Nathaniel Roger Blair Department of Pathology, Papworth Hospital, Papworth Everard, Cambridge CB3 8RE Tel: 01480 830541 — MB BS 1981 Lond.; MA Oxf. 1982; MRCPath 1989. Cons. Cardiac Histopath. Papworth & Addenbrooke's Hosps. Camb. Socs: Path. Soc. Prev: Lect (Histopath.) Char. Cross & W.m. Med. Sch. Lond.; Trustees Research Fell. Char. Cross Hosp. Lond.; Ho. Phys. & Ho. Surg. Char. Cross Hosp. Lond.

CASALE, Fabrizio Francesco 18 The Avenue, Colchester CO3 3PA Tel: 01206 579680 — MB ChB 1963 Cape Town; FFA RCS Eng. 1969; DA Eng. 1967. Cons. Anaesth. Colchester Gen. Hosp.; Cons. Anaesth. Oaks Hosp. Colchester. Socs: BMA; Roy. Soc. Med.; Pain. Soc. Prev: Regist. Addenbrooke's Hosp. Camb.; Sen. Regist. Guy's Hosp. Lond.; Cons. Anaesth. Teach. Hosp. Lusaka, Zambia.

CASALI, Giovanni 61 Newfoundland Road, Heath, Cardiff CF14 3LB — State Exam 1990 Geona.

CASANOVA COLL, Francisco Department of Anaesthetics, Royal United Hospital, Coombe Park, Bath BA1 3NG — LMS 1989 Barcelona. Prev: SHO (A & E) Bedford Hosp.

CASAPIERI, Michael 29 Woodfoot Road, Rotherham S60 3DZ Tel: 01709 366244 — MB ChB 1990 Sheff.; BSc (Hons.) Sheff. 1985, MB ChB 1990. SHO Anat. Demonst. Sheff. HA.

CASARES, Marilyn Elena Manor Oak Surgery, Horebeech Lane, Horam, Heathfield TN21 ODS Tel: 01435 812323 — MB BCh BAO 1971 Dub.; MRCGP 1993; DRCOG 1992; DCH RCP Lond. 1991.

CASASOLA, Richard James 8 Leslie Place, Edinburgh EH4 1NH — MB ChB 1990 Ed.

CASASUS BORRELL, Teresa 33 Liberia Road, London N5 1JP — LMS 1989 U Autonoma Barcelona.

CASAUBON ALCARAZ, Francisco Jose St Margarets Hospital, The Plain, Epping CM16 6TN; 14 Station Road, Epping CM16 4HN — LMS 1991 Granada.

CASBURN-JONES, Anna Ceridwen 1 Flat B, Dartmouth Park Avenue, London NW5 1JL Tel: 020 7267 9072 Email: draccj@aol.com; 1 Flat B, Dartmouth Pk Avenue, London NW5 1JL — MB BS 1992 Lond.; BSc (Med. Sci. & Sociol.) Lond. 1988; MRCP (UK) 1995. (Roy. Free Hosp. Sch. Med.) Specialist Regist. Rotat. Chase Farm Hosp. & Roy. Free Hosp.; Clin. Research Fell., Roy. Free Hosp. Socs: Fell., Roy. Soc. of Med. Prev: SHO Rotat. Roy. Sussex Co. Hosp. Brighton; SHO Rotat. (Med.) Luton & Dunstable Hosp.

CASE, Brigitta Elizabeth Tel: 0114 237 7649; PoleBrook House, Main Street, Polebrook, Peterborough PE8 5LN — MB ChB 1986 Sheff.; MRCGP 1991; DRCOG 1991; Cert. Family Plann. JCC 1989. LOCUM GP. Prev: Trainee GP Sheff. VTS.; Full time GP, Shefffield 1991-2000.

CASE, Charles Patrick Dept. Cellular Pathology, Southmead Hospital, Westbury on Trym, Bristol Tel: 0117 959 5623 Fax: 0117 959 0191; 55 Upper Cranbrook Road, Bristol BS6 7UR — MB ChB 1989 Bristol; MSc (Oxf.) 1976, DPhil 1982; MRC (Path.) 1997. Cons. Sen. Lect. in Orthopeadics with Path. Prev: Sen. Regist. & Lect. (Histopath.) Bristol Roy. Infirm.; Regist. (Histopath.) S.mead Hosp. Bristol.

CASE, Kathleen Mary Thérèse Wilmslow Health Centre, Chapel Lane, Wilmslow SK9 5HX Tel: 01625 548555 Fax: 01625 548287; Tregays, Torkington Road, Wilmslow SK9 2AE — MB ChB 1977 Manch.; BSc Manch. 1970. Socs: BMA.

CASE, Mrs Ruth Diana Weston General Hospital, Grange Road, Weston Super Mare BS23 4TQ Tel: 01934 636363; 55 Upper Cranbrook Road, Redland, Bristol BS6 7UR — BM BCh 1977 Oxf.; MA Oxf. 1977, BA 1974; FRCS Lond. 1981; FRCS Tr & Orth 1999. Locum Cons. (Orthop & Trauma) W.on Gen. Hosp., Bristol. Socs: Brit. Orthopaedic Assn. Prev: Staff Surg. (Orthop. & Trauma) S.mead Hosp. Bristol.; Specialist Regist. (Orthop. & Trauma) S.mead Hosp. Bristol.; Specialist Regist. (Orthop & Trauma) S.mead Hosp. Bristol.

CASE, Mr William George Oakroyd, 10 Turnshaw Road, Kirkburton, Huddersfield HD8 0TH; Oakroyd, 10 Turnshaws Road, Kirkburton, Huddersfield HD8 0TH Tel: 01484 603412 — BM BCh 1978 Oxf.; MA Camb. 1978; FRCS Ed. 1982; FRCS Eng. 1983. Cons. Surg. Dewsbury Dist. Hosp. Socs: Assn. Surg.; Vasc. Surgic. Soc. Prev: Sen. Regist. (Gen. Surg.) Yorks. RHA; Regist. (Surg.) St. Jas. Univ. Hosp. Leeds; Regist. (Surg.) Gen. Infirm. Leeds.

CASELEY, Jane Rosamond (retired) Windleshaw House, Withyham, Hartfield TN7 4DB — MB ChB 1956 Aberd.

CASEMENT, Enda, OBE (retired) 16 Croft Heights, Ballygally, Larne BT40 2QS Tel: 01574 583411 — MB BCh BAO 1945 Belf.; FRCPI 1976, M 1958; FRCPsych 1980, M 1971; DPM RCPSI 1954. Prev: Cons. Psychiat. & Med. Supt. Holywell Hosp. Antrim.

CASEMENT, Jonathan Rutledge The Calderdal Royal Hospital, Salterhebble, Halifax HX3 0PW North Staffs Hospital NHS Trust, City General Hospital, Stoke-on-Trent ST4 6QG Tel: 01270 874381, 01422 224077, 01782 874381 — MB ChB 1992 Birm.; FRCA 1998. (Uni.Birm.Med.Sch.) Anaesthetic SpR.

CASEMENT, Maire Edwina 27 Downview Avenue, Belfast BT15 4FB Fax: 02840 839111 — MB BCh BAO 1978 Belf.; MRCOG 1985; DRCOG 1980. Cons. Belf. City Hosp. Prev: Sen. Regist. (O & G) Roy. Matern. Hosp. Belf.

CASEMORE, Valerie Ann (retired) 19 Curtyn Close, Abingdon OX14 1SE Tel: 01235 525702 — MB BS 1966 Lond.; MRCS Eng. LRCP Lond. 1966; MFFP 1993; Cert. Family Plann. JCC 1968. Prev: SCMO (Family Plann.) Oxon. Community Health NHS Trust.

CASERO ALONSO, Francisco Javier 2 Carrongrove Road, Carron, Falkirk FK2 8NX — LMS 1985 Oviedo.

CASEWELL, Professor Mark William Medical Microbiology, King's College School of Medicine & Dentistry, Bassemer Road, London SE5 9PJ Tel: 020 7586 3181 Fax: 020 7722.1957 Email: mark@casewell.co.uk; 43 Primrose Gardens, London NW3 4UL Tel: 020 7586 3181 Fax: 020 7722 1957 Email: mark@casewell.co.uk — MB BS Lond. 1965; BSc (Physiol. Hons.) Lond. 1962, MD 1978; MRCS Eng. LRCP Lond. 1965; FRCPath 1986, M 1975; FRCP (Hons) (UK) 1998 M.1994. (St. Bart.) Emerit. Prof. of Med. MicroBiol., King's Coll., Lond. Socs: Brit. Soc. Antimicrob. Chemother.; Hosp. Infec. Soc.; Amer. Soc. Microbiol. Prev: Prof. Med. Microbiol. & Head Dulwich Pub. Health Laborat. & Med. Microbiol. King's Coll. Sch. Med. & Dent. Lond.; Reader (Med. Microbiol.) & Hon. Cons. Roy. Lond. Hosp.; Sen. Lect., Lect. (Clin. Microbiol.), Hon. Sen. Regist. & Hon. Cons. St. Thos. Hosp. Lond.

CASEY, Mr Adrian Thomas Hickman National Hospital for Neurology & Neurosurgery, Queen Square, London WC1N 3BG Tel: 020 7837 3611 Fax: 020 7813 1138 Email: athcasey@doctors.org.uk — MB BS 1985 Lond.; FRCS Eng. 1989; FRCS SN Intercoll. 1996. Cons. Neurosurg. Nat. Hosp. for Neurlogy & Neurosurg. Lond.; Cons. Neurosurg. (Spinal Unit) Roy. Nat.

Orthop. Hosp. Stanmore Middlx.; Hon. Cons. Neurosurg. Gt. Ormond St. Hosp. Lond. Socs: Brit. Cervical Spine Soc.; Soc. Brit. Neurol. Surg.; Brit. Skull Base Soc. Prev: Cons. Neurosurg. Char. Cross Hosp.; Regist. Neurosurg. Atkinson Morleys Hosp. (St. Geo.'s Hosp.); Gen. Surg. Rotat. St. Bart. Hosp.

CASEY, Dominic Raymond 6 Millicent Road, London E10 7LG — MB BS 1987 Lond.

CASEY, Francis 98 Clonmore Road, Dungannon BT71 6HX — MB BCh BAO 1985 NUI; BSc (Hons.) Belf. 1978; MRCP (UK) 1989; DCH RCPI 1987.

***CASEY, Helen Mary** 18 Marlowe Way, Colchester CO3 4JP Tel: 01206 549539 — BM BCh 1998 Oxf.; BM BCh Oxf 1998.

CASEY, Helena Bridget (retired) 153 Sheen Lane, East Sheen, London SW14 8LR — MB BCh BAO 1943 NUI; DOMS Eng. 1947. Prev: Med. Asst. Moorfields & W. Middlx. Hosps.

CASEY, Mr John Joseph 39 Merchiston Crescent, Edinburgh EH10 5AJ — MB ChB 1989 Glas.; FRCS Glas. 1994.

CASEY, Julian Michael Inaki Hickman Esperance House, Hartingdon Place, Eastbourne BN21 3BG Tel: 01323 638263 — MB BS 1985 Lond.; FCOphth 1990. Cons, (Opthalmologist), E.bourne Dist. Hosp. Trust. Prev: Sen. Regist. St. Thos. Hosp. Lond.; Regist. (Ophth.) Roy. Free Hosps. Lond.; SHO (Ophth.) Kings Coll. Hosp. Lond.

CASEY, Kevine Geraldine (retired) 108B Vassall Road, London SW9 6JA Tel: 020 7582 0718 — MB BCh BAO 1945 NUI; DObst RCOG 1949. Prev: Med. Off. Kensington, Chelsea & W.m. AHA (T).

CASEY, Leo Joseph Health Centre, Great James Street, Londonderry BT48 7DH Tel: 028 7137 8522 — MB BCh BAO 1987 Belf.; BSc (Hons.) Physiol. 1985; MRCGP 1991; DMH Belf. 1992; DRCOG 1991; Cert. Family Plann. JCC 1991; DGM RCP Lond. 1989.

CASEY, Michael Donal 20 Willow Drive, Wellesbourne, Warwick CV35 9SB Tel: 01789 840774; 1 Manor House Lane, Yardley, Birmingham B26 1PD — MB ChB Sheff. 1960; MD (Distinc.) Sheff. 1972. GP Yardley. Prev: Lect. (Human Genetics) Univ. Sheff.; Regist. (Med. & Haemat.) Walsgrave Hosp. Coventry; SHO (Med.) Warwick Hosp. & Solihull Hosps.

CASEY, Nora Elizabeth, MBE 103 Main Street, Lisnaskea, Enniskillen BT92 0JD Tel: 0136 57 21431 — LRCPI & LM, LRSCI & LM 1952; LRCPI & LM, LRCSI & LM 1952. (RCSI) Socs: BMA. Prev: Res. Med. Off. Hosp. Sick Childr. Tadworth Ct. & Belgrave Hosp.; Childr. Lond.; Ho. Surg. Univ. Coll. Hosp. Jamaica.

CASEY, Philip Anthony The Health Centre, Chapel Street, Thirsk YO7 1LG Tel: 01845 523154 Fax: 01845 526213; Low Woodcock, Woodcock Lane, Thirsk YO7 2AB — MB ChB 1981 Manch.; MRCGP 1985.

CASEY, Regina Catherine Elizabeth 25 Kings Road, Canton, Cardiff CF11 9BZ — MB BCh BAO 1989 NUI.

CASEY, Sorca Frances Flat 120 Rosemullion, RCHT, Treliske, Truro TR1 3LJ Tel: 01872 40391 Email: 101615.1002@compuserve.com — MB BCh BAO 1991 NUI. Specialist Regist. (O & G) SW Deanery Truro. Socs: BMA; Brit. Fertil. Soc.

CASEY, Valerie Claire 3 Beridge Mews, West Hampstead, London NW6 1RT — MB BS 1990 Lond.

CASEY, William Francis Cheltenham General Hospital, Sandford Road, Cheltenham GL53 7AN Tel: 01242 274143 Fax: 01242 273405 — MB ChB 1975 Liverp.; MA Camb. 1984; FFA RCS Eng. 1979. Cons. Anaesth. Cheltenham Gen. Hosp. Prev: Cons. Anaesth. Glos. Roy. Hosp. Gloucester; Sen. Lect. (Anaesth.) Univ. Jos, Nigeria; Lect. (Anaesth.) Univ. Camb.

CASEY, Yvonne Agnes Tramar Health, 391 Ormeau Road, Belfast BT7 3GP Tel: 01232 694210; 53 Queensway, Lisburn BT27 4QN Tel: 01232 627653 — MB BCh BAO 1993 Belf.; MFHom (Lond.) 1999. (Queen's University Belfast) Lecturesh.s - Qu.'s Univ. Belf. (adult Educat.).

CASH, Arthur John (retired) Institute of Child Health, Francis Road, Birmingham B16 8ET Tel: 0121 454 4851 — MB BS 1957 Lond.; MB BS (Hons.) Lond. 1957; FRCPCH 1997. Hon. Sen. Research Fell. (Paediat. & Child Health) Univ. Birm. Prev: Sen. Lect. (Community Paediat. & Child Health) Univ Birm.

CASH, Charlotte Julia Cottier Cottage Farm, Church End, Leckhampstead, Buckingham MK18 5NU Tel: 01280 860412 — MB BS 1993 Lond.; BSc Lond. 1992, MB BS 1993. SHO (Med.) N.wick Pk. Hosp. Harrow. Prev: Ho. Surg. N.wick Pk. Hosp.; Ho. Phys. Ealing Hosp.

CASH, Deborah Gail 7 Chesterwood Road, Birmingham B13 0QG — MB ChB 1994 Bristol.

CASH, George Noel, TD 77 Rothwell Road, Desborough, Kettering NN14 2NS Tel: 01536 760345 — MB BS 1959 Lond.; FRCGP 1978, M 1968. (Middlx.) Socs: Harv. Soc. & Osler Club. Prev: Ho. Off. (Radiother.) & Ho. Surg. (ENT) Middlx. Hosp.

CASH, Haydn Clifford The Villa Julia, Weston Road, Bath BA1 2XT — MB BCh 1975 Wales; PhD Lond. 1970; BSc (Hons.) CNAA 1965; Dip. Pharm. Med. RCP (UK) 1978. (Cardiff) Med. Dir. Euro Bio-Pharm. Ltd. Chippenham. Prev: Clin. Trials Manager CIBA-GEIGY Ltd.; Managing Med. Dir. ICP Ltd.; Clin. Trials Manager Pfizer Ltd. Sandwich.

CASH, Helen Theresa 39 Grassmoor Road, Birmingham B38 8BX — MB ChB 1988 Leic.; DRCOG 1992.

CASH, Ian David 24 Stoke Lane, Stoke Lodge, Patchway, Bristol BS34 6BW — BM 1995 Soton.

CASH, Professor John David 1 Otterburn Park, Edinburgh EH14 1JX Tel: 0131 443 9841 — MB ChB 1961 Ed.; PhD Ed. 1967, BSc 1959; FRCS Ed. 1995; FRCP Glas. 1994; FRCP Ed. 1970, M 1964; FRCPath 1986, M 1976. (Ed.) Nat. Med. Dir. Scott. Transfus. Serv. HQ Unit Edin.; Pres. RCP Edin.; Hon. Prof. Univ. Edin. Socs: Brit. Soc. Haematol. & Internat. Soc. Haemostasis & Thrombosis.

CASH, John Watt (retired) 7 Windmill Hill Close, Ellington Village, Morpeth NE61 5BS Tel: 01670 860371 — MB BS 1956 Durh.

CASH, Katherine Jessamy (retired) Cort House, Main Street, Arkholme, Carnforth LA6 1AX Tel: 015242 21365 — MB BS Lond. 1957 (HONS); MRCPsych 1977; BA Hons Warwick 1993. Prev: Cons. Psychiat. St. And. Hosp. N.ampton.

CASH, Margaret Elizabeth 20 Belmont Road, Twickenham TW2 5DA Tel: 020 8894 3116 — MRCS Eng. LRCP Lond. 1960; MB BS Lond., 1960; DA Eng. 1963. (Guy's)

CASH, Michael Peter Bruntsfield Medical Practice, 11 Forbes Road, Edinburgh EH10 4EY Tel: 0131 228 6081 Fax: 0131 229 4330; 18 Morningside Gardens, Edinburgh EH10 5LE Tel: 0131 447 6671 — MB ChB 1988 Bristol; MRCP (UK) 1992; MRCGP 1995; DRCOG 1993. (Bristol)

CASH, Robert Peter 152 Harley Street, London W1N; 33 Rutland Gate, London SW7 1PD Tel: 020 7923 7499 — MB ChB 1974 Birm. Med. Litigation Cons. & Forens. Med. Examr. Metrop. Police. Socs: Fell. Roy. Soc. Med.

CASH, Thomas Ivan (retired) Primrose Cottage, Portway, Upton St Leonards, Gloucester GL4 8DN Tel: 01452 371566 — MRCS Eng. LRCP Lond. 1960; FFA RCS Eng. 1967(Now FRCA); DA Eng. 1964. Prev: Cons. Anaesth. Glos. Roy. NHS Trust & E. Glos. NHS Trust.

CASH, William Jonathan 6 Old Mill Road, Scarva, Craigavon BT63 6NL — MB BCh 1998 Belf.; MB BCh Belf 1998.

CASHEL, Mary Lynn (retired) Keep Cottage, 5 Castle Lane, Carisbrooke, Newport PO30 1PH Tel: 01983 522096 — MB BS 1960 Lond.; DCH RCP Lond. 1963. Community Med. Off. I. of Wight HA. Prev: SHO Hosp. Sick Childr. Gt. Ormond St. Lond.

CASHELL, Ceri Fiona 6 Rosetta Drive, Belfast BT7 3HL — MB ChB 1998 Dund.; MB ChB Dund 1998.

CASHELL, Mary Philomena North Parade Surgery, 6 North Parade, Belfast BT7 2GG; 6 Rosetta Drive, Belfast BT7 3HL — MB BCh BAO 1973 Belf.

CASHEN, Janet Anne 72 Muirhead Avenue, Liverpool L13 0BR — MB ChB 1974 Leeds.

CASHIN, Deirdre Anne The Surgery, Marsh Gardens, Honley, Huddersfield HD9 6AG Tel: 01484 303366 Fax: 01484 303365 — MB BS 1978 Lond.; MRCP (UK) 1981.

CASHIN, Robert John Cornerways Medical Centre, 27 Woolfall Heath Avenue, Huyton, Liverpool L36 3TH Tel: 0151 489 4444 Fax: 0151 489 0528 — MB ChB 1970 Liverp.

CASHMAN, Aileen Joyce 25 Church End, Biddenham, Bedford MK40 4AR — MB BS 1944 Punjab. (Lady Hardinge Hosp. New Delhi) Assoc. Specialist (Geriat.) Bedford Gen. Hosp. Socs: Brit. Geriat. Soc. Prev: RAMC; Jun. Asst. Bacteriol. Bernhard Baron Memor. Research Laborats, Qu.; Charlotte's Hosp.

CASHMAN, Denis Vincent 4 Derwent Road, North Shields NE30 3AH — MB BS 1946 Durh.; MRCGP 1961. Socs: BMA.

CASHMAN, Jeremy Nicholas St. George's Hospital, Blackshaw Road, London SW17 0QT Tel: 020 8672 1255 — MB BS 1979 Lond.; BSc Lond. 1976; MD Lond. 1995; FFA RCS Eng. 1983. Cons. Anaesth. St. Geo. Hosp. Lond.; Hon. Sen. Lect. Univ. Lond.; Acad. Europ. Acad. Anaesth. Socs: Anaesth. Res. Soc. Prev: Lect. & Hon. Sen. Regist. (Anaesth.) Guy's Hosp. Lond.; Sen. Regist. (Anaesth.) Guy's & Lewisham Hosps. Lond.; Regist. (Anaesth.) Guy's Hosp. Lond.

CASHMAN, Mr John Philip Flat 2, 19 Marlborough Buildings, Bath BA1 2LY Tel: 01225 442126; 38 Abbotsford Road, Galashiels TD1 3HR Tel: 01896 752711 — BM 1988 Soton.; FRCS Glas. 1993; FRCS Eng. 1993.

CASHMAN, Mary Elizabeth 53 Farley Road, Selsdon, South Croydon CR2 7NG Tel: 020 8651 1222 Fax: 020 8657 9297; 11 Beech Avenue, Sanderstead, South Croydon CR2 0NN Tel: 020 8657 7599 — MB BS 1976 Lond.; MRCS Eng. LRCP Lond. 1976. (Char. Cross) Prev: GP Wallington Surrey; SHO (A & E) Mayday Hosp. Croydon; SHO (Paediat.) Sydenham Childr. Hosp. Lond.

CASHMAN, Michael David (retired) 1 Windsor Road, St Annes-on-Sea, Lytham St Annes FY8 1ET Tel: 01253 780190 Fax: 01253 780190 — MB BS 1953 Durh.; FRCP Ed. 1987, M 1963; FRCPsych 1977, M 1972; DPM Eng. 1958. Med. Panel of Ment. Health Review Tribunal. Prev: Cons. Psychiat. S. Shields Gen. Hosp. & Cherry Knowle Hosp. Ryhope & Blackpool & Fylde Hosp. Gp.

CASHMORE, Rebecca Julia 12 Hillside Crescent, Worksop S81 0JU — MB ChB 1993 Leic.

CASHYAP, Alka Davenport House Surgery, Bowers Way, Harpenden AL5 4HX Tel: 01582 767821 Fax: 01582 769285 — MB BS 1982 Delhi; MRCS Eng. LRCP Lond. 1984; MRCGP 1989; DCH RCP Lond. 1991; DRCOG 1987.

CASIE CHETTY, Lukshman William Felix 9 Kingfisher Close, Scunthorpe DN15 8EJ Tel: 01724 867942 — MB BS 1971 Ceylon. Hosp. Phys. Goole & Dist. Hosp. Goole N. Humberside.

CASIMIR, Cyril Leonard 9 Sudbrook Gardens, Ham Common, Richmond TW10 7DD Tel: 020 8940 7901 — MB BS Lond. 1946; MRCS Eng. LRCP Lond. 1945; FRCPsych 1987, M 1971; DPM Eng. 1948. (Middlx.) Cons. Psychiat. Beechcroft Bd.ing Sch. Wandsworth. Prev: Cons. Psychiat. Brixton Child Guid. Unit; Cons. Psychiat. Epsom Child & Family Consult. Clinic; Cons. Psychiat. Child Guid. Clinic, Forest Hill.

CASKEY, Fergus John 6d Deemount Terrace, Ferryhill, Aberdeen AB11 7RX Tel: 01224 582735 — MB ChB 1993 Glas.; MRCP (UK) 1996. Research Fell. (Med. & Therap.) Foresterhill Hosp. Aberd.. Prev: Research Regist. (Renal) Treliske Hosp. Truro; SHO (Med.) Treliske Hosp. Truro; Ho. Off. (Med.) Stobhill Hosp. Glas.

CASKEY, Gladys May (retired) 36 Cheltenham Park, Belfast BT6 0HR Tel: 01232 649753 — MB BCh BAO Belf. 1947. Prev: Regist. (Psychiat.) Banstead Hosp. Sutton.

CASKEY, John Faith (retired) Park Medical Centre, 164 Park Road, Peterborough PE1 2UF — MB BCh BAO 1955 Belf. Life Insur. Med.s only; Police Surg. P'boro. Prev: GP 1957-1998.

CASKEY, Michael John 10 Metchley Court, Harborne, Birmingham B17 0JP — MB ChB 1982 Birm.

CASKIE, June Peterson West Kilbride Surgery, 107B Main Street, West Kilbride KA23 9AR Tel: 01294 823607 Fax: 01294 829318 — MB ChB 1977 Glas.; FRCP Glas. 1994; MRCP (UK) 1980. Regist. (Med.) Roy. Alexandra Infirm. Paisley. Prev: SHO (Respirat. Med.) W.. Infirm. & Kt.swood Hosp. Glas.; Ho. Off. (Surg.) S.. Gen. Hosp. Glas.

CASLIN, Anthony William 39 Woodchurch Lane, Birkenhead CH42 9PJ — MB ChB 1985 Sheff.

CASON, Mr Armando Philip Ernest Oak Lodge, 25 Embercourt Road, Thames Ditton KT7 0LH — MB ChB 1972 Cape Town; FRCS Eng. 1978. (Cape Town) Cons., the Pourtney Clinic; Cons. Highgate Private Hosp. Socs: Fell., Roy. Soc. of Med.; Brit. Soc. of Cosmetic Surg.s; Fell.of Europ. Acad. of Cosmetic Surg. Prev: Research Regist. (Burns & Plastic Surg.) St. Andrews Hosp.

CASS, Hilary Dawn Wolfson centre, Mecklenburgh Square, London WC1N 2AP Tel: 020 7837 7618 Fax: 020 7833 9469 — MB BS 1982 Lond.; BSc Lond. 1979; MRCP (Paediat.) UK 1988. (Roy. Free) Cons. Paediat. Disabil. & Dir. of Postgrad. Med. Educat. at Ormond St. Hosp. Socs: Brit. Paediat. Neurol. Assn.; Brit. Paediat. Assn. Prev: Cons. Paediat. Disabil. Harper Ho. Childr.'s Serv. Herts; Sen. Regist. (Paediat.) Harper Hse. Childr. Serv. Herts.; Regist. (Paediat.) Newham Gen. Hosp. & Roy. Lond. Hosp.

CASS, Michael Andrew c/o 24 Mill Lane, Wigginton, York YO32 2PX — MB BS 1991 Lond.; FRCS (Eng.) 1995. (Char. Cross & Westm.) Specialist Regist. (Trauma & Orthop.) Hammersmith Hosps. N. W. Thames Rotat. Prev: SHO Char. Cross Surg. Rotat.

CASS, Mr Peter Leonard 127 Harley Street, London W1N 6AZ Tel: 020 7935 7341 Fax: 020 7935 7342 Email: pcass@dircon.co.uk; 23 Bryanston Mews West, London W1H 2BW — MB BS 1979 Lond.; MRCOG 1986. (Westm.) Indep. Cons. O & G Lond. Socs: Fell.Roy. Soc. of Med.; BMA; Chelsea Clin. Soc. Prev: Lect. & Sen. Regist. St. Bart. Hosp. Lond.; Research Regist. (IVF) St. Bart. Hosp. Lond.; Regist. (O & G) St. Bart. Lond.

CASS, Stephen Melbourne House Surgery, 12 Napier Court, Queensland Crescent, Chelmsford CM1 2ED Tel: 01245 354370 Fax: 01245 344476 — MB BS 1985 Lond.; DRCOG 1990; MRCGP 1995.

CASSAM, Khalid Kingstanding Circle Surgery, 26 Rough Road, Kingstanding, Birmingham B44 0UY; 22 Shrubbery Close, Sutton Coldfield B76 1WE — MB ChB 1990 Leeds. Socs: BMA; Med. Protec. Soc.

CASSAM, Samina 22 Shrubbery Close, Sutton Coldfield B76 1WE — MB ChB 1990 Leeds; JCPTGP 1995; DFFP 1995. (Leeds Univ.)

CASSAR, Carmelo 178A Wandsworth Road, London SW8 Tel: 020 7622 5947 — MD 1949 Malta; DPH Eng. 1960; DObst RCOG 1952. (Univs. Rome & Malta) Socs: BMA & Roy. Coll. GPs. Prev: SHO (Anaesth) W. Lond. Hosp.; Med. Off. Colon. Med. Serv Nigeria; Clin. Asst. St. Margt. Matern. Hosp. Sydney, Australia.

CASSAR, Emmanuel (retired) 11 Hanging Green Lane, Hest Bank, Lancaster LA2 6JB Tel: 01524 824510 — MD 1949 Malta; MRCOG 1956. Med. Off. DHSS Norcross.

CASSAR, Joseph West Middlesex University Hospital, Isleworth TW7 6AF Tel: 020 8565 5390 Fax: 020 8560 5394; 16 Queens Gardens, Ealing, London W5 1SF — MD Malta 1964; PhD (Med.) Lond. 1970; FRCP Lond. 1987; MRCP (UK) 1972; DIC (Biochem.) Lond. 1968. Cons. Phys. W. Middlx. Univ. Hosp.; Honarary Sen. Clin. Lect.. Imperial Coll. of Sci. Technol. and Med.. Socs: Endocrine Soc.; Brit. Diabetic Assn.; BMA. Prev: Sen. Regist. (Med. & Endocrinol.) Roy. Postgrad. Med. Sch. Hammersmith Hosp. Lond.; Regist. (Gen. Med.) Roy. Free Hosp. Lond.; Regist. (Diabetic Med.) King's Coll. Hosp. Lond.

CASSAR, Sarah Deborah 21 South Park Court, Park Road, Beckenham BR3 1PH — MB BS 1992 Lond.; MSc (Mental Health Studies) Lond. 1997; MRCPsych 1997. (SGHMS) Research Regist. Liaison Psychiat. UMDS Lond. Socs: Roy. Coll. Psychiat.; Brit. Holistic Med. Assn.

CASSAR-PULLICINO, Victor Nicholas Normanhurst, Queen Road, Oswestry SY11 2JB; Lares, Dr. Zammit St, Balzan, Malta — MD 1984 Malta; MRCS Eng. LRCP Lond. 1977; FRCR 1983; DMRD Lond. 1982. Cons. Radiol. Robt. Jones & Agnes Hunt Orthop. Hosp. OsW.ry.

CASSELL, Diana Margaret Constance Kingston & District Community NHS Trust, CAFC, Elm House, 84 Ewell Road, Surbiton KT6 6EX Tel: 020 8390 8151 Fax: 020 8390 4754; 2 Timbercroft, Ewell, Epsom KT19 0TD Tel: 020 8393 1040 — MB BS 1983 Lond.; MRCPsych 1987. (St.Bartholomew's, London) Cons. Child Psychiat., Child, Adolesc. & Family Centre, Surbiton. Socs: BMA; ACPP; Roy. Coll. Psychiat. Prev: Sen. Regist. (Child Psychiat.) Char. Cross Hosp. Lond.; Lect. & Regist. (Child Psychiat.) W.m. Childr. Hosp. Lond.; Regist. (Ment. Handicap) St. Lawrence's Hosp. Caterham.

CASSELL, Jacqueline Anne Mortimer Market Centre, Off Capper St., London WC1E 6AU Tel: 020 7530 5055 Fax: 020 7530 5044 Email: jcassell@gum.ucl.ac.uk; 35 Spences Lane, Lewes BN7 2HF Tel: 01273 473511 Fax: 01273 473511 — BM BCh 1988 Oxf.; Diploma n Public Health Medicine, Faculty of Public Health Medicine 1999; MSc Epidemiology, London School of Hygiene & Tropical Medicine 1999; BA (Phil.) Sussex 1992; MRCP (UK) 1996; Dip. GU Med. Soc. Apoth. Lond. 1994; Cert. Family Plann. JCC 1991. Wellcome Fell. Mortimer Market Centre Lond.; Hon. Specialist Regist. Mortimer Market Centre Lond. Socs: Diplomate DFFP; MSSVD; AGUM. Prev: Clin. Med. Off. (Family Plann.) Brighton; Specialist Regist. Genitourin. Med.

CASSELL, Mr Oliver Clive Sheldon Dept of Plastic Surgery, The Radiliffe Infirmary, Oxford OX2 6ME Tel: 01865 557927 Email: ocassell@hotmail.com; 36 Plantation Road, Walton Manor, Oxford OX2 6ME — MB ChB 1989 Sheff.; FRCS Ed. 1993. (Sheffield) Cons. Plastic & Reconstrctive Surg., Radiliffe Inf. Oxf. Socs: Brit. Assn. of Plastic Surg.s.

CASSELL, Mr Paul George (cons. rooms) South Lodge, Wexham St., Slough SL2 4HS Tel: 01753 516852 Fax: 01753 516275; Cefalu, Half Acre Hill, Chalfont Heights, Gerrards Cross SL9 9UD Tel: 01753 885137 — MB BS Lond. 1960; FRCS Eng. 1966; MRCS Eng. LRCP Lond. 1960. (St. Bart.) JP; Cons. Surg. Wexham Pk. & Maidenhead Hosps. Socs: Fell. Roy. Soc. Med.; Assn. Coloproct.; BMA & Health Care Servs. Assn. Prev: Sen. Surg. Regist. St. Bart. Hosp. Lond.; Surg. Regist. Roy. Berks. Hosp. Reading; Cons. Surg. Wexham Pk. & Maidenhead Hosps.

CASSELLS, David Alasdair Dunbar Medical Centre, Abbey Road, Dunbar EH42 1JP Tel: 01368 863226 Fax: 01368 865646; Beaconsfield House, Paterson Place, Haddington EH41 3DU — MB ChB 1981 Ed.

CASSELS, Alastair Ogilvie (retired) Milton House, Strathmore Road, Rowlands Gill NE39 1JD Tel: 01207 542353 — MB BS 1948 Durh.

CASSELS, Andrew Haig (retired) Tudor Cottage, 129 Broomhill, Downham Market PE38 9QU Tel: 01366 383018 — MB ChB 1951 Glas. Prev: Local Med. Off. Civil Serv. Dept.

CASSELS, Hilary Theresa Great Eccleston Health Centre, Raikes Road, Great Eccleston, Preston PR3 0ZA Tel: 01995 670066 Fax: 01995 671054 — MB ChB 1978 Liverp.; MRCS Eng. LRCP Lond. 1978; FRCGP 1996, M 1983; DCH 1981; DRCOG 1980. Course Organiser & Examr. for Roy. Coll. Gen. Practs.

CASSELS, Mairi Cameron Townhead Health Centre, 16 Alexandra Parade, Glasgow G31 2ES Fax: 0141 531 8935 — MB ChB 1983 Glas.; MRCGP 1987; DRCOG 1986. Princip. in Gen. Prac.

CASSELS-BROWN, Mr Andrew Dept of Ophthalmology, Clarendon Wing, Leeds General Infirmary, Belmont Grove, Leeds LS2 Tel: 0113 392 2748 — MB BS 1982 Lond.; FRCOphth 1989; FRCS (Ophth.) 1988. (St. Thos. Hosp. Med. Sch. Lond.) Cons. Ophth. Leeds Gen. Infirm. Socs: FRCOphth.

CASSELS-BROWN, Graham Cassels (retired) — MB BS 1955 Lond. Prev: Med. Off. St. Mary's Coll. (Teach. Train.) Twickenham & Normansfield Hosp.

CASSERLEY, Carmel Angela Flat 4, Jofflor Mount, 54 North Promenade, Lytham St Annes FY8 2NH — MB BCh BAO 1958 NUI.

CASSERLEY, Joan Dorothy Anne 4 Frognel Close, London NW3 6YB Tel: 020 7794 5919 — MB ChB 1953 N.Z.; FFA RCS Eng. 1959. Clin. Asst. Dept. Psychiat. St. Mary's Hosp. Lond. Prev: Regist. Char. Cross Hosp. Lond. & Tottenham Gp. Hosps.; Regist. (Anaesth.) Wellington Hosp., N.Z.

CASSIDY, Anthony Denis (retired) Flat 8, Abbeyfield Society, 237 Chesterton Rd, Cambridge CB4 1AS Tel: 01223 23500 — MB BCh BAO 1938 NUI; LM Rotunda 1945. Prev: Ho. Phys. & Ho. Surg. St. Vincent's Hosp. Dub.

CASSIDY, Caroline Alexandra 4 Kiloanin Crescent, Kiln Lane, Banbridge BT32 4NU — MB ChB 1991 Manch.

CASSIDY, Cathal Eustace Addiction Service, ST. Lukes Hospital, Armagh BT61 7NQ Tel: 02837 522381 Fax: 028 3752 6507 Email: addictionunit@adhsst.n-l.nhs.uk; Killeshil Glebe, Dungannon BT70 1TS Tel: 02887 761196 Email: cathalc@aol.com — MB BCh BAO 1981 Belf.; MMedSci (Psychother.) Belf. 1989; MRCPsych 1986. (Queens Uni. Belfast) Cons. Psychiat. (Addic.s) St. Luke's Hosp. Armagh. Socs: Roy. Coll. Psychiat.; BMA. Prev: Cons. Psychiat. (Gen.Psychiat.) S.Tyrone Hosp. Dungannon.

CASSIDY, David Michael Department of Clinical Biochemistry, Prince Charles Hospital, Merthyr Tydfil CF47 9DT Tel: 01685 728262 Fax: 01685 721911 — MB BCh 1981 Wales; BSc (Hons.) Wales 1976; MRCPath 1994; DRCPath 1993. (Welsh Nat. Sch. Med.) Cons. Chem. Path. Merthyr Tydfil; Clin. Director of Diagnnostic & Therapuetics Directorate. Socs: Fell. Roy. Soc. Med.; Assn. Clin. Biochem.; Brit. Hyperlipid. Assn. Prev: Sen. Regist. & Clin. Lect. (Clin. Biochem.) John Radcliffe Hosp. Oxf.; Research Assoc. Univ. Newc.; Regist. (Clin. Biochem.) Roy. Vict. Infirm. Newc. u Tyne.

CASSIDY, Ellen Elizabeth Bryson Street Surgery, 115 Newtownards Road, Belfast BT4 1AB Tel: 028 9045 8722 Fax: 028 9046 6766 — MB BCh BAO 1988 Belf. SHO (A & E) Belf. City Hosp. GP VTS. Prev: Ho. Off. Belf City Hsop.

CASSIDY, Professor James Institute of Medical Sciences, Foresterhill, Aberdeen AB25 2ZD Tel: 01224 681818 Fax: 01224 273066; Larig, Auchmacoy Road, Torphins, Banchory AB31 4GQ Tel: 013398 82851 Fax: 01224 273066 — MB ChB 1981 Glas.; MSc (Clin. Pharmacol.) Glas. 1988; FRCP ed. 1996; FRCP Glas. 1994; MRCP (UK) 1985. (Glas.) Prof. Oncol. Univ. Aberd.; Hon. Cons. Oncol. Aberd. Roy. Hosp. NHS Trust. Socs: (Exec.) Assn. Cancer Phys.; BMA; Amer. Assn. Cancer Research. Prev: Sen. Lect. (Med. Oncol.) Glas. Univ.; Lect. (Med. Oncol.) Univ. Edin.

CASSIDY, James Peter Main Street, Ederney, Enniskillen BT93 0D — MB BCh BAO 1976 Belf.

CASSIDY, Jane Frances 79 The Crescent, Adel, Leeds LS16 6AG — BM BS 1987 Nottm.

CASSIDY, Jane Veronica Flat 8, Priors House, Priors Haven, East St., North Shields NE30 4EB Tel: 0191 258 6355 — MB BS 1993 Lond.; MRCP (UK) 1996; MRCPCH 1997. (St. Geo. Hosp. Med. Sch.) Specialist Regist. (Paediat.) N. Tees Gen. Hosp. Prev: SHO R.V.J. Newc; SHO (Paediat.) Birm. Childr. Hosp.; Ho. Off. (Med.) St. Helier Hosp. Carshalton.

CASSIDY, Jennifer Margaret Windmill Medical Practice, Ann Street, Denton, Manchester M34 2AJ Tel: 0161 320 3131 Fax: 0161 337 8250 — MB ChB 1976 Manch.; MRCGP 1983; DRCOG 1980.

CASSIDY, John James Dow Surgery, William Street, Redditch B97 4AJ Tel: 01527 62285 Fax: 01527 596260; 37 Western Hill Close, Astwood Bank, Redditch B96 6BY — MB ChB 1985 Birm.; MRCGP 1991; DA (UK) 1988. Prev: Trainee GP Redditch.

CASSIDY, Joseph 51 Camphill Avenue, Glasgow G41 3AX — MB ChB 1987 Glas.

CASSIDY, Kirsten Anne Clinkstone Cottage, Parkhill, Kemnay, Inverurie AB51 5PL — MB ChB 1986 Aberd.; MRCGP 1990.

CASSIDY, Laura Jane — MB ChB 1968 Glas.; MRCOG 1973; Japanese Nat. Med. Cert. 1977; FRCOG 1996. (University of Glasgow) Cons. O & G Inverclyde Roy. Hosp. Greenock; Hon. Sen. Lect. Univ. of Glas. Socs: Counc. RCOG 1988-1994; Brit. Gyn. Cancer Soc.; Brit Soc. for colposcopy. Prev: Sen. Regist. Glas. Roy. Infirm. Hosp.

CASSIDY, Liam Joseph Avenue Villa Surgery, Brynmor Road, Llanelli SA15 2TJ Tel: 01554 774401 Fax: 01554 775229 Email: ljcassidy@doctors.org.uk — MB BCh 1981 Wales; DCH RCP Lond. 1985; DRCOG 1983. Clin. Asst. (Dermat.) E. Dyfed AHA. Socs: BMA & Dyfed LMC.

CASSIDY, Lorraine 20 Sycamore Mews, Orlando Road, London SW4 0SY — MB BCh BAO 1989 NUI; FRCSI 1993; FRCOphth 1993; LRCPSI 1989.

CASSIDY, Marie Therese The Dovecot, Blackwood Est., Lesmahagow, Lanark ML11 0JG — MB ChB 1978 Glas.

CASSIDY, Maureen Patten Holm, Blantyre, Glasgow G72 9UJ Tel: 0141 823354 — LRCP LRCS Ed. LRFPS Glas. 1950. (Univ. Glas.)

CASSIDY, Michael John Dolman Renal Unit, Nottingham City Hospital NHS Trust, Huknall Road, Nottingham NG5 1PB Tel: 0115 969 1169 Email: mcassidy@ncht.org.uk — MB BS 1974 Lond.; FRCP Lond. 1995; MRCP (UK) 1977. (St. Bart.) Cons. Nephrol. Nottm. Hosps. NHS Trust. Socs: Eur. Dialysis & Transpl. Assn.; S. Afr. Renal Assn.; S. Afr. Transpl. Assn. Prev: Cons. Nephrol. Hammersmith Hosp. Lond.; Cons. Nephrol. & Sen. Lect. Med.) Univ. Cape Town & Groote Schuur Hosp. Cape Town, S. Afr.

CASSIDY, Michael Patrick Eaglestone Health Centre, Standing Way, Eaglestone, Milton Keynes MK6 5AZ Tel: 01908 679111 Fax: 01908 230601 — MB BCh BAO 1980 NUI; MRCGP 1986; DObst RCPI 1983; DCH NUI 1982. Socs: BMA (Bucks. Div. Exec. Comm.); Milton Keynes Med. Soc. Prev: Ho. Off. (Med.) St. Vincents Hosp. Dub.; Regist. (Med.) St. Josephs Hosp. Clonmel Eire; Trainee GP Gillies Health Centre Basingstoke.

CASSIDY, Paul Douglas 64 Kells Lane, Gateshead NE9 5XY — MB BS 1984 Newc.; MB BS Newc. l984; MRCGP 1988.

CASSIDY, Paul Philip The Health Centre, Commercial Road, Skelmanthorpe, Huddersfield HD8 9DA Tel: 01484 863542 — MB BS 1983 Lond.; MRCGP 1992; DRCOG 1988.

CASSIDY, Rita Veronica 2 Maelors Cottage, Well Lane, Ness, South Wirral CH64 4AW — MB BCh BAO 1985 NUI.

CASSIDY, Sheila Anne Plymouth Oncology Centre, Derriford Hospital, Plymouth PL6 8DH Tel: 01752 763986 — BM BCh Oxf. 1963; MA Oxf. 1964; DSc (Hons.) Exeter 1991; DLITT (Hons.) Cheltenham 1992; Méd. Cir. Univ. Chile 1974. (Oxf.) Assoc. Specialist (Psychosocial Oncol.) Plymouth Oncol.Centre, Derriford Hosp., Plymouth; Lect. St Lukes Hospice Plymouth; Hon. Lect. Univ. of Plymouth. Socs: Brit. Psychosocial Oncol. Soc. Prev: Phys. (Palliat. Care) Plymouth Gen. Hosp.; Med. Dir. St. Luke's Hospice Plymouth; Ho. Phys. & Ho. Surg. Radcliffe Infirm. Oxf.

CASSIDY, Sheila Jean Alresford Surgery, Station Road, Alresford SO24 9JL Tel: 01962 732345 Fax: 01962 736034; High Dell Cottage, Bighton, Alresford SO24 9SE Tel: 01962 733491 — MB ChB 1978 Leeds.

CASSIDY, Timothy Patrick Newcastle General Hospital, Newcastle upon Tyne NE4 6BE Tel: 0191 273 6666 Fax: 0191 219 5049 — MB BCh BAO 1983 NUI; LRCPI & LM, LRCSI & LM 1983; MRCP (UK) 1987; FRCP Ed. 1998; FRCP 1998. (Dublin) Cons. Phys. with interest in c/o Elderly Newc. Gen. Hosp. Socs: Brit. Assn. of Stroke Phys.s; Brit. Geriat. Soc. Prev: Cons. Phys. S. Tyneside Gen. Hosp.; Sen. Regist. (Gen. & Geriat. Med.) City Hosp. Edin.; Research Fell. (Med.) Edin.

CASSIE, Mr Alistair Baxter (retired) 32 Winton Grove, Fairmilehead, Edinburgh EH10 7AS — MB ChB 1948 Ed.; FRCS Ed. 1956; FRCS Eng. 1958. Hon. Cons. Surg. Burnley HA. Prev: Sen. Regist. (Surg.) Manch. Roy. Infirm.

CASSIE, George (retired) 66 Hilton Road, Bishopbriggs, Glasgow G64 3EL — MB ChB 1952 Aberd.; DPH 1957; MFCM 1973. Prev: SCM Gt.. Glas. HB.

CASSIE, Georgina Jane 12 Cottingwood Lane, Morpeth NE61 1DU — BM BS 1998 Nottm.; BM BS Nottm 1998.

CASSIE, Mr Gordon Fordyce (retired) Lysham, Inchmarlo Road, Banchory AB31 4AH Tel: 01330 822575 — MB ChB 1944 Aberd.; ChM Aberd. 1958, MB ChB 1944; FRCS Eng. 1951. Prev: Cons. Surg. Qu. Eliz. II Hosp. Welwyn Garden City.

CASSIE, Janet Alexandra Missy Cottage, Crag Lane, Huby, Leeds LS17 0BW — MB ChB 1987 Manch.; BSc (Med. Sci.) St. And. 1984; MRCP (UK) 1993. SHO Rotat. (Palliat. Med.) Yorks.

CASSIE, Ralph Department of Gynaecology, Monklands Hospital, Airdrie G71 7AP Tel: 01236 748748; 10 Bellevue Avenue, Uddington, Glasgow G71 7AP Tel: 01698 812823 — MB ChB Aberd. 1964; FRCOG, 1983, M 1970, DObst 1966. Cons. (O & G) Bellshill Matern. & Monklands Dist. Gen. Hosps. Prev: 1st Asst. Dept. O & G Univ. Newc.

CASSIM, Sheikh Dharvesh Mohammad Avicenna Medical Centre, Oxley Shaw Lane, Leybourne, West Malling ME19 5PU Tel: 01732 841561/844676 Fax: 01732 872949; 71 Castleway, Leybourne, West Malling ME19 5HF Tel: 01732 844601 — MB BS 1967 Ceylon. (Peradeniya)

CASSIMER, Sheila Sanda 49 Fawley Road, Calderstones, Liverpool L18 9TE Tel: 0151 724 3792 & 051 928 7243 — MB BS 1968 Rangoon.

CASSON, Angela Joyce 5 Furzefield Road, Reigate RH2 7HG — LMSSA 1958 Lond. (St. Bart.)

CASSON, David Howard 68 Mild May Park, Islington, London N1 4PR Tel: 020 7241 5596; 12 Parkfield Road S., Didsbury, Manchester M20 6DB Tel: 0161 445 9744 — MB BS 1988 Lond.; BA Oxf. 1985; MRCPI 1992. Sen. Regist. & Lect. (Paediat.) Roy. Free Hosp. Lond. Prev: Regist. (Paediat.) Roy. Liverp. Childr. Hosp.; Regist. & SHO (Paediat.) Roy. Manch. Childr. Hosp.; SHO (Paediat.) Alder Hey Childr. Hosp. Liverp.

CASSON, Emma Jane Station Road Surgery, Station Road, Stalbridge, Sturminster Newton DT10 2RG Tel: 01963 362363 Fax: 01963 362866; Sovereiens, Pound Road, Thornford, Sherborne DT9 6QB Tel: 01935 373360 Email: ecasson@tip.co.uk — MB ChB 1991 Liverp.; MRCGP 1995; DFFP 1997. (Liverpool) GP Dorset; Clin. Asst. BrE. clinic, Yeocil Dist. Hosp. Socs: RCGP. Prev: Ho. Off. (Med. & Surg.) Wirral Hosp. Mersyside.; SHO (O & G); SHO (A & E).

CASSON, Ian Ferdinand The Royal Liverpool University Hospitals, Broadgreen Hospital, Thomas Drive, Liverpool L14 3LB Tel: 0151 282 6223; Pine Cottage, Pine Tree Drive, West Kirby, Wirral CH48 8AT Tel: 0151 625 2595 — MB ChB 1975 Leeds; MD Leeds 1984; FRCP Lond. 1995; MRCP (UK) 1978. Cons. Phys. Roy. Liverp. & BRd.green Univ. Hosp. NHS Trust; Clin. Lect. (Med.) Univ. Liverp.; Hon. Cons. Phys. Liverp. Wom. Hosp. Prev: Sen. Regist. (Med.) Roy. Liverp. Hosp.; Research Regist. Leeds Gen. Infirm.

CASSON, Isabel Hythe Medical Centre, Beaulieu Road, Hythe, Southampton SO45 4ZD Tel: 02380 845955 — Lic Med 1965 Lisbon; Lic Med. Lisbon 1965.

CASSON, Michael Alan 24 The Carriages, Booth Road, Altrincham WA14 4AF Tel: 0161 929 6847 Fax: 0161 928 4654 Email: miccasson@hotmail.com — MB ChB 1955 Manch.; BSc (Hons.) Manch. 1952; MRCP (UK) 1970; MRCGP 1968; DObst RCOG 1962; DCH Eng. 1959. Cons.-Asst. to the private Pract. of Dr L.A. Michael. Socs: Fell. Manch. Med. Soc. (Ex-Pres. & Ex-Sec. GP Sect.). Prev: Clin. (Path.) & Ho. Phys. Crumpsall Hosp. Manch.; Ho. Surg. Profess. Unit Manch. Roy. Infirm.

CASSON, Pamela Anne (retired) Holme Eden Vicarage, Warwick Bridge, Carlisle CA4 8RF Tel: 01228 60332 — MB ChB 1955 Liverp.; DObst RCOG 1958. Prev: Occupat. Health Phys. E. Cumbria HA.

CASSON, Peter Arthur St Mary's Vicarage, 1162 Tyburn Rd, Birmingham B24 0TB — MB BS 1995 Lond.

CASSON, Richard Trench Steventon Road Surgery, 39 Steventon Road, Drayton, Abingdon OX14 4JX Tel: 01235 531322 Fax: 01235 559385 — MB BS 1970 Lond.; MRCS Eng. LRCP Lond. 1970; MRCGP 1980; DObst RCOG 1975. Prev: SHO (Anaesth.) & Ho. Surg. St. Thos. Hosp. Lond.; Ho. Phys. Roy. Vict. Hosp. Bournemouth.

CASSON, William Robert 7 Richmondhill Place, Aberdeen AB15 5EN Tel: 01224 312044 — MB ChB 1976 Aberd.; FFA RCS Eng. 1981. Cons. Anaesth. Aberd. Teach. Hosps.; Assoc. Acad.ian Europ. Acad. of Anaesthsiol. Socs: Anaesth. Research Soc. Prev: Cons. Anaesth. Roy. Infirm. Stirling; Lect./Sen. Regist. (Anaesth.) Guy's Hosp. Lond.; Sen. Regist. (Anaesth.) Kent & Canterbury Hosp. Canterbury.

CASSONE, Anna Maria The Meyerstein Institute of Clinical Oncology, The Middlesex Hospital, Mortimer St., London W1T 3AA Tel: 020 7636 8333 Fax: 020 7436 0160; 41 Ellerton Road, Wandsworth Common, London SW18 3NQ Tel: 020 8874 5330 — MB BS 1974 Lond.; BSc Lond. 1971; FRCP Lond. 1994; FRCR 1982. (Middlx.) Cons. Clin. Oncol. Univ. Coll. Lond. Hosps. Socs: Brit. Oncol. Assn.; Brit. Inst. Radiol.; ESTRO. Prev: Sen. Lect. & Hons. Cons. Clin. Oncol. Univ. Coll. Lond. Hosps. & Middlx. Hosp. Lond.; Sen. Regist. (Radiother. & Oncol.) W.m. Hosp. Lond.; Regist. (Radiother. & Oncol.) Roy. Marsden Hosp. Lond.

CASSWELL, Mr Anthony Geoffrey Tel: 01273 779471 Fax: 01273 220919 Email: tonycasswell@hotmail.com — MB BS 1976 Lond.; FRCS Eng. 1984; FRCOphth 1993. (Lond. Hosp.) Cons. Ophth. Sussex Eye Hosp. Brighton. Prev: Vitreoretinal Fell. Moorfields Eye Hosp. Lond.; Resid. Surg. Off. Moorfields Eye Hosp. Lond.

CAST, Mr Ian Patrick (retired) Melin Llan House, Penllergaer, Swansea SA4 1GT — MB BS Lond. 1960; FRCS Ed. 1966; FRCS Eng. 1966. Cons. Neurol. Surg. W. Glam. AHA. Prev: Cons. Neurol. Surg. & Clin. Dir. (Surg. Neurol. & Neuropsychol.) Morriston Hosp. Swansea.

CAST, James Edmund Ian 3 Atkinson Drive, Brough HU15 1AH Email: james@castj.fsnet.co.uk — MB BS 1990 Lond.; BSc (Physiol.) Lond. 1987; FRCR 1997. (Charing Cross & Westminster) Cons. (Radiol.) Hull & E. Yorks. NHS Trust.

CASTALDI, Peter Unum Ltd, Milton Court, Dorking RH4 3LZ Tel: 01306 873294 Fax: 01306873450; 24 Cavendish Road, Lytham St Annes FY8 2PX Tel: 01253 713847 Fax: 01253 722907 — MB BCh 1966 Wales. Chief Med. Off. & Dir.Meds. Serv.; Company Med. Off. Hambro Assured, Guardian Roy. Exchange & UNUM UK; Med. Assesor Indep. Tribunal Serv. Socs: Fell. Roy. Soc. Med. Prev: Chief Med. Adviser DSS & Dir. Med. Servs. Benefits Agency; Med. Dir. Nat. Med. Exam. & Advisor Serv.; GP Bangor.

CASTELL, Elizabeth Olive (retired) Astonia House, High St., Baldock SG7 6 — MB BS 1953 Lond.; MRCS Eng. LRCP Lond. 1953. Prev: Hosp. Pract. Lister Hosp. Stevenage.

CASTELL, Fiona Alix 19 Oval Road, London NW1 7EA Tel: 020 7419 4788 Email: f.a.castell@btinternet — MB BS 1996 Lond.; BSc Lond. 1993. (Charing Cross & Westminister)

CASTELL, Renice London Lane Clinic, Kinnaird House, 37 London Lane, Bromley BR1 4HB Tel: 020 8460 2661 Fax: 020 8464 5041 — MB BS 1971 Lond.; MRCS Eng. LRCP Lond. 1971.

CASTELLO-CORTES, Andrew Hipolito 120 Cowley Road, London SW14 8QB — MB BS 1991 Lond.

CASTELLO CORTES, Hipolito Paul Upper Flat Right, 4 Ord St., King's Gate, Aberdeen AB15 6FT Tel: 01224 312106 — LMS 1955 Salamanca; MA Camb. 1977; MD Caracas 1969.

CASTELLS, Vicente The Health Centre, High Street, Bedworth, Nuneaton CV12 8NQ Tel: 024 7631 5827 Fax: 024 7631 0580; Blackhill, 210 Weddington Road, Nuneaton CV10 0ER — MB ChB 1987 Leic.; MRCGP 1994; DA (UK) 1992.

CASTILLO NARVAEZ, Eduardo 43 Evison Road, Rothwell, Kettering NN14 6AL — LMS 1989 Malaga.

CASTLE, Christopher Robin Southwold Surgery, York Road, Southwold IP18 6AN Tel: 01502 722326 Fax: 01502 724708; The Turrets, 71 North Road, Southwold IP18 6BH — MB BS 1986 Lond.; MRCGP 1990; DRCOG 1988. (St. Geo. Hosp. Univ. Lond.) Socs: BMA. Prev: Trainee GP Gt. Yarmouth VTS.

CASTLE, Edward Arthur Busby Road Surgery, 75 Busby Road, Clarkston, Glasgow G76 7BW Tel: 0141 644 2669 Fax: 0141 644 5171 — MB ChB 1971 Glas.; MRCGP 1977; Cert JCC Lond. 1978; Cert. Indust. Health Dund 1982. GP Clarkston; Occupat. Phys. Glas.; Dep. Chairm. E.wood Local Health Care CoOperat. Socs: Soc. Occupat. Med. Prev: Cas. Off. Vict. Infirm. Glas.; Trainee GP S.. Gen. Hosp. Glas.; Ho. Surg. Stobhill Gen. Hosp. Glas.

CASTLE, Matthew Zachary David 38b Bartholomew Villas, London NW5 2LL — MB BS 1993 Lond.

CASTLE, Nicola Anne 9 Hanover Court, Highbury St., Portsmouth PO1 2BN — BM BS 1984 Nottm.

CASTLE, Sarah Louise 82A Franklin Av, Tadley RG26 4EU — MB BS 1997 Lond.

CASTLE, Shirley Grace 25 Tennyson Avenue, London E11 2QN — MB BS 1961 Lond.; DCH RCP Lond. 1983.

CASTLEDEN, Christopher Mark University Division of Medicine for Elderly, Leicester General Hospital, Gwendolen Road, Leicester LE5 4PW Tel: 0116 249 0490 Fax: 0116 258 4666; 10 Milton Gardens, Oadby, Leicester LE2 5SA — MB BS 1969 Lond.; MD Lond. 1978; FRCP Lond. 1984; MRCP (UK) 1972; MRCS Eng. LRCP Lond. 1969. (St. Bart.) Prof. Med. for Elderly Leicester Gen. Hosp.; Hon. Cons. Geriat. Leics. HA. Socs: Brit. Geriat. Soc. Prev: Sen. Lect. (Geriat. Med.) Leicester Univ.; Lect. (Clin. Pharmacol. & Med.) Soton. Univ.; Sen. Regist. (Geriat. Med.) Soton. & S.W. Hants. Health Dist.

CASTLEDEN, Lewis Saunt Clock House Cottage, Dunmow CM6 2BB Tel: 01371 2139 — MB BS 1959 Lond.; MRCS Eng. LRCP Lond. 1942. (St. Bart.) Prev: Temp. Surg. Lt. RNVR.

CASTLES, Wilhelmina Juliette Batson Forge Close, Hayes, Bromley BR2 7LL — MB BChir 1976 Camb.; MA, MB Camb. 1976, BChir 1975; MRCP (UK) 1979; DRCOG 1977; DCH Eng. 1977. Prev: Med. Regist. King's Coll. Hosp. Lond.

CASTLETON, Beverly Ann St Peters Hospital, Guildford Road, Chertsey KT16 0PZ Tel: 01932 872000 Fax: 01932 844757; 2 Lyne Place Manor, Bridge Lane, Virginia Water GU25 4ED Tel: 01932 560797 Fax: 01932 560797 — MB 1974 Camb.; BChir 1973; FRCP Lond. 1992; MRCP (UK) 1976. Cons. Phys. c/o the Elderly & Young Physically Disabled Ashford/St Peters Hosp. & Bournewood Trusts; Med. Dir. Bournewood Trust. Socs: Brit. Geriat. Soc.; Pk.inson's Dis. Soc.; Roy. Soc. of Med.

CASTLING, Brian Hutchinson 4 Knowsley Drive, Bicton Heath, Shrewsbury SY3 5DH — MB ChB 1998 Birm.

CASTLING, Douglas Parham Paediatric Department Ronkwsood Hospital, Newtown Road, Worcester WR5 1HN Tel: 01905 763333 — MB ChB, DCH Liverp. 1982; MRCP (UK) 1992; DCH (UK) 1990. (Liverpool) Cons. Paediat., Worcester Roy. Infirm.

CASTRO, Mr John Edward (retired) The Old Vicarage, Fressingfield, Eye IP21 5PE Tel: 01379 586537 — MB BS (Distinc. Surg.) Lond. 1964; BSc (1st cl. Hons. Anat.) Lond. 1961, MS 1972; PhD CNAA 1973; FRCS Eng. 1970; FRCS Ed. 1968; MRCS Eng. LRCP Lond. 1964. Indep. Pract. (Urol.) Harley St. Lond.; Hon. Cons. Urol. St. Luke's Hosp. Clergy Lond. Prev: Sen. Lect. (Surg.) & Hon. Cons. Urol. Roy. Postgrad. Med. Sch. Lond.

CASTRO, Kenneth Andrew 7 Whitehart Road, Fair Oak, Eastleigh SO50 7JR — MB ChB 1989 Leic.; BSc (Hons.) Lond. 1983; MRCGP 1995. (Leics.)

CASWELL, Helen Jane 1 Karen Drive, Backwell, Bristol BS48 3JT — MB BS 1986 Lond.; MRCGP 1991.

CASWELL, Mr John Douglas East Street Surgery, The Old Exchange, East Street, St. Ives, Huntingdon PE27 5PB Tel: 01480 497477 Fax: 01480 497550 — MB BS 1973 Lond.; BDS 1966; FRCS Eng. 1979; FDS RCS Eng. 1972. GP St. Ives. Prev: Gen. Pract. Trainee Manch. Univ. Scheme; Regist. (Surg.) Stepping Hill Hosp. Stockport; Rotat. SHO (Surg.) Norwich.

CASWELL, Lucy Patricia 2 Grosvenor Road, Harborne, Birmingham B17 9AN — MB BS 1992 Lond.

CASWELL, Mark Department of Haematology, Royal Liverpool Childrens NHS Trust, Alder Hey, Eaton Road, Liverpool L12 2AP Tel: 0151 228 4811 Fax: 0151 252 5073 Email: mark.casell@rlch_tr.nwest.nhs.uk; Tel: 0151 348 0294 Email: mark.caswell@which.net — MB ChB 1983 Ed.; MRCP (UK) 1986; MRCPath 1995. (Edinburgh) Cons. Paediat. Haemat. Roy. Liverp. Childr. NHS Trust. Socs: Brit. Soc. Haematol.; Assn. Clin. Path. Prev: Sen. Regist. (Haemat.) Roy. Liverp. Univ. Hosp.; Clin. Research Fell. Dept. Haemat. Univ. Birm.; Regist. (Haemat.) W. Midl. RHA.

CASWELL, Sally Jane University Medical Centre, University of Kent, Giles Lane, Canterbury CT2 7PB Tel: 01227 765652 — MB ChB 1990 Leic.; BSc (Hons.) Leic. 1988; MRCGP 1994; DFFP 1994; DRCOG 1994. (Leicester) GP Princip. Socs: BMA. Prev: Trainee GP/SHO Leicester Roy. Infirm. VTS.

CASWELL, Simon John 64 Lichfield Road, Pelsall, Walsall WS3 4HL — MB 1977 Camb.; BA Camb. 1973, MB 1977, BChir 1976; MRCGP 1981; DRCOG 1979. GP Walsall.

CATALAN, José Imperial College, Psychological Medicine, Mental Health Centre, Chelsea & Westminster Hospital, London SW10 9HN Tel: 020 8746 5640 Fax: 020 8746 5648 Email: j.catalan@ic.ac.uk — Lic Med 1972 Valencia; Licentiate in Med. Valencia 1972; MSc Oxf. 1980; FRCPsych 1994, M 1977; DPM RCP Lond. 1976. Reader (Psychiat.) Imperial Coll. Sch. Med. Prev: Cons. Psychiat. Elms Clinic Horton Gen. Hosp. Banbury; Sen. Lect. (Liaison Psychiat.) Char. Cross & W.m. Med. Sch. Lond.; Lect. & Tutor (Psychiat.) Warneford Hosp. Univ. Oxf.

CATANIA AGUERO, Santiago Flat 4, Saville House, 29 Hoop Lane, London NW11 8BS — LMS 1989 Basque Provinces; MRCP (UK) 1995.

CATARINO, Pedro Alexandre Steyn Dos Reis Alves St Bartholomews Hospital, London EC1A 7BE; Ground Floor, 191 Cromwell Road, London SW5 0SE Email: catarino@doctors.org.uk — BM BCh Oxf. 1994; MA Camb. 1995; FRCS (Eng.) 1998. (Oxford University) Specialist Regist. (Cardiothoracic surrg.) St Bartholomows Hosp. Lond.; Hon. Regist. (Cardiothoracic surg) John Radcliffe Hopsital, Oxf. Prev: SHO Rotat. (Surg.) St. Geo. Hosp. Lond.; Ho. Phys. Univ. Dept. Med. Roy. Vict. Infirm. Newc.; Roy. Coll. of Surg.s of Eng. Research Fell. Oxf. Univ. 2000-2001.

CATCHPOLE, Christopher Robert Department of Microbiology, New Cross Hospital, Wolverhampton WV10 0QP; Washington Cottage, Finchfield Gardens, Wolverhampton WV3 9LT — MB ChB 1984 Birm.; MRCPI 1991; MRCPath 1993. Cons. Microbiol. New Cross Hosp. Wolverhampton. Prev: Sen. Regist. (Microbiol.) Qu. Eliz. Hosp. W. Midl. RHA.

CATCHPOLE, Michael Andrew CDSC, 61 Colindale Avenue, London NW9 5EQ Tel: 020 8200 6868 Fax: 020 8200 7868 Email: mcatchpo@phls.co.uk — MB BS 1983 Lond.; MSc (Distinc.) Lond. 1987, BSc (Hons.) 1980; FRCP Lond. 1997; MRCP (UK) 1986; MFPHM RCP (UK) 1991; FFPHM 1998. (Middlx. Hosp. Med. Sch.) Cons. Epidemiol. Communicable Dis. Surveillance Centre; Hon. Lect. St. Bart. Hosp. Med. Sch.; Sen. Med. Statistician Office for Nat. Statistics. Prev: Regist. (Community Med.) Kettering HA; SHO (Med.) Hammersmith Hosp. Lond.; Ho. Off. Middlx. Hosp. Lond.

CATER, Elizabeth Joyce Ashcroft Surgery, Benchill Medical Centre, 121 Woodhouse Lane, Benchill, Manchester M22 9WP Tel: 0161 998 4304; 16 Oaker Avenue, West Didsbury, Manchester M20 2XH Tel: 0161 445 9445 — MB ChB 1976 Birm.; DRCOG 1980; DCH RCP Lond. 1979.

CATER, Emily Victoria Ben Edar, St Cleer Road, Liskeard PL14 3HN — MB BS 1996 Lond.

CATER, John Ives (retired) Department of Child Health, Ninewells Hospital & Medical School, Dundee DD1 9SY Tel: 01382 632179 Fax: 01382 66617 — MB ChB 1978 Ed.; MB ChB Ed. 1963; MD Ed. 1978; FRCP Ed. 1983, M 1968; DCH RCPS Glas. 1965. Sen. Lect. Univ. Dundee. Prev: Lect. Univ. Aberd.

CATES, Mrs Carolyn Anne Southampton Eye Unit, Southampton General Hospital, Tremona Rd, Southampton SO16 6YD Tel: 02380 777222 Fax: 02380 794120 — MB BChir 1993 Camb.; MA Camb. 1993; FRCOphth 1997. (Cambridge) Specialist Regist. Rotat. (Ophth.) Soton Wessex. Socs: BMA; MDU. Prev: SHO (Ophth.) Addenbrooke's Hosp. Camb.

CATES, Charles Graham 36 Willow Tree Avenue, Broughton, Preston PR3 5DH — MB BS 1998 West Indies.

CATES, Christopher Joseph Manor View Practice, Bushey Health Centre, London Road, Bushey, Watford WD23 2NN Tel: 01923 225224 Fax: 01923 213270; The Ark, 6 Warneford Place, Oxhey, Watford WD19 4DP Tel: 01923 461310 Email: chriscates@msn.com — BM BCh 1980 Oxf.; MA Camb. 1981; MRCGP 1984; DRCOG 1983. Criticism Edr. Cochrane Airways Review Gp. Prev: Trainee GP Oxf. AHA (T) VTS; Ho. Off. (Gen. Surg.) Bedford Gen. Hosp.; Ho. Off. (Gen. Med.) John Radcliffe II Hosp. Oxf.

CATES, Mary Elizabeth (retired) 1 Old Sneed Cottages, 55 Stoke Hill, Bristol BS9 1EP Tel: 01179 683170 — MB ChB (1st cl. Hons. & Gold Medal) Bristol 1954; MRCGP 1980. Prev: Gen. Pract. W.bury on Trym Pract. Bristol.

CATFORD, Mr Gordon Vivian (retired) 9 St John's Wood Park, London NW8 6QP Tel: 020 7722 2168 — MB ChB Bristol 1952; FRCS Eng. 1961; FRCOphth 1988; DO Eng. 1955. Hon. Cons. Ophth. Surg. Roy. Masonic Hosp. Lond., St. Luke's Hosp. for Clergy & ILEA; Hon. Cons. Ophth. Surg. St. Geo. Hosp. Lond. & Roy. Lond. Homoeop. Hosp; Hon. Lect. & Teach. (Ophth.) Univ. Lond.; Adviser Brit. Orthop. Soc.; Assoc. Qu. Coll. Glas; Hon. Archiv. Roy. Coll. Ophth.; Mem. Med. Appeals Tribunal. Prev: Chief Clin. Asst. Moorfields Eye Hosp.

CATHCART, Abida 396a St Vincent Street, Glasgow G3 8RN Tel: 0141 226 1246; 31 Victoria Road, Lenzie, Glasgow G66 5AR — MB ChB 1995 Glas.; DRCOG Glas. 1999. (Glasgow) SHO (A&E), Yorkhill Hosp., Glas. Prev: SHO (O & G), S.ern Gen., Glas.; SHO (O & G), Roy. Matern., Glas.; SHO (O & G), Roy. Alexandra Hosp., Paisley.

CATHCART, Clare The Health Centre, Westfield Walk, Leominster HR6 8HD Tel: 01568 612084 Fax: 01568 610340; Cholstrey Cottage, Cholstrey, Leominster HR6 9AP Tel: 01568 708358 — BM BCh 1987 Oxf.; BA Oxf. 1984, BM BCh 1987; MRCGP 1993; DRCOG 1992.

CATHCART, David Berkeley 9 Halifax Road, Dewsbury WF13 Tel: 01924 465597 — MB BChir 1950 Camb.; MRCS Eng. LRCP Lond. 1948. (St. Bart.)

CATHCART, Iain Robert Viewfield Medical Centre, 3 Viewfield Place, Stirling FK8 1NJ Tel: 01786 472028 Fax: 01786 463388 — MB ChB 1974 Glas.; DRCOG 1977.

CATHCART, Jane-Mary Blair 20 Ballymoney Road, Newtownards BT23 4TG — MB BCh BAO 1977 Belf.; FRCS (Orl.) Eng. 1981.

CATHCART, John Brian Thompson Charlotte Street Surgery, 1 Charlotte Street, Dumfries DG1 2AG Tel: 01387 267626 Fax: 01387 266824 — MB ChB St. And. 1969; MRCGP 1974; DObst RCOG 1974.

CATHCART, Malcolm 104 Metchley Lane, Harborne, Birmingham B17 0HY — MB ChB 1979 Sheff.; MRCGP 1984; MFOM RCP Lond. 1991; FFOM RCP Lond. 1996. Company Med. Adviser Albright & Wilson plc Warley.

CATHCART, Mark Edward Henry Erne Health Centre, Cornagrade Road, Enniskillen BT74 6AY Tel: 028 6632 2707 — MB BCh BAO 1987 Dub.; MB BCh Dub. 1987; MRCGP 1991.

CATHCART, Russell Adair 17 Robertson Av, Dumfries DG1 4EY — MB ChB 1997 Dundee.

CATHCART, Simon James Tropical Medicine Resource, The Wellcome Trust, 210 Euston Road, London NW1 2DA Tel: 020 7611 8580 Email: s.cathcart@wellcome.ac.uk; 66 Portland Grove, Stockwell, London SW8 1JQ Tel: 020 7820 1466 — MB BCh 1987 Wales; DTM & H Liverp. 1993. Scientif. Edr. Trop. Med. Resource Wellcome Centre for Med. Sci. Lond. Socs: Roy. Soc. Trop. Med. & Hyg. Prev: Clin. Asst. Drug Dependency Unit Merseyside; SHO (Infec. Dis.) Fazakerley Hosp. Liverp.; SHO (Cas.) Univ. W. Indies Kingston, Jamaica.

CATHCART, Valerie Hazel 104 Metchley Lane, Harborne, Birmingham B17 0HY — MB ChB 1979 Sheff.; MRCGP 1984.

CATHERWOOD, Raphael Francis 'Woodlands Barn', Stackhouse Lane, Giggleswick, Settle BD24 0DL Tel: 0172 92 3053 & profess. 0532 735520 — MRCS Eng. LRCP Lond. 1964; Assoc. Fac. Occupat. Med. RCP Lond. 1979.

CATHRO, Mr Arthur James McGibbon (retired) Milton House, Newtyle, Blairgowrie PH12 8UQ Tel: 01828 650349 — MB ChB St And. 1939; FRCS Ed. 1960. Prev: Orthopaedic Cons., Livingstone Hosp., Port Hosp., Port Eliz., S. Africa.

CATLIN, Peter (retired) — MB BS 1969 Lond.

CATLIN, Robin John Oakley Chartfield Cottage, Pastens Road, Oxted RH8 0RE — MB BS 1951 Lond.; MRCS Eng. LRCP Lond. 1951; FRCCP 1974, M 1961.

CATLING, Joy Susan Anaesthetic Department, St. Helier Hospital, Carshalton SM5 1AA Tel: 020 8296 2444 — MB BS Lond. 1963; FFA RCS Eng. 1976; DA Eng. 1968; DObst RCOG 1967. (St. Mary's) Cons. Anaesth. St. Helier NHS Trust Carshalton.

CATLING, Susan Jennifer Dept. of Anaesthetics, Singleton Hospital, Swansea Tel: 01792 205666; "Broadoaks", Cilonnen Rd, Three Crosses, Swansea SA4 3PH Tel: 01792 873983 Email: s.catling@mailcity.com — MB BS 1978 Lond.; BA Camb. 1975; FFA RCS Eng. 1983. (Westminster) Cons. Anaesth. Swansea, Lead Cons. in Obstetric Anaesth. Socs: Obst. Anaesth.s Assn.; Soc. of Anaesth.s of Wales; Assn. Anaesth. GB & Irel. Prev: Sen. Regist. (Anaesth.) S. & W. Glam. HAs.; Regist. (Anaesth.) Sheff. HA; SHO (Anaesth.) W. Cumbria HA.

CATLOW, Stephen Irving Station Road Surgery, Station Road, Sowerby Bridge HX6 3AB Tel: 01422 831453/831457 — MB ChB 1980 Leeds; MRCGP 1985; DRCOG 1983.

CATNACH, Julie Liberton Medical Group, 55 Liberton Gardens, Edinburgh EH16 6JT Tel: 0131 664 3050 Fax: 0131 692 1952; 7 Wilton Road, Edinburgh EH16 5NX — MB ChB 1986 Dundee; DCCH RCP Ed. 1993; DRCOG 1992. (Dundee) GP Edin. Prev: Trainee GP/SHO (Community Paediat. & Gen. Pract.) Edin.

CATNACH, Susan Mary Hemel Hempstead General Hospital, Hemel Hempstead HP2 4AD Tel: 01442 279274 Fax: 01442 279442 — MB BS 1983 Lond.; MD Lond. 1992; MRCP (UK) 1986; FRCP 1999. (St. Bart. Hosp. Med. Sch.) Cons. Phys. & Gastroenterol. W. Herts Hosp.s NHS Trust. Socs: Brit. Soc. Gastroenterol. Prev: Lect. Inst. Liver Studies King's Coll. Hosp. Lond.

CATNACH, Thomas Burney The Surgery, 27 Minster Precincts, Peterborough PE1 Tel: 01733 54478; The Orchard House, 15 Thorpe Road, Peterborough PE3 6AB Tel: 01733 65827 — MB BS 1955 Lond.; DObst RCOG 1959. (St. Bart.) Prev: Ho. Off. Kent & Sussex Hosp. Tunbridge Wells, Ashford Hosp. Middlx. & Amersham Gen. Hosp.

CATOR, Sybil Elizabeth Glantoruaen, 5 Town Lane, Garvestone, Norwich NR9 4QR — MB ChB 1949 Bristol; MRCS Eng. LRCP Lond. 1950. (Bristol)

CATOVSKY, Professor Daniel Academic Haematology & Cytogenetics, The Royal Marsden Hospital, Fulham Road, London SW3 6JJ Tel: 020 7808 2880 Fax: 020 7351 6420 Email: d.catovsky@icr.ac.uk — Medico Buenos Aires 1961; DSc (Med.) Lond. 1986; FRCP Lond. 1990; MRCP (UK) 1985; FRCPath 1986, M 1975; F Med Sci 1999. Prof. Haemat. Inst. Cancer Research Roy. Marsden Hosp. Lond.; Hon. Cons. Phys. Roy. Marsden Hosp. Socs: Amer. Soc. Haemat.; Brit. Soc. Haematol.; Eur. Haematol. Assn. Prev: Staff Mem. MRC Leukaemia Unit RPMS.

CATT, Verity Edwina Station Approach Health Centre, Station Approach, Bradford-on-Avon BA15 1DQ Tel: 01225 866611; The Weald, Westwood Road, Trowbridge BA14 9B — MB ChB 1963 Bristol. (Bristol) Socs: BMA. Prev: Ho. Phys. St. Martin's Hosp. Bath; Ho. Surg. Roy. United Hosp. Bath.

CATTANACH, Alexander Chalmers (retired) 1 Bucklers Mews, Anchorage Way, Lymington SO41 8JL Tel: 01590 670827 Email: sandy.cattanach@lineone.net — MB ChB 1952 Glas.; MRCGP 1962. Prev: Ho. Surg. (Obst.) Ayrsh. Centr. Hosp. Irvine.

CATTANACH, Donald James Station Road Surgery, 2 Station Road, Prestwick KA9 1AQ Tel: 01292 671444 Fax: 01292 678023; Ravelston, Esplanade, Prestwick KA9 1RG Tel: 01292 478656 — MB ChB 1973 Ed.; BSc (Med. Sci.) Ed. 1970, MB ChB 1973; MRCGP 1977. Prev: Trainee GP Fife VTS.

CATTANACH, Susan Jacqueline Lochgelly Health Centre, David Street, Lochgelly KY5 9QZ Tel: 01592 780277 Fax: 01592 784044 — MB ChB 1987 Ed. Prev: Trainee GP Fife VTS; SHO (O & G) Falkirk & Dist. Roy. Infirm.; SHO (Geriat. Med.) St. Johns Hosp. Livingston.

CATTELL, Caroline Ann St Peters Street Medical Practice, 16 St Peters Street, London N1 8JG Tel: 020 7226 7131 Fax: 020 7354 9120; 24 Stanley Buildings, Clarence Passage, London NW1 2TG — MB BS 1986 Lond.; MA (Hons.) Oxf. 1987.

CATTELL, Emma Louise 40 Goldspink Lane, Sandyford, Newcastle upon Tyne NE2 1NR — MB BS 1996 Newc.; BMedSc (Hons.) Newc. 1993. SHO (Gen. Med.) S. Tees Health Care Trust Middlesbrough.

CATTELL, Howard Robert 38 Queen Elizabeth's Drive, Southgate, London N14 6RD — MB BCh 1977 Wales.

CATTELL, Victoria Department of Experimental Pathology, St. Mary's Hospital, Medical School, London W2 1NY — MB BS 1968 Lond.; MD Lond. 1977; FRCPath 1987, M 1975. Sen. Lect. (Path.) St. Mary's Hosp. Lond.

CATTELL, William Ross (retired) 30 Tavistock Terrace, London N19 4DB Tel: 020 7272 0183 Fax: 020 7272 5411 — MB ChB Ed. 1951; MD Ed. 1964; FRCP Lond. 1971, M 1956; FRCP Ed. 1969, M 1956. Prev: Sen. Phys. & Sen. Nephrol. St. Bart. Hosp. Lond.

CATTERALL, Adrian Paul Lister Hospital, Coreys Mill Lane, Stevenage SG1 4AB Tel: 01438 314333 — MB BS 1983 Lond.; MD Lond. 1996; MRCP (UK) 1986; FRCP 2000. Cons. Phys. & Gastroenterol. Lister Hosp. & Qu. Eliz. Hosp. Herts. Prev: Sen. Regist. (Gastroenterol.) St. Thos. Hosp. & Char. Cross Hosp. Lond.; Research Fell. & Hon. Regist. (Gastroenterol.) Char. Cross Hosp. Lond.

CATTERALL, Mr Anthony 149 Harley St, London W1N 2DE Tel: 020 7935 4444 Fax: 020 7486 4700; Tel: 020 7372 2166 Fax: 020 7372 4899 — MB BChir 1961 Camb.; MChir Camb. 1965; FRCS Eng. 1963. (Univ. Coll. Hosp.) Emerit. Cons. Orthop. Surg. Roy. Nat. Orthop. Hosp. Socs: Brit. Orthop. Assn.; Roy. Soc. Med.; Brit. Soc. Childr. Orthop. Surg. Prev: Sen. Regist. Roy. Nat. Orthop. Hosp.

CATTERALL, Elizabeth Ann Longhills, Sleaford Road, Branston, Lincoln LN4 1HX — MB BS 1955 Lond.

CATTERALL, Gayle Avis 56 Northern Road, Cosham, Portsmouth PO6 3DS Tel: 023 92 373321; 1 Mallard Road, Rowlands Castle PO9 6HE Tel: 023 92 412114 — MB BS 1979 Lond.; MRCS Eng. LRCP Lond. 1979; DRCOG 1984; DA Eng. 1983. (Char. Cross)

CATTERALL, James Richard Bristol Royal Infirmary, Marlborough St., Bristol BS2 8HW Tel: 0117 928 2619 Fax: 0117 928 2921; 5 The Quadrant, Redland, Bristol BS6 7JR — MB ChB 1975 Ed.; BSc Ed. 1972, MD 1987; FRCP 1994; FRCP Ed. 1992; MRCP (UK) 1978. Cons. Phys. Bristol Roy. Infirm. Socs: Sec. Brit. Thoracic Soc., 1997-2000; Memb. Eur. Thoracic Soc.; Memb. Amer. Thoracic Soc. Prev: Lect. (Respirat. Med.) City Hosp. Edin.; MRC (UK) Trav. Fell. Stanford Univ. Med. Centre, Calif. USA; Sen. Regist. Roy. Infirm. Edin.

CATTERALL, Mary (retired) — MB BS 1952 Lond.; Hon. DSc Durh. 1982; DMRT 1956; Hon. FACR 1980; FRCR 1975; FFR 1968. Prev: Cons. Radiother. Hammersmith Hosp. Lond.

CATTERALL, Michael David Dept of Dermatology, Basildon Hospital, Nether Mayne, Basildon SS16 5N2 Tel: 01268 593418 Fax: 01268 593707; Red Gable, Spring Elms Lane, Little Baddow, Chelmsford CM3 4SD Tel: 01245 225939 Fax: 01245 225939 — MB ChB 1969 St. And.; FRCP Lond. 1989; FRCP Ed. 1984; MRCP (UK) 1972. (University of St Andrews) Cons. Dermat. Basildon & Thurrock Gen. Hosp. NHS Trust; Hon. Cons. Dermat. Mid-Essex Hosps NHS Trust. Socs: Fell. Roy. Soc. Med. (Mem. Sect. Dermat.); Brit. Assn. Dermat. Mem..; Fell.St. John's Hosp. Dermatlogical Soc. Prev: Cons. Dermat. RN Med. Serv.; Surg. Cdr. RN; Hon. Cons. Dermat. Soton. Univ. Hosps.

CATTERICK, David Ian North House Surgery, North House, Hope Street, Crook DL15 9HU Tel: 01388 762945 Fax: 01388 765333 — MB BS 1985 Newc.; MRCGP 1989; DRCOG 1988. Trainee GP W. Cumbria VTS. Prev: Ho. Phys. N. Tees Dist. Gen. Hosp. Stockton-on-Tees; Ho. Surg. Freeman Hosp. Newc.

CATTERMOLE, Giles Nicholas 9 Cedar Walk, Romsey Road, Winchester SO22 5EU — BM BCh 1995 Oxf.; MA (Oxon) 1992. (Oxf.) Socs: RSM; BASICS.

CATTERMOLE, Miss Helen Ruth 15 Cross Road, Wimbledon, London SW19 1PL Email: hcattermole@hotmail.com — MB ChB 1989 Birm.; FRCS Eng. 1993; Dip. IMC RCS Ed. 1995. (Birm.) Regist. Rotat. (Orthop.) Char. Cross Hosp. Lond. Socs: BASICS; Assoc. Mem. BOA; Brit. Orthop. Research Soc. Prev: Research Fell. (Orthop.) Rugby & Leicester; SHO Rotat. (Surg.) Leicester; Lect. (Anat.) Univ. Birm.

CATTERMOLE, Roger Wilfred Over Hall, Bures St Mary, Bures CO8 5BN Tel: 01787 227058 — MB BCh 1973 Wales; FFA RCS Eng. 1983. Cons. Anaesth. W. Essex HA.

CATTERMOLE, Trevor James 13 Curlew Lane, Stockton-on-Tees TS20 1NB — MB ChB 1992 Ed.; BSc (Hons.) Ed. 1990; Dip IMC RCS Ed. 1996; MSc Robert Gordon 1998; MRCP (UK) 1998. (Edinburgh) Clin. Fell., A&E, Roy. Hosp. for Sick Childr., Edin. Socs: BMA; BASICS. Prev: SHO (Gen. Med.) Stiring Roy. Infirm.; Med. Off. Brit. Antartic Survey Rothera, Antartica; SHO (A & E) Roy. Infirm.

CATTLE, Diana Susan (retired) 29A Bennetts Road S., Keresley, Coventry CV6 2FN — MB ChB 1968 Birm.; MRCP (U.K.) 1973. Prev: GP Coventry.

CATTO, Alexander Forbes, MBE (retired) 35 Broad Street, Alresford SO24 9AS Tel: 01962 735542 — MB ChB Ed. 1945; MRCGP 1958. Prev: Ho. Surg. Stracathro Hosp. Brechin.

CATTO, Andrew John Academic Unit of Molecular and Vascular Medicine, G Floor Martin Wing, Leeds General Infirmary, Leeds LS1 3EX Tel: 0113 392 3472 Fax: 0113 242 3811 Email: a.j.catto@leeds.ac.uk — MB ChB 1989 Leeds; PhD Leeds 1999; BSc (Hons.) Leeds 1986; MRCP (UK) 1993. (Univ. Leeds) Sen. Lect. & Hon. Cons. (Med.) Univ. Leeds. Socs: Brit. Soc. Haemostasis & Thrombosis; Brit. Geriat. Soc.; Assn. Study Med. Educat. Prev: Clin. Research Fell. & Hon. Regist. Acad. Unit. of Med. Gen. Infirm. Leeds; Tutor & Hon. Regist. Leeds Gen. Infirm.; SHO (Gen. Med.) Seacroft Hosp. Leeds.

CATTO, Christopher Ewen New Lyminge Surgery, Greenbanks, Lyminge, Folkestone CT18 8NS Tel: 01303 863160 Fax: 01303 863492; Rosendale Cottage, Ridge Row, Acrise, Folkestone CT18 8JT Tel: 01303 893173 — MB ChB 1979 Manch.; BSc (Med Sci.) St. And. 1976; DRCOG 1981.

CATTO, Professor Graeme Robertson Dawson Kings College London, 57 Waterloo Road, London SE1 8WA Tel: 020 78483428 Fax: 020 78483439 Email: graeme.catto@kcl.ac.uk; 4 Woodend Avenue, Aberdeen AB15 6YL Tel: 01224 310509 Email: g.catto@doctors.org.uk — MB ChB 1969 Aberd.; Hon FRCGP 2000; ILTH 1999; FRSA 1996; FRSE 1996; DSc Aberd. 1988, MD (Hons.) 1975; FRCP Ed. 1988; FRCP Lond. 1984; FRCP Glas. 1982; MRCP (UK) 1971; F Med.Sci. 1998. (Univ. Aberd.) Pres. Gen. Med. Counc.; Vice Princip. Kings Coll. Lond. Socs: Assn. Phys. Prev: Research Fell. Dept. Med. Univ. Aberd.; Chief Scientist, Health Dept, Scott. Exec.; Vice Princip. Univ. of Aberd.

CATTO, James William Forbes 25 Moss Lane, Pinner HA5 3BB — MB ChB 1994 Leeds.

CATTO, John Vaughan Forbes, TD (retired) 25 Moss Lane, Pinner HA5 3BB Tel: 020 8868 8911 — MB BChir 1957 Camb.; MA Camb. 1958; MRCS Eng. LRCP Lond. 1957; FRCR 1975; FFR 1967; DMRD 1963; DCH Eng. 1959; DObst RCOG 1960. Prev: Cons. Radiol. W. Middlx. Univ. Hosp.

CATTO, Mary Elizabeth (retired) 20 Victoria Crescent Road, Glasgow G12 9DD Tel: 0141 334 5891 — MB ChB 1949 Glas.; MD (Hons.) Glas. 1966; FRCPath 1976, M 1964. Prev: Hon. Cons. & Reader (Orthop. Path.) Univ. Glas. at W.. Infirm. Glas.

CATTO, William Dawson (retired) 1 Earl's Court Gardens, Aberdeen AB15 4BU Tel: 01224 319312 — MB ChB Aberd. 1939. Prev: Ho. Phys. & Ho. Surg. Vict. Hosp. Burnley.

CATTON, Bessie Jean (retired) 29 The Paddock, Walbottle Village, Newcastle upon Tyne NE15 8JG Tel: 0191 267 4262 — MB ChB Ed. 1955; DPH Leeds 1965.

CATTON, Michael John, OStJ (retired) 10 Woodlands Close, Grays RM16 2GB Tel: 01375 396919 — MB BS Lond. 1949; MFOM RCP Lond. 1982; DPH Eng. 1958. Med. Adviser various indust. cos. Prev: SCMO Waltham Forest HA.

CATTY, Robert Hugh Craig University of Durham, Student Health Centre, 42 Old Elvet, Durham DH1 3JF Tel: 0191 386 5081 Fax: 0191 386 3528; 59 Hallgarth Street, Durham DH1 3AY Tel: 0191 384 7178 Fax: 0191 386 8300 Email: cattyrackham@doctors.org.uk — MB BS 1959 Lond.; MRCS Eng. LRCP Lond. 1959; FRCGP 1991, M 1971; DObst RCOG 1964. (St. Thos.) Partner GP; Fell. Centre for Health Studies Durh. Univ. Socs: BMA; RCGP; BAHSE. Prev: Med. Adviser S. of Tyne HA.

CAUCHI, Elizabeth Mary Royal Marsden Hospital, Sutton SM2 5PT; 88 Foresters Drive, Wallington SM6 9JZ Tel: 020 8288

0411 — MB BS 1994 Lond. (Char. Cross & Westm. Med. Sch.) SHO (Med.) Roy. Marsden Hosp. Sutton. Socs: BMA. Prev: SHO (Med.) Frenchay Hosp. NHS Trust; SHO (Rheum.) Nuffield Orthop. Cente Oxf.; SHO (Med.) Frimley Pk. Hosp.

CAUCHI, Paul 42 Brighton Road, Godalming GU7 1NT — MB BS 1996 Lond.

CAUDWELL, Ruth, SSStJ Wellington Way Health Centre, 1a Wellington Way, London E3 4NE Tel: 020 8980 3510 Fax: 020 8981 1441 Email: ruth.caudwell@thht.org — MB BCh 1977 Wales; FRCP (UK) 1996; MRCP (UK) 1985; MRCPCH 1996; DCP Warwick 1990; DRCOG 1981; DCH RCP Lond. 1980. (Welsh Nat. Sch. Med.) Cons. Community Paediat. Tower Hamlets Healthcare Trust. Prev: SCMO (Child Health) W. Birm. HA.

CAUFIELD, Mrs Helen Mary The Royal Free Hospital, Department of Otolaryngology, Pond Street, London NW3 2QG Tel: 020 7485 4580 — MB BS 1987 Lond.; FRCS (Otol) Ed. 1995; FRCS Lond. 1994. (UCL) Cons. Otolaryngologist Roy. Free; Hon. Sen. Lect. Roy. Free. Socs: BAOL; BAPO. Prev: Fell. Paed. Otolaryngol. Roy. Alexandra. Childr. Hosp. Sydney; Sen. Regist. Otolayngol. Roy. Nat. Throat, Nose & Ear Hosp. Lond.; Regist. Otolaryngol. Char. Cross Hosp. Lond.

CAUGHEY, David Angus AON Occupational Health, Foresterhill Road, Aberdeen AB25 2ZP Tel: 01224 669000 Fax: 01224 669030 Email: david.caughey@aers.aon.co.uk — MB ChB 1982 Aberd.; AFOM RCP Lond. 1993. Med. Adviser Liberty Occupat. Health. Socs: Soc. of Occup. Med.

CAUGHLEY, Linda Margaret Gytopathology Department, The Laboratories, Belfast City Hospital, Lisburn Road, Belfast BT9 7AD Tel: 01232 329241 Fax: 01232 263679; 9 Stormont Park, Belfast BT4 3GW Tel: 01232 483254 — MB BCh BAO 1976 Belf.; FRCPath 1995, M 1983. Cons. Cytopath. Belf. City Hosp. Trust. Socs: BMA & Brit. Soc. Clin. Cytol.; BMA; Brit. Soc. Cun. Cytol. Prev: Sen. Regist. (Histopath.) Belf. City Hosp.; Ho. Off. Ards Hosp. Newtownards, Co. Down.

CAUKWELL, Jacqueline Patricia Four Alls, Pant Caerhun, Bangor LL57 4PS Tel: 01248 354267 — MB BCh 1987 Wales. Community Med. Off. Gwynedd, Bangor & Caernarfon. Socs: Christ. Med. Fell.sh. Prev: SHO (Gen. Med. & Surg.) Ysbyby Gwynedd Bangor.

CAUKWELL, Sarah Lindsey 3 Pinewood Gardens, College Ride, Bagshot GU19 5ES — MB ChB 1991 Manch.

CAULFIELD, Heather Mary 25 Landkey Close, Northern Moor, Manchester M23 0FW — MB ChB 1995 Manch.

CAULFIELD, Mark Jonathan 17 Alberta House, Black Wall Way, London E14 9GH Tel: 020 7987 8443 — MB BS 1984 Lond.

CAULFIELD, Stephen Francis 46 Bellahouston Drive, Glasgow G52 1HQ — MB ChB 1994 Glas.

CAUN, Karenna 14 Lunesdale Court, Hornby, Lancaster LA2 8JW Tel: 015242 21977 — MB BS 1981 Lond.; MRCP (UK) 1984. Prev: Wellcome Research Fell. & Hon. Sen. Regist. (Genitourin. Med.) St. Mary's Hosp. Lond.; Regist. (Gen. Med. & Gastroenterol.) Char. Cross Hosp. Lond. & W. Middlx. Hosp. Isleworth.

CAUNT, Joseph Alan 53 Whiteley Wood Road, Sheffield S11 7FF Tel: 0114 230 5865 — MB ChB Sheff. 1965; FRCA Eng. 1969. (Sheff.) Cons. Anaesth. N. Gen. Hosp. Sheff. Socs: Obst. Anaesth. Assn.; Sheff. & E. Midl. Soc. Anaesth. Prev: Sen. Regist. (Anaesth.) Roy. Hosp. Sheff.; Vis. Asst. Prof. Anaesth. S.W. Univ. Texas, Dallas, USA; SHO (Anaesth.) N.. Gen. Hosp. Sheff.

CAUSER, Catherine Anne 10 Park Court, Castle Road, Southsea PO5 3DF — MB BS 1992 Lond. SHO Rotat. (Gen. Med.) King's Coll. Hosp. Lond.; SHO (Oncol.) Brook Gen. Hosp. Lond. Prev: SHO (Elderly Care) King's Coll. Hosp. Lond. & Worthing Gen. Hosp.

CAUSER, Jason Paul 7 Hillfield Drive, Wirral CH61 5UH — MB ChB 1992 Leeds.

CAUSER, Michael Stanley Edward Minster Practice, Greenhill Health Centre, Church Street, Lichfield WS13 6JL Tel: 01543 414311 Fax: 01543 418668; Minster House, 17 The Friary, Lichfield WS13 6QG Tel: 01543 254633 — MB ChB 1975 Birm.; DRCOG 1978. (Birmingham) GP (Parity Partner). Socs: (Treas.) Minster Research Club; (Treas.) Lichfield Med. Soc.

CAUSEY, Mr Gilbert Orchard Cottage, Bodinnick-by-Fowey, Fowey PL23 1LX Tel: 0172 687433 — MB ChB 1930 Liverp.; DSc Liverp. 1964, MB ChB (1st cl. Hons.) 1930; FRCS Eng. 1933; MRCS Eng. LRCP Lond. 1932. (Liverp.) Prof. Emerit. in Anat. Univ. Lond. Prev: Sir W. Collins Prof. of Anat. RCS Eng.; Asst. Surg. Walton Hosp. Liverp.; Lect. Anat. Univ. Coll. Lond.

CAUSTON, Alison Winter (retired) Wigmore House, Thornbury, Bristol BS12 1HD Tel: 01454 412599 — MB ChB 1952 Bristol.

CAUSTON, John Allan 12 The Roothings, Heybridge, Maldon CM9 4NA — MB ChB Leeds 1969; MRCPsych 1975; DPM Eng. 1972. (Leeds & Lond. Hosp.) Indep. Pract. Socs: Brit. Paediat. Assn.; Mem. Roy. Coll. Of Psychiat.s. Prev: Cons. Child Psychiat. Welwyn Gdn. City, Hatfield Child & Family Psychiat. Clinics & Qu. Eliz. Hosp. Welwyn Gdn. City; Sen. Regist. Tavistock Clin. Lond.; Regist. (Child Psychiat.) Hosp. Sick Childr. Gt. Ormond St. Lond.

CAUSTON, John Clifford (retired) Wigmore House, Thornbury, Bristol BS12 1HD Tel: 01454 412866 — MB ChB 1952 Bristol. Prev: Ho. Off. (Obst.) Hull Matern. Hosp.

CAUTLEY, William Gilmore (retired) Barley Croft, Kirby Lane, Chapeltown, Sheffield S35 2YX Tel: 01226 744411 — MB ChB 1958 Manch.; DObst RCOG 1962.

CAVADINO, Andrew The Westmoreland GP Centre, Fazakerley Hospital, Aintree, Liverpool L9 7AL Tel: 0151 525 6286 — MB ChB 1986 Liverp. Prev: Trainee GP/SHO (O & G) Arrowe Pk. Hosp. Wirral; SHO (Geriat. Med. & Psychiat.) Arrowe Pk. Hosp. Wirral; SHO (A & E) BRd.green Hosp. Liverp.

CAVALIERE, Vincenzo The Ridge Medical Practice, 3 Paternoster Lane, Great Horton, Bradford BD7 3EE Tel: 01274 502905 Fax: 01274 522060; 30 Church Lane, Adel, Leeds LS16 8DE Tel: 0113 261 0681 — MB ChB 1983 Manch.; T(GP) 1991. Club Doctor Bradford City AFC. Prev: Trainee GP Burnley, Pendle & Rossendale HA.

CAVALLO, Andrew Vincent 31 Crarae Avenue, Bearsden, Glasgow G61 1HY — MB BS 1985 Melbourne.

CAVAN, David Anthony Bournemouth Diabetes and Endocrine Centre, Royal Bournemouth Hospital, Castle Lane E., Bournemouth BH7 7DW Tel: 01202 704610 Fax: 01202 704759 Email: david.cavan@rbch-tr.swest.nhs.uk — BM 1985 Soton.; DM Soton. 1993; MRCP (UK) 1989; FRCP 2000. (Southampton) Cons. Phys. Roy. Bournemouth Hosp.; Clin. Director, Med., Roy. Bournemouth Hosp.; Hon. Sen. Lect. St. Thos. Hosp. Lond. Socs: Eur. Assn. Study Diabetes; Diabetes UK (Chair, Educat. and Psychosocial Care Sect.; Mem. Bd. of Trustees); Soc. for Endocrinol. Prev: Lect. & Sen. Regist. St. Thos. Hosp. Lond.; MRC Train. Fell. Univ. Birm.; Regist. (Med.) E. Birm. Hosp.

CAVANAGH, Eleanor Margaret North Methven Street, Perth PH1 5PD — MB ChB 1986 Ed.; DRCOG 1992. Prev: Trainee GP Kirkcaldy VTS.

CAVANAGH, Professor John Barr Department of Clinical Neurosciences, Institute of Psychiatry, De Crespigny Park, London SE5 8AF Tel: 020 8670 8861; 51 Chestnut Road, West Norwood, London SE27 9EZ Tel: 020 8670 8861 Email: jbc@chestnut.u-net.com — MB BS Lond. 1945; MD Lond. 1966; FRCP Lond. 1973, M 1946; FRCPath 1977. (Lond. Hosp.) Emerit. Prof. Applied Neurobiol. Univ. Lond.; Hon. Cons. Neuropathol. MRC Toxicol. Research Unit. Univ. Leicester; Hon. Research Fell. Inst. Psychiat. Univ. Lond. Socs: Path. Soc.; Brit. Neuropath. Soc. Prev: Reader (Neuropath.) & Research Fell. Guy's Hosp. Med. Sch. Lond.; Edr. Neuropath. Applied Neurobiol.; Dir. MRC Research Gp. Applied Neurobiol. Inst. Neurol.

CAVANAGH, John Gerard Joseph (retired) Health Centre, High St., Bidford on Avon, Alcester B50 4BQ Tel: 01789 773372 Fax: 01789 490380 — MB BCh BAO 1959 Belf.

CAVANAGH, Jonathan Thomas Ogilvie The Royal Edinburgh Hosptial, University Department of Psychiatry, Morningside, Edinburgh EH10 5HF Tel: 0131 537 6000 — MB ChB 1990 Glas.; MPhil Ed. 1997; MRCPsych 1995. (Glas.) Research Fell. (Dept. Psychiat.) Univ. Ed. Socs: Brit. Assn. Psychopharmacol.; Brain Res. Assn. Prev: Regist. SE Scotl. Psychiat.; SHO SE Scotl.

CAVANAGH, Joseph The Surgery, 4 Drayton Gardens, London SW10 9SA Tel: 020 7373 3356 — MB BChir 1964 Camb.; MA, MB Camb. 1964, BChir 1963. (Camb. & Univ. Coll. Hosp.) Socs: BMA. Prev: Ho. Phys. Univ. Coll. Hosp. Lond.; Ho. Surg. W. Middlx. Hosp. Isleworth; Ho. Surg. Obst. Unit W. Middlx. Hosp. Isleworth.

CAVANAGH, Julie Tayside Public Health, Medicine Service, Kings Cross Hospital, Clepington Road, Dundee DD3 8EA Tel: 01382 596984 Fax: 01382 596985 Email: jcavanagh@phm.finix.org.uk; 29

Castlefield, Cupar KY15 4DB — MB BS Newc. 1984; MFPHM RCP (UK) 1992. Cons. Pub. Health Med. Tayside HB.

CAVANAGH, Mary Clare Gosport Health Centre, Bury Road, Gosport PO12 3PN Tel: 023 9258 3302 Fax: 023 9250 1421 — MB ChB 1987 Leic.; MRCGP 1993; DA (UK) 1991.

CAVANAGH, Nicholas Patrick Conrad Tel: 020 8746 8657 Fax: 020 8746 8644; (cons. rooms), Harley Street Clinic, 35 Weymouth Street, London W1G 8BJ Tel: 020 7486 0689 Fax: 020 7837 3912 — MB BS Lond. 1969; MD Lond. 1980; MRCP (UK) 1972; MRCS Eng. LRCP Lond. 1969; FRCP 1996; FRCP CH 1997. (Guys) Cons. Paediat. Neurol. Chelsea & W.minster Hosp.and N. Thames Paediatric NeUrol..

CAVANAGH, Patricia Agnes The Surgery, 4 Drayton Gardens, London SW10 9SA Tel: 020 7373 3356 — MB ChB 1959 Liverp.

CAVANAGH, Paul John Strabane Health Centre, Upper Main Street, Strabane BT82 8AS Tel: 028 7138 4118 — MB BCh 1966 N U Irel. (N U Irel) GP Strabane, Co. Tyrone.

CAVANAGH, Paul Joseph 29 Castlefield, Cupar KY15 4DB — MB BS 1984 Newc.; MRCGP 1988; MRCPsych 1996. Specialist Regist. (Psychiat.) Roy. Dundee Liff Hosp.

CAVANAGH, Richard Andrew Deben Road Surgery, 2 Deben Road, Ipswich IP1 5EN Tel: 01473 741152 Fax: 01473 743237; Blands Place, Copdock, Ipswich IP8 3JD Tel: 01473 730426 — MB ChB 1967 Sheff.; MRCGP 1976; Dip. Pract. Dermat. Wales 1992; DObst RCOG 1975.

CAVANAGH, Sheila Ross (retired) 40 Glebe Road, Barnes, London SW13 0EA Tel: 0208876 3725 — MB ChB 1948 St. And. Prev: Regist. (Microbiol.) Char. Cross Hosp. Lond.

CAVANAGH, Mr Simon Peter St Richard's Hospital, Chichester PO19 4SE Tel: 01243 788122; Marchwood Grange, Brandy Hole Lane, Chichester PO19 4RY — MB BChir 1979 Camb.; MA Camb. 1980; FRCS Eng. 1985. Cons. Orthop. Surg. Roy. W. Sussex Hosps. Chichester & King Edwd. VII Hosp. Midhurst; Research Fell. (Hand & Micro Surg.) Singapore 1988 Europ Trav Fell.sh 1992. Socs: Fell. BOA; Brit. Orthop. Research Soc. Prev: Sen. Regist. (Orthop. Surg.) St. Mary's Hosp. Lond.; Regist. (Orthop.) Guy's Hosp. Lond.

CAVANAGH, Siobhan Anne 26 Sunningdale Park, Belfast BT14 6RU — MB BCh BAO 1997 Belf.

CAVANAGH, Mr Stephen Paul 27 Far Mead Croft, Burley-in-Wharfedale, Ilkley LS29 7RR — MB ChB 1991 Leeds; FRCS (Eng.) 1995. (Leeds Univ.) Specialist Regist. Rotat. (Gen. Surg.) Yorks.. Prev: Research Fell. (Vasc. Surg.) Leeds Gen. Infirm.

CAVANAGH, Vincent Joseph Aberfoyle Terrace Surgery, 3-5 Aberfoyle Terrace, Strand Road, Londonderry BT48 7NP Tel: 028 7126 4868; 9 Belmont Park, Londonderry BT48 7RW Tel: 01504 351535 — MB BCh BAO 1962 NUI. Med. Dir. N.lands Centre for Alcoholism Lond.derry.

CAVANNAGH, Lance Christian The Grayshott Surgery, Boundary Road, Grayshott, Hindhead GU26 6TY Tel: 01428 604343 Fax: 01428 604899; Tel: 01428 642888 — MB BS 1986 Lond.; MRCGP 1990. (Charing Cross & Westminster) Med. Off. to ELIFAR homes fcr young adults with learning disabilities.

CAVAROLI, Marco Emilio East House, Goldsmiths, South Hill, Langdon Hills, Basildon SS16 6JB Tel: 01268 542926 — MB ChB 1989 Manch.; BSc (Med. Sci.) St. And. 1986.

CAVE, Albert Mark Alexander House, 2 Salisbury Road, Farnborough GU14 7AW Tel: 01252 541155 — MB BS 1985 Lond.; MRCP (UK) 1993; MRCGP 1991; DRCOG 1993.

CAVE, Anthony Paul Drummond, Wing Cdr. RAF Med. Br. Retd. Department of Diagnostic Imaging, St Mary's Hospital, Parkhurst Road, Newport PO30 5TQ Tel: 01983 534678 Fax: 01983 821331 Email: tony.cave@iow.nhs.uk; Email: drtonycave@aol.com — MB ChB 1973 Dundee; FRCR 1982; DRCOG 1979. Cons. (Radiol.) St Mary's Hosp. Newport, Isle of wight. Socs: Magnetic Resonance Radiol. Assn. UK (Treas.); BMA; Brit. Inst. of Radiol. Prev: Cons. (Radiol.) RAF; Regist. (Radiol.) Middlx. Hosp. Lond.; Ho. Phys. & Ho. Surg. Sharoe Green Hosp. Fulwood.

CAVE, Bridgette Louise Drummond 36 Granby Grove, Highfield, Southampton SO17 3RZ — BM 1998 Soton.

CAVE, Darren Richard Morris House, Waltheof Gardens, London N17 7EB — MB BS 1994 Lond.; DRCOG 1996; DCH 1997; DFFP 1998. (St. Bartholomews London) GP Princip. Morris Ho. Surg., Tottenham. Socs: Med. Defence Union; BMA; Med. Sickness Soc. Prev: SHO (Psychiat.); SHO (Paed.); SHO (Obs).

CAVE, Deborah Louise 10 Hob Hey Lane, Culcheth, Warrington WA3 4NQ — MB BS 1992 Newc.

CAVE, Dominic Andrew The Cottage, Northfields, Bath BA1 5TN — MB BS 1994 Lond.

CAVE, Elizabeth Mary 3 Headingley Terrace, Headingley, Leeds LS6 2EE — MB BCh 1986 Wales; BSc Wales 1983; MRCP (UK) 1989; FRCR 1993. Cons. Radiol. Dewsbury & Dist. Gen. Hosp. Prev: Sen. Regist. (Radiol.) Yorks. HA.

CAVE, Georgieana Vanessa The Ridgeway Surgery, 1 The Mount Echo Avenue, Chingford, London E4 7JX — MB BS 1988 Lond.; MRCGP 1993; DRCOG 1992. GP Princip. in Chingford, Lond. E4.

CAVE, James Alan Harvard Downland Practice, East Lane, Chieveley, Newbury RG20 8UY Tel: 01635 248251 Fax: 01635 247261; 10 Sowbury Park, Chieveley, Newbury RG20 8TZ — MB BS 1985 Lond.; BSc (Hons.) Lond. 1982; MRCGP 1991; DFFP 1994; DRCOG 1988. (St.Bart.) Day News Edr. Helix plc; Mem. Berks. LMC; Chairm. Newbury PCG. Socs: BIMM; Nat. Back Pain Assn. Prev: Trainee GP Stoke Mandeville Hosp. VTS; Ho. Phys. St. Bart. Hosp. Lond.

CAVE, John David Harvard (retired) Flint House, 10b The Street, Ash, Canterbury CT3 2HJ Tel: 01227 720231 Email: dcave@dialstart.net — MB BS 1952 Lond. Prev: Ho. Surg. St. Bart. Hosp.

CAVE, Kathryn Linda Sandwell FHSA, Kingston House, 438 High St., West Bromwich B70 9LD Tel: 0121 553 1774 — MB BS 1969 Lond.; MRCS Eng. LRCP Lond. 1969. (Birm.) Med. Adviser Sandwell FHSA.

CAVE, Mark Alan (retired) Chalk House Farm, Staple, Canterbury CT3 1LE Tel: 01304 312356 — MRCS Eng. LRCP Lond. 1940; DTM & H Eng. 1941. Prev: Med. Off. Colon. Med. Serv.

CAVE, Martin Peter 31 Newport Road, Woolstone, Milton Keynes MK15 0AD Tel: 01908 677117 Email: cave@lineone.net — MB ChB 1990 Dundee; Msc (Sports Med.) Lond. 1998; DFFP RCOG 1998; T(GP) JCPTGP. Primary Care Phys. (A&E), Milton Keynes Gen. Hosp.; Sports Phys. Blackberry Orthop. Clinic, Milton Keynes; Team Doctor, Lond. Kt.s Ice Hockey Club, Lond. Socs: Brit. Inst. Musculoskel. Med.; Brit. Assn. Sport & Med.

CAVE, Michael Hamilton University Hospital of North Durham, North Road, Durham DH1 5TW Tel: 0191 333 2356 Fax: 0191 333 2747 Email: michael.cave@ndhcnt.northy.nhs.uk — MB BCh BAO 1984 Belf.; MB BCh BAO Belf. I984; MD Belf. 1994; MRCP (UK) 1987; FRCP 1999. (Qu. Univ. Belf.) Cons. Internal Med. & Cardiol. Univ. Hosp. Durh.; Hon. Cons. Cariol. James Cook Univ. Hosp. Middlesb. Socs: Brit. Cardiac Soc. Prev: Sen. Transpl. Fell. Papworth Hosp. Camb.; Career Regist. (Cardiol. & Med.) W. Midl.; Research Fell. (Cardiol.) Ulster Hosp. Belf.

CAVE, Nirmali Sandra The Surgery, 160 Streetly Road, Erdington, Birmingham B23 7BD Tel: 0121 350 2323; 18 Woodside Close, Parkhall, Walsall WS5 3LU — MB ChB 1988 Glas. GP Birm. Prev: Clin. Asst. (Diabetes) Heartlands Hosp. Birm.

CAVE, Robert John Sylvester The Abingdon Surgery, 65 Stert Street, Abingdon OX14 3LB Tel: 01235 523126 Fax: 01235 550625; 44 Victoria Road, Abingdon OX14 1DQ — MB BS Lond. 1973; MRCP (U.K.) 1975; MRCGP 1980; DPM Eng. 1978. (Univ. Coll. Hosp.) Prev: Ho. Phys. Whittington Hosp. Lond.; SHO (Med.) N.wick Pk. Hosp. Harrow; Regist. (Psychiat.) Oxon. AHA (T).

CAVE, Simon Gay Furneaux New Land Surgery, Wootton Grove, Sherborne DT9 4DL Tel: 01935 813438 Fax: 01935 817470 Email: simon.cave@ap-j81032.nhs.uk; Home Farm, Poyntington, Sherborne DT9 4LF — MB ChB 1969 Ed. (Edin.) Gen. Practitioner; Clin. Asst., Orthop., Native Hosp., Sherborne; Police Surg.

CAVE, Stephanie Briers 7 Hickton Drive, Altrincham WA14 4LZ — MB ChB 1971 Manch.; DCH Eng. 1973. Assoc. Specialist (Community Child Health) & Med. Adviser Manch. Social Servs. Adoptions/Fostering; Foundat. Mem. Fac. Community Health. Socs: Manch. Med. Soc. Prev: SHO (Paediat.) Univ. Hosp. S. Manch.

CAVE, Timothy Richard Cassam Astra Pharmaceuticals, Home Park, Kings Langley WD4 8DH; The Old Chapel, Hamptworth, Salisbury SP5 2DR — MB BS 1985 Lond.; AFPM RCP Lond. 1993. Head of Med. Affairs Astra Pharmaceut.

CAVE, William Kenneth The Ciwec Clinic Travel Medicine Centre, PO Box 12895, Kathmandu, Nepal Tel: 00977 1 228531 Fax: 00977 1 224675 Email: willcave@ciwecpc.mos.com.np; Stanford House, Priors Hill Road, Aldeburgh IP15 5EP Tel: 01728 452774

Fax: 01728 452774 — MB BS 1986 Lond.; DCH RCP Lond. 1990; DRCOG Lond. 1995; MRCGP Lond. 1995; DTM & H Liverp. 1997. (Middlx. Hosp. Med. Sch.) Staff Phys. Ciwec Travel Med. Centre Kathmandu Nepal. Socs: Roy. Coll. Gen. Pract. Prev: GP/Regist. Needham Market Suff.;; Resid. Med. Off. Brokenhill Base Hosp. Australia.

CAVE, William Peter Glenburnie, Llanwenarth Citra, Abergavenny NP7 7ET — MB BChir 1975 Camb.; MA, MB Camb. 1975, BChir 1974; FRCA 1989; DTM & H Liverp. 1978; DRCOG 1977. (Camb. & St. Thos.) Cons. Anaesth. Nevill Hall Hosp. Abergavenny. Prev: Med. Off. Kisiizi Hosp., Uganda.

CAVE-BIGLEY, Mr David Jordayne, Maj. RAMC(V) University Hospital Aintree, Longmoor Lane, Liverpool L7 9AL Tel: 0151 529 4950; Lennox Lodge, 18 Village Road, Oxton, Prenton CH43 5SR — MRCS Eng. LRCP Lond. 1969; MS Lond. 1988, MB BS 1969; FRCS Eng. 1976. (Roy. Free) Cons. Surg. Univ. Hosp. Aintree; RMO Qu. Own Yeomanry. Socs: Brit. Assn. Endocrine Surg.s. Prev: Sen. Surg. Regist. Roy. Liverp. Hosp.; Sen. Surgic. Regist. Chester Roy. Infirm.; Sen. Surg. Regist. BRd.green Hosp. Liverp.

CAVEN, Elizabeth Ann Lightburn Medical Centre, 930 Carntyne Road, Glasgow G32 6NB Tel: 0141 778 0440 Fax: 0141 778 0143; 19 Campbell Drive, Bearsden, Glasgow G61 4NF Tel: 0141 942 8366 — MB ChB 1981 Glas.; MRCGP 1986; DCH RCPS Glas. 1984; DRCOG 1985.

CAVENAGH, Alexander John McMurrough (retired) Gludy, Cradoc Road, Brecon LD3 9PE Tel: 01874 624056 — BM BCh 1954 Oxf.; FRCGP 1987; DObst RCOG 1960. Prev: GP Brecon.

CAVENAGH, James Durrell Department of Haematology, The Royal London Hospital, Whitechapel, London E1 1BB Tel: 020 7377 7180 Fax: 020 7377 7016 Email: jdcavenagh@mds.gmw.ac.uk — MB BS 1985 Lond.; MD Lond. 1996; MRCP (UK) 1988; MRCPath 1996. Sen. Lect. (Hon. Cons.).

CAVENAGH, Nicholas Francis The Hollies Surgery, The Green, Great Bentley, Colchester CO7 8PJ Tel: 01206 250691 Fax: 01206 252496; Warrens Farm, Church Road, Little Bentley, Colchester CO7 8RZ Tel: 01206 250259 — MB BS 1979 Lond. Socs: Colchester Med. Soc. Prev: Trainee GP Maidstone VTS.

CAVENAGH, William Francis (retired) 5 Colney Drive, Crin Gleford, Norwich NR4 7RH Tel: 01603 455559 — MRCS Eng. LRCP Lond. 1943; MD Lond. 1949, MB BS 1943. Prev: Res. Med. Off. Postgrad. Med. Sch. Lond.

CAVENDISH, Mr Alfred (retired) 9 Kinloss Gardens, Finchley, London N3 3DU Tel: 020 8346 7533 — MB BS Lond. 1938; FRCS Eng. 1943; MRCS Eng. LRCP Lond. 1937. Hon. Cons. Surg. Lewisham Hosp. Prev: Cons. Surg. Lewisham Hosp.

CAVENDISH, Judith Ann Supreme House, 300 Regents Park Road, Finchley, London N3 2JX Tel: 020 8346 3291/0446 — MRCS Eng. LRCP Lond. 1975; DRCOG 1977.

CAVENDISH, Mr Michael Edward 88 Rodney Street, Liverpool L1 9AR Tel: 0151 708 6070 Fax: 0151 709 7279; 195 Liverpool Road, Pewfall, St Helens WA11 9RX Tel: 01744 615486 Fax: 01744 615486 Email: mecaven@aol.com — MB BS Lond. 1961; BSc Lond. 1958; MChOrth Liverp. 1969; FRCS Eng. 1967; MRCS Eng. LRCP Lond. 1960. (Guy's) Cons. Orthop. Surg. St. Helens & Knowsley HA; Cons. Orthop. Surg. Fairfield Hosp. (p/t). Socs: Fell. BOA; Brit. Elbow & Shoulder Soc.; Eur. Soc. Elbow & Shoulder Surg. Prev: Sen. Regist. (Orthop.) United Liverp. Hosps.; Ho. Surg. (Orthop.) & Demonst. (Anat.) Guy's Hosp.

CAVENDISH, Michael Neil Hodford Road Surgery, 73 Hodford Road, London NW11 8NH Tel: 020 8905 5234 — MB BS 1979 Lond.; DRCOG 1985. (Roy. Free)

CAVES, Natalie Dawn 2F3 7 Bruntsfield Avenue, Edinburgh EH10 4EL; Flat 33C, Block 3, 10 Robinson Road, Hong Kong, Hong Kong — MB ChB 1992 Ed.; BSc Med. Sci. (Bacteriol.) Ed. 1990; MRCP UK 1998. (Edinburgh University Medical School) SHO (Anaesth.).

CAVET, James 10 Guelder Road, High Heaton, Newcastle upon Tyne NE7 7PN — MB BS 1992 Newc.

CAVILL, Gwenda School Cottage, Bothal, Morpeth NE61 6SL — MB ChB 1987 Leic.

CAVILL, Julie Dawn 7 Silk Hill Cottages, Buxworth, High Peak SK23 7NE — MB ChB 1992 Sheff.

CAVISTON, Paul Michael 54 Leswin Road, Stoke Newington, London N16 7NH Tel: 020 7254 7188 — MB BCh BAO 1979 NUI; LRCPI & LM, LRCSI & LM 1979; MRCPsych 1986; Dip. Family Ther. & Fac. Clin. Sci. Lond. 1989. (Roy. Coll. Surgs. Irel.) Lead Cons. Adolesc. Psychiat. Brookside Young Peoples Unit (Redbridge) Goodmayes; Hon. Sen. Lect. St. Bart. Hosp. Lond.; Research Regist. St. Anns Hosp. Lond.; Mem. UK Counc. for Psychother. (Mem. Psychonal. & Psychother. Sect.). Prev: Regist (Psychiat.) St. Bart. Hosp. Lond.; Sen. Regist. (Child & Family Psychiat.) Tavistock Clinic Lond.; Sen. Regist. (Child Adolesc. & Family Psychiat.) Univ. Coll. Hosp. & Middlx. Hosp. Lond.

CAVOURA, Catherine 98 Baronald Drive, Glasgow G12 0HY; 23 Hillhead Street, Hillhead, Glasgow G12 8PX Tel: 0141 339 1233 — MRCGP 1999; MB ChB 1994 Glas.; DRCOG; DFFP; Postgrad. Cert. Gen. Pract. 1998. SHO (Obst. & Gyn.). Socs: BMA,GMC. Prev: GP Regist. Glas.

CAWDELL, Graham Manley Whiston Hospital, Prescot L35 5DR Tel: 0151 430 1680 Fax: 0151 430 1335 Email: graham.cawdell@gwise.sthk-trnwest.nhs.uk; Weston, Parrs Lane, Aughton, Ormskirk L39 5BP Tel: 01695 424381 Fax: 01695 424381 Email: cawdell@doctors.org.uk — MB ChB 1975 Liverp.; FRCOG 1995, M 1982. Cons. O & G St. Helens & Knowsley Hosps. Trust & Fairfield Hosp.; Regional Coll. Adviser, Mersey Deanery, Chairm. of Specialist Train. Comm..; Hon. Clin. Lect. (Obst. & Gyn.) Univ. Liverp. Prev: Trainig Progr. Director, Mersey Deanery.; Lect. & Hon. Sen. Regist. (O & G) Liverp. Univ.; Regist. (O & G) King's Coll. & Dulwich Hosp.

CAWDERY, Hilda Muriel Department of Microbiology, Kidderminster General Hospital, Bewdley Road, Kidderminster DY11 6RJ Tel: 01562 823424; Netley House, Wombourne, Wolverhampton WV5 9HA Tel: 01902 892135 — MB BS 1966 Lond.; MRCS Eng. LRCP Lond. 1966; FRCPath 1990, M 1978. (King's Coll. Hosp.) Cons. Microbiol. Kidderminster Health Care Trust Worcs. Socs: Assn. Med. Microbiol. Prev: Sen. Regist. (Path.) King's Coll. Hosp. Lond.; Ho. Surg. (ENT) & SHO (Path.) King's Coll. Hosp. Lond.

CAWDERY, John Edward (retired) Midway, Pencoed Lane, Llanmartin, Newport NP18 2ED Tel: 01633 412117 — BM BCh 1960 Oxf.; FRCP Lond. 1980, M 1966; FRCPCH 1997; DObst RCOG 1964. Prev: Cons. Paediat. Glan Hafren NHS Trust Roy. Gwent Hosp.

CAWDRON, Bruce Alfred 10 Kings Brook Close, Rempstone, Loughborough LE12 6RR — MB BS 1979 Lond.; MRCS Eng. LRCP Lond. 1978. Med. Adviser 3M Healthcare LoughBoro.. Prev: Med. Adviser Merton, Sutton & Wandsworth FHSA.

CAWDRY, Nicholas Guy Irving (retired) 47 Victoria Park, Cambridge CB4 3EJ Tel: 01223 321045 — MB 1964 Camb.; BChir 1963; DObst RCOG 1965. Prev: GP Camb.

CAWLEY, Greta Loudoun (retired) 273 Dyke Road, Hove BN3 6PB Tel: 01273 553961 — MB BS 1949 Durh. Prev: Assoc. Specialist Dermatol. Brighton HA.

CAWLEY, Professor John Cozens University Department of Haematology, Duncan Building, Royal Liverpool Hospital, Prescot St., Liverpool L69 3BX; The Paddock, 25 Well Lane, Heswall, Wirral CH60 8NQ — MD 1980 Leeds; MB ChB Leeds 1967; PhD Camb. 1973; FRCP Lond. 1987, M 1976; FRCPath 1992, M 1982. Prof. Haemat. Univ. Liverp. Prev: Reader (Clin. Haemat.) Univ. Coll. Hosp. Lond.; Lect. (Med.) Univ. Leeds; Ellmore Research Stud. Univ. Camb.

CAWLEY, Laurence John (retired) The Old Hall, Carlton Husthwaite, Thirsk YO7 2BP — BM BCh 1947 Oxf.; MA, BM BCh Oxf. 1947. Prev: Regist. (Orthop.) Clatterbridge Gen. Hosp.

CAWLEY, Mary Elizabeth (retired) The Old Hall, Carlton Husthwaite, Thirsk YO7 2BP Tel: 01845 501246 — MB ChB 1947 Liverp. Prev: Regist. (Anaesth.) Birkenhead Gen. Hosp.

CAWLEY, Michael Ian David, RD Consulting Rooms, Wessex Nuffield Hospital, Winchester Road, Chandlers Ford, Eastleigh SO53 2DW Tel: 02380 258423 Fax: 02380 258446; Paddock Cottage, Bramshaw, Lyndhurst SO43 7JN Tel: 01794 390934 — MB BS 1958 Lond.; MD Lond. 1972; FRCP Lond. 1979, M 1964; MRCS Eng. LRCP Lond. 1958. (St. Bart.) Cons. Rheum. Soton. Univ. Hosps.; Hon. Sec. Lect. Fac. Med. Univ. Soton.; Hon. Cons. Rheum. to RN. Socs: (Heberden Roundsman 1992) Brit. Soc. Rheum. (Mem. Counc.1986-89); Amer. Coll. Rheum.; Brit. Soc. Immunol. Prev: Vis. Lect. & Cons. Univ. Kuwait; Postgrad. Clin. Tutor Univ. Soton. & RCP Tutor; Cons. Rheum. Wrightington Hosp. Lancs.

CAWLEY, Nicola The Beeches, Rickerby, Carlisle CA3 9AA — MB BS 1998 Lond.; MB BS Lond 1998.

CAWLEY, Professor Robert Hugh Edward House, Charter Nightingale Hospital, 7 Lisson Grove, London NW1 6SH Tel: (0171) 535 7901 Fax: (0171) 724 8115 — MB ChB Birm. 1955; PhD Birm. 1949, BSc 1947; FRCPsych (Hon.) 1990; FRCPsych 1971; FRCP Lond. 1975, M 1966; DPM Eng. 1959. (Birm.) Emerit. Prof. Psychol. Med. King's Coll. Sch. Med. & Dent. & Inst. of Psychiat. Lond. Prev: Chief Examr. Roy. Coll. Psychiat.; Mem. MRC & Chairm. Neurosci. Bd.; Sen. Lect. & Hon. Cons. Psychiat. Univ. Birm.

CAWOOD, John Robert Preston Grove Medical Centre, Preston Grove, Yeovil BA20 2BQ Tel: 01935 74353 — BM BCh 1966 Oxf.; MA, BM BCh Oxf. 1966; DA Eng. 1969; DObst RCOG 1968. (Lond. Hosp.) Prev: Res. Accouch. Lond. Hosp.; Ho. Phys. St. Margt.'s Hosp. Epping; Ho. Surg. Lond. Hosp.

CAWOOD, Mr Roderick Hugh The Limes, 15B Great North Road, Stibbington, Peterborough PE8 6LN Tel: 01780 782147 Fax: 01780 782147 — MB BS 1965 Lond.; FRCS Eng. 1971; MRCS Eng. LRCP Lond. 1965. (Univ. Coll. Hosp.) Cons. ENT Surg. Edith Cavell Hosp. P'boro. Socs: BMA; Brit. Assn. Otol. Prev: Sen. Regist. (ENT) Addenbrooke's Hosp. Camb.; SHO (ENT) Bristol Gen. Hosp.; SHO (Gen. Surg.) Leicester Roy. Infirm.

CAWOOD, Thomas James Woodside House, Bridgend, Linlithgow EH49 6NH — MB ChB 1998 Glas.; MB ChB Glas 1998.

CAWRSE, Nicholas Howard 5 Netherton Road, St Margarets, Twickenham TW1 1LZ — MB BS 1996 Newc.

CAWSON, Roderick Anthony 40 Court Lane, Dulwich, London SE21 7DR Tel: 020 8693 5781 — MD Lond. 1969, MB BS 1953; LMSSA Lond. 1952; BDS (Hons.) Lond. 1943; FDS RCS Eng. 1951, LDS 1943; FDS RCPS Glas. 1970; FRCPath 1977, M 1965. (King's Coll. Hosp.) Prof. Emerit. Oral Med. & Path. Guy's Hosp.; Vis. Prof. Baylor Univ. Med. Center & Dent. Coll., Dallas. Socs: BMA. Prev: RAF Dent. Br. 1944-8.

CAWSTON, Peter George Flat 12, 20 Succoth St, Glasgow G13 1DF Tel: 0141 954 7117 — MB ChB 1993 Glas.; DRCOG 1997; DGM 1998. (Glasgow) GP Princip. (Jobshare), Drumchapel Health Centre - Clin. Lect. (O.SWTE) Dept. at Gen. Pract., Glas. Univ.

CAWTE, Edwin Christopher 51 Station Road, Ibstock LE67 6JL Tel: 01530 260525 — MB BS 1956 Durh.; MRCGP 1968; DObst RCOG 1960. Prev: Clin. Teach. Fac. Med. (Community Health) Univ. Leicester; Ho. Surg. (O & G) Gen. Hosp. Newc.; Ho. Surg. Accid. Room & Ho. Phys. (Dermat.) Roy. Vict. Infirm. Newc.

CAWTHORN, Mr Simon John Department of Surgery, Frenchay Hospital, Bristol BS16 1LE Tel: 0117 970 1212; Litfield House Medical Centre, 1 Litfield Place, Clifton, Bristol BS8 3LS Tel: 0117 973 1323 Fax: 0117 973 3303 — MB BS 1973 Lond.; BSc Lond. 1973, MS 1989; FRCS Eng. 1980; MRCS Eng. LRCP Lond. 1976. Cons. Surg. Frenchay Hosp. Bristol. Socs: Fell. Roy. Soc. Med. & Mem. BMA. Prev: Sen. Regist. (Surg.) The Roy. Marsden Hosp. Lond. & Roy. Surrey Co. Hosp. Guildford; Sen. Regist. (Surg.) St. Geo. Hosp. Lond.; Regist. St. Jas. Hosp. Lond.

CAWTHORNE, Barbara Jennie 25 Preston Trust, Preston upon the Weald Moors, Wellington, Telford TF6 6DQ — MRCS Eng. LRCP Lond. 1935. (Roy. Free)

CAWTHORNE, David John (retired) 45 Clayton Road, Newcastle upon Tyne NE2 4RQ — MB BS 1947 Durh.; DObst RCOG 1952. Prev: Ho. Phys. & Ho. Surg. Newc. Gen. Hosp.

CAWTHRAY, Pamela Ann Danebridge Medical Centre, London Rd, Northwich CW9 5HR Tel: 01606 45786; Tel: 01928 791943 — MB ChB 1993 Manch.; MRCGP 2000 RCGP; DFFP 1999 RCOG; DRCOG - RCOG 1998. VTS, Chester; GP Asst. Socs: BMA.

CAWTHRON, Paul Anthony Thorneywood Adolescent Unit, Porchester Road, Nottingham NG3 6LF Tel: 0115 969 1300 Fax: 0115 955 5434 — MB BS 1980 Lond.; BSc. Lond. 1977, MB BS 1980; MRCPsych 1986. Cons. Child & Adolesc. Psychiat. Nottm. Healthcare NHS Trust.; Clin. Dir., Camus, Nottm. Healthcare NHS Trust. Prev: Cons. Adolesc. Psychiat. Longview Adolesc. Unit Colchester; Sen. Regist. Highfield Family & Adolesc. Unit Warneford Hosp. Oxf.; Regist. Bethlem Roy. & Maudsley Hosp. Lond.

CAY, Elizabeth Lorna (retired) 12 India Street, Edinburgh EH3 6EZ Tel: 0131 225 3640 — MD 1968 Ed.; MB ChB 1954; FRCP Edin. 1988; MRCP (Edin) 1985; FRCPsych 1981, M 1972; DPM Eng. 1960. Prev: Research Fell., & Hon. Lect. Dept. Psychiat. Edin. Univ.

CAY, Sarah Elizabeth Bellamy Family Planning Clinic, 18 Deanterrace, Edinburgh EH4 1NL Tel: 0131 332 7941; 250 Ferry Road, Edinburgh EH5 3AN — MB ChB 1984 Aberd.; MB ChB 1984 (Hons.) Aberd.; MRCGP 1988. Staff Grade in Family Plann. and Reproductive Healthcare.

***CAYGILL, Alexandra Christine** Homerton Hospital, Homerston Row, London E9 Tel: 020 8510 5555; 100A Newington Green Road, London N1 4RG — MB ChB 1994 Dundee.

CAYLEY, Arthur Charles Digby Central Middlesex Hospital, Acton Lane, London NW10 7NS Tel: 020 8453 2184 Fax: 020 8961 1827; 17 Conolly Road, Hanwell, London W7 3JW — MB BS 1970 Lond.; FRCP Lond. 1989; MRCP (UK) 1973. Cons. Phys. (Geriat. Med.) Centr. Middlx. Hosp. N.W.Lond. Hosp.s NHS Trust; Recognised Med. Teach. Univ. Lond.; Hon. Clin. Sen. Lect. (Geriat. Med.) Fac. of Med, Imperial Coll. of Sci., Tech. & Med. Socs: Brit. Geriat. Soc. Prev: Sen. Regist. (Geriat. Med.) Middlx. Hosp. Lond.; SHO & Ho. Phys. Middlx. Hosp. Lond.

CAYLEY, Forde Everard de Wend, MBE 67 Wish Road, Hove BN3 4LN Tel: 01273 732021 — MRCS Eng. LRCP Lond. 1939; MD Lond. 1948, MB BS 1946; FRCP Lond. 1971, M 1946. (Middlx.) Socs: Brighton & Sussex M-C Soc. Prev: Cons. Phys. in Dis. Chest Brighton & Lewes Hosp. Gp.; Sen. Regist. St. Stephen's Hosp. Chelsea; Med. Regist. Middlx. Hosp.

CAYLEY, Jeanette Ann SCMO Women's Services (Ealing), Featherstone Road Clinic, Southall UB2 5BQ Tel: 020 8574 2481 Fax: 020 8843 1482 — MSc Lond. 1985, MB BS 1970; MFFP 1993; DHMSA 1981. SCMO, Family Plann., Riverside NHS Trust. Socs: Inst. Psychosexual Med. & BMA; Lond. Soc. Family Plann. Doctors. (former Chairm.); Med. Art Soc.

CAYTON, Henry Rymer (retired) 19 The Drive, Henleaze, Bristol BS9 4LD Tel: 0117 962 8059 — MB ChB 1936 Ed.; FRCPath 1970. Hon. Cons. Bacteriol. Ham. Green Hosp. Bristol; Lect. in Bact. Univ. Bristol. Prev: Dir. Pub. Health Laborat. Serv. Bristol.

CAYTON, Ruth Margaret 8 Kingslea Road, Solihull B91 1TP — MB ChB 1968 Sheff.; MD Sheff. 1975; FRCP Lond. 1985; MRCP (UK) 1972; T(M) 1991. Cons. Phys. (Chest Med.) Birm. Heartlands Hosp.; Vis. Sen. Lect. Warwick Univ.; Hon. Sen. Lect. Birm. Univ. Prev: Lect. (Med.) Brompton Hosp. Lond.; Sen. Regist. (Med.) Lond. Hosp.

CAZES, Catherine Isabel Wake Chest Clinic, Northampton General Hospital, Northampton NN1 5BD Tel: 01604 34700; Cedar House, Yardley Hastings, Northampton NN7 1EX Tel: 01604 696230 Fax: 01604 544858 — MB BS 1969 Lond.; MRCP (U.K.) 1976; MRCS Eng. LRCP Lond. 1969. (Roy. Free) Assoc. Specialist in Respirat. Med. N.ampton Gen. Hosp. Socs: Roy. Soc. Med.; Brit. Thorac. Soc. Prev: Regist. Gen. Med. Orsett Hosp. Essex; Ho. Phys. Roy. Free Hosp.; Ho. Surg. Bedford Gen. Hosp.

CEBAGG, Charles Ernest (retired) — FRCP 1983; MRCS Eng. LRCP 1946 London; MRCP 1971; DPM 1952; MA 1946 Cambridge. Prev: Cons. Psychiat., St. John's Hosp.s, Aylesbury, Bucks.

CEBALLOS BAUMANN, Andres Otto MRC Cyclotron Unit, Hammersmith Hospital, Ducane Road, London W12 0HS Tel: 020 8740 3162 Fax: 020 8743 3987 — MD 1988 Heidelberg; State Exam Med 1987.

CEBRIAN VALENCIA, Luis 1A Park Lane, Wesham, Preston PR4 3HG — LMS 1993 Saragossa.

CECCHERINI, Andrew Francis Adrian X-ray Department, East Surrey Hospital, Canada Avenue, Redhill RH1 6RH Tel: 01737 768511 Ext: 8214 Fax: 01737 780395 — MB BChir 1987 Camb.; BA Med. Sci. Camb. 1984; MRCP (UK) 1991; FRCR 1994. Cons. Radiol. E. Surrey Hosp. Socs: BMA & Roy. Coll. Radiol.

CECIL, John Richard Brannel Surgery, 58 Rectory Road, St. Stephen, St Austell PL26 7RL Tel: 01726 822254 Fax: 01726 824450 — MB BS 1982 Lond.; MRCGP 1988; DRCOG 1988.

CECIL, Mark Rotheram 23 Cadogan Square, London SW1X 0HU — MB BS 1983 Lond.; MBA 1985; MRCS Eng. LRCP Lond. 1983; LMSSA 1983. (St. Thos.)

CECIL, Mr Thomas Desmond Cambridge House, 3 Southampton Road, Romsey SO51 8AD — BM 1990 Soton.; FRCS Eng. 1994. Regist. Rotat. (Gen. Surg.) Portsmouth & I. of Wight. Prev: SHO Rotat. (Surg.) Basingstoke & Lymington Hosps.; SHO (Orthop.) Portsmouth NHS Trust; SHO (Cardiothoracics) Frenchay Hosp. Bristol.

CEFAI, Christopher Department of Microbiology, Pathology Laboratory, Wrexham Maelor Hospital, Wrexham LL13 7TD Tel: 01978 725861 Fax: 01978 366520 Email: chriscefai@new-tr.nhs.wales.uk — MRCS Eng. LRCP Lond. 1981; MSc Lond. 1985; MRCPath 1989; FRCPath. Cons. (Microbiol.) Wrexham Maelor Hosp. NHS Trust; Hon. Sen. Lect. (Undergrad. Studies) Univ. of Wales Coll. of Med. Socs: Hosp. Infec. Soc.; Brit. Soc. Antimicrob. Chemother.; Welsh Microbiological Assn. Prev: Sen. Regist. (Microbiol.) N.. RHA.

CELA, Ester 1 Ensor Mews, London SW7 3BT Tel: 020 7373 4185 Email: e.cela@ic.ac.uk — MB BCh 1993 Wales. Clin. Research Fell. (Reproduc. Endocrinol.) Imperial Coll. Sch. Med. Lond.

CELASCHI, David Antonio 21 Lee Grove, Chigwell IG7 6AD — MB BS 1993 Lond.

CELESTIN, Mr Louis Roger (retired) Sutton House, The Promenade, Clifton Down, Bristol BS8 3HT Tel: 0117 973 7360 — MB BS 1951 Lond.; FRCS Ed. 1957; FRCS Eng. 1961. Prev: Sen. Regist. Bristol Roy. Infirm.

CELIN, Gianfranco Flat A, 34 Hans Road, London SW3 1RW Tel: 020 7225 0179 Fax: 020 7225 2016 Email: john.celin@compuserve.com — State DMS 1977 Milan. Clin. Instruc. (Plastic Surg.) Univ. Virginia Med. Sch., USA; Specialist Dip. Vasc. Surg. Univ. Milan; Specialist Dip. Angiol. Univ. Milan; Specialist Dip. Cosmetic Plastic Surg. Amer. Bd. Cosmetic Plastic Surg. Harvard; Univ. NY Univ. USA. Socs: Amer. Bd. Cosmetic Surg.; Amer. Soc. Phebology. Prev: Clin. Teachg. Fell. (Surg.) Harvard Med. Sch.

CELINSKA, Ewa — Lekarz Poznan 1968; FFPM RCP (UK) 1992; Dip. Pharm. Med. RCP UK 1979. Med. Assessor Meds. Control Agency; Hon. Sen. Regist. (Med.) UMDS Guy's & St. Thos. Hosp. Socs: Drug Informat. Assn.; Fac. Pharmaceut. Med. Prev: Clin. Asst..Med. Dir. Ciba-Geigy, UK.

CELINSKI, Michael 14 Quinn Way, Letchworth SG6 2TX — MB BS 1994 Lond.; BSc Lond. 1991. (King's Coll. Hosp. Lond.) SHO (Med.) Lister Hosp. Stevenage.

CEMBALA, Jan Antoni Wallace House Surgery, 5-11 St. Andrew Street, Hertford SG14 1HZ Tel: 01992 550541 — MB BS 1972 London; MRCS Eng. LRCP Lond. 1972 London.

CEMBROWICZ, Stefan Piotr Montpelier Health Centre, Bath Buildings, Bristol BS6 5PT Tel: 0117 942 6811 Fax: 0117 944 4182; 67 St. Michael's Hill, Bristol BS2 8DZ — MB ChB 1971 Bristol; MRCGP 1982. Teach. (Gen. Pract.) Bristol Univ.; GP Trainer; Clin. Asst. (A & E) Bristol. Roy. Infirm.

CEMLYN-JONES, Morys Wynne, TD (retired) 3 Rodney Place, Clifton, Bristol BS8 4HY — MB BS 1950 Lond.; MA Camb. 1940; MRCS Eng. LRCP Lond. 1950. Prev: Ho. Surg. Irradiat. Dept. W.m. Hosp.

CEMLYN-JONES, Patricia Mary (retired) 3 Rodney Place, Clifton, Bristol BS8 4HY — MB BS 1957 Lond. Prev: Ho. Surg. (Gyn.) Roy. Free Hosp.

CERIO, Rino Department of Dermatology, The Royal Hospitals Trust, The Royal London Hospital, Whitechapel, London E1 1BB Tel: 020 7377 7000 Fax: 020 7377 7383; 79 Court Lane, Dulwich Village, London SE21 7EF Tel: 020 8299 0360 — MB BS 1980 Lond.; BSc (1st cl. Hons.) Path. Lond. 1977; FRCP Lond. 1996; FRCP Ed. 1993; MRCP (UK) 1983; MRCS Eng. LRCP Lond. 1980; DRCPath 1993. (Guy's) Cons. Dermat., Clin. Dir. & Sen. Lect. Dermatopath. St. Bart. & Roy. Lond. Hosp. Med. Coll. Socs: Fell. Roy. Soc. Med.; Brit. Assn. Dermat.; (Treas.) Internat. Soc. Dermatopath. Prev: Sen. Regist. (Dermat. & Dermatopath.) St. John's Hosp. Lond.; Regist. (Gen. Med.) St. Thos. Hosp. Lond.; SHO (Thoracic Med.) Brompton Hosp. Lond.

CERULLO, Anthony Square Medical Practice, High Street, Godalming GU7 1AZ Tel: 01483 415141 Fax: 01483 414881 — State Exam Pisa 1990. (Univ. PISA Med. Sch.) Socs: Italitan Med. Soc. GB.

CERUNDOLO, Vincenzo 51 Copse Lane, Marston, Oxford OX3 0AT — State DMS 1984 Padua.

CERVANTES, Annabelle Jane St Johns Lane Health Centre, St. Johns Lane, Bristol BS3 5AS Tel: 0117 966 7681 Fax: 0117 977 9676 — MB BS 1985 Lond. Prev: Clin. Asst. & Research Regist. (Genitourin. Med.) Addenbrooke's Hosp. Camb.; Clin. Asst. (A & E) Addenbrooke's Hosp. Camb.; SHO (Geriat. Med.) W. Suff. Hosp. Bury St. Edmunds.

CERVENAK, Robert Francis Edward Whitburn Surgery, 3 Bryers Street, Whitburn, Sunderland SR6 7EE Tel: 0191 529 3039 Fax: 0191 529 5436; 15 Thornhill Terrace, Sunderland SR2 7JL Tel: 0191 565 8746 — MB BS 1983 Newc.; MRCGP 1988.

CERVETTO, Paul 38 Dawpool Drive, Bromborough, Wirral CH62 6DQ — MB BCh 1986 Wales.

CERVI, Paul Laurence Oliver 23 Holmwood Avenue, Shenfield, Brentwood CM15 8QS — MB BCh BAO 1984 Dub.; BA Biochem Dub. 1981; MRCPath 1993; MRCPI 1986. (Univ. Dub.) Cons. Haemat. Basildon & Thurrock Gen. Hosp. NHS Trust.

CERVILLA BALLESTEROS, Jorge Antonio Section of Epidemiology, Institute of Psychiatry, De Crespigny Park, London SE5 8AF Tel: 020 7919 3150 — LMS 1991 Granada; MRCPsych 1995. Research Fell. (Psychiat.) Sect. Epidemiol. & Gen. Pract. Inst. Psychiat. Lond. Socs: BMA; Inceptor Roy. Coll. Psychiat. Prev: Regist. Rotat. (Psychiat.) UCH Lond.

***CETTI, Edward James** 37 New St Hill, Bromley BR1 5AX Tel: 020 8857 2197 — MB BS 1998 Lond.; MB BS Lond 1998; MA CANTAB 1999.

CETTI, Mr Nicholas Edward Queen Elizabeth Hospital, Stadium, Woolwich, London SE18 4QH Tel: 020 8836 5472 Fax: 020 8836 5434 Email: www.qehospital.com; 37 New Street Hill, Bromley BR1 5AX — BM BCh Oxf. 1967; MA Oxf. 1967; FRCS Eng. 1974. (Oxf.) Cons. Urol. Qu. Eliz. Hosp. Woolwich Lond. Socs: Fell. Roy. Soc. Med. (Urol. Sect.); Brit. Assn. Urol. Surgs.; Liveryman of Soc. Apoth. Lond. and W. Kent Medico-Chirurgical Soc. Prev: Cons. Urol. RAMC; Sen. Regist. (Urol.) St. Peter's Hosps. Lond.; Regist. Birm. Accid. Hosp.

CEURSTEMONT, Maria Alice 76 Russell Drive, Wollaton, Nottingham NG8 2BE Tel: 0403 572245 — MB ChB 1998 Birm. SHO (A&E) New Cross Hosp., Wolverhampton.

CEZANNE, Helmut Hasso 1 Bellefield Avenue, Dundee DD1 4NG Tel: 01382 223490 Fax: 01382 800356 Email: hhc@drcezanne.com — State Exam Med 1986 Frankfurt; State Exam Med. Frankfurt 1986. (Frankfurt, Germany) Med. Dir. Indep. Med. Pract. Dundee; Med. Dir. Natural Health Prod. Dr. Cezanne Ltd. Dundee. Socs: Gesellschaft fur Phytotherapie, Germany, Mem.; Ordre des Medecines, France, Mem.; Nat. Ins. Of Med. Herbalists, Mem. Prev: SHO (ENT) Ninewells Hosp. & Med. Sch. Dundee; SHO (ENT) Glan Clwyd Hosp. Bodelwyddan; Hosp. Pract. Gen. Hosp. Draguignan, France.

CH'NG, Chin Lye Singleton Hospital, Swansea SA2 8QA — MB BCh BAO 1986 NUI; MRCPI 1992. (University College Galway Ireland) Specialist Regist. (Gastroenterol.) Carmarthen. Prev: Staff Grade Phys. (Gastroenterol.) Carmarthen.

CH'NG, Keng Thniah Anaesthetic Department, Pinderfield Hospital, Aberford Road, Wakefield WF1 4DG Tel: 01924 212077; 120 Thornes Moor Road, Wakefield WF2 8PX Tel: 01924 367855 — MB ChB 1985 Dundee; FFA RCSI 1994; DA (UK) 1989. (Dundee) Cons. Anaesth. Pinderfield & Pontefract Hosp. NHS Trust. Prev: Specialist Regist. (Anaesth.) Yorks. Region; Clin. Fell. (Cardiac Anaesth.) Leeds Gen. Infirm.; Regist. (Anaesth.) E. Surrey Hosp. & Warks. Train. Scheme.

CHABERT, Charles Curt 140 North Deeside Road, Milltimber AB13 0HL — MB ChB 1996 Aberd.

CHABUK, Mr Thamer Mahmoud 33 Osborne Gardens, Thornton Heath CR7 8PA Tel: 020 8771 9797 — MB ChB 1971 Baghdad; FRCS Ed. 1981.

CHACKO, Billy George 17 Cavesson Court, Cambridge CB4 3TB — MB BS 1988 Ibadan; MRCP (UK) 1994.

CHAD, Roy Kenneth Linden Centre, Woodlands Way, Broomsfield, Chelmsford CN1 5LF Tel: 01245 318844 — MB ChB 1974 Birm.; MRCPsych 1978. Cons. Psychiat. N. Essex Partnership, NHS Trust. Prev: Sen. Regist. Rotat. Roy. Free Hosp. Lond.

CHADA, Kanchan 43 Holly Drive, Waterlooville, Portsmouth — MB BCh BAO 1975 Belf.

CHADA, Naresh Kumar 1 Laburnam Way, Kings Meadow, Loughborough, Leicester LE11 2FB Tel: 01509 241371 Email: naresh1969@aol.com — MB ChB 1988 Manch.; MFPHM 1997. Cons. (Pub. Health Med.) S.ern Derbysh. Health Auth. Socs: BMA. Prev: Sen. Regist. (Pub. Health Med.) W. Midl.; SHO (Community Med.) Leicester; Ho. Surg. Leigh Infirm.

CHADA, Neta 18 Chasewood Gardens, Portadown, Craigavon BT63 5TZ — MB BCh BAO 1988 Belf.; MRCPsych 1994; DMH Belf. 1992.

CHADALAVADA, Uma Bala 3 Long Meadow, Westbury Park, Newcastle under Lyme, Newcastle ST5 4HY — MB BS 1976 Andhra.

CHADALAVADA, Venkata Subba Rao Leek Road Surgery, 1441 Leek Road, Abbey Hulton, Stoke-on-Trent ST2 8BY Tel: 01782 542266 Fax: 01782 544191; 3 Longmeadow, Westbury Park, Newcastle ST5 4HY Tel: 01782 619149 — MB BS 1972 Andhra; MS (Gen. Surg.) Andhra 1975, MB BS 1972; Dip. Urol. Lond 1986. GP Stoke-on-Trent; Clin. Asst. (Urol.) N. Staffs. Hosps. Socs: BMA & Internat. Incontinence Soc. Prev: Trainee GP Stoke-on-Trent.

***CHADDERTON, Kay Jayne** Worcester Royal Infirmary, Ronkswood, Worcester WR5 1HN Tel: 01905 763333; 59 Showell Green, The Shires, Droitwich WR9 8UE — BM 1996 Soton.

CHADDERTON, Stephen County Hospital, Lincoln LN2 5QY Tel: 01522 512512; 11 Albion Crescent, Lincoln LN1 1EB Tel: 01522 521680 — MB ChB 1967 Sheff.; Dip. GU Med. Soc. Apoth. Lond. 1993; DObst RCOG 1969. Assoc. Specialist (Geniotourin. Med.) Lincoln Co. Hosp. Socs: BMA; Soc. Study VD.; Assn. Genitourin. Med. Prev: GP Lincoln; Ho. Phys. & Ho. Surg. Roy. Hosp. Sheff.

CHADDOCK, Mark Edward Flat 5, 189 Dalkeith Road, Edinburgh EH16 5DS Tel: 0131 620 0988 Email: mark@echaddock.freeserve.co.uk — MB ChB 1994 Ed. Lats Regist. (Anaes) Edin. Prev: SHO (Anaesth.) Edin; SHO (Cardiothoracic) Edin.; SHO (A & E) St. John's Hosp. Livingston.

CHADERTON, Nicola Helen Corkallian, 10 Cold Harbour Close, Wickham, Fareham PO17 5PT — MB BS 1982 Newc.; FCAnaesth. 1989; DA (UK) 1987. (Newc. u. Tyne) Sen. Regist. (Anaesth.) Portsmouth Hosps.

CHADFIELD, Bruce Andrew Allwyn, Home Farm, Elton, Stockton-on-Tees TS21 1AG — BM BS 1984 Nottm.

CHADHA, Ashish 61 Melville Avenue, South Croydon CR2 7HZ Tel: 020 8667 0850 — MB ChB 1990 Manch.; MRCGP 1994; DFFP 1994; DPD Cardiff 1997. (Manch.) Clin. Asst. (Dermatol.). Socs: BMA.

CHADHA, Mr Avi-Nash Chander Binton Barn, Botany Hill, Sands, Farnham GU10 1LZ Tel: 0125 182310 — MB BS 1951 Lucknow; FRCS Eng. 1961. (King Geo. Med. Coll. Lucknow) Prev: Regist. Surg. Bury Gen. Hosp., Dreadnought Seamen's Hosp. Greenwich & Farnham Hosp. Gp.; Sen. Lect. & Asst. Prof. (Gen. Surg.) Postgrad. Med. Inst.

CHADHA, Dinesh Kumar Doncaster Royal Infirmary, Armthorpe Road, Doncaster DN2 5LT Tel: 01302 366666; 50 Hatchell Wood View, Bessacarr, Doncaster DN4 6UY Tel: 01302 537375 Email: chadhauk@aol.com — MB BS 1978 Delhi; MD Delhi 1981; MRCP (UK) 1986. (Maulana Azad Med. Coll., Delhi) Cons. Gen. Phys. (Elderly Care) Doncaster Roy. Infirm. & Tickhill Rd. Hosp. Doncaster; Tutor RCP. Socs: Assoc. Mem. Brit. Med. Acupunc. Soc.

CHADHA, Jagdish Chander Billinge Hospital, Billinge, Wigan WN5 7ET Tel: 01942 44000; 27 Spring Road, Orrell, Wigan WN5 8QB Tel: 01942 516756 — MB BS 1969 India; Dip. Ven. Liverp. 1978; Cert. Family Plann. JCC 1978; DTM & H Liverp. 1977.

CHADHA, Mrudula Subhash 4 Kirkham Street, London SE18 2JU Tel: 020 8854 3206 — MB BS 1966 Bombay; DO Eng. 1970.

CHADHA, Pushpinder Westfield Health Centre, Westfield Northway, Westfield, Sheffield S20 8NZ Tel: 0114 248 2498; 1 Stumperlowe Hall Chase, Fulwood, Sheffield S10 3QY — MB BS 1969 Jammu & Kashmir; DObst RCOG 1975. (Srinagar)

CHADHA, Rajinder Kumar Wilderness Road Surgery, 1 Wilderness Road, Earley, Reading RG6 7RU Tel: 0118 926 1613 Fax: 0118 926 3300 — MB BS 1970 Calcutta.

CHADHA, Sudata 7 Richmond Way, London W12 8LQ — MB BS 1997 Lond.

CHADHA, Yogesh Chandra Flat 5, Mannofield Court, 456A Great Western Road, Aberdeen AB10 6NP Tel: 01224 311992 — MB BS 1977 Poona.

CHADWICK, Alfred Edward Paul Slateford Road Surgery, 79 Slateford Road, Edinburgh EH11 1QW Tel: 0131 313 2211 — MB ChB 1980 Dundee; MB ChB Dundee 1980.; DRCOG 1982.

CHADWICK, Mr Alfred James (retired) 120 High Street, Uppermill, Saddleworth, Oldham OL3 6BT Tel: 01457 877543 — MB ChB Manch. 1957; BSc (Hons.) Manch. 1954; FRCS Ed. 1962; FRCOphth 1993; DO Eng. 1960. Prev: Cons. Ophth. Surg. Coventry & Rugby HAs.

CHADWICK, Barbara Catherine (retired) 120 High Street, Uppermill, Saddleworth, Oldham OL3 6BT Tel: 01457 877543 — MB ChB 1961 Manch.; DO Eng. 1963. Prev: Assoc. Specialist (Ophth.) S. Warks. Hosp. Gp.

CHADWICK, Benjamin David 63 Harrison Road, Southampton SO17 3TL — BM 1998 Soton.

CHADWICK, Carolyn 15 Broadway, Greasby, Wirral CH49 2NG — MB ChB 1998 Sheff.; MB ChB Sheff 1998.

CHADWICK, Cathryn Ann Leicester Royal Infirmary, Leicester LE1 5WP; 6 Stoughton Avenue, Stoneygate, Leicester LE2 2DR — MB BS 1987 Lond.; MRCP (UK) 1993; DCH RCP Lond. 1993; DRCOG 1990. Regist. (Paediat.) Leicester Roy. Infirm. Prev: SHO (Paediat.) Leicester Roy. Infirm.; Trainee GP Leicester; SHO (Paediat.) Lincoln Co. Hosp.

CHADWICK, Mr Christopher John Royal Halifax Infirmary, Free School Lane, Halifax HX1 2YP Tel: 01422 357222 Fax: 01422 342581; Westfield Farm, Warley, Halifax HX2 6DA Tel: 01422 883144 — MB ChB 1970 Liverp.; FRCS Ed. 1978. p/t Cons. Orthop. Surg., Roy. Halifax Infirm. Socs: Brit. Orth. Assn.; Brit. Elbow & Shoulder Soc.

CHADWICK, Mr David John Department of Urology, South Cleveland Hospital, Marton Road, Middlesbrough TS4 3BW Tel: 01642 854712 Fax: 01642 854708 — MB BS 1983 Newc.; MD Bristol 1994; FRCS (Urol.) 1994; FRCS Eng. 1988. (Newc. u. Tyne) Cons. (Urol.) S. Tees Acute Hosps. NHS Trust. Socs: Brit. Assn. Urol. Surgs.; Brit. Prostate Gp.; Brit. Assn. of Urological Surg. Sec. of Oncol. Prev: Sen. Regist. (Urol.) Yorks.; Regist. (Urol.) Norwich; Research Fell. (Urol.) S.mead Hosp. Bristol.

CHADWICK, Mr David Ralph 8 Forest Close, Newcastle-upon-Lyme, Newcastle ST5 3BG — BM BCh 1987 Oxf.; FRCS Ed. 1992.

CHADWICK, Professor David William Department of Neurological science, Walton Centre for Neurology-Neurosurgery., Lower Lane., Liverpool L9 7LJ — DM Oxf. 1978, MA, BM BCh 1971; FRCP Lond. 1986; MRCP (UK) 1974. Prof. Neurol. Univ. Liverp. Prev: Cons. Neurol. Walton Hosp. Liverp.; 1st Asst. (Neurol.) Roy. Vict. Infirm. Newc.; Hon. Lect. (Neurol.) Univ. Dept. Neurol., Inst. Psychiat. & King's Coll. Hosp. Med. Sch.

CHADWICK, Eliot Gordon Villas, 57 Infirmary Road, Blackburn BB2 3LP — MB ChB 1995 Manch.

CHADWICK, Elizabeth Joyce 9 Alder Lane, Balsall Common, Coventry CV7 7DZ — MB 1971 Camb.; MA Camb. 1969, MB 1971, BChir 1970; DObst RCOG 1973.

CHADWICK, Enda Thomas Willington Medical Group, Chapel Street, Willington, Crook DL15 0EQ Tel: 01388 646000 Fax: 01388 646023; Ivy House, 14 School St, Witton-le-Wear, Bishop Auckland DL14 0AS Tel: 01388 488155 Fax: 01388 488156 — MB BCh BAO 1983 NUI; MRCGP 1990; DRCOG 1989. (Univ. Coll. Cork)

CHADWICK, Fiona Dawne PO Box 809, 1 Market Street, Newcastle, NSW, 2300, Newcastle, Australia Tel: 020 8878 9078 — MB BS 1992 Lond.; FRCA 1999 Lond.; FRCA 1999. (Guy's Hosp. (UMDS) Lond.) Overseas Fell., Anaesthetics, John Hunter Hosp., Newc., NSW, Australia. Socs: RCA (Fell.); Obstetric Anaesth.s Assn.; Assn. Anaesth. Prev: Specialist Regist. (Anaesth.) St. Thomas' Hosp.Lond.; Specialist Regist. (Anaesth.) Guys Hosp., Lond.; Specialist Regist. (Anaesth.) Lewisham Hosp., Lond.

CHADWICK, Harold Alexander Talbot Medical Centre, 63 Kinson Road, Bournemouth BH10 4BX Tel: 01202 523059 Fax: 01202 533239; 23 Lonsdale Road, Bournemouth BH3 7LY — MB BChir 1971 Camb.; MA, MB Camb. 1971, BChir 1970; MRCGP 1977; DObst RCOG 1972. (Camb. & Oxf.)

CHADWICK, Harold Nordin Peppard Road Surgery, 45 Peppard Road, Caversham, Reading RG4 8NR — MB BS 1977 Lond.; BA Open 1985.

CHADWICK, Ian George Westmorland General Hospital, Burton Road, Kendal LA9 7RG — MB ChB 1987 Ed.; MRCP (UK) 1990; MD Ed. 1997. Cons. (Phys.) (Med. for Elderly) W.morland Gen. Hosp. Kendal. Prev: Lect. (Clin. Pharmacol. & Therap.) Roy. Hallamsh. Hosp. Sheff.; Sen. Regist. Geriat./ Gen. Med. N.ern Gen. Hosp., Sheff.

CHADWICK, Innes Simon Department of Anaesthetics, North Manchester General Hospital, Crumpsall, Manchester M8 5RB — MB ChB 1983 Manch.; FFA RCS Eng. 1988; DCH RCP Lond. 1987;

DA (UK) 1986. Cons. Anaesth. N. Manch. Gen. Hosp. Socs: BMA; Manch. Med. Soc. & Obst. Anaesth. Assn.; Vasc. Anaesth. Soc. Prev: Sen. Regist. Rotat. (Anaesth.).Manch. Rotat.; Regist. (Anaesth.) Manch. Roy. Infirm.

CHADWICK, Janet Madeleine Peppard Road Surgery, 45 Peppard Road, Caversham, Reading RG4 8NR — MB ChB 1976 Aberd. GP.

CHADWICK, Joanne Margaret Marches Medical Practice, Buckley Surgery, 46 Mill Lane, Buckley CH7 3HB — MB ChB 1991 Manch.; MRCGP 1995.

CHADWICK, John David Henry Botley Medical Centre, Elms Road, Botley, Oxford OX2 9JS Tel: 01865 248719 Fax: 01865 728116; Springfield, Foxcombe Road, Boars Hill, Oxford OX1 5DQ Tel: 01865 735151 — BM BCh 1978 Oxf.; MA Oxf. 1978; DRCOG 1981. (Oxford) Clin. Asst. Oxf. Blood Transfus. Serv.

CHADWICK, Julian Martin Fernlea Surgery, 114 High Road, London N15 6JR Tel: 020 8809 6445 Fax: 020 8800 4224; The South House, 2 Great North Road, Whetstone, Enfield EN5 1JS Tel: 020 8446 1066 Email: jchad@globalnet.co.uk — BM 1989 Soton. GP; PCG Chairm. Prev: SHO (O & G) Dorset Co. Hosp.; SHO (Geriat.) Poole Gen. Hosp.; SHO (Psychiat.) St. Ann's Hosp. Bournemouth.

CHADWICK, Kingsley Cameron Coach House, Manor Farm Barns, Cot Lane, Chidham, Chichester PO18 8SU Tel: 01243 573673 Fax: 01243 574305 Email: hf87@pipex.dial.com — BM BCh 1979 Oxf.; MRCGP 1984; DRCOG 1983; DCH RCP Lond. 1983.

CHADWICK, Laurence John 115 Moss Delph Lane, Ormskirk L39 5BH Tel: 01695 423554 — MB ChB 1952 Manch.; LLB 1941. (Manch.) Socs: Fell. Manch. Med. Soc. Prev: Ho. Phys. & Ho. Surg. (Orthop.) Manch. Roy. Infirm.; Research Asst. Dept. Rheum. Research, Univ. Manch.; Trainer (Gen. Pract.) Lancs.

CHADWICK, Miss Louise 1 Haddington Hill, Lisburn BT28 3AU Email: lchadw9070@aol.com — BM BCh 1986 Oxf.; BA (Hons.) Physiol. Sci. Oxf. 1983; FRCS Ed. 1991. (#Oxford) Specialist Regist. Rehabil. Med. Musgrave Pk. Hosp. Belf. Prev: Sen.Regist.Neurosurg.Roy.Victora.Hosp.Belf.

CHADWICK, Mandy 9 Hamlet Road, Wallasey CH45 6UT — MB BS 1998 Lond.; MB BS Lond 1998.

CHADWICK, Mark Highfield Farm Cottage, Upper Swanmore, Southampton SO32 2QQ; Highfield Farm Cottage, Upper Swanmore, Southampton SO32 2QQ — MB ChB 1998 Leeds.

CHADWICK, Mary Patricia (retired) 3 Greenwood, Culmore, Londonderry BT48 8NP Tel: 02871 352568 — LRCPI & LM, LRSCI & LM 1947; LRCPI & LM, LRCSI & LM 1947. Prev: Clin. Med. Off. Lond.derry, Limavady & Strabane Health Dist.

CHADWICK, Michael Anthony 15 Broadway, Greasby, Wirral CH49 2NG Tel: 0151 678 0615 — MB ChB 1996 Bristol. SHO (Gen. Vasc. Surg.) Aintree Hosps. NHS Trust Fazakerley Hosp. Liverp. Prev: SHO (A & E) Fazakerley; Ho. Off. (Gen. Med.) Bristol Roy. Infirm.; Ho. Off. (Gen. Surg.) Bristol Roy. Infirm.

CHADWICK, Michael Sinclair Ashenfell Surgery, Church Lane, Baslow, Bakewell DE45 1SP Tel: 01246 582216 Fax: 01246 583867 — MB BS 1968 Lond.

CHADWICK, Paul Robert Microbiology Department, Salford Royal Hospitals NHS trust, Hope Hospital, Salford M6 8HD — MB ChB 1987 Sheff.; BMedSci (Hons. Med. Microbiol.) Sheff. 1986, MD 1997; MRCP (UK) 1991; MRCPath 1996. (Sheff.) Cons. Microbiol. Salford Roy. Hosp. NHS Trust. Socs: Assn. Clin. Path.; Brit. Soc. Antimicrob. Chemother.; Hosp. Infec. Soc. Prev: Sen. Regist. Rotat. (Med. Microbiol.) NW Region (Manch.); Regist. (Med. Microbiol.) NW RHA; SHO (Infec. Dis. & Gen. Med.) N. Manch. Gen. Hosp.

CHADWICK, Mr Peter Charles Burnage Primary Care Resource Centre, 347 Burnage Lane, Manchester M19 1EW Tel: 0161 432 1404 Fax: 0161 442 7900; 62 Altrincham Road, Gatley, Cheadle SK8 4DP Tel: 0161 428 1004 — MB ChB 1974 Sheff.; FRCS Eng. 1980. GP Cheadle; Clin. Asst. (Endoscopy) Tameside Acute Trust.

CHADWICK, Richard Gabriel Torbay Hospital, Lawes Bridge, Torquay TQ2 7AA Tel: 01803 614567 Fax: 01803 655577 — BM BCh Oxf. 1969; DM Oxf. 1983, MA 1969; BA (Hons.) Physiol. Oxf. 1966; MRCP (UK) 1974; FRCP 1998. Cons. Phys. S. Devon Healthcare Trust. Prev: Sen. Regist. (Gen. Med., Gastroenterol. & Geriat.) Wessex RHA; Research Fell. & Hon. Lect. (Med.) Roy. Free Hosp. Lond.

CHADWICK, Rosemary Margaret 16 Haines Hill, Taunton TA1 4HW — MB ChB 1978 Sheff.; MRCGP 1984.

CHADWICK, Sharon Lorna Hemel Hempstead Hospital, West Herts NHS Trust, Hillfield Road, Hemel Hempstead HP2 4AD — MB ChB 1993 Birm.; BPharm. Nottm. 1985; MRCP (UK) 1996. p/t Specialist Regist. (Respirat. Med.) Hemel Hempstead Gen. Hosp. Socs: Brit. Thor. Soc. Prev: Research Fell. & Hon. Regist. (Respirat. Med.) Roy. Brompton Hosp. Lond.; SHO (HIV & Gen. Med.) Chelsea & W.m. Hosp. Lond.; SHO (Endocrinol. & c/o Elderly) Hammersmith Hosp. Lond.

CHADWICK, Stephanie Anne Montpelier Health Centre, Bath Buildings, Bristol BS6 5PT Tel: 0117 942 6811; 9 Rayleigh Road, Bristol BS9 2AU — MB BS 1983 Lond.; MRCGP 1989; DRCOG 1988; DCH RCP Lond. 1985.

CHADWICK, Mr Stephen John Dooley Northwick Park and St Marks NHS Trust, Watford Road, Harrow HA1 3; Woodcock Hill House, Woodcock Hill, Rickmansworth WD3 1PX — MB BS 1975 Lond.; MS Lond. 1986, MB BS 1975; FRCS Eng. 1980. Cons. Gen. & Vasc. Surg. N.wick Pk. Hosp. Harrow; Cons. Gen. & Minimally Invasive (Gastro Intestinal) Surg. & Dir. of Med. Educat. Socs: Surg. Research Soc.; Brit. Soc. Gastroenterol.; Eur. Assn. Endoscopic Surg. Prev: Sen. Regist. (Surg.) King Edwd. VII Hosp. Durban, S. Afr.; Sen. Regist. St. Mary's Hosp. & N.wick Pk. Hosps. Lond.

CHADWICK, Stephen Paul Windhill Green Medical centre, 2 Thackley Old Road, Windhill, Shipley BD18 1QB Tel: 01274 584223 — MB ChB 1991 Leeds; DRCOG 1994; MRCGP 1996. GP Specialist in Dermat., N. Bradford PCT. Prev: GP Regist. Leeds W. VTS.; Trainee GP/SHO (Ophth.) Leeds Gen. Infirm.; SHO (Med. for Elderly, O & G & Paediat.) Leeds Gen. Infirm.

CHADWICK, Terence Stanley 61 Lorne Road, Wealdstone, Harrow HA3 7NJ — MB ChB 1972 Bristol; MB ChB (Hons.) Bristol 1975; BSc (Hons.) (Microbiol.) Bristol 1972; MRCP (UK) 1977. (Bristol) Regist. (Endocrinol.) Clin. Research Centre & N.wick Pk. Hosp.; Harrow. Prev: Research Fell. Univ. Dept. Med. Bristol.

CHADWICK, Theodore Herzl (retired) 7 Elm Road, Didsbury, Manchester M20 6XB — M.B., Ch.B. Manch. 1929; F.F.A. R.C.S. Eng. 1953; D.A. Eng. 1935. Prev: Cons. (Anaesth.) N. Manch. Gp.

CHADWICK, Victoria Louise City Hospital, Dualey Road, Birmingham B18 7QH Tel: 0121 554 3801 ext. 5600; Flat 5, 58 Salisbury Road, Moseley, Birmingham B13 8JT Tel: 0121 449 8187 Email: vchadwick@compuserve.com — MB ChB 1993 Otago; DRCOG; Dpath. SHO Anaesth.

CHADWICK, William Jonathan Whitby Group Practice, Spring Vale Medical Centre, Whitby YO21 1SD; Maple Farm, Raw, Whitby YO22 4PP — MB ChB 1976 Leeds; MRCGP 2000.

CHAFER, Andrew Thomas Herbert Davenport House Surgery, Bowers Way, Harpenden AL5 4HX Tel: 01582 767821 Fax: 01582 769285; 251 Luton Road, Harpenden AL5 3DE — MB BS 1980 Lond.; MRCP (UK) 1984; MRCGP 1985; DCH RCP Lond. 1983; DRCOG 1985. Hosp. Pract. (Endoscopist) Luton & Dunstable Hosp.

CHAFFE, Ann Geraldine Mary Department of Anaesthetics, Doncaster Royal Infirmary, Armthorpe Road, Doncaster DN2 5 Tel: 01302 366666; 28 Saffron Crescent, Tickhill, Doncaster DN11 9RU — BM BS 1980 Nottm.; FFA RCS Eng. 1986. Cons. Anaesth. Doncaster Roy. Infirm.

CHAFFEY, Robert Frederick Health Centre, Priory Road, Alcester B49 5DZ Tel: 01789 763060 Fax: 01789 766545; 23 Wood Lane, Astwood Bank, Redditch B96 6NN — MB ChB 1968 Birm.; MRCGP 1978; DObst RCOG 1970. (Birm.) Prev: Ho. Surg. Selly Oak Hosp. Birm.; Ho. Phys. Ronkswood Hosp. Worcester; Ho. Off. (O & G) Dudley Rd. Hosp. Birm.

CHAGGAR, Harjinder Singh 9 Hardwyn Close, Blackberry Lea, Binley, Coventry CV3 2XL Tel: 0973 631735 Email: dochsc@hotmail.com — MB ChB 1993 Leic. A & E Med. Rotat.

CHAGGAR, Jagdish Singh Beacon Medical Practice, Churchill Avenue, Skegness PE24 2AN Tel: 01754 897000 Fax: 01754 761024 — MB ChB Sheff. 1985; MBA Sheff. 1993; BSc Sheff. 1981; MRCS Eng. LRCP Lond. 1986; MRCGP 1989; DRCOG 1988; DCH RCP Lond. 1987. Prev: Trainee GP Rotherham VTS.

CHAGGAR, Jagtar Singh Church View Surgery, 239 Halesowen Road, Cradley Heath, Cradley Heath B64 6JE Tel: 01384 66929 — MB ChB 1975 Birm.

CHAHAL, Harminder Singh 22 Avondale Crescent, Ilford IG4 5JB — MB ChB 1998 Dund.; MB ChB Dund 1998.

CHAHAL, Jagjit Kaur The Surgery, 73 Upper Wickham Lane, Welling DA16 3AF Tel: 020 8854 1910 Fax: 020 8317 3711; 1 Viewfield Road, Bexley DA5 3EE — MB BS 1960 Panjab; MB BS Panjab (India) 1960.
CHAHAL, Maninder Singh 97 Crathorne Avenue, Wolverhampton WV10 6BU — MB ChB 1998 Liverp.; MB ChB Liverp 1998.
CHAHAL, Pritpal Singh Dale Surgery, 67 Sneinton Dale, Nottingham NG2 4LG Tel: 0115 911 0256 Fax: 0115 911 0256; The Dale Surgery, 67 Sneinton Dale, Nottingham NG2 4LG — MB BS 1976 Lond.; BSc Lond. 1973, MD 1987; MRCGP 1986; MRCP (UK) 1979; FRCGP 1997. (St. Mary's) GP Princip. Nott.; SHO (Obst.) N.wick Pk. Hosp. Harrow.; Hosp. Practitioner (Diabetes); Undergrad. Tutor Nottm. Univ.; Course Organiser Nottm. VTS. Socs: Med. Chi. Soc. Nottm. Prev: Research Fell. Roy. Postgrad. Med. Sch. Lond.; Regist. (Gen. Med. & Endocrinol.) Hammersmith Hosp. Lond.; Rotat. SHO (Gen. Med.) Leic. & Groby Rd. Hosps.
CHAHAL, Rubita Chase Farm Hospitals NHS Trust, Accident & Emergency Department, 127 The Ridgeway, Enfield EN2 8JL; 38 Whitby Road, Ruislip HA4 9DP — MB BS 1986 Guru Nanak Dev India; LMSSA 1991; T(GP) 1994; DA (UK) 1991.
CHAHAL, Sarabjit Singh 5 The Avenue, Nunthorpe, Middlesbrough TS7 0AA — MB BS 1994 Newc.
CHAI, Mr David Tuck Chuen 19 Belle Meade Close, Woodgate, Chichester PO20 6YD — MB BS 1981 Lond.; FRCS Ed. 1986.
CHAIKIN, Michael Jonathan 8 Tidy Street, Brighton BN1 4EL — MB BS 1981 Lond.; BA (Hons.) CNAA 1990. (Roy. Free)
CHAIT, Ian Brian The Harrow Health Care Centre, 84-88 Pinner Road, Harrow HA1 4LF Tel: 020 8861 1221 Fax: 020 8427 4915; Fallow Cottage, 16 The Grove, Radlett WD7 7NF Tel: 01923 857090 Fax: 01923 858473 Email: millbrook@claranet.co.uk — MB ChB 1969 Birm.; MRCP (UK) 1975; MRCGP 1978; DObst RCOG 1971; 1995 Dip. Med.AC. (Birm.) Private GP, Harrow Health centre; Lect. (Gen. Pract.) Roy. Free Hosp. Med. Sch.; Hosp. Pract. (Radiother.) Barnet Gen. Hosp. Socs: Soc. Occupat. Med.; Brit. Med. Acupunct. Soc. Prev: Regist. (Med.) Harefield Hosp.; Ho. Off. (O & G) Centr. Middlx. Hosp. Lond.
CHAJED, Gautam Kingswood Medical Centre, Clayhill Road, Basildon SS16 5AD Tel: 01268 533727/280514 Fax: 01268 520513 — MB BS 1980 Karnatak; MRCP (UK) 1985; MRCPI 1984; MRCS Eng. LRCP Lond. 1984. Hosp. Pract. (Rheum.) Basildon Hosp. Essex.
CHAK, Melanie Hun Gee 1 Dorset Mews, London N3 2BN — MB BS 1997 Lond.
CHAKMA, Indu B The Surgery, 2e Canterbury Road, Handsworth, Birmingham B20 3AA Tel: 0121 356 4444 — MRCP Eng. LRCP Lond. 1974 London; MB BS 1963 Dacca; MB BS 1963 Dacca.
CHAKRABARTI, Mr Anil Department of Orthopaedics., Queen Elizabeth Hospital, Gayton Road, King's Lynn PE30 4ET Tel: 01553 613613 Fax: 01553 613613 Email: anil.chakrabarti.sec@klshosp.anglox.nhs .uk; Mill House, Newton Road, Castle Acre, King's Lynn PE32 2AZ Fax: 01760 755139 — MB BS 1988 Lond.; FRCS Eng. 1992; FRCS (Orth.) 1997. (Char. Cross & Westm. Hosp. Lond.) Cons. Orthopaedic Surg.; Orthop. Cons. Qu. Eliz. Hosp., King's Lynn. Socs: BOTA; B.O.A. Prev: Regist. Rotat. (Orthop.) St. Bart. Hosp. Lond.; SHO Rotat. (Gen. Surg.) Broomfield Hosp. Chelmsford; Percivall Pott Higher Surgic. TTrain. Rotat. (Ortho).
CHAKRABARTI, Arun Kumar The Dowlais Medical Practice, Ivor Street, Dowlais, Merthyr Tydfil CF48 3LU Tel: 01685 721400 Fax: 01685 375287 — MB BS 1967 Calcutta; FRCOG 1991, M 1967.
CHAKRABARTI, Asimes Donald Wilde Medical Centre, 283 Rochdale Road, Oldham OL1 2HG Tel: 0161 652 3184 Fax: 0161 620 2101 — MB BS 1959 Calcutta. (R.G.Kar Med. Coll.) Prev: SHO Gen. Surg. Coleraine Hosp.; Regist. Cas. Gen. Hosp Nottm.; Regist. Neuro-Surg. Crumpsall Hosp. Manch.
CHAKRABARTI, Bhaskar Walton Hall Avenue Medical Centre, 12 Walton Hall Avenue, Liverpool L4 6UF Tel: 0151 524 0267 Fax: 0151 525 9989 — MB BS 1969 Calcutta.
CHAKRABARTI, Mr Bidhan Kumar 62 Corner Fielde, London SW2 4TJ — MB BS 1958 Calcutta; FRCS Ed. 1969; DA Eng. 1962. (R.G. Kar Med. Coll.) Cons. A & E Dept. Selly Oak Hosp. Birm. Prev: Asst. Orthop. Surg. Selly Oak Hosp. Birm.; Regist. (Anaesth.) Hosp. of St. Cross Rugby; Regist. (Orthop.) Hull Roy. Infirm.
CHAKRABARTI, Biswajit 5 Sandpiper Close, Rochdale OL11 5QD — MB BS 1998 Lond.; MB BS Lond 1998.
CHAKRABARTI, Bulbul 91 Warrenwood Road, Rochester ME1 2XA — MB BS 1963 Calcutta; FRCOG 1983; MRCOG 1970.
CHAKRABARTI, Gunindra Nath Ridgewood Centre, Old Bisley Road, Frimley, Camberley GU16 9QE Tel: 01276 692919 Fax: 01276 605366; 55 Rectory Road, Farnborough GU14 7BT Tel: 01252 543776 Fax: 01252 543776 — MB BS Calcutta 1965; MRCPsych 1973; T(Psych) 1991; DPM Eng. 1972. (Calcutta Med. Coll) Cons. Psychiat. Surrey Hants. Border NHS Trust Ridgewood Centre Camberley. Prev: Cons. Psychiat. Roy. Albert Hosp. Lancaster; Cons. Psychiat. Telco Gen. Hosp. Jamshedpur, India.
CHAKRABARTI, Hashnuhanna Soma 17 Blackwood Avenue, Newton Mearns, Glasgow G77 5JY — MB ChB 1993 Glas.
CHAKRABARTI, Ilga Ursula Queen Elizabeth hospital, Gayton Road, King's Lynn PE30 4ET Tel: 01553 613613 — MB BS 1988 Lond.; MRCGP 1992; DRCOG 1992. (Char. Cross & Westm. Med. Sch.) p/t Clin. Asst., Rheum., Qu. Eliz. Hosp. King's Lynn, Norf. Prev: Trainee GP E. Lond. VTS; GP Princip., Ilford, Essex.
CHAKRABARTI, Mr Indranil Rotherham District General Hospital, Moorgate Road, Rotherham S60 2UD Tel: 01709 304579 Fax: 01709 824220 Email: indrail.chakabarti@fghj -tr trent.nhs.uk — BM BS 1984 Nottm.; BMedSci (Hons.) 1982; FRCS Ed. 1990, FRCS (Orth.) 1995. (Nottm.) Cons. (Orthop. Surg.) Rotherham Gen. Hosp. Socs: Fell. BOA; Brit. Soc. Surg. Hand (Mem.); BMA. Prev: Sen. Regist. (Orthop.) N.. RHA.
CHAKRABARTI, Nandita 106 Sheepcot Lane, Watford WD25 0EB Tel: 0192 73 72258 — MB BS 1964 Calcutta; DA Eng. 1973; DObst RCOG 1969. (Calcutta)
CHAKRABARTI, Pranab Kumar Chase Cross Medical Centre, 13-15 Chase Cross Road, Collier Row, Romford RM5 3PJ Tel: 01708 749918 Fax: 01708 742692; 78 Kingshill Avenue, Gidea Park, Romford RM5 2SB Tel: 01708 756297 — MB BS 1965 Calcutta; MFFP 1996; MRCOG 1974. (Nat. Med. Coll. Calcutta) Prev: Regist. (O & G) Wakefield Gp. Hosps.; Ho. Off. Hull Roy. Infirm.
CHAKRABARTI, Satya Ranjan (Calcutta Univ. 1969) GP, Blantyre, Glas.
CHAKRABARTI, Udayan 66 Boundary Road, London SW19 2AN — MB BS 1992 Lond.
CHAKRABARTY, Mr Bijoy Kumar (retired) Disablement Services Centre, Harold Wood Hospital, Gubbins Lane, Harold Wood, Romford RM3 0AR Tel: 01708 374121 Fax: 01708 377946 — MB BS Calcutta 1956; FRCS Eng. 1969; Dip. Rehabil. Med. RCP Lond. 1991. Sen. Lect. & Hon. Cons. St. Bart. Hosp. Lond. Prev: Cons. Rehabil. Med. N. Thames E. Region.
CHAKRABARTY, Mr Kaushik Hiraballove 17 Fownhope Avenue, Sale M33 4RE — MB ChB 1987 Manch.; FRCS Ed. 1992.
CHAKRABARTY, Sisiresh 55 Reachview Close, London NW1 0TY — MB BS 1984 Ranchi; PhD Lond. 1990; MB BS Ranchi, India 1984; MSc Cardiovasc. Studies Leeds 1986.
CHAKRABORTI, Alaka London Road Surgery, 1149 London Road, Alvaston, Derby DE24 8QF Tel: 01332 571344 Fax: 01332 757243; Strathmore, 15 Scarsdale Avenue, Littleover, Derby DE23 6ER Tel: 01332 293980 Fax: 01332 757243 — MB BS 1966 Calcutta; DObst RCOG 1969. (Nilratan Sircar) GP; Hosp. Pract. (Genitourin. Med.) Derbysh. Roy. Infirm. Socs: Derby Med. Soc.; Soc. Study VD; Obst. Gp.S. Derbys. Prev: Regist. (Obst.) Marston Green Matern. Hosp. Birm.; SHO (Gen. Surg.) Pontefract Gen. Hosp.; SHO (O & G) St. Mary's Hosp. Leeds.
CHAKRABORTI, Debabrata, MBE (retired) Park View Resource Centre, Birch Tree Close, London Road, King's Lynn PE30 5QD Tel: 01553 613613 Fax: 01553 766742 — MB BS 1962 Calcutta; FRCPsych 1992, M 1975; DPM Eng. 1974; DPM Calcutta 1965. Cons. Psychiat. (Ment. Handicap.) Pk.view Resource Centre; Regional Tutor (Psychiat. of Ment. Handicap) King's Lynn.
CHAKRABORTI, Prasanta Kumar London Road Surgery, 1149 London Road, Alvaston, Derby DE24 8QF Tel: 01332 571344 Fax: 01332 757243; Strathmore, 15 Scarsdale Avenue, Littleover, Derby DE23 6ER Tel: 01332 293980 Fax: 01332 757243 — MB BS 1965 Calcutta; Dip. Pract. Dermat. Cardiff 1994. (Nilratan Sircar) GP; Clin. Asst. (Dermat.) Derby Roy. Infirm.; Mem. Primary Care Gp. for Diabetes. Socs: Derby Med. Soc.; BMA; Derbysh. Local Med. Comm. Prev: Regist. (Med.) Hope Hosp. Salford; SHO (O & G) Marston Green Matern. Hosp. Birm.; SHO (Infect. Dis.) Seacroft Hosp. Leeds.
CHAKRABORTI, Saptarshi 4 Binham Road, South Wootton, King's Lynn PE30 3TB — MB BS 1991 Lond.

CHAKRABORTY, Aabir 38 Halstead Gardens, London N21 3DX — MB BS 1997 Lond.

CHAKRABORTY, Mr Ahindra Nath (retired) Lamorna, Old Carnon Hill, Carnon Downs, Truro TR3 6LE Tel: 01872 863261 — MB BS 1960 Calcutta; FRCS Ed. 1966; DLO Eng. 1963. Prev: Cons. Surg. (ENT) Cornw. & I. of Scilly AHA.

CHAKRABORTY, Anjan House 27A, Doctor's Residence, Hilton Road, Hartshill, Stoke-on-Trent ST4 7SE — MB ChB 1992 Birm.

CHAKRABORTY, Chanchal Clare House Surgery, Clare House, The Quadrant, Manor Park Crescent, Edgware HA8 7LU Tel: 020 8952 0004 — MB BS 1981 Lond.; Cert. Family Plann. JCC 1988; Cert. Prescribed Equiv. Exp. JCPTGP 1987; DFFP 1998. (Guy's Hospital) NHS GP Princip. Socs: Small Pract.s Assn. Prev: SHO (O & G) Bedford Gen. Hosp.; SHO (Ophth.) Ipswich Hosp.; SHO (Paediat.) Good Hope Hosp.

CHAKRABORTY, Souvik Kumar 78 Crab Lane, Trinity Fields, Stafford ST16 1SQ — MB ChB 1995 Manch.

CHAKRABORTY, Sucharu Kumar Santi, Wentedge Road, Kirk Smeaton, Pontefract WF8 3JS — MB BS 1955 Calcutta; FFA RCS Eng. 1969.

CHAKRABORTY, Sukumar (retired) High Trees, 124 Walsall Road, Perry Barr, Birmingham B42 1SG Tel: 0121 356 6135 — MB BS 1951 Calcutta.

CHAKRAPANI, Ramaswami (retired) 10 Crofton Close, Bedford MK41 8AJ — MB BS Madras 1958; FFA RCS Eng. 1972; DA 1960. Cons. Anaesth. Beds. N. Health Dist. Prev: Sen. Regist. Lond. Chest Hosp. & Middlx. Hosp.

CHAKRAVARTY, Basudeb Ballyowen Health Centre, 179 Andersonstown Road, Belfast BT11 9EA Tel: 028 9061 0611 Fax: 028 9043 1323; 66 Bristow Park, Upper Malone Road, Belfast BT9 6TJ Tel: 01232 669387 — MB BS 1971 All India Med. Scs.; MICGP 1987.

CHAKRAVARTY, Kuntal Kumar Havering Hospital NHS Trust, Haroldwood Hospital, Haroldhill, Romford Tel: 01708 746090; Rosewood House, 5 Mymms Drive, Brookmans Park, Hatfield AL9 7AE Tel: 01707 664827 Fax: 01707 664827 — MB BS 1981 India; MRCPI 1987; DGM RCP Lond. 1988; FACP USA 1992; FRCP Lond. 1998. Cons. (Rheumatol.) Havering Hosp. NHS Trust. Socs: Int. Fell. Amer. Coll. Rhematol; Brit. Soc. Rheumatol; Roy. Soc. Med. Prev: Cons. (Rheumatol.) Warrington Hosp. NHS Trust; Sen. Regist. (Rheumatol.) Addenbrooke's Hosp. Camb.; Research Regist. (Rheumatol.) Oxf. Reg. Rheumatol Dis. Research Centre, Stoke Mandeville Hosp. Aylesbury.

CHAKRAVARTY, Mark Robin 20 James Brindley Basin, Piccadilly Village, Manchester M1 2NL — MB ChB 1995 Manch.

CHAKRAVARTY, Pratima Branfill Road Surgery, 17 Branfill Road, Upminster RM14 2YX Tel: 01708 220022 Fax: 01708 640526 — MB BS 1965 Calcutta.

CHAKRAVARTY, Raj Devashis c/o Mr Sailesh Parekh, Anukhil, Pen-y-Waun, Pentyrch, Cardiff CF15 9SJ — MB BS 1978 Banaras Hindu; MB BS Banaras Hindu India 1978.

CHAKRAVARTY, Sudip Kumar 71 Daybrook Road, London SW19 3DJ — MB BS 1974 Dibrugarh; MRCOG 1984; DRCOG 1981.

CHAKRAVERTY, Mr Amaresh Chandra, Group Capt. RAF Med. Br. Nuffield Hospital, Plymouth PL6 8BG Tel: 01752 775861 Fax: 01752 768969; 7 Blue Haze Close, Glenholt, Plymouth PL6 7HR Tel: 01752 695206 Fax: 01752 695206 — MB BS 1959 Calcutta; MChOrth Liverp. 1974; FRCS Ed. 1969. Cons. Orthop. Surg. RAF. Socs: Fell. BOA; BMA; Combined Servs. Orthop. Soc. Prev: Cons. Orthop. Surg. RN; Cons. Orthop. Surg., Gibraltar.

CHAKRAVERTY, Robin Chandra Churchfields Surgery, Recreation Road, Bromsgrove B61 8DT Tel: 01527 875974 Fax: 01527 576401 Email: rob.chak@virgin.net — MB BCh 1986 Wales; MSc 1992; MLCOM 1997; DRCOG 1994; DMS Med. Soc. Apoth. Lond. 1997. (Welsh Nat. Sch. Med.) GP. Socs: BMA; Brit. Osteop. Assn.; Brit. Inst. of Musculoskeletal Med. Prev: Staff Grade A & E Roy. Shrewsbury Hosp.; Clin. Asst. Spinal Pain Serv. Dilke Hosp. Forest of Dean.

CHAKRAVERTY, Ronjon Kumar 15 St Peters Close, Cassington, Witney OX29 4DX — MB ChB 1989 Birm.; MRCP (UK) 1992.

CHAKRAVERTY, Samin Chandra Department of Radiology, Ninewells Hospital and Medical School, Dundee DD1 9SY — BM BCh 1986 Oxf.; MA Camb. 1987; MRCP (UK) 1990; FRCR 1993. Cons. Radiol., Ninewells Hosp., Dundee.; Hon. Sen. Clin. Teach., Univ. of Dundee. Prev: Cons. Radiologist, Bradford Hosp. NHS Trust; Sen. Regist. (Radiol.) Newc. Hosps.; Regist. (Respirat. Med.) Kt.swood Hosp. & W.. Infirm. Glas.

CHAKRAVORTI, Satyamohan (retired) 1 Castleview Gardens, Gants Hill, Ilford IG1 3QB Tel: 020 8554 0455 — MRCS Eng. LRCP Lond. 1943; MRCGP 1965; DIH Soc. Apoth. Lond. 1953. Div. Surg. St. John Ambul. Brig. Prev: Med. Off. I.C.I. (India) Ltd.

CHAKRAVORTY, Narendra Kumar 5 The Fairway, Fixby, Huddersfield HD2 2HU Tel: 01484 34883 — MB BS 1956 Calcutta; FRCP Ed. 1982, M 1966; DTM & H Eng. 1960. (Nilratan Sircar Med. Coll.) Cons. Phys. (Geriat. Med.) St. Luke's Hosp. Huddersfield. Prev: Sen. Regist. (Geriat. Med.) Woodend Gen. Hosp. Aberd. & Hon. Clin.; Tutor (Geriat. Med.) Univ. Aberd.; Med. Regist. Wrexham & E. Denbighsh. War Memor. Hosp.

CHAKU, Mr Shiban Krishan 74 Rectory Grove, Hampton TW12 1EE — MB BS 1968 Calcutta; FRCS Ed. 1979.

CHALABI, Gazi 111 Woodlands Avenue, Wanstead, London E11 3RB Tel: 020 8989 8908 — MD 1963 Istanbul; MSc Occupat. Med. Univ. Lond. 1985; DTM & H Liverp. 1979; DPH Eng. 1979; DCH RCPSI 1976; FRIPHH Eng. 1977. Clin. Med. Off. (Community Child Health & Occupat. Health) Newham HA. Socs: Fell. Roy. Soc. Med.; Soc. Occupat. Med.; Assoc. Mem. Brit. Paediat. Assn. Prev: SHO (Paediat.) Roy. Free Hosp. Lond.; Clin. Med. Off. (Community Child Health) Sandwell HA.

CHALABI, Nejat St John's Road Medical Centre, 1-3 St. Johns Road, East Ham, London E6 1NW — MB ChB 1974 Mosul; MFFP 1993; MRCOG 1987; Cert. Prescribed Equiv. Exp. JCPTGP 1994; FRIPHH 1990. Clin. Asst. (Gyn.) Eliz. Garrett Anderson Hosp. Lond.; GP. Socs: BMA; Med. Protec. Soc. Prev: Regist. (O & G) Qu. Mary's Hosp. Sidcup; Clin. Med. Off. (Family Plann.) Islington HA.

CHALAPATHY, Arani Sreeramulu Hainault Road Surgery, 226 Hainault Road, Leytonstone, London E11 1EP Tel: 0208 539 0261 Fax: 0208 556 1417 Email: chalapathy@aol.com — MB BS 1973 Madras; MB BS 1973 Madras. (Madras Med. College, Madras, India) G.P.; EMP for Benefit Agency; Clin. Asst. - Psychiat.; Police Surg.

CHALASANI, Ajay Kumar 10 Florey Court, Block F-23, Queen's Medical Centre, Nottingham NG7 2UH — MB BS 1983 Kakaliya, India.

CHALHOUB, Nevyne Mounir Youssef Academic Department of Child & Adolescent Psychiatry, St. Mary's Hospital Medical School, Norfolk Place, London W2 1PG Tel: 020 7725 1145; 3 Amberley Way, Uxbridge UB10 0AF — MB ChB 1983 Alexandria; MRCPsych 1993. Lect. (Child & Adolesc. Psychiat.) St. Mary's Hosp. Med. Sch. Prev: Clin. Research Fell. (Child & Adolesc. Psychiat.) Hounslow.

CHALIHA, Charlotte Dept. of OBS & GN, Kingston Hospital, Kingston upon Thames KT2 7QB; 26 Stoner Road, West Kensington, London W14 8RZ — MB BChir 1992 Camb.

CHALK, Ben-Zion 39 Armitage Road, London NW11 8QT — MB BS 1958 Durh.; DPH 1964; DA Eng. 1970. (Newc.)

CHALK, Evelyn Sarah (retired) 48 Middleway, Taunton TA1 3QJ Tel: 01823 275398 — MB BS Lond. 1948; MRCS Eng. LRCP Lond. 1947; DObst RCOG 1950. Prev: Clin. Med. Off. Som. HA.

CHALK, Jean Graham The Barn House, Hurstbourne Priors, Whitchurch — MB BS 1958 Lond.; MRCS Eng. LRCP Lond. 1958. (Lond. Hosp.)

CHALK, Mr Philip Alexander Forbes (retired) The Barn House, Hurstbourne Priors, Whitchurch RG28 7SB — MB BChir Camb. 1957; MRCS Eng. LRCP Lond. 1957; FRCS Eng. 1962; FRCOG 1978, M 1965. Prev: Cons. O & G Roy. Free Hosp. Lond.

CHALKER, Eric John 2 Lowburys, Dorking RH4 3RJ — MB BS 1952 Lond. (St. Thos.) Prev: Ho. Surg. & Ho. Phys. W. Kent Gen. Hosp. Maidstone; Ho. Surg. Obst. Unit Ronkswood Hosp. Worcester.

CHALKER, John Colson c/o R.H. Chalker, East Hayes, 29 Treverbyn Road, Padstow PL28 8DN — MB ChB 1985 Bristol; MSC (Trop. Med.) Lond. 1992; DTM & H Liverp. 1986.

CHALKIAS, Ioannis Little Common Surgery, 82 Cooden Sea Road, Bexhill-on-Sea TN39 4SP; 82 Cooden Sea Road, Bexhill-on-Sea TN39 4P — State Exam Med 1987 Frankfurt; MD 1988. SHO (Urol.) E.bourne Gen. Hosp. E. Sussex. Prev: SHO (Orthop. & Trauma) Kingston Hosp. Surrey.

CHALKLEY, Beryl Dorothy (retired) 21 Palmers Avenue, Grays RM17 5TX Tel: 01375 375871 — LRCPI & LM, LRSCI & LM 1957; LRCPI & LM, LRCSI & LM 1957.

CHALKLEY, Freda Mabel (retired) Highfield, The Common, Marlborough SN8 1DL Tel: 01672 512929 — MRCS Eng. LRCP Lond. 1935. Prev: Asst. Med. Off. (Matern. & Child Health) Nottm.

CHALKLEY, John Christopher RFDS, Mount Isa Base QLD, Australia; 44 Hale Road, Necton, Swaffham PE37 8EY — MB BS 1993 Lond.; MRCGP 2000; FRACGP (Fellow of Roy. Austral. Coll. of Gen. Practitioners) 2001; DFFP 1999; DRCOG 2000; MA (Hons.) Camb. 1994, BA (Hons.) 1990. Med. Off. Roy. Flying Doctor Serv. of Australia. Prev: Anaesthetic Regist., MaryBoro. Base Hosp., Qu.sland, Australia; Paediatric Regist., Nambour Gen. Hosp., Qu.sland Australia; Sen. Ho. Off. (Psychiat. and O & G), W.. Isles Hosp., Stornoway, Isle of Lewis, Scotl. UK.

CHALKLEY, Margaret Jane Occupational Health Unit, Sandwell Healthcare, Hallam Close, West Bromwich B71 4HU; 20 Marlborough Avenue, Bromsgrove B60 2PF — MB ChB 1969 Glas.; DRCOG 1971. Occupat. Health Phys. Sandwell Healthcare W. Bromwich. Socs: Soc. Occupat. Med.

CHALL, Davinder Boar Cottage, Grays Farm, Clift Lane, Toller Porcorum, Dorchester DT2 0EJ Tel: 01308 485044; 5 Benedictine Road, Cheylesmore, Coventry CV3 6GZ Tel: 01202 503555 — BM BCh 1996 Oxf.; BA (Oxon) 1995; DRCOG 1999; DFFP 1999. GP Regist. Dorchester. Socs: BMA; BJGP. Prev: SHO Dorset Co. Hosp. (Paediat./ Cas.).

***CHALLACOMBE, Benjamin James** 101 Mycenae Road, London SE3 7RX Tel: 020 8858 7933 Fax: 020 8858 7933 Email: benchallacombe@hotmail.com — MB BS 1998 Lond.; MB BS Lond 1998; BSc Lond 1995.

CHALLACOMBE, Christine Barbara Tel: 020 8312 6095 Fax: 020 8293 1226; 101 Mycenae Road, Blackheath, London SE3 7RX Tel: 020 8858 7933 — MB BS 1969 Lond.; MRCS Eng. LRCP Lond. 1969. (Guy's) Socs: BMA; W Kent Medico-Chir. Soc. Counc.; Assoc. Mem. RCGP. Prev: Ho. Phys. Greenwich Dist. Hosp.; Ho. Surg. Miller Gen. Hosp.

CHALLACOMBE, David Nicholas (retired) 2 Mount Terrace, Mount St., Taunton TA1 3QG Tel: 01823 337164 Email: david.challacombe@btinternet.com — MB BS 1960 Lond.; MD 1982 Lond.; FRCP 1980 Lond.; MRCP 1965 Lond; MRCS 1960 Eng.; LRCP 1960 Lond., MRCPCH 1997; FRCPCH 2000. p/t Cons. Paediat., Spec. (Allergies) at home adress. Prev: Cons. Paediat. Taunton & Som. Hosp.

CHALLAH, Sabri Naim 79 Cheyne Court, Royal Hospital Road, London SW3 — BM BCh 1979 Oxf.; MSc Lond. 1983; BA Camb. 1976. Lect. (Community Med.) St. Thos. Hosp. Lond.; Dir. EDTA Registry St. Thos. Hosp. Lond.

CHALLAND, Simon John Kagando Hospital, P.B. Kasese, Uganda; 6 North Cliffe, Leek ST13 8EW — MB BS 1987 Ncle.; MRCGP 1992; DA (UK) 1992; DRCOG 1991. Med. Supt. Community Health Uganda. Prev: Trainee GP Heaton; SHO (Anaesth.) Shotley Bridge Gen. Hosp.; SHO S.land Hosp. NZ.

CHALLANDS, Joanne Fay 35 Pondfield House, Highbury New Park, London N5 2LJ — MB ChB 1985 Birm.

CHALLANDS, Lynnette (retired) 89 Endcliffe Vale Road, Ranmoor, Sheffield S10 3ET — MB ChB 1980 Sheff.; MRCGP Lond. 1985; DCH RCP Lond. 1984.

CHALLEN, Aidan David The Medical Centre, Waterbeach Barracks, Waterbeach, Cambridge CB5 9PA Tel: 01223 204467 Fax: 01223 204437; 117 Mawson Road, Cambridge CB1 2DZ Tel: 01223 319745 Email: challen.aidan@virgin.net — MB BCh 1974 Wales; PhD Camb. 1984; MRCP (UK) 1978; AFOM RCP Lond. 1993. (Univ. Wales Sch. of Med.) GP & Occupat. Med. Camb.; Occupat.al Health Phys. (BUPA). Socs: Camb. Med. Soc.; Soc. Occupat. Med.; Roy. Soc. of Med. Prev: Sen. Med. Off. Waterbeach Barracks Camb.; Lect. (Med.) Camb. Univ. & Addenbrooke's Hosp.; Clin. Research Scientist MRC Dunn Nutrit. Unit Camb.

CHALLEN, Kesten Barbara The Surgery, 2A St. Wilfrids Square, Calverton, Nottingham NG14 6FP Tel: 0115 965 2294 Fax: 0115 965 5898; 44 Patterdale Road, Nottingham NG5 4LQ Tel: 0115 956 5044 — MB ChB 1986 Sheff.; BMedSci Sheff. 1984; MRCGP 1993; DRCOG 1991; DA (UK) 1990. (Sheffield)

CHALLEN, Peter Douglas Gilfachwydd, Islawrdref, Dolgellau LL40 1TL Tel: 01341 422664 Fax: 01341 421146 Email: onetel.net.uk — MB BS 1967 Lond.; MRCS Eng. LRCP Lond. 1967; FFA RCS Eng. 1971. (St. Bart.) Socs: Assn. Anaesth. GB & Irel.; Assn. Dent. Anaesth. Prev: Cons. Anaesth. Wythenshawe Hosp. Manch.

CHALLENER, Jill Hinchingbrooke Hospital, Huntingdon PE29 6NT Tel: 01480 416464 Fax: 01480 416698 — BM BCh 1973 Oxf.; BA Oxf. 1970; MRCP (UK) 1977. Cons. Paediat. Huntingdon HA. Prev: Sen. Regist. (Paediat.) Huntingdon HA; Regist. (Paediat.) Cambs. AHA (T); SHO (Haemat.) Addenbrookes Hosp. Camb.

CHALLENOR, John Occupational Health Support Unit, Devon and Cornwall Constabulary Headquaters, Middle moir EX2 7HQ Email: challenor@doctors.org.uk; Email: john@jchallenor.freeserve.co.uk — MB ChB 1978 Manch.; 2001 FFOM; MFOM RCP Lond. 1996; MRCGP 1982; DRCOG 1981; DCH RCPS Glas. 1980. Cons. Occupat.al Phys.; Force Med. Off., Devon and Cornw. Constab., Exeter. Socs: Fac. Occupat. Med.; Fell. Roy. Soc. Med.; Soc. Occupat. Med Pres. 2001/2002. Prev: Cons. Occup. Phys. Univ. of Plymouth; Cons. Occup. Phys. Devon Co. Counc.

CHALLENOR, Rachel May 14 Hillside Way, Yealmpton, Plymouth PL8 2NU Tel: 01752 881256 Fax: 01752 881256 Email: john@jchallenor.freeserve.co.uk — MB BS 1981 Lond.; MRCGP 1985; Dip. GU Med. Soc. Apoth. Lond. 1992; DRCOG 1984; DCH RCP Lond. 1983; DLP. Occ. Med 1999. (Middlesex Hospital Medical School) Assoc. Specialist. (Genitourin. Med.) Derriford Hosp., Plymouth.

CHALLENOR, Vivian Francis Walton House, Walton Hill, Deerhurst, Gloucester GL19 4BT — MB BCh 1977 Wales; MRCP (UK) 1982; DM Soton. 1992; FRCP 1998. (Welsh National School of Medicine) Socs: Brit. Cardiac Soc.; Brit. Pharm. Soc.; BMA.

CHALLENS, Alison Sarah 483 Warwick Road, Solihull B91 1AN — MB BCh 1997 Wales.

CHALLINER, Alistair Richard Keith — MB BS 1988 Lond.; FIMCRcsed 2001; FRCA 1995; DCH RCPS Glas. 1993; Dip IMC RCS Ed. 1992. (St. Geo. Hosp. Lond.) Cons. Anaesth. & Director ICU Maidstone Hosp, Kent; Med. Adviser, Kent fire Brig. Train. Sch., Maidstone; Hon. Med. Adviser, RNLI; Co. Controller, St Johns Ambul., Kent. Socs: Intens. Care Soc.; Resusc. Counc. UK, Regional Represen.; Intens. care Surg. Prev: Sen. Regist. (Anaesth.) St Thomas' & Roy. Brompton Hosps. Lond.; Regist. (Anaesth.) Qu. Eliz. & Birm. Accid. Hosp. Birm.; SHO (Anaesth., IC & Paediat.) Portsmouth.

CHALLINER, Jean The Old Smithy, Basford Bank, Edgton, Craven Arms SY7 8HJ Tel: 01588 680237 — MB ChB 1980 Liverp.; BSc (Hons.) Liverp. 1976 MB ChB 1980.; DIMC Ed. 1998. Clin. Assn.(A&E),Wolverhampton,NHS.Trust.New.Cross.Hosp.

CHALLINER, Rachael Ann 147 Lichfield Road, Stone ST15 8QB — MB BS 1997 Newc.

CHALLINER, Yvonne Charlotte Margaret Queen Elizabeth Queen Mother Hospital, St Peter's Road, Margate CT9 4AN Tel: 01843 22554 — MB BS 1984 Lond.; MA Oxf. 1986; MD Lond. 1995; FRCP 2000 UK. Cons. Phys. Qu. Eliz. Qu. Mother Hosp. Thanet; Hon. Sen. Lect., Univ. of Kent, Cantebury. Prev: Lect. (Geriat.) & Hon. Sen. Regist. Soton. Gen. Hosp.

CHALLINOR, John Michael (retired) Fourways, 18 West Park Drive, Leeds LS16 5AS — MB ChB 1955 Leeds. Prev: Mem. Leeds Local Med. Comm.

CHALLINOR, Peter (retired) 45 Calverley Lane, Bramley, Leeds LS13 3LP Tel: 0113 256 4149 — MB ChB 1953 Leeds. Prev: Ho. Phys. Wakefield Gen. Hosp.

CHALLIS, Andrew Luke The Health Centre, High Street, Catterick Village, Richmond DL10 7LD Tel: 01748 811475 Fax: 01748 818284; Beck Cottage, Hunton, Bedale DL8 1QZ Email: a.challis@dial.pipex.com — MB ChB 1980 Birm.; MRCGP 1984; DFFP 1988. (Birmingham) Clin. Asst.(Dermat.) Friaralee Hosp., N.allerton, N. Yorks.

CHALLIS, Denise Margaret Child Health HQ, Edgware Hospital, Burnt Oak Broadway, Edgware HA8 0AD Tel: 020 8732 6566; Lincoln House, 519 High Road, Harrow Weald, Harrow HA3 6HL Tel: 020 8954 6709 Fax: 020 8954 6709 Email: denise@exody.demon.co.uk — MB BChir 1971 Camb.; MSc Lond. 1991; MA Camb. 1972; MFCH 1989; FRCPCH 1997; DCH Eng. 1973. (Univ. Camb.) Cons. Community Paediat. Childr. Servs. Barnet; Developm. Paediat. Portland Hosp. Lond. & Edgware Hosp.

WellHo. NHS Trust. Prev: Sen. Med. Off. (Child Health) Redbridge & Waltham Forest AHA & City & E. Lond. AHA (T).

CHALLIS, Mr John Howard North London Nuffield Hospital, Cavell Drive, Enfield EN2 7PR Tel: 020 8366 2122; Belle Inc Farm, Swansea Tel: 020 8363 2129 — MB BS 1963 Lond.; FRCS Eng. 1968; MRCS Eng. LRCP Lond. 1963. (St. Bart.) Cons. Orthop. Surg. N. Lond. Nuffield & King's Hosps., Enfield; Clin. Asst. Prof. (Hon.) Univ. W. Indies 1990. Socs: Fell. (Counc.) Roy. Soc. Med. & Brit. Orthop. Assn.; Brit. Orthop. Assn.; Med. Art Soc. Prev: Cons. Orthop. Surg. N. Middlx. Hosp. Trust; Sen. Regist. (Orthop.) Lond. Hosp.; Regist. (Orthop.) Rowley Bristow Orthop. Hosp. Pyrford.

CHALLIS, Margaret Thornton (retired) The Lodge, Carrolls Farm, Bury Road, Sewardstonebury, London E4 7QN Tel: 020 8529 7624 — MB BS 1957 Lond.; MRCS Eng. LRCP Lond. 1957; DO Eng. 1963; FRCS Eng. 1967. Cons. Ophth. Regional Eye Centre & Whipps Cross Hosp. Prev: Cons.Opth. Regional Eye Centre & Whipps Cross Hosp.

CHALLIS, Rosemary Elizabeth 10 Church Lane, Funtington, Chichester PO18 9LH Tel: 01243 575585 — MB BS 1975 Lond.; MB BS (Hons.) Lond. 1975; MRCP (UK) 1978; DCH Eng. 1977. (St. Geo.)

CHALLONER, Teresa Elizabeth 27 Gloucester Avenue, Regents Park, London NW1 7AU — MD 1989 Aberd.; MB ChB Aberd. 1976; MRCP (UK) 1978.

CHALMERS, Alan Gordon Dept of Radiology, The General Infirmary at Leeds, Great George St., Leeds LS1 3EX Tel: 0113 292 3793 Fax: 0113 292 3775; 9 Park Lane, Roundhay, Leeds LS8 2EX — MB ChB 1976 Dundee; MRCP (UK) 1979; FRCR 1984. (Dundee) Cons. Radiol. Gen. Infirm. Leeds. Prev: Sen. Regist. Leeds Radiol. Train. Scheme; Regist. (Radiol.) Soton. Gen. Hosp.; Rotat. Regist. (Med.) W.. Infirm. Glas.

CHALMERS, Alastair Hugh Royal United Hospital, Combe park, Bath BA1 3NG; 2 Springfield Pl, Lansdown, Bath BA1 5RA — MB BChir 1970 Camb.; MA, MB Camb. 1970; FRCP Lond. 1989; MRCP (UK) 1972; FRCR 1975; DMRD Eng. 1974. (Guy's) Cons. Radiol. Roy. United Hosp. Bath. Prev: Sen. Regist. Radiol. King's Coll. Hosp.; Regist. (Med.) Guy's Hosp. Lond.

CHALMERS, Alexander Martin 76 Drumlin Drive, Milngavie, Glasgow G62 6NQ — MB ChB 1948 Glas. (Univ. Glas.)

CHALMERS, Alison Gillian Wemyss Dept. of Child Health, St George's Hospital Medical School, Cranmer Terrace, London SW17 0RE — MB ChB 1998 Birm.

CHALMERS, Alistair Crighton (retired) 91 King Harald Street, Lerwick ZE1 0ER Tel: 01595 693187 — MB ChB 1955 Glas.; FRCSC 1972; MRCPCH 1996; MFPHM RCP (UK) 1990; FACS 1974. SCMO (Community Child Health & Pub. Health Med.) & Dep. Dir. Pub. Health Shetland HB.

CHALMERS, Andrew John 14 Hawthorn Way, Ponteland, Newcastle upon Tyne NE20 9RU — MB BS 1987 Newc.

CHALMERS, Anthony James Mount Vernon Hospital, Rickmansworth Road, Northwood HA6 2RN Tel: 01923 826111; 4 Sheendale Road, Richmond TW9 2JJ Tel: 020 8940 4846 Email: schmooz@btinternet.com — BM BCh 1992 Oxf.; MRCP 1995. Specialist Regist. (Clin. Oncol.) Mt. Vernon Hosp. Prev: Specialist Regist. (Clin. Oncol.) Roy. Free Hosp. Lond.

CHALMERS, Archibald John (retired) Locheil, Queen's Road, Scone, Perth PH2 6QJ Tel: 01738 551444 — MB ChB 1957 St. And.; DObst RCOG 1961. Med. Off. Hillside Hosp. Perth. Prev: Ho. Phys. King's Cross Hosp. Dundee.

CHALMERS, Catherine Ann Chalmers and Partners, Cogges Surgery, Cogges Hill Road, Witney OX28 3FP Tel: 01993 700505 Fax: 01993 706610; The Gables, 36 Newland St, Eynsham, Oxford OX29 4LA Tel: 01865 881224 — MB BS Lond. 1968; MRCP (UK) 1973; MRCS Eng. LRCP Lond. 1968; MRCGP 1986; DCH Eng. 1972. (Char. Cross) Prev: Regist. (O & G) John Radcliffe Hosp.; Regist. (Chest Dis.) Ch.ill Hosp. Headington; Regist. (Geriat. Med.) Radcliffe Infirm. Oxf.

CHALMERS, Constance Mary (retired) The Mews Cottage, Egglescliffe Hall, Stockton-on-Tees TS16 9BU — MB ChB 1943 Ed. Anaesth. S. Tees Hosp. Gp. Prev: Anaesth. Roy. N.. Infirm. Inverness.

CHALMERS, David Hastings Kerr Snaefell Surgery, Cushag Road, AnaghCoar, Douglas IM2 2SU Tel: 01624 676622 Fax: 01624 674515; Ballachrink, Richmond Hill, Braddan, Douglas IM4 1JG Tel: 01624 671675 Fax: 01624 671677 — MB BChir 1979 Camb.; 2000 D.Occ.Med; MB BChir (Distinc.) Camb. 1979; MA Camb. 1980; FRCS Eng. 1985; FRCS Ed. 1984. Principle Gen. Pract. Socs: Fell. Roy. Soc. Med. Prev: SHO (Renal Transpl. & Gen. Surg.) Ch.ill & John Radcliffe Hosp. Oxf.; Cas. Off. Birm. Accid. Hosp. & Rehabil. Centre; Demonst. (Human Anat.) Univ. Oxf.

CHALMERS, Dawn Marie 2 Trentham Court, Westhill, Inverness IV2 5DF Tel: 01463 792233; 7 Sunnyside Road, Aberdeen AB24 3ND Tel: 01224 630811 — MB ChB 1996 Aberd. GPVTS. Aberd. Prev: SHO (Forens. Med.) Aberd. Roy. Hosps. NHS Trust.

CHALMERS, Douglas MacMillan Gastroenterology Department, General Infirmary of Leeds, Great George St., Leeds LS1 3EX Tel: 0113 243 2799 Fax: 0113 392 6968 Email: douglas.chalmers@leedsth.nhs.uk — MB ChB 1971 Leeds; BSc (Physiol., Hons.) Leeds 1968; FRCP Lond. 1989; MRCP (UK) 1974. Sen. Cons. Gartoenterologists. Socs: Brit. Soc. Gastroenterol.; Amer. Gastroenterol. Assn.; Brit. Assn. for Study of Liver. Prev: Sen. Regist. St. Jas. Hosp. Leeds; Hon. Sen. Regist. N.wick Pk. Hosp. Harrow.

CHALMERS, Elizabeth Anne 31 Rowallen Gardens, Broomhill, Glasgow G11 7LH — MB ChB 1984 Glas.; MD Glas. 1993; MRCP (UK) 1987; MRCPath 1993. Cons. Haemat. Roy. Hosp. Sick Childr. Glas. Prev: Cons. Haemat. Aberd. Roy. Infirm.; Sen. Regist. (Haemat.) W.. Infirm. Glas.; SHO (Med.) Stobhill Hosp. Glas.

CHALMERS, Ewan Paul David Pilgrim Hospital, Sibsey Road, Boston PE21 9QS Tel: 01205 364801 Fax: 01205 354395; Baythorpe, 25 Sibsey Road, Boston PE21 9QY Tel: 01205 362228 — MB ChB 1975 Dundee; FFA RCS Lond. 1983. Cons. (Anaesth.) Pilgrim Hosp. Boston; Assoc. Med. Director Pilgrim Hosp. Boston. Prev: Sen. Regist. (Anaesth.) Qu. Eliz. Med. Centre Birm.

CHALMERS, Fiona Alexandra 39 Cleveden Road, Glasgow G12 0PH — MB ChB 1986 Ed.; DRCOG 1989.

CHALMERS, George Lovie (retired) 23 Abbey Drive, Jordanhill, Glasgow G14 9JS Tel: 0141 959 1076 Email: george.chalmers@virgin.net — MB ChB 1957 Aberd.; FRCP Ed. 1980, M 1964; FRCP Glas. 1979, M 1965. Hon. Clin. Sen. Lect. Univ. Glas. Prev: Cons. Phys. & Clin. Dir. (Geriat. Med.) Glas. Roy. Infirm. Unit.

CHALMERS, George William Flat 1/L, 89 Hyndland Road, Hyndland, Glasgow G12 9JE — MB ChB 1990 Glas.; LLB Glas. 1985; MRCP (UK) 1994. Clin. Research Fell. (Respirat. Med.) W. Glas. Hosps. Univ. NHS Trust. Socs: Brit. Thorac. Soc.; Scott. Thoracic Soc.

CHALMERS, Gordon, Maj. 2 Swarland House, Benton, Newcastle upon Tyne NE7 7TD Tel: 0191 215 0141 Fax: 0191 284 4010; The Mill House, Killingworth Village, Newcastle upon Tyne NE12 6BL Tel: 0191 268 7145 — MB BS 1957 Durh.; DObst RCOG 1964. (Durham) Prev: SHO P.ss Mary Matern. Hosp. Newc-upon-Tyne; Maj. RAMC.

CHALMERS, Grace Constance (retired) 97 Duthie Terrace, Aberdeen AB10 7PS Tel: 01224 317294 — MB ChB Aberd. 1958; MD (Commend.) Aberd. 1963. Prev: Clin. Med. Off. Grampian HB Aberd.

CHALMERS, Hugh Andrew (retired) Colinton Surgery, 296B Colinton Road, Edinburgh EH13 0LB Tel: 0131 441 4555 Fax: 0131 441 3963 — MB ChB 1968 Ed.; DObst RCOG 1970. Sen. Med. Off. Merchiston Castle Sch. Edin.

CHALMERS, Iain David Stewart The Surgery, 20 Heneage Road, Grimsby DN32 9DY Tel: 01472 343067; 50 Weelsby Road, Grimsby DN32 0PR — MB ChB 1986 Ed. Trainee GP Grimsby VTS.

CHALMERS, Sir Iain Geoffrey The UK Cochrane Centre, NHS R&D Programme, Summertown Pavilion, Middle Way, Oxford OX2 7LG Tel: 01865 516300 Fax: 01865 516311; 22 Leckford Road, Oxford OX2 6HX Tel: 01865 554949 — MB BS Lond. 1966; MSc (Social Med.) Lond. 1975; FRCP Ed. 1996; MRCS Eng. LRCP Lond. 1966; FFPHM RCP (UK) 1986, M 1979; DCH Eng. 1971; DSc 1999; F Acad Med Sci 1999. (Middlx.) Dir. UK Cochrane Centre Oxf.; Vis. Prof. Univ. Liverp.; Vis. Prof. UCL; Vis. Prof. Univ. Exeter. Prev: Med. Off. United Nations Relief & Works Agency for Palestinian Refugees, Gaza; MRC Fell. Med. Statistics & Regist. (O & G) Welsh; Dir. Nat. Perinatal Epidemiol. Unit Oxf.

CHALMERS, Isabella Simpson (retired) c/o Crockett, 34 Hillside Crescent, Nether Hayford, Northampton NN7 3LS — MB BS 1940 Lond.; MRCS Eng. LRCP Lond. 1940.

CHALMERS, Isobel Margaret Haematology Dept, Ipswich Hospital, Heath Road, Ipswich IP4 5PD Tel: 01473 703718 Email: isobel.chalmers@ipsh-tr.ang6x.nhs.uk; 19 Brettenham Crescent, Ipswich IP4 2UB Tel: 01473 639299 Email: isobel.chalmers@btinternet.com — MB ChB 1989 Aberd.; MRCP (UK) 1992; MD 2000; MRCPath 1998. (Aberden University) Cons. Haematologista, ipswich Hosp. Socs: Brit. Soc. Haematol. Prev: SPR Roy. Hosp.s Trust, Lond.; SHO (Gen. Med.) Ysbtty Gwynedd Bangor; SHO (Gen. Med.) Aberd. Roy. Infirm.

CHALMERS, James Alastair 34 Woodside, Leigh-on-Sea SS9 4QU Tel: 01702 525403 — MB ChB Aberd. 1945.

CHALMERS, James Glidden Doctors Residence, Dumfries & Galloway Royal Infirmary, Bankend Road, Dumfries DG1 4AP — MB ChB 1994 Ed.

CHALMERS, James Walter Turnbull Information & Statistics Division, ISD, Trinity Park House, Edinburgh EH5 3SQ Tel: 0131 551 8662 Email: jim.chalmers@isd.csa.scot.nhs.uk — MB ChB 1979 Ed.; MSc Ed. 1988; MRCGP 1983; MFPHM RCP (UK) 1991; FFPHM RCP (UK) 2000. Cons. Pub. Health Med. Informat. & Statistics Div. Nat. Health Serv. in Scotl.; Hon. Sen. Lect., Dept of Pub. Health Sci.s, Univ. of Edin. Prev: Cons. Pub. Health Med. Dumfries & Galloway HB.

CHALMERS, Jane Elizabeth Oxford Terrace Medical Group, Gateshead NE8 1RQ Tel: 0191 477 2169 Fax: 0191 477 5633 Email: janechalmers@rapidial.co.uk; 14 Hawthorn Way, Ponteland, Newcastle upon Tyne NE20 9RU Tel: 01661 822081 — BM BS 1987 Nottm.; BMedSci Nottm 1985; MRCGP 1994; DRCOG 1994; Dip. Adv Gen Practice 1997. (Nottm.) Prev: Trainee GP N.umbria & Leeds E. VTS; SHO (A & E) S. Tyneside Dist. Hosp. S. Shields; Asst. GP N.umbria.

CHALMERS, Joan Maud (retired) 3 Rosemount, Hamilton Gardens, Felixstowe IP11 7ET Tel: 01394 272053 — MRCS Eng. LRCP Lond. 1945.

CHALMERS, Joanna Louise Baslow Road Surgery, 148-150 Baslow Road, Totley, Sheffield S17 4DR Tel: 0114 236 9957 Fax: 0114 262 0756; 10 Hoober Avenue, Sheffield S11 9SG — MB ChB 1990 Sheff.; MRCGP 1995; DFFP 1994; DRCOG 1994. (Univ. Sheff.)

CHALMERS, Mr John (retired) 15 Eden Lane, Edinburgh EH10 4SD Tel: 0131 447 1586 Email: jchal99503@aol.com — MD Ed. 1961, MB ChB 1950; FRCS Ed. 1963; FRCS Eng. 1953. Prev: Cons. Orthop. Surg. Roy. Infirm. & P.ss Margt. Rose Orthop. Hosp. Edin.

CHALMERS, John Medical Unit, Victoria Hospital, Hayfield Road, Kirkcaldy KY2 5AH Tel: 01592 643355 Fax: 01592 647061 Email: john.chalmers@faht.scot.nhs.uk; 65 Park View, Balmullo, St Andrews KY16 0DN Tel: 01334 870065 Email: jc@chalmers.swinternet.co.uk — MB ChB 1986 Ed.; BSc (Hons.) Ed. 1984; MRCP (UK) 1992; FRCP 2000 Edin. (Edinburgh) Cons. Phys. Vict. Hosp. Kirkcaldy; Hon. Sen. Lect., Sch. of Biological Sci.s, Univ. of St. Andrews. Prev: Sen. Regist. Diabetes Centre Ninewells Hosp. Dundee; Research Fell. Roy. Coll. Phys. Edin.; Ho. Phys. & Surg. Roy. Infirm. Edin.

CHALMERS, Mr John Adam Clelland 3 Hodgkins Close, London SE28 8NT — MB ChB 1977 Ed.; BSc Ed., MB ChB 1977; FRCS 1982.

CHALMERS, Mr John Alexander (cons. rooms), 82 Berners St., Ipswich IP1 3LU Tel: 01473 251313; Wilford Lodge, Station Road, Melton, Woodbridge IP12 1PX Tel: 013840 384514 — MB BS 1957 Lond.; FRCS Eng. 1962; FRCOG 1979, M 1966; MRCS Eng. LRCP Lond. 1957. (Westm.) Indep. Cons. Ipswich. Socs: Fell. Roy. Soc. Med.; Hunt. Soc. Prev: SHO. (Surg.) St. Jas. Hosp. Balham; SHO Qu. Charlotte's Matern. Hosp. & Chelsea Hosp. Wom. Lond.; Sen. Regist. (O & G) King's Coll. Hosp. Lond.

CHALMERS, Joyce (retired) Westcott, 13 Berwynfa, Glyn Ceiriog, Llangollen LL20 7HP — MB BS Lond. 1946; MRCS Eng. LRCP Lond. 1946.

CHALMERS, Julie Somerville The Elms Clinic, Oxford Road, Banbury OX16 Tel: 01295 229289 Fax: 01295 229282 — MB ChB 1980 Glas.; MRCPsych 1984. Cons. Psychiat. Oxf. Ment. Health Unit.; Hon. Sen. Lect., Univ. of Oxf. Prev: Sen. Regist. Rotat. (Psychiat.) Oxf. Higher Train. Scheme .

CHALMERS, Kenneth Moir (retired) The Mews Cottage, Egglescliffe Hall, Stockton-on-Tees TS16 9BU Tel: 01642 781226 — MB ChB 1943 Ed.; FRCP Lond. 1972, M 1949; FRCP Ed. 1970, M 1946. Cons. Phys. N. Tees Hosp. Gp.; Clin. Tutor Postgrad. Med., Univ. Newc-upon-Tyne. Prev: Clin. Asst. Dept. Med. Univ. Edin.

CHALMERS, Mary Ewen (retired) 64 Rubislaw Den N., Aberdeen AB15 4AN Tel: 01224 316676 — MB ChB 1943 Aberd.

CHALMERS, Nicholas Manchester Royal Infirmary, Oxford Road, Manchester M13 9WL — MB ChB 1983 Ed.; MA Camb. 1983; MRCP (UK) 1986; FRCR (UK) 1989; DMRD Ed. 1988; T(R) (CR) 1992. Cons. Vasc. Radiol. Manch. Roy. Infirm. Socs: Brit. Soc. Interven. Radiol. Prev: Sen. Regist. (Diag. Radiol.) Roy. Infirm. Edin.; Regist. (Diag. Radiol.) Univ. Edin.; Regist. (Med.) Vict. Hosp. Kirkcaldy.

CHALMERS, Reginald Burton, OStJ (retired) 19 Summerhill Road, Saffron Walden CB11 4AJ Tel: 01799 522533 — BM BCh Oxf. 1954; DObst RCOG 1957. Prev: GP & Hosp. Pract. Saffron Walden.

CHALMERS, Richard Martin Middleton Lodge Surgery, New Ollerton, Newark NG22 9SZ Tel: 01623 860668 Email: richardchalmers@doctors.org.uk; The Grey House, Main Street, Carlton-on-Trent, Newark NG23 6NW — BM BS 1985 Nottm.; BMedSci Nottm. 1983; MRCGP 1989; DRCOG 1989. (Nottm.)

CHALMERS, Richard Michael Worthing Hospital, Lyndhurst Road, Worthing BN11 2DH Tel: 01903 205111 Fax: 01903 285152 — BM BCh 1989 Oxf.; BA Oxf. 1986; MA Oxf. 1992; MRCP 1992; DM Oxf. 1997. (Oxf. Univ.) Cons. NeUrol. Worthing Hosp. and Hurstwood Pk. Neurosci.s Centre. Prev: Regist. Nat. Hosp. for Neurol. and Neurosurg., and Roy. Free Hosp., Lond.

CHALMERS, Robert James Guille Department of Dermatology, Manchester Royal Infirmary, Oxford Road, Manchester M13 9WL Tel: 0161 276 4173 Fax: 0161 276 8881 Email: r.chalmers@man.ac.uk; 16 Oaker Avenue, West Didsbury, Manchester M20 2XH Tel: 0161 445 9446 Email: r.chalmers@man.ac.uk — MB BS 1975 Lond.; MRCP (UK) 1978. (Middlx.) Cons. Dermat. Manch. Roy. Infirm. Dermat. Centre Salford & Bolton Hosps. Trust. Prev: Sen. Regist. (Dermat.) Skin Hosp. Manch.; Regist. (Dermat.) Roy. Vict. Infirm. Newc.; SHO (Gen. Med.) N. Staffs. Hosp. Centre, Stoke-on-Trent.

CHALMERS, Mr Roderick Thomas Alexander Vascular Surgery Unit, Royal Infirmary, Lauriston Place, Edinburgh EH3 9YW Tel: 0131 536 1613; 2 Buckstone Rise, Edinburgh EH10 6UW Tel: 0131 445 5622 — MB ChB 1986 Ed.; MD 1995; FRCS (Gen.) 1997; FRCS Ed. 1991. (Ed.) Cons. Vas. Surg. Roy. Infirm. of Edin. Socs: Vasc. Surg. Soc. GB & Irel. Prev: Sen. Regist. (Vasc. Surg.) St. Mary's Hosp. Lond.; Career Regist. Gen. & Train. Regist. Surg. (Lothian HB); SHO (A & E) Roy. Infirm. Edin.

CHALMERS, Roger Alistair 16 Wheatfields, Thurston, Bury St Edmunds IP31 3TE Email: rogerchalmers@ntlworld.com — MB 1980 Camb.; MRCGP 1998; MA Camb. 1980; MRCP (UK) 1982; DRCOG 1998. Gen. Practitioner Locum Work, E. Anglia. Prev: Med. Dir. Maharishi Ayurveda Health Centre Lond.; SHO Dept. Med. Hammersmith Hosp. Lond.; SHO Dept. Neurol. St. Thos. Hosp. Lond.

CHALMERS, Sarah Rosalind Milton Surgery, 132 Mountcastle Drive South, Edinburgh EH15 3LL; 16 Inverleith Avenue S., Edinburgh EH3 5QA Tel: 0131 552 3534 — MB ChB 1976 Ed. Prev: Ho. Off. (Paediat. Surg.) W.. Gen. Hosp. Edin.; Ho. Off. (Gen. Med.) E.. Gen. Hosp. Edin.

CHALMERS, Shelley Diane 20 Craigshannoch Road, Wormit, Newport-on-Tay DD6 8ND — MB ChB 1991 Dundee.

CHALMERS, Thomas Meredith 28 Barnton Gardens, Edinburgh EH4 6AE Tel: 0131 336 3705 — MB ChB 1952 Ed.; FRCP Ed. 1970, M 1959. (Ed.) Socs: Heberd. Soc. & Scott. Soc. Phys. Prev: Cons. Phys. Rheum. Dis. Unit W.. Gen. Hosp. Edin.; Sen. Lect. (Rheum.) Univ. Manch. & Hon. Cons. Phys. Manch. Roy. Infirm.; Regist. (Med.) E.. Gen. Hosp. Edin.

CHALMERS, Mr Thomas Speir (retired) Melon Park, Liberty, Elie, Leven KY9 1AU Tel: 01333 330416 — MB ChB 1939 Ed.; FRCS Ed. 1948. Prev: Cons. Surg. Dunfermline & W. Fife Hosp.

CHALMERS, William David 349 Pensby Road, Pensby, Heswall, Wirral CH61 9NL Tel: 0151 648 1193 Fax: 0151 648 2934; 127 Thingwall Road, Irby, Wirral CH61 3UD Tel: 0151 648 2298 — MRCS Eng. LRCP Lond. 1955; DObst RCOG 1968. (Liverp.) Prev: Surg. Lt. RN.

CHALMERS, William Neil 79 Clouston Street, Glasgow G20 8QW — MB ChB 1981 Glas.; MRCGP 1985.

CHALMERS-WATSON, Claire Elizabeth 42 Lauder Road, Edinburgh EH9 1UE — MB ChB 1992 Manch.

CHALMERS-WATSON, Julia Ilfra 42 Lauder Road, Edinburgh EH9 1UE — MB BS 1993 Newc. SHO N. Middlx. Hosp. Lond. Prev: SHO P'boro. Dist. Hosp.

CHALMERS-WATSON, Teresa Alice 42 Lauder Road, Edinburgh EH9 1UE — BM BS 1995 Nottm.

CHALONER, Anthony Barker 12 Ashen Green, Great Shelford, Cambridge CB2 5EY Tel: 01223 504571 — MB ChB St. And. 1959. (St. And.) Locum GP.

CHALONER, Deborah Ann Bennion Centre, Glenfield Hospital, Leicester LE3 Tel: 0116 250 2751 Fax: 0116 250 2720; Hopthorns, 28 Harborough Road, Clipston, Market Harborough LE16 9RT Tel: 01858 525271 — MB ChB 1981 Leic.; MRCPsych 1987. Cons. Old Age Psychiat. The Bennion Centre Glenfield Hosp. Leicester.

CHALONER, Mr Edmund Joseph Flat 3, 103 Rosebery Road, London N10 2LD — BM BCh 1989 Oxf.; FRCS Ed. 1994.

CHALONER, Jill Margaret Warley Hospital, Warley Hill, Brentwood CM14 5HQ Tel: 01277 302745 Fax: 01277 302748 Email: jill.chaloner@neli.nhs.uk — MB BS 1982 Lond.; MA, M Litt. Oxf. 1974; LMSSA Lond. 1981; MRCPsych 1985. (Guy's) Cons. Acute Adult Psychiat. Warley Hosp. Brentwood. Prev: Regist. (Psychiat.) Maudsley Hosp. & St. Geo. Hosp. Lond.; Ho. Phys. Hither Green Hosp.

CHALONER, John David Worcester Street Surgery, 24 Worcester Street, Stourbridge DY8 1AW Tel: 01384 371616 — MB BCh BAO Dub. 1978; MRCGP 1982; DObst 1980; DCH Eng. 1981. (TC Dub.) GP Tutor Dudley & Stourbridge; Clin. Asst. (Gastroenterol.) Dudley HA. Socs: BMA. Prev: Trainee GP Dudley VTS; Ho. Off. Adelaide Hosp. Dub.

CHALSTREY, Sir (Leonard) John, KStJ (retired) 116 Harley Street, London W1N 1AG Tel: 020 7935 7413 Fax: 020 7487 5829 — MB BChir 1957 Camb.; MA Camb. 1958, BA 1954, MD 1967; DSc (hons. causa) City Univ. 1995; FRCS Eng. 1962; MRCS Eng. LRCP Lond. 1957. Maj. RAMC (TA). Prev: Cons. Surg. St. Bart. & Roy. Lond. Hosp.

CHALSTREY, Miss Susan Elizabeth Department Otolaryngology, Princess Margaret Hospital, Okus Rd, Swindon SN1 4JU — MB BS 1983 Lond.; FRCS Eng. 1989; FRCS (Orl.) 1998. Cons. ENT Surg., P.ss Margt. Hosp., Swindon. Socs: Brit. Assn. Otol. Head & Neck Surg.; BMA; Liveryman Worshipful Soc. Apoth. Prev: Lect. (ENT Surg.) P. Wales Hosp., Hong Kong; Regist. (ENT Surg.) St. Bart. Hosp. Lond.; Sen. Regist. (ENT Surg.) Radcliffe Infirm. Oxf.

CHAMAKURI, Vijayalakshmi Belgrave Medical Centre, 116 Belgrave Road, Dresden, Stoke-on-Trent ST3 4LR Tel: 01782 593344 Fax: 01782 593344 — MB BS 1973 Andhra; T(GP) 1984; DA Eng. 1979. (Andhra Med. Coll.) Prev: Regist. (Spinal Injuries) Aylesbury Vale Health Dist.; SHO (Anaesth.) Hereford HA.

CHAMARETTE, Norman Poyntz Palmer (retired) 2 Leicester Avenue, Garstang, Preston PR3 1FH Tel: 01995 602258 — MD 1940 Manch.; MRCPsych 1973; DPM Eng. 1948. Cons. Psychiat. Manch. AHA (T) & Home Office. Prev: Res. Med. Off. OldCh. Hosp. Romford.

CHAMBERLAIN, Alexandra Sophia Elizabeth 79 Lake Road, Verwood BH31 6BX — MB BS 1996 Lond. (UCL) Trainee GP Wessex VTS (Rheumatol. Palliat. Care, ENT, Paediat. O & G) ChristCh. Hosp. Roy. Bournemouth Hosp. & Poole Hosp. Prev: SHO (A & E) Poole Hosp. Dorset; Ho. Off. (Med.) Roy. Bournemouth Hosp.; Ho. Off. (Surg.) Poole Hosp.

CHAMBERLAIN, Anna Louise 48 Kingsley Avenue, London W13 0EG — MB ChB 1998 Liverp.; MB ChB Liverp 1998.

CHAMBERLAIN, Carole Ann 71 Cavendish Road, Matlock DE4 3HD Tel: 01629 57657 — MB BS 1978 Lond.; DCH RCP Lond. 1990.

CHAMBERLAIN, Professor Douglas Anthony, CBE, Commander, British Merchant Navy (retired) 25 Woodland Drive, Hove BN3 6DH Tel: 01273 882084 Fax: 01273 566526 Email: chambda@pavillion.co.uk — MB BChir Camb. 1957; MD Camb. 1967; DSc (Hon.) Sussex 1989; FRCP Lond. 1974, M 1959; FRCA 1994; FACC 1992; FESC 1988. Hon. Cons. Cardiol. & Phys. Roy. Sussex Co. Hosp. Brighton; Prof. Resusc. (Hon. Chair) Centre for Applied Pub. Health Med. Univ. Wales Coll.of Med.; Vis. Prof. Univ. of Sussex. Prev: Asst. Resid. Med. Off. Nat. Heart Hosp. Lond.

CHAMBERLAIN, Professor Geoffrey Victor Price, RD, Surg. Cdr. RNR Retd. (retired) Department of Obstetrics & Gynaecology, Singleton Hospital, Sketty, Swansea SA2 8QA Tel: 01792 285173 Fax: 01792 208647 — MB BS Lond. 1954; MD Lond. 1968; FRCS Eng. 1960; MFFP; FFFP (Hon.) 1996; FSLCOG (Hon.) 1994; FACOG (Hon.) 1990; FRCOG 1978, M 1963; DObst 1956. Hon. Cons. Singleton Hosp. Swansea (Teachg. & Research); Examr. Univ. Lond., Liverp., Birm., Manch., Camb., Glas., Nottm., Cardiff, Lagos, Zaria, Kuala Lumpur, Sri Lanka; Edit. Contemporary Rev. Obst. & Gyn. Prev: Prof. & Chairm. O & G St. Geo. Hosp. Med. Sch. Lond.

CHAMBERLAIN, Helen Mary Flat 5, 2 Hayes Lane, Bromley BR2 9EB — MB BS 1991 Lond.; MRCP (UK) 1994. Regist. (Gen. Med. & c/o Elderly) Maidstone Hosp. Prev: SHO (Gen. Med.) Brook Gen. Hosp. Lond.; SHO (Gen. & Geriat. Med.) FarnBoro. Hosp. Orpington.

CHAMBERLAIN, Jennifer Ann (retired) 25 Woodland Drive, Hove BN3 6DH Tel: 01273 882084 Fax: 01273 566526 Email: chambda@pavilion.co.uk — MB BS 1957 Lond. Prev: Ho. Phys. & Ho. Surg. St. Martin's Hosp. Bath.

CHAMBERLAIN, Jeremy Hansard (retired) Flat C, 18 Garrick St, London WC2E 9BD Tel: 020 7228 8416 — MB BS Lond. 1961; FRCP Lond. 1992; MRCP (UK) 1967; DIC 1969. Flat 3, 40 King St., Lond. WC2E 8JS Tel: 020 7379 8216; Email: chamberlain@ukgateway.net. Prev: Dir. & Cons. Palliat. Med. Trinity Hospice Clapham Lond.

CHAMBERLAIN, Professor Jocelyn Olivia Peter Sycamores, Llanmadoc, Gower, Swansea SA3 1DB Tel: 01792 386325 — MB BS Lond. 1955; FRCP Lond. 1985; MRCS Eng. LRCP Lond. 1955; FFPHM 1976, M 1972; DCH Eng. 1959. (St. Geo.) Emerit. Prof. Community Med. Inst. Cancer Research Lond.; Chairm. Adv. Bd. of S. W. Wales Cancer Inst. Socs: Fell. Roy. Soc. Med. (Ex-Chairm. Oncol. Sect.); (Ex-Chairm.) Soc. Social Med. Prev: Dir. Cancer Screening Eval. Unit, Inst. Cancer Research Lond.; Sen. Lect. (Community Med.) Univ. Coll. Hosp. Med. Sch.; Sen. Research Fell. (Pub. Health) Lond. Sch. Hyg. & Trop. Med.

CHAMBERLAIN, Mr John Nuffield Hospital, Newcastle upon Tyne NE2 1JP Tel: 0191 281 6131 Fax: 0191 281 1379; 4 Lynwood Close, Darras Hall, Ponteland, Newcastle upon Tyne NE20 9JG Tel: 01661 822148 — MB ChB St. And. 1963; FRCS Ed. 1967; FRCS Eng. 1998. Emerit. Cons. Gen. & Vasc. Surg. Freeman Hosp. Newc. u. Tyne. Socs: Vasc. Surg. Soc. Gt. Brit. & Irel.; BMA; Eur. Vasc. Soc. Prev: Sen. Regist. (Surg.) Roy. Infirm. Edin.; Ho. Surg. Maryfield Hosp. Dundee; SHO (Surg.) Leicester Roy. Infirm.

CHAMBERLAIN, John Wilfred (retired) 21 Ladywood Road, Old Hall, Warrington WA5 9QR — MB ChB 1953 Manch. Prev: Ho. Surg. Ancoats Hosp. Manch.

CHAMBERLAIN, Jonathan Ian 28 Bemersyde Drive, Jesmond, Newcastle upon Tyne NE2 2HJ — MB BS 1990 Newc.; BDS Newc. 1985; DCH RCP Lond. 1995; DRCOG 1995. Specialist Regist. (O & G) N. Region.

CHAMBERLAIN, Malcolm Robert St. Martins Health Care, Manor Stores, Les Camos du Moullin, St Martin's, Guernsey G74 6DA Email: healthcaregroup@compuserve.com; Le Pet't Maisaon, Les Caches, St. Martins, Guernsey GY4 6PW Tel: 01481 37612 — MB ChB 1978 Birm.; MRCP (UK) 1980; DRCOG 1982. (Birmingham)

CHAMBERLAIN, Professor Marcella Anne, OBE Academic Unit of Musculo Skelelal and Rehabilitation Medicine, School of Medicine, 36 Clarendon Road, Leeds LS2 9NZ Tel: (0113) 233 4936 Fax: (0113) 243 0366 Email: m.a.chamberlain@leeds.ac.uk; 7 The Drive, Roundhay, Leeds LS8 1JF Tel: (0113) 266 7036 Fax: (0113) 266 7036 — FRCPCH 1997; MB BS Lond. 1962; BSc Lond. 1959; FRCP Lond. 1980; MRCS Eng. LRCP Lond. 1962; MRCP (UK) 1966; DCH Eng. 1964. (Guy's) CharterHo. Prof. Rehabil. Med., Univ. Of Leeds. Socs: (Ex-Pres.) Soc. Research Rehabil.; (Ex-Pres.) Brit. Soc. Rehabil. Med.; Vice-Pres. Europ. Acad. of Rehabil. Prev: Cons. Rheum. Gen. Infirm. Leeds; Sen. Regist. (Rheum.) Gen. Infirm. Leeds; Sen. Regist. (Rheum. & Rehabil.) Middlx. Hosp. Lond.

CHAMBERLAIN, Mark Edwin Department of Anaesthetics, Victoria Hospital, Whinney Heys Road, Blackpool FY3 8 Tel: 01253 303499; Red Lion Cottage, Catforth, Preston PR4 0HE Tel: 01772 690225 — MB ChB 1979 Birm.; FFA RCS Eng. 1983. Cons. Anaesth. Roy. Vict. Hosp. Blackpool. Prev: Sen. Regist. (Anaesth.) N. W.. RHA; Regist. (Anaesth.) Coventry HA; SHO (Anaesth.) E. Birm. HA.

CHAMBERLAIN, Martin Harold 18 Fulford Crescent, Willerby, Hull HU10 6NR Tel: 01482 654787 Email: drmartin@globalnet.co.uk — MB ChB 1993 Bristol; FRCS Eng. 1997. (Bristol) Regist. (Cardiothoracic Surg.) Oxf. Heart Centre, John Radcliffe Hosp., Oxf. Socs: Advanced Trauma & Life Support; MDU; BMA. Prev: Specialist SHO (Cardiothoracic Surg.) Papworth Hosp. Camb.; SHO (Gen. Surg.) Horton Gen. Banbury; SHO (Cardiothoracic Surg. & Trauma) John Radcliffe Hosp. Oxf.

CHAMBERLAIN, Mary Joanna 16 Grimsdyke Crescent, Arkley, Barnet EN5 4AG — MB BS 1978 Lond.; FFA RCS Eng. 1984.

CHAMBERLAIN, Michael Neville Bushloe End Surgery, 48 Bushloe End, Wigston, Leicester Tel: 0116 288 3477; 9 Cottage Road, Wigston Magna, Leicester LE18 3SA — MB BS 1961 Durh.

CHAMBERLAIN, Paul Francis John Nuffield Department of Obstetrics & Gynaecology, John Radcliffe Hospital, Headington, Oxford OX3 9DU Tel: 01865 221023 Fax: 01865 221164 Email: paul.chamberlain@obs-gyn.ox.ac.uk — MB BCh BAO 1976 Dub.; MA Oxf. 1989; MD Dub. 1989; FRCSC (Obst. & Gyn.) 1982; FACOG 1984. (Trinity College, Dublin) Lect. & Hon. Cons. Nuffield Dept. Obst. & Gyn. John Radcliffe Hosp. Oxf. Prev: Sen. Regist. Dept. O & G Regional Hosp. Galway; Fell. Div. Matern.-Fetal Med. Univ. Manitoba, Canada; Resid. (O & G) Qu. Univ. Kingston, Ontario, Canada.

CHAMBERLAIN, Sara Jane South Warwickshire Combined Care Trust, St. Michaels Hospital, St Michaels Road, Warwick CV34 5QW Tel: 01926 406789; Green Acre, Fern Hill Lane, Balsall Common, Coventry CV7 7AN Tel: 01676 532122 — MB BS 1986 Lond. (Middlx. Hosp. Med. Sch.) Clin. Asst. (Old Age Psychiat.) S. Warks. Combined Care Trust.

CHAMBERLAIN, Satoru Theodove Derbyshire Royal Infirmary, London Road, Derby DE1 2QY — MB BS 1986 Queensland.

CHAMBERLAIN, Simon Keith Dept. of Anaesthesia, Horton Hospital, Oxford Rd, Banbury Email: skc100@hotmail.com; 1 Town Well-End, Fritwell, Bicester OX27 7QD — MB BChir 1990 Camb.; MA Camb. 1991, MB BChir 1990; FRCA 1996. Cons. Anaesth. Oxf. Radcliffe NHS Trust.

CHAMBERLAIN, Victoria Elizabeth 39 Floral Farm, Canford Magna, Wimborne BH21 3AT Tel: 01202 889524 Email: vickychamberlain@hotmail.com — MB ChB 1996 Bristol. Surgic. SHO Rotat., Derriford Hosp.

CHAMBERLAIN, William Burt (retired) 57 Cumby Road, Newton Aycliffe DL5 5JU Tel: 01325 312238 — MB BS 1954 Durh.; DA Eng. 1956. Dent. Anaesth. Newton Aycliffe. Prev: GP Newton Aycliffe.

CHAMBERLAIN-WEBBER, James Anthony Amyas Seymour Deepdene, 47 Falmer Road, Rottingdean, Brighton BN2 7DA Tel: 01273 303787; Deepdene, 47 Falmer Road, Rottingdean, Brighton BN2 7DA Tel: 01273 303787 — MRCS Eng. LRCP Lond. 1953; MA (Hons.) Camb.; DA Eng. 1959. (Camb. & Westm.) Clin. Asst. (Anaesth.) Brighton HA. Socs: Hist. of Anasthesia. Prev: Ho. Surg. W.m. Hosp. (All St.s); Anaesth. Med. Br. RAF; Resid. Anaesth. Liverp. Roy. Infirm.

CHAMBERLAIN WEBBER, Rafe Francis Owen Cardiac Department, Bristol Royal Infirmary, Bristol BS2 8HW Tel: 0117 928 2665 Fax: 0117 928 2666 Email: mdrxcw@bristol.ac.uk — MB BChir 1985 Camb.; BA (Hons.) Camb. 1982, MD 1997; MA Camb. 1986; MRCP (UK) 1989. Specialist Regist. Bristol Roy. Infirm.; Clin. Lect. Cardiol. Univ. of Bristol. Socs: N. Amer. Soc. Pacing & Electrophysiol.; Brit. Cardiovasc. Interven. Soc.; Brit. Cardiac Soc. Prev: Fell. (Cardiol.) Indiana Heart Ins. Indianapolis, USA; Research Fell. (Cardiol.) W.m. Hosp. Lond.

CHAMBERLIN, Andrew James 17 Custom House Reach, Odessa St., London SE16 7LX — BA Oxf. 1975; BM Soton. 1985; DCH RCP Lond. 1987; MRCGP 1990; MRCPsych 1994. (Southampton) Specialist Regist. (Psychother.) Cassel & W. Middlx. Hosps.

CHAMBERLIN, Jane Elizabeth The Croft, Ashford Road, Lenham, Maidstone ME17 — MB BS 1978 Lond.; DRCOG 1980.

CHAMBERS, Alexander Noel 8 Brean Down Avenue, Bristol BS9 4JF — MB ChB 1998 Bristol.

CHAMBERS, Barbara Jill Eastholme Surgery, 2 Heaton Moor Road, Stockport SK4 4NT Tel: 0161 443 1177 Fax: 0161 442 2521 — MB BCh BAO 1981 Belf. SHO (A & E) W.. Health & Social Servs. Bd. Prev: SHO (Gen. Med.) N.. Health & Social Servs. Bd.; SHO (Chest Med.) E.. Health & Social Servs. Bd.

CHAMBERS, Camilla 3 Green Lane, Tiptree, Colchester CO5 0DA — BM BS 1992 Nottm.

CHAMBERS, Mrs Catharine Ann Department of Psychiatry, Bassetlaw District General Hospital, Kilton, Worksop; 13 Ringwood, Worksop S81 0SH Tel: 01909 472151 — MB ChB 1967 St. And.; MRCPsych 1975; DPM Ed. & Glas. 1973. (St. And.) Cons. Psychiat. (Geriat.) Trent RHA. Prev: Sen. Regist. (Psychiat.) Roy. Dundee Liff Hosp.; Regist. (Psychiat.) & SHO (Psychiat.) Roy. Dundee Liff Hosp.; SHO Trainee in Community Med. Tayside Health Bd.

CHAMBERS, Clare Alison 26 Maxwell Road, Bangor BT20 3SG — MB BCh BAO 1986 Belf.; MB BCh Belf. 1986.

CHAMBERS, Clare Helen Airedale General Hospital, Steeton, Keighley BD20 6TD Tel: 01535 652511 — MB BS 1986 Lond.; MRCPsych 1993; MRCGP 1990. Cons. (Gen. Adult Psychiat.) Airedale Gen. Hosp.

CHAMBERS, Douglas Robert (retired) Coroner's Court, Milton Court, Moor Lane, London EC2Y 9BL Tel: 020 7332 1598 Fax: 020 7601 2714 — MB BS Lond. 1953; MA Wales 1989; LLB Lond. 1960; DObst RCOG 1959. HM Coroner City of Lond.; Barrister Lincoln's Inn 1965; Hon. Sen. Lect. Legal Med. Dept. of Histopath. Roy. Free Hosp. Med. Sch. Lond.; Recognised Teach. Univ. Lond. Prev: HM Coroner Inner N. Lond.

CHAMBERS, Mr Duncan Keith Accident and Emergency Department, Leighton Hospital, Middlewich Road, Crewe CW1 4QJ Tel: 01270 612270 Fax: 01270 612004 — MB ChB 1977 Liverp.; FRCS Eng. 1982; FRCS Ed. 1982; FFAEM 1994. (Liverpool) Cons. (A & E) Leighton Hosp. Crewe.

***CHAMBERS, Eleanor Anne** 21 Rignals Lane, Chelmsford CM2 8QT Tel: 0956 268854 — MB BS 1998 Lond.; MB BS Lond 1998.

CHAMBERS, (Elizabeth) Joanna Southmead Hospital, North Bristol Trust, Westbury on Trym, Bristol BS10 5NB — MB BS 1969 Lond.; MRCS Eng. LRCP Lond. 1969; FRCR 1989; Dip. Palliat. Med. Wales 1993; DCH Eng. 1972; DObst RCOG 1971; FRCP 1999. (Roy. Free) p/t Cons. Clin. Oncol. & Palliat. Med. S.mead, N. Bristol Trust; Sen. Clin. Lect. in Clin. Oncol. and Palliat. Med., Univ. of Bristol. Socs: BMA; Bristol M-C Soc.; Assn. Palliat. Med. Prev: Sen. Regist. & Regist. (Clin. Oncol.) Bristol Roy. Infirm.; Clin. Asst. (Oncol.) Univ. Leeds & St. Jas. Hosp. Leeds; SHO (Paediat.) Roy. W. Sussex Hosp. Chichester.

CHAMBERS, Frances 12 Chorley Road, Hilldale, Parbold, Wigan WN8 7AL Tel: 01257 462058 — MB BCh BAO 1967 Belf. (Qu. Univ. Belf.) Staff Grade Paediat. (Community Child Health) Wigan. Socs: BACCH. Prev: Clin. Asst. (Venereol.) Roy. Vict. Hosp. Belf.; Med. Off. Wesley Guild Hosp. Ilesha, Nigeria; Ho. Off. Waveney Hosp. Ballymena.

CHAMBERS, Garry Crown Street Surgery, 17 Crown Street, Swinton, Rotherham S64 8LY Tel: 01709 583862 — MB ChB 1974 Sheff.; DCH Eng. 1978. GP MexBoro. & Swinton S. Yorks.

CHAMBERS, Gary Burncross Surgery, 1 Bevan Way, Chapeltown, Sheffield S35 1RN Tel: 0114 246 6052 Fax: 0114 245 0276; 21 Rocher Avenue, Grenoside, Sheffield S35 8QN Tel: 0114 246 2611 — MB ChB 1975 Sheff.; MRCGP 1979; DRCOG 1978; DCH Eng. 1977. Assoc. Adviser (Gen. Pract.) Sheff. Univ. Prev: Course Organiser Sheff. GP VTS.

CHAMBERS, Mr Gordon Manson The Manor House, Helpston Road, Ailsworth, Peterborough PE5 7AE Tel: 01733 380479 — MB BS 1957 Adelaide; FRCS Eng. 1964. Cons. Orthop. Surg. P'boro. Dist. Hosp. Socs: Fell. BOA & Roy. Soc. Med. Prev: Sen. Regist. Roy. Orthop. Hosp. Birm. & Birm. Accid. Hosp.

CHAMBERS, Harry Wigfield, TD (retired) Westcliffe Road, Ruskington, Sleaford NG34 9A Tel: 01526 834269 — MB ChB 1952 Sheff. JP. Prev: Maj. RAMC (V) Regtl. Med. Off. 5th Roy. Anglian Regt.

CHAMBERS, Helen Clare 23 Carleton Rise, Welwyn AL6 9RP — MB ChB 1995 Bristol.

CHAMBERS, Helen Heggie (retired) 28 Balbec Avenue, Leeds LS6 2BB — MB ChB 1940 Glas. Prev: Clin. Asst. Glas. Inst. of Radiother.

CHAMBERS, Herbert Neville (retired) 111 Selby Road, West Bridgford, Nottingham NG2 7BB Tel: 0115 923 1051 — MB BS 1951 Lond.; MRCS Eng. LRCP Lond. 1950; FFA RCS Eng. 1959. Prev: Cons. Anaesth. Nottm. Hosps.

CHAMBERS, Iain Robert Department of Orthopaedics, Queen Elizabeth Hospital, Gateshead NE9 6SX — MB ChB 1994 Aberd.

CHAMBERS, Jacqueline Sybil The Beanstalk, Gipsy Lane, Dordon, Tamworth B78 1SX Tel: 01827 893381 Fax: 01827 893360 — MB BS 1974 Lond.; BSc (Hons.) Lond. 1972; FFPHM RCP (UK) 1990; MFCM 1984. (Middlx.) Dir. Pub. Health Birm. HA. Prev: Chief Med. Off. Health Educat. Auth.; Dist. Med. Off. N. Birm. HA; Specialist (Community Med.) W. Midl. RHA.

CHAMBERS, Jeremy Martin John 78 Windmill Road, Hillsborough BT26 6LX — MB ChB 1988 Birm.

CHAMBERS, John Boyd Department of Cardiology, Guy's and St Thomas' Hospital, Lambeth Palace Road, London SE1 7EH Tel: 020 7928 9292 Ext: 6036 Fax: 020 7960 5680 Email: johnchambers@dial.pipex.com — MB 1980 Camb.; MB BChir Camb. 1980; MD Camb. 1990, MA 1980; MRCP (UK) 1982; FRCP 1996; FESC 1997; FACC 1997. Reader & Hon. Cons. Cardiol. Guy's & St Thomas' Hosps.; Hon. Cons. Cardiol. Maidstone Hosp. Kent. Socs: (Counc.) Brit. Soc. Echocardiogr.; Brit. Cardiac Soc.; Soc. of Heart Valve Dis. Prev: Sen. Regist. (Cardiol.) United Med. & Dent. Sch. Guys. Hosp. Lond.; Regist. (Cardiol.) St. Geo. Hosp. Lond.; Fell. Brit. Heart Foundat. Kings Coll. Hosp. Lond.

CHAMBERS, John Campbell Squirrels, Beech Close, Cobham KT11 2EN — MB BS 1991 Lond.

CHAMBERS, John Charles The Katharine House Hospice, East End, Adderbury OX17 3NC Tel: 1295 811866; 11 West Bar Street, Banbury OX16 9SD — MB ChB 1989 Ed.; MSc 2000; MRCGP 1993; DFFP 1994; DRCOG 1994. (Edin.) Macmillan Cons. and Med. Director in Palliat. Med., Banbury.

CHAMBERS, John Joseph Arrowe Park Hospital, Upton, Wirral CH49 5PE Tel: 0151 678 5111; The Knoll, Hinderton Road, Neston, South Wirral CH64 9PF — MB ChB 1967 Liverp.; FFA RCS Eng. 1972. Cons. Anaesth. Arrowe Pk. Hosp. Socs: (Hon. Sec.) Liverp. Soc. Anaesth.

CHAMBERS, John Paul c/o 21 High Beech, The Warren, Bracknell RG12 9YY — MB BChir 1990 Camb.

CHAMBERS, Jonathan The Health Centre, Albert Street, Lydney GL15 5NQ Tel: 01594 845222 Fax: 01594 845637 — MB ChB 1980 Bristol; BSc (Psychol.) Bristol 1974.

CHAMBERS, Jonathan Clifford 81 Penley House, Treliske Hospital, Treliske, Truro TR1 3LJ — MB BS 1998 Lond.; MB BS Lond 1998.

CHAMBERS, Kenneth Boyd (retired) Hillingdon, 15 Bidborough Ridge, Tunbridge Wells TN4 0UT Tel: 01892 528234 — MB BS Lond. 1947; MRCS Eng. LRCP Lond. 1947; FFA RCS Eng. 1954; DA Eng. 1952. Cons. Anaesth. Tunbridge Wells Hosp. Gp. Prev: Sen. Regist. St. Mary's Hosp. Lond.

CHAMBERS, Kenneth Henry Stony Stratford Surgery, Market Square, Stony Stratford, Milton Keynes MK11 1YA Tel: 01908 565555; 36 Wolverton Road, Stony Stratford, Milton Keynes MK11 1DX — MB ChB 1969 St. And.; DCH Eng. 1973; DObst RCOG 1971. Hosp. Pract. (Paediat.) Milton Keynes Gen. & N.ampton Gen. Hosps. Prev: Ho. Phys. Arbroath Infirm.; Ho. Off. Bushey Matern. Hosp.; Paediat. Resid. McMaster Univ. Hamilton, Canada.

CHAMBERS, Lesley Helen Tel: 01749 812310 Fax: 01749 812938; Park House, High St, Evercreech, Shepton Mallet BA4 6HZ Tel: 01749 830087 — MB BS 1982 Lond.; DRCOG 1985.

CHAMBERS, Margaret North House, Firth Home Farm, Roslin EH25 9QQ — MB ChB 1969 Aberd.

CHAMBERS, Margaret Sarah 93 Crosskeys Road, Keady, Armagh BT60 3JU Tel: 01861 538737 — MB BCh BAO 1979 Belf.; MRCGP 1983; DCH RCPI 1983; DRCOG 1982. (Qu. Univ. Belf.) Course Organiser Craigavon Area Hosp. Socs: BMA (S.. Div. N. Irel.); (Comm.) Med. Equestrian Soc.; BASICS. Prev: Hon. Sec. N.. Irel. Fac. RCGP.

CHAMBERS, Marie Theresa 21 The Boltons, London SW10 9SU — LRCP LRCS 1975 Ed.; LRCP LRCS Ed. LRCPS Glas. 1975; DCH RCP Glas. 1980. Sen. Med. Off. (Primary Health Care Progr.) Rahim Yar Khan, Pakistan. Prev: Med. Super. Jirapa Hosp., Ghana.

CHAMBERS, Mark Edwin Wigfield Penistan and Partners, Cordell Road, Long Melford, Sudbury CO10 9EP Tel: 01787 378226 Fax: 01787 311287; Wigfield House, Laurel Drive, Long Melford, Sudbury CO10 9ER Tel: 01787 378902 Email: chambo@dial.pipx.com — MB ChB 1981 Sheff.; MRCGP (Distinc.) 1985; DCH RCP Lond. 1985; DRCOG 1984; Cert. Family Plann. JCC 1984. (Sheff.) Socs: Sudbury Med. Soc. Prev: Trainee GP Lincoln VTS; Ho. Surg. Roy. Hallamsh. Hosp. Sheff.; Ho. Phys. N.. Gen. Hosp. Sheff.

***CHAMBERS, Martyn David** 2 The Square, Eynsham, Witney OX29 4HW Tel: 01865 880851; 2 The Square, Eynsham, Witney OX29 4HW Tel: 01865 880851 — MB BS 1997 Lond.; BSc (Hons.) Immunol. Lond. 1994.

CHAMBERS, Michael Fergus High Street Surgery, 60 High Street, Lurgan, Craigavon BT66 8BA Tel: 028 3832 4591 Fax: 028 3834 9000; 19 Dorchester Park, Belfast BT9 6RH — MB BCh BAO 1981 Belf.; MRCGP 1985; DCH RCPI 1983; DRCOG 1983. Socs: BMA; Ulster Med. Soc. Prev: Med. Audit Adviser S.. Health & Social Servs. Bd.

CHAMBERS, Monica Mary 8 Ramsay Road, London W3 8AZ — BM BCh 1984 Oxf.; DRCOG 1989.

CHAMBERS, Nicholas Quarter Jack Surgery, Rodways Corner, Wimborne BH21 1AP Tel: 01202 882112 Fax: 01202 882368 — BChir 1966 Camb.; MA Camb. 1966, MB 1967; DObst RCOG 1970; DA Eng. 1969. (Univ. Coll. Hosp.) Med. Off. Vict. Hosp. Wimborne. Prev: Ho. Phys., Ho. Surg. & SHO Univ. Coll. Hosp. Lond.

CHAMBERS, Philip Henry Department of Anaesthetics, Milton Keynes General Hospital, Milton Keynes MK6 5LD Tel: 01908 660033 Fax: 01908 243159 Email: phil.chambers@mks-tr.answx.nhs.uk — MB ChB 1975 Bristol; FFARCS Eng. 1980. Cons. Anaesth. Milton Keynes Dist. Gen. Hosp. Socs: BMA; Assn. Anaesth.; Intens. Care Soc. Prev: Dist. Clin. Tutor Milton Keynes Hosp.; Sen. Regist. (Anaesth.) Addenbrookes Hosp. Camb.; Regist. (Anaesth.) Univ. Hosp. Wales Cardiff.

CHAMBERS, Robert Meredith, Tibberton, Gloucester GL2 8DZ — MB BS 1952 Durh.

CHAMBERS, Robert Mark Cranford Medical Centre, 24 High Street, Cranford, Hounslow West, Hounslow TW5 9RG Tel: 020 8564 8696 Fax: 020 8564 7891 — MB BS 1983 Lond.

CHAMBERS, Ruth Florence Marlborough Family Service, 38 marlborough Place, St. Johns Wood, London NW8 0PJ Tel: 020 7624 8605 Fax: 020 7328 2185 — MB BS Lond. 1965; MRCS Eng. LRCP Lond. 1965; MRCPsych 1973. (Middlesex Hospital) p/t Cons. Child Psychiat. MarlBoro. Family Serv. Socs: Roy. Coll. Psychiat.; BMA. Prev: Sen. Regist. (Childr. & Parents) Tavistock Clinic.

CHAMBERS, Professor Ruth Margaret Primary Care Development Unit, School of Health, Staffordshire University, Beaconside, Stafford ST18 0AD Tel: 01785 353766 Fax: 01785 220290; Ivy Cottage, The Outlanes, Stone ST15 8UU Tel: 01785 815008 Fax: 01785 815008 — BM BS 1975 Nottm.; DM Nottm. 1995; BMedSci Nottm. 1973; FRCGP 1992, M 1980; DRCOG 1978. (Nottm.) Prof. Health Commiss.ing; GP Stress Fell. RCGP & DoH; GP Non Princip.; Mem. of Human Fertilisation & Embryology Auth. Socs: Counc. RCGP. Prev: GP Stone, Staffs.; GP Mobberley.

CHAMBERS, Sharon 20 Collingwood Crescent, Guildford GU1 2NS — MB BS 1975 Lond.; MSc Lond. 1981, MB BS 1975; MRCPath 1981. Dir. Pub. Health Laborat. Epsom. Prev: Cons. Microbiol. E.bourne Dist. Gen. Hosp.; Asst. Med. Microbiol. PHL St. Luke's Hosp. Guildford; Trainee Med. Microbiol. PHL Dulwich Hosp.

CHAMBERS, Shaun James 9 Stone Pits Meadow, Wilmcote, Stratford-upon-Avon CV37 9WA — MB ChB 1987 Liverp.

CHAMBERS, Sheelagh Ann Albertbridge Road Day Hospital, Belfast BT5 4PX Tel: 01232 456007 — MB BCh BAO 1981 Belf.; MRCPsych 1986. Assoc. Specialist (Psychiat.) Albertbridge Rd. Day Hosp. Belf.

CHAMBERS, Steven John Church Lane Surgery, 24 Church Lane, Brighouse HD6 1AS Tel: 01484 714349 Fax: 01484 720479; 3 Elsinore Court, Elsinore Avenue, Elland HX5 0NG — MB BS 1980 Lond.; MRCS Eng. LRCP Lond. 1980.

CHAMBERS, Susan Malago Surgery, 40 St. Johns Road, Bedminster, Bristol BS3 4JE Tel: 0117 966 3587 Fax: 0117 963 1422; 13 Redcliffe Parade, Redcliffe, Bristol BS1 6SP Tel: 0117 929 2220 — BM BS 1980 Nottm.; MSc (Gen. Pract.) Lond. 1991; BMedSci (Hons.) Nottm. 1978. Prev: GP Nottm.; Trainee GP Lincoln VTS.

CHAMBERS, Susan Jane 51 Richhill Crescent, Belfast BT5 6HF — MB BCh BAO 1996 Belf.

CHAMBERS, Professor Timothy John Department of Histopathology, St Georges Hospital Medical School, Cranmer Terrace, Tooting, London SW17 0RE Tel: 020 8725 5270 — MB BS 1972 Lond.; PhD (Lond.) 1978, BSc 1969, MB BS 1972; MRCPath 1979. (Middlx.) Prof. Histopath., Hon. Cons., Head of Dept. Histopath. St. Geo. Hosp. Med. Sch. Lond. Socs: Internat. Assn. Path. Prev: Sen. Lect. Hon. Cons. (Histopath.) St. Bart. Hosp. Lond.; Regist. (Histopath.) St. Bart. Hosp. Lond.; Ho. Surg. Middlx. Hosp. Lond.

CHAMBERS, Timothy Lachlan 2 Clifton Park, Bristol BS8 3BS Tel: 0117 906 4209 Fax: 0117 973 0887; 4 Clyde Park, Bristol BS6 6RR Tel: 0117 974 2814 Fax: 0117 907 3314 Email: chambers_home@hotmail.com — MB BS 1969 Lond.; 1995 FRCPI; 1985 FRCP Ed.; 1983 FRCP Lond. M (UK) 1972; 1969 MRCS Eng. LRCP Lond.; 1997 FRCPCH; 1993 JP. (King's Coll. & King's Coll. Hosp.) Cons. Phys. Roy. Hosp. Sick Childr. Bristol; Cons. Paediat (Civil.) RN; Sen. Clin. Lect. Univ. Bristol; Mem. Comm. on Safety of Meds.; Trustee Roy. Med. Benevolent Fund; LtCol RAMC (V); Cons. Paediat. S.mead Hosp. Bristol & W.on super Mare Gen Hosp. Socs: Correspondant De La Sociétée Française de Pédiatrie; Fell. Roy. Soc. Med. (Vice Pres.). Prev: Phys. Derbysh. Childr. Hosp. & Childr. Depts. Univ. & City Hosps. Nottm.; Sen. Regist. (Ren med.) St. Jas. Hosp. Leeds; Tutor (Paediat. & Child Health) Univ. Leeds.

CHAMBERS, William Bell P.O. Box 1117, Simpsonville SC 29681, USA Tel: 001 864 294 0655; 6 Orchard Gardens, Whitburn, Sunderland SR6 7JW Tel: 0191 529 3374 — MB BS 1953 Durh. Socs: Fell. Roy. Soc. Med.; Assoc. Mem. Roy. Coll. Gen. Pract.; Emerit. Mem. Amer. Coll. Sports Med. Prev: Vice-Pres. Med Director W.minster Research Servs. USA; Director Med. Research Brysto Myels, USA; Sen. Director Internat. Med. Dept. Producers Scherinc-Plouck Pharmaceut., USA.

CHAMBERS, William Ernest Lisburn Health Centre, Linenhall St., Lisburn BT28 1LU Tel: 01846 603203; 78 Windmill Road, Hillsborough BT26 6LX — MB BCh BAO 1958 Belf.

CHAMBERS, William Mordaunt 51E Chepstow Place, London W2 4TS — MB BS 1996 Lond.

CHAMBLER, Andrew Frank William St Mary's Hospital, Norfolk Place, Paddington, London W2 1PG Tel: 020 7725 6666; 22 Queens Mill Road, Fulham, London SW6 6JS Tel: 020 7355 9245 Email: 106435.3551@compuserve.com — MB BS 1992 Lond.; BSc Clin. Sci. Lond. 1991, MB BS 1992; FRCS Eng. 1996. (St. Mary's) Specialist. Regist. Rotat. (Orthop.) NW Thames. Socs: BOA; BOTA; Roy. Soc. Med. Prev: SHO Rotat. (Surg.) St. Mary's Hosp. Lond.; Ho. Off. (Gen. Med.) Centr. Middlx. Hosp.; Ho. Off. (Gen. Surg. & Orthop.) St. Mary's Hosp. Lond.

CHAMBLER, Mr Kenneth (retired) Norwood, Swife Lane, Broadoak, Heathfield TN21 8UR Tel: 01435 883244 — MB ChB 1951 Ed.; MCh Ed. 1969, MB ChB 1951; MD Texas 1960; FRCS Ed. 1959; FRCS Eng. 1959. Prev: Research Fell. (Burns) E. Grinstead.

CHAMINGS, Rosa Eleanor 70 Bower Mount Road, Maidstone ME16 8AT — BSc (Hons.) Lond. 1927, MD 1933, MB BS 1930; MRCS Eng. LRCP Lond. 1929. (Lond. Sch. Med. Wom.) Prev: Asst. Med. Off. Lewisham Hosp. & St. Giles Hosp. Camberwell (LCC) & Hammersmith Hosp. (Postgrad. Med. Sch.).

CHAMLEY, Mark 14 Salters Court, Gosforth, Newcastle upon Tyne NE3 5BH — MB BS 1987 Lond.

CHAMOUN, Viquar 53 Wells Street, London W1T 3PS — MB BS 1988 Lond.; BA (Hons.) Camb. 1984; MRCP (UK) 1992. Clin. Lect. Inst. Neurol. & The Nat. Hosp. for Neurol. & Neurosurg. Prev: Regist. (Med.) Mayday Hosp. Surrey.

CHAMP, Caroline Susan Dept Histopathology, Royal Glamorgan Hospital, Ynys Maerdy, Llantrisant, Pontyclun CF72 8XR Tel: 01443 443443 — MB BS 1983 Lond.; MRCPath 1991; FRCPath 2000. Cons. Histopath. E. Roy. Glam. Hosp.

CHAMP, Charles John (retired) Willowdene, Willow Lane, London Road, Amersham HP7 9DW — MD Lond. 1950, MB BS (Hons.) 1942; MRCS Eng. LRCP Lond. 1942; FRCOG 1965, M 1950. Prev: Cons. O & G Amersham & High Wycombe Area.

CHAMP, Roderick Charles Great Surries, Ellesborough Road, Butlers Cross, Aylesbury HP17 0XA Tel: 01296 623381 — MB BS 1981 Lond.; MRCS Eng. LRCP Lond. 1981; MRCGP 1985; DRCOG 1983. (St. Bart.) CMP RAF Halton; CMO Pruden. Assur Company. Socs: Fell. Assur. Med. Soc.

CHAMPION, Alan Frederick (retired) Lawnswood, Spring Hill, Ventnor PO38 1PH Tel: 01983 852696 Fax: 01983 852696 — MB BS 1953 Lond.; MRCGP 1965; DObst RCOG 1954; Cert. Av Med. MoD (Air) & Civil; Aviat. Auth. 1975. RN Surg. & Agent; Authorized Examr. Civil Aviat. Auth. Dept. of Transport. Prev: Ho. Surg. (O & G) King's Coll. Hosp.

CHAMPION, Audrey Elizabeth North Wales Cancer Treatment Centre, Glan Clwyd District General Hospital, Rhyl LL18 5UJ Tel: 01745 445148 Fax: 01745 445212 Email: dr.audrey.champion@cd_tr.wales.nhs.uk; Tel: 01745 710565 Email: rogersonjrg@aol.com — MB ChB 1974 Sheff.; FRCP Lond. 1996; MRCP (UK) 1977; FRCR 1981. Clin. Dir., N Wales Cancer Treatm. Centre Glan Clwyd Dist. Gen. Hosp. Prev: Cons. Clin. Oncol. W.on Pk. Hosp. Sheff.; SHO (Gen. Med.) Nottm. City Hosp.

CHAMPION, Christopher John Cheltenham Road Surgery, 16 Cheltenham Road, Gloucester GL2 0LS Tel: 01452 522575 Fax: 01452 304321 Email: crs@doctors.org.uk — MB BS 1976 Lond.; 2000 D.Occ.Med; MRCGP 1980.

CHAMPION, Jennifer Kirsteen Craufurd, Kevock Road, Lasswade EH18 1HX; Scottish Centre for Infection and Environmental Health, Clifton House, Clifton Place, Glasgow G3 7LN — BM BCh 1992 Oxf.; BSc (Hons) 1989; MRCGP 1997.

CHAMPION, Michael Philip Guy's Hospital, St. Thomas St., London SE1 9RT Tel: 020 7955 5000 — MB BS 1988 Lond.; MRCPCH 1996; BSc Lond. 1985; MRCP (Paediat.) UK 1991. (King's Coll. Hosp. Lond.) Cons. in Paediat. Metab. Med., Guy's Hosp., Lond. Socs: Brit. Inherited Metab. Dis. Gp.; Soc. Study of Inborn Errors of Metab. Prev: Sen. Regist. (Metab. Med.), Gt. Ormond St. Hosp.; Clin. Fell. & Hon. Sen. Regist. (Paediat. Intens. Care & Metabol. Med.) Guy's Hosp. Lond.

CHAMPION, Robert Harold (retired) 7 Doggets Lane, Fulbourn, Cambridge CB1 5BT Tel: 01223 880286 — MB BChir Camb. 1953; FRCP Lond. 1973, M 1957. Prev: Cons. Dermatol. Addenbrooke's Hosp. Camb. & E. Anglia RHA.

CHAN, Ah Wah Christopher Department of Medicine for Elderly, Basildon Hospital, Basildon SS16 5NL Tel: 01268 533911 Fax: 01268 592225 Email: chris.chan@doctors.org.uk; Tel: 01277 214153 — MB BCh 1980 Wales; MD Wales 1991; MRCP (UK) 1985. (University of Wales College of Medicine, Cardiff) Cons. Phys. (Gen. & Geriat. Med.) Basildon Hosp. Essex. Socs: Brit. Diabetic Assn.; Brit. Geriat. Soc.; Amer. Diabetes Assn. Prev: Cons. Phys. (Gen. & Geriat. Med.) S.mead Hosp. Bristol; Sen. Regist. (Geriat. & Gen. Med.) Addenbrooke's Hosp. Camb. & W. Suff. Hosp. Bury St. Edmunds; Research Regist. (Diabetes & Endocrinol.) Walton Hosp. Liverp.

CHAN, Amelia Helen Cornwall House Surgery, Cornwall Avenue, London N3 1LD Tel: 020 8346 1976 Fax: 020 8343 3809 — MB BS 1984 Lond.; MRCGP 1988.

CHAN, Andrew Chi Shing 10 Ravenfield Close, Halewood, Liverpool L26 7AQ — MB ChB 1988 Liverp.

CHAN, Antoni Tuck Yin Flat 9, Sydenham Mews, 33 Ullet Road, Liverpool L17 3AS Tel: 0151 733 3691 Email: antonichan@hotmail.com — MB ChB 1997 Aberd. (University of Aberdeen) Gen. Med. Rotat. (Specialties), Roy. Liverp. Univ. Hosp. Socs: Med. Defence Union of Scotl.; Med. Protec. Soc. Prev: Ho. Off. (Gen. Surg. & Cardiothoracic), Aberd. Roy. Infirm.; Ho. Off. (Gen. Med. & Diabetes), Aberd. Roy. Infirm.

CHAN, Cecilia Yuen-Yu 17 Hatton Gardens, Felley Mill, Nuthall, Nottingham NG16 1QT; 17 Hatton Gardens, Felley Mill, Nuthall, Nottingham NG16 1QT — BM BS 1989 Nottm. SHO (Geriat.) Sherwood Wing City Hosp. Nottm.

CHAN, Chi-Tsung Joseph Developmental Biology Unit, Institute of Child Health, 30 Guildford St., London WC1N 1EH Tel: 020 7905 2270 Fax: 020 7831 4366 Email: cchan@hgmp.mrc.ac.uk; 11 Harrow Fields Gardens, Sudbury Hill, Harrow on the Hill, Harrow HA1 3SN Tel: 020 8423 4784 Fax: 020 8930 8702 — MB ChB 1979 Manch.; PhD CNAA 1992; MSc Lond. 1987; MD Manch. 1988; MRCP (UK) 1982. Lect. Developm. Genetics Inst. Child Health. Prev: MRC Train. Fell. Recombinant DNA Technol. Nat. Inst. Med. Research Lond.

CHAN, Choong Meng The Lodge, Rickmansworth, Harefield, Uxbridge UB9 6JY — MB BS 1986 Newc.; MRCP (UK) 1991. Research Regist. (Transpl.) Harefield Hosp. Prev: Regist. (Transpl.)

Harefield Hosp.; SHO (Oncol. & Haemat.) Bradford Roy. Infirm.; Ho. Off. (Med.) Darlington Memor. Hosp.

CHAN, Christine Seung Yee Flat 16, Lowlands, 2-8 Eton Avenue, London NW3 3EJ — MB BS 1994 Lond.

CHAN, Christopher Lian Hock 17A Hermitage Road, London SE19 3QW — MB BS 1991 Lond.; BSc (Anat.) 1st cl. Hons. Lond. 1988; FRCS Eng. 1995. (UMDS) Specialist Regist. Rotat. (Gen. Surg.) S. Thames (E.). Socs: Assoc. Mem. Assn. Coloproctol. GB & Irel.; Assn. Endoscopic Surg.; Fell. Roy. Soc. Med. Prev: SHO Rotat. Addenbrooke's Hosp. Camb. PeriFell.sh.; SHO (A & E) St. Thos. Hosp. Lond.; Ho. Off. (Surg.) Guy's Hosp. Lond.

CHAN, Mr Cliff Kai Chuen 2 Redshank Grove, Leigh WN7 1LD Tel: 01976 737295 — MB ChB 1992 Manch.; FRCS Ed. 1996. (Manch.)

CHAN, Daniel Sui Leung 42 Campbell Street, Greenock PA16 8SU — MB ChB 1980 Glas.; MRCGP 1984.

CHAN, David Ho Yin Department of Ophthalmology, King's Coillege Hospital, Denmark Hill, London SE5 9RS Tel: 020 7737 4000; 27 Kelsey Crescent, Cambridge CB1 9XT — MB BChir 1991 Camb.; MA Camb. 1992, BA 1988; FRCOphth 1995. SHO (Gen. Surg.) Hammersmith Hosp. Lond. Prev: Ho. Surg. (Orthop.) Bedford Gen. Hosp.; Cas. Off. Hammersmith Hosp. Lond.; Ho. Phys. (Med. & c/o Elderly) Qu. Eliz. Hosp. King's Lynn.

CHAN, David Tak Yue 155 Fraser Road, Sheffield S8 0JJ — MB ChB 1995 Sheff.

CHAN, Dennis Dementia Research Group, The National Hospital for Neurology and Neurosurgery, Queen Square, London WC1N 3BG Tel: 020 7829 8773 Fax: 020 7209 0182 Email: d.chan@dementia.com.ucl.ac.uk — MB BChir 1993 Camb.; PhD Lond. 1992; MRCP (UK) 1997. (Cambridge) Clin. Research Fell., The Nat. Hosp. for Neurol. & Neurosurg., Lond. Prev: SHO (Neurol.) Nat. Hosp. for Neurol. & Neurosurg. Qu. Sq. Lond.

CHAN, Derrick Wei-Shih 213 Anlaby Road, Hull HU3 2PG — BM BS 1998 Nottm.; BM BS Nottm 1998.

CHAN, Elaine Yik-Lun 1 Graces Mews, 20 Abbey Road, London NW8 9AZ — MB BS 1993 Lond.

CHAN, Emma Wing-See Sherpherd's Halt, 31 West St., Godmanchester, Huntingdon PE29 2HG — MB BS 1998 Lond.; MB BS Lond 1998.

CHAN, Evelyn April Clarendon Lodge Medical Practice, 16 Clarendon Street, Leamington Spa CV32 5SS Tel: 01926 422094 Fax: 01926 331400; 66 Windy Arbour, Kenilworth CV8 2BB Tel: 01926 856850 — MB BS 1984 Lond.; Dip. Ther 1999; MRCGP 1990; DRCOG 1989; DCH RCP Lond. 1987. Prev: GP Eynsham Med. Centre Oxf.; Trainee GP/SHO Edgware Gen. Hosp. VTS; SHO (A & E) & Ho. Surg. N. Middlx. Hosp. Lond.

CHAN, Jenifer Po Ling 18 Rodney Court, 6-8 Maida Vale, London W9 1TQ — MB BS 1998 Lond.; MB BS Lond 1998.

CHAN, Joanna Lai Man 67 Wheatsheaf Road, Tividale, Oldbury B69 1SL — MB ChB 1998 Leic.; MB ChB Leic 1998.

CHAN, John Ma Wing 15 Iris Avenue, Bexley DA5 1HH — MB ChB 1992 Bristol; BSc (Hons.) Bristol 1989; MRCGP 1996.

CHAN, Joseph Chi Kong Kingsway Medical Centre, 23 Kingsway, Narborough Road South, Leicester LE3 2JN Tel: 0116 289 5081 Fax: 0116 263 0145 — MB ChB 1983 Birm.

CHAN, Joseph Jo Kau 7 Beech Close, Roehampton, London SW15 4HW — MB BS 1968 Lond.; MRCS Eng. LRCP Lond. 1965; FFA RCS Eng. 1971; DA Eng. 1970. (King's Coll. Hosp.)

CHAN, Kak Chen Glenfield Hospital, Leicester LE3 9QP Tel: 0116 287 1471; 28 Kingsmead Road, Leicester LE2 3YB Tel: 0116 288 4600 — MB BS 1979 Malaya; FRCP Lond. 1994; FRCP Ed. 1993; MRCP (UK) 1984. Cons. Paediat. (Cardiol.) Glenfield Hosp. Leicester. Prev: Cons. Paediat. (Cardiol.) Groby Rd. Hosp. Leicester.

CHAN, Kar Mun Carmen 12A Parklands, Cholmeley Pk, London N6 5FE — BChir 1997 Camb.; B Chir Camb. 1997; MB 1998. (Camb. Charing Cross& Westminster Lond.)

CHAN, Karen Guy's Hospital, St. Thomas' St., London SE1 9RT Tel: 020 7955 5000; 55 Queen of Denmark Court, Greenland Passage, Finland St, London SE16 7TB Tel: 020 7237 4307 Fax: 020 7237 4307 — MB BCh 1993 Wales. (Univ. Wales Coll. of Med.) SHO (Paediat.) Guy's Hosp. Lond.

CHAN, Karen Kar Loen 12A Parklands, Cholmeley Park, Highgate, London N6 5FE — MB BChir 1994 Camb. SHO (O & G) Guy's & St. Thos. Hosp. NHS Trust.

CHAN, Karolina Aleksandra 81 Sherbrooke Road, London SW6 7QL — LRCP LRCS Ed. LRCPS Glas. 1997.

CHAN, Karoline Kwok King 30 Craster Drive, Bulwell, Nottingham NG6 7FJ — BM BS 1996 Nottm.

CHAN, Kay Stephanie Flat 6, 77 Holden Rd, London N12 7DP — MB BS 1997 Lond.

CHAN, Mr Kong Kiong Birmingham Womens Hospital, Metchley Park Road, Edgbaston, Birmingham B15 2TG Tel: 0121 472 1377 Fax: 0121 627 2667; 81 Harborne Road, Edgbaston, Birmingham B15 3HG Tel: 0121 455 9496 Fax: 0121 455 0288 — MB BS 1970 Lond.; FRCS Eng. 1975; LMSSA Lond. 1970; FRCOG 1989, M 1977. (King's College Hospital, London University) p/t Cons. Gyn. Surg. & Gyn. Oncol. Director of Gyn. Oncol. Birm. Wom.'s Hosp.; Sen. Clin. Lect. Univ. Birm. Socs: Internat. Gyn. Cancer Soc.; Brit. Soc. Colpos. & Cerv. Path.; Brit. Gyn. Cancer Soc. Prev: Sen. Lect. & Hon. Cons. O & G Univ. Birm.; Lect. (O & G) Univ. Hong Kong; Regist. (Gen. Surg.) W.m. Hosp. Lond.

CHAN, Konstantina Xiu-Hui Portishead Health Centre, Victoria Square, Portishead, Bristol BS20 6AQ — MB BS 1992 Lond.; DRCOG; MRCGP 1997; JCPTGP 1997. GP Princip., Portishead. Socs: BMA; FFP; MRCGP. Prev: SHO (Psychiat.) Barrow Hosp. Bristol; GP Regist., Portishead; SHO (Obs & Gynae) St. Michael's Hosp. Bristol.

CHAN, Koo Hui 63 Apple Grove, Enfield EN1 3DA — BM 1995 Soton.

CHAN, Mr Koon Hung — MB BS 1993 Lond.; BSc 1990; FRCSI 1998; FRCS Ed. 1998. (LHMC) Socs: BMA; MDU.

CHAN, Mr Koon Loong Jessop Wing, Tree Root Walk, Sheffield S10 2JF Tel: 0114 2711900 Email: chan@doctors.org.uk — MB BS 1993 Lond.; MRCOG, 1999; BSc (Hons.) Lond. 1992; DFFP, 1997. (St. Mary's Hosp. Lond.) Specialist Regist. (O & G) Centr. Sheff. Univ. Hosps. NHS Trust.

CHAN, Kuen Po Hulme House Medical Centre, 175 Royce Road, Hulme, Manchester M15 5TJ — MB ChB 1979 Manch.; MRCGP 1984; DRCOG 1983. (Manchester) GP Manch.; Clin. Asst. (Rheum.) Withington Hosp. since 1993. Socs: Brit. Med. Acupunc. Soc..

CHAN, Kuen Ting 4 Sandown Drive, Hale Barns, Altrincham WA15 0BA — MB ChB 1975 Manch.; MRCOG 1986. (Manch.) Sen. Ho. Surg. (Cas. & Orthop.) N. Staffs. Roy. Infirm.; Stoke-on-Trent. Socs: BMA. Prev: Ho. Surg. & Ho. Phys. Hope Hosp. Salford.

CHAN, Kung-Kim Burnside Surgery, 365 Blackburn Road, Bolton BL1 8DY Tel: 01204 528205 Fax: 01204 386409; 62 Colchester Drive, Farnworth, Bolton BL4 0LU Tel: 01204 706436 Email: ckkoff@hyenaoffal.demon.co.uk — MB ChB 1989 Manch. (Manch.) Princip. in Gen. Pract., Burnside Surg., Bolton. Socs: Div. Surg. Astley Bridge St John Ambul. Brig.; Fell. Roy. Soc. Health.

CHAN, Kwok Ho Mark c/o Milton Lake, Milton Abbas, Blandford Forum DT11 0BJ — BM BS 1990 Nottm.

CHAN, Kwok Ning All Saints' Hospital, Chatham ME4 5NG; Upper Ground Floor, 8 Lancaster Grove, London NW3 4NX — MD 1989 Malta; PhD Lond. 1990; MRCS Eng. LRCP Lond. 1978; MRCP (UK) 1980; LMSSA Lond. 1978. (Malta & Guy's) Cons. Paediat. (s/i Neonat. Med.) All St.s' Hosp. Kent. Prev: Lect. (Child Health) Jt. Acad. Dept. Med. Coll. St. Bart. Hosp. & Lond. Hosp.; Regist. (Med.) Childr. Hosp. Sydney, Austral.; Research Fell. (Paediat.) Hammersmith Hosp. Lond.

CHAN, Louisa 18 Glamis Road, Darlington DL1 3PF — MB ChB 1996 Dundee.

***CHAN, Martin Zen-Bond** 8 Camaret Drive, St Ives TR26 2BE Tel: 01736 798888 — MB BS 1997 Lond.; BSc Lond. 1994.

CHAN, May Shiu Ramsey Group Practice Centre, Grove Mount South, Ramsey IM8 3EY Tel: 01624 813881 Fax: 01624 811921; Glen Down, Grove Hount, Ramsey IM8 3HQ Tel: 01624 816821 — MB BS 1989 Lond.; DRCOG 1993. (St. Bartholomew's)

CHAN, Mei Yoke Department of Haematology & Oncology, Hospital for Children, Great Ormond St., London WC1N 3JH Tel: 0207405 9200 Fax: (20) 7813 8588; 49 Eng Kong Crescent, Singapore 59, Singapore Tel: 00 65 4667439 — MB BS 1987 Singapore; MMed (Paediat.) Singapore 1992; MRCP (UK) 1994. (Nat. Univ. Singapore Med. Sch.) Leukaemia Research Fund Fell. & Hon. Sen. Regist. (Paediat. Oncol.) Gt. Ormond St. Hosp. Childr. Lond. Prev: Regist. (Paediat.) Alexandra Hosp., Singapore; SHO (Paediat. Oncol.) Roy. Marsden Hosp. Sutton.

CHAN, Sir Michael Chew Koon, MBE (retired) Department of Public Health, University of Liverpool, Whelan Building, Quadrangle,

Liverpool L69 3GB Email: mckchan@liv.ac.uk — MB BS Lond. 1964; MD Singapore 1969; FRCP Lond. 1986; MRCS Eng. LRCP Lond. 1964; FRACP 1975, M 1971; MFPHM (1995); FRCPCH (1996). Vis. Prof. Univ. Liverp.; Chairm Minority Ethnic Health Force N W NHS; Ethnic Health Adv. Comm. for Health Improvement; Non-Exec. Dir. Birkenhead & Wallasey PCT; Edr. Bd. Ethicity & Health. Prev: Sen. Lect. (Trop. Paediat.) & Cons. Paediat. Sch. Trop. Med. Univ. Liverp.

CHAN, Ming Wai 90 Sunnyside Road, Aberdeen AB24 3LR — MB ChB 1991 Aberd.

CHAN, Ming Wai 36 Merlinford Crescent, Dean Park, Renfrew PA4 8XW Tel: 0141 885 0128 — MB ChB 1988 Glas.; MRCGP 1995; DCH RCP Lond. 1994.

CHAN, Norman Tak-Yan The Oasks Medical Centre, Kings Road, Kingstanding, Birmingham; 3 Loughton Drive, Four Oaks, Sutton Coldfield B74 4RF — MB ChB 1989 Liverp.; MRCP (UK) 1995; DCH RCP Lond 1995. (Univ. Liverp.) Regist. (Paediat.) OldCh. Hosp. Romford. Socs: BMA; Brit. Paediat. Assn. Prev: SHO (Paediat.) Sandwell Dist. Gen. Hosp., Dudley Rd. Hosp. & Birm. Childr. Hosp.

CHAN, Mr Otto 93 Constantine Road, London NW3 2LP Tel: 020 7267 0151 — MB BS 1981 Lond.; FRCS Glas. 1984; FRCS Ed. 1984; FRCR 1988. (Roy. Free) Cons. Radiol. Roy. Lond. Hosp. Socs: Fell. Roy. Soc. Med.; Brit. Inst. Radiol. Prev: Sen. Regist. (Radiol.) St. Thos. & King's Coll. Hosps. Lond.; SHO (Cas.) Middlx. Hosp.; SHO (Orthop.) Roy. Nat. Orthop. Hosp. Stanmore.

CHAN, Peter Kwok Hong Flat 211, 372 Langside Park, Queens Park, Glasgow G42 8XK — MB ChB 1995 Glas.

CHAN, Mr Peter Siu Foon 22 College Road, Harrogate HG2 0AQ — MB ChB 1970 Leeds; MRCS Eng. LRCP Lond. 1971; FRCS Eng. 1976.

CHAN, Mr Philip Clinical Sciences Centre, Northern General Hospital, Herries Road, Sheffield S5 7AU Tel: 0114 271 4709 Fax: 0114 261 9246; 38 Cherry Tree Road, Sheffield S11 9AB Tel: 0114 255 1567 Email: p.chan@sheffield.ac.uk — MB BChir 1981 Camb.; MChir Camb. 1993; FRCS (Gen.) 1995; FRCS Eng. 1987; FRCS Ed. 1986. (Univ. of Camb.) Cons. Sen. Lect. (Vasc. Surg.) N. Gen. Hosp. Sheff. Prev: Sen. Regist. St. Mary's Hosp. Lond.; Regist. Roy. Free, Whittington Lond. Chest Hosps. & Hammersmith Hosps.Lond.; SHO Oxf. & Glos. Hosps.

CHAN, Raymond Hoi Fai 34A Seafield Road, Dundee DD1 4NP — MB ChB 1998 Dund.; MB ChB Dund 1998.

CHAN, Mr Raymond Nim-Wah (cons. rooms), Nuffield Hospital, Scraptoft Lane, Leicester LE5 1HY Tel: 0116 276 9401 Ext: 722 Fax: 0116 246 1076; 10 Knighton Road, Leicester LE2 3HH — MB BChir Camb. 1965; MA Camb. 1965; FRCS Eng. 1971. (Camb. & Univ. Coll. Hosp.) Cons. Orthop. Surg. Leicester Gen. Hosp., Rutland Memor. Hosp. & Melton Mowbray Hosp. Socs: Fell. Roy. Soc. Med.; Brit. Scoliosis Soc. Prev: Sen. Regist. Bath & Wessex & Roy. United Hosps. Bath; Regist. Robt. Jones & Agnes Hunt Orthop. Hosp. OsW.ry; Ho. Surg. Birm. Accid. Hosp.

CHAN, Richard 69 Park Head Road, Sheffield S11 9RA — MB ChB 1998 Liverp.; MB ChB Liverp 1998.

CHAN, Robert Heng Smithkline Beecham Pharm, New Fronteirs Science Park S., Third Avenue, Harlow CM19 5AW — MB BCh BAO 1988 Dub.; MB BCh Dub. 1988; MRCPI 1992.

CHAN, Roy Kwok-Yau 20 Moel Famau View, Riverside, Liverpool L17 7ET — MCPS 1979 Manitoba.

CHAN, Samuel Ka Wai 2 Bream Close, London N17 9DF — MB BS 1998 Lond.; MB BS Lond 1998.

CHAN, Miss Shirley Ying Yee 30 Wallbutton Road, London SE4 2NX — MB BS 1993 Lond.; FRSC Eng. 1997. (United Med. & Dental Schools of Guy's & St Thomas's Lond.)

CHAN, Shiu Kwan 34 Upper Malone Park, Belfast BT9 6PP — MB BCh 1998 Belf.; MB BCh Belf 1998.

CHAN, Shiu-Ping Ystradwrallt, Nantgaredig, Carmarthen SA32 7LG — MB BCh 1983 Wales.

CHAN, Shuk Wan 92 Armadale Road, Woking GU21 3LD — MB BCh 1985 Wales.

CHAN, Stephen Chak Yan 395 Victoria Road, Stoke-on-Trent ST1 3JF — MB ChB 1997 Leic.

CHAN, Stephen Ming Tak St. Pancras Coroner's Court, Camley St., London NW1 0PP Tel: 020 7387 4882 — MB BS 1978 Lond.; LLM Wales 1992; DMJ Soc. Apoth. Lond. 1988. (Char. Cross) HM Coroner Inner N. Lond. Dist. Socs: (Mem. Counc. & Ex-Treas.) Medico-Legal Soc.; Roy. Inst. Internat. Affairs; Brit. Acad. Forens. Sci. Prev: HM Dep. Coroner S.. Dist. of Gtr. Lond.; Sen. Forens. Med. Examr. Metrop. Police; GP Epsom.

CHAN, Stephen Shing Yan 3 Haughmond, Woodside Grange Rd, London N12 8ST — MB BS 1997 Lond.

CHAN, Stephen Tsung Keat 11 Gordon Road, London W4 3LU — MB BS 1993 Lond.

CHAN, Sui Yum Pathology Department, City Hospital NHS Trust, Winson Green, Birmingham B18 7QH Tel: 0121 507 4224 Fax: 0121 507 5374 Email: s.y.chan@bigfoot.com — MB BS 1977 Hong Kong; FRCPath 1996, M 1984. Cons. Path. City Hosp. NHS Trust Birm.; Hon. Sen. Clin. Lect. Univ. Birm. Socs: Fell. Hong Kong Acad. Med. (Path.) 1994; Fell. Hong Kong Coll. Path. 1994; Fell. Internat. Acad. Cytol.

CHAN, Suk Yin 21 Orchard Grove, Edgware HA8 5BL — MB ChB 1987 Leeds.

CHAN, Susan Min Hui 8 Lucerne Road, Oxford OX2 7QB — MB BS 1994 Lond.

CHAN, Sze Kin Michael (Surgery) Horfield Health Centre, Lockleaze Road, Bristol BS7 9RR Tel: 0117 969 5391; 63A Sea Mills Lane, Stoke Bishop, Bristol BS9 1DR Tel: 0117 968 1418 — MB ChB 1967 Bristol; DObst RCOG 1969. (Bristol)

CHAN, Mr Thomas Yau Kong Department of Radiology, Basildon Hospital, Nether Mayne, Basildon SS16 5NL Tel: 01268 533368 — MB BCh 1981 Wales; FRCS Eng. 1987; FRCS Ed. 1985; FRCR 1992. Cons. Radiol. Basildon Hosp. Essex. Prev: Sen. Regist. Rotat. (Radiol.) St. Geo. & Roy. Lond. Hosp.; Regist. (Radiol.) St. Thos. Hosp. Lond.; Regist. (Surg.) W.m. & King's Hosps. Lond.

CHAN, Timothy 18 Glamis Road, Darlington DL1 3PF — MB BS 1996 Newc.

CHAN, Timothy Tin Bo 26A High Street, Stonehaven AB39 2JQ Tel: 01569 764640 — MB ChB 1993 Aberd. SHO Rotat. (Med.) Qu. Eliz. Hosp. Gateshead. Prev: Ho. Off. (Gen. Med. & Gen. Surg.) Aberd. Roy. Infirm.

CHAN, Mr Tin Kin Jonathan Department of Ophthalmology, Royal Hallamshire Hospital, Glossop Road, Sheffield S10 2JF Tel: 0114 271 3056 Fax: 0114 271 3682 — MRCS Eng. LRCP Lond. 1986; BSc NUI 1988, MB BCh BAO 1986; FRCSI 1991; FRCS Ed. 1991; FCOphth. 1991, M 1990; DTM RCSI 1988; DO RCPSI 1990. (University College Dublin) Cons. Ophth., Roy. Hallamshire Hosp., Sheff. Socs: Amer. Assn. of Paediat. Ophth. And Strabismus. Prev: Regist. (Ophth.) Aberd. Roy. Infirm.; SHO (Ophth.) Addenbrooke's Hosp. Camb.; Sen. Regist. (Ophth.) Roy. Hallamshire Hosp.

CHAN, Tina Mei Lin 23 Clowser Close, Water Gardens, Sutton SM1 4TP — MB ChB 1990 Dundee.

CHAN, Vincent Ying-Chao 19 Bracken Close, Battyeford, Mirfield WF14 0HA — MB BS 1997 Lond.

CHAN, Vivian 14 Elliot Square, London NW3 3SU — MB BS 1986 Lond.

CHAN, Wai Ip 20 Llanishen Street, Heath, Cardiff CF14 3QE — MB BCh 1981 Wales; MRCP (UK) 1987.

CHAN, Wai Sun 6 Annadale Drive, Belfast BT7 3DP — MB BCh 1997 Belf.

CHAN, Wing Chuen 6B Windsor Close, Belfast BT9 6FG — MB BCh BAO 1995 Belf.

CHAN, Yan Tat Stephen Department of Clinical Oncology, City Hospital, Hucknall Road, Nottingham NG5 1PB Tel: 0115 969 1169 Fax: 0115 962 8047; The White House, Hill Top, Thurgarton, Southwell, Nottingham NG14 7GP Tel: 01636 830070 Fax: 01636 830070 — BM BS 1977 Nottm.; DM Nottm. 1987, BMedSci 1975; MRCP (UK) 1981; FRCR 1988. Cons. Clin. Oncol. Nottm. HA. Socs: Educat.al Bd. Roy. Coll. of Radiologists; ASCO, EMSMO, BGCS. Prev: Sen. Regist. (Radiother.) Christie Hosp. & Holt Radium Inst. Manch.; Regist. (Radiother.) Ch.ill Hosp. Oxf.; Clin. Sci. Ludwig Inst. Cancer Research Camb.

CHAN, Yim Yee Medical Paediatrics, Ninewells Hospital & Medical School, Dundee DD1 5SY Tel: 01382 660111; 46 Clovis Dureau Drive, Dundee DD2 5JB Tel: 01382 561906 — MB ChB 1993 Glas.; MRCP UK 1998; MRCPCH 1998. Specialist Regist. Med. Paediat. Ninewells Hosp. & Med Sch., Dundee.

CHAN, Mr Yiu-Che 42 Imperial Court, Prince Albert Road, London NW8 7PT — MB BS 1993 Lond.; BSc (Hons) 1990; FRCS (Eng) 1997. (Charing Cross and Westminster) Specialist Regist. (Surg.) S.

E. Thames Deanery. Prev: Reasearch Fell. in Vasc. Surg., St. Mary's Hosp.

CHAN, Yu-Sing University of Manchester, Department of Orthopaedic Surgery, Hope Hospital, Eccles, Salford M6 8HD; 76 Kerscott Road, Northenden, Manchester M23 0FN — MB BCh BAO 1992 Belf.; BSc (Hons) Belf. 1992; DIMCRCSEd 1995; FRCS Glas. 1996; FRCS Ed. 1996; FRCSI 1997; Dip. Sports Med. 1997; FCSHK 1997. Clin. Lect. & Hon. Specialist Regist. (Orthop. Surg.) Dept. of Orthop. Surg. Univ. of Manch. Socs: Foundat. Mem. Fac. PreHosp. Care; Roy. Coll. Surgs Edin.; Assoc. Mem. Brit. Orthop. Assoc.

CHAN, Yuk-Chun Christie 6 Waterman Way, London E1W 2QN — MB ChB 1990 Aberd.

CHAN, Yuk Keun The Surgery, The Old Orchard, Limekilns, Dunfermline KY11 3HS Tel: 01383 872201 Fax: 01383 873121 — MB ChB 1990 Ed. GP; Clin. Med. Off.; Civil. Med. Off.

CHAN CHUNG-CHI, Dr Flat 3, 3 Sandwell Crescent, London NW6 1PB — MB BS 1992 Lond.

CHAN KIN, Therese Marie (retired) 135 Browning Road, Enfield EN2 0HJ Tel: 020 8367 2021 — MB BCh BAO NUI 1956; MFCM 1974; DPH Toronto 1961. Prev: Sen. Med. Off. Enfield DHA.

CHAN LAM, Jean Marie France Dominique Department of Haematology, Barnsley District General Hospital, Gawber Road, Barnsley S75 2EP Tel: 01226 730000; 4 Hallam Grange Road, Fulwood, Sheffield S10 4BJ Email: d@dchan-lam.freeserve.co.uk — MB ChB 1984 Glas.; MRCP (UK) 1989; MRCPath 1994. Cons. Haemat. Barnsley Dist. Gen. Hosp. Prev: Sen. Regist. (Haemat. & Blood Transfus.) Plymouth HA; Regist. (Haemat.) Stobhill Gen. Hosp. Glas.

CHAN LEE GAIK, Dr 28 Hulatt Road, Cambridge CB1 8TH — MB BS 1988 Malaya; MRCP (UK) 1992.

CHAN-PENSLEY, Eric Melbury Lodge, Royal Hants County Hospital, Romsey Road, Winchester SO22 5DG — MB BS 1973 Newc.; MRCPsych 1978. Cons. (Psychiat.) Melbury Lodge Roy. Hants. Co. Hosp. Winchester. Prev: Sen. Regist. (Psychiat.) Roy. S. Hants. Hosp. Soton.; SHO (Psychiat.) W. Suff. Hosp. Bury St. Edmunds; Ho. Off. (Surg.) Kent & Canterbury Hosp.

CHAN SEEM, Chow Poo Department of Pathology, The Queen Elizabeth Hospital, Gayton Road, King's Lynn PE30 4ET Tel: 01553 613599 Fax: 01553 767742 Email: chanseem.qekl@dial.pipex.com — MB ChB 1977 Leeds; BSc Leeds 1974; MRCP (UK) 1981; FRCPath 1986. (Leeds)

CHAN SEUNG CHI, Stephen 16 Lowlands, 2-8 Eton Avenue, London NW3 3EJ — MB BS 1992 Lond.

CHAN TUN LUN, Ah-Fee 12 Alford Court, Shepherdess Walk, London N1 7JW — MB BS 1984 Delhi; FFA RCSI 1992.

CHANA, Gurvinder Singh The Yiewsley Family Practice, Yiewsley Health Centre, 20 High Street, Yiewsley, West Drayton UB7 7DP Tel: 01895 435328 Fax: 01895 444672; 10 Gervaise Close, Cippenham, Slough SL1 5NQ Tel: 01753 576552 Fax: 01753 773560 Email: gschana@msn.com — MB ChB 1989 Dundee. GP Princip.

CHANA, Mr Jagdeep Singh 102 Lambourne Road, Chigwell Row, Chigwell IG7 6EJ — MB BS 1991 Lond.; MB BS (Hons.) Lond. 1991; BSc (Immunol.) 1st cl. Hons. Lond. 1988; FRCS Eng. 1995. SHO (Plastic Surg.) Mt. Vernon Hosp. Lond. Prev: SHO Rotat. (Surg.) Univ. Coll. & Middlx. Hosp.; SHO (Plastic Surg.) Yorks. Regional Burns Unit Wakefield; Demonst. (Anat.) Univ. Oxf.

CHANA, Lorna Valerie The Crossroads Surgery, 449 Warrington Road, Rainhill, Prescot L35 4LL Tel: 0151 430 9989; West Winds, 58 Springfield Lane, Eccleston, St Helens WA10 5HA — MB ChB 1975 Liverp.; DRCOG 1977. Socs: Assoc. Mem. Fac. Homoeop.

CHANA, Navnit Singh The Surgery, 1 Church Road, Mitcham CR4 3YU Tel: 020 8648 2579 Fax: 020 8640 4013; 13 The Park, Carshalton SM5 3BY — MB BS 1986 Lond.; BSc Lond. 1983; MRCGP 1991; DA (UK) 1988. GP Course Organiser St. Geo Hosp. Lond.

CHANA, Previna 230 Ridge Road, Sutton SM3 9LY — MB BS 1994 Lond.; MRCGP 2000; BSc (Hons.) Lond. 1991; DRCOG RCP. 1998; DCH RCP. 1998. (Charing Cross & Westminster Med. Sch.) Salaried Gen. Practitioner, Balham Pk. Surg., Balham. Socs: MDU; BMA; MRCGP. Prev: GP Regist., Canbury Health Centre, Kingston upon Thames; Clin. Asst. GP, Esme Ho. Surg., Putney; GP Regist., Canbury Health Centre, Kingston Upon Thames.

CHANA, Som Singh Health Centre, Station Road, Haydock, St Helens WA11 0JN Tel: 01744 22272; West Winds, 58 Springfield Lane, Eccleston, St Helens WA10 5HA — MB ChB 1975 Liverp.; MFHoM 1987; DRCOG 1977.

CHANA, Treena 230 Ridge Road, Sutton SM3 9LY — MB BS 1995 Lond.

CHANARIN, Israel (retired) 11 Fitzwilliam Avenue, Richmond TW9 2DQ — MD Cape Town 1953, MB ChB 1947; DCP Lond 1955; FRCPath 1964; FRCP 1998. Prev: Cons. Haemat. Clementine Ch.ill Hosp.

CHANARIN, Louise Mary 18 Peppercorn Close, Colchester CO4 5WS — BM 1989 Soton.

CHANARIN, Nicholas 18 Peppercorn Close, Colchester CO4 5WS — MB ChB 1987 Bristol; MRCP (UK) 1990. Regist. Flinders Adelaide, Austral. Prev: SHO Soton & SW Hants. HA.

CHANCE, Barry (retired) (Surgery), 12 Cleveland Road, St Helier, Jersey JE1 4HD — MB ChB Birm. 1960; DObst RCOG 1962. Prev: Ho. Phys. (Paediat.) Childr. Hosp. Birm.

CHANCE, Patrick Sebastien Guillaume 22 Bankfields, Headcorn, Ashford TN27 9RA; Flat 3, 52 Sallsbury Road, Moseley, Birmingham B13 8JT Tel: 0121 249 1521 Email: patchance@tesco.net — MB ChB 1995 Birm.; ChB Birm. 1995; MB CLB Birm. 1995. SHO Regist., Al Birm. Psychiat. Train. Rotat.

CHANCELLOR, Christina Isabella Keppoch Road Surgery, Keppoch Road, Culloden, Inverness IV2 7LL Tel: 01463 793400 Fax: 01463 793060; 16 Beaufort Road, Inverness IV2 3NP Tel: 01463 224034 — MB ChB 1979 Aberd. Gen. Pract. Culloden Med. Pract.; Gen. Pract. Culloden Med. Pract. Prev: Wom.'s Retainer Scheme Highland Region; GP Culloden; Princip.

CHAND, Anjuman Diwan Hasland Surgery, 66 Storforth Lane, Hasland, Chesterfield S41 0PW Tel: 01246 277973 Fax: 01246 203645; Fairways, Matlock Road, Walton, Chesterfield S42 7LD — MB BS 1970 Dacca; DRCOG 1978. (Dacca Med. Coll.) GP Chesterfield. Prev: SHO (Anaesth.) Law Hosp. Carluke.

CHAND, Deep Sandwell District General Hospital, West Bromwich B71 4HJ Tel: 0121 607 3340 Fax: 0121 607 3403; Tabley, Roman Road, Little Aston Park, Sutton Coldfield B74 3AT Tel: 0121 353 9755 — MB BS 1972 Rajasthan; MD Chandigarh 1976; FFR RCSI 1981; DMRD Eng. 1980; FACA 1998. (S.P. Med. Coll., Bilsaner) Cons. Radiol. Sandwell Dist. Gen. Hosp.; Sen. Mem. Amer. Inst. Ultrasound Med.; Dep. Govr. Amer. Biographic Inst. Research Assn.; Lt. Col. RAMC (V); Off. Commanding Clin. Squadron 202 field Hosp. Socs: Fell. Roy. Soc. Med.; Soc. Magnetic Resonance USA (Mem. Brit. Chapter); Magnetic Resonance Radiol. Assn. Prev: Chairm. Div. Radiol. Sandwell Dist. Gen. Hosp.; Chairm. BMA (Sandwell Div.).

CHAND, Govardhan Tripuraneni The Surgery, 22 Rosslyn Road, Longton, Stoke-on-Trent ST3 4JD Tel: 01782 332626 — MB BS 1976 Osmania; LRCP LRCS Ed. LRCPS Glas. 1984.

CHAND, Kailash Stamford House, Stamford Street, Ashton-under-Lyne OL6 6QH Tel: 0161 344 0803 Fax: 0161 339 8243 — MB BS 1974 Punjabi.

CHAND, Muhammad Younus 44 Glenn Avenue, Purley CR8 2AG; St. Thomas' Health District (Teaching), Community Health Centre, Bromfelde Road, London SW4 Tel: 020 7720 6551 — MB BS 1965 Punjab; MB BS Punjab (Pakistan) 1965; DTM & H Eng. 1971; DCH RCPSI 1971; Cert FPA (IUD) 1975. Instruc. Doctor Family Plann. Assn. Lond.; Clin. Med. Off. & Sch. Med. Off. St. Thos. Health Dist. (T). Socs: Assoc. Mem. Brit. Paediat. Assn.

CHAND, Raj Garden City Surgery, 59 Station Road, Letchworth SG6 3BJ Tel: 01462 624000; 4 Schoolfields, Letchworth SG6 2TZ — MB ChB 1986 Sheff.; BMedSci 1985 (Hons.) Pharmacol. & Therap. Sheff. (Sheffield) Prev: Trainee GP Nuneaton VTS.

CHAND, Ruhita Ashoka, MBE (retired) 92 Linden lea, Compton, Wolverhampton WV3 8BE Tel: 01902 710246 — MB ChB Birm. 1943. Prev: Cons. Chest Phys. Wolverhampton & Dudley & Stourbridge Hosp. Gps.

CHAND, Tripuraneni Govardhana Westfields, West Paddock, Leyland, Preston PR25 1HR Tel: 01772 622777 — MB BS 1972 Andhra; MSc Manch. 1982; MRCPysch 1979. Cons. Psychiat. Leyland. Prev: Sen. Regist. W. Midl.

CHANDA, Monica Woodley Health Centre, Hyde Road, Woodley, Stockport SK6 1ND Tel: 0161 430 4166 Fax: 0161 406 8218 — MB ChB 1992 Manch.; MRCGP 1997; DRCOG 1996; DCH RCP Lond. 1994. GP Manch. Socs: RCGP; RCOG. Prev: GP/Regist.

Stockport; SHO (Psychiat.) Trafford Gen. Hosp.; SHO (O & G) Hope Hosp. Manch.

CHANDARANA, Vinodrai Chhotalal Weston Favell Health Centre, Weston Favell Centre, Northampton NN3 8DW Tel: 01604 785027 Fax: 01604 414880; 50 Thorburn Road, Weston Favell, Northampton NN3 3DA Tel: 01604 414549 — MB BS Bombay 1970. (Grant Med. Coll.) Clin. Asst. (Young Disabled Unit) Manfield Hosp. N.ampton.

CHANDE, Chetan 22 The Square, Ringley Chase, Whitefield, Manchester M45 7UL Tel: 0161 796 2944 Fax: 0161 766 3150; 22 The Square, Ringley Chase, Whitefield, Manchester M45 7UL Tel: 0161 796 2944 Fax: 0161 766 3150 — MB ChB 1991 Manch.; MRCGP 1995; DRCOG 1995. (Manch.) Locum Gen. Practitioner, Manch. Prev: SHO (Psychiat.) Stepping Hill Hosp. Stockport VTS; Trainee GP Marple Stockport; Ho. Off. (Surg.) Manch. Roy. Infirm.

CHANDER, Ajay 45 Stanley Avenue, Harborne, Birmingham B32 2HA — MB ChB 1995 Birm.; BDS Wales 1986.

CHANDER, Rajesh 18 Roydale Close, Loughborough LE11 5UW — MB ChB 1994 Leeds.

CHANDER, Somesh South Tyneside Health Care Trust, Flagg Court Health Centre, Flagg Court, South Shields NE33 2PG Tel: 0191 456 0791 Fax: 0191 451 6447 — MB BS 1970 Panjab. (Panjab) GP S. Shields, Tyne & Wear.

CHANDHOK, Vinod Raj 58 Lynton Mead, London N20 8DJ — MB BS 1977 Kanpur.

CHANDI, Alka Grand Drive Surgery, 132 Grand Drive, London SW20 9EA Tel: 020 8542 5555 Fax: 020 8542 6969; 13 Rheingold Way, Wallington SM6 9NA — MB ChB 1993 Glas.; DRCOG 1995; MRCGP 1997. (Glasgow University)

CHANDIOK, Swatantrata University Hospital of South Manchester, Withington Hospital, West Didsbury, Manchester M20 2LR Tel: 0161 291 4939 Fax: 0161 447 4604; Aran, 43 King's Road, Wilmslow SK9 5PW Tel: 01625 536161 — MD Chandigarh 1972; MB BS Punjab 1967; FRCOG 1991, M 1975; RCOG Lond. Cons. Phys. Genitoturin. Med. Withington Hosp. Manch; Hon. Clin. Lect. in Genito Urin. Med. in the Depts. of Med. & Obst. & Gyn. Univ. of Manch. Socs: MSSVD; BMA; RCOG. Prev: Cons. Phys. Genitourin. Med. Derby Roy. Infirm.; Sen. Regist. (Genitourin. Med.) Roy. Infirm. Manch.; Hon. Clin. Lect. (Genitourin. Med.) Univ. Manch.

CHANDIRAMANI, Mr Vijay Alim Flat 4, 35 Central Road, Manchester M20 4YE — MB BS 1986 Bombay; FRCS Ed. 1992.

CHANDLER, Alison May (retired) — MB BS 1975 Newc.; MRCGP 1980; DRCOG 1978. Prev: GP Newc. u. Tyne.

CHANDLER, Andrew Main Road Surgery, Main Road, Parson Drove, Wisbech PE13 4LF Tel: 01945 700223 Fax: 01945 700915 — MB ChB 1982 Manch.

CHANDLER, Barbara Janet Regional Neurological Rehabilitation Centre, Hunters Road, Newcastle upon Tyne NE2 4NR; 176 Darras Road, Ponteland, Newcastle upon Tyne NE20 9AF — MD 1993 Newc.; FRCP 2000; BMedSc (Hons.) 1979, MB BS 1982; MRCP (UK) 1989. p/t Cons. Rehabil. Med. Regional Rehabil. Centre Huntersmoor Hosp. Newc.; Hon. Sen. Lect. Newc. Univ. Socs: Brit. Soceity of Rehabil. Med.; Soc. for Research in Rehabil.; Inst. of Psychosexual Med.

CHANDLER, Charles Crispin David (retired) 4 Grimbly Place, Harpes Road, Oxford OX2 7LT Tel: 01865 514951 — MB BS Lond. 1954; MRCS Eng. LRCP Lond. 1950; FFA RCS Eng. 1955, FRCA; DA Eng. 1953. Prev: Cons. Anaesth. Nuffield Orthop. Centre Oxf. & United Oxf. Hosps.

CHANDLER, Christopher John Wingates House, Wingates Road, Leyland Mill Lane, Wigan WN1 2SH Tel: 01942 44665 Email: chrischand@aol.com — MB ChB 1975 Leeds; FRCOG 1992, M 1980. Cons. O & G Wigan HA. Socs: BMA & Brit. Fertil. Soc.; Brit. Soc. of Gynne Endoscopy.

CHANDLER, Mr Christopher Lloyd Department of Neurosurgery, Kings College Hospital, Denmark Hill, London SE5 9RS Tel: 020 7346 3020 — MB BS Lond. 1986; BSc Newc. 1981; FRCS Eng. 1990; FRCS (SN) 1996. (Westm.) Cons. Neurosurg. Kings Coll. Hosp. Socs: Fell. Roy. Soc. Med.; Soc. of Brit. Neurosurg. Prev: Sen. Regist. Frenchay Hosp., Bristol; Regist. (Neurosurg.) Atkinson Morley's Hosp. Lond.; SHO (Gen. Surg.) St. Geo., St. Bart. & Whipps Cross Hosps. Lond.

CHANDLER, Douglas Alton (retired) Bryntirion, Kingstone, Hereford HR2 9HJ Tel: 01981 250246 — MRCS Eng. LRCP Lond. 1945. Prev: Cas. Off. W.m. Hosp.

CHANDLER, Geoffrey Noel (retired) BUPA Hospital, Roundhay Hall, Jackson Avenue, Roundhay, Leeds LS8 1NT Tel: 0113 269 3939 — BM BCh 1946 Oxf.; MA Oxf. 1948, DM 1958; FRCP Lond. 1968, M 1948. Cons. Phys. BUPA Hosp. Roundhay Hall Leeds. Prev: Cons. Phys. Leeds (St. Jas.) Univ. Hosp. & Chapel Allerton Hosp. Leeds & Sen. Clin. Lect. Univ. Leeds.

CHANDLER, Graeme Peter, TD 103 Thorne Road, Doncaster DN2 5BE Tel: 01302 701128 Fax: 01302 701128 Email: gchand343@wahoo.co.uk; White House, High St, Campsall, Doncaster DN6 9AF Tel: 01302 701128 Email: gchand343@netscape.net — MB ChB Sheff. 1968; FRCOG 1992, M 1973. (Univ. Sheff.) Cons. O & G Doncaster Roy. & Montagu Hosp. NHS Trust; Col. Late RAMC (TA) CVHQ Reserve of Offs. Socs: N. Eng. Obst. & Gyn. Soc.; NINES; Trent SOAP. Prev: Cons. O & G Doncaster Roy. Infirm; Sen. Regist. (O & G) Ninewells Hosp. Dundee; Regist. (O & G) Dundee Roy. Infirm.

CHANDLER, Henry Arthur, Group Capt. RAF Med. Br. 29 Hodson Road, Chiseldon, Swindon SN4 0LN Tel: 01793 740994 Fax: 01793 741664 Email: drhenryc@hachan. demon.co.uk — MRCS Eng. LRCP Lond. 1968; MSc Surrey 1973; BSc (Engin. & Chem. Engin.) Lond. 1962; MB BS 1968; FRCPath 1988, M 1976. (King's Coll. Hosp.) Cons. in Chem. Path., St Geo.s Hosp.. Blackshaw Rd, Lond..; Adviser in Chem. Path. Nuffield Hosp. Socs: Fell. RSM; Soc. Occupat. Med.; Clin. Biochem. Prev: Sen. Regist./Lect. Soton. Gen. Hosp.; Ho. Phys. King's Coll. Hosp. Lond.; Ho. Surg. St Giles' Hosp. Lond.

CHANDLER, Ian Peter 84 Treza Road, Porthleven, Helston TR13 9UQ Tel: 01326 562468 — MB BS 1998 Lond.; MB BS Lond 1998. Socs: Fell.of Roy. Soc. of Med.

CHANDLER, James Alan 6 Mellor Lane, Mellor, Blackburn BB2 7JR — MB ChB 1996 Leic.; ALS; ATLS. (Leicester) SHO (Anaesth.) Norf. & Norwich Hosp. Prev: SHO (A & E) Jersey; SHO (Surg.) Jersey; SHO (Med.) Leicester Gen. Hosp.

CHANDLER, John Edward Department of Haematology, The James Cook University Hospital, Maston Way, Middlesbrough Tel: 01642 854139 Fax: 01642 854381 — MB BS 1973 Lond.; FRCP Lond. 1992; MRCP (UK) 1977; FRCPath 1994, M 1982. Cons. Haemat. S. Tees NHS Trust, The James Cook Univ. Hosp. Prev: Sen. Regist. (Haemat.) Nottm. Univ. Hosp.; Regist. (Haemat.) Leicester Roy. Infirm.

CHANDLER, Katharine Elizabeth 28A Goldhurst Terrace, London NW6 3HU — MB BChir 1991 Camb.

CHANDLER, Lisa Jane 3 Dell Rise, Park St., St Albans AL2 2QJ — MB BS 1998 Lond.; MB BS Lond 1998.

CHANDLER, Owen John Home Farm, Riddlesworth, Diss IP22 2TD — MB ChB 1997 Manch.

CHANDLER, Paul Anthony 11 Bank Street, Cheadle, Stoke-on-Trent ST10 1NR — BM BS 1997 Nottm.

CHANDLER, Richard James The Stokes Medical Centre, Braydon Avenue, Little Stoke, Bristol BS34 6BQ Tel: 01454 616767 — MB ChB 1965 Bristol.

CHANDLER, Sarah Edith Flat C, 76 Fairhazel Gardens, London NW6 3SR — MB BS 1993 Queensland.

CHANDLER, Sylvia Irene Joyce The Medical Centre, Tanhouse Lane, Church Hill, Redditch B98 9AA Tel: 01527 67715 — MB ChB 1975 Birm.

CHANDLER, William George 1 St Andrews Road, Stogursey, Bridgwater TA5 1TE — MB BS 1990 Lond.

CHANDNA, Mr Arvind 98 Brynland Avenue, Bishopston, Bristol BS7 9DX Tel: 0117 421681 — MB BS 1978 Delhi; FRCS Ed. 1985; DO RCS Eng. 1985.

CHANDNANI, Mohini Tarachand (retired) Gateshead Health Centre, Prince Consort Road, Gateshead NE8 1NR Tel: 0191 478 3550 Fax: 0191 478 3501 — MB BS 1961 Rajasthan. GP Gateshead, Tyne & Wear.

CHANDOK, Harbikramjit Singh 32 College Drive, Ruislip HA4 8SB — MB BS 1996 Lond.

CHANDOK, Rajpreet Singh 32 College Drive, Ruislip HA4 8SB — MB BS 1996 Lond.

CHANDOLA, Asha 24 Northcote Road, New Malden KT3 3HG Tel: 020 8255 7342 — MB BS 1993 Lond.; BSc Lond. 1990; DCH RCP

Lond. 1996; DRCOG 1996; DFFP 1998; MRCGP 1998. (St. Geo. Hosp. Lond.) GP Asst. Socs: BMA; MDU. Prev: GP Regist. Raynes Pk.; SHO (Elderly Care) Mayday Hosp. Thornton Heath.

CHANDOO, Amirali Hassanali 15 Clare Road, Lancaster LA1 2LX Tel: 01524 60705 — MD 1974 Dar-Es-Salaam, Tanzania; MCOphth. 1991; DO RCPSI 1991. Clin. Asst. (Ophth.) Lancaster Acute Hosps.

CHANDR-RUANG-PHEN, Pornpat Flat 8, Ares Court, Homer Drive, London E14 3UL — MB BS 1991 Lond.

CHANDRA, Aninda 106 Denham Lane, Chalfont St Peter, Gerrards Cross SL9 0QJ Tel: 01753 886902 — MB BS 1996 Lond.; MA (Hons.) Oxf. 1993. (Guy's) SHO Rotat. (Basic Surg.) Kent & Canterbury Hosp.

CHANDRA, Ashok Kumar Shanti-Niketon, 106 Denham Lane, Chalfont St Peter, Gerrards Cross SL9 0QJ Tel: 01753 886902 — MB BS 1963 Calcutta; DMRD Eng. 1979; DMRD Calcutta 1967. (Calcutta Med. Coll.) Assoc. Specialist (Radiol.) Stoke Mandeville Hosp.

CHANDRA, Ekambaram Flat 23a, Block 4, Wordsley Hospital, Stream Road, Stourbridge DY8 5QX — LMSSA 1987 Lond.; MB BS Madras 197; MRCGP 1990; DRCOG 1988; DGO 1981.

CHANDRA, Girish 36 Lloyd Park Avenue, Croydon CR0 5SB — MB BS 1961 Lucknow.

CHANDRA, Latika Yiewsley Health Centre, High Street, Yiewsley, West Drayton UB7 7DP Tel: 01895 422292 Fax: 01895 422134; 106 Denham Lane, Gerrards Cross SL9 0QJ — MB BS 1971 Calcutta; BSc Calcutta 1962, MB BS 1971.

CHANDRA, Mahesh Blackburn Road Surgery, 283 Blackburn Road, Bolton BL1 8HB Tel: 01204 524770 Fax: 01204 380914 — MB BS 1964 Lucknow; MB BS 1964 Lucknow.

***CHANDRA, Malika** West Riding, Lambourne Road, Chigwell IG7 6JN — MB BS 1998 Lond.; MB BS Lond 1998.

CHANDRA, Venkataraman Department of Obstetrics & Gynaecology, Victoria Hospital, Whinney Heys Road, Blackpool FY3 8NR; 109 Gawsworth Road, Sale M33 2UZ — LRCP LRCS 1983 Ed.; LRCP LRCS Ed. LRCPS Glas. 1983.

CHANDRA MOHAN, Alagar Ramanujam 327 Wingletye Lane, Hornchurch RM11 3BU — MB BS 1986 Madras.

CHANDRA MOHAN, Veeriah Jetty (Surgery) 5 Michael House, Bath St., Coventry CV1 5AA; 94 Kenilworth Road, Coventry CV4 7AH Tel: 02476 418310 — MB BS 1971 Osmania; DRCOG 1977. (Ghandi Med. Coll. Hyderabad)

CHANDRA RAJ, Ivan 52 Roundwood Park, Harpenden AL5 3AF — MB BS 1977 Madras; LRCP LRCS Ed. LRCPS Glas. 1980.

CHANDRA REDDY, Perumal Swan Lane Surgery, 66 Swan Lane, Wickford SS11 7DD Tel: 01268 735951 Fax: 01268 570849 — MB BS 1970 Madras. Princip GP Basildon. Prev: Trainee GP Natwich; SHO (Orthop.) N. Tees Gen. Hosp. Stockton.

CHANDRACHUD, Mr Hari Raghunath (retired) 15 Blackwood Road, Milngavie, Glasgow G62 7LB Tel: 0141 956 3041 — MB ChB 1958 St. And.; FRCS Glas. 1965; FRCS Ed. 1965. Prev: Hon. Clin.. Lect. Univ.Glas.

CHANDRADEVA, Kanagasbapathy 7 Horner Lane, Mitcham CR4 3QY — MB BS 1982 Peradeniya; MRCS Eng. LRCP Lond. 1988.

CHANDRAKER, Anil Kumar 97 Marsland Road, Sale M33 3HS — MB ChB 1987 Glas.

CHANDRAKUMARAN, Mr Kandiah 33A Castle Road, Hythe CT21 5HB — LRCP LRCS Ed. LRCPS Glas. 1984; FRCS Ed. 1983.

CHANDRALINGHAM, Nagalingam Kathirgamalingam Sealyham Flat-C, Withybush General Hospital, Haverfordwest SA61 2PZ — MB BS 1975 Sri Lanka; LRCP LRCS Ed. LRCPS Glas. 1985.

CHANDRAMANI, Syamala Manor Hospital, Moat Road, Walsall WS2 9PS Tel: 01922 721172; 2 Hollyhedge Close, Northfield, Birmingham B31 5SN Tel: 0121 476 9991 — MB BS 1969 Kerala; Dip. Ven. Soc. Apoth. Lond. 1976. (Kottayam) Assoc. Specialist & Asst. (Genitourin. Med.) Manor Hosp. Walsall; Sen. Clin. Med. Off. (Family Plann.) Birm. Soc. NHS Comm. Trust. Prev: Sen. Regist. (Venereol.) Gen. Hosp. Birm. & Stoke on Trent.

CHANDRAMOHAN, Sundaram c/o Dr Rangareddy, 394 St Albans Road, Nottingham NG6 9FP — MB BS 1972 Bangalor; MB BS Bangalore 1972.

CHANDRAN, Babu Siddharthan 14 Whitehall Gardens, London W4 3LT — BM 1990 Soton.; MRCP (UK) 1993.

CHANDRAN, Qudsia Pantiles Medical Centre, Church Street, Sutton-in-Ashfield NG17 1EX Tel: 01623 557646 Fax: 01623 557646 — MB BS 1962 Punjab; MB BS Punjab (Pakistan) 1962; Cert. Family Plann. JCC 1969; DObst RCOG 1968. (Fatima Jinnah Med. Coll. Lahore) Socs: BMA; Overseas Doctors Assn.; Conserv. Med. Soc.

CHANDRAN, Thambiturai Raj Pantiles Medical Centre, Church Street, Sutton-in-Ashfield NG17 1EX Tel: 01623 557646 Fax: 01623 557646; 53 Sheepwalk Lane, Ravenshead, Nottingham NG15 9FD Tel: 01623 792531 Fax: 01623 557646 — MB BS 1964 Ceylon; DObst RCOG 1968. (Ceylon Med. Coll.) Maj. RAMC (V); Commr. Commiss. for Racial Equality. Socs: Fell. Roy. Soc. Med.; BMA (Ex-Hon. Sec. & Ex-Chairm. Dukeries Div.); ODA (Ex-Hon. Jt. Sec.). Prev: Mem. Bd. Trent Fac. RCGP; Mem. Assn. Police Surgs.

CHANDRAN, Vallathol S Hollies Health Centre, Swan Street, Merthyr Tydfil CF47 8ET Tel: 01685 721266 Fax: 01685 375787.

CHANDRAN, Velayudhan Fryent Medical Centre, 331 Church Lane, London NW9 8JD Tel: 020 8205 6262 — MB BS 1975 Madras; MRCS Eng. LRCP Lond. 1982.

CHANDRANI, Reshma 215 Mackintosh Place, Roath, Cardiff CF24 4RP — MB BCh 1998 Wales.

CHANDRAPAL, Kandasamy Ernest 1 Stanhope Avenue, Finchley Central, London N3 3LX Tel: 020 8346 3247 — MB BS 1966 Madras; DPH Lond. 1979; DLO RCS Eng. 1975.

CHANDRAPPA, Madannavar Hanumanthappa 161 Armadale Road, Bolton BL3 4TP — MB BS 1966 Mysore.

CHANDRARAJ, Regina 52 Roundwood Park, Harpenden AL5 3AF — MB BS 1973 Madurai.

CHANDRARAJAN, Chelliah Subramaniam 69 Beach Road, Littlehampton BN17 5JH — MB BS 1975 Sri Lanka; DPM Eng. 1982; DAB Lond.1998.

CHANDRASEGARAM, Wimala Woodsmoke, 1 Bramfield Lane, Waterford, Hertford SG14 2QE — MB BS 1970 Ceylon.

CHANDRASEKARA, Bernadette Shyama Dodampegama 22A Birchen Grove, London NW9 8SA; 94 Girton Avenue, Kingsbury, London NW9 9UD Tel: 020 8204 8652 — MB ChB 1995 Dundee. (Dundee)

CHANDRASEKARAN, Badrinathan 6 Ashenden Road, Guildford GU2 7UU — MB BS 1998 Lond.; MB BS Lond 1998.

CHANDRASEKARAN, Mr Sankaran c/o Mr N. Balaji, 55 Clarence Gardens, Hyndland, Glasgow G11 7JW — MB BS 1984 Madras; FRCS Ed. 1990.

CHANDRASEKARAN, Mr Thipparajapura Venkatraman 91 Queens Hill Crescent, Newport NP20 5HF — MB BS 1986 Madras; FRCS Ed. 1992.

CHANDRASEKARAN, Mr Venkatchalam Knightsbridge Wing, St George's Hospital, Blackshaw Road, Tooting, London SW17 0QT Tel: 020 8725 3962; 2 Privet Close, Reading RG6 4NY Tel: 0118 901 8806 Email: v.chandra@onet.co.uk — MB BS 1978 Madras; FRCS Glas. 1992; FRCS CCTL 1995. (Thanjavur Medical Collegem, India) Cons. Cardiothoracic Surg. Socs: Roy. Coll. Surgs. & Phys. Glas.; BMA. Prev: Locum Cons., Leeds Gen. Infirm., Leeds; Locum Cons., John Radcliffe Hosp., Oxf.; Sen. Regist. (Cardiothoracic Surg.) Harefield Hosp. Uxbridge.

CHANDRASEKHAR, Turuvekere Veerappa Doncaster Royal Infirmary, Armthorpe Road,, Doncaster DN2 5LT Tel: 01302 366666 Ext: 3516; 9 Stirling Drive, Gourock PA19 1AH Tel: 01475 636984 — MB BS 1969 Bangalor; BSc Mysore 1958; LLB Bangalore 1970, MB BS 1969; FFA RCSI 1980; DA Eng. 1975. (Bangalore Med. Coll.) Cons. Anaesth. K. Khaled Hosp. Tabuk Saudi Arabia.; Doncaster Roy. Infirm. Armthorpe Rd. Doncaster DN2 5LT; Locum Cons.. Dept Anaesth.s. Prev: Regist. (Anaesth.) Roy. Alexandra Infirm. Paisley.

CHANDRASEKHARAN, Shankar 78 Onslow Road, Sheffield S11 7AG — MB ChB 1996 Sheff.

CHANDRASENA, Tiththagalle Gamage De Silva R N Greenwich Health Authority, King William Walk, London SE10 9JH Tel: 020 8858 8090; 113 Donaldson Road, London SE18 3JZ Tel: 020 8856 3630 — MB BS 1978 Sri Lanka; MRCP (UK) 1986; MRCS Eng. LRCP Lond. 1985; DCH RCP Lond. 1983.

CHANDRASHEKHAR, M N Earle Road Medical Centre, 131 Earle Road, Liverpool L7 6HD Tel: 0151 733 7172.

CHANDRASIRI, Rajapakse Bahagothra Chitra MWP General Hospital, Bishop Auckland DL14 6AD — MB BS 1974 Sri Lanka; FFA RCSI 1984.

CHANDRATRE, Pratima Sanjiv General Hospital, Salterhebbel, Halifax HX3 0PW — MB BS 1977 Poona; FRCA 1996.

CHANDRATRE, Sanjiv Narayan General Hospital, Salterherbel, Halifax HX3 0PW Tel: 01422 357171 — MB BS 1974 Poona; MRCP (UK) 1984; MRCPI 1983.

CHANDRE GOWDA, Hanumanahalli Kade Garlands Hospital, Carlisle CA1 3SX Tel: 01228 31081 — MB BS 1966 Mysore.

CHANDY, John Radiology Department, University Hospitals Coventry & Warwickshire NHS Trust, Stoney Stanton Road, Coventry CV1 4FH Tel: 024 7684 4150 Fax: 024 7684 4150; 27 Long Furlong, Rugby CV22 5QS Tel: 01788 813316 Email: john@chandy.freeserve.co.uk — MB BS 1970 Madras; FRCR 1982; DMRD Eng. 1980. (Christian Medical College Vellore, South India) p/t Cons. Radiol. Univ. Hosp. Coventry& Warwicks. NHS Trust Hosps. Socs: Fell. Roy. Soc. Med.; Brit. Soc. Skeletal Radiol.; Eur. Soc. Musculo-Skeletal Radiol. Prev: Cons. Radiol. Coventry & Rugby Hosps.; Sen. Regist. (Radiol.) Leics. Gp. Hosps.; Regist. (Radiol.) Leics. Gp. Hosps.

CHANDY, Joseph Shinwell Medical Centre, Fourth Street, Horden, Peterlee SR8 4LE Tel: 0191 586 3859 Fax: 0191 586 0748 — MB BS 1966 Kerala; MRCP (UK) 1973; MRCGP 1977. (Trivandrum Med. Coll.) Prev: Med. Regist. Gen. Hosp. Middlesbrough.

CHANDY, Joseph The Surgery, 69 Stockingate, South Kirkby, Pontefract WF9 3PE Tel: 01977 642251 Fax: 01977 645515 — MB BS 1966 Kerala. (Kerala) GP Pontefract, W. Yorks.

CHANDY, Joseph Betula, 3 Pine Meadows, Kirk Ella, Hull HU10 7NS — MB BS 1998 Lond.; MB BS Lond 1998.

CHANG, Bernard 2 Newlay Wood Fold, Horsforth, Leeds LS18 4HJ Tel: 0113 258 7030 Email: wendy.lum_hee@virgin.net — MB ChB Bristol 1993; FRCS (Ed.) 1997; FRCOphth Lond. 1998.

CHANG, Carl Tsang Nin Bush Hill Park Medical Centre, 25 Melbourne Way, Bush Hill Park, Enfield EN1 1XG Tel: 020 8366 5858 Fax: 020 8366 8514 — MB BS 1980 Lond.; MRCGP 1984. (Middlesex Hospital)

CHANG, Daniel See Kuan Hall Green Surgery, 164 Ormskirk Road, Upholland, Skelmersdale WN8 0AB Tel: 01695 624999 Fax: 01695 622241; 1 Rectory Farm, Rectory Lane, Standish, Wigan WN6 0XD Email: dchang@onetel.net.uk — MB ChB 1980 Manch.; MRCGP 1984; Cert. Family Plann. JCC 1986; DRCOG 1983.

CHANG, Mr David Department of Surgery, Addenbrooke's Hospital, Hills Road, Cambridge CB2 2QQ — MD 1993 Manch.; MB ChB 1982; FRCS Eng. 1987; FRCS Ed. 1986. Sen. Regist. (Gen. Surg.) Addenbrooke's Hosp. Camb. Prev: Research Regist. Univ. Dept. Surg. Roy. Liverp. Hosp.; Regist. (Surg.) W.m. Hosp. Lond.; SHO Rotat. (Surgic.) Manch. Roy. Infirm.

CHANG, Jacqueline Margaret Meyer Street Surgery, 20 Meyer Street, Cale Green, Stockport SK3 8JE Tel: 0161 480 2882 Fax: 0161 480 0583 — MB BCh BAO 1969 Dub.; BA, MB BCh BAO Dub. 1969; DO Eng. 1974. (TC Dub.) Founding Dir. Addic. Recovery Train. Servs.

CHANG, James Christie Hospital, Wilmslow Road, Manchester M20 4BX Tel: 0161 446 3271 Fax: 0161 446 3300; 13 Manor Road, Cheadle Hulme, Cheadle SK8 7DQ Tel: 0161 485 5028 — MB BCh Dub. 1968; BA Dub. 1966; MRCP (UK) 1973; MRCPath 1975; FRCP 1992. (TC Dub.) Cons. Christie Hosp. Manch. Socs: Brit. Soc. Haematol.

CHANG, John Winston 80 Millhouse Crescent, Kelvindale, Glasgow G20 0UE — MB ChB 1988 Glas.; BSc St. And. 1985.

CHANG, Lydia Pei-Yu 39 Elm Park Road, Pinner HA5 3LE — MB BS 1991 Lond.

CHANG, Mathew Khai Laing The Surgery, 121-123 The Grove, Stratford, London E15 1EN Tel: 020 8534 5300 Fax: 020 8534 3273; 33 Patridge Close, West Beckton, London E16 3TB Tel: 020 7511 6718 — MB BS 1980 Ranchi; LMSSA Lond. 1987.

CHANG, Pun Hon Fax: 0117 931 5743 Email: pun.chang@gp-l81028.nhs.uk; 19 School Road, Frampton Cotterell, Bristol BS36 2DB Tel: 01454 776808 — MB ChB 1981 Bristol; MRCGP 1985; DRCOG 1985.

CHANG, Mr Rene Wen Suen Renal Medicine & Transplantation, St. George's Hospital, Blackshaw Road, London SW17 0QT Tel: 020 8725 3869 Fax: 020 8725 2068 Email: rene.change@stgeorges.nhs.uk — MB BS 1968 Lond.; MS 1978; BSc (Special) Lond. 1965; FRCS Eng. 1974. (Westm.) Cons. Transpl. Surg. St. Geo.'s Hosp. Lond. Socs: Roy. Soc. of Med.; Brit. Transpl.ation Soc.; Soc. of Critical Care Med. Prev: Sen. Cons. Surg. Riyadh Armed Forces Hosp. Saudi Arabia; Surg. Regist. St. Stephen's Hosp. Lond.; Ho. Surg. Whittington Hosp. Lond.

CHANG, Sarah Lai-Lai (Surgery), 229 West Barnes Lane, New Malden KT3 6JD Tel: 020 8336 1773 Fax: 020 8395 4797; 12 Lower Green Road, Esher KT10 8HD — MB BS 1986 Lond.; MRCGP 1990; DCH RCP Lond. 1989; DRCOG 1988. Prev: SHO (Palliat. Med. & Geriat.) St. Catherine's Hospice Crawley; Trainee GP Wolverhampton VTS; Trainee GP E. Molesey Surrey.

CHANG, Sebastian Hsueh-ping Tresholme, 39 Elm Park Road, Pinner HA5 3LE Tel: 020 8866 2915 Fax: 020 8459 6965; Tresholme, 39 Elm Pk Road, Pinner HA5 3LE Tel: 020 8866 2915 Fax: 020 8459 6965 — MB BS 1995 Lond. (Royal Free Hospital, London University) SHO(Urol.), Sunderland Roy. Hosp. Socs: MDU; Brit. Med. Assn. Prev: SHO (Orthop.) S.end Hosp.; SHO, (Cardiothoracic) Roy. Brompton Hosp.; Sen. Ho. Off. (A & E), Lister Hosp., Stevenage.

CHANG, Serene Hsi-Lin 301 Cardamom Building, 31 Shad Thames, London SE1 2YR — MB BS 1998 Lond.; MB BS Lond 1998. (UMDS Guy's & St Thomas' Hosp.) Med.HO.Joyce Geem Hosp.Dartford.

CHANG, Yang How St Charles Hospital, Parkside Health NHS Truat., Exmoor Street,, London W10 6DZ Tel: 0208 962 4051 Fax: 0208 962 4056/4243 Email: chang.yang@ukgateway.net; 43 Hazelmere Road, St Albans AL4 9SA Tel: 01727 862438 Fax: 01727 862438 Email: changyh@doctor.org.uk — MB BS 1971 Adelaide; MRCPsych 1986. Cons. (Psychiat.) Horizon NHS Trust Radlett, Herts. Prev: Cons. (Psychiat.) Barnet Healthcare Trust.

CHANG, Yen-Ch'ing Rosemullion, Woodlands Road, Bromley BR1 2AP — MB BS 1996 Lond.

CHANG, Yok Fun 10 Matlock Road, Brighton BN1 5BF — MB ChB 1983 Dundee; Cert. Prescribed Equiv. Exp. JCPTGP 1988; DRCOG 1988. GP Brighton.

CHANG, Yuk Lun Department of Paediatrics, Mayday University Hospital, London Road, Croydon CR7 7YE Tel: 020 8401 3397 Fax: 020 8401 3398 Email: john.chang@mhc-tr.sthames.nhs.uk; 53 Southlands Drive, Wimbledon, London SW19 5QJ Email: jylchang@yahoo.com — MB ChB 1982 Bristol; BSc Bristol 1979; MRCP (UK) 1986; FRCP (Ed); FRCPCH. (Bristol) Cons. Paediat. (Neonat.) Mayday Hosp. Croydon; Hon. Sen. Lect. (Paediat.) St. Geo. Med. Sch. Lond. Prev: Sen. Regist. (Neonat.) Mater Childr. Hosp. S. Brisbane, Austral.; SHO (Paediat.) Warrington Dist. Gen. Hosp.; Sen. Regist. (Paediat.) Kingston Hosp. & Char. Cross Hosp. Lond.

CHANG CHAU-LAP, Charlie 6 Ty To Maen Close, St. Mellons, Cardiff CF3 5EY Tel: 029 2079 5295 — MB BCh 1969 Wales; DCH Eng. 1980. (Cardiff)

CHANG KIT, Hong Ling c/o Department of Anaesthetics, York District Hospital, Wigginton Road, York YO31 8HE — MB BS 1987 West Indies; BSc Mathematics & Physics, Univ West Indies, 1980. Staff Grade in Anaesthetics; Locum Staff Grade (Anaesth.) York Dist. Hosp. Socs: Assn. of Anaesthetics of Gt. Britain & Irel. Prev: Vis. Specialist Regist. (Anaesth.) Roy. Oldham Hosp.; Vis. Regist. (Anaesth.) MusGr. Pk. Hosp. Taunton, Som.

CHANGIZI, Rouhollah 16 Upper Belgrave Road, Bristol BS8 2XH Tel: 0117 973 7173 — MD 1958 Teheran. (Teheran Med. Sch. & Guy's Hosp. Lond.) Clin. Asst. Day Hosp. & Manor Pk. Hosp. Bristol.

CHANKUN, Tony Siak Lam Queens Road Medical Practice, The Grange, St. Peter Port, Guernsey GY1 1RH Tel: 01481 724184 Fax: 01481 716431 — MB BS 1986 Lond.; BSc (Hons.) Lond. 1983; MRCGP 1992; DRCOG 1991; DCH RCP Lond. 1990. (King's Coll. Sch. Med. & Dent. Lond.) Socs: Assoc. Mem. Brit. Med. Acupunc. Soc.

CHANNELL, Sonia (retired) 36 York Road, Edinburgh EH5 3EQ Tel: 0131 551 1177 — MB BChir 1962 Camb.; MB Camb. 1962, BChir 1961; DCH Eng. 1965. Prev: Princip. Gen. Pract. Ed.

CHANNER, Judith Lois — MB ChB 1978 Manch.; MRCPath 1990; Cert. Family Plann. JCC 1980; FRCPath 1999. Prev: Loum Cons. (Histopath.); Sen. Regist. & SHO (Histopath.) S.mead Hosp. Bristol; Sen. Regist. (Histopath.) N.. Gen. Hosp. Sheff.

CHANNER, Kevin Stephen 6 Ranmoor Rise, Ranmoor, Sheffield S10 3HU — MD 1985 Manch.; MB ChB 1978; MRCP (UK) 1980. Cons. Phys. & Cardiol. Roy. Hallamsh. Hosp. Sheff. Prev: Sen. Regist. (Cardiol.) Bristol Roy. Infirm.; Regist. (Cardiol., Diabetes/Gen. Med. & Cardiol./Gen. Med.) Bristol Roy. Infirm.

CHANNING, Abigail Ruth — BM 1995 Soton.; MRCGP 2000. Gen. Practitioner. Prev: GP Regist. Exeter VTS.

CHANNING, Rev. Edward William Mason (retired) Coombe Cottage, Sandgate, Exeter EX2 7JL Tel: 01392 874644 — MB BS 1968 Lond.; MA Manch. 1992; DA Eng. 1970. Prev: Princip. GP Bideford.

CHANNING, Giles Matthew 61 Birchfield Road, Ceadle Heath, Stockport SK3 0SY — BM 1994 Soton.

CHANNING, Nigel Adrian The Surgery, 124 New Church Road, Hove BN3 4JB Tel: 01273 729194 Fax: 01273 881992; Applejack Cottage, Plumpton Lane, Plumpton, Lewes BN7 3AH — MA (Hons.) Camb. 1981; MB BS Lond. 1980; FRCGP 1993, M 1984; DRCOG 1983. (Guy's) Socs: Treas. SE Thames Fac. RCGP; BMA. Prev: SHO St. Augustine's Hosp. Chartham & Buckland Hosp. Dover; SHO (A & E) William Harvey Hosp. Ashford.

CHANNON, Claude Edward (retired) 8 Wilson Gardens, Newcastle upon Tyne NE3 4JA Tel: 0191 285 5764 — MRCS Eng. LRCP Lond. 1952; MA Camb. 1948. Prev: Ho. Surg. Taunton & Som. Hosp.

CHANNON, Mr Geoffrey Michael Department of Orthopaedic Surgery, Wycombe General Hospital, Queen Alexandra Road, High Wycombe HP11 2TT Tel: 01494 425002; Hundridge House, Great Missenden HP16 0RW Tel: 01494 863690 Fax: 01494 863589 Email: g.m.channon@talk21.com — MB ChB 1970 Ed.; BSc Ed. 1967; FRCS Ed. 1976. (Edinburgh) Cons. Orthop. Surg. High Wycombe; Hon. Cons. Nuffield Orthop. Centre, Oxf. Prev: Research Fell. Univ. Toronto, Canada; Sen. Regist. (Orthop. Surg.) Cardiff; Lect. (Orthop. Surg.) Welsh Nat. Sch. Med. Cardiff.

CHANNON, Lola Vivian (retired) 8 Wilson Gardens, Newcastle upon Tyne NE3 4JA Tel: 01632 855764 — MB BS 1950 Durh. Prev: Ho. Surg. Roy. Vict. Infirm. Newc.

CHANNON, Michael Edward Kingston Park Avenue Surgery, Newcastle upon Tyne Tel: 0191 286 0022 — MB BS 1981 Lond.; MRCGP 1986.

CHANRAI, Madhvi Flat 2, 11 Adamson Road, Swiss Cottage, London NW3 3HX Tel: 020 7483 4327 — MB BChir 1986 Camb.; BA Camb. 1984; MRCGP 1993. Retainer GP Lond. Prev: Trainee GP Hampstead Lond.; SHO (Med.) Bedford Gen. Hosp. & Bristol Gen. Hosp.

CHANT, Brian Worth 64 Spon Lane, Grendon, Atherstone CV9 2PD Tel: 01827 714325; Polesworth/Dordon, Tamworth Tel: 01827 892893 — MB ChB 1956 Manch. (Manch.)

CHANT, Darren John 4 Burreed Close, Watersedge, St Mellons, Cardiff CF3 0RL Tel: 029 2036 3458 — MB BCh 1995 Wales; BSc (Hons.) Wales 1992. (Univ. Wales Coll. Med.) SHO Rotat. (Surg.) Roy. Gwent Hosp. Newport.

CHANT, Mr Harvey James Vascular Studies Unit, Department of Surgery, South Manchester University Hospitals, Withington Hospital, Nell Lane, Manchester M20 2LR Email: h.chant@fs.with.man.ac.uk — MB BS 1992 Lond.; BSc (Hons) Lond. 1987; FRCS Eng. 1997. (St Georges London) Research Fell. (Vasc. Surg.) RCS. Socs: Rouleaux Club.

CHANTARASAK, Mr Nopdol Don 78 Harley Street, London W1N 1AE Tel: 020 7255 1308 Fax: 020 8421 1288 Email: nd-chantarasak@foh.co.uk; 2 Badgers Meadow, Pwllmeyric, Chepstow NP16 6UE Tel: 07831 790568 — MB BS 1980 Lond.; BSc Lond. 1977; FRCS Ed. 1986; MRCS Eng. LRCP Lond. 1980. (Char. Cross Hosp. Med. Sch.) Indep. Surg. Lond. Prev: Cons. Surg. Highgate Private Hosp. Lond.; Regist. (Gen. Surg.) Walton Hosp. Liverp.; Regist. (Plastic Surg.) Mersey Reg. Plastic Unit Whiston Hosp.

CHANTLER, Sir Cyril (retired) 22 Benbow House, New Globe Walk, London SE1 9DS Tel: 0207 401 3246 Email: cyril.chantler@kcl.ac.uk — MB Camb. 1964, BChir (Distinc. Med.) 1963; MD Camb. 1973, MA 1964; FRCP Lond. 1977, M 1967. Prev: Chair of Gt. Ormond St. Hosp. for Childr. Trust.

CHANTLER, Ilona Wanda Charles Salt Research Unit, Robert Jones & Agnes Hunt Orthopaedic &, District Hospital NHS Trust, Oswestry SY10 7AG Tel: 01691 404476; Ochr, The Llawnt, Rhydycroesau, Oswestry SY10 7HY — MB ChB 1973 Bristol. Doctor i/c Clin. Trials Chas. Salt Research Unit., Robt. Jones & Agnes Hunt Orthop. & Dist. Hosps. NHS Trust OsW.ry. Socs: Brit. Menopause Soc. Prev: GP OsW.ry; GP & Clin. Med. Off. (Sch. of Community Med.) Newc.; GP Camden & Islington & Clin. Med. Off. (Family Plann.) Camden & Islington.

CHANTLER, Jonathan Mark 60 Herne Hill, London SE24 9QP — BChir 1991 Camb.

CHANTLER, Susan Stapleford Cottage, Burton Road, Stapleford, Tarporley CW6 0ET — MB BS 1984 Lond.; MRCGP 1989; DRCOG 1988. (Roy. Free) Prev: Trainee GP Lister Hosp. Stevenage VTS; SHO (Paediat.) Arrowe Pk. Hosp. Wirral; Ho. Surg. Barnet Gen. Hosp.

CHANTRY, Andrew Douglas 48 Stainton Road, Sheffield S11 7AX — MB ChB 1998 Sheff.; MB ChB Sheff 1998.

CHANTRY, Jane Elizabeth Falkland House Surgery, Falkland Road, Sheffield S11 7PL Tel: 0114 266 0285; 22 Marsh House Road, Ecclesall, Sheffield S11 9SP — MB ChB 1974 Sheff.

CHAO, David Roayl Free Hospital, Hampstead, London NW3 2QG — BM BCh 1990 Oxf.; DPhil 1987 Oxford; MRCP (UK) 1993. Med. Oncol. Cons., Dept. of Oncol., Roy. Free and N. Middlx. Univ. Hosps., Lond. Socs: Assn. of Cancer Phys.s; Roy. Soc. of Med.

CHAO, Mark Anthony 18 Kenyon Mansions, Queens Club Gardens, London W14 9RN; 2nd Floor, 9C Broom Road, Happy Valley, Hong Kong Tel: 00 852 8920601 — MB BS 1993 Lond. Prev: SHO (Radiother. & Oncol.) Middlx. Hosp. Lond.

CHAO, Richard Pai Wang 19 Corfton Road, London W5 2HP — MRCS Eng. LRCP Lond. 1965; DPM Leeds 1970.

CHAO, William Sai-Chik 99 Harley Street, London W1N 1DF Tel: 020 7487 3204; 53 Meadowbank, Primrose Hill, London NW3 3AY Tel: 020 7722 4745 — MD 1965 Chiba Univ. Japan; LAH Dub. 1969. (Chiba Univ.) Assoc. Endoscopist i/c Endoscopy Unit Gastroenterol. Dept. P. of; Wales Hosp. Lond. & St. Ann's Hosp. Lond. Socs: Japanese Soc. Gastroenterol. & Brit. Soc. Digestive Endoscopy. Prev: Regist. (Gen. Surg.) P. of Wales & St. Ann's Hosps. Lond.; Resid. in Gen. Surg. Univ. Hosp. Chiba, Japan; Ho. Off. Gen. Surg. W. Middlx. Hosp.

CHAOUAT, Ari 71 Tamarin Gardens, Cambridge CB1 9GQ — MD 1992 Strasbourg.

CHAPARALA, Bharaati C Holyhead Primary Health Care Centre, 1 St James Road, Handsworth, Birmingham B21 0HL Tel: 0121 554 8516 Fax: 0121 523 5306 — LRCP LRCS Ed. LRCPS Glas. 1982 Edinburgh/Glasgow; MB BS 1974 Andhra; MB BS 1974 Andhra.

CHAPE, Calvin Tel: 01292 886622 Fax: 01292 614303 — MB ChB 1987 Dundee; DRCOG 1991. Clin. Asst. (Diabetes) Ayr. Prev: SHO (Psychiat.) Murray Roy. Hosp. Perth; SHO (Cas.) Vict. Hosp. Kirkcaldy.

CHAPEL, Andrew John South Point, Somerford Road, Cirencester GL7 1TX Tel: 01285 2260 — MB BS Lond. 1963; MRCS Eng. LRCP Lond. 1963. (St. Geo.) Assoc. Specialist (Gen. Surg.) Cirencester Hosp.; Assoc. Specialist (Gen. Surg.) Cirencester Hosp.

CHAPEL, Helen Margaret Department Immunology - Level 7, John Radcliffe Hospital, Oxford OX3 9DU Tel: 01865 221769 Fax: 01865 742180 — MB BChir 1969 Camb.; MA Camb. 1969, MD 1976; FRCP (UK) 1997; FRCPath 1989, M 1977. (Univ. Camb. & St. Thos. Hosp.) Cons. Immunol. Oxf. Radcliffe Hosp.; Sen. Clin. Lect. Univ. Oxf. Med. Sch. Prev: Lect. Univ. Birm. Med. Sch.

CHAPEL, Hendrikus Heligan Manor Cottage, Pentewan, St Austell PL26 6EN Tel: 01726 844050 — MD 1986 Louvain; MSc Pub. Health Med. Univ. Lond. 1993. Sen. Regist. (Pub. Health Med.) Cornw. & Isle of Scilly HA's St. Austell.

CHAPELA, Jesús Manuel Marfleet Group Practice, 350 Preston Road, Hull HU9 5HH Tel: 01482 701834 Fax: 01482 784757 — 1994 Licentiate in Medicine & Surgery; 1997 Dip. Faculty of Family Planning; 1999 Certificate of Prescibed Experience. (Universidad de Santiago de Compostela, Spain) Princip. GP, Marfleet Gp. Pract., Hull. Prev: SHO in A & E, P. Chas. Hosp. Merthyr Tydfil, S. Wales; SHO in Gen. Med., Roy. Gwent Hosp. Newport, Gwent; SHO in Dermatalogy, Roy. Gwent Hosp.

CHAPELHOW, Sharon Jane 247 The Glen, Palace Fields, Runcorn WA7 2TF — MB ChB 1991 Leic.

CHAPLAIN, William, BEM 4 Bell Avenue, Aston-on-Trent, Derby DE72 2BE Tel: 01332 792473 — MB ChB St. And. 1954. Prev: Emerit. Cons. Psychiat. Aston Hall Hosp. Aston-on-Trent.; Cons. Psychiat. Aston Hall Hosp. Aston-on-Trent; Ho. Phys. (Psychiat. & Geriat.) Maryfield Gen. Hosp. Dundee.

CHAPLAIS, Janet de Zouche 92 Ivy Park Road, Ranmoor, Sheffield S10 3LD — BM BCh 1971 Oxf.; MRCP (UK) 1976; DCH Eng. 1975.
CHAPLIN, David Andrew New Cumnock Surgery, 67 Afton Bridgend, New Cumnock, Cumnock KA18 4BA Tel: 01290 338242 Fax: 01290 332010; 8 The Leggate, New Cumnock, Cumnock KA18 4NG — MB ChB 1985 Glas.; DRCOG (UK) 1988. (Glas.)
CHAPLIN, David Andrew 8 Roseworth Avenue, Gosforth, Newcastle upon Tyne NE3 1NB Tel: 0191 213 1550 Email: d.a.chaplin@newcastle.ac.uk — MB BS 1991 Newc.; MRCP (UK) 1994; Dip. Epidemiol. 1997. (Newcastle-upon-Tyne) Specialist Regist. (Elderly Care) N. Region. Socs: RCP (Lond.); BGS. Prev: Research Regist. (Med. & Elderly Care) N. Tyneside Gen. Hosp.; SHO (Med. & Elderly Care) N. Tyneside Gen. Hosp. & Carlisle.
CHAPLIN, Jane Victoria 93 Dringthorpe Road, York YO24 1LF Tel: 01904 704753; 67 Graveney Road, London SW17 0EG Tel: 020 8672 7634 — MB ChB 1993 Leeds. SHO (Paediat.) Lewisham Childr.s Hosp. Prev: SHO (A & E) St. Helier Hosp.; SHO (O & G) Hull; GP Regist. Hull.
CHAPLIN, Robert Henry Springfield Hospital, 61 Glenburnie Road, London SW17 7DJ; 24 Gordon Dale Road, London SW19 8EN — MB ChB 1986 Leic.; MRCPsych 1991. Sen. Regist. (Psychiat.) Roy. Pk. Hosp. Vict., Austral. Prev: Regist. Rotat. (Psychiat.) Leics. Train. Scheme.
CHAPLIN, Simon Callington and Gunnislake Group, Health Centre, Haye Road, Callington PL17 7AW Tel: 01579 382666 Fax: 01579 383345; North Park House, Lower Calstock Road, Gunnislake PL18 9AN — BM BS 1980 Nottm.; BMedSci (Hons.) 1978.
CHAPLIN ROGERS, Simon Paul Park Surgery, Park Surgery, Hursley Road, Chandlers Ford, Eastleigh SO53 2ZH Tel: 023 8026 7355 Fax: 023 8026 5394; Carterlands, Southdown Road, Shawford, Winchester SO21 2BY — MB BS 1985 Lond.; BDS (Hons.) Lond. 1979; LDS RCS Eng. 1979. (Univ. Coll. Hosp.)
CHAPMAN, Alexander Lewis Stonecroft, Bredon, Tewkesbury GL20 7EL — MB BS 1997 Newc.
CHAPMAN, Alison Redbriggs Croft, Greeness, Cuminestown, Turriff AB53 8HY — MB ChB 1988 Aberd.; MRCGP 1992.
CHAPMAN, Alison (retired) 11 Dunton Close, Sutton Coldfield B75 5QD Tel: 0121 308 6705 — MB ChB 1948 St. And. Prev: Clin. Asst. (Dermat.) Good Hope Hosp. Sutton Coldfield.
CHAPMAN, Allan — MB ChB 1981 Glas.; MRCP (UK) 1994. Cons. Paediat.Dumfries and Gallway Roy. Infirm., Bankend Rd, Dumfries, D01 4AP. Socs: RCPCH. Prev: Regist. (Paediat.) Roy. Hosp. Sick Childr. Edin.
CHAPMAN, Andrea Denise Department of Pathology, Medical School Buildings, Aberdeen Royal Infirmary, Foresterhill, Aberdeen AB25 2ZD Tel: 01224 553000 Fax: 01224 663002 Email: Andrea.chapman@arch.graupian.scot.nhs.uk; Tel: 01224 703099 Email: mail@adchapman.com — MB ChB 1994 Aberd.; 2001 MRCPath. (Aberdeen) Cons., Path., Aberd. Roy. Infirm. Socs: Path. Soc.; Train. Mem. Assn. Clin. Path.; Internat. Acad. Path. Prev: SHO (Path.) Aberd. Roy. Infirm.; Ho. Off. (Plastic, Neurosurg., Cardiol. & Gen. Med.) Aberd. Roy. Infirm.; Specialist Regist., Path., Aberd. Roy. Infirm.
CHAPMAN, Andrew Charles Holt Medical Practice, High Street, Holt NR25 6BH Tel: 01263 712461 Fax: 01263 713211 — MB BS 1973 Lond.; MRCS Eng. LRCP Lond. 1973; MRCGP 1980.
CHAPMAN, Andrew John (retired) Stonecroft, Bredon, Tewkesbury GL20 7EL Tel: 01684 772272 — MB BS Lond. 1968; FRCGP 1987, M 1974; DObst RCOG 1972; DA Eng. 1970. RCGP Tutor Cheltenham.
CHAPMAN, Andrew John Milman Road Health Centre, Milman Road, Reading RG2 0AR Tel: 0118 968 2285 Fax: 0118 975 5033; 28 Brading Way, Purley-on-Thames, Reading RG8 8BS Tel: 0118 943 1388 — MB ChB 1986 Leeds; BSc (Hons.) (Path.) Leeds 1983. Princip. GP. Socs: BMA. Prev: Princip. GP Withernsea & Milnthorpe.
CHAPMAN, Ann Lynn Noble Heartlands Hospital, Bordesley Green E., Birmingham B9 5ST Tel: 0121 766 6611; 2 Bull Street, Harbourne, Birmingham B17 0HH Tel: 0121 680 8805 Email: a.l.noble@bham.ac.uk — BM BCh 1991 Oxf.; BA (Hons.) Camb. 1988; MRCP (UK) 1994; DTM & H RCP Lond. 1995. Specialist Regist., Gen. Med. & Infect. Dis.s, Heartlands Hosp., Birm. Prev: MRC Clin. Research Fell. Univ. Birm.; Regist. (Infec. Dis.) City Gen. Hosp. Stoke on Trent & Birm. Heartlands Hosp.
CHAPMAN, Anthony Hugh 46 North Park Grove, Roundhay, Leeds LS8 1EW — MB BS 1969 Lond.; MRCP (UK) 1974; MRCS Eng. LRCP Lond. 1968; FRCR 1978; DMRD Eng. 1977; DObst RCOG 1975; DCH Eng. 1972. (St. Bart.) Cons. (Radiol.) St. Jas. Univ. Hosp. Leeds. Prev: Sen. Regist. (Radiol.) Hammersmith Hosp. Lond.; Med. Regist. P.ss Alexandra Hosp. Harlow.
CHAPMAN, Arthur John Sunderland Royal Hospital, Sunderland SR4 7TP; Woodthorn, Strathmore Road, Rowlands Gill NE39 1HZ — MD 1987 Birm.; MB ChB 1975; MRCP (UK) 1978; FRCP Lond. 1995. Cons. Diabetes & Endocrinol. Socs: Brit. Diabetic Assn.; Soc. Endocrinol.; Soc. for the Study of Fertil.
CHAPMAN, Aubrey Bruce Carey Blackwater Medical Centre, Princes Road, Maldon CM9 7DS Tel: 01621 854204 Fax: 01621 850246; 25 Fish Street, Goldhanger, Maldon CM9 8AT Tel: 01621 788211 Fax: 01621 788718 — MB BS Lond. 1966; BSc (Anat.) (Hons.) Lond. 1963; MRCS Eng. LRCP Lond. 1966. (Lond. Hosp.) Hosp. Pract. Geriat. Day Hosp. St. Peter's Hosp. Maldon Essex. Prev: Ho. Phys. (Cardiac) & Ho. Surg. (Neurosurg.) Lond. Hosp.; Ho. Surg. (Obst.) Qu. Mary's Matern. Home Hampstead.
CHAPMAN, Brian John 42 Alnwickhill Road, Edinburgh EH16 6LW Tel: 0131 664 6208 Email: brian.chapman@talk21.com — MB ChB 1981 Ed.; BSc (Hons.) Ed. 1978; FRCP Ed. 1993; MRCP (UK) 1985. Cons. Gen. & Geriat. Med. Roy. Infirm. & Liberton Hosps. Edin.; Pat. Serv.s Director for Med. of the Elderly Directorate, Lothian Univ. Hosp.s NHS Trust. Prev: Sen. Regist. (Gen. & Geriat. Med.) Roy. Infirm. Edin.
CHAPMAN, Bridget Maud (retired) 2B Luttrell Road, Sutton Coldfield B74 2SR — MB ChB 1954 Birm.; DObst RCOG 1956. SCMO Community Med. (Family Plann.) Birm. HA; Clin. Asst. (Obst. & Gyn.) Good Hope Matern. Hosp. Sutton Coldfield. Prev: Ho. Surg. Surgic. Profess. Unit Qu. Eliz. Hosp. Birm.
CHAPMAN, Callum Michael 16 Fifth Cross Road, Twickenham TW2 5LG — MB BS 1987 Lond.
CHAPMAN, Catherine Eluned National Blood Service, Holland Drive, Barrack Road, Newcastle upon Tyne NE2 4; Woodthorn, Strathmore Road, Rowlands Gill NE39 1HZ — MD 1987 Birm.; BSc (Hons.) Birm. 1973, MD 1987, MB ChB 1976; MRCP (UK) 1982; MRCPath 1990. Cons. Admin. Charge of Med. Servs. Nat. Blood Serv. Newc. u. Tyne. Prev: Clin. Lect. Immunol. Univ. Birm.
CHAPMAN, Charles David Cobweb Cottage, Silver St., Barrow-upon-Humber DN19 7DN — MB ChB 1989 Leeds.
CHAPMAN, Mr Charles William, OBE, OStJ Plastic Surgery Unit, Derriford Hospital, Derriford Road, Plymouth PL6 8DH Tel: 01752 792110 — MB ChB 1955 Sheff.; FRCS Eng. 1968. Cons. Plastic Surg. Derriford Hosp. Plymouth & Torbay Hosp Torquay. Socs: Brit. Assn. Plastic Surgs. & Brit. Assn. Aesthetic Plastic Surgs.
CHAPMAN, Christine Michele Holmwood Corner Surgery, 179 Malden Road, New Malden KT3 6AA Tel: 020 8942 0066 Fax: 020 8336 1377; 64 Cromford Way, New Malden KT3 3BA Tel: 020 8942 1073 — MB ChB 1979 Liverp.; MRCGP 1983. (Liverpool University)
CHAPMAN, Claire Louise 94 Penrhyn Road, Sheffield S11 8UN — MB ChB 1996 Sheff.
CHAPMAN, Claire Sian Department of Haematology, Leicester Royal Infirmary, Leicester LE1 5WW Tel: 0116 258 6603 Fax: 0116 258 5093 — MB BS 1979 Lond.; MRCP (UK) 1983; MRCPath 1986. (St. Thos.) Cons. Haemat. Leicester Roy. Infirm.
CHAPMAN, Colin James Daniel Chapman and Partners, 370-372 Cregagh Road, Belfast BT6 9EY Tel: 028 9049 2214 Fax: 028 9049 2214 — MB BCh BAO 1978 Belf.
CHAPMAN, Cynthia Margaret 15 Edgar Road, Winchester SO23 9TW — BChir 1971 Camb.; MB; DO Eng. 1974.
CHAPMAN, Cyril James Oxford Clinical Genetics Service, Churchill Hospital, Old Road, Headington, Oxford OX3 7LJ Tel: 01865 226015 Fax: 01865 226011 Email: cyril.chapman@orh.anglox.nhs.uk — MB ChB Otago 1970; PhD Auckland 1981; BSc Wellington 1965; BMedSci Otago 1969; FRCP 1998. (Otago) Cons. Clin. Genetics Ch.ill Hosp. Oxf. Socs: (Hon. Sec.) Clin. Genetics Soc. Prev: Sen. Lect. Univ. Auckland, NZ; Cons. Clin. Genetics Wellington Hosp., NZ.
CHAPMAN, David Eric Hollow Way Medical Centre, 58 Hollow Way, Cowley, Oxford OX4 2NJ Tel: 01865 777495 Fax: 01865 771472 Email: david.chapman@gp-k86048.nhs.uk — MB BS 1986 Lond.; MA Camb. 1983; MD Lond. 1996; MRCP (UK) 1989;

MRCGP 1996; DRCOG 1997; DCH 1998. (Roy. Lond. Hosp.) p/t GP (Partner) Hollow Way Med. Centre. Prev: MRC Research Fell. John Radcliffe Hosp. Oxf.; Regist. (Nephrol. & Gen. Med.) John Radcliffe Hosp. Oxf.; SHO (Med.) N.wick Pk. Hosp. Harrow.

CHAPMAN, Mr David Frederick 5 Broad Elms Lane, Bents Grove, Sheffield S11 9RQ — MB ChB 1967 Leeds; MB ChB (Hons.) Leeds 1967; FRCS Ed. 1976; FRCS Eng. 1974. Cons. Otolaryngol. Roy. Hallamsh. Hosp. Sheff. Prev: Cons. Otolaryngol. N.. Gen. Hosp. Sheff.; Sen. Regist. (Otolaryngol.) Radcliffe Infirm. Oxf..

CHAPMAN, David Geoffrey (retired) 372 Cregagh, Belfast BT6 9EY Tel: 01232 792214 — MB BCh BAO 1944 Belf.; MRCGP 1971. Prev: Res. Med. Off. City Hosp. Belf.

CHAPMAN, David John (retired) 3 Walker Close, Eastbourne BN23 6AQ Tel: 01323 411729 — LMSSA Lond. 1945; FRCPC 1980; MRCS Eng. LRCP Lond. 1945; DMRD Lond. 1950. Prev: Radiol. Henderson Gen. Hosp. Hamilton Ontario, Canada.

CHAPMAN, Denise Chantal Moonhill, Crippetts Lane, Leckhampton, Cheltenham GL51 4XT Tel: 01242 862445 Email: denisecapman@yahoo.com — MB BCh 1994 Wales; MRCGP 2001. (University of Wales College of Medicine, Cardiff) Gen. Practitioner, Swansea. Prev: GP Regist., Swansea 1999; GP UTS Swansea Bay; Med. Rotat.al SHO, Morriston Hosp., Swansea.

CHAPMAN, Desmond John (retired) 17 Goldstone Crescent, Hove BN3 6LQ — MB BS 1947 Lond.; MRCS Eng. LRCP Lond. 1947.

CHAPMAN, Donald Weatherby (retired) Lane Head, Muggleswick, Consett DH8 9DN Tel: 01207 255244 Fax: 01207 255244 — MB BS 1959 Durh. Prev: SHO (Paediat.) Childr. Hosp. Sunderland.

CHAPMAN, Dorothy Garrett 42 Alnwickhill Road, Edinburgh EH16 6LW Tel: 0131 664 6208 — MB ChB 1981 Ed.; BSc (Hons.) Ed. 1978; MRCGP 1985; DRCOG 1984. (Edinburgh) Med. Adviser Benefits Agency Med. Servs. Prev: GP Edin.; Regist. (Geriat. Med.) Longmore Hosp. Edin.; Clin. Asst. (Haemat.) Roy. Infirm. Edin.

CHAPMAN, Elizabeth Ann Queen Mary's Hospital, Sidcup DA14 6LT — MB ChB 1996 Cape Town.

CHAPMAN, Elizabeth Philippa Brocklebank Health Centre, 249 Garratt Lane, London SW18 4UE Tel: 020 8870 1341/871 4448; 132 Lower Ham Road, Kingston upon Thames KT2 5BD — MB ChB 1986 Bristol; MRCGP 1992; DCH RCP Lond. 1990; DObst Auckland 1988. (Bristol)

CHAPMAN, Fiona Margaret Sunderland Eye Infirmary, Queen Alexandra Rd, Sunderland SR2 9HP — MB BS 1986 Newc.; MA Camb. 1983; FRCOphth. 1992; DO RCS Eng. 1988. p/t Cons. (Opth) Sunderland City Hosp.s Sunderland. Prev: Sen. Regist. (Ophth.) Newc. HA; Regist. (Ophth.) Newc. HA; SHO (Ophth.) Roy. Vict. Infirm. Newc.

CHAPMAN, Gillian Patricia Radcliffe Infirmary Day Hospital, Woodstock Road, Oxford OX2; 37 Sandfield Road, Headington, Oxford OX3 7RN — MB BS 1973 Lond.; BSc (Hons.) Lond. 1971, MB BS 1973; MRCP (UK) 1974; DObst RCOG 1976. Clin. Asst. (Geriat.) Oxf. RHA.; Clin. Asst. (Endoscopy).

CHAPMAN, Glyn Bradley Sunbury Health Centre Group Practice, Green Street, Sunbury-on-Thames TW16 6RH Tel: 01932 713399 Fax: 01932 713354; 47 Harfield Road, Sunbury-on-Thames TW16 5PT — MB BS 1984 Lond.; MRCGP 1989. Prev: Trainee GP Watford VTS.

CHAPMAN, Harry Richard (retired) Clifton Hampden, 25 Clifton Road, Tettenhall, Wolverhampton WV6 9AN — MB ChB 1939 Birm.

CHAPMAN, Ian Cross Road Surgery, Cross Road, Rodwell, Weymouth DT4 9QX Tel: 01305 768844 Fax: 01305 760686; 53 Broughton Crescent, Weymouth DT4 9AR — MB BS 1980 Lond.; MRCP (UK) 1983; MRCGP 1988. Prev: Regist. (Med.) N. Manch. Gen. Hosp.

CHAPMAN, Ian Robert 5 Broad Elms Lane, Ecclesall, Sheffield S11 9RQ — BM BS 1994 Nottm.

CHAPMAN, Jacqueline 40 Cambridge Street, London SW1V 4QH — MB BS 1969 Lond.; FFA RCS 1974. (St. Geo.) Med. Off. Dept. Social Security Sutton. Prev: Regist. (Anaesth.) Guy's Hosp.; Ho. Phys. St. Geo. Hosp. Lond.; SHO (Anaesth.) Harold Wood Hosp.

CHAPMAN, Mr James Anthony 124 Lake Road E., Roath Park, Cardiff CF23 5NQ Tel: 029 2075 5023 — MB BChir 1968 Camb.; MA, MB Camb. 1968, BChir 1967; FRCS Eng. 1974. (Camb. & Middlx.) Accid. Surg. Rotat. Addenbrooke's Hosp. Camb. Prev: Ho. Phys. Redhill Gen. Hosp.; Ho. Surg. Middlx. Hosp. Lond.

CHAPMAN, James Stevenson 12 Middleshade Road, St Andrews KY16 9NA Tel: 01334 473687 — MB ChB Glas. 1943. (Univ. Glas.)

CHAPMAN, Jane Ellen Darnall Health Centre, 2 York Road, Sheffield S9 5DH Tel: 0114 244 1681 Fax: 0114 242 1160 — MB ChB 1967 Leeds. (Leeds)

CHAPMAN, Janet Sara 1F2, 23 Livingstone Place, Edinburgh EH9 1PD — MB ChB 1998 Ed.; MB ChB Ed 1998.

CHAPMAN, Janette Parkside Group Practice, 27 Wyche Grove, South Croydon CR2 6EX Tel: 020 8680 2588; 'April Cottage', 7 Upper Woodcote Village, Purley CR8 3HE — MB ChB 1978 Aberd.; MRCGP 1982; DRCOG 1981. p/t GP.

CHAPMAN, Jennifer Anne Department of Community Child Health, Battle Hospital, Oxford Road, Reading RG30 1AG; 75 Hilmanton, Lower Earley, Reading RG6 4HN — MB ChB 1970 Birm.; BSc (Hons.) Physiol. & Zool. Lond. 1966; MRCP (UK) 1974; FRCPCH 1997; DCH RCP Lond. 1973; DRCOG 1972; FRCP Lond. 1999. (Univ. Birm.) Cons. Paediat. Battle Hosp., Reading. Socs: Fell. Roy. Soc. Trop. Med. & Hyg. Prev: Regional Princip. Specialist Paediat. Natal Provin. Admin. Seconded to Kwazulu Govt., S. Afr.

CHAPMAN, Jennifer Margaret The Old Surgery, Gloucester St., Painswick, Stroud GL6 6QR Tel: 01452 812310 — MB ChB Cape Town 1969; MFFP 1994. (Cape Town) SCMO Seven NHS Trust in Family Plann. & Reproductive Health Care.

CHAPMAN, Jeremy Neil 178A Portobello Road, London W11 2EB — MB BChir 1990 Camb. SHO Rotat. (Med.) Roy. Lond. Hosp. Prev: Ho. Surg. Hinchingbrooke Hosp. Huntingdon; Ho. Phys. Addenbrookes Hosp. Camb.

CHAPMAN, Jeremy Robert Department Medicine, Renal Unit, Westmead Hospital, Westmead, Sydney NSW 2145, Australia Tel: 61 2 633 6962 Fax: 61 2 893 7440; c/o Four Wents, Ivy Hatch, Sevenoaks TN15 0NN — MB BChir 1978 Camb.; MD Camb. 1987, MA 1979; FRCP Lond. 1995; FRACP 1989. Director Renal Med. W.mead Hosp. & Sydney Univ., Austral.; Assoc. Prof. Univ. Sydney; Dir. Red Cross Tissue Typing Laborat. Sydney, Austral.; Chairm. Austral. Bone Marrow Donor Registry. Socs: Pres. Transpl. Soc. Austral. & NZ. Prev: MRC Research Fell. NDS Oxf. Univ.; Regist. (Med.) John Radcliffe & Ch.ill Hosps. Oxf.; SHO Brompton Hosp. Lond.

***CHAPMAN, Joel Edward** Bridgegate Surgery, 43 Bridgegate, Retford DN22 7UX Tel: 01777 702381/2 Fax: 01777 711880 — MB ChB 1994 Sheff.; MRCGP 1998; DRCOG 1998.

CHAPMAN, Mr John (retired) (cons. rooms) Three Shires Hospital, The Avenue, Cliftonville, Northampton NN1 5DR Tel: 01604 20311 Fax: 01604 29066 — MB BS 1960 Lond.; BSc Lond. 1957; FRCS Eng. 1967. Cons. Urol. N.ampton Gen. Hosp. Prev: Cons. Urol., N.ampton Gen. Hosp..

CHAPMAN, John Andrew 3 Bryn Estate, Morfa Nefyn, Pwllheli LL53 6DD — MB ChB 1993 Sheff.

CHAPMAN, John Brian (retired) Grey Ladies, White Lane Close, Sturminster Newton DT10 1EJ — MB BChir 1952 Camb.; FRCGP 1987; DObst RCOG 1956. Counc. Mem. Joseph Weld Hosp.

CHAPMAN, John Montgomerie 8 Penlee Gardens, Stoke, Plymouth PL3 4AN Tel: 01752 559366 — MB BS Lond. 1969; MRCS Eng. LRCP Lond. 1969; FFA RCS Eng. 1977; DObst RCOG 1972. (Roy. Free) Cons. Anaesth. Plymouth Gen. Hosp. Socs: Assn. Anaesth. Prev: Surg. Lt. CDR. RNR; Sen. Regist. (Anaesth.) Brist. Health Dist. (T); Vis. Asst. Prof. Univ. Virginia Charlottesville USA.

CHAPMAN, John Philip Oakley Jockey Road Surgery, 519 Jockey Road, Sutton Coldfield B73 5DF Tel: 0121 354 3050 Fax: 0121 355 1840 — MB ChB Birm. 1975; MRCP (UK) 1980; MRCGP 1984.

CHAPMAN, Jonathan Andrew Widcombe Surgery, 3-4 Widcombe Parade, Bath BA2 4JT Tel: 01225 310883 Fax: 01225 421600 — MB BS 1988 Lond.; DRCOG 1992. (Guy's Hosp. Med. Sch.) Hon. Teach. (Gen. Pract.) Univ. Bristol.

CHAPMAN, Jonathan Roy The Towers Surgery, 163 Holton Road, Barry CF63 4HP Tel: 01446 734131 Fax: 01446 420002 — MB BS 1979 Lond.; BSc (Pharmacol.) Lond. 1976; DRCOG 1984; DCH RCP Lond. 1983. (St. Bart.) Socs: BMA & Med. Defence Union. Prev: SHO City Hosp. Nottm.; Ho. Surg. Crawley Hosp.; Ho. Phys. St. Bart. Hosp. Lond.

CHAPMAN, Julia Tina Vance 34 Ainger Road, Hampstead, London NW3 3AT — MB BS 1986 Lond.

CHAPMAN, Katherine 61 Mill Street, Eynsham, Witney OX29 4JY — MB BS 1994 Lond.

CHAPMAN, Katherine Mary Abbey Medical Centre, Lonend, Paisley PA1 1SU Tel: 0141 889 4088; 54 Balgonie Avenue, Paisley PA2 9LP — MB BS 1974 Newc.

CHAPMAN, Kathryn Mary 17 Bishops Cleeve, Austrey, Atherstone CV9 3EU — MB BS 1986 Lond.; DCH RCP Lond. 1989. SHO (Paediat.) Qu. Mary's Univ. Hosp. Roehampton. Prev: SHO Rotat. (Med.) W.m. Hosp. Lond.; SHO Rotat. (Paediat.) St. Geo. Hosp. Lond.

CHAPMAN, Keith Alexander 1 West Mill Wynd, Lasswade EH18 1LZ — MB ChB 1981 Ed.

CHAPMAN, Kenneth Suite 10, 103-105 Harley St., London W1G 6AJ Tel: 020 7224 3011 Fax: 020 7487 3680 Email: yi28@dial.pipex.com; Barham House, East Hoathly, Lewes BN8 6QL Tel: 01825 840032 Fax: 01825 840032 — MB ChB 1955 Ed.; FRCOG 1984, M 1965; FRANZCOG 1978; FAGO 1977; MMSA 1962; DObst RCOG 1958. Cons. O & G Lond. Socs: Fell. Roy. Med. Soc. Edin.; Fell. Roy. Soc. Med. Prev: Cons. O & G Univ. Isfahan Iran, Tokoroa Hosp. NZ & Sydney Adventist Hosp. Austral.

***CHAPMAN, Kim Erica** 166 Crookesmoor Road, Sheffield S6 3FS — MB ChB 1997 Sheff.

CHAPMAN, Laura Jane 14 Lucan Road, Liverpool L17 0BS — MB ChB 1994 Liverp.

CHAPMAN, Leslie 74 The Avenue, Sunbury-on-Thames TW16 5EX Tel: 0193 27 83800 — LMSSA 1953 Lond.; ARIC 1944; MPS 1934. (St. Bart.) Hon. Chem. Path. Sutton & W. Merton Health Dist. Prev: Chem. Path. Sutton & W. Merton Health Dist.; Med. Biochem. W. Lond. Hosp.; Ho. Phys. (Paediat.) St. Albans City Hosp.

CHAPMAN, Liam Edward 34 Grove Crescent, Kingsbury, London NW9 0LP Tel: 020 8905 8552 Fax: 020 8200 8878 Email: lecjjchapman@lineone.net; 13 Titus Street, Saltaire, Bradford Tel: 01274 599593 — MB BS 1993 Lond.; DTM & H RCP Lond. 1995. p/t GP Regist. Lond. VTS - GP Retainee. Socs: Med.Defence.Union, St. Paul's. Prev: SHO (c/o Elderly) Chase Farm Hosp. Enfield; SHO (O & G) Whittington Hosp. Lond.; SHO (Paediat.) N. Middlx. Hosp. Edmonton.

CHAPMAN, Linda The Ruddington Medical Centre, Church Street, Ruddington, Nottingham NG11 6HD Tel: 0115 921 1144 Fax: 0115 940 5139; Meadow End Cottage, 21 Curzon St, Gotham, Nottingham NG11 0HQ Tel: 0115 983 0705 — BM BS 1981 Nottm.

CHAPMAN, Malcolm 126 Harley Street, London W1N 1PA Tel: 020 7935 1918; Kestrels, Sunset Lane, West Chiltington, Pulborough RH20 2NY — MB BS 1956 Lond.; BSc (Hons. Physiol.) Lond. 1953, MB BS 1956; FFR 1965; DMRD Eng. 1962. (Middlx.) Prev: Cons. Radiol. Middlx Hosp & Univ Coll Hosp Lond.; Roy. Nat. Orthop. Hosp. Lond.

CHAPMAN, Malcolm Graham Terrence Blackbrook Farm, 15 Ashbourne Road, Blackbrook, Belper DE56 2LD — MRCS Eng. LRCP Lond. 1967; MRCPsych 1973; DPM Eng. 1971. (Sheff.) Cons. Child Psychiat. Trent RHA. Socs: Soc. Clin. Psychiat.

CHAPMAN, Mark Angus Scott 5 Bare Lane, Ockbrook, Derby DE72 3RG Email: mark.chapman@nottingham.ac.uk — MB BS 1987 Lond.; MA (Hons.) Camb. 1988; MS Lond. 1995; FRCS Eng. 1991; FRCS (Gen.) 1997. (London Hospital Medicine College) Lect. in Surg. Gastroenterol. Socs: Assn. of Coloproctol. of GB & Irel.; Caius Med. Assn.

CHAPMAN, Melanie Elizabeth 4 North East Circus Place, Edinburgh EH3 6SP; 108 Thirlestane Road, Edinburgh EH9 1AS — MB ChB 1981 Dundee; MRCP (UK) 1985; FRCR 1990; T(R) (CR) 1993; DMRD Ed. 1989. Cons. Radiol. W.. Gen. Hosp. NHs Trust, Edin. Socs: Roy. Coll. Radiols.

CHAPMAN, Michael David Market Street Practice, Ton-y-Felin Surgery, Bedwas Road, Caerphilly CF83 1PD Tel: 029 2088 7831 Fax: 029 2086 9037; 7 Bryn Aur, Coed-y-Cwm, Ynysybwl, Pontypridd CF37 3JE Tel: 01443 791448 — MB BCh 1989 Wales; MRCGP 1993.

CHAPMAN, Michael Huw 1 Lawman Court, 262 Kew Road, Richmond TW9 3EF — MB BS 1997 Lond.

CHAPMAN, Miriam Vance 34 Ainger Road, London NW3 3AT; Flat 3, 50 Dartmouth Pk Road, London NW5 1SN — MB ChB 1990 Bristol; MRCP (UK) 1993. SHO (Anaesth.) Roy. Free Hosp. Lond.

CHAPMAN, Murray John Top Flat, 124 Upper St., London N1 1QP — MB BS 1988 Lond.; BSc (Hons.) Anthropol. Lond. 1985, MB BS 1988. Ho. Phys. St. Bart. Hosp. Lond.

CHAPMAN, Naomi 26 Thornleigh Dr, Lisburn BT28 2DA Tel: 01846 672307 — MB BCh BAO 1997 Belf.

CHAPMAN, Nicola Clare 11 Comely Bank Avenue, Edinburgh EH4 1EW Tel: 0131 332 0207 — MB BS 1986 Lond.; MRCP (UK) 1990. Sen. Regist. (Geriat. Med.) Edin. Prev: Regist. (Geriat. Med.) Edin. Roy. Infirm.; SHO (O & G) Falkirk & Dist. Roy. Infirm; SHO (Med.) Wolverhampton HA.

CHAPMAN, Nigel Dennis The Quild Hall, Burton St., Nottingham NG1 4BN Tel: 01159 412322 Fax: 01159 500141; 27 Hollies Drive, Edwalton, Nottingham NG12 4BZ Tel: 01159 235440 — MB ChB 1994 Leeds; MB ChB (Hons. Distinc. Surg.) 1974; BSc (Biochem.) (Hons.) Leeds 1971; MRCGP 1979; DObst RCOG 1976; Cert. Av. Med. 1983. ((Leeds)) HM Coroner Notts.; Lect. Nottm. Univ. Socs: Vice-Pres. E. Midl. Coroners Soc.; Nottm. Med-Leg. Soc. Prev: HM Coroner Lincoln; Med. Off. Lincoln Hospice; GP Saxilby.

CHAPMAN, Oliver Guy 70 Stoke Valley Road, Exeter EX4 5ER — MB BS 1994 Lond.

CHAPMAN, Patricia Jean Valerie 71 Raven Road, Stokenchurch, High Wycombe HP14 3QW Tel: 01494 483669 — BM BCh Oxf. 1968; BA Oxf. 1968; MFFP 1993; Dip. Venereol. Soc. Apoth. Lond. 1986. (Oxf. & Middlx.) Assoc. Specialist Phys. (Genitourin. Med.) Aylesbury Vale Community Healthcare NHS Trust Aylesbury. Socs: Med. Soc. Study VD; Brit. Menopause Soc.; Assn. Genitourin. Med. Prev: Clin. Asst. (Genitourin. Med.) Radcliffe Infirm. Oxf.

CHAPMAN, Mr Patrick Lee Farm, New Lane, Sutton Green, Guildford GU4 7QF — MB BS Lond. 1968; FRCS Eng. (Orl.) 1977; MRCS Eng. LRCP Lond. 1968. (Roy. Free Hosp. Sch. Med.) Cons. Otolaryngol./ead & Neck Surg. St. Peter's Hosp. Chertsey & Roy. Surrey Co. Hosp. Guildford & Ashford Hosp. Middlx. Socs: Fell. Roy. Soc. Med.; Assn. Head & Neck Oncol.; Brit. Soc. Audiol. Prev: Cons. Otolaryngol./Head & Neck Surg. St. Luke's Hosp. for Clergy & W. Middlx. Univ. Hosp. Isleworth; Sen. Regist. (ENT) St. Mary's Hosp. Lond. & Head & Neck Unit Roy. Marsden Hosp. Lond.; Regist. Roy. Nat. Throat, Nose & Ear Hosp. & Hosp. Sick Childr. Lond.

CHAPMAN, Percy Jeffrey 23 Glyn-y-Mel Road, Lower Town, Fishguard SA65 9LY — MB ChB 1947 Bristol; MRCS Eng. LRCP Lond. 1946. (Bristol) Prev: Med. Off. Nat. Coal Bd. Pneumoconiosis Field Research Scheme; Sen. Med. Off. Antarctic Pelagic Whaling Season 1949-50; Sen. Cas. Off. Bristol Roy. Infirm.

CHAPMAN, Peter The Blackheath Hospital, 40-42 Lee Terrace, London SE3 9UD Tel: 020 8463 0019 Fax: 020 8463 0019 Email: chapmanp@aol.com; The Blackheath Hospital, 40-42 Lee Terrace, London SE3 9UD Tel: 020 8304 6647 Fax: 020 8463 0019 Email: chapmanp@aol — MB ChB 1976 Dundee; FRCS Ed. 1982. Cons. Plastic Surg. Guy's & St. Thos. Trust. Socs: Fell. Roy. Soc. Med.; Brit. Assn. Aesthetic Plastic Surgs.; Brit. Assn. Plastic Surg. Prev: Cons. Burns & Plastic Surg. Qu. Eliz. Milit. Hosp. Woolwich; Sen. Regist. (Plastic Surg.) W. Norwich Hosp.; Regist. (Plastic Surg.) Addenbrooke's Hosp. Cambs.

CHAPMAN, Peter GP Suite, Cannock Community Hospital, Brunswick Road, Cannock WS11 1JP Tel: 01543 576660 Fax: 01543 576663 — MRCS Eng. LRCP Lond. 1964. (Birm.) Socs: Cannock Med. Soc. Prev: Mem. Local Med. Comm. & Mid Staffs. Health Dist. Managem. Comm.

CHAPMAN, Peter Alexander (retired) Home Farm, Boultham Park, Lincoln LN6 7ST Tel: 01522 686052 — MB BS 1951 Lond.; MRCS Eng. LRCP Lond. 1951. Prev: GP Lincoln & Hosp. Pract. (ENT) Lincoln Co. Hosp.

CHAPMAN, Mr Peter Geoffrey Department of Orthopaedics, Norfolk & Norwich Hospital, Brunswick Road, Norwich NR1 3SR Tel: 01603 286861 — MB BS 1985 Lond.; MA Camb. 1985; FRCS (Orth.) 1994; FRCS Eng. 1989. Cons. Orthop. & Trauma Norf. & Norwich Hosp. Socs: Brit. Soc. Of Surg. for the Hand; Brist. Orthopaedic Assn. Prev: Sen. Regist. St. Bart. Hosp. Lond.; Regist. (Orthop.) Addenbrooke's Hosp. Camb.

CHAPMAN, Peter John 16 de Vere Close, Wivenhoe, Colchester CO7 9AX — MB BS 1950 Lond. (Lond. Hosp.) Prev: Ho. Phys. &

Ho. Surg. Lond. Hosp.; Ho. Surg. (Obst.) City of Lond. Matern. Hosp.

CHAPMAN, Peter John Carnell Brookedale Medical Centre, 79, Povey Cross Road, Horley RH6 0AE Tel: 01293 776996 Fax: 01293 820259 Email: avmed@drchapman.co.uk, avmed@drehapman.co.uk; Whitestone, Highbrook, West Hoathly, East Grinstead RH19 4PL Tel: 01444 892261 — MB BS 1952 Lond.; MRCS Eng. LRCP Lond. 1948; MFOM RCP Lond. 1982; DPH Eng. 1958. (St. Bart.) Cons. Aviat. Med. Gatwick Horley, Surrey; Med. Adviser Bristow Helicopters Ltd., Cathay Pacific. Socs: Ex-Chairm. Internat. Advis. Comm. on Aviat. Med. IAOPA; FRAeS. Prev: Mem. IATA Med. Comm. & Europ. Airlines Med. Dirs. Soc.; Chief Med. Off. Brit. Caledonian Airways; Med. Off. 615 (Co. Surrey) Squadron, Roy. Aux. Air Force.

CHAPMAN, Peter John Lorraine (retired) St Ann's Hospice, St Ann's Road N., Heald Green, Cheadle SK8 3SZ Tel: 0161 437 8136 Fax: 0161 498 9640 — MRCS Eng. LRCP Lond. 1951. Med. Dir. St. Ann's Hospice Cheadle.

CHAPMAN, Peter Timothy Royal Postgraduate Medical School (Department of Rheumatolog, Hammersmith Hospital, Du Cane Road, London W12 0NN Tel: 020 8743 2030; Flat 714, William Goodenough House, Mecklenburgh Square, London WC1N 2AN Tel: 020 7837 8888 — MB ChB 1984 Otago; BSc Otago 1979; FRACP 1993. Research Fell. Roy. Postgrad. Med. Sch. Hammersmith Hosp. Lond. Socs: Brit. Soc. Rheum. Prev: Sen. Med. Resid. & Sen. Regist. (Rheum.) ChristCh. Hosp., NZ.

CHAPMAN, Philippa Joan The Health Centre, High St., Bedworth, Nuneaton CV12 8NQ Tel: 01203 315432 — MB BS 1990 Lond.; BSc (Immunol.) Lond 1984.

CHAPMAN, Phillip Charles Symes (retired) Pipers Moon, Brampton, Norwich NR10 5AA Tel: 01603 279370 — MB BS 1959 Lond.; MRCS Eng. LRCP Lond. 1959; DObst RCOG 1961. Prev: SHO (Cas.) Leicester Roy. Infirm.

CHAPMAN, Richard Douglas 43 The Paddock, Beverley HU17 7HQ — MB ChB 1998 Ed.; MB ChB Ed 1998.

CHAPMAN, Richard James 4 Newton Drive, West Kirby, Wirral CH48 9UP — BM BCh 1996 Oxf.

CHAPMAN, Robert Anthony Eye Department, St. James's University Hospital, Leeds LS9 7TF Tel: 0113 206 5746 Fax: 0113 206 5028 Email: eyedoc2020@excite.com; 522 Nottingham Road, Chaddesden, Derby DE21 6QL Tel: 01332 662304 Fax: 01332 678264 Email: lechwaba.chapman@cwcom.net — MB ChB 1975 Bristol; MRCGP 1979; DRCOG 1979; DO Eng. 1977. Community Eye Phys. St. Jas. Univ. Hosp. Leeds. Prev: Ophth. Elim Hosp. S. Afr.; Superintendent Jane Furse Hosp. S. Afr.; GP Co. Durh.

CHAPMAN, Robert Charles Forensic Medicine Unit (Department of Histopathology), St George's Hospital Medical School, Cranmer Terrace, Tooting, London SW17 0RE Tel: 020 8725 0015 Fax: 020 8725 0017; Lane End, Warfied St, Warfield, Bracknell RG42 6AR — MB ChB 1982 Birm.; MRCPath 1994; DMJ (Path.) Soc. Apoth. Lond. 1990. Sen. Lect. (Forens. Med.) & Hon. Cons. Forens. Path. St. Geo. Hosp. Lond. Socs: Fell. Roy. Soc. Med. (Clin. for Med.); BMA; Brit. Assn. Forens. Med. Prev: Sen. Lect. (Forens. Med.) & Hon. Cons. Forens. Path. Guy's Hosp. Lond.

CHAPMAN, Robert Cleaver 502 Upper Newtownards Road, Belfast BT4 3HB — MB BCh BAO 1941 Belf.; BDS 1952, LDS 1939; FDS RCS Eng. 1953.

CHAPMAN, Robert Oliver Oakwood Medical Centre, Oakwood Lane, Barnton, Northwich CW8 4HE Tel: 01606 74718 Fax: 01606 784529; 18 Longmeadow, Weaverham, Northwich CW8 3JH Tel: 01606 852067 Fax: 01606 854852 — MB ChB 1972 Sheff.; MRCGP 1976.

CHAPMAN, Robert Sutherland (retired) 10 Douglas Muir Place, Milngavie, Glasgow G62 7RS Tel: 0141 955 0171 — MB ChB (Hons.) Aberd. 1962; FRCP Glas. 1986, M 1984; FRCP Lond. 1984, M 1967; FRCP Ed. 1977, M 1965. Prev: Cons. Dermat. Stobhill NHS Trust.

CHAPMAN, Mr Robin Heath 10 Harley Street, London W1 Tel: 020 7486 9018; Kingston Hospital, Wolverton Avenue, Kingston upon Thames KT2 7QB Tel: 020 8546 7711 — MB BS 1967 Lond.; FRCS Eng. 1972. (Lond. Hosp.) Cons. Orthop. Surg. Kingston Hosp. & New Vict. Hosp. Kingston. Socs: Fell. BOA & Roy. Soc. Med.; Brit. Soc. Surg. of the Hand; Soc. Expert Witnesses. Prev: Sen. Regist. (Orthop.) Roy. Lond. Hosp.; Sen. Resid. (Orthop.) Vanderbilt Univ. Hosp.; Regist. (Surg.) Roy. Lond. Hosp.

CHAPMAN, Roderick MacDonald 4 Moor Road, Milngavie, Glasgow G62 8AT — MB ChB 1997 Glas.

CHAPMAN, Roger 29 Pilleys Lane, Boston PE21 9RA — MB ChB 1951 Sheff.; DPH Liverp. 1967. (Sheff.) Emerit. Cons. Phys. Pilgrim Hosp. Boston. Prev: Cons. Phys. (Geriat.) E. Lincs. Hosps.

CHAPMAN, Roger Geoffrey Bassett Road Surgery, 29 Bassett Road, Leighton Buzzard LU7 1AR Tel: 01525 373111 Fax: 01525 853767; Woodland End, 3 Woodland Avenue, Leighton Buzzard LU7 3JW Tel: 01525 375248 Fax: 01525 854054 Email: roger@rgclbgp.demon.co.uk — MB BS 1971 Lond.; BSc (Hons., Biochem.) Lond. 1968; MRCS Eng. LRCP Lond. 1971; FRCGP 1987, M 1976; DObst RCOG 1974. (St. Bart.) GP Princip. Prev: Trainee GP Aylesbury VTS; SHO (Obst.) Roy. Berks. Hosp. Reading; Ho. Surg. Profess. Unit & Gyn. Dept. St. Bart. Hosp. Lond.

CHAPMAN, Roger Laurence Kenneth Grandell, 16 South Drive, Mickleover, Derby DE3 5AN Tel: 01332 514080 — MB BS 1968 Lond.; MRCS Eng. LRCP Lond. 1968; FRCOG 1988, M 1973; DObst 1970. (Univ. Coll. Hosp.) Cons. O & G Derby City Hosp. Prev: Lect. (O & G) Univ. Coll. Hosp. Lond.; Scientif. Asst. Nuffield Inst. Med. Research; Regist. (O & G) W. Middlx. Hosp. Isleworth.

CHAPMAN, Roger William Gibson Department of Gastroenterology, John Radcliffe Hospital, Oxford OX3 9DU Tel: 01865 741166 Fax: 01865 751100; 37 Sandfield Road, Headington, Oxford OX3 7RN Tel: 01865 761354 — MB BS 1973 Lond.; MD Lond. 1983, BSc (Hons.) (Physiol.) 1970, MB BS 1973; FRCP Lond. 1992; MRCP (UK) 1976. (St. Bart.) Cons. Phys. Gastroenterol. John Radcliffe Hosp. Oxf.; Hon. Sen. Lect. Oxf. Univ. Socs: Brit. Soc. Gastroenterol.; Sec. Brit. Assn. Study of the Liver; Amer. Assn. Study Liver Dis. Prev: Hon. Lect. Med. Roy. Free Hosp. Lond.; Ho. Phys. St. Bart. Hosp. Lond.; Regist. (Med.) Soton. Gen. Hosp.

CHAPMAN, Roxana Suite 10, 103-105 Harley St., London W1G 6AJ Tel: 020 7224 3011 Fax: 020 7487 3680 Email: yi28@dial.pipex.com; Barham House, East Hoathly, Lewes BN8 6QL Tel: 01825 840032 Fax: 01825 840032 — MD Tehran 1963; LMSSA Lond. 1975; FRCOG 1984, M 1967; FRANZCOG 1978; FAGO 1977; Acamedician of Russian Acad. of Laser Sc 1997. Cons Gyn in private Pract; Vis. Cons. Obst. & Gyn. Cromwell Hosp. Socs: BMA; Fell. Hunt. Sco.; Fell. Europ. and Amer. Laser Societies. Prev: Cons. O & G P.ss Leyla Pahlavi Hosp. Tehran Iran, Tokoroa Hosp. NZ & Sydney Adventist Hosp. Austral.

CHAPMAN, Ruth 34 Elson Road, Formby, Liverpool L37 2EQ — MB ChB 1991 Leic.; BSc Leic. 1988, MB ChB 1991.

CHAPMAN, Ruth Alice Mary The Rectory, Theydon Mount, Epping CM16 7PW — MB BS 1992 Lond.

CHAPMAN, Sheila Jane Childrens Unit, Royal Surrey County Hospital, Gill Avenue, Park Barn, Guildford GU2 7XX Tel: 01483 571122 Fax: 01483 450742 Email: pbenton@royalsurrey.nhs.uk; Tel: 01483 277307 Fax: 01483 267528 — BM BCh Oxf. 1969; MA Oxf. 1969; FRCP Lond. 1991; MRCP (UK) 1972; FRCPCH 1997. (Oxf.) p/t Cons. Paediat. Roy. Surrey Co. Hosp. Trust. Prev: Sen. Regist. (Paediat.) Guy's Hosp. Lond.

CHAPMAN, Simon Charles, TD Mulberry Cottage, Mill Lane, Henley-on-Thames RG9 4HB Tel: 01491 414422 Fax: 01491 414402 Email: schapman@i-way.co.uk — MB ChB 1977 Birm.; MFPM RCP (UK) 1989; Dip. Pharm. Med. RCP (UK) 1986; DRACOG 1980; FFPM RCP (UK) 1995. (Birm.) Chairm. The Essenta Govt. Ltd. Glas.; Chairm. HCC de Gado Govt. PLC, Lond. Socs: Fell. Roy. Soc. Med.; Fell. Roy. Soc. Arts; Inst. Biol. Prev: Managing Dir. The Med. Gp. (Educat.) Ltd. Abingdon; Dir. Med. Operats. Boehringer Ingelheim Ltd.; Clin. Asst. (Radiother.) Ch.ill Hosp. Oxf..

CHAPMAN, Stanley Waters Crawcrook Medical Centre, Back Chamberlain Street, Crawcrook, Ryton NE40 4TZ Tel: 0191 413 2243 Fax: 0191 413 8098 — MB BS 1977 Newc. GP Ryton, Tyne & Wear.

CHAPMAN, Stephen St Johns Road Surgery, 10 St. Johns Road, Newbury RG14 7LX Tel: 01635 40160 — MB ChB 1971 Ed.; MRCGP 1976; DObst RCOG 1974.

CHAPMAN, Stephen Birmingham Children's Hospital NHS Trust, Steelhouse Lane, Birmingham B4 6NH Tel: 0121 333 9731 Email: stevechapman@doctors.org.uk; 26 Greenland Road, Selly Park, Birmingham B29 7PN Tel: 0121 471 4125 Fax: 0121 471 3310

Email: docchapman@msn.com — MB BS 1976 Lond.; FRCP Lond. 1996; MRCP (UK) 1979; MRCS Eng. LRCP Lond. 1976; FRCPCH 1997; FRCR 1982. Cons. Paediat. Radiol. Birm. Childr. Hosp.; Sen. Clin. Lect. Univ. Birm. Socs: Eur. Soc. Paediat. Radiol.; Brit. Nuclear Med. Soc.; Brit. Soc. Of Paediat. Radiol.

CHAPMAN, Stephen James Aldern Bridge Lodge, Basingstoke Road S., Newbury RG20 4HQ — BM BCh 1998 Oxf.; BM BCh Oxf 1998.

CHAPMAN, Stephen Paul 47 Romsey Road, Winchester SO22 5DE — MB BS 1989 Lond.; BSc (Biochem.) Lond. 1986; MRCGP 1995; DRCOG 1993.

CHAPMAN, Susan Elizabeth (retired) Whitestone, Highbrook, West Hoathly, East Grinstead RH19 4PL Tel: 01444 892261 Fax: 01444 892261 — MB ChB 1949 Ed.; DCH Eng. 1952. Prev: Assoc. Specialist Genitourin. Med. Brighton, Sussex.

CHAPMAN, Suzanne Telford Department of Microbiology, St. Mary's Hospital, Newport PO30 5TG Tel: 01983 524081 Fax: 01983 825437; The Old House, Bucks Farm, Shorwell, Newport PO30 3LP — MB BCh BAO 1976 Dub.; MA 1992; MRCPath 1985; DTM & H Liverp. 1979. Cons. (Microbiol.) St. Mary's Hosp. Newport, I. of Wight. Socs: Assoc. Of Med. Microbiologies (AMM) Hon. Treas. Prev: Sen. Regist. (Microbiol.) S.mead Hosp. Bristol & Bristol Roy. Infirm.; Regist. (Microbiol.) S.mead Hosp. Bristol; Ho. Surg. St. Bernard's Hosp. Gibraltar.

CHAPMAN, Terence Telford (retired) 54 Vandon Court, Petty France, London SW1H 9HF Tel: 020-7222 2504 — MB BCh BAO Dub. 1946; MA BAO Dub. 1992, MD 1951; MD 1952 MD Dublin 1952. Prev: Cons. Phys. Roy. City of Dub. Hosp.

CHAPMAN, Thomas William Lawson Old Rectory, Stourport Road, Great Witley, Worcester WR6 6JP — MB ChB 1998 Bristol.

CHAPMAN, Timothy Hugh Manarddwylan, Station Road, St Clears, Carmarthen SA33 4DQ — MB BS 1998 Lond.; MB BS Lond 1998.

CHAPMAN, Victoria Jane 57 Willow Vale, London W12 0PA — MB BS 1988 Lond.; BA Oxf. 1985.

CHAPMAN, Wendy Alison 1 Yaldham Cottages, Kemsing Road, Wrotham, Sevenoaks TN15 6NN — MB BS 1986 Lond. SHO (Gen. Surg. & A & E) Maidstone Hosp. Prev: SHO (Elderly Care & Cas.) Mayday Hosp. Croydon & Guy's Hosp. Lond.; SHO (Cardiothoracic Surg.) N. Gen. Hosp. Sheff.; SHO (Orthop.) Leicester HA.

CHAPMAN, Wilfrid Ernest (retired) 5 Southend House, South Road, Durham DH1 3TG Tel: 0191 384 2747 — MB BS Durh. 1939; DObst RCOG 1947.

CHAPMAN-SHEATH, Mr Philip James 47 Merrivale Square, Oxford OX2 6QX — MB BS 1992 Lond.; FRCS 1996. Specialist Regist. (Trauma & Orthop. Surg.) Oxf. Regional Train. Progr.

CHAPPATTE, Mr Oliver Arnold 27 Waldemar Avenue, London SW6 5LB Tel: 020 7736 5887 — MB BS 1979 Lond.; FRCS Eng. 1984; MRCOG 1989. (St. Thos.)

CHAPPEL, David Barrington Department of Epidemiology and Public Health, University of Newcastle, Newcastle upon Tyne NE2 4HH Tel: 0191 222 8899 Fax: 0191 222 6746 Email: d.b.chappel@newcastle.ac.uk; 42 Cavendish Place, Newcastle upon Tyne NE2 2NH Tel: 0191 281 9145 — MB BS 1985 Lond.; MSc Lond. 1992; MA Camb. 1986; MFPHM RCP (UK) 1994. Lect. (Pub. Health Med.) Univ. Newc. u. Tyne; Hon. Sen. Regist. N. & Yorks. Region. Socs: Soc. Social Med.; Fell.Roy. Inst. Pub. Health and Hyg. & Soc. of Pub. Health. Prev: Sen. Regist. & Regist. (Pub. Health Med.) Oxf. RHA Train. Scheme; Med. Teach. Islamic Aid Health Centre Afghan Refugees Med. Train. Course, Pakistan; Regist. Rotat. (Med.) King Geo. Hosp. Ilford. & Lond. Hosp.

CHAPPEL, Elizabeth Catherine (Taylor) Chantry Lane Health Centre, 17 Chantry Lane, Grimsby DN31 2LP Tel: 01472 342063 Fax: 01472 242066; 10 Fairfield Road, Scartho, Grimsby DN33 3DP Email: l1331c65@hotmail.com — MB BS 1991 Lond. (Char. Cross and Westm.) GP Princip. Socs: BMA.

CHAPPEL, John Anthony (retired) 52 King Edward Avenue, Aylesbury HP21 7JE — MB BS 1955 Lond.; MRCS Eng. LRCP Lond. 1955. Prev: Med. Regist. Stoke Mandeville Hosp. Aylesbury.

CHAPPEL, William Alan 2 Old Talbot House, High St., Cuckfield, Haywards Heath RH17 5JX — MB ChB 1971 Cape Town.

CHAPPELL, Alfred Guy, OBE Kenfig Farmhouse, Kenfig, Bridgend CF33 4PT Tel: 01656 742556 — MB ChB 1954 Birm.; FRCP Lond. 1975, M 1962. Hon. Cons. Phys., P.ss of Wales Hosp, Bridgend; Med. Mem. Indep. Tribunal Serv.; Regional Respirat. Adviser, Healthcall. Socs: (Ex-Chairm., Treas. & Sec. Regional Represen.s SubComm.) Soc. Phys. Wales; Brit. Thorac. Soc. Prev: Sen. Regist. (Med.) Brompton Hosp. Lond.

CHAPPELL, Mr Andrew Martin 1/1, 23 Kelvindale Gardens, Glasgow G20 8DW Tel: 0141 945 1643 Email: 106131.3110@compuserve.co.uk — MB ChB 1989 Aberd.; FRCS Glas. 1995. Specialist Regist. (Orthop.) W. Scotl. Train. Scheme.

CHAPPELL, Barnaby Garner 122 Addison Gardens, London W14 0DS Fax: 020 7371 6942 Email: barry@chappell.demon.co.uk; 76 Chapelfields, Charterhouse Road, Godalming GU7 2AA — MB BS 1997 Lond. Surg. STTO Rotat. St. Richards Hosp. Chicheter.

CHAPPELL, Gillian Margaret The Health Centre, Park Road, Tarporley CW6 0BE Tel: 01829 733456 — MB ChB 1988 Liverp.; DRCOG 1993.

CHAPPELL, Lucy Charlotte Dept of Obstetrics, St Thomas Hospital, Lambeth Palace Road, London SE1 7EH; 22Frognall Lane, London NW3 7DT — MB ChB 1992 Camb.; BSc Lond. 1990; MBBChir. Camb. 1992. Research Regist. (Obst.) St. Thos. Hosp. Lond.

CHAPPELL, Margaret Elizabeth Department of Histopathology, Southend Hospital, Prittlewell Chase, Westcliff on Sea SS0 0RY Tel: 01702 221210 Fax: 01702 221059; 5 Sandbanks, Benfleet SS7 2AW Tel: 01702 428827 — MB BS 1980 Lond.; MSc Trop. Med. Lond. 1985; FRCPath 1996. Cons. Histopath. S.end HA. Prev: Lect. &Hon. Sen. Regist. (Histopath.) Roy. Free Hosp. Lond.

CHAPPELL, Mr Richard Hollis Health Building Surgery, 1 Bentsbrook Close, North Holmwood, Dorking RH5 4HY Tel: 01306 885802 — BM 1976 Soton.; FRCS Eng. 1981; MRCGP 1987; DRCOG 1987. (Soton.) Prev: Trainee GP Soton. VTS; SHO (Obst.) City Hosp. Nottm.; Regist. (Surg.) Char. Cross Hosp. Lond.

CHAPPELOW, Elizabeth Mary The Health Centre, 20 Cleveland Square, Middlesbrough TS1 2NX Tel: 01642 246138 Fax: 01642 222291; Low Cottage, Ingleby Arncliffe, Northallerton DL6 3LN — MB BS 1985 Newc.; BMedSc (Hons.) Newc. 1982; MRCGP 1990; DRCOG 1988. (Newc. u. Tyne) Prev: GP Willington Med. Gp.

CHAPPELOW, Steven 660 Scott Hall Road, Leeds LS17 5PB — MB ChB 1985 Leeds; MB ChB Leeds 1988; BSc (Hons.) Med. Microbiol. Leeds 1985. Staff Grade (A & E) St. Jas. Univ. Hosp. Leeds. Socs: BASICS; Brit. Assn. Accid. & Emerg. Med. Prev: SHO (Orthop. & A & E) Airedale Gen. Hosp.

CHAPPITI, Shankar Sreenivas 58 Montpelier Road, London SE15 2HE — MB BS 1993 Lond.

CHAPPLE, Mr Christopher Reginald Department of Urology, Royal Hallamshire Hospital, Glossop Road, Sheffield S10 2JF Tel: 0114 271 1900 Fax: 0114 279 7841 Email: c.r.chapple@shef.ac.uk — MB BS 1980 Lond.; BSc Lond. 1977, MD 1990; FRCS (Urol.) Eng. 1990; FRCS Eng. 1985. (Middlx.) Cons. Urol. Roy. Hallamsh. Hosp. Sheff. Socs: Brit. Assn. Urol. Surgs.; Internat. Continence Soc.; Director of Educat. The Europ. Assn. of Urol. Prev: Arris & Gale Lect. Roy. Coll. Surgs.

CHAPPLE, Mr David Charles Lyon 1 Green Lane Cottages, Haslemere GU27 3LE Email: big.dave@dial.pipex.com — MB BS 1990 Lond.; MSc 1985, BSc Lond. 1984; FRCS 1994. Regist. Rotat. (Orthop.) St. Geo. Hosp. Lond. Socs: BOTA & OEMS. Prev: SHO (Gen. Surg. & Plastics) St. Geo. Hosp. Lond.; SHO (Orthop.) Roehampton.

CHAPPLE, Jean Catherine Public Health Directorate, Kensington, Chelsea & Westminster Health Authority, 50 Eastbourne Terrace, London W2 6LX Tel: 020 7725 3401 Fax: 020 7725 3259 Email: jean.chappie@ha.kcw-ha.ntnames.nhs.uk; 39 Lammas Park Road, Ealing, London W5 5JD Tel: 020 8567 8270 Email: 101330.2113@compuserve.com — MB ChB 1973 Liverp.; MCommH Liverp. 1977; MFFP 1993; FFPHM RCP (UK) 1987, M 1981; DCH Eng. 1976; DObst RCOG 1975; FRCP 1998. (Liverpool) Cons. Obst. & Perinat. Epidemiol. N. Thames Region; Hon. Sen. Lect. (Epidemiol. & Pub. Health) Imperial Coll. Sch. Med. St Mart'y Hosp Lond. Prev: Cons. Obst. & Perinat. Epidemiol. N.wick Pk. Hosp. Harrow; Hon. Lect. (Community Child Health) Liverp. Univ.; Sen. Regist. (Community Med.) Mersey RHA.

CHAPPLE, Mr Keith Stewart West Barn, Wepham, Arundel BN18 9RD — MB ChB 1993 Sheff.; FRCS Eng. 1997. (Sheffield)

CHAPPLE, Mrs Mary Ruth Department of Haematology, Dewsbury District Hospital, Halifax Road, Dewsbury WF13 4HS Tel: 01924

512000 Fax: 01924 816083 — MB BS 1980 Lond.; BSc Lond. 1977, MD 1992; MRCP (UK) 1983; MRCPath 1990. (Middlx.) Cons. Haemat. Dewsbury Dist. Hosp. W. Yorks. Socs: Brit. Soc. Haematol.

CHAPPLE, Michael John Tel: 01582 491122 — MB BS 1965 Lond.; FRCP Lond. 1990; MRCP (UK) 1975; MRCS Eng. LRCP Lond. 1965; DMRD Eng. 1973. (Middlx.) Socs: Fell. Of Roy. Coll. Of Paediat. & Child Health. Prev: Lect. Child Health Univ. Soton.; Regist. (Paediat.) Newc. Gen. Hosp.; Regist. (Radiol.) Bristol Health Dist. (T).

CHAPPLE, Robert, CB, Air Vice-Marshal RAF Med. Br. Retd. (retired) Hazel House, Withington, Cheltenham GL54 4DA Tel: 01242 890374 — MB BS 1958 Lond.; MRCS Eng. LRCP Lond. 1958; MFOM Lond. 1980; MFCMI 1978; DPH Bristol 1973. Prev: Princip. Med. Off. HQ RAF Support Command.

CHAPPLE, Robert David St George's Surgery, St Pauls Medical Centre, 121 Swindon Road, Cheltenham GL50 4DP Tel: 01242 707755 Fax: 01242 707749 — MB ChB 1986 Sheff.; MRCGP 1991; AFOM RCP Lond. 1993; DRCOG 1991; DCH RCP Lond. 1989. Socs: Soc. Occupat. Med. & BMA. Prev: Trainee GP Cheltenham & Glos. VTS; Occupat. Med. Off. Unilever plc Lond.

CHAPPLE, Sarah-Jane Student Health Centre, De Montfort University, The Gateway, Leicester LE1 9BH Tel: 0116 257 7594 Fax: 0116 257 7614 — MB ChB 1989 Leic.; MRCGP 1999. GP De Montfort Surg., Leiester. Socs: MRCGP (BMA).

CHAPPLE, Simon Andrew Springwood, Felcourt Road, Felcourt, East Grinstead RH19 2LD — MB ChB 1995 Manch.; BSc St. And. 1992. HM Forces (RAF).

CHAPPLE, Susan Olivia 1 Green Lane Cottages, Haslemere GU27 3LE Email: pr35@dial.pipex.com — MB BS 1990 Lond.; DRCOG 1994. (St Thomas's) GP Retainer Haslemere Health Centre. Prev: GP Regist. Haslemere Health Centre; Trainee GP/SHO Roy. Free Hosp. VTS.

CHAPUT DE SAINTONGE, David Michel (retired) The London Hospital Medical College, Turner St., London E1 2AD Tel: 020 7377 7105 Fax: 020 7377 7449 Email: d.m.chaputdesaintonge@mds.qmw.ac.uk — MB BS 1966 Lond.; PhD Lond. 1978, BSc (Hons.) 1963; FRCP Lond. 1986; MRCP (UK) 1969; MFPM 1999. Cons. Phys. & Dir. Clin. Skills St. Bart. & Roy. Lond. Hosp. Med Coll.; Assoc. Lect. Univ. Surrey; Hon. Research Fell. Unit. Internat. Health Care Research Karolinska Inst., Stockholm; Hon. Sen. Lect. (Clin. Pharmacol.) St. Bart. Hosp.; Research Assoc. Inst. Cognitive Scs. Boulder, Colorado. Prev: Sen. Lect. (Clin. Pharmacol. & Therap.) Lond. Hosp.

CHAR, Dwarka Nath Char and Aggarwal, Plumstead Health Centre, Tewson Road, Plumstead, London SE18 1BH Tel: 020 8854 8027 Fax: 020 8317 3030 — MB BS 1970 Agra.

CHARD, Declan Tarn 2A Bushey Avenue, London E18 2DS — MB BS 1994 Lond.

CHARD, Michael Denis Worthing Hospital, Lyndhurst Road, Worthing BN11 2DH Tel: 01903 205111 Fax: 01903 285045 — MB BS 1977 Lond.; MD Lond. 1991; FRCP Lond. 1997; MRCP (UK) 1980. (The London Hospital Medical College) Cons. Rheum. Worthing & S.lands Hosp. Trust. Socs: Brit. Soc. Rheum. Prev: Sen. Regist. (Rheum.) Addenbrooke's Hosp. Camb.

CHARD, Professor Timothy 171 Lauderdale Tower, Barbican, London EC2Y 8BY Tel: 020 7628 5662 Fax: 020 7600 1439 Email: tim_chard@compuserve.com — MB BS 1960 Lond.; MD Lond. 1968; FRCOG 1977, M 1966. (St. Thos.) Prof. O & G St. Bart. & Roy. Lond. Sch. Med. & Dent. Lond.

CHARE, Mr Michael John Bruton Swansea NHS Trust, Morriston Hospital, Morriston, Swansea SA6 6NL Tel: 01792 703 579; Tyn-y-Dderwen, Fforest Goch, Pontardawe, Swansea SA8 3JB Tel: 01792 863011 — BM BCh 1969 Oxf.; FRCS Eng. 1974. (Oxf. & St. Mary's) Cons. Surg. Swansea NHS Trust. Prev: Sen. Regist. (Gen. Surg.) S. Glam. & Clwyd HA; Rotat. Surg. Regist. Univ. Hosp. Wales Cardiff.; Cons. Surg. W. Glam. HA.

CHARFARE, Mr Gulam Habib Gulam Mohemad Bedford Hospital, Kempston Road, Bedford MK42 9JD Tel: 01234 355122; Flat 803 Endsleigh House, Bedford Hospital, Kempston Road, Bedford MK42 9DJ Tel: 01234 795823 Fax: 01234 795823 — MB BS 1986 Bombay; FRCS Glas. 1993. (Grant Medical College, Bombay, India) Staff Grade Surg., Bedford Hosp.

CHARI, Premila 33 Avondale Avenue, London N12 8EP — MB BS 1994 Lond.

CHARI, Sarla 16 Woodberry Grove, London N12 0DL — MB BS 1959 Rangoon. (Rangoon) Clin. Med. Off. (Community Health Servs.) Lancs. AHA. Prev: SHO & Cas. Med. Off. Rangoon Gen. Hosp.; Asst. Med. Off. Matern. & Child Health Welf. Centre, Gt.er Rangoon; Health Scheme.

CHARIDEMOU, Charalambos Farnworth Health Centre, Frederick St., Farnworth, Bolton BL4 9AH Tel: 01204 795170 Fax: 01204 572787; 14 Sandfield Drive, Lostock, Bolton BL6 4DU — MB ChB 1983 Manch.; DRCOG 1991. (Manch.) Socs: Manch. Med. Soc.; Brit. Assn. Rally Doctors. Prev: SHO (A & E & O & G) N. Manch. HA; SHO Rotat. (Surg.) Centr. Manch. HA; SHO (Gen. Surg.) Oldham HA.

CHARIG, Mr Clive Robin Epsom General Hospital, Dorking Road, Epsom KT18 7EG Tel: 01372 735154 Fax: 01372 277494 Email: cchark@aol.com; 6 Mayfield, Fortyfoot Road, Leatherhead KT22 8RS Tel: 01372 377997 — MB BS 1978 Lond.; MA Oxf. 1978; FRCS (Urol.) 1991; FRCS Ed. 1984. (Oxf. & Middlx.) Cons. Urol. Epsom Gen. Hosp. Prev: Sen. Regist. (Urol.) St. Geo. Hosp. Lond.; Lect. (Urol.) Inst. Urol. Lond.; Regist. (Urol.) St. Peter's Gp. Hosp. Lond.

CHARIG, Eileen May The Belmont Medical Centre, 53-57 Belmont Road, Uxbridge UB8 1SD Tel: 01895 233211 Fax: 01895 812099; Paddocks, Chapel Lane, Stoke Poges, Slough SL2 4QJ Tel: 01753 662900 Fax: 01753 662900 — MB BCh BAO 1979 NUI. (RCS Dub.) Prev: GP Deddington, Oxon.; Research Regist. Littlemore Hosp. Oxf.; Trainee GP Windsor VTS.

CHARIG, Mark Julian X-Ray Department, Wexham Park Hospital, Slough SL2 4HL Tel: 01753 633548/9; Paddocks, Chapel Lane, Stoke Poges, Slough SL2 4QJ Tel: 662900 Fax: 01753 664286 Email: mark.charig@which.net — MB BS 1981 Lond.; BSc Lond. 1978; MRCP (UK) 1984; FRCR 1987. (King's Coll. Hosp.) Cons. Radiol. Heatherwood & Wexham Pk. Hosps. Trust. Prev: Sen. Regist. (Diag. Radiol.) John Radcliffe Hosp. Oxf.; SHO (Radiother.) Hammersmith Hosp. Lond.; SHO (Gen. & Chest Med.) Kingston Gen. Hosp. Kingston-upon-Thames.

CHARITOU, Alexandros 8 Queens Walk, London W5 1TP — MB BS 1997 Lond.

CHARITY, Katharine Merle (retired) 64 Ravenscourt Gardens, Ravenscourt Park, London W6 0TU — MB BS Lond. 1953; MRCS Eng. LRCP Lond. 1953; DCH Eng. 1955. Asst. to Dr Alwin Latham (now Retd.). Prev: Ho. Off. Qu. Eliz. Hosp. Childr. Lond.

CHARITY, Richard Mark 130 Northfield Lane, Wickersley, Rotherham S66 2HW — MB ChB 1996 Liverp.

CHARKIN, Steven Mark The Surgery, 22 St. Anne's Terrace, London NW8 6PH Tel: 020 7722 7389; Silverdale, Vale of Health, Hampstead, London NW3 1AN Tel: 020 7794 1160 — MB BS 1983 Lond.

CHARLES, Anne Louise 17 Arlington Court, Old Swinford, Stourbridge DY8 1NN — MB BS 1997 Lond. GP VTS, Black Country (O & G). Socs: MPS. Prev: Psychiat.; A&E.

CHARLES, Brendan Marcus Carteknowle and Dore Medical Practice, 1 Carterknowle Road, Sheffield S7 2DW Tel: 0114 255 1218 Fax: 0114 258 4418; 75 Rosamond Avenue, Bradway, Sheffield S17 4LS Tel: 0114 236 8956 — MB ChB 1978 Sheff.; MRCGP 1983. (Sheffield) GP Partner. Socs: BMA; Sheff. M-C Soc. Prev: SHO (Accid. Emerg.) N.. Gen. Hosp. Sheff.; Ho. Phys. Sheff. Childr. Hosp.; Ho. Off. A & E Dept. Hallamshire Hosp. Sheff.

CHARLES, Catherine Patricia 14 Glencroft Avenue, Comber, Newtownards BT23 5UN Tel: 01247 872396 — MB BCh BAO 1997 Belf. (Queen's Belfast) SHO & GP Rotat. Ulster Hosp. Dundonald Belf.

CHARLES, David 24 Castle Street, Tutbury, Burton-on-Trent DE13 9JF — MB ChB 1985 Manch.

CHARLES, David Lindsay Gable House, 46 High Street, Malmesbury SN16 9AT Tel: 01666 825825; St Leonards Cottage, School Lane, Lea, Malmesbury SN16 9NQ — BM BCh 1979 Oxf.; MA Oxf. 1980, BA 1976, BM BCh 1979; MRCGP 1984; DRCOG 1982. Prev: Ho. Surg. Roy. United Hosp. Bath; Ho. Phys. John Radcliffe II Hosp. Oxf.; Trainee GP Bath VTS.

CHARLES, David Peter Harrowside Surgery, 72 Harrowside, Blackpool FY4 1LR Tel: 01253 341793 Fax: 01253 46969 — MB ChB 1976 Manch. GP Princip.; Med. Adviser to DSS; Indep. Clin. Expert to LoftHo.s of Fleetwood.

CHARLES, Dorothea Patricia Joy The Health Centre, High Street, Bedworth, Nuneaton CV12 8NQ Tel: 024 7631 5827 Fax: 024

7631 0580; The Pantiles, 35 Coventry Road, Bulkington, Nuneaton CV11 4NL Tel: 01203 312626 — MB ChB 1959 Manch. (Manch.) Prev: Ho. Surg. Salford Roy. Hosp.; Ho. Phys. Manch. N.. Hosp.

CHARLES, Elizabeth Jean 114 Waterpark Road, Birkenhead CH43 0RS — MB ChB 1994 Liverp.

CHARLES, Eric The Pantiles, 35 Coventry Road, Bulkington, Nuneaton CV12 9LY Tel: 01203 312626 — MB ChB 1958 Manch. (Manch.) Prev: Ho. Surg. & Ho. Phys. Manch. Roy. Infirm.; Cas. Off. Ancoats Hosp. Manch.

CHARLES, Francis William (retired) 128 Nab Lane, Stocksbank Road, Mirfield WF14 9QJ Tel: 01924 51 32 39 — MB BCh BAO 1949 Belf.; BSc, MB BCh BAO Belf. 1949.

CHARLES, Heather Jane Elsdale Street Surgery, 28 Elsdale Street, London E9 6QY Tel: 020 8985 2719 — MB BS 1985 Lond.

CHARLES, Huw Myrddin John Ely Bridge Surgery, 23 Mill Road, Ely, Cardiff CF5 4AD Tel: 029 2056 1808 Fax: 029 2057 8871; 14 Bishops Road, Whitchurch, Cardiff CF14 1LZ — MB BCh 1980 Wales; MRCGP 1986; DRCOG 1984.

CHARLES, Ian Philip Valentine Road Surgery, Valentine Road, Hunstanton PE36 5DN Tel: 01485 532859 Fax: 01485 534608; 2 Hastings Drive, Hunstanton PE36 6HB Tel: 01485 532906 — MB BCh 1983 Wales; D.Occ.Med. RCP Lond. 1995; MRCGP 1987. Occupat. Phys. Dow Chem. Co. King's Lynn; Local Med. Off. Civil Serv. & DVLA; Med. Off. Hunstanton Lifeboat (RNLI). Socs: Soc. Occupat. Med.

CHARLES, Ian Robert Flat 7, Grosvenor Court, 29 Grosvenor Road, Southport PR8 2ES — MB ChB 1993 Liverp.

CHARLES, Kenneth Sterling Flat 19, Block 1, 5 Beech Hill Road, Sheffield S10 2RA — MD BS 1988 West Indies; MRCP (UK) 1994.

CHARLES, Leighton Mossford 77 Harley Street, London W1N 1DE Tel: 020 7487 5271; Hunters Moon, 1 Ashley Pk Road, Walton-on-Thames KT12 1JU Tel: 01932 222182 — MB BCh 1951 Wales; BSc, MB BCh Wales 1951. Fell. Brit. Soc. Med. & Dent. Hypn. Prev: Sub-Dean & Adviser of Studies Fac. Med. Sc. & Med. Off. King's Coll.; Strand.

***CHARLES, Lesley Ann** 6 North Farm Road, Hebburn NE31 1LX — MB ChB 1998 Ed.; MB ChB Ed 1998; BSc (Med Sci), 1995.

CHARLES, Mrs May Davies (retired) Woodside, Frith Common, Tenbury Wells WR15 8JX — MB BS 1940 Lond.; MRCS Eng. LRCP Lond. 1940; MRCOG 1946. Prev: Ho. Surg. & Ho. Phys. Roy. Free Hosp.

CHARLES, Rachel 41 Appleton Way, Hucclecote, Gloucester GL3 3RP — BM BS 1994 Nottm.

CHARLES, Richard Geoffrey Cardiothoracic Centre - Liverpool NHS Trust, Thomas Drive, Liverpool L14 3PE Tel: 0151 228 1616 Fax: 0151 220 8573 Email: richardgcharles@cs.com; (cons. rooms), 45 Rodney St, Liverpool L1 9EW Tel: 0151 708 0316 Fax: 0151 709 5679 — MB ChB 1969 Bristol; BSc (Physiol. Hons.) Bristol 1966; FRCP Lond. 1986; MRCP (UK) 1972; MRCS Eng. LRCP Lond. 1969; FESC 1994; FACC 1983. (Univ. Bristol) Cons. Cardiol. Cardiothoracic Centre Liverp. NHS Trust; Clin. Lect. (Cardiol.) Univ. Liverp.; Cons. Med. Off. Roy. Sun Alliance, Liverp. Socs: Fell. Europ. Soc. Cardiol.; Brit. Cardiac Soc.; (Imm. Past Pres.) Brit. Pacing & Electrophysiol. Gp. (BPEG). Prev: Sen. Regist. (Cardiol) Groote Schuur Hosp. Cape Town, S. Afr. & Sefton Gen. Hosp. Liverp.; Regist. (Cardiol.) United Bristol Hosps.

CHARLES, Robert Henry George, TD Benefits Agency, Medical Services, Olympic Way, Wembley HA9 0DL Tel: 020 8795 8938 — MB BChir 1962 Camb.; MB BChir Camb. 1961; MA Camb. 1961, BA 1958; MFCM 1972; DPH Eng. 1971; DCH Eng. 1969. (Camb. & Westm.) Med. Adviser Benefits Agency Med. Servs. DSS; Edr. Catering & Health; FRIPHH. Socs: BMA. Prev: Sen. Med. Off. Head Food & Environ. Health Br. DHSS; Maj. RAMC(V); PMO Lond. Boro. Hounslow.

CHARLES, Sandra Jayne 7 Birch Drive, Little Aston, Sutton Coldfield B74 4HW — MB BS 1992 Lond.

CHARLES, Stephen John Royal Eye Hospital, Nelson St., Manchester M13 9WH Tel: 0161 276 1234 Fax: 0161 272 6618 — MB BS 1983 Lond.; MA Oxf. 1983; MD Lond. 1993; FRCS Glas. 1988; FCOphth 1989; DO RCS Eng. 1987. Cons. Vitreoretinal Surg. Roy. Eye Hosp. Manch. Socs: Med. Protec. Soc. Prev: Cons. Vitreoretinal Surg. Ulleval Univ. Hosp. Oslo, Norway; Fell. (Vitreoretinal Surg.) Manch. Roy. Eye Hosp.; Sen. Regist. Manch. Roy. Eye Hosp.

CHARLES, Thomas Henry Seymour 22 Kingston Road, Leicester LE2 1QB — MB ChB 1997 Leic.

CHARLES, Thomas John Abergele Hospital, Llanfair Road, Abergele LL22 8DP Tel: 01745 832295 — MB BCh 1969 Wales; FRCP Lond. 1991; MRCP (UK) 1972. Cons. Phys. Abergele Hosp. & Glan Clwyd Hosp.

CHARLES, William Jackson Department of Psychiatry, Victoria Hospital, Blackpool FY3 8NR Tel: 01253 303687 — MB BCh BAO 1967 Belf.; MRCPsych 1973; DPM Eng. 1970. Cons. Psychiat. Vict. Hosp. Blackpool.

CHARLES-CHILLCOTT, Richard John 2 St Edmunds Farmhouse, Lower Vobster, Bath BA3 5RJ Tel: 01373 812177 — MB ChB 1972 Ed.; BSc (Chem.) Wales 1967; DPM 2001 (Diploma in Prime Medicine). Med. Off. HMP Portland Dorset; Mem. Prison Med. Coll. Prev: SHO (O & G) Friarage Hosp. N.allerton.

CHARLES-JONES, Huw Dann The School of Primary Care, University of Manchester, Rusholme Health Centre, Walmer St., Manchester M14 5NP Tel: 0161 256 3015 Fax: 0161 256 1070 Email: huw.charles-jones@man.ac.uk; Dee Fords Avenue, Chester CH3 5UP — MB BS 1984 Lond.; MRCGP 1989; DRCOG 1988; DCH RCP Lond. 1987. (The London Hospital) N.W. Reg. NHS Exec. R &D Train. Fell.; R & D lead Chester City PCG; Asst. Health La. Med. Centre. Chester. Prev: GP Princip. Upton Village Surg. Chester.

CHARLES-JONES, John Edward Dann Three Greens, Lodge Gardens, Wealstone La., Upton-by-Chester, Chester CH2 1HG Tel: 01244 383884 Fax: 01244 370521 — MB BS Lond. 1955; MRCGP 1968; DAvMed. FOM RCP Lond. 1997; Cert. Av Med. MoD (Air) & CAA 1975; FRAeS 1997. (Char. Cross) Med. Adviser Air Tours Internat. Airways; Authorised Med. Examr. Civil Aviat. Auth., Federal Aviat. Auth. & Canad.; Aviat. Examr. Socs: Fell. Roy. Soc. Med.; Chester & N. Wales Med. Soc.; Aeromed. Gp. Roy. Aeronautical Soc. & Assoc. Aviat. Med. Examrs. Prev: GP Upton Village Surg. Chester; Ho. Off. Char. Cross Hosp. Lond.; RAMC.

CHARLES-JONES, Shirley Madeleine Dann (retired) Three Greens, Lodge Gdns., Wealstone Lane, Upton-by-Chester, Chester CH2 1HG Tel: 01244 383884 Fax: 01244 370521 — MB BS Lond. 1955; DMJ (Clin.) Soc. Apoth. Lond. 1994. Prev: GP & Trainer Chester.

CHARLESON, Frank Hamilton Medical Group, 4 Queens Road, Aberdeen AB15 4ZT Tel: 01224 622345 Fax: 01224 627426 — MB ChB 1992 Aberd.

CHARLESTON, Mervyn Threlfall (retired) The Health Centre, Ferndown, Wimborne Tel: 01202 897000 Fax: 01202 897888 — MB ChB 1955 Bristol. Prev: GP Wimborne.

CHARLESWORTH, Arthur Clive (retired) Mount Easy Farmhouse, School House Lane, Horsmonden, Tonbridge TN12 8BT — MB BS 1973 Lond.; MRCPsych 1978. Prev: Cons. Child Adolesc. Psychiat. E.bourne Health Dist.

***CHARLESWORTH, Bruce Richard** Oakdene, Poole Lane, Burton Salmon, Leeds LS25 5JU Tel: 01977 679179 — MB ChB 1996 Leeds.

CHARLESWORTH, Carolyn Heather Department of Radiology, Wycombe General Hospital, High Wycombe HP11 2TT Tel: 01494 425445; Long Meadow, High Road Eastcote, Pinner HA5 2HJ Tel: 020 8429 1682 — MB BS Lond. 1970; MRCP (UK) 1973; FRCR 1990. (St. Thos.) Cons. Radiol. Wycombe Gen. Hosp. High Wycombe. Socs: Roy. Coll. Radiol.; BMA; MRRA.

CHARLESWORTH, Professor David Withington Hospital, Manchester M20 2LR Tel: 0161 445 8111; Alexandra Hospital, Cheadle SK8 2PX Tel: 0161 428 3656 — MB ChB Manch. 1959; DSc Manch. 1983, MD 1970; FRCS Eng. 1967. Prof. Surg. Withington Hosp. Manch.

CHARLESWORTH, Dineli Nirmaleen 175 Bradford Road, Winsley, Bradford-on-Avon BA15 2HN Tel: 01225 868864 — MB BS 1992 Lond.; MRCGP 1997; DRCOG 1995. (Roy. Free Hosp. Sch. Med.)

CHARLESWORTH, Elizabeth Anne (retired) 20 Ploughmans Way, Macclesfield SK10 2UN Tel: 01625 511352 — MB BS 1967 Lond.; MSc Manch. 1986; BSc (Hons. Physiol.) Lond. 1964; MRCS Eng. LRCP Lond. 1967; MFCM RCP (UK) 1986. Prev: Cons. Pub. Health Med. N. Derbysh. HA.

CHARLESWORTH, John Philip Eborall and Partners, Fountain Medical Centre, Sherwood Avenue, Newark NG24 1QH Tel: 01636 704378/9 Fax: 01636 610875; Cold Harbour, Caunton, Newark NG23 6BE Tel: 01636 86610 — MB ChB 1969 Leeds; DA Eng.

1972. Mem. Race Course Med. Offs. of Gt. Brit. Socs: Fac. Anaesths. & Brit. Assn. Sport & Med. Prev: Surg. Lt. RN.

CHARLESWORTH, Justin Paul 10 Oaks Road, Tenterden TN30 6RD Tel: 01580 766522 — MB BS 1992 Lond.; MRCGP 1997; DRCOG 1995. (Roy. Free Hosp. Sch. Med.) Clin. Asst. Dermat.

CHARLESWORTH, Michael (retired) Glentarff, Ringford, Castle Douglas DG7 2AT Tel: 01557 820275 — MB BS 1958 Lond.; MRCS Eng. LRCP Lond. 1958; FRCR 1975; FFR 1972; DMRD Eng. 1969. Radiol., The Lond. Clinic. Prev: Cons. Neuroradiologist, St. Bart. Hosp., Lond.

CHARLESWORTH, Philippa Helen 127 Broadway, Southbourne, Bournemouth BH6 4EJ — BM 1985 Soton.

CHARLESWORTH, Rosemary (retired) Glentarff, Ringford, Castle Douglas DG7 2AT — MRCS Eng. LRCP Lond. 1959.

CHARLESWORTH, William George West Kent Health Authority, Preston Hall, Aylesford ME20 7NJ Tel: 01622 710161 Fax: 01622 719802; 22 Woodlands Avenue, Sidcup DA15 8HA Tel: 020 8300 0238 — MB ChB 1956 Ed.; FFPHM RCP (UK) 1989; DObst RCOG 1966; DPH Liverp. 1963. Cons. Communicable Dis. Control W. Kent. HA. Prev: Dir. of Pub. Health Dartford & Gravesham DHA; Area Specialist Community Med. Lambeth, S.wark & Lewisham AHA (T); Capt. RAMC.

CHARLETT, Pauline Jane 65 Camphill Road, Broughty Ferry, Dundee DD5 2LY — MB ChB 1996 Manch.

CHARLEWOOD, Alison Mary The Park Medical Group, Fawdon Park Road, Newcastle upon Tyne NE3 2PE Tel: 0191 285 1763 Fax: 0191 284 2374 — BM BS 1988 Nottm.; BMedSci Nottm. 1986. Trainee GP Newc. u Tyne VTS.

CHARLEWOOD, John Edward (retired) 31 Wilson Gardens, Newcastle upon Tyne NE3 4JA Tel: 0191 285 7398 — MB BS 1954 Durh.; FRCGP 1978, M 1965; DCH Eng. 1959; DObst RCOG 1957. Ex-Provost N. Engl. Fac. RCGP. Prev: RCGP Examr.

CHARLEY, Andrew Roger Newington Road Surgery, 100 Newington Road, Ramsgate CT12 6EW Tel: 01843 595951 Fax: 01843 853387 — MB BS 1986 Newc.; DRCOG 1990.

CHARLEY, David James, OBE (retired) 22 Orville Gardens, Headingley, Leeds LS6 2BS Tel: 0113 275 6139 — MB BS 1946 Lond.; MD Lond. 1951; FRCP Lond. 1973, M 1952; MRCS Eng. LRCP Lond. 1942. Prev: Hon. Clin. Dir., Wheatfields Hospice Leeds.

CHARLEY, Helen Grace The Old Mill, 1 Marine Terrace, Rosemarkie, Fortrose IV10 8UL Tel: 01381 626273 Email: charley.robinson@dial.pipex.com — MB ChB 1978 Dundee; Cert. Family Plann. JCC 1981; MRCGP Lond. 1984; DRCOG Lond. 1980. (Dundee) MacMillan GP Facilitator in Palliat. Care. Prev: Trainee GP Hammersmith Hosp. & Roy. Postgrad. Med. Sch. VTS; GP Princip. Acton, Lond. N1; GP Princip. ST. Ives, Cambs.

CHARLICK, Bruce Jack (retired) The Nessit, Mill Lane, Ness, South Wirral CH64 4BQ Tel: 0151 336 2009 — MB ChB 1954 Liverp.; MFOM RCP Lond. 1983, AFOM 1978; DIH Eng. 1977. Cons. Occupat. Med. Mersey RHA. Prev: Employm. Med. Advisor EMAS.

CHARLIER, Anthony Raymond Salen Surgery, Aros, Isle of Mull PA72 6JL Tel: 01680 300327; Dunmoine, Salen, Isle of Mull PA72 6JL Tel: 0168 03 327 — MB BS 1975 Lond.; PhD Exeter 1973; BSc Lond. 1969. Prev: Ho. Surg. King's Coll. Hosp. Lond.; SHO (A & E) Lond. Hosp.; SHO (Ophth.) Roy. N.. Infirm. Inverness.

CHARLSON, Michael John, Capt. RAMC 2 Welton Low Road, Elloughton, Brough HU15 1HR — MB BChir 1988 Camb.; MA Camb. 1988, MB BChir 1989. RMO Roof of the Americas Expedition Lond. Prev: RMO 2nd Bn. Parachute Regt.; RMO 1st Bn. Worcs. & Sherwood Foresters Regt.; Ho. Phys. W. Cumbld. Hosp. Whitehaven.

CHARLSON, Paul Barry Brough and South Cave Medical Practice, 4 Centurion Way, Brough HU15 1AY Tel: 01482 667108 Fax: 01482 665090; Frisia, Westfield Park, Elloughton, Brough HU15 1AN Fax: 01482 665728 Email: needles999@aol.com — MB BS 1983 Lond.; MRCGP 1987; DRCOG 1986; Cert. Family Plann. JCC 1985; Dip Med Acupunc 1998. (St. Geo.) GP Trainer & Course Organiser E. Riding GPEC; Bd. Mem. E. Yorks. PCG. Socs: Accred. Mem. Brit. Med. Acupunc. Soc. Prev: GP Asst. Turangi N. Is., NZ; SHO (Geriat., Paediat. & O & G) Frimley Pk. Hosp. Camberley.

CHARLTON, Alan 25 Eaton Road, Handbridge, Chester CH4 7EN Tel: 01244 680169 Email: accharlton@cs.com — MB ChB 1965 Leeds; DObst RCOG 1971. Prev: SHO Roy. Infirm. & Matern. Hosp. Hull.

CHARLTON, Alfred Ian Alexander The Old Manse, North Sunderland, Seahouses — MRCS Eng. LRCP Lond. 1951.

CHARLTON, Avril Eleanor Marjory (retired) 22 Shaftesbury Crescent, North Shields NE30 3LR — MB BS 1948 Durh.; FFA RCS Eng. 1954; DPM Eng. 1980; DA Eng. 1951. Prev: Cons. Anaesth. Newc. Gen. Hosp.

CHARLTON, Bettyanne Cosham Health Centre, Vectis Way, Cosham, Portsmouth PO6 3AW Tel: 023 92 381117; Pint House, 17 Fraydene, Prinsted, Emsworth PO10 8HU Tel: 01243 374012 — BM 1977 Soton.; DObst 1979; MFHom 1993; MRCGP 1983; MRCGP 1983; DObst 1979.

CHARLTON, Bruce Graham Department of Psychology, Newcastle University, Newcastle upon Tyne NE1 7RU Tel: 0191 222 6247 Fax: 020 8222 5622 Email: bruce.charlton@ncl.ac.uk — MB BS 1982 Newc.; MB BS (Hons.) Newc. 1982; MA Durh. 1989; MD Newc. 1988. (Newcastle) Reader in Evolutionary Psychiat.- Dept. of Psychol.; Vis. Prof. UEL Centre for Health Serv. Research, St Bartholemews Hosp., Lond. 1999-2001. Prev: Lect. (Pub. Health) Newc.Univ.; Lect. (Anat.) Glas. Univ.; Wellcome Fell.sh. MRC Neuroendocrinol. Unit Newc. u. Tyne.

CHARLTON, Charles Paul Jeremy Department of Paediatrics, University Hospital, Queens Medical Centre, Nottingham NG7 2UH Tel: 0115 924 9924 — MB ChB 1980 Sheff.; BMedSci (Hons.) Sheff. 1979; MRCP (UK) 1985; FRCPCH 1997. (Univ. Sheff.) Cons. Paediat. Gastroenterol. Univ. Hosp. Qu. Med. Centre Nottm. Socs: Fell. Roy. Coll. Paediat. & Child Health; Med. Interview Teachg. Assn.; Paediatric Educat. s/i Gp. (Treas.). Prev: Lect. (Child Health) Med. Coll. of St Bartholomews & Roy. Lond.; Research Fell. (Gastroenterol.) Inst. Child Health Univ. Birm.

CHARLTON, Mr Clive Arthur Cyril (retired) Radford Villa, Timsbury, Bath BA2 0QF Tel: 01761 470658 Fax: 01761 470658 — MB BS Lond. 1958; MS Lond. 1967; FRCS Eng. 1963. Mem. Bath & Wessex Med. Hist. Gp.; Med. Chairm. Pens. Appeal Tribunals. Prev: Cons. Urol. Bath Health Dist.

CHARLTON, Clive David Alan Royal Berkshire Hospital, London Road, Reading RG1 5AN Tel: 0118 987 7871 Fax: 0118 987 7877; 36 Rances Lane, Wokingham RG40 2LH — MB BS 1977 Lond.; FRCR 1988; T(R) (CO) 1991; DCH RCP Lond. 1982; DRCOG 1982. (Westm.) Cons. Clin. Oncol. Berks. Cancer Centre Reading. Prev: Sen. Regist. (Clin. Oncol.) W.m. Hosp. Lond. & St. Luke's Guildford; Research Fell. (Oncol.) W.m. Hosp. & Char. Cross & W.m. Med. Sch.

CHARLTON, Fraser Graham Department of Pathology, Royal Victoria Infirmary, Queen Victoria Road, Newcastle upon Tyne NE1 4LP Tel: 0191 282 4445 Email: fraser.charlton@ncl.ac.uk; 26 The Firs, Gosforth, Newcastle upon Tyne NE3 4PH Tel: 0191 213 1624 — MB BS 1991 Newc.; MB BS (Hons.) Newc. 1991; BMedSc. (Hons.) Newc. 1988; PhD. Newc. 1999. Lect. (Histopath.) Roy. Vict. Infirm. Newc.

CHARLTON, Gareth Ashley Clovelly, Danes Road, Awbridge, Romsey SO51 0HL — MB BCh 1983 Witwatersrand; BSc Witwatersrand 1979, MB BCh 1983; FRCA 1988. Cons. Anaesth. Soton. Gen. Hosp.

CHARLTON, Heather Margaret The Health Care Surgery, 63 Palgrave Road, Sheffield S5 8GS Tel: 0114 234 1200 Fax: 0114 231 4591; 12 Endcliffe Vale Road, Sheffield S10 3EQ Tel: 0114 266 5635 — MB ChB 1984 Sheff.; MRCGP 1991; DRCOG 1991.

CHARLTON, Jeremy Stuart 27 Hessle View, Leeds LS6 1ER — MB ChB 1994 Leeds.

CHARLTON, Joanne 20 Milvain Avenue, Newcastle upon Tyne NE4 9JA — MB BS 1993 Newc.

CHARLTON, John Alexander Vicarage Road Medical Centre, Vicarage Road, Mickleover, Derby DE3 5EB Tel: 01332 513283 Fax: 01332 518569; Apple Acre, Adam's Road, Kirk Langley, Ashbourne DE3 5EB Tel: 01332 824238 Fax: 01332 518569 Email: jcharlton@lineone.net — MB ChB 1979 Leeds; MRCGP 1983; DRCOG 1983. Princip. GP Mickleover; Med. Off. King's Lodge Young Disabil. Unit Derby City Hosp.; Clin. Asst. (Rheum.) Derby Roy. Infirm; Med. Off. To John Port Sch. Etwall; Med. Off. To Derby Evening Telegraph. Socs: Derby Med. Soc.

CHARLTON, John Clement (retired) The Hawthorns, 179 Station Road, Mickleover, Derby DE3 5FH Tel: 01332 513224 — MB BCh BAO 1946 Belf.

CHARLTON, John Edmond Department of Anaesthesia, Royal Victoria Infirmary, Queen Victoria Road, Newcastle upon Tyne NE1 4LP Tel: 0191 282 4412 Fax: 0191 282 0466 Email: j.e.charlton@ncl.ac.uk — MB BS Durh. 1965; FRCA 1971; DObst. RCOG 1967. Cons. Pain Managem. Anaesth. Pain mgt.Unit Roy. Vict. Infirm. Newc. Socs: Europ. Amer. Soc. Regional Anaesth.; Pain Soc.; Assn. Anaesth. GB & Amer. Soc. Anaesth.
CHARLTON, Jonathan Samuel The Elmcroft Surgery, 5 Elmcroft Crescent, North Harrow, Harrow HA2 6HL Tel: 020 8863 1337 Fax: 020 8863 6826 — MB BS 1978 Newc.; MRCP (UK) 1981; DRCOG 1983. (Newcastle) Clin. Asst. (Dermat.) Mt. Vernon Hosp. N.wood. Prev: Clin. Asst. (Rheum.) Char. Cross Hosp. Lond.; GP Harlesden Lond.; SHO (Med.) Roy. Vict. Infirm. Newc.
CHARLTON, Keith Merton Lodge Surgery, West Street, Alford LN13 9DH Tel: 01507 463262 Fax: 01507 466447 — MRCS 1980 Eng.; LRCP 1980 Lond.
CHARLTON, Mrs Margaret (retired) 61 Plantation Road, Oxford OX2 6JE Tel: 01865 54248 — BM BCh 1965 Oxf.; MA Oxf. 1967, BM BCh 1965. Prev: GP Oxf.
CHARLTON, Mary Helen 31 Meriden Road, Hampton in Arden, Solihull B92 0BS — MB BS 1983 Lond.; BSc Lond. 1980; MRCP (UK) 1986. (Univ. Coll. Lond.) Staff Grade Phys. (Diabetes) Birm. Heartland Hosp. Prev: Staff Grade Phys. (Diabetes) Derbysh. Roy. Infirm.; SHO (Med.) Qu. Med. Centre Nottm.
CHARLTON, Maura Alexandra Magherafelt Health Centre, 1 Fairhill Road, Magherafelt BT45 6BD Tel: 028 7930 2904 — MB BCh BAO 1987 Belf.; MRCGP 1991; DMH Belf. 1991; DRCOG 1990; DCH Dub. 1990. Gen. Med. Practitioner; N.. Local Med. Comm. Mem.; GP Represen. on the N.. Bd. Cervical Screening Advis. Comm.; N.. Area Med. Advis. Comm. Socs: N.. Bd. Female GP Soc. (former Treas.).
CHARLTON, Paul Nicholas Department of Anaesthetics, St James's University Hospital, Beckett Street, Leeds LS9 7TF Tel: 0113 206 5789 Fax: 0113 206 5630; 3 Woodland Croft, Horsforth, Leeds LS18 5NE Tel: 0113 258 3624 — MB ChB 1983 Leeds; MRCGP 1987; FRCA 1994; DGM RCP Lond. 1987; DRCOG 1986. Cons. (Anaesth.) St James Univ. Hosp. Leeds. Prev: Sen. Regist. (Anaesth.) Leeds Gen. Infirm.; Sen. Regist. & Regist. Rotat. (Anaesth.) Yorks. Region.
CHARLTON, Paul Philip The Whitehorse Practice, 87 Whitehorse Road, Croydon CR0 2JJ Tel: 020 8684 1162 Fax: 020 8665 1454 — MB BS 1977 Lond.; BSc (Hons.) Lond. 1974; MRCGP 1983; DRCOG 1983; Cert. Family Plann. JCC 1982. (St. Thos.) Clin. Dir. Croydon Gen. Pract. Link Off.; Mem. Croydon LMC; Bd. Mem. PCG. Socs: Croydon Med. Soc. Prev: Trainee GP Croydon VTS; SHO (Gen. Med., Neurol. & Cardiol.) Mayday Hosp. Thornton Heath.
CHARLTON, Robert Stephen Orchard Court Surgery, Orchard Court, Orchard Road, Darlington DL3 6HS Tel: 01325 465285 Fax: 01325 284034; Sunnyside, Oakdene Avenue, Darlington DL3 7HR — MB BS 1979 Newc.; MRCGP 1983; DRCOG 1982.
CHARLTON, Ruth McKechnie 16 Cypress Crescent, Blyth NE24 2NB Tel: 01670 353680 — MB BS 1989 Lond.; MRCP (UK) 1994. Paediat.Cons. Epsom Surrey. Prev: Regist. (Paediat.) Hillingdon & Roy. Brompton Nat. Heart & Lung Hosp.; SHO (Paediat.) Qu. Charlottes Hosp., Brompton Hosp., Hosp. for Sick Childr. Gt. Ormond St. & Hammersmith Hosp.
CHARLTON, Shelagh Margaret Department of Anaesthetics, Royal Free Hospital NHS Trust, Pond St., London NW3 — MB BS 1979 Lond.; BSc Lond. 1976; FFA RCS Eng. 1985. (Univ. Coll. Hosp.) Cons. Anaesth. & Hon. Sen. Lect. Roy. Free Hosp. NHS Trust Lond. Prev: Cons. Anaesth. Whittington Hosp. NHS Trust Lond.; Lect. & Hon. Sen. Regist. (Anaesth.) Lond. Hosp. Med. Coll. Lond.
CHARLTON, Susanne Christa Jackson and Partners, Port View Surgery, Higher Port View, Saltash PL12 4BU Tel: 01752 847131 Fax: 01752 847124 — MB BS 1988 Lond.; MRCGP 1993; DRCOG 1993. GP & Clinc. Asst., ept. Radiother. Derriford Hosp., Plymouth. Prev: Trainee GP Saltash Health Centre.
CHARLWOOD, Mr Andrew Philip 423 Antrim Road, Newtownabbey BT36 5EE — MB BCh BAO 1989 Belf.; FRCS Ed. 1993.
CHARLWOOD, Cheryl Ann 21 Ascot Drive, Bebington, Wirral CH63 2QP — MB ChB 1991 Liverp.
CHARLWOOD, George Paul Burnham Medical Centre, Love Lane, Burnham-on-Sea TA8 1EU Tel: 01278 795445 Fax: 01278 793024; 4 Golf Links Road, Burnham-on-Sea TA8 2PW Tel: 01278 783282 — MB BCh BAO 1987 Belf.; MRCGP 1992; DCH RCP Lond. 1990.
CHARLWOOD, Gillean Penelope Grosvenor Medical Centre, 23 Upper Grosvenor Road, Tunbridge Wells TN1 2DX Tel: 01892 544777 Fax: 01892 511157; 50 Frant Road, Tunbridge Wells TN2 5LJ Tel: 01892 538577 — MB BS 1971 Lond.; MRCS Eng. LRCP Lond. 1971; DObst RCOG 1973; DCH Eng. 1973. (Char. Cross)
CHARLWOOD, Graham John Grosvenor Medical Centre, 23 Upper Grosvenor Road, Tunbridge Wells TN1 2DX Tel: 01892 544777 Fax: 01892 511157; 50 Frant Road, Tunbridge Wells TN2 5LJ Tel: 01892 538577 — MB BS Lond. 1969; MRCP (UK) 1974; MRCS Eng. LRCP Lond. 1969; DObst RCOG 1973; DCH Eng. 1972. (Char. Cross) Sen. Partner; Hosp. Practitioner, Endoscopy, Maidstone and Tunbridge Wells NHS Trust. Prev: Regist. (Med.) St. Stephen's Hosp. Lond.; SHO (Paediat.) Char. Cross Hosp. Lond. & Hosp. Sick Childr. Gt. OrmondSt.
CHARLWOOD, Lucy Miranda Uma 34 High Oaks Road, Welwyn Garden City AL8 7BH — MB ChB 1998 Bristol.
CHARLWOOD, Ronald Robert (retired) Timbertoft, Hensting Lane, Fishers Pond, Eastleigh SO50 7HH Tel: 01962 777436 Email: ronaldcharlwood@hensting.freeserve.co.uk — MA, BM BCh Oxf. 1954; MRCGP 1974; DObst RCOG 1957.
CHARMAN, Carolyn Rachel West Wind, Porthpean Beach Road, St Austell PL26 6AU; Flat 2, 10 Peveril Drive, The Park, Nottingham NG7 1DE Tel: 0115 947 2691 — BM BCh 1993 Oxf.; MRCP Part II 1996; MRCP Part I 1995. Research Fell. (Dermatol.) Qu.'s Med. Centre Nottm. Socs: BMA; MDU; BAD.
CHARMANDARI, Evangelia Flat 46, 49 Hallam St., London W1W 6JW — Ptychio Iatrikes 1988 Thessalonika; MRCP (UK) 1996; MSc (Clinical Paediatrics) 1998. Research Fell. (Paediat. Endocrinol.), Middlx. Hosp., Lond. Socs: BMA; BES.
CHARMANTAS, Maria Ghoula The Medical Centre, 24 Laurie Grove, London SE14 6NH Tel: 020 8692 6427 Fax: 020 8691 9698; 71 Hervey Road, Blackheath, London SE3 8BX — MRCS Eng. LRCP Lond. 1980; MRCGP 1986; DRCOG 1984.
CHARNAUD, Arthur Benjamin Trengneath Hospital, Penryn St., Redruth TR15 2SP Tel: 01209 219232 — MB ChB 1972 Bristol; BSc (Psychol.) Bristol 1968, MB ChB 1972; MRCPsych 1978.
CHARNLEY, Mr Godfrey James Derriford Hospital, Derriford Road, Plymouth PL6 8DH Tel: 01752 763777 Fax: 01752 768976 — MB BS 1983 Lond.; FRCS (Orth.) 1996; FRCS Ed. 1988; FRCS Eng. 1988. (St. Thos.) Cons. Orthop. & Trauma Surg. Derriford Hosp. Plymouth; Hon. Sen. Lect. 1998. Socs: Fell. BOA; Assoc. Mem. French Soc. of Orthop. & Traumat.; Soc. Internat. Orthop. & Traumatol. Prev: Sen. Regist. (Orthop. Surg.) Bristol; Regist. (Orthop. Surg.) Middlx., Roy. Free & Whittington Hosps. Lond.; Regist. (Surg.) Barnet Gen. Hosp.
CHARNLEY, Janet Borchardt Medical Centre, 62 Whitchurch Road, Withington, Manchester M20 1EB Tel: 0161 445 7475 Fax: 0161 448 0466; 47 Beverly Road, Ladybarn, Manchester M14 6TH Tel: 0161 224 3851 — MB ChB 1980 Manch.; BSc (Hons.) Manch. 1972; MRCGP 1984; DRCOG 1984; DCH RCP Lond. 1982. (Manchester) GP, S. Manch.; Hosp. Practitioner, Diabetes Dept., Manch. Roy. Infirm., Manch.. Prev: Miss. Doctor, Pakistan.
CHARNLEY, Natalie Grace Flat 5, 7 Glengyle Terrace, Edinburgh EH3 9LL — MB ChB 1996 Ed.
CHARNLEY, Mr Richard Michael Freeman Hospital, High Heaton, Newcastle upon Tyne NE7 7DN Tel: 0191 284 3111; 10 Woodlands, Gosforth, Newcastle upon Tyne NE3 4YN — MB BChir 1982 Camb.; MA Camb. 1983; DM Nottm 1990; FRCS Eng. 1986. Cons. Gen. Surg. (Hepatobiliary & Pancreatic Surg.) Freeman Hosp. Newc. u. Tyne. Prev: Lect. (Surg.) Univ. Nottm.; Regist. (Surg.) Nottm. HA.
CHARNOCK, Mr Frederick Mark Luckhoff Women's Centre, Oxford Radcliffe Trust, Headington, Oxford OX3 9DU Tel: 01865 221625 Fax: 01865 221188; Manor Farm House, Bletchingdon, Kidlington OX5 3DP Tel: 01869 350149 Fax: 01869 350728 — MB ChB (Hons.) Cape Town 1968; FRCS Eng. 1975; FRCS Ed. 1975; FRCOG 1990, M 1977. (Cape Town) Cons. O & G Oxf. AHA (T); Hon. Sen. Lect. Univ. Oxf. Socs: Fell. Roy. Soc. Med.; Internat. Gyn. Cancer Soc.; Brit. Gyn. Lawcer Soc. Prev: Sen. Regist. (O & G) St. Bart. Hosp. Lond.; SHO (Gyn.) Samarit. Hosp. Wom. Lond.; SHO (Obst.) Qu. Charlotte's Matern. Hosp. Lond.

CHARNOCK, Raymond Barker (retired) 25 Norman Road, Hatfield, Doncaster DN7 6AF — MB ChB 1948 Manch. Prev: Ho. Phys. & Ho. Surg. Withington Hosp. Manch.

CHARNY, Mark Campbell Translucency Ltd, 21 St Georges Square, Worcester WR1 1HX Tel: 01905 726779 Fax: 0870 052 3511 Email: marktranslucency.co.uk; 21 St Georges Square, Worcester WR1 1HX Fax: 0870 052 3511 Email: mark@translucency.co.uk — MB BChir 1975 Camb.; PhD Wales 1987; MA, MB BChir Camb. 1975; FFPHM RCP UK 1991, M 1989; MFCM 1985; T(PHM) 1991. Indep. Cons Transllucency Ltd, Worcester. Prev: Dir., Nat. Centre for Clin. Audit; Sen. Med. Off. NHS Exec., Leeds; Dir. (Pub. Health) Wilts. Health Auth. Health Commiss.

CHARON, Jean-Pierre Marc 54 Sunnymead Road, Birmingham B26 1LJ; 20 Thirlestane Road, Edinburgh EH9 1AN — MB ChB 1993 Dundee. Specialist Regist. (Radiol.) Roy. Infirm. of Edin.

CHARRETT, Macdonald Arthur (retired) 33 Denham Lodge, Oxford Road, New Denham, Uxbridge UB9 4AB Tel: 01895 234840 — MRCS Eng. LRCP Lond. 1940; MFCM 1972; DPH Lond. 1947. Prev: Dist. Community Phys. E. Berks. Health Dist.

CHARTER, Michael (retired) 2 Well House Close, Whitsbury, Fordingbridge SP6 3QZ Tel: 01725 518552 Fax: 01725 518552 — MB BS 1964 Lond.; MRCS Eng. LRCP Lond. 1962. Prev: Med. Dir. Roy. Bournemouth Hosp. Occupat. Health Servs.

CHARTERIS, Mr David Graham Moorfields Eye Hospital, City Rd, London EC1V 2PD Tel: 020 7253 3411 Fax: 020 7253 4696; 29 Barnsbury Square, London N1 1JP Tel: 020 7609 1365 — MB ChB 1983 Ed.; FRCS Ed. 1988; FRCOphth 1989; MD Ed. 1994. Cons. Ophth. Surg. Moorfields. Eye Hosp. Lond.; Hon. Sen. Research. Fell. Dept. Clin. Ophth. Prev: Fell.Viteoretinal.Surg.Moorfields.Eye.Hosp.; Sen.Regist/Viteoretinal.Fell.Manc.Roy.Eye.Hosp.; Wellcome.Research.Fell.

CHARTERS, Andrew John Withington Hospital, West Didsbury, Manchester M20 2LR Tel: 0161 445 8111 — BSc Lond. 1979, MB BS 1982; DCH RCP Lond. 1987; DRCOG 1987. SHO Rotat. (Psychiat.) Withington Hosp. Prev: Trainee GP Lond. VTS; SHO (Paediat.) Centr. Manch. & Lothian HB; SHO (A & E) King's Coll. Hosp. Lond.

CHARTERS, Freda Kelman Burnfield Medical Practice, Harris Road, Inverness IV2 3PF Tel: 01463 220077 Fax: 01463 714588; 34 Broadstone Park, Inverness IV2 3LA — MB ChB 1984 Aberd.; MRCGP 1989.

CHARTERS, John William University of Durham, Student Health Centre, 42 Old Elvet, Durham DH1 3JF Tel: 0191 386 5081 Fax: 0191 386 3528; Woodside Cottage, Shincliffe, Durham DH1 2NB Tel: 0191 386 8896 — MB ChB 1979 Manch.; Dip. Ther. Newc. 1996; MRCGP 1987; DRCOG 1982. Med. Off. Univ. Durh.

CHARTERS, Peter Fazakerley Hospital, Longmoor Lane, Liverpool L9 7AL Tel: 0151 529 5153 Fax: 0151 529 5155; 31 Heathbank Avenue, Irby, Wirral CH61 4XD Email: petchart@argonet.co.uk — MB ChB 1971 Liverp.; BA (Hons.) (Pure & Appl. Math.) Open 1987; MD Liverp. 1984; MRCP (UK) 1976; FFA RCS Eng. 1978. (Liverp.) Cons. Anaesth. & Intens. Care Aintree Hosps. Liverp. Prev: Cons. Anaesth. & Pain Roy. Liverp. Hosp. & Walton Hosp Liverp.; Cons. Anaesth. & Intens. Care Clatterbridge & Arrowe Pk. Hosps. Wirral; Hon. Research Coordinator NW Emerg. Recompression & Med. Hyperbaric Unit.

CHARTRES, John Crispin (retired) Haven View, 19 The Rath, Milford Haven SA73 2QA Tel: 01646 692052 — BM BCh Oxf. 1944; MA Oxf. 1944; DMRD Eng. 1953; DTM & H Liverp. 1947. Prev: Cons. Radiol. Dyfed HA.

CHARWAY, Christiansen Laryea Anaesthetic Department, Southport & Formby District General Hospital, Town Lane, Kew, Southport PR8 6PN Tel: 01704 579713; 9 Tavistock Drive, Ainsdale, Southport PR8 2RU Tel: 01704 579713 — MB ChB 1972 Ghana; FFA RCSI 1979; DA Eng. 1977. (Liverpool University (Post Grad.) Univ. Ghana Med. Sch.) Cons. Anaesth. Mersey RHA. Socs: Intens. Care Soc.; Assn. Anaesth. GB & Irel.; Obst. Anaesth. Assn. Prev: Sen. Regist. (Anaesth.) Mersey RHA.

CHASE, Alexander James Forest House, Bishops Down Park Road, Tunbridge Wells TN4 8XS — MB BS 1993 Lond.

CHASE, Anne Elizabeth 8 Poplar Road, West Winch, King's Lynn PE33 0NH — MB ChB 1971 Glas.; DCCH RCP Ed. 1984; DCH RCPS Glas. 1973. Clin. Med. Off. NW Anglia Healthcare NHS Trust.

CHASE, Anthony Oswald (retired) Milton, Corscombe, Dorchester DT2 0NU — MB BChir 1947 Camb.; MRCS Eng. LRCP Lond. 1946; MRCGP 1979; DA Eng. 1972. Prev: Mem. Ch. Miss. Soc. 1950-66.

CHASE, David Robert (retired) Cassiobury House, Laxfield Road, Fressingfield, Eye IP21 5PY Tel: 01379 586300 — MB BS 1953 Lond.; DObst RCOG 1955. Prev: Sen. Cas. Off. & Ho. Phys. Paediat. & Skin Depts. Char. Cross Hosp.

CHASE, George Harold Godwin (retired) 49 Roman Bank, Stamford PE9 2ST Tel: 01780 62366 — MRCS Eng. LRCP Lond. 1940; BA Camb. 1936. Prev: Ho. Phys. & Surg. Guy's Hosp. Sector 10.

CHASE, Harold Derek Cavendish Health Centre, 53 New Cavendish Street, London W1G 9TQ Tel: 020 7487 5244 Fax: 020 7224 4577; 12 Aynhoe Road, London W14 0QD Email: derek@chasehom.demon.co.uk — MB BChir 1979 Camb.; MA Camb. 1979; MRCGP 1983; DRCOG 1983; Cert. Family Plann. JCC 1983. (St Mary's, Cambridge) Socs: (Ex-Sec.) Brit. Holistic Med. Assn. Prev: Chairm. Centr. Lond. Multifund; Course Organiser St. Mary's Hosp. Lond.; Lect. (Gen. Pract.) St. Mary's Hosp. Lond.

CHASE, Jeremy Chester Centlivres 7 Bickerton Road, London N19 5JU — MB ChB 1977 Cape Town; MRCPsych. 1985; DCH Eng. 1980. (Cape Town) Cons. Psychiat. Watford Gen. Hosp.; Mem. Soc. Psychosomat. Res. Prev: Sen. Regist. (Psychiat.) Middlx. Hosp. Lond.; Regist. (Psychiat.) Middlx. Hosp., Univ. Coll. Hosp. & Maudsley Hosp. Lond.

CHASE, Nicholas John c/o 143 Broomhill, Downham Market PE38 9QU — MB ChB 1991 Manch.; BA Camb. 1985.

CHASE, Norah Beatrice Ann (retired) 24 Court Road, Eltham, London SE9 5NW Tel: 020 8850 4095 — MB BS Lond. 1954.

CHASE, Philip Norman 55 Little Heath Road, Bexleyheath DA7 5HL Tel: 01322 430129 Fax: 01322 440949; 175 Green Lane, Eltham, London SE9 3SZ Tel: 020 8850 6522 — MB BS 1968 Lond.; BA Bristol 1951; MRCS Eng. LRCP Lond. 1968. (St. Bart.)

CHASE, Richard Paterson Guildhall Surgery, High Street, Clare, Sudbury CO10 8NY Tel: 01787 277523 Fax: 01787 278628; 12 Ashen Road, Clare, Sudbury CO10 8LQ — MB ChB 1975 Dundee. (Dundee) Prev: Ho. Surg. Addenbrookes Hosp. Camb. & Middlemore Hosp. Auckland; Surg. Regist. Dunedin Pub. Hosp.

CHASE, Sarah Beatrice Albion Surgery, Pincott Road, Bexleyheath DA6 7LP Tel: 020 8304 8334 Fax: 020 8298 0408 — BM 1987 Soton.; BSc (Phys. & Biol.) Soton. 1983.

CHASSELS, Mirrlees Ramsay (retired) Thorndale 15 Shore Road, Skelmorlie PA17 5EQ Tel: 01475 520233 — MB ChB 1939 Glas.; DPH 1947. Prev: Med. Mem. Pens. Appeal Tribunals For Scotl.

CHASTELL, David J M (retired) 45 Callis Court Road, Broadstairs CT10 3AU — MB BS Lond. 1957; MRCS Eng. LRCP Lond. 1956. Prev: Sen. Police Surg. Thames Police.

CHASTENEY, Margaret Laura Everson (retired) 3 Birchwood Drive, Rushmere St Andrew, Ipswich IP5 1EB Tel: 01473 723426 — MRCS Eng. LRCP Lond. 1961; DObst RCOG 1963. Prev: Gyn. Ho. Surg. Roy. Free Hosp.

CHASTY, Richard Christopher 9 Cocksheadhey Road, Bollington, Macclesfield SK10 5QZ — MB BS 1987 Lond.; BSc Lond. 1984; MRCP (UK) 1990; MRCPath 1996; DRCPath 1995. (St. Thos. Hosp.) Cons. Haemat. N. Staffs. NHS Trust. Prev: Sen. Regist. (Haemat.) Derriford Hosp. Plymouth & Bristol Childr. Hosp; Research Regist. & Hon. Regist. (Haemat.) Manch. Roy. Infirm.; Tutor (Haemat.) Univ. Manch. & Manch. Roy. Infirm.

CHATAKONDU, Srinivasa Chakravarti 17 Cranleigh Gardens, Stoke Bishop, Bristol BS9 1HD — MB BS 1992 Lond.

CHATAKONDU, Srisaila 17 Cranleigh Gardens, Stoke Bishop, Bristol BS9 1HD — MB BS 1996 Lond.

CHATAMRA, Mr Krisna Department Surgical Science, Royal College of Surgeons, Lincoln's Inn Fields, London WC2A 3PE; Homefield, St Loes Pitch, Culvery Hill, Amberley, Stroud GL5 5BB — MB BS 1969 Lond.; MD Lond. 1982; FRCS Eng. 1976; MRCS Eng. LRCP Lond. 1969. (Westm.) Buckston Browne Lect. & Medallist 1982; Sec. Lect. Dept. Surg. Sci. RCS Lond.; Hon. Lect. Dept. Applied Physiol. & Surg. Sci. RCS Eng.; Vice-Pres. Harveian Soc. Lond. Socs: Physiol. Soc. Prev: Sen. Regist. (Surg.) Char. Cross Hosp. Lond.; Bernard Sunley Surg. Fell. RCS Lond.; Regist. (Surg.) W.m., St. Stephen's & Roy. Marsden Hosps. Lond.

CHATAWAY, Anna Marie Garden Flat, 17 Talbot Road, Highgate, London N6 4QS Email: jc33@btinternet.com — MB BS 1993 Lond.;

BDS Lond. 1987; FRCA 1999. (Univ. Coll. Hosp. Lond.) (Specialist Regist. Anaesth.),UCLH Lond.

CHATAWAY, Simon Jeremy Stovold Garden Flat, 17 Talbot Road, Highgate, London N6 4QS Email: jc33@bt.internet.com; Garden Flat, 17 Talbot Road, Highgate, London N6 4QS — BM BCh 1989 Oxf.; MA Camb. 1990; MRCP (UK) 1993. (Oxford) Specialist Regist. (5) Neurol., Nat. Hosp. for Neurol., Qu. Sq., Lond.

CHATER, Nichola Carla Livingston Drive Health Centre, Livingston Drive, Liverpool L17 8XY Tel: 0151 283 4040 Fax: 0151 283 3311; 140 Brodie Avenue, Mossley Hill, Liverpool L18 4RJ Tel: 0151 724 3597 — MB ChB 1985 Liverp.; BSc (Hons.) Liverp. 1979, MB ChB 1985; MRCGP 1991; DCH RCPS Glas. 1988. Cons. Rehabil. Med. N. Mersey Community (NHS) Trust. Socs: Brit. Soc. Rehabil. Med.; Inst. Psychosexual Med. 1997; Inst. Health Serv. Managem. 1994.

CHATER, Stuart Nigel Royal Halifax Infirmary, Free School Lane, Halifax HX3 0LJ Fax: 01422 357222 — MB BS 1977 Lond.; FFA RCSI 1983; FFA RCS Eng. 1983. Cons. Anaesth. Roy. Halifax Infirm.; Director Post Grad. Med. Educat., Calendale NHS Trust. Socs: Obst. Anaesth. Assn.; Anaesth. Research Soc. Prev: Sen. Regist. (Anaesth.) Leeds Gen. Infirm.; Regist. (Anaesth.) Roy. Hallamsh. Hosp. Sheff.; SHO (Anaesth.) Glos. Roy. Hosp.

CHATFIELD, Andrew Howard 18 Hill Top View, Farmhill, Braddan, Douglas IM2 2LD — MB BS 1981 Lond.; Dip. Pract. Dermat. Wales 1995. Med. Dir. Regency Crown Clinics Lond.

CHATFIELD, Mary McIndeor 56 Carlaverock Road, Glasgow G43 2QN — MB ChB 1963 Glas.

CHATFIELD, Simon Tel: 01462 683051 Fax: 01462 485650; Tel: 01462 433841 — MB BS 1980 Lond.; MRCGP 1984; DRCOG 1983.

CHATFIELD, Susan Lesley Bradford Royal Infirmary, Duckworth Lane, Bradford BD9 6RJ Tel: 01274 542200 Fax: 01274 382259 Email: secretarychatfield@bradfordhospitals.nhs.uk — MB BS 1980 Lond.; MRCP (UK) 1985; Cert. Community Paediat. Warwick 1987; DCH RCP Lond. 1983. (St. Bart.) Cons. Neonat. Paediat. Bradford Hosp. NHS Trust. Socs: Mem. of Brit. Assn. of Perivatal Med., Med. Wom.'s Federat.; Fell. of Roy. Coll. of Paediat. & Child Health.

CHATFIELD, Terence Herbert Peter (retired) 17 Tavistock Road, Manadon Hill, Plymouth PL5 3DG Tel: 01752 771469 — MB ChB 1954 Bristol.

CHATFIELD, Mr William Robertson 56 Carlaverock Road, Glasgow G43 2QN — MD 1972 Glas.; MB ChB 1963; FRCS Glas. 1979; FRCS Ed. 1968; FRCOG 1981, M 1968. (Glas.) Cons. O & G Qu. Mother's Hosp. Glas. & W.ern Infirm. Glas. Prev: Hall Tutorial Fell. in Midw. Univ. Glas.; Lect. Univ. Coll. Nairobi, Kenya; Sen. Lect. ChristCh. Clin. Sch. Univ. Otago, N.Z.

CHATLANI, Mr Prakash Thakurdas 26 Christchurch Gardens, Harrow HA3 8NR — MB ChB Ed. 1976, BSc (Med. Sci) 1973; FRCS Eng. 1981; FRCS Ed. 1980; DCH RCP Lond. 1993.

CHATOO, Mr Minhal Hussein Bashir 32 Bishop's Avenue, Northwood HA6 3DG Tel: 01923 841344 Email: minhalbchatoo@msn.com; 11 Belgrave Close, Mill Hill, London NW7 3QG Tel: 020 8906 3195 Fax: 020 8906 3195 Email: minhal.chatoo@btinternet.com — MB BS 1992 Lond.; FRCS Eng. 1996. (St. Geo. Hosp. Med. Sch.) Specialist Regist. Rotat. (Orthop.); Roy. Nat. Orthop. Hosp. & Roy. Free Hosp. Socs: BMA; Med. Med. Protec. Soc.; Brit. Orthop. Train. Assn. Prev: Regist. (Orthop.) Centr. Middlx. Hosp.; SHO Rotat. (Surgic.) Char. Cross Hosp. Lond.

CHATOO, Shelina Bashir 59 Downton Avenue, London SW2 3TU Tel: 020 8674 1493 — MB BS 1990 Lond.; MRCGP 1994; DFFP 1994; DRCOG 1993; DCH RCP Lond. 1992. SHO (Paediat.) Whipps Cross Hosp. Lond. Prev: Trainee GP/SHO St. Helier VTS.

CHATOOR, Roger 13 Peri Court, St Mildred's Place, Canterbury CT1 3TH — MB BS 1990 West Indies; MRCP (UK) 1993. SHO (Cardiol.) Kent & Canterbury Hosp.; Clin. Fell. (Cardiol.) Papworth NHS Trust Camb. Prev: SHO (Nephrol.) Kent & Canterbury Hosp.

CHATRATH, Anil Madangopal 25 Thorncliffe Road, Southall UB2 5RJ Tel: 020 8540 0782 — MB BS 1973 Patna. (P. of Wales Med. Coll.) Ho. Phys. Gen. Hosp. Jersey.

CHATRATH, Vina Madan Station Road Surgery, 42 Station Road, London NW4 3SU Tel: 020 8202 3733 Fax: 020 8203 8096 — MB BS 1973 Patna; MB BS 1973 Patna.

CHATRATH, Virinder Kumar Denham Medical Centre, Tilehouse Way, Denham, Uxbridge UB9 5JA Tel: 01895 832012; 2 Norgrove Park, Gerrards Cross SL9 8QT — MB ChB 1970 Ed.; MRCGP 1978.

CHATTERIS, Denise Joan The Lodge, Station Road, Earl Shilton, Leicester LE9 4LU — MB ChB 1976 Manch.; BSc St. And. 1973; DRCOG 1978.

CHATTERJEA, Amares (retired) 12 Highlands Road, Rochdale OL11 5PD Tel: 01706 368492 — MB BS 1954 Calcutta; BSc (Hons.) Calcutta 1948. Prev: Resid. (Surg.) Ottawa Gen. Hosp., Canada.

CHATTERJEE, Mr Amal Kumar (retired) 65 Harrison Road, Fulwood, Preston PR2 9QJ Tel: 01779 718088 — MB BS Calcutta 1951, DGO 1954; FRCS Ed. 1968. Prev: Assoc. Specialist (Neurosurg.) Roy. Preston Hosp.

CHATTERJEE, Amit Kumar Collingwood Surgery, Hawkeys Lane, North Shields NE29 0SF Tel: 0191 257 1779 Fax: 0191 226 9909; 28 Mast Lane, North Shields NE30 3DE — MB ChB 1989 Ed.; MRCGP 1993; DCH RCP Lond. 1992.

CHATTERJEE, Anita 21 The Lea, Trentham, Stoke-on-Trent ST4 8DY — MB ChB 1996 Dundee.

CHATTERJEE, Anupam 101 The Avenue, Sale M33 4XZ Tel: 0973 255580 Fax: 0161 833 4272 Email: 100527.2065@compuserve.com — MB ChB 1986 Bristol; FRCS (Ophth.) Ed. 1991. Ophth. Surg. Optimax Laser Eye Clinics Manch. Socs: Fell. Manch. Med. Soc.; Fell. Amer. Soc. Cararact & Refractive Surg.; Fell. Assn. Research in Vision & Ophth. Prev: Research Regist. (Ophth.) Manch. Roy. Eye Hosp.; SHO (Ophth.) Manch. Roy. Eye Hosp. & Leicester Roy. Infirm.; SHO (Neurosurg.) Qu. Med. Centre Nottm.

***CHATTERJEE, Anwesh Kumar** 1 Rydal Cl, Burnley BB10 2SL — MB ChB 1997 Manch.

CHATTERJEE, Arup Prakash 70 Well Street, Hackney, London E9 7JA Tel: 020 8985 3806 Fax: 020 8525 5891 Email: goodlad@innocent.com — MB BS 1984 Calcutta; MB BS Calcutta, India 1984; LMSSA Lond. 1986; MRCGP 1996; DPM RCPSI 1990. (Med. Coll. Calcutta India) GP Regist. Lond.

CHATTERJEE, D K Dunninc Road Surgery, 28 Dunninc Road, Shiregreen, Sheffield S5 0AE Tel: 0114 257 0788 Fax: 0114 257 0069.

CHATTERJEE, Debabrata 26 Aldwickbury Crescent, Harpenden AL5 5RR Tel: 01582 764513 — MB BS 1960 Calcutta; FRCS Eng 1973; DObst RCOG 1963; FRCS Ed. 1965; ChM Liverp. 1973; MRCS Eng. 1973 LRCP Lond. 1973; FICS Geneva 1973. Cons. Surg. BUPA Hosp. Harpenden. - Retd. / W. Isles Health Bd. - Retd. Socs: Sen. Fell. Assn. Snog. GB & I; Fell. RSM; Mem. Lap. Soc., GB & I, Europe, USA. Prev: Cons. Surg., N. W. Thames RHA; Cons. Surg., Univ. Hosp. W. Indies; Cons. Surg., Roy. Infirm. Edin.

CHATTERJEE, Durga Sankar Ford Motor Company Ltd., Warley, Brentwood CM13 3BW Tel: 01277 252729 Fax: 01277 253066 — MB BS 1960 Calcutta; FFOM RCP Lond. 1990, MFOM 1979; DIH Soc. Apoth. Lond. 1974. Chief Med. Off. Ford Motor Co. Ltd. Brentwood; Golden Jubilee Research Schol. Som. 1986. Socs: Soc. Occupat. Med. Prev: Med. Off. Brit. Steel Corpn. Med. Asst. (Orthop.) Gen. Hosp. S.end; Regist. (Orthop.) War Memor. Hosp. Scunthorpe; Sen. Med. Off. Ford Motor Co. Ltd.

CHATTERJEE, Haradhan 563 New North Road, Hainault, Ilford IG6 3TF — MB 1941 Calcutta.

CHATTERJEE, Jagadis Prasad 126 Elizabeth Street, Blackpool FY1 3QN — MB BS 1964 Calcutta; MB BS 1964 Calcutta.

CHATTERJEE, John Hari Keighley Road Surgery, Keighley Road, Illingworth, Halifax HX2 9LL Tel: 01422 244397/248308 Fax: 01422 241101; 26 Savile Park, Free School Lane, Halifax HX1 3EW — MB ChB 1979 Manch.; MRCGP 1983.

CHATTERJEE, Kanai Lal The Health Centre, Stock Road, Billericay CM12 0BJ Tel: 01277 658071 Fax: 01277 633261; 151 Western Road, Billericay CM12 9JE Tel: 01277 658914 — MB BS Calcutta 1960. (R. G. Kar Med. Coll.) Prev: Maj. Indian Army Med. Corps; Regist. (Geriat.) Barncoose Hosp. Redruth & Leicester Gen. Hosp.

CHATTERJEE, Lalit Mohan Southend Road Surgery, 271A Southend Road, Stanford-le-Hope SS17 8HD Tel: 01375 679316 Fax: 01375 679335 — MB BS 1962 Calcutta; DTM & H RCP Lond. 1968.

CHATTERJEE, Maureen 1 Oakhurst Terrace, Benton, Newcastle upon Tyne NE12 9NY — MB BS 1961 Durh. Prev: Ho. Phys. Sunderland Roy. Infirm.; Ho. Surg. Sunderland Gen. Hosp. & Qu. Eliz. Hosp. Gateshead.

CHATTERJEE, Miss Modhusree 34 Ford End, Woodford Green IG8 0EG — MB 1990 Camb.; MA Camb. 1991, MB 1990, BChir Camb. 1989; FRCOphth.

CHATTERJEE, Nilima (retired) 65 Harrison Road, Fulwood, Preston PR2 9QJ Tel: 01772 718088 — MB BS Calcutta 1954, DGO 1956; DA Eng. 1963. Prev: Clin. Asst. (Anaesth.) Roy. Preston Hosp.

CHATTERJEE, Paul Prodip Kumar 87 Allington Drive, Billingham TS23 3UE — MB ChB 1993 Liverp.

CHATTERJEE, Petula Christine The Orchard, 18A Chapel Lane, Wilmslow SK9 5HX — MB ChB 1976 Manch.; BSc St. And. 1973.

CHATTERJEE, Mr Saktidas (retired) 33 St. Albans Avenue, Ashton-under-Lyne OL6 8DF Tel: 0161 330 5359 — MB BS 1951 Calcutta; FRCS Eng. 1958; FRCS Ed. 1955; FRCOphth 1993; DO Eng. 1955; DOMS Calcutta 1952. Locum Ophthamic Med. Practitioner, Rayner optition, Oldham. Prev: Cons. Ophth. Oldham & Tameside AHAs.

CHATTERJEE, Mr Sandip Department of Neurosurgery, Walton Hospital, Rice Lane, Liverpool L9 1AE Tel: 0151 525 3611 — MB BS 1988 Calcutta; FRCS Ed. 1989.

CHATTERJEE, Santana 151 Western Road, Billericay CM12 9JE — MB BS 1994 Lond.

CHATTERJEE, Satya Saran, OBE 15 Hunters Mews, Macclesfield Road, Wilmslow SK9 2AR Tel: 01625 522559 Fax: 01625 548321; 15 Hunters Mews, Wilmslow SK9 2AR Tel: 01625 548321, 01738 560301 — MB BS 1944 (Hnrs Anat.) Patna; FRCP Ed. 1973, M 1972; FRCP Lond. 1973, M 1949; FCCP 1973. (Patna & Birm.) JP; Cons. Chest Phys. Altrincham Chesh. Socs: Europ. Soc. Clin. Respirat. Physiol.; Fell. RCP Lond. & Edin. Prev: Sen. Regist. Baguley Hosp. Manch.; Jun. Asst. Dept. Med. Albany Med. Coll., U.S.A.; Capt. IAMC.

CHATTERJEE, Swades Chandra 79 Pilleys Lane, Boston PE21 9RA — MB BS 1959 Calcutta; FFA RCS Eng. 1970.

CHATTERJEE, Tarun Kumar (retired) 83 Broad Walk, Pownall Park, Wilmslow SK9 5PN Tel: 01625 525473 — MB BS 1961 Calcutta; FRCOG 1986, M 1966; DObst 1965; DCH NUI 1966. Prev: Cons. Genitourin Med. Manch. Roy. Infirm. & St. Thos. Hosp. Stockport.

CHATTERJEE, Professor Vengalil Krishna Kumar Department of Medicine, Level 5, Addenbrooke's Hospital, Hills Road, Cambridge CB2 2QQ Tel: 01223 336842 Fax: 01223 336846 Email: kkc1@mole.bio.cam.ac.uk; 15 Algers Road, Loughton IG10 4NG — BM BCh 1982 Oxf.; FRCP Lond. 1996. Proffessor of Endocrinol., Hon. Cons. Phys. Addeerbroske's Hosp., Camb. Socs: Assn. Phys. Endocrine Soc.; Exec. Euro. Thyroid Assn. Prev: Wellcome Sen. Fell. & Hon. Cons. Phys. Addenbrooke's Hosp. Camb.; Regist. Hammersmith Hosp. Lond.; SHO Hammersmith, Brompton & St. Thos. Hosps. Lond.

CHATTERJI, Mr Subroto 3 Fford y Briallu, Abergwili, Carmarthen SA31 2JU — MB BS 1981 Calcutta; MSc Orth Lond. 1991; FRCS Ed. 1986. Cons. Orthop. Surg. Camb. Milit. Hosp. Aldershot. Socs: Brit. Orthop. Assn. Prev: Regist. (Orthop.) Chase Farm Hosp. Enfield.

CHATTERJI, Urjit 12 Summer Road, Harrow HA1 4BU — MB BS 1993 Lond.

CHATTERTON, Barry James Radiology Department, Waikato Hospital, Hamilton, New Zealand Tel: 00 64 7 8398605 Fax: 00 64 7 8398779; 255 Passfield Avenue, Eastleigh SO50 9NB Tel: 01703 612088 — MB BS 1979 Lond.; BSc (Biochem.) Lond. 1976; FRCR 1986. Cons. Radiol. Waikato Hosp. Hamilton, NZ. Prev: Sen. Regist. (Diag. Radiol.) St. Jas. Univ. Hosp. & Leeds Gen. Infirm.

CHATTHA, Ejaz Ahmed Wesham Park Hospital, Wesham, Krikham, Preston PR4 3AL; 43 Montcliffe Crescent, Manchester M16 8GR — MB BS 1974 Punjab; MRCS Eng. LRCP Lond. 1980.

CHATTOPADHYAY, Asok Kumar 63 Broadway, Walsall WS1 3EZ — MB BS 1972 Calcutta.

CHATTOPADHYAY, Bilwanath Public Health Laboratory & Department Microbiology, Whipps Cross Hospital, London E11 1NR Tel: 020 8539 5223 Fax: 020 8556 2855 — MB BS 1964 Calcutta; FRCPath 1985, M 1973. Dir. & Cons. Med. Microbiol. Whipps Cross Hosp. Lond.; Hon. Lect. (Med. Microbiol.) St. Barts. Hosp. Lond. Socs: Brit. Soc. Antimicrob. Chemother.; Brit. Soc. Study of Infec.; Hosp. Infec. Soc. Prev: Sen. Regist. (Med. Microbiol.) St. Bart. Hosp. Lond. & Qu. Mary's Hosp. Lond.; Regist. (Chem. Path.) Qu. Mary's Hosp. Lond.

CHATTOPADHYAY, Chandra Bhusan Wrightington Hospital, Hall Lane, Appley Bridge, Wigan WN6 9EP Tel: 01257 256238 Fax: 01257 256375; 9 Brandreth Delph, Parbold, Wigan WN8 7AQ Tel: 01257 462229 — MB BS 1971 Calcutta; AIIMS (N. Delhi) 1975; FRCP Lond. 1996; MRCP (UK) 1981. Cons. Rheum. Wrightington Hosp. NHS Trust, Roy. Preston Hosp. & Chorley Hosp.; Clin. Dir. (Rheum. & Med.) Wrightington Hosp.; Hon. Sen. Lect. Univ. of Centr. Lancs. Socs: Brit. Soc. Rheum. Prev: Research Fell. Inst. Immunol. & Rheum. Nat. Hosp. Norway, Oslo; Clin. Tutor (Rheum.) Univ. Manch.; Sen. Regist. (Rheum.) NW RHA.

CHATTOPADHYAY, Hena 9 Brandreth Delph, Parbold, Wigan WN8 7AQ — MB BS 1972 Calcutta; MD (Microbiol.) Chandigarh 1975.

CHATTOPADHYAY, Mr Prabhat Kumar 113 Ingleway Avenue, Blackpool FY3 8LH — MB BS 1966 Calcutta; FRCS Ed. 1978; MRCOG 1973.

CHATTOPADHYAY, Pranab Kumar Doclands Medical Centre, Blanche Street, Ashton-on-Ribble, Preston PR2 2RL Tel: 01772 723222 Fax: 01772 726619 — MB BS 1964 Calcutta; MB BS 1964 Calcutta.

CHATTOPADHYAY, Sakti 4 Whiston Green, Whiston, Rotherham S60 4JX — MB BS 1972 Calcutta.

CHATTOPADHYAY, Swapan K George Street Medical Centre, 10 George Street, Aberaman, Aberdare CF44 6RY Tel: 01685 874120 Fax: 01685 881581.

CHATTOPADHYAY, Tapan Kumar 14 Framingham Road, Sale M33 3SH — MB BS 1976 Calcutta; MRCP (UK) 1985.

CHATTOPADHYAY, Tapaskumar 5 The Coppice, Blackburn BB2 7BQ — MB BS 1970 Calcutta.

CHATTOPADHYAY, Ushashi 15 Ely Place, Chigwell IG8 8AG Tel: 020 8504 1034 — MB BS Calcutta 1967; DTM & H Eng. 1971; DCH Calcutta 1969. (Calcutta Med. Coll.) Staff Grade Pract. Camden & Islington Community Health Servs. NHS Trust. Prev: Clin. Med. Off. Islington HA; SHO (Paediat.) St. Helen's Hosp. Hastings; SHO (Paediat.) Childr. Hosp. Stockton-on-Tees.

CHATTREE, Sunita 78 Rogersfield, Langho, Blackburn BB6 8HD — MB BS 1975 Ranchi; MB BS Ranchi, India 1975.

CHATURVEDI, Krishna Kant Southbourne Grove Surgery, 314 Southbourne Grove, Westcliff on Sea SS0 0AF Tel: 01702 344074; 11A Crosby Road, Westcliff on Sea SS0 8LF — MB BS 1974 Indore. Clin. Asst. G.U. Med. S.end Trust Hosp., S.end on Sea; Clin. Goremance lead, Ment. Health, S.end on Sea Primary care Trust.; Exec. Mem., S.O.S. PCT.; Mem.. Local Med. Comm., S. Essex. L.M.C. Socs: Clin., Gornance lead, Ment. Health PCT Exec..; Small Pract.s- Forum lead S.end PCT; Med. Protec. Soc.

CHATURVEDI, Nishi Department of Epidemiology & Public Health, University College London, 1-19 Torrington Place, London WC1E 7HB — MB BS 1985 Lond.; MD Lond. 1994; MRCP 1988. Regist. (Pub. Health) Hampstead HA. Prev: SHO (Med.) Waltham Forest HA.; SHO (Med.) Bloomsbury & Riverside HA; SHO (A & E) Lewisham & N. S.wark HA.

CHATURVEDI, Rainu Margaret Stanhope Centre, Outwoods, Belvedere Road, Burton-on-Trent DE13 0QL; 41 Newton Road, Burton-on-Trent DE15 0TX — MB BS 1986 Lond.; DRCOG 1992; MRCGP 1996. (St Thomas') CMO Adult Ment. Health. Prev: GP Princip., Walsall.

CHATURVEDI, Rajiv Ranjan 3 Moss Bawn, Magherafelt BT45 5BY — MB BChir 1990 Camb.; MRCP (UK) 1993.

CHATWIN, Helen Catherine 7 Green Hollow Close, Fareham PO16 7XP — MB ChB 1998 Leic.; MB ChB Leic 1998.

CHATZIGRIGORIS, Petros Health Care Internatrional (Scotland) Ltd., Beardmore St., Clydebank G81 4DY — Ptychio Iatrikes 1982 Athens.

CHAU, Boon Ling 73 Chase Road, London N14 4QY — MB ChB 1992 Leic.

CHAU, Edmond Ping Wa 18 New Wokingham Road, Crowthorne RG45 6JL Tel: 01344 773418 Fax: 01344 762753; Pinegrove, 100 Ellis Road, Crowthorne RG45 6PH Tel: 01344 762714 — BM 1984 Soton.; MRCGP 1989; DCH RCP 1988 Lond.; BM Soton l984; MRCGP 1989; DCH RCP Lond. 1988. (Soton.) GP. Prev: Clin. Med. Off. Frimley Childr. Centre; Trainee GP Elsenham; SHO (A & E) P.ss Alexandra Hosp. Harlow.

CHAU, Mr Gordon Kwok-On 22 The Marlowes, St. John's Wood, London NW8 6NA — MB ChB 1985 Ed.; FRCS Eng. 1990; FCOphth 1990; DO RCS Eng. 1989.

CHAU, Ha Nguyen 12 Bramley Av, Barlby, Selby YO8 5EY — MB BS 1997 Lond.

CHAU, Ian Tat Man Flat 48, Millbrooke Court, Keswick Road, London SW15 2RA Tel: 020 8877 1460 Email: ianchan@btinternet.com — MB BS 1994 Lond.; MRCP (UK) 1998. (UMDS) Specialist Regist. (Med. Oncol.), Roy. Marsden Hospita, Lond.

CHAU, Noan-Minh 45 Gables Close, London SE5 7QE — MB BS 1997 Lond.

***CHAU, Pak-Lee** Department of Biochemistry, University of Cambridge, Cambridge CB2 1QW — MB BChir 1993 Camb.; PhD Camb. 1991, MA 1990, MB BChir 1993.

CHAU, Simon Kwan Ho 8 The Pines, Leigh WN7 3JS — BM BS 1994 Nottm.

CHAU, Wai Fong 102 Wolverton Road, Bournemouth BH7 6HX Tel: 01202 303439 — MB ChB 1991 Bristol; MRCP (UK) 1995. Regist. (Gen. Med. & Endocrinol.) W.on & UBHT.

CHAUBAL, Nalini Dwarkanath The Long Barn, Drayton Beauchamp, Aylesbury HP22 5LS — MB BS 1959 Bombay; DA Eng. 1963. (Grant Med. Coll.) Asst. (Anaesth.) Specialist Stoke Mandeville Hosp. Prev: Regist. (Anaesth.) St. Luke's Hosp. Bradford & Roy. Hosp.; Wolverhampton.; SHO Qu. Eliz. Hosp. Birm.

CHAUBEY, Sanjay 15 Violet Gardens, Carluke ML8 5TJ — MB ChB 1997 Glas.

CHAUDARY, Aqil Haider 76 City Road, Birmingham B16 0HQ — MB ChB 1993 Manch.

CHAUDARY, Mr Murid Ahmed Watford General Hospital, Vicarage Road, Watford WD18 0HB Tel: 01923 217690 Fax: 01923 217778 — MRCS Eng. LRCP Lond. 1971; ChM Leeds 1984, MB ChB 1971; FRCS Eng. 1976. Cons. BrE. Surg. Watford Gen. Hosp. Prev: Sen. Lect. & Hon. Cons. (BrE. Dis.) Guy's Hosp. Lond.; ICRF Research Fell. & Hon. Sen. Reigst. BrE. Unit Guy's Hosp. Lond.; Regist. Dept. Urol. & Kidney Transpl. Hammersmith Hosp.

CHAUDERY, Noureen 4 Brownlow Road, Parkhill, Croydon CR0 5JT Tel: 020 8688 3311 — MB BS 1985 Punjab; MRCS Eng. LRCP Lond. 1990; MRCGP 1995; DCH RCP Lond. 1993; DGM RCP Lond. 1992.

CHAUDHARI, Imran 191 Clarendon Park Road, Leicester LE2 3AN — MB ChB 1998 Leic.; MB ChB Leic 1998.

CHAUDHARI, Milind Pralhad 104 Beechwood House, Melville Grove, Newcastle upon Tyne NE7 7AG — MB BS 1990 Poona.

CHAUDHARI, Shabana Asghar 51 Wavertree Road, London SW2 3SL — MB BS 1996 Lond.

CHAUDHARY, Arun Kumar Department of Mental Health, Scunthorpe General Hospital, Cliff Gardens, Scunthorpe DN15 7BH Tel: 01724 290071 Fax: 01724 290419; 7 Sandfield Close, Silica Lodge, Scunthorpe DN17 2XE Tel: 01724 351482 Fax: 01724 277169 Email: chaudhary.chaudary@nflworld.com — MB BS 1980 Ranchi; MRCPysch 1986; FRCPsych 1998. Cons. Psychiat. Scunthorpe Gen. Hosp.; Hon. Lect. Sheff. Med. Sch. Prev: Regist. (Psychiat.) E. Glam. Gen. Hosp. Pontypridd; Regist. Rotat. (Psychiat.) Warley Hosp. Brentwood; Regist. Rotat. & SHO (Psychiat.) Bridgend.

CHAUDHARY, Bashir Ahmad 457 Newark Road, Lincoln LN6 8RT Tel: 01522 522552 — MB BS 1951 Punjab; BSc Punjab (Pakistan) 1944, MB BS 1951; DTM & H Liverp. 1954; DO Eng. 1963. (King Edwd. Med. Coll.) Sen. Ho. Med. Off. (Ophth.) Co. Hosp. Lincoln.

CHAUDHARY, Deepak 4 Sturmer Court, Scunthorpe DN16 3TX — MB BS 1974 Patna.

CHAUDHARY, Mohamed Farooq 55 Woodfield Avenue, London SW16 1LE — LRCPI & LM, LRSCI & LM 1970; LRCPI & LM, LRCSI & LM 1970.

CHAUDHARY, Mr Rajendra 37 Cranborne Road, Cosham, Portsmouth PO6 2BG Tel: 023 92 351253 — MB BS 1982 Delhi; FRCS Eng. 1989; FRCS Ed. 1988; Dip. Urol. Lond 1991.

CHAUDHARY, Rehanna Parveen 20 Whitton Close, West Bessacarr, Doncaster DN4 7RD — MB ChB 1995 Sheff.

CHAUDHARY, Mr Shuaib Mohamma 55 Richmond Hill Road, Edgbaston, Birmingham B15 3SA Tel: 0121 454 8686 — MB BS 1978 Punjab; FRCS Ed. 1989; FCOphth 1989; DO RCPSI 1989. Regist. (Ophth.) Singleton Hosp. Swansea.

CHAUDHARY, Sumrana Naeem 44 Daniel Street, Cardiff CF24 4NY — MB BCh 1993 Wales.

CHAUDHRI, Babar Bashir Flat 5, Paxton Court, Adamsrillm Road, London SE26 4AY — MB BChir 1992 Camb.

CHAUDHRI, Fayyaz Latif Anneburgh House, Ewanrigg Rd, Maryport CA15 8EL Tel: 01900 815544 — MB BS 1983 Lond.; MRCGP 1989; DCH RCP Lond. 1988.

CHAUDHRI, Kaiser Broadway Surgery, 2 Broadway, Fulwood, Preston PR2 9TH — MB ChB 1985 Manch.; LLM Cardiff 1995; MRCGP 1990. Medico-Legal Examr. for Various Solicitors. Socs: BMA; The Medico-Legal Soc.; UK Register of Expert Witnesses. Prev: Trainee GP/SHO Vict. Hosp. Blackpool VTS.

CHAUDHRI, Omar Saleem 163 Byres Road, Glasgow G12 8TS — MB ChB 1996 Glas.

CHAUDHRI, Qamar Clinical Neurophysiology Department, Queens Medical Centre, University Hospital, Nottingham NG7 2; 52 Wollaton Vale, Wollaton, Nottingham NG8 2PB — MB ChB 1978 Manch.; MRCGP 1985. Assoc. Specialist (Clin. Neurophysiol.) Qu. Med. Centre Nottm.

CHAUDHRI, Sheevan Mary Bernadette 6 Ladyrigg, Darras Hall, Ponteland, Newcastle upon Tyne NE20 9QS — MB BS 1996 Newc.

CHAUDHRI, Sofia Royal Alexandra Hospital, Corsebar Road, Paisley PA2 4HX — MB ChB 1982 Glas.; FRCA 1988. Cons. Anaesth. Roy. Alexandra Hosp. Paisley.

***CHAUDHRY, Aafia** Flat 35, Dene House Court, Leicester Place, Leeds LS2 9BS — MB ChB 1998 Manch.; MB ChB Manch 1998.

CHAUDHRY, Adil Anthony 1 Swann Grove, Cheadle Hulme, Cheadle SK8 7HW — MB BS 1988 Newc.; MRCP Lond. 1992. Regist. (Paediat.) Qu. Charlotte's & Hammersmith Special HA.

CHAUDHRY, Afzal Niaz 149 Regent-on-the-River, William Morris Way, Fulham, London SW6 2UU — MB BS 1991 Lond.; BSc Biomed. Sci. (Hons.) Lond. 1988; MRCP (UK) 1994. (St. Geo. Hosp. Med. Sch. Lond.) Regist. Rotat. MRC Res. Fell. Renal Unit Hammersmith Hosp. Lond. Socs: Roy. Soc. Med. Prev: Regist. Renal Unit Char. Cross Hosp. & Hammersmith Hosp.; SHO Rotat. Guy's Hosp. Lond.

CHAUDHRY, Ahmad Yar Faculty of Medicine, Walsgrave Hospital NHS Trust, Clifford Bridge Road, Coventry CV2 2DX Tel: 024 76 60202002476 538848 Fax: 024 76 535166 — MB BS Punjab 1969; FRCP Glas. 1992; FRCP Ed. 1991; FRCP Lond. 1990; MRCP (UK) 1979. (Nishtar Multan Pakistan) Cons. Phys./Cardiol. Walsgrave Hosp. Coventry; Cons. Phys. (Cardiol.) Shalamar Hosp. Lahore, Pakistan; Cons. Cardiol. King Fahid Hosp. Jeddah, Saudi Arabia; Vis. Cons. to BUPA Pk.way Solihull & Priory Hosp. Birm.

CHAUDHRY, Mr Bhupinder Singh Oakfield Road Surgery, 1 Oakfield Road, North Ormesby, Middlesbrough T53 6EZ Tel: 01642 244990 Fax: 01642 248714 — MB BS 1965 Punjab; FRCS Ed. 1973. (Govt. Med. Coll. Patiala) Prev: Regist. (Gen. Surg.) N. Ormesby Hosp. Middlesbrough; Regist. (Neurosurg.) & Regist. (Orthop.) Middlesbrough Gen. Hosp.

CHAUDHRY, Farah 31 Beagle Avenue, Huddersfield HD4 7AP; Flat 24, Wilton Place, Goyton Road, Harrow HA1 2HJ Tel: 020 8537 9440 Email: farahchaudhry@hotmail.com — MB BS 1997 Lond.; MA 1998. (UMDS London/ Cambridge University) SHO (A&E), Leeds Gen. Infirm. Prev: SHO (Paediat.) Puderfields, Wakefield; Ho. Off. (Orthop.) Lewisham Hosp., Lond.; Ho. Off. (Med.) Greenwich Gen. Hosp., Lond.

CHAUDHRY, Hemendra Mohan (retired) Hill Crest Medical Centre, 86 Holt Road, Wrexham LL13 8RG Tel: 01978 262193 Fax: 01978 310193 (Call before faxing) — MB BS 1968 Delhi.

CHAUDHRY, Mr Maqsood Ahmed — MB BS 1978 Punjab; FRCS Glas. 1988.

CHAUDHRY, Mohammed Tashfeen 78 Nether Currie Crescent, Currie, Edinburgh EH14 5JG — MB ChB 1990 Ed.

CHAUDHRY, Mubarak Ahmad Univ.Dept of Cardiac Surgery, Glasgow Royal Infirmary, 10 Alexandra parade, Glasgow G31 2ER Tel: 0141 711 4731 Email: m.chaudhry@clinmedogla.ac.uk; 3 Invergarry Place, Thornliebank, Glasgow G46 8UT Tel: 0141 638 0657 — BChir 1990 Camb.; MB Camb. 1990; FRCS (Eng.) 1995. (Camb.) Lect. Cardiothoracic Surg., Univ. of Glas.; Hon Specialist Regist. Cardiothoracic Surg. Glas. Roy. Infirm. Socs: Brit. Assn. of Cardiothoracic Surg. Prev: Regist. (Cardiothoracic Surg.) Wessex Carbiothoracic Unit Soton. Gen. Hosp.

CHAUDHRY, Muhammad Afzal The Medical Centre, 29 Bryant Street, Chatham ME4 5QS Tel: 01634 848911 — MB BS 1958 Punjab; MB BS Punjab (Pakistan) 1958; DPM Eng. 1966. (Lahore) Socs: BMA. Prev: Ho. Off. St. Alfege's Hosp. Lond.; Regist. Belmont Hosp.

CHAUDHRY, Quratulain 18 Rothwell Road, Savile Park, Halifax HX1 2HA Tel: 01422 340096 — MB ChB 1990 Dundee.

CHAUDHRY, Sahil 6 Danes Brook Court, Ingleby Barwick, Stockton-on-Tees TS17 0QX — MB ChB 1985 Manch.

CHAUDHRY, Satya Harish 22 Whitby Road, Slough SL1 3DQ Tel: 01753 527988; 60 Stoke Poges Lane, Slough SL1 3PD Tel: 01753 535356 — MB BS 1952 Bombay. Socs: MDU. Prev: Clin. Asst. (O & G) Upton & K. Edwd. VII Hosp.

CHAUDHRY, Mr Shahid Mahmood 71 Montagu Avenue, Gosforth, Newcastle upon Tyne NE3 4JN Tel: 0191 285 7722 Fax: 0191 241 0374 Email: shahid@chaudhry.u-net.com — MB BS 1983 Punjab; FRCSI 1989.

CHAUDHRY, Sohail Raza Keir Street Surgery, 42 Keir Street, Glasgow G41 2LA Tel: 0141 423 3335 Fax: 0141 423 9883 — MRCS Eng. LRCP Lond. 1981.

CHAUDHRY, Mr Tajammal Ahmad Flat 7, 14 Herbert Crescent, London SW1X 0HB — MB BS 1981 Punjab; FRCS Ed. 1985.

CHAUDHRY, Mr Tanveer Anjum Eye Department, Barnsley District General Hospital, Gawber Road, Barnsley S75 2EP Tel: 01226 777750 Fax: 01226 777946 — MB BS 1985 Karachi; FRCS Ed. 1991; MCOphth 1991; DO RCPSI 1991. (Dow Medical College, Karachi University) Cons. Ophth. Surg. Barnsley Dist. Gen. Hosp. Barnsley.

CHAUDHRY, Tariq Saeed Ward 4, Renal Medicine, Freeman Hospital, Newcastle upon Tyne NE7 7AG Tel: 0191 284 3111 Fax: 0191 223 1233; 2 Sturdee Gardens, Jesmond, Newcastle upon Tyne NE2 3QT Tel: 0191 285 9313 — MB BS 1975 Punjab; MRCP (UK) 1989; Dip. Nephrol. & Hypertens. RPMS Lond. 1991. (Nishtar Multan, Pakistan) Assoc. Specialist Nephrol. Freeman Hosp. Newc. u-Tyne. Prev: Nephrol. King Faisal Specialist Hosp. Riyadh, Saudi Arabia.

CHAUDHRY, Waseem Nayyar 157 Donald Street, Roath, Cardiff CF24 4TP — MB BCh 1989 Wales.

CHAUDHURI, Ajay Kumar Ray (retired) 58 North Grange Road, Bearsden, Glasgow G61 3AF Tel: 0141 942 4649 Email: chaudhuria@aol.com — MB BS 1956 Calcutta; FRCP Glas. 1975, M 1964. Prev: Cons. Phys. (Communicable Dis.) Monklands Dist. Gen. Hosp. Airdrie.

CHAUDHURI, Anjan Kumar 10 North Road, Gloucester GL1 3JX; 130 Fairwater Drive, Woodley, Reading RG5 3JF Tel: 0118 969 0479 — MB BS 1988 Calcutta. (Calcutta Medical College) Staff Grade in Haemat. Wexham Pk. Hosp. Slough. Prev: Sen. SHO (Med.) E. Glam. Gen. Hosp.; SHO (Med.) James Paget Hosp. Gt. Yarmouth; SHO (Haemat.) Wythenshire Hosp. Manch.

CHAUDHURI, Anup Kumar Camphill Road Surgery, 10 Camp Hill Road, Nuneaton CV10 0JH Tel: 024 7639 3388 Fax: 024 7639 7907 — MB BS 1968 Calcutta; MB BS 1968 Calcutta.

CHAUDHURI, Arup Kumar 10 North Road, Gloucester GL1 3JX Tel: 01452 520462; 5 Heathville Road, Gloucester GL1 3DP Tel: 01452 528299 Fax: 01452 387917 — MB BS 1961 Calcutta; MRCP (UK) 1972. Hosp. Pract. (Geriat. Med.) Glos. Acute NHS Trust; Police Surg. Glos. Socs: Brit. Geriat. Soc. & RCP Lond. Prev: Clin. Tutor Glos. Postgrad. Med. Centre.

CHAUDHURI, Benu Bhushon The Surgery, 85 Stopford Road, Plaistow, London E13 0NA Tel: 020 8472 3901 Fax: 020 8503 4818; 16A Seagry Road, London E11 2NQ Tel: 020 8989 0716 — MB BS 1965 Karachi; DA Eng. 1967; DPH Eng. 1978. (Dow Med. Coll.) Princip. GP City & E. Lond. FPC; Cons. Anaesth. NE Thames RHA; Counc.lor Community health Counc. Lond. Boro. Tower Hamlets; Chairm. Tower Hamlet Commiss. for Racial Equality. Socs: FRIPHH. Prev: Regist. (Anaesth.) Herts. & Essex Gen. Hosp. Bishop's Stortford, Roy.; Infirm. Edin., Addenbrookes Hosp. Camb., & Bethnal Green Hosp.; Lond.

CHAUDHURI, Himadri 59 Buckingham Road, Chorlton, Manchester M21 0SB — MB BS 1972 Calcutta.

CHAUDHURI, Mr Jagodindra Kumar 37 Butt Hill, Kippax, Leeds LS25 7JU Tel: 0113 286 2044 — MB BS 1955 Calcutta; FRCS Eng. 1967. (N.R.S. Med. Coll.) Clin. Asst. (Plastic Surg.) Pinderfields Gen. Hosp. Wakefield; Assoc. Mem. Brit. Assn. Plastic Surgs.

CHAUDHURI, Mira 10 North Road, Gloucester GL1 3JX Tel: 01452 20462 — MB BS 1962 Calcutta; FRCP Lond. 1995; FRCP Ed. 1989; MRCP (UK) 1974; DCH RCPS Glas. 1968. (Calcutta) Cons. Phys. (Geriat. Med.) Glos. Roy. Hosp. Socs: Brit. Geriat. Soc. Prev: Regist. (Med. & Geriat.) & SHO (Med.) Glos. Roy. Hosp.

CHAUDHURI, P S High Street Surgery, 28 High Street, Prescot L34 6HE Tel: 0151 426 2890.

CHAUDHURI, Praphullachandra (retired) 463 Newchurch Road, Rawtenstall, Rossendale BB4 7TG Tel: 01706 213373 — MB 1951 Calcutta; DGO Dub. 1953; DObst RCOG 1953.

CHAUDHURI, Ranjana Department of Radiology, Whittington Hospital NHS Trust, Highgate Hill, London N19 5NF Tel: 020 7288 5680 Fax: 020 7288 5133; 22 Hoop Lane, London NW11 8JL Tel: 020 8201 9752 — BChir 1980 Camb.; MA Camb. 1981; FRCR 1987. (King's Coll. Camb. & Roy. Lond. Hosp.) Cons. (Radiol.) Whittington Hosp. Lond. Socs: Roy. Coll. Radiol.; Brit. Inst. Radiol.; Internat. Soc. for magnetic resonance in Med. Prev: Cons. Radiol. Hillingdon Hosp. 1994-98; Sen. Regist. & Regist. (Radiol.) Guy;s Hosp.; SHO (Med.) Roy. Marsden Hosp. Sutton.

CHAUDHURI, Sanjay The Natural Health Service, 50 Angelica Way, Whiteley, Fareham PO15 7HZ Tel: 01489 881823 — MB BS 1991 Lond.; BSc (Hons.) Lond. 1988, MB BS 1991.

CHAUDHURI, Sourja The High Street Surgery, 100 High Street, Dover CT16 1EQ Tel: 01304 206463; Valentica, 99 Sandwich Road, Whitfield, Dover CT16 3LU Tel: 01304 823294 — MB BS 1977 Lond.

CHAUDHURY, Abdul Jabbar Health Clinic, Ashgrove, Blackburn, Bathgate EH47 7LL Tel: 01506 652956 Fax: 01506 634790 — MB BS 1968 Dacca. (Dacca) GP Bathgate.

CHAUDHURY, Gopal Bandhu Longview Health Care Centre, 132 Longview Drive, Huyton, Liverpool L36 6EQ Tel: 0151 489 2833 Fax: 0151 480 1133; resid., 29 Ormskirk Road, Knowsley, Prescot L34 8HB — MB BS 1965 Calcutta; DCH 1967. (Nat. Med. Coll.)

CHAUDHURY, Maya Huyton Family Health Practice, 71 Longview Drive, Huyton, Liverpool L36 6EB Tel: 0151 480 6214; resid., 29 Ormskirk Road, Knowsley, Prescot L34 8HB — MB BS 1969 Calcutta; DObst DRCOG 1974; DGO Calcutta 1971. (Calcutta Med. Coll.) Prev: SHO (O & G) & Ho. Off. Warrington Health Dist.

CHAUDHURY, Mr Sib Das 120 Cotswold Gardens, London NW2 1PN Tel: 020 8455 7854 — FRCS Ed. 1975.

CHAUDOIR, Peter John Stanmore House, Linden Avenue, Kidderminster DY10 3AA Tel: 01562 822647 Fax: 01562 827255; 43 Chester Road S., Kidderminster DY10 1XJ Tel: 01562 824129 — MB ChB 1955 Birm.; DObst RCOG 1960; DCH Eng. 1965. (Birm.) Prev: Flight Lt. RAF Med. Br.; Ho. Surg. (Obst.) Ronkswood Hosp. Worcester; Ho. Phys. (Paediat.) Dudley Rd. Hosp.

CHAUDRI, Mazhar Bashir 1 Foxhill Road, Burton Joyce, Nottingham NG14 5DB Tel: 01159 314424 Fax: 01159 313457 — MB ChB 1991 Leeds; MRCP (UK) 1996. Specialist Regist. Rotat. (Respirat. Med.) Nottm. Socs: BMA.

CHAUDRI, Mohammad Bashir The Willows Medical Centre, Church Street, Carlton, Nottingham NG4 1BJ Tel: 0115 940 4252 Fax: 0115 956 9976 — MS BS DRCOG. (King Edward Medical College, Lahore, Pakistan)

CHAUDRY, Irfan Ashraf 21 Saxon Av, Manchester M8 4QH — MB ChB 1997 Dundee.

CHAUDRY, Iskander Hayat South Field, Congleton Road, Alderley Edge SK9 7AL — MB ChB 1996 Manch.

CHAUDRY, Nusrat Begum 21 Saxon Avenue, Manchester M8 4QH — MB BS 1964 Punjab; MB BS Punjab (Pakistan) 1964. Prev: Ho. Off. Mulago Hosp. Kampala, Uganda; Med. Off. Tabora Regional Hosp. Tanzania; SHO Bedford Gen. Hosp.

CHAUDRY, Zia Raseeb 84 Kingsley Road, Southampton SO15 8QN — MB ChB 1991 Leic.

CHAUDURY, Farakh Rehana Alexandra Park Health Centre, 2 Whitswood Close, Manchester M16 7AP Tel: 0161 226 2710 — MB ChB 1975 Aberd. SHO (Paediat.) Qu. Pk. Hosp. Blackburn. Prev: SHO (O & G) Falkirk Roy. Infirm.; Ho. Off. (Surg.) Aberd. Roy. Infirm.; Ho. Off. (Med.) Falkirk Roy. Infirm.

CHAUHAN, Alpha 433 Gleneagles Avenue, Leicester LE4 7YJ — MB ChB 1996 Leic.

CHAUHAN, Anilkumar Amberley, Takeley, Bishop's Stortford CM22 6QJ — MB BCh 1979 Wales; MRCP (UK) 1982; FRCR 1986;

DMRD Eng. 1984. Cons. (Radiol.) W. Essex HA. Prev: Sen. Regist. & Regist. (Diagn. Radiol.) St. Bart. Hosp. Lond.

CHAUHAN, Anoop 52 Kerrysdale Avenue, Leicester LE4 7GH — MB ChB 1987 Manch.

CHAUHAN, Balwant Clarendon Park Road Health Centre, 296 Clarendon Park Road, Leicester LE2 3AG Tel: 0116 270 5049; Santosh, 40 Ingarsby Drive, Evington, Leicester LE5 6HA — MB ChB 1977 Manch.; MRCGP 1989.

CHAUHAN, Bhupendra 4 Fairfield Street, Leicester LE5 5BF — MB ChB 1993 Sheff.

CHAUHAN, Chatenya 90 Lidgett Lane, Moortown, Leeds LS8 1LQ Tel: 0113 288 8283 Fax: 0113 216 3504 Email: chet@btinternet.com — MB ChB 1989 Dundee; BMSc (Hons.) Dund 1986; FRCS Ed. 1994; USMLE Step I & II; ECFMG Cert 1995. (Dundee) Specailist Regist. Orthop. Leeds Deamers; Expert witness approved by THT Law Soc. Socs: Cartilage Repair Soc. Mem.; MDDU; BOA. Prev: Peri-Fell.sh. Surgic. Rotat. N.. Gen. Hosp.; Lect. (Biomed. Sci.) Univ. Sheff.; SHO (Neurosurg.) Roy. Hallamsh. Hosp. Sheff.

CHAUHAN, Devinder Singh 5 Vincent Close, London SE16 6QL — MB BS 1989 Lond.

CHAUHAN, Ghanshyam Singh Clifton House Medical Centre, 263-265 Beverley Road, Hull HU5 2ST Tel: 01482 341423 — MB BS 1982 Lond.; DCH RCPS Glas. 1986.

CHAUHAN, Mr Mahipatsinh Laxmanbhai Kellaway Pharmacy, 18 Kellaway Avenue, Bristol BS6 7XR — MB BS 1977 Saurashtra; FRCS Ed. 1983.

CHAUHAN, Mayursingh 7 Etherley Grange, Bishop Auckland DL14 0JY — MRCS Eng. LRCP Lond. 1981; MD Liverp. 1990, MB ChB 1981; MRCOG 1986. Cons. O & G Bishop Auckland Dist. Gen. Hosp.

CHAUHAN, Nagendrakumar Dalpatbhai Clarendon Medical, 35 Northland Avenue, Londonderry BT48 7JW; 16 Millbrook Park, Drumahoe, Londonderry BT47 3QH Tel: 01504 265391 — MB BCh BAO Dub. 1968; MA Dub. 1968. (TC Dub.) GP Geriat. Waterside Hosp. Lond.derry; Police Surg.; Med. Off. Univ. Ulster. Prev: Med. Off. Stradreagh Hosp. Lond.derry.

CHAUHAN, Naresh 559B Lordship Lane, London SE22 8LB — MB BS 1993 Lond.

CHAUHAN, Nilesh 66 Egerton Avenue, Leicester LE4 0DN — MB ChB 1995 Bristol.

CHAUHAN, Sandeep Kumar Flat 1, 33 Adelaide Crescent, Hove BN3 2JJ — MB BS 1992 Lond.; FRCS Eng. 1996. (UMDS Guy's & St. Thos.)

CHAUHAN, Sanjay The Surgery, 2 Littlefield Lane, Grimsby DN31 2LG Tel: 01472 342250 — MB ChB 1987 Manch.

CHAUHAN, Sarbjit — MB ChB 1994 Dundee; BMSc (Hons.) Dund 1992. (Dundee) Trainee GP/SHO (Paediat.) Lond. VTS. Socs: BMA. Prev: Ho. Off. (Gen. Med.) Qu. Mary's Hosp. Kent; Ho. (Gen. Surg.) Newham Gen. Hosp. Lond.

CHAUHAN, Umesh 2A Helmshore Road, Haslingden, Rossendale BB4 4BG — MB ChB 1990 Manch.; MRCGP 1994.

CHAUHDRY, Mr Muhammad Saleem Southey Hill Surgery, 11 Southey Hill, Sheffield S5 8BB Tel: 0114 232 6420 Fax: 0114 234 2990; 18 Belgrave Road, Sheffield S10 3LN Tel: 0114 230 2229 — MB BS Punjab (Pakistan) 1964. (Nishtar Med. Coll. Multan) GP Sheff. Police Surg.; Area Steward Med. Charitable Soc. W. Riding Co. York; Med. Office S. Yorks. Br. Brit. Red Cross Soc. Socs: BMA (Chairm. & Hon. Treas. Sheff. Div.); Overseas Doctors Assn. (Sec. Sheff. Div.); Life Mem. Brit. Red Cross Soc. Prev: Regist. (Neurosurg.) N. Staffs. Hosp. Centre Stoke-on-Trent; Regist. (Psychiat.) Middlewood Hosp. Sheff.; SHO (Gen. Surg.) Ryhope Gen. Hosp.

CHAVASSE, Steven John, Surg. Lt. RN 1 Mill Street, Torrington EX38 8AL — MB BS 1985 Lond.; BA Oxf. 1982.

CHAVDA, Dinesh Bawalal Harperbury Hospital, Radlett WD7 9HQ — MB BS Rajasthan 1970; DPM Eng. 1981. (Sardar Patel Med. Coll. Bikaner) Assoc. Specialist (Psychiat.) Honzon NHS Trust Harperbury Radlett WD7 9HQ; Locum Cons. Psychiat. S. Beds Community Trust Luton. Socs: Assoc. Fell. Internat. Coll. Psychosomatic Med.; Indian Doctors Assn. Prev: Regist. (Psychiat.) Horton Hosp. Epsom & Luton & Dunstable Hosp.

CHAVDA, Jagdishchandra Lavjibhai Royal Halifax Infirmary, Free School Lane, Halifax HX1 2YP Tel: 01422 357222 Fax: 01422 360525; 21 Ambleton Way, Queensbury, Bradford BD13 2DZ Tel: 01274 884060 Fax: 01274 884060 Email: jagdish.chavda@tesco.net — MB BS 1977 Gujarat; MS (Orthop.) Gujarat 1982; LMSSA Lond. 1985; DRCOG 1987; Cert Managem Health.Servs.OU 1998. (B.J. Med. Coll. Ahmedabad, India) Staff Grade Hosp. Pract. (A & E) Roy. Halifax W.Yorks Infirm. Socs: Assoc. Fell. Fac. Accid. & Emerg. Med.; Brit. Assn. Emerg. Med.; Fell.Roy.Soc.Med.Lond. Prev: Princip. GP St. Leonards Lincs; Regist. (Orthop. & Spinal Injuries) Civil Hosp. India.

CHAVDA, Swarupsinh Vinodchandra Tel: 0121 627 2577 Fax: 0121 627 2578 Email: svchavda@doctors.org.uk; West Barn, Whitehouse Farm, Lutley Lane, Hayley Green, Halesowen B63 1EZ — MB ChB 1975 Nairobi; FRCR Eng. 1983; DMRD Eng. 1982. Cons. Radiol. W. Midl. RHA.

CHAVE, Helen Sally Salisbury Health Carer NHS Trust Hosp, Odstock, Salisbury Tel: 01722 336262, 020 2040 2402; 40 Wilman Way, Harvard Heights, Salisbury SP2 8QS Email: h.s.chave@btinternet.com — MB BS 1987 Lond.; DM 2000 Southampton; FRCS 2000 Gen Surg.; FRCS Eng. 1992. (St. Geo. Hosp. Med. Sch.) Cons. (Gen. Surg.) Salisbury NHS Health Care Trust. Socs: Roy. Soc. Med. Prev: Wessex Registra Rotat.

CHAVE, Toby Alexander Department of Dermatology, Leicester Royal Infirmary, Infirmary Square, Leicester LE1 5WW — MB ChB 1994 Sheff.; MRCP Ryal Coll. Of Phys., Lond. 1999. Specialsit Regist., Dermat., Leicester Roy. Infirm.. Prev: Sen. Ho. Off., Dermat., Univ. Hosp. of Wales; Sen. Ho. Off., (Med.) Roy. Devon & Exeter Hosp., Exeter; Res. Med. Off. Bundaberg Base Hosp. Qu.sland, Australia.

CHAVE-COX, Clement (retired) 1 Rayleigh Road, Harrogate HG2 8QR — MB BS 1949 Lond.; MRCS Eng. LRCP Lond. 1949. Prev: Ho. Phys. W.m. Hosp.

CHAVE-COX, Richard Vernon The Leeds Road Practice, 49-51 Leeds Road, Harrogate HG2 8AY Tel: 01423 566636; 6 Kenilworth Avenue, Harrogate HG2 8DB Tel: 01423 872333 Email: rchavecox@aol.com — MRCS Eng. LRCP Lond. 1980; Cert. Family Plann. JCC 1983. Forens. Med. Examr. (N. Yorks. Police). Socs: BMA; Assn. Police Surg.; Harrogate Med. Soc. Prev: Community Med. Off. Medway HA; Trainee GP Medway HA VTS; SHO (Paediat.) All St.s Hosp. Chatham.

CHAWDA, Nilesh Jayantilal Whitwick Road Surgery, Whitwick Road, Coalville LE67 3FA Tel: 01530 836507 — MB ChB 1990 Leeds; BSc (Biochem.) Leeds 1987; MRCGP 1994; DRCOG 1994. Princip. in Gen. Pract.; Trainee GP Syston Leic. Prev: SHO (Gen. Med.) Leicester Gen. Hosp.; SHO (O & G & Paediat.) Leicester Roy. Infirm.; SHO (Geriat.) Leicester Gen. Hosp.

CHAWDA, Sanjiv Jayantilal Department of Neuroradiology, National Hospital for Nervous Diseases, Queen Square, London WC1N 3BG; 35 Howberrry Road, Edgware HA8 6SS — MB BCh 1990 Wales; BSc (Hons.) Wales 1987, MB BCh 1990; MRCP Ed. 1993; FRCR 1996. Specialist Regist. (NeuroRadiol.). Prev: Regist. (Radiol.) Welsh Train. Scheme; SHO Rotat. (Med.) Leeds Gen. Infirm.

CHAWDHARY, Satish Burton Hospital NHS Trust, Belvedere Road, Burton-on-Trent DE13 0RB; 19 Scalpcliffe Close, Burton-on-Trent DE15 9AX — MB BS 1977 Delhi; MB BS New Delhi 1977; FRCS Ed. New Delhi 1989; FCOphth. Lond. 1989. Cons. Ophth.

CHAWDHERY, Mr Muhammad Zafar Renal Transplant Unit, Royal London Hospital, Whitechapel, London E1 1BB Tel: 020 7377 7289 Fax: 020 7377 7003; St. Bartholomews Hospital, West Smithfield, London EC1A 7BE Tel: 020 7601 8281 Fax: 020 7601 8529 — MB ChB 1984 Dundee; FRCS Ed. 1990; FRCS Eng. 1989. (Univ. Dundee) Cons. Gen. & Transpl. Surg. Roy. Lond. Hosp. Socs: Fell. Roy. Soc. Med.; Brit. Transpl. Soc. Prev: Sen. Regist. (Surg.) Addenbrooke's Hosp. Camb.; Regist. & Research Fell. Wessex Transpl. Unit St. Mary's Hosp. Portsmouth; Ho. Surg. Ninewells Hosp. Dundee.

CHAWISHLY, Mr Soran Akram Barnet General Hospital, Wellhouse Lane, Barnet EN5 3DJ Tel: 020 8440 5111; 8 Salmon Street, Kingsbury, London NW9 8PN — MB ChB 1973 Baghdad; FRCS Ed. 1994; LMSSA Lond. 1988; DLO RCS 1986. Assoc. Specialist (ENT) Barnet. Gen. Hosp.

CHAWLA, Harpal Singh The Surgery, 176 Milcote Road, Smethwick B67 5BP Tel: 0121 429 1572 Fax: 0121 434 4518 — MB BS 1972 Kashmir.

CHAWLA, Mr Hector Bryson Moray Consulting Rooms, 14 Moray Place, Edinburgh EH36DT Tel: 0131 225 8059 Fax: 0131 225 6749; 73 Morningside Drive, Edinburgh EH3 5NJ Tel: 0131 447 2932 Fax: 0131 447 8110 — MB ChB 1961 St. And.; FRCS Ed. 1968; DO Eng. 1967; DObst RCOG 1964. Cons. Ophth. Roy. Infirm. Edin.; Examr. (Ophth.) RCS Edin. & RCPS Glas. Socs: Ophth. Soc. UK; Club Jules Gonin. Prev: Fell. Retina Serv. N. W.. Univ. Chicago, USA.

CHAWLA, Mr Jagdish Chander Royal Alexandra Hospital NHS Trust, Corsebar Road, Paisley PA2 9PN Tel: 0141 887 9111 Fax: 0141 887 6701; Maryfield, 15 High Calside, Paisley PA2 6BY Tel: 0141 887 3505 — MB BS 1960 Punjab; MB BS Punjab (India) 1960; DO Eng. 1965; FRCS Ed. 1968; FRCOphth 1988. (V.J. Hosp. Amritsar) Hon. Clin. Sen. Lect. Univ. Glas.; Cons. Ophth. Surg. & Clin. Dir. Roy. Alexandra Hosp. Paisley; Examr. for Final FRCS Exam in Ophths. Glas. Socs: Fell. Coll. Ophths.; Panel of Ophth. Med. Pract. to Serve on the NHS; Ophth. Oxf. Congr. & Brit. Med. Assoc. Prev: Sen. Regist. (Ophth.) W.. Infirm. Glas.; Resid. Surg. Off. (Ophth.) Birm. & Midl. Eye Hosp.

CHAWLA, Mr Jagdish Chandra Rookwood Hospital, Fairwater Road, Cardiff CF5 2YN Tel: 029 2056 6281 Fax: 029 2056 6355; 36 Ty Gwyn Road, Penylan, Cardiff CF23 5JG Tel: 029 2048 0103 — MD 1973 Bristol; MB BS Osmania 1956; FRCS Eng. 1965. (Osmania Med. Coll. Hyderabad) Cons. incharge Rehabil. & Spinal Injuries & Sen. Lect. (Rehabil.) Rookwood Hosp. Cardiff. Socs: Internat. Med. Soc. Paraplegia; Brit. Soc. Rehabil. Med. (Counc. Mem.). Prev: Dep. Dir. Avon Stroke Unit Frenchay Hosp. Bristol; Sen. Regist. (Neurosurg.) Frenchay Hosp. Bristol; Assoc. Prof. Surg. Univ. Malaya.

CHAWLA, Mr Jagmohan Singh Consultant Ophthalmic Surgeon, North East London Eye DepartmentGubbing Lane, Harold Wood Hospital, Gubbins Lane, Harold, Romford RM3 0BE — MB BS 1978 Delhi; FRCOphth 2001; FRCS Glas. 1994. Cons. Opthalmologist Roy. N.E. Lond. Eye Partnership - Harold Wood Hosp. Romford - Whipps Cross Univ. Hosp., Leytomstone, Lond. Socs: UK & Irel. Soc. Cataract & Refractive Surg.; Amer. Soc. of Cataract & Refractive Surg.; Europ. Soc. of Cataract & Refractive Surg. Prev: Cons. Ophth. Surg. Roy. Albert Edwd. Infirm. Wigan.

CHAWLA, Kishore Kumar 73 Bower Way, Cippenham, Slough SL1 5HJ Tel: 01628 545647 — MB BS 1985 Punjab; MB BS Punjabi 1985. Assoc. Specialist Community Alcohol Team, Merton, Sutton & Wandsworth HA. Prev: Staff Grade Psychiat. Community Alcohol Team Merton, Sutton & Wandsworth HA; Regist. (Psychiat.) M. Glam. HA.

CHAWLA, N K Breckfield Road North Surgery, 141 Breckfield Road North, Liverpool L5 4QU Tel: 0151 263 6534.

CHAWLA, Mr Om Parkash Luton & Dunstable Hospital NHS Trust, Lewsey Road, Luton LU4 0DZ Tel: 01582 497102 Fax: 01582 497031; Lotus Lodge, Hicks Road, Markyate, St Albans AL3 8LW Tel: 01582 497102 Fax: 01582 84009 — MB BS 1973 Panjab; MB BS Panjab l973; MS Chandigrh 1976; FRCS Ed. 1983; MNAMS 1979. Cons. ENT Surg. Luton & Dunstable NHS Hosp. Socs: Joseph Soc. Europ. Acad. Facial Surg.; BMA; Brit. Assn. Otol. Head & Neck Surg. Prev: Sen. Regist. Soton. Univ. Hosp. & Poole Gen. Hosp.

CHAWLA, Mr Om Prakash Derbyshire Fire Authority, Occ. Health Unit, The Old Hall, Burtan Road, Derby DE23 6EH Tel: 01332 771221 Fax: 01332 270360; 98 Chartwell Avenue, Wingerworth, Chesterfield S42 6SP Tel: 01246 558242 — MB BS Lucknow 1963; MS Delhi 1971; FRCS Ed. 1978; T(GP) 1991; AFOM RCP Lond. 1989. (King Geo. Med. Coll. Lucknow) Sen. Occupat. Health Phys. Derbysh. Fire Auth., Derby. Socs: Soc. Occupat. Med.; Assn. Local Auth. Med. Advisor. Prev: Occupat. Health Phys. & SCMO N. Derbysh. HA; Regist. (Gen. Surg.) Barnsley Dist. Gen. Hosp.; Regist. & SHO (Gen. Surg.) Chesterfield Roy. Hosp.

CHAWLA, Punita Tanya 41 The Meadows, Lyndhurst SO43 7EJ — MB BS 1990 Lond.; FRCR 1999; MRCP (UK) 1994; MRCGP 1994; DRCOG 1992. Cons. (Radiol.) Portsmouth Hosps. NHS Trust. Prev: Trainee GP Soton. VTS; Regist. (Radiol.) Soton. Univ. Hosps.

CHAWLA, Rajinder Lal The Surgery, 262 Stanstead Road, Forest Hill, London SE23 1DE Tel: 020 8699 8261 — MB BS 1956 Punjab; MB BS Punjab (India) 1956; DPH Eng. 1963, DIH 1964; DTM & H Liverp. 1964. (Amritsar) Prev: SHO Gen. Hosp. Ashton-under-Lyne, W. Hill Hosp. Dartford & Gravesend Hosp.

CHAWLA, Suman The Surgery, 176 Milcote Road, Smethwick B67 5BP Tel: 0121 429 1572 Fax: 0121 434 4518 — MB BS 1974 Jammu & Kashmir; MB BS 1974 Jammu & Kashmir.

CHAWLA, Vimla Chawla, 1A Welbeck Drive, Wingerworth, Chesterfield S42 6SN Tel: 01246 276590; 98 Chartwell Avenue, Wingerworth, Chesterfield S42 6SP Tel: 01246 558242 — MD 1970 (Padeat.) Delhi; MB BS Jabalpur 1966; DCH Dub. RCPSI 1977; T(GP) 1991. Prev: Clin. Med. Off. (Community Paediat.) N. Derbysh. HA; Regist. (Paediat.) Roy. Hosp. Chesterfield.

CHAWNER, Judith Mary (retired) 35 St Faith's Road, St. Cross, Winchester SO23 9QD Tel: 01962 868128 — MRCS Eng. LRCP Lond. 1961. Clin. Med. Off. Winchester HA. Prev: Clin. Med. Off. Gwynedd AHA.

CHAY, Siew Tuck Stephen 58 Shotley Avenue, Sunderland SR5 1PS — MB BS 1989 Newc.

CHAYTOR, Robert Geoffrey (retired) Flat 3 Heatherlea, Allendale, Hexham NE47 9BT Tel: 01434 683605 — MB BS 1944 Durh.; DLO Eng. 1951. Prev: Cons. (ENT) Newc. AHA (T).

CHAZAN, Albert Anthony (retired) Flat 8, Matlock Crt., 45 Abbeyy Road, London NW8 0AB Tel: 020 7624 1470 — MB ChB 1947 Glas.; FRCPath 1970. Prev: Med. Off. Dept. Clin. Path. Lond. Clinic.

CHAZAN, Nathaniel 28 Broomburn Drive, Newton Mearns, Glasgow G77 5JF — MB ChB 1952 Glas.

CHE ABDULLAH, Shahrin Tarmizi 11 Wimberley Houses, Glamis Dr, Dundee DD2 1UP — MB ChB 1997 Dundee.

CHEADLE, Brian Department of Medicine For The Elderly, St. Thomas's Hospital, Shaw Heath, Stockport SK3 8BL Tel: 0161 483 1010; 102 Grange Road, Bramhall, Stockport SK7 3QB — MB ChB 1978 Sheff.; MRCP (UK) 1984. Cons. Phys. Stockport HA. Socs: Brit. Geriat. Soc.; BMA. Prev: Sen. Regist. (Geriat. Med.) Stockport HA.; Regist. (Geriat. Med.) St. Geo. Hosp. Lond.; Regist. (Gen. Med.) Wharfedale Dist. Gen. Hosp. Otley.

CHEADLE, Colin Reeve (retired) Chilcomb, Jubilee Hill, Pelynt, Looe PL13 2JZ — MB BS Lond. 1947; DObst RCOG 1950. Prev: Exam. Med. Off. DHSS.

CHEAH, Edson Kit Leng Department of Obstetrics and Gynaecology, Kings College Hospital, Bessemer Road, London N12 8HP Email: edson@psionworld.net; 7 Holden Road, North Finchley, London N12 8HP Email: edson.psionworld.net — MB BS 1989 Lond.; MRCOG 19975. (Guy's Hosp. Lond.) Specialist Regist. Kings Coll. Hosp. Lond.

CHEAH, Eu-Gene 54 Apsley House, Finchley Road, London NW8 0NY — BM BCh 1990 Oxf.; MRCP (UK) 1994; FRCOphth 1996. (Oxf.)

CHEAH, Fook Sen 463 Falls Road, Belfast BT12 6DD — MB BCh BAO 1963 Belf.; DObst RCOG 1965.

CHEAH, Mr Kevin Seng Khoon Hartshill Orthopaedic Centre, Hartshill Road, Stoke-on-Trent ST4 7NZ — MB ChB 1984 Sheff.; MB ChB Sheff. l984; FRCS Eng. 1988. Regist. (Orthop.) Robt. Jones & Agnes Hunt Hosp. OsW.ry.

CHEAH, Ping Ye Paediatric Cardiology Department, Royal Hospital for Sick Children, Yorkhill, Glasgow G3 8SJ — MB BS 1989 Malaya.

CHEAH, Sow Shen 6 Killynure Wood, Enniskillen BT74 6FR — MB BCh BAO 1979 Dub. (TC Dub.)

CHEAH, Teng-Siam 54 Carlton Road, Hale, Altrincham WA15 8RL — MB ChB 1967 Ed.; MRCPsych 1977; DPM Ed. 1974. Cons. (Child & Adolesc. Psychiat.) Stockport AHA. Prev: SHO (Psychiat.) Bangour Village Hosp. Broxburn.

CHEAL, (Angela) Carol Wells Park Practice, 1 Wells Park Road, London SE26 6JQ Tel: 020 8699 2840 Fax: 020 8699 2552 Email: carol.cheal@GP-g85114.nhs.uk — MB BChir 1980 Camb.; MFFP 1993; MB BChir Camb. 1979; MA Camb. 1980; DRCOG 1982; DCH Eng. 1981. (Camb. Univ. & King's Coll. Hosp. Lond.) p/t Gen. Practitioner; Family Plann. Instruc. Doctor MFFP. Socs: MEDACT; Fell. RSM; Mem. NHS Support Federat.

CHEAL, Heather Jane Bethel, 46 Greenhill Way, Haywards Heath RH17 7SQ Tel: 01444 457263 — MB BS 1994 Lond.; DFFP 1997; DRCOG 1996. GP Retainer, Silverdale Rd. Surg., Burgess Hill. Socs: Fac. Family Plann. Prev: SHO (Psychiat.) P.ss Roy. Hosp. Haywards Heath; SHO (Paediat.) Roy. Alexandra Hosp. for Sick Childr. Brighton; SHO (A & E) & (Med.) P.ss Roy. Hosp. Haywards Heath.

CHEALE, Susan Margaret Park Surgery, 25 The Park, Yeovil BA20 1DG Tel: 01935 474196 Fax: 01935 411429; The Long House, Orchard Corner, West Mudford, Yeovil BA21 5TJ — MB BCh 1972 Wales; BSc (Hons.) Bristol 1969; DObst RCOG 1974.

CHEALES, Nicholas Alexander Woodlands Health Centre, Allington Road, Paddock Wood, Tonbridge TN12 6AR Tel: 0189 283 3331; 127 Bush Road,, East Peckham, Tonbridge TN12 5LL Tel: 01622 871914 — MB BS 1981 Lond.; MRCGP 1986; DRCOG 1985; DCH 1984.

CHEAM, Eddy Wooi Su Department of Anaesthetics, Chesterfield & North, Derbyshire Royal Hospital, Chesterfield S44 5BL — MB ChB 1987 Bristol. SHO (Anaesth.) Hillingdon Hosp. Prev: SHO (A & E) Frenchay Hosp. Bristol; SHO (Gen. & Geriat. Med.) Hemel Hempstead Gen. Hosp.; Ho. Phys. (Gen. Geriat. Med. & Infec. Dis.) Ham Green Hosp. Bristol.

CHEANG, Pei Pei 45 Merthyr Street, Cathays, Cardiff CF24 4JL — MB BCh 1998 Wales.

CHEATER, Lyndsay Susan 9 Frost Dr, Irby, Wirral CH61 4XL — MB ChB 1997 Birm.

CHEATLE, Mr Timothy Ross 121 The Street, Old Costessey, Norwich NR8 5DF — MB ChB 1980 Dub.; MCh Dub. 1992; FRCSI 1985. (Univ. Dub. Trinty Coll.) Cons. Gen. & Vasc. Surg. Norf. & Norwich Hosp. Socs: Surgic. Research Soc.; Eur. Soc. Vasc. Surg.; Roy. Soc. Med. Prev: Sen. Regist. Univ. Coll. & Middlx. Hosps.

CHECINSKI, Kenneth Michael Department of Addictive Behaviour, St. George's Hospital Medical Schoool, Cranmer Terrace, London SW17 0RE Tel: 020 8725 2626 Fax: 020 8725 2914 Email: k.checinski@sghms.ac.uk; Department of Psychiatry, Epsom General Hospital, Dorking Road, Epsom KT18 7EG Tel: 01372 204164 Fax: 01372 202524 — MB BS 1983 Lond.; MA Camb. 1984; MRCPsych 1988. Sen. Lect. (Addic. Behaviour) Univ. Lond. & St. Geo. Hosp. Med. Sch. Lond.; Hon. Cons. (Psychiat.) Pathfinder NHS Trust & Surrey Oaklands NHS Trust. Socs: (Hon. Treas.) Brit. Assn. Social Psychiat.; Soc. Study Addic. Prev: Sen. Regist. (Psychiat.) St. Geo. Hosp. Lond.; Research Fell. (Psychiat.) St. Geo. Hosp. Med. Sch. Lond.; Regist. (Psychiat.) Springfield Hosp. Lond.

CHECKETTS, Matthew Roger University Department of Anaesthesia, Ninewells Hospital & Medical School, Dundee DD1 9SY Tel: 01382 632427 Fax: 01382 644914; The Coach House, Crawford Park, Perth Road, Dunblane FK15 0HA Tel: 01786 825045 Email: m.r.checketts@dundee.ac.uk — MB ChB 1987 Glas.; FRCA 1994. (Glas.) Clin. Lect. (Anaesth.) Ninewells Hosp. & Med. Sch. Dundee. Socs: Assn. GB & Irel. & Europ. Soc. Regional Anaesth. Prev: Research Fell. & Career Regist. (Anaesth.) Univ. Glas.

CHECKETTS, Mr Roger Gilbert 19 The chesters, West Denton, Newcastle upon Tyne NE5 1AF Tel: 0191 565 3973 Email: rogerthebone@yahoo.co.uk — MD 1967 Sheff.; MB ChB 1962; FRCS Eng. 1969. (Sheff.) Hon. Clin. Lect. Univ. Newc.; Cons. (Orthop. Surg.) N.. RHA; Vis. Prof. Sch. Health Sci. Univ. Sunderland. Socs: Fell. Brit. Orthop. Assn. Prev: Sen. Regist. Dept. Orthop. W.. Infirm. Glas.; Research Asst. Dept. Surg. Univ. Sheff.; Rotating Surg. Regist. United Sheff. Hosps.

CHECKLAND, Katherine Harriet Marple Cottage Surgery, 50 Church Street, Marple, Stockport SK6 6BW Tel: 0161 426 0011 Fax: 0161 427 8160.

CHECKLEY, Barbara Hannah Bridget 27 Grampian Court, Aviemore PH22 1TB — MB ChB 1994 Leic.

CHECKLEY, Eleanor Jane 4 Dovecote Mews, Chorlton Cum Hardy, Manchester M21 9HN Tel: 0161 881 7957 Email: ejcheckley@doctors — MB ChB 1993 Manch.; FRCA 1999 Lond. Specialist Regist. (Anaesth.). Socs: Intens. Care Soc.; Assn. of Anaesth.s; Manch. Med. Soc. Prev: Med. Regist.; SHO (Neonat. Surg.); SHO (Anaesth.).

CHECKLEY, Professor Stuart Arthur Deans Office, Institute of Psychiatry, De Crespigny Park, London SE5 8NP Tel: 020 7848 0153 Fax: 020 7703 1646 Email: s.checkley@iop.kcl.ac.uk — BM BCh 1970 Oxf.; BA Oxf. 1967; MRCP (UK) 1973; MRCPsych 1977. Prof. Psychoneuroendocrinol. Inst. Psychiat. Lond. Socs: Fell. Roy. Coll. Psychiat.; Fell. Roy. Coll. Phys. Eng. Prev: Hon. Sen. Lect. Inst. Psychiat. Lond.; Hon. Cons. Maudsley Hosp.

CHEDUMBARUM PILLAY, Ouma Devi 30 Challands Way, Hasland, Chesterfield S41 0ER — MB ChB 1996 Sheff.

CHEE, Lew Chin c/o Department of Anaesthetics, Royal Alexandra Hospital, Paisley Tel: 0141 887 9111 — MB ChB 1992 Glas. SHO (Anaesth.) Roy. Alexandra Hosp. Paisley.

CHEE, Tony Oon Cheok 23 Martinville Park, Belfast BT8 7JH — MB BCh BAO 1994 Belf.

CHEE, Yen Lin Department of Haematology, Aberdeen Royal Infirmary, Aberdeen Tel: 01224 681818 — MB ChB 1993 Glas.; MRCP 1996. Specialist Regist. (Haemat.) Aberd. Roy. Infirm.

CHEE KENG JIN, Anthony 12 Godolphin House, 76 Fellows Road, London NW3 3LG — MB BS 1986 Singapore.

CHEE KWAN YOUNG, Dr Inverclyde Royal Hospital, Greenock PA16 0X Tel: 01475 633777; 33 Eriskay Avenue, Glasgow G77 6XB — MB ChB 1990 Glas. SHO (O & G) Inverclyde Roy. Hosp. Greenock.

CHEEK, Bradley Norman Well Close Square Surgery, Well Close Square, Berwick-upon-Tweed TD15 1LL Tel: 01289 356920 Fax: 01289 356939; Magdalene Fields House, Berwick-upon-Tweed TD15 1NE Tel: 01289 305453 Fax: 01289 356939 — MB ChB 1981 Dundee; FRCGP 1992, M 1985; DRCOG 1984. Clin. Asst. (Rheum.) Berwick; Trainer GP N.umbria VTS; Regional Adviser for Fell.sh. Assessm. N. of Eng. Fac. RCGP. Prev: GP Ldr. N.umbria VTS; Trainee GP Doncaster VTS.

CHEEK, Clare Margaret 142 Wembdon Hill, Wembdon, Bridgwater TA6 7QB — MB BCh 1987 Wales; FRCS Ed. 1992.

CHEEK, Stephen Philip Rocklands, Cannongate Road, Hythe CT21 5PX — MB BS 1975 Lond.; MRCP (UK) 1978. (St. Geo.) Cons. Phys. (Geriat.) Cuckfield Hosp. Sussex. Socs: Brit. Geriat. Soc. Prev: Sen. Regist. (Geriat.) St. Geo. Hosp. Lond.; Regist. (Gen. Med. & Nephrol.) St. Mary's Hosp. Portsmouth; Regist. (Oncol). St. Bart. Hosp. Lond.

CHEEL, Christine Bartley Green Health Centre, Romsley Road, Bartley Green, Birmingham B32 3PR Tel: 0121 477 4300; 18 Margaret Road, Harborne, Birmingham B17 0EU — MB ChB 1980 Birm.; DRCOG 1984.

CHEEMA, Mr Ahmad Masood c/o Dr Naeem Ahmad, Anaesthetic Department The James Paget Hospital, Lowestoft Road Gorleston, Great Yarmouth NR31 6LA — MB BS 1975 Punjab; FRCS Glas. 1988.

CHEEMA, Asad Akram 179 Sorrel Bank, Linton Glade, Croydon CR0 9LZ — MB BS 1994 Lond.

CHEEMA, Harpreet Singh 31 Cumberland Avenue, Fixby, Huddersfield HD2 2JJ — MB BCh 1985 Wales. Trainee GP Huddersfield.

CHEEMA, Joginder Singh 112 Villiers Street, Leamington Spa CV32 5YE Tel: 01926 39460 — MB BS 1974 Jammu & Kashmir. (Govt. Med. Coll. Srinagar)

CHEEMA, Mohammad Nusrullah Hawkesley Health Centre, 375 Shannon Road, Kings Norton, Birmingham B38 9TJ Tel: 0121 486 4200 Fax: 0121 486 4201 — MB BS 1977 Punjab; MB BS 1977 Punjab.

CHEEMA, Mr Rizwan Ahmad 2 Greystone Avenue, Manchester M21 7RP — MB BS 1983 Punjab; FRCS Ed. 1987.

CHEEMA, Saroj Amersham Hospital, Whielden Street, Amersham, Bulk, Cardinal Clinic,, Oakley Speen Road,, Windsor; 4 The Rushes, Maidenhead SL6 1UW Tel: 01628 635960 Fax: 01628 781328 Email: saroj9@aol.com — MRCS Eng. LRCP Lond. 1974; Cert. Prescribed Equiv. Exp. JCPTGP 1981; MRCPsych 1994. (Roy. Free Lond.) Cons., Gen. Adult Psychiat. Socs: Fell. Roy. Soc. Med.; BMA; MPS.

CHEEMA, Surinder Paul Singh 22 Warrenside, Deighton, Huddersfield HD2 1LP — MB BCh 1981 Wales; FRCA 1992; FFA RCSI 1991; DA (UK) 1986.

CHEEROTH, Sajeev Ravi 40 Rushgrove Avenue, London NW9 6QS — MB BS 1994 Lond.

CHEEROTH, Sheila Ajantha 40 Rushgrove Avenue, Colindale, London NW9 6QS — MB BS 1988 Lond.; DCH RCP Lond. 1993. SHO Rotat. (Paediat.) W.m. Childr. Hosp. Lond. Prev: SHO (Cas.) Roy. Free Hosp. Lond.; Ho. Off. (Med.) King Geo. & Barking Hosps. Essex; Ho. Off. (Surg.) Roy. Free Hosp. Lond.

CHEESBROUGH, Andrew John Macfarlane Doctors Surgery, Bates Green Health Centre, Bates Green, Norwich NR5 8YT Tel: 01603 749921 Fax: 01603 741718 Email: wvmpbg@aol.com — MB ChB 1981 Birm.; MRCGP 1995; DTM & H Liverpool.Uni. GP Princ.

CHEESBROUGH, John Stephen Public Health Laboratory, Royal Preston Hospital, Preston PR2 9HG Tel: 01772 710107 Fax: 01772 710152 — MB BS 1977 Lond.; BSc Lond. 1974; MRCP (UK) 1981; MRCPath 1989. Cons. Microbiol. Roy. Preston Hosp. Socs: Brit. Soc. For Antimicrobial Chemother.; Brit. Infec. Soc.; Hosp. Infec. Soc. Prev: Lect. (Med. Microbiol.) Univ. Liverp.; Specialist (Med.) Qu. Eliz. Centr. Hosp. Blantyre, Malawi; Research Fell. Beth Israel Hosp. Boston, USA.

CHEESBROUGH, Marion Frances North West Child & Family Services Team, Seymour House, Seymour Terrace, Liverpool L3 5PE Tel: 0151 707 0101 — BM BS 1979 Nottm.; BMedSci Nottm. 1977; MRCPsych 1983. Cons. Child & Adolesc. Psychiat. Roy. Liverp. Childr. Hosp. Prev: Lect. (Child & Adolesc. Psychiat.) Univ. Liverp.; Sen. Regist. (Child & Adolesc. Psychiat.) Liverp. HA; Gov. Psychiat. Malawi Africa.

CHEESBROUGH, Michael John 4 Occupation Road, Lindley, Huddersfield HD3 3AZ — LMSSA 1968 Lond.; MB BChir Camb. 1969; MA Camb. 1969, BA 1965; FRCP Lond. 1988; MRCP (UK) 1973. (Guy's) Cons. Dermat. Huddersfield NHS Trust. Socs: BMA. Prev: Cons. Dermat. Notts. AHA (T).

CHEESE, John Ayrton (retired) Oakworth, 60 London Road, Canterbury CT2 8JZ Tel: 01227 462901 — MB BS Lond. 1948; MRCS Eng. LRCP Lond. 1948; MRCGP 1962; DCH Eng. 1954. Prev: Ho. Phys. Hosp. Sick Childr. Gt. Ormond St. & Middlx. Hosp.

CHEESE, Nicholas Edward The Lanes Medical Practice, Plough Lane, Stoke Poges, Slough SL2 4JW Tel: 01753 662244 Fax: 01753 665200; Roselea, 18 Rylett Crescent, London W12 9RL Tel: 020 8746 2146 Fax: 020 8746 2116 — MB BS 1981 Lond.; MRCS Eng. LRCP Lond. 1981. (Middlx. Hosp.) Private Gen. Practitioner at the La.s Med. Pract., Plough La., Stoke Poges. Socs: Brit. Travel Health Assn. Prev: Princip. in Gen. Pract.; In Partnership, Crown St. Surg., Acton, Lond.

CHEESEMAN, Sarah Jane 28 Alexandra Close, Framwellgate Moor, Durham DH1 5ED — MB ChB 1998 Ed.; MB ChB Ed 1998.

CHEESEMAN, Susan Lara 7 Derby Road, Eastwood, Nottingham NG16 3PA — MB ChB 1991 Leeds.

CHEESMAN, Ann Louise 11 Lancastre Grove, Leeds LS5 3DY — MB ChB 1994 Leeds. SHO (Med.) York Dist. Hosp.

CHEESMAN, Professor Anthony David ENT Unit, Wellington Hospital, Wellington Place, London NW8 9LE Tel: 020 7483 5084 Fax: 020 7483 5052 Email: drtonycheesman@cs.com; Tel: 020 7837 0709 Fax: 020 7837 1067 Email: drtonycheesman@cs.com — BSc (Hons.) Physiol. Lond. 1962, MB BS 1965; FRCS (Otolarngol.) Eng. 1970; MRCS Eng. LRCP Lond. 1965; FRCSLT (Hon.) 1996. (Char. Cross) p/t Cons. Neurotologist Nat. Hosp. for Neurol. and Neurosurg., Qu. Sq., Lond.; Hon. Sen. Lect. Gough Cooper Dept. Neurosurg. Nat. Hosp. Lond.; Hon. Cons. & Vis. Prof. Dept. OtoLaryngol., Barts & The Lond. NHS Trust. Socs: Fell. Roy. Soc. Med. (Ex Pres. Sect. of Laryngol. & Rhinology); Internat. Skull Base Soc. (Ex. Hon. Sec.); Brit. Skull Base Soc. (Ex Pres.). Prev: Gen. Manager Roy. Nat. Throat Nose & Ear Hosp.; Med. Dir. Roy. Throat Nose & Ear Hosp. NHS Trust; Lect. Otolaryng. Univ. W. Indies & Cons. Otolaryngol. Univ. Hosp. W. Indies, Jamaica.

CHEESMAN, Anthony Morgan 2 Hambledon Road, Bournemouth BH6 5PH — MB BS 1998 Lond.; MB BS Lond 1998.

CHEESMAN, Benjamin Paul Riverview Practice, Wick Medical Centre, Martha Terrace, Wick KW1 5EL Tel: 01955 602355 Fax: 01955 602434; Hazelrigg, Coronation St, Wick KW1 5LS — MB ChB 1992 Aberd.; MRCGP 1996. (Aberd.)

CHEESMAN, Caroline Anne 11 Murrayfield Gardens, Edinburgh EH12 6DG — MB ChB 1998 Manch.; MB ChB Manch 1998.

CHEESMAN, Clare Ann Spring House, St Mary's Lane, Hertford SG14 2LF — MB BS 1993 Lond.

CHEESMAN, Mark Geoffrey Department of Medicine for the Elderly, Southmead Hospital, Westbury-on-Trym, Bristol BS10 5NB Tel: 0117 959 5376 Fax: 0117 959 5376 Email: cheeseman_m@southmead.swest.nhs.uk; 16 Russell Grove, Westbury Park, Bristol BS6 7UE Tel: 0870 133 1255 Fax: 0870 133 1255 Email: mark@stilton54.freeserve.co.uk — MB BCh 1977 Wales; MD Leic. 1993; FRCP Lond. 1996; MRCP (UK) 1980. (Univ. Wales Coll. Med.) Cons. Phys. (Geriat.) S.mead Health Servs. NHS Trust Bristol; Hon. Sen. Lect. (Med. & Geriat.) Univ. Bristol. Socs: (Exec. Comm. & Regional Sec.) Christian Med. Fell.sh.; Fell. Roy. Soc. Med.; Brit. Soc. Echocardiogr. Prev: Sen. Regist. (Geriat. & Med.) Frenchay Hosp. Bristol; Lect. (Med.) Univ. Hosp. Wales Cardiff; Clin. Research Fell. Groby Rd. Hosp. Leicester.

CHEESMAN, Toby Steven 264 Clarendon Park Road, Leicester LE2 3AG — MB ChB 1995 Leic.

CHEESMOND, Eugenie Hilda Dorothy (retired) 1 Deardengate, Haslingden, Rossendale BB4 5QN Tel: 01706 216215 — MB ChB 1944 Cape Town; DPH Manch. 1962.

CHEETHAM, Anna Marie 18 Florence Close, Atherstone CV9 1HR — BM BS 1997 Nottm.

CHEETHAM, Anne Carol Hellesdon Medical Practice, 343 Reepham Road, Hellesdon, Norwich NR6 5QJ Tel: 01603 486602 Fax: 01603 401389 — MB ChB 1979 Sheff.; MRCGP 1983.

CHEETHAM, Carolyn Elizabeth Westover Surgery, Western Terrace, Falmouth TR11 4QJ Tel: 01326 212120 — MB BS 1978 Newc.; DCH Lond. 1980.

CHEETHAM, Catherine 99 South Mossley Hill Road, Liverpool L19 9BQ — MB ChB 1997 Sheff.

CHEETHAM, Christine Marion 'Pantiles', 34 Deepdale Avenue, Scarborough YO11 2UF — MB ChB 1947 Manch. (Manch.)

CHEETHAM, Christopher Henry Breezemount, Pretoria Road, High Wycombe HP13 6QW Tel: 01494 528692 Fax: 01494 528692 — MB BChir 1963 Camb.; FRCP Lond. 1980, M 1969; MRCPCH 1996; DObst RCOG 1966; DCH Eng. 1967. (St. Thos.) Cons. Paediat. Wycombe Gen. Hosp. Prev: Sen. Regist. (Paediat.) King's Coll. Hosp.; Regist. (Paediat.) Fulham Hosp.; Resid. Med. Off. Qu. Eliz. Hosp. Childr. Hackney.

CHEETHAM, David Reynolds 14 Burlington Road, Isleworth TW7 4LY — MB BS 1971 Lond.; BA Manch. 1959; MRCOG 1979.

CHEETHAM, Drostan Ralph 11 Christchurch Road, Cheltenham GL50 2NY — MB BS 1994 Lond.

CHEETHAM, Edward Dixon 8 Church Green, Warburton, Lymm WA13 9SS — MB ChB 1988 Liverp.; FRCA 1994.

CHEETHAM, Emma Jane 50 Brock End, Portishead, Bristol BS20 8AS — BM 1991 Soton.; MRCGP 1996; DFFP 1995; DRCOG 1995. GP Asst.

CHEETHAM, Jane Elizabeth 23 Christchurch Road, Winchester SO23 9SU — MB BS 1986 Lond.; BA Oxf. 1983; MRCP (UK) 1991; FRCR 1993. Cons. Radiol. Roy. Hants. Co. Hosp. Winchester. Prev: Sen. Regist. (Diagn. Radiol.) Soton. Univ. Hosps. Trust; Regist. (Radiol.) St. Geo. Hosp. Lond.

CHEETHAM, Jeffrey Nigel Humphrey 38 Linthurst Road, Blackwell, Bromsgrove B60 1QH — MB ChB 1983 Birm.; MRCGP 1987; DRCOG 1986.

CHEETHAM, Marjorie Evelyn The Shieling, Mill Lane, Rainhill, Prescot L35 6NG — MB ChB 1930 Liverp.; MB ChB (Hons.) Liverp. 1930. (Liverp.) Mem. Liverp. Med. Inst. Prev: Ho. Surg. & Cas. Off. Roy. Infirm. Liverp.; Res. Med. Off. Alder Hey Childr. Hosp.

CHEETHAM, Mark James 30 Glentworth Avenue, Oswestry SY10 9PZ — MB BS 1993 Lond.

CHEETHAM, Mary 91 Ferry Road, New Marston, Oxford OX3 0EX — MB ChB 1961 Ed.; DPM Eng. 1967, DA 1963. Prev: Sen. Regist. Child Guid. Clinic King's Coll. Hosp. Lond.; SHO Roy. Edin. Hosp.; Regist. Springfield Hosp. Lond.

CHEETHAM, Paul Veor Surgery, South Terrace, Camborne TR14 8SN Tel: 01209 612626 — MB BS Lond. 1968. (St. Bart.)

***CHEETHAM, Philippa Jayne** 26 The Grove, Little Aston, Sutton Coldfield B74 3UB Tel: 0121 353 4190 — MB ChB 1996 Bristol; MB ChB (Hons.) Bristol 1996.

CHEETHAM, Robert Benjamin Midtown Farm House, Beckermet CA21 2YB — MB BS 1991 Lond.

CHEETHAM, Timothy David Department of Child Health, Royal Victoria Infirmary, Queen Victoria Road, Newcastle upon Tyne NE1 4LP — MB ChB 1985 Leic.; BSc Leic. 1981, MD 1996; MRCP (UK) 1989. Sen. Lect. (Paediat.) Dept. Child Health Univ. Newc. Prev: Regist. (Paediat.) Hull Roy. Infirm.; Research Fell. John Radcliffe Hosp. Headington; Clin. Lect. (Paediat.) Univ. Camb.

CHEFFINS, Edward Michael (retired) St. Fillans, 30 Common Lane, Hemingford Abbots, Huntingdon PE28 9AN Tel: 01480 469947 — MB BS 1941 Lond.; MB BS (Hons., Dist. Applied Pharmacol. & Therap.) Lond. 1941; FRCPI 1957, M 1951. Hon. Cons. Phys. (Chest Dis.) Addenbrooke's Hosp. Camb. Prev: Cons. Chest Phys. Cambs. AHA (T).

CHEGWIDDEN, Richard John Donald 25 Barrow Hedges Way, Carshalton SM5 3LL; 153 Cannon Hill Lane, London SW20 9BZ — MB BS 1969 Lond.; MRCS Eng. LRCP Lond. 1969; DObst RCOG 1972. (King's Coll. Hosp.) Med. Off. Carter Hse. Home Lond. Boro. Merton; Sen. Tutor (Gen. Pract.) St. Geo. Hosp. Med. Sch. Lond.; Course Organiser Trainee Half Day Release Course St. Geo. Hosp. Med. Sch. Lond.; Local Civil Serv. Med. Off.; Chairm. LMC (Merton, Sutton & Wandsworth); Vice-Chairm. FHSA. Socs: GMSC; AUTGP; BMA. Prev: Ho. Surg. (A & E) King's Coll. Hosp. Lond.; Ho. Phys. (Gen. Med.) Dreadnought Seamen's Hosp. Lond.; Ho. Surg. (Obst.) Kingston Hosp.

CHEHATA, Joseph Chehata Gouda The Haywood Hospital, High Lane, Bunslem, Stoke-on-Trent ST6 7AG; 32 Stanbrook Road, Shirley, Solihull B90 4UT — MB ChB 1983 Alexandria; MRCP (UK) 1995. Staff Grade - Rheum. - The Haywood Hosp. - Stoke-On-Trent. Socs: Mem. of BMA; Mem. of Brit. Soc. of Rheum.; Mem. of W. Midl.s Rheum. Soc. Prev: Regist. (Gen. Med. & Rheum.) City Hosp. Birm.; SHO Rotat. (Med.) Mid. Staffs. Hosp.; SHO (c/o Elderly) Aberystywyth Bronglais Gen. Hosp.

CHELL, Mr Julian 21 Elm Avenue, Long Eaton, Nottingham NG10 4LR — BM BS 1988 Nottm.; FRCS Ed. 1993.

CHELL, Paul Barrington Birchdene, 2 Kington Rise, Claverdon, Warwick CV35 8PN Tel: 01926 843833 Fax: 01926 843833 — MB ChB 1986 Birm.; FRCOphth 1991, M 1991; DO RCSI 1990. Specialist Private Surg. (Ophth.). Socs: Amer. Soc. Cataract & Refractive Surgs.; Eur. Soc. Cataract & Refractive Surgs.; UK & Irish Soc. Cataract & Refractive Surgs. Prev: Fell. (Refractive Surg. Cataract Surg. & Cornea) Moorfields Eye Hosp. Lond.

CHELLAPPAH, Mandalanayagam Department of Geriatric Medicine, Pembury Hospital, Tunbridge Wells TN2 4QJ Tel: 01892 823535; Greenacres, 63 Sandown Park, Tunbridge Wells TN2 4RT — MB BS Ceylon 1968; FRCP Lond. 1995; MRCP (UK) 1976; MRCS Eng. LRCP Lond. 1977. (Univ. Ceylon, Peradeniya) Cons. Phys. (Geriat. Med.) Kent & Sussex Weald NHS Trust Tunbridge Wells. Socs: Fell. Roy. Soc. Med.; Brit. Geriat. Soc. Prev: Sen. Regist. (Geriat. Med.) W. Middlx. Univ. Hosp. Isleworth; Sen. Regist. (Geriat. Med.) NW (St. Mary's) Health Dist. (T); Resid. (Internal Med.) Mercy Hosp. Buffalo, USA.

CHELLARAM HATHIRAMANI, Karuna Gillaine 48 Australia Road, Gabalfa, Cardiff CF14 3DB — MB BCh 1998 Wales.

CHELLIAH, Janet Vasanthi No 92 Flat 5 The Cut, Waterloo, London SE1 8LN — MB BS 1993 Flinders; DRCOG RCOG 1998; MRCOG RCOG 1999.

CHELLIAH, Patrick Jogendran 18 Caversfield Close, Littleover, Derby DE23 7SR Tel: 01332 517644 — MB BS 1966 Ceylon; FRCOphth 1990, M 1980; DO Eng. 1980. Assoc. Specialist (Ophth.) Derbysh. Roy. Infirm. Derby. Socs: Med. Protec. Soc.; Intraocular Implant Soc. Prev: Regist. (Ophth.) Roy. Surrey Co. Hosp. Guildford; SHO (Ophth.) Qu. Mary's Hosp. Sidcup & Roy. Surrey Co. Hosp. Guildford.

CHELLINGSWORTH, Miriam Claire (retired) Helen Ley Court, Bericote Road, Blackdown, Leamington Spa CV32 6QP Tel: 01926 303909 — BM 1979 Soton.; DM Soton. 1992; FRCP Lond. 1996; MRCP (UK) 1982. Prev: Cons. Phys. (c/o Elderly) M. Staffs. Gen. Hosp. NHS Trust.

CHELVARAJAH, Ramesh 9 Addison House, Kings Drive, Eastbourne BN21 2YD — MB BS 1996 Lond.

CHEN, Alexander Wai Ying 7 Ruxley Lane, West Ewell, Epsom KT19 0JB — MB BS 1997 Lond.

CHEN, Benadict 7 Ruxley La, Epsom KT19 0JB — BM 1997 Soton.

CHEN, Cong Xiao Flat 14, 53 Kent Road, Glasgow G3 7BL — MB ChB 1993 Ed.

CHEN, Constance Elizabeth Chorlton Health Centre, 1 Nicolas Road, Chorlton, Manchester M21 9NJ Tel: 0161 881 7941 Fax: 0161 861 7567; 54 Woburn Drive, Hale, Altrincham WA15 8NA — MB ChB 1979 Manch.; DRCOG 1982; DCH Eng. 1982. Prev: Trainee GP Timperley; SHO (O & G) Pk. Hosp. Manch.; SHO (Paediat.) Pk. Hosp. Manch.

CHEN, Fabian Fu Fah Flat 2, 20 Lennard Road, Croydon CR0 2UL — MB BS 1986 Lond.

CHEN, Mr Hean Choon Derbyshire Royal Infirmary, London Road, Derby DE1 2QY — MB BS 1985 Lond.; FRCS Eng. 1989; FCOphth. 1989; DO RCS Eng. 1989. (Char. Cross Hosp. Medical School) Cons. Ophth. Derbysh. Roy. Infirm. Prev: Sen. Regist. (Ophth.) Manch. Roy. Eye Hosp.; Research Fell. & Hon. Sen. Regist. (Ophth.) Roy. Postgrad. Med. Sch. Hammersmith Hosp. Lond.; Regist. (Ophth.) Char. Cross Hosp. Lond.

CHEN, Klaus Department of Histopathology, Walsgrave Hospital, Clifford Bridge Road, Coventry CV2 2DX — MB ChB 1978 Liverp.; MRCPath 1986.

CHEN, Ruth Pin Tze East London & City Health Authority, Tredegar House, 97-99 Bow Road, London E3 2AN — MRCS Eng. LRCP Lond. 1966. SCMO E. Lond. & The City HA.

CHEN, Simon Derk Meng 87A Sinclair Road, London W14 0NR Tel: 0958 345844 Email: s-chen@rocketmail.com — MB BS 1996 Lond.; BSc (Hons.) Biomed. Science Lond. 1994. (St. George's Hospital Medical School) SHO (Opht.) Addenbrookes Hosp. Camb.

CHEN, Suet Ching Jeanette Neuadd Meirionnydd, Heath Park, Cardiff CF14 4YS — MB BCh 1994 Wales.

CHEN, Terng Fong Worcester Royal Infirmary NHS Trust, Newtown Road, Worcester WR5 1HN Tel: 01905 763333 Fax: 01905 760767; Parkfield Nurseries, Hallow Road, Hallow, Worcester WR2 6PH Tel: 01905 641979 — MB BS 1983 Lond.; MS Lond. 1993; FRCS (Urol.) 1995; FRCS Eng. 1987. Cons. Urol. Surg. Worcester Roy. Infirm. Socs: Brit. Assn. Urol. Surgs.; BAUS. Prev: Sen. Regist. (Urol.) W.. Gen. Hosp. Edin.; Regist. (Urol.) Manch. Roy. Infirm.; Research Regist. (Urol.) & Regist. Rotat. (Surg.) Addenbrooke's Hosp. Camb.

CHEN, Timothy Michael Chi Hoong 15 West Road, Elgin IV30 1SA — MB BS 1996 Lond.

CHEN, Wai 26 Belsize Park, London NW3 4DU — BM 1983 Soton.; MPhil Camb. 1989; MRCP (UK) 1994; MRCPsych 1996; MRCGP 1987; DRCOG 1986; DCH RCP 1985.

CHENEY, Geoffrey Thomas, RD Department of Postraduate Dental Education, Clinical School, Addenbrooke's Hospital, Hills Road, Cambridge CB2 2SP — MB BS 1970 Lond.; BDS 1962; MRCS Eng. LRCP Lond. 1970; FDS RCS Eng. 1966, LDS 1962. (Guy's) Cons. Oral & Maxillofacial Surg. Norf. & Norwich Hosp.; Regional Dir. Postgrad. Dent. Educat.; Surg. Cdr. (D) RNR. Socs: Fell. Brit. Assn. Oral & Maxillofacial Surg.; Fell. Europ. Assn. Cranio Maxillofacial Surg.; BMA. Prev: Sen. Regist. (Oral Surg.) Postgrad. Dent. Inst. E.man Dent. Hosp.; Sen. Regist. (Oral Surg.) E.man Dent. Hosp. & Qu. Vict. Hosp. E. Grinstead.

CHENG, Alfred Flat 15, 55 Shepherds Hill, Highgate, London N6 5QP Fax: 020 8341 0360 — MB BS 1982 Lond.; MD Lond. 1994; MRCP (UK) 1985. Socs: Fell. Roy. Soc. Med.

CHENG, Ben (retired) 8 Rose Garden Close, Edgware HA8 7RF — MB BS 1953 Lond.; MRCP Lond. 1960; FRCPath 1980, M 1968. Prev: Cons. Chem. Path. Watford Gen. Hosp. & Brompton Hosp. Lond.

CHENG, Christine Jih Ching Morriston Hospital, Morriston, Swansea SA2 0QT Tel: 01792 703280; 14 Jervois Lane, Singapore 109190, Singapore Tel: 00 65 65 479 4408 Email: ffioncheng@aol.com — MB BCh 1993 Wales. (University of Wales College of Medicine) Specialist Regist. (Anaesth.) Morriston Hosp. Prev: SHO (Anaesth.) Morriston Hosp.; SHO (Anaesth.) Singleton Hosp.; SHO (Anaesth.) P.ss of Wales Hosp.

CHENG, Chun-Wai Danny 101a Colney Hatch Lane, Muswell Hill, London N10 1LR — MB BS 1997 Lond.

CHENG, Gerald Cheuk Wai 3 Straffan Lodge, 1 Belsize Grove, London NW3 4XE — MB BS 1990 Lond.

CHENG, Mr Hung (cons. rooms), 23 Banbury Road, Oxford OX2 6NX Tel: 01865 513483 Fax: 01865 56303; 199 Woodstock Road, Oxford OX2 7AB Tel: 01865 557826 — MB BChir 1961 Camb.; FRCS Eng. 1967; MRCS Eng. LRCP Lond. 1960; DO Eng. 1964. (Westm.) Cons. Ophth. Oxf. Eye Hosp. Socs: Fell. Roy. Soc. Med. (Ex-Pres. Ophth. Sect.). Prev: Resid. Surg. Off. Moorfields Eye Hosp.; Research Fell. Brit. Diabetic Assn.; Cons. Ophth. Tunbridge Wells Health Dist.

CHENG, Kamen Carolyn 2 Newham Close, Leicester LE4 9NE — BM BS 1994 Nottm.

CHENG, Professor Kar Keung Public Health & Epidemiology Medical School, University of Birmingham, Edgbaston, Birmingham B15 2TT Tel: 0121 414 6757 Fax: 0121 414 7878 Email: k.k.cheng@bham.ac.uk — MB BS 1984 Hong Kong; PhD Camb. 1994; BSc Hong Kong 1982; MRCGP 1991; MFCM 1989; MFPHM RCP (UK) 1989; FFPHM RCP (UK) 1997. Prof. Epidemiol. Univ.

Birm.; Hon. Cons. Community Med. Hong Kong Govt.; Hon. Cons. Pub. Health Med. W. Midl. Health. Prev: Sen. Lect. (Pub. Health & Epidemiol.) Univ. Birm.; Lect. (Community Med.) Univ. Hong Kong.

CHENG, Karen 83 Sandbanks Road, Poole BH14 8BT — MB ChB 1995 Manch.

CHENG, Katharine Yuen Mei Respiratory Unit, Alder Hey Childrens Hospital, Gaton Road, Liverpool L12 2AP Tel: 0151 228 4811 Fax: 0151 252 5929 Email: kcheng@liv.ac.uk; 18 Huntersfield, Shavington, Crewe CW2 5FB Tel: 01270 668508 — MB ChB 1987 Manch.; MRCPI 1992. Specialist Regist. (Paediat.) Mersey Deanery.

CHENG, Kok Ee 19 The Crescent, Belfast BT10 0GJ — MB BCh 1998 Belf.; MB BCh Belf 1998.

CHENG, Mr Koon-Sung 28 Skeggles Close, Huntingdon PE29 6SN Tel: 01480 450526 Fax: 01480 450526 Email: kscheng@huntingdon28.freeserve.co.uk — MB BChir 1990 Camb.; FRCS 2000 (Gen. Surg.); MA Camb. 1991. BA 1987; FRCS Eng. 1996; FRCSI 1994. (Univ. Camb.) Regist. Rotat. (Gen. Surg.) & Specialist Regist. Rotat. N. Thames (E.). Socs: Life Mem. Camb. Univ. Med. Soc. Prev: SPR (Gen. Surg.) Chase Farm Hosp. Enfield; SPR (Gen. Surg.) Roy. Free Hosp. Lond.; SPR (Gen. Surg.) P.ss Alexandra Hosp. Harlow.

CHENG, Mr Leo Hurk-Hang Department of Oral & Maxillofacial Surgery, York District Hospital, Wigginton Rd, York YO31 8HE Tel: 01904 453904; 8 Manor Court, Shadwell, Leeds LS17 8JE Tel: 0113 273 0875 — MB ChB 1991 Birm.; ChB Birm. 1991; FRCS Glas. 1995; BDS Ed. 1985; FDS RCS Eng. 1990; FRCS 1999. Specialist Regist. Rotat. (Oral & Maxillofacial Surg.) Yorks. Socs: BMA & Brit. Soc. Dent. Research; Fell. Brit. Assn. Oral & Maxillofacial Surg. Prev: SHO (Paediat. Neurosurg.) Birm. Childr. Hosp.; SHO Rotat. (Gen. Surg.) Worcester Roy. Infirm.; Ho. Surg. Worcester Roy. Infirm.

CHENG, Muk-Noong Child & Family Psychiatric Clinic, Burgess Hill Clinic, The Brow, Burgess Hill RH15 9BW Tel: 0144 46 248901 Email: mn@chengs.freeserve.co.uk — MB BS Hong Kong 1968; MRCPsych 1972; DPM Eng. 1971. Med. Dir. Ment. Health, Mid-Sussex NHS Trust. Prev: Sen. Regist. (Child & Adolesc. Psychiat.) Wessex Unit for Childr. & Parents Portsmouth; Regist. (Child Psychiat.) Child Guid. Train. Centre Tavistock Clinic Lond.; Regist. (Psychiat.) W Middlx. Hosp. Middlx.

CHENG, Susan Elizabeth 31 Langham Way, Ely CB6 1DZ — MB ChB 1980 Manch.

CHENG, Wei Apartment 4, 89-91 St George's Square, London SW1V 3QW — MB BS 1984 New South Wales.

CHENG, William Chung Wing The Surgery, 241 Westbourne Grove, London W11 2SE Tel: 020 7229 5800 Fax: 020 7243 2058 — MB BS 1973 Lond.; FFOM 2001 (Dublin); LLM 2000 (Cardiff); MD 1999 (Lond.); FRCP 2001 (Lond.); MRCP (UK) 1977; MRCS Eng. LRCP Lond. 1973; MFOM RCPI Dub. 1995; AFOM RCP Lond. 1994; DTM & H RCP Lond. 1996; MBA Open Univ. 1996. (Univ. Coll. Hosp.) Hon. Cons. in Occupat.al Med., Medway NHS Trust (Gillingham, Kent) 2001.

CHENG, Zelda 83 Sandbanks Road, Poole BH14 8BT — MB BCh 1992 Wales.

CHENGAPPA, Kokkalera Subbaiah (retired) 95 Coombe Lane, London SW20 0BD — MB BS 1953 Madras. Prev: Assoc. Specialist (A & E) N. Manch. HA.

CHENNELLS, Paul Michael 2A Grange View Gardens, Leeds LS17 8NL — MB BS 1975 Newc.; FRCR 1981; DMRD Eng. 1980. Cons. Radiol. Leeds Gen. Infirm.; Hon. Lect. Univ. Leeds.

CHEONG, Benjamin Yau Chuen 20 Muel Famall View, Otterspool, Liverpool L17 5ET — MB ChB 1994 Liverp.; MRCP (UK) 1997. (Univ. Liverp. Med. Sch.) Clin. Asst. (Cardiol.) Aintree Cardiac Centre Fazakerley Hosp. Liverp.; Specialist Regist. Cardiol. Roy. Hallamshire Hosp., Sheff. Socs: Founding Mem. Brit. Soc. Heart Failure. Prev: SHO & Ho. Off. Fazakerley Hosp. Liverp.; Hon. Clin. Fell. Regional Cardiothoracic Centre Liverp.

CHEONG, Fook Meng 20 Chandos Way, Golders Green, London NW11 7HF Tel: 020 8458 4941 — MB BS 1990 Lond. SHO (Ophth.) Roy. Lond. Hosp. Prev: SHO (Neurosurg.) Nat. Hosp. Neurol. & Neurosurg. Qu. Sq. Lond.; SHO (A & E) W.m. Hosp. Lond.

CHEONG, Percy John Hing (retired) 1230 Yardley Wood Road, Shirley, Solihull B90 1JX Tel: 0121 474 3020 — LMSSA 1952 Lond. Prev: GP Birm.

CHEONG-LEEN, Mr Philip The Croft, West Drive, Carshalton SM5 4EL — MB ChB 1964 Aberd.; FRCS Ed. 1971. Cons. Orthop. Surg. Epsom Gen. Hosp. Socs: Fell. BOA. Prev: Sen. Regist. (Orthop.) St. Geo. Hosp. Lond.; Clin. Lect. Univ. Hong Kong; Ho. Surg. Aberd. Roy. Infirm.

CHEONG-LEEN, Richard Central Eye Service, Central Middlesex Hospital, Deton Lane, London NW10 7NS Tel: 020 8965 5733; Flat 6, 9-11 Bloomsbury Square, London WC2A 2CP Tel: 020 7831 6985 Fax: 020 7831 4775 Email: riccleen@easynet.co.uk — MB BS 1996 Lond. SHO Ophth. Sch. Centr. Middlx. Hosp. Prev: SHO Ophthlmology, St Thomas Hosp.; SHO A&E Mayday Hosp.

CHEONGVEE, Evelyn Siang Lean Cardinal Clinic, Bishop's Lodge, Oakley Green, Windsor SL4 5UL — MB BCh BAO 1962 NUI; MRC Psych 1981; DPM Eng. 1967. (Univ. Coll. Dub.) Prev: Sen. Regist. (Psychiat.) St. Clement's Hosp. Lond. & Lond. Hosp.

CHEOW, Heok Keong 18 Tolkien Way, Kingswood, Stoke-on-Trent ST4 7SJ — MB ChB 1993 Dundee; MRCP 1997. Specialist Regist. (Clin. Radiol.) Bristol. Roy. Infirm. Socs: Med. Protec. Soc. Prev: SHO (Gen. Med.) Manch. Roy. Infirm.; SHO (Gen. Med.) Preston Acute Hosps.; Ho. Off. (Med.) Ninewells Hosp. Dundee.

CHERIAN, Annie 79 Pimmcroft Way, Sale M33 2LA Tel: 0161 969 9911 — MB ChB 1990 Ed. SHO (Haemat.) Qu. Eliz. Hosp. Birm. Socs: BMA & Christian Med. Fell.sh. Prev: SHO Rotat. (Med.) Wrightington Trust Hosp. & Leigh Infirm.; SHO (Gen. Med. & Acute Geriat.) W.morland Gen. Hosp. Kendal; Ho. Off. (Gen. Med.) Blackburn.

CHERIAN, Ruby 79 Pimmcroft Way, Sale M33 2LA — MB ChB 1995 Manch.

CHERIDJIAN, Victor-Elie Pepe Dimitri C (retired) Somerville Medical Practice, 4 Somerville, Poulton Road, Wallasey CH44 9ED Tel: 0151 638 9333 Fax: 0151 637 0291 — MB BCh 1969 Ain Shams; MRCS Eng. LRCP Lond. 1973; FRCOG 1998. Clin. Asst. (Colposcopy) Arrowe Pk. Hosp. Wirral. Prev: Dep. Police Surg. Merseyside Police.

CHERIYAN, Joseph Addenbrooke's Hospital NHS Trust, Hills Road, Cambridge CB2 2QQ Email: cheriyanj@aol.com; 26 Heathcroft, London W5 3EZ — MB ChB 1997 Sheff.; MRCP. UK. (Sheff.) Spec. Reg. At Addenbrooke's Hosp. NHS Trust. Socs: BMA; Med. Protec. Soc.; MDU.

CHERIYAN, Mr Joseph Kottukapally (retired) 37 Lethbridge Road, Wells BA5 2FW Tel: 01749 672935 — MB ChB Aberd. 1960; FRCS Ed. 1967. Private Consultations. Prev: Sen. Med. Off. (Surgic. Servs.) Kuwait Oil Company.

CHERIYAN, Kovoor Elias P.A.N.D.A. Centre, Hawkhead Hospital, Paisley PA2 7BL Tel: 0141 889 8151 Fax: 0141 842 1614 Email: renvet-pet.scot.nhs.uk — MB BS 1974 Kerala; FRCPCH 1997; FRIPHH 1987; DFM Glas. 1987; DCCH RCP Ed. 1984; DCH Eng. 1977. (Kottayam Medical college) Cons. Paediat. (Community Child Health)Renfrewsh. & Inverclyde Primary Healthcare NHS Trust Paisley; Hon. Sen. Lect. Univ. Glas. 1993. Socs: Soc. Pub. Health Med.; BMA. Prev: SCMO (Child Health) Hairmyres Hosp. E. Kilbride; Regist. (Paediat.) Dumfries & Galloway Roy. Infirm.; SHO Sheff. Childr. Hosp.

CHERIYAN, Sarah 19 Blairston Avenue, Bothwell, Glasgow G71 8RZ — MB BS 1977 Kerala. Clin. Med. Off. (Child Health) Lanarksh. Healthcare NHS Trust. Socs: BMA; Med. Protec. Soc. Prev: SHO (Psychiat.) Stobhill Hosp. Glas.; SHO (Psychiat) Woodike Hosp., Lenzie, Glas.

CHERRILL, Gary Crown House Surgery, Chapelgate, Retford DN22 6NX Tel: 01777 703672 Fax: 01777 710534; Tithe Farm House, Church Lane, Clarborough, Retford DN22 9NA — MB ChB 1978 Sheff.; MRCP (UK) 1980; MRCGP 1982; DRCOG 1982. GP Retford.

CHERRY, Ann Willoughby Family Practice, 75 Cardiff Road, Dinas Powys CF64 4JT Tel: 029 2051 5455 Fax: 029 2051 5177 — MB BS 1977 Lond.; DRCOG 1980.

CHERRY, Elizabeth Margaret Stepping Hill Hospital, Poplar Grove, Stockport SK2 7JE Tel: 0161 483 1010 Fax: 0161 419 4040; 93 Peregrine Road, Offerton, Stockport SK2 5UP Email: lizcherry@which.net — MB ChB 1989 Manch.; BSc St. And. 1986. Staff Grade (A & E) Stepping Hill Hosp. Stockport. Prev: SHO (A & E) N. Manch. Gen. Hosp.; SHO (A & E) Roy. Oldham Hosp.; SHO (Anaesth.) N. Manch. Gen. Hosp.

CHERRY, Jack (retired) 44 Park Road, Abingdon OX14 1DS Tel: 01235 520415 — MB BS 1952 Lond. Prev: Ho. Phys. & Ho. Surg. Lond. Hosp.

CHERRY, James Muirhead 2 Sparks Close, Chester CH3 5RB — MB BS 1985 Adelaide.

CHERRY, Jane Elizabeth Northampton Lane North Surgery, 120 Northampton Lane North, Moulton, Northampton NN3 7QP Tel: 01604 790108 Fax: 01604 670827; 21 Rushmere Road, Northampton NN1 5RZ Tel: 01604 38143 — MB ChB 1977 Leeds.

CHERRY, Mr John Robert ENT Department, Blackburn Royal Infirmary, Blackburn BB2 3LR Tel: 01254 294409; Artlebeck House, Caton, Lancaster LA2 9RG Tel: 01524 770442 Fax: 01524 770442 — MB BS 1975 Lond.; FRCS Eng. 1982. (St. Bart.) Cons. Otolaryngol., Head & Neck Surg. Blackburn Roy. Infirm., Burnley Gen. Hosp. Socs: Brit. Assn. Otol. Head & Neck Surg.; N. Eng. Otorhinolaryng. Soc.; Otorhinolarynol. Research Soc. Prev: Cons. Otolaryngol. Lancaster Acute Hosps. NHS; Sen. Regist. (ENT Surg.) Roy. Free Hosp. Lond. & Roy. Surrey Co. Hosp.; Vis. Instruc. (Otolaryngol.) & Special Fell. (Facial Plastic Surg.) Oregon Health Scs. Univ. Portland, USA.

CHERRY, John Stewart The Medical Centre, 7 Hill Place, Arbroath DD11 1AE Tel: 01241 431144 Fax: 01241 430764; 10 Waulkmill Village, Letham Grange, Colliston, Arbroath DD11 4QU Tel: 01241 72483 — MB ChB 1981 Ed.; BSc (Med. Sci.) Ed. 1978, MB ChB 1981; MRCGP 1986; DRCOG 1985. GP Arbroath.

CHERRY, Linda Anne Allander Street Surgery, 124 Allander Street, Glasgow G22 5JH Tel: 0141 336 8038 Fax: 0141 336 3440 — MB ChB 1988 Glas.

CHERRY, Mr Paul Martin Hempsall The Clementine Churchill Hospital, Sudbury Hill, Harrow HA1 3RX Tel: 020 8872 3872 Fax: 020 8872 3871 — MB BS Lond. 1969; FRCS Ed. 1975; FRCS Eng. 1975; FRCSC 1975; MRCS Eng. LRCP Lond. 1969; FRCOphth 1988. (Univ. Lond. & St. Mary's Hosp.) Cons. Ophth. GainsBoro. Clin. Lond., Clementine Ch.ill Hosp. Harrow, Harley St. Clin. Lond. & BUPA Hosp. Bristol; Staff (Ophth.) Toronto Hosp; Asst. Prof. Ophth. Univ. Toronto; Cons. Ophth Ultralase. Socs: Brit. Soc. Refractive Surg.; Canad. Ophth. Soc.; Canad. Med. Assn. Prev: Lect. (Ophth.) Univ. Toronto, Canada; Assoc. (Ophth.) Toronto Gen. Hosp.

CHERRY, Mr Richard John University Hospital Coventry & Warwickshire NHS Trust, Coventry & WarwickShire Hospital, Coventry CV1 4FH Tel: 02476 224055 Email: richard.cherry@wh-tr.wmids.nhs.uk — MB BS 1967 Lond.; FRCS Eng. 1972. (Lond. Hosp.) Cons. Orthop. Surg. Univ. Hosps. Coventry & Warwicks. NHS Trust; Sen. Lect. (Orthop.) Warwick Univ. Prev: Cons. Orthop. Surg. E. Birm. Hosp.; Sen. Regist. (Orthop.) W. Midl. AHA.; Regist. (Orthop.) Coventry & Warks. Hosp.

CHERRY, Russell Charles Jiggins Lane Medical Centre, 17 Jiggins Lane, Bartley Green, Birmingham B32 3LE Tel: 0121 477 7272 Fax: 0121 478 4319 — MB ChB 1980 Birm.; MRCGP 1984; DRCOG 1983. Hon. Lect. (Gen. Pract.) Univ. of Birm.

CHERRY, Timothy John Sipling Tel: 01295 259484 Fax: 01295 279293; Wallow Bank Farm House, Chipping Warden, Banbury Tel: 01295 86739 — MB BS 1980 Lond.; DRCOG 1983.

CHERRY, Trudi 12 Station Road, Aston Juxta, Mondrum, Nantwich CW5 6DW — BM BS 1994 Nottm.

CHERRY, William James Bruce (retired) The Mount, Park Terrace, Barnard Castle DL12 8NN Tel: 01833 31903 — MB BS 1957 Durh.

CHERRYMAN, Professor Graham Robert Department of Radiology, University of Leicester, Leicester Royal Infirmary, Leicester LE1 5WW Tel: 0116 258 6719 Fax: 0116 258 6721 Email: gcherryman@lvi.org.uk; Tane House, 108 Burton Road, Melton Mowbray LE13 1DL Tel: 01664 500553 — MB ChB 1975 Cape Town; FRCR 1981. Prof. Radiol. & Head of Dept. Univ. Leicester. Prev: Cons. Radiol. Univ. Hosp. Nottm.; Cons. Radiol. Roy. Marsden Hosp. Lond.; Sen. Research Fell. (Med.) & Hon. Cons. Radiol. Aberd.

CHERSICH, Natalie Elizabeth 30 Broyle Road, Chichester PO19 4BA — MB BCh 1996 Witwatersrand.

CHERUKURI, Anil Kumar Department of Gastroenterology, Royal Sussex County Hospital, Eastern Road, Brighton BN2 5BE — MB BS 1981 Andhra; MRCPI 1990.

CHESHIRE, Christopher Michael Manchester Royal Infirmary, Oxford Road, Manchester M13 9WL Tel: 0161 276 1234; 38 The Crescent, Davenport, Stockport SK3 8SN Tel: 0161 483 2972 Email: jamike38@cheshirec.freeserve.co.uk — MB ChB 1976 Manch.; MB ChB (Hons.) Manch. 1976; BSc (Hons.) (Pharm.) Manch. 1969; FRCP Lond. 1990; DCH Eng. 1979. (Manchester) Cons. Phys. Geriat. & Gen. Med. Manch. Roy. Infirm.; Dir. of Educat. Centr. Manch. Healthcare Trust; Chairm. Brit. Geriat. Soc. N. & W. Socs: (Counc.) Assn. Study Med. Educat.; Brit. Geriat. Soc.; Fell.of Inst. of Med. , Law & Ethics. Prev: Dean of Clin. Studies Manch. Univ.; Med. Dir. Centr. Manch. Healthcare Trust; Lect. & Sen. Regist. (Geriat. Med.) Univ. of S. Manch.

CHESHIRE, Professor David Joseph Edward, SBStJ, Squadron Ldr. RAF Med. Br. Retd. (retired) Cardigan House, 93 Stonegate, Spalding PE11 2PQ Tel: 01775 713640 Fax: 01775 713640 — MB BS 1947 Lond.; MRCS Eng. LRCP Lond. 1947; PhD (Neurol. & Orthop.) USA 1987; DPhysMed Eng. 1954. Prev: Med. Dir. SW System for Spinal Injuries Phoenix,USA.

CHESHIRE, Elizabeth Rose Diana 95 Dawes Road, London SW6 7DU — MB BS 1998 Lond.; LLB(hons) 1985. (UMDS) Ho.. Surg. St.Helier Hosp. Carshalton. Socs: MDU. Prev: Ho..Phys.Guy's Hosp.Lond.

CHESHIRE, Mary Elisabeth (retired) 10 Marton Dale Court, Dixons Bank, Marton in Cleveland, Middlesbrough TS7 8NU — MB BS 1959 Durh.; FFA RCS Eng. 1964; DA Eng. 1961. Prev: Cons. Anaesth. N. & S. Tees Health Dists.

CHESHIRE, Mr Nicholas John William Regional Vascular Unit, St. Mary's Hospital, Paddington, London W2 1NY Tel: 020 7886 1068 Fax: 020 7886 2213 Email: n.cheshire@ic.ac.uk; Orchard House, Bradford Road, Birkenshaw, Bradford BD11 2DS Tel: 01274 682761 — MB ChB 1985 Leic.; MD Leic. 1994; FRCS (Gen.) 1997; FRCS Eng. 1995; FRCS Ed. 1989. (Univ. Leicester Med. Sch.) Cons. Vasc. Surg. St. Mary's Hosp. NHS Trust Lond.; Tutor (Vasc. Surg.) Coll. Surg. Eng. & Vasc. Surg. Soc. GB & Irel. RCS Lond. Educat. Dept. Socs: Surgic. Research Soc.; Assn. Endoscopic Surgs.; Vasc. Surgic. Soc. GB & Irel. Prev: Regist. Rotat. (Surg.) St. Mary's Hosp. Lond.; Regist. Rotat. (Surg.) Edin.; SHO Rotat. Leicester.

CHESLYN-CURTIS, Sarah The Luton & Dunstable Hospital NHS Trust, Lewsey Road, Luton LU4 0DZ Tel: 01582 497104; Deerhurst, Whipsnade, Dunstable LU6 2LH — MB BS 1979 Lond.; MS Lond. 1989; FRCS (Gen.) 1991; FRCS Eng. 1984; T(S) 1993. (St. Mary's Hospital London) Cons. Gen. Surg. Luton & Dunstable Hosp. NHS Trust; Clin. Dir. Socs: Assn. Upper GI Surgs. (Counc. Mem. & Hon. Treas.). Prev: Sen. Regist. (Surg.) St. Mary's & Hammersmith Hosp. Lond.; Clin. Research Fell. (Surg.) St. Mary's Hosp. Lond.; Regist. Rotat. (Surg.) & SHO Middlx. & Centr. Middlx. Hosps. Lond.

CHESNER, Ian Michael 125 Darley Green Road, Dorridge, Solihull B93 8PU — MB ChB 1973 Liverp.; MRCP (UK) 1977.

CHESNEY, David Grosvenor Road Surgery, 4 Grosvenor Road, Dorchester DT1 2BB Tel: 01305 251004 Fax: 01305 250684; Cowden, Charminster, Dorchester DT2 9RN Tel: 01305 265450 — MRCS Eng. LRCP Lond. 1966. (St. Bart.) Prev: Ho. Phys. & Ho. Surg. Addenbrooke's Hosp. Camb.

CHESNEY, David Stirling Whiteladies Health Centre, Whatley Road, Clifton, Bristol BS8 2PU Tel: 0117 973 1201 Fax: 0117 946 7031 — MB ChB 1978 Bristol; MRCGP 1982; AFOM RCP Lond. 1989; DRCOG 1980. (Bristol Univ.)

CHESNEY, Robert CGNU P.L.C., St. Helen's, 1 Undershaft, London EC3P 3DQ Tel: 020 7662 2789 Fax: 020 7662 2977; Oak Cottage, Shalstone, Buckingham MK18 5LX Tel: 01280 700971 — MRCS Eng. LRCP Lond. 1971. (St. Barts.) Chief Med. Off. CGNU Grp. Plc. Co. Ltd, Alder's Life, J. D. Basset & Plant Safety Ltd; Med. Examr. Med. Bureau for Occupat. Dis. S. Africa & Pneumoconiosis; Med. & Research Bureau Zambia.; Med. Examr. NGRNYCH union. Socs: Fell. Assur. Med. Soc.; Soc. Occupat. Med. & Fell. Roy. Soc. Med. Prev: Asst. Med. Adviser Chartered Consolidated Serv. Ltd. & Diamond TradingCo. Lond.; Cons. Phys. BUPA; Res. Med. Off. King Edwd. VII Hosp. for Offs. Lond.

CHESNEY, Mr Robert Buchan 69 Osborne Place, Aberdeen AB25 2DD — MB ChB 1968 Glas.; FRCS Ed. 1973; FRCS Ed. (Orthop.) 1979. Cons. (Orthop. Surg.) Aberd. Hosps. Prev: Sen. Regist. (Orthop. Surg.) Aberd. Roy. Infirm.; SHO (Surg. Rotat.) W.. Infirm Glas.; Ho. Surg. (Orthop.) Raigmore Hosp. Inverness.

CHESOVER, David Frederick Thornhills Medical Group, 732 London Road, Larkfield, Aylesford ME20 6BQ Tel: 01732 843900 Fax: 01732 872633 — MB BS 1981 Lond.; LLM 2000 Dist.; MRCGP 1986; DRCOG 1984; FRCGP 1998. (The Royal London Hospital) Regional Trainer/ UnderGrad. Tutor St. Barts & The Roy.

Lond.; Cons. to RELATE.; Assoc. Risk Cons., Med. Protec. Soc.; GP Clinic Risk Adviser, Maidstone & Malling PCT.

CHESOVER, Jack (retired) 2 Bridge Close, Walton-on-Thames KT12 1DX Tel: 01932 253383 — MRCS Eng. LRCP Lond. 1950; BDS Lond. 1960. Prev: Cas. Off. Stratford-on-Avon Hosp.

CHESS, Erika Jane 3 Redgate Terrace, London SW15 2ES — MB BS 1993 Lond.

CHESSELLS, Professor Judith Mary Institute of Child Health, 30 Guilford St., London WC1N 1EH Tel: 020 7813 8190 Fax: 020 7813 8100 Email: j.chessells@ich.ucl.ac.uk; 50 Northchurch Road, London N1 4EJ Tel: 020 7254 8562 Fax: 020 7923 2945 — MB BS 1962 Lond.; MD Lond. 1971; FRCP Lond. 1978, M 1965; FRCPCH 1997; FRCPath 1990, M 1987; DObst RCOG 1965. (Lond. Hosp.) Leukaemia Research Fund Prof. Haemat. & Oncol. Inst. Child Health Lond. Prev: Cons. Clin. Haemat. Hosp. for Sick Childr. Gt. Ormond St. Lond.; Lect. (Haemat.) Inst. Child Health Lond.; Clin. Research Fell. (Child Health) Hammersmith Hosp. Lond.

CHESSER, Alistair Mark Sloan Undergraduate Teaching Centre, 7th Floor, Ragmore Hospital, Inverness IV2 6AF Tel: 01463 704066 — BChir 1990 Camb.; MRCP (UK) 1993. Clin. Teachg. FRCOW, Ragmore Hosp., Inverness.

CHESSER, Donald Thomas Sloan (retired) North Lodge, Shabden Park, High Road, Chipstead, Coulsdon CR5 3SF Tel: 01737 551693 — MB BS 1960 Lond.; DObst RCOG 1963. Prev: GP Carshalton.

CHESSER, Edward Stewart 39 Page's Lane, London N10 1PU — MB BChir 1958 Camb.; MA, MB Camb. 1958, BChir 1957; FRCP Lond. 1987, M 1961; FRCPsych 1980, M 1973; DPM Lond. 1965. (Univ. Coll. Hosp.) Sen. Lect. & Hon. Cons. Acad. Dept. Psychiat. Univ. Coll. Middlx. Sch.Med. Lond. Socs: Fell. Roy. Soc. Med.; Soc. Psychosomat. Research. Prev: Sen. Regist. & Regist. Bethlem Roy. & Maudsley Hosps.; Sen. Regist. (Psychol. Med.) Hammersmith Hosp.

CHESSER, John Jule Sloan The Surgery, 121 Wrythe Lane, Carshalton SM5 2RT Tel: 020 8644 2727 Fax: 020 8641 7994 — MB BS 1959 Lond.; DObst RCOG 1961. (St. Thos.)

CHESSER, Samuel Guy Sloan 23 Thornville Street, Headingley, Leeds LS6 1RP — MB ChB 1996 Leeds.

CHESSER, Mr Timothy John Sloan Dept of Orthopaedics, Frenchay Hospital, Frenchay, Bristol BS32 4DF — MB BS 1990 Lond.; FRCS Eng. 1994; FRCS (Tr.& Orth.) 1999. (St. Thomas' Hospital London) Cons. Trauma & Orthopaedic Surg.

CHESSHIRE, Arthur 2 College Fields, Marlborough SN8 1UA Tel: 01672 516865 — MB BS Durh. 1950; DA Eng. 1969.

CHESSHIRE, Daphne Golland 2 College Fields, Marlborough SN8 1UA Tel: 01672 516865 — MB BS Durh. 1951; DCH Eng. 1957.

CHESSHIRE, John Stanley I'Anson, MC Burford House, Tenbury Wells WR15 8HQ Tel: 01584 819820 — MB ChB Birm. 1939; DObst RCOG 1947. (Birm.) Prev: Chief Med. & Health Off. Trengganu, Malaysia.

CHESSHIRE, Nicholas James Top Flat, 30 Aldebert Terrace, London SW8 1BJ Tel: 020 7582 2201 — MB BS 1990 Lond.

CHESSHYRE, Matthew Henry Highgate Group Practice, 44 North Hill, London N6 4QA Tel: 020 8340 6628 Fax: 020 8342 8428; 1 Grasmere Road, London N10 2DH Tel: 020 8883 0634 Email: matthewchesshyre@compuserve.com — MB BChir 1969 Camb.; MA Camb. 1971, BA 1966; MRCGP 1974; FFA RCS Eng. 1976; DObst RCOG 1972. (Camb. & St. Thos.) GP Trainer Lond. Socs: BMA. Prev: Regist. (Anaesth.) Aberd. Roy. Infirm.; Med. Off. Vila Base Hosp. Port Vila Vanuata; Ho. Surg. St. Thos. Hosp. Lond.

CHESTER, Alan Waugh (retired) 4 Hartley Close, Bromley BR1 2TP Tel: 020 8467 3996 — MD Durh. 1940, MB BS 1935; FRCOG 1966, M 1948. Prev: Cons. (O & G) Dartford & Gravesham Health Dist.

CHESTER, Darren Lee 38 Brooklands Drive, Gedling, Nottingham NG4 3GU Tel: 0973 384903 — MB ChB 1995 Birm.; ChB Birm. 1995; MB Birm. 1995. (Birm. Univ. Med. Sch.) SHO (Surg. Rotat.) N. Staffs. Hosp. NHS Trust.

CHESTER, David William Riverside Surgery, Barnard Avenue, Brigg DN20 8AS Tel: 01652 650131 Fax: 01652 651551 — MB BS 1971 Lond.; MRCS Eng. LRCP Lond. 1971. GP Brigg. Prev: Regist. (Paediat. Cardiol.) Roy. Liverp. Childr. Hosp.; Regist. (Paediat.) Poole Gen. Hosp.

CHESTER, Elizabeth Mary Flat 1, Sutton House, Quay St., Woodbridge IP12 1BX — MB ChB 1949 St. And.

CHESTER, Mr Graeme Hughbert 197 Huntingdon Road, Cambridge CB3 0DL; 8 Emerald Terrace, West Perth 6005, Australia — MB BS 1969 Western Australia; FRCS Eng. 1974; FRACS 1978; FRACO 1978; DO RCS Eng. 1973.

CHESTER, John David St. James' University Hospital, Beckett St., Leeds LS9 7TF Tel: 0113 243 3144 Fax: 0113 242 9886 — MB BS 1993 Lond.; PhD Glas. 1988; BA (Hons.) Oxf. 1985; MRCP (UK) 1996. (St. Mary's Hosp. Med. Sch. Lond.) Specialist Regist. (Med. Oncol.) St. Jas. Univ. Hosp. Leeds. Socs: Assn. of Cancer Phys.s; Amer. Assn. of Cancer Research; Amer. Soc. of Gene Ther. Prev: SHO (Med.) John Radcliffe Hosp. Oxf.

CHESTER, Mr John Frederick Email: chest_jf@tst.nhs.uk; The Court House, Bradford-on-Tone, Taunton TA4 1HG Tel: 01823 461502 Fax: 01823 343204 — BM 1978 Soton.; MS Soton. 1986; FRCS Eng. 1982; MRCP (UK) 1983; T(S) 1991. Cons. Gen. & Vasc. Surg. Taunton & Som. Hosp.; Undergrad. Teachg. Co-ordinator; Examr., RCS Engl. Socs: Vasc. Surgic. Soc.; Eur. Soc. Vasc. Surg. Prev: Sen. Regist. (Vasc. Surg.) St Geo. Hosp. Lond.; Clin. Fell. (Surg.) Harvard Med. Sch.; Regist. (Surg.) Roy. United Hosp. Bath.

CHESTER, John Harold 12 Eastville Avenue, London NW11 0HD — MB BCh BAO Dub. 1958; DObst RCOG 1964. Prev: Ho. Surg. & Ho. Phys. W. Herts. & St. Paul's Hosps. Hemel Hempstead.

CHESTER, Kate Elizabeth 10 Southcot Place, Bath BA2 4PE — MB BS 1998 Lond.; MB BS Lond 1998.

CHESTER, Michael Roy Cardiothoracic Centre, Thomas Drive, Liverpool L14 3PE Tel: 0151 228 1616 Fax: 0151 220 8573 Email: ali@angina.org — MB BS 1983 Lond.; MD Lond. 1992; MRCP (UK) 1986. (St Georges) Cons. (Cardiol.) Cardiothoracic Centre Liverp.; Sen. Lect. Dept. Human Anat. & Cell Biol. Liverp. Univ. Socs: Brit. Cardiac Interven. Soc.; Pain Soc.; Brit. Cardiac Soc. Prev: Sen. Regist. (Cardiol.) Cardiothoracic Centre Liverp.; Lect. (Cardiol.) St. Geo. Hosp. Lond.; Fell. Nat. Heart & Lung Inst. & Harefield.

CHESTER, Paul Giles Rutherford House, Langley Park, Durham DH7 9XD Tel: 0191 373 1386 Fax: 0191 373 4288; 35 Deanery View, Lanchester, Durham DH7 0NH Tel: 01207 529229 — MB BS 1987 Newc.; MRCGP 1992; DRCOG 1991.

CHESTER, Sonia Kay Castellet, Gibraltar Rd, Skegness PE25 3BB — MB BS 1996 Lond.

CHESTER, Susan Chapman Nuffield Road Medical Centre, Nuffield Road, Chesterton, Cambridge CB4 1GL Tel: 01223 423424 Fax: 01223 566450; 32 Gough Way, Newnham, Cambridge CB3 9LN — MB BChir 1976 Camb.; MRCGP 1980; DRCOG 1978; DCH Eng. 1977. GP Princip.

CHESTERFIELD, Marcus Peter Packsaddle House, Leys Lane, Frome BA11 2JX — MB BS 1996 Lond.

CHESTERMAN, Laurence Paul 2 Elliott House, Arbuthnot Road, London SE14 5LT — MB BS 1979 Lond.; BSc (Hons. Physiol.) Lond. 1976, MB BS 1979; MRCP (UK) 1983; MRCPsych 1988. (Univ. Coll. Hosp.) Sen. Regist. (Clin. Neurophysiol.) Maudsley Hosp. Lond. Prev: SHO Univ. Coll. Hosp.; Research Regist. Univ. Dept. Neurol. Inst. Psychiat. King's Coll.; Hosp. Lond.

CHESTERMAN, Margaret Sheila (retired) 66 Chorley Drive, Sheffield S10 3RR Tel: 0114 303536 — MRCS Eng. LRCP Lond. 1939. Prev: Asst. Med. Off. Sheff. Matern. & Child Welf. Serv.

CHESTERS, Edward William (retired) Palmfield, Church Hill, Crook DL15 9DN Tel: 01388 762945 — MB BS 1962 Durh. Prev: GP Co. Durh.

CHESTERS, Susan Ann Parkfield Health Centre, Sefton Road, New Ferry, Wirral CH62 5HS Tel: 0151 644 0055 Fax: 0151 643 1679; 2 Sunningdale Road, Wallasey CH45 0LU — MB ChB 1975 Liverp.; DRCOG 1980; Cert IHSM 1997. GP Wirral Merseyside. Prev: SHO (O & G) Mill Rd. Matern. Hosp. Liverp.; Trainee GP Liverp.

CHESTERTON, Mr James Ralph (cons. rooms) The Blackheath Hospital, Blackheath, London SE3 9UD Tel: 020 8318 7722 Fax: 020 8318 2542; (cons. rooms), 148 Harley St., London W1N 1AH Tel: 020 7935 1900 Fax: 020 7935 1900 — MB BChir 1962 Camb.; MB BCh Camb. 1962; MA Camb. 1962; FRCS Eng. 1969; DO Eng. 1964. (St. Thos.) Cons. Ophth. Surg. Greenwich Eye Unit & Guy's Gp. Hosps. Socs: FRCOphth; Fell. Roy. Soc. Med.; BMA. Prev: Sen. Regist. Guy's Hosp. Lond.; Resid. Surg. Off. Moorfields Eye Hosp. Lond.; Ho. Surg. St. Thos. Hosp. Lond.

CHESTERTON, Lindsay Jennifer 3 Castle Cr, Shellingford, Faringdon SN7 7PX — BM BS 1997 Nottm.

CHESTNUT, Rachel Jane 132 Bentinck Drive, Troon KA10 6JB Tel: 01292 318789 — MB ChB 1980 Glas.; FFA RCS Eng. 1985. Cons. Anaesth. CrossHo. Hosp. Kilmarnock. Prev: Cons. Anaesth. St. John's Hosp. Howden.

CHESTNUTT, John Alastair James Station Road Surgery, 32 Station Road, Ballyward, Castlewellan BT31 9TU Tel: 028 4064 4217 — MB BCh BAO 1982 Belf.; MRCGP 1986; DCCH RCP Ed. 1988; DRCOG 1986.

CHESTNUTT, William Norman Bella Vista, 2 Ardlough Road, Drumahoe, Londonderry BT47 5SW Tel: 01504 42366 — MB ChB 1977 Ed.; FFA RCSI 1981. Cons. Anaesth. Altnagelvin Area Hosp. Lond.derry. Socs: Soc. Of Anaesth., N.Z. Prev: Cons. Anaesth. Erne Hosp. Ewnishillew.

CHESWORTH, Alexandra Jane September Cottages, Hervines Road, Amersham HP6 5HS — MB BS 1991 Lond.

CHESWORTH, Claire Jan September Cottage, Hervines Road, Amersham HP6 5HS — MB BS 1988 Lond.

***CHESWORTH, Jennifer Anne** Flat 58, St. Andrews Wharf, 12 Shad Thames, London SE1 2YN Tel: 020 7378 0595 — MB BS 1996 Lond.; BMedSci Lond. 1995; DCH 1998.

CHESWORTH, Phyllis Marion c/o P.H. Bowes,Rollit Farrell & Bladon Solicitors, Rowntree Wharf, Navigation Road, York YO1 9WE Tel: 01904 625790 Fax: 01904 625807 — MB BS 1974 Lond.; MRCS Eng. LRCP Lond. 1974; DRCOG 1977. (Roy. Free) Med. Off. St. Philip's Coll. Kongwa, Dodoma, Tanzania. Prev: GP Kidderminster; Med. Off. Mvumi Hosp. Dodoma, Tanzania; Ho. Phys. Coppetts Wood Br. Roy. Free Hosp.

CHESWORTH, Raymond John Hambleton Lytham Road Surgery, 2 Lytham Road, Fulwood, Preston PR2 8JB Tel: 01772 716033 Fax: 01772 715445 — MB BS 1975 Lond. (Middlx.)

CHESWORTH, Timothy John The Barn, Shepreth Road, Barrington, Cambridge CB2 5SB — MB ChB 1998 Bristol.

CHETCUTI, Phillip Andrew John The Old Chapel, Knaresborough Road, Follifoot, Harrogate HG3 1DT — MB BS 1982 Nottm.

CHETTER, Ian Clifford 13 Cossack Avenue, Orford, Warrington WA2 9PB — MB ChB 1990 Leeds.

CHETTY, Muthyala Chinna Pulliah (retired) 19 Ravensdale Gardens, Ellesmere Park, Eccles, Manchester M30 9JD Tel: 0161 789 6976 — MB BS 1951 Madras; 1951 BSc Madras 1944, MB BS 1951; 1973 MRCP (U.K.) 1973; 1957 DTM & H Ed. 1957; 1960 DCH Eng. 1960. Prev: Assoc. Specialist (Gen. Med.) Hope Hosp. Salford.

CHETTY, Muthyala Narendra X-Ray Department, The Hillingdon Hospital, Pield Heath Road, Uxbridge UB8 3NN Tel: 01895 279710 — MB ChB 1982 Manch.; BSc (Hon.) (Physiol.) 1979 Manch.; FRCR 1989; MRCP 1985 (UK); BSc (Hons.) (Physiol.) Manch. 1979; MRCP (UK) 1985; FRCR 1989. Cons. Radiol. Hillingdon Hosp. Uxbridge. Socs: Brit. Soc. Interven. Radiol.; Roy. Coll. of Radiologists BrE. Gp. Prev: Sen. Regist. & Regist. (Diag. Radiol.) Hammersmith Hosp. Lond.; Regist. (Diag. Radiol.) Gen. Infirm. & St. Jas. Univ. Hosp. Leeds.

CHETTY, Muthyala Santhi Hope Hospital, Stott Lane, Salford M6 8HD Tel: 0161 787 5107 Fax: 0161 787 4677 Email: schetty@hope.srht.nwest.nhs.uk; 27 Winton Road, Bowden, Altrincham WA14 2PE Tel: 0161 926 8556 — MB ChB 1985 Ed.; BSc (Hons.) Ed. 1983; MRCP (UK) 1988; FRCA. (Ed.) Cons. Anaesth. Hope Hosp. Salford. Socs: Manch. Med. Soc. Prev: Sen. Regist. & Regist. (Anaesth.) NW RHA; SHO (Anaesth.) Withington Hosp. Manch. & Roy. Infirm. Edin.

CHETTY, Mr Utheshtra 6 Merchiston Park, Edinburgh EH10 4PN — MB ChB 1970 Ed.; FRCS Ed. 1975; MRCP (U.K.) 1976. Sen. Lect. & Cons. Surg. Lothian Health Bd.

CHEUK, Chifan 88 Greenwood Hill, Belfast BT8 7WF — MB BCh BAO 1996 Belf.

CHEUK, Mun Sze 12 Penshurst Mews, Norwich NR4 6JJ — MB BS 1982 Hong Kong.

CHEUNG, Betty Yuen Yee 25 Pytchley Crescent, Upper Norwood, London SE19 3QT — MB BS 1996 Lond.

CHEUNG, Brian 22 Elvaston Place, London SW7 5QE — MB BCh BAO 1982 Belf.

CHEUNG, Chi Cheong 4 Eilen Gardens, Windsor Park, Belfast BT9 6FW — MB BCh BAO 1977 Belf.; MRCOG 1984, D 1980. Regist. (O & G) Belf. City Hosp.

CHEUNG, Ching Wai 97 Gadlys Road, Aberdare CF44 8AB — MB ChB 1997 Bristol.

CHEUNG, Chui Ming Gemmy Undergraduate Centre, Whittington Hospital, St Marys Win, Highgate Hillg, London N19 5NF — MB BS 1997 Lond.

CHEUNG, Mr David Lik Ching 43 Ovington Street, London SW3 1LJ — MB 1965 Camb.; MChir Camb. 1978, MB 1965, BChir 1964; FRCS Eng. 1972; MRCP Lond. 1968. (Westm.) Research Surg. Regist. Brompton Hosp. Lond. Socs: Fell. Roy. Soc. Med. Prev: Ho. Phys. & Ho. Surg. W.m. Hosp.

CHEUNG, David Ming Wai 20 Rose Road, Birmingham B17 9LJ — MB ChB 1994 Bristol.

CHEUNG, David Sai-Ho 38 Pemberton Close, Aylesbury HP21 7NY Email: drdimble@hotmail.com — MB BS 1996 Lond. (St George's Hospital Medical School) SHO (Med. Rotat.) Luton & Dunstable Hosp.

CHEUNG, Elaine Siu-Kwok 27 Southernhay Road, Leicester LE2 3TN — MB ChB 1995 Leic. (Leic.)

CHEUNG, Grace Wai Yan 25 Victoria Road, Harborne, Birmingham B17 0AQ — MB ChB 1993 Liverp.

CHEUNG, Helen 22 Elvaston Place, London SW7 5QE — MB BCh BAO 1986 Belf. Trainee GP Lond. VTS. Prev: Trainee GP/SHO (Gen. Med./O & G/A & E) Lond. VTS.

CHEUNG, Hing Cheong 60 School Road, Killough, Downpatrick BT30 7QL — MB BCh BAO 1984 Belf.; MB BCh Belf. l984.

CHEUNG, Joanna Suk-Yee 42 Rankeillor Street, Edinburgh EH8 9HZ — MB ChB 1997 Ed.

CHEUNG, Kathy Yuen Ping Spaedwell Clinic, Torrington Park Health Centre, Torrington Park, London N12 9SS Tel: 020 8445 7061 Fax: 020 8343 9122; 43 Cotswold Gardens, Golders Green Estate, London NW2 1QT Tel: 020 8455 8872 Email: kathy.cheung@virgin.net — MB BS 1985 Lond.; LicAc (Hon.) 1994; DFFP 1993. (Royal Free Hosp. Sch. Of Med.) GP Retainee; EMO Family Plann., Woms. Health, Barret HA.; Acupunc. Prev: Trainee GP Med. Centre Willesden Lond.; Research Regist. NW Thames RHA; SHO (Haemat. & Paediat.) Barnet Gen. Hosp.

CHEUNG, Kim-Kwong Welford House, Ingatestone Road, Blackmore, Ingatestone CM4 0NZ — MB ChB 1984 Sheff. Nuffield Dept. O & G John Radcliffe Hosp. Oxf. Prev: SHO (O & G) Lond. Hosp.

CHEUNG, King-On 30 Barn Rise, Wembley Park, Wembley HA9 9NJ — MB ChB 1972 Glas.; MRCP (UK) 1976; DCH RCPS Glas. 1974.

CHEUNG, Linda Choi Beak 7 Rowley Road, Boston PE21 6JE — MB BS 1998 Lond.; MB BS Lond 1998.

CHEUNG, Moira Shang-Mei 28 Elgar Avenue, Crowthorne RG45 6QP — MB BS 1998 Lond.; MB BS Lond 1998.

CHEUNG, Ruth Chung-Yan 25 Victoria Road, Harborne, Birmingham B17 0AQ — MB BS 1997 Lond.

CHEUNG, S T H The Doctors Centre, 41 Broomwood Road, Orpington BR5 2JP Tel: 01689 832454 Fax: 01689 826165.

CHEUNG, Stephen Chee-Kin 27 Spa Road, Radipole, Weymouth DT3 5EP — MB BS 1996 Lond.

CHEUNG, Vivian Yee Nin 26 Driffield Road, Bow, London E3 5NF — MB BS 1988 Lond.; FRCA 1996; DA (UK) 1992. Specialist Regist. (Anaesth.), N. Lond. Sch. of Anaesth. Prev: Specialist Regist. (Anaesth.) Roy. Free Hosp. Lond.; Regist. (Anaesth.) Roy. Free Hosp. Lond.; SHO (Anaesth.) St. Bart. Hosp. Lond.

CHEUNG, Wing Keung Calvin 5 Rogersons Green, Liverpool L26 7ZL — MB ChB 1990 Liverp.

CHEUNG CHUN WAH, Nap Tai Queen Mary's Hospital, Sidcup DA14 6LT Tel: 020 8302 2678 Email: nap.cheung@kci.ac.uk — MB ChB 1985 Sheff.; MRCP (UK) 1991; MD 2000. Cons. Rheum., Qu. Mary's Hosp., Sidcup, Kent. Prev: Sen. Regist. (Rheum. & Med.) Guy's Hosp. Lond.; Research Fell. (Rheum.) Staffs. Rheum. Centre Stoke-on-Trent; Regist. Rotat. (Gen. Med. & Rheum.) Dudley Rd. Hosp. Birm.

CHEUNG MING HON, Michael 9 Julian Road, Bristol BS9 1NQ — MB ChB 1992 Bristol.

CHEVASSUT, Timothy James Telfer Department of Haematology, Western General Hospital, Edinburgh EH4 2XU Email: chevassut@hotmail.com; 17/2 Claredence Street, Stockbridge EH3 5AE Tel: 0171 5572729 Email: chevassut@hotmail.com — BM

BCh 1993 Oxf.; MA Oxf. 1993, BA 1989; MRCP Lond. 1996; MPH Harvard 1998. (Oxford University) Specialist Regist. in Clin. Haemat., Lothian Univ. Hosp. NHS Trust; Research Fell., Fac. of Med., Univ. of Edin. Prev: Regist. (Haemat.) Roy. Devon & Exeter Hosp.; Research Fell., Harvard Med. Sch., Boston USA.

CHEVERTON, Peter Douglas Daiichi Pharmaceuticals UK Ltd., International Press Centre, 76 Shoe Lane, London EC4A 3JB Tel: 020 7936 2850 Fax: 020 7583 6035 Email: peter.cheverton@daiichi-pharma.co.uk; 17 Out Westgate, Bury St Edmunds IP33 3NZ Tel: 01284 702859 Fax: 01284 763195 Email: cheverton@classic.msn.com — MB ChB 1970 Cape Town; M. Med.Rad. T. Cape Town 1975. Dir. of Med. Oncol., Daiich Pharmaceut. UK, Ltd. Prev: Med. Dir. Asta Medica Ltd UK; Cons. Radiotherapist Durban, S. Africa; Med. Dir. Lederle Laboratries, S. Africa.

CHEVERTON, Sian Gwynne Oakham Medical Centre, Cold Overton Road, Oakham LE15 6NT — BM BCh 1978 Oxf.; MA Oxf. 1979; MRCP (UK) 1980; MRCGP 1983; T(GP) 1991; DRCOG 1983. (Oxford) GP Oakham; Clin. Asst. (Diabetes) Rutland Memor. Hosp. Prev: GP Bradford; Research Regist. (Diabetes) Radcliffe Infirm. Oxf.; SHO (Med.) Radcliffe Infirm. & John Radcliffe Hosp. Oxf.

CHEVES, Peter Bruce (retired) Vicarage Farm, Mendlesham, Stowmarket IP14 5RS Tel: 01449 766317 — MRCS Eng. LRCP Lond. 1951.

CHEVRETTON, Miss Elfy Brigitte Department ENT Surgery, Guy's & St Thomas Hospital Trust, Lambeth Palace Road, London SE1 7EH Tel: 020 7928 9292 Ext: 3684 Fax: 020 7922 8088; 5th Floor, Emblem Hse, London Bridge Hospital, 27 Tooley St, London SE1 2PR Tel: 020 7403 4501 Fax: 020 7357 6122 — MB BS 1978 Lond.; MS Lond. 1990, BSc 1974; FRCS (Otol.) Eng. 1985; MRCS Eng. LRCP Lond. 1978. (St. Geo. Hosp. Med. Sch.) Cons. ENT Surg. Guy's & St. Thos. Hosp. Trust 1993-Present; Hon. Sen. Lect. (Surg.) Guy's Campus UMDS 1996-Present; Hon. Cons. Dept. Oral & Maxillofacial Surg., kings Health Care NHS trust, 1998-2001. Socs: Roy. Soc. Med.; BMA; HCSA. Prev: Sen. Regist. Rotat. Roy. Lond. Hosp., Whitechapel, Lond. & N.wick Pk. Hosp. Harrow, Middlx.; Lect. (ENT)Roy. Lond. Hosp., Whitechapel, Lond.

CHEW, Ai-Lean 72 Park W., Edgware Road, London W2 2QJ — MB ChB 1997 Glas.

CHEW, Carolyn Anne Robert Darbishire Practice, Rusholme Health Centre, Walmer St., Rusholme, Manchester M14 5NP Tel: 0161 225 6699; Alvor, 7 Millwood Close, Eden Park, Cheadle Hulme, Cheadle SK8 6SU — MB ChB 1984 Manch.; MB ChB (Hons.) Manch. 1984; BSc (Hons.) Manch. 1981; MRCGP (Distinc.) 1989; DRCOG 1988; DGM RCP Lond. 1986. Sen. Lect. (Gen. Pract.) Univ. Manch. Socs: Fell. Manch. Med. Soc.; Brit. Med. & Dent. Hypn. Soc.

CHEW, Mr Christopher Kit Seong 60 Great Clarendon Street, Oxford OX2 6AX — MB BS 1977 Melbourne; FRCS Glas. 1988; FCOphth 1988.

CHEW, David Chesterfield & North Derbyshire Royal Hospital, Calow, Chesterfield S44 5BL Tel: 01246 277271; Holly Bank, Main St, Great Longstone, Bakewell DE45 1TF — MB ChB 1980 Liverp.; FRCP Lond. 1995; MRCP (UK) 1983. Cons. Phys. (special responsibil. for Elderly) N. Derbysh. HA. Prev: Sen. Regist. (Geriat. & Gen. Med.) Mersey RHA.

CHEW, Eng-Wooi Regional Cardiology Centre, Belfast City Hospital, Lisburn Road, Belfast BT9 7AB Tel: 01232 329241 Fax: 01232 263581; 6 Woodlands Close, off Knockmore Road, Lisburn BT28 2XR — MB BCh BAO Belf. 1985; MD Belf. 1990; MRCP (UK) 1988. (Qu. Univ. Belf.) Cons. Cardiol. Belf. City Hosp. Socs: Brit. Cardiac Soc.; RCP Edin.; BMA.

CHEW, Ghee Kheng Aberdeen Royal Infirmary, Foresterhill, Aberdeen AB25 2ZN Tel: 01224 681818; 26A Ferryhill Place, Aberdeen AB11 7SE Tel: 01224 572728 — MB BS 1992 Adelaide. SHO (Gen. Surg.) Aberd. Roy. Infirm.

CHEW, Iain Shing Hee Craiglockhart Surgery, 161 Colinton Road, Edinburgh EH14 1BE Tel: 0131 455 8494 Fax: 0131 444 0161; 120 Greenbank Crescent, Edinburgh EH10 5SZ Tel: 0131 447 8383 Fax: 0131 447 8383 Email: ichew@dircon.co.uk — MB ChB 1974 Ed.; MRCGP 1978. GP Princip. Socs: Brit. Soc. Experim. & Clin. Hypn.; Brit. Med. Acupunct. Soc.; Assoc. Mem. Fac. Homeopath.

CHEW, Mr Kean Seong Accident & Emergency Department, Middlesbrough General Hospital, Ayresome Green Lane, Middlesbrough TS5 5AZ Tel: 01642 854253 Fax: 01642 854251 Email: kean.chew@email.stahnhurst.northy.nhs.uk — MB BCh BAO 1986 Belf.; FRCS Ed. 1993; DRCOG 1991; FFAEM 1997. Cons. A & E Med. Middlesbrough Gen. Hosp. Socs: N. Region Rep. Of Brit. Assn. Of Acc. & Emerg. med.; Med. Informatics.

CHEW, Li-Ching 1 Winnipeg Quay, Salford M5 2TY; 53 Applecross Close, Rochester ME1 1SQ Tel: 01634 848780 — BM BS 1997 Nottm. SHO Gen. Med./ c/o Elderly Medway Hosp. (KENT). Socs: Med. Defence Union; BMA. Prev: SHO (A & E) Hope Hosp. Salford; Ho. Off. in Med. Derby Roy. Infirm.; Qu.s Med. Centre Ho. Off. in Surg./ O & Gac.

CHEW, Min Wei Room 233, Biggart House, Broadway, Belfast BT12 6HG — MB BCh 1998 Belf.; MB BCh Belf 1998.

CHEW, Robert Eric 21 Tycehurst Hill, Loughton IG10 1BX Tel: 020 8508 1537 — MB BS 1988 Lond.; DRCOG 1993; MRCGP 1997.

CHEW, Ruth Littleborough Health Centre, Featherstall Road, Littleborough OL15 8HF; 32 Rooley Moor Road, Rooley Moor, Rochdale OL12 7AX — MB BS 1987 Newc.; MB BS (Hons.) Newc. 1987; MRCGP (Distinc.) 1991; DRCOG 1990; Cert. Family Plann. JCC 1990.

CHEW, Shern-Lin Department of Endocrinology, St. Bartholomew's Hospital, West Smithfield, London EC1A 7BE Tel: 020 7601 8343 Fax: 020 7601 8505 — MB BChir 1985 Camb.; MD (Sir Lionel Whitby Medal) Camb. 1997; MB BChir (Distinc. Med) Camb. 1985; BSc (Hons.) Leeds 1983; MRCP (UK) 1989; FRCP Lond. 1998. (Camb.) Sen. Lect. & Cons. Phys. St Bartholomews & Roy. Lond. Sch. of Med. & Dent.; Cons. Endocrinologist Lond. Clinic Centre for Endocrinol., Lond.; Vice-chair, ELCHA Research Ethics Comm. Socs: Counc. Mem./Fell., Roy. Soc. of Med.; Mem., Amer. and Brit. Endocric Societies. Prev: Wellcome Trust Advanced Fell., Cold Spring Harbor Laborat., New York, USA; MRC Train. Fell. & Hon. Sen. Regist. (Endocrinol.) & Asst. Lect. ICRF (Med. Oncol.) St. Bart. Hosp. Lond.; Asst. Univ. Hosp. Leuven, Belgium & AZ Stuivenberg, Antwerp, Belgium.

CHEW, Timothy Martin Crocketts Farm, Abberley, Worcester WR6 6BS Tel: 0129 921760 — MB ChB 1971 Birm.

CHEW, Mr Yoon Heng 10 Beaufort Crescent, Beechill Road, Newtownbreda, Belfast BT8 7UA Tel: 01232 692901 — MB BCh BAO 1989 Belf.; FRCS Ed. 1994. SHO Rotat. (Surg.) E. Health & Social Security Bd. Prev: Cas. Off. & SHO Rotat. (Surg.) E. Health & SS Bd.; Ho. Off. Roy. Vict. Hosp. Belf.

CHEYNE, Alexander Ian (retired) Bridge of Frew, Kippen, Stirling FK8 3JA Tel: 0178 870678 — MB ChB 1954 Aberd.; FRCP Glas. 1989; FRCPsych 1986, M 1971; DPM Eng. 1966. Prev: Cons. Psychiat. Nuffield Hosp. Glas. & Stud. Health Servs. Univ. Glas.

CHEYNE, Alison Jane 39 Polwarth Street, Hyndland, Glasgow G12 9UE — MB ChB 1985 Glas.; MRCPsych 1996; MRCGP 1991. (Univ. Glas.) Specialist Regist. (Psychol.) W. of Scotl. Prev: Regist. (Psychiat.) Argyll & Clyde Rotat. Hartfield Clinic Dumbarton; SHO (A & E) W.. Infirm. Glas.; SHO (Med.) Aberd. Roy. Infirm.

CHEYNE, Mr Christopher (retired) 30 Knighton Road, Little Aston, Sutton Coldfield B74 4NX Tel: 0121 353 1291 — MB ChB 1957 Liverp.; MChOrth 1968; FRCS Eng. (ad eund.) 1979; FRCS Ed. 1966. Prev: Cons. Orthop. Surg. Good Hope Hosp. Sutton Coldfield.

CHEYNE, David Brian Ormeau Park Surgery, 281 Ormeau Road, Belfast BT7 3GG Tel: 028 9064 2914 Fax: 028 9064 3993 — MB BCh BAO 1989 Belf.; DCH RCPS Glas. 1992; DRCOG 1992.

CHEYNE, Elizabeth Henrietta Louise 37 Chapel Lane, Halebarns, Altrincham WA15 0AG — MB ChB 1993 Bristol.

CHEYNE, George Young (retired) Woodlee, Innerleithen Road, Peebles EH45 8BD Tel: 01721 721811 — MB ChB 1950 Ed.

CHEYNE, Louis Richard Patrick Li 37 Chapel Lane, Hale Barns, Altrincham WA15 0AG — MB ChB 1994 Birm.

CHEYNE, Malcolm Fulton Mackinnon Memorial Hospital, Broadford, Isle of Skye Tel: 01471 822491 — MB ChB 1970 St. And.; MRCGP 1978; Dip Human Sexuality 1989 Lond.; 1992 Diploma in GUM Soc. of Apothelaries; Dip Pract Derm 1994 Wales.

CHEYNE, William Gordon 73 Regent Street, Stonehouse GL10 2AA Tel: 01453 822145; Beech House, Kings Stanley, Stonehouse GL10 3HW Tel: 01453 823551 — MRCS Eng. LRCP Lond. 1959. Socs: BMA; Dispensing Doctors Assn.; Stroud GP Assn. Prev: Capt. RCAMC.

CHHABDA, Prithipal Surjitsingh Flat 8 Doctors' Residence, Law Hospital, Carluke ML8 5ER — MB BS 1983 Saurashtra; MS (Orth.) Saurashtra 1987.

CHHABRA, Dev Raj Chhabra's Surgery, 3 Eden Terrace, Durham Road, Sunderland SR2 7PF Tel: 0191 567 5673 Fax: 0191 514 7462; 11 Thornfield Grove, Sunderland SR2 7UZ Tel: 0191 567 5673 — MB BS 1973 Delhi. (Maulana Azad Med. Coll.) Prev: GP Stourbridge; Regist. (Psychiat.) Burton Rd. Hosp. Dudley; SHO Psychiat. Highcroft Hosp. Birm.

CHHABRA, Ramesh Kumar Broadley House, Broadley Road, Margate CT9 3UL Tel: 01843 67192 — MD 1959 Agra; MD (Med.) Agra 1959, MB BS 1956. (Agra) Assoc. Specialist (Geriat. Med.) Canterbury & Thanet Health Dist.

CHHABRA, Saroj South Tyneside District Hospital, Harton Lane, South Shields NE34 0PL Tel: 0191 202 4031 Fax: 0191 202 4146; Elm Tree, 11 Thornfield Grove, Sunderland SR2 7UZ Tel: 0191 565 4206 — MB BS 1975 All India Inst. Med. Scs.; MRCPsych. Lond. 1981; FRCPsych. 1999. (All India Inst. Med. Scs.) Cons. Psychiat. S. Tyneside Health Care NHS Trust & Hon. Clin. Lect. Newc. Univ. Socs: Assn. Brit. PsychoPharmacol.; Old Age Sect. RCP. Prev: Sen. Regist. (Psychiat.) Mersey RHA.; Regist. Psychiat. Roy. Liverp. Hosp.; SHO (Paediat.) New Cross Hosp. Wolverhampton.

CHHAYA, Bhanushankar Chandrashankar 16 Kelso Close, Worth, Crawley RH10 7XH — LAH Dub. 1956.

CHHAYA, Sanjiv Carl 14 Newquay Close, Walsall WS5 3EP — MB BS 1994 Lond.; FRCA 2000 Dublin; 2000 FFARCSI Dublin; BSc (1st. cl. Hons.) Lond. 1990. (UMDS Guy's & St. Thos. Hosps.) Specialist Regist. (Anaesth.) Univ. Coll. Lond. Roy. Free Hosp. Trust, Rotat.; Provisional Fell. in Anaesth., Austin & Repatination Med. Centre, Melbourne, Australia. Prev: SHO Rotat. (Anaesth.) Univ. Coll. Lond. Hosp. Trust.

CHHETRI, Mr Prem Chandra Kumar c/o 3 Clevely Drive, Nuneaton CV10 0JZ — MB BS 1966 Kerala; FRCSI 1993.

CHHIBBER, Arvind Devraj Nuffield House Surgery, The Stow, Harlow CM20 3AX Tel: 01279 425661 Fax: 01279 427116; 17 Hilly Field, Harlow CM18 7HU Tel: 01279 420566 — MB ChB 1968 East Africa. (Makerere Univ. Coll. Kampala)

CHHIBBER, Farkhanda Akhtar 17 Hillyfield, Harlow CM18 7HU — MB BS 1967 Punjab.

CHHINA, Navjyoat 107 Heathcote Road, Whitnash, Leamington Spa CV31 2LX — BM BCh 1998 Oxf.; BM BCh Oxf 1998.

CHIA, Hendrick Miah Yang Guy's Hospital, St Thomas St., London SE1 9RT; 40 Napier Road, Bromley BR2 9JA — MB BS 1987 Lond.; MRCPI 1993.

CHIA, Kee Vui Department of Gynaecology, Bolton General Hospital, Minerva Road, Farnworth, Bolton BL4 0JR — MB ChB 1981 Liverp.

CHIA, Peng Sang 28 Murray Crescent, Cottingham HU16 5ED — MB ChB 1985 Aberd.; MRCGP 1990; T(GP) 1991; DRCOG 1990. Prev: Trainee GP Cleveland VTS; SHO (O & G) Cameron Hosp. Hartlepool; SHO (Paediat.) Middlesbrough Gen. Hosp.

CHIA, Stanley 16/8 East Parkside, Edinburgh EH16 5XL — MB ChB 1997 Ed. SHO.

CHIAH, Keong Seng Govanhill Health Centre, 233 Calder Street, Glasgow G42 7DR Tel: 0141 531 8385 Fax: 0141 531 4432 — MB ChB 1981 Glas.; MRCGP 1985; DRCOG 1984; Cert. Family Plann. JCC 1985.

CHIAH, Seonaid Anne Arran, 40 Admiral Street, Glasgow G41 1HU Tel: 0141 429 2626 Fax: 0141 429 2331 — MB ChB 1981 Glas.; DRCOG 1983; Cert. Family Plann. JCC 1983.

CHIAM, Tow Kwung 3 Longdon Drive, Four Oaks, Sutton Coldfield B74 4RF Tel: 0121 353 9381 — MB ChB 1988 Birm; DRCOG 1992.

CHIANAKWALAM, Mr Chiledu Ijeoma William Harvey Hospital, Ashford TN23 0LZ Tel: 01233 633331 — MB BS 1980 U. of Nigeria; FRCSI 1990. Resid. Surg. William Harvey Hosp. Ashford. Prev: Regist. (Urol.) William Harvey Hosp. Ashford; Regist. Univ. Hosp. Maiduguri, Nigeria.

CHIANELLI, Marco 15 Colebrooke Row, London N1 8DB — State Exam 1990 Rome.

CHIANG, Catherine Cross Prentice 36 Southesk Ave, Bishopsbriggs, Glasgow G64 3AD — MB ChB 1984 Aberd.; DRCOG 1991; DCH RCPS Glas. 1989; MPH Glas. 1997. Specialist Regist. (Pub. Health) Argyll & Clyde Health Bd. Socs: BMA; Soc. Pub. Health; Fac. of Pub. Health Med. Prev: CMO (Child Health) Ayrsh. & Arran Health Bd.

CHIANG, Min Sein Keighley Road Surgery, Keighley Road, Illingworth, Halifax HX2 9LL Tel: 01422 244397/248308 Fax: 01422 241101; Whitegate Lodge, Whitegate, Siddal, Halifax HX3 9AE Tel: 01422 344348 — MB BS 1974 Patna.

CHIAPPE, Karen Nicola Oak Tree Lodge, Yeoland Down, Yelverton PL20 6BY — BM BCh 1988 Oxf.; MRCGP 1992; DRCOG 1992. Prev: Trainee GP W.on Super Mare & Exeter VTS; Ho. Off. (Surg.) Dernford Hosp. Plymouth; Ho. Off. (Med.) Truro Hosp. Treliske.

CHIAPPE, Nicholas Paul Budshead Health Centre, 433 Budshead Road, Whitleigh, Plymouth PL5 4DU Tel: 01752 773492 Fax: 01752 775657; Oak Tree Lodge, Yeoland Down, Yelverton PL20 6BY Tel: 01822 853963 — BM BCh 1988 Oxf.; MA Camb. 1989; MRCGP 1992; DRCOG 1992; DGM RCP Lond. 1991. (Oxford) GP Princip. Prev: Trainee GP Exeter VTS.

CHIB, Satish Chander Rossington Practice, Grange Lane, New Rossington, Doncaster DN11 0LP Tel: 01302 868421 Fax: 01302 863622 — MB BS Punjab, India 1954. (Amritsar, India) GP.

CHICK, Christopher Michael 5 Hunts Close, Doddington, March PE15 0LQ — MB BCh 1998 Wales.

CHICK, Jonathan Dale Royal Edinburgh Hospital, Edinburgh EH10 5HF Tel: 0131 537 6442 Fax: 0131 537 6866 Email: jchick@compuserve.com — MB ChB 1971 Ed.; MA Camb. 1966; MPhil Ed. 1978; FRCP Ed. 1990; MRCP (UK) 1973; FRCPsych 1988, M 1976. Cons. Psychiat. Roy. Edin. Hosp.; Sen. Lect. Edin. Univ. Socs: Plinius Maior Soc.; Soc. for the Study of Addic.; Eur. Soc. Biomed. Res. Alcoholism. Prev: Mem. Scientif. Staff (Epidemiol. Studies in Psychiat.) MRC; Regist. Roy. Edin. Hosp.; SHO Roy. Infirm. Edin.

CHICK, Veronica Hazel 62 Pevensey Road, London SW17 0HR — MB BS 1994 Lond.; DRCOG 1997; MRCGP 98; BSc Hons 91.

CHIDAMBARAM, Mr Alagappan 241 Burges Road, Eastham, London E6 2EU — MB BS 1983 Madras; FRCS Ed. 1993.

CHIDAMBARAM, Mr Muthiah 227 Alexandra Avenue, South Harrow, Harrow HA2 9DL — MB BS 1972 Madras; FRCS Glas. 1978. (Madurai Med. Coll.) Asst. Prof. & Cons. (Cardiac Surg.) King Saud Univ. Hosp. Riyadh. Socs: Soc. Thoracic & Cardiovasc. Surgs. Gt. Brit. & Irel.; Fell. Amer. Coll. Chest Phys.

CHIDAMBARAM, Velayudham Bury General Hospital, Walmersley Road, Bury BL9 6PG Tel: 0161 764 6081; 10 Swallow Fields, Blackburn BB1 8NR Tel: 01254 53916 — MB BS 1974 Madurai; DA Eng. 1981. (Madurai Med. Coll.) Assoc. Specialist (Anaesth.) Bury Gen. Hosp. Prev: Trainee GP Blackburn Hyndburn Ribble Valley HA; Regist. (Anaesth.) Blackburn Roy. Infirm. & Vict. Hosp. Kirkcaldy; SHO (Anaesth.) Blackburn Roy. Infirm.

CHIDDICK, Sopiie Helen 25 Coleshill Close, Hunt End, Redditch B97 5UN — MB BCh 1996 Wales.

CHIDGEY, Monica Anne Market St Practice, Tonyfelin Surgery, Bedwas Road, Caerphilly CF83 1PD Tel: 029 2088 7831; 31 Beatrice Road, Whitchurch, Cardiff CF14 1DT — MB BS 1984 Lond.; MRCGP 1990. (Char. Cross) Prev: Trainee GP Merthyr Tydfil Mid. Glam. VTS.

CHIDLEY, Kay Estelle 20 Kidderminster Road, Bromsgrove B61 7JS — BM 1990 Soton.

CHIDRAWAR, Mr Mukunda Murlidhar c/o Dr K. B. Swain, 16 Royal Lodge Road, Belfast BT8 7UL — MB BS 1977 Bombay; MS (Gen. Surg.) 1980; FRCSI 1992.

CHIDRAWAR, Uywala Mukunda c/o Dr K. B. Swain, 10 Glenside Park, Drumbo, Lisburn BT27 5LG — MB BS 1980 Bombay; MRCP (UK) 1993.

CHIDWICK, David Andrew Springfield Surgery, Springfield Way, Brackley NN13 6JJ Tel: 01280 703431 Fax: 01280 703241; Astwick House, Queens St, Farthinghoe, Brackley NN13 5NY — MB BS 1978 Lond.; BA Camb. 1975; MRCGP 1983; DRCOG 1981.

CHIEN, Fan Wui c/o W. Collins, 175 Muirfild Drive, Glenrothes KY6 2PX — MB ChB 1986 Dundee.

CHIESA, Marco Cesare The Cassel Hospital, 1 Ham Common, Richmond TW10 7JF Tel: 020 8940 8181 Fax: 020 8332 6424; 140 Palewell Park, East Sheen, London SW14 8JH Tel: 020 8878 4273 Fax: 020 8332 6424 Email: marco@cassel.ftech.co.uk — MD 1978 Milan; MRCPsych 1983. Cons. Psychother. Cassel Hosp. Richmond; Sen. Tutor & Hon. Cons. Psychother. Inst. Psychiat. Maudsley Hosp.

Lond. Prev: Sen. Regist. (Psychother.) Cassel Hosp. & Char. Cross Hosp. Lond.; Sen. Regist. Cassel Hosp. & St. Bernard's Hosp.; Regist. (Psychiat.) Char. Cross. Hosp. Lond.

CHIEVELEY-WILLIAMS, Sarah Ann 30 Dulwich Road, Herne Hill, London SE24 0PA — MB BS 1989 Lond.; MRCP Lond.1992; FRCA Lond.1995. Cons. Anaesth., Univ. Coll. Hosp.s, NHS Trust, Lond.

CHIEW, Yoke Fong Department of Medical Microbiology, The Royal London Hospital Medical School, Turner St., London E1 2AD — MB BS 1979 Singapore.

CHIGARU, Mr Clifford 37 Moubray Road, Dalgety Bay, Dunfermline KY11 9JP — MB ChB 1979 Rhodesia; FRCS Ed. 1984; LRCP LRCS Ed. LRCPS Glas. 1979.

CHIGNELL, Mr Anthony Hugh 44 Wimpole Street, London W1M 7DG Tel: 020 7935 7022 Fax: 020 7224 3722 — MB BS 1962 Lond.; FRCS Eng. 1968; DO Eng. 1966. (St. Thos.) Cons. Ophth. St. Thos. Hosp. Lond. & King Edwd. VII Hosp. Offs. Lond.; Hon. Cons. Ophth. to the Army. Socs: Fell. Roy. Soc. Med. Prev: Res. Regist. (Surg.) Moorfields Eye Hosp.; Sen. Regist. & Ho. Surg. (Ophth.) St. Thos. Hosp. Lond.

CHIJIOKE, Pascal Chioli Department of Pharmacology & Therapeutics, University of Nigeria Teaching Hospital, Enugu PMB 01129, Nigeria Tel: 00 234 42 459171 Fax: 00 234 42 253397; 163 Winchester Road, Edmonton, London N9 9EX — MB BChir 1980 Camb.; MA Camb. 1980, BA (Pharmacol.) 1977; MRCP (UK) 1983. (Camb.) Sen. Lect. (Pharmacol. & Therap.) & Hon. Cons. Phys. Univ. Nigeria Teachg. Hosp. Enugu, Nigeria. Socs: Nigerian Med. Assn.; Fell. Roy. Soc. Med. Prev: Research Regist. (Clin. Pharmacol.) St. Bart. Hosp. Lond.; Regist. (Med.) N. Middlx. Hosp. Lond.; SHO (Gen. Med.) P. of Wales Hosp. & Sheppey Gen. Hosp.

CHIKANZA, Ian Cletos Department of Rheumatology, Royal London Hospital, Bancroft Road, London E1 4DG Tel: 020 7377 7865 Fax: 020 7377 7763 Email: i.c.chikanza@mds.qmw.ac.uk — MB ChB 1983 Zimbabwe; MRCP (UK) 1986; MD; LRCP LRCS Ed. LRCPS Glas. 1982; FRCPCH. Cons. Rheum. Roy. Lond. Hosp. & Newham Hosp.; Sen. Lect. St. Barts & Roy. Lond. Hosp. Sch. of Med. & Dent., Lond. Socs: Amer. Coll. Rheum.; Brit. Soc. Rheum.; Brit. Paediat. Rheumatol. Gp. Prev: Sen. Regist. Guy's Hosp. Lond.; Regist. & Lect. Univ. Zimbabwe.

CHIKHALIKAR, Gautam Tukaram Kingsfold Medical Centre, Woodcroft Close, Penwortham, Preston PR1 9BX Tel: 01772 746492 Fax: 01772 909141 — MB BS 1970 Gujarat. (B.J. Med. Sch.) Clin. Assist. Opthalmology, Chorley & S. Ribble NHS Trust, Chorley Lancs.

CHIKHALIKAR, Geetisha 3 Castle Walk, Penworthham, Preston PR1 0BP — MB ChB 1997 Liverp.

CHIKHANI, Mr Claude Gabriel Aziz Doncaster Royal Infirmary, Thorne Road, Doncaster DN2 5LT Tel: 01302 366666 — MB BCh 1973 Ain Shams; FRCS Ed. 1983; FFAEM 1994. Cons. (A & E) Doncaster Roy. Infirm. Prev: Sen. Regist. (A & E) N.. RHA; Regist. (A & E) Oxf. RHA.

CHIKWE, Joanna Dripshill House, Hanley Castle, Worcester WR8 0AG — BM BCh 1997 Oxf.

CHILAKA, Victor Ngozi Dept of Obstetrics and Gynaecology, Queen Elizabeth Hospital, Sheriff Hill, Gateshead NE9 6SX — MB BS 1982 Ibadan; MRCOG 1994.

CHILCOTT, Jessica Lowri The Oaks, Windyridge, Dinas Powys CF64 4AW Tel: 01222 515942 — MB BCh 1996 Wales.

CHILCOTT, Richard Christian Seven Stones, St. Peters Rd, Hayling Island PO11 0RT — BM 1997 Soton.

CHILD, Anne Hawthorne Cardiological Sciences, St. George's Hospital Medical School, Cranmer Terrace, London SW17 0RE Tel: 020 8725 5248 Fax: 020 8767 7141; 24 Oakfield Lane, Keston BR2 6BY Tel: 01689 856765 — MD 1988 Leic.; MPhil Lond. 1983; MD Toronto 1966; Specialist Accredit. Clin. Genetics JCHMT 1985. (Toronto) Research Fell. Nat. Heart & Lung Inst. Lond. Socs: Clin. Genetics Soc.; Brit. Connective Tissue Soc. Prev: Clin. Lect. (Cardiol. Sci.) St. Geo. Hosp. Med. Sch. Lond.; Med. Off. Guy's Hosp. Med. Sch.; Sci. Research Off. Inst. Child Health Lond.

CHILD, Barry Gordon 5 Bowling Street, Sandwich CT13 9HA — MB BS 1956 Lond.; MB BS (Hons. Surg.) Lond. 1956. (Char. Cross.) Prev: Cas. Off. Char. Cross Hosp. Lond.; Obst. Off. Char. Cross Hosp. Obst. Unit Kingsbury; Med. Off. Grenfell Assn.

CHILD, Christopher Simon Flat 1, 44 Clapham Common North Side, London SW4 0AA — MB BS 1996 Lond.

CHILD, Christopher Stuart Baron Department of Anaesthesia, Royal Sussex County Hospital, Eastern Road, Brighton BN2 5BE — MB BS 1977 Lond.; FFA RCS Eng. 1981; LMCC 1986. Cons. Paediat. Anaesth. Roy. Alexandra Hosp. for Sick Childr. & Roy.; Sussex Co. Hosp. Prev: Sen. Regist. (Anaesth.) Univ. Coll. Hosp. Lond.; Vis. Asst. Prof. Montreal Childr. Hosp. Canada.

CHILD, David Francis Maelor Hospital North East Wales Trust, Wrexham LL13 7TD Tel: 01978 291100 Fax: 01978 727124; Whitegate Farm, Gyfelia, Wrexham LL13 0YH — MB ChB 1967 Birm.; FRCP Lond. 1988; MRCP (UK) 1972. Cons. Phys. Maelor Hosp. Wrexham. Socs: Diabetes UK; Vice Chairm. Welsh Commitee Diabetes UK. Prev: Lect. (Med.) Univ. Manch.; Regist. (Med.) Hammersmith Hosp. Lond. & Worcester Roy. Infirm.

CHILD, David Laurie 2 Eastern Road, Birmingham B29 7JP — MB BS 1970 Lond.; MB BS Lond. 19970; BSc Lond. 1967; FRCGP 1992, M 1980; MRCP (UK) 1974. (St. Thos. Hosp.) Prev: Regist. (Rheum.) St. Thos. Hosp. Lond.; Med. Off. Wusasa Hosp., Nigeria.

CHILD, Donald Alan York District Hospital, Wiggington Rd, York YO31 8HE — MB ChB 1967 Sheff.; FFA RCS Eng. 1971. (Sheff.) Cons. Anaesth. York Hosps. Prev: Sen. Regist. (Anaesth.) United Leeds Hosps.; Regist. (Anaesth.) United Sheff. Hosps.

CHILD, Dorothy Royds House, Heptonstall, Hebden Bridge HX7 7LN; 3/5 Rocheid Park, East Fettes Avenue, Edinburgh EH4 1RP — MB ChB 1957 Ed.; FFA RCSI 1963; FFA RCS Eng. 1964. Cons. Anaesth. Roy. Infirm. & W.. Gen. Hosp. Edin.

CHILD, Fiona Jane King's College Hospital, Denmark Hill, London SE5 9RS Tel: 020 7346 3258 Fax: 020 7346 3616 — MB BS 1991 Lond.; BSc Lond. 1988; MRCP (UK) 1994. Regist. (Dermat.) King's Coll. Hosp. Lond. Prev: SHO Rotat. (Med.) St. Geo. Hosp. Lond.; SHO (Dermat. & Genitourin. Med.) Guy's Hosp. Lond.

CHILD, Geoffrey Vincent 24 Oakfield Lane, Keston BR2 6BY — MB BS 1965 Lond.; MSc McGill 1971. (Westm.)

CHILD, Helen Frances North Staffordshire Royal Infirmary, Newcastle rd, Stoke-on-Trent ST4 6QG; 60 Ashley Drive, Swinton, Manchester M27 0AX — BM 1991 Soton.; MRCP (UK) 1995; MRCPCH 1997. (Southampton) Socs: MRCPCH. Prev: Secialist Regist. (Paediat.), Manch. Childr.'s Hosp.; Specialist Regist. (Paediat.) Booth Hall Hosp., Manch.; Regist. (Paediat.) Qu.'s Pk. Hosp. Blackburn & Roy. Preston Hosp.

CHILD, James Anthony Department of Haematology, The General Infirmary, Leeds LS1 3EX Tel: 0113 392 6643 Fax: 0113 392 6349; St. John's House, Wetherby Road, Roundhay, Leeds LS8 2LE Tel: 0113 265 9321 — MB BS 1963 Lond.; MD Lond. 1971; FRCP Lond., M 1967; FRCPath 1995. (Guy's) Cons. Haemat. Leeds Gen. Infirm.; Hon. Sen. Lect. Univ. Leeds; Chairm. Myeloma sub-Gp.; Mem. MRC Adult Leukaemia Working Party; Mem. Scientif. Advis. Bd., Internat. Myeloma Found. Socs: Chairm. UK Myeloma Forum; Brit. Soc. Haematol.; (Comm.) Centr. & S. Lymphoma Gp. Prev: MRC Fell. & Lect. St. Bart. Hosp. Lond.; Regist. (Med.) Centr. Middlx. Hosp. Lond; Regist. & Ho. Off. Guy's Hosp. Lond.

CHILD, Jennifer Ann Dept.Microbiology, Surrey & Sussex Healthcare Trust, Crawley Hospital, West Green Drive, Crawley RH11 7DH Tel: 01293 600300 Ext: 3093 Email: ja.child@doctors.org.uk — MB BS 1987 Lond.; MRCPath 1999. (Charing Cross and Westminster) Cons. Microbiologist.Surrey&Sussex. Healthcare Trust.; Infec. control doctor and Hon. Cons. microbiologist, Qu. Vict. hos[pital, E. Grinstead. Socs: Brit. Assn. Antimicrobial Chemother.; Amer. Soc. Microbiol.; Assn. of Med. Microbiologists. Prev: Hon. Clin. Lect. Dept. Infec. Univ. Birm. Med. Sch.; SPR (Med.Micro) Birm. Childr.s' Hosp.; Specialist Regist. (Med.Micro.)Qu. Elizebeth. Hosp.Birm.

CHILD, Nicolas John Child & Family Clinic, 49 Airbles Road, Motherwell ML1 2TJ Tel: 01698 254551 Email: childs@compuserve.com; 8 Lee Crescent, Portobello, Edinburgh EH15 1LW Tel: 0131 669 2184 Fax: 0131 669 2184 — MB ChB 1971 Ed.; MPhil Ed. 1976, BSc (Med. Sci.) 1968; MRCPsych 1975. (Ed.) Cons. Child & Adolesc. Psychiat. Lanarksh. Primary Care NHS Trust. Prev: Sen. Regist. (Child & Adolesc. Psychiat.) Roy. Edin. Hosp. & Roy. Hosp. Sick Childr. Edin.

CHILD, Rev. Peter David (retired) Carmel, 2 Pennine Way, Broadmeadows, Biddulph, Stoke-on-Trent ST8 7EJ Tel: 01782 513590 Email: dchildocds@aol.com — MRCS Eng. LRCP Lond. 1964. Prev: GP.

***CHILD, Rowan Jane** Mill Cottage, 19 Old Dey Lane, Brigstock, Kettering NN14 3HY — MB BS 1997 Lond.; BSc Hons. (Pharmacol.) 1994.

CHILD, Sarah Claire Chantal 24 Oakfield Lane, Keston BR2 6BY — BM 1996 Soton.

CHILD, Simon Richard — MB ChB 1980 Bristol; MRCGP 1984; Cert. Family Plann. JCC 1983; DRCOG 1982. Gen. Practitioner. Socs: BMA. Prev: Trainee GP Bury VTS; Ho. Surg. Yeovil Dist. Hosp.; Ho. Phys. Roy. Devon & Exeter Hosp.

CHILD, Stuart William Fronks Road Surgery, 77 Fronks Road, Dovercourt, Harwich CO12 3RS Tel: 01255 556868 Fax: 01255 556969; Bessbrook, Harwich Road, Great Oakley, Harwich CO12 5JR Tel: 01255 886455 Fax: 01255 886455 — MB ChB 1972 Leeds. (Leeds) GP. Socs: Colchester Med. Soc. Prev: SHO (Paediat.) & SHO (Obst.) Pontefract Gen. Infirm.

CHILD, Timothy John 72 Westgate, Chichester PO19 3HH — MB BS 1993 Lond.; MA Camb. 1994. (Lond. Hosp. Med. Coll.) Specialist Regist. (O & G) Oxf. Region. Prev: SHO (O & G) John Radcliffe Hosp. Oxf.

CHILD, Vivien Mary 2 Eastern Road, Birmingham B29 7JP — MB BS 1973 Lond.; DO Eng. 1976. (St. Thos.) Clin. Asst. (Ophth.) Selly Oak Hosp. Birm. & Wolverhampton Eye Infirm. Prev: SHO (Paediat.) Mayday Hosp. Thornton Heath; SHO (Ophth.) Croydon Eye Unit.

CHILDS, Amanda Jillian The Ferry, Chatteris PE16 6SG Tel: 01353 3110; 47 St Mark's Road, Teddington TW11 9DE Tel: 020 8943 3424 — MB BS 1982 Lond.; MRCGP 1988; DRCOG 1985. GP Teddington. Prev: Trainee GP N.wick Pk. Hosp. Harrow; Ho. Surg. King Edwd. VII Hosp. Midhurst; Ho. Phys. W. Middlx. Hosp. Isleworth.

CHILDS, Anne-Marie 1 Tern Park, Linton Road, Collingham, Wetherby LS22 5LY — MB ChB 1989 Bristol; BSc (Hons.) Pharmacol. Bristol 1986; MRCP (UK) 1992. Lect. & Hon. Sen. Regist. (Paediat. & Child Health) Univ. Leeds. Prev: Regist. (Paediat.) Clarendon Wing Leeds Gen. Infirm.

CHILDS, Anthony Frederick Sydney (retired) Leaside, Filmer Grove, Godalming GU7 3AB Tel: 01483 423234 Fax: 01483 423234 — MB BChir Camb. 1960; MRCS Eng. LRCP Lond. 1959; DObst RCOG 1964. Prev: GP Godalming.

CHILDS, Austin John (retired) Fernfield, Park Lane, Baldwin's Gate, Newcastle ST5 5ET — MB ChB 1951 Glas.; DPH 1958; DIH Soc. Apoth. Lond. 1960. Prev: GP Newc. under Lyme.

CHILDS, David The Cedar House, Townfield Lane, Mollington, Chester CH1 6NJ — MB ChB 1979 Manch.; FFA RCS Eng. 1983; DObst. RCOG 1981. Cons. Anaesth. Chester Dist. Hosp. Prev: Sen. Regist. Rotat. (Anaesth.) Mersey RHA; Vis. Asst. Prof. Oregon Health Sci. Univ. Portland, USA.

CHILDS, David Ruston (retired) 243 Berrow Road, Burnham-on-Sea TA8 2JQ — MB 1956 Camb.; BChir 1955; DObst RCOG 1956. Prev: GP Burnham-on-Sea.

CHILDS, Frances Eleanor Mary Worcestershire Community Healthcare NHS Trust, Child Health Department, Isaac Maddox House, Shrub Hill Road, Worcester WR4 9RW Tel: 01905 763333; Windmill Hill House, Main Road, Kempsey, Worcester WR5 3LW — MB ChB 1982 Birm.; MRCP (Paediat.) (UK) 1991; MRCGP 1987; MSc (Warwick) 1997. (Birmingham) Cons. Community Paediat. S. Worcs. Community NHS Trust. Prev: Sen. Regist. (Community Paediat.) N.. Birm. Community NHS Trust.

CHILDS, Joan Daphne Meskell (retired) 2 Tiddy Brook Road, Whiteacres, Whitchurch, Tavistock PL19 9BZ Tel: 01822 614328 — MB BS 1947 Lond.; MB BS (Hons.) Lond. 1947; DPM Eng. 1973. Prev: Med. Asst. (Child & Family Psychiat.) S. W.. RHA.

CHILDS, Katharine Jane Leaside, Filmer Grove, Godalming GU7 3AB — MB BS 1990 Lond.

CHILDS, Robert Austin Bute House, Grove Medical Centre, Wootton Grove, Sherborne DT9 4DL Tel: 01935 810900 Fax: 01935 810901; Newhay, Corton Denham, Sherborne DT9 4LS Tel: 01963 220752 — BM 1987 Soton.; MRCGP 1992; DRCOG 1991.

CHILDS, Wendy Jane Bury Hall Farm House, 110 The Avenue, Alverstoke, Gosport PO12 2JY — BM 1989 Soton.; MRCP (UK) 1993; MRCGP 1997. Prev: GP/Regist. Penryn, Cornw.

CHILKA, Sameer Yeshawant 1 Lawnheads Avenue, Littleover, Derby DE23 6DR — MB BS 1996 Lond.

CHILL, Caroline Samantha Grimble and Partners, 20 Pepys Road, Raynes Park, London SW20 8PF Tel: 020 8946 3074/8249 Fax: 020 8296 0145; 18 Ranelagh Garden Mansions, Ranelagh Gardens, London SW6 3UG Tel: 020 7731 1453 Fax: 020 7731 1453 Email: docchill@aol.com — MB BS 1982 Lond.; DRCOG 1984. (Charing Cross)

CHILLAL, Balaji Bridge Street Surgery, Bridge Street, Aberfan, Merthyr Tydfil CF48 4RB Tel: 01443 693250 Fax: 01443 693249. GP Aberfan, M. Glam.

CHILLALA, Jay 5 Huntly Drive, Solihull B91 3FL — MB ChB 1993 Manch.; BSc (Med. Sci.) St. And. 1990; MRCP Lond. 1998. Specialist Regist. (Geriats. & Gen. Med.) The Roy. Oldham Hosp. Oldham. Prev: SHO (Med.) Walsall Manor Hosp. Walsall; Hse. Off. (Med.) Wordsley Hosp. Stourbridge.

CHILLALA, Shekhar Dept of A&E, Leicester Royal Infirmary, Leicester LE1 5WW; 5 Hutley Drive, Solihull B91 3FL — MB ChB 1985 Birm.

CHILLINGWORTH, Thomas Herbert (retired) 16 Glencoe Park, Newtownabbey BT36 7PT Tel: 02890773147 Fax: 02890773147 — LRCPI & LM, LRSCI & LM 1953; LRCPI & LM, LRCSI & LM 1953; LAH Dub. 1952; CIH Dund 1976; DA Eng. 1956. Prev: Med. Off. Social Security Agency N. Irel.

CHILLISTONE, Daniel James David Newcome, Battery La, Portishead, Bristol BS20 7JD — MB ChB 1997 Leic.

CHILTON, Andrew Phillip 104 Oxford Road, Moseley, Birmingham B13 9SQ — MB BS 1992 Newc.

CHILTON, Mr Christopher Paul East Midland Nuffield Hospital, Rykneld Road, Littleover, Derby DE23 7SN Tel: 01332 521227 Fax: 01332 512481; Serendipity, Tanners Lane, Repton, Derby DE65 6FP Tel: 01283 701855 Fax: 01283 701856 Email: chilts01@globalnet.co.uk — MB BS Lond. 1971; FRCS Eng. 1977. Cons. Urol. Derby City Gen. Hosp. Socs: Fell. Roy. Soc. Med.; Derby Med. Soc. Prev: Sen. Regist. (Urol.) St. Peter's Hosps. Lond.; Hunt. Prof. Roy. Coll. Surg. Eng.

CHILTON, Margaret Helen (retired) 14 Ralliwood Road, Ashtead KT21 1DE Tel: 01372 272457 — MB ChB Birm. 1951; DObst RCOG 1954; MRCGP 1966. Prev: GP Ashtead.

CHILTON, Stewart Anthony Martonside Medical Centre, 1a Martonside Way, Middlesbrough TS4 3BY; 2 York Road, Nunthorpe, Middlesbrough TS7 0EX Tel: 01642 313508 — MB ChB 1976 Liverp.; Med. Dipl. 2000 AL; MRCGP 1980; DRCOG 1979. Socs: Brit. Med. Acupunct. Soc.

CHILVERS, Mr Antony Stuart St. Anthonys Hospital, London Road, North Cheam, Sutton SM3 9DW Tel: 020 8337 6691 Fax: 020 8335 3325; 3 Palmerston Court, 2-8 Palmerston Road, Sutton SM1 4QL Tel: 020 8395 7776 Fax: 020 8715 3435 — MB BChir 1964 Camb.; BA Camb. 1961, MChir 1972, MA 1964; FRCS Eng. 1966. (St. Thos.) Cons. Surg. St. Helier Hosp. Carshalton; Sen. Lect. & Hon. Cons. St. Geo. Hosp. Socs: Mayo Clinic Alumni & Chesleden Club. Prev: Regist. & Sen. Regist. St. Thos. Hosp. Lond.; Research Asst. Mayo Clinic, USA.

CHILVERS, David Michael 15 Cottes Way, Hillhead, Fareham PO14 3NB Email: davidc@interalpha.co.uk — MB BS 1986 Lond.; MRCGP 1993; T(GP) 1993; DRCOG 1992. Regist. (Geriat.) Summerlands Hosp. Yeovil.

CHILVERS, Professor Edwin Roy Respiratory Medicine Division, Department of Medicine, University of Cambridge School of Clinical Medicine, Level 5, Box 157, Addenbrooke's Hospital, Hills Road, Cambridge CB2 2QQ Tel: 01223 762007 Fax: 01223 762007 Email: erc24@hermes.cam.ac.uk — BM BS 1982 Nottm.; BMedSci. Nottm. 1980; PhD Lond. 1991; FRCP Ed. 1995; MRCP (UK) 1985; FRCP 1999. (Nottingham) Prof. (Respirat. Med.) Univ. Camb.; Hon. Cons. Psys.Addenbrooks & Papworth.Hosp. Prev: Hon. Cons. Phys. & Wellcome Sen. Research Fell. (Clin. Sci.) Roy. Infirm. Edin.

CHILVERS, Julian Paul 109 Queens Park Road, Harborne, Birmingham B32 2LB Tel: 0121 426 2633 Fax: 0121 312 7700 Email: j.chilvers@lineone.net — MB ChB 1993 Leic.; DA (UK) 1996. Specialist Regist. (Anaesth.) Birm./W. Midls. Rotat.

CHILVERS, Neal Andrew Flat 3, 16 The Green, Ashton-on-Trent, Derby DE72 2AA Tel: 01332 799669 — MB BS 1991 Lond.; BSc (Hons.) Lond. 1988; MRCP (UK) 1995. (Charing Cross & Westminster) Regist. Rotat. (Paediat.) Nottm. & Derby. Prev: SHO Rotat. (Paediat.) Leics. HA.

CHIN, Alan Kie Loong 25 Meadowbrook, Islandmagee, Larne BT40 3UG — MB BCh BAO 1971 Belf.; MSc (Data Processing)

Ulster 1988. (Belf.) Prev: SHO & Jun. Clin. Tutor in Therap. & Pharmacol. Qu. Univ. Belf. & N.; Irel. Hosps. Auth.

CHIN, Anthony Tet Lin (retired) 3 The Oaks, Wimbledon Hill Road, London SW19 7PB — MB BCh BAO 1975 Dub.; MSc Surrey 1981; MA Dub. 1979; FRCPath 1994, M 1982. Prev: Cons. Med. Microbiol. St. Helier Hosp. Carshalton.

CHIN, Christopher Augustus 89E Oxford Gardens, London W10 5UL — MB BS 1986 Lond.; MRCP (UK) 1992.

CHIN, David Mun Foo 50 Clerwood Park, Edinburgh EH12 8PP — MB BCh 1985 Wales.

CHIN, Derek Tze-En Cardiac Department, King's College Hospital, Denmark Hill, London SE5 9RS — MB BS 1988 Lond.; MRCP (UK) 1991. (Royal Free Hospital School of Medicine University of London) Regist. Rotat. (Cardiol.) Brighton King's Coll.

CHIN, Dominic 78 Sycamore Close, Bradford BD3 0EA — MB BChir 1989 Camb.; MA Camb. 1990; MRCGP 1993; DFFP 1994.

CHIN, Jacqueline Elizabeth Flat 4, 35 Queens Gardens, London W2 3AA — MB BS 1989 Lond.; DRCOG 1992.

CHIN, Kian Heung Flat . 23 Greenlands, Holloway Hill, Ottershaw, Chertsey KT16 0RN — MB ChB 1993 Bristol.

CHIN, Kin-Fah Flat 2/1, Westcliffe Court, Sutcliffe Road Anniesland, Glasgow G13 1AP — MB ChB 1993 Aberd.

CHIN, Pe-Loong 174 Lowry Hill Road, Carlisle CA3 0EZ — MB BS 1965 Lond.; FRCP Ed. 1981, M 1968; MRCS Eng. LRCP Lond. 1965. (Lond. Hosp.) Cons. Phys. Dept. Geriat. Med. Cumbld. Infirm. Carlisle.

CHIN, Pearl Chen Choo Westbourne Grove Medical Centre, 241 Westbourne Grove, London W11 2SE Tel: 020 7229 5800 — BM 1991 Soton.; MRCGP 1998.

CHIN, Sarah Cheh-Ping Chells Way Surgery, 265 Chells Way, Stevenage SG2 0HN Tel: 01438 313001 Fax: 01438 362322; 85 London Road, Knebworth SG3 6HG — MB BCh BAO 1976 Belf.

CHIN, Saw Sian 23 Dogfield Street, Cardiff CF24 4QJ; 108A Lerong 1B, Jalan Sungai Maong Tengah, 93150 Kuching, Sarawak 93150, Malaysia Tel: 00 60 082 416026 — MB ChB 1996 Dundee. Ho. Off. (Med.) Qu. Eliz. Hosp. Birm. Socs: BMA. Prev: Ho. Off. (Surg.) W. Cumbld. Hosp.

CHIN, Su Kiun Loanhead Court, Loanhead Place, Aberdeen AB25 2TT — MB ChB 1996 Aberd.

CHIN, Teck Meng Melvin 48 Broadway Tower, Broadway, Belfast BT12 6HG — MB BS 1996 New South Wales. SHO (Med.) Roy. Vict. Hosp. Prev: SHO (A & E) Daisy Hill Hosp.; Pr. Ho. Off. Roy. Vict. Hosp.

CHIN, Tshun Leong Nicholas Flat 3, 50 Roman Road, London E2 0LT — MB ChB 1994 Sheff.

CHINA, Joan Marie (retired) Cross Cottage, Duck Lane, Barford St Martin, Salisbury SP3 4AN Tel: 01722 744094 — MRCS Eng. LRCP Lond. 1948.

CHINDULURI, Chandra Mohan Raju The Surgery, 76 Herbert Road, London SE18 3PP Tel: 020 8854 3964 Fax: 020 8317 8512 — MB BS 1972 Banaras; MRCP (UK) 1984. Prev: Cons. Phys. King Fahd Hosp. Al Hamrah Jeddah, Saudi Arabia.

CHINEGWUNDOH, Mr Francis Ikechukwu Tel: 020 7601 8391 Fax: 020 7601 7844 Email: francis-chinegwundoh@msn.com; 56 Redbridge Lane W., London E11 2JU Email: francis_chinegwundoh@msn.com — MB BS 1984 Lond.; MS Lond. 1994; FRCS Eng. 1989; FRCS Ed. 1989; FRCS (Urol.) 1995 Intercoll Surg Bd UK; FEBU 1997. (St. Geo. Hosp. Med. Sch. Lond.) Cons. Urol. Roy. Hosps. NHS Trust & Newham Healthcare NHS Trust Lond. Socs: Fell. Roy. Soc. Med.; BMA; Brit. Assn. Urol. Prev: Sen. Regist. (Urol.) Univ. Hosp. Birm. & Roy. Hosp. Shrewsbury.

CHINEGWUNDOH, John Okechukwu Magbogu 34 Shakespeare Road, London SE24 0LB — BChir 1994 Camb.; MB Camb. 1994; MRCP Lond. 1997. (Camb./UMDS) Specialist Regist. (Ger./Respirat. Med.) Univ. Coll. Hosp. Socs: RCP Lond. Prev: Research Fell., Div. of Pulm., Allergy & Critical Care Med., Columbia Univ., New York, USA.

CHINERY, Christopher Graham Roebuck House, High Street, Hastings TN34 3EY Tel: 01424 420378 Fax: 01424 719234; Guestling Surgery, Stream Farm House, Chapel Lane, Guestling, Hastings TN35 4HN Tel: 01424 813661 Fax: 01424 452824 — MB BS 1974 Lond.; MRCS Eng. LRCP Lond. 1974; DRCOG 1977. (Guy's Lond.)

CHING, Mr Hin San 28 Hulatt Road, Cambridge CB1 8TH — MB BS 1987 Malaya; FRCS Ed. 1993; FRCS Glas. 1992.

CHING, Teresa Veronica The Halo, Unity Road, Porthleven, Helston TR13 9DA — MB BCh 1995 Wales.

CHINN, Graham Lester Lower Road Surgery, 17 Lower Road, Fetcham, Leatherhead KT22 9EL Tel: 01372 378166 Fax: 01372 374734 — MB BS 1973 Lond.; DObst RCOG 1975. (St. Geo.) Prev: Trainee GP Epsom VTS; Ho Off. (Gen. Med. & Surg.) Epsom Dist. Hosp.

CHINN, Julia Denise Nightingale Surgery, Greatwell Drive, Cupernham Lane, Romsey SO51 7QN Tel: 01794 517878 Email: nigalesurg@tep.co.uk; 20 Godfrey Pink Way, Bishops Waltham, Southampton SO32 1PB — MB BS 1981 Lond.; MRCGP 1988. (St Mary's Hospital)

CHINN, Richard Ernest Wexham Park Hospital, Wexham, Slough SL2 4HL Tel: 01753 633000; 19 Harecourt Close, Dorney Beach, Maidenhead, Slough SL6 0DY — MB BCh 1976 Birm.; MRCPsych 1981. Cons. Psychiat. Prev: Maj. RAMC 1981-6.

CHINN, Richard Harrison Havant Health Centre Suite B, PO Box 41, Civic Centre Road, Havant PO9 2AQ Tel: 023 9248 2124 Fax: 023 9247 5515; Priory Cottage, 2 Long Copse Lane, Emsworth PO10 7UL Tel: 01243 374148 — MB ChB Glas. 1966; MRCP (U.K.) 1971. (Glas.) Prev: Lect. in Med. Univ. Soton. St. Mary's Gen. Hosp. Portsmouth; Hon. Med. Regist. MRC Blood Pressure Research Unit W.. Infirm. Glas.

CHINN, Roger John Stuart Chelsea & Westminster Hospital, X-Ray Department, 369 Fulham Road, London SW10 9NH Email: r.chinn@ic.ac.uk — MB BS Lond. 1986; MRCP (UK) 1990; FRCR 1994. (St Mary's Hospital Med School, London) Cons. Radiol. Chelsea & W.m. Hosp. Socs: BMA. Prev: Sen. Regist. (Radiol.) Middlx. & Univ. Coll. Hosps. Lond.; Research Fell. MRI Unit Middlx. Hosp.; SHO (Gen. Med.) St. Mary's Hosp. Lond.

CHINN, Sarah Ellen Lyndhurst Surgery, 2 Church Lane, Lyndhurst SO43 7EW Tel: 023 8028 2689 Fax: 023 8028 2918 — BM Soton. 1981; MRCP (UK) 1984.

CHINNECK, Peter John Elston Meadows, Whittonditch Road, Ramsbury, Marlborough SN8 2PX — BM 1980 Soton.

CHINNERY, Patrick Francis Department of Neurology, University of Newcastle upon Tyne, The Medical School, Framlington Place, Newcastle upon Tyne NE2 4HH Tel: 0191 222 8334 Fax: 0191 222 8553 Email: p.f.chinnery@ncl.ac.uk; 167 Beaconside, South Shields NE34 7PT Tel: 0191 455 8944 — MB BS 1992 Newc.; MB BS (Hons.) Newc. 1992; BMedSc (1st cl. Hons.) Newc. 1989; MRCP (UK) 1995. Regist. (Neurol.) Roy. Vict. Infirm. Newc.; Clin. Research Assoc. Univ. Newc. u. Tyne; Wellcome Research Fell. Newc. upon Tyne. Prev: SHO (Gen Med.) Roy. Vict. Infirm., Freeman Hosp. & Newc. Gen. Hosp. Newc.

CHINNOCK, John Henry (retired) Sunningdale, New Wood, Stourbridge DY7 6RX Tel: 01384 393894 — MB ChB 1959 Aberd.; DObst RCOG 1962. Prev: Clin. Asst. (Gyn.) Dudley Guest Hosp.

CHINOY, Virendra Jayantilal 23 Vicarage Field, Worthing BN13 3SF Tel: 01903 262116 — MB BS Indore 1968.

CHINTAPATLA, Srinivas Department of Surgery, Trafford Healthcare NHS Trust, Manchester M41 5SL — MB BS 1988 Bangalore.

CHINWALA, Abu-Talib Mohammed 153 Montagu Mansions, London W1U 6LQ — BM 1996 Soton.

CHINYAMA, Nyaya Catherine 3A Blackstock Road, London N4 2JF — MB ChB 1986 Zimbabwe; MRCPath 1995, D 1993. Clin. Research Fell. Univ. Bristol. Socs: BMA; Brit. Div. Acad. of Internat. Path. Prev: Sen. Regist. & Regist. (Histopath.) St. Bart. Hosp.

CHIODINI, Peter Leslie The Hospital for Tropical Diseases, Mortimer Market, Capper St., London WC1E 6AU Tel: 020 387 9300 Ext: 5418 Fax: 0207 383 0041; 9 Lavenham Drive, Biddenham, Bedford MK40 4QR — MB BS 1978 Lond.; PhD Lond. 1973, BSc (1st cl. Hons.) 1970; FRCP Lond. 1992; MRCP (UK) 1980; MRCS Eng. LRCP Lond. 1978; FRCPath 1996. (King's Coll. Hosp.) Cons. Parasitol. Hosp. for Trop. Dis. Lond.; Hon. Sen. Lect. Lond. Sch. Hyg. & Trop. Med. Socs: Fell. Roy. Soc. Trop. Med. & Hyg.; Brit. Soc. Antimicrob. Chemother.; Amer. Soc. Trop. Med. & Hyg. Prev: Vis. Prof. (Parasitol.) Univ. Chicago; Sen. Regist. (Communicable & Trop. Dis.) E. Birm. Hosp.; Regist. (Med.) St. Geo. Hosp. Lond.

CHIOTAKAKOU, Efterpi Flat E, 95 Westbourne Terrace, London W2 6QT — Ptychio Iatrikes 1989 Athens.

CHIPCHASE, Barry Benjamin Kolvin Unit, General Hospital, Newcastle upon Tyne NE4 6BE Tel: 0191 256 3103 Fax: 0191 219 5052 Email: barry@kolvin.org — MB ChB 1986 Birm.; MRCPsych 1992; MBA (Durham) 1998. Cons. (Forens. Adolesc. Psychiat.) Kolvin Unit Newc. Gen. Hosp. Socs: Amer. Acad. of Child & Adolesc. Psychiat. Prev: Sen. Regist. (Forens. Adolesc. Psychiat.) N.. & Yorks. RHA; Regist. (Psychiat.) Barnsley Hall Hosp. BromsGr..

CHIPCHASE, Jeremy Giles Addison 30 The Lawns, Northampton NN5 6AF — MB BS 1990 Lond.

CHIPPENDALE, John Houghton (retired) — MB ChB 1957 Leeds; DObst RCOG 1959. Prev: GP Lancaster.

CHIPPENDALE, Susan Mary Ashington House, Ashington Way, Westlea, Swindon SN5 7XY; Agecroft, Lodersfield, Lechlade — MB ChB 1980 Dundee; BSc Dund 1976.

CHIPPERFIELD, Alex Old Cottage, Burcot, Abingdon OX14 3DP — MB BS 1997 Lond.

CHIPPERFIELD, Robert Ayton 16 Beechpark Way, Watford WD17 3TY — BM BS 1997 Nottm.

CHIPPERFIELD, Ruth Susan 284 Cottingham Road, Hull HU6 8QA — MB BChir 1994 Camb.; MA Camb. 1995; MRCPsych 1998. (Addenbrooke's, Cambridge) Specialist Regist. (Psychiat) Lucille Van Geest Centre, PeterBoro. Prev: SHO (Psychiat.) Fulbourn Hosp. Camb.; SHO (Psychiat.) Hinchingbrooke Hosp. Huntingdon.

CHIPPINDALE, Andrew James Portland Lodge, West Road, Hexham NE46 3JU; Royal Victoria Infirmary, Newcastle upon Tyne NE1 4LP — MB ChB 1980 Leeds; BSc (Anat.) Leeds 1977, MB ChB 1980; MRCP (UK) 1983; FRCR 1987. Cons. Radiol.

CHIPPINDALE, Lorna (retired) 19 St Just Close, Ferndown BH22 9EA — MB ChB 1950 Sheff.; FFA RCS Eng. 1959; DA Eng. 1954. Prev: Cons. Anaesth. Whittington Hosp. Lond.

CHIPPINDALE, Patricia (retired) 6A Rowlands Hill, Wimborne BH21 1AN Tel: 01202 880732 — MB BS 1946 Lond.; MRCP Lond. 1949; MRCS Eng. LRCP Lond. 1946; DCH Eng. 1950. Prev: Med. Regist. & Ho. Surg. Univ. Coll. Hosp.

CHIPPINDALE, Ruth Marian (retired) 83 High Street, Harlton, Cambridge CB3 7ES Tel: 01223 262170 — MB BChir Camb. 1941; MRCS Eng. LRCP Lond. 1940; DCH Eng. 1943; MA 1990. Prev: Ho. Surg. Univ. Coll. Hosp.

CHIPPING, Patricia Margaret Trust Headquarters, Royal Infirmary, Princess Road, Hartshill, Stoke-on-Trent ST4 7PS Tel: 01782 555414 Fax: 01782 555414 Email: pd-chipping@nstaffsh.wmids.nhs.uk — MB BS 1973 Lond.; FRCP Lond. 1991; MRCP (UK) 1977; FRCPath 1992, M 1980. (Roy. Free) Cons. Haemat. N. Staffs. Hosp. NHS Trust; Med. Director, N. Staffs. Hosp. NHS Trust. Prev: Sen. Regist. (Haemat.) Hammersmith Hosp. Lond.

CHIPPINGTON, Samantha Jane 8 Hewson Road, Lincoln LN1 1RX — BM BS 1994 Nottm.

CHIQUITO-LOPEZ, Mr Plutarco Elias 2 Valebrooke Gardens, Sunderland SR2 7HU — D Med y Cir 1980 Guayaquil Ecuador; FRCSI 1990. Prev: Clin. Research Fell. (A & E Med.) John Radcliffe Hosp. Oxf.

CHIRAYATH, Henry Geriatrics, Lurgan Hospital, Lurgan BT66 8NX Tel: 028 38 323262 Fax: 028 38 329483 Email: chirayath@hotmail.com; 66 Lyndale Grange, Craigavon, Portadown BT63 5XB — DPM 1978 R.C.P. London; MBBS 1965 Kerala University, India; FRCP 1994 R.C.P. Edinburgh; MD 1969; MRCP 1983 R.C.P. UK. (Calicui Medical College, Calicui, India) Locum Cons. in Geriat.s with on-call and O.P. comitments in Gen. Med. Socs: Fell., Roy. Coll. of Phys.s, Edin.; Brit. Geriat. Soc.; Stroke Soc. of N.ern Irel. Prev: Cons. Phys. and NeUrol. Airbase Hosp., Dhahran, Saudi Arabia.

CHIRGWIN, Margaret Elizabeth c/o BHC Lagos, King Charles St., London SW1A 2AH Tel: 00 234 445 33066 Fax: 00 234 445 33067 Email: benuefund@compuserve.com; Vine Cottage, Winterborne Stickland, Blandford Forum DT11 0NT Tel: 01258 880406 — BM BCh 1986 Oxf.; BA Camb. 1983. Specialist (Primary Healthcare Specialist) Benue Health Fund Project, Nigeria, Dept. Internat. Develop. Lond. Socs: MPA Harvard 1989. Prev: Health & Populat. Field Manager Bolivia Overseas Developm. Admin. Lond.; Regist. (Pub. Health Med.) Leics. HA; Project Ldr. Primary Health Care Progr. Cambodia Health UnLtd. Lond.

CHIRODIAN, Mr Nishan Red House, 101 Kingsway, Mildenhall, Bury St Edmunds IP28 7HS Tel: 01638 716513 Fax: 01638 716513 — MB BChir 1993 Camb.; FRCS Eng. 1998. (Cambridge (Addenbrookes)) Specialist Regist. Rotat. (Trauma & Orthop.) E. Anglian.

CHISHAM, (Alice Jane) Mary The Drey, Roundhill Way, Cobham KT11 2EX Tel: 01372 842021 — MB BS Lond. 1962; MRCPsych 1984; DObst RCOG 1964. (Char. Cross) Cons. Psychiat. Mid-Surrey HA; Cons. Psychist. Qu. Eliz.'s Foundat. for the Disabled, Leatherhead. Socs: BMA. Prev: Ho. Surg. Bromley Hosp.; Ho. Phys. (Radiother. & Radiodiag.) Char. Cross Hosp. Lond.; Asst. MOH City of Cardiff Pub. HA.

CHISHICK, Alice Rebecca Tipper Down, Tipper Lane, South Harting, Petersfield GU31 5LH Tel: 01730 825788 — MB ChB 1987 Bristol; MRCGP 1993; DFFP 1993; DRCOG 1991. Prev: Trainee GP Basingstoke Dist. Hosp. VTS.

CHISHICK, Harry Benjamin James Postern Gate Surgery, Cinque Ports Street, Rye TN31 7AP Tel: 01797 223333/224924 Fax: 01797 226858; Tower Cottage, Winchelsea TN36 4EA Tel: 01797 226653 — MB BCh 1978 Wales; MRCGP 1983; DRCOG 1981; Cert. Family Plann. JCC 1981. (Cardiff) Surg. Lt. Cdr. RNR. Socs: BMA. Prev: Trainee GP Frimley Pk. Hosp. VTS; SHO (Accid. Serv.) John Radcliffe Hosp. Oxf.; Ho. Phys (Neurol.) & Ho. Surg. Profess. Surg. Unit Univ. Hosp. Wales Cardiff.

CHISHOLM, Alexander Gordon (retired) Greencroft, Forest Lane, Kirklevington, Yarm TS15 9ND — MB ChB 1952 Aberd.; DPM Leeds 1962; MRC Psych 1972. Prev: SHMO & Regist. De la Pole Hosp. Willerby.

CHISHOLM, Andrew Douglas (retired) Flat 10, Servite House, Kinbrae Park Gardens, Newport-on-Tay DD6 8JX — LRCP LRCS Ed. LRFPS Glas. 1939. Prev: Dep. PMO Sch. Health Serv. Glas.

CHISHOLM, Cecilia Janette Simpson, Capt. RAMC (retired) Failte, 3 Machrie Drive, Helensburgh G84 9EJ Email: chisholm@failte.prestel.co.uk — MB ChB Glas. 1961; DCH Eng. 1965; DObst RCOG 1963. SCMO Bedford & Shires Health & Care NHS Trust; Locum Community Paediat., Renfrewsh. & Inverclyde Primary Care NHS Trust. Prev: Asst. MOH Lond. Boro. Harringey.

CHISHOLM, David George Royal Marsden NHS Trust, Fulham Road, London SW3 6JJ; 87 Woodside, Wimbledon, London SW19 7BA — MB BS 1986 Lond.; MRCP (UK) 1990; FRCA 1993. (Char. Cross Hosp. Med. Sch.) Cons. Anaesth. Roy. Marsden NHS Trust Lond. Socs: Assn. Anaesth. GB & Irel.; BMA. Prev: Sen. Regist. (Anaesth.) Univ. Coll. Hosp. NHS Trust; Regist. (Anaesth.) Gt. Ormond St. Hosp., UCH & Middlx. Hosps. Lond.; SHO (Anaesth.) St. Geo. Hosp. Lond.

CHISHOLM, Diana Morag (retired) Seagulls, Church Road, Binstead, Ryde PO33 3SY Tel: 01983 563780 Email: seagulls@tcp.co.uk — MB ChB Cape Town 1955; MD Cape Town 1970; FRCPath 1986, M 1974. Sen. Lect. (Haemat.) Univ. Soton. Prev: Cons. Haematologist Emenities (Retd. June 1998).

CHISHOLM, Donald (retired) 1 Swans Walk, Saltern's Lane, Hayling Island PO11 9TX — MRCS Eng. LRCP Lond. 1940; DMRD Eng. 1949. Prev: Cons. Radiol. Wessex RHB.

CHISHOLM, Mr Elliot McNab The Woking Nuffield Hospital, Shores Road, Woking GU21 4BY Tel: 01483 763511; Urquhart House, Aviary Road, Pyrford, Woking GU22 8TH — MB ChB 1977 Ed.; ChM Ed. 1988; FRCS Eng. 1981. Cons. Gen. Surg. St Peter's Hosp. Chertsey. Prev: Sen. Regist. (Gen. Surg.) Yorks. RHA; Cancer Research Fell. Yorks. RHA; Post Fell.sh. Surgic. Rotat. St. Jas. Hosp. Leeds.

CHISHOLM, Helen Kennedy (retired) 15 Lothian Terrace, Newtongrange, Dalkeith EH22 4QL — MB ChB 1945 Glas. Prev: Res. Ho. Phys. Roy. Infirm. Glas.

CHISHOLM, Mr Iain Hampden Southampton Eye Unit, Southampton General Hospital, Tremona Road, Southampton SO16 6YD Tel: 02380 794445; Oakfield, Farley Chamberlayne, Braishfield, Romsey SO51 0QR Tel: 01794 368250 — MB Camb. 1966, BChir 1965; MA Camb. 1966; FRCS Eng. 1972; FRCOphth 1988; DO Eng. 1970. (St. Thos.) Cons. Ophth. Soton. Eye unit, S.ampton Gen. Hosp. Socs: Macular Soc.; Club Jules Gonin; Oxf. Congr. Prev: Ho. Off. (Neurosurg.) Nat. Hosp. Nerv. Dis. Lond.; Resid. Surg. Off. Moorfields Eye Hosp. (City Rd. Br.) Lond.; Postgrad. Fell. Bascom Palmer Eye Inst. Miami, USA.

CHISHOLM, Ian Duncan (retired) The Manor House, Stratton-on-the-Fosse, Bath BA3 4QU Tel: 01761 232064 — MB BS 1960 Lond.; MA Oxf. 1955, BA 1953; FRCP Lond. 1980, M 1963; FRCPsych 1981, M 1971; DPM Lond. 1966. Prev: Cons. Psychiat. S.mead HD & Clin. Lect. (Ment. Health) Univ. Bristol.

CHISHOLM, Ian Graham (retired) April Cottage, Church cliff, Kingsdown, Deal CT14 8AT Tel: 01304 373050 — MB BChir 1960 Camb.; MB Camb. 1960, BChir 1959; MRCS Eng. LRCP Lond. 1959; DObst RCOG 1960. Prev: Ho. Phys. (Experim. Med.) & Resid. Obst. Guy's Hosp. Lond.

CHISHOLM, Ian McGregor Alison Lea Medical Centre, Calderwood, East Kilbride, Glasgow G74 3BE Tel: 01355 236444 — MB ChB Glas. 1969; DObst RCOG 1971.

CHISHOLM, Mr Ian Thomas Tel: 01384 402327 Fax: 01384 270306; Jasmine Cottage, 18 School Road, Wombourne, Wolverhampton WV5 9ED — MB ChB 1973 Leeds; FRCS Eng. 1978; FRCS Ed. 1977. (Univ. Leeds) Prev: Regist. (Surg.) Guest Hosp. Dudley; Regist. Roy. Berks. Hosp. Reading; Fell. (Vasc. Surg.) Austin Hosp. Univ. Melbourne, Austral.

CHISHOLM, James Kenneth (retired) 8 Green Street, Bothwell, Glasgow G71 8RN Tel: 01698 852214 — MB ChB Glas. 1945.

CHISHOLM, Jennifer Margaret 51 Enfield Road, Brentford TW8 9PA — MB ChB 1992 Glas.

CHISHOLM, John William Twyford Health Centre, Loddon Hall Road, Twyford, Reading RG10 9JA Tel: 0118 934 0112 Fax: 0118 934 1048; 30 Crisp Road, Henley-on-Thames RG9 2EP Tel: 01491 575343 Fax: 01491 572413 — MB 1975 Camb.; BA Camb. 1971, MB 1975, BChir 1974; MRCGP 1978; DRCOG 1977. (Camb. & Westm. Hosp.) Socs: BMA (Counc. Gen. Med. Servs. & Other Comms.); GMSC Dep. Chairm. & Negotiator. Prev: Ho. Surg. & Ho. Phys. Croydon Gen. Hosp.; Trainee GP Reading VTS.

CHISHOLM, Julia Clare Department of Paediatric Oncology, Great Ormond St. Hospital, Great Ormond St, London WC1N 3JH Tel: 0207 4056 9200 Fax: 0207 813 8588; 29 Cornwall Road, Sutton SM2 6DU — BM BCh 1989 Oxf.; PhD Camb. 1987, MA 1987, BA 1983; MRCP (UK) 1992. (Oxford) Cons., Paediat. Oncol., Gt. Ormond St. Hosp. Socs: MRCPCH; UKCCSG. Prev: Specialist Regist. Paediat., Epsom Gen. Hosp.; Specialist Regist. Paediat. Oncol., Gt. Ormond St. Hosp.

CHISHOLM, Lindsey Jane 29 Snowdon Terrace, Seamill, West Kilbride KA23 9HN — MB BS 1991 Lond.; BSc Lond. 1988.

CHISHOLM, Margaret (retired) Holly Cottage, 29 Shelt Hill, Woodborough, Nottingham NG14 6DG Tel: 0115 965 2511 — MB BCh BAO 1923 Belf.

CHISHOLM, Roger Alexander Department of Radiology, Hope Hospital, Stott Lane, Salford M6 8HD Tel: 0161 787 5474 Fax: 0161 787 5009; Avondale, 15 Brackley Road, Monton, Eccles, Manchester M30 9LG Tel: 0161 707 5547 — MB BChir 1980 Camb.; MA Camb. 1977; MRCP (UK) 1983; FRCR 1986. (Cambridge) Cons. Diagn. Radiol. Hope Hosp. Univ. Manch. Sch. Med. Salford. Socs: Brit. Med. Ultrasound Soc.; Roy. Coll. Radiol.; Brit. Inst. Radiol. Prev: Sen. Regist. (Diagn. Radiol.) Addenbrooke's Hosp. Camb.

CHISHOLM, Ronald Ian Bruachan, Methlick, Ellon AB41 7JS; The Old School, The Square, Tarves, Ellon AB41 Tel: 0165 15 777 Fax: 0165 15 805 — MB ChB 1982 Aberd.; MRCGP 1986; DRCOG 1985. Prev: Trainee GP/SHO Aberd. VTS; Ho. Off. Falkirk & Dist. Roy. Infirm. & Raigmore Hosp. Inverness.

CHISHOLM-BATTEN, Roger Edmund Harold Road Surgery, 164 Harold Road, Hastings TN35 5NG Tel: 01424 720878/437962 Fax: 01424 719525 — MB BS 1973 Lond.; DRCOG 1977.

CHISHOLM-BATTEN, Walter Rodolphe (retired) Apple Tree Cottage, Bedwyn Common, Marlborough SN8 3LJ Tel: 01672 870289 — MRCS Eng. LRCP Lond. 1958; LMSSA Lond. 1951; LM Rotunda 1953. Prev: Sen. Regist. (Psychiat.) St. Francis Hosp. Haywards Heath & Brighton Gen. Hosp.

CHISHTI, Ahmad Dustghir 4 Balmoral Terrace, South Gosforth, Newcastle upon Tyne NE3 1YH Email: ax@chishti1.freeserve.co.uk — MB ChB 1988 Dundee; BMSc (Hons.) Dund 1984; FRCA 1996; MRCGP 1992; DRCOG 1992. (Univ. Dundee Med. Sch.) Specialist Regist. Rotat. (Anaesth.) Newc. Gen. Hosp.; Research Fell. Brit. Jl. of Anaesths.

CHISHTI, Jamal Muhammad 30 The Glen, Heaton, Chorley New Road, Bolton BL1 5DB — MB BS 1962 Punjab; FFA RCS Eng. 1970; DA Eng. 1968.

CHISHTI, Mr Muhammad Khalid Naseem 22 Harrow Street, Manchester M8 5RZ — MB BS 1981 Karachi; FRCS Glas. 1987; FRCS Ed. 1986.

CHISHTI, Mustafa Kamel The Health Centre, Rossland Place, Kinghorn, Burntisland KY3 9RT Tel: 01592 890217 Fax: 01592 890456 — MB BS 1965 Punjab.

CHISHTI, Sarah 4 Balmoral Terrace, South Gosforth, Newcastle upon Tyne NE3 1YH — MB BS 1994 Newc.

CHISHTI, Shahed Kaleem Kim 41 Seafield Road, Dundee DD1 4NL — MB ChB 1997 Dundee.

CHISHTI, Zeba Jasmin 2 Ross Place, Kinghorn, Burntisland KY3 9SQ — MB ChB 1997 Ed.

CHISNALL, Andrew South Street Surgery, 83 South Street, Bishop's Stortford CM23 3AP Tel: 01279 710800 Fax: 01279 710801 — MB BS 1986 Lond.; MRCGP 1995; DCH RCP Lond. 1989. Police Surg. Herts.

CHISNALL, David Philip 24 Edale Road, Allerton, Liverpool L18 5HR — MB ChB 1990 Liverp.; MRCGP 1995.

CHISNALL, Joseph Leonard, MC 4 Fairfield Gardens, Crank, St Helens WA11 7SL Tel: 01744 26650 — MB ChB 1938 Liverp. (Liverp.)

CHISNELL, Paul Thomas Valkyrie Road Surgery, 20 Valkyrie Road, Westcliff on Sea SS0 8BX Tel: 01702 331255 Fax: 01702 437050 — MB BS 1983 Lond.; DA (UK) 1986.

CHISSELL, Mr Hugh Richard Department of Orthopaedics, Frimley Park Hospital, Portsmouth Road, Frimley, Camberley GU16 7UJ Tel: 01276 604575 Email: hehissell@doctors.org.uk; Greystones, Bentley, Farnham GU10 5NE Tel: 01420 23117 — MB BS 1985 Lond.; FRCS (Orth.) 1994; FRCS Eng. 1989; FRCS Ed. 1989. (St. Bartholomew's Hospital) Cons. Orthop. Surg. Frimley Pk. Hosp. Camberley Surrey. Prev: Sen. Regist. (Orthop. & Trauma) Char. Cross Hosp.

CHISSELL, Sarah Anne William Harvey Hospital, Ashford TN24 0LZ — MB ChB 1986 Bristol; MRCOG 1991. Cons. (Obst & Gyn) William Harvey Hosp., Ashford, Kent. Prev: Sen. Regist. (O & G) Poole Hosp. Dorset; Research Fell. (Gyn.) St. Michael's Hosp. Bristol; Regist. (O & G) S.mead Hosp. Bristol.

CHISWELL, Richard James Novartis Pharmaceutials UK Ltd, Frimley Business Park, Frimley, Camberley GU16 5SG Tel: 01276 698673 Fax: 01276 698317 Email: richard.chiswell@pharma.novartis.com; Wild Thyme, Gorse Bank Close, Storrington, Pulborough RH20 3AQ — MB BS 1969 Lond.; MRCS Eng. LRCP Lond. 1969; DPharm Med. (Guy's) Med. Adviser Novartis Pharmaceut., UK Ltd. Prev: Med. Adviser Ciba Geigy Pharmaceut. Horsham.

CHISWICK, Derek Royal Edinburgh Hospital, Morningside Place, Edinburgh EH10 5HF Tel: 0131 537 5854 Fax: 0131 537 5857 Email: derek.chiswick@lpct.scot.nhs.uk; 6 St. Catherines Place, Edinburgh EH9 1NU Tel: 0131 667 2444 Fax: 0131 662 8913 — MB ChB Liverp. 1969; MPhil Ed. 1978; FRCPsych 1989, M 1976. (Univ. Liverp.) Cons. Forens. Psychiat. Lothian Primary care. NHS Trust; Hon. Clin. Sen. Lect. (Forens. Psychiat.) Univ. Edin. Prev: Mem. Indep. homicide inquiry into care & treat. of Darren Carr.; Mem. Home Off. Advis. Bd. Restricted Pats.; Mem. MacLean Comm. On Serious Violent & Sexual Offenders.

CHISWICK, Professor Malcolm Leon St. Mary's Hospital, Whitworth Park, Manchester M13 0JH Tel: 0161 276 6331 Fax: 0161 276 6536 Email: m.chiswick@man.ac.uk; Highclere, Parkfield Road, Altrincham WA14 2BT Tel: 0161 928 8579 Fax: 0161 929 5564 Email: m.chiswick@btinternet.com — MB BS 1965 Newc.; MD Newc. 1974; FRCP Lond. 1980, M 1969; FRCPCH 1997; DCH Eng. 1967. (Univ. Newc. u. Tyne) Cons. Paediat. N. W.. Regional Perinatal Centre St. Mary's Hosp. Manch.; Prof. Child Health & Paediat. Univ. Manch. Socs: (Ex-Hon. Sec.) Brit. Assn. Perinatal Med.; Neonat. Soc.; Roy. Soc. Med. Prev: Research Assoc. (Child Health) St. Mary's Hosp. Manch.; Regist. (Paediat.) St. Geo. Hosp. Lond. & Soton. Childr. Hosp.

CHITA, Balbir Singh Paisley Road West Surgery, 532 Paisley Road West, Glasgow G51 1RN Tel: 0141 427 2504; 42 Dudley Drive, Hyndland, Glasgow G12 9RZ Tel: 0141 334 0965 — MB ChB 1982 Aberd.

CHITALE, Mr Sudhanshu Vinayak Norfolk & Norwich Univ. Hospital NHS Trust, Colney Lane, Norwich NRG 7UY Tel: 01603 286286; Tel: 01603 812015 — MBBS 1982; FRCS 1998 (Gen. Surg.) Royal Coll. Surg. London; Dip Urol 1995 Univ. Coll. London; FICS 1995 (Surg) Int. Coll. Of Surg. Chicago USA; MS 1986 (Gen. Surg.) Shivasi Univ. India. (DRVM Med. Coll. Solapur, India '82 & Shivasi Univ. Kolhapur, Indis '86) Staff Urol., Norf. & Norwich Univ. Hosp. NHS Trust, Norwich. Socs: BMA; Race & Culture Awareness Gp., Norf. & Norf. Hosp.; Urol. Soc. Of India (USI). Prev: Regist. Urol., Norf. & Norwich Hosp. Norwich; Regist. Surg. / Urol. Bedford Hosp. Bedford.

CHITHILA, Charles James Martyn 41 Binghill Crescent, Milltimber AB13 0HP — MB ChB 1983 Manch.; BSc Malawi 1977. SHO (Gen. Med. & Geriat.) Clwyd HA. Prev: SHO (Rheum.) W. Lancs. HA; Ho. Off. (Surg.) Oldham HA; Ho. Off. (Med.) Blackburn, Hyndburn & Ribble Valley HA.

CHITHIRAMOHAN, Ramalingam Nirmalakumar Lucy Baldwin Hospital, Olive Grove, Bewdley Road, Stourport-on-Severn DY13 8XZ Tel: 01299 827327; 37 Marlborough Avenue, Bromsgrove B60 2PH Tel: 01527 576295 — MB BS 1983 Colombo; MRCPsych 1989. Sen. Regist. (Adult Gen. Psychiat.) W. Midl. Prev: Regist. (Psychiat. & Forens Psychiat.) Reaside Clinic Birm.

CHITKARA, Mr Deepak Kumar Department of Ophthalmology, Walton Hospital, Rice Lane, Liverpool L9 1AE Tel: 0151 529 4044 Fax: 0151 529 4283 Email: dkc@roseneyecentre.co.uk — MB ChB 1982 Manch.; FRCOphth 1989; DO RCS Eng. 1988. (Univ. Manch.) Cons. Ophth. Surg. Walton Hosp. Liverp. Socs: Exec. Comm. Mem. UKISCRS; ASCRS; AAO. Prev: Sen. Regist. (Ophth.) N.. Region Newc.; Regist. (Ophth.) Roy. Vict. Infirm. Newc. u. Tyne & N. Riding Infirm. Middlesbrough.

CHITKARA, Neelam Kings College Hospital, Denmark Hill, London SE5 9RS Tel: 020 7737 4000; 4 Shelley Close, Coulsdon CR5 2LT — MB BS 1976 Delhi; FRCA 1993; DA (UK) 1989; DObst RCPI 1981; DO RCPSI 1979. Staff Grade & Research Fell. Intens. Care Unit (Anaesth.) Medway Hosp. Gillingham.

CHITKARA, Subhash Chander Tollers Lane Surgery, 59 Tollers Lane, Old Coulsdon, Coulsdon CR5 1BF Tel: 01737 556880 — MB BS 1971 Panjab; MRCPI 1981.

CHITNAVIS, Bhupal Prabhakar 85 Firs Drive, Hounslow TW5 9TA — MB BS 1989 Lond.; BSc Lond. 1986, MB BS 1989.

CHITNAVIS, Diptila Haematology Department, John Radcliffe Hospital, Headington, Oxford OX3 9DU — MB BChir 1991 Camb.; MA Camb. 1991; MRCP (UK) 1994; Dip RCPath 1997. (Downing Coll. Univ. Camb. UMDS Guy's & St. Thos. Hosps. Lon) Regist. (Haemat.) John Radcliffe Hosp. Oxf. Socs: Assn. Clin. Paths. Prev: SHO Oxf. Haemophilia Centre Oxf. Radcliffe NHS Trust; SHO (Renal) Guy's & St. Thos. Hosps. NHS Trust Lond.; SHO (Gen. Med.) Qu. Mary's Hosp. Sidcup Kent.

CHITNAVIS, Mr Jaisingh Prabhakar 40 French Laurence Way, Chalgrove, Oxford OX44 7YF — MB BChir 1989 Camb.; FRCS 2001 (Tr & Orth); MChir 2000; MA Camb. 1991; FRCS Ed. 1993; FRCS Eng. 1993; LMSSA Lond. 1988. (Charing Cross & Westminster) Specialist Regist. Rotat. (Trauma & Orthop.) Oxf. Socs: Med. Protec. Soc.; Brit. Orthop. Assn.; Brit. Orthopaedic Trainees Assn. Prev: M. E. Davis Research Fell. Roy. Coll. Surgs. Eng.; PeriFell.sh. Rotat. Surg. W.m. & Watford Hosps.; Knee Surg. Fell. Sydney, Australia.

CHITNAVIS, Sarojini Prabhakar 85 Firs Drive, Hounslow TW5 9TA — MB BS 1955 Osmania.

CHITNIS, Anand John Castle Practice, 2 Hawthorne Road, Castle Bromwich, Birmingham B36 0HH Tel: 0121 747 2422 Fax: 0121 749 1196 Email: anand.chitnis@gp-m89026.nhs.uk — MB ChB 1987 Manch.; BSc St. And. 1984; MRCGP 1992; T(GP) 1992; DRCOG 1991; Cert. Family Plann. JCC 1990. Clin. Asst. (ENT) Good Hope Hosp. Sutton Coldfield; Assessor for Confidential Enquiry into Stillbirths & Deaths in Infancy W. Midl; Child Health Surveillance Trainer Solihull; GP Trainer W. Midls. Region; Tutor Med. Studs. Birm. Univ. Socs: Liaison Comm. E. Birm. Matern. Servs.; Midl. Fac. Roy. Coll. GP (Dist. Represen. Solihull); BMA. Prev: Trainee GP Cheadle Hulme; SHO (Paediat.) Withington & Wythenshawe Hosps. Manch.; SHO (O & G) St. Mary's Hosp. Manch.

CHITNIS, Jay-Gopal (retired) Solihull Health Authority, 6th Floor, Mell House, 46 Drury Lane, Solihull B91 3BU Tel: 0121 712 8332 Fax: 0121 712 8302 Email: jai.chitnis@solihull-ha.wmids.nhs.uk — MB ChB Birm. 1955; MRCS Eng. LRCP Lond. 1955; FRCGP 1991, M 1962; DObst RCOG 1958. Med. Adv. Solihull Health Auth. Prev: Hosp. Pract. ENT Dept. Qu. Eliz. Hosp. Birm.

CHITNIS, Mr Sanjeev Lakshaman Consultant Orthopaedic Surgeon, Royal Alexandra Hospital, Corsebar Road, Paisley PA2 9PN Tel: 0141 887 9111 Fax: 0141 580 4898; 4 Lynton Avenue, Whitecraigs, Glasgow G46 7JP Tel: 0141 571 6808 Fax: 0141 571 6808 Email: shreyas@chitniss.freeserve.co.uk — MB BS 1978 Delhi; MSC (Orth.) Lond. 1988; MRCS Eng. LRCP Lond. 1983; FRCS Glas. 1985; FRCS Ed. 1985. (Univ. Coll. Med. Sciences, Delhi) Cons. Orthop. Surg. Roy. Alexandra Hosp. Paisley. Socs: BMA; Fell. BOA; Brit. Soc. for the Surg. of the Hand. Prev: Cons. Orthop. Surg. Social Insur. Hosp. Riyadh, Saudi Arabia.

CHITRA, Alex 17 Anderson Close, London N21 1TH — MB BS 1996 Lond.

CHITRA, Gopinathan 17 Whitehall Close, Chigwell Row, Chigwell IG7 6EQ Tel: 020 8559 9897 — MB BS 1984 Kerala; FRCA 1994; FFA RCSI 1993; DA (UK) 1990. Cons. Anaesth. Barking, Havering & Redbridge Hosp.s NHS Trust, Romford. Socs: OAA; BMA; AAGBI. Prev: Sen. Regist. King's Coll. Hosp. & Roy. Sussex Co. Hosp.; Regist. Rotat. (Anaesth.) King's Coll. Hosp. & Medway Hosp. Kent; Regist. (Anaesth.) OldCh. Hosp. Romford.

CHITRAPU, Raghuram Kiran 5 Jerbourg Close, Newcastle ST5 3LR — MB ChB 1996 Liverp.

CHITSABESAN, Praminthra 20 Roundwood, Shipley BD18 4JP — MB BS 1997 Newc.

CHITSABESAN, Prathiba 20 Roundwood, Shipley BD18 4JP — MB ChB 1996 Manch.

CHITSABESAN, Sabanathan Sai Medical Centre, 59 St. Pauls Road, Manningham, Bradford BD8 7LS Tel: 01274 543464 Fax: 01274 490003 — MB BS 1964 Ceylon; DPM Eng. 1974. (Ceylon)

CHITTENDEN, Keith Frederick (retired) 17 The Droveway, Hove BN3 6LF — MB BS 1961 Lond.; MRCS Eng. LRCP Lond. 1960; DObst RCOG 1963. Prev: GP Hove.

CHITTICK, David George Hubert 20A Longbeach Road, London SW11 5ST — MB BS 1988 Lond.; BSc Lond. 1985, MB BS 1988; MRCGP 1992; DRCOG 1990.

CHITTY, John Robert New Court Surgery, 39 Boulevard, Weston Super Mare BS23 1PF Tel: 01934 624242 Fax: 01934 642608; 155 Old Mixon Road, Hutton, Weston Super Mare BS24 9QB — MB ChB 1984 Manch.; MB ChB Manch. l984; MRCGP 1989; T(GP) 1991. (Manch.)

CHITTY, Roger Noel West Cheshire Hospital, Liverpool Road, Chester CH2 1BQ Tel: 01244 365000 Fax: 01244 364251 Email: sharon.walker@mta.wwirraicc-tr.nhs.uk; 9 Kingsway, Heswall, Wirral CH60 3SN — MB ChB 1971 Liverp.; Dip. Psychother. 1983; FRCPsych 1994, M 1980; DCH RCPSI 1976; DObst. RCOG 1975, DFFP 1994; Cert. Family Plann. JCC 1976; Cert. Prescribed Equiv. Exp. JCPTGP 1981. Cons. (Psychiat.) W. Ches. Hosp.; Hon. Clin. Lect. Univ. Liverp. Socs: Liverp. Psychiatr. Soc. (Ex-Pres.); Mem. Liverp. Med. Inst. Prev: Trainee GP Wirral VTS; Lect. & Hon. Sen. Regist. (Clin. Psychiat.) Univ. Liverp. & Mersey RHA.

CHITTY, William Alexis (retired) 17 St Quentin Rise, Bradway, Sheffield S17 4PR — MB BS 1951 Lond.; MRCGP 1976. Prev: Hosp. Pract. Dept. Geriat. Med. N.. Gen. Hosp. Sheff.

CHIU, Catherine Ka Fu 106 Denbigh Street, London SW1V 2EX — MB BS 1998 Lond.; MB BS Lond 1998.

CHIU, Chung Tai 37 St Werburghs Road, Manchester M21 0TL — MB ChB 1979 Manch.; BSc St. And. 1976.

CHIU, Dong Ching 91 Wilkinson Way, Chiswick, London W4 5XF — MB BS 1991 Lond.; MRCGP 1996; DFFP 1996. Prev: SHO (Paediat., ENT & O & G) Centr. Middlx. Hosp. Lond.; GP/Regist. Lond. VTS; SHO Rotat. (Radiother. & Oncol.) Char. Cross Hosp. & Mt. Vernon Hosp. Lond.

CHIU, Irene Hau-Ming Room 3, 51 Park Avenue, Worthing BN11 2HX — MB BS 1998 Lond.; MB BS Lond 1998.

CHIU, Tor Wo 8 Kingsley Avenue, Stretford, Manchester M32 0UB Email: gola04@udcf.gla.ac.uk — BM BCh 1993 Oxf.; MA Oxf. 1994, BA 1990. SHO (ENT) Vict. Infirm. Glasg. Socs: Roy. Soc. Med. Prev: Lect. (Anat.) Hunt. Inst. Univ. Glas.; Prosector (Anat.) Roy. Coll. Surgs. & Phys. Glas.; Ho. Phys. W. Infirm. Glas.

CHIU, Yu Siu 45 Baldwin Avenue, Childwall, Liverpool L16 3GD; 22B Fu Bon Court, 32 Fortress Hill Road, North Point, Hong Kong — MB ChB 1990 Liverp. Socs: BMA & MPS.

CHIVATE, Mr Jayant Gajanan 15 Manor Court, Moat Road, Walsall WS2 9XS — MB BS 1977 Poona; MS Poona 1982; FRCS Glas. 1987.

CHIVATE, Vandana Jayant Flat 15, Manor Court, Manor Hospital, Moat Road, Walsall WS2 9XS — MB BS 1979 Poona.

CHIVERS, Charles Andrew Jericho Health Centre, Walton Street, Oxford OX2 6NW Tel: 01865 558861; 12 Apsley Road, Oxford OX2 7QY Tel: 01865 310350 — MB BS 1975 Lond.; MRCGP 1983; DRCOG 1981; DA Eng. 1978. Prev: GP Trainee Saltash; Med. Off. RRS Discovery; Med. Off. All St.'s Hosp. Transkei, S. Africa.

CHIVERS, Charles Peter, MBE (retired) Heyridge, 17 Warrington Road, Cuddington, Northwich CW8 2LH Tel: 01606 883093 — MB ChB Manch. 1946; MFOM RCP Lond. 1978; DIH Soc. Apoth. Lond. 1953. Med. Adviser Various Cos. Chesh. Prev: Med. Off. I.C.I. (Paints/Mond).

CHIVERS, Margaret Esther (retired) 20 Bridgwater Road, Llanrumney, Cardiff CF3 5TF Tel: 01222 210260 — MB BS Lond. 1950; MRCS Eng. LRCP Lond. 1950; DObst RCOG 1952.

CHIVERS, Steven Edward 16 Duffryn Close, Coychurch, Bridgend CF35 5TA — MB BCh 1997 Wales.

CHIVERTON, Mr Stephen Gregory 8 Spring Grove, Strand on the Green, Chiswick, London W4 3NH — BM BCh 1981 Oxf.; MA Oxf. 1981; FRCS Eng. 1986. Asst. Urol. Lond. Clin.; Lect. UCL. Prev: Research Fell. Div. Gastroenterol. McMaster Univ. Hamilton, Canada.

CHIYENDE, Judith Kombe St. Albans City Hospital, Normandy Road, St Albans AL3 5PN Tel: 01727 66122; 21 Brooklands Court, Hatfield Road, St Albans AL1 3NS — MB ChB Zambia 1979; BSc Zambia 1976; MRCP UK 1987; DCH Glas. 1987.

CHMIELEWSKI, Andrew Trevor Pain Relief Clinic, Northampton General Hospital NHS Trust, Northampton NN1 5BD Tel: 01604 545065 Fax: 01604 544668 Email: atchmielewski@btinternet.com; The Old House, 123 High St, Flore, Northampton NN7 4LW Tel: 01327 340429 Fax: 01327 340272 — MB BS 1973 Lond.; FFA RCS Eng. 1978. (Guy's) Cons. Anaesth. & Pain Relief Gen. Hosp. N.ampton. Socs: BMA; Assn. Anaesth.; Internat. Assn. Study of Pain.

CHOA, Mr Dennis Ian Tel: 020 7915 1313 Fax: 020 7915 1541; The London Otological Centre, 66 New Cavendish St, off Harley St, London W1G 8TD Tel: 020 7580 9746 Fax: 020 7580 9749 Email: dchoa@tiscali.co.uk — BM BCh 1976 Oxf.; MA Camb. 1976; MA Oxf. 1977; FRCS Eng. 1981. (Oxf.) Cons. ENT Surg. & Roy. Nat. Throat, Nose & Ear Hosp., Univ. Coll. Hosp & Middlx. Hosp. Lond. Whittington Hosp.; Hon. Sen. Lect. Inst. Otol. & Laryngol. & Feren's Inst.; Hon. Research Sec. Oriole Soc. Socs: Head and Neck Surg.s; Oriole Soc., Hon. Research Sec.; Brit. Assn. of Otohinolaryngologists. Prev: Sen. Regist. (ENT) Hosp. Sick Childr. Gt. Ormond St. & Roy. Nat. Throat Nose & Ear Hosp. Lond.; Regist. (Otorhinolaryng.) Radcliffe Infirm. Oxf.; Lect. (Surg.) Univ. Hong Kong.

CHOA, Mr Robert Gerald Yennadon House, Dousland, Yelverton PL20 6NA — MB BS 1973 Newc.; FRCS Ed. 1978. (Newc.) Cons. Urol. S. W.. RHA. Socs: Brit. Assn. Urol. Surgs. Prev: Sen. Regist. (Urol.) W. Midl. RHA; Regist. (Urol.) Norf. AHA; Lect. Surg. Univ. Hong Kong.

CHOAT, David Julian Michael Shepperton Health Centre, Shepperton Court Drive, Laleham Road, Shepperton TW17 8EJ Tel: 01932 220524 Fax: 01932 244948 — MB BS 1969 Lond.; MRCS Eng. LRCP Lond. 1969; DObst RCOG 1973; DCH Eng. 1972. (Guy's) Hosp. Practioner Cardiol. Prev: SHO (Med., Paediat. & Obst.) Farnham Hosp.

CHODERA, Jennifer Claire 103 Kempton Grove, Cheltenham GL51 0JU — BM BS 1998 Nottm.; BM BS Nottm 1998.

CHODERA, Joseph Dezider 19 Buxton Drive, New Malden KT3 3UX Tel: 020 8942 2303 — MUDr 1950 Charles Univ. Prague; MUDR Charles U. Prague 1950; MS Prague 1968. (Charles Univ.) Hon. Cons. Rehabil., Electrodiagn, Orthop., Prosthesis & Orthotics Qu. Mary's Univ. Hosp. Lond.; Mem. APO Correspondent (Switz.). Socs: Brit. Assn. Rheum.; Assn. Czech Phys. (Prague). Prev: Princip. Research Fell. DoH; Dir. of Prostetic Research Centre Prague; Scientist of CE Acad. of Sc. Prague.

CHOHAN, Bishan Paul Singh 185 North Street, Coventry CV2 3FR — MB BChir 1990 Camb.; PhD Biochem. Wales 1979, BSc (Hons.) Biochem 1976.

CHOHAN, Jilesh 2 Beverley Avenue, Leicester LE4 6JB; The Flat, Goodlands Cottage, Bagatelle Road, St Saviour, Jersey JE2 7TY Tel: 01534 615913 Email: jilesh@epulse.net — MB ChB 1993 Manch. Socs: RCGP.

CHOHAN, Muhammad Masud HM Young Offenders Institute/Remand Centre, Brinsford, New Road, Featherstone, Wolverhampton WV10 7WA — MB BS 1967 Punjab; DPM Eng. 1972. Prev: Sen. Regist. Rotat. (Psychiat.) S. Glam. AHA (T) & M. Glam. AHA.

CHOHAN, Nishat Shafiq Chohan Medical Centre, 407 Little Horton Lane, Bradford BD5 0LG Tel: 01274 740400 Fax: 01274 726680; 2 Colston Close, Bradford BD8 0BN Tel: 01274 409400/225400 — MB BS 1965 Punjab; DA (UK) 1977. (Fatima Jinnah Lahore, Pakistan)

CHOHAN, Sanjiv Singh 36 Raymond Road, London E13 0SW — MB ChB 1993 Aberd.; BSc (Med. Sci.) Hons. Aberd. 1992. SHO (Anaesth.) Aberd. Roy. Infirm.

CHOHAN, Shamsher Singh Rosemead Drive Health Centre, 103 Rosemead Drive, Oadby, Leicester LE2 5PP Tel: 0116 271 3020 — BM BS 1989 Nottm.

CHOHAN, Zahid Latif Flat No 31, Glan Clwyd Hospital, Rhyl LL18 5UJ — MB BS 1986 Punjab.

CHOI, Arnwald Young Sydney Flat 1 Shield House, 22A Sutton Place, London E9 6EH — MB BS 1996 Lond.

CHOI, Bernard Chingford Health Centre, 109 York Road, London E4 8LF Tel: 020 8524 8422 Fax: 020 8559 3538; 13 Essex Road, Chingford, London E4 6DG Tel: 020 8529 4077 — MB BS 1991 Lond.; MRCGP Lond. 1996; DCH Lond. 1996; DRCOG Lond. 1997. (Charing Cross & Westminster) GP Partner.

CHOI, Chi Fai 49 Blackburn Street, Trinity Riverside, Manchester M3 6AS — MB ChB 1994 Birm.; ChB Birm. 1994. SHO (A & E) Hope Hosp. Salford. Socs: BMA. Prev: SHO (Gen. Med.) S.end Gen. Hosp.

CHOI, David 2 Brooklyn Avenue, Flixton, Manchester M41 6PF — MB ChB 1992 Ed.

CHOI, Desiree May Annette Shield House, 22A Sutton Place, London E9 6EH — MB BS 1991 Lond. (St. Bart.) Specialist Regist. (Anaesth.) St. Bart. Hosp., Lond.; Clin. Research Fell., BC Woms. Hosp., Vancouver. Prev: Regist. (Anaesth.) Qu. Eliz. Hosp. Adelaide, S. Austral.

CHOI, Peter 2 Brooklyn Avenue, Flixton, Manchester M41 6PF — BChir 1990 Camb.

CHOI, Sieu Pang 27F Winchester Road, London NW3 3NR — MD 1991 Louvain.

CHOI, William Hong 128 Selhurst Close, Parkside, Wimbledon, London SW19 6AZ — MB BS 1991 Lond. SHO (Gen. Surg.) Kingston Hosp.

CHOJNACKI, Adrian GlaxoSmithKline, North Lonsdale Road, Ulverston LA12 9DR Tel: 01229 482187 Fax: 01229 482580 Email: ac28178@gsk.com; Birkdale, 92 Pk Road, Swarthmoor, Ulverston LA12 0HJ Tel: 01229 586561 — MB ChB 1976 Manch.; MFOM 1992, A 1987; MRCGP 1980; DRCOG 1979; Cert JCC Lond. 1979. Director, Employee Health Managem., GlaxoSmithKline. Socs: Soc. Occupat. Med. Prev: GP Dalton-in-Furness; SHO (Paediat.) Bolton Gen. Hosp.

CHOJNOWSKA, Emma Isbael 56 Lakewood Road, Eastleigh SO53 5AA — MB BChir 1989 Camb.; BA Camb. 1986, MB BChir 1989. Ho. Off. (Gen. Med. & Geriat.) Addenbrooke's Hosp. Camb.

CHOJNOWSKI, Adrian Julian 56 Lakewood Road, Eastleigh SO53 5AA — BChir 1992 Camb.; MA Camb. 1995; MB Camb. 1993; FRCS Lond. 1997. (Camb.) Specialist Regist. (Orthop.) E. Anglia.

CHOK, Shera Li-May Island Health, 145 East Ferry Road, London E14 3BQ — MB BS 1993 Lond.

CHOKSEY, Apurva Bhagwandas 6 Frampton Walk, Clifford Park, Coventry CV2 2JE — MB BS 1988 Bombay.

CHOKSEY, Mr Munchi Soli Department of Neurosurgery, Walsgrave Hospital, Coventry CV2 2DX Tel: 024 76 538955 Fax: 024 76 538744 Email: munchi@choksey.freeserve.co.uk; Fillongley Lodge, Tamworth Road, Fillongley, Coventry CV7 8EA Tel: 01676 542884 Fax: 01676 549017 Email: munehi@choksey.freeserve.co.uk — BM BCh 1979 Oxf.; 1993 MD Camb. 1993; 1980 MA 1980; 1993 FRCS (Surg. Neurol.) 1993; 1984 FRCS Ed. 1984. (Camb.) Cons. Neurosurg. Walsgrave Hosp. NHS Trust Coventry. Socs: BMA;

Soc. of Brit. Neurol. Surg. Prev: Sen. Regist. (Neurosurg.) Newc. Gen. Hosp.

CHOKSHI, Nalinikant Chimanlal Selly Oak Hospital, Raddlebarn Road, Birmingham B29 6JD Tel: 0121 627 1627 Fax: 0121 627 8103 Email: ncchokshi@yahoo.co.uk; 17 Winchfield Drive, Harborne, Birmingham B17 8ST Tel: 0121 429 1467 — MB BS Bombay 1958; DGO CPS Bombay 1959; MRCS Eng. LRCP Lond. 1981; MRCGP 1968; FRCR 1977; DMRD Eng. 1976. (Grant Med. Coll.) Cons. Radiol. Selly Oak Hosp. Birm.; Hon. Sen. Lect. Univ. Birm. Med. Sch.; Extern. Examr. for Master of Med. in Diagnostic Radiol., Mulago Hosp., Makerere Univ., Kampala Uganda 2000 & 2001. Socs: (Ex-Pres. & Ex-Sec.) Uganda Med. Soc.; (Ex-Sec.) Uganda Med. Assn.; BMA (Exec. Mem. Birm. Div.& Past Chairm.). Prev: Ho. Off. (Paediat.) J.J. Gp. Hosps. Bombay, India; Med. Off. (O & G) Motlivai Hosp. Bombay, India; Med. Off. King Geo. VI Hosp. Nairobi, Kenya.

CHOKSHI, Urmila Nalinikant 17 Wichfield Drive, Birmingham B17 8ST — MRCS Eng. LRCP Lond. 1975; DCP Warwick 1985. Assc. Specialist Comm. Paediat. Birm. Childr.s. Hosp. NHS. Trust. Prev: SHO (O & G) Marston Green Matern. Hosp. Birm.; SHO (Paediat.) Birm. Childr. Hosp.; Ho. Off. (Surg.) Gen. Hosp. Walsall.

CHOKSI, Sushmi Mala Desiree Bay Tree Cottage, 19 Winchester St., Botley, Southampton SO30 2EB — MB BS 1990 Lond.

CHOKSY, Sohail Ahmed 36 Cambridge Road, Cambridge CB3 0PJ Tel: 01223 277883 Fax: 01223 277883 Email: schoksy@aol.com — MB BS 1992 Lond.; BSc Lond. 1989; FRCS Lond. 1996. (St. Barts. Hosp.) Specialist Regist. E. Anglian Gen. Surg. Rotat. Socs: Fell. Roy. Coll. Surgs.; Affil. Assn. Surgs.

CHONG, Alena Yu-Lene 77 Sandringham Gardens, London N12 0PA — MB BS 1996 Lond.; BSc (1st cl. Hons.) Med. Sci. & Biochem. Lond. 1993; MRCOG (Pt. I) 1998. (United Medical and Dental Schools of Guy's and St Thomas') SHO (O & G) St Bart. & the Roy. Lond. Hosps. Lond.

CHONG, Aun Yeong Department of General Medicine, Hereford Hospitals NHS Trust, County Hospital, Union Walk, Birmingham HR1 2ER; 256F Lorong Satu, Jalan Semabok, Melaka 75050, Malaysia — MB BS 1998 New South Wales.

CHONG, Camilla, C 26 Cornwall Terrrace Mews, Regents Park, London NW1 5LL — MB BS 1990 Lond.; Dip. M. 1997; AFPM 1999. (Roy. Free Hosp. Sch. Med. Lond.) Head of Scientif. Relations, Cardiovasc.- Europe & Overseas. Socs: BMA; Brit. Cardiac Soc. Prev: Cardiovasc. Sen. Med. Adviser - BMS; Product Strategy Manager, Glaxowellcome; Clin. Research Phys. Guy's Hosp.

CHONG, Chean Leung Hestia Drive Flat, Selly Oak Hospital, Birmingham B29 6JT Tel: 01723 365363 — MB ChB 1994 Bristol. Prev: Resid. Med. Off. Belvedere Hosp. ScarBoro.; Ho. Off. W. Cornw. Hosp.; Ho. Off. Bristol Roy. Infirm.

CHONG, Chee Fui 32 Ironmongers Place, London E14 9YD — MB BS 1993 Lond.

CHONG, David 18 Beaton Road, Pollokshields, Glasgow G41 4LA Email: dcschong@msn.com; 339 Kilmarnock Road, Newlands, Glasgow G43 2DS — MB ChB 1992 Glas.; FRCS Ed. 1996. Specialist Regist., W. of Scotl. Higher Surgic. Train. Scheme.

CHONG, Edward Min Fong 17 The Spinney, Elston, Newark NG23 5PE — MB ChB 1982 Dundee; MRCP (UK) 1985. Regist. (Cardiol.) Glas. Roy. Infirm. Prev: Med. Regist. Ninewells Hosp. Dundee.

CHONG, Giap Wang 16 The Atrium, 30 Vincent Square, London SW1P 2NW Tel: 020 7834 3493 — MB BS 1988 Lond.; MBA Lond. 1995. Regist. (Gen. Med. & Endocrinol.) Char. Cross Hosp. Lond., Hemel Hempstead Gen. Hosp. & Watford Gen. Hosp. Prev: SHO (Gen. Med.) Kent & Sussex Hosp. & Pembury Hosp. Tunbridge Wells; SHO (Clin. Oncol. & Radiother.) St. Bart. Hosp. Lond.; SHO (A & E) Watford Gen. Hosp.

CHONG, Heong Pung 5 Collingwood Court, 46 Eastworth Road, Chertsey KT16 8DP — MB BCh BAO 1986 Belf.

CHONG, Irene 10 Lynton Avenue, London NW9 6PD — MB BS 1998 Lond.; MB BS Lond 1998.

CHONG, Jillia Ann 52 Watermint Quay, Craven Walk, London N16 6DD — MB BS 1989 West Indies.

CHONG, Kah Kiong Unit of Metabolic Medicine, Mint Wing, St. Mary's Hospital, Praed St., London W2 1NY; 24 Moat Lodge, London Rd, Harrow HA1 3LU — MB ChB 1985 Dundee; BMSc 1982; MRCP (UK) 1989. Sen. Regist. in Diabetes & Endocrinol. Prev: Research Fell. Univ. Dundee.

CHONG, Mun Seng Kings College Hospital, Mapother House, London SE5 9A2 — MB BS 1986 Lond.; BSc Lond. 1983; MD Lond. 1993; MRCP (UK) 1989. Cons. Neurol. Medway Hosp. gillingham, King's Coll. Hosp. Lond. Prev: Regist. (Neurol.) Roy. Free Hosp. Lond.; Regist. & SHO Rotat. (Med.) Lond. Hosp.; Lect. (Clin. Neurol.) Univ. Birm.

CHONG, Mr Ngai Hang Victor Department of Ophthalmology, King college Hoospital, Denmark Hill, London SE5 9RS Tel: 020 77374000 Fax: 020 73463738 Email: v.chong@ucl.ac.uk; 7 Langford Green, London SE5 8BX — MB ChB 1988 Glas.; FRCS Ed. 1993; DO RCPSI 1992; FRCOphth 1994; PhD Lond. 1999. (Glasgow) Cons. Opthalmic Surg., Kings Coll. Hosp. Lond. Prev: Molecular Opthalmology Fell., Univ. Of IOWA, USA; MRC/Med. Retinal Fell., Moorfields Eye Hosp., Lond.; Acad. Specalist Regist., Moorfields Eye Hosp., Lond.

CHONG, Mr Patrick Fon Sen 53 St Katharine's Way, St. Katharine-by-the-Tower, London E1W 1LP Email: pfs.chong@btinternet.com — MB BS 1993 Lond.; FRCS Eng. 1998. (Lond. Hosp. Med. Coll.) Clin. Research Fell., Imperial Coll. Sch. Med. Lond. Socs: Assn. Surg.; Christ. Med. Fell.sh.; Assn. Surg. Train. Prev: SHO (Gen. & Vasc. Surg.) Whipps Cross Hosp. Lond.; SHO (Orthop. & Trauma Surg.) Chelsea & W.m. Hosp.; SHO (Cardiothoracic Surg.) Roy. Brompton Nat. Heart & Lung Hosp.

CHONG, Peter Stephen 18 Beaton Road, Glasgow G41 4LA — MB ChB 1996 Glas.

CHONG, Philomena 11 Beechwood Grove, London W3 7HX — MB BS 1990 Tasmania.

CHONG, Toh-Yong (retired) 30 Russell Drive, Glasgow G61 3BD — MB ChB 1959 Glas.; DCH RFPS Glas. 1961.

CHONG, William Chew Coon Parkfield Health Centre, Sefton Road, New Ferry, Wirral CH62 5HS Tel: 0151 644 6665; 15 Dunham Close, Eastham, Wirral CH62 9EP — MB ChB 1978 Birm.; BSc (Hons.) Birm. 1975, MB ChB 1978.

CHONG, Wui Heung Department of Histopathology, GKT Medical School, St Thomas Hospital, London SE1 7EH; 43 Hillgate Place, London W8 7SS — BM BCh 1987 Oxf.; PhD. Lond. 1997; BA Camb. 1984; MRCP (UK) 1990; MRCPath 1999; DGM RCP Lond. 1989. (Oxford) Lect. (Histopath.). Prev: Asst. Lect. (Histopath.) UMDS St. Thos. Hosp. Lond.; SHO (Med.) St. Geo. Hosp. Lond.; Clin. Research Fell. Imperial Cancer Research Fund.

CHONG, Wui Khean Department of Radiology, Great Ormond St. Hospital for Children, London WC1N 3JH Tel: 020 7405 9200 Fax: 020 7829 8665 Email: kchong@ich.ucl.ac.uk; 2 Vane Close, Hampstead, London NW3 5UN — MD 1994 Sheff.; BMedSci 1984, MB ChB 1985; MRCP (UK) 1988; FRCR 1991. (university of Sheffield) Cons. Paediat. Neuroradiol. Gt. Ormond St. Hosp. for Childr. Lond.; Hon. Sen. Lect. Inst. Child Health. Prev: Sen. Regist. (Neuroradiol.) Nat. Hosps. Neurol. & Neurosurg. Lond.; Sen. Regist. (Radiol.) Middlx. Hosp. Lond.; Regist. (Radiol.) St. Mary's Hosp. Lond.

CHONG, Yuen Ming 35C Blackness Avenue, Dundee DD2 1EY — MB ChB 1998 Dund.; MB ChB Dund 1998.

CHONG SIEW FOON, Elizabeth 6 Hunter House, Ward Road, London N19 5QE — MB BS 1988 Lond.; BSc Lond. 1985; DCH RCP Lond. 1992.

***CHOO, Chin Hung_** 22/11 Parkside Terrace, Edinburgh EH16 5XW — MB ChB 1998 Ed.; MB ChB Ed 1998.

CHOO, Diana Siew Foong 18 Upper Malone Gardens, Belfast BT9 6LY Tel: 01232 616031 — MB BCh BAO 1991 Belf.; DRCOG 1993. (Qu. Univ. Belf.) SHO Dermat. W.ern Infirm. Glas. Socs: BMA; Roy. Coll. Phys. Edin.

CHOO-KANG, Alan Tat Wing Middlesbrough General Hospital, Ayresome Green Lane, Middlesbrough TS5 5AZ Tel: 01642 850850; 41 Lakeside Road, Kirkcaldy KY2 5QJ Tel: 01592 268717 Email: achookang@bigfoot.com — MB ChB 1993 Ed.; BSc (Med Sci.) Ed. 1991; MRCP (UK) 1997. (Univ. Ed.) Specialist Regist. Diabetes & Endocrinol. Middlesbrough Gen. Hosp. Socs: Brit. Diabetic Assn. (Med. and Scientif. Sect.). Prev: Sen. SHO (Gen. Med.) Countess of Chester Hosp.; SHO Rotat. (Gen. Med.) Hull Roy. Infirm.; Ho. Off. (Med.) Falkirk & Dist. Roy. Infirm.

CHOO-KANG, Yhen Foo James 41 Lakeside Road, Kirkcaldy KY2 5QJ — MB ChB 1964 Ed.; BSc (Hons.) Ed. 1961, MB ChB

1964; FRCP Ed. 1981, M 1968. (Ed.) Cons. Phys. Respirat. Dis. Fife. Health Bd. Prev: Sen. Regist. City Hosp. Edin.

CHOON, Siew Cheong West of England of Eye Unit, Royal Devon & Exeter Hospital, Exeter EX1 2ED — MB BCh BAO 1987 NUI; FCOphth 1991. Regist. (Ophth.) W. of Eng. Eye Unit Roy. Devon & Exeter Hosp. Prev: SHO (Ophth.) Roy. Vict. Eye Hosp. Bournemouth & Manch. Roy. Eye Hosp.

CHOONARA, Professor Imtiaz Ahmed Academic Division of Child Health, Derbyshire Children's Hospital, Uttoxeter Road, Derby DE22 3NE Tel: 01332 625635 Fax: 01332 625636 — MD 1987 Liverp.; MB ChB 1977; MRCP UK 1981. Prof. in Child Health.

CHOONG, Beverley Helen 1 Fairbank Avenue, Orpington BR6 8JY Tel: 01689 857288 — MB BS 1990 Lond.; BSc Lond. 1987; DRCOG 1994; DCH RCP Lond. 1993. SHO Qu. Mary's Hosp. Sidcup. Prev: Trainee GP FarnBoro. Hosp. VTS.

CHOONG, Khuat Siew Simon 10 Elliott Square, London NW3 3SU — MB BS 1989 Lond.; FRCS (Eng) 1994; FRCS Ed 1994; MS (Lon) 1997 (UCL).

CHOONG, Michael Loke Onn Red Hill Surgery, 11 Redhill, Chislehurst BR7 6DB Tel: 020 8467 7419 Fax: 020 8295 1270; 1 Fairbank Avenue, Orpington BR6 8JY Email: mloc@lineone.net — MB BS 1992 New South Wales; MRCGP 1995; DFFP 1995. GP. Prev: Trainee GP FarnBoro.

CHOONG KAM CHONG, Lin Sun Flat 8, 75 Laundry Road, Southampton SO16 6SJ — MB BCh BAO 1984 Dub.; MRCPsych 1990.

CHOPDAR, Mr Amresh East Surrey Hospital, Canada Avenue, Redhill RH1 5RH Tel: 01737 768511 Fax: 01737 761395; Tel: 01372 721360 — MB BS Utkal 1964; FRCS Ed. 1973; FRCOphth 1989; DO Eng. 1970. (SCB Med. Coll. Cuttack) Cons. Ophth. E. Surrey Hosp. Socs: Roy. Soc. Med.; Hon. Cons. to Macular Dis. Soc.; BMA. Prev: Sen. Regist. W.. Ophth. Hosp. & Moorfields Eye Hosp. Lond.; Fell. Ocular Vasc. Serv. Univ. Iowa, USA.

CHOPIN, Karin Teresa Southgrounds Farm, Slapton, Kingsbridge TQ7 2QW — MB ChB Bristol 1992; MA Geneva 1981. (Bristol)

CHOPPING, Barry Michael (retired) Holker Lea, High Lea Road, New Mills, High Peak SK22 3DT Tel: 01663 744395 Email: barry@chopping.org.uk — MB ChB 1966 Liverp.; MSc Manch. 1997; AFOM RCP Lond. 1994; MRCGP 1978. Prev: Occupat.al Phys., mediscreen, Helsby, Chesh..

CHOPRA, Amarjit Singh Barking Medical Group Practice, 130 Upney Lane, Barking IG11 9LT Tel: 020 8594 4353/5709 Fax: 020 8591 4686; Russells, 43 Stradbroke Drive, Chigwell IG7 5RA Tel: 020 8500 8748 Fax: 020 8257 0359 — MB BS 1960 Patna; FRCP Ed. 1994; MRCP Ed. 1964; MRCP Glas. 1964. (Patna Med. Coll.) Socs: Primary Care Rheum. Soc.; BMA. Prev: SHO (Infec. Dis. & Chest) W.. Hosp. Lond.; Regist. (Med.) Highlands Gen. Hosp. Lond.; Med. Off. Ranchi Med. Coll., India.

CHOPRA, Anil Whitmore Way Surgery, Aegis Medical Centre, Felmores Centre, Basildon SS15 5LE Tel: 01268 520641 Fax: 01268 271057 — MB BS 1982 Lond.; MRCGP 1986; DRCOG 1985. (St. Thos.) GP Basildon; Chairm. Basildon & Wickford GP Locality Forum; Co-Chair Basildon Commiss.ing Pilot. Prev: Trainee GP Bottisham Camb.; SHO (Cas.) St. Thos. Hosp. Lond.; SHO (Obst.) Watford.

CHOPRA, Mr Bhavnesh Datt 25 Parkstone Avenue, Hornchurch RM11 3LX Tel: 014024 51455 — MB BS 1964 All India Inst. Med. Scs.; MB BS All India Inst. of Med. Sciences 1964; FRCS Ed. 1974; DLO Eng. 1970. Cons. ENT Surg. Rush Green, Vict. & OldCh. Hosps. Romford; Cons. ENT Surg. Essex Nuffield Hosp., BUPA Hartswood Hosp Brentwood & BUPA Roding Hosp. Redbridge.

CHOPRA, Gargi Boughton Surgery, 60 The Street, Boughton-under-Blean, Faversham ME13 9AS Tel: 01227 751217 — MB BS 1972 Banaras Hindu. (Inst. Med. Scs. Varanasi)

CHOPRA, Mr Jaison 9 Slades Hill, Enfield EN2 7DL Tel: 020 8366 0143 — MB BS 1977 Aligarth Muslim; BSc Punjab 1970; FRCS Ed. 1989.

CHOPRA, Mahendra Paul Tameside General Hospital, Fountain Road, Ashton-under-Lyne OL6 9RW Tel: 0161 330 8373; Little Beeches, Compstall Road, Romiley, Stockport SK6 4JG Tel: 0161 427 6555 — MB BS 1960 Lucknow; MPhil. Leeds 1971; FRCPI 1985, M 1976; MRCGP 1975. (GSVM Coll. Kanpur) Cons. Phys. Tameside Gen. Hosp. Ashton-under-Lyne. Socs: Brit. Thorac. Soc.& Brit. Cardiac Soc. Prev: Research Regist. Coronary Care Unit Sefton Gen. Hosp. Liverp.; Research Fell. & Regist. Cardiac Unit Hull; Med. Regist. Glas. Roy. Infirm.

CHOPRA, Mickey 113 Faraday Avenue, Sidcup DA14 4JE — BM 1992 Soton.

CHOPRA, Mr Mohendra Singh Boughton Surgery, 60 The Street, Boughton-under-Blean, Faversham ME13 9AS Tel: 01227 751217 — MB BS 1968 Banaras Hindu; MS (Obst. & Gyn.) Banaras Hindu 1971, MB BS 1968.

CHOPRA, Mr Narinder Bhushan 28 Lingwood Park, Peterborough PE3 6RX — MB BS 1973 Gura Nanak India; MB BS Guru Nanak, India 1973; FRCS Ed. 1981.

CHOPRA, Pawaninder Singh 43 Stradbroke Drive, Chigwell IG7 5RA — MB BS 1991 Lond.; DRCOG 1993. (UCH)

CHOPRA, Preeti Little Beeches, Compstall Road, Romiley, Stockport SK6 4JG — MB BCh 1998 Wales.

CHOPRA, Pushpa Kumari Dr P Chopra, 75 Sunnyside Gardens, Upminster RM14 3DP Tel: 01708 223156 Fax: 01708 640967; 25 Parkstone Avenue, Hornchurch RM11 3LX Tel: 01708 451455 Fax: 01708 451455 — MB BS 1963 Panjab, India; DRCOG 1970. (Christian Med. Coll. Punjab, India) Socs: Indian Med. Assn.; Overseas Doctors Assn.; BMA.

CHOPRA, Rajesh Kay Kendall Laboratories, Patterson Inst. for Cancer Research, Christie Hospital, Wilmslow Road, Manchester M20 Tel: 0161 446 3000 — MB BS 1985 Lond.; PhD Lond. 1996, BSc 1982; MRCPath 1996; MRCP (UK) 1988. Director of Haemat. Oncol. Christie Hosp. Gp. Ldr. Paterson Inst. For Cancer Research and Univ. Manch. Prev: Leukaemia Research Fund Research Fell. (Bone Marrow Transpl.) Univ. Coll. Hosp. Lond.; MRC Research Fell. & Hon. Sen. Regist. Univ. Coll. & Middlx. Hosp. Med. Sch.; Brit. Soc. Haemat. & Berkeley Fell. Cancer Research Unit Walter & Eliza Hall Inst. Roy. Melbourne Hosp., Austral.

CHOPRA, Rakesh 6 Warcop Court, Kingston Park, Newcastle upon Tyne NE3 2TA — MB BS 1984 Newc.; MB BS Newc. I984.

CHOPRA, Rakeshwar Cowes Health Centre, 8 Consort Road, Cowes PO31 7SH Tel: 01983 295251 Fax: 01983 280461 Email: rakesh.chopra@gp-j84015.nhs.uk; Tel: 01983 296232 — MB BS 1974 Poona; FRCS Ed. 1987; T(GP) 1994. (Armed Forces Med. Coll.) Prev: Trainee GP St. Mary's Hosp. Newport I. of Wight; Regist. (Orthop.) Falkirk & Dist. Roy. Infirm.; Regist. (Gen. Surg.) Rotherham Dist. Gen. Hosp.

CHOPRA, Raksha 38A Lovelace Avenue, Solihull B91 3JR — MB BS 1968 Panjab.

CHOPRA, Ram Karan (retired) 49B Bexley Road, Erith DA8 3SH Tel: 01322 340614 — MB BS 1955 Patna; DTM & H Eng. 1957, DCH 1958. Prev: Med. Regist. Swansea Gen. Hosp.

CHOPRA, Sarita Royal Crescent and Preston Road Practice, 25 Crescent Street, Weymouth DT4 7BY Tel: 01305 774466 Fax: 01305 760538; 1 Sutton Close, Sutton Poyntz, Weymouth DT3 6LJ Tel: 01305 832945 — MB BS 1988 Lond.; BSc (Pharmacol.) Lond. 1985, MB BS 1988; MRCGP 1993; DRCOG 1991. (University College Hospital) Prev: Ho. Off. (Surg.) Univ. Coll. Hosp. Lond.; Ho. Off. (Med.) Qu. Alexandra Hosp. Portsmouth; Resid. Med. Off. Brisbane, Austral.

CHOPRA, Satish Kumar Chopra, Meir Health Centre, Saracen's Way, Meir, Stoke-on-Trent ST3 7DS Tel: 01782 312360 Fax: 01782 593257; White Oaks, Saverley Green, Stoke-on-Trent ST11 9QX Tel: 01782 397886 Fax: 01782 397886 — MB BS 1967 Jiwaji; DLO RCS Eng. 1973; Dip. Acupunc. (G. R. Medical School Gwaliob India) GP Stoke on Trent. Socs: Med. Protec. Soc. Prev: Regist. (ENT) Neath Gen. Hosp.

CHOPRA, Sunil 52 Queens Road, Feltham TW13 5AR — MB BS 1990 Lond.

CHOPRA, Usha Chopra, Meir Health Centre, Saracen's Way, Meir, Stoke-on-Trent ST3 7DS Tel: 01782 312360 Fax: 01782 593257; 'White Oaks', Fulford Road, Saverley Green, Stoke-on-Trent ST11 9QX Tel: 01782 397886 Fax: 01782 397886 — MB BS 1967 Ranchi; MRCOG 1973; DObst RCOG 1969. (Rajendra Medical School Ranchi (India)) GP Stoke-on-Trent. Socs: Med. Protec. Soc. Prev: Regist. (O & G) Bridgend Gen. Hosp.

CHOR, Che Chuan Flat 15 Ascot Court, Grove End Road, London NW8 9RY — MB ChB 1992 Dundee.

CHORARIA, Bhim Raj Tameside General Hospital, Fountain St., Ashton-under-Lyne OL6 9RW Tel: 0161 331 6000 Fax: 0161 331 6553 — MB BS 1961 Calcutta; MD (Radiodiag.) Gujarat 1974;

DMRD Aberd. 1980; FFR RCSI Dub. 1984. (Calcutta Med. Coll.) Cons. Radiol. Ashton-under-Lyne. Socs: Roy. Coll. Radiol.; Overseas Doctors Assn. Prev: Sen. Regist. Glas. Roy. Infirm. & Inst. Neurol. Sci. Glas.

CHORBACHI, Mr Mohammed Raouf Great Ormond Street Hospital for Children, Great Ormond St., London WC1N 3JH Tel: 020 7405 9200; 66 Willowfield, Pk Avenue, Dublin 4, Republic of Ireland — MB BCh BAO 1987 NUI; FRCS Ed. 1992; LRCPSI 1987; MSc 1997. Sen. Regist. (Audiological Med.) N. Thames. Socs: BMA; BAAP; BAOL.

CHORLEY, Susan Jane The Surgery, 50 The Glade, Furnace Green, Crawley RH10 6JN — MB BS 1986 Lond.; BSc Lond. 1983; MRCGP 1991; DRCOG 1991. (Charing Cross) GP Princip. Prev: Trainee GP Redhill VTS.

CHORLTON, Ian (retired) Fern Cottage, Hunsley Road, Walkington, Beverley HU17 8SZ — MB BS 1961 Durh.; FRCPath 1983, M 1971; DCP Lond 1969. Cons. Histopath. Castle Hill Hosp. Cottingham. Prev: Wing Cdr. RAF Med. Br. Cons. (Histopath.) i/c Histol, Cytol. & Electron Microscopy Inst. Path. & Trop. Med. RAF Halton.

CHORLTON, Michael Iain The Cabin Surgery, High St., Rishton, Blackburn BB1 4 Tel: 01254 884217; 11 Arnside Close, Off Collingwood, Clayton le Moors, Blackburn Tel: 01254 877581 — MB BS Lond. 1993; BSc (Hons.) Basic Med. Sci. & Pharm. Lond. 1990, MB BS 1993; MRCGP 1997. (King's Coll. Sch. Med. & Dent.) Partner GP. Prev: Trainee GP Blackburn VTS.

CHOU, Christy Wah Keung Whinfield Surgery, Whinbush Way, Darlington DL1 3RT Tel: 01325 481321 Fax: 01325 380116 — MB ChB 1985 Dundee. GP Darlington.; Police Surg.

CHOUCRI, Moheb Choucri Aziz Clare Road Surgery, 51 Clare Road, Halifax HX1 2JP Tel: 01422 365460 Fax: 01422 348706 — MB BCh 1969 Ain Shams; MB BCh 1969 Ain Shams.

CHOUDARY, Adusumilli Abbulu c/o Dr S. R. Yannamani, 85 Comberford Road, Tamworth B79 8PE — MB BS 1971 Andhra.

CHOUDARY, Mr Vemulpall Raghavendra 31 Birch Hill Crescent, Rochdale OL12 9QF — MB BS 1982 Madras; FRCS Ed. 1994.

CHOUDHARY, Bikram Pratap 5 Maindy Croft, Ton Pentre, Pentre CF41 7ET — MB BS 1998 Lond.; MB BS Lond 1998.

CHOUDHARY, Bineeta 259 Hoyles Lane, Cottam, Preston PR4 0LD — MB BS 1995 Lond.

CHOUDHARY, Binod Prasad Burbage Surgery, Tilton Road, Burbage, Hinckley LE10 2SE Tel: 01455 634879 — MB BS 1975 Ranchi; Cert. Community Paediat. Warwick 1991; DTCD Patna 1977. Clin. Asst. (Genitourin. Med.) Leicester Roy. Infirm. Prev: Clin. Asst. (A & E) St. Cross Hosp. Rugby.

CHOUDHARY, Hari N St David's Street Surgery, St. David's Street, Ton Pentre, Pentre CF41 7NE Tel: 01443 435846 Fax: 01443 431480.

CHOUDHARY, Manorma St David's Street Surgery, St. David's Street, Ton Pentre, Pentre CF41 7NE Tel: 01443 435846 Fax: 01443 431480.

CHOUDHARY, P Speke Health Centre, North Parade, Liverpool L24 2XP Tel: 0151 448 1293.

CHOUDHARY, Prasoon Chandra St Tydfil's Hospital, Merthyr Tydfil CF47 0SJ Tel: 01685 723244 — MB BS 1969 Bihar; MRCPsych 1978; DPM Eng. 1975. Cons. Psychiat. Tydfil's Hosp. Merthyr Tydfil.

CHOUDHARY, Sita Ram Blackhills Surgery, 16 Blackhills Road, Horden, Peterlee SR8 4DN Tel: 0191 518 3646 Fax: 0191 586 2773 — MB BS 1974 Patna.

CHOUDHERY, Vincent Paul 8 Melville Gardens, Glasgow G64 3DF — MB ChB 1990 Glas.

CHOUDHRI, Abdul Haq Department of Radiology, Trafford General Hospital, Moorside Road, Davyhulme, Manchester M41 5SL Tel: 0161 746 2001; Department of Radiology, Altrincham General Hospital, Market St, Altrincham WA14 1PE Tel: 0161 928 6111 — MB ChB 1978 Manch.; MRCP (UK) 1982; FRCR 1987; DMRD 1986. Cons. Radiol. Trafford Healthcare NHS Trust. Prev: Cons. Radiol. Mid Essex Hosps. NHS Trust; Regist. & Sen. Regist. (Radiol.) St. Mary's Hosp. Lond.; Fell. (Paediat. Radiol.) UCLA Med. Centre Calif., USA.

CHOUDHRY, Haroon Khaliq 19 Prestbury Road, Wilmslow SK9 2LJ — MRCS Eng. LRCP Lond. 1992.

CHOUDHRY, Semiya Omur Flat 3, Milton Avenue, Highgate, London N6 5QF; Flat 3, 1 Milton Ave, Highgate, London N6 5Q1 Email: semiyachoudry@hotmail.com — MB BS 1996 Lond.

CHOUDHRY, Tahir Ahmed 18 Wentworth Way, Bletchley, Milton Keynes MK3 7RW Tel: 01908 75341 — LRCPI & LM, LRSCI & LM 1965; LRCPI & LM, LRCSI & LM 1965; Cert JCC Lond. 1979. Med. Off. Bletchley Matern. Unit.

CHOUDHRY, Tanzila Waheed St. James Medical Centre, Burnley Road, Rawtenstall, Rossendale BB4 8HH Tel: 01706 213060 Fax: 01706 213060 Email: tanzilachoudhry@totalise.co.uk — MB ChB 1992 Manch.; MRCGP 1996; AFOM 2000; DFFP 1995; DRCOG 1994. (Manch.) Gen. Practitioner, 3/4-time; Specialist Regist. Occ. Med., Medischeen, Oldham Trust, Oldham. Prev: SHO (Med., Paediat. & Psychiat.) Qu. Pk. Hosp. Blackburn.

CHOUDHURI, Abdul Mosaver 25 Ashford Road, Stockport SK4 5JX — MB ChB 1997 Liverp.

CHOUDHURI, Debdas Chiswick Health Centre, Fishers Lane, London W4 1RX Tel: 020 8994 2465 Fax: 020 8994 9497 — MB BS 1962 Calcutta; MRCP (UK) 1976; DCH Delhi 1965.

CHOUDHURI, Kaushik First Floor Flat, 35 Gauden Road, London SW4 6LR — MB BS 1998 Lond.; MB BS Lond 1998.

CHOUDHURI, Naginah Jabeen 41 Marple Road, Stockport SK2 5EL — MB BCh 1992 Wales.

CHOUDHURI, Mr Sutanu Kumar Tydehams Meads, Tydehams, Newbury RG14 6JT — MBBS Calcutta 1961; FRCS Ed. 1969.

CHOUDHURI, Mr Ujjal Kumar 43 Albury Place, Ferryhill, Aberdeen AB11 6TQ Tel: 01224 581000 Email: u.chondhuri@abdn.ac.uk — MB BS 1986 Madras; FRCS Ed. 1992; MCh (Orth.) Aberd. 1997. Staff (Orthop. Surg.) Aberd. Roy. Infirm. Socs: Fell. Roy. Coll. Surg.

CHOUDHURY, A High Street Surgery, 28 High Street, Prescot L34 6HE Tel: 0151 426 2890.

CHOUDHURY, Abdul Haque 10 Winey Close, Chessington KT9 2SP Tel: 020 8397 6333 — MB BS Dacca 1967; Dip. Ven. Liverp. 1969. Clin. Asst. (Psychiat.) D.O.P. Langley Wing Epsom Gen. Hosp. Surrey.

CHOUDHURY, Mr Abdur Rashid 58A Burton Road, Repton, Derby DE65 6FN — MB BS 1961 Gauhati; ChM Aberd. 1973; FRCS Eng. 1971; FRCS Ed. 1971; FRCS Glas. 1971.

CHOUDHURY, Mr Amit Kumar Victoria Hospital, Whinney Heys Road, Blackpool FY3 8NR — MB BS 1983 Poona; FRCS Glas. 1995.

CHOUDHURY, Ananya 68 View Road, Rainhill, Prescot L35 0LS — BChir 1995 Camb.

CHOUDHURY, Arun 105 North Park Brook Road, Callands, Warrington WA5 9ST — MB BS 1974 Dibrugarh.

CHOUDHURY, Asit Kumar Ilford Medical Centre, 61-63 Cleveland Road, Ilford IG1 1EE Tel: 020 8514 7761/8478 0367 Fax: 020 8478 4448; 4 Dickens Rise, Chigwell IG7 6PA Tel: 020 8500 4663 — B BS Calcutta, 1958. GP Essex. Prev: Regist. (Gyn.) King Geo. Matern. Hosp. Ilford; SHO (Midw.) Matern. Hosp. Notts.; Regist. (Gyn.) N. Ormsby Hosp. Middlesbrough.

CHOUDHURY, Mr Bhuban Mohan 43 Bateman Road, London E4 8ND — MB BS 1967 Gauhati; MB BS Gauhati, India 1967; FRCS Glas. 1982.

CHOUDHURY, Mr Gautam 3 Batemill Close, Macclesfield SK10 3EA — MB BS 1978 Gauhati; FRCS Glas. 1992; FRCS Ed. 1991.

CHOUDHURY, Ghazi Shafiqul Alam (Surgery), 886 Garratt Lane, London SW17 Tel: 020 8672 1948; The Grantchester, Coombe Bank, Kingston upon Thames KT2 7DN Tel: 020 8949 2771 Fax: 020 8682 2752 — MB BS 1967 Dacca; MRCGP Roy. Coll. GPs 1998; MRCOG 1971; DObst RCOG 1969; DTM & H Liverp. 1968. (Dacca Med. Coll.) Hosp. Pract. (Gyn.) St. Jas. Hosp. Lond. Socs: BMA. Prev: Regist. (O & G) Poole Gen. Hosp. & Mothers' Hosp. Lond.

CHOUDHURY, Girija S Greenfield Surgery, 12 Porth Street, Porth CF39 9RP Tel: 01443 682644 Fax: 01443 682291.

CHOUDHURY, Mr Kanmull 401 Louth Road, Grimsby DN36 4PX — MB BS 1958 Calcutta; FRCS Ed. 1968; MRCOG 1963. (Calcutta Med. Coll.) Prev: GP Cleethorpes.

CHOUDHURY, Marina Mou 422 Lewisham High Street, London SE13 6LJ — MB BS 1993 Lond.

CHOUDHURY, Mohammad Abul Quasem 34 Tabor Road, London W6 0BW — LMSSA 1963 Lond.

CHOUDHURY, Mohammed Abdul Hoque 42 Millais Road, London E11 4HD — MB BS 1963 Dacca; FRCOG 1992, M 1978.

CHOUDHURY, Namit Kumar Crossgates Medical Practice, 2 Windmill Knowe, Crossgates, Cowdenbeath KY4 8AT Tel: 01383 511398 Fax: 01383 611586 — MB BS 1963 Gauhati.

***CHOUDHURY, Nancy Nahar** 139A Barlow Moor Road, West Didsbury, Manchester M20 2DY — MB BS 1996 Lond.; BSc (Biomed. Sci.) Lond. 1993.

CHOUDHURY, Nasimul Gani 28 The Wynd, Kenton, Newcastle upon Tyne NE3 4LA — MB ChB 1985 Leic.

CHOUDHURY, Nilima Hollies Health Centre, Swan Street, Merthyr Tydfil CF47 8ET Tel: 01685 723363 Fax: 01685 350106 — MB BS 1963 Calcutta. (Calcutta) GP Merthyr Tydfil, Mid Glam.

CHOUDHURY, Probha 18 Grimsby Road, Cleethorpes DN35 7AD Tel: 01472 42859; 2 Alexandra Road, Cleethorpes DN35 8LH Tel: 01472 691560 — MB BS 1959 Calcutta; MRCOG 1965. (Calcutta Med. Coll.)

CHOUDHURY, Rabindranath Das, TD, KStJ (retired) Occupational Health Depaertment, Whelley Hospital, Bradshaw St., Whelley, Wigan WN1 3XD Tel: 01942 822643 Fax: 01942 822630 — MRCS Eng. LRCP Lond. 1952; FFOM RCP Lond. 1993; MFOM RCP Lond. 1980; MRCGP 1964; DMJ (Clin.) Soc. Apoth. Lond. 1963; DIH Eng. 1962; DPH Liverp. 1955. Prev: Cons. Occupat. Phys. Wigan DHA & Chorley DHA.

CHOUDHURY, Robin Patrick Department of Cardiology, Charing Cross Hospital, Fulham Palace Road, London W6 Email: r.choudhury@rpms.ac.uk; 83c Ashley Gardens, London SW1 1HG Email: rchoudhry@aol.com — BM BCh 1992 Oxf.; BA Oxf. 1989; MRCP (UK) 1995. Specialist Regist. (Cardiol.) Char. Cross Hosp. Lond. Socs: Balliol Med. Soc. Prev: Regist. (Med.) Hammersmith Hosp. Lond.

CHOUDHURY, Romit Peacehaven, Inverkeithing Road, Crossgates, Cowdenbeath KY4 8AL — MB ChB 1998 Glas.; MB ChB Glas 1998.

CHOUDHURY, Sadhan K Church Street, Merthyr Tydfil CF47 0AY — MB BS 1963 Calcutta. (Calcutta) GP Merthyr Tydfil.

CHOUDHURY, Sarala Shafiqul Alam The Grantchester, Coombe Bank, Kingston upon Thames KT2 7DN Tel: 020 8949 2771 — MB BS 1966 Bombay; DA Eng. 1971. (Grant Med. Coll.) Clin. Asst. (Anaesth.) Sutton Hosp. & Banstead Hosp. Prev: Regist. (Anaesth.) St. Jas. Hosp. Lond.; SHO (Anaesth.) Dudley Rd. Hosp. Birm.

CHOUDHURY, Zinatun Nahar 27 Rodney Road, New Malden KT3 5AB Tel: 020 8949 9352 — MB BS 1973 Dacca; DA 1979. (Sylhet Medical College Bangladesh)

CHOUDREE, Abhimanyu Chandrasakar Holbrook Lane Surgery, 268 Holbrook Lane, Coventry CV6 4DD Tel: 024 7668 8340 Fax: 024 7663 7526 — LRCPSI 1963.

CHOUDREE, Sangamithra Urvashi Dharini 72 Cardross Street, London W6 0DR Tel: 020 8741 4466 — MB ChB 1970 Ed.; BSc Ed. 1970. (Ed.) Research Psychother. (Psychiat.) Guy's Hosp. Lond. Socs: BMA. Prev: Princip. GP Lond.; Med. Off. (Volun. Serv. Overseas) Sierra Leone; Regist. (Radiol.) Glostrup Hosp. Denmark & Roy. Infirm. Edin.

CHOUDRY, Ammara Aziz 8 Chinnor Crescent, Greenford UB6 9NU — MB BS 1998 Lond.; MB BS Lond 1998.

CHOUDRY, Ansar Ali 75 Floyer Road, Birmingham B10 9PY — MB ChB 1991 Leeds.

CHOUDRY, Guzanfar Ali 75 Floyer Road, Small Heath, Birmingham B10 9PY — MB ChB 1991 Leeds.

CHOUDRY, Kamran Munsif 12 James Drive, Hyde SK141RQ — MB ChB 1995 Manch.

CHOUDRY, Nas St. Ann's Hospital, Haven Road, Canford Cliffs, Poole BH13 7LN Tel: 01202 492059 Fax: 01202 492069 Email: nas.choudry@dorset-tr.swest.nhs.uk; Woodland House, 19 Western Avenue, Branksome Park, Poole BH13 7AN Tel: 01202 700613 Fax: 01202 707895 — MB ChB 1972 Bristol; FRCPsych 1991, M 1976; T(Psychiat.) 1991. p/t Cons. (Adult Ment. Illness) St. Ann's Hosp. Poole, Dorset. + Cons. Addic. Serv.s E. Dorset.; Clin. Teach. Univ. Soton.; Clin. Teach. Prof. And Assoc. Chairm. of Psychiat., St. Geo. Univ. Sch. Med. Grenada W. Indies (UK Fac). Prev: Sen. Regist. (Psychiat.) Bristol Univ.; Staff Psychiat. Regional Psychiat. Centre Saskatoon, Canada.

CHOUHAN, Mr Ashok Kumar Worthing Hospital, Worthing BN11 2DH Tel: 01903 205111 Email: akchouham@hotmail.com — MB BS 1977 Bhopal; FRCS Ed. 1989. Staff Grade (Surg.) Worthing Hosp. W. Sussex. Prev: Regist. (Gen. Surg.) W. Cumbld. Hosp. Whitehaven.

CHOUHAN, Mr Mohammad Ashraf P.O. Box 1021, Kingston upon Thames KT1 3AW; 79 Clarence Avenue, New Malden KT3 3TY — MB BS 1982 Punjab; FRCSI 1989. Assoc. Specialist (Orthop.). Socs: BMA; Brit. Orthop. Assn.

CHOUKROUN, Catherine Top Foor Flat, 32 Copley Park, London SW16 3DD — MD 1992 Lyons.

CHOW, Arthur Eric Thin Acre, 15 Vinery Road, Bury St Edmunds IP33 2JT Tel: 01284 764900 — MB BS 1963 Lond.; FRCA 1970; DA Eng. 1967; DObst RCOG 1965. (St. Mary's) Cons. Anaesth. W. Suff. Gen. Hosp. Socs: Assn. Anaesths. Prev: Sen. Regist. & Regist. Anaesth. Dept. St. Geo. Hosp. Lond.; Clin. Fell. in Anaesth. Mass. Gen. Hosp. Boston, U.S.A.

CHOW, Carl 36 Walkerscroft Mead, London SE21 8LJ — MB BS 1992 Lond.

CHOW, Gabriel Chi Shiu 17 Westbourne Grove, Barnsley S75 1AE — MB BChir 1988 Camb.; MRCPI 1993; MRCPCH 1997; DCH RCP Lond. 1992. (Middlx. Hosp. & Camb.) Specialist Regist. (Paediat. Neurol.) Qu.'s Med. Centre Nottm. Socs: Med. Defence Union; MRCPCH. Prev: Regist. (Paediat.) Doncaster; SHO (Adult Neurol.) Roy. Hallamshire Hosp. Sheff.; Regist. St. Piers Lingfield Surrey.

CHOW, Julianna Yim-Nam 264 Green Lanes, London N4 2HE Tel: 020 8809 6642 — MB BS 1996 Lond. SHO (Paediat.) Kings Coll. Lond. Prev: SHO Paediat. Brighton; Ho. Off. (Med.) Whittington Hosp. Lond.; Ho. Surg. Stafford Hosp.

CHOW, Kar Yee 8 Astonville Street, London SW18 5AL — MB BS 1995 Lond.

CHOW, Peter Chiu Man 94 Hermitage Court, Knighton St., London E1W 1PW — MB ChB 1984 Glas.; MRCP (UK) 1990.

CHOW, Pok Yu 86 The Drive, Golders Green, London NW11 9UL — MB ChB 1987 Glas.

CHOW, Teresa Wai Ping 10 Kenilworth Close, Liverpool L25 7XQ — MB ChB 1986 Liverp.

CHOW, Wai Cheong 40 Lowman Road, London N7 6DB — MB BS 1990 Lond.; BSc Lond. 1987; MRCP (UK) 1993.

CHOW, Mr Wai Man Department of Urology, Scarborough Hospital, Woodland Drive, Scarborough YO12 6AF Tel: 01723 368111; 41 North Stead Manor Drive, Scarborough YO12 6AF Tel: 01723 365774 — MB BCh 1981 Wales; FRCS (Urol.) 1992; FRCS Glas. 1988; Dip. Urol. Lond 1992. Cons. Urol. ScarBoro. Hosp. Socs: Foundat. Fell. Acad. Med. Hong Kong 1993; Foundat. Fell. Hong Kong Coll. Surgs. 1990. Prev: Sen. Med. Off. & Clin. Lect. (Surg.) Univ. Hong Kong.

CHOW, Wei Mun Jade Department of Cellular Pathology, St. Georges Hospital Medical School, Cranmer Terrace, London SW17 0RE Tel: 020 8725 5278 Fax: 020 8725 0064 Email: jchow@sghms.ac.uk — MB BCh BAO 1983 Dub.; PhD Lond. 1992; MA Dub. 1992; MRCPath 1989. (Trinity Coll. Dub.) Reader & Hons. Cons. (Histopath.) St. Geo. Hosp. Med. Sch. Lond. Socs: Internat. Assn. Path. (Brit. Div.); Bone & Tooth Soc.; Amer. Soc. Bone & Mineral Research. Prev: Lect. (Histopath.) St. Geo. Hosp. Med. Sch. Lond.; Regist. & SHO (Histopath.) Univ. Coll. Hosp. & Middlx. Med. Sch. Lond.

CHOW, Wing Chow Stephen 33 Perystreete, London SE23 2LF — MB ChB 1990 Ed.

CHOWANIEC, Anne Maria 38 Auchinloch Road, Lenzie, Glasgow G66 5HA — MB ChB 1976 Dundee; MRCPCH 1997; MFFP 1994; MRCGP 1980; DCH Eng. 1980; DRCOG 1979. (Univ. Dundee) SCMO Lanarksh. Primary Care (NHS) Trust.

CHOWCAT, Naomi Loretta Department of Surgery, District General Hospital, King's Drive, Eastbourne BN21 2UD Tel: 01323 417400; 87 Wannock Lane, Lower willingdon, Eastbourne BN20 9SQ Tel: 01323 485005 — MB BS 1975 Lond.; MS FRCS Eng. 1983; BSc Lond. 1972, MS 1991, MB BS 1975. (Univ. Coll. Hosp.) Assoc. Specialist (Gen. Surg.) E.bourne Dist. Gen. Hosp.; Vasectomy Surg. E.bourne & Co. Healthcare. Socs: Assn. Surg. Prev: Regist. Rotat. (Surg.) Guy's Hosp. Lond.; Research Asst. (Surg.) Univ. Coll. Lond.; Regist. (Gen. Surg.) Univ. Coll. Lond.

CHOWDARY, Kamineni Venugopal Wolverton Health Centre, Gloucester Road, Wolverton, Milton Keynes MK12 5DF Tel: 01908 316633 Fax: 01908 225397; 40 Calverton Road, Stony Stratford, Milton Keynes MK11 1HL — MB BS 1967 Bangalore; DA Eng. 1970. (Bangalore Med. Coll.) Prev: Clin. Asst. Day Hosp. Wolverton Milton Keynes; Regist. (Anaesth.) Croydon & Warlingham Pk. Gp. Hosps.

CHOWDARY, Narasetty Prabhakara c/o Dr B.K. Rao, 8 Horton Road, Springwood, King's Lynn PE30 4XU — MB BS 1971 Karnatak.

CHOWDHARY, Saqib Department of Cardiovascular Medicine, Queen Elizabeth Hospital, Birmingham Tel: 0121 472 1311; 64 Jacoby Place, Edgbaston, Birmingham B5 7UW Tel: 0121 249 3231 Email: xcz26@dial.pipex.com — MB BS 1990 Lond.; MRCP (UK) 1993. Research Fell. (Cardiol.) Qu. Eliz. Hosp. Birm. Prev: Regist. (Cardiol.) Qu. Eliz. Hosp. Birm.; Regist. (Cardiol.) Geo. Eliot Hosp. Nuneaton; Regist. (Cardiol.) Heartlands Hosp. Birm.

CHOWDHARY, Mr Upendra Mohan The Onion Loft, The Fields, Lower Caldecote, Biggleswade SG18 9AX — MB BS 1963 Agra; FRCS Glas. 1969; FRCS Ed. 1969; LMSSA Lond. 1980; T(S) 1991.

CHOWDHARY, Mr Zimran Ahmed Doctors Mess, Ipswich General Hospital, Heat Road, Ipswich IP4 5PD; 3 Godbold Close, Kesgrave, Ipswich IP5 2FE Email: zimram@zac25.freeserve.co.uk — MB BS 1986 Karachi; FRCS Ed. 1993.

CHOWDHURY, Abul Mohsin Department of Public Health Medicine, Bexley Health Authority, 221 Erith Road, Bexleyheath DA7 6HZ Tel: 020 8298 6180 Fax: 020 8298 6183; 53 Orchard Drive, Cassiobury Park, Watford WD17 3DX Tel: 01923 246219 — MB BS 1962 Dacca; FRCPCH 1997; DTCH Liverp. 1972; Dip Nutrit. Lond. 1970. (Dacca) Cons. Communicable Dis. Control. Pub. Health Dept. Greenwich & Bexley HAs. Socs: Fell. Roy. Inst. Pub. Health & Hyg.; Fell. Soc. Pub. Health; Fac. Community Health. Prev: DMO & DPH NW Herts.; Dist. Sen. Med. Off. NW Herts. HA; Cons. Pub. Health Med. Herts.

CHOWDHURY, Avneet Singh 3 Greystone Gardens, Kenton, Harrow HA3 0EF — MB BS 1990 Lond.

CHOWDHURY, Belal Arif 8 Belgrave Avenue, Victoria Park, Manchester M14 5DL — MB ChB 1996 Manch.

CHOWDHURY, Mr Chitta Ranjan, Lt.-Col. RAMC Retd. (retired) Juni, 18 Elm Grove, Hornchurch RM11 2QX Tel: 01708 442268 Fax: 01708 200128 Email: crchowdhury@hotmail.com — MB BS Dacca 1970; FRCS Ed. 1979; FICS 1990; Accredit. Otolaryngol. RCS Ed. 1988; FCS Hong Kong; MBIM. Cons. Ent/Head & Neck Surg. Havering Hosp. NHS Trust Romford Essex. Prev: Cons. Ear, Nose & Throat Surg. Harold Wood Hosp. & OldCh. Hosp. Romford.

CHOWDHURY, Delowar Husain 99 Carlingford Road, London N15 3EJ Tel: 020 8889 1734 — MB BS 1966 Dacca. (Dacca Med. Coll.) Socs: BMA. Prev: SHO Bradford Roy. Infirm.; SHO Oldham Roy. Infirm.; Ho. Surg. & Asst. Surg. Dacca Med. Coll. Hosp.

CHOWDHURY, Emyr Abdul Hafiz 16 Cambridge Square, Wrexham LL11 2YG — MB ChB 1992 Liverp.

CHOWDHURY, Fahmid Ul-Haque Glenfield General Hospital, Groby Road, Leicester LE3 9QP Tel: 0116 287 1471 Fax: 0116 258 3950; 11 Eden Road, Oadby, Leicester LE2 4JP Tel: 0116 271 6029 Fax: 0116 271 6029 — MB ChB 1996 Leic. SHO Rotat. (Gen. Med.) Glenfield Gen. & Leicester Roy. Infirm. Socs: BMA. Prev: Ho. Off. (Surg.) Walsgrave Hosp. Coventry; Ho. Off. (Gen. Med.) Glenfield Gen. Leicester.

CHOWDHURY, Fateha Banu 2 Barbauld Road, Stoke Newington, London N16 0SS; The Luton and Dunstable Hospital NHS Trust, Lewsey Road, Luton LU4 0DZ Tel: 01582 598990 — MB BS 1997 Lond.; BSc Hons. (St. Bartholomew's and The Royal London School of Medicine) SHO Rotat. Luton & Dunstable Hosp.

CHOWDHURY, Hari Ranjan Lower Broughton Health Centre, Great Clowes Street, Salford M7 1RD Tel: 0161 839 2725 Fax: 0161 832 1210 — MB BS 1967 Dacca. (Dacca) SHO & Regist. (Gen. Med.) Gen. Hosp. Ashton-under-Lyne. Prev: SHO (Med. & Geriat.) Hope & Ladywell Hosps. Salford; SHO (Cas. & Orthop.) Blackburn Roy. Infirm.; SHO & Ho. Off. (Med.) Dacca Med. Coll. Hosp.

CHOWDHURY, Hasina 99 Carlingford Road, London N15 3EJ Tel: 020 8889 1734 — MB BS 1968 Dacca. (Dacca) Prev: SHO (Anaesth.) Oldham Gen. Hosp.; Ho. Off. Surg. & Paediat. Dacca Med. Coll. Hosp. Bangladesh; SHO Anaesth. Ashton Gen. Hosp.

CHOWDHURY, Md Waseaur Rahman Ysbyty Gwynedd, Penrhosgarnedd, Bangor LL57 2PW Tel: 01248 355568 Fax: 01248 355568; 'Cartref', Penrhosgarnedd, Bangor LL57 2NL Tel: 01248 355568 Fax: 01248 355568 Email: wrchowdhury@e.mail.com — MB BS 1965 Dhaka; DLO RCS Eng. 1972. Assoc. Specialist (ENT-Head & Neck Surg.) Gwynedd Hosp. NHS Trust Bangor.

CHOWDHURY, Mina Mohil Maqsood 37 Glasgow Street, Glasgow G12 8JR — MB ChB 1998 Glas.; MB ChB Glas 1998.

CHOWDHURY, Minto 4 Ashcott Close, Lostock, Bolton BL6 4RW; Alistair Ross Health Centre, Breightmet Fold Lane, Bolton BL2 6NT Tel: 01204 385206 — MB ChB 1985 Manch.; BSc (Hons.) Manch. 1983; MRCGP 1991; DRCOG 1991. Socs: BMA. Prev: Trainee GP Bolton; SHO Rotat.(Gen. Med.) Blackburn Roy. Infirm.; SHO (A & E) Blackpool Vict. Hosp.

CHOWDHURY, Mohammad Ali Pana 12 Rogersfield, Langho, Blackburn BB6 8HB Tel: 01254 240473 Fax: 01254 240473 — MB BS 1965 Dacca; DPM Eng. 1980. Substantive Locum Cons. Gen. Adult Psych. Wigan & Leigh Health Serv.s NHS Trust. Socs: Soc. Clin. Psychiat. Prev: Sen. Regist. Trent HA; Regist. Hope Hosp. Salford & Prestwich Hosp. Manch.; Assoc. Specialist (Psychiat.) Calderstone NHS Trust Whalley.

CHOWDHURY, Mohammed Habibullah 3 Rectory Field, Harlow CM19 4HD — MB BS 1967 Dacca. (Dacca Med. Coll.) Clin. Asst. (Psychiat.) Herts. & Essex Hosp. Bishop's Stortford; Police Surg. Harlow & Epping Area. Socs: Fell. Roy. Soc. Med.; BMA. Prev: Med. Off. Harlow Family Plann. Serv.; Coroners Path. E. Berks.

CHOWDHURY, Mohammed Ikram The Surgery, 209 Wells Road, Knowle, Bristol BS4 2DF Tel: 0117 968 1182 Fax: 0117 962 6408 — MB BS 1965 Karachi; MB BS 1965 Karachi.

CHOWDHURY, Mohammed Mahbub Ul-Haque University Hospital of Wales, Department of Dermatology, Box 100, Cardiff CF14 4XW Tel: 029 2074 7747 Fax: 029 2074 5161 Email: mabs@chowdhurym.freeserve.co.uk; 10 Kinsale Close, Cardiff CF23 8PQ — MB ChB 1991 Leic.; MRCP (UK) 1996. (Leic.) Cons. Dermatol., Univ. Hosp. of Wales, Cardiff; Hon. Clin. Teach. in Dermat., Univ. of Wales Coll. of Med., Cardiff CF14 4XN; Specialist Reg. (Dermat.) Univ. Hosp. of Wales. Socs: Brit. Assn. Dermat.; The Dowling Club; Roy. Soc. Med. Prev: Regist. (Dermat.) Newc. Roy. Vict. Infirm. & Sunderland Roy.

***CHOWDHURY, Mohua** The Knoll, Windsor Road, Oldham OL8 1RG Tel: 0161 652 6371; 94 Linwood Close, Camberwell, London SE5 8UX Tel: 020 7737 6904 — MB BS 1996 Lond.

CHOWDHURY, Moti 37 Glasgow Street, Glasgow G12 8JR — MB ChB 1996 Glas.

CHOWDHURY, Muhammad Rezwan 3 Glyn Coli Close, Treorchy, Cardiff CF42 6SU — BM BCh 1990 Oxf.

CHOWDHURY, Muhammad Sakhawat Husain Friary House Surgery, Friary House, 2a Beaumont Road, Plymouth PL4 9BH Tel: 01752 663138 Fax: 01752 675805; 33 Goosewell Hill, Eggbuckland, Plymouth PL6 5TJ Tel: 01752 704975 — MB BS 1963 Dacca; DTM & H Liverp. 1968; DCH RCPSI 1968. (Dacca) Prev: Ho. Phys. (Paediat.) Whipps Cross Hosp. Lond.; SHO (Orthop) & Regist. (Paediat.) Roy. Cornw. Hosp. Truro.

CHOWDHURY, Muntasir Rafique 9 The Dell, Netheroyd Park, Fixby, Huddersfield HD2 2FD — MB BS 1996 Lond.

CHOWDHURY, Nadira Barbara Castle Health Centre, Broadley Road, Harlow CM19 5SJ Tel: 01279 308888 Fax: 01279 308080 — MB BS 1970 Dacca; MB BS 1970 Dacca.

CHOWDHURY, Nawroze Iqbal 22 East End Road, London N3 3QT Tel: 020 8346 5242 — MRCS Eng. LRCP Lond. 1982.

***CHOWDHURY, Nojrul Amin** 23 Reservoir Street, Rochdale OL16 2XH Tel: 01706 653674 — MB ChB 1997 Manch.

CHOWDHURY, Paramit Dept. of Renal Medicine and Transplantation, 5th Floor, Thomas Guys House, Guy's Hospital, St. Thomas St., London SE1 9RT Tel: 0209 955 5000; 13 Langford Green, Champion Hill, Camberwell, London SE5 8BX Tel: 020 7274 5448 — MB BS 1992 Lond.; MRCP (UK) 1996. (King's Coll. Lond.) Specialist Regist., Renal Meicine, S. Thames Region.; Research Regist. Renal Unit Guy's Hosp. Lond. Socs: Renal Assn.; Brit. Transpl. Soc. Prev: Specialist Regist. Renal Guy's Hosp.; Specialist Regist. Renal Kings Coll. Hosp.; Specialist Regist. Renal Kent and Canterbury Hosp.

CHOWDHURY, Peter Abdul Halim 39 West Avenue S., Chellaston, Derby DE73 1HS — MB BCh 1995 Wales.

CHOWDHURY, Rana Surajit Mannford Way Health Centre, Mannford Way, Hainault, Ilford IG6 3HS — MB BS 1986 Lond.; BSc (Hons.) Lond. 1983; MRCP (UK) 1989. Trainee GP Hainault VTS. Prev: SHO (Gen Med. & Diabetol.) K. Geo. Hosp. Ilford; SHO (Chest Med.) Barking Hosp.; SHO (Neurol.) OldCh. Regional Neurosci. Centre.

CHOWDHURY, Rebecca Yasmin 33 Goosewell Hill, Plymouth PL6 5TJ — BM 1997 Soton.

CHOWDHURY, Shafiqul Bar c/o Mr A. M. Tarafdar, 19 Thorn Lane, Bradford BD9 6LU — MB BS 1984 Dacca; MRCP (UK) 1993.

CHOWDHURY, Shah Mazharul Islam Derby Road Surgery, 17 Derby Road, Chellaston, Derby DE73 1SA Tel: 01332 700309; 39 West Avenue South,, Chellaston, Derby DE73 1SH Tel: 01332 702744 — MB BS 1962 Dacca. (Dacca Med. Coll.) Prev: SHO (O & G) King's Mill Hosp. Sutton-in-Ashfield; SHO (Gen. Surg.) City Hosp. Nottm.; Regist. (O & G) Pilgrim Hosp. Boston.

CHOWDHURY, Sharmin 94 Fircroft Road, London SW17 7PW Tel: 020 8672 0422 — MB BS 1997 Lond.; BSc (Hons) 1994. (St. Mary's Hospital Medical School) SHO Ophth. Prev: A & E SHO; Med. HO; Surgic. HO.

CHOWDHURY, Shawkatur Reza 6 Jessica Mews, Canterbury CT1 1HL Tel: 01227 454706 — MB BS 1951 Dacca; DLO RCS Eng. 1967.

CHOWDHURY, Simon 7 Holland Park Avenue, London W11 3RH — MB BS 1994 Lond.

CHOWDHURY, Sunilkumar Das 'Eithinfa,', Carmel, Holywell CH8 8QP — LRCPI & LM, LRSCI & LM 1964; LRCPI & LM, LRCSI & LM 1964.

CHOWDHURY, Susanne 3 St Barnabas Street, Oxford OX2 6BG — MB 1985 Camb.; BChir 1984.

CHOWDHURY, Tahseen Ahmad 64 Christopher Road, Selly Oak, Birmingham B29 6QJ Tel: 0121 472 2644 Fax: 0121 472 2644 Email: t.a.chowdhury@bham.ac.uk — MB ChB 1990 Birm.; MD 1998; MRCP (UK) 1993. (Birm.) Lect. (Gen. Med., Endocrinol., Diabetes) Birm. Heartlands Hosp. Socs: Brit. Diabetic Assn.; Eur. Assn. for Study Diabetes. Prev: Lect. (Gen. Med., Endocrinol., Diabetes) Qu. Eliz.'s Hosp. Birm.; Sen. Regist. (Gen. Med., Diabetes & Endocrinol.) Selly Oak Hosp. Birm.; Clin. Research Fell. Univ. Birm.

CHOWDHURY, Tanzina 53 Orchard Drive, Watford WD17 3DX Email: tanzina@doctors.org.uk — MB BS 1994 Lond.; MRCP 1997 (London). (UCLH (London)) Paediat. Regist., N. Thames.

CHOWDHURY, Uttom Kumar Family Consultant Clinic, Camus, Dunstable Health Centre, Priory Gardens, Church Street, Dunstable LU6 3SU — MB ChB 1990 Manch.; MRCPsych 1996. (Manch.) Cons. Child Psychiat. Prev: Regist. (Psychiat.) N. Lond. Teachg. Hosps.; SHO (Psychiat.) Leics. HA; Ho. Phys. E. Birm. Hosp.

CHOWDHURY, Vijoy 20 Bulstrode Gardens, Hounslow TW3 3AJ — MB BS 1982 Lond.; MB BS (Distinc. Path.) Lond. 1982; MRCP (UK) 1986; MRCPath 1991. (St. Mary's)

CHOWDRY, Akhund Shahab 36 Abercorn Road, Newton Mearns, Glasgow G77 6NA — MB ChB 1991 Ed.

CHOWIENCZYK, Philip Jan 6 Grotes Place, London SE3 0QH — MB BS 1988 Lond.

CHOWINGS, Jeremy Stephen 13 Cargil Terrace, Edinburgh EH5 3ND — MB ChB 1992 Liverp.

CHOWN, Charles Stanley Malcolm Minafon, Betws-y-Coed LL24 0AS — MRCS Eng. LRCP Lond. 1952. (Liverp.) Socs: BMA. Prev: Ho. Surg. N.. Hosp. Liverp.; SHO Monkmoor Childr. Hosp. Shrewsbury; SHO (O & G) St. Asaph Hosp.

CHOWN, Sally Rebecca Gloucester Royal Hospital, Great Western Rd, Gloucester GL1 3NN Tel: 01452 395251 Fax: 01452 395273 Email: sally-chown@glour-tr.swest.nhs uk — MB BS 1988 Lond.; BSc (Hons.) Lond. 1985, MB BS 1988; MRCP (UK) 1991; MRCPath 1997. p/t Cons. Haematologist.

CHOWNS, Jonathan Clive Department of Genito-Urinary Medicine, St. Georges Hospital, Blackshaw Road, Tooting, London SW17 0QT — MB 1982 Camb.; BChir 1981.

CHOY, Ernest Ho Sing Clinical and Academic Rheumatology, King's College Hospital, Bessemer Road, Denmark Hill, London SE5 9RS Tel: 020 7346 6195 Fax: 020 7346 6475 Email: ernest.choy@kcl.ac.uk; 124 Loudoun Road, St John's Wood, London NW8 0ND — MB BCh 1985 Wales; MD Wales 1995; MRCP (UK) 1988. Cons. Sen. Lect. (Rheum.) GKT Sch. of Med., King's Coll. Lond. Socs: Amer. Coll. Rheum.; Fell. Roy. Soc. Med. (Counc. Mem. Standing Comm. Div. Rheum. & Rehabil.); Brit. Soc. Rheum. Prev: Lect. (Rheum.) Guy's & King's Coll. Hosp. Lond.; Research Fell. & Regist. (Rheum.) Guy's Hosp. Lond.

CHOY, Mr Leong Sing Alfred Royal Liverpool University Hospital, Department of Surgery, PO Box 147, Liverpool L69 3BX Tel: 0151 706 2000; 14 Eton Drive, Thornton-Hough, Wirral CH63 1JS Tel: 0151 336 6827 — MB BChir 1988 Camb.; MA 1988; FRCS Eng. 1992. Research Fell. (Surg.) Univ. Liverp.

CHOY, Yiok-Seong Lister House, 11-12 Wimpole St., London W1M 7AB Tel: 020 7436 2135 Fax: 020 7323 1022 — MB BS 1974 Singapore. (Singapore) GP (Allergy & Nutrit.al Med.); Hon. Clin. Asst. (Immunol.) Middlx. Hosp. Lond.

CHOYCE, Andrew 55C Central Hill, Upper Norwood, London SE19 1BS; 104 Broom Leys Road, Coalville, Leicester LE6 3AB — MB ChB 1988 Aberd.; FRCA 1996; DA (UK) 1996. Specialist Regist. (Anaesth.) Kings Healthcare NHS Trust Lond. Socs: MRCAnaesth.; Assn. Anaesth.

CHOYCE, Jonathan The Surgery, 130 Knights Hill, London SE27 0ST Tel: 020 8670 2940 — MB 1978 Camb.; BChir 1977.

CHOYCE, Mr Matthew Quentin Accident & Emegency Department, Royal Victoria Infirmary, Newcastle upon Tyne Tel: 0191 232 5131; 6 Hambledon Gardens, High Heaton, Newcastle upon Tyne NE7 7AL — BM BCh 1987 Oxf.; FRCS Eng. 1992. Sen. Regist. (A & E) Roy. Vict. Infirm Newc. u. Tyne. Socs: BMA & Brit. Accid. & Emerg. Med. Prev: Regist. (A & E) Roy. Vict. Infirm. Newc.; SHO (Plastic Surg.) Frenchay Hosp. Bristol; SHO Rotat. (Surg.) Roy. United Hosp. Bath.

CHRISPIN, Kathleen Hilary (retired) 1 Forge Lane, Headcorn, Ashford TN27 9QG Tel: 01622 890540 — MB ChB 1952 Sheff.; MFFP 1993. Prev: SCMO Canterbury & Thanet Health Dist.

CHRISTENSEN, Donna Marie Catherine Loveys The Mermaid Centre, Royal Cornwall Hospitals Trust-Treliske, Truro TR1 3LJ Tel: 01872 253778 Fax: 01872 252898; Lamanver Farm, Argal Cross, Penryn TR10 9BJ Fax: 01326 374539 — MD 1981 Massachusetts; BA Boston 1971; EdM Harvard 1975. BrE. Clinician Cornw.; Dir. of BrE. Screening Unit, Cornw. Socs: BMA; Assoc. Mem. Roy. Coll. Radiol.; Past (Pres.) Assn. BrE. Clinicians. Prev: Cons. Gen. Surg. & Chief Resid. Surg. Beth Israel Hosp. Harvard Univ. Boston, USA.

CHRISTIAN, Ann Sheila 50 Gledhow Wood Grove, Leeds LS8 1PA — MB ChB 1975 Leeds; FFA RCS Eng. 1984. Cons. Anaesth. Pontefract Gen. Infirm.

CHRISTIAN, Edward Clifford 22 Chilmark Road, London SW16 5HB — MB BCh BAO 1957 NUI; MD NUI 1964; FRCPath 1980, M 1964.

CHRISTIAN, Martin Tremayne 15 Apsley Street, Partick, Glasgow G11 7ST Email: mtc3q@clinmed.gla.ac.uk — MB ChB 1992 Ed.; MRCP (UK) 1995. Research Fell. (Human Nutrit.) Univ. Glas. Prev: SHO Yorkhill NHS Trust, Leicester Roy. Infirm. & Glas. Roy. Matern. Hosp.

CHRISTIAN, Mary Sheila 18 Upton Court Road, Slough SL3 7LY Tel: 01753 520135 — MB ChB 1949 Glas.; FRCS Glas. 1962; FRFPS Glas. 1961. (Glas.) Cons. A & E Wexham Pk. Hosp. Slough; Mem. Transport Comm. Med. Commiss. Accid. Preven. Socs: BMA (Hon. Sec. E. Berks. Div.); Hon. Life Mem. Brit. Assn. Accid. & Emerg. Med. Prev: Cons. A & E Roy. Free Hosp. Lond.; Cons. Surg. Govt. Hosp. Arabian Gulf; Sen. Regist. (Surg.) Wexham Pk. Hosp. Slough.

CHRISTIAN, Meryl Ann Fountain Cottage, High St., Scalby, Scarborough YO13 0QT Tel: 01723 363572 — MB BS 1950 Durh. (Durh.) Prev: Ho. Surg. Roy. Vict. Infirm. Newc.

CHRISTIAN, Paul Bryan (retired) Pittwater, 105 Satchell Lane, Hamble, Southampton SO31 4HL — MB BS 1961 Lond.; MRCS Eng. LRCP Lond. 1961. Prev: Nuffield Pract. Soton. Hosp. Gp.

CHRISTIAN, Peter Kevin Dukes Avenue Surgery, 1 Dukes Avenue, London N10 2PS Tel: 020 8883 9149 — MB BS 1979 Lond.; BSc 1974 (Hon.) Lond.; MRCGP 1984.

CHRISTIAN, Robert Philip Thorburn, Tynwald Road, Peel IM5 1JP Tel: 01624 842808 — MB ChB 1958 Liverp. (Liverp.) p/t Police Surg. I. of Man; HMA Peel Lifeboat; HMO Brit. Red Cross Soc. (I. of Man Br.); War Pens. Agency Comm. Mem. Socs: I. of Man Med. Soc. Prev: Sen. Partner Peel Med. Gp. Pract.; Squadron Ldr. RAF Med. Br., Specialist O & G; Regtl. Med. Off. 3rd Green Jackets, Rifle Brig.

CHRISTIAN, Steven Stable Cottage, Greys Mallory, Banbury Road, Warwick CV34 6SX — MB ChB 1995 Dundee.

CHRISTIAN, Wendy June The Surgery, 82 Lillie Rd, Fulham, London SW6 1TN — MB BS 1993 Lond.; MRCGP 2001; BSc (Hons.) Physiol. Lond. 1988; DFFP 1998; MRCP 1986 (pt. 1 only). (Charing Cross & Westminster) p/t GP Principle. Socs: BMA. Prev: GP Regist. Fulham; Clin. Asst. GUM St. Stephens Centre.

CHRISTIE, Alastair Malcolm (retired) 48 Thame Road, Warborough, Wallingford OX10 7DA Tel: 01865 858549 — MB ChB 1940 Ed. Prev: Gen. Practitioner.

CHRISTIE, Albert (retired) Flat 46, Muirfield Court, 20 Muirend Road, Muirend, Glasgow G44 3QD Tel: 0141 637 8114 — MB ChB 1936 Aberd.; MA Aberd. 1936; FFA RCS Eng. 1953; DA Eng. 1942. Prev: Anaesth. Vict. Infirm. Glas.

CHRISTIE, Alexander Barlas (retired) 17 Corberry Park, Dumfries DG2 7NG Tel: 01387 254855 Email: achristie8@compuserve.com — MB ChB Ed. 1958; FRCP Glas. 1980, M 1966; FRCPsych 1984, M 1972; DPM Eng. 1969. Prev: Cons. Psychiat. Crichton Roy. Hosp. Dumfries.

CHRISTIE, Alexander James Glebe Medical Centre, Abbeygreen, Lesmahagow, Lanark ML11 0EF Tel: 01555 892328 Fax: 01555 894094; 1 Broompark Drive, Lesmahagow, Lanark ML11 0DH Tel: 01555 894746 — MB ChB 1980 Ed.; BSc Ed. 1977.

CHRISTIE, Andrew Leslie Munro (retired) The Street, Old Costessey, Norwich NR8 5OB — MSc NZ; PhD, MB BS Lond. 1943; MRCS Eng. LRCP Lond. 1942; FRCPath 1954.

CHRISTIE, Anne Winthrop (retired) 11 Townsend Lane, Lower Almondsbury, Bristol BS32 4EQ Tel: 01454 613212 — MB ChB 1952 Bristol; DA Eng. 1955. Assoc. Specialist (Anaesth.) Frenchay Hosp. Bristol. Prev: Assoc.Specialist (Anaesth.) Frenchley Hosp., Bristol.

CHRISTIE, Barbara Anne Acorn Practice Group, St. Johns Health Centre, Oak Lane, Twickenham TW1 3PH Tel: 020 8891 0073 Fax: 020 8744 0060 — MB ChB 1988 Glas.; MRCGP 1995; DRCOG 1994. Prev: Trainee GP Glas.

CHRISTIE, Basil George Bagot (retired) St Giles Lodge, Kingston, Canterbury CT4 6HY Tel: 01227 830156 — MB BS 1949 Lond.; MD Lond. 1959; FRCP Lond. 1975, M 1959; MRCS Eng. LRCP 1949; DPhysMed. Eng. 1955. Cons. Phys. (Rheum. & Rehabil.) Canterbury, Thanet & S.E. Kent Health. Prev: Regist. Dept. Physical Med. & Rheum. Middlx. Hosp.

CHRISTIE, Caroline Anne Drumchapel Road Surgery, 242 Drumchapel Road, Glasgow G15 6EG Tel: 0141 944 4453 — MB ChB 1976 Glas.

CHRISTIE, Carolynne Leslie Elborough Street Surgery, 81-83 Elborough Street, Southfields, London SW18 5DS Tel: 020 8874 7113 Fax: 020 8874 3682 — MB ChB 1984 Aberd.; MB ChB Aberd. I984.

CHRISTIE, Catherine Swan Surgery, Swan Street, Petersfield GU32 3AB Tel: 01730 264011 Fax: 01730 231093 — BM BS 1989 Nottm.; BMedSci (Hons.) 1987; MRCP (UK) 1993; MRCGP 1997; DFFP 1996; DRCOG 1995. (Nottingham) GP Princip. Swan Surg. Petersfield; Clin. Asst. (Dermat.) St. Mary's Hosp. Portsmouth; Clin. Med. Off. Family Plann. St. Mary's Hosp. Portsmouth. Prev: GP/Regist. Portsmouth; SHO (O & G) St. Richards Hosp. Chichester; SHO (Med.) Withington Hosp. Manch. & Addenrooke's Hosp. Camb.

CHRISTIE, Constance Florence (retired) Scott's Mill, Ann St., Gatehouse of Fleet, Castle Douglas DG7 2HU — MB ChB 1941 St. And.; BSc St. And. 1938, MB ChB 1941. Prev: Med. Off. Dept. Health & Social Security Centr. Office for Scotl.

CHRISTIE, Diane Cranleigh Health Centre, 18 High Street, Cranleigh GU6 8AE Tel: 01483 273951 Fax: 01483 275755 — MB BS 1988 Lond.; MRCGP 1994; DRCOG 1992. GP Cranleigh.

CHRISTIE, Elizabeth Ann St Margarets Surgery, 29 Bridge Street, Bradford-on-Avon BA15 1BY Tel: 01225 863278 Fax: 01225 868648; 23 The Pastures, Lower Westwood, Bradford-on-Avon BA15 2BH Tel: 01225 867820 — MB ChB 1974 Aberd.; BMedBiol Aberd. 1971; MRCPsych 1979. (Aberd.) Prev: Hon. Research Fell. (Clin. Psychiat.) Qu. Eliz. Med. Centre Birm.; Regist. (Child & Adolesc. Psychiat.) Crichton Roy. Hosp. Dumfries; Asst. GP NW Herts. HA.

CHRISTIE, Elizabeth Margaret Albertbridge Road Surgery, 189 Albertbridge Road, Belfast BT5 4PW Tel: 028 9045 7109 Fax: 02890 225666; 11 Fort Road, Dundonald, Belfast BT16 1XR — MB BCh BAO 1980 Belf.; Certificate of Prescribed Experience in General Practice. (Queens University of Belfast) Gen. Med. Practitioner, Belf. Socs: Ulster Med. Soc. Prev: Ho. Off. Ulster Hosp. Dundonald.

CHRISTIE, Gordon Lindsay 76 Knowe Park Avenue, Carlisle CA3 9EL — MB ChB 1989 Ed.; BSc (Hons.) Ed. 1987; MRCP (UK) 1992. Regist. (Respirat. Med.) Carlisle. Prev: Research Fell. (Child Health) Med. Sch. Aberd.

CHRISTIE, Grant Irwin Gordon 232 Westbourne Park Road, London W11 1EP — MB ChB 1994 Otago.

CHRISTIE, Harry Donald (retired) Forest Hill, Stonehaven AB39 2LN Tel: 01569 762548 — MB ChB Aberd. 1926. Prev: Ho. Surg. & Res. Med. Off. Gravesend & N. Kent Hosp.

CHRISTIE, Hilary Joscleyn Eveleigh (retired) 48 Thame Road, Warborough, Oxford OX10 7DA Tel: 01865 858549 — BM BCh 1945 Oxf.; BM BCh Oxon. 1945; DA Eng. 1947. Prev: Ho. Phys. & Ho. Surg. Radcliffe Infirm.

CHRISTIE, Iain Rochford Health Centre, 14 Market Place, Carluke ML8 4BP Tel: 01555 771012 — MB ChB 1978 Glas.; DRCOG 1982.

CHRISTIE, Iain Thomson The Health Centre, 2 The Tanyard, Cumnock KA18 1BF Tel: 01290 421157 Fax: 01290 425444; Hartfield, 48 Ayr Road, Cumnock KA18 1DW Tel: 01290 421380 — BSc Ed. 1967, MB ChB 1970; DObst RCOG 1972; LFHom. 1996. (Edinburgh)

CHRISTIE, Iain Winston Royal United Hospital, Coombe Park, Bath BA1 3NG; 15B Bury Hill, Winterbourne Down, Bristol BS36 1AB — MB BCh 1988 Witswatersrand; FRCA 1994. Regist. Rotat. (Anaesth.) Bristol. Prev: SHO (Anaesth.) N.ampton & Baragwanath.

CHRISTIE, Ian Gordon Dalapples, 123 Titchfield Road, Stubbington, Fareham PO14 3HD Tel: 01329 662149 Email: dalapples@btinternet.com; 8 Burgess Park Mansions, Fortune Green Road, London NW6 1DP Tel: 020 8435 7118 — MB BChir 1958 Camb.; MA Camb. 1959, BA 1955; LLB Lond. 1989; FRCP Ed. 1985, M 1966; MRCS Eng. LRCP Lond. 1958; FRCPsych 1984, M 1971; DPM Eng. 1961. (Camb. & Guy's) Mem. Ment. Health Review Trib. Socs: RCPsych. (Gen. Psychiat., Forens., Subst. Misuse, Social & Community & Psychother Sects); MRCPsych. Prev: Cons. Lead Clin. (Psychiat.) & Med. Dir. Worthing Priority Care NHS Trust; Cons. Psychiat. & Dir. Servs. (Sub-Unit Gen. Manager) Knowle Hosp. Fareham; Founder & 1st Dir. Alpha Ho. & Culverlands Hse. Therap. Communities.

CHRISTIE, Mr James Royal Infirmary of Edinburgh, Lauriston Place, Edinburgh EH3 9YW Tel: 0131 536 3790 Fax: 0131 536 3413; Ferniehaugh, Dolphinton, West Linton EH46 7HJ — MB ChB 1965 St. And.; FRCS Ed. 1970. Cons. Edin. Roy. Infirm.

CHRISTIE, James McFarlane The Gables, Bellevue Avenue, Kirkintilloch, Glasgow G66 1AJ — MB ChB 1972 Glas.; BDS 1968; FDS RCPS Glas. 1978.

CHRISTIE, James Patrick 50 Cliffefield Road, Sheffield S8 9DL — MB ChB 1987 Sheff.; BMedSci Sheff. 1985. Prev: Trainee GP/SHO Barnsley VTS.

CHRISTIE, James Stuart West Meon Surgery, Doctors Lane, West Meon, Petersfield GU32 1LR Tel: 01730 829666 Fax: 01730 829229; East Broom, Hemplands Lane Privett, Alton GU34 3NT Tel: 01730 828280 — MB ChB 1977 Leeds; MRCGP 1989; DRCOG 1981. Prev: P'boro. Dist. Hosp. VTS.

CHRISTIE, Janice Elizabeth The Royal Edinburgh Hosp, Morningside Terrace, Edinburgh EH10 5HF Tel: 0131 537 6000; Tel: 0131 447 5167 — MB ChB 1973 Aberd.; M Phil Ed. 1980; MRCPsych 1977. Cons. Psychia trist Gen. Psychiat. Prev: Clin.Scientist & Hon.Cons. Psychiatric.; MRC Brain Metab. Unit Roy. Edin. Hosp.

CHRISTIE, John Lownie, Wing Cdr. RAF Med. Br. Retd. Department of Histopathology, Russells Hall Hospital, Dudley DY1 2HQ Tel: 01384 244033 Fax: 01384 244066; Wendover House, 4 Roberts Lane, Redlake Drive, Stourbridge DY9 0YZ Tel: 01562 884725 — MB ChB Ed. 1964; BSc (Hons.) Ed. 1961; FRCPath 1986, M 1973; DMJ (Path.) Soc. Apoth. Lond. 1978; DCP Lond 1971. (Ed.) Cons. Histopath. Russells Hall Hosp. Dudley; Mem. CCSC. Socs: Assn. Clin. Path. (Ex. Counc.); BMA (Mem. CCSC, Chairm. Path. Subcomm.); Renal Assn. Prev: Cons. Histopath. RAF Inst. Path. Halton; Path. Armed Forces Inst. Path. Washington DC, USA; Path Roy. Postgrad. Med. Sch. Lond.

CHRISTIE, John Michael Landale 35 Clyde Road, Redland, Bristol BS6 6RH — BM 1989 Soton.; MRCP (UK) 1993. Research Regist. (Gastroenterol.) John Radcliffe Hosp. Oxf. Socs: BMA. Prev: Regist. (Gastroenterol.) Bristol Roy. Infirm.

CHRISTIE, John Stewart 6C Rosebery Avenue, Harpenden AL5 2QP — MB ChB 1967 Liverp.; MRCPsych 1973; DPM Eng. 1972. Cons. Psychiat. Stockport DHA. Socs: Fell. Manch. Med. Soc. Prev: Cons. Psychiat & Sen. Regist. Cheadle Roy. Hosp.; Regist. (Psychiat.) Walton Hosp. Liverp.

CHRISTIE, Julie Helen Hartfield, 48 Ayr Road, Cumnock KA18 1DW Tel: 01290 421380 Email: julchr@hotmail.com; Hartfield, 48 Ayr Road, Cumnock KA18 1DW Tel: 01290 421380 — MB ChB 1996 Aberd. SMO Obst. & hynecology, Toyal Devon & Exeter Hosp., Exeter. Prev: SHO Totan, Logan Hosp., QLD, Australia; SHO A&E, The Yur Hosp., Scotl.

CHRISTIE, Lesley Catriona Westbourne, 46 Station Road, Carluke ML8 5AD — MB ChB 1977 Ed.

CHRISTIE, Lesley Jane Flat 1, Ruthven St., Glasgow G12 9BT — MB ChB 1997 Glas.

CHRISTIE, Louise Hodge 48 Ayr Road, Cumnock KA18 1DW — MB ChB 1994 Aberd.

CHRISTIE, Lynne Catherine Muiredge Surgery, Merlin Crescent, Buckhaven, Leven KY8 1HJ Tel: 01592 713299 Fax: 01592 715728 — MB ChB 1986 Ed.

CHRISTIE, Mairi Catherine 3 Inkerman Terrace, Whitehaven CA28 7TY Tel: 01946 693907 — MB ChB 1948 Glas.

CHRISTIE, Maureen Lyon (retired) 17 Corberry Park, Dumfries DG2 7NG Tel: 01387 254855 Email: achristie8@compuserve.com — MB ChB Glas. 1958; DObst RCOG 1960. Prev: SCMO (Family Plann.) & Clin. Med. Off. (Community Child Health) Dumfries & Galloway HB.

***CHRISTIE, Nicola Theda** The Horton Hospital, Oxford Road, Banbury OX16 9AL Tel: 01295 275500 — MB ChB 1998 Leic.; MB ChB Leic 1998.

CHRISTIE, Pamela Ann 5 Roseneath Street, Edinburgh EH9 1JH — MB ChB 1993 Ed.

CHRISTIE, Peter Nicholas Maple Childrens Centre, 28-34 Wolverhampton Avenue, Kingston upon Thames KT2 7QB Tel: 020 8546 7711; 9 Ashdown Road, Epsom KT17 3PL Tel: 01372 720727 — MB BS 1963 Lond.; FRCPCH 1997; FRCP Lond. 1994; MRCP (UK) 1974; MFPHM 1989; MFCM 1974; DCH Eng. 1968; DPH Lond. 1967; DObst RCOG 1966. (St. Thos.) Cons. Paediat. Kingston Hosp. NHS Trust.; Hon. Cons. Paediat. St Geo.'s Hosp. Tooting. Socs: BMA. Prev: Hon. Sen. Regist. MRC Statist. Research & Servs. Unit. Univ. Coll. Hosp. Lond.; Lect. (Developm. Paediat.) Inst. Child Health Lond.; Med. Advis. Family Plann. Assoc. Tanzania.

CHRISTIE, Peter Riddell Tel: 0141 300 1100 Fax: 0141 300 1170; 6 Ledcameroch Crescent, Bearsden, Glasgow G61 4AD — MB ChB 1985 Glas.; PhD 1980 Glas.; BSc 1976 Glas.; MFPHM RCP (UK) 1992; MPH Glas. 1992; FFPHM RCP (uk) 2000; FFPHM 2000 UK. (Glasgow) Cons. Epidemiol. Scott. Centre for Infec. & Environm. Health Glas.

CHRISTIE, Raymond Purvis (retired) 4 Red Hall Court, Felixstowe IP11 7AQ Tel: 01394 279757 — MB BS 1962 Durh. Prev: SHO (O & G) Preston Hosp. N. Shields.

CHRISTIE, Robin Andrew Stark Tel: 01462 434246; 28 Chiltern Road, Hitchin SG4 9PJ Tel: 01462 437824 — MB ChB 1977 Manch.; MRCGP 1982; DRCOG 1980. GP Trainer N. Thames Region; GP Tutor N. Herts.; Mem. Herts. LMC; Managing Partner Portmill Surg. Prev: Trainee GP Banbury VTS; SHO Booth Hall Childr. Hosp. Manch.; Ho. Phys. & Ho. Surg. N. Manch. Gen. Hosp.

CHRISTIE, Sharon Norma 37 Old Holywood Road, Belfast BT4 2HJ — MB BCh BAO 1989 Belf.; MB BCh BAO NUI Belf. 1989.

CHRISTIE, Sheila Mary Boghead of Orrock, Balmedie, Aberdeen AB23 8YA — MB ChB 1994 Aberd.

CHRISTIE, Simon William 2 Kings Head Street, Harwich CO12 3EG — MB ChB 1995 Glas.

CHRISTIE, Suzanne Frances 2/R, 34 Hillhead Street, Glasgow G12 8PZ Tel: 0141 334 0572 — MB ChB 1994 Glas.

CHRISTIE, Thomas Alfred 2 Glenorchil Place, Auchterarder PH3 1LR Tel: 01764 664093 — LRCP LRCS Ed. LRFPS Glas. 1942. (Anderson & St. Mungo's Coll. Glas.)

CHRISTIE, Thomas Hildred Wick Place, Ditchling, Hassocks BN6 8XE Tel: 0179 182175 — MB BS 1951 Lond.; MRCS Eng. LRCP Lond. 1950; FFA RCS Eng. 1954. (King's Coll. Hosp.) Cons. Anaesth. Brighton & Lewes Hosp. Gps. Prev: Sen. Regist. Dept. Anaesth. St. Thos. Hosp.; Surg. Lt. RNVR.

CHRISTIE BROWN, Jeremy Robin Warrington 127 Harley Street, London W1N 1DJ Tel: 020 7486 3631 Fax: 020 8265 2026; Rotherwood, 11 Sydenham Hill, London SE26 6SH Tel: 0208 670 1071 Fax: 0208 265 2026 — BM BCh Oxf. 1960; MA Oxf. 1965, BA 1957; FRCP Lond. 1983, M 1964; FRCPsych 1979, M 1971; DPM Lond. 1967. (Oxf. & Univ. Coll. Hosp.) Emerit. Cons. Psychiat. Maudsley Hosp. Lond. Prev: Cons. Psychiat. Maudsley Hosp. Lond.; Cons. Psychiat. Univ. Coll. Hosp. & Friern Hosp.

CHRISTIE BROWN, Jonathan Stafford 11 Sydenham Hill, London SE26 6SH — MB BS 1991 Lond.

CHRISTIE BROWN, Margaret Elizabeth Rotherwood, 11 Sydenham Hill, London SE26 6SH Tel: 020 8670 1071; 127 Harley Street, London W1 Tel: 020 486 3631 — MB BS 1961 Lond. (Univ. Coll. Hosp.) Prev: Cons. Psychotherap. Qu. Charlottes & Chelsea Hosps. Wom. Lond.; Assoc. Mem. Assn. Psychotheraps.

CHRISTISON, Mr David (retired) Lea Rig, 21 Eastcote Avenue, Glasgow G14 9LQ Tel: 0141 959 5376 — MB ChB Glas. 1938; FRCS Glas. 1980; FRCOphth Lond. 1993; DOMS Eng. 1947. Prev: Surg. Glas. Eye Infirm.

CHRISTISON, Joan Rae (retired) 32 Green Drive, Inverness IV2 4EU Tel: 01463 230288 — MB ChB 1947 Glas.; MRCPsych 1972; DPM Eng. 1960.

CHRISTISON, Margaret Kyle Lea Rig, 21 Eastcote Avenue, Glasgow G14 9LQ Tel: 0141 959 5376 — M.B., Ch.B. Glas. 1939. (Glas.)

CHRISTLEY, Howard Michael Gemini Research Limited, 162 Science Park, Milton Road, Cambridge CB4 0GH Tel: 01223 424260; 58 John Amner Close, Ely CB6 1DT — MB BS 1982 Lond.; MA Camb. 1983; FFPM RCP (UK) 1991; Dip. Pharm. Med. RCP (UK) 1990.

CHRISTMAS, Anthony Randolph Wagtails, Crooksbury Road, Runfold, Farnham GU10 Tel: 0125 182598 — MB BS 1954 Lond. (St. Thos.) Prev: Ho. Phys. Farnham Hosp.; Ho. Surg. Hertford Co. Hosp.

CHRISTMAS, David Department of Anaesthetics, Princess Royal Hospital NHS Trust, Apley Castle, Telford TF1 6TF Tel: 01952 641222 Email: david.christmas@prh-tr.wmids.nhs.uk; 41 Kennedy Road, Shrewsbury SY3 7AA Email: dxmas@hospital-doctor.net — MB ChB 1976 Birm.; MBA Wolverhampton 1996; FFA RCS 1980. (Birm.) Cons. Anaesth. P.ss Roy. Hosp. NHS Trust Telford; Med. Director, P.ss Roy. Hosp. NHS Trust, Telford. Socs: Assn. Anaesth. GB & N.. Irel.; Intens. Care Soc.; Eur. Soc. Intens. Care Med. Prev: Cons. Anaesth. Dudley Rd. Hosp. Birm.; Sen. Regist. Yorks. Scheme for Higher Profess. Train.

CHRISTMAS, David Mackinnon Barrett Flat 6, 16 Speirs Wharf, Glasgow G4 9TB — MB ChB 1996 Glas.

CHRISTMAS, Emma Rosalind 6 Chapel Villas, Dalgety Bay, Dunfermline KY11 9UD — MB ChB 1994 Ed. SHO (Gen./Geriat. Med.) Moodlands Hosp. Edin.; SHO (Paediat.) Newc.

CHRISTMAS, Raymond John 4 Roseland Avenue, Manchester M20 3QY — LRCPI & LM, LRSCI & LM 1958; LRCPI & LM, LRCSI & LM 1958.

CHRISTMAS, Rowena Severnbank Surgery, The Health Centre, Lydney Tel: 01594 845222; Spring Cottage, Pen-y-Fan Green, Nr. Monmouth, Monhantshire NP25 4RA Tel: 01600 860446 — MBBS 1996 (London); MRCGP 1999; DFFP 2000; DCH 1998. GP Princip. Socs: BMA; Roy. Coll. of GPs.

CHRISTMAS, Steven College Road Surgery, 50/52 College Road, Maidstone ME15 6SB Tel: 01622 752345 Fax: 01622 758133 — MB BS 1975 Lond.; BSc (Hons.) Lond. 1972; DRCOG 1981; DCH Eng. 1980. (London Hospitals)

CHRISTMAS, Mr Timothy John 15th Floor, Charing Cross Hospital, Fulham Palace Road, London W6 8RF Tel: 020 8846 1966 Fax: 020 8846 7696 Email: tctristmas@compuserve.com; 14 Coniger Road, London SW6 3TA Tel: 020 7371 9131 Email: tchristmas@compuserve.com — MB BS 1980 Lond.; MD Lond. 1992; FRCS (Urol.) 1991; FRCS Eng. 1984. (Middlx. Hosp. Med. Sch.) Cons. Surg. inUrol. Oncol., Caring Cross Hosp., \\the \Roy. Marsden Hosp., Chelsea & W.minster Hosp..; Hon. Cons. Surg., Mt.

Vernon Hosp., N.wood, Roy. Brompton Hosp., Chelsea. Socs: Fell. Roy. Soc. Med.; Brit. Assn. Surgic. Oncol.; Americal Urological Assn. Prev: Sen. Regist. St. Bart. Hosp. Lond.; Research Fell. (Surg.) Univ. Coll. & Middlx. Sch. Med.; Regist. (Surg.) Lond. Hosp. Whitechapel.

CHRISTMAS, Trudy Karen Jane Melrose, The Park, Cheltenham GL50 2SG Tel: 01242 570797 — MB BS 1996 Lond.; BSc (Hons) Lond. 1993. (St Georges Tooting)

CHRISTODOULOU, Aristophanes Andrea Fernbank, Finchley Way, London N3 1AB Tel: 020 8349 3426 Email: dr_a_christodoulou@msn.com; The Oxford, 6 Green Meadow, Little Heath, Potters Bar EN6 1LL Tel: 01707 857273 — MB BS 1985 Lond. Chief Exec. Diagnostics Div. W.minster Health Care Holdings Plc Lond.

CHRISTODOULOU, Chris Christodoulos PO Box 68, Kent & Canterbury Hospital, Ethelbert Road, Canterbury CT1 3NG — MB ChB 1992 Stellenbosch.

CHRISTODOULOU, Christakis 7C Amberley Court, Hestia Drive, Selly Oak Hosp., Raddlebarr Road, Birmingham B29 6JD — BM BS 1997 Nottm.

CHRISTODOULOU, Christos Flat 1, 32 Park Road, Coventry CV1 2LD — Ptychio Iatrikes 1986 Athens.

CHRISTOFOROU, Christos 33 Lyndhurst Road, Wood Green, London N22 5AX — MB ChB 1979 Manch.; MRCP (UK) 1983.

CHRISTOPHER, Mr Andrew Nimal 9 Greenhill Gardens, Guildford GU4 7HH — MB BS 1987 Lond.; FRCS Glas. 1993.

CHRISTOPHER, Anne Vimala 51 Oxford Road, Cowely, Oxford OX4 2ER — MB BS 1991 Newc.

***CHRISTOPHER, Antony Stephen** Doctors' Mess, Royal Devon & Exeter Hospital, Barrack Road, Exeter EX2 5DW — MB ChB 1998 Bristol; BEng (Hons.) CNAA Plymouth 1992.

CHRISTOPHER, Bryan Wilfrid Cosby Carmichael Moatfield Surgery, St. Michaels Road, East Grinstead RH19 3GW Tel: 01342 327555 Fax: 01342 316240 — MB BChir 1963 Camb.; MA Camb. 1963. (Middlx.) Socs: BMA. Prev: Ho. Surg. & SHO (Cas.) Middlx. Hosp.; Ho. Off. (O & G) Cuckfield Hosp.

CHRISTOPHER, Erpys 35 Wood Vale, London N10 3DJ Tel: 020 8883 0085 — MB BS 1961 Lond.; MRCS Eng. LRCP Lond. 1961; MFFP 1993; DCH Eng. 1965; DObst RCOG 1964. (Univ. Coll. Hosp.) Cons. Family Plann. & Reproduc. Health Haringey Healthcare NHS Trust; Domicil. Med. Off. Family Plann. Lond. Boro. Haringey; Med. Off. Psychosexual Clinic Univ. Coll. Hosp. Lond., Margt. Pyke; Centre Lond. & N. Middlx. Hosp. Lond. Socs: BMA; Founder Mem. Inst. Psychosexual Med.; Soc. Pub. Health. Prev: Clin. Asst. (Obst. & Med.) Ho. Phys. Eliz. G. Anderson Hosp. Lond.; Ho. Surg. Mile End Hosp.

CHRISTOPHER, Jason Brett Salehurst House, Blackham, Tunbridge Wells TN3 9UB — MB ChB 1997 Sheff.

CHRISTOPHER, Judith Anne St George's Hospital, Department Child Health, Blackshaw Road, Tooting, London SW17 0QT; 11 Seymour Gardens, Surbiton KT5 8QE — MB BS Lond. 1983; MRCP (UK) Paediat. 1988; FRCPCH 1997. (Middlx. Hosp.) Cons. Paediat. St. Geo. Hosp. Lond. Prev: Sen. Regist. (Paediat.) St. Peters Hosp. Chertsey.

CHRISTOPHER, Peter Miles The Surgery, High Street, Fenny Compton, Leamington Spa CV47 2YG Tel: 01295 770855 Fax: 01295 770858; Knotts Cottage, Bridge St, Fenny Compton, Leamington Spa CV47 2XY — MB BS 1970 Lond. (Roy. Free)

CHRISTOPHER, Susan Kathleen Knotts Cottage, Bridge St, Fenny Compton, Leamington Spa CV47 2XY Tel: 01295 770627 — MB BS 1972 Lond.; MRCS Eng. LRCP Lond. 1972. (Roy. Free) Med. Off. (p/t) BrE. Screening, Coventry & Warwick Hosp., Coventry.

CHRISTOPHERS, Joella Warders Medical Centre, 47 East Street, Tonbridge TN9 1LA Tel: 01732 770088 Fax: 01732 770033 — MB BChir 1991 Camb.; MA Camb. 1992; MRCGP 1995; DCH RCP Lond. 1994; DFFP 1994; DRCOG 1993.

CHRISTOPHERSON, Thereza Anne Patricia Maybury Villa, The Ridge, Woking GU22 7EG — MB BS 1998 Lond.; MB BS Lond 1998.

CHRISTOPHI, George 7 Emerald Court, Slough SL1 2JZ — MB ChB 1988 Manch.

CHRISTOU, Takis Craven Road Medical Centre, 60 Craven Road, Leeds LS6 2RX Tel: 0113 295 3531 — MB ChB 1966 Leeds; MRCGP 1984. (Leeds)

CHRISTY, Joan Rachel Olive 92 Groomsport Road, Bangor BT20 5NT Tel: 01247 458344 — MB BCh BAO 1982 Belf.

CHRISTY, Michael William Donnachie Saintfield Health Centre, Fairview, Saintfield, Ballynahinch BT24 7AD Tel: 028 9751 0575 Fax: 028 9751 1895; Tel: 01238 519061 — MB BCh BAO 1989 Belf.; MA Camb. 1985; MRCGP 1993; DFFP 1993; DCH RCP Lond. 1992; DRCOG 1991. Med. Assessor Indep. Tribunal Serv.

CHRISTYS, Andrew George Nicklyn House, Wadborough, Worcester WR8 9HA — MB ChB 1973 Dundee.

CHRISTYS, Ann Rosemary Anaesthetic Department, General Infirmary at Leeds, Great George St., Leeds LS1 3EX Tel: 0113 392 6672; 33 Danefield Terrace, Otley LS21 1HU Tel: 01943 461672 — MB ChB 1976 Ed.; FFA RCS Eng. 1986; PhD Leeds 1999. Assoc. Specialist Anaesth. Leeds Teachg. Hosps. NHS Trust.

CHRONNELL, Peter Kevin (retired) 138 Kingsbrook Road, Manchester M16 8WG Tel: 0161 881 6801 — MB ChB Manch. 1963; DObst RCOG 1966.

CHRYSOPOULO, Minas Theodore 189 Friern Barnett Lane, London N20 0NN — MB BS 1996 Lond.

CHRYSTAL, Kathleen May Robertson 17 Ashgrove Road W., Aberdeen AB16 5BB Tel: 01224 483118; 21 The Close, Shotley Bridge, Consett DH8 0DS — MB ChB 1958 Aberd.; MB ChB (Hons.) Aberd. 1958; FRCS Ed. 1965. Cons. Plastic Surg. N. RHA. Socs: Cons. Mem. Brit. Assn. Plastic Surgs.; Roy. Soc. Med. Prev: Sen. Regist. (Plastic Surg.) Bangour Gen. Hosp. W. Lothian; Regist. (Plastic Surg.) Qu. Mary's Hosp. Roehampton; Research Asst. Scott Hosp. Endowments Research Trust.

CHRYSTALL, Dorothy Mitchell (retired) 46/6 Inverleith Gardens, Edinburgh EH3 5QF Tel: 0131 551 1120 — MB ChB 1935 Aberd. Prev: Ho. Phys. Roy. Aberd. Hosp. Sick Childr.

CHU, Anthony Christopher Imperial College of Science, Technology and Medicine, Unit of Dermatology, Hammersmith Hospital, London W12 0NN Tel: 020 8383 3264 Fax: 020 8383 2345 Email: achu@rpms.ac.uk; The Cedars, 6 Hengrave Road, Honor Oak Park, London SE23 3NW Tel: 020 8699 1313 — MRCS Eng. LRCP Lond. 1975; BSc Lond. 1972, MB BS 1975; FRCP Lond. 1993; MRCP (UK) 1977; FRCP (UK) 1993. (Guy's Hospital) Sen. Lect. Dermat. Imperial Coll. of Sci., Technol. & Med. Hammersmith Hosp. Lond. Socs: Histiocyte Soc. (Chairm. Scientif. Comm.).; Roy. Soc. Med.; Brit. Assn. Dermatol. Prev: Welcome Sen. Clin. Research Fell. & Sen. Lect. Cons. Dermat. Hammersmith Hosp. Lond.; Sen. Regist. (Dermat.) St John's Hosp. Lond.; Sen. Staff Assoc. Columbia Prespretarian Hosp. New York.

CHU, Carol Elaine Department Clinical Genetics, Ashley Wing, St James's University Hospital, Beckett St., Leeds LS9 7TF Tel: 0113 206 4020 Fax: 0113 246 7090 Email: medcec@stjames.leeds.ac.uk; Tel: 01937 557608 Email: medcec@stjames.leeds.ac.uk — MB ChB 1976 Sheff.; MSc (Med. Genetics) Glas. 1991; MD Sheff. 1995; MRCPI 1993. (Sheffield University) Cons. (Clin. Genetics) Leeds. Socs: BMA; Brit. Soc. Human Gen.

CHU, Cheuk Hung Peter Ching Silver Lane Surgery, 1 Suffolk Court, Yeadon, Leeds LS19 7JN Tel: 0113 250 4953 Fax: 0113 250 9804 — MB ChB 1971 Leeds; MRCS Eng. LRCP Lond. 1972; DCH Eng. 1974; DObst RCOG 1973. GP Yeadon.

CHU, Henson 191 Icknield Way, Letchworth SG6 4TT Email: familyphysician@usa.net — LRCP LRCS Ed. LRCPS Glas. 1989; MCFP 2001; Dip Derm RCPS Glas. 2000; Dip. Pract. Dermat. Univ. Wales 1994; DFFP 1993; DGM RCPS Glas. 1992; DFFP 1993; DRANZCOG 2001; FRACGP 1998; DABFP 1998; MICGP 1996; MRCGP 1993; Dip. GU Med. Soc. Apoth. Lond. 1996; DCH RCPSI 1996; Dip. Clin. Psychiat. RCPSI 1995; Dip. GU Med. Ven. Liverp. 1994. GP Far E. Med. Serv.s, Hong Kong. Socs: Amer. Acad. of Family Phys.; Hong Kong Med. Assn. Prev: Instruc. Dept. of Family Med. Univ. of Rochester New York, USA; Chief Resid. Dept. of Family Pract. Mt. Sinai Hosp. Chicago, USA; SHO (Dermatol.)Skin Hosp. & Ladywell Hosp. Salford.

CHU, Sau Kwan Flat 5, 19 Elvaston Place, London SW7 4QF — MB BS 1987 Hong Kong; FRCS Ed. 1992.

CHU, Stephanie Yin Yiu 21 Albert Road, Lenton, Nottingham NG7 2EX — BM BS 1993 Nottm.

CHU, Welgent Wai-Ching c/o Dr De Munshi's Secretary, High Croft Hospital, PO Box 267, Birmingham B23 6AX; A2 Dragon Heights, 12 Eastbourne Road, Kowlom Tong, Hong Kong Tel: 3369 355 — MB ChB 1990 Glas. SHO (Psychiat.) Highcroft Hosp. Birm.

Prev: SHO (Cas.) StoneHo. Hosp. Lanarksh.; SHO (O & G & Med.) Solihull Hosp. W. Midl.

CHU CHI-MAI, Patrick Department of Haematology, Royal Liverpool University Hospital, Prescot Road, Liverpool L7 8XP — MB BS 1978 Hong Kong; FRCP Lond.; FRCP Ed.; FRCPath. Cons. Haemat. Roy. Liverp. Univ. Hosp. Socs: Protec. Soc.

CHUA, Mr Chong Beng 25 Queen Mary Court, Derby DE22 1BB — BM BS 1988 Nottm.; BMedSci (Hons.) Nottm. 1986; FRCS Ed. 1994. Regist. (Urol.) City Hosp. Nottm. Prev: SHO (Transpl. Surg.) Leicester Gen. Hosp.; SHO Rotat. (Surg.) Derby.

CHUA, Chung Nen Eye Unit, Royal Berkshire Hospital, Reading RG1 5AN — BM BS 1990 Nottm.

CHUA, Dorothy Poh Luan (retired) 15 Fairdale Gardens, London SW15 6JW Tel: 020 8789 3431 — MB ChB 1958 Aberd. Med. Asst. Kingston & Long Gr. Hosps.; Med. Assoc. Indep. Tribunal Serv. Prev: Assoc. Specialist (Geriat. Med.) Kingston & Long Gr. Hosps.

CHUA, Eddy Soon Kheng Department of medicine for the elderly, Northwick Park Hospital, Watford Road, Harrow HA1 3UJ Tel: 0208 869 3407; The Little House, London Road, Harrow-On-Hill, Harrow HA1 3JQ Email: eddy.chua@hhh-tr.nthames.nhs.uk — MB ChB 1987 Glas.; BSc (Hons.) Biochem. Liverp. 1981; MD 1998; MSc (Human Nutrit.) Lond. 1982; MRCP (UK) 1990. (Glasgow)

CHUA, Mr Hock Beng 239 Minster Court, Edgehill, Liverpool L7 3QH — MB ChB 1988 Liverp.; FRCS Ed. 1993.

CHUA, Ignatius Chung-I 231 Providence Road, Sheffield S6 5BH — MB ChB 1998 Sheff.; MB ChB Sheff 1998.

CHUA, Richard Kok Wah 109 Wellesley Avenue, Belfast BT9 6DH — MB BCh BAO 1994 Belf.

CHUA, Sak Eng B63 Staff Residence, St. James's University Hospital, Beckett St., Leeds LS9 7TF — MB BS 1992 Melbourne.

CHUA, Seok Mee 31 Beryl Road, London W6 8JS — MB BS 1991 Lond.

CHUA, Shareen Shih Wei 59/6 Cockburn Street, Edinburgh EH1 1BS — MB ChB 1998 Ed.; MB ChB Ed 1998.

CHUA, Siew Chen Room 2, 68 St Stephens Road, Norwich NR1 3RE — MB BS 1997 New South Wales.

CHUA, Siew-Eng 25 Deep Dale, London SW19 5EZ — BM BCh 1990 Oxf.

CHUA, Tuan Peng Royal Surrey County Hospital, Egerton Road, Guildford GU2 7XX Tel: 01483 571122 — MB BS 1987 Lond.; MD Lond. 1996; BSc (1st cl. Hons.) Lond. 1984; MRCP (UK) 1990. Cons. Cardiol. Roy. Surrey Co. Hosp., Guildford; Cons. Cardiol., St.Geo. Hosp., Lond. Socs: Med. Res. Soc.; Brit. Cardiac Soc.; Assoc. Fell., Amer. Coll. of Cardiol. Prev: Sen. Regist. Hammersmith Hosp., Lond.; Sen. Regist., Roy. Brompton Hospita, Lond.; Regist., Roy. Free Hosp., Lond.

CHUA, Victor Wee Teck 10 St George's Court, Cavendish Avenue, Cambridge CB1 7UP Email: victor.chua@iname.com — MB BChir 1995 Camb.; MB BChir Camb. 1994; MA Camb. 1996, BA 1992. (Camb.) SHO (Ophth.) Leicester Roy. Infirm.

CHUA, Wan Lian 87 Middleton Boulevard, Wollaton Park, Nottingham NG8 1FX — BM BS 1995 Nottm.; BMedSci Nottm. 1993. SHO Rotat. (Psychiat.) High Royds Hosp. Mewston Near Ilkley. Prev: SHO (Med.) St. Mary's Hosp. Isle of Wight; SHO (Pschiatry) St. Mary's Hosp. Isle of Wight; Ho. Off. (Med.) Kings Mill Hosp. Mansfield Notts.

CHUA, Wei Mei 25 Becket House, Becket St., London SE1 4XY — MB BS 1996 Lond.

CHUAH, Seong Som Cardiology Department, Stepping Hill Hospital, Poplar Grove, Stockport SK2 7JE Tel: 0161 483 1010 Fax: 0161 419 5478; 2 Hilton Road, Grovesnor Park, Sharston, Manchester M22 4ZD Tel: 0161 945 5580 — MB BCh 1993 Wales; MRCP (Lond.) 1996. (Univ. Wales Coll. Med.) Research Regist. Cardiol. Stepping Hill Hosp. Stockport. Prev: SHO (Med. & ICU) Hope Hosp. Salford; SHO (Med.) S. Bucks. NHS Trust; SHO (Med. for Elderly) S.end Healthcare NHS Trust.

CHUAH, Taik Pin 58A Mount Pleasant, Norwich NR2 2DQ — MB ChB 1988 Dundee. Ho. Off. Dundee Roy. Infirm. Tayside HB.

CHUAQUI, Paz Bernadita 24 Tibbets Close, Inner Park Road, London SW19 6EF — MSc Neurochem. 1977; Medico Cirujano Chile 1972; MRCPsych. 1978.

CHUBB, Charles Henry Thomas The Health Centre, Base Street, Thame OX9 3JZ Tel: 01844 261066; 32 Park Town, Oxford OX2 6SJ Tel: 01865 552877 — MBBS Lond. 1978; MRCGP 1982; DRCOG 1981. GP Thame.

CHUBB, Edward Alexander 11 Oldbury Close, Horsham RH12 5JZ — MB BCh 1998 Wales.

CHUBB, Helen Lindsay Whitchurch Hospital, Cardiff CF14 7XB; 63 Waterloo Gardens, Penylan, Cardiff CF23 5AB — MB BCh 1987 Wales; MSc Wales 1995; MRCGP 1991; MRCPsych 1993; DRCOG 1991. (Univ. Wales Coll. Med.)

CHUBB, Lindsay Vaughan 1 Bronwydd Close, Cardiff CF23 5RA — MB BCh 1952 Wales; FRCGP 1984.

CHUBB, Sarah Elizabeth Mary 6 Scarcroft Hill, York YO24 1DE Tel: 01904 644120 — DFFP 2001; BM BS Nottm. 1988; MRCGP 1993; DRCOG 1991.

CHUBB, Suzanne Atlasta, Low Ham, Langport TA10 9DS Tel: 01458 250728 — MB ChB 1997 Bristol; MB ChB (Hons.) Bristol 1997. (Bristol) SHO. (Med.) Gloucester Roy Hosp. Prev: SHO (A & E) Torbay Hosp. Torquay Devon; PRHO (Surg.) S.mead Hosp.; PRHO (Med.) W.on Gen. Hosp.

CHUCK, Alexis Josephine Department of Rheumatology, Dryburn Hospital, North Road, Durham DH1 5TW Tel: 0191 333 2333 Fax: 0191 333 2581 — MB ChB 1977 Liverp.; FRCP Lond. 1996; MRCP (UK) 1981; FRCP Ed 1998. Cons. Rheum. N. Durh. Healthcare NHS Trust. Prev: Sen. Regist. (Rheum.) Nottm. & Mansfield Hosps.; Tutor (Rheum.) Univ. Manch.; Regist. (Med.) Wythenshawe Hosp. Manch.

CHUDGAR, Nitin Ochchhavlal Doctors Mess, Tameside General Hospital, Fountain St., Ashton-under-Lyne OL6 9RW — MB BS 1970 Gujarat; MB BS Gujarat India 1970.

CHUDLEY, Sylvia Marion Jiggins Lane Medical Centre, 17 Jiggins Lane, Bartley Green, Birmingham B32 3LE Tel: 0121 477 7272 Fax: 0121 478 4319; 16 Ashmore Road, Cotteridge, Birmingham B30 2HA — MB ChB 1979 Birm.

CHUE HONG, Mr Philippe Tacklam Tel: 01592 890217 Fax: 01592 890456; Ranfurly, Queen Margaret St, Kinghorn, Burntisland KY3 9SP Tel: 01592 890724 — MB ChB 1975 Ed.; BSc (Med. Sci.) Ed. 1972; FRCS Ed. 1981. Sen. Partner, Kinghorn Med. Pract., Kinghorn; Clin. Asst., Gastroenterol., Vict. Hosp., Kirkcaldy. Prev: Ho. Surg. Roy. Infirm. Edin.; Ho. Phys. Chalmers Hosp. Edin.

CHUGH, Satwant Kumar (retired) Walkley House Medical Centre, 23 Greenhow Street, Sheffield S6 3TN Tel: 0114 234 3716 — MB BS 1963 Punjab.

***CHUI, Daniel Tak Yiu** 42/8 Parkside Terrace, Edinburgh EH16 5XR Tel: 0131 667 2866 Email: danielchui@campurserve.com — BM BS 1998 Nottm.; B.Med. Sci (Hons.) 1996; BM BS Nottm 1998.

CHUI, David Kwan Chi Eastbourne District General Hospital, Kings Drive, Eastbourne BN21 2UD — MB ChB 1984 Leic. Cons. Obst. and Gynaecologist, E.bourne Hosptals NHS Trust.

CHUI, Ei-Cheng 1F3 43 Balcarres Street, Edinburgh EH10 5JG — MB ChB 1998 Ed.; MB ChB Ed 1998.

CHUI, Shyr Lin 8 Gilbey Close, Uxbridge UB10 8TD — BM BCh 1993 Oxf. SHO (Med.) Watford Gen. Hosp.

CHUI, Siu Hang Billy 4 Marlcroft Avenue, Stockport SK4 3LZ — MB ChB 1988 Manch.

CHUI WAN CHEONG, Pak Lim 49 Park Road, Glasgow G4 9JD — MB ChB 1974 Glas.

CHUI YEW CHEONG, Chan Yoong Garden City Surgery, 1A Garden City, Holcombe Brook, Bury BL0 9TN Tel: 01204 884710 Fax: 01204 888334; 373 Holcombe Road, Greenmount, Bury BL8 4HF Tel: 01204 887351 — MB ChB 1976 Manch.; DRCOG 1978.

CHUKWUEMEKA, Andrew Okechukwu 17 Luxor Street, London SE5 9QN — MB BS 1992 Lond.; FRCS Eng. (UMDS) Specialist Regist.

CHUKWUEMEKA, Sylvia Ogechi 12 Illingworth, Windsor SL4 4UP — MB BS 1994 Lond.

CHUKWULOBELU, Rosemary Ngozi 63 Berberry Close, Bournville, Birmingham B30 1TB — LMSSA 1995 Lond.

CHULAKADABBA, Mr Adhisabandh Cherry Gate, 2 Dodnor Lane, Newport PO30 5TB — MD 1986 Thailand; FRCS Ed. 1994.

CHUMAS, Mr Paul Dominic Flat 4, 4 Bank St., Barrhead, Glasgow G78 2RA — MB BS 1984 Lond.; FRCS Ed. 1988.

CHUN, Pik Kwan 57 Gulduthel Park, Inverness IV2 4RU — MB ChB 1993 Dundee; DRCOG 1997. (University of Dundee.) GP

Regist. Burnfield Med Pract. Inverness. Socs: BMA & Med. Protec. Soc. Prev: SHO (Gen. Med.) Torbay Hosp. Torquay; Ho. Off. (Surg.) Stirling Roy. Infirm.; Ho. off. (Med.) Ninewells Hosp. & Med. Sch. Dundee.

CHUNDRIGAR, Mr Tariq Lamorna, 4 Bar Hill, Medely, Crewe CW3 9QD — MB BS 1987 Karachi; FRCS Ed. 1992.

CHUNG, Andrene Suzanne Hamersmith House, Hammersmith Hospital, Du Cane Road, London W12 0NN — MB BS 1986 W. Indies.

CHUNG, Andrew Ka Kin 11 Buckingham Avenue, Headingley, Leeds LS6 1DJ — MB ChB 1996 Leeds; BSc (Hons.) Leeds 1994. SHO (Ophth.) ScarBoro. Gen. Hosp. Prev: Ho. Off. (Med.) St. Jas. Univ. Hosp. Leeds; Ho. Off. (Surg.) ScarBoro. Gen. Hosp.

CHUNG, Angela Sinman 62 Gorse Bank Road, Halebarns, Altrincham WA15 0AX — MB ChB 1998 Manch.; MB ChB Manch 1998.

CHUNG, Ching Wa Ambledon, Silverhillock, Cornhill, Banff AB45 2AY — MB ChB 1993 Ed.

CHUNG, David Anthony Flat 3/1, 136 Woodlands Road, Glasgow G3 6LF — MB ChB 1996 Glas.

CHUNG, Eddie Man Kuen Hawthorn Close, Watford WD17 4SB — MB ChB 1985 Dundee; MRCP (UK) 1990; MD 1995. Sen. Lect. & Hon. Cons. Paediat.

CHUNG, Gawun Jah-Hung 12 Martingales Close, Richmond TW10 7JJ — MB BS 1994 Lond.

CHUNG, George Ka Keung Department of Transplant Medicine, Harefield Hosptial, Harefield, Uxbridge UB9 6TH Tel: 01895 823737; 37 Burlington Close, Pinner HA5 2TP — MB ChB 1991 Liverp.; MRCP (UK) 1994. (Liverp.) Regist. (Cardiol.) Harefield Hosp. Socs: Brit. Soc. Echocardiogr. Prev: Regist. (Gen. Med.) Barnet Gen. Hosp.; Regist. (Cardiol.) Norf. & Norwich Hosp.

CHUNG, Helen Elizabeth 5 Slough Road, Datchet, Slough SL3 9AP Tel: 01753 542654 — MB BS 1997 Lond.; BMedSci, Lond. 1996. (Char. Cross & Westm.)

CHUNG, Mr Hugh Maurice 5 Slough Road, Datchet, Slough SL3 9AP Tel: 01753 542654 — MB ChB 1957 Leeds; Specialist Register 1996; FRCS Ed. 1961; FCOphth 1988. Ophth. Med. Practitioner Windsor & Bracknell. Prev: Cons. Ophth. Surg. Bedford Gen. Hosp.; Cons. Ophth. Surg. & Head, Dept. Ophth. Kingston Pub. Hosp., Jamaica.

CHUNG, Kenneth Yee Kin Gordon and Partners, The Redwell Medical Centre, 1 Turner Road, Wellingborough NN8 4UT Tel: 01933 400777 Fax: 01933 671959; 5 Cross Lane, Aldwincle, Kettering NN14 3EG Tel: 01832 720730 — MRCS Eng. LRCP Lond. 1985.

CHUNG, Kenneth Yiu Kwan 32 The Friary, Nottingham NG7 2PB — BM BS 1992 Nottm.

CHUNG, Professor Kian Fan National Heart & Lung Institute, Imperial College School of medicine, Dovehouse St, London SW3 6LY Email: f.chung@ic.ac.uk — MB BS 1975 Lond.; DSc Lond. 2001; MD Lond. 1983; FRCP Lond. 1992; MRCP (UK) 1977. (Middlx. Hosp. Med. Sch.) Prof. (Thoracic Med.) & Hon. Cons. Dept. Thoracic Med. Nat. Heart & Lung Inst. & Roy. Brompton Hosp. Lond.; MRC Trav. Fell. Cardiovasc. Research Inst. Univ. Calif., San Francisco, USA. Socs: Brit. Pharm. Soc.; Amer. Thoracic Soc.; Eur. Respirat. Soc. Prev: Lect. & Hon. Sen. Regist. (Med.) Char. Cross Hosp. Med. Sch. Lond.; Regist. Clinique Univ. Med. Geneva, Switz.; SHO Hammersmith Hosp. Lond.

CHUNG, Kit Oi Vauxhall Health Centre, Limekiln Lane, Liverpool L5 8XR Tel: 0151 298 2246 — MB BCh BAO 1982 Belf.; MRCGP 1987.

CHUNG, Kong Meng Park Street Surgery, Park Street, Bootle L20 3DF Tel: 0151 922 3577 Fax: 0151 933 6098; 144 Moor Lane, Liverpool L23 2UQ Email: kong.chung@which.net — MB ChB 1988 Aberd. Bootle & Litherland PCG Bd. Mem.

CHUNG, Margaret Mary Chung, Colville Health Centre, 51 Kensington Park Road, London W11 1PA Tel: 020 7727 8212 Fax: 020 7792 8084 — MB BS 1974 Lond.; BSc (Hons.) Liverp. 1968; MRCS Eng. LRCP Lond. 1974; MRCGP 1978. (Univ. Coll. Hosp.) Prev: SHO (Chest Med.) & (Paediat.) St. Chas. Hosp. Lond.; SHO (O & G) Centr. Middlx. Hosp. Lond.

CHUNG, Natali Anne Yenfah Ipswich Hospital, Heath Road, Ipswich IP4 5PD; 139 Gleneldon Road, London SW16 2BQ — MB BS 1996 Lond.; BSc Lond. 1995. (St George's Hospital Medical School) SHO Rotat. (Med.) Ipswich Hosp.

CHUNG, Peter Wai-Ming 21 Bodmin Drive, Bramhall, Stockport SK7 2HX — MB ChB 1990 Sheff.

CHUNG, Pui-Ching David 5 Bolehill Lane, Crookes, Sheffield S10 1SA — MB ChB 1992 Sheff.

CHUNG, Raymond Arthur Heath Place, Blackham, Tunbridge Wells TN3 9TY — MB BS 1983 Lond.; BSc Lond. 1980, MB BS 1983.

CHUNG, Tin Tak 8 Ridgetor Road, Woolton, Liverpool L25 6DQ — MB ChB 1980 Liverp.; MRCS Eng. LRCP Lond. 1980.

CHUNG, Tommy Wing Hong 18 Welbeck Ave, Aylesbury HP21 9BH Email: tomandlisa@aol.com — MB BCh 1993 Wales; DFFP 1995; MRCOG 1999. (Univ. Wales Coll. Med.) GP Regist. Trainee. Stoke Mandeville Hosp. Bucks. Prev: Regist. (O & G) St. Helier's Hosp. Lond.; SHO (Surg.) Crawley Hosp. W. Sussex; SHO (Urol.) St. Geo. Hosp. Lond.

CHUNG, Tung Yau 5 Grangewood Close, Cardiff CF23 8PP — MB ChB 1998 Leic.; MB ChB Leic 1998.

CHUNG, Wai Kui 259 Yew Tree Road, Manchester M14 6BS — MB ChB 1974 Sheff.

CHUNG-FAYE, Guy Allen 28 Richard Cooper Road, Shenstone, Lichfield WS14 0NL — MB ChB 1991 Leic.; MRCP. Specialist Regist. (Gastroenterol.) Qu. Eliz. Hosp. Edgbaston, Birm.; Inst. of cancer studies, univ. of Birm.

CHUNG HUNG TSEUNG, Chung Ying Choong The Medical Unit, The Manor Drive, Worcester park KT4 7LG Tel: 020 7703 6050 — MB BS 1976 Lond.; MRCS Eng. LRCP Lond. 1975. (Guy's Hospital Medical School)

CHURCH, Adrian William Edmund 10 Barnside Road, Dullaghy, Kilrea, Coleraine BT51 5YB — MB BCh BAO 1984 Belf.; MB BCh Belf. I984.

CHURCH, Alistair Colin flat 3/1, 71 Ashley St., Woodlands, Glasgow G3 6HW Tel: 0141 331 0321 — MB ChB 1997 Glas.; BSc (Hons.) Glas. 1995. (Glasgow) SHO Med. Rotat. Glas. Roy. Infirm. Glas.

CHURCH, Armorel Barbara Guy's Hospital (Department of Anaesthesia), 2nd Floor, New Guys House, St Thomas St., London SE1 9RT Tel: 020 7955 4051 Fax: 020 7955 8844; 16 Passmore Street, London SW1W 8HP Tel: 020 7730 2802 Fax: 020 7730 2802 — MB BS 1966 Lond.; FRCA 1971; DA Eng. 1968. (St. Thos.) p/t Cons. Anaesth., Guy's Hosp. Prev: Cons. Anaesth., Greenwich Dist. Hosp.

CHURCH, Carol Parkwater Farm, Whiteparish, Salisbury SP5 2QR Tel: 017948 84357 — MB BS 1967 Lond.; DCH Eng. 1970. (St. Bart.) SCMO Hants. AHA (T). Prev: Ho. Off. (Paediat.) Whipps Cross Hosp. Lond.; Asst. Co. Med. Off. Hants. CC; Garrison Med. Off. Dhekelia, Cyprus.

CHURCH, Catherine Ann Langdale, Southam Lane, Southam, Cheltenham GL52 3NY Tel: 01242 520238 — MB ChB 1964 Glas.; DPH 1967. (Glas.) Clin. Med. Off. E. Glos. NHS Trust. Socs: BMA. Prev: Ho. Off. Thoracic Surg. Unit Ch.ill Hosp. Oxf.; Ho. Off. Paediat. Dept. Addenbrooke's Hosp. Camb.; Asst. Co. MOH & Sch. Med. Off. Gloucester.

CHURCH, Catherine Jayne 42 Valley View, Jesmond, Newcastle upon Tyne NE2 2JS — MB BS 1997 Newc.

CHURCH, David Samuel The Health Centre, Pier Road, Tywyn LL36 0AT Tel: 01654 710238 — MB ChB 1990 Leeds; BSc Leeds 1987; MRCGP 1995; DRCOG 1994. (Leeds) GP Tywyn, Meinrioneth.; Locum GP. Socs: (Stud.) Leeds Med. Soc.; BMA; RCGP. Prev: Med. Off., Gore Hosp., NZ; SHO, Tauranga, Bay of Plenty, NZ; SHO, Bronglais, Aberystwyth.

CHURCH, Elaine Natalie Liverpool Health Authority, Hamilton House, Pall Mall, Liverpool L3 6AL Tel: 0151 285 2062 Fax: 0151 285 2007 Email: elaine.church@liverpool-ha.nwest.nhs.uk; Yew Tree Farm, Greenhill Lane, Lower Whitley, Warrington WA4 4JD Fax: 01925 730317 — MB ChB 1984 Liverp.; MPH (Distinc.) Liverp. 1992; MFPHM London 1997. (Liverpool) Cons. (Pub. Health Med.) Liverp. HA / Sefton HA. Prev: Cons. Pub. Health NHS Exec. NW; Cons. Pub. Health NW RHA; Locum Cons. Pub. Health NW RHa.

CHURCH, Elizabeth Jane Whittington Moor Surgery, Scarsdale Road, Chesterfield S41 8NA Tel: 01246 453717 — MB ChB 1994 Birm.; MRCGP 1998; DRCOG 1997; DFFP 1998. Partner:GP.Whittington. Moor.Surg. Chesterfield. Prev: Trainee

GP/SHO Chesterfield & N. Derbysh. Roy. Hosp. VTS; Ho. Phys. Burton Dist. Hosp.; Ho. Surg. Selly Oak Hosp. & Gen. Hosp. Birm.

CHURCH, Elize 96 Lyes Green, Corsley, Warminster BA12 7PA — MB ChB 1988 Orange Free State.

CHURCH, Henry (retired) 21 Glen Shee, St. Leonards, E. Kilbride, Glasgow G74 2JH — MB ChB 1952 Glas.

CHURCH, Howard David Vivian Spring House, Hunton, Bedale DL8 1PX — MB ChB 1982 Leeds; MRCPsych 1987.

CHURCH, Ian Cochrane (retired) 1 Humber View, Swanland, North Ferriby HU14 3ND Tel: 01482 633568 — MRCS Eng. LRCP Lond. 1946; MRCPsych 1971; DPM Eng. 1954. Prev: Cons. Psychiat. Humberside AHA.

CHURCH, Jacqueline Ann Ardersier, 59 Langside Drive, Newlands, Glasgow G43 2QX — MB ChB 1983 Glas.; FRCA 1989; FFA RCSI 1988. Cons. Anaesth. Glas. Roy. Infirm. Univ. NHS Trust.

CHURCH, James Robert Matthew Glenseaton Lodge, Balgownie Road, Bridge of Don, Aberdeen AB22 8LS — MB ChB 1998 Ed.; MB ChB Ed 1998.

CHURCH, Jane Elizabeth Department of Cardiology, Ninewells Hospital, Dundee; Castlegate House, Castlegate, Ceres, Cupar KY15 5NG Tel: 01334 828792 Fax: 01334 828792 — MB ChB 1981 Dundee. Staff Grade (Cardiol.) Ninewells Hosp. Dundee.

CHURCH, Jeremy John Parkwater Farm, Whiteparish, Salisbury SP5 2QR Tel: 017948 84357 — MB BS 1967 Lond.; MRCS Eng. LRCP Lond. 1967; FFA RCS Eng. 1975; DA Eng. 1971. (St. Bart.) Cons. Anaesth. Salisbury Gen. Hosp.; Dir. Day Surg. Socs: BMA & Assn. Anaesths. Prev: Sen. Regist. (Anaesth.) Soton. Gen. Hosp.; Staff Specialist Anaesth. Dept. P. of Wales Hosp. Sydney, Australia.

CHURCH, Mr John Christian Tracey (retired) Abney Court, Bourne End SL8 5DL Tel: 01628 522668 Fax: 01628 531990 Email: jctchurch@online.rednet.co.uk — MD 1968 Camb.; MB 1956, BChir 1955; FRCS Ed. 1968; DTM & H Antwerp 1958; DObst RCOG 1957. Cons. Surg. Orthop. Bucks. Prev: Cons. Surg. A & E High Wycombe Health Dist.

CHURCH, Mr John David (retired) — MB BS Lond. 1964; FRCS Eng. 1970; MRCS Eng. LRCP Lond. 1964. Prev: Hosp. Pract. (Surg.) Axminster Hosp.

CHURCH, Jonathon Paul Hackwood Partnership, Essex House, Essex Road, Basingstoke RG21 7T; 38 Newbury Gardens, Stoneleigh, Epsom KT19 0NX Email: drjchurch@hotmail.com — MB BS 1996 Lond.; MRCGP 2001; BSC Lond. 1995; DRCOG 1998. (St George's Lond.) GP Locum, Overton Surg., Overton. Prev: GP Regist. Kingswood Surg.,Swin.

CHURCH, Katherine Elizabeth 19 St James Road, Ilkley LS29 9PY — MB BS 1995 Newc.

CHURCH, Laurence 11 Court House Mansions, The Eastway, Epsom KT19 8SF — MB ChB 1998 Birm.; ChB Birm. 1998.

CHURCH, Lyndon Daborn (retired) Langdale, Southam Lane, Southam, Cheltenham GL52 3NY — LMSSA Lond. 1955; BSc Wales 1950; MRCGP 1971. Prev: GP High Wycombe.

CHURCH, Martin Richard Tracey Lambdens, Abney Court, Bourne End SL8 5DL — MB ChB 1988 Birm.; BSc Physiol. Sheff. 1984.

CHURCH, Mary Veronica Blantyre Health Centre, 64 Victoria Street, Blantyre, Glasgow G72 0BS Tel: 01698 826331; 5 Belmont Avenue, Uddingston, Glasgow G71 7AX — MB ChB 1976 Glas.

CHURCH, Michael Alan (retired) 407 Lanark Road W., Currie EH14 5SL Tel: 0131 449 3399 — MA, MB Camb. 1965, BChir 1964; FFCM 1983, M 1974; DTPH Lond 1971. Prev: Med. Adviser Scott. Health Educat. Gp. Edin.

CHURCH, Mr Robert Douglas 35 Mount Street, Breaston, Derby DE72 3AJ Tel: 01332 873174; 2 Clipper View, The Moorings, Edgbaston, Birmingham B16 9DJ Tel: 0121 455 7829 Fax: 0121 454 8627 Email: robert.church@virgin.net — MB ChB 1991 Sheff.; FRCS Eng. 1996. Specialist Regist. Rotat. W. Midl.; Specialist Regist. Shrewsbury Roy. Hosp. Shrewsbury. Socs: ASIT. Prev: SHO Sunderland Roy. Hosp.; SHO Rotat. (Surg.) Birm. Heartlands Hosp.; Specialist Regist. N. Staffs. Roy. Infirm.

CHURCH, Robin Birdwood The Health Centre, Ashen Green, Great Shelford, Cambridge CB2 5EY Tel: 01223 843661 Fax: 01223 844570; East Lodge, Two Bridge Lane, Little Shelford, Cambridge CB2 5HE Tel: 01223 842243 — MA Camb. 1957, MB 1960, BChir 1959; MRCGP 1986; DObst RCOG 1961. (Camb. & St. Bart.) Socs: BMA. Prev: Med. Supt. Kabarole Hosp. Fort Portal, Uganda; Surg. (Gyn.) Mengo Hosp. Uganda; Ho. Surg. Luton & Dunstable Hosp.

CHURCH, Ronald Edward 3 Centre Cliff, Southwold IP18 6EN Tel: 01502 723637 — MRCS Eng. LRCP Lond. 1945; MA Camb. 1947, MD 1953, MB BChir 1945; FRCP Lond. 1985; FRCP Ed. 1961, M 1951. (St. Bart.) Emerit. Cons. Dermat. Sheff. HA (T). Socs: Hon. Mem. (Ex-Pres.) Brit. Assn. Dermat. Prev: Hon. Clin. Lect. (Dermat.) Univ. Sheff.; Cons. Dermatol. Roy. Hallamsh. Hosp. Sheff.

CHURCH, Rosalind Susan Stockwell Group Practice, 107 Stockwell Road, London SW9 9TJ Tel: 020 7274 3225 Fax: 020 7738 3005; 43 West Square, London SE11 4SP — MB BS Lond. 1976; BA Oxf. 1972. (St. Barts.) Prev: Trainee GP St. Geo. Hosp. Lond. VTS.

CHURCH, Stephen Morriss 100C Portnall Road, London W9 3BE — MB ChB 1989 Bristol.

CHURCH, Susan Edith St Helens & Knowsley, NHS Trust, Whiston Hospital, Warrington Road, Prescot L35 5DR Tel: 0151 426 1600; 25 Park Lane, Hartford, Northwich CW8 1PZ — MB ChB Liverp. 1979; MD Liverp. 1987; MRCP (UK) 1982; FRCP 1999 (UK). Cons. Respirat. Phys. Whiston Hosp Merseyside.

CHURCH, Susannah Margaret Abney Court, Bourne End SL8 5DL — MB BChir 1991 Camb.

CHURCH, Vivian Arthur Ashby Health Centre, North St., Ashby-de-la-Zouch, Leicester LE65 1HU Tel: 01530 414131 — MB BCh 1961 Wales; MRCGP 1973. (Cardiff) Prev: Ho. Phys. LLa.lly Gen. Hosp.; SHO (Anaesth.) E. Glam. Hosp. Ch. Village.

CHURCH, William Edward Mannering House, Bethersden, Ashford TN26 3DJ — MRCS Eng. LRCP Lond. 1941; MA, MB BChir Camb. 1942; MRCP Lond. 1947. (St. Thos.) Socs: Fell. Soc. Geneal. Prev: Ho. Phys. St. Thos. Hosp.; Regtl. Med. Off. 3rd Parachute Brig.; Sen. Med. Regist. St. Helier Hosp. Carshalton.

CHURCH, Mr William Henry Glenseaton Lodge, Balgownie Road, Bridge of Don, Aberdeen AB22 8LS Tel: 01224 702381 — MB BS Lond. 1970; FRCS Eng. 1983; MRCP (UK) 1975; FCOphth 1991. Cons. Ophth. Aberd. Roy. Hosps. NHS Trust.

CHURCHER, Anthony 10 Park Avenue, Eastbourne BN22 9QN Tel: 01323 503822 — MB BS 1950 Lond.; MRCS Eng. LRCP Lond. 1950. (Univ. Coll. Hosp.) Doctor Grand Hotel E.bourne. Socs: Fell. Roy. Soc. Med. Prev: Obst. Ho. Off. St. Thos. Hosp.; Sen. Ho. Off. Chest Unit & Ho. Surg. Surgic. Unit, Univ. Coll. Hosp.

CHURCHER, Gillian Mary (retired) 25 Vapron Road, Mannamead, Plymouth PL3 5NJ Tel: 01752 668728 — MRCS Eng. LRCP Lond. 1953; MB BS Lond. 1953, Dip. Bact. 1963; FRCPath 1980, M 1968. Prev: Cons. Cytopath. Plymouth Clin. Area.

CHURCHER, Julian Duncan The Surgery, 3 Austin Road, Battersea, London SW11 5JP Tel: 020 7498 0232 Fax: 020 7498 0271; 6 Broadgates Road, Wandsworth Common, London SW18 3NL Tel: 020 8875 9177 Email: jchurcher@compuserve.com — MB BS 1983 Lond.; MRCS Eng. LRCP Lond. 1982; MRCGP 1987; DRCOG 1987. (St. Thos.) Prev: Ho. Surg. St Thos. Hosp.

CHURCHER, Mark Duncan (retired) Lower Barn, Coarsewell, Ugborough, Ivybridge PL21 0HP — MB BS 1956 Lond.; FFA RCS Eng. 1961; DA Eng. 1959. Hon. Cons. Anaesth. Plymouth Health Dist. Prev: Sen. Regist. (Anaesth.) St. Thos. Hosp.

CHURCHER, Sally Jane Dyneley House Surgery, Newmarket Street, Skipton BD23 2HZ Tel: 01756 799311 Fax: 01756 707203 — MB ChB 1985 Leeds; BSc (Physiol.) Leeds 1982; MRCGP 1991; DCH RCP Lond. 1990; DRCOG 1990. Prev: Trainee GP Airedale VTS; Ho. Off. Wharfedale Gen. Hosp.

CHURCHER-BROWN, Christopher John Villakin, Hawthorn Road, Denmead, Waterlooville PO7 6LJ Tel: 02392 257622 Fax: 02392 257622 Email: churcher-brown@doctors.org.uk — MRCS Eng. LRCP Lond. 1972; MRCPsych 1978; DPM Eng. 1978; FRCPsych 1999. (Westminister) Head of Psychiat. Dept. The Roy. Hosp. Haslar, Gosport; Regional Adviser Med. Counc. Alcoholism; Cons. Adviser Psychiat. to Med. Dir. Gen. (Navy). Socs: Brit. Med. Assn.; Med. Counc. on Alcoholism; Mem. Expert Witness Inst.

CHURCHILL, Amanda Jane Bristol Eye Hospital, Lower Maudlin St, Bristol B51 2LX — MB ChB 1986 Leeds; PhD 1999 Leeds; PhD 1986 BChD Leeds 1976,; BSc Leeds 1983; FRCOphth 1992. Cons. Sen. Lect.,Bristol Uni, Bristol (Ophth). Socs: Bd. Mem. Europ. Vision & Eye Research Soc. Prev: Sen. Regist. Rotat. (Ophth.) Leeds Gen. Infirm.; Wellcome Research Fell. (Molecular Med) Leeds Uni Leeds).

CHURCHILL, David Department of Obsteterics & Gynaecology, Good Hope NHS Trust, Sutton Coldfield B75 7RR Tel: 0121 378 2211; 17 London Road, Lichfield WS14 9EQ Tel: 01543 419417 — MB ChB 1985 Birm.; MD Birm. 1995; MRCOG 1990. Cons. Good Hope Hosp.; Clin. Cons. W. Midl. Perinatal Audit Unit. Socs: Brit. Hypertens. Soc.; Blair Bell Res. Soc.; Internat. Soc. Study Hypertens. in Pregn. Prev: Sen. Regist. Rotat. W. Midl. RHA; Research Fell. (Med. & Fetal Med.) Univ. Birm.; Regist. (O & G) Centr. & W. Birm.

CHURCHILL, David Andrew Grovelands Medical Centre, 701 Oxford Road, Reading RG30 1HG Tel: 0118 958 2525 Fax: 0118 950 9284; British Airways Travel Clinic, 701 Oxford Road, Reading RG30 1HG Tel: 0118 957 5101 Fax: 0118 950 9284 — MB BS 1969 Lond.; Acad. Dip. Gen. Biochem. Lond. 1966. (St. Thos.) Prev: Trainee GP Reading VTS; Ho. Surg. Harrow Hosp.; Ho. Phys. Metrop. Hosp. Lond.

CHURCHILL, Duncan Robert Royal Sussex County Hospital, Eastern Road, Brighton BN2 5BE Tel: 01273 664720 Fax: 01273 664720 Email: duncan.churchill@brighton-healthcare.whs.uk — MB BS 1985 Lond.; BA (Hons.) Oxf. 1982; MRCP (UK) 1989; DTM & H RCP Lond. (Middlx. Hosp. Med. Sch.) Cons. (HIV & Genitourin. Med.), Roy. Sussex Co. & Brighton Gen. Hosp. Socs: Med. Soc. Study VD; (Exec. Comm.) Brit. HIV Assn.; Asscoiation of Genitourin. Med. Prev: Regist. (HIV Med.) Middlx. Hosp. Lond.; Regist. (Trop. Med.) Hosp. for Trop. Dis.s Lond.; Regist. (Med.) Middlx. Hosp. Lond.

CHURCHILL, Mr Mark Alexander Bergerhorf, 30 Camborne Road, Sutton SM2 6RQ — MB BS 1981 Lond.; BSc (Hons.) Lond. 1977, MB BS (Hons.) 1981; FRCS Ed. 1986; MRCS Eng. LRCP Lond. 1981. Cons. Orthop. St. Helens Hosp. Carshalton.

CHURCHILL, Martin Peter 165 Seaforth Gardens, Epsom KT19 0LW — MB BS 1991 Lond.; DRCOG 1996. (St. Geo. Med. Sch. Lond.)

CHURCHILL, Richard David Department of General Practice, University of Nottingham Medical School, Queen's Medical Centre, Nottingham NG7 2UH Tel: 0115 970 9901 Email: dick.churchill@nottingham.ac.uk; 32 Kingrove Avenue, Beeston, Nottingham NG9 4DQ — BM BS 1989 Nottm.; BSc (Clin. Biochem.) Surrey 1980, MSc 1982; BMedSci Nottm. 1987; MRCGP 1993; DFFP 1993. (Nottm.) GP Princip.; Lect. (Gen. Pract.) Univ. Nottm. Med. Sch. Socs: RCGP (Fac. Hon-Sec.). Prev: Trainee GP Nottm. VTS.

CHURCHILL, Robert Simson (retired) Benchmark Cottage, East Dean, Salisbury SP5 1HJ — MB BS Lond. 1958; DObst RCOG 1960. Prev: Ho. Phys. (Paediat. & Dermat.) & Ho. Surg. (Gyn.) Char. Cross Hosp. Lond.

CHURCHILL-DAVIDSON, Mr Dudley, RD (retired) 1 Montagu Mews S., off George St., London W1H 7ER — MB BChir 1952 Camb.; MA, MB BChir Camb. 1952; FRCS Eng. 1958. Hon. Cons. Orthop. Surg. Roy. Lond. Homoeop. Hosp.; Hon. Col. Roy. Marines Reserve. Prev: Hon. Surg. to HM the Qu.

CHURCHMAN, Imogen Ruth 5 Hill Rise, Chalfont St Peter, Gerrards Cross SL9 9BN — BM BCh 1992 Oxf.

CHURCHWARD, Hedley Cole Vickers Churchward and Partners, Croft Medical Centre, 2 Glen Road, Oadby, Leicester LE2 4PE Tel: 0116 271 2564 Fax: 0116 272 9000; Threeways, 373 Scraptoft Lane, Scraptoft, Leicester LE7 9SE Tel: 0116 243 2277 Fax: 0116 243 2277 — MB BS 1969 Lond.; MRCGP 1976; DObst RCOG 1973. (Univ. Coll. Hosp.) Trainer GP Leicester VTS. Socs: Leic. Med. Soc. Prev: Course Organiser Leicester VTS; Trainee GP Stoke-on-Trent VTS; Cas. Off. Qu. Mary's Hosp. Roehampton.

CHURCHYARD, Andrew John c/o The Parkinson's Disease Society, Brain Tissue Bank, Institute of Neurology, 1 Wakefield St., London WC1N 1PJ Tel: 020 7837 8370 Fax: 020 7278 4993 — MB BS 1984 Melbourne; PhD Melbourne 1996; FRACP 1991. Research Fell. Inst. Neurol. Lond. Socs: Austral. Assn. Neurol.

CHURMS, Barbara Kathleen Alconbury and Brampton Surgeries, The Surgery, School Lane, Alconbury, Huntingdon PE28 4EQ Tel: 01480 890281 Fax: 01480 891787; 3 Fielding Court, Eaton Ford, St. Neots, Huntingdon PE19 7LP Tel: 01480 474028 — MB BS 1968 Newc.; MFFP. (Newc. upon Tyne) GP Alconbury. Prev: Ho. Surg. Qu. Mary's Hosp. Sidcup; Ho. Phys. LLa.lli Gen. Hosp.

CHURN, Mark John 2 Heath Road, Holtspur, Beaconsfield HP9 1DD — MB ChB 1987 Ed.; MRCP (UK) 1994.

CHUTER, Graham Stephen Jonathan Mabuhay, Brownlow Road, Berkhamsted HP4 1HB — MB ChB 1998 Dund.; MB ChB Dund 1998.

CHUTER, Patrick John Stirchley Medical Practice, Stirchley Health Centre, Stirchley, Telford TF3 1FB Tel: 01952 660444 Fax: 01952 415139; Hillside, Worfield, Bridgnorth WV15 5LW Tel: 0174 64 411 — MA, BM BCh Oxf. 1970; MRCP (UK) 1974; MRCGP 1987. (Oxf. & Westm.) Course Organiser Shrewsbury VTS. Prev: SHO (Oncol.) Char. Cross Hosp. Lond.; Resid. (Med.) Montreal Gen. Hosp., Canada; Ho. Off. (Gen. Med.) W.m. Hosp. Lond.

CHYC, Anthony David 65 Longmeadow Road, Prescot L34 0HW Tel: 0151 546 6030 — MB BS 1983 Lond.; MA Oxf. 1989, BA 1980. GP Liverp.

CIAMPOLINI, Iacopo 126 Kimberley, Cardiff CF2 5EF Email: iacopo.ciampolini@virgin.net; Wound Healing Research Unit, University of Wales College, Cardiff — State DMS 1989 Florence; FRCS (Eng.) 1997. (Florence) Research Regist. Wound Healing Research Unit Univ. of Wales Coll. of Med. Prev: SHO (Plastic Surg.) Morriston Hosp.

CIANCHI, Frank Richard (retired) The Whittern, Brilley, Whitney-on-Wye, Hereford HR3 6JH — MRCS Eng. LRCP Lond. 1959; DObst RCOG 1961. Prev: Anaesth. Regist. Roy. Vict. Hosp. Boscombe.

CIANCHI, Marian Frances Highmede, Great Brickhill, Milton Keynes Tel: 01908 75111 — MB BCh BAO 1951 Dub.; BA Dub. 1949, MB BCh BAO 1951. (Dub.) Prev: Ho. Off. (O & G) Mile End. Hosp.; Regist. (Med.) Neasden Hosp.; Regist. (Physical Med.) St. Jas. Hosp. Balham.

CIANFARANI, Stefano Department of Surgery, Level 7, Bristol royal Infirmary, Bristol BS2 8HW; 35 Emperor's Gate, London SW7 4JA Tel: 020 7370 1798 — State Exam Rome 1982. Research Fell. (Paediat. & Endocrinol.) St. Bart. Hosp. Lond.

CIAPPARA, Joseph (retired) 510 Wellingborough Road, Northampton NN3 3HX Tel: 01604 404614 — MD 1958 Malta; BPharm. 1955. Hosp. Pract. (A & E) N.ampton Gen. Hosp.; Club Surg. N.ampton Town Football Club.

CIBULSKIS, Raymond Peter 12 Brewer Street, London W1R 3FS — MB BS 1987 Western Austral.

CICCONE, Graham Keith Anaesthetic Dept, QEQM Hospital, St Peters Road, Margate CT9 4AN Tel: 01843 225544 — MB BS 1990 Lond.; BSc (Hons.) Lond. 1984; FRCA 1995. (Charing Cross and Westminster) Cons. Anaesth. Qu. Eliz. The Qu. Mother Hosp. Margate Kent.

CICHON-FELDMAN, Beate Maria 13 Tuckfield House, Residential Village, Bovemoors Lane, Exeter EX2 5DS — State Exam Med 1994 Aachen.

CICLITIRA, Professor Paul Jonathan Gastroenterology Unit, UMDS, Rayne Institute, St Thomas Hospital, London SE1 7EH Tel: 020 7928 9292 Fax: 020 7620 2597 Email: p.ciclitira@rayne.umds.ac.uk; 35 Elgin Crescent, London W11 2JD — MB BS Lond. 1971; PhD Lond. 1986, MD 1982; FRCP Lond. 1991; MRCP (UK) 1974. (St. Bart.) Prof. Gastroenterol. UMDS & Cons. Phys. Guy's & St. Thos. Hosp. Lond. & Rayne Inst.; Hon. Cons. Phys. (Gastroenterol.) Guy's & St. Thos. Hosps. Lond.; Lilly & Brit. Soc. Gastrolenterol. UK & Eire. Socs: Eur. Soc. Clin. Investig.; Brit. Soc. Gastroenterol.; Assn. Phys. Prev: Wellcome Sen. Research Fell. Clin. Sc. & Head Research Unit Rayne Inst. St. Thos. Hosp. Lond.; Research Fell. MRC Laborat. Molecular Biol. Camb.; Hon. Sen. Regist. (Gen. Med.) Addenbrooke's Hosp. Camb. & Guy's Hosp. Lond.

CIECIERSKI, Andrzej Jan Krzysztof Emmer Green Surgery, 4 St Barnabas Rd, Emmer Green, Reading RG7 8RA Tel: 0118 447 8123 Fax: 0118 446 3341 — MB BS 1992 Lond.; DLO 1997; MRCGP 1999. (Char. Cross & Westm.) Gen. Practitioner, Emmer Green Surg. Reading; Clin. Asst., ENT Dept., Roy. Berks. Hosp., Reading.

CIENSKA, Paulina 2 Castlebar Road, London W5 2DP Tel: 020 8997 2005 — MB ChB 1948 Polish Sch. Med.; MB ChB Polish Sch. of Med. Ed. 1948; LLB Lwow 1938.

CIESLICKI, Susan Helen 6 Longholm, Chequers Lane, Tadworth KT20 7RD — MB BS 1991 Lond.

CIETAK, Mr Krzysztof Alexander 11 Dalton Road, Earlsdon, Coventry CV5 6PB Tel: 024 767443/4 Fax: 024 76 622197 — MB ChB 1971 Birm.; MD Birm. 1984; FRCOG 1990, M 1978. Cons. O & G Walsgrave Hosp. Coventry. Socs: ISUOG; BMUS; BMFMS. Prev:

Sen. Regist. & Regist. (O & G) Birm. Matern. Hosp. & Birm. & Midl. Hosp. Wom.; Regist. (O & G) Roy. Berks. Hosp. Reading.

CIEZAK, Richard Frank Highview Surgery, 20 Southgate Road, Potters Bar EN6 5DZ Tel: 01707 871980 Fax: 01707 871995 — MB BS 1972 Lond.; MRCS Eng. LRCP Lond. 1972; MRCGP 1980; DObst RCOG 1975. Prev: Trainee GP Swindon VTS; Ho. Phys. St. Mary's Hosp. (Harrow Rd. Br.) Lond.; Ho. Surg. Whipps Cross Hosp. Leytonstone.

CIKO, Vjera Danica Riverhouse, St. Clement, Truro TR1 1SZ Tel: 01872 272000 Fax: 01872 272000 Email: vjerac@hotmail.com — MB BS 1990 Sydney; BSc Sydney 1987; FRACGP 1995; DRACOG 1994; Cert of Equiv Exp JCPTGP 1999. (University of Sydney) GP Locum.

CIKUREL, Katia 30 Ufton Road, London N1 5BX Tel: 020 7254 3053 Fax: 020 7684 1861 Email: cbaker6751@aol.com; 30 Ufton Road, London N1 5BX Tel: 020 7254 3053 Fax: 020 7684 1861 — MB BS 1990 Lond.; BSc Hons. (Psychol.) Lond. 1987; MRCP (UK) 1993. (Charing Cross and Westminster) Specialist Regist. (Neurol.) Nat. Hosp. for Neurol. & Neurosurg. Prev: Specialist Regist. (Neurol.) Roy. Lond. Hosp.; Research Regist. (Neurophysiol.) Nat. Hosp. Neurol. & Neurosurg. Lond.; SHO (Neurol.) Roy. Free Hosp. Lond.

CILASUN, Ozlem 19 Cobthorn Way, Congresbury, Bristol BS49 5BJ — MB BS 1991 Lond. Prev: SHO (c/o Elderly) Centr. Middlx. Hosp. Lond.

CIMA, Peter Harington (retired) 2 Springhill Gardens, Lyme Regis DT7 3HL — MB BS 1950 Lond.; MRCS Eng. LRCP Lond. 1949; DPH Lond. 1967. Prev: PMO W. Berks. HA.

CINCOTTA, Robert Bartolo 40 Holley Road, London W3 7TS — MB BS 1985 Melbourne.

CINKOTAI, Kornelia Ilona Department of Clinical Haematology, The Royal Infirmary, Oxford Road, Manchester M13 9WL Tel: 0161 276 1234 — MD 1967 Budapest; MRCPath 1981. Assoc. Specialist Manch. Roy. Infirm. Socs: Internat. Soc. Haemat. & Brit. Soc. Haematol. Prev: Regist. (Haemat.) Manch. Roy. Infirm.; Regist. (Blood Transfus.) NBTS, Budapest; Research Asst. ICI Pharmaceut. Alderley Pk.

CINNAMOND, Professor Michael James Department of Otorhinolaryngology, University Floor, Tower Block, Belfast City Hospital, Belfast BT9 7AB Tel: 01232 329241 Fax: 01232 247895; 10 Governor's Ridge Park, Carnreagh, Hillsborough BT26 6LD Tel: 01846 683090 — MB BCh BAO 1967 Belf.; FRCS Ed. 1974; FRCSI 1985. Prof. Otorhinolaryng. Qu. Univ. Belf.; Cons. Paediat. Otolaryngol. Belf. City Hosp. & Roy. Belf. Hosp. Sickm Childr. Socs: Fell. Roy. Soc. Med.; Irish Otolaryngol. Soc. Prev: Sen. Regist. (Otolaryngol.) Roy. Vict. Hosp. Belf.; Clin. Fell. (Otolaryngol.) Hosp. Sick Childr. Toronto, Canada.

CIROLLI, Riccardo Giuseppe Mario 40 Falcon Way, London E14 9UP — State Exam Catania 1990.

CITRON, Ivor, SJM (retired) 18 Fletsand Road, Wilmslow SK9 2AB — Lic Med 1946 Dub.; Lic. Med., Lic. Surg. Dub. 1946. Prev: Qu.s Silver Jubilee Medal.

CITRON, Kenneth Michael 4 Riverside Drive, Esher KT10 8PG Tel: 01372 464696 Email: ken.suecitron@ukgateway.net — MB BS (Hons. Med.) Lond. 1948; MD Lond. 1952; FRCP Lond. 1968, M 1952; MRCS Eng. LRCP Lond. 1949. (Guy's) p/t Hon. Cons. Phys. Roy. Brompton Nat. Heart & Lung Hosp. Lond. Socs: (Ex-Pres.) Brit. Thoracic Soc.; (Ex-Pres) Brit. Soc. of Allergy & Clin. Immunol. Prev: Sen. Regist. (Med.) Brompton Hosp. Lond.; Ho. Phys. Guy's Hosp.

CITRON, Leslie Harold (retired) Flat 55, Devonshire Court, New Hall Road, Broughton Park, Salford M7 4JT Tel: 0161 792 3091 — MB BCh BAO 1952 Dub.; Lic. Med., Lic. Surg. Dub. 1941.

CITRON, Mr Neil David St Helier Hospital, Wrythe Lane, Carshalton SM5 1AA; 4 Dudley Road, Wimbledon, London SW19 8PN Tel: 020 8542 2612 — MB 1976 Camb.; MChir Camb. 1986, MB 1976, BChir 1975; FRCS Eng. 1979. Cons. Orthop. Surg. St. Helier NHS Trust. Socs: Fell. Roy. Soc. Med.; Brit. Soc. Surg. Hand. Prev: Sen. Regist. Roy. Nat. Orthop. Hosp. Stanmore; Lect. Anat. King's Coll. Lond.

CLAASEN, Gabriella Salcombe Gardens, 8 Salcombe Gardens, Mill Hill, London NW7 2NT Tel: 020 8959 6592 Fax: 020 8959 0112 — Laurea 1971 Rome; Laurea in Medicini e Chirurgia Rome 1971.

CLACEY, Robert Peter Cairnsmoor, Nunney Road, Frome BA11 4LA Tel: 01373 451109 — MB ChB 1976 Birm.; MRCPsych 1981. Cons. in Gen. Adult Psychiat., Som. Partnership NHS Trust. Prev: Sen. Regist. (Psychiat.) Trent RHA.

CLACK, Glen Ivan Sidney Leneca Pharmaceuticals, Alderley Park, Macclesfield SK10 4TG Tel: 01625 518280 Fax: 01625 516904 Email: glen.clack@alderley.zeneca.com; 5 Lioncroft Cottages, Upwood Road, Bury, Huntingdon PE26 2PA Tel: 01487 812249 — MB BS 1992 Lond. (Royal Free) Med. Adviser (Oncol.) Zeneca Pharmaceut. Chesh. Prev: Basic Surgic. Train. N. E.

CLAFF, Harold Raymond Steels Lane Health Centre, 384-398 Commercial Road, London E1 Tel: 020 7791 0831 — MRCS Eng. LRCP Lond. 1941. (Westm.) BMA Sir Chas. Hastings Award. Prev: Ho. Surg., Sen. Cas. Off. & Supernum. Regist. Childr. Dept. W.m.; Hosp; Med. Fell. Counc. Europe.

CLAFFERTY, Robert Anthony Forth Valley Primary Care NHS Trust, Westbank Clinic, Falkirk FK1 5RQ — MB ChB 1990 Glas.; Dip FMS 2001 (Soc. of Apoth.) London; MRCPsych 1995; DGM RCPS Glas. 1992. (Glas.) Cons.

CLAGUE, Howell William Chest Clinic, Sunderland General Hospital, Sunderland SR4 7TP Tel: 0191 565 6256 Fax: 0191 569 9292 Email: howell.clague.chs.northy.nhs.uk — MB BCh 1973 Wales; BSc, MD Wales 1983; FRCP Lond. 1992; MRCP (UK) 1976. Cons. Phys. (s/i Chest Dis.) Sunderland Gen. Hosp. Prev: Cons. Phys. (s/i Chest Dis.) Bishop Auckland Gen. Hosp.; Sen. Regist. Fazakerley Walton & Roy. Liverp. Hosps. Liverp.; Clin. Research Fell. Univ. W.. Ontario, Canada.

CLAGUE, John Edward 71 Crescent Road, Walton, Liverpool L9 2AW — MB ChB 1982 Liverp.

CLAGUE, Roy Bridson Nobles Hospital, Westmoreland Road, Douglas IM1 4QA Tel: 01624 642129 Fax: 01624 642527; 33, King Edward Bay Apts, Sea Cliff Road, Onchan, Douglas IM3 2JG Tel: 01624 621102 Email: r.b.clague&talk21.com — MB BS 1971 Newc.; MD Newc. 1979; FRCP Lond. 1989; MRCP (UK) 1974. Cons. Phys. (Rheum. &Gen. Med..) Noble's Hosp. Douglas, I. of Man. Socs: Brit. Soc. Rheumatol.; Amer. Coll. Rheumatol. Prev: Cons. Rheum. Withington Hosp. Manch.; Cons. Rheum. Manch. Roy. Infirm.; MRC Train. Fell.

CLAIDEN, Mandy The Medical Centre, The Brow, Burgess Hill RH15 9BS Tel: 01444 246162 Fax: 01444 232199 — MB BS 1985 Lond.; BA Oxf. 1979.

CLAIN, Mr Allan (retired) Lace Cottage, Off High St., Great Missenden HP16 9AB Tel: 01494 866820 — MB ChB Cape Town 1944; FRCS Eng. 1949. Prev: Cons. Surg. & Surg. Tutor Dudley Rd. Hosp. Birm.

CLAISSE, Alison Zoe Carnegie Clinic, Pilmuir St., Dunfermline KY12 7AX Tel: 01383 722911; 9 Cameron Street, Dunfermline KY12 8DP — MB ChB 1981 Ed.; DRCOG 1987; DA (UK) 1985. Clin. Med. Off. Fife Healthcare.

CLAMP, Andrew Robert 27 Wiltshire Close, Exeter EX4 1LU — BM BCh 1996 Oxf.; MA Camb 1997. SHO Med. Birm. heartlands Hosp.

CLAMP, Henry Hollybank Bungalow, The Beck, Elford, Tamworth B79 9BT Tel: 0182 785354 — MB ChB 1954 Birm. (Birm.) Sen. Med. Off. LST Clinics Nuneaton; Corr. Fell. Amer. Acad. Cosmetic Surg. Socs: Amer. Soc. Cosmetic Surgs.

CLAMP, Iain James The Health Centre, High Street, Bedworth, Nuneaton CV12 8NQ Tel: 024 7631 5827 Fax: 024 7631 0580 — MB ChB 1992 Sheff.; MRCGP 2001; DRCOG 1996; DFFP 1997. (Sheff. Univ.) GP. Prev: Trainee GP/SHO (Paediat.) Geo. Eliot Hosp. Nuneaton VTS.

CLAMP, John Richard 26 Victoria Square, Clifton, Bristol BS8 4EW Tel: 0117 973 6222 — MB ChB 1954 Bristol; PhD Bristol 1962, BSc (Biochem.) 1958, MD 1968; FRCP Lond. 1983, M 1977; FRSC 1979; FRIC 1966. (Bristol) Prof. Experim. Med. Univ. Bristol.

CLAMP, Margaret Health Centre, Main Road, Radcliffe-on-Trent, Nottingham NG12 2GD Tel: 0115 933 2948; 131A Shelford Road, Radcliffe-on-Trent, Nottingham NG12 1AZ Tel: 0115 933 2368 — BM BS 1980 Nottm.; MRCGP 1984. GP Trainer Nottm. VTS. Prev: Trainee GP Nottm. VTS.

CLAMP, Philip Alan 66 Monarch Drive, Worcester WR2 6ES — BM BCh 1992 Oxf.

CLAMPITT, Lisa Beth 42 Marston Ferry Court, Marston Ferry Road, Oxford OX2 7XH — MB ChB 1998 Ed.; MB ChB Ed 1998.

CLANCY, Adrian 9 Hall Lane, Baguley, Manchester M23 1AQ Tel: 0161 437 0975; 5 The Aspens, Brookside Road, Gatley, Cheadle SK8 4BA Tel: 0161 428 4709 — MB ChB Ed. 1960.

CLANCY, Anne Elizabeth (retired) 4 Beauford House, The Hollow, Bamford, Hope Valley S33 0AU — MB BCh BAO 1957 NUI; DO Eng. 1961. Prev: Regist. Ophth. Roy. Infirm. Sheff.

CLANCY, Brendan Flat 1/L, 76 Thornwood Drive, Glasgow G11 7PR — MB ChB 1989 Ed.

CLANCY, Joan Marian Patricia 7 Hitches Lane, off Wheeley's Road, Edgbaston, Birmingham B15 2LS — MB BCh BAO 1977 NUI; FRCSI 1985. Research Fell. Skin Culture Laborat. Accid. Hosp. Birm.

CLANCY, Marc James 48 Rosefield Road, Liverpool L25 8TF — BM BCh 1994 Oxf. SHO Rotat. (Surg.) Roy. Free Hosp. Prev: Demonst. (Anat.) Univ. Bristol; Ho. Off. (Med.) N.ampton Gen. Hosp.; Ho. Off. (Surg.) Oxf. Radcliffe Hosp.

CLANCY, Mr Michael James Accident & Emergency Department, Southampton General Hospital, Tremona Road, Southampton SO16 6YD — MB ChB 1981 Sheff.; FRCS Eng. 1987; FRCS Ed. 1986; MSc 1998 Sheffield. Cons. A & E Med. S.ampton. Prev: Vis. Research Fell. Yale Univ., Conn., USA; Sen. Regist. (A & E) St. Jas. Univ. Hosp. Leeds; SHO Rotat. (Surg.) Roy. United Hosp. Bath.

CLANCY, Ruth Frances Clare 9 Hall Lane, Manchester M23 1AQ Tel: 0161 998 5711 — MB ChB 1962 St. And. (Queen's Coll. Dundee) Clin. Asst. in Drug Dependence, Manch. Drug Servs.; Clin. Asst. in Alcohol Dependence, ATU, Withington Hosp., Manch.

CLANCY, Ruth Mary 1 Damson Way, Orchard Hill, Fountain Drive, Carshalton SM5 4NR Tel: 020 8770 8000 Fax: 020 8770 8370 — MB ChB 1980 Leeds; DRCOG 1983; MRCGP 1986; MFFP 1993. (Leeds University) Cons. Family Plann. & Reproductive Health S. W. Lond. Community NHS Trust. Socs: Inst. Psychosexual Med. 1992.

CLANCY, Thomas 19 The Headway, Ewell Village, Epsom KT17 1UN — MB BCh BAO 1946 NUI. (Univ. Coll. Dub.)

CLANDILLON, Edmund John (retired) 128 Oxford Road, Macclesfield SK11 8JG — MB BS 1956 Durh.

CLAOUE, Mr Charles Marie Philippe Alexis The Cromwell Hospital, Cromwell Road, London SW5 0TU Tel: 020 7460 2000 Fax: 020 7460 5555; The Blackheath Hospital, 40-42 Lee Terrace, London SE3 9UD Tel: 020 8318 7722 Fax: 020 8318 2542 — MB BChir Camb. 1982; MA Camb. 1981, BA 1978; MD Bristol 1987; FRCS Eng. 1987; FRCOphth 1989; FICS 1992; DO RCS Eng. 1984. (Camb.) Cons. Ophth. Surg. (Corneal, Refractive & Cataract) Cromwell Hosp. Lond. Prev: Corneal Fell. & Sen. Regist. Moorfields Eye Hosp. Lond.; Regist. St. Thos. Hosp. Lond.; Hon. Regist. Bristol Eye Hosp.

CLAPHAM, Anthony Nicholas Oak Orchard, Stonebyres, Lanark ML11 9UP Tel: 01555 664886 — MB BS Durh. 1966; DObst RCOG 1969. (Newc.)

CLAPHAM, Charles Cornell (retired) 34 Priory Close, Tavistock PL19 9DJ Tel: 01822 613452 — MB BChir 1949 Camb.; MA Camb. 1950, MB BChir 1949; DObst RCOG 1950. Prev: Specialist in Obst. RAMC.

CLAPHAM, Ciaran Mary Highbridge Medical Centre, Pepperall Road, Highbridge TA9 3YA Tel: 01278 783220 Fax: 01278 795486; Appletree Cottage, Downend Crescent, Puriton, Bridgwater TA6 4TH — MB ChB 1977 Sheff.; MRCGP 1986; DRCOG 1979.

CLAPHAM, Michael Charles Cornell 113 Sharmans Cross Road, Solihull B91 1PH — MB BS 1976 Lond.; MRCS Eng. LRCP Lond. 1976; FFA RCS Eng. 1980. Cons. Intens. Care Med. & Anaesth. Univ. Hosp. Birm. Prev: Cons. Anaesth. Solihull Hosp.

CLAPHAM, Peter 16 Dudley Drive, Glasgow G12 9SB — MB ChB 1996 Glas.

CLAPP, Brian Richard 4 Morris Road, Marlborough SN8 1TJ — MB BS 1994 Lond. SHO (Respirat. Med.) Lond. Chest Hosp.

CLAPP, Richard Mark Macdonald Stowmarket Health Centre, Violet Hill Road, Stowmarket IP14 1NL Tel: 01449 776000 Fax: 01449 776005 — MB ChB 1986 Ed. Prev: SHO (Paediat.) N. Devon Dist. Hosp.; SHO (ENT) Roy. Cornw. Hosp.; SHO (Gen. Med. & Geriat.) Roodlands Hosp. Haddington.

CLAPPEN, John Angus 23 Boston Avenue, Southend-on-Sea SS2 6JH Tel: 01702 342589; 8 Beresford Gardens, Hadleigh, Benfleet SS7 2SA Tel: 01702 554963 — MB BS 1952 Lond.; MRCS Eng. LRCP Lond. 1952. (St. Bart.) Prev: Ho. Phys. & Ho. Surg. (Obst.) Rochford Gen. Hosp.

CLAPPISON, Douglas Peter Department of Health, Quarry House, Quarry Hill, Leeds LS2 7UE Tel: 0113 254 6280 Fax: 0113 254 6342 Email: peter.clappison@doh.gsi.gov.uk; East View, Stead Lane, Thorner, Leeds LS14 3EA Tel: 0113 289 2939 Fax: 0113 289 2939 — MB ChB 1971 Sheff.; MRCGP. (University of Sheffield) Sen. Med. Off. DoH Leeds; Chairm. UK Drug Utilisation Research Gp. Socs: BMA; Internat. Soc. Pharmacoepidemiol; Chairm. of Regulat. Counicil UK Drug Utilisation Research Gp., Chairm. Prev: Med. Adviser Beds. FHSA; Regional Med. Off. Regional Med. Serv.; GP LoW.oft.

CLAPTON, Keith John Plympton Health Centre, Mudge Way, Plymouth PL7 1AD Tel: 01752 341474 — MB ChB 1963 Sheff.; MRCGP 1971. (Sheff.) JP. Prev: Maj. RAMC, Specialist in Med. Camb. Milit. Hosp. Aldershot.

CLARAMUNT ROMERO, Maria del Carmen Leagrave Surgery, 37A Linden Road, Luton LU4 9QZ Tel: 01582 572817 Fax: 01582 494675 — LMS 1987 Valencia; MRCGP 1996. GP Princip.

CLARANCE, Gillian Ann (retired) Morningside, Chub Tor,, Yelverton PL20 6HY Tel: 01822 853591 — MB BS 1957 Lond.; LMCC 1960 Canada; DCH Eng. 1961; DObst RCOG 1961. Prev: Gen. nMwdical Practtittioner yelverton devon, Regist. (Paedit) Roy. Hosp.; fro Sick Childr., Bristol/ Plymouth Gen. Hosp. Regist. (Paediatric) Gen. Hosp. Plymouth. Sen. Ass. Res. Hosp for Sick Childr., Toronto, Canada.

CLARE, Charlotte Mary 72 Bentley Lane, Leeds LS6 4AJ — MB ChB 1996 Leeds.

CLARE, Corinne Anne Little Manor, Sheffield Park, Uckfield TN22 3RB — MB BS 1996 Lond.

CLARE, Dilis The Health Centre, 2A Forest Road, Edmonton, London N9 8RZ Tel: 020 8804 0121 — MB BCh BAO 1980 NUI.

CLARE, Fiona Brigit 5 Davidson Gardens, Glasgow G14 9JH — MB BChir 1986 Camb.; MRCGP 1991.

CLARE, Josephine Green Hill, Raper View, Aberford, Leeds LS25 3AF Email: joe.devlin@talk21.com — MB ChB 1991 Leeds; MRCP 1996. Specialist Reg. (Geiatrics) Leeds.

CLARE, Keith Anthony Boswer, Pill Creek, Feock, Truro TR3 6SE Tel: 01872 862746 — MB BS 1954 Lond.; AFOM RCP Lond. 1982; DA (UK) 1968; DRCOG 1956. Prev: Regional Med. Dir. Far E. Mobil Oil Corp. New York; Med. Dir. Mobil Oil Corp., Indonesia; Sen. Med. Advisor Shell Int. Petroleum Co. Ltd Lond.

CLARE, Patrick Andrew Burson Baildon Cottage, Outwood Lane, Horsforth, Leeds LS18 4HR — MB ChB 1990 Leeds.

CLARE, Richard George 7 South Meade, Manchester M21 8EB — MB ChB 1980 Liverp. GP Sale.

CLARE, Thomas David 1 Orchard Drive, Aston Clinton, Aylesbury HP22 5HR — MB BS 1992 Lond.

CLARIA-OLMEDO, Marcelo Jose 14 Sinclair Drive, Liverpool L18 0HN Tel: 0151 722 3981 — Medico Buenos Aires 1969; MRCPsych 1978. (Buenos Aires) Cons. (Psychiat.) Mersey RHA.

CLARIDGE, Anne Jeanette Briston Lodge, Briston, Melton Constable NR24 2HR — MB BS 1986 Newc.

CLARIDGE, Geoffrey Braham The AshLea Medical Practice, Gilbert House, 39 Woodfield Lane, Ashtead KT21 2BQ Tel: 01372 276385 Fax: 01372 279530; Savernake, 63 Harriotts Lane, Ashtead KT21 2QE Tel: 01372 277288 Fax: 0870 568536 Email: gbclaridge@netscapeonline.co.uk — BM BCh 1972 Oxf.; MA, BM BCh Oxf. 1972; MRCGP 1986; MRCOphth 1989; DO RCS Eng. 1984. (Oxford and St. George's) Princip. GP; Hosp. Pract. (Ophth.) Epsom Dist. Hosp.; Ophth. Med. Practitioner Trainer. Socs: Fell. Roy. Soc. Med,. Prev: Lect. Inst. Urol. Lond.; Regist. (Med.) Croydon Gen. Hosp.; Regist. (Neurosurg.) Atkinson Morley's Hosp. Lond.

CLARIDGE, Katharine Georgina c/o Department of Ophthalmology, Taunton & Somerset Trust Hospitals, Musgrove Park, Taunton TA1 5DA Tel: 01823 342950 Fax: 01823 342943 Email: clari_k@tst.nhs.uk — MB BS 1985 Lond.; MA Oxf. 1985; FCOphth 1989; DO RCS Eng. 1988. Cons. Ophth. Taunton & Som. Trust. Socs: BMA. Prev: Sen. Regist. Bristol Eye Hosp.; Lect. (Ophth.) St. Thos. Hosp. Lond.; Regist. Croydon Eye Unit Thornton Heath & St. Geo. Hosp. Lond.

CLARIDGE, Maria Teresa 1 Oldhams Cottages, Ebford, Exeter EX3 0QY Tel: 01392 877687; Loganstones, Lustleigh, Newton Abbot TQ13 9SQ — MB BS 1986 Lond.; BSc 1984; MRCGP (Distinc.) 1990; DGM RCP Lond. 1988. Asst. GP Exeter; Clin. Asst. (Med.) Exeter.

CLARIDGE, Mr Martin St Martin's House, St. Martin's Avenue, Canterbury CT1 1QQ Tel: 01227 464241 Fax: 01227 464241 — BM BCh 1951 Oxf.; MCh Oxf. 1964, BM BCh 1951; FRCS Eng. 1956. (Oxf. & St. Thos.) Hon. Cons. Urol. Surg. Kent & Canterbury Hosp. Socs: Fell. Roy. Soc. Med.; Brit. Assn. Urol. Surgs. Prev: Res. Surg. Off. St. Peter's Hosp. For Stone Lond.; Sen. Surg. Regist. St. Thos. Hosp. Lond.; Surg. Regist. W.m. Hosp.

CLARIDGE, Martin Walton Charles Sycamore Cottage, Ferndew Heights, Fernden Lane, Haslemere GU27 3LA — MB BS 1996 Lond.

CLARIDGE, Patricia Margaret Wimpole Road Surgery, 52 Wimpole Road, Colchester CO1 2DL Tel: 01206 794794 Fax: 01206 790403 — MRCS Eng. LRCP Lond. 1980 London.

CLARK, Agnes (retired) Carr Field House, Carr Head Lane, Poulton-le-Fylde FY6 8JB Tel: 01253 883401 — MB ChB Ed. 1952; MRCOG 1957; DObst RCOG 1954. Prev: Regist. (O & G) Crumpsall Hosp. Manch.

CLARK, Alan Stanley Grainger Trenchard House, Edde Cross St., Ross-on-Wye HR9 7BZ Tel: 01989 763500 — MB BS 1963 Lond.; MRCS Eng. LRCP Lond. 1962; DObst RCOG 1964. (Guy's) Socs: BMA. Prev: Ho. Surg. & Ho. Phys. Hereford Hosps.; Ho. Phys. (Paediat.) Worcester Roy. Infirm.

CLARK, Alasdair Ronald Buxton Whitefields Surgery, Hunsbury Hill Road, Camp Hill, Northampton NN4 9UW Tel: 01604 760171 Fax: 01604 708528; The Surgery, 17A Church Lane, Kislingbury, Northampton NN7 4AD Tel: 01604 760171 — BM BCh 1973 Oxf.; MA Camb. 1970; DRCOG 1976. (Oxford) GP.

CLARK, Alexa Kay 69 Woodlands Grange, Forest Hall, Newcastle upon Tyne NE12 9DG — BM BS 1989 Nottm.; BMedSci Nottm. 1987; MRCGP 1993; DRCOG 1992. Regist. (Palliat. Med.) Newc. u. Tyne. Prev: SHO (Palliat. Med.) St. Oswald's Hospice Newc.; SHO (Psychiat.) W.on Gen. Hosp.; Trainee GP Lincoln VTS.

CLARK, Alexander Aitken (retired) Springfield, Duntocher Road, Dalmuir, Clydebank G81 3LP Tel: 0141 952 3128 — MB ChB 1942 Glas. Vice-Pres. BMA & Ex-Chairm. BMA Charities Trust. Prev: Chairm. Represen. Body BMA.

CLARK, Alexander Stewart Whincroft, 2A Upper Colquhoun St., Helensburgh G84 9AQ Tel: 01436 672647 — MB ChB 1966 Glas.; FRCOG 1983, M 1970. Cons. (O & G) Vale of Leven Hosp. Alexandria; Civil Cons. RN Scotl.

CLARK, Alistair Hamilton Department of Histopathology, Arrowe Park Hospital, Upton, Wirral CH49 5PE Tel: 0151 678 5111 Fax: 0151 504 1733 — MB ChB 1976 Glas.; MRCPath 1984; DRCOG 1978; FRCPath 1996. Cons. Histopath. Arrowe Pk. Hosp. Upton, Wirral. Prev: Sen. Regist. (Histopath.) St. Thos. Hosp. Lond.; Sen. Regist. (Histopath.) St. Mary's Hosp. Portsmouth; SHO/Regist. (Histopath.) Vict. Infirm. Glas.

CLARK, Andrea Katherine Tel: 01264 773704 — MB ChB 1985 Bristol; MRCGP 1990; DCH RCP Lond. 1988. p/t GP Locum.

CLARK, Andrew David HMP Frankland, Brasside, Durham DH1 1YD Tel: 0191 384 5544 — MB BS 1979 Lond.; BSc Lond. 1976; MRCS Eng. LRCP Lond. 1979; MRCGP 1986. Med. Off. HM Prison Serv. HMP Frankland.

CLARK, Andrew Douglas 18 Kilnburn, Newport-on-Tay DD6 8DE — MB ChB 1991 Ed.

CLARK, Andrew Frederick McGuinness Unit, Mental Health Services of Salford, Bury New Road, Prestwich, Manchester M25 3BL Tel: 0161 772 3648 Fax: 0161 772 3593 Email: andrew.clark@man.ac.uk — MB BS 1982 Newc.; FRCPsych 2001; MA Camb. 1983; MRCPsych 1987. Sen. Lect. (Adolesc. Psychiat.) Univ. Manch.; Hon. Cons. Adolesc. Psychiat. Ment. Health Servs. Salford NHS Trust. Prev: Cons. Adolesc. Psychiat. S. Birm. Ment. Health NHS Trust; Sen. Regist. (Child & Adolesc. Psychiat.) N.. RHA; Regist. (Psychiat.) Roy. Vict. Infirm. Newc. u. Tyne.

CLARK, Andrew John Kingthorne Group Practice, 83A Thorne Road, Doncaster DN1 2EU Tel: 01302 342832 Fax: 01302 366995 — MB ChB 1993 Birm.

CLARK, Andrew John Edward Flat 3FL/23 Lauriston Gardens, Edinburgh EH3 9HH — MB ChB 1997 Ed.

CLARK, Andrew Jonathan Brandis Psychotherapy Unit, Avon and Western Wiltshire Mental Health Partnership Trust, Blackberry Hill Hospital, Manor Road, Fishponds, Bristol BS16 2EW Tel: 0117 918 6811 Fax: 0117 975 4832 Email: andrew.clark@awp.swest.nhs uk — MB BS 1986 Lond.; MA Camb. 1987; MRCPsych 1992. Cons. Psychotherap. Blackberry Hill Hosp. Bristol. Prev: Sen. Regist. (Psychother.) Roy. S. Hants. Hosp. Soton.; Regist. (Psychiat.) Bethlem Roy. & Maudsley Hosps. Lond.; SHO (Haemat.) Warwick Hosp.

CLARK, Andrew Lawrence Academic Cardiology, Castle Hill Hospital, Castle Road, Cottingham HU16 5JQ Tel: 01482 624087 Fax: 01482 624085 Email: 4.l.clarke@medschool.hull.ac.uk; Tel: 01482 631532 — MB BS 1984 Lond.; MA Camb. 1985, BA 1981; MD Lond. 1994; MRCP (UK) 1988. (Westminster) Sen. Lect. & Hon. Cons. Cardiol., Univ. of Hull & Hull and E. Yorks. NHS Trust. Socs: Brit. Cardiac Soc.; Brit. Soc. Echocardiogr.; Brit. Soc. Heart Failure. Prev: Robt. Luff Fell. (Cardiol.) Nat. Heart & Lung Inst.; Sen. Regist. (Cardiol.) W.ern Infirm., Glas. HB.

CLARK, Andrew Malcolm Public Health Department, East Lancashire Health Authority, 31-33 Kenyon Road, Nelson BB9 5SZ Tel: 01282 610240 Fax: 01250 610213; 149 Leeds Road, Harrogate HG2 8EZ Tel: 01423 872305 Email: andrew.clark@virgin.net — MB BS 1975 Lond.; MPH Leeds 1996; MFPHM 1998. (Middlx.) Cons. Pub. Health Med., E. Lancs Health Auth.; Pub. Health Director, NW Cervical Screening QARC. Prev: Cons. Pub. Health Med., E. Lancs. Health Auth.; Sen. Med. Off. DoH; GP Worthing.

CLARK, Andrew Thomas Dept. Allergy & Clinical Immunology, Box 40, Addenbrooke's Hopsital, Hills Rd, Cambridge CB2 2HT — MB BS 1992 Lond.; MRCP (UK) 1996. Clin. Research Fell. in Allergy Univ. of Camb.; Regist. (Paediat.) Addenbrooke's Hosp. Camb. Prev: SHO (Paediat.) Guy's & St. Thos. Hosp. Lond.

CLARK, Mr Andrew William 55 New Church Road, Hove BN3 4BG Tel: 01273 720217 Fax: 01273 694886; (cons. rooms), 55 New Church Road, Hove BN3 4BG Tel: 01273 720217 Fax: 01273 220919 — MB BS Lond. 1964; MS Lond. 1977; FRCS Eng. 1969. (King's Coll. Hosp.) Hon. Cons. Surg. Brighton Healthcare; Hunt. Prof. RCS Eng. Socs: Roy. Soc. Med.; Brit. Soc. Gastroenterol. Prev: Sen. Regist. King's Coll Hosp. Lond.; Research Fell. Harvard Med. Sch., USA.

CLARK, Angela Marion 48 Holmcliffe Avenue, Huddersfield HD4 7RN — MB ChB 1982 Leeds; MSc Sheffield 1997. SCMO (Family Plann. & Genitourin. Med.) Huddersfield. Socs: Assoc. Mem. Inst. Psychosexual Med; Fac. Fam. Plann.; Brit. Assn. Sexual & Marital Ther.

CLARK, Anna Lucy Lawn Cottage, Bromsgrove Rd, Clent, Stourbridge DY9 9PY — MB BS 1996 Lond.

***CLARK, Annalisa** Bourne House, Chatley, Droitwich WR9 0AP — MB BS 1996 Lond.

CLARK, Anne Lyndon, Poynders Road, London SW4 8PS Tel: 020 8671 8667 — MB BCh BAO 1948 NUI; DPM Eng. 1963. (Univ. Coll. Dub.)

CLARK, Anne Ethelwyn The Grove, Thorner, Leeds LS17 Tel: 0113 289 2228 — MRCS Eng. LRCP Lond. 1957. (Middlx.) Prev: Ho. Surg. & Ho. Phys. Ashford Hosp. Middlx.

CLARK, Annie Simpson Ruthrieston House, 199 Broomhill Road, Aberdeen AB10 7LN Tel: 01224 316862 — MB ChB 1924 Aberd. Prev: Ho. Surg. Aberd. Sick Childr. Hosp.; Ho. Phys. Edin. Hosp. Wom. & Childr.; Sen. Ho. Surg. Roy. E. Sussex Hosp. Hastings.

CLARK, Anthony David Clifton House, Park Place, Wickham, Fareham PO17 5EZ Tel: 01329 832283 — MB ChB 1964 Bristol; MB ChB (Hnrs.) Bristol 1964; FRCOG 1983, M 1970. (Bristol) Cons. O & G St. Mary's Hosp. Portsmouth. Prev: Sen. Regist. (O & G) Roy. Postgrad. Med. Sch. Hammersmith Hosp.

CLARK, Anthony John Urmston Lane Surgery, 134 Urmston Lane, Stretford, Manchester M32 9DF Tel: 0161 865 3400 Fax: 0161 865 4429; 57 Broad Road, Sale M33 2ES Tel: 0161 286 1361 Email: tclark.sale@compuserve.com — MB ChB 1978 Manch. GP Stretford.

CLARK, Anthony Neville Gordon (retired) 23 Cavendish House, Kings Road, Brighton BN1 2JH Tel: 01273 24569 — MD 1951 Leeds; MB ChB 1948; FRCP Lond. 1973, M 1959. Prev: Regist. (Neurol.) Gen. Infirm. Leeds.

CLARK, Anthony Robert 2 The Stables, Millcroft, Crosby, Liverpool L23 9YT Tel: 0151 931 1582 — MB ChB 1996 Liverp.; MB ChB Liverp. 1996 (with commendation). (Liverp.) SHO Rotat. (O & G) Wirral NHS Trust; SHO (Neonat. Paediat. & Oncol.) & Sen. SHO (Obst. & Gyn.) Wirral NHS Trust. Socs: BMA; MPS. Prev: SHO (O & G) Arrowe Pk. Hosp. Wirral.

CLARK, Arthur Godfrey Boulton Guy's & St Thomas Medical & Dental School, Kings College, Floor 12, Guy's Tower, Guy's Hospital., London SE1 9RT Tel: 020 7955 4018 Fax: 020 7357 6037 — MB BS 1979 Lond.; MA Camb. 1978, BA 1974; MRCP (UK) 1982; FRCP 1998. (St. Mary's Hospital Medical School London) Sen. Lect. & Hon. Cons. Paediat. (Nephrol.) Guy's Hosp. Lond. Socs: Eur. Soc. Paediat. Nephrol.; Internat. Paediat. Nephrol. Assn; Brit.Assn.Paediat. Nephrol. Prev: Lect. (Paediat. Nephrol.) Guy's Hosp. Lond.; Eden Research Fell. Roy. Coll. Phys.

CLARK, Arthur Robert Leonard (retired) 24 Fitzroy Avenue, Kingsgate, Broadstairs CT10 3LS Tel: 01843 862499 — MB BS 1955 Lond.; MSc (Occupat. Med.) Lond. 1975; MFOM RCP Lond. 1978; DHMSA 1984; Accredit. Specialist (Occupat. Med.) 1984; DIH Eng. 1975. Prev: Chief Med. Off. Transmanche-Link.

CLARK, Barbara Mary Caroline Alder Cottage, 48A Peel St., Macclesfield SK11 8BH — MB ChB 1990 Sheff.

CLARK, Brian Edgar (retired) The Health Centre, West Pottergate, Norwich NR2 4BX Tel: 01603 628705 Fax: 01603 766789 — MB BS 1966 Lond.; LRCP MRCS Eng. 1966. Prev: Sen. Regist. (Haematol.) W. Dorset Gp. Hosps.

CLARK, Brian John 26 Wick Avenue, Wheathampsetead, St Albans AL4 8QB Tel: 0141 211 2473 — MB ChB 1989 Glas.; BSc (Hons.) Glas. 1986, MB ChB 1989. SHO (Path.) W.. Infirm. Glas. Prev: SHO (Ophth.) Ayr Hosp.; Roy. Coll. Prosector Dept. Anat. Univ. Glas.

CLARK, Bruce Rae 1 Grantham Court, Eleanor Close, London SE16 6PT Tel: 020 7252 2966 — MB ChB 1992 Ed.; BSc (Hons.) Path. Ed. 1989; MRCPsych 1997. (Ed.) Wellcome Clin. Train. Fell. The Inst. of Psychiat. Lond.; Hon. Specialist Regist. Bethlem & Maudsley NHS Trust. Socs: Life Mem. Roy. Med. Soc. Prev: Regist. (Psychiat.) Bethlem/Maudsley Hosps.; SHO (Gen. Med.) Roy. Lond. Hosp. Trust.

CLARK, Callum Ian McMillan 189 Church Road, Frampton Cotterell, Bristol BS36 2BJ — MB BChir 1994 Camb.

CLARK, Caroline Anne X Ray Departments, Kirkcaldy Acute Hospitals N H S Trust, Victoria Hospital, Kirkcaldy KY2 5AH — MB BS 1985 Lond.; BSc (Hons.) Lond. 1982, MB BS 1985; MRCP (UK) 1990; DMRD 1993; FRCR 1995. (King's Coll. Hosp.) Cons.(Radiol.) Vic Hosp. Kirkcaldy. Prev: Regist. (Radiol.) Roy. Infirm. Edin.; SHO (Gen. Med.) Addenbrookes Hosp. Camb.; Ho. Off. Liver Unit King's Coll. Hosp. Lond.

CLARK, Caroline Margaret Child Health Department, Dunoon General Hospital, 360 Argyll St., Dunoon PA23 7RL Tel: 01369 704341 — MB ChB 1980 Glas.; DCH RCP Lond. 1983; DRCOG 1982. (Glas.) Assoc. Specialist (Community Child Health) Argyll & Bute NHS Trust. Socs: BMA; SACCH; Assoc. Mem. RCPCH. Prev: Community Med. Off. (Community Child Health) Grampian N.; Trainee GP Paisley; SHO (Paediat.) S.. Gen. Hosp. Glas.

CLARK, Catherine Jayne 321 Clarendon Park Road, Leicester LE2 3AQ — MB ChB 1998 Leic.; MB ChB Leic 1998.

CLARK, Cecilia Marie 64 Rubislaw Den S., Aberdeen AB15 4AY — MB ChB 1962 Aberd.

CLARK, Mr Charles Edward 84 Springkell Avenue, Glasgow G41 4EH Tel: 0141 427 0859 — MB ChB 1974 Birm.; FRCS Ed. 1979; MPH Glas. 1989; MFPHM 1996. Cons. Pub. Health Med. Lanarksh. HB. Prev: Med. Dir. Yorkhill NHS Trust Glas.; Cons. Surg. Belford Hosp. Fort William; Demonst. (Anat.) Univ. Bristol.

CLARK, Charles Justin Mullin (retired) 31 The Avenue, Branksome Park, Poole BH13 6LH Tel: 01202 763147 — MB BS Lond. 1945; MD (Distinc.) Lond. 1949; FRCP Lond. 1969, M 1946. Hon. Cons. Phys. (Gen. Med.) Roy. Bournemouth Gen. Hosp.; Hon. Clin. Teach. Med. Univ. Soton. Med. Sch., Char. Cross & W.m. Med. Sch. Prev: Sen. Regist. (Med.) W.m. Hosp.

CLARK, Christine 1 Seafield Avenue, Heswall, Wirral CH60 4SJ — MB ChB 1991 Liverp.

CLARK, Christine Elizabeth Accident & Emergency Department, Blackburn Royal Infirmary, Bolton Road, Blackburn BB2 3LR; 4 Berkeley Colonnade, 69 Watling Street Road, Fulwood, Preston PR2 8AG Tel: 01772 774901 — MB ChB 1989 Ed. Staff Grade (A & E) Blackburn Roy. Infirm. Socs: Roy. Med. Soc. Edin.

CLARK, Christopher Elles School Surgery, Fore St., Witheridge, Tiverton EX16 8AH Tel: 01884 860205 Fax: 01884 860887; Oakfield, Witheridge, Tiverton EX16 8AN Tel: 01884 860248 Email: ceclark@sol.co.uk — MB ChB 1986 Bristol; BSc (Hons.) Bristol 1983; MRCP (UK) 1991; MRCGP 1993; DFFP 1993. GP Educat. Facilitator, Inst. of Gen. Pract., Exeter. Prev: Trainee GP Newton Abbot; Regist. (Med.) Roy. Devon & Exeter NHS Trust; SHO (Med.) Torbay Hosp. Torquay.

CLARK, Christopher James Hairmyres Hospital, East Kilbride, Glasgow G15 8RD; 30 Buckingham Terrace, Glasgow G12 8ED — MB BCh BAO 1974 Dub.; BSc Glas. 1969; BA, MD Dub. 1985, MB BCh BAO 1974; FRCP Glas. 1988; MRCP (UK) 1976. Cons. Phys. Hairmyres Hosp. Glas.; Hon. Sen. Clin. Lect. (Med.) & Hon. Lect. (Physiol.) Univ. Glas.

CLARK, Christopher John 36 The Street, Capel St Mary, Ipswich IP9 2EE Tel: 01473 310203; Acacia Farm, Great Wenham, Colchester CO7 6PP Tel: 01473 311498 — BM BCh 1968 Oxf.; MA Oxf. 1968.

CLARK, Christopher Robert 2 Southhouse Avenue, Edinburgh EH17 8EA Tel: 0131 664 1601 — MB ChB 1988 Dundee; MRCPsych 1994. Specialist Regist. Rotat. (Forens. Psychiat.) W. Midl. Prev: Sen. Regist. Rotat. (Gen. Psychiat.) Sheff.; Regist. Rotat. (Psychiat.) St. Geo. Hosp. Lond.; SHO (Psychiat.) St. Lawrence's Hosp. Bodmin.

CLARK, Christopher Thomas Lady Bay Surgery, 195A Trent Boulevard, West Bridgford, Nottingham NG2 5BX Tel: 0115 981 6100 Fax: 0115 981 7709 — MB BS 1973 Lond.; MRCS Eng. LRCP Lond. 1973; DRCOG 1978. (St. Mary's)

CLARK, Colette 99 East Kilbride Road, Clarkston, Glasgow G76 8JE — MB ChB 1978 Glas.; FFA RCS Eng. 1982.

CLARK, Colin Alison Lea Health Centre, Calderwood, Glasgow; Juniper Gate, 7 Cairnryan, Stewartfield, Glasgow G74 4RT — MB ChB 1983 Glas.; MRCGP 1988.

CLARK, Colin Maitland Wishaw Health Centre, Kenilworth Avenue, Wishaw ML2 7BQ Tel: 01698 372201 Fax: 01698 371051; 68 Avonbridge Drive, Hamilton ML3 7EJ Tel: 01698 372201 — MB ChB 1975 Glas. Med. Adviser Orgavon Laboratories NewHo. Lanarksh. Socs: Exec. Comm. Mem. Lanarksh. Div. BMA.

CLARK, Mr Darren 11 Holly Street, Smethwick, Smethwick B67 7BS — MB ChB 1991 Birm.; FRCS Ed. 1996. Specialist Regist. Rotat. (Orthop. & Trauma) W. Midl. Socs: BOTA. Prev: Regist. (Orthop. & Trauma Surg.) S. Birm. Trauma Unit Univ. Hosp. Trust Birm.; SHO (Spinal Surg.) Roy. Orthop. Hosp. Birm.; SHO (Vasc. Surg. & Urol.) Birm. Heartlands Hosp.

CLARK, David 21 Nethermains Road, Milngavie, Glasgow G62 6NL — M.B., Ch.B. Glas. 1942. (Glas.)

CLARK, David 119 Hardie Drive, West Boldon, East Boldon NE36 0HA — BM BCh 1992 Oxf.

CLARK, David Ernest 122 Churchway, Weston Mill, Plymouth PL5 1AJ — MB ChB 1960 Leeds; MSc (Community Med.) Manch. 1982; DIC (Engin in Med.) Imperial Coll. Lond. 1963. Sen. Research Fell. (Med. Informatics) Univ. Manch.; Hon. Sen. Regist. (Community Med.) N. W.. RHA. Prev: Clin. Asst. (Pulm. Physiol.) Bury Gen. Hosp.; Ho. Surg. (Orthop.) Leeds Gen. Infirm.; May & Baker Research Fell. Dir. Med. Computing Unit Univ. Manch.

CLARK, David Gowan Cresswell 27 Hollymead Close, Colchester CO4 5JU — MB ChB 1990 Cape Town.

CLARK, David Graham 122 Munro Road, Jordanhill, Glasgow G13 1SE — MB ChB 1997 Glas.

CLARK, David Hazell (retired) 5 High Street, Grantchester, Cambridge CB3 9NF Tel: 01223 841255 — MD 1967 Ed.; PhD Camb. 1972, MA 1946, BA 1941; MB ChB 1943; FRCP Ed. 1958, M 1948; FRCPsych 1971; DPM Lond. 1949. Prev: Cons. Psychiat. Fulbourn Hosp. & Addenbrooke's Hosp. Camb. & Assoc.

CLARK, Mr David Iain Department of Phythalmology, Walton Hospital, Rice Lane, Liverpool L9 Tel: 0151 529 4353 — BM 1977 Soton.; FRCOphth 1989; FRCS Ed. 1983; DO Eng. 1981. Cons. Ophth. Aintree Hosps. Liverp.; Cons. Ophth. Dept. Of Neonatology Liverp. Wom.s Hosp. Prev: Cons. Ophth. Walton Hosp. & St. Pauls Eye Hosp. Liverp.

CLARK, Mr David Ian Derbyshire Royal Infirmary, Dept. of Orthopaedics, London Road, Derby DE1 2QY Email: clark.sec@sdah-treit-nhs.uk; The Old School House, Over Lane, Hazelwood Tel: 01642 360180 Email: dandclark7@compuserve.com — MB ChB 1988 Sheff.; FRCS 1998 (Ortho.); BMedSci. Hons. (Orthop. Bioengin.) Sheff. 1987; FRCS Eng. 1993. Cons. Orthopaedic & Upper Limb Surg. Derbysh. Roy. Infirm. Derby. Socs: Brit. Orthop. Assn.; Brit. Shoulder and Elbow Soc.; Brit. Trauma Soc. Prev: SHO

(Orthop.) N.. Gen. Hosp. Sheff.; SHO (Cardiothoracic & Gen. Surg.) Groby Rd. Hosp. Leicester; SHO (Orthop., Cas. & Neurosurg.) Qu. Med. Centre Nottm.

CLARK, David John 5 Chester Street, Edinburgh EH3 7RF — MB ChB 1987 Ed.

CLARK, Mr David Llewellyn 7 Sherwood Park Road ., Sutton SM1 2SQ Tel: 020 8642 5993 — MB BS 1990 Lond.; FRCS Eng. 1995.

CLARK, David Martin The Darley Dale Medical Centre, Two Dales, Darley Dale, Matlock DE4 3FD Tel: 01629 733205 — MB ChB 1980 Ed.; MRCGP 1984; DRCOG 1982. GP Matlock; Clin. Asst. (Geriat.) Whitworth Hosp.

CLARK, David Michael Beech House, Bridge Road, Airmyn, Goole DN14 8LJ Tel: 01405 4208 — MB ChB 1953 Leeds.

CLARK, Mr David Phillips Bank Street Surgery, 46-62 Bank Street, Alexandria G83 0LS Tel: 01389 752419 Fax: 01389 710521; Nether Haldane, Stirling Road, Balloch, Alexandria G83 8EP — MB ChB 1981 Glas.; FRCS Glas. 1985; MRCGP 1987.

CLARK, Mr David William Southlands Hospital, Shoreham-by-Sea BN43 6TQ; 60 Salvington Hill, Worthing BN13 3BB — MRCS Eng. LRCP Lond. 1976; BSc Lond. 1973, MB BS 1976; FRCS Eng. 1980. Cons. (Orthop.) S.lands Hosp. Shoreham-by-Sea. Socs: Provin. Fell. Roy. Soc. Med.; Assoc. Mem. Brit. Orthop. Assn. Prev: Regist. (Orthop.) Heatherwood Hosp. Ascot; Regist. (Orthop.) Wexham Pk. Hosp. Slough; Regist. (Orthop.) Roy. Free Hosp. Lond.

CLARK, Deborah Harvie 6 Enfield Street, Nottingham NG9 1AL Email: deborah.clark@nottingham.ac.uk — MB ChB 1988 Leic.; MRCGP 1992; MRCPsych 1996. Lect. & Hon. Specialist Regist. (Psychiat.) Univ. Nottm.

CLARK, Deborah Jane 24 Watergate Way, Liverpool L25 8TP — MB ChB 1989 Liverp.

CLARK, Deborah Jane Royal Hospital, Chesterfield S44 5BL Tel: 01246 277271; 146 Homebush Road, Strathfield, New South Wales 2135, Australia — MB ChB 1970 Sheff.; MRCPath 1976; FRCP Lond. 1994; MRCP (UK) 1982. Cons. (Haemat.) Chesterfield Roy. Hosp.

CLARK, Mr Donald Robert City General Hospital, Fusehill St., Carlisle CA1 2HG Tel: 01228 23444 — MB ChB 1979 Birm.; FRCS Eng. 1984. Cons. Otol. N. RHA.

CLARK, Donna 19 Kelvindale Gardens, Kelvindale, Glasgow G20 0XD — MB ChB 1997 Glas.

CLARK, Drew Accident & Emergency Department, Airedale General Hospital, Keighley BD20 6TD; Bent Clough Farm, Keighley Road, Colne BB8 7HF Tel: 01282 866749 — MB ChB 1974 Ed.; BSc Ed. 1971; Cert JCC Lond. 1978.

CLARK, Edmund Greenwood (retired) 2 Deer Park, Wollaton, Nottingham NG8 2NX — MB ChB 1951 Sheff.; FFOM RCP Lond. 1993; DIH Soc. Apoth. Lond. 1960. Prev: Sen. Med. Adviser John Player & Son Nottm.

CLARK, Edwin Charles Ballards, Knotting Green, Bedford MK44 1AA — MB BChir 1994 Camb.

CLARK, Elaine 175 Lonsdale Drive, Enfield EN2 7JY — MB BS 1993 Lond.

CLARK, Elizabeth 20 Claremont Crescent, Edinburgh EH7 4HX Tel: 0131 557 0742 — MB ChB 1946 Glas. (Glas.)

CLARK, Elizabeth Ann 33 Manor Road, Caddington, Luton LU1 4EE Tel: 01582 725673; Christmas Cottage, Pipers Lane, Aley Green, Luton LU1 4DS Tel: 01582 841391 Email: billashford@talk21.com — MB ChB 1984 Leic.; DRCOG 1988; DCH RCP Lond. 1987. Prev: Trainee GP Leicester VTS.

CLARK, Elizabeth Jane 23 Townhill Bank, Padiham, Burnley BB12 8DH — MB BCh 1992 Wales.

CLARK, Elizabeth Jennifer 318 Hempstead Road, Watford WD17 4NA — MB BS 1990 Lond.

CLARK, Elizabeth Young Hercus Loan House, 24 Hercus Loan, Musselburgh EH21 6AY Tel: 0131 665 3510 — MB ChB 1949 Ed. Socs: Affil. Mem. RCPsych. Prev: Regist. Bellsdyke Hosp. Larbert; SHO (Surg.) Hemlington Hosp. Middlesbrough; SHO Rosslynlee Hosp. Roslin.

CLARK, Emma Margaret 26 Pople Street, Wymondham NR18 0PS — MB BS 1996 Lond.; BSc Lond. SHO Med. Rotat. Norf. & Norwich Hosp.

CLARK, Ewan Dryden Portlethen Group Practice, Portlethen Health Centre, Bruntland Road, Portlethen, Aberdeen AB12 4QL Tel: 01224 780223 Fax: 01224 781317; Mill of Findon, Portlethen, Aberdeen AB12 4QQ Tel: 01224 780176 — MB ChB 1985 Aberd.; MRCGP 1991.

CLARK, Fiona Catherine Elizabeth 1 Jura Quadrant, Netherton, Wishaw ML2 0TD — MB ChB 1996 Dundee; DRCOG 1999. SHO. Hartwood Hosp. Shotts. Lanarksh..

CLARK, Fiona Jane 84 Oak Hill Road, Sevenoaks TN13 1NT — MB ChB 1991 Birm.; ChB Birm. 1991.

CLARK, Francis Denside, Murtle Den Road, Milltimber AB13 0HS Tel: 01224 861109 — MB ChB 1949 Aberd.

CLARK, Francis Ronald (retired) Carrick, Abbotsford Road, North Berwick EH39 5DB — MB ChB 1951 Ed.; FRCS Ed. 1964; FRCOG 1971, M 1960. Prev: Cons. O & G W.. Gen. Hosp. Edin. & Roy. Inf. Edin.

CLARK, Frederick (retired) Cauto, 15 Fawdon Walk, Brunton Bridge, Newcastle upon Tyne NE13 7AW Tel: 0191 271 5673 Fax: 0191 232 4280 Email: b.willisclark@btinternet.com — MB BS 1955 Durh.; MB BS (Hons.) Durh. 1955; FRCP Lond. 1973, M 1961. Cons. Phys. Freeman Gp. of Hosps. NHS Trust; Sen. Lect. (Med.) Univ. Newc. Prev: 1st Asst. Dept. Med. Univ. Newc.

CLARK, Gareth Peter 45 Pant-y-Dwr, Three Crosses, Swansea SA4 3PG — BM 1995 Soton. SHO (A & E) Hereford. Prev: Ho. Off. (Surg.) Basingstoke; Ho. Off. (Med.) Bath.

CLARK, Geoffrey Stephen 49 Castle Rise, Cardiff CF3 4BB — MRCS Eng. LRCP Lond. 1973; BSc Lond. 1970, MB BS 1973; FRCA 1977. (Guy's) Cons. Anaesth. Roy. Gwent Hosp. Newport. Prev: Sen. Regist. (Anaesth.) Univ. Hosp. Wales Cardiff; Clin. Fell. (Anaesth.) Univ. Toronto Canada; Regist. (Anaesth.) Roy. Berks. Hosp. Reading.

CLARK, Mr Geoffrey William Barton 12 Bingley Bank, Bardsey, Leeds LS17 9DW — MB ChB 1984 Manch.; MB ChB Manch. I984; BSc St. And. 1981; MD Manch. 1994; FRCS Ed. 1989. Hon. Sen. Regist. (Gen. Surg.) Univ. Hosp. Wales Cardiff; Lect. (Gen. Surg.) Univ. Wales Coll. of Med. Socs: BMA. Prev: Regist. (Gen. Surg.) Bolton Gen. Hosp.; Research Fell. Univ. S.. Calif., USA; Regist. (Vasc. Surg.) Manch. Roy. Infirm.

CLARK, Mr George Logan (retired) 4 Charlotte Place, Perth PH1 5LS Tel: 01738 635945 — MB ChB 1942 Glas.; FRFPS Glas. 1948; FRCS Glas. 1962; FRCS Ed. 1948. Prev: Cons. in Admin. Charge (Orthop.) & Orthop. Surg. Bridge of Earn Hosp.

CLARK, Mr George Ogilvie (retired) Woodlands, 15 Muchall Road, Wolverhampton WV4 5SE Tel: 01902 341424 — MB ChB 1946 Aberd.; FRCS Eng. 1957; FRCS Ed. 1953; DLO Eng. 1952. Prev: Hon. Cons. Surg. (ENT) Wolverhampton HA.

CLARK, George Philip Malcolm anaesthetic Department, Northern General Hospital, Sheffield S5 7AU Tel: 0114 271 4818; ST. Helena Cottage, I5a topside, Grenoside, Sheffield S35 8RD Tel: 0114 246 0732 — MB 1972 Camb.; MA; BChir 1971; MRCP (U.K.) 1974; FFA RCS Eng. 1976. (Cambridge) Cons. N.ern Gen. Hosp. NHS Trust. Prev: Sen. Regist. & Regist. Sheff. AHA; Lect. Nairobi Univ. Kenya.

CLARK, Gerald Andrew (retired) Popses, The Street, Kirby-le-Soken, Frinton-on-Sea CO13 0EE Tel: 0125 564373 — MB BS 1957 Lond. Prev: Cas. Off. W.m. Hosp.

CLARK, Gilbert Winston (retired) Hugo Bank, 13 West Drive, Porthcawl CF36 3LS Tel: 01656 783739 Email: eric@ebowers.netlineuk.net — MB BCh Wales 1951; BSc Wales 1946; FRCGP 1971, M 1958; DIH Soc. Apoth. Lond. 1966. Prev: Ho. Phys. Med. Unit & Paediat. Unit Welsh Nat. Sch. Med.

CLARK, Gillian Paris 140 High Street, Tillicoultry FK13 6DU — MB ChB 1991 Dundee; DRCOG 1994.

CLARK, Glenys Rosemary (retired) 4 Arethusa Way, Bisley, Woking GU24 9BZ Tel: 01483 481753 — MB ChB Bristol 1958; MRCS Eng. LRCP Lond. 1958; DObst. RCOG Lond. 1960; DTM & H Lond. 1962.

CLARK, Gordon 3 Green Lane, Roxwell, Chelmsford CM1 4NA — MB BS 1974 Lond.; BSc (Hons.) Lond. 1971, MB BS 1974; FFA RCS Eng. 1979. (Lond. Hosp.) Cons. Anaesth. Chelmsford Hosps. Socs: Assoc. Anaesth. Prev: Sen. Regist. Roy. Free Hosp.; Lect. Lond. Hosp. Med. Coll.; Regist. (Anaesth.) Lond. Hosp.

CLARK, Gordon Angus (retired) 70 Victoria Park Drive N., Glasgow G14 9PJ Tel: 0141 959 4004 — MB ChB Glas. 1956; MRCGP 1965; DObst RCOG 1959. Prev: GP Glas.

CLARK, Gordon Robert, MC (retired) Belvoir Cottage, Main St., Caythorpe, Nottingham NG14 7ED — MB ChB 1942 Ed.

CLARK, Graham Stuart Church Plain Surgery, Church Plain, Loddon, Norwich NR14 6EX Tel: 01508 520222 Fax: 01508 528579; The Old Sun Inn, Loddon Road, Broome, Bungay NR35 2RJ Tel: 01986 896724 — MB BChir 1988 Camb.; MA Camb. 1992, BA (Hons.) 1985, BSc (Hons.) 1983; LMSSA Lond. 1988. (Camb. Addenbrooke's) Clin. Asst. (A & E) Norf. & Norwich Hosp. Prev: SHO (A & E O & G& Paediat.) Norf. & Norwich Hosp.; SHO (Chest Med.) W. Norwich Hosp.

CLARK, Heather Jane — MB BS 1988 Lond.; FFAEM 2001; MSc (Sports Medicine) 2000; BSc (Hons.) Lond. 1985, MB BS 1988; MRCP Lond. 1996; DA 1991. (St. Mary's Hosp.) p/t Specialist Regist. Accid.s & Emerg., Hillingdon Hosp.; Club Med. Off., QPR football Club. Lond. Prev: Specialist Regist. A & E Char. Cross Hosp. Lond.; Specialist Regist. Accid & Emerg. Chelsea & W.minster; Specialist Regist. HEMS, Roy. Lond. Hosp.

CLARK, Helen Blackwood 21 Nethermains Road, Milngavie, Glasgow G62 6NL — MB ChB 1942 Glas. (Glas.) Prev: Jun. Asst. ENT Dept. Vict. Infirm. Glas.; Ho. Off. Mearnskirk EMS Hosp.

CLARK, Helen Elizabeth 3 Lucas Road, High Wycombe HP13 6QE — BM BS 1986 Nottm.; MRCP (UK) 1989; MRCGP 1996. (Univ. Nottm.) Prev: GP/Regist. Oxf. VTS.

CLARK, Helen Mary 25 Leigh Road, Street BA16 0HB Tel: 01458 442200 — MB BS 1964 Lond.; MRCS Eng. LRCP Lond. 1964. (Roy. Free) Cas. Off. Bridgwater Gen. Hosp. Socs: Med. Acupunct. Soc. Prev: Ho. Surg. Louth Co. Hosp. Dundalk; Ho. Phys. Roy. Free Hosp.

CLARK, Herbert, Capt. RAMC (retired) Fyvie, 90 Montrose Road, Arbroath DD11 5JW Tel: 01241 872749 — MB ChB 1946 Glas.; CIH Dund 1970. Prev: GP Arbroath.

CLARK, Hester Sarah Georgina 'Ard-Na-Greina', 88 Annaghmore Road, Castledawson, Magherafelt BT45 8DU — MB BCh BAO 1975 Belf.; MRCOG 1982, D 1977; FRCOG 1995. Cons. O & G Mid Ulster Hosp. Magherafelt.

CLARK, Hilary Lottie Maria 118 Coventry Road, Warwick CV34 5HH — BM 1994 Soton.

CLARK, Iain MacDonald (retired) 24 Hercus Loan, Musselburgh EH21 6AY Tel: 0131 665 3510 — MB ChB 1950 Ed.; DPM Ed. 1971; DObst RCOG 1954; MRCGP 1968. Prev: Sen. Regist. Roy. Edin. Hosp.

CLARK, Ian Western Isles Hospital, Macauley Road, Stornoway, Isle of Lewis HS1 2AF Tel: 01851704704 Fax: 01851 706240 Email: ian.clarke@wihb.scot.nhs.uk; Erisort House, Goathill Crescent, Stornoway, Isle of Lewis HS1 2TB Tel: 01851 704974 Email: driclark@hotmail.com — MB ChB 1972 St. And.; FRCPsych 1996, M 1977. Cons. Psychiat. W.. Isles HB; Med. Dir. W.. Isles HB. Prev: Cons. Psychiat. Cheadle Roy. Hosp.; Lect. (Psychiat.) Univ. Dundee.

CLARK, Ian Douglas East Surrey Health Authority, West Park Road, Horton Lane, Epsom KT19 8PH Tel: 01372 731111 Fax: 01372 729841 Email: ian.clark@esurrey-ha.sthames.nhs.uh; 147 Green Lanes, Ewell, Epsom KT19 9TN Tel: 020 8786 7207 — MB ChB 1982 Glas.; MFPHM RCP (UK) 1992. Dir. (Pub. Health & Informat.) E. Surrey HA. Prev: Cons. Pub. Health Med. Berks. HA & FHSA; Sen. Regist. (Pub. Health Med.) SE Thames RHA.

CLARK, Ian James (retired) Wilmar, Irthington, Carlisle CA4 6NJ — MB ChB Ed. 1962; DObst RCOG 1965. Prev: GP. Brampton.

CLARK, Ian Walker 47 East Green, Anstruther KY10 3AA — MB ChB 1946 Ed. (Ed.) Local Treasury Med. Off.

CLARK, Jacqueline Tracey Rose Cottage, Newsham, Richmond DL11 7RA — MB BS 1985 Lond.; MRCGP 1993. GP Armed Forces (Army).

CLARK, Mr James Alexander Lamb (retired) Rosewell, 15 Scott Crescent, Hillside, Montrose DD10 9EL Tel: 0167 483429 — MB ChB 1947 Ed.; ChM Ed. 1958, MB ChB 1947; FRCS Ed. 1952. Prev: Cons. Surg. Stracathro Hosp. Brechin.

CLARK, James Francis (retired) 28 Drumry Road, Clydebank G81 2LL — LRCP LRCS 1937 Ed.; LRCP LRCS Ed. LRFPS Glas. 1937.

CLARK, James Struthers (retired) 64 Princes Road, Brunton Park, Newcastle upon Tyne NE3 5AN Tel: 0191 236 4194 — MB BS 1951 Durh.

CLARK, James Timothy McHardy Broomhill Cottage, Harford Road, Harford, Ivybridge PL21 0JG — MB BS 1989 Lond. Specialist Regist. (Obstet. & Gyn.) Devon. Prev: Demonst. (Anat.) Univ. Birm.

CLARK, Jane Allison The Medical Centre, Lynfield Mount Hospital, Heights Lane, Bradford BD9 6DP Tel: 01274 494194 Fax: 01274 363206 — MB ChB 1988 Aberd.; MRCPsych 1995. Cons. Rehabil. Psychiat. Bradford Community and Ment. Health Trust. Prev: Regist. (Psychiat.) Airedale Gen. Hosp. Keighley W. Yorks.; SHO (Psychiat.) Train. Scheme Bradford HA; SHO (O & G) Wellington Area HB, NZ.

CLARK, Jane Erskine Willesborough Health Centre, Bentley Road, Willesborough, Ashford TN24 0HZ Tel: 01233 621626 Fax: 01233 622930; Field Cottage, Faversham Road, Boughton Aluph, Ashford TN25 4PQ — MB ChB 1980 Leeds; MRCGP 1985; DCCH RCP Ed. 1985; DRCOG 1984.

CLARK, Janet Mackenzie (retired) 69 Hallam Grange Crescent, Sheffield S10 4BB — MB ChB Ed. 1960. Prev: Assoc. Specialist (Histopath.) Sheff.

CLARK, Jason Charles Derwent Swanage Health Centre, Railway Station Approach, Station Road, Swanage BH19 1HB Tel: 01929 422231; 17 Walrond Road, Swanage BH19 1PB — MB BS 1982 Lond.; MRCGP 1987; DRCOG 1987; DCH RCP Lond. 1986. Prev: SHO (O & G) Poole Gen. Hosp.; SHO (Paediat.) Poole Gen. Hosp.; SHO (Geriat. Med.) Whipps Cross Hosp. Lond.

CLARK, Jean Elizabeth (retired) 6 Beechacres, Gloucester Road, Thornbury, Bristol BS35. 1BE — MB BS Lond. 1955; DObst RCOG 1958; FRCPCH 1997.

CLARK, Jean Mary Creighton, MBE, SSStJ Roseland, Clifton, Severn Stoke, Worcester WR8 9JF Tel: 01905 371259 — MB ChB St. And. 1943.

CLARK, Jeffrey Brian Brooklea Clinic, Wick Road, Bristol BS4 4HU Tel: 0117 971 1211 Fax: 0117 972 3370 — BM 1981 Soton.; MRCGP 1985; DRCOG 1983. GP Bristol.

CLARK, Jennifer Grace Thornhill, Alnmouth Road, Alnwick NE66 2QG Tel: 01665 602464 — MB ChB 1962 Ed.; DCH RCPS Glas. 1971; DObst RCOG 1965. (Ed.) Prev: SCMO (Family Plann.) Albion Rd. Clinic N. Shields.

CLARK, Jeremy Stuart 7 Oakland Drive, Robertsbridge TN32 5EX — MB BS 1993 Lond.

CLARK, Joan Elizabeth 9 Bonhard Road, Scone, Perth PH2 6QL — MB ChB 1976 Ed.

CLARK, Joan Margaret Linnmill Cottage, By Clackmannan, Alloa FK10 3PY — MB ChB 1980 Aberd. GP Alloa.

CLARK, Joan Patricia 11 The Woodlands, Cottingham HU16 5RP Tel: 01482 841490 — MB ChB 1977 Ed.; DRCOG 1979. Prev: GP. Princ. GP Princ.

CLARK, Johanna Pamela, Squadron Ldr. RAF Med. Br. (retired) The Surgery, 6 Middlerich Road, Sandbach CW11 1DL Tel: 01270 759305 — MB BS Lond. 1989. Prev: Med. Off. RAF.

CLARK, Mr John Glan Clwyd District General NHS Hospital Trust, Rhyl LL18 5UJ Tel: 01745 583910 Fax: 01745 583143; Rhondda, 57 Orme View Drive, Prestatyn LL19 9PG Tel: 01745 886739 Fax: 01745 886739 — MB ChB 1968 Liverp.; ChM Liverp. 1981; FRCS Eng. 1973. Cons. Surg. Glan Clwyd Hosp. Conwy & Denbignshire NHS Trust; Hon. Clin. Teach. Univ. Wales Coll. Med. Socs: Brit. Soc. Gastroenterol.; Brit.Assoc. Surg. Oncol.; Assoc. Upper Gastro Intestinal Surg.s.

CLARK, John Adrian Rutherford House, Langley Park, Durham DH7 9XD Tel: 0191 373 1386 Fax: 0191 373 4288; Hawkshill House, Cornsay Colliery, Durham DH7 9BP Tel: 0191 373 4133 — MB BS 1979 Newc.

CLARK, John Adrian 16 Coast Road, North Shields NE29 8ND — MB BS 1994 Newc.; BDS Newc. 1988.

CLARK, John Alexander (retired) 44 marchbank Gardens, Paisley PA1 3JD Tel: 0141 883 3927 — MB ChB Glas. 1950. Prev: Clin. Asst. Johnstone Hosp.

CLARK, John Alexander Erskine (retired) 17 Selsey Avenue, Southsea PO4 9QL Tel: 01705 731363 — BA, MB BChir Camb. 1951; MRCGP 1966. Prev: GP S.sea.

CLARK, John Chalmers Department of Forensic Pathology, University of Sheffield, Medico-Legal Centre, Watery St., Sheffield S3 7ES Tel: 0114 273 8721 Fax: 0114 279842 Email: forensic.path@sheffield.ac.uk; 29 Botanical Road, Sheffield S11 8RP — MB ChB 1975 Aberd.; FRCPath 1994, M 1982; DFM 1991. Sen. Lect. (Forens. Path.) Univ. Sheff. Socs: (Sec.) Brit. Assn. Forens.

Med.; Assn. Clin. Pathol. Prev: Sen. Lect. (Forens. Med. & Sci.) Univ. Glas.; Lect. (Forens. Path.) Univ. Sheff.; Lect. (Path.) Univ. Aberd.

CLARK, John David Alastair Department of Medicine, West Suffolk Hospital, Bury St Edmunds IP33 Tel: 01284 713000 — MD 1989 Glas.; MB ChB 1979; FRCP Glas. 1993, FRCP Lond. 1996; MRCP (UK) 1982. Cons. Phys. W. Suff. Hosp. Bury St. Edmonds; Grad. Course Supervisor, Clin. Sch., Univ. of Camb. Socs: Brit. Diabetic Assn. & Soc. Endocrinol. Prev: Lect. (Med.) & Hon. Sen. Regist. Univ. Bristol; Regist. (Med.) Addenbrooke's Hosp. Camb.; SHO (Med.) Stobhill Hosp. Glas.

CLARK, John David Farrimond 63 Cinderhill Lane, Grenoside, Sheffield S35 8NG — MB ChB 1963 Liverp. Med. Asst. Nat. Blood Transfus. Serv. Lancaster. Socs: Fell. Manch. Med. Soc. Prev: Regist. (Path.) Withington Hosp. Manch. & Roy. Lancaster Infirm.; Regist. Nat. Blood Transfus. Serv. Manch.

CLARK, John Douglas 21 Radford Park Road, Plymstock, Plymouth PL9 9DN Tel: 01752 402150 — MRCS Eng. LRCP Lond. 1957; MFFP 1993. SCMO (Family Plann.) Plymouth Community Trust NHS Serv. Prev: GP Plymouth.

CLARK, John Edward Marshes, Butt Lane, Snaith, Goole DN14 9DY Tel: 01405 860111 Fax: 01405 863901 — MB ChB 1974 Sheff.

CLARK, John Howard West Kirby Health Centre, Grange Road, Wirral CH48 4HZ Tel: 0151 625 9171 Fax: 0151 625 9171 — MB ChB 1975 Liverp. (Liverpool) Med. Supt. W. Kirby Resid.ial Sch. Wirral; Bd. Mem., Bebington & W. Wirral PCG. Socs: BMA. Prev: Dep. Police Surg. Merseyside Police Force.

CLARK, John Martin Savernake, The Lanes, Tetney, Grimsby DN36 5LX Tel: 01472 816427 Fax: 01472 816427 Email: john-m.clark@virgin.net; savernake, The Lanes, Tetney, Grimsby DN36 5LX Tel: 01472 816427 Fax: 01472 816427 Email: john-m.clarke@virgin.net — MB ChB 1972 Bristol; BSc Bristol 1969, MB ChB 1972; FFA RCS Eng. 1976. (Bristol University) Cons. Anaesth. Grimsby HA. Socs: Roy. Coll. Anaesth. (Fell.); Assn. of Anaesth.s (Full Mem.); Pain Soc. of GB & Irel. Prev: Cons. Anaesth. N.E Lincs Hosp. Trust.

CLARK, John Victor (retired) Holly House, 7 Church Road, Spratton, Northampton NN6 8HR Tel: 01604 847350 Fax: 01604 841926 — MRCS Eng. LRCP Lond. 1963; BSc Lond. 1960, MB BS 1963; FRCPath 1983, M 1971; DObst RCOG 1965. Prev: Cons. Pathol. N.ampton Gen. Hosp.

CLARK, Jon Roy Hurst End House, Hurst Common Lane, Sheffield S6 1EX — MB ChB 1993 Sheff.

CLARK, Julia Elizabeth Department of Paediatrics, Newcastle General Hospital, Westgate Road, Newcastle upon Tyne NE4 6BE Tel: 0191 273 8811 Email: julia.clark@nuth.northy.nhs.uk; Garden House, Throckley Hall, Coach Road, Throckley, Newcastle upon Tyne NE15 9RH Tel: 0191 264 6226 — BM BS 1987 Nottm.; MRCP (UK) 1991; DCH RCP Lond. 1990. (Nottm.) Cons. in Paediatric Infec. Dis.s and Immunol., Newc. Gen. Hosp, Newc. Socs: Roy. Coll. Paediat. and Child Health; Europ. Soc. of Paediatric and Infec. Dis.s.

CLARK, Julia Rosemary 36 Christchurch Road, Norwich NR2 2AE — MB BS Lond. 1966; MRCPsych. 1982; DPM Eng. 1979; DCH Eng. 1969. Assoc. Specialist (Psychiat.) Hellesdon Hosp. Norwich Norf. Ment. Health Care NHS Trust. Socs: Assn. Cognitive Analytic Therapists.

CLARK, Julian David Tel: 01472 342325 Fax: 01472 251739 — MB ChB 1985 Leic.; DGM; MRCGP 1989; DGP RCP Lond. 1987.

CLARK, Juliet Maynard Plas Newydd, Rectory Road, Crumlin, Newport NP1 — MB ChB 1958 Bristol. (Bristol.)

CLARK, Mrs June Ritchie The Health Centre, Victoria Road, Leven KY8 4ET Tel: 01333 425656 Fax: 01333 422249; Swainsfield, Star of Markinch, Glenrothes KY7 6LE — MB ChB 1979 Dundee.

CLARK, Karen Helen The Manse, Stenness, Stromness KW16 3HH — MB ChB 1993 Aberd.

CLARK, Kathryn Flat 1/1, 7 Clavering Street E., Paisley PA1 2PU — MB ChB 1998 Glas.; MB ChB Glas 1998.

CLARK, Mr Kenneth 11 Masonfield Crescent, Newton Stewart DG8 6QS — MB ChB 1951 Ed.; MB ChB (Hons.) Ed. 1951; FRCS Ed. 1957; DMRD Eng. 1970. (Ed.) Cons. Radiol. Stafford Gp. Hosps. Socs: W Midl. Surg. Soc. & Midl. Urol. Club. Prev: Cons. Surg. Birm. RHB; Surg. Regist. W.. Infirm. Glas.; SHO Profess. Surg. Unit Roy. Infirm. Edin.

CLARK, Kenneth Andrew Castle Street Surgery, 67 Castle Street, Salisbury SP1 3SP Tel: 01722 322726 Fax: 01722 410315; Malvern House, 125 Castle Road, Salisbury SP1 3RP Tel: 01722 323113 Fax: 01722 410315 Email: kenclark@castlesurg.clara.net — MB BS 1974 Lond.; DRCOG 1979. Chair S. Wilts. PCG; Police Surg. Wilts. Constab.; Med. Off. Wilts. Fire Brig. Socs: Assn. Police Surg. Prev: Resid. Med. Off. Armidale & New Eng. Hosp. Australia & Ryde Hosps.ydney Australia.

CLARK, Kenneth George Alfred Guys Drug Research Unit, 6 Newcomen St., London SE1 1YR; 7 Dry Bank Court, Dry Bank Road, Tonbridge TN10 3BP Tel: 01732 355602 Fax: 01732 355602 Email: kennethcark@doctors.org.uk — MB BS Lond. 1960; MD Lond. 1975; MRCS Eng. LRCP Lond. 1960; FRCPath. 1981, M 1969. (King's Coll. Hosp.) Indep. Cons Haemat.; Hon. Cons. Haemat. Bethlem & Maudsley NHS Trust. Socs: Brit. Soc. Haematol.; Assn. Clin. Pathol. Prev: Cons. Haemat. Guy's Hosp.; Sen. Lect. Dept. Haemat. King's Coll. Hosp. Med. Sch.; Cons. Haemat. King's Coll. Hosp.

CLARK, Laura Anne 52 Esher Road, Hersham, Walton-on-Thames KT12 4LG — MB BS 1989 Lond.; BSc Lond. 1986; MRCP (UK) 1995.

CLARK, Leon Jude 62 Vicars Hall Gardens, Boothstown, Manchester M28 1HU — MB BS 1997 Lond.

CLARK, Lesley (retired) 3 Bryn y Coed, Llanfair Caereinion, Welshpool SY21 0SQ Tel: 01938 811098 Email: htonyhalliday@aol.com — MB ChB 1963 Liverp.; MSc (Med. Audiol.) Manch. 1991. Prev: SCMO (Audiol.) St. Helens & Knowsley HA.

CLARK, Liane Chestnut House, Broad Drove W., Tydd St Giles, Wisbech PE13 5NU Tel: 01945 871025 Fax: 01945 871030 — MB BS 1984 Lond.; MSc Community Med. Lond. 1989; MFFP 1993; MFPHM RCP (UK) 1991; DRCOG 1987. (Middlx.) Clin. Asst. (Genitourin. Med.) Stoke Mandeville, Milton Keynes Gen. & N.ampton Gen. Hosps. Prev: SCMO (Family Plann.) Milton Keynes HA; SHO (O & G) Roy. N.., Whittington Hosps. Lond. & Ch.ill Hosp. Oxf.; SHO (Accid. Serv.) John Radcliffe Hosp. Oxf.

CLARK, Lindsay Ann Old Mill Surgery, 100 Old Mill Road, Uddingston, Glasgow G71 7JB Tel: 01698 817219; Juniper Gate, 12 Anderson Court, Dunblane FK15 9BE — MB ChB 1984 Glas.; MB ChB Glas. l984; MRCGP 1988.

CLARK, Lisa-Jayne 8 Randall Road, Chandlers Ford, Eastleigh SO53 5AL Tel: 01703 253600 — MB BS 1997 Lond.; BSc. London 1994. (Char. Cross & Westm. Med. Sch.) SHO Med., Roy. Bournemouth Hosp., Bournemouth; Ho. Off. Med. W. Middlx. Univ. Hosp. Prev: Char. Cross & W.m. Med. Sch.; Ho. Off. Surg. N. Devon Dist. Hosp. Barnstaple.

CLARK, Lorna Anne Holly House, Church Road, Spratton, Northampton NN6 8HR Tel: 01604 847350 — MB ChB 1966 Ed.

CLARK, Louise 10 Satley Gardens, Sunderland SR3 1AL Tel: 0191 520 3282 — MB BS 1997 Newc.

CLARK, Louise Jayne Beatson Inst. for Cancer Research, Garscube Est., Switchback Road, Bearsden, Glasgow G61 1BD Tel: 0141 942 9361; 83 Hawthorn Avenue, Bearsden, Glasgow G61 3NF — MB ChB 1982 Leeds; FRCS (ENT) Ed. 1987. Prev: Clin. Research Fell. Beatson Inst. Cancer Glas.; Regist. (Otolaryngol.) Gartnavel Hosp. & W.. Infirm. Glas.

CLARK, Malcolm Brian Plas Newydd, Rectory Road, Crumlin, Newport NP1 — MB ChB 1959 Bristol; DObst RCOG 1962.

CLARK, Malcolm Walker Gartcosh, 6 Dryburn View, Durham DH1 5AP Tel: 0191 386 4776 — MB ChB 1947 Glas.

CLARK, Margaret (retired) Carrick, Abbotsford Road, North Berwick EH39 5DB — MB ChB 1956 Ed.; DObst RCOG 1958.

CLARK, Margaret Ann 17 Glenmarsh Way, Formby, Liverpool L37 8DX — MB BS 1996 Newc.

CLARK, Margaret Mary (retired) 55 Parkside Drive, Edgware HA8 8JU Tel: 020 8958 4627 Fax: 020 8958 4627 — MB ChB Leeds 1959; FFA RCS Eng. 1966; DA Eng. 1962. Volun. Acupunc., Cherry Lodge Cancer Care, Elmbank Barnet Herts, EN5 5HD. Prev: Cons. Anaesth. Barnet Dist. HA.

CLARK, Marguerite Elisabeth Whitchurch Health Centre, Armada Road, Bristol BS14 0SU Tel: 01275 835625 Fax: 01275 540035; 9 Russell Road, Westbury Park, Bristol BS6 7UB Tel: 0117 942 2539 — MB BS 1974 Lond.; MRCS Eng. LRCP Lond. 1973; DRCOG 1976. (St. Marys)

CLARK, Maria 18 Temple Fortune Lane, London NW11 7UD Tel: 020 8455 5226 — MB BChir 1989 Camb.; MRCP (UK) 1991. Sen. Regist. (Paediat. & Paediat. Neurol.) Gt. Ormond St. & Univ. Coll. Hosps. Lond. Prev: Sen. Regist. (Paediat.) St Mary's & Centr. Middlx. Hosps.; Regist. (Paediat.) Qu. Charlottes & Hammersmith Hosps.; SHO (Paediat.) Gt. Ormond St. Lond.

CLARK, Marianna Irene Hanka 16 Lansdown Place E., Bath BA1 5ET Tel: 01225 310983 — MB ChB 1947 Ed. (Ed.)

CLARK, Marinatu Onaiwu 90 Manor Farm Road, Wembley HA0 1BW — MB BS 1979 Lond.

CLARK, Marion Lithgow 47 East Green, Anstruther KY10 3AA — MB ChB 1949 Ed. (Ed.)

CLARK, Martin Clifford Stag Medical Centre, 162 Wickersley Road, Rotherham S60 4JW Tel: 01709 379285 Fax: 01709 820431; 1 Hallam Road, Moorgate, Rotherham S60 3BT — MB ChB 1969 Birm.; MB ChB (Hons.) Birm. 1969; BSc (Hons.) Birm. 1969; DObst RCOG 1971. (Birm.) Hon. Lect. (Gen. Pract.) Sheff. Univ. Prev: Local Radio Doctor; SHO. (Surg.) Friarage Hosp. N.allerton; Ho. Off. Profess. Med. Unit Qu. Eliz. Hosp. Birm.

CLARK, Martin Fraser 8 Balmachie Road, Carnoustie DD7 7SR — MB ChB 1996 Dundee.

CLARK, Martin Hugh 35 Rhymney Street, Cardiff CF24 4DH — MB BCh 1993 Wales.

CLARK, Mary Pauline 153 Blythe Road, London W14 0HL — MB BS 1976 Lond.; DCH RCP Lond. 1983; DRCOG 1981. GP Lond.

CLARK, Mat Halley (retired) 24 Horwood Avenue, Derby DE23 6NX Tel: 01332 342139 — MB ChB Liverp. 1945; DObst RCOG 1948. Prev: GP Derby.

CLARK, Matthew James 374 Psalter Lane, Banner Cross, Sheffield S11 8UW — MB ChB 1997 Leeds.

CLARK, Matthew Lucas Cranleigh Health Centre, 18 High Street, Cranleigh GU6 8AE Tel: 01483 273951 Fax: 01483 275755 — MB BS 1991 Lond.; MB BS (Distinc.) Lond. 1991; BSc (Hons.) Lond. 1988; MRCGP 1995; DFFP 1994; DRCOG 1994. (Lond. Hosp.) Socs: MIA. Prev: Trainee GP E. Surrey VTS; SHO (Paediat., Psychiat. & O & G) E. Surrey Hosp.

CLARK, Matthew Paul Alexander 3A Loom Lane, Radlett WD7 8AA — MB BS 1996 Lond.

CLARK, Michael David Anthony 86 Park Road, Hindley, Wigan WN2 3RX Tel: 01942 258240 — MB ChB 1995 Manch. (Univ. Manch.) SHO (Urol.), Stepping Hill Hosp., Stockport. Socs: BMA. Prev: SHO Rotat. (A & E Med.) Roy. Oldham Hosp. Manch.; Ho. Off. (Surg.) Roy. Albert Edwd. Hosp. Wigan; Ho. Off. (Med.) Qu. Pk. Hosp. Blackburn.

CLARK, Michael John Alresford Group Surgery, Station Road, Alresford SO24 9JL Tel: 01962 732345 Fax: 01962 736034 — MB 1969 Camb.; BChir 1968; MRCGP 1974; DObst RCOG 1970. (St. Geo.) GP Trainer Winchester VTS. Prev: Ho. Phys. & Ho. Surg. Roy. Hants. Co. Hosp. Winchester.

CLARK, Michael Llewellyn Princess Grace Hospital, 45-52 Nottingham Place, London W1M 3FD Tel: 020 7486 1234; 7 Sherwood Park Road, Sutton SM1 2SQ Tel: 020 8642 5993 — MB BS 1958 Lond.; MD Lond. 1970; FRCP Lond. 1975, M 1960. (St. Geo.) Hon. Sen. Lect. St. Bart. Med. Coll. Lond. Socs: Brit. Soc. Gastroenterol. & Assn. Phys. Prev: Sen. Regist. (Med.) St. Geo. Hosp. Lond.; Research Asst. Univ. Pennsylvania Hosp., USA; Ho. Off. St. Geo. Hosp. Lond.

CLARK, Michael Richard Simon Fairfields, 16 Arkwright Road, Marple, Stockport SK6 7DE — MB BS 1979 Lond.

CLARK, Moyna Gladys North Lakeland Health Care, Central Clinic, Victorial Place, Carlisle CA1 1HM Tel: 01228 603200; Applegarth, Irthington, Carlisle CA6 4NN Tel: 016977 3121 Fax: 016977 3121 Email: moyna.clark@btinternet.com — MB ChB 1967 Leeds; DCH RCPS Glas. 1984; Cert. Family Plann. JCC 1975. (Leeds) Assoc. Specialist, Designated Doctor, Child Protec. for N. Cumbria; Police Surg. Child Abuse; Lect. Child Protec. Socs: BMA; Assoc. Mem. BPA; Brit. Assn. Study & Preven. Child Abuse & Neglect. Prev: Clin. Med. Off. (Comm. Child Health), Cumbria; Clin. Research Asst., (Cardio-Vasc. & Nephrol.), Cumbld. Infirm.; Clin. Med. Off. Derbysh. AHA.

CLARK, Natasha School House, Combe Hay, Bath BA2 7EG; Flat 13, Conn Aught House, Queen Alexandra Hospital, Cosham, Portsmouth PO6 3LY — BM 1996 Soton.; BSc (Hons) Soton. 1995. (Southampton) Med. SHO Rotat. Qu. Alexandra Hosp. Portsmouth. Socs: BMA; MDU.

CLARK, Neale Hudson Dourado and Partners, Maybush Medical Centre, Belle Isle Health Park, Portobello Road, Wakefield WF1 5PN Tel: 01924 328132 Fax: 01924 328130; 27 Walton Station Lane, Sandal, Wakefield WF2 6HP Tel: 01924 328162 Fax: 01924 328130 — MB BCh 1973 Wales; MRCGP 1978; T(GP) 1991; DCH Eng. 1980; DRCOG 1977; Cert JCC Lond. 1977. (Welsh Nat. Sch. of Med.) Clin. Asst. (Palliat. Care) Wakefield Hospice. Socs: (Vice Pres.) Wakefield Dyslexia Assn.

CLARK, Nicola Louise Applegarth, Irthington, Carlisle CA6 4NN Tel: 016977 3121 Email: clark@drnicky.freeserve.co.uk — BM BS 1994 Nottm.; BMedSci Nottm. 1992. Specialist Regist. N. Thames Rotat. (Paediat.). Socs: RCPCH. Prev: Ho. Off. (Med.) St. Geo. Hosp. Lincoln; Ho. Off. (Surg.) Furness Gen. Hosp.; SHO (Paediat.) City Gen. Hosp. Stoke-on-Trent.

CLARK, Nigel Andrew Denis The Surgery, Branksomewood Road, Fleet GU51 4JX Tel: 01252 613624 Fax: 01252 816489 — MB BS 1984 Lond.; MRCGP 1989; DRCOG 1988. (Char. Cross Hosp.) GP; Medico-Legal Cons. Socs: BMA; Brit. Assn. Sport & Med. Prev: Trainee GP Havant VTS; SHO (Paediat.) St. Marys Hosp. Portsmouth; SHO (Psychiat.) St. Jas. Hosp. Portsmouth.

CLARK, Norman MacDonald 2 Ronaldshaw Park, Ayr KA7 2TJ Tel: 01292 263534 — MB ChB 1966 St. And.; MRCPsych 1972; DPM Ed. & Glas. 1971; DObst RCOG 1968. Cons. Forens. Psychiat. Douglas Inch Centre Glas.

CLARK, Norman Stuart (retired) Kinnord, Partridge Road, Brockenhurst SO42 7RZ Tel: 01590 623695 — MB ChB Aberd. 1936; BSc Aberd. 1933, MD (Hons.) 1955; FRCP Lond. 1964, M 1945; MRCP Ed., 1962; DCH Eng. 1939. Prev: Reader (Child Health) Univ. Aberd.

CLARK, Pamela Jobling 21 Louth Road, Sheffield S11 7AU — MB ChB 1984 Sheff.; MB ChB Sheff. l984.

CLARK, Patricia Mary Rubie 17 Walrond Road, Swanage BH19 1PB — MB BS 1983 Lond.; BSc Lond. 1981; MRCP (UK) 1990; DCH RCP Lond. 1986. Staff Community Paediat. E. Dorset. Socs: MRCPCH. Prev: Regist. (Paediat.) Poole Gen. Hosp.; SHO (Paediat.) Poole Gen. Hosp.; SHO (Paediat.) Dorset Co. Hosp. Dorchester & Soton. Gen. Hosp.

CLARK, Paul 26C Montgomerie Street, Ardrossan KA22 8EQ — MB ChB 1978 Glas.

CLARK, Peter 6 Crown Terrace, Dowanhill, Glasgow G12 9HA — MB ChB 1986 Glas.; BSc Glas. 1983, MB ChB 1986; MRCP (UK) 1990.

CLARK, Peter Alan (retired) Boreas House, 66A North Road, Southwold IP18 6BH Tel: 01502 724604 — MB BS 1960 Lond.; MRCS Eng. LRCP Lond. 1957; FRCPath 1976, M 1963. Prev: Cons. Haemat. Barnet HA.

CLARK, Peter Irving Clatterbridge Centre for Oncology, Clatterbridge Road, Bebington, Wirral CH63 4JY Tel: 0151 334 1155 Fax: 0151 482 7675; Glenelg, Park W., Lower Heswall, Wirral CH60 9JE Tel: 0151 342 9403 Fax: 0151 342 9478 — MB BS 1981 Lond.; MA Camb. 1982; MD Lond. 1989; FRCP Lond. 1995. Cons. Phys. Med. Oncol. Clatterbridge Centre for Oncol.; Med. Dir. Clatterbridge Centre for Oncol.; Chairm. Clatterbridge Cancer Research Trust. Prev: Imperial Cancer Research Fund Fell. St. Bart. Hosp. Lond.

CLARK, Peter John 34 Toberwine Street, Glenarm, Ballymena BT44 0AP — MB BCh BAO 1989 Belf.

CLARK, Mr Philip Beckford (retired) The Grove, Thorner, Leeds LS14 3DN Tel: 0113 289 2228 — MB BChir 1951 Camb.; MA Camb. 1952, MD 1962, MChir 1963; FRCS Eng. 1956. Prev: Cons. Urol. Surg. Gen. Infirm., St. Jas. Hosp. & Seacroft Hosp. Leeds.

CLARK, Raymond Martin 11 The Avenue, Stone ST15 8DG — MB BS 1967 Lond.; FFA RCS Eng. 1973. (Roy. Free)

CLARK, Rebecca Sandringham Practice, Sandringham Road Health Centre, Sandringham Road, Intake, Doncaster DN2 5JH Tel: 01302 321521 Fax: 01302 761792 — MB ChB 1993 Birm.; ChB Birm. 1993.

CLARK, Rebecca South Park Surgery, 19 St Catherines, Lincoln LN5 8LW — MB ChB 1993 Manch.; DRCOG 1995; DCH 1997; MRCPG 1997. GP Princip.

CLARK, Richard 243 Mottram Road, Stalybridge SK15 2RF Tel: 014576 3263 — MRCS Eng. LRCP Lond. 1953; DObst RCOG 1958.

(Leeds) Assoc. MRCGP; Clin. Asst. (Med.) Tameside Gen. Hosp. Ashton-under-Lyne. Socs: BMA. Prev: Ho. Surg. & Ho. Phys. Doncaster Roy. Infirm.; Ho. Obstetr. Green Bank Matern. Hosp. Darlington; SHO Obst. Preston Roy. Infirm.

CLARK, Richard Elles University Department of Haematology, 2nd Floor, Duncan Building, Royal Liverpool Hospital, Prescot St., Liverpool L7 8XP Tel: 0151 706 4344 Fax: 0151 706 5810 — MB BS 1978 Lond.; MA Camb. 1982, BA 1975; MD Lond. 1986; FRCP Lond.1994; MRCP (UK) 1981; MRCPath 1987; FRCPath 1996. (Westm.) Cons.(Haemat.); Reader (Haemat.) Univ. of Liverp. Prev: Sen. Lect. (Haemat.) Univ. Wales Coll. Med.; Sen. Regist. (Haemat.) S. Glam. HA; Leukaemia Research Fund Train. Fell. Welsh Nat. Sch. Med. Cardiff.

CLARK, Richard Ferguson 1 Elms Avenue, Eastbourne BN21 3DN Tel: 01323 411017 — LRCP LRCS 1940 Ed.; LRCP LRCS Ed., LRFPS Glas. 1940; LDS RCS Ed. 1939. (Ed.) Socs: BDA; BMA.

CLARK, Richard Russell Burnside House, Howwood, Johnstone PA9 1DG — MB ChB 1998 Glas.; MB ChB Glas 1998.

CLARK, Mr Robert Charles, Surg. Capt. RN (retired) 52 Mancroft Avenue, Stubbington, Fareham PO14 2BG Tel: 01329 664062 — MB BS 1957 Lond.; FRCS Ed. 1968. Cons. Orthop. Surg. RN.

CLARK, Robert Lindsay 1 Pennine Grove, Cross Stone Road, Todmorden OL14 8AU — MB ChB 1959 Ed.; MFOM RCP Lond. 1979; DIH Soc. Apoth. Lond. 1968. Dir. Tynestead Ltd. Rochdale.

CLARK, Robert Nigel Wake Les Forfaitures, La Ruette des Forfaitures, Castel GY5 7XS; 10A The Strand, St Peter Port, Guernsey GY1 1AY — MB BCh 1994 Wales; BDS (Lond.) 1974; FDS RCS UK 1980; FRCS Ed. 1998. (Guy's Hospital/Uni.Wales.Coll.Med) Cons. Oral & Maxillofacial Surg. HM. Forces. Socs: Fell.Roy.Coll.Surg.Eng.; Fell.Roy.Coll.Surg.Ed.; Fell.Roy.Soc.Med. Prev: Sen.Regist.Morriston.Hosps.wansea.

CLARK, Robert Stewart Scarborough Hospital, Scarborough YO12 6QL; Candler House, 73 Garth End Road, West Ayton, Scarborough YO13 9JJ — MB ChB 1976 Glas.; MRCP (UK) 1979; FRCPS Glas. 1991. Cons. Phys. ScarBoro. Hosp. Socs: Brit. Cardiac Soc. Prev: Lect. (Med.) Ninewells Hosp. Dundee; Regist. (Cardiol.) Glas. Roy. Infirm.; Regist. (Med.) Vict. Infirm. Glas.

CLARK, Mr Robert Vaughan (retired) 14 Howard Place, St Andrews KY16 9HL — MB ChB 1957 St. And.; FRCS Ed. 1964. Hon. Sen. Lect. (Anat.) Univ. St. And. Prev: Cons. Surg. St. Bernard's Hosp. Gibraltar.

CLARK, Robert William (retired) 10 The Mill, Mill Green, Turvey, Bedford MK43 8ET Tel: 01234 888896 — MB BS 1955 Lond.; FRCGP 1989, M 1974; DObst RCOG 1958.

CLARK, Robin John Respiratory Centre, St Mary's Hospital, Portsmouth PO3 6AD Tel: 02392 286000 Fax: 02392 866735 — MB BS 1978 Lond.; MB BS (Hons.) Lond. 1978; FRCP Lond. 1995; MRCP (UK) 1983. (King's Coll. Hosp.) Cons. Phys. Gen. & Respirat. Med. Portsmouth Hosps. NHS Trust. Socs: Brit. Thorac. Soc. & Amer. Thorac. Soc. Prev: Cons. Phys. Roy. Hopsital Haslar; SR RNH Haslar; Hon. Sen. Regist. Hammersmith Hosp. Lond.

CLARK, Roderic Lawrance Herschel Medical Centre, 45 Osborne Street, Slough SL1 1TT Tel: 01753 520643 Fax: 01753 554964; 95 Rogers Lane, Stoke Poges, Slough SL2 4LP — MB BS 1985 Lond.; BSc Biochem. Lond. 1981, MB BS 1985; MRCGP 1988; DRCOG 1987. (Char. Cross) Prev: Trainee GP Bath VTS; Ho. Phys. Char. Cross Hosp. Lond.; Ho. Surg. W. Middlx. Univ. Hosp.

CLARK, Roger Thornton Medical Centre, 4 Craven Avenue, Bradford BD13 3LG Tel: 01274 832110 Fax: 01274 831694 — MB ChB 1971 St. And.

CLARK, Roger David Rothesay Health Centre, Townhead, Rothesay PA20 9JL Tel: 01700 502290 Fax: 01700 505692; Mount View, 42 Mount Stuart Road, Rothesay PA20 9EB Tel: 01700 505362 — MB ChB 1991 Leic.; MRCGP 1995. (Leicester)

CLARK, Roger John Mount View Practice, London Street Medical Centre, London Street, Fleetwood FY7 6HD Tel: 01253 873312 Fax: 01253 873130 — MB ChB 1978 Manch.; MRCGP 1986; DRCOG 1985; DCH RCP Lond. 1984. Socs: Small Pract. Assn. Prev: Sen. Med. Off. RAF Binbrook.

CLARK, Roland Arthur Department of Medicine, Ninewells Hospital, Dundee DD1 9SY Tel: 01382 660111; 4 Lawhead Road E., St Andrews KY16 8ND Tel: 01334 477025 — MB ChB 1965 Ed.; BSc (Hons.) Ed. 1962; FRCP Glas. 1995; FRCP Lond. 1993; FRCP Ed. 1981; MRCP (UK) 1971. (Ed.) Cons. Phys. King's Cross & Ninewells Hosps. Dundee; Hon. Sen. Lect. & Head (Respirat. Dis.) Univ. Dundee. Socs: Brit. Thorac. Soc.; Amer. Thoracic Soc.; Eur. Respirat. Soc. Prev: Cons. Phys. Lodge Moor & N.. Gen. Hosps. Sheff.; Regist. (Cardiol. & Gen. Med.) Roy. Infirm. Edin.; Research Schol. (Respirat. Dis.) City Hosp. Edin.

CLARK, Ronald George (retired) 71 Wilson Street, Perth PH2 0EY Tel: 01738 623649 — MB ChB St. And. 1956; DObst RCOG 1960. Prev: Ho. Surg. Craigtoun Matern. Hosp. St. And.

CLARK, Professor Ronald George Brookline, 2 Chesterwood Drive, Sheffield S10 5DU Tel: 0114 266 3601 — MB ChB 1956 Aberd.; MD Sheff. 1996; FRCS Glas. 1997; FRCS Eng. 1982; FRCS Ed. 1960. Emerit. Prof. Surg. Sheff.; Scientif. Governor Brit. Nutrit. Foundat.; Dep. Chairm. Rev. Bd. Overseas Qualified Practitioners. Socs: (Vice-Pres.) Europ. Soc. Parenteral & Enteral Nutrit.; Counc. Mem. & Hon. Mem. Nutrit. Soc.; Assn. Surg. Prev: Dean Univ. Sheff. Fac. Med. & Dent.; Pro Vice-Chancellor Univ. Sheff.

CLARK, Ronald McDonald New Milton Health Centre, Spencer Road, New Milton BH25 6EN Tel: 01425 621188 Fax: 01425 620646 — MB ChB 1973 Glas.; MRCGP 1977; DObst RCOG 1975. (Glasgow) Prev: Ho. Off. (Surg.) Stirling Roy. Infirm.; Ho. Off. (Med.) Stobhill Hosp. Glas.; Trainee Gen. Pract. Bath Vocational Train. Scheme.

CLARK, Rose Marion 8 Oxford Terrace, Edinburgh EH4 1PX — MB ChB 1956 Ed. Med. Off. (Child Health & Family Plann.) Fife Health Bd. Prev: Ho. Phys. S.field Hosp. Edin. & Roy. Infirm. Edin.

CLARK, Ross Doctors Residency, Royal Preston Hospital, Shoroe Green Lane, Fulwood, Preston PR2 9HT — MB ChB 1988 Ed.

CLARK, Sarah Lazy End, 25b Newark Road, Windlesham GU20 6NE — MB BS 1993 Lond.; MRGCP 1997. (King's College Hospital Medical School) GP Retainee, Ash Vale Health Centre, Surrey. Socs: BMA; MDU.

CLARK, Sarah Jane 30 Kingscroft Road, Leatherhead KT22 7BU Tel: 01372 375800; 67 Holly Bush Lane, Hampton TW12 2QY Tel: 020 8979 0206 — BM BS 1991 Nottm. Clin. Research Fell. Inst. of Liver Studies Kings Coll. Hosp. Lond.

CLARK, Shane Patrick 33 Kirkhill Avenue, Haslingden, Rossendale BB4 6UB — MB ChB 1998 Birm.

CLARK, Sheena Helen Riverside Surgery, Water Street Health centre, Water St., Port Talbot SA12 6LF Tel: 01639 891376; 98 Penshannel, Neath Abbey, Neath SA10 6PP Tel: 01792 815532 — MB BS 1991 Newc.; MRCGP 1996; DRCOG 1995.

CLARK, Sheila Anne Dept. Of Anaesthesia, Blackburn Royal Infirmary, Blackburn BB2 3LR; 254 Sharoe Green Lane N., Fulwood, Preston PR2 9HD — MB ChB 1967 Glas.; FRCPCH; FRCP; MRCP (U.K.) 1972; DObst RCOG 1969; DCH Eng. 1970. (Glas.) Cons. Paediat. Preston & Chorley Hosp. Prev: Sen. Regist. & Regist. (Paediat.) Childr. Hosp. Sheff.; Med. Regist. Dumfries & Galloway Roy. Infirm.

CLARK, Sheila Juliet Samuel 144 Bunning Way, Frederica St., Islington, London N7 Tel: 020 7607 0116; 60 Bunning Way, Frederica St, Islington, London N7 9UP Tel: 020 7700 3671 — MD 1979 Madras; MB BS Shivaji 1973; MSc (Med. Microbiol.) Lond. 1992; MRCPath 1993; DTM & H Liverp. 1992. Sen. Regist. (Microbiol.) Univ. Coll. Hosp. Middlx., Whittington, & Hosp. Trop. Dis. Lond. Prev: Regist. (Microbiol.) St. Mary's Lond.

CLARK, Sheila Margaret Dermatology Dept, Leeds General Infirmary, Great George Street, Leeds LS1 3EX Tel: 0113 392 5724 Fax: 0113 392 3565 — MB ChB 1989 Leeds; MRCP (UK) 1992. Cons. Dermatol., Leeds & Pontefract Gen. Infirm. Socs: Brit. Assn. Dermat.; BMA; Brit. Assn. of Paediat. Dermatol. Prev: Sen. Regist. (Dermat.) Univ. Hosp. Wales; Regist. (Dermat.) Leeds Gen. Infirm.; SHO (Geriat. Med.) Seacroft Hosp. Leeds.

CLARK, Simon John 27 Regent Drive, Mossley, Ashton-under-Lyne OL5 9NZ — MB ChB 1989 Birm.; MRCGP 1995; DRCOG 1993.

CLARK, Simon John 2 Ascol Drive, Plumley, Knutsford WA16 0UD Tel: 01606 46177 Fax: 01606 46177 Email: rvecho@yahoo.com — BM 1992 Soton.; MRCP (UK) 1995; MRCPCH 1996. Specialist Regist. Mersey Deanery. Socs: BMA; Brit. Paediat. Assn. Prev: Regist. (Paediat.) Alder Hey Childr. Hosp. Liverp.

CLARK, Simon Richard 13 Gretna Road, Newcastle upon Tyne NE15 7PE — MB ChB 1998 Sheff.; MB ChB Sheff 1998.

CLARK, Stella Anne Murray Royal Hospital, Perth PH2 7BH Tel: 01738 21151; Pleasance House, Pleasance, Falkland, Cupar

KY15 7AW Tel: 01337 57041 — MB ChB 1982 Aberd.; MPhil Ed. 1990; MRCPsych 1986.

CLARK, Mr Stephen Charles The Cardiothoracic Centre, Freeman Hospital, Newcastle upon Tyne NE7 7DN Tel: 0191 223 1417, 0191 284 3111; 69 Woodlands Grange, Forest Hall, Newcastle upon Tyne NE12 9DG — BM BS 1989 Nottm.; BMedSci (Hons.) Nottm. 1987; FRCS Eng. 1993; DM Nottingham 1999; FRCS C-Th 1999. (Nottingham) Cons. cardiothorac Surg., Regional cardiothorac, Freeman Hosp., Newc. upon Tyne. Socs: Soc. of Cardiothor. Surg. of GB & Irel.; Europ. Assn. of Cardiothor. Surg.; Internat. Soc. for Heart and Lung Transpl.ation. Prev: Regist. (Cardiopulm. Transpl.) Freemans Hosp. Newc.; Sen. Regist./cardoiothorac Surg. freeman Hosp., Newc. upon tyne; Fell. in cardiac Surg., Toronto Gen. Hosp., Ontario. Canada.

CLARK, Stephen John Austin Lovemead Surgery, 11 The Halve, Trowbridge BA14 8SD Tel: 01225 2752 — MB BS 1972 Lond.; DRCOG 1981. (St. Thos.)

CLARK, Stuart 45 Kenton Road, Newcastle upon Tyne NE3 4NH — MB ChB 1994 Aberd.

CLARK, Susan Jane 105A Cadogan Gardens, London SW3 2RF — MB 1982 Camb.; MB BChir Camb. 1982; PhD Melbourne 1989; MA Camb. 1983. Socs: Brit. Hypertens. Soc. Prev: Clin. Lect. & Research Regist. (Cardiovasc. Med.) John Radcliffe Hosp. Oxf.

CLARK, Miss Susan Katharine 25 Kelso Place, London W8 5QG Tel: 020 7937 7411 — MB BChir 1990 Camb.; MA Camb. 1990, MB BChir 1990; FRCS Eng. 1994; MD Camb. 1999. Specialist Regist. (Gen. Surg.) S. Thames W.

CLARK, Thomas Antony 116 Salisbury Road, Moseley, Birmingham B13 8JZ — MB ChB 1994 Birm.

CLARK, Thomas Bradley Falmouth Road Surgery, 78 Falmouth Road, London SE1 4JW Tel: 020 7407 4101/0945 Fax: 020 7357 6170; 74 Ferndene Road, Herne Hill, London SE24 0AB Tel: 020 7733 6942 — MB BS 1966 Lond.; T (GP) 1991. (St. Bart.) Prev: Ho. Off. (Paediat.) PeterBoro. Dist. Hosp.

CLARK, Thomas James The Health Centre, 68 Pipeland Road, St Andrews KY16 8JZ Tel: 01334 477477 Fax: 01334 466512 — MB ChB 1965 Edinburgh; MB ChB Edin. 1965. (Edinburgh) GP St. Andrews, Fife.

CLARK, Thomas Justin 1 Hallam Road, Rotherham S60 3BT Tel: 01709 364879 Email: tjusclark@aol.com — MB ChB 1993 Birm.; MRCOG 1999; RCOG London. Clin. Research Fell. (Obst & Gyn) Birm. Wom.'s Hosp. & Univ. of Birm. Socs: Med. Defense Union; BMA. Prev: SHO (O & G) Leicester Gen. Hosp.; Specialist Regist. (O & G) Welsgrave Hosp. Coventry; Specialist Regist. (O & G) Birm. Wom.'s Hosp.

CLARK, Professor Timothy John Hayes (retired) Imperial College, London SW7 2AZ Email: t.clark@ic.ac.uk — MB BS 1960 Lond.; MB BS (Hons.) Lond. 1961; BSc (Hons.) Lond. 1958, MD 1967; FRCP Lond. 1973, M 1962; MRCS Eng. LRCP Lond. 1960; FCGI 1997. Prof. Pulm. Med. Nat. Heart & Lung Inst. Imperial Coll.; Pro Rector (Admissions) Imperial Coll. Prev: Dean Nat. Heart & Lung Inst.

CLARK, Tristan William School House, Combe Hay, Bath BA2 7EG — BM 1998 Soton.

CLARK, Vicki Alana Department of Anesthetics, Royal Infirmary, 1 Lauriston Place, Edinburgh EH3 9YW Tel: 0131 536 3651 Email: vaclark@ed.ac.uk; Tel: 0131 660 6681 Email: vickiaclark@yahoo.co.uk — MB ChB 1978 Ed.; FFA RCS Eng. 1983. (Edinburgh) Cons. Anaesth. Roy. Infirm. Edin.

CLARK, Victoria Jane (Hill) Fenton and Partners, Medical Centre, Burgage Green, Southwell NG25 0EW Tel: 01636 813561 Fax: 01636 816453; Mayfield Lodge, 32 Caythorpe Rd, Caythorpe, Nottingham NG14 7EA Tel: 0115 966 5365 — BM BS 1990 Nottm.; BMedSci (Hons.) Nottm. 1988; MRCGP 1994; DRCOG 1992. (Nottm.) GP.

CLARK, Wendy Angela 4 Belvedere Place, Norwich NR4 7PP — MB BS 1989 Lond.

CLARK, Wendy Angela 12 Alum Chine Road, Bournemouth BH4 8DX — MB BS 1949 Lond.; FFA RCS Eng. 1957. (Roy. Free) Cons. Anaesth. Chelsea & Kensington Hosp. Gp. Prev: Sen. Anaesth. Regist. King's Coll. Hosp. & Woolwich Hosp. Gp.; Anaesth. Regist. Brompton Hosp. Lond. & Roy. Free Hosp.

CLARK, William Cuthbertson (retired) 3 Bell Court, The Maltings, Lillington Avenue, Leamington Spa CV32 5FH Tel: 01926 315374 — MB ChB 1940 Ed. Prev: Chairm. Indust. Injuries & War Pens. Med. Bds.

CLARK, William Iain Cuthbertson Horn Street Surgery, 24 Horn Street, Winslow, Buckingham MK18 3AL Tel: 01296 714504 Fax: 01296 715195; Hill Farm House, 1 High St, North Marston, Winslow, Buckingham MK18 3PD Tel: 01296 670359 — MB BChir 1977 Camb.; MA Camb. 1975; MRCS Eng. LRCP Lond. 1976. (St. Bart.) Med. Off. Swanbourne Hse. Sch.; Hon. Adviser Counc. for InVolun. Tranquiliser Addic. Prev: Trainee GP Oxon. VTS; Surgic. Off. Frimley Pk. Hosp.; Ho. Off. (Med.) St. Luke's Hosp. Guildford.

CLARK-JONES, Alan 9 Great Spilmans, Dulwich, London SE22 8SZ Tel: 020 8693 5031 — MB BS 1953 Lond.; MRCS Eng. LRCP Lond. 1953; MRCGP 1977; DCH Eng. 1956; DObst RCOG 1955. (King's Coll. Hosp.) Med. Adviser to Overseas Dept. Save the Childr. Fund; Hon. Sec. & Treas. Mary Minet Trust. Prev: GP Princip. Camberwell; SHO (Med.) Qu. Mary's Hosp. Sidcup; Ho. Surg. & Ho. Phys. King's Coll. Hosp.

CLARK-MAXWELL, Priscilla Anne (retired) Mackworth House Farm, Mackworth Village, Derby DE22 4NF Tel: 01332 344187 — BM BCh 1953 Oxf.; MA Oxf. 1953; DObst RCOG 1955; DCH Eng. 1959. Sen. Med. Off. Slough & Dist. Family Plann. Clinic.; Clin. Asst. (Venereol.) Upton Hosp. Slough. Prev: Ho. Surg. (O & G) City Gen. Hosp. Stoke-on-Trent.

CLARK-WILSON, Leslie James 7 Lansdowne Road, Luton LU3 1EE Tel: 01582 732385 — MB BS 1952 Lond.

CLARKE, Aileen Elizabeth Health Services Research Unit, London School of Hygience & Tropical Medicine, 1 Keppel St., London WC1E 7HT — BM BCh 1979 Oxf.; MSc Lond. 1988, MD 1993; MRCGP 1985; MFPHM RCP (UK) 1990; DCH RCP Lond. 1983. Sen. Lect. Health Serv. Research Unit Lond. Socs: Fell. of the Fac. of Pub. Health Med.

CLARKE, Alan David The Medical Centre, Cranwell Road, Driffield YO25 6UH Tel: 01377 208208 — MB ChB 1975 Leeds; BSc (1st cl. Hons. Physics) Manch. 1970; Cert. Family Plann. JCC 1978. Gen. Practioner; Clin. assitant, Alfred Bean Hosp. Driffield. Socs: Assoc. Mem. Univ. Manch. Inst. Sci. & Technol.

CLARKE, Alan Thomas Flat 19b Hospital Residences, Inverclyde Royal Hospital, Larkfield Road, Greenock PA16 0XN — MB ChB 1996 Ed.

CLARKE, Alison (retired) 10 Eglinton Drive, Skelmorlie PA17 5AE — MB ChB 1941 Aberd.; DObst RCOG 1944; Hon. FRCGP 1970.

CLARKE, Amanda Lucy 111 Cambridge Gardens, London N10 2LW — MB BS 1998 Lond.; MB BS Lond 1998.

CLARKE, Andrea Jane 9 Orchard Road, Rowlands Gill, Gateshead NE9 1ED — MB BS 1996 Newc.

CLARKE, Mr Andrew Dunsbee 154 Wythenshawe Road, Northern Moor, Manchester M23 0PF; 'Coronet' Morley Green Road, Wilmslow SK9 59O Tel: 01625 530854 Email: andrew.clarke@btinternet.com — MB ChB 1988 Manch.; BSc St. And. 1985; FRCS Glas. 1993. (St. Andrew's/ Manchester) Specialist Regist. in Surg., Wythenshaw Hosp., Manch. Socs: Med. Defence Union. Prev: SHO (O & G) Wythenshawe Hosp. Manch.; Specialist Regist. Gen. Surg., N. MC Genral; Research Regist., Glas. Roy. Infirm.

CLARKE, Andrew Melville Thomas Department of Histopathology, York District Hospital, Wigginton Road, York YO31 8HE Tel: 01904 631313 — MB BS Lond. 1986; MRCPath 1995. Cons. Histopath. York Dist. Hosp. Prev: Sen. Regist. (Histopath.) Yorks. Regional Train. Scheme; Regist. (Histopath.) Leeds Gen. Infirm.; Regist. (Histopath.) St. Mary's & Qu. Alexandra Hosps. Portsmouth.

CLARKE, Mr Andrew Michael Orthopaedic Department, Taunton & Somerset Hospital, Musgrove Park, Taunton TA1 5DA Tel: 01823 342961 Fax: 01823 342474 — MB BS 1984 Lond.; FRCS (Orth) 1994; FRCS Eng. 1988. (Middlx.) Cons. Orthop. Taunton & Som. Hosp. Prev: Sen. Regist. (Orthop.) Sheff. Hosps.

CLARKE, Andrew Stuart The Pease Way Medical Centre, 2 Pease Way, Newton Aycliffe DL5 5NH Tel: 01325 301888; Midhill Cottages, Auckland Park, Bishop Auckland DL14 8RN — MB BS 1988 Newc.; MRCGP 1992; DRCOG 1992. Forens. Med. Examr. Co. Durh. Police.

CLARKE, Professor Angus John Department Medical Genetics, University of Wales College of Medicine, Heath Park, Cardiff CF14 4XN Tel: 029 2074 4057 Fax: 029 2074 7603 Email:

clarkeaj@cardiff.ac.uk — BM BCh 1979 Oxf.; MA Camb. 1980, BA 1976; DM Oxf. 1989; FRCP Lond. 1994; MRCP (UK) 1982; FRCPCH 1997. Clin. Reader (Med. Genetics) Univ. Wales Coll. Med.

CLARKE, Ann Jean 3 Fordwell, Llandaff, Cardiff CF5 2EU — MB ChB 1979 Liverp. (Liverpool)

CLARKE, Anna The Vicarage, 12 Fairfax Gardens, Menston, Ilkley LS29 6ET — MB BS 1997 Lond.

CLARKE, Anna Luise (retired) 21 Grange Road, Edinburgh EH9 1UQ — MD 1950 Munster; LAH Dub. 1959. Clin. Med. Off. Herts. AHA. Prev: GP Edin.

CLARKE, Anne Mary Drs Spicer, Allan & Clarke, Woodside Health Centre, 3 Enmore Road, South Norwood, Croydon SE2 5NT Tel: 020 8656 5790 Fax: 020 8656 7984 Email: administrator@gp-h83025.sthames.nhs.uk; 73 The Heights, Foxgrove Road, Beckenham BR3 5BZ — MB BS 1966 Lond.; MRCS Eng. LRCP Lond. 1966. (Roy. Free) GP; Clin. Asst. Child & Adolesc. Ment. Health Serv. Croydon. Socs: Founder Mem. Croydon Medico-Legal Soc. Prev: SHO (Anaesth.) FarnBoro. Hosp.; Div. Med. Off. S.. Region Brit. Rail; Med. Off. Bromley AHA.

CLARKE, Anthony Hugh Sydenham 103 New Church Road, Hove BN3 4BD Tel: 01273 732856, 01883 343333 — DCH 1976; DRCOG 1978; MB BS 1976; DA 1980; FRCGP 1997. (St. Bartholomews Hosp.) GP Princip.; Med. Off., Caterham Sch.; Med. Off., Woldingham Sch. Socs: Med. Off.s of Sch. Assn. (MOSA). Prev: Course Organiser, GP Vocational Train. Scheme, E. Surrey Hosp '90-'00.

CLARKE, Anthony James (retired) 1 Saffron Park, Kingsbridge TQ7 1RL — MRCS Eng. LRCP Lond. 1950. Prev: Clin. Asst. Sherwood Hosp. Nottm.

CLARKE, Anthony John The Medical Centre, Station Avenue, Bridlington YO16 4LZ Tel: 01262 670686 Fax: 01262 401685 — MB BS 1981 Lond.; MA Camb. 1982; MRCGP 1985; DRCOG 1986; DCH RCP Lond. 1984. (Westm.) Gen. Practitioner; Clin. Asst., Obst., Bridlington Dist. Hosp. Socs: Christian Med. Fell.sh.; BMA. Prev: GP Oxf.; Trainee GP Oxf. VTS; SHO (O & G) Oxf.

CLARKE, Anthony Keith Royal National Hospital For Rheumatic Diseases, Upper Borough Walls, Bath BA1 1RL Tel: 01225 465941 Fax: 01225 421202 Email: clarkea@rnhrd.swest.nhs.uk; Charcoal House, Market Place, Colerne, Chippenham SN14 8DF Tel: 01225 743215 Fax: 01225 743215 Email: aclarkefrcp@cs.com — MB BS Lond. 1968; BSc (Special, Physiol.) Lond. 1965; FRCP Lond. 1987; MRCP (UK) 1972. (Lond. Hosp.) Cons. Rheum. & Rehabil. & Med. Dir. Roy. Nat. Hosp. Rheum. Dis. Bath.; Civil. Cons. Rheum. & Rehabil. RAF; Co. Med. Off., Wilts. St. John Ambul. Socs: Brit. Soc. Rheum.; (Ex-Chairm.) Brit. Soc. Rehabil. Med.; BMA (Pres. Bath & Dist. Div.). Prev: Sen. Regist. (Rheum. & Rehabil.) King's Coll. Hosp. Lond.; Research Fell. Bone & Jt. Resarch Unit Lond. Hosp. Med. Coll.; Regist. (Med.) Bethnal Green Hosp.

CLARKE, Basil Frank (retired) 1 Clarendon Crescent, Edinburgh EH4 1PT Tel: 0131 332 9524 — MB ChB 1955 N.Z.; FRCP Ed. 1970, M 1960. Cons. Phys. (Phys. Diabetic & Dietetic Dept.) Roy. Infirm. Edin.; Sen. Lect. Univ. Edin. Med. Sch. Prev: Sen. Regist. Dept. Med. Roy. Infirm. Edin.

CLARKE, Bernadette Bridget Thatcham Health Centre, Bath Road, Thatcham, Newbury RG18 3HD Tel: 01635 67171 Fax: 01635 76395; Tangle Cottage, Turners Grove, Upper Bucklebury, Reading RG7 6RD — MB ChB 1984 Bristol; MRCGP 1988.

CLARKE, Bernard University Department of Cardiology, Manchester Heart Centre, Manchester Royal Infirmary, Manchester M13 9WL Tel: 0161 276 4143 Fax: 0161 276 8904 Email: bernard.clarke@man.ac.uk — MB ChB 1980 Sheff.; MD (Distinc.) Sheff. 1989; BSc (Hons.) Human Biol. & Anat. 1976; FRCP Lond. 1995; MRCP (UK) 1984; FESC 1997; FACC 1997; FRCP 2000 Edinburgh. (Sheff.) Cons. Cardiol. Manch. Roy. Infirm.; Hon. Lect. (Med.) Univ. Manch. Socs: Brit. Cardiac Soc.; Brit. Cardiovasc. Interven. Soc.; Brit. Pacing & Electrophysiol. Gp. Prev: Sen. Regist. (Cardiol.) Wessex Cardiothoracic Centre Soton. Gen. Hosp.; Brit. Heart Foundat. Fell. (Cardiol. & Clin. Pharmacol.) Brompton Hosp. Lond.; Regist. (Med.) Hammersmith Hosp. Lond.

CLARKE, Brenda Mary (retired) The Haven, Shop Lane, East Lavant, Chichester PO18 0BA — MB BS 1951 Lond. Prev: Med. Off. (Family Plann.) Slough.

CLARKE, Brenda Winifred Hafiz and Clarke Health Centre, Albion St., Brierley Hill DY5 3EE Tel: 01384 77628 — MB ChB 1949 Birm. (Birm.) Prev: Obst. Ho. Surg. Qu. Eliz. Hosp. Birm.; Ho. Phys. Gen. Hosp. Birm.; Cas. Off. Corbett Hosp. Stourbridge.

CLARKE, Brian Marvin Greenwood (retired) 226 Ferry Road, Felixstowe IP11 9RU Tel: 01394 283415 Fax: 01394 283415 — MB BS Lond. 1954; MRCS Eng. LRCP Lond. 1955; DObst RCOG 1958. Prev: Clin. Asst. (Orthop.) Ipswich Hosp.

CLARKE, Brian Patrick The Surgery, Mile Elm, Calne SN11 0NE Tel: 01249 2091; Wayside, Mile Elm, Calne SN11 0NE Tel: 01249 2093 — MB ChB 1961 Ed. (Ed.) Socs: BMA. Prev: SHO Forth Pk. Matern. Hosp. Kirkcaldy; Flight Lt. RAF Med. Br.

CLARKE, Carl Edward Department of Neurology, Hull Royal Infirmary, Anlaby Road, Hull HU3 2JZ — MD 1988 Manch.; BSc (Hons.) Manch. 1979, MB ChB 1982; MRCP (UK) 1985.

CLARKE, Catherine Margaret Health Centre, Gort Walk, Hulme, Manchester M15 5FR Tel: 0161 226 5211 Fax: 0161 227 9754; 21 Musbury Avenue, Cheadle Hulme, Cheadle SK8 7AT Tel: 0161 485 8909 — MB ChB 1964 Ed.; DA Eng. 1968; DObst RCOG 1967. Staff Grade Pract. Mancunian Community NHS Trust. Prev: SHO (Obst.) & Ho. Off. (Anaesth.) W.. Gen. Hosp. Edin.; Med. Off. Methodist Miss. Soc.

CLARKE, Charles Richard Astley 152 Harley Street, London W1N 1HH Tel: 020 7359 6412 Fax: 020 7359 6412 — MB BChir 1970 Camb.; MB Camb. 1970, BChir 1969; FRCP Lond. 1984; MRCP (UK) 1972. (Guy's) Cons. Neurol. Nat. Hosp. Neurol., Neurosurg. & Whipp's Cross Hosp. Lond. Prev: Cons. Neurol. St. Bart. Hosp. Lond.; Sen. Regist. (Neurol.) Nat. Hosps. Nerv. Dis. Lond.; Med. Off. Brit. Everest Expedit. 1975 & 1982.

CLARKE, Christopher William New Court Surgery, 39 Boulevard, Weston Super Mare BS23 1PF Tel: 01934 624242 Fax: 01934 642608; Half Acre, Main Road, Hutton, Weston Super Mare BS24 8QG Tel: 01934 814878 — BM 1979 Soton.; MRCGP 1984.

CLARKE, Christopher William Marshall Intensive Care Unit, Victoria Hospital, Whinneys Heys Road, Blackpool FY3 8NR Tel: 01253 300000; 107 Victoria Road E., Thornton Cleveleys, Blackpool Tel: 01253 858357 — MB BCh BAO 1982 Dub.; FFA RCS Eng. 1986; DA (UK) 1984. Cons. Anaesth. & Intens. Care Wyre & Fylde HA Blackpool. Prev: Sen. Regist. (Anaesth.) Univ. Hosp. S. Manch.

CLARKE, Colin Blair Roselea, Dawbers Lane, Euxton, Chorley PR7 6EW — MB ChB 1997 Liverp.

CLARKE, Cyril Patrick Charles Medeval Ltd., University of Manchester, Skelton House, Manchester Science Park, Lloyd Street N., Manchester M15 6SH Tel: 0161 226 6525 Fax: 0161 226 8936 Email: c.clarke@medeval.com — MB BS 1989 Lond.; BSc (Hons.) Lond. 1986; Dip. Pharm. Med. 1996; RCP Lond. (Univ. Coll. Lond.) Clin. Research Phys. Medeval Ltd. Univ. Manch.; Clin. Asst. (Neurol.) Manch. Roy. Infirm. Socs: Brit. Soc. Allergy & Clin. Immunol.

CLARKE, Daphne Cicelyn Kempe 77 Elers Road, Ealing, London W13 9QB Tel: 020 8567 8817 — MB BS Lond. 1958; MRCS Eng. LRCP Lond. 1958; DObst RCOG 1960. (Middlesex Hospital London) GP.

CLARKE, Mr David 17 Woodlands Drive, Yarm TS15 9NU Tel: 01642 786182 — MB BS 1966 Durh.; MD Newc. 1995, MS (Commend.) 1977; FRCS Eng. 1971. (Newc.) Cons. Gen. Surg. S. Cleveland Hosp. Middlesbrough. Socs: N. Eng. Surg. Soc. & Vasc. Surg. Soc.; Assn. Surg. Prev: Sen. Regist. (Surg.) Newc. Univ. Hosps.; Research Fell. (Surg.) Harvard Univ.; Ho. Off. Roy. Vict. Infirm. Newc.

CLARKE, Mr David Barry (retired) Hill Cottage, Hillhead, Colyton EX24 6NJ Tel: 01297 552289 — MB ChB 1953 Birm.; FRCS Eng. 1959; MRCS Eng. LRCP Lond. 1953. Mem. Ct. of Examrs. RCS Eng. Prev: Cons. Cardiothoracic Surg. Qu. Eliz. Hosp. Birm.

CLARKE, Mr David Glyn Lambeth, Southwark & Lewisham Health Commission, 1 Lower Marsh, London SE1 7NT Tel: 020 7716 7000 Fax: 020 7716 7018; 26 Abbotsleigh Road, London SW16 1SP Tel: 020 8769 5117 — MB BS 1974 Lond.; BSc (Anat.) Lond. 1971; FRCS Glas. 1981; FRCS Eng. 1980; DMRT Ed. 1982. Project Off. Pub. Health & Health Policy Lond.

CLARKE, David John Queen Elizabeth Psychiatric Hospital, Mindelsohn Way, Birmingham B15 2QZ Tel: 0121 627 2840; Holly Cottage, Hallow, Worcester WR2 6NP — MB ChB 1982 Birm.; MRCPsych 1986. Sen. Lect. (Developm. Psychiat.) Univ. Birm.; Med. Soc. Study Behavioural Phenotypes. Prev: Sen. Regist. Ledbury Rd. Hereford; Regist. Hollymoor Hosp. Birm.

CLARKE, David Norman Stirling Royal Infirmary, Livilands, Stirling FK8 2AU Tel: 01786 434000; 101 Ochiltree, Dunblane FK15 0PA — MB ChB 1970 Leeds; MB ChB (Hons.) Leeds 1970; FRCP Glas. 1988; MRCP (UK) 1974. Cons. Phys. Stirling Roy. Infirm. Socs: Brit. Soc. Gastroenterol. & Caledonian Soc. Gastroenterol. Prev: Sen. Regist. Grampian HB Aberd.; Research Fell. Clin. Genetics Johns Hopkins Hosp. Baltimore, USA.

CLARKE, David Philip Radiology Department, Warwick Hospital, Lakin Road, Warwick CV34 5BW Tel: 01926 495321; Broad Marston Priory, Priory Lane, Broad Marston, Stratford-upon-Avon CV37 8XZ Tel: 01789 721575 — MB ChB 1977 Liverp.; FRCR 1983; DMRD Liverp. 1981. Cons. Radiol. Warwick Hosp. Socs: Fell. Roy. Soc. Med.; Brit. Med. Ultrasound Soc. Prev: Sen. Regist. (Ultrasound & Nuclear Med.) Roy. Marsden Hosp. Lond.; Sen. Regist. (Radiol.) Mersey RHA.

CLARKE, David Robert The Bramblefield Clinic, Grovehurst Road, Sittingbourne ME10 2ST Tel: 01795 431266 Fax: 01795 431277; Hospital Farm Oast, Church Hill, Harbledown, Canterbury CT2 9AH Tel: 01227 761180 Fax: 01227 784702 — MB BS 1969 Lond.; MRCGP 1987; Cert. Family Plann. JCC 1975; DObst RCOG 1975; DA Eng. 1974. (Middlx.) Med. Dir. Bramblefield Clinic Sittingbourne. Prev: GP Sittingbourne, Kent; Clin. Med. Off. Croydon AHA; Resid. Med. Off. King Edwd. VII Hosp. Off.

CLARKE, David Stewart The St Lawrence Surgery, 79 St. Lanewrence Avenue, Worthing BN14 7JL Tel: 01903 237346; The Limes, Durrington Hill, Worthing BN13 2PU — MB ChB 1983 Dundee; MRCGP 1994.

CLARKE, Derek Herbert (retired) 199 Andover Road, Newbury RG14 6NB Tel: 01065 581341 — MB BS 1949 Lond.; DO RCS Eng. 1965. Prev: Civil. Ophth. RAF Biggin Hill Kent.

CLARKE, Dominic Peter 13 Troutbeck Grove, Littleover, Derby DE23 7XT — MB BS 1986 Lond.

CLARKE, Dorothy Rosemary (retired) Annex Rushmoor Cottage, Dunsbridge Turnpike, Shepreth, Royston SG8 6RB — MB BS Lond. 1937; MRCS Eng. LRCP Lond. 1937. Prev: Resid. Med. Off. Bearstead Memor. Hosp. Underwood Rd. & Horton Gen. Hosp. Banbury.

CLARKE, Douglas James 14 The Spinney, Epsom Downs, Epsom KT18 5QU — BM 1991 Soton.

CLARKE, Douglas James Arthur Blakeney, High St., Hampton TW12 2SX Tel: 020 8979 8990 — MB BS 1953 Lond.; MRCGP 1968. (St. Bart.) Socs: Balint Soc.; Med. Protec. Soc.; BMA. Prev: SHO W. Middlx. Hosp.; Ho. Surg. (Gyn.) Kent & Canterbury Hosp.; Ho. Phys. Barnet Gen. Hosp.

CLARKE, Eamonn James Upwell Health Centre, Townley Close, Upwell, Wisbech PE14 9BT Tel: 01945 773671 Fax: 01945 773152; Wyndhurst, 80 New Road, Upwell, Wisbech PE14 9BP Tel: 01945 772062 — MB ChB 1985 Leic.; MB ChB (Hons.) Leic. 1985; MRCGP 1990; DRCOG 1990. Prev: Trainee GP Leics. VTS; SHO Rotat. (Med.) Leics. HA.

CLARKE, Edward Granville Woodchurch, MC (retired) Little Glebe, Hungerford Lane, Shurlock Row, Reading RG10 0PB Tel: 01734 343609 — BM BCh Oxon. 1940.

CLARKE, Edward Thomas 52 Stanley Road, Hoylake, Wirral CH47 1HY — MB ChB 1997 Leeds.

CLARKE, Eileen Marjorie 'Woodside', 44 West Beeches Road, Crowborough TN6 2AG — MB ChB 1975 Bristol; MRCS Eng. LRCP Lond. 1975. SCMO (Adult Ment. Handicap) Tunbridge Wells HA.

CLARKE, Eileen Mary (retired) 6 Croft House Fold, Addingham, Ilkley LS29 0LS Tel: 01943 831313 — MB BCh BAO NUI 1948.

CLARKE, Eleanor Adrienne (retired) 45 Bendemeer Road, Putney, London SW15 1JX Tel: 020 8788 9097 Fax: 020 8788 9097 — MB ChB 1985 Bristol; BSc Bristol 1982, MD 1991. Prev: Lect. (Anat.) Univ. Coll. Lond.

CLARKE, Eleanor Mary (retired) 27 Solesbridge Lane, Chorleywood, Rickmansworth WD3 5SN Tel: 01923 284427 Fax: 01923 282 619 Email: eleanor.clarke@btinternet.com — MB BChir Camb. 1956; DObst RCOG 1958. p/t occasional GP locum work. Prev: Med. Off. Bucks. AHA.

CLARKE, Elizabeth Anne 1 Ash Road, Parkhall, Clydebank G81 3PN — MB ChB 1990 Sheff.

CLARKE, Elizabeth Ellis (retired) 16 Kings Hall Road, Beckenham BR3 1LU Tel: 020 8325 0275 — MB BS Lond. 1964; DIH Eng. 1970; AFOM London 1978. Occupat. Phys. Prev: Occupat. Health Adviser King's Coll. Hosp. Lond.

CLARKE, Ellis Whiteside 47 Deramore Drive, Belfast BT9 5JS — MB ChB 1949 Birm.

CLARKE, Elspeth Dow 74 London Road, Datchet, Slough SL3 9LQ — MB BS 1981 Lond. (Roy. Free) Socs: Assn. Anaesth. GB & Irel. Prev: Sen. Med. Off. Europ. Asst. Croydon; Regist. (Anaesth.) Univ. Coll. Middlx. Hosps. Lond.; SHO (Anaesth.) Roy Free & Char. Cross Hosps. Lond.

CLARKE, Emma Jayne Caswell Clinic, Glanrhyd Hospital, Bridgend CF31 4LN — MB BCh 1991 Wales; 1996 MRCPsych; 1996 MSc. Specialist Regist. in Forens. Psychiat., Bridgend. Prev: Specialist Regist. Gen. Psychiat. Cardiff.

CLARKE, Eric David 333 Unthank Road, Norwich NR4 7QA — BM BS 1996 Nottm.

CLARKE, Farine Haymarket Publishing, 174 Hammersmith Road, London W6 7JP Tel: 020 7413 4357 Fax: 020 7413 4513; Flat 83, Scotts Sufferance Wharf, Mill St, London SE1 2DF Tel: 020 7252 2684 Fax: 020 7252 2684 — MB BS 1986 Lond.; T(Gp) 1997. (St Geo. Hosp.) Managing Dir. Haymarket Med. Publishing Lond. Prev: Edr. GP Newspaper; Med. Edr. Pulse Newspaper; Trainee GP St. Helier Hosp. VTS.

CLARKE, Fiona James Cook University Hospital, Marton Road, Middlesbrough TS4 3BW Tel: 01642 854195 Fax: 01642 854661; 17 Ellington Close, Ryhope, Sunderland SR2 0LG — MB BS 1986 Newc.; FRCP 2001; MRCP (UK) 1992. Cons. Rheum. S. Cleveland Hosp. Middlesbrough; Tutor in Med. Educat. Postgrad. Inst. for Med. & Dent. Univ. Of Newc.-upon-Tyne. Socs: Brit. Paediatric Rheum. Gp.; Brit. Soc. For Rheum. Prev: Sen. Regist. (Rheum.) S. Cleveland Hosp. Middlesbrough; Research Regist. (Rheum.) Freeman Hosp. Newc.; Regist. (Rheum.) Roy. Vict. Infirm. & Freeman Hosp. Newc.

CLARKE, Fiona Laura Department of Anaesthesia, South Cleveland Hospital, Marton Road, Middlesbrough TS4 3BW Tel: 01642 854600 Fax: 01642 854335; Tel: 01642 710080 Email: fiona.clarke@email.stahnhst.northy.nhs.uk — MB BS 1985 Newc.; FRCA 1991. (Newc. u. Tyne) Cons. Anaesth. & Intens. Care S. Tees Acute Trust. Prev: Sen. Regist. Rotat. (Anaesth.) Newc. VTS; Fell. (Intens. Care) Academisch Ziekenhuis Groningen Netherlands; Lect. (Anaesth.) Univ. Sheff.

CLARKE, Fiona Rose Breffni, Spicer Stone, Leek ST13 7DS — MB ChB 1988 Manch.; BSc Manch. 1985; MRCOG 1993. Clin. Research Fell. (Immunol.) Paterson Inst. Christie Hosp. Withington.

CLARKE, Fitzroy Alexander 14 Park Road, Ilford IG1 1SD — MB BS 1995 West Indies.

CLARKE, Francis Joseph Bonnyrigg Health Centre, High Street, Bonnyrigg EH19 2DA — MB BCh BAO 1987 NUI; MRCGP 1992; DRCOG 1991; DCH RCPI 1991. (Univ. Coll. Dublin, Irel.)

CLARKE, Geoffrey Charles Maxwell (retired) 32 Briavels Court, Downs Hill Road, Epsom KT18 5HP Tel: 01372 722824 — MB ChB 1955 Cape Town; FRCOG 1982, M 1963.

CLARKE, Geoffrey Johnston Queens Road Medical Group, 6 Queens Road, Aberdeen AB15 4NU Tel: 01224 641560 Fax: 01224 642773; 8 Hilltop Drive, Westhill AB32 6PL Tel: 01224 740699 Email: geoff.clarke@qrmg.grampian.scot.nhs.uk — MB ChB 1979 Aberd.; MRCGP 1984; DRCOG 1981. (Aberdeen) Session. Med. Off. Occupat.al Med. A.O.W Health Solutions Aberd.

CLARKE, Geoffrey Reginald Department of Rheumatology, Harold Wood Hospital, Gubbins Lane, Romford RM3 0BE — MB BChir 1962 Camb.; MA Camb. 1962; FRCP Lond. 1990; MRCP (UK) 1967; MRCS Eng. LRCP Lond. 1962. (Camb. & Roy. Lond. Hosp.) Cons. Rheum. Barking, Havering & Brentwood HA. Socs: BMA; Brit. Soc. Rheum.; RSM. Prev: Clin. Lect. & Sen. Regist. Nuffield Orthop. Centre; Regist. (Med.) Kettering Gen. Hosp.; Sen. Regist. & Regist. (Rheum.) St. Thos. Hosp. Lond.

CLARKE, Gerald Bedford (retired) 1 Bricknell Avenue, Hull HU5 4EP Tel: 01482 342392 — MRCS Eng. LRCP Lond. 1954. Prev: GP Hull.

CLARKE, Gerald John Reginald (retired) Berries, Milford Road, Elstead, Godalming GU8 6HE Tel: 01252 703068 — MB BS 1953 Lond. Prev: Ho. Surg. Orpington Hosp.

CLARKE, Gillian Anne South Road Health Centre, 19 South Road, Lerwick ZE1 0RB Tel: 01595 693201 Fax: 01595 697113; 57 King

Harald Street, Lerwick ZE1 0ER — MB BS 1986 Lond.; MRCGP 1992; DRCOG 1990. Assoc. Adviser & Postgrad. Tutor.
CLARKE, Gillian M St Marys Surgery, Applethwaite, Windermere LA23 1BA Tel: 01539 488484 Fax: 01539 442838 — MB ChB 1978 Liverpool; MB ChB 1978 Liverpool.
CLARKE, Gillian Ruth Selly Oak Hospital, Oak Tree Lane, Birmingham B30 1UB Tel: 0121 627 1627; 236 Lickey Road, Rednal, Birmingham B45 8TE Tel: 0121 453 7604 — MB ChB Leeds 1997; PhD Leeds 1994; BSc (Hons.) Leeds 1992. SHO Gen. Med. Rotat. Selly Oak Hosp. Birm.
CLARKE, Gillian Sarah Elizabeth 14 Marmont Park, Belfast BT4 2GR — MB BCh BAO 1994 Belf.
CLARKE, Gordon Keith (retired) Deers Leap, Hampton Lane, Meriden, Coventry CV7 7JR Tel: 01676 522410 — MB ChB Birm. 1953. Prev: Ho. Surg. & Ho. Phys. Gen. Hosp. Birm.
CLARKE, Gregory James Thornbury Health Centre, Eastland Road, Thornbury, Bristol BS35 1DP Tel: 01454 412599 Fax: 01454 41911 — BM 1991 Soton.; MRCGP 1996; DCH RCP Lond. 1995; DRCOG 1994.
CLARKE, Heather Julia Martin 'Glenwood', Barff Road, Potterhanworth, Lincoln LN4 2DU — MB ChB St And. 1969; FFA RCS Eng. 1977.
CLARKE, Hedley Latham (retired) 70 Wymington Road, Rushden NN10 9JX — MB BS Lond. 1952; MRCS Eng. LRCP Lond. 1952; FFA RCS Eng. 1964; DA Eng. 1958. Prev: Cons. Anaesth. W. Middlx. Hosp.
CLARKE, Helen Catherine 21 Bindon Road, Exeter EX4 9HN — MB BS 1993 Lond.
CLARKE, Helen Elizabeth 5 Cross Hillocks Lane, Widnes WA8 4PN — MB ChB 1988 Liverp.
CLARKE, Henry Grosvenor 2 Fox Hill Close, Birmingham B29 4AH — MB ChB 1952 Ed.
CLARKE, Henry Joy The Arlington Road Medical Practice, 1 Arlington Road, Eastbourne BN21 1DH Tel: 01323 727531; 3 Fairway Close, Eastbourne BN20 8DB — MB BS 1953 Lond.; MRCS Eng. LRCP Lond. 1953; DObst RCOG 1955. (Middlx.) Med. Off. St. Wilfride Hospice E.bourne. Prev: Ho. Surg. (ENT) & Ho. Off. (Radiother.) Middlx. Hosp.; Ho. Surg. Sussex Matern. Hosp. Brighton.
CLARKE, Hester Louise Alberts Dairy, Heathfield Farm, Whippingham Road, East Cowes PO32 6NQ — MB BS 1981 Lond.
CLARKE, Hilary Alison 5 Creechberry Orchard, Bathpool, Taunton TA1 2EX Tel: 01823 324125 — BM 1987 Soton. Clin. Asst. (Psychiat.) W.on Area Health Trust. Prev: SHO (A & E) Salisbury Gen. Hosp.
CLARKE, Hilary Margaret Ramsey Group Practice Centre, Grove Mount South, Ramsey IM8 3EY Tel: 01624 813881 Fax: 01624 811921 — MB BCh BAO 1986 Belf.
CLARKE, Hilary Mary Mytton Oak Medical Practice, Racecourse Lane, Shrewsbury SY3 5LZ Tel: 01743 362223 Fax: 01743 244 5811 — MB ChB 1985 Birm.; MRCGP 1993; DRCOG 1992; DCH RCP Lond. 1990; DA (UK) 1990. (Birm.)
CLARKE, Mr Hugh James Queen Alexandra Hospital, Department of Orthopaedics, Cosham, Portsmouth PO6 3LY Tel: 023 92 286570 Fax: 023 92 286570 — MB BS 1980 Lond.; FRCS Lond. 1984. (Middlx.) Cons. Orthop. Qu. Alexandra Hosp. Portsmouth. Socs: Fell. BOA; Fell. RCS Lond. Prev: Fell. Reconstuc. Hip & Knee Surg. John Hopkins Univ. Baltimore, USA; Sen. Regist. & Regist. (Orthop.) Soton. Dist. Hosps.; Regist. (Surg.) Middlx. Hosp. Lond.
CLARKE, Ian Alexander (retired) Granly, Deepdene Avenue, Dorking RH5 4AE Tel: 01306 882517 — MB BS 1944 Lond.; MRCS Eng. LRCP Lond. 1941; MRCGP 1968. Prev: Anaesth. Dorking Gen. Hosp.
CLARKE, Ian Stewart 9 Inchfad Road, Balloch, Alexandria G83 8SY — MB ChB 1985 Aberd.; MRCPsych 1990. Regist. (Psychiat.) Aberd.; Inceptor Roy. Coll. Psychiat.
CLARKE, Irene Lorraine (retired) Milnthird, Rhonehouse, Castle Douglas DG7 1TA Tel: 01556 680426 — MB ChB 1951 Ed.; DObst RCOG 1956; LMCC 1972. Prev: Aberystwyth; Regist. (O & G) Chester City Hosp.
CLARKE, Irene Robertson 34 Chantry Road, Bishop's Stortford CM23 2SF Tel: 01279 653161; 34 Chantry Road — MB ChB Glas. 1957; FFPHM RCP (UK) 1991; MFCM RCP (UK) 1974; DPH Glas. 1960; DObst RCOG 1959; FR; FRIPHH. (Univ. Glas.) Med. Housing Adviser Boro. of Broxbourne, Welwyn, Hatfield Dist. Counc., Riversmead & Stort Valley Housing Assns. Socs: (Ex-Pres.) Soc. Pub. Health; BMA (Hon. Ex-Pres. E. Herts. Div.). Prev: Cons. Pub. Health Herts. FHSA; Dir. (Pub. Health) E. Herts. HA.
CLARKE, Jacqueline Stowe Hill House, Weedon, Northampton NN7 4SF — MB BS 1971 Lond.; BSc Lond. 1968, MB BS 1971; FRCP Lond. 1991; MRCP (UK) 1974. (Roy. Free) Cons. (Dermat.) N.ampton Health Dist. Prev: Regist. (Dermat.) St. Thos. Hosp. Lond.; Sen. Regist. (Dermat.) Middlx. Hosp. Lond.
CLARKE, Jacqueline Isabella Mabel Belvoir Park Hospital, Belfast BT8 8JR Tel: 01232 491942 Fax: 01232 492554; 171 Ballylesson Road, Belfast BT8 8JU Tel: 01232 826571 — MB BCh BAO 1985 Belf.; MRCP Ed. 1988; FRCR 1992; FFR RCSI 1991. Cons. Clin. Oncol. Belvoir Pk. Hosp. Belf. Socs: Brit. Gyn. Cancer Soc. Prev: SHO (Radiother.) Belvoir Pk. Hosp. Belf.
CLARKE, James 119 Wendover Road, Aylesbury HP21 9LW Tel: 01296 25635 — MB ChB 1962 Ed. (Ed.)
CLARKE, James Anthony (retired) 22 Copse Hill, London SW20 0HG — MB BCh BAO 1946 NUI; FFA RCS Eng. 1954; DA Eng. 1951. Sen. Cons. Anaesths. St. Jas. Hosp. Balham; Cons. Anaesth. St. Anthony's Hosp. Cheam; Hon. Cons. Anaesth. New Vict. Hosp. Kingston-on-Thames & St. Teresa's Matern. Hosp. Wimbledon. Prev: Sen. Ho. Surg. St. Vincent's Hosp. Dub.
CLARKE, James Camac (retired) 550 Upper Newtownards Road, Belfast BT4 3HE Tel: 01232 673405 — MB BCh BAO Belf. 1949; FFA RCS Eng. 1953; DA RCPSI 1951. Prev: Cons. Anaesth. Ulster Hosp. Belf.
CLARKE, James Camac Main X-Ray Dept, Rotal Victoria Hospital, Grosvenor Road, Belfast BT12 6BA Tel: 028 90 240503; 16 Sheepshill, Old Galgorm Road, Ballymena BT42 1QW Tel: 028 25 655416 — MB BCh BAO 1982 Belf.; FRCR 1990; FFR RCSI 1990. Cons. Radiol. Roy. Vict. Hosp..; Lect. Sch. Radiol. Univ. Ulster. Socs: BMA; Ulster Radiol. Soc. Prev: Regist. (Radiol.) Roy. Vict. Hosp. Belf.; SHO Rotat. (Surg.) Roy. Vict. Hosp. & Ulster Hosp.; Ho. Off. Belf. City Hosp.
CLARKE, James Fitzgerald Blair Roselea, Dawbers Lane, Euxton, Chorley PR7 6EW Tel: 01257 453546 — MB ChB Liverp. 1965; FRCOG 1984, M 1971, DObst 1968. Cons. (O & G) Sharoe-Green Hosp. Preston & Chorley & Dist, Hosp. Socs: N. Eng. Obst. & Gyn. Soc. Prev: Lect. O & G Liverp. Univ.; Regist. (O & G) Clatterbridge Hosps. & Liverp. AHA (T).
CLARKE, Mr James Malcolm Furber Norfolk & Norwich Hospital, Brunswick Road, Norwich NR1 3SR Tel: 01603 286286 Fax: 01603 286434 Email: jim.clarke@norfolk-norwich.thenhs.com — MB BS Lond. 1970; MS Lond. 1985; FRCS Eng. 1975; MRCS Eng. LRCP Lond. 1970. Cons. Surg. Norf. & Norwich Health Care NHS Trust. Socs: BMA; Vasc. Surg. Soc.; Eur. Soc. Vasc. Surg. Prev: Sen. Regist. Middlx. Hosp.
CLARKE, James Terence 39 Merton Hall Road, London SW19 3PR — MB BS 1976 Lond.; MRCS Eng. LRCP Lond. 1976; FFA RCS Eng. 1982. Cons. Anaesth. St. Geo. Hosp. Lond.
CLARKE, Jane Rebecca Department of Respiratory Medicine & Cystic Fibrosis, Birmingham Children's Hospital NHS Trust, Steelhouse Lane, Birmingham B4 6NH Tel: 0121 333 8199 Fax: 0121 333 8201 Email: jane.clarke@bhamchildrens.wmids.nhs.uk; 33 Michael Drive, Edgbaston, Birmingham B15 2EL Tel: 0121 440 8017 — MB BS 1983 Lond.; MD Lond. 1996; MRCP (UK) 1987; FRCPCH 1997. (Univ. Coll. Hosp. Med. Sch. Lond.) Cons. (Respirat. Paediat.) Birm. Childr. Hosp. Prev: Sen. Regist. (Paediat.) Hosp. Childr. NHS Trust Gt. Ormond St. Lond.; Clin. Research Fell. Roy. Childr. Hosp. Melbourne; Research Fell. & Regist. Hammersmith Hosp. Lond.
CLARKE, Janet Patricia Tanworth Lane Surgery, 2 Tanworth Lane, Shirley, Solihull B90 4DR Tel: 0121 744 2025 Fax: 0121 733 6890; 66 Oxford Road, Moseley, Birmingham B13 9SQ Tel: 0121 449 2131 — MB ChB 1978 Liverp.; MRCGP 1983; DRCOG 1980. (Liverpool) GP Solihull.
CLARKE, Janet Winifred Child Development Unit, Peterborough District Hospital, Thorpe Road, Peterborough PE3 6DA Tel: 01733 874718 Fax: 01733 874718; Two Gates, Old North Road, Wansford, Peterborough PE8 6LB Tel: 01780 784182 Fax: 01780 784182 Email: j.w.clarke@btinternet.com — MB BChir 1977 Camb.; MSc (Community Child Health) Warwick 1996; MA Camb. 1977; DCH RCP Lond. 1987. SCMO NW Anglia Health Care Trust

P'boro.; Med. Co-ordinator Child Developm. Centre. Socs: Brit. Assn. Community Child Health; Assoc. Mem. Roy. Coll. Paediat. Child Health.

CLARKE, Janette Department of Genitourinary Medicine, Clayton Hospital, Wakefield WF1 3JS Tel: 01924 214421 Fax: 01924 814447 Email: janette.clarke@panp_tr.northy.nhs.uk; 24 Woodbourne Avenue, Moortown, Leeds LS17 5PQ — MB ChB 1981 Leeds; MB ChB (Hons.) Leeds 1981; BSc (Hons.) Leeds 1981; FRCP Lond. 1995; MRCP (UK) 1984. (Leeds) Cons. Phys. Genitourin. Med. Pinderfields & Pontefract Hosps. NHS Trust Wakefield. Socs: Med. Soc. Study VD & Genitourin. Phys. Colposcopy Gp.; Brit. HIV Assn.; Amer. Sexually Transm. Dis. Assoc. Prev: Sen. Regist. (Genitourin. Med.) Leeds Gen. Infirm.

CLARKE, Jayne Elizabeth 84 Framingham Road, Sale M33 3RJ Tel: 0161 972 0171 — MB BCh BAO 1988 Belf.; MRCGP 1993; DCH Dub. 1992; DRCOG 1991.

CLARKE, Jayne Louise 70 Central Avenue, Beeston, Nottingham NG9 2QP — BM BS 1996 Nottm.

CLARKE, Jeffrey James Sylvan Corner, Milton Abbas, Blandford Forum DT11 0BL — MB BS 1990 Lond.

CLARKE, Joan Mary Hopkins 22 Copse Hill, Wimbledon, London SW20 0HG — MRCS Eng. LRCP Lond. 1946.

CLARKE, Joan Mildred (retired) 15 Wharncliffe Gardens, Highcliffe, Christchurch BH23 5DN Tel: 01425 271100 — MD Liverp. 1968, MB ChB 1962; FFPM RCP (UK) 1989. Prev: Cons. Pharmaceut. Med.

CLARKE, Joan Millicent 55 Silverdale Road, Yealand Redmayne, Carnforth LA5 9TB — MB BS 1952 Lond.; MRCS Eng. LRCP Lond. 1951; DPH Eng. 1962, DCH 1953.

CLARKE, Joanne Boehringer Ingelheim Pharma KG, Birkendorfer Strasse 65, Biberach an der Riss 88397, Germany Tel: 00 49 7351 545065 Fax: 00 49 7351 544611; Wardley, High St, Rowde, Devizes SN10 2ND — MB BChir 1985 Camb.; MA Camb. 1987. Head of Oncol. Clin. Research, Boehringer Ingelheim Pharma KG. Prev: Research Phys. Simbec Research Ltd. Merthyr Tydfil; Clin. Asst. (Paediat. Oncol.) Glos. Roy. Hosp.; Trainee GP Glos. VTS.

CLARKE, Joanne Natalie 85 The Cr, Southwick, Brighton BN42 4LB — MB ChB 1997 Sheff.

CLARKE, John 20 Belgrave Avenue, Off Park Lane, Wesham, Preston PR4 3JN — MB ChB 1992 Manch.

CLARKE, John (retired) Mill Cottage, Mill Lane, Wrea Green, Preston PR4 2WP Tel: 01772 681634 — MD 1962 Manch.; MB ChB 1952; MRCPsych 1971; DPM Eng. 1959. Prev: Cons. Psychiat. Heref. Hosp. Gp.

CLARKE, John Aitken (retired) 34 Chantry Road, Bishop's Stortford CM23 2SF Tel: 01279 653161 — MD 1965 Glas.; DSc Glas. 1971, MD (Hons.) 1965, MB ChB 1957. Supervisor Emmanuel & Pembroke Coll. Camb.; Vis. Prof. Univ. Belgrade & Novi Sad, Yugoslavia. Prev: Reader (Anat.) Qu. Mary & W.field Coll. Lond. Univ.

CLARKE, John Alexander North House Surgery, North House, Hope Street, Crook DL15 9HU Tel: 01388 762945 Fax: 01388 765333 — MB ChB Liverp. 1969; MRCGP 1974; DObst RCOG 1974; Cert FPA 1981. (Liverp.) Socs: BMA. Prev: Maj. RAMC.

CLARKE, Mr John Antony 96 East Sheen Avenue, London SW14 8AU Tel: 020 8876 5152 — MB BS 1963 Lond.; FRCS Eng. 1973; MRCS Eng. LRCP Lond. 1963. (Guy's) Cons. Plastic Surg. Chelsea & W.m. Hosp. Lond. Socs: Brit. Assn. Plastic Surg. & Brit. Burn Assn. Prev: Cons. Plastic Surg. Qu. Mary's Hosp. Roehampton i/c Regional Burns Unit, Croydon Gp. Hosp. & Guy's Hosp. Lond.; Regist. (Surg.) Brit. Med. Team Saigon, Vietnam; Fell. Hosp. Sick Childr. Toronto, Canada.

CLARKE, John Arthur Tel: 01323 410088 Fax: 01323 644638 — MB ChB 1970 Manch.; Dip. Pract. Dermat. Wales 1994; Cert. JCC Lond. 1977; DObst RCOG 1972. (Manch.) Bd. Mem. E.bourne Downs PCG; Lead Clinician E.bourne Osteoporosis Centre. Prev: Mem. (Sec & Pres.) E.bourne Med. Soc.; Mem. (Chairm.) BMA.

CLARKE, John Colin Group Practice Centre, Rosemary St., Mansfield NG19 6AB Tel: 01623 23600 & 27070 — MB ChB 1956 Sheff.; DObst RCOG 1958. Med. Off. Indust. Injuries Bd. DHSS. Socs: BMA. Prev: Ho. Off. & SHO (Cas./Orthop.) Mansfield Gen. Hosp.; SHO (O & G) King's Mill Hosp. Sutton-in-Ashfield.

CLARKE, John David St Mary's Medical Centre, Vicarage Road, Strood, Rochester ME2 4DG Tel: 01634 291299/291266 Fax: 01634 295752; 58 Maidstone Road, Rochester ME1 3BS — MB ChB 1974 Manch.; DRCOG 1976. Prev: Ho. Phys. & Ho. Surg. Bury Gen. Hosp.; Trainee GP Medway VTS, Gillingham.

CLARKE, John Edward Park Surgery, Albion Way, Horsham RH12 1BG Tel: 01403 217100; Ranfold Farm House, Toat Hill, Slinfold, Horsham RH13 7RL — MB BS 1975 Lond.; MRCS Eng. LRCP Lond. 1974; MRCGP 1984; FFA RCSI 1979. (Guy's) Socs: Brit. Soc. Med. & Dent. Hypn.

CLARKE, John Howard 8 Chiltern Drive, Upper Hopton, Mirfield WF14 8PZ — MB ChB 1971 Leeds.

CLARKE, John James Tel: 01702 463333 Fax: 01702 603026; 73 St. Mary's Road, South Benfleet, Benfleet SS7 1NL Tel: 0137 453058 — MB BS 1955 Lond. (Char. Cross) Socs: BMA. Prev: SHO Off. Plaistow Hosp.; Ho. Phys. E. Ham Memor. Hosp.; Ho. Surg. Char. Cross Hosp. Lond.

CLARKE, John James 160 Wincobank Avenue, Sheffield S5 6BB Tel: 0114 238 6126 — MB BCh BAO 1952 NUI; LAH Dub. 1952. (Univ. Coll. Dub.) Socs: BMA. Prev: Cas. Off. Rotherham Hosp.; Ship Surg. B.I.S.N. Co.; Res. Med. Off. Bishop's Stortford Hosp.

CLARKE, John Martin Medical Centre, Prince of Wales Barracks BFPO 1 — MB BS 1988 Lond. SHO (Surg.) Plymouth.

CLARKE, John Otway (retired) 1a Sewdley Street, London E5 0AX Tel: 020 8533 7700 — MB BS Lond. 1967; MRCS Eng. LRCP Lond. 1967. Prev: Ho. Surg. & Ho. Phys. W. Middlx. Hosp. Lond.

CLARKE, John Picton James 2 Heol Tir Coch, Efail Isaf, Pontypridd CF38 1BW — MB ChB 1955 Bristol; MFCM 1972; DPH Wales 1964. (Bristol) Cons. Pub. Health Med. Gwent HA. Prev: Asst. Princip. Med. Off. & Asst. Princip. Sch. Med. Off. Glam. CC; Dep. Boro. MOH & Dep. Boro. Sch. Med. Off. Rhondda Boro.; Cas. & Ho. Surg. (Orthop.) Bristol Roy. Infirm.

CLARKE, Mr John Raymond North Riding Infirmary, Newport Road, Middlesbrough TS1 5JE Tel: 01642 854057 Fax: 01642 854064; The Orchard, Woodhouse Farm, Little Ayton, Middlesbrough TS9 6HZ Tel: 01642 723181 Fax: 01642 724956 — MB BS 1975 Newc.; FRCS Glas. (Ophth.) 1983; FRCOphth 1988; DO RCS Eng. 1980. (Newc.) Cons. Ophth. S. Tees Acute Hosps. Trust.

CLARKE, John Wilson (retired) 2A Brown's Brae, Holywood BT18 0HL — MB BCh BAO 1960 Belf.; MB BCh BAO Belf. 1956; BSc (1st cl. Hons. Anat.) Belf. 1960; DObst RCOG 1958. Prev: Sen. Lect. (Anat.) Qu. Univ. Belf.

CLARKE, Jonathan Charles Kenyon 1 Yarrell Mansions, Queens Club Gardens, London W14 9TB — MB BS 1996 Lond.

CLARKE, Jonathan Neil Birchwood Medical Centre, 15 Benson Road, Birchwood, Warrington WA3 7PJ Tel: 01925 823502 Fax: 01925 852422; 25 Birchall Avenue, Culcheth, Warrington WA3 4DB Tel: 01925 762979 — MB ChB 1982 Birm.; MRCGP 1986; DCH RCP Lond. 1987; Cert. Prescribed Equiv. Exp. JCPTGP 1986. Prev: Trainee GP Sandwell HA VTS.

CLARKE, Josephine Mary (retired) Gardenstone Farm, Hutton Rudby, Yarm TS15 0HZ Tel: 01642 700270 — MB ChB Sheff. 1962; DO Eng. 1979.

CLARKE, Judith 3 Calder House Cottages, Calder House Lane, Garstang, Preston PR3 1ZE — BM BS 1989 Nottm.; MRCPsych 1996.

CLARKE, Judith Fisher Medical Centre, Millfields, Coach Street, Skipton BD23 1EU — MB BS 1979 Lond.; MRCGP 1984; DRCOG 1983. Prev: Trainee GP Dover VTS.

CLARKE, Judith Gertrude Flat 2 Left, 37 Cairo Drive, Glasgow G11 5PX — MB ChB 1993 Glas.

CLARKE, Judith Heather Cwmbach, Dyffryn Gwyn, Happy Valley, Tywyn LL36 9HY; Cwmbach, Dyffryn Gwyn, Happy Valley, Tywyn LL36 9HY — MB ChB 1980 Leeds.

CLARKE, Julian Harry Tel: 01342 327555 Fax: 01342 316240 — MB BS 1981 Lond.; MRCP (UK) 1985; MRCGP 1988. Clin. Asst. Qu. Vict. Hosp. E. Grinstead. Prev: Regist. S.end & Rochford Hosps. S.end-on-Sea; Research Fell. (Chest Med.) Lond. Hosp. Whitechapel.

CLARKE, Julie Ponteland Medical Group, Thornhill Road, Ponteland, Newcastle upon Tyne NE20 9PZ Tel: 01661 825513 Fax: 01661 860755; 29 Oaklands, Gosforth, Newcastle upon Tyne NE3 4YQ Tel: 0191 284 1473 Fax: 0191 213 5003 Email: julie.clarke@newcastle.ac.uk — MB BS 1984 Newc.; MB BS Newc. l984; MRCGP 1988; DRCOG 1986. (Newc. u. Tyne) Educat. Fell. RCGP Alzheimers Dis. Dept. Primary Health Care Med. Sch.; Univ.

Newc. u. Tyne. Prev: Princip. GP Gateshead; SHO (O & G & A & E) Newc. Gen. Hosp.

CLARKE, Karen Elizabeth Carryduff Surgery, Hillsborough Road, Carryduff, Belfast BT8 8HR Tel: 028 9081 2211 Fax: 028 9081 4785; 37 Front Road, Drumbo, Lisburn BT27 5JX — MB BCh BAO 1978 Belf.; DRCOG 1981; MRCGP (Distinc.) 1982; DCH Dub. 1981. Socs: Ulster Med. Soc.

CLARKE, Karen Louise The Surgery, Lower Quinton, Stratford-upon-Avon CV37 8SJ Tel: 01789 720820; Nail Cottage, 243 High St, Henley-in-Arden, Solihull B95 5BG Email: johnson.clarke@virgin.net — MB ChB 1993 Birm.; DRCOG 1996; DFFP 1996. (Birm.) GP Partner Lower Quinton Stratford-upon-Avon. Socs: RCGP Assoc. Mem. Prev: Henley-in-Ardon M/C, GP Regist.

CLARKE, Karen Wendy Aintree Cardiac Centre, University Hospital Aintree, Lower Lane, Liverpool L9 7AL Tel: 0151 529 2584 Fax: 0151 529 2724 Email: karen.clarke@aht.nwest.nhs.uk — MB ChB 1986 Manch.; MRCP (UK) 1990; DM (Nottingham) 1996. Cons. Cardiol.

CLARKE, Katharine Mary 172 Bradshaw Meadows, Bolton BL2 4ND — MB ChB 1993 Leeds.

CLARKE, Kathleen, TD, OBE (retired) 91 Moorside N., Fenham, Newcastle upon Tyne NE4 9BX Tel: 0191 272 1901 — MB BS Durh. 1962; FFA RCS Eng. 1972; DA Eng. 1968. Cons. Anaesth. City Hosp. Sunderland Trust; DL. Prev: Cons. Anaesth. Newc. Gen. Hosp.

CLARKE, Kofi 17A Kempshott Road, Streatham, London SW16 5LG — MB ChB 1989 Ghana; MRCP (UK) 1992.

CLARKE, Leslie William (retired) West Willows, 66 Beanacre, Melksham SN12 7PY Tel: 01225 708236 — MA Camb. 1947, MB BChir 1946; MRCS Eng. LRCP Lond. 1946. Prev: Ho. Surg. St. Bart. Hosp.

CLARKE, Linda Winifred Anne 3 Somerset Court, Coleraine BT51 3LQ; 3 Somerset Court, Coleraine BT51 3LQ — MB BCh BAO 1994 Belf.; DMH Belf. 1996.

CLARKE, Lucy Caeren 35 Buston Terrace, Jesmond, Newcastle upon Tyne NE2 2JL — MB BS 1996 Newc.

CLARKE, Malcolm Cardiology Department, City General Hospital, Stoke-on-Trent Tel: 01782 718344; Springfield House, The Avenue, Endon, Stoke-on-Trent ST9 9BY — MB BS 1965 Lond.; FRCP Lond. 1984, M 1969; MRCS Eng. LRCP Lond. 1965; FACC 1984. (Roy. Free) Cons. Cardiol. N. Staffs. Hosp. Centre Stoke-on-Trent; Vis. Hon. Assoc. Prof. Clin. Med. Univ. S. Florida, USA; Sec. Brit. Pacing & Electrophysiol. Gp. Socs: Brit. Cardiac Soc. Prev: Sen. Regist. St. Bart. Hosp. Lond.; Ho. Phys. Roy. Free Hosp. Lond.; Research Fell. Hosp. Sick Childr. Toronto, Canada.

CLARKE, Margaret Anna 36 Lidderdale Road, Liverpool L15 3JG — MB ChB 1994 Liverp.

CLARKE, Margaret Patricia Hawthorns Surgery, 331 Birmingham Road, Sutton Coldfield B72 1DL Tel: 012 373 2211 Fax: 0121 382 1274; 5 Parklands Drive, Sutton Coldfield B74 2QU Tel: 0121 323 3408 — MB ChB 1979 Birm.; MRCGP 1985; DRCOG 1983.

CLARKE, Maria Theresa 15 The Pastures, Coulby Newham, Middlesbrough TS8 0UJ — MB ChB 1986 Sheff.

CLARKE, Mary Davina (retired) 9 Elliswick Road, Harpenden AL5 4TP — MB BS 1955 Lond.

CLARKE, Mary Frances Department Haematology, St Helier NHS Trust, Wrthe Lane, Carshalton SM5 1AA Tel: 020 8296 2216 Email: mclarke@sgms.ac.uk; 6 Stanton Road, London SW20 8RL — MB BS 1973 Lond.; FRCPath 1993, M 1981. (Charing Cross Hospital) Cons. (Haemat.) St. Heliers Hosp. Carshalton Surrey & St. Anthony's Hosp. Cheam; Hon. Sen. Lect. (Haemat.) St. Geo. Hosp. Med. Sch. Lond. Socs: Brit. Soc. of Haemat.; Fell. Roy. Soc. Med. & Merton Med. Soc.

CLARKE, Matthew Dickon 33 West Park Drive E., Leeds LS8 2EE Tel: 0113 266 6836 — MB BS 1993 Lond.; BSc Lond. 1990.

CLARKE, Professor Michael University of Leicester, Department Epidemiology & Public Health, 22-28 Princess Road W., Leicester LE1 6TP Tel: 0116 252 3201 Fax: 0116 252 3272 Email: mc69@leicester.ac.uk; 9/10 Westbridge Close, Leicester LE3 5LW Tel: 0116 253 2533 — MB BS Lond. 1965; FRCP Lond. 1991; MRCS Eng. LRCP Lond. 1965; FFPHM RCP (UK) 1979, M 1974; DPH Lond. 1968; FRCP (Hons.) Ed. 1996. (Middlx.) Prof. Dept. Epidemiol. & Pub. Health Univ. Leicester; Dir. Trent Inst. for Health Servs. Research; Vice-Pres Fac. Pub. Health Med.; Hon. Cons. (Pub. Health Med.), Leics. HA; Co-ord. Dir., Trent Inst. For Health Serv. Research. Socs: Soc. Social Med.; Internat. Epidemiol. Assn.; Centr. R & D Comm. of DOH. Prev: Lect. (Clin. Epidemiol. & Social Med.) St. Thos. Hosp. Lond.; Vis. Scientist USA Pub. Health Servs.; Ho. Surg. Middlx. Hosp. Lond.

CLARKE, Michael Anthony Tree House Childrens Centre, Stepping Hill Hospital, Poplar Ground, Stockport SK2 7JE Tel: 0161 741 5044 Fax: 0161 741 5044 — MB ChB Bristol 1976; BSc (Psychol.) Bristol 1972; FRCP Lond. 1993; DCH RCP Lond. 1981; MRCS PRCPch 1997. (Bristol) Cons. Paediat. NeuroPhysiol.; Paediat. Med. Director, David Lewii Special centre for Surg., Alclerly edge, Chesh.. Prev: Sen. Regist. (Paediat. Neurol.) Booth Hall & Roy. Manch. Childr. Hosps.; Regist. (Neurol.) Gen. Infirm. Leeds; Regist. (Paediat.) Leicester Roy. Infirm.

CLARKE, Michael George 8 Highbury Road, Hitchin SG4 9RW — MB BS 1969 Lond.; MRCP (U.K.) 1973; MRCPsych 1976. (Westm.) Cons. Psychiat. Lister Hosp. Stevenage. Prev: Lect. Dept. Psychiat. Leicester Univ.

CLARKE, Michael John 15 Basil Mansions, Basil St., London SW3 1XA Tel: 020 7584 6719 Fax: 020 7581 0244 — BM BCh Oxf. 1970; MA Oxf. 1970; MRCP (UK) 1974; D.Occ.Med. RCP Lond. 1996; FRCP 1998. (Oxf. & St. Mary's) Med. Off. Legal & Gen. Life Assur. Soc., Barclays Bank, BAT Indust. The Economist. Socs: Assur. Med. Soc. & Soc. Occupat. Med. Prev: Regist. Stoke Mandeville Hosp. Aylesbury; SHO (Gen. Med.) Radcliffe Infirm. Oxf.

CLARKE, Michael John Holmes Chapel Health Centre, London Road, Holmes Chapel, Crewe CW4 7BB Tel: 01477 533100 Fax: 01477 532563 — MB BS 1987 Lond.; BSc Lond. 1984; MRCGP 1993; DCCH RCGP 1992; DRCOG 1991. (Char. Cross & Westm.)

CLARKE, Mr Michael Joseph Northern Vascular Centre, Freeman Hospital, Newcastle upon Tyne NE7 7DN — MB ChB 1989 Ed.; MD 2001 Univ. of Newc. upon Tyne; FRCS 2001 (Gen. Surg.); FRCS Ed. 1994. (Ed.) Cons. Vasc. Surg., Freeman Hosp., Newc. Upon Tyne. Prev: Research Regist. (Surg.) Freeman Hosp. Newc.; SHO Rotat. (Surg.) Newc. Gen. Hosp.; Specialist Regist., Gen. Surg., N.. Deanary.

CLARKE, Mr Michael Patrick Department of Ophthalmology, Royal Victoria Infirmary, Queen Victoria Road, Newcastle upon Tyne NE1 4LP Tel: 0191 282 4002 Fax: 0191 227 5276 Email: m.p.clarke@ncl.ac.uk; 192 Western Way, Darras Hall, Ponteland, Newcastle upon Tyne NE20 9NB Tel: 01661 872073 — MB BChir 1981 Camb.; FRCS Eng. 1986; FCOphth. 1988; T(Ophth.) 1991. Cons. Ophth. Roy. Vict. Infirm. Newc.; Sen.. Lect. Univ. Newc. Prev: Sen. Regist. Qu. Med. Centre Nottm.; Fell. Dept. Ophth. Hosp. for Sick Childr. Toronto, Canada.

CLARKE, Myles Desmond Beckett Glenhead, Auchencairn, Castle Douglas DG7 1RL Tel: 01556 640322 Fax: 01556 640222 Email: mylesclarke@ukgateway.net — MB ChB 1956 Liverp.; MRCS Eng. LRCP Lond. 1956; MRCGP 1965; DMJ Soc. Apoth. Lond. 1968. (Liverp.) Cons. Forens. Phys. Socs: Forens. Sci. Soc.; Assn. Police Surg.; Brit. Acad. Forens. Sci. Prev: Hon. Lect. (Forens. Med.) Univ. Liverp.; Vis. Lect. Merseyside Police Train. Sch. Liverp.; Sec. Merseyside Medico-Legal Soc.

CLARKE, Nicholas Alexander Howard Sevenoaks Hospital, Hospital Road, Sevenoaks TN13 3PG Tel: 01732 221 8241 Fax: 01732 228243 — MB BS Lond. 1984; MRCPsych 1990; MD 1999 Md London 1999. Cons. Psychiat. (Old Age Psychiat.), Invicta Community Care NHS Trust, Maidstone; Consg. Psychiat.: Golden Greenclinic, Sevenoaks; Private Cons Psych Ticehurst Priory Hosp. Brain Injury Serv.s, E. Sussex; Cons Psych Cromwell Hosp., Lond.. Socs: Brit. Assn. Psychopharmacol.; Acad. Old Age Psychiat. Assn. Prev: Sen. Regist. (Psychiat. of Old Age) Guy's & Lewisham NHS Trust Lond.

CLARKE, Mr Nicholas Martin Parry Department of Orthopaedic Surgery, Southampton General Hospital, Shirley, Southampton SO16 6YD Tel: 02380 796769; Awbridge Farm, Dunbridge Lane, Awbridge, Romsey SO51 0GQ — MB ChB 1975 Bristol; ChM Bristol 1987; FRCS Eng. 1979; FRCS Ed. 1979; T(S) 1991. Cons. Orthop. Surg. Soton. Gen. Hosp.; Hunt. Prof. RCS. Socs: Fell. BOA; Brit. Soc. Childr. Orthop. Surg. Prev: Cons. Sen. Lect. (Orthop. Surg.) Bristol Roy. Infirm. & Bristol Roy. Hosp. for Sick Childr.; Sen. Regist. (Orthop. Surg.) Roy. Orthop. Hosp. Birm.; Research Fell. (Paediat. Orthop.) A.I. du Pont Inst. Delaware, USA.

CLARKE, Nigel Robert Alexander 14 The Paddocks, Yarnton, Oxford OX1 5JD; 14 The Paddocks, Oxford OX1 5JD — BM BCh 1989 Oxf.; MA Oxf. 1990; MRCP (UK) 1992. (Oxf.) Consultnat Cardiol. & Phys., Warwick Gen. Hosp. Prev: Regist. (Transpl. Med.) Harefield Hosp.; SHO (Cardiol.) Lond. Chest Hosp.; SHO Rotat. (Gen. Med.) Bournemouth & Poole.

CLARKE, Mr Noel William Department of Urology, Hope Hospital, Salford Royal Hospital NHS Trust / Christie Hospital NHS Trust, Eccles Old Road, Salford M6 8HD Tel: 0161 787 5568 Fax: 0161 787 5814; Riversdale, 39 Bury New Road, Ramsbottom, Bury BL0 0AR Fax: 01706 826372 — MB BS 1981 Lond.; ChM Manch. 1990; FRCS (Urol.) 1992; FRCS Eng. 1985. Cons. Urol. Salford Roy. Hosps. NHS Trust & Christie Hosp. NHS Trust; Hon. Sen. Lect. Manch. Univ. Inst. Cancer Studies. Socs: Brit. Assn. Urol. Surgs.; Europ. Assn. Urol.s; Europ. Sch. of Urol. Prev: Lect. (Urol.) Manch. Univ.; Sen. Regist. (Urol.) Manch.

CLARKE, Norah Helen Colquhoun (retired) 1 Beuzeville Avenue, Summerheath Road, Hailsham BN27 3PB Tel: 01323 848018 — MB BS Lond. 1937; FRCS Ed. 1947; MRCS Eng. LRCP Lond. 1937; DObst RCOG 1943; DCH Eng. 1944, DTM & H 1948. Prev: Ho. Surg. Eliz. G. Anderson Hosp.

CLARKE, Norman Fison, MBE 152 Harley Street, London W1 Tel: 020 7935 8762 — MRCS Eng. LRCP Lond. 1941; LDS RCS Eng. 1939. (Guy's) Socs: BDA & Brit. Soc. Study Orthodont. Prev: Sen. Hosp. Dent. Off. New End Hosp. Hampstead.

CLARKE, Patricia Jane Department of Surgery, John Radcliffe Hospital, Oxford OX3 9DU; Ryvoan, Church Lane, Horton cum Studley, Oxford OX33 1AW — MB BS 1979 Lond.; MD Lond. 1989; FRCS Eng. 1983. Cons. Surg. John Radcliffe Hosp. Oxf.

CLARKE, Patricia Teresa 14 Thorn Road, Bearsden, Glasgow G61 4PP — MB BS 1979 Lond.; MRCP (UK) 1983; FRCPath. 1998.

CLARKE, Patrick Desmond 21 The Avenue, Summersdale, Chichester PO19 4PX Tel: 01243 528347 — MB BS 1996 Lond.; BSc (Hons.) Lond. 1993. (Char. Cross & Westm.) SHO (A & E) Chelsea & W.m. Hosp. Lond.

CLARKE, Mr Patrick Reginald Rudland 10 Con Owl Close, Helmsley, York YO62 5DU Tel: 01439 771030 — MB BS 1944 Lond.; FRCS Eng. 1949. (St. Mary's) Socs: Fell. Roy. Soc. Med.; Emerit. Mem. Soc. Brit. Neurol. Surgs. (Ex Pres.); N. of Eng. Surg. Soc.(Ex Pres.). Prev: Cons. Neurosurg. Middlesbrough Gen. Hosp.; Surg. Specialist MoH Sudan Govt.; Capt. RAMC.

CLARKE, Paul 1A Belair Park, Newtownards BT23 4UX — MB BCh BAO 1986 Belf.

CLARKE, Paul Regional Neonatal Unit, Hope Hospital, Scott Lane, Salford M6 8HD Tel: 0161 7875278 Fax: 0161 7875786 Email: paul.clarke@srht.nhs.uk; 23 Delph Way, Whittle0le-Woods, Chorley PR6 7TG Tel: 01257 277606 Email: drpaulclarke@yahoo.co.uk — MB ChB 1990 Manch.; MRCP (UK) 1995; DCH RCP Lond. 1994; DCCH RCP Ed. 1994. (University of Manchester) Clin. Research Fell. (Neonat. Med.), Hope Hosp., Salford. Socs: Guild Catholic Doctors; The Neonat. Soc., Brit. Assn. of Perinatal Med. Prev: Regist. (Paediat.) Wigan Roy. Albert Edwd. Infirm. & Billinge Hosp.; Regist. (Paediat.) Ormskirk & Dist. Gen. Hosp.; Specialist Regist. (Neonat.) Regional Neonat. Intens. Care Unit, Hope Hosp. Salford.

CLARKE, Paul Douglas 29, Harley Street, London W1G 9QR Tel: 0207 323 5840 Fax: 0207 323 5843 Email: paul.clarke@masta.org; 201 East Dulwich Grove, London SE22 8SY Tel: 020 8488 8982 Fax: 020 8488 8983 — MA Oxf. 1966, BM BCh 1968; FRCP Lond. 1986; MRCP (UK) 1974. (Oxf. & St. Bart.) Med. Dir. Med. Advisery Serv. Travellers AbRd. (MASTA); Med.Adviser Boots Travel Clinics. Socs: Fell. Roy. Soc. Trop. Med. & Hyg. Prev: Cons. Adviser Trop. Med. to Med. Dir.-Gen. (Navy); Cons. Phys. RN Hosp. Haslar.

CLARKE, Paul Russell Academic Unit of Anaesthesia, St. James University Hospital, Leeds Tel: 0897 69679 — MB ChB 1991 Leeds; MMed Sc 2001 Leeds; MRCP (UK) 1995; FRCA 1999. (Leeds) Lect. in Anaesth., Univ. of Leeds.

CLARKE, Mr Peter Bayliss, OBE, TD (retired) Hillhead, Tarland, Aboyne AB34 4TJ Tel: 01224 81949 — BSc Birm. 1948; MB ChB Birm. 1951; BDS Birm. 1953; LDS Birm. 1952; Hon. FDS RCPS Glas. 1967; Hon. FDS RCS Ed. 1962; FDS RCS Eng. 1957. Prev: Cons. Oral & Maxillofacial Surg. Aberd. Roy. Infirm.

CLARKE, Peter Frederick Franz Yardley Wood Health Centre, 401 Highfield Road, Yardley Wood, Birmingham B14 4DU Tel: 0121 474 5186 Fax: 0121 436 7648 — MB ChB 1979 Birm.; MRCGP 1986; DRCOG 1984.

CLARKE, Peter John Wickersley Health Centre, Poplar Glade, Wickersley, Rotherham S66 2JQ Tel: 01709 549610 Fax: 01709 702470; 21 Shafton Road, Rotherham S60 3JG — MB ChB 1983 Sheff.; MRCGP 1988. Prev: Trainee GP Rotherham VTS.

CLARKE, Peter Murray ENT Department, Charing Cross Hospital, Fulham Palace Road, London W6 8RF Tel: 020 8846 7798 Fax: 020 8846 1070; 45 Bendemeer Road, Putney, London SW15 1JX — MB ChB 1985 Bristol; BSc Bristol 1982, MB ChB 1985; FRCS Eng. 1991; FRCS (Orl.) 1995. Cons. ENT Char. Cross Hosp. Lond.; Attend. ENT Cons. to Roy. Hosp. for Neuro-disabil., Putney; Cons. ENT Unit, Cromwell Hosp. Lond.

CLARKE, Petronella Cornelia 264 Alexandra Park Road, London N22 7BG — MB ChB 1962 Liverp.; MD Lond. 1978; FRCS Ed. 1969; FRCOG 1983, M 1968. (Liverp.)

CLARKE, Philip James White House Surgery, Weston Lane, Weston, Southampton SO19 9HJ Tel: 023 8044 9913 Fax: 023 8044 6617; The White House, Weston Lane, Southampton SO19 9HJ Tel: 0191 449913 — BM 1976 Soton.; DRCOG 1979; DA Eng. 1978. Hosp. Pract. (Anaesth.) Soton. Gen. Hosp.

CLARKE, Phillip Denis Radiology Department, Castle Hill Hospital, Cottingham HU16 5JR Tel: 01482 623205; 113 West Ella Road, Kirk Ella, Hull HU10 7QS Tel: 01482 653922 Email: pclarke@karoo.co.uk — MB BS 1979 Newc.; MRCP (UK) 1985; FRCR 1990; FRCP 1998. Cons. (Radiol.) E. Yorks. Hosps. Trust. Socs: Fell.Roy. Coll. of Pysicians (Edin.); RSNA. Prev: Fell. (Radiol.) PA Hosp. Brisbane; Sen. Regist. (Radiol.) Newc. HA.; Med. Regist. Aberd. Teach. Hosps.

CLARKE, Rachel Limeleigh Medical Group, 434 Narborough Road, Leicester LE3 2FS Tel: 0116 282 7070 Fax: 0116 289 3805 — MB ChB 1989 Leic.

CLARKE, Rachel Peartree Lane Surgery, 110 Peartree Lane, Welwyn Garden City AL7 3XW Tel: 01707 329292 — MB BS 1988 Lond.; DRCOG 1990.

CLARKE, Rachel Lisa 55 Swanston Gardens, Edinburgh EH10 7DE — MB ChB 1996 Ed.

CLARKE, Mr Raymond William Mary Ear, Nose & Throat Department, Royal Liverpool University Hospital, Prescot St., Liverpool L7 3BX Tel: 0151 706 5847; 46 Southgate, Honley, Huddersfield HD9 6NT Email: rayclarke@aol.com — MB BCh BAO 1981 NUI; BSc (Hons.) Path. NUI 1983; FRCS (Orl.) 1996; FRCS Eng. 1990; DCH NUI 1983. (Univ. Coll. Dub.) Cons. (OtoLaryngol.) Roy. Liverp. Childr.'s Hosp.; Cons. (OtoLaryngol.) Roy. Liverp. Univ. Hosp.; Clin. Tutor, Roy. Liverp. Childr.'s Hosp.; Progr. Director, OtoLaryngol., Mersey Deanery. Socs: Otolaryngol. Research Soc.; Brit. Assn. Paediat. Otol. (Counc.).; Brit. Assn. Otol. Prev: JLO Trav. Fell. (Rhinological Surg.) State Univ. New York, Brooklyn, USA; Regist. (Otolaryngol.) Mersey Region; Research Fell. (Nasal) Liverp. Univ.

CLARKE, Richard Anthony Chanctonbury Community Mental Health Team, 24 Old Mill Square, Storrington RH20 4NQ Tel: 01903 741414 — MB BS 1990 Lond.; MRCPsych 1994. (Char. Cross and Westm.) p/t Cons. Gen. Adult Psychiat., Worthing Priority Care NHS Trust.

CLARKE, Professor Richard Samuel Jessop (retired) 78 King's Road, Knock, Belfast BT5 6JN Tel: 028 9079 7155 — MB BCh BAO 1954 Belf.; PhD Belf. 1969, BSc (Hons.) 1951, MD 1958; FFA RCS Eng. 1961. Hon. Archiv. Roy. Vict. Hosp. Belf. Prev: Prof. Anaesth. Qu. Univ. Belf.

CLARKE, Robert Christopher Neill 17 Halftown Road, Augher BT77 0BT — MB BCh BAO 1989 Belf.

CLARKE, Robert Geoffery 3 Elm Cottages, Northchapel, Petworth GU28 9HR — MB BS 1998 Lond.; MB BS Lond 1998.

CLARKE, Robert Gravely Benson Highview Surgery, 20 Southgate Road, Potters Bar EN6 5DZ Tel: 01707 871980 Fax: 01707 871995 — MB ChB 1980 Birm.; MA Camb. 1981; MRCP (UK) 1985; MRCGP 1990; Cert. Family Plann. JCC 1990. Assoc. Dean Postgrad. Gen. Pract. N. Thames. Prev: Course Organiser Postgrad. Centre Barnet Gen. Hosp. VTS; Tutor (Gen. Pract.) Barnet; Regist. (Med.) Barnet Gen. Hosp.

CLARKE, Mr Robert Jeffery (retired) Meerhay Manor, Beaminster DT8 3SB Tel: 01308 862305 — ChM Bristol 1972, MB ChB 1960; FRCS Eng. 1966. Prev: Sen. Surg. Regist. United Birm. Hosps.

CLARKE, Robert Joseph The Clinical Trial Service Unit, Nuffield Department of Clinical Medicine, The Radcliffe Infirmary, Woodstock Road, Oxford OX2 6HE Tel: 01865 57241 Fax: 01865 58817 — MB BCh BAO 1979 NUI; MSc (Epidemiol.) Univ. Lond. 1993; MD NUI 1991; MRCP (UK) 1985; MRCPI 1986. Sen. Research Fell., Clin. Trial Serv. Unit. Radcliffe Infirm. Oxf; Hon. Cons. in Pub. Health Med. Oxf. Health Auth.; Inaugural David Mitchell Lect. RCP Irel. Prev: Research Fell. (Clin. Pharmacol.) Vanderbilt Univ. Nashville Tennessee, USA; Research Fell. (Cardiol.) Adelaide Hosp. Dub.

CLARKE, Ronald Gibb West End Surgery, 10 West End, Swanland, North Ferriby HU14 3PE Tel: 01482 633570; 52 Dale Road, Swanland, North Ferriby HU14 3QJ Email: user@clarke-run.kaboo.co.uk — MB ChB 1978 Manch.; DCH.

CLARKE, Ross 7 Elgin Gardens, Dundee DD3 8NJ; 1st Floor Left, 38 Thompson St, Aberdeen AB25 2QP — MB ChB 1995 Aberd. SHO (Anaesth.) Aberd. Roy. Hosp. NHS Trust. Prev: SHO (A & E) Inverness; SHO (Orthop.) Elgin.

CLARKE, Sally Anne The Medical Centre, 12 East King Street, Helensburgh G84 Tel: 01436 673366 — BM 1988 Soton.; DRCOG 1999 (UK); MRCGP 1999 (UK); MRCP (UK) 1991. (Southampton University) GP Helensburgh. Socs: MRCGP - Mem.

CLARKE, Mr Samuel Henry Creighton Bourneside, High St., St Mary Bourne, Andover SP11 6AY Tel: 01264 738014 — MRCS Eng. LRCP Lond. 1936; FRCS Eng. 1946. (St. Bart.) Cons. Surg. (Urol.) Brighton & Cuckfield & Crawley Health Dists. Socs: (Ex-Mem. Counc.) Brit. Assn. Urol. Surgs.; Fell. Roy. Soc. Med. (Ex-Mem. Counc. Sect. Urol., Mem. Sects. Urol. & Proctol & Surg). Prev: Surg. Chief Asst. St. Bart. Hosp. Lond.; Sen. Regist. St. Peter's Hosp. For Stone Lond.; Maj. RAMC, Surg. Specialist.

CLARKE, Sarah Ann 3 Hatfield Road, London W13 9DG — MB BS 1982 Lond.; MFPM RCP (UK) 1987. Indep. Pharmaceut. Phys. UK.

CLARKE, Sarah Catherine 17 Romney Close, Chessington KT9 1BP — MB BChir 1990 Camb.

CLARKE, Sarah Jane Woodside, Brockhall Village, Old Langho, Blackburn BB6 8AY — MB ChB 1987 Manch. Regist. (Anaesth.) Manch. Roy. Infirm.

CLARKE, Sarah Virginia Ferndown Health Centre, St. Mary's Road, Ferndown, Wimborne Tel: 01202 897000 Fax: 01202 897888 — BM 1980 Soton.; MRCGP 1987.

CLARKE, Sean Heaton Moor Medicine, 32 Heatonmoor Road, Heaton Moor, Stockport SK4 4NX; 6 Royle Street, Manchester M14 6RN — MB ChB Manch. 1994; DFP. (Manchester) GP Register at Heaton Moor MC.

CLARKE, Shane Royal United Hospital, Coombe Park, Bath BA1 3NG; 4 Hughenden Road, Clifton, Bristol BS8 2TT — MB BS 1991 Lond.; BSc (Hons.) Bristol 1982; MRCP (UK) 1994. SHO (Med.) Roy. United Hosp. Bath. Socs: BMA & Brit. Assn. Sports Med.

CLARKE, Sheila 17A Kempshott Road, Streatham, London SW16 5LG — MB ChB 1990 Univ. Ghana; MRCP (UK) 1994.

CLARKE, Mr Simon Andrew Flat 8, 1/2 Percival Terrace, Brighton BN2 1FA Email: sclarke305@aol.com — MB BS 1990 Lond.; BSc Hons. Lond. 1987; FRCS 1996. (London) Regist. (Paediat. Surg.) Lewisham Lond.

CLARKE, Mr Simon Francis Jackson 7 Aldrin Close, Beaconside, Stafford ST16 3SZ — MB ChB 1989 Sheff.; DA (UK) 1993; FRCS (Ed) 1999. Specialist Regist. Rotat. (A&E), Manch. Prev: SHO Rotat. (Surg.) Birm. City Hosp.; GP VTS, Chesterfield; SHO (Anaesth.) Roy. Hallamsh. Hosp. Sheff. & Doncaster Roy. Infirm.

CLARKE, Simon Geoffrey Email: sclarke@doctors.org.uk; Little Orchards, 6 Layters Way, Gerrards Cross SL9 7QY Tel: 0208 838 5381 Email: sclarke@doctors.org.uk — MB ChB 1991 Manch.; DA (UK) 1995; FRCA 1998. (Manch.) Sen. Regist. Anaesthetics N. W. Thames Rotat. (Imperial Coll.) Lond. Socs: RSA; World Anaesth.; AAGBI. Prev: Sen. Regist. Anaesth. Fremantle Hosp. W. Australia.

CLARKE, Simon Peter 13 Kennington Avenue, Bishopston, Bristol BS7 9EU — MB BS 1984 West. Austral.

CLARKE, Sinead Eileen Owl Cottage, 1 Goosehill, Castleton, Sheffield — MB ChB 1997 Manch.

CLARKE, Sonji Deloraine 9 Adamsrill Road, Sydenham, London SE26 4AL — MB BS 1989 Lond.; MRCOG 1996. (Guy's Hospital UMDS) Flexible Specialist Regist. (O & G) King's Coll. Hosp.; Clin. Asst. City of Lond. Migraine Clinic. Prev: Flexible Regist. (O & G) Qu. Charlotte's Hosp.; Flexible Regist. (O & G) Pembury Hosp.

CLARKE, Stephen Ernest 51 Moss Road, Portadown, Craigavon BT62 1NB — MB BCh BAO 1997 Belf.

CLARKE, Stephen John Institute of Cancer Research, 15 Cotswold Road, Belmont, Sutton SM2 5NG Tel: 020 8643 8901 Fax: 020 8770 7885; 1 Cheviot Close, Sutton SM2 5SB Tel: 020 8661 1082 — MB BS 1983 Sydney; FRACP 1990. Sen. Lect. Inst. Cancer Research Drug Developm. Sect. Sutton. Prev: Sen. Regist. (Med.) Roy. N. Shore Hosp. Sydney, Austral.

CLARKE, Stephen Lee Caskgate Street Surgery, 3 Caskgate Street, Gainsborough DN21 2DJ Tel: 01427 612501 Fax: 01427 615459 — MB BS 1976 Lond.; MRCS Eng. LRCP Lond. 1976. (Guy's)

CLARKE, Steven Alexander The Surgery, Branksomewood Road, Fleet GU51 4JX Tel: 01252 613624 Fax: 01252 816489; 7 Polmear Close, Church Crookham, Fleet GU52 8UH Tel: 01252 615252 — BM 1986 Soton.; BM Soton 1986; MRCGP 1997; DRCOG 1991; Cert. Family Plann. JCC 1991; DCH RCP Lond. 1990; DFFP 1998. (Soton.) GP Fleet; Chairm. Hart PCG. Prev: SHO (Psychiat., Paediat. & O & G) Frimley Pk. Hosp.

CLARKE, Mr Stewart Desmond (retired) King Edward VII Hospital, Midhurst GU29 0BL — MB BCh BAO 1955 Belf.; MCh (Hons.) Belf. 1960; FRCS Ed. 1960, FRCS Eng. 1961. Prev: Cons. Surg. King Edwd. II Hosp. Midhurst.

CLARKE, Stewart William (retired) 13 Hadley Grove, Hadley Green, Barnet EN5 4PH Tel: 020 8449 2416 — MD (Hons.) Birm. 1969, MB ChB 1959; FRCP Lond. 1974, M 1965. Cons. Phys. Roy. Free Hosp., Brompton Hosp., King Edwd. VII Hosp.; Off. Lond. & King Edwd. VII Hosp. Midhurst. Prev: Joseph Sen. White Research Fell. RCP Lond.

CLARKE, Stuart Paul West Kirby Health Centre, The Concourse, Grange Road, West Kirby, Wirral CH48 4HZ Tel: 0151 625 9171 Fax: 0151 625 9499 — MB ChB 1985 Liverp. GP. Prev: Ships Phys., Carnival Cruise Lines, Miami, Florida; SHO (Sen. Surg.) Warrington Dist. Gen. Hosp.; SHO (Orthop.) Arrowe Pk. Hosp. Wirral.

CLARKE, Susan O'Donnell and Partners, Farnham Health Centre, Brightwells, Farnham GU9 75A Tel: 01252 737387; 1 Shortheath Road, Farnham GU9 8SR Tel: 01372 274561 Email: h.s.lumley@doctors.org.uk — BM 1986 Soton. p/t Gen. Practitioner; Health Screening, DupaClare Pk., Crondall, Surrey. Prev: Trainee GP Guildford VTS; SHO (A & E & ENT) Guildford HA.

CLARKE, Susan Elizabeth Meadowcroft House, 24 Bradley Lane, Rufforth, York YO23 3QJ — MB BCh 1980 Wales; FRCS Ed. 1988. Regist. (ENT) York Dist. Hosp.

CLARKE, Susan Elizabeth Mary Department of Nuclear Medicine, Guy's Hospital, St Thomas St., London SE1 9RT Tel: 020 7955 4592 Fax: 020 7955 4657 Email: sue.clarke@kcl.ac.uk; 26 Abbotsleigh Road, London SW16 1SP Tel: 020 8769 5117 — MB BS 1974 Lond.; BSc (Anat.) Lond. 1971, MB BS 1974; MSc (Nuclear Med.) 1981; MRCP (UK) 1977; FRCP (UK). Cons. Phys. Nuclear Med. Guy's Hosp. Lond.; Sen. Lect. Radiol. Sci. GRT Sch. of Med. and Dent.. Socs: Fell. Roy. Coll. Phys.; (Ex-Pres.) Brit. Nuclear Med. Soc.; Eur. Assn. Nuclear Med. (Advisery Counc.). Prev: Sen. Regist. (Nuclear Med. & Gen. Med.) St. Thos. Hosp. Lond.

CLARKE, Susan Mary Mount Street Health Centre, Mount Street, Diss IP22 4QG Tel: 01379 642023 Fax: 01379 643320; Old Leaf Cottage, Earsham Road, Hedenham, Bungay NR35 2DF Tel: 01508 482581 Email: greg@paston.co.uk — MB BS 1979 Lond.; DRCOG 1996; DCH RCP Lond. 1995. (Guy's) GP Partner Diss Norf. Prev: GP/Regist. Norwich VTS; Clin. Med. Off. (Child Health) Norwich HA.

CLARKE, Suzanne Kathleen Ruth (retired) Bickley Cottage, 4 Main Road, Cleeve, Bristol BS49 4NU Tel: 01934 838672 — MB ChB Bristol 1948; MD Bristol 1956; MRCS Eng. LRCP Lond. 1948; FRCPath 1972, M 1963. Prev: Cons. Microbiol. Pub. Health Laborat. Serv. & Bristol Roy. Infirm.

CLARKE, Terence Kilian, OBE (retired) 4 Periam Close, Henley-on-Thames RG9 1XN Tel: 01491 577778 Fax: 01491 576020 Email: tr_clarke@compuserve.com — MB BS Lond. 1957; FFPM RCP (UK) 1989; DA Eng. 1961. Prev: Specialist (Anaesth.) RAMC.

CLARKE, Thomas Anthony Piers (retired) 2 Robin's Court, Upton Pyne, Exeter EX5 5HZ Tel: 01392 541536 Fax: 01392 841530 Email: taclarke@lineone.net — MB BS Lond. 1953. Prev: GP Exeter.

CLARKE, Thomas John Department of Histopathology, Royal Devon & Exeter Hospitals (Wonford), Exeter EX2 5DY Tel: 01392 402982 Fax: 01392 402964; Tel: 01404 811109 — MB BChir 1982 Camb.; MA, MB Camb. 1982, BChir 1981; MRCPath. 1988; FRCPath 1998. (Lond. Hosp.) Cons. Histopath. & Cytopath. Exeter HA. Prev: Sen. Regist. (Histopath.) Plymouth & Exeter HA; Regist. (Histopath.) Derriford Hosp. Plymouth; SHO (Path.) Centr. Middlx. Hosp.

CLARKE, Thomas John 13 Fox Road, Holmer Green, High Wycombe HP15 6SE — MB BCh BAO 1976 Belf.

CLARKE, Thomas Neville Scamander Department of Anaesthesia & ITU, Newcastle General Hospital, Westgate Road, Newcastle upon Tyne NE4 6BE Tel: 0191 273 8811 Fax: 0191 256 3154 Email: staff@nghgas.demon.co.uk; 22 The Drive, Gosforth, Newcastle upon Tyne NE3 4AH Tel: 0191 284 8977 — BM BCh 1977 Oxf.; MA Oxf. 1974, DPhil 1974; FFA RCS Lond. 1981. (Oxf.) Cons. Anaesth. Newc. Hosps. NHS Trust; Med. Adviser N. E. Ambul. Serv. NHS Trust; Jt. Hon. Sec. JCALC (Jt. Roy. Coll. Ambul. Servs. Liais. Comm.); Hon. Prof. Fac. Health Studies Chas. Sturt Univ., NSW, Austral.; Roy. Coll. Anaesth.s Mem., CPSM Paramedic Bd. Prev: Chairm. N. Region ODP Train. Panel.

CLARKE, Timothy John 12 The Walnuts, Branksome Roa, Norwich NR4 6SR — MB ChB 1992 Birm.

CLARKE, Trevor Peter Andrew 43 Alson Avenue, Worcester Park KT4 7EG — MB BS 1968 Lond.

CLARKE, Ursula Styring (retired) St Michaels Nursing Home, 9 Chesterfield Road, Brimington, Chesterfield S43 1AB — MB ChB 1933 Sheff.; MSc Sheff. 1932. Prev: Lect. (Optics) Sheff. Sch. Orthoptics.

CLARKE, Victoria Ann 2 Beacon Hill, Woking GU21 1QR — MB ChB 1993 Leic.

CLARKE, Vinedhini 67 Uplands Crescent, Llandough, Penarth CF64 2PS — MB BS 1984 Madras; MRCP (UK) 1993.

CLARKE, William Barrington Buckley Health Centre, Padeswood Road, Buckley CH7 2JL Tel: 01224 550555 Fax: 01224 545712; Rose Cottage, Rose Lane, Mynydd, Mold CH7 6UA — MB ChB 1961 Liverp.; BSc (1st cl. Hons. Anat.) Liverp. 1961, MB ChB 1965. (Liverp.)

CLARKE, William Henry Chadwell House, Chadwell St Mary, Grays RM16 4DJ Tel: 0137 522103 — BM BCh 1956 Oxf.; MA, BM BCh Oxf. 1956; DO Eng. 1959. (Oxf. & Lond. Hosp.) SHMO (Ophth.) Surg. & Surg. i/c Contact Lens Dept.; Centre OldCh. Hosp. Romford, Orsett Hosp. Grays. Socs: Fell. Roy. Soc. Med.; BMA. Prev: Sen. Ho. Off. (Ophth.) OldCh. Hosp. Romford; Ho. Phys. St. John's Hosp. Chelmsford; Ho. Surg. Ophth. & Plastic Dept. Lond. Hosp.

CLARKE, William Leo Ide Lane Surgery, Ide Lane, Alphinton, Exeter EX2 8UP Tel: 01392 439868 Fax: 01392 493513; Southfields, 5A Elm Grove Road, Topsham, Exeter EX3 0EQ Tel: 01392 874435 Email: leo.clarke@plymouth.swis.net — MB ChB 1983 Leic.; BSc Norwich 1978; MRCGP 1987; DRCOG 1989; Dip. Palliat. Med. Wales 1998. (Univ. Leic. Med. Sch.) Socs: Accred. Mem. & Lect. Brit. Soc. Med. & Dent. Hypn.; Assn. Palliat. Med.; Roy. Coll. Gen. Pract.

CLARKE-SMITH, Elizabeth Mary Helene 18 Cambrian Place, Swansea SA1 1RG — MB BCh 1993 Wales; BSc (Hons.) Wales 1990. (Univ. Wales Coll. Med.) SHO (Psychiat.) Cefn Coed Hosp. Swansea. Prev: SHO (O & G & Gen. Med.) Singleton Hosp. Swansea; SHO (Cardiol.) Univ. Hosp. Wales Cardiff.

CLARKE THOMAS, Anna-Jane Bargoed Hall Family health Centre, Cardiff Rd, Bargoed CF81 8NN; Fax: 029 2061 9898 Email: ajandgt@aol.com — MB BCh 1996 Wales. (University of Wales College of Medicine)

CLARKE-WALKER, Alastair Robert 82 Maralyn Avenue, Waterloo Village, Waterlooville PO7 7LL — LMSSA 1996 Lond.; MD St. Geo. W. Indies 1995; BSc (Hons. Pharmacol.) Portsmouth 1982; LRCP LRCS 1996. GP Regist. Portsmouth; SHO (Psychiat.) St James. Hosp. Portsmouth. Prev: SHP (A & E) Roy. Bournemouth Hosp.

CLARKE-WILLIAMS, Jane Elizabeth Forest End Surgery, Forest End, Waterlooville PO7 7AH — MB ChB 1985 Birm.; DRCOG 1989. Prev: Clin. Asst. (Radiotherap. & Oncol.) St. Richards Hosp. Chichester; Clin. Asst. (Geriat.) Trevor Howell Day Hosp. & Qu. Alexandra Hosp. Portsmouth; Clin. Asst. (Family Plann.) St. Mary's Hosp. Portsmouth.

CLARKE-WILLIAMS, Michael James (retired) 15 Teapot Row, Clocktower Drive, Southsea PO4 9YA Tel: 023 9286 3010 — MB BChir Camb. 1953; MA Camb. 1951; FRCP Lond. 1984; FRCP Ed. 1972, M 1962; MRCS Eng. LRCP Lond. 1951. Prev: Cons. Phys. (Geriat.) Portsmouth & SE Hants. Health Dist.

CLARKSON, Adrian Grant Outwood Surgery, 581A Leeds Road, Outwood, Wakefield WF1 2JL Tel: 01924 822626 Fax: 01924 870975; 66 Wrenthorpe Lane, Wrenthorpe, Wakefield WF2 0PT Tel: 01924 290908 Fax: 01924 784843 Email: asclark@epulse.net — MB ChB 1980 Leeds; DRCOG 1983. (Leeds) Prev: Mem. Wakefield VTS; Ho. Surg. Clayton Hosp. Wakefield; Ho. Phys. Leeds Gen. Infirm.

CLARKSON, Alan David 18 High Wood, Ilkley LS29 8SB — MB ChB 1964 Leeds; DPM 1968.

CLARKSON, David Gregory Derwent House Surgery, Derwent House, Wakefield Road, Cockermouth CA13 0HZ Tel: 01900 324100 Fax: 01900 324106; 2 Jennys Croft, Eaglesfield, Cockermouth CA13 0SF — MB ChB 1978 Leeds; MA 2000 Durh.; MRCGP 1982; DRCOG 1981; DCH RCPS Glas. 1982. (Leeds) Prev: Course Organiser W. Cumbria VTS.

CLARKSON, Guy Christopher Bridge Street Practice, 21 Bridge Street, Driffield YO25 6DB Tel: 01377 253441 Fax: 01377 241962; Barncroft, West End, Kilham, Driffield YO25 4RR — MB BS 1979 Newc.; DRCOG 1983.

CLARKSON, Ian Paul Ballyclare Group Practice, Ballyclare Health Centre, George Avenue, Ballyclare BT39 9HL Tel: 028 9332 2575 Fax: 028 9334 9897; 67 Kensington Road, Belfast BT5 6NL Tel: 01232 796026 — MB BCh BAO 1990 Belf. Med. Off. N. Irel. Hospice Belf.

CLARKSON, Jane Elizabeth Bankfield Surgery, 15 Huddersfield Road, Elland HX5 9BA Tel: 01422 375537 Fax: 01422 370776 — MB ChB 1977 Birm.; DCH Eng. 1979.

CLARKSON, Jill-Marie 2 Ballards Close, Mickleton, Chipping Campden GL55 6RL; 2 West View, Wylam NE41 8DT — MB BS 1992 Newc. p/t Specialist Regist. in Anaesthetics Newc. Sch. of Anaesth.. Socs: BMA; Assn. of Anaesth.s; Obsteric Anaesth. Assn. Prev: Specialist Regist. in Anaesthetics Cleveland Sch. of Anaesth.; SHO in Anaesthetics Newc. & Gateshead Rotat..

CLARKSON, Jonathan David 37 Woodlands Road, Aigburth, Liverpool L17 0AJ — MB ChB 1991 Liverp.

CLARKSON, Judith Mary Nappings Paddock, Morlands Drive, Cheltenham GL53 8LP — MB BS 1980 Lond.; DRCOG 1983. Prev: Trainee GP Harrogate VTS; Ho. Surg. Roy. Free Hosp.; Ho. Phys. Harrogate Gen. Hosp.

CLARKSON, Karen Susan 432 Meanwood Road, Leeds LS7 2LP — MB ChB 1994 Leic.

CLARKSON, Kathleen Gwyneth (retired) 74 Magdalen Road, Exeter EX2 4TR Tel: 01392 73242 — BA Dub. 1958, MB BCh BAO 1960; DObst RCOG 1963; LM Rotunda 1962. Prev: Med. Off. (Urol.) Roy. Devon & Exeter Hosp.

CLARKSON, Kenneth Shaw (retired) 2 King Alfreds Way, Wedmore BS28 4BB Tel: 01934 713102 — MB BS 1945 Lond.; MRCS Eng. LRCP Lond. 1945; BDS Lond. 1957; LDS RCS Eng. 1957.

CLARKSON, Kevin Richard Sixways Clinic, London Road, Charlton Kings, Cheltenham GL52 6HS Tel: 01242 583520 — MB ChB 1978 Leeds; MRCGP 1984; DRCOG 1980.

CLARKSON, Lesley 14 Tardree Road, Kells, Ballymena BT42 3PE — MB BS 1996 Lond.

CLARKSON, Marianne Vera The Verdin Arms, Wimboldsley, Middlewich CW10 0LW — MB ChB 1989 Liverp.

CLARKSON, Michael E The Laurie Pike Health Centre, 95 Birchfield Road, Handsworth, Birmingham B19 1LH Tel: 0121 554 0621 & 021 523 8111 — MB ChB 1968 Birm. (Birm.)

CLARKSON, Nigel Charles The Surgery, Kinmel Avenue, Abergele LL22 7LP Tel: 01745 833158 Fax: 01745 822490; Gwelfryn, Rhyd-y-Foel, Abergele LL22 8DY Tel: 01942 517667 — MB ChB 1977 Leeds; BSc Leeds 1974, MB ChB 1977. GP Abergele.

CLARKSON, Nora (retired) 101 Watchfield Court, Sutton Court Road, London W4 4ND — MRCS Eng. LRCP Lond. 1942.

CLARKSON, Peter Falmer House, Barcombe, Lewes BN8 5DL — MB BS 1988 Lond.; BSc (Hons.) Lond. 1985; MRCP (UK) 1991.

CLARKSON, Peter John 118/120 Stanford Avenue, Brighton BN1 6FE Tel: 01273 506361; Calcot Farm House, Steyning

BN44 3AA — MB BS Lond. 1961; MRCS Eng. LRCP Lond. 1962; MRCGP 1966; DCH Eng. 1964; DObst RCOG 1964. (St. Mary's) Chairm. Brighton Postgrad. Med. Centre.

CLARKSON, Richard Llewellyn 74 Magdalen Road, Exeter EX2 4TR — MB ChB 1997 Birm.

CLARKSON, Stephen George The Old Dispensary, 8 Castle Street, Warwick CV34 4BP Tel: 01926 494137 Fax: 01926 410348 — MB ChB 1973 Bristol.

CLARKSON, Sushila Montague Health Centre, Oakenhurst Road, Blackburn BB2 1PP Tel: 01254 268410 Fax: 01254 268450; The Sycamores, 84 Mellor Brow, Mellor, Blackburn BB2 7EX — MB BS 1987 Lond.; BSc Lond. 1985; Cert. Family Plann. JCC 1990. Socs: BMA; RCGP. Prev: Clin. Med. Off. Blackburn; Trainee GP Lt. Harwood Health Centre Blackburn; SHO (Paediat. & O & G) Qu. Pk. Hosp. Blackburn.

CLARKSON, Suzanne Jane, Surg. Lt. RN 24 Dairymoor, Wickham, Fareham PO17 5JR — MB BCh 1995 Wales. (Univ. Wales Coll. Med.) Surg. Lt. (Gen. Duties) RN Portsmouth. Socs: Med. Protec. Soc. Prev: Ho. Off. Roy. Hosp. Haslar; Ho. Off. Roy. Gwent Hosp. Newport.

CLARKSON, Walter Brian (retired) 74 Magdalen Road, Exeter EX2 4TR Tel: 01392 73242 — MB ChB St. And. 1956; FFA RCS Eng. 1962. Prev: Cons. Anaesth. Devon & Exeter Clin. Area.

CLARKSON WEBB, William Douglas (retired) Hersham House, Kelvedon Road, Little Braxted, Witham CM8 3LD Tel: 01621 891480 — MRCS Eng. LRCP Lond. 1945; LDS RCS Eng. 1946. Prev: Dent. Surg. St. And. Hosp.

CLARVIS, Mark Christian Kingsteignton Surgery, Whiteway Road, Kingsteignton, Newton Abbot TQ12 3HN Tel: 01626 883312 Fax: 01626 336406; 12 Vale Road, Decoy, Newton Abbot TQ12 1DZ — MB ChB 1987 Bristol; DCH RCP Lond. 1990. (Bristol University) Clin. Asst. (Upper GI Endoscopy) Torbay Hosp. Prev: Trainee GP Newton Abbot; Ho. Phys. Roy. Cornw. Hosp.; Ho. Surg. Torbay Hosp.

CLASON, Mr Alexander Ernest Darlington Memorial Hospital, Hollyhurst Road, Darlington DL3 6HX Tel: 01325 380100; Oakwood House, Dalton Road, Croft on Tees, Darlington DL2 2SY — MB ChB 1975 Glas.; PhD Glas. 1971, BSc 1968, MB ChB 1975; FRCS Glas. 1979. Cons. Gen. Vasc. Surg. Darlington Memor. Hosp. Socs: Vasc. Soc. GB & Irel. (N. Eng. Vasc. Gp.).

CLASON THOMAS, David Howell 371 Chepstow Road, Newport NP19 8HL Tel: 01633 277771 — MB BS 1953 Lond.; MRCS Eng. LRCP Lond. 1949; DObst RCOG 1967. (St. Bart.) Civil Serv. Med. Off.; Police Surg.; Admiralty Surg. & Agent. Prev: SHO (Obst.) Middlesbrough Matern. Hosp.; Sen. Ho. Phys. W. Hartlepool Gen. Hosp.; Squadron Ldr. RAF Med. Br.

CLASPER, Mr Jonathan Charles 7 Bodmin Close, Belmont, Hereford HR2 7ZB — MB ChB 1986 Glas.; FRCS Ed. 1992; Dip. IMC RCS Ed. 1989.

CLASPER, Paul 65 Station Road, Stanley DH9 0JP — MB ChB 1986 Dundee.

CLASPER, Susan Walker Medical Group, Church Walk, Walker, Newcastle upon Tyne NE6 3BS; 2 Sovereign Court, Jesmond Road, Jesmond, Newcastle upon Tyne NE2 1JZ Email: jmbarua@aol.com — MB BS 1993 Newc.; MRCGP 1999; DFFP 1999; DCH RCP Lond. 1995; DRCOG RCOG Lond. 1998. (Newc. u. tyne) p/t GP Retainee. Walker Med.Gp. Ch. Walk.Newc. Socs: BMA; MPS. Prev: GP. Regist.Cruddas Pk. Newc.; SHO(OBS) Sunderland Dist. Gen.; SHO (Med.) S. Tyneside Dist. Hosp.

CLATWORTHY, Mary Audrey — MB BS 1994 Lond.; MRCGP 2001; MA Camb. 1996; MRCP 1998 (UK). GP Princip.

CLATWORTHY, Menna Ruth Crud-yr-Awel, St. Illtyd, Abertillery NP13 2AY — MB BCh 1996 Wales.

CLAVERT, Katrina Lee Flat 2, 48 Belmont Road, St Andrews, Bristol BS6 5AT — MB ChB 1996 Ed.

CLAXTON, Alison New Hollins, Brackenthwaite, Loweswater, Cockermouth CA13 9UX — MB ChB 1981 Glas.

CLAXTON, Alleyna Pascale Department of Microbiology, Chelsea and Westminster Hospital, Fulham Road, London SW10 9NH Tel: 020 8846 8273 Fax: 020 8746 8270 Email: a.claxton@ic.ac.uk; 86C Tollington Park, Stroud Green, London N4 3RA Tel: 020 7263 6494 — MB BS 1994 Lond.; MA Camb. 1995; MRCP (Lond.) 1998. (Gonville and Caius/St Bartholomews MC) Specialist Regist. (MicroBiol.) Chelsea & W.minster & Char. Cross Hosps. Prev: SHO (Respirat. & Gen. Med.) Homerton Hosp. Lond.; SHO Rotat. (Nephrol. & Med. Oncol.) Roy. Free Hosp. Lond.; SHO (Trop. & Infec. Dis.s) Coppetts Wood Hosp. Lond.

CLAXTON, Andrew Robert 36 Priory Street, Bowdon, Altrincham WA14 3BQ Tel: 0161 928 4984 — MB ChB 1988 Manch.; BSc St. And. 1985. Specialist Regist. (Anaesth.) Stoke-on-Trent Sch. Anaesth. Socs: Brit. Med. Soc.; Assn. Anaesth. Prev: Clin. Research Fell. Univ. Toronto, Canada; Helicopter Emerg. Med. Serv. Regist. Roy. Lond. Hosp.

CLAXTON, Bret Andrew 7 The Orchards, Bingley BD16 4AZ — MB ChB 1994 Aberd.

CLAXTON, Nicola Brigitte 23 The Regina, Bath BA1 2QE — MB ChB 1995 Bristol.

CLAY, Albert Arthur, OBE (retired) Blue Waters, Mortehoe, Woolacombe EX34 7ED Tel: 01271 870685 — MRCS Eng. LRCP Lond. 1939.

CLAY, Andrea Elizabeth The Surgery, Reading Road, Hook RG27 9ED Tel: 01256 762125 — MB ChB 1990 Sheff.; MRCGP 1996; DFFP 1995. p/t Princip. GP, Hook Surg.

CLAY, Anita Royal Devon & Exeter Hospital, Barrack Road, Exeter EX4 5DW Tel: 01392 411611 — MB BS 1982 Lond. Clin. Asst. (A & E) Devon. Socs: Nat. Inst. Med. Herbalist.

CLAY, Barbara Ellen Maire (retired) Elm Rise, Greens Lane, Wroughton, Swindon SN4 0RJ Fax: 01793 845957 Email: barbara.clay@virgin.net — MRCS Eng. LRCP Lond. 1961; FRCR 1974; FFR 1973; Dip. Med. Educat. Dund 1993; DMRD Eng. 1969; DObst RCOG 1964 BA(open) April 1999. Prev: Cons. (Radiol.) P.ss Margt. Hosp. Swindon.

***CLAY, Beverley Elizabeth** 63 Green Lane, Bournemouth BH10 5LE — MB BS 1994 Lond.; BSc (Hons.) Lond. 1991.

CLAY, Charles Brian (retired) Fairhurst, 38 Rawson Avenue, Halifax HX3 0LR Tel: 01422 349504 — BM BCh 1956 Oxf.; MA, BM BCh Oxf. 1956. Prev: GP Halifax 1961 - 1992.

CLAY, Jennifer Caroline Department of Genitourinary Medicine, Pilgrim Hospital, Sibsey Road, Boston PE21 9QS; The White Horse House, Sea Lane, Old Leake, Boston PE22 9JH Tel: 01205 871185 — MB BS 1968 Lond.; MRCS Eng. LRCP Lond. 1967; FRCOG 1991, M 1976; Dip. Midw. Coll O&G. S. Afr. 1971. (Roy. Free) Cons. Genitourin. Med. S. Lincs. HA. Socs: BMA & Med. Soc. Study Venereal Dis. Prev: Cons. & Hon. Sen. Clin. Lect. (Genitourin. Med.) Gen. Hosp. Birm. & Univ. Birm.; Hosp. Med. Off. (O & G) Mpilo Hosp. Bulawayo, Rhodesia; Med. Off. (Med.) Baragwanath Hosp. Johannesburg, S. Africa.

CLAY, Michael Joseph (retired) The Croft, Blencarn, Penrith CA10 1TX Tel: 01768 88693 — MB BS 1942 Durh.; LLB Durh. 1937; LMCC 1957. Prev: Ho. Surg. (ENT) Roy. Vict. Infirm. Newc.

CLAY, Mollie Elizabeth 15 Cornwall Road, Dorchester DT1 1RU Tel: 01305 251752; 62 Monmouth Road, Dorchester DT1 2DG — MB ChB 1968 Sheff. (Sheff.) Prev: SHO (Cas.) Roy. Hosp. Sheff.

CLAY, Mr Nigel Robert c/o Department Orthopaedic Surgery, Glan Clwyd Hospital, Rhyl LL18 5UJ Tel: 01745 534997 Fax: 01745 534997 Email: nigel.clay@cd-tr.wales.nhs.uk — MB ChB 1977 Dundee; FRCS Ed. 1983. (Dundee) Cons. Orthop. Surg. Glan Clwyd Hosp. Rhyl. Socs: Fell. Brit. Orthop. Assoc.; BMA. Prev: Sen. Regist. (Orthop. & Trauma) Cardiff Roy. Infirm; Regist. (Orthop. & Traumat.) Univ. Hosp. Nottm.

CLAY, Philip Rhodes (retired) Chiltington, 35 Blanford Road, Reigate RH2 7DP — BM BCh 1946 Oxf.; FRCP Lond. 1973, M 1950; DCH Eng. 1952. Prev: Cons. Paediat. E. Surrey, & Cuckfield & Crawley HAs.

CLAY, Richard Antony King Georges Hospital, Eastern Avenue, Newbury Park, Redbridge, Ilford IG3 8YB Tel: 020 8554 8811; 4 Waverley Close, South Woodford, London E18 1HY Tel: 020 8505 6835 — MB BS 1951 Lucknow; MFCM 1973; DPH Eng. 1964. (King Geo. Med. Coll. Lucknow) Phys. Occupat. Health Dept. King Geo. Hosp. Ilford. Prev: Dist. Community Phys. MOEH Redbridge; Act. Dir. Health Servs. Roy. Boro. Kensington & Chelsea; Dist. Med. Off. Brit. W. Indies.

CLAY, Ruth Susan 72 Priory La, Macclesfield SK10 4AF — BM 1997 Soton.

CLAY, Simon Nicholas Poplars Surgery, 17 Holly Lane, Erdington, Birmingham B24 9JN Tel: 0121 373 4216 Fax: 0121 382 9576; 101 Darnick Road, Sutton Coldfield B73 6PF Tel: 0121 354 7530 Email: simonnclay@aol.com — MB ChB 1986 Birm.; MRCGP 1990;

Cert. Family Plann. JCC 1990. Clin. Asst. (Dermat.) Good Hope Hosp., Sutton Coldfield. Prev: SHO (Paediat.) Wellington Hosp., NZ; Trainee GP Sutton Coldfield VTS; SHO (Geriat. & Med.) Good Hope Hosp. Sutton Coldfield.

CLAY, Stephen John Charles Quorn Medical Centre, 1 Station Road, Quorn, Loughborough LE12 8BP Tel: 01509 412232 Fax: 01509 620652 — BM BS 1985 Nottm.; BMedSci (1st cl. Hons.) Nottm. 1983; MRCGP (Distinc.) 1991; DCH RCP Lond. 1990; DRCOG 1990. Clin. Asst. (Paediat. & A & E) Qu. Med. Centre Nottm. Prev: SHO Rotat. (Paediat.) Qu. Med. Centre Nottm.; SHO (O & G) Leicester Roy. Infirm.; SHO Rotat. (Med.) Leicester HA.

CLAYDEN, Graham Stuart Paediatric Unit, St. Thomas Hospital, Lambeth Palace Road, London SE1 7EH Tel: 020 7928 9292; 41 Beckenham Road, Beckenham BR3 4PR Tel: 020 8658 3709 — MB BS 1970 Lond.; MB BS (Hons.) Lond. 1970; MD Lond. 1981; FRCP Lond. 1984; MRCP (UK) 1972; MRCS Eng. LRCP Lond. 1970. (Westm.) Reader (Paediat.) United Med. & Dent. Sch. of Guy's & St. Thos. Hosps. Lond.; Hon. Cons. Paediat. St. Thos. Hosp. & Hosp. for Childr. Gt. Ormond. St. Lond. Socs: Acad. Bd. Mem. Brit. Paediat. Assn. Prev: Sen. Regist. (Paediat.) Hosp. Sick Childr. Gt. Ormond St. Lond.; Lect. (Paediat.) & Hon. Sen. Regist. St. Thos. Hosp. Med. Sch. Lond.; SHO (Paediat.) Soton. Univ. Gp. Hosps.

CLAYDEN, Lady Gwendoline Edith 61 Wimpole Street, London W1M 7DE Tel: 020 7935 3117; 8 Walton Street, London SW3 1RE Tel: 020 7589 1300 — MB BCh 1946 Witwatersrand. (Witwatersrand) Socs: Assoc. Mem. Brit. Assn. Plastic Surgs; Internat. Soc. Aesthetic Plastic Surg. & Brit. Assn. Aesthetic. Prev: Clin. Asst. Plastic Surg. St. Thos. Hosp. Lond.; Regist. Plastic Surg. Baragwaneth Hosp. Johannesburg; Cons. Plastic Surg. Harari Hosp. Salisbury, Zimbabwe.

CLAYDEN, John Richard Elmwood Health Centre, Huddersfield Road, Holmfirth, Huddersfield HD9 3TR Tel: 01484 689111 Fax: 01484 689333; Jomari, 25 Binns Lane, Holmfirth, Huddersfield HD9 3BL Tel: 01484 683851 Fax: 01484 686139 Email: jclayden@familydoc.win.uk.net — MB ChB 1969 Liverp.; DFFP 1994; DRCOG 1981. Edr. Kirklees MAAE Magazine. Socs: BMA & Liverp. Med. Inst.; Disp. Drs. Assn. Prev: Ho. Phys. Ormskirk & Dist. Gen. Hosp.; Ho. Surg. Bradford Roy. Infirm. & St. Luke's Hosp. Bradford.

CLAYDON, Adrian Hepton 90 Juniper, Bracknell RG12 7ZF Email: aclaydon@doctors.org.uk — MB ChB 1990 Leic.; MRCP (UK) 1995. Research Fell. (Gastroenterol.) Centr. Middlx. Hosp., Pk. Roy. Prev: Regist (Gastroenterol) W. Bay Health, NZ.

CLAYDON, Elizabeth Joanne The Exmoor Unit, North Devon District Hospital, Raleigh Park, Barnstaple EX31 4JB Tel: 01271 322483 Fax: 01271 322370 — MB ChB 1979 Birm.; FRCP 1996. Cons. Genitourin. Med. and HIV, N. Devon Dist. Hosp. Barnstaple; Cons. Genitourin. Med., Roy. Devon and Exeter Healthcare NHS Trust, Exeter; Med. Director, N.ern Devon Health Care NHS Trust. Prev: Cons. Genitourin. & HIV St. Marys Hosp. Lond.

CLAYDON, Peter John Barnsley Hospital, Gawber Rd, Barnsley S75 2EP Tel: 01226 730000; 31 Huddersfield Road, West Bretton, Wakefield WF4 4JP Tel: 01924 830327 — MB BS 1989 Newc.; FRCA. 1996. Cons.(Anaes.) Barnsley Dist Hosp. Prev: Regist. (Anaesth.) Sheff. (N. Trent).

CLAYDON, Peter John Orr Whiteparish Surgery, Common Road, Whiteparish, Salisbury SP5 2SU Tel: 01794 884269 Fax: 01794 884109; Dairy House Farm, Whiteparish, Salisbury SP5 2SF Tel: 01794 884500 — MRCS Eng. LRCP Lond. 1969; MA Camb. 1969; DA Eng. 1971. (King's Coll. Hosp.) Prev: Clin. Asst. (Anaesth.) Salisbury Health Dist.; SHO (O & G & Anaesth.) Salisbury Gp. Hosps.; Ho. Off. King's Coll. Hosp. Gp. Hosps.

CLAYDON, Philippa Elizabeth 5 Mill Gardens, Ringmer, Lewes BN8 5JD — MB ChB 1998 Sheff.; MB ChB Sheff 1998.

CLAYDON, Susan Margaret Dept. of Pathology, Algernon Firth Building, Leeds Gen. Infirmary, Great George St., Leeds LS1 3EX Tel: 0113 392 3936 Fax: 0113 247 0072; White House, High Street, Campsall, Doncaster DN6 9AF Tel: 01302 701128 — MB BS 1979 Lond.; MRCS Eng. LRCP Lond. 1979; MRCPath 1986; DMJ (Path.) Soc. Apoth Lond. 1985; FRCPath 1997. (Char. Cross) Cons. Anat. Path. To Leeds Gen. Inf./ Hon. Sen. Lect., Leeds Uni.; Cons. Path. To the Home Office. Socs: Brit. Assn. Forens. Med. Mem.; BMA Mem.; Med. Protec. Soc. Mem. Prev: Sen. Lect. (Forens. Path.) Univ. Wales Coll. Med. Cardiff; Regist. (Path.) Char. Cross Hosp. Lond.; Ho. Phys. W. Middlx. Hosp. Isleworth.

CLAYSON, Mr Anthony David North Manchester General Hospital, Delavneys Road, Crumpsall, Manchester M8 6RL Tel: 0161 720 2305; 52 Crossfield Drive, Worsley, Manchester M28 2QQ — MB ChB 1982 Manch.; FRCS (Orth.) 1993; FRCS Ed. 1987.

CLAYSON, Christopher William, CBE Cockiesknowe, Lochmaben, Lockerbie DG11 1RL Tel: 01387 810231 — MD (Gold Medal) Ed. 1936, MB ChB 1926; FRCP (Hon.) Ed. 1990; FRCP Ed. 1951, M 1948; FRCP Lond. 1968; DPH Ed. & Glas. 1930; Hon. FACP 1968; Hon. FRACP 1969; Hon. FRCPS Glas. 1970; Hon. FRCGP 1971. (Ed.) Socs: Hon. Mem. Scott. Soc. Phys. & Thoracic Soc. Prev: Pres. RCP Ed.; Chairm. Scott. Counc. Postgrad. Med. Educat.; Phys. i/c Area Dept. Tuberc. & Chest Dis. Dumfries & Galloway.

CLAYSON, Helen The Surgery, Askew Gate, Kirkby-in-Furness LA17 7TE Tel: 01229 889247 Email: drclayson@aol.com; Prospect House, Kirkby-in-Furness LA17 7UB — MB BS 1973 Lond.; FRCP 2001; MRCP (UK) 1977; FRCGP 1991, M 1979; DRCOG 1979. (Roy. Free) Gen. Practitioner, Kirkby in Furness; Med. Director, The Hospice of St Mary of Furness, Ulverston, Cumbria; Hon. Research Fell., Univ. of Sheff. Socs: BMA; Assn. of Palliat. Med. Prev: Non-Exec. Mem. Morecambe Bay HA; GP Tutor S. Cumbria; Med. Off. St. Mary's Hospice Ulverston.

CLAYSON, Mark Christopher Peel Medical Practice, 2 Aldergate, Tamworth B79 7DJ Tel: 01827 50575 Fax: 01827 318911 Email: mclayson@mclayson.freeserve.co.uk — MB BS 1986 Lond.; BSc (Hons.) Lond. 1983; MRCGP 1990; Dip. Med. Educat. Dundee 1995; DRCOG 1990. (King's Coll. Lond.) GP; Fell. Essex Univ.; Mem. Essex Fac. Bd./Mag. Ed.; GP Tutor N. Essex HA; Police Surg. Essex Constab.; Chairm. Nat. Asthma Campaign (Tendring Coastal Br.); GP Educat. & Train. Comm.; Mem. Local Educat. Bd.; Examr. Roy. Coll. Gen. Pract.; Reviewer for Med. Educat. Review. Socs: Nat. Assn. GP Tutors; BMA.

CLAYTON, Alison Jane Dept. of Medical Oncology, Christie Hospital, Wilmslow Road, Withington, Manchester M20 4BX Email: ackayton@picr.man.ac.uk; 54 School Lane, Didsbury, Manchester M20 6RT — BM BCh 1992 Oxf.; MRCP, 1996. (Oxford) Clin. Research Fell. in Med. Oncol., Christie Hosp., Manch.; Specialist Regist., Med. Oncol., Christie Hosp., Manch. Socs: MRCP. Prev: SHO Heamatology, Soton.; SHO Med./Oncol., Poole, Dorset; SHO Med. Rotat., S.U.H. NHS Trust, Soton.

CLAYTON, Andrew Robert 129 Whitaker Road, Derby DE23 6AQ Tel: 01332 625586 — BM BS 1980 Nottm.; BMedSci Nottm. 1978; MRCPsych 1985. Med. Dir. & Cons. Psychiat. (Liaison Psychiat.) S.. Derbysh. Ment. Health Trust. Prev: Sen. Regist. (Psychiat.) Qu. Med. Centre Nottm.

CLAYTON, Professor Dame Barbara Evelyn, DBE, CBE Geriatric Medicine, University of Southampton, Room AC 19, Southampton General Hospital, Tremona Road, Southampton SO16 6YD Tel: 02380 796800; 16 Chetwynd Drive, Bassett, Southampton SO16 3HZ Tel: 02380 769937 — MB ChB Ed. 1946; PhD Ed. 1949, MD 1953; Hon. DSc Soton. 1992; Hon. DSc Ed. 1985; Hon. FRCPI 1987; FRCP Ed. 1985; FRCP Lond 1972, M 1964; PRCPath 1984, F 1971, M 1965; FRCPCH (Hon) 1997, 1963. (Univ. Ed.) Hon. Research Prof. Metab. Univ. Soton.; Chairm. Standing Comm. on Postgrad. Med. & Dent. Educat.; Governor Brit. Nutrit. Foundat.; Chairm. Med. & Sci. Panel Leukaemia Reserch Fund; Hon. Pres. Brit. Dietetic Assoc. Socs: Hon. Fell. Amer. Soc. Clin. Path.; Hon. Mem. Assn. Clin. Biochem.s; Hon. Mem. Soc. for Study of Inborn Errors of Metab. Prev: Pres. Roy. Coll. Path.; Dean Fac. Med. Univ. Soton.; Prof. Chem. Path. & Human Metab. Univ. Soton.

CLAYTON, Charles Philip Lawrence Hounsfield Way Surgery, Hounsfield Way, Sutton-on-Trent, Newark NG23 6PX Tel: 01636 821023 Fax: 01636 822308; Wilton House, Mill Lane, Normanton on Trent, Newark NG23 6RW — MB BS 1976 Lond.; DCH Eng. 1982; DRCOG 1982. (St. Thos.)

CLAYTON, Claire Lorraine Norfolk and Norwich University Hospital, Brunswick Road, Norwich NR1 3SR — MB BS 1982 Lond.; T(GP) 1991. (Guy's) p/t Clin. Asst.

CLAYTON, Colin 144 Wigan Road, Hindley, Wigan WN2 3DF — MB ChB 1985 Leeds; BSc Leeds 1982, MB ChB 1985.

CLAYTON, David Alistair The Surgery, Glapthorn Road, Oundle, Peterborough PE8 4JA Tel: 01832 273408; The Old Forge, Church St, Polebrook, Peterborough PE8 5LP Tel: 01832 275316 — MB ChB 1986 Birm.; DCH RCP Lond. 1991; DRCOG 1989. (Birmingham) Med. Off. Oundle Sch.

CLAYTON, David John The Loddon Vale Practice, Hurricane Way, Woodley, Reading RG5 4UX Tel: 0118 969 0160 Fax: 0118 969 9103 — MB BCh 1978 Wales.

CLAYTON, Donna Linda 10 Loch Ard Cottages, Kinlochard, Aberfoyle, Stirling FK8 3TL Tel: 01877 387347 Fax: 01877 387347 — MB ChB 1995 Leic. (Univ. Leic.) SHO (Anaesth.) S.. Gen. Hosp. NHS Trust, Glas. Socs: Train. Mem.,Glas. & W. of Scotl. Soc. Anaesth. Prev: SHO (A & E) Vale of Leven DGH.

CLAYTON, Francis Godfrey 17 Nursery Road, Hoddesdon EN11 9LA Tel: 01992 465221 — MB BS Lond. 1955. (Middlx.)

CLAYTON, Frank David Calderstones, 7 Paddock Drive, Parkgate, Neston CH64 6TQ — MB ChB 1964 Liverp.; DPM Eng. 1967. (Liverp.) p/t Locum GP. Prev: Regist. (Psychiat.) Sefton Gen. Hosp. Liverp.; Princip. GP.

CLAYTON, Geoffrey Meikle The Old Rectory, Colney, Norwich NR4 7TX Tel: 01603 454314 Email: gmc@takeheart.co.uk — BSc Lond. 1952, MB BS 1955; MB CS 1980; FRCGP 1982, M 1968. (Middlx.) Socs: Brit. Computer Soc. Prev: Ho. Surg. (O & G) & Ho. Phys. Middlx. Hosp. Lond.; Ho. Off. GP Path. Laborat. Kingston.

CLAYTON, Gillian Sarah 10 Larkhill Lane, Formby, Liverpool L37 1LX — MB BS 1994 Lond.

CLAYTON, Guy Lawrence Lockwood Road Surgery, 30 Lockwood Road, Molescroft, Beverley HU17 9GQ Tel: 01482 888689 — MB ChB 1989 Manch.; BSc (Med. Sci.) St. And. 1986; DA 1991 Lond.; DCH 1993 Glas.; MRCGP 1994 Lond. Gen. Pract., Lockwood Rd., Beverley.

CLAYTON, Helen Mary Flat 1, 33A Fladgate Road, London E11 1LX — MB BS 1991 Lond.; DGM RCP Lond. 1994. SHO (Palliat. Care) MacMillan Hse. Qu. Eliz. II Hosp. Welwyn Gdn. City. Prev: SHO (O & G & c/o the Elderly) Newham Gen. Hosp.

CLAYTON, Janet Marilyn Maternity Ultrasound Department, Royal Berkshire Hospital, London Road, Reading RG1 5AN Tel: 0118 987 7279 Fax: 0118 987 8044; 5 Melksham Close, Lower Earley, Reading RG6 4AU Tel: 0118 975 5211 — MB BCh Wales 1978. (Welsh Nat. Sch. Med.) Assoc. Specialist (O & G Ultrasound) Roy. Berks. Hosp. Reading.

CLAYTON, John Pilkington, CVO (retired) Knapp House, Market Lavington, Devizes SN10 4DP Tel: 01380 813827 — MB BChir 1957 Camb.; MA Camb. 1951; MRCS Eng. LRCP Lond. 1945. Prev: Surg.Apoth. HM Ho.hold at Windsor & HM the Qu. Mother's Ho.hold at Roy. Lodge.

CLAYTON, John Sunderland Dodington Surgery, 29 Dodington, Whitchurch SY13 1EU Tel: 01948 662033 Fax: 01948 663428 — MB ChB 1951 Sheff.; MRCS Eng. LRCP Lond. 1951; MRCGP 1974; DObst RCOG 1955. (Sheff.) Prev: Ho. Surg. (O & G) Qu.'s Pk. Hosp. Blackburn; Ho. Phys. City Gen. Hosp. Sheff.; Capt. RAMC.

CLAYTON, Keith Campbell 10 Casita Grove, Kenilworth CV8 2QA — MB ChB 1975 Leeds; FRCA (Eng.) 1980; LLM Cardiff 1996. Cons. (Anaesth.) Walsgrave Hosp. Coventry.; Hon. Sen. Lect. Univ. of Birm.; Hon. Sen. Lect. Univ. of Warwick.

CLAYTON, Mr Malcolm Ian 3 The Chase, Llangybi, Usk NP15 1TY Tel: 01633 450296 — MB BChir 1980 Camb.; BDS Ed. 1974; FRCS Ed. 1984. Cons. Surg. (ENT) Roy. Gwent Hosp. Newport. Prev: Sen. Regist. (ENT) Yorks. RHA.; Regist. (ENT) Univ. Hosp. Wales Cardiff; SHO (Oral Surg.) Univ. Hosp. S. Manch.

CLAYTON, Mark Ramsay Bideford Medical Centre, Abbotsham Road, Bideford EX39 3AF Tel: 01237 476363 Fax: 01237 423351; 1 Lower Winsford Court, Abbotsham Road, Bideford EX39 3QP — MB BS 1984 Lond.; MRCGP 1991; DRCOG 1990. (Char. Cross Hosp. Med. Sch.) Approved Gen. Pract. Trainer Devon & Cornw.

CLAYTON, Martyn Keith Glenwood Health Centre, Napier Road, Glenrothes KY6 1HL Tel: 01592 611171 Fax: 01592 611931 — MB ChB 1987 Manch.; BSc St. And. 1984; MRCGP 1991; DCCH RCP Ed. 1991.

CLAYTON, Michael Graham Gerrard Lower Moor Hey Farm, Pinfold Lane, Huddersfield HD2 2EN — MB 1971 Camb.; MA Camb. 1970, MB 1971, BChir 1970; MRCGP 1980. Cons. (A & E Med.) Huddersfield Roy. Infirm.

CLAYTON, Michael Robert Longton Medical Centre, 451 Warrington Rd, Rainhill, Prescot L35 4LL Tel: 0151 430 0333 Fax: 0151 431 0017 — MB ChB 1992 Bristol; BSc Bristol 1984; MRCGP 1996; DRCOG 1995; DCH RCP Lond. 1994. (Bristol) GP Princip. Socs: BMA & Christian Med. Fell.sh. Prev: Ho. Off. S.mead & Bristol Roy. Infirm.; Preston V.T.S.

CLAYTON, Pamela Blanche Two Rivers, Cargreen, Saltash PL12 6PA — MB BS Lond. 1955; DA Eng. 1959; Cert. Family Plann. JCC 1970. (Roy. Free) Clin. Med. Off. Mid Downs. Prev: SHO (Anaesth.) Redhill Gen. Hosp.; Ho. Surg. King's Lynn Hosp.; Ho. Phys. St. John's Hosp. Chelmsford.

CLAYTON, Peter Horsford Medical Centre, 77 Holt Road, Horsford, Norwich NR10 3DX Tel: 01603 891122 Fax: 01603 891139 — MB BS 1981 Lond.; MRCGP 1985; DCH RCP Lond. 1990; Cert. Family Plann. JCC 1990. (Guy's) Police Surg. Norwich & S12 Approved Doctor Ment. Health. Socs: Assoc. of Police Surg.s.

CLAYTON, Peter Ellis Royal Manchester Childrens Hospital, Manchester M27 4HA Tel: 0161 727 2585 Fax: 0161 727 2583 Email: peter.clayton@man.ac.uk — MB ChB 1984 Manch.; BSc (Hons.) Manch. 1981, MD 1991; MRCP (UK) 1989; FRCPCH 1998. Sen. Lect. (Child Health & Paediat. Endocrinol.) Roy. Manch. Childr. Hosp. Socs: Brit. Soc. Paediat. Endocrinol.; Eur. Soc. Paediat. Endocrinol.; Amer. Endocrine Soc. Prev: Lect. (Child Health) Univ. Manch.; Regist. Rotat. (Paediat.) Bolton Gen. Hosp. & Roy. Manch. Childr. Hosp.; MRC Train. Fell. (Endocrinol.) Univ. Virginia, USA.

CLAYTON, Professor Peter Theodore Biochemistry Unit, Institute of Child Health, 30 Guilford St., London WC1N 1EH Tel: 020 7242 9789 Fax: 020 7404 6191 Email: pclaytonich.ucl.ac.uk; 6 Priory Gardens, Highgate, London N6 5QS Tel: 020 8348 7052 — MB BChir 1974 Camb.; MD Camb. 1984, MA 1975; FRCP Lond. 1992; MRCP (UK) 1977; FRCPCH 1997. Prof. Inst. Child Health & Hon. Cons. Phys. Gt. Ormond St. Hosp. for Childr. & Univ. Coll. Hosps., Lond. Socs: FRCPCh.; Fell.Roy. Coll. of Phys.s (Lond.).

CLAYTON, Philip Clayton and Partners, 45 Castle Street, Dumfries DG1 1DU Tel: 01387 252848 Fax: 01387 248096 — MB ChB 1975 Dundee; BSc (Med. Sci.) St. And. 1972; MRCGP 1982.

CLAYTON, Philip Frank Alton Street Surgery, Alton Street, Ross-on-Wye HR9 5AB Tel: 01989 563646 Fax: 01989 769438; Merrivale House, Merrivale Lane, Ross-on-Wye HR9 5JL Tel: 01989 768594 — MB BS 1986 Lond.; BSc Lond. 1983, MB BS 1986; MRCGP 1990. (Mem. Brit. Med. Acupuncture Soc.) Prev: Trainee GP Som. VTS.

CLAYTON, Philip Peter Hilbre, Layters Way, Gerrards Cross SL9 7QY — MB BS 1997 Lond.

CLAYTON, Richard David 22 Prenton Lane, Birkenhead CH42 9NX — MB ChB 1990 Leeds.

CLAYTON, Richard Nigel North Staffordshire NHS Trust, Ward 60, Nines Block, City General Hospital, Stoke-on-Trent ST4 6QG Tel: 01782 553424 Fax: 01782 553427 — MD Birm. 1978; BSc Lond. 1967, MB BS 1970; FRCP Lond. 1985, M 1974. Cons. Phys. Endocrinol. & Prof. of Med. Univ. Keele N. Staffs. Hosp. Centre Stoke on Trent. Prev: Sen. Clin. Sci., Cons. Phys. & Endocrinol. Cancer Research Centre Harrow.

CLAYTON, Ruth 29 Dodington, Whitchurch SY13 1EN Tel: 01948 662033 Fax: 01948 663428 — MB BS 1987 Lond. Prev: SHO (A & E) Weymouth Dist. Hosp.; Ho. Off. (Surg.) Roy. Shrewsbury Hosp.; Ho. Off. (Med.) Yeovil Dist. Hosp.

CLAYTON, Stephen John Station Road Surgery, Station Road, Stalbridge, Sturminster Newton DT10 2RG Tel: 01963 362363 Fax: 01963 362866 — MB ChB 1984 Leic.; MB ChB Leic. l984; MRCGP 1991. SHO (Med.) Rotat. Leics. HA.

CLAYTON, Susan Dawn West Lawn, 42 Nab Lane, Shipley BD18 4HH — MB ChB 1968 Leeds; DA Eng. 1971. Clin. Asst. (Anaesth.) Bradford HA.

CLAYTON, Tracey Jane Overbridge Cottage, 38 Brook St., Chipping Sodbury, Bristol BS37 6AZ Email: tewaring@hotmail.com — MB ChB 1991 Leeds; MRCP (UK) 1995; FRCA 1998. Specialist Regist. Anaesth., Bristol. Socs: Intens. Care Soc. Prev: SHO (Anaesth.) Glos. Roy. Hosp.

CLAYTON, Wendy Mary (retired) 70 Collisdene Road, Orrell, Wigan WN5 8RL Tel: 01695 622073 — MB ChB Liverp. 1957. Prev: Cas. Off. Whiston Hosp. Prescot.

CLAYTON, William George 93 Whitefield Road, Stockton Heath, Warrington WA4 6ND Tel: 01925 263073 — MB ChB 1957 Liverp.; FFA RCS Eng. 1967.

CLAYTON, William John Department of General Practice & Primary Care, Royal Free Hospital School of Medicine, Rowland Hill St., London NW3 2PF — MB BS 1980 Lond. (Middx.)

CLAYTON-JOLLY, Alexander James 12 Jubet Court, Green Lanes, London N16 9ED — MB BS 1993 Lond.

CLAYTON-PAYNE, Barrie John (retired) Bencista, Oak Hill Cross Road, Teignmouth TQ14 8TN Tel: 01626 772265 Fax: 01625 779299 — MB BS Lond. 1955; MRCS Eng. LRCP Lond. 1955; MRCGP 1963; DObst RCOG 1957. Prev: Ho. Phys. W. Lond. Hosp. Hammersmith.

CLAYTON PAYNE, Christopher David Gold Street Surgery, Gold Street, Saffron Walden CB10 1EJ Tel: 01799 525325 Fax: 01799 524042; School Street Surgery, Great Chesterford, Saffron Walden CB10 1NN Tel: 01799 530950 Fax: 01799 524042 — MB BS 1978 Lond.; MRCGP 1983; DCH RCP Lond. 1982; DRCOG 1981. Clin. Asst. St. Jas. Hosp. Saffron Walden; Clin. Asst. (Ment. Handicap) Saffron Walden; GP Trainer E. Anglia Region. Prev: GP Trainee Wessex VTS; Ho. Phys. St. Johns Hosp. Chelmsford; Ho. Surg. Lond. Hosp. Whitechapel.

CLAYTON-SMITH, Jill Department Medical Genetics, St Mary's Hospital, Whitworth Park, Manchester M13 0JH Tel: 0161 276 6264 Fax: 0161 276 6145 Email: jcs@central.cmnt.nwest.nhs.uk; 1 Broomfield Road, Heaton Moor, Stockport SK4 4NB — MD 1993 Manch.; MB ChB (Hons.) 1982; MRCP (UK) 1985; FRCP (UK) 1999; FRCPCH 1997. Cons. Clin. Geneticist Manch. Prev: Sen. Regist. (Clin. Genetics) Manch.

CLAYTON-STEAD, Andrew John Shelf Health Centre, Shelf Moor Road, Shelf, Halifax HX3 7PQ Tel: 01274 691159; 68 Poplar Grove, Bradford BD7 4LJ — MB ChB 1976 Manch.

CLEAK, Mr David Kenneth 2 Manor Close, Droitwich WR9 8HG — MB ChB 1970 Birm.; FRCS Eng. 1976. Cons. Orthop. Surg. Worcs. Health Trust. Prev: Sen. Regist. (Orthop.) Roy. Orthop. Hosp. Birm. (Woodlands).

CLEAK, Victoria Elizabeth 26 Earls Road, Bevois Valley, Portswood, Southampton SO14 6SH Tel: 02380 221453 — MB ChB 1996 Sheff.

CLEAL, David John Park Avenue Medical Centre, 166-168 Park Avenue North, Northampton NN3 2HZ Tel: 01604 716500 Fax: 01604 721685 — MB BS 1979 Lond.; DSM 2001 Bath Univ.; BSc (Hons.) Lond. 1976; MRCP (UK) 1982; MRCS Eng. LRCP Lond. 1979; MRCGP 1986; DRCOG 1984. (Char. Cross) Trainer (Gen. Pract.) N.ampton VTS.

CLEANTHIS, Telemachos Marios 12 Russell Av, London N22 6PP — MB BS 1997 Lond.

CLEAR, Daniela Brigid 103 Malvern Road, St Johns, Worcester WR2 4LJ — MB ChB 1989 Bristol; MRCP (UK) 1993; DTM & H Liverp. 1992. Clin. Research Fell. Univ. Dept of Neurol. Sci. Walton Centre for Neurol. & Neurosurg. Liverp.

CLEAR, John Davidson Taunton and Somerset Hospital Dept of Anaesthetics, Musgrove Park, Taunton TA1 5DA Tel: 01823 342114 Fax: 01823 344936 Email: john.clear@tst.nhs.uk — MB ChB 1986 Birm.; BSc (Med. Biochem. Studies) Birm. 1983; FRCA 1993. Cons. (Anaesth.) Taunton & Som. Hosp. Socs: Obst. Anaesth. Assn.; Assn. Anaesthetics.; Vasc. Anaesth. Soc. Prev: Sen. Regist. Rotat. (Anaesth.) Soton. Salisbury & Winchester; Regist. (Anaesth.) St. Thos. Hosp. Lond.; Regist. (Anaesth.) Odstock Hosp. Salisbury.

CLEAR, Mary Rosina Nunwell Surgery, 10 Pump Street, Bromyard HR7 4BZ Tel: 01885 483412 Fax: 01885 488739; 186 West Malvern Road, Malvern WR14 4AZ — MB ChB 1981 Birm.; DRCOG 1986; DCH RCP Lond. 1984. GP. Prev: Trainee GP Hereford Co. Hosp. VTS.

CLEAR HILL, Bridget Gytha Rose Billericay Health Centre, Stock Road, Billericay CM12 0BJ Tel: 01277 658071 Fax: 01277 631892 — MB BS 1980 Lond.; MRCP (UK) 1984; MRCGP 1985. (Middlx.)

CLEARE, Anthony James Institute of Psychiatry, De Crespigny Park, London SE5 8AF Tel: 020 7848 5130 Fax: 020 7848 5129 Email: a.cleare@iop.kcl.ac.uk — MB BS 1990 Lond.; BSc (Hons.) Lond. 1987; MRCPsych 1994; PHD London, 1998. Sen. Lect. (Psychol. Med.) Inst. of Psychiat.; Hon. Cons. Maudsley Hosp. Lond. Prev: Sen. Regist. (Psychiat.) Maudsley Hosp. Lond.; Regist. (Psychiat.) Maudsley Hosp. Lond.

CLEARKIN, Mr Louis Gerard Arrowe Park Hospital, Upton, Wirral CH49 5PE Tel: 0151 604 7047 — MB ChB 1978 Sheff.; ChM 1992 Sheff.; FRCS Eng. (Ophth.) 1983; FCOphth 1989; DO RCS Eng. 1982. Cons. Ophth. Surg. Wirral NHS Trust; Hon. Lect. (Ophth.) Univ. Liverp. Socs: N. Eng. Ophth. Soc. & UK Intraocular Implant Soc. Prev: Sen. Regist. Mersey RHA; Clin. Fell. Moorfields Eye Hosp. Lond.

CLEARKIN, Peter Michael 47 Cobbett Road, Bitterne Park, Southampton SO18 1HJ — MB BCh BAO 1953 Belf.; DPH NUI 1959.

CLEARKIN, Ronald James Kettering General Hospital NHS Trust, Rothwell Road, Kettering NN16 8UZ — MB BS 1982 Lond.; BSc (Hons.) Lond. 1979; MRCP (UK) 1986; FRCA 1991; DTM & H RCP Lond. 1992. (Westm.) Cons. Phys. Kettering Gen. Hosp. NHS Trust. Prev: Sen. Regist. (Med.) N.. RHA.

CLEARY, Brian James 9 Norbeck Avenue, Manchester M21 8TG — MB ChB 1990 Manch.; BSc (Med. Sci.) St. And. 1987; MRCP (UK) 1996. Specialist Regist. Diagnostic Radiol. Univ. Manch. Train. Scheme.

CLEARY, Colman Valentine 4 Rugosa Road, West End, Woking GU24 9PA — MB BCh BAO 1971 NUI; MFPM 1989. (Univ. Coll. Dub.) Unit Manager & Sen. Med. Off. Med. Control Agency Lond. Socs: Fell. Roy. Soc. Med.; BMA. Prev: Med. Adviser Pharma Industry; Dep. Sec. Gen. Irish Med. Assn.; Resid. Surg. Off. Moorfields Eye Hosp. Lond.

CLEARY, Mr John Eric The Nuffield Hospital, Birkby Hall Road, Huddersfield HD2 2BL Tel: 01484 533131; Lower Binns Barn, Binns Lane, Holmfirth, Huddersfield HD7 1BL — MB ChB 1967 Liverp.; MChOrth Liverp. 1974; FRCS Eng. 1973; FRCS Ed. 1972.

CLEARY, John Joseph Laurence Carlton Street Surgery, Carlton Street, Horninglow, Burton-on-Trent DE13 0TE Tel: 01283 511387 Fax: 01283 517174 — MB BCh BAO 1987 NUI.

CLEARY, John William (retired) 30 Pinchbeck Road, Spalding PE11 1QD Tel: 01775 712862 — MB BChir 1974 Camb.; MA Camb. 1986, BA 1970; FRCP Lond. 1995; MRCP (UK) 1976. Prev: Cons. Phys. (Med. for Elderly) P'boro. Dist. Hosp.

CLEARY, Mary Marion Foston Lodge, Foston, York YO60 7QE Tel: 0165381 297 — MB ChB 1961 Sheff. (Sheff.) GP York. Socs: York Med. Soc.

CLEARY, Mary Patricia Goodmayes Hospital, Goodmayes, Ilford IG3 8XJ Tel: 020 8970 8391 Fax: 020 8970 5705 — MB BCh BAO 1974 NUI; MSc Clin. Psychother. Lond. 1985; MRCPI 1981; MRCPsych 1982; MRCPsych 1982. (Univ. Coll. Dublin) Cons. Psychiat. Good Mayes Hosp. Ilford Essex; Med. mem. Ment. HEALTH Review Tribunal; Second opinion Apptd. doctor Ment. HEALTH ACT Commiss., 1998 - 2001. Prev: Cons. Psychiat. Claybury Hosp.; Cons. Psychiat. Basildon Dist. Gen. Hosp.; Sen. Regist. Claybury Hosp. & The Lond. Hosp.

CLEARY, Maureen Anne Willink Biochemical Genetics Unit, Royal Manchester Childrens Hospital, Hospital Road, Pendlebury, Manchester M27 4HA Tel: 0161 727 2137 Fax: 020 7727 2137 Email: maureen@willink.demon.co.uk; 14 Derbyshire Road, Sale M33 3EG — MB ChB 1985 Glas.; MRCP (UK) 1989; MD Glas. 1997. (Glasgow) Cons. Paediat. with s/i in Metab. Dis. Roy. Manch. Childr.s Hosp. Socs: BMA; Manch. Med. Soc. Prev: Sen. Regist. (Paediat.) Roy. Manch. Childr. Hosp. Manch.; Research Fell. Roy. Manch. Childr. Hosp.; Regist. Rotat. (Paediat.) NW RHA.

CLEARY, Paul Robert 133 Church Street, Milnthorpe LA7 7DZ — MB ChB 1991 Ed.

CLEARY, Pauline Mary Peel Health Centre, Angouleme Way, Bury BL9 0BT Tel: 0161 764 0311 Fax: 0161 761 7548; 12 Ribbleton Close, Seddons Farm, Bury BL8 2TH — MB ChB 1979 Sheff.

CLEASBY, Morgan Joseph 374 Moor Green Lane, Birmingham B13 8QP — MB ChB 1992 Birm.; BSc (Physiol.) Birm. 1989; MRCP (UK) 1995. Regist. Rotat. (Radiol.) W. Midl. RHA Train. Scheme. Prev: SHO Rotat. (Gen. Med.) S. Birm. HA.

CLEASBY, Steven John 15 Green Close, Burnley BB11 3QL — MB ChB 1995 Leeds.

CLEATOR, Pamela Jean Gill Medical Centre, 5 Harriet Street, Walkden, Worsley, Manchester M28 3DR Tel: 0161 790 3033 Fax: 0161 702 9544; 6 Hazelfields, Worsley, Manchester M28 2LS Tel: 0161 728 2599 — MB ChB 1971 Manch.; MSc Manch. 1976. (Manchester)

CLEATOR, Susan Jane Persimmon Lodge, Collaroy Road, Cold Ash, Newbury RG18 9PB Tel: 01635 863734; 85 Sulgrave Road, London W6 7QH — BM BCh 1992 Oxf.; BA Oxf. 1989; MRCP (UK) 1995. SHO (Anaesth. & ITU) St. Mary's Hosp. Lond. Socs: BMA; Med. Wom. Federat. Prev: SHO Rotat. (Gen. Med.) N.wick Pk. Hosp. Harrow.

CLEAVE, Mr Hugh Latimer, CBE, Surg. Capt. RN Retd. 21 Chapel Meadow, Buckland Monachorum, Yelverton PL20 7LR Tel: 01822 852389 — FRCS Eng. 1935; MRCS Eng. LRCP Lond. 1931. (Middlx. & Bristol) Prev: Hon. Surg. to H.M. The Qu.; Cons. Surg. RN Hosp. Plymouth; Res. Med. Off. Putney Hosp.

CLEAVE, Nicola Jane 25 Elmsleigh Gardens, Southampton SO16 3GE — BM 1991 Soton.

CLEAVER, Christopher Patrick The White House, Frome St Quintin, Dorchester DT2 0HF — MB ChB 1990 Leic.

CLEAVER, Maxine Helen 40 Newland Lane, Coventry CV7 9BA — MB BS 1998 Newc.; MB BS Newc 1998.

CLEDWYN-DAVIES, Alann (retired) Birchwood, 9 Nicholas Way, Northwood HA6 2TR Tel: 01923 824206 — MRCS Eng. LRCP Lond. 1947. Prev: Capt. RAMC.

CLEE, Martin David Conquest Hospital, The Ridge, St Leonards-on-Sea TN37 7RD Tel: 01424 755255; Hedgeside, 98 Hastings Rd, Battle TN33 0TQ — MB ChB 1975 Ed.; BSc (Hons.) Med. Sci. Ed. 1973; FRCP Glas. 1989; MRCP (UK) 1977. (Edinbirgh) Cons. Phys. with interest in Respirat. Med. conquest Hosp., Hastings.; Hon. Sen. Lect. Glas. Univ. Prev: Sen. Regist. Ninewells Hosp. Dundee; Cons. Phys. StoneHo. Hosp.S, Lanarksh..

CLEE, William Benjamin The Park Canol Group Practice, Park Carnol Surgery, Central Park, Church Village, Pontypridd CF38 1RJ Tel: 01443 203414 Fax: 01443 218218; 40 Heol-y-Pentre, Pentyrch, Cardiff CF15 9QE Tel: 01222 892344 — MB BCh 1978 Wales; BSc (Hons.) Wales 1975; MRCP (UK) 1982. (Welsh National School of Medicine) GP; Vice-Chairm. Taff-Ely Drug Support Gp.; Clin. Asst. Endoscopy Clinic E. Glam. Hosp.; Mem. Mid Glam. Subst. Misuse Forum; Mem. Advis. Counc. on the Misuse of Drugs; Chairm. Welsh Advis. Comm. on Drug & Alcohol Misuse; Mem. Preven. Working Gp. ACMD; Mem. Clin. Guidelines Working Gp. Dept. of Health. Socs: Brit. Soc. Study Addic. Prev: Regist. (Med.) E. Glam. Dist. Gen. Hosp.

CLEELAND, Jonathan Alan Private Health Care, Bredon House, 321 Tettenhall Road, Wolverhampton WV6 0JZ Tel: 01902 753651 Fax: 01902 754210 Email: jonahthan.cleeland@private-healthcare.co.uk — MB ChB 1980 Liverp.; BSc (Hons.) Liverp. 1976; MFOM RCP Lond. 1991, AFOM 1989; Spec. Accredit. Occupat. Med. 1991. Cons. Occupat. Phys.& Partner. Socs: Soc. Occupat. Med.; BMA; M.I.O.S.H. Prev: Med. Dir., Corporate Med. Managem. Ltd. N.wich, Chesh.; Sen. Employm. Med. Adviser Health & Safety Exec. Leeds.

CLEEVE, Henry James William (retired) 67 Christchurch Mount, Epsom KT19 8LZ Tel: 01372 812487 — MB BS 1953 Lond.; BSc (Special) Lond. 1950; FRCPath 1976, M 1964; DCH Eng. 1958. Prev: Sen. Lect. & Hon. Cons. Chem. Path. St. Geo. Hosp. Lond.

CLEEVE, Stewart James 1 Hollybush Row, Chesham Road, Wigginton, Tring HP23 6HL — MB ChB 1997 Bristol.

CLEEVE, Victoria Jane 18 Warnington Drive, Doncaster DN4 6SS — MB BS 1998 Newc.; MB BS Newc 1998.

CLEGG, Alison Jane Ashburton Surgery, 1 Eastern Road, Ashburton, Newton Abbot TQ13 7AP Tel: 01364 652731 Fax: 01364 654273; Vicarage Bench, Bowden Hill, Ashburton, Newton Abbot TQ13 7RA — MB BS 1984 Lond.; DCH RCPS 1988.

CLEGG, Anthony Taleb and Partners, The Surgery, Burton Road, Woodville, Swadlincote DE11 7JG Tel: 01283 217036 Fax: 01283 552308; Higham, 25 Kilwardby St, Ashby-de-la-Zouch LE65 2FR — MB ChB 1977 Liverp.; Cert. Family Plann. JCC 1983; DRCOG 1982. Mem. S. Derbysh. Gen. Pract. Gp. Socs: NW Leics. Med. Soc. Prev: SHO (O & G) Warrington Dist. Gen. Hosp.; SHO (Paediat. Surg. & Urol.) Alder Hey Childr. Hosp.; SHO (Surg. & Cas.) Roy. Liverp. Hosp.

CLEGG, Brian Douglas Clydebank Health Centre, Kilbowie Road, Clydebank G81 2TQ Tel: 0141 531 6400 Fax: 0141 531 6465; 48 Munro Road, Jordanhill, Glasgow G13 1SF — MB ChB 1975 Aberd.

CLEGG, Brian Vincent (retired) 8 Holly Tree Close, Ley Hill, Chesham HP5 3QT Tel: 01494 785755 — MB BChir Camb. 1965; MA Camb. 1965; FFR 1972; DMRD Toronto 1968. Prev: Cons. Radiol. Hemel Hempstead Gen. Hosp. Lond.

CLEGG, David Francis Goude (retired) The Dower House, Bonehill, Tamworth B78 3HX Tel: 01827 289538 Email: clegg@sowerhse.force9.co.uk — MB ChB 1954 Manch.; FRCGP 1978, M 1972. Prev: GP Tamworth.

CLEGG, Donald Stuart Valentine House, 1079 Rochdale Road, Manchester M9 8AJ Tel: 0161 740 2524 Fax: 0161 795 2531; 33 Hilton Lane, Prestwich, Manchester M25 9SA — MB ChB 1974 Manch. Prev: Regist. (Anaesth.) Manch. Roy. Infirm.

CLEGG, Professor Edward John Dept. of Biomedical Sciences, University of Aberdeen, Marischal College, Aberdeen AB10 1YS Tel: 01224 274324 Fax: 01224 274329 Email: e.clegg@abdn.ac.uk; 22 Woodburn avenue, Aberdeen AB15 8JQ Tel: 01224 317132 Email: ejsdclegg@talk21.com — MB ChB Sheff. 1948; PhD Liverp. 1957; MD Sheff. 1964; FIBiol. 1975. (Sheff.) Emerit. Prof. Biol. Anthropol. Univ. Aberd. Socs: Hon. Mem. (Ex-Chairm.) Soc. Study Human Biol.; Life Mem. (Ex-Pres.) Anat. Soc. of GB & Irel. Prev: Regius Prof. Anat. Univ. Aberd.; Reader (Human Biol.) Univ. Sheff. & Lect. (Anat.) Univ. Liverp.; Ho. Surg. Roy. Infirm. Sheff.

CLEGG, Gareth Roger 14 Spottiswoode Street, Edinburgh EH9 1ER Tel: 0131 229 4118 Email: gareth@cleggs.demon.co.uk — MB ChB 1993 Ed.; MRCP (UK) 1996. (Univ. Ed.) SHO (A & E) Edin. Roy. Infirm.

CLEGG, Jane Moura 42 Cloncurry Street, Fulham, London SW6 6DU Tel: 020 7736 3445 — MB BS 1960 Lond.; DPM Eng. 1969. (Univ. Coll. Hosp.) Prev: Sen. Regist. Child. Psychiat. Lond. Hosp., Whipps Cross Hosp. & Leytonstone Child Guid. Clinic.

CLEGG, Mr John 20 Old Mill Avenue, Cannon Park, Coventry CV4 7DY Tel: 024 76 414602 — MB ChB 1965 Leeds; FRCS Eng. 1971. (Leeds) Cons. (Orthop. & Traum. Surg.) Coventry & Warks. Hosp. Prev: Sen. Regist. (Orthop.) Roy. Orthop. Hosp. Birm. & Coventry & Warks.; Hosp.; SHO (Orthop.) Marguerite Hepton Hosp. Boston Spa.

CLEGG, Mr John Fawcett (retired) Whitethorne, The Crescent, Hartford, Northwich CW8 1QS Tel: 01606 76400 Fax: 01270 251214 — MB BChir Camb. 1964; MA Camb. 1964; FRCS Eng. 1969; FRCS Ed. 1967. Prev: Sen. Regist. Manch. Roy. Infirm.

CLEGG, Jonathan Peter Harvey House Surgery, 13-15 Russell Avenue, St Albans AL3 5ES Tel: 01727 831888 Fax: 01727 845520; Doctors Surgery, 13-15 Russell Avenue, St Albans AL3 5HB — MB BS 1980 Lond.; DRCOG 1983; DFOM 1997. (Middlesex) Clin. Asst. (Minor Surg.); HSE Apptd. Doctor. Socs: Soc. Occupat. Med.

CLEGG, Nancy Grace (retired) 18 Walden Avenue, Arborfield, Reading RG2 9HR Tel: 0118 976 0256 — MB BChir Camb. 1940; MA Camb. 1939; MRCS Eng. LRCP Lond. 1939; DObst RCOG 1948. Prev: Sen. Scientif. Off. Rd. Research Laborat. Crowthorne.

CLEGG, Mr Raymond Thomas 7 Ladyfield Road, Thorpe Salvin, Worksop S80 3JS Tel: 01909 771544 Fax: 01909 771544 Email: rtclegg@tesco.net; 7 adyfield Road, Thorpe Salvin, Worksop S80 3JS Tel: 01909 771544 Fax: 01909 771544 Email: rtclegg@tesco.net — MB ChB 1968 Sheff.; FRCS Eng. 1974. Cons. ENT Surg. Roy. Hallamsh. Hosp. Hosps. Sheff.(Retd. Awarded Hon. Cons. Prev: Cons. ENT Surg. Chesterfield Roy. Hosp.

CLEGG, Sarah Katie 9 Lumsden Street, Top Right Flat, Yorkhill, Glasgow G3 8RQ — MB ChB 1996 Glas.

CLEGG, Susan 1 Highmoor Crescent, Oldham OL4 2SN — MB ChB 1985 Ed.

CLEGG, William Hardy (retired) Columcille, Strongarbh, Tobermory, Isle of Mull PA75 6RA Tel: 01688 302493 — MRCS Eng. LRCP Lond. 1959. Prev: Ho. Phys. & Ho. Surg. (Obst.) Halifax Gen. Hosp.

CLEGHORN, Mrs Jean (retired) Glenlee, Dalginross, Comrie, Crieff PH6 2EG Tel: 01764 670237 Email: arthur.cleghorn@btinternet.com — MB ChB 1943 Birm.; DCH Eng. 1948; DObst RCOG 1949. Prev: Med. Off. (Family Plann.) Forth Valley HB.

CLEGHORN, Nicola Jane 2 Cartington Court, Fawdon, Newcastle upon Tyne NE3 2JU — MB BS 1997 Newc.; BSc (Hons.) Newc. 1989; MPhil, Newc. 1994. SHO Paediat.

CLEIN, Emmanuel Morris 49 Southway, London NW11 6SB — MB BCh BAO Dub. 1948. (Univ. Dub.) Prev: GP Lond.; Capt. RAMC; Ho. Surg. Roy. E. Sussex Hosp.

CLEIN, Geoffrey Peter Poole Hospital NHS Trust, Longfleet Road, Poole BH15 2JB Tel: 01202 665511; 17 Bingham Avenue, Poole BH14 8ND Tel: 01202 707209 — MB BChir Camb. 1961; MA Camb. 1964; MD Camb. 1969; FRCP Lond. 1975, M 1963. (King's Coll. Hosp.) Cons. Phys. Poole Gen. Hosp. Socs: Brit. Soc. Haematol. Prev: Lect. (Med.) Univ. Camb.; Sen. Regist. Roy. Vict. Infirm. Newc.; Cons. Phys. St. Geo. Hosp. Lond.

CLEIN, Lewis John 80 Harley Street, London W1N 1AE Tel: 020 7935 4647 — MB BCh BAO 1949 Dub.; MD Dub. 1960; MRCP Lond. 1953; FRCPsych 1977; DPM Lond. 1959. (T.C. Dub.) Cons. Psychiat. Charter Nightingale Hosp. Lond. Socs: Fell. Roy. Soc. Med. Prev: Cons. Psychiat. Long Gr. Hosp. Epsom & Roy. Hosp. Richmond; Lect. (Ment. Health) Qu. Univ. Belf.; Sen. Regist. Maudsley Hosp. Lond.

CLELAND, Elinor Margaret (retired) 24 North Parade, Aberystwyth SY23 2NF Tel: 01970 612983 — MB ChB 1951 Ed.; DObst RCOG 1955. Prev: SHO (Obst.) St. David's Hosp. Cardiff.

CLELAND, Jennifer Ann 1 The Spires, Church Road, Holywood BT18 9DY Tel: 01232 421725 — MB BCh BAO 1988 Belf.; FRCOphth 1992.

CLELAND, Jennifer Rosemary 9 Glebe Avenue, Mauchline KA5 6AF — MB ChB 1969 Aberd.; Dch Eng. 1971. (Aberd.) SCMO Community Med. Ayrsh. & Arran HB. Prev: SHO W.. Infirm. Glas.; SHO (Paediat.) Hillingdon Hosp. Uxbridge.

CLELAND, John Ballochmyle Medical Practice, Institute Avenue, Catrine, Mauchline KA5 6RU Tel: 01290 551237 Fax: 01290 552784; 9 Glebe Avenue, Mauchline KA5 6AF Tel: 01290 50777 — MB ChB 1970 Glas.; FRCP Glas. 1994; MRCP (UK) 1974. Prev: SHO Med. Glas. Roy. Infirm.

CLELAND, Lorna Catherine Top Left, 19 Highburgh Road, Glasgow G12 9YF — MB ChB 1995 Glas.

CLELAND, Peter George 45 Montagu Avenue, Gosforth, Newcastle upon Tyne NE3 4JJ Tel: 0191 284 8844 — MB 1973 Camb.; BChir 1972; FRCP Lond. 1991; FRCP Ed. 1991; MRCP (UK) 1975. Cons. Neurol. Sunderland Roy. Hosp.; Cons. Neurol. Regional Neurol. Centre, Newc. Gen. Hosp.; Clin. Lect. in Neurol. to the Univ. of Newc. Socs: Worshipful Soc. of Apoth. Prev: Sen. Regist. (Neurol.) Newc. Gen. Hosp.; Regist. (Neurol.) Newc. Gen. Hosp.; SHO (Neurol.) Nat. Hosp. Lond.

CLELAND, Philip Ralph The Surgery, The Meads, Kington HR5 3DQ Tel: 01544 230302 Fax: 01544 230824; School Green, Huntington, Kington HR5 3PQ Tel: 01544 370650 — MB ChB 1967 Birm. (Birm.) Prev: Med. Off. Chas. Johnson Memor. Hosp., Zululand; Regist. (Anaesth.) Groote Schuur Hosp. Cape Town, S. Afr.; SHO (O & G) Harari Hosp. Salisbury, Zimbabwe.

CLELAND, Mr William Paton (retired) Green Meadows, Goodworth Clatford, Andover SP11 7HH Tel: 01264 324327 — MB BS 1934 Adelaide; FRCP Lond. 1966, M 1939; FRCS Eng 1946; FACS 1969. Hon. Cons. Surg. King's Coll. Hosp. & Roy. Brompton & Nat. Heart & Lung Hosp. Lond.; Adviser (Cardiothoracic Surg.) DoH. Prev: Cons. Thoracic Surg. Postgrad. Med. Sch. & Hammersmith Hosp. Lond.

CLELLAND, Colin Andrew Ravenwood, 12 St Georges Road, Stowlangtoft, Bury St Edmunds IP31 3JP Tel: 01359 31269 — MB ChB 1981 Leeds. Sen. Regist. (Histopath.) N. Gen. Hosp. Sheff.; Assoc. Mem. ACP. Prev: Hon. Regist. (Histopath.) Papworth Hosp. Camb.

CLELLAND, Ian Alan Young and Partners, The Ryan Medical Centre, St. Marys Road, Bamber Bridge, Preston PR5 6JD Tel: 01772 335136 Fax: 01772 626701 — MB ChB 1980 Dundee.

CLEMANS-GIBBON, Tracey Matilda South Street Surgery, 83 South Street, Bishop's Stortford CM23 3AP Tel: 01279 710800 Fax: 01279 710801; The Barn, Boyton End, Thaxted, Dunmow CM6 2RB Tel: 01371 831133 — MB BS 1985 Lond.

CLEMENS, Nicholas John The Health Centre, Bowers Place, Crawley Down, Crawley RH10 4HY Tel: 01342 713031 Fax: 01342 718715 — MB BS 1973 Lond.; MRCGP 1978; DRCOG 1978. Hon. Med. Off. Qu. Vict. Hosp. E. Grinstead.

CLEMENSON, Colin James (retired) 33 Rowson Street, Wallasey, Wirral — MRCS Eng. LRCP Lond. 1958. Prev: Chief Med. Off. Travancore Med. Fund Kerala, India.

CLEMENT, Mr Andrew Department of Obstetrics & Gynaecology, Queen Mary's University Hospital, Roehampton Lane, London SW15 5PN Tel: 020 8789 6611 Fax: 020 8355 2871; Upton House, Warboys Road, Kingston upon Thames KT2 7LS Tel: 020 8549 0137 — MB BChir 1973 Camb.; MA Camb. 1973; FRCS Eng. 1982; FRCOG 1995, M 1978. Cons. O & G Qu. Mary's Univ. Hosp. Lond. & Kingston Hosp. Socs: BMA; (Sec.) Sociéte Clinique Française. Prev: Sen. Regist. (O & G) Kingston, W.m. & St. Stephen's Hosps.; Regist. (O & G) St. John Radcliffe Hosp. Oxf. & St. Bart. Hosp. Lond.; Ho. Phys. & Ho. Surg. St. Bart. Hosp. Lond.

CLEMENT, Mr David Alun Morriston Hospital, Morriston NHS Trust, Swansea SA6 6NL Tel: 01792 703738; The Manor House, Highpool Lane, Newton, Swansea SA3 4TX Tel: 01792 361608 Fax: 01792 511102 Email: alun.clement@virgin.net — MB BS 1976 Lond.; DPhil Sussex 1972; BSc Lond. 1968; FRCS Eng. 1981; FRCS Ed. 1980. Cons. Orthop. Surg. Morriston NHS Trust. Prev: Sen. Regist. (Orthop.) P.ss Margt. Rose Orthop. Hosp. Edin.; Regist. (Orthop.) Nottm. HA.

CLEMENT, Frances Mary 2 Derriman Grove, Sheffield S11 9LE — BChir 1992 Camb.; DFFP 1996; DCH 1997. (Cambridge University)

CLEMENT, Joanna Merrill Orchard Surgery, Blackhorse Way, Horsham RH12 1SG Tel: 01403 253966/7 — MB BS 1987 Lond.

CLEMENT, John Alan Iestyn Thomas Royal Infirmary, Upper Maudlin St., Bristol BS2 8HW Tel: 0117 928 2163; (cons. room), Litfield House, Litfield Place, Clifton, Bristol BS8 Tel: 0117 973 1323 — MB BS 1957 Lond.; FFA RCS Eng. 1964; DA Eng. 1961. (Guy's) Cons. Anaesth. United Bristol Hosps.; Clin. Lect. Univ. Bristol. Socs: Assn. Anaesths.; Soc. Anaesth (Ex-Pres. SW Region). Prev: Sen. Regist. & Tutor, & Regist. (Anaesth.) United Bristol Hosps.; Regist. (Anaesth.) Leicester Roy. Infirm.

***CLEMENT, Jonathan Daniel** 1B Dunswin Court, Dalmuir, Clydebank G81 4AL Tel: 0141 941 1068 — MB BS 1997 Lond.; BSc Lond. 1994.

CLEMENT, Michael Hugh (retired) Littlecroft, Ringland Road, Taverham, Norwich NR8 6TG — MB BChir 1947 Camb.; MRCS Eng. LRCP Lond. 1943. Prev: Ho. Surg. W.m. Hosp.

CLEMENT, Michael John Gloucester Road Medical Centre, Tramway House, 1A Church Road, Horfield, Bristol BS7 8SA Tel: 0117 949 7774 Fax: 0117 949 7730 — MB BS 1981 Lond.; MRCP (UK) 1986; MRCGP 1988; DCH RCP Lond. 1986.

CLEMENT, Michèle Ingrid Department of Dermatology, Orpington Hospital, Sevenoaks Road, Orpington BR6 9JU Tel: 01689 815261 Fax: 01689 815268 Email: michele.clement@bromleyhospitals.nhs.uk — MB BS 1975 Lond.; BSc Lond. 1972; FRCP Lond. 1994; MRCP (UK) 1978. (Univ. Coll. Hosp.) p/t Cons. Dermat. And Clin. Director Bromley Hosps. NHS Trust. Prev: Sen. Regist. (Dermat.) King's Coll. Hosp. Lond.

CLEMENT-JONES, Mark Trefor 10 Roseworth Avenue, Gosforth, Newcastle upon Tyne NE3 1NB Tel: 0191 284 5582 — MB BS 1990 Newc. SHO (Neonat. Paediat.) John Radcliffe Hosp. Oxf. Prev: SHO (O & G) Jersey Gen. Hosp., P.ss Mary Matern Hosp. & Roy. Vict. Infirm. Newc.; Newc. u. Tyne.

CLEMENTE MEORO, Maria Del Carmen 6 West Hill Court, Millfield Lane, London N6 6JJ — LMS 1987 Valencia; MRCPsych 1992.

CLEMENTS, Adrian Charles Holford Lodge, Plumley Moor Road, Plumley, Knutsford WA16 9RS Tel: 01565 722197 — MB ChB 1990 Manch. Demonst. (Anat.) Univ. Leeds.

CLEMENTS, Amanda Louise 14 Windsor Road, Cambridge CB4 3JW — MB BS 1998 Lond.; MB BS Lond 1998.

CLEMENTS, Antony John Peter The Barton Surgery, Barton Terrace, Dawlish EX7 9QH Tel: 01626 888877 Fax: 01626 888360; The Old Vicarage, Cofton Hill, Cockwood, Exeter EX6 8RB Tel: 01626 891981 — MB BS Lond. 1988; BSc Lond. 1985; MRCP (UK) 1993; MRCGP 1992; DGM RCP Lond. 1995; DCH RCP Lond. 1991. (Guy's Hosp. Med. Sch.) GP Princip. Prev: Trainee GP Exeter VTS.

CLEMENTS, Brian William East Cleveland Hospital, Alford Road, Brotton, Saltburn-by-the-Sea TS12 2FF Tel: 01287 676215 Fax: 01287 678121; 7 High Street, Brotton, Saltburn-by-the-Sea TS12 2SP — MB BCh BAO 1978 Belf.

CLEMENTS, Catherine Louise Pinhoe Surgery, Pinn Lane, Exeter EX1 3SY Tel: 01392 469666 Fax: 01392 464178; Ilex House, Starcross, Exeter EX6 8QY Tel: 01626 891981 — MB BS 1988 Lond.; MRCGP 1992; DRCOG 1992; DCH RCP Lond. 1991. (Royal Free) Prev: Trainee GP Plymouth VTS.

CLEMENTS, Mr David Blakeley Silver Birches, 3 Thornhill Close, Granville Park, Aughton, Ormskirk L39 5HB Tel: 01695 423841 —

MB ChB 1960 Manch.; BSc Manch. 1957, MB ChB 1960; FRCS Ed. 1966; FRCS Eng. 1966; DO Eng. 1963. Cons. Orthop. Surg. St. Helens & Knowsley Trust. Socs: Liverp. Med. Inst. & Ophth. Soc. Prev: Ho. Surg. Roy. Eye Hosp. Manch.; Sen. Regist. St. Paul's Eye Hosp. Liverp.; Cons. Orthop. Surg. Alder Hey Hosp.

CLEMENTS, David Graham Endoscopy Unit, Airedale General Hospital, Skipton Road, Keighley BD20 6TD Tel: 01535 292347 Fax: 01535 295234; Tel: 01756 797122 — MB ChB 1980 Birm.; MD Birm. 1993; MRCP (UK) 1983; FRCP Lond. 1998. Cons. Gastroenterol. Airedale Gen. Hosp. Keighley. Socs: Brit. Soc. Gastroenterol.; Brit. Assn. Study Liver. Prev: Sen. Regist. (Med. & Gastroenterol.) Univ. Hosp. of Wales Cardiff; Regist. Gen. Hosp. Birm.; Sheldon Fell. Liver Unit Qu. Eliz. Hosp. Birm.

CLEMENTS, Deborah Mary 64 Pengors Road, Llangyfelach, Swansea SA5 7JF — MB BCh 1998 Wales. SHO Surg., Cardiff.

CLEMENTS, Duncan Millroy Churchill Medical Centre, Clifton Road, Kingston upon Thames KT2 6PG Tel: 020 8546 1809 Fax: 020 8549 4297; 18 Woodlands Avenue, New Malden KT3 3UN — MB BS 1974 Lond.; DRCOG 1977.

CLEMENTS, Elizabeth Anne Frances 13 Canonbury Park N., London N1 2JZ Tel: 020 7226 0876 — MB BS 1964 Lond.; MRCS Eng. LRCP Lond. 1965; FFA RCS Eng. 1974; DA Eng. 1967. (St. Bart.) Cons. Anaesth. Whipps Cross Univ. Hosp. Prev: Sen. Regist. (Anaesth.) Lond. Hosp. Whitechapel.

CLEMENTS, Elizabeth Jocelyn Fontana and Partners, Silsden Health Centre, Elliott Street, Silsden, Keighley BD20 0DG Tel: 01535 652447 Fax: 01535 657296; Raikes Close, 10 Grassington Road, Skipton BD23 1LL Tel: 01756 797122 — MB ChB 1980 Birm.; MRCGP 1984; DRCOG 1983; DCH RCP Lond. 1982. (Birm.)

CLEMENTS, Geoffrey Baverstock (retired) — MB BChir 1968 Camb.; PhD Glas. 1972; MA Camb. 1969, BA 1965, MB BChir 1968; FRCPath 1997. Hon Sen. Lect. Univ. Glas. 1989. Prev: Dir. Regional Virus Laborat. W. Glas. Hosps. Univ. NHS Trust.

CLEMENTS, Gillian Mary Old Farm, Burlton, Shrewsbury SY4 5SZ — MB ChB 1981 Manch.; MFPHM RCP (UK) 1994; DGM RCP Lond. 1988; DCH RCP Lond. 1985. Cons. Pub. Health Med. Shrops. HA.

CLEMENTS, Guy Charles 225 Osborne Road, West Jesmond, Newcastle upon Tyne NE2 3LB — MB BS 1997 Newc.

CLEMENTS, Helena Department of Child Health, Queens Medical Centre, Nottingham NG7 2UH Tel: 0115 924 9924; 1 Mystery Hill, Gables Drive, Hockerton, Southwell NG25 0QU Tel: 01636 815715 — BM BS 1988 Nottm.; MRCP (UK) 1991; MRCPCH 1997. Specialist Regist. City Hosp. Nottm. Socs: Paediat. Research Soc. Prev: Specialist Regist. Lincoln Co. Hosp.; Clin. Research Fell. (Child Health) Univ. Nottm.; SHO (Neonat. Paediat.) Nottm. City Hosp.

CLEMENTS, James Eagle House Surgery, Eagle House, White Cliff Mill Street, Blandford Forum DT11 7DQ Tel: 01258 453171 — DRCOG 1990; DA (UK) 1990. Prev: Trainee GP Honiton Devon; SHO (O & G) Exeter Gen. Hosp.; SHO (Anaesth.) Exeter Gen. Hosp.

CLEMENTS, Jeanne Mary (retired) 5 Lower Road, Stoke Mandeville, Aylesbury HP22 5XA Tel: 0129 661 3522 — MB BS 1948 Lond.; MRCS Eng. LRCP Lond. 1947; DObst RCOG 1951. Prev: GP Aylesbury.

CLEMENTS, John Garvin Dunluce Health Centre, 1 Dunluce Avenue, Belfast BT9 7HR — MB BCh BAO 1975 Belf.; MRCGP 1979.

CLEMENTS, John Marcus Murray 129 Croesonen Parc, Abergavenny NP7 6PF — MRCS Eng. LRCP Lond. 1968.

CLEMENTS, Melanie Jayne Norfolk and Norwich Health Care Trust, Brunswick Road, Norwich NR1 3SR Tel: 01603 286286; 90 North Brink, Wisbech PE13 1LN Tel: 01945 589918 — MB BS 1992 Lond.; MRCP (UK) 1996. Specialist Regist. (Paediat.) Norf. & Norwich Hosp. Prev: Regist. (Paediat.) Qu. Eliz. Hosp. King's Lynn; SHO (Paediat. & Neonat. Intens. Care) Addenbrooke's Hosp. Camb.; SHO (Paediat.) Qu. Eliz. Hosp. Kings Lynn.

CLEMENTS, Michael Reginald Watford General Hospital, Vicarage Road, Watford WD1 8HB Tel: 01923 217696 Fax: 01923 217455; Corner Cottage, Kings Lane, Chipperfield, Kings Langley WD4 9EN Tel: 01923 267697 Fax: 01923 267697 Email: m.clements@connect-2.co.uk — MB BS 1976 Lond.; BSc (Hons.) Lond. 1973; MD Lond. 1987; FRCP Lond. 1995; MRCP Lond. 1979; MRCS Eng. LRCP Lond. 1976. (Westm.) Cons. Phys. (Diabetes & Endocrinol.) W. Herts. NHS Trust incorporting the Mt. Vernon Cancer Centre; Prof. Clin. Med. St. Geo. Sch. Med. Univ. Grenada. Socs: Brit. Diabetic Assn.; Bone & Tooth Soc.; Roy. Soc. Med. (Mem. of Steering Comm. of Endocrine Sect.). Prev: Lect. (Med.) Manch. Roy. Infirm.; MRC Research Fell. Dunn Nutrit. Laborat. Camb.; Regist. (Med.) Addenbrooke's Hosp. Camb.

CLEMENTS, Nicholas David 102 St Davids Road, Otley LS21 2RQ — MB ChB 1981 Leic.; DRCOG 1983.

CLEMENTS, Paul Walter (retired) 12 Orchard Avenue, Parkstone, Poole BH14 8AJ Tel: 01202 745437 — MB BS 1947 Lond.; MRCS Eng. LRCP Lond. 1946; DObst RCOG 1952. Prev: GP Poole.

CLEMENTS, Peter Wreford (retired) Kalafrana, 28 Cranford Avenue, Exmouth EX8 2PZ Tel: 01395 273401 — MA Camb. 1958, MB 1959, BChir 1958; MRCS Eng. LRCP Lond. 1958; DObst RCOG 1964. Prev: Ho. Phys. Guy's Hosp. Lond.

CLEMENTS, Philip Augustine Harris (retired) Meadow Saffron, 4A Oldfield Road, Bath BA2 3NB Tel: 01225 422435 Email: meadowsaff@aol.com — MRCS Eng. LRCP Lond. 1943; MFPHM 1989; MFCM 1972. Prev: Area Med. Off Wilts.

CLEMENTS, Philip John 27 Fairthorne Way, Shrivenham, Swindon SN6 8EA Tel: 01793 782408 — MB BS 1969 Lond.; MRCS Eng. LRCP Lond. 1969; DA Eng. 1971.

CLEMENTS, Raymond Derek (retired) 12 Craigmore Avenue, Bletchley, Milton Keynes MK3 6HD Tel: 01908 372503 Email: rdclements@aol.com — MB BS (Hnrs. Med.) Lond. 1954; MRCGP 1964. Prev: Ho. Phys. Profess. Med. Unit, Ho. Surg. Profess. Surg. Unit & Obst.

CLEMENTS, Richard Department of Clinical Radiology, Royal Gwent Hospital, Newport NP20 2UB Tel: 01633 234346; 13 Fields Park Road, Newport NP20 5BA — BM BCh 1975 Oxf.; MA Oxf. 1976, BA (Physiol. Sc., 1st cl. Hons.) 1972; FRCS Eng. 1981; FRCR 1984. (Oxford & St. Thomas) Cons. Radiol. Roy. Gwent Hosp. Newport. Socs: Eur. Soc. Urogenital Radiol. Prev: Regist. (Radiol. & Gen. Surg.) Univ. Hosp. Wales Cardiff; SHO (Gen. Surg.) Poole Gen. Hosp.; Ho. Phys. St. Thomas Hosp. Lond.

CLEMENTS, Richard Andrew Bryson Street Surgery, 115 Newtownards Road, Belfast BT4 1AB Tel: 028 9045 8722 Fax: 028 9046 6766 — MB BCh BAO 1979 Belf.; MRCGP 1984; DCH Dub. 1983; DRCOG 1983. GP Belf.

CLEMENTS, Robert 18 Holmwood Avenue, Uddington, Glasgow G71 7AJ — MB ChB 1977 Glas.; MRCGP 1988.

CLEMENTS, Mr Roger Varley 111 Harley Street, London W1N 1DG Tel: 020 7637 0701 Fax: 020 7224 3852 Email: roger.clements@dial.pipex.com; 18 Lanchester Road, Highgate, London N6 4TA Tel: 020 8883 4734 — BM BCh 1960 Oxf.; MA Oxf. 1963; FRCS Ed. 1972; FRCOG 1980, M 1967; DObst RCOG 1962. (Univ. Coll. Hosp.) Risk Managem. Cons. QRM Healthcare Ltd.; Hon. Lect. (Obst. & Gyn.) Roy. Free Hosp. Lond.; Hon. Cons. Obst. & Gyn. Hammersmith Hosp. Lond.; Clin. Asst. Prof. Obst. & Gyn. UK. Fac. St. Geo. Univ. Sch. Med Grenada, W Indies; Examr. Univ. Lond. Roy. Free Hosp.; Examr. RCOG, W. Afr. Coll. Surgs. Postgrad. Med. Coll. Nigeria Bd & Univ Ibadan Nigeria; Lect. & Examr. Centr. Midw. Bd.; Edr.-in-Chief Clin. Risk. Socs: Fell. Roy. Soc. Med.; BMA; Fell. Acad. Experts. Prev: Med. Exec. Dir. & Clin. Dir. (O & G) N. Middlx. Hosp. NHS Trust; Sen. Regist. (O & G) Univ. Coll. Hosp. Ibadan, Nigeria; Lect. (O & G) St. Mary's Hosp. Med. Sch. Lond.

CLEMENTS, Sanja 46 Peplins Way, Brookmans Park, Hatfield AL9 7UU — LMSSA 1995 Lond.

CLEMENTS, Sarah Dawn 26 Worsley Road, Cowes PO31 8JN — BM BS 1994 Nottm.

CLEMENTS, Stephen le Harival Alexander 6 Stoke Road, Ashton, Northampton NN7 2JN Tel: 01604 862080 — MB BS 1945 Lond. (King's Coll. Hosp.) Prev: Ho. Phys. Leatherhead Emerg. Hosp.; Ho. Surg. Horton Emerg. Hosp. & Sutton Emerg. Hosp.

CLEMENTS, Steven Alan Christopher The J's Bungalow, Gwaunfarren Farm, Galon Uchaf, Merthyr Tydfil CF47 8AP — MB BCh 1987 Wales.

CLEMENTS, Mr William Desmond Barry Upper G1/ HPB Unit, Royal Victoria Hospital, Grosvenor Road, Belfast BT12 6BA Tel: 02890 263324 Fax: 02890 263325 Email: barryclements@royalhospitals.n-i.nhs.uk; Tel: 02892 622997 Fax: 02892 662117 — MB BCh BAO (Hons.) Belf. 1985; BSc (Hons.) Belf. 1982; FRCSI 1989; MD 1997; FRCS (Gen) 1997. (Queen's Univ Belfast) Cons Upper GI/ HPB/ Laparoscopic Surg., Roy. Vict.

Hosp., Belf.; Hon. Clin Lect Qu.'s Univ of Belf.; Fac. of Minimal Access Ther. Train. Guildford, The Roy. Surrey Co. Hosp. Socs: Euro Assn. of Endoscopic Surg.s (EAES); Irish Soc. Gastroenterol. (ISG/ USG); Surg. Research Soc. (SRS).

CLEMENTS, William Ian Church Street Surgery, 1 Church Street, Newtownards BT23 4FH Tel: 028 9181 6333 Fax: 028 9181 8805 — MB BCh BAO 1971 Belf.; MRCGP 1975.

CLEMENTSON, Douglas Westwood (retired) Beechcroft, 31 Woodlands Road, Motherwell ML1 2PX Tel: 01698 263235 — MB ChB 1951 Glas. Prev: Ho. Surg. Glas. Roy. Infirm.

CLEMENTSON, Gerald 14 Lloyd Park Avenue, Croydon CR0 5SA Tel: 020 8688 9055 — MB BS Lond. 1951. (St. Geo.) p/t RMAO Emerg. Bed. Serv.; Clin. Tutor (Gen. Pract.) St. Geo. Hosp. Med. Sch. Lond. Socs: (Ex-Pres.) Croydon Med. Soc.; Croydon Medico-Legal Soc.; BMA (Ex-Chairm. Croydon Div.). Prev: Resid. Sen. Cas. Off. Hampstead Gen. Hosp.; Ho. Surg. & Cas. Off. St. Geo. Hosp. Lond.; Capt. RAMC.

CLEMENTSON, Michael Richard Parkside Group Practice, 27 Wyche Grove, South Croydon CR2 6EX Tel: 020 8680 2588 Fax: 020 8680 1415 — MB BS 1983 Lond. Prev: GP to the Homeless Croydon; Clin. Asst. (Rheum.) Purley Hosp.; Trainee GP St. Helier VTS.

CLEMINSON, Foster Bruce The Surgery, Scalloway, Shetland ZE1 0UX Tel: 01595 880219; Ingaville, Scalloway, Lerwick ZE1 0UX Tel: 0159 588340 — MB ChB 1971 Manch.; MRCGP 1977; DRCOG 1976. Prev: SHO (O & G) Airedale Gen. Hosp. Steeton; SHO (Gen. Med.) W.mld. C. Hosp. Kendal; SHO Terminal Care St. Christophers Hospice Lond.

CLEMMEY, William Robert Lionel 156 Westminster Way, North Hinksey Village, Oxford OX2 0LR — MB BS Lond. 1975; MRCS Eng. LRCP Lond. 1967; LMCC 1980; FRCPC 1979; MRCPsych 1973; DPM Eng. 1971. Asst. Clin. Prof. Dept. Psychiat. Fac. Med. Univ. Alberta Canada. Prev: Sen. Regist. Bethlem & Maudsley Hosps.; Cons. Psychiat. Alberta Hosp. Edmonton Alberta, Canada.

CLEMO, Joan Tudor Cottage, New Lane, Dereham NR20 3JX — MB BS 1975 Newc.

CLEMONS, Kate Rebecca Snowford House, Leamington Road, Long Itchington, Rugby CV23 8QE — MB ChB 1993 Bristol.

CLEMONS, Michael John 12 Warwick Drive, Atherstone CV9 3AS — MB BCh 1989 Wales; T(GP) 1993.

CLENAGHAN, Stephen Dominic 102 Ballinderry Road, Lisburn BT28 2NW — MB BCh BAO 1996 Belf.

CLENDINNEN, Mr Brian Guy The Old Hall, Malpas SY14 8HB Tel: 01948 860414 — MB ChB 1963 Birm.; BSc Birm. 1960, ChM 1971, MB ChB 1963; FRCS Eng. 1967. (Birm.) Prev: Cons. Surg. Roy. N.. Hosp. & Whittington Hosp. Lond.; Sen. Lect. Surg. Univ. Bristol; Research Fell. Dept. Surg. Harbor Gen. Hosp. Calif..

CLENSHAW, Joanna Elizabeth Eleanor Linwood CMHC, Butlers Green Road, Haywards Heath RH19 3RU Tel: 01444 441881; Craigmore, 9 Savile Park, Halifax HX13EA — MB BS 1992 Newc.

CLENTON, Susan Jane 17 Goldsmith Avenue, Warwick CV34 6JA — MB ChB 1996 Sheff.

CLEOBURY, John Frank (retired) 23 River Court, The Green, Chartham, Canterbury CT4 7JN Tel: 01227 731357 — MB BS Lond. 1946; FRCPsych 1973, M 1971; FRCP Ed. 1971, M 1959; MRCS Eng. LRCP Lond. 1946; DCH Eng. 1954. DPM 1959. Med. Examr. & Assessor UKCC. Prev: Med.Examnr.&Assessor UKCC.

***CLERIHEW, Linda Jane** 1A Bencroft Avenue, Biggar ML12 6EU — MB ChB 1994 Dundee.

CLERKIN, Pauline Margaret Mary The Surgery, 221 Whaddon Way, Bletchley, Milton Keynes MK3 7EA Tel: 01908 373058 Fax: 01908 630076; Lees Folly, Watling St, Littel Brickhill, Milton Keynes MK17 9NB — MB BCh BAO 1987 NUI.

CLESHAM, Desmond John 14 Hardwick Drive, Shrewsbury SY3 8UZ — MB ChB Liverp. 1978; DRCOG 1981.

CLESHAM, Gerald James Department of Cardiology, Broomfield Hospital, Court Road, Chelmsford CM1 7ET Tel: 01245 514232 Fax: 01245 514867 — BM BCh 1987 Oxf.; MA Camb. 1988; MRCP (UK) 1990; PhD Camb. 1998. Cons. Cardiol. Broomfield Hosp., Chelmsford; Cons. Cardiol. St Bartholomews Hosp., Lond. Prev: MRC Train. Fell. Addenbrooke's Hosp. Camb.; Regist. (Cardiol.) Hammersmith Hosp. Lond.; Ho. Off. John Radcliffe Hosp. Oxf.

CLEUGH, Patricia Anne Medical Support Services, Royston House, 34 Upper Queen St., Belfast BT1 6FD; 10 Park View, Old Eglish Road, Dungannon BT71 7JP — MB ChB 1981 Aberd.; MRCP (UK) 1985; DCH RCP Lond. 1990. (Aberdeen) Med. Off. (Health & Social Servs.) Belf. Prev: Clin. Med. Off. (Child Health) Lurgan Gen. Hosp.; GP New Brighton; Occupat. Health Phys. Wallasey.

CLEVELAND, Mr Trevor John Department of Radiology, Northern General Hospital, Herries Road, Sheffield S5 7AU Tel: 0114 271 5108 Fax: 0114 271 4747 Email: t.cleveland@breathemail.net — BM BS 1985 Nottm.; BMedSci Nottm. 1983; FRCS Eng. 1990; FRCR 1994. Cons. Vasc. Radiologist, Sheff. Vasc. Inst. Prev: Sen. Regist. & Regist. (Radiol.) Sheff. Hosps.

CLEVENGER, Eve Olga Stirchley Medical Practice, Stirchley Health Centre, Stirchley, Telford TF3 1FB Tel: 01952 660444 Fax: 01952 415139; The Cottage, 1 Wrekin Course, Telford TF6 5AJ Tel: 01952 740287 — MB ChB 1973 Birm.

CLEVERLEY, Huw Rhys St Annes Group Practice, 161 Station Road, Herne Bay CT6 5NF Tel: 01227 742226 Fax: 01227 741439; 62 Gordon Road, Herne Bay CT6 5QT Tel: 01227 365571 — MB ChB 1984 Birm.; MRCGP 1989.

CLEVERLEY, Joanne Rita 6B Oak Court, St Albans Villas, London NW5 1QU — MB BS 1986 Lond.; MRCP (UK) 1991; FRCR 1996.

CLEVERLEY, Sarah Jane Lintonville Medical Group, Old Lane, Ashington NE63 9UT Tel: 01670 812772 Fax: 01670 521573; 16 Rectory Park, Morpeth NE61 2SZ — MB BS 1975 Newc.; MRCGP 1979; DRCOG 1978.

CLEWER, Glenn John Ton Farm, Glascoed, Pontypool NP4 0UA — MB BCh 1998 Wales.

CLEWES, Adrian Robert 21 Gainsborough Road, Wavertree, Liverpool L15 3HU — MB ChB 1992 Liverp.; MRCPI 1998, (Dublin). Specialist Regist. (Rheum.), Mersy Deanery. (N. W.).

CLEWETT, Vanessa Park View, Tathall End, Hanslope, Milton Keynes MK19 7NF — MB BS 1997 Lond.

CLEWLOW, Robert Michael (retired) 93 Shaftesbury Avenue, Blackpool FY2 9UZ Tel: 01253 353838 — MB ChB 1959 Birm.; MRCGP 1981; DCH Eng. 1962. Prev: Cas. Off. Gen. Hosp. Birm.

CLEWS, James William The Health Centre, Alfred Squire Road, Wednesfield, Wolverhampton WV11 1XU; 17 Enderby Drive, Penn, Wolverhampton WV4 5QU — MB ChB 1968 Birm.; BSc Aston 1967. Socs: BMA. Prev: Clin. Asst. (Urol.) New Cross Hosp. Wolverhampton; Ho. Surg., Ho. Phys. & SHO (Paediat.) Roy. Hosp. Wolverhampton; Clin. Asst. (Dermat.) New Cross Hosp.Wolverhampton.

CLIBBON, Jonothan James 2 Grove Road, Bury St Edmunds IP33 3BE — MB ChB 1992 Leeds.

CLIFF, Mr Andrew Michael 29 Glanaber Park, Chester CH4 8LE Tel: 01244 683645; 29 Glenaber Park, Chester CH4 8LE Email: acliff@talk21.com — MB ChB 1991 Manch.; FRCS 2000 (Urol.); FRCS Eng. 1995. Specialist Regist. (Urol.) Mersey Region. Prev: SHO Rotat. (Surg.) MusGr. Pk. Hosp. Taunton.

CLIFF, George Bastian Valehurst, St. Helen's Park Road, Hastings TN34 2JH — MB ChB 1942 Birm.; BSc McGill 1948; MRCS Eng. LRCP Lond. 1942. (Birm.)

CLIFF-PATEL, Sandeep 101 Woodlands, Harrow HA2 6EN — MB BS 1991 Lond.; MRCP (UK) 1994.

CLIFFE, Alison Margaret James Paget Hospital, Lowestoft Road, Gorleston, Great Yarmouth NR31 6LA Tel: 01493 600611; 48 Lynn Grove, Gorleston, Great Yarmouth NR31 8AR — MB ChB 1973 Dundee; FRCS Ed. 1984; FCOphth 1989; DO Eng. 1980. Assoc. Specialist Ophth. Jas. Paget. Hosp. Gorleston. Prev: Regist. (Ophth.) Roy. N.. Infirm. Inverness; Regist. (Ophth.) & Ho. Off. (Therap.) Ninewells Hosp. Dundee.

CLIFFE, Derek John Heston Health Centre, Cranford Lane, Heston, Hounslow TW5 9EP; Everglades Lindale Close, Wentworth, Virginia Water GU25 4NT Tel: 01344 842729 — MB BS 1951 Lond.; MRCS Eng. LRCP Lond. 1951; DObst RCOG 1957. (Guy's) Prev: Act. Squadron Ldr. RAF Med. Br.; Ho. Surg. Obst. Bromely Hosp.

CLIFFE, Ian Village Farm House, Main St, Wach, Ripon HG4 5EN Tel: 01765 640504 — MB ChB Leeds 1959; DObst RCOG 1961. (Leeds)

CLIFFE, Jane Margaret The Surgery, The Gardens, London SE22 9QU Tel: 020 8693 4715 Fax: 020 8299 4418; 21 Champion Grove, London SE5 8BN Tel: 020 7326 1687 — MB BS 1981 Newc.; DCH RCP Lond. 1987. Clin. Asst. (Dermat.) Kings Coll. Hosp. Prev: Community Med. Off. Lambeth HA.

CLIFFE, Peter Andrew Harvey The Surgery, East Grinstead Road, Lingfield RH7 6ER Tel: 01342 833456 Fax: 01342 836347; Stone Hill House, West Hoathly Road, East Grinstead RH19 4HW — MB BS 1984 Lond.; MRCGP 1991; Cert. Family Plann. JCC 1989. (Guy's Hosp. Med. Sch. Lond.) Med. Staff Qu. Vict. Hosp. E. Grinstead & Edenbridge Memor. Hosp. Prev: Trainee GP Windsor VTS; SHO (Neonat. & Paediat.) Wexham Pk. Hosp. Slough.

CLIFFE, Robert John Oak Mead, Golly, Burton Green, Rossett, Wrexham LL12 0AW — MB BCh 1980 Wales; MRCGP 1985; Cert. Family Plann. RCOG 1983; DRCOG 1983.

CLIFFORD, Adrian Alexander Ralston Osier Holt, Louth LN11 7UD Tel: 01507 473483 Fax: 01507 478865 Email: dracliffmb@aol.com — MB ChB 1979 Ed.; BSc Ed. 1976; MRCGP 1985; DRCOG 1985. (Ed.) Prev: Med. Off. Anglo Amer. Mustagh Expedition 1984; Med. Off. Scott. Nuptse Expedition 1981.

CLIFFORD, Alan David The Health Centre, Bowers Place, Crawley Down, Crawley RH10 4HY Tel: 01342 713031 Fax: 01342 718715 — MB BS 1983 Lond.; MRCGP 1988; DRCOG 1987. (St. Bart. Lond.) Hon. Med. Off., Qu. Vict. Hosp., E. Grinstead. Socs: BMA. Prev: SHO. (O & G) Crawley Hosp.; SHO. (ENT) Roy. Sussex Co. Hosp.; SHO (Psychiat.) Crawley Hosp.

CLIFFORD, Christopher Piers 27 Bradmore Park Road, London W6 0DT — MB BS 1987 Lond.; BA (Hons.) Oxf. 1984; MRCP (UK) 1990.

CLIFFORD, David Graham Chastleton Surgery, Newton Drive, Framwellgate Moor, Durham DH1 5BH Tel: 0191 384 6171 Fax: 0191 386 3743 — MB ChB 1990 Leic. GP. Prev: SHO (Gen. Med.) Preston Hosp. N. Shields.

CLIFFORD, Denis Joseph Abronhill Health Centre, Pine Road, Cumbernauld, Glasgow G67 3BE Tel: 01236 727654; 7 Braes O' Yetts, Kirkintilloch, Glasgow G66 3RP Tel: 0141 777 8373 — MB ChB 1988 Glas. Socs: Med. & Dent. Defence Union Scotl. & BMA.

CLIFFORD, Elizabeth Margaret Wexham Park Hospital, Wexham Street, Slough SL2 4HL Tel: 01753 633000 Fax: 01753 624204 — MB BS 1987 Lond.; BSc (Hons.) Lond 1984; MRCPsych 1994. (Middlx. Hosp.) Hon. Sen. Regist. (Psychiat.) Univ. Oxf. Cons. in Adult Gen., and Liaison Psychiat.. Cons., Psychiat., Wrexham Pk. Hosp., Slough, E. Berks. Prev: Regist. Rotat. (Psychiat.) Oxf. Train. Scheme; SHO Rotat. (Psychiat.) Leicester; SHO Rotat. (Med.) N.ampton.

CLIFFORD, Gregory John Park Crescent New Surgery, 1A Lewes Road, Brighton BN2 3JJ Tel: 01273 603531/680135 Fax: 01273 698863 — MB BS 1985 Lond. (Univ. Coll. Lond.) Prev: Trainee GP Brighton VTS.

CLIFFORD, Guy Neil 15 Kingsley Road, Stafford ST17 9BU — MB ChB 1991 Leeds.

CLIFFORD, John Student Health Service, University of the West of England, Coldharbour Lane,Frenchay, Bristol BS16 1QY Tel: 0117 965 6261; High Barn, Winford Road, Chew Magna, Bristol BS40 8QQ Tel: 01275 332924 — MB ChB 1968 Manch.; DObst RCOG 1971. Med. Off. i/c Stud. Health Serv. Univ. of W. of Eng. Socs: Brit. Assn. Sport & Med.

CLIFFORD, John Marsden (retired) Nancy Row, Burton Pidsea, Hull HU12 9DL — MSc Lond. 1972; MSc Soton. 1969; MB BChir Camb. 1953. Prev: Head (Clin. Pharmacol.) Pharmaceut. Div. Reckitt & Colman Hull.

CLIFFORD, John Michael Flat 5, 29 Knowsley Road, Liverpool L19 0PF — MB ChB 1994 Liverp.

CLIFFORD, Katy Anne St Mary's Hospital, Praed Street, London W2 1NY; 96 Fulham Road, London SW3 6HS — MB BChir 1986 Camb.; MB Camb. 1986, BChir 1985; MRCOG 1991; MD 2000. Cons. Dept. of Obst. and Gyn. St Mary's Hosp. Lond.

CLIFFORD, Kevin Martin Andrew 9 Levenside, Hutton Rudby, Yarm TS15 0EX — MB BS 1972 Lond.; MRCS Eng. LRCP Lond. 1972; FRCR 1982. Cons. Radiol. S. Tees HA.

CLIFFORD, Peter David College Street Surgery, 5 College Street, Higham Ferrers, Wellingborough NN10 8DX Tel: 01933 412777 Fax: 01933 419013 — MB BS 1971 Newc.; MRCGP 1976; DObst RCOG 1976; DA Eng. 1973. (Newcastle)

CLIFFORD, Mr Robert Paul The Little Grove Clinic, Rue de Haut, St Lawrence, Jersey JE3 1JZ Tel: 01534 32496 Fax: 01534 89463; Castle Green House, Gorey, St Martin, Jersey JE3 6DR Fax: 01534 855151 Email: paulclif@super.net.uk — MB ChB 1973 Manch.; FRCS Glas. 1994; FRCS Eng. 1979; FFAEM 1994. Cons. Orthop. & Trauma Surg. Gen. Hosp. St. Helier Jersey, Cl. Socs: Fell. BOA; Brit. Trauma Soc.; Brit. Assn. Accid. & Emerg. Med. Prev: Clin. Fell. Sunnybrook Med. Centre Toronto, Canada; Sen. Regist. (Orthop.) Wessex; Regist. (Orthop.) Qu.'s Med. Centre Nottm.

CLIFFORD, Rollo David Kingfisher Ward, Dorset County Hospital, Williams Avenue, Dorchester DT1 2JY Tel: 01305 254240/9 Fax: 01305 254289 Email: rollo.clifford@wdgh.nhs.uk — MB BS 1979 Lond.; MRCS Eng. LRCP Lond. 1979; DM Soton. 1990; MRCP (UK) 1984; FRCPCH 1996. (Westm.) Cons. Paediat.Dorset Co. Hosp. Dorchester. Socs: Brit. Paediat. Assn.; Brit. Thorac. Soc.; Brit. Assn. Perinatal Med. Prev: Lect. (Child Health) Hosp. Sick Childr. Bristol; Regist. (Paediat.) N.wick Pk. Hosp. Harrow; Research Fell. (Asthma) Univ. Soton.

CLIFFORD, Wayne Anthony 80 Barnsdale Road, Clifton, Nottingham NG11 9JB — MB BS 1977 Lond.

CLIFFORD, William Francis (retired) Dan-y-Graig, Vicarage Road, Penygraig, Tonypandy CF40 1HR Tel: 01443 433261 — LRCPI & LM, LRSCI & LM 1951; LRCPI & LM, LRCSI & LM 1951.

CLIFFORD-JONES, Edward (retired) 25 South Ridge, Brunton Park, Gosforth, Newcastle upon Tyne NE3 2EJ Tel: 0191 236 7345 — MB BS 1941 Lond.; MRCS Eng. LRCP Lond. 1938. Prev: Cons. Chest Phys. Welsh Hosp. Bd.

CLIFFORD-JONES, Robert Edward Neurology Department, Worthing Hospital, Lyndhurst Rd, Worthing BN11 2DH Tel: 01908 205111 Fax: 01908 285152 Email: robert.clifford-jones@wash-tr.sthames.nhs.uk; Mount Place, 40 Goring Road, Steyning BN44 3GF Email: rhcj@aol.com — BM BCh 1972 Oxf.; DM Oxf. 1983; FRCP Lond. 1991; MRCP (UK) 1975. Cons. Neurol. Worthing & Mid Downs HAs. Prev: Sen. Regist. (Neurol.) St. Mary's Hosp. & Nat. Hosp. Nerv. Dis. Lond.

CLIFFORD-JONES, Mr William Eric, OStJ, Group Capt. RAF Med. Br. Retd. (retired) Nara, Haycrafts Lane, Harmans Cross, Swanage BH19 3EB Tel: 01929 480816 — MB BS 1953 Lond.; MRCS Eng. LRCP Lond. 1953; FRCOphth 1990; DO Eng. 1967. Prev: Cons. Ophth. W. Wales Gen. Hosp. Carmarthen & P. Philip Hosp. LLa.lli.

CLIFT, Anthony David (retired) Broomfield, 151 Manchester Old Road, Middleton, Manchester M24 4DZ Tel: 0161 643 8081 Email: adelift@doctors.org.uk — MB ChB 1953 Manch.; MD Manch. 1971; FRCGP 1980, M 1965; DObst RCOG 1957. Occupat. Phys.; Med. Adviser Xaverian Coll. Manch. Prev: Sen. Partner Gen. Pract. Peterloo Med. Centre Middleton. M24 4DZ.

CLIFT, Mr Benedict Anthony Tel: 01382 660111 Fax: 01382 496201 Email: ben.clift@tuht.scot.nhs.uk; Email: baclift@hotmail.com — MB ChB 1986 Dundee; BMSc (Hons.) Dund 1983; FRCS (Orth.) 1995; FRCS Ed. 1991. Cons. Orthop. & Trauma Surg. Dundee Teachg. Hosps.; Hon. Sen. Lect. Univ. of Dundee. Socs: Fell. of BOA; BMA. Prev: Sen. Lect. (Orthop. & Trauma Surg.) Univ. Dundee; Regist. Rotat. (Orthop.) Raigmore Hosp. Inverness.

CLIFT, David Lloyd Brookfield, Robin Lane, Parbold, Wigan WN8 7BE — MB BS 1996 Lond.

CLIFT, Dorothy Cecily (retired) Kirk Hammerton, 23 Durham Avenue, Bromley BR2 0QH Tel: 020 8460 5776 — MB ChB Leeds 1943. Prev: Clin. Asst. (Dermat.) St. Bart. Hosp. Lond.

CLIFT, John Lawrence 3 The Chapel, Edward St., Normanton WF6 2QU — MB ChB 1989 Leeds.

CLIFT, Michael Raymond (retired) 9 Glevum Close, Longlevens, Gloucester GL2 9JJ Tel: 01452 532515 Fax: 01452 532515 — MB ChB 1956 Bristol. Gen. Sec. Lect. & Med. Adviser Brit. Soc. for the Turin Shroud; Med. Off. Amateur Boxing Assn., 1983; Proctor & Examr. Disabled Candiates MENSA 1987. Prev: Surg. P & O/BI Gp.

CLIFT, Simon PO Box 2094, Doddma, Tanzania; 20 Wainwrights, Long Crendon, Aylesbury HP18 9DT Tel: 01844 201073 — MB BS 1986 Lond.; MRCGP 1991; DTM & H RCP Lond. 1994; DGM RCP Lond. 1991; DRCOG 1989.

CLIFTON, Andrew George Atkinson Morley's Hospital, Copse Hill, Wimbledon, London SW20 0NE — MB BS 1981 Lond.; MA Oxf. 1983, BA (Hons.) 1978; MRCP (UK) 1985; FRCR 1989. Cons. Neuroradiol. Atkinson Morley's Hosp. Lond. Prev: Regist. (Radiol.) Roy. Free Hosp. Lond.; Sen. Regist. Nat. Hosp. Neurol. & Neurosurg., Gt. Ormond St. & Hammersmith Hosps. Lond.; Sen. Regist. (Radiol.) Univ. Coll. Hosp. Lond.

CLIFTON, Angela Springfield Hospital, Glenburnie Road, London SW17 7DJ Tel: 020 8672 9911; 631 Upper Richmond Road W.,

Richmond TW10 5DU Tel: 020 8876 0751 — MB BS 1972 Lond.; MRCPsych 1987. (Guy's) Assoc. Specialist (Rehabil.) Springfield Hosp. Lond.

CLIFTON, Charlotte Jane 23 Scott Close, Ashby-de-la-Zouch LE65 1HT — MB BS 1982 Lond. Sen. Med. Adviser (Nutrit.) Peter Black Healthcare Ltd Swadlincote. Socs: Roy. Soc. Med. Prev: Healthcare Relations Phys. Merck, Sharp & Dohme Ltd Hoddesdon.

CLIFTON, David Ivan Barnsley District General Hospital, Gawber Road, Barnsley S75 2EP — MB BS 1975 Lond.; MRCP (UK) 1978; MRCS Eng. LRCP Lond. 1974. (St. Mary's) Internist, Chief of Med., Dir. Intens. Care Thompson Gen. Hosp. Socs: Brit. Thoracic Soc. & Manitoba Med. Assn. Prev: Assoc. Specialist BMH Hong Kong; Cons. Gen. & Thoracic Med. AFHSR, Saudi Arabia; Regist. (Thoracic Med.) Llandough Hosp. Cardiff.

***CLIFTON, Ian James** Huddersfield Royal Infirmary, Lindley, Huddersfield HD3 3EA Tel: 01484 422191 Email: ian.clifton@doctors.org.uk; 132 Burton Acres Lane, Kirkburton, Huddersfield HD8 0QR Tel: 01484 604090 — MB ChB 1998 Dund.; MB ChB Dund 1998; BMSc (Hons) Dund. 1996.

CLIFTON, Julia The Health Centre, Manor Road, Beverley HU17 7BZ — MB BS 1991 Lond.; MRCGP 2000; BSc Lond. 1988; DFFP 1994; MRCOG 1997. (University College Middlesex London) G.P,Beverley. Prev: Specialist Regist. (O & G) York; Specialist Regist. (O & G) Grimsby; SHO (O & G) N.wick Pk. Hosp. Harrow Middlx.

CLIFTON, Mr Martin Anthony 2 Amwell Place, Hertford Heath, Hertford SG13 7SE Tel: 01992 505123 Fax: 01992 553180 Email: martinc@mclif.demon.co.uk — MB BS 1969 Lond.; MS Lond. 1984; FRCS Eng. 1975; FRCS Ed. 1975; MRCS Eng. LRCP Lond. 1969. (St. Bart.) Cons. Surg. P.ss Alexandra Hosp. Harlow & St. Margt. Hosp. Epping. Socs: Fell. Roy. Soc. Med. (Mem. Surg. & Coloproctol. Sects.); Brit. Soc. Gastroenterol. Prev: Sen. Regist. (Surg.) Lond. Hosp.; Hon. Clin. Asst. St. Marks Hosp. Lond.; Lect. (Surg.) Lond. Hosp.

CLIFTON, Martin Richard Oaklands, Middlewich Medical Centre, St. Anns Walk, Middlewich CW10 9BE Tel: 01606 836481 — MB ChB 1976 Liverp. Prev: SHO (Paediat.) Birkenhead Childr. Hosp.; SHO (O & G) Walton Hosp. Liverp.; SHO (Psychiat.) Clatterbridge Hosp. Bebington.

CLIFTON, Phillip James McKinley 17 Manor Road N., Edgbaston, Birmingham B16 9JS — MB ChB 1975 Birm.; FFA RCSI 1982. Cons. Anaesth. Selly Oak Hosp. Birm.

CLIFTON-BROWN, Angela Florence Whites Farm, Helions Bumpstead, Haverhill CB9 7AB — MB BS 1980 Lond.; MRCGP 1984; DRCGP 1983.

CLIMIE, Paul Brian 9 Elie Street, Dowanhill, Glasgow G11 5HJ Tel: 0141 339 4486 Email: paul4jags@aol.com — MB ChB 1994 Glas.; BSc (Hons.) Pharmacol. Glas. 1991.

CLIMIE, Robert Philip 34 Leverson Street, London SW16 6DD — MB BS 1986 Lond. SHO (O & G) St. Helier Hosp. Carshalton. Prev: SHO (Med.) St. Helier Hosp. Carshalton; SHO (Med.) Kingston Hosp.; SHO (Paediat.) All St.'s Hosp. Chatham.

CLINCH, Jacqueline Georgina 39 Priestman Point, Rainhill Way, London E3 3EY — MB BS 1991 Lond.

CLINE, Wendy Adfer Unit Ward W.I., Whitchurch Hospital, Whitchurch, Cardiff CF14 7XB Tel: 029 2069 3191 Fax: 029 2061 4799; 10 Oakdene Close, Cyncoed, Cardiff CF23 6HJ Tel: 029 2075 0944 — MB BS 1965 Lond.; MRCS Eng. LRCP Lond. 1965; DPM Eng. 1973. (Roy. Free & Cardiff) Assoc. Specialist (Alcohol & Subst. Misuse) Adfer Unit WhitCh. Hosp. Cardiff. Socs: BMA & Cardiff Med. Soc.

CLINKENBEARD, Janette McKay Riccarton Practice, Heriot Watt University Health Centre, The Avenue, Riccarton, Currie EH14 4AS Tel: 0131 451 3010 Fax: 0131 451 3503; Bavelaw Tower, 40 Harlaw Road, Balerno, Edinburgh EH14 7AX — MB ChB 1977 Glas.; FRCGP 1993, M 1981; DRCOG 1980. Research Convenor Brit. Assn. Health Servs. in Higher Educat.

CLINT, Simon Anthony 119 The Meadows, Cherry Burton, Beverley HU17 7RL — MB BS 1998 Lond.; MB BS Lond 1998.

CLINTON, Carl Accident & Emergency Department, Jersey General Hospital Gloucester St., St Helier, Jersey Tel: 01534 59000; Chamonix, Route Oranfe, St-Brelade, Jersey JE3 8JP Tel: 01534 491489 — MB ChB 1986 Sheff.; FFAEM 1994; Dip. Sports Med. Lond. 1991. Cons. A & E & Sports Med. Jersey Gen. Hosp.; Mem. Family Pract. Comm. Sheff. Socs: BMA; BASM; BAEM. Prev: Assoc. Specialist (A & E & Sports Med.) Jersey Gen. Hosp.; Regist. (A & E, Gen. Med. & Endocrinol.) Jersey Gen. Hosp.; SHO (O & G) Rotherham Dist. Gen. Hosp.

CLINTON, Elizabeth Flat 27, 46 Speirs Wharf, Glasgow G4 9TB — MB ChB 1988 Glas.

CLINTON, Sean Terence 20 Stock Grove, Milnrow, Rochdale OL16 3XB — MB ChB 1992 Manch.

CLINTON-JONES, Geoffrey Bryan (retired) Spearbed Copse, Dock Lane, Beaulieu, Brockenhurst SO42 7YJ Tel: 01590 612226 Fax: 01590 612480 Email: spearbed@btinternet.com — MA, MB BChir Camb. 1956; DObst RCOG 1961. Prev: Ho. Phys. & Ho. Surg., & Res. Med. Off. Nuffield Ho. Guy's Hosp.

CLISH, David 50 Grosvenor Road, Billingham TS22 5HQ — MB ChB 1967 St. And.

CLISSOLD, Elmer (retired) Cliff Cottage, Coldharbour, Dorking RH5 6HE Tel: 01306 712006 Fax: 01306 712006 — MB BS 1956 Lond.; MRCGP 1965; DA Eng. 1958. Prev: Her Majesty's Insp. of Anat. for Eng., Wales & Scotl.

CLITHEROE, Donald Graham (retired) Newkyn, 127 Sutton Road, Huthwaite, Sutton-in-Ashfield NG17 2NF Tel: 01623 517004 — MB ChB Birm. 1941.

CLITHEROE, Edna Gwendoline Woodland Lea, Cold Overton, Oakham LE15 7QB — MRCS Eng. LRCP Lond. 1946; BA Camb. 1943, MB BChir 1946. (Camb. & Birm.) Prev: Ho. Surg., Ho. Phys. & Obst. Ho. Surg. Dudley Rd., Hosp. Birm.

CLITHEROE, Maurice Benedict 2 Somerby Road, Cold Overton, Oakham LE15 7QB — MB ChB 1944 Birm.

CLIVE, Sally ICRF Medical Oncology Unit, MRC Building, Western General Hospital, Crewe Road, Edinburgh EH4 2XU Tel: 0131 332 2471 Ext: 2403 Email: s.clive@icrf.icnet.uk; 26/5 Inverleith Place, Edinburgh EH3 5QB Tel: 0131 551 6637 — MB ChB 1992 Aberd.; MB ChB (Hons.) Aberd. 1992; BSc (Med. Sci.) Hons. Aberd. 1991; MRCP (UK) 1995. (Aberdeen) Clin. Research Fell. (Med. Oncol.) ICRF Med.Oncol.Unit, W.ern Gen. Hosp. Edin. Prev: Hon. Regist. & Lect. (Med. Oncol.) Univ. Edin. W.. Gen. Edin.; SHO (Med.) Aberd. Roy. NHS Trust.

CLOAK, Brian Joseph Southwick Health Centre, The Green, Southwick, Sunderland SR5 2LT Tel: 0191 548 6634 Fax: 0191 548 1281 — MB BCh 1982 NUI; MB BCh N U I 1982. GP Sunderland.

CLODE-BAKER, Edward George 33 Francis Street, Leicester LE2 2BE — MB ChB 1996 Leic.

CLOGHER, Charlotte Anne Princess Royal, Community Health Centre, Greenhead Road, Huddersfield HD1 4EW — MB ChB 1979 Birm.; MSc (Med. Audio.) Manch. 1996; DCH Glas. 1982; DRCOG 1981. Assoc. Specialist, (Community Paediat.), Huddersfield NHS Trust. Prev: SCMO Solihull HA.; Clin. Med. Off. Huddersfield HA.

CLOGHER, Luke Calderdale Royal Hospital, Salterhebble, Halifax HX3 0PW; Clay House Farm, Saddleworth Road, Barkisland, Halifax HX4 0DX — MB ChB BAO 1973 NUI; MRCPI 1980; DCH RCPSI 1976. Cons. Paediat. Halifax Gen. Hosp. Socs: FRCPCH.

CLOHERTY, Mr John Kirwan, OStJ (retired) The Coach House, Dobbins Lane, Wendover, Aylesbury HP22 6BZ Tel: 01296 624187 — MB BCh 1955 NUI; FRCS Ed. 1976; FRCOphth 1988; DO Eng. 1964. Prev: Sen. Regist. St. John Ophth. Hosp., Jerusalem.

CLOKE, Ashwiney Ram Hill Farmhouse, Meadway, Oving, Aylesbury HP22 4HA — MB BS 1983 Lond. (St. Thos. Hosp. Lond.) Socs: BMA. Prev: Regist. Med. Nuffield Det. of Med. John Radcliffe Hosp. Oxf.

CLOKE, David James 24 Cherry Tree Avenue, Dover CT16 2NL — MB BS 1997 Newc.

***CLOKEY, Graeme James** 21 Ashlea Drive, Giffnock, Glasgow G46 6BH; 21 Viaduct Road, Clarkston, Glasgow G76 8BN Tel: 0141 644 3799 — MB ChB 1996 Glas.

CLOOTE, Alison Helen Bristol Royal Hospital for sick Children, St. Michael's Hill, Bristol BS2 8BJ; Garden Flat, 2 Cotham Side, Bristol BS6 5TP — MB BS 1986 Lond.; FRCA 1992. Cons. in (Paediat. Anaesth. & IC), Bristol Roy. Hosp. for sick Childr..

CLOSE, Alan Richard The Health Centre, Hermitage Road, St John's, Woking GU21 1TD Tel: 01483 723451 Fax: 01483 751879 — MB ChB 1970 Birm.; MRCS Eng. LRCP Lond. 1970; LMCC 1972; DA Eng. 1973.

CLOSE, Carol Teresa 9 Broad-Dykes Place, Kingswells, Aberdeen AB15 8UB — MB ChB 1987 Glas.; MRCGP 1991.

CLOSE, Colin Frank Taunton & Somerset Hospital, Musgrove Park, Taunton TA1 5DA Tel: 01823 342037 — MB BS 1980 Lond.; BA Oxf. 1977; MD Lond. 1991; MRCP (UK) 1984; FRCP 1999. (Guy's Hosp. Lond.) Sen. Regist. (Diabetes & Endocrinol.) W. Midl. RHA. Socs: Brit. Diabetic Assn.; Soc. Endocrinol.; Brit. Hypertens. Soc. Prev: Regist. (Med.) Roy. Hallamsh. Hosp. Sheff.; Research Fell. Unit for Metab. Med. UMDS Guy's Hosp. Lond.

CLOSE, George Colin Alexandra Hospital, Woodrow Drive, Redditch B98 7UB Tel: 01527 512069/ 503030 — MB ChB 1972 Sheff.; FRCPCH 2000; FRCP (1994); MRCP (UK) 1978; DCH RCP Lond. 1976. Cons. (Paediat.) with interest in Community Paediat. BromsGr. & Redditch. Prev: Cons. Paediat. Commonw. of Dominica, W. Indies.

CLOSE, Howard James Newstead House, 2 Newstead Road, Otley LS21 3JB Tel: 01943 462079 — MB BS 1970 Newc.; FRCR 1980. Cons. (Radiother. & Oncol.) Regional Radiother. Centre Cookridge; Hosp. Leeds. Prev: Sen. Regist. (Radiother.) Regional Radiother. Centre Cookridge Hosp.; Leeds; GP Middlesbrough.

CLOSE, Jacqueline Clare Therese Dept Health Care of the Elderly, Dulwich Hospital, E. Dulwich Grove, London SE22 8PT Tel: 020 7346 6073 Fax: 020 7346 6370 Email: jacqueline.close@kcl.ac.uk — MB BS 1989 Lond.; MRCP (UK) 1993. Lect.l. Clin. Age Research Unit King's Coll. Hosp. Lond. Prev: Research Fell. Clin. Age Research Unit King's Coll. Hosp. Lond.

CLOSE, James Brooks The Ashlea Medical Practice, 30 Upper Fairfield Road, Leatherhead KT22 7HH Tel: 01372 375666 Fax: 01372 360117 — MB BS 1972 Lond.; BSc Lond. 1969; MRCP (UK) 1975; MRCS Eng. LRCP Lond. 1972; MRCGP 1985; DRCOG 1980. (St. Bart.) GP Trainer; Clin. Asst., Diabetes. Socs: Fell. Roy. Soc. Med. Prev: Regist. St. Thos. Hosp. Lond.; SHO Nat. Hosp. Qu. Sq. & Whittington Hosp. Lond.; Ho. Phys. Med. Profess. Unit. St. Bart. Hosp. Lond.

CLOSE, Lydia Pauline Fairfield, Fairfield Lane, West End, Woking GU24 9QX — MB BS 1998 Lond.; MB BS Lond 1998.

CLOSE, Margaret Elaine 202 Hillhall Road, Lisburn BT27 5JA — MB BCh BAO 1984 Belf.; MB BCh Belf. 1984; MRCGP 1991; DFFP 1993; DCH Dub. 1990; DRCOG 1987; DFFP 1999. Clin. Med. Off. (Community Child Health) Down & Lisburn HSS Trust; Clin. Med. Off. (Family Plann.) N. & W. Belf. HSS Trust; Instruc. Family Plann. Doctor. Prev: Trainee GP Centr. Servs. Agency N. Irel.

CLOSE, Peter Justin The Red House, Brook, Newport PO30 4EJ — MB ChB 1983 Liverp.; MRCP (UK) 1987; FRCR 1991; DMRD Liverp. 1989. Cons. Radiol. St. Mary's Hosp. NHS Trust Newport I. of Wight. Prev: Sen. Regist. Rotat. (Radiol.) Mersey RHA; Fell. (Diagn. Radiol.) P.ss Alexandria Hosp. Brisbane, Austral.

CLOSE, Steven Andrew 35 Kirkwood Avenue, Redding, Falkirk FK2 9UF — MB ChB 1996 Aberd.

CLOSE, Virginia May Department of Orthopaedics, Tygerberg Academic Hospital, PO Box 3, Tygerberg 7505, Western Cape 7505, South Africa Tel: 00 27 021 9384136 Fax: 00 27 021 9311451; 242 Merville Garden Village, Newtownabbey BT37 9TT — MB BCh BAO 1986 Belf.; FRCS Eng. 1991; FRCSI 1991; FRCS Ed. 1991; FCS(SA) Orth. (Queens Belfast) Cons. Orthop. Surg. Tygerberg Acad. Hosp. W.. Cape, S. Afr.; Lect. (Orthop.) Univ. of Stellenbosch W. Cape, S. Africa. Socs: Full Mem. S. Afr. Orthop. Assoc. Prev: Sen. Regist. (Orthop.) Univ. Natal Durban, S. Afr.

CLOSS, Susan Patricia Ty Olwen Palliative Care Service, Morriston Hospital, Swansea NHS Trust, Swansea SA6 6NL Tel: 01792 703412 Fax: 01792 703695 Email: susan.closs@morriston-tr.wales.nhs.uk — MB BS 1975 Lond.; MRCP (UK) 1979; MRCS Eng. LRCP Lond. 1975; FRCPath 1995, M 1983; FRCP 1998. (St. Bart.) Cons. Palliat. Med.and Clin. Director of Cancer Serv.s. Swansea NHS Trust. Socs: Assn. Palliat. Med.& Pallative Med. of Gt. Britain and Irel. Prev: Cons. (Palliat. Med.) Blackburn, Hyndburn & Ribble NHS Health Care Trust.

CLOTHIER, Mr John Campbell Ivy Cottage, Water Lane, West Bromwich B71 3SA Tel: 0121 588 4164 — BM BCh 1970 Oxf.; FRCS Eng. 1976; MRCS Eng. LRCP Lond. 1969. (Oxf.) Cons. Orthop. Surg. Sandwell Healthcare Trust W. Bromwich. Socs: BMA & Mem. Brit. Orthop. Assn.

CLOTHIER, Mr John Guthrie Isleden, St. Michael's, Tenterden TN30 6DH Tel: 015806 3247 — MRCS Eng. LRCP Lond. 1935; MD Lond. 1938, MB BS 1935; FRCS Eng. 1938; MFOM RCP Lond. 1978; FACS 1945. (King's Coll. Hosp.) Socs: Fell. Roy. Soc. Trop. Med. & Hyg. & Roy. Soc. Med. Prev: Chief Med. Off. & Cons. Surg. Brit. Petroleum Co. Lond.; Cons. Surg. Nat. Iran. Oil Co. Abadan; Surg. Specialist RAMC.

CLOTHIER, Mr Peter Robert Tameside General Hospital, Fountain St., Ashton-under-Lyne OL6 9RW Tel: 0161 331 6317; 30 Greenhurst Lane, Ashton-under-Lyne OL6 9DR — MB ChB 1973 Liverp.; FRCS Eng. 1978. (Liverpool) Cons. Surg. Tameside & Glossop Acute Servs. NHS Trust. Socs: Brit. Assn. Surgic. Oncol. Prev: Cons. Surg. RAF Med. Br.; Hon. Sen. Regist. (Surg.) P'boro Dist. Gen. Hosp. & St. Stephen's Hosp. Lond.

CLOUD, Geoffrey Christopher Department of Clinical Neurosciences, St. Georges Hospital Medical School, Cranmer Terrace, London SW17 0RE Email: g.cloud@sghms.ac.uk — MB BS 1992 Lond.; BSc (Hons.) Lond. 1989; MRCP (UK) 1997. (St. Bartholomew's Hospital) Specialist Regist. (Gen. Med.) N. W. Thames Region; Stroke Assn. Clin. Fell. St. Geo.s Hosp. Med. Sch. Socs: Brit. Soc. Geriat. Med. Prev: SpR The Hammersmith Hosp., Lond.

CLOUGH, Christopher George King's College Hospital, Denmark Hill, London SE5 9RS Tel: 020 7346 3667 Fax: 020 7346 5319; 17 Blenheim Road, Bickley, Bromley BR1 2EX — MB ChB 1975 Manch.; MRCP (UK) 1978; FRCP 1992. Cons. Neurol. King's Coll. Hosp. Lond.; Med. Dir. KCH Lond.

CLOUGH, Deborah Louise 3 Beaufort House, Beaufort Avenue, Manchester M20 1LL — MB ChB 1994 Manch.

CLOUGH, Fiona Constance Wilkinson and Partners, Carterton Surgery, 17 Alvescot Road, Carterton OX18 3JL Tel: 01993 844567 Fax: 01993 841551; The Mill, Alvescot, Bampton OX18 2RX Tel: 01993 841196 — MB ChB 1983 Manch.; MRCGP 1988; DRCOG 1986. Socs: BMA. Prev: Trainee GP Woking Surrey; SHO (Psychiat.) Ashford Hosp. Middlx.; SHO (Med.) Dorking Gen Hosp. Surrey.

CLOUGH, Harriet Anne Cumberland Infirmary, Newtown Road, Carlisle CA2 7HY — MB BS 1982 Lond.; MRCP (UK) 1989; DGM RCP Lond. 1988; DPM RCP Lond. 1993. Staff Off. (Geriat. & Rehabil. Med.) Cumbld. Infirm.

CLOUGH, Mr James Robert (retired) Rock Ridge, The Street, Olveston, Bristol BS35 4DA Tel: 01454 617540 — MB BS 1957 Lond.; FRCS Eng. 1962. Prev: Cons. Orthop. & Traum. Surg. Frenchay Hosp. & Winford Orthop. Hosp. Bristol.

CLOUGH, Janet Virginia Haematology Department, Countess of Chester Hospital, Liverpool Road, Chester CH4 9NN — MB ChB Birm. 1972; FRCP Lond. 1992; MRCP (U.K.) 1975; FRCPath. 1991, M 1980. Cons. Haemat. Countess of Chester Hosp.

CLOUGH, Joanne Barbara Child Health, Southampton General Hospital, Southampton SO16 6YD Tel: 02380 796867 Fax: 02380 796378 Email: jbc@soton.ac.uk; 51 Bugle Street, Southampton SO14 2AG — MB BS 1978 Lond.; DM Soton. 1992; MRCP (UK) 1986; FRCA 1983. Sen. Lect. (Paediat. & Respirat. Med.) Soton. Gen. Hosp.

CLOUGH, Lesley Anne The Surgery, Outings Lane, Doddinghurst, Brentwood CM15 0LS Tel: 01277 821699 Fax: 01277 821226; Roothings Rise, Shellow Road, Willingale, Ongar CM5 0SS Tel: 01277 896224 Email: laclough@aol.com — MB BChir 1980 Camb.; MRCGP 1985; MMedSci Birm. 1998. (Cambridge University) GP Princip. Socs: RCGP Essex Fac. (Bd. Mem.).

CLOUGH, Peter Howard The David Lewis Centre for Epilepsy, Mill Lane, Warford, Alderley Edge SK9 7UD Email: peterc@davidlewis.org.uk — MB ChB 1994 Manch.; MSc 1988 Manch. (Faculty of Medicine). Sedior Clin. Med. Off. (Epileptology); Clin. Assitant (Neurol.) Centre for Neurosci.s, Hope Hosp. & S. Manch.

CLOUGH, Richard Kenneth (retired) 27 Cockey Moor Road, Bury BL8 2HD Tel: 0161 764 4609 — MB ChB 1933 Manch.; DCH Eng. 1936. Prev: Surg. Lt. RNVR.

CLOUGH, Simon Christopher 10 Hilltop View, Meppershall, Shefford SG17 5QE — MB BS 1990 Lond.

CLOUGH, Timothy Martin 19 Beechfield, Grasscroft, Oldham OL4 4EN — MB ChB 1992 Manch.; BSc 1989 St. Andrtass; FRCS 1996. Specialist Regist. (Orthop.) N. W. Deanery.

CLOUGHLEY, Eric Dalgleish (retired) Springwood, Cauldwell Road, Mansfield NG18 5BL Tel: 01623 631845 — LRCP LRCS 1946 Ed.; LRCP LRCS Ed. LRFPS Glas. 1946; MRCGP 1968. Prev: Regional Med. Off. DHSS.

CLOUT, Audrey (retired) Ewhurst Place, Ifield Drive, Crawley RH11 0AD — MB BS 1953 Lond.; MRCS Eng. LRCP Lond. 1951.

CLOUT, Catherine Diagnostic Imaging, Northern General Hospital, Herries Road, Sheffield S5 7AU Tel: 01142434343 — BM 1982 (Hons.) Soton.; MRCP (UK) 1986; FRCR 1990. Cons.(Radiol.) N.ern Gen. Hosp. Socs: Roy. Coll. Radiol.; Brit. Med. Ultrasound Soc.; BMA. Prev: Cons. Radiol. Huddersfield Roy. Infirm.; Sen. Regist. & Regist. (Radiol.) Sheff. Hosps.; SHO Rotat. (Med.) Soton. Hosps.

CLOUT, Ivan Reginald, OBE (retired) Ewhurst Place, Ifield Drive, Crawley RH11 0AD Tel: 01293 22278 — MRCS Eng. LRCP Lond. 1944; MA Camb.; FRCGP 1980, M 1965. Prev: Surg. Lt. RN.

CLOUTER, Carole Angela Grove Medical Practice, Shirley Health Centre, Grove Road, Shirley, Southampton SO15 3UA Tel: 023 8078 3611 Fax: 023 8078 3156; 44 Brookvale Road, Southampton SO17 1RA — BM Soton. 1981; MRCGP 1986; DCH RCP Lond. 1984; DRCOG 1984. GP Shirley. Prev: Trainee GP Soton.; SHO (Paediat.) Univ. Hosp. Nottm.

CLOUTER, Gabriela Barton House Health Centre, 233 Albion Road, London N16 9JT Tel: 020 7249 5511 Fax: 020 7254 8985 — MB BS 1993 Lond.

CLOUTER, Marjorie Audrey 1 St Mark's Place, Portobello, Edinburgh EH15 2QB Tel: 0131 669 1017 — MB ChB 1968 Ed. (Ed.)

CLOUTING, Elizabeth Marie Milbourne House, 3 Deerhurst Close, Mill Lane, Calcot, Reading RG31 7RX — MB BS 1997 Lond.

CLOVER, Anne Maureen 5 Olivey Place, Mylor Bridge, Falmouth TR11 5RX Tel: 01326 374996 Fax: 01326 374996; 5 Olivey Place, Mylor Bridge, Falmouth TR11 5RX — MB BS Lond. 1963; MRCS Eng. LRCP Lond. 1963; FFHom 1980, M 1977; DPM Eng. 1970; DObst RCOG 1965. (Roy. Free) Prev: Cons. Homoeop. Phys, Tunbridge Wells; Cons. Homoeop. Phys Roy. Lond. Homoeop. Hosp.; Sen. Regist. Cheadle Roy. Hosp.

CLOVER, Anthony James Peterson 13 Claremont Hill, Shrewsbury SY1 1RD — BM BS 1995 Nottm.; BMedSci (Hons.) Nottm. 1993. (Univ. Nottm. Med. Sch.) SHO Rotat. (Surg.) Char. Cross Hosp. Lond.

CLOVER, Judy Ann Southampton General Hospital, Tremona Road, Southampton SO16 6YD; The Vicarage, 402 Hinkler Road, Thornhill, Southampton SO19 6DF — MB BS 1984 Lond.; MRCOphth 1994. Staff Grade Soton. Eye Unit; Clin. Asst. Soton. Eye Unit. Prev: SHO (Cas.) Guy's Hosp. Lond.; SHO (Ophth.) Croydon Eye Unit; SHO (O & G) Ashford Hosp. Middlx.

CLOW, David James Department of Paediatrics, Dumfries & Galloway Royal Infirmary, Bankend Road, Dumfries DG1 4AP Tel: 01387 46246; 27 Dalbeattie Road, Dumfries DG2 7PJ Tel: 01387 52706 — MB ChB 1965 Glas.; FRCP Glas. 1979; MRCP (UK) 1970. Cons. Community Paediat. & Cons. Paediat. Dumfries & Galloway Area HB. Socs: (Exec. Comm.) Scott. Paediat. Soc.; Brit. Paediat. Assn. Prev: Cons. Community Paediat. Dumfries & Galloway HB; Cons. Paediat. Kingdom of Tonga S. Pacific; Regist. (Paediat.) Falkirk & Stirling Roy. Infirm.

CLOW, Elizabeth Crawford Montgomery (retired) Tigh Beag, Boat og Garten, Inverness IV2 5XQ — MB ChB 1928 Glas.; Foundat. MRCGP. Prev: Res. Phys. & Surg. Glas. Roy. Infirm.

CLOW, Eric (retired) 12 Abbey Drive W., Grimsby DN32 0HH — MB 1961 Camb.; BChir 1960; BChir 1960 Camb.; FRCGP 1988, M 1977. Prev: Ho. Phys., Ho. Surg. & Sen. Ho. Phys. (Chest Dis.) St. Helier Hosp. Carshalton.

CLOW, William Menzies Dept, Obstetrics and Gynaecology, Withybush Hospital, Fishguard Rd, Haverfordwest SA61 2PZ Tel: 01437 773254 Fax: 01437 773391; 149 Haven Road, Haverfordwest SA61 1DL Tel: 01437 763841 — MB ChB 1965 Ed.; FRCOG 1984, M 1971, DObst 1967. (Ed.) Cons. O & G Withybush Gen. Hosp. HaverfordW.; Honaray Lect.. (Obst&Gyn) Univ. of Wales, Coll. of Med.; Lead Colposcopist, Pembrokesh. Cervical Screening Wales, Cardiff. Socs: Welsh Obst. & Gyn. Soc.; Brit. Soc. Colposcopy & Cervical Path.; Brit. Soc. Gynaecol. Endoscopy. Prev: Sen. Regist. (O & G) Manch. AHA (T).; Ho. Surg. Bangour Gen. Hosp.; Ho. Phys. Roy. Infirm. Edin.

CLOWES, Carl Iwan Powys Health Care NHS Trust, Ysbyty Bronllys, Bronllys, Brecon LD3 0LS Tel: 01874 711661 Fax: 01874 711611; Y Wigoedd, Rhoscefnhir, Pentraeth LL75 8YT Tel: 0124 8450 305 — MB ChB Manch. 1967; MSc Social Med. Lond. 1980; FFPHM RCP (UK) 1994; MFCM RCP (UK) 1981; DTM & H RCPSI 1985; Cert. Health Economics Aberd. 1982. Dir. of Med. Servs. Powys NHS Trust. Socs: Welsh Med. Soc.; Coun. Of Europe Fell.ship. Prev: Dir. Plann. Powys HA; GP Llanaelhaearn; Specialist Community Med. Gwynedd HA.

CLOWES, Mr Charles Brian Eildon Bank, High Cross Avenue, Melrose TD6 9SE — MB ChB 1969 Ed.; FRCS Ed. 1975.

CLOWES, Christopher Tobias Cubbington Road Surgery, 115 Cubbington Road, Leamington Spa CV32 7AJ Tel: 01926 425131 Fax: 01926 427254; 4 Purcell Close, Eastfield Road, Leamington Spa CV32 4XS Tel: 01926 886490 — MB BS 1983 Lond.; DRCOG 1987. Clin. Asst. Ment. Handicap W.on Hosp. Leamington Spa; Clin. Asst. Phys. Handicap. Castel Froma Home for Disabled Leamington Spa.

CLOWES, David Peter Howletts Farm, Fernhill Lane, Balsall Common, Coventry CV7 7AN — MRCS Eng. LRCP Lond. 1961. (Manch.) Prev: Ho. Surg. Manor Hosp. Nuneaton; Ho. Phys. & SHO (Obst.) Geo. Elliot Hosp. Nuneaton.

CLOWES, Jackie Anne 113 Cross Lane, Sheffield S10 1WN — MB ChB 1992 Sheff.; BSc (Hons.) Sheff. 1987, MB ChB 1992.

CLOWES, Jonathan Rafe St. Lukes House, Blackmoorfoot Road, Huddersfield HD4 5RH Tel: 01484 466027 Fax: 01484466111 Email: jclowes@doctors.org.uk — BM BCh 1987 Oxf.; MRCGP, 1992; MFPHM, 1999. Locum Cons.. (Pub. Health Med.) Huddersfield. Socs: BMA.

CLOWES, Martin Anthony Eye Department, Royal Halifax Infirmary, Free School Lane, Halifax HX1 2YP — MB BS 1978 Lond.; MRCS Eng. LRCP Lond. 1978.

CLOWES, Nicholas William Beaufoy The Old Vicarage, Doddington, Nantwich CW5 7PS Tel: 01270 520327 — MB ChB 1976 Birm.; FFA RCS Eng. 1982. Cons. Anaesth. N. Staffs. Hosp. Prev: Sen. Regist. (Anaesth.) W. Widl. RHA; Regist. (Anaesth.) Leics. AHA (T); SHO (Anaesth.) Walsgrave Hosp. Coventry.

CLOWES, Peter Mount Pleasant Medical Centre, Ditherington Road, Shrewsbury SY1 4DQ Tel: 01743 235111; The Brambles, Darville, Shrewsbury SY1 2UG — MB BS 1977 Lond.; DRCOG 1980.

CLOWES, Rachel Laura Howletts Farm, Fernhill Lane, Balsall Common, Coventry CV7 7AN — MB ChB 1994 Birm. Prev: SHO (Med.) Good Hope Hosp. Sutton Coldfield; SHO (Surg.) Solihull Hosp.

CLUBB, Alan Stuart Eskbridge Medical Centre, 8A Bridge Street, Musselburgh EH21 6AG Tel: 0131 665 6821 Fax: 0131 665 5488; 15 Windsor Gardens, Musselburgh EH21 7LP Tel: 0131 665 5177 — MB ChB 1971 Ed.; MRCGP 1978. (Edinburgh)

CLUBB, Alexander William The Clubb House, Granville Terrace, Stone ST15 8DF Tel: 01785 812 663 Fax: 01785 814985 Email: vestbright@aol.com — MB ChB 1955 Aberd.; FRCOG 1977; MRCOG 1964. (Aberdeen) Locum Work (Partly Retd.). Socs: N. Eng. Obst. & Gyn. Soc.; Birm. & Mid. O&G Soc. Prev: Sen. Regist. (O & G) United Birm. Hosps. & Birm. RHB; Regist. O & G City Gen. Hosp. Sheff.; Ho. Surg. Aberd. Roy. Infirm.

CLUBB, Augusta Stanley (retired) 20 Fields Park Court, Newport NP20 5BD — MB ChB Ed. 1932; DPH Ed. & Glas. 1935.

CLUBB, Catriona 17 Craigenbay Crescent, Lenzie, Kirkintilloch, Glasgow G66 5JW — MB ChB 1998 Aberd.; MB ChB Aberd 1998.

CLUBB, Dawson Robert 'Houlland', Brae, Shetland ZE2 9QJ — MB ChB 1964 Aberd. (Aberd.)

CLUBB, Elizabeth Mary Fitz-Simon Clitherow House, 1 Blythe Mews, Blythe Road, London W14 0NN Tel: 020 7371 1341 Fax: 020 7371 4921; Holmwood, Foxcombe Road, Boar's Hill, Oxford OX1 5DL Tel: 01865 739994 Fax: 01865 327386 — MB BS 1947 Lond.; FRCGP 1986, M 1954. (W. Lond.) Med. Dir. Natural Family Plann. Serv. Lond. Socs: BMA.

CLUBB, John Meredyth Holmwood, Foxcombe Road, Boars Hill, Oxford OX1 5DL Tel: 01865 739994 — MRCS Eng. LRCP Lond. 1947; FRCGP 1983, M 1953. (King's Coll. Hosp.) JP; Chairm. Med. Insur. Agency. Socs: BMA.

CLUBB, Richard Anthony North End Medical Centre, 211 North End Road, West Kensington, London W14 9NP Tel: 020 7385 7777 Fax: 020 7386 9612 — MB BCh 1973 Wales; DCH Eng. 1975.

CLUBB, Timothy Colin The Surgery, High Street, Barley, Royston SG8 8HY Tel: 01763 848244 Fax: 01763 848677; St. Peters Hill, Meeting Lane, Litlington, Royston SG8 0QF Tel: 01763 853084 —

MB BS 1989 Lond. (St. Geo. Hosp. Med. Sch.) Prev: Trainee GP Camb. VTS.

CLUBB, Vincent James 17 Arnstones Cl, Colchester CO4 3AS — MB ChB 1997 Sheff.

CLUCAS, Alan Thomas Cird Galderma, BP 87, 06902 Sophia Antipolis, France Tel: 33 9395 7148 Fax: 33 9395 7071; 75 Tattenham Crescent, Epsom KT18 5NY Tel: 01737 359321 — BM BCh 1980 Oxf.; MA Oxf. 1983, BA 1977, BM BCh 1980; MFPM 1989; MRCP (UK) 1983; Dip. Pharm. Med. RCP (UK) 1985. Director Clin. Research & Developm. Cird Galderma, France. Prev: Med. Director Rhone-Poulenc Rorer, Austral.; Clin. Research Phys. Pfizer Sandwich; Regist. (Med.) Treliske Hosp. Truro.

CLUETT, Barbara Elisabeth North Swindon Practice, Home Ground Surgery, Thames Avenue, Haydon Wick, Swindon SN25 1QQ Tel: 01793 705777; 27 Stone Lane, Lydiard Millicent, Swindon SN5 3LD — BM 1978 Soton.

CLUETT, David Medical Centre, High Street, Ruabon, Wrexham LL14 6NH Tel: 01978 823717 Fax: 824142; 3 Mountfields, Bangor Isycoed, Wrexham LL13 0BZ Tel: 780966 — MB BCh 1977 Wales; MRCGP 1981.

CLULEY, Sarah 24 Avon Green, Wyre Piddle, Pershore WR10 2JE — MB ChB 1985 Liverp.

CLULOW, Catherine Psychiatric Unit, Derby City General Hospital, Uttoxeter Road, Derby DE22 3NE Tel: 01332 625580 — MRCS Eng. LRCP Lond. 1979. (Liverpool) Clin. Med. Off. (Gen. Psychiat.) Derby City Gen. Hosp.

CLULOW, George Edward (retired) 308 Crewe Road, Willaston, Nantwich CW5 6NJ Tel: 01270 568612 Fax: 01270 568612 Email: hilted@ukgateway.net — MB BS Lond. 1951.

CLUNE, Fergus Anthony Martin 177 High Street, Sheerness ME12 1UH — MB BCh BAO 1962 NUI; LDS RCSI. (Univ. Coll. Dub.)

CLUNIE, Fiona Spence Sunnyside Royal Hospital, Hillside, Montrose DD10 9JP Tel: 01674 830361 Fax: 01674 830361 Ext.251 — MB ChB 1988 Aberd.; MRCPsych 1993. Cons. Psychiat. Sunnyside Roy. Hosp. Montrose.

CLUNIE, Gavin Peter Ross Rheumatology Department, Royal Free Hospital, Pond St, London NW3 Email: g.clunie@ucl.ac.uk; 56 Gastein Road, London W6 8LU — MB BS 1988 Lond.; BSc Lond. 1984; MD Lond. 1996; MRCP (UK) 1991. Sen. Regist. (Rheum.) Univ. Coll. Hosps. Socs: Brit. Soc. Rheum. Prev: Lect. (Rheum.) Univ. Coll. Lond.

CLUNIE, Jason Matthew John Surgery, 28 Gloucester Road, Cheriton Bishop, Exeter EX6 6JA Tel: 01647 24272; Kennick Barn, Christow, Exeter EX6 7NZ — MB BS 1991 Lond. (University College Hospital London) GP.

CLUNIE, John Corner Place Surgery, 46A Darmouth Road, Paignton TQ4 5AH Tel: 01803 557458 Fax: 01803 524844 — MB BS 1957 Lond.; DObst RCOG 1962. (Univ. Coll. Hosp.) Socs: Assoc. RCGP; BMA. Prev: SHO (Cas. & Orthop.) Peace Memor. Hosp. Watford; Ho. Phys. Whittington Hosp.; Ho. Surg. N. Middlx. Hosp.

CLUNIE, Roger William Duncan (retired) Riverlea Cottage, Mottisfont, Romsey SO51 0DR Tel: 01794 341164 Fax: 01794 341154 — MB ChB 1965 Birm.; FFA RCSI 1973; DA RCPSI 1971. Cons. Anaesth. Roy. Hants. Co. Hosp. Winchester. Prev: Sen. Regist. Rotat. (Anaesth.) Kings Coll. Hosp. Lond. & Qu. Vict. Hosp. E. Grinstead.

CLUTTERBUCK, Daniel John Hawick Health Centre, Teviot Road, Hawick TD9 9DT Tel: 01450 372076; PF2, 3 Maxwell Street, Edinburgh EH10 5HT — MB ChB 1992 Liverp. GP Regist. Hawick Health Centre Roxburghsh. Prev: SHO (Med.) Roy. Infirm. Edin.

CLUTTERBUCK, Elaine Joyce Dept. Of Renal Medicare, Hammersmith Hospital, Du Cane Road, London W12 0NN Tel: 020 8383 3152 Fax: 020 8383 2062 — MB ChB 1980 Leeds; PhD Brunel 1989; BSc (Hons.) Leeds 1977; FRCP Lond. 1995; MRCP (UK) 1983. (Leeds) Cons. Nephrologist, Hammersmith Hosp., Lond. Prev: Sen. Regist. (Renal Med.) Guy's Hosp. Lond.; MRC Train. Fell. Nat. Inst. Med. Research Lond.

CLUTTON, Hayley Amanda 6 Darnley Av, Worsley, Manchester M28 7UG — MB ChB 1997 Manch.

CLUTTON-BROCK, Thomas Henry Department of Anaesthesia & Intensive Care Medicine, The Queen Elizabeth Hospital, Norht 5A, Edgbaston, Birmingham B15 2TH Tel: 0121 627 2060 Fax: 0121 627 2062 — MB ChB 1980 Bristol; MRCP (UK) 1983; FFA RCS Eng. 1985. Sen. Lect. (Anaesth. & IC) Univ. Birm. & Hon. Cons. W. Midl. RHA. Prev: Lect. (Anaesth.) Univ. Birm.; Regist. (Anaesth.) Bristol & W.on HA; SHO (Intens. Care) Middlx. Hosp. Lond.

CLYBURN, Paul Anthony Department of Anaesthetics, University Hospital of Wales, Cardiff CF14 4XW Tel: 029 2074 7747 Fax: 029 2074 7203 Email: clyburn@cf.ac.uk; 9 The Rise, Llanishen, Cardiff CF14 0RA Tel: 029 2076 2932 — MB BS 1978 Lond.; MRCP (UK) 1982; FFA RCS Eng. 1984. (St. Mary's Hosp. Med. Sch. Lond.) Cons. Anaesth.Cardiff and the Vale NHS Trust.

CLYDE, Christine Ann Austhorpe View Surgery, 5 Austhorpe View, Leeds LS15 8NN Tel: 0113 260 2262 Fax: 0113 232 8090 — MB ChB 1987 Leeds; DCH 1991; DRCOG 1980; PhD Leeds 1982.

CLYDE, Elizabeth Margaret Stanley Venlaw View, Connor St., Peebles EH45 8HD — MB ChB 1967 Ed.; DFFP 1997; DPM Eng. 1976; DObst RCOG 1969.

CLYDE, Heather Christine Orchard Farm, 75 Niblock Road, Antrim BT41 2RH — MB BCh BAO 1982 Belf. Clin. Med. Off. N. Health & Social Servs. Bd. Prev: Clin. Med. Off E. Health & Social Servs. Bd. Belf.

CLYDE, John Wilson Charlotte Street Surgery, 1 Charlotte Street, Dumfries DG1 2AG Tel: 01387 267626 Fax: 01387 266824 — MB ChB 1991 Ed.; MRCP (UK) 1994. SHO (A & E) Roy. Devon & Exeter Hosp. Prev: SHO (Nephrol.) Roy. Liverp. Univ. Hosp. NHS Trust; SHO (Med.) NE Warks. HA.

CLYDE, Ronald John Cambria Surgery, Ucheldre Avenue, Holyhead LL65 1RA — MB BCh BAO 1976 Belf.; MRCGP 1983; DRCOG 1985; DCH RCP Lond. 1984. (Qu. Univ. Belf.) GP Holyhead. Socs: Brit. Med. Acupunct. Soc. Prev: Med. Off. Gen. Petroleum Corpn., Qatar.; GP Holyhead. - Again.

CLYMO, Andrew Batten Whittington Old House, Horsebridge Lane, Kinver, Stourbridge DY7 6NX Tel: 01384 873693 Fax: 01384 873693 Email: andrew@clymo.screaming.net — MB BS 1959 Lond.; FRCP Lond. 1982, M 1965; MRCS Eng. LRCP Lond. 1959; FRCPCH 1997; Cert. Av. Med. 1994; DCH Eng. 1964. (Roy. Free) Socs: Assn. Clin. Path.; BMA; Brit. Med. Pilots Assn. Prev: Cons. Paediat. Wolverhampton Gp. Hosps.; Sen. Regist. (Paediat.) Soton. Gp. Hosps.; Research Regist. (Paediat.) Qu. Charlotte's Matern. Hosp.

CLYNE, Jeffrey Robert, MBE 65 Glebelands Road, Prestwich, Manchester M25 1WH Tel: 0161 773 2281 Fax: 0161 773 2281 — MB ChB Manch. 1954; FRCGP 1981, M 1968. (Manch.) Indep. Med. Pract. Manch.; Indust. Med. Off. (Occupat. Health) Salford; JP. Socs: Fell. Manch. Med. Soc.; BMA. Prev: Princip. GP Manch; Lect. (Gen. Pract.) Manch. Univ.; Capt. RAMC.

CLYNE, Michael James Sankyo Co. Ltd., London Representative Office, Ana House, 6-8 Old Bond St., London W1S 4PH Tel: 020 7409 0317 Fax: 020 7493 1409; 17 Kings College Road, Ruislip HA4 8BQ — MB ChB Ed. 1966; MFPM 1989; DObst RCOG 1971. UK Med. Dir. Sankyo Company Ltd Lond. Socs: Fell. Roy. Soc. Med.; BMA. Prev: Managing Dir. Panpharma Ltd. Amersham; Ho. Surg. & Ho. Phys. Qu. Mary's Hosp. Sidcup; Maj. RAMC.

CLYNES, Don (retired) — MB ChB 1952 Manch.; MRCGP 1965.

CLYNICK, Francis Edward 117 Harley Street, London W1G 6AS Tel: 020 7935 0723; Melinsey, Veryan, Truro TR2 5PX Tel: 0187 250543 — MB ChB 1941 St. And.; FFA RCS Eng. 1953; DA Eng. 1947. Prev: Cons. Anaesth. Qu. Charlotte's St. Mark's & Roy. N.. Hosps.

CNATTINGIUS, Jacob Anders Scandanavian Medical Centre, 15 Harvey Street, London W1G 9QQ Tel: 020 7636 7780 Fax: 020 7636 7790; Ashlands, Belmont Road, Combe Down, Bath BA2 5JR Tel: 020 7636 7780 Fax: 020 7636 7790 — Lakarexamen 1981 Lund.

COACKLEY, Alison 22 Osborne Road, Southport PR8 2RJ — MB ChB 1987 Aberd.

COAD, Nigel Anthony Gregory Walsgrave Hospital, Coventry CV2 2DX Tel: 024 76 602020 Fax: 024 76 197622; The Manor, Church Lane, Cubbington, Leamington Spa CV32 7JT — MB ChB 1973 Liverp.; FRCP Lond. 1976; FRCPCH 1997. (Liverp.) Cons. Paediat. Walsgrave Hosp. Coventry.

COAD, Nigel Robin Millhouse, Totley Grove, Totley, Sheffield S17 3AX — BM 1981 Soton.; FFA RCS Eng. 1986. Cons. Anaesth & Intens. Care N. Gen Hosp. Sheff.

COAD, Wendy Mary 8 Clifton Terrace, Liskeard PL14 4HN — MB ChB 1977 Bristol.

COADY, Andrew Terence Pathway House, 11 Copperkins Lane, Amersham HP6 5QB — MB BS 1979 Lond.; MRCPath 1991. Cons. Path. Mt. Vernon & Watford Hosps. NHS Trust.

COADY, Anne Mary Haematology Department, Royal Liverpool Hospital, Prescott St., Liverpool L7 8XP; 36 Digg Lane, Wirral CH46 6AQ — MB BCh BAO 1986 Dub. Regist. (Haemat.) Roy. Liverp. Hosp.

COADY, David Andrew 39 Park Avenue, Crosby, Liverpool L23 2SR — MB BS 1993 Newc.

COADY, Mr Martin Stephen Edward Department of Plastic Surgery, Middlesbrough General Hospital, Ayresome Green Lane, Middlesbrough TS5 5AZ Email: martincoady:compuserve.com — MB BS 1987 Lond.; FRCS Eng. 1991; FRCS (Plast) 1998. (Guy's Hosp. UMDS) Cons. (Plastic Surg.) Middlesbrough; Clin. Dir., plastic Surg., S. Tees Acute Hosp.s. Socs: Brit. Assn. Plastic Surgs.

COADY, Thomas John 4 Crofton Road, Ipswich IP4 4QS — MB ChB 1956 Glas.

COAKER, Martin Julian Geoffrey Street Health Centre, Geoffrey Street, Preston PR1 5NE Tel: 01772 401760 Fax: 01772 401766 — MB ChB 1981 Manch.; MRCGP 1986; DRCOG 1985.

COAKES, James Rainald 24 The Chase, Tadworth KT20 6JD — BM 1998 Soton.

COAKES, Mr Roger Lawrie 148 Harley Street, London Tel: 020 7935 1207 Fax: 020 8761 7229 — MB BS Lond. 1967; FRCS Eng. 1974; MRCS Eng. LRCP Lond. 1967; FRCOphth 1989; DO Eng. 1971. (St. Geo.) Cons. Ophth. Surg. King's Coll. Hosp. Lond.; Recognized Teach. (Ophth.) Univ. Lond. Socs: Fell. Roy. Soc. Med. Prev: Sen. Resid. Off. Moorfields Eye Hosp. Lond.; Research Fell. Mayo Clin. USA; Sen. Regist. St. Geo. Hosp. Lond.

COAKHAM, Professor Hugh Beresford Department of Neurosurgery, Frenchay Hospital, Bristol BS16 1LE Tel: 0117 973 1323 Fax: 0117 973 3303; Mansion House Stables, Litfield Road, Clifton, Bristol BS8 3LL Email: hcoakham@aol.com — MB BS 1968 Lond.; MRCS Eng. LRCP Lond. 1968; BSc Lond. 1964; FRCP Lond. 1991; FRCS Eng. 1975; MRCP (UK) 1971. (Univ. Coll. Hosp.) Cons. Neurosurg. Frenchay Hosp. & Roy. Infirm. Bristol; Prof. Neurosurg. Univ. Bristol; Dir. Imperial Cancer Research Fund Brain Tumour Gp. Socs: Soc. Brit. Neurol Surgs.; Brit. Neuropath. Soc. Prev: Regist. (Surg.) Univ. Coll. Hosp. Lond.; Sen. Regist. (Neurosurg.) Maudsley Hosp. Lond. & SE Regional Centre, Brook Hosp. Lond.; Neurosurg. Fell. Mass. Gen. Hosp. & Harvard Univ. Boston.

COAKLEY, Anthony Joseph Willow House, Beech Hill, Bridge, Canterbury CT4 5AU Tel: 01227 830869 — MSc Lond. 1976; MB ChB Manch. 1970; FRCP Lond. 1987; MRCP (UK) 1973; FRCR 1993. Cons. Phys. Nuclear Med. Kent & Canterbury Hosp. Socs: Fell. Roy. Soc. Med.; (Ex-Pres.) Brit. Nuclear Med. Soc. Prev: Assoc. Dean Postgrad. Med. SE Thames; Sen. Regist. Addenbrooke's Hosp. Camb.; Regist. (Med.) & Research Regist. St. Thos. Hosp. Lond.

COAKLEY, Fergus Vincent Department of Radiology, Leicester Royal Infirmary, Leicester LE1 5WW Tel: 0116 254 1414 Fax: 0116 258 6062; 1233 York Avenue, Apartment 9M, New York NY 10021, USA Tel: 00 1 212 6397000 Fax: 00 1 212 7944010 Email: fergus-coakley@msn.com — MB BCh BAO 1988 NUI; MRCPI 1990; FRCR 1994. (Univ. Coll. Cork, Irel.) Sen. Regist. (Radiol.) Leicester Roy. Infirm.; Fell. (Body Imaging) Memor. Sloan-Kettering Cancer Center, NY.

COAKLEY, John Hugh Intensive Care Unit, St. Bartholomew's Hospital, West Smithfield, London EC1A 7BE Tel: 020 7601 7526 Fax: 020 7601 7528 Email: coakley@dial.pipex.com; 62 North Road, Highgate Village, London N6 4AA Tel: 020 8341 2145 — MB ChB 1980 Liverp.; MD Liverp. 1993; FRCP Lond. 1996; MRCP (UK) 1983. (Liverp.) Cons. Phys. (Intens. Care) St. Bart. & Homerton Hosp. Lond.; Med. Dir. Homerton Hosp. Socs: (Ex-Pres.) Green Dragon Med. Soc.; Intens. Care Soc.; Eur. Soc. Intens. Care Med. Prev: Sen. Regist. (Intens. Ther.) NE Thames RHA; Englert Clin. Lect. & Research Fell. (Med.) Univ. Liverp.; Regist. (Med.) Whiston Hosp.

***COAKLEY, Margaret Nora** 30 Windermere Avenue, Roath Park, Cardiff CF23 5PR — MB ChB 1995 Birm.; ChB Birm. 1995.

COAKLEY, Peter Gerald Leyland Queens Elizabeth Hopsital, Stadium Road, London SE18 4QH Tel: 020 88365025 Fax: 020 88364958 Email: pglcoakley@aol.com — MB BS 1989 Lond.; PHD Lond. 2000; MRCP (UK) 1992. (Royal London Hospital) Specialist Regist. (Rheum.) Lond.; Cons. Phys. and Rheumatologist, Qu. Eliz. Hopsital, Lond. Socs: Brit. Soc. Rheum.; Brit. Soc. Histocompatibility & Immunogen. Prev: ARC Research Fell. Guy's Hosp.; Regist. (Rheum.) Middlx. Hosp. & Whittington Hosp. Lond.; SHO (Med.) Univ. Hosp. Nottm.

COALES, Una Francesca 32 Stockwell Park Road, London SW9 0AJ Tel: 020 7207 8432 Email: ufcmd@aol.com — MD 1991 Oregon Health Sci. Univ.; FRCS Ed.; DRCOG. GP Regist. SW. Thames Lond. Deanery. Socs: Roy. Soc. Med. (Young Fell.); BMA; MDU.

COALS, Mr John (retired) 1 Pump Cottages, Brown Heath Road, Christleton, Chester CH3 7PW Tel: 01244 335322 — MB BS 1953 Lond.; FRCSC 1968; FRCS Eng. 1961. Prev: Cons. A & E Countess of Chester Hosp. Chester.

COAN, Anita Chesterton 29 Frickley Road, Nether Green, Sheffield S11 7EX — MB ChB 1988 Sheff.; MRCPsych 1991. Regist. (Psychiat.) N. Trent RHA.

COAN, Kristine Marie Flat 2, 63-71 Rye Hill Park, London SE15 3JR — MB ChB 1980 Sheff.

COAPES, Christopher Matthew 16 Hunt Lea, Whickham, Newcastle upon Tyne NE16 5TU — MB ChB 1996 Ed.

COARD, Kathleen Cecile Maria c/o Dr Bruce Lyons, Histopathology Department, Derriford Hospital, Plymouth PL6 8DH — MB BS 1978 Univ. W. Indies.

COAST-SMITH, Richard Coast (retired) Highfield, Back Lane, Bradford Abbas, Sherborne DT9 6SQ Tel: 01935 429260 — MB ChB Ed. 1961; FRCGP 1988, M 1974; DObst RCOG 1962.

COATE, Christopher Ernest Henry Cedar Close, Holloway Road, Duffield, Belper, Derby DE56 4FE; Cedar Close, Holloway Road, Duffield, Derby DE56 4FE Tel: 01332 842242 — MB BS 1973 Lond.; BDS Lond. 1967; FDS RCS Eng. 1976, LDS 1967. (Middlx.) GP Belper. Prev: Regist. (Dent. Surg.) Bristol Dent. Hosp.; Ho. Phys. & Ho. Surg. Harefield Hosp.

COATES, Amanda Jane Woodhill Surgery, Station Road, Mayfield TN20 6BW; Ormonde House, Orchard Rise, Tunbridge Wells TN3 9RX Tel: 01892 864016 Email: amandacoates@btinternet.com — BM 1981 Soton.; DRCOG 1985; Dip. ther. 1997 Wales. (Soton. Univ.) Princip., Woodhill Surg., Station Rd., Mayfield E. Sussex.

COATES, Andrew John Merrill Lydbrook Health Centre, Lydbrook GL17 9LG Tel: 01594 860219 Fax: 01594 860987; 5 Abbots View, Abbots Wood, Cinderford GL14 3EG Tel: 01594 825583 — MB ChB 1975 Birm. p/t Clin. Asst. (Elderly Care).

COATES, Anna Patricia Mawby Ash Tree Farm, Ashby La, Bitteswell, Lutterworth LE17 4SQ — MB ChB 1997 Birm.

COATES, Professor Anthony Robert Milnes Department of Medical Microbiology, St. Georges Hospital Medical School, University of London, Cranmer Terrace, London SW17 0RE Tel: 020 8725 5725 Fax: 020 8672 0234 Email: a.coates@sghms.ac.uk — MRCS Eng. LRCP Lond. 1973; MD Lond. 1984, BSc 1970, MB BS 1974; MRCP (UK) 1978; FRCP 1998; FRCPath 1999. (St. Thos.) Prof. & Chairm. Med. Microbiol. St. Geo. Hosp. Med. Sch. Univ. Lond.; Hon. Cons. Med. Microbiol. St. Geo. Healthcare Lond. Prev: Sen. Lect. (Med. Microbiol.) Lond. Hosp. Med.; MRC Train. Research Fell. Dept. Bact. Hammersmith Hosp. Lond.; Sen. Regist. Dept. Bact. Hammersmith Hosp. Lond.

COATES, Brenda Mary Manor Farmhouse, 23 Burrough St., Ash, Martock TA12 6NZ Tel: 01935 822378 — MB BS 1962 Lond.; MRCS Eng. LRCP Lond. 1962; DObst RCOG 1964. Clin. Med. Off. (Community Med. & Child Health) Som. HA.

COATES, Mr Christopher John Mount Alvernia Hospital, Harvey Road, Guildford GU1 3LX Tel: 01483 576020 Fax: 01483 565950 Email: cjcoates@uk.consultants.co.uk; Amberley, 22 Orchard Road, Shalford, Guildford GU4 8ER Tel: 01483 567898 Email: chriscoat@aol.com — MB BS 1976 Lond.; FRCS Lond. 1981. Cons. Roy. Surrey Co. Hosp. Guildford. Prev: Sen. Regist. Rotat. (Orthop.) Char. Cross Hosp. Lond.; Lect. (Orthop.) Char. Cross Hosp.

COATES, David Andrew Twyford Surgery, Hazeley Road, Twyford, Winchester SO21 1QY Tel: 01962 712202 Fax: 01962 715158; Water Farm House, Twyford, Winchester SO21 1QE Tel: 01962 712067 — MB ChB 1968 Bristol; BSc Ed. 1963; DObst RCOG 1970. Socs: BMA. Prev: Med. Off. S. Pacific Health Serv. (Fiji).

COATES, David Peter Department of Anaesthesia, Bristol Royal Infirmary, Bristol BS2 8HW Tel: 0117 928 2163 Fax: 0117 928 2098; 47 Glenavon Park, Stoke Bishop, Bristol BS9 1RW Tel: 0117

968 4686 Fax: 0117 968 4686 — MB BS 1976 Lond.; MRCS Eng. LRCP Lond. 1976; FRCA 1981. (Guy's Hospital, London) Cons. Anaesth. United Bristol Healthcare Trust .; Med. Director Site Remediation Servs. Ltd.; PostGrad. Examr. Roy. Coll. of Anaesths. Socs: Past Pres. Soc. IV Anaesth.; Treas. Brit. Orthopaedic Anaesth.s Soc.; Mem. of Inst. of Directors. Prev: Clin. Director of Anaesth. UBHT; Sen. Regist. (Anaesth.) S. W.. RHA; Regist. & SHO (Anaesth.) Oxf. RHA.

COATES, Douglas Mandall, TD (retired) 543 Chester Road, Woodford, Bramhall, Stockport SK7 1PR — MB ChB Manch. 1941; DMRD Eng. 1948. Prev: Ho. Surg. Manch. Roy. Infirm.

COATES, Edward Malcolm (retired) 5 Clifton Lane, Meltham, Huddersfield HD9 4AQ — MB ChB 1951 Manch.; DA Eng. 1956. Prev: Res. Anaesth. Macclesfield Gp. Hosps.

COATES, Florence Shirley 294 Ecclesall Road S., Sheffield S11 9PT — MB ChB Leeds 1959. (Leeds) Princip. Clin. Med. Off. (Community Health) Sheff. AHA; Med. Adviser to Sheff. Local Auth. Adoption Agency & Sheff. Family & Community Servs. Prev: Ho. Phys. Wakefield Gen. Hosp.; Ho. Surg. & Ho. Phys. St. Jas. Hosp. Leeds.

COATES, Gina 29 Crescent Road, Rowley Park, Stafford ST17 9AL — MB ChB 1988 Leic. Clin. Asst. (Psychiat.) Stafford. Prev: Clin. Asst. (Community Psychiat.) Cardiff; Regist. Rotat. (Psychiat.) Gwent & Powys.

COATES, John Adrian Halkett Place Surgery, 84 Halkett Place, St Helier, Jersey JE1 4XL Tel: 01534 736301 Fax: 01534 887793; Belle Vue, La Route de St Jean, Le Couvent, St Lawrence, Jersey JE3 1ND Tel: 01534 860880 Fax: 01534 887793 — MB ChB 1978 Leeds; MRCGP 1983; DCH RCP Lond. 1985; DRCOG 1982. (Leeds) Socs: Jersey Med. Soc. Prev: GP Mapplewell Barnsley S. Yorks.

COATES, John William Rotherham Priority Health NHS Trust, Mental Health Department, Rotherham District General Hospital, Moorgate Road, Rotherham S60 2UD Tel: 01709 304333 Fax: 01709 304105; Email: jcoat1@doctors.org.uk — MB BCh BAO 1983 Belf.; MRCPsych 1992. Cons. Psychiat. Rotherham Ment. Health Dept.; Hon. Clin. Lect., Univ. of Sheff. Prev: Cons. Psychiat. Newry Ment. Health Dept. 1995-1998.

COATES, Leonie Elizabeth Prospect House Medical Group, Prospect House, Prospect Place, Newcastle upon Tyne NE4 6QD Tel: 0191 273 4201 Fax: 0191 273 0129; 1A Westwood Gardens, Kenton, Newcastle upon Tyne NE3 3DA Tel: 0191 285 7596 — MB BS 1984 Newc.; MRCGP 1992; MRCOG 1989.

COATES, Lucy Elizabeth (retired) 5 Madeley Close, Hale, Altrincham WA14 3NJ Tel: 0161 928 5155 — MB BS 1947 Durh.; MRCGP 1965.

COATES, Marjorie (retired) 5 Clifton Lane, Meltham, Huddersfield HD9 4AQ — MB ChB 1952 Manch.; DObst RCOG 1954.

COATES, Mark John 19 Moorland Rise, Haslingden, Rossendale BB4 6UA — MB ChB 1986 Manch.

COATES, Martin Brevitt Anaesthetic Department, Level 4, Derriford Hospital, Plymouth PL6 8DH Tel: 01752 792365 Fax: 01752 763287 Email: martin.coates@phnt.swest.nhs.uk; 133 Looseleigh Lane, Derriford, Plymouth PL6 5HW — MB ChB 1968 Bristol; FRCA 1992; FFA RCS Eng. 1976; DA Eng. 1971; DObst RCOG 1970. (Bristol) Cons.(Anaesth.) Plymouth NHS Trust; Regional Adviser, S.W. Region, for Roy. Coll. of Anaesth.s 1999; Mem., Deans Advis. Panel, S.W. Region 2001. Socs: Assn. Anaesth.; Soc. Anaesth. SW Region; Brit. Soc. Orthopaedic Anaesth. Prev: Cons. Anaesth. Colonial War Memor. Hosp. Suva, Fiji; Med. Off. (Anaesth.) P.ss Margt. Hosp. Nassau, Bahamas; Asst. Prof. (Anaesth.) Univ. Virginia U.S.A.

COATES, Muriel Dean House, Park Bridge, Ashton-under-Lyne OL6 8AJ Tel: 0161 330 2420 — MB ChB 1947 Manch.; DIH Soc. Apoth. Lond. 1969; DPH 1964; DMRT Eng. 1953; MRCGP 1969. (Manch.) SCMO (Occupat. Health) Oldham AHA (Oldham Boro.). Socs: Assoc. Fac. Occupat. Med. RCP Lond; BMA. Prev: Clin. Asst. (Neurol.) United Sheff. Hosps.; Research Fell. Med. Care Research Unit Manch. Univ.; Dep. Admin. Med. Off. Town Hall Manch.

COATES, Olive Alethea 6 Shepherds Close, Fen Ditton, Cambridge CB5 8XJ Tel: 01223 292275 — MB BS 1963 Lond.; MB BS (Hons.) Lond. 1963; MRCS Eng. LRCP Lond. 1963; AFOM RCP Lond. 1990; DCH Eng. 1966; DObst RCOG 1965. (St. Bart.)

COATES, Peter Bolitho Haematology Department, Queen Elizabeth Hospital, Gayton Road, King's Lynn PE30 4ET — MB ChB 1973 Liverp.; MRCP (UK) 1981; MRCPath 1987; DCH Eng. 1980. Cons. Haemat. Qu. Eliz. Hosp. King's Lynn. Prev: Sen. Regist. Rotat. (Haemat.) Univ. Coll. Hosp. Lond.; Regist. (Haemat.) Univ. Coll. Hosp. Lond.; Regist. (Med.) Qu. Mary's Hosp. Sidcup.

COATES, Philip Anthony Andrew Metabolic Unit, Staffordshire General Hospital, Weston Road, Stafford ST16 3SA Tel: 01785 257731 Ext: 4222 — MB ChB 1986 Leic.; BSc Leics. 1984; MRCP (UK) 1990; MD 1995. (Leicester) Cons. Phys. (Diabetes & Endocrinol.). Prev: Sen. Regist. (Diabetes) Univ. Hosp. Wales, Cardiff; Research Regist. (Diabetes Research) Univ. Wales Coll. Med. Cardiff; Regist. (Med.) Univ. Hosp. Wales Cardiff.

COATES, Philip James Barton 137 Chessfield Park, Little Chalfont, Amersham HP6 6RU — MB BS 1998 Lond.; MB BS Lond 1998.

COATES, Sheila Margaret The Surgery, 114 Walm Lane, London NW2 4RT Tel: 020 8452 0366 Fax: 020 8450 3816; 11 Pattison Road, London NW2 2HL Tel: 020 7794 9911 — MB BS 1982 Lond.; BA (Hons.) Camb. 1962; MRCGP 1986. (Royal Free Hospital)

COATES, Steven James 77 St Kenelms Road, Romsley, Halesowen B62 0PG — MB ChB 1998 Sheff.; MB ChB Sheff 1998.

COATES, William Edward (retired) Wern-y-Wylan, Dinas Dinlle, Llandwrog, Caernarfon LL54 5TW Tel: 01286 830249 — MB ChB 1939 Liverp. Prev: Resid. Med. Off. (Obst.) BRd.green Hosp. Liverp.

COATESWORTH, Mr Andrew Peter Tel: 01904 631313 — MB ChB 1988 Birm.; FRCS (Orl & HNs) 2000; FRCS Eng. 1995. (Birmingham) Specialist Regist. (ENT) Yorks. & N. RHA, Cons..Ent. York and Harrogate. Socs: BAOL - HNS.

COATESWORTH, Audrey 42 Manor Park, Maids Moreton, Buckingham MK18 1QX Tel: 01280 812462 Fax: 01280 816927 — MB ChB 1962 Ed.; MRCPsych 1978. Indep. Cons. Psychiat. Bucks. Socs: Fell. RSM.

COATHUP, Paul Alexander University of East Anglia Health Centre, University of East Anglia, Earlham Road, Norwich NR4 7TJ Tel: 01603 592172; 85 Earlham Road, Norwich NR2 3RE — MB BS 1973 Lond.; BSc Lond. 1970; Cert. Family Plann. JCC 1978. (Middlx. Hosp. Med. Sch. Univ. Lond.) Univ. Phys. Univ. E. Anglia Health Centre Norwich.; Clin. Med. Off. E. Norf. Health Family Plann. Clinic Auth. Prev: Trainee GP Norwich VTS; Ho. Phys. & Ho. Surg. Basildon Hosp.; Clin. Fell. (Psychiat.) SUNY Upstate Med. Centre Syracuse, New York.

COATS, Alison Elizabeth Johnstone Health Centre, 60 Quarry Street, Johnstone PA5 8EY Tel: 01505 324348 Fax: 01505 323710 — MB ChB 1988 Glas.; DRCOG 1991.

COATS, Professor Andrew Justin Stewart Department of Cardiac Medicine, National Heart & Lung Institute, Dove House St., London SW3 6LY Tel: 020 7351 8164 Fax: 020 7351 8634 Email: a.coats@ic.ac.uk; 105a Cadogan Gardens, London SW3 Tel: 020 7730 5950 — MB BChir 1981 Camb.; MA Oxf. 1984, DM 1992; FRCP Lond. 1994; MRCP (UK) 1986; FACC 1995; FRACP 1988; FESC 1995; T(M) 1991. (Cambridge) Prof. Cardiol. Imperial Coll. Lond.; Hon. Cons. Cardiol. Roy. Brompton Hosp. Lond. Socs: Fell. Amer. Heart Assn. (Mem. Circulat. Counc.); Internat. Soc. Hypertens. Prev: Clin. Lect. (Cardiovasc. Med.) John Radcliffe Hosp. Oxf.; Fell. Pembroke Coll. Oxf.; Research Fell. (Cardiac) John Radcliffe Hosp. Oxf.

COATS, Eileen Hamilton (retired) 8 Myrtle Close, Dousland, Yelverton PL20 6NZ — MB BChir Camb. 1951. Prev: GP Bethnal Green Med. Mission Lond.

COATS, Neith Lucy Bruce 8 The Square, Cathedral Views, Crane Bridge Road, Salisbury SP2 7TW — MB ChB 1941 Aberd. (Aberd.) Socs: BMA. Prev: Ho. Surg. & Ho. Phys. Grantham Hosp.; Ho. Surg. Roy. Hosp. Richmond; Ho. Off. Harold Wood Hosp.

COATS, Mr Percy Murray, Surg. Lt. RN Retd. (cons. rooms), Nuffield Hospital, Stirling Road, Guildford GU2 7RF Tel: 01483 555812 Fax: 01483 555921 Email: percycoats@consultants.co.uk — MB BS Lond. 1965; FRCS Ed. 1974; MRCP (UK) 1971; MRCS Eng. LRCP Lond. 1965; FRCOG 1988, M 1975; DCH Eng. 1969; FRSH 1993. (St. Geo.) Examr. Univ. Lond. & RCOG; Indep. Assessor NHS complaints. Socs: Fell. Roy. Soc. Med- Vice Pres. OTG Sect.; BMA; Blair Bell Res. Soc. Prev: Cons. O & G Roy. Surrey & St. Luke's Hosp. Trust Guildford; Sen. Regist. (O & G) King's Coll. Hosp. Lond.; Resid. Surg. Off. Qu. Charlotte's Hosp. & Chelsea Hosp. Wom. Lond.

COATS, Mr Timothy John Royal London Hospital, Whitechapel, London E1 1BB Tel: 020 7377 7728 Fax: 020 7377 7014 Email: t.j.coats@mds.qmw.ac.uk; 2 Forest Heights, Epping New Road, Buckhurst Hill IG9 5TE — MB BS 1986 Lond.; BSc Lond. 1983; FRCS Eng. 1990; MD Lond. 1998; FFAEM 1997. Sen. Lect. St. Bart. & The Roy. Lond. Sch. of Med. & Dent., Qu. Mary & W.field Coll.; Hon. Cons. Roy. Hosps. NHS Trust; Hon. Cons. Homerton Hosp. Prev: Research Fell. (Neurosurg.) Roy. Lond. Hosp.; Regist. (A & E) Leeds Gen. Infirm.; Regist. (Helicopter Emerg. Med. Serv.) Roy. Lond. Hosp.

COBAIN, Esther Jean Spylaw Bank Road Surgery, 26 Spylaw Bank Road, Edinburgh EH13 0JW — MB ChB 1988 Ed.; DRCOG 1992; DGM RCP Glas. 1991.

COBAIN, Timothy Greer 120 Main Street, Conlig, Newtownards BT23 7PT — MB BCh BAO 1985 Belf.; MRCGP 1990; DRCOG 1990; Dip. IMC RCS Ed. 1989.

COBB, Mr Andrew Grant Ashtead Hospital, The Warren., Ashtead KT21 2SB Tel: 01372 278037; Downsview, The Ridge, Epsom KT18 7ET Tel: 01372 274888 Fax: 01372 274888 — MB BS 1977 Lond.; BSc (Hons.) Lond. 1974; FRCS Ed. 1983; FRCS Eng. 1983. (Middlx.) Cons. Orthop. Surg. Epsom Health Care NHS Trust; Hon. Cons. Surg. St. Lukes Hosp. for Clergy Lond.; Hon. Sen. Lect. Inst. Orthop. Univ. Lond.; Examr. Univ. Lond. (MB BS), & RCS (FRCSOrth); Intercollegiate Exam. Bd. (FRCS Orth.); Clin. Dir. Epsom & St Helier NHS Trust. Socs: Girdlestone Orthop. Soc.; Percivall Pott & Seddon Socs.; ABC Club. Prev: Hon. Cons. Surg. Orthop. Roy. Nat. Orthop. Hosp. Stanmore; Sen. Lect. Inst. Orthop. Univ. Lond.; Sen. Regist. (Orthop. Surg.) St. Bart. Hosp. Lond.

COBB, Andrew Myhill The Royal London Hospital (St. Clements), 2A Bow Road, London E3 4LL Tel: 020 7377 7959 Fax: 020 7377 7963 Email: andrewcobb@compuserve.com — MB ChB 1981 Birm.; MRCPsych 1987. (Birm.) Cons. Psychiat. Tower Hamlets Healthcare Trust; Cons. Psychiat.. E. Lond. and the City Ment. Health Trust. Prev: Hon. Cons. N.. Birm. Ment. Health Trust; Sen. Regist. Rotat. (Psychiat.) Oxf.

COBB, Mr Benjamin Blackheath Hospital, 40 Lee Terrace, London SE3 9UD Tel: 020 8318 7722; 15 Westgrove Lane, London SE10 8QP Tel: 020 8691 1148 — MB BS Lond. 1955; FRCS Eng. 1967. (St. Thos.) Hon. Cons. Ophth. Greenwich & Lewisham Hosps. Socs: Fell Roy. Soc. Med.; Brit. Microcirculat. Soc. Prev: Sen. Regist. Eye Dept. St. Thos. Hosp.; Sen. Resid. Off. Moorfields Eye Hosp. Lond.; Ophth. Roy. Commonw. Soc. For Blind Survey (1962) N. Rhodesia.

COBB, Carol Anne Sandwell General Hospital, Sandwell Healthcare, Lyndon, West Bromwich B71 4HJ Tel: 0121 553 1831, 0121 607 3938 Fax: 0121 607 3265; 9 Charlotte Road, Edgbaston, Birmingham B15 2NQ Tel: 0121 440 8258 — MB BS 1982 Lond.; BSc Lond. 1979; MRCP (UK) 1986; FRCP 1999. (St. Thomas') Cons. Phys. (Gastroenterol.) Sandwell Healthcare W. Bromwich. Socs: BSG; BASL; MWF. Prev: Sen. Regist. (Gastroenterol.) Birm. & Oxf.

COBB, Caroline Joan 3 Station Road, Kingsbarns, St Andrews KY16 8TB — MB ChB 1993 Ed.

COBB, Elizabeth Iona Little Venice Medical Centre, 2 Crompton Street, London W2 1ND Tel: 020 7723 1314 Fax: 020 7723 8580; 16 Provost Road, London NW3 4ST Fax: 020 7916 2201 — MB BS 1984 Lond.; DRCOG 1989; DCH RCP Lond. 1986. Prev: Trainee GP St. Bart. VTS; SHO (Paediat.) N.wick Pk. Hosp.

COBB, Emily Jane Riverview Practice, Wick Medical Centre, Martha Terrace, Wick KW1 5EL; Strathallan, Milton, Wick KW1 5SR — MB ChB 1991 Ed.; BSc (Hons.) Ed. 1989; MRCGP 1995; DRCOG 1993. (Ed.) Prev: Trainee GP Caithness.

COBB, Helen Elizabeth 103 Wayland Avenue, Brighton BN1 5JL — MB BS 1994 Lond. Trainee GP/SHO Ealing Hosp. S.all VTS. Prev: Ho. Off. (Med.) K. Geo. Hosp. Ilford; Ho. Off. (Surg.) Newham Gen. Hosp. Plaistow.

COBB, Jacqueline Ann 327 Ecclesall Road S., Sheffield S11 9PW Tel: 0114 235 1293 — MB BS 1962 Lond.; AFOM RCP Lond. 1988; DA Eng. 1964. (Char. Cross) Mem. Pneumoconiosis Med. Panel DHSS. Prev: Regist. Miners' Chest Dis. Treatm. Centre & Scientif. Off. MRC; Pneumoconiosis Research Centre Llandough Hosp. Penarth; Regist. (Chest Dis.) Tindal Gen. Hosp. Aylesbury.

COBB, John Pern Dean House, Park Lane, Teddington TW11 0HY Tel: 020 8977 5633 — BM BCh 1966 Oxf.; MRCP Lond. 1969; FRCPsych 1984, M 1975. Cons. Psychiat. & Clin. Tutor Priory Hosp. Lond. Prev: Sen. Lect. & Cons. Psychiat. St. Geo. Hosp. Lond.

COBB, Johnathan James 10 Westbank Drive, Anston, Sheffield S25 5HT Email: jjc@anston.demon.co.uk — MB BS 1988 Lond.; BSc Lond. 1985; MRCP (UK) 1991; MRCGP 1993. (St. Mary's Hosp. Med. Sch. Lond.) Prev: Regist. (Med.) Middlx. Hosp. Lond.

COBB, Mr Justin Peter 149 Harley Street, London W1N 2DE Tel: 020 7224 0326 Fax: 020 7487 5997 Email: j.cobb@ucl.ac.uk; 16 Provost Road, London NW3 4ST Tel: 020 7722 9292 Fax: 020 7916 2201 Email: cobbfamily@usenet.co.uk — BM BCh 1982 Oxf.; MCh Oxf. 1991; FRCS Eng. 1986. Cons. Orthop. Surg. UCL Hosp. & King Edwd. VII Hosp. Offs.; Hunt. Prof. Surg. & Osteosarcoma 1991. Socs: Fell. Roy. Soc. Med.; Fell. BOA. Prev: Sen. Regist. (Orthop.) Middlx. Hosp. Lond.; Regist. (Orthop.) Roy. Sussex. Co. Hosp. Brighton & St. Thos. Hosp.

COBB, Kathleen Bannatyne Massetts, Church Path, Cowfold, Horsham RH13 8DA Tel: 0140 386328 — MB ChB 1934 Ed.; MA Camb. 1929; MRCPsych 1972; DPM Ed. 1939. (Ed.) Prev: Cons. Psychotherap. Gen. Hosp. Newc.; Asst. Phys. Dept. Psych. Med. Roy. Infirm Aberd.; Fell. in Paediat. Psychiat. Colorado Psychopathic Hosp. (Univ.

COBB, Mr Nigel John (retired) Laws Close, Whiston, Northampton NN7 1NN Tel: 01604 890353 — MB ChB Bristol 1952; FRCS Eng. 1963; LMCC 1958. N.ampton. Prev: Sen. Res. Off. Bristol Roy. Infirm.

COBB, Peter Crispin (retired) Saxonbury House, Croft Road, Crowborough TN6 1DP Tel: 01892 652266 Fax: 01892 668607 — MB BChir 1970 Camb.; BChir 1969; MRCS Eng. LRCP Lond. 1968; DObst RCOG 1970.

COBB, Rachel Anne Downsview, The Ridge, Epsom KT18 7ET Tel: 01372 274888 — MB BS 1982 Lond.; DRCOG 1985. (St. Mary's)

COBB, Mr Richard Alan Birmingham Heartlands Hospital, Birmingham B9 5SS Tel: 0121 424 2000 Email: cobbr@heartsol.wmids.nhs.uk — MB BS 1978 Lond.; MS Lond. 1987; FRCS Eng. 1982. (St. Thos.) Cons. Surg. Birm. Heartlands Hosp. Socs: Fell. Assn. Surgs.; Assn. Coloproctol. - Counc. Mem.; Brit. Soc. Gastroenterol. Prev: Sen. Regist. (Surg.) Oxf.; Regist. (Surg.) Roy. Berks. & Battle Hosp. Reading; Regist. Rotat. (Surg.) Soton. & Salisbury.

COBBAN, Kenneth McLean, TD (retired) Broomhill, Venlaw Quarry Road, Peebles EH45 8RJ — MB ChB MB ChB Liverp. 1927; MB BS Lond. 1928; MD Liverp. 1930, BSc (Hons.) 1922; FRCGP 1969; BSc (Hons) 1922. Prev: Head, Dept. Gen. Pract. Univ. Coll. Hosp. Ibadan, Nigeria.

COBBE, Anne Tel: 020 8992 1963/0530/2010 Fax: 020 8579 4519 Email: anne.cobbe@ge-e85019.nhs.uk — MB BS 1966 Lond.; MRCS Eng. LRCP Lond. 1966; MRCGP 1985; DCH Eng. 1969; DObst RCOG 1969. (Roy. Free) Clin. Tutor (Gen. Pract.) Middlx. Hosp. Med. Sch., Char. Cross & St. Mary's Hosps. Lond. Socs: BMA. Prev: SHO & Resid. Med. Off. Qu. Eliz. Hosp. Childr. Hackney; Ho. Phys. Roy. Free Hosp.; Ho. Off. (Obst.) S. Lond. Hosp.

COBBE, John Mortimer Myra House, Bisley, Stroud GL6 7BL — MB 1974 Camb.; BChir 1973.

COBBE, Professor Stuart Malcolm Department of Medical Cardiology, Royal Infirmary, 10 Alexandra Parade, Glasgow G31 2ER Tel: 0141 211 4722 Fax: 0141 552 4683 Email: stuart.cobbe@clinmed.gla.ac.uk — MD 1981 Camb.; MB BChir 1972; FRCP Lond. 1986; FRCP Glas. 1986; MRCP (UK) 1974. (St. Thos.) Walton Prof. of Med. Cardiol. Roy. Infirm. Glas. Prev: Clin. Reader & Hon. Cons. Cardiol. John Radcliffe Hosp. Oxf.; Sen. Regist. (Cardiol. & Gen. Med.) John Radcliffe Hosp. Oxf.; Research Fell. Cardiothoracic Inst. Nat. Heart Hosp. Lond.

COBBETT, Mr John Robey (retired) Springhill, Beeches Lane, Ashurstwood, East Grinstead RH19 3RN Tel: 01342 321881 — MB BChir 1955 Camb.; MB BChir Camb. 1956; FRCS Eng. 1962; MRCS Eng. LRCP Lond. 1954. Hon. Cons. Plastic Surg. Qu. Vict. Hosp. E. Grinstead. Prev: Cons. Plastic Surg. Qu. Vict. Hosp. E. Grinstead.

COBBETT, Susan Ann 11 Avon Close, Rochford SS4 3AB Tel: 01702 540069 — MB BS 1978 Lond.; MRCS Eng. LRCP Lond. 1978.

COBBLEDICK, Christine Ann (retired) 123 West Park Drive, Nottage, Porthcawl CF36 3RN Tel: 01656 788768 — MB BCh 1977 Wales; DRCOG 1981.

COBBLEDICK, Michael Fairfield Medical Centre, Julian Terrace, Port Talbot SA12 6UQ Tel: 01639 890916; 123 West Park Drive, Nottage, Porthcawl CF36 3RN Tel: 0165671 8768 — MB BCh 1977 Wales; DRCOG 1981. Med. Off. B. O. C., W. Glam.

COBBOLD, Mrs Stephanie Seton Woodlands Cottage, Penmaen, Gower, Swansea SA3 5BD Tel: 01792 371210 — MB BS 1969 Lond.; MB BS (Hons.) Lond. 1969; FRCP Lond. 1995; MRCS Eng. LRCP Lond. 1969. (St. Mary's) Med. Adviser DVLA Swansea. Prev: Ho. Phys. St. Mary's Hosp. Lond.; Ho. Surg. Singleton Hosp. Swansea.

COBBY, Mark Jonathon Dominic Accident & Orthpaedic Radiology Department, Frenchay Hospital, Frenchay, Bristol BS16 1LE Tel: 0117 970 1212 — MB ChB 1981 Bristol; FRCR 1988; MRCP (UK) 1984. Cons. Radiol. Frenchay Hosp., Bristol. Prev: Sen. Regist. (Clin. Radiol.) Bristol Roy. Infirm.

COBBY, Timothy Francis 18 Holmes Grove, Henleaze, Bristol BS9 4EE — MB ChB 1987 Bristol.

COBDEN, Irving North Tyneside General Hospital, North Shields NE29 8NH Tel: 0191 259 6660 Fax: 0191 296 0281; The Bungalow, Hartford Bridge Farm, Hartford Bridge, Bedlington NE22 6AH Tel: 01670 820903 — MD 1980 Newc.; MB BS 1973; FRCP 1991; MRCP (UK) 1976. Cons. Phys. N.umbria Health Care; Hon. Clin. Lect. (Med.) Univ. Newc.; Hon. Cons. Phys. Freeman Hosp. Newc.; Med. Dir. N. Tyneside Hosp. N.umbria Healthcare. Prev: 1st Asst. (Gastroenterol.) Univ. Newc.; Sen. Regist. (Med.) N.. RHA; Research Regist. (Gastroenterol.) Leeds Gen. Infirm.

***COBERMAN, Miranda** 28 Brockley Avenue, Stanmore HA7 4LX — MB BS 1997 Lond.

COBLEY, Margaret 31 Victoria Road, Penarth CF64 3HY — MB BS 1980 Lond.; MRCS Eng. LRCP Lond. 1980; FFA RCS Eng. 1985; FRCA 1985 Eng. Cons. Anaesth. Univ. Hosp. Wales Cardiff. Prev: Lect. & Regist. (Anaesth.) Univ. Hosp. Wales Cardiff.

COBLEY, Thomas Dennis David Elford Farm, Dalwood, Axminster EX13 7HB — MB ChB 1993 Manch.; BDS Newc. 1985; FRCS Ed 1997; FDSRCPS Glas. 1988.

COBNER, Paul Grant Nurses Home, Alder Hey Children's Hospital, Eaton Road, Liverpool L12 2AP — MB ChB 1975 Bristol.

COBURN, Peter Richard 24 West Street, Chichester PO19 1QP Tel: 01243 789630 Fax: 01243 536591 Email: peter.coburn@connecttres.co.uk; Martins, Dyers Lane, Slindon, Arundel BN18 0RE Tel: 01243 814540 Email: peter.coburn@talk21.com — MB BS Lond. 1969; MRCP (UK) 1973; FRCP (UK) 1985. (St. Bart.) Cons. Dermat. Worthing & Chichester Hosps. Socs: Fell. RCP; Brit. Assn. Dermatol.; Brit. Assn. Dermatol. Surg. Prev: Sen. Regist. (Dermat.) Char. Cross Hosp. Lond.; Regist. (Dermat.) Roy. Vict. Infirm. Newc.; Regist. (Cardiol.) Manch. Roy. Infirm.

COBURN, Sheila Alice (retired) The Beeches, Talbot Road, Glossop SK13 7DP Tel: 0145 742355 — MRCS Eng. LRCP Lond. 1942. Prev: JP.

COCHEME, Manuel Alfred Xavier 9 Grange Road, Cambridge CB3 9AS — MB BChir 1939 Camb.; MA, MB BChir Camb. 1939; MRCPsych 1971; DTM & H Eng. 1941; DPM Bristol 1948. (Camb. & St. Thos.) Prev: Cons. Psychiat. Brookwood Hosp. Knaphill; Sen. Psychiat. Specialist Federat. of Malaya.

COCHLIN, Dennis Llewellyn X-Ray Department, University Hospital of Wales, Heath Park, Cardiff CF14 4WZ Tel: 029 2074 7747; Thornton Hough, Cardiff Road, Creigiau, Cardiff CF15 9NL — MB BCh 1970 Wales; FRCR 1975. Cons. Radiol. Univ. Hosp. Wales Cardiff & Cardiff Roy. Infirm.; Hon. Clin. Teach. Univ. Wales Coll. Med.; Lect. & Mem. Bd. of Studies Postgrad. Dip. Med. Ultrasound Univ. Wales Coll. Med. Socs: Brit. Med. Ultrasound Soc. & Amer. Inst. Ultrasound Med. Prev: Cons. Radiol. E. Glam. Gen. Hosp.

COCHRAN, Mr David Farquharson MacBeth Linlithgow Health Centre, 288 High Street, Linlithgow EH49 7ER Tel: 01506 670027; 62 Kettil'stoun Mains, Linlithgow EH49 6SL Tel: 01506 845865 — MB ChB 1977 Ed.; FRCS Ed. 1982; Dip. Forens. Med. Glas 1993; DRCOG 1992. Examr. (Forens. Med.) Lothian & Borders Police. Socs: BMA; Forens. Sci. Soc. Prev: Med. Off. i/c., Cayman Is. Govt.

COCHRAN, Diarmid Anthony Lancaster Royal Infirmary, Ashton Road, Lancaster LA1 4RP Tel: 01524 65944; 16 Bulloch Avenue, Giffnock, Glasgow G46 6NF Tel: 0141 638 0285 — MB ChB 1990 Glas. SHO (Med.) Lancaster Roy. Infirm.

COCHRAN, Dominic Paul 61 Deanwood Avenue, Netherlee, Glasgow G44 3RQ — MB ChB 1985 Glas.; MRCP (UK) 1990. Cons. Paediat. (Neonat. & Respirat. Med.) Roy. Hosp. Sick Childr. Glas. Socs: Paediat. Research Soc. Prev: Sen. Regist. (Paediat. Med.) Roy. Hosp. Sick Childr. Edin.; Research Fell. (Paediat. Respirat. Med.) Roy. Liverp. Childr. Hosp.; SHO (Paediat. Cardiol.) Brompton Hosp. Lond.

COCHRAN, Duncan Stuart Wright's Barn, Town St., Lound, Retford DN22 8RT — MB BS 1996 Lond.

COCHRAN, Gordon Oliver Burney Street Practice, 48 Burney Street, London SE10 8EX Tel: 020 8858 0631 Fax: 020 8293 9616; 68 Crescent Road, Alverstoke, Gosport PO12 2DN Tel: 01705 501689 — MB BS 1963 Lond.; MRCS Eng. LRCP Lond. 1962. (Univ. Coll. Hosp.)

COCHRAN, John Bell (retired) Oakdene, Maxwelltown, Dumfries — MB ChB 1944 Glas.; BSc Glas. 1940, MB ChB 1944; FRCP Glas. 1973, M 1962; FRFPS Glas. 1948; MRCP Lond. 1949. Prev: Surg. Lt. RNVR.

COCHRAN, Kenneth Douglas (retired) Viewfield, Blebocraigs, Cupar KY15 5UG Tel: 01334 850307 Fax: 01334 850307 — MB ChB 1944 Glas.; Dip. Ven. Liverp. 1976. Prev: Venereol. Tayside HB.

COCHRAN, Kenneth James West Beckton Health Centre, Lawson Close, London E16 Tel: 020 7445 7720; 30 Seagry Road, London E11 2NH — MB BS 1982 Lond.; BSc Hons. Aston 1978; MRCGP 1996; DCH RCP Lond. 1985; Dip Therapeutics Cardiff 1998. (Univ. Coll. Hosp. Lond.)

COCHRAN, Professor Kenneth McMillan Department of Postgraduate Medicine, 124 Observatory Road, Glasgow G12 8UZ Tel: 0141 330 4736 Fax: 0141 330 6298; 33 Upper Glenburn Road, Bearsden, Glasgow G61 4BN Tel: 0141 942 5310 — MB ChB Glas. 1967; FRCP Ed. 1996; FRCP Lond. 1991; FRCP Glas. 1983, M 1971; DObst RCOG 1969. (Univ. Glas) Dean. Postgrad. Med Educat. Glas.; Regist. MRCP (UK) Exam. RCPS Glas.; Chairm. MRCP (UK) Policy Comm.; Cons. Phys. (Gastroenterol.) Vict. Infirm. Glas. Socs: AGA; BSG. Prev: Mem. Counc. RCPS Glas.; Hon. Clin. Sub-Dean Univ. Glas.; Specialty Advisor (Med.) Postgrad Dept. Univ. Glas.

COCHRAN, Lynn Blyth Health Centre, Thoroton Street, Blyth NE24 1DX Tel: 01670 396560 Fax: 01670 396579; 41 Humford Way, Bedlington NE22 5ET — MB BS 1986 Newc.; MRCGP 1990. Prev: Trainee GP N.umbria VTS; SHO (Community Paediat.) Dept. Community Med. & Child Health Sunderland; Ho. Off. (Med. & Surg.) Hexham Gen. Hosp.

COCHRAN, Mr William (retired) — MB ChB 1949 Aberd.; FRCS Glas. 1978; FRCS Ed. 1957. Indep. Cons. Paediat. Surg. Prev: Cons. Paediat. Surg. & Cons. i/c A & E Dept. Roy. Hosp. Sick Childr. Glas.

COCHRANE, Alexander Auld, VRD (retired) 37 Glenesk Road, Eltham, London SE9 1AG Tel: 020 8850 8425 — MB BS 1944 Lond. Prev: Mem. Med. Bd. Panel for Indust. Inj. DHSS.

COCHRANE, Alexandra Flat 1/2, 55 Wilton St, Glasgow G20 6RP Tel: 0141 946 3410 Email: alexormin@aol.com — MB ChB 1994 Ed.; Dip. Trop. Med. RCPI 1996; MRCP 1999. SHO3 Infec. Dis.s Garbravel Gen. Hosp., Glas. Prev: SHO (Med.) Groote Schuur Hosp. Cape Town, RSA.; SHO (A & E) Falkirk Roy. Infirm.; SHO (Paediat.) City Gen. Hosp. Stoke-on-Trent.

COCHRANE, Allan Johnstone Upper Rockcliffe, Shore Road, Aberdour, Burntisland KY3 — MB ChB 1973 Glas.; MRCGP 1977; DRCOG 1976.

COCHRANE, Barbara Anne 10 Slievecoole Park, Belfast BT14 8JN — MB BCh BAO 1977 Belf.

COCHRANE, Brenda Osborne House, The Green, Olveston, Bristol BS35 4EJ Tel: 01454 613409 — MB BS Lond. 1966; MRCS Eng. LRCP Lond. 1966; DA Eng. 1968. (King's Coll. Hosp.) Prev: Clin. Asst. (Anaesth.) Avon AHA (T).; Regist. (Anaesth.) Plymouth Gen. Hosp.; Ho. Phys. King's Coll. Hosp. Lond.

COCHRANE, Caroline Louisa Tel: 01491 575988 — MB BS 1967 Lond.; DCH Eng. 1969. (Middlx.) Clin. Med. Off. (Family Plann.). Prev: Gen. Practitioner, Lond. N12.

COCHRANE, David Frank Osborne House, The Green, Olveston, Bristol BS35 4EJ Tel: 01454 613409 — MB ChB 1967 Bristol; MRCS Eng. LRCP Lond. 1967; FFA RCS Eng. 1972; DA Eng. 1969. (Bristol) Cons. Anaesth. Frenchay Hosp. Bristol.

COCHRANE, David James Ulster Hospital, Dundonald, Belfast BT16 1RH Tel: 029 9056 1398 Email: david.cochrane@ucht.n-i.nhs.uk — MD 1994 Belf.; MB BCh (Hons.) 1986; BSc (1st cl. Hons.) Biochem. 1983; MRCP (UK) 1989. (Queens Belfast) Cons. Cardiol. Ulster Hosp. Dundonald.

COCHRANE, Ernest McGregor (retired) The Old Rectory, Manthorpe, Grantham NG31 8NF Tel: 01476 564454 — BA Dub. 1937, MD 1945, MB BCh BAO 1937. Prev: Sen. Ho. Surg. Vict. Centr. Hosp. Wallasey.

COCHRANE, Gail Alison St Peters Street Medical Practice, 16 St Peters Street, London N1 8JG Tel: 020 7226 7131 Fax: 020 7354 9120; 26 Almeida Street, London N1 1TD — MB BS 1984 Lond.; LMSSA Lond. 1983. Prev: Trainee GP Hastings VTS; Ho. Off. (Med.) St. Albans City Hosp.

COCHRANE, Mr Geoffrey William King George Hospital, Barley Lane, Goodmayes, Ilford IG3 8YB Tel: 020 8970 8060 Fax: 020 8970 8085 Email: geoffrey.cochrane@rbhc-tr.nthames.nhs.uk; 8 Dove's Yard, Cloudesley Place, London N1 0HQ — MB BS 1972 Lond.; FRCOG 1989, M 1977; MFFP 1995. (Roy. Free) Cons. O & G King Geo. Hosp. Goodmayes; Jt. Assoc. Med. Director - Educat. Chair NTE STC in O & G. Socs: Fell. Roy. Soc. Med.; Internat. Continence Soc.; Brit. Soc. Gyn. Endoscopy. Prev: Sen. Regist. St. Bart. Hosp. Lond.; Regist. Roy. Free Hosp. Lond.; Resid. Med. Off. Qu. Charlotte's Matern. Hosp. Lond.

COCHRANE, George MacKenzie (retired) Braeside, Symonds Yat W., Ross-on-Wye HR9 6BW Tel: 01600 890207 — MB BChir 1953 Camb.; MA, MB BChir Camb. 1953; FRCP Lond. 1985; FRCP Ed. 1975, M 1962; DPhysMed. 1959. Cons. Phys. Rehabil. Med. Oxon. HA. Prev: Cons. Rheum. & Rehabil. Derbysh. Roy. Infirm.

COCHRANE, Gordon McLellan Department of Thoracic Medicine, Guy's Hospital, London SE1 9RT Tel: 020 7955 4147 Fax: 020 7403 8288; 27 Ulundi Road, Blackheath, London SE3 7UQ — MB BS 1969 Lond.; BSc (Physiol.) Lond. 1966, MB BS 1969; FRCP Lond. 1985; MRCP (UK) 1972. Cons. Phys. & Sen. Clin. Adviser UMDS Guy's Hosp. Lond. Socs: Brit. Thorac. Soc. (Exec. Chairm. Manpower & Resources Comm.).

COCHRANE, Hugh Robin Department of Pathology, Sunderland Royal Hospital, Kayll Road, Sunderland SR4 7TP Tel: 0191 565 6256 — BM 1981 Soton.; MRCPath 1992; DRCPath 1994. Cons. Histopath. & Cytopath. City Hosps. Sunderland.

COCHRANE, James Halliday (retired) High Green House, Troutbeck, Windermere LA23 1PN Tel: 0153 94 34421 — MB ChB 1957 Ed.; DObst RCOG 1960. Prev: Ho. Surg. (Obst.) Simpson Memor. Matern. Pavil. & Ho. Surg. Roy. Infirm. Edin.

COCHRANE, James Murray The Worcester Street Surgery, Stourbridge DY8 Tel: 01384 371616; 89 Greyhound Lane, Stourbridge DY8 3AD Tel: 01384 396098 — MB ChB 1958 Ed.; DObst RCOG 1962.

COCHRANE, John David The Medical Centre, Tanhouse Lane, Church Hill, Redditch B98 9AA Tel: 01527 67715; 23 Sandhills Road, Barnt Green, Birmingham B45 8NP Tel: 0121 445 2816 — MB ChB 1969 Ed. (Ed.) Prev: SHO (Paediat.) & SHO (O & G) Copthorne Hosp. Shrewsbury; Med. Off. (Methodist Miss. Soc.) Nixon Memor. Hosp. Segbwema, Sierra; Leone.

COCHRANE, John Graeme 2 Ashburnham Road, Ampthill, Bedford MK45 2RH Tel: 01525 840775 — MB BS 1954 Lond.; DObst RCOG 1961. (St. Bart.) Locum Gen. Practioner. Socs: BMA; Med. Equestrian Assn. Prev: Hosp. Pract. Luton Matern. Hosp.; Ho. Phys. & Ho. Surg. Luton & Dunstable Hosp.; Ho. Off. (Obst.) Luton Matern. Hosp.

COCHRANE, Mr John Patrick Stuart 19 Wimpole Street, London W1M 7AD Tel: 020 7637 9755 Fax: 020 7637 2789; 22 Woodside Avenue, Highgate, London N6 4SS Tel: 020 8444 9180 — MB BS 1967 Lond.; MS Lond. 1981; FRCS Eng. 1972; MRCS Eng. LRCP Lond. 1967. (Middlx.) Cons. Surg. Whittington Hosp.; Hon. Cons. Hosp. of St. John & St. Eliz. Lond. Socs: Fell. Roy. Soc. Med.; Fell. Assn. Surgs. Prev: Sen. Regist. (Surg.) Centr. Middlx. Hosp.; Regist. (Surg.) Leicester Gen. Hosp; Lect. (Surg.) Middlx. Hosp. Lond.

COCHRANE, Mr Jonathan George (retired) Kilbruach, Nisbet Rd, Gullane EH31 2BQ Tel: 01620 842839 Fax: 01620 842839 — MB BS 1965 Lond.; FRCS Ed. 1983; FRCS Eng. 1970; MRCS Eng. LRCP Lond. 1965. Indep. Cons. Orthop. Scotl. Prev: Cons. Orthop. Surg. St. John's Hosp. Howden & P.ss Margt. Rose Orthop. Hosp. Edin.

COCHRANE, Laura Mary Flat 3/2, 71 Woodford St., Glasgow G41 3HW — MB ChB 1995 Dundee.

COCHRANE, Lindsay 16 Thornton Avenue, Macclesfield SK11 7UG — MB ChB 1991 Leeds.

COCHRANE, Lorna Maeve Hairmyres Hospital, East Kilbride, Glasgow G75 8RG Tel: 0141 220292 — MD 1991 Glas.; MB ChB 1982. Staff Grade Respirat. Med. Socs: Scott. Thoracic Soc.; Brit. Thorac. Soc.; Scott. Soc. Experim. Med.

COCHRANE, Margaret Ann Department of Community Child Health, Edenhall Hospital, Pinkieburn, Musselburgh EH21 7TZ; Laverocklaw, Elvingston, Haddington EH41 3SX Tel: 01875 852444 — MB BCh 1965 Wales; MRCP (U.K.) 1970; DCH Eng. 1967. SCMO.

COCHRANE, Margaret Elizabeth Mary The Surgery, 1 Church Road, Mitcham CR4 3YU Tel: 020 8648 2579 Fax: 020 8640 4013; 37 Murray Road, London SW19 4PD — MB BChir 1974 Camb.; BA Camb. 1970; DCH RCP Lond. 1981. (Camb. & St. Thos.)

COCHRANE, Martha Christine Laigh Woodston, Maybole KA19 7JH Tel: 01655 82262 — MB ChB 1953 Glas. (Glas.) Clin. Med. Off. Community Health Ayrsh. & Arran Health Bd. Prev: Dep. Med. Off. Clydebank Dunbartonsh.; SHO Orthop. Law Hosp. Carluke.

COCHRANE, Murray James Barclay Parkhead Hospital, 81 Salammanca St., Glasgow G33 Tel: 0141 211 8300; The Knoll, 47A Colquhoun St, Helensburgh, Helensburgh G84 9LQ — MB ChB 1994 Glas. SHO (Psychiat.) Pk.head Hosp. Gt.er Glas. Community & Ment. Health NHS Trust. Prev: SHO (Psychiat.) Cross Ho. Hosp. Ayrsh. & Arran Community & Ment. Health NHS Trust.

COCHRANE, Paul Telford Oak Hall Surgery, 41-43 High Street, New Romney TN28 8BW Tel: 01797 362106 Fax: 01797 366495 — MRCS Eng. LRCP Lond. 1975; D.Occ.Med. RCP Lond. 1995. (Char. Cross) Hon. Med. Advisor RNLI Dungeness Lifeboat; Med. Off. Brit. Energy. Socs: BMA; Soc. Occupat. Med.; Fell. of the Roy.Soc. Of Med. Prev: Capt. RAMC; Trainee GP Army VTS.

COCHRANE, Peter (retired) Quaker Barn, Oving Road, Whitchurch, Aylesbury HP22 4JF — MB ChB 1958 Liverp.; MD Liverp. 1971; FRCP Lond. 1979, M 1967; DCH Eng. 1963; DObst RCOG 1960. Prev: Cons. Phys. Stoke Mandeville Hosp. NHS Trust.

COCHRANE, Richard Alexander Flat 8, Medical Residences, Ysbyty Glan Clwyd, Rhuddlan Road, Rhyl LL18 5UJ — MB BChir 1989 Camb.

COCHRANE, Rosemary Anne 24 Manse Road, Bearsden, Glasgow G61 3PR — MB ChB 1985 Glas.; BSc (Hons.) Glas. 1983, MB ChB 1985; DA (UK) 1986.

COCHRANE, Ruth Margaret Department of Obstetrics & Gynaecology, St. Mary's Hospital, Praed St., London W2; 27 Buckingham Gardens, Edgware HA8 6NB — MB ChB 1981 Wales; MRCOG 1987; DA (UK) 1984. Sen. Regist. (O & G) St Mary's Hosp. Lond.

COCHRANE, Sheila (retired) 11 Stade Street, Hythe CT21 6BD — MB BS 1943 Lond.; MRCS Eng. LRCP Lond. 1942; DCH Eng. 1944.

COCHRANE, Sheila Mary (retired) West Bank, Queen's Road, Kendal LA9 4PL Tel: 01539 720044 — MB ChB 1951 Liverp.; BA (Hons.) Camb. 1945, MA 1951; DObst RCOG 1954. Prev: GP Kendal.

COCHRANE, Mr Thomas Drysdale (retired) Old Posingford, Hartfield TN7 4HA Tel: 01892 770366 — MB BS 1957 Lond.; FRCS Ed. 1965; MRCS Eng. LRCP Lond. 1957. Hon. Cons. Plastic Surg. Qu. Vict. Hosp. E. Grinstead; Hon. Adviser The Guinea Pig Club. Prev: Hon. Cons. Plastic Surg. King Edwd VII Hosp. for Offs. Lond.

COCHRANE, Thomas John Dundas 29 Bassett Road, Leighton Buzzard LU7 1AR Tel: 01525 373111 Fax: 01525 853767; Quince House, Heath Pk Road, Leighton Buzzard LU7 3BB Tel: 01525 372391 — BM BCh 1954 Oxf.; MA, BM BCh Oxf. 1954.

COCHRANE, Thomas Robert Cedric Church Grange Health Centre, Bramblys Drive, Basingstoke RG21 8QN Tel: 01256 329021 Fax: 01256 817466; 61 Fennel Close, Chineham, Basingstoke RG24 8XF Tel: 01256 63803 — MB BCh BAO 1984 Belf.; MB BCh Belf. I984; MRCGP 1989.

COCHRANE, William Henry St James Surgery, 89 Wash Lane, Clacton-on-Sea CO15 1DA Tel: 01255 222121; Islay House, 198 Frinton Road, Holland on Sea, Clacton-on-Sea CO15 5UU Tel: 01255 815705 — MB ChB 1954 Glas.; DObst RCOG 1962; DA Eng. 1957; Cert JCC Lond. 1978. Anaesth. Clacton & Dist. Hosp.

COCHRANE-DYET, Claire Elizabeth Thornhills Medical Group, 732 London Road, Larkfield, Aylesford ME20 6BQ Tel: 01732 843900 Fax: 01732 872633 — MB ChB 1990 Bristol; MRCGP 1995; DGM RCP 1992. Gen. Pract. Princip., Thornhills Med. Gp., Larkfield.

COCHRANE-SMITH, Ronald Alexander William (retired) 125 Richard Heights, Flint CH6 5BS — MB ChB Aberd. 1952.

COCK, Christina Elsbeth Oxford Terrace Medical Group, Oxford Terrace, Gateshead NE8 1RQ Tel: 0191 477 2169 Fax: 0191 477 5633; 16 Rectory Terrace, Gosforth, Newcastle upon Tyne NE3 1YB Tel: 0191 213 2863 Fax: 0191 213 1050 Email: christina@dpcc.demon.co.uk — MB BS 1979 Lond.; MRCGP 1984; FRCGP 1997. (Univ. Coll. Hosp.) Prev: Trainee GP Newc. VTS; Princip. Guidepost Med. Gp.

COCK, Hannah Rutherford Department Neurological Science, Royal Free Hospital, Pond St., London NW3 Tel: 020 7794 0500 Fax: 020 7431 1577; 10 Derbin Court, 68-70 Queens Drive, London N4 2XR Tel: 020 8800 0625 Fax: 020 8800 0625 Email: hannah_c@compuserve.com — MB BS 1989 Lond.; BSc (1st cl. Hons.) Lond. 1986; MRCP (UK) 1992; MD (Lond.) 1996. (Univ. Coll. Lond.) Specialist Regist. (Neurol.) Roy. Free Hosp. Lond. Socs: Assoc. Mem. Assn. Brit. Neurol. Prev: Research Fell. (Neurosci.) Roy. Free Hosp. Lond.; Regist. (Med.) Hillingdon Hosp. Uxbridge; SHO (Neurol.) Roy. Free Hosp. Lond.

COCK, Sylvie Flat 9, 9 Grosvenor Hill, London SW19 4RU — MD 1987 Louvain.

COCKAYNE, Edward Ernest (retired) Green Farm House, Woolpit, Bury St Edmunds IP30 9RQ Tel: 01359 240792 Fax: 01359 242632 Email: ecock86486@aol.com — MB BS Lond. 1963; MRCS Eng. LRCP Lond. 1963; FRCGP 1991, M 1969; DObst RCOG 1966. Prev: Ho. Surg. Guy's Hosp.

COCKAYNE, Lucinda Mary Group Surgery, Wood St., Middleton, Manchester M24 Tel: 0161 643 5385 Fax: 0161 653 6430; 12 Shelley Road, Reddish, Stockport SK5 6JG Tel: 0161 442 0594 — MB ChB 1989 Manch.; MRCGP 1993; DRCOG 1994. Socs: Manch. Med. Soc.

COCKAYNE, Sarah Elizabeth Royal Hallamshire Hospital, Glossop Road, Sheffield S10 2JF Tel: 0114 271 1900 Fax: 0114 271 3763; Tel: 0114 268 4459 — MB BS 1989 Lond.; MRCP (UK) 1995. (Guy's Hosp.) Cons. (Dermat.) Roy. Hallamsh. Hosp. Sheff.

COCKBAIN, Jonathan Michael Richard The Surgery, 121 Wrythe Lane, Carshalton SM5 2RT Tel: 020 8644 2727 Fax: 020 8641 7994 — MB BS 1992 Lond.; DRCOG 1996; MRCGP 1997. (St. Georges Hospital Medical School) GP.

COCKBAIN, Roger Gordon The Cottage, Hatch Lane, Weston, Hitchin SG4 7EB Tel: 01462 790228 Email: rogercockbain@hotmail.com — Hon. Member Chinese Medicine Institute & Register; BSc (Hons.) Lond. 1964, MB BS 1967; MRCS Eng. LRCP Lond. 1967; MRCGP 1974; DCH Eng. 1971; Dip. Med. Acupunc. 1996. (Univ. Coll. Hosp.) Div. Police Surg. Herts. Constab. Socs: Assn. Police Surg.; Fell.Roy. Soc. of Med.; Mem. of Roy. Coll. of Gen. Practitioners. Prev: Ho. Surg. Poole Gen. Hosp.; Ho. Phys. (Paediat.) St. Albans City Hosp.; GP Princip. 1969-1997.

COCKBURN, Alison Fisher Newhills Practice, Easterhouse Health Centre, 9 Auchinlea Road, Glasgow G34 9HQ Tel: 0141 771 0781; 53 Hamilton Drive, Glasgow G12 8DP — MB ChB 1959 Ed.

COCKBURN, Andrew Syme 30 Southways Avenue, Hampstead Garden Suburb, London NW11 6RU Tel: 020 8731 7887 Fax: 020 8731 7887 — MB BS 1954 Adelaide; MRCPsych 1972; DPM Eng. 1962. (Adelaide)

COCKBURN, Ann Patricia Stenhouse Medical Centre, Furlong Street, Arnold, Nottingham NG5 7BP Tel: 0115 967 3877 Fax: 0115 967 3838; 70 Watcombe Circus, Nottingham NG5 2DT Tel: 0115 960 9556 Email: pagecockburn@msn.com — MB ChB 1982 Bristol; MRCGP 1989; DRCOG 1986. (Univ. Bristol)

COCKBURN, Beatrice Mary (retired) — MB ChB 1968 Liverp. Prev: Ho. Off. (Surg.) Chester Roy. Infirm.

COCKBURN, Douglas Clement (retired) The Roundel, 34 Main St, Kilconquhar, Leven KY9 1LQ Tel: 01333 340307 — MB ChB 1946 Ed.; BA Camb. 1944; DObst RCOG 1963. Prev: GP Grantown-on-Spey, Moray.

COCKBURN, Elizabeth Anne 65 Abbey Road, Scone, Perth PH2 6LL — MB ChB 1986 Aberd. Clin. Med. Off. Perth.

COCKBURN, Professor Forrester, CBE Department of Child Health, Royal Hospital Sick Children, Yorkhill, Glasgow G3 8SJ Tel: 0141 201 0236 Fax: 0141 201 0837; 53 Hamilton Drive, Glasgow G12 8DP Tel: 0141 339 2973 — MB ChB Ed. 1959; MD Ed. 1966; FRCP Glas. 1979, M 1978; FRCP Ed. 1971, M 1963; DCH RFPS Glas. 1961; FRCPCH (Hons) 1997; FRSE 1999; FRCS Ed (Hon) 1999. Chairm. Yorkhill NHS Trust Glas.; Emerit. Prof. Child Health Dept. Child Health Univ. Glas; Hon. Sen. Research Fell. Dept. Child Health Univ. Glas. Socs: (Ex-Pres.) Europ. Assn. Perinatal Med.; (Ex-Pres.) Brit. Assn. Perinatal Med.; (Ex-Pres.) Soc. Study Inborn Errors of Metab. Prev: Samson Gemmell Prof. Child Health Univ. Glas.; Nuffield Fell. Nuffield Inst. Med. Research Univ. Oxf.; Research Fell. (Paediat. Metab. Dis.) Boston Univ., USA.

COCKBURN, Hazel Agnes Christina Flat 1, 14 Montagu Square, London W1H 2LD — MB ChB Glas. 1964; FFA RCS Eng. 1970. (Glas.) Prev: Sen. Regist. Dept. Anaesth. St. Mary's Hosp. Lond. W9.

COCKBURN, Iain Timothy Robin Bayer plc, Stoke Court, Stoke Poges, Slough SL2 4LY Tel: 01635 566768 Fax: 01635 566785; Burgess House, Church Path, Stokenchurch, High Wycombe HP14 3TJ Tel: 01494 484989 — MB ChB 1975 Liverp.; MRCGP 1979. Head Europ. Drug Safety. Socs: Fell. Roy. Soc. Med.; Fac. Pharmaceut. Phys.; Soc. Pharmacoepidemiols. Prev: Head Med. Affairs Innovex (UK) Ltd; Sen. Dir. Worldwide Drug Safety Surveillance RW Johnson Pharmaceut. Research Inst.; Med. Advisor Drug Monitoring Centre, Sandoz.

COCKBURN, Irene Ruth 23 Derry Road, Omagh BT78 5DY — MB BCh BAO 1992 Belf.

COCKBURN, James Joseph Tolworth Hospital, (Villiers House) Red Lion Road, Tolworth, Surbiton KT6 7QU Tel: 020 8390 0102 Fax: 020 8390 3877 — MB BCh BAO 1955 Dub.; FRCPI 1973, M 1958; FRCPsych 1976, M 1971; T(Psych) 1991; DPM Lond. 1962. (T.C. Dub.) Cons. Psychiat. Kingston & Dist. NHS Trust Surrey; Mem. Ment. Health Rev. Tribunal. Socs: Fell. Roy. Soc. Med. Prev: Sen. Regist. St. Clement's Hosp. Lond.; Regist. Bethlem Roy. & Maudsley Hosps. Lond.; Asst. Lect. (Physiol.) Univ. Dub.

COCKBURN, Jayne Elizabeth Frimley Park Hospital, Portsmouth Road, Frimley, Camberley GU16 7UJ Tel: 01276 692777; Beechbank, Lake Road, Deepcut, Camberley GU16 6RD — MB BS 1983 Lond.; MRCOG 1988. Cons. O & G Frimley Pk. Hosp. Socs: Roy. Soc. Med. & Wom. in Gyn. & Obst. Soc. Prev: Sen. Regist. & Lect. St. Geo. Hosp. Lond.

COCKBURN, John Jeffrey Hilton House, Moss St., Liverpool L6 1HF — MB ChB 1967 Liverp.

COCKBURN, John Michael Seaford Health Centre, Dane Road, Seaford BN25 1DH Tel: 01323 490022 Fax: 01323 492156 — MB BS 1970 Lond.; MRCS Eng. LRCP Lond. 1969; MRCGP 1997. (Guy's) GP Trainer/Course Organiser E.bourne VTS.

COCKBURN, Katrina Jane 1 Pasture Drive, Croft, Warrington WA3 7LH — MB BS 1992 Newc. Regist. (Psychiat.) N. & Yorks. RHA.

COCKBURN, Matthew Keith Francis The Surgery, Astonia House, High Street, Baldock SG7 6BP Tel: 01462 892458 Fax: 01462 490821 — MB BS 1984 Lond.; 2000 M.stud Camb. Homerton sch. Of health studies; MRCGP 1990; DCH RCP Lond. 1988; DA (UK) 1986. (St. Bart.) GP Baldock; Chairm. Synapse.; Course organiser for Lister VTS; Course organiser for sen. Registra in Gen. Pract. Lond. Deanery.; Clin. Assist. In colonoscopy.

COCKBURN, Richard Antony 57 St Marys Avenue, Whitley Bay NE26 1TB — MB ChB 1997 Ed.

COCKBURN, Thomas Anderson (retired) Meadowbank, 4 Arran Drive, Airdrie ML6 6NJ Tel: 01236 62018 — MB ChB 1942 Glas.

COCKBURN, Thomas Rodney Masefield Road Surgery, 40 Masefield Road, The Scotlands, Wolverhampton WV10 8RZ Tel: 01902 731907 Fax: 01902 727118; 357 Stafford Road, Wolverhampton WV10 6EA — MB ChB 1963 Ed.; MRCGP 1978; DRCOG 1976.

COCKBURN, Mrs Una (retired) 14 Kessington Drive, Bearsden, Glasgow G61 2HG Tel: 0141 942 2482 — MB ChB 1947 Aberd.; DPH Aberd. 1952. Prev: Asst. M.O.H. Notts. Co.

COCKCROFT, Anne Elizabeth Occupational Health and Safety Unit, Royal Free Hospital, Pond St., London NW3 2QG Tel: 020 7794 2522 Fax: 020 7794 2512 Email: 100411.3315@compuserve.com — MB BS 1975 Lond.; MD Lond. 1985; FRCP Lond. 1992; MRCP (UK) 1977; FFOM RCP Lond. 1992,

MFOM (Distinc.) 1987; DIH Eng. 1982. (St. Bart.) Cons. & Sen. Lect. (Occupat. Med.) Roy. Free Hosp. & Sch. Med. Lond.; Edr. Occupat. & Environm. Med.; Sen. Research Fell. CIET InterNat. Socs: Brit. Thorac. Soc.; Soc. Occupat. Med. Prev: Lect. & Hon. Sen. Regist. Char. Cross Hosp. Lond.; Research Sen. Regist. MRC Pneumoconiosis Unit Llandough Hosp. Penarth; SHO (Gen. Med.) Roy. Sussex Co. Hosp. Brighton.

COCKCROFT, Gerald Anthony (retired) Elland BUPA Hospital, Elland Lane, Elland HX5 9EB Tel: 01422 375557 — LMSSA 1962 Lond. Prev: Ho. Phys. & Ho. Surg. W. Lond. Hosp.

COCKCROFT, John Henry James Billericay Health Centre, Stock Road, Billericay CM12 0BJ Tel: 01277 658071 Fax: 01277 631892; 5 Sadlers Close, Billericay CM11 1SB Tel: 01277 632181 — MB BS 1986 Lond.; BSc Basic Med. Scs. & Pharmacol. Lond. 1983, MB BS 1986; MRCGP 1992; DCH RCP Lond. 1991; DRCOG 1991; DGM RCP Lond. 1990. (Lond. Hosp.) Prev: Trainee GP Lymm VTS; SHO (Paediat.) Roy. Liverp. Childr. Hosp.; SHO (A & E) N. Manch. Gen. Hosp.

COCKCROFT, John Ronald Department of Cardiology, University Hospital, Heath Park, Cardiff CF14 4XW Tel: 029 2074 3489 Fax: 029 2074 3500 Email: cockcroftjr@cf.ac.uk — MB ChB 1980 Leics.; BSc Lond. 1975; FRCP 1997; MRCP (UK) 1984. Sen. Lect. & Hon. Cons. (Cardiol.) Univ. Hosp. Cardiff. Socs: Med. Res. Soc. & Internat. Soc. Hypertens.; Brit. Pharm. Soc. (Mem. Comm. Clin. Sect.). Prev: Sen. Lect. (Clin. Pharmacol.) Qu.s Med. Centre Nottm.; Lect. (Clin. Pharmacol.) Guy's Hosp. Lond.; Sen. Regist. Roy. Postgrad. Med. Sch. & Hammersmith Hosp. Lond.

COCKCROFT, Michael The Surgery, 17B Warmdene Road, Brighton BN1 8NL Tel: 01273 508811 Fax: 01273 559860; Sunwayes, 2 Radinden, Manor Road, Hove BN3 6NH — MB BS 1970 Lond.; MRCGP 1977; DObst RCOG 1975. (Middlx.) Prev: Trainee Gen. Pract. Brighton & Lewes Vocational Train Scheme; Ho. Phys. & Ho. Surg. Mt. Vernon Hosp. N.wood.

COCKCROFT, Paul Michael Public Health Laboratory, St. Mary's Hospital, Milton Road, Portsmouth PO3 6AQ Tel: 023 92 866201 Fax: 023 92 824652 Email: paul.cockcroft@smail01.porthosp.swest.nhs.uk; 11 Brookmead Way, Langstone, Havant PO9 1RT Tel: 023 9279 1907 — MB BS 1975 Lond.; BSc Lond. 1972; FRCPath 1994, M 1982. (Middlx.) Cons. Med. Microbiol. St Mary's Hosp. Portsmouth. Prev: Sen. Regist. Univ. Coll. Hosp. Lond.; Regist. Whittington Hosp. Lond.; Ho. Surg. Middlx. Hosp. Lond.

COCKEL, Roy 78 Park Hill, Moseley, Birmingham B13 8DS Tel: 0121 449 0197 Email: roycockel@compuserve.com — MB Camb. 1963, BChir 1962; FRCP Lond. 1978, M 1965. (Camb. & St. Thos.) Cons. Phys. Univ. Hosp. Birm. (Selly Oak Hosp.); Hon. Cons. Gastroenterol. Qu. Eliz. Hosp. Birm.; Sen. Clin. Lect. (Med.) Univ. Birm. Socs: Brit. Soc. Gastroenterol.; Pancreatic Soc.; W Midl.s Phys.s Assn. (Ex-Pres). Prev: Dep. Dean Bd. Postgrad. Med. & Dent. Educat. Univ. Birm.; Sen. Regist. (Med.) Qu. Eliz. Hosp. Birm.; Ho. Phys. St. Thos. Hosp. Lond.

COCKELL, Anna Patricia 12 Eaton Mews N., London SW1 — MB BS 1988 Lond.; MRCOG 1993. Research Fell. (Fetal Health) St. Thos. Hosp. Lond. Prev: Regist. (O & G) St. Mary's Hosp. Lond. & Watford Gen. Hosp.; SHO (O & G) Qu. Charlotte's & Chelsea Hosp. Lond.

COCKELL, Jacqueline Lesley Beverley 53 Farley Road, South Croydon CR2 7NG Tel: 020 8651 1222 Fax: 020 8657 9297; 5 Rockfield Mount, Rockfield Road, Oxted RH8 0EL Tel: 01883 730687 — MB BChir 1991 Camb.; MA; MRCGP 1995. (Camb.)

COCKER, Darren Phillip Weybridge Health Centre, 22 Church Street, Weybridge KT13 8DW — MB BS 1995 Lond.

COCKER, James (retired) Department of Pathology, Derbyshire Royal Infirmary, Derby DE1 2QY — MB BChir 1953 Camb.; MD Camb. 1963, MA,; MRCS Eng. LRCP Lond. 1953; FRCPath 1979, M 1967. Cons. (Histopath.) S. Derbysh. HA. Prev: Sen. Regist. (Path.) United Sheff. Hosps.

COCKER, Margaret Broad Mead, Westwell Leacon, Charing, Ashford TN27 0EN Tel: 0123 371 2437 — MB ChB 1941 Manch. (Manch.) Prev: Asst. Med. Off. Childr. Hosp. Manch.

COCKERAM, Joanne Halcyon, Hillside-West, Hutton, Weston Super Mare BS24 9TX — MB BS 1994 Lond.

COCKERAM, Stephen Forester 47 Bearcroft Avenue, Great Meadow, Worcester WR4 0DR — MB ChB 1998 Birm.; ChB Birm. 1998.

COCKERAM-PARANAVITANA, Mayanthi Neluni Shamela 47 Bearcroft Avenue, Great Meadow, Worcester WR4 0DR — MB ChB 1996 Birm.

COCKERELL, Oliver Charles 30 Lime Court, 2 Gypsy Lane, London SW15 5RJ — MB BS 1987 Lond.; BSc Lond. 1984; MRCP (UK) 1989. Research Fell. Inst. Neurol. Qu. Sq. Lond.

COCKERHAM, Rowena Dept of Anaesthetics, City Hospital, Dudley Road, Birmingham B18 7QH; Honeysuckle Cottage, Long St, Williton, Taunton TA4 4QY — BM BCh 1996 Oxf. (Oxford) SHO (Anaesth.) Birm. City Hosp. Prev: SHO (Integrated Med.) Leicester Gen. Hosp.; SHO (A & E) N.ampton Gen. Hosp.; PRHO (Gen. Surg.) John Radcliffe Hosp. Oxf.

COCKERILL, Kathryn Joyce Castle Street Surgery, 39 Castle Street, Luton LU1 3AG Tel: 01582 729242 Fax: 01582 725192; Flinders, 23A Snowhill, Maulden, Bedford MK45 2BP Tel: 01525 404803 — MB BS 1987 Newc.; MRCGP 1992. Socs: MRCGP.

COCKERILL, Marcus John Kensington Road Surgery, 148 Kensington Road, Coventry CV5 6HY Tel: 024 7667 2466 Fax: 024 7671 7311 — MB ChB 1985 Birm.; BSc (Hons. Biochem.) Birm. 1982; MRCGP 1997; DRCOG 1988. Clin. Asst. Gen. Med. Prev: Trainee GP Balsall Common; Trainee GP/SHO Coventry HA VTS.

COCKERILL, Richard John (retired) The Orchard, 9 Greenhurst Lane, Oxted RH8 0LD Tel: 01883 712307 — MB BChir Camb. 1961; BA Camb 1957. Prev: Ho. Surg., Cas. Off. & Asst. Ho. Phys. Guy's Hosp. Lond.

COCKERSOLE, Francis James (retired) The Lilacs, Broughton Park, Great Broughton, Cockermouth CA13 0XW Tel: 01900 827068 Fax: 01900 827068 Email: cockersole@msn.com — MB ChB 1942 Birm.; BA Open 1978; MRCS Eng. LRCP Lond. 1942; FRCOG 1964, M 1951; MMSA Lond. 1955. Examr. Roy. Coll. O & G; Examr. Centr. Midw. Bd. Prev: Cons. O & G W. Cumbria HA.

COCKERSOLE, Gillian Marjorie Glencoe, 100 Buxton Road, Disley, Stockport SK12 2HE Tel: 01663 765565 — MB BS 1967 Lond.; MRCS Eng. LRCP Lond. 1967. (Roy. Free) Clin. Asst. Nat. Blood Auth.; Clin. Asst. (Occupat. Health) Stockport Acute Servs. NHS Trust. Prev: Regist. (Gen. Med.) N.. Gen. Hosp. Sheff.; Med. Asst. Nat. Blood Transfus. Serv. Regional Transfus. Centre Sheff.; Ho. Surg. (Gyn.) Roy. Free Hosp. Lond.

COCKETT, Alan David Orchard Lodge Young Peoples Unit, Cotford St Luke, Taunton TA4 1DB Tel: 01823 432211 Fax: 01823 432541 — MB ChB 1978 Birm.; MRCPsych 1983. (Birm.) Cons. Child & Adolesc. Psychiat. Orchard Lodge Young Peoples Unit Taunton; Edr. Europ. Eating Disorders Review. Prev: Sen. Regist. (Child & Adolesc. Psychiat.) Inst. Family Psychiat. Ipswich; Regist. (Psychiat.) Burton Rd. Hosp. Dudley; SHO (Psychiat.) Barnsley Hall Hosp. BromsGr.

COCKETT, Mr Frank Bernard (retired) 14 Essex Villas, Kensington, London W8 7BN Tel: 020 7937 9883 — MB BS 1941 Lond.; BSc (1st cl. Hons.) Lond. 1937, MS 1953; FRCS Eng. 1947; MRCS Eng. LRCP Lond. 1940. Examr. Surg. Univ. Lond. Prev: Cons. Surg. St. Thos. Hosp. & King Edwd. VII Hosp. Offs. Lond.

COCKILL, Simon Mount Pleasant Medical Centre, Ditherington Road, Shrewsbury SY1 4DQ Tel: 01743 235111 — MB ChB 1986 Birm.; MRCGP 1992; DRCOG 1993.

COCKING, John Brian (retired) East Kent Hospitals NHS Trust, Queen Elizabeth The Queen Mother Hospital, St Peters Road, Margate CT9 4AN Tel: 01843 225544 Fax: 01843 220048 — MB BChir 1962 Camb.; MA Camb. 1962; FRCP Lond. 1979, M 1967. Hon Cons. Phys. Qu. Eliz., The Qu. Mother Hosp. Margate. Prev: Cons.Phys.Qu. Eliz., Qu. mother Hosp.Margate.

COCKINGS, Garth Francis (retired) Signal House Surgery, 82 Riverside Walk, Midland Road, Olney MK46 4BP — MB BS 1958 Lond.; MRCS Eng. LRCP Lond. 1957; MRCGP 1965; DObst RCOG 1960.

COCKINGS, Jerome Garth Lineham 82 Riverside Walk, Midland Road, Olney MK46 4BP — MB BS 1986 Lond.; FCAnaesth 1991. Regist. (Anaesth.) St. Thos. Hosp. Lond. Prev: SHO (Anaesth.) St. Bart. Hosp. Lond.

COCKMAN, Nigel George (retired) Child & Family Therapy Services, Gosport Health Centre, Bury Road, Gosport PO12 3PN Tel: 01705 584201 — MB BS 1961 Lond.; MRCPsych 1974; DObst

RCOG 1969. Cons. Child & Adolesc. Psychiat. Child & Family Ther. Servs., Gosport. Prev: Sen. Regist. Hosp. Sick Childr. Lond.

COCKMAN, Philippa Jane St Stephen's Health Centre, Bow Community Hall, William Place, London E3 5ED Tel: 020 8980 1760 Fax: 020 8980 6619 — MB BS 1991 Lond.; BA (Hons.) Camb. 1982; MRCGP 1996; DCCH RCP Ed. 1995; DFFP 1995; DRCOG 1994. (Univ. Coll. Lond.) Princip. in Gen. Pract. and Trainer, St. Stephen's Health Centre, Bow, E. Lond.

COCKRELL, Nigel Brian Stanmore House Surgery, Linden Avenue, Kidderminster DY10 3AA Tel: 01562 822647 Fax: 01562 827255; The Gables, Neweys Hill, Worcester WR3 7DZ — MB ChB 1987 Liverp.; MRCGP. Clin. Asst. (Dermat.) Kidderminster Hosp.

COCKRILL, John Strelley Health Centre, 116 Strelley Road, Strelley, Nottingham NG8 6LN Tel: 0115 929 9219 Fax: 0115 929 6522; Wyvill Cottage, Private Road, Sherwood, Nottingham NG5 4DB — BM BS 1983 Nottm.

COCKRILL, John Noel (retired) 27 Admiralty Mews, The Strand, Walmer, Deal CT14 7AZ Tel: 01304 239439 Fax: 01304 239904 — MB BCh BAO Dub. 1950; MA Dub. 1954. Prev: Indep. GP Rainham Kent.

COCKROFT, Stephen Department of Anaesthetics, Salisbury District Hospital, Odstock, Salisbury SP2 8BJ Tel: 01722 336262; New Hall Hospital, Bodenham, Salisbury SP5 4EY Tel: 01722 422333 — MB BChir 1984 Camb.; MA Camb. 1985, BA 1982; FRCA 1990. (Girton Coll., Univ. Camb.) Cons. Anaesth. & Intens. Care Salisbury Dist. Hosp. Socs: Intens. Care Soc.; Assn. Anaesth. Prev: Sen. Regist. (Anaesth.) Soton. Gen. Hosp.; Lect. (Anaesth. & Intens. Care) & Regist. Roy. Lond. Hosp. Med. Sch.; SHO (Anaesth.) St. Bart. Hosp. Lond.

COCKS, David William Nathan Foy and Partners, 106 Splott Road, Splott, Cardiff CF24 2XY Tel: 029 2046 2848 Fax: 029 2045 2123 — MB ChB 1990 Leic.

COCKS, Elizabeth Mary (Tanner) Stour Cottage, 10 Westgate Grove, Canterbury CT2 8AA; Stour Cottage, 10 Westgate Grove, Canterbury CT2 8AA — MB BS 1976 Lond.; MRCS Eng. LRCP Lond. 1975. (Roy. Free) Assoc. Specialist Community Paediat. Prev: GP Canterbury.

COCKS, George Robert Windy Ridge, 29 Ballymoney Road, Banbridge BT32 4DX — MB BCh BAO Belf. 1955.

COCKS, Helen Catherine 12 Tanglewood Close, Quinton, Birmingham B32 1RG; 12 Tanglewood Close, Quinton, Birmingham B32 1RG Tel: 0121 423 3096 — MB ChB 1993 Leeds; FRCS (Otol.) Eng. 1998. (Leeds University) Research Fell., OtorhinoLaryngol., Univ. of Birm. Socs: Otorhinolaryngol. Research Soc.; Brit. Assn. Otol.; Head and Neck Surgs. Prev: SHO (Otorhinolaryngol.) Qu. Med. Centre Nottm.

COCKS, Norman Martin (retired) Shelton Hospital, Shrewsbury SY3 8DN — Lic Med, Lic Surg Dub. 1957; DPM RCPSI 1966. Cons. Psychiat.(p/t; semi-Retd.). Prev: Sen. Regist. SW Metrop. RHB.

COCKS, Raymond Arthur Westrop Surgery, Highworth, Swindon SN6 7DN Tel: 01793 762218 — MB BS 1968 Lond.; MRCS Eng. LRCP Lond. 1968. (Lond. Hosp.)

COCKS, Robert Anthony (retired) 12 Firshill, Highcliffe-on-Sea, Christchurch BH23 4RE Tel: 01425 273055 Email: racocks@argonet.co.uk — MB BS Lond. 1950; MRCS Eng. LRCP Lond. 1946; MRCPath 1965. Prev: Cons. Path. & Cytol. E. Dorset Health Dist. at ChristCh. Hosp.

COCKS, Thomas (retired) Yew Tree Cottage, Great Milton, Oxford OX44 7NF Tel: 01865 279592 — MB BS 1933 Durh.

COCKSEDGE, Simon Hugh Thornbrook Surgery, Thornbrook Road, Chapel-en-le-Frith, Stockport SK23 0RH Tel: 01298 812725 Fax: 01298 816221 — BM BCh 1981 Oxf.; BSc 1978; FRCGP 1996, M 1985; DRCOG 1985; DCH RCP Lond. 1984. (Oxford) Lect. (Primary Care) Univ. Manch.; Hon. Lect. (Primary Care) Univ. Liverp. Prev: Med. Adviser High Pk. Hospicecare.

COCKSHOOT, David Locks Hill Surgery, 95 Locks Hill, Frome, Bath Tel: 01373 454446 Fax: 01373 454447 Email: david@tnhconsult.demon.co.uk; 24 Green Park, Bath BA1 1HZ Tel: 01225 480760 Fax: 01373 454447 — MB ChB 1989 Leeds; MRCGP 1993; DRCOG 1992; DCH RCP Lond. 1992.

COCKSHOTT, Aysha Mary Wangford Surgery, Church St., Wangford, Brandon IP27 — MB ChB 1981 Wales.

COCKSHOTT, Christine Una Furness General Hospital, Dalton Lane, Barrow-in-Furness LA14 4LF Tel: 01229 870870 — MB ChB 1965 Manch.; MRCPsych 1978. Cons. Psychiat. Furness Gen. Hosp. Barrow in Furness. Prev: Cons. Psychiat. Highcroft Hosp. Birm.; Sen. Regist. (Psychiat.) Uffculme Clin. Birm. & Centr. Hosp. Warwick; Regist. (Psychiat.) Walsgrave Hosp. Coventry.

COCKWELL, Kristian La Paz, Tangle Wood Drive, Great Horkesley, Colchester CO6 4EZ — MB BS 1998 Lond.; MB BS Lond 1998.

COCKWELL, Paul Department of Nephrology, Queen Elizabeth Medical Centre, Birmingham B15 2TH Tel: 0121 472 1311 Fax: 0121 627 2527; 69 Lightwoods Hill, Smethwick B67 5EA — MB BCh 1987 Wales; MRCP (UK) 1990; PH.D (B/ham) 1999. (Cardiff) Cons. Phys. and Nephrologist, Univ. Hosp. NHS Trust, Birm..; Hon. Sen. Lect., Div. of Med. Sci.s, Univ. of Birm.. Socs: Renal. Assn; Brit. Transpl. Soc.; Roy. Coll. of Phys.s - Coll. Tutor. Prev: Sen. Regist. (Me. & Nephrol.) Univ. Hosp., Birm.; Sheldon Clin. Research Fell. Univ. Birm.; Regist. (Med. & Nephrol.) Heartlands Hosp. Birm.

COCUZZA, Clementina Elvezia Anna 21 Lakeside, Oxford OX2 8JF — MB BS 1987 Lond.; BSc Lond. 1984, MB BS 1987. SHO (Infec. Dis.) St. Ann's Hosp. Lond. Prev: Ho. Off. (Gen. Med. & Infec. Dis.) Rushgreen Hosp.; Ho. Off. (Gen. Surg. & Orthop.) Newham Gen. & St. And. Hosp.

CODD, Alan Charles Mindham (retired) Salter's Cottage, Lower Sandydown, Boldre, Lymington SO41 8PP Tel: 01590 622237 — MRCS Eng. LRCP Lond. 1954. Prev: GP Soton.

CODD, Anthony Arthur 213A Western Way, Darras Hall, Ponteland, Newcastle upon Tyne NE20 9ND — MD 1972 Bristol; MB ChB 1958; Dip. Bact. Lond 1964. (Bristol) Cons. Microbiol. Pub. Health Laborat. Serv. Newc. Upon Tyne.

CODD, Isabel Mary Macintosh The Health Centre, High St., Aberdare CF44 7DD; Rockleaze, Abernant, Aberdare CF44 0RR — MB ChB 1945 Bristol. (Bristol)

CODD, Katherine Lois (retired) 9 South Street, Exmouth EX8 2SX Tel: 01395 271573 — MRCS Eng. LRCP Lond. 1959; DObst RCOG 1962.

CODDINGTON, Rosemary Histopathology Department, Royal Hospital Haslar, Gosport PO12 2AA Tel: 02392762228 Fax: 02392 762549 Email: rosecodd@dsca.mod.uk — MB BS 1976 Lond.; FRCPath. Cons. Histopath. Roy. Hosp. Haslar. Prev: Sen. Regist. (Histopath.) Soton. Gen. Hosp.

CODDINGTON, Terence Birmingham DSC, Oak Tree Lane Centre, Oak Tree Lane, Selly Oak, Birmingham B29 6JA Tel: 0121 627 1627 Fax: 0121 627 8210; The Old Rectory, Lower Strensham, Strensham, Worcester WR8 9LW — MB BS 1977 Lond.; BSc (Elect. Engin.) City Univ. 1969; MRCS Eng. LRCP Lond. 1977; LMSSA Lond. 1977. (St. Bart.) Cons. Rehabil. Med. (Bioeng. Servs.) W. Midl. RHA & S. Birm. HA; Vis. Specialist (Prosth.s & Bioeng.) Char. Cross Hosp.; Hon. Research Fell. Char. Cross Hosp. Med. Coll.; Envirom. Control Assessor. Prev: Sen. Med. Off. Disabem. Serv. Auth.; Med. Off. DHSS (Prosth. Surg. & Rehabil. Med.) Qu. Mary's Hosp. Roehampton; SHO (Surg.) Hosp. Sick Childr. Gt. Ormond St. Lond.

CODDINGTON, Mr William Grosvenor Springwood, Whitmore Heath, Newcastle ST5 5JA — MD Liverp. 1965, MB ChB 1959; FRCS Eng. 1970; FRCOphth. 1993 (Ex Officio). Prev: Ho. Off. Liverp. Roy. Infirm.; Sen. Regist., Manch. Roy. Eye Hosp.; Cons. Ophth. Surg. N. Staffs. Gp. Hosps.

CODEN, Bernard (retired) 7 Park Court, 325/327 Preston Road, Harrow HA3 0QR Tel: 020 8904 5375 — MB ChB 1927 Ed.; FFA RCS Eng. 1953; DA Eng. 1936. Prev: Cons. Anaesth. W. Lond. Hosp., P.ss Beatrice Hosp. & Highlands.

CODEN, Mr John Anthony, Capt. RAMC 92 Harley Street, London W1G 7HU Tel: 020 7487 4816 Fax: 020 7486 5684; 66 Trevelyan Crescent, Harrow HA3 0RJ Tel: 020 8907 0839 — MB BS 1961 Lond.; MRCOG 1969; DObst RCOG 1963. (London Hospital) Specialist O & G. Socs: Roy. Soc. Med. (Obst. & Gyn. Sect.); Brit. Colposcopic Soc. Prev: Cons. O & G Ludshott Manor Hosp.; Regist. (O & G) Hillingdon Hosp. Uxbridge & Char. Cross Gp. Hosps.; Capt. RAMC, RARO.

CODLIN, Rita Maria Sylvia 88 The Fairway, Dymchurch, Romney Marsh TN29 0QP — MB BS 1994 Lond.

CODLING, Bernard William University of West of England, Frenchhay Campus, Coldharbour Lane, Bristol BS16 1QY Tel: 01452 28555 Fax: 01452 395285 Email: ben.codling@uwie.ac.uk; Crantock, Deans Quarry, Burleigh, Stroud GL5 2PQ Tel: 01453 884229 Fax: 01453 884229 Email: bcodl@aol.com — MB ChB

1966 Birm.; MD Birm. 1977; MRCS Eng. LRCP Lond. 1966; FRCPath 1985, M 1973. Sen. Research Fell. Univ. of W. of Eng.; Hon. Cons. in Epidemiol. Socs: BSCC; Path. Soc.; Assn. Clin. Path. Prev: Cons. Path. Glos. Roy. Hosp.; Lect. (Path.) Univ. Birm.; SHO (Clin. Path.) United Birm. Hosps.

CODY, Matthew William Joseph Edward Coolyermer House, Aughanaugh, Letterbreen, Enniskillen — MB BCh BAO 1981 Dub.

COE, Andrew Julian Scunthorpe General Hospital, Cliff Gardens, Scunthorpe DN15 7BH — MB ChB 1982 Liverp.; FFA RCS Eng. 1987. Cons. Anaesth. Scunthorpe Gen. Hosp.

COE, Andrew William Walsgrave Hospital, Clifford Bridge Road, Coventry CV2 2DX Tel: 024 76 538893; Inchford House, 28 Castle Road, Kenilworth CV8 1NG — MB ChB 1978 Bristol; FRCP Lond. 1985; FRCPCH 1997. (Bristol) Cons. Paediat. & Neonat. Walsgrave Hosp. Coventry.; Commiss.er (Child Health) Co. HA. Prev: Sen. Regist. (Paediat.) Hosp, for Sick Childr., Lond.; Fell. (Neonat.) Hosp. for Sick Childr. Toronto, Canada.

COE, Conrad Desmond (retired) 18 Withdean Crescent, Brighton BN1 6WH Tel: 01273 553514 — MB ChB 1937 Manch. Prev: Asst. Med. Off. Hope Hosp. Salford.

COE, Daphne Frances 2 Sovereign Close, Ruislip HA4 7EF Tel: 01895 636233 — MB BS 1962 Lond.; MRCS Eng. LRCP Lond. 1962; DCH Eng. 1965. (King's Coll. Hosp.)

COE, Glyn John 32 Grangethorpe Road, Urmston, Manchester M41 9HT — MB ChB 1965 Manch.; MRCS Eng. LRCP Lond. 1965; MRCGP 1975; DObst RCOG 1969; DCH Eng. 1971.

COE, Kirsten Isobel The Surgery, 32 Clifton, York YO30 6AE Tel: 01904 653834 Fax: 01904 651442; 1 Usher Park Road, Haxby, York YO32 3RX — MB ChB 1986 Leeds; DRCOG 1990. (Leeds) Prev: Trainee GP Wakefield VTS.

COE, Nicola Louise 210 Silverdale Road, Earley, Reading RG6 7NB — MB ChB 1998 Birm.

COE, Peter Alan Department of Anaesthetics, Perth Royal Infirmary, Perth PH1 1NX Tel: 01738 623311; 21 Comely Bank, Perth PH2 7HU — MB ChB 1979 Leeds; FFA RCS Eng. 1984. Cons. Anaesth. Perth Roy. Infirm. Socs: Assn. Anaesth. GB & Irel.; Pain Soc.; N. Brit. Pain Soc. Prev: Sen. Regist. (Anaesth.) Guy's Hosp. Lond.; Regist. (Anaesth.) St. James' Hosp. Leeds.; SHO (Anaesth.) Harrogate Dist. Gen. Hosps.

COE, Sara Maxwell Westlands, Boughton Hall Avenue, Send, Woking GU23 7DF — MB ChB 1988 Bristol.

COE, Susan MacVicar 21 Comely Bank, Perth PH2 7HU — MB ChB 1979 Manch.; FFA RCS Eng. 1985; DRCOG 1981. Doctors Retainer Scheme Perth Roy. Infirm.

COE, Trevor Roy Flat 1, Murray Court, 14 Handsworth Wood Road, Birmingham B20 2DR Email: heywoodcoe@compuserve.com — LMSSA 1984 Lond.; MA Camb. 1985, MB 1984, BChir 1985; FRCA 1993; DA (UK) 1989. Specialist Regist. (Anaesth.) Univ. Hosp. Birm. NHS Trust. Prev: Staff Grade (Anaesth.) S. Devon Healthcare.; Regist. (Anaesth.) Torbay HA; SHO (Gen. Med.) Torbay HA.

COE, Wendy Jacqueline Tel: 0117 986 3063 Fax: 0117 986 5061 — MB ChB 1975 Bristol; DRCOG 1977; MRCGP 1982; DCH 1981. Gen. Practitioner, Princip. Prev: Regist. (Gen. Med. & Paediat.) Yeovil Hosp. Som.; SHO (Neonat. Paediat.) Bristol Matern. Hosp.

COEKIN, Sian Elizabeth 77 Cyncoed Road, Cyncoed, Cardiff CF23 5SB — MB BS 1985 Lond.

COFFEY, Anthony Julian Dobson 15 Auriol Park Road, Worcester Park KT4 7DP — MB ChB 1998 Bristol.

COFFEY, Catherine Joseph 3 Hartopp Road, Leicester LE2 1WE — MB BCh BAO 1981 Dub.

COFFEY, Desmond Patrick Clapham Family Practice, 51 Clapham High Street, London SW4 7TL Tel: 020 7622 4455 Fax: 020 7622 4466 — MB BCh BAO 1975 NUI.

COFFEY, Francis Michael Accident & Emergency Department, Queen's Medical Centre, University Hospital, Nottingham NG7 2UH — MB BCh BAO 1987 NUI; LRCPSI 1987.

COFFEY, Ian William Admin Block, Bangour Village Hospital, Broxburn EH52 6LW Tel: 01506 419666 — MB BCh BAO 1986 NUI.

COFFEY, John (retired) 128 Wigan Road, Standish, Wigan WN6 0AY Tel: 01257 473092 — MB BCh BAO NUI 1951; LM Rotunda 1957; DCH RCPSI 1957. Prev: GP Wigan.

COFFEY, John Francis Boultham Park Medical Practice, Boultham Park Road, Lincoln LN6 7SS Tel: 01522 874444 Fax: 01522 874466 — MB ChB 1987 Leic.; MRCGP (Distinc.) 1992; DRCOG 1992. Course Organiser, Lincoln Vocational Train. Scheme 1997. Socs: BMA; R.C.G.P.

COFFEY, John Patrick X-Ray Department, Manchester Royal Infirmary, Oxford Road, Manchester M13 9WL — MB BCh BAO 1986 NUI; FFR RCSI 1993.

COFFEY, Julie Teresa 98 Sackville Road, Crookes, Sheffield S10 1GW — MB ChB 1994 Sheff.

COFFEY, Margaret Susanna 46 Nursery Road, London N14 5QB — BM BS 1987 Nottm.; MRCGP 1991.

COFFEY, Michele Therese Mary c/o Mr Michael Harkin, Battersea Court, Rich House, University of Surrey, Guildford GU2 7XH — MB BCh BAO 1980 NUI.

COFFEY, Patrick Edward (retired) Coffey, Baunton House, Cirencester GL7 7BD Tel: 01285 652911 — BA Oxf. 1938, BM BCh 1941. Prev: Anaesth. Cirencester Hosp. Surg. Lt.-Cdr. RNVR.

COFFEY, Paul Patrick Sutterton, Horn's Lane, Combe, Oxford OX29 8NH — MB BS 1975 Lond.; MRCP (UK) 1979; MRCGP 1985.

COFFEY, Thomas Anthony Brocklebank Health Centre, 249 Garratt Lane, London SW18 4UE Tel: 020 8870 1341/871 4448; 18 Gracedale Road, London SW16 6SW Tel: 020 8870 1341 — BSc (Hons.) Lond., MB BS 1988; MRCP (UK) 1991; MRCGP 1993; DRCOG 1992; DCH RCP Lond. 1992. Prev: Trainee GP Lond.; SHO (Psychiat.) Kingston Hosp.; SHO (O & G) St. Geo. Hosp. Lond.

COFFIELD, Mary-Jo Crosbie, Moredon Road, Paisley PA2 9LJ — MB ChB 1994 Glas.

COFFIN, Christopher John (retired) Oakfield House, 10 Norwood road, Tiverton EX16 6BD — MB BS 1967 Lond.; MRCS Eng. LRCP Lond. 1967.

COFFIN, Mr Frank Robert (retired) 4 Emery Cottages, West Wittering, Chichester PO20 8QF Tel: 01243 511060 — MRCS Eng. LRCP Lond. 1949; FRCS Eng. 1958, FDS 1953. Hon. Cons. Oral Surg. Roy. Marsden Hosp., St. Bart. Hosp. & St. Geo. Hosp Lond. Prev: Cons. Maxillofacial Surg. Ashstead Hosp. Surrey.

COFFIN, John Pennell The Coach House Surgery, High Street, Stock, Ingatestone CM4 9BD Tel: 01277 840267 Fax: 01277 841568; 33 Birch Lane, Stock, Ingatestone CM4 9NA Tel: 01277 841270 — MB BS 1977 Lond.; BSc (Pharmacol.) Lond. 1974. (Lond. Hosp.) GP Princip. Socs: Roy. Coll. Gen. Pract. Prev: Trainee GP Chelmsford VTS.

***COFFIN, Matthew David** Chapner Farm, Witheridge, Tiverton EX16 8PS — BM 1997 Soton.

COFFMAN, Derek Anthony Law Medical Group Practice, 9 Wrottesley Road, London NW10 5UY Tel: 020 8965 8011 Fax: 020 8961 6239; 63 Mount Pleasant Road, London NW10 3EH Tel: 020 8459 6478 Email: dercom@aol.com — MB BCh 1962 Wales; FRCGP 1980, M 1971. GP Trainer; Clin. Asst. (Gastroenterol.) St Mary's Hosp. Lond. Socs: BMA. Prev: Resid. Med. Off. Roy. Free Hosp.; SHO (Paediat.) Cardiff United Hosps.; Ho. Phys. (Med. Unit) Cardiff Roy. Infirm.

COGAN, Brian Dermot Michael Fenham Hall Surgery, Fenham Hall Drive, Fenham, Newcastle upon Tyne NE4 9XD; 11 Linden Road, Gosforth, Newcastle upon Tyne NE3 4EX Tel: 0191 213 2448 — MB BCh BAO 1977 NUI; DRCOG 1980. Prev: GP Elswick Health Centre; GP Fenham Hall GP Fenham Hall Med. Gp.

COGAN, Fiona Margaret Leesbrook Surgery, Mellor Street, Lees, Oldham OL4 3DG — MB ChB 1981 Manch.; BSc (Hons.) St. And. 1978. (Manchester) Socs: Oldham Med. Soc.

COGAN, Mr John Farnon (retired) Timbers, Wedhampton, Devizes SN10 3QE Tel: 01380 840729 — MB ChB Manch. 1946; FRCS Eng. 1961; FRCS Ed. 1961; MRCS Eng. LRCP Lond. 1946; DO Eng. 1951. Cons. Ophth. Surg. Chester Roy. Infirm. & Wrexham Hosp. Gp. Prev: Lect. in Ophth. Liverp. Univ.

COGAN, Robert 4 Blurton Road, London E5 0NL Tel: 020 8985 6471 — MB BS 1977 Lond.; BSc Lond. 1974, MB BS 1977.

COGBILL, Kevin Lloyd, Lt.-Col. RAMC 22 Keynston Down Road, Blandford Camp, Blandford Forum DT11 8AQ — MB ChB 1974 Birm.; DRCOG 1984.

COGBILL, Peter Graham Northbrook Health Centre, 93 Northbrook Road, Shirley, Solihull B90 3LX Tel: 0121 746 5000 Fax: 0121 746 5020 — MB ChB 1975 Birm. Prev: SHO (Obst.)

Walsgrave Hosp. Coventry; Ho. Surg. Walsgrave Hosp. Coventry; Ho. Phys. & SHO (Gen. Med.) Geo. Eliot Hosp. Nuneaton.

COGGAN, Alison Mary The Simpson Health Centre, 70 Gregories Road, Beaconsfield HP9 1PS Tel: 01494 671571 Fax: 01494 680219; 17 Barrards Way, Seer Green, Beaconsfield HP9 2YZ — MB BS 1985 Lond.; MRCGP 1989; DRCOG 1988; DCH RCP Lond. 1987. (St. Bart.) Prev: SHO (Geriat.) N.ampton Gen. Hosp.; SHO (Paediat. & O & G) N.ampton Gen. Hosp.; Trainee GP Long Buckby N.ants.

COGGER, Valerie Ellen Scott Southend Lodge, Moorend Grove, Leckhampton, Cheltenham GL53 0EX — BM 1979 Soton.; BM Soton 1979; DFFP 1993; DRCOG 1983; DCH RCP Lond. 1982. (Soton.) Asst. GP S. & W. RHA Retainer Scheme. Prev: Asst. GP Doctors Retainer Scheme Mid Surrey HA; Community Med. Off. Mid Surrey HA.

COGGINS, Maureen Mary Occupational Health Unit, Leicestershire County Council, County Hall, Glenfield, Leicester LE3 8RP Tel: 0116 265 6121 Fax: 0116 265 6265; 3 Main Street, Cadeby, Nr. Market Bosworth, Nuneaton CV13 0AX — MB BS 1969 Newc.; MFOM RCP Lond. 1984, AFOM 1980; DIH Eng. 1980. Co. Med. Adviser Leics. Socs: Soc. Occupat. Med. Prev: Co. Med. Adviser Notts.; Employm. Med. Adviser EMAS (Nottm.); Med. Off. Brit. Steel Corpn. Consett Works.

COGGINS, Mr Ronald Paul 1 Railway Terrace, Fishponds, Bristol BS16 4LP Tel: 0117 956 5439; 3 Prestwich Avenue, Culcheth, Warrington WA3 4NA Tel: 01925 764358 — MB ChB 1990 Liverp.; FRCS Ed. 1995. (Liverp.) Specialist Regist. NW Region. Socs: BMA. Prev: SHO (Surg.) Countess of Chester Hosp.; SHO Rotat. (Surg.) Mersey Region.

COGGON, Professor David Noel Murray MRC Environmmental Epidemiology Unit, Southampton General hospital, Southampton SO16 6YD — BM BCh 1976 Oxf.; PhD Soton. 1984; MA Camb. 1976; DM Oxf. 1993; FRCP Lond. 1992; MRCP (UK) 1978; FFOM RCP Lond. 1993, M 1987. Prof. (Occupat. & Environm. Med.) MRC Environm. Epidemiol. Unit Soton.; Hon. Cons. (Occupat. Med.) Soton. HA.

COGGON, Sarah Gosport War Memorial Hopitals, Bury Road, Gosport PO12 3PW; Wembury, Romsey Road, Awbridge, Romsey SO51 0HG — MB BS 1976 Lond.; DCH Eng. 1978. (Lond. Hosp.) Regist. Brookvale Adolesc. Unit Soton. Prev: Regist. Ravenswood RSU Knowle Hosp.; Regist. Psychother. Roy. S. Hants. Hosp. Soton.; Regist. Community Psychiat. Gosport War Memor. Hosp.

COGHILL, Helen Mary Orchard Lane Surgery, Orchard Lane, Denton, Northampton NN7 1HT Tel: 01604 890313 Fax: 01604 890143 — MB ChB 1977 Birm.; MRCGP 1986; DRCOG 1979.

COGHILL, Jonathan Christopher Derriford Hospital, Department of Anaesthesia, Level 07, Derriford Road, Plymouth PL6 8DH Tel: 01752 792692; Overdeer, 1 Deer Leap, Down Road, Tavistock PL19 9AG Tel: 01822 612904 Fax: 01822 615858 Email: coghill@easynet.co.uk — MB ChB 1974 Bristol; FFA RCS Eng. 1978. (Bristol) Cons. (Anaesth.) Plymouth HA. Socs: Obst. Anaesth. Assn.; Brit. Assn. Obst. Surg.; Soc. Anaesth. SW Region. Prev: Cons. (Anaesth.) Bassetlaw HA; Sen. Regist. (Anaesth.) Sheff.; Regist. (Anaesth.) Bristol.

COGHILL, Nelson Fuller (retired) 28 The Grove, Ealing, London W5 5LH Tel: 020 8567 1072 — MB BChir 1937 Camb.; MA Camb. 1937; FRCP Lond. 1960, M 1938; MRCS Eng. LRCP Lond. 1937; T(M) 1991. Prev: Phys. W. Middlx. Hosp. Isleworth & S. Middlx. Hosp. Twickenham.

COGHILL, Stuart Burnett Department of Cellular Pathology, Northampton General Hospital NHS Trust, Northampton NN1 5BD Tel: 01604 545407 Fax: 01604 545575; Email: stuart-coghill@doctors.org.uk — MB ChB 1979 Dundee; BMSc (Hons.) Dund 1976; MRCPath 1985; FRCPath 1995. Cons. Cytol. & Histopath. N.ampton Gen. Hosp. NHS Trust. Prev: Cons. Histopath. N.ampton Gen. NHS Trust; Sen. Regist. (Histopath. & Cytol.) Oxf. RHA; Lect. & Hon. Sen. Regist. Univ. Dundee.

COGHLAN, Mr Brian Anthony Department of Plastic Surgery, Chelsea & Westminster Hospital, 369 Fulham Road, London SW10 9NH Tel: 020 8746 8000 — MB ChB 1987 Bristol; BSc Bristol 1984; FRCS (Plast) 1995; FRCS Eng. 1991; MD Bristol 1996. (Bristol) Cons. Plastic Surg. Chelsea & W.minster Hosp.; Cons. Plastic Surg. St. Richard's Hosp. Chichester. Prev: Sen. Regist. (Plastic Surg.) Gt. Ormond St. Hosp. Lond.; Sen. Regist. Rotat. (Plastic Surg.) St. Jas. Univ. Hosp. Leeds; Regist. (Plastic Surg) Hosp. Glas.

COGHLAN, Brian Patrick Woodley Health Centre, Hyde Road, Woodley, Stockport SK6 1ND Tel: 0161 430 2466 Fax: 0161 406 8217 — MB ChB 1961 Manch.; MRCS Eng. LRCP Lond. 1961; DCH Eng. 1964; DObst RCOG 1963.

COGHLAN, Cherrie Anne Hillingdon Hospital, Pield Heath Road, Uxbridge UB8 3NN Tel: 01895 206809 — MB BCh BAO 1979 Dub.; MRCPsych 1984. (Trinity College, Dublin) Cons. Psychiat. Hillingdon Hosp. Uxbridge.; Vis. Cons. Psychiat. Bowden Hosp. Clinic, ST. Andrews at Harrow, Harrow-on-the-hill, Middlx. Prev: Cons. Psychiat. St. Bernard's & Mt. Vernon Hosps. Middlx.; Sen. Regist. Univ. Coll. & The Middlx. Hosps. Lond.

COGHLAN, Hugo Donal 3 Westfield Road, Winnersh, Wokingham RG11 — LRCPI & LM, LRSCI & LM 1949; LRCPI & LM, LRCSI & LM 1949.

COGHLAN, Mr Kieran Mary The Royal London Hospital, Dept. of Oral Omaxillofacial Surgery, 3rd Floor Alex House, Whitechapel, London E1 1BB Tel: 01708 688344, 020 7377 7051 Fax: 020 7377 7095; 47 Lyndhurst Avenue, Twickenham TW2 6BQ Tel: 020 8898 2839 Fax: 020 8288 9485 — MB BCh BAO 1977 NUI; BDS NUI 1972; FRCS Ed. 1985; FFD RCSI 1982. Cons. Oral & Maxillofacial Surg. Roy. Lond. Hosp. Trust & St. Margt. Hosp. Epping. Socs: Brit. Assn. Oral & Maxillofacial Surg.; Craniofacial Soc. Prev: Sen. Regist. (Oral & Maxillofacial Surg.) Univ. Coll., Gt. Ormond St. & E.man Hosp. Lond.

COGHLAN, Mary Catherine 12 Bickerton Road, Headington, Oxford OX3 7LS Tel: 01865 61859 — MB BCh BAO 1951 NUI; FRCPsych 1979, M 1972; DPM Lond. 1962; DCH Eng. 1954. (Dub.) Socs: Fell. Roy. Soc. Med.; Profess. Mem. Soc. Analyt. Psychol. Prev: Sen. Lect. (Child Psychiat.) Roy. Postgrad. Med. Sch. Lond.; Sen. Regist. (Child Psychiat.) St. Mary's Hosp. Lond.; Regist. Bethlem Roy. & Maudsley Hosp.

COGHLAN, Stefan Frederick Edmund 15 Green Lane, Vicars Cross, Chester CH3 5LA Tel: 01244 341433 — MB ChB 1985 Liverp.; Dip. Obst. Otago 1988. Regist. (Anaesth.) Mersey RHA. Prev: SHO (Anaesth.) Chester HA.

COGILL, Geoffrey Owen 60 Ranelagh Road, London W5 5RP — BM 1997 Soton.

COGMAN, David Michael Healy (retired) Kenwood Nursing Home, 32 Alexandra Grove, London N12 8HG — MB BS Lond. 1942; MD Lond. 1952; FRCPath 1965, M 1963. Prev: Cons. Bact. Barnet & Finchley Health Dist.

COGMAN, Mary Monica Healy (retired) 36 Parkside, Mill Hill, London NW7 2LP — MB BS Lond. 1947; MRCS Eng. LRCP Lond. 1947; MFCM 1972. Prev: Dist. Community Phys. Barnet & Finchley Health Dist.

COGSWELL, Charlotte Campbell 7 Somerton Court, Gosforth, Newcastle upon Tyne NE3 2QZ — MB BS 1990 Newc.

COGSWELL, Diana Frances The Keep, 7 Castle Avenue, Warblington, Havant PO9 2RY Tel: 01705 486169 — MB BS 1967 Lond.; MRCS Eng. LRCP Lond. 1967; MFFP 1994. (Middlx.) SCMO Portsmouth Healthcare NHS Trust. Socs: Founder Mem. Brit. Menopause Soc.; BMA. Prev: Deptm. Med. Off. Havant UD; Ho. Phys. Soton. Gen. Hosp.; Ho. Surg. Tilbury Hosp.

COGSWELL, Jeremy John (retired) Department of Paediatrics, Poole Hospital, Longfleet Road, Poole BH15 2JB Tel: 01202 865511 — MD Camb. 1975, MB BChir 1963; FRCP Lond. 1980, M 1967; MRCS Eng. LRCP Lond. 1962; DCH RCP Lond. 1965; FRCPCH 1997. Cons. Paediat. Poole Gen. Hosp. Prev: Sen. Regist. (Paediat.) Guy's Hosp. Lond.

COGSWELL, Lucy Katherine 7 Castle Avenue, Havant PO9 2RY — BM BCh 1997 Oxf.

COHEN, Abraham (retired) 168 Queens Drive, Liverpool L15 6XX Tel: 0151 722 1964 — MSc Sheff. 1927, BSc (1st cl. Hons.) 1926, MB ChB 1929.

COHEN, Alan 3 Burton Close Mews, Bakewell DE45 1AG — MB ChB 1967 Sheff.; FRCR 1977; DMRD Eng. 1972.

COHEN, Alan Charles The Rowans Surgery, 1 Windermere Road, Streatham, London SW16 5HF Tel: 020 8764 0407; 130 Pepys Road, London SW20 8NS Tel: 020 8947 3895 — MB BS 1977 Lond.; BSc (Hons.) Lond. 1973, MB BS 1977; FRCGP 1993, M 1982; DCH Eng. 1980. (Char. Cross)

COHEN, Alan Mark Anaesthetic Dept, Bristol Royal Infirmary, Bristol BS2 8AW Tel: 0117 928 2163 Fax: 0117 428 2098 Email: alan.cohen@ubht.swest.nhs.uk — MB BS 1984 Lond.; BSc (Hons.) Lond. 1981; MRCP (UK) 1987; FRCA 1991. (Royal Free) Cons. Anaesth. Bristol Roy. Infirm. Socs: Assn. of Cardioth. Anaesth. - Full Mem.; Roy. Coll. Of Anaesth. - Full Mem.; Assn. of Anaesth. - Full Mem. Prev: Sen. Regist. (Anaesth.) St. Geo. Hosp. Lond.; Clin. Fell. (Anaesth.) P. Chas. Hosp. Brisbane, Australia; Sen. Regist. (Anaesth.) Roy. Brompton Hosp. Lond.

COHEN, Alexander Thomas King's College Hospital, Department of Medicine, Denmark Hill, London SE5 9PJ Tel: 020 7346 3015 Fax: 020 7346 3927 Email: alexander.cohen@kol.ac.uk — MB BS 1980 Melbourne; MSc Lond. 1991; FRACP 1990; MD Melbourne 1999. Phys. & Epidemiol. Dept. of Med, King's Coll. Hosp. Lond. Socs: Internat. Soc. Thrombosis & Haemostasis; Internat. Union Angiol.; Med. Res. Soc. Prev: Dir. Clin. Studies Thrombosis Research Inst. King's Coll. Hosp. Lond.; Lect. (Thrombosis Research) King's Coll. Sch. Med. & Dent.

COHEN, Andrew c/o Royal Free Hospital, Hampstead, London NW3 2QG Email: aco@globalnet.co.uk — MB ChB 1994 Leeds; MBChB (Hons.) Leeds 1994; BSc (Hons.) Leeds 1991. Specialist Regist. (Anaes), Stevenage Hosp., Herts. Socs: BMA & Med. Protec. Soc.; RCA. Prev: SHO (Anaes) Bristol Roy. Infirm.; SHO (Anaes) W.on Gen. Hosp.; SHO (Cas, Anaes/ITU) Australia.

COHEN, Andrew Edward Burmantofts Health Centre, Cromwell Mount, Leeds LS9 7TA Tel: 0113 295 3700 Fax: 0113 295 3701 — MB ChB 1989 Leeds.

COHEN, Andrew Edward Doctors Surgery, 2 Padnell Road, Waterlooville PO8 8DZ Tel: 023 9226 3138 Fax: 023 9261 8100; 51 Loxwood Road, Waterlooville PO8 9TY — BChir 1992 Camb.; MB BChir Camb. 1993; MA Camb. 1997; MRCGP 1997. (Univ. Camb.)

COHEN, Mr Andrew Peter 82 Templenewsam Road, Leeds LS15 0LP — MB BS 1989 Newc.; FRCS Ed. 1994.

COHEN, Andrew Rupert Merton Child, Adolescent & Family Service, Cricket Green Polyclinic, 4 Birches Close, Cricket Green, Mitcham CR4 4LQ Tel: 020 8770 8828 Fax: 020 8770 8848 — MB BS 1992 Lond. (UMDS (St. Thos. Campus)) Cons. Child & Adolesc. Psychiat., S. W. Lond. & St. Geo.'s Ment. Health Trust.

COHEN, Andrew Sidney 117 Stafford Court, Phillimore Gardens, London W8 7DR — MB BS 1989 Lond.; FRCS Eng. 1993. Specialist Regist. (Cardiotheracic Surg.) Lond. Chest. Hosp. Prev: Specialist Regist. (Cardiotheracic Surg.) St. Mary's Hosp. Lond.; SHO (Cardiothoracic Surg.) John Radcliffe Hosp. Oxf.; SHO (Orthop. & Gen. Surg.) Roy. Berks. Hosp.

COHEN, Andrew Timothy The Intensive Care Unit, St. James's University Hospital, Beckett St., Leeds LS9 7TF Tel: 0113 206 6813 Fax: 0113 206 4141 Email: a.t.cohen@leeds.ac.uk — MB ChB 1975 Leeds; FFA RCS Eng. 1979; DRCOG 1977. (Leeds) Cons. Anaesth. & Intens. Care St. Jas. Univ. Hosp. Leeds - Hon. Sen. Anaesth. Care St. Jas. Univ. Hosp. Leeds; Cons. Anaesth. St. Jas. Hosp. Leeds; Hon. Sen. Clin. Lect. Univ. Leeds; Mem. Bd. of Exam. RCA. Socs: BMA; Assn. Anaesth.; (Counc.) Intens. Care Soc. Prev: Mem. Counc. Intens. Care Soc.; N.. & Yorks. Clin. Lead, Health Care.

***COHEN, Anna Shelli** 10 Sandhill Drive, Alwoodly, Leeds LS17 8DX Email: annascohen@hotmail.com — BM BCh 1998 Oxf.; BM BCh Oxf 1998.

COHEN, Anne Frances Chapeloak Practice, 347 Oakwood Lane, Leeds LS8 3HA; 6 Parkwood Gardens, Leeds LS8 1JR — MB ChB 1977 Leeds.

COHEN, Arnold 27 Ravenscroft Avenue, Golders Green, London NW11 8BH — BA Oxf. 1947, MA 1952, DM 1964, BM BCh 1949; FRCPath. 1972, M 1964; DObst RCOG 1954. (Oxf. & Univ. Coll. Hosp.) Emerit. Reader Virol. Univ. of Lond. Socs: BMA; Path. Soc. Prev: Hons. Cons. Virologist Univ. Coll. Hosp.; Ho. Surg. (Obst.) Kingston Hosp.; Med. Off. RAF.

COHEN, Mr Ben London Otological Centre, 66 New Cavendish St., London W1G 8TD; 716 Endsleigh Court, Upper Woburn Place, London WC1H 0HW Tel: 020 7387 6805 — MB ChB 1937 Glas.; FRCS Eng. 1953; DLO Eng. 1947. (Glas.) Prev: Cons. (ENT) N. Middlx. Hosp. Lond. & Barnet Gen. Hosp.; Sen. Regist. Roy. Nat. Throat, Nose & Ear Hosp. Lond.

COHEN, Mr Brian Department of Orthopaedic Surgery, The Middlesex Hospital, Mortimer St., London W1T 3AA Tel: 020 7380 9034 — MB BS 1982 Lond.; FRCS (Orth.) 1995; FRCS Ed. 1987; MD 1997. (Roy. Lond. Hosp.) Cons. Orthop. Surg. Middlx. & Univ. Coll. Hosps.; Hon. Sen. Lect. Inst. of Human Performance Univ. of Lond. Socs: Fell. BOA; Brit. Shoulder & Elbow Soc.; Eur. Shoulder & Elbow Soc. Prev: Sen. Regist. Addenbrooke's Hosp. Camb.

COHEN, Cecil Baron (retired) 11 Birchfields, Off Park Road, Hale, Altrincham WA15 9LW Tel: 0161 980 7024 — MB ChB 1955 Manch. Prev: Ho. Surg. Clayton Hosp. Wakefield.

COHEN, Charles (retired) 37 Crosslea Avenue, Sunderland SR3 1LT — MB BChir Camb. 1956; MA Camb. 1952; MRCS Eng. LRCP Lond. 1951. Prev: Med. Regist. Roy. Infirm. Sunderland.

COHEN, Mr Charles Richard Graham 31 Curzon Road, Muswell Hill, London N10 2RB Tel: 020 8444 9858 Fax: 020 8442 0594 Email: richard.cohen@tesco.net — MB BChir 1985 Camb.; BSc (2nd cl. Hons.) Lond. 1983; MD Camb. 1995; FRCS Eng. 1990; FRCS Eng (Gen Surg) 1996 (Camb). Cons. Surg. St. Mark's Hosp. (Middlx.) / Centr. Middlx. Hosp. Prev: Sen. Regist. Rotat. Guy's Hosp. Lond.

***COHEN, Charlotte Elizabeth Maria** 117 Stafford Court, Phillimore Gardens, Kensington, London W8 7DR Tel: 020 7937 2111 — MB BS 1997 Lond.; MB BS (Hons.) Lond. 1997; BSc Lond. 1994.

COHEN, Cyril, OBE (retired) Mansefield, Aberlemno, Forfar DD8 3PD Tel: 01307 830259 — MB ChB 1949 Manch.; FRCP Glas. 1972, M 1962; FRCP Ed. 1972, M 1961; FRFPS Glas. 1961. JP.; Hon. Fell. Dundee Univ. Prev: Cons. Phys. (Geriat. Med.) Tayside HB.

COHEN, David Granville 10 St Stephens Terrace, Vauxhall, London SW8 1DH Tel: 020 7840 0123 Fax: 020 7840 0123 — MB BS 1973 Lond.; FFA RCS Eng. 1980. (Westm. Hosp.) Cons. Anaesth. Mayday Hosp. NHS Trust Thornton Heath Croydon Surrey. Prev: Lect. (Anaesth.) Lond. Hosp. Med. Coll.; Hon. Sen. Regist. (Anaesth.) Tower Hamlets & Newham HA's; Asst. Prof. Anaesth. TuLa. Univ. Med. Centre New Orleans Louisiana, USA.

COHEN, David Leonard 8 Ashbourne Grove, Salford M7 4DD — MB BCh 1983 Witwatersrand.

COHEN, David Leslie Northwick Park Hospital, Watford Road, Harrow HA1 3UJ Tel: 020 8869 2451 Fax: 020 8869 2241 Email: david.cohen@which.net — MB BS 1979 Lond.; FRCP Lond. 1996; MRCP (UK) 1981. (Roy. Free) Cons. Phys. N.wick Pk. Hosp. Harrow; Mem. Disabil. Living Allowance Advis. Bd.; Cons. Phys., Clementine Ch.ill Hosp. Socs: Brit. Geriat. Soc. & Brit. Diabetic Assn. Prev: Cons. Phys., Nottm. City Hosp.; Sen. Regist. (Gen. & Geriat. Med.) Radcliffe Infirm. Oxf.; Research Regist. Unit for Metab. Med. Guy's Hosp. Lond.

COHEN, Deborah Anne Four Hedges, Castle Hill, Llanblethian, Cowbridge CF71 7JB — MB BS 1981 Lond.; MRCGP 1986; D.Occ.Med. RCP Lond. 1996; DRCOG 1984. (Char. Cross) Asst. GP Cowbridge.

COHEN, Elizabeth Frances 11 King's Road, Ilkley LS29 9AE Tel: 01943 817894 — MB ChB 1976 Manch.

COHEN, Elizabeth Mary 82 Templenewsam Road, Leeds LS15 0LP — MB BS 1991 Newc.

COHEN, Geoffrey Frith Derby City General Hospital NHS Trust, Uttoxeter New Road, Derby DE22 3NE Tel: 01332 340131 Fax: 01332 290559; Hope Coltage, Alstonefield, Ashbourne DE6 2GE Tel: 01335 310381 Email: frithc@aol.com — MB BChir 1959 Camb.; MA Camb. 1959; FRCP Lond. 1977, M 1964; MRCS Eng. LRCP Lond. 1958; BSC Loughborough 1999. (Camb. & Westm.) Emerit. Cons. Phys. Derby City Gen. Hosp.; Clin. Teach Univ. of Nottingh.; Examr., RCP. Lond. Socs: Fell. BMA; Renal Assn. & IC Soc. Prev: Clin. Fell. Montreal Gen. Hosp., Canada; Sen. Regist. Derbysh. Roy. Infirm.; Regist. (Med.) Roy. Free Hosp. Lond.

COHEN, Mr Geoffrey Leonard 63 Westbourne Road, Sheffield S10 2QT Tel: 0114 268 6558 — MB ChB 1966 Liverp.; ChM Liverp. 1983, MB ChB 1966; FRCS Ed. 1972; FRCS Eng. 1973. (Liverp.) Cons. Surg. Roy. Hallamsh. Hosp. Sheff. Prev: Lect. in Surg. Univ. Dept. Surg. Manch. Roy. Infirm.; Tutor (Surg.) Univ. Manch. & Hon. Sen. Regist. Manch. Roy. Infirm.; Surg. Regist. Leicester Gen. Hosp.

COHEN, Hannah Department of Haematology, University College London Hospitals NHS Trust, Grafton Way, London WC1E 6DB Tel: 020 7387 9300 Ext: 8563 Fax: 020 7380 9911 Email:

h.cohen@academic.uclh.nthames; 36 Aberdare Gardens, London NW6 3QA Tel: 020 7624 8599 — MB ChB 1974 Manch.; MD Manch. 1989; FRCP Lond. 1995; MRCP (UK) 1980; FRCPath 1996, M 1984. Cons. Haematologist. Socs: Fell. Roy. Coll. Phys.; Fell. Roy. Coll. Path.; Brit. Soc. Haematol. Prev: Sen. Lect. & Hons. Cons. Imperial Coll. Sch. of Med. @St. Mary's Hosp. & St. Mary's NHS Trust, Lond.; Clin. Lect. (Haemat.) Univ. Coll. & Middlx. Sch. Med. Lond.; Lect. & Hon. Sen. Regist. (Haemat.) Middlx. Med. Sch. Lond.

COHEN, Harold (retired) 35 Meadowbank, Primrose Hill Road, London NW3 3AY Tel: 020 7483 0420 — MB ChB 1947 Sheff.; MD Sheff. 1962; FRCP Lond. 1974, M 1953. Prev: Cons. Phys. Salford Roy. Hosp. & Hope Hosp. Salford.

COHEN, Helen Elizabeth Shumwood Farm, Ashbrittle, Wellington TA21 0HX — MB BCh 1995 Wales.

COHEN, Howard Clive Woodcote Group Practice, 32 Foxley Lane, Purley CR8 3EE Tel: 020 8660 1304 Fax: 020 8660 0721; The Woodcote Group Practice, 140 Chipstead Valley Road, Coulsdon CR5 3BB Tel: 020 8660 1305 — MB ChB 1985 Bristol; MRCGP 1990; DRCOG 1990; DCH RCP Lond. 1988. Prev: Trainee GP Avon VTS; SHO Rotat. Bristol; Ho. Phys. Frenchay Hosp. Bristol.

COHEN, Howard Newman Hairmyres Hospital, E. Kilbride, Glasgow G75 8RG Tel: 0141 20292; 32 Milverton Road, Whitecraigs, Glasgow G46 7JN — MB ChB 1972 Liverp.; MD Liverp. 1982; FRCP Ed. 1992; FRCP Glas. 1988; MRCP (UK) 1976. Cons. Phys. & Endocrinol. Hairmyres Hosp. E. Kilbride. Socs: Scott. Soc. Experim. Med.; Scott. Soc. Phys. Prev: Vis. Prof. Pediat. Endocrinol. Univ. Calif. San Francisco, USA; Sen. Regist. Glas. Roy. Infirm.; Regist. & SHO Mersey RHA.

COHEN, Jeremy 32 Harman Drive, London NW2 2ED — MB BS 1990 Lond.; BSC Lond. 1988, MB BS 1990; MRCP Lond. 1993.

COHEN, Jill Maidstone Road Surgery, 262 Maidstone Road, Chatham ME4 6JL Tel: 01634 842093 Fax: 01634 842151 — MB ChB 1969 Cape Town; MB ChB 1969 Cape Town.

COHEN, Johnson David, CBE (retired) 33 Temple Fortune Hill, London NW11 7XL Tel: 0208 455 7817 — MB BS Lond. 1966; MA Oxf. 1957, BA 1954; MRCS Eng. LRCP Lond. 1966; FRCGP 1979, M 1971; T(GP) 1991. GP Lond., Retd.; Hon. Fell. Lincoln Coll. Oxf.; Fell. Roy. Free Hosp. Sch. Med.; Hon. Guildhall Sch. Music. Prev: Vis. Teach. Tavistock Clinic Lond.

COHEN, Professor Jonathan Brighton & Sussex Medical School, Westlain House University of Brighton, Village Way, Falmer BN1 9PH Tel: 020 8383 3243 Fax: 020 8383 3394 Email: j.cohen@bsms.ac.uk — MB BS 1974 Lond.; MSc Lond. 1981, BSc 1971; FRCP Lond. 1987; FRCPath 1996; FRCPE 1997. (Char. Cross) Prof. & Head Infec. Dis. & Microbiol, Imperial Coll. Sch. of Med. Hammersmith Hosp. Lond. Socs: Brit. Infec. Soc.; Brit. Soc. Antimicrob. Chemother.; Infect. Dis. Soc. Amer.

COHEN, Jonathan Charles Yeovil District Hospital, Higher Kingston, Yeovil BA21 4AT; Manor Farm, Chillington, Ilminster TA19 9JA — MB BS 1978 Lond.; MSc (Neurochem.) Lond. 1982, MB BS 1978; MRCPsych 1983. Cons. Yeovil Dist. Hosp.

COHEN, Jonathan Marc 2 Primley Park Court, Leeds LS17 7LQ — BM BCh 1998 Oxf.; BM BCh Oxf 1998.

COHEN, Joseph South Woodford Health Centre, 114 High Road, London E18 2QS Tel: 020 8491 3303 Fax: 020 8559 2451; 4 Piercing Hill, Theydon Bois, Epping CM16 7JN Tel: 01992 812000 — MB BS 1975 Lond.; MRCP (UK) 1978; MRCGP 1982. Socs: Fell. Med. Soc. Lond. Prev: Resid. Med. Off. W.m. Hosp. Lond.

COHEN, Judith Rosalind Hillcroft, Saltway, Muzzyhill, Feckenham, Redditch B96 6JU — MB ChB 1971 Birm. Sen. Med. Off. (Family Plann.) W. Midl. RHA; Sen. Clin. Med. Off. (Family Plann.) N. Worcs. HA.

COHEN, Juliet Rose 26 Tierney Road, London SW2 4QR — MB BS 1986 Lond.; MA Oxf. 1983; MRCGP 1996; DRACOG 1990. (Lond. Hosp.)

COHEN, Keith David James William 3 South Gillsland Road, Edinburgh EH10 5DE — MB ChB 1998 Dund.; MB ChB Dund 1998.

COHEN, Kenneth Max (retired) 6 Meadowfield Drive, Cleadon Village, Sunderland SR6 7QW — LRCP LRCS 1956 Ed.; LRCP LRCS Ed. LRFPS Glas. 1956. Prev: Ho. Phys. Darlington Memor. Hosp.

COHEN, Lester Maes Y Ffynnon, Caemorgan Road, Cardigan SA43 1QU Tel: 01239 614700 Fax: 01239 614700 — MB BS 1955 Lond.; MD Lond. 1968; DObst RCOG 1957. (St. Bart.) Socs: Roy. Coll. Gen. Pract.; Med. Soc. Study VD. Prev: Cons. Venereol. Univ. Hosp. of Wales & SE Glam. Hosp. Gp.; Ho. Phys. & Ho. Surg. (O & G) St. Bart. Hosp. Lond.

COHEN, Margaret Elizabeth Lendrum (retired) Hope Cottage, Alstonefield, Nr Ashbourne, Derby DE6 2GE Tel: 01332 340730 — MB BS 1963 Lond.; MRCS Eng. LRCP Lond. 1963; FFR 1969; DMRD Eng. 1966. Clin. Dir. & Cons. Radiol. BrE. Unit Derby City Gen. Hosp. Prev: Sen. Regist. (Radiol.) Derbysh. Roy. Infirm.

COHEN, Mark Adrian 81A Sulgrave Road, London W6 7QH — MB ChB 1994 Birm.

COHEN, Mark Thomas 49A High Street, Lochwinnoch PA12 4AB — MB ChB 1987 Glas.

COHEN, Merton 119 Mather Avenue, Liverpool L18 6JY Tel: 0151 724 2476 — MB ChB 1960 Liverp.; FFA RCS Eng. 1964. Liverp. AHA (T).

COHEN, Michael 29 Edgeworth Avenue, London NW4 4EX — MB BS 1997 Lond.

COHEN, Michael Adam Hart The Surgery, 60 Falcondale Road, Westbury-on-Trym, Bristol BS9 3JY Tel: 0117 962 3406 Fax: 0117 962 1404; 31 Elmlea Avenue, Westbury on Trym, Bristol BS9 3UU Tel: 0117 962 3706 Fax: 0117 962 1404 Email: mcohen@mcmail.com — MB BS 1979 Lond.; BSc (Hons.) Lond. 1975; MRCP (UK) 1984; MRCGP 1991; DRCOG 1986. (London Hospital Medical College) Princip. GP; Hosp. Practitioner Gastroenterol. S.mead Hosp. Bristol. Socs: Primary Care Soc. Gastroenterol. Prev: Lect. Clin. Pharmacol. Chinese Univ. Hong Kong; Regist. Med. Ipswich Hosp.

COHEN, Michael Barry 6 Sandhill Grove, Leeds LS17 8ED Tel: 0113 268 5864 — MRCS Eng. LRCP Lond. 1961; DObst RCOG 1962. (Leeds) Socs: BMA & W. Riding M-C Soc. Prev: Ho. Phys. Halifax Gen. Hosp.; Obst. Ho. Off. P.ss Roy. Matern. Home, Huddersfield.

COHEN, Michael Stephen Daisy Hill House, Heights Lane, Bradford BD9 6DP Tel: 01274 363832 — MB ChB 1976 Manch.; MRCPsych 1982. Cons. Psychiat. Bradford Community Health NHS Trust. Prev: Cons. Psychiat. Bexley Hosp.

COHEN, Neville Howard (retired) 3 Duchy Road, Hadley Wood, Barnet EN4 0HX Tel: 020 8449 2522 — MRCS Eng. LRCP Lond. 1957; DObst RCOG 1966. Prev: JP.

COHEN, Mr Nicholas Paul Department of Urology, Ward 44, Aberdeen Royal Infirmary, Cornhill Road, Aberdeen AB25 2ZN Tel: 01224 681818 Fax: 01224 840726; 6 Fetteresso Castle, Fetteresso, Stonehaven AB39 3UR Tel: 01569 767617 — MB ChB 1984 Birm.; FRCS (Urol.) 1996; FRCS Eng. 1990; FEBU 1998. Cons. Urol. Surg. Aberd. Roy. Infirm. Socs: Fell. Roy. Soc. Med.; Brit. Assn. Urol. Surgs. Prev: Sen. Regist. Rotat. (Urol.) W. Midl.; Career Regist. (Urol.) Aberd. Roy. Infirm.; Research Regist. (Urol.) St. Bart. Hosp. Lond.

COHEN, Norman Albert 32 Harman Drive, London NW2 2ED Tel: 020 8452 1611 — MRCS Eng. LRCP Lond. 1942; BSc 1940; MRCPsych 1971; DPM Eng. 1948. (Cardiff) Hon. Cons. Psychother. W. Middlx. Hosp. Socs: Brit. Psychoanal Soc. Prev: Psychiat. Cassel Hosp. Richmond.

COHEN, Paul Robert 10 Curlew Close, Bamford, Rochdale OL11 5PX — MB ChB 1992 Liverp.

COHEN, Raymond Chapman (retired) 14 Chipping Hill, Witham CM8 2DE Tel: 01376 513262 — MB BS 1932 Lond.; MD Lond. 1934; MRCS Eng. LRCP Lond. 1931; DPH Lond. 1933. Hon. Cons. Thoracic Med. Colchester & Chelmsford Dist. Hosps. Prev: Cons. Dis. of Chest NE Metrop. RHB.

COHEN, Professor Robert Donald, CBE (retired) St. Bartholomew's and the Royal London School of Medicine & Dentistry, Dept of Diabetes & Metabolic Med, The Royal London Hospital, Whitechapel Road, London E1 1BB Tel: 020 7377 7110 Fax: 020 7377 7636 Email: rcohen@doctors.org.uk — MB BChir 1958 Camb.; F Med. Sci 1998; MD Camb. 1966, MA 1958; FRCP Lond. 1971, M 1960; MRCS Eng. LRCP Lond. 1958. Prev: Prof.Med. Lond. Hosp.. Med Coll.. (Sch. of Med. & Dent., Qu. Mary and W.hall Coll., Univ. of Lond..

COHEN, Robert Ian St Andrew's at Harrow, Bowden House Clinic, London Road, Harrow-on-The-Hill, Harrow HA1 3JL Tel: 020 8966 7000 Fax: 020 8864 6092; 10 Harley Street, London W1N 1AA Tel: 020 7467 8300 Fax: 020 7467 8312 — MB BS 1976 Lond.; MRCS Eng. LRCP Lond. 1976; MRCPsych 1984; Dip. Criminol. Lond. 1990;

DRCOG 1980. (Roy. Free) Cons. Psychiat. & Med. Dir. St. And. at Harrow Bowden Hse. Clinic; Cons BUPA Hosp. Herts. Prev: Cons. Psychiat. Hillingdon Hosp.; Sen. Regist. (Psychiat.) Lond. Hosp.; Hon. Sen. Regist. (Forens. Psychiat.) Friern Hosp. Barnet.

COHEN, Robert Maurice East London + City, Mental Health, NHE Trust, Homerton DDU, Homerton Hospital, Homerton Row, London E9 6SR Tel: 020 8510 8629 Fax: 020 8510 8270 — MB BS 1985 Lond.; MA Camb. 1983; MRCPsych 1990. Cons. Psychiat. (Drugs & Alcohol) E. Lond. + City Ment. Health NHS Trust. Prev: Sen. Regist. (Psychiat.) Char. Cross & W.m. Med. Sch. Lond.; Regist. (Psychiat.) Chase Farm Hosp.; Ho. Surg. Watford Gen. Hosp.

COHEN, Ronald Jack 54 Willifield Way, Hampstead Garden Suburb, London NW11 7XT Tel: 0208 455 0905 Fax: 0208 455 0905 Email: rjc-cdb@dircon.co.uk — MB ChB 1970 Cape Town; FFA RCS Eng. 1976. Private Anaesth. Pract. Socs: Roy. Soc. Med. Prev: Lect. (Anaesth.) Lond. Hosp. Med. Coll.; Sen. Regist. (Anaesth.) Brompton Hosp. Lond.; Cons. Anaesth. Harefield Hosp. Middlx.

COHEN, Professor Samuel Isaac 9 Heathcroft, Hampstead Way, London NW11 7HH Tel: 020 8455 4781 — MB BCh (Distinc. Surg.) 1948; BSc (Distinc. Anat.) Wales 1946; MD Lond. 1953, MB BS 1949; FRCP Lond. 1970, M 1954; FRCPsych 1971; DPM Eng. 1958. (Cardiff) Emerit. Prof. Psychiat. Univ. Lond. & Hon. Cons. Psychiat. Roy. Lond. Hosp. Prev: Prof. Psychiat. Lond. Hosp. Med. Coll.; Hon. Cons. Psychiat. Brompton Hosp. Lond.; Lect. (Med.) Med. Unit. Cardiff.

COHEN, Mr Samuel Joseph (retired) 14 St John Street, Manchester M3 4DZ Tel: 0161 835 1465 — MB BCh 1947 Witwatersrand; FRCP Lond. 1994; MRCP Ed. 1952; FRCS Eng. 1956. Hon. Cons. Surg. & Paediat. Urol. Booth Hall Childr. Hosp. Blackley, Roy. Manch. Childr. Hosp. & St. Mary's Hosp. Manch. Prev: Vis. Prof. (Paediat. Urol.) Bielenson Hosp. Tel Aviv, Israel, Univ. Michigan, USA & Bogota Univ. Med. Sch., Colombia.

COHEN, Sheila Flat 3, 132 Harley St., London W1N 1AH — MB BS 1959 Durh.; DCH Eng. 1963.

COHEN, Shoshana Sarah 7 Winchester Avenue, Penylan, Cardiff CF23 9BT — MB BS 1996 Lond.

COHEN, Simon Aaron 12 Sandmoor Lane, Alwoodley, Leeds LS17 7EA — MB ChB 1996 Leeds.

COHEN, Simon Lionel University College Hospital, Gower St., London WC1E 6AU Tel: 020 7388 3894 Fax: 020 7380 9816 Email: simon.cohen@ucl.ac.uk; 175 West Heath Road, London NW3 7TT Tel: 020 8458 7988 Email: kushi@dircon.co.uk — MB BS Lond. 1961; FRCP Lond. 1979, M 1964; MRCS Eng. LRCP Lond. 1961; DObst RCOG 1963. (Univ. Coll. Hosp.) Cons. Phys. Univ. Coll. Hosp. & Middlx. Hosp. Lond.; Sen. Lect. Univ. Coll. Hosp. Med. Sch. Lond.; Hon. Cons. Nephrol. St. Peter's Hosps. Lond.; Hon. Sen. Lect. (Nephrol.) Inst. Urol. Lond. Socs: Europ. Soc. Intens. Care Med.; Chairm. Ethics Working Party Chairm.; Renal. Assn. Prev: Sen. Regist. & Regist. (Med.) St. Mary's Hosp. Lond.; Instruct. (Med.) Univ. Minnesota Med. Sch., USA.

COHEN, Stanley Bernard 30 Countisbury Drive, Liverpool L16 0JJ — MB ChB Liverp. 1961; MD Liverp. 1979; FRCP Lond. 1980, M 1967. p/t Cons. Phys. Walton & Fazakerley Hosps. Liverp.; Hon. Clin. Lect. Univ. Liverp. Socs: Liverp. Med. Inst. Prev: Fell. (Med.) Johns Hopkins Hosp.; Sen. Regist. (Med.) Liverp. AHA.

COHEN, Stephen Jeremy Kings Langley Surgery, The Nap, Kings Langley WD4 8ET Tel: 01923 261035 Fax: 01923 269629; 57 Valley Road, Chorleywood, Rickmansworth WD3 4DT Email: dodoco1@cs.com — MB BS Lond. 1968; MRCP (UK) 1973; MRCS Eng. LRCP Lond. 1968; DA Eng. 1971; DObst RCOG 1970; DCH Eng. 1970. (Roy. Free) Socs: Brit. Med. Acupunc. Soc. Prev: Regist. (Paediat.) Ahmadu Bello Univ. Zaria, Nigeria; Regist. (Anaesth.) Hillingdon Hosp. Uxbridge; SHO Neonat. Unit Whittington Hosp. Lond.

COHEN, Susan Lee 14 Alvanley Gardens, London NW6 1JD — MB BS 1982 Lond.

COHEN, Sydney (retired) Linwood, Ashbrooke Range, Sunderland SR2 9BP Tel: 0191 528 4110 — MB BCh 1951 Witwatersrand; FRCOG 1972, M 1959, DObst 1956. Cons. O & G Sunderland Hosp. Gp. Prev: Sen. Regist. (O & G) United Newc. Hosps.

COHEN, Sydney, CBE 4 Frognal Rise, London NW3 6RD Tel: 020 7435 6507 — MD 1954 Witwatersrand; FRS; PhD Lond. 1959; Hon. DSc Witwatersrand 1987, MD 1954, MB BCh 1944; FRCPath 1964. (Witwatersrand) Emerit. Prof. Chem. Path. Guy's Hosp. Med. Sch. Lond.; Mem. Immunol. Soc. & Roy. Soc. Trop. Med. & Hyg. Lond. Prev: Reader in Immunol. St. Mary's Hosp. Lond.; on Scientif. Staff Nat. Inst. Med. Research; Nuffield Dominion Fell. in Med.

COHEN, Victoria Mary Lendrum 21 Sale Hill, Sheffield S10 5BX — BChir 1995 Camb.

COHEN, Vivienne (retired) 9 Heathcroft, Hampstead Way, London NW11 7HH Tel: 020 8455 4781 — MB BS Lond. 1951; MRCS Eng. LRCP Lond. 1951; FRCPsych 1977, M 1971. Hon.Cons.. Israel Inst. of Gp. Anal., Tel Aviv, Israel. Prev: Sen. Lect. & Hon. Cons. Psychother. (Psychol. Med.) St. Bart. Hosp. Lond.

COHN, Anthony Simon 40 England's Lane, London NW3 4UE Tel: 020 7483 0925 — MB BS 1989 Lond.; MRCP (UK) 1992. (St. Geo.) Regist. (Neonatol.) UCLH Lond. Prev: Regist. (Paediat.) Whipps Cross Hosp. Lond.; SHO (Paediat.) Hosp. Sick Childr. Lond.

COHN, Michael Richard Hereford County Hospital, Hereford HR1 2ER Tel: 01432 364062; The Stone House, Fownhope, Hereford HR1 4PJ Tel: 01432 860635 Email: cohnee@ukonline.com — BM BS 1981 Nottm.; DM Nottm. 1993; MRCOG 1986. Cons. O & G Hereford Hosps. NHS Trust. Socs: Birm. Midl.s Obst. & Gyn.; Brit. Soc. Coloposcopy & Cervical Path. Prev: Sen. Regist. Leicester Hosps.; Lect. Chinese Univ. of Hong Kong; Research Regist. N.. Gen. Hosp. Sheff.

COIA, Denise Assunda Florence Street Day Hospital, 28 Florence St., Gorbals, Glasgow G5 Tel: 0141 429 2878 Fax: 0141 420 3464 — MB ChB 1976 Glas.; MRCPsych 1981; DRCOG 1978; FRCPsych 1997. (Glas.) Cons. Psychiat. Gtr. Glas. HB / Adviser Ment. Health Gtr. Galsgow Health Bd.; Hon. Sen. Lect. (Psychol. Med.) Glas. Univ.; Research Fell. (Pub. Health) Glas. Univ.; Mem. Nat. Standards Bd. Scotl. Socs: Roy. Coll. Psychiat. (Sec. Scott. Div.) (1997-2001); Chairm. Scott. Div.

COIA, John Eugenio Department of Clinical Microbiology, Western General Hospital, Crewe Road, Edinburgh EH4 2XU Tel: 0131 537 1927 Fax: 0131 537 1024 Email: john.coia@ed.ac.uk; 17 Braehead Avenue, Barnton, Edinburgh EH4 6QN Tel: 0131 339 5701 — MB ChB 1984 Glas.; BSc (1st cl. Hons. Molecular Biol.) Glas. 1981, MD 1991; MRCPath 1991. Cons. Med. Microbiol. W.. Gen. Hosp. Edin.; Director Scott. E.Coli 0157 Refer. Liboratory. Socs: Brit. Soc. Study of Infec.; Hosp. Infec. Soc.; Assn. Med. Microbiol. Prev: Sen. Regist. (Med. Microbiol.) Glas. Roy. Infirm.; Regist. (Med. Microbiol.) Glas. Roy. Infirm.

COID, Donald Routledge Department of Epidemiology & Public Health, Ninewells hospital & Medical school, Dundee DD2 9SY Tel: 01382 632124 Fax: 01382 644197 Email: drcoid@eph.dundee.ac.uk; 1 Miur Gardens, St Andrews KY16 9NH Tel: 01334 472710 Fax: 01334 472710 Email: dcoid@hotmail.com — BM BS 1976 Nottm.; MSc Lond. 1981; BMedSci (Hons.) Nottm. 1974; MRCP (UK) 1979; FFPHM RCP (UK) 1996, M 1989; MFCM 1985; FRCP Ed. 1997; FRIPHH 1997. (Nottm.) Cons. (Health Servs. Research) Dundee Univ.; Hon. Sen. Lect. Dundee Univ. Socs: Fell. Roy. Austral. Coll. Med. Adminstrators; Foundat. Fell. Austral. Fac. Pub. Health Med.; Soc. for Social Med. Prev: Chief. Admin. Med. Off., Dir. Pub. Health & Exec. Dir. Tayside HB; Asst. Gen. Manager Fife HB; Regional Dir. (Pub. Health) E.ern Goldfields Pub. Health Region, W.ern Australia.

COID, Professor Jeremy Weir Forensic Psychiatry Research Unit, St. Bartholomews Hospital, William Harvey House, 61 Bartholomew Close, London Tel: 020 7601 8138 Fax: 020 601 7969 Email: j.w.coid@mds.qmw.ac.uk — MB ChB 1974 Sheff.; MPhil Lond. 1983; MD Univ. Lond. 1996; MRCPsych 1978; Dip. Criminol. Lond. 1983; DPM 1981. Cons. Forens. Psychiat. E. Lond. & City HA; Prof. Forens. Psychiat. St. Bart. & Roy. Lond. Sch. Med. & Dent.

COIGLEY, Michael Harold Farnham (retired) The Woodlands, Alveston, Stratford-upon-Avon CV37 7QR Tel: 01789 293158 Fax: 01789 293158 — MB BS Lond. 1947; MRCS Eng. LRCP Lond. 1947; FRCGP 1974, M 1971. Prev: Hosp. Pract. (Cardiol.) Coventry HA.

COIPEL, Pamela Marie Westerhope Medical Group, 377 Stamfordham Road, Westerhope, Newcastle upon Tyne NE5 2LH Tel: 0191 243 7000 Fax: 0191 243 7006 — MB ChB 1987 Leeds; MRCGP 1991; DRCOG 1991. (Univ. Leeds Med. Sch.) Socs: BMA; Roy. Coll. Gen. Pract.

COKER, Adeyemi Akintola Harold Wood Hospital, Gubbins Lane, Romford RM3 0BE — MB BS 1982 Lagos; CPE Pg.D. Law

(Middlesex); Cert. BSCCP; Cert. Lap. Surg. (RCOG); MRCOG 1993. Cons. O & G Barking, Havering & Redbridge NHS Trust; Cons. in Obst. & Gyn. Early Pregn./Acute Gyn. Prev: Sen. Regist. St. Mary's Hosp., Lond.; Sen. Regist. Hillingdon Hosp., Uxbridge; Sen. Regist. Lister Hosp., Stevenage.

COKER, Mr Akinoso Ebunoluwa Olujimi 69 Woodholm Road, Sheffield S11 9HS Fax: 0114 225 7042 Email: aderupoko1@compuserve.com — MB BS 1984 Ibadan; FRCS Glas. 1990; FRCS (Gen) 1999. (University College Hospital College of Med. Ibadan Nigeria) Specialist Regist. N.ern Gen. Hosp. Sheff. Socs: Affil. Fell. Assn. Surgs. GB & Irel.; Fell. Roy. Soc. Med. Prev: Staff Surg. Rotherham DGH NHS Trust Rotherham S. Yorks.

COKER, Mr Babatunde Julian Tel: 07970 795343 Email: juliancoker@gol.com; Email: juliancoker@gol.com — MB BS 1984 Lagos; MS 1999 Lond.; FRCS 1999 (Intercollegiate); DIC 2000 Lond.; MSc 2000 (Dist) Imperial Coll. Lond.; FRCS Eng. 1992. Regist. (Gen. Surg.) P.ss Alexandra Hosp. Harlow.; Cons. Gen. and Vasc. Surg. to Barking Havering and Redbridge Hosps. NHS Trust; Cons. Gen. and Vasc. Surg. to OldCh. Hosp. Romford; Cons. Gen. and Vasc. Surg. to King Geo. V Hosp. Ilford. Socs: Mem. Vasc. Surgic. Soc. of GB & Irel.; Mem. Europ. Vasc. Surgic. Soc.; Mem. Assn. of Surg.s of GB & Irel. Prev: Regist. (Gen. Surg.) Whittington Hosp. Lond.; Sen. Regist. (Gen./Vasc. Surg.) Roy. Lond. & Barts NHS Trust Lond. 2000; Sen. Regist. (Vasc. Surg.) Roy. Free Hosp. Lond. 2001.

COKER, Charles Babatunde Akintola Olarewaju Flat 2, 18 Louvaine Road, London SW11 2AG — MB BS 1985 Lond.

COKER, David Martin Department of Genito-Urinary Medicine, Furness General Hospital, Barrow-in-Furness LA14 4LF Tel: 01229 870870; 1 Church Close, Levens, Kendal LA8 8QE Tel: 015395 60057 Fax: 015395 60057 — MB ChB 1982 Manch.; FRCP Lond. 1997; MRCP (UK) 1985. Cons. Genitourin. Med. Bay Community Trust. Prev: Sen. Regist. (Genitourin. Med.) Roy. Liverp. Hosp.; Regist. (Genitourin. Med.) Middlx. Hosp. Lond.; Regist. (Gen./Genitourin. Med.) St. Thos. Hosp. Lond.

COKER, Frederick Baptist Adeniyi c/o 8 Elstow Grange, 40 Brondesbury Park, London NW6 7DW — LRCPI & LM, LRSCI & LM 1958; LRCPI & LM, LRCSI & LM 1958; FRCOG 1980, M 1965.

COKER, Robina Kate Respiratory Medicine, Hammersmith Hospital, Du Cane Road, London W12 0HS Tel: 020 8383 3329 Fax: 020 8383 4957 Email: robina.coker@ic.ac.uk — MB BS 1986 Lond.; BSc Lond. 1983; MRCP (UK) 1989; PhD Lond. 1997; CCST 1998. (St. Thos. Hosp. Med. Sch. Lond.) Sen. Lect. + Hon. Cons. in Respirat. Med., Imperial Coll. Fac.l of Med., Hammersmith, Lond..; Asst. Director of Research + Developm. Hammersmith Hosp.s NHS Trust. Socs: Christ. Med. Fell.sh. (Pub.at. Comm.); Am. Thoracic Soc.; Brit.Thoracic Soc. Prev: Sen. Regist. (Thoracic Med.) Whipps Cross Hosp. Lond.; Locum Cons. (Thoracic Med), Whipps Cross Hosp. , Lond.; Wellcome Research Fell. (Thoracic Med.)Nat. Heart & Lung Inst. and... Univ. Coll. Lond.

COKER, Timothy Charles The Surgery, Stowe Drive, Southam, Leamington Spa CV47 1NY Tel: 01926 812577 Fax: 01926 817447; Fieldgate View, Pillory Green, Napton, Rugby CV47 8LN Tel: 01926 815739 Email: tcoker@napton.softnet.co.uk — MB BS 1984 Lond.; DRCOG 1989; DA (UK) 1989. Med. Dir. Nightcall (S. Warks.) GP CoOperat. Prev: Co-ordinator Mangochi Malaria Research Project Atlanta, USA; Trainee GP Stratford upon Avon; SHO (Anaesth.) John Radcliffe Hosp. Oxf.

COKER, Mr Timothy Patrick Old Orchard, Briar Patch Lane, Letchworth SG6 3LY — MB BS 1979 Lond.; FRCS Ed. 1987; MRCP (UK) 1985; FRCOphth 1991. Cons. Ophth. N. & E. Herts. Prev: Sen. Regist. (Ophth.) Leeds Gen. Infirm.

COKER, William John, OBE, Group Capt. RAF Med. Br. Headquarter Personnel & Training Command, Royal Air Force Innsworth, Gloucester GL3 1EZ Tel: 01452 712612 Ext: 5862 Email: avmed@ddavmed.demon.co.uk; Eastcott, Upavon, Pewsey SN9 6DU Tel: 01980 630803 Email: bill.coker@btinternet.com — MB ChB 1972 Birm.; BA (Hons.) Open 1994; BSc (Hons.) Birm. 1967; FRCP Lond. 1993; MRCP (UK) 1975; DAvMed. (RCP) 1998. (Univ. Birm. Med. Sch.) Dep. Director Aviat. Med. (RAF)- HQ Personnel and Train. command Innesworth, Gloucester. Socs: Aerospace Med. Assn.- Edr.ial Advisery Panel Mem.; BMA. Prev: Chief Flight Med. Air Force Surg. Gen.'s Office Bolling AFB Washington DC 20332; Cons. Phys. & Head Med. Assessm. Progr. for GW Veterans; Cons. Phys. P.ss Alexandra Hosp. RAF Wroughton.

COKILL, Bernard Michael Cockill and Partners, Group Surgery, Church St, Ossett WF5 9DE Tel: 01924 273118 Fax: 01924 261321 — MB ChB 1965 Leeds.

COKKINOS, Philip 55B Warwick Avenue, London W9 2PR — Ptychio Iatrikes 1991 Patras.

COLABAWALLA, Homai Merherji 153 Lordswood Road, Birmingham B17 9BP — MB BS 1946 Bombay. Med. Asst. (Psychiat.) All St.s' Hosp. Birm.

COLACO, Cecil Bernard Rheumatology Unit, Central Middlesex Hospital Unit NHS Trust, Acton Lane, Park Royal, London NW10 Tel: 020 8453 2237/2243 Fax: 020 8453 2236 — MB ChB 1975 Bristol; BSc (Hons.) Bristol 1972; MRCP (UK) 1979; FRCP 2000. (University of Bristol) Cons. Rheum. Centr. Middlx. Hosp. NWL NHS Trust. Socs: Brit. Soc. Rheum.; Brit. Soc. Immunol. Prev: Sen. Regist. (Rheum. & Rehabil.) & Hon. Clin. Lect. (Immunol.) Middlx. Hosp. Lond.; Sen. Regist. (Rheum. & Rehabil.) N.wick Pk. Hosp. Harrow; ARC Research Fell. Middlx. Hosp. Lond.

COLACO, Thelma Doris Cecilia 12 Sutcliffe Road, Welling DA16 1NL — MB BS 1986 Lond.

COLADANGELO, Rino Casmira Lower Gatley, Steeple Morden, Royston SG8 0NR Tel: 01763 852211 — MB BS 1974 Lond.; MRCP (UK) 1978. (Middlx.) p/t Blossoms Inn Med. Centre 21-26 Garlick Hill, Lond. EC4V 2AU; Chief Exec., Medix UK plc, Steeple Morden, Herts. Prev: Managing Dir. Clin. Servs. N. Herts. NHS Trust; Regist. (Med.) Lister Hosp. Stevenage; Ho. Phys. Middlx. Hosp. Lond.

COLBACK, Raymond John Henry Hill (retired) 31 Rectory Terrace, Newcastle upon Tyne NE3 1YB Tel: 0191 285 1850 Fax: 0191 285 1850 Email: raycolgw@waitrose.com — MB ChB 1955 Cape Town; BA (Hons.) Open 1987; FRCA 1967; DA Eng. 1958; DTM & H Liverp. 1958. Prev: Cons. Anaesth. Newc. DHA.

COLBECK, Mr Roger Anthony Department of Urology, Northwick Park Hospital, Watford Road, Harrow HA1 3UJ Tel: 020 8869 2616 — MRCS Eng. LRCP Lond. 1973; BSc Lond. 1970, MB BS 1973; FRCS Eng. 1978. (Char. Cross) Assoc. Specialist (Urol.) N.wick Pk. Hosp. Harrow. Prev: Research Regist. Dept. Comparative Med. N.wick Pk. Hosp. Harrow; Regist. (Surg.) N.wick Pk. Hosp. Harrow; Regist. (Surg. & Orthop.) Mt. Vernon Hosp. N.wood.

COLBECK, William John (retired) 183 Warning Tongue Lane, Doncaster DN4 6TT Tel: 01302 535361 — MB BChir 1952 Camb.; MA Camb. 1960; FFA RCS Eng. 1960. Prev: Cons. Anaesth. Doncaster Roy. Infirm.

COLBERT, Timothy Simon City Way Surgery, 67 City Way, Rochester ME1 2AY Tel: 01634 843351 Fax: 01634 830421 — MB BS 1981 Lond.; DRCOG 1984; AFOM 1998. (St George's Hospital Medical School)

COLBORN, Roderick Phillip Figges Marsh Surgery, 41 Streatham Road, Mitcham CR4 2AD Tel: 020 8648 2611 Fax: 020 8640 4617 — MB ChB 1988 Cape Town.

COLBOURN, Carole Ystwyth Medical Group, Ystwyth Primary Care Centre, Parc Y Llyn, Llanbadarn Fawr, Aberystwyth SY23 3TL Tel: 01970 613500 Fax: 01970 613505; Nant Gau, Bow St, Aberystwyth — MB BS 1975 Lond.; DRCOG 1977. Prev: Clin. Med. Off. E. Dyfed HA & Oxf.; GP Tyne & Wear Family Pract. Comm.

COLBRIDGE, Mark Jacques 21 Harley Terrace, Newcastle upon Tyne NE3 1UL — MB BS 1989 Newc.; MRCP Ed. 1992.

COLBRIDGE, Thomas Jacques (retired) Aysgarth, 58 Southwood Road, Cottingham HU16 5AH Tel: 01482 846148 — MB BS 1960 Lond.; MRCS Eng. LRCP Lond. 1960; DObst RCOG 1962. Prev: Ho. Obstetr. Lewisham Hosp.

COLBROOK, Paul Vincent 16 Dogwood Road, Poole BH17 7PA — MB BS 1987 Lond.; MRCGP 1992; DA (UK) 1992; T(GP) 1992. Prev: SHO (A & E) Basingstoke Dist. Hosp.

COLBURN, David Drummond 4 Bowfield Road, West Kilbride KA23 9JY — MB ChB 1977 Glas.

COLBURN, Murray The Surgery, 63 Rowley Road, Orsett, Grays RM16 3ET Tel: 01375 892082 Fax: 01375 892487; Ivydene, High Road, Orsett, Grays RM16 3ER — MB BS 1975 Lond.; BSc Lond. 1972; MRCGP 1982; D.Occ.Med. RCP Lond. 1995; Dip. Pract. Dermat. Wales 1992; DRCOG 1982; DCH RCP Lond. 1978. (St Mary's Hospital Medical School) Hosp. Pract. (Dermat.) Orsett & Basildon Hosps.

COLBURN, William Frederick 33 Alderton Road, Orsett, Grays RM16 3DZ Tel: 01375 892604 — MB BCh BAO 1945 Belf.

COLBY, Elizabeth Mary 25 Underlane, Plympton, Plymouth PL7 1QU Tel: 01752 339882; 29 Fairfield Avenue, Edgware HA8 9AG — MB ChB 1991 Bristol; MRCGP 1996; DRCOG 1995. SHO (Psychiat.) Glenbourne Unit Plymouth. Prev: GP/Regist. Plymouth; SHO (O & G, Paediat. & A & E) Derriford Hosp. Plymouth; SHO (Psychiat.) Glenbourne Unit Plymouth.

COLBY, Robert Vange Health Centre, Southview Road, Vange, Basildon SS16 4HD — MRCS Eng. LRCP Lond. 1968; DObst RCOG 1970. (St. Bart.) Prev: SHO (Obst.) Gen. Hosp. Rochford; Trainee Gen. Pract. Chelmsford Vocational Train. Scheme.

COLCHESTER, Professor Alan Charles Francis Kent Institute of Medicine & Health Sciences, Electronic Engineering Laboratories, University of Kent, Canterbury CT2 7NT Tel: 01227 827200; The Old Rectory, Stowting, Ashford TN25 6BE Tel: 01303 862474 — BM BCh 1974 Oxf.; PhD Lond. 1985; BA Oxf. 1970; FRCP Lond. 1993; MRCP (UK) 1977. (Univ. Coll. Hosp.) p/t Cons. Neurol., Guys and St Thomas' Hosp. and E. Kent Hosp.Trust. Socs: Fell. Roy. Soc. Med.; Assn. Brit. Neurol. Prev: Sen. Lect. (Neurol.) Guy's Hosp. United Med. & Dent. Sch. Lond.; Sen. Regist. (Neurol.) Atkinson Morley's & St. Geo. Hosps. Lond.; Regist. (Neurol.) Lond. Hosp. Whitechapel.

COLCLOUGH, Angela Betty Department of Histopathology, Chestnut Villa, Severalls Hospital Site, 2 Boxted Road, Colchester CO4 5HG Tel: 01206 744848; Planter's Gap, Main Road, Lower Somersham, Ipswich IP8 4QD Tel: 01473 831661 Fax: 01473 832116 — MB ChB 1976 Manch.; FRCPath 1995, M 1982. Cons. Histopath. Essex Rivers Healthcare Trust Severalls Hosp. Site Colchester. Prev: Cons. Histopath. Bolton Gen. Hosp.

COLDMAN, Karl Peter 53 Glazebury Drive, Westhoughton, Bolton BL6 5SL — MB ChB 1997 Manch.

COLDREY, David Arthur Old Court House Surgery, Throwley Way, Sutton SM1 4AF Tel: 020 8643 8866 — MB BS 1986 Lond.; BA Coll of Anaesths 1989. (Barts)

COLDREY, John Bartholomew (retired) Waterside, Riverside Road, Shaldon, Teignmouth TQ14 0DJ Tel: 01626 873476 — MB BS 1951 Lond.; MRCS Eng. LRCP Lond. 1951; DObst RCOG 1956. Prev: O & G Ho. Surg. S. Devon & Cornw. Hosp. Plymouth.

COLDREY, Peter Arthur (retired) 16 Meadow Lane, Abergavenny NP7 7AY Tel: 01873 852142 — MB BS Lond. 1951; FFA RCS Eng. 1963; DA Eng. 1955. Prev: Cons. Anaesth. Gwent AHA.

COLDREY, Richard Plant 12 Main Street, Ravenglass CA18 1SG Tel: 01229 717685 — MB BS 1939 Lond.; MRCS Eng., LRCP Lond. 1938. (Univ. Coll. Hosp.) Surg. Lt.-Cdr. RNR. Socs: BMA; W Cumbld. Med. Soc. Prev: Ho. Surg. Lincoln Co. Hosp.

***COLDWELL, Christopher Howard** Royal Albert Edward Infirmary, Wigan Lane, Wigan WN1 2NN Tel: 01942 244000 — MB ChB 1998 (Hons) Manch.; BSc 1995 (Hons) Manch.

COLDWELL, Peter Herbert (retired) Minstrels, Woodlands Road, Harpsden, Henley-on-Thames RG9 4AB Tel: 01189 403133 — MRCS Eng. LRCP Lond. 1948; DMRD Eng. 1954. Prev: Cons. Radiol. Reading & Dist. Hosp. Gp.

COLDWELL, Susan 91 Warren Road, Worthing BN14 9QU — MB BCh 1977 Wales; MSc Community Paediat. Lond. 1992; DCP Warwick 1990; DRCOG 1981; DCH Eng. 1979. (Welsh Nat. Sch. Med. Cardiff) Cons. Community Child Health Worthing; Cons. in Paediatric Diabetes, Worthing. Socs: Roy. Coll. Paediat. & Child Health; BACCH; Soc. Pub. Health.

COLE, Adrian John The Surgery, 1 Kimberworth Road, Rotherham S61 1AH Tel: 01709 561442/562319 Fax: 01709 740690; 23 Queensway, Moorgate, Rotherham S60 3EE — MB ChB 1977 Sheff.; DRCOG 1981.

COLE, Adrian Marcus Lockswood Surgery, Centre Way, Locks Heath, Southampton SO31 6DX Tel: 01489 576708 Fax: 01489 576185; Silver Ley, Hadrian Way, Chilworth, Southampton SO16 7HY Tel: 02380 768160 — BM 1981 Soton.; MRCGP 1988; DRCOG 1986; Cert. Family Plann. JCC 1985. (Southampton) Prev: Trainee GP Winchester VTS; SHO Rotat. (O & G) St. Bart. Hosp. Lond.; SHO Roy. Nat. Orthop. Hosp. Lond.

COLE, Alan David (retired) Mulberry Cottage, Grafton, Bampton OX18 2RY Tel: 01367 810556 — MB BS Lond. 1953; MRCS Eng. LRCP Lond. 1953; DObst RCOG 1958. Prev: GP Oxf.

COLE, Alison Barbara Jane, Maj. 6 Roundwood Gardens, Harpenden AL5 3AJ — MB BChir 1992 Camb.; DRCOG 1997.

COLE, Allan Gordon Halliwell University Hospitals of Leicester, Groby Road, Leicester LE3 9QP Tel: 0116 256 3871 Fax: 0116 250 2700; Manor Farm House, The Green, Anstey, Leicester LE7 7FT Tel: 0116 236 2660 — MB BS 1973 Lond.; MRCS Eng. LRCP Lond. 1973; FFA RCS Eng. 1979; T(Anaes) 1991. (St. Bart.) Med. Dir. & Cons. Anaesth. Univ. Hosp.s of Leicester NHS Trust. Socs: Brit. Assn. Med. Managers (Bd. Mem.); Intens. Care Soc.; Bd. Mem. Assn. Trust Med. Directors. Prev: Sen. Regist. (Anaesth.) Nuffield Dept. Anaesth. Oxf.; Regist. (Anaesth.) St. Bart. Hosp. Lond.

COLE, Andrew James The Grange, Grange Avenue, Benton, Newcastle upon Tyne NE12 9PN Tel: 0191 215 1799; 29 Kenton Road, Newcastle upon Tyne NE3 4NH — MB BS 1984 Lond.; MA Camb. 1985; MRCPsych 1989. Cons. Newc. Ment. Health NHS Trust. Prev: Regist. Nuffield Child Psychiat. Unit Newc.; Regist. St Nicholas Hosp. Gosforth; Lect. (Psychiat.) Univ. Newc.

COLE, Andrew John New Cross Street Health Centre, New Cross Street, Bradford BD5 7AW Tel: 01274 728909 — MB BS 1984 Newc.; MB BS Newc. l984; MRCGP 1988. Prev: Trainee GP N.umbria VTS.; Ho. Job at Tyneside.

COLE, Andrew Spencer 57B St Mary's Grove, London W4 3LW — MB BS 1990 Lond.

COLE, Andrew Timothy Derby City General Hospital, Uttoxeter Road, Derby, Derby DE22 3NE Tel: 01332 625639 — MB BS 1982 Lond.; MRCP (UK) 1985; DM Nott 1998. (Cambridge, U.C.N.) Cons. Phys. (Gastroenterol. & Gen. Med.) Derby City Gen. Hosp. Socs: BSG; AGA. Prev: Lect. (Gastroenterol.) Qu. Med. Centre Univ. Nottm.; Research Fell. Qu. Med. Centre Univ. Nottm.; Regist. (Med.) Leicester HA & Glenfield Hosp. Leicester.

COLE, Andrew Timothy Easterhouse Health Centre, 9 Auchinlea Road, Glasgow G34 9HQ Tel: 0141 531 8170 Fax: 0141 531 8110 — MB ChB 1985 Leic.

COLE, Andrew Timothy Church Grange Surgery, Bramblys Drive, Basingstoke RG25 Tel: 01256 389786; The Pump House, Preston Candover, Basingstoke RG25 2EH Tel: 01256 389786 Email: atlmcole@aol.com — MB BS 1985 Lond.; BSc Lond. 1982; DRCOG 1989. (Barts.)

COLE, Anne (retired) Moorhouse, Rickerby, Carlisle CA3 9AA — MB ChB 1960 St. And.; DCH Eng. 1964. Prev: SCMO Centr. Clinic Carlisle.

COLE, Mr Ashley Antony Northern General Hospital, Sheffield S5 — BM BS 1991 Nottm.; FRCS (Tr. & Orth.) 2001; BMedSci Nottm. 1989; FRCS Eng 1997. Socs: BACA; BOA; BOTA.

COLE, Brian Forum Health Centre, 1A Farren Road, Wyken, Coventry CV2 5EP Tel: 024 7626 6370 Fax: 024 7663 6518; Hillside, Tunnel Road, Galley Common, Nuneaton CV10 9PE Tel: 024 76 392019 — MB ChB 1969 Birm. Asst. Dep. Coroner Warks.

COLE, Brian Stephen Oak Street Medical Practice, Norwich NR3 3DL Tel: 01603 613431 Fax: 01603 767209 Email: brian.cole@gp-d82047.nhs.uk; 27 West Parade, Norwich NR2 3DN Tel: 01603 624706 — MB BS 1968 Lond.; BSc Lond. 1965; FRCGP 1988, M (Distinc.) 1973. (King's Coll. Hosp.) Prev: Trainee GP Ipswich VTS; Vis. Asst. Prof. Dept. Family Med. Univ. W.. Ontario; Vis. Assoc. Prof. Dept. Family Med. Univ. Minnesota.

COLE, Brian Wilson (retired) 126 Allerton Road, Bradford BD8 0AQ Tel: 01274 543632 — MRCS Eng. LRCP Lond. 1953; MA Camb. 1953, BA (Hons. Nat. Sc. Trip. Pt. I) 1949. Prev: Capt. RAMC.

COLE, Bruce Wallis 6 Alexanders Walk, Caterham CR3 6DT — BM BCh 1948 Oxf.; MA, BM BCh Oxf. 1948; DObst RCOG 1953. (Oxf. & Guy's) Prev: Surg. Lt. RN.

COLE, Carolyn Marie 95 Wandsworth Road, Belfast BT4 3LT — MB BCh BAO 1977 Belf.; DRCOG 1979; Dip. (Pract. Dermatology) .Wales 1996. Clin. Asst./Hosp. Practitioner, Belf. City Hosp. (p/t) & Ulster Hosp., Dundonald; Med. Ref.

COLE, Catherine Anne 81 Clumber Road, Poynton, Stockport SK12 1NW Tel: 01625 875176; 165 Fortis Green Road, Muswell Hill, London N10 3LX Tel: 020 8444 1009 — MB ChB 1995 Birm.; MB ChB (Hons.) Birm. 1995; MRCPsych. 1999. (Birmingham) SHO (Forens. Psychiat.) Hammersmith & Fulham Ment. Health NHS Trust, Middx. Prev: SHO (Child Psychiat) Edgware Hosp. Middx; SHO (Psychiat.) Watford Gen. Hosp. Watford; SHO (Psychiat.) Highcroft Hosp. Birm.

COLE, Christopher Charles Birchwood Practice, Birchwood Medical Centre, Northmead Drive, Poole BH17 7XZ Tel: 01202 697639 Fax: 01202 659323 — MB BS 1992 Lond.

COLE, Christopher John 46 Mitchell Road, Havant PO9 3QB — MB BS 1996 Lond.

COLE, Christopher Kersley (retired) Low Mill, Bainbridge, Leyburn DL8 3EF Tel: 01969 650416 — MB BS 1940 Lond.; MRCS Eng. LRCP Lond. 1939; DObst RCOG 1946. Prev: Squadron Ldr. RAFVR.

COLE, Clive Rhys Thistle Lodge, Haverfield Road, Spalding PE11 2XP — MB ChB 1993 Aberd. Trainee GP Dumfries & Galloway Roy. Infirm. VTS. Prev: Ho. Off. (Surg.) Dumfries & Galloway Roy. Infirm.; Ho. Off. (Med.) York Dist. Hosp.

COLE, Cordelia Joy Heatherley, Quickley Rise, Chorleywood, Rickmansworth WD3 5PE Tel: 01923 282741 Email: dillycole@mcmail.com; Flat 102, Park South Austin Road, Battersea, London SW11 5JN Tel: 020 7622 0735 Email: dillycole@hotmail.com — MB BS 1996 Lond.; BSc Immunol. 1993. (UMDS Guy's & St. Thos. Hosps.) SHO (Opthalmology), Hillingdon Hosp.; SHO (Ophth.) The N. Hants. Trust Basingstoke. Socs: MPS; BMA; CMF. Prev: SHO (A & E) St. Geos. Hosp. Tooting.

COLE, David John Department Radiotherapy & Oncology, Churchill Hospital, Headington, Oxford OX3 7LJ Tel: 01865 225686/7 — MB BS 1976 Lond.; FRCP Lond. 1997, M 1980; MRCS Eng. LRCP Lond. 1976; FRCR 1986; FRCP 1997. (Guy's) Cons. Radiother. & Oncol. Ch.ill Hosp. Oxf. Prev: Sen. Regist. (Radiother. & Oncol.) Ch.ill Hosp. Oxf.; Hon. Sen. Regist. & Clin. Lect. (Pharmacol. & Mat. Med.) Welsh Nat. Sch. Med. Cardiff; Research Fell. (Radiat. Oncol.) Mass. Gen. Hosp. Boston, USA.

COLE, David Roger Derllys, Cenarth, Newcastle Emlyn SA38 9JY — MB BS 1985 Lond.

COLE, David Ross (retired) 291 Walmersley Road, Bury BL9 6NX — MB ChB 1953 Liverp.

COLE, David Roy 2 Glamis Gardens, Longthorpe, Peterborough PE3 9PQ — MB ChB 1982 Sheff.; FRACP 2001 Austalian Colleges of Physicians; MD Sheff. 1992, BMedSci 1979; MRCP (UK) 1984. Cons. Phys. & Specialist ChristCh. hosp. ChristCh., NZ; Diabetologist Ashburton Hosp. Ashburton, NZ; Clin. Sen. Lect. Univ. Otago. Socs: Europ. Assoc. Study Diabetes; NZ Med. Assn.; Internal Med. Soc. New Zealand. Prev: Sen. Regist. Roy. United Hosp. Bath; Research Fell. & Hon. Sen. Regist. Soton. Gen. Hosp.; Regist. W.. Gen. Hosp. Edin.

COLE, Eleanor Doris Ekundayo Jenner Maudsley Hospital, Denmark Hill, London SE5 8AZ Tel: 020 7919 2925 Fax: 020 7919 2086 Email: e.cole@slam-tr.nhs.uk — MB BS 1983 Lond.; MRCPsych 1989. (Roy. Free) Cons. Psychiat. Maudsley Hosp. Lond. Socs: Med. Defence Union; MRCPsych. Prev: Sen. Regist. Maudsley Hosp. Lond.; Res. Fell. Roy. Free Hosp. Sch. Med. Lond.; Regist. Roy. Free/Friern Psychictry Train. Scheme.

COLE, Ethel Patricia Wendean, 3 Ashley Heights, Armagh BT60 1HG Tel: 01861 523552 — MB BCh BAO 1951 Dub. Prev: Asst. Med. Pract. Armagh City Hosp.

COLE, Frances Roberta Gibson Court, Medical Centre, New Road, Boldon Colliery NE35 9AN Tel: 0191 519 3000; 40 Moorside S., Fenham, Newcastle upon Tyne NE4 9BB Tel: 0191 226 0768 — MB BS 1977 Lond.; MRCS Eng. LRCP Lond. 1977; MRCGP 1982. (St. Mary's) Clin. Tutor Univ. Newc. Med. Sch. Socs: Brit. Med. Accupunc. Soc. Prev: Ho Phys. Oxon. AHA (T); Ho. Surg. & SHO (Obst.) Leics. AHA (T).

COLE, Frank Eden Court Medical Practice, Tangmere Drive, Castle Vale, Birmingham B35 7QX Tel: 0121 747 2671 — MRCS Eng. LRCP Lond. 1968; MRCGP 1976. (Liverp.)

COLE, Gaynor Frances Shropshire's Community and Mental health Trust,, Cross Houses site, Shrewsbury SY5 6JN Fax: 01743 761242; Inchgarth, Clive Avenue, Church Stretton SY6 7BL Tel: 01224 861030 Fax: 01694 723827 — MB ChB 1974 Liverp.; PhD Wales 1967, BSc 1964; FRCP Ed. 1994; MRCP (UK) 1979; FRCPCH 1997. Cons. Community Paediat. with Maj. interest I neuroDevelopm. and Rehabil. Shrops.'s Community & Ment. Health Trust; Cons. Paediatric NeUrol. Robt. Jones and Agnes Hunt Hospita OsW.ry.l. Prev: Cons. Paediatric Neorologist, Roy. Aberd., Childr.s Hosp., Aberd.; Sen. Regist.. Hosp. for Sick Childr., Lond.

COLE, Gillian Clarice (retired) — MB ChB 1960 Cape Twon; MB ChB Cape Town 1960; MD Witwatersrand 1977; FRCPath. 1992, M 1981; DPM Witwatersrand 1968. Prev: Sen. Lect. & Hon. Cons. Neuropath. Univ. Wales Coll. Med. Cardiff.

COLE, Graham 65 High Street, Clayton West, Huddersfield HD8 9NS — MB BS 1987 Lond.; MSc Lond. 1984, BSc 1983; DRCOG 1991. Pharmaceut. Phys. Besselaar Leeds. Prev: Clin. Pharmacol. Fisons plc.

COLE, Graham John The Orchard Medical Centre, Fairmead, Cam, Dursley GL11 5NE Tel: 01453 548666 Fax: 01453 548124; 26 Cam Green, Cam, Dursley GL11 5HN — MB BS 1983 Lond.; MSc Lond. 1978, BSc 1977, MB BS 1983; DRCOG 1986.

COLE, Gwenhwyfar (retired) Gwen Cole, Merrow, Glebe Road, Merstham, Redhill RH1 3AB Tel: 01737 553276 — MB BChir Camb. 1951; MRCS Eng. LRCP Lond. 1948.

COLE, Heather Kim Cruess New Cross Street Medical Centre, Bradford BD5 7AW — MB BS 1984 Newc.; MRCGP 1988. Prev: Trainee GP N.ld. VTS; SHO (Psychiat.) St. Nicholas Hosp. Gosforth.

COLE, James Sanderson (retired) 1/2 Craigmillar Castle Road, Edinburgh EH16 4BX Tel: 0131 661 7272 — MB ChB 1954 St. And.

COLE, Joan Mary 134 Staples Road, Newport PO30 2DP — MB BS 1960 Lond. (St. Thos.)

COLE, John George Latham (retired) 128 Tamworth Road, Sutton Coldfield B75 6DH Tel: 0121 378 2570 — MB ChB 1942 Birm.; MRCS Eng., LRCP Lond 1942; FRCR 1973; DMRD Eng. 1948; DMR Lond 1948. Prev: Cons. Radiol. i.c. Dudley Rd. Hosp. Birm.(Now City Hosp.).

COLE, John Hugh Wellington Medical Centre, Bulford, Wellington TA21 8PW Tel: 01823 663551 Fax: 01823 660650; Rosemount, Mount St, Taunton TA1 3QE Tel: 01823 284180 Fax: 01823 350293 Email: johnhcole@aol.com — MB BS 1959 Lond.; MRCS Eng. LRCP Lond. 1959; DObst RCOG 1961. (St. Thos.) Socs: BMA; BAPAM. Prev: Ho. Phys. & Cas. Off. & Ho. Surg. Cirencester Memor. Hosp.; Ho. Surg. (Obst.) Lambeth Hosp.

COLE, Kathryn Elizabeth 42 Coryton Crescent, Whitchurch, Cardiff CF14 7EQ — MB BCh 1995 Wales.

COLE, Lorraine Melony The Pump House, The Green, Preston Candover, Basingstoke RG25 2EH — MB BS 1984 Lond.

COLE, Mary Margaret The Maple Young People's Service, Shaftsbury Road, Brintous Terrace, Poole BH15 2 — MB ChB Sheff. 1982; DRCOG 1985; MRCPsych 1998. Specialist Regist. Child & Adolesc. Psychiat. Maple Young Peoples Servive, Poole. Prev: SHO (Psychiat.) Springfield Hosp. Lond.; Clin. Asst. (Ophth.) Soton. Eye Hosp.; Regist. Roy. S.ants Soton.

COLE, Michael Arthur Health Centre, Iveldale Drive, Shefford SG17 5AD Tel: 01462 814899 Fax: 01462 815322; Marywell House, Meppershall, Shefford SG17 5ND — MB ChB 1956 Birm.; MRCGP 1965; DObst RCOG 1961. Socs: BMA (Ex-Sec. N. Beds. Div.). Prev: SHO (O & G) Lister & N. Herts. Hosps. Hitchin; Ho. Surg. & Ho. Phys. Hallam Hosp. W. Bromwich.

COLE, Michael Linley 5 Kensington Place, London W8 7PT Tel: 020 7229 7111/9686 Fax: 020 7221 3069; Church Farm, Framsden, Stowmarket IP14 6HR Tel: 01473 890324 — MB BChir 1980 Camb.; BA Camb. 1974.

COLE, Nicholas Martin (retired) 3 The Link, East Dean, Eastbourne BN20 0LB Tel: 01343 423106 — MB BS 1960 Lond.; DMJ (Clin.) Soc. Apoth. Lond. 1975; DObst RCOG 1962. Prev: Cons. & Med. Dir. Earl Mt.batten Hospice Newport I. of Wight.

COLE, Nigel Clive Samuel Minster Practice, Greenhill Health Centre, Church Street, Lichfield WS13 6JL Tel: 01543 414311 Fax: 01543 418668; 8 Cloister Walk, Whittington, Lichfield WS14 9LN — MB ChB 1980 Birm.

COLE, Owen James c/o The Renal Unit, Nottingham City Hospital, Hucknall Road, Nottingham NG5 1PB; Flat 11, Gladstone Court, 1 Cavendish Crescent S., The Park, Nottingham NG7 1EN Tel: 0115 988 1355 — MB BS 1991 Lond.; FRCS (Eng.) 1995. (St. Mary's) Renal Transpl. Research Fell.

COLE, Professor Peter John Royal Brompton Hospital, Sydney Street, London SW3 6NP Tel: 020 7935 5609 Fax: 020 7486 9166 Email: yrz87@dial.pipex.com; 25 Beaumont Street, London W1G 6DQ Tel: 020 7935 5609 Fax: 020 7486 9166 Email: yrz87@dial.pipex.com — MB BS Lond. 1967; BSc Lond. 1964; FRCP Lond. 1981; MRCP (UK) 1970; MRCS Eng. LRCP Lond. 1967; FRCPath 1991, M 1984. (Char. Cross) p/t Prof. Respirat. Med. Roy. Brompton Hosp., Lond.; Hon. Cons. Phys. Roy. Brompton Hosp. &

Harefield NHS TrustLond.; Prof. Respirat. Med. Imperial Coll. Sch. of Med. At Nat. Heart & Lung Inst. Socs: Fell. Roy. Soc. Med. (Ex-Pres. Sect. Clin. Immunol. & Allergy); Amer. Thoracic Soc. (Mem. Long Range Plann. & Program Comm.); Eur. Respirat. Soc. (Chairm. Long Range Plann. Comm. of Infec. Scientif. Gp.). Prev: Sen. Lect. & Reader (Thoracic Med.) Cardiothoracic Inst. Lond.; Mem. Scientif. Staff MRC & Hon. Sen. Regist. (Med.) N.wick Pk. Hosp. Harrow; Regist. (Med.) Middlx. Hosp. Lond.

COLE, Peter John Anaesthetic Department, D - Floor Infirmary at Leeds, Great George Street, Leeds LS1 3EX Tel: 0113 392 6672 Email: pjcoley@hotmail.com; 100 Knaveshire Crescent, York YO23 1EU Tel: 01904 637335 Email: pjcoley@hotmail.com — MB BS 1991 Lond.; DA 1995 Lond.; MMed Sc 1999 Leeds; FRCA 1997. (Lond. Hosp. Med. Coll.) Cons. Anaesth. The Gen. Infirm. at Leeds. Socs: Pain Soc.; Obstetric Assn. of Anaesth.y; Assn. of Anaesth.s. Prev: Specialist Regist. (Anaesth.) Leeds; SHO (Intens. Care) Addenbrooke's Hosp. Camb.; SHO (Anaesth.) Roy. Lond. Hosp.

COLE, Peter Vernon (retired) 7 Canonbury Park S., London N1 2JR Tel: 020 7226 6207 — MB ChB 1954 St. And.; FFA RCS Eng. 1959. Cons. Anaesth. St. Bart. Hosp.; Hon. Sen. Lect. (Anaesth.) St. Bart. Hosp. Med. Coll. Prev: Research Fell. Nuffield Dept. Anaesth. Univ. Oxf.

***COLE, Radrie** 42 Hawthorn Brookway, Birmingham B23 5LF — MB BS 1998 Lond.; MB BS Lond 1998.

COLE, Richard Barrett (retired) The Old Post Office, Maer, Newcastle ST5 5EF Tel: 01782 680789 — MB BChir Camb. 1958; MD Camb. 1965; FRCP Lond. 1973, M 1959. Prev: Cons. Phys. N. Staffs. Hosp. Centre.

COLE, Mr Richard Philip Department of Plastic Surgery, Salisbury District Hospital, Salisbury SP2 8BJ — MB ChB 1982 Sheff.; ChM Sheff. 1993; FRCS (Plast Surg.) 1994; FRCS Eng. 1987; FRCS Ed. 1986. Cons. Plastic Surg. Salisbury Dist. Hosp. Prev: Sen. Regist. (Plastic Surg.) Qu. Mary's Hosp. St Thomas.Hosp Roy. Morden Hosp; Lond.; Regist. (Plastic Surg.) Wessex Regional Centre for Plastic & Maxillofacial Surg. Salisbury; SHO (Plastic Surg.) St. Thos. Hosp. Lond.

COLE, Robert Andrew Burnbank House, 8 Allanbank Road, Larbert FK5 4AU Tel: 01324 553230 & profess. 24000 — MB ChB 1968 Glas.; FRCOG 1989, M 1973. (Glas.) Cons. O & G Falkirk & Dist. Roy. Infirm.

COLE, Mr Robert Benjamin Wellesley 30 Burghill Road, Sydenham, London SE26 4HN Tel: 020 8778 2091 — MB BS 1927 Durh.; BA (Hons.) Philos. Lond. 1928; BA Durham 1927, MA, MD 1943, MS 1944; MB BS (1st cl. Hons., Distinc. Med. & Surg.) 1934; FRCS Eng. 1944; FRCS Ed. 1944; DOMS Eng. 1950. (Durh.) Socs: Fell. Roy. Soc. Med. Prev: Sen. Surg. Specialist Min. Health W.. Nigeria; Surg. Cons. to Govt.; & Dir. Clin. Studies Min. Health Sierra Leone; Ophth. Surg.; Lambeth, S.wark & Lewisham AHA.

COLE, Mr Robin Sanford St Peter's Hospital, Guildford Road, Ottershaw, Chertsey KT16 0PZ Tel: 01932 872000; 4 The Mead, Beckenham BR3 5PE Tel: 020 8650 1012 — MB BS 1979 Lond.; MS Lond. 1992, BSc (Hons.) 1976; FRCS Eng. 1983. (St. Thos. Hosp. Med. Sch.) Cons. Urol. Surg. St. Peter's Hosp. Chertsey. Socs: Fell. Roy. Soc. Med. Prev: Sen. Regist. (Urol.) St. Thos. Hosp. Lond.; Asst. Dir. Lithotripter Centre St. Thomas Hosp. Lond.

COLE, Roger Henry Leslie Hakeford Farm, Chelfham, Barnstaple EX32 7LB Tel: 01271 850222 — MB BChir 1956 Camb.; MB Camb. 1956, BChir 1955; DCH Eng. 1959; DObst RCOG 1960. (St. Thos.)

COLE, Roger John Barn House, West Buckland, Kingsbridge TQ7 3AQ — MB BS 1965 Lond.

COLE, Sarah 5 Hillcrest Avenue, Kirkcaldy KY2 5TU Tel: 01592 208941 — MB ChB 1998 Glas.; MB ChB Glas 1998. SHO (O & G), CrossHo. & Ayreshire Centr. Hosps. Prev: PRHO (Surg.), Inverclyde Roy. Hosp., Greenock.

COLE, Mr Simon John 7 Spinnaker Court, Becketts Place, Kingston upon Thames KT1 4EW — MB BS 1989 Lond.; FRCS Eng. 1993. (St. George's) Specialist Regist. (Gen. Surg.) S. Thames (E.) Region. Socs: Fell. Roy. Soc. Med. Prev: Research Fell./Hon. Regist. (Dept. Gastroenterol. & Nutrit. Centr. Middlx Hosp. Lond.; SHO (Acad. Surg. Unit, Roy. Lond. Hosp.; SHO (Surg.) Roy. Hants. Co. Hosp. Winchester.

COLE, Stella Josephine Ayodele South Reddish Medical Centre, The Surgery, Reddish Road, Stockport SK5 7QU — MB ChB 1979 Manch.; MB ChB (Hons.) Manch. 1979; MRCP (UK) 1982; DObst 1980; Cert. Family Plann JCC. Prev: Cas. Off. Booth Hall Childr. Hosp. Manch.; SHO (Paediat.) Roy. Manch. Childr. Hosp. & Hope Hosp.; SHO (Paediat.) Booth Hall Hosp. Manch.

COLE, Stephen James — MB ChB 1991 Dundee; BSc (Hons.) Dund 1986; FRCA 1996. Cons. Anaesth. & Intens. Care, Lincoln Co. Hosp., Lincoln. Socs: Intens. Care Soc.; Europ. Soc. Anaesthesology; Scott. Intens. Care Soc.

COLE, Susan Katharine 31 Granby Road, Edinburgh EH16 5NP — MB ChB 1962 Ed.; MSc (Soc. Med.) Lond. 1977; MD Ed. 1971; FRCP Ed. 1993; MFCM 1978; MRCOG 1968, DObst 1966. (Ed.) Community Med. Specialist (Informat. Servs. Div.) Common Servs.; Agency Edin.

COLE, Thomas Baird Rockcrest Farm, 65 Killynure Road W., Carryduff, Belfast BT8 8EA — MB BCh BAO 1976 Belf.

COLE, Mr Thomas Peter (retired) Moorhouse, Rickerby, Carlisle CA3 9AA Tel: 01228 25701 — MB ChB 1957 Birm.; FRCS Eng. 1964. Prev: Cons. Surg. E. Cumbld. Gp. Hosps.

COLE, Trevor Rodney Philip Clinical Genetics Unit, Birmingham Womens Hospital, Edgbaston, Birmingham B15 2TG Tel: 0121 627 2639; 10 Clive Road, Bromsgrove B60 2AY — MB ChB 1984 Birm.; FRCP 1998; FRCP 1998. Cons. Clin. Genetics Birm. Matern. Hosp. Prev: Research Fell. Hosp. for Sick Childr. Toronto; Sen. Regist. (Med. Genetics) Univ. Hosp. Wales; Action Research Fell. Inst. of Med. Genetics Univ. Hosp. of Wales.

COLE-KING, Alys Department Psychiatry, St. Cadoc's Hospital, Caerleon, Newport NP18 3XQ Tel: 01633 421121; Bryn Mynach, Barmouth LL42 1RG — MB BCh 1990 Wales; MRCPsych 1995; DGM RCP Lond. 1992. Research Regist. (Liasion Psychiat.) St. Cadoc's Hosp. Gwent. Socs: BMA. Prev: SHO Rotat. (Psychiat.) St. Cadoc's Hosp. Gwent.

COLEBROOK, Martin (retired) 11 Crofton Close, Bedford MK41 8AJ Tel: 01234 355402 — MB 1959 Camb.; BChir 1958.

COLEBROOK, Robert David Sheringham Medical Practice, Health Centre, Cromer Road, Sheringham NR26 8RT Tel: 01263 822066 Fax: 01263 823890; 4 Primrose Lane, Sheringham NR26 8UP Tel: 01263 821127 Fax: 01263 821127 Email: rob@bumblepest.freeserve.co.uk — MB ChB 1987 Leeds; DFFP 1995. Clin. Asst. Kelling Hosp. Norwich DHA. Prev: SHO (Gen. Med., O & G & Paediat.) Huddersfield Roy. Infirm.

COLEBY, Elizabeth Mary Cambrook House, Eastcourt Road, Temple Cloud, Bristol BS39 5BU — MB BS 1986 Lond.; DGM RCP Lond. 1992; DRCOG 1992; DCH RCP Lond. 1991.

COLEBY, Marian Doreen The Childrens Centre, St Marks Hospital, St Marks Road, Maidenhead SL6 6DU Tel: 01793 638629 — MB ChB 1976 Leeds; MSc Newc. 1991; MRCP (UK) 1979. Cons. Community Child Health E. Berks. Socs: p/t Cons. Paediat. Community Child Health Sheff.

COLECLOUGH, Gillian The Medical Centre, Hall Close, Marske-by-the-Sea, Redcar TS11 6BW Tel: 01642 482725 Fax: 01642 483334 — MB ChB 1990 Dundee; DRCOG 1994. Trainee GP Cleveland VTS.

COLEIRO, Denise Ann 45/18 Maritime Street, Leith, Edinburgh EH6 6SA Tel: 0131 555 5177 — MB ChB 1993 Ed.; DRCOG 1997; DFFP 1998. (Univ. Ed.) SHO Community Child Health, Edin. Socs: BMA. Prev: GP Regist. Calverton Pract.; GP/Regist. Plains View Surg. Nottm.; SHO (Paediat.) Qu.s Med. Centre Nottm.

COLEIRO, Joseph Anthony Department of Ophthalmology, Ninewells Hospital, Dundee DD1 9SY Tel: 01382 660111 Fax: 01382 660130 Email: jo.coleiro@tuht.scot.nhs.uk; 20 Grove Road, Broughty Ferry, Dundee DD5 1JL Tel: 01382 779111 — MD Malta 1967; FRCS Ed. 1973; FRCOphth 1988; DO Eng. 1971. (Roy. Univ. Malta) Cons. Ophth. Ninewells Hosp. Dundee; Sen. Lect. Univ. Dundee; Examr. RCS Edin., Roy. Coll. Ophth. & RCPS Glas.; Exam. Nat. Univ. Singapore; Exam. Coll. Ophth. Hong Kong. Socs: Fell. Roy. Soc. Med.; BMA (Ex-Chairm. Dundee Div.); Amer. Acad. Ophth. Prev: Sen. Regist & Regist. Roy. Infirm. Edin.

COLEMAN, Anthony John 43 Wieland Road, Northwood HA6 3QX — MB BS 1958 Lond.; FFA RCS Eng. 1964. (St. Geo.) Cons. Anaesth. N.wick Pk. Hosp. & Clin. Research Centre Harrow. Prev: Prof. Anaesth. Fac. Med. Univ. Natal, S. Africa.

COLEMAN, Cabrini Mary 205 Park Road, Cowes PO31 7NP — MB BS 1994 Lond.

COLEMAN, Catherine Mary 59 Bournemouth Road, Wimbledon, London SW19 3AR — MB ChB 1988 Glas.

COLEMAN, Clare Judith Bramble Cottage, Shelton, Norwich NR15 2SJ — MB ChB 1995 Ed. (Ed.)

COLEMAN, Collette Mary 4 The Owlers, Whaley Bridge, High Peak SK23 7DE — MB BS 1984 Newc.; MB BS Newc. l984.

COLEMAN, David John 25 Highfield Drive, Ickenham, Uxbridge UB10 8AW Tel: 01895 36070 — MB BS 1951 Lond.; MRCS Eng. LRCP Lond. 1950; FFA RCS Eng. 1954; DA Eng. 1953. (St. Geo.) Hon. Cons. Nat. Hosp. Socs: Assn. Anaesths. & BMA. Prev: Sen. Cons. Anaesth. Nat. Hosps. Qu. Sq. Roy. Masonic & St. Geo. Hosp.; Sen. Examr. & Dir. of Studies SMAE Inst.

COLEMAN, Mr David John Department of Plastic & Reconstructive Surgery, The Radcliffe Infirmary, Woodstock Road, Oxford OX2 6HE Tel: 01865 224465 Fax: 01865 311673 Email: david.coleman@nds.ox.ac.uk; 33 Victoria RoaD, Oxford OX2 7QF Tel: 01865 557226 Fax: 01865 556515 Email: djcplast@aol.com — BM 1979 Soton.; MS Soton. 1991; FRCS (Plast) 1991; FRCS Eng. 1983. Cons. Plastic & Reconstruc. Surg. Radcliffe Infirm. NHS Trust & P.ss Margt. Hosp. Swindon; Hon. Clin. Sen. Lect. Univ. Oxf. Socs: Brit. Assn. Plastic Surg. Coun. 2000; Brit. Assn Aesth.Plastic Surg.s. Prev: Sen. Regist. (Plastic Surg.) W. Midl. Region; Regist. (Plastic Surg.) Leeds & Bradford; Research Fell. (Plastic Surg. & Burns) Univ. Bradford.

COLEMAN, Professor Dulcie Vivien Department of Histopathology and Cytopathology, Hammersmith Hospital, London W12 0NN Tel: 020 8383 8142 Fax: 020 8383 8143 Email: d.v.coleman@ic.ac.uk; Flat 12, 24 Hyde Park Square, London W2 2NN Tel: 020 7262 0240 — MB BS 1956 Lond.; MD Lond. 1972; FRCPath 1992, M 1980. (St. Bart.) Prof. Emerit. (Cytopath.)Imperial Coll. Med. Sch., Univ. Lond.; Cons. Cytopath. Hammersmith Hosp., Lond. Socs: Fell. Roy. Soc. Med.; (Chairm.) Brit. Soc. Clin. Cytol. Prev: Cons. (Cytopath), St Mary's Hosp. Lond.

COLEMAN, Eileen Mount Sandel Surgery, 4 Mountsandel Road, Coleraine BT52 1JB — MB BCh BAO 1972 Belf. Socs: BMA.

COLEMAN, Eric Norman (retired) — MB ChB Glas. 1948; MD (Commend.) Glas. 1961; FRCP Ed. 1968, M 1956; FRFPS Glas. 1954; FRCP Glas. 1965; FRCPCH 1996. Med. Adviser, Soc. for Cardiol. Sci. and Technol. (SCST). Prev: Cons. Phys., Cardiol. & Postgrad. Adviser Roy. Hosp. Sick Childr. Glas.

COLEMAN, Francis Bernard Department of Haematology, The District Hospital, Peterborough; Eglesfield, Stamford Road, Market Deeping, Peterborough PE6 8AB Tel: 01778 343407 — BM BCh 1957 Oxf.; MA, BM BCh Oxf. 1957; DObst RCOG 1961. Clin. Asst. (Haemat.) P'Boro. Dist. Hosp. Prev: Cas. Off. & Ho. Surg. (O & G) Lewisham Hosp.

COLEMAN, Gerald Michael The Surgery, 105 Wake Green Road, Moseley, Birmingham B13 9US Tel: 0121 449 0385 — LRCPI & LM, LRSCI & LM 1959; LRCPI & LM, LRCSI & LM 1959; LM Rotunda 1960. Prev: Chairm. Birm. LMC; Ho. Surg. St. Laurence's Hosp. Dub.; Intern. Rotunda Hosp. Dub.

COLEMAN, Gordon Arthur Wycliffe (retired) 469 Streetsbrook Road, Solihull B91 1LA Tel: 0121 705 1641 Fax: 0121 705 1641 Email: gordonjulia@itakephotos.co.uk — MB BS 1974 Lond.; DTM & H Eng. 1976. Locum Gen. Practitioner - contact via home tel. Number.

COLEMAN, Grahame Paul Woodlands, 13 Glen Eyre Drive, Bassett, Southampton SO16 3NQ Tel: 023 8076 0149; Woodlands, 13 Glen Eyre Drive, Bassett, Southampton SO16 3NQ Tel: 023 8076 0149 Fax: 023 8076 0149 — MB BS 1960 Lond.; 1995 Dip Med Ac; FLCOM 1984; MRCS Eng. LRCP Lond. 1960; MRCGP 1974; DMS Med. Soc. Apoth. Lond. 1995; DObst RCOG 1962; DCH Eng. 1962. (Guy's) p/t Osteopath. (Musculoskeletal Med.) Wessex Nuffield Hosp. Chandlers Ford. Socs: Brit. Med. Acupunct. Soc.; Brit. Assn. Manip. Med.

COLEMAN, Grahame Philip The Health Centre, Market Drayton TF9 3BS Tel: 01630 652158 Fax: 01630 652322 — MB ChB 1981 Birm. Prev: Trainee GP Dudley Rd. Hosp. VTS.

COLEMAN, Helen Plunkett House, 8 Park Lane, Fareham PO16 7JR Tel: 01329 286700 — MB ChB 1979 Leeds; MRCP 1988 (UK); DCH RCP 1982 Lond. Cons. Community Child Health Portsmouth NHS Healthcare Trust. Prev: Regist. (Paediat.) N. Tees Hosp. Stockton; Sen. Regist. Community Child Health Soton. Univ. Trust.

COLEMAN, Helen Elizabeth 6 Watson Close, Woodloes Park, Warwick CV34 5SW — BM BS 1990 Nottm.

COLEMAN, Jaimie Paul 81 Brunswick Street, Broomhall, Sheffield S10 2FL — MB ChB 1996 Sheff.

COLEMAN, Mr James Eugene 8 Vicarage Road, Twickenham TW2 5TS — MB BCh BAO 1982 NUI; MCh NUI 1991, MB BCh BAO 1982; FRCSI 1986; LRCPSI 1982.

COLEMAN, Jean Isabel (retired) 9 Barbourne Terrace, Worcester WR1 3JS Tel: 01905 23519 — MB ChB 1949 Birm.; MRCS Eng. LRCP Lond. 1949; MRCPsych 1975; DPM Eng. 1973. Cons. Psychiat. Rubery Hill Hosp. Birm.

***COLEMAN, Jill Elizabeth** Marshwood House, Ruckinge, Ashford TN26 2PB — BM 1996 Soton.

COLEMAN, Joan Mary (retired) Derrysbourne, Wonersh, Guildford GU5 0QZ Tel: 01483 898600 Fax: 01483 894960 — MB ChB Ed. 1956; MRCPsych 1975; DPM Eng. 1974. Founder Mem. (Mem. Co-ordinator) Ritual Abuse Informat. Network & Support RAINS. Prev: Assoc. Specialist (Psychiat.) Heathlands Ment. Health Trust SW Surrey.

COLEMAN, John Richard Southernhay House Surgery, 30 Barnfield Road, Exeter EX1 1RX Tel: 01392 211266 Fax: 01392 204407; 23 St Leonard's Road, Exeter EX2 4LA — MB ChB 1962 Bristol; MD Bristol 1967; DObst RCOG 1973. Prev: Ho. Off. (Obst.) S.mead Hosp. Bristol; Ho. Surg. Bristol Roy. Infirm.; Ho. Phys. S.mead Hosp. Bristol.

COLEMAN, Rev. John Wycliffe (retired) 25 Southborough Road, London E9 7EF Tel: 0208 985 7525 Email: johnaudreyco@cs.com — MB BChir Camb. 1946; FRCS Eng. 1969. Prev: Dir. Christian Hosp. Shiraz Iran.

COLEMAN, Jonathan Charles, TD The Old Manse, Ponsanooth, Truro TR3 7EE Tel: 01872 865072 Fax: 01872 865072 — MB BS Lond. 1962; BSc (Anat.) Lond. 1959; MRCS Eng. LRCP Lond. 1962; FRCPath 1981, M 1969. (Char. Cross) Emerit. Reader (Med. Virol.) Char. Cross & W.m. Med. Sch. Lond.; Vis. Prof. Kuwait Univ. Prev: Sen. Lect. (Med. Microbiol.) Lond.; Lect. (Bact.) Char. Cross Hosp.; Regist. (Path.) Char. Cross. Hosp. Lond.

COLEMAN, Jonathan David 8 Foxdell, Dene Road, Northwood HA6 2BH — MB ChB 1991 Auckland.

COLEMAN, Mrs Joyce Esme (retired) Tisle Downs, New House Farm, Ilton, Ilminster TA19 9HL — MB ChB 1955 Bristol. Prev: Med. Off. Regional Transfus. Centre S.mead.

COLEMAN, Julie Margaret The Westmoreland GP Centre, Fazakerley Hospital, Aintree, Liverpool L9 7AL Tel: 0151 525 6286 — MB ChB 1991 Sheff.

COLEMAN, Katherine Ann 26 Dickenson Road, London N8 9ET Tel: 020 8348 0322 — MB BS 1993 Lond.; BSc Lond. 1989; DCH RCP Lond. 1995. GP Regist. Lond.

COLEMAN, Kathryn Elizabeth 100 Leconfield Road, Loughborough LE11 3SQ Tel: 01509 238892 Email: stephen.coleman@virgin.net — MB BS 1993 Lond. (Kings College London)

COLEMAN, Kathryn Lesley Flat 57, 8 Selsdon Way, London E14 9GR — MB ChB 1997 Manch.

COLEMAN, Lorna Jane St Thomas Health Centre, Cowick Street, St. Thomas, Exeter EX4 1HJ Tel: 01392 676677 Fax: 01392 676677; 3 Exeleigh, Starcross, Exeter EX6 8PB Tel: 01626 890396 Email: asm@freenet.co.uk — MB BS 1990 Lond.; MRCGP 1996; DCH RCP Lond. 1995. (St. Mary's Hosp. Med. Sch.) Prev: Trainee GP Liskeard.

COLEMAN, Mark Giles 34 St Faith's Road, Winchester SO23 9QD — MB ChB 1988 Leic.

COLEMAN, Martin Albert Timothy Porthceri Surgery, Park Crescent, Barry CF62 6HE Tel: 01446 735365 Fax: 01446 700682 — MB BS 1981 Lond.; MRCGP 1985; DRCOG 1987. GP Barry.

COLEMAN, Martyn Crawford Kingthorne Group Practice, 83A Thorne Road, Doncaster DN1 2EU Tel: 01302 342832 Fax: 01302 366995 — MB BS 1982 Lond. GP Doncaster.; CME Tutor.

COLEMAN, Matthew Anthony Gerard Wessex Fetal Medicine Unit, E Level Princess Anne Hospital, Oxford Road, Southampton SO16 5YA Email: matthew.coleman@suht.swest.nhs.uk; 402A Brighton Road, Shoreham-by-Sea BN43 6RF — MB ChB 1987 Liverp.; MD 2000; MRCP (UK) 1992; MRCOG 1994. Fetal and Matern. Med. Cons. Prev: Sub Speciality Trainee Fetal Matern.

Med., Soton.; Regist. (O & G) Worthing; Research Regist., Nat. Wom.'s Hosp., Auckland, NZ.

COLEMAN, Michael Charles St Peters Surgery, St. Peters Street, Carmarthen SA31 1LN Tel: 01267 236241 Fax: 01267 236241; Montrose, Bolahaul Road, Cwmffrnd, Carmarthen SA31 2LP — MB BCh 1980 Wales; DRCOG 1984.

COLEMAN, Michel Philippe Dept of Epidemiology and Public Health, London School of Hygiene and Tropical Medicine, London WC1E 7HT; 14 Montague Road, London SW19 1SY — BM BCh 1975 Oxf.; MSc Lond. 1981; MFCM 1985. Hd. Cancer and Pub. Health Unit, Lond. Sch. Hyg. & Trop. Med.

COLEMAN, Neil Samuel Avenue Medical Centre, Wentworth Avenue, Slough SL2 2DG Tel: 01753 524549 Fax: 01753 552537 Email: neil.coleman@gp-k81039.nhs.uk; 73 Burnham Lane, Slough SL1 6JY Tel: 01628 664988 — MB ChB 1982 Birm.; MA Thames Valley Univ.; 2000 Dip Pol Gov't (Open); MRCGP 1987; DRCOG 1987; DFFP 1997. GP Princip. Socs: Roy. Soc. of Med. (Fell.); Anglo-French Med. Soc. (Mem.); Windsor Med. Soc.(Mem.).

COLEMAN, Nicholas Department of Histopathology, Addenbrooke's Hospital, Cambridge CB2 2QQ Tel: 01223 217163 Fax: 01223 216980 Email: nc109@cam.ac.uk; Downing College, Regent St, Cambridge CB2 1DQ — MB ChB 1986 Bristol; PhD Camb. 1994; BSc Bristol 1983; MRCPath 1994. Lect. (Path.) Univ. Camb.; Hon. Cons. Path. Addenbrooke's Hosp. Camb. Prev: Sen. Regist., Regist. & SHO (Path.) Addenbrooke's Hosp. Camb.; Ho. Surg. & Ho. Off. (Med.) Bristol Roy. Infirm.

COLEMAN, Nicholas Alexander 59 Manor Road, Crosby, Liverpool L23 7XH — MB ChB 1988 Liverp.

COLEMAN, Nicholas Stephen 135 Park Hill Road, Harborne, Birmingham B17 9HE — MB ChB 1991 Leeds; MRCP (UK) 1994. Research Fell., Gastroenterol, Univ. Hosp. Nottm. Prev: Specialist Regist. Gen. Med. & Gastroenterol, Heartlands Hosp. Birm.; Specialist Regist. Gen. Med. & Gastroenterol, Selly Oak Hosp. Birm.; Specialist Regist. Gen. Med. & Gastroenterol, Walsgrave Hosp. Coventry.

COLEMAN, Nicola Jane 7 Church Path, Little Wymondley, Hitchin SG4 7JE — MB BS 1983 Lond.

COLEMAN, Norman Harold 19 Corbridge Road, Childwall, Liverpool L16 7QN — LRCPI & LM, LRSCI & LM 1954; LRCPI & LM, LRCSI & LM 1954; DCH RCPSI 1960.

COLEMAN, Paul Denley 44 Raleigh Road, Bristol BS3 1QT — MB ChB 1994 Bristol.

COLEMAN, Peter The General Hospital, St Helier, Jersey JE2 3QS Tel: 01534 59000 — MB ChB 1978 Liverp.; FFA RCS Eng. 1982. Cons. Anaesth. Jersey. Prev: Cons. Anaesth. Walton & Fazakerley Hosps. Liverp.; Sen. Regist. (Anaesth.) Mersey RHA; Lect. Univ. Calgary, Canada.

COLEMAN, Peter Alan Ventnor Medical Centre, 3 Albert Street, Ventnor PO38 1EZ Tel: 01983 852787 Fax: 01983 855447 — MB ChB 1981 Leic.; MRCGP 1985; DRCOG 1984. (Leicester) PCG Bd. Mem. Socs: BMA; Roy. Coll. Gen. Pract.

COLEMAN, Richard John Department of Neurology, Aberdeen Royal Infirmary, Foresterhill, Aberdeen AB25 2ZN Tel: 01224 681818; 96 Cornhill Road, Aberdeen AB25 2EH — MB BS 1981 Lond.; BSc Lond. 1978, MD 1989; FRCP Ed. 1995; MRCP (UK) 1984. Cons. Neurol. Aberd. Roy. Infirm. Socs: Assn. Brit. Neurols. Prev: Sen. Regist. (Neurol.) Leeds & Wakefield HAs; Research Fell. (Neurol.) Nat. Hosp. Nerve Dis. Qu. Sq. Lond.; Regist. (Neurol.) Lond. Hosp.

COLEMAN, Robert Andrew 2 Marsh Lane, Gillingham, Beccles NR34 0LQ — MB ChB 1995 Manch.; DFFP 1999. GPVTS. Socs: MSS; BMA; FRSM.

COLEMAN, Professor Robert Edward YCR Department of Clinical Oncology, Weston Park Hospital, Sheffield S10 2SJ Tel: 0114 226 5213 Fax: 0114 226 5678 Email: r.e.coleman@sheffield.ac.uk; 48 School Green Lane, Sheffield S10 4GQ Tel: 0114 230 5474 — MB BS 1978 Lond.; MD Lond. 1989; FRCP Ed. 1996; FRCP Lond. 1995; MRCP (UK) 1981. (King's Coll. Hosp. Med. Sch.) Prof. & Hon. Cons. Med. Oncol. W.on Pk. Hosp. Sheff. Socs: Assn. Cancer Phys.; Amer. Soc. Clin. Oncol.; Eur. Soc. Med. Oncol. Prev: Reader & Hon. Cons. Med. Oncol. W.on Pk. Hosp. Sheff.

COLEMAN, Rosalind Lucy Old Granary Farm House, Ourseburn, York YO26 9TD Tel: 01904 735421 Fax: 01904 735512 Email: rcoleman@mrc.gm — MB BS 1989 Lond.; MRCP (UK) 1992; DTM & H Lond. 1998; MSc (Public Health Develop. Countries) Lond. 1997. (Char. Cross & Westm. Hosp. Lond.) Assoc. Researcher MRC, The Gambia; Med. Off. Farafenni Dist. Health, The Gambia. Prev: Masters Stud. Lond. Sch. Hyg. & Trop. Med. Pub. Health in Developing Countries; Med. Off. Hlabisa, S. Afr.

COLEMAN, Rosalyn Mary Shrodells Unit, Watford General Hospital, Vicarage Road, Watford WD18 0HB — MB ChB 1976 Bristol; MRCPsych 1987. Cons. Psychiat. Gen. Adult & Subst. Abuse, Shrodells Unit Watford Gen. Hosp.

COLEMAN, Rosemary St John's Institute of Dermatology, Guy's Hospital, St. Thomas Street, London SE1 9RT Tel: 020 7955 5000 — MB BCh BAO 1987 Dub.; MD Dub. 1994; MRCPI 1990. Sen. Regist. (Dermat.) St John's Inst. Dermat. Lond. Prev: Clin. Research Fell. Inst. Child Health Lond.

COLEMAN, Sarah Patricia Flat 79, Halliard Court, Barquentine Place, Cardiff CF10 4NH — MB ChB 1995 Leic.

COLEMAN, Susan Anne Anaesthetic Department, Hexham General Hospital, Hexham NE46 1QJ Tel: 01434 606161; 4 Hollin Hill Terrace, Riding Mill NE44 6HR — MB ChB 1980 Leeds; MB ChB (Hons.) Leeds 1980; FRCA 1984. Cons. Anaesth. Hexham Gen. Hosp. Prev: Cons. Anaesth. Freeman Hosp. Newc.

COLEMAN, Timothy John Public Health Laboratory, County Hospital, Hereford HR1 2ER Tel: 01432 277117 Fax: 01432 351396 — MB BS 1969 Lond.; DPhil. Sussex 1974; MSc (Med. Immunol.) Lond. 1988; MSc (Med. Microbiol.) Lond. 1976; FRCPath 1990, M 1977. (St.Mary's) Dir. Hereford PHL & Head of Leptospira Refer. Unit. Prev: Sen. Lect. (Microbiol.) Univ. Surrey & Cons. Microbiol. Guildford Pub. Health Laborat. St. Luke's Hosp.; Sen. Microbiol. Epsom Pub. Health Laborat.; Research Regist. Roy. Sussex Co. Hosp. Brighton.

COLEMAN, Timothy John Division of General Practic, School of Community Health Sciences, University of Nothingham, Queens Medical Centre (Med. School), Nottingham NG7 2UH — MB ChB 1988 Leeds; MRCGP 1992; MD Leic. 1998. (Leicester) Clin. Lect.; Asst. in Gen. Pract.

COLEMAN, Trevor Douglas Pinfold Health Centre, Field Road, Bloxwich, Walsall WS3 3JP Fax: 01922 775132; 22 Wallington Heath, Bloxwich, Walsall WS3 3NP — MB BCh 1981 Wales.

COLEMAN-SMITH, Iola The Knoll Surgery Partnership, 46 High Street, Frodsham, Warrington WA6 7HF Tel: 01928 733249 Fax: 01928 739367; Birchwood, Hill Road S., Helsby, Warrington WA6 9PT — MB ChB 1977 Manch.; FRCS Eng. 1982; FRCS Ed. 1982; MRCGP 1988.

COLENSO, Susan Mary Old Mill House, Mill Lane, Calcot, Reading RG31 7RS — MB BS 1970 Lond.; MRCP (U.K.) 1973; FRCR 1977; DMRD Eng. 1975. (Westm.) Cons. Radiol. King Edwd. VII Hosp. Windsor & Wexham Pk. Slough. Prev: Sen. Regist. King Edwd. VII Hosp. Windsor & Wexham Pk.; Sen. Regist. (Radiol.) Middlx. Hosp. Lond. & Harefield Hosp.

COLERIDGE, Hugh Cedric Clifford Phoenix Surgery, 9 Chesterton Lane, Cirencester GL7 1XG Tel: 01285 652056 Fax: 01285 641562; 6 Hampton Grove, Meysey Hampton, Cirencester GL7 5JN Tel: 01285 851973 Fax: 01285 851973 — MB BS Lond. 1965; MRCGP 1984; DCH Eng. 1971; Cert. Av. Med. 1985. (St. Bart.) Hosp. Pract. Rehabil. Unit Cirencester Hosp.; Clin. Asst. Orthops. Cirencester Hosp. Socs: BMA. Prev: SHO (Geriat.) P.ss Margt. Hosp. Swindon; Gen. Duties Med. Off. Kalulushi Mine Hosp., Zambia; Dist. Med. Off. (Ankole & Kigezi Dists.) Uganda MoH.

COLERIDGE, Judith Mary 3 Middle Spillmans, Rodborough, Stroud GL5 3RU Tel: 01453 759302 Email: judithmcol@aol.com — MB BChir 1971 Camb.; MA Camb. 1971; DObst RCOG 1973. Holistic Med. Counsellor. Prev: Med. Counsellor Bristol Cancer Help Centre; Sen. Med. Off. (Family Plann.) Soton.; Lect. (Human Reproduc.) Soton. Univ.

***COLERIDGE, Simon Derwent** Highland View, Dunsford, Exeter EX6 7AE Tel: 01802 415079 Fax: 01179 282099 — MB ChB 1995 Bristol.

COLERIDGE SMITH, Mr Philip David Department of Surgery, University College London Medical School, London W1N 8AA Tel: 020 7636 8333 Fax: 02075049413 Email: p.coleridgesmith@ucl.ac.uk — BM BCh 1977 Oxf.; DM Oxf. 1996; FRCS Eng. 1981. Reader (Surg.) & Cons. Surg. Univ. Coll. & Middlx. Sch. Med. Lond.; Edr. Jl. Phlebol. Socs: Fell. Roy. Soc. Med.; BMA;

Amer. Verons Forum. Prev: Research Fell. Middlx. Hosp. Lond.; Regist. (Gen. Surg.) Roy. Free Hosp. Lond. & W.m. Hosp. Lond.

COLES, Alasdair John Department of Neurology, Addenbrooke's Hospital, Mill's Road, Cambridge CB2 2QQ Tel: 01223 216751 Fax: 01223 336941 Email: alasdair_coles@hotmail.com — BM BCh 1990 Oxf.; MRCP (UK) 1993; PHD 1997. (Oxford) Specialist Regist.(Neurol).Anglian.Deanery. Prev: Research Regist. (Neurol.) Addenbrooke's Hosp. Camb.; SHO Rotat. (Med.) Qu. Med. Centre Nottm.

COLES, Charlotte Elizabeth Chelwood House, 1D Ness Road, Burwell, Cambridge CB5 0AA — MB ChB 1993 Leic.

COLES, Christopher John Lawrence Hill Health Centre, Hassell Drive, Bristol BS2 0AN Tel: 0117 955 5241 Fax: 0117 941 1162 — MB ChB 1992 Bristol; DFFP 1996. GP Bristol; Clin. Asst. (Rheum.) Univ. Dept. Med. Bristol Roy. Infirm.

***COLES, Clare Penelope** 60 Nash Gardens, Circus Mews, Bath BA1 2PW — MB BS 1998 Lond.; MB BS Lond 1998.

COLES, Duncan Robert 97 Brunswick Quay, Greenland Dock, London SE16 7PX — MB BS 1998 Lond.; MB BS Lond 1998.

COLES, Edward Cecil University of Wales College of Medicine, Heath Park, Cardiff CF14 4XN Tel: 029 2074 2311 Fax: 029 2074 3664 Email: coles@cf.ac.uk; Pentwyn House, Pendoylan, Cowbridge CF71 7UJ — MB BS 1965 Lond.; MRCS Eng. LRCP Lond. 1964; MTech Brunel 1971; FFPHM RCP (UK) 1990; MFCM 1980. (Lond. Hosp.) Head Of Dept. Med. Comput. & Stastistics.; Hon. Cons. Bro Taf, HA; Hon. Cons. Pub. Health Laborat. Serv. Socs: Fell. Brit. Computer Soc. 1977. Prev: Ho. Off. Qu. Eliz II Hosp. Welwyn Gdn. City & Lond. Hosp.

COLES, Gerald Anthony Suite 18, Renel Office, University Hospital of Wales, Meeth Park, Cardiff CF4 4XW — MB BS Lond. 1963; MD Lond. 1971; MRCP Lond. 1965; MRCS Eng. LRCP Lond. 1963. (Westm.) Cons. Phys. Univ. Hosp. Wales.

COLES, John Sydney Portugal Place Health Centre, Portugal Place, Wallsend NE28 6RZ Tel: 0191 262 5252 Fax: 0191 262 0241; 188 Doncaster Road, Newcastle upon Tyne NE2 1RB — MB BS 1966 Durh. (Newc.) Socs: BMA; Anat. Soc. Prev: Ho. Off. (Surg. & Child. Health) Roy. Vict. Infirm. Newc.; Lect. (Anat.) Univ. Newc. u. Tyne.

COLES, Jonathan Peter Chelwood House, 1D Ness Road, Burwell, Cambridge CB5 0AA — MB ChB 1993 Leic.

COLES, Judith Anne Dept. of Geriat. Med., St. Georges Hospital, Blackshaw Road, London SW17 0QT Tel: 020 8725 3502 — MB ChB 1972 Sheff.; FRCP Lond. 1994; MRCP (UK) 1975; DTM & H Eng. 1977. (Sheffield) Cons. Phys. Geriat. Med. St. Geo. Hosp. Lond. Socs: Fell. Roy. Soc. Trop. Med. & Hyg.; Brit. Geriat. Soc. Prev: Sen. Regist. Middlx. Hosp. Lond.

COLES, Keith Ridgway Davis (retired) Postern Park Stable, Postern Lane, Tonbridge TN11 0QT Tel: 01732 773333 — MRCS Eng. LRCP Lond. 1933. Prev: Med. Ref. Bournemouth Corp. Transport.

COLES, Margaret Edith (retired) 12 St James Drive, Burton, Carnforth LA6 1HY Tel: 01524 782231 — MB ChB 1958 Leeds. Prev: SCMO (Child Health) Lancaster.

COLES, Michael Kyte (retired) 19 Torton Hill Road, Arundel BN18 9HF — MB BS 1951 Lond.; MRCS Eng. LRCP Lond. 1951; MFOM RCP Lond. 1980. Prev: Sen. Mem. & Sen. Med. Off. Stoke-on-Trent & Birm. Pneumoconiosis Med. Panels.

COLES, Patricia Frances de Carteret (retired) Pont Sioni, Aberedw, Builth Wells LD2 3SQ Tel: 01982 560205 — MB BS 1945 Lond.; FFA RCS Eng. 1953; DA Eng. 1948. Prev: Sen. Regist. (Anaesth.) Middlx. Hosp.

COLES, Peter Fraser 46 Cardiff Road, Taffs Well, Cardiff CF15 7PQ — MB BCh 1989 Wales.

COLES, Peter Keith Lindsay, Group Capt. RAF Med. Br. Medigold Health Consultancy Ltd, Preston Lodge Court, Preston Deanery, Northampton NN7 2DS Tel: 01604 870888 Fax: 01604 870780 Email: peter.coles@medigold-health.com — MB ChB 1970 Manch.; MRCGP 1977; AFOM RCP Lond. 1987; DAvMed Eng. 1979; DObst RCOG 1974. (Manchester) Socs: Soc. Occupat.al Med.

COLES, Richard John Forth Valley Primary Care Trust, Kildean Hospital, Drip Raod, Stirling FK8 1PA Tel: 01786 446615 — MB BS 1980 Lond.; MRCPsych 1986. Cons. Psychiat. (Old Age). Prev: Sen. Regist. (Psychiat.) St. Thos. Hosp. & Guys Hosp. Lond.; Sen. Regist. (Psychiat.) St. Augustines Hosp. Canterbury & SE Kent Health Dist.; Regist. (Psychiat.) St. Thos. & Tooting Bec Hosps. Lond.

COLES, Robert Ross Adlard, Surg. Cdr. RN Retd. 22 Humber Road, Beeston, Nottingham NG9 2EF Tel: 0115 925 1372 Fax: 0115 951 8503 — MB BChir 1952 Camb.; FRCP Ed. 1978, M 1971; DLO Eng. 1957. (Univ. Camb. & St. Mary's Hosp. Lond.) Emerit. Cons. Audiol. Med. Nottm. HA; Retd. Mem. Staff MRC Inst. Hearing Research Nottm.; Med. Adviser Brit. Tinnitus Assn. Socs: Fell. Roy. Soc. Med. (Ex-Pres. Otol. Sect.); Hon. Life Mem. (Ex Chairm.) Brit. Soc. Audiol.; Hon. Life Mem. Brit. Assn. Otolaryngol. Prev: Dep. Dir. MRC Inst. Hearing Research Nottm.; Vis. Prof. Univ. Soton.; Med. Off. RN. Med. Serv.

COLES, Roger William Beech Lodge, 16 Manor Rd, Scarborough YO12 7RZ Tel: 01307 467604, 01723 367021; 5 Viewmount, Forfar, Forfar DD8 1LJ — MB BS 1967 Lond.; BSc (Hons.) Wales 1960; MSc Lond. 1963; MRCS Eng. LRCP Lond. 1967; MRCGP 1978; DObst RCOG 1969; DCH Eng. 1969. (St. Bart.) Locum Gen. Practitioner. Socs: Brit. Med. Acupunct. Soc. Accredit. Mem.; Mem. Roy. Coll. of GP's. Prev: Med. Off. Ituk Mbang Methodist Hosp. Uyo, Nigeria & Nixon Memor. Methodist Hosp. Segbwema, Sierra Leone.

COLES, Ruth Elizabeth (retired) 1 Holmes Grove, Henleaze, Westbury-on-Trym, Bristol BS9 4ED Tel: 0117 962 3747 — MB ChB 1951 Bristol. Clin. Med. Off. Family Plann. & Pregn. Advis. Serv. Bristol & W.on HA. Prev: Med. Dir. Brook Advis. Centre Avon.

COLES, Ruth Ethel Ashurst (retired) Green's Farmhouse, Wortham, Bury St Edmunds IP22 1PW Tel: 01379 788044 — MB ChB Bristol 1956; FRCOG 1976, M 1962. Prev: Cons. O & G Whittington Hosp. Lond.

COLES, Simon Richard 41 Rookery Road, Wyboston, Bedford MK44 3AX — MB BS 1997 Lond.

COLES, Stephen Ridgway Davis Postern Park Oast, Tonbridge TN11 0QT Tel: 01732 773322 Fax: 01734 773344 Email: drstephencoles@aol.com; Postern Park Oast, Tonbridge TN11 0QT Tel: 01732 773322 Fax: 01734 773344 — MB BS 1971 Lond.; MRCS Eng. LRCP Lond. 1971; DObst RCOG 1974. (Guy's) E. M. P. Benefits Agency Sutton. Prev: Clin. Asst. (Occupat. Health) Kent & Sussex Weald NHS Trust; Med. Off. Spastics Soc. Sch. Tonbridge; Gen. Practitioner, Tonbridge 1976-1998.

COLES, Victoria Ruth 29 Mayfield Close, Catshill, Bromsgrove B61 0NR — MB ChB 1995 Birm.

COLEY, Andrew Nicholas McIlvride Medical Practice, 5 Chester Road, Poynton, Stockport SK12 1EU Tel: 01625 872134 Fax: 01625 859748 — MB ChB 1983 Sheff. Prev: Trainee GP Stockport VTS.

COLEY, John Charles McIlvride Medical Practice, 5 Chester Road, Poynton, Stockport SK12 1EU Tel: 01625 872134 Fax: 01625 859748; 11 Thorn Road, Bramhall, Stockport SK7 1HG — MB ChB 1976 Manch.

COLEY, Kuldip Dr Coley, Pollard Park Health Centre, 190 Otley Road, Bradford BD3 0DQ Tel: 01274 306346 — MB BS Osmania 1960.

COLEY, Stuart Charles The Royal Hallamshire Hospital, Glossop Rd, Sheffield S10 2JF Tel: 0114 271 2957 — MB ChB 1990 Birm.; FRCR 1996; MRCP (UK) 1993. Cons. NeUrol., Roy. Hants. Hosp., Sheff. Socs: Brit. Soc. of NeUrol.s; Roy. Coll. of Radiologists.

COLEY, Susan — MB BS 1978 Newc.; FFA RCS Eng. 1984. Cons. Anaesth. Leicester.

COLEY, Veronica Paulette 23 Sheepmoor Close, Harborne, Birmingham B18 8TD — MB ChB 1969 Birm.; MRCPsych 1976.

COLFOR, Ann Mathona 77 Esmond Road, Chiswick, London W4 1JE — MB BCh BAO 1984 Dub.; MB BCh Dub. 1984; MRCPI 1986; MRCPath 1994. Prev: Sen. Regist. (Histopath.) Roy. Marsden Hosp. Lond.

COLFORD, Carole Anne 8 Cedars Avenue, Rickmansworth WD3 7AN — MB BS 1992 Lond.

***COLFOX, Lucinda Sheila Mary** Dorset County Hospital, Williams Avenue, Dorchester DT1 2JY Tel: 01305 251150; Lankham Cottage, Cattistock, Dorchester DT2 0HY Tel: 01300 320484 Fax: 01300 321552 — BM 1998 Soton.; BM Soton 1998.

COLGAN, Brendan Joseph Colgan, 463 Falls Road, Belfast BT12 6DD Tel: 028 9024 3593 Fax: 028 9023 6454; 45 Vauxhall Park, Belfast BT9 5HB — MB BCh BAO 1991 Belf.

COLGAN, Jane Madelaine 7 Glenmore Drive, Bonnybridge FK4 1EU — MB ChB 1989 Glas.; DTM & H LSTMH 1991; MRCP Glas. 1997. SHO Microbiol.

COLGAN, John Frederick Jubilee Unit, Springfield Hospital, Glenburnie Road, London SW17 7DJ Tel: 020 8682 6320 Fax: 020 8682 6723 — MB BS 1977 Lond.; BSc Lond. 1972, MB BS 1977. Cons. Psychiat. Springfield Hosp. Lond.; Clin. Dir. Elderly Serv. Socs: Roy. Coll. Psychiat.

COLGAN, Simon John 16 Ardaluin Heights, Newcastle BT33 0RA — MB BCh 1997 Belf.

COLGAN, Stephen Mark 73 Frances Street, Cheadle SK8 2AL — MB ChB 1981 Manch.; MSc Manch. 1987, MB ChB 1981; MRCPsych 1986. Sen. Regist. Dept. Psychiat., Manch. Roy. Infirm. Prev: Regist. (Psychiat.) Univ. Hosp. S. Manch.

COLGATE, Elizabeth Julia Fullwell Cross Health Centre, 1 Tomswood Hill, Barkingside, Ilford IG6 2HG Tel: 020 8500 0231 Fax: 020 8491 1598 — MB BS 1980 Lond.; BSc (Hons.) Lond. 1977, MB BS 1980; MRCGP 1984; DRCOG 1982; Cert. Family Plann. JCC 1982. (Univ. Coll. Hosp.) Prev: Trainee GP Edgware Gen. Hosp. VTS.

COLGATE, Robert Edmond Thomas PO Box 439, Cardiff CF11 9XN — MB BCh 1986 Wales; MRCPsych 1992. Cons. (Old Age Pschiat.) Bro Morgannwg NHS Trust. Prev: Sen. Regist. Rotat. (Psychiat.) S. Wales; Regist. Rotat. (Psychiat.) M. Glam. HA; SHO (Gen. Med.) New Cross Hosp. Wolverhampton.

COLIN, Mr John Fitzmaurice 419 Unthank Road, Norwich NR4 7QB Tel: 01603 259925 Fax: 01603 259525 — MRCS Eng. LRCP Lond. 1965; MS Lond. 1977, MB BS 1965; FRCS Eng. 1971; FRCS Ed. 1970. (Westm.) Cons. Surg. Norwich Health Dist. Socs: Counc. Assn. Surg. Gt. Brit. & Irel.; Europ. Vasc. Soc.; Vasc. Soc. Gt. Brit. & Irel. Prev: Lect. (Surg.) Univ. Nairobi, Kenya; Sen. Regist. W.m. Hosp. Lond.; SHO Accid. Serv. Radcliffe Infirm. Oxf.

COLIN-JONES, David Duncan 63 St Peter's Road, Margate CT9 4AL — MB BS 1990 Lond.

COLIN-JONES, Professor Duncan Gadsby Queen Alexandra Hospital, Cosham, Portsmouth PO6 3LY Tel: 023 92 286255 Fax: 023 92 286054; Downland, Station Road, Soberton, Southampton SO32 3QU — MB BS Lond. 1962; MD Lond. 1971; FRCP Lond. 1978, M 1966; MRCS Eng. LRCP Lond. 1962; DObst RCOG 1964. (St. Bart.) Cons. Phys. Qu. Alexandra Hosp. Portsmouth; Prof. Gastroenterol. & Personal Chair Univ. Soton.; Mem. Edit. Bd. Endoscopy; Mem. Appraisal Comm. Of Nat. Inst. For Clin. Excellence (NICE). Socs: Brit. Soc. Gastroenterol. Hon. Mem.. Prev: Vice-Pres. Europ. Soc. Gastrointestinal Endoscopy; Mem. Advis. Comm. Drugs (DoH); Treas. Brit. Soc. Gastroenterol.

COLIN-THOME, David Geoffrey, OBE Castlefields Health Centre, Chester Close, Castlefields, Runcorn WA7 2HY Tel: 01928 566671 Fax: 01928 581631; Higher View, Newton-by-Frodsham, Frodsham, Warrington WA6 6TN Tel: 01928 788396 — MB BS 1966 Newc.; MHSM 1998; MFPHM 1994; FRCGP 1990, M 1973; DCH Eng. 1971; DObst RCOG 1969. Dir. of Primary Care (p/t) Lond. Regional Office NHSE; Primary Care Adviser (p/t) N. W. Regional Office NHSE; Hon. Fell. Health Serv. Managem. Unit Manch. Univ. Prev: Sen. Med. Off. (p/t) NHSRE Scott. Office; Dir. of Primary Care (p/t) N. W. Regional Office NHSE; Sen. Lect. (Gen. Pract.) Univ. Liverp.

COLL, Alison Jane Family Doctor Unit Surgery, 92 Bath Road, Hounslow TW3 3LN Tel: 020 8577 9555 Fax: 020 8570 2266; 144 Sutton Court Road, Chiswick, London W4 3HT Tel: 020 8995 0683 Fax: 020 8747 9258 Email: alicoll@blueyonder.co.uk — MB BCh 1980 Wales; MRCGP 1985; DRCOG 1984.

COLL, Leonora Kilmarnock Road Surgery, 123 Kilmarnock Road, Glasgow G41 3YT Tel: 0141 649 6231 Fax: 0141 632 2012; 8 Southbrae Drive, Glasgow G13 1PX — MB ChB 1977 Glas.; MFHom RCP Lond. 1996; DRCOG 1982. Assoc. Specialist Homoeop. W. Glas. Hosp. Univ. NHS Trust.

COLLACOTT, Richard Anthony Western Isles Hospital, Stornoway, Isle of Lewis HS1 2AF Tel: 01851 704704 — BM BCh 1971 Oxf.; PhD Leic. 1983; BA (Hons.) Oxf. 1968, DM 1979, MA 1971; FRCPsych 1996, M 1985; MRCGP (Distinc.) 1977; DObst RCOG 1973. (Oxf.) Cons. Psychiat. W.ern Isles. Prev: Cons. Psychiat. (Learning Disabil.) Fosse NHS Trust Leicester; Sen. Lect. (Psychiat.) Leicester Univ. Med. Sch.; Lect. (Psychiat. & Gen. Pract.) Leicester Univ. Med. Sch.

COLLAR, Brenda (retired) 2 Wade Street, Littleover, Derby DE23 6BH — MRCS Eng. LRCP Lond. 1941.

COLLARD, John Martin The Surgery, 352 College Road, Erdington, Birmingham B44 0HH Tel: 0121 373 1244 — MB ChB 1982 Leeds; MRCGP 1986; DRCOG 1986. Prev: Trainee GP Leeds VTS; Ho. Off. (Med.) Leeds Gen. Infirm.

COLLAS, David Martin Department of Geriatrics, Watford General Hospital, Vicarage Road, Watford WD18 0HB Tel: 01923 217172 Fax: 01923 217715 Email: dmcollas@aol.com — MB BS 1974 Lond.; BSc Lond. 1971; MRCP (UK) 1977. (University College Hospital) Cons. Phys. Geriat. Med. Watford Gen. Hosp. Socs: Brit. Geriat. Soc.; BMA; Internat. Continence Soc. Prev: Sen. Regist. (Geriat. & Gen. Med.) Univ. Coll. Hosp. Lond.; Research Fell. (Cardiol.) St. Geo.'s Hosp. Lond.; Regist. (Med.) St. Geo.'s Hosp. Lond.

COLLEARY, Gerald 151 Dunluce Ave, Belfast BT9 7AX — MB BCh BAO 1996 Belf.

COLLEDGE, Julian David The Surgery, Ruckinge Road, Hamstreet, Ashford TN26 2NJ Tel: 01233 732262 Fax: 01233 733097 — MB ChB 1972 Bristol; MRCPsych 1979; MRCGP 1977; DRCOG 1986.

COLLEDGE, Nicola Rosemary Geriatric Medicine Unit, Liberton Hospital, Lasswade Road, Edinburgh EH16 6UB Tel: 0131 536 7800 Fax: 0131 536 7896 — MB ChB 1984 Ed.; BSc (Hons.) Ed. 1981; FRCP Ed. 1994; MRCP (UK) 1987. (Edin.) Cons. Geriat. Liberton Hosp. & Roy. Infirm. Edin.; Hon. Sen. Lect. Univ. Edin. Socs: Brit. Geriat. Soc. Prev: Sen. Lect. (Geriat. Med.) Univ. Edin.; Sen. Regist. (Geriat.) City Hosp. Edin.; Regist. (Med.) Milesmark Hosp. Dunfermline.

COLLEDGE, Ruth Elizabeth Joan The Surgery, Hamstreet, Ashford TN26 2NJ Tel: 0123 373 2262 — MB BCh BAO 1977 Belf. GP Ashford Kent.

COLLEE, George Galbraith Department of Anaesthesia, The Royal Free Hospital, Pond St., London NW3 2QG Tel: 020 7794 0500 — MB ChB 1981 Ed.; FFA RCS Eng. 1987; Europ. Dip. Intens. Care Med. 1993. Cons. Anaesth. Roy. Free Hosp. Lond. Prev: Sen. Regist. (Anaesth.) St. Bart. Hosp. Lond.; Clin. Fell. (Intens. Care) Harvard Univ. Dept. Anaesthiol. Mass. Gen. Hosp. Boston, USA.

COLLEE, Professor John Gerald, CBE (retired) 27b Drummond place, Edinburgh EH3 6PN Tel: 0131 557 5234 Email: gerrycolllee@compuserve.com — MB ChB 1951 Ed.; MD (Gold Medal) Ed. 1962; FRCP Ed. 1979, M 1977; FRCPath 1975, M 1964; FRSE. Edit. Bd. Mackie & McCartney's Pract. Med. Microbiol. 14th Edn. Prev: Prof. (Med.Microbiol.) Univ. Edin. Med. Sch.

COLLERTON, Joanna Clare 30 Osborne Avenue, Jesmond, Newcastle upon Tyne NE2 1JR — BM BCh 1988 Oxf.; MRCP (UK) 1991; MRCGP 1993; DRCOG 1992. Clin. Lect. (Primary Care) Dept. Gen. Pract. King's Coll. Sch. Med. & Dent. Lond.

COLLETT, Alan Litcham Health Centre, Manor Drive, Litcham, King's Lynn PE32 2NW Tel: 01328 701568 Fax: 01328 700632; Blenheim House, Tittleshall, King's Lynn PE32 2PF Tel: 01328 700276 Email: collett@cd-online.co.uk — MB BS 1976 Lond.; MRCS Eng. LRCP Lond. 1976; DRCOG 1978. (Guy's)

COLLETT, Anne Susan 26 Clarendon Road, Redland, Bristol BS6 7EU — BM 1998 Soton.

COLLETT, Beverly Jane Pain Management Service, University Hospitals of Leicester NHS Trust, Leicester Royal Infirmary, Infirmary Square, Leicester LE1 5WW Tel: 0116 258 5653 Fax: 0116 258 7528 Email: wreake@aol.com; Tel: 01664 424502 Fax: 01664 424502 Email: wreake@aol.com — MB BS 1976 Lond.; FRCA 1981. (King's Coll.) Cons. Anaesth. (Pain Managem.) Leicester Roy. Infirm.; Assessor & Reviewer for Brit. Jl. Anaesth, Europ. Jl. Pain, Europ. Jl. of anaesthesiology, Pain. Socs: Internat. Assn. Study Pain; Assn. of Anaesth.s. Mem.; Roy. Coll. Anaesth. Pat. Liason Gp. Prev: Cons. Anaesth. i/c Pain Relief Whipps Cross Hosp. Lond.; Lect. (Anaesth.) Chinese Univ. Hong Kong; Sen. Regist. (Anaesth.) King's Coll. Hosp. Lond.

COLLETT, Cheryl Ann Family Planning, Weston Hospital, Grange Road, Uphill, Weston Super Mare BS26 Tel: 01934 636363; The Old Vicarage, Sparrow Hill Way, Weare, Axbridge BS26 2LE Tel: 01934 732731 — MB BS 1975 Lond.; MRCS Eng. LRCP Lond. 1975; MFFP 1993; Instruc. Doctor Family Plann. 1985; Cert. Family Plann. JCC 1980. (St. Mary's) p/t SCMO (Family Plann.) W.on Area Health Trust. Prev: Med. Adviser & Underwriter WPA; SCMO (Psychosexual Med.) E.bourne HA; Med. Off. (Family Plann.) E.bourne & Mid Downs HAs.

***COLLETT, Claire Natalie** 2 East Brook Way, Southwick, Brighton BN41 1PS Tel: 01273 597335 Email: cncollet@hotmail.com — MB BS 1998 Lond.; MB BS Lond 1998.

COLLETT, Elizabeth The Bell Surgery, York Road, Henley-on-Thames RG9 2DR; Whistling Cottage, Russells Water, Henley-on-Thames RG9 6EU Tel: 01491 641436 Fax: 01491 641436 — MB BS 1977 Lond.; MRCGP 1990; DRCOG 1982. (The London Hospital Medical College) GP. Socs: MOSA & Path. Soc. Prev: GP Lond.; Trainee GP Lisson Gr. Health Centre; SHO (O & G) St. Mary's Hosp. Lond.

COLLETT, Keith Anthony The Surgery, 2 Littlefield Lane, Grimsby DN31 2LG Tel: 01472 342250; 4 Queen's Parade, Cleethorpes DN35 0DF Tel: 01472 692797 — MB BS 1977 Lond.; MRCP (UK) 1980; MRCS Eng. LRCP Lond. 1977; MRCGP 1983; DRCOG 1982. (Guy's) Prev: Regist. (Clin. Haemat.) Univ. Hosp. Nottm.

COLLETT, Lesley Ann 7 Ogilvy Square, Worcester WR3 7LU — MB ChB 1975 Ed.; MRCGP 1981; DCP (Distinc.) 1990.

COLLETT, Pauline Rio Gabrielle Fairmile Hospital, Cholsey, Wallingford OX10 9HH Tel: 01491 651281 — MRCS Eng. LRCP Lond. 1964; MRCPysch 1978. Cons. Psychiat. Health Commiss. Vict., Australia.

COLLETT, Philip Michael Rene 46 Station Way, Buckhurst Hill IG9 6LN Tel: 020 8504 4830 Fax: 020 8504 3303 Email: eye-q1@doctors.org.uk — MB BS 1983 Lond.; MRCOphth 1991; Dip. Law City Univ. 1990; DO RCS Eng. 1988. (Middlx.) Ophth. Med. Pract. Buckhurst Hill; Legal Adviser Denticare Gp. Socs: Hon. Soc. Inner Temple; Soc. Doctors in Law.

COLLETT, Philip Murray 26 College Close, Rowlands Castle PO9 6AJ — MB BS 1977 Lond.

COLLETT, Robert William Cecil Twyford Health Centre, Loddon Hall Road, Twyford, Reading RG10 9JA Tel: 0118 934 0112 Fax: 0118 934 1048; 56 New Road, Twyford, Reading RG10 9PT Tel: 0118 934 1532 — MB BS 1966 Lond.; MRCS Eng. LRCP Lond. 1966; DObst RCOG 1972. (St. Bart.) Prev: Med. Off. RAF; SHO P'boro. Dist. Hosp.; Ho. Phys. Qu. Mary's Hosp. Sidcup.

COLLETT, Stuart Mark 56 New Road, Twyford, Reading RG10 9PT — BM 1997 Soton.

COLLETT, Mrs Suzanne 83 Platts Lane, London NW3 7NL Tel: 020 7435 6297 — LRCP LRCS 1938 Ed.; LRCP LRCS Ed. LRFPS Glas. 1938; MFCM 1974; DPH Lond. 1963. (Roy. Colls. Ed.) Sen. Med. Off. Haringey Health Dist. Socs: BMA. Prev: Princip. Med. Off. Guy's Health Dist. (T); Med. Off. Sehiras, Iran; Asst. MOH Beckenham & Croydon.

COLLEY, Charles Michael Chemical Pathology Department, Princess Margaret Hospital, Okus Road, Swindon SN1 4JU — MB BChir 1978 Camb.; PhD Camb. 1973; MRCS Eng. LRCP Lond. 1977; FRCPath. 1997. (Camb. & Char. Cross) Cons. Chem. Path. P.ss Margt. Hosp. Swindon. Prev: Sen. Regist. (Chem. Path.) Roy. Berks. Hosp. Reading; Lect. (Chem. Path.) Char. Cross Hosp. Med. Sch. Lond.; Hon. Regist. (Chem. Path.) Char. Cross Hosp. Lond.

COLLEY, Ian Harris, OBE, CStJ, Surg. Rear-Admiral Retd. c/o The Royal Bank of Scotland plc, Church Square, Inveraray PA32 8TY — MB BS 1948 Lond.; MRCS Eng. LRCP Lond. 1948; FFCM 1978, M 1974; MFOM RCP Lond. 1979; DPH Lond. 1960. (King's Coll. Hosp.) Prev: Chairm. Med. & Survival Comm. Roy. Nat. Lifeboat Inst.; Hon. Phys. to HM the Qu..

COLLEY, Jennifer Jane 93 Hanging Lane, Northfield, Birmingham B31 5DA — MB BS 1998 Lond.; MB BS Lond 1998.

COLLEY, Professor John Richard Thomas Jubbs Court Farm, Failand Lane, Lower Failand, Bristol BS8 3SS Tel: 01275 374809 — MB BS 1955 Lond.; MB BS (Hons.) Lond. 1955; BSc (Physiol.) Lond. 1952, MD Lond. 1969; FRCP Lond. 1985; MRCS Eng. LRCP Lond. 1955; FFCM 1977, M 1972. (St. Thos.) Emerit. Prof. Pub. Health Med. Univ. Bristol. Prev: Prof. Pub. Health Med. Univ. Bristol; Reader Paeidat. Epidemiol. Dept. Med. Statistics & Epidemiol. Lond. Sch. Hyg. & Trop. Med.; Hon. Cons. Clin. Epidemiol. Hosp. Sick Childr. Gt. Ormond St. Lond.

COLLEY, Joy Kathleen c/o The Royal Bank of Scotland plc, Church Square, Inveraray PA32 8TY — MB BChir Camb. 1947; MA Camb. 1947; DCH Eng. 1950. (Kings College Hospital London)

COLLEY, Margaret Siriol Vaughan 3 Manor Court, Bramcote, Beeston, Nottingham NG9 3DR Tel: 0115 922 7351 — MB ChB 1948 St. And.; DObst RCOG 1950. Mem. Med. Comm. Brit. Sub-aqua Club; Indust. Injury Bds. DHSS; BUPA. Prev: Ho. Phys. & Obst. Ho. Off. P.ss Beatrice Hosp. Lond.; Cas. Off. Dreadnought Seamen's Hosp.; Ho. Off. (Obst.) All St.s' Hosp. Chatham.

COLLEY, Nigel Vivien Royal Devon & Exeter Hospital (Heavitree), Gladstone Road, Exeter EX1 2ED Tel: 01392 411611 — MB BS 1978 Lond.; MD Lond. 1988; MRCS Eng. LRCP Lond. 1978; FRCOG 1997, M 1984. (St. Bart's) Cons. O & G Roy. Devon & Exeter Hosp. Prev: Sen. Regist. King's Coll. Hosp. Lond.; Regist. Univ. Coll. Hosp. Lond.; Resid. Surg. Off. Chelsea Hosp. for Wom.

COLLEY, Patricia Joan Old School Medical Centre, School Lane, Greenhill, Sheffield S8 7RL Tel: 0114 237 8866 Fax: 0114 237 3400; Parsons Croft, 190 Carr Lane, Dronfield Woodhouse, Sheffield S36 7GB Tel: 0114 289 1331 — MB ChB 1957 Sheff. (Sheff.) Prev: Ho. Surg., Ho. Phys. & Sen. Ho. Surg. Roy. Infirm. Sheff.

COLLEY, Stephen John Woodland Practice, Holmwood Health Centre, Franklin Avenue, Tadley RG26 4ER Tel: 0118 981 4166 Fax: 0118 981 1432; 18 Spring Lane, Mortimer, Reading RG7 3RT Tel: 0118 933 2042 Email: sixcolleys@aol.com — MB BS 1976 Lond.; MB BS (Hons.) Lond. 1976; BSc (Hons.) Lond. 1973; MRCP (UK) 1979. (Kings Coll. Lond.) GP; Hosp. Pract. (Endoscopy) Basingstoke DHA. Prev: Regist. (Med.) Hants. HA; SHO N.wick Pk. Hosp. Harrow.

COLLEY, Steven Peter Chequers Lodge, Thrandeston Road, Brome, Eye IP23 8AT — MB ChB 1998 Bristol.

COLLEYPRIEST, Benjamin John 20 Clarendon Way, Chislehurst BR7 6RF — BM 1998 Soton.

COLLIE, Edna Hillside, 5 Cargill Road, Maybole KA19 8AF — MB ChB 1955 Glas.

COLLIE, Ian Fisher John Rose House, Hampton Court Road, Hampton Court, East Molesey KT8 9BW Tel: 020 8 979 1752 — MRCS Eng. LRCP Lond. 1944; DPM Eng. 1961. (Middlx.) Prev: Cons. Psychiat. Springfield Hosp. Lond. & St. Geo. Hosp. Lond.; Psychiat. Regist. W.m. Hosp. Lond.; Sen. Regist. St. Francis Hosp. Haywards Heath.

COLLIE, Mhairi Helen Stewart Basement Flat, 39 Aberdeen Road, London N5 2UG — MB ChB 1991 Ed.; FRCS Ed. 1995. (Ed.) Research Fell. (Surg.) Roy. Free Hosp. Lond.

COLLIE, Shirley Jane Western Infirmary, Dumbarton Road, Glasgow G11 6NT; 12 Grosvenor Terrace, Glasgow G12 0TB — MB ChB 1991 Glas. Specialist Regist. (Anaesth.) W.. Infirm. Glas. Socs: Roy. Coll. Anaesth.; BMA; Assn. Anaesth. GB & Irel. Prev: SHO (Anaesth.) Vict. Infirm. Glas.; SHO (Anaesth.) Kilmarnock; SHO (A & E) Ayr.

COLLIE, Wilma Marie Hamilton Medical Group, 4 Queens Road, Aberdeen AB15 4ZT Tel: 01224 622345 Fax: 01224 627426 — MB ChB 1991 Glas.

COLLIE-KOLIBABKA, Edmund (retired) 30 Oakeshott Avenue, London N6 6NS — MB ChB 1944 Polish Sch. of Med. Prev: Med. Regist. Harold Ct. Hosp. & Brentwood Chest Clinic.

COLLIE-KOLIBABKA, Gertrude Anna 30 Oakeshott Avenue, London N6 6NS Tel: 020 8340 9259 — MB ChB 1949 Polish Sch. of Med.; MA Ed. 1943; CPH Lond. 1954; DObst RCOG 1959. Med. Off. Kensington, Chelsea & W.m. AHA (T). Socs: BMA. Prev: GP Lond.; Asst. Med. Off. Matern. & Child Welf. & Sch. Med. Off. Essex CC.

COLLIER, Abigail Davina 33 Elsdon Road, Gosforth, Newcastle upon Tyne NE3 1HY — MB BS 1996 Newc.

COLLIER, Andrew James The Stewart Medical Centre, 15 Hartington Road, Buxton SK17 6JP Tel: 01298 22338 Fax: 01298 72678; 93 Green Lane, Buxton SK17 9DJ Tel: 01298 23161 — MB BS 1980 Newc.; MRCGP 1984; DRCOG 1984. Prev: GP Pyramid Hill Vict., Austral.; GP Carlisle.

COLLIER, Mr Andrew Mark 209 High Street, Boston Spa, Wetherby LS23 6AA Tel: 01937 842521 Email: a.collier@bigfoot.com; 5 Church Street, Godalming GU7 1EQ Tel: 01483 421630 — MB ChB 1988 Aberd.; FRCS Ed. 1994. Specialist Regist. (Orthop.) Yorks. Regional Train. Progr.. Prev: Regist. (Orthop.) City Hosp. Birm.; SHO (Orthop.) Roy. United Hosp. Bath; SHO (Orthop.) Avon Orthop. Centre.

COLLIER, Barbara Beryl (retired) 14D John Spencer Square, Canonbury, London N1 2LZ Tel: 020 7359 2030 — MB BS 1955 Lond.; FFA RCS Eng. 1965; DA Eng. 1959. Prev: Cons. Anaesth. Whipps Cross Hosp. Lond.

COLLIER, Brian Romer Tanglewood, Streethay, Lichfield WS13 8LR Tel: 01543 263154; 25 Burton Road, Streethay, Lichfield WS13 8LR — MB BS 1960 Lond.; LMSSA Lond. 1960; DObst RCOG 1962. (St. Bart.) Ref. DHSS (W.. Div.). Socs: BMA. Prev: SHO

(Anaesth.) & Obst. Ho. Surg. Kent & Canterbury Hosp.; Ho. Phys. Bedford Gen. Hosp.

COLLIER, Caroline Joy 21 Bell Lane, Ludlow SY8 1BN — MB BCh 1975 Wales; MRCGP 1980; DRCOG 1980. Sen. Med. Off. DoH; AIDS Lect. & Resource Off. Lond. Prev: GP Stourbridge; SHO (Obst.) High Wycombe Gen. Hosp.; SHO (Paediat.) Amersham Gen. Hosp.

COLLIER, Catherine Jane XX Place Surgery, 2 Stainers Road, London E1 4AH; 5 Edenbridge Road, Hackney, London E9 7DR — MB BS 1991 Lond.; MRCGP 1997; DCH 1995; DRCOG 1994; DFFP 1993. (St. Bart.) GP Princip.

COLLIER, Charles Nicholas Glebe House Surgery, 19 Firby Road, Bedale DL8 2AT Tel: 01677 422616 Fax: 01677 424596; 9 Kirkby Road, Ripon HG4 2EY — MB ChB 1977 Leeds; BSc (Hons.) Leeds 1974, MB ChB 1977; MRCGP 1987; DRCOG 1981; DCH Eng. 1980. GP Bedale. Prev: SHO (Psychiat.) Warlingham Pk. Hosp. Surrey; SHO (Paediat.) Redhill Gen. Hosp. Surrey; GP Trainee Caterham.

COLLIER, Christian 23 Munden Street, West Kensington, London W14 0RH — MB BS 1997 Lond.

COLLIER, David Andrew Winton 24 Chalmers Road, Ayr KA7 2RQ Tel: 01292 610555 Fax: 01292 288952 — MD 1991 Ed.; MB ChB Ed. 1980; BSc (Hons.) Ed. 1977, MD 1991; FRCP Glas. 1995; FRCP Eng. 1994; MRCP (UK) 1983. (Univ. Ed.) Cons. Phys. (Gen. Med., Diabetes & Endocrinol.) S. Ayrsh. Trust; Hon. Clin. Sub-Dean & Hon. Sen. Lect. Ayrsh. Socs: Brit. Diabetic Assn.; BMA; (Sec. Treas.) Strathclyde Diabetic Gp. Prev: Sen. Regist. (Gen. Med., Diabetes & Endocrinol.) Gtr. Glas. HB.

COLLIER, David John Flat 3, 32 Queensdown Road, London E5 8NN — MB BS 1992 Lond.

COLLIER, David John Fitzroy Regis Medical Centre, Darby Street, Rowley Regis, Warley B65 0BA Tel: 0121 559 3957 Fax: 0121 502 9117 — MB ChB 1978 Birm.; MRCGP (Distinc.) 1984; DRCOG 1983; DCH RCP Lond. 1981.

COLLIER, Mr David St John Basildon Hospital, Nether Mayne, Basildon SS16 5NL Tel: 01268 533911 Fax: 01268 280548; Regal Lodge, Gazeley Road, Kentford, Newmarket CB8 7QA Tel: 01638 751359 — MB BS 1977 Lond.; MA Camb. 1990; MS Lond. 1989; BChD Leeds 1971; FRCS Eng. 1981; MRCS Eng. LRCP Lond. 1977; FDS RCS Eng. 1975, L 1971; T(S) 1991. (Guy's) Cons. Gen. Surg. Basildon Hosp. Prev: Clin. Lect. (Surg.) Univ. Camb.; Research Fell. (Surg.) Addenbrooke's Hosp. Camb.; Ho. Surg. & Ho. Phys. Guy's Hosp. Lond.

COLLIER, Fiona West Johnstone Street, Alva FK12 5BD — MB ChB 1984 Aberd.; MRCGP 1990; DRCOG 1988; DCH RCP Glas. 1987. GP Princip., Alva; Clin. Asst. Dermat. Qu. Margt. Hosp. Dunfermline. Prev: Clin. Asst. (Dermat.) Qu. Margt. Hosp. Dunfermline; Clin. Asst. (Ment. Handicap) Roy. Scott. Nat. Hosp. Larbert; GP Alloa, Clackmannansh.

COLLIER, Florence Ivy (retired) The Priory, Frensham, Farnham GU10 3BQ Tel: 0125 125 2938 — MRCS Eng. LRCP Lond. 1936. Prev: Med. Supt. Ch. Miss. Soc.

COLLIER, Gareth Morgan 76 Gelligaer Street, Cardiff CF24 4LB — MB BCh 1997 Wales.

COLLIER, Gilbert Hoyles (retired) 706 Frobisher House, Dolphin Square, London SW1V 3LW — MRCS Eng. LRCP Lond. 1935; MRCGP 1969. Prev: Cas. Off. Preston Roy. Infirm.

COLLIER, Gillian Mary St. Annes Surgery, 161 Station Road, Herne Bay CT6 5NF Tel: 01227 742427 Fax: 01227 741439; The Water Mill, Littlebourne, Canterbury CT3 1QJ Tel: 01227 721269 — MB BS 1968 Lond.; MRCS Eng. LRCP Lond. 1968; DRCOG 1988. (Roy. Free) Counsellor Waymark Trust Canterbury; Co-ordinator Options Crisis Pregn. Counselling Serv. Canterbury. Prev: Clin. Asst. (Geriat. Med.) Qu. Vict. Centre Herne Bay; Trainee GP Canterbury VTS.

COLLIER, Ian Peter Ashfield Surgery, 8 Walmley Road, Sutton Coldfield B76 1QN Tel: 0121 351 7955 Fax: 0121 313 2509; 26 Old Acre Close, Walmley, Birmingham B76 1WF Tel: 0121 382 0064 — MB ChB 1982 Birm.; DRCOG 1986. GP Sutton Coldfield.

COLLIER, Isobel Felicity 11 East Churchfield Road, London W3 7LL — MB BCh BAO 1965 Belf.; FFA RCS Eng. 1976. Cons. Anaesth. Centr. Middlx. Hosp., Lond.

COLLIER, James Fredrick Lisburn Road Surgery, 10-12 Lisburn Road, Belfast BT9 6AA Tel: 028 9032 3035 — MB BCh BAO 1972 Belf.

COLLIER, Jane Davina Bishops Lodge, Old Weston Road, Bishopswood, Stafford ST19 9AG — MD 1994 Newc.; MB ChB Bristol 1986; MRCP (UK) 1989. Sen. Regist. (Hepatol. & Gastroenterol.) Addenbrooke's Hosp. Camb. Prev: Research Fell. CRC Med. Molecular Biol. Gp. Univ. Newc.; SHO Rotat. (Med.) Newc.; Regist. Rotat. (Gastroenterol.) N.. Region.

COLLIER, Jane Sarah 51 The Ridings, Portsmouth PO2 0UF — MB BS 1992 Lond.

COLLIER, Jim Hamish Nicholas Dept of Anaesthesia, Northampton General Hospital, Northampton Tel: 01604 34700; 5 Penn Gardens, East Hunsbury, Northampton NN4 0QX Tel: 01604 762588 — MB ChB 1981 Sheff.; DRCOG 1988. SHO (Anaesth.) N.ampton Gen. Hosp. Prev: SHO/Trainee GP Chesterfield Derbysh.; SHO (Anaesth.) Leics. Roy. Infirm.

COLLIER, Joanne Elizabeth Apartment 20, Chervil Close, Manchester M14 7DP — MB ChB 1997 Leeds.

COLLIER, John 11 Church Street, St Paul's, Canterbury CT1 1NH Tel: 01227 464936 Email: johncoll@aol.com — MB BS Lond. 1968; MRCP (UK) 1974; MRCS Eng. LRCP Lond. 1967; FFPM RCP (UK) 1994; Dip. Pharm. Med. RCP (UK) 1978. (Roy. Free) Freelance Cons. Pharmaceut. Med. Canterbury. Prev: Dir. (Clin. Research & Developm.) Pfizer Sandwich.

COLLIER, John Douglas Barn Surgery, Christchurch Medical Centre, Purewell Cross Road, Christchurch BH23 3AF Tel: 01202 486456 Fax: 01202 486678 — BM 1989 Soton.; DFFP 1994.

COLLIER, Jonathon Marc 127 Bouverie Avenue S., Salisbury SP2 8EA — BM BCh 1996 Oxf. SHO BST St.Geo.s.

COLLIER, Joseph Gavin Department Pharmacology & Clinical Pharmacology, St. George's Hospital Medical School, London SW17 0RE Tel: 020 8725 5607 Fax: 020 8682 0487 Email: jcollier@sghms.ac.uk — MB BChir Camb. 1968; MA Camb. 1968, MD 1975; FRCP Lond. 1978. (Camb. & St. Geo.) Hon. Cons. (Clin. Pharmacol..) & Prof. of Meds. Policy, St. Gerges. Hosp., Lond.; Edr. Drug & Therap. Bull. Socs: Meds. Commiss. Prev: Expert Adviser (Med.) to Ho. of Commons Health Select Comm.

COLLIER, Joyce Barbara Ashfurlong Health Centre, 233 Tamworth Road, Sutton Coldfield B75 6DX Tel: 0121 308 6311; 26 Old Acre Close, Sutton Coldfield B76 1WF Tel: 0121 382 0064 — MB ChB 1982 Birm.; MRCGP 1986; DCH RCP Lond. 1987; DRCOG 1984. GP Sutton Coldfield. Prev: Trainee GP Kidderminster VTS.

COLLIER, Judith Annette Boyer Barn Surgery, 22 Ferring Street, Ferring, Worthing BN12 5HJ Tel: 01903 242638 Fax: 01903 700574 — BM BCh 1981 Oxf.; MRCGP 1985; DRCOG 1984. GP Ferring.

COLLIER, Professor Leslie Harold 8 Peto Place, Regents Park, London NW1 4DT Tel: 020 7487 4848 Fax: 020 7224 2939 — MB BS Lond. 1947; DSc Lond. 1968, MD 1953; FRCP Lond. 1980, M 1969; MRCS Eng. LRCP Lond. 1943; FRCPath 1975. (Univ. Coll. Hosp.) Emerit. Prof. (Virol.) Univ. Lond. Socs: Fell. Roy. Soc. Med. Past Pres. & Hon. Mem. Sec. Path.; Soc. Gen. Microbiol.; Path. Soc. Prev: Prof. Virol. & Sen. Lect. Jt. Dept. Virol. Lond. Hosp. Med. Coll. & St. Bart. Hosp. Med. Coll. Lond.; Hon. Cons. Tower Hamlets HA; Dir. Vaccines & Sera Laborats. Lister Inst. Elstree.

COLLIER, Mary Kathleen Manse Road Surgery, 142 Manse Road, Ardersier, Inverness IV2 7SR Tel: 01667 462240 Fax: 01667 462912; Grianan, Balnaroid, Cawdor, Nairn IV12 5QY — MB BS 1970 Lond.; MRCS Eng. LRCP Lond. 1968. (St. Bart.)

COLLIER, Pamela Ann Claremont Medical Centre, 91 Claremont Road, Salford M6 7GP Tel: 0161 743 0453 Fax: 0161 743 9141; 13 Brackley Road, Monton, Eccles, Manchester M30 9LG Tel: 0161 281 2502 — MB ChB 1968 Manch. Socs: Manch. Med. Soc.; Brit. Menopause Soc.

COLLIER, Patrick Terence Launceston Medical Centre, Landlake Road, Launceston PL15 9HH Tel: 01566 772131 Fax: 01566 772223; Trelakes, Roydon Road, Launceston PL15 8HL Tel: 01566 773977 — MB BS 1968 Lond.; DObst RCOG 1972. (Char. Cross) Prev: Med. Off. RAF.

COLLIER, Peter Michael AON, 8 Devonshire Square, London EC2M 5PL Tel: 020 7623 5500; 52 Randolph Avenue, London W9 1BE Tel: 020 7221 0552 — MB ChB Aberd. 1971.

COLLIER, Robert Graham St Ann Street Surgery, 82 St. Ann Street, Salisbury SP1 2PT Tel: 01722 322624 Fax: 01722 410624 — BM BCh 1968 Oxf.; MA; MRCP (U.K.) 1974; DCH Eng. 1970. (Oxf. & St. Thos.)

COLLIER, Simon Gregory 11 Juniper Row, Newport TF10 7RT — MB ChB 1984 Birm.; FRCPS Glas. 1992.

COLLIER, Stephen Leonard Gordon Street Surgery, 72 Gordon Street, Burton-on-Trent DE14 2JB Tel: 01283 563175 Fax: 01283 500638; 35 Field Lane, Horninglow, Burton-on-Trent DE13 0NH — MB ChB 1978 Bristol; DRCOG 1982.

COLLIER, Susan Deborah Glaxo Smith Kline, Stockley Park West, Uxbridge Tel: 0120 484 6514 Fax: 0120 484 6514; 5 Lumwood, Smithills, Bolton BL1 6TZ Tel: 01204 493481 — MB ChB 1984 Manch.; BSc (Physiol.) Manch. 1981; DRCOG 1987. Regional Med. Adviser, Glaxo Smith Kline; Hon. Clin. Asst., Manch. Diabetes Centre. Prev: GP Princip., Shalford; SHO GP Trainee Wigan HA VTS.

COLLIER, Susan Jennifer The Surgery, Pound Close, Oldbury, Warley B68 8LZ Tel: 0121 552 1632 Fax: 0121 552 0848; 9 Sir Richards Drive, Harborne, Birmingham B17 8SA — MB ChB 1978 Birm.; MRCGP 1982; DRCOG 1980; DCH Eng. 1981.

COLLIER, Susan Margaret (retired) 12 St Helen's Road, Dringhouses, York YO24 1HP — MB 1973 Camb.; BChir 1972. Prev: Med. Dir. St. Leonards Hospice York.

COLLIGAN, Denis Whitley Road Medical Centre, 1 Whitley Road, Collyhurst, Manchester M40 7QH Tel: 0161 205 4407 Fax: 0161 203 5269 — MB ChB 1986 Manch.; BSc (Hons.) Med. Biochem. Manch. 1983; MRCGP 1991; DRCOG 1991; DCH RCP Lond. 1989.

COLLIGHAN, Stephen James Brook House, Heap Road, Norden, Rochdale OL12 7SN Tel: 01706 38095 — MB ChB 1965 Ed.; DMRD Ed. 1970. (Ed.) Cons. (Radiodiag.) Oldham Dist. Hosps. Prev: Sen. Regist. (Radiodiag.) Roy. Infirm. Dundee; Regist. (Radiodiag.) Roy. Infirm. Edin.

COLLIN, Christine Frances Rehabilitation Medicine, Battle Hospital, Oxford Road, Reading RG30 1AG Tel: 0118 958 3666 Fax: 0118 963 6751; 2 Abberbury Avenue, Iffley, Oxford OX4 4EU Tel: 01865 779340 — MB BS 1973 Newc.; MB BS (Hons.) Newc. 1973; FRCP Lond. 1996; MRCP (UK) 1976. Cons. Phys. (Neurol. Rehabil. Med.) Battle Hosp. Reading. Socs: Brit. Soc. Rehabil. Med.; Soc. Research Rehabil. Prev: Sen. Regist. (Geriat. Med. & Rehabil.) Oxf. RHA; Research Regist. John Radcliffe Hosp.; Regist. (Gen. Med.) Roy. Vict. Infirm. Newc.

COLLIN, Mr Jack Tel: 01865 221282 Fax: 01865 221117 Email: jack.collin@nds.ox.ac.uk — MB BS 1968 Newc.; MD 1976 (Commend.) Newc.; FRCS 1973 Eng; MA 1980 Oxf. Cons. Surg. John Radcliffe Hosp.; Cons. Surg. John Radcliffe Hosp.; Profess. Fell. Trinity Coll. Oxf.; Europ. Fell. Surgic. Research Soc. Socs: Vasc. Surg. Soc.; Assn. of Surg. of GB & Irel. (Elected Mem. of Counc.); Euro. Surgic. Assn. (Elected Mem.). Prev: Demonst. (Anat.) Univ. Newc.; Sen. Research Assoc. Dept. Surg. Univ. Newc.; Mayo Foundat. Fell. Mayo Clinic Rochester, USA.

COLLIN, Mr John Richard Olaf 67 Harley Street, London W1G 8QZ Tel: 020 7486 2699 Fax: 020 7486 8626 — MB BChir 1968 Camb.; FRCOphth 1993; FRCS Eng. 1973; MRCS Eng. LRCP Lond. 1967; DO Eng. 1971. (Camb. & Westm.) Cons. Surg. Moorfields Eye Hosp. Lond. & Inst. Ophth. Univ. Lond.; Cons. Ophth. Surg. King Edwd. VII Hosp. Lond.; Hon. Cons. Ophth. Surg. Hosp. Childr. Gt. Ormond St. Lond. Socs: Eur. Soc. Ophth. Plastic & Reconstruc. Surg.; Amer. Soc. Ophth. Plastic & Reconstruc. Surg.; Roy. Coll. Ophth. Prev: Sen. Lect. (Clin. Ophth.) Moorfields Eye Hosp. Lond.; Sen. Regist. Moorfields Eye Hosp. Lond. (High Holborn Br.); Fell. (Ophth. Plastic & Reconstruc. Surg.) Univ. Calif. Med. Sch. San Francisco, USA.

***COLLIN, Marian Beth** 2 Abberbury Avenue, Iffley, Oxford OX4 4EU — BM BCh 1998 Oxf.; BM BCh Oxf 1998; BA (Hons.) Oxf.

COLLIN, Peter Gregory 190 Fields New Road, Chadderton, Oldham OL9 8NT — MB ChB 1988 Liverp.

COLLIN, Roderick Christopher Lovell Sippel Department of Haematology, Chesterfield & North Derbyshire Royal Hospital, Calow, Chesterfield S44 5BL Tel: 01246 277271 — MB ChB 1978 Sheff.; MA Oxf. 1972; MRCP (UK) 1983; MRCPath 1986. Cons. Haemat. Chesterfield & N. Derbysh. Roy. Hosp.

COLLING, Lois Edith Tavistock Clinic, 120 Belsize Lane, London NW3 Tel: 020 7435 7111; 103 Milton Grove, Stoke Newington, London N16 8QX Tel: 020 7923 3370 — MB BCh 1983 Wales; BSc Hons. Wales 1978, MB BCh 1983; MRCPsych. 1993. Sen. Regist. (Child & Adolesc. Psychiat.) Tavistock Clinic Lond.

COLLING, Patrick Neil 117 Carr Manor Road, Leeds LS17 5AB — MB ChB 1992 Leeds.

COLLING, William Aubrey (retired) Rounton House, East Rounton, Northallerton DL6 2LA Tel: 01609 882339 Fax: 01609 882339 Email: aubrey@c0lling.freeserve.co.uk — MD 1964 Newc.; MB BS Durh. 1952; FRCGP 1972, M 1960. Prev: Chairm. N.E. Eng. Fac. RCGP.

COLLINGE, Professor John MRC Prion Unit & Department of Neurogenetics, Imperial College School of Medicine, St Mary's Campus, Norfolk Place, London W2 1PG Tel: 020 7594 3760 Fax: 020 7706 7094 Email: j.collinge@ic.ac.uk — MB ChB 1984 Bristol; BSc (Hons.) Bristol 1981, MD 1992; MRCP (UK) 1988; FRCP 1998; FRCPath 1999. Wellcome Princip. Research Fell. (Clin. Scis.) St. Mary's Hosp. Med. Sch. & Hon. Cons. Neurol. & Molecular Genetics St. Mary's Hosp. Lond. Dir., MRC Prion Unit; Prof. Molecular Neurogenetics Imperial Coll. Sch. of Med. at St. Mary's 1994; Hon. Cons. Neurol. Nat. Hosp. for Neurol. & Neurosurg., Qu. Sq. Lond. Socs: Brit. Pharm. Soc.; Assoc. of Brit. Neurols.; Founder Fell. Acad. Med. Sci.

COLLINGE, John Deane Sleaford Medical Group, Riverside Surgery, 47 Boston Road, Sleaford NG34 7HD Tel: 01529 303301 Fax: 01529 415401 — MB ChB 1966 Sheff.; FRCGP 1987; DObst RCOG 1968. GP Sleaford; Hosp. Pract. (A & E) Lincoln Co. Hosp. Prev: SHO (Profess. Unit) Childr. Hosp. Sheff.; Ho. Surg. (Profess. Unit) Jessop Hosp. Wom. Sheff.; Ho. Off. Roy. Hosp. Sheff.

COLLINGHAM, Kathryn Elizabeth Public Health Laboratory, Birmingham Heartlands Hospital, Birmingham B9 5SS; 24 Oldway Drive, Solihull B91 3HP — MB ChB 1974 Bristol; MSc (Med. Microbiol.) Lond. 1981; FRCPath 1995, M 1983.

COLLINGHAM, Neil Talbert Flat 1F2, 24 Argyle Place, Edinburgh EH9 1JJ — MB ChB 1996 Ed.

COLLINGS, Anna Karen 16 Middlemass Green, Pewsey SN9 5AZ — MB BS 1992 Lond.; DCH RCP Lond. 1996. (Char. Cross & Westm. Med. Sch.) GP Regist. Lambourn.

COLLINGS, Anthony Denis Southend Hospital, Prittlewell Chase, Westcliff on Sea SS0 0RY Tel: 01702 435555 Fax: 01702 221377; 65 Silversea Drive, Westcliff on Sea SS0 9XD Tel: 01702 472855 Fax: 01702 719885 Email: adcollings@aol.com — MB BS 1973 Newc.; MB BS (Hons.) Newc. 1973; FRCP Lond. 1993. Cons. Phys. (Gen. & Geriat. Med.) S.end Hosps. Socs: Fell.Roy. Soc. Med.; Brit. Geriat. Soc.; BMA. Prev: Sen. Regist. (Gen. & Geriat. Med.) Manch. Univ. Hosp.; Regist. Rotat. (Med. & Neurol.) Newc. Univ. Hosp.; Ho. Phys. & Ho. Surg. Roy. Vict. Infirm. Newc.

COLLINGS, Brian Roy Marylebone Road Health Centre, Marylebone Road, March PE15 8BG — MB BCh 1975 Witwatersrand.

COLLINGS, Elizabeth Mavis (retired) Apothecary House, 32 Fowler's Road, Salisbury SP1 2QU Tel: 01722 333512 — MB BS 1958 Lond.; MRCS Eng. LRCP Lond. 1958. Liveryman Soc. Apoth. Lond.

COLLINGS, Frank Lindley Walter (retired) Apothecary House, 32 Fowler's Road, Salisbury SP1 2QU Tel: 01722 333512 — MB BS Lond. 1956; MRCS Eng. LRCP Lond. 1956; MRCGP 1982; DCH Eng. 1959; MMSA Lond. 1960. Prev: Med. Off. RAF St. Kilda 1958.

COLLINGS, Paul Anthony James Highfield Hospital, Newcastle Road, Chester-le-Street DH3 3UD Tel: 0191 333 3730; 1 Low Green, Shincliffe, Durham DH1 2NF — MB BS 1982 Lond.; BSc Lond. 1979; MRCPsych 1987. Cons. Psychiat. Old Age Co. Durh. & Darlington Priority Servs. NHS Trust.

COLLINGS-WELLS, James Stanhope North Street House Surgery, 6 North Street, Emsworth PO10 7DD Tel: 0143 373538; 5 Clovelly Road, Emsworth PO10 7HL Tel: 01243 376679 — MB BS 1988 Lond.; MRCGP 1991; DRCOG 1991. (King's Coll. Lond.)

COLLINGS-WELLS, John Arthur Rivercroft, Undershore Road, Lymington SO41 5SA Tel: 01590 672144 Fax: 01590 672144 — MB BS Lond. 1954; MRCS Eng. LRCP Lond. 1954; DObst RCOG 1956. (King's Coll. Hosp.) Hon. Med. Off. Jubilee Sailing Trust Soton. Prev: Ho. Phys. Belgrave Hosp. Childr.; Ho. Surg. (Midw.) W. Middlx. Hosp. Isleworth.

COLLINGTON, Anthony George (retired) .11,St Annes View, Worksop S80 3QQ — MB ChB 1954 Ed.; DObst RCOG 1956.

COLLINGWOOD, Gerard Anthony (retired) Haigh Hall Medical Centre, Haigh Hall Road, Greengates, Bradford BD10 9AZ Tel: 01274 613326 — MB ChB 1960 Leeds.
COLLINGWOOD, Karen Elaine 140 Cherrydown Avenue, London E4 8DZ — MB BS 1998 Lond.; MB BS Lond 1998.
COLLINGWOOD, Paul Irving Eastgate Medical Group, 37 Eastgate, Hornsea HU18 1LP Tel: 01964 532212 Fax: 01964 535007; Hall Farm, Sigglesthorne, Hull HU11 5QH Tel: 01964 535395 Fax: 01964 535395 Email: emaildocpaull@aol.com — MB ChB 1976 Birm.; MSc (Sports & Exercise Med.) Nottm. 1997. Socs: Assoc. Fac. Homoeop. Prev: Regist. (Gen. Med.) Clwyd N. Hosp.; Regist. (Dermat.) Clwyd N. Hosp.; Regist. (Chest. & Rheumat.) Clwyd N. Hosp.
COLLINGWOOD, Peter Dodgson, OBE Old School, Nayland, Colchester CO6 4JH Tel: 01206 262401 Fax: 01206 262401 Email: peter@plysplit.demon.co.uk — MRCS Eng. LRCP Lond. 1947. (St. Mary's)
COLLINI, Paul John 5 Highfield Road, Surbiton KT5 9LP — MB ChB 1998 Ed.; MB ChB Ed 1998.
COLLINO, Colin Edward 41 Glycena Road, London SW11 5TP — MB BS 1981 Lond.
COLLINS, Alison Jane Flat 2, 32 Portland St., York YO31 7EH — MB BS 1985 Lond.; MRCGP 1990. Prev: Trainee GP York; SHO (Psychiat.) ScarBoro. Gen. Hosp.; SHO (Paediat.) King Geo. Hosp. Ilford.
COLLINS, Alison Jane 63 Falcons Way, Shrewsbury SY3 8ZG Tel: 01743 359780 Email: alison.mike@btinternet.com — MB BChir 1994 Camb.; MA Camb. 1995; BA Camb. 1991; DCH RCP 1996; MRCGP (RCPG) Dec. 1998; DFFP (RCOG) 1999. (Camb.) GP Retainer, Ellesmere Med. Pract. Prev: GP Regist. Ellesmere Med. Pract. Ellesmere, Shrops.; SHO O & G Roy. Shrewsbury Hosp.; SHO Paediat. Roy. Shrewsbury Hosp.
COLLINS, Andrew David 11 Sheridan House, Wincott St., London SE11 4NY — MB BS 1991 Lond.
COLLINS, Andrew Thomas 9 Little Wenham, Moira, Craigavon BT67 0NN — MB BCh BAO 1995 Belf.
COLLINS, Anne Kirkman 35 Elmfield Grove, Gosforth, Newcastle upon Tyne NE3 4XA Tel: 0191 284 0569 — MB BS 1962 Lond.; MRCS Eng. LRCP Lond. 1962; MRCPath 1976. (Roy. Free) Cons. Haemat. Regional Transfus. Centre Newc. u Tyne. Prev: Res. Asst. Pathol. Roy. Free Hosp. Lond.; Regist. (Clin. Path.) Roy. Marsden Hosp. Lond.
COLLINS, Anthony John 8 Rosslyn Road, Bath BA1 3LH — MD 1990 Bristol; PhD 1968; BSc Bath 1965; MB ChB 1980. Sen. Lect. (Pharmacol.) Univ. Bath; Assoc. Specialist Roy. Nat. Hosp. for Rheum. Dis. Bath.
COLLINS, Anthony John Westleigh, Hazeley Heath, Hook RG27 8NA Tel: 0118 932 6472; 29 Essex Way, Purdis Farm, Ipswich IP3 8SN Tel: 01473 272061 — BChir 1996 Camb.; MB Camb. 1997. (Camb.) SHO (Paediat.). Ipswich. Hosp Suff.. Prev: SHO (O & G).Ipswich.Hosps.uffolk; SHO (Med. & c/o the Elderly) W. Suff. Hosp. Bury St. Edmunds, Suff.; SHO (A & E) Ipswich Hosp. Ipswich Suff.
COLLINS, Anthony Joseph 286 Falls Road, Belfast BT12 6AN — MB BCh BAO 1992 Belf.
COLLINS, Barrie Patrick Crich House, 738 Mansfield Road, Woodthorpe, Nottingham NG5 3FY Tel: 0115 960 4678 — MRCS Eng. LRCP Lond. 1962. (Sheff.) Prev: SHO (Accid. & Orthop.), Ho. Surg. & Ho. Phys. Sheff. Roy. Infirm.
COLLINS, Barry George The Surgery, 1 Rowner Road, Gosport PO13 9UA Tel: 023 9258 0093 Fax: 023 92 504060 — MB BS 1966 London; MB BS 1966 London; MRCS Eng. LRCP Lond. 1970 London.
COLLINS, Brian Bernard (retired) Glendevon, Harwich Road, Little Oakley, Harwich CO12 5JD Tel: 01255 886216 Email: borucol@clara.net — MB BS 1954 Lond.; MRCS Eng. LRCP Lond. 1954. Prev: Ho. Surg. (Obst.) FarnBoro. Hosp.
COLLINS, Carol Ann St Andrew's Surgery, The Old Central School, Southover Road, Lewes BN7 1US Tel: 01273 476216 — MB BCh BAO 1988 NUI; DRCOG 1993; T(GP) 1992; DCH RCP Lond. 1990. BrE. Phys. Roy. Sussex Co. Hosp.
COLLINS, Carole Anne Maud 73 Nindum Road, Stratton, Swindon SN3 4BB; UNICEF (HARGEISA), BP 583, Djibouti — MB BCh 1981 Wales.
COLLINS, Carole Elizabeth West Middlesex University Hospital, Twickenham Road, Isleworth TW7 6AF Tel: 020 8560 2121 — MB BS 1986 Lond.; MA Camb. 1987; MD 1996 Lond.; MRCP (UK) 1990. Cons. Gastroenterologist, W. Middlx. Univ. Hosp., Isleworth, Middlx. Prev: Sen. Regist. (Gastroenterol.) St. Mary's Hosp. Lond.; Clin. Research Fell. Gastrointestinal Research Unit Roy. Lond. Hosp.
COLLINS, Charles David (retired) Lych Gate House, Pitland St., Holmbury St Mary, Dorking RH5 6NB Tel: 01306 730726 — MB BS 1954 Lond.; FRCR 1975; DMRT Eng. 1961. Prev: Cons. Radiother. St. Thos. Hosp. Lond.
COLLINS, Mr Charles Douglas Taunton & Somerset Hospital, Musgrove Park, Taunton TA1 5DA Tel: 01823 342100 Fax: 01823 323691; Crowcombe House, Crowcombe, Taunton TA4 4AE Tel: 01984 618266 Fax: 01984 618448 — MB BChir (Distinc. Surg.) Camb. 1963; MB ChB (Hons.) Sheff. 1963; MA Camb. 1963; ChM Sheff. 1973; FRCS Eng. 1967. (Camb. & Sheff.) Cons. Surg. Taunton & Som. Hosp. Socs: Fell. Assn. Surgs.; BSG; (Counc.) RCS Eng. Prev: Sen. Regist. (Surg.) United Bristol Hosps. & SW RHA; Regist Rotat. (Surg.) Roy. Infirm. Sheff.; Research Asst. Dept. Surg. Univ. Sheff.
COLLINS, Christine Janice Gilder Lodge, Fambridge Road, Althorne, Chelmsford CM3 6BZ — MB BS 1985 Lond.
COLLINS, Christopher Joseph 12 Denewood Park, Belfast BT11 8FS — MB BCh BAO 1980 Belf.
COLLINS, Christopher Martin Priestley 14 Fleetwood Street, London N16 0ND — BChir 1974 Camb.; MB 1975.
COLLINS, Clare Louise 78 Old Odiham Road, Alton GU34 2HS — MB ChB 1996 Dundee.
COLLINS, Clare Mary Howard (retired) Samarkand, Camden Park, Tunbridge Wells TN2 4TW Tel: 01892 528379 — MB BCh BAO NUI 1950; DCH NUI 1952; DPH NUI 1956. Prev: SCMO Hounslow & Spelthorne HA.
COLLINS, Daniel Denis Michael (retired) 31 Dunlambert Gardens, Belfast BT15 3NN — MB BCh BAO 1958 NUI. Asst. Psychiat. E. Special Care Hosp. Gp. Muckamore Abbey. Prev: Ho. Phys. & Ho. Surg. Jervis St. Hosp. Dub.
COLLINS, David Anthony Department of Rheumatology, Princess Margaret Hospital, Okus Road, Swindon SN1 4JU Tel: 01793 426467 — MB BS 1982 Lond.; BSc Lond. 1979, MD 1993; MRCPI 1986. (St. Geo.) Cons. (Rheum.) P.ss Margt. Hosp. Swindon, Cirencester Hosp. Gloucester & Cheltenham Gen. Hosp. Gloucester. Socs: Fell. Roy. Soc. Med.; Brit. Soc. Rheum. Prev: Sen. Regist. (Rheum.) St. Geo.s Hosp. Lond.
COLLINS, David Jonathan The Surgery, Welbeck St., Creswell, Worksop S80 4HA Tel: 01909 721206 Fax: 01909 722011 — MB ChB 1986 Sheff.; BMedSci (Med. Microbiol.) Sheff. 1985, MB ChB 1986; MRCGP 1990.
COLLINS, David Michael Stuart Greenway, Knoll Road, Godalming GU7 2ER Tel: 01483 415605 — MB BS 1980 Lond.; MRCGP 1993. (St Thomas's Hospital, London)
COLLINS, David Roland (retired) — MB BS 1972 Lond.; BSc Lond. 1969; MRCPath. 1982. Prev: Cons. (Haemat.) Oxf. Regional Transf. Centre.
COLLINS, David Roy Department Clinical Chemisty, Northwick Park Hospital, Watford Road, Harrow HA1 3UJ Tel: 020 8869 2120; 15/17 Cornwall Crescent, London W11 1PH — MB BS 1980 Lond.; MD Lond. 1991; MSc Clin. Biochem. Lond. 1985, BSc (Immunol.) 1976; MRCPath 1986. Sen. Regist. Rotat. (Chem. Path.) N.wick Pk. Hosp. Harrow & St. Mary's Hosp. Paddington. Socs: Assn. Clin. Biochem. & Clin. Molecular Genetics Soc. Prev: Regist. (Chem. Path.) Roy. Free Hosp. Lond.; Demonst. (Path.) King's Coll. Lond.
COLLINS, David William Walter 7 Suffolk Street, Helensburgh G84 8EJ — MB ChB 1974 Manch. Prev: SHO (Rotat. Surg.) & Ho. Surg. & Ho. Phys. Manch. Roy. Infirm.
COLLINS, Declan Patrick Medlars, Station Road, Castle Cary BA7 7PA — MB BS 1998 Lond.; MB BS Lond 1998.
COLLINS, Donal Malachy 9 Lloyd Close, Galmington, Taunton TA1 5QU — MB BCh BAO 1992 Dub.
COLLINS, Dorothy Evelyn Margaret (retired) 19 South Lodge, Fareham PO15 5NQ Tel: 01329 843053 Email: drdemocollins@lineone.net — MB ChB 1946 Bristol; DCH Eng. 1952. Prev: GP Fareham.
COLLINS, Dorothy Roxane Leggatts, Fishbourne, Chichester PO18 8AP Tel: 01243 2106 — MB ChB 1947 Leeds. (Leeds) Clin.

Asst. Dept. Neurol. St. Richard's Hosp. Chichester. Prev: Cas. Off. Roy. W. Sussex Hosp. Chichester.

COLLINS, Edwyn Patrick (retired) 21 Daintree, Needingworth, Huntingdon PE27 4SP Tel: 01480 300657 — MB ChB 1956 Aberd.; MRCGP 1974; MFOM 1980. Prev: Commandant RAF Centr. Med. Estab.

COLLINS, Erika Hanway Road Surgery, 2 Hanway Road, Buckland, Portsmouth PO1 4ND Tel: 023 9281 5317 Fax: 023 9289 9926; 81 Stubbington Avenue, North End, Portsmouth PO2 0JD Tel: 023 92 660153 — MD 1972 Vienna; MRCS Eng. LRCP Lond. 1976; DCH Eng. 1977; DRCOG 1976. (Vienna) GP. Socs: Portsmouth Med. Soc.; Anglo-German Med. Soc. Prev: GP Portsmouth; SHO (Paediat. & O & G) St. Mary's Hosp. Portsmouth.

COLLINS, Fiona Margaret 41 Wolveleigh Terrace, Gosforth, Newcastle upon Tyne NE3 1UP Tel: 0191284 0578 — MB ChB 1997 Ed. (Ed.) SHO Med. Rotat., Sunderland Roy. Infirm. Sunderland. Socs: MDU; BMA & MDDUS. Prev: PRHO (Med.) Roy. Infirm. Edin. NHS Trust; PRHO (Surg.) Borders Gen. Hosp. Melrose.

COLLINS, Fiona Mary The Moorings, Valley Road, Kenley CR8 5DG Tel: 020 8660 6104 Fax: 020 8763 2280; 47 Selcroft Road, Purley CR8 1AJ Tel: 020 8668 1719 — MB BS 1983 Lond.; DRCOG 1988. (Westminster)

COLLINS, Florence Jean Shankhill Health Centre, 135 Shankill Parade, Belfast BT13 1SD Tel: 028 9024 7181; 39 Lisnoe Road, Lisburn BT27 5LT Tel: 01846 672977 — MB BCh BAO 1977 Belf.

COLLINS, Gail Chesterfield & North Derbyshire Royal Hospital, Calow, Chesterfield S44 5BL Tel: 01246 277271 — BM BS 1988 Nottm.; CCST; MRCP (UK) 1992. Sen. Regist. (Cons. Paediat.) Chesterfield & N. Derbysh. Roy. Hosp. Prev: Regist. Rotat. (Paediat.) Derby & Nottm.

COLLINS, Mr Gerald Nicholas Department of Urology, Stepping Hill Hospital, Stockport SK2 7JE Tel: 0161 419 4299 Fax: 0161 419 5699; Newfy, Gillbrook Mews, Gillbrook Road, Didsbury, Manchester M20 6WH Tel: 0161 446 1303 Email: gerald.collons@stockport-tr.nwest.nhs.uk — MB BCh BAO 1983 NUI; FRCS Ed. 1989; FRCS Glas. 1989; MD 1993; FRCS (Urol.) 1997. (UniversityCollege Cork) Cons. Urol. Stepping Hill Stockport. Socs: Brit. Assn. Urol. Surg.; BHA. Prev: Sen. Regist. (Urol.) Christie Hosp. Manch., Stepping Hill Stockport and; + Manch. Roy. Infirm.

COLLINS, Geraldine Louise — MB BCh BAO 1989 NUI; LRCP & LRCSI 1989.

COLLINS, Glenn William Beccles Medical Centre, 7-9 St. Marys Road, St. Marys Road, Beccles NR34 9NQ Tel: 01502 712662 Fax: 01502 712906; 55 Lowestoft Road, Beccles NR34 7RD — MB BS 1982 Lond.; DCH RCP Lond. 1986; MRCGP 1987; DRCOG 1985.

COLLINS, Graham Campbell 23 Dover Road, PO Box 399, Bellevue Hill, Sydney NSW 2029, Australia Tel: 012 371 6000; 28 Cranmore Gardens, Belfast BT9 6JL — MB BCh BAO 1980 Belf.; MRCGP 1986; DCCH RCP Ed. 1986; DRCOG 1986.

COLLINS, Graham David 37 Wadborough Road, Sheffield S11 8RF — MB ChB 1995 Sheff.

COLLINS, Graham Peter 217a Banbury Road, Oxford OX2 7HQ — MB BS 1998 Lond.; MB BS Lond 1998.

COLLINS, Harold Alphonsus (retired) Westbrook House, Windsor Road, Ascot SL5 7LF Tel: 01344 625257 — MB BCh BAO NUI 1956; DIH Eng. 1959, DPH 1959. Prev: GP Staines.

COLLINS, Harriet Frances Bulley and Partners, Hamdon Medical Centre, Matts Lane, Stoke-sub-Hamdon TA14 6QE Tel: 01935 822236 Fax: 01935 826565 — MB BS 1984 Lond.; MRCGP 1989; T(GP) 1991; DRCOG 1990; Cert. Family Plann. JCC 1986.

COLLINS, Helen Elaine 109 Station Road, Lower Stondon, Henlow SG16 6JJ Tel: 01462 850305 Fax: 01462 581858 — MB ChB 1985 Sheff. (Sheffield) GP.

COLLINS, Henry Antony (retired) 45 Chetwynd Road, London NW5 1BX — MRCS Eng. LRCP Lond. 1952.

COLLINS, Ian Peter Clackmannan County Hospital, Alloa Tel: 01324 570700 — BM 1986 Soton.; MRCGP 1991; MRCPsych 1993; Cert. Av. Med. 1992. Prev: Cons. St Lawrences Hosp. Bodmin; Sen. Regist. Camb.; Regist. (Psychiat.) Roy. Edin. Hosp.

COLLINS, Iona Elizabeth 21 Pennygroes, Groesfaen, Pontyclun CF72 8PA — MB BS 1996 Lond.

COLLINS, Jake Alexander 41 Wynndale Road, London E18 1DY — MB BS 1989 Lond.

COLLINS, James Donald Ashworth Hospital, Parkbourn, Maghull, Liverpool L31 1HW Tel: 0151 472 4554 Fax: 0151 471 2494 — MB ChB 1978 Bristol. Cons. Forens. Psychiat. Ashworth Hosp. Liverp.

COLLINS, James Wyper (retired) 2 Garwhitter Drive, Milngavie, Glasgow G62 8DT Tel: 0141 956 1732 — MB ChB 1957 Glas.; FFA RCS Eng. 1963. Prev: Cons. Anaesth. Roy. Hosp. Sick Childr. & W.. Infirm. Glas.

COLLINS, Jane Elizabeth Great Ormond St. Hospital NHS Trust, London WC1N 3JH Tel: 0207 813 8330 — MB ChB 1978; MD Birm. 1988; MSc Lond. 1985; FRCP Lond. 1994; FRCPCH 1997. (Birmingham) Chief Exec. Gt. Ormond St. Hosp. Lond.

COLLINS, Janine Gwenda Medical Defence Union, 3 Devonshire Place, London W1G 6HE Tel: 020 7486 6181; Highcroft House, Hollies Hill, Nailsworth, Stroud GL6 0AW — MB BS 1981 Lond.; LLM Cardiff 1997. (St. Geo. Hosp. Med. Sch.) Secretariat Med. Defence Union. Prev: GP Wilts.; Med. Advisor BCA Swindon.

COLLINS, Jason Edwin — BM 1992 Soton.; MRCGP 1998; MRCP (UK) 1996; DGM RCP Lond. 1995; DTM & H Liverp. 1993. (Soton.)

COLLINS, Jeremy Steven 220 Chipping House Road, Nether Edge, Sheffield S7 1DR Tel: 0114 258 9394 — MB ChB 1988 Aberd. Regist. (Anaesth.) Yorks. HA. Prev: SHO (Anaesth.) Sheff. HA.

COLLINS, Joan Rose (retired) Polyn, Trevellan Road, Mylor Bridge, Falmouth TR11 5NE Tel: 01326 373782 — MB ChB 1943 Birm.; MRCGP 1954.

COLLINS, John Bartholomew (retired) 279 New Birmingham Road, Dudley DY2 7SA Tel: 0121 557 4739 — MB BCh BAO 1943 NUI; MRCGP 1967; LM 1943.

COLLINS, John Patrick 64 Beechgrove Park, Belfast BT6 0NR; 19 Cheltenham Park, Belfast BT6 0HR Tel: 01232 645341 — MB BCh BAO 1991 Belf.; DCH Dub. 1995; MRCGP Ed. 1996. (Queens University Belfast)

COLLINS, John Samuel Andrew 39 Lisnoe Road, Lisburn BT27 5LT Tel: 01846 672977 Fax: 01232 263360 Email: collins.lisburn@dnet.co.uk — MB BCh BAO 1976 Belf.; MD Belf. 1988; FRCPI 1996; FRCP Lond. 1994; FRCP Ed. 1994; MRCPI 1994; MRCP (UK) 1980. (Qu. Univ. Belf.) Cons. Phys. (Gastroenterol.) Roy. Vict. Hosp. Belf. Socs: Irish & Brit. Soc. Gastroenterol.; Amer. Soc. Gastrointestinal Endoscopy; Assn. Phys. Prev: Sen. Regist. Roy. Vict. Hosp. Belf.; Sen. Specialist. (Med.) RAF Med. Br.; Asst. Vis. Prof. Med. Coll. Wisconsin Milwaukee, USA.

COLLINS, John Vincent Chelsea & Westminter Hospital, London SW10 9NH Tel: 020 7351 8030 Fax: 020 7351 8085 — MB BS 1966 Lond.; MD Lond. 1974; BDS Lond. 1961; FRCP Lond. 1981, M 1969. (Guy's) Cons. Phys. Chelsea & W.m. Hosps. Lond. & Roy. Brompton; Hon. Sen. Lect. Heart & Lung Inst. Lond.; Hon. Cons. Phys. Roy. Hosp. Chelsea; Sen. Med Adviser Benenden Healthcare Soc. Prev: Sen. Lect. And Cons. Phys. St. Bart. Hosp. Med. Coll.

COLLINS, John William Wapping Health Centre, 22 Wapping Lane, London E1W 2RL Tel: 020 7481 9376 — MB ChB 1978 Aberd.; MRCGP 1984; DRCOG 1982. GP Lond.; GP Co-ordinator City & E. Lond. Homeless Team. Prev: Trainee GP St. Bart. & Hackney Hosps. Lond. VTS; Regist. Macmillan Serv. St. Joseph's Hospice Lond.; Phys. City & E. Lond. Homeless Health Project.

COLLINS, Jonathan Brierley Low Moor House, 167 Netherlands Avenue, Low Moor, Bradford BD12 0TB Tel: 01274 606818 Fax: 01274 691684; Thornleigh, Village St, Norwood Green, Halifax HX3 8QG — MB ChB 1974 Manch. Prev: SHO (O & G) & Ho. Off. Birch Hill Hosp. Rochdale.

COLLINS, Jonathan Douglas Licensing Division, Medicines Control Agency, Market Towers, 1 Nine Elms Lane, London SW8 5NQ Tel: 020 7273 0000; 3 Barkestone Close, Emerson Valley, Milton Keynes MK4 2AT Tel: 01908 502054 — MD 1991 Newc.; MB BS Lond. 1977; MRCP (UK) 1981; MFPM 1990; DPM Eng. 1987. (Middlx. Hosp.) Med. Assessor Meds. Control Agency Lond.; Clin. Asst. (Dept. Med.) Milton Keynes Gen. Hosp. Socs: Brit. Thorac. Soc. & Milton Keynes Med. Soc. Prev: Head (Clin. Pharmacol.) Hoechst Marion Roussel UK Ltd. Milton Keynes.

COLLINS, Karilyn Jane The Village, Bodenham, Hereford HR1 3JX Tel: 01568 797434 Email: doctorcollins@ereal.net — MB BS 1969 Lond.; DObst RCOG 1972; DTM & H Liverp. 1995. (St. Thos.) Socs: Inst. Psychosexual Med. Prev: Ho. Phys. S. Lond. Hosp. Wom.; Ho. Surg. Croydon Gen. Hosp.; GP Princip. 1976-98.

COLLINS, Katherine Mary Mount Vernon Hospital, Rickmansworth Road, Northwood HA6 2RN — MB BS 1975 Lond.; MRCS Eng. LRCP Lond. 1975; FFA RCS Eng. 1979. (St. Geo.) Cons. Anaesth. & Pain Managem. Specialist Mt. Vernon Hosp. N.wood. Prev: Cons. Anaesth. N. Middlx. Hosp.; Sen. Regist. (Anaesth.) St. Thos. Hosp. Lond.

COLLINS, Kathleen Mary Springfield Road Surgery, 66-70 Springfield Road, Belfast BT12 7AH Tel: 028 9032 3571 Fax: 028 9020 7707 — MB BCh BAO 1975 Belf.

COLLINS, Kenneth Edward Midlock Medical Centre, 7 Midlock Street, Glasgow G51 1SL Tel: 0141 427 4271 Fax: 0141 427 1405; 3 Glenburn Road, Giffnock, Glasgow G46 6RE Tel: 0141 638 7462 Fax: 0141 638 1848 — MB ChB 1972 Glas.; MPhil (Med. Law & Ethics) Glas. 1992; PhD Glas. 1987, MB ChB 1972; MRCGP 1980. Prev: Regist. (Psychiat.) & SHO (Med.) S.. Gen. Hosp. Glas.; Ho. Off. (Med. & Surg.) S.. Gen. Hosp. Glas.

COLLINS, Kenneth George (retired) 154 High Street, Portishead, Bristol BS20 6PY Tel: 0117 984 2406 — MB ChB 1955 Bristol. p/t Med. Attache Canad. Govt.; Med. Off. Brit. Boxing Bd. of Control (S.W.); Authorised Examr. Civil Aviat. Auth.

COLLINS, Kenneth John (retired) Windhover, 12 Albury Road, Guildford GU1 2BU Tel: 01483 564185 Email: kenjcollins@hotmail.com — MB BS 1974 Lond.; DPhil Oxf. 1960; BSc (Physiol.) Lond. 1954; FRCP Lond. 1992; MRCP (UK) 1985; MRCS Eng. LRCP Lond. 1973. Prev: on Staff MRC.

COLLINS, Lisa Ann Larwood Health Centre, 56 Larwood, Worksop S81 0HH Tel: 01909 500233 Fax: 01909 479722; Rowan House, Budby Road, Cuckney, Mansfield NG20 9JW — MB ChB 1985 Sheff.; DRCOG 1989.

COLLINS, Lisa Simone 25 Marine Court, Southsea PO4 9QU — MB BS 1998 Lond.; MB BS Lond 1998.

COLLINS, Louis 139 Oakwood Court, Abbotsbury Road, London W14 8JS — MRCS Eng. LRCP Lond. 1937. Prev: Local Treasury Med. Off.

COLLINS, Luke Joseph (retired) The Castle, 254 Manchester Road, Burnley BB11 4HF Tel: 01282 428668 — MB BCh BAO NUI 1943; MFCM RCP (UK) 1974; MFPHM 1989; DPH Dub. 1946; LM 1944; Dip. Med. Acupunc. 1997. Prev: MoH Princip. Sch. Med. Off.

COLLINS, Malcolm Richard 18A Eastfields, Eastcote, Pinner HA5 2SR Tel: 020 8868 8066 — State DMS 1989 Bologna. (Univ. Rome, La Sapienza) SHO (Psychiat.) Chase Farm Hosp. Socs: Roy. Soc. Trop. Med. Prev: SHO (O & G) King Geo. Hosp. Goodmayes; Resid. Med. Off. St. Francis Hosp. Katete, Zambia; SHO (Paediat.) Hillingdon Hosp.

COLLINS, Margaret Towl (retired) 11 St Peter's Road, Aldeburgh IP15 5BG Tel: 01728 453166 — MB BS 1937 Lond.

COLLINS, Mark Nathaniel Priory Hospital, Priory Lane, Roehampton, London SW15 5JJ Tel: 020 8392 4205 Fax: 020 8392 8995 Email: drmcollins@prioryhealthcare.co.uk — MB BS Lond. 1976; MA Oxf. 1977; MRCP (UK) 1979; MRCPsych 1986. (Univ. Coll. Hosp. Med. Sch.) Cons. Psychiat. Priory Hosp. Lond.; Hon. Sen. Lect. St. Geo. Hosp. Lond. Prev: Lect. (Psychiat.) St. Geo. Hosp. Lond.

COLLINS, Martin Damian (retired) Leggatts, Fishbourne, Chichester PO18 8AP Tel: 01243 572106 Fax: 01243 572567 — MB BS 1944 Lond.; MRCS Eng. LRCP Lond. 1944. Prev: Res. Med. Off. Roy. W. Sussex Hosp. Chichester.

COLLINS, Mary Margaret Annwen 17 Sandrock Road, Marford, Wrexham LL12 8LT — MB ChB 1972 Birm.; Cert. Family Plann. JCC 1974. Community Health Phys. (Family Plann., Well Wom. & Child Health) Clwyd HA; Asst. Genitourin. Med. Maelor Hosp. Wrexham; Diplomat Fac. Family Plann. & Reproduc. Healthcare. Socs: Assn. Genitourin. Med.; NW Soc. Sexual Med.

COLLINS, Miss Melanie Margaret 20 Windsor Terrace, South Gosforth, Newcastle upon Tyne NE3 1YL Tel: 0191 284 6316 — MB BS 1987 Lond.; BSc Lond. 1984; FRCS (Otol.) 1995; FRCS Eng. 1991; MRCGP 1994; DRCOG 1993. (St. Bart. Hosp. Med. Sch.) Specialist Regist. (Otorhinolaryng.) Freeman Hosp. Newc. Prev: Regist. (ENT) N. Riding Infirm. MiddlesBoro.; SHO (ENT) Roy. Nat. Throat Nose & Ear Hosp. Lond.; SHO (Surg.) Char. Cross Hosp. Lond.

COLLINS, Michael Collins and Partners, The Health Centre, Maison Dieu Road, Dover CT16 1RH Tel: 01304 865555 Fax: 01304 201161; Meadowside, Forge Lane, Whitfield, Dover CT16 3LA — MB ChB 1977 Aberd.; MRCGP 1981; DRCOG 1979.

COLLINS, Michael Anthony Baslow Road Surgery, 148-150 Baslow Road, Totley, Sheffield S17 4DR Tel: 0114 236 9957 Fax: 0114 262 0756; Shoreham Street Surgery, 251 Shoreham St, Sheffield S1 4SS Tel: 0114 272 1717 — MB ChB 1968 Bristol; DObst RCOG 1969.

COLLINS, Michael Anthony The Royal Wolverhampton Hospital, New Cross Hospital, Wolverhampton WV10 0QP Tel: 01902 307999; 24 Parklands, Stourbridge DY9 7JT — MB ChB 1985 Birm.; BSc (Hons.) Birm. 1982; MRCP (UK) 1989; FRCR 1992. Cons. Radiol. Roy. Wolverhampton Hosp. Socs: Brit. Inst. Radiol. Prev: Sen. Regist. (Radiol.) W. Midl. Train. Scheme.

COLLINS, Michael Barnaby (retired) 42 Burlington Road, Dore, Sheffield S17 3NQ Tel: 0114 364906 — MB ChB 1952 Sheff. Prev: Ho. Phys. Wharncliffe Hosp. Sheff.

COLLINS, Michael Columba Radiology Department, Royal Hallamshire Hospital, Glossop Rd, Sheffield S10 2JF Tel: 0114 271 3405 Fax: 0114 271 3766 Email: michael.collins@csuh.nhs.uk; 31 Cavendish Ave, Dore, Sheffield S17 3NJ Tel: 0114 236 5865 Email: collinss@btinternet.com — MB BCh BAO 1973 NUI; FRCR 1980; DMRD Eng. 1978; DCH RCPSI 1976. Cons. Radiol. Roy. Hallamsh. & N. Gen. Hosp. Sheff.; Progr. Director, N. Trent Radiol. Train. Progr., Roy. Hallamshire Hosp., Sheff. Socs: Roy. Coll. Radiol.; Brit. Inst. of Radiologists; 25 Radiological club. Prev: Sen. Regist. & Regist. (Radiol.) Sheff.; SHO Regional Hosp. Galway; SHO Drogheda Irel.

COLLINS, Michael Edward The Surgery, 356 Southborough Lane, Bromley BR2 8AA Tel: 020 8468 7081; 2 St. Kilda Road, Orpington BR6 0ES — BM 1979 Soton.; MRCGP. (Soton.) Course Organiser FarnBoro. VTS. Prev: Dir. EMDOC; Bd. Mem. Orpington PCG.

COLLINS, Michael John Merrett Penn Hill Surgery, St. Nicholas Close, Yeovil BA20 1SB Tel: 01935 74005 Fax: 01935 421841; Thurlands, Chetnole, Sherborne DT9 6PE Tel: 01935 872414 — MRCS Eng. LRCP Lond. 1973; BSc (Hons.) Lond. 1969, MB BS 1973; DRCOG 1976. (St. Bart.) GP Yeovil.

COLLINS, Michael Lawrence 144 Harley Street, London W1N 1AH; Maple Down, Lockton Chase, Ascot SL5 8TP — MB ChB 1969 Leeds; MRCS Eng. LRCP Lond. 1969. Socs: Fell. Roy. Soc. Med. Prev: Specialist (Gyn., Endocrinol. & Infertil.) McMaster Univ. Med.; Centre Hamilton Ontario Canada.

COLLINS, Niamh Sarah 35 Elmfield Grove, Newcastle upon Tyne NE3 4XA — MB BS 1997 Newc.

COLLINS, Nicholas Peter 24 Clerks Croft, Bletchingley, Redhill RH1 4LH; 1/11 Kidman Street, Coogee, Sydney NSW 2034, Australia — MB BS 1987 Lond.; MRCGP 1995. (Char. Cross & Westm.) Regist. (IC) Wollongong Hosp. NSW, Australia. Prev: GP/Regist. SW Thames Region; Family Med. Progr. Illawarra Health Serv. NSW, Austral.; SHO (O & G) Luton & Dunstable.

COLLINS, Owen Desmond Gruffydd, OBE Bayer plc, Bayer House, Strawberry Hill, Newbury RG14 1JA Tel: 01635 563103 Fax: 01635 563103 Email: owen.colllins.oc@bayer.co.uk; Bewley Cottage, Bowden Hill, Lacock, Chippenham SN15 2PW Tel: 01249 730356 — MB BCh 1987. (University of Cambridge) Med. Adviser, Bayer plc; Sen. Lect. Keele Univ. Research Fell. in Gen. Pract., Regional GP Unit, Birm.; Med. Adviser to C.E. Andersons & Sons Ltd., Barclays Bank Ltd. & other Cos.; Primary Care Phys. (UK & abRd.); Vis. Cons. Learning Assessm. Centre, Horsham, W. Sussex; HS RSCH Guildford; RAF Med. Pract. Prev: Regt.. Med. Off., Grenadier Guards.

COLLINS, Pamela Anne AON Ltd Occupational Health, Winfrith Technology Centre, Winfrith, Dorchester DT2 8DH Tel: 01305 203460 Fax: 01305 203546; Marsh Farmhouse, Pound Road, Leigh, Sherborne DT9 6JD Tel: 01935 873503 Fax: 01935 873503 — MB ChB 1982 Manch.; MFOM 2002; DRCOG 1985; MRCGP 1986; DFOM 1996. Specialist Regist. Occupat. Med. Dorchester. Socs: Soc. Occupat. Med.; BMA. Prev: GP Princip. Petersfield Hants.

COLLINS, Patrick 6 Elm Close, Weston Turville, Aylesbury HP22 5SS — MRCS Eng. LRCP Lond. 1962; MD Lond. 1976, MB BS 1962; FRCP Lond. 1983, M 1967. (St. Bart.) Cons. Phys. Stoke Mandeville Hosp. Aylesbury. Prev: Sen. Regist. (Gen. Med.) Leicester Roy. Infirm. & Sheff. Roy. Hosp.; Reg. (Cardiol.) Gen. Infirm. Leeds.

COLLINS, Paul Antony Andover Health Centre, Charlton Road, Andover SP10 3LD Tel: 01264 350270 Fax: 01264 336701 Email:

paul.collins1@virgin.net; 61 Borkum Close, Andover SP10 4LE Tel: 01264 337044 — BM 1979 Soton.; DFFP 1993; DRCOG 1983. Prev: Trainee GP Frimley Pk. Hosp. VTS; Ho. Surg. Weymouth & Dist. Hosp.; Ho. Phys. Basingstoke & Dist. Hosp.

COLLINS, Paul Dominic 4 Oakwood Avenue, Cyncoed, Cardiff CF23 9HA — MB BCh 1998 Wales.

COLLINS, Paul John Newton Lodge Regional Secure Unit, Ouchthorpe Lane, Wakefield WF1 3SP — MB BCh BAO 1982 Dub.; MRCPsych 1987. Cons. Forens. Psychiat. Yorksh. Regional Serv. Wakefield. Prev: Sen. Regist. (Forens. Psychiat.) Ashworth Hosp. Liverp. & NW RHA; Sen. Regist. (Gen. Psychiat.) Trent RHA; SHO & Regist. Mapperley Hosp. Nottm.

COLLINS, Professor Peter National Heart & Lung Institute, Faculty of Medicine, Imperial College of Science, Technology and Medicine, and Royal Brompton Hospital, Dovehouse St., London SW3 6LY Tel: 020 7351 8112 Fax: 020 7823 3392 Email: peter.collins@ic.ac.uk — MB BChir 1980 Camb.; MA Camb. 1983; MD Camb. (Sir Walter Langdon-Brown Prize) 1992; FRCP Lond. 1994; MRCP (UK) 1982; FACC 1994; FESC 1993. (St. Thos.) Prof. of Clin. Cardiol., Nat. Heart and Lung Inst., Fac. of Med., Imperial Coll. of Sci., Technol. and Med., & Hon. Cons. Cardiol. & Roy. Brompton Hosp. Lond. Socs: Fell. Europ. Soc. Cardiol.; Brit. Cardiac. Soc.; Assn. Phys. Prev: Sen. Regist. & Regist. (Cardiol.) Nat. Heart & W.m. Hosp. Lond; Regist. (Med.) Roy. Free Hosp. Lond.

COLLINS, Peter Douglas 44 West Street, Stourbridge DY8 1XN — MB ChB 1983 Bristol.

COLLINS, Peter Leslie 7 The Morelands, West Heath, Birmingham B31 3HA — MB ChB 1995 Dundee. Specialist Regist. (Gastroenterol.) Merseyside Deanery Liverp.

COLLINS, Peter William University Hospital of Wales, Heath Park, Cardiff CF4 4XN Tel: 029 2074 2155 Fax: 029 2074 5085; 54 Britway Road, Dinas Powys CF64 4AF — MB BS Lond. 1986; BA (Hons.) Camb. 1983; MD Lond. 1993; MRCP (UK) 1988; MRCPath 1995. (St. Bart.) Cons. Haemat. & Dir. of Haemophilia Univ. Hosp. Wales. Socs: Brit. Soc. Haematol.; Brit. Soc. Thrombosis & Haemostasis. Prev: Lect. (Haemat.) & Hon. Sen. Regist. Roy. Free Hosp. Lond.; SHO (Haemat.) Lond. Hosp.; SHO Rotat. (Med.) OldCh. Hosp. Romford.

COLLINS, Rachel Kay 128 Alexandra Road, Sheffield S2 3EG — MB ChB 1989 Leeds.

COLLINS, Richard Andrew Widbrook Surgery, 72 Wingfield Road, Trowbridge BA14 9EN Tel: 01225 752412 — MB BS 1981 Lond.; LMSSA Lond. 1981. (Roy. Free)

COLLINS, Mr Richard Edward Charles Kent & Canterbury Hospitals NHS Trust, Canterbury CT1 3HS Tel: 01227 766877 Fax: 01227 783024; Seatonden, Ickham, Canterbury CT3 1SL Tel: 01227 721033 — MB BS 1967 Lond.; FRCS 2000 Ed.; FRCS Eng. 1971; MRCS Eng. LRCP Lond. 1967. (St. Geo.) Cons. Surg. Canterbury & Thanet Hosps.; Chairm. Intercollegiate Exam. Bd. - Gen. Surg. 1998-2001.; Mem. SAC Gen. Surg. 1995-2001. Socs: Fell. Roy. Soc. Med.; FACS.; Assn. of Surg.s GB & Irel.. Fell.and Exec. Comm. Mem. 1997-2001. Prev: Sen. Regist. Guy's Hosp. Gp.; Regist. (Surg.) Wycombe Gen. Hosp. High Wycombe; Cas. Off. & Ho. Phys. St. Geo. Hosp. Lond.

COLLINS, Richard James 2 Jacomb Road, Lower Broadheath, Worcester WR2 6QW — MB BS 1998 Lond.; MB BS Lond 1998.

COLLINS, Richard John Department of Diabetic Medicine, County Hospital, Union Walk, Hereford HR1 3SR Tel: 01432 364131; The Village, Bodenham, Hereford HR1 3JX Tel: 01568 797434 Email: druncollins@ereal.net — MB BS 1971 Lond.; MA Camb. 1967; MRCP (UK) 1974; MRCS Eng. LRCP Lond. 1971; DTM & H Liverp. 1995; DObst RCOG 1973. (St. Thos.) Staff Grade, Phys. in Diabetes & Endocrinol., Hereford Co. Hosp. Prev: GP Princip.; Regist. (med.) & SHO (Obst. & Gyneacology & Paediat.) at Hereford Co. Hosp.

COLLINS, Robert John Felixstowe Road Surgery, 235 Felixstowe Road, Ipswich IP3 9BN Tel: 01473 719112; 8 Belgrave Close, Albany Gardens, Ipswich IP4 2TT Tel: 01473 254038 — MB BS 1974 Lond.; MRCP (UK) 1977; MRCGP 1991. (Middlx.) Dep. Force Surg. Suff. Constab. Prev: SHO (Gen. Med.) Nottm. Gen. Hosp.; SHO (Med.) Ipswich Hosp.; Ho. Phys. Middlx. Hosp.

COLLINS, Robin Elspeth Thurlands, Chetnole, Sherborne DT9 6PE — MB BS 1972 Lond.; DA Eng. 1975. (St. Bart.)

COLLINS, Mr Ronald Leslie Leopold 8 Lynnwood Avenue, Fenham, Newcastle upon Tyne NE4 6XB — MB BS 1968 W. Indies; FRCS Ed. 1975.

COLLINS, Professor Rory Edwards Clinical Trial Service Unit & Epidemiological Studies Unit, Radcliffe Infirmary, Oxford OX2 6HE Tel: 01865 404834 Fax: 01865 558817; 41 Southmoor Road, Oxford OX2 6RF Tel: 01865 557636 — MB BS 1981 Lond.; MA Oxf. 1986, MSc (Statistics) 1983; BSc (Statistics) George Washington Univ. USA 1977; LMSSA Lond. 1980. (St. Thos.) Prof. Med. & Epidemiol. Univ. Oxf.; Hon. Cons. Cardiac Dept. John Radcliffe Hosp. Oxf.; Co-Dir. BHF/MRC/ICRF Clin. Trial Serv. Unit Radcliffe Infirm. Oxf. Socs: Fell. Europ. Soc. Cardiol.; Brit. Cardiac Soc.; Fell. Amer. Coll. Cardiol.

COLLINS, Rupert Jamie Christopher Cubbington Road Surgery, 115 Cubbington Road, Leamington Spa CV32 7AJ Tel: 01926 425131 Fax: 01926 427254 — MB ChB 1985 Dundee; MRCGP 1990.

COLLINS, Ruth Margaret Eastfield Medical Centre, Eastfield Drive, Penicuik EH26 8EY Tel: 01968 675576 Fax: 01968 674395; Cranley House, 1/9 Ettrick Road, Edinburgh EH10 5BJ — MB ChB 1970 Aberd.

COLLINS, Simon John 5 Minton Mews, Carlyle Road, Bromsgrove B60 2PN — MB ChB 1990 Liverp.

COLLINS, Stephen Christopher Philip Highcliffe Medical Centre, 248 Lymington Road, Highcliffe, Christchurch BH23 5ET Tel: 01425 272203 Fax: 01425 271086; 17 Falcon Drive, Mudeford, Christchurch BH23 4BA Tel: 01425 277378 — MB ChB 1984 Leic.; MB ChB Leic. l984; DRCOG 1988. Prev: Trainee GP Leicester VTS; SHO (A & E, Gen. Med. & Paediat.) Canterbury Hosp. Bd. ChristCh. Hosp. NZ.

COLLINS, Stephen Russell Oleuffynnon, Glyn-Brochan, Llanidloes SY18 6PJ — MB BS 1989 Lond.

COLLINS, Stuart James Cherry House, Hillcommon, Taunton TA4 1DY — BM BS 1983 Nottm.; BMedSci Nottm. 1981; FRCA. 1990. Cons. Anaesth. MusGr. Pk. Hosp. Taunton & Som. NHS Trust Taunton. Prev: Sen. Regist. (Anaesth.) Milton Keynes Hosp.

COLLINS, Terence McQueen Maryport Group Practice, Alneburgh House, Ewanrigg Road, Maryport CA15 8EL Tel: 01900 815544 Fax: 01900 816626 — BM BCh 1972 Oxf.; BVetMed Lond. 1966; MA Oxf. 1973, BA 1969; MRCGP 1983; DObst RCOG 1976; DCH Eng. 1975; FRCGP 1997. (Oxf.) Clin. Asst., Gen. Med., W. Cumbria Primary Care Trust, Whitehaven, Cumbria. Socs: Fac. Bd., Cumbria Fac. RCGP.

COLLINS, Tony Michael Vodena, Vine Lane, Clent, Stourbridge DY9 9PH; 19 Tennyson Avenue, Rock Ferry, Birkenhead CH42 2DJ — MB ChB 1979 Sheff.; MFPHM RCP (UK) 1990. Cons. Pub. Health Med. Dudley HA. Prev: Sen. Regist. (Pub. Health Med.) W. Midl. RHA; Regist. (Radiother.) Cookridge Hosp. Leeds.

COLLINS, Tracey Margaret Whiteleigh, St Johns Hill Road, Woking GU21 1RW — MB BCh BAO 1987 Belf.

COLLINS, Vanessa Carolyn Anne 9 Windsor Avenue, Belfast BT9 6EE — MB ChB 1998 Dund.; MB ChB Dund 1998.

COLLINS, Professor Vincent Peter Department Histopathology, Box 235, Addenbrooke's Hospital, Hills Road, Cambridge CB2 2QQ Tel: 01223 336072 Fax: 01223 216980 Email: vpc20@cam.ac.uk — MB BCh BAO 1971 NUI; MD Karolinska Inst., Stockholm 1978; FRCPath 1996, M 1988. (Dublin) Prof. Histopath. Univ. Camb.; Hon. Cons. Path. Addenbrooke's Hosp. Camb.; Foreign Adjunct Prof., Karolinska Inst., Stockholm, Sweden. Prev: Prof Tumour Path. Karolinska Inst., & Sen. Cons. Path. Karolinska Hosp., Stockholm; Prof. Neuropath. Univ. Gothenberg, Sweden.

COLLINS, Violet Mary (retired) Coomberry, 2 Chapel Lane, Bodmin PL31 2LH Tel: 01208 74464 — MB BS Lond. 1947; MFCM 1973; DObst RCOG 1948. Prev: Sen. Med. Off. DHSS.

COLLINS, Wendy Elizabeth Mill Cottage, Menadarva, Kehelland, Camborne TR14 0JH — MB BS 1984 Lond. (Westm.) Clin. Asst. Child Psychiat. Truro. Prev: Trainee GP Redruth VTS; Regist. (Geriat.) Cornw. & I. of Scilly HA; SHO (A & E & Anaesth.) Cornw. & I. of Scilly HA.

COLLINS, Yvonne Dorothy Goldsworth Park Health Centre, Denton Way, Woking GU21 3LQ Tel: 01483 767194 Fax: 01483 766042; 72 Lovelace Drive, Pyrford, Woking GU22 8QY Tel: 0193 23 46767 — MB ChB 1972 Leeds; DObst RCOG 1974; Cert Family

Plann. RCOG, RCGP & Family Plann; Assn. 1975. Prev: Ho. Phys. & Ho. Surg. Wharfedale Gen. Hosp. Otley.

COLLINSON, Aileen Agnes Robertson (retired) Markham Cottage, 112 Westgate, Southwell NG25 0LT Tel: 01636 813920 — MB ChB 1955 Leeds. p/t Learning Disabilty Serv.-Nottm. health care trust. Prev: Assoc. Specialist Balderton Hosp. Newark.

COLLINSON, Andrew Station Road Surgeries, Station Road, Haworth, Keighley BD22 8NL Tel: 01535 642255/6 Fax: 01535 645380; 38 Gledhow Drive, Oxenhope, Keighley BD22 9SA — MB ChB 1970 Sheff.; DObst RCOG 1972.

***COLLINSON, Anna Jane** 41 Dark Lane, Backwell, Bristol BS48 3NT Tel: 01275 462626 — MB BS 1996 Lond.

COLLINSON, Barbara The Surgery, 201 Queensbower Road, Bestwood Park, Nottingham NG5 5RB Tel: 0115 920 8615 Fax: 0115 966 6073 — MB BS 1978 Newc.; MRCGP 1983; DCH Eng. 1982; DRCOG 1980; Cert. Family Plann. JCC 1982.

COLLINSON, Deborah Jane 46 Bury Hill, Hemel Hempstead HP1 1SP — MB ChB 1997 Leic.

COLLINSON, Derek Geoffrey Priory Medical Group, Cornlands Road, Acomb, York YO24 3WX Tel: 01904 781423 Fax: 01904 784886 — MB BChir 1969 Camb.; MRCS Eng. LRCP Lond. 1968.

COLLINSON, Iris Buchanan Fraser (retired) 5 North Dunes, Hightown, Liverpool L38 0BS — MRCS Eng. LRCP Lond. 1945. Med. Off. (Sch. Med. & Family Plann.) Sefton AHA. Prev: Cas. Off. Bootle Gen. Hosp.

COLLINSON, Janet Elizabeth 3 Grange Farm Close, Abbotsley, St Neots, Huntingdon PE19 6XA — MB BS Lond. 1958. (Middlx.) Company Doctor, Aircraft Research Assoc., Bedford. Prev: Ho. Phys. & Ho. Surg. & Ho. Surg. (O & G) Bedford Gen. Hosp.

COLLINSON, Janet Gaye 2 Spinney Close, Gilmorton, Lutterworth LE17 5PR — BM BS 1987 Nottm.

COLLINSON, John Alexander 3 Gleneagles Drive, Widnes WA8 9JH — MB ChB 1992 Ed.

COLLINSON, John David Parkstone Health Centre, Mansfield Road, Poole BH14 0DJ Tel: 01202 741370 Fax: 01202 730952; 45A East Avenue, Bournemouth BH3 7BT Tel: 01202 766074 — MB BChir 1975 Camb.; MB BChir Camb. 1974; MA Camb. 1975; MRCGP 1980. Socs: Brit. Med. Acupunct. Assn.

COLLINSON, Julian Rupert 12 Copped Hall Way, Camberley GU15 1PA — MB BS 1992 Lond.; BSc Lond. 1989; MRCP (UK) 1995.

COLLINSON, Martin Andrew Princess Street Surgery, Princess Street, Gorseinon, Swansea SA4 4US Tel: 01792 895681 Fax: 01792 893051 — MB BS 1978 Lond.

COLLINSON, Matthew Peter 105 Ingleden Court, Leeds LS17 8TP — MB BS 1988 Lond.; MRCP (UK) 1993.

COLLINSON, Nicholas Edward The New House, 7 King Henry's Walk, Dalston, London N1 4NX — MB ChB 1992 Sheff.; MB ChB (Hons.) Sheff. 1992.

COLLINSON, Paul Ormandy Department of Chemical Pathology, Level 2, Jenner Wing, St George's Hospital, Blachshaw Road, Tooting, London SW17 0Q7 Tel: 0208 725 5934 Fax: 020 8401 3189 Email: collinsonpaul@hotmail.com — MB BChir 1980 Camb.; MA, MB Camb. 1981 BChir 1980; BA Camb. 1977; MRCPath 1988; MD 1994; FRCPath 1997. Cons. Chem. Path. & Metab. Med.St Geo.'s Hos[pital; Sen. Vis. Fell. MIM Centre City Univ.

COLLINSON, Peter Charles, VRD (retired) 10 Cortworth Lane, Wentworth, Rotherham S62 7SB Tel: 01226 743174 — MRCS Eng. LRCP Lond. 1939. Prev: Surg. Lt.-Cdr. RNR Retd.

COLLINSON, Rachel 8 Freshfields Drive, Padgate, Warrington WA2 0QY — MB BCh 1995 Wales. SHO (Elderly Care), Barnstable, N. Devon. Socs: BMA. Prev: SHO (O & G), Ashington, N.umberland.

COLLINSON, Robert Charles Adair Greenside Surgery, Greasbrough, Rotherham S61 4PT Tel: 01709 560773; 49 Clayfield Lane, Wentworth, Rotherham S62 7TD Tel: 01226 745486 — MB BChir 1978 Camb.; MA Camb. 1978. (Cambridge and St Bartholomews) GP Rotherham. Prev: Regist. (Path.) Vict. Hosp. Blackpool; Regist. (Surg.) Stoke on Trent Hosp.

COLLINSON, Victor Foster (retired) The Bower Farm, Grosmont, Abergavenny NP7 8HS Tel: 01981 240219 Fax: 01981 240219 — MB BS Lond. 1958; MRCGP 1966. Prev: Ho. Surg. & Ho. Phys. Bedford Gen. Hosp.

COLLIS, Anthony Arthur (retired) 2 St Leonards Road, Bridgend CF31 4HF Tel: 01656 653238 — MB BS 1948 Lond.; LMSSA Lond. 1947; FFA RCS Eng. 1964; DA Eng. 1954. Prev: Cons. Anaesth. Mid-Glam. Hosp. Gp.

COLLIS, Antony James Belmont Surgery, St. James Square, Wadhurst TN5 6BJ Tel: 01892 782121 Fax: 01892 783989 — MB BS 1974 Lond. (Char. Cross) Prev: Trainee GP Maidstone VTS; Ho. Phys. (Cardiol.) & Ho. Surg. (ENT, Plastic & Genitourin. Surg.) Char. Cross Hosp. Lond.

COLLIS, Antony Thomas Gurney Knightwick Surgery, Knightwick, Worcester WR6 5PH Tel: 01886 21279 Fax: 01886 821516 — MB BChir 1970 Camb.

COLLIS, Christopher Henry Penshurst, 118A Kew Road, Richmond TW9 2AU Tel: 020 8940 6384 — MB BChir 1972 Camb.; MD Camb. 1981, MA 1973; MRCP (UK) 1975; FRCR 1984; FRCP Lond. 1998. (Guy's) Cons. & Hon. Sen. Lect. (Radiother. & Oncol.) Roy. Free Hosp. & Sch. Med. Lond. Prev: Sen. Regist. (Radiother. & Oncol.) Bristol Roy. Infirm.; Lect. & Regist. (Radiother. & Oncol.) Inst. Cancer Research & Roy. Marsden Hosp. Sutton & Lond.; Regist. (Med. Oncol.) St. Bart. Hosp. Lond.

COLLIS, Ian Department of Psychological Medicine, University College Hospital, Grafton Way, London WC1E 6AU Tel: 020 7387 9300; St. Luke's-Woodside Hospital, Woodside Avenue, London N10 3HU Tel: 020 8219 1812 — MB BS 1986 Lond.; MRCPsych 1990. Cons. Gen. Adult Psychiat. St. Luke's-Woodside & Univ. Coll. Hosps.; Hon. Sen. Lect. UCL. Prev: Sen. Regist. Rotat. (Gen. Psychiat.) Univ. Coll. Hosp. Lond.; Research Regist. Roy. Free Hosp. Lond.

COLLIS, Professor John Leigh 26 Hayfield Road, Moseley, Birmingham B13 9LF Tel: 0121 449 3179 — MB ChB 1935 Birm.; MB ChB (1st cl. Hons.) Birm. 1935; BSc Birm. 1932, MD (Hons.) 1943; FRCS Eng. 1937; MRCS Eng. LRCP Lond. 1935. (Birm.) Emerit. Prof. Thoracic Surg. Univ. Birm. Socs: (Ex-Pres.) Soc. Thoracic Surgs.; Thoracic Soc. Prev: Lt.-Col. RAMC; Thoracic Surg. W. Midl. RHA; Surg. Qu. Eliz. Hosp. Birm.

COLLIS, John William The Medical Centre, 15 Cawley Road, Chichester PO19 1XT Tel: 01243 786666/781833 Fax: 01243 530042; Dawtreys, Mill Lane, Sidlesham, Chichester PO20 7NB Tel: 01243 641289 Fax: 01243 641289 Email: johncollis@talk21.com — MB BS 1965 Lond.; MRCS Eng. LRCP Lond. 1965; DObst RCOG 1968. (Char. Cross) Prev: Cas. Off. W. Lond. Hosp; SHO (Paediat.) St. John's Hosp. Chelmsford; Ho. Surg. (Obst.) Camb. Matern. Hosp.

COLLIS, Kathleen Valerie 19 Aireville Crescent, Bradford BD9 4EU Tel: 01274 592580 — MB ChB 1970 Leeds; DA Eng. 1973. Clin. Asst. (Anaesth.) Airedale Gen. Hosp. Steeton.

COLLIS, Lynne Jean 8A Cedar Court, North Tyneside General Hospital, Rake Lane, North Shields NE29 8NH — MB ChB 1997 Sheff.

COLLIS, Peter John (retired) Francesca, Old Hall Lane, Whitwell S80 4QX Tel: 01909 723197 — MB ChB 1960 Birmingham; MRCGP 1976; DObst RCOG 1962.

COLLIS, Rachel Elinor University Hospital of Wales, Cardiff CF14 4XW Tel: 02920 747747; 54 Britway Road, Dinas Powys, Cardiff CF64 4AF Tel: 02920 514741 — MB BS 1986 Lond.; FRCA. 1992; FFA RCS Eng. 1988; FRCA 1988 Eng. (St. Bart.) Cons. Anaes. Roy. Lond. Hosp. Prev: Regist. (Anaesth.) Univ. Coll. Hosp. & Middlx. Hosp.; SHO (Cardiothoracics) St. Bart. Hosp. Lond.; SHO (Anaesth.) Whittington Hosp. Lond.

COLLIS, Rebecca Jane Hartcliffe Health Centre, Hareclive Road, Bristol BS13 0JP Tel: 0117 964 2839 — MB ChB 1984 Bristol; MB ChB Bristol l984; DRCOG 1986; MRCGP 1988; DGM 1987. Prev: Trainee GP Avon VTS.

COLLISTER, Gillian Catherine 88 Loudoun Road, Newmilns KA16 9HQ — MB ChB 1986 Glas.

COLLISTER, Ruby May (retired) c/o Collister, The Forge, Chobham, Woking GU24 8QP — LRCP LRCS Ed. LRFPS Glas. 1948; DM Leiden 1952. Prev: Home Office Insp. (Cruelty to Animals Act 1876).

COLLIVER, Daniel William 28 Jermayns, Lee Chapel N., Basildon SS15 5EZ — MB ChB 1998 Leeds.

COLLOBY, Peter Stanley Department of Pathology, City Hospital NHS Trust, Dudley Road, Birmingham B18 7QH Tel: 0121 507 4268 Fax: 0121 507 5374 Email: cht.hist@which.net; 100 Forest House Lane, Leicester Forest E., Leicester LE3 3PY Tel: 0116 239 0855

Fax: 0116 239 0856 Email: peter@pcolloby.freeserve.co.uk — MB BS 1985 Lond.; MA (Hons.) Camb. l986; MRCPath 1992. Cons. Path. (Histopath.) City Hosp. NHS Trust Birm.; Mem. Roy. Coll. Path.; Hon. Clin. Sen. Lect. Birm. Univ. Socs: Assn. Clin. Paths. Prev: Clin. Lect. (Path.) Leicester Univ.; Regist. (Histopath.) Leicester Roy. Infirm.; SHO (Path.) E. Birm. Hosp.

COLLOMOSSE, Mr John Roland William Newel House, 46 Hayes Lane, Kenley CR8 5LA Tel: 020 8763 0804 — MB BS 1978 Lond.; FRCS Eng. 1984; DRCOG 1987.

COLLYER, Andrew John Wareham Health Centre, Streche Road, Wareham BH20 4PG Tel: 01929 553444 Fax: 01929 550703; Mill House, Organford, Poole BH16 6ET Tel: 01202 625000 — MB BS 1967 Lond.; MRCS Eng. LRCP Lond. 1967; MRCGP 1977; DObst RCOG 1973. (Roy. Free) Prev: Orthop. Ho. Surg. Roy. Free Hosp.; Ho. Phys. St. Peter's Hosp. Chertsey.

COLLYER, David Robin Wonford House Hospital, Dryden Road, Exeter EX2 5AF Tel: 01392 403629; The Old Vicarage, Kenton, Exeter EX6 8NG — MB BS 1963 Lond.; FRCPsych 1996, M 1972; DPM Eng. 1967. (St. Mary's) Locum at Wonford Ho. Hosp. Socs: BMA. Prev: Cons. Psychiat. Exeter Ment. Health Unit Wonford Hse. Hosp. Exeter; Sen. Regist. (Psychiat.) W.m. Hosp. Lond.; Sen. Regist. Holloway Sanat., Virginia Water.

COLLYER, Geoffrey Brice 37 Torwood Lane, Whyteleafe CR3 0HD Tel: 020 8660 4636 — MB BS 1939 Lond.; MRCS Eng. LRCP Lond. 1938; DOMS Eng. 1942. (Guy's) Prev: Chief Clin. Asst. Moorfields Eye Hosp.

COLLYER, Ian Timothy 33 Church Street, Marple, Stockport SK6 6BW Email: icol@globalnet.co.uk — BM BCh 1996 Oxf.; BA (Hons.) 1993. (Oxf.)

COLLYER, Jane Dell Cottage, Beeches Hill, Bishops Waltham, Southampton SO32 1FE Tel: 01489 890788 — MB BS 1993 Lond.; DRCOG 1996; MRCGP 1998. GP Princip. Prev: Locum GP; GP VTS.

COLLYER, John 15 Parkfields, Putney, London SW15 6NH Tel: 020 8788 6682 — MB BS 1968 Lond.; FFA RCS Eng. 1976. (St. Mary's) Cons. Anaesth. Croydon AHA. Prev: Sen. Regist, (Anaesth.) St. Geo. Hosp. Lond. & Hosp. Sick. Childr.; Gt. Ormond St. Lond.; Regist. (Anaesth.) W.m. Hosp. Lond.

COLLYER, Stephen Patrick Corinthian Surgery, St Paul's Medical Centre, 121 Swindon Road, Cheltenham GL50 4DP Tel: 01242 707777 Fax: 01242 707776 — MB BS 1987 Lond.

COLLYER, Thomas Charles 32 Downsview Avenue, Storrington, Pulborough RH20 4PS — MB ChB 1998 Leeds.

COLLYER-POWELL, Katherine Janet 50 Binghams Road, Crossways, Dorchester DT2 8BW — MB BS 1986 Lond.

COLLYER-POWELL, Mr Richard Graham Forest Keep, 5 Castle Woods, Redlynch, Salisbury SP5 2PY — MB BCh 1975 Wales; FRCS Eng. 1980; FRCOphth 1993. Cons. Ophth. Salisbury Dist. Hosp. NHS Trust. Prev: Sen. Regist. (Ophth.) Soton. & Portsmouth; Lect. (Ophth.) Univ. Soton.

COLLYNS, Timothy Anthony 78 Boreham Road, Warminster BA12 9JN — BChir 1990 Camb.

COLMAN, Andrew William 14 Lynton Avenue, Chanterlands Avenue, Hull HU5 3TH Email: acolman@clara.net — MRCS Eng. LRCP Lond. 1986; MSc Manch. 1994; PhD UMIST 1996. Vis. Med. Informatics Dept. Computation Univ. of Manch. Inst. Sci. & Technol.

COLMAN, Anthony Richard Stokes Medical Centre, Braydon Avenue, Little Stoke, Bristol BS34 6BQ Tel: 01454 616767 Fax: 01454 616189; The Organ Wing, Hill House, Hill House Road, Staplehill, Bristol Tel: 0117 956 4361 — MB ChB 1966 Bristol.

COLMAN, Bernard Harold, VRD Department of Otolaryngology, Radcliffe Infirmary, Oxford OX2 6HE Tel: 01865 249891 — MB ChB 1947 Ed.; MSc Oxf. 1984, BSc 1971, MA 1967; ChM Ed. 1967, MB ChB 1947; FRCS Ed. 1953. (Ed.) Cons. ENT Surg. Oxon AHA (T); Clin. Lect. (Otolaryng.) Univ. Oxf. Socs: Coll. Otorhinolaryngol. Amicitiae Sacrum; Fell. (Pres. Sect. Otol.) Roy. Soc. Med. Prev: Sen. Regist. (ENT) Roy. Infirm. Edin.; Surg. Lt.-Cdr. RNR; Schuknecht Research Fell.

COLMAN, Gary 12 Garsdale, Birtley, Chester-le-Street DH3 2EY — MB ChB 1992 Leic.

COLMAN, Jennifer Elaine Rita Dale Lodge, Sandy Lane, Dereham NR19 2EA — LMSSA 1984 Lond.

COLMAN, Richard Douglas 156 Fulford Road, York YO10 4DA Tel: 01904 620091 Fax: 01751 432342 Email: richardcol@doctors.org.uk; Cowl House, Bransdale, Fadmoor, York YO62 7JW Tel: 01751 432342 Fax: 01751 432342 — MB BChir 1976 Camb.; MA Camb. 1976; MRCGP 1980; Dip. Occ. Med. RCP Lond. 1997; DRCOG 1979. (St. Bart.) Indep. GP York; York DSS Bd.ing Doctor; Occupat. Health Phys. Socs: Soc. Occupat. Med.; Assur. Med. Soc.

COLMER, John Philip (retired) 9 Monmouth Hill, Topsham, Exeter EX3 0JQ Tel: 01392 874436 — MB BS 1954 Lond. Prev: Ship's Surg. Cable & Wireless (Marine) Ltd.

COLMER, Mr Malcolm Richard (retired) 50 Dudlow Lane, Liverpool L18 2EZ Tel: 0151 722 4523 — MB BChir Camb. 1962; MA Camb. 1963, MChir 1975; FRCS Eng. 1966. JP. Prev: Cons. Surg. Whiston & St. Helens Hosp. Liverp.

COLMSEE, Manfred Rudiger Park Surgery, Park Surgery, Hursley Road, Chandlers Ford, Eastleigh SO53 2ZH Tel: 023 8026 7355 Fax: 023 8026 5394; 4 Weardale Road, Chandlers Ford, Eastleigh SO53 3BH Tel: 01703 254317 — BM Soton. 1982; MRCGP 1986; DRCOG 1985; DCH RCP Lond. 1984. Prev: Trainee GP VTS Roy. Hants. Co. Hosp. Winchester; Ho. Phys. (Gen. Med.) Roy. Hants. Co. Hosp. Winchester; Ho. Surg. (Gen. Surg.) Salisbury Gen. Infirm.

COLOVER, Jack (retired) Dept. of Neurology, Lamberth Wing, St Thomas Hospital, London SE1 7EH Tel: 020 7722 4523 Email: jack@colover.fsnet.co.uk — MB BS Lond. 1939; MD Lond. 1947; FRCP Lond. 1972, M 1946; MRCS Eng. LRCP Lond. 1937. Brook & Greenwich Dist. Hosps. & Medway & Gravesend Hosp. Gps.; Research Assoc. Rayne Inst. St. Thos. Hosp. Lond.; Mem. Research Gp. Neurogenetics & Neuro-Ophth. World Federat. Neurol. Prev: Cons. Neurol. SE Metrop. Regional Neurol. & Neurosurg. Centres.

COLQUHOUN, Alexander Davidson Directorate Anaesthesia & Intensive Care, The Royal Infirmary, University NHS Trust, Glasgow G31 3ER Tel: 0141 211 4620 Fax: 0141 211 5920 Email: a.d.colquhouu@clinmed.gla.ac.uk; 39 Moorfoot Way, Bearsden, Glasgow G61 4RL Tel: 0141563 7453 — MB ChB 1978 Glas.; MRCGP 1983; FRCA 1985; DRCOG 1982. Cons. Anaesth. Glas. Roy. Infirm.; Hon.Clin. Sen. Lect. in Anaesth., Glas. Univ.,; ACTA Treas.; Director, Glas. ANAESTHETIC Serv.s Ltd. Socs: Assn. Cardio-Thoracic Anaesth.; Assoc Dent. Anaesth.s; Assoc. Anaesth.s GB& Irel. Prev: Instruc. (Anaesth.) Med. Coll. Virginia Richmond, USA; Sen. Regist. (Anaesth.) Leicester Roy. Infirm.; Regist. (Anaesth.) W.. Infirm Glas.

COLQUHOUN, Alexandra Jane 28 Wollaston Road, Irchester, Wellingborough NN29 7DE — MB ChB 1997 Leic.

COLQUHOUN, Anne Brodie Plantly Moss Farm, Lochwinnoch PA12 4DW Tel: 01505 842205 — MB ChB 1971 Glas.; DObst RCOG 1973.

COLQUHOUN, Helen Anne Pleiad, Balmoral Suite, Royal British House, Leonard Street, Perth PH2 8HA Tel: 01738 563777 Fax: 01738 563778 Email: hac@pleiad.co.uk — MB ChB 1984 Ed.; BSc Ed 1979; MRCGP 1988; Dip. Pharm. Med. RCP (UK) 1991; FFPHM 2000 UK. Cons. Pharmaceut. Phys. Pleiad Ltd. Perth; Non-Princip. GP, Peripatetic. Prev: Assoc. Med. Dir. Syntex Pharmaceuts.

COLQUHOUN, Iain Robert Department of Radiology, Charing Cross Hospital, Fulham Palace Road, London W6 8RF — MB BS 1977 Lond.; FRCS Eng. 1981; MRCS Eng. LRCP Lond. 1977; FRCR 1985. (Guy's) Cons. Neuroradiol. Char. Cross Hosp. Lond. Prev: Sen. Regist. (Neuroradiol.) Newc. Gen. Hosp.; Sen. Regist. (Radiol.) Soton. Gen. Hosp.; Regist. (Radiol.) John Radcliffe Hosp. Oxf.

COLQUHOUN, Mr Ian William Consultant Cardiothoracic Surgeon, Directorate of Cardiothoracic Surgery, Glasgow Royal Infirmary, Alexander Parade, Glasgow G31 2ER Tel: 0141 211 4733; 19 Easdale Place, Newton Mearns, Glasgow G77 6XD — MB ChB 1982 Glas.; FRCS (Cth) Glas. 1994; FRCS Glas. 1987. Cons. Cardiothoracic Surg.Roy. Infirm. Glas. Socs: Soc. Thoracic & Cardiovasc. Surgs. GB & Irel. Prev: Sen. Regist. (Cardiothoracic Surg.) Roy. Infirm. Glas.; Cardiopulmn. Transpl. Fell. Freeman Hosp. Newc.; Regist. (Cardiothoracic) Gtr. Glas. HB.

COLQUHOUN, John Hubert Carr Runkerry, 72 St John's Road, Clacton-on-Sea CO15 4BT Tel: 01255 424010 — MB BCh BAO 1953 Dub. (TC Dub.) Med. Assessor for Mobility Allowances. Prev: Ho. Surg. King Edwd. VII Hosp. Windsor; Obst. Ho. Surg. S.lands Hosp. Shoreham; Capt. RAMC.

COLQUHOUN, Katherine Barbara Margaret Greeta, North Road, Sandwich Bay, Sandwich CT13 9PJ — MB BS 1996 Lond.

COLQUHOUN, Margaret Kirk (retired) 5 Balmyle Road, West Ferry, Dundee DD5 1JJ Tel: 01382 778195 — MB ChB 1956 St. And.

COLQUHOUN, Marigilka Cunha e Silva 30 Ceylon Road, London W14 0PY — Medico Federal Univ. Bahia, Brazil 1978.

COLQUHOUN, Michael Charles The Court Road Surgery, Court Road, Malvern WR14 3BL Tel: 01684 573161 Fax: 01694 561593 — MB BS 1974 Lond.; BSc Lond. 1971; MRCP (UK) 1977; MRCGP 1989; DRCOG 1984; FRCP 1998. (St. Mary's) Clin. Asst. (Cardiol.) Hereford Co. Hosp.; Examr. RCS Edin.; Sec. Resusc. Counc. UK; Vice Chairm. Resusc. Counc. UK. Socs: Exec. Mem. Europ. Resusc. Counc.; Brit. Cardiac Soc. Prev: Regist. (Cardiol.) Guy's Hosp. Lond.; Regist. (Med. & Cardiol.) Roy. Free Hosp. Lond.

COLQUHOUN, Paul Simon 38 Cole Park Road, Twickenham TW1 1HS — MB BS 1992 Lond.

COLQUHOUN, Roisin Geraldine 1A Riley Bank Mews, Manley Road, Frodsham, Warrington WA6 6HP Tel: 01928 740756 — MB BCh BAO 1984 Belf.; MB BCh Belf. l984; MRCGP 1989; DRCOG 1986; AFPM 1996. (Queen's University Belfast) Socs: Brit. Assn. Pharmaceut. Phys.

COLQUHOUN FLANNERY, Mr William 11 Suffolk Drive, Whiteley, Fareham PO15 7DE Email: kelly@soton.ac.uk — BM 1988 Soton.; FRCS Eng. 1993. (Soton. Univ. Med. Sch.) Regist. (ENT Surg.) Soton. Gen. Hosp. Prev: SHO (Head & Neck) Roy. Marsden Hosp.; SHO (Gen. & Vasc. Surg.) Roy. Bournemouth Hosp.; SHO (Paediat. Surg.) Wessex Regional Paediat. Surg. Centre.

COLQUITT, Hugh Richard (retired) 9 Ranmoor Court, Graham Road, Sheffield S10 3DW — MB BS 1946 Lond.; MD Lond. 1952; MRCP Lond. 1949; FCPath 1967. Prev: Regist. Path. & Ho. Phys. Univ. Coll. Hosp.

COLSON, Hugh William (retired) Pendragon, St. Mawes, Truro TR2 5AZ Tel: 01326 270593 — MRCS Eng. LRCP Lond. 1946; MRCVS Ed. 1942. Prev: Res. Obst. Off. St. Mary's Hosp.

COLSON, Simon James 19 Queen Anne's Grove, Bedford Park, London W4 1HW — MB ChB 1985 Manch.; MBA Lond. 1991. Prev: Ho. Surg. St. Helier Hosp. Carshalton; Ho. Phys. Mayday Hosp. Thornton Heath.

COLT, Joan Margaret Roper (retired) Mulberries, Mavelstone Road, Bromley BR1 2PD Tel: 020 8460 9745 — MB ChB Aberd. 1959; MA Aberd. 1953. Prev: Occupat. Health Med. Adviser Bromley HA.

COLTART, Douglas John Department of Cardiology, Guy's & St Thomas' Trust, St. Thomas' Hospital, London SE1 7EH Tel: 020 7928 9292 Fax: 020 7960 5673 Email: john.coltart@gstt.sthames.nhs.uk; (cons. rooms), 15 Upper Wimpole St, London W1M 2TB Tel: 020 7486 5787 Fax: 020 7486 5470 Email: john@coltarts.demon.co.uk — MB BS Lond. 1967; MD Lond. 1972; FRCP Lond. 1983, M 1969; MRCS Eng. LRCP Lond. 1967; FESC 1985; FACC 1977. (St. Bart.) Clin. Director of Cardiac Serv. - Cons. Phys., Hon. Sen. Lect. & Cardiol. Guy's & St Thos. Hosps.; Clin. Dir. of Cardiac Servs.; Cons. Phys. Metrop. Police; Hon. Cons. Phys. St. Luke's Hosp. for Clergy; Civil. Cosultant in Cardiol. to the army; Cons. Cardiol., King Edwd. VII Hosp.; Cons. Cardiol. Roy. Navy Assn. Socs: Fell. Amer. Coll. Cardiol.; Brit. Cardiac Soc.; Brit. Pharm. Soc. Prev: Regist. (Cardiol.) Hammersmith Hosp. (Roy. Postgrad. Med. Sch. St. Bart. Hosp. Lond.; Fell. (Cardiol.) Stanford Univ., USA.

COLTART, Robert Stewart Kent & Canterbury Hospital, Ethelbert Road, Canterbury CT1 3NG Tel: 01227 766877; Field House, Station Road, Bridge, Canterbury CT4 5AJ Tel: 01227 830896 — MB BS 1976 Lond.; FRCP Lond. 1996; FRCR 1985; DCH Eng. 1980. (St. Bart.) Cons. Clin. Oncol. Kent & Canterbury Hosp. NHS Trust. Prev: Sen. Regist. Velindre Hosp. Cardiff; MRC Train. Fell. Camb.

COLTART, Mr Timothy McCallum Lister Hospital, Chelsea Bridge Road, London SW1W 8RH Tel: 020 7730 8522 Fax: 020 7730 7391 — MB BChir 1963 Camb.; PhD Lond. 1968; MA Camb. 1969; FRCS Ed. 1970; FRCOG 1983, M 1970. (St. Bart.) Cons. Socs: Roy. Soc. Med. (Ex-Pres. Sect. Obst. & Gyn.). Prev: Cons. O & G Guy's Hosp. .; Cons O&G Qu. Charlottes &Chelsea Hosp.

COLTER, Elizabeth Frances 163 Milwards, Hatfield AL10 8UU — MB ChB 1983 Leic.

COLTER, Margaret 1 Beechacre, Ramsbottom, Bury BL0 9LS — MB ChB 1978 Manch. (Manchester) GP.

COLTHURST, Mr James Richard 19 High Stree, Hungerford RG17 0NL Tel: 01488 684008 Fax: 01488 684008; Balsdon Farm House, Folly Road, Inkpen, Hungerford RG17 9DH — MB BS 1981 Lond.; BSc Lond. 1978; MBA Brunel 1992; FRCS Ed. 1986; MFHom 1995. (St. Thos.) Indep. Med. Practitioner; Indep. Managem. Cons. Hungerford. Socs: Old Etonian Med. Soc. Prev: Managing Dir. Oxycare Ltd.; Regist. (Radiol.) St. Thos. Hosp. Lond.; Regist. (Surg.) Watford.

COLTMAN, Mr David Brompton King Street Surgery, 38 King Street, Lancaster LA1 1RE; Forge Mill House, Forge Mill, Canton, Lancaster LA2 9NB — MB BS 1967 Newc.; FRCS Ed. 1974. Prev: Regist. (Surg.) Sunderland Gen. Hosp.; Regist. (Cardiothoracic Surg.) Shotley Bridge Gen. Hosp.; Regist. (Surg.) Roy. Vict. Infirm. Newc.

COLTMAN, Katharine Margaret Dawson (retired) Galloway Rise, West Burton, Leyburn DL8 4JW Tel: 01969 663507 — MB ChB Leeds 1945; DCH Eng. 1946; DObst RCOG 1948. Prev: Ho. Phys. (Childr.) & Ho. Surg.(Orthop.) Gen. Infirm. Leeds.

COLTMAN, Timothy Patrick, Surg. Lt. RN Royal Hospital Haslar, Gosport PO12 2AA Tel: 01705 762510; 3 The Gate House, Clocktower Drive, Royal Gate, Southsea PO4 96A Tel: 01705 839274 — MB BS 1994 Lond. (Lond. Hosp. Med. Coll.) SHO (A & E) Roy. Hosp. Haslar SHO Gen. Surg. Prev: Med. Off. HMS N.d.; Force Med. Off. Cdr. Standing Naval Force (Channel); SHO (A & E) Derriford Hosp. Plymouth.

COLTON, Professor Christopher Lewis Toft Barn, Farmer St., Bradmore, Nottingham NG11 6PE Tel: 0115 921 3331 Fax: 0115 921 3113 Email: cxcolton@cs.com — MB BS 1960 Lond.; FRCS Ed. (Orth.) 1979; FRCS Eng. 1963; MRCS Eng. LRCP Lond. 1960. (St. Thos.) Cons. Emerit. Nottm. Univ. Hosp.; Special Prof. Orthop. & Accid. Surg. Nottm. Univ. Socs: Fell. (Ex-Pres.) BOA; Hon. Mem. Deutsche Gesellschaft für Unfallchirurgie; Hon. Mem. Hellenic Assn. for Orthop. Surg. & Traumatol. Prev: Lect. (Orthop. Surg.) Roy. Nat. Orthop. Hosp. Lond.; Regist. (Gen. Surg.) Frenchay Hosp. Bristol.; Regist. (Orthop. Surg.) Bristol Roy. Infirm.

COLTON, Fiona Mary Elizabeth Ballyowen Health Centre, 179 Andersonstown Road, Belfast BT11 9EA Tel: 028 9061 0611 Fax: 028 9043 1323 — MB BCh BAO 1986 Belf.; MRCGP 1991; DObst. RCPI 1990; DCH RCPS Glas. 1990; DMH Belf. 1989. Socs: BMA & MPS.

COLUMB, Malachy Oliver Department Anesthesiology, Univ.of Michigan Medical Center, 1500 East Medical Center Drive, IG323 University Hospital, Box 0048, Ann Arbor MI 48109, USA; 4 Courtenays, The Green, Seacroft, Leeds LS14 6JZ — MB BCh BAO 1985 NUI; FCAnaesth. 1990; DA (UK) 1988. Fell. (Cardiothoracic Anaesth.) Gen. Infirm Leeds.

COLVER, Allan Froggatt Burnbrae, Hepscott, Morpeth NE61 6LH Tel: 01670 517199 — MB BS 1976 Lond.; MA Camb. 1970; MD Newc. 1993; FRCP Ed. 1995; FRCP Lond. 1991; MRCP (UK) 1980; FRCPCH 1997. Sen. Lect. (Community Child Health) Univ. Newc. u. Tyne.

COLVER, Doreen Christine Boyd 17 Stumperlowe Park Road, Sheffield S10 3QP — MB ChB St. And. 1940; DCH Eng. 1946. (St. And.) Socs: BMA. Prev: Clin. Asst. Centre for Human Genetics Sheff.; Ho. Phys. Hosp. Sick Childr. Gt. Ormond St. Lond.; Surg. Lt. RNVR 1944-46.

COLVER, Graham Borland Department of Dermatology, Chesterfield & North Derbyshire Royal Hospital, Chesterfield S44 5BL; Oakwood, 1 Ryecroft Glen Road, Sheffield S17 3NG — BM BCh 1974 Oxf.; DM Oxf. 1990, BM BCh 1974; FRCP Ed. 1993; MRCP (UK) 1979. Cons. Dermat. Chesterfield & N. Derbysh. Roy. Hosp.; Hon. Clin. Lect. (Med. & Pharmacol.) Sheff. Univ. Prev: Sen. Regist. (Dermat.) Roy. Infirm. Edin.; Regist. (Med.) Whipps Cross Hosp. Lond.; Regist. (Dermat.) Slade Hosp. Oxf.

COLVER, Hilary Moira Community Child Health Services, Edinburgh University Hospital NHS Trust, 10 Chalners Way, Edinburgh EH9 1TS Tel: 0131 536 0000; 2 Eglinton Crescent, Edinburgh EH12 5DH — BM BS 1975 Nottm.; BMedSci Nottm. 1973; DCH Eng. 1978. (Nottm.) SCMO Edin. Univ. Hosps. NHS Trust.

COLVER, Patricia Anne Morpeth Health Centre, Gas House Lane, Morpeth NE61 1SR Tel: 01670 513657 Fax: 01670 511966; Burnbrae, Hepscott, Morpeth NE61 6LH Tel: 01670 517199 — MB BS 1976 Lond.; MRCGP 1982; DCH Eng. 1981; DA Eng. 1980. (St Bartholomews Hospital) Prev: GP Heaton Newc.

COLVER, Sally Elizabeth Avenue Medical Practice, 7 Reney Avenue, Sheffield S8 7FH Tel: 0114 237 7649; Oakwood, 1 Ryecroft Glen Road, Sheffield S17 3NG Tel: 0114 236 1438 — MB BS 1979 Lond.; MRCP (UK) 1982; MRCGP 1985; DRCOG 1984; DCH RCP Lond. 1983. (Middlesex Hospital)

COLVILLE, Alaric Public Health Laboratory, Church Lane, Heavitree, Exeter EX2 5AD Tel: 01392 402977 Fax: 01392 412835 Email: acolville@phls.org.uk — BM BCh 1981 Oxf.; FRCpath 1998; MSc Lond. 1987; MA Camb. 1982; MRCP (UK) 1985; MRCPath 1990; MBA 2000 Durham. Cons. Microbiologist, Pub. health Laboratary Serv. Exeter. Prev: Asst. Microbiol. (Sen. Regist.) Pub. Health Laborat. Serv. Nottm.; Cons. Microbiol. Pub. Health Laborat. Carlisle. Pub. Health Lab.

COLVILLE, Barry (retired) Pool Foot, Clappersgate, Ambleside LA22 9NE Tel: 015394 34067 — MB BS Durh. 1953; FRCGP 1971, M 1965. Prev: Tutor (Gen. Pract.) Univ. Leeds.

COLVILLE, Caroline Cecelia Histopathology Department, Rockefeller Building, University St., London WC1E 6JJ Tel: 020 7209 6033 — MB BS 1996 Lond. (Char. Cross and Westm. Lond.) Specialist Regist.(Histopath.) Univ. Coll. Lond. Prev: SHO, (Path.) Trafford Gen. Hosp. Manch.; Ho. Off. (Med.) Guildford; Ho. Off. (Surg.) Redhill.

COLVILLE, Douglas Robert Rutherglen Health Centre, 130 Stonelaw Road, Rutherglen, Glasgow G73 2PQ Tel: 0141 531 6030 Fax: 0141 531 6031 — MB ChB 1979 Dundee.

COLVILLE, Elizabeth Ann (retired) Poolfoot, Clappersgate, Ambleside LA22 9NE — MB BS 1953 Durh. Prev: Med. Off. Univ. Health Serv. Univ. Leeds.

COLVILLE, Ivor Alan (retired) 33 St Marks Road, Bath BA2 4PA Tel: 01225 310883 — MB ChB 1950 Ed.

COLVILLE, Mr John (retired) 3 Church Close, Belmore, Ballylesson, Belfast BT8 8JX Fax: 02890 826935 — MB BCh BAO Belf. 1955; FRCSI 1981, FRCS Ed. 1962; DObst RCOG 1958. Cons. Plastic Surg. Ulster Hosp. Dundonald, Roy. Vict. Hosp. Belf. & Roy. Belf. Hosp. Sick Childr. Prev: Pres. Brit. Sco. Surg. of Hand.

COLVILLE, John Colin Holly House, 5 Holly Road, Macclesfield SK11 8JA — MB ChB 1983 Liverp.; MRCP (UK) 1988; DA (UK) 1990. Regist. (Anaesth.) Liverp. Prev: SHO (Anaesth.) Roy. Liverp. Hosp.

COLVILLE, John Fergus (retired) Brierley, Little Green, Mells, Frome BA11 3QZ — MB BS 1954 Durh. Prev: GP Radstock & Dist.

COLVILLE, John Robertson (retired) (cons. rooms), 10 Harley St., London W1N 1AA Tel: 020 7580 4280 — MB BS 1959 Melbourne; MRCPsych 1972; T(Psychiat.) 1991; DPM Eng. 1965. Hon. Med. Off. Roy. Irish Regt. TA Duke of York's HQ Chelsea. Prev: Cons. (Child & Adolesc. Psychiat.) Oxf. RHA, Bloomfield Clinic Guy's Hosp. Lond & King Edwd. Hosp. Windsor.

COLVILLE, Linda Jean 36 Cherry Vale, Liverpool L25 5PX Tel: 0151 428 5848 — MB BS 1979 Lond.; FFA RCS Eng. 1986. Cons. Anaesth. Aintree Trust Hosp. Liverp.

COLVILLE, Robert Lawson Kellock (retired) 34 Fairfield Drive, Clarkston, Glasgow G76 7YH Tel: 0141 644 1664 — MB ChB 1953 Glas.; DObst RCOG 1954; FRCGP 1978, M 1968. Phys. (Occupat. Health), CocaCola & Schweppes Beverages plc; Hon. Clin. Lect. Univ. Glas. Prev: Non-Exec. Dir. Vict. Infirm. NHS Trust. Glas.

COLVILLE, Wesley Creighton (retired) 8 Homewood Road, Northenden, Manchester M22 4DN Tel: 0161 998 8866 — MB ChB 1938 Glas.

COLVIN, Andrew Paul Central Surgery, Sussex Road, Gorleston-on-Sea, Great Yarmouth NR31 6QB Tel: 01493 414141 Fax: 01493 656253; 5 Yallop Avenue, Gorleston, Great Yarmouth NR31 6HA Tel: 01493 442179 — MB ChB 1982 Glas.; MRCGP 1989; Dip. IMC RCS Ed. 1990; DRCOG 1987; AFOM 1997. (Univ. Glas.) GP; Occupat. Phys. Dep. Clin. Dir., James Paget Hosp. Hyperbaric Unit. Socs: Soc. Occupat. Med.; (Chairm.) Brit. Hyperbaric Assn.; Fac. Pre-hosp. Care. Prev: Trainee GP RAMC VTS; RMO 7 Ghurka Rifles, Hong Kong.

COLVIN, Bernard Alexander John 3 Inverary Terrace, Dundee DD3 6BS — MB ChB 1996 Dundee.

COLVIN, Mr Bernard Charles (retired) 3 Inverary Terrace, Dundee DD3 6BS — MB ChB 1957 Glas.; FRCS Ed. 1970; FRCS Glas. 1970. Hon. Sen. Lect. (Orthop. & Traum. Surg.) Univ. Dundee. Prev: Cons. Orthop. Surg. Roy. Infirm. Dundee.

COLVIN, Brian Trevor Department of Haematology, The Royal London Hospital, Whitechapel Road, London E1 1BB Tel: 020 7377 7455 Fax: 020 7377 7016; White Croft, South Hill, Chislehurst BR7 5EF Tel: 020 8467 3833 — MB BChir Camb. 1970; MA Camb. 1970; FRCP Lond. 1990; MRCP (UK) 1972; FRCPath 1988, M 1976. (Camb. & Lond. Hosp.) Sen. Lect. & Hon. Cons. Haemat. St. Bart. & Roy. Lond. Sch. Med. & Dent.; Asst. Warden (Stud. Affairs) St. Bart. & Roy. Lond. Sch. Med. & Dent. Socs: Roy. Soc. Med. (Pres. Sect. Path.); BMA; Brit. Soc. Haematol. Prev: Regist. (Gen. Med., Haemat. & Cardiol.) Lond. Hosp.; Lect. (Haemat.) Lond. Hosp. Med. Coll.; Ho. Phys. & Ho. Surg. Lond. Hosp.

COLVIN, David Wylie 35C Church Road, Richmond TW9 1UA Tel: 020 8940 0528 — MB ChB 1989 Glas.; MRCP (UK) 1995.

COLVIN, Deborah Rosalind The Lawson Practice, 85 Nuttall Street, London N1 5HZ Tel: 020 7739 9701; 35 Andrews Road, London E8 4RL — MB BS 1982 Lond.; MRCGP 1985; DRCOG 1985.

COLVIN, Douglas Abraham The Surgery, 37 Ongar Road, Abridge, Romford RM4 1UH Tel: 01992 761387 Fax: 01992 716163 — MB BS 1988 Lond.; BSc Lond. 1985; MRCGP 1994. (London Hospital Medical College) p/t Clin. Asst. (Dermat.) King Geo. Hosp. Ilford. Prev: Trainee GP Redbridge HA VTS.

COLVIN, Ian Benjamin 9 Fallowfield, Stanmore HA7 3DF — BM BS 1998 Nottm.; BM BS Nottm 1998.

COLVIN, Ian George Scotsburn Road Health Centre, Scotsburn Road, Tain IV19 1PR Tel: 01862 892203 Fax: 01862 892165; Cromdale, Knockbreck Road, Tain IV19 1BW — MB ChB 1977 Glas.; DRCOG 1980. (Glas.) Prev: SHO (Chest & Gen. Med.) Heathfield Hosp. Ayr.; SHO (O & G) Ayrsh. Centr. Hosp. Irvine.

COLVIN, John Russell Ninewells Hospital and Medical School, Dundee DD1 9SY Tel: 01382 632175 Email: j.r.colvin@dundee.ac.uk — MB ChB 1982 Aberd.; FFA RCSI 1987; FRCA 1987. Cons. Anaesth. & Intens. Care Ninewells Hosp. & Hon. Sen. Lect. Dundee. Socs: Scott. Soc. Anaesth. & Assn. Anaesth. Prev: Sen. Regist. (Anaesth.) Ninewells Hosp. Dundee; Research Fell. Univ. (Anaesth.) Glas.; Regist. (Anaesth.) W.. Infirm. Glas.

COLVIN, Joyce Wylie (retired) 27 Gartcows Drive, Falkirk FK1 5QQ Tel: 01324 622760 — MB ChB Glas. 1952; DA Eng. 1957. Prev: Assoc. Specialist (Anaesth.) Falkirk & Dist. Roy. Infirm.

COLVIN, Laura Juliet 4 Hardy Road, London SE3 7NR Tel: 020 8858 0373 — MB ChB 1998 Leic.; MB ChB Leic 1998. Med. Ho. Off., Geo. Elliot Hosp., Nuneaton. Socs: MDU; BMA. Prev: Ho. Off. (Urol.), Leicester.

COLVIN, Lesley Anne 8 Leslie Place, Edinburgh EH4 1NH Tel: 0131 332 8521 — MB ChB 1990 Ed.; BSc (Med. Sci.) Ed. 1988; FRCA 1994. Clin. Research Fell. (Anaesth.) Roy. Infirm. Edin. Univ. Edin.

COLVIN, Michael Andrew 3 Inverary Terrace, Dundee DD3 6BS — MB ChB 1992 Dundee.

COLVIN, Michael Peter Dept. of Anaesthesia, Royal London Hospital, Whitechapel, London E1 1BB Tel: 020 7377 7787 Email: mpcol@lineone.net; 4 Hardy Road, Blackheath, London SE3 7NR Tel: 020 8858 0373 Email: mpcol@lineone.net — MB BS 1965 Lond. Univ.; BSc Lond. 1962; MRCS Eng. LRCP Lond. 1965; FRCA Eng. 1969. (Lond. Hosp.) Cons. Anaesth. Barts and The Lond. NHS Trust; Clin. Director Support Serv.s, Barts and The Lond. NHS Trust. Socs: Assn. Anaesths. & Intens. Care Soc.; Soc. of Apoth. Prev: Sen. Lect. (Anaesth.) Lond. Hosp. Med. Coll.; Clin. Instruc. (Anaesth.) Univ. Calif. San Diego, U.S.A.; Hon. Anaesth. Sydney Hosp., Australia.

COLVIN, Peter William Booth The Archway Surgery, Dobbin Lane, Armagh BT61 7QP Tel: 028 3752 1400 Fax: 028 3752 1444 Email: archway@talk21.com; 27 Drumilly Road, Hockley, Armagh BT61 8RG — MB BCh BAO 1979 Belf.; MRCGP 1983; DCH Dub. 1982; FRCGP 1997.

COLVIN, Susan The Clarendon Surgery, 213 Burrage Road, London SE18 7JZ Tel: 020 8854 0356 Fax: 020 8855 5484; 4 Hardy Road, Blackheath, London SE3 7NR Tel: 020 8858 0373 — MB BS Lond. 1969; DCH Eng. 1971; DObst RCOG 1970. (Lond. Hosp.) Princip. GP Greenwich & Bexley HA.

COLWELL, Rex Arthur (retired) Rossyln, 3 Croft Road, Evesham WR11 4NE Tel: 01386 442283 — MB BS 1957 Lond.; MRCS Eng. LRCP Lond. 1956; DObst RCOG 1958. Hosp. Pract. (Obst.) Avonside Hosp. Prev: Receiv. Room Off. Lond. Hosp.

COLWILL, Rebecca Catherine Dingle Farm, Little Witley, Worcester WR6 6LF — MB ChB 1991 Leeds; Primary FFA Irel. 1998.

COLYER, Elizabeth Emily Stuart Grayshott Surgery, Boundary Road, Hindhead GU26 6TY; Tremont House, Linden Chase, Sevenoaks TN13 3JT — BM 1990 Soton.; BSc (Hons.) Biol. Sc. Exeter 1986; MRCGP 1996; DRCOG 1994. (Soton.) GP Locum (long term) Grayshott Surg. Socs: Med. Defence Union. Prev: GP/Regist. Grayshoot Surrey; RMO Psychiat. ChristCh. New Zealand; RMO Surg. ChristCh. New Zealand.

COLYER, Perihan Eva Claremont Surgery, 2 Cookham Road, Maidenhead SL6 8AN — MB BS 1984 Lond.; BSc Lond. 1981; MRCGP (Distinc.) 1988; DRCOG 1988; Cert. Family Plann. 1988; DCH RCP Lond. 1987. (Univ. Coll. Hosp.) Prev: Trainee GP Windsor VTS.

COMAISH, Barbara (retired) Hallington Mill, Hallington, Newcastle upon Tyne NE19 2LJ Tel: 01434 672311 — MB BS Lond. 1958; DCH Eng. 1962.

COMAISH, Ian Francis University Hospital, Queen's Medical Centre, Nottingham NG7 2UH — BM BCh 1991 Oxf.; MA Camb. 1992. Specialist Regist., Univ. Hosp. Qu.'s Med. Centre, Notts. Prev: SHO (Ophth.) Roy. United Hosp. Bath.

COMAISH, James Stanley Department of Dermatology, Royal Victoria Infirmary, Newcastle upon Tyne NE1 4LP; Hallington Mill, Hallington, Newcastle upon Tyne NE19 2LJ Tel: 01434 672311 — MB ChB 1954 Liverp.; MD Liverp. 1975; FRCP Lond. 1974, M 1960. Emerit. Cons. Dermat. Roy. Vict. Infirm. Newc. u. Tyne; Med. Mem., appeals tribunals. Socs: Brit. Soc. of Dermatlogfical Surg. (Hon.LifeMem.); Internat. Soc. for Dermatol. Surg. (Ex-Treas.); BMA (Ex-Chairm. Newc. Br.). Prev: Vis. Prof. (Dermat.) Univ. Pennsylvania, USA; Sen. Lect. (Dermat.) Univ. Newc.; Vis. Research Assoc. Duhring Laborats. Univ. Pennsylvania, USA.

COMAS, Antonio 27 Beech Court, Liverpool L18 3JZ — LMS 1991 Saragossa.

COMBE, Amanda Jayne 17 College Terrace, Brighton BN2 2EE — MB ChB 1993 Sheff.

COMBE, Elizabeth Anne Charing Cross Hospital, Fulham Palace Road, London W6 8RF Tel: 020 8846 1234 — MB BS 1989 Lond.

COMBE, Gillian Margaret The Basement Flat, 6 Worcester Terrace, Bristol BS8 3JW — MB ChB 1995 Bristol.

COMBE, John Roderick Springfield Farm, Polton, Lasswade EH18 1DY — MB ChB 1973 Ed.

COMBE, William Alexander Dunlop, CStJ c/o Lloyds Bank, High St., High Wycombe — MRCS Eng. LRCP Lond. 1946; BA (Applied Sc.) Open 1986; DA Eng. 1953. (St. Mary's) Assoc. Anaesth. St. John Ophth. Hosp. Jerusalem, Israel. Prev: Asst. Anaesth. Moorfields Eye Hosp. Lond.; Regist. (Anaesth.) Hosp. Sick Childr. Gt. Ormond St. Lond. & Roy. Hosp. Sick Childr. Edin.

COMBER, Edward Weybridge Health Centre, Church Street, Weybridge KT13 8DW Tel: 01932 853366 Fax: 01932 859851 — MB BCh BAO 1979 NUI; MRCGP 1985; DCH NUI 1983; DObst RCPI 1981. Div. Surg. Metrop. Police.

COMBER, Margaret Grace Tapmoor Cottage, Moorlinch, Bridgwater TA7 9BZ — MB BS 1966 Lond. (Middlx.) Clin. Asst. Cas. Yeovil Dist. Hosp. Prev: SHO (Traum. Surg.) Yeovil Dist. Hosp.; SHO (Cas.) Dorset Co. Hosp. Dorchester; SHO (Obst.) Yeovil Dist. Hosp.

COMBES, Nicholas John 17 Millhaven Avenue, Birmingham B30 2QH — MB ChB 1988 Birm.

COMBES, Shirley Genevieve 6 Gray Court, Parkleys, Ham, Richmond TW10 5LU — MB BS 1973 Lond.; MRCS Eng. LRCP Lond. 1973.

COMER, Christine Elizabeth 13 Dingwall Drive, Greasby, Wirral CH49 1SG — MB BCh 1974 Wales.

COMER, Desmond Joseph 13 Dingwell Drive, Greasby, Wirral CH49 1SG — MB ChB 1976 Manch.

COMER, Marie Brigid 250 St George's Road, Preston PR1 6NQ — MB ChB 1986 Manch.; MRCP (UK) 1989. Research Regist. (Rheum.) St. Bart. Hosp. Lond.

COMER, Ulrike Darvell Bruderhof, Robertsbridge TN32 5DR — State Exam Med 1989 Hamburg.

COMERCI, Giuseppe Department of Gynaecological Oncology, Queen Elizabeth Hospital, Gateshead NE9 9SX — State Exam 1991 Bologna.

COMERFORD, Mr David Graham (retired) The Yorkshire Council, Bradford Road, Bingley BD18 1TW Tel: 01274 500311 — MB ChB 1962 Leeds; FRCS Ed. 1969. Prev: Cons. Ent. Surg., Bradford Roy. Infirm.

COMERFORD, Michael Brian Elmore, Grande Route de Rozel, St Martin, Jersey JE3 6AP Tel: 01534 854296 — MB BS 1949 Lond.; DObst RCOG 1950. (St. Mary's) Sen. Research Fell. Waller Cardiopulm. Unit. St. Mary's Hosp. Lond.; Med. Adviser Clin. Research Dept. AB Hassle. Prev: Research Regist. (Obst.) St Mary's Hosp.

COMFORT, Alexander Chacombe House, Chacombe, Banbury OX17 2SL Tel: 01295 478 0089 — MB BChir Camb. 1944; PhD Lond. 1963, MA 1944; DSc Lond. 1963; MRCS Eng. LRCP Lond. 1944; DCH Eng. 1945. (Lond. Hosp.) Socs: (Ex-Pres.) Brit. Soc. Research on Ageing; Roy. Soc. Med. Prev: Adjunct. Prof. Neuropsychiat. Inst. Univ. Calif. Los Angeles; Dir. of Research (Gerontol.) Univ. Coll. Lond.; Lect. Physiol. Lond. Hosp. Med. Coll.

COMINOS, Mathilda 3 Ray Court, Somerset Road, London W13 9PA — MB BS 1994 Lond.

COMINS, Michael Edward 55 Humbolt Road, London W6 8QQ — MB BS 1996 Lond.

COMISKEY, Genevieve Ann Mayfield Road Surgery, 125 Mayfield Road, Edinburgh EH9 3AJ Tel: 0131 668 1095 Fax: 0131 662 1734 — MB BCh BAO 1987 NUI; MB BCh NUI 1987.

COMISKEY, Mary Claire Marie Curie Centre, Marie Curie Drive, Elswick Road, Newcastle upon Tyne NE4 6SS Tel: 0191 219 5560 Fax: 0191 256 5719 Email: mcomiskey@newcastlecentre.mariecurie.org.uk — MB BCh BAO 1985 NUI; FRCP 1999; MRCPI 1990. Cons. Palliat. Med. Marie Curie Centre Newc. & N. Centre for Cancer Treatm. Prev: Sen. Regist. (Palliat. Med.) Newc.

COMLEY, Lysbeth Ann 3 Lawton Close, Hinckley KE10 0YG — MB ChB 1964 St. And.; MRCP (U.K.) 1972. Cons. Paediat. Geo. Eliot Hosp. Nuneaton. Socs: FRCP; FRCPCH; BMA. Prev: Sen. Regist. Childr. Hosp. Birm.; Lect. Dept. Paediat. Univ. Rhodesia; Med. Regist. Walsgrave Hosp. Coventry.

COMMANDER, Martin John 55 Pereira Road, Birmingham B17 9JB — MB ChB 1985 Birm.

COMMANDER, Richard Anthony Dorian Prasad, Blackford and Commander, 6 Dyas Road, Great Barr, Birmingham B44 8SF Tel: 0121 373 1885; 16 Edge Hill Road, Sutton Coldfield B74 4NU — MB ChB 1979 Birm.; DRCOG 1982. GP Kingstanding Birm.

COMMON, Mr John Dermot Ainslie 11 King Street, Newcastle ST5 1EH Tel: 01782 614174 Fax: 01782 714957 — MRCS Eng. LRCP Lond. 1971; FRCS Eng. 1981; FRCOphth. (Westm.) Cons. Ophth. Surg. N. Staffs. Roy. Infirm. Prev: Sen. Regist. Birm. & Midl. Eye Hosp.; Regist. W.. Ophth. Hosp.

COMPER, John Wilbert (retired) 122 Mayfield Avenue, Orpington BR6 0AG — MB BS 1951 Lond.; MRCS Eng. LRCP Lond. 1951; MRCGP 1960. Prev: Surg. Lt. RNVR.

COMPER, Susan Janet 85 Kingswood Road, Bromley BR2 0NG Tel: 020 8464 0284 — MB BS 1978 Lond.; DCH RCP Lond. 1982. (Guy's)

COMPITUS, Barbara Ann 7 Beech Grove, South Bank, Middlesbrough TS6 6ST — MB ChB 1998 Birm.; ChB Birm. 1998.

COMPSON, Mr Jonathan Paul Orthopaedic Department, King's College Hospital, Denmark Hill, London SE5 9RS Tel: 020 7346 3388 Fax: 020 7346 3445 — MB BS 1980 Lond.; BSc Lond. 1977; FRCS (Orth.) 1994; FRCS Eng. 1987; FRCS Ed. 1986. (St. Mary's) Cons. Trauma & Orthop. King's Coll. Hosp. Lond.

COMPSON, Lindsey Jane Mauve Practice, Drumhar Health Centre, North Methven Street, Perth PH1 5PD Tel: 01738 622421 Fax: 01738 444077; Croft-An-Righ Farm House, Kinrossie, Perth PH2 6AU Tel: 01821 650492 — MB BS 1984 Lond.; DFFP 1987. Prev: GP Medway VTS; Clin. Med. Off. Medway.

COMPSTON, Juliet Elizabeth Department of Medicine, University of Cambridge Clinical Sch, Addenbrooke's Hospital, Hills Road, Cambridge CB2 2QQ Tel: 01223 336867 Fax: 01223 336846; Tel: 01223 893414 — MB BS Lond. 1970; BSc (Physiol.) Lond. 1967, MD 1979; FRCP Lond. 1988; MRCP (UK) 1973; FRCPath 1996, M 1989. (Middlx.) Lect. in Med. & Hon. Cons. Phys. Univ. Camb. Clin. Sch. Addenbrooke's Hosp. Camb.; Reader in Metab. Bone Dis. Socs: Pres. Bone & Tooth Soc.; Med. Res. Soc.; Amer. Soc. Bone & Mineral Research. Prev: Sen. Lect. (Path.) & Hon. Cons. (Med.) Univ.

Hosp. Wales Cardiff; Regist. (Med.) St. Thos. Hosp. Lond.; SHO Brompton Hosp. Lond.

COMPTON, Christopher Harold SmithKline Beecham Pharmaceuticals, New Frontiers Science Park (South), Third Avenue, Harlow CM19 5AW Tel: 01279 644715; 56 Walnut Way, Buckhurst Hill IG9 6HX — MB BCh 1988 Wales; MRCP (UK) 1991; Dip. Pharm. Med. RCP (UK) 1995. Pharmaceut. Phys. (Respirat. Research) SmithKline Beecham Pharmaceut. Harlow. Prev: Regist. (Gen. Med.) Roy. Gwent Hosp.; SHO (Renal Med.) Cardiff Roy. Infirm.

COMPTON, Desmond Michael Portaferry Health Centre, Ann Street, Portaferry, Newtownards BT22 1LX; 5 Richmond Park, Ballymoney BT53 7AE — MB BCh BAO 1974 Belf.

COMPTON, Mr Edward Hugh Medico-Legal Practice Independent, The Granary at Cotton Mill Farm, Farnsfield, Newark NG22 8ED Tel: 01623 883277 Fax: 01623 883277 Email: compton.ortho@virgin.net.uk — MB BS 1967 Lond.; MRCS Eng. LRCP Lond. 1967; FRCS Eng. 1972; HTC. Orthop. RCS Eng. 1981. (St. Geo. Lond.) Indep. Pract. Socs: Brit. Orthop. Assn.; Acad. Experts; Brit. Assn. Surg. Knee. Prev: Cons. Orthop. Surg. King's Mill Centre for Health Care Servs.; Sen. Regist. (Orthop.) Harlow Wood & Notts. AHA; Regist. (Orthop.) Lord Mayor Treloar Orthop. Hosp. Alton.

COMPTON, Miss Jacqueline The Old Forge, St Cross, South Elmham, Harleston IP20 0NZ Tel: 01986 782255 — MB BS 1992 Lond.; BSc Hons Lond 1989; MRCOG 1998. Specialist Regist. O & G E. Anglian Rotat.s.

COMPTON, Nicola Jane Penhill Farm, Fremington, Barnstaple EX31 2NG — MB BS 1981 Lond. Clin. Asst. N. Devon Health Trust.;Staff Grade Med.; OrthoGeriat.

COMPTON, Stephen Andrew Mater Hospital Trust, Crumlin Road, Belfast BT41 6AB Tel: 01232 741211 Email: sacompton@aol.com; 49 Castlehill Road, Belfast BT4 3GP Tel: 01232 763344 — MB BCh BAO 1976 Belf.; FRCPsych. 1997. Cons. Psychiat. of Old Age Mater Hosp. Trust. Socs: Ment. Health Act Comm. N Irel.

COMYNS, Malcolm John 121 Starlane, Canning Town, London E16 4QH Tel: 0207 476 4862 Fax: 0207 546 5306 — MRCS Eng. LRCP Lond. 1960. (Lond. Hosp.)

CONACHER, Eiona Innes (retired) 17 Braehead Road, Barnton, Edinburgh EH4 6BN Tel: 0131 339 1932 — MB ChB 1955 Ed.; MA, MB ChB Ed. 1955. Prev: Ho. Phys. Roy. N.. Infirm. Inverness.

CONACHER, Ruth Shepherd Reoch 25 Burnham Close, Enfield EN1 3RA — MB ChB Glas. 1956.

CONACHER, William Dawson Hamilton (retired) 17 Braehead Road, Edinburgh EH4 6BN — MB ChB (Commend.) Glas. 1946; FRCP Ed. 1965, M 1952; FRCP Glas. 1969, M 1962. Prev: Cons. Phys. Bangour Gen.. Hosp.

CONATY, Derek John The Surgery, Abbotswood Road, Brockworth, Gloucester GL3 4PE Tel: 01452 863200 Fax: 01452 864993; Yew Tree Cottage, Green St, Brockworth, Gloucester GL3 4RT Tel: 01452 864442 — MB BChir 1980 Camb.; MA Camb. 1981; MRCGP 1985; DRCOG 1985. Prev: SHO (O & G, Gen. Med. & Psychiat.) Basingstoke Gen. Hosp.

CONATY, Terence Anthony Smallfield Surgery, Wheelers Lane, Smallfield, Horley RH6 9PT Tel: 01342 843382 Fax: 01342 844080 — MB ChB 1978 Leeds.

CONBOY, Aileen Olga The Coach House, Broomleigh, Booth Road, Altrincham WA14 4AU — MB ChB 1993 Manch.

CONBOY, Peter John 21 Spencer Street, Oadby, Leicester LE2 4DQ — MB ChB 1994 Leic. SHO (A & E) Leicester Roy. Infirm.; Demonst. (Anat.) Univ. Leicester.

CONBOY, Veronica Bridget Lewis 34 Blanche Street, Roath, Cardiff CF24 1QT — MB BCh 1987 Wales.

CONCHA, Eduardo Marcelino Department of Anaesthetics, Nevill Hall Hospital, Brecon Road, Abergavenny NP7 7EG — LMS 1988 Cadiz.

CONCHIE, Alan Frederic (retired) 149 Thorne Road, Doncaster DN2 5BH Tel: 01302 326556 — MB ChB 1954 Sheff.; MRCS Eng. LRCP Lond. 1954; DCH Eng. 1962, DA 1958. Cons. Paediatr. Doncaster Roy. Infirm. Prev: Research Asst. Dept. Child Heath Univ. Sheff. Regist. (Paediat.).

CONDE FERNANDEZ, Fernando 239 Hoblands, Haywards Heath RH16 3NA — LMS 1985 Santiago de Compostela.

CONDELL, Helen Michelle 55 Farley Hill, Luton LU1 5EG — MB BS 1997 Lond.

CONDIE, Peter Waddell Department Pathology, Hexham General Hospital, Hexham NE46 1QJ Tel: 01434 655005 Fax: 01434 655017 — MB ChB 1972 Dundee; FRCPath 1994. Cons. Haemat. N.umbria Healthcare NHS Trust; Cons. Haematologist, Nat. Blood Serv., Newcaslte Upon Tyne. Socs: Brit. Soc. Haematologists; Founder Mem. Brit. Blood Transfus. Soc.; Assn. Clin. Pathol. Prev: Sen. Regist. (Blood Transfus. & Haemat.) N. RHA; Regist. (Haemat.) Nottm. City Hosp.

CONDIE, Robert (retired) Dalhousie Grange, Cockpen, Bonnyrigg EH19 3HX Tel: 0131 663 5177 Fax: 0131 663 5177 — MB ChB 1954 Ed.; DObst RCOG 1958.

CONDIE, Roy Gordon Department of Obstetrics & Gynaecology, City Hospital (NHS Trust), Birmingham B18 7QH Tel: 0121 554 3801 Fax: 0121 507 5467; 13 Hardwick Road, Streetly, Sutton Coldfield B74 3BY Tel: 0121 353 7333 — MD Aberd. 1975, MB ChB 1966; FRCOG 1984, M 1971, DObst 1968. (Aberd.) Cons. O & G City Hosp. (NHS Trust) Birm.; Clin. Sen. Lect. (Obst. & Gyn.) Univ. Birm. Socs: Fell. Birm. & Midl. Obst. & Gyn. Soc.; Internat. Continence Soc. Prev: Sen. Clin. Lect. (O & G) Univ. Qu.sld., Austral.; Sen. Regist. (O & G) Grampian HB; Regist. (O & G) Tayside HB.

CONDIE, William Hall Longrigg Medical Centre, Leam Lane, Wardley, Gateshead NE10 8PH — MB ChB 1945 St. And. (Dundee) Prev: Cas. Off. & Ho. Phys. Roy. Infirm. Perth; Med. Off. RAMC, 70th Brit. Gen. Hosp. Vienna.

CONDILLAC, David Louis 2 Berwick Drive, Blundellsands, Liverpool L23 7UH — MB BS 1969 Mysore; MRCOG 1978.

CONDLEY, Matthew 229 Foden Road, Birmingham B42 2EH — MB ChB 1998 Manch.; MB ChB Manch 1998.

CONDLIFFE, Alison Mary Addenbrooke's Hospital, Dept. of Medicine, Level 5, hill's Rd, Cambridge CB2 2QQ; 75 Fulbourn Road, Teversham, Cambridge CB1 5AJ — MB BS 1987 Lond. Hon.Cons.Respirat.Med.Addenbrook's. Hosp.; Wellcome Intermediate.Fell.

CONDLIFFE, Honor Alexandra 6 Carrwood, Halebarns, Altrincham WA15 0EE — MB BS 1998 Lond.; MB BS Lond 1998; BX Oxon 1995. (St Mary's Hospital Medical School)

***CONDLIFFE, Robin Anthony** 62 Marple Road, Stockport SK2 5QH — MB ChB 1998 Ed.; MB ChB Ed 1998; BSc Lond. 1995.

CONDON, Henry Arthur (retired) 88 Southborough Road, Bickley, Bromley BR1 2EN Tel: 020 8467 2373 — MRCS Eng. LRCP Lond. 1944; FFA RCS Eng. 1954; DA Eng. 1949. Prev: Cons. Anaesth. Roy. Nat. Throat, Nose & Ear Hosp. Lond.

CONDON, Hugh Charles The Old Granary, Charlton, Chichester PO18 0HU Tel: 01243 811296 — MB BS 1979 Lond.

CONDON, John Adrian 39 Lister House, Restell Close, London SE3 7UL — MB BS 1992 Lond.; DRCOG 1995; DFFP 1995. (Univ. Coll. Lond.) Prev: Trainee GP Greenwich VTS.

CONDON, John Rhys 14 Highfield Hill, London SE19 3PS — MB BCh 1957 Wales; BSc Wales 1954; FRCP Lond. 1980, M 1965. (Cardiff) Cons. Phys. Brook Hosp. & Greenwich Dist. Hosp. Lond. Socs: Fell. Roy. Soc. Med.; Fell. Hunt. Soc.; Osteoporosis Soc. Prev: Cons. Phys. St. Mary's Hosp. E.bourne; Sen. Regist. St. Geo. Hosp. Lond.; Regist. (Med.) Unit W.m. Hosp. Lond.

CONDON, Katherine Helen The White House, 24 Kingsway, Bognor Regis PO21 4DH Tel: 01243 265451 — MB BS 1980 Lond.

CONDON, Neil Ignatius 48 Welbeck Avenue, Hove BN3 4JN — LM 1955 Rotunda; MB BCh BAO NUI 1952; MFCM 1973; DPH 1957. (NUI) Specialist Community Med. Brighton HA. Prev: MOH Hove Boro. Counc. & Portslade UD; Dep. MOH & Dep. Princip. Sch. Med. Off. City of Lincoln; Asst. Admin. Med. Off. Birm.

CONDON, Mr Richard William Nuffield Hospital, Shores Road, Woking GU21 4BY; Westmarch, Burnhams Road, Little Bookham, Bookham, Leatherhead KT23 3BA Tel: 01372 450212 — MB BCh BAO 1973 NUI; FRCS Ed. 1983; FCOphth 1989; DO RCS Eng. 1980. (Univ. Coll. Dub.) Cons. Ophth. Surg. St. Peter Hosp. & Runnymede Hosp. Chertsey, Nuffield Hosp. Woking & Mt. Alvernia Hosp.; Cons. Ophth. Surg. Roy. Surrey Hosp. Guildford. Socs: Glaucoma Soc.; Amer. Acad. Ophth. Oxf. Congr. Prev: Sen. Regist. (Ophth.) Moorfields Eye Hosp. Lond.; Sen. Regist. (Ophth.) Char. Cross Hosp. Lond.

CONDON, Robert Nicholas Harford Park Lane Surgery, 8 Park Lane, Broxbourne EN10 7NQ Tel: 01992 465555 — MB BS 1976 Lond.; MRCS Eng. LRCP Lond. 1976.

CONDRON, Claire Kathleen 7 Carol Park, Newtownabbey BT36 6SF — MB BCh BAO 1997 Belf.

CONE, Andrew Mark 31 Endeavour Way, Hythe Marina, Hythe, Southampton SO45 6DX — MB BS 1985 Lond.

CONEY, Suzanne 39 Larkfield Lane, Southport PR9 8NN — MB ChB 1995 Dundee.

CONEYS, Thomas David DeVere 11 Spencer Parade, Northampton NN1 5AQ — LRCPSI 1973.

CONGDON, Audrey Mary Hampton Grange, 21 Hampton Lane, Solihull B91 2QJ Tel: 0121 705 4547 — MB ChB 1963 Liverp. (Liverp.) Clin. Asst. (Genitourin. Med.) Birm. Gen. Hosp. Prev: SHO (Ophth.) Qu. Eliz. Hosp. Birm. & Manch. Roy. Eye Hosp.; Ho. Surg. Birkenhead Gen. Hosp.

CONGDON, Helena Mary 301 Leeds Road, Bramhope, Leeds LS16 9JX Tel: 0113 267 4784 — MB ChB Leeds 1970; MRCOG 1994; DObst RCOG 1972. (Leeds) Specialist Regist. (O & G) St Jas. Hosp. Leeds.

CONGDON, Rachel Mary Hampton Grange, 21 Hampton Lane, Solihull B91 2QJ Tel: 0121 705 4547; 28 Albany Gardens, Hampton Lane, Solihull B91 2PT Tel: 0121 705 4547 — BM 1990 Soton. SHO (Paediat.) Torbay Hosp. Devon; SHO (Adult Psychiat.) All Birm. Rotat.al Train. Scheme & All St.s Psychiat. Hosp. Birm. Prev: SHO (Neonat.) Roy. Devon & Exeter Hosp.; Trainee Rotat. (Psychiat. - Old Age & Adult) Solihull Hosp. in Midl. 1997-1998; Trainee Rotat. (Gen. Adult Psychiat.) Highcroft Hosp. Birm. 1998.

CONGDON, Roger George 1 Shepherd's Croft, Southview Road, Findon, Worthing BN14 0UA Tel: 01903 873152 — MB BS 1955 Lond.; FRCP Canada 1972; FRCPsych 1989, M 1971; FFPHM 1979, M 1972; DMJ Soc. Apoth. Lond. 1968; DPM Eng. 1963. (King's Coll. Lond. & King's Coll. Hosp.) Cons. Psychiat. Mid Downs HA; Vis. Cons. Psychiat. HM Prison Serv. Prev: Asst. Prof. (Psychiat.) Qu. Univ. Kingston, Canada; Cons. Psychiat. Walsgrave Hosp. Coventry.

CONGERA, Gina Pinucia 1 Oxford Terrace, Bensham, Gateshead NE8 1RQ Tel: 0191 477 2169; 11 Queens Road, Jesmond, Newcastle upon Tyne NE2 2PQ Tel: 0191 281 1450 — MB BS 1988 Newc.; MRCGP 1993; DCH RCP Lond. 1992. (Newc.)

CONGLETON, Joanne Elizabeth Worthing General Hospital, Lyndhurst Rd, Worthing BN11 2DH Tel: 01903 205111 Fax: 01903 285045 Email: jo.congleton@wash-tr.sthames.nhs.uk — MB BS 1987 Lond.; MRCP (UK) 1990. Cons. Gen.& Respir. Med. Worthing Gen. Hosp. Socs: Brit. Thorac. Soc. Prev: Sen. Regist. (Respirat. Med.) Roy. Brompton Hosp. Lond.; Clin. Tutor (Respirat. Med.) Nat. Heart & Lung Inst. Lond.; Regist. (Respirat. Med.) Killingbeck Hosp. Leeds & Pontefract Gen. Infirm.

CONGREVE, Katharine Andrea Mary 39 Blomfield Road, London W9 2PF — MB ChB 1997 Bristol.

CONI, Hugh John Adolphus 12 The Green, Rowlands Castle PO9 6BN — MB BS 1991 Lond.; BSc Clin. Sci. Lond. 1990; DRCOG 1996; Dip. IMC RCS Ed. 1994. (Char. Cross & Westm.)

CONI, Nicholas Keith (retired) 26 Brookside, Cambridge CB2 1JQ Tel: 01223 361614 Fax: 01223 361614 Email: nickconi@btinternet.com — MB BChir Camb. 1962; FRCP Lond. 1984, M 1964; FRCPC 1968. Assoc. Lect. Fac. Clin. Med. Camb. Univ. Prev: Cons. Phys. Geriat. Med. Addenbrooke's NHS Trust.

CONIAM, Stephen William Department of Anaesthetics, Frenchay Hospital, Bristol BS16 1LE Tel: 0117 970 2020; 26 Cotham Grove, Bristol BS6 6AN — MB BChir 1975 Camb.; MB Camb. 1975, BChir 1974; MA Camb 1975; FFA RCS Eng. 1978. (Westm.) Cons. Anaesth. & Pain Relief Frenchay Hosp. Bristol. Socs: Assn. Anaesth. GB & Irel.; Internat. Assn. Study of Pain; Pain Soc. Prev: Cons. Anaesth. Dryburn Hosp. Durh.; Sen. Regist. Sheff. AHA (T); SHO (Anaesth.), Ho. Surg. & Ho. Phys. York Co. Hosp.

CONLAN, Bernadette Rosemary 30 Oaklands, Newcastle upon Tyne NE3 4YP — MB BS 1987 Newc.; DRCOG 1991.

CONLAN, Mr David Patrick Department of Orthopaedics, Addenbrooke's NHS Trust, Cambridge CB2 2QQ Tel: 01223 216854 Fax: 01223 217307 — MB ChB 1981 Leic.; BSc Hull 1975; FRCS Ed. 1986; FRCS Eng. 1986. Cons. Trauma & Paediat. Orthop. Addenbrooke's Hosp. Camb.; Assoc. Lect. Univ. Camb. Socs: Fell. Brit. Scoliosis Soc.; Brit. Orthop. Assn.; Brit. Soc. Childr. Orthop. Surg. Prev: Sen. Regist. (Orthop.) N.. RHA; Clin. Lect. (Orthop.) Univ. Leics.; Vis. Sen. Regist. Adelaide Childr. Hosp., Austral.

CONLAN, Enda Fergus 173 Belfast Road, Newry BT34 1QY — MB BCh BAO 1993 Dub.

CONLAN, Patrick Thomas Mary Thameside Community Healthcare NHS Trust, Thurrock Community Hospital, Long Lane, Grays RM16 2PX Tel: 01375 364544 Fax: 01375 394970 — MB BCh BAO 1972 NUI; MRCP (UK) 1981; DCH Lond. 1976; FRCP 1999. Cons. (Paediat.) Community Child Health Basildon & Thurrock.

***CONLAN, Richard Ciaran Peter** 10 Collinward Avenue, Newtownabbey BT36 6DY Tel: 01232 587747 — MB ChB 1998 Dund.; MB ChB Dund 1998.

CONLON, Christopher Francis 73 (2F3) Slateford Road, Slateford, Edinburgh EH11 1PR Email: cfconlon@doctors.org.uk — MB BS 1993 Lond.; DRCOG RCOG. 1999. (King's Coll. Sch. Med. & Dent.) GP Regist. May Lodge.Health.Centre.Borders. Prev: SHO (O & G) Monklands & Bellshill Hosps.; SHO (Gen. Med.) Law Hosp. Carluke; SHO (Gen. & Renal Med.) Qu. Margt. Hosp. Dunfermline.

CONLON, Christopher Peter Nuffield Department of Medicine, John Radcliffe Hospital, Oxford OX3 9DU Tel: 01865 741166 Fax: 01865 222962 — MB BS 1980 Lond.; MA 1996 Oxf.; BA Oxf. 1977; MD Lond. 1991; MRCP (UK) 1983; FRCP 1996. Cons. Phys. Infec. Dis. John Radcliffe Hosp. Oxf. Socs: Brit. Infec. Soc.; Assn. of Phys.s.

CONLON, Daphne Elsie Grace 2 Bradda Court, Port Erin IM9 6PQ — MB BCh BAO 1964 NUI.

CONLON, Delia Mary Netherton Health Centre, Halesowen Road, Dudley DY2 9PU Tel: 01384 254935 Fax: 01384 242468; 16 Brunswick Gate, Pedmore, Stourbridge DY8 2QA Tel: 01384 295896 — MB BCh 1975 Wales.

CONLON, Fiona Veronica 36 Heath Halt Road, Cardiff CF23 5QF — MB BCh 1997 Wales. (University of Wales, College of Medicine, Cardiff)

CONLON, Maurice Hugh Ridgacre House Surgery, 83 Ridgacre Road, Quinton, Birmingham B32 2TJ Tel: 0121 422 3111 — MB ChB 1988 Birm.; MRCGP Lond. 1997; DRCOG 1991. (Univ. of Birm.) Prev: Trainee GP Smethwick, W. Midl.; SHO St. Giles Hospice Lichfield; SHO Dudley Rd. Hosp. Birm. VTS.

CONLON, Michael Brendan 2 Bradda Court, Port Erin IM9 6PQ — MD 1949 NUI; MB BCh BAO 1945; MRCPI 1949.

CONLON, William Patrick Bushey Fields Hospital, Bushey Fields Road, Russells Hall, Dudley DY1 2LZ Tel: 01384 244951; 16 Brunswick Gate, Pedmore, Stourbridge DY8 2QA — MB BCh 1974 Wales; MRCPsych 1980. Cons. Psychiat. Bushey Fields Hosp. Dudley.; Med. Dir.; Postgrad. Clin. Tutor for Worcs. Rotat.al Train. Scheme in Psychiatr. Prev: Sen. Regist. Midl. Nerve & Qu. Eliz. Hosps. Profess. Unit Birm.; Sen. Regist. (Psychiat.) Uffculme Clin. Moseley, Birm.; Hon. Lect. Birm. Univ. Med. Sch.

CONLONG, Philip John Mark 21 Breeze Mount, Prestwich, Manchester M25 0AH — MB ChB 1989 Manch.

CONMEY, Margaret Mary Hednesford Street Surgery, Cannock Tel: 01543 503121; 6 Steps Gardens, Haughton, Stafford ST18 9NS Tel: 01780 780864 Email: marjo@john-mcara.supanet.com — MB ChB 1988 Glas.; MRCGP 1994; DFFP 1994; DRCOG 1995. (Glasgow University)

CONN, Agnes Kirkland (retired) 1 Dumgoyne Avenue, Milngavie, Glasgow G62 7AL Tel: 0141 956 1316 — MB ChB St. And. 1945; MA St. And. 1940, MD 1956. Prev: Cons. Bacteriol. & Dep. Dir. The City Laborat. Glas. Bacteriol. Centr. Microbiol. Laborats. Edin.

CONN, Alan Gordon Wansbeck Hospital, Wood Horn Lane, Ashington NE63 9JJ Tel: 01670 521212; 7 Chantry Mews, Bridge St., Morpeth NE61 1PT Tel: 01670 503904 — MB ChB 1978 Ed.; BSc (Med. Sci.), Ed. 1975; FRCA 1983. Cons. Anaesth. Cheviot & Wansbeck NHS Trust. Socs: Intens. Care Soc. Prev: Sen. Regist. (Anaesth.) Roy. Infirm. Edin.; Cons. Intens. Ther. Unit Khoula Hosp., Muscat, Oman.

CONN, Andrew John 36 Bryansglen Park, Bangor BT20 3RS — BM BS 1996 Nottm.

CONN, David Arthur Department of Anaesthetics, Royal Devon & Exeter Hospital, Barrack Road, Exeter EX2 5DW Tel: 01392 402473 Fax: 01392 402472; Channons Farm, Silverton, Exeter EX5 4HU — MB ChB 1982 Glas.; FRCA 1990; MRCGP 1986; DRCOG 1985. Cons. Anaesth. & Pain Managem. Roy. Devon & Exeter Hosp. Prev:

Sen. Regist. (Pain Managem.) Flinders Med. Centre, Adelaide; Sen. Regist. (Anaesth.) Newc. u. Tyne; Trainee GP Argyll & Clyde HB Paisley Dist. VTS.

CONN, George Eric Medical Centre, George House, 1 Oxford Drive, Ruislip HA4 9EY; 1 Oxford Drive, Ruislip HA4 9EY Tel: 020 8866 3430 — MB BS 1961 Lond.; MRCS Eng. LRCP Lond. 1961; DObst RCOG 1963. (Guy's) Med. Off. 1st Nat. Bank & N.wood & Pinner Cott. Hosp. Prev: Ho. Surg. (O & G) W. Hill Hosp.; Ho. Phys. Mt. Vernon Hosp. N.wood.

CONN, Hellen Stephen (retired) 422 Kingsbridge Drive, Rutherglen, Glasgow G73 2BX Tel: 0141 647 4106 — MB ChB 1958 Glas.; MFPHM 1989; MFCM 1972; DPH Glas. 1965; DObst RCOG 1961. Prev: Cons. Pub. Health Med. (Child Health) Lanarksh. HB.

CONN, Ian Gordon (retired) Hilton, Fraser Avenue, Johnstone PA5 8JE Tel: 01505 322106 — MB ChB 1951 Glas.; MRCGP 1968. Prev: Sen. Regional Med. Off. Scott. Home & Health Dept.

CONN, Mr Ian Graeme Department of Urology, South Glasgow University Hospital NHS Trust, 1345 Govan Road, Glasgow G51 4TF; Dornoch, Lawmarnock Road, Bridge of Weir PA11 3AP — MB ChB 1980 MB Ch B Glas.; MD 1988 Glass; FRCS Glas. 1984. Cons. Urol. Surg. S.. Gen. Hosp. Glas.; S. Glas. Univ. Hosp. NHS Trust. Socs: Fell. Europ. Bd. Urol. Prev: Cons. Urol. Surg. Aberd. Roy. Infirm.; Sen. Regist. (Urol.) St. Woolos Hosp. Newport Gwent; Lect. (Urol.) W.. Gen. Hosp. Edin.

CONN, Jane Susan 16 The Orchard, Hepscott, Morpeth NE61 6HT Tel: 01670 510802 — MB ChB 1978 Leeds; DFFP 1995; DA (UK) 1980. Staff Grade (Haemat. & Blood Transfus.) Newc.

CONN, Paul Chandler Department Histopathology, Chestnut Villa, 2 Boxted Road, Colchester CO4 5HG Tel: 01206 744848 Email: paul.conn@essexrivers.nhs.uk — MB BS 1977 Lond.; MRCP (UK) 1981; FRCPath 1997, M 1986. (Middlx.) Cons. Histopath. Colchester Hosp. Prev: Sen. Regist. (Histopath.) Addenbrookes Hosp. Camb. & Norf. & Norwich Hosp.; Med. Off. Chas. Johnson Memor. Hosp. Kwa-Zulu, S. Africa; Regist. (Med.) Vaiola Hosp. Tonga.

CONN, Paul Gilbert Ballygomartin Road Surgery, 17 Ballygomartin Road, Belfast BT13 3BW; 1A Marnabrae, Belsize Road, Lisburn BT27 4LD — MB BCh BAO 1983 Belf.; MRCGP 1988; DRCOG 1987.

CONN, William Guthrie The Health Centre, Redcar TS10 1RP; Ladywell House, 92 Corporation Road, Redcar TS10 1PA Tel: 01642 482734 — MB ChB 1958 Glas.; DA Eng. 1960. ((Glas.)) Socs: Fell. Roy. Soc. Med.; Assoc. Mem. RCGP; Fac. Anaesth. RCS Eng. Prev: Sen. Med. Off. Anglo Amer. Corp. (C.A.) Ltd.; Chief (Gen. Pract.) MoD & Aviat. Hosp., Jeddah.

CONNACHER, Alan Alexander Medical Unit, Perth Royal Infirmary, Perth PH1 1NX Tel: 01738 623311 Fax: 01738 473510 Email: aconnacher@pri.tucht.scot.nhs.uk; Hatton House, Hatton Road, Perth PH2 7DB Tel: 01738 440743 — MB ChB 1981 Dundee; FRCP Glasgow 2000; MD (Hons.) Dundee 1992; FRCP Ed. 1994; MRCP (UK) 1984. (University of Dundee) Hon. Sen. Lect. (Med.) Univ. Dundee. Prev: Clin. Lect. W.. Gen. Hosp. Edin.; Regist. (Med.) Ninewells Hosp. & Med. Sch. Dundee.

CONNAN, Alexandra Louise Mayfield Road Surgery, 125 Mayfield Road, Edinburgh EH9 3AJ Tel: 0131 668 1095 Fax: 0131 662 1734; 52 Bonaly Road, Edinburgh EH13 0EQ Tel: 0131 441 7679 — MB BS 1984 Lond.; MFFP 1993; MRCGP 1988; DRCOG 1986.

CONNAN, Daniel (retired) Garden House, Cromwell Walk, Huntingdon PE29 3HR Tel: 01480 52520 Fax: 01480 52520 Email: dan@dial.drakken.com — MB BS Lond. 1958; BSc Lond. 1955; MRCS Eng. LRCP Lond. 1958; MRCGP 1976; DMJ (Clin.) Soc. Apoth. Lond. 1970; DObst RCOG 1960. Prev: GP Huntingdon.

CONNAN, Frances Helen Eating Disorder Unit, Maudsley Hospital, Denmark Hill, London SE5 8AZ Tel: 020 7919 3183 Email: f.connan@iop.kcl.ac.uk — MB BS 1992 Lond.; BSc (Hons.) Lond. 1989; MRCPsych 1996. (King's Coll. Lond.) MRC Clin. Train. Fell. Inst. of Psychiat. Lond.; Hon. Sen. Regist. (Psychiat.) Maudsley Hosp. Lond.

CONNAUGHTON, Jennifer Ann The State Hospital, Carstairs, Lanark ML11 8RP Tel: 01555 840293 Fax: 01555 840112 Email: Jenni.Connaughton@tsh.scot.nhs.uk — MB BS 1967 Lond.; MPhil Glas. 1995; MRCS Eng. LRCP Lond. 1967; MRCPsych 1983; DCH RCP Lond. 1969. (Roy. Free) Med. Director State Hosp. Carstairs. Prev: Med. Off. Ment. Welf. Commiss. for Scotl.

CONNAUGHTON, Josephine Theresa Brick Lane Surgery, 28 Brick Lane, Enfield EN3 5BA Tel: 020 8443 0413 Fax: 020 8805 9097 — MB BS 1976 Lond.

CONNAUGHTON, Kevin Joseph Bridgeton Health Centre, 201 Abercromby Street, Glasgow G40 2DA Tel: 0141 550 3822 — MB ChB 1983 Glas.

CONNAUGHTON, Mark Department of Cardiology, St. Thomas' Hospital, Lambeth Palace Road, London SE1 7EH — MB BS 1987 Lond.; BA Psychol. & Physiol. Oxf. 1982; MRCP (UK) 1991. Regist. (Cardiol.) St. Thos. Hosp. Lond. Prev: Regist. (Med.) Medway Hosp. Gillingham; Regist. (Med.) Derriford Hosp. Plymouth.

CONNEALLY, Padhraic Radiology Department, Erne Hospital, Enniskillen BT74 6HY Tel: 0286 638 2602 — MB BCh BAO 1981 NUI; BSc (Med.) NUI 1978; FFR RCSI 1995; FRCR 1991; DMRD (RCR) 1988. (University College Galway) Cons. Radiol. Erne Hosp. Enniskillen & Tyrone Co. Hosp. Omagh. Prev: Sen. Regist. (Radiol.) Char. Cross Hosp. Lond.; Regist. (Radiol.) Univ. Coll. Hosp. Middlx. Hosp. Lond.; Cons. (Radiol.) S. Tyrone Hosp. Dungannon.

CONNELL, Alexander Cochrane (retired) 14 Varna Road, Glasgow G14 9NE Tel: 0141 959 2905 — MB ChB 1945 Glas.

CONNELL, Anne Frances 36 Aursbridge Crescent, Barrhead, Glasgow G78 2TJ — MB ChB 1989 Glas. SHO (A & E) Yorkhill NHS Trust Glas.

CONNELL, Anthea Mary Stewart (retired) 3 Lifford Gardens, Broadway WR12 7DA Tel: 01386 853303 Fax: 01386 853303 Email: aconnell.dowglass@virgin.net — MB ChB Birm. 1952; FRCS Eng. 1964; FRCOphth 1989. Dir. Barbados Eye Study State Univ. NY. Prev: Sen. Cons. & Head of Depart. Ophth. Barbados.

CONNELL, David Blackall (retired) Lower Wreyland, Lustleigh, Newton Abbot TQ13 9TS Tel: 01647 277262 Fax: 01647 277262 Email: dbconnell@doctors.org.uk — MB BS 1956 Lond.; ECFMG Cert. 1976; FLEX Lic. (USA) 1976; MRCGP 1966. Prev: GP Partner Magnolia Ho., Sunningdale, Ascot Berks.

CONNELL, David Garden Barnyards, Lumphart Farm, Daviot, Inverurie AB51 0HX — MB ChB 1982 Ed.; BSc Med. Sci. Ed. 1979, MB ChB 1982; MRCGP 1986; DRCOG 1985.

CONNELL, Frances Elizabeth Albinia Dept. Psychiatry, Royal London Hospital, Whitechapel, London E1 — MB BS 1988 Lond.; MRCPsych 1995.

CONNELL, Helen Elisabeth Fir Trees, Cloves Hill, Morley, Ilkeston DE7 6DH — MB ChB 1995 Manch. SHO (Paediat.). Prev: SHO Med.

CONNELL, Henry c/o George Connell Esq., Old Catherdral Vicarage, St James Row, Sheffield S1 1XA — MB ChB 1975 Sheff.; FFA RCS Eng. 1982. Sen. Regist. (Anaesth.) Bristol & Plymouth Hosps.

CONNELL, Jane Emma 70 Beech View Road, Kingsley, Warrington WA6 8DG — BM BS 1993 Nottm.

CONNELL, Professor John Muir Cochrane Department of Medicine and Therapeutics, Western Infirmary, Glasgow G11 6NT Tel: 0141 211 2108 Fax: 0141 211 1763 Email: jmcclm@clinmed.gla.ac.uk — MB ChB 1977 Glas.; MB ChB (Commend.) Glas. 1977; MD Glas. 1986; FRCP Lond. 1989; MRCP (UK) 1979. Prof. Endocrinol. Univ. Glas.; Hon. Cons. Phys. W. Glas. Hosps. Univ. NHS Trust. Socs: Endocrine Soc. & Brit. Hypertens. Soc.; (Treas.) Scott. Soc. Experim. Med. Prev: Sen. Clin. Sci. MRC Blood Pressure Unit. Glas.; Research Fell. Howard Florey Inst. Melbourne, Austral.; Sen. Regist. MRC Blood Pressure Unit W.. Infirm. Glas.

CONNELL, Lesley Elizabeth Tollcross Medical Centre, 1101-1105 Tollcross Road, Glasgow G32 8UH Tel: 0141 778 2717 Fax: 0141 778 6880; 68 Newlands Road, Glasgow G43 2JH Tel: 0141 649 9229 — MB ChB 1977 Glas. SCMO (Family Plann.) Gtr. Glas. HB. Prev: Trainee GP Kirkintilloch; SHO Stobhill Hosp. Glas.; Ho. Off. Glas. Roy. Infirm.

CONNELL, Michael Charles (retired) Midtown House, Caldbeck, Wigton CA7 8EL Tel: 016974 78133 — MB BChir 1943 Camb.; MA Camb. 1943; MRCS Eng. LRCP Lond. 1943; DMR Lond 1946; MSR (Hon). Prev: Cons. Radiol. N.ampton & Dist. Hosps.

CONNELL, Paul Richard Millwood Surgery, Mill Lane, Bradwell, Great Yarmouth NR31 8HS Tel: 01493 661549 Fax: 01493 440187; 35 Seaview Rise, Hopton-on-Sea, Great Yarmouth NR31 9SE Tel: 01502 730580 — MB BS 1985 Lond.; DFFP 1993; DRCOG 1990;

DA (UK) 1987. Gen. Practitioner, Dr Dooldeniya and Partners, Gt. Yarmouth. Prev: SHO (Anaesth., Gen. Med., Accid & Emerg.) Norf. & Norwich Hosps.; SHO (O & G) Jas. Paget Hosp. Gt. Yarmouth.

CONNELL, Peter Alan Medical Defowof Union, 230 Blackfriars Road, London SE1 8PJ Tel: 0207 202 1500 — MB ChB 1971 Bristol; MRCS Eng. LRCP Lond. 1971; DObst RCOG 1973. Medico Legal Adviser. Prev: GP Partner Downond Bristol.

CONNELL, Peter Andrew The Surgery, 344 Long Lane, Hillingdon, Uxbridge UB10 9PN Tel: 01895 237411 Fax: 01895 812875 — MB BS 1964 Lond.; BSc Lond. 1961, MB BS 1964. (Middlx.)

CONNELL, Philip Geoffrey Ridgewood House, Macclesfield Road, Wilmslow SK9 2AJ — MRCS Eng. LRCP Lond. 1991; MRCS Eng LRCP Lond. 1991; BDS Lond. 1986; FRCS Eng 1997.

CONNELL, Rebecca 28 Elm Road, Hale, Altrincham WA15 9QW — MB ChB 1992 Leic.

CONNELL, Richard Antony 81 Danes Dr, Glasgow G14 9EN — MB ChB 1997 Glas.

CONNELL, Rowan James 52 Bollo Lane, London W4 5LT — MB BS 1991 Lond.

CONNELL, Simon John 2 Queen Square LA1 1RP Tel: 01524 843333 — MB ChB 1993 Manch.; MRCGP 1997; DCH RCP 1997. (Manch.) GP Pricipal Lancaster Area. Prev: SHO (Psychiat.) Macclesfield; SHO (Cas., Paediat. & Gen. Med. & Obst.) Roy. Lancaster Infirm.; GP Regist. Lancaster.

CONNELL, Susan Elizabeth 6 Beechwood Avenue, Ruislip HA4 6EN — MB BS 1993 Lond.

CONNELL, Treldon Everet 87 Auriel Avenue, Dagenham RM10 8BU — MRCS Eng. LRCP Lond. 1974.

CONNELLAN, Esther Zoe 31 Warwick Crescent, Sittingbourne ME10 1TG — MB ChB 1992 Leic.

CONNELLAN, Sarah-Ann 12 St Davids Road, Manor Park, Miskin, Pontyclun CF72 8PW Tel: 01443 222000 — MB ChB 1988 Leic.; MRCGP 1993; Cert. Family Plann. JCC 1990. SHO Rotat. (Psychiat.) M. Glam. Prev: SHO (O & G) Llandough Hosp. Penarth; SHO (Paediat.) Cardiff Roy. Infirm; Ho. Surg. Leicester Roy. Infirm. & Glenfield Gen. Hosp.

CONNELLAN, Stephen John Yew Tree Cottage, 56 Kiddemore Green Road, Brewood, Stafford ST19 9BQ Email: 101542.2417@compuserve.com — MB BS 1971 Lond.; MRCP (UK) 1976; FRCP 1993. (St. Mary's) Cons. Phys. Newcross Hosp. Wolverhampton. Socs: Brit. Thorac. Soc. & Brit. Soc. Allergy & Clin. Immunol. Prev: Sen. Regist. (Thoracic Med.) Wythenshawe Hosp. Manch.; Research Fell. (Respirat. Med.) Roy. Postgrad. Med. Sch. Hammersmith Hosp. Lond.; Regist. (Respirat. Med.) Papworth & Addenbrooke's Hosp. Camb.

CONNELLY, Anne Wishaw Health Centre, Kenilworth Avenue, Wishaw ML2 7BQ Tel: 01698 365420; 4A Elvan Court, Motherwell ML1 3EL — MB ChB 1978 Ed.

CONNELLY, Derek Thomas The Cardiothoracic Centre, Thomas Drive, Liverpool L14 3PE Tel: 0151 228 1616 Fax: 0151 220 8573 Email: connelly@liv.ac.uk; 26 Stowe Close, Liverpool L25 7YE Tel: 0151 486 4958 — MB ChB 1984 Glas.; BSc (Hons.) Glas. 1981; MD Glas. 1994; MRCP (UK) 1987; FRCP 1998. Sen. Lect. (Cardiol.) Univ. Liverp.; Hon Cons. (Cardiol.) The Cardiothoracic Centre Liverp. Socs: Fell.Roy. Coll. Phys.s & Surg.s Glas.; Brit. Cardiac Soc.; Brit. Pacing & Electrophysiol. Gp. Prev: Sen. Regist. (Cardiol.) Cardiothoracic Centre Liverp.; Electrophysiol. Fell., Mid America Heart Inst.; Research Fell. Roy. Brompton & Nat. Heart Hosp.

CONNELLY, Helen Rhoda Devonshire Green Medical Centre, 126 Devonshire Street, Sheffield S3 7SF Tel: 0114 272 1626 — MB ChB 1991 Sheff.; DFFP 1994; DRCOG 1993; MRCGP 1995. (Sheffield) p/t Asst. Genral Practitioner; Locum Family Plann. Doctor.

CONNELLY, Peter John Murray Royal Hospital, Perth PH2 7BH Tel: 01738 562335 Fax: 01738 440431 Email: peter@connelly@pk.tpct.scot.nhs.uk; Tel: 01382 580286 — MB ChB 1979 Glas.; MRCPsych 1984; FRCPsych 1998. Cons. Old Age Psychiat. Murray Roy. Hosp. Perth. Prev: Clin. Director Ment. Health Serv.s. Perth & Kinross Healthcare NHS Trust.

CONNER, Mr Alan Nelson (retired) 14 Ballater Drive, Bearsden, Glasgow G61 1BY Tel: 0141 942 5576 — MB ChB 1960 Glas.; FRCS Ed. 1965; FRCS Glas. 1965. Prev: Consult. Orthop. Surg., Roy. Hosp. For Sick Childr.

CONNER, Anne Marie Broompark, Whauphill, Newton Stewart DG8 9QB — MB ChB 1980 Glas.

CONNER, Christine Evelyn Department of Obstetrics & Gynaecology, Aberdeen Royal Infirmary, Aberdeen AB25 2ZN Tel: 01224 314535; 97 Forest Avenue, Aberdeen AB15 4TN Tel: 01224 314535 — MB ChB 1987 Ed.; MRCOG 1993; MD 1999. (Edinburgh) Sen. Regist. Aberd. Roy. Infirm.; Subspeciality trainee in FetoMatern. Med. Socs: Brit. Matern. and Fetal Med. Soc. Prev: Wellbeing Research Fell. Univ. Dundee; Regist. Aberd. Roy. Infirm.; SHO W.. & Qu. Mothers Hosp. Glas.

CONNER, Jane Trail (retired) 14 Ballater Drive, Bearsden, Glasgow G61 1BY Tel: 0141 942 5576 — MB ChB 1961 Glas.; DA Eng. 1968. Prev: Comm. Dent. Anaesth.

CONNER, Sylvia Tel: 01702 230555 Fax: 01702 231207 — MB BS 1983 (Hons.) Lond.; BSc (Hons.) Lond. 1980; MRCGP 1988; DRCOG 1987.

CONNER, Thomas Alexander Eric 62 The Hollow, Bath BA2 1LZ — MB BCh BAO 1981 Belf.; MB BCh Belf.1981.

CONNERY, Julie Ann 164 Ballynahinch Road, Dromore BT25 1EA — MB BCh BAO 1997 Belf.

CONNERY, Timothy Philip Victoria Health Centre, Glasshouse Street, Nottingham NG1 3LW Tel: 0115 948 3030 Fax: 0115 911 1074 — MB ChB 1980 Dundee; MA Oxf. 1967; MRCGP 1984; DCH RCP Lond. 1984. (Dundee) GP Tutor Nottm. Univ. Med. Sch.

CONNETT, Gary James Southampton General Hospital, Dept. of Paediatrics, Tremona Road, Southampton SO16 6YD, 01703 798973 Email: garyconnett@suht.freeserve.co.uk; Vine Cottage, Pikes Hill Avenue, Lyndhurst SO43 7AX Tel: 02380 7989 8973 — MB ChB 1985 Bristol; MD Bristol 1993; MRCP (UK) 1989; DCH RCP Lond. 1988. Cons. Paediat. (Respirat.) Soton. Univ. Hosp. Trust. Prev: Sen. Regist. Birm. Childr. Hosp.; Acad. Regist. (Cystic Fibrosis) Soton. Univ. Hosp.; Overseas Fell. (Paediat.) & Lect. Nat. Univ. Hosp., Singapore.

CONNING, Professor David Michael, OBE (retired) Blacksmith's Cottage, Totnor, Brockhampton, Hereford HR1 4TJ — MB BS 1955 Durh.; FRCPath 1982, M 1979; FIBiol. 1985. Prev: Dir.-Gen. Brit. Nutrit. Foundat.

CONNOLLY, Ann Marie Flat 1, 49 Lordship park, London N16 5UN — MB BCh BAO 1984 NUI; MRCGP 1991.

CONNOLLY, Anne Lesley The Ridge Medical Practice, 3 Paternoster Lane, Great Horton, Bradford BD7 3EE Tel: 01274 502905 Fax: 01274 522060; Smith Avenue Medical Centre, 93 Smith Avenue, Bradford BD6 1HA Tel: 01274 676224 — MB ChB 1983 Birm.; MBChB Birm. 1983; MRCGP 1987; DRCOG 1985.

CONNOLLY, Art Austin Patrick Neurosurgery, The London Hospital, London E1 1BB Tel: 020 7377 7000; Flat C, 176 Tooting High St, London SW17 0SF — BM BCh 1987 Oxf.; MSc Oxf. 1984, MA 1987, BA 1982, BM BCh 1987; FRCPS Glas. 1992. SHO (Neurosurg.) The Lond. Hosp. Prev: Demonst. (Cas.) St. Thos. Hosp. Lond.; Ho. Surg. Ch.ill Hosp. Oxf.

CONNOLLY, Brigid Penelope Stack Horizon, 12 New Road, Bolehill, Matlock DE4 4GL — MB ChB 1981 Sheff. Adjuc. Med. Off. DHSS; Clin. Asst. Derbysh.

CONNOLLY, Carol Elizabeth 9 Gibbon Crescent, East Kilbride, Glasgow G74 3HU; 36 Pearl Street, Newtown NSW 2042, Australia — MB ChB 1989 Glas.; MRCGP 1994; DRCOG 1993. Socs: BMA.

CONNOLLY, Carol Nessa Margaret 19 Highfield Avenue, Harpenden AL5 5UB — MB ChB 1976 Cape Town.

CONNOLLY, Catherine Anne Southgates Medical Centre, 41 Goodwins Road, King's Lynn PE30 5QX Tel: 01553 692333 Fax: 01553 692555 — MB BCh BAO 1981 NUI; MRCGP 1987.

CONNOLLY, Catherine Mary Islington House, 3 Islington Square, Liverpool L3 8DD Tel: 0151 207 0848 — MB BCh BAO 1946 NUI; DPH Liverp. 1953. (NUI)

CONNOLLY, Catherine Mary 7 Manor Road, Jordanhill, Glasgow G14 9LG — MB ChB 1980 Glas.; MRCP (UK) 1984.

CONNOLLY, Catherine Veronica Freckleton Health Centre, Douglas Drive, Freckleton, Preston PR4 1RY Tel: 01772 632403; 9 Blackpool Road, Ansdell, Lytham St Annes FY8 4EH Tel: 01253 737308 — MB ChB 1984 Manch.; MB ChB Manch. l984; MRCGP 1988; DRCOG 1987.

CONNOLLY, Catriona Mary Noelle Department of Anaesthetics, Ninewells Hospital, Dundee DD2 Tel: 01382 632175; 43 Bay Road, Wormit, Newport-on-Tay DD6 8LW — MB BS 1988 Lond.; FRCA 1996. Specialist Regist. (Anaesth.) Ninewells Hosp. Dundee. Prev: SHO (Anaesth.) Law Hosp. Lanarksh.

CONNOLLY, Charles Kevin, TD 39 Stanhope Road, Darlington DL3 7AP Tel: 01325 462593 Fax: 01325 743435; Aldbrough House, Aldbrough St John, Richmond DL11 7TP Tel: 01325 374244 — MB BChir 1962 Camb.; MA Camb. 1962, MB BChir 1962, BA (Nat. Sc. Trip. Part I 1st cl.; Hons. & Part II Path.) 1958; FRCP Lond. 1977, M 1964. (Camb. & Middlx.) Cons. Phys. Darlington & N.allerton NHS Trusts; Hon. Clin. Lect. (Med.) Univ. Newc.; Med. Mem., The Appeals Serv. Socs: Med. Res. Soc. & (Counc.) Brit. Thoracic Soc. Prev: Sen. Regist. (Med.) St. Geo. Hosp. Lond.; Resid. Med. Off. Brompton Hosp. Lond.; Ho. Phys. Middlx. Hosp. Lond.

CONNOLLY, Mr Christopher Kevin 76 Greer Park Heights, Newtown Breda Road, Belfast BT8 7YG Tel: 01232 492948 Email: christopher@connolly36.freeserve.co.uk — MB BCh BAO 1994 Belf.; BSc (Hons. Path.) Belf. 1992, MB BCh BAO 1994; FRCSI 1997. (The Queen's University of Belfast)

CONNOLLY, Clare Mary Little Horton Lane Surgery, 482 Little Horton Lane, Bradford BD5 0PA Tel: 01274 394277; 35 Heaton Grove, Bradford BD9 4DZ Tel: 01274 534126 — MB ChB 1982 Manch.; MRCGP 1986; DRCOG 1985.

CONNOLLY, Daniel James Anthony 75 Old Road, Headington, Oxford OX3 7LA — MB ChB 1991 Leeds.

CONNOLLY, Derek Leslie Cardiac Unit, Papworth Hospital, Cambridge CB3 8RE Tel: 01480 830541 Email: atrium@btinternet.com; 3 Ballard Close, Milton, Cambridge CB4 6DW Tel: 01223 440917 — MB ChB 1988 Ed.; BSc (1st cl. Hons.) Ed. 1986; PhD (Cantab) 1999; MRCP (UK) 1991. (Edinburgh) Sen. Regist. Cardiac Unit Papworth Hosp. Socs: Brit. Cardiac. Soc.; BPEG. Prev: Hon. Sen. Regist. (Cardiol.) Addenbrooke's Hosps. Camb.; SHO (Cardiol.) Hammersmith Hosp. Lond.; Ho. Phys. Profess Med. Unit Roy. Infirm. Edin.

CONNOLLY, Dermot Francis Waterside Health Centre, Glendermolt Road, Londonderry BT47 6AU Tel: 028 7132 0100 — MB BCh BAO 1982 NUI; MB BCh NUI 1982; MRCGP 1986; DRCOG 1985; DCH 1984. Socs: MRCGP & BMA.

CONNOLLY, Desmond Michael 164 Sellincourt Road, Tooting, London SW17 9SA Tel: 020 8672 8530 Email: desconol@globalnet.co.uk — MB BS 1982 Lond.; MRCGP 1988; DAvMed FOM RCP 1991; MA 1998. (Middlesex Hospital Medical School)

CONNOLLY, Dominic Francis Addictions Unit, Tyrone & Fermanagh Hospital, Hospital Road, Omagh BT79 0NS Tel: 01662 249156; 1 Retreat Heights, Ballynamullan Road, Omagh BT79 0HH — MB BCh BAO 1978 NUI; MRCPsych 1983. Cons. Psychiat. Addic.s Specialist Tyrone & Fermanagh Hosp.

CONNOLLY, Elizabeth Angela 1 Neath Way, Chandlers Ford, Eastleigh SO53 4SU — MB BCh BAO 1987 NUI; FRCSI 1991.

CONNOLLY, Francis Gerard 82 Brunswick Road, Bangor BT20 3DN — LRCPI & LM, LRSCI & LM 1955; LRCPI & LM, LRCSI & LM 1955; LAH Dub. 1955; DA RCPSI 1959. (RCSI) Asst. Anaesth. N. Down Hosp. Gp. Socs: Assn. Anaesths. Prev: Regist. N. Irl. Hosp., Auth. & Wigan & Leigh Hosp. Gp.

CONNOLLY, Francis Hugh Queen Anne House, Woodcote Road, Epsom KT18 7QS — MB ChB 1960 Sheff.; MRCPsych 1972; DPM Eng. 1970. Prev: Cons. Psychiat.

CONNOLLY, Geraldine Anne 90 High Street, Barkway, Royston SG8 8EF — MB BCh BAO 1986 NUI.

CONNOLLY, Gerard Michael Marian 15 Maxwell House, Palmerston Road, London N22 8QW — MB BCh BAO 1978 NUI.

CONNOLLY, Helen Mary Catherine 48 Crabtree Lane, Harpenden AL5 5NS — BM BS 1989 Nottm.; DCH RCP Lond. 1991; MRCGP 1993; Dip SportsMed RCP&S. Glas. 1998.

CONNOLLY, Helena Mary Frances Trent House, 32 Marske Mill Lane, Saltburn-by-the-Sea TS12 1HR Tel: 01287 22636 — MB ChB 1973 Liverp.; DCH RCPS Glas. 1976.

CONNOLLY, Mr James Anthony Queen's Medical Centre, Nottingham NE7 2UH Tel: 0115 924 9924 — MB BS 1988 Newc.; FRCS Ed. 1993; FRCS Glas. 1993. Cons. in A8E.

CONNOLLY, James Denis Rentoul 25 Upper Malone Road, Belfast BT9 6TY Tel: 01232 615462; Green Park Healthcare Trust, Stockman's Lane, Belfast BT9 7JB Tel: 01232 669501 — MB BCh BAO Belf. 1969; FFA RCSI 1973. (Queen's University Belfast) Cons. Anaesth. Musgrave Pk. & Belf. City Hosps.; Med. Dir. Green Pk. Healthcare Trust. Socs: Life Mem. Europ. Soc. Regional Anaesth. (GB & Irel. Zone Comm. Mem.); N. Irel. Soc. Anaesth.; Amer. Soc. Regional Anesth. Prev: Cons. Anaesth. Lagan Valley Hosp. Lisburn.

CONNOLLY, Professor John Henry (retired) Regional Virus Laboratory, Royal Victoria Hospital, Belfast BT12 6BN Tel: 01232 240503 Fax: 01232 439181 — MB BCh BAO 1954 Belf.; MD Belf. 1958; FRCPath 1978, M 1966; FRCPI 1975, M 1964. Hon. Prof. Sch. Clin. Med. Qu. Univ. Belf. Prev: Vis. Asst. Prof. Biochem. Johns Hopkins Univ. Sch. Hyg. & Pub. Health Baltimore, USA.

CONNOLLY, Mr John Kevin Royal Liverpool Hospital, Liverpool L7 8XP Tel: 0151 706 2000; 8 Willow Way, Didsbury, Manchester M20 6JS — MB BCh BAO 1983 Dub.; FRCSI 1987. Sen. Regist. (Surg.) Roy. Liverp. Hosp. Prev: Tutor (Surg.) Roy. Infirm. Univ. Manch.; Regist. (Surg.) Wrexham Maelor Hosp. Clwyd.

CONNOLLY, John Michael The Ridge Medical Practice, 3 Paternoster Lane, Great Horton, Bradford BD7 3EE Tel: 01274 502905 Fax: 01274 522060 — MB ChB 1983 Birm.; MRCGP 1987; DRCOG 1986. (Birmingham)

CONNOLLY, John Oliver 75 Oakley Road, London N1 3LW — MB BCh BAO 1988 Belf.; MRCP (UK) 1991. Regist. (Renal Med.) Dulwich Hosp. Lond.

CONNOLLY, John Paul DHSS, Northern Ireland Civil Service, Castle Buildings, Stormont, Belfast BT4 3SQ; 25 Chatsworth, Bangor BT19 7WA Tel: 01247 472226 — MB BCh BAO 1987 Belf.; MRCGP 1991; MD Belfast 1997. Med. Off. DHSS N.ern Irel. Civil Serv. Castle Buildings Stormont Belf. Prev: Clin. Research Fell. (Therap. & Pharmacol.) Qu.'s Univ. Belf.; Trainee GP Dunluce Health Centre Belf.; SHO & Ho. Off. Roy. Vict. Hosp. Belf.

CONNOLLY, Joseph (retired) 3 Meare Close, Tadworth KT20 5RZ Tel: 01737 814582 — MB BS Lond. 1956; MPhil Lond. 1972; FRCP Lond. 1984, M 1960; MRCS Eng. LRCP Lond. 1956; FRCPsych 1981, M 1973; DPM Eng. 1971; DObst RCOG 1958; DCH Eng. 1958. Cons. Psychiat. Bethlem Roy. & Maudsley Hosps. Lond. Prev: Sen. Lect. (Psychiat.) & Hon. Cons. W.m. Med. Sch. & Hosp. Lond.

CONNOLLY, Katherine Margaret Flat 25 Easingwold, Regent Road, Altrincham WA14 1RT — MB BCh BAO 1943 NUI.

CONNOLLY, Kathryn Clare Flat 1, 7 Glengyle Terrace, Edinburgh EH3 9LL Tel: 0131 229 4889 Email: kconn72121@aol.com — MB ChB 1998 Ed.; MB ChB Ed 1998. (Edinburgh) Ho. Off. (Surg.), St. John's Hosp., Howden Rd., W. Livingston, W. Lothian. EH54 6PP.

CONNOLLY, Kieran Banbridge Medical Group Centre, Linenhall Street, Banbridge BT32 3EG; Downhill, Newry Road, Banbridge BT32 3HF — MB BCh BAO 1968 NUI; MRCGP 1975.

CONNOLLY, Mr Leo Patrick 21 St John Street, Manchester M3 4DT Tel: 0161 834 3851; Moor Howe, 95 Hill Top Avenue, Cheadle Hulme, Cheadle SK8 7JA Tel: 0161 485 4355 — MB ChB Sheff. 1959; FRCS Eng. 1968; FRCS Ed. 1968; MRCS Eng. LRCP Lond. 1959; Dip. IMC RCS Ed. 1990. p/t Cons. Surg. (Trauma & Orthop. Surg.) Manor Lodge Consg. Suite. Socs: Fell. BOA; Brit. Trauma Soc.; Guild Catholic Doctors. Prev: Cons. Surg. (Traum. & Orthop. Surg.) Tameside Gen. Hosp. Ashton-under-Lyne; Sen. Regist. (Orthop. Surg.) Manch. N.. Hosp. & United Manch. Hosps.; Regist. (Orthop.) Addenbrooke's Hosp. Camb.

CONNOLLY, Margaret Rose 26 Dunes Drive, Formby, Liverpool L37 1PF — LRCP LRCS 1943 Ed.; LRCP LRCS Ed. LRFPS Glas. 1943.

CONNOLLY, Mary Anne Gartnaval Royal Hospital, 1055 Great Western Rd, Glasgow G12 0XH Tel: 0141 211 1437 Fax: 0141 211 1444; 12 Elm Walk, Bearsden, Glasgow G61 3BQ Tel: 0141 942 4979 — MB BCh BAO 1985 Belf.; MRCGP 1989; MRCPsych 1991; DGM RCP Lond. 1988; DCH Dub. 1987; DRCOG 1987. (Queens University Belfast) Cons. Psychiat., Gartnaval, Roy. Hosp., Glas. Prev: Regist. (Psychiat.) Crichton Roy. Hosp. Dumfries; Sen. Regist. in Psychiat., W. of Scotl. Train. Scheme.; Trainee GP Roy. Vict. Hosp. Belf. VTS.

CONNOLLY, Maurice Declan (retired) 16 Holford Way, Newton-le-Willows WA12 0BZ — LM 1945 Rotunda; BSc, NUI 1945, MB BCh BAO 1941 DPH 1945. Prev: Ho. Phys. Richmond, Whitworth & Hardwicke Hosps. Dub. & St. Kevin's.

CONNOLLY, Michael Gilford Health Centre, Castleview, Gilford, Craigavon BT63 6JS Tel: 028 3883 1225; Grove House, Moyallan, Portadown, Craigavon BT63 5JX Tel: 01762 831225 — MB BCh BAO NUI 1966. (University College Dublin)

CONNOLLY, Michael James 56 Credinhill Park, Upper Dumurry Lane, Belfast BT17 0ES — MB BCh BAO 1990 Belf.; DCH RCPS

Dub. 1992; DRCOG 1992. (Qu. Univ. Belf.) Socs: Roy. Austral. Coll. GPs; Med. Protec. Soc. Prev: GP Brisbane, Austral.

CONNOLLY, Nicholas Paul 25 Upper Malone Road, Belfast BT9 6TY — MB ChB 1996 Dundee.

CONNOLLY, Noel Brendan 19 Lisbeg Park, Crossmaglen, Newry BT35 9DA — MB BCh BAO 1993 Belf.

CONNOLLY, Pamela Mary (retired) Fir View, 85 Kirklake Road, Formby, Liverpool L37 2DA — MB ChB 1961 Liverp.; MRCS Eng. LRCP Lond. 1961.

CONNOLLY, Patrick Joseph 10 Fairfax Avenue, Glasgow G44 5AL — MB ChB 1936 Glas. (Glas.)

CONNOLLY, Patrick Thomas 95 Hill Top Avenue, Cheadle Hulme, Cheadle SK8 7JA — MB ChB 1997 Sheff. SHO Rotat. (Surg.) N. Staffs. Socs: MDU; BMA. Prev: Ho. Rotat. (Gen. Surg., Cardiothoracic Surg. & Respirat. Med., c/o the Elderly).

CONNOLLY, Mr Rainier Campbell (cons. rooms), 149 Harley St., London W1N 2DH Tel: 020 7935 4444; Manor Lodge, Rickmansworth Road, Northwood HA6 2QT Tel: 019274 21085 — MRCS Eng. LRCP Lond. 1941; FRCS Eng. 1947. (St. Bart.) Hon. Consg. Neurosurg. St. Bart. Hosp. Lond. Socs: (Ex-Pres.) Neurol. Sect. Roy. Soc. Med.; Soc. Brit. Neurol. Surgs. Prev: Cons. Neurosurg. Midl. Centre for Neurosurg., Birm. Accid. Hosp. & Roy. Nat. Orthop. Hosp. Lond.; Maj. RAMC, Specialist Neurosurg, (Mentioned in Despatches).

CONNOLLY, Sally Amanda 57 Darras Road, Darras Hall, Ponteland NE20 9PD — MB ChB 1990 Dundee; MRCP CH; MRCP (UK) 1994. p/t Sen. Regist. (Paediat.) Newc.-upon-Tyne. Socs: MRCPCH.

CONNOLLY, Simon Andrew Coatbridge Health Centre, 1 Centre Park Court, Coatbridge ML5 3AP Tel: 01236 422311 Fax: 01236 437787 Email: simon.connolly@coatbridge.lampct.scot.nhs.uk — MB ChB 1985 Glas.; MA Camb. 1976, BA 1973; MRCGP 1989. Waverley Med. Pract., Coatbridge Health Centre, Coatbridge, Lanarksh. ML5 3AP; Med. Director Medihelp Ltd. Socs: Brit. Assn. of Cosmetic Doctors. Prev: Trainee GP/SHO Inverclyde Roy. Hosp. Greenock VTS.; SHO (Med.) Inverclyde Hosp.; SHO (Surg.) StoneHo. Hosp.

***CONNOLLY, Sylvia** 75 Melling Way, Old Hall Estate, Kirkby, Liverpool L32 1TW; Lancaster Royal Infirmary, Ashton Road, Lancaster LA1 4RP Tel: 01524 65944 Fax: 01524 846346 — MB ChB 1997 Leeds; MB ChB (Hons.) Leeds 1997.

CONNOLLY, Thomas Patrick Omagh Health Centre, Mountjoy Road, Omagh BT79 7BA Tel: 028 8224 3521; 11, Crevenagh Road, Omagh BT79 0EW Tel: 028 8224 2739 — MB BCh BAO 1965 NUI.

CONNOLLY, Vincent Mark Tel: 01642 850850 Fax: 01642 854327; 107 Turnberry, Ouston, Chester-le-Street DH2 1LR — MB ChB 1987 Glas.; MRCP (UK) 1990; MD 1998. (Univ. Glas.) Cons. Phys. Diabetes Care Centre Middlesbrough Gen. Hosp. Socs: Eur. Assn. Study Diabetes; Brit. Diabetic Assn.; Brit endocrine Soc. Prev: Sen. Regist. (Gen. Med., Diabetes & Endocrinol.) N.. Region; Regist. (Gen. Med., Diabetes & Endocrinol.) W. of Scotl.; Regist. (Gen. Med., Diabetes, Endocrinol. & Metab. Med.) N.wick Pk. Hosp. Harrow.

CONNON, Eunice Ann Farquhar Queens Road Medical Group, 6 Queens Road, Aberdeen AB15 4NU Tel: 01224 641560 Fax: 01224 642773; 18 Gordondale Road, Aberdeen AB15 5LZ Tel: 01224 634735 — MB ChB 1984 Aberd.; MRCGP 1988.

CONNOR, Adam James Martin 20 Beeston Close, South Oxhey, Watford WD19 6LF — BM BS 1996 Nottm.

CONNOR, Augustine Patrick 4 Buckingham Vale, Bristol BS8 2BU — MB BCh BAO 1981 NUI.

CONNOR, Brian William Desmond Garvagh Health Centre, 110 Main Street, Garvagh, Coleraine BT51 5AE Tel: 028 2955 8210 Fax: 028 2955 7089 — MB ChB 1989 Bristol; MRCGP 1993.

CONNOR, Daniel James 21 Summerhill Road, Cowplain, Waterlooville PO8 8XD — BM BS 1991 Nottm.

CONNOR, Elaine Erne Health Centre, Cornagrade Road, Enniskillen BT74 6AY Tel: 028 6632 2707; 22 Castle Wood, Castlecoole Road, Enniskillen BT74 6BF Tel: 028 6632 7885 — MB BCh BAO 1978 Belf.; MRCGP 1983.

CONNOR, Gregory John Parkview Surgery, Rear of Goldsworth Centre, Sprotbrouth Road, Doncaster DN5 8BP; 19 Fairburn Croft Crescent, Barlborough, Chesterfield S43 4UU — MB ChB 1988 Sheff.; DFPHM 2001; MRCGP 1993. Gen. Practitioner.

CONNOR, Henry County Hospital, Hereford HR1 2ER Tel: 01432 364131 Fax: 01432 364193 — MB 1971 Camb.; BChir 1970; MD Camb. 1980; FRCP Lond. 1985; MRCP (UK) 1972. (Westm.) Cons. Phys. Co. Hosp. Hereford. Socs: Brit. Diabetic Assn. Prev: Lect. (Therap.) Univ. Sheff.; Regist. (Med.) Radcliffe Infirm. Oxf.

CONNOR, Hilary Elaine 43 Inverness Street, London NW1 7HB — MB BS 1997 Lond.

CONNOR, Professor James Michael Institute of Medical Genetics, Yorkhill, Glasgow G3 8SJ Tel: 0141 201 0365 Fax: 0141 357 4277 Email: j.m.connor@clinmed.gla.ac.uk; East Collarie Farm, Waterside, By Fenwick, Kilmarnock KA3 6JJ — MB ChB 1975 Liverp.; BSc (Hons.) Liverp. 1973, DSc 1995, MD 1981; FRCP Ed. 1990; FRCP Glas. 1988; MRCP (UK) 1977. (Liverpool) Prof. Med. Genetics & Dir. of The W. of Scotl. Regional Genetics Serv. Inst. Med. Genetics Glas. Socs: Brit. Soc. Human Genetics; Eur. Soc. Human Genet.; Amer. Soc. Human Genetics. Prev: Assoc.Dean (Research) Fac.Med. Univ.Glas; Wellcome Trust Sen. Lect. (Med. Genetics) Univ. Glas.; Instruc. Internal Med. Johns Hopkins Hosp. Baltimore, USA.

CONNOR, Jeannette Ann Department of Radiodiagnosis, Sunderland Royal University Hospital, Kayll Road, Sunderland SR4 7TP Tel: 0191 565 6256 Email: jenny.connor@chs.northy.nhs.uk; Dalton Moor Farm, Dalton Le Dale, Seaham SR7 9JY Tel: 0191 517 3692 — MB ChB 1982 Dundee; FRCR 1990. Cons. Radiol. Sunderland Roy. Univ. Hosp..; Cons. Radiologist BUPA Hosp. Washington, Washington. Prev: Sen. Regist. (Radiol.) Roy. Infirm. Glas.; Regist. (Radiol.) Vict. Infirm. Glas.

CONNOR, Jennifer Ann 135 All Saints Street, Hastings TN34 3BG — MB BS 1963 Lond.; DCH Eng. 1965. (Char. Cross)

CONNOR, Jillian Margaret 10E Brisbane Court, Braidpark Drive, Giffnock, Glasgow G46 6LX — MB ChB 1993 Glas.

CONNOR, John Haslett Western Elms Surgery, 317 Oxford Road, Reading RG30 1AT Tel: 0118 959 0257 Fax: 0118 959 7950 — MB BS 1975 Lond.; MRCS Eng. LRCP Lond. 1975; MRCGP 1979; DRCOG 1979; DCH Eng. 1978. (Char. Cross) Prev: Regist. (Med.) Waikato Hosp. Hamilton NZ; Trainee GP King's Lynn VTS; Ho. Phys. Char. Cross Hosp.

CONNOR, Martin Paul, Squadron Ldr. RAF Med. Br. Royal Naval Hospital (Haslar), Gosport PO12 2AA Tel: 01705 584255 — MB ChB 1988 Glas.; MSc Lond. 1994; DTM & H Liverp. 1996; MRCPath 1997. Cons. (Microbiol.) Roy. Naval Hosp. Haslar. Socs: Assn. Clin. Path.; Assn. Med. Microbiol.; BMA. Prev: Specialist Regist. St. Thomas' & Guy's Hosps. NHS Trust; Regist. (Microbiol.) Stoke Mandeville Hosp. Aylesbury & John Radcliffe Hosp. Oxf.; RAF Med. Off. Belize Centr. Amer.

CONNOR, Mary Elizabeth Jessop Wing, Royal Hallamshire Hospital, Sheffield S10 2SF Tel: 0114 226 1060; 22 Redcar Road, Crookes, Sheffield S10 1EX Tel: 0114 268 0738 — MB ChB 1980 Birm.; MD Birm. 1992; MRCOG 1985; DCH RCP Lond. 1983; FRCOG 1999. p/t Cons. O & G Roy. Hallamshire Hosp. Socs: N. Eng. Obst. & Gyn. Soc.; Brit. Soc. Gyn. Endoscopy. Prev: Clin. Research Fell. Paterson Inst. for Cancer Research Christie Hosp. & Holt Radium Inst. Manch.; Sen. Regist. (O & G) N.. Gen. Hosp. Sheff.

CONNOR, Nicola Ruth 25 Chandos Road, London N2 9AR — MB BS 1991 Lond.; BSc (Pharmacol.) Lond. 1988; MFPHM London 1999. (University College Hospitall School of Medicine) Sen. Regist. in Pub. Health.

***CONNOR, Philip Peter** 123 Vanner Road, Witney OX28 1LQ — MB BS 1997 Lond.

CONNOR, Rachel Alyson Clare Department of Radiology, Hairmyres Hospital, Hairmyres, East Kilbride, Glasgow G75 8RG Tel: 0135 52 20292; East Collarie Farm, Waterside, Kilmarnock KA3 6JJ — MB ChB 1979 Liverp.; VQE 1979; FRCR 1985. Cons. (Radiol.) StoneHo. Hosp. & Hairmyres Hosp. E. Kilbride. Socs: Brit. Med. Ultrasound Soc.; Fell. Roy. Coll. Radiol. Prev: Resid. (Diag. Radiol.) Johns Hopkins Hosp. Baltimore, USA; Sen. Regist. (Radiol.) W.. Infirm. Glas.

CONNOR, Stephen Edmund John Neuroadiology Dept, Kings College Hosp, Denmark Hill, London SE5 9RS Tel: 020 7737 4000; 68 Farquhar Road, Upper Norwood, London SE19 1LT Email: s.connor@talk121.com — MB ChB 1992 Birm.; MRCP (UK) 1995;

FRCR 1996. Specialist Regist. (Neuroradiol.) King Coll.. Lond. Socs: RCR; BMA; BIR. Prev: Regist. Rotat. (Radiol.) W. Midl.; SHO (Med. & Geriat.) City Hosp. Birm.; SHO (Anaesth.) Worcester Roy. Infirm.

CONNOR, Terrence Powell Kerami, Pontac, St Clement, Jersey JE2 6FU Tel: 01534 854649 — MB BS Lond. 1954; LMCC 1962; FRCPC 1966; CRCP(C) 1963; DMR 1963; DABR(D) 1963; CCPS(Q) 1964. (St. Thos. Hosp. & McGill Univ.) Assoc. Prof. Univ. Toronto 1975-89. Socs: Ontario Med. Assn. Prev: Assoc. Specialist Jersey Gen. Hosp. St. Helier; Chief Radiol. Wom. Coll. Hosp. Toronto, Canada.

CONNOR, William Campbell Wallace Medical Practice, Wallace House, Maxwell Place, Stirling FK8 1JU Tel: 01786 448900 — MB ChB 1973 Glasgow. (Glasgow) GP Stirling.

CONOCHIE, Bruce Campbell, MBE (retired) 89 Bartlow Road, Linton, Cambridge CB1 6LY Tel: 01223 894460 — MB ChB 1944 Glas.

CONOD, Kevin Charles 5 Birmingham Road, Walsall WS1 2LX Tel: 01922 20303; 18 Charlemont Road, Walsall WS5 3NG — MB ChB 1983 Birm.

CONRAD, Mr George Jurek 29 Chain Walk Drive, Kenwyn, Truro TR1 3ST — MD 1959 Silesian Med. Acad. Katowice; FRCS Ed. 1973; DLO Eng. 1967. Cons. (ENT Surg.) Roy. Cornw. Hosp. Truro. Socs: Fell. Roy. Soc. Med.; BMA. Prev: Regist. ENT Surg. Aberd. Roy. Infirm.; Clin. Tutor (ENT Dis.) Univ. Aberd.; Sen. Regist. (ENT Surg.) Radcliffe Infirm. Oxf.

CONRAD, Jerome Julian Alexander The Acorns Surgery, 85 Wheelock Street, Middlewich CW10 9AE Tel: 01606 837400 — MB ChB 1981 Manch.

CONRAD, Jerzy Marek The Willow Surgery, Coronation Road, Downend, Bristol BS16 5DH Tel: 0117 970 9500; First floor Flat, 22 Beaufort Road, Clifton, Bristol BS8 2JY Tel: 0117 974 3446 Email: george.conrad@connectfree.uu — MB ChB 1972 Bristol.

CONRAD, Kitty Kate (retired) 30 Brim Hill, London N2 0HG — MB BS 1933 Lond.; DPH 1937.

CONRAD, Konrad Wladislaw Osborne Avenue Surgery, 5 Osborne Avenue, Jesmond, Newcastle upon Tyne NE2 1PQ Tel: 0191 281 0041 Fax: 0191 281 1474; 26 Oakfield Road, Gosforth, Newcastle upon Tyne NE3 4HS Tel: 0191 284 1252 Email: conrad@rapidial.co.uk — MB BS 1979 Newc.; MFOM 2000; MRCGP 1983; AFOM 1988; DRCOG 1983. Gen. Practitioner; Sen. Clin. Med. Off. (Occupat. Med.) Newc. Primary Care Trust. Socs: Soc. Occupat. Med.

CONRAD, Roderick James Department of Histopathology, Royal Free Hospital, Pond St., Hampstead, London NW3 2QG Tel: 020 7794 0500 — MB BS 1985 Queensland.

CONRAD, Virginia Ann 223 Groveley Lane, Birmingham B31 4QB — MB ChB 1995 Leeds.

CONRAN, Gordon Eric Victor (retired) 1 Sheenewood, London SE26 6BH — MB BS 1948 Madras; MRCGP 1968. Prev: Regist. (Thoracic Surg.) Brook Gen. Hosp.

CONRAN, Michael Bernard 29 Hamilton Gardens, St. John's Wood, London NW8 9PU Tel: 020 7286 3454 — MRCS Eng. LRCP Lond. 1947; MD Lond. 1971, MB BS 1950. (Guy's) Socs: Assoc. Mem. Brit. Psycho-Analyt. Soc; Fell. Roy. Soc. Med. Prev: Cons. Psychotherap. Friern Hosp. & Halliwick Ho. Lond.; Univ. Lect. Bact., Med. Sch. Birm.; Med. Asst. Shenley Hosp.

CONRAN, Thomas Martin Good and Conran, The Health Centre, Tavanagh Avenue, Portadown, Craigavon BT62 3BU Tel: 028 3835 1497 Fax: 028 3835 1246 — MB BCh BAO 1972 Belf.

CONROY, Brian, Surg. Lt.-Cdr. RN (retired) c/o Pathology Department, St. Richard's Hospital, Spitalfield Lane, Chichester PO19 4SE Tel: 01243 788122 Fax: 01243 536259 — MB ChB 1975 Dundee; FRCPath 1994, M 1982. Cons. Histopath. & Cytopath. St. Richard's Hosp. Chichester. Prev: Cons. Histopath. RN Hosp. Haslar.

CONROY, Desmond Patrick Joseph Lane View, Coverhill Road, Grotton, Oldham OL4 5RF — MB BCh BAO 1948 NUI. (Univ. Coll. Dub.) Dir. Med. Emerg. Duty Serv. Manch.; Chairm. Healthcare Managem. Consults.

CONROY, James Isaac 3 Hawstone Avenue, Whitefield, Manchester B45 7PK Tel: 0161 766 5063 — MRCS Eng. LRCP Lond. 1932; MRCGP 1967. (King's Coll. Lond.) Prev: Res. Med. Off. Qu. Mary's Hosp. Sidcup & Jewish Matern. Hosp. Lond.

CONROY, Jonathan Lee Woodview, Smith Lane, Mobberley, Knutsford WA16 7QD — MB ChB 1995 Manch.

CONROY, Julia Margaret St Richards Hospital, Spitalfield Lane, Chichester PO19 4SE Tel: 01243 788122; 2 Stanton Drive, Summersdale, Chichester PO19 4QN Tel: 01243 771607 — MB BS 1980 Newc.; MRCPath 1989. Cons. (Histopath.) St. Richards Hosp. Chichester. Prev: Sen. Regist. (Histopath.) Soton. Gen. Hosp.

CONROY, Mark, OStJ, Brigadier late RAMC Jutland House, Jutland Road, Catterick Garrison DL9 3AT — MB BCh BAO NUI 1968; FRCGP 1986, M 1975; DCH Eng. 1978; DObst RCOG 1973. (Univ. Coll. Dub.) Sen. Partner, Gmc Catterick. Prev: Direct.Army-Gen.Pract.

CONROY, Mary Catherine Hewelsfield, 19 Heol Wen, Rhiwbina, Cardiff CF14 6EG Tel: 029 2062 0828 — LRCPI & LM, LRCSI & LM 1948; LM Nat. Matern. Hosp. Dub. 1949; TDD Wales 1952. (RCSI Dublin) Mem. Pneumoconiosis Med. Panel & Silicosis Med. Bd. Socs: Thoracic Soc. Wales. Prev: Asst. Chest Phys. Caerphilly; Sen. Asst. Med. Off. Grosvenor Sanat. Ashford; Res. Ho. Phys. Meath Hosp. Dub.

CONROY, Philip Thomas 2 Apsley Close, Bowdon, Altrincham WA14 3AJ — MB ChB 1978 Manch.; FFA RCS Eng. 1982. Cons. Anaesth. Wythenshawe Hosp. Manch.

CONROY, Sandra Jane Garden City Practice, 11 Guessen Road, Welwyn Garden City AL8 6QW Tel: 01707 321166 Fax: 01707 391911 — MB BCh BAO 1986 NUI.

CONROY, Simon Paul Bedford Hopsital, Hempston Road, Nottingham Tel: 01234 355122 — MB ChB 1995 Leic.; MRCP 1998. (Leicester) SPR Geriat.s, E. Anglia. Socs: (Sec.) Anglo-French Med. Soc.; Brit. Geriat.s Soc. Prev: SHO (Med.), Derbysh. Roy. Infirm.; SHO Qu.s Med, Nottm.; SHO, Med.Leicester Hosp.

CONROY, Stephen Alison Lea Medical Centre, Calderwood, East Kilbride, Glasgow G74 3BE Tel: 01355 233981; 7 Woodyett Park, Busby, Glasgow G76 8SJ Tel: 0141 644 5095 — MB ChB 1990 Glas. (Glasgow) Clin. Asst. (Paediat., A & E) Roy. Hosp. for Sick childr. Socs: BMA; MDDUS. Prev: SHO Bellshill Matern. Hosp. Lanarksh.; SHO (Cas.) Hairmyres Hosp. Glas.; Resid. (Surg.) Dumfries & Galloway Roy. Infirm.

CONROY, Thomas Aidan 4 The Serpentine, Grassendale, Liverpool L19 9DT Tel: 0151 427 1740 — MB BCh BAO 1959 NUI; MRCPsych 1972; DPM Eng. 1970; DPH Liverp. 1962. Cons. Psychiat. Walton Hosp. Liverp. Prev: Sen. Regist. (Psychiat.) Rainhill Hosp. Liverp.; Psychiat. Regist. Walton Hosp. Liverp.; Asst. Port Med. Off. Liverp.

CONRY, Brendon Gerard Lidwells House, Goudhurst, Cranbrook TN17 1JJ Tel: 01580 211149 Fax: 01580 212303 Email: b.conry@virgin.net — MB BS 1979 Lond.; MRCS Eng. LRCP Lond. 1979; MRCP (UK) 1982; DMRD Eng. 1984; FRCR 1986. (St. Bart.) Cons. Radiol.Tumbridge Wells Hosp.s, Maidstone & Tumbridgewells NHS Trust. Prev: Sen. Regist. & Regist. (Radiol.) St. Bart. Hosp. Lond.; Ho. Surg. & SHO (Med.) St. Bart. Hosp. Lond.

CONSIDINE, Mr John (retired) 8 Reddings Road, Moseley, Birmingham B13 8LN Tel: 0121 449 3153 — MB BCh BAO 1949 NUI; FRCS Eng. 1960. Prev: Cons. Urol. E. Birm. HA & Solihull HA.

CONSIGLIO, Ramon Victor Threlfall's Farm, Bilsborrow, Preston PR3 0RN Tel: 01995 40489 — MD 1955 Malta; BSc, BPharm. Malta 1952, MD 1955; FFA RCS Eng. 1962; DA Eng. 1958. (Malta) Cons. Anaesth. Roy. Preston Hosp. Prev: Sen. Lect. in Anaesth. Univ. E. Africa; Sen. Regist. Dept. Anaesth. Roy. Infirm. Manch.

CONSTABLE, Anne Bradlea, Durham Road, Wolviston, Billingham TS22 5LP — MB ChB 1977 Manch.; MRCGP 1981.

CONSTABLE, Frank 25 Battleton, Dulverton TA22 9HU — MRCS Eng. LRCP Lond. 1939.

CONSTABLE, Frank Leonard, TD, KStJ (retired) 17 Roseworth Avenue, Gosforth, Newcastle upon Tyne NE3 1NB Tel: 0191 285 1223 — MB BS 1951 Durh.; BSc (Hons.) Durham. 1942, MD 1960; FRCPath 1963. Hon. Phys. to HM the Qu.; DL. Prev: Cons. Bacteriol. Roy. Vict. Infirm. Newc.

CONSTABLE, Gary Lee Institute of Human Nutrition, Southamton Genral Hospital, Mail Point 113, Tremona Road, Southampton SO16 6YD Tel: 0238 794968 — MB BS 1991 Lond.; MRCP (UK) 1996. (Lond. Hosp. Med. Coll.) Regist. (Gastroenterol.) St Richards. Chichester; Clin. Fell. in Human Nutrit.; Honarary Specialist Registar in Gastroenterol. Prev: SPR (Gastroenterol) S.amton Gen. Hosp.; SPR (Gastroenterol) St. Richards Hosp., Chichester.

CONSTABLE, George Doig Christmas Cottage, High St., Stogursey, Bridgwater Tel: 01278 331 — MB ChB 1956 St. And.
CONSTABLE, Guy Nicholson (retired) Westwood, 8 Hazel Close, Ashbourne DE6 1HX — MB BCh BAO 1948 Dub.; MA, MD Dub. 1953; FFPHMI 1984, M 1979. Prev: Dir. Pub. Health Bolton HA.
CONSTABLE, Jean Margaret (retired) 17 Roseworth Avenue, Gosforth, Newcastle upon Tyne NE3 1NB Tel: 0191 285 1223 — MB BS 1951 Durh. JP. Prev: SHO (Microbiol.) Roy. Vict. Infirm. Newc.
CONSTABLE, Peter Hadley 35 Wiseton Road, London SW17 7EE — BM BCh 1988 Oxf.; MA Camb. 1989; FRCOphth 1992. Regist. Inst. Ophth. & Moorfields Eye Hosp. Socs: Assn. for Research in Vision & Ophth.; Roy. Soc. Med.; Glaucoma Soc. Prev: Regist. (Ophth.) OldCh. Hosp.; SHO (Ophth.) Char. Cross & W.m. Hosp.; SHO (Ophth.) Roy. Lond. & Moorfields Eye Hosp. Lond.
CONSTABLE, Peter John, CBE (retired) Lilley House, Lilley, Luton LU2 8LH Email: peterconstable@lilleyhouse.freeserve.co.uk — MB BS 1954 Lond.; MSc Lond. 1981, MD 1966; FRCGP 1983, M 1965; FFOM RCP Lond. 1987, M 1982; DIH Soc. Apoth. Lond. 1978; DObst RCOG 1958. Prev: Cons. Occupat. Phys. Centr. Pub. Health Laborat. Colindale & N. Herts. NHS Trust.
CONSTABLE, Trevor John 6 Thorney Road, Sutton Coldfield B74 3HT — MB ChB 1970 Ed.; MRCP (U.K.) 1973. Cons. Phys. Walsall Manor Hosp. Socs: Brit. Soc. Rheum. Prev: Sen. Regist. (Med.) Qu. Eliz. Hosp. Birm.; Sen. Regist. Rheum. Dis. Unit N.. Gen. Hosp. Edin.; Sheldon Clin. Research Fell. Dept. Experim. Path. Birm. Univ. Med.
CONSTANCE, Nicholas David 6 Trelawney Road, Padstow PL28 8EQ Tel: 01841 532766 — MB BS 1986 Lond.; MRCGP 1992; DRCOG 1991; DCH RCP Lond. 1991. Prev: Regist. (Paediat.) NE Surrey Hosp. Redhill.
CONSTANT, Mr Christopher Robert Clinic One, Box 37, Addenbrooke's Hospital, Hills Road, Cambridge CB2 2QQ Tel: 01223 216229 Fax: 01223 217307 Email: constant@psilink.co.uk; 4 Fennec Close, Cherry Hinton, Cambridge CB1 9GG Tel: 01223 249556 Fax: 01223 410247 Email: crc@constant-cr.co.uk — MB BCh BAO NUI 1975; LLM Cardiff 1994; MCh NUI 1987; FRCSI 1979; MA 2000 Camb. (Cork) Cons. Orthop. Surg. Addenbrooke's Hosp. Camb. Socs: Fell. BOA; Founder Mem. Brit. Elbow & Shoulder Soc. Prev: Sen. Regist. (Orthop. & Traum. Surg.) Addenbrooke's Hosp. Camb.; Clin. Fell. (Orthop. Surg.) Toronto, Canada; Regist. (Neurosurg.) Radcliffe Infirm. Oxf.
CONSTANTIN, Annette Mary Lucie (retired) 38 Parkdale, Danbury, Chelmsford CM3 4EH Tel: 01245 224671 — MB BS Lond. 1949.
CONSTANTINE, Claire Elizabeth Department of Microbiology, Worcester Royal Infirmary, Castle Street Branch, Worcester WR1 3AS Tel: 01905 763333 Fax: 01905 22343 — MB ChB 1981 Birm.; MSc Lond. (Med. Microbiol.) 1985; MA Oxf. 1984, BA 1978; FRCPath 1999. Cons. Microbiol. Worcester Roy. Infirm. Prev: Cons. Microbiol. Pub. Health Laborat. Serv. Addenbrooke's Hosp. Camb.
CONSTANTINE, George Meadowbrook Road Surgery, 4 Meadowbrook Road, Halesowen B63 1AB Tel: 0121 550 1034 Fax: 0121 550 4758; 33 Manor Road N., Edgbaston, Birmingham B16 9JS — MB ChB 1964 Alexandria; LMSSA Lond. 1969; DObst RCOG 1970. Socs: BMA.
CONSTANTINE, Glyn 37 Walsall Road, Little Aston, Sutton Coldfield B74 3BA — MB ChB 1980 Liverp.; BSc (1st cl. Hons.) Manch. 1974; MB ChB (Hons.) Liverp. 1980; MRCP Lond. 1983; MRCS Eng. LRCP Lond. 1980; MRCOG 1985. Cons. O & G Good Hope Hosp. Sutton Coldfield. Prev: Sen. Regist. Dudley Rd. Hosp. Birm.; Regist. (Obst. Gyn.) Birm. & W. Midl. Hosp. for Wom.; SHO (O & G) Withington Hosp. Manch.
CONSTANTINE, Sarah Jane 35 Greenway Lane, Chippenham SN15 1AE — BM 1991 Soton.
CONSTANTINIDES, Costas PO Box 50155, Limassol 3601, Cyprus Tel: 00357 345147; 316 Broomhill Road, Aberdeen AB10 7NE Tel: 01224 316950 — MB ChB 1956 Aberd.; FRCS Glas. 1965; FRCS Ed. 1966; FRCOphth. 1989; DO Eng. 1961. (Aberd.) Indep. Pract. Limassol, Cyprus. Prev: Sen. Ophth. Surg. Min. of Health Abu Dhabi.; Sen. Regist. (Ophth.) Glas. Eye Infirm.
CONSTANTINIDES, Helena Hall Floor Flat, 124A Redland Road, Redland, Bristol BS6 6XY Tel: 0117 973 3364 Email: hels1999@aol.com; 50 Hunstanton Avenue, Herborne, Birmingham B17 8TA Tel: 0121 429 6785 — MB ChB 1995 Bristol; MRCS (Eng) June 1999. (Bristol) SHO (OtorhinoLaryngol.).
CONSTANTINIDES, Savvas 25 Ramsbury Road, Leicester LE2 6HR; PO Box 1520, Limassol, Cyprus — MB ChB 1993 Leic.; MRCP (Lond.) 1997. (Cardiol. Research Regist.) Walsgrave Hosp., Coventry. Socs: B.M.A (Full Mem.).
CONSTANTINIDOU, Maria Wellington Health Centre, 16 Wellington Road, St John's Wood, London NW8 9SP Tel: 020 7722 3382 Fax: 020 7722 2390; 30 Rochester Road, London NW1 9JJ Tel: 020 7482 1761 — MB BS 1970 Lond.; MRCP (UK) 1980; MRCS Eng. LRCP Lond. 1970; DCH Eng. 1973.
CONSTANTINOU, Jason Top Flat, 81 Shirland Road, London W9 2EL — MB BS 1996 Lond.
CONSTERDINE, Eric, Maj. RAMC Retd. 5 Adelaide House, 23 Grand Parade, St Leonards-on-Sea TN37 6DN — MRCS Eng. LRCP Lond. 1943; DPH Bristol 1970. (Manch. & Bristol) Chief Med. Off. Trinidad & Tobago Oil Co. Ltd. Socs: Soc. Community Med. Prev: Sen. Med. Off. Caroni Ltd. Trinidad; MOH Jamaican Govt.; Sen. Med. Off. Foreign Off. (Anglo-Egyptian Sudan).
CONTARDI, Peter Alan 12 Holme Park Avenue, Uppernewbold, Chesterfield S41 8XB — MB BS 1986 Lond.
***CONTELL, Faith Nerine** 45A Portnall Road, London W9 3BA Tel: 020 8 969 8759; 50 Raphael Crescent, Gelvan Park, Port Elizabeth 6020, South Africa Tel: 00 27 414 24444 Fax: 00 27 414 24444 — MB ChB 1994 Cape Town; BSc Cape Town 1989.
CONTRACTOR, Abid Saleh Blackburn Street Health Centre, Radcliffe, Manchester M26 1WS; 365 Manchester Road, Bury BL9 9QS Tel: 0161 723 2062 — MB BS 1956 Karachi; DTM & H Liverp. 1957. (Dow Med. Coll.)
CONTRACTOR, Mr Bhadresh Ramanlal The Health Centre, Trenchard Avenue, Thornaby, Stockton-on-Tees TS17 0DD Tel: 01642 762636 Fax: 01642 766464; Over Dinsdale Hall, Neasham, Darlington DL2 1PW Tel: 01325 332478 Fax: 01325 332478 — MB BS 1972 Gujarat; FRCS Ed. 1977. Hosp. Pract. (Gastroenterol.) S. Cleveland Hosp.
CONTRACTOR, Hansa Bhadresh Department of Anaesthesia, North Tees General Hospital, Hardwick, Stockton-on-Tees TS19 8PE Tel: 01642 617617 Fax: 01642 602995; Over Dinsdale Hall, Neasham, Darlington DL2 1PW Tel: 01325 332478 — MB BS 1972 Gujarat; FFA RCS Eng. 1977; DA Eng. 1975. Cons. Anaesth. N. Tees. Gen. Hosp. Stockton-on-Tees. Prev: Sen. Regist. (Anaesth.) Newc. AHA (T).
CONTRACTOR, Nasreen 365 Manchester Road, Bury BL9 9QS — MB BS 1990 Lond.
CONTRACTOR, Noshirwan Kaikhushro (retired) 14 Cyncoed Road, Cardiff CF23 5SG Tel: 01443 495544 — MRCS Eng. LRCP Lond. 1942; MFCM 1973; DPH Wales 1956. Prev: Sen. Admin. Med. Off. S. Glam. AHA.
CONTRERAS, Professor Marcela National Blood Service - North London, Colindale Avenue, London NW9 5BG Tel: 020 8258 2705 Fax: 020 8205 5017 Email: marcela.contreras@nbs.nhs.uk; 2 Middleton Road, London NW11 7NS — MD Chile 1968; BSc Chile 1961; FRCP Ed. 1992; MRCPath 1988; FRCPath 1997; FRCP Lond. 1998. (Univ. Chile) Nat. Dir. For Diagnostics Developm. & Research; Prof. Transfus. Med. Roy. Free Hosp. Med. Sch.; Hon. Sen. Lect. St. Mary's Hosp. Med. Sch.; Edr.-in-Chief Vox Sanguinis. Socs: Fell. Roy. Soc. Med. (Ex-Pres. Sect. Path.); Fell. Roy. Coll. Pathol.; Expert Advis. Gp. on Hepatitis & UK NBTS/NIBSC Liaison Gp. Prev: Mem. (Pres.) Internat. Soc. Blood Transfus.; Chief Exec. & Med. Dir. N. Lond. Blood Transfus. Centre Colindale; Exec. Dir. Lond. SE Zone of Nat. Blood Serv.
CONVERY, Alistair Dunbeath Health Centre, Kingussie Medical Practice, Ther Surgery, Ardvonie Park, Kingussie Tel: 01540 661233 — MB ChB 1986 Ed.; MRCGP 1990. GP Partner in Kingussie Med. Pract., Ardvonie Pk., Kingussie, Invernesshire. Socs: BASICS; RCSP. Prev: GP Princip. Dunbeath Caithness 1993-2001; Asst. GP Cuminestown.
CONVERY, Cormac Accident and Emergency Department, Glasgow Royal Infirmary, 84 Castle Street, Glasgow G4 0SF — MB ChB 1996 Dundee.
CONVERY, Kathryn Anne Burnield Medical Practice, Harris Road, Inverness IV2 3 — MB ChB 1984 Aberd.; DA (UK) 1987. GP Inverness Retainer Scheme; GP Caithness Retainer Scheme; Clin.

Asst. in Chest Med. Raigmore Hosp. Inverness. Prev: Trainee GP Glas.

CONVERY, Philip Niall 77 Marlborough Park S., Belfast BT9 6HS — MB BCh BAO 1989 Belf.; MB BCh BAO NUI Belf. 1989.

CONVERY, Rory Peter 3 Craigadick Park, Maghera BT46 5DD — MB BCh BAO 1990 Belf.; MB BCh Belf. 1990.

CONWAY, Alison Susan Woodland Centre, Hillingdon Hospital, Pield Heath Road, Uxbridge UB8 3NN Tel: 01895 279837 Fax: 01895 279718 Email: alison.conway@152.hillingh-tr.nthames.nhs.uk — MB BS 1985 Lond.; MRCPsych 1990. Cons. Psychiat. of Old Age Hillingdon Hosp. Uxbridge. Prev: Sen. Regist. Rotat. (Adult & Gen. Psychiat.) St. Geo. Hosp. Lond.; Research Worker St. Thos. Hosp. Lond.; SHO & Regist. Rotat. St. Geo. Hosp. Lond.

CONWAY, Annie Royal Liverpool Childrens Hospital, Eaton Road, Alder Hey, Liverpool L12 2AP Tel: 0151 228 4811; 56 Rosslyn Road, Vicars Cross, Chester CH3 5HP Tel: 01244 328962 — MB BCh BAO 1962 NUI; MCommH Liverp. 1979; DPH Liverp. 1969. SCMO (Community Child Health) Roy. Liverp. Childr. NHSTrust Alder Hey; Med. Adviser to Liverp. LA Adoption & Fostering Panels.

CONWAY, Bernadette Elizabeth 27 Bowhouse Drive, Kirkcaldy KY1 1SB — MB BCh BAO 1977 Belf. Assoc. Specialist (Cytopathol.) Forth Pk. Hosp. Kirkcaldy.

CONWAY, Brian Martin Newbridge Surgery, 129 Newbridge Hill, Bath BA1 3PT Tel: 01225 425807 Fax: 01225 447776; Thorncliffe, The Batch, Saltford, Bristol BS31 3EN — MB BS 1973 Lond.; MRCP (UK) 1976; MRCS Eng. LRCP Lond. 1973. (Roy. Free)

CONWAY, Bryan Ronald 8 Sharman Drive, Belfast BT9 5HL — MB BCh BAO 1996 Belf.

CONWAY, Christine Ann Halifax Road Surgery, 9 Halifax Road, Dewsbury WF13 2JH — MB ChB 1982 Leeds; MRCGP 1986. (Leeds) p/t GP Dewsbury.

CONWAY, Damian Patrick 157 Loughmacrory Road, Sixmilecross, Omagh BT79 9LF — MB BCh BAO 1994 Belf.

CONWAY, David Ian Glasgow Nuffield Hospital, Beaconsfield Road, Glasgow G12 0PJ Tel: 0141 334 9441 Fax: 0141 339 1352; 53 Kirkintilloch Road, Lenzie, Glasgow G66 4LB Tel: 0141 776 1463 Fax: 0141 776 1463 — MB ChB Manch. 1970; MD Manch. 1983; FRCOG 1992, M 1977; DObst RCOG 1972. (Manch.) Cons. O & G Bellshill Matern. Hosp. & Monklands Dist. Gen. Hosp. Airdrie; Family Plann Doctor Centr. Health Clinic Cumbernauld; Hon. Sen. Lect. Glas. Univ. Socs: Brit. Soc. Med. & Dent. Hypn.; Brit. Fertil. Soc. Prev: Lect. & Sen. Regist. (O & G) Bristol Matern. Hosp.; Tutor (O & G) Hope Hosp. Salford.

CONWAY, Dwayne Sean Gavin 56 Rosslyn Road, Vicars Cross, Chester CH3 5HP — MB ChB 1995 Birm.; MRCP Part I 1997. (Birm.) SHO (Gen. Med.) Derriford Hosp. Plymouth. Prev: SHO (Elderly Care) York Dist. Hosp.; SHO (A & E) York Dist. Hosp.; Ho. Off. (Gen. Surg.) Warwick Hosp.

CONWAY, Edith Margaret (retired) Craigniche House, Glenlia, Foyers, Inverness IV2 6YA Tel: 01456 486394 — MB ChB Aberd. 1948. Prev: Resid. Med. Off. Hse. of Daviot, Inverurie.

CONWAY, Elizabeth Jane (retired) 27 Bowhouse Drive, Kirkcaldy KY1 1SB — LRCPI & LM, LRSCI & LM 1946; LRCPI & LM, LRCSI & LM 1946. Prev: Assoc. Specialist Ment. Handicap. Hensol Hosp. Pontyclun.

CONWAY, Ellen Ita (retired) 27 St Georges Terrace, Herne Bay CT6 8RH Tel: 01227 373107 — MB BCh BAO 1968 NUI. Prev: Clin. Asst. (Palliat. Med.) Kent.

CONWAY, Eunice Jean 22 Polwarth Street, Glasgow G12 9TY — MB ChB 1990 Manch.

CONWAY, Gareth Leon 4 Linseys Hill, Armagh BT61 9HD — MB BCh BAO 1997 Belf.

CONWAY, Gerard Stephen The Middlesex Hospital, Mortimer St., London W1T 3AA Tel: 020 7380 9201 Fax: 020 7380 9201 Email: g.conway@ucl.ac.uk — MB BS 1981 Lond.; MD Lond. 1992; FRCP 1997, M 1985. (Lond. Hosp. Med. Sch.) Cons. Endocrinol. UCL Hosps. NHS Trust. Prev: Sen. Regist. (Diabetes & Endocrinol.) Whittington Hosp., Univ. Coll. Hosp. & Middlx. Hosp. Lond.; Regist. (Med.) Unit Middlx. Hosp. Lond.; Sen. Lect. (Endocrinol.) Univ. Coll. Lond. Sch. Med. UCL Hosp.

CONWAY, Henry Paul Ashton Health Centre, 67-69 Pedders Lane, Ashton-on-Ribble, Preston PR2 1HR Tel: 01772 726839; 185 Tulketh Road, Ashton, Preston PR2 1ER Tel: 01772 727238 — MB BCh BAO 1972 NUI; BAgrSc NUI 1965, MB BCh BAO 1972; MRCP UK 1980; MRCGP 1981; DCH RCPSI 1977; DObst RCPI 1975. (Univ. Coll. Dub.) GP. Socs: BMA & Preston Medico-Ethical Soc. Prev: SHO (Med.) Roy. Shrewsbury Hosp.; SHO (Paediat.) Devonsh. Rd. Hosp. Barrow-in-Furness; SHO (O & G) Coombe Lying-in Hosp. Dub.

CONWAY, Hugh (retired) Flat 65, Kelburne Court, 51 Glasgow Road, Paisley PA1 3PD Tel: 0141 889 0939 — MB ChB 1940 Glas.; BSc Glas. 1937; MB ChB (Hons.) Glas. 1940; FRCP Lond. 1966, M 1947; FRCP Glas. 1964, M 1962; FRFPS Glas. 1960; FRCP Ed. 1974, M 1971. Cons. Phys. P.ss Louise Scott. Hosp. Erskine. Prev: Sen. Phys. Roy. Alexandra Infirm. Paisley.

CONWAY, Ian Michael Somerset Health Authority, Wellsprings Road, Taunton TA2 7PQ — MB BS Lond. 1979; MRCS Eng. LRCP Lond. 1978. (Roy. Free)

CONWAY, Jacqueline Loraine Charlotte Basement Flat, 196 Camberwell Grove, London SE5 8RJ — MB BS 1987 Lond.; MRCPsych 1992. Socs: Transcultural Psychiat. Soc.

CONWAY, James Vincent Psychiatric Unit, Northern General Hospital, Sheffield S5 7AU Tel: 0114 226 1529 Fax: 0114 226 1533; 10 Clumber Road, Sheffield S10 3LE Tel: 0114 230 3993 — MB BCh BAO 1967 NUI; MRCPsych 1974; DPM Dub. 1971; FRCPsych 1997. Cons. Psychiat. N. Gen. Hosp. Sheff.; Lect. Univ. Sheff. Prev: Sen. Regist. Univ. Manch.

CONWAY, Janet Deborah The X-ray Dept., Halton Hospital, North Cheshire Hospitals Trust, Hospital Way, Runcorn WA7 2DA Tel: 01928 753291 Fax: 01928 753192; The Vicarage, Demage Lane, Upton-by-Chester, Chester CH2 1EL Tel: 01244 370549 — MB ChB 1970 Liverp.; MRCS Eng. LRCP Lond. 1970; FRCR 1977; DMRD Liverp. 1974. (Liverpool) Cons. Radiol. Halton Gen. Hosp. Runcorn. Prev: Cons. Radiol. Halton Gen. Hosp. Runcorn & Warrington Gen. Hosp.; Sen. Regist. (Radiol.) Chester Health Dist. & Clatterbridge Hosp. Bebington; Regist. (Radiol.) Liverp. Roy. Infirm.

CONWAY, John Clifford Stockwell Lodge Medical Centre, Rosedale Way, Cheshunt, Waltham Cross EN7 6HL Tel: 01992 624408 Fax: 01992 626206 — MB BCh; LRCPI; LRCSI; MRCGP. (Royal College of Surgeons in Ireland)

CONWAY, John Finbarr (retired) Barclays Bank Chambers, Tudor Square, West Bridgford, Nottingham NG2 6BT Tel: 01159 811341 Fax: 01159 815808 — MB BCh BAO NUI 1961; MLitt TC Dub. 1991; BA Open 1984; MICGP 1984; MRCGP 1969. Prev: SHO (O & G) Tyrone Co. Hosp. Omagh.

CONWAY, Mr Joseph Shoel Hospital of St John & St Elizabeth, 60 Grove End Road, London NW8 9NH Tel: 020 8455 5698 Fax: 020 8455 5698; 30 Middleway, Hampstead Garden Suburb, London NW11 6SG Tel: 020 8455 5698 Fax: 020 8455 5698 — MRCS Eng. LRCP Lond. 1945; FRCS Eng. 1956; FRCOphth 1988; DOMS Eng. 1948. (St. Mary's) Hon. Cons. Ophth. Surg. Roy. Free Hosp. Lond.; Expert Witness in Ophth. Socs: Fell. Roy. Soc. Med.; Oxf. Ophth. Congr.; Lond. Jew. Med. Soc. (Ex. Pres). Prev: Cons. Ophth. Surg. Lond. Jewish Hosp.; Cons. Ophth. Surg. Roy. Free Hosp. Hampstead & Whipps Cross Hosp. Lond.; Chief Clin. Asst. Moorfields Eye Hosp. & W.m. Hosp. Lond.

CONWAY, Julia Anne Le Petit Belot, Le Vier Beaumont, St Peter, Jersey JE3 7EA — MB ChB 1985 Manch.; MRCGP 1990; T(GP) 1991. Trainee GP Blackburn VTS.

CONWAY, Kathryn Mary 7 Kingsway Drive, Harrogate HG1 5NJ — MB BCh 1991 Wales.

CONWAY, Kathryn Rachel Hagley, Walwyn Road, Colwall, Malvern WR13 6EG — MB ChB 1985 Dundee; DRCOG 1988.

CONWAY, Kevin Patrick 3 Easton Avenue, Belfast BT14 6LL — MB BCh 1997 Wales.

CONWAY, Malachy Sutton View, 24 Shaftesbury Avenue, Hull HU8 9BH Tel: 01482 75215 — MB BCh BAO 1954 NUI. (Cork.) Prev: SHO Hosp. Sick Childr. Derby; SHO (Obst.) Gulson Hosp. Coventry; Regist. Infec. Dis. Castle Hill Hosp. Cottingham.

CONWAY, Marion Frances Oldpark Road Surgery, 460 Oldpark Road, Belfast BT14 6QG Tel: 028 9074 6535 Fax: 028 9074 7768 — MB BCh BAO 1992 Belf.; MRCGP 1996; DMH Belf. 1997; DFFP 1996; DRCOG 1995; DCH Dub. 1995. GP Princip. Belf.

CONWAY, Mary Ellen Broomhanger, Crown Lane N., Ardleigh, Colchester CO7 7RB Tel: 01206 231550 — MB BS 1985 Lond.; BSc Lond. 1982; MRCP (UK) 1988; MFPHM RCP (UK) 1995. Cons. Pub. Health Med. S. Essex HA.

CONWAY, Mavis Mary St. James' Close, St. James' Villas, Winchester SO23 9SN Tel: 01962 854651 — MB ChB 1955 Bristol; DCH Eng. 1958; DObst RCOG 1957. (Bristol) Socs: Inst. Psychosexual Med.; Fac. Fam. Plann. & Reproduc. Health Care& Roy. Coll. Obst. & Gyn. Prev: SCMO Winchester HA; Sen. Resid. Off. Roy. Hosp. Sick Childr. Bristol; Ho. Phys. Bristol Roy. Infirm.

CONWAY, Michael 21 Oldfield Drive, Heswall, Wirral CH60 6SS — MB ChB 1966 Liverp.; FFA RCS Eng. 1970.

CONWAY, Michael John (retired) 39 Willow Park, Willow Bank, Manchester M14 6XT Tel: 0161 224 5253 — MB ChB 1956 Manch.; DCH Eng. 1958.

CONWAY, Miranda Philomena c/o Sefton General Hospital, Smithdown Road, Liverpool L15 2HE; 6 Bryanston Road, Prenton, Birkenhead CH42 8PU — MB BCh BAO 1978 NUI; MRCPsych 1983.

CONWAY, Neville (retired) St. James Close, St James Villas, Winchester SO23 9SN Tel: 01962 854651 — MB BS 1956 Lond.; FRCP Lond. 1975, M 1962; MRCS Eng. LRCP Lond. 1956. Prev: Cons. Cardiol. Wessex Regional Cardiac & Thoracic Centre W.. Hosp. Soton.

CONWAY, Nicholas Thomas 10 Transy Grove, Dunfermline KY12 7QP — MB ChB 1998 Ed.; MB ChB Ed 1998.

CONWAY, Paul Gerard 2 Rufford Close, Prescot L35 5HS — MB ChB 1990 Liverp.; MRCGP 1994; DRCOG 1993.

CONWAY, Paul John Health Centre, Victoria Sq, Portishead, Bristol BS20 6AQ Tel: 01275 847474 Fax: 01275 817516; Holcombe, 8 Watercress Close, Wraxall, Bristol BS48 1HN Tel: 01275 856504 — MB ChB 1967 Bristol; BSc Bristol 1963. (Bristol)

CONWAY, Sarah Katherine 19 Kingsley Road, Wimbledon, London SW19 8HF Tel: 020 8540 1951 — MB BS 1992 Lond.; BSc (Hons.) Human Biol. Univ. Lond. 1989; MRCGP 1996; DRCOG 1995. (Univ. Coll. Hosp. Sch. Med.)

CONWAY, Shaun Baxter and Conway, The Surgery, Hardingham Street, Hingham, Norwich NR9 4JB Tel: 01953 850237 Fax: 01953 850581; Elm Barn, The Fields, Hingham, Norwich NR9 43G — BM BS 1984 Nottm.; BMedSci Nottm. 1982; MRCGP 1990; DCH RCP Lond. 1990; DRCOG 1989; Cert. Family Plann. JCC 1989. (Nottm.)

CONWAY, Steven Philip Seacroft Hospital, York Road, Leeds LS14 6UH Tel: 0113 206 3513 Fax: 0113 206 3738 Email: steven.conway@leedsth.nhs.k; 36 Ash Hill Drive, Leeds LS17 8JP Tel: 0113 273 7367 — MB BS 1978 Lond. Cons. Paediat. St Jas. & Seacroft Univ. Hosp. Leeds; Sen. Clin. Lect. Paediat. & Child Health Univ. of Leeds. Socs: RCPCH Immunol. & Infec. Dis. Gp. Prev: Cons. in Paediat. in Infec. Dis.s, St Jas. & Seacroft Hosp., Leeds.

CONWAY, Stewart Colin Kildean Hospital, Drip Road, Stirling FK8 1RW Tel: 01786 446615 — MB ChB 1984 Ed.; MSc Manch. 1992; BSc (Hons.) Ed. 1982, MB ChB 1984; MRCPsych 1991. Cons. Psychiat. Kildean Hosp. Centr. Scotl. Prev: Sen. Regist. (Psychiat. of Old Age) Roy. Edin. Hosp.

CONWAY, Valerie Anne 87 Barrington Drive, Glasgow G4 9ES Tel: 0141 339 0894; 10 Dunvegan Drive, Newton Mearns, Glasgow G77 5EB Tel: 0141 639 5318 — MB ChB 1977 Glas.; MFHom 1979. (Univ. Glas.) Indep. Cons. Homoeopath. Med. Glas. & Ayr.

CONWAY, Vyvian Gordon The Surgery, Cross Road, Sacriston, Durham DH7 6LJ Tel: 0191 371 0232; Manor Dene, 36 North End, Durham DH1 4NJ Tel: 0191 386 1348 — MB BS 1963 Durh.; DObst RCOG 1966; Mem. BMA. Prev: Ho. Phys. & Ho. Surg. Roy. Vict. Infirm. Newc-upon-Tyne.

CONWAY, Zoe Frances 7 Kilfillan Gardens, Berkhamsted HP4 3LU — MB BS 1987 Lond.

CONYBEARE, Mr Martin Edward (retired) 74 London Road, Canterbury CT2 8LS Tel: 01227 454097 Fax: 01227 764871 — MB BS Lond. 1963; FRCS Eng. 1968; MRCS Eng. LRCP Lond. 1963. Cons. Surg. Orthop. & Trauma Canterbury & Thanet Hosps. Trust. Prev: Sen. Regist. (Orthop.) Nuffield Orthop. Centre & Radcliffe Infirm. Oxf.

CONYERS, Anthony Berkeley St Richards, Chichester PO1 S04 Tel: 01243 788122 ext 5290 Email: abcon@doctors.org.uk; Elmstead House, Elms Lane, West Wittering, Chichester PO20 8LW Tel: 01243 515562 Email: obcon@doctors.org.uk — MRCS Eng. LRCP Lond. 1963; FFA RCS Eng. 1969; DA Eng. 1967; DObst RCOG 1965; LMCC 1972; ECFMG Cert 1969. (St. Thos.) Cons. Anaesth. St. Richards Hosp. Chichester & Vis. Cons. King Edwd. VII Hosp. Midhurst. Socs: BMA; Assn. Anaesth.s; Intens. Care Soc. Prev: Sen. Regist. (Anaesth.) Soton. Univ. Hosps. Gp.; Deans Exchange Fell. Montreal Gen. Hosp. Canada; Regist. (Anaesth.) St. Bart. Hosp. Lond.

COODE, Peter Edward 73 Geffers Ride, Burleigh Road, Ascot SL5 7JZ — MB ChB 1970 Birm.; MRCPath 1976.

COODE, William Kristian 37 Cornwal Road, Dorchester DT1 1RY — MB BS 1994 Lond.

COOGAN, John Stephen Vincent St Roch, Lt.-Col. RAMC The Ladywell Unit, University Hospital, Lewisham, London SE13 6LH Tel: 020 8333 3000 Ext: 8167 Fax: 020 8333 3402; 47 Kenilworth Gardens, London SE18 3JB Tel: 020 8856 0183 — MB BCh BAO 1972 NUI; FRCPsych 1992, M 1980; T(Psych) 1991; DPM Eng. 1980. (Galway) Cons. Gen. Adult Psychiat. S. Lond. & Maudsley NHS Trust; Sen. Lect. UMDS Guy's Hosp. Socs: (Chairm. BFG Sub-Comm. Child Guid. & BFG Sub-Comm. Child Health& Welf. & Child Protec.); Brit. Assn. Study & Preven. Child Abuse & Neglect; Med. Counc. Alcholism. Prev: Sen. Cons. (Psychiat.) Brit. Army of the Rhine.; Cons. Adviser Psychiat. Brit. Forces, Middle E.; Cons. Psychiat. Command Psychiat. Unit BAOR BMH Hanover.

COOGAN, Kathleen c/o Dungannon Clinic, Thomas St., Dungannon BT70 1HS — MB BCh BAO 1976 NUI; DRCOG 1980; MRCGP 1980.

COOGAN, Maureen 53 Garnock Hill, Belfast BT10 0AW — MB BCh BAO 1987 Belf.; MB BCh Belf. 1987. Trainee GP Berwicksh.

COOK, Alan Moray Department of Radiology, Ninewells Hospital, Dundee DD1 9SY — MB ChB 1981 Glas.; BSc (Hons. Immunol.) Glas. 1978; FRCR 1987. Cons. Radiol. Prev: Cons. Radiol. Hull Roy. Infirm.

COOK, Alastair John Caldwell 48 Kirk Road, Bathgate EH48 1BP — MB ChB 1988 Ed.

COOK, Alexander Wilson (retired) 21 Over Links Drive, Poole BH14 9QU Tel: 01202 700283 — MB BS Lond. 1948; FRCGP 1974, M 1960; DObst RCOG 1952. Prev: SHO (Obst.), Ho. Phys. & Ho. Surg. Guy's Hosp. Lond.

COOK, Alison Elizabeth 23 The Dell, Vernham Dean, Andover SP11 0LF — MB BS 1984 Lond.

COOK, Alison Louise 6 The Rise, Cherry Grove, Haverfordwest SA61 2PA — MB ChB 1998 Birm. (Birm.)

COOK, Allan Montague (retired) c/o Alastrean House, Tarland, Aboyne AB34 4TA — MB ChB 1950 Aberd.; MRCPsych 1971; DPM Eng. 1954. Hon. Cons. Psychiat. Grampian HB. Prev: Phys. Supt. Ladysbridge Hosp. Banff.

COOK, Andrew Grant Central Surgery, Brooksby Drive, Oadby, Leicester LE2 5AA Tel: 0116 271 2175 Fax: 0116 271 4015 — MB ChB 1992 Leic.; DRCOG 1995; MRCGP 1996. (Leics.) GP Leicester. Prev: Trainee GP/SHO (Psychiat. A & E & O & G) Kettering VTS.

COOK, Andrew James 40 Enys Road, Eastbourne BN21 2ED — MB BS 1994 Lond.

COOK, Andrew Paul The Health Centre, Trenchard Avenue, Thornaby, Stockton-on-Tees TS17 0DD Tel: 01642 762921 Fax: 01642 760608; 7 Longshaw Close, Ingleby Barwick, Stockton-on-Tees TS17 0UF — MB ChB 1984 Leeds; BSc (Hons.) Leeds 1981; MRCGP 1988; DRCOG 1988. (Leeds)

COOK, Andrew Stephen, Maj. RAMC Retd. Binscombe Medical Centre, 106 Binscombe Lane, Godalming GU7 3PR Tel: 01483 415115 Fax: 01483 414925 — MB BS 1986 Lond.; MRCGP 1993; DRCOG 1992; DCH RCP Lond. 1991. (Char. Cross Hosp. Med. Sch.) GP Trainer. Socs: BMA.

COOK, Miss Anne Elizabeth The Packet House, 2 The Boat Steps, Bartow Rd, Worsley, Manchester M28 2PB — MB ChB 1993 Manch.; FRCS Ed. 1997. (Manchester) Research Fell. (Ophth.) St. Paul's Eye Unit RLHH Liverp. Socs: MDDHS; MSJ. Prev: SHO (Ophth.) St. Paul's Eye Unit Liverp.; SHO (Ophth.) Countess of Chester Hosp.

COOK, Anthony Raymond (retired) 1 Selwyn House, The Close, Alrewas, Lichfield WS13 7LD — MRCS Eng. LRCP Lond. 1960; DPM Eng. 1965. Locum Cons. Psychiat., S.ern Derbysh. Ment. Health Trust, Derby City Gen. Hosp., Derby. Prev: Cons. Psychiat. St. Matthew's Hosp. Burntwood.

COOK, Mr Antony Ian Muir 3 Valeside, Back Western Hill, Durham DH1 4RF Tel: 01384 44278 — MB ChB 1967 Liverp.; FRCS Eng. 1973; FRCS Ed. 1972. (Liverp.) Cons. Surg. Dryburn Hosp. Durh. Prev: Sen. Surg. Regist. Mersey RHA.

COOK, Arthur Thompson, Maj.-Gen. late RAMC Retd. (retired) The Old Cricketers, Cricket Hill Lane, Yateley GU46 6BA Tel: 01252

879452 Fax: 01252 871763 — MB BS 1946 Lond.; FRCP Lond. 1975, M 1955; FRCP Ed. 1965, M 1954; MRCS Eng. LRCP Lond. 1946; DCH Eng. 1955; DTM & H Eng. 1954. Prev: Dir. of Army Med.

COOK, Audrey Mary Staffordshire Oncology Centre, Royal Infirmary, Princes Road, Hartshill, Stoke-on-Trent ST4 7LN — MB BS 1989 Lond.; BSc Lond. 1986; MRCP (UK) 1992; FRCR 1996. (St Thoms's Hospital) Cons. Clin. Oncol., N. Staffs. NHS Trust and Roy. Shrewsbury Hosp.

COOK, Barbara Anne 38 Broadwater Road, Worthing BN14 8AB Tel: 01903 231701; Easter Cottage, 52 Salvington Hill, High Salvington, Worthing BN13 3AZ Tel: 01903 831247 — MB BS 1983 Lond.; DRCOG 1988; DA (UK) 1985.

COOK, Brian Terry Skewen Medical Centre, Queens Road, Skewen, Neath SA10 6UL Tel: 01792 812316 Fax: 01792 323208; 98 Penshannel, Neath SA10 6PP — MB BCh 1976 Wales.

COOK, Caroline Jane 39 Eastmoor Park, Harpenden AL5 1BN — MB BS 1997 Lond.

COOK, Mr Charles Alfred George, MC, GM 13 Clarence Terrace, Regents Park, London NW1 4RD Tel: 020 7723 5111 — DSc (Hons.) Birm. 1983; FRCS Eng. 1950; MRCS Eng. LRCP Lond. 1939; DOMS Eng. 1947. (Guy's) Prev: Emerit. Cons. Ophth. Surg. Moorfields Eye Hosp. & Guy's Hosp.; Cons. Ophth. Surg. W. Middlx. Hosp. Isleworth; Vice Dean Inst. Ophth. Lond.

COOK, Charles Malcolm Manse Road Surgery, 142 Manse Road, Ardersier, Inverness IV2 7SR Tel: 01667 462240 Fax: 01667 462912 — MB ChB 1971 Leeds. (Leeds) Prev: Sen. Med. Off. RAF Med. Br.; SHO (Obst.) Manygates Hosp. Wakefield; Ho. Surg. Pontefract Gen. Infirm.

COOK, Rev. Professor Christopher Charles Holland Kent Insititute of Medicine & Health care, University of Kent at Canterbury, Canterbury CT2 7PD Tel: 01227 824063 Fax: 01227 824054 Email: c.c.h.cook@ukc.ac.uk — MB BS 1981 Lond.; BSc Lond. 1977, MD 1995; MRCPsych 1986; Cert. Av. Med. 1991. (St George's Med. Sch.) p/t Prof. Psychiat. of Alcohol Misuse; Cons. Psychiat., Civil Aviat. Auth., Gatwick. Socs: (Ex-Comm.1996-2000) Soc. Study Addic. (Sec.1997-2000); Med. Counc. Alcholism. Prev: Cons. Psychiat. & Sen. Lect. (Addic.) Nat. Addic. Centre; Lect. (Drug & Alcohol Dependence) Univ. Coll. & Middlx. Sch. Med. Lond.; Regist. & SHO Rotat. Psych. Train. Scheme Guy's Hosp. Lond.

COOK, Christopher Ian Murray Lattice Barn Surgery, 14 Woodbridge Road East, Ipswich IP4 5PA Tel: 01473 726836 Fax: 01473 273567; Sunfield Cottage, Playford Road, Little Bealings, Woodbridge IP13 6ND Tel: 01473 611324 — MB ChB 1980 Birm.; MRCGP 1986; DA (UK) 1982. (Birm.) GP Trainer Ipswich.

COOK, Christopher Keith Lewis 1 Westfield Place, Bristol BS8 4AY — MB BChir 1989 Camb.; MA 1990 Camb.; FRCR 2000; MRCP (UK) 1993. Cons., W.on Dist. Hosp. Radiol. (Interven.). Prev: Regist. (Radiol.) Brit. Roy. Infirm.; Regist. (Med.) Winchester; SHO (Med.) Addenbrooke's and Soton.

COOK, Professor Colin Burford 5 Albert Bridge Road, London SW11 4PX; 373 Strawberry Hill Avenue, Stamford CT 06902, USA Tel: 203 348 9091 — MB BS 1951 Lond.; FLEX Lic (USA) 1952; Dip. Amer. Bd. Psychiat. & Neurol. 1979. (Middlx.) Indep. Psychiat. Stamford Connecticut; Assoc. Clin. Prof. Psychiat. Columbia Univ. NY City. Socs: Amer. Med. Assn., Amer. Psychiat. Assn. & Soc.; Psychoanalytic Phys. Prev: Post-Grad. Fell. Nat. Hosp. Nerv. Dis. Lond.

COOK, David Angus Graham (retired) 27 Julian Road, Sneyd Park, Bristol BS9 1JY — BM BCh 1971 Oxf.; FRCPsych 1994, M 1976; DPM Eng. 1975. Prev: Cons. Psychiat. Avon & W. Wilts. Ment. Health Care NHS Trust.

COOK, David Henry Matthew OMS Ltd., 12 Sunnybank Road, Aberdeen AB24 3NG Tel: 01224 492884 Fax: 01224 487812; 38 Westfield Drive, Forfar DD8 1EQ — MB ChB 1987 Dundee. Sen. Med. Off. OMS Ltd. (Internat.) Baku Azer Za-Jan. Socs: BMA & Soc. Occupat. Phys.

COOK, David Mark 10 Thomson Avenue, Birmingham B38 8YD — MB ChB 1994 Leeds.

COOK, David Markham (retired) 7 Park Road, Broadstairs CT10 1ED Tel: 01843 862566 — MB BS Lond. 1963; FRCP Lond. 1987, M 1968; DCH Eng. 1965; FRCPCH 1998. Cons. Paediat. Thanet Healthcare Trust. Prev: Sen. Regist. (Paediat.) United Sheff. Hosps.

COOK, Deborah Susan Department of Histopathology, UHWHC NHS Trust, Heath Park, Cardiff CF14 4XW — BM BS 1995 Nottm.; BMed Sci Nott. 1993; DMJ (Path) 2001; MSc Toxicology, 1997. (Nottingham) Specialist Regist. (Histopath.), Cardiff.

COOK, Denis Rochester (retired) Greengates, Redburn, Bardon Mill, Hexham NE47 7EA Tel: 0149 84 244 — MB BS 1948 Durh.; FRCGP 1973, M 1958; DMJ (Clin.) Soc. Apoth. Lond. 1962. Prev: Sec. Lond. Local Med. Comms.

COOK, Donald Edward, Wing Cdr. RAF Med. Br. Defence Radiological Protection Service, Institute of Naval Medicine, Alverstoke, Gosport PO12 2DL Tel: 01705 768126 Fax: 01705 511065; 13 Fullerton Way, Tadley RG26 3YN Email: 106152.3301@compuserve — MB ChB 1979 Aberd.; MMedSc Birm. 1994; AFOM RCP Lond. 1987; DAvMed FOM RCP Lond. 1989; DIH Lond. 1987; MRAeS 1989. (Aberd.) Sen. Med. Off. (Occupat & Radiat. Med.) Inst. Naval Med. Alverstoke; Adviser (Radiat. Med.) DGMS (RAF). Socs: Aberd. M-C Soc.; Soc. Occup. Med.; Roy. Aeronaut. Soc. Prev: Chief Instruc. RAF Aviat. Med. Train. Centre; Sen. Med. Off. RAF Kinloss Moraysh.; Ho. Phys. Lewis Hosp. Stornoway.

COOK, Eileen Margaret 1 Ludlow Close, Oadby, Leicester LE2 4SU — MB ChB 1993 Leic.; DRCOG 1998. Trainee GP Leic.; GP Regist. Leic. GP.VTS.

COOK, Elaine Julie Lambert Medical Centre, 2 Chapel Street, Thirsk YO7 1LU Tel: 01845 523157 Fax: 01845 524508; Fairlawn, 1 Croft Heads, Sowerby, Thirsk YO7 4JP — MB BS 1984 Newc.

COOK, Elizabeth Anne Canton Health Centre, Wessex Street, Cardiff CF5 1XU Tel: 029 2022 6016 Fax: 029 2039 4846 — MB BCh 1986 Wales.

COOK, Frederick Health Centre, Burscough, Ormskirk Tel: 01704 895566 — MB ChB 1969 Liverp.; DRCOG 1971. Med. Off. HMP Garth Lancs.

COOK, Gary Arnold Depart. Of Epidemiology, Stepping Hill Hospital, Poplar Grove, Stockport SK7 6HE Tel: 0161 419 5985 Email: gary.cook@stockport-tr.nhs.uk — MB ChB 1975 Bristol; LLB 1999 (Man. Metropolitan Univ.); MFPHM 1985 (Lond.); MRCP (Lond., UK) 1980. Cons. Epidemiologist; Hon. Research Fell. Socs: BMA; Manch. Med. Soc.; Soc. for Social Med. Prev: Cons. in Pub. Health Med., N. W. RHA; Cons. in Pub. Health Med., W. Berks. HA.

COOK, Gary John Russell Department of Nuclear Medicine, Guy's Hospital, London SE1 9RT Tel: 020 7955 4855 Fax: 020 7955 4657 Email: g.cook@umds.ac.uk — MB BS 1986 Lond.; MSc Lond. 1994; MRCP (UK) 1989; FRCR 1994. (Guy's Hosp.) Hon. Cons. Nuclear Med. Guy's Hosp. Lond. Prev: Sen. Regist. (Nuclear Med.) Guy's Hosp. Lond.; Regist. (Radiol.) St. Mary's Hosp. Lond.; Regist. (Gen. & Nuclear Med.) Greenwich Dist. & Guys Hosp.

COOK, Geoffrey David Limeleigh Medical Group, 434 Narborough Road, Leicester LE3 2FS Tel: 0116 282 7070 Fax: 0116 289 3805; 33 Swithland Lane, Rothley, Leicester LE7 7SG Email: gdcook@dircon.co.uk — MB BCh 1974 Wales; MFFP 1993; DRCOG 1977. Sen. Partner; Course Organiser Leicester Univ.; Clin. Teach. Leicester Univ. Med. Sch. Socs: BMA. Prev: Sen. Regist. & Regist. (Gyn.) Univ. Hosp. Wales Cardiff; Regist. (Paediat.) & SHO (Med.) Univ. Hosp. Wales Cardiff; Ho. Off. (Surg.) Gen. Hosp. Nottm.

COOK, Geoffrey William (retired) Kings Corner Surgery, Sunninghill, Ascot SL5 0PS Tel: 01990 23181 — MB BChir 1962 Camb.; MRCS Eng. LRCP Lond. 1962; DObst RCOG 1964. Prev: Ho. Off. (O & G) FarnBoro. Hosp. Kent.

COOK, George Robert Grassendale Medical Practice, 23 Darby Road, Liverpool L19 9BP Tel: 0151 427 1214 Fax: 0151 427 0611; Lea House, 33 Ashfield Road, Liverpool L17 0BY Tel: 0151 291 9111 Fax: 0151 291 9112 Email: george@33ashfield.freeserve.co.uk — MRCS Eng. LRCP Lond. 1979; Cert. Family Plann. JCC 1984. (Liverp.) Med. Dir.NW Med. Serv. Liverp.; Clin. Lead. Undergrad. Univ Liverp. Med. Sch. Prev: Clin. Asst. (Genitourin. Med.) Roy. Liverp. Univ. Hosp.

COOK, Gillian 4 Beckside Cottages, The Green, Millom LA18 5HL — MB ChB 1987 Liverp.

COOK, Glynis Elizabeth St John's Hill Surgery, 39 St John's Hill, Sevenoaks TN13 3NT Tel: 01732 747203; Tylers, 47 Kippington Road, Sevenoaks TN13 2LL Tel: 01732 452110 Fax: 01732 464299 — MB ChB 1977 Aberd. Asst. GP St. John's Hill Surg. Sevenoaks.

COOK, Gordon Department of Haematology, Glasgow Royal Infirmary, Castle St., Glasgow G4 0SF — MB ChB 1988 Glas.;

MRCPI 1993; DRCPath 1995; MRCPath 1997. Sen. Regist. (Haemat.). Prev: LRF Clin. Fell., Career Regist. & BMT Clin. Co-Ordinator Glas.

COOK, Gordon Charles Wellcome institutefor the History of Medicine, 183 Euston Road, London NW1 1BE Tel: 020 7611 8615 Fax: 020 7611 8562 Email: g.cook@wellcome.ac.uk; 11 Old Street Road, St Albans AL1 1QE Tel: 01727 869000 — MB BS 1957 Lond.; DSc Lond. 1976, BSc (Hons. Physiol.) 1955, MD 1965; FRCP Lond. 1972, M 1960; MRCS Eng. LRCP Lond. 1957; FRACP 1978, FLS 1989. (Roy. Free) Hon. Sen. Lect. Med. Univ. Coll. Lond. & Research Assoc. Wellcome Inst. for the Hist. Med. Lond.; Examr. Med. Makerere Univ. Uganda, Lond. Univ. & RCP Lond.; Examr. Trop. Med. Lond. Univ.; Med. Adviser Overseas Developm. Admin. & Internat. Bk. Developm.; Edit. Bd. Postgrad. Med. Jl. & Jl. of Infec. & Transactions of the Roy. Soc. of Trop. Med. & Hyg.; Hon. Lect. (Clin. Parasitol.) Med. Coll. St. Bart. Hosp. Lond.; Hon. Cons. Phys. St. Luke's Hosp for Clergy & Help Age; Vis. Prof. Med. Univ. Basrah & Mosul, Iraq & Qatar; Mem. Exec. Comm. Fac. Hist. & Philosophy of Med. & Pharmacy, Worshipful Soc. of Apoth. of Lond. Socs: Fell. (Former Pres.) Roy. Soc. Trop. Med. & Hyg.; Life Mem. Roy. Soc. Med. (Vice-Pres. Hist. Med. Sect.); (Former Pres.) Osler Club of Lond. Prev: Prof. Med. & Chairm. Clin. Sc. Dept. Univ. Papua New Guinea Port Moresby; Prof. Med. Univ. Zambia Lusaka & Riyadh Univ., Saudi Arabia.

COOK, Graham Alexander The Health Centre, Queen Street, Jedburgh TD8 6EN Tel: 01835 863361 Fax: 01835 864273; Fairview Cottage, Nenthorn, Kelso TD5 7RY — MB ChB 1981 Glas.; MRCGP 1985; DRCOG 1985. GP Adviser Borders Community Health Serv. Trust.

COOK, Mr Graham Edward Accident & Emergency Department, Maidstone General Hospital, Hermitage Lane, Maidstone ME16 9QQ Tel: 01622 723003 Fax: 01622 723003; 11 Ridgewood, New Barn, Longfield DA3 7LS Tel: 01474 834443 — MB BS 1976 Lond.; FRCS Ed. 1986; FFAEM 1993. (Char. Cross) Clin. Dir. for Surg. Socs: Fell. Med. Soc. Lond. Prev: Cons. & Dir. A & E Servs. Maidstone Gen. Hosp.; Cons. A & E Med. Qu. Mary's Hosp. Sidcup; Sen. Regist. (A & E) Ealing Hosp. Lond.

COOK, Graham Patrick Station Drive Surgery, Station Drive, Ludlow SY8 2AR Tel: 01584 872461 Fax: 01584 877971; Meadow House, Ashford Carbonell, Ludlow SY8 4DA Tel: 01584 831162 Fax: 01584 877972 — MB BS Lond. 1981; MRCGP 1985; DRCOG 1983. (Guy's) Clin. Asst. Ludlow Community Hosp. Socs: BMA. Prev: Trainee GP FarnBoro. VTS; Med. Off. Occupat. Health Servs. Manzini, Swaziland.

COOK, Graham Thomas John Square Surgery, 66 The Square, Hartland, Bideford EX39 6BL Tel: 01237 441200 — MB ChB 1962 Birm.; MSc (Health Care Sciences) Exeter 1992. Prev: Lect. (Physiol.) Birm. Univ.; Cas. Surg. St. Mary's Hosp. Lond.; Ho. Off. (Surg.) Harrow Hosp.

COOK, Miss Helen Louise Castle Lodge, Castlegate, Kirkbymoorside, York YO62 6BW Email: helenlcook@aol.com — MB BS 1991 Newc.; MD (Lond.) 2001; FRCOphth 1997. (Newc. u. Tyne) Specialist Regist. (Opthalmology), N.Thames Rotat. Socs: Roy. Soc. Med.; Fell. Roy. Coll. Ophths. Prev: Research Assoc. (Ophth.) UMDS/St. Thos. Hosp. Lond.; SHO (Ophth.) Roy. Lond. Hosp. Trust.; SHO (Ophth.) Greenwich Dist. Dist. Hosp. Lond.

COOK, Professor Herbert Terence Department of Histopathology, Imperial College Hammersmith Hospital, Du Cane Road, London W12 0NN Tel: 020 8383 3223 Email: t.cook@ic.ac.uk — MB BS 1980 Lond.; MRCP (UK) 1983; FRCPath 1997. (St Marys Hospital Med School) Prof. of Renal Path., Imperial Coll. Lond.

COOK, Ian Stewart 24 Churchill Road, Langley, Slough SL3 7QZ — BM 1996 Soton.

COOK, Isabel Jane Dr D J McNie and Partners, 4 St. Barnabas Road, Caversham, Reading RG4 8RA Tel: 0118 478123 — BM BCh 1992 Oxf.; BA Oxf. 1989, BM BCh 1992; MRCGP 1996; DRCOG 1995. GP Reading; Clin. Asst. (Palliat. Care) Henley on Thames. Prev: Trainee GP/SHO N.ampton Gen. Hosp. VTS.; SHO (A & E) Kent & Canterbury Hosps.

COOK, Jacqueline Ann Department of Human Genetics, Sheffield Children's Hospital, Western Bank, Sheffield S10 2TH — MB BS 1986 Lond.; BA (Hons.) Oxf. 1983; FRCP. Cons. Clin. Genetics Sheff. Childr. Hosp. Socs: Brit. Soc. Human Genetics. Prev: Sen. Regist. (Clin. Genetics) St. Jas. Hosp. Leeds.

COOK, James 82 Bournbrook Road, Birmingham B29 7BU — MB ChB 1989 Birm.

COOK, Mr James Anthony Consultant ENT Surgeon Neurotologist, Leicester Royal Infirmary, Leicester LE1 5WW Tel: 0116 258 6021 Fax: 0116 258 6882 Email: jcook@lri.org.uk; 8 Beaumanor Drive, Woodhouse, Loughborough LE12 8TX Email: jim.cooki=i@virgin.net — MB BChir 1982 Camb.; MA, MB BChir Camb. 1982; FRCS (Otol.) Eng. 1987. (Cambridge/Middlesex) Cons. Ent. Surg/Neurotologist Leicester Roy. Infirm. Leics.; Clin. Teach. Leis. Uni.; Hon. Lec. De Montfort.Univ.; Hon. Sen. Lect., Dept Surg., Leicester Univ.. Socs: Prosper. Meniere Soc.; Roy. Soc. Med. Counc. (Sec.Otol.); Otorhinolary.Soc. Prev: Sen. Regist. (ENT) Mersey Regional Train. Scheme; Skullbase/NeurOtol.Fell.St.Vincents.Hosp.Sydney.Austr.; Regist. (ENT) Whipps Cross Hosp. & St. Bart. Hosp. Lond.

COOK, Jane Easdale (retired) 6 Alexandra Avenue, Stepps, Glasgow G33 6BP Tel: 0141 779 2884 — MB ChB 1942 Glas. Prev: Res. Ho. Surg. Glas. Roy. Matern. & Wom. Hosp.

COOK, Jane Valmai 9 Alleyn Road, Dulwich, London SE21 8AB — MB BCh 1980 Wales; MRCP (UK) 1983; FRCR 1986. Cons. Radiol. St. Helier Hosp. Surrey. Prev: Sen. Regist. (Radiol.) Rotat. St. Geo. Hosp. Lond.

COOK, Jennifer Anne Markham 7 Park Road, Broadstairs CT10 1ED — MB BS 1990 Lond.

COOK, Jennifer Margaret Galen Lodge, Eastfield Road, Ross-on-Wye HR9 5AN Tel: 01989 764378 — BM BCh 1973 Oxf.; BA Oxf. 1969, BM BCh 1973. Clin. Asst. (Dermat.) Co. Hosp. Hereford.; Clin. Med. Off. (Family Plann.) Severn NHS Trust. Prev: Ho. Surg. N. Middlx. Hosp. Lond.; Ho. Phys. Whipps Cross Hosp. Lond.

COOK, Joan Esther (retired) 10 Ennerdale Road, Wallasey CH45 0LY — LRCP LRCS Ed. LRFPS Glas. 1944. Prev: Med. Off. CMS Hosp. Omdurman, Sudan.

COOK, Joanne Norma Robin Lane Medical Centre, Robin Lane, Pudsey LS28 7BR — MB ChB 1996 Leeds; BDS Ed. (Hons.) 1989; FDS RCS Ed. 1993. (Univ. Leeds)

COOK, Mr John (retired) — MB ChB 1949 Ed.; FRSE; ChM Ed. 1963, MB ChB 1949; FRCS Ed. 1954. Prev: Cons. Surg. E. Gen. Hosp. Edin. & Edenhall Hosp. Musselburgh.

COOK, John David Cooper (retired) The white House, Martham, Great Yarmouth NR29 4PA Tel: 01493 740449 — MB BS Lond. 1953; DObst RCOG 1955. Prev: Mem. Norwich M-C Soc. & Med. Club Gt. Yarmouth.

COOK, Mr John Holford 18 The Brow, Friston, Eastbourne BN20 0ES — MB BS 1968 Lond.; FRCS Eng. 1975; MRCS Eng. LRCP Lond. 1968; FFA RCS Eng. 1978; DO Eng. 1972. (Roy. Free) Cons. Anaesth. E.bourne Dist. Gen. Hosp.

COOK, John Peter Fletcher (retired) 16 Bieston Close, Wrexham LL13 9SZ Tel: 01978 354351 — M.B., Ch.B. Leeds 1947. Prev: GP Stalybridge.

COOK, John Robert (retired) Top Farm, 2 Harrowden Road, Orlingbury, Kettering NN14 1JB — MB BS 1960 Lond.

COOK, John Sutherland, DFC (retired) 23 Fleming Close, Langney, Eastbourne BN23 7AF — MB ChB 1955 St. And.; DTM & H Liverp. 1956.

COOK, Joseph Paul Welbeck Road Surgery, 1A Welbeck Road, Bolsover, Chesterfield S44 6DF Tel: 01246 823742; The Swallows, Astnith, Chesterfield S45 8AN — MB ChB 1981 Birm.; MRCP (UK) 1985; MRCGP 1988. Mem., Professional Exec., N. E.. PCT. Prev: Trainee GP Nottm. VTS.

COOK, Judith Highgate Group Practice, 44 North Hill, London N6 4QA Tel: 020 8340 6628; 32 Bartholomew Villas, London NW5 2LL Tel: 020 7267 6905 Fax: 020 7267 6905 Email: nick.alex@virgin.net — MB BChir 1966 Camb.; BA (Nat. Scs.) Camb. 1962, MA 1966; Dip. Tropical Med. & Hygiene (London) 2000. (St. Thos.) GP Sessions with Primary Care for Homeless People Team, Camden and Islington Health Auth. Prev: Princip. in GP Enfiled & Haringay HA; Ho. Surg. (ENT) St. Thos. Hosp. Lond.; Ho. Phys. Eliz. G. Anderson Hosp. Lond.

COOK, Kathleen Macdougall Marieville, Askomil Road, Campbeltown PA28 6EN Tel: 01586 552364 — MB ChB 1983 Glas.; DA (UK) 1985.

COOK, Laurence Brian Department of Anaesthesia, Royal Oldham Hospital, Oldham OL1 2JH Tel: 0161 627 8828 — MB BS 1984 Newc.; FRCA 1990. Cons. Anaesth. Roy. Oldham Hosp.

COOK, Lawrence John 52 Southleigh Road, Havant PO9 2QH Tel: 01705 484904 — MB BCh 1972 Wales; FRCP Lond. 1989; MRCP (U.K.) 1975. Cons. (Dermat.) Portsmouth & S.E. Hants. Health Dist. & I. of Wight; HA. Prev: Sen. Regist. (Dermat.) Roy. Vict. Infirm. Newc.

COOK, Leonard 37 Highfield Road, Sheerness ME12 3BA Tel: 01795 662430 — MRCS Eng. LRCP Lond. 1958; DA Eng. 1961; Cert. Av. Med. MoD (Air) & CAA 1979. (Guy's) Med. Off. HMP Elmley, Isle of Sheppey, Kent. Socs: BMA. Prev: Regist. (Anaesth.) Brighton & Lewes Gp. Hosps.; SHO (Anaesth.) Leicester Roy. Infirm.; SHO (Cas.) Kent & Canterbury Hosp.

COOK, Louise West Wing, Dipple Medical Centre, Wickford Avenue, Basildon SS13 3HQ Tel: 01268 555115 — MB BCh 1986 Wales; MRCGP 1991; DRCOG 1990.

COOK, Lucinda Anne Smallfield Surgery, Wheelers Lane, Smallfield, Horley RH6 9PT Tel: 01342 843382 Fax: 01342 844080 — MB BS 1991 Lond.; MRCGP 1996; DFFP 1996; DRCOG 1995; DGM RCP Lond. 1994; DCH RCP Lond. 1994. (Char. Cross & Westm. Hosp. Lond.)

COOK, Lucy Rebecca Hillside, Clive Avenue, Church Stretton SY6 7BL — MB ChB 1998 Liverp.; MB ChB Liverp 1998.

COOK, Margaret Katherine Department of Haematology, St. John's Hospital at Howden, Livingston EH54 6PP Tel: 01506 419666 Fax: 01506 460301; The Mill, Oak Lane, Foxcovert Grove, Edinburgh EH12 6XH Tel: 0131 339 0012 Fax: 0131 339 0012 Email: margaret.cook@wlt.scot.nhs.uk — MB ChB 1968 Ed.; FRCP Ed. 1981, M 1972; FRCPath. 1987, M 1975. (Edinburgh University) Cons. Haemat. St. John's Hosp. Livingston; Hon. Sen. Lect. (Fac. Med.) Univ. Edin. Socs: Brit. Soc. Haematol.; Assn. Clin. Pathol.

COOK, Marilyn Anne Oxleas NHS Trust, Green Parks House, Farnborough Hospital, Orpington BR6 8NY — MB ChB Bristol 1980; MRCPsych 1985; T(Psych) 1991. Cons. Psychiat. Oxleas NHS Trust, Bromley, Kent. Prev: Sen. Regist. (Psychiat.) St. Geo. Hosp. Lond.; Regist. (Psychiat.) Maudsley Hosp. Lond.; SHO (Psychiat.) N.wick Pk. Hosp. Lond.

COOK, Mark Adrian Birmingham Blood Centre, Vincent Drive, Edgbaston, Birmingham B15 2SG Tel: 0121 253 4007 Fax: 0121 253 4003 Email: mark.cook@nbs.nhs.uk — MB ChB 1988 Bristol; MRCPI 1995, Royal College of Physicians of Ireland; Dip RCPath 1998, RCPath. Specialist Regist. (Haemat. & Transfus. Med.), Nat. Blood Serv., Birm.

COOK, Martin Charles Carleton Surgery, 9 Castle Gardens Crescent, Poulton-le-Fylde FY6 7NJ Tel: 01253 895545 Fax: 01253 899350; 61 Garstang Road W., Poulton-le-Fylde FY6 8AA — MB ChB 1980 Manch.; DRCOG 1982. Prev: Trainee GP Burnley VTS.

COOK, Professor Martin Gerald Department of Histopathology, Royal Surrey County Hospital, Egerton Road, Guildford GU2 7XX Tel: 01483 464065 Fax: 01483 452718 Email: mgcook@globalnet.co.uk; Park Farm, Blackdown, Haslemere GU27 3BT Tel: 01428 656003 — MD Lond. 1979, MB BS 1966; FRCPath 1986, M 1973; MRCS Eng. LRCP Lond. 1966; FRCPA 1981. (Charing Cross) Cons. Histopath. Roy. Surrey Co. Hosp. Guildford; Hon. Cons. Dermatopathologist St. Geo. Hosp. Lond.; Sen. Lect. Univ. Lond.; Mem. WHO Melanoma Panel; Sec. Melanoma Club; Mem. EORTC Melanoma Pathol. Gp.; Prof. (Pathol.), Univ. of Surrey. Socs: Internat. Acad. Path.; Brit. Soc. Dermatopath.; Brit. Assn. Dermatol. Prev: Sen. Lect. Univ. Adelaide; Sen. Regist. & Lect. Lond. Hosp.; Regist. Hammersmith Hosp. Lond.

COOK, Martin James Tatton, Swallowcliffe, Salisbury SP3 5PW — MB ChB 1994 Birm. (Birm.)

COOK, Mr Michael Anthony Thomas 75 Vincent Drive, Chester CH4 7RQ — MB ChB 1966 Birm.; MSc Liverp. 1990; FRCS Eng. 1975. Cons. A & E Med. Wrexham Maelor Hosp.

COOK, Michael Edward Massey (retired) 38 Barnfield Road, Exeter EX1 1RZ Tel: 01392 274257 Fax: 0870 131 6316 Email: memcook@hotmail.com — MA, BM BCh Oxf. 1955. Prev: GP Exeter.

COOK, Michael Hugh 9 Constitution Hill, Ipswich IP1 3RG Tel: 01473 251498 — MRCS Eng. LRCP Lond. 1962; FFA RCS Eng. 1969. (St. Thos.) Cons. Anaesth. Ipswich Hosp. NHS Trust. Socs: Fell. Roy. Soc. Med.; Assn. Anaesths. Prev: Assoc. Prof. Anaesth. Pk.land Memor. Hosp. Texas, USA; Regist. (Anaesth.) United Sheff. Hosps. & Hereford Hosp. Gp.; Ho. Surg. (O & G) & Ho. Phys. Co. Hosp. Hereford.

COOK, Miranda 26 Criffel Avenue, London SW2 4AZ — MB ChB 1991 Leeds.

COOK, Miriam Clare 42 Browning Avenue, Boscombe, Bournemouth BH5 1NW — MB BS 1985 Lond.

COOK, Nicholas James High Street Medical Centre, 19 High Street, Staveley, Chesterfield S43 3UU Tel: 01246 472296 Fax: 01246 471665 — MB ChB 1983 Sheff. GP Chesterfield. Prev: GP Trainee Chesterfield VTS; Jun. Ho. Phys. & Jun. Ho. Surg. Chesterfield & N. Derbysh. Roy. Hosp.

COOK, Nicholas James Central Surgery, Corporation Street, Rugby CV21 3SP Tel: 01788 574335 Fax: 01788 547693; 19 Vicarage Lane, Dunchurch, Rugby CV22 6QP — MB ChB 1987 Sheff.; MRCGP 1996; MRCOphth. 1991; DTM & H. Liverp. 1995; DCH RCP Lond. 1993. Gen. Practitioner, Rugby; Assoc. Specialist (Ophth.) Hinchley Hosp. Leics; Primary Care Ophth., Rugby; Retinal Screening Ophth., Coventry and Rugby. Prev: Demonst. (Med.) Dept. Biochem. Sci. Univ. Sheff.; Ophth. Kissy Eye Hosp. Freetown, Sierra Leone.

COOK, Nigel Kenneth Dalton Square Surgery, 8 Dalton Square, Lancaster LA1 1PP Tel: 01524 842200; Spring Bank, Chapel Lane, Ellel, Lancaster LA2 0PN — MB BS 1981 Lond.; MRCGP 1986; DRCOG 1984. (St. Bart) Prev: SHO (Psychiat.) Roy. Preston Hosp.; SHO (O & G) P.ss Anne Hosp. Soton.; SHO (Accid. & Emerg. Orthop.) Soton. Gen. Hosp.

COOK, Noelin Catherine (retired) St Faiths, Woodford, Bude EX23 9HZ — MB BCh BAO NUI 1963; MCh (Otol.) NUI 1970; FRCS Eng. 1969. Prev: Cons. Otolaryngol. Worcs. Roy. Infirm. NHS Trust.

COOK, Norman John (retired) 590 Wells Road, Knowle, Bristol BS14 9BD Tel: 01275 832124 — MB ChB 1945 Bristol; DCH Eng. 1946. Prev: Ho. Phys. Bristol Roy. Infirm.

COOK, Paul Jonathan Stables Cottage, Hopton Lane, Alfrick, Worcester WR6 5HP — MB BCh 1995 Wales.

COOK, Paul Russell Department of Anaesthesia, Royal Oldham Hospital, Rochdale Road, Oldham OL1 2JH Tel: 0161 627 8828 Fax: 0161 627 8831 Email: paul.cook@oldham-tr.nwest.nhs.uk — MB ChB 1979 Birm.; MA Oxf. 1983; FRCA 1984; DA Eng. 1983. (Oxford/Birmingham) Cons. Anaesth. Roy. Oldham Hosp.; Hon. Cons. (Palliat. Care) Roy. Oldham Hosp. Socs: Manch. Med. Soc. (Anaesth. Div.); Yorksh. Soc. Anaesth.; The Pain Soc.

COOK, Penelope Ann 111 Chorley Road, Heath Charnock, Chorley PR6 9JT Tel: 01257 480924 Fax: 01257 480924 — MB ChB Liverp. 1966; FRCPsych 1996, M 1974; DPM Eng. 1973; DObst RCOG 1970; DCH Eng. 1969. Socs: Fell. Manch. Med. Soc. Prev: Child Psychiat. Wigan & Leigh NHS Trust.

COOK, Peter Howard Ellis Gledhill The Surgery, 25 St Mary's Road, Tickhill, Doncaster DN11 9NA Tel: 01302 742503 — FRCGP 2001; MB ChB Sheff. 1970; MRCGP 1983; DObst RCOG 1973. GP Trainer Doncaster VTS. Prev: Ho. Surg. N.. Gen. Hosp. Sheff.; SHO (A & E) Nottm. Gen. Hosp.; Trainee GP Birm. VTS.

COOK, Mr Peter John, TD (retired) 123 Bishopton Road, Stockton-on-Tees TS18 4PN Tel: 01642 678741 — MB BS 1952 Lond.; FRCS Glas. 1967; MRCS Eng. LRCP Lond. 1950. Prev: Cons. Surg. (A & E Serv.) N. Tees Gen. Hosp. Stockton-on-Tees.

COOK, Peter John Clinical Geratology Department, Radcliffe Infirmary, Woodstock Road, Oxford OX2 6HE Fax: 01865 224815 — MD Bristol 1984, BSc (Hons. Physiol.) 1966, MB ChB 1969; FRCP Lond. 1991; MRCP (UK) 1973. (Bristol) Gen. Phys. with Special Responsibil. for Elderly John Radcliffe Hosp. & Radcliffe Infirm. Oxf.; Hon. Clin. Lect. (Med.) Oxf. Univ. Socs: Brit. Geriat. Soc. Prev: Sen. Regist. (Geriat. Med.) St. Thos. Hosp. Lond.; Hon. Lect. & Sen. Regist. (Gen. Med. & Clin. Pharmacol.) Roy. Free Hosp. Lond.; Regist. (Gen. Med.) Univ. Coll. Hosp. Lond.

COOK, Peter Jorn Department of Respiratory Medicine, Dryburn Hospital, North Rd, Durham DH1 5TW Tel: 0191 333 2333 Email: peter.cook@doctors.org.uk — MB BS 1983 Lond.; BSc Lond. 1981; MSc Lond. 1993; MD Lond. 1998; MRCP (UK) 1988; DA (UK) 1986; DTM & H (Lond.) 1998. (London Hospital Medical College) Cons. Phys. (Respirat. Med), Dryburn Hosp., Durh.; Sen. Lec. (Med.) Univ. Newc. Prev: Cystic Fibosis Fell.,Birm.Heartlands Hosp.; Specialist Regist. (Respirat. &Gen.Med)Birm.; Regist. (Infec. Dis.) City Hosp. Edin.

COOK, Peter Lionel (retired) The White House, 122 Highfield Lane, Southampton SO17 1NP Tel: 01703 556794 — MB BS 1956 Lond.; MRCS Eng. LRCP Lond. 1956; FRCR 1975; FFR 1967; DMRD Eng. 1964; DObst RCOG 1958. Cons. Neurolradiol. Wessex Neurol. Centre Soton.; Hon. Clin. Lect. & Postgrad. Clin. Tutor Univ. Soton. Prev: Sen. Regist. (Radiol.) Middlx. & St. Bart. Hosp. Lond.

COOK, Philip George Department of Radiology, Royal Cornwall Hospital (Treliske), Truro TR1 3LJ — MB ChB 1981 Birm.; FRCR 1987. Cons. Radiol. Roy. Cornw. Hosp. Truro. Socs: FRCR. Prev: Sen. Regist. (Radiol.) Bristol Roy. Infirm.; Regist. (Radiol.) Plymouth Hosps.

COOK, Philippa Waulkmill House, By Charlestown, Dunfermline KY12 8JU Tel: 01383 873070 — MB BS 1994 Lond.; BMSc St. And. 1991; DRCOG 1996; DFFP 1995. (St. Bartholomew's)

COOK, Mr Richard Charles Millward (retired) 26 North Road, Grassendale Park, Liverpool L19 0LR Tel: 0151 427 7206 Fax: 0151 427 7206 Email: richardcmcook@netscapeonline.co.uk — BM BCh 1958 Oxf.; FRCS Eng. 1966. Prev: Cons. Paediat. Surg. Roy. Liverp. Childr. Hosp.

COOK, Richard Ian Mid Sussex Health Care, The Health Centre, Trinity Road, Hurstpierpoint, Hassocks BN6 9UQ Tel: 01273 834388 — MB ChB 1989 Birm.; MRCGP 1994; DCH RCP Lond. 1993.

COOK, Richard James 1 Burgoyne Road, Camberley GU15 1LS — MB ChB 1997 Birm.; FDS RCS Eng 1993; BDS Hons Lond. 1989. (Birmingham Dental School, Guys) Gen. Surg. Rotat., Heartlands Hosp., Birm. Prev: Ho. Surg. & Ho. Off. Med.; Lect. in Dent. Surg.; SHO Maxillo Facial Surg.

COOK, Richard John Alton Street Surgery, Alton Street, Ross-on-Wye HR9 5AB Tel: 01989 563646 Fax: 01989 769438; Galen Lodge, Eastfield Road, Ross-on-Wye HR9 5AN Tel: 01989 764378 — BM BCh 1973 Oxf.; BA Oxf. 1969, BM BCh 1973; MRCGP 1978. Prev: Ho. Off. (Med.) & SHO (Neurosurg.) St. Bart. Hosp. Lond.; SHO (Paediat.) Heref. Co. Hosp.

COOK, Robert Charles Saltash Health Centre, Callington Road, Saltash PL12 6DL Tel: 01752 842281 Fax: 01752 844651; Roscarrick, Higher Port View, Saltash PL12 4BU Tel: 01752 846970 — MB ChB 1976 Dundee; MRCGP 1980; DRCOG 1978. Clin. Tutor (Gen. Pract.) Univ. Bristol; Chairm. Cornw. Clin. Research Gp. Prev: Course Organiser Plymouth GP VTS.

COOK, Robert Edward 9/144 White House Loan, Edinburgh EH9 2AN — MB BChir 1992 Camb.

COOK, Robert Magnus Markham 7 Park Road, Broadstairs CT10 1ED — MB BS 1994 Lond.

COOK, Robert Swales (retired) 2C Aughton Road, Birkdale, Southport PR8 2AF Tel: 01704 67234 — MB ChB 1941 Liverp. Cons. Phys. (Geriat. Med.) Mersey RHA. Prev: SHMO (Geriat.) S.port Hosp. Gp.

COOK, Rosalind 26 Abbotshall Crescent, Cults, Aberdeen AB15 9JP — MB ChB 1994 Aberd.

COOK, Rosemary Jane Airdrie Health Centre, Monkscourt Avenue, Airdrie ML6 0JU Tel: 01236 769333; Acharn, 38 Victoria Place, Airdrie ML6 9BX — MB ChB 1983 Glas.; MRCGP 1987; DRCOG 1987. Socs: BMA. Prev: SHO (Gen. & Geriat. Med.) E. Riding Gen. Hosp. Driffield; SHO (Obst.) Bellshill Matern. Hosp.; SHO (Psychiat.) CrossHo. Dist. Gen. Hosp.

COOK, Sangita 11 Ridgewood, New Barn, Longfield DA3 7LS — MB BS 1980 Lond. (Char. Cross Hosp. Med. Sch.) SHO (Psychiat.) Maidstone Hosp. Prev: Clin. Med. Off. (Child Health) Hertsmere AHA, Herts.; SHO (Anaesth.) Chase Farm Hosp. Enfield.

COOK, Shelley Louise 98 Great North Road, Eaton Socon, St Neots, Huntingdon PE19 8EJ — BM BS 1997 Nottm.

COOK, Stephanie Jayne Royal United Hospital, Combe Park, Bath BA1 3NG; College Farm House, Common Road, Weston Colville, Cambridge CB1 5NS Tel: 01223 290039 Email: steph-cook@hotmail.com — BM BCh 1997 Oxf.; BA (Hons.) Cantab. 1994; HA Cantab 1999. (Cambridge and Oxford) SHO Roy. United Hosp. Bath; Res. Fell. In Vasc. Surg., Dept of Vasc. Surg., Roy. Surrey Co. Hosp. Prev: Pre Regist. Ho. Off. (Surg.)John Radcliffe Hosp. Oxf.; Pre Regist Ho. Off. (Med.) Poole Hosp., Poole.

COOK, Stephen George 21 Widford Grove, Chelmsford CM2 9AT Tel: 01245 257377 — MB BS 1985 Queensland; MRACOG 1991.

COOK, Steven 4 Melrose Close, West Denton, Newcastle upon Tyne NE15 7SU Tel: 01632 678635 — MB BS 1969 Newc.; MRCP (UK) 1976; FFA RCS Eng. 1978. Sen. Regist. (Anaesth.) Newc. AHA (T). Prev: Regist. (Anaesth.) & SHO (Med.) Roy. Vict. Infirm. Newc.; Ho. Phys. & Ho. Surg. Newc. Gen. Hosp.

***COOK, Stuart Alexander** 9A Grove Road, Bladon, Woodstock OX20 1RQ — MB BS 1994 Lond.; BSc Lond. 1991; MRCP 1997.

COOK, Mr Stuart Douglas Bristol Eye Hospital, Lower Maudlin St., Bristol BS1 2LX Tel: 0117 923 0060 Fax: 0117 928 4686 Email: evelyn.mooney@ubht.swest.nhs.uk; 31 Oakfield Road, Clifton, Bristol BS8 2AT — MB ChB 1979 Glas.; PhD Glas. 1988, MB ChB 1979; FRCS Ed. 1984; FRCOphth. 1988. Cons. Ophth. Bristol Eye Hosp.; Cons. (Ophth) W.on Gen. Hosp.; Cons. Sen. Lect. Univ. Bristol.

COOK, Tabitha 2 Northfield Close, South Cave, Brough HU15 2EW — MB ChB 1993 Liverp.

COOK, Tessa 42 Sefton Park Road, Bristol BS7 9AJ — MB ChB 1983 Bristol; MRCP (UK) 1986; MRCPsych 1988. Prev: Clin. Asst. (Psychother.), Blackberry Hill Hosp. Bristol; Clin. Asst. (Forens. Psychiat.), Fromeside Clinic, Bristol.

COOK, Mr Timothy Alan Gloucester Royal Hospital, Great Western Road, Gloucester G21 3NN Tel: 01452 395615 Fax: 01452 394813 — DM 2000 (Oxf.); FRCS 2000 (Gen. Surg.); BM BCh Oxf. 1989; MA Oxf. 1994, BA 1986; FRCS Eng. 1993. Cons. Colorectal Surg., Gloucestershire Roy. Hosp. Gloucester. Prev: RSO, St Mark's Hosp. Harrow; Specialist Regist., Oxf. Reg.; Roy. Coll. Of Surg. Research Fell, Dept. Of Pharmacol. Oxf.

COOK, Timothy Mark Department of Anaesthesia, Royal Perth Hospital, GPO X2213, Perth 6001, Australia; 12 Sunningdale, Bristol BS8 2NF — MB BS 1987 Lond.; BA (Hons.) Camb. 1984; MB BS (Hons.) Lond. 1987; FRCA 1993; DA (UK) 1989. Regist. (Anaesth.) Roy. United Hosp. Bath. Prev: Regist. (Anaesth.) Frenchay Hosp. Bristol.

COOK, Victoria Ann Mills 94 Whitton Road, Twickenham TW1 1BS — MB BS 1989 Lond.; MRCOG 1994.

COOK, William Bernard (retired) 2 Hailsham Road, Polegate BN26 6NL — LMSSA 1949 Lond. Prev: Clin. Asst.(Med) King's Coll. Hosp. Lond.

COOK, William Ronald 10 Blackwood Avenue, Kilmarnock KA1 1SW — MB ChB 1970 Glas.

COOKE, Albert 26 Wynmore Avenue, Bramhope, Leeds LS16 9DE Tel: 0113 267 5540 — MB ChB 1954 Leeds; MRCGP 1971; DObst RCOG 1955. (Leeds) Fact. Med.Off. Leeds. Prev: GP 1966-1993.

COOKE, Alfred Hunt (retired) 74 Brent Street, London NW4 2ES Tel: 020 8202 8414 — M.R.C.S. Eng., L.R.C.P. Lond. 1935. Prev: R.A.M.C.

COOKE, Anthea Margaret 691 Coventry Road, Birmingham B10 0JL Tel: 0121 773 4931 Fax: 0121 753 2210; 50 Hazelwood Road, Acocks Green, Birmingham B27 7XP Tel: 0121 706 1779 Fax: 0121 753 2210 — BM BCh 1962 Oxf.

COOKE, Bernard John Edward (retired) The Ridings, 36 Dudsbury Avenue, Ferndown, Wimborne Tel: 01202 893825 — MRCS Eng. LRCP Lond. 1956; BSc (Hons. Anat.) Lond. 1952, MB BS 1955; FRCOG 1977, M 1964, DObst 1961. Prev: Cons. O & G E. Dorset Health Dist.

COOKE, Brian Edwin Mayfield, Whalley Road, Simonstone, Burnley BB12 7HT Tel: 01282 771238 — MRCS Eng. LRCP Lond. 1953. (Leeds) Socs: Assn. Occupat. Med. RCP Lond. Prev: Med. Adviser (N.) Philips Electronics; Ho. Phys., Ho. Surg. & SHO (Anaesth.) Burnley Gen. Hosp.; Squadron Ldr. RAF Med. Br.

COOKE, Brian Ernest Dudley (retired) 21 Redwood Court, Station Road, Llanishen, Cardiff CF14 5RD Tel: 029 2074 7167 — MRCS Eng. LRCP Lond. 1949; MDS Lond. 1959; FDS RCS Eng. 1952, LDS 1942; FRCPath 1974, M 1965. Vis. Prof. Univ. Sydney Dent. Sch. 1986. Prev: Prof. Oral Med. & Oral Path. & Dean Dent. Sch. Welsh Nat. Sch. Med. Univ. Wales.

COOKE, Brian Roy Barrington Gallery House, 10 High Street, Totnes TQ9 5RY Tel: 01803 840053 Fax: 01803 864343 Email: bcooke@bc1.org.uk — MB BS 1977 Lond.; MRCS Eng. LRCP Lond. 1977; MFCM 1986, MFPHM 1989. (Roy. Free) Cons. in Pub. Health Med., S. W. Peninsula. Prev: Cons. Pub. Health Med. Health Educat. Auth. Lond.; Cons. Pub. Health Med. NE Thames RHA.

COOKE, Carole Anne 70 Derry Road, Strabane BT82 8LD Tel: 01504 886739 Email: c.cooke@ukgateway.net — MB BCh BAO 1997 Belf. SHO (Opthalmology).

COOKE, Caroline Miguette Department of Medicine, Leicester General Hospital, Gwendolen Road, Leicester LE5 4PW Tel: 0116

249 0490; 17 Scotland Lane, Houghton on the Hill, Leicester LE7 9GH — MB BS 1985 Lond.; BSc Lond. 1982, MB BS 1985; MRCGP 1992. Regist. (Palliat. Med.) Leicester Gen. Hosp. Prev: Clin. Asst. (Palliat. Med.) Leics. Hospice; Trainee GP N.ampton VTS; SHO (Radiother. Oncol.) Leicester Roy. Infirm.

COOKE, Christine Ann 35 Kingsfield Drive, Manchester M20 6JA — MB ChB 1993 Sheff.

COOKE, Conrad Justin Gowrie House, Chelmsford Road, Hatfield Heath, Bishop's Stortford CM22 7BH — BM BCh 1989 Oxf.; BA Camb. 1986; MRCP (UK) 1993.

COOKE, David Alun Winch Lane Surgery, Winch Lane, Haverfordwest SA61 1RN Tel: 01437 762333 Fax: 01437 766912; Ysgubor Hen, Honeyhook, Llangwm, Haverfordwest SA62 4JR — MB BCh 1989 Wales; MRCGP 1993; DFFP 1994; DCH RCP Lond. 1993; DRCOG 1992. (Univ. Wales Coll. Med.) Socs: Cymdeithas Feddygol. Prev: Trainee GP Cardiff VTS; Ho. Off. (Surg.) Univ. Hosp. Wales Cardiff; Ho. Phys. Cardiff Roy. Infirm.

COOKE, Mr David Antony Philip St Helier Hospital, Carshalton SM5 1AA Tel: 020 8 296 2775 Fax: 020 8 288 1838; 7 Keith Street, Maryborough Qld 4650, Australia Tel: 00 61 71230124 Fax: 00 61 71230124 — MB BS 1976 Lond.; BSc (Hons.) Lond. 1973, MS 1994; FRCS Eng. 1982; FRCS Ed. 1982. (St. Bart.) Cons. Surg. (Gen. & Vasc. Surg.) St. Helier Hosp. Carshalton; Research Regist. St. Thos. Hosp. Lond. Socs: Fell. Roy. Soc. Med.; Harveian Soc.; Med. Soc. Lond. (Ex-Counc.). Prev: Sen. Regist. St. Geo. Hosp. Lond.; Surg. Specialist Internat. Red Cross, Geneva; Demonst.(Anat.) St. Bart. Hosp. Med. Coll. Lond.

COOKE, David Ian Hillbarn House, Dancing Hill, North Petherton, Bridgwater TA6 6NG Tel: 01278 662271 — MB ChB 1975 Bristol; BSc (Med. Microbiol.) Bristol 1975, MB ChB (Hons.) 1978; MRCP (UK) 1981; FRCR 1988. Cons. Radiol. Musgrave Pk. Hosp. Taunton. Prev: Sen. Regist. (Radiol.) Leeds Gen. Infirm.; Regist. Univ. Dept. Med. Brist. Roy. Infirm.; Regist. Dept. Med. King Edwd. VIII Hosp. Durban.

COOKE, Derek Riversdale, 59 Bridge St., Belper, Derby DE56 1AY Tel: 01332 822386 — MB BS 1975 Lond.; MRCS Eng. LRCP Lond. 1974. (St. Mary's)

COOKE, Diana Lynn 6 Icen Road, Weymouth DT3 5JJ — MB BS 1968 Lond.; DObst RCOG 1971; DCH Eng. 1970. (Westm.) SCMO Dorset Ha.

COOKE, (Edith) Mary, OBE (retired) 12 The Pryors, East Heath Road, London NW3 1BS Tel: 020 7431 0165 Fax: 020 7431 0165 Email: bmcooke@talk21.com — MB BS Lond. 1959; BSc (Physiol.) Lond. 1955; MD Lond. 1967; FRCP Lond. 1994; MRCS Eng. LRCP Lond. 1958; MRCP (UK) 1992; FRCPath 1979, M 1967; MCRS Eng. LRCP Lond. 1958. Vice Pres. Med. Defence Union. Prev: Dep. Dir. Pub. Health Laborat. Serv. HQ.

COOKE, Mr Edward Andrew 39 Inishowen Drive, Belfast BT10 0EW — MB BCh BAO 1988 Belf.; FRCSI 1992.

COOKE, Edward Thomas Michael Elizabeth House, 30 Ednam Road, Goldthorn Park, Wolverhampton WV4 5BW Tel: 01902 338722 — MB ChB 1965 Leeds; DLO Eng. 1975. Hosp. Pract. (ENT) E. Birm. Hosp. Prev: Clin. Asst. (ENT) E. Birm. Hosp.;'Eval. of Severe Epistaxsis Treated by Arterial Ligation' Jl. Laryngol. & Otol. 1985.

COOKE, Ernest Davidson Clinical Microvascular Unit, St. Bartholomew's Hospital, London EC1A 7BE Tel: 020 7601 8498 Fax: 020 7601 8499; 79 Woodland Rise, Muswell Hill, London N10 3UN Tel: 020 8883 1050 — MD 1978 Dub.; MB BCh BAO Dub. 1951. (T.C.Dub.) Dir. Clin. Microvasc. Unit St. Bart. Hosp. Lond.; Hon. Sen. Research Fell. St. Bart. Hosp. Lond. & The Lond. Hosp. Socs: Fell. Roy. Soc. Med.; BMA. Prev: Clin. Asst. Hosp. Sick Childr. Gt. Ormond St. Lond.; Regist. (Med.) S.mead Hosp. Bristol; Ho. Phys. Roy. City of Dub. Hosp.

COOKE, Francis James 27 St Pauls Avenue, Lytham St Annes FY8 1ED — MB BS 1996 Lond.

COOKE, Fraser James 90 Repton Road, West Bridgford, Nottingham NG2 7EL — BM BCh 1997 Oxf.

COOKE, George Alastair King's Mill Hospital, Mansfield Road, Sutton-in-Ashfield NG17 4SL — MB ChB 1989 Manch.; MO 1998; MRCP (UK) 1992. (Manch.) Cons. Cardiol., King's Mill Hosp., Notts.

COOKE, Graham Stephen Cranmore, Bridle Lane, Rickmansworth WD3 4JH — BChir 1994 Camb.

COOKE, Heather Marie Gupta 70 Almshill Road, Sheffield S11 9RS — MB BS 1992 Lond.; PhD Lond. 1987; BSc Manch. 1982; MRCGP 1996; DCH RCP Lond. 1995; DFFP 1995; DRCOG 1996. (Char. Cross & Westm. Lond.) SHO (Psychiat.) Hellesden Hosp. Norwich. Prev: GP/Regist. Cirencester; SHO (A & E) Roy. Hallamsh. Hosp. Sheff.; SHO (Paediat.) Qu. Mary's Hosp. Sidcup.

COOKE, Hilary Barbara Joy (retired) 20 Kelmscott Road, Harborne, Birmingham B17 8QN Tel: 0121 426 2354 Fax: 0121 681 2265 — MB ChB 1944 Birm. Prev: Clin. Asst. Dudley Rd. Hosp. Birm.

COOKE, Professor Ian Douglas (retired) University Department Obstetrics & Gynaecology, Jessop Hospital for Women, Sheffield S3 7RE Tel: 0114 226 8281 Fax: 0114 275 2153 Email: i.d.cooke@sheffield.ac.uk — MB BS MB BS Sydney 1958; DGO Sydney 1962; FRCOG 1974, M 1963. Prof. O & G Univ. Sheff. at Jessop Hosp. Wom. Sheff. Prev: Wellcome Trav. Fell. Karolinska Hosp. Stockholm, Sweden.

COOKE, Janet Elizabeth 20 Crescent Walk, West Parley, Wimborne; 440 Kinson Road, Bournemouth BH10 5EY Tel: 574604 — MB ChB 1978 Ed.; MRCGP 1982; DRCOG 1980.

COOKE, Janine Brenda Invicta Community NHS Trust, Homeopathic Hospital, 41 Church Road, Tunbridge Wells TN1 1JU Tel: 01892 539144 Fax: 01892 535522; 30Great Bounds Drive, Southborough, Tunbridge Wells TN4 0TR Tel: 01892 528993 Email: jcooke9391@aol.com — MB ChB 1972 Bristol. (Bristol) SCMO Invicta Community Care NHS Trust; Asst. (Gen. Pract.). Socs: Diplomate Fac. Family Plann. & Sexual Health; MRCPCH.

COOKE, John Nigel Carlyle, CB, OBE, Air Vice-Marshal RAF Med. Br. Retd. Civil Aviation Authority, Medical Department, Aviation House, Gatwick Airport S., Gatwick RH6 0YR Tel: 01293 573685 Fax: 01293 573995; 4 Lincoln Close, Stoke Mandeville, Aylesbury HP22 5YS Tel: 01296 613852 Fax: 01296 613852 — MB BS Lond. 1945; MD Lond. 1950; FRCP Ed. 1968, M 1950; FRCP Lond. 1967, M 1950; MRCS Eng. LRCP Lond. 1945; MFOM RCP Lond. 1982. (St. Mary's) Cons. to Civil Aviat. Auth. Prev: Cons. Adviser to Sultan of Oman's Air Force 1985-1991; Prof. Aviat. Med.; Dean of Air Force Med.

COOKE, John Tristram (retired) Morn Hill Lodge, Alresford Road, Winchester SO21 1HL Tel: 01962 878306 — MB BS 1959 Lond.; BA Camb. 1952; MRCGP 1976. Prev: GP Winchester.

COOKE, Juanita-Lyn 30 Cabin Hill Gardens, Belfast BT5 7AP — MB BCh BAO 1991 Belf.; MRCGP 1995.

COOKE, Juliette Christine 2 Beechlawn, Guildford GU1 3PE Tel: 01483 568985 — MB BS 1978 Lond.; MRCP (UK) 1982; FRCR 1985. (St. Bart.) Clin. Dir. Jarvis BrE. Screen Centre Guildford. Prev: Sen. Regist. (Radiol.) W.m.

***COOKE, Karen Christine** 21 Shaws Drive, Wirral CH47 5AP — MB ChB 1995 Sheff.

COOKE, Leila Beatrice BANES PCT, New Friends Hall,, Heath House Lane, Stapleton, Bristol BS16 1EQ Tel: 01179 585666 Fax: 01179 586048 — MB ChB 1973 Bristol; MRCPsych 1980; FRCPsych 1999. Cons. Psychiat. (Learning Disabil.) BANES PCT; Clin. Lect. (Ment. Health) Univ. Bristol. Socs: (Forum) Roy. Soc. Med.; BMA.

COOKE, Louise Michelle 24 Townsend Road, Eaton Rise, Norwich NR4 6RG; Low Barn, Brocket View, Acaster Malbis, York YO23 2PY — MB BS 1993 Newc.; DFFP 1996; DRCOG 1996; MRCGP 1998. GP Retainer. Socs: BMA; Roy. Coll. Gen. Pract.; MDU. Prev: SHO (Paediat. Psychiat. & O & G) N. Tees; GP/Regist. Stockton; SHO (Med.) N. Tees.

COOKE, Lucy Helen 14 Potters Lane, Polesworth, Tamworth B78 1HE — BM BS 1993 Nottm.

COOKE, Mrs Lynn Denise Gartnaval General Hospital, 1053 Great Western Road, Glasgow G12 0YN Tel: 0141 211 3000 Fax: 0141 357 4725; Westdel, Queens Place, Glasgow G12 9DQ — BM 1982 Soton.; DM Soton. 1993; FRCS (Orl.) Eng. 1993; FRCS (ENT) Eng. 1987. Cons. Ent. Surg. Gartnaval Gen. Hosp. Glas.; Hon. Sen. Lect. Glas. Univ.

COOKE, Margaret Lowri The Street Lane Practice, 12 Devonshire Avenue, Leeds LS8 1AY Tel: 0113 295 3838 Fax: 0113 295 3842; 5 Wedgewood Drive, Roundhay, Leeds LS8 1EF Tel: 0113 266 1383 — MB ChB 1970 Ed.; BSc Ed. 1967. (Edinburgh)

COOKE, Matthew William Accident and Emergency Department, Coventry and Warwickshire Hospital, Stoney Stanton Road, Coventry

CV1 4FH Tel: 024 760844090 Fax: 0870 055 8087 Email: mwc@emerg.demon.co.uk — MB ChB 1982 Birm.; FRCS Ed. 1987; Dip. IMC RCS Ed. 1989; FFAEM 1995. Sen. Lect. (A & E Med.) Univ. Warwick; Dir., Emerg. Med. Research Gp.; Cons. A & E Walsgrave Hosp., Coventry; Edr. Pre-Hosp. Immediate Care, BMJ Publishing Gp. Socs: Fell. & Bd. Mem. Fac. Accid. & Emerg. Med.; Brit. Assn. Accid. & Emerg. Med.; Brit. Assn. Immed. Care Schemes. Prev: Cons. (A & E), City Hosp., Birm.; Regist. (A & E Med.) Kings Coll. Hosp. Lond.; Sen. Regist. (A & E Med.) W. Midl.

COOKE, Michael John 26 Northumberland Avenue, Gosforth, Newcastle upon Tyne NE3 4XE — MB ChB 1980 Sheff.

COOKE, Michael John Wilbraham Road Surgery, 515 Wilbraham Road, Chorlton, Manchester M21 0UF Tel: 0161 881 6120 Fax: 0161 861 7796 — MB ChB 1984 Manch.

COOKE, Michael Joseph 12 Bell Meadow, Worcester Lane, Pedmore, Stourbridge DY9 0YY Tel: 01562 885431 — MB ChB 1973 Bristol; MRCGP 1977; DCH Eng. 1976; DObst RCOG 1975.

COOKE, Morris Arthur 20 Kelmscott Road, Harborne, Birmingham B17 8QN Tel: 0121 427 2370 Fax: 0121 681 2265 Email: morris_cooke@compuserve.com — MB ChB Birm. 1943; MRCS Eng. LRCP Lond. 1943; FFOM RCP Lond. 1979, M 1978; CBiol, MIBiol. 1984. (Birm.) Cons. Occupat. Phys. & Toxicol. Birm.; Cons. Occupat. Phys./Toxicol. Firmenich & other companies; Hon. Sen. Clin. Lect. Inst. Occupat. Health. Socs: Fell. Roy. Soc. Med. (Ex-Pres. Sect. Occupat. Med.); (Ex-Pres.) Soc. Occupat. Med.; Brit. Assn. Dermatol. Prev: Cons. Chief Med. Adviser Albright & Wilson Ltd; Vis. Prof. Dept. Product. Mechanical & Elec. Engin. (Health & Safety Unit) Aston Univ.; Capt. RAMC.

COOKE, Nicholas Peter Bow Wood Barn, Botton House Farm Lane, Chalfont St Giles HP8 4EE — MB BS 1983 Lond.

COOKE, Nigel James (retired) 5 Wedgewood Drive, Leeds LS8 1EF — MB ChB 1967 Ed.; BSc (Hons. Physiol.) Ed. 1964, MB ChB 1967; FRCP Lond. 1982, M 1971; FRCP Ed. 1982. Prev: Sen. Regist. Respirat. Dis. Unit N.. Gen. Hosp. Edin.

COOKE, Nigel Trevor St Helier Hospital NHS Trust, Wrythe Lane, Carshalton SM5 1AA Tel: 020 8644 4343 — MB BS 1975 Lond.; MB BS (Hons. Distinc. Therap. & Obst. & Gyn.) Lond. 1975; MD Lond. 1983, BSc 1972; FRCP Lond. 1992; MRCP (UK) 1978. (Middlx.) Cons. Phys. (Gen. & Respirat. Med.) St. Helier Hosp. Carshalton. Prev: Sen. Regist. (Gen. & Respirat. Med.) Char. Cross Hosp. Lond.; Regist. (Med.) & Research Fell. (Med.) Middlx. Hosp. Lond.; Regist. Gen. Infirm. Leeds.

***COOKE, Olga Helen Charlotte** 29 The Avenue, Kew, Richmond TW9 2AL Tel: 020 8940 6712 — MB ChB 1996 Ed.

COOKE, Mr Paul Hamilton Nuffield Orthopaedic Centre, Headington, Oxford OX3 7LD Tel: 01865 227359 Fax: 01865 227320 — MB ChB 1977 Sheff.; ChM 1990; FRCS Eng. 1981. Cons. Orthop. Surg. Nuffield Orthop. Centre NHS Trust Oxf. Socs: Coun. Mem., Europ. foot and ankle Surg. Soc. Prev: Regist. (Orthop. Surg.) Bristol Hosps.; Sen. Regist. (Orthop. Surg.) Oxf.; Vis. Fell. Roy. Childr. Hosp. Melbourne, Austral.

COOKE, Mr Peter William Fax: 0709 218 6287 Email: peter.cooke@virgin.net — MB ChB 1989 Birm.; FRCS Eng. 1994; FRCSI 1993. (Birmingham) Specialist Regist. (Urol.) W. Midl. Regional Train. Scheme. Socs: BMA; BAUS (Assoc. Mem.). Prev: Urol. Res. Fell. (Urol.) Birm. Univ.; Jun. Regist. Qu. Eliz. Hosp., E. Birm. Hosp. & Good Hope Hosp. Birm.; SHO (A & E) Gen. Hosp. Birm.

COOKE, Rachel Somerset 25 Westfield Terrace, Newport-on-Tay DD6 8HX — MB ChB 1982 Leeds; MRCGP 1986; DRCOG 1985. (Leeds) Prev: Med. Off. P & O Lines.

COOKE, Richard Andrew Cardiothoracic Centre, 6th Floor, East Wing,, St Thomas Hospital, London SE1 7EM Tel: 020 7928 9292 Email: cookmo@aol.com — MB BCh BAO 1985 Belf.; Ba (Law) Durham 1978; MRCP London 1988; MD Thesis 1996; FRCP 2000. (Queens University Belfast.) Cons. Cardiol. Guys & St Thomas, Lond. Prev: Specialist Regist. in Cardiol., Guys Hosp., Lond. 1989-1995.

COOKE, Richard Arthur Long View, Castle Rise, Spittal, Haverfordwest SA62 5QW Tel: 01437 741291 — BSc (Hons.) (Physiol.) Lond. 1972, MB BS 1975; FFA RCS Eng. 1981. (Univ. Coll. Lond. & Univ. Coll. Hosp.) Cons. (Anaesth.) Withybush Hosp. HaverfordW.. Prev: Sen. Regist. (Anaesth.) Univ. Hosp. Nottm.; Regist. (Anaesth.) St. Ja's. Univ. Hosp. Leeds.

COOKE, Richard Joseph Newcastle General Hospital, Westgate Road, Newcastle upon Tyne NE4 6BE Tel: 0191 273 8811 Fax: 0191 272 2641; Ward 35, Leazes Wing (SCBU), Floor 2, Royal Victoria Infirmary, Queen Victoria Road, Newcastle upon Tyne NE1 4LP Tel: 0191 227 5168 Fax: 0191 227 5238 — MB BCh BAO 1970 NUI; MRCPI 1978.

COOKE, Richard Peter Davidson Microbiology Department, Eastbourne District General Hospital, Kings Drive, Eastbourne BN21 2UD Tel: 01323 417400 Fax: 01323 414928 Email: richard.cooke@ed.ebh-tr.sthames.nhs.uk — MB BS 1979 Lond.; FRCP 2000; Dip. Bact. Manch. 1988; BSc (Hons.) Lond. 1976; MRCP (UK) 1984; MRCPath. 1989; FRCPath. 1997. (Univ. Coll. Hosp.) Cons. Microbiol. E.bourne Dist. Gen. Hosp. E. Sussex. Prev: Sen. Regist. (Microbiol.) N. W.. Regional Train. Scheme; Regist. (Microbiol.) W. Midl. Regional Train. Scheme; Regist. (Med.) Harefield Hosp. Middlx.

COOKE, Mr Richard Stephen Department of Neurosurgery, Royal Victoria Hospital, Belfast BT12 6BA Tel: 01232 240503 Fax: 01232 237733 Email: rscooke@neurorvh.dnet.co.uk — MB BCh BAO 1986 Belf.; FRCS (SN) 1995; FRCSI 1990. (Qu. Univ. Belf.) Cons. Neurosurg. Roy. Vict. Hosp. Belf.

COOKE, Professor Richard William Ingram Institute of Child Health, Royal Liverpool Childrens Hospital, Alder Hey, Liverpool L12 2AP Tel: 0151 228 4811 Fax: 0151 228 2024 Email: mc19@liv.ac.uk; 11 Western Drive, Liverpool L19 0LX Tel: 0151 427 3337 — MRCS Eng. LRCP Lond. 1971; MD Lond. 1979, MB BS 1971; FRCP Lond. 1986; MRCP (UK) 1973; FRCPCH 1996; DCH Eng. 1973. (Char. Cross) Prof. Paediat. Med. Univ. Liverp. Socs: Brit. Assn. Paediat. Neurol.; (Pres. and Past Sec.) Neonat. Soc.; Vice-Pres. RCPCH. Prev: Paediat. Dept. Cardiol. Sophiakinder-ziekenhuis Rotterdam; Research Fell. Dept. Paediat. Oxf. Univ.; Lect. Paediat. Univ. Oxf.

COOKE, Robert Thomas Reginald 1 Rosa Cottages, Heronsgate Road, Chorleywood, Rickmansworth WD3 5BB — MB BCh BAO 1967 Belf.; DObst RCOG 1969. (Belf.) Socs: BMA; Assoc. RCGP. Prev: Clin. Med. Off. Dept. Health & Social Servs. N. Down & Ards Dist.; Obst. Ho. Off. Belf. City Hosp.; Paediat. Ho. Off. Ulster Hosp. Dundonald.

COOKE, Roger Anthony Performance Through Health Ltd., 19 The Crescent, Ednall Lane, Bromsgrove B60 2DS Tel: 01527 577242 Fax: 01527 832618; Summers Place, Badley Wood Common, Whitbourne, Worcester WR6 5ST Tel: 01886 821644 Fax: 01886 821944 Email: rogerpth@cs.com — MB ChB 1975 Birm.; Dipimc (RCS Edin) 1997; FFOM RCP Lond. 1990, MFOM 1987, AFOM 1982; DIH Soc. Apoth. Lond. 1982. (Birm.) Cons. Occupat. Phys. Worcs.; Dir., Performance Through Health Ltd, Health & Safety Press. Socs: Soc. Occupat. Med.; Brit. Assn. Immed. Care Schemes. Prev: Cons. Occupat. Med. Worcs. & DHA; Chief Med. Off. GKN plc; Regional Med. Off. BT (Midl. Region).

COOKE, S Shirley Crawford (retired) 40 Greenfield Road, Little Sutton, Ellesmere Port CH66 1QR Tel: 0151 339 3334 — MB ChB Liverp. 1948. Prev: Sen. Med. Off. Chester DHA.

COOKE, Sarah Louise 11A Moor Lane, Wilmslow SK9 6AG — BM BS 1989 Nottm.; MRCGP 1995; DCH RCP Lond. 1994.

COOKE, Sheila Margaret Silver University Department of Obstetrics & Gynaecology, Jessop Hospital for Women, Leavygreave Road, Sheffield S3 7RE Tel: 0114 276 6333 Fax: 0114 275 2153; 80 Grove Road, Millhouses, Sheffield S7 2GZ Tel: 0114 262 0718 — MB ChB 1962 Aberd.; DObst RCOG 1965. Clin. Asst. (O & G) Jessop Hosp. for Wom. Sheff. Prev: Ho. Phys. Woodend Hosp. Aberd.; Ho. Surg. Whipps Cross Hosp. Lond. & Matern. Hosp. Aberd.

COOKE, Simon Stuart Fordingbridge Surgery, Bartons Road, Fordingbridge SP6 1RS Tel: 01425 652123 Fax: 01425 654393 — MB ChB 1988 Liverp.; DRCOG 1996; DFFP 1996; Dip Ther 1997 Wales. (Liverp.) GP/Regist. Poole. Prev: SHO (O & G & Med.) Derriford Hosp. Plymouth; MO to 40 Commando RM; Squadron Med. Off. 8th Frigate Squadron.

COOKE, Siobhan Dolores The Blithedale Medical Centre, 3 Jersey Street, Bethnal Green, London E2 0AW; 18 Queens Road, Leytonstone, London E11 1BB — MB BS 1984 Lond.; DCH RCP Lond. 1990. Trainee GP Lond. VTS. Prev: Regist. (Radiother.) Guy's, St. Thos. & Kings Coll. Hosp.; SHO (Obst.) Nat. Matern. Hosp. Dub.; SHO (Paediat.) Hillingdon Hosp.

COOKE, Stephen David Sigrist Whiteley and Partners, 4 Market Place, Billesdon, Leicester LE7 9AJ Tel: 0116 259 6206 Fax: 0116 259 6388 — MB BS 1984 Lond.; MRCGP 1988; DRCOG 1989. (Charing Cross Hospital Medical School) Prev: Trainee GP Char. Cross Hosp. Lond. VTS.

COOKE, Stephen Gavin Gloucestershire Royal Hospital, Radiology Department, Great Western Road, Gloucester GL1 3NN Tel: 01452 394532 Fax: 01452 394535 — MB BS 1978 Lond.; MRCP (UK) 1982; FRCR 1987. (St. Mary's) Cons. Radiol. Glos. Roy. Hosp. Prev: Sen. Regist. (Diag. Radio.) Bristol Roy. Infirm. & Plymouth Gen. Hosp.; Regist. (Endocrinol. & Nuclear Med.) Guy's Hosp. Lond.; Ho. Phys. St. Mary's Hosp. Lond.

COOKE, Mrs Susan Margaret (retired) 26 Wynmore Avenue, Bramhope, Leeds LS16 9DE Tel: 0113 267 5540 — MB ChB Manch. 1963.

COOKE, Mr Theodore John Cameron (cons. rooms), New Hall Hospital, Bodenham, Salisbury Tel: 01722 422333; The Manor House, Church Lane, Fovant, Salisbury SP3 5LA Tel: 01722 714765 Fax: 01722 714765 — MB BS Lond. (Hon. Surg.) 1965; MS Lond. 1977; MBA (Distinc.) Warwick 1993; FRCS Eng. 1969; MRCS Eng. LRCP Lond. 1965. (St. Bart.) Cons. Gen. Endocrine & Vasc. Surg. Salisbury Gen. Infirm. Socs: Fell. Roy. Soc. Med.; Brit. Assn. Endocrin. Surgs. Prev: Sen. Regist. (Surg.) Hammersmith Hosp. Lond. & Roy. Berks. Hosp. Reading; Regist. (Surg.) St. Thos. Hosp. Lond.; Ho. Surg. Surgic. Profess. Unit & Thoracic Dept. St. Bart. Hosp. Lond.

COOKE, Timothy David Botesdale Health Centre, Back Hills, Botesdale, Diss IP22 1DW Tel: 01379 898295 — MB BChir 1985 Camb.; BA Camb. 1983; BSc Lond. 1981; DRCOG 1990.

COOKE, Mr Timothy Gordon Department of Surgery, Glasgow Royal Infirmary, 10 Alexandra Parade, Glasgow G31 2ER Tel: 0141 552 3535; West Del, Queens Place, Glasgow G12 9DQ — MD 1980 Liverp.; MB ChB 1973; FRCS Glas. 1984; FRCS Eng. 1977. (Liverp.) St. Mungo Prof. Surg. Univ. Glas. & Cons. Surg. Glas. Roy. Infirm. Prev: Sen. Lect. & Cons. Surg. Roy. Hosp. Liverp.; Sen. Lect. & Cons. Surg. Char. Cross Hosp. Lond.; Lect. (Surg.) Soton. Univ.

COOKE, Victor Alan 35 Kingsfield Drive, Manchester M20 6JA — MB ChB 1998 Sheff.; MB ChB Sheff 1998. SHO Gen. Med., Barnsley Dist. Gen. Hosp., S.Yorks.

COOKE, Victoria Anne Holmwood, 7 Tangier Road, Guildford GU1 2DE — MB BS 1983 Lond.; BSc Lond. 1981, MB BS 1983; MRCGP 1987; DRCOG 1986. (Guy's) BrE. Phys. Jarvis Centre, Guildford; Clin. Asst. (Geriat. Med.) Roy. Surrey Co. Hosp. Guildford. Prev: Trainee GP Beaconsfield VTS.

COOKE, Mr William Michael South Cleveland Hospital, Middlesbrough TS4 3BW Tel: 01642 854863 — BM BCh 1962 Oxf.; MA Oxf. 1962; FRCS Eng. 1967. (Oxf. & St. Mary's) Cons. Surg. S. Tees Acute Health Trust; Assoc. Clin. Lect. (Surg.) Univ. Newc; Hon. Clin. Tutor Char. Cross & W.m. Med. Sch. Lond. Socs: Brit. Soc. Gastroenterol.; Assn. Surg.; Assn. Endoscopic Surgs. Prev: Sen. Regist. (Surg.) Hammersmith Hosp. Lond.; Cas. Off. St. Thos. Hosp. Lond.; Ho. Surg. Radcliffe Infirm. Oxf.

COOKE-YARBOROUGH, Claire Mary 65 Lyncroft Gardens, Hounslow TW3 2QU Tel: 020 8894 3005 — MB BS 1986 New South Wales; MB BS (Hons.) New South Wales 1986.

COOKEY, Harford Gbalafama Great North Road Surgery, 164 Great North Road, Gosforth, Newcastle upon Tyne NE4 5AB; 76 Moor Road N., Newcastle upon Tyne NE3 1AB Tel: 0191 285 3229 — LMSSA 1988 Lond.; MB BCh Nigeria 1977. GP Princip. Socs: Brit. Med. Assn.; Med. Defence Union; Med. Assn. of Nigerian Spacialist and Gen. Practitioners.

COOKEY, Ibelema Patricia Sexual Health Department, Avenue House, The Avenue, Eastbourne BN21 3XY Tel: 01323 444166 Fax: 01323 444165 — MB ChB 1980 Birm.; MFFP 1993. (Birm.) SCMO (Family Plann. & Reproduc. Healthcare) E.bourne & Co. Trust; Clin. Asst. (Genitourin. Med.).

COOKEY, Nnenna Chimelu North Durham Health Care NHS Trust, The Health Centre, Newcastle Road, Chester-le-Street DH3 3UR Tel: 0191 333 3884 Fax: 0191 333 3890 Email: nnennacookey@ndch.demon.co.uk; The Limes, 76 Moor Road N., Gosforth, Newcastle upon Tyne NE3 1AB Tel: 0191 285 3229 — MB BS 1979 Ahmadu Bello Univ. Nigeria; MB BS Ahmadu Bello 1979; MRCP (UK) 1986; DCH RCP Lond. 1985; FRCPCH 1997. (Ahmadu Bello Univ. Nigeria) Cons. Paediat. Socs: MRCPCH; BMA; Roy. Coll. Phys. Prev: Sen. Regist. (Paediat.) Community Child Health Newc.; Regist. (Paediat.) Sunderland Dist. Gen. Hosp. & Roy. Vict. Infirm. Newc.

COOKLIN, Alan Ivor Fax: 020 8374 2577 Email: alancooklin@cs.com — MB ChB 1965 Ed.; FRCPsych 1981, M 1972; DPM Ed. & Glas. 1968. (Ed.) Cons. Univ. Coll. Lond. Paediat. Liaison Serv.; Recognised Teach. Univ. Lond.; Family Project Camden & Islington Ment. Health NHS Trust; Hon. Sen. Lect. UCL. Prev: Dir. Inst. Family Ther. Lond.; Director MarlBoro. Family Serv.; Director MarlBoro. family Serv.

COOKLIN, Michael 6 Canons Court, Edgware HA8 7ST — MB ChB 1985 Manch.; BSc (Hons.) Manch. 1982, MB ChB 1985; MRCP (UK) 1988. Research Fell. & Hon. Regist. (Cardiol.) St Mary's Hosp. Lond. Prev: Regist. (Cardiol. & Gen. Med.) St. Marys Hosp. Lond.; SHO (Renal & Gen. Med.) Hope Hosp. Salford; Ho. Phys. & Ho. Surg. Univ. Hosp. S. Manch. HA.

COOKLIN, Ruth Simone Email: ruthcooklin@doctors.org.uk — MB ChB 1973 Manch.; MRCPsych 1978. (Manchester) Professional Adviser to Child and Adolesc. Ment. Health Charity, "YoungMinds". Socs: Fell. Roy. Soc. Med. Prev: Cons. in Private Pract.; Staff Cons. Psychiat., Gr.lands Priory Hosp., Lond.; Clin. Lect. & Hon. Sen. Regist. (Ment. Health) Univ. Coll. Lond.

COOKLIN, Sidney (retired) 42 Stoneygate Court, London Road, Leicester LE2 2AJ Tel: 0116 270 1802 — MRCS Eng. LRCP Lond. 1953.

COOKSEY, Mr Graeme Castle Hill Hospital, Cottingham, Hull — MB ChB 1976 Bristol; DM Nottm. 1991; FRCS Eng. 1981. Cons. Urol. Hull & E. Yorks. HA.

COOKSLEY, Donald Eric (retired) 3 Seymour Drive, Mannamead, Plymouth PL3 5BG Tel: 01752 664355 — MB ChB 1960 Liverp.; MRCS Eng. LRCP Lond. 1960. Assoc. Specialist (Health c/o Elderly) Mt. Gould Hosp. Plymouth. Prev: Regist. (Path.) Radcliffe Infirm. Oxf.

COOKSLEY, Rachel Milford, Parkway Road, Chudleigh, Newton Abbot TQ13 0LF — MB BS 1991 Lond.

COOKSON, Adam John 1 Ribchester Avenue, Blackpool FY4 4SD — MB BCh 1995 Wales; BSc (Hons.) St. And. 1990.

COOKSON, Anna Gillian Isobel 300 Leicester Road, Cropston, Leicester LE7 7GT — MB ChB Ed. 1967; DCH Eng. 1971; DObst RCOG 1970. (Ed.) Clin. Med. Off. Leics. HA.

COOKSON, Professor Barry David Laboratory of Hospital Infection, Central Public Health Laboratory, 61 Colindale Avenue, London NW9 5HT Tel: 020 8200 4400 Fax: 020 8200 7449 Email: bcookson@phls.nhs.uk — MB BS 1975 Lond.; BDS 1971 (Hons); MRCP 1979 UK; FRCPath 1994; MRCPath 1982; MSc 1981 Lond.; 1999 (Hon. DipHic). (Lond. Hosp) Dir.Laborat. of Hosp. Infec., Centr. Pub. Health Laborat. Servs., Lond.; Hon. Sen. Lect. (Microbiol.) Roy. Free Hosp. Lond.; Vis. Prof. Lond. Sch. Of Hyg. and Trop. Med. Socs: Chairm. Hosp. Infec. Standards Gp. (HIS,AMM,DH,ICNA,PHMEG); Assn. Med. Microbiol. Clin. Serv. Sub Comm.; Chairm. Glycopeptide resistant enterococeal working party (HIS, RCNA, BSAC). Prev: Sen. Lect. St. Thos. Hosp. Lond.; Lect. & Ho. Phys. & Ho. Surg. Lond. Hosp.

COOKSON, Daniel Thomas 2FL/31 India Street, Edinburgh EH3 6HE — MB ChB 1997 Ed.

COOKSON, Frederick Brian (retired) Ingleside Farm, Church Lane, Rudford, Gloucester GL2 8DT Tel: 01452 790470 — MA Camb. 1962, MB BChir 1961; FRCGP 1990, M 1981; DObst RCOG 1965. Prev: Princip. GP & Sen. Partner Gloucester.

COOKSON, Gregory Anthony Hugh (retired) Cherry Tree Farm, 280 Gorefield Road, Leverington, Wisbech PE13 5TB Tel: 01945 870408 — MB BCh BAO 1952 Dub.; DPH Lond. 1962. Prev: Med. Off. Oversea Civil Serv. (Kenya).

COOKSON, Ian Blair 8 Redstone Rise, Noctorum, Birkenhead CH43 7NT — MB BCh BAO 1964 Dub.; MA Dub. 1986, BA, MB BCh BAO 1964; MPsychMed Liverp. 1986; FRCPsych 1986, M 1972; DPM Eng. 1971. (T.C. Dub.) Cons. Psychiat. N. Mersey Community NHS Trust; Clin. Lect. Univ. Liverp.; Mersey Regional Represen. Rehabil. RCPsych. Socs: (Ex-Pres.) Liverp. Psychiat. Soc. Prev: Ho. Off. Roy. City Dub. Hosp.

COOKSON, Professor John Bernard Glenfield Hospital, Groby Road, Leicester LE7 7GT Tel: 0116 287 1471 — MB ChB Birm. 1968; MD Birm. 1977; FRCP Lond. 1985; MRCP (UK) 1971; DObst RCOG 1970. (Birm.) Cons. Phys. Glenfield Gen. Hosp. Leics.; Dir.

Clin. Studies Univ. Leicester. Socs: Thoracic Soc. Prev: Lect. & Sen. Lect. Dept. Med. Univ. Rhodesia; Ho. Phys. Gen. Hosp. Birm.

COOKSON, John Charles Royal London Hospital, 2A Bow Road, London E3 4LL Tel: 020 7377 7957 Fax: 020 7377 7963 — BM BCh 1972 Oxf.; DPhil Oxf. 1972, BA 1966; FRCP Lond. 1992; MRCP (UK) 1975; FRCPsych 1987, M 1978. (Oxf. & Univ. Coll. Hosp.) Cons. Psychiat. The Roy. Lond. Hosp., St. Clements's. Socs: Fell. Roy. Soc. Med. Prev: Regist. (Psychiat.) Maudsley Hosp. Lond.; Lect. (Psychiat.) St. Bart. Hosp. Lond.; Ho. Phys. Univ. Coll. Hosp. Lond.

COOKSON, Judith Fiona Jean 300 Leicester Road, Cropston, Leicester LE7 7GT — MB ChB 1997 Bristol.

COOKSON, Neil Mathew Peacock Villa Medical Centre, Roman Road, Prenton CH43 3DB Tel: 0151 608 4702 Fax: 0151 609 0067 — MB ChB 1986 Liverp.

COOKSON, Robert Power (retired) Myrtledene, 6 Trafalgar Crescent, Bridlington YO15 3NR — LRCP LRCS Ed. LRFPS Glas. 1943; MRCGP 1963. Prev: Ho. Surg. The Infirm. Arbroath.

COOKSON, Susan Frances The Medical Centre, 24-28 Lower Northam Road, Hedge End, Southampton SO30 4FQ Tel: 01489 785722 Fax: 01489 799414 — MB BS 1976 Western Australia; MRACGP 1983 Western Australia. (Western Australia) p/t GP Soton.

COOKSON, Timothy William Tinshill Lane Surgery, 8 Tinshill Lane, Leeds LS16 7AP Tel: 0113 267 3462 Fax: 0113 230 0402; The Hawthorns, 40a Heathfield, Adel, Leeds LS16 7AB Tel: 0113 677714 — MB ChB 1963 Leeds; MRCGP 1971; DA Eng. 1967.

COOKSON, Tobias William Sebastian Bradford Road Surgery, 60 Bradford Road, Trowbridge BA14 9AR Tel: 01225 754255 Fax: 01225 774391 Email: brmc@globalnet.co.uk; 224 Great Chalfield, Atworth, Melksham SN12 8NL Tel: 01225 782538 Email: toby.cookson@virgin.net — MB BS 1988 Lond.; MRCGP 1996. (Char. Cross & Westm.)

COOKSON, Professor William Osmond Charles Wellcome Trust Centre, Human Genetics, Rodsevelt Drive,, Headington, Oxford OX3 7BN Tel: 01865 287607 Email: wocc@well.ox.ac.uk — MB BS 1975 West. Austral.; MD West. Austral. 1986, MB BS 1975; DPhil Oxf. 1994; FRACP 1985; FRCP 2000; Fmedsci 1999. Wellcome Sen. Clin. Research Fell. Univ. of Oxf., Oxf.; Hon. Cons. Oxf. RHA. Oxf.

COOLE, Colin William (retired) 3 Shoreham Place, Shoreham, Sevenoaks TN14 7RX Tel: 01959 522697 — MB BS 1952 Lond.; AFOM RCP Lond. 1979. Prev: Civil Serv. Local Med. Off.

COOLE, Louise 53 Cannon Hill Road, Coventry CV4 7BT — MB ChB 1988 Leic.; MPH 1997 Nottm.; MFPHM 2001; MSc (Clin. Microbiol.) Lond. 1994; BSc (Hons.) Biol. Sci. Leic. 1982. Regist. (Pub. Health Med.) Doncaster Health; Regist. (Pub. Halth Med.) Leics. Health. Prev: SHO (Cas. & Microbiol.) Leicester Roy. Infirm.

COOLEDGE, Jacqueline Sarah Market Cross Surgery, 7 Market Place, Mildenhall, Bury St Edmunds IP28 7EG Tel: 01638 713109 Fax: 01638 718615; Conewood House, 10 Parklands Green, Furnham St. Genevieve, Bury St Edmunds IP28 6UH — MB BS 1980 Lond.; BSc Lond. 1977; DCH RCP Lond. 1984; DRCOG 1986. (St. Bart.) Prev: Trainee GP Bury St. Edmunds; SHO (A & E & Orthop.) W. Suff. Hosp. Bury St. Edmunds; SHO (O & G) Guy's Hosp. Lond.

COOLEDGE, Roderic Charles Barrow Hill Surgery, Barrow Hill, Barrow, Bury St Edmunds IP29 5DX; Conewood House, 10 Parklands Green, Fornham St. Genevieve, Bury St Edmunds IP28 6UH — MB BS 1977 Lond.; DA Eng. 1984. Prev: Regist. (Anaesth.) Middlx. Hosp. & Whipps Cross Hosp. Lond.; SHO (Anaesth.) N.wick Pk. Hosp. Harrow.

COOLEY, Ashleigh Anne 25 St Rualds Close, Wallingford OX10 0XE Tel: 01491 832025; 5 Mellings Wood, Kilnbhouse Lane, Lytham St Annes FY8 3DW Tel: 01491 832025 — BM BCh 1991 Oxf.; DRCOG 1994; DFFP 1994; DCH RCP Lond. 1993. Trainee GP Wallingford Med. Centre. Prev: Trainee GP W. Berks. VTS.

COOLICAN, Michael Anthony 16 John Grace Street, Cheylesmore, Coventry CV3 5GZ — MB BS 1988 Lond.

COOLING, Mr Cyril Ivor (retired) 3 Hales Court, Hales Close, Tenterden TN30 6RJ — MB BS 1946 Lond.; FRCS Eng. 1951. Hon. Surg. Post. Office & Civil Serv. Sanat. Soc.; Hon. Surg. Roy. Marsden Hosp. Lond. Prev: Sen. Regist. (Surg.) Roy. Marsden Hosp. Lond. & W.m. (Gordon) Hosp.

COOLING, Hilary Susan Central Health Clinic, Tower Hill, Bristol BS2 0JD Tel: 0117 927 6781 Fax: 0117 927 2180; 25 Fairlawn Road, Montpelier, Bristol BS6 5JS Tel: 0117 955 7730 Fax: 0117 927 2180 — MB ChB 1975 Bristol; MFFP 1993; DRCOG 1979. SCMO (Family Plann.) United Bristol Healthcare NHS Trust; Sen. Clin. Med. Off. (Family Plann.) Bath & W. Community NHS Trust; Fac. Family Plann. Instruc. Doctor; Hon. Clin. Lect. (Obst. & Gyn.) Univ. of Bristol. Prev: GP Asst. Avon Health Homelessness Med. Project; Dep. Police Surg. Avon & Som. Constab.

COOLING, Nicholas John Huddersfield Nuffield Hospital, Huddersfield HD2 2BL Tel: 01484 533131 Fax: 01484 452467 — MB BS 1981 Lond.; MRCPsych 1986; Dip. Clin. Psychother. 1992. Cons. Psychiat. Huddersfield Nuffield Hosp. Huddersfield. Prev: Cons. Psychiat. Altrincham Priory Hosp.; Cons. Psychiat. St. Luke's Hosp. Huddersfield; Sen. Regist. (Psychiat.) Fulbourn & Addenbrooke's Hosps. Camb.

COOLING, Nicola Jayne 23 Phillip Street, Risca, Newport NP11 6DF Email: nick_j_coo@hotmail.com — MB ChB 1993 Manch.; MRCP 1997.

COOLING, Richard Andrew Cheam Family Practice, The Knoll, Parkside, Cheam, Sutton SM3 8BS Tel: 020 8770 2012 Fax: 020 8770 1864 Email: richard.cooling@nelson-pct.nhs.uk — MB BS 1978 Lond.; DRCOG 1982. (King's Coll. Hosp.) GP Med. Off. Orchard Hill Resid. Unit for Adults with Learning Disabil Carshalton; Clin. Director, Nelson and W. Merton Primary Care Trust. Prev: Trainee GP St. Helier Hosp. Carshalton VTS; Ho. Surg. Sutton Hosp.; Ho. Phys. Dulwich Hosp.

COOLING, Mr Robert James Moorfields Eye Hospital, City Road, London EC1V 2PD Tel: 020 7566 2720 Fax: 020 7566 2843 — MB ChB 1970 Liverp.; MB ChB (Hons.) Liverp. 1970; FRCS Eng. 1977; FRCOphth 1988; DO RCS Eng. 1974. Med. Dir. & Cons. Surg. Moorfields Eye Hosp. Lond.; Cons. Surg. St. Dunstan's Lond.; Civil. Cons. RN; Clin. Teach. Inst. Ophth. Lond. Prev: Sen. Lect. Inst. Ophth. Lond.; Demonst. (Anat.) Univ. Oxf.

COOLING, Rosalind Mary West Bay Health Consultancy, 21 Station Road, Teignmouth TQ14 8PE Tel: 01626 777730; Highfield, Picket Head Hill, Torquay Road, Shaldon, Teignmouth TQ14 0BB Tel: 01626 873512 — MB ChB 1951 Ed. (Ed.) Prev: GP Oxf.; Sch. Med. Off. Oxf. City Health Dept.

COOMANSINGH, David Patrick Aberdeen Royal Infirmary, Aberdeen AB21 9ZX Tel: 01224 681818; 17 Laburnum Walk, Aberdeen AB16 5EL Tel: 01224 591871 — MB BS 1989 West Indies; MRCP (UK) 1994. Staff Grade (Gastroenterol.) Aberd. Roy. Infirm.

COOMARASAMY, Dharini 121 Aveling Pk Road, London E17 4NS — MB ChB 1997 Manch.

COOMBE, Anthony David Brynteg Surgery, Brynmawr Avenue, Ammanford SA18 2DA Tel: 01269 592058 — MB BCh 1971 Wales; MRCGP 1980; DObst RCOG 1973. Prev: Ho. Phys. Dept. Child Health St. David's Hosp. Cardiff; Ho. Surg. Caerphilly Dist. Miners' Hosp.

COOMBE, David Horst, Brigadier late RAMC Retd. 17 Glebe Court, Fleet GU51 4NJ Tel: 01252 624039 — MB BS 1960 Lond.; MSc (Social Med.) Lond. 1979; MRCS Eng. LRCP Lond. 1960; FFPHM 1989, M 1980; DTM & H Eng. 1963. (St. Geo.) Prev: Dir. Army Pub. Health Med. & Cdr. Army Med. Servs. Train. Gp.; Dep. Dir. Gen. Army Med. Servs. MOD Lond.

COOMBER, Antony Sylvester Grovelands Medical Centre, 701 Oxford Road, Reading RG30 1HG Tel: 0118 958 2525 Fax: 0118 950 9284; 28 Mansfield Road, Reading RG1 6AJ Tel: 0118 957 6599 — MB BS 1969 Lond.; DA Eng. 1974. (Lond. Hosp.) Socs: Reading Path. Soc. Prev: SHO (Paediat. & Anaesth.) Roy. Berks. Hosp. Reading.

COOMBER, Sarah (Sally) Ellen Louise Suffolk Occupational Health, The Ipswich Hospital, Heath Road, Ipswich IP4 5PD Tel: 01473 704011 Fax: 01473 704241; Stable Barn, Langham, Bury St Edmunds IP31 3EE Tel: 01359 259059 Fax: 01359 259059 — MB BS 1988 Newc.; AFOM RCP Lond. 1995; MRCGP 1992; DRCOG 1991; MFOM 1997. (Newcastle upon Tyne) p/t Cons. Occupat. Phys. Socs: Elected Ordinary Bd. Mem. of the Fac. of Occupat.al Med. 2000. Prev: Sen. Regist. (Occupat. Med.) Addenbrooke's Hosp. Camb.; Trainee GP Ipswich Hosp.

COOMBER, Simon John Strudwick Bewicke Health Centre, 51 Tynemouth Road, Wallsend NE28 0AD Tel: 0191 262 3036 Fax: 0191 295 1663 — MB BS 1984 Newc.; MB BS Newc. l984; MRCGP 1988. GP Wallsend.

COOMBES, Andrew Gordon Archer High Croft Farm, Bramble Crescent, Benfleet SS7 2XA — MB BS 1991 Lond.; BSc Lond. 1990, MB BS 1991. SHO (Ophth.) Soton. Univ. NHS Trust Hosp. Socs: Fell. Roy. Soc. Med. (Mem. Ophth. Sect.).

COOMBES, Andrew Mark Alban 4 Harrow Place, Maulden, Bedford MK45 2DG — MB BS 1996 Lond.

COOMBES, Anthony Henry Reginald, MBE (retired) Jessamine Cottage, The Street, Framfield, Uckfield TN22 5NL Tel: 01825 890394 — MRCS Eng. LRCP Lond. 1937; DPH Lond. 1951; DTM & H Eng. 1946. Prev: Dep. Dir. Med. & Health Dept. Hong Kong.

COOMBES, Mr Gary Bayley Doncaster Royal Infirmary, Armthorpe Road, Doncaster DN2 5LT Tel: 01302 366666 Fax: 01302 553167 Email: gcoombes@drimh-tr.trent.nhs.uk; The Old Forge, Low Road, Scrooby, Doncaster DN10 6AJ Tel: 01302 710281 Fax: 01302 710281 Email: coombes358@netscapeonline.co.uk — MB BS Lond. 1964; FRCS Eng. 1972; FRCS Ed. 1971; MRCS Eng. LRCP Lond. 1964. (Char. Cross) Cons. Surg. Doncaster + Bassetlan. NHS Trust; Med. Reviewer. Commiss. For Health Improvement. Socs: Fell. Assn. Surgs.; E. Midl. Surg. Soc. Prev: Sen. Regist. (Surg.) Addenbrooke's Hosp. Cambs; Regist. (Surg.) Char. Cross Hosp. Lond.; Short Serv. Commiss. RN.

COOMBES, Jane Louise 32 Warrender Park Terrace, Marchmont, Edinburgh EH9 1ED — MB ChB 1988 Sheff.; MRCGP 1996. Socs: Med. Defence Union; BMA. Prev: Trainee GP Sheff. & Edin.; Regist. (Psychiat.) Dunedin Infirm., NZ; SHO (Psychiat.) Doncaster Roy. Infirm. & Sheff.

COOMBES, Raoul Charles Dalmedo Stuart Medical Oncology, Imperial College School of Medicine, Charing Cross Hospital, Fulham Palace Road, London W6 8RF Tel: 020 8846 1478 Fax: 020 8846 1433 Email: c.coombes@ic.ac.uk — MB BS 1971 Lond.; PhD Lond. 1978, MD 1981; FRCP Lond. 1990; MRCP (UK) 1973. (St. Geo.) Prof. Med. Oncol. Imperial Coll. Sch. Med. Char. Cross Hosp.; Dir. Cancer Servs. Hammersmith Hosp. Trust Lond. Socs: Director and Chairm. ICCG; Amer. Assn. of Cancer Research; Brit. Assn. of Cancer Research. Prev: Hon. Cons. Phys. Roy. Marsden Hosp. Sutton & Med. Oncol. St. Geo. Hosp. Lond.; Hon. Sen. Lect. Inst. Cancer Research.

COOMBES, Sarah Jane 2 Lower Church Street, Cuddington, Aylesbury HP18 0AS Tel: 01844 291979 — MB BS 1992 Lond.; BSc Lond. 1989; FRCS (Eng.) 1997. (London Hospital Medical College) Specialist Regist. Rotat. (A & E) Oxf. Socs: Brit. Assn. Accid. & Emerg. Med. Prev: SHO (Orthop. & IC) N.ampton Gen. Hosp.; SHO (Gen. Surg.) John Radcliffe Hosp. Oxf.

COOMBES, Susan St Peters Hill Surgery, 15 St. Peters Hill, Grantham NG31 6QA Tel: 01476 590009 Fax: 01476 570898; 14 Sandon Road, Grantham NG31 9AZ Tel: 01476 562301 — MB ChB 1976 Dundee.

COOMBES, Sydney Kenneth 35 New St. Hill, Bromley Tel: 020 8857 6364 — MB BS 1947 Punjab; FFA RCS Eng. 1963; DA Eng. 1957. (Lahore) Cons. Anaesth. St. Andrews & Newham Gen. Hosps. Prev: Anaesth. Regist. St. Stephen's Hosp. Chelsea & Hull (A) & (B) Hosp.; Gps.; Ho. Surg. & Cas. Off. Mayo Hosp. Lahore.

COOMBS, David Mark Victoria Park Health Centre, Bedford Avenue, Birkenhead CH42 4QJ Tel: 0151 645 8384 Fax: 0151 644 9561 — MB ChB 1980 Leeds; MRCP (UK) 1984; MRCGP 1985; DRCOG 1985. Clin. Asst. Dermat., Arrowe Pk. Hosp., wirral.

COOMBS, Elizabeth Belmont Health Care Centre, Eastholme Avenue, Belmont, Hereford HR2 7UX Tel: 01432 354366 Fax: 01432 340434; 4 Dishley Court, Leominster HR6 8QD Tel: 01568 616255 — MB ChB Dundee 1971; MRCGP 1980; DCCH RCP Ed. 1990; DRCOG 1988.

COOMBS, Geoffrey Alwyn 1 Hicks Road, Markyate, St Albans AL3 8LJ Tel: 01512 840288 Fax: 01512 840919 — MBChB Sheff. 1983; DCH. (St. Bart. Sheffield) Socs: BMA; MDU. Prev: Jun. Ho. Off. Surg. Doncaster; Jun. Ho. Off. Med. Barnsley; SHO A&E Hemel Hempstead.

***COOMBS, Henri Michael Christopher** 4 The Covert, Woodstock OX20 1UU Tel: 01993 811567 — MB ChB 1998 Manch.; MB ChB Manch 1998.

COOMBS, Ian Campbell (retired) 25 Higher Knutsford Road, Grappenhall, Warrington WA4 2JS Tel: 01925 261695 Fax: 01925 261695 — MB ChB Ed. 1963.

COOMBS, Ian Phillip 8 Beaufort Drive, Kittle, Swansea SA3 3LD — BM BS 1994 Nottm.

COOMBS, Joan Rosemary (retired) 47 Hanson Drive, Fowey PL23 1ET — MB ChB 1958 Bristol. Sen. Clin. Med. Office, Cornw. Healthcare Trust. Prev: SCMO (Family Plann.) Leeds HA.

COOMBS, Mr Laurence Michael 23 Hilltop Lane, Wakefield WF3 1HT — MB BS 1978 Lond.; MD Lond. 1993; FRCS Eng. 1985; FRCS (Urol.) 1994; MRCS Eng. LRCP Lond. 1978.

COOMBS, Martin Charles Danes Camp Surgery, Rowtree Road, Northampton NN4 0NY Tel: 01604 709426 Fax: 01604 709427 — MB BS 1985 Lond.; MA Oxf. 1982; MRCGP 1989; DRCOG 1987. (St. Mary's Hosp. Med. Sch.)

COOMBS, Nathan John The Royal South Hampshire Hospital, Southampton; 86 Wilton Gardens, Upper Shirley, Southampton SO15 7QR — BM 1992 Soton.; BSc (Hons.) Soton. 1991. Ho. Surg. Profess. Surg. Unit. Roy. S. Hants. Hosp. Socs: BMA. Prev: Ho. Phys. (Gastroenterol.) Bournemouth Gen. Hosp.

COOMBS, Mr Richard Robert Harvey Fairlight, Coombe Park, Kingston Hill, Kingston upon Thames KT2 7JB Tel: 020 8546 1778 Fax: 020 8549 1254; 22 Harley Street, London W1N 1AA Tel: 020 7637 0491 — BM BCh 1969 Oxf.; MA, BM BCh (1st cl. Hons.) Oxf. 1969; DM 1981, MCh Oxf. 1982; FRCS Eng. 1974; MRCP (UK) 1974; FRCS Ed. Orth. 1980. (Oxf. & Univ. Coll. Hosp.) Cons. Orthopaedic, Surg., Char. Cross Hosp., Imperial Coll. of Sci. Technol. & Med. Socs: Fell. Roy. Soc. Med.; Brit. Orthopaedic Assn.; Amer. Acad. of Orthopaedic Surg.s. Prev: Sen. Regist. St. Mary's Hosp. Lond.; Ho. Phys. Med. Unit & Ho. Surg. Surgic. Unit. Univ. Coll. Hosp. Lond.

COOMBS, Robert Christopher Jessop Wing, Sheffield Teaching Hospitals, Trust, Tree Root Walk, Sheffield S10 2SF Tel: 0114 226 8000 Email: r.c.coombs@sheffield.ac.uk; Hillside, Back Lane, Hathersage, Hope Valley S32 1AR Tel: 01433 651958 — MB BS 1979 Lond.; BSc Lond. 1976, MB BS 1979; BSc 1976 Lond.; MRCP (UK) 1982; DCH RCP Lond. 1981; FRCPCH 1998. (London) Cons. Neonat. Paediat., Jessop Wing, STH Sheff. Socs: Brit. Soc. Paediat. Gastroenterol. & Nutrit.; Paediat. Research Soc. Prev: Lect. (Child Health) Univ. Birm.; Regist. (Paediat.) John Radcliffe Hosp. Oxf.

COOMBS, Sarah Emily 9 St Thomas Avenue, Hayling Island PO11 0ET Tel: 01705 464879 — MB ChB 1997 Bristol. SHO (Paediat.), MillGr. Pk. Hosp., Taunton. Prev: Ho. Off. (Med.) Bristol Roy. Infirm.; Ho. Off. (Surg.) N. devon Dist. Hosp., Barnstaple; SHO (A&E) N. Devon Dist. Hosp., Barnstable.

COOMBS, Stephen John 10 Moorfield Road, Manchester M20 2UY — MB BS 1978 Lond.

COOMES, Edward Nelson Charing Cross Hospital, Fulham Palace Road, London W6 8RF Tel: 020 8846 1990; Cromwell Hospital, Cromwell Road, London SW5 — MB BS 1951 Lond.; MD Lond. 1963; FRCP Lond. 1976, M 1955. (St. Thos.) Cons. Phys. Char. Cross Hosp. Riverside HA; Clin. Tutor Brit. Postgrad. Med. Federat.; Recognised Teach. (Med.) Char. Cross & W.m. Med. Sch. Lond. Univ. Socs: Brit. Diabetic Assn. (Mem. Scientif Sect.); BMA. Prev: Regist. St. Thomas's Hosp.; Sen. Regist. Roy. Infirm. Manch.; Ho. Phys. Nat. Hosp. Qu. Sq.

COONAN, Brendan The Surgery, 66-68 Stoke Road, Gosport PO12 1PA Tel: 023 9258 1529 Fax: 023 9250 1417 — MB BCh BAO 1974 Dub.; BA.

COONER, Bhupinder Singh The Surgery, Wharf Road, Gnosall, Stafford ST20 0DB Tel: 01785 822220 Fax: 01785 822776 — MB ChB 1991 Manch.

COONEY, John Martin Guy's and Lewisham NHS Trust, The Ladywell Unit, Lewisham Hospital, London SE13 6LH Tel: 020 8333 3000 Fax: 020 8333 3402 Email: j.m.cooney@lineone.net — MB BCh BAO NUI 1986; MRCPI 1989; LRCPSI 1986; MRCPsych 1992; MD NUI 1997. Lect. & Hon. Sen. Regist. (Psychiat.) St. Bart. Hosp. Lond.; Cons. & Sen. Lect. (Psychiat.). Prev: Locum Cons. (Community Psychiat.) The Maudsley Hosp. Lond.; Sen. Regist. (NeuroPsychiat.) The Maudsley Hosp. Lond.; Lect. & Hon. Sen. Regist. (Psychiat.) St Bart. Hosp. Lond.

COONEY, Joseph Andrew Abbots Hill, Chapel Hill, Speen, Princes Risborough HP27 0SP — MB BS 1990 Lond.

COONEY, Joseph Arthur Willesborough Health Centre, Bentley Road, Willesborough, Ashford TN24 0HZ Tel: 01233 621626 Fax: 01233 622930; Corner Hill House, Woolpack Hill, Smeeth, Ashford TN25 6QJ — MB BS 1980 Lond.; MRCGP 1988; DRCOG 1984.

COONEY, Kieron Daniel Upper Green Road Medical Centre, Upper Green Road, St. Helens, Ryde PO33 1UG Tel: 01983 872772 Fax: 01983 874800 — MB BChir 1988 Camb.; DRCOG 1990.
COONEY, Maire Kathleen 30 Clerk Road, Penicuik EH26 9HB — MB ChB 1994 Manch.
COONEY, Seamus Addison Road Medical Practice, 12-14 Addison Road, London E17 9LT Tel: 020 8520 4708 Fax: 020 8520 6266 — MB BCh BAO 1982 Dub.
COONEY, Veneta Bernadette 51 Canterbury Avenue, Redbridge, Ilford IG1 3NE Email: veneta.cooney@medix-uk.com — MB BS 1991 Lond.; AFOM 2000; MRCGP Lond. 1996. (St. George's London) Specialist Regist., Occupat. Med., FarnBoro., Hants.
COONJOBEEHARRY, Kurunandan Rathawrsingh The Doctors Centre, 41 Broomwood Road, Orpington BR5 2JP Tel: 01689 832454 Fax: 01689 826165 — MB BS 1986 Lond.; MRCGP 1991; DCH RCP Lond. 1990. Director & Sec. for Emdoc, Bromley doctors on call. Prev: Clin. Commiss.ing Dir. Bromley Health; PCG Bd. Mem.
COOP, David John Glentworth Surgery, Dalton Terrace, York YO24 4DB Tel: 01904 658542 Fax: 01904 671979 — MB ChB 1975 Ed.; DRCOG 1977.
COOP, John Alexander Seaton and Colyton Medical Practice, Seaton Health Centre, 148 Harepath Road, Seaton EX12 2DU Tel: 01297 20877 Fax: 01297 23031; Marlee, Gully Shoot, Colyford, Colyton EX24 6HF Tel: 01297 52058 — MB BS 1978 Lond.; MRCS Eng. LRCP Lond. 1978; MRCGP 1982 (Lond.). Locality Med. Dir. E. Devon Locality; Chairm. E. Devon PCG.
COOPAMAH, Lalida Devi 51 Landsdown Road, Canterbury CT1 3J Tel: 01227 459173; 32 Avenue Des Manguiers, Quatre Bornes, Mauritius Tel: 00 230 4547698 — MB ChB 1994 Leeds. SHO Rotat. (Paediat.) SE Kent.
COOPE, Anthony Michael The Old Woking Grange natural therapy and education centre, High St., Woking GU22 8LB Tel: 01483 772269; Wren Cottage, 6 Allendale, Thursley Road, Elstead, Godalming GU8 6DL Tel: 01252 702465 Fax: 01252 703442 Email: doctc@dircon.co.uk — MB ChB 1968 St. And.; DRCOG 1971. Indep. Med. Practitioner (Nutrit.al Holistic Med.). Prev: Phys. Forest Mere Health Hydro Liphook.; Sen.par.GP.
COOPE, Bernard John 67 Love Lane, Stourbridge DY8 2DZ — MB ChB 1987 Birm.
COOPE, Beryl Margaret (retired) Tighnacleirich Foss, Pitlochry PH16 5NQ Tel: 01882 634224 Email: coope@foss5.freeserve.co.uk — MB ChB 1955 Manch.; DObst RCOG 1957. Prev: GP Worcs.
COOPE, Gerald Arrowsmith Bollington Medical Centre, Wellington Road, Bollington, Macclesfield SK10 5JL Fax: 01625 575650 Email: gerald.coope@gp.n81022.nhs.uk; 5 Springbank, Bollington, Macclesfield SK10 5LQ — MB ChB 1978 Manch.; MRCP (UK) 1983; MRCGP 1986. Prev: SHO Fairfield Hosp. Bury; Traine GP Manch.; Regist. Doncaster Roy. Infirm.
COOPE, Jean Katharine Mary (retired) Plant Cottage, Beeston Brow, Bollington, Macclesfield SK10 5PR Tel: 01625 573494 Fax: 01625 575650 — MB ChB 1951 Manch.; MD Manch. 1980; FRCGP 1985; DObst RCOG 1953. Prev: Ho. Phys. Manch. Roy. Infirm. & Crumpsall Hosp. Manch.
COOPE, John Raisley, MBE (retired) The Waterhouse, Bollington, Macclesfield SK10 5PR Tel: 01625 572481 — MB ChB 1952 Manch.; FRCGP 1986, M 1963. Prev: Ho. Phys. & Ho. Surg. Clatterbridge Hosp. Nr. Birkenhead.
COOPE, Katrina Brown Tel: 01954 231550 Fax: 01954 231573; Horse-Shoe House, School Road, Broughton, Huntingdon PE28 3AT Tel: 01487 822352 — MB ChB 1968 St. And. GP 1 Dring's Cl., Over, Camb. Prev: GP P'boro.; Clin. Med. Off. (Community Child Health) P'boro.
COOPE, Maurice Leeming Bollington Medical Centre, Wellington Road, Bollington, Macclesfield SK10 5JL Tel: 01625 572481 — MB ChB 1963 Birm.
COOPE, Sarah Ruth 23 Exeter Street, Cottingham HU16 4LU — MB ChB 1998 Ed.; MB ChB Ed 1998.
COOPER, Adam Leighton Rashid and Partners, Havercroft Health Centre, Cow Lane, Ryhill, Wakefield WF4 2AX Tel: 01226 725555 Fax: 01226 700051; 16 Crab Lane, Newmillerdam, Wakefield WF2 7SU — MB BS 1984 Newc.; MB BS Newc. l984.
COOPER, Alan (retired) 7 Herons Reach, West Charlton, Kingsbridge TQ7 2TT Tel: 01548 531871 — MB ChB 1961 Liverp.; DObst RCOG 1963; DCH Eng. 1964.
COOPER, Alan Frederick Arthur Pennington Lockswood Surgery, Centre Way, Locks Heath, Southampton SO31 6DX Tel: 01489 576708 Fax: 01489 576185; Email: flyingdoc90@hotmail.com — BM 1980 Soton.; DRCOG 1984. GP Warsash & Locks Heath; Med. Off. Coll. of Maritime Studies, Warsash; Local Med. Off. Civil Serv. Med. Advis. Serv.; Examr. United Kingdom Offshore Operat. Assn.; Approved Med. Examr. Health & Safety Exec. Basingstoke, Hants; Examr. Maritime & Coastguard Agency. Prev: SHO (O & G) P.ss Anne Hosp. Soton.; SHO (Gen. Med.) Roy. S. Hants. Hosp. Soton.; SHO (Paediat.) Soton. Gen. Hosp.
COOPER, Alan Stanley The Lodge, Rodlewood, Nr. Liphook GU30 7LA Tel: 01730 821372 Fax: 01730 821372; The Lodge, Rondlewood, Nr. Liphook GU30 7LA Tel: 01730 821372 — MB BS Lond. 1960; MRCS Eng. LRCP Lond. 1960. (Guy's) Private GP; Med. Off. to various Equestrien events. Prev: Ho. Surg. & Ho. Phys. Guy's Hosp.; Hon. Med. Off. Brit. Equestrian Federat.; Med. Off. Brit. Olympic Equestrien Team.
COOPER, Alexander Fraser (retired) 35 Windsor Avenue, Newton Mearns, Glasgow G77 5NU Tel: 0141 639 3566 — MD 1976 Dundee; MD (Commend.) Dundee 1976; MB ChB St. And. 1963; FRCP Glas. 1984; FRCP Ed. 1982; MRCP (UK) 1971; FRCPsych 1984, M 1972; DPM Ed. & Glas. 1966. Prev: Cons. Psychiat. Leverndale Hosp., Glas.
COOPER, Alfred Kenneth (retired) Cloud-Edge, Red Lane, Colne BB8 7JR Tel: 01282 864944 — MB ChB 1951 Leeds. JP.
COOPER, Alison Elizabeth 8 Agden Road, Sheffield S7 1LY — MB ChB 1982 Sheff.; FFA RCSI 1988. Cons. Anaesth. Rotherham Dist. Hosps. Trust. Prev: Regist. (Anaesth.) Sheff. HA; SHO (Anaesth.) Sheff. HA; SHO (A & E) N.. Gen. Hosp. Sheff.
COOPER, Alison Louise Medical Defence Union, 230 Blackfriars Road, London SE1 8PJ; 40 Therapia Road, East Dulwich, London SE22 0SE — MB ChB 1983 Bristol; FFA RCS Eng. 1988. Sen. Med. Claims Handler, Med. Defence Union, Lond.. Prev: Cons. Anaesth., Kings Healthcare, Lond..
COOPER, Alun Lewis Bridge Medical Centre, Wassand Close, Three Bridges Road, Crawley RH10 1LL Tel: 01293 526025 — MB BS 1979 Lond.; BSc Lond. 1975, MB BS 1979; MRCGP 1984.
COOPER, Andrew Boyson South Road Health Centre, 19 South Road, Lerwick ZE1 0RB Tel: 01595 693201 Fax: 01595 697113; Mountfield House, Lerwick ZE1 0QA Tel: 01595 3201 — BM BCh 1977 Oxf.; MRCGP 1994; DA (UK) 1982; DRCOG 1978. Ltd. Specialist (Anaesth.) Shetland HB. Socs: BMA & Assn. Anaesth.
COOPER, Andrew Michael Fairwater Health Centre, Plasmawr Road, Fairwater, Cardiff CF5 3JT Tel: 029 2056 6291 Fax: 029 2057 8870; Twyn-y-Geirwen, Mountain Road, Pentyrch, Cardiff CF15 9QP — MB ChB 1982 Leeds; FRCGP 1999; MRCGP 1986; DRCOG 1986. Course Organiser S. Glam. VTS. Prev: Trainee GP/SHO Cardiff VTS; Ho. Off. Leeds Gen. Infirm.
COOPER, Andrew Paul 11 The Foundry, Castle Eden, Hartlepool TS27 4SQ — BM BS 1981 Nottm.
COOPER, Andrew Ronald 26 College Park, Castlerock Road, Coleraine BT51 3HE Tel: 01265 43896 — MD 1992 Belf.; MB BCh BAO 1981; DRCOG 1983; DA (UK) 1986; FFA RCSI 1988. Cons. Anaesth. & Pain Relief Coleraine Hosp. Socs: Assn. Anaesth. Gt. Brit. & Irel.; Pain Soc. Prev: Sen. Regist. (Anaesth.) Qu. Univ. Belf.;Hosp. Ballymena; Regist. (Anaesth.) Gen. Hosp. St Helier, Cl.
COOPER, Angela Mary Clarice 48 Hall Lane, Werrington, Peterborough PE4 6RA — MB BS 1976 Lond.; FFARCS Eng. 1981; DRCOG 1978. Cons. Anaesth. & Intens. Care P'boro Dist. Hosp. Prev: Research Fell. Assn. Anaesth. Gt. Brit. & Irel.; Sen. Regist. (Anaesth.) New Addenbrooke's Hosp. Camb.
COOPER, Angus Jonathan 81 Brighton Place, Aberdeen AB10 6RT Email: angus.cooper@which.net — BM 1987 Soton.; MRCP (UK) 1993; Dip. IMC RCS Ed. 1994; FFAEM 1998. (Soton.) Specialist Regist. (IC) Aberd. Roy. Infirm. Prev: Regist. (A & E), Ipswich Hosp.; Specialist Regist. (A&E), E. Angluia Rotat.
COOPER, Anne Cardiorespiratory Medicine Hope Hospital, Stott Lane, Salford, Manchester M16 8HD Tel: 0161 787 5040 Fax: 0161 787 4328 Email: a. cooper@crm.srht.nwest.nhs.uk; 24 Rowley Way, Knutsford WA16 9AU — MB BChir 1988 Camb.; MA Camb. 1989; MRCP (UK) 1990; MD Manch. 1997. (University of Cambridge) Cons. Cardiol. Hope Hosp. Manch. Prev: Clin. Lect. (Cardiovasc.

Med.) Wythenshawe Hosp. Manch.; Clin. Lect. (Cardiovasc. Med.) Withington Hosp. Manch.

COOPER, Anne Margaret Airedale General Hospital, Skipton Road, Steeton, Keighley BD20 6TD Tel: 01535 652511 Fax: 01535 292068 — MB ChB 1981 Sheff.; FRCP 2001 (UK); DRCOG 1983; MD 1998 (Sheffield). (Univ. Sheff.) p/t Cons. Rheum. Airedale Gen. Hosp. Keighley (p/t) & Cons. Rheum. Bradford Roy. Infirm. (p/t). Socs: Brit. Soc. for Rheum.; Nat. Osteoporosis Soc. Prev: Clin. Research Fell. (Human Metab. & Clin. Biochem.) Sheff.; Sen. Regist. (Rheum.) Cardiff; Regist. (Rheum.) Cardiff.

COOPER, Anne Marie 25 Park Street, Bath BA1 2TF — MB ChB 1990 Bristol.

***COOPER, Ashley John** Princess Margaret Hospital, Okus Road, Swindon SN1 4JU Tel: 01793 426693 Email: ash_qq1@hotmail.com — BM 1997 Soton.

COOPER, Barbara Ann The Surgery, 29 Woodcock Road, Norwich NR3 3UA Tel: 01603 425989; 31 Lowther Road, Eaton Rise, Norwich NR4 6QN Tel: 01603 425989 — MB ChB 1975 Leeds. Prev: Ho. Phys. St. Luke's Hosp. Bradford; Ho. Surg. Bradford Roy. Infirm.; Trainee Gen. Pract. Norwich Vocational Train. Scheme.

COOPER, Barrington Spencer 10 Devonshire Place, London W1N 1PB Tel: 020 7935 9335 Fax: 020 7935 1093 — MB BS 1946 Lond.; BA (Hons.) Lond. 1942; PhD Col. Pacific 1979; MRCGP 1964. (St. Bart.) Cons. Phys. Langham Clinic Psychother.; Vis. Lect. Strang Inst. Preven. Med. NYC, USA 1975-90; WHO Vis. Lect. Psychosomatic Research 1978; Vis. Lect. Boston Univ. Med. Sch.; Chairm. & Cons. AMCHC Ltd.; Med.: Skyy Spirits Inc.; Adviser to: Caplin Systems Ltd., Caplin Systems Inc., Internet Consultancy Ltd., New Media Med. Univ. Socs: Fell. Roy. Soc. Med.; Fell. Soc. Clin. Psych.; Affil. Roy. Coll. Psych. Prev: Regist. (Gen. Med.) Oster Hse. St. Albans; Clin. Asst. (Psychol. Med.) St. Bart. Hosp. Gp.; Cons. Psychother. Bowden Hse. Clinic Harrow.

COOPER, Barry Hunter Health Centre, Andrew Street, East Kilbride, Glasgow G74 1AD Tel: 01355 906643 — MB ChB 1976 Glas.; Dip Obst Auckland 1978.

COOPER, Beatrice Johanna Cheyne Child Development Service, Ground Floor, Chelsea & Westminster Hospital, 369 Fulham Road, London SW10 9NH Tel: 020 8846 1634/5 Fax: 020 8846 1284 Email: beatricecr@chelwest.nhs.uk; 61 Drakefell Road, New Cross, London SE14 5SH Tel: 020 7639 1574 — MB ChB 1979 Manch.; BSc Manch. 1976; MRCP (UK) 1982; DCH RCP Lond. 1981; FRCPCH 1997. (Manchester) Cons. Paediat. (Community Paediat.) Chelsea & W.m. Healthcare Lond. Socs: RCPCH; ACPP; ISPCAN. Prev: SCMO Lewisham & N. S.wark HA; Regist. (Paediat.) Kings Coll. Hosp. Lond. & All St.s Hosp. Chatham.

COOPER, Beatrice Marie Sophie Occupational Health Care Ltd, Occupational Health Centre, Platform 14, London Bridge Station, London SE1 9SP Tel: 020 7234 1861 Fax: 020 7234 1243; 57 Manor Way, Beckenham BR3 3LN Tel: 020 8658 2801 — MD 1977 Paris; MFOM RCP Lond 1992, AFOM 1988; T(OM) 1993. Cons. Occupat. Phys., Occupat. Health Care Ltd. Lond. Prev: Sen. Occupat. Phys. Wellcome Foundat. Ltd. Beckenham.

COOPER, Carol Anne Holly Court, Summerlands Hospital, Preston Road, Yeovil BA20 2BX; 105 South Street, Crewkerne TA18 8AA Tel: 01460 72739 — BM 1985 Soton.; BM Soton 1985; MRCPsych 1994; MRCGP 1989; DCH RCP Lond. 1988. Clin. Med. Off. (Psychiat.) Avalon Trust Yeovil. Prev: Regist. Som. Psychiat. Train. Scheme; Trainee GP Yeovil VTS.

COOPER, Carol Marie Dermatology Department, Royal Hospital, Chesterfield; 242 Longedge Lane, Wingerworth, Chesterfield S42 6PS Tel: 01246 278355 — MB ChB 1965 Manch. Assoc. Specialist (Dermat.) Chesterfield & N. Derbysh. Roy. Hosp.

COOPER, Caroline Mary 8 Collier Way, Stapleford, Cambridge CB2 5DZ; 8 Collier Way, Stapleford, Cambridge CB2 5DZ Tel: 01223 845651 — MB ChB 1986 Bristol; MRCGP 1991; DGM RCP Lond. 1990; Dip. Obst. Otago 1988.

COOPER, Catherine Anne Clifton Lane Health Centre, Clifton Lane, Doncaster Road, Rotherham S65 1DU Tel: 01709 382315 Fax: 01709 512646 — MB ChB 1981 Sheff.; MRCGP 1986; DRCOG 1985.

COOPER, Celia 22 St Dennis House, Melville Road, Birmingham B16 9NE — MB BS 1972 Lond.; MRCS Eng. LRCP Lond. 1972; FFA RCS Eng. 1978.

COOPER, Charles Michael Steward 8 Agden Road, Sheffield S7 1LY — MB BS 1980 Lond.; BSc (Hons.) Lond. 1977; FRCA 1987. (St. Mary's, London) Cons. Anaesth. Chesterfield & N. Derbysh. Roy. Hosp.; Assoc. Postgrad. Dean, Mid-trent. Prev: Sen. Regist. & Regist. (Anaesth.) Sheff. Teach. Hosps.; SHO Rotat. (Gen. Med.) Leicester Teach. Hosps.

COOPER, Christine Muriel Harris High Lodge, Vicarage Road, East Budleigh, Budleigh Salterton EX9 7EF Tel: 01395 445329 — MB ChB Bristol 1944; MRCS Eng. LRCP Lond. 1944. Prev: on Staff Cossham Memor. Hosp. Bristol.

COOPER, Christopher Brian 123 Queens Road, Bury St Edmunds IP33 3ES — BM 1995 Soton.

COOPER, Christopher David Royal Albert Edward Infirmary, Wigan Lane, Wigan WN1 2NN Email: chris.cooper@wiganlhs-tr.nwest.nhs.uk — MB ChB 1990 Manch.; MRCP (UK) 1996; DTM & H Liverpool 1997. (Univ. Manch.) Cons. Paediat. Roy. Albert Edwd. Infirm. Wigan; Hon. Cons. Roy. Manch. Childr.'s Hosp. Prev: Sen. Regist. (Paediat.) Manch.

COOPER, Christopher John South Staffordshire Healthcare NHS Trust, St. George's Hospital, Stafford ST16 3AG Tel: 01785 257888 — MB ChB 1971 Liverp.; MRCPsych 1975. Cons. Psychiat.S. Staffs. Healthcare NHS Trust Stafford. Prev: Cons. Psychiat. St. Geo. Hosp. Stafford; Sen. Regist. (Psychiat.) Notts. AHA; Regist. (Psychiat.) Liverp. AHA.

COOPER, Clare 45 Wellington Square, Hastings TN34 1PN — MB BS 1979 Lond.; Dip. Pract. Dermat. Wales 1990. (Char. Cross.) Assoc. Specialist (Dermat.) Conquest Hosp. Hastings. Socs: Fell. Roy. Soc. Med.; Brit. Assn. Dermatol. Prev: Clin. Med. Off. Hastings AHA; Ho. Surg. Sutton Hosp.; Ho. Phys. Cuckfield Hosp.

COOPER, Claudia Ariane 55 Manor Road, Wokingham RG41 4AR — BM 1998 Soton.

COOPER, Colin Paul Apex Lodge, Fitzroy Park, London N6 6JA Tel: 020 8340 9200 — MB BS 1959 Lond.; MRCS Eng. LRCP Lond. 1959; FRCR 1975; FFR 1972; DMRD Eng. 1970; DIH Soc. Apoth. Lond. 1967. (Roy. Free) Cons. Radiol. Roding & Holly Hse. Private Hosps. Prev: Cons. Radiol. Whipps Cross & Wanstead Hosps. Lond.; Sen. Regist. Univ. Coll. Hosp. Lond.; Sen. Cas. Off. Roy. Free Hosp.

COOPER, Professor Cyrus MRC Environmental Epidemiology Unit, Southampton General Hospital, Southampton SO16 6YD Tel: 02380 777624 Fax: 02380 704021; 344 Hill Lane, Upper Shirley, Southampton SO15 7PH Tel: 02380 512125 — MB BS 1980 Lond.; MA Camb. 1980; DM Soton. 1989; FRCP Lond. 1996; MRCP (UK) 1983. (Camb. & St. Bart.) Prof. Rheum. MRC Environm. Epidemiol. Unit Soton. Gen. Hosp.; MRC Sen. Clin. Scientist & Cons. Rheum. Soton. Prev: Sen. Regist. (Rheum.) Bristol Roy. Infirm.; Asst. Prof. Epidemiol. Mayo Clinic, USA; Regist. (Gen. Med.) & SHO (Med.) Soton. Gen. Hosp.

COOPER, Damien David Leven Surgery, 29 High Stile, Leven, Beverley HN17 5NL Tel: 01864 542155 — BM BS 1976 Nottingham; BM BS 1976; BMedSci 1974 Nottingham; MRCGP 1981; DRCOG 1981. (Nottingham)

COOPER, David (retired) — MRCS Eng. LRCP Lond. 1968.

COOPER, David Inverurie Medical Group, 1 Constitution Street, Inverurie AB51 Tel: 01467 621345; 45 Wallacebrae Crescent, Danestone, Aberdeen AB22 8YE Tel: 01224 707519 Email: cooper@davido.freeserve.co.uk — MB ChB 1997 Aberd. (Aberdeen) GP Regist., Inverurie Med. Gp., Inverurie. Socs: Ass. Mem. RCGP. Prev: SHO (A&E), Vict. Infirm., Glas.; SHO (A&E) Aberd. Roy. Infirm.; SHO (Dermatol.) Aberd. Roy. Infirm.

COOPER, David Glenn 14 Burnham Grove, East Boldon NE36 0DU — BChir 1996 Camb.

COOPER, David Ian (retired) The Surgery, High St., Lowestoft NR32 1JE Tel: 01502 589151 Fax: 01502 566719 — MB ChB 1967 Glas.; DA Eng. 1969; DObst RCOG 1969. Prev: Hosp. Practitioner (Anaesth.) Gt Yarmouth & Waveney Health Dist.

COOPER, David Norman Montagu Hospital, Adwick Road, Mexborough S64 0AZ Tel: 01709 585171 Fax: 01709 571689; 45 Meadow Drive, Tickhill, Doncaster DN11 9ET Email: david.cooper@ukonline.co.uk — MB ChB 1974 Dundee; FRCP Lond. 1994; MRCP (UK) 1979. Cons. Phys. Montagu Hosp. MexBoro. Socs: Brit. Thorac. Soc.; Brit. Geriat. Soc. Prev: Sen. Regist. (Gen. & Geriat. Med.) City Gen. Hosp. Stoke-on-Trent; Tutor (Med.) Univ. Dept. Med. Hope Hosp. Salford; SHO (Med.) Stepping Hill Hosp. Stockport.

COOPER, David William Leven Valley, Hutton Rudby, Yarm TS15 0EZ — MB BS 1983 Newc.; FRCA 1989. Cons. Anaesth. S. Cleveland Hosp. Middlesbrough.

COOPER, Dorothy Joyce 157 Bradford Road, Combe Down, Bath BA2 5BS Tel: 01225 832636 — MRCS Eng. LRCP Lond. 1940; FFHom 1982, M 1972; DCH Eng. 1949. (Lond. Sch. Med. Wom.) Socs: Life Fell. Roy. Soc. Med.; BMA. Prev: Maj. RAMC, Med. Specialist; Ho. Phys. Roy. Free Hosp; Ho. Surg. Roy Devon & Exeter Hosp.

COOPER, Edgar Arthur (retired) Craigshield Farm, Wark, Hexham NE48 3DT Tel: 01434 230235 — MB BChir 1949 Camb.; PhD Birm. 1956; MA Camb. 1951, MD 1961; FFA RCS Eng. 1954; DA Eng. 1952. Prev: Prof. Anaesth. Univ. Newc.

COOPER, Edith No. 3 Staff Residences, Uphill Road S., Weston Super Mare BS23 4TQ — MB BCh BAO 1970 Belf.

COOPER, Edwin Jon 53 Park Drive, London N21 2LT — MB BS 1998 Lond.; MB BS Lond 1998.

COOPER, Elaine Kathleen Hawthorn Lodge, Moorgreen Hospital, West End, Southampton SO30 3JB Tel: 023 8047 5157 Fax: 023 8047 5160 — MB ChB Birm. 1960; MRCS Eng. LRCP Lond. 1960; MFFP 1993. (Birm.) Psychosexual Counseller Contracep. and Sexual Health. Serv. & Learning Cons. Adviser in SEXUALITY issues Disabil. Team S.ampton Community Health. Socs: Assoc. Mem. Inst. Psycho-Sexual Med. Prev: Dir. Family Plann. Serv. Soton. Community Health Serv. Trust.

COOPER, Elizabeth 13 Hartside Gardens, Jesmond, Newcastle upon Tyne NE2 2JR; 13 Hartside Gardens, Jesmond, Newcastle upon Tyne NE2 2JR — MB BS 1993 Newc.; MRCP UK 1996. Specialist Regist. (Rehabil. Med.). Socs: Brit. Soc. Rehab. Med.

COOPER, Elizabeth Sarah 3FR, 6 Leslie Place, Edinburgh EH4 1NQ — MB ChB 1989 Ed.

COOPER, Elspeth Jean 2 Corbiehill Park, Davidson's Mains, Edinburgh EH4 5EQ — MB ChB Ed. 1968; Dip. Pract. Dermat. Wales 1996. (Ed.) Assoc. Specialist (Dermat.) Roy. Infirm. Edin. Prev: Research Asst. N.. Gen. Hosp. Edin.; GP Princip.

COOPER, Felicity The Portmill Surgery, 114 Queen Street, Hitchin SG4 9TH Tel: 01462 434246 Fax: 01462 441246; Bury Farm House, St. Paul's Walden, Hitchin SG4 8BP — MB BS 1984 Lond.; MRCGP 1996; DRCOG 1988. (Roy. Free Hosp. Sch. Med.) Trainer.

COOPER, Fiona Alexandra Group Medical Practice, Glodwick Health Centre, 137 Glodwick Road, Oldham OL4 1YN Tel: 0161 909 8377 Fax: 0161 909 8414; 10 Bramhall Close, Milnrow, Rochdale OL16 4BX — MB ChB 1986 Manch.; MRCGP 1990; DRCOG 1989. Prev: Trainee GP Birch Hill Hosp. Rochdale.

COOPER, Geoffrey Harold 9 Banks Hill, Barnoldswick BB18 5XA Tel: 01282 813368 — MB ChB 1965 Manch.; MRCS Eng. LRCP Lond. 1965. Prev: Capt. RAMC; Ho. Phys. Birch Hill Hosp. Rochdale; Ho. Surg. Burnley Gen. Hosp.

COOPER, Gillian Mary Woodside Medical Centre, Jardine Crescent, Coventry CV4 9PL Tel: 024 7669 4001 Fax: 024 7669 5639; 89 Cromwell Lane, Coventry CV4 8AQ — MB ChB 1976 Leeds; DRCOG 1983; DA Eng. 1982.

COOPER, Gillian Ruth Elgar House Surgery, Church Road, Redditch B97 4AB Tel: 01527 69261 Fax: 01527 596856 — MB ChB 1977 Glas.; DCH Eng. 1982; DRCOG 1981; DFFP 1997. GP, Elgar Ho., Redditch; Med. Adviser Worcs. HA. Prev: Regist. (Paediat.) & SHO (A & E) Frimley Pk. Hosp. Camberley; SHO (Paediat.) Roy. Hosp. Sick Childr. Glas.

COOPER, Gisu Rosemount Medical Practice, 1 View Terrace, Aberdeen AB25 2RS Tel: 01224 638050 Fax: 01224 627308 — MB BS 1988 Lond. Regist. (Med. for Elderly) Hemel Hempstead Hosp. Herts. Prev: SHO Rotat. Roy. Free Hosp. Lond.

COOPER, Mr Graham Geoffrey Aberdeen Royal Infirmary, Aberdeen AB25 2ZN Tel: 01224 681818 — MD 1988 Aberd.; MB ChB 1976; FRCS Glas. 1980. Cons. Vasc. Surg. Grampian HB Aberd. Prev: Sen. Regist. (Surg.) E. Health & Social Servs. Bd. Belf.

COOPER, Mr Graham John Department of Cardiothoracic Surgery, Northern General Hospital, Sheffield S5 7AU Tel: 0114 271 4954 Fax: 0114 261 0350; 29 Carsick View Road, Ranmoor, Sheffield S10 3LZ — MB ChB 1984 Leeds; MD Leeds 1995; FRCS (C Th) 1995; FRCS Ed. 1988. Cons. Cardiothoracic Surg. N. Gen. Hosp. Sheff.; Clin. Director,Cardiothoracic Serv.s. Prev: Sen. Regist. (Cardiothoracic Surg.) St. Thos. Hosp. Lond.

COOPER, Graham Leggatt Quantanova Asia Pacific, c/o Scotia Pharmaceuticals, Scotia House, Castle Business Park, Stirling FK9 4TZ Tel: 01786 895100 Fax: 01786 895450; Ballabeg Dykehead, Port of Menteith, Stirling FK8 3JY Tel: 01877 385216 — MB ChB St. And. 1970; MFPM RCP (UK) 1991; MRCGP 1977; Dip. Pharm. Med. RCP (UK) 1982; DObst RCOG 1973; DA (UK) 1972. (St. And.) Managing Dir. Quantanova Asia Pacific, (Scotia Singapore). Prev: Med. Dir. Scotia Drug Discovery, Scotia Pharmaceut.; Med. Manager (Far E.) Zeneca Pharmaceut.; Med. Dir. (Far E.) Glaxo Pharmaceut.

COOPER, Harris (retired) 6 Naseby Close, London NW6 4EY Tel: 020 7372 0510 — MB BS Lond. 1938; MRCS Eng. LRCP Lond. 1938. Prev: Cas. Off. Roy. Sussex Co. Hosp. Brighton.

COOPER, Helen Barlow 377 Stamfordham Road, Westerhope, Newcastle upon Tyne NE5 2JH Tel: 0191 286 9178; 48 Moorside S., Fenham, Newcastle upon Tyne NE4 9BB — MB ChB 1962 Aberd. Prev: Regist. (Dermat.) Glas. Roy. Infirm.

COOPER, Helen Mary Frankley Health Centre, 125 New St., Frankley, Birmingham B45 0EU Tel: 0121 453 8211; 40 Witherford Way, Birmingham B29 4AX — MB ChB 1992 Birm. Prev: SHO (A & E & Paediat.) Selly Oak Hosp.; SHO (O & G) Birm. Matern. Hosp.

***COOPER, Hywel Lloyd** 26 Bryn Gwyn Road, Cyncoed, Cardiff CF23 6PQ — BM 1996 Soton.; MBedSci Soton. 1995.

COOPER, Ian Charles Bedford Hospital, Kempston Road, Bedford MK42 9DJ Tel: 01234 355122 Fax: 01234 792222; 11 Rothsay Gardens, Bedford MK40 3QA Tel: 01234 262806 — MB BS 1978 Lond.; MD Lond. 1991; FRCP Lond. 1997; MRCP (UK) 1980. (Univ. Coll. Hosp. Lond.) Cons. Cardiol. Bedford & Papworth Hosps. Prev: Sen. Regist. Rotat. (Cardiol. & Gen. Med.) St. Thos. Hosp. & Greenwich Dist. Hosp. Lond.

COOPER, Jacqueline Anne 12 Tivoli Road, Crouch End, London N8 8RE Tel: 020 8341 9948 — MB BS 1989 Lond.; BSc (Intercalated) Genetics 1986; MRCP (UK) 1993; FRCA 1996. (Roy. Free Hosp. Sch. Med.) Cons. Anaesth. Roy. Free Hosp. Lond. Prev: SHO Rotat. (Anaesth.) St. Thos. Hosp. Lond.; SHO Rotat. (Med.) Guy's Hosp.; Regist. Rotat. (Anaesth.) Middlx. & Univ. Coll. Hosp. Lond.

COOPER, James Allan Mill of Fortune Farm, Comrie, Crieff PH6 2JE — MB ChB 1955 St. And.; Dip. Community. Med. Ed. 1975; MFCM RCPI 1978. Unit CMS W.. Gen. Hosp.; CMS Capital Serv. Lothian Health Bd. Prev: ADMO N. Lothian Dist. LHB.

COOPER, James David Trinity Palliative Care Services, Trinity - The Hospice in the Fylde, Low Moor Road, Bispham, Blackpool FY2 0BG Tel: 01253 358881 Fax: 01253 352771; 62 Warbreck Hill Road, Blackpool FY2 9UQ Tel: 01253 591541 — MB ChB 1973 Manch. (Manch.) Med. Dir. (Palliat. Med.) Trinity - The Hospice in the Fylde Blackpool.; Hon. Cons. Blackpool Vict. Hosp. NHS Trust.; Hon. Sen. Lect. (Palliat. Med.) Univ. of Centr. Lancs. Socs: Assn. Palliat. Med.

COOPER, James Graham Grosvenor Medical Centre, Grosvenor Street, Crewe CW1 3HB Tel: 01270 256348 Fax: 01270 250786 — MB ChB 1986 Manch.; MRCGP 1991; T(GP) 1991.

COOPER, James Joylon Flat 3, 8 Royal York Crescent, Clifton, Bristol BS8 4JZ — BM BS 1986 Nottm.; BMedSci Nottm. 1984, BM BS 1986; FRCA 1993.

COOPER, Jamie Gray 85 Leslie Terrace, Aberdeen AB25 3XB — MB ChB 1996 Aberd. SHO (Surg.) Aberd. Roy. Hosps. Socs: BMA.

COOPER, Jane Elizabeth Queen Marys Hospital, Sidcup DA14 6LT Tel: 020 8302 2678 — MB BChir 1979 Camb.; MA, MB Camb. 1980, BChir 1979; MRCPath 1986. Cons. Histopath. Qu. Mary's Hosp. Kent. Prev: Lect. (Histopath.) Inst. Child Health Univ. Lond.; Asst. Lect. (Path.) St. Thos. Hosp. Med. Sch.

COOPER, Jane Elsie Susan 67 Southdown Road, Hersham, Walton-on-Thames KT12 4PJ Tel: 01932 246407 Email: jane.doc@virgin.net — MB BS 1979 Lond.; DFFP 1997; Dip. Gestalt Psychother. Sherwood Psychother. Train. 1998. (St. Bart.) Psychotherapist & Psychosexual Med. Pract. Surrey; Mem. Sherwood Psychother. Train. Inst. Socs: Inst. Psychosexual Med. Prev: Clin. Med. Off. Bournewood NHS Trust Surrey; SHO (Gyn.) Hackney Hosp. Lond.; Ho. Surg. Pr. of Wales Hosp. Lond.

COOPER, Jane Harvey c/o Wildwoods, Trimpley, Bewdley DY12 1NH — MB ChB 1980 Birm.; MSC London 1997.

COOPER, Jane Lesley Chapelthorpe Surgery, Hall Lane, Chapelthorpe, Wakefield WF4 3JE Tel: 01924 255166 Fax: 01924

257653; Hall Lane, Chapelthorpe, Wakefield WF4 3JE Tel: 01924 255166 — MB ChB 1986 Leeds; MRCGP 1993; Dip. Obst. Otago 1989; DA Eng. 1988. GP. Socs: BMA. Prev: Trainee GP Harrogate VTS.

COOPER, Jason Crawford Department of Obstetrics & Gynaecology, North Staffordshire Hospital, City General Newcastle Road, Stoke-on-Trent ST4 6QG Tel: 01782 715444 Fax: 01782 740164 — MB BS 1986 Lond.; BSc Lond. 1983, MD 1997; MRCOG 1992; MD 1997. (St. Geo. Hosp. Med. Sch.) Cons. O & G N. Staffs. Hosp.'. Prev: Sen. Regist. (O & G) Addenbrooke'sHosp. Camb.; Research Fell. Univ. Camb.

COOPER, Jayne Deborah Holt Medical Practice, High Street, Holt NR25 6BH — MB BS 1980 Lond.; MRCP (UK) 1985. (St. Bart.) Prev: Regist. (Med.) Roy. Hallamsh. Hosp. Sheff.; SHO (Endocrinol.) Roy. Postgrad. Med. Sch. & Hammersmith Hosp. Lond.; SHO (Thoracic Med.) Brompton Hosp. Lond.

COOPER, Jean Lilias 54 Allison Drive, Carnwath, Lanark ML11 8HF — MB ChB 1957 Glas.; DPH Glas. 1967.

COOPER, Jessie Ross McCutcheon (retired) 17 Killasser Court, Station Approach Road, Tadworth KT20 5AN Tel: 01737 812954 — MB ChB (Hons.) Ed. 1938.

COOPER, Joan (retired) 16 Trumpington Road, Cambridge CB2 2AQ Tel: 01223 350171 — MRCS Eng. LRCP Lond. 1920; FRCA 1992; FFA RCS Eng. 1953; DA Eng. 1935. Hon. Consg. Anaesth. United Camb. Hosps. & E. Anglian RHB. Prev: Ho. Phys., Ho. Surg. & Res. O & G Off. Char. Cross Hosp.

COOPER, John (retired) 4 North Circular Road, Belfast BT15 5HB Tel: 01232 777057 Fax: 01232 777057 — MB BCh BAO 1955 Belf.; FFA RCSI 1964; FFA RCS Eng. 1965. Prev: Cons. Anaesth. Mater Infirm. Hosp. Belf.

COOPER, John Earnswood Medical Centre, 92 Victoria Street, Crewe CW1 2JR Tel: 01270 257255 Fax: 01270 501943; 45 Bridge Street, Wybunbury, Nantwich CW5 7NE Tel: 01270 841954 — MB ChB Bristol 1959. Socs: BMA.

COOPER, John Andrew Locke, MC Highrigg Drive, Durton Lane, Broughton, Preston PR3 5LJ Tel: 01772 2525 — MRCS Eng. LRCP Lond. 1942; FFA RCS Eng. 1954; DA Eng. 1948. (Manch.) Cons. Anaesth. Preston & Chorley Hosp. Gp. Prev: Cons. Anaesth. Roy. Infirm. Bradford; RAMC.

COOPER, John Anthony (retired) Chydaw, Kenwyn, Truro TR4 9BY Tel: 01872 274494 — MB BS Lond. 1956; LMSSA Lond. 1956; FRCOG 1978, M 1965, DObst 1962. Prev: Cons. O & G Cornw. & I. of Scilly Trust.

COOPER, Mr John Charles Rotherham District General Hospital, Moorgate Road, Rotherham S60 2UD — MB ChB 1978 Sheff.; ChM Sheff. 1987, MB ChB 1978; FRCS Eng. 1982. Cons. Gen. Surg. Rotherham Dist. Gen. Hosp. Prev: Sen. Regist. (Surg.) Sheff.; Research Fell. (Surg.) Leeds Gen. Infirm.; Regist. Rotat. (Surg.) Sheff. HA.

COOPER, John Edward Meadow Cottage, 25 Ireton Grove, Attenborough, Nottingham NG9 6BJ Tel: 0115 925 6493 Fax: 0115 967 7719 — BM BCh 1953 Oxf.; BA (Physiol.) Oxf. 1950, BM BCh 1953; FRCP Lond. 1973, M 1958; DPM Lond. 1961; FRCPsych 1972, M 1971. (Oxf. & Univ. Coll. Hosp.) Emerit. Prof. Psychiat. Univ. Nottm.; Mem. WHO Expert Panel on Ment. Health. Socs: Fell. Roy. Soc. Med. Prev: Prof. Psychiat. Univ. Nottm.; Cons. Psychiat. Roy. Bethlem & Maudsley Hosps.; Vice-Dean Inst. Psychiat. Lond.

COOPER, John Graham Glenfield Surgery, 111 Station Road, Glenfield, Leicester LE3 8GS Tel: 0161 233 3604 Fax: 0161 233 2674 Email: cooperjg@gp-c82056.nhs.uk; 8 Flaxland, Rothley Lodge, Rothley, Leicester LE7 7RJ Tel: 0116 237 4871 — MB ChB 1980 Leic.; FRCGP 2000; BSc (Hons.) Lond. 1975; MRCGP 1985; DRCOG 1984. (Leicester)

COOPER, John Peter Dept Cardiology, Bedford Hospital, Kempston Road, Bedford MK42 2LL Tel: 01234 795946 Fax: 01234 792222 — MB BS 1984 Lond.; MD 1997; BSc (1st cl. Hons.) Lond. 1981; FRCP (UK) 2000. Cons. Cardiol. & Gen. Phys. Bedford Hosp.; Roy. Coll. Phys.s Tutor Bedford Hosp. Socs: Brit. Cardiac Soc.; Brit. Cardiac Interenhon Soc.; Brit. Roy. Coll. Phys.s.

COOPER, John Richard Campbell (retired) Middle Cottage, The Green, Sarratt, Rickmansworth WD3 6AY Tel: 01923 263140 — MRCS Eng. LRCP Lond. 1944; LDS Durh. 1949. Prev: Ho. Surg. (Thoracic Surg.) St. Bart. Hosp. Lond.

COOPER, John Robert Dept. Diagnostic Imaging, Northern General Hospital, herries Road, Sheffield S57AU Tel: 0114 271 5432 Email: robert.cooper@sth.nhs.uk; 112 Stannington View Road, Sheffield S10 1SS — MB BS 1987 Lond.; BSc Lond. 1984; MRCP (UK) 1992; FRCR 1997. Cons. Diagnostic Radiol. Sheff. Teachg. Hosp. NHS Trust.

COOPER, John Robert Baxter Unilever House, Blackfriars, London EC4P 4BQ Tel: 020 7822 5871 Fax: 020 7822 6334 Email: john.cooper@unilever.com; 1 Horse Pastures, Little Hawkwell Farm, Maidstone Road, Pembury, Tunbridge Wells TN2 4AQ Tel: 01892 824523 — MB BS 1975 Lond.; FFOM RCP Lond. 1997, M 1988, A 1982. (St. Thos.) Socs: Fell. Roy. Soc. Med.; Soc. Occupat. Med. Prev: Med. Dir. Mobil Europe & Afr.; Med. Off. Brit. Petroleum; SHO (Rheum. & Neurol.) & Ho. Surg. (ENT) St. Thos. Hosp. Lond.

COOPER, Jonathan Ferguson 23 Mayfield Crt., Mayfield Road, Moseley, Birmingham B13 9HS — MB ChB 1978 Birm.; BSc, MB ChB (Hons.) Birm. 1978.

COOPER, Joseph Emery 134 Sutton Court, Sutton Court Road, London W4 3EF — MB BS 1984 Lond.

COOPER, Josephine Evelyn Mary 15 Clarendon Road, Fulwood, Sheffield S10 3TQ Tel: 0114 230 2716 — MB ChB 1955 Liverp.; MRCPsych 1973; DPM Eng. 1972. (Liverp.) Prev: Cons. Psych. Hosps. for Ment. Sub.-N. Sheff. Area; Clin. Lect. (Psychiat.) Univ. Sheff.; Regist. Belle Vue Ment. Hosp. Kingston, Jamaica.

COOPER, Joyce (retired) 54 Roman Road, Failsworth, Manchester M35 9JZ Tel: 0161 681 1667 — MB ChB 1939 Manch.; MRCS Eng. LRCP Lond. 1939. Prev: Hon. Med. Off. Oldham & Dist. Cerebral Palsy Centre.

COOPER, Mr Julian Paul 119 Wynn Road, Penn, Wolverhampton WV4 4AW Tel: 01902 330040 — MB ChB 1990 Birm.; BSc (Hons.) Anat. Birm. 1987, MB ChB (Hons.) 1990; FRCS Eng. 1994. SHO (Orthop.) Roy. Orthop. Hosp. Birm.; Lect. (Anat.) Univ. Birm. Med. Sch. 1991-92. Prev: SHO Rotat. (Surg.) Birm.; Ho. Surg. Birm. Accid. Hosp.; Ho. Phys. E. Birm. Hosp.

COOPER, Julie Christina Elizabeth 74 Mountfield Gardens, Kenton, Newcastle upon Tyne NE3 3DD — MB ChB 1983 Ed.; MRCP (UK) 1987; FRCR 1991. Sen. Regist. (Radiol.) Newc. HA.

COOPER, Juliet Kim 85 Leslie Terrace, Aberdeen AB25 3XB — MB ChB 1996 Aberd.; BSc MedSci 1995. (Aberd.) GP VTS Aberd. Socs: BMA; MDDUS.

COOPER, June Brierley (retired) Four Seasons, Column Park, Llanfairpwllgwyngyll LL61 5NJ Tel: 01248 714604 — MB ChB 1964 Liverp.; FFA RCS Eng. 1974; DObst RCOG 1966. Prev: Cons. Anaesth. Ysbyty Gwynedd, Bangor.

COOPER, Mr Kenneth Veitch (retired) 66 Poulters Lane, Worthing BN14 7SZ Email: kcooper66@aol.com — MB BS Lond. 1951; FRCS Ed. 1961; FRCOG 1972, M 1959. Prev: Cons. O & G Worthing Hosp. Gp.

COOPER, Kevin 100 Newminster Road, Newcastle upon Tyne NE4 9LJ — MB BS 1994 Newc.

COOPER, Kevin Gary Albyn Hospital, 21-24 Albyn Place, Aberdeen AB10 1RW — MB ChB 1986 Ed.; MRCOG.

COOPER, Khorshed Sarosh 95 Station Road, Hendon, London NW4 4PA Tel: 020 8202 7983 — MB BS 1952 Bombay; MFFP 1993; DGO CPS Bombay 1954. (G.S. Med. Coll.) SCMO Margt. Pyke Centre Lond.

COOPER, Lesley Dorothea 16 Stakesby Road, Whitby YO21 1HS Tel: 01947 604824 — MB ChB 1949 Ed. Prev: Clin. Asst. (Geriat.) Whitby Hosp.

COOPER, Leslie Charles George South Hill Lodge, Deopham Green, Wymondham NR18 9DQ — MB ChB 1979 Leeds.

COOPER, Linda Carol Chorleywood Health Centre, 7 Lower Road, Chorleywood, Rickmansworth WD3 5EA Tel: 01923 287100 Fax: 01923 287120 — MB BChir 1976 Camb.; MA Camb. 1976; MRCP (UK) 1981; T(GP) 1991. GP Herts. Socs: Vice-Chairm. Med. Jl.ists Assn.; Multiple Births Foundat. Prev: Sen. Regist. (Rheum.) Canad. Red Cross Hosp. Taplow; Regist. (Med.) Hillingdon Hosp.; Regist. (Surg.) Qu. Eliz. II Hosp. Welwyn Gdn. City.

COOPER, Lorna Alice Hall 1 Laburnum Crescent, Wishaw ML2 7EH — MB ChB 1997 Glas.

COOPER, Louise Rosalind 27 The Fairway, Alwoodley, Leeds LS17 7QP — MB ChB 1995 Leeds. GP/Regist. Airedale Hosp. VTS. Prev: Ho. Off. (Gen. Med.) Airedale Hosp.; Ho. Off. (Gen. Surg.) Pinderfields Hosp. Wakefield.

COOPER, Manisha 66 Furnival Road, Manchester M18 8DQ Tel: 0161 231 1337 — MB ChB 1994 Manch. Trainee GP N. Manch. Gen. Hosp. VTS. Prev: Ho. Off. (Med.) Manch. Infirm.; Ho. Off. (Surg.) Roy. Oldham Hosp.

COOPER, Margaret Elizabeth 1 Evergreen Close, Woolmer Green, Knebworth SG3 6JN — MB BCh BAO 1973 Belf.; DRCOG 1976. SCMO (Wom. Serv.) N. Herts. NHS Trust.

COOPER, Margaret Highstead (retired) 2 The Manor Close, Shincliffe Village, Durham DH1 2NS Tel: 0191 386 5818 — MB ChB 1955 Ed.; MRCPsych 1981; Dip. Psychother. Leeds 1985. Cons. Psychogeriat. SW Durh. & S. Tees HA. Prev: Clin. Asst. Winterton Hosp. Sedgefield.

COOPER, Mark Goldcoast Medical Imaginary Ltd., P.O. Box 382, Southport, Queensland 4215, Australia Tel: 00 61 7 32537029 Fax: 00 61 7 32531049 Email: markc@gem.com.au; 2 Greens Meade, Woodfalls, Salisbury SP5 2NL Email: mcooper3@bigpond.net.au — MB BS 1984 Lond.; BSc (Hons.) Lond. 1981; MRCP (UK) 1988; FRCR 1993; FRCR 1998. (St. Mary's) Partner-Private Radiol. Gp. Socs: Soc. Cardiovasc. & Interven.al Radiol. Prev: Sen. Regist. Rotat. (Diag. Radiol.) Wessex RHA; Regist. (Diag. Radiol.) Addenbrooke's Hosp. Camb.; Regist. Rotat. (Gen. Med. & Cardiol.) Soton. & Salisbury HA.

COOPER, Mr Mark Angus Crewes Stuart Morriston Hospital, Swansea SA6 6NL Tel: 01792 702222 Fax: 01792 703867; Glanmor, 4 Brynfield Road, Langland, Swansea SA3 4SX Tel: 01792 361390 — MB BS 1979 Lond.; FRCS (Plast) Eng. 1993; FRCS Eng. 1983. (Char. Cross Hosp.) Cons. Plastic Surg. Morriston Hosp. Swansea. Prev: Sen. Regist. St. And. Hosp. Billericay; Regist. (Plastic Surg.) Univ. Hosp. S. Manch.; SHO (Plastic Surg.) Frenchay Hosp. Bristol.

COOPER, Mark Hayden 11 Gloucester Road, Walsall WS5 3PL — MB ChB 1989 Leeds; BSc Leeds 1986, MB ChB Leeds 1989. (University of Leeds) Fell. (CT Surg.) Univ. of Wisconsin, Madison, WI, USA; Vis. Lect. (Surg.) Univ. Soton. Socs: Brit. Transpl. Soc. & Cell Transpl. Soc. Prev: Chief Resid. (Gen. Surg.) Texas A & M Coll. of Med., Temple, TX, USA; Resid. (Gen. Surg.) Univ. Med. Center E.. N. Carolina, Greenville, USA; Research Fell.sh. (Transpl. Sci.) Univ. Pittsburgh, PA, USA.

COOPER, Mark Stuart 20 Brierley Street, Crewe CW1 2AY — BM BCh 1994 Oxf.

COOPER, Mr Martin John Exeter Nuffield Hospital, Wonford Road, Exeter EX2 4UG Tel: 01392 262125 Fax: 01392 425147; Neopardy House, Neopardy, Crediton EX17 5EP Tel: 01363 772611 Email: martincooper@talk21.com — MB BS 1971 Lond.; MS Lond. 1982; FRCS Eng. 1976; MRCS Eng. LRCP Lond. 1971. (Roy. Free) Cons. Surg. Roy. Devon & Exeter Hosp. Wonford; Dir. Cancer Servs., Exeter Cancer Centre; Lead Clinician, Peninjsula Cancer Network. Socs: Fell. Assn. Surgs.; Brit. Soc. Gastroenterol.; Brit. Assn. Surg. Oncol. Prev: Cons. & Sen. Lect. Surg. Univ. Bristol.

COOPER, Martin Paul Brockhurst Medical Centre, 139-141 Brockhurst Road, Gosport PO12 3AX — MB BS 1981 Lond.; MRCGP 1985; DGM RCP Lond. 1986; DRCOG 1983. (St. Geo.) Prev: Med. Off. Mambilima Mission Hosp., Zambia.

COOPER, Martin William 148 Loxley Road, Sheffield S6 4TE — MB ChB 1988 Sheff.; MRCP (UK) 1991. SHO (Med.) Good Hope Gen. Hosp. Sutton Coldfield. Prev: Ho. Phys. Rotherham Dist. Gen. Hosp.; Ho. Surg. Roy. Hallamsh. Hosp. Sheff.

COOPER, Mary Wilhelmina (retired) 15 Linwood Grove, Darlington DL3 8DP Tel: 01325 468225 — MB BS 1936 Durh.

COOPER, Matthew 21 Lower Street, Pulborough RH20 2BH — MB 1980 Camb.; BChir 1979. Assoc. Specialist Sussex Eye Hosp.

COOPER, Matthew Ian 4 Fife Place, Fairlie, Largs KA29 0BU — MB ChB 1994 Manch.

COOPER, Matthew Jason 23 Monks Walk, Penwortham, Preston PR1 0AQ — MB ChB 1996 Leeds.

COOPER, Maxwell John Francis 1 Granby Grove, Highfield, Southampton SO17 3RY — BM 1997 Soton.; BSc (Hons) Soton 1996.

COOPER, Mehrengise Keki 23 Countess Weir, Exeter EX2 6CR Tel: 01392 275436 Email: mehrengise-cooper@compuserve.com — MB BS 1991 Lond.; MRCP (UK) 1995. (St. Mary's Hosp. Med. Sch.) Specialist Regist. Paediat. Roy. Devon & Exeter Hosp. Socs: Roy. Coll. Paediat. & Child Health; Med. Protec. Soc.; MRCPCH. Prev: Regist. (Paediat.) Roy. Devon & Exeter Hosp.; Regist. (Paediat.) S.mead Hosp. Bristol.

COOPER, Michael Adrian New Cross Hospital, Wolverhampton Road, Wolverhampton WV10 0QP Tel: 01902 307999 Ext: 2424 Fax: 01902 642993 Email: dr.cooper"rwh-tr.wmids.nhs.uk; 50 Jordan Road, Sutton Coldfield B75 5AB — MB ChB 1986 Sheff.; FRCPath 2001; MRCPath 1992. (Sheff.) Cons. Microbiol. Roy. Wolverhampton Hosps. NHS Trust. Prev: Sen. Regist. & Regist. (Microbiol.) W. Midl. Regional Health Auth.

COOPER, Michael Andrew Mill Stile, Spark Bridge, Ulverston LA12 8BS — MB ChB 1994 Ed.; BSc (Hons.) Ed. 1992, MB ChB 1994.

COOPER, Michael Andrew East Gloucester NHS Trust, Garden Wing, Delancey Hospital, Leckhampton, Cheltenham GL53 9DU Tel: 01242 272125 Fax: 01242 272128 — MB ChB 1977 Aberd.; MRCPsych 1985; Cert. Prescribed Exp Gen Pract, Roy. Coll. GP 1981. Cons. Psychiat. Learning Disabil. E. Glos. NHS Trust; Clin. Teach. (Ment. Health) Univ. Bristol. Socs: Fell. Roy. Soc. Med. Prev: Resid. (Path.) Univ. of Iceland; Trainee GP Montrose; Regist. (Psychiat.) Fulbourn Hosp. Camb.

COOPER, Michael Blinman Steward (retired) 74 The Hill, Wheathampstead, St Albans AL4 8PS Tel: 01582 629578 — MB BChir 1950 Camb.; MB BChir Camb.1950; MA Camb. 1950; DObst RCOG 1956. Prev: Ho. Surg. (Cas., A & E & Gen. Surg.) St. Bart. Hosp. Lond.

COOPER, Michael James Community Health Sheffield NHS Trust, Fulwood House, Old Fulwood Road, Sheffield S10 3TH — MB ChB 1992 Leic. SHO (Psychiat.) Community Health Sheff. NHS Trust. Prev: Trainee GP/SHO (O & G) Rugby VTS.

COOPER, Michael Marchant 14 Georges Lane, Horwich, Bolton BL6 6RT Tel: 01204 692760 Fax: 01204 692760 — MB ChB 1975 Manch.; MRCGP 1979; DRCOG 1978. Gen. Practitioner, Granville Ho., Med. Centre, Adlington, Chorley; Clin. Asst. (Wom. Health Care) Bolton Gen. Hosp. Socs: Bolton Med. Soc.; Chorley Med. Soc. Prev: GP Bolton; Clin. Tutor (Gen. Pract.) Bolton.

COOPER, Michael Richard (Surgery), 104 New Road, Rubery, Birmingham B45 9HY Tel: 0121 453 3584 — MB ChB 1967 Birm.

COOPER, Michael Thomas 76 Bradley Street, Crookes, Sheffield S10 1PB — MB ChB 1989 Sheff.

COOPER, Monica Frieda The Oaks, Monkmead Lane, West Chiltingdon, Pulborough RH20 2NH Tel: 01798 812600 Fax: 01798 812600 — MB BS 1973 Lond.; MRCS Eng. LRCP Lond. 1973.

COOPER, Monica Mary Law Street Surgery, 49-51 Laws Street, Pembroke Dock SA72 6DJ Tel: 01646 683113 / 682002 Fax: 01646 622273; Jameston Court, Jameston, Tenby SA70 8QD Tel: 01834 871616 — MB BCh BAO 1977 NUI; MRCGP 1982; Dip. Pract. Dermat. Wales 1995; Dip. Palliat. Med. Wales 1993. (Cork) Clin. Asst. (Dermat. & Genitourin. Med.) Wales. Prev: Trainee GP Roy. Infirm. Doncaster; SHO (Geriat.) St. Mary Abbot's Hosp. Lond.; Intern St. Finbarr's Hosp. Cork.

COOPER, Neil Christopher Water Meadow Surgery, Red Lion Street, Chesham HP5 1ET Tel: 01494 782241 — MB ChB 1984 Bristol; MRCGP 1988; DRCOG 1988; DCH RCP Lond. 1987. GP Chesham. Prev: Trainee GP/SHO Wycombe Gen. Hosp. VTS.

COOPER, Nicholas Anthony 4 Wells Drive, Stafford ST17 0PL — MB ChB 1987 Leic.

COOPER, Nicholas Ian Lee House, Eves Corner, Danbury, Chelmsford CM3 4QA Tel: 01245 225522 Fax: 01245 222196; Redholme, The Ridge, Little Baddow, Chelmsford CM3 4RT Tel: 01245 224436 Fax: 01245 222196 — MB BS 1978 Lond.; PGD 2000 Middlesex University (Tavistock Clinic). Med. Asst. Chelmsford Hospice.; Cancer Lead, Malden and S. Chelmsford PCT. Prev: SHO (Psychiat.) Warley Hosp.; SHO (Gen. Med., Rheum., O & G & Cas.) Harold Wood Hosp.; Ho. Phys. & Ho. Surg. St. Margt. Hosp. Epping.

COOPER, Mr Nicholas Keith SO1 Prev Med., Medical Branch, HQ UKSC (G), BFPO 140 — MB BCh BAO 1976 Belf.; FRCS Ed. 1984; MFOM RCP Lond. 1994; T(OM) 1994.

COOPER, Nicola Ann 25 Thornville Street, Burley, Leeds LS6 1RP Tel: 0113 224 9046 Email: dnacooper@aol.com — MB ChB 1994 Leeds. SHO Rotat. (Med.) Bradford Roy. Infirm.

COOPER, Nicolas Anthony Catherine House Surgery, New Walk, The Plains, Totnes TQ9 5HA Tel: 01803 862073 Fax: 01803 862056; Conygar House, Jubilee Road, Totnes TQ9 5BP Tel: 01803 864763 Fax: 01803 864670 — MB BS 1976 Lond.; BSc Lond.

1973; MRCP (UK) 1979; DFFP 1993; ECFMG Cert. 1976; MRCPCH 1997; Mmed 1998(Dundee). (Lond. Hosp) Trainer (Gen. Pract.) Totnes; Univ. Clin. Tutor (Gen. Pract.) Torbay Postgrad. Educat. Dept. Torquay; Hon. Lect. (Med. Educ.) Plymouth Postgrad. Med. Sch.; Mem. Edit. Bd. Child Abuse Review; Med. Columnist W.. Morning News, Your Health; Research Fell. Dept. Primary Health Care Univ. Plymouth; Educator Train. the Trainers Fac. RCS Engl.; Hon. Lect. Med. Educat., Plymouth Postgrad. Med. Sch. Socs: Assn. Study Med. Educat.; Assn. Child Psychol. & Psychiat.; (Sec.) GP Writers Assn. Prev: SHO (Obst.) N.wick Pk. Hosp. Harrow; SHO. (Paediat.) Qu. Eliz. Hosp. Childr. Lond.; SHO (Paediat.) Guy's Hosp. Med. Sch. Lond.

COOPER, Nigel Frederick Draisey (retired) 21 Forge Lane, Little Aston, Sutton Coldfield B74 3BE Tel: 0121 352 0453 — MB ChB Birm. 1952. Prev: GP Sutton Coldfield.

COOPER, Norna (retired) Tullymet, Carslogie Road, Cupar KY15 4HY — MB ChB 1948 Aberd.; DPH 1955. Prev: SCMO Fife Health Bd.

COOPER, Owen Gynaecology Office, University Hospital of Wales, Heath Park, Cardiff CF14 4XW — MB BS 1990 Lond.

COOPER, Paul Douglas 66 Fern Avenue, Jesmond, Newcastle upon Tyne NE2 2QY Tel: 0191 281 0086 Fax: 0191 281 0086 Email: p.d.cooper@ncl.ac.uk — MB BS 1980 Lond.; FFA RCS Eng. 1984. (Char. Cross) Cons. Anaesth. N. Tyneside Dist. Gen. Hosp. Socs: (Treas.) N. of Eng. Soc. Anaesth. Prev: Cons. Cardiothoracic Anaesth. Freeman Hosp. Newc.; Sen. Regist. N.. RHA; Regist. (Anaesth.) Sheff. HA.

COOPER, Paul Hayes Fernwood House, Hoxne Rd, Syleham, Eye IP23 4LT — BM 1997 Soton.

COOPER, Paul Nicholas 16 St John Street, Manchester M3 4EA Tel: 0161 832 9954 Email: pcooper@man.ac.uk — BM BCh 1983 Oxf.; DM Oxford 1996; FRCP Lond. 2000; MA Camb. 1983; MRCP (UK) 1987. (Cambridge & Oxford) Cons. (Neurol.) Hope Hosp. Gt.er Manch.; Lect. (Neurol.) Univ. Manc.; Med. Dir. David Lewis Centre Warford, Chesh. Socs: Mem. of Counc., N. Eng. Neurol. Assoc.; Mem. & Regional Rep., Assoc. of Brit. Neurol.; Mem. Brit. Neuropsychiatric Assoc. Prev: Sen. Reg. (Neurol) Walton Centre Liverp.; Reg. (Neurol.) Manch. Roy. Infirm.

COOPER, Peter Baskerville Stirling (retired) Mirador, The Ball, Minehead TA24 5JJ Tel: 01643 703827 — MRCS Eng. LRCP Lond. 1944; BA, MB BChir Camb. 1945. Prev: Temp. Capt. RAMC.

COOPER, Peter Henry Westgate Practice, Greenhill Health Centre, Church Street, Lichfield WS13 6JL Tel: 01543 414311 Fax: 01543 256364; 62 Wentworth Road, Lichfield WS14 9HN Tel: 01543 263542 Fax: 01543 256364 — MB ChB 1974 Bristol; MRCGP 1979; DCH Eng. 1977. (Bristol)

COOPER, Peter John Mid Wales Hospital, Talgarth, Brecon LD3 0DS Tel: 01874 711671 Fax: 01874 711671 — MB ChB 1976 Birm.; MRCPsych 1986. Cons. Psychiat. (Adult Ment. Illness with s/i in Psychother.) Kidderminster Gen. Hosp. Prev: Sen. Regist. (Psychiat. Forens.) Reaside Clinic & Uffculm Clinic Birm.

COOPER, Peter Nigel Department of Pathology, Royal Victoria Infirmary, Newcastle upon Tyne Tel: 0191 222 7169 Fax: 0191 227 5119 — MB BS 1983 Lond.; BA (Hons.) Camb. 1980; MRCPath 1990; DMJ (Path.) Soc. Apoth. Lond. 1992. Sen. Lect. in Forens. Path., Univ. of Newc. - upon-Tyne. Socs: Assn. Clin. Path.; Brit. Assn. Forens. Med.

COOPER, Philip John 28 Christchurch Mount, Epsom KT19 8NB — MB BS 1977 Lond.; BSc Lond. 1974, MB BS 1977; DRCOG 1980.

COOPER, Philip Jonathan Foster Windsor Cottage, 29 High St., Stanwell, Staines TW19 7LJ — MB BS 1982 Lond.; FCAnaesth. 1990; DA (UK) 1984. Regist. Rotat. (Anaesth.) St. Geo. Hosp. Lond. Socs: Jun. Mem. Assn. Anaesth. Prev: Regist. (Anaesth.) St. Richard's Hosp. Chichester; SHO (Anaesth.) Soton Gen. Hosp.; SHO (Gen. Med. & A & E) St. Richard's Hosp. Chichester.

COOPER, Rachel Ann 33 Bank Hall Road, Stockport SK4 3JR — MB ChB 1989 Birm.; MRCP (UK) 1992; FRCR 1997. Clin. Oncol. Christie Hosp. Manch.

COOPER, Richard Charles 4 Ridge Lane, Watford WD17 4TD Tel: 01923 226745 — MB BS 1992 Lond.; BSc Clin. Pharmacol. & Toxicol. Lond. 1989. (St. Thos. Hosp. Med. Sch.) Regist. Rotat. (Radiol.) N. Region. Prev: SHO Rotat. (Med.) S. Tyneside Dist. Hosp.

COOPER, Richard Maurice 51 St Leoanard's Avenue, Lostock, Bolton BL6 4JE — MB ChB 1989 Manch.; BSc (Hons.) Manch. 1986; FRCA 1995. Regist. (Anaesth.) NW RHA. Socs: BMA; Manch. Med. Soc.; Assn. Anaesth. GB & Irel. Prev: SHO (Anaesth.) N. Manch. Gen. Hosp. & Pk. Hosp. Manch.; SHO (Cas.) S. Manch. Hosps.

COOPER, Richard Michael 17 Harley Street, London W1N 1DA Tel: 020 7580 3324 Fax: 020 7436 0661; 35 West Hill Park, Highgate, London N6 6ND Tel: 0208 342 8818 Fax: 0208 342 8828 — MB BS 1964 Lond.; MRCS Eng. LRCP Lond. 1964. (Char. Cross) Cons. Med. Off. Pinnacle Insur. Co.; Memorex Computer Products Ltd. & other Cos.; Sen. Med. Examr. Scott. Widows, Gen. Accid. & Other Insur. Cos.; Med. Cons. WPP plc, Korn Ferry Serv. Team. Socs: Fell. Roy. Soc. Med.; Counc. Mem. Indep. Doctors Forum. Prev: Ho. Surg. Char. Cross Hosp.; Ho. Phys. Mt. Vernon Hosp.

COOPER, Robert Andrew (retired) Taylors Cottage, Little Wittenham, Abingdon OX14 4RD Tel: 01865 407887 — MB BS 1954 Lond.; LMSSA Lond. 1953. Prev: SHO N. Devon Infirm. Barnstaple.

COOPER, Robert Forbes Solihull Health Authority, 21 Poplar Road, Solihull B91 3AH Tel: 0121 704 5191 Fax: 0121 705 9541 — MB ChB 1980 Birm.; MA Camb. 1980; MFCM 1987; FFPHM RCP (UK) 1994, M 1989. Dir. Pub. Health Solihull HA; Hon. Sen. Clin. Lect. Univ. Birm. Socs: BMA; Assn. Pub. Health. Prev: Sen. Regist. (Community Med.) W. Midl. RHA; Cons. Pub. Health Med. Birm. Centr.

COOPER, Robert Gary (retired) 48 Moorside S., Fenham, Newcastle upon Tyne NE4 9BB — MB ChB 1961 Aberd.; FRCP Lond. 1984; MRCP (UK) 1970. Cons. Phys. Freeman Hosp. Newc.

COOPER, Robert Geoffrey Rheumatic Diseases Centre, Hope Hospital, Stott Lane, Salford M6 8HD Tel: 0161 787 4367 Fax: 0161 787 4367 Email: rcooper@fs1.ho.man.ac.uk; Burford, 27 Broad Oak Rd, Worsley, Manchester M28 2TL Tel: 0161 727 8706 Fax: 0161 728 5404 — MB ChB 1977 Manch.; MD Manch. 1986; FRCP Lond. 1997; MRCP (UK) 1980. Cons. And Hon. Sen. Lecturtr in Rheum. Hope Hosp. Salford. Socs: Physiol. Soc. & Brit. Soc. Rheum.; Amer. Coll. of Rheum. Prev: Cons. Rheum. & Gen. Phys. Pinderfields Gen. Hosp. Wakefield; Sen. Regist. (Med. Rheum.) Salford HA.

COOPER, Robin Ashley Nightingales, North Road, Leigh Woods, Bristol BS8 3PL — MB BS 1990 Lond.; FRCA 1996. Specialist Regist. Rotat. S. W. Eng.

COOPER, Rosemary Claypath Medical Practice, 26 Gilesgate, Durham DH1 1QW Tel: 0191 333 2838 Fax: 0191 333 2836 — MB BS 1982 Newc.; MRCGP 1987; Dip. Ther. Newc. 1996; DRCOG 1986. (Newc. u. Tyne) Prev: Trainee GP N.umbria VTS; SHO (Paediat. & O & G) Sunderland Dist. Gen. Hosp.

COOPER, Rosemary Anne (retired) Granida, 9 East St., Hambledon, Waterlooville PO7 4RX Tel: 01705 632382 Fax: 01705 241448 — MB BChir Camb. 1951; MA Camb. 1951; FRCP Lond. 1977, M 1953. Prev: Cons. Phys. Dept. Clin. Neurophysiol. N. Staffs. Hosp. Centre.

COOPER, Ruth Elizabeth Staffa Health Centre, 85 High St., Tibshelf, Derby Tel: 01773 872252; Aled House, Stansley House Gardens, Tansley, Matlock DE4 5HQ Tel: 01692 581500 — MB ChB 1987 Birm. Prev: Trainee GP Chesterfield.

COOPER, Sally Ann Queensbridge Group Practice, 24 Hollt Street, London E8 3XP Tel: 0207 254 1101 Fax: 0207 923 1541 — MB BS 1993 Lond.; DRCOG 1997; DFFP 1997; DCH RCP Lond. 1996; MRCGP CRCGP 1998. (St. Bart. Hosp. Lond.) Gen. Pract. Principle; GP Tutor - UnderGrad. Med. Stud.s QMW, Lond.

COOPER, Professor Sally-Ann Department of Psychological Medicine, University of Glasgow, Academic Centre, Gartnavel Royal Hospital, 1055 Great Western road, Glasgow G12 0XH Tel: 0141 211 3701 Email: sacooper@clinmed.gla.ac.uk — MB BS 1985 Lond.; 2001 FRCPsych; BSc Lond. 1982; MRCPsych 1989; MD Lond. 1997. Prof. of Learning Disabilities, Univ. of Glas. and Hon. Cons. in Learning Disabilities Psychiat., Gt.er Glas. Primary Care NHS Trust.

COOPER, Samantha Jane 1 College Park Drive, Westbury-on-Trym, Bristol BS10 7AN — MB BS 1998 Lond.; MB BS Lond 1998.

COOPER, Sarosh Hormasji 95 Station Road, Hendon, London NW4 4PA — MB BS 1952 Bombay. (G.S. Med. Coll. Bombay)

COOPER, Sheldon Charles 76 Dawlish Road, Birmingham B29 7AA — MB ChB 1996 Birm. (Birm.)

COOPER, Sian Michelle 30 Barnet Lane, Barnet EN5 2DN Tel: 020 8447 0380 — MB ChB 1994 Manch.; MRCP (UK) 1998. (Manchester) Paediat. SpR Paediatric Intens. Care Unit St Mary's Hosp. Paddington. Socs: BMA; MDU; RCPCH. Prev: SHO (Community Paediat.) Nottm. Community NHS Trust; Snr SHO, Ealing; SHO (Paediat. A & E, Neurol. & Neurosurg.) QMC Nottm.

COOPER, Simon Charles Taunton and Somerset Health Trust, Musgrove Park Hospital, Taunton TA1 5DA — MB BS 1985 Lond.; MRCP (UK) 1989. Cons. Phys. Socs: Brit. Geriat. Soc. Prev: Sen. Regist. Rotat. (Med. & Geriat. Med.) Yorks. Region; Regist. (Med. & Geriat.) Bristol Roy. Infirm.; SHO Rotat. (Med.) St. Mary's Hosp. Lond.

COOPER, Simon Freeth Theatre Royal Surgery, 27 Theatre Street, Dereham NR19 2EN Tel: 01362 852800 Fax: 01362 852819 — MB BS 1977 Lond.; FRCP 2001; MRCP (UK) 1980; MRCGP 1987; DTM & H Liverp. 1984. (Char. Cross)

COOPER, Simon Peter 2 Eccles Close, Whaley Bridge, High Peak SK23 7RS — MB BS 1993 Newc.

COOPER, Stanley James (retired) 24 Corton Long Lane, Corton, Lowestoft NR32 5HA — MB ChB Ed. 1956; DObst RCOG 1959. Assoc. Specialist (Med.) James Paget Hosp. Gt. Yarmouth.

COOPER, Stephen Jason Department of Mental Health, Queen's University of Belfast, Whitla Medical Building, 97 Lisburn Road, Belfast BT9 7BL Tel: 01232 335791 Fax: 01232 324543 Email: s.cooper@queens-belfast.ac.uk — MD 1984 Belf.; MB BCh BAO 1975; MRCPsych 1980; FRCPsych 1996. (Queen's University of Belfast) Sen. Lect. Dept. Ment. Health Qu.'s Univ. Belf. Socs: Brit. Assn. Psychopharmacol.; CINP; Fell. Roy. Coll. Psychiat.

COOPER, Stephen Michael 10 Main Avenue, Totley, Sheffield S17 4FG — MB ChB 1987 Liverp.

COOPER, Susan Jill Newbridge Surgery, 129 Newbridge Hill, Bath BA1 3PT Tel: 01225 425807 Fax: 01225 447776 Email: susan.cooper@gp.181070.nhs.uk; Scotts Farm, Bury Lane, Bratton, Westbury BA13 4RD Tel: 01380 830955 — BM 1982 Soton.; MRCGP 1986; DRCOG 1984; Cert. Family Plann. JCC 1984. Prev: Trainee GP Portsmouth VTS.

COOPER, Susan Margaret Fenwick Road Surgery, 261 Fenwick Road, Giffnock, Glasgow G46 6JX Tel: 0141 531 6993 Fax: 0141 531 6997 — MB ChB 1989 Glas.; MRCGP Glas. 1995; DFFP 1995. (Glas.)

COOPER, Susan Mary Dermatology Department, Churchill Hospital, Oxford Tel: 01865 228232 — MB ChB 1984 Bristol; Certificate of Vocational Training in General Practice 1993; MRCP 1997; MRCGP 1994; DRCOG 1992. Specialist Regist. Oxf. Rotat. in Dermat. Prev: Trainee GP/SHO Wycombe & Amersham Gen. Hosps. Oxf. VTS.

COOPER, Susan Rebecca Rheumatology Dept, Kings College Hospital, Dulwich, London SW5 Tel: 020 7346 6191 Email: susieadams@compuserve.com; 108 Dora Road, Wimbeldon, London SW19 7HJ Tel: 020 8946 7822 — MB BS 1993 Lond.; BSc (Hons.) Lond. 1992; MRCP 1997. (St. Mary's Hosp. Med. Sch.) Specialist Regist. Rheum. Kings Coll. Hosp. Lond. Socs: MRCP; BSR. Prev: Clin. Research Fell. (Rheum.) King's Coll. Hosp. Lond.; SHO (Haemat. & Gen. Med.) Lewisham Hosp. NHS Trust; Whittington Hosp. NHS Trust.

COOPER, Tara Kerr St Johns Hospital, Livingston EH54 6PP Tel: 01506 419666 Fax: 01506 415269; 18A Blackford Road, Edinburgh EH9 2DS — MB BCh BAO 1980 Belf.; MRCOG (Gold Medal) 1985. Cons. St. John's Hosp. Livingston W. Lothian.

COOPER, Thomas Francis Michael 45 Wellington Square, Hastings TN34 1PN Tel: 01424 722066 Fax: 01424 718385 — MB BS 1979 Lond.; 1999 St Georges,London; MRCGP 1984; DRCOG 1981. (Char. Cross) Princip GP Hastings; GP Trainer Hastings. Socs: Christ. Med. Fell.sh. Prev: Trainee GP Crawley; Asst. Med. Dir. St. Catherines Hospice Crawley.

COOPER, Tracey Anne 4 Clent Drive, Hagley, Stourbridge DY9 9LN — BM 1990 Soton.

COOPER, Valerie Margaret Whitworth Road Surgery, 9 Whitworth Road, South Norwood, London SE25 6XN Tel: 020 8653 1414 Fax: 020 8771 3038; 9 Rayleigh Rise, South Croydon CR2 7AN Tel: 020 8653 2589 Fax: 020 8771 3038 — MB BS Med. Inst. (I) Rangoon 1965; DA Eng. 1970. Socs: BMA. Prev: SHO (Anaesth.) Dartford Gp. Hosps.; Ho. Surg. Margate Gen. Hosp.; Ho. Phys. Ramsgate Gen. Hosp.

COOPER, Vincent Waterhouses Medical Practice, Waterfall Lane, Waterhouses, Stoke-on-Trent ST10 3HT Tel: 01538 308207 Fax: 01538 308653 — MB ChB 1973 Bristol.

COOPER, Wendy Jane Kingsbridge Medical Practice, Kinsbridge Avenue, Newcastle ST5 LHP Tel: 01782 427361; 31 Redhills, Eccleshall, Stafford ST21 6JW — BM BS 1992 Nottm.; BMedSc Nottm. 1990, BM BS 1992; DRCOG 1995. GP Newc.-U-Lyme. Prev: Trainee GP N. Staffs. HA.

COOPER, William Albert Bruce (retired) 2 Parklands Drive, Fulwood, Preston PR2 9SH Tel: 01772 862731 — MB BS 1938 Durh.; MRCGP 1952. JP. Prev: Surg. Lt.-Cdr. RNVR.

COOPER, Wilson Gilmore 15 Clarendon Road, Fulwood, Sheffield S10 3TQ Tel: 0114 230 2716 — MB ChB 1953 Liverp.; FFA RCS Eng. 1963; DA Eng. 1961; DTM & H Liverp. 1955. (Liverp.) Cons. (Anaesth) N. Gen., Lodge Moor, King Edwd. VII Orthop. & Nether Edge Hosps. Sheff.; Clin. Lect. in Anaesth. Univ. Sheff. Socs: BMA. Prev: Sen. Regist. Anaesth. Roy. Liverp. Childr. Hosp. & Alder Hey Childr. Hosp. Liverp.; Regist. Anaesth. BRd.green Hosp. & Aintree Chest Unit Liverp.

COOPER, Yvonne Wandsworth Borough Council (Occupat. Health Unit), Wandsworth Town Hall, Wandsworth High St., London SW18 2PU Tel: 020 8871 8501 Fax: 020 8871 8502 — MB BS 1979 Lond.; DRCOG 1982. (Roy. Free) Indep. Occupat. Health Phys. Lond.

COOPER-SMITH, John Howard Room 6124B, War Pensions Agency, Norcross, Thornton-Cleveleys FY5 3TA — MB BS 1972 Lond.; MRCS Eng. LRCP Lond. 1972; DAvMed FOM RCP Lond. 1986; DObst RCOG 1974. (Char. Cross.) Med. Off. DSS. Blackpool. Prev: Civil. Instruc. Aviat. Med. RAF Aviat. Med. Train. Centre Leics.; Ho. Phys. W. Lond. & Char. Cross Hosps.; Ho. Surg. (Obst.) S.mead Hosp. W.bury On Trym.

COORAY, Gaston Marius Letchmore Road Surgery, 8 Letchmore Road, Radlett WD7 8HT Tel: 01923 856017 Fax: 01923 856017 — MB BS 1964 Ceylon; FFOM RCP Lond. 1994, MFOM 1980; DPH Eng. 1972; DIH Eng. 1972; DIH Soc. Apoth. Lond. 1972; Cert. Av Med. Eng. 1981. Cons. Occupat. Health W. Herts. NHS Trust; Maj. RAMC TA; Mem. Social Security Appeals Tribunal. Socs: BMA; Soc. Occupat. Med.; Mem.ANHOPS. Prev: Cons. Epidemiol. WHO Geneva; Postgrad. Research Fell. Lond. Sch. Hyg. & Trop. Med.; Employm. Med. Adviser EMAS.

COORAY, Patabendige Gamini 20 Wentworth Drive, Bedford MK41 8BB Tel: 01234 343734 — MRCS Eng. LRCP Lond. 1981; MB BS Ceylon 1967. (Peradeniya Med. Sch. Sri Lanka) Staff Doctor (Paediat.).

COORAY, Sherva Elizabeth 8 Letchmore Road, Radlett WD7 8HT Tel: 01923 856017 Fax: 01923 856017 Email: gmcooray@bizonline.co.uk — MB BS 1968 Ceylon; MRCPsych 1975; DPM Eng. 1974; FRCPsych 1999. (Univ of ceylon) Cons. Psychiat. Pk.side Health Trust, Kingsbury Hosp. Lond., Centr. Middlx. Hosp. Lond. & Lond. Boro. Brent; Hon. Sen. Lect. Learning Disabil.Imperial Coll. Socs: BMA. Prev: Regist. Harperbury Hosp. Shenley; Med. Asst. Shenley Hosp.; Cons. WHO Geneva.

COORE, Juliette Rani Department of Chemical Pathology, General Infirmary, Leeds LS2 9JT Tel: 0113 292 2798 Fax: 0113 233 5672 Email: julieco@pathology.leeds.ac.uk; 5 Earlswood Avenue, Roundhay, Leeds LS8 2BR Tel: 0113 269 6439 — MB ChB 1985 Birm.; ChB Birm. 1985; MRCPI 1992; MRCPath 1997. Sen. Regist. (Chem. Path.) Leeds Gen. Infirm. Socs: Assn. Clin. Biochem. Prev: Regist. (Chem. Path.) Qu. Med. Centre & City Hosp. Nottm.; SHO Rotat. (Med.) E. Birm. Hosp.

COORSH, Mr Jonathan Charles Queen Elizabeth Hospital, Sheriff Hill, Gateshead NE9 6SX; Stella House, 353 Durham Road, Low Fell, Gateshead NE9 5AJ Tel: 0191 440 3189 — MB BS 1988 Lond.; FRCS (Tr. & Orth.) 1999; FRCS Eng. 1993. Cons. Orthopaedic Surg.

COOTE, Annabel Louise 55 Kiln Road, Fareham PO16 7UH — MB ChB 1996 Sheff.

COOTE, Elizabeth Anne Cadbury Heath Health Centre, Parkwall Road, Cadbury Heath, Bristol BS30 8HS Tel: 0117 980 5705 Fax: 0117 980 5707 Email: drcoote.partners@gp-l81130.nhs.uk; Ground Floor Flat, Southwood House, Bannerleigh Road, Leigh Woods, Bristol BS8 3PF Tel: 0117 973 8716 Email:

anne@leighwoods.junglelink.co.uk — BM BCh 1984 Oxf.; MA Oxf. 1986. (Oxf.) Socs: BMA. Prev: SHO (O & G) Torbay Hosp. Torquay; Trainee GP Torbay HA.

COOTE, Jacqueline Margaret Dept of Radiology, Royal Devon and Exeter Hospital, Barrach Road, Exeter EX2 5DW Tel: 01392 403791 Fax: 01392 402330 Email: jmcoote@doctors.net.uk — MB BS 1986 Lond.; BSc (Hons.) Lond. 1983; MRCP (UK) 1989; FRCR 1994. (St George's hosp Med School London) p/t Sen. Regist. SW Rotat.; Cons in clin Radiol. Radiol. Dept Roy. Devon & Exeter Hosp (Wonford) Exeter. Prev: Sen Regist Radiol. SW Rotat., S.; Sen Regist Radiol. S W Rotat.; Regist. (Radiol.) Univ. Hosp. Wales Cardiff.

COOTE, Joanna Helen 150 Stockport Road, Mossley, Ashton-under-Lyne OL5 0RQ — MB ChB 1998 Manch.; MB ChB Manch 1998.

COOTE, Marie Josephe Arlette Nadia 4 Paddock Close, Blackheath Park, London SE3 0ES Tel: 020 8852 8008 — MB BCh BAO NUI 1960; FFA RCSI 1975; DA Eng. 1962. p/t Cons. in Pain Relief, The Blackheath Hosp. 40-42 Lee Terr., Lond. SE3 9UD. Socs: Assn. Anaesth.; Pain Soc.; BMA. Prev: Cons. Anaesth. Greenwich Health Dist.

COOTE, Nicola Mary Ann 43 Bouverie Road, London N16 0AH — MB ChB 1989 Leeds; MRCP (UK) 1993.

COOTE, Suzanne Elizabeth Tree Tops, Redman, Cockermouth CA13 0PZ — BM BS 1996 Nottm.

COOZE, Peter Huw 5 Adam Walk, Cwrt Herbert, Neath SA10 7DA — MB BCh 1983 Wales.

COPCUTT, Eva Gwendolen Crooked Thatch, East End, Hook Norton, Banbury OX15 5LG Tel: 01608 737498 — MB BS 1939 Lond.; MRCS Eng. LRCP Lond. 1939; MRCGP 1975. (Univ. Coll. Hosp.)

COPE, Alison 26 Grasmere Road, Royton, Oldham OL2 6SR — MB ChB 1996 Leic.

COPE, Andrew Ian The Avenue Surgery, 71 The Avenue, Wivenhoe, Colchester CO7 9PP Tel: 01206 824447 Fax: 01206 827973 — MB BS 1989 Lond.; DRCOG 1995; MRCGP 1995. (St. Mary's) Socs: Colchester Med. Soc.

COPE, Andrew Paul The Kennedy Institute of Rheumatology, Immunology Division, 1 Aspenlead Road, London W6 8LH Tel: 0802 383 4444 Fax: 0802 383 4499 Email: a.cope@ic.ac.uk; 1 Telegraph Lane, Claygate, Esher KT10 0DT Tel: 01372 463485 — MB BS 1985 Lond.; MB BS (Hons.) Lond. 1985; PhD Lond. 1994, BSc (Hons.) 1982; MRCP (UK) 1988; ECFMG 1985. Wellcome Sen. Fell. In Clini. Sci.; Sen. Lect. In Rheum. (Imperial Coll. Sch. Of Med).; Hon. Cons. Rheum. (Hammersmith Hosp. Trust). Socs: Roy. Soc. Med. (Hom. Sec. Clini immunol & Allergy Sect.); Amer. Coll. Of Rheum; Brit. Soc. Rheum. Prev: Wellcome Postdoctoral Research Schol. (Immunol.) Stanford Univ. Sch. Med.; Wellcome Clin. Research Fell. & Hon. Regist. (Rheum.) Char. Cross Hosp. Lond.; Regist. (Rheum.) Char. Cross Hosp. Lond.

COPE, Mr Andrew Robert Accident & Emergency, Peterborough District Hospital, Thorpe Road, Peterborough PE3 6DA — MB BS 1976 Lond.; MRCS Eng. LRCP Lond. 1976; FRCS Eng. 1983. Cons. A & E P'boro. Dist. Hosp.; Lt. Col. RAMC (V); ATLS Instruc., RCS 1988; ALS Instruc., Europ. Resusc. Counc. Socs: Brit. Assn. Accid. & Emerg. Med. & Emerg. Med. Research Soc. Prev: ATLS Instruc. RCS 1988; Sen. Specialist (Surg.) RAMC; Sen. Regist. St. Bart. Hosp. Lond.

COPE, Arthur Gwyn (retired) 4 Lucas Road, High Wycombe HP13 6QE — MRCS Eng. LRCP Lond. 1953. Prev: Med. Off. Ment. Retarded Old People Residen. Homes Bucks CC.

COPE, Denise Alderney Hospital, Ringwood Road, Poole BH12 4NB Tel: 01202 735537 — MB ChB 1982 Manch.; BSc St. And. 1979; MRCPsych 1988; MRCGP 1987; DRCOG 1986. Cons. Old Age Psychiat. Dorset Healthcare Trust. Prev: Sen. Regist. Rotat. (Psychiat.) Wessex; Regist. (Psychiat.) Roy. S. Hants. Hosp. Soton.

COPE, Derek Hubert Patrick (retired) 2 Bingham Place, London W1U 5AT Tel: 020 7935 1015 — MB BS 1945 Lond.; MRCS Eng. LRCP Lond. 1945; FFA RCS Eng. 1953; DA Eng. 1950. Hon. Anaesth. Hosp. SS. John & Eliz. Lond. Prev: Adviser in Anaesth. Proc. King Edwd. VII Hosp. Offs. Lond.

COPE, Edward (retired) Pond Side, Cumnor Village, Oxford Tel: 01865 862488 — MB ChB 1939 Leeds; MD (Distinc.) Leeds 1948; FRCOG 1960, M 1949. Cons. O & G Oxon. HA; Clin. Lect. Univ. Oxf.; Examr. Obst. & Gyn. Univ. Sheff., Birm., Leeds, & Oxf.; Mem. Counc. Examr. RCOG. Prev: Cons. O & G Dudley Rd. Hosp. Birm.

COPE, Elizabeth Mary Squire and Partners, Market Place, Hadleigh, Ipswich IP7 5DN Tel: 01473 822961 Fax: 01473 824895 — BM BS 1984 Nottm.; MRCGP 1988; DRCOG 1988.

COPE, Helen Margaret The Wellcome Trust, 183 Euston Road, London NW1 2BE Tel: 020 7611 8888 Fax: 020 7611 8687 — MB ChB 1985 Ed.; MRCPsych 1990. Scientif. Prog. Manager, Career Developm. Grp. Wellcome Trust; Hon. Sen. Lect. Inst. Psychiat. Lond. Prev: Clin. Lect. (Neuropsychiat.) Inst. Psychiat. & Inst. Neurol. Lond.

COPE, Ivor James 9 Ridgway Road, Barton Seagrave, Kettering NN15 5AQ — MRCS Eng. LRCP Lond. 1954; MFCM 1973; DPH Lond. 1967. Prev: SCMO Kettering Health Dist.

COPE, James (retired) 19 Hillside Gardens, Barnet EN5 2NG Tel: 020 8449 0757 — MB BS 1957 Lond. Prev: Med. Adviser Insur. & other Cos.

COPE, John Thomas (retired) Craven House, Swineshead, Boston PE20 3LR Tel: 01205 820355 — MB BS 1950 Lond.; MRCS Eng. LRCP Lond. 1950.

COPE, Lance Henry South Tyneside District Hospital, South Shields NE34 0PL Tel: 0191 254 8888; Stone Villa, Lansdowne Road, Forest Hall, Newcastle upon Tyne NE12 9BL — MB BS 1980 Lond.; MA Camb. 1981; MRCP (UK) 1983; FRCR 1987. Cons. Radiol. S. Shields Gen. Hosp.

COPE, Marcus Robert 36 Valley View, Jesmond, Newcastle upon Tyne NE2 2JS — MB BS 1996 Newc.

COPE, Margaret Anne St John's Group Practice, 1 Greenfield Lane, Balby, Doncaster DN4 0TH — MB ChB 1980 Sheff.; DRCOG 1983.

COPE, Mr Martin Russell Humberside Maxillofacial Unit, Hull Royal Infirmary, Anlaby Road, Hull HU3 2JZ Tel: 01482 4793 Fax: 01482 5064 — MB BS 1989 Lond.; BChD Leeds 1980; FRCS Ed. 1994; FDS RCS Eng. 1984; FRCS 1995 (Maxfac intercollegiate). Cons. (Oral & Maxillofacial Surg.) Hull Roy. Infirm. Kingston Upon Hull. Socs: Fell. Brit. Assn. Oral & Maxillofacial Surg. Prev: Sen. Regist. (Maxillofacial Surg.) Canniesburn Hosp. Glas.; SHO (A & E & Orthop.) St. Richards Hosp. Chichester; Ho. Off. Roy. Surrey Co. Hosp.

COPE, Martin Terry 12 Ravenscourt Place, Gateshead NE8 1PP; 30 Saltwell View, Gateshead NE8 4NT — MB ChB 1973 Leeds.

COPE, Nansi Margaret (retired) 26 Constitution Hill, Sudbury CO10 2PT Tel: 01787 70122 — MB ChB 1949 Sheff.

COPE, Nichola Jane 3 Rosebarn Avenue, Pennsylvania, Exeter EX4 6DY — MB ChB 1987 Bristol. Regist. (Histopath.) Roy. Devon. & Exeter Hosp.

COPE, Paul Gough Lowesmoor Medical Centre, 93 Lowesmoor, Worcester WR1 2SA Tel: 01905 723441; Whittington Grange, Worcester WR5 2RD Tel: 01905 356425 — MB BS 1960 Lond. (Middlx.)

COPE, Rosemarie Vivienne Reaside Clinic, Birmingham Great Park, Rubery, Birmingham B45 9BE Tel: 0121 678 3000 Fax: 0121 678 3041 — MB ChB 1969 Birm.; FRCPsych 1989, M 1974; DPM Eng. 1972. Clin. Dir. & Cons. Forens. Psychiat. Reaside Clinic Birm.; Mem. Ct. of electors, Roy. Coll. Psychiat.; Regional Adviser in Psychiat. for registration; Midl. Region, Roy. Coll. Psychiat.; Hon. Sen. Clin. Lect. Birm. Prev: Sen. Regist. & Regist. (Psychiat.) All St.s' Hosp. Birm.; SHO (Psychiat.) Qu. Eliz. Hosp. Birm.

COPE, Sally Jane Ashfield Surgery, 8 Walmley Road, Sutton Coldfield B76 1QN Tel: 0121 351 7955 Fax: 0121 313 2509; 1 Blakesley Close, Walmley, Sutton Coldfield B76 1EF — MB ChB 1985 Manch.; BSc St. And. 1982.

COPE, Mr Simon Andrew — MB BCh 1990 Wales; DFFP 1993; FRCS Eng. 1997. (Univ. Wales, Coll. Med.) Specialist Regist. (A&E). MusGr. Pk. Hosp. Taunton.; SHO (Anaesth.) Yeovil Dist. Hosp. Prev: SHO (Thoracic Surg.) Frenchay Hosp. Bristol; SHO (Gen. Surg. & Urol.) W.on Gen. Hosp.; SHO (A & E) Derriford Hosp. Plymouth.

COPE, Stephen Frederick James Street Surgery, 2 James Street, Boston PE21 8RF Tel: 01205 362556 Fax: 01205 359050; Beaulieu, London Road, Frampton, Boston PE20 1BP — MB ChB 1973 Sheff.; MRCGP 1977; DRCOG 1978. (Sheff.) Prev: Trainee GP Boston VTS; Ho. Off. (Gen. Med.) Lodge Moor Hosp. Sheff.; Ho. Off. (Orthop. & Cas.) N.. Gen. Hosp. Sheff.

COPE, Susan Janet South London & Maudsley NHS Trust, Ladywell Unit, University Hospital Lewisham, London SE13 Tel: 020 8833 3000 Email: susan.cope@slam-tr.nhs.uk — MB BChir 1975 Camb.; MA; FRCPsych 1996, M 1980. Cons. Psychiat. & Sen. Lect.S. Lond. and Maudsley NHS Trust. Prev: Sen. Regist. Rotat. Lond. Hosp. & Maudsley Hosp. Lond.

COPE, Tristan Mark 53 Whitchurch Road, Chester CH3 5QB — MB ChB 1992 Aberd.

COPE, Victor 8 Oak Lea Avenue, Fulshaw Park, Wilmslow SK9 1QL Tel: 01625 527120 — MB BChir 1956 Camb.; FFR 1965; DMRD Eng. 1960. (Camb.) Cons. Radiol. Manch. Roy. Infirm. Prev: Ho. Phys. & Ho. Surg. & Sen. Regist. (Radiol.) Radcliffe Infirm. Oxf.

COPELAND, Basil Irwin 87-89 Prince of Wales Road, London NW5 3NT Tel: 020 7267 0067; Flat 1, 16 Lyndhurst Road, London NW3 5NL Tel: 020 7435 8121 — MRCS Eng. LRCP Lond. 1951. (Guy's) Prev: Asst. (ENT.) St. Stephens Hosp. Lond.; Ho. Phys. St. Alfege's Hosp. Greenwich.

COPELAND, Claire Louise 1 Calais Burn Place, Dunfermline KY11 4RD — MB ChB 1998 Dund.; MB ChB Dund 1998.

COPELAND, Goetz Guy Flat 6, Hunter Court, 5 Swynford Gardens, London NW4 4XL — MB ChB 1956 Liverp.

COPELAND, Mr Graham Paul BUPA North Cheshire, Fir Tree Close, Stretton, Warrington WA4 4LU; 1 Heyes Grove, Rainford, St Helens, St Helens WA11 8BW Tel: 0115 925502, 01744 889021 — MB BS 1976 Lond.; ChM Liverp. 1987; FRCS Lond. 1981. Cons. Gen. Surg. Warrington Dist. Gen. Hosp.; Hon. Lect. Univ. Liverp.; Chairm. Clin. Audit. Warrington; Clin. Governance Lead, Warrington. Prev: Sen. Regist. (Gen. Surg.) Liverp.

COPELAND, Jenifer Ann Marie Ryan Purvis and Partners, The Hart Surgery, York Road, Henley-on-Thames RG9 2DR Tel: 01491 843204 Fax: 01491 411296; Woodlands, Woodlands Road, Harpsden, Henley-on-Thames RG9 4AA — MB BS Lond. 1970; MRCS Eng. LRCP Lond. 1970. (St. Bart.) Prev: Ho. Phys. St. Leonard's Hosp. Lond.; Ho. Surg. Surgic. Profess. Unit St. Bart. Hosp. Lond.

COPELAND, Professor John Richard Malcolm (retired) University Of Liverpool Department of Psychiatry Academic Unit, St Catherine's Hospital, Birkenhead, Wirral CH42 0LG Tel: 0151 604 7333 Fax: 0151 653 3441 Email: jrmcop@liverpool.ac.uk — MB MB BChir Camb. 1957; MA, BA Camb. 1953, MD 1975; FRCP Lond. 1980, M 1963; MRCS Eng. LRCP Lond. 1956; FRCPsych 1978, M 1971; DPM Lond. 1966. Dir. Inst. Human Ageing Liverp.; Hon. Cons. Psychiat. N. Mersey Community Trust. Prev: Prof. & Head Dept. Psychiat. Univ. Liverp.

COPELAND, Linda Elsa Kathleen Springburn Health Centre, 200 Springburn Way, Glasgow G21 1TR Tel: 0141 531 9671 Fax: 0141 531 6705; 6 Muirhead Way, Bishopbriggs, Glasgow G64 1YG — MB ChB 1975 Glas.; MRCGP 1979; DRCOG 1977.

COPELAND, Paul Francis (retired) 21 Moorside S., Fenham, Newcastle upon Tyne NE4 9BD — MB BS 1964 Durh.; FFA RCS Eng. 1969. Cons. Anaesth. Freeman Hosp. NHS Trust. Prev: Sen. Regist. (Anaesth.) Regional Neurosurg. Unit Newc. Gen. Hosp.

COPELAND, Mr Stephen Andrew Berkshire Independent Hospital, Wensley Road, Reading RG1 1UZ Tel: 0118 902 8063 Fax: 01734 757790 Email: stephen.copeland@btinernet.com; Woodlands, Woodlands Road, Harpsden, Henley-on-Thames RG9 4AA Tel: 01189 402114 Fax: 01189 401255 Email: s.copeland@msn.com — MB BS 1970 Lond.; FRCS Eng. 1975; MRCS Eng. LRCP Lond. 1970. (St. Bart.) Cons. Orthop. Surg. Roy. Berks. Hosp. Reading; Dir. Internat. Bd. Shoulder Surg.; Pres. Europ. Shoulder & Elbow Soc. Socs: Fell. BOA; Fell. (Counc. Mem.) Roy. Soc. Med.; Ex Pres. & Founder Mem. Brit. Elbow & Shoulder Surg. Soc. Prev: Sen. Regist. (Orthop.) St. Bart. Hosp. Lond.; Clin. Lect. Inst. Orthop. Lond.; Hon. Sen. Regist. Roy. Nat. Orthop. Hosp. Lond.

COPEMAN, Annabel Jane Long Cliff, Bates Lane, Helsby, Warrington WA6 9LJ — MB BS 1993 Lond.

COPEMAN, Peter William Monckton 82 Sloane Street, London SW1X 9PA Tel: 020 7245 9333 Fax: 020 7245 9232; 20 Spencer Park, London SW18 2SZ Tel: 020 8874 7549 — MB BChir Camb. 1957; MD Camb. 1972, MA 1956; FRCP Lond. 1974, M 1962. (Camb. & St. Thos.) Hons. Cons. Dermat. St. Luke's Hosp. for Clergy Lond. Socs: Fell. Europ. Soc. Clin. Investig.; Brit. Assn. Dermat. (Willan Librarian); Fell. Med. Soc. Lond. Prev: Cons. Phys. (Dis. of Skin) W.m. Hosp. Lond., W.m. Childr. Hosp. & Qu. Mary'sHosp. Roehampton; Research Fell. Mayo Clinic Rochester, Minn. USA 1968; Regist. (Med.) St. Thos. Hosp. Lond.

COPEMAN, Richard Alwyn 5 Platt Street, London NW1 1RN Tel: 020 7387 4669 — MB BS 1976 Lond.; MRCS Eng. LRCP Lond. 1976; MFOM 1990; MRCGP 1980; DCH Eng. 1979; DRCOG 1978. (Westm.) Cons. Occupat. Phys. BMI Occupat.al Health, Lond. Prev: GP Lond.; Cons. Occupat. Phys. Roy. Lond. Hosp. Whitechapel Lond.

COPENHAGEN, Harald John Farnell House Medical Centre, 25 Spring Grove Road, Hounslow TW3 4BE Tel: 020 8570 0143 Fax: 020 8572 2888; 132 Argyle Road, London W13 8ER Tel: 020 8998 6646 Fax: 020 8998 9995 — MB ChB 1960 Cape Town; MRCGP 1993. (Univ. of Cape Town) Clin. Asst. (Plastic & Reconstruc. Surg.) W. Middlx. Univ. Hosp.; Freeman of the City of Lond. Socs: Fell. Roy. Soc. Med.; Allied Assoc. Brit. Assn. Plastic Surg. Prev: Wellcome Trust Research Fell. & Regist. (Surg.) Hammersmith Hosp. Lond.; Regist. (Surg.) Groote Schuur Hosp. Cape Town; Ho. Surg. Profess. Unit Hammersmith Hosp. Lond.

COPITHORNE, Richard Ernest Cornish, VRD (retired) Keri, 237 Oulton Road, Lowestoft NR32 4QX — MRCS Eng. LRCP Lond. 1933; MRCS Eng. LRCP, Lond. 1933; DCH Eng. 1936, DPH 1950. Prev: PMO (Sch. Health) GLC.

COPLAND, Allan McKenzie Ashbank, Church St., Monifieth, Dundee DD5 — MB ChB 1990 Dundee.

COPLAND, Derek Robert The Belmont Medical Centre, 53-57 Belmont Road, Uxbridge UB8 1SD Tel: 01895 233211 Fax: 01895 812099 — MB ChB 1975 Aberd. Prev: Trainee GP Lond. (St. Thos.) VTS; Ho. Surg. St. Stephen's Hosp. Chelsea; Ho. Phys. Aberd. Roy. Infirm.

COPLAND, Elizabeth June (retired) 25 Belgrave Crescent, Edinburgh EH4 3AL Tel: 0131 343 6743 — MB BS 1948 Durh. Prev: Ho. Surg. Newc. Gen. Hosp.

COPLAND, John Lanark Doctors, Health Centre, South Vennel, Lanark ML11 7JT Tel: 01555 665522 Fax: 01555 666857; 41 Albany Drive, Lanark ML11 9AF Tel: 01555 664106 Email: janniecop@aol.com — MB ChB 1977 Glas.; MRCGP 1981. (glasgow)

COPLAND, Mhairi Aberdeen Royal Hospitals NHS Trust, Foresterhill, Aberdeen AB25 2ZB Tel: 01224 681818; 111 Sunnyside Road, Aberdeen AB24 3LS Tel: 01224 482139 — MB ChB 1996 Aberd.; BSc (Med. Sci.) Aberd. 1994. SHO (Med.) Aberd. Roy. Hosps. NHS Trust.

COPLAND, Mr Robert Frank Paul Chase Farm Hospital, The Ridgeway, Enfield EN2 8JL Tel: 020 8366 6600 — MB BS 1969 Lond.; FRCS Eng. 1973; MRCS Eng. LRCP Lond. 1969; Acad. Dipl. Gen. Biochem. Univ. Lond. 1967. (St. Mary's) Cons. Urol. Enfield & Haringey AHA. Prev: Sen. Regist. (Urol.) St. Mary's Hosps. Lond.; Regist. (Gen. Surg. & Urol.) Sheff. Roy. Hosp.; Regist. (Gen. Surg.) Nottm. Univ. Gp. Hosps.

COPLAND, Shirley Ann Aberdeen Royal Hospitals NHS Trust, Aberdeen Royal Infirmary, Foresterhill, Aberdeen AB25 2ZN Tel: 01224 681818; 64 Newburgh Circle, Bridge of Don, Aberdeen AB22 8QZ — MB ChB 1980 Aberd.; MB ChB (Hons.) Aberd. 1980; MRCP (UK) 1984. Staff Grade (Gen. Med., Endocrinol. & Diabetes) Aberd. Roy. Infirm. Socs: BMA; Scott. Soc. Experim. Med.; Brit. Diabetic Assn. Prev: Research Regist. Grampian HB & Rowett Research Inst. Aberd.

COPLAND, Mr William Alexander, VRD (retired) 25 Belgrave Crescent, Edinburgh EH4 3AL Tel: 0131 343 6743 — MB ChB 1946 Aberd.; FRCS Ed. 1975; FRCR 1975; FFR 1956; DMRD Bristol 1952; DMRD Eng. 1952. Prev: Cons. Radiol. Admin i/c W.. Gen. Hosp. Edin.

COPLEY, Ernest Lionel (retired) 7 Chestnut Grove, Carleton, Pontefract WF8 3NG Tel: 01977 702817 — MB ChB 1949 Leeds. Prev: Dermat. Ho. Phys. Gen. Infirm. Leeds.

COPLIN, Jacqueline Clare 13 Shutehay Drive, Willow Rise, Cam, Dursley GL11 5UU Tel: 01453 548636 — MB BS 1963 Lond. (Roy. Free) Clin. Med. Off. Severn NHS Trust. Prev: Clin. Med. Off. Surrey AHA.; Ho. Surg. & Ho. Phys. Amersham Gen. Hosp.

COPP, Professor Andrew John Institute of Child Health, 30 Guilford St., London WC1N 1EH Tel: 020 7242 9789 Fax: 020 7831 4366 Email: a.copp@ich.ucl.ac.uk — MB BS 1983 Lond.; DPhil, MA Oxf. 1978. Prof. & Hon. Cons. Inst. Child Health Gt. Ormond St. Hosp. Sick Childr. Lond. Socs: (Pres.) Developm. Path. Soc. Prev: Research Sci. Head of Med. Embryol. Research Laborat.

Imperial Cancer Research Fund Oxf.; Fogarty Internat. Research Fell. Dept. Stanford Univ. Med. Centre, USA.

COPP, Edward Peter (retired) Alderley, 11 Park Road, Disley, Stockport SK12 2NA Tel: 01663 766409 Fax: 01663 766409 Email: coppep@doctors.org.uk — MB ChB Manch. 1955; MD Manch 1965; DPhysMed 1962. Hon. Cons. Rheum. & Rehabil. Manch. Centr. Hosp. Trust.

COPP, Louise Victoria Gardens Surgery, Victoria Gardens, Neath SA11 1HW Tel: 01639 643786 Fax: 01639 640018 — MB BCh 1988 Wales; BSc (Anat.) Cardiff 1985; MRCGP 1992; DCH RCP Lond. 1991. (Univ. Wales Coll. Med.) GP Princip. Prev: Staff Grade (A & E) P. Philip Hosp. LLa.lli.; Trainee GP/SHO W. Wales Hosp. Carmarthen VTS.

COPP, Michael Vivian Department of Anaesthesia, Cheltenham General Hospital, Sandford Road, Cheltenham GL53 7AN Tel: 01242 274143 Fax: 01242 273405 Email: michael.copp@egnhst.co.uk — MB BS 1983 Lond.; FRCA 1990. (King's College Hospital) Cons. Anaesth. Cheltenham Gen. Hosp. Prev: Sen. Regist. (Anaesth.) Soton.; Research Regist. (Anaesth.) Lond. Chest. Hosp.; Regist. (Anaesth.) Middlx. Hosp. Lond.

COPP, Peter Alexander James Dalkeith Medical Centre, 24-26 St Andrew St., Dalkeith EH22 1AP Tel: 0131 663 2461; 46 Lauder Road, Edinburgh EH9 1UE Tel: 0131 667 6313 Fax: 0131 662 8949 Email: gp.plus@virgin.net — MB ChB 1984 Ed.; MRCGP 1989; DFFP 1994; DCCH RCS Ed. 1989; DRCOG 1988. Private.GP. Med.Dir.GP Plus. Socs: Primary Care Rheum. Soc.; Med. Dent. Hypn. Soc.

COPP, Sydney, CStJ (retired) Tredale, 11 Despenser Road, Sully, Penarth CF64 5JX Tel: 029 2053 1526 — MRCS Eng. LRCP Lond. 1945; FRCGP 1981. Prev: Regional Med. Off. Welsh Office.

COPP, Thomas Arthur (retired) 115 Surrenden Road, Brighton BN1 6WB Tel: 01273 553653 — MRCS Eng. LRCP Lond. 1943; FFA RCS Eng. 1953; DA Eng. 1945. Prev: Cons. Anaesth., Brighton.

COPPACK, James Samuel Nesfield Cottage, 96 Main St., Ebberston, Scarborough YO13 9NJ — MB BS 1989 Lond.; MRCGP 1993.

COPPACK, Jeremy John Norwood House Surgery, Belle Vue Street, Scarborough YO12 7EJ Tel: 01723 374485 Fax: 01723 501517 — MB ChB 1985 Leeds.

COPPACK, Simon Ward Alexandra Wing, Medical Unit, Royal London Hospital, Whitechapel, London E1 1BB Email: s.w.coppack@qmul.ac.uk; 23 Ingram Road, East Finchley, London N2 9QA — MB BS 1980 Lond.; MB BS (Hons.) Lond. 1980; MD Lond. 1993, BSc 1977; FRCP Glas. 1994; MRCP (UK) 1983; FRCP Lond. 1998. (Westminster) Reader, St. Bartholemews & Roy. Lond. Sch. of Med. Prev: Sen. Lect., Univ. Coll. Lond. Med. Sch.; Sen. Regist. Radcliffe Infirm. Oxf.; Vis. Scientist Mayo Clinic Rochester, USA.

COPPEL, Dennis Leslie (retired) 34 Deramore Park S., Belfast BT9 5JY — MB BCh BAO 1960 Belf.; FFA RCSI 1967. Cons. Anaesth. Roy. Vict. Hosp. Belf. Prev: Asst. Vis. Prof. Univ. Texas, Dallas.

COPPEN, Alec James 5 Walnut Close, Downs Road, Epsom KT18 5JL Tel: 01372 720800 Fax: 01372 742602 — MB ChB Bristol 1953; DSc Bristol 1979, MD 1958; FRCP Lond. 1980, M 1975; Hon FRCPsych 1995; DPM Lond. 1957. Emerit. Psychiat. W. Pk. Hosp. Epsom; Hon. Fell. Coll. Internat. Neuropsychopharmacol.; Hon. Mem. (Ex-Chairm.) Europ. Collegium Neuropsychopharmacologicum; Corr. Mem. Deutsche Gesellschaft fur Psychiatrie und Nervenheilkunde. Socs: Disting. Fell. Amer. Psychiat. Assn.; (Ex-Pres.) Brit. Assn. Psychopharmacol. (lifetime achievement gold medal). Prev: Hon. Sen. Regist. & Regist. Bethlem Roy. & Maudsley Hosp. Lond.; Ho. Surg. & Ho. Phys. Bristol Roy. Infirm.

COPPEN, Michael James Department of Histopathology, Mayday University Hospital, London Road, Croydon CR7 7YE; Five Furlong House, 97 Tattenham Crescent, Epsom KT18 5NY Tel: 0737 357559 Fax: 01737 218364 Email: regina.coppen@kcl.ac.uk — MB BS 1978 Lond.; MRCPath 1985; FRCPath 1996. Cons. Histopath. Mayday Healthcare NHS Trust Croydon. Socs: Assn. Cin. Path. & Brit. Soc. Clin. Cytol.; Internat. Acad. Path.; FRCPath. Prev: Sen. Regist. (Histopath.) Univ. Coll. & Whittington Hosps. Lond.; Regist. (Path.) Guy's Hosp. Lond.; Ho. Surg. Roy. Free Hosp. Lond.

COPPEN, Richard John Paediatric Department, Poole General Hospital, Longfleet Road, Poole BH15 2JB Tel: 01202 442382 Fax: 01202 442822 Email: rcoppen@ poole-tr.swest.nhs.uk; Tel: 01202 708601 — MB ChB 1974 Bristol; MRCP (UK) 1976; FRCP UK 1995; FRCPCH 1997. Cons. Paediat. Community Child Health Poole Hosp. NHS Trust. Prev: Regist. (Paediat.) Stroke Mandeville Hosp. Aylesbury; Sen. (Clin. Med. Off.) Dorset HA.

COPPENS, Marc 20 Charles Avenue, Lenton Abbey, Nottingham NG9 2SH — MD 1990 Antwerp.

COPPER, James Robert Department Health Care of Elderly, Derriford Hospital, Plymouth PL6 8DH Tel: 01752 792890 Fax: 01752 792894; 82 Stentaway Road, Plymstock, Plymouth PL9 7EE Tel: 01752 407678 Fax: 01752 481160 — BM BCh 1970 Oxf.; MA Oxf. 1970; FRCP Lond. 1992; FRCP Ed. 1985; MRCP (UK) 1977. (Univ. of Oxford) Cons. Phys. (Gen. Med. & c/o Elderly) Plymouth Hosps. NHS Trust & Plymouth Primary Care Trust; Hon. Lect. Univ. St. John's Newfld., Canada; Hon. Lect. Plymouth Postgrad. Med. Sch.; Hon. Lect. Coll. St. Mark & St. John Plymouth; Med. Dir. Plymouth Primary Care Trust Reviewer, Health Advis. Serv. Lond. Socs: Fell. Roy. Soc. Med.; Brit. Geriat. Soc.

COPPIN, Alan Frank Cyril (retired) 8 Warfield Avenue, Waterlooville PO7 7JJ Tel: 023 9226 2375 — MB BS 1952 Lond.; MRCGP 1960.

COPPIN, Brian David 21 Wryneck Close, Lordswood, Southampton SO16 8FJ — MB ChB 1988 Cape Town; MRCP (UK) 1995; DA (SA) 1990. Research Fell. (Clin. Genetics) Wessex Clin. Genetics Serv. Prev: Regist. (Paediat.) St. Geo. Hosp. Lond.; SHO (Paediat. Cardiol.) Soton. Gen. Hosp.; SHO (Neonat.) John Radcliffe Hosp. Oxf.

COPPIN, Charles Michael Stevenson (retired) 33 Park Lawn, Church Road, Farnham Royal, Slough SL2 3AP Tel: 01753 646807 Fax: 01753 642223 — BM BCh 1954 Oxf.; MA Oxf. 1954; FFOM RCP Lond. 1982, MFOM 1978; Dip Occ Hyg Lond. 1962; DIH Soc. Apoth. Lond. 1960. Prev: Med. Dir. Slough Occupat. Health Serv.

COPPIN, Richard John Oakley and Overton Partnership, Overton Surgery, Station Road, Overton, Basingstoke RG25 3DU Tel: 01256 770212 Fax: 01256 771581; Hazeldown, Hatchgate, Steventon, Basingstoke RG25 3BJ Tel: 01256 397361 — BM BS 1975 Nottm.; BMedSci Nottm. 1973; DRCOG 1977. (Nottm.) Prev: SHO (Paediat.) Basingstoke Dist. Hosp.; SHO (O & G) Odstock Hosp. Salisbury; Ho. Phys. Nottm. Gen. Hosp.

COPPING, David Matthew Lazybed, Headley Fields, Headley, Bordon GU35 8PS — MB BS 1991 Lond.

COPPING, Joanna Ruth 15 Henry Road, West Bridgford, Nottingham NG2 7NA — BM BS 1992 Nottm.; BMedSci Nottm. 1990; DRCOG 1995; DFFP 1998; MRCGP 1998. (Nottingham)

COPPINGER, Mr Stephen William Valentine Department of Urology, Royal Shrewsbury Hospital NHS Trust, Mytton Oak Road, Shrewsbury SY3 8XQ Tel: 01743 261441 Fax: 01743 261062; 23 The Crescent, Town Walls, Shrewsbury SY1 1TH Tel: 01743 233 3421 Fax: 01743 353774 Email: stephen.coppinger@virgin.net — MB BS 1979 Lond.; FRCS (Urol.) 1995; FRCS Ed. 1984; FRCS Eng. 1984; MS Lond. 1997. (Middlx.) Cons. Urol. Roy. Shrewsbury Hosp. & P.ss Roy. Hosp. Shrops. Socs: Brit. Assn. Urol. Surgs.; Fell. Roy. Soc. Med. (Prev. Counc. Mem. Sect. Urol.). Prev: Cons. Urol. N. Staffs. (NHS) Trust Stoke-on-Trent; Sen. Regist. (Urol.) St. Peter's Hosp. Lond.

COPPLESTONE, John Adrian Department of Haematology, Derriford Hospital, Derriford Road, Plymouth PL6 8DH Tel: 01752 777111 Fax: 01752 792400 Email: adrian.copplestone@phnt.swest.nhs.uk — MB BS 1978 Lond.; MB BS (Hons.) Lond. 1978; FRCP Lond. 1994; MRCP (UK) 1980; MRCS Eng. LRCP Lond. 1978; FRCPath 1995, M 1986. (St Bartholomew's) Cons. Haemat. Derriford Hosp. Plymouth.

COPPLESTONE, John Francis B10 Shirley Towers, Vane Hill Road, Torquay TQ1 2BX — MB BS 1954 Lond.

COPPLESTONE-BRUCE, Jeremy Charles 30 Broadway, Fulwood, Preston PR2 9TH — MB ChB 1998 Leeds; BSc (Hons.); Dphil (Oxon.).

COPPOCK, Janet Mary (retired) The White House, Groesffordd, Brecon LD3 7SN Tel: 01874 665284 — MB BCh 1951 Wales. Prev: Asst. Ystradgynlais GP Powys.

COPPOCK, Jennifer Eileen 115 Beechwood Avenue, Earlsdon, Coventry CV5 6FQ Tel: 024 76 679020 — MB BS 1977 Lond.; DA

Eng. 1979. (Univ. Coll. Hosp.) SCMO Blood Transfus. (Apheresis) Birm.

COPPOCK, John Stuart Department of Rheumatology, Walsgrave Hospital, Phase 4: Ground Floor, Clifford Bridge Road, Walsgrave, Coventry CV2 2DX; 115 Beechwood Avenue, Earlsdon, Coventry CV5 6FQ — MB BS 1977 Lond.; BSc (Hons.) (Biochem.) Lond. 1974; FRCP Lond. 1994; MRCP (UK) 1982. Cons. Rheum. Walsgrave Hosps. NHS Trust Coventry & Geo. Eliot NHS Trust Nuneaton; Hon. Vis. Sen. Clin. Lect. (Rheum.) Univ. Warwick. Prev: Sen. Regist. (Rheum. & Gen. Med.) St. Barts. & Whipps Cross Hosps. Lond.; Sheldon Clin. Research Fell. Qu. Eliz. Hosp. Birm.

COPPOCK, Lee Alexander 11 Bleasdale Close, Aughton Green, Ormskirk L39 6RU — MB ChB 1991 Sheff.

COPPOCK, Phillipa Jane Greasby Surgery, Greasby Health Centre, Greasby Road, Greasby, Wirral CH49 3NH Tel: 0151 678 3000 Fax: 0151 604 1813; Breeze How, Mill Hey Road, Caldy, Wirral CH48 1ND Tel: 0151 625 7467 — MB BS 1981 Lond.; MRCS Eng. LRCP Lond. 1981; DRCOG 1984. (Guy's Hosp.) GP Wirral. Socs: MRCGP.

COPPOCK, William Arthur The White House, Groesfford, Brecon LD3 7SN Tel: 01874 86284 — MB BS 1986 Lond.; MRCGP 1991; DRCOG 1990.

COPPOLA, Anne Mary Tate 17 Greville Road, Southampton SO15 5AW — BM 1998 Soton.

COPPOLA, William Gerald Tate Department of Primary Care & Population Sciences, Archway Resource Centre, 2nd Floor,, Holborn union Building, Highgate Hill, London N19 5LW Tel: 020 7288 3469 Fax: 020 7281 8004 Email: w.coppola@pcps.ucl.ac.uk; 16 Huddleston Road, London N7 0AP Tel: 020 7607 0501 Fax: 020 7609 6159 Email: will@coppola.co.uk — BM BCh 1987 Oxf.; BA (Hons.) Camb. 1983; MRCGP 1992; DRCOG 1991. Lect. Univ. Coll. Lond.; Asst. in Gen. Pract. Socs: Soc. Social Med.; Roy. Inst. GB. Prev: Lect. Roy. Free Sch. of Med.; Trainee GP Oxf. VTS.

COPPOLO, Marisa Bilbrook Medical Centre, Brookfield Road, Bilbrook, Wolverhampton WV8 1DX Tel: 01902 847313 Fax: 01902 842322 — MB BS 1977 Lond.; DRCOG 1981. (St. Mary's)

COPPS, Caroline Anne Overton Park Surgery, Overton Park Road, Cheltenham GL50 3BP Tel: 01242 580511 — MB ChB 1990 Sheff.; DFFP; Dip. (Ther) Cardiff 2000; DRCOG 1996. (Sheffield)

COPSEY, Alan Parklands Surgery, 4 Parklands Road, Chichester PO19 3DT Tel: 01243 782819/786827; Shirley Lodge, Ratham Lane, Bosham, Chichester PO18 8NH Tel: 01243 572150 Email: alancopsey@aol.com — MB BS Lond. 1970; MRCGP 1977; DObst RCOG 1974; DCH Eng. 1973; FRCGP 1999. (St. Geo.) VTS Course Organiser for Chichester & Worthing. Prev: SHO (Paediat.) Roy. W. Sussex Hosp. Chichester; Ho. Surg. St. Geo. Hosp. Lond.

COPSEY, Matthew David 23 Arundel Way, Billericay CM12 0FL — MB BS 1984 Lond.

COPSON, Ellen Roxane Poppies, Longhills Rd, Church Stretton SY6 6DS Tel: 01694 723150 — MB BS 1996 Lond.; BSc Lond. 1993. (UMDS)

COPSON, Steven Grant Newmarket Road Surgery, 7 Newmarket Road, Norwich NR2 2HL Tel: 01603 621006; 11 Oakfields Road, Cringle Ford, Norwich NR4 6XE Tel: 01603 505623 — MB ChB 1985 Leic. Prev: Trainee GP Gt. Yarmouth & Waveney VTS.

CORAL, Anthony Paul Harrogate District Hospital, Harrogate HG2 7SX Tel: 01423 553708 Fax: 01423 555360 Email: anthony.coral@hhc-tr.northy.nhs.uk; Hill Top Cottage, Hill Top Lane, Pannal, Harrogate HG3 1PA Tel: 01423 871435 Email: anthony.coral@virgin.net — MB BS 1979 Lond.; MRCP (UK) 1983; FRCR 1986. Cons. Radiol. Socs: Brit. Inst. Radiol.; Fell. Roy. Soc. Med.; Brit. Soc. Skeletal Radiol. Prev: Cons. Radiol. St. Jas. Univ. Hosp. Leeds.; Lect. (Radiol.) Univ. Michigan, USA; Sen. Regist. (Radiol.) Middlx. Hosp. Lond.

CORALL, Ian Mitchell PO Box 3261, London SW1V 3XB Tel: 020 7233 6464 Fax: 020 7233 6469 — MRCS Eng. LRCP Lond. 1969; FFA RCS Eng. 1973. (St. Bart.) Cons. Anaesth. King's Coll. Hosp. Lond.; Hon. Sen. Lect. (Anaesth.) KCH Sch. Med. & Dent. Lond.; Examr. Final FDS, RCA Eng. Socs: Roy. Soc. Med. (Past Mem. Counc. Anaesth. Sect.); Harveian Soc. Prev: Examr. FRCA 1983-95; Beckwith-Smith Research Fell. (Anaesth.) Kings Coll. Hosp. Med. Sch. Lond.; Asst. Edr. Anaesth.

CORALL, John Mitchell 13 Marshall Road, Rainham, Gillingham ME8 0AR Tel: 01634 31171 — MB ChB 1936 Aberd.; DMR Lond 1947. Hon. Cons. Radiol. Maidstone & Medway Health Dists. Socs: Fell. Roy. Soc. Med.; Brit. Inst. Radiol. Prev: Sen. Asst. Radiodiagnostician Hammersmith Hosp.; ADMS SE Asia Command (HQ) mentioned in despatches.

CORBET BURCHER, Elizabeth Anne Atwood House, Old Green Lane, Camberley GU15 4LG — BM BCh 1977 Oxf.; MA, BM BCh Oxf. 1977; DO Eng. 1979. (St. Thos.) GP Kennington, Lond.; Regist. (Neurosurg.) Nat. Hosp. Nerv. Dis. Lond.; Regist. Oxf. Eye Hosp. Prev: Ho. Surg. Nuffield Dept. Surg. & SHO (Accid. Serv.) Radcliffe Infirm.; Oxf.; SHO (Ophth.) Roy. Berks. Hosp. Reading.

CORBETT, Alan Lewis (retired) The British Home, Crown Lane, London SW16 3JB Tel: 020 8670 8261 — MB BS Lond. 1957; FRCGP 1982, M 1966. Prev: Sec. Educat. Comm. S. Lond. Fac. RCGP.

CORBETT, Alexander Cooke (retired) 1 Penhale Road, Golden Bank, Falmouth TR11 5UZ Tel: 01326 311781 — MB BCh BAO 1939 Dub.; BA Dub. 1937, MA, MD 1968; MRCGP 1959. Prev: Ho. Phys. & Resid. Surg. Off. N. Ormesby Hosp. Middlesbrough.

CORBETT, Brian Patrick Village Medical Centre, 400-404 Linthorpe Road, Middlesbrough TS5 6HF Tel: 01642 851234 Fax: 01642 820821; 12 The Crescent, Linthorpe, Middlesbrough TS5 6SQ — MB BCh BAO 1983 NUI. Clin. Asst. (Psychogeriat.) Caster Bequest Hosp. & E.erside Day Centre Middlesbrough.

CORBETT, Mr Charles Richard Rainford The Princess Royal Hospital, Lewes Road, Haywards Heath RH16 4EX Tel: 01444 441881 Fax: 01444 455895; 39 Beckworth Lane, Haywards Heath RH16 2EH Tel: 01444 484524 Fax: 01444 484524 Email: crrcorbett@doctors.org.uk — MB BChir 1970 Camb.; MA, MChir Camb. 1981; FRCS Eng. 1973. (Camb. & St. Thos.) Cons. Surg. P.ss Roy. Hosp. Haywards Heath. Socs: Fell. Roy. Soc. Med.-Past Hon Sec Venous Forum of RSM; Fell. Assn. Surgs.; Vasc. Surg. Soc. GB & Irel. Prev: Sen. Regist. (Surg.) St. Thos. Hosp. Lond.; Sen. Resid. Univ. Calif. Irvine, USA; Regist. (Surg.) Leicester Gen. Hosp.

CORBETT, Christopher Laurence Pelham House, Pelham Road, Retford DN22 7BJ Tel: 01777 706223 — MD 1977 Manch.; MB ChB 1970; FRCP Lond. 1990; MRCP (UK) 1973. Cons. Phys. Bassetlaw Health Dist. Socs: Brit. Soc. Gastro Enterol. Prev: Sen. Regist. Roy. Hallams. Hosp. Sheff.; Hon. Lect. (Med.) Roy. Free Hosp. Sch. Med.

CORBETT, David John Richard Dartford West Health Centre, Tower Road, Dartford DA1 2HA Tel: 01322 228032/223960; 53 Joydens Wood Road, Bexley DA5 2HU — BSc (Hons. Psychol.) Lond. 1977, MB BS 1980; MRCGP 1985; DCH RCP Lond. 1984; DRCOG 1982. (Guy's) GP Trainger Organizer, Dartford and Gravesham Ms.; Dartford and Gravesham Pcl Excutive Comm. Mem.

CORBETT, Dennis Stephen 18 Gillman House, Pritchards Road, London E2 9BL — MB BS 1988 Lond.

CORBETT, Elizabeth Ann Barn End Cottage, Austrey Lane, No Mans Heath, Tamworth B79 0PE — MB ChB 1980 Sheff.; DRCOG 1984.

CORBETT, Elizabeth Lucy London School of Hygiene &Tropical Medicine, Keppel St, London WC1E 7HT Tel: 020 7927 2116 Email: elizabeth.corbett@ishtm.ac.uk; 58 Rainhana Road, London NW10 5DY — MB BChir 1990 Camb.; BA Camb. 1985; MRCP 1992; DTMSH 1996. (Cambridge) Specialist Regist.(Infec. Dis.s.) Hammersmith Hosp.; Hon Lect. Lond Sch of Hyg. & Trop. Med.

CORBETT, Emma Jane Louise Tremodrett Mill, Roche, St Austell PL26 8LP — MB ChB 1992 Leeds.

CORBETT, Gail Treharne Whinpark Medical Centre, 6 Saughton Road, Edinburgh EH11 3RA Tel: 0131 455 7999 Fax: 0131 455 8800; 7 Glenlockhart Bank, Edinburgh EH14 1BL Tel: 0131 443 8683 Fax: 0131 455 8118 — MB ChB 1978 Aberd.; DRCOG 1984. GP Asst.

CORBETT, Geoffrey David Austin Badger Hill, 23 Magherabeg Road, Dromore BT25 1RS — MB BS 1998 Lond.; MB BS Lond 1998.

CORBETT, George Francis (retired) 87a Red Lion Lane, Little Sutton, South Wirral CH66 1HQ Tel: 0151 339 2213 — MB BCh BAO Dub. 1945.

CORBETT, Harriet Jane Royal Manchester Children's Hospital, Hospital Road, Pendelbury, Manchester Email: hcorbett@doctors.org.uk; 40 Kensington Road, Chorlton, Manchester M21 9AX — MB ChB 1996 Liverp.; MRCS 1999 Eng. (Univ. of Lond.) p/t SpR Paediatric Surg. Manch. Childr.'s Hosp.s.

CORBETT, Henry Vincent (retired) 31 Lifford Gardens, Broadway WR12 7DA Tel: 01386 852280 — MB ChB Liverp. 1932; MSc Liverp. 1936, MD 1934; FRCS Ed. 1950; MRCS Eng. LRCP Lond. 1934; MMSA 1942; FRCOG 1960, M 1947. Prev: Cons. O & G St. Helens & Dist. Hosps. Gp.

CORBETT, Jill Marilyn Edna (retired) 5 Cherry Tree Close, High Salvington, Worthing BN13 3QJ Tel: 01903 261040 — MB ChB Sheff. 1961. Clin. Asst. Child Psychiat.

CORBETT, Joanne Rumney Medical Practice, 840-842 Newport Road, Rumney, Cardiff CF3 4LH Tel: 029 2079 7751 Fax: 029 2036 1971; The Old Mill, Penllyn, Cowbridge CF71 7RQ — MB BS 1983 Lond.; BSc Lond. 1980; MRCGP 1989; DFFP 1993; DRCOG 1989. (University College Hospital)

CORBETT, Professor John Anthony (retired) 88 Holtye Road, East Grinstead RH19 3HU Tel: 0385 782846, 01342 324996 Fax: 01342 324996 Email: j.a.corbett@amserve.net — MB BS 1960 Lond.; FRCP Lond. 1988, M 1963; MRCS Eng. LRCP Lond. 1959; FRCPsych 1978, M 1971; DCH Eng. 1963; DPM 1966; DPM Acad. Eng. 1965; AKC 1960; FRCPCH 1996. Prev: Phys. Maudsley & Bethlem Roy. Hosps.

CORBETT, John Thomas, OBE (retired) Home Farm House, Twywell, Kettering NN14 3AH Tel: 01832 732628 — MB ChB 1935 Birm.; MB ChB (Hons.) Birm. 1935; MRCS Eng. LRCP Lond. 1935; LLB (Hons.) Lond. 1955; FRCGP 1970, M 1956. Mem. Gray's Inn; Med. Ref. Guardian Roy. Exchange Assur. Gp. & other Insur. Cos. Prev: Med. Off. H.M. YCC WellingBoro.

CORBETT, Katherine Goldie 112 Frinton lodge, The Esplanade, Frinton-on-Sea CO13 9HE — MB ChB 1944 Glas. (Glas.) Socs: Colchester Med. Soc. Prev: Ho. Surg. (Obst.) Roy. Infirm. Stirling; Ho. Phys. Mearnskirk E.M.S. Hosp.

CORBETT, Lynn Branch End Surgery, Stocksfield NE43 7LL Tel: 01661 842626 Fax: 01661 844392 — MB BS 1988 Newc.; MRCGP 1992; DRCOG 1991; DFFP 1996. (Newcastle upon Tyne) GP N.umbria. Prev: Trainee GP N.umbria VTS; Ho. Phys. Preston Hosp. N. Shields; Ho. Surg. Ashington Hosp.

CORBETT, Margaret Frances (retired) 102 Chesterton Road, Cambridge CB4 1ER Tel: 01223 467865 Fax: 01223 316390 Email: mcorbett@dial.pipex.com — MB BS Lond. 1953; BA Open 1974. Prev: Sen. Clin. Research Fell. (Dermat.) Addenbrooke's Hosp. Camb.

CORBETT, Martin Gerard Health Centre, Newgate Street, Worksop S80 1HP; Newgate Street, Worksop S80 1HP Tel: 01909 500288 Fax: 01909 479564 Email: gerard.corbett@gp-c84083.nhs.uk — MB BCh BAO 1977 NUI; MRCGP 1981; DObst. NUI 1980; DCH Irel. 1979.

CORBETT, Mary (retired) 12 Blomfield Road, London W9 1AH Tel: 020 7286 1915 Fax: 020 7286 1915 — MB BS Lond. 1957; FRCP Lond. 1977, M 1962; MRCS Eng. LRCP Lond. 1957. Prev: Cons. Phys. (Rheum.) Middlx. Hosp. Lond.

CORBETT, Megan Jane 23A Rustat Road, Cambridge CB1 3QR — MB ChB 1992 Auckland.

CORBETT, Miss Melanie Caroline The Western Eye Hospital, Marylebone Road, London NW1 5YE Tel: 020 886 3265 Fax: 0207 886 3259 — MB BS 1987 Lond.; BSc (Hons.) Lond. 1984; MRCOphth 1991; FRCS Glas. 1992; MD 1997 London. (Roy. Lond. Hosp. Med. Coll.) Cons. Opthalmic Surg., The W.ern Eye Hosp.. (St Mary's NHS Trust) and Caring Cross Hosp. (Hammersmith Hosp.s NHS Trust) Lond.; Hon. Sen. Lect.. Imperial Coll. Sch. of Med., Lond.; Cons. Ophthalnic Surg., Th Lister Hosp., Chelsea Bridge, Lond. Socs: Roy. Coll. Ophth. (Ex-Chair. Ophth. Trainees Gp.); Soc. Cataract & Refractive Surg. Of UK & Irel.; Hon. Sec. of The Med. Contact Lens & Ocular Surface Assoc. Prev: Sen. Regist. (Ophth.) St. Thomas' Hosp. Lond.; Sen. Regist. (Ophth.) King's Coll. Hosp. Lond.; Corneal Fell. (Opth), Moorfields Eye Hosp., Lond.

CORBETT, Michael James 20 Pirehill Lane, Stone ST15 0JN — MB BS 1990 Lond.

CORBETT, Patricia Clare Abingdon Medical Centre, 88-92 Earls Court Road, London W8 6EG Tel: 020 8746 5959 Fax: 020 7746 5960; Beaufort House, 17 The Butts, Brentford TW8 8BJ Tel: 020 8560 3837 — MB BS 1978 Lond.; BA Camb. 1975; MRCGP 1982; DRCOG 1980; DCH RCP Lond. 1980. (St. Mary's Hosp.)

CORBETT, Robert Andrew Grace Cottage, Milton of Cultoquhey, Crieff PH7 3QX Tel: 01764 2967 — MB ChB 1940 Glas. (Univ. Glas.) Prev: Apptd. Fact. Doctor; Local Treasury Med. Off.

CORBETT, Robert Harcourt Department Diagnostic Radiology, Hairmyres Hospital, East Kilbride, Glasgow G75 8RG Tel: 01355 585782 — MB ChB 1970 Glas.; FRCR 2001; DMRD Eng. 1973. (Univ. Glas.) Cons. Radiol. Hairmyres Hosp. E. Kilbride; Hon. Clin. Sn Lect., U of Glas. 1996-. Socs: BMA (Dep. Chairm. Lanarksh. Div.) 1999/2000; Mem. Scott. Counc. 1997 - Curr.; Soc. Radiol. Protec. (Chair. Internat. Comm.); Brit. Inst. Radiol. (Edr., Bir News). Prev: Sen. Regist. (Diag. Radiol.) Vict. Infirm. Glas.

CORBETT, Rory Department of Dermatology, Royal Hospitals Trust, Grosvenor Road, Belfast BT12 6BA Tel: 028 9089 4635; Tel: 028 9269 2067 — MB BCh BAO 1970 Belf.; FRCP 1988; MRCP (UK) 1975. Cons. Dermat. Roy. Vict. Hosp. & Belf. City Hosp.

CORBETT, Simon Jonathan 109 Sandycombe Road, Kew, Richmond TW9 2EP — BChir 1997 Camb.

CORBETT, Mr Steven Andrew 135 Woodwarde Road, Dulwich, London SE22 8UP — MB BS 1990 Lond.; PhD 2000 Lond.; FRCS (Tr & Orth) 2002; BSc (Hons.) Biochem. Lond. 1986; FRCS Eng. 1995; FRCS Ed. 1995. (St. Thomas's Hospital, London) Specialist Regist. (Orthop.) Rotat., Chelsea & W.minister Hosp. Lond. Prev: Regist. (Orthop.) Hammersmith Hosp. Lond.; SHO (Gen. Surg. & Orthop.) St. Bart. Hosp. Lond.

CORBETT, Timothy James 49 Burleigh Road, St Albans AL1 5DH Tel: 01727 846932 — MB BS 1990 Lond.; BSc (Hons.) Lond. 1987, MB BS 1990; MRCP (UK) 1993. SHO (Haemat.) Roy. Free Hosp. Lond. Prev: SHO (Gen. Med.) Lister Hosp. Stevenage.

CORBETT, Valere 10 Station Road, Kibworth, Leicester LE8 0LN — MB ChB 1969 Birm.; DObst RCOG 1973.

CORBETT, Mr William Anthony Ivy Lodge, Tanton Dykes, Stokesley, Middlesbrough TS9 5JS Tel: 01642 710877; james Cook Univ. Hospital, Marton Road, Middlesbrough TS4 3BW Tel: 01642 854893 — MB ChB 1974 Liverp.; BSc Liverp. 1971; FRCS Eng. 1978. Cons. Colorecial Surg. James Cook Univ. Hosp. Middlesbrough; Prof. Med. Computing Univ. Teeside.; Hon. Lect. Dept. of Surg. Univ. Newc. Prev: Research Fell. Cornell Univ.; Lect. (Surg.) Univ. Liverp.

CORBEY, Martyn Thomas 51 Waverley Road, Rugby CV21 4NN — BM BS 1979 Nottm.

CORBIN, Christopher John Milton House Surgery, Doctors Commons Road, Berkhamsted HP4 3BY Tel: 01442 874784 Fax: 01442 877694; Fernwood, Chesham Road, Wigginton, Tring HP23 6JD Tel: 01494 758827 Fax: 08700 567872 Email: med@corbins.demon.co.uk — MRCS Eng. LRCP Lond. 1976. Princip. in Gen. Pract.; Assoc. Specialist (Palliat. Care), The Hospice of St. Francis, Berkhamsted. Socs: Fell. Roy. Soc. Med.; Roy. Coll. Radiol. Prev: Off. i/c Dept. Radiol. P.ss Mary's RAF Hosp., Halton.

CORBIN, David Orlando Christopher 57 Wolverhampton Road, Olbury, Oldbury B68 0NF — MB 1979 Camb.; BA Camb. 1975, MB 1979, BChir 1978; MRCP (UK) 1982. Regist. (Neurol.) Qu. Eliz. Hosp. Birm. Prev: Regist. (Med.) Roy. Infirm. Edin. & Vict. Hosp. Blackpool; SHO Hope Hosp. Salford.

CORBIN, Michael John Havant Health Centre Suite B, PO Box 43, Civic Centre Road, Havant PO9 2AQ Tel: 023 9248 2124 Fax: 023 9247 5515; 24 Westbourne Avenue, Emsworth PO10 7QU — MB BS 1968 Lond.; MRCS Eng. LRCP Lond. 1968; DObst RCOG 1970.

CORBISHLEY, Catherine Marian Department of Histopathology, St. George's Hospital Medical School, Cranmer Terrace, Tooting, London SW17 0RE Tel: 020 8725 5277 Fax: 020 8767 7984; 96 Mostyn Road, Merton Park, London SW19 3LP — MB ChB 1976 Bristol; MB ChB Bristol 1979; BSc (Microbiol. 2.1. Hons.) Bristol 1976; FRCPath 1996; MRCPath (Histopath.) 1985. Cons. & Sen. Lect. Histopath. St. Geo. Hosp. & Med. Sch. Lond. Prev: Lect. & Sen. Regist. (Histopath.) St. Geo. Hosp. Tooting; Regist. (Histopath.) Frenchay Hosp. Bristol.

CORBITT, Nicola Elizabeth 5 Melbury, Whitley Bay NE25 9XP — MB BS 1988 Newc. SHO (A & E) N. Tyneside Gen. Hosp. Prev: Ho. Off. (Gen. Surg.) N. Tyneside Gen. Hosp.; Ho. Off. (Gen. Med.) Preston Hosp.

CORBLE, Gillian 21 Lancaster Gardens, Beltinge, Herne Bay CT6 6PU — MB ChB 1973 Manch.; BSc Manch. 1970, MB ChB 1973; MRCP (UK) 1975; MRCGP 1987. GP Kent Co. FPC. Prev: Sen. Med. Off. Solomon Is.s/ODA; Med. Dir. Brit./Nepal Trust.

CORBRIDGE, Jennifer Susan — MB ChB 1978 Leeds; MRCGP 1982.

CORBRIDGE, Luisa Jane 44 Dedmere Road, Marlow SL7 1PG — MB BS 1989 Lond.; MRCGP 1994.

CORBRIDGE, Rogan John 44 Dedmere Road, Marlow SL7 1PG — MB BS 1990 Lond.

CORBYN, Christopher Norman 41 Harvey Road, Mansfield, Nottingham NG8 3BB — MB ChB 1978 Sheff. GP Rainworth; Police Surg. Notts. Constab.

CORCORAN, David 3 Queens Road, London N11 2QJ Tel: 020 8889 6375 — MB ChB 1985 Sheff.; PhD Leicester 1994; BMedSci Sheff. 1984. Research Fell (Biochem.) Univ. Reading. Prev: Asst. Lect. (Histopath.) UMDS St. Thos. Hosp. Lond.

CORCORAN, Eamonn (retired) Trevene, Caerau Lane, Ely, Cardiff CF5 5HJ Tel: 01222 591855 — MD 1948 NUI; MB BCh BAO 1942. Prev: Asst. Dept. Path. Univ. Coll. Cork.

CORCORAN, Gerard Daniel Department of Clinical Microbiology, Western Infirmary, Dumbarton Road, Glasgow G11 6NT Tel: 0141 211 2364 Fax: 0141 211 2138 Email: corcoran@clinmed.gla.ac.uk — MB BCh BAO 1982 NUI; FRCPath 1999; FRCPI 1997; MRCPI 1986; MRCPath 1991; DTM & H RCP Lond. 1994. (Dublin) Cons. Bact. W.. Infirm. Glas.; Hon. Clin. Sen. Lect. (Bact.) Univ. Glas. 1995. Socs: Hosp. Infec. Soc. Prev: Sen. Regist. (Med. Microbiol.) Univ. Coll. & Middlx. Hosps. Lond.; Regist. (Microbiol.) St. Jas. Hosp. Dub. & Univ. Coll. Hosp. Galway.

CORCORAN, Mr Gerard David Aintree Hospitals (NHS) Trust, University Hospital, Aintree, Liverpool L9 7AL Tel: 0151 529 2098 Fax: 0151 529 3762 Email: fazhosp@infopct.u-net.com; 17 Brows Lane, Formby, Liverpool L37 3HY Tel: 01704 873723 Email: hcorcoran1@aol.com — MB BS 1975 Lond.; BSc (Hons.) Lond. 1972, MS 1989; FRCS Eng. 1981. (Lond. Hosp.) Macmillan Cons. Palliat. Med. Aintree Hosps. NHS Trust. Liverp.; Med. Dir. Woodlands Hospice Liverp. Prev: Cons. Palliat. Med. St Gemma's Hospice Leeds.

CORCORAN, Helen Margaret 133 Thame Road, Haddenham, Aylesbury HP17 8EQ Tel: 01844 292386 Email: cocoran@dial.pipex.com — BM BCh 1989 Oxf.; BA Oxf. 1986; MRCGP 1993; DFFP 1993; DRCOG 1992; DCH RCP Lond. 1991. GP Asst. Socs: Nat. Assn. Non-Princip.s; Guild Catholic Doctors; Christ. Med. Fell.sh. Prev: Med. Off. Mutomo Hosp. Kenya; Trainee GP Aylesbury.

CORCORAN, James Michael (retired) 6 Queensway, Lincoln LN2 4AH Tel: 01522 22939 — MB BCh BAO 1946 NUI. Prev: Gen. Pract. Clin. Asst. Lincoln Co. Hosp.

CORCORAN, John David Klinik Medikaloka Rep. Oddice SOS, Kuningham Plaza, South Tower Ground Floor, Jlhr Rasuna Said Kav C1114, Jakarta 12940, Indonesia; Monksgarden, Limpley Stoke, Bath BA3 6HR Tel: 0122 122 3153 — MB ChB 1956 Manch.; DObst RCOG 1958.

CORCORAN, John David Ross Royal Belfast Hospital for Sick Children, 180-184 Falls Road, Belfast BT12 6BE; 43 Willesden Park, Belfast BT9 5GY — MB BCh BAO 1985 NUI; BSc (Hons.) Dub. 1987; MRCPI 1990; DCH Dub. 1988. Socs: Paediat. Research Soc.; (Young Investigator) Europ. Soc. Paediat. Research.

CORCORAN, John Stephen Torrington Park Health Centre, Torrington Park, North Finchley, London N12 9SS Tel: 020 8445 7261 Fax: 020 8343 9122; 50 Avondale Avenue, London N12 8EN Tel: 020 8445 7102 — MB BCh BAO 1977 NUI; MRCP (UK) 1982; DRCOG 1988; DCH RCP Lond. 1987. Prev: Lect. (Med.) Whittington Hosp. Lond.; Regist. (Med.) Geo. Eliot Hosp. Nuneaton; Ho. Off. Mater Miser. Hosp. Dub.

CORCORAN, Mark Timothy Kingston 24 Upper Cranbrook Road, Redland, Bristol BS6 7UN Tel: 0117 924 8594 — MB BS 1985 Lond.; MRCGP 1989; DCH RCP Lond. 1988.

CORCORAN, Mary Elizabeth 133 Melton Road, Nottingham NG2 6FG — MB ChB 1975 Liverp.; MFCM 1986. (Liverp.) Epidemiol. Uganda Nat. Expanded Progr. on Immunisation Save The Childr. Fund (UK). Socs: Fell. Roy. Soc. Med.; BMA. Prev: Trainee (Community Med.) Wessex & Trent RHAs; Med. Off. Mvumi Hosp., Tanzania.

CORCORAN, Raymond Hayward House Macmillan, Specialist Palliative Care Unit, City Hospital NHS Trust, Nottingham NG3 1PB Tel: 01159 627619 — MB ChB 1960 Liverp.; FRCOG 1981, M 1968. Cons. & Med. Dir. Hayward Hse. Macmillan Palliat. Care Unit City Hosp. Nottm.; Clin. Teach. Univ. Nottm. Socs: Fell. N. Eng. Obst. & Gyn. Soc.; Assn. Palliat. Med. Prev: Cons. & Med. Tutor St. Joseph's Hospice Lond.; Cons. O & G St. Catherine's Hosp. Birkenhead; Lect. (Obst.) Univ. Liverp.

CORCOS, Christopher Daniel Flat 4, 30 Highbury Road, Weston Super Mare BS23 2DN Email: corcoscol@a1.com.au — MB BS 1987 Lond.; BSc Birm. 1977; MRCPsych. 1992; FRANZCP 1998. (Char Cross & West.)

CORCUERA MAZA, Maria Angeles 11 Netley Street, London NW1 3EJ — LMS 1985 Basque Provinces.

CORDEAUX, William Locking (retired) The Chapel House, Botesdale, Diss IP22 1BU Tel: 01379 898286 — MB BChir Camb. 1954; BA Camb. 1951; FRCGP 1985, M 1965; DObst RCOG 1959. Prev: GP Botesdale, Diss.

CORDEIRO, Maria Francesca Wound Healing Research Unit, Moorfields Eye Hospital, Bath St., London EC1V 9EL Tel: 020 7608 6887 Fax: 020 7608 6887 Email: m.cordeiro@ucl.ac.uk — MB BS 1987 Lond.; MRCP (UK) 1990; FRCOphth 1992; PhD Lond. 1998. (London) Wellcome Vision Research Fell. Inst. Ophth. Lond.; Acad. Specialist Clin. Lect. Moorfields Eye Hosp. Lond. Socs: Roy. Soc. Med.; Med. Res. Soc.; Assn. Research in Vision & Opthalmology.

CORDEIRO, Nuno Jorge Velloza c/o Medical Post Graduate Office, Falkirk & District Royal Infirmary, Majors Loan, Falkirk FK1 5QE — MB ChB 1997 Ed.

CORDELL, Andrew John Horfield Health Centre, Lockleaze Rd, Bristol BS7 9RR Tel: 0117 969 5391 — BM BCh 1985 Oxf.; MA Camb. 1986; T (GP) 1991; MRCGP 1990; DRCOG 1989; DCH RCP Lond. 1988. Gen. Practitioner, Bristol; Med. Off., Internat. Nepal Fell.sh., Nepal. Prev: GP Norwich.

CORDELL, Richard James 6 Woodhill Park, Pembury, Tunbridge Wells TN2 4NN — MB ChB 1992 Bristol.

CORDELL, Robin Francis, Lt.-Col. RAMC 'Hollybush', 51 New Abbey Road, Dumfries DG2 7LZ Tel: 01387 253696 — MB BS 1983 Lond.; BSc Lond. 1980; MRCGP 1987; Dip. IMC RCS Ed. 1992; DFFP 1994; T(GP) 1991; DCH RCP Lond. 1986; DRCOG 1986. (St. Geo.) Gen. Practitioner with interest in Occupat.al Med. Prev: GP Winchester; Trainee GP/SHO (Gen. Med.) St. Richard's Hosp. Chichester.; Med. Off. RAMC.

CORDELL-SMITH, James Anthony Byxfield House, 21 Station Crescent, Cold Norton, Chelmsford CM3 6HY — MB ChB 1996 Leic.

CORDEN, David (retired) 11 Badgers Rise, Caversham, Reading RG4 7QA Fax: 01189 543667 Email: david.corden@dtn.ntc.com — MB ChB Birm. 1959.

CORDER, Mr Allan Paul County Hospital, Union Walk, Hereford HR1 2ER — MB BS 1978 Lond.; MS Soton. 1989; FRCS Eng. 1983.

CORDER, Christine Elizabeth Manchester Road Surgery, 57 Manchester Road, Southport PR9 9BN Tel: 01704 532314 Fax: 01704 539740; 38 Lynton Road, Hillside, Southport PR8 3AW — MB BS 1993 Lond.; DRCOG Birm 1996. (University College and Middlesex School of Medicine) Princip. in Gen. Pract. (p/t); Med. Off. at Qu.sCt. Hospice, S.port.

CORDERY, Rebecca Jane Dementia Research Group, Institute of Neurology, The National Hospital for Neurology and Neurosurgery, Queen Square, London WC1N 3BG Tel: 020 7837 3611 Email: dementia.ion@ucl.ac.uk; 9 Crouchmans Close, Dulwich Wood, London SE26 6ST — MB BS 1994 Lond.; BSc (Hons.) Lond. 1991; MRCP (UK) 1997. (King's Coll. Lond.) Clin. Research Fell. Inst. Neurol. & The Nat. Hosp. for Neurol. & Neurosurg. Lond. Prev: SHO (Neurol.) Char. Cross Hosp. Lond.; SHO (Gen. Med.) Kings Coll. Hosp. Rotat.

CORDERY, Roger Adrian 9 Crouchmans Close, London SE26 6ST — MB BS 1994 Lond. Specialist Regist. (Anaesth.) Chase Farm Hosp., Enfield, Lond. Prev: SHO (Anaesth.) Lewisham Hosp.; SHO (Anaesth.) Guys Hosp. Lond.; Resid. Med. Off. (ITU) Harley St. Clinic. Lond.

CORDESS, Professor Christopher Charles Rampton Hospital, Retford DN22 0PD Tel: 01777 247719 Fax: 01777 247737; The University of Sheffield, Regent Court, 30 Regent St, Sheffield S1 4DA Tel: 0114 222 0807 Fax: 0114 272 4095 Email: c.c.dordess@sheffield.ac.uk — MB BCh BAO 1970 Dub.; MPhil Lond. 1984; MA Dub. 1971; MRCP (UK) 1973; FRCPsych 1997, M 1981; FRCP 1998. (Trinity Coll. Dub. Univ. Dub.) Prof. Forens. Psychiat., Sheff. Univ.; Hon. Cons. Psychiat. Rampton Hosp. Notts. Socs: Roy. Soc. Med.; Fell. Roy. Coll. Psychiat. Lond. (Hon. Sec. Forens. Sect.); Assoc. Mem. Brit. Psychoanal. Soc. Prev: Hon. Sen.

Lect. Char. Cross & W.m. Med. Sch.; Vis. Prof. Psychother. Kyushu Univ. Fukuoka City, Japan; Sen. Regist. (Psychiat.) Bethlem Roy. Hosp. & Maudsley Hosp. Lond.

CORDESS, Wendy Susanne Clare The Lodge, Church Road, Rochford SS4 3HY — MB BS 1994 Lond.; BSc Physiol. 1991.

CORDIN, Charlotte Winifred (retired) Flat 1, 8 Chesterfield Road, Eastbourne BN20 7NU Tel: 01323 739777 — MB ChB Ed. 1948; DPH 1954. Prev: Clin. Asst. S. W.. RHB.

CORDINER, Carolyn Mary 1 Kenmore Gardens, Bearsden, Glasgow G61 2BA — MB ChB 1976 Glas.; FRCR 1982; DMRD Eng. 1980. Cons. Radiol. BrE. Screening Serv. Glas. Prev: Cons. Radiol. Hairmyres Hosp. Lanarksh.

CORDINER, David Stuart 16 Woodcot Park, Stonehaven AB39 2HG — MB ChB 1993 Aberd.

CORDINER, Mr James Wilson 1 Kenmore Gardens, Bearsden, Glasgow G61 2BA — MB ChB 1969 Glas.; FRCS Glas. 1984; FRCOG 1986; MRCOG 1974, DObst 1971. Hon. Clin. Lect. Univ. Glas.; Cons. Obst. Qu. Mother Hosp. Glas.; Cons. Gynaecol. W.. Infirm. Glas. Socs: Vice-Pres. Brit. Soc. Colpscopy & Cerv. Path. Prev: Sen. Lect. Dept. Midw. Univ. Glas.

CORDING, Vicky Louise 8 Robbins Terrace, Featherstone, Pontefract WF7 6LN — MB ChB 1998 Liverp.; MB ChB Liverp 1998.

CORDINGLEY, Jeremy John 18 Mansel Close, Guildford GU2 9RF — MB BS 1986 Lond.; MRCP (UK) 1991; FRCA 1993. (Charing Cross and Westminister)

CORDINGLEY, John Louis Post Cottage, Milton, Banbury OX15 4HH Tel: 01295 720862 Fax: 01295 722169 Email: john.cordingley@virgin.net; Post Cottage, Milton, Banbury OX15 4HH Tel: 01295 720862 Fax: 01295 722169 Email: john.cordingley@virgin.net — DSc (Univ. of Hertfordshire) Hon. Causa 2000; MB BS Sydney 1952; PhD Lond. 1966. p/t Clin. Anatomist Dept. of Anat. Univ. of Oxf.; Emerit. Reader (Anat.) Univ. Lond.; Div. Surg. St. John Ambul. Brig. Socs: Fell. Roy. Soc. Med.; Anat. Soc.; Brit. Assn. Clin. Anatomists. Prev: Pub. Health Phys. N.ampton HA; Reader (Anat.) Univ. Lond. (King's Coll.); Lect. (Anat.) Univ. Coll. Ibadan, Nigeria.

CORDINGLEY, Rosemary Anne Jarvis Breast Screening, Training & Diagnostic Centre, Stoughton Road, Guildford GU1 1LJ Tel: 01483 783200 Fax: 01483 783299 — MB BS 1986 Lond. (Char. Cross & Westm. Hosp. Lond.) p/t Cons. BrE. Diagnostician Jarvis BrE. Screening Train. & Diag. Centre Guildford. Socs: (Sec.) Assn. BrE. Clinicians; Assoc. Mem. Roy. Coll. Radiol. BrE. Gp.

CORDINGLY, Anthony John (retired) 6 Prince Arthur Road, Hampstead, London NW3 6AU Tel: 020 7794 9459 — MB BS Lond. 1964; FRCPsych 1989, M 1972; DPM Eng. 1970. Prev: Cons. Psychiat. Napsbury Hosp.

CORDINGLY, Katherine Alison Marshall 24 Park End, Croughton, Brackley NN13 5LX — MB BS 1998 Lond.; MB BS Lond 1998. (Imperial college) SHO Rotat. Paediat St Guys hosp. Prev: Jun. Ho. Off. Med. Ealing Hosp.

CORDINGLY, Matthew Robin 2 Vine Place, Brighton BN1 3HE — MB BS 1998 Lond.; MB BS Lond 1998.

CORDLE, Janet Elizabeth The Warren, 6 Fairlands Park, Coventry CV4 7DS Tel: 024 76 419416 — MB ChB 1981 Bristol. Med. Off., Warren Pearl Hospice, Solihull. Prev: Clin. Asst. (Clin. Oncol.) Glenfield Hosp. Leicester; Med. Off. (Palliat. Med.) Myton Hospice Warwick; Clin. Asst. (Haemat.) Solihull Hosp.

CORDNER, Duane Edward Stuart Mayfield Medical Centre, Park Road, Jarrow NE32 5SE Tel: 0191 489 7183 Fax: 0191 483 2001 — MB BCh BAO 1990 Belf.; MB BCh Belf. 1990; MRCGP 1995; Dip. Psychiat. Lond. 1993. (Qu. Univ. Belf.)

CORDUFF, Michael Benignus (retired) Haul-a-Gwynt, Rhoscolyn, Holyhead LL65 2NQ Tel: 01407 860470 — MB BCh BAO NUI 1949. Prev: GP Trentham Stoke-on-Trent.

CORDWELL-SMITH, Claire Bremner Deerwood House, Doune FK16 6AD — MB ChB 1991 Ed.

CORE, Andrew William Mitchell — LRCP LRCS Ed. LRFPS Glas. 1955; DObst RCOG 1959. (Glas.) Socs: BMA. Prev: Ho. Surg. Hairmyres Hosp. Lanark; Ho. Phys. Falkirk & Dist. Roy. Infirm.; Ho. Off. Midw. S. Gen. Hosp. Glas.

CORE, Jessica Braidwood (retired) St. Ives, Doncaster Road, Rotherham S65 2DD Tel: 01709 851414 — MB ChB 1943 Ed.; DCH Eng. 1949. Princip. GP Rotherham.; Med. Off. Child Welf. Clinics Rotherham AHA. Prev: Ho. Phys. Newc. Gen. Hosp.

COREIRA, Moushumi Christine 42 Abbots Grove, Stevenage SG1 1NR — MB BS 1998 Lond.; MB BS Lond 1998.

COREN, Anne .2, St Katherines Precinct, London NW1 4HH Tel: 020 7935 4933 — MB BS 1964 Lond.; MRCS Eng. LRCP Lond. 1964; FFA RCS Eng. 1969. (Roy. Free.) Cons. Anaesth. Moorfields Eye Hosp. Lond. Socs: Fell. Roy. Soc. Med.; Assn. Anaesth. Prev: Sen. Regist. (Anaesth.) Middlx. Hosp. Lond.; Regist. Nat. Heart Hosp. & Char. Cross. Hosp. Lond.

COREN, Michael Elias Department of Paediatrics, St Marys Hospital, Praed St., London W2 1NY Tel: 020 728866249 Email: m.coren@ic.ac.uk; 32 Elms Avenue, Hendon, London NW4 2PG Email: mcoren@doctors.org.uk — MB BS 1989 Lond.; BSc Lond. 1986; MRCP (UK) 1993. (University College and Middlesex School of Medicine) Cons. Paediat. St. Mary's Hosp. Lond. Prev: Sen. Regist. (Paediat.) St. Mary's Hosp. Paddington & N.wick Pk. Hosp. Harrow; Regist. (Paediat.) Roy. Brompton Hosp. & Hillingdon Hosp.

COREY, Oran Isabel Mary The Avenue Surgery, 14 The Avenue, Warminster BA12 9AA Tel: 01985 846224 Fax: 01985 847059; 12 Penleigh Close, Corsham SN13 9LE — MB BCh BAO 1988 Belf.; DRCOG 1992; DGM RCPS Glas. 1991; MRCGP DEC Lond. 1994. (Queen's University Belfast) GP f/t Partner, Warminster.

CORFAN, Elinor 8 Viceroy Close, Bristol Road, Edgbaston, Birmingham B5 7UR Tel: 0121 446 6781 — MB ChB 1944 Ed.; DCH Eng. 1946. SCMO Birm. AHA (T); Clin. Asst. Midl. Nerve Hosp. Birm. Prev: Asst. MOH Middlx. CC; Ho. Surg. (O & G) Addenbrooke's Hosp. Camb.; Asst. Med. Off. Alder Hey Childr. Hosp. Liverp.

CORFE, Jeremy Frank Court Lodge, West Peckham, Maidstone ME18 5JN — MB ChB 1998 Birm. (Birm.)

CORFE, Sarah Eleanor Flat 1, Hartley Court, 12 Winn Road, Southampton SO17 1EN Tel: 07971 437367 — MB ChB 1993 Birm. (Univ. Birm.) SHO (Psychiat.), E. Surrey Hosp., Redhill. Prev: SHO (Paediat.) Sandwell W. Bromwich; SHO (A & E) Wolverhampton; Ho. Off. (Surg.) Stoke-on-Trent.

CORFIELD, Alasdair Ross Flat Top/Left, 19 Highburgh Road, Glasgow G12 9YF Email: al.corfield@com100.freeserve.co.uk — MB ChB 1995 Glas.; MRCP (UK) 1998.

CORFIELD, Alastair Robert Henry Jackson and Partners, Glastonbury Surgery, Feversham Lane, Glastonbury BA6 9LP Tel: 01458 833666 Fax: 01458 834536; 14 Read Mead, Glastonbury BA6 8DN — MB BChir 1991 Camb.; MA Camb. 1992; MRCGP 1995; DFFP 1995; DRCOG 1994. (Univ. Camb./Addenbrooke's Hosp.) Prev: GP Regist. Camb. Univ. VTS.

CORFIELD, Alison Judith (Solomon) Child & Family Service, Bourne House, Radbrooke College Campus, Radbrooke Road, Shrewsbury SY3 9BL Tel: 01743 272569 — MB ChB 1969 Birm.; MRCPsych. 1980; DCH Eng. 1971. Cons. Child & Adolesc. Psychiat. Shrops. Ment. Health NHS Trust. Prev: Sen. Regist. (Child Adolesc. Psychiat.) W. Midl. Train. Scheme; Regist. (Psychiat.) Roy. Shrewsbury Hosp. (Shelton).

CORFIELD, Mr Andrew Peter County Hospital, Union Walk, Hereford HR1 2ER Tel: 01432 355444; Hinton, Elm Road, Hereford HR1 2TH Tel: 01432 271808 — MB BS 1974 Lond.; FRCS Eng. 1979; MRCS Eng. LRCP Lond. 1974. (Char. Cross) Cons. Gen. Surg. Co. Hosp. Hereford. Prev: Sen. Regist. (Surg.) Exeter & Bristol Hosps.; Regist. (Surg.) Roy. United Hosp. Bath; Ho. Surg. & Ho. Phys. Char. Cross Hosp. Lond.

CORFIELD, Lorraine Frances 26 Argyle Street, Oxford OX4 1SS — MB BS 1996 Lond. (St. Mary's Hospital)

CORFIELD, Michael Hamilton Finchampstead Road Surgery, 474 Finchampstead Road, Finchampstead, Wokingham RG40 3RG Tel: 0118 973 2678 Fax: 0118 973 3689 — MB BS 1980 Lond.; MRCGP 1987.

CORFIELD, Norman Stanley Willesborough Health Centre, Bentley Road, Willesborough, Ashford TN24 0HZ Tel: 01233 621626 Fax: 01233 622930; Cloud End, Forge Hill, Aldington, Ashford TN25 7DT Tel: 01233 720241 Fax: 01233 720241 Email: corfield_cloudend@compuserve — MB ChB 1969 St. And. Hosp. Pract. (Surg.) S. Kent Hosps.

CORFIELD, Mr Peter William David (retired) 17 College Court, Ludlow SY8 1BZ Tel: 01584 872233 — MB BS 1946 Lond.; MS

Lond. 1952, MB BS 1946; FRCS Eng. 1950. Prev: Cons. Surg. Mt. Vernon, Harefield, Wembley & N.wood & Pinner Hosps.

CORFIELD, Richard McKinlay (retired) Bramley Cottage, 1 Bridge Place, Nether Compton, Sherborne DT9 4QF Tel: 01935 814818 — MB BS Lond. 1953; DObst RCOG 1955.

CORFIELD, Mrs Rosemary Anne The Queen's Hospital, Belvedere Road, Burton-on-Trent DE13 0RB Tel: 01283 566333; 109 Palmerston Street, Derby DE23 6PF — MB ChB 1979 Liverp.; ChM Liverp. 1991; FRCS Eng. 1984; FRCS Ed. 1984. Cons. Urol. The Qu.s Hosp. Burton upon Trent; Assoc. Med. director Clin. risk Qu.'s Hosp Buton Burton Upon Trent. Prev: Cons. Urol. Chesterfield & N. Derbysh. Roy. Hosp.; Sen. Regist. (Urol.) Freeman Hosp. Newc. u. Tyne.

CORK, Michael John University Dept of Dermatology,Division of moleculor & Genetic medicine, Floor O, The Royal Hallamshire Hospital, Glossop Road, Sheffield S10 2JF Tel: 0114 276 6222 Fax: 0114 275 6574 Email: m.j.cork@sheffield.ac.uk — MB BChir 1983 Camb.; PhD St. And. 1984, BSc (Hons.) 1979; MRCP (UK) 1989; FRCP 1999. Sen. Lect. & Hon. Cons. Dermat. Roy. Hallamshire Hosp. Socs: Brit. Soc. Investig. Dermat.; Brit. Assn. Dermat. Prev: Sen. Regist., Lect. & Regist. (Dermat.) Roy. Hallamsh. Hosp. Sheff.; Regist. (Respirat. & Gen. Med.) Leeds Gen. Infirm.; SHO (Rotat.) Regional Cardiothoracic Centre Wythenshawe Hosp. Manch.

CORKAN, Elizabeth Joanne Department of Radiodiagnosis, Royal Albert Edward Infirmary, Wigan Lane, Wigan WN1 2NN; 8 The Limes, Standish, Wigan WN6 0BJ — MB ChB 1974 Sheff.; FRCR 1981; DMRD Eng. 1979. Cons. Radiol. Wigan NW RHA. Socs: Brit. Nuclear Med. Soc.

CORKE, Alison Ruth 100 Whyke Lane, Chichester PO19 2AT — MB BS 1996 Lond.

CORKE, Philip John 68 Broad Square, Norris Green, Liverpool L11 1BS — MB ChB 1986 Sheff.

CORKE, Richard Thomas Briercliffe Road Surgery, 357 Briercliffe Road, Burnley BB10 1TX Tel: 01282 424720 Fax: 01282 429055 — MB ChB 1976 Liverp. Dir. Burnley & Pendle Primary Care Centre Ltd.

CORKER, Robert Morrison (retired) Summerhill, East View, Kendal LA9 4JY — LMSSA 1938 Lond.

CORKERY, Ann Patricia West Sussex HA, 1 The Causeway, Durrington, Worthing BN12 6BT Tel: 01903 708649; 4 Church Grove, The Hollows, West Chiltington, Pulborough RH20 2QL Tel: 01798 813962 Fax: 01798 813962 — MB BS 1985 Lond.; BSc (Hons) Lond. 1982; MFPHM 1993; MPH Liverp. 1990; FFPHM 2000. (St. Geo. Hosp. Med. Sch.) Cons. Pub. Health Med. W. Sussex Health Auth. Socs: Hon. Sec. (Epidemiol. and Pub. Health) Roy. Soc. Med. (1993-5); Off. and Mem. of Counc. (Epidemiol. and Pub. Health); Roy. Soc. Med. Prev: Sen. Regist. (Pub. Health Med.) S. W. Thames Rotat.; Regist. (Pub. Health Med.) Mersey Region Rotat.

CORKERY, Fiona Margaret 43 Ventress Farm Court, Cambridge CB1 8HD — MB BCh BAO 1990 NUI.

CORKERY, Mr John Joseph The Children's Hospital, Steelhouse Lane, Birmingham B4 6NH Tel: 0121 333 8077 Fax: 0121 333 8141 Email: sean.corkery@bhamchildrens.wmids.nhs.uk; 20 Hamilton Avenue, Birmingham B17 8AJ Tel: 0121 429 4165 Email: sean.corkery@talk21.com — MB BCh BAO NUI 1960; MCh NUI 1965; FRCS Eng. 1965; FRCSI 1964; DObst RCOG 1962. (Cork) Cons. Paediat. Surg. Childr. Hosp. Birm. Socs: (Ex-Pres.) Brit. Assn. Paediat. Surgs.; BMA. Prev: Sen. Regist. (Surg.) Childr. Hosp. Sheff.; Research Fell. (Ainsworth Schol.) Hosp. Sick Childr. Toronto Canada; Hon. Sec. Brit. Assn. Paediat. Surg.

CORKERY, Patricia Bridget Cadwgan Surgery, Old Colwyn, Colwyn Bay LL29 9NP; Greenacres, Peulwys Lane, Old Colwyn, Colwyn Bay LL29 Tel: 01492 55964 — MB ChB 1957 Liverp.

CORKERY, Mr Patrick Henry (retired) Greenacres, Peulwys Lane, Old Colwyn, Colwyn Bay LL29 8YF Tel: 01492 515964 — MB BCh BAO 1951 NUI; MCh Orth Liverp. 1958; FRCS Ed. 1957. Prev: Sen. Orthop. Regist. Profess. Unit Roy. S.. Hosp. Liverp.

CORKEY, Christopher Laurence Ormeau Road Practice, 485 Ormeau Road, Belfast BT7 3GR Tel: 028 9064 1506; 3 Broomhill Park Central, Belfast BT9 5JD Tel: 01232 667906 — MB BCh BAO 1971 Belf. Occupat. Health Phys. N. & W. Belf. Health & Social Serv. Trust. Prev: Staff Med. Off. Belvoir Pk. Hosp. Belf.; Cas. Off., Ho. Off. & SHO Belf. City Hosp.

CORKEY, Christopher William Boyd Daisy Hill Hospital, Hospital Road, Newry BT34 8DR Tel: 02830 835000 Fax: 02830 262407; 11 Kilbroney Road, Rostrevor, Newry BT34 3BH Tel: 028302 38398 Email: corkey@globalnet.com — MB BCh BAO 1972 Belf.; FRCPI 1992; FRCP Ed. 1988; MRCPI 1990; MRCP (UK) 1975; FRCPCH. Cons. Paediat. Daisy Hill Hosp. Newry & Craigavon Area Hosp. Socs: Brit. Paediat. Assn.; Fell. Fac. Paediat. RCP Irel.; Irish Perinatal Soc. Prev: Sen. Regist. Roy. Belf. Hosp. for Sick Childr. Belf.; Fell. Respirat. Dis. Hosp. for Sick Childr. Toronto.

CORKEY, Elizabeth Phyllis Mary Killiney, 14 Circular Road E., Holywood BT18 0HA Tel: 01232 422227 — MB BCh BAO 1962 Dub.; MA Dub. 1992, MB BCh BAO 1962; Cert FPA 1968. (TC Dub.) Assoc. Specialist (Blood Transfus.) N. Irel. Socs: Fell. Ulster Med. Soc.; BMA. Prev: Clin. Med. Off. EHSSB; SHO (Anaesth.) Roy. Vict. Hosp. Belf.; Ho. Phys. Sir. P. Dunn's Hosp. Dub.

CORKHILL, Susan Elizabeth Yorkshire Street, 80 Yorkshire Street, Burnley BB11 3BT — MB ChB 1972 Liverp.; DObst RCOG 1974. GP; Med. Officier, Pendleside Hospice, Colne Rd. Burnley, Lancs.

CORKILL, Richard John Flat 1, 8 Spicer Road, Exeter EX1 1SY Tel: 01392 411093 — LMSSA 1994 Lond. SHO (Med.) Roy. Devon & Exeter Health Trust.

CORKILL, Robin Guy Dept. Of Neurology, Preston Royal Hospital, Sharoe Green Lane, Preston PR2 — MB BS 1992 Lond.; BSc (Hons. Biochem.) Lond. 1989; MRCP (UK) 1997. Specialist Regist. Neurol. Socs: Med. Protec. Soc. Prev: Regist. (Gen. Med.) Horton Gen. Hosp. Banbury; Regist. (Neuropsychiat.) Maudsley Hosp. Lond.; SHO (Med.) Roy. Devon & Exeter (Wonford) Hosp.

CORKILL, Rufus Anthony 4 Cedar Walk, Romsey Road, Winchester SO22 5EU — MB BS 1993 Lond.

CORLESS, Mr David James 19 Pimms Grove, High Wycombe HP13 7EE — MB ChB 1985 Birm.; MD Birm. 1996; FRCS Eng. 1990; FRCS (Gen) 1997. Cons. Surg., Leighton Hosp., Crewe; Hon. Lect. Char. Cross & W.m. Med. Sch. Lond. Prev: Regist. (Gen. Surg.) Chelsea & W.m. Hosp. Lond.; Sen. Regist. (Hon.Lect), Chelsea W.minster Hosp.; Sen. Regist., Roy. Marsden Hosp.

CORLESS, Derek 16 Ship Road, Burnham-on-Crouch CM0 8JX — MB BS 1960 Lond.; BSc (Anat.) Lond. 1957; FRCP Lond. 1979, M 1965; FRCP Ed. 1982, M 1964. (Univ. Coll. Hosp.) p/t Clin. Asst., Mid Essex Hosp. Servs. & Maldon & S. Chelmsford NHS Primary Care Trust. Socs: Brit. Geriat. Soc. Prev: Cons. Phys. (Geriat. & Gen. Med.) Lewisham & N. S.wark Dist. DHA (T); Cons. Phys. Geriat. St. Bart. Hosp. & Hackney Gp. Hosps.; Cons. Phys. c/o the Elderly Mid Essex DHA.

CORLESS, John Andrew 21 Arnside Avenue, Rainhill, Prescot L35 9JH Email: j.coreless@bigfoot.com — MB ChB 1992 Dundee; MRCP (UK) 1996. Specialist Regist. (Thoracic.Med.) Univ. Hosp. Aintree. Socs: Liverp. Med. Inst.; Roy. Coll. Phys. Edin. Prev: Specialist Regist.(Thoracic&Gen.Med.).Roy. Liverp. Univ. Hosp.; Specialist.Regist.(Thoracic&Gen.Med.)Arrowe.Part.Hosp.Wirral.; SHO (Cardiol.) Cardiothoracic Centre Liverp.

CORLETT, Alison Jane York District hospital, Wigginton Road, York YO31 8HE Tel: 01904 631313; 9 Royal Chase, Dringhouses, York YO24 1LN Tel: 01904 701810 — MB ChB 1988 Birm.; MRCP (UK) 1993. Cons. in Med. for the Elderly York Dist. Hosp.

CORLETT, Amanda Jane 19 St Marks Avenue, Oldfield Brow, Altrincham WA14 4JB — MB ChB 1977 Liverp.; DRCOG 1989. (Liverpool) Sessional Clin. Med. off. (Well Adults & Family Plann.) Trafford NHS Trust. Prev: GP Timperley; Trainee GP Timperley; Regist. & SHO (Gen. Med.) Trafford AHA.

CORLETT, David Ernest (retired) Apple Tree Cottage, Main St., Kirklington, Newark NG22 8NL Tel: 01636 814908 — MB BChir Camb. 1954; MRCGP 1968; DObst RCOG 1957; DCH Eng. 1956. Prev: Ho. Surg. Lond. Hosp.

CORLETT, David John Church Street Surgery, Church Street, Spalding PE11 2PB Tel: 01775 722189 Fax: 01775 712164; 15 The Chantry, Spalding PE11 3LF — MB ChB Leic. 1981; MRCGP 1985.

CORLETT, Helen Mary Auldyn, The Slype, Gustard Wood, Wheathampstead, St Albans AL4 8SA — MB BS 1987 Lond.

CORLETT, John Robert The Scott Practice, 1 Greenfield Lane, Balby, Doncaster DN4 0TG Tel: 01302 850546 Fax: 01302 855338; Karagoth, St. Bartholomews Rise, Bessacarr, Doncaster DN4 6LS — MB ChB 1984 Sheff.; MB ChB Sheff. l984; MRCGP Lond. 1988; DCH RCP Lond. 1986. Socs: BMA; RCGP.

CORLETT, Mr Jonathan Charles Richard Salisbury District Hospital, Salisbury SP2 8BJ Email: jcorlett@luna.co.uk — MB ChB 1981 Birm.; FRCS Ed. 1992. (Univ. Birm.) Staff Surg. Salisbury Dist. Hosp. Wilts.

CORLETT, Katharine Joyce Hanscombe House Surgery, 52A St. Andrew Street, Hertford SG14 1JA Tel: 01992 582025 Fax: 01992 305511; 35 Chadwell, Ware SG12 9LD — MB ChB 1980 Liverp.; MRCGP 1985; DRCOG 1982. GP Hertford. Socs: Christian Med. Fell.sh.

CORLETT, Mr Michael Peter Department of Surgery, Worcester Royal Infirmary, Newtown Road, Worcester WR5 1HN Tel: 01905 760678 Fax: 01905 760768; Oak House Farm, Himbleton, Droitwich WR9 7LF Tel: 01905 391240 Email: mpcorl@globalnet.co.uk — MB BS 1981 Lond.; MS Lond. 1992; FRCS Eng. 1986; FRCS Ed. 1985; MRCS Eng. LRCP Lond. 1982. (Guy's) Cons. Surg. Worcester Roy. Infim. Socs: Assn. Surg.; Assn. Endoscopic Surg.; Brit. Assn. of Surg. Oncol. Prev: Sen. Regist. (Gen. Surg.) W. Midl. Surg. Train Scheme; Career Regist. W. Midl. Surg. Train. Scheme; Research Assoc. (Surg.) Washington Univ. Med. Sch. St. Louis., USA.

CORLETT, Rowena Jane 3 Baring Close, East Stratton, Winchester SO21 3DY Tel: 01962 774569 — MB ChB 1973 Ed. BrE. Clinician N. Hants. Hosp. Basingstoke.

CORLETT, Sarah Katharine Central London Multifund, The Acrow Building, London W2 1NY Tel: 020 7706 8811 Fax: 020 7706 4211; 47 Corrance Road, London SW2 5RD Tel: 020 7737 0770 — MB ChB 1983 Leic.; MSc (Pub. Health Med.) Lond. 1992; MFPHM RCP (UK) 1995. Sen. Regist. (Pub. Health Med.) N. Thames. Prev: Med. Off. Christian Outreach, Sudan; SHO (O & G) Char. Cross Hosp. Lond.; SHO (Paediat.) Geo. Eliot Hosp. Nuneaton.

CORLEY, Margaret (retired) 7 Monkfrith Way, Southgate, London N14 5LY Tel: 020 8368 4608 Email: mcorley@u.k.packardbell.org — MB BCh 1964 Liverp.; FFA RCS Eng. 1970. Clin. Med. Off. E. Herts. NHS Trust.

CORMAC, Irene Dove Reaside Clinic, Birmingham Great Park, Bristol Road S., Birmingham B45 8BE Tel: 0121 453 6161 Fax: 0121 453 7181 — MB BS 1971 Lond.; MRCS Eng. LRCP Lond. 1971; MRCPsych 1996; DA Eng. 1973. (Guy's)

CORMACK, Ailsa Susan Rose Street, Todmorden OL14 5AT — BM BS 1987 Nottm.; MRCGP 1991.

CORMACK, Andrew James Ross 58 Torr Lane, Plymouth PL3 5PD — MB ChB 1997 Aberd.

CORMACK, Andrew Sutherland 93 Usk Road, Pontypool NP4 8AF — MB BS 1984 Lond.; DRCOG 1988.

CORMACK, Anne Morris 38 Scotstoun Park, South Queensferry EH30 9PQ Tel: 0131 319 1189 — MB ChB 1952 Glas.; MA Glas. 1947, MB ChB 1952; DObst RCOG 1956. Clin. Med. Off. (Community Med.) Family Plann. with FVHB.

CORMACK, Caroline Rosemary Helen 11 Montpelier, Edinburgh EH10 4LZ — MB ChB 1994 Ed.

CORMACK, Elisabeth Charlotte Warren Childrens Centre, 61 Woodland Park, Lisburn BT28 1LQ Tel: 01846 666695; 4 Botanic Court, Belfast BT7 1QY — MB BCh BAO 1979 Belf.; MMSc Belf. 1992; MRCPsych 1988. Cons. Child & Adolesc. Psychiat. Down & Lisburn Trust.

CORMACK, Mr George Carl Addenbrooke's Hospital, Cambridge CB2 2QQ Tel: 01223 245151; Pulteney House, Scotts Gardens, Whittlesford, Cambridge CB2 4NR Tel: 01223 836865 Fax: 01223 837282 — MB ChB 1976 Aberd.; MA Camb. 1983; FRCS Ed. 1981. Cons. Plastic, Reconstruc. & Hand Surg. Camb. HA. Socs: Brit. Assn. Plastic Surg. & Brit. Soc. Surg. Hand. Prev: Sen. Regist. (Plastic Surg.) Qu. Vict. Hosp. E. Grinstead; Regist. (Plastic Surg.) Lothian HB.

CORMACK, Hugh Sutherland Braemore, Usk Road, Pontypool NP4 8AF — MB BChir 1959 Camb.; BA, MB Camb. 1959, BChir 1958; MRCS Eng. LRCP Lond. 1959; DObst RCOG 1966.

CORMACK, Ian Sutherland 79 Lon Masarn, Sketty, Swansea SA2 9EX — MB BS 1994 Lond.

CORMACK, James Dennis, Col. (retired) Grainish, Main Road, Carr Bridge PH23 3AA Tel: 01479 841386 — MB ChB 1952 Ed.; FRCP Ed. 1969, M 1959. Prev: Cons. Med. Army Med. Serv.

CORMACK, John Francis Greenwood Surgery, Tylers Ride, South Woodham Ferrers, Chelmsford CM3 5XD Tel: 01245 322443 Fax: 01245 321844; Deben House, Chapel Row, Woodham Ferrers, Chelmsford CM3 8RN Tel: 01245 322443 Email: jwrmacr@btinternet.com — MB BS 1975 Lond.; BDS Lond. 1970; MRCS Eng. LRCP Lond. 1975. (Lond. Hosp.) GP Sen. Partner; Elected Mem. BMA Press Spokesman; Founder Mem. Media Medics. Socs: (Hon. Sec.) BMA.

CORMACK, Mr John George Rigfoot, 22 Southside Road, Inverness IV2 3BG — MB ChB 1965 Ed.; BSc (2nd cl. Hons.) (Physiol.) Ed. 1965, MB ChB 1968; FRCS Ed. 1973; DO Eng. 1971.

CORMACK, John James Callender (retired) 5 Gordon Road, Edinburgh EH12 6NB Tel: 0131 334 3266 Email: sscormack@aol.com — MB ChB Ed. 1959; MD Ed. 1970; FRCP Ed. 1992; FRCGP 1978, M 1967; DObst RCOG 1964. Prev: Lect. (Gen. Pract.) Univ. Edin.

CORMACK, Louise Elizabeth Hinchingbrooke Healthcare, Intergrated Children's Services, Primrose Lane, Huntingdon PE29 1WG Email: lcormack@aol.com; Pulteney House, Scotts Gardens, Whittlesford, Cambridge CB2 4NR Tel: 01223 836865 Fax: 01223 837282 — MB BS 1979 Lond.; MRCP (UK) 1982; FRCPCH. Cons. Community Paediat. Hinchingbrooke NHS Trust Huntingdon. Prev: Sen. Regist. (Community Paediat.) Camb.; SCMO (Community Child Health) E. Surrey; Sen. Regist. (Paediat.) Edin.

CORMACK, Margaret Alison (retired) 112 Savernake Road, London NW3 2JR Tel: 020 7485 7843 — MB BCh 1949 Witwatersrand; BSc, MB BCh Witwatersrand 1949; DPM Eng. 1968. Prev: Cons. Psychiat. (Ment. Handicap.) Essex Hall Colchester.

***CORMACK, Thomas Graham McMorrow** 22 Southside Road, Inverness IV2 3BG Tel: 01463 230593 — MB ChB 1994 Aberd.

CORMIE, Carolyn Anne Department of Paediatrics, Ninewells Hospital, Dundee DD1 9SY Tel: 01382 660111; 9 Oxford Street, Dundee DD2 1TJ — MB ChB 1987 Aberd.; MRCGP 1993; DCCH RCP Ed. 1992; DRCOG 1990; MRCP (UK) 1996. Specialist Regist. (Paediat.) Ninewells Hosp. Dundee. Prev: SHO (Paediat.) Ninewells Hosp. Dundee; Research Fell. (Community Paediat.) Dumfries & Galloway HA; Trainee GP Dumfries & Galloway VTS.

CORMIE, Catherine Mary Community Paediatric Dept., Borders General Hospital, Melrose TD6 9BS; Cragdale, 31 Craigend Road, Stow, Galashiels TD1 2RJ — MB BS 1987 Newc.; DFFP 1996; MRCGP 1991; DCH RCP Lond. 1991; DRCOG 1990. Staff Grade (Community Child Health) Borders HB; SCMO in Family Plann., Primary Care NHS Trust, Borders. Prev: Trainee GP Earlston Health Centre; SHO (O & G & Psychiat.) S. Shields Gen. Hosp.; SHO (Paediat.) Borders Gen. Hosp.

CORMIE, Paul Julian Stow Surgery, 144 Galashiels Road, Stow, Galashiels TD1 2RA Tel: 01578 730245 Fax: 01578 730731; Cragdale, 31 Craigend Road, Stow, Galashiels TD1 2RJ Tel: 01578 730410 — MB ChB 1984 Aberd.; MB ChB Aberd. l984; MRCGP 1988; DRCOG 1986; DFFP 1997. (Aberdeen) GP. Socs: BMA; BASICS. Prev: Trainee GP Inverness VTS; SHO (A & E) Ingham Infirm. S. Shields; SHO (Geriat. Med.) Milesmark Hosp. Dunfermline.

CORMIE, Peter John Penalverne Surgery, Penalverne Drive, Penzance TR18 2RE Tel: 01736 363361 Fax: 01736 332118; Badgers Lodge, Badgers Cross, Gulval, Penzance TR20 8XE — MB ChB 1983 Bristol; MRCP (UK) 1987; MRCGP 1994; DRCOG 1993. (Univ. Bristol) Prev: Trainee GP Truro; Regist. (Med.) Hope Hosp. Manch.; SHO (Paediat.) Treliske Hosp. Truro.

CORN, Timothy Henry Glaxo Wellcome Research & Development, Greenford UB6 0HE Tel: 020 8422 3434 Fax: 020 8966 2701 Email: thc9571@ggr.co.uk — MB BS 1978 Lond.; MSc Lond. 1972, BSc 1971; FFPM RCP (UK) 1996; MRCPsych 1983. (King's Coll. Hosp.) Sen. Clin. Research Phys. Glaxo Gp. Research; Hon. Cons. Psychiat. Maudsley Hosp. Lond.; Hon. Sen. Lect. Inst. Psychiat. Lond. Socs: (Hon. Treas.) Brit. Assn. Psychopharmacol. Prev: Sen. Med. Off. Meds. Control Agency.

CORNABY, Mr Andrew John Department of Urology, West Dorset Hospital, Damers Road, Dorchester DT1 2JY Tel: 01305 255470 Fax: 01305 255469 — MB BS 1980 Lond.; FRCS Glas. 1984. (Westminster, London) Cons. Urol. W. Dorset Gen. Hosps. NHS Trust. Prev: Sen. Regist. (Urol.) Roy. Free Hosp. & Whipps Cross Hosp. Lond. & Cardiff Hosps. Wales.

CORNAH, Mr John Fulwood Hall Hospital, Midgeley Lane, Preston PR2 5SZ Tel: 01772 704111 Fax: 01772 795131 — MB ChB 1977 Liverp.; BDS 1968; FDS RCS Eng. 1979. Cons. Oral Surg. (Oral/Maxillo-Facial Surg.) Roy. Preston Hosp.

CORNAH, Lesley Jean Dalton House Surgery, 66 Edgcumbe Avenue, Newquay TR7 2NN Tel: 01637 873209; Lerryn, 20 Elm Close, Newquay TR7 2LN Tel: 01637 871035 Email: lesleytaylortr@freeserve.co.uk — MB BS 1985 Lond.; DCH RCP Lond. 1990; DRCOG 1989. Retained GP. Prev: SHO (Paediat.) Roy. Cornw. Hosp. Truro; Trainee GP Newquay; SHO (O & G) Roy. Cornw. Hosp. Truro.

CORNAH, Mr Michael Scott 4 Forest Gate, Blackpool FY3 9AW Tel: 01253 398742 Fax: 01253 304306 Email: mnls@btinternet.com — MB ChB Liverp. 1966, MChOrth 1973; FRCS Eng. 1971; FRCS Ed. 1971. (Liverp.) Cons. Orthop. Surg. Vict. Hosp. Blackpool. Socs: Fell. BOA. Prev: Sen. Regist. (Orthop.) Hartshill Orthop. Hosp. Stoke-on-Trent; Regist. (Orthop.) Wrightington Hosp.; Lady Jones Research Fell. (Orthop. Surg.) Univ. Liverp.

CORNAH, Peter Robert Radiology Department, West Wales Hospital, Carmarthen SA31 2AF; Brywllan, Cilycwm, Llandovery SA20 0SY — MB ChB 1975 Liverp.; FFR RCSI 1982; DMRD Lond. 1979. (Liverp.) Cons. Radiol. W. Wales Hosp. Carmarthen. Prev: Cons. Radiol. Horton Gen. NHS Trust. Banbury.; Sen. Regist. (Diag. Radiol.) Sheff.; Regist. (Diag. Radiol.) Edin.

CORNAH, Robert Alan 42 Theobalds Road, Holborn, London WC1 8NW — MB BCh 1993 Witwatersrand.

CORNALL, Richard John The Old Cottage, 73 South End, Garsington, Oxford OX44 9DJ — MB BCh 1986 Oxf.; BA Camb. 1983; DPhil Oxf. 1993; MRCP (UK) 1990. Wellcome Career Developm. Award Fell. Oxf. Univ. Prev: Regist. (Renal Med.) Hammersmith Hosp. Lond.; MRC Train. Fell. Oxf. Univ.

CORNBLEET, Michael Alan Fairmile Marie Curie Centre, Frogston Road W., Edinburgh EH10 7DR Tel: 0131 445 2141 Fax: 0131 445 5845 Email: med@mcccfairmile.u-net.com; 10 Donibristle Gardens, Dalgety Bay, Dunfermline KY11 9NQ Tel: 01383 823995 Email: macbleet@aol.com — MB BS 1973 Lond.; BSc (Hons., Biochem.) Lond. 1970, MD 1981; FRCP Lond. 1994; FRCP Ed. 1989; MRCP (UK) 1976; T(M) 1991. (Univ. Coll. Lond. & Univ. Coll. Hosp.) Med. Dir. & Cons. Palliat. Med. Fairmile Marie Curie Centre Edin.; Hon. Cons. Med. Oncol. W.. Gen. Hosp. Edin.; Hon. Sen. Lect. Univ. Edin. Socs: Assn. Palliat. Med.; Assn. Cancer Phys.; Amer. Soc. Clin. Oncol. Prev: Cons. & Sen. Regist. (Med. Oncol.) W.. Gen. Hosp. Edin.; Roy. Marsden Fell. Inst. Cancer Research Sutton.

CORNBLOOM, Mark Lionel Simon Sandhurst Group Practice, 72 Yorktown Road, Sandhurst GU47 9BT Tel: 01252 872455 Fax: 01252 872456 — MB BS 1981 Lond.; BSc (Psychol.) Lond. 1978; MRCGP 1985; DRCOG 1986. Prev: Trainee GP Roehampton VTS.

CORNE, Jonathan Michael Tel: 0115 924 9924 Fax: 0115 942 4554 Email: jonanthan.corne@mail.qmcuh-tr.trent.nhs.uk; 66 The Ropewalk, The Park, Nottingham NG1 5DW Tel: 0115 950 4906 — MB BS 1987 Lond.; MA Camb. 1987; Phd (Soton) 1999; MRCP (UK) 1992. (Cambridge university & Kings College School of Medicine) Cons. Phys. (Respirat. Med.), Qu.'s Med. Centre, Nottm. Socs: Roy. Soc. Med.; Brit. Thorac. Soc.; Brit. Soc. Allergy & Clin. Immunol. Prev: Assoc., Yale Univ. Sch. of Med.; Sen. Regist. Soton; MRC Train. Fell.

***CORNELISSEN, Piers Louis** Psychology Department, Ridley Building, Newcastle University, Newcastle upon Tyne NE1 7RU Tel: 0191 222 5622 Email: p.l.cornelissen@ncl.ac.uk; 11 Moor Place, Gosforth, Newcastle upon Tyne NE3 4AL — MB BS Lond. 1988; BA (Oxon) 1984; DPhil (Oxon) 1992.

CORNELIUS, Janet McClure 1 Whinfield Road, Prestwick KA9 2BQ Tel: 01292 74765 — MB ChB 1969 Glas.; MRCP (UK) 1974; MRCPath. (Haemat.) 1978.

CORNELIUS, Paul George 54 Sturry Road, Canterbury CT1 1HT — MB BS 1983 Lond.; MRCP (UK) 1988.

CORNELL, Jacqueline Mary Wallingford Medical Centre, Reading Rd, Wallingford OX10 9DU Tel: 01491 835577; Herries, Reading Road, Wallingford OX10 9DT Tel: 01491 832387 — MB BS 1982 Lond.; DRCOG 1985; DCH 1988. p/t Asst. GP - Retainer Scheme.

CORNELL, Mr Mark Simon Queen Elizabeth The Queen Mother Hospital, St. Peter Rd, Margate CT9 4AN Tel: 01843 225544 Ext: 62860 Email: mscornell@aol.com; 2 Birkdale Colse, Chestfield, Whitstable CTS 3PY Email: mscornell@ad.com — BM 1987 Soton.; FRCS Eng. 1991; FRCS (Orth.) 1998. (Soton.) Cons. in Trauma and Orthop. Hosps. NHS Trust, Qu. Eliz. the Qu. Mother Hosp., Margate, Kent; Fell. (Paediat. Orthop.) Sydney, Australia. Socs: Brit. Orthop. Assn.; Brit. Soc. for Childr.s Orthop. Surg. Prev: Specialist Regist. (Orthop.) Kent & Canterbury; Specialist Regist. (Orthop.) St. Thos. Hosp. Lond.; Regist. (Orthop.) Maidstone Hosp., Guy's & St Thos. Hosp. & Lewisham Hosp. Lond.

CORNELL, Michael Norman Page 75 Bushwood Road, Richmond TW9 3BG — MB BS 1970 Lond.; MRCP (UK) 1975; MRCS Eng. LRCP Lond. 1970; DRCOG 1977; DCH Eng. 1975. (Char. Cross)

CORNELL, Stuart John 28 Pennine View, Stocksbridge, Sheffield S36 1ER — MB ChB 1975 Manch.; MMedSci Sheff. 1993; FRCS Eng. 1980; FRCS Ed. 1980; MRCGP 1983; MPH 1996; MFPHM 1997. (Manchester) Cons. (Pub. Health Med) Doncaster HA. Prev: Sen. Regist. (Pub. Health Med.) Sheff; GP Stocksbridge.

CORNER, Andrew Jonathan Dept of Anaesthetics, Royal Sussex County Hospital, Easter Road, Brighton BN2 5BE — MB BS 1992 Lond.; MRCP (UK) 1996; FRCA 1999.

CORNER, Beryl Dorothy Flat 4 Chartley, The Avenue, Sneyd Park, Bristol BS9 1PE Tel: 0117 968 5308; Flat 4 Chartley, The Avenue, Sneyd Park, Bristol BS9 1PE Tel: 0117 968 5308, 01428 713017 — Hon. DSc. (UWE) 2000; MB BS Lond. 1934; MD Lond. 1936; Hon. MD Bristol 1996; FRCP Lond. 1953, M 1936; MRCS Eng. LRCP Lond. 1934; Hon. FRCPCH 1997. (Lond. Sch. Med. Wom.) Emerit. Cons. Paediat. Bristol, W.on-super-Mare & S.mead Health Dists. Socs: Fell. Roy. Soc. Med. (Ex-Pres. & Hon. Mem. Paediat. Sect.); Hon. Mem. Brit. Paediat. Assn.; (Ex-Pres.) Med. Wom. Internat. Assn. Prev: Lect. (Child Health) Univ. Bristol; Ho. Phys. Roy. Free Hosp. & Brompton Hosp. Consump.; Ho. Surg. Bristol Roy. Infirm.

CORNER, Roderick William MacLean (retired) Hawthorn Hill, 36 Wordsworth St., Penrith CA11 7QY Tel: 01768 863660 Fax: 01768 862445 — MB ChB 1961 Ed.; MRCGP 1973; DObst RCOG 1966. Prev: GP Penrith.

CORNER, Timothy Robin Jeremy Kenneth Macrae Medical Centre, 32 Church Road, Rainford, St Helens WA11 8HJ Tel: 01744 882606 Fax: 01744 883546; The Beeches, 10 Rainford Road, St Helens WA10 6BS Tel: 01744 739247 Fax: 01744 739247 — MB BS 1972 Lond.; MRCS Eng. LRCP Lond. 1972; LMSSA Lond. 1972. (St. Bart.) p/t Gen. Med. Practitioner. Socs: St. Helens Med. Soc. Prev: Ho. Off. David Lewis N.. Hosp. Liverp.; Cas. Off. Providence Hosp. St. Helens; SHO (Geriat. & Gen. Med.) Newsham Gen. Hosp. Liverp.

CORNES, Brian (retired) 2 Poundisford Close, Taunton TA1 4TF Tel: 01823 330657 — LRCP LRCS Ed. LRFPS Glas. 1952; MRCPsych 1971; DPM Durham. 1960. Prev: Cons. Psychiat. St. And., Hellesdon, Norf. & Norwich Hosps.

CORNES, John Selwyn 2 Westbury Park, Bristol BS6 7JB Tel: 0117 973 8168 — MB BS 1951 Lond.; BSc (Special Physiol., 1st cl. Hons.) Lond. 1948, MD 1961; FRCPath 1974, M 1963; DCP Lond 1957; AKC 1948. (Westm.) Emerit. Cons. Path. United Bristol Hosps. NHS Trust; Clin. Lect. Univ. Bristol; Acad. Chaplain Univ. Bristol. Socs: Fell. Roy. Soc. Med.; Assn. Clin. Pathols. Prev: Cons. Path. & Dir. Dept. Cytol United Bristol Hosps.; Lect. (Path.) W.m. Hosp.; Regist. (Path.) Postgrad. Med. Sch.

CORNES, Maureen (retired) 2 Poundisford Close, Hovelands, Taunton TA1 4TF Tel: 01823 330657 — MB ChB 1954 Birm.; DPM Eng. 1967; DObst RCOG 1956. Prev: Assoc. Specialist (Psychiat.) Little Plumstead Hosp. Norwich.

CORNES, Paul Graham Sheffield Bristol haematology and Oncology Centre, Horfield Road, Bristol BS2 8ED Tel: 0117 923 0000 — BM BCh 1984 Oxf.; BA Oxf. 1981, MA 1987; MRCP (UK) 1991; FRCR 1994. (Oxford, UK) Cons. Oncologist, Bristol, UK; Hon. Sen. Regist. Acad. Unit of Radiother. Roy. Marsden Hosp.; Clin. Research Fell. Inst. Cancer Research Belmont, Surrey; Cons. Oncologist Roy. United Hosp., Bath, UK. Prev: Jun. Lect. Roy. Marsden Hosp. Lond.

CORNEY, Charles Edward 84 Wigginton Road, York YO31 8JQ Tel: 01904 349362 — MB BS 1962 Char. Cross; FRCR 1975; FFR 1973; DMRD Eng. 1969. Cons. Radiol.; Med. Cons. Socs: Founder Mem. Brit. Assn. Continence Care.; UK Register of Med. Expert Witnesses and Single Jt. Experts. Prev: Sen. Regist. (Radiol.) Middlx. Hosp., Lond.; Regist. (Med.) Epsom Dist. Hosp.; Cas. Off. Char. Cross Hosp. Lond.

CORNEY, Gerald (retired) 56 Russell Court, Woburn Place, London WC1H 0LW — MB ChB 1952 Liverp.; MD Liverp. 1966; DObst RCOG 1958; DCH Eng. 1960. Hon. Research Fell. Galton Laborat.

UCL. Prev: Mem. Scientif. Staff MRC Human Biochem. Genetics Unit.

CORNFORD, Charles Stanley Newlands Surgery, Newlands Road, Middlesbrough TS1 3E Tel: 01642 247029; Alpha House, 133 Guisborough Road, Nunthorpe, Middlesbrough TS7 0JE Tel: 01642 712869 Email: charles.cornford@mongxnet.co.uk — MB BS 1980 Newc.; MSc Lond. 1992; MRCGP 1986; DCH RCP Lond. 1985; MD Newcastle University 1999. GP; Research Fell. in Educat. Newc. Univ.

CORNFORD, Mr Philip Andrew 109 Sandhurst Street, Aigburth, Liverpool L17 7BU Tel: 0151 727 3385 — MB BS 1990 Lond.; BSc Lond. 1987, MB BS 1990; FRCS Eng. 1994. Regist. (Urol.) Leighton Hosp. Crewe.

CORNFORD, Stanley Edward (retired) 17 Wheatlands Road, Harrogate HG2 8BB Tel: 01423 562427 — MB ChB 1957 Leeds; FRCGP 1978, M 1968. Prev: Ho. Surg. (Obst.) St. Mary's Hosp. Leeds.

***CORNFORTH, Belinda Mary** 7 Rutland Road, West Bridgford, Nottingham NG2 5DH Tel: 0115 914 3405 — BM BS 1995 Nottm.

CORNFORTH, Brenda Mary The Knares Surgery, Great Berry Surgery, Nightingales, Langdon Hills, Basildon SS16 6SA; Ladywell House, Ladywell Lane, Great Baddow, Chelmsford CM2 7AE — MB BS 1968 Lond.; MRCS Eng. LRCP Lond. 1968. (Roy. Free) Prev: SHO (Anaesth.) Roy. Free Hosp. Sch. Med. Lond.; Ho. Phys. W. Kent Gen. Hosp. Maidstone; Ho. Surg. Roy. Free Hosp. (New End Hosp.) Lond.

CORNFORTH, Charles Montague 5 Selkirk Drive, Chester CH4 8AQ Tel: 01244 672499 — MB ChB 1943 Ed. (Ed.)

CORNISH, Candida June Rock House, 9 Beach Road, Penarth CF64 1JX — MB BS 1991 Newc.

CORNISH, Charles Andrew Christmas Maltings Surgery, Camps Road, Haverhill CB9 8HF Tel: 01440 702203 Fax: 01440 712198 — MB BS 1977 Lond.; MRCGP 1988.

CORNISH, Douglas Cecil 38 West End, Long Whatton, Loughborough LE12 5DW Tel: 01509 843708 — MB BS Lond. 1953; MRCS Eng. LRCP Lond. 1953; AFOM RCP Lond. 1982; DObst RCOG 1955. (St. Geo.) Sen. Med. Off. Rolls Royce Ltd. Midl. Gp. Socs: Rugby Med. Soc. Prev: Employm. Med. Adviser EMAS Coventry; Ho. Phys. & Res. Obst. Asst. St. Geo. Hosp.

CORNISH, Elizabeth Lucinda 32D Lapwing Lane, Didsbury, Manchester M20 2NS — MB ChB 1995 Manch.; MRCP Part I 1997; MRCP UK Part 2 1999. (Manch.)

CORNISH, Errol Malcolm 11 Holmbury Park, Bromley BR1 2QS — MB ChB 1977 Cape Town; MSc Oxf. 1979; BSc (Hons.) Natal (Durban) 1971; BSc Natal (Pietermaritzburg) 1970; DA (SA) 1995. (Cape Town) Sen. Regist. (Cardiac Surg. & Anaesth.) Groote Schuur Hosp. Cape Town; Fleet Med. Adviser, Hebridean Is. Cruises, Skipton c/o Holmbury Pk., Bromley, Kent BR1 2QS. Socs: Fell. Roy. Soc. Med.; Roy. Soc. S. Afr. Prev: Sen. Regist. (Anaesth.) Groote Schuur Hosp. Cape Town; SHO (O & G) Groote Schuur Hosp. Cape Town; Clin. Research Fell. Nuffield Dept. O & G Univ. Oxf. & John Radcliffe Hosp. Oxf.

CORNISH, Fiona Elizabeth Newnham Walk Surgery, Wordsworth Grove, Cambridge CB3 9HS Tel: 01223 366811 Fax: 01223 302706; 151 Huntingdon Road, Cambridge CB3 0DH Tel: 01223 323087 Fax: 01223 323087 — MB BChir 1985 Camb.; MRCGP 1990; DCH RCP Lond. 1989; DRCOG 1986.

CORNISH, Gabrielle Rosemarie Louise Preston Grove Medical Centre, Preston Grove, Yeovil BA20 2BQ Tel: 01935 474353 Fax: 01935 425171 — MB BS 1990 Lond.; DRCOG Lond. 1993; DFFP Lond. 1995. (St. Geo. Hosp. Med. Sch.)

CORNISH, Glenn Francis 9 Porteridges, Oak Ridge, Dorking RH4 2NT — MB BS 1991 Lond.; MRCPsych 1998. Specialist Regist. Psych. Rotat. Univ. Coll. Lond.

CORNISH, Jacqueline Margery Mary Tresilian, Woodland Grove, Claverton Dowm, Bath BA2 7AT — MB ChB 1972 Bristol.

CORNISH, Jennifer Frances 57 Trelawney Road, Plympton, Plymouth PL7 4LJ — BM 1981 Soton. Hosp. Practitioner in BrE. Med.

CORNISH, Jeremy William Michael Haslemere Health Centre, Church Lane, Haslemere GU27 2BQ Tel: 01483 783023 Fax: 01428 645065; Edgewood, Bunch Lane, Haslemere GU27 1AE Tel: 01428 642801 — MB BS 1975 Lond.; MRCS Eng. LRCP Lond. 1975; DRCOG 1982. (St. Thos.)

CORNISH, Matthew Yeovil District Hospital, Higher Kingston, Yeovil BA21 4AT Tel: 01935 384246 Email: medic@eiowen.demon.co.uk — MB BS 1990 Lond.; BSc (Hons.) Lond. 1987; FRCA 1998. (St Georges London) Staff Grade, Anaesth. E. Som. NHS Trust, Yeovil. Socs: Mem. - Obstetric Anaesth.s Assn.; Fell. - Roy. Coll. of Anaesth.s.

CORNISH, Simon Richard Tristram Winswood, Sanctuary Road, Holsworthy EX22 6DQ Tel: 01409 254081 Fax: 01409 253326 — MB BS 1988 Lond.

CORNISH, Virginia Margaret Regis Medical Centre, Darby Street, Rowley Regis, Warley B65 0BA Tel: 0121 559 3957 Fax: 0121 502 9117; 39 Kelmscott Road, Harbourne, Birmingham B17 8QW Tel: 0121 559 1118 Fax: 0121 426 4101 — MB BS 1988 Lond.; MRCGP 1992. GP Princip.; GP Trainer. Socs: MDU & BMA.

CORNMELL, Carol Anne Tottington Health Centre, 16 Market Street, Tottington, Bury BL8 4AD Tel: 01204 885106 Fax: 01204 887717; 12 Chale Green, Harwood, Bolton BL2 3NJ — MB ChB 1983 Manch.; MRCGP 1987. GP Tottington Health Centre. Prev: Trainee GP Bury VTS; Trainee GP/SHO Rotat. (Med.) Bury Gen. Hosp. Lancs.; Ho. Off. (Surg. & Orthop.) Roy. Preston Hosp.

CORNOCK, Sarah Jane 10 Wellstones Close, Ivybridge PL21 0FE — MB ChB 1990 Sheff.; DA (UK) 1995; DFFP 1998; DRCOG 1998. Gen. Pract. Regist., Plymouth VTS. Prev: Data Standards Admin. (Clin.) UK Transpl. Support Serv. Auth.; SHO (A & E) Qu. Eliz. II Hosp. Welwyn Gdn. City.

CORNES, Peter Stanley Riverside Medical Centre, 175 Ferry Road, Hullbridge, Hockley SS5 6JH Tel: 01702 230555 Fax: 01702 231207; 10 Beauchamps, Burnham-on-Crouch CM0 8PR Email: user240132@aol.com — 2001 MRAes; MB BS (Hons.) Lond. 1976; Cert. Av. Med. 1990. (Lond. Hosp. Med. Coll.) Socs: Anglo-French Med. Soc.; BMA; Assn. Of Aviat. Med. Examr.s. Prev: Ho. Surg. St. John's Hosp. Chelmsford; Ho. Phys. Lond. Hosp.; Capt. RAMC.

CORNWALL, Louise Jane Lehman and Partners, Hightown Surgery, Hightown Gardens, Banbury OX16 9DB Tel: 01295 270722 Fax: 01295 263000; 1 Crouch Hill Road, Banbury OX16 9RG Tel: 01295 265547 — MB BS 1989 Lond.; BSc (Hons.) Lond. 1986; MRCGP 1995; DCH RCPS Glas. 1993. (King's Coll. Sch. Med. & Dent. Lond.) Prev: Trainee GP Banbury, Oxon.; SHO (O & G) Bishop Auckland Gen. Hosp.; SHO (Community Paediat.) Sunderland Dist. Gen. Hosp.

CORNWALL, Peter Leonard Fern Lodge CMHC, 153 High Street, Eston TS6 9JQ Tel: 01642 452091 Email: lenny.cornwall@tney.northy.nhs.uk — MB BS 1986 Newc.; MRCPsych 1992; Dip. Med. Sci. (Newcastle) 1986. Cons. Psychiat., Tees @ Nort E. Yorks. NHS Trust; Hon. Sen. Lect., Univ. of Newc. upon Tyne. Prev: Clin. Research Assoc. (Psychiat.) Univ. Newc.; Sen. Regist. & Regist. Rotat. (Gen. Psychiat.) N.. RHA; SHO Rotat. (Psychiat.) Newc. Scheme.

CORNWELL, Carol-Ann Flat 4, 141 Lenton Boulevard, Lenton, Nottingham NG7 2BT — BM BS 1981 Nottm.

CORNWELL, Graeme Albyn Medical Practice, 30 Albyn Place, Aberdeen AB10 1NW Tel: 01224 586829 Fax: 01224 213238 — MB ChB 1990 Aberd.; MRCGP 1994. Clin. Sen. Lect. Univ. Dept. Gen. Pract. Univ. Aberd.

CORNWELL, Johanna Gabriella Miranda Oak Farm, Scaldwell, Northampton NN6 9JY — MB BS 1991 Lond.; BSc (Hons.) Lond. 1989. Acad. Fell. (Gen. Pract.) St. Bart. & Roy. Lond. Sch. Med. & Dent. Socs: Roy. Coll. Gen. Pract. Prev: Trainee Lond. Acad. Scheme; Trainee GP E. Lond. VTS.

CORNWELL, John Court (retired) 12 Knoll Hill, Sneyd Park, Bristol BS9 1RA Tel: 0117 909 2182 Fax: 0117 909 2182 — MB BS 1951 Lond.; MA Oxf. 1949; MFOM RCP Lond. 1983; DPH Bristol 1973; DTM & H Liverp. 1964; DObst RCOG 1956. Prev: Sen. Occupat. Phys. Co. Avon.

CORNWELL, Martina 164 Portland Street, Southport PR8 6RB — MB ChB 1987 Liverp.

CORNWELL, Winifred Betty (retired) 50 Romney Drive, off Sundridge Avenue, Bromley BR1 2TE Tel: 020 8290 6488 — MB BS 1950 Lond.; MRCS Eng. LRCP Lond. 1950; FFA RCS Eng. 1969; DA Eng. 1954. Prev: Cons. Anaesth.. Lond.. Chest Hosp.

CORP, Nigel The Surgery, 166 New Road, Croxley Green, Rickmansworth WD3 3HD Tel: 01923 778277 — MB 1978 Camb.; MA; BChir 1977; MRCP (UK) 1981. (Camb. & Westm.) GP

Rickmansworth. Prev: SHO (Med.) N.wick Pk. Hosp. Harrow. SHO (Cardiol.) W.m. Hosp.; Ho. Surg. S.W. Surrey (Guildford) Health Dist.

CORPS, Mr Barry Varndell Michael (retired) Builg, Charnes Road, Ashley, Market Drayton TF9 4LQ Tel: 01630 2040 — MB ChB 1956 St. And.; ChM Birm. 1970; FRCS Ed. 1962. Prev: Cons. Plastic Surg. N. Staffs. Roy. Infirm. Stoke on Trent.

CORPS, David John Oak Tree Health Centre, Tyne Ave, Didcot OX11 7GD Tel: 01235 810099 Fax: 01235 815181 Email: david.corps@doctors.org.uk — BM BCh 1982 Oxf.; MA, BM BCh Oxf. 1982; MRCGP 1993; DRCOG 1992. (Oxf.) GP Princip. Oak Tree Health Centre, Didcot.

CORR, Conor James 72 Perry Street, Northampton NN1 4HW — MB BCh BAO 1994 Belf.

CORR, Fiona Maria 188 Bush Road, Dungannon BT71 6EZ — MB BCh BAO 1994 Belf.

CORR, John Francis 6 Finaghy Road S., Belfast BT10 0DR — LRCP LRCS 1956 Ed.; LRCP LRCS Ed. LRFPS Glas. 1956.

CORR, Laura Anne Cardiac Department, St. Thomas' Hospital, Lambeth Palace Road, London SE1 7EH Tel: 020 7960 5611 Fax: 020 7960 5680 Email: i.corr@gstt.sthames.nhs.uk; 32 Eccleston Street, London SW1W 9PY Tel: 020 7730 1905 Fax: 020 7730 1906 — MB BS 1981 Lond.; PhD Lond. 1991; FRCP Lond. 1997; MRCP (UK) 1984; FESC 1995. Cons. Invasive Cardiol. Guy's & St. Thos. Hosps. Trust Lond.; Assoc. Edr. Europ. Heart Jl.; Assoc. Edr., Europ. Heart Jl. Socs: Fell. Europ. Soc. Cardiol.; Brit. Cardiac Interven. Soc.; Brit. Soc. Echocardiogr. Prev: Fell. Hôpital Cardiologique Lille, France; Sen. Regist. (Cardiol.) Hammersmith Hosp. Lond.; MRC Research Regist. (Cardiol.) Brompton Hosp. & Nat. Heart & Lung Inst. Lond.

CORRADO, Hector Aldo (retired) The Whitehouse, Cichle Hill, Cadnant, Menai Bridge LL59 5TA Tel: 01248 712461 — MD 1949 Malta. Prev: Cons. Chest Phys. Gwynedd AHA.

CORRADO, Karin Maria Brookvale Practice, Hallwood Health Centre, Hospital Way, Runcorn WA7 2UT Tel: 01928 718182 Fax: 01928 790716 — MB ChB 1976 Manch.; MRCGP 1980; DRCOG 1979.

CORRADO, Oliver John Leeds General Infirmary, Great George St., Leeds LS1 3EX Tel: 0113 392 2662 Fax: 0113 392 6557 Email: oliver.corrado@leedsth.nhs.uk; 17 Lidgett Park Road, Leeds LS8 1EE — MB BS Lond. 1976; FRCP Lond. 1994; MRCP (UK) 1979; MRCS Eng. LRCP Lond. 1976. Cons. Geriat. Gen. Infirm. & Chapel Allerton Hosp. Leeds. Prev: Sen. Regist. Rotat. (Geriat. & Gen. Med.) Leeds & Bradford; Research Fell. (Thoracic Med.) St. Bart. Hosp. Lond.; Regist. (Gen. & Thoracic Med.) Roy. Free Hosp. Lond.

CORRALL, Roger James Martin Royal Infirmary, Bristol B52 8HW; 64 Pembroke Road, Bristol BS8 3DX Tel: 0117 974 2505 Fax: 0117 928 2768 — MB ChB 1968 Ed.; BSc (Hons.) Ed. 1965, MD 1977; FRCP Lond. 1985; FRCP Ed. 1983; MRCP (UK) 1970. (Ed.) Cons. Phys. & Endocrinol. Bristol Roy. Infirm; Hon. Sen. Lect. (Med.) Univ. Bristol. Socs: Brit. Diabetic Assn.; Soc. Endocrinol.; Eur. Soc. Clin. Investig. Prev: Sen. Regist. N.. Gen. Hosp. Gp. Edin.; Regist. (Gen. Med. & Metab. Disorders) Roy. Infirm. Edin.; Clin. & Research Fell. Case W.. Reserve Univ., USA.

CORREA, Mr Jonathan Benedict Southampton General Hospital, Tremona Road, Southampton SO16 6YD; 78 Pacific Close, Ocean Village, Southampton SO14 3TY Tel: 01703 226777 — MB BS 1977 Bombay; MS (Gen. Surg.) Bombay 1981; FRCS Glas. 1987. Staff Grade (Gen. Surg.) Soton. Hosps. NHS Trust. Prev: Assoc. Specialist (Gen. & Vasc. Surg.) Roy. Sussex Co. Hosp. Brighton; Regist. (Gen. Surg. & Urol.) Crawley Hosp.; Regist. (Gen. Surg.) Joyce Green Hosp. Dartford.

CORRIDAN, Bryan James Patrick 51 Woodside Avenue, London N10 3HY — BChir 1984 Camb.

CORRIDAN, Nora Patricia 51 Woodside Avenue, London N10 3HY Tel: 020 8883 4902 — MB ChB 1947 St. And.; DO Eng. 1952. (St. And.) Prev: Med. Asst. W.. Ophth. Hosp. & Ophth. Dept. Char. Cross Hosp. Lond.; SHO Eye Dept. OldCh. Hosp. Romford; Ho. Surg. Dundee Roy. Infirm.

CORRIDAN, Mr Patrick Gerard Joseph 8 Summerfield Road, Wolverhampton WV1 4RR — MB BCh BAO 1981 NUI; FRCS 1988; FRCOphth 1988. (Univ. Coll. Cork) Cons. Ophth. Wolverhampton Eye Infirm. & Walsall Manor Hosp. Socs: Oxf. Ophth. Congr.; Amer. Acad. Ophth.; BMA. Prev: Fell. Glaucoma Unit Moorfields Eye Hosp. Lond.; Regist. (Ophth.) Birm. & Midl. Eye Hosp. Birm.; SHO (Ophth.) Sussex Eye Hosp. Brighton.

CORRIE, Gordon Raymond 22 Blyth Road, Maltby, Rotherham S66 7LF — MB ChB 1976 Sheff.

CORRIE, Lindsay Anne Cordwent The Chelsea Practice, Violet Melchett Clinic, 30 Flood Walk, London SW3 5RR Tel: 020 8237 2544 — MB BS 1985 Lond.; MRCGP (Distinc.) 1990; DRCOG 1989; DCH RCP Lond. 1989. GP Lond. Prev: GP Hong Kong.

CORRIE, Paul Richardson Crumlin Road Health Centre, 130-132 Crumlin Road, Belfast BT14 6AR Tel: 02890 741188 Fax: 02890 758811; 9-11 Cherryvalley, Knock Road, Belfast BT5 6PH — MB BCh BAO 1979 Belf.; MRCGP 1983; DRCOG 1981. (Queen's University, Belfast) Socs: Soc. Occupat. Med. & Assur. Med. Soc.

CORRIE, Philippa Gail Oncology Centre, Addenbrooke's Hospital, Cambridge CB2 2QQ; 43 High Street, Teversham, Cambridge CB1 5AF — BM BCh 1989 Oxf.; PhD Lond. 1986, BSc (1st cl. Hons.) 1984; MRCP (UK) 1992; FRCP Lond. 2000. Cons. (Med. Oncol.) Addenbrooke's Hosp. Camb. Socs: ASCO; AACR; BACR. Prev: Lect. & Hon. Sen. Regist. (Med. Oncol.) CRC Inst. Cancer Studies Qu. Eliz. Hosp. Birm.

CORRIE, Thomas 20 Fiery Hill Road, Barnt Green, Birmingham B45 8LG — LRCP LRCS 1946 Ed.; LRCP LRCS Ed. LRFPS Glas. 1946. (St. Mungo's Coll. Glas.) Prev: Temp. Surg. Lt. RNVR; Ho. Surg. & Surgic. Regist. Accid. Hosp. Birm.

CORRIGALL, Richard James Snowsfields Adolescent Unit, Thomas Guy House, Guys Hospital, 47 Weston St., London SE1 3RR Tel: 020 7955 2043 Fax: 020 7955 2049 Email: rcorrigall@slam-tr.nhs.uk — MB BS 1988 Newc.; MRCPsych 1992. Cons. Child & Adolesc. Psychiat. & Sen. Lect. Guy's Hosp. Lond. Prev: Cons. Child & Adolesc. Psychiat. Simmon's Ho. Adolesc. Unit Lond.; Sen. Regist. (Child & Adolesc. Psychiat.) Maudsley & Bethlem Hosp. Lond.; Regist. (Psychiat.) Maudsley & Bethlem Hosp. Lond.

CORRIGAN, Christopher Brunswick House Medical Group, 1 Brunswick Street, Carlisle CA1 1ED Tel: 01228 515808 Fax: 01228 593048 — MB ChB 1987 Sheff.; MRCGP 1991; DCH RCP Lond. 1991. Prev: SHO (O & G) Qu. Eliz. Hosp. Gateshead, Tyne & Wear.; SHO (A & E) Roy. Vict. Infirm. Newc. u. Tyne.

CORRIGAN, Christopher John Dept of Respiratory Medicine & Allergy, 5th Floor Thomas Guy house, guy's Hospital, London SE1 9RT Tel: 0207 955 4571 Fax: 0207 403 8640 Email: c.corrigan@cxwms.ac.uk; The Chrannies, Meesons Lane, Grays RM17 5EE Tel: 01375 373801 Email: chris.anne.corrigan@cwcom.net — MB BS 1983 Lond.; PhD Lond. 1990; MSc Oxf. 1981, MA 1985, BA 1977; MRCP (UK) 1986; FRCP 1998. Clin. Sen. Lect. & Hon. Cons. Phys. (Gen. Internal & Respirat. Med.) Imperial Coll. Sch. of Med. (Char. Cross Campus) Lond. Socs: Brit. Soc. Immunol.; (Counc.) Brit. Soc. Allergy & Clin. Immunol. Prev: Clin. Sen. Lect. & Hons. Cons. Phys. Nat. Heart & Lung Inst. Roy. Brompton Hosp. Lond.

CORRIGAN, Diane Bernadette Southern Health & Social Services Board, Tower Hill, Armagh BT61 9DR Tel: 01861 410041 Fax: 01861 414550 Email: dianeco@shssb.n-i.nhs.uk; Linden House, 61 Newry Road, Armagh BT60 1ER Tel: 01861 524701 — MB BCh BAO 1981 Dub.; BA, MB BCh BAO Dub. 1981; MFPHM 1989; MPH NUI 1985; FFPHM 1998. (Trinity College, Dublin) Cons. Pub. Health Med. S.. Health & Social Servs. Bd.

CORRIGAN, Donna Lynette Royal Hospital for Sick Children, Yorkhill, Glasgow G41 4QJ Tel: 0141 201 0000; 1 Newark Drive, Pollockshields, Glasgow G41 4QJ Tel: 0141 424 4327 Email: donna@nc-dc.demon.co.uk — MB ChB 1990 Manch.; BSc (Med. Sci.) St. And. 1987; DRCOG 1993; DFFP 1993; DCH RCP Lond. 1993; MRCP 1995. (St. Andews & Manch.) Specialist Regist. (Paediat.) Roy. Hosp. Sick Childr. Yorkhill Glas. Prev: SHO (Paediat.) Inverclyde Roy. Hosp. Greenock; SHO (Paediat.) Alder Hey Hosp. Liverp., St. Mary's Hosp. Manch. & Booth Hall Childr. Hosp. Manch.

CORRIGAN, Francis Martin Argyll & Bute Hospital, Lochgilphead PA31 8LD Tel: 01546 602323 Fax: 01546 604914 Email: fmcorrigan@aol.com — MD 1989 Aberd.; MB ChB Glas. 1976; MRCPsych 1981. Cons. Psychiat. Argyll & Bute Hosp. Lochgilphead. Prev: Lect. Univ. Aberd.

CORRIGAN, John Charles 18 Molesworth Road, Cookstown BT80 8NR — MB BCh BAO 1993 NUI; LRCPSI 1993.

CORRIGAN, John Kyran Tudhoe Village, Spennymoor, Durham Tel: 01388 814867 — MB BCh BAO 1938 NUI; DPH 1940. (Dub.)

SBStJ. Socs: BMA (Mem. Counc. N. Eng. Br. & Ex-Chairm. Bishop Auckland Div.); Assn. Indust. Med. Offs. Prev: Asst. Surg. & Res. Surg. Off. Co. Hosp. Durh.; Orthop. Ho. Surg. Darlington Memor. Hosp.

CORRIGAN, Luke Daniel Kingsholm Surgery, Alvin Street, Gloucester GL1 3EN Tel: 01452 522902 Fax: 01452 387819 — MB BS 1984 Lond.; MRCGP 1990.

CORRIGAN, Margaret Mary 10 Glebe Gardens, Newtownabbey BT36 6ED — MB BCh BAO 1986 Belf.; MRCGP 1992; DMH Belf. 1989; DRCOG 1990; DGM RCP Lond. 1989. GP Glengormley. Prev: SHO (Paediat.) Roy. Belf. Hosp. for Sick Childr.; SHO (O & G) Mid Ulster Hosp. Magherafelt.

CORRIGAN, Neil Peter 25 Seafield Park, Portstewart BT55 7JU — MB BCh BAO 1986 Belf.

CORRIGAN, Mr Neil Thomas 17 Brook Road, Heaton Chapel, Stockport SK4 5BZ — MB ChB 1989 Glas.; BSc Glas. 1989, MB ChB 1989; FRCS Ed. 1994.

CORRIGHAN, Graham Alexander Dovecot Health Centre, Longreach Road, Liverpool L14 0NL Tel: 0151 228 3336 Fax: 0151 220 3225 — MB BCh 1981 Wales. (Cardiff) Princip. in Gen. Pract. Davecot Health Centre, Liverp.. Socs: BMA.

CORRIN, Professor Bryan Histopathology Department, Royal Brompton Hospital, Sydney St., London SW3 6NP Tel: 020 7351 8420 Fax: 020 7351 8293; 14 Foxgrove Road, Beckenham BR3 5AT Tel: 020 8650 7029 — MB BS Lond. 1956; FRCPath 1977, M 1965. (St. Mary's) Emeritas Prof. Thoracic Path. Nat. Heart & Lung Inst. Imperical Coll., Univ. Lond.; Hon. Cons. Path. Roy. Brompton Hosp. Lond. Socs: (Ex-Pres.) Internat. Acad. Path. (Brit. Div.); Path. Soc.; Assn. Clin. Path. Prev: Reader (Morbid Anat.) St. Thos. Hosp. Med. Sch. Lond.; Lect. (Path.) Univ. Manch.; Resid. Clin. Path. Birm. Childr. Hosp.

CORRIN, Christine Elizabeth 6 Swallow Close, Pool-in-Wharfedale, Otley LS21 1RR Tel: 0113 284 1008 — MB BS 1984 Lond.; MRCGP 1988; DRCOG 1987. (Roy. Free Hosp. Sch. Med.) GP Asst. Headingley Leeds; Clin. Asst. (Obst. & Gyn.) Leeds Gen. Infirm. Prev: Trainee GP Lond. VTS.

CORRIN, Sheila Ann 14 Foxgrove Road, Beckenham BR3 5AT Tel: 020 8650 7029 — MB BS 1960 Lond.; MRCS Eng. LRCP Lond. 1960; DObst RCOG 1961. (Roy. Free & Manch.) Sessional Off. Croydon Community Health. Socs: Inst. Psychosexual Med. Prev: Asst. Lect. (Physiol.) Manch. Univ.; Ho. Phys. Manch. Roy. Infirm.; Ho. Surg. St. Mary's Hosps. Manch.

CORRIN, Susan Elizabeth Dr Iddon & Partners, Eastgate Surgery, 31 York Place, Knaresborough HG5 0AD Tel: 01423 557200; 12 ST. Robert's Road,, Knaresborough HG5 8EQ Tel: 01423 867901 — MB ChB 1993 Liverp.; BSc Liverp. 1990; DRCOG 1995; DFFP 1997; MRCGP 1997; Cert. Prescribed Equiv. Exp. JCTGP 1998. GP/Occupat. Health Care Doctor.

CORRIS, Professor Paul Anthony Regional Cardiothoracic Centre, Freeman Hospital, Newcastle upon Tyne NE7 7DN Tel: 0191 284 3111 Fax: 0191 223 1321 Email: paul.corris@ncl.ac.uk; 36 Reid Park Road, Jesmond, Newcastle upon Tyne NE2 2ES Tel: 0191 281 3904 — MB BS 1976 Lond.; FRCP Lond. 1991; MRCP (UK) 1979; MRCS Eng. LRCP Lond. 1976. (Westm.) Director Pulm. Vasc. Unit Freeman Hosp.; Prof. Thermal Med. Univ. Newc.; Assoc. Med. Director CardioPulm. Transpl. Freeman Hosp.; Reader (Thoracic Med.) Univ. Newc. Socs: Assn. Phys.; (Counc.) Brit. Thoracic Soc.; Internat. Soc. Heart & Lung Transpl. Prev: Sen. Regist. (Respirat. & Gen. Med.) Newc. Hosp.; Ho. Phys. W.m. Hosp.

CORRY, Dominic Gerard Flat 1, 5 Stockwell Park Road, London SW9 0AP — MB BS 1989 Lond.

CORRY, Ian Stanley 13 Ulsterville Avenue, Belfast BT9 7AS Tel: 028 9066 5517 Fax: 028 90 663328 Email: iancorry@unite.co.uk — MB ChB 1984 Ed.; BSc (Physiol.) Ed. 1982; FRCS Ed. 1988; Dip. Sports Med. Ed. 1992; FRCS Ed (Orth.) 1995; MBChB Ed. 1984; MD Belf. 1995; Dip. Sports Med. Ed. 1992. (Univ. Edin.) Cons. (Orthop. Surg.) Roy. Vict. Hosp. Belf. Musgrave Pk. Hosp. Belf. Antrim Area Hosp. Antrim. Socs: BASEM; BOA; BOSTA. Prev: Sen. Regist. (Orthop. Surg.) Belf.; Regist. (Orthop. Surg.) Belf.

CORRY, Martin Joseph Carrickmore Health Centre, Termon Road, Carrickmore, Omagh BT79 9JR Tel: 028 8076 1242 — MB BCh BAO 1990 Belf.; MRCGP 1993; DRCOG 1992; DCH Dub. 1992; DGM RCP Lond. 1991.

CORRY, Peter Cecil Child Development Centre, St. Luke's Hospital, Bradford BD5 0NA Tel: 01274 365461 Fax: 01274 365465; 8 Dale Close, Guiseley, Leeds LS20 8JL Tel: 01943 879190 Fax: 01943 879190 Email: peter@pccorry.demon.co.uk — MB BCh BAO 1972 Belf.; FRCP Lond. 1994; MRCP (UK) 1980; DCH Eng. 1980; DCH RCPSI 1979; FRCPCH 1997. (Queens University Belfast) Cons. Community Paediat. St. Luke's Hosp. Bradford; Hon. Lect. (Paediat. & Child Health) Univ. Leeds; Hon. Clin. Lect. (Paediat.) Univ. of Sheff. Socs: Eur. Acad. Childh. Disabil.; Brit. Assn. Community Child Health; Brit. Paediat. Neurol. Assn. Prev: Sen. Regist. & Sen. Tutor (Paediat.) Roy. Belf. Hosp. for Sick Childr.; Sen. Regist. (Paediat.) Altnagelvin Hosp. Lond.derry & Ulster Hosp. Dundonald.

CORSE, John Oliver Gilbert Road Medical Group, 39 Gilbert Road, Bucksburn, Aberdeen AB21 9AN Tel: 01224 712138 Fax: 01224 712239; 24 Overton Circle, Dyce, Aberdeen AB21 7FR Tel: 01224 723221 — MB ChB 1968 Aberd. (Aberd.) Prev: SHO (Geriat.), Ho. Surg. (Plastic Surg.) & SHO (Gen. Surg.) Woodend; Gen. Hosp. Aberd.

CORSER, Anthea Jane Hall Grove Surgery, 4 Hall Grove, Welwyn Garden City AL7 4PL Tel: 01707 328528 Fax: 01707 373139; 133 Verulam Road, St Albans AL3 4DN Tel: 01727 832800 Fax: 01727 832902 Email: rich.anth@eclipse.co.uk — MB BS 1993 Lond.; BSc Lond. 1991; DGM RCP Lond. 1997; DRCOG 1998. (Lond. Hosp. Med. Coll.) Trainee GP/SHO Qu. Eliz II Hosp. Welwyn Gdn. City VTS; GP Regist. Hall Gr. Surg. Socs: BMA. Prev: SHO (Med.) Lister Hosp. Stevenage; SHO (A & E) Lister Hosp. Stevenage; Ho. Off. (Surg. & Orthop.) Basildon Hosp. Essex.

CORSER, Geoffrey Charles Department Anaesthetics, Princess Royal Hospital, Apley Castle, Telford TF1 6TF — MB BS 1976 Lond.; FFA RCS Eng. 1981. (St. Geo.) Cons. Anaesth. W. Midl. RHA; PostGrad. Clin. Tutor, P.ss Roy. Hosp. Socs: Assn. Anaesth. Gt. Brit. & Irel. & Brit. Prev: Sen. Regist. (Anaesth.) W. Midl. RHA.

CORSER, Percy Joseph Ward (retired) Ivanhoe, Caldbec Hill, Battle TN33 0JY Tel: 01 424 773827 — MRCS Eng. LRCP Lond. 1944.

CORSER, Robert Bidlake Flat 13, Twyford House, Hulse Road, Southampton SO15 2LB — MB ChB 1992 Dundee; PhD Dundee 1988; BSc Manch. 1983. SHO Dundee Teach. Hosp. Socs: BMA.

CORSON, Jeremy David Institute of Medical & Social Care Research, Wheldon Building, University of Wales, Bangor LL57 2UW Fax: 01248 681832; Glasfryn, Lon Pobty, Bangor LL57 1EJ — MB ChB 1979 Bristol; MRCGP 1983; FFPHM RCP (UK) 1997, MF 1988; DRCOG 1983. p/t Independant cons. In Pub. Health; Hon. Sen. Lect. Univ. of Wales Bangor. Prev: Dep. Director of Pub. Health, N. Wales HA; Med. Dir. Gwynedd Community Trust; Dir. Pub. Health Health Promotion Wales.

CORSON, Mr John George (retired) Irstead Manor, Neatishead, Norwich NR12 8XP Tel: 01692 630274 Fax: 01692 630274 — MB BS Lond. 1950; FRCS Eng. 1955. Prev: Cons. Gen. Surg. Jas. Paget Hosp. Norf.

CORSON, Mr Robert John Sunderland Royal Hospital, Kayau Road, Sunderland SR4 7TP Tel: 0191 565 6256 — MB ChB 1984 Glas.; MB ChB Glas. l984; FRCS Ed. 1988; MD Manch. 1996; FRCS (Gen.) 1997. Cons. (Surg.) Sunderland Roy. Hosp. Socs: Fell. Assn. Surgs.; Fell. Assn. ColoProctol.; BMA. Prev: Sen. Regist. NW Regional Health Auth.; Regist. Rotat. (Surg.) N. Manch. & Univ. Hosp. S. Manch.; Research Fell. Univ. Hosp. S. Manch. & N. W.. Injury Research Centre.

CORSTON, Patricia Betty (retired) 13 Berrylands, Milton Road, Cambridge CB4 1XW — MB BChir 1949 Camb.; DObst RCOG 1952.

CORSTON, Richard Norman Glenthorne, 64 Finchfield Road W., Finchfield, Wolverhampton WV3 8BA; Small Heath Cottage, Ashford Bank, Claverly, Wolverhampton WV5 7DY — MB BChir 1972 Camb.; MD Camb. 1983, MA 1972, BA 1968, MB 1972, BChir 1971; MRCP (UK) 1974. Cons. Neurol. Midl. Centre Neurol. & Neurosurg. & New Cross Hosp.; Wolverhampton. Socs: Assoc. Brit. Neurols.

CORSTON, Sarah Helen The Fairfield Centre, Fairfield Grove, Charlton, London SE7 8TX Tel: 020 8858 5738 Fax: 020 8305 3005; 51 Lewisham Park, London SE13 6QZ — MB BS 1987 Lond.; MRCGP 1994; DRCOG 1991. GP Charlton. Prev: SHO (Paediat.)

Brook Hosp. Lond.; SHO (Med., A & E, O & G & Psychiat.) Guy's Hosp. Lond. VTS.

CORSTORPHINE, Wendy Jayne 145 Sycamore Close, Burghfield, Reading RG30 3SW — MB BCh 1998 Wales.

CORT, Jonathan Mark 79 Marshall Road, Wood Seats, Sheffield S8 0GP — MB ChB 1993 Sheff.

CORTAL PEDRA, Marcos Hillingdon Hospital, Accident & Emergency Department, Pield Health Road, Uxbridge UB8 3NN; 10 Honiton Road, London NW6 6QE — LMS 1994 U Autonoma Barcelona.

CORTI, Kathleen Donatia Florence Whitecliff, 9 Queens Avenue, Broadstairs CT10 1EH Tel: 01843 866065 — MB BS 1953 Lond.

CORTISSOS, Eric 17 Church Street, Bridgwater TA6 5AT — Artsexamen 1991 Amsterdam.

CORVIN, Darach Joseph Latham House Medical Practice, Sage Cross Street, Melton Mowbray LE13 1NX Tel: 01664 854949 Fax: 01664 501825; 18 Gartree Drive, Melton Mowbray LE13 0AE Tel: 01664 69301 — MB BCh BAO 1970 NUI; MRCGP 1982; MRCOG 1975, DObst 1973; DCH RCPSI 1972. (Univ. Coll. Dub.) Hosp. Pract. (Gyn.) War Memor. Hosp. Melton Mowbray. Prev: Regist. (O & G) Leicester Roy. Infirm. & Bolton Gen. Hosp.; Ho. Off. (Med.) & Ho. Off. (Paediat.) Internat. Miss. Train. Hosp. Drogheda.

CORY, Mr Christopher Charles 43 Alma Road, Reigate RH2 0DN Tel: 01737 247855 Fax: 01737 247855 Email: coryeye@memail.com — MA, MB BChir Camb. 1957; FRCS Eng. 1968; MRCS Eng. LRCP Lond. 1956; FCOphth. 1988; DO Eng. 1968. (King's Coll. Hosp.) Cons. Ophth. BUPA Gatwick Pk. Hosp.; Cons. Ophth. BUPA Gatwick Pk. Hosp. Socs: Fell. Roy. Soc. Med.; BMA. Prev: Clin. Dir. Optimax Laser Eye Clinic; Cons. Ophth. E. Surry DHA; 1st Asst. Dept. Ophth. Roy. Vict. Infirm. Newc.

CORY, Clive Edmund 23 North Parade, Grantham NG31 8AT Tel: 01476 593808 Fax: 01476 593808 Email: doctor@cory.bytenet.co.uk — MB ChB 1968 Liverp.; FFA RCS Eng. 1973. (Liverp.) Cons. Anaesth. Grantham Hosp.; Clin. Tutor & Dir. Postgrad Med. Educat. Grantham Hosp. Socs: Obst. Anaesth. Assn.; Assn. Anaesth. GB & Irel.; Liverp. Med. Soc. Prev: Specialist (Anaesth.) Tanzanian Min. Health & Overseas Developm. Agency; Extern. Examr. (Physiol. & Clin. Measurem.) Dares Salaam Univ.

CORY, Jill Elizabeth Sophronia 29 Clockhouse Place, London SW15 2EL — MB BS 1996 Lond.

CORY, Pamela 40 The Oval, Harrogate HG2 9BA; The Old Barn, Church Green, Roxwell, Chelmsford CM1 4NZ Tel: 01245 248222 — MB BCh 1979 Wales; FRCR 1986. Cons. Radiol. Basildon & Thurrock Gen. Hosps.

COSBIE ROSS, Mr James Andrew South Cleveland Hospital, Marton Road, Middlesbrough TS4 3BW Tel: 01642 854854 Fax: 01642 854854; 31 North End, Hutton Rudby, Yarm TS15 0DG Tel: 01642 700258 Fax: 01642 700258 — MB ChB 1965 Liverp.; FRCOG 1983, M 1970. (Liverp.) Cons. O & G S. Tees Health Dist. Hosps.; Hon. Sen. Lect. Univ. Dundee; Hon. Lect. Univ. Newc. Socs: N. Eng. Soc. Obst. & Gyn.; Internat. Continence Soc. Prev: Sen. Regist. (O & G) United Leeds Hosps.; Regist. (O & G) Mill Rd. Matern. Hosp. Liverp.

COSFORD, Paul Anthony North Bedfordshire Health Authority, Department of Public Health, 3 Kimbolton Road, Bedford MK40 2NU Tel: 01234 355122 — MB BS 1987 Lond.; BSc Lond. 1984; MRCPsych 1991. Regist. (Train. Progr. Pub. Health Med.) NW Thames RHA. Prev: Lect. (Psychiat.) St. Mary's Hosp. Med. Sch. Lond.; Regist. (Psychiat.) Pk.side HA Train. Scheme.

COSGRAVE, Eileen Nora Colonsay Prouds Lane, Bilston Tel: 01902 42268 — MB BCh BAO 1946 NUI. (Cork) Asst. MOH Staffs. CC.

COSGROVE, Mr Aidan Patrick Musgrave Park Hospital, Belfast BT9 7JB Tel: 01232 669501 Fax: 01232 683816; 51 Rugby Road, Belfast BT7 1PT Email: aidan.cosgrove@doctors.org.uk — MD 1992 Belf.; BSc (Hons.) Belf. 1982, MD 1992, MB BCh BAO 1985; FRCSI 1989; FRCS (Orth.) 1995. Cons. Paediat. Orthop. Surg. Musgrave Pk. Hosp. & Roy. Belf. Hosp. for Sick Childr. Socs: Fell.Brit. Othopaedic Assn.; Mem. Brit. Soc. Childr.s Othopaedic Surg.

COSGROVE, Carmel Therese 6 Demesne Road, Holywood BT18 9DQ — MB BCh BAO 1978 Belf.; MRCGP 1982; DCH RCPI 1982.

COSGROVE, Catherine Alison Morrington Hosptital, Swansea; Laurel Cottage, Lower Kingsdown Road, Kingsdown, Corsham SN13 8BB — MB BS 1994 Lond.; MRCP Lond. 1998. SHO Med., Morrington Hosp. Swansea.

COSGROVE, David Owen Hammersmith Hospital, Du Cane Road, London W12 0HS Tel: 020 8383 4942 Fax: 020 8382 1700 — BM BCh 1963 Oxf.; MRCP Lond. 1968. Cons. Radiol. Hammersmith Hosp. Lond. Socs: Fell. Roy. Coll. Radiol.; Fell. Roy. Coll. Phys. Prev: Cons. Nuclear Med. Roy. Marsden Hosp. Sutton.

COSGROVE, Eileen Elizabeth Huntly Health Centre, Jubilee Hospital, Bleachfield Street, Huntly AB54 8EX Tel: 01466 792116 Fax: 01466 794699; Wilmount, Gladstone Road, Huntly AB54 8BW — MB ChB 1981 Aberd.; DRCOG 1984.

COSGROVE, Helen 88 Peverell Park Road, Plymouth PL3 4ND — MB BS 1987 Lond.; FRCS Ed. 1994.

COSGROVE, Helen Catherine Overstrand, Norfolk Drive, Mansfield NG19 7AG — MB BS 1983 Newc.; MRCGP 1988; DRCOG 1989.

COSGROVE, Ian Michael (retired) Butts Road Medical Centre, Butts Road, Bakewell DE45 1ED Tel: 01629 812871 Fax: 01629 814958 — MB BCh BAO 1965 Dub.; BA 1963 Dub.; DObst. RCOG 1969; MRCGP 1974. Prev: Ho. Phys. & Ho. Surg. Roy. United Hosp. Bath.

COSGROVE, James Mackie Old Machar Medical Practice, 526 King Street, Aberdeen AB24 5RS Tel: 01224 480324 Fax: 01224 276121; 175 Broomhill Road, Aberdeen AB10 6JQ Tel: 01224 313664 — MB ChB 1972 Aberd. (Aberd.) Prev: Ho. Off. Aberd. Roy. Infirm. & Woodend Gen. Hosp. Aberd. (Glenburn Wing).

COSGROVE, James Paul Quayside Medical Practice, 82-84 Strand Road, Londonderry BT48 7NN Tel: 028 7126 2790 Fax: 028 7137 3729; 100 Culmore Road, Londonderry BT48 8JE — MB BCh BAO 1973 Belf.

COSGROVE, Joan Monica 44 Talbot Park, Londonderry BT48 7TA — MB BCh BAO 1975 Dub.; FRCS Eng. 1983; FRACS 1981; Obst. (NI) 1977.

COSGROVE, John Joseph 22 Culmore Road, Londonderry BT48 7RS Tel: 01504 351386 — MB BCh BAO 1940 NUI; DPH, BSc (PH) 1942. (Dub.) Prev: Sen. Ho. Surg. Belf. Emerg. Hosp.

COSGROVE, John Lawrence (retired) St Giles Surgery, Townfield Lane, Chalfont St Giles HP8 4QG Tel: 01494 874006/7 Fax: 01494 871223 — MB BS 1968 Lond. Prev: Regist. Rheumat. Dept. Lond. Hosp.

COSGROVE, Joseph Finbarr 22 Castleside Road, Newcastle upon Tyne NE15 7DS; 47 Fernwood Avenue, Gosforth, Newcastle upon Tyne NE3 5DL Tel: 0191 284 1448 — MB BS 1988 Newc. SHO (Med.) Bishop Auckland; SHO (Neo-Natal IC) P.ss Mary Matern. Hosp. Newc.; SHO (Anaesth.) Roy. Vict. Infirm. Newc. & Gateshead; Trainee Mem. Assn. Anaesth. Prev: SHO (Anaesth.) Sunderland; SHO (A & E) Sunderland; Ho. Off. (Gen. Med.) Dryburn Hosp. Durh.

COSGROVE, Kevin Joseph Quayside Medical Practice, 82-84 Strand Road, Londonderry BT48 7NN Tel: 028 7126 2790 Fax: 028 7137 3729; 35 Upper Galliagh Road, Londonderry BT48 8LW — MB BCh BAO 1974 NUI; MRCGP 1980; DRCOG 1979; DCH RCPSI 1978. (Univ. Coll. Dub.) GP Lond.derry; Chairm. Med. Bd.ing Panel for Indust. Injur. Prev: GP Trainee N. Irel. VTS; Ho. Off. Mater Miser. Hosp. Dub.; Intern St. Joseph's Hosp. Pk.ersburg, U.S.A.

COSGROVE, Lindsay Elaine Flat TFR, 12 Church Hill Place, Edinburgh EH10 4BD — MB ChB 1998 Ed.; MB ChB Ed 1998.

COSGROVE, Martin Paul Brookfields Health Centre, Seymour Street, Cambridge CB1 3DQ Tel: 01223 723160 Fax: 01223 723089 — MB ChB 1983 Sheff.; AFOM RCP Lond. 1993; MRCGP 1988; DRCOG 1996; DCH RCP Lond. 1995; DFFP 1994; DGM RCP Lond. 1987. (Sheff.) Occupat. Health Phys. Harris; Occupat.al Health Physics Consignia. Prev: Sen. Med. Off. RAF Halton Aylesbury; Sen. Med. Off. RAF AlderGr., Sek Kong; Regtl. Med. Off. Qu. Ghurkha Engineer Regt.

COSGROVE, Michael Singleton Hospital, Sketty, Swansea SA2 8QA Tel: 01792 285043 Fax: 01792 285244 Email: mike.cosgrove@swansea-tr.wales.nhs.uk — BM BS 1985 Nottm.; BMedSci Nottm. 1983; MRCP (UK) 1988. Cons. Paediat. Singleton Hosp. Swansea. Socs: Fell. Roy. Coll. of Paediat. and Child Health (FRCPCH). Prev: Lect. (Child Health) Univ. of Wales Coll. of Med. Cardiff; Tutor (Child Health) Univ. of Manch.

COSGROVE, Patrick James 44 Talbot Park, Londonderry BT48 7TA — MB BCh BAO 1944 NUI. (Univ. Coll. Dub.)

COSGROVE, Patrick Vernon Finn The Bristol Priority Clinic, PO Box 2043, Bath BA2 5YD Tel: 01225 835755 Fax: 01225 835755 — MB BS 1968 Lond.; MRCP (UK) 1972; MRCS Eng. LRCP Lond. 1968; MRCPsych 1977; DPM Eng. 1974. (Guy's) Cons. Child & Adolesc. Psychiat. Bristol Priority Clinic, Bath. Socs: Brit. Assn. Psychopharmacol. Prev: Cons. Child Psychiat. & Ment. Handicap Bath Health Dist; Sen. Regist. Wessex Regional Unit for Childr. & Parents, Portsmouth; Research Regist. (Ment. Health) Univ. Bristol.

COSGROVE, Pauline Anne Waterside Health Centre, Glendermot Road, Londonderry BT47 6AU Tel: 028 7132 0100 Fax: 028 7134 9323 — MB BCh BAO 1988 NUI.

COSGROVE, Sean Damian 18 Prince Edward Drive, Belfast BT9 5GB — MB BCh BAO 1990 Belf.; MB BCh Belf. 1990.

COSH, John Arthur (retired) Mead Court, Maudlin Road, Totnes TQ9 5EX Tel: 01803 863939 — MD Camb. 1951, MB BChir 1940; FRCP Lond. 1964, M 1947; MRCS Eng. LRCP Lond. 1940. Prev: Lect. Med. Univ. Bristol.

COSIMINI, Antony Joseph The Almshouse Surgery, Trinity Medical Centre, Thornhill Street, Wakefield WF1 1PG Tel: 01924 327150 Fax: 01924 327165; 4 Newlyn Drive, Wakefield WF2 7DX — MB ChB 1990 Manch.; MRCGP 1995; DRCOG 1994; OFFP 1995. (Manch.) GP Princip. Prev: Trainee GP Wakefield VTS.

COSKERY, Gail Moyna 3 Belt Road, Maghera BT46 2LP — BM BS 1990 Nottm.

COSSAR, Dora Frances Department of Neuroanaesthesia, Southern General Hospital, 1345 Govan Road, Glasgow G51 4TF Tel: 0141 201 1989; Email: d.cossar@ntlworld.com — MB ChB 1971 Glas.; FRCA Eng. 1975. p/t Cons. Neuroanaesth. S.. Gen. Hosp. Glas.; Hon. Sen. Lect. Glas. Univ. Socs: Assn. Anaesth. Gt. Brit. Irel.; Scott. Soc. Anaesth.; Neuroanesth. Soc. Prev: Sen. Regist. (Anaesth.) S. Gen. Hosp. Glas.; Med. Off. (Neuroanaesth.) S.. Gen. Hosp. Glas.; Regist. Anaesth. W.. Infirm. Glas.

COSSAR, Jonathan Harvey Queens Crescent Surgery, 10 Queens Cresent, Glasgow G4 9BL Tel: 0141 332 3526 Fax: 0141 332 1150; Ramla, 9 Mar Drive, Bearsden, Glasgow G61 3LY Tel: 0141 942 8262 — MD 1988 Glas.; MB ChB Glas. 1970; Cert FPA 1973. (Glas.) Research Assoc. Scott. Centre for Infec. & Environm. Health, Clifton Ho., Glas.; Hon. Clin. Sen. Lect. Univ. Glas.; Miller Trav. Fell.sh. 1983. Socs: Brit. Soc. Study of Infec. & Soc. Occupat. Med.; Internat. Soc. Travel Med. Prev: Ho. Off.(Med., Surg. & Obst.) S.. Gen. Hosp. Glas.; Ho. Off. (Med. Paediat.) Roy. Hosp. Sick Childr. Glas.

COSSEY, Andrew James 35 Wiclif Way, Nuneaton CV10 8NH — MB BS 1992 Lond.

COSSHAM, Paul Scobell Garden House, Stafford Place, Weston Super Mare BS23 2QZ Tel: 01934 628641 — MB ChB 1964 Bristol; FFA RCS Eng. 1969. (Bristol) Cons. Anaesth. W.on Gen. Hosp. Prev: Cons. Anaesth. Leicester Hosps.; Sen. Regist. (Anaesth.) United Sheff. Hosps.; Regist. (Anaesth.) S.mead Hosp. Bristol.

COSSHAM, Thomas Robert 8 Moorgate Avenue, Sheffield S10 1EQ — MB ChB 1994 Sheff.

COSSLETT, Anna Krisha 15 Moore Cl, Claypole, Newark NG23 5AU — MB ChB 1997 Birm.

COSSLETT, Nancy May (retired) 56 Greenhill Road, Halesowen B62 8EX Tel: 0121 421 2870 — MB ChB 1948 Manch. Asst. Med. Off. Matern. & Child Welf. Worcs. CC. Prev: Ho. Off. (Obst.) St Mary's Hosp. Manch.

COSTA, Dominic South Lambeth Road Practice, 1 Selway House, 272 South Lambeth Road, London SW8 1UL Tel: 020 7622 1923 Fax: 020 7498 5530 — MB BS 1967 Melbourne; MRCP (UK) 1974; MRCGP 1993.

COSTA, Stephen 48 Chilcomb Road, Harefield, Southampton SO18 5GQ — MB BS 1996 Lond.

COSTA-MICHAEL, Michael 6 Waterfall Terrace, London SW17 9LT — MB BS 1996 Lond.

COSTALES, Eleanor Layga 34 East Hill, London SW18 2HH — MB BS 1997 Lond.

COSTELLO, Anthony Mark De Lacy Centre for International Child Health, Institute of Child Health, 30 Guilford St., London WC1N 1EH Tel: 020 7242 9789 — MB BChir 1978 Camb.; MA Camb. 1978; FRCP Lond. 1994; MRCP (UK) 1980. (Middlx.) Cons. Paediat. & Sen. Lect. Internat. Child Health Inst. Child Health Lond.; Hon. Cons. Hosp. Trop. Dis. Lond.; Hon. Sen. Lect. UCL Med. Sch. Prev: Sen. Regist. (Paediat.) Univ. Coll. Lond.; Field Dir. Save the Childr. Fund, Nepal.

COSTELLO, Bernard 3 Ruskin Avenue, Saltburn-by-the-Sea TS12 1QB — MRCS Eng. LRCP Lond. 1973; MRCGP 1977.

COSTELLO, Mr Callaghan Brendan 14 St John Street, Manchester M3 4DZ Tel: 0161 834 2768 Fax: 0161 835 1465 Email: cbcostello@gconnect.com — MB BCh BAO NUI 1966; MD NUI 1985; FRCS Eng. 1972; FRCS Ed. 1972. (Cork) Cons. Urol. N. Manch. Gen. Hosp. Prev: Sen. Lect. (Urol.) Manch. Univ.

COSTELLO, Caroline Helen 23 Grandpont Place, Longford Close, Oxford OX1 4NH — BChir 1996 Camb.; MB Bchir Camb. 1996.

COSTELLO, Christine Ellen MacGregor Department of Haematology, Chelsea and Westminster Hospital, 369 Fulham Road, London SW10 9NH Tel: 020 8746 8000 — MB ChB Liverp. 1968; FRCP Lond. 1989; MRCP (UK) 1972; FRCPath 1993; MRCPath 1981; DObst RCOG 1970. (Liverp.) Cons. Haemat. Chelsea & W.m. Hosp. Lond. Prev: Sen. Regist. (Haemat. & Blood Transfus.) St. Geo. Hosp. Lond. & S.; Lond. Transfus. Centre.

COSTELLO, Christopher Sketty Surgery, De la Beche Road, Sketty, Swansea SA2 9EA Tel: 01792 206862; 71 Gabalfa Road, Derwen Fawr, Swansea SA2 8NA Tel: 01792 204659 — MB BCh 1981 Wales; MRCGP 1986; DCH RCP Lond. 1983; DRCOG 1983. Prev: Trainee GP Morriston, Swansea; Ho. Surg. & Ho. Phys. Singleton Hosp. Swansea.

COSTELLO, Darren Philip 227 Aylestone Road, Leicester LE2 7QJ — MB ChB 1998 Leic.; MB ChB Leic 1998.

COSTELLO, Donald Francis Anthony 9 Baroness Close, Princess Gardens, Hull HU6 9UB — MB ChB 1984 Leeds; DRCOG 1997. (Leeds)

COSTELLO, Francis Thomas The Medical Centre, Lancaster Road, Preesall, Blackpool FY1 4NF; Primrose House, Daggers Lane, Preesall, Blackpool Tel: 01253 812243 — MB ChB 1975 Manch.; BSc Manch. 1970, MB ChB 1975; MRCP (UK) 1981. Prev: Regist. (Med.) Vict. Hosp. Blackpool; SHO Booth Hall Hosp., Blackpool; Ho. Off. Manch. Roy. Infirm.

COSTELLO, John Department of Respiratory Medicine & Allergy, Kings College Hospital, Bessemer Road, London SE5 9PJ Tel: 020 7346 3165 Fax: 020 7346 3589 — MD 1987 NUI; MB BCh BAO NUI 1968; FRCP (I) Lond. 1996; FRCP Lond. 1983; MRCP (I) (UK) 1995; MRCP (UK) 1972. (Univ. Coll. Dub.) Cons. Phys. Gen. & Respirat. Med. King's Coll. Hosp.; Clin. Dir. Med. (Respirat. Med.) Kings Coll. Hosp.; Sen. Lect. Guy's, King's & St. Thomas' Med. Sch. Socs: Brit. Pharmacol. Soc.; Amer. Thoracic Soc. & Brit. Thoracic Soc. (Mem. Counc.); Fell. Roy. Soc. Med. (Ex-Pres. Resp. Sect.). Prev: Asst. Prof. Med. Univ. Calif. Serv. San Francisco Gen. Hosp., USA; Lect. Univ. Edin. Dept. Med. Roy. Infirm. Edin.; Regist. Brompton Hosp. Lond.

COSTELLO, Julian Paul Bellevue Surgery, Bellevue Terrace, Newport NP20 2WQ Tel: 01633 256337 Fax: 01633 222856; Bettws Health Centre, 500 Monnow Way, Bettws, Newport NP20 7TD Tel: 01633 855121 — MB BCh 1978 Wales; MRCGP 1982; DRCOG 1981. GP Newport. Socs: BMA; Eur. Undersea Biomed. Soc.; Assoc. Mem. Fac. Homeop. Lond. Prev: Clin. Asst. (Psychiat.) St. Cadocs Hosp. Caerleon Gwent.

COSTELLO, Julie Christine 9 Victoria Terrace, Paulton, Bristol BS39 7NY; 21 St Lawrence Avenue, Bidborough, Tunbridge Wells TN4 0XA — BM BS 1990 Nottm.; MRCGP 1995; DRCOG 1994. (Nottm.) Occasional Locum, Clin. Asst. work in A&E, Roy. United Hosp., Bath. Prev: Staff Grade (A & E) Roy. United Hosp. Bath; VTS Lincoln Co. Hosp.

COSTELLO, Lorna Margaret Dungannon Health Clinic, 38 Thomas St., Dungannon BT70 1HS Tel: 01868 723101 Fax: 01868 752458; 11 Bushvale, Bush Road, Dungannon BT71 6QA Tel: 01868 724769 — MB BCh BAO 1983 Belf.; Dip. Mem. Roy. Coll. Family Plann. & Reproduc. Health Care. (The Queen's University of Belfast) Staff Grade Community (Paediat.) Dungannon; Clin. Med. Off. (Family Plann.) Dungannon. Socs: BMA; BACCH; NIFPDA. Prev: GP Antrim.

COSTELLO, Mary Cecilia de lacy The Surgery, The Gardens, London SE22 9QU Tel: 020 8693 4715 Fax: 020 8299 4418 — BM BS 1980 Nottm.; BMedSci (Hons.) Nottm. 1978; DA Eng. 1982.

COSTELLO, Mary Margaret 418 Northolt Road, Harrow HA2 8EZ — MB ChB 1989 Aberd.

COSTELLO, Paul Anthony 22 Seggielea Road, Glasgow G13 1XJ — MB ChB 1992 Aberd.

COSTELOE, Kathleen Louise Homerton Hospital, Homerton Row, London E9 6SR Tel: 020 8919 5555 Fax: 020 8919 7850; Alexandra House, Royal London Hospital, Whitechapel, London E1 1BB Tel: 020 7377 7000 Fax: 020 7377 7619 — MB BChir 1973 Camb.; MA Camb. 1977; FRCP Lond. 1989; MRCP (UK) 1974; FRCPCH 1997. Reader (Neonat. Paediat.) St. Bart. & Roy. Lond. Sch. Med. & Dent.; Hon. Cons. Paediat. Homerton Hosp. NHS Trust & Roy. Hosps. NHS Trust.

COSTEN, Mark Timothy James Flat 17, Foresterhill Court, Aberdeen AB25 2WA Email: mtjrac@aol.com — MB BS Lond. 1993; BSc (Hons) 1990; FRCOphth 1998. (London Hospital Medical College) SHO Ophth. Dept. Aberd. Roy. Infirm. Socs: Christ. Med. Fell.sh. Prev: SHO Opthalmology Greenwich Dist. Hosp.

COSTEN, Peter David Maxwell (retired) La Broderie, La Claire Mare, St Peters, Guernsey GY7 9QA Tel: 01481 264500 Email: pcosten@guernsey.net — MB ChB 1970 Leeds; MA (Philosophy & Health Care) Wales 1991; LLM Wales 1996; FFA RCS Eng. 1975; Dip. Health Care Law Wales 1992; Cert. Av. Med. 1978; DA Eng. 1974; MSc Portsmouth 1999. Prev: Anaesth. P.ss Eliz. Hosp. Guernsey.

COSTIGAN, Helen Mary Stepping Hill Hospital, Poplar Grove, Stockport SK2 7JE; 17 Hall Road, Rushouse, Manchester M14 5HN — MB ChB 1995 Manch. SHO (Med.).

COSTIGAN, Kevin Joseph 13 Ilford Avenue, Liverpool L23 7YE — MB ChB 1993 Liverp.

COSTIGAN, Patricia Stephanie Gyleburn, St Mungo, Lockerbie DG11 1BY — MB ChB 1981 Liverp.; FRCS (Orth.) 1993; FRCS Ed. 1986. Cons. Orthop. Dumfries & Galloway Roy. .Infirm. Socs: Brit. Orthop. Assn.; BMA; SPOC. Prev: Sen. Regist. (Orthop.) Roy. Infirm. Glas.; Regist. (Orthop. & Accid. Surg.) Qu. Med. Centre Nottm.

COSTIN, Sylvia Beatrice Bude House, Eaton Bray Road, Totternhoe, Dunstable LU6 2BN Tel: 01525 220317 — M.R.C.S. Eng. L.R.C.P. Lond. 1943. (Lond. Sch. Med. Wom.) Clin. Asst. Accid. Serv. Luton & Dunstable Hosp. Prev: Asst. Surg. Orthop. & Fract. Clinic Luton & Dunstable Hosp.; Res. Surg. Off. E.M.S. Plastic Unit Glouc.; Ho. Surg. Luton & Dunstable Hosp.

COSTLEY, William Buchanan c/o James Paget Hospital, Gorleston, Great Yarmouth NR31 6LA; Hill House, Beccles Road, Fritton, Great Yarmouth NR31 9HB — MB BS 1962 Lond.; MRCS Eng. LRCP Lond. 1962; FRCOG 1982, M 1970, DObst 1965. Cons. (O & G) James Paget Hosp. Gorleston. Prev: Regist. (O & G) Groote Schuur Hosp. Cape Town S. Africa.

COTA, Mr Allwyn Martinho 102 Murchison Avenue, Bexley DA5 3LL — MB BS 1988 Bombay; FRCS Glas. 1994.

COTES, John Everard 9 Almoner's Barn, Durham DH1 3TZ Tel: 0191 383 2489 Fax: 0191 383 9859 Email: cotes@coterie.globalnet.co.uk — BM BCh 1948 Oxf.; MA Oxf. 1948, DSc 1989, DM 1966; FRCP Lond. 1969, M 1949; FFOM RCP Lond. 1981. (St. Bart.) Vis. Phys. Sci. Univ. Newc. Socs: Brit. Thorac. Soc.; Eur. Respirat. Soc. Prev: Reader Univ. (Occupat. Health) & Hon. Cons. Clin. Respirat. Physiol. Univ. Newc.; Mem. Scientif. Staff MRC Pneumoconiosis Unit; Rockefeller Fell. Johns Hopkins Hosp. Baltimore, USA.

COTES, Phoebe Mary (retired) 16 Wildwood Road, London NW11 6TB — MB BS 1957 Lond.; PhD Lond. 1950, BSc 1947; MRCS Eng. LRCP Lond. 1957. Prev: Mem. Scientif. Staff MRC Clin. Research Centre .

COTES, Susan Carole Northampton General Hospital, Cliftonville, Northampton NN1 5BD Tel: 01604 34700 — MB BS 1992 Lond. (King's Coll. Lond.) SHO (Paediat.) N.ampton Gen. Hosp. Prev: Sen. Med. Off. (Emerg.) Townsville, Qu.sland, Austral.; SHO (Med.) N.ampton Gen. Hosp.

COTGROVE, Andrew John Pine Lodge Young Peoples Centre, 79 Liverpool Road, Chester CH2 1AW Tel: 01244 364776 Fax: 01244 364778 — MB ChB 1982 Sheff.; MSc Brunel 1993; MRCPsych 1989. Cons. Adolesc. Psychiat. Regional Adolesc. Unit Chester.

COTHAY, Miss Delia Margaret Helen Hernaman Gorsedene West, The Long Road, Rowledge, Farnham GU10 4EB Tel: 01252 792628 — MB BS 1951 Lond.; FRCS Eng. 1960. (Westm.) Emerit. Cons. Orthop. & Traum. Unit. A & E Roy. Surrey Co. Hosp. Guildford. Socs: Sen. Fell. BOA. Prev: Regist. Lord Mayor Treloar Hosp. Alton; Ho. Surg. W.m. Hosp. & Roy. Nat. Orthop. Hosp. Stanmore.

COTTA, Reis Gualberto c/o Yvonne Evans, 16 Ravensdale, Basildon SS16 5HS — MB BS 1988 Bombay.

COTTAM, Christopher Gerard 25 Old Hall Road, Ulverston LA12 7DQ — MB ChB 1992 Liverp.

COTTAM, David Chadwick 124 Preston Old Road, Freckleton, Preston PR4 1HD — MB ChB 1980 Liverp.; BSc (Hons.) Manch. 1967; PhD Lond. 1972; DRCOG 1982; DCCH RCP Ed. 1984.

COTTAM, Deborah Jane 103 Coed Camlas, The Highway, New Inn, Pontypool NP4 8RP — MB BCh 1995 Wales.

COTTAM, Rachel Marjorie Pentwyn, Dorstone, Hereford HR3 6AD Tel: 01981 550305; 7 Rattray Road, Brixton, London SW2 1AY Tel: 020 7733 1871 — BM BCh 1991 Oxf.; MA York 1993; MA Camb. 1988; DPhil Sussex 1996. Prev: SHO (O & G) Roy. Sussex Co. Hosp.

COTTAM, Sara-Lisa Gresham The Surgery, 3 Chequers Drive, Prestwood, Great Missenden HP16 9DU — MB ChB 1990 Manch.; BSc (Hons.) Manch. 1987; MRCGP 1994; DRCOG 1992. (Manch.) Princip. in Gen. Pract., High Wycombe. Prev: Trainee GP Preston VTS.

COTTAM, Simon Jasper Charles King's College School of Medicine & Dentistry, Bessemer Road, London SE5 9PJ Email: simon.cottam@kcl.ac.uk; Woodhall House, 23 Woodhall Drive, Dulwich, London SE21 7HJ — MB ChB 1983 Liverp.; FFA RCS Eng. 1988. Cons. Anaesth. King's Coll. Sch. Med. & Dent. Lond.

COTTAM, Stephen Nicholas Great Eccleston Health Centre, Raikes Road, Great Eccleston, Preston PR3 0ZA Tel: 01995 670066 Fax: 01995 671054 — MB ChB 1985 Birm.; MRCP (UK) 1988; MRCGP 1993; DRCOG 1994. Prev: Trainee GP Scunthorpe VTS; SHO (Gen. Med.) Walton & Fazakerley Hosps. Liverp.; Ho. Phys. Walsall Manor Hosp.

COTTEE, Charlotte Ann 207 Clarendon Park Road, Leicester LE2 3AN — MB ChB 1998 Leic.; MB ChB Leic 1998.

COTTEE, Christina Susannah Weston Surgery, 36 Combe Park, Bath BA1 3NR Tel: 01225 446089 Fax: 01225 465690; Rush Hill Surgery, 20 Rush Hill, Bath BA2 2QH Tel: 01225 446087 — MB ChB 1984 Ed.; MRCGP (Distinc.) 1988; DRCOG 1986. Prev: GP Camb.

COTTEE, Mark Andrew St. George's Hospital Medical School, Blackshaw Road, London SW17 — MB BS 1986 Lond.; MRCP (UK) 1989. Cons. & Sen. Lect. (Geriat. Med.) St. Geo. Hosp. Lond. Socs: Brit. Geriat. Soc.

COTTEE, Raymond Leonard (retired) 63 Sheen Lane, London SW14 8AB Tel: 020 8876 9230 Fax: 020 8878 3231 — MB BS 1956 Lond. Prev: Med. Examr. Insur. Company.

COTTELL, Henry Colin Fenton and Partners, Medical Centre, Burgage Green, Southwell NG25 0EW Tel: 01636 813561 Fax: 01636 816453; 17 Newark Road, Southwell NG25 0ES — BM BS 1978 Nottm.

COTTELL, Kathryn Mary Tmorneloe Lodge, 29 Barbourne Road, Droitwich WR1 RU Tel: 01905 22445 — BM BCh 1974 Oxf.

COTTER, Arthur Gerald Purcell (retired) Fallowfield, 150 Strabane Road, Castlederg BT81 7JD Tel: 0166 26 71664 — MB BCh BAO 1954 Dub.

COTTER, Mr Duncan Harold George Skipton General Hospital, Keighley Road, Skipton BD23 2RJ Tel: 01756 792233 Fax: 01756 700485 — MB BS 1974 Lond.; FRCS Eng. 1980; MRCS Eng. LRCP Lond. 1974; FRCP 1999 London. (Westm.) Cons. Rehabil. Med. Airedale NHS Trust; Hon. Research Fell. Univ. Leeds Research Sch. Med. Socs: Brit. Soc. Rehabil. Med.; (Ex-Pres.) Amputee Med. Rehabil. Soc.; Internat. Soc. Prosth.s & Orthotics. Prev: Med. Off. DHSS Artific. Limb Serv. Leeds.

COTTER, Professor Finbarr Edward St. Bartholemew's and Royal London School of Medicine and Dentistry, Turner St., London E1 2AD Tel: 020 7377 7076 Fax: 020 7377 7629 Email: f.e.cotter@qmw.mds.ac.uk; Marringdean, St. Leonard's Park, Horsham RH13 6EG — MB BS 1978 Lond.; PhD Lond. 1991 MB BS 1978; MRCP (UK) 1981; MRCPath 1985; FRCP (UK) 1996; FRCPath 1996. Prof. of Experim. Haemat. Socs: Brit. Soc. of Haemat. ; Counc. Mem. Prev: Clin. Research Fell. Imperial Cancer Research Fund; Lect. (Haemat.) Lond. Hosp. Med. Coll.; Reader in Haemat. & Oncol., Inst.of Child Health.

COTTER, Helena Mary Josephine (retired) 61 Appleton Road, Upton, Chester CH2 1JH Tel: 01244 344117 — MB BS 1960 Lond.; MRCS Eng. LRCP Lond. 1960; DObst RCOG 1962. Prev: SCMO Countess of Chester Health Trust.

COTTER, Jerome The London Hospital, Whitechapel, London E1 1BB Tel: 020 7377 7000 — MB BS 1965 Lond.; MRCS Eng. LRCP Lond. 1965; FFA RCS Eng. 1970. (Lond. Hosp.) Cons. Anaesth. Lond. Hosp.

COTTER, John Alfred 23 Park Avenue, Wrexham LL12 7AL — MB BCh BAO 1949 NUI.

COTTER, Julia Roseberry Topping, Westgate Drive, Bridgnorth WV16 4QF Tel: 0174 625663 — MB BS 1968 Lond.; DA Eng. 1971. (Roy. Free) Regist. Anaesth. Salisbury Gen. Infirm. Socs: Fac. Anaesth. RCS Eng. Prev: Ho. Phys. Hampstead Gen. Hosp.; Ho. Surg. Gen. Hosp. Nottm.; SHO (Anaesth.) Sheff. RHB.

COTTER, Lawrence St. Tydfil's, Wesley Place, Merthyr Vale, Merthyr Tydfil CF48 4RS — MB ChB 1971 Manch.; MRCP (U.K.) 1975. SHO (Neurol.) Ch.ill Hosp. Oxf. Prev: Ho. Phys. & Ho. Surg. Manch. Roy. Infirm.; SHO (Clin. Cardiol.) Hammersmith Hosp. Lond.

COTTER, Margaret Mary Geraldine Histopathology Department, Prince Of Wales Hospital, Bridgend Tel: 01656 752600 Email: margaret.cotter@bromor.wales.nhs.uk — MB BCh BAO 1979 NUI; MRCPath 1987. Cons. Histopath./ Cytopathologist, P. of Wales Hosp.. Bridgend. Prev: Cons. Histopath. & Cytopath. Orpington Hosp.; Sen. Regist. Rotat. (Histopath.) N. Middlx. & Roy. Free Hosps. Lond.; Cons. Cytopath Llandough Hosp.

COTTER, Mary 7 Heol Wen, Rhiwbina, Cardiff CF14 6EF Tel: 029 2061 4907 — MB BCh Wales 1966; FFPHM RCP (UK) 1992; MFCM Lond. 1983; DObst RCOG 1968. (Welsh Nat. Sch. Med.) Med. Advis. Welsh Health Common Servs. Auth.; Med. Dir. Wales Cancer Registry; Med. Adviser Health Intelligence Unit WHCSA. Prev: Med. Dir. Wales Cancer Registry; Sen. Med. Off. Welsh Office.

COTTER, Paul Anthony 29A Fitzgeorge Avenue, London W14 0SZ — MB BCh BAO 1981 NUI.

COTTER, William Anthony The Surgery, 174 Bellegrove Road, Welling DA16 3RE Tel: 020 8856 1770 Fax: 020 8319 8951 — MB BCh BAO 1989 Dub.; DFFP 1994. (TC Dub.) Socs: BMA. Prev: Regist. (Psychiat.) St. Vincent Hosp. Dub.; GP Regist. Lond.

COTTERELL, Stephen John Chancery Lane Surgery, Green Lane, Thrapston, Kettering NN14 4QL Tel: 01832 732456 Fax: 01832 736939 Email: stephen.cotterell@gp-k83065.nhs.uk — MB BS 1985 Lond.; MA Camb. 1982; DCH RCP Lond. 1989. Prev: Regist. (Geriat.) & SHO (Paediat.) Addenbrooke's Hosp. Camb.; SHO (Gen. Med.) Newmarket.

COTTERHILL, Athena Tanya 52 Jesson Road, Walsall WS1 3AX — MB BCh 1996 Witwatersrand.

COTTERILL, Andrew Michael 38 Wellington Road, London E11 2AU Tel: 020 8989 0056 — MB BS 1978 Lond.; MD Lond. 1992; MRCP (UK) 1981. Sen. Lect. (Paediat. Endocrinol.) St. Bart. Hosp. Med. Coll. Prev: Wellcome Research Fell. (Paediat. Endocrinol.) St. Bart. Hosp. Lond.

COTTERILL, Mr Cecil Paul 84 Fitz Roy Avenue, Harborne, Birmingham B17 8RQ Tel: 0121 427 1063 — MB ChB 1947 Birm.; MCh (Orthop.) Liverp. 1958; FRCS Ed. 1957; MRCS Eng. LRCP Lond. 1948.

COTTERILL, Jeffery William Central Surgery, Corporation Street, Rugby CV21 3SP Tel: 01788 574335 Fax: 01788 547693; 116 Percival Road, Rugby CV22 5JU Tel: 01788 575341 — MB BS 1982 Lond.; BA Oxf. 1979; MRCGP 1987.

COTTERILL, John Anthony (retired) 56 Broomfield, Adel, Leeds LS16 7AD Tel: 0113 267 1447 Fax: 0113 267 1447 — MD Newc. 1972; BSc (1st cl. Hons.) Durham 1960, MB BS 1963; FRCP Lond. 1981, M 1969. Prev: Ho. Surg. & Ho. Phys. (Dermat.) Roy. Vict. Infirm. Newc-upon-Tyne.

COTTERILL, Stephen Leslie Department of Medical Microbiology, East Somerset NHS Trust, Yeovil District Hospital, Yeovil BA21 4AT Tel: 01935 707427 Fax: 01935 410753 Email: cotts@gwise.esomerset-tr.swest.nhs.uk — BM BS 1984 Nottm.; BMedSci (Hons.) Nottm. 1982; MRCPath 1993. Cons. Microbiol. Yeovil dist. Hosp. Yeovil. Prev: Sen. Regist. (Microbiol.) Birm. Childr. Hosp.; Sen. Regist. (Microbiol.) PHLS Laborat. Newcross Hosp. Wolverhampton & City Hosp. Birm.

COTTIER, Brian Clatterbridge Centre for Oncology NHS Trust, Wirral; 7 Elm Road, Prenton, Birkenhead CH42 9NY — MD 1983 Liverp.; MB ChB 1974; FRCP Lond. 1993; MRCP (UK) 1978; FRCR 1985. Chief Exec. & Cons. Clin. Oncol. Clatterbridge Centre Oncol. Prev: Sen. Lect. & Hon. Cons. Radiother. & Oncol. Liverp. Univ.

COTTIER, Frederick Martineau, OStJ Roslea, 51 Station Road, Bamber Bridge, Preston PR5 6PE Tel: 01772 35128; Rawstorne House, Pope Lane, Whitestake, Preston PR4 4BA Tel: 01772 743964 — MB ChB 1964 Glas. (Glas.) Hon. Med. Off. Lancs. Co. Ambul. Serv.; Co. Surg. St. John Ambul. Brig. Lancs. Socs: Intens. Care Soc. & Brit. Assn. Immediate Care.

COTTINGHAM, Dan Pickering Medical Practice, Southgate, Pickering YO18 8BL Tel: 01751 472441 — MB ChB 1993 Aberd.; MRCGP 1997; DRCOG 1996. (aberdeen)

COTTINGHAM, Rowland Lovat Accident & Emergency Unit, Royal Sussex County Hospital, Eastern Road, Brighton BN2 5BE Tel: 01273 696955 Fax: 01273 680627 Email: rowley.cottingham@brighton-healthcare.nhs.uk — MB BS 1979 Lond.; BSc Lond. 1976; FRCS Ed. 1992; FFAEM 1997; DA (UK) 1985. (St. Thos.) Cons. A & E Roy. Sussex Co. Hosp.; Med. Off. Roy. Automobile Club. Socs: BMA; Brit. Assn. Emerg. Med.; BASICS. Prev: Sen. Regist. (A & E) Roy. Free Hosp. Hosp. Lond.; Regist. (A & E) Guy's & Lewisham Hosp.; Regist. (Anaesth.) Roy. Surrey Co. Hosp. Guildford.

COTTLE, Anne Gillian Grove House Surgery, West Shepton, Shepton Mallet BA4 5UH Tel: 01749 344016; Hill House, Winterfield Road, Paulton, Bristol BS39 7QR — MB ChB 1964 Manch.

COTTMAN, Stella Barbara Hillview Lodge, Royal United Hos[pital, Coombe, Bath BA1 3NG — MB BS 1968 Lond.; MRCS Eng. LRCP Lond. 1968; MRCPsych 1973. Cons. Psychother. Avon & Wilts. Ment. Health Partnership NHS.

COTTON, Brian Richard c/o Anaesthetic Department, Leicester Royal Infirmary, Infirmary Road, Leicester LE1 5DL; 14 Meadowcourt Road, Leicester LE2 2PB — MRCS Eng. LRCP Lond. 1973; BSc Lond. 1970, MB BS 1973; FFA RCS Eng. 1979. (St. Bart.) Cons. Anaesth. Leic. Roy. Infirm.

COTTON, Dennis William Keith Department of Pathology, University of Sheffield Medical School, Beech Hill Road, Sheffield S10 2RX Tel: 0114 276 6222 — BM 1979 Soton.; PhD Lond. 1973, BSc 1968; MD Sheff. 1988; MRCPath 1988. Reader (Path.) Univ. Sheff. Med. Sch.; Hon. Cons. Roy. Hallamsh. Hosp. Sheff.; Examr. Roy. Coll. Paths., RCS Eng. & Roy. Inst. Pub. Health & Hyg.; Edit. Bd. Jl. Path. & Dep. Edr. Histopath.; Comm. Mem. Melanoma Study Gp. Socs: BMA; (Counc.) Path Soc. GB & Irel.; Internat. Acad. Path.

COTTON, Elisabeth Marjorie (retired) — MB ChB 1968 Liverp.; DObst RCOG 1970.

COTTON, Geoffrey David 10 Burchett Coppice, Wokingham RG40 4YA — MB BS 1994 Lond.; BSc Lond. 1993; MRCP (UK) Lond. 1998. (St. George's Lond.) Med. Advisor, Boehringer Ingelheim Ltd, Bracknell (Pharmaceut. Med.

COTTON, Helen Margaret The Surgery, 13 Camberwell Green, London SE5 7AF Tel: 020 7703 3788 — MB BS 1979 Lond.; MRCGP 1984; DRCOG 1984. (Guys)

COTTON, Helen Tracy — MB BS Lond. 1990; BSc Lond. 1987; MRCP 1997; DCH RCP Lond. 1993. Specialist Regist. in Paediat., Epsom and St. Helier NHS Trust.

COTTON, James Nut Tree Farm, North Wootton, Shepton Mallet BA4 4AG — MB BS 1991 Lond.

COTTON, James Paul 27 Burntwick Drive, Lower Halstow, Sittingbourne ME9 7DX — MB ChB 1996 Dundee.

COTTON, Joanna Mary St Thomas Court Surgery, Church St., Axminster EX13 5AG Tel: 01297 32126 Fax: 01297 35759; The Old Vicarage, Higher St, Bradpole, Bridport DT6 3JA — MB BS 1985 Lond.; MRCGP 1992; MRCPsych 1990. GP Retainer. Prev: Princip. GP Plymouth; SHO (O & G) Freedom Fields Hosp. Plymouth; Trainee GP Exeter VTS.

COTTON, John Lawrence (retired) Lane End, 26 Meadow Park, Irwell Vale, Ramsbottom, Bury BL0 0QB Tel: 01706 821227 — MB ChB 1948 Manch.; MRCS Eng. LRCP Lond. 1948; MFCM 1972; DPH Liverp. 1952. Prev: Med. Off. E. Sussex AHA.

COTTON, Kerryn Marie Tel: 01332 766762 Fax: 01332 272084 — MB ChB 1984 Leeds; DRCOG 1988; DGM RCP Lond. 1986. Prev: SHO (O & G) St. Helier Hosp. Carshalton; SHO (Paediat.) N.ampton Gen. Hosp.; Trainee GP Banstead Surrey VTS.

COTTON, Mark Maclean Flat 2/3, St Andrews Square, Glasgow G1 5PP — MB BS 1985 Lond.

COTTON, Mary-Anne 1 Regent Road, Surbiton KT5 8NN — MB BS 1997 Lond.

COTTON, Mr Michael Henry 1 Rodenhurst Road, London SW4 8AE; 59 Circular Drive, Burnside, Bulawayo, Zimbabwe Tel: 00 263 9 245240 Fax: 00 263 9 60048 Email: mikeytha@mweb.co.zw — MB BS 1979 Lond.; MA Oxf. 1979; FRCS Eng. 1983; FACS 1999. (St. Thomas's Hospital, London) Cons. Surg. United Bulawayo Hosps.; Cons. Surg. Mater Dei Hosp., Bulawayo.; Vis. Dist. Surg, MAF, Matabeleland; Director A&E Dept, Mafer Dei Hosp. Bulawayo. Socs: Fell. Assn. Surg. E. Afr.; Internat. Surg. Soc.; Zimbabwe Assn. Surg. Prev: Sen. Regist. (Surg.) Harare Centr. Hosp.; Med. Off. (Surg.) Umtata Gen. Hosp., Transkei; Regist. (Surg.) Warneford Hosp. Leamington Spa.

COTTON, Patrick Anthony Beacon Medical Practice, 40 Algitha Road, Skegness PE25 2AJ Tel: 01754 897000 Fax: 01754 761024 — BM BS 1981 Nottm.

COTTON, Philip Dept. of general Practice, 4 Lancaster Crescent, Glasgow G12 0RR Tel: 0141 211 1666 — MB ChB 1989 Glas.; BSc (Hons.) St. And. 1984. Clin. Lect. Univ. Glas. Socs: MRCGP.

COTTON, Professor Roger Ernest 50 Broadgate, Beeston, Nottingham NG9 2FW Tel: 0115 925 8565 — MB BS Lond. 1949; MD Lond. 1961; FRCPath 1972, M 1963. (Middlx.) Emerit. Cons. Path. City Hosp. Nottm. Socs: (Ex-Pres.) Internat. Acad. Path.; (Ex-Pres.) Brit. Div. Internat. Acad. Path. Prev: Special Prof. Path. Univ. Nottm.; Foundat. Edr. Histopath.; Asst. Path. Bland-Sutton Inst. Path. & Ho. Surg. Middlx. Hosp.

COTTON, Roy Charles 34 Meadow Drive, Prestbury, Macclesfield SK10 4EZ — MD 1962 Leeds; MB ChB 1955. (Leeds) Med. Adviser Imperial Chem. Indust. Pharmaceut. Div. Alderley Pk. Socs: Brit. Soc. Haematol. Prev: Research Fell. (Haemat.) Roy. Infirm. Manch.

COTTON, Sandra Anne School Road Surgery, School Road, Praze-An-Beeble, Camborne TR14 0LB Tel: 01209 831386; 1 Ivy Court, Red Lane, Rosudgeon, Penzance TR20 9PU Tel: 01736 762594 — MB BCh 1981 Wales. Clin. Med. Off. (Family Plann.) Cornw. Healthcare Trust.

COTTON, Stephen John, Flight Lt. RAF Med. Br. 436 Oundle Road, Orton Longueville, Peterborough PE2 7DB — MB ChB 1991 Liverp.; BSc Liverp. 1988; DFFP 1995; DRCOG 1995. Med. Off. RAF.

COTTON, Susan Gillian (retired) 2 Bowers Lea, Cam, Dursley GL11 5PR Tel: 01453 519061 — MB BS 1962 Lond.; MB BS (Hons.) Lond. 1962; FRCP Lond. 1980, M 1964; MRCS Eng. LRCP Lond. 1962. Cons. Phys. Roy. Gwent Hosp. Newport; Clin. Teach. for UWCM at Roy. Gwent Hosp. Newport; Med. Mem. of The Appeals Serv. Tribunals Wales and S. W. Region. Prev: Sen. Regist. (Med.) Univ. Hosp. Wales Cardiff.

COTTON, Timothy George Riverside Practice, Friarsgate Medical Centre, Winchester SO23 8EF Tel: 01962 853599 Fax: 01962 849982; 82 Hatherley Road, Winchester SO22 6RR Email: tgcotton@msn.com — MB BS 1987 Lond.; MRCGP 1994. Prev: Trainee GP Avon Valley Pract. Wilts. VTS; Trainee GP Odstock Hosp. Salisbury VTS.

COTTON, William John (retired) Flat 37 Cedar Manor, 19-21 Poole Road, Bournemouth BH4 9DE — MRCS Eng. LRCP Lond. 1929; BA, BM BCh Oxon. 1931. Prev: Asst. Ho. Surg., Out-pat. Off. & Ho. Phys. Childr. Guy's Hosp.

COTTRALL, Khursheed Mayday Hospital, Croydon CR7 7YE Tel: 020 8401 3398 Fax: 020 8401 3372; 4 Edith Terrace, Chelsea, London SW10 0TQ Tel: 020 7352 6631 Fax: 020 7352 6631 — MB BS All India Inst. of Med. Sciences 1964; FRCP Lond. 1994; MRCP (UK) 1971; DCH Eng. 1967; FRCP 1991; FRCPCH 1997. Cons. Paediat. Mayday Hosp. Thornton Heath; Med. Adviser Catholic Childr. Soc. Socs: Fell. Roy. Soc. Med.; Action for Sick Childr. (Mem. Counc. Croydon Br.). Prev: Research Fell. & Hon. Sen. Regist. (Child Health) King's Coll. Hosp. Med. Sch. Lond.; Sen. Regist. (Paediat.) Hosp. Sick Childr. Gt. Ormond St. Lond.

COTTRELL, Andrew John Bishop Auckland General Hospital, Bishop Auckland DL14 6AD Tel: 01388 454000 Fax: 01388 454107 Email: andrew.cottrell@smtp.sdhe-tr.northy,nhs.uk; 4 Dene Hall Drive, Bishop Auckland DL14 6UG Tel: 01388 661413 — MB BS 1974 Newc.; BSc Newc. 1971; FRCP Ed. 1989; MRCP (UK) 1977; FRCPCH 1997. (Univ. Newc. u. Tyne) Cons. Paediat. Bishop Auckland Gen. Hosp. Socs: Brit. Assn. Perinatal Med. Prev: Sen. Regist. (Paediat.) Childr. Hosp. Sheff.; Regist. (Paediat.) Newc. AHA (T); Research Regist. (Paediat. Cardiol.) Freeman Hosp. Newc.

COTTRELL, Cheryl Kim Flat 5, Fitzwilliam Heights, 21 Taymount Rise, London SE23 3UG — MB BS 1998 Lond.; MB BS Lond 1998.

COTTRELL, David Alfred 17 Castle Street, Cupar KY15 4AU — MB ChB 1994 Ed.

COTTRELL, Mr David George Eye Department, Claremont Wing, Royal Victoria Infirmary, Queen Victoria Road, Newcastle upon Tyne NE1 4LP Tel: 0191 232 5131 Fax: 0191 227 5246 Email: d.g.cottrell@ncl.ac.uk — MB BS 1977 Newc.; BA Oxf. 1974; FRCS Ed. (Ophth). 1982; FRCOphth 1988; DO Eng. 1980. (Oxf. & Newc.) Cons. Ophth. Roy. Vict. Infirm. Newc. u. Tyne; Hon. Clin. Tutor, Med. Sch. Univ. of Newc. Socs: Trustee N. Eng. Ophth. Soc.; UK & Irel. Soc. Cataract & Refractive Surgs.; Oxf. Ophth. Congr. Prev: Regist. (Ophth.) Roy. Hallamsh. Hosp. Sheff.; SHO (Neurol) Roy. Hallamsh. Hosp. Sheff.; Ho. Surg. Roy. Vict. Infirm. Newc.

COTTRELL, Professor David John Academic Unit of Child & Adolescent Mental Health, 12A Clarendon Road, Leeds LS2 9NN Tel: 0113 295 1760 Fax: 0113 295 1761 Email: d.j.cottrell@leeds.ac.uk — MB BS 1979 Lond.; MA Oxf. 1984; FRCPsych. (Westm.) Prof. Child & Adolesc. Psychiat. Sch. Med. Univ. Leeds. Prev: Sen. Lect. (Child & Adolesc. Psychiat.) Lond. Hosp. Med. Coll.; Lect. (Child & Adolesc. Psychiat.) St. Geo. Hosp. Med. Sch. Lond.

COTTRELL, George Robert (retired) 10 Hastings Avenue, Benton, Newcastle upon Tyne NE12 9NX Tel: 0191 266 2075 Email: george-cottrell@mail.com — MB BS 1945 Durh. GP Wallsend Tyne & Wear. Prev: GP Wallsend, Tyne and Wear (Retd.).

COTTRELL, Juliette Sara 85 Kennylands Road, Sonning Common, Reading RG4 9JT; 6 Bickley Moss, Oakwood, Derby DE21 2LJ — MB BChir 1992 Camb.; BA (Hons.) Camb. 1990. (Camb.)

COTTRELL, Katherine Ann 31 Mount Road, Heaton Norris, Stockport SK4 2NB — MB ChB 1990 Ed.

COTTRELL, Martin Andrew Corner Place Surgery, 46A Dartmouth Road, Paignton TQ4 5AH Tel: 01803 557488 — MB BS 1983 Lond. Gen. Practitioner,Corner Pl. Surg., Paignton.

COTTRELL, Paul William Arnold Crosby, Skene and Partners, College Way Surgery, Comeytrowe Centre, Taunton TA1 4TY Tel: 01823 259333 Fax: 01823 259336 — MB BS 1973 Lond.; MRCS Eng. LRCP Lond. 1972; DRCOG 1978. (St. Bartholomew's) Socs: BMA; BASICS; Primary Care Spec. Gp. of Brit. Computer Soc. Prev: Trainee GP Exeter VTS; SHO Rotat. Childr. Hosp. Bristol.

COTTRELL, Peter Richard St Andrews Medical Centre, St. Andrews Court, Pinewood Gardens, Southborough, Tunbridge Wells TN4 0LZ Tel: 01892 515455 Fax: 01892 514019 — MB BChir 1983 Camb.; MA, MB Camb. 1983, BChir 1982; MRCGP 1986; DRCOG 1984. GP Tunbridge Wells.

COTTRELL, Serena Mary Paediatric Intensive Care Unit, Royal Childrens Hospital, Melbourne, Australia Tel: 01556 610220; Strath-Urr, Dalbeattie DG5 4JB Tel: 01556 610220 — MB BS 1992 Lond.; MMed Sc 1999; BSc (Hons.) Leic. 1987; MRCPI 1996. (Char. Cross & Westm. Med. Sch.) Specialist Regist. (Paediat.) W. Midl.; Paediat. Intens. Care. Prev: SHO Anaesthetics Worcester & Hereford Hosp.; SPR Paediat. Intens. Care Birm. Childr.'s Hosp.

COTTRILL, Alfred Clement 3 Wootton Green Lane, Balsall Common, Coventry CV7 7EZ Tel: 016765 35774 — MB ChB 1958 Birm. (Birm.) Med. Off. (Occupat. Health) Brooklands Birm. Prev: Ho. Surg. (Urol.) Qu. Eliz. Hosp. Birm.; Ho. Phys. Gen. Hosp. Birm.; Ho. Phys. Profess. Unit, Childr. Hosp. Birm.

COTTRILL, Christopher Paul Department of Radiotherapy and Clinical Oncology, St Bartholomew's Hospital, London EC1A 7BE Tel: 020 7601 8355 Fax: 020 7601 8364 — MB BS 1988 Lond.; PhD (Nat. Sci.) Lond. 1985, BSc 1st cl. Hons. Anat. 1982; MRCP (UK) 1991; FRCR 1995. Cons. Clin. Oncol. Barts and Lond. NHS Trust; Cons. Clin. Oncologist, Whipps Cross Univ. Hosp. NHS Trust. Prev: Sen. Regist. (Radiother.) Roy. Marsden NHS Trust; Regist. (Radiother.) Mt. Vernon Hosp. N.wood Middlx.; Regist. (Clin. Oncol.) W.m. & Char. Cross Hosps. Lond.

COTTRILL, Mark Richard Bruce Brook Mill Medical Centre, College Street, Leigh WN7 2RB Tel: 01942 681880 Fax: 01942 262578; The Moat House, Lymm Hall, Lymm WA13 0AJ Tel: 01925 754097 Email: dr.m.cottrill@gpinternexus.uk — MRCS Eng. LRCP Lond. 1975. (Guy's Hosp.) Hosp. Pract. (Endoscopy) Lancs. Socs:

(Hon. Sec.) Anglo-French Med. Soc.; Primary Care Gastroenterol. Soc.; Brit. Soc. Gastroenterol.

COTTRILL, Paul Nicholas John Brookfield Surgery, Whitbarrow Road, Lymm WA13 9DB Tel: 01925 756969 Fax: 01925 756173 — MB BS 1974 Lond.; MRCS Eng. LRCP Lond. 1974. (Roy. Free)

COTTRILL, Philip Hedley (retired) Yewtree House, Allington Park, Bridport DT6 5DD — MB ChB 1960 Bristol; DObst RCOG 1962.

COTZIAS, Christina Sophia 9 Southborough Close, Surbiton KT6 6PU — MB ChB 1993 Birm. (Univ. Birm.) Research Regist. Qu. Charlottes Hosp. Lond. Prev: SHO (Obst.) St. Mary's Hosp. Lond.

COUCH, Alan Henry Clift (retired) 6 Judges Drive, Norwich NR4 7QQ — MB BS 1943 Lond.; MD Lond. 1947; FRCP Lond. 1971, M 1943; DCH Eng. 1949. Prev: Cons. Chest Phys. United Norwich Hosps.

COUCH, Anna Louise 54 Planatation House, Amersham HP6 6HL — MB BS 1997 Lond. (Roy Free Hosp Sch of Med)

COUCH, Audrey (retired) 4 Westheath Court, Gerald Road, West Kirby, Wirral CH48 4ES Tel: 0151 342 4137 — MB ChB 1953 Liverp.; FFR 1963; DMRD Liverp. 1957. Cons. Radiol. Roy. Liverp. Hosp. & Roy. Liverp. Childr. Hosp.; Mem. Liverp. Med. Inst. & Roy. Coll. Radiol. Prev: Sen. Regist. (Radiol.) Liverp. Roy. Infirm.

COUCH, David William (retired) Cobwebs, 5 Racing Reach, Horning, Norwich NR12 8JR Tel: 01692 631004 — MB BChir 1953 Camb.; MA Camb. 1954, MB BChir 1953; DObst RCOG 1959. Prev: Ho. Phys. N. Middlx. Hosp. Lond.

COUCH, Jane Caroline Beaumont Villa Surgery, 23 Beaumont Road, St Judes, Plymouth PL4 9BL Tel: 01752 663776 — MB ChB 1987 Otago; MRCGP 1992. Prev: Trainee GP Plymouth.; Clin. Asst. (Psychiat.) Plymouth.

COUCH, John Roderick Studholme Medical Centre, 50 Church Road, Ashford TW15 2TU Tel: 01784 420700 Fax: 01784 424503 — MB BS 1976 Lond.; MRCS Eng. LRCP Lond. 1976; DRCOG 1979. (St. Marys) Prev: SHO (Paediat.) Paddington Green Childr. Hosp. Lond.; SHO (Psychiat. & O & G) St. Mary's Hosp. Lond.; SHO (O & G) St. Mary's Hosp. Lond.

COUCH, Richard Michael (retired) Rick Barton House, Chideock Hill, Chideock, Bridport DT6 6JW Tel: 01297 489677 Email: richard.couch@which.net — MB ChB 1966 Sheff. Prev: Sen. Partner, Sutton Med. Centre.

COUCHER, John Richard 84 Pursewardens Close, Ealing, London W13 9PW — MB BS 1992 Lond.

COUCHMAN, Denis Ronald 9 Heatherlands, Thakeham Road, Storrington, Pulborough RH20 3NE — MB BS 1957 Lond.; MRCS Eng. LRCP Lond. 1957; DObst RCOG 1961; DA Eng. 1959. (King's Coll. Hosp.) Cons. Anaesth. N. Downs Hosp. Caterham. Socs: Fac. Anaesth. RCS Eng. Prev: SHO (O & G) Scarsdale Hosp. Chesterfield; Capt. RAMC; Ho. Off. E. Surrey Hosp. Redhill.

COUCHMAN, John Malcolm, DSC (retired) Bramshaw Lodge, Bramshaw, Lyndhurst SO43 7JE — MRCS Eng. LRCP Lond. 1939; MA, BM BCh Oxon 1939. Prev: Cons. (Genito-Urin. Med.) St. Mary's Hosp. Portsmouth & Bedford Gen. Hosp.

COUGAN, Catherine Ann Dept. of Community Child Health, Lower Hospital, Berrydon Rd, Aberdeen AB25 3HG Tel: 01224 557734 — MB BCh BAO 1985 Belf.; MRCGP 1990. (Queen's Univ. Belfast) p/t Staff Grade Paediat., Community Child Health, Grampian Univ. Hosps. Trust, Aberd. Prev: SHO (A & E) Roy. Aberd. Childr. Hosp.; GP Kirkcaldy Fife VTS; SHO (Paediat.) Roy. Belf. Hosp. Sick Childr.

COUGHLAN, John Bonaventure (retired) 1 Hawthorn Close, Aller Park, Newton Abbot TQ12 4TG Tel: 01626 351973 — MB BCh BAO 1949 NUI. Prev: SHO (Surg.) S. Infirm. Cork & Falmouth Hosp.

COUGHLIN, Lynda Bernadette Countess of Chester Hospital, Chester CH2 1UL; 19 Woodsorrel Way, Lowton, Warrington WA3 2GX Tel: 01942 272966 — MB ChB 1994 Liverp. SHO (O & G) Countess of Chester. Prev: SHO (O & G) Liverp. Wom.s. Hosp.; SHO (A & E) Roy. Liverp. Univ. Hosp.; Ho. Off. (Gen. Med. & Surg.) S.port & Formby NHS Trust.

COUGHLIN, Mary Jarvis and Partners, Westbrook Medical Centre, 301-302 Westbrook Centre, Westbrook, Warrington WA5 8UF; Brantingham, Chester Road, Higher Walton, Warrington WA4 5LP — MB ChB 1980 Leics.; MRCGP 1985; DRCOG 1984; DCH RCP Lond. 1983. (Leicester) Prev: Ho. Off. (Med. & Surg.) Leic. Gen. Hosp.

COUGHLIN, Patrick Anthony Newstead, Catforth Rd, Catforth, Preston PR4 0HE Email: pacoughlin@aol.com — MB ChB 1997 Leeds.

COUGHLIN, Sean Patrick Great Eccleston Health Centre, Raikes Road, Great Eccleston, Preston PR3 0ZA Tel: 01995 670066 Fax: 01995 671054; Newstead, Catforth Road, Catforth, Preston PR4 0HE Tel: 01772 690071 — MB ChB 1970 Manch.; MMedSc Leeds 1986; FRCGP 1994, M 1976; DObst RCOG 1972. Assoc. Adviser NW Eng. Prev: SHO (O & G) Sharoe Green Hosp. Preston; Ho. Surg. & Phys. Ancoats Hosp. Manch.

COULDEN, Richard Anthony Ross Lantern House, 94 High St., Great Abingdon, Cambridge CB1 6AE — MB BS 1981 Lond.; MRCP (UK) 1984; FRCR 1987. Cons. Cardiac Radiol. Papworth & Addenbrooke's Hosps. Camb. Prev: Sen. Regist. (Radiol.) Addenbrooke's Hosp. Camb.

COULDERY, Mr Anthony David Norfolk & Norwich Hospital, Brunswick Road, Norwich NR1 3SR Tel: 01603 628377 — MB BS 1955 Melbourne; FRCS Eng. 1964; FRCS Ed. 1962. Cons. ENT Surg. Norf. & Norwich Hosp. & Jas. Paget Hosp. Gorleston. Prev: Sen. Regist. (ENT) Univ. Coll. Hosp. Lond.; Sen. Regist. (Surg.) W. Middlx. Hosp.; Regist. (Surg.) Hammersmith Hosp. Lond.

COULDRICK, Mark William The Surgery, Station Road, Hemyock, Cullompton EX15 3SF — MB BS 1985 Lond.; MRCGP 1991; DRCOG 1990; DCH RCP Lond. 1989.

COULDRICK, William Gerald Richard Didcot Health Centre, Britwell Road, Didcot OX11 7JH Tel: 01235 512288 Fax: 01235 811473; Close Barn, Townsend, Harwell, Didcot OX11 0DX Tel: 01235 835329 Fax: 01235 835329 — MB BS 1959 Lond.; MRCS Eng. LRCP Lond. 1959; MRCGP 1972; Dip. Sports Med. Lond 1985; DObst RCOG 1961. (King's Coll. Hosp.) Staff Didcot Cott. Hosp. Socs: BMA. Prev: Hosp. Pract. Diabetic Dept. Roy. Berks. Hosp. Chairm. Oxon. LMC; SHO (Paediat.) Leicester Roy. Infirm.

COULDWELL, Andrew Beverley Cawood Mosborough Health Centre, 34 Queen Street, Mosborough, Sheffield S20 5BQ Tel: 0114 248 7488; 43 King Ecgbert Road, Totley Rise, Sheffield S17 3QR Tel: 0114 236 9318 Email: andy@snowhole.u-net.com — MB ChB 1985 Sheff.; MRCGP. (Sheffield) Socs: Roy. Coll. Gen. Pract.

COULL, Alexander Bruce Parkstone House, 108 The Broadway, Thorpe Bay, Southend-on-Sea SS1 3HH Tel: 01702 582700 Fax: 01702 589153 — MB ChB 1957 Aberd.; DObst RCOG 1962. GP.

COULL, Andrew John 15 North Drive, Aylesbury HP21 9AN Tel: 01296 336448 — MB ChB 1993 Ed.; BSc (Med. Sci.) Ed. 1992; MRCP (UK) 1996. (University of Edinburgh) Specialist Regist. (Gen. & Geriat. Med.) Oxf. Socs: BMA; BGS; MDU. Prev: SHO III (Geriat.) Falkirk Dist. & Roy. Infirm.

COULL, David Bruce The Surgery, Mount Avenue, Hutton, Brentwood CM13 2NL Tel: 01277 224612 Fax: 01277 200169 — MB BS 1969 Lond.; MA Camb. 1959; DObst RCOG 1971. (Lond. Hosp.) Prev: Ho. Phys. Lond. Hosp.; Ho. Surg. Harold Wood Hosp. Romford; SHO (Obst.) St. And. Hosp. Billericay.

COULL, Mr John Taylor, CB Monaltrie House, 6 Badger Way, Ewshot, Farnham GU10 5TE Tel: 01252 851061 — MB ChB Aberd. 1958; FRCS Eng. 1990; FRCS Ed. 1965. (Aberd.) Cons. Orthop. Surg. Socs: Fell. BOA (Exec. Counc. Mem.); Fell. Milit. Surg. Soc.; Fell. Roy. Soc. Med. Prev: Director .Med -Leg Serv. (Army); Dir. Army Surg.; Cons. Adviser Orthop. Surg. (Army).

COULL, Robert Stewart c/o 47 Blair Road, Coatbridge ML5 1JQ — MB ChB 1993 Manch.

COULL, Mr Roderick Email: rodcoull@hotmail.com — BM 1991 Soton.; FRCS (ORTH) 2001; BA Stanford 1986; FRCS Lond. 1996. (Southampton) Specialist Regist. Rotat. (Orthop.). Socs: BOA (Assoc. Fell.); MPS.

COULL, Sharon Louise Nethergate Medical Schooll, 2 Tay Square, Dundee DD1 1PB Tel: 01382 221527 Fax: 01382 226772 Email: scoullenethergate.finix.org.uk — MB ChB 1992 Aberd.; MRCGP 1996; DRCOG 1994. (Aberdeen) Principle; Hon. Lect. Dept. Gen. Pract., Univ. Dundee Tayside Centr. Pract.,Dundee. Socs: BMA; Forfarshire Med. Assn. Prev: Trainee GP Dundee; Higher Train. Fell. (Gen. Pract.) Tayside Centre for Gen. Pract. Dundee.

COULSHED, Norman (retired) 33 Woolton Hill Road, Liverpool L25 6HU Tel: 0151 428 3664 — MD 1956 Liverp.; MB ChB 1945; FRCP Lond. 1971, M 1951. Prev: Cons. Phys. (Cardiol.) Liverp. Regional Adult Cardiothoracic Centre BRd.green Hosp. Liverp.

COULSON, Alan James 78 Claymore Drive, Stirling FK7 7UP — MB ChB 1994 Glas.

COULSON, Andrew Whiteladies Health Centre, Whatley Road, Clifton, Bristol BS8 2PU Tel: 0117 973 1201 Fax: 0117 946 7031 — MB ChB 1975 Bristol; DRCOG 1977.

COULSON, Ann Manor Health Centre, Liscard Village, Wallasey CH45 4JG Tel: 0151 638 8221 Fax: 0151 639 6512; 64 Meols Parade, Meols, Wirral CH47 5AX Tel: 0151 632 1728 — MB ChB 1979 Liverp.; Cert. Family Plann. JCC 1986. (Liverp.) Socs: Wallasey Med. Soc.

COULSON, Catherine Centro Reproductive Medicine, 4 Priory Road, Clifton, Bristol BS8 1TX Tel: 0117 902 1100 Fax: 0117 902 1101; The Towers, Church Road, Stoke Bishop, Bristol BS9 1JS Tel: 0117 968 4837 — MB ChB 1976 Bristol; DRCOG 1978. Clin. Asst. (Infertil.) Univ. Bristol; Sen. Clin. Med. Off. (Psychosexual Med.) St. Michael's Hosp. Bristol. Socs: Inst. Psychosexual Med.; Accred. Mem. Brit. Soc. Med. & Dent. Hypn.

COULSON, Ethnea Anne Mary New Hayesbank Surgery, Cemetery Lane, Kennington, Ashford TN24 9JZ Tel: 01233 624642 Fax: 01233 637304; Braeside, Stowting, Ashford TN25 6BD — BM BCh 1971 Oxf.; MA Oxf. 1971; DCH Eng. 1975; DObst RCOG 1974. Prev: Regist. (Paediat.) William Harvey Hosp. Ashford & W. Middlx. Hosp. Isleworth; SHO (Paediat.) Ashford Hosp. Middlx.

COULSON, Ian Halliday Dermatology Unit, Burnley General Hospital, Casterton Avenue, Burnley BB10 2PQ Tel: 01282 474819 Fax: 01282 474809 — MB BS 1978 Lond.; BSc Lond. 1975; FRCP Lond. 1995; MRCP (UK) 1981. (St. Thos. Hosp. Med. Sch.) Cons. Dermat. Burnley Gen. Hosp. & Rossendale Gen. Hosp. Lancs. Socs: Roy. Soc. Med.; N. Eng. Dermat. Soc. Prev: Sen. Regist. Skin Dept. St. Helier Hosp. Carshalton & St. Geo. Hosp. Lond.; Regist. St. Geo. Hosp. Lond.; SHO St. John's Hosp. Dis. of the Skin Lond.

COULSON, Miranda Lucy 14 Badgerwood Drive, Frimley, Camberley GU16 8UF — MB BS 1993 Lond.; Pharm.BSC.Hons.Uni.Coll.Lond. 1990. (Uni.Coll.Lond.Med.Sch.) Regist. Anaest.&Intens..Care.Maroondah.Hosp.Melbourne.Austr.

COULSON, Raymond Ademola 28 Maple Drive, Vicarage Heights, Kendal LA9 5BN — LRCP LRCS Ed. LRCPS Glas. 1979; MFFP 1993; MRCOG 1981; FRCOG 1998. Prev: Regist. (O & G) Liverp. HA; Lect. Univ. Zimbabwe 1986-88.

COULSON, Richard William Stephen Mersea Road Surgery, 272a Mersea Road, Colchester CO2 8QY Tel: 01206 764374 Fax: 01206 765667 — BM BS 1983 Nottm.

COULSON, Susan Mary 27 Upper Green, Dunmurry, Belfast BT17 0EL — MB ChB 1991 Manch.; MRCGP 1995; DRCOG 1994. (Manch.)

COULSON, Timothy John Overnhill Family Practice, 14 Overnhill Road, Staple Hill, Bristol BS16 5DN Tel: 0117 970 1656 Fax: 0117 987 2479 Email: overnhill@callnet.uk.com — MB BCh 1980 Wales; DRCOG 1987. (Welsh National School of Medicine, Cardiff) GP Principal; Police Surg. A& S Police; Bd. Mem. E. Bristol PCG. Prev: Trainee GP Brit. Milit. Hosp. Rinteln VTS, W. Germany; Med. Off. Traing. Depot Brig. of Gurkhas Hong Kong.

COULSON, Warwick James Albany House Medical Centre, 3 Queen Street, Wellingborough NN8 4RW Tel: 01933 222309 Fax: 01933 229236 — BM BS 1987 Nottm.; BMedSci Nottm. 1985; MRCGP 1991; DRCOG 1990. Clin. Asst. (Cardiol.) Kettering Gen. Hosp.

COULSTING, Dorothy Rogers Ryecroft, Narbeth Road, Tenby SA70 8HT Tel: 01834 842447 — MB ChB Manch. 1946. (Manch.) Prev: Pub. Health.

COULSTING, Hugh Stuart Ryecroft, Narberth Road, Tenby SA70 8HT Tel: 01834 842447 — MB ChB Manch. 1946; MRCS Eng. LRCP Lond. 1946; MRCPsych 1971; DPM Manch. 1951. (Manch.) Prev: Family Psychiat. (Cons.).

COULTAS, Ann Patricia Applegarth, Delville Avenue, Keyworth, Nottingham NG12 5JA — MB BS 1964 Durh.

COULTAS, Helen Winifred Harvey (retired) 1 White House Grove, Elvington, York YO41 4AL Tel: 01904 608288 — MB ChB Birm. 1955. Prev: SCMO York HA.

COULTAS, Robert John Applegarth, Delville Avenue, Keyworth, Nottingham NG12 5JA — MB BS 1962 Durh.; FFA RCS Eng. 1968. Cons. Anaesth. Nottm. Gp. Hosps. Prev: Sen. Regist. Newc. Univ. Hosps.; Lect. Anaesth. Unit Lond. Hosp. Med. Coll.

COULTER, Carmel Anne Elizabeth Department of Oncology, St. Mary's Hospital, Praed St., London W2 1NY Tel: 020 7886 1132 Fax: 020 7886 1840 — MB BS 1970 Lond.; FRCP Lond. 1991; FRCR 1977. (Roy. Free) Cons. Clin. Oncol. St. Mary's Hosp. Lond. & Middlx. Hosp. Lond.; Hon. Cons. King Edwd. VII & Qu. Eliz. II Hosp. Welwyn Gdn. City. Prev: Sen. Regist. (Radiother.) St. Bart. Hosp. Lond.

COULTER, David Frew (retired) The Gables, Corntown Road, Corntown, Bridgend CF35 5BG — MD 1968 Glas.; MB ChB 1946; FRCGP 1970. Prev: Course Organiser Bridgend VTS.

COULTER, Fiona Victoria Infirmary Main Building, East King St., Helensburgh G84 7BU Tel: 01436 655038 Fax: 01436 655035 — MB ChB 1982 Dundee; MRCPsych 1988. Cons. Gen. Adult Psychogeriat. Lomond Trust Dunbartonsh.

COULTER, Gary George c/o Barclays Bank, 1 Manvers St., Bath BA1 1JZ — MB BS 1981 Lond.; BA (Hons.) Oxf. 1978.

COULTER, James Edwin Martin Holywood Arches Health Centre, Westminster Avenue, Belfast BT4 1NS Tel: 028 9056 3354 Fax: 028 9065 3846; 1 Castlehill Manor, Belfast BT4 3QH Tel: 01232 760244 Email: e.coulter@virgin.net — MB BCh BAO 1987 Belf.; MRCGP 1991; DRCOG 1991; DCH RCPSI 1989. Prev: Trainee GP N. Irel. VTS.

COULTER, John Brian Stuart 11A Fulwood Park, Liverpool L17 5AA Tel: 0151 727 3238; Liverpool School of Tropical Medicine, Pembroke Place, Liverpool L3 5QA Tel: 0151 708 9393 Fax: 0151 708 8733 — MB BCh BAO Dub. 1964; BA Dub. 1964, MD 1986; FRCPI 1987, M 1971; DCH RCP Glas. 1967. (Trinity College University of Dublin) Hon. Cons. Paediat. Roy. Liverp. Childr. Hosps.; Sen. Lect. (Trop. Paediat.) Liverp. Sch. of Trop. Med.; Lect. (Child Health) Univ. Liverp. Prev: Cons. & Lect. Ahmado Bello Univ., Nigeria; Lect. (Child Health) Univ. Aberd.; Assoc. Prof. Paediat. & Child Health Univ. Khartoum, Sudan.

COULTER, Margaret Elizabeth Castle Place Surgery, Tiverton EX16 6RR Tel: 01884 252333; Cartref, 20 Uplowman Road, Tiverton EX16 4LU Tel: 01884 256159 — MB BCh BAO 1979 Belf. (Qu. Univ. Belf.) p/t GP Tiverton Retainer Scheme. Prev: GP Ecclefechan; Clin. Asst. Mid Devon Practive, Witheridge, Devon.

COULTER, Michael David (retired) 3 West Road, Gamlingay, Sandy SG19 3JT Tel: 01767 651193 — MB BS Lond. 1955; DObst RCOG 1960. Prev: Maj. RAMC i/c Med. Centre GHQ FARELF Singapore.

COULTER, Nichola Claire 30 Tullynore Road, Hillsborough BT26 6QE — MB BCh 1998 Belf.; MB BCh Belf 1998.

COULTER, Ruth Sarah 12 Mid Island Park, Greyabbey, Newtownards BT22 2SZ — MB ChB 1997 Dundee.

COULTER, Samuel Arthur The Surgery, 4 Station Road, Frimley, Camberley GU16 5HF Tel: 01276 62622 Fax: 01276 683908; Southwood Cottage, 126 Ively Road, Cove, Farnborough GU14 0LJ Tel: 01252 520859 — MB BS 1975 Lond.; DA Eng. 1978. (Roy. Free) Prison Med. Off. HMP Coldingley; Police Surg. Guildford. Prev: Trainee GP Watford; Regist. (Anaesth.) Qu. Eliz. Hosp. Bridgetown, Barbados; SHO (Rotat.) Armidale Hosp., Australia.

COULTER, Simon Kenneth 9 Thornhill Mews, Thornhill Parade, Belfast BB5 7AF — MB BCh 1998 Belf.; MB BCh Belf 1998.

COULTER, Susan Wendy 36 Gordon Street, Southport PR9 0LY Tel: 01704 537584 — MB ChB 1990 Liverp.; MA Oxf. 1989, BA (Hons.) 1982; DFFP 1995; DRCOG 1994; T (GP) 1995. Salaried pms GP. Socs: Med. Protec. Soc.; BMA; Assoc. Roy. Coll. of Gen. Practitioners. Prev: Clin. Fell. (A & E) Chorley DGH; Trainee GP Stockton Heath; SHO (A & E) N. Manch. Gen. Hosp. & Warrington Dist. Gen. Hosp.

COULTHARD, Mr Alan Royal Victoria Infirmary, Queen Victoria Road, Newcastle upon Tyne NE1 4LP Tel: 0191 282 5950 Fax: 0191 282 4818 Email: alan.coulthard@ncl.ac.uk — MB BS 1982 Newc.; BMedSc (1st cl. Hons.) Newc. 1979, MB BS 1982; FRCS Ed. 1987; FRCR 1991. (Newcastle University) Cons. Radiol. Roy. Vict. Infirm. Newc. u. Tyne; Sen. Lect. (Radiol.) Univ. Newc. U. Tyne. Prev: Sen. Regist. (Diag. Radiol.) Newc. HA; Regist. (Gen. Surg.) Roy. Vict. Infirm. Newc.

COULTHARD, Colin William Steven Threewaters House, Nanstallon, Bodmin PL30 5LL — MB BS 1996 Lond.

COULTHARD, Dudley Spion Kop, 68 South View, West Denton, Newcastle upon Tyne NE5 2BQ Tel: 0191 243 1491 — MB BS

1949 Durh. (Newc.) Apptd. Exam. Surg. & Div. Surg. St. John Ambul. Brig.; Civil Serv. Dept. Local Med. Off.

COULTHARD, Malcolm George Children;s Kidney Unit, Royal Victoria Infirmary, Queen Victoria Road, Newcastle upon Tyne NE1 4LP Tel: 0191 282 4778 Fax: 0191 261 5881 Email: malcolm.coulthard@ncl.ac.uk — MB BS 1970 Lond.; BSc (Physiol., 1st cl. Hons.) Lond. 1970; FRCP Lond. 1990; MRCP (UK) 1977; DCH Eng. 1975; FRCPCH 1997. (The London Hospital) Cons. Paediat. (Nephrol.) Roy. Vict. Infirm. Newc. u. Tyne; Hon. Sen. Lect. (Child Health) Univ. Newc.

COULTHARD, Michael The Coppice, Herne Lane, Rustington, Littlehampton BN16 2BY Tel: 01903 783178; Rushtine, Huntsmans Hill, Rugeley WS15 1QE — MB BS 1964 Durh.; DObst RCOG 1970. (Newc.) Clin. Asst. (Rehabil.) Zachary Merton Community Hosp. Rustington. Prev: Ho. Phys. Dept. Paediat. Roy. Vict. Infirm. Newc.; Med. Off. RAMC; Med. Adviser Organon Laborats.

COULTHARD, Richard Andrew 154 Bridgetown Road, Stratford-upon-Avon CV37 7JA — BM 1997 Soton.

COULTHWAITE, Pauline Mary (retired) Barrow Coombe, Appleby-in-Westmorland CA16 6AA Tel: 0176 835 1444 — MB ChB 1960 Ed.; DObst RCOG 1963.

COULTON, Eric Richard Kinmel Bay Medical Centre, The Square, Kinmel Bay, Rhyl LL18 5AU Tel: 01745 353965 Fax: 01745 356407 — MB ChB 1972 Sheff.; DObst RCOG 1974.

COUMBARIDES, Angela Margaret 100 Vicarage Lane, Great Baddow, Chelmsford CM2 8JB — MB ChB 1997 Manch. Surgic. SHO, Train. Rotat., Hope Hosp.,Salford.

COUMBE, Adam Department of Histopathology, Farnborough Hospital, Farnborough Common, Orpington BR6 8ND Tel: 01689 814291 Fax: 01689 814293 Email: acoumbe@doctors.org.uk — MB BS 1984 Lond.; MA Camb. 1987, BA 1981; MRCPath 1991; FRCPath 1999. (Guy's) Cons. Histopath. Bromley Hosps. NHS Trust. Socs: Assn. Clin. Path.; Path. Soc.; Brit. Soc. Clin. Cytol. Prev: Sen. Lect. & Hon. Cons. Morbid Anat. & Rheum. Lond. Hosp. Med. Coll.; Sen. Regist. (Histopath.) Hosp. for Sick Childr. Gt. Ormond St. Lond.; Regist. (Histopath.) St. Mary's Hosp. Lond.

COUNDON, Helen 13 Brighton Grove, Whitley Bay NE26 1QH — MB ChB 1987 Ed.

COUNIHAN, Richard Glynn 7 Revelstoke Road, Wimbledon Park, London SW18 Tel: 020 8946 1400 — MB BCh BAO 1952 NUI; DObst RCOG 1957; LM Nat. Matern. Hosp. 1955. Prev: Ho. Surg. & Ho. Phys. St. Vincents' Hosp. Dub.; Ho. Phys. (O & G) Univ. Coll. Hosp. Kingston, Jamaica; Sen. Ho. Off. (Obst.) Dulwich Hosp.

COUNSELL, Barbara Rachel Anne 32 Foxley Lane, Purley CR8 3EE Tel: 020 8660 1304; 48 Sanderstead Hill, South Croydon CR2 0HA — MB BCh 1976 Wales; MRCGP 1983; Dip. Ther. Wales 1998.

COUNSELL, David John c/o Anaesthetic Department, Victoria Hospital, Whinney Heys Road, Blackpool FY3 8NR Tel: 01253 303499 Fax: 01253 303510; Moor End Barn, Stricklands Lane, Stalmine, Poulton-le-Fylde FY6 0LL Tel: 01253 702528 — MB ChB 1982 Leic.; FRCA 1987. Cons. Anaest. Blackpool Vict. Hosp. (Cardio-thoracic Anaesth. & Acute Pain).

COUNSELL, Garth Forrest (retired) Seascape, 17 Bybrook Field, Sandgate, Folkestone CT20 3BQ Tel: 01303 248691 — MB ChB 1957 Bristol; MRCGP 1966; DObst RCOG 1960; DCH Eng. 1959. GP Trainer Folkestone.; Vis. Med. Off. Dept. Geriat. Roy. Vict. Hosp. Folkestone. Prev: GP Faversham.

COUNSELL, Gillian Ann 4 St Michaels Avenue, Bolton BL3 2LP — MB ChB 1988 Sheff.

COUNSELL, Pamela (retired) Corner, 1 Birch Close, Wedmore BS28 4BG Tel: 01934 712637 — MB ChB 1945 Bristol; FRCA 1959; DA Eng. 1948. JP.; Cons. Anaesth. Bristol Roy. Hosp.; Clin. Teach. (Anaesth.) Univ. Bristol. Prev: Regist. (Anaesth.) Hosp. Sick Childr. Gt. Ormond St.

COUNSELL, Radhika East Gloucestershire NHS Trust, Gloucestershire Oncology Unit, Sandford Road, Cheltenham GL53 7AN Tel: 01242 273610 Fax: 01242 273506 Email: radhika.counsell@egnhs.org.uk — MB BS 1981 Lond.; FRCP 1999; BSc (Hons) Lond. 1978, MD 1993; MRCP (UK) 1984; FRCR 1988; MD 1992. (Univ. Coll. Hosp. Lond.) p/t Cons. Clin. Oncol. E. Glos. NHS Trust Cheltenham. Socs: Roy. Coll. Radiol.; Brit. Gyn. Cancer Soc.; Roy. Coll. Phys.s. Prev: Sen. Regist. (Clin. Oncol.) Addenbrooke's NHS Trust Camb.; MRC Clin. Research Fell. & Hon. Sen. Regist. (Clin. Oncol.) Ch.ill Hosp. Oxf.; Regist. (Clin. Oncol.) Ch.ill Hosp. Oxf.

COUNTER, Lois 1 Beacon Park, Penrith CA11 7UB — MB BS 1997 Newc.

COUNTER, Paul Richard, Surg. Lt. RN Medical Mess, Royal Naval Hospital, Haslar, Gosport PO12 2AA — MB BS 1993 Lond. Prev: Ho. Phys. RNH Plymouth; Ho. Surg. RNH Haslar.

COUP, Andrew 25 St John Close, Walton, Chesterfield S42 7HH — MB ChB 1994 Sheff. Specialist Regist. (Histopath) Qu. Med. Centre, Nottm. Prev: SHO (Histopath.) Roy. Preston Hosp.; SHO (Med. & c/o Elderly) Chesterfield Roy. Hosp. Derbysh.

COUP, Anthony John Barnsley District General Hospital, Gawber Road, Barnsley S75 2EP — MB ChB 1969 Sheff.; FRCPath 1987, M 1975. Cons. (Histopath.) Barnsley Dist. Gen. Hosp. Socs: Assn. Clin. Path. & Brit. Div. Internat. Acad. Path. Prev: Lect. (Path.) Univ. Sheff.; Ho. Surg. & Ho. Phys. Doncaster Roy. Infirm.

COUPE, Anthony Settle Kiltearn Medical Centre, Hospital St., Nantwich CW5 5RL Tel: 01270 610200; Shropshire Gate Farm, Old Woodhouses, Whitchurch SY13 4EH — MB ChB 1962 St. And. Prev: SHO Roy. Nat. Orthop. Hosp. Lond.; Resid. Clin. Path. Birchill Hosp. Rochdale; Ho. Phys. Arbroath Infirm.

COUPE, Leila Catherine 19 Northwold, Ely CB6 1BG — MB ChB 1994 Liverp.

COUPE, Madelaine Jane 16 Eythorne Road, Shepherdswell, Dover CT15 7PB Tel: 01304 830419 — BM BS 1990 Nottm.; FRCA 1997. Career Regist. (Anaesth.) Guy's Hosp., Lond. Socs: BMA; Assn. Anaesth. Prev: Regist. (Anaesth.) Kent & Canterbury Hosp.; SHO (Anaesth.) Univ. Hosp. Nottm. & Sutton-in-Ashfield; SHO (Paediat.) King's Mill Hosp.

COUPE, Michael Howard 73A Commercial Road, Poole BH14 0JB — MB ChB 1995 Birm.; ChB Birm. 1995.

COUPE, Michael Owen Healey Office, Birch Hill Hospital, Rochdale OL12 9QB Tel: 01706 755671; Higher Stoodley Farm, Lee Bottom Road, Mankinholes, Todmorden OL14 6HD Tel: 01706 819516 — MD 1989 Manch.; MB ChB 1981; MRCP (UK) 1984. Cons. Phys. Cardiol. Ryl Oldham Hsp. Socs: NW Cardiol. Gp (Sec.). Prev: Cons. Phys. Cardiol. Rochdale HA.; Research Fell. Brit. Heart Foundat. Cardiac Dept. Brompton Hosp.; Regist. (Med.) Hammersmith Hosp. Lond.

COUPE, Robert Mathew 42 Whittaker Lane, Little Eaton, Derby DE21 5AT — MB ChB 1992 Leeds. SHO Rotat. (Surg.) Derby Roy. Infirm.

COUPE, Simon Charles Stour Surgery, 49 Barrack Road, Christchurch BH23 1PA Tel: 01202 464500 Fax: 01202 464529; 3 Old Barn Road, Christchurch BH23 2QY — MB ChB 1983 Birm. GP ChristCh..

COUPE, Mrs Susan Margaret 38 Craighouse Avenue, Morningside, Edinburgh EH10 5LN — MB ChB 1977 Dundee; FFA RCS Eng. 1982.

COUPER, David Michael The Oaks Surgery, Applegarth Avenue, Park Barn, Guildford GU2 8LZ Tel: 01483 563424 Fax: 01483 563789; Milford Cottage, Portsmouth Road, Milford, Godalming GU8 5HX Tel: 01483 414540 — MB BS 1978 Lond.; DRCOG 1983.

COUPER, Donald MacLennan Ashcroft Surgery, 803 Stockport Road, Levenshulme, Manchester M19 3BS Tel: 0161 224 1329 Fax: 0161 224 0094 — MB ChB 1974 Aberd.; MRCGP 1982; DA (UK) 1980. G.S.M.

COUPER, Edward Hayes (retired) 8 Park Hill, Bromley BR1 2JH Tel: 020 8467 5004 — MB BS 1944 Lond. Prev: Clin. Asst. (Med.) Erith Hosp.

COUPER, Mr Graeme William 3 Keyes Gardens, Jesmond, Newcastle upon Tyne NE2 3RA — MB ChB 1991 Aberd.; FRCS Ed. 1995. (Univ. Aberd.)

COUPLAND, Christine Rhoda Calthorpe House, Acle, Norwich NR13 3QR Tel: 01493 750573 — MB ChB 1947 Glas.; DObst RCOG 1950. (Glas.) Prev: SCMO (Audiol.) Gt. Yarmouth & Waveney HA; Res. Med. Off. Qu. Charlotte's Matern. Hosp. Lond.; Ho. Surg. Roy. Hosp. Sick Childr. Glas.

COUPLAND, Maria del Carmen 1 Bonaly Brae, Colinton, Edinburgh EH13 0QF — MB ChB 1977 Dundee; BMSc (Hons.) 1974. SHO (Anaesth.) Ninewells Hosp. Dundee. Prev: Temp. Lect. Path. Ninewells Hosp. & Med. Sch. Dundee.

COUPLAND, Michael Peter Moore (retired) 10 Ropers Court, Lavenham, Sudbury CO10 9PU Tel: 01787 248237 — MB BS 1952 Lond.; FRCGP 1986, M 1963; LMSSA Lond. 1949; MRCGP 1963. Prev: Ho. Surg. Canad. Red Cross Memor. Hosp. Taplow.

COUPLAND, Rex Ernest Fox Hollow, Quaker Lane, Farnsfield, Newark NG22 8EE Tel: 01623 882028 — MB ChB 1947 Leeds; FRSE 1960; DSc Leeds 1970, PhD 1954; MD (Distinc.) 1952. (Leeds) Emerit. Prof. Human Morphol. Univ. Nottm. Socs: BMA (Ex-Chairm. Nottm. Br.). Prev: Hon. Cons. Trent RHA; Chairm. MRC Non-Ionizing Radn. Comm.; Mem. Trent RHA & Med. Sub-Comm. Univ. Grants Comm.

COUPLAND, Mr Robin Michael 8 Belvedere Place, Norwich NR4 7PP — MB 1981 Camb.; BChir 1980; FRCS Eng. 1985; FRCS Ed. 1985.

COUPLAND, Terence Graham c/o 129 Farnhurst Road, Barnham, Bognor Regis PO22 0LL — MB BS 1968 Lond.; FFA RACS 1975; MRCS Eng. LRCP Lond. 1968.

COURIEL, Jonathan Michael Respiratory Unit, Royal Liverpool Childrens Hospital, Alder Hey, Liverpool L12 2AP Tel: 0151 252 5911 Fax: 0151 252 5929 Email: jcouriel@rlch-tr.nwest.nhs.uk — MB BChir 1973 Camb.; FRCPCH 1997; FRCP Lond. 1990; MRCP (UK) 1976; MA Camb. 1973; BA (Hons.) 1970. (UCH Lond. Camb.) Roy. Liverp. Childr. Hosp.; Clin. Lect., Dept child health, Univ. of Liverp. Socs: (Counc.) RCPCH 1994-1998; Brit. Thorac. Soc. (Counc. 2001-); Brit. Paediat. Respirat. Soc. (Chairm. 2001-). Prev: Cons. Paediat. Respirat. Med. Manch.; Univ. Postgrad. Tutor (Paediat.) Univ. Manch.; Research Fell. Asst. Phys. (Thoracic Med.) Roy. Childr. Hosp., Melbourne.

COURRIER, Mr Michel Youssef 51 Burnham Way, London W13 9YB — MD 1972 Damascus; FRCSI 1987.

COURT, Bruce Vincent NHS Executive, West Midlands Regional Office, Bartholomew House, 142 Hagley Road, Birmingham B16 9PA Tel: 0121 224 4677 Fax: 0121 224 4680 — MB BS 1977 Lond.; MFPHM RCP (UK) 1995; MRCGP 1986; DFFP 1993. Cons. Pub. Health Med. NHS Exec. W. Midl. Regional Off.; Hon. Clin. Sen. Lect. Med. Sch. Univ. Birm. Socs: Fell. Roy. Soc. Med. Prev: Sen. Regist. & Hon. Lect. Inst. Pub. & Environm. Health Univ. Birm.; Sen. Med. Off. Berlin Gp. Pract., Germany; GP Lond.

COURT, Caroline Sarah 23 Brunswick Terrace, Hove BN3 1HJ — MB BS 1992 Lond.

COURT, Fiona Geradine 6 Church Lane, Ratcliffe on the Wreake, Leicester LE7 4SF — MB ChB 1996 Dundee; BMSc (Hons. Forens. Med.) Dund. 1993. (Dund.) SHO Univ. Dund.; Anat. Demonst. Dund.

COURT, Mr Geoffrey Alden (retired) 69 St Martin's Road, Coventry CV3 6FD Tel: 01203 412579 — MB BChir 1949 Camb.; FRCS Eng. 1959. Prev: Cons. Surg. Geo. Eliot Hosp. Nuneaton.

COURT, Juliet Elizabeth 283 Bramhall Lane S., Bramhall, Stockport SK7 3DW — MB ChB 1979 Manch.; MRCP (UK) 1983; T (M) (Paediat.) 1993. Bliss Fell. Neonat. Med. St. Mary's Hosp. Manch.

COURT, Michael Cardio Pulmonary Therapeutic Unit, ClinR & D Medical Affairs, (Europe) SmithKline Beecham Pharmaceuticals,, New Frontiers Science Park, Third Avenue, Harlow CM19 5AW; 32 Green End, Comberton, Cambridge CB3 7DY Tel: 01223 263900 — MB ChB 1974 Birm.; MRCGP 1978; Dip. Pharm. Med. RCP (UK) 1992. Dir. (Cardio Pulm.) Ther. Unit SmithKline Beecham. Socs: Fac. Pharmaceut. Med.; Brit. Assn. Pharmaceut. Phys. Prev: Head Clin. Affairs Pk.e Davis & Co.; Sen. Med. Adviser Napp Pharmaceut. Gp.; Princip. GP, Trainer & VTS Course Organiser I. of Wight.

COURT, Sarah Jane Greyfriars, Greyfriars Avenue, Hereford HR4 0BE — MB ChB 1990 Ed.

COURT, Simon Community Paediatric Department, Newcastle General Hospital, Westgate Road, Newcastle upon Tyne NE4 6BE Tel: 0191 273 8811 Ext: 23363 Fax: 0191 219 5072 Email: jackie.baxter@ncnt.nortuy.nhs.uk; 13 Elmfield Road, Gosforth, Newcastle upon Tyne NE3 4AY Tel: 0191 285 1682 Email: simon.court@ncl.ac.uk — MB ChB 1970 Bristol; MSc (Comm. Med.) Newc. 1994; BSc (Biochem.) Bristol 1967; FRCP Lond. 1986; MRCP (UK) 1974; DCH Eng. 1972. Cons. Comm. Paediat. Newc. upon Tyne Hosp.s Trust. Socs: Fell. Roy. Call. Paediat. & Child Health; Fell. Roy. Coll. Phys.

COURT, Stephen Alistair 16 Harmont House, 20 Harley St., London W1G 9PH Tel: 020 7580 5411 Fax: 020 7323 3418 — MB ChB 1975 Bristol; BSc (Physiol.) Bristol 1972; MRCP (UK) 1977. Indep. GP Lond.; Clin. Asst. (Endoscopy) N.wick Pk. Hosp. Harrow.

COURT, Susan Elizabeth The Surgery, 2 Crescent Bakery, St. Georges Place, Cheltenham GL50 3PN Tel: 01242 226336 Fax: 01242 253587; 8 Harvesters View, Bishops Cleeve, Cheltenham GL52 7WD Tel: 01242 679306 Email: sue@wongo.prestel.co.uk — MB BS 1986 Lond.; BSc (Biol.) Soton. 1977. (Westm.) Prev: Trainee GP/SHO (Geriat. Med.) Delancey Hosp. Cheltenham VTS; Trainee GP/SHO (O & G) Glos. Roy. Hosp. VTS; SHO (Radiother. & Oncol.) Cheltenham Gen. Hosp.

COURT BROWN, Professor Charles Michael Craigesk House, Lothianbridge, Dalkeith EH22 4TP — MD 1985 Ed.; BSc Aberd. 1970; MB ChB 1975; FRCS (Orthop.) Ed. 1984; FRCS Ed. 1979. Cons. Orthop. Surg. Lothian HB. Prev: Sen. Lect. (Orthop. Surg.) Univ. Edin.

COURTENAY, Harold Logan Marsden Road Health Centre, South Shields NE34 6RE Tel: 0191 454 0457 Fax: 0191 427 1793; 6 West Meadows Road, Cleadon Village, Sunderland SR6 7TX Tel: 0191 519 0936 — MB BCh BAO 1950 Belf.; DObst RCOG 1962. (Qu. Univ. Belf.) Socs: Fell. Ulster Med. Soc.; Newc. & N.. Cos. Med. Soc. Prev: Regist. (Med.) St. Helens Hosp. Lancs.; Ho. Surg. Musgrave Pk. Hosp. Belf.; Ho. Phys. Ulster Hosp. Dundonald.

COURTENAY, Kenneth Patrick 28 Seely Road, London SW17 9QS — MB BCh BAO 1987 Dub.; MB BCh Dub. 1987; MRCGP 1992; DRCOG 1991; DGM RCP Lond. 1990. (Univ. Dub., Trinity Coll.) Reg. (Psychiat.) St. Geo. Hosp. Lond.; Collegiate Trainees Comm. Roy. Coll. Psychiat. (S. Thames Rep.). Socs: BMA; Brit. Assn. Psychopharmocol. Prev: Regist. (Child Psychiat.) Epsom, Surrey; Regist. (Gen. Adult Psychiat.) Epsom, Surrey; Regist. (Learning Disabil.) Mitcham, Surrey.

COURTENAY, Michael John Francis (retired) Flower Pot Cottage, Manor Road, Adderbury, Banbury OX17 3EJ Tel: 01295 811039 — MB BChir 1952 Camb.; FRCGP 1981, M 1960. Prev: Sen. Med. Adviser Advis. Counc. for Ch.'s Min.

COURTENAY, Richard Treloar, Wing Cdr. Retd. Sherbourne Medical Centre, 40 Oxford Street, Leamington Spa CV32 4RA Tel: 01926 333500 Fax: 01926 470884; 25 Avonlea Rise, Leamington Spa CV32 6HS Tel: 01926 330085 — MB BS 1983 Lond.; DipAvMed 1993; DFFP 1997. Princip. GP Leamington Spa; AME for CAA. cl. one and Two. Socs: AAME. Prev: SMO RAF Odiham; Gp. Flt. Med. Off. HQ38Gp; SMO RAF Chivenor.

COURTENAY, Tamsin Mary Andres Coombe's Cottage, 16 Ash Walk, Henstridge, Templecombe BA8 0QD — BM 1995 Soton.

COURTENAY-EVANS, Patricia Anne (cons. rooms), Gatwick Park Hospital, Povey Cross Road, Horley RH6 0BB Tel: 01293 785511; Starrock Court, Starrock Lane, Chipstead, Coulsdon CR5 3QB — MB BS 1966 Lond.; MRCS Eng. LRCP Lond. 1966; FRCOG 1989; MRCOG 1973. (St. Mary's) Assoc. Specialist (O & G) Crawley Hosp.

COURTENAY-EVANS, Rupert James A & E Department, Mayday University Hospital, Croydon CR7 7YE Tel: 020 8401 3137; Starrock Court, Chipstead, Coulsdon CR5 3QB Tel: 017375 54049 — MB BChir 1963 Camb.; MA Camb. 1964; FRCP Lond. 1981, M 1967. (Camb. & St. Bart.) p/t Cons. Phys. (Gen.and A & E Med.) Mayday Health Care NHS Trust. Socs: BMA; Soc. for Acute Med. (UK).

COURTENAY-MAYERS, Bryan Bernard Pellew, MC 51 Brook Green, London W6 7BJ Tel: 020 7602 8420 Fax: 020 7371 2147 — MD Paris 1939; MRCS Eng. LRCP Lond. 1951; DTM & H Eng. 1948. (Westm.) Phys. French Consulate-Gen. Lond. Socs: Fell. Roy. Soc. Med. Prev: Capt. RAMC.

COURTENEY-HARRIS, Mr Robert George City General Hospital, Stoke-on-Trent ST4 6QC — MB BS 1982 Lond.; FRCS Otolaryngol. Eng. 1989; FRCS (ORC) 1996. (St.Bartholomews) Cons. ENT Surg., City Gen. Hosp., Stoke-on-Trent. Prev: Sen. Regist. Rotat. (ENT) St. Thos., Gt. Ormond St. Hosps. Lond. & Norf. & Norwich Hosps.

COURTMAN, Mr Nigel Harvey Department of Orthopaedics, Furness General Hospital, Dalton Lane, Barrow-in-Furness LA14 4LF Tel: 01229 870870 — MB ChB 1984 Manch.; MB ChB Manch. I984; BSc St. And. 1981; FRCS (Orth.) 1996; FRCS Eng. 1988. (Manch.) Cons. Orthop. Surg. Furness Hosps. NHS Trust. Prev: Sen. Regist. & Regist. (Orthop. Surg.) NW RHA; Research Fell. Arthritis & Rheum. Counc. Univ. Salford.

COURTMAN, Simon Paul 16 Roots Lane, Wickham Bishop, Witham CM8 3LS — BM BS 1991 Nottm.

COURTNEY, Aisling Elisabeth 6 Willow Bank, Ballynahinch BT24 8TL Tel: 01238 564947 — MB BCh 1998 Belf.; MB BCh Belf 1998.

COURTNEY, Carol Ann 2/R, 116 Dundrennan Road, Glasgow G42 9SH — MB ChB 1996 Glas.

COURTNEY, Christopher Hamish 28 Ashburn, Ballynahinch BT24 8DQ — MB BCh BAO 1992 Belf.

COURTNEY, David, OStJ Occupational Health Unit, 151 Belfast Road, Carrickfergus BT38 8PL Tel: 028 9070 0718 Fax: 028 9070 0731 — MB BCh BAO 1971; MD Belf. 1979; MRCGP 1977; FFOM RCPI 1984, M 1979; FFOM RCP Lond. 1991, M 1979; Spec. Accredit. Occupat. Med. JCHMT 1979; DIH Eng. 1978; DObst RCOG 1973; FRCPI 1997; FRCP 1999. Med. Adviser PANI. Socs: Soc. Of Occup. Med.; Ulster Med. Soc. Prev: Med. Off. Standard Telephones & Cable Ltd.

COURTNEY, Mr David John Oral & Maxillofacial Surgery Department, Derriford Hospital, Plymouth Tel: 01752 763209 Email: djc@facial-surgery.com — BM 1992 Soton.; BDS Bristol 1986; FRCS 1995 (OMFS). (University of Southampton) Cons. Oral & Maxillofacial Surg., Derriford Hosp.; Cons. Oral & Maxillofacial Surg., Nuffield Hosp., Plymouth. Socs: Brit. Assn. of Head & Neck Oncol.; Brit. Assn. of Oral & Maxillofacial Surg.; Brit. Med. Assn. Prev: Sen. Reg. O & M Surg., S. W.ern Rotat.

COURTNEY, Diana Bowyer Woodchurch Road Surgery, 270 Woodchurch Road, Prenton, Birkenhead CH43 5UU Tel: 0151 608 3475 — MB ChB 1970 Liverp. Socs: Liverp. Med. Inst.; Birkenhead Med. Soc.

COURTNEY, Edward Douglas James 48 Navigation Way, Victoria Dock, Hull HU9 1SW — MB ChB 1996 Leeds.

COURTNEY, Elaine 61 The Ferns, Lostock Hall, Preston PR5 5QT — MB ChB 1991 Manch. Doctor Medico-Legal Consultancy Gloucester. Prev: SHO (Gen. Med. & A & E) Leighton Hosp. Crewe; SHO (A & E) Roy. Albert Edwd. Infirm. Wigan.

COURTNEY, Elaine Margaret 51 St Agatha Road, Heath, Cardiff CF14 4EA — MB BCh BAO 1978 Belf.; DRCOG 1980.

COURTNEY, Hugh Adair (retired) Tabgha, 17 Coldstream Avenue, Leven KY8 5TN Tel: 01333 429034 — MB BCh BAO 1948 Belf.; FRCGP 1971; DObst RCOG 1951. Prev: Hosp. Pract. (Geriat.) Cameron Hosp. Windygates.

COURTNEY, James Ronald Priory Surgery, 26 High Street, Holywood BT18 9AD Tel: 028 9042 6991 Fax: 028 9042 3643; 2 Croft Manor, Holywood BT18 0QD Tel: 01232 428304 Email: courtney@priory.dnet.co.uk — MB BCh BAO 1981 Belf.; MRCGP 1986; DRCOG 1984. Socs: BMA; Ulster Med. Soc. Prev: Trainee GP St.field; SHO (Paediat.) Roy. Belf. Hosp. Sick Childr.; SHO (Psychiat.) Craigavon Hosp.

COURTNEY, Jayne Margaret Academy Street Surgery, 2 Academy Street, Hurlford, Kilmarnock KA1 5BU Tel: 01563 525314 Fax: 01563 573561; 9 Howard Street, Kilmarnock KA1 2BP — MB ChB 1980 Glas.; MRCGP 1984; DRCOG 1983.

COURTNEY, Julia Margaret 6 Willow Bank, Ballynahinch BT24 8TL — MB BCh BAO 1996 Belf.

COURTNEY, Mary Elizabeth Department of Psychological Medicine, Barnsley district General Hospital, Gawber Road, Barnsley S75 2EP Tel: 01226 777958; 95 Huddersfield Road, Skelmanthorpe, Huddersfield HD8 9AR Tel: 01484 866131 Email: marty.courtney&virgin.net — MB ChB 1975 Ed.; MMedSc Leeds 1983; FRCPsych 1995, M 1982; MRCGP 1979; Dip. Psychother. Leeds. 1985; MA Leeds 1997. Cons. Psychiat. Barnsley DGH. Prev: Cons. Psychiat. St. Jas. Univ. Hosp.; Sen. Clin. Lect. Univ. Leeds.; Cons. Psychiat. Airedale Hosp. Steeton.

COURTNEY, Paul Michael Desborough House, 1 Desborough Road, Eastleigh SO50 4NY Tel: 01703 615729; 52 Hyde Street, Winchester SO23 7DY — MB ChB 1981 Manch.; MRCPsych 1988. Cons. Psychiat. Winchester HA.

COURTNEY, Philip Alexander Site 30, Hawthorn Hill, Hannahstown, Belfast BT17 0NX — MB BCh BAO 1992 Belf.

COURTNEY, Philip Arthur 1 Glenard Road, Omagh BT78 5BE — MB BCh BAO 1985 Dub.; MRCGP 1994; MICGP 1994.

COURTNEY, Philip Terence The Surgery, Marlpits Road, Honiton EX14 2NY Tel: 01404 41141 Fax: 01404 46621; Avenhayes, Buckerell, Honiton EX14 3EH — MB BS 1976 Lond.; MRCGP 1981; DA (UK) 1986; DRCOG 1980. Prev: GP Motueka, Nelson, NZ; Trainee GP Univ. Exeter VTS; Dist. Med. Off. Rumph Dist. Hosp. Malawi, Afr.

COURTNEY, Rosemary Madeleine 35 Rickmansworth Road, Watford WD1 3AY Tel: 01923 223232 Fax: 01923 235028; 89 Parkside Drive, Watford WD17 3AY Tel: 01923 221715 — MB ChB 1970 Bristol; DObst RCOG 1972. (Bristol) Prev: GP Abbots Langley.

COURTNEY, Mr Stephen Philip Royal Berkshire Hospital, London Road, Reading RG1 5AN Tel: 0118 987 7418 Fax: 0118 987 7881; 36 Pound Lane, Sonning, Reading RG4 6GG Tel: 0118 969 5110 Fax: 0118 969 8351 Email: steve.courtney@cmcom.net — MB BCh 1978 Wales; MCh Wales 1990; FRCS (Gen.) 1993; FRCS Eng. 1983; FRCS Ed. 1983. Cons. Surg. (BrE. & Endocrine Surg.) Roy. Berks. Hosp. Reading. Socs: Brit. Assn. Surgic. Oncol.; Eur. Soc. Mastol.; Brit. Assn. Endocrin. Surgs. Prev: Sen. Regist. Rotat. (Surg.) Bangor & Cardiff; Regist. (Surg.) Bristol Roy. Infirm. & Frenchay Hosp. Bristol.

COURY, John Charles (retired) Green Pastures, Willow Lane, Wargrave, Reading RG10 8LH Tel: 0118 940 1407 — MB BS 1952 Lond. Prev: GP Reading.

COUSENS, Anne Rachel Wildgoose Chase, Broad St., Weobley, Hereford HR4 8SA — MB ChB 1995 Manch.

COUSIN, Mr Gary Craig Smith 18 Vale Coppice, Ramsbottom, Bury BL0 9FJ Email: gcscousin@rcsed.ac.uk — MB ChB 1993 Glas.; BDS Glas. 1985; FRCS Ed. 1996; FDS RCS Ed. 1989; FRCS 2000. Sen. Regist. (Oral & Maxillofacial Surg.) Manch.Roy.Infirm.; Hon. Doc. Bury Rangers Jun. FC. Socs: BMA; Jun. Fell. Brit. Assn. Oral & Maxillofacial Surg.; Train. Mem. Euro. Assc. Cranio-Maxillofacial.Surg. (EACMFS). Prev: Basic Surgic. Trainee Roy. Oldham Hosp. & Bury NHS Trust; Sen. Regist. (Oral & Maxillofacial Surg.) E. Lancs. Maxillofacial Serv. Blackburn Roy. Infirm.; Sen. Regist. (Oral & Maxillofacial Surg.) N. Manch. Gen. Hosp.

COUSINS, Anna Louise Orchard Cross, Stonegate, Whixley, York YO26 8AS — MB ChB 1990 Dundee.

COUSINS, Bernard Andrew (retired) West Hill, Victoria Road, Douglas IM2 6AQ Tel: 01624 622057 — MB BCh BAO 1941 NUI; MSc (Biochem.) NUI 1943, MD 1954; MRCGP 1962; Cert Av Med. 1980. Prev: Authorised Med. Examr. Civil Aviat. Auth.

COUSINS, Cecil Herbert (retired) 90 Humber Avenue, South Ockendon RM15 5JN Tel: 01708 856243 — MB 1938 Calcutta. Prev: Gen. Pract. - Essex.

COUSINS, Christine Gillian 37 Kings Avenue, Poole BH14 9QG — MB ChB 1973 Bristol; FFA RCS Eng. 1978.

COUSINS, Claire 9 Carisbrooke Avenue, Burton Pastures, Gedling, Nottingham NG4 2RD — BM BS 1984 Nottm.; BM BS Nottm. l984; MRCP (UK) 1987; FRCR 1990. Cons. Radiol. Hammersmith Hosp. Lond.

COUSINS, Michael Antony 12 Burnside, Kinloss, Forres IV36 3XL — MB ChB 1982 Leeds.

COUSINS, Paul Grovehurst Surgery, Grovehurst Road, Kemsley, Sittingbourne ME10 2ST Tel: 01795 430444 Fax: 01795 410539; 6 Hadleigh Court, Hempstead, Gillingham ME7 3SW — MB BS Lond. 1986; MRCGP 1992; DRCOG 1991.

COUSLAND, Gary Department of Psychiatry, Southern General Hospital, 1345 Govan Road, Glasgow G51 4TF; 17 Forth Road, Glasgow G61 1JT — MB ChB 1987 Dundee; PhD Ed. 1983; BSc Microbiol.) Hons. Glas. 1980. SHO (Psychiat.) S. Glas. Train. Scheme.

COUSLEY, Florence Mavis Braeyside, 17 Cookstown Road, Moneymore, Magherafelt BT45 7QF Tel: 01648 48209 — MB BCh BAO 1953 Belf.; DObst RCOG 1955. (Belf.) SCMO (Cervical Cytol & Family Plann.); Cookstown Magherafelt Dist.; Med. Off. Cervical Cytol. Dungannon Dist. Prev: Ho. Off. Roy. Vict. Hosp. Belf. & Roy. Matern. Hosp. Belf.; Med. Off. Cervical Cytol. Clinics (Tyrone Co. Health; Comm.).

COUTINHO, Elias Joseph 6 St,. Mary's Road, Bexley DA5 — MB BS 1960 Madras.

COUTINHO, Maria de Lourdes Pamela Medical Practice, 58 Roman Way, London N7 8XF Tel: 020 7607 7502 — MB ChB Aberd. 1963; BSc Bombay 1956; DTM & H Liverp. 1965. (Aberd.) p/t GP Princip.; Med. Mem. for the InDepend. Tribunal Serv. Prev: Community Med. Off. Hampstead HA; Regist. (Infec. Dis.) Coppetts Wood Hosp. Lond.; Regist. (Paediat.) Whittington Hosp. Lond.

COUTINHO, Melchiades Christopher Arnold Royal Preston Hospital, Sharoe Green Lane, Fulwood, Preston PR2 9HT — MB BS

1974 Bangalore; FRCR 1986; DMRD Lond. 1983. Cons. Radiol. Roy. Preston Hosp.

COUTS, Ben (retired) 121a Rosebank, Guisborough Road, Nunthorpe, Middlesbrough TS7 0JD Tel: 01642 315546 — MD Glas. 1947, MB ChB 1937; DPH Glas. 1940. Prev: Chest Phys. S. Tees (Middlesbrough) Health Dist.

COUTTS, Alan Stuart Four Oaks Medical Centre, Carlton House, Mere Green Road, Sutton Coldfield B75 5BS Tel: 0121 308 2080 Fax: 0121 323 4694; 145 Mere Green Road, Sutton Coldfield B75 5DD — MB ChB 1981 Liverp.; MRCGP 1986.

COUTTS, Mr Alastair Gordon Gilbert Bain Hospital, Lerwick ZE1 0TB Tel: 01595 5678; Marovo, 17 Sandy Loch Drive, Lerwick ZE1 0SR Tel: 01595 2242 — MB ChB 1973 Dundee; FRCS Ed. 1979. Cons. Surg. Gilbert Bain Hosp. Lerwick.

COUTTS, Elizabeth Helena Anne South Road Health Centre, 19 South Road, Lerwick ZE1 0RB Tel: 01595 693201 Fax: 01595 697113; Marovo, 17 Sandy Loch Drive, Lerwick ZE1 0SR Tel: 01595 2242 — MB ChB 1973 Aberd.; DRCOG 1975.

COUTTS, Fiona Stenhouse Medical Centre, 66 Furlong Street, Arnold, Nottingham NG5 7BP Tel: 0115 967 3877 Fax: 0115 967 3838; 12 Mapperley Orchard, Arnold, Nottingham NG5 8AG — MB ChB 1968 Aberd.; DObst RCOG 1970. (Aberd.)

COUTTS, Gillian Mary The Surgery, 5 Enys Road, Eastbourne BN21 2DQ Tel: 01323 410088 Fax: 01323 644638; 12 Park Avenue, Eastbourne BN22 9QN Tel: 01323 504429 — MB BS 1987 Lond.; Cert Family Plann. JCC 1992. Prev: Trainee GP E.bourne VTS.

COUTTS, Ian Ingram Penair Vean, St. Clement, Truro TR1 1TD Tel: 01872 241326 — MB ChB 1972 Liverp.; MD Liverp. 1982; FRCP Lond. 1992; MRCP (UK) 1975. Cons. Phys. Roy. Cornw. Hosp. Treliske Truro.

COUTTS, James Francis 81 High Street, Botley, Southampton SO30 2ES — BM BCh 1989 Oxf.; MRCP (UK) 1993.

COUTTS, Jonathan Alexander Phillips Paediatric Department, Queen Mother's Hospital, Yorkhill, Glasgow G3 8SJ Tel: 0141 201 0532 Fax: 0141 201 0524 Email: jonathan.coutts@yorkhill.scot.nhs.uk; Tel: 0141 956 5420 — MB ChB 1984 Glas.; MRCP (UK) 1988. (Univ. Glas.) Cons. Neonat. Paediat., Qu. Mother's Hosp. Yorkhill Glas.; Hon. Clin. Sen. Lect. (Child Health) Univ. Glas. Socs: Scott. Paediat. Soc.; Fell. Roy.Coll. Phys.s (Glas.); FRCPCH. Prev: Sen. Regist. (Paediat.) Roy. Hosp. Sick Childr. Glas.; Lect. (Paediat.) Univ. Hong Kong; Neonat. Fell. Univ. Brit. Columbia Vancouver, Canada.

COUTTS, Marjorie Annette Barnardos New Families Project, 54 Head St., Colchester CO1 1PB Tel: 01206 562438; Street Cottage, The Hill, Polstead, Colchester CO6 5AH Tel: 01206 263405 — MB ChB Bristol 1961. Med. Adviser Barnardo's New Families Project Colchester. Prev: Ho. Phys. Frenchay Hosp. Bristol.

COUTTS, Michael Anthony Department of Histopathology, King's College Hospital, Bessemer Road, Denmark Hill, London SE5 9RS; Gabwell Court, Lower Gabwell, Stokeinteignhead, Newton Abbot TQ12 4QS Email: mikecou@hotmail.com — MB BS 1993 Lond.; MA (Hons.) Oxf. 1990; Dip RCPath Lond.1998. (Oxford and St. Bartholomew's) Specialist Regist. (Histopath.) King's Coll. Hosp. Lond.

COUTTS, Norman Alexander (retired) 1 Elm Gardens, Bearsden, Glasgow G61 3BH Tel: 0141 942 7194 — MB ChB 1958 Glas.; BSc (Hons. Physiol.) Glas. 1955; FRCP Lond. 1982, M 1967; FRCP Ed. 1978, M 1966; FRCP Glas. 1974, M 1965; DCH Eng. 1961.

COUTTS, Sheila Rachel Jane 12 Mapperley Orchard, Arnold, Nottingham NG5 8AG — MB ChB 1996 Ed.; BSc MedSci 1993. (Ed.) SHO (Med.) Roy. Infirm. Edin.

COUTTS, Shelagh Brown 7 Spence Street, Glasgow G20 0AW — MB ChB 1997 Ed.

COUTTS, Shiona Murray 7 Spence Street, Glasgow G20 0AW — MB ChB 1998 Ed.; MB ChB Ed 1998; BSc 1995. (Edinburgh) SHO (O & G), Roy. Infirm. of Edin.

COUTTS, Vera Cecile (retired) 20 Spens Crescent, Perth PH1 1PE — MB ChB 1953 Aberd.; MFCM 1972; DPH St. And. 1959. Prev: SCMO Fife HB.

COUTTS, William Ernest 24 Albany Road, Cardiff CF24 3YY — MB ChB 1937 Aberd.; MA, MB ChB Aberd. 1937. (Aberd.) Prev: Squadron Ldr. RAFVR.

COVE, David Hugh Dorset County Hospital, Dorchester DT1 2JY Tel: 01308 251150; Duffryn, 1 Herringston Road, Dorchester DT1 2BS Tel: 01308 265239 Email: david.cove@dorch.wdgh-tr — MB ChB 1972 Birm.; BSc (Hons.) Birm. 1969, MD 1980; FRCP Lond. 1988, M 1975. (Birmingham) Cons. Phys. Dorset Co. Hosp. Weymouth & Dist. Hosp. Socs: Roy. Soc. Med.; RCP; Diabetics UK. Prev: Roy. Coll. of Phys.s, Wessex, Regional Afdvisor; Sen. Regist. (Med.) Dudley Rd. Hosp. Birm.; Sheldon Research Fell. & Hon. Regist. (Med.) Qu. Eliz. Hosp.

COVE, Peter, OStJ, TD (retired) Peter Cove OStJ FDS RCS LRCP LRCS, Consultant Maxillofacial Surgeon, Alne Cross, York YO61 1SD Tel: 01347 838346 — LRCPI & LM, LRSCI & LM 1971; LRCPI & LM, LRCSI & LM 1971; FDS RCS Eng. 1967; FFD RCSI 1967. Prev: Rotating Sen. Regist. (Oral Surg.) Guy's Hosp. & Qu. Vict. Hosp. E. Grinstead.

COVE, Richard David 1 Herringston Road, Dorchester DT1 2BS — MB ChB 1998 Bristol.

COVE-SMITH, John Rodney James Cook University Hospital, Middlesbrough TS4 3BW Tel: 01642 850850; Kirby House, Kirby-in-Cleveland, Middlesbrough TS9 7AN Tel: 01642 712618 — MB BChir 1968 Camb.; MA Camb. 1968, MD 1979; FRCP Lond. 1983; MRCP (UK) 1972; FRCP 2000 Edinburgh. (St. Thos.) Cons. Phys. & Nephrol. S. Tees Acute Hosp. Trust; Hon. Clin. Lect. Univ. Newc.; Assoc. Med. Dir. S. Tees Hosp. NHS Trust; Chief of Serv., Acad. Div., S.Tees Hosp. NHS Trust. Socs: BMA; Renal Assn.; Brit. Transpl.ation Soc. Prev: Sen. Regist. (Med.) Nottm. & Guy's Hosp. Lond.; Regist. (Med.) Nottm. City Hosp.; Roy Coll. Of Phys.s Reg. Adviser, N. Region.

COVE-SMITH, Penelope Ann Stanbury, 76 Shinfield Road, Reading RG2 7DA Tel: 0118 954 7676 — MB BS Lond. 1961; MRCS Eng. LRCP Lond. 1961; DObst RCOG 1962. (King's Coll. Hosp.) Assoc. Specialist Paediat. Dept. Roy. Berks. Hosp. Reading. Prev: Ho. Phys. (Neurosurg. & Paediat.) Whittington Hosp. Lond.; Ho. Phys. (Diabetic) King's Coll. Hosp.

COVELL, Brian 26 Westwood Avenue, Kendal LA9 5BB Tel: 01539 737049 — MB ChB Ed. 1968; MFCM RCP (UK) 1979; Dip. Soc. Med. Ed. 1973. Med. Off. St. And. Ambul. Assn. Edin. Prev: Lect. Dunfermline Coll. Phys. Educat. Edin.; Sen. Regist. (Community Med.) Lothian HB; Med. Off. Health Dept. Edin.

COVELL, Bruce Robert Parkbury House Surgery, St. Peters Street, St Albans AL1 3HD Tel: 01727 851589 — MB BS 1981 Lond.; DA Eng. 1984; DRCOG 1983; MRCGP 1998; PGCE 1998. (Royal London Hospital) GP; Clin. Asst. (c/o Elderly) St. Albans.; GP Trainer.

COVELL, Kenneth John (retired) 19 Longs Field, North Curry, Taunton TA3 6NN Tel: 01823 490039 — MB BS 1949 Lond.; MRCS Eng. LRCP Lond. 1947; FFA RCS Eng. 1964; DTM & H Eng. 1952, DA 1955. Prev: Cons. Anaesth. Som. HA.

COVELL, Robert Gordon c/o GPO, Lymington — MRCS Eng. LRCP Lond. 1950; BA (Hons.) Camb. 1946, MB 1974, BChir 1973; FFCM 1985; DPH Lond. 1961. (Camb. & Lond. Hosp.) Sen. Research Fell. Dept. Med. Roy. infirm. Edin.; Clin. Researcher Communicable Dis. (Scotl.) Centre Ruchill Hosp. Glas. Prev: Sen. Med. Off. Scott. Home & Health Dept.; Gp. Capt. RAF Med. Br.; Orthop. Ho. Surg., Ho. Phys. & Receiv. Room Off. Lond. Hosp.

COVELL, Tracey 2 Hamstead Meadow, Chidham, Chichester PO18 8TJ — BM 1991 Soton.; DRCOG 1996; DFFP 1996. GP Regist. Hants. Socs: Med. Protec. Soc.; BMA. Prev: Med. Off. Bay of Is.s Hosp., New Zealand; SHO (O & G) St. Richard's Hosp. Chichester; SHO (A & E) St. Richard's Hosp. Chichester.

COVENTRY, Claire Louise 34 Leegomery Road, Wellington, Telford TF1 3BP — MB BS 1990 Lond. SHO (A & E) P.ss Roy. Hosp. Telford.

COVENTRY, David MacDonald Department of Anaesthesia, Ninewells Hospital, Dundee DD1 9SY Tel: 01382 60111 — MB ChB 1981 Aberd.; FFARCS Eng. 1985. Cons. Anaesth. Ninewells Hosp. Dundee. Prev: Regist. (Anaesth.) Vict. Infirm. Glas.

COVENTRY, Keith (retired) 1 Alde House, Alde House Drive, Aldeburgh IP15 5EE Tel: 01728 453679 — MB BChir 1953 Camb.; DObst RCOG 1954. Prev: Obst. Ho. Surg. St. Thos. Hosp. Lond.

COVENTRY, Peter John 2 Besford Square, Belle Vue Road, Shrewsbury SY3 7PG — MB BS 1990 Lond.; MRCGP (UK) 1993; DRCOG 1995. GP Regist. Telford Shrops.

COVENTRY, Stanley William James (retired) The Bungalow, Kenstone Hodnet, Market Drayton TF9 3JL — MB ChB 1950 Liverp.

COVERLEY, Carolyn Teresa Child & Family Service, 14 Byron Road, St Helier, Jersey JE2 4LQ Tel: 01534 89861 Fax: 01534 280079 Email: family@ih.net; Le Hurel, La Rue de Cambrai, Trinity, Jersey JE3 5AL — BM BCh 1981 Wales; MRCPsych 1986. Cons. Child & Adolesc. Psychiat. States of Jersey Health & Social Servs. Prev: Cons. Child & Adolesc. Psychaitrist Tameside & Glossop Community & Priority Servs. NHS Trust; Sen. Regist. (Child & Adolesc. Psychiat.) N. W.. RHA; SHO & Regist. (Psychiat.) Exeter HA.

COVERLEY, Stuart Robson 20 Culme Road, Mannamead, Plymouth PL3 5BJ Tel: 01752 662972 Fax: 01752 662972 — BM BCh Oxf. 1957; MA Oxf. 1955; MRCS Eng. LRCP Lond. 1956. (Oxf. & St. Thos.) Socs: Plymouth Med. Soc. & BMA. Prev: Ho. Phys. & Ho. Surg. S. Devon & E. Cornw. Hosp. Plymouth; Ho. Surg. (Obst.) Herts. & Essex Gen. Hosp. Bishop's Stortford.

COVINGTON, Anne Elizabeth Bishop's Lodge, 1 Folly Court, Sibford Ferris, Banbury OX15 5RH Tel: 01295 780734 — MB ChB 1980 Sheff.; MRCGP 1984; Cert. Community Paediat. Warwick 1989; DCH RCP Lond. 1987; DRCOG 1983; DFFP 1998. (Sheffield University)

COVINS, Christopher Mark The Surgery, Fordyce Memorial Institute, Gardenstown, Banff AB45 3YJ; 3 High Shore, Macduff AB44 1SL — MB ChB 1985 Birm.; MRCGP 1992.

COWAN, Mr Andrew Robert 10 Cotsalls, Botley Road, Eastleigh SO50 7HP Tel: 01703 601226 Email: andrew@vascsurg.freeserve.co.uk; 64 Park Road, Hale, Altrincham WA15 9LG Tel: 0161 980 6891 — MB BS 1987 Lond.; FRCS Eng. 1993; FRCS (Gen. Surg.) 1999. (Roy. Free Hosp. Sch. Med.) Regist. Rotat. Wessex Post Fell.sh. Prev: Regist. & SHO (Cardiothoracic Surg.) St. Bart. Hosp. Lond.; SHO (A & E) Newham Gen. Hosp. Lond.; SHO Rotat. (Surg.) Derriford Hosp. Plymouth.

COWAN, Bevyl Bruce Rake House, Burton, South Wirral CH64 5TE — MB ChB 1949 Ed. (Ed.) JP; Mem. Liverp. Med. Inst. Prev: Clin. Med. Off. Wirral HA; Ho. Phys. & Ho. Surg. Roy. Liverp. Childr. Hosp.; Clin. Asst. Dept. Psychol. Med. Roy. Liverp. Childr. Hosp.

COWAN, Catherine Ann 75 Montrose Drive, Bearsden, Glasgow G61 3LF — MB ChB 1976 Ed.; DRCOG 1978. Clin. Asst. (Geriat.) Drumchapel Hosp. Glas.

COWAN, Catherine Lesley Highfield Health Centre, 2 Proctor Street, off Tong Street, Bradford BD4 9QA Tel: 01274 227700 Fax: 01274 227900; 51 Creskeld Lane, Bramhope, Leeds LS16 9EP — BM BCh 1977 Oxf.; DRCOG 1981; DCH Eng. 1979. Prev: GP Gateshead; Trainee GP Banbury VTS.

COWAN, Catriona Department of Pathology, Western General Hospital, Crewe Road, Edinburgh EH4 2XU Tel: 0131 537 1962 — MB ChB 1991 Glas.; MRCPath 1999; BSc (Hons.) Glas. 1988. Cons., Path. Dept., W.. Gen. Hosp., Edin. Prev: Specialist Regist. (Path.), Glas. Roy. Infirm.; SHO (Path.) Glas. Roy. Infirm.

COWAN, Colin Bruce All Saints Hospital, Lodge Road, Hockley, Birmingham B18 5SD — MB ChB 1984 Glas.; BSc Glas. 1981, MB ChB 1984.

COWAN, Constance Margaret (retired) 7 West Road, Emsworth PO10 7JT Tel: 01243 373147 — BM BCh Oxf. 1942; MA Oxf. 1942; MFCM 1974; DCH Eng. 1951; DObst RCOG 1946. Prev: SCM (Child Health) W. Sussex HA & Croydon HA.

COWAN, Craig McCallum Flat 6, 59 Parkfield Road, Aigburth, Liverpool L17 4LE — MB ChB 1994 Liverp.

COWAN, Mr David Lockhart 14 Moray Place, Edinburgh EH3 7DT Tel: 0131 225 4843 Fax: 0131 225 6749; Kellerstane House, Gogar Station Road, Edinburgh EH12 9BS Tel: 0131 339 0293 — MB ChB Ed. 1965; FRCS Ed. 1970. (Ed.) Cons. Surg. (ENT) Roy. Hosp. Sick Childr. Edin., W.. Gen. Hosp. Edin. & City Hosp. Edin.; Hon. Sen. Lect. Dept. Otolaryngol. Univ. Edin. Socs: Roy. Soc. Med.; Brit. Assoc. of OtoLaryngol. Head & Neck Surg.; Scott. Otolaryngol. Soc. Prev: Cons. Surg. (ENT) Bangour Gen. Hosp. Broxburn; Sen. Regist. (ENT) City Hosp. Edin.; Ho. Phys. & Ho. Surg. Roy. Infirm. Edin.

COWAN, Denis Leventon 22 Caroline Place, London W2 4AN Tel: 020 7229 1671 Fax: 020 7229 2671 — MB BCh BAO 1951 Dub.; MA Dub. 1953, MB BCh BAO 1951; LAH Dub. 1950; MFOM RCP Lond. 1983. (T.C. Dub.) Socs: Fell. Inst. Pub. Health & Hyg.; MPS Irel.; Fell. Roy. Soc. Health. Prev: Apptd. Fact. Doctor; Mem. Bd. Governors Hosps. for Dis. of Chest.

COWAN, Derek 7 Westfield Court, Mirfield WF14 9PT — MB BS 1961 Durh.; MB BS Lond. 1961; BSc Durham. 1964. Cons. Dermat. Huddersfield Roy. Infirm.

COWAN, Mr Dickinson Bergius Portland Hospital, 214 Great Portland St., London W1W 5QT Tel: 020 7390 8433 Fax: 020 7383 4162 Email: j.beckerleg@uk.medsecs.co.uk or ww.doctorcowan.co.uk — BM BCh Oxf. 1970; FRCS Ed. 1976; FRCOG 1992, M 1976. Med. Dir. Fertil. Unit Portland Hosp. Lond.; Cons. Obst. & Gyn. Portland Hosp. Lond. Socs: Fell. Roy. Soc. Med.; Brit. Fertil. Soc. Prev: Cons. Gyn. Bourn Hall Clinic Camb.; Cons. O & G Edw. VIII Hosp. Durban, SA; Sen. Regist. (O & G) St. Bart. Hosp. Lond.

COWAN, Dilys Ann Ampthill Square Medical Centre, 219 Evershott Street, London NW1 1DE Tel: 020 7387 6161 Fax: 020 7387 0420 — MB BS 1976 Lond.; BSc Lond. 1973; MRCP (UK) 1979; MRCGP 1987. Prev: Regist. (Clin. Haemat.) Univ. Coll Hosp. Lond.; Rotating SHO (Med.) Whittington Hosp. Lond.; Ho. Phys. & Ho. Surg. Ipswich & E. Suff. Hosp.

COWAN, Elizabeth Margaret McMurray 85 Farquhar Road, Edgbaston, Birmingham B15 2QP Tel: 0121 454 2584 — MB ChB 1955 Ed.; DObst RCOG 1959; DPH Lond. 1960.

COWAN, Elizabeth Williamson Hunter Whitaker Road No.2, Coventry CV5 9JE; Holmby House, 8 Eastnor Grove, Leamington Spa CV31 1LD Tel: 01926 339203 — MB ChB 1980 Manch.; MRCGP 1984; DRCOG 1984. (St. Andrews and Manchester) GP Coventry.

COWAN, Ephraim Brodie (retired) 5A Fairfield Court, Eaglesham Road, Clarkston, Glasgow G76 7YG Tel: 0141 644 4900 — LRCP LRCS Ed. LRFPS Glas. 1946; FBOA 1964; Dip. Inst. Optic Sc. Glas. 1950. Director of Exams. Assn. Contact Lens Practs. Prev: Tutor Postgrad. Contact Lens Pract. Stow Coll. Glas.

COWAN, Mr Eric Cecil 27 Cultra Ave, Holywood BT18 0AZ Tel: 02890 423311 Fax: 02890 425224 — MB BCh BAO 1952 Belf.; PhD Belf. 1994, LLM 1993; MCh Belf. 1972; FRCS Ed. 1959; FRCSI 1981; FACS 1977; DLITT 1995. (Qu. Univ. Belf.) Socs: Fell. Roy. Soc. Med.; Ophth. Soc. UK; Fell. Int. Soc. Refractive Surg. Prev: Cons. Ophth. Surg. Roy. Vict. Hosp. Belf. City Hosp.; Sen. Regist. Benn Hosp. Belf.; Regist. Corneo-Plastic Unit Qu. Vict. Hosp. E. Grinstead.

COWAN, Fiona Jane Dept. of Paediatrics, Southmead Hospital, Westbury-on-Trym, Bristol BS10 5NB Tel: 0117 959 5327 Fax: 0117 959 5282 Email: cowan_fj@hotmail.com — MB BCh 1986 Wales; MRCP (UK) 1992; MRCGP (Distinc.) 1991; DCH RCP Lond. 1990. (University of Wales College of Medicine) Cons. (Paediat.), S.mead Hosp., Bristol. Prev: Sen. Regist. (Paediat.) Univ. Hosp. Wales Cardiff; Regist. (Paediat.) S.mead Hosp. Bristol; SHO (Paediat.) Bristol Childr. Hosp.

COWAN, Fiona Mary Central Surgery, Sussex Road, Gorleston-on-Sea, Great Yarmouth NR31 6QB Tel: 01493 414141 Fax: 01493 656253 Email: 106144.41@compuserve.com; Oaklands, Priory Road, St. Olaves, Great Yarmouth NR31 9HQ Tel: 01493 488626 — MB ChB Glas. 1966; DObst RCOG 1969.

COWAN, Frances Mary Department of Sexually Transmitted Diseases, University College London, Gower St., London WC1E 6BT Tel: 020 7380 9300 Ext: 9893 Email: fcowan@gum.ucl.ac.uk — MB BS 1984 Lond.; FRCPE 2000; FRCP 2001; MSc Epidemiol. Lond. 1990; MRCP (UK) 1987; MD 1995. (Med. Coll. of St Bart's Hosp.) Hon. Cons. & Sen. Lect. (Genitourin. Med.) Univ. Coll. Med. Sch. Lond. Socs: Roy. Coll. Phys. Edin. & Med. Soc. Study VD. Prev: Lect. (Genitourin. Med.) UCL; Research Fell. (Infec. Dis.) City Hosp. Edin.; Regist. (Med. & Genitourin. Med.) St. Thos. Hosp. Lond.

COWAN, Frances Mary Department of Paediatrics, Imperial College School of Medicine, Hammersmith Hospital, London W12 0HS Tel: 020 8743 2030 Fax: 020 8740 8281; 107 College Road, Isleworth TW7 5DP — MB BS 1972 Lond.; PhD Oslo 1987; MRCP (UK) 1975; LRCPI & LM, LRCSI & LM 1972; MRCGP 1982; DCH Eng. 1976. Sen. Lect. & Hons. Cons. Paediat. Hammersmith Hosp. Lond. Prev: Neonat. Research Fell. Hammersmith Hosp. Lond. & Oslo; Lect. (Neonat. Phys.) Lond. Hosp. Whitechapel.

COWAN, George Osborne, OBE, OStJ, Maj.-Gen. late RAMC Retd. JCHMT, 5 St Andrews Place, Regent's Park, London NW1 4LB Tel: 0207 935 1174 Ext: 439 Fax: 0207 692 3383 — MB ChB 1963 St. And.; FRCP Lond. 1983, M 1967; FRCP Ed. 1978, M

1967; DTM & H Eng. 1968. p/t Med Dir JCHMT; Cohen Lect. Univ. Liverp. 1991. Socs: Roy. Soc. Trop. Med. & Hyg. (Ex-Pres.); Brit. Soc. Gastroenterol. Prev: Commandant Roy. Army Med. Coll.; Prof. Milit. Med. RAMC; Postgrad. Dean N. Thames.

COWAN, James Campbell Department of Cardiology, Leeds General Infirmary, Great George St., Leeds LS1 3EX Tel: 0113 392 2643 Fax: 0113 392 3981; 51 Creskeld Lane, Bramhope, Leeds LS16 9EP — BM BCh 1980 Oxf.; DPhil Oxf. 1978, MA 1978; FRCP Lond. 1995; T(M) 1991. Cons. Cardiol. Leeds Gen. Infirm. Prev: Sen. Lect. & Lect. (Cardiovasc. Studies) Univ. Leeds; Squibb Cardiovasc. Research Fell. Freeman Hosp. Newc.; Regist. (Cardiol.) & SHO (Gen. Med.) Freeman Hosp. Newc.

COWAN, James Temple Firrhill Medical Centre, 167 Colinton Mains Drive, Edinburgh EH13 9AF Tel: 0131 441 3119 Fax: 0131 441 4122; Torcraik House, North Middleton, Gorebridge EH23 4QX — MB ChB 1979 Ed.

COWAN, Jane Royal Edinburgh Hospital, Morningside Terrace, Edinburgh EH10 5HF; 21, Chalybeate, Haddington, Edinburgh EH41 4NX Tel: 0162 082 4958 — MB ChB Aberd. 1994; MRCP 1999. Adolesc. Psych. Young Peoples Unit Roy. Edin. Hosp.. Socs: Inceptor Roy. Coll. Psychiat. Prev: SHO Child Psychiat. Edin. Sick Childr.s. Hosp.; SHO (Psychiat. Old Age) Roy. Edin. Hosp.; SHO (Gen. Adult Psychiat.) Rosslynlee Hosp.

COWAN, Jean Bowman 4 Raughmere Court, Lavant, Chichester PO18 0DT — MB ChB 1945 Glas.; DObst RCOG 1948. (Glas.)

COWAN, John Balfour 4 Norwood Drive, Whitecraigs, Glasgow G46 7LR Tel: 0141 638 9921 — MB ChB 1965 Glas. (Glas.)

COWAN, John Duncan 8 Carpenters Wood Drive, Chorleywood, Rickmansworth WD3 5RJ — MB BS 1968 Newc.; MRCGP 1979; DObst RCOG 1971. (Newc.) Prev: Assoc. Med. Dir. E.L.W.A. Hosp. Monrovia Liberia; SHO (Paediat.) MusGr. Pk. Hosp. Taunton; Ho. Surg. (O & G) Roy. Vict. Hosp. Bournemouth.

COWAN, John Francis (retired) Laurel Cottage, School Road, Erpingham, Norwich NR11 7QY Tel: 01263 761553 — MB ChB 1941 Ed.

COWAN, John Frederick Eldred, MC (retired) 16 Sandykeld, 26 Manor Road, East Cliff, Bournemouth BH1 3EZ — LRCPI & LM, LRSCI & LM 1939; LRCPI & LM, LRCSI & LM 1939. Prev: Med. Off. A.R.P. Metrop. Boro. Shoreditch.

COWAN, John Livingstone (retired) 45 Victoria Road, Gorleston, Great Yarmouth NR31 6ED Tel: 01493 664128 — MRCS Eng. LRCP Lond. 1949; DTM & H Ed. 1966. Prev: GP Bradwell.

COWAN, Joseph Manuel Arnold Royal National Orthopaedic Hospital, Brockley Hill, Stanmore HA7 4LP Tel: 020 8954 2300; 28 Green Lane, Watford WD19 4NJ Tel: 01923 226740 — MB ChB 1974 Glas.; MRCP (UK) 1976; FRCP 1998. Dir. (Rehabil.) Roy. Nat. Orthop. Hosp. Stanmore; Cons. Neurophys. Mt. Vernon Hosp. N.wood.

COWAN, Kenneth Alec, Col. late RAMC Retd. Chase View, Tittensor Road, Barlaston, Stoke-on-Trent ST12 9DN Tel: 0178 139 2392 — MB ChB 1953 Birm.; MRCS Eng. LRCP Lond. 1947; FFA RCS Eng. 1954; DA Eng. 1949. (Birm.) DL Co. of Staffs.; Hon. Life Fell. N. Staffs. Med. Inst. Prev: Cons. Anaesth. N. Staffs. Gp. Hosps.; Anaesth. Sen. Regist. Stoke-on-Trent Hosp. Gp.

COWAN, Margaret Macmillan Centre, Strathcathro Hospital, Brechin DD9 7QA Tel: 01674 76161 Fax: 01674 673151 — MB ChB 1984 Dundee; MRCGP 1988. (Dundee) Clin. Med. Off. Prev: GP Montrose, angus.

COWAN, Margaret Geddes (retired) 123 Craigleith Road, Edinburgh EH4 2EH Tel: 0131 332 7666 — MB ChB 1948 Aberd. Prev: Child Health Med. Off. Lothian HB.

COWAN, Margaret Smith Springfield Medical Practice, 9 Springfield Road, Bishopbriggs, Glasgow G64 1PJ Tel: 0141 772 4744 Fax: 0141 772 3035; 30 Brackenbrae Avenue, Bishopbriggs, Glasgow G64 2BW — MB ChB 1976 Glas.; MRCGP 1985; DRCOG 1978.

COWAN, Mary Gertrude Bertha Lisburn Health Centre, Linenhall Street, Lisburn BT28 1LU Tel: 028 9260 3203 Fax: 028 9250 1311; Knockrath, Fort Hill, Lisburn BT28 3BB — MB BCh BAO 1966 Dub.; MRCGP 1972; DObst RCOG 1968. Prev: SHO Lagan Valley Hosp. Lisburn; Ho. Off. Tyrone Co. Hosp. Omagh.

COWAN, Maurice Anthony (retired) 85 Farquhar Road, Edgbaston, Birmingham B15 2QP Tel: 0121 454 2584 — MRCS Eng. LRCP Lond. 1954; MD Sheff. 1965, MB ChB 1954; FRCP Lond. 1978, M 1958. Cons. Panel DHSS Med. Appeals Tribunal. Prev: Cons. Dermat. United Birm. Hosps., & E. Birm. Hosp.

COWAN, Michael Douglas 75 Montrose Drive, Bearsden, Glasgow G61 3LF — MB ChB 1971 St. And.; MRCP (UK) 1976; FRCR 1978; DMRD Eng. 1975. Cons. (Diag. Radiol.) W.. Infirm. & Kt.swood Hosp. Glas. Socs: Scott. Radiol. Soc. & Scott. Thoracic Soc. Prev: Sen. Regist. (Diag. Radiol.) Dundee Health Dist.; Regist. Gen. Med. Peel Hosp. Galashiels; Regist. Radiol. W.. Infirm. Glas.

COWAN, Michael Louis 126 Harley Street, London W1 1AH Tel: 020 7935 4797; 10 Anns Close, London SW1X 8EG — LAH Dub. 1959. (T.C. Dub.) PhC Dub. 1962; Clin. Asst. Roy. Nat. Throat, Nose & Ear Hosp. Lond.; Med. Adviser Ogilvy Benson & Mather Ltd., Assoc. Merchandising Corp.; PLN Partners, Scott. Life Assur. & other Cos.; Med. Staff BUPA Med. Centre. Socs: Anglo-Amer. Med. Soc. & BMA. Prev: Rotating Ho. Phys. & Ho. Surg. Roger Williams Gen. Hosp. Providence; R.I., U.S.A.

COWAN, Nicholas Robert Laurence South Street Doctors Surgery, South Street, Cockermouth CA13 9QP Tel: 01900 324123 Fax: 01900 324122 — MB ChB 1983 Bristol; MRCGP 1988; DRCOG 1987. (Bristol)

COWAN, Nicola Anne c/o Mr and Mrs O'Mordha, Touchwood, Hadlow Park, Tonbridge TN11 0HY — MB ChB 1988 Sheff.

COWAN, Norman Michael Cummertrees House, Marley Heights, Haslemere GU27 3LU Tel: 01428 641098 — MB ChB 1950 Ed. Socs: W Lond. M-C Soc. Prev: Ho. Phys. Roy. Infirm. Edin.

COWAN, P Jane Medical Protection Society, Granary Wharf House, Leeds LS11 5PY Tel: 0113 243 6436; 51 Handforth Road, Wilmslow SK9 2LX Tel: 01625 525465 Fax: 01625 540504 — MB BS 1980 Lond.; MRCPI 1989; DCP Sheff. 1991; DCH RCP Glas. 1988; FRCPCH 1997. (St. Geo.) Medico-Legal Adviser,Risk Managem. Serv.s. Prev: Cons.Paediat..Macclesfield,E. Chesh.NHS Trust; Med. Secretariat. MDU.

COWAN, Patrick Jonathan 59 The Oaks, West Byfleet KT14 6RW — MB ChB 1986 Sheff.

COWAN, Richard Andrew 51 Handforth Road, Wilmslow SK9 2LX Tel: 01625 525465 — MB BS 1980 Lond.; MD Lond. 1990; MRCP (UK) 1984; FRCR 1990. (Westm.) Cons. Radiother. Christie Hosp. & Holt Radium Inst. Manch. Prev: Clin. Research Fell. (Med. Oncol.) Manch.

COWAN, Russell Edgar Colchester General Hospital, Turner Road, Colchester CO4 5JL Tel: 01206 742382 Fax: 01206 742384; Rochfords, Wormingford, Colchester CO6 3AQ Tel: 01206 242264 Email: cowans@btinternet.com — MB BS 1969; MD Lond. 1979; FRCP Lond. 1989; MRCP (UK) 1972; MRCS Eng. LRCP Lond. 1969. (Guy's) Cons. Phys. & Gastroenterologist Colchester Gen. Hosp.; Mem., Bd. of Examr.s, Roy. Coll. of Phys.s, Lond.; Extern. Assessor, Roy. Coll. of Phys.s, Lond. Socs: Brit. Soc. Gastroenterol. (Previous Hon. Treas. Endoscopy Comm.); Fell.Roy. Soc. Med. (Counc. Mem. and vice-Pres., sect. Coloproctol.).; Fell. Europ. Brd. Gastroenterol. Prev: Sen. Regist. (Med.) Lond. Hosp.; MRC Clin. Research Fell. St. Thos. Hosp. Lond.; Regist. (Med.) Guy's Hosp. Lond.

COWAN, Shona 53 East London Street, Edinburgh EH7 4BW — MB ChB 1993 Aberd.; DFFP 1995. SHO (Paediat.) Neonat. Unit. Edin. Prev: SHO (O & G) E. Gen. Hosp.; SHO (O & G) Jersey; Ho. Off. (Med.) Aberd.

COWAN, Thomas Robert 14 Ryelands Park, Easington, Saltburn-by-the-Sea TS13 4PE — MB BS 1973 Newc.

COWAN, William Keith (retired) Priestfield House, Burnopfield, Newcastle upon Tyne NE16 6AF Tel: 01207 270308 — MB ChB 1950 Liverp.; PhD Newc. 1994; MD Liverp. 1961; FRCP Ed. 1971, M 1961; FRCPath 1977, M 1965. Hon. Cons. Histopath. Gateshead AHA.; Hon. Research Assoc. Path. Univ. Newc. Prev: Cons. Path. Gateshead AHA.

COWAP, Jane Alison 34 Reckitt Road, London W4 2BT — MB BCh 1988 Witwatersrand; BSc Hons. 1985, MB BCh Witwatersrand 1988.

COWAP, Nicola Anne Lee Fax: 020 7702 8023; Email: sambache@lineone.net — MB BS 1988 Lond. p/t Gen. Practioner Princip.

COWARD, Allen Edgar Brian Nadra and Partners, The Surgery, Gardden Road, Rhosllanerchrugog, Wrexham LL14 2EN Tel: 01978 840034 Fax: 01978 845782; Fair View, Cloy Lane, Overton on Dee, Wrexham LL13 0HR Tel: 01978 710063 — MB ChB 1983 Liverp. (Liverp.)

COWARD, Andrew David King's Norton Surgery, 66 Redditch Road, Kings Norton, Birmingham B38 8QS Tel: 0121 458 2550; 3 Beaks Hill Road, Birmingham B38 8BJ — MB ChB 1986 Birm.; MRCGP 1991.

COWARD, Catherine Margaret Anne King's Norton Surgery, 66 Redditch Road, Kings Norton, Birmingham B38 8QS Tel: 0121 458 2550 — MB ChB 1991 Birm.

COWARD, Frances Beth (retired) Stepgates Family Health Centre, Stepgates, Chertsey KT16 8HZ Tel: 01932 565655 — MB BS 1985 Lond.; MA Camb. 1986; MRCGP 1989; DCH RCP Lond. 1989; DRCOG 1988.

COWARD, Jeremy Health Centre, Pier Road, Tywyn LL36 0AT Tel: 01654 710238 Fax: 01654 712143 — MB BS 1988 Lond.; MRCGP 1994; DRCOG 1993; DFFP 1993; DCH RCP Lond. 1992. (Roy. Free Hosp. Sch. Med., Univ. Lond.) Clin. Asst. (A & E) Hosp. St. Cross Rugby. Socs: Assoc. Mem. Brit. Med. Acupunc. Soc.; Brit. Assn. Immed. Care Schemes; Brit. Computer Soc. (Mem. Primary Healthcare Specialist Gp.). Prev: Trainee GP Warks.

COWARD, Jermaine Ian George 12 Kirton Grove, Wolverhampton WV6 8RX — MB BS 1998 Lond.; MB BS Lond 1998.

COWARD, Lucy Jane 51 Halstow Way, Pitsea, Basildon SS13 2NY — MB BS 1997 Lond.

COWARD, Nigel Harrison J D Lansdowne and Partners, Helston Medical Centre, Trelawney Road, Helston TR13 8AU Tel: 01326 572637 Fax: 01326 565525 — MB ChB 1969 Bristol; DA Eng. 1972; DObst RCOG 1971.

COWARD, Richard John Mark 4 Kenilworth Road, Bristol BS6 6ER — MB ChB 1992 Bristol.

COWARD, Robert Alan Renal Unit, Royal Preston Hospital, Sharoe Green Lane, Preston PR2 9HT Tel: 01772 710744 Fax: 01772 710744; 18 Briksdal Way, Lostock, Bolton BL6 4PQ Tel: 01204 495569 Email: robert@rcoward.freeserve.co.uk — BM BS 1975 Nottm.; DM Nottm. 1985, BMedSci (Hons.) 1973; FRCP Ed. 1996; FRCP Lond. 1993; MRCP (UK) 1978. (Nottingham) Cons. Phys. & Nephrol. Roy. Preston Hosp. Socs: Fell. Manch. Med. Soc.; Renal Assn.; Internat. Soc. Nephrol. Prev: Sen. Regist. (Renal Med.) Roy. Hallamsh. Hosp. Sheff.; Research Fell. Manch. Roy. Infirm.; Regist. (Renal & Gen. Med.) Manch. Roy. Infirm.

COWBURN, John Edward Ridgeway Surgery, 6-8 Feckenham Road, Astwood Bank, Redditch B96 6DS Tel: 01527 892418; 1344 Evesham Road, Astwood Bank, Redditch B96 6BD Tel: 01527 892544 — MB ChB 1980 Birm.; DRCOG 1984.

COWBURN, Peter James Western Infirmary, Glasgow G11 6NT; 18 Church Lane, Romsey SO51 8EP — MB BS 1990 Newc.; MRCP (UK) 1993. Research Fell. (Cardiol.) W.. Infirm. Glas. Prev: SHO (Cardiol.) W.. Infirm. Glas.

COWBURN, Philip John 108 Panfield Lane, Braintree CM7 5RL — MB ChB 1993 Glas.

COWDEN, Fiona John Howard Unit, 2 Crozier Terrace, Hackney, London E9 6AT Tel: 020 8919 8996; 7 Lomand Road, Wemyss Bay PA18 6BE — MB ChB 1993 Glas.; MRCPsych Lond. 1998. Clin. Research Fell. Qu. Mary & W.field Coll. Univ. of Lond. Prev: Regist. (Psychiat.) Univ. Coll. Hosp. Psychiat. Train. Scheme Lond.

COWDEN, John Morton SCIEH, Clifton House, Clifton Place, Glasgow G3 7LN Tel: 0141 300 1150 Fax: 0141 300 1172 Email: jcowden@scieh.csa.scot.nhs.uk — MB ChB 1977 Sheff.; MFPHM 1989; FFPHM 1998. Cons. Epidemiol. Scott. Centre for Infec. & Environm. Health; Honory Clin. Sen. Lect. Univ. of Glas.

COWE, Alexander May (retired) — MB ChB 1958 Aberd. Prev: GP Ilkeston.

COWE, Linda The Clinic, Mill Isle, Craignair Street, Dalbeattie DG5 4HE Tel: 01556 610331; 58 Maxwell Park, Dalbeattie DG5 4LS — MB ChB 1975 Aberd.; MRCGP 1979; DCCH RCGP & FCM 1983; DRCOG 1979; DCH RCPS Glas. 1979. (Aberdeen)

COWE, Margaret Elizabeth Clifton Cottage, Kirk Yetholm, Kelso TD5 8PH Tel: 0157 382250 — MB ChB 1938 Ed. (Univ. Ed.) Prev: Ho. Surg. Elsie Inglis Matern. Hosp. Ed. & Roy. Infirm. Sunderland; Med. Regist. Stracathro E.M.S. Hosp.

COWELL, Elizabeth Wynn Mela, 27 Meiriadog Road, Old Colwyn, Colwyn Bay LL29 9NR — MB BCh 1983 Wales.

COWELL, Gordon Grant Henrietta Street Health Centre, Henrietta Street, Girvan KA26 9AN Tel: 01465 712281 Fax: 01465 712187 — MB ChB Glas. 1969; MRCGP 1974. (Glasgow) Med. Adviser Benefits Agency Med. Serv.

COWELL, Hannah 24 Deuchar Street, Jesmond, Newcastle upon Tyne NE2 1JX — MB BS 1996 Newc.

COWELL, James Malcolm Munro Medical Centre, West Elloe Avenue, Spalding PE11 2BY Tel: 01775 766181 Fax: 01775 766168; Hawthorn House, 68 Hawthorn Bank, Spalding PE11 1JQ Tel: 01775 724224 — MB ChB 1969 Glas.; Cert. Family Plann. JCC 1979; DObst RCOG 1976. (Glas.) Dep. Police Surg. Spalding Hosp. Pract. (Geriat.) Welland Hosp. Spalding. Socs: Lincoln Med. Soc.; P'boro. Med. Soc. Prev: SHO (Obst.) Qu. Mother's Hosp. Glas. & Roy. Matern. Hosp. Glas.; SHO (Gyn.) Glas. Roy. Infirm.; SHO (Surg.) Vict. Infirm. Glas.

COWELL, Marte Maria Wester Hailes Health Centre, 7 Murrayburn Gate, Edinburgh EH14 2SS Tel: 0131 537 7300 Fax: 0131 537 7337 — MB ChB 1988 Ed.; MRCGP 1995. Socs: BMA; MRCGP. Prev: SHO (Gen. Profess. Train.) St. John's at Howden, Livingston.

COWELL, Mary Alexa Clayton (retired) 33 Eaveslea, New Road, Kirkby Lonsdale, Carnforth LA6 2AB — MB ChB 1935 Manch.; MD (Commend.) Manch. 1938; FRCR 1975; FFR 1971; FFR RCSI 1963; DMR Eng. 1941. Prev: Cons. Radiotherap. Glas. W.. Infirm. & Roy. Beatson Memor. Hosp. Glas.

COWELL, Richard Pennant Wynn Wrexham Maelor Hospital, Croesnewydd Road, Wrexham LL13 7TD Tel: 01978 725134 — MB BS 1985 Lond.; BSc (Hons.) Lond. 1982; MRCP (UK) 1988; MD Lond. 1998. (Guy's Hospital) Cons. Cardiol. Wrexham Maelor Hosp. Clywd. Socs: Brit. Cardiac. Soc.; Brit. Soc. Cardiac; Pacing and Electrophysiol. (BPEG). Prev: SHO Rotat. (Gen. Med.) Guy's Hosp. Lond.; Research Fell. (Cardiol.) Harefield Hosp. Middlx.; Regist. (Cardiol.) N.wick Pk. Hosp. Lond.

COWELL, Sarah Joanna 31 Hitherwood Drive, London SE19 1XA Tel: 020 8670 5806 — BM 1991 Soton.; BSc Psychol. Soton. 1990; MRCP (UK) 1995. (Southampton University) Specialist Regist. (Geriat. & Gen. Med.); Research Fell. Cardiol. Dept. Roy. Infirm. Edin. Prev: Specialist Regist. (Geriat. & Gen. Med.) S. E. Scotl.

COWELL, Thomas Robert Wynn (retired) Mela, 27 Meiriadog Road, Old Colwyn, Colwyn Bay LL29 9NR — MB ChB 1953 Liverp. Prev: Ho. Phys., Ho. Surg. & Sen. Ho. Off. O & G Clatterbridge Hosp.

COWEN, Charles Johnstone Rose Cottage, Littel Shurdington, Shurdington, Cheltenham GL51 4TX — BM BS 1990 Nottm.; BMedSci. 1988.

COWEN, David 27 Elston Close, Chapel House Est., Newcastle upon Tyne NE5 1JZ Tel: 0191 267 5757 — MB ChB 1984 Dundee; Dip. Obst. Auckland 1987. SHO Rotat. (Anaesth.) Newc. u Tyne Hosps. Prev: Auckland Hosp. Bd., NZ.

COWEN, David Stephen Northfield Avenue Surgery, 61 Northfield Avenue, West Ealing, London W13 9QP Tel: 020 8567 1612 Fax: 020 8579 2593 — MB BS 1973 Lond.; DObst RCOG 1975; Cert. Family Plann. JCC 1975. (Lond. Hosp.) Socs: BMA; Assoc. Mem. RCGP. Prev: SHO St. Thos. Hosp. Lond.; Ho. Surg. St. Albans City Hosp.; Ho. Phys. Worthing Hosp.

COWEN, Dennis David (retired) 11 Broadlands Lodge, Broadlands Road, Highgate, London N6 4AW Tel: 020 8341 4100 — MB BS 1947 Lond.; MRCGP 1959. Prev: Med. Ref., Dept of Social Servs.

COWEN, Jennifer Mary Wexham Park Hospital, Wexham Street, Slough SL2 4HL Tel: 01753 633000; Batchwood, Camp Road, Gerrards Cross SL9 7PB — MB BS (Hons.) Lond. 1972; FRCP Lond. 1993; MRCP (UK) 1974; FRCPCH 1997. (Roy. Free) p/t Cons. Paediat. Heatherwood and Wexham Pk. Hosp.s Trust. Prev: Lect. (Child Health) Univ. of Liverp.; Regist. (Paediat.) N.wick Pk. Hosp. Harrow; SHO (Neonat. Paediat.) Hammersmith Hosp. Lond.

COWEN, John Cowen and Ashe, 51 Sloane Street, London SW1X 9SW Tel: 020 7838 9422 Fax: 020 7259 5409; The Flat, 51 Sloane St, London SW1X 9SW Tel: 0207 245 6574 — MB BChir 1975 Camb.; MA 1975; DRCOG 1976. (Camb. & St. Thos.) Private Gen. Pract. Socs: Fell. Med. Soc. Lond. Prev: Resid. Med. Off. King Edwd. VII Hosp. Offs. Lond.; Cas. Off. & SHO (O & G) St Thos. Hosp. Lond.; Asst. Div. Police Surg. Metrop. Area.

COWEN, Julius (retired) 93 Grange Gardens, The Bourne, Southgate, London N14 6QW — MB ChB 1935 Glas. Prev: Capt RAMC.

COWEN, Mr Michael Edward Humberside Cardiothoracic Surgical Centre, Castle Hill Hospital, Cottingham HU16 Tel: 01482 875875; Moorhill Farm, 83 Main St, Etton, Beverley HU17 7PG Tel: 01430 810458 — MB ChB 1982 Leeds; BSc (Phys.) Leeds 1979, MB ChB 1982; FRCS Lond. 1987. Cons. Cardiothoracic Surg. Humberside.

COWEN, Michael John The Manor House, The Green, Woughton-on-the-Green, Milton Keynes MK6 3BE Tel: 01908 665777 — MB ChB 1964 Liverp.; FFA RCS Eng. 1978; MRCGP 1971; DA Eng. 1971; DObst RCOG 1966. Cons. Anaesth. Milton Keynes NHS Trust; Med. Dir. Milton Keynes. Socs: Obst. Anaesth. Assn.; Pain Soc. Prev: Sen. Regist. Nuffield Dept. Anaesth. Radcliffe Infirm. Oxf.; Ship's Surg. P & O SN Company; Med. Off. Shell Internat. Petrol Company.

COWEN, Professor Philip John University Dept of Psychiatry, Warneford Hospital, Oxford OX3 7JX Tel: 01865 226 3094 Fax: 01865 251076 Email: phil.cowen@psychiatry.ox.ac.uk; 92 Southend, Garsington, Oxford OX44 9DL — MB BS 1974 Lond.; BSc 1971 Lond.; FRCPsych 1991; MD 1984; M 1979; BSc Lond. 1971, MD 1984; FRCPsych 1991, M 1979. (Univ. Coll. Hosp.) MRC Clin. Scientist & Hon. Cons. Psychiat. Warneford Hosp. Oxf.; Prof. Psychophasmacology Univ. of Oxf. Socs: Fell. of Acad. of Med. Sci.s. Prev: Research Fell. (Clin. Psychopharmacol.) Radcliffe Infirm. Oxf.; Regist. (Psychol. Med.) King's Coll. Hosp. Lond.

COWEN, Philip Nathan (retired) 22 Congreve Way, Bardsey, Leeds LS17 9BG Tel: 01937 572881 — MB BS 1955 Durh.; PhD Lond. 1950; BSc Edin. 1945; FRCPath 1976. Prev: Sen. Lect. (Path.) Univ. Leeds.

COWEN, Stuart Victor Tel: 01902 341409 Fax: 01902 620527 — MB ChB 1977 Leeds.

COWEN, Vanessa Isabelle Email: vanessacowen@hotmail.com — MB ChB 1994 Sheff.; DRCOG 1997; MRCGP 1998. (Sheffield Medical School) GP Non-Princip., Lond.; Acad. Train. Fell., Sheff. Prev: GP Non-Princip.

COWEY, Alexander John 1 Wealden Cottages, Heathfield Road, Burwash Weald, Etchingham TN19 7LA — MB ChB 1998 Manch.; MB ChB Manch 1998.

COWEY, Ruth Victoria 79 Spooner Road, Sheffield S10 5BL — MB ChB 1998 Sheff.; MB ChB Sheff 1998.

COWIE, Mr Alfred George Adam . Esperance House, .Hjartington Place, Eastbourne BN21 3BG Tel: 01323 737100 Fax: 01323 414954; .7 Chesterfield Road, ., Eastbourne BN20 7NT Tel: 01323 734972 Fax: 01323 730313 Email: cowie@mistral.co.uk — MB BChir Camb. 1963; MA Camb. 1963; FRCS Eng. 1967; FICS 1990; DObst RCOG 1965. (Univ. Coll. Hosp.) Emerit. Cons. Surg. UCL Hosps. Trust; Hon. Cons. Urol. E.bourne Dist. Gen. Hosp. Trust; Mem. Ct. Examrs. RCS Eng. Socs: Eur. Assn. Urol. Surgs. & Brit. Assn. Urol. Surgs.; Assn. Surg. Prev: Cons. Urol. Univ. Coll. Hosp. & Middlx. Hosp. Lond.; Resid. Asst. Surg. & Tutor (Surg.) Univ. Coll. Hosp.; Resid. Surg. Off Brompton Hosp. Lond.

COWIE, Mr Alistair George 400 Parrs Wood Road, East Didsbury, Manchester M20 5GP Tel: 0161 445 8981 — MB ChB 1988 Manch.; FRCS Ed. 1992. Specialist Regist. (Diagn. Radiol.) Manch. Roy. Infirm. Prev: Specialist Regist. (Gen. Surg.) Bury Gen. Hosp.; MRC Research Regist. John Radcliffe Hosp. Oxf.

COWIE, Andrew James Henderson Elizlea, High St., Errol, Perth PH2 7QJ — MB ChB 1992 Ed.

COWIE, Andrew Simon Porch Surgery, Beechfield Road, Corsham SN13 9DL Tel: 01249 712232 Fax: 01249 701389; Gatesgarth, Lacock Road, Corsham SN13 9HS Tel: 01249 713025 — MB ChB 1979 Birm.; MRCGP 1984; DRCOG 1983; DA Eng. 1981. Prev: SHO (Accid. Emerg. & Paediat.) Bath Roy. United Hosp.; SHO (Geriat.) Ham Green Hosp. nr. Bristol; SHO (Anaesth.) Bath Roy. United Hosp.

COWIE, Carol Mackenzie (retired) 90 Park Road, Chiswick, London W4 3HL Tel: 020 8994 1140 — MB ChB 1958 Aberd.

COWIE, Charlotte Myong Barbican health Plc., 3 White Lyon Court, London EC2Y 8EA Tel: 020 7588 3146; 4a Camberwell Church Street, London SE5 8QU Tel: 020 7703 0034 — MB BS 1990 Lond.; Dip. Sports Med. Lond 1993; DM-S Med. 1995; MRO 1995. Sports Med. Specialist Barbican Health Plc.; Clin Asst. Brit. Olympic Med. Centre. Socs: Coun. Mem., Brit. Inst. of Musculoskeletal Med.; Treas. Sout-E. Br. Brit. Assn. Sport & Med. Prev: Clin. Asst. (Sports Med.) Roy. Lond. Hosp.; Med. Off. Millwall FC. & Eng. Ladies' Football Squad; Med. Off. GB Running Squad.

COWIE, David Bruce Hare The Medical Defence Union Ltd, 3 Devonshire Place, London W1G 6HE Tel: 020 7486 6181 — MB ChB 1984 Birm.; DRCOG 1992; MA (Medical Law and Ethics) 1997. (University of Birmingham) Medico-Legal Adviser Med. Defence Union Lond.

COWIE, David Horace George (retired) White Rose Cottage, Whitehall Lane, Checkendon, Reading RG8 0TN Tel: 01491 682327 — MB BS Durh. 1956; FRCOG 1977, M 1964; DObst RCOG 1960. Cons. O & G Pk. Hosp. Davyhulme. Prev: Cons. O & G Trafford DHA.

COWIE, Fiona Annette Moreton Medical Centre, 27 Upton Road, Wirral CH46 0PE Tel: 0151 677 2327 Fax: 0151 604 0419; Hooton Hey, Chester Road, Great Sutton, South Wirral CH66 3PX Tel: 0151 339 2601 — MB ChB 1985 Sheff.; DFFP (IUD) 1990. (Sheffield) Princip. GP; GP Trainer. Family Plann. & Reproductive Health Care. Trainer in Child Health Surveillance. Socs: BMA. Prev: SHO (O & G/Psychiat.) Arrowe Pk. Hosp. Wirral; Trainee GP Moreton Wirral.

COWIE, Fiona Jane Beatson Oncology Centre, Western Infirmary, Dumbarton Road, Glasgow G11 6NT; Cartenvoch, Bardowie, Glasgow G62 6ES Tel: 01360 620434 — MB BS 1987 Lond.; MD Lond. 1995; MRCP (UK) 1991; FRCR 1998. (University College London) Regist. (Clin. Oncol.) W.. Gen. Infirm. Glas. Prev: Research Fell. (Paediat.) Roy. Marsden Hosp. Sutton.

COWIE, George (retired) Offerton Health Centre, 10 Offerton Lane, Offerton, Stockport SK2 5AR Tel: 0161 480 0324 — MB ChB 1955 Aberd.; DObst RCOG 1960. Prev: Ho. Phys. Aberd. Roy. Infirm.

COWIE, Mr George Henry 53 Ballycoan Road, Belfast BT8 8LL — MD 1983 Belf.; MB BCh BAO 1973; FRCS Eng. 1979; FRCS Ed. 1979. Cons. Orthop. E. Health & Social Servs. Bd.

COWIE, Heather Suzanne 14 Hazelmere Road, Sketty, Swansea SA2 0SN — MB BCh 1998 Wales.

COWIE, Iain Dudley Stuart Rosevale, 1 Albany Lane, Dumfries DG1 1JL Tel: 01387 54083 — MB ChB 1954 Ed.; DObst RCOG 1956.

COWIE, Ian Watson Ramsay Grove House Surgery, Soothill, Batley WF17 5SS Tel: 01924 476363 Fax: 01924 474119; 127 High Street, Hanging Heaton, Batley WF17 6DR Tel: 01924 469328 — MB ChB 1976 Dundee.

COWIE, James The Old Mill, Horrabridge, Yelverton PL20 7QE — MB ChB 1969 Aberd.; BSc Aberd. 1964, MB ChB 1969; FRCP (UK) 1983, M 1972. (Aberd.) Cons. Phys. (Gen. & Chest Med.) S. W.. RHA.

COWIE, John Bardsley (retired) 17 Craignabo Road, Peterhead AB42 2YE Tel: 01779 471651 — MB ChB Liverp. 1947.

COWIE, Mr John William (retired) Mayfield, Hag Farm Road, Burley-in-Wharfedale, Ilkley LS29 7AB Tel: 01943 862095 — MB ChB 1944 Ed.; FRCS Ed. 1947; FRCR 1984; DMRD Eng. 1955. Prev: Cons. Radiol. Bradford Roy. Infirm.

COWIE, Professor Martin Richard Cardiac Medicine, National Heart + Lung Institute, Faculty Of Medicine, Imperial College, Dovehouse Sreet, London SW3 6LY Tel: 0207 351885 Email: m.cowie@ic.ac.uk — MB ChB 1989 Aberd.; BMedBiol. Aberd. 1988; MRCP (UK) 1992; MSc (Epidemiol.) Lond. 1997; MD 1999 Aberdeen. Prof. Cardiol.; Hon. Cons. Cardiol. Roy.Brompton and Harefield NHS Trust. Socs: Eur. Soc. of Cardiol.; Med. Research Soc. (Mem. Scientif. Comm.); Roy. Coll. Phys.s Lond. (Collegiate Mem.). Prev: Regist. (Cardiol.) Middlx. Hosp. Lond.; Wellcome Research Fell. (Clin. Epidemiol.) Nat. Heart & Lung Inst. Lond.; Specialist Regist. (Cardiol.) Hillingdon Hosp. Lond.

COWIE, Mr Richard Alfred Neuroscience Unit, Alexandra Hospital, Mill Lane, Cheadle SK8 2PX Tel: 0161 491 1606 Fax: 0161 491 1645; Laurel House, Delamer Road, Bowdon, Altrincham WA14 2NQ — MB ChB 1970 Ed.; BSc (Med. Sci.) (Hons.) (Bact.) Ed. 1970; ChB MB 1973; FRCS (SN) 1981; FRCS Ed. 1977. Cons. Neurosurg. Hope Hosp. Salford & Roy. Manch. Childr. Hosp. Socs: Soc. Brit. Neurol. Surgs. & N. Eng. Neurol. Assn. Prev: Sen. Regist. Midl. Centre Neurosurg. & Neurol.; Regist. (Surg. Neurol.) W.. Gen. Hosp. Edin.

COWIE, Mr Ronald Skae Broxton, 21 Kennedy Road, Shrewsbury SY3 7AB Tel: 01743 232990 — LRCP LRCS 1947 Ed.; FRFPS Glas. 1953; LRCP LRCS Ed. LRFPS Glas. 1947; FRCS Ed. 1954. (Anderson Coll. Glas.) Socs: Fell. Brit. Orthop. Assn.; BMA. Prev: Cons. Orthop. Surg. Robt. Jones & Agnes Hunt Orthop. Hosp. OsW.ry &

Shrewsbury Hosp.; Resid. Surg. Off. Roy. Nat. Orthop. Hosp. Stanmore; Clin. Fell. Mass. Gen. Hosp. Boston, USA.

COWIE, Rosemary Geraldine 73 Wordsworth Way, Bothwell, Glasgow G71 8QS — MB ChB 1989 Glas.

COWIE, Stephen 334 Horsley Road, Washington NE38 8HU — MB ChB 1998 Ed.; MB ChB Ed 1998.

COWIE, Thomas Newlands (retired) 7 Murray Place, Luss, Alexandria G83 8PG Tel: 01436 860289 — MB ChB 1944 Glas.; BSc Glas. 1941, MD (Commend.) 1948; FRCR 1979; DMRD Eng. 1948. Prev: Cons. Radiol. P.ss Louise Hosp. Erskine.

COWIE, Professor Valerie Aileen 15 Woodthorpe Road, Putney, London SW15 6UQ Tel: 020 8789 7583 — MB ChB 1948 Aberd.; MB ChB (cum laude) Aberd. 1948; PhD Lond. 1967; MD (cum laude) Aberd. 1951; FRCPsych (Foundat. Fell.) 1972; DPM Lond. 1954. (Univ. Aberd.) Emerit. Prof. Personal Chair. (Ment. Handicap) Univ. Wales Conferred 1986. Prev: Asst. Dir. MRC Psychiat. Genetics Research Unit Maudsley Hosp.; Vis. Scientist Nat. Inst. of Health Bethesda, USA; Cons. Psychiat. Fountain & Carshalton Gp. Hosps.

COWIE, Valerie Joan Flat 21 Thorne House, 279 Wilmslow Road, Manchester M14 6HW — MB ChB 1973 Dundee; BMSc (Hons.) Dund 1970, MD (Commendat.) 1986, MB ChB 1973; FRCR 1982.

COWIN, George Stewart (retired) 2 Henson Grove, Newton Aycliffe DL5 4NJ Tel: 01325 313289 — MB BS 1954 Durh. Prev: Ho. Phys. S. Shields Gen. Hosp.

COWIN, Simon Williams Silverthorns, Bradshaw Lane, Mawdesley, Ormskirk L40 3SE — MB ChB 1996 Liverp.; BSc (Hons) Pharmacol. Liverp. 1994. SHO GP VTS.

COWLAM, Simon Robert 57 Dinsdale Road, Sandyford, Newcastle upon Tyne NE2 1DN — MB BS 1996 Newc.

COWLAND, Geoffrey Nicholas David Stokenchurch, High Wycombe HP14 3TG Tel: 01494 483633 — MB BS 1983 Lond.; MRCGP 1987; DRCOG 1985. (Guy's Hospital) Prev: Trainee GP Mid Downs VTS; Ho. Phys. Cuckfield Hosp.; Ho. Surg. William Harvey Hosp. Ashford.

COWLARD, James Dennis 70 Promenade Gardens, Riverside Drive, Liverpool L17 7EU — MB ChB 1983 Manch.

COWLARD, Richard John Old Cottage Hospital Surgery, Alexandra Road, Epsom KT17 4BL Tel: 01372 724434 Fax: 01372 748171; 1 Norman Avenue, Epsom KT17 3AB — MB BS 1983 Lond.; MRCGP 1989; Dip. Occ. Med. 1995. GP Practitioner; GP Trainer Epsom.; Med. Off. W.S. Arkins Engin. RAC Co. Club Epsom. Socs: Epsom Med. Soc.; Roy. Coll. Gen. Pract.

COWLES, Stephen Michael Hobs Moat Medical Centre, Ulleries Road, Solihull B92 8ED Tel: 0121 742 5211 Fax: 0121 743 4217; 30 Winchcombe Road, Solihull B92 8PJ Tel: 0121 742 5211 — MB ChB 1981 Birm.; MRCGP 1987; DRCOG 1984.

COWLEY, Andrew David Willows, Sunnyside Lane, Balsall Common, Coventry CV7 7FY — MB BCh 1998 Wales.

COWLEY, Catherine Paxton Cottage, 17 South Road, Saffron Walden CB11 3DG — BM BS 1982 Nottm.; BMedSci Nottm. 1980; DCH RCP Lond. 1984. (Nottingham University)

COWLEY, Catherine 154 Canterbury Road, Kennington, Ashford TN24 9QE — MB BS 1997 Lond.

COWLEY, Mr David Jon (retired) 2 Whitewood Close, Lytham St Annes FY8 4RN — MB ChB St. And. 1960; ChM (Commend.) Dund 1970; FRCS Eng. 1964. Cons. Surg. Vict. Hosp. Blackpool. Prev: Hon. Cons. & Sen. Lect. (Surg.) Univ. Manch. & Univ. Hosp. S. Manch.

COWLEY, Edward Julian 1 Old Pond Cottage, Howland Road, Marden, Tonbridge TN12 9HA — MB BS 1992 Lond.

COWLEY, Gerard Patrick 69 Fordwich Rise, Hertford SG14 2BW — MB BS 1989 Lond.

COWLEY, Hugh Craig Addenbrook's Centre for Clinical Investigation, Addenbrook's Hospital, Hills Rd, Cambridge CB2 2GG Tel: 01223 296000 Fax: 01223 296002 — MB BCh 1986 Oxf.; BA Pharm. Camb. 1983; FCAnaesth. 1991; Dip. Pharm. Med. 1997. Dir. (Clin. Pharm.) Smithkline Beecham Pharmaceut. Prev: Sen. Regist. E. Anglia HA.

COWLEY, Leslie Clifford Ramsey Group Practice Centre, Bowring Road, Ramsey IM8 Tel: 01624 813881; Fairfield, Ramsey IM8 Tel: 01624 812247 — BM BCh 1961 Oxf.; MA 1961; MRCS Eng. LRCP Lond. 1962; DA Eng. 1965; DCH Eng. 1964; DObst RCOG 1963. Assoc. Specialist (Anaesth.) I. of Man Health Servs. Bd. Socs: I. of Man Med. Soc. Prev: Ho. Surg. (Surgic. & Obst.) St. Mary's Hosp. Lond.; Resid. Med. Off. P.ss Louise Childr. Hosp. Lond.

COWLEY, Martin Lewis Cumberland Infirmary, Carlisle CA2 7HY Tel: 01228 523444; Hilcote, Kirkbride, Wigton CA7 5JB Email: martin@hilcote.freeserve.co.uk — MB ChB 1978 Birm.; MRCP (UK) 1984; FRCP 1996; FRCP Ed 1998. Cons. (Cardiol.) Cumbld. Infirm. Carlisle. Socs: Brit. Cardiac Soc. Prev: Cons. (Phys. & Cadiology) RN Hosp. Plymouth & Derriford Hosp. Plymouth; Sen. Regist. (Cardiol.) Killingbeck Hosp. Leeds; Sen. Regist. (Cardiol.) Lond. Hosp. Whitechapel.

COWLEY, Neil Department of Radiotherapy, Poole General Hospital, Poole — MB ChB 1970 Liverp.; FRCR 1975. Cons. Radiother. Poole Gen. Hosp. Prev: Lect. Dept. Radiother. Univ. Leeds.

COWLEY, Nigel Mark Denmark Road Medical Centre, 37 Denmark Road, Winton, Bournemouth BH9 1PB Tel: 01202 521111; 4 Berwick Road, Bournemouth BH3 7BB Tel: 01202 765983 Fax: 01202 555037 — MB ChB 1983 Birm.; MRCGP 1988; Cert. Family Plann. JCC 1988; DRCOG 1986; DCH RCP Lond. 1989. Prev: Princip. GP Salisbury; Trainee GP Stroud VTS; Jun. Med. Off. Goulburn Valley Base Hosp. Shepperton, Vict. Austral.

COWLEY, Norman (retired) 3 Tynedale Road, South Shields NE34 6EX Tel: 0191 455 4974 — MB BS Durh. 1942; MRCGP 1952. Prev: Ho. Surg. Accid. Room, Roy. Vict. Infirm. Newc.

COWLEY, Mr Rowland, OBE (retired) 27 Cornfield Road, Linthorpe, Middlesbrough TS5 5QJ Tel: 01642 819695 — MB BS 1947 Durh.; FRCS Ed. 1958; FRCOphth 1988; DO Eng. 1952. Prev: Cons. Ophth. Surg. N. Riding Infirm. Middlesbrough.

COWLEY, Sarah Jane The London Fields Medical Centres, 38-44 Broadway Market, London E8 4QJ Tel: 020 7254 2883 Fax: 020 7254 2066 — BM Soton. 1987. GP Princip. Prev: GP Woolwich; Trainee GP Beckton, Lond.

COWLING, Betty Edwina 3 Corchester Towers, Corbridge NE45 5NR Tel: 0143471 2850 — MB BS 1952 Durh.

COWLING, Hannah Emily 3 Garden Cottages, Tabley Park, Tabley, Knutsford WA16 0HB — MB ChB 1997 Sheff.

COWLING, Mark Graham Guy's Hospital, St. Thomas' St., London SE1 9RT Tel: 020 7955 5000 ext 2461; 24 Arthur Road, New Malden KT3 6LX — MB BS 1988 Lond.; BSc Lond. 1985; MRCP (UK) 1991; FRCR 1994. Lect. (Interven.al Radiol.) Guy's Hosp. Lond.

COWLING, Rebecca Jane Southport & Formby NHS Trust, Town Lane, Southport PR8 6NJ; 67 Oakwood Drive, Bolton BL1 5EH — MB ChB 1991 Manch. SHO (Paediat.) S.port & Formby NHS. Prev: Ho. Off. (Med. & Surg.) S.port & Formby NHS Trust.

COWLING, Richard Ernest (retired) 3 Lodge Gardens, Oakham LE15 6EP — MB BS 1950 Lond.; BSc (Hons.) Lond. 1940, MB BS 1950. Prev: Ho. Surg. Lond. Hosp.

***COWLISHAW, David** Flat 8, Carlisle Court, 42 St Edmunds Rd, Southampton SO16 4FS Tel: 02380 786140 Email: dave@doctor.prestel.co.uk — BM 1997 Soton.

COWLISHAW, Phillip James 16 Cornhill, Allestree, Derby DE22 2FT — MB ChB 1995 Birm. (Birm.)

COWMAN, Joanna Elizabeth Flat 2 Kingsley House, North Devon District Hospital, Raleigh Park, Barnstaple EX31 4JB Tel: 01271 322577; Old Barn, Angel Court, West Down, Ilfracombe EX34 8NH Tel: 01271 879114 — MB ChB 1995 Aberd. (Aberdeen) Basic Surg. rotat. N. Devon Dist. Hosp. Barnstaple. Prev: Sen. SHO (A & E) Roy. Hants. Co. Hosp. Winchester; SHO (Paediat. & Neonatology) Aberd. Roy. Infirm.; SHO (A & E) Aberd. Roy. Infirm.

COWMEADOW, Florence Pauline .45 Beauval Road, ., Dulwich, London SE22 8UG Tel: 020 8693 1812; 45 Beauval Road, Dulwich, London SE22 8UG Tel: 020 8693 1812 — MB BS 1981 Lond.; MA Lond. 1973; BA (Hons.) Leeds 1971; MRCPsych 1987. Prev: Sen. Regist. (Psychother.) Guys' Hosp.; Hon. Sen. Regist. Maudsley Hosp.; Cons. Psychother. Guy's Hosp. Lond.

COWPE, Janine 146 West Drive, Thornton-Cleveleys FY5 2EG — MB ChB 1998 Sheff.; MB ChB Sheff 1998.

COWPE, Mr Oliver Ormrod Mill House, Arley, Aston by Budworth, Northwich CW9 6LZ Tel: 01606 383 — MB ChB 1943 Manch.; BSc Manch. 1943; FRCS Eng. 1949. (Manch.) Prev: Cons. Orthop. Surg. Univ. Hosp. S. Manch. & Altrincham Gen. Hosp.; Sen. Regist. Salford Roy. Hosp. & Manch. Roy. Infirm.

COWPE, Thomas Varley Colne Health Centre, Market Street, Colne BB8 0LJ Tel: 01282 862451 Fax: 01282 871698; Old Laithe,

Hill Lane, Colne BB8 7EF Tel: 01282 866257 — MB BChir 1975 Camb.; MA, MB BChir Camb. 1975; D.Occ.Med. RCP Lond. 1995; MRCGP 1979. Div. Med. Off. Smith & Nephew Fabrics Div.; Med. Off. Rolls Royce (Barnoldswick).

COWPER, David Milne Fulham Clinic, 82 Lillie Road, London SW6 1TN Tel: 020 7386 9299 Fax: 020 7610 0635; 43 Rosaville Road, London SW6 7BN Tel: 020 7385 7449 Fax: 020 7385 9243 — MB BCh BAO 1962 Dub.; MRCGP 1973. (T.C. Dub.) Course Organiser Riverside VTS. Socs: BMA. Prev: Regist. (Med.) Joyce Green Hosp. Dartford; SHO (Med.) Qu. Mary's Hosp. E. End Lond.; Ho. Surg. (O & G) Freedom Fields Hosp. Plymouth.

COWPER, Robert Astley Department of Genitourinary Medicine, Northampton General Hospital, Northampton NN1 5BD Tel: 01604 633536 Fax: 01604 622296 — MB ChB 1968 Bristol. (Bristol) Cons. Phys. Genitourin. Med. N.ampton Gen. Hosp. Socs: Med. Soc. Study VD; BMA; Assoc for genito-Urin. Med. (AGUM). Prev: Sen. Regist. (Venereol.) Bristol Roy. Infirm.; Research SHO Roy. Nat. Hosp. Bath.

COWPER, Scott Gladstone, TD (retired) Ground Floor Flat, 6 Townfield Road, West Kirby, Wirral CH48 7EZ Tel: 0151 625 7846 — MRCS Eng. LRCP Lond. 1938; DSc Reading 1955, BSc 1930; MRCPath 1965; DTM Liverp. 1938, DTH 1939; FIBiol 1982, M 1969. Prev: Prof. Parasitol. Univ. Ibadan.

COWPER, William Binns 4 Grange Villas, Wallsend-on-Tyne, Wallsend NE28 7PN Tel: 0191 263 4352 — LRCP LRCS Ed. LRFPS. Glas. 1943. (Ed.) Prev: Cas. Surg. & Ho. Surg. Guest Hosp. Dudley; Capt. R.A.M.C.

COWSER, Julie The Health Centre, Coatham Road, Redcar TS10 1SX Tel: 01642 475157 Fax: 01642 470885 — MB ChB 1986 Leeds.

COX, Alan 17 Vincent Close, Bromley BR2 9ED — MB BS Lond. 1958; MRCS Eng. LRCP Lond. 1958. (King's Coll. Hosp.)

COX, Mr Alan Gyth (retired) 20 De Moulham Road, Swanage BH19 1NY — MB ChB 1958 Sheff.; MD Sheff. 1962; FRCS Eng. (ad eund.) 1977; FRCS Ed. 1965. Prev: Cons. Surg. N.wick Pk. Hosp.

COX, Alan Herbert, Wing Cdr. RAF Med. Br. Retd. (retired) Appledore Cottage, 4 Brewer's Court, Abingdon OX14 5BG Tel: 01235 526791 — MB BS 1950 Lond. Prev: Civil. Med. Pract. RAF Abingdon.

COX, Alan Leslie 5 Kidston Drive, Helensburgh G84 8QA — MB ChB 1992 Aberd.

COX, Amanda Louise East Street Medical Centre, East Street, Okehampton EX20 1AY Tel: 01837 52233 — MB ChB 1982 Bristol; MRCGP 1986. Prev: Trainee GP Exeter VTS; SHO (Obst.) Morriston Hosp. Swansea.

COX, Andrew David Accident and Emergency Department, Aberdeen Royal Infirmary, Foresterhill, Aberdeen Tel: 01224 681818; 10 Meadowlands Drive, Westhill AB32 6EJ Tel: 01224 749994 — MB ChB 1994 Aberd.; BSc (Hons.) St. And. 1989. SHO Rotat. (Surg.) Aberd. Roy. Infirm.; SHO (A & E) Aberd. Roy. Infirm. Prev: SHO (Surg.) Aberd. Roy. Infirm.

COX, Andrew Edward Ashton Road Surgery, 58 Ashton Road, Droylsden, Manchester M43 7BW Tel: 0161 370 1610 Fax: 0161 371 1258 — MB ChB 1989 Manch.

COX, Andrew James 29 Park Road, Buckden, St Neots, Huntingdon PE19 5SL — MB ChB 1997 Birm.

COX, Ann-Marie Leckhampton Surgery, Lloyd Davies House, 17 Moorend Park Road, Cheltenham GL53 0LA Tel: 01242 515363 Fax: 01242 253512; 16 Leckhampton Road, Cheltenham GL53 0AY Tel: 01242 526423 — MB ChB 1991 Bristol; MRCGP 1995; DRCOG 1993. Clin. Asst. (Oncol.) Cheltenham Gen. Hosp. Socs: Med. Protec. Soc.

COX, Antony Dawson Department of Child & Adolescent Psychiatry, Bloomfield Centre, Guy's Hospital, St Thomas St., London SE1 9RT Tel: 020 7955 4286 Fax: 020 7403 7601; Flat 11, 92-94 Great Titchfield St, London W1W 659 — MB BChir 1963 Camb.; MPhil Lond. 1969; MA Camb. 1964; FRCP 1987, M 1966; FRCPCH 1997; FRCPsych 1979, M 1972. (St. Thos.) Socs: Fell. Roy. Soc. Med. (Pres. Psychiat. Sect. 1966-67); BMA. Prev: Emerit. Prof. Child & Adolesc. Psychiat. Lond. Univ., UMDS Guy's & St. Thos. Hosps. Lond.; Prof. Child & Adolesc. Psychiat. Liverp. Univ.; Sen. Lect. Inst. Psychiat.

COX, Arthur Geoffrey (retired) — MB BS 1954 Lond.; MRCS Eng. LRCP Lond. 1954. Prev: Ho. Surg. King Geo. Hosp. Ilford.

COX, Barbara Gillian Waterloo Medical Centre, 178 Waterloo Road, Blackpool FY4 3AD Tel: 01253 48619 & 44219; Copper Beeches, 39 High Cross Road, Poulton-le-Fylde, Blackpool Tel: 01253 884122 — MB ChB 1959 Birm.; DA Eng. 1961. (Birm.) Clin. Asst. Dept. Anaesth. Vict. Hosp. Blackpool.

COX, Mr Charles Walter Francis Mowbray 29 Newbridge Crescent, Wolverhampton WV6 0LN Tel: 01902 751367 — MB BS 1970 Lond.; FRCS Ed. 1979; MRCS Eng. LRCP Lond. 1970; MRCOG 1976. (St. Geo.) Cons. (O & G) New Cross Hosp. Wolverhampton.

COX, Christopher John Charlton Courthouse Practice, Ton-y-Felin Surgery, Bedwas Road, Caerphilly CF83 1XN Tel: 029 2088 7316 Fax: 029 2088 4445; 4 Kidwelly Court, Hendredenny, Caerphilly CF83 2TY — MRCS Eng. LRCP Lond. 1970. (Guy's) Prev: SHO (O & G) N. Staffs. Matern. Hosp. Stoke-on-Trent; Ho. Phys. Roy. Devon & Exeter Hosp. Exeter; Ho. Surg. Birm. Accid. Hosp.

COX, Claire Margaret Swan Surgery, Swan Street, Petersfield GU32 3AB Tel: 01730 264011 Fax: 01730 231093; Rowan Garth, 71 Bell Hill, Petersfield GU32 2EA Tel: 01730 262517 — MB ChB 1985 Bristol; MSc 2001; MRCGP 1989; DRCOG 1987. GP Trainer; Course Organiser. Prev: Trainee GP Portsmouth VTS.

COX, Colleen Agnes (retired) 7 Dormywood, Ruislip HA4 7UW Tel: 01895 478927 — MB ChB Sheff. 1956; MD Sheff. 1963; MRCPCH 1997; DCH Eng. 1959. Prev: Cons. Paediat. (Community Child Health) Hounslow & Spelthorne Community & Ment. Health Trust.

COX, Craig Martin 43 Hazalwood Road, Sneyd Park, Bristol BS9 1PS — MB BS 1985 Lond.; FRCA 1994. (Lond.) SHO (Anaesth.) Broomfield Hosp. Chelmsford.; Sen. Regist. (Anaesth.) Bristol Roy. Infirm.

COX, Dale Antony Dennis and Partners, The Medical Centre, Folly Lane, Bewsey, Warrington WA5 0LU — MB ChB 1981 Birm. (Birm.) Gen. Pract. The Med. Centre, Fours La., Warrington.

COX, David Anthony 29 Clive Road, Cardiff CF5 1HF — MB BCh 1993 Wales.

COX, David Edward The Surgery, 15 West Town Road, Backwell, Bristol BS48 3HA Tel: 01275 850600 Email: davidcox@gp-l81060.nhs.uk; Apple Acre, 105 Main Road, Cleeve BS49 4PN — MB BS 1985 Lond.; MRCGP 1990; DRCOG 1989. (University College Hospital) Vis. Med. Off. (Learning Difficulties); GP Trainer, S. W. Region. Prev: Ho. Off. (Med.) Univ. Coll. Hosp. Lond.; Ho. Off. (Surg.) MusGr. Pk. Hosp. Taunton.

COX, Mr David Richard 24 Princes Road, Richmond TW10 6DH — MB BS 1981 Lond.; FRCS Eng. 1987; LRCP MRCS 1981. Regist. (Orthop.) W. Middlx. Univ. Hosp. Isleworth. Prev: Surg. Rotat. King's Coll. Hosp. Lond.

COX, David Truscott (retired) 3 Somerset Road, Ferring, Worthing BN12 5QA — MA Camb. 1948; MRCS Eng. LRCP Lond. 1948. Prev: Res. Med. Off. St. And. Hosp. Dollis Hill.

COX, Dennis Charles Anthony The Spinney Surgery, The Spinney, Ramsey Road, St. Ives, Huntingdon PE27 37P Tel: 01480 492501 Fax: 01480 356159; Elmers End, Colne Road, Bluntisham, Huntingdon PE28 3LT Email: dennis_cox@msn.com — MB BS 1980 Lond.; MA (Med. Law & Ethics.) Lond. 1994; MRCGP 1986; DRCOG 1984. (Roy. Free) Asst. Dir. (Studies Gen. Pract.) Univ. Camb. Gen. Pract. & Primary Care Research Unit, Inst. Pub. Health Addenbrooke's Hosp. Camb. Prev: Trainee GP Basingstoke VTS; Ho. Phys. St. And. Hosp. Lond.; Ho. Surg. Roy. N.. Hosp. Lond.

COX, Diana Elizabeth The London Medico-Legal Centre, 40 Stockwell St., Greenwich, London SE10 8EY Tel: 020 8293 3080 Fax: 020 8858 3043 — MB BS 1984 Lond.; MA Camb. 1984; MRCPath 1996. Forens. Path. Lond. Medico-Legal Centre.

COX, Dominic Howard Department of Academic Cardiology, Freeman Hospital, Newcastle upon Tyne Tel: 0191 284 3111 Email: dom.cox@ncl.ac.uk; 203 Cheviot Court, Melville Grove, High Heaton, Newcastle upon Tyne NE7 7DF Tel: 0191 284 3111 — MB ChB 1994 Aberd.; BSc (Hons) (Physiol.) 1989; MRCP 1997. (Aberd.) Clin. Lect. in Cardiol. Univ. Newc. u. Tyne. Socs: MRCP (Ed.). Prev: SHO Rotat. in Gen. Med. - Aberd. Roy. Hosp. NHS Trust.

***COX, Donna Michelle** Ipswich Hospital, Leath Road, Ipswich IP4 5PD Tel: 01473 712233; 33 Chewton Common Road, Highcliffe, Christchurch BH23 5LX Tel: 0956 942919 — BM BCh 1998 Oxf.; BM BCh Oxf 1998.

COX, Doreen Amanda The Apple Cart, Birmingham Road, Bacons End, Kingshurst, Birmingham B37 6RB Tel: 0121 779 4057 — MB ChB 1993 Bristol. (Bristol) Specialist Regist. (Radiol.) Birm. Prev: SHO Rotat. (Med.) Warwick Hosp. & Gloucester Roy. Hosp.; Ho. Surg. & Phys. Bristol Roy. Infirm.

COX, Eileen Margaret Sprinbank Surgery, Green Hammerton, York YO26 8BN Tel: 01423 330030 Email: eileen.cox@virgin.net; Heathside, 18 Otley Road, Harrogate HG2 0DN Email: eileen.cox@virgin.net — MB ChB 1981 Leic. p/t Asst. in Gen. Pract.; Clin. Asst., Urol., Harrogate Dist. Hosp.

COX, Elizabeth (retired) Mawingo, Brentor Road, Mary Tavy, Tavistock PL19 9PY — MB BS 1952 Durh.

COX, Elizabeth Jane Chave Lensfield Medical Practice, Lensfield Road, Cambridge CB2 1EG Tel: 01223 352779; Manor Farm, Brook Lane, Coton, Cambridge CB3 7PY Tel: 01954 210756 — MB BS 1978 Lond.; BSc (Pharmacol.) Lond. 1975; MRCGP 1983; DRCOG 1982. (St. Bart.) Asst. Gen. Pract. 48 Lensfield Rd. Camb.; Clin. Asst. (Oncol.) Addenbrooke's Hosp. Camb. Prev: Trainee GP Lond.; SHO (Radiother. & Gen. Med.) St. Bart. Hosp. Lond.; SHO (O & G) The Lond. Hosp.

COX, Eric Vincent (retired) Conygree, Carbinswood Lane, Upper Woolhampton, Reading RG7 5TS Tel: 0118 971 3826 Email: eric.cox@virgin.net — MB BS 1948 Durh.; BSc (Hons. Physiol.) Durham. 1945, MD 1958; FRCP Lond. 1972, M 1955. Prev: Cons. Phys. BUPA & Roy. Berks. Hosp. Reading.

COX, Freda May 2 West Mead, Woodhall Park CrescentW., Stanningley, Leeds — MRCS Eng. LRCP Lond. 1948; DPH Leeds 1965; Co. Asst. Med. Off. Batley Div. W. Riding.

COX, Frederick Campbell Shetland HB, Brevik House, Lerwick ZE1 0RB Tel: 01595 743072 Fax: 01595 695200 Email: 106231.1532@compuserve.com; 29 Burgh Road, Lerwick ZE1 0LA Tel: 01595 696466 — MB ChB 1968 Glas.; MRCP (U.K.) 1972. Chief Admin. Med. Off./Dir. of Pub. Health Shetland HB. Socs: RCPS Glas. Coll. Prev: GP Shetland HB; Sen. Med. Off. Falkland Is.s Govt. Med. Dept.; Regist. (Gen. Surg.) Bignold Hosp. Wick.

COX, Giles Michael 20 Adbolton Grove, West Bridgford, Nottingham NG2 5AR — MB BS 1990 Lond.; MRCP (UK) 1994.

COX, Gillian Lynda William Budd Health Centre, Leinster Avenue, Knowle West, Bristol BS4 1NL Tel: 0117 963 6201; 35 Ashton Road, Ashton, Bristol BS3 2EQ Tel: 0117 963 4853 — BM 1979 Soton.; MRCGP 1983; DRCOG 1983. Prev: Trainee GP Newham VTS; Ho. Surg. Roy. Hants. Co. Hosp. Winchester; Ho. Phys. St. Helen's Hosp. Hastings.

COX, Glenice Hazel 52 Cranesbill Drive, Bicester OX26 3ZF Tel: 01869 357124 — MB ChB 1990 Leeds; DA (UK) 1993. (Leeds) SHO Forens. Psychiat. Three Bridges RSU, Ealing, Hammersmith & Fulham NHS Trust. Prev: SHO (Psychiat.) Ashford Hosp., Middlx.; SHO (Psychiat.) Napsbury Hosp. Barnet; SHO (Psychiat.) Watford Gen. Hosp.

COX, Gordon Andrew 12 Church Hill, Newcastle BT33 0JU — MB BS 1991 Lond.

COX, Gordon Andrew Oakley House, Manor Road, Penn, High Wycombe HP10 8JA Tel: 01494 816594 — MB BCh 1971 Wales; BDS Birm. 1964. (Cardiff) Clin. Pharmacol. Dept. Roche Products Ltd. Welwyn Garden City. Prev: Med. Dept. Roche Products Ltd. Welwyn Garden City & Syntex Pharmaceut. Maidenhead; Ho. Surg. Cardiff Roy. Infirm.; Ho. Phys. Llandough Hosp. Cardiff.

COX, Graham John The Surgery, 319 Westdale Lane, Carlton, Nottingham NG3 6EW Tel: 0115 952 5320 Fax: 0115 952 5321 — BM BS 1980 Nottm.; MRCGP 1992; DTM & H Liverp. 1986. Princip. in Gen. Pract.

COX, Mr Graham John Department of Otolaryngology, Stoke Mandeville Hospital, Aylesbury Tel: 01296 315771 Fax: 01296 315772; Holton House, Holton, Oxford OX33 1PR Tel: 01865 875983 Fax: 01865 875983 — MB BS 1985 Lond.; BDS (Hons.) Lond. 1981; FRCS (Orl.) 1993; FRCS Eng. 1989. Cons. Otolaryngol. Stoke Mandeville Hosp. Aylesbury; Cons. Head & Neck Surg. Radcliffe Infirm. Oxf. Prev: Sen. Regist. (ENT) Radfcliffe Infirm. Oxf. & Roy. Berks. Hosp. Reading; Regist. (ENT) Soton. Univ. Hosp.

COX, Gregory Mark 6 Monkbarns Drive, Arbroath DD11 2DS — MB ChB 1985 Dundee; BMSc (Hons.) Pharmacol. Dund 1982; DO Eng. 1990. Arbroath & Friockheim LHCC Bd.

COX, Helen 2/3 Riverside, Dalvait Road, Balloch, Alexandria G83 8LN — MB ChB 1988 Birm.; MRCP (UK) 1996; MRCPCH 1996; DCH RCP Lond. 1993. (Univ. Birm.) Specialist Regist. (LAT) Clin. Genetics, St. Mary's Hosp. Manch. Prev: Specialist Regist. (Paediat.) Birm. Childr. Hosp.

COX, Helen Storer Road Medical Centre, 2A Storer Road, Loughborough LE11 5EQ Tel: 01509 212120; 169 Main Street, Willoughby on the Wolds, Loughborough LE12 6SY Tel: 01509 880861 — BM BCh 1972 Oxf.; MA Oxf. 1972; MRCP Lond. 1995; DCH RCP Lond. 1990; DTM & H Liverp. 1974; DObst RCOG 1974. Clin. Asst. (Paediat.) Leicester Roy. Infirm.; Med. Off., Rainboroe Childr.'s Hospice LoughBoro. Prev: Trainee GP LoughBoro. VTS; SHO (Gen. Med.) Glenfield Hosp. Leicester; Med. Off. Zomba Gen. Hosp., Malawi.

COX, Helen Elizabeth 100A Denbigh Street, London SW1V 2EX — MB ChB 1985 Cape Town; MRCP (UK) 1992.

COX, Helen Elizabeth 36 Oak Tree Terrace, Fenay Bridge, Huddersfield HD8 0DA — MB ChB 1997 Leeds.

COX, Hella Staion Road Surgery, Haworth BD22 8 NL — MB ChB 1989 Leic.

COX, Hubert John Edwin, TD Sozo Clinic, 14 Ayleswater, Watermead, Aylesbury HP19 0FB Tel: 01296 399317 Fax: 01296 399291 — MB ChB 1951 Birm.; MRCS Eng. LRCP Lond. 1952; MRCGP 1968; DCH Eng. 1955; DObst RCOG 1953. (Birm.) Socs: Fell. Roy. Soc. Med.; BMA; Brit. Soc. Ecol. Med. Prev: Asst. Med. Dir. G.D. Searle & Co.; Asst. Phys. Burnley Gp. Hosps.; Regist. (Med.) Crumpsall Hosp. Manch.

COX, Hugh Jeremy Dorset County Hospital, Williams Avenue, Dorchester DT1 2JY Tel: 01305 254205 Email: hjcox@tinyonline.co.uk; Lambert Cottage, White Lackington, Piddletrethide, Dorchester DT2 7QU — MB BS 1980 Lond.; FRCS Eng. 1986 Gen. Surg.; FRCS 1988 (Ent)England. (Westm.) Cons. Otorhinolarynciologist Dorset Couynty Hosp. Dorcherster.; Cons. Otorhinlaryngologist, Yeovil Dist. Hosp. Yeovil. Prev: Sen. Regist. Soton. Univ. Hosps.; Sen. Regist. Roy. Marsden Hosp. Lond.; Sen. Regist. Roy. Devon & Exeter Hosp.

COX, Ian David Dalton St George's Hospital, Blackshaw Road, London SW17 0QT — BM BCh 1989 Oxf.; MRCP (UK) 1992.

COX, Ian Douglas Pangbourne Medical Practice, The Boat House Surgery, Whitchurch Road, Pangbourne, Reading RG8 7DP Tel: 0118 984 2234 Fax: 0118 984 3022; 1 Emery Down, Upper Basildon, Reading RG8 8PA — MB BChir 1977 Camb.; BA Camb. 1973; MRCP (UK) 1979; MRCGP 1984. (Camb. & Lond. Hosp.) Chief Med. Off. Pruden. Assur. Prev: Wellcome Research Fell. & Regist. (Med.) Lond. Hosp.

COX, Ivan George 8 Goldieslie Road, Sutton Coldfield B73 5PQ Tel: 0121 354 9237 Email: ivan.cox@btinternet.com — MB ChB 1968 Birm.; MRCP (UK) 1972; FRCGP 1988, M 1981; DCH Eng. 1971. (Birm.) p/t Salaried GP Birm. Socs: Assn. Palliat. Med.; Roy. Coll. Gen. Pract. (Bd. Birm. Sub-Fac.). Prev: Macmillan Adviser in Cancer & Palliat. Care, Lond.; Princip. in Gen. Pract., Lanrie Pike Health Centre, Birm.

COX, Ivan Michael 19 Gainsborough Road, Littledown, Bournemouth BH7 7BD Tel: 01202 460165 Fax: 01202 460165 Email: wfas@sportsfirstaid.com — BM 1991 Soton. (Soton. Univ.) Managing Director, Wessex 1st Aid for Sport Ltd. Bournemouth, Dorset. Socs: Fell. Roy. Soc. Med.; Amer. Coll. of Sports Med.; Internat. Federat. of Sports Med. Prev: GP Regist. Bournemouth; ATLS Provider RCS Eng.

COX, Jacqueline Ballantyne Drumdelnies, Inverness Road, Nairn IV12 5NT — MB BS 1981 Lond. Clin. Asst. (Gen. Psychiat.) St. Geo. Hosp. Stafford.

COX, James Doctors Surgery, Friar Row, Caldbeck, Wigton CA7 8DS; The Barn, Caldbeck, Wigton CA7 8DP — MB BS 1972 Newc.; MD Newc. 1993; FRCP Ed. 1997; FRCGP 1991, M 1976; Dip. IMC RCS Ed. 1989; DObst RCOG 1974. Med. Adviser, Cumbria Ambul. Serv., NHS Trust. Prev: Asst. Prof. Dept. Family Pract. S.. Illinois Univ. Springfield, USA; Assoc. Adviser Gen. Pract. Univ. Newc.

COX, James George Charlton Wansbeck General Hospital, Ashington NE63 9JJ Tel: 01665 711201; 3 Castle Street, Warkworth, Morpeth NE65 0UW — MB BChir 1977 Camb.; FRCP Lond. 1994; FRCP Ed. 1993; MRCP (UK) 1980. (Cambridge St. Thomas's) Cons. Phys. (Med. for Elderly, Intermediate Care. & Gen. Med.) Wansbeck Geneneral Hosp. N.d. Prev: Sen. Regist. (Med. for

Elderly & Med.) Hull Roy. Infirm.; Regist. (Med.) St. Thos. Hosp. Lond.

COX, Jennifer Ann Winsley Barn, Winsley, Bradford-on-Avon BA15 2LB — MB BS 1970 Lond.

COX, Jennifer Anne Town Medical Centre, 25 London Road, Sevenoaks TN13 1AR Tel: 01732 454545/458844 Fax: 01732 462181; Shire Lane Farm House, Stalisfield Green, Faversham ME13 0HY Tel: 01795 890366 Fax: 01795 890136 — MB BS 1983 Lond.; MRCGP 1988; DCH RCP Lond. 1986; DRCOG 1985. (St. Geo. Hosp. Med. Sch.) Hosp. Pract. (Genitourin. Clinic) Kent & Sussex Hosp.; Clin. Asst. (Psychiat.) Pembury Hosp. Prev: SHO (Psychiat.) Maidstone Hosp.; SHO (Cas. & O & G) Guy's Hosp. Lond.; SHO (Paediat. & Community Child Health) N.. Gen. Hosp. Sheff.

COX, Jeremy Patrick Halton Orford Lodge Surgery, 100 Bancroft, Hitchin SG5 1ND Tel: 01462 432042 Fax: 01462 436505 — MB BS 1984 Lond.

COX, Jeremy Philip Douglas Thornton Goose Cottage, Yeabridge, South Petherton TA13 5LW Tel: 01460 240779 — MB BS 1991 Lond.; BA Physiol. Sci. Oxf. 1988; MRCP (UK) 1995. (Oxf. Univ. & St. Bart. Hosp. Lond.) MRC Train. Fell. (Molecular Endocrinol.) Hammersmith Hosp. Lond. Prev: SHO Nat. Hosp. Neurol. Lond.; SHO (Gen. Med.) N.wick Pk. Hosp. Harrow.

COX, Jeremy Stewart, MBE, Lt.-Col. RAMC Retd. 4 Lampton Close, Wool, Wareham BH20 6EW Tel: 01979 467785 Email: jeremy@starlight66.freeserve.co.uk, jermery@starlight66.freeserve.co.uk; 4 Lampton Close, Wool, Wareham BH20 6EW Tel: 01929 462785 Email: starlight_aden@yahoo.com — MB BS 1960 Lond.; MRCGP 1974; DTM & H Eng. 1973. (Univ. Coll. Hosp.) Locum- GP. Socs: Wessex Med. Soc.; Ordinary. Prev: Sen. Med. Off. Med. Centre Bovington Camp; Sen. Med. Off. Roy. Armoured Corps Centre; SHO (Surg.) Vict. Hosp. Romford.

COX, Joanna Elizabeth 19B Eslington Terrace, Newcastle upon Tyne NE2 4RL — BM BCh 1990 Oxf.

COX, Joanna Winifred Nailsea Health Centre, Somerset Square, Nailsea, Bristol BS48 1RR Tel: 01275 856611 Fax: 01275 857074 — MB BS 1985 Lond.; MRCGP 1990; DRCOG 1988. Prev: Trainee GP Bristol VTS; Ho. Phys. Whittington Hosp. Lond.; Ho. Surg. Roy. United Hosp. Bath.

COX, Joanne 49 Longnor Road, Heald Green, Cheadle SK8 3BW Tel: 0161 282 2609 — BM BS 1988 Nottm.; BMedSci Nottm. 1986; MRCOG 1995. Research Regist. Qu. Charlotte's & Chelsea Hosp. Lond.; Regist. (Obst. & Gyn.) W. Middlx. Hosp. Middlx. Prev: Regist. (O & G) Chelsea & W.minster Hosp. Lond.

COX, John 19 Belle Vue Road, Weymouth DT4 8RZ — MB ChB 1944 Birm.

COX, John Desmond (retired) Horsepool Meadow, Chulmleigh EX18 7BW Tel: 01769 580400 — MB BChir Camb. 1948; BA Camb. 1946. Prev: Ho. Off. (ENT) & Cas. Off. (Surg.) Middlx. Hosp.

COX, John Lee Department of Psychiatry, School of Postgraduate Medicine, Thornburrow Drive, Hartshill, Stoke-on-Trent ST4 7QB Tel: 01782 554019 Fax: 01782 747319 Email: pca02@keele.ac.uk; 104 Horwood Houses, Keele, Newcastle ST5 5BH Tel: 01782 637526 — BM BCh Oxf. 1965; MA, DM Oxf. 1978; FRCP Ed. 1985; MRCP (UK) 1970; FRCPsych 1987, M 1973; DPM Eng. 1971; FRCP (Lond.) 1997. Prof. Psychiat. Sch. Postgrad. Med. Univ. Keele, Staffs.; Cons. Psychiat. City Gen. Hosp.; Head of Dept. Psychiat. 1997-2000; Pres. Roy. Coll. Psychiat. 1999-2002. Prev: Sen. Lect. (Psychiat.) & Hon. Cons. Roy. Edin. Hosp.; Lect. (Psychiat.) Makerere Univ. Kampala, Uganda; Dean Roy. Coll. Psychiat. - 1993-1998.

COX, John Parry Westlake Surgery, High Street, West Coker, Yeovil BA22 9AH Tel: 01935 862212 Fax: 01935 865105; The Warren, Weston Street, East Chinnock, Yeovil BA22 9EQ Tel: 01935 863304 — BChir 1976 Camb.; BChir 1976 MB 1977 Camb.; MRCP (UK) 1979; MRCGP 1980; DRCOG 1979; DCH RCP Lond. 1978.

COX, John Rex 1 Ivy Grove, Ripley, Derby — MB BS 1958 Durh.; DObst RCOG 1962.

COX, John Rodgers (retired) 80 Slayleigh Lane, Sheffield S10 3RH Tel: 0114 230 5443 — MB ChB 1954 Sheff.; MD Sheff. 1961; FRCP Lond. 1981, M 1973; MRCS Eng. LRCP Lond. 1954; MRCPsych 1971; MRCGP 1962. Prev: Cons. Phys. (Med. & Rehabil.) Nether Edge & Lodge Moor Hosps. Sheff.

COX, John Stanley Lake Road Health Centre, Nutfield Place, Portsmouth PO1 4JT Tel: 023 92 821201 — MB BS 1950 Lond.; MRCS Eng. LRCP Lond. 1949; DObst RCOG 1951. (St. Bart.) Prev: Ho. Surg. St. Bart. Hosp. Lond.; Ho. Surg. (Obst.) N. Middlx. Hosp. Lond.; on Med. Staff. Gen. Hosp. Regina, Canada.

COX, Jonathan The Park Medical Centre, Maine Drive Clinic, Maine Drive, Chaddesden, Derby DE21 6LA Tel: 01332 665522 Fax: 01332 678210 — MB BChir 1985 Camb.; BSc Lond. 1982; MRCGP 1991; DRCOG 1989.

COX, Jonathan Karll The Paddock, Raunds, Wellingborough NN9 6EE — MB BChir 1992 Camb.; MA Camb. 1993. GP Princip. Prev: GP Regist. O & G Camb.; SHO (O & G) King's Lynn; SHO (A & E) King's Lynn.

COX, Julian Robert 10 Manor Road, Solihull B91 2BH Tel: 0121 705 3258 — MB ChB 1988 Birm.; BSc (Hons) Bristol 1982; MRCP (UK) 1995; DCH RCP Lond. 1991. Regist. (Paediat.) Sandwell Healthcare NHS Trust W. Bromwich.

COX, Julie Elizabeth Margaret 11 Castle Farm Mews, Jesmond, Newcastle upon Tyne NE2 3RG — MB BS 1993 Newc.

COX, Karen Anne 24 Mayton Avenue, Frettenham, Norwich NR12 7LH — MB ChB 1994 Manch.

COX, Karina Louise 140 Antill Road, London E3 5BN — MB BS 1998 Lond.; MB BS Lond 1998.

COX, Leonard Edward c/o Doctors Mess, Ipswich Hospital, Heath Road, Ipswich IP4 5PD — MB BS 1991 Queensland.

***COX, Lucy Julia** 4 College Farm Court, Barton, Cambridge CB3 7AL Tel: 01223 264282 — MB ChB 1998 Leeds.

COX, Margaret Lissant (retired) 6 High View Road, Leek ST13 5BS Tel: 01538 383146 — MB BChir 1949 Camb.; MRCS Eng. LRCP Lond. 1943; DObst RCOG 1950. Prev: GP Partner Leek.

COX, Maria Louise Watford General Hospital, Vicarage Road, Watford WD18 0HB Tel: 01923 217172 Fax: 01923 217715; The Shires, 14 Beechwood Road, Beaconsfield HP9 1HP — MB BS 1975 Lond.; FRCP Lond. 1994; MRCP (UK) 1980.

COX, Mark Aylwin The Corner House, 443 Streetsbrook Road, Solihull B91 1RB — MB BS 1986 Lond.; MRCP (UK) 1991. Cons. Gastroenterol., Manor Hosp., Walsall.

COX, Mark Lissant Magill Department of Anaesthesia, Chelsea & Westminster Hospital, 369 Fulham Road, London Tel: 020 8746 8026; 14A Queens Avenue, Muswell Hill, London N10 3NR Tel: 020 8444 0925 Email: marklcox@aol.com — MB BS 1990 Lond.; BSc Lond. 1987; FRCA 1995. Cons. Anaesth., Chelsea & W.m. Hosp. Socs: BMA; Assn. of Anaesth.s; Roy. Coll. of Anaesth.s. Prev: Specialist Regist. Roy. Brompton Hosp. Lond.

COX, Mark Timothy The General Hospital, St Helier, Jersey Tel: 01580 200391 — MB BS 1979 Lond.; MPhil Lond. 1993; MRCPsych 1984. (St. Thos.) Cons. Psychiat. Gen. Hosp., Jersey. Prev: Cons. Psychiat. Qu. Eliz. Milit. Hosp. Woolwich; Sen. Regist. (Psychiat.) P.ss Wales Hosp. Ely; Regist. (Psychiat.) Univ. Hosp. S. Manch.

COX, Meredydd Owen St Oswalds Surgery, The Parade, Pembroke SA71 4LD Tel: 01646 682374 Fax: 01646 622424; The Wells, St. Twynells, Pembroke SA71 5EE Tel: 01646 661317 — MB BCh 1982 Wales; MRCP (UK) 1985; MRCGP 1991; DCH RCP Lond. 1990.

COX, Michael Christopher Langton 26 Cherry Garden Avenue, Folkestone CT19 5LD Tel: 01303 275465 Fax: 01303 275465 — MRCS Eng. LRCP Lond. 1954. (Lond. Hosp.) Med. Adviser Goldshield Gp. Socs: Fell. Roy. Soc. Med. Prev: Ho. Surg. (Orthop.) St. Bart. Hosp. Rochester; Ho. Phys. (Radiother.) & Res. Anaesth. Lond. Hosp.; Dir. Clin. Research Laborat. (GB) Ltd.

COX, Michael Ievers (retired) Becksteps, Caldbeck, Wigton CA7 8EU Tel: 016974 78407 — MRCS Eng. LRCP Lond. 1946.

COX, Michael Jeffrey The Health Centre, Merstow Green, Evesham Tel: 01386 765600 — MB BS 1955 Lond.; MRCGP 1972. (Lond. Hosp.) Prev: Orthop. & Plastic Ho. Surg. Hosp. Sick Childr. Gt. Ormond St. Surg.; Regist. Vict. Hosp. Blackpool; Surg. Lt. RN.

COX, Mr Michael Llewellin (retired) Yew Tree Lodge, Main St., Higham-on-the-Hill, Nuneaton CV13 6AJ Tel: 01455 212799 Fax: 01455 212799 — MB ChB 1954 Bristol; MFFP 1993; FRCOG 1977, M 1964, DObst 1956.

COX, Natasha Mireille 35/6 Dean Street, Stockbridge, Edinburgh EH4 1LN — MB ChB 1996 Ed.

COX, Neil Harrison Department of Dermatology, Cumberland Infirmary, Carlisle CA2 7HY Tel: 01228 523444 Fax: 01228 814849 — MB ChB 1980 Liverp.; BSc (Hons.) Liverp. 1978; FRCP Lond. 1994; FRCP Ed. 1994. Cons. Dermat. N. Cumbria Acute Hosps. NHS Trust. Socs: Brit. Soc. Dermat. (completed term of office); Roy. Soc. Med. Counc. Mem. Dermatol. Sect.

COX, Niall 6 Beehive Close, Nine Elms, Swindon SN5 5UL — MB BS 1996 Lond.

COX, Niall Lawrence Thomas Dewsbury Hospital Tel: 01924 512000; 20 Westcombe Avenue, Leeds LS8 2BS Tel: 0113 266 3676 Email: niallcox@doctors.org.uk — MB BCh BAO 1987 Belf.; MRCP (UK) 1993.

COX, Nicholas Charles Mason (retired) 25 Hulse House, The Garden Village, Richmond DL10 4NS Email: nick@nocholascox.free-online.co.uk — MB BS 1981 Lond.

COX, Nigel Leigh Royal Hampshire County Hospital, Winchester SO22 5DG Tel: 01962 824919; The Old Vicarage, Colden Common, Winchester SO21 1TL Tel: 01962 712268 — BM BCh 1970 Oxf.; BA Oxf. 1970; MRCP (UK) 1973; MRCS Eng. LRCP Lond. 1970. Cons. Rheum. & Rehabil. Roy. Hants. Co. Hosp., Winchester.; Cons. Rheumatologist, Roy. Nat. Hosp. for Rheumatic Dis., Upper Boro. Walls, Bath.

COX, Paul William Miller Street Surgery, Miller Street, Off Kings Street, Newcastle ST5 1JD Tel: 01782 711618 Fax: 01782 713940; 11 Wymondley Grove, Trentham, Stoke-on-Trent ST4 8TW — MB ChB 1971 Birm.; MRCGP 1980; DObst RCOG 1974; DCH Eng. 1976. Prev: Trainee GP Birm. VTS; SHO (Anaesth.) United Birm. Hosps.

COX, Penelope Jane (retired) 25 Euston Road, London NW1 2SD Tel: 020 7713 6028 Fax: 020 7713 6035 — MB ChB 1985 Birm. Wom. Min. Ldr. Lond. Internat. Ch. of Christ.

COX, Peter Anthony 14 Kings Close, Kings Heath, Birmingham B14 6TP — BM 1979 Soton.

COX, Mr Peter John West Cornwall Hospital, St. Clare St., Penzance TR18 2PF Tel: 01736 874137 Fax: 01736 350134 Email: peter.cox@rcht.swest.nhs.uk; The Retreat, Polmennor Road, Heamoor, Penzance TR20 8UW Tel: 01736 330101 Email: retreat@retreat.free-online.co.uk — MB BS 1973 Lond.; BSc (1st cl. Hons.) Lond. 1969, MS 1990, MB BS 1973; FRCS Eng. 1979; MRCS Eng. LRCP Lond. 1973. (Char. Cross) Cons. Surg. W. Cornw. Hosp. Penzance. Prev: Sen. Regist. Rotat. (Surg.) W.m. Hosp. Lond.; Sen. Regist. (Surg.) Roy. Vict. Hosp. Bournemouth; Regist. Rotat. (Surg.) Newc. AHA (T).

COX, Mr Peter John Anthony Princess Elizabeth Orthopaedic Centre, Royal Devon and Exeter Hospital, Barrack Road, Exeter EX2 5DW Tel: 01392 411611; 5 Otter Court, Ingsdon, Bickington, Newton Abbot TQ12 6NW Tel: 01626 821628 Email: pja.cox@lineone.net.uk — MB BS 1983 Lond.; MS Lond. 1994; FRCS Ed. 1988; FRCS (Orth) 1995. (Char. Cross) Cons. Surg. (Orthop.) Roy. Devon & Exeter Health Care Trust; Childr. Orthop. Surg. Prev: Sen. Regist. Orthop. Soton.

COX, Peter John Raymond Lower Mulberry Cottage, Nanstallon, Bodmin PL30 5LJ Tel: 01208 831272 — MB BS Lond. 1965; MRCS Eng. LRCP Lond. 1964; DObst RCOG 1967. (Guy's) Socs: BMA & Brit. Assn. Immediate Care. Prev: SHO (O & G), Cas. Off. & Ho. Off. Hereford Gen. Hosp.

COX, Mr Peter Talbot High Brake, Favordale Road, Colne BB8 7AG — MD 1974 Manch.; MB ChB 1966; FRCS Eng. 1971. (Manch.) Cons. Orthop. Surg. Burnley Health Dist. Prev: Sen. Regist. (Orthop. Surg.) Manch. AHA (T); Ho. Phys. & Ho. Surg. Manch. Roy. Infirm; Sen. Research Assoc. (Surg.) Dept. Surg. Roy. Vict. Infirm. Newc.

COX, Philip John The New Surgery, Buxton Road, Tideswell, Buxton SK17 8NS Tel: 01298 871292 Fax: 01298 872580 — MB ChB 1980 Sheff.; BMedSci 1976, MB ChB Sheff. 1980; MRCGP 1985; DCH RCP Lond. 1984; DRCOG 1983. (Sheffield)

COX, Phillip Martin Department of Histopathology, ICSM, Hammersmith Hospital, Du Cane Road, London W12 0HS Tel: 020 8383 3280 Fax: 020 8740 7417 Email: pcox@rpms.ac.uk; 73 Sutherland Chase, Ascot SL5 8TE — MB BS 1984 Lond.; PhD Lond. 1994, MB BS 1984; MRCPath 1993. Sen. Lect. & Hon. Cons. RPMS. Socs: Internat. Acad. Path. & Assn. Clin. Path.; Brit. Paediat. Path. Assn. Prev: Sen. Regist. (Histopath.) St. Geo. Hosp. Lond. & Roy. Surrey Co. Hosp. Guildford; Clin. Research Fell. Marie Curie Cancer Research.

COX, Phyllis Marjorie Coppice House, 16 Wick House Close, Wick, Pershore WR10 3NT — MB ChB 1960 Ed.

COX, Pippa Marie 27 Tillingham Gardens, Clanfield, Waterlooville PO8 0XQ Tel: 01705 421027 — MB BS 1997 Lond. SHO (O & G), St.Mary's Hosp. Portsmouth. Prev: SHO (A&E), Qu. Alexandra Hosp., Portsmouth.

COX, Mr Quentin George Nelson Raigmore Hospital, Old Perth Road, Inverness IV2 3UJ Tel: 01463 704000 Fax: 01463 705568; Drumdelnies, Nairn IV12 5NT Tel: 01667 454175 — MB BS 1981 Lond.; FRCS Ed. (Orth.) 1992; FRCS Eng. 1986; FRCS Ed. 1986; FRCS Ed. Ortho. 1992. Cons. Orthop. Surg. Raigmore Hosp. Inverness. Socs: Fell. BOA; Assoc. Mem. Brit. Soc. Surg. Hand. Prev: Cons. Orthop. Surg. Leicester Roy. Infirm. & Leicester Gen. Hosp.; Sen. Regist. (Orthop. Surg.) Derby Roy. Infirm. & Harlow Wood Orthop. Hosp.; Research Fell. (Orthop.) John Hopkins Univ. Baltimore, USA.

COX, Rachel Michelle 1 Fitzgerald Road, Sheffield S10 1GX — MB ChB 1995 Sheff.

COX, Mr Robert Department of Urology, Royal Cornwall Hospital, Truro TR1 3LJ Tel: 01872 252562 Fax: 01872 252417 Email: robert.cox@rcht.swest.nhs.uk; Tresevern House, Stithians, Truro TR3 7AR Tel: 01209 860130 Fax: 01209 860661 Email: rc@treseverh.demon.co.uk — MB BS 1972 Lond.; MD Lond. 1985; FRCS Eng. 1977. (St. Thos.) Cons. Urol. Roy. Cornw. Hosps. Trust. Socs: Brit. Assn. Urol. Surg. Prev: Cons. Urol. Cornw. & I. of Scilly HA; Sen. Regist. (Urol.) Cardiff; Regist. St. Peter's Gp. Hosps. Lond.

COX, Robert Ramsay X-Ray Department, Nuffield Hospital, Plymouth PL6 8BG Tel: 01752 703710; 22 Cranmere Road, Higher Compton, Plymouth PL3 5JY Tel: 01752 772403 — MRCS Eng. LRCP Lond. 1957; MA Oxf. 1954; DMRD Eng. 1965. (Guy's) Cons. Radiol. Plymouth HA. Socs: Fell. Roy. Soc. Med. Prev: Sen. Regist. (Radiol.) St. Mark's, Brompton & Roy. Nat. Orthop. Hosps.

COX, Robin Anthony Frederick Linden House, Long Lane, Fowlmere SG8 7TG Tel: 01763 208636 Fax: 01763 208549 Email: rafcox@lineone.net; Linden House, Long Lane, Fowlmere SG8 7TG Tel: 01763 208636 Fax: 01763 208549 Email: rafcox@lineone.net — MB BChir Camb. 1960; MA Camb. 1960; FRCP Lond. 1988; FFOM RCP Lond. 1984, MFOM 1980. (Camb. & Guy's) p/t Indep. Occupat.al Med. Cons. Socs: Fell. Roy. Soc. Med. (Ex-Pres. Sect. Occupat. Med.); Ex-Vice Dean Fac. Occupat. Med.; Soc. Occupat. Med. Prev: Chief Med. Off. Nat. Power plc; Chief Med. Off. Centr. Electricity Generating Bd.; Med. Dir. Phillips Petroleum Co. Europe & Afr.

COX, Rosamond Andree (retired) The Old Rectory, Ashley, Market Harborough LE16 8DH Tel: 01858 565518 Fax: 01858 565518 — BM BCh 1971 Oxf.; MRCPath 1984; FRCPath 1996. Prev: Cons. Med. Microbiol. Kettering & Dist. Gen. Hosp.

COX, Ruth Angela 10 Bewick Road, Gateshead NE8 4DP Tel: 0191 477 1536; 7 Glenbrooke Terrace, Low Fell, Gateshead NE9 6AJ — MB BS 1971 Newc.; MRCGP 1975; DCH RCPS Glas. 1973.

COX, Sarah Medical Day Unit, Chelsea and Westminster Hospital, 369 Fulham Rd, London SW10 9NH Tel: 0208 237 5054 Email: sarah.cox@chelwest.nhs.uk — MB BS 1989 Lond.; BSc (Hons) Lond. 1986; MRCP (UK) 1992. Cons. (Palliat. Med.) Chelsea & W.minister Hosp., Lond. & Trinity hospice, Lond. Prev: Sen. Regist. (Palliat. Med.) Eden Hall Hospice & Roy. Free Hosp., Lond.; Sen. Regist. (Palliat. Med.) St Bartholomews Hosp., Lond.; Sen. Regist. (Palliat. Med.) Whipps Cross Hosp., Lond.

COX, Simon North Road Surgery, 17 North Road, Great Clacton, Clacton-on-Sea CO15 4DA Tel: 01255 224600 Fax: 01255 224617; Burnsall, 754 St John's Road, Clacton-on-Sea CO16 8BN Tel: 01255 820749 — MB BS 1966 Lond.; MRCS Eng. LRCP Lond. 1966; DObst RCOG 1969. (King's Coll. Hosp.) Gen. Pract. Phys. Clacton & Dist. Hosp.; Sen. Police Surg. Essex (Tendring Div.). Socs: BMA. Prev: SHO (O & G) Ipswich & E. Suff. Hosp.; Ho. Surg. (A & E) King's Coll. Hosp. Lond.; Ho. Surg. (Paediat.) Brook Gen. Hosp. Lond.

COX, Mr Simon James 63 High Road, Bushey Heath, Watford WD2 1EE — MB BS 1965 Lond.; FRCS Eng. 1970; MRCS Eng. LRCP Lond. 1965. (St. Thos.) Cons. Surg. Watford Gen. Hosp. Socs:

Assn. Surgs. Prev: Regist., Hon. Lect. & Sen. Regist. (Surg.) St. Thos. Hosp. Lond.

COX, Stephen Andrew Melbourne Park Medical Centre, Melbourne Road, Aspley, Nottingham NG8 5HL Tel: 0115 978 6114 Fax: 0115 924 9334; 8 Killisick Road, Arnold, Nottingham NG5 8DB Tel: 0115 955 4258 — MB ChB 1977 Birm.; MRCGP 1981; DRCOG 1980. Police Surg. Notts. Constab.; Trainer Nottm. VTS.

COX, Stephen James The Spinney Medical Centre, 23 Whittle Street, St Helens WA10 3EB Tel: 01744 758999 Fax: 01744 758322 — MB ChB 1987 Liverp.; T(GP) 1992; DGM RCP Lond. 1991. Mem. St Helens & Knowsley Young Princips. in Gen. Pract.

COX, Mr Stephen Nigel Barn's Piece, Barrack Hill, Nether Winchendon, Aylesbury HP18 0DU — MB BS 1976 Lond.; FRCS Eng. (Ophth.) 1983; FCOphth 1989; DO Eng. 1980. (ST. Thos.) Cons. Ophth. High Wycombe & Stoke Mandeville. Prev: Jt. Sen. Regist. (Ophth.) Lond. Whitechapel & Moorfields Hosps.; Lect. (Clin. Ophth.) Moorfields Eye Hosp. Lond.; Regist. (Ophth.) Greenwich & Dist. & St. Thos. Hosps. Lond.

COX, Stephen Philip The Surgery, Ivy Court, Tenterden TN30 6RB Tel: 01580 763666/764022 Fax: 01580 766199; 12 Westwell Court, Tenterden TN30 6TS Tel: 01580 764556 Fax: 01580 765981 Email: scox@avnet.co.uk — BM 1986 Soton.; BA (Hons.) (CNAA) 1977; MRCGP 1990; Cert. Av. Med. 1998. (Soton.) Hon. Med. Off. Kent & E. Sussex Steam Railway. Prev: SHO John Radcliffe Hosp. Oxf. VTS; Ho. Phys. Roy. S. Hants. Hosp. Soton.; Ho. Surg. Stafford Dist. Gen. Hosp.

COX, Stephen Ronald Giletts Surgery, Deanland Road, Balcombe, Haywards Heath RH17 6PH Tel: 01444 811948; Downsview, 23 College Road, Ardingly, Haywards Heath RH17 6TU — MB BS 1982 Lond.; MSc 2000 Oxf.; LMSSA Lond. 1982; MRCGP 1986; DRCOG 1987. Prev: Trainee GP Measham Med. Unit; SHO (O & G) New Cross Hosp. Wolverhampton; SHO (Med. & Geriat.) Burton-on-Trent Gen. Hosp.

COX, Steven Alan Lissant The Simpson Health Centre, 70 Gregories Road, Beaconsfield HP9 1PS Tel: 01494 671571 Fax: 01494 680219; The Shires, 14 Beechwood Road, Beaconsfield HP9 1HP — MA; BM BCh Oxf. 1974; MRCGP 1979; DCH Eng. 1978; DRCOG 1977.

COX, Stuart James (retired) 29 Berengrave Lane, Rainham, Gillingham ME8 7LS Tel: 01634 366775 — MB BCh BAO 1953 Belf.; BA 1998. JP.; Chairm. Kent Social Servs.; Chairm. Kent Jt. Consultative Comm. for Personal Servs.; Mem. Bd. Age Concern Eng.; Dir. Bridge Wardens Coll. Univ.Kent. Prev: Charm. Medway HA.

COX, Stuart Jeremy 30 New End Square, London NW3 1LS — MB BS 1987 Lond.; BA Oxf. 1978; MRCPsych 1992. Clin. Lect. & Hon. Sen. Regist. Rotat. Univ. Coll. Lond. Prev: Regist. Rotat. NW Thames.

COX, Susan Mary Marine Parade Surgery, 1 Marine Parade, Lowestoft NR33 0QL Tel: 01502 257 4072; 19 Silverwood Close, Lowestoft NR33 7LX — MB ChB 1971 Sheff. (Sheff.) GP LoW.oft; Clin. Asst. (Geriat.) LoW.oft & N. Suff. Hosp.; Chairperson LoW.oft PCG. Socs: Suff. Local Med. Comm.; Chairperson Waveney GP Forum. Prev: Clin. Med. Off. Norf. AHA; Ho. Phys. & Cas. Off. Roy. Hosp. Sheff.

COX, Susan Nicola Allison 16 Whitefield Road, Whitecliff, Poole BH14 8DD — MB ChB 1984 Bristol; MRCP (UK) 1987. Prev: Trainee GP/SHO (Med.) Torbay.

COX, Thomas James (retired) 11 Penydarren Park, Merthyr Tydfil CF47 8YW Tel: 01685 376582 — MB BCh BAO 1946 NUI. Prev: Asst. Med. Off. St. Otterns Ment. Hosp. Waterford.

COX, Timothy Charles Southam Great Ormond Street Hospital for Children, London WC1 Email: t.cox@ich.ucl.ac.uk; 20 Hamilton Road, Ealing, London W5 2EH Tel: 020 8567 3926 — MB BS 1973 Lond.; FRCR 1980. (Middlx. Hosp. Med. Sch.) Cons. Neuroradiologist The Nat. & Gt. Ormond St. Hosps. Prev: Cons. (Neuroradiol.) Guy's, Bethlem Roy. & Maudsley Hosps. Lond.

COX, Timothy John Coleridge Medical Centre, Ottery St Mary EX11 1EQ Tel: 01404 814447 Fax: 01404 815971; Moneyglass Cottage, Colestocks, Honiton EX14 3JR Tel: 01404 850005 — MB BS 1973 Lond.; MRCP (UK) 1975; MRCS Eng. LRCP Lond. 1973; DRCOG 1980. (Guy's) Prev: SHO Rotat. (Med.) Brighton Health Dist.; Resid. (Paediat.) Edwd. VII Hosp. Bermuda; Regist. (Med.) Auckland Health Dist.

COX, Professor Timothy Martin Department of Medicine, Level 5, Addenbrooke's Hospital, Hills Road, Cambridge CB2 2QQ Tel: 01223 336864 Fax: 01223 336846 Email: jbg20@medschl.cam.ac.uk — MB BS 1971 Lond.; FMedSci 1998; MSc Lond. 1978, MD 1979; MD Camb. 1991; FRCP Lond. 1984; MRCP (UK) 1973. (Lond. Hosp.) Prof. Med. Univ. Camb. Sch. Clin. Med. Addenbrooke's Hosp.; Hon. Cons. Phys. Addenbrooke's Hosp. Socs: Comm. Mem. Med. Research Soc.; Assn. Phys.; Brit. Soc. of Gastroentology. Prev: Sen. Lect. (Haemat.) & Cons. Phys. (Med.) Roy. Postgrad. Med. Sch. Hammersmith Hosp. Lond.; Wellcome Sen. Lect. (Clin. Sc.) & Cons. Phys. (Med.) Roy. Postgrad. Med. Sch. Hammersmith Hosp. Lond.; Vis. Scientist (Biol.) Mass. Inst. Technol. Mass., USA.

COX, Victoria Alison 2 Ford Lane, Frilford, Abingdon OX13 5NS — MB ChB 1998 Leeds.

COX, Victoria Margaret Harewood Medical Practice, Richmond Road, Catterick Garrison DL9 3JD Tel: 01748 833904 Fax: 01748 834290 — BM BS 1980 Nottm.; MRCGP 1986. (Nottingham) Co-Dir. Nurse Practitioner Progr. (Health Studies) Univ. of York; Med. Adviser N. Yorks. HA.

COX-MAKSIMOV, Desiree Cheryl Thelma Wolfson College, Cambridge University, Cambridge CB3 9BB — BM BCh 1992 Oxf.; MPhil (Hist. Med.) Camb. 1993; BSc (Hons.) Chem. & Physics McGill Univ. Montreal 1986. PhD Stud. (Hist. Med.) Camb. Univ. Prev: Tutor Physiol. Clare Coll. Camb. Univ.

COX MCNEIL LOVE, Robin Michael 42A Castle Road, Southsea PO5 3DE — MB BS 1984 Lond. (Lond. & Roy. Free)

COXALL, Susan Jane 4 Chilton Road, Hitchin SG4 9PL — MB ChB 1988 Sheff.

COXHEAD, Mihiri Saman 20 The Glade, Welshwood Park, Colchester CO4 3JD — MRCS Eng. LRCP Lond. 1990.

COXHEAD, Neil Birchwood, King Coel Road, Colchester CO3 5AG — MB BS 1980 Lond. Cons. Psychiat. Linden Centre Chelmsford. Socs: Roy. Coll. Psychiat.

COXON, Alan (retired) 11 Kenton Road, Gosforth, Newcastle upon Tyne NE3 4NE — MB BS 1952 Durh.; FRCOG 1977, M 1964, DObst 1957. Prev: Cons. O & G Newc. & N.d HAs.

COXON, Ann Yvonne 121 Harley Street, London W1G 7AZ Tel: 020 7486 2534 Fax: 020 7637 1665 Email: coxon@easynet.co.uk; 18 Ladbroke Gardens, London W11 2PT Tel: 0207 229 7849 — MB BS 1963 Lond.; MRCP Lond. 1968; DCH Eng. 1965. (Guy's) Indep. Pract. Socs: Harveian Soc. & Med. Soc.; Roy. Soc. Med. Prev: Research Dir. Howard Foundat. Camb.; Sen. Regist. Nat. Hosp. Nerv. Dis. Qu. Sq. Lond. & St. Bart. Hosp. Lond.

COXON, Fareeda Yasmine (Ahmed) Northern Centre for Cancer Treatment, Newcastle General Hospital, Newcastle NE4 6BE Tel: 0191 219 4208 — MB BS 1988 Lond.; MRCP (UK) 1992. (Charing Cross and Westminster Medical School) Cons. Med. Oncol., NCCT, Newc. Gen. Hosp., Newc.-upon-Tyne; Hon. Clin. Lect. Prev: Specialist Regist. (Med. Oncol.) Anchor Unit Aberd. Roy. Infirm. Aberd.; Clin. Research Fell. & Hon. Regist. Roy. Marsden Hosp. Lond.; ICRF Research Fell. ICRF Colorectal Cancer Unit St. Marks Hosp. Lond.

COXON, Ian David Glenlyn Medical Centre, 115 Molesey Park Road, East Molesey KT8 0JX Tel: 020 8979 3253 Fax: 020 8941 7914; Magnolia Cottage, Giggs Hill Road, Thames Ditton KT7 0BT Tel: 020 8398 3642 — MB ChB 1969 St. And.; DObst RCOG 1973. (St. And.) Prev: SHO (Orthop. & A & E) Centr. Middlx. Hosp. Lond.; SHO (Obst.) City of Lond. Matern. Hosp.; SHO (Paediat.) W.m. Childr. Hosp. Lond.

COXON, Mr John George (retired) — MB BS Lond. 1943; FRCS Eng. 1947; MRCS Eng. LRCP Lond. 1943. Prev: Urol. Calderdale Hosps.

COXON, Jonathan Philip 62 Blue Waters Dr, Paignton TQ4 6JF — BM BCh 1997 Oxf.

COXON, Nicholas Richard 4 Walter Scott Avenue, Wigan WN1 2RH — BM BS 1996 Nottm.

COXON, Thomas Charles Old Fletton Surgery, Rectory Gardens, Peterborough PE2 8AY Tel: 01733 315141 Fax: 01733 894739 Email: charles.coton@gp-d81029.nhs.uk — MB 1981 Camb.; MA Camb. 1981, BChir 1980; DRCOG 1984. (St. Thos.) GP P'Boro. Prev: SHO (Anaesth.) St. Thos. Hosp. Lond.; GP W. Suff. Hosp. VTS.

COY, Aisling Anne Christina 21 Mill Lane, Heswall, Wirral CH60 2TE — MB ChB 1993 Birm.

COY, Sarah Elizabeth 33 Merrygreen Place, Stewarton, Kilmarnock KA3 5EP — MB ChB 1995 Glas.

COYER, Anthony Brian (retired) Elmleaze, 86 Wyke Road, Weymouth DT4 9QJ Tel: 01305 785224 — MB BS 1942 Durh.; DPhysMed. Eng. 1953. Prev: Cons. Phys. Rahab & Rheum. W.Dorset Hosp.s 1956-1985.

COYER, John (retired) Southwood, Southwood Avenue, Ottershaw, Chertsey KT16 0LH — MB ChB 1953 Birm.; DObst RCOG 1960. Prev: Ho. Surg. Hull Matern. Hosp.

COYLE, Ann Christina 216 Carmunnock Road, Glasgow G44 5AP Tel: 0141 637 5379 — MB ChB 1950 Glas.; DObst. RCOG 1952.

COYLE, Catherine Ann Department of Clinical Oncology, UCCO Cookridge Hospital, Leeds LS16 6QB Tel: 0113 392 4082 Fax: 0113 392 4052 — MB BCh BAO 1985 Belf.; MRCP 1990; FRCR 1995. Cons. Clin. Oncol. Cookridge Hosp. Leeds.

***COYLE, Christopher John** Haafgarn House, Browhouses, Annan DG12 6TG Tel: 01461 40070 — MB ChB 1994 Sheff.

COYLE, Denis John 1 Rosepark E., Dundonald, Belfast BT5 7RL — MB BCh BAO 1976 Belf.

COYLE, Edward Francis 1 Llwyn-y-pia Road, Cardiff CF14 0SX — MB ChB 1978 Manch.; MFPHM RCP (UK) 1988; MRCGP 1983; FFPHM 1994. Dir. Pub. Health Med. Gwent HA; Dir. Pub. Health Gwent HA. Prev: Cons. Pub. Health Med. S. Glam. HA.

COYLE, Fintan Maurice Albion Street Health Centre, 87 Albion St., Rotherhithe, London SE16 7JX Tel: 020 7237 2092 Fax: 020 7231 1435; 59 Speldhurst Road, London W4 1BY Tel: 020 8747 1347 Fax: 020 8747 1347 — MB BS 1987 Lond.; DRCOG 1992. Med. Edr. 'Geriat. Med.'. Prev: Trainee GP Lond.; SHO (Genitourin. Med. & O & G) Char. Cross Hosp. Lond.; SHO (Paediat.) Greenwich Hosp. Lond.

COYLE, Frances Mary 15 Porth y Castell, Barry CF62 6QA — MB BCh 1993 Wales.

COYLE, Hugh Edward Hunter Health Centre, Andrew Street, East Kilbride, Glasgow G74 1AD Tel: 01355 906655 — MB ChB 1975 Glas.; MRCP (UK) 1979; DRCOG 1981.

COYLE, Jeanette Margaret Anne 15 Porth Y Castell, Barry CF62 6QA — MB ChB 1993 Birm.

COYLE, John Benjamin 143 Langer Lane, Chesterfield S40 2JP — MB ChB 1998 Leic.; MB ChB Leic 1998.

COYLE, John Manus 7 Strathmore Park S., Antrim Road, Belfast BT15 5HJ — MB BCh BAO 1990 Belf.; MB BCh Belf. 1990.

COYLE, Mervyn Edward 16 Cofton Road, West Heath, Birmingham B31 3QP — MB BS 1982 Lond.; MRCP (UK) 1988; DRCOG 1990. GP Perth, W. Austral.

COYLE, Mr Patrick Joseph Bro Morgannwg NHS Trust, 71 Quarella Road, Bridgend CF31 1YE Tel: 01656 752968 Email: patrick.coyle@bromor-tr.wales.nhs.uk; 20 Long Oaks Court, Sketty, Swansea SA2 0QH Tel: 01792 290516 Fax: 01792 290516 Email: patjcoyle@aol.com — MRCS Eng. LRCP Lond. MRCS Eng. LRCP Lond. 1969; FRCS Eng. 1976; DObst RCOG 1972. (Char. Cross) Med. Dir. Bro Morgannwg NHS Trust, Bridgend and Neath Port Talbot; Cons. Surg. Bro Morgannwg NHS Trust. Socs: Brit. Assn. Surg. Oncol.; Roy. Soc. Mem. Roy. Soc. Med.; Guild Catholic Doctors. Prev: Cons. Co-ordinator & Advisor Med. Audit Wales; Cons. Surg. W. Glam. HA, Neath; Sen. Regist. (Surg.) Univ. Hosp. Wales, Cardiff & Singleton Hosp. Swansea.

COYLE, Paula Rose 26 Clifford Drive, Chester CH4 7PA — BM 1987 Soton.; DRCOG 1991. Clin. Med. Off. (Community Paediat.) Countess of Chester Hosp. Prev: Volun. Work AbRd. Action Health 2000; Trainee GP Chester VTS.

COYLE, Peter James Mawney Road Practice, 34 Mawney Road, Romford RM7 7HD Tel: 01708 743627 Fax: 01708 738244 — MB BS 1959 Lond.; DObst. RCOG 1962. (Lond. Hosp.)

COYLE, Peter Valentine 9 Archvale Park, Newtownabbey BT36 6LL — MB BCh BAO 1979 Belf.

COYLE, Victoria Mary 25 Upper Lisburn Road, Balmoral, Belfast BT10 0GX — MB BCh 1998 Belf.; MB BCh Belf 1998.

COYLE-GILCHRIST, Margaret Mercedes (retired) Stoneleigh, Church St., Farndon, Chester CH3 6QU Tel: 01829 270258 — MB ChB 1955 Liverp.; MD Liverp. 1958; FRCPath 1976, M 1966. Prev: Cons. Path. Maelor Gen. Hosp. Wrexham.

COYNE, Helen Margaret Walker Medical Group, Walker Health Centre, Walker, Newcastle upon Tyne NE6 3BS Tel: 0191 220 5905 Fax: 0191 220 5904; 58 Moor Road North, Gosforth, Newcastle upon Tyne NE3 1AB Tel: 0191 285 7795 — MB BS 1976 Newc.; MRCGP 1980; DRCOG 1978. (Newcastle upon Tyne) Gen. Practitioner, Walker Med. Gp., Walker Healthcare, Newc. upon Tyne. Prev: Clin. Asst. Diabetes Centre Newc. Gen. Hosp.

COYNE, John Dermot Department of Histopathology, University Hospital of South Manchester, West Didsbury, Manchester M20 8LR Tel: 0161 445 8111 — LRCPI & LM, LRSCI & LM 1977; LRCPI & LM, LRCSI & LM 1977; MRCPath 1987; DCH NUI 1979. Cons. Histopath. S. Manch. HA. Prev: Ho. Off. (Med.) St. Luke's Hosp. Kilkenny; Regist. (Histopath.) Reg. Hosp. Cork; Lect. Histopath. Univ. Hosp. of S. Manch.

COYNE, Linda Anne The Health Centre, Penstone Park, Lancing BN15 9AG Tel: 01903 763144; 32 Ring Road, Lancing BN15 0QE Tel: 01903 753536 — MB BS 1974 Lond.; LRCPI & LM, LRCSI & LM 1972; DCH RCPSI 1973.

COYNE, Philip Michael Forest Hall Medical Centre, Station Road, Forest Hall, Newcastle upon Tyne NE12 9BQ Tel: 0191 220 5800 Fax: 0191 220 5814 — MB BS 1976 Newc.; MRCGP 1980; DRCOG 1980.

COZENS, Alison Lenise (3F2) 10 Marchmont Crescent, Edinburgh EH9 1HN — MB ChB 1996 Ed.

COZENS, John Alastair Woodend Hospital, Eday Road, Aberdeen AB15 6XS — MB BS 1985 Newc.; MD Newc. 1996, BMedSc 1982; FRCS Ed. 1990. Cons. Rehabil. Med. Woodend Hosp. Aberd. Prev: Sen. Regist. (Rehabil.) Leeds; Regist. (Neurosurg.) Roy. Hallamsh. Hosp. Sheff.; Research Regist. Univ. Newc.

COZENS, Neil James Alan Department of Radiology, Derbyshire Royal Infirmary, London Road, Derby DE1 2QY Tel: 01332 347141; Park View, 1 Ashbourne Road, Kirk Langley, Derby DE6 4NS — MB ChB 1986 Birm.; FRCR 1992; DMRD Ed. 1991. Cons. Radiol. Derbysh. Roy. Infirm. Derby. Prev: Sen. Regist. (Radiol.) Roy. Infirm. Edin.

COZZI, Emanuele .Department of Surgery, .University of Cambridge, Addenbrooke's Hospital, Cambridge CB2 2AH Tel: 01223 336986 Fax: 01223 410772; 15 Barbraham Road, Cambridge CB2 2AH Tel: 0498 847906 — State DMS 1989 Padua; State DMS Padua 1984. (University of Padua) Clin. Research Assoc., Univ. of Camb. Socs: Soc. Italiana Di Immunologia Immunopath.; Soc. Italiana Di Allergologia.

CRABB, Godfrey Reynold Bonar Bridge Surgery, Library Buildings, Bonar Bridge, Ardgay IV24 3DH Tel: 01863 766383 Fax: 01863 766671 — MB ChB 1968 Ed.; BSc (Hons.) Lond. 1964. Socs: Accred. Mem. Brit. Soc. Med. & Dent. Hypn.

CRABB, Herbert Henry (retired) Southcott House, Pewsey SN9 5JF Tel: 01672 63408 — MRCS Eng. LRCP Lond. 1939; DObst RCOG 1947. Prev: Ho. Surg. Roy. S. Hants. Hosp.

CRABB, Ian Jonathan Department of Anaesthetics, Gloucestershire Royal Hospital, Great Western Road, Gloucester GL1 3NN Tel: 01452 394442 Email: ian.crabb@gloucs-tr.swest-nhs.uk — MB BS 1983 Lond.; FCAnaesth. 1991; DA (UK) 1987. Cons. (Anaesth. Inrensive Care), Gloucestershire Roy. Hosp. Prev: Clin. Fell. (Anaesth.), Roy. N. Shore Hosp., Sydney, NSW.

CRABB, Keith Andrew 22 Church Street, Taunton TA1 3JF Tel: 01823 51247 — MB BS 1979 Lond.; MRCGP 1984; DRCOG 1983; DCH RCP Lond. 1982; DA (UK) 1985. Prev: SHO (Anaesth.) Mt. Vernon Hosp. Middlx.; SHO (Anaesth.) Watford Gen. Hosp.

CRABB, Simon John Tarbet Croft, Marringdean Rd, Billingshurst RH14 9HD — MB BS 1996 Lond.

CRABBE, Mr David Christopher Geoffrey Department of Paediatric Surgery, Leeds General Infirmary, Great George St., Leeds LS2 9NS Tel: 0113 243 2799 Fax: 0113 392 6609 — MB BS 1983 Newc.; MD Newc. 1994; FRCS Eng. 1988; FRCS Ed. 1987; FRCS (Paediat.) 1995. (Newcastle upon Tyne) Cons. Paediat. Surg. Leeds Gen. Infirm.; Hon. Sen. Lect. (Paediat. Surg.) Univ. of Leeds. Prev: Sen. Regist. (Paediat. Surg.) Hosp. Sick Childr. Lond.; MRC Research Fell. Childr. Hosp. Los Angeles, Calif., USA; Regist. Rotat. (Surg.) Newc. u. Tyne.

CRABBE, George Geoffrey (retired) Church Farm, Ryhall, Stamford PE9 4HR Tel: 01780 62227 — MB ChB 1954 Bristol; FFA RCS Eng. 1965. Prev: Cons. Anaesth. P'boro. & Dist. Hosps.

CRABBE, Ian Frank Palms Medical Centre, 97-101 Netley Road, Newbury Park, Ilford IG2 7NW Tel: 020 8554 9551 Fax: 020 8518 2045; 24 Sylvan Way, Chigwell Row, Chigwell IG7 4QB Tel: 020 8501 0783 Fax: 020 8518 2045 — MB BS 1969 Lond.; FRCGP 1995, M 1976; DObst RCOG 1972. (St. Bart.) Course Organiser Ilford VTS sine 1984; Mem. Redbridge & Waltham Forest LMC. Socs: World Org. Family Doctors. Prev: Trainer GP Ilford VTS; Redbridge & Waltham Forest LMC 74-99.

CRABBE, Michael George Andrew Brook Bushes, Bramshaw, Lyndhurst SO43 7JB — MB ChB 1988 Leic.

CRABBE, Rachel Mary Gomer Church View Surgery, School La, Collingham, Wetherby LS22 5BQ Tel: 01937 573848 Fax: 01937 574754; 9 Tudor lawns, Roundhay, Leeds LS8 2JR Tel: 0113 265 7415 — MB BS 1983 Newc.; MRCGP 1987; DRCOG 1986. (Newcastle) p/t GP Princip.; Clin. Asst. Combined BrE. Clinic Leeds Gen. Infirm.; Health Screening Phys. BUPA Hosp. Leeds; Asst. GP Ch. View Surg. Collingham, Leeds. Prev: Asst. GP Hemel Hempstead & Princip. GP S. Shields; Trainee GP N.d. VTS.

CRABBE, Raymond William 61 Avondown Road, Durrington, Salisbury SP4 8ET — MB ChB 1984 Leeds; BSc (Hons.) Leeds 1981, MB ChB I984; MRCP (UK) 1990. Regist. (Diag. Radiol.) Guy's Hosp. Lond.; Regist. (Diag. Radiol.) Qu. Eliz. Milit. Hosp. Lond.

CRABBE, Sharon Ann Chapel Street Clinic, Chapel St., Widnes WA8 7RE Tel: 0151 424 2156; 102 Townfield Lane, Oxton, Birkenhead CH43 2LH Tel: 0151 652 7762 — MB ChB 1989 Liverp.; MRCPsych 1994. Sen. Regist. (Psychiat.) Mersey RHA.

CRABBE, Susan Jean The Almshouse Surgery, Trinity Medical Centre, Thornhill Street, Wakefield WF1 1PG Tel: 01924 327150 Fax: 01924 327165; 10 Wellhead Mews, Chapelthorpe, Wakefield WF4 3JG Tel: 01924 254355 Fax: 01924 200614 — MB ChB 1976 Sheff.

CRABBIE, Elizabeth Morag Balmuick Farm, Comrie, Crieff PH6 2LY Tel: 01764 70286 & profess. 70217 — MB ChB 1970 Aberd. (Aberd.)

CRABTREE, Barbara Jane Fore Street, Wellington, Taunton TA21 8AB Tel: 01823 662836 Fax: 01823 660955 — MB BS 1976 Lond.; BSc Lond. 1972; DRCOG 1978; Cert. Family Plann. JCC 1979. (Roy. Free) GP Wellington.

CRABTREE, Claire 10 Central Drive, Rainford, St Helens WA11 8DE — MB BS 1998 Lond.; MB BS Lond 1998.

CRABTREE, Helen Louise Beaufront, Beaufront Terrace, East Boldon NE36 0PN — MB BS 1990 Lond.; MRCP (UK) 1994.

CRABTREE, Janet Mary 35 Water Meadow Way, Wendover, Aylesbury HP22 6RS Tel: 01296 623545 — MB BS 1987 Lond.; MRCP (UK) 1991; MRCGP 1995; DRCOG 1994.

CRABTREE, John 11 Hillcroft Close, Darrington, Pontefract WF8 3BD — MB ChB 1983 Leeds; T(GP) 1991.

CRABTREE, John David (retired) Bullace Grange, Millhouse Green, Penistone, Sheffield S36 9NS — MB ChB 1949 Sheff.; MFOM RCP Lond. 1980.

CRABTREE, Nicholas Alexander 7 New Laithe Close, Skipton BD23 6AZ — MB ChB 1998 Manch.; MB ChB Manch 1998.

CRABTREE, Mr Norman Lloyd (retired) 57 Wellington Road, Edgbaston, Birmingham B15 2ER Tel: 0121 440 2841 Fax: 0121 440 2783 — MRCS Eng. LRCP Lond. 1939; FRCS Eng. 1947; DLO Eng. 1941. Hon. Cons. Otolaryngol. Birm. Centr. HA; Mem. (Ex-Pres.) Midl. Inst. Otol. Prev: Cons. Otolaryngol. Qu. Eliz. & Childr. Hosp. Birm.

CRABTREE, Paul Gary Egryn Llys Meddyg, Llys Meddyg, Victoria Road, Penygroes, Caernarfon LL54 6HD Tel: 01286 880207 Fax: 01286 880859; Dolau Gwyn, Rhostryfan, Caernarfon LL54 7PW Tel: 01286 830635 — MB BCh 1983 Wales; BDS Wales 1977.

CRABTREE, Roger Edmund Woodgate-Jones and Partners, The Surgery, Mount Street, Bishops Lydeard, Taunton TA4 3LH Tel: 01823 432361 Fax: 01823 433864; Herons Reach, Bishops Lydeard, Taunton TA4 3LJ — MB BS 1977 Lond.; DRCOG 1980. (Roy. Free) Prev: SHO St. Helier Hosp. Carshalton; Ho. Surg. & Ho. Phys. Roy. Free Hosp. Lond.

CRACK, Lindsay Anne Beechcroft, Aydon Road, Corbridge NE45 5EG Tel: 01434 633216 — BM BS 1977 Nottm.; MRCGP 1981; Dip. Palliat. Med. Wales 1995; DRCOG 1980. Cons. Palliat. Med. Marie Curie Centre Newc.; Hon. Cons. (Palliat. Med.) City Health Trust Newc. Prev: Sen. Regist. St. Oswalds Hospice Gosforth; Regist. Teeside Hospice; GP Ponteland.

CRACKETT, Geoffrey Group Practice Surgery, Middle Chare, Chester-le-Street DH3 3QD Tel: 0191 388 4857 Fax: 0191 388 7448 — MB ChB 1989 Leeds; DRCOG 1993; MRCGP 1993.

CRACKNELL, Bridget Dinah 15 West Way, Lymington SO41 8DZ Tel: 01590 671832 — MB ChB 1985 Bristol. Trainee GP Wigan Infirm. VTS.

CRACKNELL, Derek Douglas, MBE Sivam, 134 Hartford Road, Huntingdon PE29 1XQ Tel: 01480 52502 — MB BS Lond. 1951. (St. Bart.)

CRACKNELL, Ian Douglas Maples Family Medical Practice, 35 Hill Street, Hinckley LE10 1DS Tel: 01455 234576 Fax: 01455 250506; 27 Highfield St, Stony Stanton, Leicester LE9 4JD — MB BS 1976 Lond.; MRCS Eng. LRCP Lond. 1974. Hosp. Pract. Gen. Surg., Hinkley & Dist. Hosp.

CRACKNELL, Mary Gwyneth Woodley Centre Surgery, 106 Crockhamwell Road, Woodley, Reading RG5 3JY Tel: 0118 969 5011 Fax: 0118 944 0382 — MB ChB 1979 Birm.

CRACKNELL, Michael Maurice Bideford Medical Centre, Abbotsham Road, Bideford EX39 3AF Tel: 01237 476363 Fax: 01237 423351 — MB BS 1966 Lond.; MRCS Eng. LRCP Lond. 1966; DA Eng. 1970; DObst RCOG 1969. (St. Thos.)

CRACKNELL, Paul Killamarsh Medical Practice, 209 Sheffield Road, Killamarsh, Sheffield S21 1DX Tel: 0114 251 0000 — MB ChB 1989 Bristol; BSc (Hons.) Bristol 1986; MRCGP 1994; DRCOG 1994. (Bristol Univ.) Prev: Trainee GP Chesterfield VTS; SHO Chesterfield Roy. Hosp.

CRADDOCK, Charles Frank Department of Haematology, Hammersmith Hospital, London W12 0NN Tel: 020 8383 4017 Fax: 020 8742 9335 Email: c.craddock@rpms.ac.uk — BM BCh 1982 Oxf.; MRCP (UK) 1985; DPhil. Oxf. 1994; MRC Path. 1995. (Oxf. Univ.) Cons. (Haematol.) Hammersmith Hosp. Lond. Prev: Bone Marrow Transpl. Co-ord. Hammersmith Hosp. Lond.; Fell. (Haematol.) Univ. Washington USA; Wellcome Trust Clin. Fell. Inst. Molec. Med. Univ. Oxf.

CRADDOCK, Darren James 2 Grange Park, Stratford-upon-Avon CV37 6XH — MB ChB 1996 Dundee.

CRADDOCK, Denis (retired) 36 Lackford Road, Chipstead, Coulsdon CR5 3TA Tel: 01737 552746 — MB ChB Liverp. 1944; MD Liverp. 1967; FRCGP 1977, M 1953; DObst RCOG 1950. Prev: Hon. Librarian RCGP.

CRADDOCK, Kenneth Harold Old Grove Cottage, Llangrove, Ross-on-Wye HR9 6HA — MB ChB 1970 Birm.; FFA RCS Eng. 1975; DA Eng. 1974.

CRADDOCK, Professor Nicholas John University of Birmingham, Queen Elizabeth Psychiatric Hospital, Edgbaston, Birmingham B15 2QZ Tel: 0121 6782358 Fax: 0121 6782351 Email: n.craddock@bham.ac.uk — MB ChB 1985 Birm.; MB ChB (Hons.) Birm. 1985; PhD Wales 1995; MA Camb. 1984; MMedSci. Birm. 1991; MRCPsych 1989. Prof. of molecular prychiatry and head of univ. Dept. of prychiatry; Prof. (Molecular Psychiat.) & Hon. Cons. Psychiatr. Socs: Internat. Soc. for psychiatric genetics, (Mem.); Amer. Soc. of Human Genetics, (Mem.); Brit. Assn. of PsychoPharmacol., (Mem.). Prev: Wellcome Trust Sen. Res. Fell. Univ. Wales Coll. Med. Cardiff; Wellcome Trust Research Fell. & Vis. Lect. (Psychiat.) Washington Univ. St. Louis, USA; Wellcome Trust Train. Fell. (Psychol. Med.) Univ. Wales Coll. Med. Cardiff.

CRADDOCK, Stephen Clive 38 Briardene, Lanchester, Durham DH7 0QD Tel: 01207 520749 Email: sccofcmf@aol.com — MB BS 1966 Newc.; FFA RCS Eng. 1970. Cons. Anaesth. N. Durh. Acute Hosp. Trust. Socs: Christ. Med. Fell.sh. (Regional Sec. N..).

CRADDUCK, Graham William Station Road Surgery, 24 Station Road, Long Buckby, Northampton NN6 7QB Tel: 01327 842360 Fax: 01327 842302 — MB ChB 1973 Dundee; MRCGP 1979; DRCOG 1978.

CRADICK, Neil Henry Station Road Surgeries, Haworth, Keighley BD22 8NL — BM BS 1989 Nottm.

CRADOCK-WATSON, John Edgecombe (retired) La Maison du Menage, St Ouen, Jersey JE3 2LS — BM BCh Oxf. 1952. Prev: Med. Off. Pub. Health Laborat. Serv.

CRADWICK, Jeremy Charles c/o Department of Radiology, Peterborough District Hospital, Thorpe Road, Peterborough PE3 6DA — BM 1976 Soton.; FRCR 1985. Cons. Radiol. P'boro. Dist. Hosp.

CRAFT, Professor Alan William 2 Ruthven Court, Adderstone Crescent, Newcastle upon Tyne NE2 2HH — MD Newc. 1978, MB

BS 1969; FRCP Lond. 1984; MRCP (UK) 1972; T(M) (Paediat.) 1991. (Newc.) Prof. Child Health Univ. Newc. u. Tyne. Socs: Vice-Pres. Coll. Paediat. and Child Health; Pres. Paediatric Oncol. Soc. Prev: Cons. Paediat. Roy. Vict. Infirm. Newc.; MRC Train. Fell. (Paediat. Oncol.) Roy. Marsden Hosp. Lond.

CRAFT, Professor Ian Logan London Gynaecology & Fertility Centre, Cozens House, 112A Harley St., London W1N 1AF Tel: 020 7224 0707 Fax: 020 7224 3102 Email: info@lfc.or.uk; 5 Devonshire Mews N., London W1G 7BJ — MB BS 1961 Lond.; FRCS Eng. 1966; MRCS Eng. LRCP Lond. 1961; FRCOG 1986, M 1970. (Westm.) Dir. Lond. Gyn. & Fertil. Centre; Vis. Prof. UCL. Prev: Dir. Fertil. & Obst. Studies Humana Hosp. Wellington, Lond.; Prof. O & G Roy. Free Hosp. Lond.; Sen. Lect. & Hon. Cons. Inst. O & G Qu. Charlotte's Hosp. & Chelsea Hosp. Wom. Lond.

CRAFT, Isobel Albion Terrace Surgery, 13 Albion Terrace, Lynemouth, Morpeth NE61 5SY Tel: 01670 860212 Fax: 01670 860669; 12 Coquet Drive, Highthorne Est., Ellington, Morpeth NE61 5LN Tel: 01670 860187 — MB BS Durh. 1964. (Newcastle)

CRAFT, Naomi 11 Leverton Street, Kentish Town, London NW5 2PH Tel: 020 7267 9066 Fax: 020 7918 0892 Email: 100725.1525@compuserve.com — MB BS 1988 Lond.; BSc Lond. 1985; MRCGP 1994. Freelance Med. Jl.ist; GP Locum. Prev: Edit. Regist. BMJ Lond.; Trainee GP Muswell Hill Lond.; SHO (Genitourin. Med.) Roy. Lond. Hosp.

CRAFT, Timothy Michael Department of Anaesthesia, Royal United Hospital, Combe Park, Bath BA1 3NG Tel: 01225 825057 Fax: 01225 825061; Stockland, Beechen Cliff Road, Bath BA2 4QR Fax: 01225 482295 Email: tim@bathanaesthesia.demon.co.uk — MB BS 1983 Lond.; FRCA 1990. Cons. Anaesth. & Intens. Care Roy. United Hosp. Bath; Clin. Dir. (Anaesth., Theatres, Day Surg., IC & Pain Servs.) Roy. United Hosp Bath. Prev: Sen. Regist. (Anaesth. & Intens. Care) Bristol Roy. Infirm.; Vis. Asst. Prof. Univ. Maryland Baltimore, USA; Regist. (Anaesth.) Nuffield Dept. Anaesth. Oxf.

CRAFTER, Paul Francis 44 Davenport Avenue, Hessle HU13 0RP — MRCS Eng. LRCP Lond. 1989.

CRAGG, David Kevin South Park Surgery, 250 Park Lane, Macclesfield SK11 8AD; 21 Altrincham Road, Gatley, Cheadle SK8 4EL — MB ChB 1988 Sheff.; MD 1997; MRCGP 1992; Cert Family Plann JCC 1991; DRCOG 1991. GP. Prev: Lect. (Gen. Pract.) Univ. Manch.

CRAGGS, Alison Margaret Stewart Warren Garth, Brindley Brae, Kinver, Stourbridge DY7 6LR Tel: 01384 872237 — MB ChB 1982 Birm.; DRCOG 1987; DCH RCP Lond. 1985. Clin. Asst. (Diabetes) Wordsley Hosp.; Clin. Med. Off. (Family Plann.) Dudley HA. Prev: Trainee GP Dudley VTS.

CRAGGS, David Frederick The Priory Hospital, Priory Lane, Roehampton, London SW15 5JJ Tel: 020 8876 8261 Fax: 020 8392 2632; The Priory Hospital, Priory Lane, London SW15 5JJ — MB BS 1954 Lond.; FRCPsych 1983, M 1971; DPM Eng. 1960. Cons. Psychiat. The Priory Hosp. Roehampton; Med. Dir. Galsworthy Lodge Alcoholic Treatm. Centre. Prev: Med. Dir. St. Brendan's Hosp. Bermuda; Cons. Psychiat. Hellingly Hosp. Sussex & Kent & Sussex Hosp. Tunbridge; Wells; Chairm. Counc. on Alcoholism in Bermuda.

CRAGGS, Deborah Anne Royal Hampshire County Hospital, Romsey Road, Winchester SO22 5DG Tel: 019627 863535; 5 Fernlea Gardens, Bassett, Southampton SO16 7BJ — BM 1978 Soton. Staff Grade (Dermat.) Winchester & E.leigh Healthcare Unit Roy. Hants. Co. Hosp. Prev: Sen. Med. Off. Family Plann. Soton.

CRAGGS, Ian Frank Albion House Suegery, Albion Street, Brierley Hill DY5 3EE Tel: 01384 70220 Fax: 01384 78284 Email: albion.house@bigfoot.com — MB ChB 1982 Birm; MRCGP 1986; DRCOG 1985. Prev: Trainee GP Dudley VTS.

CRAGGS, James Ernest Russells Hall Hospital, Dudley DY1 2HQ; 22 Greening Drive, Edgbaston, Birmingham B15 2XA — MB BS 1983 Lond.; MSc Aston 1991; MRCP (UK) 1990; FRCA 1994; DA (UK) 1986. Cons. The Dudley Gp. of Hosp. NHS Trust.

CRAGGS, John Christopher Wickham Market Medical Centre, Chapel Lane, Wickham Market, Woodbridge IP13 0SB Tel: 01728 747101 Fax: 01728 747580 — MB BS 1960 Lond.; DObst RCOG 1964. (St. Bart.)

CRAGGS, Linda Ann Spring Hill Medical Centre, Spring Hill, Arley, Coventry CV7 8FD Tel: 01676 540395 Fax: 01676 540760; 65 Shanklin Drive, Weddington, Nuneaton CV10 0BG — MB BCh 1988 Wales; DCH RCP Lond. 1993; DRCOG 1993.

CRAGGS, Margaret Elizabeth Crosswood, Wood Lane, Aspley Guise, Milton Keynes MK17 8EL — MB ChB 1986 Leic.; MRCGP 1992; DCH RCP Lond. 1991.

CRAGGS, Richard Anthony Orchard Street Health Centre, Ipswich IP4 2PU Tel: 01473 213261; Hall Cottage, Church Road, Ashbocking, Ipswich IP6 9LG Tel: 0473 890127 — MRCS Eng. LRCP Lond. 1974.

CRAGHILL, Dawn Marcia Briarwood Medical Centre, 514 Blackpool Road, Ashton-on-Ribble, Preston PR2 1HY Tel: 01772 726186 Fax: 01772 768823; 24 Watling St Road, Fulwood, Preston PR2 8DY — MB BS 1993 Lond.; BSc (Psychol. & Basic Med. Sc.) Lond. 1990; DRCOG 1997; DCH 1997; MRCGP 1998. (Univ. Coll. Lond.) GP Princip.

CRAIG, Adam Raymond 29 Hadley Road, Enfield EN2 8JT — MB BS 1991 Lond.; BSc (Hons.) Lond. 1988; MRCP (UK) 1994; MRCPH 1996. (Char. Cross & Westm.) Trainee Fell. MRC (Paediat.) St. James Univ. Hosp. Leeds. Prev: Lect. & Hon. Specialist Regist. (Paediat.) St. Jas. Univ. Hosp. Leeds; Regist./Tutor (Paediat.) St. Jas. Univ. Hosp. Leeds; SHO (Paediat.) Derbysh. Childr. Hosp.

CRAIG, Aileen Dorothy 20 Robsland Avenue, Ayr KA7 2RW — MB ChB 1988 Ed.

CRAIG, Alan Douglas (retired) 9 Muirfield Meadows, Castlepark, Bothwell, Glasgow G71 8NT Tel: 01698 854522 — MB ChB 1948 Glas.; MRCGP 1962. Prev: Ho. Surg. Glas. Roy. Cancer Hosp. & Radium Inst.

CRAIG, Alastair John Abbey House Surgery, Golding Close, Daventry NN11 5RA Tel: 01327 877770 Fax: 01327 708585; 5 London Road, Daventry NN11 4DA Tel: 01327 878741 Email: scottydoc4@cs.com — MB ChB 1977 Glas.; MRCGP 1982; DRCOG 1979. (Glas.) Gen. Practitionor,Daventry; Course organiser, N.ampton VTS.

CRAIG, Alastair William (retired) 3 Stepney Drive, Scarborough YO12 5DP Tel: 01723 375869 — MB ChB 1955 Ed.; FRCOphth 1993; T(Ophth) 1991; FCOphth 1988; DO Eng. 1961. Prev: Cons. Ophth. ScarBoro. & Bridlington Hosps.

CRAIG, Albert Victor (retired) 183 Maidstone Road, Chatham ME4 6JG Tel: 01634 842462 — MB BS 1945 Lond.; DObst RCOG 1954. Prev: Ho. Surg. Univ. Coll. Hosp. & Edgware Gen. Hosp.

CRAIG, Alexander, Surg. Rear-Admiral 21 Barfield, Ryde PO33 2JP Tel: 01983 611518 — MB ChB 1967 Ed. p/t Criminal Injuries Compensation Appeal Panel. Socs: Fell. Roy. Soc. Med. Prev: Med. Dir. Gen. (Naval); SRA Support Med. Serv.; Med. Off. i/c Inst. Naval Med. Gosport Hants.

CRAIG, Alexis Elmbank Group, Foresterhill Health Centre, Westburn Road, Aberdeen AB25 2AY Tel: 01224 696949 Fax: 01224 691650 — MB ChB 1982 Aberd.; MRCGP 1987; MRCPsych 1990.

CRAIG, Alison Dorothy Ashley Department of Haematology, Ysbyty Glan Clwyd, Sarn Lane, Bodelwyddan, Rhyl LL18 5UJ; Penrallt, Allt y Powls, Llanfairtalhaiarn, Abergele LL22 8TP — MB ChB 1977 Bristol; MB ChB Bristol 1977.; MRCP (UK) 1982; FRCPath 1997, M 1987.

CRAIG, Alison Elizabeth St Nicholas Health Centre, Saunder Bank, Burnley BB11 2EN Tel: 01282 831249 Fax: 01282 425269 — MB ChB 1984 Manch.; MB ChB Manch. I984. Prev: SHO (Paediat.) Burnley Gen. Hosp.; SHO (Med.) Salford HA.

CRAIG, Alison Mary Larne Health Centre, Gloucester Avenue, Larne BT40 1PB Tel: 02828 261919; 105 Glenarm Road, Larne BT40 1DY Tel: 02828 260495 — MB BCh BAO 1982 Belf.; MB BCh Belf. 1982; MRCGP 1987; DRCOG 1986; DCH Dub. 1986.

CRAIG, Amanda Polly Staverton Surgery, 51 Staverton Road, London NW2 5HA Tel: 020 8459 6865 Fax: 020 8451 6897; 50 Ossulton Way, Hampstead Garden Suburb, London N2 0LB Tel: 020 8883 2160 Email: warner@lineone.net — MB BS 1980 Lond.; DRCOG 1982.

CRAIG, Andrew (retired) Melbost, 4 Lakeland Park, Keswick CA12 4AT Tel: 017687 72235 Email: cpt-craig@hotmail.com — MB ChB 1958 Glas.; DFFP 1993. Co. Med. Off. St. John Ambul. Brig. Cumbria. Prev: Capt. RAMC.

CRAIG, Andrew John 17 Dudley Road, Grantham NG31 9AA; 20/27 Cocks Barn Lane, Stockton-on-Tees TS20 1LR — BChir 1991 Camb.; MA Cantab. 1989; MRCP (UK) 1995; MRCGP 1996. (Cambridge)

CRAIG, Andrew Mark Swinburn c/o 32 Westwood Road, Newcastle upon Tyne NE3 5NN — MB BS 1997 Newc.
CRAIG, Angela Bridget 4 Roffey Close, Purley CR8 4BH — MB ChB 1997 Otago.
CRAIG, Mr Barry Francis 83 Balmoral Avenue, Belfast BT9 6NZ — MB BCh BAO 1972 Belf.; FRCS Ed. (Orth.) 1981; FRCS Ed. 1976.
CRAIG, Betty Royden Trewen, The Avenue, Llandaff, Cardiff CF5 2L — MB BCh 1952 Wales. (Cardiff)
CRAIG, Brian George Royal Belfast Hospital for Sick Children, 180 Falls Road, Belfast BT12 6BE Tel: 028 9026 3031 Fax: 028 9026 3491 Email: brian.craig@royalhospitals.n-i.nhs.uk; 10 Plantation Avenue, Lisburn BT27 5BL Tel: 028 9267 1587 — MB BCh BAO 1977 Belf.; MD Belf. 1986; FRCP Lond. 1994; MRCP (Paediat.) (UK) 1980; FRCPCH 1997. Cons. Paediat. Cardiol. Roy. Belf. Hosp. Sick Childr. Socs: Brit. Cardiac Soc.; Assn. Europ. Paediat. Cardiol.; Brit. Paediat. Cardiol. Assn. Prev: Clin. Fell. (Cardiol.) Hosp. Sick Childr. Toronto, Canada.
CRAIG, Catriona Margaret 64 Esslemont Avenue, Aberdeen AB25 1SR — MB ChB 1998 Aberd.; MB ChB Aberd 1998.
CRAIG, Christine Valerie 154 Canterbury Road, Urmston, Manchester M41 0QR — MB ChB 1998 Leeds.
CRAIG, Christopher Joseph Dyneley House Surgery, Newmarket Street, Skipton BD23 2HZ Tel: 01756 799311 Fax: 01756 707203; 15 Kirk Lane, Eastby, Skipton BD23 6SF Tel: 01756 792999 Fax: 0870 055 3846 Email: chris@skipton.demon.co.uk — MB BS 1970 Lond.; MRCGP 1974. (St. Mary's) GP. Socs: N. Yorks. Emerg. Doctors Assn.; BMA; (Ex-Pres.) Keighley & Dist. Med. Soc. Prev: GP Trainer N. Yorks.; Trainee GP Airedale VTS.
CRAIG, Clare Louise Holywood Arches Health Centre, Westminster Avenue, Belfast BT4 1NS Tel: 028 9056 3358 — MB BCh BAO 1990 Belf.; MRCGP 1994.
CRAIG, Mr Colin McKean (retired) Peasmarsh Palce, Peasmarsh, Rye TN31 6XE Tel: 01797 230936 — MB BS Lond. 1940; FRCS Eng. 1948; MRCS Eng. LRCP Lond. 1938. Prev: Cons. Surg. LoW.oft & N. Suff. Hosp.
CRAIG, David Duncan (retired) 3 Britten Street, London SW3 3TY — MRCS Eng. LRCP Lond. 1959; MA, MB Camb. 1959. BChir 1958; MRCGP 1967; DObst RCOG 1961. Local Treas. Med. Off.
CRAIG, Mr David McKean The Downs, 92 Salvington Hill, High Salvington, Worthing BN13 3BD — MB BS 1970 Lond.; FRCS Eng. 1975; MRCS Eng. LRCP Lond. 1970. Cons. Orthop. Worthing Hosp. & S.lands Hosp. Shoreham. Prev: Sen. Regist. Rotat. (Orthop.) St. Bart. Hosp. Lond.; Regist. Lord Mayor Treolar Hosp. & Portsmouth Gp. Hosps.
CRAIG, Donald Gwynvor (retired) Pentecost, Veryan, Truro TR2 5QA Tel: 01872 501450 Fax: 01872 501450 Email: donald.craig@tesco.net — BM BCh 1954 Oxf.; MA 1954 Oxf.; MRCP 1963; 1996 D.Occ.Med. RCP Lond.; 1987 Dip. Ven. Soc. Apoth. Lond.; DMJ 1969 Soc. Apoth. Lond.; FRCP 1985; DRCOG 1958. Prev: Sen. Lect. (Gen. Pract.) Guy's Hosp. Med. Sch. Lond.
CRAIG, Donald Henry 1463 London Road, Leigh-on-Sea SS9 2SQ Tel: 01702 710131 Fax: 01702 471154 — MB BS 1962 Durh.
CRAIG, Douglas Liddle Castlegait Surgery, 32 Castle Street, Montrose DD10 8AG Tel: 01674 672554 Fax: 01674 675025; Castlegate, 25 Bridge St, Montrose DD10 8AE Tel: 01674 676364 — MB ChB 1972 Ed.; DA Eng. 1982.
CRAIG, Douglas Stuart 79 Avenue Road, Leicester LE2 3EA Tel: 0116 244 8084 — MB BChir Camb. 1948; DObst RCOG 1954. Indust. Med. Off. Gent & Co. Ltd. Leicester. Prev: Ho. Surg. (Obst.) BRd.green Hosp. Liverp.; Demonst. (Anat.) Univ. Liverp.; Med. Off. RAMC.
CRAIG, Elizabeth (retired) Smithy Croft, Manbeen, Elgin IV30 8TN Tel: 01343 546415 — BA Open 1992; MB ChB Glas. 1957.
CRAIG, Elizabeth Sara Talbot Medical Centre, 63 Kinson Road, Bournemouth BH10 4BX Tel: 01202 523059 Fax: 01202 533239; 20 Penn Hill Avenue, Poole BH14 9LZ Tel: 01202 743651 — MB BS 1985 Lond.; DRCOG 1992. (Char. Cross)
CRAIG, Mr Ewan Alastair Royal Shrewsbury Hospital, Mytton Oak Road, Shrewsbury SY3 8XQ Tel: 01743 261000 — MB ChB 1985 Leeds; DO RCS Eng. 1988; FRCOphth 1990, M 1988. Cons. Ophth. Roy. Shrewsbury Hosp., Shrewsbury & P.ss Roy. Hosp. Telford. Prev: Fell. Moorfields Eye Hosp. Lond.; Sen. Regist. & Regist. (Ophth.) Ninewells Hosp. Dundee; SHO (Ophth.) Manch. Roy. Eye Hosp.
CRAIG, Finella 36 Hatherley Court, Hatherley Grove, London W2 5RE — MB BS 1988 Lond.
CRAIG, George Leith Mount, 46 Ferry Road, Edinburgh EH6 4AE Tel: 0131 554 0558 Fax: 0131 555 6911; 29 Murrayfield Avenue, Edinburgh EH12 6BA — MB ChB 1983 Glas.; MB ChB (Commend.) Glas. 1983; MRCP (UK) 1986; MRCGP (Distinc.) 1990; FCOphth. 1992; DRCOG 1990; DO RCS Glas. 1989. Prev: Trainee GP Glas.; Regist. (Ophth.) W.. Infirm. Glas.; Regist. (Med.) & SHO (Obst.) Stobhill Gen. Hosp. Glas.
CRAIG, Gillian Mary (retired) 118 Cedar Road East, Abington, Northampton NN3 2JF — MB BS Lond. 1963; MD Lond. 1974; FRCP Lond. 1990, M 1967. Prev: Cons. Phys. Geriat. Med. N.ampton HA.
CRAIG, Gillian Mary 101 Copse Hill, Wimbledon, London SW20 0NR Tel: 020 8947 4858 — MB BS Lond. 1955. (St. Mary's)
CRAIG, Gordon Robert 9 Kingswood Avenue, Bexhill-on-Sea TN39 4EJ — BM 1982 Soton.; MRCP (UK) 1991; FCAnaesth 1990. Socs: Fell. Coll. Anaesth.; RCP.
CRAIG, Gordon William Globetown Surgery, 82-86 Roman Road, London E2 0PG Tel: 020 8980 3023 Fax: 020 8983 4627; Appartment 3, Sebastian House, 2-4 Sebastian St, London EC1V 0HE Fax: 020 7253 5076 Email: tonyandg@aol.com — MB ChB 1985 Manch. (Manchester) GP Princip. Prev: SHO (Med.) & Regist. (c/o Elderly) St. Mary's Hosp. Lond.; Ho. Off. (Surg.) Manch. Roy. Infirm.; Ho. Off. (Med.) Vict. Hosp. Blackpool.
CRAIG, Harry Lindsay (retired) Cobbetts, Bournefields, Twyford, Winchester SO21 1NY Tel: 01962 712314 Fax: 01962 712314 Email: harrycraig@onetel.net.uk — BM BCh 1956 Oxf.; MA Oxf. 1956; FRCGP 1981, M 1965; DObst RCOG 1957; BA Oxf 1953; MRACGP 1965. Prev: Med. Off. Winchester Coll. 1967-87.
CRAIG, Henry Jeremy Lee (retired) Craigdarragh, 517 Glenshawe Road, Claudy, Londonderry BT47 4BT Tel: 01504 338255 — MD Belf. 1968, MB BCh BAO 1955; FFA RCSI 1971; FFA RCS Eng. 1961; DA Eng. 1957. Prev: Cons. Anaesth. Roy. Vict. Hosp. Belf.
CRAIG, Iain Fergusson Dennycross Medical Centre, Duke Street, Denny FK6 6DB Tel: 01324 822330 Fax: 01324 824415 — MB ChB 1985 Dundee; PhD Biochem. Ed. 1979; BSc Biochem. Strathclyde 1975; MRCGP 1989; DRCOG 1988. Prev: Research Fell. Baylor Coll. Med.
CRAIG, Ian Donaldson 3 Blunts Hall Drive, Witham CM8 1LZ Tel: 01376 513696 — MRCS Eng. LRCP Lond. 1953; DMJ (Clin.) Soc. Apoth. Lond. 1970; DObst RCOG 1955. (Leeds) Clin. Tutor in Forens. Med. Socs: Roy. Coll. Gen. Pract.; Assn. Police Surg.; Fell. Roy. Soc. Med. Prev: Ho. Phys. Gen. Infirm. Leeds; Ho. Surg. & SHO (Obst.) St. John's Hosp. Chelmsford.
CRAIG, Ian George Logan 'Parkside', 43 Corringham Road, Stanford-le-Hope SS17 0NU Tel: 01375 674234 — MB ChB 1942 Aberd. (Aberd.) Prev: Surg. Regist. I. of Wight Hosp. Gp.; Orthop. Regist. Bradford Roy. Infirm.; Ho. Surg. & Ho. Phys. Aberd. Roy. Infirm.
CRAIG, Ian Robert Dewsbury & District Hospital, Healds Road, Dewsbury WF13 4HS Tel: 01924 465105 — MB ChB 1984 Leeds.
CRAIG, James Arthur 25 St Leonards Road, Ayr KA7 2PS Tel: 01292 282382 — MB ChB 1969 Glas.; MRCP (UK) 1972. Cons. Dermat. CrossHo. Hosp. Kilmarnock. Prev: Cons. Dermat. Chester & Clwyd S. HAs.; Sen. Regist. (Dermat.) Roy. Vict. Infirm. Newc.; Sen. Lect. (Dermatovenereol.) Univ. Nairobi.
CRAIG, James David Gourock Health Centre, 181 Shore Street, Gourock PA19 1AQ Tel: 01475 634617; The Health Centre, 181 Shore St., Gourock PA19 Tel: 01475 34617 — MB ChB 1971 Glas.; DObst RCOG 1973. (Glas.) Prev: Jun. Ho. Off. (Surg.) W.. Infirm. Glas.; Jun. Ho. Off. (O & G) Robroyston Hosp. Glas.; SHO (Psychiat.) Gartnavel Roy. Hosp. Glas.
CRAIG, Mr James Oscar Max Clark The White House, 18 Sandy Lane, Cheam, Sutton SM2 7NR Tel: 020 8642 2696 — LRCPI & LM, LRCSI & LM 1950; DMRD Eng. 1959; FHKCR (Hon) 1995; FRCP Lond. 1994; FRCS Eng. 1982; FRCSI 1956; MRCP (UK) 1989; FRCGP 1991; FRCR 1975; FFR 1962; Hon. FFR RCSI 1986. Hon. Cons. Radiol. St. Mary's Hosp. Lond. (Emerit.); Vis. Prof. Univ. Brit. Columbia; Vis. Prof. Univ. Qu.sld. Austral.; Vis. Prof. Concord Hosp. Sydney, Austral.; Hon. Sen. Clin. Lect. & Lect. (Radiol., Anat. & Clin. Radiol.) St. Mary's Hosp. Med Sch Lond. Socs: Hon. Mem. Radiol. Soc. N. Amer.; (Pres. Advis. Bd.) Med. Protec. Soc.; & Roy. Soc.

Med. Prev: Dir. (Clin. Studies & Diag. Radiol.) St. Mary's Hosp. Med. Sch. Lond.; Pres. Roy. Coll. Radiol.

CRAIG, James Robert 10 Lulworth Road, Lee-on-the-Solent PO13 9HU — BM 1995 Soton.

CRAIG, Jane 14 Dransfield Road, Sheffield S10 5RN Email: nandjcraig@btinternet.com — MB ChB 1992 Sheff.; MRCGP 1996. Walkley Ho. Med. Centre, Greenmon St.

CRAIG, Jane Catherine Trinity Street Surgery, 1 Trinity Street, Norwich NR2 2BG Tel: 01603 624530; 5 St. Bartholomew's Close, Norwich NR2 4DX Tel: 01603 633211 — MB BS 1990 Lond.; DCH 1997; MRCGP 1998.

CRAIG, Jane Marie Royal Hallamshire Hospital, Sheffield S10 2JF Tel: 0114 276 6222; 111B Glebe Road, Cambridge CB1 7TE Tel: 01223 212148 — MB ChB 1989 Manch.; MRCP (UK) 1992. Regist. (Genitourin. Med.) Roy. Hallamsh. Hosp. Sheff.

CRAIG, Jean Veronica (retired) 15 Old Sneed Park, Bristol BS9 1RG Tel: 0117 968 2909 — MRCS Eng. LRCP Lond. 1942; MD Lond. 1947, MB BS 1945; MRCP Lond. 1946; DMRT Eng. 1974. Prev: Assoc. Specialist (Radiother.) Bristol Roy. Infirm.

CRAIG, Jenny Isabelle Ogilvie Department of Haematology, Box 234 Addenbrooke's Hospital, Cambridge CB2 2QQ Tel: 01223 217071 Email: jioc2@cam.ac.uk; 40 Fendon Road, Cambridge CB1 7RT — MB ChB 1981 Ed.; MD Ed. 1991; MRCP (UK) 1984; MRCPath 1992; FRCP 2000 (path); FRCP 1999 Edin. Cons. Haematologist Addenbrooke's Hosp. Camb. Prev: Sen. Regist. & Regist. (Haemat.) Roy. Infirm. Edin.; Regist. (Gen. Med.) Milesmark Hosp. Dunfermline.; Assoc. Specialist Haemat. & Blood Transfus. Serv. Roy. Infirm. Edin.

CRAIG, John Gavin Westcliffe Surgery, Westcliffe Road, Shipley BD18 3EE Tel: 01274 580787; Valley Cottage, Spitalcroft, Knaresborough HG5 8JB Tel: 01423 864896 — MB BCh BAO 1970 Belf.; FRCP 1998; MRCP (UK) 1973; MRCGP 1985.

CRAIG, John Joseph 46 Casaeldona Rise, Belfast BT6 9RA — MB BCh BAO 1991 Belf.; BSc (Med. Genetics) Belf. 1989; MRCP (UK) 1994. Regist. (Neurol.) Roy. Vict. Hosp. Belf.

CRAIG, John Scott Jarman (retired) Partridge Cottage, Redpale, Dallington, Heathfield TN21 9NR — MB BCh BAO 1974 Belf.; FRCR 1982. Cons. Radiol. Hastings & Rother NHS Trust. Prev: Sen. Regist. (Radiodiagn.) Bristol Roy. Infirm.

CRAIG, John Stanley Ulster Hospital, Dundonald, Belfast BT16 1RH Tel: 0028 9048 4511; 51 Millars Forge, Dundonald, Belfast BT16 1UT Tel: 028 9041 0899 — MB ChB 1989 Aberd.; MRCP (UK) 1993. Sen. Regist. (Paediat.) Ulster Hosp., Dundonald; Research Fell., Dept of Child Health, Qu.'s Univ. of Belf. Socs: (Collegiate) Roy. Coll. Phys. & Surg. Glas.; Roy. Coll. Paediat. & Child Health; Nutrit. Soc. Prev: Lect. in Paediat. Univ. Coll. Dub..; Regist. in Paediat. our Lady's Hosp. fro Sick Childr. Dub. & The Nat. Matern. Hosp., Dub..; Sen. Regist. in Paediat., Antrim Area Hosp..

CRAIG, John Thompson Kilkeel Health Centre, Kilkeel, Newry BT34 4BS Tel: 016937 62601; Goleen, Newcastle Road, Kilkeel, Newry BT34 4AQ Tel: 016937 717 — MB BCh BAO 1951 Belf.

CRAIG, Jonathan Paul The Surgery, Station Road, Attleborough NR17 2AS Tel: 01953 452394 Email: jon.craig@lineone.net — MB ChB Manch. 1992; MRCGP 1997; DRCOG 1996. (Manch.) GP, AttleBoro. Surgeries, Norf. Prev: Roy. Air Force Med. Off.

CRAIG, Mr Joseph Kevin 26 Mayfields, Keynsham, Bristol BS31 1BW; Hope Cove, Druidston Broad Haven, Haverfordwest SA62 3NE Tel: 01437 781053 Fax: 01437 781053 — MB ChB 1946 Manch.; FRCS Eng. 1953; FRCS Ed. 1951; FRCOG 1974, M 1956. (Manch.) Cons. O & G Bath Clin. Area. Socs: N. Eng. Obst. & Gyn. Soc.; SW Obst. & Gyn. Soc.; UK Counc.lor - Internat. Phys. for Preven. of Nuclear War. Prev: Sen. Regist. (O & G) United Bristol Hosps.; Tutor (O & G) Univ. Bristol.

CRAIG, Judy Howard Albany House Medical Centre, 3 Queen Street, Wellingborough NN8 4RW Tel: 01933 222309 Fax: 01933 229236; Howard's End, 16A Doddington Road, Earl's Barton, Northampton NN6 0NF Tel: 01604 811045 — MB BS 1981 Lond.; MRCGP 1985; DRCOG 1983. Prev: Trainee GP N.ampton VTS; Ho. Off. Roy. Free Hosp. Lond. & St. Margt. Hosp. Swindon.

CRAIG, Kenneth David, Wing Cdr. RAF Med. Br. Retd. Norfolk Mental Health NHS Trust, Kingfisher House, Wensum Meadows, Hellesdon Hospital, Norwich NR11 7DW Tel: 01603 421677 Fax: 01603 421342 Email: dr@kencraig.freeserve.co.uk; Pond Farm, Banningham, Norwich NR11 7DU Tel: 01263 737687 Fax: 01263 735687 Email: dr@kencraig.freeserve.co.uk — MB BCh BAO 1974 Belf.; FRCPsych 1993, M 1981; DFFP 1993; T (Psych) 1991. (Belf.) Cons. Psychiat.; Hon. Cons. Ex-Servs. Ment. Welf. Soc. Socs: Fell. Roy. Soc. Med.; (Pres.) Anglo-Amer. Med. Soc.; Camb. Med. Soc. Prev: Cons. Adviser Psychiat. RAF; Cons. Psychiat. RAF Hosp. Ely & RAF Hosp. Wegberg.

CRAIG, Laura Joyce Boghall Farmhouse, Stannington, Morpeth NE61 6BB — MB BS 1944 Durh.

CRAIG, Lesley May 19 Collieston Drive, Bridge of Don, Aberdeen AB22 8SN — MB ChB 1979 Aberd.

CRAIG, Leslie MacDonald, MBE (retired) Camus, Furnace, Inveraray PA32 8XU Tel: 01499 500630 — MB ChB 1952 Glas.

CRAIG, Louise Burleigh (retired) The White House, 18 Sandy Lane, Cheam, Sutton SM2 7NR Tel: 020 8642 2696 — LRCPI & LM, LRSCI & LM 1950; LRCPI & LM, LRCSI & LM 1950.

CRAIG, Malcolm Doclands Medical Centre, Blanche Street, Ashton-on-Ribble, Preston PR2 2RL Tel: 01772 723222 Fax: 01772 726619; 20 Fulwood Hall Lane, Fulwood, Preston PR2 8DB Tel: 01772 700539 — MB ChB 1972 Birm.; MRCGP 1991.

CRAIG, Margaret Barbour Allander Street Surgery, 124 Allander Street, Glasgow G22 5JH Tel: 0141 336 8038 Fax: 0141 336 3440; 41 Queen Square, Glasgow G41 2BD — MB ChB 1982 Ed. Prev: Trainee GP Glas. VTS.

CRAIG, Marjorie Simmonds Altnacraig, Glenbuchat, Strathdon AB36 8UB — MB ChB Aberd. 1942. (Aberd.)

CRAIG, Mark Frederick 57 Eastwood Road, Leigh-on-Sea SS9 3AH — MB ChB 1998 Ed.; MB ChB Ed 1998.

CRAIG, Michael Flat 3, 12 Lindfield Gardens, London NW3 6PU Tel: 020 7435 7154 Email: mcraig2323@aol.com — MB BS 1996 Lond.; BSc (Hons.) Psychol. Bristol 1991; MRCOG (Pt I) 1998. (Royal Free Hospital) SHO (O & G) UMDS Lond.; Sen. Sen. Ho. Off. (Acting Regisrar) UMDS Lond. Socs: Roy. Soc. Med. Prev: SHO (Gyn.) St. Mary's Hosp. Lond.

CRAIG, Michael Stewart Talbot Medical Centre, Stanley Street, South Shields NE34 0BX Tel: 0919 455 3867 Fax: 0191 454 3825; 18 Underhill Road, Cleadon Village, Sunderland SR6 7RS — MB ChB 1978 Aberd.; MRCGP 1982.

CRAIG, Michelle 36 Ballymena Road, Doagh, Ballyclare BT39 0QR — MB BCh BAO 1997 Belf.

CRAIG, Myrtle Ogilvy 6 Braid's Walk, Kirk Ella, Hull HU10 7PA — MB ChB 1962 Ed.; DA Eng. 1966.

CRAIG, Niall John Angus Top Floor Flat, 9 Colville Place, Aberdeen AB24 5LY — MB ChB 1992 Aberd.; FRCS Ed 1998. Specialist Regist. (Orthop.) Aberd. Roy. Infirm., Aberd.

CRAIG, Nicholas John The Priory Surgery, 326 Wells Road, Bristol BS4 2QJ Tel: 0117 949 3988 Fax: 0117 778250; Tel: 0117 927 9530 — MB BS 1985 Lond.; BSc (Hons.) (Pharm.) Lond. 1982; DRCOG 1991. (St. Bart.) Socs: Med. Protec. Soc. Prev: SHO (Orthop.) Winford Hosp. Bristol; SHO (Geriat.) Frenchay Hosp. Bristol; SHO (ENT & A & E) S.mead Hosp. Bristol.

CRAIG, Patricia Maureen Orchard Hill, Corston, Bath BA2 9AN Tel: 01225 218 — MB BS 1953 Lond.; MRCS Eng. LRCP Lond. 1953. (St. Mary's) Course Tutor Open Univ. Socs: Soc. Social Hist. Med. Prev: Brit. Emp. Cancer Campaign Research Worker Dept. Surg. Univ. Bristol; Regist. Path. Frenchay Hosp. Bristol & Gen. Infirm. Leeds.

CRAIG, Paul James 57 Eastwood Road, Leigh-on-Sea SS9 3AH — MB BS 1996 Lond.; BSc (Hons) Lond. 1993. Specialist Regist. in Histopath., Roy. Hosps. Trust, Lond.

CRAIG, Richard (retired) Cladach, 5 Miller Place, Ardrossan KA22 8PP Tel: 01294 466159 — MB ChB 1951 Glas.; MFOM RCP Lond. 1980; DIH Soc. Apoth. Lond. 1975.

CRAIG, Richard Garrett 27 Grainger Road, Isleworth TW7 6PQ — MB BS 1987 Lond.; FRCA 1994. Regist. (Anaesth.) Ealing Hosp.

CRAIG, Mr Robert Dominic Peter (retired) Consulting Suite, Alexandra Hospital, Mill Lane, Cheadle SK8 2PX Tel: 0161 428 3656 Fax: 0161 491 3867 — MB ChB Manch. 1954; MD Manch. 1972; FRCS Eng. 1958. Prev: Hon. Lect. (Plastic Surg.) Univ. Manch.

CRAIG, Robert James Loganlea Centre, 76 John St., Penicuik EH26 8NF Tel: 01968 679407 Fax: 01968 677698 — MB ChB 1971 Ed.; MPhil Ed. 1978, MB ChB 1971; MRCPsych 1976; FRCPsych 1997. (Edinburgh) Cons. (Psychiat.) Rosslynlee Hosp. Roslin.; Assoc. Med. Director (Clin. Effectiveness) Lothian Primary Health Care NHS Trust. Prev: Sen. Regist. (Psychiat.) Roy. Edin.

Hosp.; Regist. (Psychiat.) Rosslynlee Hosp. Roslin; SHO (Gen. Med.) Edenhall Hosp. Pinkieburn.

CRAIG, Mr Robert Peter, OStJ, QHS, Maj.-Gen. late RAMC Retd. 24 Trafalgar Avenue, London SE15 6NR Tel: 071 252 5504 Fax: 020 7252 5344 Email: rpcraig@yahoo.co.uk — MB BS Durh. 1964; MD Newc. 1987; FRCS Eng. 1972; FFAEM 1994. (Durh.) p/t Med. Mem. Pens. Appeal tribunals; Med. Mem. Tribunal Appeals Serv. Socs: BMA; Assn. Accid. & Emerg. Med.; Fell. Fac. Accid. & Emerg. Med. Prev: Cons. A & E Med. Wansbeck Gen. Hosp. N.d.; Cdr. Med. UK Land Forces; Dir. Army Surg.

CRAIG, Roderic Burnhouse Surgery, 15 Burnhouse Road, Wooler NE71 6BJ Tel: 01668 281575 Fax: 01668 282442; 15 Burnhouse Road, Wooler NE71 Tel: 01668 281575 Fax: 01668 282442 — MB BS 1968 Newc.; DObst RCOG 1971. Prev: SHO (O & G & Paediat.) Newc. Gen. Hosp.; SHO (O & G) Hexham Gen. Hosp.; Ho. Phys. Newc. Gen. Hosp.

CRAIG, Ruth Winifred (retired) 3 St David's Crescent, Oadby, Leicester LE2 2RL Tel: 0116 274 5659 — LRCP LRCS 1949 Ed.; LRCP LRCS Ed. LRFPS Glas. 1949; DObst RCOG 1956. Prev: Med. Off. Vict. Hosp. Damascus.

CRAIG, Sarah Kathyrn Lloyd Royal Bolton Hospital, Minerva Road, Bolton BL4 0JR; 15 Oughtrington Crescent, Lymm WA13 9JD Tel: 01925 757762 — MB ChB 1984 Sheff.; MSc Manch. 1998; MRCPsych 1994; DRCOG 1986. Cons. Old Age Psychiat.

CRAIG, Sheila Wood 47 Powis Terrace, Aberdeen AB25 3PP Tel: 01224 52459 — MB ChB 1951 Aberd. Prev: Ho. Phys. Woodend Gen. Hosp. Aberd. & Roy. Aberd. Hosp. Sick Childr.; Ho. Surg. Aberd. Matern. Hosp.

CRAIG, Sonya Elizabeth 78 Dobbin Road, Portadown, Craigavon BT62 4EZ — BChir 1995 Camb.

CRAIG, Stuart William Blackbird Leys Health Centre, 63 Blackbird Leys Road, Oxford OX4 6HL Tel: 01865 778244; 116 Southend, Garsington, Oxford OX44 9DL — BM BCh 1976 Oxf.; BA Oxf. 1973, BM BCh 1976; MRCGP 1985; DRCOG 1984. GP Oxf.

CRAIG, Susan Valerie Lance Lane Medical Centre, 19 Lance Lane, Liverpool L15 6TS Tel: 0151 737 2882 Fax: 0151 737 2883 — MB ChB 1970 Liverp.; DObst RCOG 1972.

CRAIG, Susannah Mary 85 Redmoor Close, Tavistock PL19 0ER — MB ChB 1985 Liverp. Prev: SHO (A & E Psychiat. & Geriat. Med.) Arrowe Pk. Hosp. Wirral; SHO (O & G) Whiston Hosp. Prescot.

CRAIG, Thomas John Montgomery Foyleside Family Practice, Bridge Street Medical Centre, 30 Bridge Street, Londonderry BT48 6LA Tel: 028 7126 7847 Fax: 028 7137 0723; 50 Carmoney Road, Coolafinney, Eglinton, Londonderry BT47 3PH Tel: 028 7181 0488 Fax: 028 7181 2077 Email: tom.craig@lineone.net — MB BCh BAO Belf. 1970; MICGP 1990; DFFP 1990.

CRAIG, Mrs Veronica Ashley Medical Centre, 140 Groomsport Road, Bangor BT20 5PE — MB BCh BAO 1983 Belf.; MRCGP 1989; DRCOG 1989. (Belf.) Prev: SHO (Paediat.) Roy. Belf. Hosp. for Sick Childr.; SHO (Gen. Med.) Belf. City Hosp.; SHO (Haemat.) Belf. City Hosp.

CRAIG, Virginia Anne St Luke's Hospice, Fobbing Farm, Nethermayne, Basildon SS16 5NJ Tel: 01268 524973 Fax: 01268 282483 — MB ChB 1987 Ed.; PhD Camb. 1984; BSc Leeds 1978; MRCP (UK) 1992. (Edinburgh) Med. Dir., St. Luke's Hospice, Basildon. Prev: Regist. (Palliat. Med.) St. Luke's Hospice Basildon.

CRAIG-MCFEELY, Patrick Michael Hillbrow Surgery, Hill Brow Road, Liss GU33 7LE Tel: 01730 892262 Fax: 01730 895779 Email: patrick mcfeely@gp-j82164.nhs.uk; Epstocks, Church St, Farnham Road, Liss GU33 6JY — MB BS 1982 Lond.; MA Oxf. 1983; MRCGP 1987; DRCOG 1989; DCH RCP Lond. 1987; Dip. Thera. Wales 1998. (St. Thomas' Hospital) GP; Assoc. GP Tutor Hants; Clin. Asst. (Rheum.) Portsmouth; GP Teach. Univ. Soton. Med. Sch.; Hon. Research Fell. Drug safety research Unit, Univ. S.ampton.; Therap. portfolio, SE Hants. PCT. Socs: Soc. Apoth. Lond. Prev: SHO (Rheum. & Rehabil.) St. Richards Hosp. Chichester; Med. Off. RN.

CRAIGEN, Anthony Allan (retired) Arden House, 29 Coppice Avenue, Great Shelford, Cambridge CB2 5AQ Tel: 01223 844709 — MB BS Lond. 1950; MRCS Eng. LRCP Lond. 1948; DObst RCOG 1954. Prev: Sen. Med. Off. leys & St. Faith's Camb.

CRAIGEN, Mr Michael Alan Charles Department of Orthopaedic Surgery, The Royal Orthopaedic Hospital, Woodlands, Northfield, Birmingham B31 2AP Tel: 0121 685 4000 Fax: 0121 627 8211; Wellgate, Rowney Green Lane, Rowney Green, Alvechurch, Birmingham B48 7QS Tel: 0121 445 1429 Fax: 0121 445 4072 — MB BS 1981 Lond.; FRCS (Orth.) 1994; FRCS Eng. 1987; FRCS Ed. 1986; Dip. Hand Surg. (Euro.) 1996. (Guy's Hospital London) Cons. Orthop. Surg. Roy. Orthop. Hosp. & Selly Oak Hosp. Birm.; Hon. Sen. Lect. Univ. of Birm. Socs: Fell. BOA; Fell. BSSH. Prev: Sen. Lect. (Orthop. Trauma & Hand Surg.) Qu. Med. Centre Nottm.; Fell. Christine M. Kleinert Inst. for Hand & Microsurg. Louisville, Kentucky, USA; Lect. Orthop. Soton. Univ.

CRAIGHEAD, Iain Bruce Fern Hill Practice, Coxwell Road, Faringdon SN7 7ED Tel: 01367 242407; 6 Chestnut Avenue, Faringdon SN7 8BB Email: craighead@btinternet.com — MB ChB 1992 Aberd.; BMedBiol. Aberd. 1989; MRCGP 1996; DRCOG 1995. (Aberdeen) GP Princip. Socs: Christian Med. Fell.sh. Prev: SHO (Surg.) Belford Hosp. Fort William; GP/Regist. Peterculter; Trainee GP/SHO Aberd. Roy. Hosps. NHS Trust VTS.

CRAIGHEAD, Isobel Beatrice (retired) 8 Sycamore Street, Springwood Village, Kelso TD5 8NH Tel: 01573 223483 — MB ChB Ed. 1949, DPH 1952; FFCM 1984,; MFPHM 1972. Prev: Specialist (Community Med.) S. Tees HA.

CRAIGHEAD, Susan Kathleen Medical Research Council Unit, Hertford County Hospital, North Road, Hertford SG14 1LP — MB ChB 1976 Liverp.; DCH 1995; MRCGP 1981; MRCP (UK) 1979. Clin. Research Doctor - MRC Environm. Epidemiol. Unit, Soton. Gen. Hosp. Prev: GP Potters Bar; SHO (Neonat. Paediat.) Lond. Hosp. (Whitechapel); SHO (Med.) Warneford Hosp. Leamington Spa.

CRAIGHILL, Anthony Richard 21 Enmore Gardens, London SW14 8RF — MB BChir 1976 Camb.

CRAIGIE, David McIntosh (retired) Sandyleaze, Prinsted Lane, Prinsted, Emsworth PO10 8HT Tel: 01243 371031 Email: dpcprinsted@aol.com — MB ChB 1955 Ed.

CRAIGIE, Ian Tyrie The Surgery, 114-116 Carden Avenue, Brighton BN1 8PD Tel: 01273 500155 Fax: 01273 501193 — MB ChB 1970 Liverp.; MRCS Eng. LRCP Lond. 1970; MRCGP 1977; DObst RCOG 1973.

CRAIGMILE, Doris Angus (retired) 26 Fernleigh Road, Winchmore Hill, London N21 3AL Tel: 020 8882 4589 — MB BS 1943 Lond.; MD Lond. 1949; MFCM 1972; DObst RCOG 1946; CPH Lond. 1948. Prev: Med. Adv. Home Finding Team Dr. Barnardos Lond. Div.

CRAIGMILE, Judith Anne 34 Redford Road, Edinburgh EH13 0AA — MB ChB 1987 Ed.

CRAIGMYLE, David Walford Mill Medical Centre, Knobcrook Road, Wimborne BH21 1NL Tel: 01202 886999 Fax: 01202 840049; Grange Farm, Grange, Wimborne BH21 4HX Tel: 01202 884426 — MB BCh 1979 Wales; MRCGP 1985.

CRAIGMYLE, Elizabeth Bryn y Mor, Berea, St Davids, Haverfordwest SA62 6DD Tel: 01348 831426 Email: tyddewi@clara.net — MB BCh Wales 1983. (University of Wales College of Medicine) Princip. in Gen. Pract., at Solva Surg. Solva. Prev: Job sharing Partner at Solva Surg., Pembrookshire.

CRAIGMYLE, Marshall Buchanan Lang 49 Bettws y Coed Road, Cyncoed, Cardiff CF23 6PJ Tel: 029 2075 8633 — MB ChB 1948 Glas.; MD Glas. 1960. Prev: Prof. & Chairm. Dept. of Anat. Fac. Med. & Health Sci. Al Ain, UAE.

CRAIK, Ian Fraser (retired) 20 Balrymonth Court, St Andrews KY16 8XT Tel: 01334 75025 — MB ChB 1951 Ed.; DPH 1957; MFCM 1972. Prev: Dep. MOH City of Edin.

CRAIK, John Elliot (retired) Cuilbeag, Carrick Castle, Lochgoilhead, Cairndow PA24 8AF Tel: 01301 703372 — MB ChB 1934 Glas.; FRCPath 1963. Prev: Cons. Admin. Charge Path. Vict. Infirm. & Chairm. Glas. SE Dist. Med. Comm.

CRAIK, John Ireland O'Brien Ravendene, 23 Brighton Road, Crawley RH10 6AE Tel: 01293 523383 Email: craik@lineone.net — MB ChB 1977 Glas.; DRCOG 1979.

CRAIK, Marie Clare The Bell Surgery, York Road, Henley-on-Thames RG9 2DR Fax: 01491 411295; 34 College Crescent, Oakley, Aylesbury HP18 9RA — BM BCh 1992 Oxf.; PhD Newc. 1989, BSc 1984; MRCGP 1996. (Oxford) Clin. Asst. ENT. Socs: Roy. Coll. Gen. Pract.

CRAIK, Mary Catherine Albyn Medical Practice, 30 Albyn Place, Aberdeen AB10 1NW Tel: 01224 586829 Fax: 01224 213238 — MB ChB 1988 Aberd.; MRCGP 1992.

CRAIL, Robert Brownfield 19 Pennington Drive, Oatlands Chase, Weybridge KT13 9RU — B.M., B.Ch. Oxon. 1942.

CRAIL, Susan Margaret Liverpool Hospital, PO Box 103, Sydney, Sydney NSW 2170, Australia Tel: 00 612 98 28 3000; 83 Lindsay Park, Burnley BB10 3SQ Tel: 01282 431531 — MB BS 1994 Lond.; BSc Brighton 1986. (Roy. Tree) Regist. (Med.) Liverp. Hosp., Sydney, Austral. Socs: Roy. Coll. Paediat. Prev: SHO (Med.) Norf. & Norwich Hosp.; Ho. Off. (Med.) Roy. Free Hosp.

CRAKE, Thomas St. Bartholomew's Hospital, West Smithfield, London EC1A 7BE Tel: 020 7601 7800; Garden Flat, 30 Willow Road, Hampstead, London NW3 1TL Tel: 020 7431 3299 Fax: 020 7431 3299 — MB BS 1980 Newc.; MD Newc. 1990; MRCP (UK) 1983; FRCP. Cons. Cardiol. St. Bart. & N. Middlx. Hosps. Lond.; Hon. Sen. Lect. Med. Coll. St. Bart. Hosp. Lond. Socs: Fell. Europ. Soc. Cardiol.; Brit. Cardiac Soc. Prev: Sen. Regist. (Cardiol.) St. Mary's & Hammersmith Hosps. Lond.; Research Fell. Cardiothoracic Inst. Lond.; Regist. (Med.) Roy. Vict. Infirm. Newc. & Nat. Heart Hosp. Lond.

CRAM, Lester Pollock 10 Dunvegan Drive, Newton Mearns, Glasgow G77 5EB — MB ChB 1976 Glas.

CRAM, Lisa Anne 39 Malborough Hill, London NW8 0NG — MB ChB 1987 Glas.

CRAMER, Elenor Jane Selly Oak Hospital, Raddlebarn Road, Selly Oak, Birmingham B29 6JD Tel: 0121 627 1627 Email: elliecramer@hotmail.com — BM BS 1996 Nottm. (Nottingham) SHO Anaesth., Selly Oak Hosp., Birm. Socs: BMA. Prev: SHO, A & E, Selly Oak; JHO, Surg., Glas. Roy. Infirm.; JHO, Med., Shrewsbury, Roy.

CRAMMER, John Lewis South Grange, Fenway, Steeple Aston, Bicester OX25 4SP — MRCS Eng. LRCP Lond. 1946; MA Camb.; FRCPsych 1974, M 1971; DPM Eng. 1956. (Univ. Coll. Hosp.) Emerit. Reader (Biol. Psychiat.) Univ. Lond. Socs: Fell. Roy. Soc. Med. Prev: Hon. Cons. Maudsley Hosp. Lond.; Cons. Psychiat. St. John's Hosp. Stone; Edr. Brit. Jl. Psychiat.

CRAMOND, Patricia Mary Currie Road Health Centre, Currie Road, Galashiels TD1 2UA Tel: 01896 752419 Fax: 01896 753876 — MB ChB 1981 Edinburgh; MB ChB Edin. 1981. (Edinburgh) GP Galashiels, Selkirksh.

CRAMOND, Susan Ann Cameron 19 Argyle Crescent, Edinburgh EH15 2QQ Tel: 0131 669 0685 — MB ChB 1979 Ed.

CRAMP, Celia Edith Royal Shrewsbury Hospital, Mytton Oak Road, Shrewsbury SY3 8XQ Tel: 01743 261631 Fax: 01743 261444; The Windmill, Vennington, Westbury SY5 9RG Tel: 01743 884576 — BM BCh 1971 Oxf.; FRCPCH 1998; FRCP Lond. 1975; DCH Eng. 1974. (Univ. Oxf. & Univ. Coll. Hosp. Lond.) Socs: Fell.of Roy. Coll. of Paediat. & Child Health. Prev: Cons. Paediat., Whiston Hosp., Merseyside; Sen. Regist. (Paediat.) Roy. Manch. Childr.s Hosp. & Wigan Infirm.; Regist. (Paediat.) Roy. Manch. Childr.s Hosp.

CRAMP, Geoffrey Joseph Drumcannach, Arisaig PH39 4NJ — MB ChB 1991 Dundee.

CRAMP, Harry Edward, MBE (retired) Milton House, Castle St., Torrington EX38 8EZ — MB ChB 1956 Bristol; DObst RCOG 1960; MRCGP 1969.

CRAMP, Hilary Alison 41B Beauchamp Road, London SW11 1PG — MB BS 1988 Lond.; MRCP (UK) 1991. Research Fell. St. Bart. Hosp. Lond.

CRAMP, Jessica Chloe Whiston Hospital, Warrington Road, Prescot L35 5DR — MB ChB 1998 Liverp.; MB ChB Liverp 1998.

CRAMP, Matthew Edward 41B Beauchamp Road, Clapham, London SW11 1PG — MB BS 1987 Lond.; MRCP (UK) 1990. Clin. Research Fell. Inst. Liver Studies King's Coll. Hosp. Lond. Prev: SHO (Med.) Lister Hosp. Stevenage; Ho. Surg. Homerton Hosp. Lond.; Ho. Phys. St. Bart. Hosp. Lond.

CRAMP, Paul Graham Willard Depoartment of Anaesthetics, Bradford Royal Infirmary, Duckworth Lane, Bradford BD9 6RJ Tel: 01274 364065 Fax: 01274 366542 Email: paulcramp@bradfordhospitals.nhs.uk; Upper Longbottom Farm, Warley Wood Lane, Luddendenfoot, Halifax HX2 6BW — MB ChB 1982 Manch.; BSc St. And. 1979; MRCP (UK) 1986; FRCA 1989. Cons. Anaesth., Bradford Roy. Infirm., Bradford.

CRAMPIN, Amelia Catharine Karonga Prevention Study, PO Box 46, Chilumba, Karonga District, Malawi Tel: 00 265 364256 Fax: 00 265 364256 Email: kpschill@aol.com; London School of Hygiene & Tropical Medicine, Keppel St, London WC1E 7HT Tel: 020 7436 4230 — MB ChB 1989 Manch.; MSc Lond. 1995; MFPHM 1997; DTM & H Liverp. 1993. Field Epidemiol., Karonga Preven. Study, Malawi; Lect. Communicable Dis. Epidemiol. Unit. Lond. Sch. Hyg. & Trop. Med. Prev: Lect. (Communicable Dis. Control) Kings Coll. Sch. Med. & Dent. Lond.; Sen. Regist. (Pub. Health) Lond.

CRAMPSEY, Fiona Margaret Feeney and Partners, 29 Glasgow Road, Paisley PA1 3PA Tel: 0141 889 3356 Fax: 0141 887 5526; 116 Mt Annan Drive, Glasgow G44 4RX — MB ChB 1984 Glas.; MRCGP 1988; DRCOG 1987. (Glasgow University) Clin. Asst. (Dermat.) Vict. Infirm. Socs: BMA & S.. Med. Soc.; BMA; S.ern Med. Soc.

CRAMPSEY, Veronica Rose 15 Myrtle Park, Glasgow G42 8UQ Tel: 0141 423 2735 — MB ChB 1956 Glas.; MA Glas. 1950, MB ChB 1956.

CRAMPTON, Anne Heath Hill Practice, Heath Hill Road South, Crowthorne RG45 7BN Tel: 01344 777915; 40 Spring Meadow, Bracknell RG12 2JP Tel: 01344 411583 — MB ChB 1985 Sheff.; MRCGP 1992. Prev: Trainee GP Windsor VTS.

CRAMPTON, Gillian Mary Williams, Crampton and Hanip, Carters Green Medical Centre, 396-400 High Street, West Bromwich B70 9LB Tel: 0121 553 0385 Fax: 0121 525 9770; 16 Ravenhurst Drive, Great Barr, Birmingham B43 7RS Tel: 0121 357 6243 — MB ChB 1979 Birm.; MRCGP 1983; DCH Eng. 1981; DRCOG Eng. 1981. (Birm.)

CRAMPTON, Shelley Anne 10 Wesley Cl, Mattishall, Dereham NR20 3NY — MB ChB 1997 Leeds.

CRAMPTON SMITH, Professor Alexander Flat 1, 15 Rawlinson Road, Oxford OX2 6UE Tel: 01865 512954 — MB ChB 1941 Ed.; MA Oxf. 1961; FFA RCS Eng. 1954; DA Eng. 1947. (Ed.) Emerit. Prof. Anaesth. Univ. Oxf. Socs: Anaesth. Research Soc. Prev: Nuffield Prof. Anaesth. Oxf. Univ.; Civil Cons. Anaesth. RN.

CRAN, Eva Margaret (retired) 21 Carrisbrooke House, Courtlands, Sheen Road, Richmond TW10 5AZ Tel: 020 8948 6952 — MA, MB ChB Aberd. 1936; DPH Lond. 1939. Prev: Dep. Div. Med. Off. LCC & Dep. MOH Boro. Camberwell.

CRAN, James (retired) Chreag Bheag, Rhynie, Huntly AB54 4HD — MB ChB 1941 Aberd. Prev: Geriatr. Barnet Gen. Hosp.

CRAN, John Shaw Cran, Gripper, Bolton and Evers, Health Centre, Chacewater, Truro TR4 8QS Tel: 01872 560346 Fax: 01872 561184; The Surgery, Quay Road, Devoran, Truro TR3 6PN Tel: 01872 863189 — MB BS 1973 Lond.

CRANE, Barrie John Gable House, 46 High Street, Malmesbury SN16 9AT Tel: 01666 825825; Woodhayes, Little Somerford, Chippenham SN15 5JW Tel: 01666 823287 — MB ChB 1960 Liverp.; DA Eng. 1966. Socs: BMA. Prev: Regist. (Anaesth.) Bath Clin. Area; Ho. Phys. (Paediat.) Roy. United Hosp. Bath; Ho. Surg. (O & G) St. Woolos Hosp. Newport.

CRANE, Professor Jack State Pathologists Department, Institute of Forensic Medicine, Grosvenor Road, Belfast BT12 6BS Tel: 01232 894648 Fax: 01232 237357; 173 Malone Road, Belfast BT9 6TB — MB BCh BAO 1977 Belf.; FRCPath 1995, M 1984; FFPath RCPI 1985; DMJ Soc. Apoth. Lond. 1982. (Qu. Univ. Belf.) State Path. N. Irel.; Prof. Forens. Med. Qu. Univ. Belf.; Cons. Path. N. Irel. HSSB. Socs: Fell. Brit. Assn. Forens. Med. Prev: Lect. (Forens. Med.) Qu. Univ. Belf.; Asst. State Path. N. Irel.

***CRANE, Jeremy Samuel** 112 Park Road, Prestwich, Manchester M25 0DU Tel: 0161 740 0222 — MB ChB 1997 Liverp.

CRANE, John Anthony 9 Maes-y-Rhedyn, Creigiau, Cardiff CF15 9JX; 9 Maes-y-Rhedyn, Creigiau, Cardiff CF15 9JX Tel: 01222 891221 Fax: 01222 891331 — MB BS 1992 Lond.; BSc 1989; DCH 1996; MRCGP 1997. (St. Georges Hospital, London) Socs: Britsih Med. Acupunc. Soc.

CRANE, John Emlyn (retired) 9 Penllwyn Park, Carmarthen SA31 3BU Tel: 01267 236370 — MB BCh 1942 Wales; BSc Wales, MB BCh 1942; FRCGP 1976.

CRANE, John Lewis 70 Camberwell Road, London SE5 0EG Tel: 020 7703 8010 — MB ChB Liverp. 1955; Dip. Sports Med. Glas. 1992. Med. Adviser Arsenal Football Club & Football Assn. Socs: Football Assn. Regional Med. Soc. SE; Past Chairm. FARMSE. Prev: Princip. GP S.E. Lond.; Chairm. S.E. Div. BMA.

CRANE, Michael David Rectory Lane Surgery, 44 Rectory Lane, Prestwich, Manchester M25 1BL Tel: 0161 773 1803 Fax: 0161 773 3292 — MB ChB 1971 Manch.

CRANE, Michael David Hillcroft, Heol-y-Cawl, Dinas Powys CF64 4AH — MB BCh 1970 Wales; MRCP (UK) 1972; FRCR 1975; DMRD Eng. 1974.
CRANE, Raymond Granville 4 St Edwards Meadow, Winterbourne Dauntsey, Salisbury SP4 6JD — MB BS 1975 Lond.; MFOM RCP Lond. 1992, A 1989, F 1997.
CRANE, Steven Derek 10 Sheridan Way, Pudsey LS28 9NU — BM BS 1992 Nottm.; FFAEM 2000; MRCP (UK) 1995. Specialist Regist. (A & E) Gen. Infirm. Leeds.
CRANE, Timothy Paul 4 Poney Chase, Wickham Bishops, Witham CM8 3NX — MB ChB 1996 Birm.
CRANE, William Paton Old Meadow, 25 Ayot Green, Welwyn AL6 9BA — MB ChB 1947 Glas.; MB ChB (Commend.) Glas. 1947. Med. Adviser Roche Products Ltd. Welwyn Gdn. City.
CRANER, Matthew John, Surg. Lt.-Cdr. RN St Malo, 1 South Hill, Felixstowe IP11 2AA — MB ChB 1992 Bristol; MRCP (UK) June 1998. SHO (Cardiol.) Plymouth. Prev: SHO (Gen. Med. & Gastroenterol.) Essex.
CRANFIELD, Frances Mary Hall Grove Surgery, 4 Hall Grove, Welwyn Garden City AL7 4PL Tel: 01707 328528 Fax: 01707 373139; Standhill Cottage, 43 London Road, Hitchin SG4 9EW Tel: 01462 435332 Fax: 01462 436407 — MB BS 1976 Lond.; MRCS Eng. LRCP Lond. 1976; DRCOG 1980; FRCGP 1996. (St. Mary's) RCGP/Astra Research Award 1980; Asst. Dep. Coroner Hitchin Jurisdiction; Chairm. Herts. LMC. Socs: Founder Mem. Expert Witness Inst.; Medico-Legal Soc.
CRANFIELD, Frederick Roger 153 Risca Road, Newport NP20 3PP Tel: 01633 244088 — MB BCh 1972 Wales; MRCP (UK) 1977; DCH Eng. 1974.
CRANFIELD, Karen Anne West Anaesthetic Department, Aberdeen Royal Infirmary, Forester Hill, Aberdeen AB25 2XF Tel: 01224 681818 — MB BS 1987 Lond.; FRCA 1993; DA (UK) 1989. (Roy. Free Hosp. Sch. Med.) Cons. Anaesth. Aberd. Roy. Infirm. Socs: Assn. Anaesth. Prev: Sen. Regist. (Anaesth.) UCL Hosp.; Regist. (Anaesth.) Chelsea & W.m. Hosp. Lond.; SHO (Anaesth.) Roy. Infirm. Glas.
CRANFIELD, Tanya Georgina Department of Haematology, Queen Alexandra Hospital, Cosham, Portsmouth PO6 3LY Tel: 023 92 286311 Fax: 02392 374204 Email: tanyacrawford@qmail01.porthosp.swest.nhs.uk — MB BS 1978 Lond.; MRCP Lond. 1981; MRCPath 1989. (Charing Cross Hospital) Cons. Haemat. Qu. Alexandra Hosp. Portsmouth.
CRANITCH, Julia Ann 254 Liverpool Road, London N1 1LG — MB BS 1982 Lond.
CRANK, Andrew Avondale Health Centre, Avondale St., Bolton BL1 4JP Tel: 01204 840153 — MB ChB 1979 Manch.; MRCGP 1987; DRCOG 1987.
CRANKSON, Mr Staenley John E18 Stratham Place, Oldbrook, Milton Keynes MK6 2HD — MB ChB 1973 Ghana; FRCS Ed. 1981.
CRANLEY, Mr Brian Daisy Hill Hospital, Newry BT35 8DR Tel: 02830 835238 Fax: 028302 68869 Email: brian.cranley@ahh.n-i.nhs.uk; Ballinran House, 95 Shore Road, Rostrevor, Newry BT34 3AB Tel: 016937 38774 Email: brca1@aol.com — MB BCh BAO 1972 Belf.; MD (Hons.) Belf. 1981; FRCSI 1995; FRCS Ed. 1976. (Qu. Univ. Belf.) Cons. (Surg.) Daisy Hill Hosp. Newry. Socs: Fell. Assn. Surgs.; Vasc. Soc. GB & Irel.; Chairm. N. Irel. Surgic. Train. Com.
CRANMER-GORDON, Cynthia Rosemary Lyndhurst, 20 Beach Road, Hartford, Northwich CW8 4BB Tel: 01606 75533 — MB ChB 1953 Liverp. (Liverp.) Prev: Paediat. Ho. Phys. Chester City Hosp.; Ho. Surg. Alder Hey Childr. Hosp.; Paediat. Regist. Clatterbridge Hosp. Wirral.
CRANMORE, Fiona Jean Wotton Lawn, Horton Road GL1 3WL — BM BS 1983 Nottm.; MRCPsych 1988. p/t Staff Carade (Psychiat.) Wotton Lawn Hosp. Gloucester. Prev: Regist. (Psychiat.) Barrow Hosp. Bristol.
CRANNA, Frederick Maxwell (retired) Tanglewood, Balcarras Road, Charlton Kings, Cheltenham GL53 8QG Tel: 01242 580983 Fax: 01242 580983 — MB ChB 1956 Glas. Prev: GP Charlton Kings, Cheltenham.
CRANNA, Robert Allister (retired) 40 Smith Lane, Egerton, Bolton BL7 9EZ Tel: 01204 304582 — MRCS Eng. LRCP Lond. 1944.
CRANNEY, Mike Oak Vale Medical Centre, 158-160 Edge Lane Drive, Liverpool L13 4AQ Tel: 0151 259 1551 Fax: 0151 252 1121; 17 Villies Crescent, Eccleston, St Helens WA10 5HP Tel: 01744 617243 — MB ChB 1978 Liverp.; MRCGP 1994; DRCOG 1993; DGM RCP Lond. 1992; DCH RCP Lond. 1991. Research Fell. (Pharmacol.) Liverp. Univ.
CRANSHAW, Julius Harry 9 Third Acre Rise, Botley, Oxford OX2 9DA — MB ChB 1992 Bristol.
CRANSTON, Christopher John 29 Waterlow Road, Maidstone ME14 2TR — MB BS 1994 Lond.
CRANSTON, David Peter 10 West Common Way, Harpenden AL5 2LF Tel: 01582 764673 Fax: 01582 765409 Email: david@drcranston.demon.co.uk — MB BS Lond. 1970; BSc (Hons.) Lond. 1967; Cert. Av Med. 1977; DA Eng. 1973. (Univ. Coll. Hosp.) Anaesth. NW Herts. & S. Beds. Health Dist.; Sen. Aviat. Med. Examr. Federal Aviat. Admin. & CAA; Chief Med. Off. Brit. Racing Drivers Club & Silverstone Circuit Ltd. Socs: RACMSA Med. Comm.; (Vice Chairm.) RAC MSA Med. Comm.
CRANSTON, David Scott (retired) Chelmsley View, 40 Gilson Way, Kingshurst, Birmingham B37 6BE — MB ChB 1946 Glas. Prev: O & G Ho. Surg. Falkirk & Dist. Roy. Infirm.
CRANSTON, Mr David William Department of Urology, Churchill Hospital, Oxford OX3 7LJ Tel: 01865 225941 Fax: 01865 226086 — MB ChB 1975 Bristol; DPhil Oxf. 1986; FRCS Eng. 1980. Cons.Surg. (Urol. Transpl.) Univ. Oxf. & Ch.ill Hosp. Socs: Brit. Assn. Urol. Surgs.; Eur. Assn. Urol.; Amer. Urol. Assn. Prev: Clin. Lect. (Urol. & Transpl.) Univ. Oxf. & Ch.ill Hosp. Oxf.; Hanson Research Fell. & Hon. Clin. Lect. Nuffield Dept. Surg. Univ. Oxf.; Regist. (Surg.) Roy. United Hosp. Bath.
CRANSTON, Iain Charles Pearson St. Thomas' Hospital, Department of Medicine, 4th Floor North Wing, Lambeth Palace Road, London SE1 7EH Email: i.cranston@umds.ac.uk; 1C Sydenham Avenue, Sydenham, London SE26 6UL — MB BS 1986 Lond.; MRCP (UK) 1990. Lect. & Hon. Sen. Regist. (Med.) St. Thos. Hosp. Lond. Prev: Research Regist. (Endocrinol.) Guy's Hosp. Lond.
CRANSTON, John 10 Grangethorpe Drive, Burnage, Manchester M19 2LG — MB ChB 1984 Birm.
CRANSTON, Ross Douglas 74B Glengarry Road, London SE22 8QD — MB ChB 1990 Ed.; MRCP (UK) 1995; DRCOG 1992; DFFP 1993. (Ed.) Specialist Regist. GUM/HIV St. Ths. Hosp. Lond. Socs: BMA; Collegiate Mem. RCP Edin.; MSSVD.
CRANSTON, Professor William Ian (retired) 31 Berrylands, Surbiton KT5 8JT Tel: 020 8399 2790 Email: cran_hill@hotmail.com — MB ChB 1949 Aberd.; MB ChB (Hons.) Aberd. 1949; MA Oxf. 1962; MD Aberd. 1957; FRCP Lond. 1965, M 1952. Prev: Prof. Med. United Med. Sch. Guy's & St Thos. Lond.
CRANSWICK, George Noel Harvard Consulting Rooms, Fitzroy Nuffield Hospital, 10-12 Bryanston Square, London W1H 8BB Tel: 020 7723 1288; 4 Stanton Road, Barnes, London SW13 0EX Tel: 020 8876 5782 — MB BS 1942 Sydney; MRCGP 1966; DCH RCP Lond. 1952. Socs: BMA. Prev: Sen. Regist. (Med.) Roy. Marsden Hosp. Lond.
CRASKE, David Anthony 2 Fairhill Close, Penrith CA11 8RD Tel: 01768 863084 Email: dcraske@aol.com — BM BS 1992 Nottm.; BMedSci Nottm. 1990. Specialist Regist. (Anaesth.) Leeds Gen. Infirm. Socs: Train. Mem. Assn. Anaesth.
CRASKE, Elizabeth 8 Tracey Court, Hibbert St., Luton LU1 3XH — MB BS 1989 Lond.
CRASKE, John (retired) 15 Higher Downs, Altrincham WA14 2QL Tel: 0161 928 2898 Fax: 0870 164 0471 Email: john@omp-tickok.demon.co.uk — MB BChir 1959 Camb.; BA Camb. 1955; Dip. Bact. Lond. 1966; MRCPath 1968. Sen. Research Fell. Med. MicroBiol. Univ. Liverp. Prev: Cons. Microbiol. Pub. Health Laborat. Poole Gen. Hosp.
CRASKE, Stephen Endsleigh, Mark Way, Godalming GU7 2BQ — MB BS 1958 Lond.; MRCS Eng. LRCP Lond. 1958; FRCPsych 1990, M 1971; DPM Eng. 1962. (King's Coll. Hosp.) Cons. Psychiat. NW Surrey Gp. Hosps. Prev: Ho. Surg. (ENT) King's Coll. Hosp.; SHO Acad. Unit Psychiat. Middlx. Hosp; Sen. Regist. (Psychiat.) Roy. Free Hosp.
CRATCHLEY, Mollie Doreen (retired) 3A Woods Orchard Road, Tuffley, Gloucester GL4 0BT Tel: 01452 309558 — MB ChB St. And. 1957. Locum GP Gloucester area. Prev: GP Addlestone, Surrey & Stourbridge. W. Midl.s.
CRATE, Mr Ian Duncan Bassetlaw District General Hospital, Kilton, Worksop S81 0BD Tel: 01909 502163 Fax: 01909

506492/502598 Email: idcrate@msn.com; 33 Boscombe, Worksop S81 7SB Tel: 01909 506491 Fax: 01909 506492 Email: idcrate@msn.com — MB BS 1979 Lond.; FRCS Ed. 1986; MRCS Eng. LRCP Lond. 1979; FRCS Eng. 1999. (Guy's) Cons. Surg. (Colorectal Surg.) Bassetlaw Dist. Gen. Hosp. Socs: Milit. Surg. Soc.; ASGBI; RSM. Prev: Cons. Surg. (Army).

CRAUFURD, David Ivor Orme Department of Medical Genetics, St. Mary's Hospital, Haversage Road, Manchester M13 0JH — MB BS 1976 Lond.; MSc Manch. 1985; MRCPsych 1983. Wellcome Trust Lect. (Psychiat.) Univ. Manch. Prev: Sen. Regist. (Psychiat.) N. W.. RHA Manch.

CRAVEN, Alison Riversdale Surgery, Riversdale House, Merthyrmawr Road, Bridgend CF31 3NL Tel: 01656 766866 Fax: 01656 668659 — MB BS 1983 Lond. GP Trainee Bridgend VTS. Prev: Ho. Phys. Thanet Dist. Hosp.; Ho. Surg. E.bourne Dist. Gen. Hosp.

CRAVEN, Andrew John Meadowside Medical Practice, 1-3 Meadowside, Lancaster LA1 3AQ Tel: 01524 32622 Fax: 01524 846353; 2 Prospect Drive, Hest Bank, Lancaster LA2 6HX Tel: 01524 824290 Fax: 01524 825074 Email: cravenaj@aol.com — MB ChB 1987 Leeds; FRCGP 1999; MRCGP 1992. Trainer (Gen. Pract.) Lancaster; Assoc. Dir. Post Grad. GP Educat.; GP Lancaster. Prev: Trainee GP Airedale Hosp. VTS.

CRAVEN, Anne Frances High Street Health Centre, High Street, Burton Latimer, Kettering NN15 5RH Tel: 01536 723566 Fax: 01536 420226; The Old Rectory, Hardwick, Wellingborough NN9 5AL Tel: 01933 678221 — MB ChB 1976 Manch.

CRAVEN, Barbara Margaret Boughton Medical Group, Boughton Health Centre, Hoole Lane, Chester CH2 3DP Tel: 01244 325421; Spy Hill Farm, Woodside, Ashton, Chester CH3 8AG Tel: 01829 751388 — MB BS 1961 Durh. Socs: (Comm.) Chester & N. Wales Med. Soc. Prev: Clin. Med. Off. Chesh. AHA; Ho. Off. (Paediat.) Newc. Gen. Hosp.; Ho. Off. Roy. Vict. Infirm. Newc.

CRAVEN, Eric Robert Brookside House, Brook Lane, Great Easton, Market Harborough LE16 — MB BS 1966 Lond.; FRCPath 1986, M 1975. (Univ. Coll. Hosp.) Cons. Haemat. Kettering Gen. Hosp. Prev: Sen. Regist. Haemat. Middlx. Hosp. Lond.; Regist. Lond. Hosp. & Hammersmith Hosp.; Ho. Phys. & Ho. Surg. Barnet Gen. Hosp.

CRAVEN, Mr John Leonard (retired) 20 Main Street, Nether Poppleton, York YO26 6HS Tel: 01904 794896 Email: j.craven@btinternet.com — MD 1965 Manch.; BSc Manch. 1956, MD 1965, MB ChB 1960; FRCS Eng. 1967. Prev: Cons. Surg. York Dist. Hosp.

CRAVEN, John Rennie Nettleham Medical Practice, 14 Lodge Lane, Nettleham, Lincoln LN2 2RS Tel: 01522 751717 Fax: 01522 754474; The Sonnets, Church Lane, Sudbrooke, Lincoln LN2 2QH — MB ChB 1974 Leeds; ECFMG Cert. 1974; MRCGP 1980. (Leeds) Trainer (Gen. Pract.) Lincoln VTS; Nuffield Health Screening Lincoln Nuffield Hosp. Socs: Lincoln Med. Soc.; Christian Med. Fell.sh.; Lincoln Med. Golf Soc. Prev: Hosp. Pract. (A & E) Lincoln. Co. Hosp.

CRAVEN, Judith Mary Community Drug Problem Service, 22-24 Spittal St., Edinburgh EH3 9DU; 40 Warrender Park Terrace, Edinburgh EH9 1EB Email: webber@compuserve.com — MB BS 1984 Newc.; MB BS Newc. l984; MRCGP 1989. Clin. Asst. (Psychiat. & Subst. Misuse) Roy. Edin. Hosp.

CRAVEN, Kenneth William Edward 8 Melander Close, York YO26 5RP Tel: 01904 782851 — MRCS Eng. LRCP Lond. 1961; MA Camb. 1965, MB 1961, BChir 1960; DA Eng. 1965; DCH Eng. 1963; DObst RCOG 1962. (Camb. & St. Mary's)

CRAVEN, Marcus James Flat 132, Clare Court, Judd St., London WC1H 9QR — MB BS 1998 Lond.; MB BS Lond 1998.

CRAVEN, Nicholas Martyn Burnley General Hospital, Casterton Avenue, Burnley BB10 2PQ Tel: 01282 474818 Fax: 01282 474809; Email: nickcraven@supanet.com — BM BCh 1989 Oxf.; MA Camb. 1990; MRCP (UK) 1992. Cons.(Dermat.) Burnley Gen. Hosp., Burnley.; Hon. Cons. Dermatol.: Hope Hosp. Salford. Socs: Brit. Med. Assn.; Brit. Assn. of Dermatol.s; Brit. Soc. for Investigative Dermat. Prev: Clin. Lect. (Dermat.) Univ. of Manch..

CRAVEN, Phillip John 4 Snaithing Lane, Sheffield S10 3LG — MB ChB 1982 Sheff.

CRAVEN, Rachael Mary Abbots Cottage, Abbots Way, Merrow, Guildford GU1 2XP — BM BCh 1994 Oxf. SHO (Anaesth.) Bristol Roy. Infirm.

CRAVEN, Richard Mark Woodlands Medical Centre, 106 Yarm Lane, Stockton-on-Tees TS18 1YE Tel: 01642 607398 Fax: 01642 604603; Cherwell, 25 The Grove, Marton in Cleveland, Middlesbrough TS7 8AF — MB ChB 1985 Sheff.; MRCGP 1989; DRCOG 1989. GP Stockton-on-Tees.

CRAVEN, Sarah Brunswick Health Centre, 139-140 St. Helens Road, Swansea SA1 4DE Tel: 01792 643001 / 643611; 58 Waverley Drive, Coltshill, Mumbles, Swansea SA3 5SY Tel: 01792 368465 — MB BS 1987 Lond.; MRCGP 1991. Prev: SHO (Med. for Elderly) Morriston Hosp. Swansea; SHO (Ophth.) Singleton Hosp. Swansea; SHO (O & G) Morriston Hosp. Swansea.

CRAVEN, Sarah Elisabeth 3 Wharfedale Terrace, Linton Road, Collingham, Wetherby LS22 5BT — MB BS 1994 Lond.; MB BS Lond.; BSc (Hons.) Lond. 1992. SHO (O & G), Harrogate Dist. Hosp. Prev: SHO (O & G), Chelsea & W.minster; SHO (Paediat.), Qu. Eliz. Hosp., Hackney.

CRAW, Nicholas Ian 75 Orchard Road, Lytham St Annes FY8 1PG — MB ChB 1998 Manch.; MB ChB Manch 1998.

CRAWFORD, Adrian Neil The Medical Centre, Cranwell Road, Driffield YO25 6UH Tel: 01377 253334 Fax: 01377 241728 — MB ChB 1978 Birm.; MRCGP 1982. GP Driffield. Socs: BMA & Roy. Coll. Gen. Pract. Prev: Trainee N.allerton VTS; Ho. Surg. Birm. Gen. Hosp.; Ho. Phys. BromsGr. Gen. Hosp.

CRAWFORD, Ainslie Sanderson (retired) 9 Royal Crescent, Edinburgh EH3 6PZ — MB ChB 1936 Ed.; MD Ed. 1948; FRCA 1953; DA Eng. 1950; DPH Ed. & Glas. 1939. Prev: Cons. Anaesth. Roy. Infirm. Edin. & Roodlands Hosp. Haddington.

CRAWFORD, Alexa Clare The Surgery, Victoria Gardens, Lockerbie DG11 2BJ Tel: 01576 203665 Fax: 01576 202773 — MB ChB 1986 Aberd.

CRAWFORD, Alistair Daniel (retired) The Health Centre, Oliver St., Ampthill, Bedford MK45 2SB Tel: 01234 402641 — MB 1959 Camb.; BChir 1958; DObst RCOG 1960.

CRAWFORD, Alistair Hogg Bodreinallt Surgery, Bodreinallt, Conwy LL32 8AT Tel: 01492 593385 Fax: 01492 573715 — MB BS 1987 Lond.; MRCGP 1991; DGM RCP Lond. 1990. Trainee GP Gwynedd VTS.

CRAWFORD, Andrew 20 Edward Road, Market Harborough LE16 7AD — MB BS 1994 Lond.

CRAWFORD, Anne Isabel Murdoch 8 Greenacre Road, Hest Bank, Lancaster LA2 6HD Tel: 01524 822946 — MB ChB Sheff. 1965; DObst RCOG 1967. (Sheffield University) Clin. Asst. (Dermat.) Qu. Vict. Hosp. Morecambe; Clin. Asst. (Psychiat.) Ridge Lea Hosp. Lancaster; JP. Socs: BMA; Lancaster Med. Bk. Club. Prev: Med. Off. Lancaster Univ. Health Centre Lancaster; SHO (O & G) & Ho. Surg. Scarsdale Hosp. Chesterfield; Ho. Phys. Roy. Hosp. Chesterfield.

CRAWFORD, Anthony David St Clements Partnership, Tanner Street, Winchester SO23 8AD Tel: 01962 852211 Fax: 01962 856010; 1 Prior's Barton, Kingsgate Road, St. Cross, Winchester SO23 9QF Tel: 01962 62168 — MB BS 1972 Lond.; MRCP (U.K.) 1975; MRCS Eng. LRCP Lond. 1972. (Guy's) Prev: Lect. in Med. Univ. Soton.; Regist. (Med.) Frenchay Hosp. Bristol.

CRAWFORD, Barbara (retired) 68 Brownsea View Avenue, Poole BH14 8LQ Tel: 01202 707011 — MB ChB 1950 Sheff. Prev: Gen. Practitioner POOLE DORSET.

CRAWFORD, Mr Bernard Searle (retired) 9 Springfield Glen, Sheffield S7 2HL Tel: 0114 236 6616 — MB ChB 1943 Sheff.; FRCS Eng. 1950. Cons. Plastic Surg. United Sheff. Hosps. Prev: Resid. Surg. Off. & Ho. Surg. Sheff. Roy. Hosp.

CRAWFORD, Brian James Findlay Silver Street Surgery, 26 Silver Street, Great Barford, Bedford MK44 3HX Tel: 01234 870325 Fax: 01234 871323 Email: doc.b.crawf@talk21.com; Yew Tree Cottage, Wilden Road, Colmworth, Bedford MK44 2NN Tel: 01234 376201 Email: doc.b.crawf@talk21.com — MB ChB 1974 Glas.; Dip. Palliat. Med. Wales 1992; DObst RCOG 1976.

CRAWFORD, Brian Wolstan Dixie (retired) 4 Little Dene, Gateshead NE9 5AF Tel: 0191 491 0995 — MB BS 1949 Durh.; MRCGP 1972.

CRAWFORD, Catherine Elizabeth Jeanne Marden House, Sherston, Malmesbury SN16 0PZ Tel: 01666 8400PZ; Karia Medical Centre, Kibris Sehitleri Cad, No. 59, Bodrum 48400, Turkey Tel: 00 902 52 Fax: 313 6233 — MB BS 1990 Lond.; BSc (Hons.) Psychol. Manch. 1972. GP Karia Med. Centre. Prev: SHO (Cas.) Barnet Dist.

Gen. Hosp.; SHO (Oncol.) Roy. Free Hosp.; SHO (Infec. Dis.) Coppetts Wood Hosp.

CRAWFORD, Cedric Dawson Horsefair Practice, Horse Fair, Rugeley WS15 2EL Tel: 01889 582244 Fax: 01899 582244; Star Croft, Gaia Lane, Lichfield WS13 7LW Tel: 01889 58244 — MB ChB 1962 Birm.; MRCS Eng. LRCP Lond. 1962; MRCGP 1972; Cert. Family Plann. JCC 1972; DObst RCOG 1964. (Birm.) Train. Pract. W. Midl. Regional VTS; Chairm. Staffs. LMC; Chairm. Dist. Med. Advis. Comm.; Sec. Mid-Staffs. Dist. Med. Sub-Comm. Socs: BMA & GMSC. Prev: SHO (Cas.) Dudley Rd. Hosp. Birm.; Ho. Surg. Loveday St. Matern. Hosp. Birm. & Birm. & Midl. Hosp. Wom.

CRAWFORD, Christine McCallum Argyle Street Surgery, 1119 Argyle Street, Glasgow G3 8ND Tel: 0141 248 3698 Fax: 0141 221 5144; 100 Douglas Park Crescent, Bearsden, Glasgow G61 3DW — MB ChB 1979 Glas.; MRCP (UK) 1985; MRCGP 1984; DCH RCPS Glas. 1981. (Univ. Glas.)

CRAWFORD, Christopher Ewan Hamish Brown and Partners, 35 Saughton Crescent, Edinburgh EH12 5SS Tel: 0131 337 2166 Fax: 0131 313 5059; 12 Orchard Brae Gardens, Edinburgh EH4 2HJ Fax: 0131 332 2405 Email: cehcraw@aol.com — MB ChB 1981 Ed.; MRCGP 1986. (Edinburgh) Socs: Brit. Sleep Soc. Prev: Trainee GP W. Lothian VTS.

CRAWFORD, Colin Keith (retired) 68 Brownsea View Avenue, Poole BH14 8LQ Tel: 01202 707011 Email: c.ckc.crawford@talk21.com — MB ChB 1950 Sheff.; MRCGP 1968. Fact. Med. Adviser Plessey Controls Ltd & Whitecap Internat. (Metal Box) Poole. Prev: Pk.; Med. Regist. Rheum. Research Unit Nether Edge Hosp. Sheff.

CRAWFORD, Colin Leithead 23 Grafton Road, London W3 6PB — MB ChB 1957 New Zealand.

CRAWFORD, Colley Elizabeth 13 Sunbury Avenue, London NW7 3SL — MB BS 1998 Lond.; MB BS Lond 1998.

CRAWFORD, David Charles 1 Beechfield Road, Gosforth, Newcastle upon Tyne NE3 4DR Tel: 0191 285 8362 — MB BS 1979 Newc.; FRCP; FRCA. Cons. Anaesth. Newc. Gen. Hosp. Prev: Sen. Regist. (Anaesth.) N.. RHA; Lect. (Anaesth.) Univ. Leic.; SHO (Med.) Roy. Vict. Infirm. Newc.

CRAWFORD, David Stephen New Gregory's, Gregories Farm Lane, Beaconsfield HP9 1HJ — MB ChB 1984 Leeds; FRCS (Ed.); FRCS (Plast). Cons. Plastic Surg. Heatherwood & Wexham Pk. Hosps. Trust Slough.

CRAWFORD, Mr Derek James Oaklands, 31 Yerburgh Avenue, Colwyn Bay LL29 7NB — MB ChB 1976 Glas.; FRCS Glas. 1980. Cons. Surg. Ysbyty Gwynedd Bangor & Llandudno Gen. Hosp.

CRAWFORD, Desmond George (retired) 56 Glenfield Drive, Kirkella, Hull HU10 7UL Tel: 01482 651410 — MB BCh BAO 1953 Dub. Prev: Ho. Phys. & Ho. Surg. Kingston Gen. Hosp. Hull.

CRAWFORD, Diane Eastside Surgery, 7-8 Eastside, Hutton Rudby, Yarm TS15 0DB Tel: 01642 700993 Fax: 01642 701857; Lockerbie Cottage, Swainby, Northallerton DL6 3DW Tel: 01642 700050 Fax: 01642 701857 — MB ChB 1985 Sheff.; MRCGP 1989; DGM RCP Lond. 1990; Cert. Family Plann. JCC 1989; DRCOG 1989. (Univ. Sheff.) GP Princip. Socs: Brit. Diabetic Assn. Prev: SHO (O & G) Roy. Vict. Infirm. & P.ss Mary Matern. Hosp. Newc.; SHO (Med. & Geriat. Med.) Shotley Bridge Gen. Hosp.

CRAWFORD, Professor Dorothy Hanson Huph Robson Building, Edinburgh University Medical School, George Square, Edinburgh EH8 9XD Tel: 0131 650 3142 Fax: 0131 650 3711 Email: d.crawford@ed.ac.uk — MB BS 1968 Lond.; PhD Bristol 1976; DSc Lond. 1992; MD Lond. 1987; FRCPath 1994, M 1981. (St. Thos.) Prof. Med. Microbiol. Univ. Edin.; Hon. Sen. Lect. Lond. Sch. Hyg. & Trop. Med. Socs: Fell. of the Roy. Soc. of Edinbrugh. Prev: Prof. Microbiol. Lond. Sch. Hyg. & Trop. Med.; Reader (Virol.) Roy. Postgrad. Med. Sch. Lond.; Research Assoc. & Hon. Lect. Univ. Coll. Hosp. Lond.

CRAWFORD, Edward Gavin Byrne, 33 Dumbuck Crescent, Dumbarton G82 1EJ — MB ChB 1995 Glas. Arrocharmoutain rescue team,argyll.

CRAWFORD, George Marshall (retired) 8 Drums Terrace, Greenock PA16 7TH Tel: 01475 632820 — MB ChB 1943 Glas.; MRCGP 1955. Prev: GP Greenock.

CRAWFORD, Gerald Norman Cullen (retired) 67 Sandfield Road, Headington, Oxford OX3 7RW — MB BS 1944 Lond.; MA Oxf. 1952, DM 1973; MRCS Eng. LRCP Lond. 1943. Prev: Prof. & Assoc. Postgrad. Dean Med. Sch. & Dept. Human Biol. & Anat.

CRAWFORD, Gordon Andrew 10 Hayford Place, Cambusbarron, Stirling FK7 9JX — MB ChB 1988 Aberd.

CRAWFORD, Gordon MacDonald Clydebank Health Centre, Kilbowie Road, Clydebank G81 2TQ Tel: 0141 531 6400 Fax: 0141 531 6336; 24 Moorfoot Way, Bearsden, Glasgow G61 4RL Tel: 0141 942 8052 — MB ChB 1978 Glas.; BSc (Hons.) (Biochem.) Glas. 1975, MB ChB 1978; MRCGP 1982; DRCOG 1981.

CRAWFORD, Graeme Michael Bangor Health Centre, Newtownards Road, Bangor BT20 4LD Tel: 02891 515215 Fax: 02891 515397 — MB BCh BAO 1982 Belf.; MRCGP 1988; DRCOG 1987; DCH RCPSI 1986. (Qu. Univ. Belf.) Gen. Med. Practitioner, Bangor, Co. Down; Chairm. GP Exec., Ards & Bangor Community Hosps. Socs: Ulster Med. Soc.

CRAWFORD, Gregor 14 Cuttyfield Place, Carronshore, Falkirk FK2 8TA — MB ChB 1990 Ed.

CRAWFORD, Heath Penrose Glencairn, South Dean Road, Kilmarnock KA3 7RE — MB ChB 1952 Glas.; DA Eng. 1958.

CRAWFORD, Hugh Fleming, TD, Col. late RAMC (retired) Malden, White Post Lane, Sole St., Gravesend DA13 9AX Tel: 01474 812659 — MRCS Eng. LRCP Lond. 1952; AFOM RCP Lond. 1985. Prev: Occupat. Health Phys. Lucas Industries.

CRAWFORD, Iain Granby Place, Northfleet, Gravesend DA11 9EY Tel: 01474 352447; 5 Elm Close, Higham, Rochester ME3 7NH — MB BS 1955 Lond.; DCH Eng. 1958. (St. Thos.) Prev: Sen. Ho. Off. (Med.) All St.s' Hosp. Chatham; Res. Med. Off. Jenny Lind Childr. Hosp. Norwich.

CRAWFORD, Ian Brown (retired) 43 Sweetcroft Lane, Hillingdon, Uxbridge UB10 9LE — MB BS 1949 Lond.; DObst RCOG 1957. Prev: Chairm. Med. Staff Comm. Hayes Cott. Hosp.

CRAWFORD, Ian Campbell, CBE, Maj.-Gen. late RAMC Retd. The Arbour, Coldharbour Lane, Bobbing, Sittingbourne ME9 8NN Tel: 01795 842292 Fax: 01795 843753 — MB ChB 1956 Ed.; FRCP Lond. 1986; FRCP Ed. 1972, M 1961. (Ed.) Indep. Cons. Cardiol. BUPA Alexandra Hosp. Walderslade. Socs: Brit. Cardiac Soc.; Fell.Roy. Soc. of Med.; Brit. Nuclear Cardiol. Soc. Prev: Dir. of Army Med. & Cons. Phys. to Army; Sen. Cons. Phys. Qu. Eliz. Milit. Hosp. Lond.

CRAWFORD, Ian Patrick, GM, OStJ, Maj.-Gen. late RAMC (retired) Mill Cottage, Mill Lane, Cocking, Midhurst GU29 0HJ Tel: 01730 817982 — MRCS Eng. LRCP Lond. 1959; FFOM 1987, M 1981; FFCM 1982, M 1973; DIH Soc. Apoth. Lond. 1968; DPH Lond. 1967; DTM & H Eng. 1966. Prev: Commandant & Postgrad. Dean RAMC.

CRAWFORD, Isabelle Elisabeth Muriel Department of Psychiatry, Addenbrooke's Hospital, Hills Road, Cambridge CB2 2QQ; Kenilworth Cottage, 57 Pierce Lane, Fulbourn, Cambridge CB1 5DJ Tel: 01223 881266 — MB ChB 1991 Manch.; BSc (Med. Sci.) St. And. 1988. SHO (Psychiat.) Fulbourn Hosp. Cambs. Prev: Regist. (Paediat.) Bruntsfield Med. Edin. Pract.; GP/Regist. - Esk Med. Centre, Musselborgh; SHO (ENT) City Hosp. Edin.

CRAWFORD, Jacqueline Andrews 24 Moorfoot Way, Bearsden, Glasgow G61 4RL — MB ChB 1980 Glas.; MRCGP 1984; Cert. Family Plann. JCC 1984; DRCOG 1983. Research (Phys.) Community Pharmacol. Servs. Ltd Clydebank; Chief Med. Off. Nat. Australia Life Clydebank.

CRAWFORD, Jacqueline Leslie New Gregory's, Gregories Farm Lane, Beaconsfield HP9 1HJ — MB ChB 1986 Leeds.

CRAWFORD, James Alan Bentley (retired) The Millstream, 8 Templemill Cottages, Temple, Marlow SL7 1SA Tel: 01628 824875 — MB BS Lond. 1955; MRCS Eng. LRCP Lond. 1955; MFOM RCP Lond. 1980; DIH Eng. 1960. p/t Cons. Occupat. Health Marlow. Prev: Gp. Med. Adviser Mobil-UK.

CRAWFORD, James Alexander 17 Oakleigh Road, Bexhill-on-Sea TN39 4PY — LRCP LRCS 1935 Ed.; LRCP LRCS Ed. LRFPS Glas. 1935; MRC Psych. 1967; DPM Eng. 1947.

CRAWFORD, Joan Frances Mortimer Surgery, Victoria Road, Mortimer Common, Reading RG7 1HG Tel: 0118 933 2436 Fax: 0118 933 3801; Forest Lodge, West End Road, Mortimer, Reading RG7 3TP Tel: 01734 332010 — MB ChB 1974 Bristol; MRCGP 1991; DRCOG 1976.

CRAWFORD, John Gerard 5 Finlayson Quad, Airdrie ML6 8LT Tel: 01236 767521 — MB ChB 1987 Glas.; MRCGP 1993.

CRAWFORD, John Mackay c/o Crawford, Houston Head, Bridge of Weir PA11 3SU — MB ChB 1992 Glas.

CRAWFORD, Kathleen Patricia Evelyn (retired) 5 Church Lane, Westbere, Canterbury CT2 0HA Tel: 01227 710632 — MB BCh BAO 1947 Dub. Prev: Ho. Surg. Sir P. Dun's Hosp. Dub.

CRAWFORD, Kenneth Paul 42 School Lane, Walton, Wakefield WF2 6PA; 22 Midland Road, Royston, Barnsley S71 4QP Tel: 01226 722418 — MB BCh BAO 1976 Belf.; BSc Belf. 1974, MB BCh BAO 1976.

CRAWFORD, Kenneth Stewart (retired) 6 Hillside Road, Radcliffe-on-Trent, Nottingham NG12 2GZ Tel: 0115 933 2394 — MB ChB 1938 Aberd.; FFA RCS Eng. 1953; DA Eng. 1946.

CRAWFORD, Laura Alice 50 Nasmyth Avenue, Bearsden, Glasgow G61 4SQ — MB ChB 1987 Glas.; MRCGP 1992; DRCOG 1991. BA Med. Servs. Glas.. Prev: GP Princip. Borders Health Bd.

CRAWFORD, Leonora Annetta (retired) 1 Wain Close, Little Heath, Potters Bar EN6 1NF Tel: 01707 55324 — MB BS 1940 Lond.; MRCS Eng. LRCP Lond. 1940; FFCM 1981, M 1973; DPH Eng. 1944; DCH Eng. 1950.

CRAWFORD, Lesley Margaret 14 Derby Street, Cambridge CB3 9JE — MB ChB 1985 Glas.; MRCGP 1992.

CRAWFORD, Louis (retired) 7 Menlove Mansions, Menlove Gardens W., Liverpool L18 2HY Tel: 0151 737 1087 — MB ChB 1942 Leeds; MRCGP 1960. Prev: Mem. Med. Bd.ing Panel DHSS Merseyside.

CRAWFORD, Lynsay Elspeth Flat 4, 26 Athole Gardens, Glasgow G12 9BB — MB ChB 1991 Glas.

CRAWFORD, Mairi Elspeth Lyle Glen Orchy, Glenorchy Road, North Berwick EH39 4PE — MB BS 1998 Newc.; MB BS Newc 1998.

CRAWFORD, Margaret Joan Pilgrim Hospital, Sibsey Road, Boston PE21 9QS Tel: 01205 364801 Fax: 01205 365062; Highfield, 39 Sibsey Road, Boston PE21 9QY Tel: 01205 353957 — FRCPCH 1997; MB ChB Ed. 1970; FRCP Lond. 1992; MRCP (UK) 1974; DCH Eng. 1972. Cons. Paediat. Pilgrim Hosp. Boston.

CRAWFORD, Marjorie Catherine 44 Cramond Road N., Edinburgh EH4 6JA — MB ChB 1970 Glas.; FFA RCS Eng. 1980; DA Eng. 1978. Regist. (Anaesth.) Roy. Free Hosp. Lond.

CRAWFORD, Mary (retired) 4 Little Dene, Gateshead NE9 5AF Tel: 0191 491 0995 — MB BS 1949 Durh.; DObst RCOG 1950. Prev: GP Gateshead.

CRAWFORD, Michael Department of Anaesthesia, Hairmyres Hospital, East Kilbride, Glasgow G75 8RG Tel: 01355 220292 — MB ChB 1985 Glas.; FFA RCSI 1990. (University of Glasgow) Cons. Anaesth., Hairmyres Hosp., E. Kilbride. Prev: Cons. Anasethetist, Aberd. Roy. Infirm.

CRAWFORD, Michael Jeremy Ash Grove Barn, Shawbridge St., Clitheroe BB7 1LZ — MB BS 1982 Lond.

CRAWFORD, Michael Joseph 6 Beech Park, Liverpool L12 1LP — MB BS 1988 Lond.

CRAWFORD, Nigel Patrick Somerville University Hospital Aintree, Longmoor Lane, Liverpool L9 7AL; Orchard Cottage, Elfordleigh, Plympton, Plymouth PL7 5EB Email: yni46@dial.pipex.com — MB ChB 1998 Liverp.; MB ChB Liverp 1998; BSc (Hons) Liverpool 1996. (Liverpool) SHO.

CRAWFORD, Norman Henry Booth (retired) Derry-Nane, 18 Dales Lane, Whitefield, Manchester M45 7WW Tel: 0161 766 2053 — MB BCh BAO 1954 Belf. Prev: Res. Med. Off. Roy. Vict. & Roy. Matern. Hosps. Belf.

CRAWFORD, Pamela Anne 41 Kilmany Road, Wormit, Newport-on-Tay DD6 8PG — MB ChB 1990 Dundee. GP Regist. Dundee. Prev: Trainee GP Kirkaldy VTS; SHO (Geriat.) Law Hosp.; Regist. (Microbiol.) W.. Gen. Hosp. Edin.

CRAWFORD, Pamela Jane 23a Aytoun Road, Pollokshields, Glasgow G41 5HW — MB ChB 1991 Glas.; MRCP (UK) 1995.

CRAWFORD, Professor Pamela Mary York NHS Trust, Department of Neurosciences, York District Hospital, York YO31 8HE Tel: 01904 454106 Fax: 01904 453477 — MB ChB 1978 Liverp.; MD Liverp. 1986; FRCP Lond. 1995; MRCP (UK) 1981. Cons. Neurol. Special Centre for Epilepsy York, York Dist. Hosp.; Med. Adviser Tuberous Sclerosis Soc. & Migraine Trust; Edit. Bd. Seizure.; Patron York Against Motorneurone Dis.; Vis. Prof. (Community Neurol. Studies) Leeds Metrop. Univ. Prev: Neurol. Edr. Drugs & Therap. Bull.; Sen. Regist. (Neurol.) Atkinson Morley's Hosp. Lond.; Regist. (Neurol.) Manch. Roy. Infirm.

CRAWFORD, Paul Ian, Surg. Lt. RN 30D Smugglers Way, RHU, Helensburgh G84 8JA Tel: 01436 4321 — MB BS 1983 Newc. Med. Off. 10th Submarine Squadron.

CRAWFORD, Pauline Lehman and Partners, Hightown Surgery, Hightown Gardens, Banbury OX16 9DB Tel: 01295 270722 Fax: 01295 263000; Fax: 0208 959 6311 Email: david.wood@ellernmede.org — BM 1990 Soton.; MRCGP 1995. p/t GP Banbury; Locum In Family Plann. Oxforshire.

CRAWFORD, Mr Peter John Department of Neurology, Regional Neurosciences Centre, Newcastle General Hospital, Newcastle upon Tyne NE4 6BR Tel: 0191 273 8811 Fax: 0191 272 0872; 16 Pinegarth, Darras Hall, Ponteland, Newcastle upon Tyne NE20 9LF Tel: 01661 822686 — MB BS 1974 Lond.; BSc Durham. 1966; FRCS Eng. 1978. (Lond. Hosp.) Cons. Neurosurg. Newc. Gen. Hosp.; Head (Neurosurg.); Clin. Lect. (Surg.) Univ. Newc. Prev: Sen. Regist. Atkinson Morley's Hosp. Lond. & Nat. Hosp. Qu. Sq. Lond.; Regist. Addenbrooke's Hosp. Camb.

CRAWFORD, Peter Macdonald, LVO (retired) Eleanburn, Bridge of Gairn, Ballater AB35 5UD Tel: 013397 55894 Email: petermeg@eleanburn.freeserve.co.uk — MB ChB 1948 Glas.; DObst RCOG 1953. Prev: Apoth. to HM Ho.hold at Balmoral.

CRAWFORD, Philippa Holmwood Corner Surgery, 179 Malden Road, New Malden KT3 6AA Tel: 020 8942 0066 Fax: 020 8336 1377; 60 Villiers Avenue, Surbiton KT5 8BD Tel: 020 8390 6482 — MB BS 1970 Lond.; MRCGP 1984; DObst RCOG 1975; DCH Eng. 1973. (Univ. Lond., Lond. Hosp.)

CRAWFORD, Robert Cameron Department of Radiology, Ysbyty, Bangor LL57 2PW Tel: 01248 370007; Preswylfa, Llandegfan, Menai Bridge LL59 5TA Tel: 01248 712320 — MB BCh 1969 Wales; FRCR 1978. Cons. Radiol. Gwynedd Health Auth.

CRAWFORD, Robert Graham (retired) 34 Avondale Road, Shipley BD18 4QX Tel: 01274 581423 — MB ChB 1936 Ed. Prev: Sen. Med. Off. Bradford AHA.

CRAWFORD, Mr Robert James Norfolk & Norwich Hospital, Brunswick Road, Norwich NR1 3SR — MB ChB 1976 Bristol; ChM Bristol 1991; FRCS Eng. 1981. Cons. Orthop. Surg. Norf. & Norwich Hosp. Prev: Regist. & Sen. Regist. OsW.ry Orthop. Train. Progr.

CRAWFORD, Robert Malcolm 25 Glen Road, Holywood BT18 0HB — MB BCh BAO 1979 Belf.

CRAWFORD, Mr Robin Alfred Florian Addenbrooke's NHS Trust, Hills Road, Cambridge CB2 2QQ Tel: 01223 216251 Fax: 01223 217666 Email: robin.crawford@addenbrookes@nhs.uk; 5 The Cenacle, Merton St, Cambridge CB3 9JS Tel: 01223 354408 — MB BChir 1986 Camb.; MA, MB Camb. 1986, BChir 1985; FRCS Eng. 1989; MRCOG 1991; MD 1998. (Cambridge/St Thomas') Cons. Gyn. Oncol. Addenbrooke's Hosp. Camb. Socs: Counc. mem. of Brit.Gyn. Cancer Soc. Prev: Fell. (Gyn. Oncol.) St Bartholomews Hosp. & Roy. Marsden; Lect. (O & G) Med. Coll. St. Bart. Hosp. Lond.; Regist. (O & G) Whittington & Univ. Coll. Hosps. Lond.

CRAWFORD, Mr Rudy Accident & Emergency Department, Royal Infirmary, Glasgow G4 0SF Tel: 0141 211 5007 Fax: 0141 552 5384 Email: rudy.crawford@northglasgow.scot.nhs.uk — MB ChB 1978 Glas.; BSc (Hons.) Glas. 1976, MB ChB 1978; FRCS Glas. 1982; FFAEM 1993. (University of Glasgow) Cons. A & E Glas. Roy,. Infirm.; Hon. Clin. Sen. Lect. Univ. Glas. Socs: Roy. M-C Soc. & Brit. Assn. of Accid. & Emerg. Med.; Fell. Roy Coll. Phys. & Surg. Glas. (Convener Accid. & Emerg. Subcomm.). Prev: Sen. Regist. (A & E) Aberd. Roy. Infirm.; Regist. (A & E) Glas. Roy. Infirm.; Regist. (Surg.) Univ. Dept. Surg. Glas. Roy. Infirm.

CRAWFORD, Sarah Louise Birmingham Heartlands Hospital, 45 Bordesley Green E., Birmingham B9 5ST — BM 1992 Soton.; MRCP (UK) 1995. Regist. (A & E) Univ. Hosp. (Selly Oak) Birm. Prev: SHO (Med.) Good Hope Hosp. Salford; SHO (A & E) Soton. Gen. Hosp.; Ho. Off. (Gen. Med.) St. Mary's Hosp. Portsmouth.

CRAWFORD, Shirley Elizabeth 1 Ranmoor Rise, Ranmoor, Sheffield S10 3HU Tel: 0114 230 3922 — BM BS Nottm. 1985, BMedSci 1983; MRCGP 1991; Cert. Community Paediat. Sheff. 1990; DCH RCPS Glas. 1989; DRCOG 1987.

CRAWFORD, Mr Simon Callander 23A Aytoun Road, Pollokshields, Glasgow G41 5HW — MB ChB 1991 Glas.; BSc (Hons.) Molecular Biol. Glas. 1988; FRCS Ed. 1995; MRCOG 1996.

(Glas.) Specialist Regist. (O & G) The Qu. Mother's Hosp. Glas. Socs: Glas. Obst. & Gyn. Soc.; Brit. Soc. of Gyn. Endoscopy.

CRAWFORD, Stephen Giles Wilson 22 Keyberry Park, Newton Abbot TQ12 1BZ — MB BS 1998 Lond.; MB BS Lond 1998.

CRAWFORD, Stuart Michael Airedale General Hospital, Skipton Road, Steeton, Keighley BD20 6TD Tel: 01535 652511 Fax: 01535 295319; Honfleur, 50 Falcon Road, Bingley BD16 4DW Tel: 01274 566520 Fax: 01274 566520 Email: moncam@cix.compulink.co.uk — MB ChB 1975 Liverp.; MB ChB (Distinc. Organic Chem. & Histol.) Liverp. 1975; MD Liverp. 1987; FRCP Lond. 1994; FRCP Ed. 1990; MRCP (UK) 1978; T(M) 1991. Cons. Med. Oncol. Airedale Gen. Hosp. Keighley & St. James Univ. Hosp. Leeds; Croom Lect. RCP Edin. Socs: Brit. Assn. Cancer Research; Amer. Soc. Clin. Oncol.; Assn. Cancer Phys. Prev: Sen. Regist. (Med. Oncol.) Char. Cross Hosp.; Lect. (Med. Oncol.) Guy's Hosp. Lond.; SHO (Cardiol.) Sefton Gen. Hosp. Liverp.

CRAWFORD, Susan Patricia The Millstream, 8 Templemill Cottages, Temple, Marlow SL7 1SA Tel: 01628 824875 — MB BS 1987 Lond.; BA Oxf. 1984; MRCP (UK) 1991.

CRAWFORD, Tanya Anne The Bloomfield Centre, Guys Hospital, St Thomas St., London Bridge, London N5 1UP — BM 1991 Soton.; MRCPsych 1996; MSC 1996.

CRAWFORD, Tiffany Elizabeth Greenview Surgery, 129 Hazeldene Road, Northampton NN2 7PB Tel: 01604 791002 Fax: 01604 721822; 15 Colonial Drive, Collingtree Park, Northampton NN4 0BL Tel: 01604 767205 — BM BS 1991 Nottm.; MRCGP 1996; DRCOG 1994. (Univ. Nottm.) Prev: Trainee GP N.ampton.

CRAWFORD, Veronica Ann Testvale Surgery, 12 Salisbury Road, Totton, Southampton SO40 3PY Tel: 02380 866999 — MB BChir 1967 Camb.; MA Camb. 1968, MB 1967, BChir 1966. (Camb. & St. Bart.) Prev: Ho. Surg. & Ho. Phys. Roy. Vict. Hosp. Bournemouth.

CRAWFORD, Vivienne Helen Greenbank Drive Surgery, 8 Greenbank Drive, Sefton Park, Liverpool L17 1AW Tel: 0151 733 5703 — MB ChB 1980 Liverp.

CRAWFORD, William Allen, SBStJ (retired) Harbour House, Cliff St, Ramsgate CT11 9HY Tel: 01843 592517 — MB BS 1957 Lond.; MRCS Eng. LRCP Lond. 1956; FRCGP 1989, M 1965. Prev: Asst. (Occupat. Health) Pfizer Ltd. Sandwich.

CRAWFORD, William Sturgess 142 Rosemary Hill Road, Little Aston, Sutton Coldfield B74 4HN Tel: 0121 353 7428 — MB BCh BAO 1954 Dub.; DTM & H. Liverp. 1957; FRCOG 1978, M 1965. (T.C. Dub.) Cons. O & G Good Hope Matern. Hosp. Sutton Coldfield. Socs: Fell. Roy. Soc. Trop. Med. & Hyg. Prev: Sen. Regist. (O & G) Postgrad. Med. Sch. Hammersmith Lond.; Off. Govt. Kenya; Regist. Rotunda Hosp. Dub.

CRAWFORD, Yvonne Elizabeth Barbara Tranent Medical Practice, Loch Road, Tranent EH33 2JX Tel: 01875 610697 Fax: 01875 615046 — MB BCh BAO 1978 Belf.; DA RCS Eng. 1982; DRCOG 1983.

CRAWFORD CLARKE, Karen Elizabeth Henfield Medical Centre, Deer Park, Henfield BN5 9JQ; Staples Barn House, Staples Barn Lane, Henfield BN5 9PR Tel: 01273 493444 — MB ChB 1989 Ed.; BSc Ed. 1987; MRCGP 1994. (Ed.) GP.

CRAWFURD, Anthony Raymond Ivy Court, Tenterden TN30 6RB Tel: 01580 763666 Fax: 01580 766194 Email: ivycourt@doctors.org.uk; Seymour House, Shoreham Lane, St. Michaels, Tenterden TN30 6EH Tel: 01580 762967 Fax: 01580 766194 — BM BCh Oxf. 1966; MA 1966; MRCP (UK) 1974; LMSSA Lond. 1966; Dip. Sports Med. Scotl. 1993; DObst RCOG 1970; DCH Eng. 1969; FRCP 1998. (Oxf. & King's Coll. Hosp.) Med. Off. W. View Hosp. Tenterden; Hon. Med. Off., Brit. Fencing Assn. Socs: (Liveryman) Soc. Apoth. Prev: SHO King's Coll. Hosp. Lond. & Kent & Canterbury Hosp.

CRAWFURD, Mr Edward John Payne Northampton General Hospital, Billing Road, Northampton NN1 5BD Tel: 01604 634700 — MB BS 1980 Lond.; FRCS Eng. 1984. (Westminster) Cons. N.ampton Gen. Hosp. Socs: Fell.Roy. Soc. of Med.; Fell.Brit. Orthopaedic Soc.; Brit. Assn. Knee Surg.s. Prev: Sen. Regist. W.m. Hosp. & Univ. Coll. Hosp. Lond.

CRAWFURD, Martin d'Auvergne (retired) Compton, Ivy House Lane, Berkhamsted HP4 2PP Tel: 01442 863202 — MB BS Lond. 1953; FRCPath 1976, M 1963; DPath Eng. 1959. Indep. Consg. Pract. Genetics Herts. Prev: Hon. Sen. Lect. Char. Cross Hosp. Med. Sch.

CRAWFURD-PORTER, Vera Elizabeth (retired) Glenmayne, Killinghall, Harrogate HG3 2DQ Tel: 01423 2185 — MB ChB 1953 Leeds. Prev: Med. Off. Marks & Spencer Ltd., Leeds, Bradford, Harrogate & Wakefield.

CRAWLEY, Arthur Patrick The Mount, Fordbrook Lane, Pelsall, Walsall WS3 4BW Tel: 01922 682666 — MB ChB Glas. 1950. (Glas.) Clin. Asst. (Dermat.) Walsall AHA. Socs: BMA.

CRAWLEY, Brian Edward Wychwood, The Drove, Fordwich, Canterbury CT2 0DE Tel: 01227 711695 — MB BS 1959 Lond.; FFA RCS Eng. 1966; DA Eng. 1964. (St. Mary's) Cons. Anaesth. Kent & Canterbury Hosp. Socs: Assn. Anaesths.; Fell. Roy Soc. Med. Prev: Sen. Regist. W.m. Hosp. Lond. & Qu. Mary's Hosp. Roehampton; Clin. Asst. Nat. Hosp. Qu. Sq. Lond.; Chairm. Dept. Anaesth. K. Faisal Hosp. Riyadh, Saudi Arabia.

CRAWLEY, Deborah Elizabeth Tel: 0114 242 6411 Fax: 0114 249 1551 Email: deborahcrawley@gp-c88047.nhs.uk; 53 Alms Hill Road, Ecclesall, Sheffield S11 9RR Tel: 0114 236 6230 Email: deborahcrawley@doctors.org.uk — MB ChB 1979 Ed.; MRCGP 1984; DRCOG 1983; Cert FPA. 1983; DCH Lond. 1981. (Ed.) p/t GP. Prev: SHO (Paediat.) Roy. Hosp. Sick Childr. & Simpson Mem. Matern. Pavil. Edin.; Trainee GP Chelmsford, OldCh., Rushgreen, Warley Hosps. & Romford VTS.

CRAWLEY, Esther Madeleine Molecular Pathology, 3rd Floor, Windeyer Building, UCLMS, 46 Cleveland St., London W1T 4JF Tel: 020 7636 8333 Email: rekgemc@ucl.ac.uk; Flat 7, Sutherland House, 133-135 Queenstown Road, London SW8 3RJ Tel: 020 7622 6695 Email: rekgemc@ucl.ac.uk — BM BCh 1991 Oxf.; BA (Hons.) Oxf. 1988; MRCP (UK) 1994. (Oxf.) Clin. Research Fell. Molecular Rheum. UCL; Hon. Regist. Gt. Ormond St. Hosp. Socs: Roy. Coll. Paediat. & Child Health. Prev: Regist. (Paediat.) Mersey Region; SHO Rotat. (Paediat.) Childr. Hosp. Birm.; Ho. Surg. E. Birm. Hosp.

CRAWLEY, Francesca Anne-Marie 12 Cavendish Road, London W4 3UH Tel: 020 8995 89970 Email: creepy@crawley.u-net.com — BM BCh 1991 Oxf.; MRCP (UK) 1994; MD. (Cambridge and Oxford) Specialist Regist. (Neurol.) Char. Cross Hosp., Lond. Prev: Specialist Regist. (Neurol.) Atkinson Morley's Hosp. Lond.; Lect. (Clin. Neurosci.) St. Geo. Hosp. Med. Sch. Lond.

CRAWLEY, Helen Elizabeth Wells Health Centre, Glastonbury Road, Wells BA5 1XJ Tel: 01749 672137 Fax: 01749 679833 — BM 1990 Soton.; MRCGP 1995; DRCOG 1994. (Soton.) Socs: BMA.

CRAWLEY, Helen Susan Twyford Health Centre, Loddon Hall Road, Twyford, Reading RG10 9JA Tel: 0118 934 0112 Fax: 0118 934 1048; Little Orchard, Blakes Road, Wargrave, Reading RG10 8LA Tel: 0118 940 2853 — BM BCh 1984 Oxf.; MRCGP 1988; DRCOG 1987; DCH RCP Lond. 1986. Prev: GP Clapham; Trainee GP Reading VTS.

CRAWLEY, Henry Burton Holt Medical Practice, High Street, Holt NR25 6BH Tel: 01263 712461 Fax: 01263 713211 — MB 1978 Camb.; BChir 1977; MRCGP 1982.

CRAWLEY, Jane Margaret Stewart Wellcome Trust Research Laboratories, Box 230, Kilifi, Kenya; 6 Bath Street, St. Clements, Oxford OX4 1AY Tel: 01865 72153 — MB BS 1981 Lond.; MRCP (UK) 1987; DTM & H RCP Lond. 1990. Clin. Lect. Wellcome Trust Research Laborat. Kilifi, Kenya. Prev: Clin. Research Fell.sh. (Gastroenterol.) Roy. Childr. Hosp. Melbourne, Austral.; Regist. (Paediat.) John Radcliffe Hosp. Oxf.; SHO (Paediat.) Hosp. Sick Childr. Gt. Ormond St. Lond.

CRAWLEY, Joan Elizabeth (retired) Garth House, Hertingfordbury, Hertford SG14 2LG Tel: 01992 582963 — MB ChB 1942 Ed.; FRCP Ed. 1994; MRCP Ed. 1948. Prev: Asst. GP Hereford.

CRAWLEY, Linda Carol The Grange, Highfield Road, Hemsworth, Pontefract WF9 4DP Tel: 01977 610009 Fax: 01977 617182 — MB ChB 1984 Liverp.; MRCGP 1989.

CRAWLEY, Maurice Anthony Medicines Control Agency, Market Towers, 1 Nine Elms Lane, London SW8 5NQ Tel: 020 7273 0273 Fax: 020 7273 0293; 39 Barn Meadow Lane, Great Bookham, Leatherhead KT23 3EZ Tel: 01372 454985 — MB ChB 1957 Sheff.; MRCP (UK) 1972; DPhysMed Eng. 1969. Sen. Med. Assessor Nat. Variations Unit, Med. Control Agency. Socs: Roy. Soc. Med.; Brit. Soc. Rheum. Prev: Head Clin. Drug Safety Roche Products Ltd. Welwyn Gdn. City; Cons. Phys. Rheum. & Rehabil. New Addenbrooke's Hosp. Camb.; RAF Cons. Adviser (Rheum. & Rehabil.).

CRAWLEY, Philip Samuel Hints Gate House, Coreley, Ludlow SY8 3QU Tel: 01584 890732 — MB BS 1966 Lond.; MRCP (UK) 1972; MRCS Eng. LRCP Lond. 1966. (St. Bart.) Cons. Paediat. Lea Castle Hosp. Kidderminster.

CRAWLEY, Simon John Tudor Lodge, 8 Oak Hill Road, Surbiton KT6 6EH — MB BS 1997 Lond.

CRAWLEY, Una Cinzia 288 Stanmillis Road, Belfast BT9 5DZ — MB BCh BAO 1986 Belf.

CRAWLEY-BOEVEY, Emma Elizabeth (Browne) Public Health Sciences Department, St. Georges Hospital Medical School, Cranmer Terrace, London SW17 0RE; Email: e.crawley-boerey@doctors.org.uk, e.crawley-boevey@doctors.org.uk — MB BS 1994 Lond.; BSc 1991; DFPHM 2001. (University College London)

CRAWSHAW, Amanda Louise 94 Bentley La, Leeds LS6 4AJ — MB ChB 1997 Leeds.

CRAWSHAW, Ann 92 Talfourd Road, Peckham, London SE15 5NZ Tel: 020 7703 6572 — MB BS 1971 Lond. (St. Thos.) Assoc. Specialist (Clin. Oncol.) St. Thos. & Guy's Trust. Socs: BOA; Roy. Soc. Med.; Linnean Soc. Prev: Sen. Regist. & Regist. (Radiother.) King's Coll. Hosp. Lond.

CRAWSHAW, Mr Charles Christian De Villiers Winfield Hospital, Tewkesbury Road, Gloucester GL2 9WH — MB BS 1974 Lond.; FRCS Eng. 1981; MRCS Eng. LRCP Lond. 1974. (Guy's) Cons. Orthop. Surg. Glos. Roy. Hosp. Prev: Sen. Regist. (Orthop.) St. Geo.s Hosp, Lond.; Research Fell. Harlow Wood Hosp Nott.

CRAWSHAW, Everard George Aitken Now y Dom, Allington Park, Bridport DT6 5DD Tel: 01308 23267 — MB BChir 1942 Camb.; MRCP Lond. 1947; DCH Eng. 1948. (Lond. Hosp.) Prev: Paediat. Regist. Soton. Childr. Hosp.; Asst. Med. Regist. Hosp. Sick Childr. Gt. Ormond St.; Maj. RAMC.

CRAWSHAW, Howard Martyn 5 Crescent Parade, Ripon HG4 2JE Tel: 01765 607346 — MB ChB 1972 Ed.; BSc (Med. Sci., Hons.) Ed. 1969; FRCS Ed. 1977. (Ed.) Prev: Cons. Surg. E. Gen. Hosp. Edin.

CRAWSHAW, James William Aitken Riverbanks, Kiln Lane, Brockham, Betchworth RH3 7LZ Email: jgjc@jgjc.screaming.net — MB BS 1997 Lond. (Charing Cross & Westminster Medical School) SHO.Urol. (Kent & Canterbury). Prev: SHO Orthopae. Kent&W.minster; SHO(A&E) Kent&W.minster.

CRAWSHAW, Joanna Mary The Surgery, The Meads, Kington HR5 3DQ Tel: 01544 230302; Mill Cottage, Gladestry, Kington HR5 3NY Tel: 01544 22649 — MB ChB 1964 Birm.

CRAWSHAW, John Andrew The New Surgery, River Street, Mevagissey, St Austell PL26 6UE Tel: 01726 843701 Fax: 01726 842565; Hill Top House, Mevagissey, St Austell PL26 6RY Tel: 01726 842453 — MB BS 1968 Lond.; MRCS Eng. LRCP Lond. 1967; FRCGP 1986, M 1974; DObst RCOG 1969. (Guy's) Hosp. Pract. (Geriat.) Penrice Hosp. St. Austell; Sec. MEDACT (Cornw. Br.). Socs: BMA. Prev: Resid. Obst. Roy. Cornw. Hosp. (Treliske) Truro; Ho. Phys. & Ho. Surg. Orpington Hosp.

CRAWSHAW, Paul Anthony Gerard Children's Unit, St. Peters Hospital, Guildford Road, Chertsey KT16 0PZ Tel: 01931 872000 — MB ChB 1982 Manch.; MRCP (Paediat.) (UK) 1987; DCCH RCP Ed. 1987; MD Leic. 1997. (Manch.) Cons. Paediat. St. Peter's Hosp. Chertsey. Prev: Sen. Regist. Soton.; Research Fell. Brit. Paediat. Assn.; Regist. (Paediat.) Nottm.

CRAWSHAW, Peter John Salthouse X-Ray Department, Furness General Hospital, Barrow-in-Furness LA14 4LF Tel: 01229 870870; The Old Vicarage, Broughton-in-Furness LA20 6HS Tel: 01229 716789 — MB ChB 1974 Manch.; FRCR 1983; DMRD Eng. 1979. Cons. Radiol. Morecambe Bay NHS Trust. Socs: FRCR; Fell. Manch. Med. Soc.; Brit. soc. Interven. Radiologists. Prev: Rotat. Sen. Regist. Dept. Radiol. Univ. Manch.; Trainee Regist. Univ. Dept. Diag. Radiol. Univ. Manch.; Rotating SHO (Paediat.) Booth Hall Hosp. Manch.

CRAWSHAW, Sheila Margaret Tanton Cottage, Kirklevington, Yarm — MRCS Eng. LRCP Lond. 1958.

CRAXFORD, Patricia Anne 49 Brierdene Crescent, Whitley Bay NE26 4AD Tel: 0191 253 3554 — MB BS 1977 Newc.; BMedSc (Hons.) Newc. 1974; FFA RCS Eng. 1982. Cons. Anaesth. N. Tyneside HA. Socs: Assn. Anaesths. & BMA. Prev: Sen. Regist. (Anaesth.) N.ern RHA; Regist. (Anaesth.) Newc. HA; SHO (Anaesth.) Newc. & Durh. HAs.

CRAY, Edith Beryl 48 Fernhill Close, Mayals, Swansea SA3 5BX Tel: 01792 68150 — MB BCh 1955 Wales; BSc, MB BCh Wales 1955. (Cardiff) Prev: JHMO (Cas.), Ho. Phys. & SHO Neurosurg. Unit, Morriston Hosp.

CRAY, Steven Harvey Department of Anaesthetics, Newcastle General Hospital, Newcastle upon Tyne NE4 6BE Tel: 0191 273 8811; 10 West Avenue, Gosforth, Newcastle upon Tyne NE3 4ES Tel: 0191 285 4781 — MB BS 1987 Lond.; FRCA 1993. Sen. Regist. Rotat. N. Region. Prev: Clin. Fell. Leeds Gen. Infirm.; Regist. Blackpool & Hope Hosp.

CRAYFORD, Timothy John Benjamin Department of Epidemiology & Public Health Medicine, King's College Hospital, Denmark Hill, London SE5 9RS Tel: 020 7346 3559 Email: tim.crayford@kcl.ac.uk; 133 Choumert Road, Peckham, London SE15 4AP — MB BS 1988 Lond.; MSc Lond. 1994; MFPHM 1997. (St. Bartholomew's) Sen. Lect. (Epidemiol. & Pub. Health) King's Coll. Hosp. Sch. Med. & Dent. Lond. Prev: Clin. Research Fell. (O & G) King's Coll. Hosp. Lond.; SHO (Gyn.) Hammersmith Hosp. Lond.; Hon. SHO (Environm. & Preven. Med.) St. Bart. Hosp. Med. Coll. Lond.

CRAZE, Andrew Leslie Magnolia House Practice, Magnolia House, Station Road, Ascot SL5 0QJ Tel: 01344 637800 Fax: 01344 637823; Garden Cottage, Church Road, Windlesham GU20 6BH Tel: 01276 477301 — MB ChB 1986 Aberd.; MRCGP 1992; DA (UK) 1988. GP Princip.; Clin. Asst. BrE. Clinic Windsor; Occupat. Health Phys. Surrey Ambul. Serv. Socs: Brit. Med. Acupunct. Soc. Prev: Regist. (Med.) Roy. Perth Hosp. Austral.

CRAZE, Janet Lindsey Department of Paediatrics, Level 4, John Radcliffe Hospital, Oxford OX3 9DU Email: janet.craze@orh.nhs.uk; 4 River View, Sandford-on-Thames, Oxford OX4 4YF Tel: 01865717604 — MB BS 1986 Lond.; MRCP (UK) 1990. Cons. Padiat. John Radcliff Hosp. Oxf. Prev: Specialist Regist. (Paediat.) Whittington Hosp. Lond.

CREABY, Gaynor Elizabeth Smada, Main Street N., Aberford, Leeds LS25 3AH — MB ChB 1994 Liverp.

CREABY, Mary Majella Whitchurch Hospital, Whitchurch, Cardiff CF14 7XB Tel: 029 2069 3191 — MB BCh BAO 1985 NUI; MRCPsych 1990. (Galway, Irel.) Cons. Psychiat. with Special Responsibil. for Rehabil. Psychiat. WhitCh. Hosp. Cardiff.

CREAGH, Fionuala Mary 199 Ecclesall Road S., Sheffield S11 9PN — MB BS 1977 Lond.; MD Lond. 1985; MRCP (UK) 1980.

CREAGH, Michael Desmond Department of Haematology, The Royal Cornwall Hospital NHS Trust, Treliske Hospital, Truro TR1 3LJ Tel: 01872 252524 — MB ChB 1981 Manch.; MRCP (UK) 1986; MRCPath 1994; MD (Sheffield) 1996. Cons. Haemat. Roy. Cornw. Hosp. NHS Trust. Prev: Sen. Regist. Rotat. NW RHA.

CREAGH, Michael Francis 5 Kerrison Road, Ealing, London W5 5NW — BChir 1981 Camb.; MRCP (UK) 1985; FRCR 1988. Cons. Radiol. St Peters Hosp. Chertsey, Surrey. Prev: Sen. Regist. (Radiol.) St. Thos. Hosp. Lond.; Regist. (Radiol.) St. Thos. Hosp. Lond.; Regist. (Gen. Med.) Battle Hosp. Reading.

CREAGH, Teresa Mary Department of Histopathology, St Peters Hospital, Chertsey KT16 0PZ; Tennings Croft, Franksfield, Peaslake, Guildford GU5 9SR — MB BS 1981 Lond.; MRCPath 1991. Cons. Histocytopath. St. Peter's Hosp. Chertsey. Prev: Cons. Histocytopath. St. Geo. Hosp. Lond.; Sen. Regist. (Histopath.) St. Mary's Hosp. Lond.

CREAGH, Theresa Mary Long Barn View, Weald, Sevenoaks TN14 — BM 1991 Soton.

CREAGH, William Joseph (retired) 41 Lutterworth Road, Leicester LE2 8PH — MB BCh BAO 1946 NUI.

CREAGH-BARRY, Michael James William Little Rams Island, Shapwick, Blandford Forum DT11 9LB — MB BS 1977 Lond.; MRCS Eng. LRCP Lond. 1977; FRCR 1985. (St. Bart.) Cons. Radiol. Poole Gen. Hosp.

CREAGH-BARRY, Patrick Charles Philip 58 Saughall Road, Blacon, Chester CH1 5EY — MB BS 1976 Lond.; MRCS Eng. LRCP Lond. 1976; FFA RCS Eng. 1983. (St. Bart.)

CREAK, David Robert Peartree Lane Surgery, 110 Peartree Lane, Welwyn Garden City AL7 3XW Tel: 01707 329292; 41 Barleycroft Road, Welwyn Garden City AL8 6JX — MB ChB 1974 Bristol; MRCGP 1994; DRCOG 1977. Prev: Clin. Asst. (Neurol.) Qu. Eliz. II

Hosp. Welwyn Gdn. City; Trainee GP Welwyn Gdn. City VTS; Ho. Phys. & Ho. Surg. Frenchay Hosp. Bristol.

CREAM, Jeffrey Joseph 152 Harley Street, London W1G 7LH Tel: 020 7935 2477 Fax: 020 7224 2574; 19 Temple Sheen, London SW14 7RP Tel: 020 8876 7142 Fax: 020 8876 7142 — MB ChB 1961 Manch.; BSc Manch. 1958, MD 1972; FRCP Lond. 1978, M 1965. (Manch.) Cons. Dermat. Char. Cross Hosp., Chelsea & W.m. Hosp. & W. Middlx. Univ. Hosp. Prev: Sen. Regist. (Dermat.) Middlx. Hosp. Lond.; Lect. (Immunol.) Inst. Dermat.; Regist. (Dermat.) St. Thos. Hosp. Lond.

CREAMER, Brian (retired) Vine House, Highfields, East Horsley, Leatherhead KT24 5AA Tel: 01483 283320 — MB BS 1948 Lond.; MD Lond. 1952; FRCP Lond. 1966, M 1950. Prev: Cons. Phys. St. Thos. Hosp. Lond.

CREAMER, Ian Stephen, MC, Brigadier late RAMC Tel: 01276 412905 Fax: 01276 412737; Owl Corner, 4 Parkhill Road, Torquay TQ1 2AL Email: owlman@doctors.org.uk — MRCS Eng. LRCP Lond. 1966; MSc (Community Med.) Lond. 1984; MFPHM RCP (UK) 1989; FFPHM RCP(UK) 2000; MFCM Lond. 1988; DFFP 1994. (Liverpool) Cons. Pub. Healthmed, Army Med. Servs. Director Army Health Policy Team. Socs: Fell. Roy. Soc. Med. Prev: COMD Med HQ 5 Div.; Comd Med. 3 (UK) Div.; DACOS Med. HQ UKLF.

CREAMER, John Daniel 32 Alfriston Road, London SW11 6NN — MB BChir 1989 Camb.; BSc St. And. 1987; MRCP (UK) 1992.

CREAMER, John Edward Department of Cardiology, North Staffordshire Hospital Centre, Newcastle Road, Stoke-on-Trent ST4 6QG Tel: 01782 552341 Fax: 01782 713071; Key Cottage, Smith Lane, Mobberley, Knutsford WA16 7QH Email: jon.creamer@btinternet.com — MB ChB 1978 Manch.; BSc Manch. 1975; FRCP Lond. 1997; MRCP (UK) 1982; DRCOG 1980. Cons. Cardiol. N. Staffs. Hosp. Centre. Socs: Brit. Cardiac Soc.; Amer. Coll. Cardiol. Prev: Sen. Regist. (Cardiol.) Manch. Roy. Infirm.; Regist. (Cardiol.) St. Bart. Hosp. Lond.; Regist. (Gen. Med.) Roy. Shrewsbury Hosp.

CREAMER, Katherine Louise 32 Alfriston Road, London SW11 6NN — MB BS 1994 Lond.; BSc (Hons.) St. And. 1987.

CREAMER, Kenneth Archibald (retired) Meadowfield Cottage, Courtway, Bridgwater TA5 1DR Tel: 01278 671620 — MRCS Eng. LRCP Lond. 1951. Prev: Family Doctor, High Bridge Som..

CREAMER, Paul Southmead Hospital, Southmead Road, Bristol BS10 5NB; 5 Fiddes Road, Bristol BS6 7TN Tel: 0117 924 8024 — MB BS 1981 Lond.; MRCP (UK) 1986. Sen. Regist. (Rheum.) Bristol Roy. Infirm. Prev: Research Fell. (Rheum.) Bristol Roy. Infirm.; Research Fell. (Boots/ARC Fell.sh.) St. Geo. Hosp. Sydney, Austral.; Regist. (Med.) Bristol Roy. Infirm.

CREAN, Andrew Michael 2 (IFI) Merchiston Place, Edinburgh EH10 4NR Tel: 0131 228 9443 Email: crean67@hotmail.com — BM 1992 Soton.; BSc Soton. 1990, BM 1992; MRCP (UK) 1996. (Soton.) Specialist Regist. (Radiol.) Roy. Infirm. Edin. Prev: Clin. Fell. (Cardiol.) Roy. Infirm. Edin.; SHO (IC) W.ern Gen. Edin.

CREAN, Dermot Michael, Surg. Capt. RN Retd. 22 St Mark's Close, Alverstoke, Gosport PO12 2DB Tel: 01705 527125 — MB BCh BAO 1965 NUI; FRCP Ed. 1994; DPhysMed Eng. 1973; MPhil. Loughborough 1989. (Cork) Socs: Brit. Assn. Rheum. Prev: Sen. Specialist Rheum & Rehabil. RN.

CREAN, Ernest Eugene St Andrews Surgery, The Old Central School, Southover Road, Lewes BN7 1US Tel: 01273 476216 Fax: 01273 487587; 23 The Avenue, Lewes BN7 1QS — MB BCh BAO 1973 NUI; FRCOG 1994, M 1979. (Univ. Coll. Dub.) Hosp. Practitioner, Colposcopy, Brighton; Hosp. Practitioner Urodynamics, Lewes.

CREAN, Gerard Patrick (retired) Ross Hall Hospital, 221 Crookston Road, Glasgow G52 3NQ Tel: 0141 810 3151 — MB BCh BAO NUI 1953; PhD Ed. 1965; FRCPI 1988; FRCP Glas. 1978, M 1976; FRCP Ed. 1966, M 1956. Cons. Phys. (Gastroenterol.) Ross Hall Hosp. Glas. Prev: Cons. Phys. & Phys. i/c Gastrointestinal Centre & Research Centre Diag. Methodol. S.. Gen. Hosp. Glas.

CREAN, James Peter (retired) 32 Shakespeare Drive, Shirley, Solihull B90 2AL Tel: 0121 744 7022 — LRCPI & LM, LRSCI & LM 1948; LRCPI & LM, LRCSI & LM 1948. Prev: Ho. Surg. Mercer's Hosp. Dub.

CREAN, Peter Michael 16 Gracemount Park, Belfast BT8 6GS — MB BCh BAO 1976 Belf.; MB BCh Belf. 1976; FFA RCSI 1980. Cons. Anaesth. Roy. Belf. Hosp. for Sick Childr. Socs: Assoc. Paediat. Anaesth. Gt. Brit. & Irel.; N. Irel. Soc. Anaesth. Prev: Fell. Dept. Anaesth. Hosp. for Sick Childr. Toronto Canada; Fell. Dept. Neonat. & Paediat. Intens. Care Hosp. for Sick Childr. Toronto.

CREAN, Mr Vincent St John Department of Oral and, Maxillofacial Dental Institute, 256 Gray's Inn Road, London WC1X 8LD Tel: 020 7915 1056 Fax: 020 7915 1259 Email: s.crean@eastman.ucl.ac.uk; 5 Oldfield Mews, Highgate, London N6 5XA — MB BS 1992 Lond.; BDS Lond. 1981; FRCS Eng. 1996; FDS RCS Eng. 1994; FRCS 2000 FRCS (OMFS) UK 2000. (UCL) Sen. Lect./Hon. Cons. E.man Dent. Inst., UCL Hosp.s, Hosp. for Sick Childr., Gt. Ormond St, + Whittington Hosp. Lond..; UCL Hosp. E.man Inst. for Oral Health Care Sci.

CREANE, Julie Grace 57 Parkmore, Knockmenagh, Craigavon BT64 2AE — MB BCh 1998 Belf.; MB BCh Belf 1998. SHO, CIP Rotat., Ulster Hosp., Dundonald. Prev: Ho. Off., Craigavon Area Hosp.

CREANEY, Jane 14 Racecourse Close, Downpatrick BT30 6US — MB BCh BAO 1993 Belf.; DCH Dub. 1996; DGM RCPS Glas. 1995; DRCOG Lond. 1996; MRCGP 1997. Socs: BMA; MRCGP. Prev: GP Trainee; Trainee GP Daisy Hill Hosp. VTS.

CREANEY, Karen Lynne Drongan Surgery, 74 Mill O'Shields Road, Drongan, Ayr KA6 7AY Tel: 01292 591345 Fax: 01292 590782 — MB ChB 1986 Liverp.; MRCGP 1992; Dip. Ven. Liverp. 1989.

CREANEY, William John Ailsa Hospital, Dalmellington Road, Ayr KA6 6AB Tel: 01292 610556; High Abbothill Farm, Ayr KA6 6AQ — MB BCh BAO 1984 Belf.; MB BCh Belf. l984; MRCPsych 1991. (Qu. Univ. Belf.) Cons. Psychiat. (Old Age) Ailsa Hosp. Ayr. Socs: BMA; Alzheimer's Soc. Scotl. Prev: Sen. Regist. Sub. Acad. Dept. Psychiat. Ysbyty Gwynedd; Regist. (Psychiat.) N. Wales Hosp. Denbigh; Regist. Gwynfa Resid. Unit N. Wales.

CREASE, George Alexander Graham Practice Centre, Auchterarder PH3 1AH Tel: 01764 62275; 5 Glenorchill Terrace, Auchterarder PH3 1PZ — MB ChB 1952 Ed. (Ed.) Prev: Ho. Surg. Craigtoun Matern. Hosp.; Ho. Phys. Roy. Infirm. Perth & City Fev. Hosp. Edin.

CREASEY, David Peter 99 Bradford Road, Bournemouth BH9 3PL — MB BS 1991 Lond.

CREASEY, John Moray (retired) 2 Leadhall View, Harrogate HG2 9PF — MB ChB 1951 Leeds. Prev: S.M.O. Dept of Social Security.

CREASY, Jillian Margaret Heeley Green Surgery, 302 Gleadless Road, Sheffield S2 3AJ Tel: 0114 250 0309 Fax: 0114 250 7185; 22 Clarke Street, Broomhall, Sheffield S10 2BS Tel: 0114 272 7886 — MB BS 1982 Lond.; MPhil Sheff. 1995; MA Camb. 1983; MRCGP 1986; DRCOG 1986; DCH RCP Lond. 1984. (Kings Coll. Hosp. Med. Sch.) Trainer (Gen. Pract.) Sheff. Socs: Med. Pract. Union; Assn. Community Based Care; Med. Act. Prev: Research Fell. (Gen. Pract.) Sheff.

CREASY, Mr Terry Stephen Department of Radiology, The Royal Bournemouth Hospital, Bournemouth BH7 7DW Tel: 01202 303626 Fax: 01202 309538 — MB BChir 1982 Camb.; MA Oxf. 1992; MA Camb. 1983, MB BChir 1982; FRCS Ed. 1989; FRCR 1990. Cons. Radiol. Roy. Bournemouth Hosp. Prev: Sen. Regist. & Regist. (Radiol.) John Radcliffe Hosp. Oxf.; SHO Rotat. (Gen. Surg.) Leicester Roy. Infirm.; SHO (Cas.) Bristol Roy. Infirm.

CREBER, Christopher John South Queensferry Group Practice, The Health Centre, Rosebery Avenue, South Queensferry EH30 9HA Tel: 0131 331 1396 Fax: 0131 331 5783 — MB ChB 1983 Dundee. (Dundee) GP S. Qu.sferry, W. Lothian.

CREE, Professor Ian Alexander Department of Pathology, Translational Oncology Research Centre, Dept of Histopathology, Queen Alexandra Hospital, Cosham, Portsmouth PO6 3LY — MB ChB 1982 Dundee; PhD Dundee 1987, BMSc (Hons.) 1979; FRCPath 1997, M 1988; FRCOphth 2000 FRCOphth 2000. (Dundee) Cons. Histopath.; Hon. Cons. Moorfields Eye Hosp. Lond.; Hon. Prof., Inst. of Ophth.; Edit. Bd. Anti-Cancer Drugs; Regional Edr. Pathol. Oncol. Research. Socs: Fell. Roy. Soc. Trop. Med. & Hyg.; Assn. Clin. Paths.; (Vice-Pres.) Internat. Soc. Chemosensitivity Testing. Prev: Clin. Sen. Lect., Inst. of Oplithalmology UCL, Lond.; Sen. Lect. (Clin. Path.) Ninewells Hosp. Dundee.

CREE, Joan Alys (retired) 56 Platts Lane, Hampstead, London NW3 7NT — MB ChB 1952 Glas. Prev: GP 25 Edgenbury La., Edgware, Miiddx.Prinipal.

CREE, Joanna Mary 62 Woodstock Road, Broxbourne EN10 7NS — MB ChB 1985 Dundee; MRCGP 1989; DCH RCP Lond. 1989. Prev: Med. Off. (Community Child Health) Tayside HB.

CREE, Nicola Victoria 42 Hyde Terrace, Newcastle upon Tyne NE3 1AT — MB BS 1997 Newc.

CREE, Richard Timothy James 23B Akenside Terrace, Jesmond, Newcastle upon Tyne NE2 1TN — MB BS 1993 Newc.

CREE, Sylvia Joan (retired) 17 The Crescent, Brinklow, Rugby CV23 0LG Tel: 01788 833263 — MB BS Lond. 1957; MRCS Eng. LRCP Lond. 1957; DA Eng. 1962; DObst RCOG 1960. Prev: Gen. Practitioner.

CREED, Anthony Lowry Nicholson West Croft House, 66 Main Street, Egremont CA22 2DB Tel: 01946 820348 Fax: 01946 821611; Orchard House, Rottington, Whitehaven CA28 9UR Tel: 01946 822205 — MB BChir 1975 Camb.; MA Camb.; DIH Eng. 1980; DRCOG 1977. (St. Thos.) Med. Off. Stead McAlpin Carlisle. Socs: AFOM RCP Lond. Prev: Med. Off. Brit. Nuclear Fuels Ltd. Windscale; SHO (Med.) Kingston Hosp.; Ho. Surg. St. Thos. Hosp. Lond.

CREED, David Stuart 1 Woodland Terrace, Redland, Bristol BS6 6LR — MB ChB 1993 Bristol.

CREED, Professor Francis Hunter The Mount, 67 Kinder Road, Hayfield, High Peak SK22 2HS — MB BChir 1972 Camb.; MD Camb. 1985, MA 1972; FRCP Lond. 1991; MRCP (UK) 1974; FRCPsych 1991, M 1976. Prof. Psychol. Med. Univ. Manch. & Hon. Cons. Psychiat. Manch. Roy. Infirm. Prev: Sen. Lect. Univ. Manch. & Hon. Cons. Psychiat. Manch. Roy. Infirm.; Ment. Health Research Fell. Lond. Hosp.; Sen. Regist. (Psychiat.) Lond. Hosp.

CREED, Helen Sherida Beechwood Cottage, 25 Brattlewood, Sevenoaks TN13 1QS — BChir 1996 Camb.

CREED, Julia Jane 23 Westgarth Avenue, Edinburgh EH13 0BB — MB BS 1998 Lond.; MB BS Lond 1998.

CREED, Maureen Evelyn Department of Histopathology South Block, Royal Berkshire Hospital, Redlands Road, Reading RG1 5AN Tel: 01189 875111 — MB ChB Sheff. 1969. (Sheff.) Clin. Asst. (Histopath.) Roy. Berks. Hosp. Socs: BMA. Prev: Clin. Med. Off. (Sch. Health) Hope Clinic; Regist. (Gyn. Path.) Jessop Hosp. Wom. Sheff.; Regist. (Clin. Path.) Sheff. Roy. Infirm.

CREED, Thomas Julian Stockwell Hill, Malthouse Lane, Wolverhampton WV6 9PB — MB BS 1994 Lond.

CREEDON, Jane 69 Blackscotch Lane, Mansfield NG18 4PF — MB ChB 1982 Sheff. GP Sutton-in-Ashfield.

CREEDON, Richard Joseph Tameside General Hospital, Fountain St., Ashton-under-Lyne OL6 9RW — MB BCh BAO 1977 NUI.

CREEK, Ian Michael Peas Ash Farm, Burgate, Fordingbridge SP6 1NB — MB BS 1988 Lond. Prev: Regist. ; Middleware Hosp., Auckland NZ.

CREELY, Steven James 6 Hartland Close, Widnes WA8 9FB — MB ChB 1998 Liverp.; MB ChB Liverp 1998.

CREER, Dean David 9A Loring Road, London N20 0UJ — MB ChB 1991 Cape Town.

CREERY, Robert Desmond Gibson, VRD (retired) La Jaonière des Hougues, Rue des Choffins, St Saviours, Guernsey GY7 9XW Tel: 01481 265758 — MB BCh BAO 1943 Belf.; MB BCh BAO (Gold Medal Paediat.) Belf. 1943; MD (Commend.) Belf. 1947; FRCP Lond 1971, M 1951; DCH Eng. 1948. Prev: Community Paediat. Guernsey.

CREESE, Katherine Helen Paedriatric Department, Llandough Hospital, Penlan Rd, Llandough, Cardiff Tel: 02920 711711; 7 Denbigh Street, Pontcanna, Cardiff CF11 9JQ Tel: 02920 230407 Email: katecreese@netscapeonline.co.uk — MB BCh 1990 Wales; 2000 MRCPCH; DCH RCP Lond. 1993; DRCOG 1992. (Welsh Nat. Sch. Med. Cardiff) Specialist Regist., Paediat., Univ. of Wales.

CREESE, Richard, TD (retired) 128 Boileau Road, London SW13 9BP Tel: 020 8748 1990 — MB BS 1944 Lond.; PhD Lond. 1952. Mickle Fell. Univ. Lond. Prev: Prof. Physiol. Univ. Lond. St. Mary's Hosp. Med. Sch.

CREHAN, Philippa Oughtibridge Surgery, Church Street, Oughtibridge, Sheffield S35 0FW Tel: 0114 286 2145 Fax: 0114 286 4031; 33 Blackbrook Avenue, Lodge Moor, Sheffield S10 4LT — MB ChB 1990 Leeds.

CREIGHTON, Francis James Tameside General Hospital, Fountain St., Ashton-under-Lyne OL6 9RW — MB BChir 1978 Camb.; MRCP (UK) 1982; MRCPsych 1986. Cons. Psychiat. Tameside & Glossop HA.

CREIGHTON, Miss Jane Elizabeth 17 Arran Drive, Horsforth, Leeds LS18 5SW — BM BS 1992 Nottm.; BMedSci 1990; FRCS 1996. (Nottingham) Research Fell. (Hepato-Pancreatic-Billiary Surg.), Freeman Hosp., Newc.

CREIGHTON, Paul Anthony South Broomhill Health Centre, Hadyson Rd, South Broomhill, Morpeth NE65 9SF Tel: 01670 760229, 01670 761094; 1 Elm Grove, Warkworth, Morpeth NE65 0SR Tel: 01665 711206 Fax: 01665 713275 — MB BS 1972 Newc.; FRCGP 1990, M 1976; DObst RCOG 1974. Assoc. Dir of Postgrad., Gen. Pract. Edu. Univ of Newc. upon Tyne; Jt. Hosp. Vis. Convenor N. Eng. Fac. Bd. RCGP; Ldr. Visitor JCPTGP. Prev: Scheme Organiser (Gen. Pract.) N.umbria VTS.

***CREIGHTON, Sarah Irina Josephine** 114 Park Avenue, Hull HU5 3ET — MB BS 1993 Lond.; BSc Lond. 1990.

CREIGHTON, Sarah Margaret University College Hospital, Grafton Way, London W1 — MB BS 1984 Lond.; FRCOG 2001; MD Lond. 1992; MRCOG 1989. Cons. O & G Univ. Coll. Hosp. Lond.

CREIGHTON GRIFFITHS, Patrizia Marina Creighton Sunfold, Lisvane Road, Lisvane, Cardiff CF14 0SG — MB BCh 1985 Wales.

CRELLIN, Adrian Mark Yorkshire Centre for Clinical Oncology, Cookridge Hospital, Leeds LS16 6QB Tel: 0113 292 4257 Fax: 0113 292 4052 — LMSSA 1979 Lond.; MA Camb. 1980, BChir 1980, MB 1979; FRCP 1997, M (UK) 1984; FRCR 1988. (Lond.) Cons. Clin. Oncol.; Dir. Yorks. Centre for Clin. Oncol. Socs: Brit. Oncol. Assn.; Europ. Soc. Therap. Radiol. and Oncol.; Roy. Soc. Med. Prev: Sen. Regist. Middlx. Hosp. Lond. & Mt. Vernon Hosp. N.wood.

CRELLIN, David Wilson (retired) 22 Basset Road, Camborne TR14 8SN Tel: 01209 712208 — MB ChB 1962 Manch. Prev: Med. Regist & SHO Bedford Gen. Hosp.

CRELLIN, Robert Perric Department of Clinical Oncology, Poole Hospital, Longfleet Road, Poole BH15 2JB Tel: 01202 442492 Fax: 01202 442825; Rushall House, Rushall Lane, Lytchett Matravers, Poole BH16 6AJ — MB BS 1979 Lond.; FRCS Ed. (ENT) 1986; FRCS Eng. (ENT) 1986; FRCS Eng. 1983; FRCR 1991. Cons. (Clin. Oncol.) Poole Hosp. Poole, Dorset. Socs: Brit. Oncol. Assn.; Brit. Assn. Head & Neck Oncol.; RAD Soc. Prev: Sen. Regist. (Clin. Oncol.) City Hosp. Nottm.; Lect. (Clin. Oncol.) W.. Gen. Hosp. Edin.; Regist. (Radiother.) W.. Gen. Hosp. Edin.

CREMADES TUDELA, Emilio Northgate Hospital, Northgate St., Great Yarmouth NR30 1BU; 28 Association Way, Norwich NR7 0TQ — LMS 1980 Valencia.

CREMASCHINI, Giuliana Paediatric Surgery Division, The Hospital for Children, Great Ormond St., London WC1N 3JH — State Exam 1991 Milan.

CREME, Irvine (retired) 186 Canterbury Road, Davyhulme, Urmston, Manchester M41 0GR Tel: 0161 748 5559 Fax: 0161 747 1997 — MB ChB 1962 Birm.; MA Manch. 1999.

CRÈME, Melinda Leonie 5 Yale Court, Honeybourne Road, West Hampstead, London NW6 1JF Tel: 020 7794 3744 — MB ChB 1992 Birm.; MRCGP Lond. 1997; DFFP 1997. (Birm.) GP Partner Lisson Gr. Health Centre Lond. Socs: Med. Protec. Soc. Prev: GP Asst. Lisson Gr. Health Centre.

CREMER, Mary Patricia (retired) High Trees, The Wood End, Wallington SM6 0RA Tel: 020 8669 0665 — MB BCh BAO 1949 NUI; DA Eng. 1955. Prev: Clin. Med. Off. RAF Biggin Hill.

CREMER, Richard John (retired) High Trees, The Wood End, Wallington SM6 0RA — MB BS 1950 Lond.; DCH Eng. 1956. Prev: GP Wallington.

CREMIN, Dermot Damien Royal Glamorgan Hospital, Ynysmaerdy, Llantrisant, Pontyclun CF72 9XR Tel: 01443 443600 — MB BCh BAO 1987 NUI; FFARCSI 1993. (University College Galway, National Uni Ireland.) Cons.(Anaesth) Roy. Glamotgan Hosp. Ynyshaerdy, Llantrisant.

CREMIN, Mr Michael Desmond (retired) Whitewell, Broadway, Hale, Altrincham WA15 0PQ Tel: 0161 980 4652 — MB BS 1944 Lond.; FRCS Eng. 1950; DLO Eng. 1948. Prev: Cons. ENT Surg. Stockport & Buxton Gp. Hosps.

CREMIN, Patricia Mary Fairbrook Medical Centre, Fairway Avenue, Borehamwood WD6 1PR — MB BCh BAO 1990 NUI; DCH 1996; MRCGP 1997. GP Practitioner.

CREMIN, William Desmond Park Road Surgery, Park Road, Bournemouth BH8 8HS Tel: 01202 551535 — MB BS 1964 Lond.;

MRCS Eng. LRCP Lond. 1964. (Lond. Hosp.) Med. Adviser Chase Manhattan Bank Bournemouth. Socs: BMA. Prev: Med. Off. Cunard Line Soton.; SHO (Surg.) Harold Wood Hosp.; Resid. Anaesth. & Ho. Phys. Lond. Hosp.

CREMONA, Andrew Newbyres Medical Group, Gorebridge Health Centre, Gorebridge EH23 4TP Tel: 01875 820405 Fax: 01875 820269; 135 Craiglea Drive, Edinburgh EH10 5PP — MB ChB 1984 Sheff.; MRCP (UK) 1989. GP Princip. New Byres Med. Gp. Gorebridge. Prev: Research Fell. (Rheum.) W.. Gen. Hosp. Edin.; Regist. (Gen. Med.) Law Hosp. Carluke.

CREMONA, Fiona Ruth 135 Craiglea Drive, Edinburgh EH10 5PP — MB ChB 1987 Glas.; DCH RCP Glas. 1990. GP Retainer Edin. Prev: Trainee GP Lanarksh; SHO (Paediat.) CrossHo. Hosp. Kilmarnock; SHO (Obst.) Bellshill Matern. Hosp.

CREMONA-BARBARO, Anne Adamson Centre, St Thomas' Hospital, Lambeth Palace Road, London SE1 7EH Tel: 020 928 9292 Ext: 2386 Fax: 020 922 8294 — LRCP 1975 Lond.; MRCS 1975 Eng.; FRCPsych 1996; MRCPsych 1980. Cons. Psychiat., S. Lond. & Maudsley Hosp. NHS Trust; Cons. Psychiat. Florence Nightingale Hosp. Lond.; Cons. Psychiat. Finsbury Healthcare Lond. Prev: Cons. Psychiat. Brunel Univ. Uxbridge; Cons. Psychiat. Hillingdon Hosp. Uxbridge; Cons. Psychiat. Wexham Pk. Hosp. Slough.

CREMONESINI, David Paolo 122 Warwick Road, Kenilworth CV8 1HS Tel: 01926 511494; 44 Fairway, Raynes Park, London SW20 9DN Tel: 020 8543 2909 — MB BS 1996 Lond.; BS Oxon. (St George's Hospital) SHO Paediat. Lewisham Hosp. Prev: SHO Paediat. St Helier Hosp. Carshalton; Med. Ho. Off. E. Surrey Hosp. Redhill; Ho. Off. Surgic. Frimley Pk. Hosp.

CRERAND, Mr John Department of Orthopaedics, Noble's Isle of Man Hospital, Westmoreland Road, Douglas IM1 4QA Tel: 01624 642109 Fax: 01624 642280 Email: crerand@totalise.co.uk; Brookvale House, Main Road, Union Mills, Douglas IM4 4AJ — MB BCh BAO 1983 NUI; MChOrth Liverp. 1992; FRCSI 1987. (Univ. Coll. Dub.) Cons. Orthop. Surg. Noble's I. of Man Hosp. Douglas; Cons. in adminstrative charge, A&E Dept, noble'n Isle of Mann Hosp. douglas,10m.

CRERAR-GILBERT, Agnieszka Joanna 51 New Caledonian Wharf, 6 Odessa St, London SE16 7TN Tel: 020 7394 9499 Email: 100637.3173@compuserve.com — Lekarz 1988 Warsaw; MA Biology, Warsaw 1985; MD of Warsaw, 1988; FRCA Lond. 1997. (Med. Sch. Warsaw) Specialist Regist. (Anaesth. Rotat.) Roy. Hosp. Trust. Socs: BMA; MRCAnaesth.; Internat. Trauma Anaesth. & Critical Care Soc.

CRESSALL, Stuart Frederick Moseley Hodsoll House, High St., Farningham, Dartford DA4 0DH Tel: 01322 863356 — MA Oxon. 1937, BM BCh 1941; MFOM RCP Lond. 1979; DPH Lond. 1961. (St. Thos.) Socs: Soc. Occupat. Med.; Emerit. Mem. Internat. Commiss. on Occupat. Health. Prev: PMO Briggs Motor Bodies; Sen. Med. Off. Ford Motor Co.; Occupat. Health Expert Internat. Labour Office.

CRESSEY, Anna Frances — MB ChB 1993 Bristol; MRCGP 2001 London; MRCP (UK) 1996; DTM & H Liverp. 1997; DRCOG 1999. GP. Prev: Med. Relief Worker, Kenya with Merlin; SHO Paediat. Roy. Alexandra Hosp. For Childr., Brighton; GP Locum.

CRESSEY, David Martin 3 Pleasant View, Station Road, Hathersage, Sheffield S32 1DD — MB BS 1990 Newc.; BSc (Marine Biol.) Newc. 1985. Specialist Regist. (Anaesth.) Centr. Sheff. Hosps. Trust. Prev: SHO (Anaesth.) Qu. Med. Centre & City Hosp. Nottm.

CRESSEY, Jillian Margaret 6 Meeres Lane, Kirton, Boston PE20 1PS — BM BS 1992 Nottm.; FRCA 1996. (Nottm.) Specialist Regist. (Anaesth.) N. Region. Socs: Med. Defence Union; BMA. Prev: SHO (Anaesth.) Newc. Hosps. & Chester; SHO (Med.) Stafford Dist. Gen. Hosp.

CRESSEY, Pamela Freda The Surgery, 1 Dring's Close, Over, Cambridge CB4 5NZ Tel: 01954 31550; The Principals Lodge, Westminster College, Madingley Road, Cambridge CB3 0AB Tel: 01223 354720 — MB BS 1956 Lond.; DObst RCOG 1958. (Char. Cross.) Sen. Med. Off. Family Plann. Camb. Health Auth.

CRESSEY-RODGERS, Justin Fraser Derwen NHS Trust, St. David's Hospital, Jobswell Road, Carmarthen SA31 3HB Tel: 01267 237481; Efail Caerlleon, Llanboidy, Whitland SA34 0DL — MB BS 1996 Lond.; BSc Lond. 1990; PhD Lond. 1995. (UMDS London) SHO Rotat. (Psychiat.) St. David's Hosp. Carmarthen. Prev: PRHO (Surg.) Kingston; PRHO (Med.) Salisbury; SHO (Psychiat.) Carmarthen.

CRESSWELL, Andrew David Netherfield Court, Eaton Road, Chester CH4 7EW — MB ChB 1985 Bristol.

CRESSWELL, Barbara Elizabeth The Surgery, Myatts Field Health Centre, Patmos Road, London SW9 6SE Tel: 020 7411 3573; 2A Alleyn Road, Dulwich, London SE21 8AL — MB ChB Bristol 1979; MRCGP 1983. (Bristol)

CRESSWELL, Douglas (retired) 5 Cherry Hill Avenue, Barnt Green, Birmingham B45 8LA Tel: 0121 445 1002 Email: cresswell@cherrylease.fsnet.co.uk — MB ChB Birm. 1957; MRCGP 1968; DObst RCOG 1959. Prev: SHO (Anaesth.) W. Bromwich & Dist. Hosp. Gp.

CRESSWELL, Graham John, Squadron Ldr. RAF Med. Br. Retd. bmi british midland, Ground Floor, The Queens Building, London Heathrow Airport, Hounslow TW6 1DY Tel: 020 8990 5347 Fax: 020 8990 5348 Email: graham.cresswell@bigfoot.com; Ann Cottage, Kilmeston, Alresford SO24 0NW Tel: 01962 771472 Fax: 01962 771899 — MB ChB 1975 Sheff.; DAvMed FOM RCP Lond. 1986. (Sheffield) Aeromed. Specialist Pilot Brit. Midl. Airways; Vis. Lect. (Aviat. Med.) RAF Sch. Aviat. Med.; Aviat. Med. Adviser Europ. Regional Airlines Assn.; Mem. Airline Med. Advisers Comm. Socs: Fell. Roy. Aernautical Soc. (Aviat. Med. Gp.); Mem. Aerospace Med. Assn.; Aeronautical Soc. Prev: Aeromed Specialist Pilot Dan Air Serv.; Med. Off. (Pilot) RAF Inst. Aviat. Med. FarnBoro.

CRESSWELL, Jane Evelyn Community Child Health Services, 10 Chalmers Crescent, Edinburgh EH9 1TS Tel: 0131 556 0492 Fax: 0131 536 0570; 7 Penicuik Road, Roslin EH25 9LJ — MB ChB 1979 Bristol; MRCP (UK) 1983; MRCGP 1989; DCH RCP Lond. 1989; DRCOG 1988. (Univ. Bristol) p/t Cons. Paediat., Lothian Univ. Community NHS Trust. Prev: Trainee GP Midlothian VTS.

CRESSWELL, Miss Janet Lisa Chesterfield and North Derbyshire Royal Hospital, Calow, Chesterfield S44 5BL Tel: 01246 277271 Email: janet.cresswell@cndrh-tr.trent.nhs.uk; Hilltop Cottage, Hill Lane, Holymoorside, Chesterfield S42 7EP Tel: 01246 566161 Email: janetcresswell@holymoorside.com — MB ChB 1987 Sheff.; MRCOG 1992. Cons. (O & G Chesterfield & N. Derbysh. Roy. Hosp. Socs: Fac. Fam. Plann. Brit. Matern. and Fetal Med. Soc. Organising Comm.; Brit. Menopause Soc. Prev: Sen. Regist. (O & G) Sheff.; Research Fell. (O & G) Univ. Sheff. N.. Gen. Hosp.; Regist. Rotat. (O & G) Sheff.

CRESSWELL, Jon Peter — MB ChB 1975 Dundee; MSc Ed. 1985; BSc St. And. 1972; FFPHM 2001; MRCOG 1980; FRCOG 1997, M 1980; Instruc. Doctor's Cert. JCC 1984. Cons. Pub. Health Med. Grampian HB; Hon. Clin. Sen. Lect. Univ. Aberd. Socs: BMA. Prev: Sen. Regist. (Community Med.) Grampian HB; Research Lect. (O & G) St. Geo. Hosp. Tooting; Clin. Med. Off. (Family Plann.) Wandsworth HA.

CRESSWELL, Murray Allan Flat 2, 49 Kenilworth Road, St Leonards-on-Sea TN38 0JL — MB ChB 1963 Sheff.; FRCP 1983, M 1971; DObst RCOG 1965; DCH Eng. 1966. Cons. Paediat. N. Beds. HA. Prev: Cons. Paediat. N. Derbysh. (Chesterfield) HA.; Sen. Regist. Paediat. Childr. Hosp. & Univ. Nottm.; Regist. Paediat. Hillingdon Hosp.

CRESSWELL, Patricia Anne Newcastle & North Tyneside Health Authority, Benfield Road, Newcastle upon Tyne NE6 4PF Tel: 0191 219 6000 Fax: 0191 219 6066; 42 Reid Park Road, Jesmond, Newcastle upon Tyne NE2 2ES — MB BS 1979 Newc.; FRCS Ed. 1984; MFPHM RCP (UK) 1996; MRCGP 1987. Dir. Pub. Health Newc. & N. Tyneside Health Auth. Prev: GP Newc.; Cons. Pub. Health Med. NHS Exec. N.. & Yorks. Durh.

CRESSWELL, Susan Margaret 3 Ashfield Grove, Whitley Bay NE26 1RT Tel: 0191 253 2233 — MB BS 1976 Lond.; MFFP 1993. (Char. Cross) SCMO (Family Plann.) N. Tyneside; Clin. Asst. (Urol.) Freeman Hosp. Newc.; Clin. Asst. Nat. Blood Serv. Newc. Prev: Family Plann. Off. Newc. & N. Tyneside HA; Clin. Research Asst. (O & G) Preston Hosp. N. Shields.

CRESSWELL, Mr Timothy Roger Cross Lane Farm, Riber, Matlock DE4 5JD Email: tim.cresswell@lineone.net — BM 1991 Soton.; FRCS (Ed) 1998. (Soton.) Specialist Regist. (Ortho) Sheff. Rotat. Prev: Sen. SHO (Orthop. & Trauma) Chesterfield; SHO (Orthop.) Sheff.; SHO (Ortho & Hand Surg.) Macclesfield.

CRETNEY, Eric James (retired) 73 Alvington Way, Market Harborough LE16 7NF Tel: 01858 432836 — MB BChir 1953

Camb.; BA, MB BChir Camb. 1953. Prev: Ho. Surg. W. Suff. Gen. Hosp.

CRETNEY, Julie Denise Palatine Group Practice, Murray's Road, Douglas IM2 3TD Tel: 01624 623931 Fax: 01624 611712; 14 Ard Reayrt, Ramsey Road, Laxey IM4 7PZ — MB ChB 1989 Sheff.

CRETNEY, Philip Neil 22 Northfield Road, Blaby, Leicester LE8 4GU Tel: 0116 277 2597 — MB BS 1952 Lond.; DCH Eng. 1958. (St. Bart.)

CREW, Alan David Meadowbank, 19 Hall Drive, Bramhope, Leeds LS16 9JF — MB ChB 1955 Leeds; FFA RCS Eng. 1960; DObst RCOG 1957. Cons. Anaesth. Killingbeck Hosp. Leeds.

CREW, Mr Jeremy Paul Kirtlands Cottage, Weston Road, Bletchingdon, Kidlington OX5 3DH Tel: 01865 7622 9976 — MB BChir 1989 Camb.; MA Camb. 1990, MB BChir Camb. 1989; FRCS Eng. 1993. Regist. (Urol.) Oxf. Radcliffe Hosp. Trust. Socs: Brit. Assn. Urol. Surgs.; BMA. Prev: Regist. Rotat. (Surg.) St. Geo. Hosp. Lond.; SHO Rotat. (Surg.) Roy. Surrey Co. Hosp. Guildford & St. Geo. Hosp. Lond.

CREWDSON, John Francis (retired) Winster House, Winster, Windermere LA23 3NU — MB Camb. 1956, BChir 1955; DO Eng. 1961. Hon. Cons. Ophth. St. Thos. Hosp. Lond. Prev: Chief Clin. Asst. Moorfields Eye Hosp. Lond.

CREWE, Hilary Jean (retired) Flat 17, Whitegates, Wilmslow Road, Cheadle SK8 1HG Tel: 0161 491 3900 — MB ChB 1940 Manch.; MFPHM RCP Lond. 1972. Prev: Sen. Sch. Med. Off. Stockport.

CREWS, John Richard (retired) Southfield, 24 Fir Tree Close, Hilton, Yarm TS15 9JZ — MRCS Eng. LRCP Lond. 1951; MRCGP 1962.

CREYKE, Mary 10 Rossett Garth, Harrogate HG2 9NB Tel: 01423 871548 — MB BS Durh. 1954. (Durh.)

CRIBB, Clare Teslin 568 Gower Road, Upper Killay, Swansea SA2 7DR — MB ChB 1997 Manch.

CRIBB, George Thomas 1 Blackdown Road, Knowle, Solihull B93 9HP Tel: 0156 45 773612 — MB ChB 1941 Bristol. (Bristol)

CRIBB, Gillian Louise Royal Shrewsbury Hospital, Shrewsbury SY3 8QX; 7 Greenhill Avenue, Copthorne, Shrewsbury SY3 8NR — MB ChB 1996 Manch.

CRIBB, Janette Sarah Linton House, Cann Lane, Appleton, Warrington WA4 5NF — MB ChB 1992 Birm. SHO (Psychiat.) Barrow Hosp. Bristol.

CRIBB, John Morgan (retired) 1 Kempnough Hall Road, Worsley, Manchester M28 2QP Tel: 0161 799 6449 — MRCS Eng. LRCP Lond. 1935; BA Oxf. 1934; DA Eng. 1944. Prev: Sen. Med. Off. (Wales) Min. of Pens. & Nat. Insur.

CRIBB, Pamela Elspeth Bellevue Surgery, Bellevue Terrace, Newport NP20 2WQ Tel: 01633 256337 Fax: 01633 222856 — MB ChB 1989 Bristol; MRCGP (Distinc.) 1994; DFFP 1993; DCH RCP Lond. 1993; DRCOG 1992.

CRIBB, Rachel Jane 42 Uxbridge Road, Hampton TW12 3AD — MB BCh 1998 Wales.

CRIBB, Richard Alan Alresford Surgery, Station Road, Alresford SO24 9JL Tel: 01962 732345 Fax: 01962 736034 — MB ChB 1983 Liverp.; MRCGP 1991; T(GP) 1991; DRCOG 1991. Prev: Sen. Med. Off. Submarine Escape Train. Tank; Sen. Med. Off. RN Coll. Greenwich; Sen. Med. Off. 8th Frigate Squadron.

***CRIBBIN, Laurence James** 7 Sylvan Court, School Lane, Woolton, Liverpool L25 7AJ — MB ChB 1995 Liverp.

CRICHLOW, Mr Thomas Peter Kenneth Robert The Princess Royal Hospital, Apley Castle, Telford TF1 6TF Tel: 01952 641222 Fax: 01952 242218; Pendleton, 58 Port Hill Road, Shrewsbury SY3 8RN Tel: 01743 344102 — MB BS 1977 Lond.; FRCS Eng. 1981. (Middlx.) Cons. Orthop. Surg. P.ss Roy. Hosp. Telford. Socs: Fell. Hunt. Soc.; Fell. BOA; BMA.

CRICHTON, Alan 86 Inverleith Place, Edinburgh EH3 5PA — MB BChir 1993 Camb.

CRICHTON, Anne-Marie Forth View Practice, Dean Road, Bo'ness EH51 9BB; Middle Strath Mill, Strathloanhead, By Avonbridge, Falkirk FK1 2LA — BM BS 1990 Nottm.; MRCGP 1995; DRCOG 1994. (Univ. Nottm.) GP Princip. Prev: GP Bury St. Edmunds; Clin. Asst. (Psychogeriat.) Bury St. Edmunds.

CRICHTON, Ashley Robert Crawford The Surgery, 1 The Ridgway, Woodingdean, Brighton BN2 6PE Tel: 01273 307555 Fax: 01273 304861; Ellinge Hall, Glynde, Lewes BN8 6SX Tel: 01273 858042 — BM BCh 1977 Oxf.; BA (Hons.) Oxf. 1974, MA 1978; DRCOG Auckland 1981. (Univ. Oxf. (Oriel) & King's Coll. Hosp. Med. Sch.) Prev: SHO (Orthop.) Middlemore Hosp. Auckland, NZ; SHO (Neonat. Paediat.) St. Jas. Univ. Hosp. Leeds; SHO (Anaesth.) Roy. Sussex Co. Hosp. Brighton.

CRICHTON, Blair McKendrick 107 Dora Road, Wimbledon Park, London SW19 7JT — MB BS 1970 Lond.; MRCS Eng. LRCP Lond. 1970; DIH Eng. 1978; Mem. FOM RCP Lond. 1982. (Guy's) Sen. Med. Off. Lond. Regional Transport. Socs: Fell. Roy. Soc. Med.; Soc. Occupat. Med. Prev: SHO (Psychiat.) Guy's Hosp. Lond.

CRICHTON, Brian Eric Hobs Moat Medical Centre, Ulleries Road, Solihull B92 8ED Tel: 0121 742 5211 Fax: 0121 743 4217 — MB ChB 1988 Birm.

CRICHTON, Charles Lachlan Portree Medical Centre, Portree IV51 9BZ Tel: 01478 612013 Fax: 01478 612340 — MB ChB 1979 Aberd.; MRCGP 1986.

CRICHTON, Christina Mary Portree Medical Centre, Portree IV51 9BZ; Tigh-na-Craig, Staffin Road, Portree IV51 9HS — MB ChB 1982 Aberd.

CRICHTON, David Angus James Fisher Medical Centre, 4 Tolpuddle Gardens, Bournemouth BH9 3LQ Tel: 01202 522622 Fax: 01202 548480 — MB ChB 1977 Ed.; MRCGP 1981; DGM RCP Lond. 1988; DRCOG 1981; DA, DCH 1982.

CRICHTON, David George 17 Minorca Road, Deepcut, Camberley GU16 6ST — MB ChB 1994 Leeds.

CRICHTON, Fiona Jean Baillie 42 Polmont Road, Laurieston, Falkirk FK2 9QT Tel: 01324 623446; Department of Obstetrics and Gynaecology, Falkirk and District Royal Infirmary NHS Trust, Majors Loan, Falkirk FK1 5QE Tel: 01324 624000 — MB ChB 1983 Dundee; MRCOG 1990. Cons. O & G Falkirk & Dist. Roy. Infirm. Prev: Sen. Regist. & Regist. (O & G) Tayside; Clin. Research Fell. (O & G) Tayside HB; SHO (Haemat.) Tayside HB.

CRICHTON, Isobel Shiona 4 Kilnford Drive, Dundonald, Kilmarnock KA2 9ES — MB ChB 1981 Glas.

CRICHTON, Jane Alison 15 School Road, Wellbank, Broughty Ferry, Dundee DD5 3PL — MB ChB 1998 Aberd.; MB ChB Aberd 1998.

CRICHTON, John Hugh McDiarmid Orchard Clinic, Edinburgh EH10 5HF Tel: 0131 5378858 Fax: 0131 537 5857 Email: john.clinchton@lpct.scot.nhs.uk — BM BS 1990 Nottm.; PhD (Criminol.) Camb. 1996; BMedSci Nottm.1988; MRCPsych. 1996; Cert. Forens. Psychother. Lond. 1995. (Nottingham) Cons. (Forens. Psychiat.); Hon. Fell. in Law, Univ. Edin. Socs: Internat. Assn.Law & Ment..Health; Acad. Forens. Sci. Prev: Nightingale Research Schol. Trinity Hall & Inst. Criminol. Camb.; Lect. (Developm. Psychiat.) Camb. Univ.; Lect. (Forens. Psychiat.) Edin. Univ.

CRICHTON, John Lawson Borders General Hospital, Melrose TD6 9BS Tel: 01896 4333; The Banks, Newstead, Melrose TD6 9DE Tel: 01896 822407 — MB ChB 1955 St. And.; FRCOG 1985, M 1972; DRCOG 1966. Cons. O & G Borders HB. Socs: Brit. Med. Ultrasound Soc.; Assoc. Mem. RCGP. Prev: Cons. (O & G) W.. I. HB.; Cons. (O & G) Canad. Armed Forces Europe.

CRICHTON, Neil Rothnie Whitchurch Health Centre, Armada Road, Bristol BS14 0SU Tel: 01275 832285 Fax: 01275 540035; 10 Druid Road, Stoke Bishop, Bristol BS9 1LH Tel: 0117 968 4688 Fax: 0117 907 1608 Email: nrcrichton@compuserve.com — MB ChB 1978 Aberd.; MRCGP 1982; DRCOG 1983; DCH RCP Lond. 1981. (Aberdeen) Socs: BMA.

CRICHTON, Paul The Royal Marsden Hospital, Fulham Road, London SW3 6JJ — MD 1984 Munich; MA Oxf. 1974; MRCPsych 1990. Cons. & Sen. Lect. (Psychiat.) Roy. Marsden Hosp. Socs: BMA; Brit. Neuropsychiat. Assn. Prev: Sen. Regist. (Psychiat.) Maudsley Hosp.; Regist. (Psychiat.) Char. Cross Hosp.; Hon. Asst. Ho. Phys. Nat. Hosp. Neurol. & Neurosurg. Lond.

CRICHTON, Thomas Ingram (retired) 86 Inverleith Place, Edinburgh EH3 5PA Tel: 0131 478 0676 — MB ChB 1944 Ed.; DObst RCOG 1951.

CRICK, Aerona Margaret Agnes Kelvin House, Bridgwater Road, Winscombe BS25 1NW — MB ChB 1961 Bristol.

CRICK, Alexandra Pitts 16 Spencer Road, Poole BH13 7EU — MB BS 1992 Lond.

CRICK, Anthony Frederick 6 Overcliffe, Gravesend DA11 0EF Tel: 01474 357071 Fax: 01474 560219 — MB BChir 1947 Camb.; BA Camb. 1944, MB BChir 1947. (Guy's & Camb.) Clerk to Kent

LMC's. Socs: Med. Bd. War Pens. & Indust. Injuries. Prev: Dep. Resid. Med. Off. & Sen. Cas. Off. Roy. N.. Hosp. Lond.; Ho. Surg. (Neurosurg.) Joyce Green Hosp. Dartford; Asst. Med. Off. St. Bernard's Hosp. S.all.

CRICK, David Louis Anthony Faith House Surgery, 723 Beverley Road, Hull HU6 7ER — MB ChB 1976 Leeds; MRCGP 1980. GP Hull.

CRICK, Jonathan Charles Pitts Department of Cardiology, Bristol Royal Infirmary, Marlborough St., Bristol BS2 8HW Tel: 0117 928 2664 Fax: 0117 928 2666; Burnett House, Burnett, Bristol BS31 2TF Tel: 0117 986 0242 — MRCS Eng. LRCP Lond. 1973; DPhil Sussex 1984; FRCP Lond. 1994; MRCP (UK) 1979. (King's Coll. Hosp.) Cons. Cardiol. Bristol Roy. Infirm.; Hon. Clin. Lect. (Med.) Univ. Bristol. Socs: Brit. Cardiac Soc. & Brit. Cardiovasc. Interven. Soc. Prev: Sen. Regist. (Cardiol.) Hammersmith Hosp. Lond.; Regist. (Cardiol.) Guy's Hosp. Lond.; Hon. Regist. (Cardiol.) Roy. Sussex Co. Hosp. Brighton.

CRICK, Jonathan Mark James High Meadows, Bardon Hill, Hexham NE47 7BN — MB BCh 1993 Wales.

CRICK, Mr Martin Denys Pitts 16 Spencer Road, Canford Cliffs, Poole BH13 7EU — MB BS 1966 Lond.; FRCS Eng. 1973; MRCS Eng. LRCP Lond. 1966; DO Eng. 1971. (St. Thos.) Cons. Ophth. Surg. Bournemouth & E. Dorset Hosp. Gp. Prev: Sen. Regist. St. Thos. Hosp. Lond.; Resid., Moorfields Eye Hosp. Lond.; Regist. St. Thos. Hosp. Lond.

CRICK, Michael James Kelvin House, Bridgwater Road, Winscombe BS25 1NW — MB ChB 1961 Bristol; DObst RCOG 1963.

CRICK, Michael Robert North Caister Medical Centre, Brandford Road, Great Yarmouth NR30 5NE Tel: 01493 720618; 5 Rollesby Gardens, Rollesby, Great Yarmouth NR29 5HD Tel: 01493 748281 — MB ChB 1982 Sheff.; MRCGP 1987. Prev: Trainee GP E. Cumbria VTS.

CRICK, Mr Ronald Pitts International Glaucoma Association, Ophthalmic Department, King's College Hospital, Denmark Hill, London SE5 9RS Tel: 020 7737 3265 Fax: 020 7737 3265; 10 Golden Gates, Sandbanks, Poole BH13 7QN Tel: 01202 707560 Fax: 01202 707560 — MRCS Eng. LRCP Lond. 1939; FRCS Eng. 1950; FRCOphth 1988; DOMS Eng. 1946. (King's Coll. Hosp.) p/t Hon. Ophth. Surg. King's Coll. Hosp. Lond.; Emerit. Lect. King's Coll. Sch. of Med. & Dent. Lond. Socs: Fell. Roy. Soc. Med. (Vice-Pres. Ophth. Sect.).; (Pres.) Internat. Glaucoma Assn.; Internat. Perimetric Soc. Prev: Ophth. Surg. King's Coll. Hosp. Lond.; Recogn. Teach. (Ophth.) King's Coll. Hosp. Med. Sch.; Chairm. Ophth. Postgrad. Train. Comm. SE Thames RHA.

CRICKMAY, Jennifer Robin 2 Garfield Place, Maudlin Road, Totnes TQ9 5TB — MB BS 1965 Lond.; MRCPsych 1980; DPM Lond. 1969. (Univ. Coll. Hosp.) Cons. Child & Adolesc. Psychiat. Young People's Centre Mt. Gould; Hosp. Plymouth.

CRICKMORE, Carolyn Tracy Mount Farm Surgery, Lawson Place, Bury St Edmunds IP32 7EW; 118 Crowland Way, Cambridge CB4 2LT — MB BChir 1990 Camb.; MA Camb. 1991, MB 1990. BChir 1989. Trainee GP Suff. HA. Prev: Trainee GP/SHO (Gen. Med., Paediat. & O & G) W. Suff. HA; SHO (A & E & Orthop.) W. Suff. Hosp. Bury St. Edmunds; Ho. Phys. (Gen. Med.) P'boro. Dist. Hosp.

CRIDDLE, John Walter Willowbeck, Estcourt Road, Darrington, Pontefract WF8 3AJ — MB BS 1993 Lond.

***CRIDLAND, Gail** Flat 41, 20 Abbey Road, London NW8 9BJ — MB BS 1998 Lond.; MB BS Lond 1998.

CRIGGIE, William Robert Lanark Doctors, Health Centre, South Vennel, Lanark ML11 7JT Tel: 01555 665522 Fax: 01555 666857 — MB ChB 1978 Ed.

CRIGHTON, Alexander James Unit of Oral Surgery & Medicine, Dundee Dental Hospital & School, Park Place, Dundee DD1 4HR Tel: 01382 660111 Fax: 01382 635998 Email: a.j.crighton@dundee.ac.uk — MB ChB 1993 Ed.; FDS OM RCSEd 1999; BDS Ed. 1984; FDS RCS Ed. 1988. Cons. in Oral Med. Tayside Uni Hosp.s Trust; Cons. in Oral Med., Feinbrae Private Clinic, Dundee; Cons. in Oral Med., Albyn Hosp., Aberd. Socs: Brit. Med. Assn.; Brit. Assn. of Oral Med.; Europ. Assoc of Oral Med.

CRIGHTON, Andrew Damien 27 Adelaide Place, Dundee DD3 6LE — MB ChB 1994 Glas.

CRIGHTON, Ian Leuchars Sunderland Royal Hospital, Kayll Road, Sunderland SR4 7TP; 2A The Crescent, Cleadon, Sunderland SR6 7QZ — MB ChB 1978 Sheff.; FRCS Eng. 1983, Gen. 1995. Cons. (Gen. Surg.) Sunderland Roy. Hosp. Prev: Sen. Regist. NW RHA.; Research Fell. Roy. Marsden Hosp. Lond.; Regist. (Surg.) Roy. Hallamsh. Hosp. Sheff.

CRIGHTON, Isla Margaret The Old Stables, Church Gate, Colston Basset, Nottingham NG12 3FE Tel: 01949 81675 — MB ChB 1989 Manch.; FRCA. Cons. (Anaesth.), Qu.'s Med. Centre, Nottm. Prev: Regist. (Anaesth.) Nottm.

CRIGHTON, James Leuchars (retired) Apartment 1, 24 North Avenue, Leicester LE2 1TL — MB ChB 1951 St. And.; PhD Leic. 1994. Prev: Phys. Stud. Health Serv. Univ. Leics. & Leics. Polytechnic.

CRILL, David Hocquard (retired) The Farm, L'Etacq, St Ouen, Jersey JE3 2FB Tel: 01534 481029 — BM BCh Oxf. 1954; MA Oxf. 1954. Prev: Ho. Surg. High Wycombe War Memor. Hosp.

CRILLEY, Paul Francis 12 Langley Avenue, Whitley Bay NE25 9DF — MB ChB 1990 Sheff.

CRILLY, Catherine Una 16 Dogwood Road, Poole BH17 7PA — MB BS 1988 Lond. Trainee GP Dorset VTS. Prev: SHO (Psychiat.) St. Ann's Hosp. Poole; SHO P.ss Anne Hosp. Soton.; SHO (O & G & Paediat.) Basingstoke Dist. Gen. Hosp.

CRILLY, Damian 11 Hempstall, Welwyn Garden City AL7 3LY — MB BCh BAO 1984 Belf.; MB BCh Belf. l984; MRCP (UK) 1987.

CRILLY, Desmond Daniel (retired) Plas Gwyn, Llanfaelog, Anglesey, Tycroes LL63 5SY Tel: 01407 810334 — MB BCh BAO Dub. 1944. Prev: Ho. Surg. Sir P. Dun's Hosp. Dub.

CRILLY, Heather Margaret Old School House, Over Norton, Chipping Norton OX7 5PU Tel: 01608 644693 — MB ChB 1986 Liverp.; MRCGP 1992; T(GP) 1992. GP Princip. Prev: Trainee GP Maghull, Merseyside; SHO (Community Paediat.) Liverp.; GP Retainer Maghull.

CRILLY, Michael Anthony 42 Colinmander Gardens, Ormskirk L39 4TF — MB ChB 1987 Liverp.; MRCGP 1991; MPH Liverp. 1993; MFPHM 1996; DGM RCP Lond. 1990; T (GP) 1992; CCST (PHM) 1998. (Liverp.) Sen. Lect. Pub. Health Meds. Liverp. Uni.; Hon. Cons. in Pub. Health Med., Liverp. HA. Prev: Regist. (Pub. Health Med.) Mersey RHA Liverp.; Trainee GP S. Sefton VTS; Sen. Regist. (Pub. Health Med.) & Clin. Research Fell. (Gen. Pract.) Manch. Univ.

CRIMLISK, Helen Lesley Schwanallee 14, Marburg 35037, Germany; 14 Long Lane, Aughton, Ormskirk L39 5AT Tel: 01695 421602 — MB BS 1988 Lond.; BSc (Hons.) Lond. 1985; MRCP (UK) 1991; MRCPsych 1995. (UMDS Lond.) Sen. Regist. Maudsley Hosp. Prev: Research Fell. Inst. Neurol. Lond.; Regist. (Psychiat.) Maudsley & Roy. Bethlem Hosp. Lond.; SHO (Neurol.) Nat. Hosp. Neurol. & Neurosurg. Lond.

CRIMLISK, Susan Nicola 23 Poplar Grove, Hammersmith, London W6 7RF Tel: 020 7602 8884; c/o 14 Long Lane, Aughton, Ormskirk L39 5AT Tel: 01695 421602 — MB BS 1991 Lond.; BSc (Hons.) Lond. 1988; MRCPsych. (University College London) Specialist Regist. Child&Adolesc.. Psychiat.St. Mary's.Hosp. Paddington.

CRIMMINS, Geoffrey John Eryl Surgery, Eryl, Station Road, Llantwit Major CF61 1ST Tel: 01446 793444 Fax: 01446 793115; Ty Croeso, West End, Llantwit Major CF61 1SL — MB BChir 1974 Camb.; MA, MB Camb. 1974, BChir 1973; MRCP (UK) 1977. (Cambridge & St Bartholomews London)

CRINALL, Fiona Jane 33 Northcote Road, Sidcup DA14 6PN Tel: 020 8309 0415 — MB BS 1981 Lond.; FFARCS Lond. 1988. Prev: Regist. (Anaesth.) Middlx. & Whittington Hosp. Lond.; SHO (Anaesth.) Roy. Free Hosp. Lond.

CRINION, Anthony Robert 11 Newport Drive, Fishbourne, Chichester PO19 3QQ — MB ChB 1973 Liverp.

CRINNION, Mr James Nicholas Windsor Edge, 86 Church Road, London W7 3BE — MB ChB 1987 Leeds; FRCS Lond. 1991. Research Fell. (Gen. Surg.) Leeds Gen. Infirm. Prev: SHO Rotat. PeriFell.sh. (Surg.) N.. Gen. Hosp. Sheff.

CRINYION, Ian James Garden Lane Medical Centre, 19 Garden Lane, Chester CH1 4EN Tel: 01244 346677 Fax: 01244 310094; Keewaydin, Hooton Road, Willaston, South Wirral CH64 1SN Tel: 0151 327 5432 — MRCS Eng. LRCP Lond. 1968. (Liverp.) Local Med. Off. Civil Serv. Med. Advis. Serv.; Racecourse Med. Off. Chester; Med. Off. Univ. Coll. Chester. Socs: Brit. Stud. Health Assn.; Racecourse Med. Offs. Assn. Prev: SHO (O & G & Gen. Med.)

Chester City Hosp.; Ho. Off. (Gen. Surg.) Chester Roy. Infirm.; Clin. Asst. (Surg.) Chester Roy. Infirm.

CRIPPS, Colin Malcolm (retired) Abbey House, Golding Close, Daventry NN11 5RA Tel: 01327 877770 — MB BChir 1963 Camb.; MB BChir Camb. 1964; MA Camb. 1964; DObst RCOG 1965. Clin. Asst. (Dermat.) N.ampton Gen. Hosp. Prev: Regist. (Path.) & Ho. Surg. (Gyn.) St. Bart. Hosp.

CRIPPS, David Frank Moss Grove Surgery, 15 Moss Grove, Kingswinford DY6 9HS Tel: 01384 277377 Fax: 01384 402329; 22 Chingford Close, Wordsley, Stourbridge DY8 5PA Tel: 01384 296172 — MB BS 1972 Lond.; MRCS Eng. LRCP Lond. 1972; MRCGP 1977; DCH Eng. 1976; DObst RCOG 1974. (Guy's) Socs: BMA. Prev: Trainee GP Dudley & Stourbridge VTS; Ho. Surg. Roy. Surrey Co. Hosp. Guildford; SHO (O & G) W. Suff. Hosp. Bury St. Edmunds.

CRIPPS, Diana Lesley Zeneca Pharma UK, Kings Court, Water Lane, Wilmslow SK9 5AZ Tel: 01625 712213 Fax: 01625 712598; The Orchard, Warrington Road, Mickle Trafford, Chester CH2 4EA Tel: 01244 300474 — MB ChB 1989 Bristol; Dip. Pharm. Med. RCP (UK) 1995; DA (UK) 1991. Sen. Med. Adviser. Socs: AFPM. Prev: Med. Dir. Cortecs Ltd.

CRIPPS, Elizabeth Jean 21 Marjorie Street, Cramlington NE23 6XQ Tel: 01670 734814 — MB BS 1981 Newc.

CRIPPS, John Roger 84 Warwick Park, Tunbridge Wells TN2 5EN Tel: 01892 30550 — MB BS 1965 Lond.; BPharm Lond. 1960, MB BS 1965; DMRD Eng. 1970; FFR 1972. (Char. Cross) Cons. Radiol. Pembury Hosp. Prev: Sen. Regist. (Diag. Radiol.) King's Coll. Hosp. Lond.; Regist. (Diag. Radiol.) Middlx. Hosp. Lond.

CRIPPS, Jonathan William — MB BS Lond. 1988; BA Oxf. 1985; MRCPsych 1992. (Charing Cross/Westminster) Cons. Forens. Psychiat. Prev: Sen. Regist. (Forens. Psychiat.) Maudsley Hosp.; Registar (Psychiat), Epsom.

CRIPPS, Matthew Graham Barnes Close Surgery, Barnes Close, Sturminster Newton DT10 1BN Tel: 01258 474500 Fax: 01258 471547; Branch Surgery, Ranelagh Cottage, New St, Marnhull, Sturminster Newton DT10 1QA Tel: 01258 820015 — MB BS 1983 Lond.; FRCGP 1996, M 1987; DFFP 1993; DCH RCP Lond. 1987; DRCOG 1986; Cert. Family Plann. JCC 1986; DGM RCP Lond. 1985. (Univ. Coll. Lond. & Westm. Med. Sch.) GP & Trainer Sturminster Newton; W. Dorset Represent. Wessex Fac. RCGP; NHS Provider for Acupunc.; GP Clin. Governance Lead, Prescribing Lead and Exec. Comm. Mem. N. Dorset Primary Care Trust. Socs: BMA; Accred. Mem. Brit. Med. Acupunc. Soc. Prev: SHO (Psychiat. & Geriat.) E.bourne Hosps.; SHO (A & E) Worthing Hosp.; SHO (O & G) Roy. Sussex Co. & Brighton Gen. Hosps.

CRIPPS, Mr Neil Philip James (retired) Department of Surgery., St Richards Hospital, Spitalfields Road, Chichester PO19 4SE Tel: 01243 831593 Fax: 01243 831683 — MB ChB 1982 Manch.; ChM Manch. 1996; FRCS Eng. 1989; FRCS Ed. 1988; FRCS (Gen.) 1997. Cons. Colorectal Surg. St Richard's Hosp. Chichester. Prev: Cons. Surg., Roy. Hosp.. Haslar Gosport & QA Hosp. Portsmouth.

CRIPPS, Thomas Philip Department of Anaesthesia, Borders General Hospital, Melrose TD6 9BS Tel: 01896 754333 Email: t.cripps@borders.scot.nhs.uk; Email: tomcripps@aol.com — MB ChB 1979 Ed.; BA Oxf. 1976; FFA RCS Eng. 1983. Cons. Anaesth. Prev: Lect. Univ. Leeds.

CRIPPS, Timothy Roy Cardiology Department, Bristol Royal Infirmary, Bristol BS2 8HW Tel: 0117 928 2665 Fax: 0117 928 2666 Email: tim.cripps@bris.ac.uk; Elwell Farm House, Winford Lane, Dundry, Bristol BS41 8LT Tel: 0117 964 6493 Email: tim-cripps@bristol.ac.uk — BM BCh 1980 Oxf.; DM Oxf. 1989; MRCP (UK) 1983; FRCP 1999 FRCP 1999. (Oxf.) Cons. Cardiol. Bristol Roy. Infirm.; Mem. Brit. Pacing & Electrophysiol. Gp. Socs: Brit. Cardiac Soc.; Brit. Cardiac Interven. Soc. Prev: Internat. Electrophysiol. Fell. W.mead Hosp. Sydney, Austral.; Sen. Regist. (Cardiol.) John Radcliffe Hosp. Oxf.; Regist. (Cardiol.) St. Geo. Hosp. Lond.

CRIPWELL, Michael Trease Goodinge Health Centre, Goodinge Close, North Road, London N7 9EW Tel: 020 7530 4940; 24 Archibald Road, London N7 0AL Tel: 020 7607 5762 Email: 106104.557@compuserve.com — MB BS 1973 Lond.; MRCGP 1979; DCH Eng. 1976. (Middlx.) Prev: Regist. (Psychiat.) Watford Gen. Hosp.; SHO (Paediat.) Hemel Hempstead Gen. Hosp.; SHO (O & G) Barnet Gen. Hosp.

CRISP, Adrian James Addenbrooke's Hospital, Hills Road, Cambridge CB2 2QQ Tel: 01223 216254; Arran House, 19 Cambridge Road, Little Abington, Cambridge CB1 6BL Tel: 01223 891141 — MB BChir 1974 Camb.; MA Camb. 1975, MD 1985; FRCP Lond. 1991; MRCP (UK) 1977; DRCOG 1977. (Camb. & Univ. Coll. Hosp.) Cons. Rheum. Addenbrooke's Hosp. Camb.; Dir. of Studies Clin. Med. & Fell. Ch.ill Coll. Camb.; Assoc. Dean Camb. Univ. Clin. Sch. Socs: Brit. Soc. Rheum. & Bone & Tooth Soc. Prev: Sen. Regist. (Rheum.) Guy's Hosp. Lond.; Research Fell. Mass. Gen. Hosp. & Harvard Med. Sch. Boston, USA; Regist. (Med.) Univ. Coll. Hosp. Lond.

CRISP, Andrew John Radiology Department, Royal Victoria Infirmary, Queen Victoria Road, Newcastle upon Tyne NE1 4LP — MB BS 1981 Newc.; MD Newc. 1991, MB BS 1981; MRCP (UK) 1984; FRCR 1993.

CRISP, Professor Arthur Hamilton 113 Copse Hill, London SW20 0NT Tel: 020 8946 0976 — MB BS 1956 Lond.; DSc Lond. 1980, MD 1967; FRCP Lond. 1975, M 1970; FRCP Ed. 1972, M 1961; MRCS Eng. LRCP Lond. 1956; FRCPsych 1971; DPM Eng. 1960; Hon. FRCPsych 1996. (Westm.) Emerit. Prof. Psychol. Med. Univ. Lond. St. Geo. Hosp. Med. Sch.Lond. SW17 0RE; Hon. Fell. St. Geo. Hosp. Med. Sch. Socs: Fell. Roy. Soc. Med. Prev: Chairm. Adv. Comm. Med. Tr. to EC 1963-66; Chairm. Educat. Comm. GMC 1982-88; Dean Fac. Med. Univ. Lond. 1976-1980.

CRISP, Jennifer Anne Ranellie, Tinkers Lane, Brewood, Stafford ST19 9DD — MB BChir 1975 Camb.; BA Camb. 1975, MB BChir 1975; MRCPsych 1982. Cons. Psychiat. including Psychodynamic Psychother. City Gen. Hosp. & Richmond Lodge Stoke-on-Trent.

CRISP, Mr John Charles BUPA Hospital Bushey, Heathbourne Road, Bushey, Watford WD23 1RD Tel: 020 8950 9090; 4 Elmhurst Close, Bushey, Watford WD23 2QB Tel: 01923 225514 Fax: 01923 225514 Email: crispyjc@aol.com — MB BS Lond. 1967; FRCS Eng. 1972; MRCS Eng. LRCP Lond. 1967. (Guy's) Cons. Urol. W. Herts. Hosp. Trust. Socs: Roy. Soc. Med. (Sect. Urol.). Prev: Cons. Urol. Watford Gen. Hosp.; Sen. Regist. (Urol.) Guy's Hosp. Lond.; Regist. (Urol.) Norf. & Norwich Hosp.

CRISP, Katherine Elizabeth The Binfield Practice, Binfield Health Centre, Terrace Road North, Binfield, Bracknell RG42 5JG Tel: 01344 425434 Fax: 01344 301843; 21 Greenham Wood, North Lake, Bracknell RG12 7WJ — MB BS 1980 Lond.

CRISP, Matthew David 30 Fearon Road, North End, Portsmouth PO2 0NJ — BM 1993 Soton.

CRISP, Stuart Ronald Cockburn 6 Eyres Close, Ewelme, Wallingford OX10 6LA — MB BChir 1992 Camb.; MRCP (Paediat.) 1996. (Camb.) Specialist Regist. Paediat. John Radcliffe Hosp. Oxf. Socs: Coll. of Paediat. & Child Health Christ. Med. Fell.sh.

CRISP, Thomas Alexander, TD The Chestnuts, 242 Ongar Road, Writtle, Chelmsford CM1 3NZ Tel: 01245 421517 Fax: 01245 461777 Email: comcrisp@aol.com — MB BS 1973 Lond.; BSc Lond. 1970, MB BS 1973; Dip. Sports Med. Lond. 1987. (Lond. Hosp.) Sports Phys. Roy. Lond. Hosp.; Sports Phys. Springfield Med. Centre; Lect. Univ. E. Lond.; Med. Off. Chelmsford Sports Injuries Centre. Socs: Brit. Assn. Sport & Med. (Sec. E.. Region); Amer. Coll. Sports Med. Prev: Clin. Asst. (Sports Med.) Lond. Hosp.; GP Chelmsford; SHO (Obst & Gyn., Gen. Med. & Cas. Harold Wood Hosp.

CRISP, Mr William John Stafford District General Hospital, Weston Road, Stafford ST16 3SA — MB BS 1980 Newc.; MD Newc. 1993; FRCS Ed. 1986. Cons. Surg. Stafford Dist. Gen. Hosp. Prev: Sen. Regist. (Gen. Surg.) N.. RHA; Vis. Lect. Chinese Univ. Hong Kong; Post. Fell.sh. Regist. (Gen. Surg.) Freeman Hosp. Newc.

CRISPIN, Helen 4 Green Park Close, Winchester SO23 7HG — BM 1998 Soton.

CRISPIN, Jane Doreen Princess Alexander Eye Pavilion, Chalmers St., Edinburgh EH3 9HA Tel: 0131 536 1000; 4 Ormidale Terrace, Edinburgh EH12 6EQ Tel: 0131 337 3565 — MB ChB 1968 Ed.; MRCOphth 1995. (Ed.) Clin. Asst. (Ophth.) P.ss Alexandra Eye Pavil. Edin. Prev: Med. Off. (Family Plann.) Lothian HB & Brook Advis. Centre Edin.

CRISPIN, John Richard Whin Park Medical Centre, 6 Saughton Road, Edinburgh EH11 3RA Tel: 0131 455 7999 Fax: 0131 455 8800; 4 Ormidale Terrace, Edinburgh EH12 6EQ Tel: 0131 337 3565 — MB ChB 1968 Ed.; FRCGP 1997; MRCGP 1977; FRCS Ed. 1974; DObst RCOG 1971. (Ed.)

CRISPIN, Susan Ann Chaldon Road Surgery, Chaldon Road, Caterham CR3 5PG Tel: 01883 345466 Fax: 01883 330942 — MB BS 1988 Lond.; DCH RCP Lond. 1993. (Kings College London)

CRISPIN, Zona Lesley Guild Community Heathcare Trust, Guild Lodge, Guild Park, Whittingham, Preston PR3 2JH — MB ChB 1982 Leeds; MMedSci 1988; MRCPsych 1986. Cons. Forens. Psychiat. Guild Lodge, Whittingham, Preston. Prev: Cons. (Forens. Psychiat.) Ashworth Hosp. Merseyside; Sen. Regist. (Psychiat.) N.. RHA; Regist. (Psychiat.) Lynfield Mt. Hosp. Bradford.

CRISTOFANI, Peita Joan 55 Avondale, Ash Vale, Aldershot GU12 5NE — MB BS 1978 Lond.; MRCS Eng. LRCP Lond. 1978.

CRISTOFOLI, Lia Elizabeth Gallions Reach Health Centre, Bentham Road, Thamesmead, London SE28 8BE Tel: 020 8333 5001 Fax: 020 8333 5020 — MB BS 1986 Lond. Trainee GP Greenwich VTS.

CRISWELL, Michael Iain Fordie House, 82 Sloane St., London SW1X 9PA Tel: 020 7235 1117 Fax: 020 7235 3721; 4 Lysias Road, London SW12 8BP — MB ChB 1985 Manch.; BSc St. And. 1982; MRCGP 1993; DCCH RCP Ed. 1990; DRCOG 1988. Prev: Trainee GP/SHO (Paediat.) Roy. Hosp. Sick Childr. Edin.; SHO (A & E) Char. Cross Hosp. Lond.

CRITCHFIELD, Timothy Owen The Surgery, The Coppice, Herne Lane, Rustington, Littlehampton BN16 3BE Tel: 01903 783178 Fax: 01903 859027 — MB ChB 1984 Sheff.

CRITCHLEY, Anne Therese 18 Elmet Road, Barwick-in-Elmet, Leeds LS15 4HE — MB BS 1980 Newc.

CRITCHLEY, Edmund Michael Rhys 5518 Merlin Road, Blackburn BB2 7BA Tel: 01254 260342 Fax: 01254 260342 — BM BCh 1957 Oxf.; DM Oxf. 1974, MA 1957; FRCP Lond. 1977, M 1964; FRCP Ed. 1975, M 1964. (King's Coll. Hosp.) Cons. Neurol. Preston Roy. Hosp.; Counc. Mem. & Examr. RCP Lond.; Hon. Prof. Neurol. Univ. Centr. Lancs. 1993; Emerit. Prof. Clin. Neurol.; Med. Assessor Licensing Div. of the Meds. Control Agency from (August 1997). Socs: Fell. Roy. Soc. Med.; Assn. Brit. Neurols.; (Ex Pres.) N. Eng. Neurosci. Assn. Prev: Instruc. (Neurol.) Univ. Kentucky Med. Center, USA; Sen. Regist. Univ. Coll. Hosp. Lond.; Regist. (Neurol.) Roy. Free Hosp.

CRITCHLEY, Eustasia 2 Hurstbourne Avenue, Highcliffe, Christchurch BH23 4RQ — Ptychio Iatrikes 1972 Athens.

CRITCHLEY, Mr Giles Roderic Flat 6, Neville Court, 22 Graces Mews, London SE5 8HE — MB BChir 1990 Camb.; FRCS Eng. 1993.

CRITCHLEY, Professor Hilary Octavia Dawn Department of Obstetrics & Gynaecology, Centre for Reproductive Biology, University of Edinburgh, 37 Chalmers St., Edinburgh EH3 9EW Tel: 0131 229 2575; 17 Viewforth Terrace, Edinburgh EH10 4LJ — MB ChB 1981 Manch.; MD Manch. 1991; FRcog 1998; Franzcog 1991. Prof. of Reproductive Med. Univ. of Edin.

CRITCHLEY, Hugo Dyfrig 18 Merlin Road, Blackburn BB2 7BA; 1 Neville Court, 22 Graces Mews, London SE5 8HE — MB ChB 1990 Liverp.; BSc (Hons.) Physiol. 1987; DPhil (Psychol Stud) Oxiensis 1996; MRC Psych. Research Fell. FIL Wellcome Dept, Cognitive Neurol., Inst.of Neurol.; Hon. Clin. Contracts Neurovasc. Med. St. Mary's Hosp. Paddington; Autonomic Unit Nat. Hosp. Neurol. & Neurosurg. Qu. Lond. Socs: MRCPsych; Roy. Soc. Med. Prev: Hon. Regist. Bethlem & Maudsley NHS Trust; SHO Psychiat. Rotat. St Geo.s Hosp.; Lect. Inst. of Psychiat. Dept. of Psychol. Med.

CRITCHLEY, Isobel Vernon (retired) Hollin House Farm, Glasshouses, Harrogate HG3 5QQ Tel: 01423 711345 — MB ChB 1948 Leeds. Prev: Ho. Surg. Leeds Matern. Hosp. & Hosp. Wom. Leeds.

CRITCHLEY, James Michael Allis (retired) Hollin House Farm, Glasshouses, Harrogate HG3 5QQ — MB ChB 1948 Leeds; DObst RCOG 1951. Prev: Ho. Surg. Leeds Matern. Hosp. & Hosp. Wom. Leeds.

CRITCHLEY, Jane Marushka 49 Emperor's Gate, London SW7 4HJ Tel: 020 8237 5333 Fax: 020 8237 5344; Flat 1, 88A Cromwell Road, London SW7 4EN Tel: 020 7584 9756 — MB BS 1958 Lond.; MRCS Eng. LRCP Lond. 1958; DObst RCOG 1960. (King's Coll. Hosp.) Socs: (Ex-Sec. & Pres.) Anglo US Med. Soc.; Soc. Apoth. Lond.; Med. Soc. Lond. Prev: Regist. (Med.) St. Mary Abbot's Hosp. Lond.; Fell. (Gastroenterol. & Endocrinol.) Univ. Virginia Hosp., USA; Resid. Med. Off. Tadworth Br. of Hosp. Sick Childr. Lond.

CRITCHLEY, John Parade Surgery, The Parade, Liskeard PL14 6AF Tel: 01579 342667 Fax: 01579 340650; High Wynard, Old Road, Liskeard PL14 6DW Tel: 01579 343698 — MB BS 1966 Lond.; MRCS Eng. LRCP Lond. 1966; DA Eng. 1970; DObst RCOG 1969. (St. Thos.) Prev: Regist. (Anaesth.) Portsmouth Gp. Hosps.

CRITCHLEY, Mair 18 Merlin Road, Blackburn BB2 7BA Tel: 01254 260342 Fax: 01254 260342 — MB BS 1962 Lond.; MD Lond. 1974; MRCS Eng. LRCP Lond. 1962; FRCR 1988; DA Eng. 1965. (Roy. Free) Cons. & Clin. Dir. (Nuclear Med.) Roy. Liverp. Univ. Hosp.; Lect. (Radiol Diagn. Med.) Univ. Liverp.; Mem. Edit. Brit. Jl. Radiol. Socs: (Counc.) Brit. Nuclear Med. Soc.; Brit. Inst. Radiol. (Sub-Comm. Nuclear Med.); Liverp. Med. Inst. Prev: Sen. Regist. (Nuclear Med.) Manch. Roy. Infirm.; Research Fell. (Pulm. Physiol. Med.) Univ. Med. Centre Lexington Ky., USA.

CRITCHLEY, Mark Alan Mount Pleasant Medical Centre, Ditherington Road, Shrewsbury SY1 4DQ Tel: 01743 235111 — MB ChB 1984 Leic.; MRCGP 1990; DRCOG 1990; DGM RCP Lond. 1987. Occupat.al Phys.; Medico-Legal Expert.

CRITCHLEY, Michael James (retired) 8 St Mary's Road, Bexley DA5 2DD — MB ChB 1960 Birm.; MRCGP 1968; AFOM RCP Lond. 1981; DObst RCOG 1961. Local Med. Off. Civil Serv. Med. Advis. Serv. Swanley. Prev: Med. Off. Remploy Woolwich.

CRITCHLEY, Patricia Ann (Surgery), 103 South Norwood Hill, London SE25 6BY Tel: 020 8771 0742; 57 South Croxted Road, Dulwich, London SE21 8BA Tel: 020 8761 4962 — BM 1977 Soton.

CRITCHLEY, Mr Paul Stephen 19 Siskin Close, Stockton-on-Tees TS20 1SG Tel: 01642 550116; 31 High Street, Chinnor OX39 4DJ Tel: 01844 353558 — BM BS 1990 Nottm.; FRCS (Plast.) 2001; BMedSci Nottm. 1988; FRCS Eng. 1995. (Nottingham) Specialist Regist. (Plastic Surg.) Salisbury Dist. Hosp. Prev: Specialist Regist. (Plastic Surg.) Stoke Mandeville Hosp.; Specialist Regist. (Plastic Surg.) Radcliffe Hosp. Oxf..; SHO (Plastic Surg.) Salisbury Dist. Hosp.

CRITCHLEY, Peter Henry Stuart Leicester Royal Infirmary, Infirmary Square, Leicester LE1 5WW Tel: 0116 258 6630 Fax: 0116 258 6192; 1 The Old Rectory, Main St, Saddington, Leicester LE8 0QH Tel: 0116 240 2587 — MB BS 1978 Lond.; MA Camb. 1979, BA 1975, MD 1991; FRCP Lond. 1996. Cons. Rehabil. Med. & Neurol. Leicester Roy. Infirm. NHS Trust. Socs: Assn. Brit. NeUrol.s; Brit. Soc. Rehabil. Med. Prev: Lect. (Disabil. Med.) Univ. Soton.

CRITCHLOW, Barbara Mary Summer Hill, 68 Sandy Lane, Romiley, Stockport SK6 4NH — MRCS Eng. LRCP Lond. 1962.

CRITCHLOW, Brian William Marine Avenue Medical Centre, 64 Marine Avenue, Whitley Bay NE26 1NQ Tel: 0191 252 5317 — MB BS 1975 Lond.; MRCS Eng. LRCP Lond. 1975. (Univ. Coll. Hosp.) Prev: SHO (Paediat.) Preston Hosp. N. Shields; SHO (O & G) S. Shields Gen. Hosp.; Ho. Surg. (ENT) Univ. Coll. Hosp. Lond.

CRITCHLOW, Denise Gail Institute of Psychitry, ASB, 4 Windsor Walk, Denmark Hill, London SE5 8BB Tel: 0207 7848 0369 Fax: 01270 627220 Email: d.critchlow@10p.kcl.ac.uk; 26 Mornington Terrace, Camden, London NW1 7RS Tel: 0207 387 6947 — MB ChB 1990 Liverp.; MRCPsych 1995. (Liverp.) Sen. Regist. Subst. Abuse Unit City Gen. Hosp. Stoke-on-Trent W. Midl. RTS; Locum Cons. in Addic.s, Maudsley hosital, Denmark Hill, Lond.

CRITCHLOW, Jeremy Ian Derbyshire Lane Practice, 213 Derbyshire Lane, Sheffield S8 8SA Tel: 0114 255 0972 — MB BS 1991 Lond.

CRITCHLOW, Margaret Rosalind c/o 14 Clonroot Road, Portadown, Craigavon BT62 4HG — MB BCh BAO 1977 Belf.

CRITCHLOW, Stephen Green Holywell Hospital, Steeple Rd, Antrim BT 41 2RJ Tel: 02894 413376 — MB BChir 1977 Camb.; MB Camb. 1977, MA, BChir 1976; MRCPsych 1986; DCH RCPSI 1980. Cons. Psychiat. of Old Age, Holywell Hosp. Antrim. Socs: Mem. Roy. Coll. Psychiat.s. Prev: Regist. (Psychol. Med.) St. Bart. Hosp. Lond.; Specialist Regist. Psychiat. N.. Irel. 1997-1999.

CRITTENDEN, Frederick Kenneth (retired) Manor Croft, Kings Bromley, Burton-on-Trent DE13 7HZ Tel: 01543 472220 — MRCS Eng. LRCP Lond. 1942. Prev: Med. Off. & Anaesth. Meynell Ingram Cott. Hosp. Yoxall.

CRITTENDEN, Gemma Higden Cottage, Valley Road, Hughenden, High Wycombe HP14 4PF — MB BS 1993 Lond.

CRNIC, Vladimir c/o Kidderminster General Hospital, Bewdley Road, Kidderminster DY11 6RJ — State Exam Med 1991 Heidelberg.

CRO, Roger John West Street Surgery, 89 West Street, Dunstable LU6 1SF Tel: 01582 664401 Fax: 01582 475766; 26 High Street, Edlesborough, Dunstable LU6 2HS Tel: 01525 221528 Fax: 01582 475766 — MRCS Eng. LRCP Lond. 1969; MA Camb. 1967. (Sheff.)

CROAL, Bernard Lewis Department of Clinical Biochemistry, Aberdeen Royal Infirmary, Forester Hill, Aberdeen AB25 2ZN Tel: 01224 681818 Fax: 01224 694378 Email: b.l.croal@abdn.ac.uk; 36 Donald Avenue, Kemnay, Inverurie AB51 5JE Tel: 01467 642049 — MB ChB 1992 Glas.; BSc (Hons.) Glas. 1989; DRCPath 1997; MRCP (UK) 1988. (Glas.) Specialist Regist. (Clin. Biochem.) Aberd. Roy. Infirm.; Hon. Clin. Lect. (Clin. Biochem.) Univ. Aberd. Socs: Roy. Coll. Phys. Surg. of Glas.; Diplomate Mem. Roy. Coll. Pathologists; Assn. Clin. Biochems. Prev: SHO III (Clin. Biochem.) Vict. Infirm. NHS Trust Glas.; Regist. Clin. Biochem.ry at Glas. Roy. Infirm.

CROALL, John — MB ChB 1982 Glas.; 2001 Open; 1997 Open; MRCPath 1989; FRCPath 1997. (Glas.) Cons. Microbiologist, Trafford Gen. Hosp., Manch.. Socs: Brit. Soc. Antimicrob. Chemother.; Assn. Med. Microbiol.; Hosp. Infec. Soc. Prev: Cons. Microbiologist Liverp. Pub. Health Lab.

CROCK, Mr Henry Vernon, AO Cromwell Hospital, Cromwell Road, London SW5 0TU Tel: 020 7460 5646 Fax: 020 7460 5648 Email: spinadisorders@breathemail.net — MB BS 1953 Melbourne; MS Melbourne 1978, MD 1968; FRCS Eng. 1957; FRACS 1961; FRCS Ed. (Hon). Dir. Spinal Disorders Unit & Cons. Spinal Surg. Cromwell Hosp. Lond.; Hon. Cons. Roy. Postgrad. Med. Sch. & Hon. Sen. Lect. Hammersmith Hosp.; Hon. Cons. Spinal Surg. Lond. Socs: Fell. BOA; Fell. Austral. Orthop. Assn.; Corres. Mem. Japanese Orthop. Assn. Prev: Sen. Surg. & Profess. Assoc. (Orthop.) St. Vincent's Hosp. Univ. Melbourne, Austral.

CROCKARD, Professor Hugh Alan Department of Surgical Neurology, National Hospital for Neurology & Neurosurgery, Queen Square, London WC1N 3BG Tel: 020 7636 4191 Fax: 020 7722 3141 Email: a.crockard@ion.ucl.ac.uk — MB BCh BAO 1966 Belf.; FDS RCS 2001; FRCS Eng. 1971; FRCS Ed. 1970; D.sc 2000. (Belfast) Cons. Neurosurg. Nat. Hosp. Neurol. & Neurosurg. Lond.; Dir. Surg. Educat., RCS; Dir. Raven. Dept. Ed. RCS.; Prof. Surg. Neuro. Univ. W.ern. Australia; Pres. Cervical Spine Research Soc. (Europ. Br.). Socs: Counc.mem.Brit.Soc.Neurog.Surg.; Amer. Acad. Neurosurgs.; Austral. Spine Soc. Prev: Past pres.Brit.Cervical spine.soc.; Hunt. Prof. RCS Eng. 1973.

CROCKARD, Margaret Caroline Ann 49 Hillway, Highgate, London N6 6AD — MB BCh BAO 1970 Belf.; DCH RCPS Glas. 1974; DObst RCOG 1972.

CROCKATT, David Ralph, Group Capt. RAF Med. Br. Retd. Brook Lodge, Buckworth, Huntingdon PE28 5AR — MRCS Eng. LRCP Lond. 1955; DAvMed Eng. 1968. (Leeds)

CROCKATT, Robin Howard Ian Priory Medical Centre, Cornlands Road, Acomb, York YO24 3WX Tel: 01904 781423 Fax: 01904 784886; Priory Medical Group, 45 Heworth Green, York YO31 7SX Tel: 01904 425241 — MRCS Eng. LRCP Lond. 1958; DObst RCOG 1964. (Leeds) Prev: Ho. Surg. Pinderfields Gen. Hosp. Wakefield; Ho. Phys. Gen. Infirm. Leeds & St. Jas. Hosp. Leeds.

***CROCKER, Alison Rosemary** 36 Eaton Road, Norwich NR4 6PZ Tel: 01603 454457 Fax: 01603 456031 — BM BCh 1998 Oxf.; BM BCh Oxf 1998; BA Oxf 1995.

CROCKER, Catherine Barbara 30 Westfield Road, Acocks Green, Birmingham B27 7TL Tel: 0121 706 5131; Tel: 0121 704 4160 — MB BChir 1975 Camb.; MA Camb. 1975; MRCGP 1982; DCH Eng. 1979. GP Principle; GP Tutor to S. Birm, PCG. Prev: GP Solihull; SHO (Paediat.) E. Birm. Hosp. & Solihull Hosp.; Ho. Phys. & Ho. Surg. Hull Roy. Infirm.

CROCKER, Clive Simeon Poplars Surgery, 17 Holly Lane, Erdington, Birmingham B24 9JN Tel: 0121 373 4216 Fax: 0121 382 9576 — MB ChB 1978 Birm.; BSc Birm. 1975, MB ChB 1978; DRCOG; MRCGP.

CROCKER, Professor John Department of Histopathology, Birmingham Heartlands Hospital, Bordesley Green East, Birmingham B9 5SS Tel: 0121 424 1188 Fax: 0121 424 0196 Email: crockej@heartsol.wmids.nhs.uk — MB BChir 1975 Camb.; MD Camb. 1983, MA 1974; FRCPath 1993, M 1981; MRCP Lond. 1998. Cons. Histopath. Birm. Heartlands Hosp. & Prof. (Path.) Univ. Birm.; Edr.-in-Chief, Molecular Path.; Prof. Birm. Univ.; Vis. Sen. Lect. Univ. Warwick. Socs: Brit. Lymphoma Path. Gp.; Path. Soc.; Assn. Clin. Paths. Prev: Lect. (Path.) Univ. Birm.; SHO (Path.) E. Birm. Hosp.; Ho. Surg. & Ho. Phys. Hull Roy. Infirm.

CROCKER, Kirsty Louise 84 Nutbush Lane, Chelston, Torquay TQ2 6SD — MB BS 1998 Lond.; MB BS Lond 1998.

CROCKER, Peter David Risca Surgery, St. Mary Street, Risca, Newport NP11 6YS Tel: 01633 612666; 4 Marigold Close, Rogerstone, Newport NP10 9AZ — MB BS 1980 Lond.; MRCGP 1984.

CROCKER, Mr Simon Geoffrey 36 Eaton Road, Norwich NR4 6PZ Tel: 01603 454451 Fax: 01603 456031 — MB BS Lond. 1968; MRCS Eng. LRCP Lond. 1968; FRCOG 1986, M 1974; DObst 1970. (St. Barthomew's Hospital Medical College, University of London) Cons. O & G Norf. & Norwich Univ. Hosp.; Hon. Sen. Lect., Univ. of E. Anglia. Socs: Brit. Med. Assn.; Fell.Roy. Soc. of Med.; Brit. Gyn. Soc. Prev: Sen. Lect. & Cons. O & G St. Bart. Hosp. Med. Coll. Lond.; Sen. Lect. (O & G) Univ. Singapore & Kandang Kerbau Hosp. Singapore.

CROCKET, Aysel Alva Medical Practice, West Johnstone St., Alva FK12 5BD Tel: 01259 760331; Glenisla, Longrow, Menstrie FK11 7EA — MB ChB 1988 Glas.; PhD Glas. 1978; MRCGP 1993. Post-Doct. Research Fell. Univ. Cincinnati, USA. Socs: BMA. Prev: Trainee GP/SHO VTS.

CROCKET, Beatrice Margaret (retired) Garlands Cottage, Bourne Road, West Bergholt, Colchester CO6 3EL Tel: 01206 240239 — MB ChB 1947 Ed.; MRCPsych 1971; Dip. Psych. Ed. 1952. Prev: Cons. Child Psychiat. N.E. Essex Child Guid. Clinic Colchester.

CROCKET, George Thomas Parkhead Hospital, 81 Salamanca St., Glasgow G31 5ES Tel: 0141 554 7951; 14 Burntbroom Gardens, Mount Vernon, Glasgow G69 7HX — MB ChB 1973 Glas.; MBA Strathclyde 1990; MRCPsych 1977. Cons. Psychiat. Pk.head Hosp. & Roy. Infirm. Glas.; Hon. Clin. Sen. Lect. (Psychol. Med.) Univ. Glas.

CROCKET, Richard Wilfred 4A Osler Road, Headington, Oxford OX3 9BJ Tel: 01865 68925 — MD 1965 Glas.; MB ChB 1937; FRCP Glas. 1970; FRFPS 1941; FRCP Ed. 1962; FRCPsych 1971; DPM Lond. 1939. (Glas. & Ed.) Socs: Soc. Clin. Psychiat. Prev: Cons. (Psychol. Med.) OldCh. Hosp. Romford & Ingrebourne Centre St. Geo. Hosp. HornCh.; Sen. Regist. & Tutor Psychiat. Univ. Leeds & United Leeds Hosp.

CROCKETT, Adrienne Louise Priestly Unit, Dewsbury District Hospital, Halifax Road, Dewsbury WF13 4HS Tel: 01924 512000; 19 Crown Point Road, Kingsway, Ossett WF5 8RG Tel: 01924 278112 — MB BS 1985 Lond.; DRCOG 1989. (St. Bart.) Staff Grade Psychiat.; Clin. Asst. (Psychiat.) Dewsbury. Prev: GP Princip. Homestead Clinic Wakefield.

CROCKETT, Antony William Basil Elm Tree Surgery, High Street, Shrivenham, Swindon SN6 8AG Tel: 01793 782207 Fax: 01793 784429; Elm Tree House, Shivenham, Swindon SN6 8AA Tel: 01793 782608 Email: crockett@dial.pipex.com — BM 1980 Soton.; MRCGP 1986; DRCOG 1985; DA Eng. 1984. (Soton.) GP Princip.; Clin. Asst. Chest Clinic Swindon & MalBoro. Health Trust. Socs: GP Asthma Gp.; GP Writers Assn. Prev: Trainee GP Portsmouth; SHO (Anaesth.) St. Bart. Hosp. Lond.; SHO Portsmouth VTS.

CROCKETT, Charles Stephen Central Buchan Medical Group, The Surgery, School Street, New Pitsligo, Fraserburgh AB43 6NE Tel: 01771 653205 Fax: 01771 653294 — MB ChB 1955 Aberd.; MRCGP 1968.

CROCKETT, Clifden John Northbourne Surgery, 1368 Wimborne Road, Bournemouth BH10 7AR Tel: 01202 574100 Fax: 01202 590030; 22 Queens Road, Christchurch BH23 3HH — MB BS 1975 Lond. (Westm.)

CROCKETT, Mr David John (retired) 34 Hillside Crescent, Nether Heyford, Northampton NN7 3LS Tel: 01327 342390 — MB BChir 1946 Camb.; BA; FRCS Eng. 1952. Prev: Cons. Plastic Surg. St. Luke's Hosp. Bradford.

CROCKETT, Janice (retired) 17 Merthyr Mawr Road, Bridgend CF31 3NN — MB BCh 1965 Wales. Cons. Community Paediat. M. Glam. Prev: Ho. Phys., Ho. Surg. & Ho. Surg. (O & G) Bridgend Gen. Hosp.

CROCKETT, Lindsey 19 Tolworth road, Surbiton KT6 7TA — MB BS 1998 Lond.; MB BS Lond 1998; BSc (hons.) Lond. 1995. (Barts & the Royal London Hospitals) Socs: BMAS.

CROCKETT, Philip Stephen 31 Ladhope Drive, Galashiels TD1 2BL; 10 Foruie Court, Collieston, Ellon AB41 8SB — MB ChB 1993 Aberd.; MRCGP. SHO (Psychiat.).

CROCKFORD, Anne 78 Claygate Lane, Hinchley Wood, Esher KT10 0BJ Tel: 020 8398 7474 — MB BS Lond. 1955. (Westm.)

CROCKFORD, Tracey Kathryn Tree Tops, Peckforton Hall Lane, Spurtstow, Tarporley CW6 9TF — MB ChB 1988 Manch.; DRCOG 1991. Staff Grade (Community Paediat.) Countess of Chester NHS Trust. Prev: Trainee GP Chester.

CROCOMBE, Juli Margaret 11 Court Road, Whitchurch, Cardiff CF14 1HN Tel: 029 2069 3557 — MB BCh 1988 Wales; DRCOG 1991; MRC Psych 1998. (University of Wales) Staff Grade Psychiat. in Learning Disabilities, Wonford Ho. Hosp., Exeter. Socs: Fell.Roy. Soc. of Med.; Founder Mem. Brit. Assn. of Ment. Health Law.

CROCOMBE, Marie Joyce The Grantham Centre, Grantham Road, London SW9 9DL Tel: 020 7733 6191 Fax: 020 7737 2870 — MB BS 1987 Lond.; DRCOG 1992.

CROCOMBE, Sarah Jane 233 Moorside Road, Urmston, Manchester M41 5SJ — MB ChB 1989 Bristol.

CROFT, Andrew Malcolm Old Springfields, Lelant Downs, Hayle TR27 6LL — MB ChB 1989 Leeds.

CROFT, Ashley Marcel John, Lt.-Col. RAMC 17 Keogh Close, Ash Vale, Aldershot GU12 5RJ — MB BS 1985 Lond.; FFPHM 2001 UK; MSc Lond. 1990; MA Oxf. 1984; MFPHM RCP (UK) 1995; DMCC Lond. 1995. (Guy's Hosp. Med. Sch. Lond.) Cons. Pub. Health Med. MoD. Socs: Brit. Travel Health Assn.; Fell. Roy.Soc. Of Trop. Med & Hyg.; Fell., Roy. Soc. Med. Prev: Cons. Pub. Health Med. Operat. Resolute, Bosnia.

CROFT, Barbara Ashley 50 Otho Court, Brentford Dock, Brentford TW8 8PY — MB BS Lond. 1959; MRCS Eng., LRCP Lond. 1959. (Roy. Free) Cons. Community Paediat. Richmond, Roehampton Twickenham HA; Trustee of Project for Childr. with special needs, Richmond. Socs: Fell. Fac. Community Health F. of Roy. Inst. of Pub. Health and Hyg.; Fell. Roy. Soc. Med.; Fell. of Roy. Coll. of Paediat. and Child Health. Prev: Sen. Med. Off. Child Health Hereford & Worcester AHA; Asst. MOH & Sch. Med. Off. Worcester; Princip. GP., Malvern.

CROFT, Charles Beresford 55 Harley Street, London W1N 1DD Tel: 020 7580 2426 — MB ChB 1965 Leeds; FRCS Ed. 1972; FRCS Eng. 1970; Dip. Amer. Bd. Otolaryngol. 1979. (Leeds) Cons. ENT Surg. Roy. Nat. Throat, Nose & Ear Hosp. Lond. & The Roy. Free Hosp.; Civil Cons. (Laryngol.) RAF; Examr. RCS Edin. & DLO Lond. Socs: Fell. Roy. Soc. Med.; BMA. Prev: Attend. Head & Neck Surg. Montefiore Hosp. New York, USA; Assoc. Prof. (Otolaryng.) Albert Einstein Med. Sch. New York, USA; Sen. Regist. (ENT) Leeds. Gen. Infirm.

CROFT, Desmond Nicholas Bourne House, Hurstbourne Priors, Whitchurch RG28 7SB Tel: 01256 892665 Fax: 01256 893659 — BM BCh 1956 Oxf.; DM Oxf. 1966, MA 1956; FRCP Lond. 1975; MRCP (UK) 1959; Hon. FRCR 1986. (Oxf. & St. Thos.) Emerit. Cons. Phys. St. Thos. Hosp. Lond. Socs: (Ex-Pres.) Brit. Nuclear Med. Soc.; Founding Mem. Europ. Assn. of Nuclear Med.; Eur. Union Med. Specialists (Ex-Pres. Nuclear Med. Sect.). Prev: Sen. Regist. (Med.) & Ho. Phys. (Med. & Neurol.) St. Thos. Hosp. Lond.; Nuffield Foundat. Med. Fell. (Gastroenterol.) Boston Univ., USA; Specialist (Med.) BMH Tripoli, Libya.

CROFT, Duncan 25 Horsebrass Drive, Bagshot GU19 5RB — MB BChir 1991 Camb.; MA Camb. 1992, BA 1988, MB BChir 1991.

CROFT, Eirian 5 Bigwood Road, London NW11 7BB — MB BCh 1942 Wales; BSc Wales 1939; MRCS Eng. LRCP Lond. 1941. (Cardiff.)

CROFT, Frederick Ferdinand (retired) Middle House, 11 Arnworth Avenue, Fauvic, Grouville JE3 — MRCS Eng. LRCP Lond. 1935. Prev: Cons. to Air Crew Selection Bd. RAF HornCh.

CROFT, Giles Peter 9 Berkeley Close, Hucclecote, Gloucester GL3 3TG Email: gpcroft@doctors.org.uk — MB ChB 1998 Leeds; BSc. (Leeds) Med.PRHO.York.Dist.Hosp. Prev: Orthop.Surg.PRHO.St.James'.Uni.Hosp.Leeds; Gen. Surgic. PRHO. St.James'. Hosp. Leeds.

CROFT, Gita Angelika Department of Child Health, Royal Free Hospital, Pond Street, London NW3 2QQ Tel: 0141 425 2841, 020 7794 0500; 5 Dolphin Road, Pollokshields, Glasgow G41 4LE Tel: 0141 425 2841, 020 7794 0500 — MB ChB 1985 Aberd.; MRCP (Paediat.) (UK) 1992; MRCGP 1990; DCH RCPS Glas. 1989. p/t Specialist Regist. (Med. Paediat.) N. Thames. Prev: Specialist Regist. (Med. Paediat.) Roy. Hosp. Sick Childr. Glas.; Regist. Roy. Hosp. Sick Childr. Edin.; SHO Rotat. (Paediat.) Aberd.

CROFT, Graham The Hollies, High St., Hinderwell, Whitby YO21 2AQ Tel: 01947 840281 — MB BS 1984 Lond.; BSc Lond. 1981; DRCOG 1990. (St. Bart.)

CROFT, Hilary Diana Russel Bourne House, Hurstbourne Priors, Whitchurch RG28 7SB Tel: 01256 892665 — MB BS 1958 Lond.; MRCS Eng. LRCP Lond. 1957. (St. Thos.)

CROFT, Jeremy Andrew Yew Tree Medical Centre, 100 Yew Tree Lane, Solihull B91 2RA Tel: 0121 705 8787 Fax: 0121 709 0240; Sunset Lodge, 9 Benson Road, Stratford-upon-Avon CV37 6UU Tel: 01789 204904 — MB ChB 1974 Birm.; MRCGP 1990; DRCOG 1977. Clin. Asst. (Elderly Med.). Prev: Med. Off. Sunhaven Old Peoples Home.

CROFT, John Andrew 11 Ambleway, Walton-le-Dale, Preston PR5 4JF — MB ChB 1998 Liverp.; MB ChB Liverp 1998.

CROFT, Justine Joanne 9 Berkeley Close, Cranhamgate, Hucclecote, Gloucester GL3 3TG — MB ChB 1992 Birm.

CROFT, Keith Frederick, Wing Cdr. RAF Med. Br. Retd. Croft Medical Associates, 12 Sands Lane, Carlton Le Moorland, Lincoln LN5 9HJ Tel: 01522 788730 Fax: 01522 789291 Email: keithfcroft@doctors.org.uk; 12 Sands Lane, Carlton le Moorland, Lincoln LN5 9HJ Tel: 01522 788730 Fax: 01522 789291 Email: keithfcroft@talk21.com — MB ChB 1977 Manch.; BSc (Biochem. Hons.) Manch. 1969, MB ChB 1977; DRCOG 1981. (Manchester) GP Locum. Prev: Med. Adviser (Biological Warefare), Min. of Defence.

CROFT, Marion Selina 2A Turquand Street, London SE17 1LT — MB BS 1998 Lond.; MB BS Lond 1998.

CROFT, Michael Downton Gateways Surgery, Andrew Close, Shenley WD7 9PL; 15 York Road, St Albans AL1 4PL — MB BS 1980 Lond.; DRCOG 1983; DCH RCP Lond. 1985.

CROFT, Nicholas Michael Department of Paediatric Gastroenterology, Queen Mary and Westfield College, St Bartholomew's Hospital, London EC1A 7BE — MB BS 1986 Lond.; MRCP (UK) 1989; DCH RCPS Glas. 1990; PhD Ed. 1996. Sen. Lect. (Paediat. Gastroenterol.). Prev: Sen. Regist. RHSC Glas.; Research Fell. & Hon. Regist. Gastrointestinal Laborat. W.. Gen. Hosp. Edin.; Regist. (Med.) Roy. Hosp. For Sick Childr. Edin.

CROFT, Peter Reginald School of Postgraduate Medicine, University of Keele, Stoke-on-Trent ST4 7NY — MB ChB 1974 Birm.; MSc Lond. 1987; MD Birm. 1994. Prof. Epidemiol. Univ. Keele.

CROFT, Rebecca Susan 70 The Avenue, Tadworth KT20 5DE — MB BS 1997 Lond. (London)

CROFT, Richard James 17 Sandringham Avenue, Benton, Newcastle upon Tyne NE12 8JX — MB ChB 1995 Glas.

CROFT, Richard Paul 82 Mount Crescent, Brentwood CM14 5DD Tel: 01277 219984 Email: richard@rcroft.demon.co.uk; 70 Culver Lane, Reading RG6 1DY Tel: 0118 926 0672 — BM BCh 1980 Oxf.; MA Oxf. 1980; MRCGP 1984; DTM & H RCP Lond. 1985; DRCOG 1983. GP Regist., Reading. Socs: Internat. Leprosy Assn. Prev: Project Dir. Danish Bangladesh Leprosy Mission; Project Dir. Lamb Hosp. Dinajpur, Bangladesh.

CROFT, Richard Thomas — MB BS 1978 Lond.; MRCS Eng. LRCP Lond. 1977; DFFP 1994; Dip. Pract. Dermat. Wales 1991; DRCOG 1979. (Roy. Free Hosp.) Princip. GP Kent Family Pract. Comm.; Hosp. Practitioner Diabetes Kent & Sussex Hosp. Prev: Ho. Surg. Whipps Cross Hosp. Lond.; Ho. Phys. W. Kent Gen. Hosp. Maidstone.

CROFT, Mr Rodney John 144 Harley Street, London W1N 1AH Tel: 020 7935 0023; 127 Queens Road, Buckhurst Hill IG9 5BH — MB BChir 1968 Camb.; MA Camb. 1969, MChir 1982; FRCS Eng. 1973; FACS 1984. (Camb. & Middlx.) Cons. Gen. & Vasc. Surg. N. Middlx. Hosp. Lond.; Roy. Free Hosp. Med. Sch. Clin. Sub-Dean N. Middlx. Hosp. Lond.; Hon. Sen. Lect. (Surg.) Roy. Free Hosp. Med. Sch.; Hon. Sen. Lect. (Surg.) Med. Coll. St. Bart. Hosp. Lond.; Examr. Final MB BS Univ. Lond.; Recognised Teach. Univ. Lond.; Assoc. Prof. Surg. St. Geo. Univ. Grenada; Liveryman Worshipful Soc. Apoth. Socs: Fell. Assn. Surgs.; Fell. Roy. Soc. Med.; Vasc. Surgic. Soc GB & Irel. Prev: Sen. Regist. (Surg.) Middlx. Hosp. & Centr. Middlx. Hosp. Lond.; Regist. (Surg.) Ipswich & E. Suff. Hosp.; Regist. (Neurosurg.) Nat. Hosp. Nerv. Dis. Maida Vale.

CROFT, Rosemary Anne 70 Culver Lane, Reading RG6 1DY Tel: 0118 961 6807 Email: richard@rcroft.demon.co.uk — MB BCh 1981 Oxf.; MA Camb. 1981; MRCGP 1985; DRCOG 1984. Locum GP. Prev: Regist. (GP) Chalfont Surg., Reading; TB Progr. Dir., Danish Bangladesh Leprosy Mission, Bangladesh.

CROFT, Russell Dominic The Child Development Centre, Danestrete, Stevenage SG1 1HB Tel: 01438 314333 Ext: 2587 Fax: 01438 781470; 9 Pirton Road, Hitchin SG5 2BD Tel: 01462 636350 — MB ChB 1979 Birm.; BA Oxf. 1970; MRCP (UK) 1983. (Birm. Univ.) Cons. Community Paediat. N. Herts. NHS Trust. Socs: BMA; Fell. Roy. Coll. Paediat. & Child Health; BAPSCAN. Prev: SCMO E. Berks. NHS Trust; Regist. (Community Paediat.) Lewisham & N. S.wark HA.

CROFTON, Eileen Chris, MBE (retired) 13 Spylaw Bank Road, Edinburgh EH13 0JW — BM BCh 1943 Oxf. Prev: Med. Dir. Scott. Comm. Action Smoking & Health.

CROFTON, Sir John Wenman, KBE (retired) 13 Spylaw Bank Road, Edinburgh EH13 0JW Tel: 0131 441 3730 Fax: 0131 441 5105 Email: eapretty@breathemail.net — MRCS Eng. LRCP Lond. 1936; MD Camb. 1947, MB BChir 1937; FRCP Ed. 1957, M 1954; FRCP Lond. 1951, M 1939; Hon. FRCP Ed. 1987; Hon. FFCM 1984; Hon. FRCPI 1976; Hon. FRACP 1976; Hon. FACP 1976. Hon. Pres.Tbalert, Lond.; Hon Fell. UMDs Guys & St. Thos. Prev: Dean Fac. Med. & Prof. Respirat. Dis. & Tuberc. Univ. Edin.

CROFTON, Mary Elizabeth St. Mary's Hospital, Praed St., London W2 1NY Tel: 020 7886 6125 Fax: 020 7725 6669 Email: mary.crofton@st_marys.nhs.uk; 7 Ascott Avenue, Ealing, London W5 3XL Tel: 020 8567 0830 — MB BS 1973 Lond.; MRCP (UK) 1975; FRCR 1981; FRCP Lond. 1996. (St. Mary's Hosp. Med. Sch.) Cons. Radiol. St. Mary's Hosp. Lond. Socs: Brit. Inst. of Radiol.; Brit. Med. Ultrasound Soc. Prev: Sen. Regist. (Radiol.) Hammersmith Hosp. Lond.; Regist. (Gen. Med.) St. Mary's Hosp. Lond.

CROFTON-BIWER, Catherine Joan Yorkstones, 10 Elmete Avenue, Roundhay, Leeds LS8 2JX — MB BS 1967 Lond.; MRCS Eng. LRCP Lond. 1967. (Roy. Free)

CROFTS, Barbara Joan Cutteslowe Farmhouse, Oxford OX2 8ES Tel: 01865 513784 — MB BS 1971 Lond.; MRCS Eng. LRCP Lond. 1971; DO Eng. 1978. Med. Off. Oxf. Eye Hosp. Prev: Ho. Phys. & Ho. Surg. Roy. Free Hosp. Lond.; Regist. (Ophth.) Groote Schuur Hosp. Cape Town, S. Afr.

CROFTS, Catherine Frances 6 The Downlands, Warminster BA12 0BD Tel: 01985 213327 — MB BS 1944 Lond. (Roy. Free) Prev: Ho. Surg. Roy. Free Hosp.; Ho. Phys. Memor. Hosp. Woolwich.

CROFTS, Charles Bertram, Maj. RAMC Retd. (retired) 27 Hamilton Drive, Radcliffe on Trent, Nottingham NG12 1AG Tel: 0160 732473 — MRCS Eng. LRCP Lond. 1927. Prev: Med. Ref. Pruden. & Pearl Assur. Cos.

CROFTS, Frances Margaret 2 St Margarets Road, Edinburgh EH9 1AZ — MB BS 1974 Lond.; MRCS Eng. LRCP Lond. 1973.

CROFTS, Harold Robert 23 Carnegie Crescent, Aberdeen AB15 4AU — MB ChB 1959 Aberd.

CROFTS, Kenneth Harold McLintock Pear Tree Surgery, 28 Meadow Close, Kingsbury, Tamworth B78 2NR Tel: 01827 872755 Fax: 01827 874700 — MB ChB 1951 Ed. (Ed.) Prev: Ho. Surg. Roy. Infirm. Edin.; Ho. Off. E. Surrey Hosp. Redhill.

CROFTS, Norman Fortrey (retired) The Old Vicarage, Ospringe, Faversham ME13 8XS Tel: 01795 532621 — MB BChir 1942 Camb.; MA Camb. 1942; FRCP Lond. 1972, M 1948; MRCS Eng. LRCP Lond. 1942. Hon. Cons. Chest Phys. Canterbury Gp. Hosps. Prev: Clin. Asst. Brompton Hosp.

CROFTS, Peter Kenelm Savernake Hospital, Marlborough SN8 3HL Tel: 01793 425429 — MB ChB 1973 Birm.; MRCPsych 1978. (Birm.) Cons. Psychiat. E. Wilts Health Care MarlBoro. Socs: Brit. Assn. Behavioural Psychother. Prev: Sen. Regist. W. Midl. RHA; Regist. (Psychiat.) Qu. Eliz. Med. Centre Birm.

CROFTS, Sally Louise 26 Shaftesbury Road, Dundee DD2 1HF Tel: 01382 66219 — MB ChB 1985 Dundee.

CROFTS, Mr Trevor-John c/o Department of Surgery, Royal Infirmary of Edinburgh., Lauviston Place, Edinburgh Tel: 0131 536 1609 Fax: 0131 536 1509 Email: croftsline@aol.com; 2 St. Margarets Road, Edinburgh EH9 1AZ Tel: 0131 447 6357 Fax: 0131 447 0614 Email: croftline@aol.com — MB BS 1970 Lond.; MS Lond. 1983; FRCS Eng. 1977; MRCS Eng. LRCP Lond. 1970; FRACS 1983; FRCS 1997 FRCS (EDIN) 1997. Cons. Surg.Roy. Infirm. Edin. Socs: Fell. Hong. Kong Coll. Surgs.; Roy. Soc. Med. Prev: Sen. Lect. (Surg.) Aberd. Roy. Infirm.; Sen. Lect. (Surg.) P. of Wales Hosp. Shatin, Hong Kong (New Chinese Univ.).

CROKE, Winifred Mary (retired) Manor House Hospital, Aylesbury HP20 1EG — MB ChB 1948 Otago; MRCPsych 1972; DPM Eng. 1971. Cons. Psychiat. of Ment. Handicap & Child Psychiat.

CROKER, Graham Howie The Surgery, Blendworth Lane, Horndean, Portsmouth Tel: 023 92 599430 — MB ChB 1972 Liverp.; DRCOG 1985.

CROKER, John Richard 152 Harley Street, London W1N 1HH Tel: 020 7935 8868 Fax: 020 7224 2574; 26 Montagu Gardens, Wallington SM6 8ER — BM BCh 1970 Oxf.; MA BM BCh Oxf. 1970; FRCP Lond. 1990; MRCP (UK) 1973. (St. Thos.) Cons. Phys. Gen. Med. Univ Coll.; Cons. Geriat. Middlx. Hosp.; Hon. Sen. Lect. Univ. Coll. & Middlx. Sch. Med. Lond. Socs: Brit. Geriat. Soc. & Mem. Brit. Soc. Gastroenterol. Prev: Sen. Regist. (Geriat.) Middlx. Hosp.; Research Hon. Sen. Regist. (Gastroenterol.) Middlx. Hosp.; Regist. Lond. Hosp.

CROKER, Lucinda Rose 8 The The Green, Walton-le-Wolds, Loughborough LE12 8HR — MB ChB 1994 Bristol.

CROLLICK, Avril Janet 2 The Mall, London SW14 7EN — MB ChB 1965 Leeds; DCH Eng. 1980. (Leeds) Clin. Asst. in Paediat. Seacroft Hosp. Leeds. Prev: Ho. Surg. & Ho. Phys. Otley Gen. Hosp.

CROMAR, Doreen Margaret 95 Tromode Park, Douglas IM2 5L Tel: 01624 24833 — MB BCh 1942 Liverp. (Liverp.) Prev: Ho. Surg., Res. Surg. Off. & Orthop. Regist. Roy. S.. Hosp.; Liverp.

CROMARTY, James Irvine, OBE, QHP, Group Capt. RAF Med. Br. Retd. (retired) Waterfield, Orphir, Orkney KW17 2RA Tel: 0185 681327 — MB ChB Ed. 1951; FFPHM RCP (UK) 1994, M 1974; DPH Ed. 1962. Prev: Gen. Manager, Chief Admin. Med. Off. & Dir. of Pub. Health Orkney Bd.

CROMBIE, Mr Alan 12 Millhouse Close, Glasgow G20 0UD Tel: 0141 946 9502 Email: alancrombie@lineone.net — MB ChB 1992 Glas.; BSc (Hons.) Glas. 1989; FRCS Ed. 1997.

CROMBIE, Professor Alexander Leaster (retired) 19 Graham Park Road, Gosforth, Newcastle upon Tyne NE3 4BH Tel: 0191 285 2378 — MB ChB Ed. 1959; FRCS Ed. 1964; FRCOphth 1988; FRCOpth. (Hon.) 1998. Prev: Dean Med. Sch. & Prof. Ophth. Univ. Newc.

CROMBIE, Catriona Margaret Wake Green Surgery, 7 Wake Green Road, Moseley, Birmingham B13 9HD Tel: 0121 449 0300 — MB ChB 1989 Leic.

CROMBIE, Jillian Lesley 6 Lockside, Narrow St., Lime House, London E14 8EH — MB BS 1988 Lond.

CROMBIE, Richard David 144 Howard Road, Clarendon Park, Leicester LE2 1XJ Tel: 0116 270 7917 — MB ChB 1989 Leic.

CROMBIE, Robert Black 50 Tetney Lane, Holton Le Clay, Grimsby DN36 5AT — MB ChB 1945 Ed. (Ed.) Prev: Capt. RAMC.

CROMBIE, Robert Nicolson David and Partners, Clee Medical Centre, 363 Grimsby Road, Cleethorpes DN35 7XE Tel: 01472 697257 Fax: 01472 690852; 53 Bolingbroke Road, Cleethorpes DN35 0HF Tel: 01472 509653 — MB ChB 1979 Leeds; BSc (Hons.) Anat. Leeds 1976, MB ChB 1979.

CROMBIE SMITH, Harry John Christopher Memorial Medical Centre, 2 Edinburgh Road, Lauder TD2 6TW Tel: 01578 722267 Fax: 01578 718667 — MB ChB 1968 Ed.; BSc (Med. Sci., Hons. Biochem.) Ed. 1968, MB ChB 1971; DObst RCOG 1973. Prev: SHO (Obst.) Elsie Inglis Matern. Hosp. Edin.; Ho. Off. (Surg.) Leith Hosp.; Ho. Off. (Med.) Roy. Infirm. Edin.

CROMBY, James William 22 Bathwick Hill, Bath BA2 6EW; 4600 Post Oak Place, Suite 211, Houston Texas 77027, USA — MB BS 1956 Durh.; ECFMG Cert 1977; LMCC 1966. Med. Dir. AMD Clinic & Houston Vein Center Texas, USA. Socs: Soc. Française de Phlebologie; N. Amer. Soc. Phlebol. Prev: on Active Staff N. York Branson Hosp. Toronto, Canada; on Ct.esy Staff N. York Gen. Hosp. Toronto; on Med. Staff. Faith Hosp. St. Louis Missouri, USA.

CROME, Professor Ilana Belle School of Health Sciences, University of Wolverhampton, 62-68 Lichfield St., Wolverhampton WV1 1DJ Tel: 01902 321166 Fax: 01902 321161; Wyke House, 62 Sutherland Drive, Westlands, Newcastle ST5 3NZ Tel: 01782 633168 Fax: 01782 660733 — MB ChB 1975 Birm.; MPhil Lond. 1982; MA Camb. 1974; MD Birm. 1996; MRCPsych 1981; T(Psych) 1991; FRCPsych 1997. Prof. Psychiat. Univ. Wolverhampton; Head Dept. of Psychiat. Univ. Wolverhampton; Mem. Edit. Bd. Drug &

Alcohol Dependence; Mem. Dep. Ed. Drugs: Educat. Preven. Policy. Socs: (Exec. Counc.) Soc. Study Addic.; Roy. Soc. Med.; Exec. Comm. (Subst. Misuse Sect.) Roy. Coll. Psychiat. Prev: Cons. & Sen. Lect. (Psychiat.) Sch. Postgrad. Med. Keele Univ. N. Staffs. Hosp.; Hon. Cons. Psychiat. Maudsley & Bethlem Roy. Hosps. & King's Coll. Hosp. Lond.; Sen. Lect. (Psychiat.) & Research Psychiat. Inst. Psychiat. Lond.

CROME, Professor Peter Wyke House, 62 Sutherland Drive, Newcastle ST5 3NZ Tel: 01782 633168 Fax: 01782 718071 Email: p.crome@keele.ac.uk — MB BS 1970 Lond.; T(M) 1991; DObst RCOG 1973; PhD Lond. 1995; MD Lond. 1980; FRCP Glas. 1995; FRCP Lond. 1990; FRCP Ed. 1988; MRCP (UK) 1974; MRCS Eng. LRCP Lond. 1970; FFPM RCP (UK) 1992. (King's Coll. Hosp.) Prof. Geriat. Med. Keele Univ.; Cons. Geriat. Combined Healthcare City Gen. Hosp. Stoke. Prev: Sen. Lect. King's Coll. Sch. Med.; Hon. Cons. Bromley, King's Coll. & Guy's Hosps.

CROMEY, George Martin Ormeau Road Practice, 485 Ormeau Road, Belfast BT7 3GR Tel: 028 9064 1506; 1 The Hermitage, Drumbeg Road, Dunmurry, Belfast BT17 9NH — MB BCh BAO 1977 Belf.; DRCOG 1980. GP Belf. Socs: Assoc. MRCGP; BMA; Fell. Ulster Med. Soc. Prev: SHO (Obst.) Ulster Hosp. Dundonald; SHO (Med.) & Jun. Ho. Off. Roy. Vict. Hosp. Belf.

CROMEY, Roger Swanston 1 Jordanstown Heights, Newtownabbey BT37 0NN Tel: 01232 864563 — MB BCh BAO 1970 Belf.; DObst RCOG 1972; MRCGP 1974.

CROMIE, Alan John Department of Forensic Medicine, Institute of Pathology, Grosvenor Road, Belfast BT12 6BL; 53 Cotswold Avenue, Belfast BT8 6NA Tel: 02890 702778 — MB BCh BAO 1982 Belf.; MB BCh Belf. 1982. Trainee Forens. Path. Dept. Foren. Med. Inst. Path. Qu. Univ. Belf.

CROMIE, Brian William (retired) 14 Park Street, King's Cliffe, Peterborough PE8 6XN Tel: 01780 470754 Fax: 01780 470754 — MB BS Lond. 1954; FRCP Ed. 1971, M 1958; FFPM 1993.

CROMIE, David Thompson Lanarkshire Health Board, 14 Beckford St., Hamilton ML3 0TA Tel: 01698 281313 Fax: 01698 424316 Email: david.cromie@lanarkshirehb.scot.nhs.uk — MB BCh BAO 1986 Belf.; MPH Glas. 1996; MRCGP 1990; DMH Belf. 1992; MFPHM 1998. (Queen's University Belfast) Cons (Pub. Health Med.) Lanarksh. HB; Hon Clin Sen. Lec. Glas. Univ Glas. Prev: Sen. Regist. (Pub. Health Med.) Lanarksh. HB.

***CROMIE, Nicholas Alexander** Ninewells Hospital, Dundee DD1 9SY; Sketrick Island, Killinchy, Newtownards BT23 6QH Tel: 01238 541564 — MB ChB 1998 Dund.; MB ChB Dund 1998.

CROMIE, William Neville Brookeborough Surgery, Tanyard Lane, Brookeborough, Enniskillen BT94 4AB Tel: 028 8953 1225 — MB BCh BAO 1987 Belf.; MRCGP 1992.

CROMPTON, Mr Archibald Clifford 28 Park Avenue, Leeds LS8 2JH Tel: 0113 265 8950 — MB ChB 1960 Manch.; MD Manch. 1971; FRCS Ed. 1965; FRCOG 1981, M 1968; DObst. 1962. (Manch.) Cons. O & G St. Jas. Univ. Hosp. Leeds; Sen. Clin. Lect. (Obst. & Gyn.) Univ. Leeds. Socs: N. Eng. Obst. & Gyn. Soc. Prev: Clin. Lect. (O & G) Univ. Manch.; Regist. (Obst.) Withington Hosp. Manch.; William Walter Research Fell. Univ. Dept. O & G Manch.

CROMPTON, Brian Anthony Health Place, Wrawby Road, Brigg DN20 8GS Tel: 01482 659659; Fergus Hill, Skendleby, Spilsby PE23 4QE Tel: 01754 890609 Email: briancrompton@lineone.net — MB ChB 1977 Birm.; MRCGP 1985; DRCOG 1980; DCH RCPS Glas. 1980. Med. Director/Director of Clin. Governance, N. lines P.C.t; Clin. Med. Off.Family Plann.; Gen. practitioner, Grimsby. Prev: Head of Primary Care United Health; Med. Dir. Humberside FHSA; GP Skegness.

CROMPTON, Douglas Ewan 2/B Haldane Terrace, Newcastle upon Tyne NE2 3AN — MB BS 1998 Newc.; MB BS Newc 1998.

CROMPTON, Graham Kenneth Western General Hospital, Crewe Road, Edinburgh EH4 2XU Tel: 0131 537 1778 Fax: 0131 343 3989 Email: g.crompton@ed.ac.uk; 14 Midmar Drive, Edinburgh EH10 6BU Tel: 0131 447 1022 Email: gcromp@aol.com — MB ChB Ed. 1959; FRCP Ed. 1974; MRCP (UK) 1963; FCCP 1990. Cons. Phys. W.. Gen. Hosp. Edin.; Sen. Lect. (Med.) Dept. Med. Univ. Edin. Socs: (Ex-Pres.) Brit. Thoracic Soc.; (Ex-Pres.) Scott. Thoracic Soc.

CROMPTON, Jane Louise 440 Manchester Road, Leigh WN7 2NP — MB ChB 1994 Liverp. SHO (A & E) Ormskirk Dist. Gen. Hosp. Prev: Ho. Off. (Surg. & Med.) Warrington Dist. Gen. Hosp.

CROMPTON, John Gordon Overdale Medical Practice, 207 Victoria Avenue, Borrowash, Derby DE72 3HG Tel: 01332 280800 Fax: 01332 669256; 50 Draycott Road, Breaston, Derby DE72 3DA Tel: 01332 872672 Fax: 01332 669256 — MB BS 1965 Lond. (Char. Cross) Med. Off. Trent Coll. Sch. Long Eaton; Clin. Asst. (Rheum.) Derbysh. Roy. Infirm. Socs: Derby Med. Soc.; Primary Rheum. Soc.; Midl. Rheum. Soc. Prev: Ho. Surg. (Gen. Surg. & Orthop.) Harrow Hosp.; Ho. Phys. Edgware Gen. Hosp.

CROMPTON, John William Church Lane Surgery, Church Lane, Boroughbridge, York YO51 9BD Tel: 01423 322309; Coverpoint, Scarah Lane, Burton Leonard, Harrogate HG3 3RS Tel: 01765 676566 — BM BS 1989 Nottm.; BMedSci Nottm. 1987; MRCGP 1993; DRCOG 1991.

CROMPTON, M Rufus (retired) 6 High Cedar Drive, Copse Hill, Wimbledon, London SW20 0NU Tel: 0208 947 3987 Fax: 0208 947 3987 — MRCS Eng. LRCP Lond. 1954; MB BS Lond. 1954; PhD Lond. 1965, MD 1963; FRCPath 1976, M 1964; DMJ Soc. Apoth. Lond. 1972. Hon. Cons. Path. St. Geo. Hosp. Prev: Sen. Lect. (Forens. & Neuropath.) St. Geo. Hosp. Med. Sch.

CROMWELL, Sheila Margaret Monkhams Cottage, Aimes Green, Galley Hill, Waltham Abbey EN9 2AU Tel: 01992 893405 — MB ChB 1950 Leeds; DCH Eng. 1955. Cons. Paediat. Epping Forest Spastics Assn.

CRON, Alison Mary Springburn Health Centre, 200 Springburn Way, Glasgow G21 1TR Tel: 0141 531 9641 Fax: 0141 531 9642; 4 Ralston Road, Bearsden, Glasgow G61 3SS — MB ChB 1980 Glas.; MRCGP 1984. Gen. Practitioner.

CRONAN, William Stanley St Clements Surgery, 39 Temple Street, Oxford OX4 1JS Tel: 01865 248550 — MB ChB 1970 Glas.

CRONAU, Gillian Margaret (Smith) 12 Wyvern Close, Dartford DA1 2NA Tel: 01322 225551 — MB BS 1985 Lond.; DRCOG 1989; DTM & H RCP Lond. 1988; DCH RCP Lond. 1987. GP Puthoe Med. Pract. Bedford. Socs: MPS. Prev: Trainee GP Dartford & Gravesham VTS.

CRONE, Agnes Andrew 4 Weetwood Manor, Weetwood Court, Leeds LS16 5QU Tel: 0113 275 2070 — MB ChB 1943 Leeds; DCH Eng. 1947. Asst. MOH Leeds AHA.

CRONE, Agnes Mary (retired) Dept of Dermatology, North hants Hospital, Basingstoke RG24 9NA Tel: 01256 314784 — MB BCh BAO 1972 Belf.; MRCP (UK) 1979; DCH Eng. 1974. Cons. Dermat. N. Hants. Hosp. Basingstoke.

CRONE, Malcolm David Musgrave Park Hospital, Stockmans Lane, Belfast BT9 7JB Tel: 02890 669501 Fax: 02890 582509; 21 Station Road, Craigavad, Holywood BT18 0BP — MB BCh BAO 1979 Belf.; FRCR 1986. Cons. Radiol. Musgrave Pk. Hosp. Belf.

CRONE, Nora Moralee 10 Meadow Lane, E. Herrington, Sunderland SR3 3RQ — MB BS 1938 Durh. (Newc.) Med. Asst. Cherry Knowle Hosp. Ryhope. Prev: Regist. St. Nicholas Hosp. Gosforth; Ho. Phys. Childr. Hosp. Sunderland.

CRONE, Peter Bernhard 10 Meadow Lane, E. Herrington, Sunderland SR3 3RQ — MD 1947 Durh.; MB BS 1937; Dip. Bact. Lond 1947. (Durh.)

CRONIN, Anthony Joseph Child Development Centre, Scott Hospital, Beacon Park Road, Plymouth PL2 2PQ Tel: 01752 314358; 10 Hartley Park Gardens, Plymouth PL3 5HU — MB BS 1974 Lond.; FRCP Lond. 1996; MRCP (UK) 1981; FRCPCH 1997; DCH RCP Lond. 1980. (Char. Cross Hosp. Med. Sch.) Cons. Paediat. Community Child Health Child Developm. Centre Plymouth & Derriford Hosp. Plymouth; Mem. Europ. Acad. Childh. Disabil. Socs: BMA; BACCH. Prev: Sen. Regist. Char. Cross Hosp. Lond.; Regist. King's Coll. Hosp. Lond.

CRONIN, Antonia Jane 89 Glyn Road, London E5 0JA Tel: 020 8519 8894 — MB BS 1996 Lond.

CRONIN, Brian Ilford Medical Centre, 61 Cleveland Road, Ilford IG1 1EE Tel: 020 8478 0367 — MB BCh BAO 1959 Dub.; LAH Dub. 1958; DObst RCOG 1964.

CRONIN, Denis Patrick (retired) 51 Broadway, Bramhall, Stockport SK7 3BU Tel: 0161 440 7791 — LRCPI & LM, LRCSI & LM 1948; FRCPsych 1974, M 1971; DPM Eng. 1957. Prev: Cons. Psychiat. Warley Hosp. Brentwood & Harold Wood Hosp.

CRONIN, Emmanuel (retired) 4 Arundel Lodge, Salisbury Avenue, Finchley, London N3 3AL Tel: 020 8349 0157 — MB BChir 1938 Camb.; MA Camb. (1st cl. Hons. Nat. Sc. Trip. Pts. I & II) 1935, MD 1945; MRCS Eng. LRCP Lond. 1938; MRCP Lond. 1946; MD 1945. Prev: Hon. Clin. Asst. P.ss Eliz. of York Hosp. Childr. & Centr. Lond. ENT Hosp.

CRONIN, Etain (retired) 4 Harley Place, London W1G 8QB Tel: 020 7580 7072 — MB BS 1952 Lond.; FRCP Lond. 1971, M 1957. Cons. Phys. St. John's Hosp. Dis. Skin. Prev: Ho. Surg. Char. Cross Hosp.

CRONIN, Hannah Mary Bernadette St Triduanas Medical Practice, 54 Moira Park, Edinburgh EH7 6RU Tel: 0131 657 3341 Fax: 0131 669 6055; 6 Nelson Street, Edinburgh EH3 6LG Tel: 0131 556 2775 — MB ChB 1975 Ed.; MRCGP 1982; DRCOG 1978.

CRONIN, Hawys Sydney 73 Cemetery Road, Porth CF39 0BH Tel: 01443 682835 Fax: 01443 682835 — MB BCh 1961 Wales; DObst RCOG 1963. Assoc. Specialist (Anaesth.) E. Glam. Hosp. Pontypridd.

CRONIN, Heather Fay Home Farm, Newton Kyme, Tadcaster LS24 9LS — MB BS 1982 Newc.; MRCPsych 1988. Regist. (Psychiat.) Leeds HA.

CRONIN, Mr Kevin (retired) Abbots Lea, Litchborough, Towcester NN12 8JA Tel: 01327 830323 — MS Lond. 1966, MB BS 1947; FRCS Eng. 1955. Prev: Arris & Gale Lect. RCS.

CRONIN, Marianne Therese Longfield Medical Centre, Princes Road, Maldon CM9 7DF; 6 Bower Gardens, Maldon CM9 6HJ — MB BCh 1989 Wales.

CRONIN, Melanie Anne Pendleside Medical Practice, Clitheroe Health Centre, Railway View Road, Clitheroe BB7 2JG Tel: 01200 421888 Fax: 01200 421887 — MB ChB 1985 Liverp.; DRCOG 1987; LFHom Glasgow 1998. (Liverp.) GP. Prev: Trainee GP W. Lancs. HA; SHO (A & E) S. Sefton HA; SHO (Paediat.) W. Lancs. HA.

CRONIN, Morven Sheridan Peacock House, Coppy Lane, Beamish, Stanley DH9 0RQ — MB ChB 1990 Manch. Clin. Med. Off. (Community Child Health) Gateshead HA.; Staff Grade (Community Child Health) Sunderland.

CRONIN, Patricia May Cherry Knowle Hospital, Ryhope, Sunderland SR2 0NB Tel: 0191 569 9414 Fax: 0191 569 9429 — MB BS 1981 Lond.; MRCPsych 1987. Cons. Old Age Psychiat. Sunderland.

CRONIN, Paul Anthony Carmel Middlewich Road Surgery, 163-165 Middlewich Road, Northwich CW9 7DB Tel: 01606 43850 — MB ChB 1985 Manch.; BSc St. And. 1982; DA (UK) 1987. Socs: BMA. Prev: Trainee GP Withington & Manch. VTS; SHO (Chest Med.) Wythenshawe; SHO (Anaesth.) Leighton Hosp. Crewe.

CRONIN, Stephen Michael Department of Child Health, South Tyneside District Hospital, Harton Lane, South Shields NE34 0PL Tel: 0191 454 8888 Fax: 0191 202 2170 Email: s.m.cronin@ncl.ac.uk; Stobbilee House, Near Witton Gilbert, Durham DH7 6TW Tel: 0191 373 6132 Fax: 0191 373 6977 Email: s.m.cronin@ncl.ac.uk — MB ChB 1983 Manch.; BSc St. And. 1980; MRCP (Paediat.) (UK) 1991; MRCPCH 1996; FRCPCH 1997; Fell Paed. Intens. Care Univ. Brit. Columb 1990. (St. Andrews and Manchester) Cons. Paediat. (Respirat. Med.) S. Tyneside Dist. Hosp.; Hon. Sen. Lect. Child Health, The Med. Sch., Univ. Newc. upon Tyne. Socs: Fell. Roy. Coll. Paediat. & Child Health. Prev: Sen. Regist. Rotat. (Paediat.) Soton. Univ. Hosp. Trust; Regist. (Paediat. IC) Roy. Childr.s Hosp. Melbourne, Australia; Research Assoc. (Child Health) Univ. Newc.

CRONIN POZWOLSKI, Myriam Jeannine 15 Abinger Road, Bedford Pk, London W4 1EY Tel: 020 8994 0185 — MD 1966 Paris. (Paris) Clin. Asst. (Psychiat.) Ealing, Hammersmith & Hounslow AHA (T).

CRONJE, Wilhelm Heinrich Flat 5 Stafford House, 1 Maida Avenue, London W2 1TE — MB ChB 1992 Stellenbosch.

CRONK, Peter Gregson (retired) Elizabeth's Orchard, Sandhurst, Gloucester GL2 9NP — MB BChir Camb. 1951; MA Camb. 1951; MRCGP 1960. Prev: Sen. Med. Off. Roy. Fleet Auxil.

CRONLY, John Paul The Surgery, High Street, Rawmarsh, Rotherham S62 6LW Tel: 01709 522888 — BM BS 1986 Nottm.

CRONSHAW, Susan Janette 3 Beaumont Place, Greenbank, Plymouth PL4 8EA — MB ChB 1991 Bristol; DCH RCP Lond. 1995. GP Regist. Chaddlewood Surg. Plymouth. Prev: SHO (O & G & Paediat.) Derriford Hosp. Plymouth; SHO (Psychiat.) Glenbourne, Plymouth.

CROOK, Ann Elizabeth 18 Eden Park Drive, Batheaston, Bath BA1 7JJ — MB ChB 1965 Bristol. (Bristol) Prev: Gyn. Ho. Surg. Bristol Gen. Hosp.; Ho. Phys. Ham Green Hosp.

CROOK, Anthony, MC, Brigadier late RAMC Retd. Colly Farm, Dottery, Bridport DT6 5PU Tel: 01308 422978 — MRCS Eng. LRCP Lond. 1938; MFCM 1975. (Guy's) Prev: DDMS N.. Command; Commandant RAMC Train. Centre Keogh Barracks Ash Vale; OC Milit. Hosp. Tidworth.

CROOK, Anthony James Wellfield Surgery, 291 Oldham Road, Rochdale OL16 5HX Tel: 01706 355111 Fax: 01706 341859; Bryn, Manchester Road, Rochdale OL11 3EL Tel: 01706 631996 — MB ChB 1960 Manch.; DObst RCOG 1963. (Manch.) Prev: Ho. Surg. Ancoats Hosp. Manch.; Ho. Phys. Crumpsall Hosp. Manch.; Ho. Off. (Obst.) Oldham & Dist. Gen. Hosp.

CROOK, Beresford Roger Melville (retired) Oakfield Cottage, 12 The Avenue, Sneyd Park, Bristol BS9 1PA Tel: 0117 968 5103 — MB BChir 1962 Camb.; MA Camb. 1962; MRCP Lond. 1967; MRCS Eng. LRCP Lond. 1961. Hon. Clin. Fell. S.mead Hosp. Bristol. Prev: Cons. Cardiol. Schieland Ziekenhuis, Schiedam, Holland.

CROOK, David Hugh Brookside, 48 Westgate, Louth LN11 9YD Tel: 01507 602176 — MB BS 1947 Lond.; MRCS Eng. LRCP Lond. 1942; DObst RCOG 1948. Prev: Obst. Off. Jessop Hosp. Wom. Sheff.; Res. Obstetr. Guy's Hosp.

CROOK, Gwynneth Claire ParkView Group Practice, 2 Longford Road W., Reddish, Stockport Tel: 0161 431 9339; Sunnydale, New Mills Road, Hayfield, High Peak SK22 2EX — MB ChB 1977 Dundee; MRCGP 1981; DRCOG 1979.

CROOK, Hilary Eleanor Skillan 3 Brookland Road, Whitley, Wigan WN1 2QG Tel: 01942 46814 — MB BS 1953 Lond. (Roy. Free)

CROOK, Ivor 58 Ashton Road, Droylsden, Manchester M43 7BW — MB ChB 1982 Manch.; DRCOG 1986.

CROOK, James Cooper, Maj.-Gen. late RAMC Retd. (retired) Egloshayle, Fore St., Kingsand, Torpoint PL10 1NB Tel: 01752 823666 — MB BS 1946 Lond.; MD Lond. 1953; FRCPath 1968, M 1963; DTM & H Eng. 1952. Prev: Dir. of Army Path. & Cons. Path. To The Army.

CROOK, Joan Bennet (retired) 7 Matlock Avenue, Marton, Middlesbrough TS7 8LW — MB ChB Glas. 1944. Prev: Med. Asst. St. Luke's Hosp. Middlesbrough.

CROOK, John (retired) 3 Brookland Road, Whitley, Wigan WN1 2QG — MB BChir 1954 Camb.; MA Camb. 1953; MRCS Eng. LRCP Lond. 1953; FFA RCS Eng. 1964; DA Eng. 1961; DObst RCOG 1958. Prev: Cons. Anaesth. Wigan & Leigh Hosp. & Wrightington Hosp. Appley Bridge.

CROOK, John Michael London Lane Clinic, Kinnaird House, 37 London Lane, Bromley BR1 4HB Tel: 020 8460 2661 Fax: 020 8464 5041 — MB BS 1964 Lond.; MRCGP 1977. (Lond. Hosp.) Socs: BMA. Prev: Resid. Obst. Off. Roy Vict. Hosp. Bournemouth; SHO (Paediat.) Roy. W. Sussex Hosp. Chichester; SHO St. Francis Hosp. Haywards Heath.

CROOK, John Robert 5 Creechberry Orchard, Taunton TA1 2EX — MB BS 1987 Lond.; BSc (Pharm.) Lond. 1984, MB BS 1987; MRCP (UK) 1990. Regist. (Med.) MusGr. Pk. Hosp. Taunton. Prev: SHO (Cardiol.) Bristol Roy. Infirm.; SHO (Med.) Frenchay Hosp. Bristol; SHO (Renal) S.mead Hosp. Bristol.

CROOK, Martin Andrew Chemical Pathology Department, Guy's Hospital, St Thomas' St., London SE1 9RT Tel: 020 7955 4012 Fax: 020 7955 4781 — MB BS 1983 Lond.; PhD Lond. 1988, BSc (1st cl. Hons. Biochem. & Basic Med. Sci.) 1981; MRCPath 1991. Sen. Lect. & Hon. Cons. (Chem. Path.) Guy's & Lewisham Hosps. Lond. Socs: Brit. Hyperlipid. Assn. Prev: Sen. Regist. & Hon. Lect. (Clin. Chem.) Guy's Hosp. Lond.; Regist. & SHO (Chem. Path.) St. Bart's Hosp. Lond.; Brit. Heart Foundat. Researcher Hunt. Inst. Lond.

CROOK, Martin Clifford St Katherines Surgery, High Street, Ledbury HR8 1DZ Tel: 01531 633271 Fax: 01531 632410; Wylde House Cottage, Gloucester Road, Ledbury HR8 2JE Tel: 01531 633363 — MB BS 1980 Lond.; MA Camb. 1981; MRCGP 1986; DRCOG 1983; Cert. Family Plann. JCC 1983. (Lond. Hosp.) Cas. Off. Ledbury Cottage Hosp.; Chairm. Ledbury Cottage Hosp. Staff Comm. Prev: Trainee GP Cheltenham & Glouc. VTS; SHO (Obst.) Basildon Gen. Hosp.; SHO (A & E) Lond. Hosp. Whitechapel.

CROOK, Nicholas John Kendal Torbay Hospital, Lawes Bridge, Torquay TQ2 7AA Tel: 01803 614567; 2 Linden Terrace, Newton Abbot TQ12 1LL — MB ChB 1992 Aberd.; MRCP (UK) 1997. Specialist Regist. (Diabetes & Endocrinol.) Torbay Hosp. Torquay.

CROOK, Paul David 18 Edenpark Drive, Bath Easton, Bath BA1 7JJ — MB BS 1994 Lond.; MRCP Lond. 1997; DMH Liverp 1998. (Royal London Hospital) SHO Hosp. for Trop. Dis.s. Socs: Roy. Soc. Hyg. And Trop. Med.

CROOK, Paul Reginald Wansbeck General Hospital, Woodhorn Lane, Ashington NE63 9JJ Tel: 01670 521212 Fax: 01670 529458 Email: paul.crook@northumbria-healthcare.nhs.uk — MB ChB 1972 Birm.; FRCP Lond. 1991; MRCP (UK) 1975. Cons. Rheum. Wansbeck Hosp. & Freeman Hosp. Trust.

CROOK, Perrie Sue — MB ChB 1981 Leic.; DRCOG 1983. (Leicester) GP; War Pens. Examr. for the Benefits Agency.

CROOK, Peter Austin 3 Thorn Park, Mannamead, Plymouth PL3 4TG Tel: 01752 661846 — MB ChB 1952 Bristol. Prev: GP Plymouth.

CROOK, Sarah Marian Dorset Health Authority, Victoria House, Princes Road, Ferndown BH22 9JR Tel: 01202 851272 Fax: 01202 851273 Email: sarah.crook@dorset-ha.swest.nhs.uk; 656 Dorchester Road, Upwey, Weymouth DT3 5LE Tel: 01305 813271 Fax: 01305 815643 Email: dr_crook@hotmail.com — MB BS 1977 Lond.; MRCS Eng. LRCP Lond. 1977; MRCpath 1988. (St. Mary's) Cons. Communicable Dis. Control. Dorset HA.

CROOK, Stephen Anthony The Surgery, 58 Ashton Road, Droylsden, Manchester M43 7BW Tel: 0161 370 1610; 63 Bagslate Moor Road, Rochdale OL11 5YH Tel: 01706 353552 — MB ChB 1987 Manch. Prev: Trainee GP/SHO (Gen. Med.) Birch Hill Hosp. Rochdale VTS; Ho. Phys. Salford Roy. Hosp.; Ho. Surg. Birch Hill Hosp. Rochdale.

CROOK, Susan Jill 11 Dunstall Road, London SW20 0HP — MB BS 1977 Lond.; MRCPath (Microbiol.) 1984; Cert. Family Plann. JCC 1979. (St. Bart.) Prev: Sen. Lect./Hon. Cons. Microbiol. Roy. Postgrad. Med. Sch. Lond.; Sen. Regist. (Microbiol.) St. Bart. Hosp. Lond.

CROOK, Timothy George Rother House Medical Centre, Alcester Road, Stratford-upon-Avon CV37 6PP Tel: 01789 269386 Fax: 01789 298742; Rother House Medical Centre, Alcester Road, Stratford-upon-Avon CV37 6PP Tel: 01789 269386 — BM 1987 Soton.; MRCGP 1994; Dip IMC RCS Ed. 1992; DRCOG 1991; DCH RCP Lond. 1990. GP Clin. Asst. (Ophth.) S. Warks. Hosp.; Mem. W. Middl. C.A.R.E. Team.

CROOK, Timothy John Churchill Hospital, Headington, Oxford OX3 7LE; Jupiter Cottage, 11 Watlington St, Nettlebed, Henley-on-Thames RG9 5AA Tel: 01491 641673 — MB BS 1994 Lond.; BSc (Hons.) Lond. 1991. SHO Rotat. (Surg.) Roy. Berks. Hosp.; SHO (Urol.) Ch.ill Hosp. Oxf. Socs: BMA; Reading Path. Soc.; BAUS. Prev: Ho. Off. (Med.) Battle Hosp. Reading; Ho. Off. (Surg.) Bromley Hosp.

CROOK, Tina Louise The Medical Centre, 24-28 Lower Northam Road, Hedge End, Southampton SO30 4FQ Tel: 01489 785722 Fax: 01489 799414 — MB BS 1994 Lond.; MRGCP (distinction) 1998; DRCOG 1998; DFFP 1998. (UMDS) GP Hedge End, Soton.; Family Plann. Off., Winchester; Benefits Agency Med. Off., Winchester. Socs: BMA; MPS. Prev: GP Regist., Cookham, Berks.; SHO O & G, High Wycombe, Bucks.; GP VTS Scheme, High Wycombe, Bucks.

CROOK, Tonya Jane 39A Axminster Road, London N7 6BP — MB BS 1990 Lond.; MRCP (UK) 1994; DTM & H RCP Lond. 1995.

CROOK, Victoria Ann Whiston Hospital, Warrington Road, Prescot L35 5DR — MB ChB 1998 Liverp.; MB ChB Liverp 1998.

CROOK, William Simon Hellesdon Hospital, Drayton High Road, Norwich NR6 5BE — MB BS 1983 Lond.

CROOKALL, Peter Robert 10 Hopton Close, Plymouth PL6 5JJ Tel: 01752 706202 — MB BS 1993 Lond.; MRCGP 1997; DRCOG 1996; DCH RCP Lond. 1995. (St Thos. Hosp. (OMDS))

CROOKE, James William 361 Wavertree Nook Road, Wavertree Garden Suburb, Liverpool L15 7LJ Tel: 0151 722 7751 — MB ChB 1990 Liverp.; FRCA 1997. Specialist Regist. (Anaesth.) Mersey Region . Socs: Liverp. Soc. Anaesth.

CROOKE, John Walter (retired) The Pingles, 12 Park Avenue, Great Crosby, Liverpool L23 2SP Tel: 0151 924 5758 — MB BS (Hons.) Lond. 1957; BSc (Physiol.) Lond. 1954; FRCA 1965; DA Eng. 1959. Prev: Cons. Anaesth. Roy. Liverp. & BRd.green Univ. Hosp. Trust.

CROOKENDEN, David 4 Warley Road, Blackpool FY1 2JU — MB BCh BAO 1960 Dub.; LRCP LRCS Ed. LRFPS Glas. 1960; DObst RCOG 1961; DA Eng. 1964. Socs: Anglo-Amer. Med. Soc.

CROOKES, David Paul Parkgrove Terrace Surgery, 22B Parkgrove Terrace, Edinburgh EH4 7NX Tel: 0131 312 6600 Fax: 0131 312 7798 — MB ChB 1983 Leeds; MRCGP 1990; DObst Auckland 1988. GP Edin.

CROOKES, Peter Miles Bailey, SBStJ (retired) Apple Acre, 240 Beacon Hill Road, Newark NG24 2JP — MB Camb. 1960, BChir 1959. Prev: Ho. Phys. St. Luke's Hosp. Guildford.

CROOKES, Ruth Elizabeth 35 Marlborough Heights, Church Road, Belfast BT6 9QR — MB BCh BAO 1992 Belf.; MRCGP 1996; DGM RCPS Glas. 1995; DRCOG 1994; DCH Dub. 1994.

CROOKS, Andrew John Robinson 22 Deansway Road, Mitcheldean GL17 0BJ; Point House, Aston Crews, Ross-on-Wye — MB BCh BAO 1965 Belf.; MRCOG 1977, DObst 1974. Cons. O & G P.T. Caltex Pacific Sumatra, Indonesia. Prev: Regist. (O & G) Wigan & Leigh Gp. Hosps. & N. Manch. Gen. Hosp.; Gen. Duties Med. Off. & Specialist. (O & G) Nchanga.

CROOKS, Barbara Anne — MB ChB 1992 Glas.; 1997 (FFARCS) Ire; DA (UK) 1995.

CROOKS, Bruce Neville Dept of Paediatrics, Newcastle General Hospital, Westgate Road, Newcastle upon Tyne NE4 6BE Tel: 0191 273 8811 Fax: 0191 273 0183 Email: b.n.a.crooks@ncl.ac.uk; 15 Upleatham Street, Saltburn-by-the-Sea TS12 1LA Tel: 01287 625347 — MB ChB 1990 Birm.; MB ChB (Hons.) Birm. 1990; BSc (Hons.) Birm. 1987; MRCP (UK) 1994; MRCPCH (UK). Clin. Research Assoc. & Hon. Specialist Regist. (Paediat.) Newc. Gen. Hosp. Socs: MRCPCH. Prev: Regist. (Paediat.) Roy. Vict. Infirm. Newc.; Regist. (Neonat.) Roy. Vict. Infirm. Newc. u. Tyne; Regist. (Paediat.) S. Cleveland Hosp. Middlesbrough.

CROOKS, Daniel Antonio Hull Royal Infirmary, Anlaby Road, Kingston upon Hull, Hull HU3 2JZ Tel: 01482 675038 Fax: 01482 675522 Email: user@dacrooks.karoo.co.uk; Quinta Sarmiento, 10 Hambling Drive, Molescroft, Beverley HU17 9GD Tel: 01482 888390 Fax: 01482 888914 — MD 1982 Panama; MPhil Lond. 1991; MRCPath 1993. (Univ. Panama) Cons. Neuropath. Roy. Hull Hosp. NHS Trust, Hull. Socs: Brit. Neuropath. Soc.; Internat. Soc. Neuropath. Prev: Sen. Regist. (Neuropath.) Walton Centre for Neurol. & Neurosurg. Liverp.

CROOKS, George William 62 Bay Road, Wormit, Newport-on-Tay DD6 8LZ — MB ChB 1977 Aberd.

CROOKS, Gillian Mary Templepatrick Surgery, 80 Castleton, Templepatrick, Ballyclare BT39 0AZ Tel: 028 94 432202 Fax: 028 94 433707; 30 Rickamore Road, Templepatrick, Ballyclare BT39 0ET Tel: 0184 94 32813 — MB BCh BAO 1982 Belf.; MD Belf. 1992; MRCP (UK) 1985; MRCGP 1986; DRCOG 1986. GP Templepatrick; Commiss.ing GP NHSSB. Socs: Ulster Med. Soc.; Roy. Coll. Gen. Pract. (N. Irel. Fac.); BMA. Prev: Research Fell. (Gen. Pract.) Qu. Univ. Belf.

CROOKS, Jane (retired) Department Child & Family Psychiatry, Downend Clinic, Buckingham Gardens, Bristol BS16 5TW Tel: 0117 956 6025 — MB ChB 1978 Manch.; MRCP UK 1981; MRCPsych 1987. Prev: Cons. Child & Family Psychiat. Frenchay Healthcare Trust.

CROOKS, Janina 53 Delamere Road, Ealing, London W5 3JL — Med. Dipl. Kiev 1940.

CROOKS, Mr John Edward Dept of Urology, Stobhill Hospital, Balornock Road, Glasgow G21 3UW Tel: 0141 201 3000 Fax: 0141 201 3779; 6 Laurel Avenue, Lenzie, Kirkintilloch, Glasgow G66 4RU — MB ChB 1987 Glas.; FRCPS Glas. 1991. Cons. Urol. Surg. StobhillHosp., Glasg.

CROOKS, Lesley Wynne Eastside Farmhouse, Maryculter, Aberdeen AB12 5FA — MB ChB 1977 Aberd.

CROOKS, Mark Philip 25 Wentworth Drive, Blackwell, Bromsgrove B60 1BE Tel: 0121 445 5409 — MB ChB 1978 Birm.; MRCGP 1986; DA Eng. 1982.

CROOKS, Richard Neville Bawtry Health Centre, Station Road, Bawtry, Doncaster DN10 6RQ Tel: 01302 710326 — MB ChB 1972 Ed.; MRCGP 1976; DCH Eng. 1976; DObst RCOG 1975. (Edinburgh) GP; Chairm. E. PCT Professional Exec. Comm. Prev: Dir. Primary

Care Developm. Lincs. Health; Asst. Adviser (Gen. Pract.) Univ. Sheff.; GP Facilitator Notts. FHSA.

CROOKS, Rosalind Alison Jane Department of Radiology, UCLH & Middlesex NHS Trust, The Middlesex Hospital, Mortimer Street, London W1N 8TT; 65 Albert Road, Alexandra Park, London N22 7AA Email: ros@peakbp.force9.co.uk — MB ChB 1995 Liverpool; MRCP 1999 London. (Liverpool) SPR, Radiol., UCLH & Middlx. Hosp.s, Lond. Prev: SHO Med., Barnet Hosp., Lond.; SHO Infec. Dis.s, Coppetts Wood Hosp., Roy. Free, Lond.; SHO Renal Med., Guy's Hosp. Lond.

CROOKS, Stephen, Surg. Lt.-Cdr. RN Retd. (retired) Hideaway, Bissoe Road, Carnon Downs, Truro TR3 6GB Tel: 01872 865485 — MRCS Eng. LRCP Lond. 1970; AFOM RCP Lond. 1982; DAvMed Eng. 1976. Prev: Aviat. Med. Specialist RN.

CROOKS, Stephen William Department of Respiratory Medicine, Heartlands Hospital, Bordesley Green E., Birmingham B9 5SS Tel: 0121 766 6611 Fax: 0121 772 0292 Email: stephen.crooks@virgin.net; 142 Park Hill Road, Harborne, Birmingham B17 9HD — MB BCh BAO 1981 Belf.; MRCP (UK) 1985; DCH RCPS Glas. 1985. Specialist Regist. (Respirat. Med.). Socs: Brit. Thorac. Soc.; Eur. Respirat. Soc.; Amer. Thoracic Soc. Prev: Phys. Nazareth Hosp., Israel; Regist. (Gen. Med.) St. Geo. Hosp. Lond.

CROOKSTON, Alexander Muirlands, 71 Bellsdyke Road, Falkirk FK1 — MB ChB 1975 Glas.

CROOM, Alexandra Judith 63 Green Ridges, Headington, Oxford OX3 8PL — MB BS 1987 Lond.; MRCP (UK) 1994. Research Regist. Osler Chest Unit Ch.ill Hosp. Oxf.

CROOT, Gillian Mary Orchard House, Mill Road, Old Buckenham, Attleborough NR17 1SG — MB BS 1994 Lond.

CROOT, Lorraine Michele Dept.of Rheumatology, B. Floor, Royal Hallamshire Hospital, Glossop Rd, Sheffield S10 2JF Fax: 0114 271 1844 Email: l.mcroot@sheffield.ac.uk; 3 Lionel Hill, Crane Moor, Sheffield S35 7AQ Tel: 0114 288 6312 Fax: 0870 054 8731 Email: lorraine@reuber.demon.co.uk — BM BS 1992 Nottm.; BMedSci Nottm. 1990; MRCP (UK) 1996. Specialist Regist. N. Trent Rheum. Rotat.

CROPLEY, Ian Martin 31 Montserrat Road, London SW15 2LD Tel: 020 8789 2385 Email: ian.cropley@ndirect.co.uk — MB BS 1985 Lond.; MA Camb. 1986; MRCP (UK) 1988. Locum Cons. Clin. St Mary's Hosp. Lond. Prev: Sen. Regist. Infec. Dis.s, St Mary's Hosp., Lond.; Sen. Regist., Infec. Dis.s, Norhtwich Pk., Harrow.

CROPP, James Edward New Place House, School Lane, Welwyn AL6 9QA — BM 1994 Soton.

CROPPER, Margaret Windmill Medical Practice, Ann Street, Denton, Manchester M34 2AJ Tel: 0161 320 3929; 75 Staley Road, Mossley, Ashton-under-Lyne OL5 9PL Tel: 01457 833553 Fax: 01457 838426 — MB ChB 1966 Ed.; DFFP 1993; Cert. Family Plann. JCC 1972; DA Eng. 1969. (Ed.) GP Princip.; JP; Mem. W.pennine LMC. Socs: Brit. Menopause Soc.; Int. Menopause Soc. Prev: Sen. Regist. (Anaesth.) Liverp. S.. Hosp.

CRORIE, John Watson Mount Florida Medical Centre, 183 Prospecthill Road, Glasgow G42 9LQ Tel: 0141 632 4004 Fax: 0141 636 6036 — MB ChB 1979 Glas.

CRORY, George Albert Charles Larne Health Centre, Gloucester Avenue, Larne BT40 1PB Tel: 028 2826 1922 Fax: 028 2827 9560; 109A The Roddens, Larne BT40 1PY Tel: 01574 278468 — MB BCh BAO 1976 Belf.; MRCGP 1980.

CROSBIE, Andrew Denis Brookfields Health Centre, Seymour Street, Cambridge CB1 3DQ Tel: 01223 723160 Fax: 01223 723089 — MB BCh 1990 N U Irel; MB BCh 1990 N U Irel.

CROSBIE, Belinda Jane St Michaels, Sheiling Rd, Crowborough TN6 1BJ — MB BS 1982 Lond. Regist. (Anaesth.) Poole Gen. Hosp. Prev: SHO (Anaesth.) W.m. Hosp. Lond.; Hosp. Med. Off. i/c Anaesth. Mpilo Centr. Hosp. Zimbabwe.

CROSBIE, David Innes 187C Stonelaw Road, Burnside, Rutherglen, Glasgow G73 3PD — MB ChB 1995 Glas.; BSc (1st cl. Hons. Pharmacol.) Glas. 1992. SHO (Gen. Med.) S.. Gen. Hosp. Glas.

CROSBIE, Eilean Gail 10 Knowles Lane, Gomersal, Cleckheaton BD19 4LE — MB ChB 1989 Dundee; MRCP (Lond.) 1996.

CROSBIE, James Joseph Department of Pathology, Altnagelvin Hospital, Londonderry BT47 Tel: 01504 45171; 21 Colby Avenue, Cullmore Road, Londonderry BT48 8PF Tel: 01504 359992 — MB BCh BAO 1975 Belf.; MRCPath 1990. Cons. Histopath. & Cytopath. Altnagelvin Hosp. Lond.derry.

CROSBIE, John Paul Bellevue Surgery, Bellevue Terrace, Newport NP20 2WQ Tel: 01633 256337 Fax: 01633 222856 — MB BCh BAO 1987 NUI.

CROSBIE, Patrick Joseph Whiteabbey Health Centre, 95 Doagh Road, Newtownabbey BT37 9QW Tel: 028 9086 4341 Fax: 028 9086 0443; 19 Greenacres, Glebe Road, Carnmoney, Glengormloy, Newtownabbey BT36 6NL — MB BCh BAO 1977 Belf.

CROSBIE, Philip Alexander John 42/2F2 Dalkeith Road, Edinburgh EH16 5BS — MB ChB 1997 Ed.

CROSBIE, Mr Reginald Benjamin (retired) The Nook, 64 Spital Road, Bromborough, Wirral CH62 2AH Tel: 0151 334 2729 — M.B, Ch.B (E distinction) Liverpool 1955; BSc (Chem., 1st cl. Hons.) A.R.I.C. Lond. 1949; MB ChB (Distinc.) Liverp. 1955; FRCS Ed. 1962; FRCS Eng. 1962. Mem. Interview Bd., Lord Chancellors Dept. Prev: Tutor (Surg.) Roy. Coll. Surg. & Univ. Liverp.

CROSBIE, Shaun Stephen The Haven, Beaufort Road, Tredegar NP22 4NR — MB ChB 1984 Leic.; MB ChB Leic. l984.

CROSBIE, William Alexander (retired) Oak Tree Cottage, Besselsleigh, Abingdon OX13 5PX Tel: 01865 863905 — MB ChB 1955 Glas.; FRCP Lond, 1987, M 1965; FRCP Ed 1982, M 1963. Prev: Chief Med. Off. UK Atomic Energy Auth.

CROSBY, Mr Alan Courtney Northern General Hospital, Herries Road, Sheffield S5 7AU Tel: 01234792119 Email: ian.cooper@bedhos.anglox.nhs — MB ChB 1974 Sheff.; FRCS Ed. 1979. Cons. (A & E) N. Gen. Hosp. Sheff. Prev: Sen. Regist. (A & E) Roy. Hallamsh. Hosp. Sheff.; Regist. (Orthop.) Roy. Infirm. Stoke on Trent; Regist. (Surg.) Singleton Hosp. Swansea.

CROSBY, Colin Peter Department of Sport and Exercise Medicine, The Garden Hospital, Sunny Gardens Road, Hendon, London NW4 1RX Tel: 020 8457 4500 Fax: 020 8457 4567; 12 Old Manor Court, 40 Abbey Raod, London NW8 0AR Tel: 020 7604 3464 Fax: 020 7604 3464 Email: cpcrosb@aol.com — MB BS 1979 Lond.; MA Oxf. 1980; MRCS Eng. LRCP Lond. 1979. (St. Mary's) Med. Dir. (Dept of Sport & Exercise Med.) Garden Hosp. Lond.; Med. Dir. Champneys Gp.; Sports Med. Cons. Anglo-Japanese Health Centre; Lect. (Sports Med.) Univ. Herts.; Lect. (Sports Med.) Univ. Middlx. Socs: Reg. Chairm. Brit. Assn. Sport & Med.; Brit. Assn. Sport & Exercise Sci.s; RSM. Prev: Demonst. (Human Anat.) Univ. Oxf.; SHO (Gen. Surg. & Orthop.) St. Albans City Hosp.; Ho. Surg. Cardiovasc. Unit St. Mary's Hosp. Lond.

CROSBY, Mr David Lewis, OBE 15 Pencisely Road, Llandaff, Cardiff CF5 1DG Tel: 029 2022 0200 Fax: 029 2022 0200 — MB BCh 1953 Wales; FRCS Eng. 1960. Cons. Surg. Univ. Hosp. of Wales Cardiff.

CROSBY, Francis Robert Gordon Carnoustie Medical Group, The Health Centre, Dundee Street, Carnoustie DD7 7RB Tel: 01241 859888 Fax: 01241 852080 — MB ChB 1977 Aberd.; MRCGP 1983; DRCOG 1982.

CROSBY, Gail Lois Watlington Surgery, Thieves Bridge Road, Watlington, King's Lynn PE33 0HL Tel: 01553 810253 — MB BCh 1986 Witwatersrand; MFFP 1994.

CROSBY, Gwenda 15 Pencisely Road, Llandaff, Cardiff CF5 1DG — MB BCh 1957 Wales. Clin. Asst. Rehabil. Rookwood Hosp. Llandaff. Prev: SHO Med. Rockwood Hosp. Llandaff; Ho. Off. & SHO (Anaesth.) Morriston Hosp. Swansea.

CROSBY, Mary Elizabeth 28 Creyke Close., Cottingham HU16 4DH Tel: 01482 843577 — MB ChB 1972 Manch. p/t SCMO Sexual & Reprod Health Serv.s Hull & E. riding Community Health NHS Trust, Conifer Hse, 32-36 Prospect St., Hull HU2 8PX. Socs: Inst. Psychosexual Med.; & Instruc. Doctor Fac. Family Plann.; Med. Wom.'s Federat.

CROSBY, Patricia Sabina Arbury Medical Centre, Cambridge Drive, Stockingford, Nuneaton CV10 8LW Tel: 024 7638 8555 Fax: 024 7635 2396; Champfleurie, 9 Slade Close, Whitestone, Nuneaton CV11 6UW — MB ChB 1961 Ed.; MRCGP 1970; DObst RCOG 1964. (Ed.) Socs: BMA; Lourdes Med. Assn. Prev: SHO & Ho. Surg. W.. Gen. Hosp. Edin.; Ho. Phys. Roy. Infirm. Edin.

CROSBY, Paul Shangri-La, 1 Wood Lane, Chendri Wood, Hayfield, High Peak SK22 2PA Tel: 01663 745386 — MB BS Bombay 1951; LCPS Bombay 1939; FRCP Ed. 1977, M 1954; DTM & H Ed. 1953. (Grant. Med. Coll. Bombay & Ed.) Hon. Cons. Phys. N. W.. RHA.

Socs: BMA; Fell. Roy. Soc. Med. Prev: Cons. Phys. Macclesfield Infirm.; Edr. Quar. Med. Review Bombay; Maj. IAMC.

CROSBY, Philip Ann Burrow Thomas Health Centre, South William Street, Workington CA14 2ED Tel: 01900 603985 Fax: 01900 871131; Arden Lea, Moresby Parks, Whitehaven CA28 8UU — MB BS 1983 Lond.; MRCGP 1988.

CROSBY, Richard Robert Church Place Surgery, 6 Church Place, Moffat DG10 9ES Tel: 01683 220197 Fax: 01683 221320 — MB ChB 1988 Sheff.; MRCGP 1993. Dist. Med. Off. Malawi.

CROSBY, Stephen John The Village Surgery, Elbow Lane, Liverpool L37 4AW Tel: 01704 878661 Fax: 01704 832488; 8 Wrigleys Close, Freshfield, Formby, Liverpool L37 7DT Tel: 01704 877373 — MB ChB 1976 Birm.

CROSBY, Thomas David Lewis Elscott House, Llysworney, Cowbridge CF71 7NQ — MB BS 1988 Lond.

CROSBY, Vincent Linden Palliative Care Unit, E Floor East Block, Queen's Medical Centre, University Hospital, Nottingham NG2 7UH — MB BS 1989 Lond.; MRCGP 1995. Cons. in Palliat. Med., Univ. Hosp., Nottm. Prev: Clin. Research Fell. (Palliat. Med.) Hayward Hse. Macmillan Palliat. Care Unit Nottm. City Hosp.

CROSBY, Zoe Vanessa 22 Shirley Grove, Rusthall, Tunbridge Wells TN4 8TJ — MB BS 1993 Lond.; BSc Hons. Lond. 1990.

CROSER, David Hans St Michaels Cottage, Paradise, Painswick, Stroud GL6 6TN — BM BS 1994 Flinders.

CROSFIELD, Caroline Eleanor High Street Surgery, 75 High Street, Minster, Ramsgate CT12 4AB Tel: 01843 821333 Fax: 01843 823146; Little Santon Farm, Preston, Canterbury CT3 1JF — MB BS 1981 Lond.; MRCGP 1985; DTM & H Liverp. 1987; DRCOG 1985. (St. Thos. Hosp. Med. Sch.)

CROSFILL, Fiona Marjorie Heronsyke Cottage, Burton in Kendal, Carnforth LA6 1LG — MB BS 1984 Lond.; MRCOG 1989.

CROSFILL, Mr Martin Lawson (retired) Polmennor Farmhouse, Heamoor, Penzance TR20 8UL Tel: 01736 365424 — MB BS (Hnrs.) Lond. 1953; FRCS Eng. 1961; DHMSA 1991.

CROSHER, Richard Frank Department of Maxillofacial Surgery, Rotherham General Hospitals NHS Trust, Moorgate Road, Rotherham S60 2UD Tel: 01709 307296 Fax: 01709 307220 Email: richardcrosher@hotmail.com; 32 Slayleigh Avenue, Fulwood, Sheffield S10 3RB Tel: 0131 446 9861 Email: richardcrosher@hotmail.com — MB ChB 1991 Sheff.; BDS Lond. 1979; FRCS Ed. (Max. Fac) 1994; FDS RCPS Glas. 1985. (Sheffield University) Cons. (Oral & Maxillofacial Surg.). Socs: Brit. Ass. Of Oral and maxillofacial Surg.s; Brit. Assn. of head and neck oncologists. Prev: Cons., oral & Mayillofacial Surg., W. Lothian Health care trust; Speciallist Regist., oral & mayillofacial Surg., Scotl. Edin.; SHO, Gen. Surg., borders Gen. Hosp., Melrose.

CROSKERY, Sidney Elisabeth, OBE (retired) 22 Malton Fold, Malton Drive, Taughmonagh, Belfast BT9 6PZ Tel: 01232 _ 615884 — MD 1927 Ed.; BSc Ed. 1922, MD (Commend.) 1927, MB ChB 1925. Prev: Med. Off. i/c Aden Port Trust Families Clinic.

CROSLAND, John Michael The Surgery, 112 Weoley Park Road, Selly Oak, Birmingham B29 5HA Tel: 0121 472 1965; 36 Bunbury Road, Northfield, Birmingham B31 2DP Fax: 0121 680 3848 Mobile: 07092 127514 Email: gp@brum.com — MB BS 1965 Newc.; MSc Surrey 1968; MRCP (U.K.) 1972.

CROSLAND, Margaret Mary (retired) Carnanes, Surby Mooar, Port Erin IM9 6TD Tel: 01624 832581 Fax: 01624 832581 — MB ChB Manch. 1944; MCPS 1938. Prev: Div. Surg. St. Johns Assoc.

CROSLAND, Sarah Joanne 49 Manor Way, Petts Wood, Orpington BR5 1NN — MB BS 1987 Lond.; DRCOG 1991; DGM RCP Lond. 1989.

CROSLAND, Sheila Margaret Gilmour (retired) Priory Croft, School Road, Leominster HR6 8NJ Tel: 01568 613974 — MB BS Lond. 1951; DPH Lond. 1965. Mem. Fac. Community Health. Prev: Sen. Med. Off. (Audiol.) Hereford Dist. HA.

CROSLAND, Susan Jane Pendeen Surgery, Kent Avenue, Ross-on-Wye HR9 5AL Tel: 01989 763535 Fax: 01989 768288; 8 Fisherman's Reach, Wilton, Ross-on-Wye HR9 6BE Tel: 01989 763178 — MB ChB 1984 Glas.; DRCOG 1987. p/t GP Princip. Socs: Christian Med. Fell.sh. Prev: Trainee GP Hereford VTS.

CROSLAND-TAYLOR, Paul James (retired) Primrose Cottage, West Looe Hill, Looe PL13 2HW Tel: 01503 263784 — MD Camb. 1967, MB BChir 1949; MRCS Eng. LRCP Lond. 1949; FRCPath 1975, M 1967; MRCS LRCP 1967. Sen. Lect. Middlx. Hosp.

CROSS, Alexander 18 Whitecraigs, Kinnesswood, Kinross KY13 9JN — MB ChB 1944 Glas.

CROSS, Andrew Paul St Lukes Surgery, Warren Road, Guildford GU1 3JH Tel: 01483 572364 Fax: 01483 304379 — MB BS 1984 Lond.; MRCGP 1988; DCH RCP Lond. 1990. Prev: SHO Rotat. W.m. Childr. Hosp.; Trainee GP Guildford VTS.

CROSS, Mr Anthony Theodore 8 Grange Terrace, Stockton Road, Sunderland SR2 7DF Tel: 0191 510 0555; The Old Vicarage, Tudhoe Village, Spennymoor DL16 6JY Tel: 01388 816520 Fax: 01388 816529 Email: atx.ortho@onyxnet.co.uk — MB BS 1968 Lond.; FRCS Eng. 1973. (Univ. Coll. Hosp.) Cons. Orthop. City Hosps. Sunderland; Hon. Clin. Lect. (Orthop.) Univ. Newc.; Dep. regional Specialty Adviser othopaedics; Roy. Coll. Surgic. Tutor, City Hosp.s Sunderland. Socs: Fell. BOA; (Counc.) Brit. Orthop. Assn.1997-2000; Brit. Trauma Soc. Prev: Clin. Dir. (Orthop., Trauma & A & E) City Hosps.(1994-1996); Sen. Regist. St. Geo. Hosp. Lond.; Regist. (Surg.) St. Stephens Hosp. Lond. & Roy. Lond. Homeop. Hosp.

CROSS, Arthur Percival (retired) Waipori Lodge, 69 Carr Hill Lane, Sleights, Whitby YO21 1RS Tel: 01947 810431 — MB ChB 1951 Ed.; MRCGP 1969. Prev: Mem. ScarBoro. DHA.

CROSS, Brian William The Health Centre, Church St., Mansfield Woodhouse, Mansfield NG19 8BL Tel: 01623 633111 Fax: 01623 423480; 26 The Avenue, Mansfield NG18 4PD Tel: 01623 21696 Fax: 01623 21696 — MB BCh BAO 1980 Belf.; MICGP 1987; DCH RCP Lond. 1984; DRCOG 1983. (Belf) Prev: Med. Off. (A & E) Ulster Hosp. Dundonald.

CROSS, Deborah Ann Grange Farm, East Cottingwith, York YO42 4TB — MB BS 1998 Lond.; MB BS Lond 1998.

CROSS, Mr Frank William Department of General Surgery, Royal London Hospital, Whitechapel Road, London E1 1BB Tel: 020 7377 7020 Fax: 020 7375 3646 Email: f.cross@dial.pipex.com — MB BS 1975 Lond.; MS Lond 1988; FRCS Eng. 1979. (Char. Cross) Cons. Surg. Vasc. Surg. & Trauma Roy. Lond. Hosp.; Hon. Cons. St. Lukes Hosp. for the Clergy; Hon. Sen. Lect. St. Bart. & Roy. Lond. Hosp. Med. Coll.; Assoc. Edr., European Jl. of Vasc. & EndoVasc. Socs: Fell. Roy. Soc. Med.; Assn. Surg.; Vasc. Surg. Soc. GB & Irel. Prev: Sen. Regist. Middlx. Hosp. & United Norwich Hosps.; Research Fell. Nat. Med. Laser Centre Dept. Surg. Univ. Coll. Lond.; Regist. (Surg.) Croydon Gen. Hosp.

CROSS, Gordon David 22 Faraday Road, Maidstone ME14 2DB — MB BS 1976 Lond.; MRCS Eng. LRCP Lond. 1976; FFA RCS Eng. 1985.

CROSS, Helen McCallum Thorn Chase, Greenhill, Evesham WR11 — MB ChB 1966 Glas.

CROSS, Hilary Ann, Maj. RAMC Medical Centre, AAC Centre, Middle Wallop, Stockbridge SO20 8DY Tel: 01264 384209; Officers Mess, AAC Centre, Middle Wallop, Stockbridge SO20 8DY — MB ChB 1987 Manch.; BMedSci St. And. 1984; DRCOG 1991. Trainee GP Middle Wallop VTS.

CROSS, James Anthony 3 Burrows Close, Bookham, Leatherhead KT23 3HB Tel: 01372 457143 — MB ChB 1995 Manch.; BSc St. And. 1992. SHO Anaesth., W.on-Super Mare. Prev: SHO Orthop./A & E, Oldham; RMO Perth, W. Australia; SHO Med., Warwick.

CROSS, Jane Amanda 129 Clarence Road, London SW19 8QB — MB BS 1991 Lond.; BSc (Hons.) Biochem. Lond. 1988; MSc (Immunol.) Lond. 1996; MRCP (UK) 1994.

CROSS, Jeffrey Schuyler Cardiothoracic Centre, Thomas Drive, Liverpool L14 3PE — MD 1985 Brown University Providence, USA; MD Brown University Providence USA 1985.

CROSS, Joanna Chambers of J.M. Collins, 9 Woodhouse Square, Leeds LS3 1AD Tel: 0113 245 1986 Fax: 0113 244 8623; The Old Vicarage, 45 Westfield Road, Tockwith, York YO26 7PY — MB ChB 1987 Manch.; BSc St And. 1984.

CROSS, John McMurtry 39 Harefield, Hinchley Wood, Esher KT10 9TG Tel: 020 8398 3950 Fax: 020 8398 3950; 39 Harefield, Hinchley Wood, Esher KT10 9TG Tel: 020 8398 3950 Fax: 020 8398 3950 — MB BCh BAO Belf. 1961; DO Eng. 1969; DObst RCOG 1965.

CROSS, Judith Helen The Wolfson Centre, Mecklenburgh Square, London WC1N 2AP Tel: 020 7837 7618 Fax: 020 7833 9469 Email: h.cross@ich.ucl.ac.uk; 39 Bedford Road, St Albans AL1 3BH — MB ChB 1984 Birm.; MRCP (UK) 1987. Cons. Paediat. Neurol. Gt. Ormond St. Hosp. Childr. NHS Trust Lond. Socs: Brit. Paediat.

Assn.; Brit. Paediat. Neurol. Assn. Prev: Clin. Research Fell. (Paediat. Neurol.) Inst. Child Health Lond.; Regist. (Neurol.) Hosp. Childr. Gt. Ormond St. Lond.; Regist. (Paediat.) Centr. Birm. HA.

CROSS, Justin John Laidlaw Hospital For Sick Children, 555 University Avenue, Toronto ON M5G 1X8, Canada Tel: 416 813 1500 Email: jjcross@yahoo.com; 4 Coombe Hill Glade, Beverley Lane, Kingston upon Thames KT2 7EF Email: jjcross@yahoo.com — MB BChir 1989 Camb.; MA Camb. 1991; MRCP (UK) 1992; FRCR 1996. (Camb.) Fell.NeuroRadiol., Univ. of Toronto, Canada. Prev: Specialist Regist. in NeuroRadiol., Addenbrooke's Hosp., Camb.; Specialist Regist. In Radiol., Addenbrooke's Hosp., Camb.

CROSS, Kathryn Ann Monkseaton Medical Centre, Cauldwell Avenue, Whitley Bay NE25 9PH Tel: 0191 252 1616 — MB BS 1985 Newc.; MB BS (2nd. Cl. Hons.) Newc. 1985; MRCGP 1992; DRCOG 1988; Cert. Family Plann. JCC. 1988. Prev: Partner Priory Med. /Gp.; Partner Killingworth Health Centre.

CROSS, Mr Keith Simon Howard Vascular Surgery Unit, Ward 36, Aberdeen Royal Infirmary, Aberdeen AB25 2ZQ Tel: 01224 681818 Ext: 52781 Fax: 01224 840519; Ardgathen, 4 Golfview Road, Bieldside, Aberdeen AB15 9DQ — MB BCh BAO 1981 Dub.; MD Dub. 1991; MMedSci NUI 1986; FRCSI (Gen.) 1994; FRCSI 1986; FRCS Ed. 1986. (Dublin) Cons. Vasc. Surg. Aberd. Roy. Infirm. Socs: BMA; Eur. Soc. Vasc. Surg.; SRS. Prev: Sen. Regist. Beaumont Hosp. Dub.; Sen. Regist. Matern. Hosp. Dub.; Sen. Regist. Meath & Adelaide Hosps. Dub.

CROSS, Linda Carole 122 Kyverdale Road, London N16 6PR — MB BS 1983 Lond.

CROSS, Mark Richard 15 Huguenot Court, 64-68 Princelet St., London E1 Email: markx@dial.pipex.com — MB ChB 1990 Cape Town; MRCPsych 1998. (Cape Town) Sen. Regist. Homerton Hosp. Lond. Socs: Roy. Soc. Med.; RCPsych. Prev: Albany Lodge, St Albans; Regist. (Psychiat.) Centr. Middlx. Hosp. Lond.

CROSS, Melanie Dawn Boleside House, Galashiels TD1 3NT — MB ChB 1997 Aberd.

CROSS, Michael Hugh The Old Vicarage, Westfield Road, Tockwith, York YO26 7PY Tel: 01423 359224 — MB ChB 1986 Manch.; BSc St. And. 1983. Cons. (Anaesth.) Leeds Gen. Infirm.

CROSS, Nicholas Charles Nevill Hall Hospital, Becon Road, Abergavenny NP7 7EG Email: nick.cross@gwent.wales.nhs.uk — BM 1989 Soton.; MRCP (UK) 1993; FRCR 1998. (Soton.) Cons. Radiologist, Nevill Hall Hosp., Abergavenny. Prev: Regist. (Radiol.) Univ. Hosp. Wales Cardiff.

CROSS, Nicholas Peter Flat 5, 2 Mannering Road, Liverpool L17 8TR — MB ChB 1998 Liverp.; MB ChB Liverp 1998.

CROSS, Norman (retired) Whickham Hill N., Whickham Highway, Gateshead NE11 9QL Tel: 0191 488 1255 — MB ChB 1957 Leeds. Prev: Clin. Asst. (Geriat.) Gateshead & Dist. Hosp. Gp.

CROSS, Pamela Lesley Wylcwm Street Surgery, 3 Wylcwm Street, Knighton LD7 1AD Tel: 01547 528523 Fax: 01547 529347 — MB ChB 1983 Dundee; MRCGP 1990; DA (UK) 1987; DRCOG 1986. Prev: SHO (Geriat.s) Nevill Hall Hosp. Abergavenny; Trainee GP Brecon; Med. Off. Bamalete Lutheran Hosp., Botswana.

CROSS, Patricia Anne 79 Albert Road W., Heaton, Bolton BL1 5HW — MB BCh 1987 Wales; MRCGP 1994.

CROSS, Paul Anthony Department of Pathology, Queen Elizabeth Hospital, Gateshead NE9 6SX Tel: 0191 403 2273 — MB BS 1983 Newc.; BMedSc (Hons.) Newc. 1982; MRCPath 1989. (Newc. u. Tyne) Cons. Histopath. Qu. Eliz. Hosp. Gateshead. Prev: Cons. Histopath. Bury Gen. Hosp.

CROSS, Rachel Anne Boleside House, Galashiels TD1 3NT — MB ChB 1994 Ed.

CROSS, Richard Cranleigh, Dale Road, Haverfordwest SA61 1HZ Tel: 01437 766195 — MB ChB 1972 Birm.; FFA RCS Eng. 1978; DObst RCOG 1974. Cons. Anaesth. Pembrokesh. & Derwen NHS Trust.

CROSS, Richard Andrew 3 Burrows Close, Bookham, Leatherhead KT23 3HB Tel: 01372 457143 — MB ChB 1993 Manch.; BSc (Med. Sci.) St. And. 1990. (St. And. & Manch.) SHO (Anaeth.) Manch. Roy. Infirm. Prev: Med. Off. (Anaesth.) Ngwelezana Hosp. Empangenu, Kwalezulu Natal, S. Afr.

CROSS, Richard Latta Merstow Green Medical Practice, Merstow Green, Evesham WR11 4BS Tel: 01386 765600 Fax: 01386 446807 — MB ChB 1967 Glas.; DObst RCOG 1968.

CROSS, Russell John Pinfold Surgery, Pinfold Lane, Methley, Leeds LS26 9AB Tel: 01977 515203 Fax: 01977 551062; 14 Westfield Grove, Wakefield WF1 3RS Tel: 01924 366625 — MB ChB 1971 Leeds; BSc (Hons.) (Anat.) Leeds 1968, MB ChB 1971. Prev: Clin. Asst. (Urol.) & Research Asst. (Urol.) Castleford Hosp.; Head of Dept. Gen. Pract. King Khalid Hosp. Jeddah.

CROSS, Simon Sayers Department of Pathology, University of Sheffield Medical School, Beech Hill Road, Sheffield S10 2RX Tel: 0114 272 2683 Fax: 0114 278 0059 Email: s.s.cross@sheffield.ac.uk — MB BS 1984 Lond.; BSc (Hons.) Lond. 1981; MD Sheff. 1995; MRCPath 1990. (Guy's) Sen. Lect. (Path.) & Hon. Cons. Histopath. Univ. Sheff. Med. Sch.; Mem. Brit. Div. Internat. Acad. Path. Socs: Assn. Clin. Path; Brit. Soc. Clin. Cytol.; Path. Soc. Prev: MRC Train. Fell.; Sen. Regist. (Histopath.) Sheff.; Regist. (Histopath.) Univ. Hosp. Wales Cardiff.

CROSS, Stephen Jeremy Cardiac Department, Aberdeen Royal Infirmary, Aberdeen AB9 2ZN Tel: 01224 681818; 8 Broomhill Terrace, Aberdeen AB10 6JN Tel: 01224 321176 — MB ChB 1985 Sheff.; MRCP (UK) 1988. Regist. (Cardiol.) Aberd. Roy. Infirm. Prev: Regist. (Gen. Med.) Raigmore Hosp. Inverness; Regist. (Gen. Med. & Diabetes) Centr. Middlx. Hosp. Lond.

CROSS, Susan Jill Anaesthetic Department, Worcester Royal Infirmary, Ronkswood Branch, Newtown Road, Worcester WR5 1HN — MB ChB 1984 Manch.; MB ChB Manch. I984; FRCA 1993. Staff Grade (Anaesth.) Worcester Roy. Infirm. Prev: Regist. (Anaesth.) N. Staffs. Gen. Hosp. & Shrewsbury Roy. Hosp.; SHO (Anaesth.) Wrexham Maelor Hosp.; SHO (Med.) Ysbyty Gwynedd Bangor.

CROSS, Tanya Julia Appletree Cottage, Nuffield, Henley-on-Thames RG9 5SS Tel: 01491 641900 — MB ChB 1995 Bristol. SHO (Paediat.) Frenchay Hosp., Bristol. Prev: SHO (Paediat.) Gloucester Roy. Hosp.; SHO (Paediat.) Bristol Childr. Hosp.; SHO (Paediat.) S.mead Hosp. Bristol.

CROSS, Tarquin Gordon 508 Streatham High Road, Streatham, London SW16 3QB — MB BS 1997 Newc.

CROSS, Thomas William, TD 4 Malcolm Street, Crawford Gardens, Motherwell ML1 3HY Tel: 01698 252435 — MB ChB Glas. 1958; DPH Glas. 1971; DORCOG Lond. R. Coll.; MFPHM RCP (UK) 1988; MFOM RCPI 1980; MFCMI 1978; MFOM RCP Lond. 1978; MFCM 1974; DPA Scott. Bus Educat. Counc. 1978; DIH Dund 1973; DObst RCOG 1972; FFOM 1999. (Glasgow) Dist. Med. Off. Lanarksh. HB; Asst. Med. Off. Health Dept. Glas. Dist. Counc; Maj. T & AVR. Socs: BMA; BSSI. Prev: Flight Lt. RAF Med. Br; Community Med. Specialist Lanarksh. HB; Ho. Phys. Strathclyde Hosp. Motherwell.

CROSS, Timothy James 88-90 Emscote Road, Warwick CV34 5QJ — MB ChB 1987 Glas.; BSc (Hons.) (Anat. & Experim. Path.) St. And. 1983.

CROSS, Timothy James Scott Cherrytrees, 50 Wergs Rd, Tettenhall, Wolverhampton WV6 8TD — MB BS 1996 Lond.

CROSS, Victor Herbert Bournbrook Medical Practice, 480 Bristol Road, Selly Oak, Birmingham B29 6BD Tel: 0121 472 0129; 53 Kelmscott Road, Harborne, Birmingham B17 8QW — MB ChB 1978 Birm. Occupat. Health Off. S.. HA. Prev: Postgrad. Clin. Tutor S. Birm. HA.

CROSS, William Alexander School House 2, Fordell, Crossgates, Cowdenbeath KY4 8EY Tel: 01383 510440 — MB ChB 1979 Ed.

CROSS, William Richard Rosslyn, Cumeragh Lane, Whittingham, Preston PR3 2AN — BM BS 1995 Nottm.

CROSS, Xanthe Helen Colchester General, Hosp., Turner Road, Colchester CO4 5JL; 29 Parkside Estate, Rutland Road, Hackney, London E9 7JU Tel: 020 8985 9595 — MB BS 1997 Lond.; BMedSci Lond. 1996. (St. Bar. & Roy. Lond. Sch. Med. Dent.) SHO (Surg.) Colchester. Prev: Ho. Off. (Surg.) Whipps Cross Hosp. Lond.; Ho. Off. (Med.) Roy. Lond. Hosp.

CROSS, Zoe Elizabeth 40 Finsen Road, London SE5 9AW — MB BS 1997 Lond.

CROSSAN, Clare Bernadette The Surgery, The Green, Parbold, Wigan WN8 7DN Tel: 01257 463126 — MB BS 1987 Lond.; DRCOG 1991; DCH RCP Lond. 1990.

CROSSAN, Elaine Mary Carluke H.C., Market Place, Carluke ML8 4AZ Tel: 01555 771012 — MB ChB 1978; DGM Glasgow; DRCOG Glasgow; MRCGP Edinburgh; DFFP Glasgow. (Univ. of Glasgow) p/t GP, Carluke H.C.

CROSSAN, Isabella 67 Craigstown Road, Randalstown, Antrim BT41 2NS — MB ChB 1993 Leic.

CROSSE, Barbara Anne Greenlea Oncology Unit, Huddersfield Royal Infirmary, Lindley, Huddersfield HD3 3EA Tel: 01484 342999 — MB ChB 1983 Leeds; BSc (Hons.) Leeds 1980; MRCP (UK) 1986. p/t Cons. Med. Oncol. Calderdale & Huddersfield NHS Trust, Huddersfield. Socs: Assn. in Calver Phys.s; Brit. Oncological Assn. Prev: Sen. Regist. (Infec. Dis.) Seacroft Hosp. Yorksh. HA; Sen. Regist. (Gen. Med.) St. Jas. Hosp. Trust Leeds; Sen. Regist. Med. Oncol. Yorks. Rotat.

CROSSE, John Ormandy, Col. late RAMC Retd. (retired) 8 Hicks Lane, Girton, Cambridge CB3 0JS Tel: 01223 276650 — MB BChir 1963 Camb.; MB Camb. 1963, BChir 1962; BA Camb. 1958; MRCS Eng. LRCP Lond. 1962; DTM & H Eng. 1965. Prev: Sen. Med. Off. Dover Shorncliffe Garrison.

CROSSE, Judith Margaret Trent Meadows Surgery, Wood Street, Burton-on-Trent Tel: 01283 845555 — MB ChB 1984 Manch.; MRCGP 1996; DRCOG 1995. (Univ. of Manch.)

CROSSE, Mark Mortimer Shackleton Department Anaesthetics, Southampton General Hospital, Southampton SO16 6YD Tel: 02380 777222 Fax: 02380 794348; Clare House, Southdown Road, Shackleford, Winchester SO21 2BY — MRCS Eng. LRCP Lond. 1965; MA Camb. 1964, BA 1961, MB 1966, BChir 1965; FRCA Eng. 1970. (Camb. & St. Bart.) Cons. Dept. Anaesth. Soton. Univ. Gp. Hosps. Socs: Assn. Anaesths. Prev: Sen. Regist. (Anaesth.) W.m. Hosp. & Soton. Univ. Gp. Hosps.; SHO (Anaesth.) St. Geo. Hosp. Lond. & St. Bart. Hosp. Lond.

CROSSE, Stephen Macdonald Watercress Medical Group, Dean Surgery, Ropley, Alresford SO24 0BQ Tel: 01962 772340 Fax: 01962 772551 — MB BChir 1973 Camb.; MA, MB Camb. 1973, BChir 1972. (Camb. & St. Bart.) Clin. Asst. (Geriat. Med.) Lord Mayor Treloar Hosp.; Div. Med. Off. Alresford Div. St. John Ambul. Socs: BMA. Prev: Trainee GP Basingstoke VTS; SHO (Paediat.) Basingstoke Dist. Hosp.; Ho. Surg. & Ho. Phys. Crawley Hosp.

CROSSIN, Clare Mary Carrick Hill Medical Centre, 1 Carrick Hill, Belfast BT1 2JR Tel: 028 9043 973 — MB BCh BAO 1989 Belf.; MRCGP 1993. Socs: BMA.

CROSSIN, Jane Dolores 10 Adelaide Avenue, Belfast BT9 7FY — MB BCh BAO 1989 Belf.

CROSSIN, Thomas Christopher Carrick Hill Medical Centre, 1 Carrick Hill, Belfast BT1 2JR Tel: 028 9043 973; 9 Broomhill Manor, Belfast BT9 5HG — MB BCh BAO 1953 Belf.

CROSSKEY, Henry Evelyn (retired) St. Jean de Luz, 56 Main Road, Biggin Hill, Westerham TN16 3DU Tel: 01959 572344 — MB ChB 1948 Birm.; DObst RCOG 1952.

CROSSKEY, Katherine Sheila Mildred (retired) St. Jean de Luz, 56 Main Road, Biggin Hill, Westerham TN16 3DU — MB ChB 1948 Birm.

CROSSKEY, Philip Harben (retired) Rose Cottage, Little Cowarne, Bromyard HR7 4RH Tel: 01885 400291 — MB BChir Camb. 1951; MA Camb. 1951; DObst RCOG 1955. Prev: Ho. Phys. (Paediat.) & Ho. Off. (Obst.). MusGr. Pk. Hosp. Taunton.

CROSSLAND, David Steven 18B Lawson Road, Broomhill, Sheffield S10 5BW — MB ChB 1995 Sheff.

CROSSLAND, Graeme John 8 Somerville Green, Leeds LS14 6AY — MB ChB 1997 Manch.

CROSSLAND, John Steven Pendre Surgery, Clayton Road, Mold CH7 1SS Tel: 01352 759163 Fax: 01352 758255 — MB ChB 1968 Manch.

CROSSLAND, Julie Ann 5 Beeley Street, Salford M6 6BW — MB ChB Manch.; MB ChB Manch. 198.

CROSSLAND, Pauline Elizabeth Gowerton Medical Centre, Mill St, Gowerton, Swansea SA4 3ED Tel: 01792 872404 — MB BCh 1980 Wales; MRCGP 1987.

CROSSLAND, William Davies Rooley Lane Medical Centre, Bradford BD4 7SS Tel: 01274 728009; Lucarne House, 56 Farnley Road, Menston, Ilkley LS29 6JP Tel: 01943 874607 — MB ChB 1960 Leeds; Mem. BMA. Prev: Ho. Phys., Ho. Surg. & Ho. Surg. (O & G) St. Luke's Hosp.; Bradford.

CROSSLEY, Alan Norton Medical Centre, Forest Road, Hay-on-Wye, Hereford HR3 5DS Tel: 01497 822110 Fax: 01497 822110; Sundew Cottage, Clyro, Hereford HR3 5SW — MB ChB 1970 Birm.; MRCGP 1977; DA Eng. 1973; DObst RCOG 1972. (Birm.) Prev: Ho. Phys. Birm. Gen. Hosp.; SHO (Obst.) Good Hope Matern. Hosp. Sutton Coldfield; SHO (Anaesth.) Roy. Cornw. Hosp. (Treliske) Truro.

CROSSLEY, Angus Wallace Adamson 364 Duffield Road, Darley Abbey, Derby DE22 1ER — MB ChB 1977 Glas.; FFA RCS Eng. 1985. Sen. Lect. (Anaesth.) Univ. Nottm.; Hon. Cons. Anaesth. Derby City Hosp. Prev: Regist. (Anaesth.) Vict. Infirm. Glas.; 1st Asst. (Anaesth.) Univ. Newc.; Research Asst. (Pharmacol.) Univ. Glas.

CROSSLEY, Damayanthi Ruckmala Thornley Street Surgery, 40 Thornley Street, Wolverhampton WV1 1JP Tel: 01902 688500 Fax: 01902 444074 Email: tim.crossley@virgin.net — MB BS 1980 Lond.; 1999 Mmed sci, Birm. GP, Wolverhampton. Prev: Clin. Med. Off. Drug Addic. Unit Wolverhampton; Trainee GP Aylesbury VTS.

CROSSLEY, David John Anaesthetic Department, Princess Alexandra Hospital, Hamstel Road, Harlow CM20 1QX Tel: 01279 444455 — MB BS 1988 Lond.; FRCA 1993. (St. George's Med. Sch.) Cons. (Anaesth. & IC) P.ss Alexandra Hosp. Harlow.

CROSSLEY, David Richard Ruthwaite, Skelwith Bridge, Ambleside LA22 9NP — MB ChB 1987 Manch.; MA Camb. 1983; MRCGP 1991.

CROSSLEY, Gillian Evelyn Marian (retired) Lower Farm, Tockington, Bristol BS2 4LE Tel: 01454 612337 — MB BS Lond. 1952.

CROSSLEY, Helen Connaught Surgery, 144 Hedge Lane, Palmers Green, London N13 5ST Tel: 020 8886 2284 Fax: 020 8372 7246; 52 Park Drive, Winchmore Hill, London N21 2LS Tel: 020 8372 7246 — MB BS Lond. 1962; MRCS Eng. LRCP Lond. 1961. (Roy. Free) GP in Palmers Green. Socs: BMA. Prev: Ho. Surg. Lambeth Hosp.; Ho. Phys. Miller Hosp.; Ho. Surg. (Orthop.) Roy. Free Hosp. Lond.

CROSSLEY, Ian Brian 29A New Beacon Road, Grantham NG31 9JS — BM BCh 1992 Oxf.

CROSSLEY, Ian Roger Boxgrove House, Beckford Hall, Beckford, Tewkesbury GL20 7AA Tel: 01386 881844; Department of Gastroenterology, Cheltenham General Hospital, Sandford Road, Cheltenham GL53 7AN Tel: 01242 274099 — MD 1981 Sheff.; MB ChB 1971; MRCP (UK) 1974; FRCP (UK) 1995. Cons. Phys. & Gastroenterol. Cheltenham Gen. Hosp. Socs: Brit. Soc. Gastroenterol.; Med. Res. Soc.; Brit. Assn. Study Liver. Prev: Sen. Regist. Roy. Devon & Exeter Hosp.; Lect./Sen. Regist. Liver Unit King's Coll. Hosp. Lond.; Research Fell. (Gastroenterol.) Univ. Toronto.

CROSSLEY, Mr John (retired) Lower Farm, Tockington, Bristol BS32 4LE Tel: 01454 612337 — MB BChir Camb. 1947; FRCS Eng. 1950; FRCOG 1964, M 1954, DObst 1948. Prev: Cons. (O & G) S.mead Hosp. Gp.

CROSSLEY, John Marvale (retired) 20 Somerville Road, Sutton Coldfield B73 6JA Tel: 0121 354 2428 — MB ChB 1945 Birm.; DObst RCOG 1950. Prev: Ho. Surg. Qu. Eliz. Hosp. Birm.

CROSSLEY, John Neil The Health Centre, Madeira Road, West Byfleet KT14 6DH Tel: 01932 336933 Fax: 01932 355681; 16 Dean Close, Pyrford, Woking GU22 8PA Tel: 01932 345553 Fax: 01932 355681 — MB BS Lond. 1962; BSc (Hons.) Lond. 1959; MRCS Eng. LRCP Lond. 1962. (Guy's) Hosp. Pract. (Gastroenterol.) St. Peter's Hosp. Chertsey. Socs: Brit. Soc. Gastroenterol. Prev: Lect. (Physiol.) Guy's Hosp. Med. Sch. Lond.; Ho. Surg. & Ho. Phys. Guy's Hosp. Lond.

CROSSLEY, John Withers (retired) 21 Heol Serth, Ty Isaf, Caerphilly CF83 2AN Tel: 029 20 882377/20861172 — MB ChB 1959 Manch. Prev: Med. Advisor Benefits Agency Med. Serv. Cardiff.

CROSSLEY, Margaret Catriona A & E Department, Hull Royal Infirmary, Anlaby Road, Hull; Tel: 01273 416225 Email: ann@familydoctors.co.uk — MB BS 1991 Newc.; MRCP (UK) 1996. (Newc.) Specialist Regist. (A & E) Hull Roy. Infirm.

CROSSLEY, Neil Roderick The Abingdon Surgery, 65 Stert Street, Abingdon OX14 3LB Tel: 01235 523126 Fax: 01235 550625 — MB ChB 1976 Liverp.; MRCGP 1980; Cert. Family Plann. JCC 1980; DRCOG 1978. Med. Off. Henley RFC; GP Trainer.

CROSSLEY, Nicola Ann Wroughton Health Centre, Barrett Way, Wroughton, Swindon SN4 9LW — BM BS 1990 Nottm.; BMedSci Nottm. 1987; MRCGP 1994; DRCOG 1996. GP Princip. Prev: Trainee GP/SHO Exeter VTS.

CROSSLEY, Robert Anthony 5 Kings Road, Windsor SL4 2AD — MB BS 1997 Lond.
CROSSLEY, Robert Brian (retired) 36 Mayfair Gardens, Southampton SO15 2TW Tel: 01703 236900 Fax: 01703 236900 Email: rbcrossley@hotmail.com — MB BCh BAO 1955 Belf.; FRCPsych 1984, M 1971; DPM Eng. 1962. Med. Mem., Mentla Health Review Tribunal. Prev: Cons. Psychiat. Soton. & SW Hants. HA.
CROSSLEY, Sarah Lynne 270 Spendmore Lane, Coppull, Chorley PR7 5DE — MB ChB 1998 Dund.; MB ChB Dund 1998.
CROSSLEY, Timothy Martin Thornley Street Surgery, 40 Thornley Street, Wolverhampton WV1 1JP Tel: 01902 26843 Fax: 01902 688500 — BM BCh 1980 Oxf.; BA Oxf. 1980; MRCGP 1985. GP Wolverhampton. Prev: Trainee GP Aylesbury VTS.
CROSSLING, Mr Frank Turner (retired) 28 North Grange Road, Bearsden, Glasgow G61 3AF Tel: 0141 563 8535 — MB ChB 1949 Aberd.; FRCS Glas. 1969; FRCS Eng. 1954. Prev: Cons. Surg. Stobhill Hosp. Glas.
CROSSMAN, Professor David Christopher University of Sheffield, Cardiovascular Research Group, Clinical Sciences Centre, Northern General Hospital, Herries Road, Sheffield S5 7AU Tel: 0114 271 5815 Fax: 0114 261 9587 Email: d.c.crossman@sheffield.ac.uk — MB BS 1982 Lond.; MD Univ. Lond. 1991; BSc (1st. cl. Hons. Physiol.) Lond. 1979; MRCP (UK) 1985; T(M) 1993; FRCP (Lond) 1998; FACC 1999; FESC 2000. (ST. Bartholomew's) Prof. Clin. Cardiol. Univ. Sheff. Socs: Brit. Pharm. Soc.; Brit. Cardiac Soc.; Assn. Phys. Prev: Sen. Regist. Hammersmith Hosp. Lond.; MRC Clin. Train. Fell.
CROSSMAN, Helen Mary 83 Dunstan Crescent, Worksop S80 1AG — MB ChB 1979 Sheff.
CROSSMAN, Mr Ian Geoffrey Orthodontic Department Royal Alexandra Hospital, Dyke Road, Brighton BN1 3JN Tel: 01273 328145 Fax: 01273 774858; 53 Tongdean Avenue, Hove BN3 6TN Tel: 01273 556858 — MB BS 1968 Lond.; BDS (Hons.) Lond. 1961; FDS RCS Eng. 1966, DOrth 1964. (Guy's) Cons. Orthodont. Roy. Alexandra Hosp. Brighton. Socs: BDA; BMA; (Pres.) Brit. Soc. Study Orthodont. Prev: Ho. Phys., Ho. Surg., Regist. & Sen. Regist. (Orthodont.) Guy's Hosp. Lond.; Dent. Tutor Sussex Postgrad. Med. Centre.
CROSSMAN, John Edward 18 Brady and Martin Court, Northumberland Road, Newcastle upon Tyne NE1 8SG — MB BS 1992 Lond.
CROSSMAN, Lucy Caroline 50 Sandringham Road, South Gosforth, Newcastle upon Tyne NE3 1PY Tel: 0191 285 3084 — BM BS 1996 Nottm. SHO (Med.) Freeman Hosp. Newc. Prev: SHO (Surg.) DRI, Derby; SHO (Med.) City Hosp. Nottm.
CROSSMAN, Mr Paul Thomas 53 Tongdean Avenue, Hove BN3 6TN — BM BCh 1994 Oxf.; MA Camb. 1995; FRCS Eng. 1998.
CROSSMAN, Richard Paul 11 Harberton Crescent, Chichester PO19 4N — MB BS 1990 Lond.
CROSSTHWAITE, David Ian Wallace House Surgery, 5-11 St. Andrew Street, Hertford SG14 1HZ Tel: 01992 550541 — MB ChB 1977 Manch.; MRCGP 1981; DRCOG 1980. Princip. Gen. Pract. Hertford. Prev: Gen. Pract. Train. Scheme Reading.
CROSSWAITE, Alastair Gordon 19 West Werberside, Edinburgh EH4 1SZ — MB BS 1987 Lond.
CROSTHWAITE, Jeremy David London Road Medical Centre, 2 London Road, Uppingham, Oakham LE15 9TJ Tel: 01572 823531; 2 London Road, Uppingham, Oakham LE15 9TJ Tel: 01572 822623 — MB BS 1976 Lond.; MRCGP 1981; DRCOG 1980. (Middlx.) Med. Off. Uppingham Sch.
CROSTHWAITE, Olivia Susan 'Seaward', 17 Lingdale Road, West Kirby, Wirral CH48 5DG Tel: 0151 632 3757 — MB ChB Liverp. 1939. (Liverp.)
CROTCH-HARVEY, Michael Antony 1 Pipit Avenue, Newton-le-Willows WA12 9RG Tel: 01925 225397 — MB ChB 1985 Liverp.; MRCP (UK) 1988. Regist. Rotat. (Radiol.) Mersey RHA. Prev: Regist. Rotat. (Med.) Mersey RHA; SHO (Med.) Whiston & St. Helens Hosps.
CROTHERS, Elizabeth Dorothy Old School Surgery, 54 Station Road, Greenisland, Carrickfergus BT38 8TP Tel: 028 9086 4455 Fax: 028 9036 5367 — MB BCh BAO 1982 Belf.; MB BCh Belf. 1982; MRCGP 1988. (Qu. Univ. Belf.)
CROTHERS, Joseph Graham Radiology Department, Royal Victoria Hospital, Grosvenor Road, Belfast BT12 6BA Tel: 01232 894962 Fax: 01232 310920; 1 Tudor Park, Holywood BT18 0NX Tel: 01232 424009 — MB BCh BAO 1973 Belf.; FFR RCSI 1988; FRCR 1982; DMRD Eng. 1981; DRCOG 1976. (Belf.) Cons. (Radiol.) Roy. Vict. Hosp. Belf. Socs: Amer. Inst. of Ultrasound in Med. & Ulster Med. Soc.
CROTON, Christopher Stanley (retired) The Surgery, Overstrand Road, Cromer NR27 0AJ Tel: 01263 513148 Email: chriscroton@ukgetaway.net.net — MB ChB 1970 Sheff.; MB ChB (Hons.) Sheff. 1970; MRCP (UK) 1972. Prev: Med. Off. Norwich City FC.
CROTON (MRS ENTWISHE), Jean Lindsay Lyle (Baker) Manchester Road Surgery, 280 Manchester Road, Warrington WA1 3RB Tel: 01925 230022 Fax: 01925 575069; Cogshall Lane Farm, Cogshall Lane, Comerbach, Northwich CW9 6BW Tel: 01606 891363 Fax: 01606 891363 — MB ChB 1971 Sheff.; DObst RCOG 1973; Cert FPA 1974.
CROTTY, Isabel Mary (retired) 12 Hazel Grove Gardens, Hazel Grove Road, Haywards Heath RH16 3DY Tel: 01444 451738 — MB BCh BAO 1945 Dub.; MA Oxf. 1954; LM Coombe 1946; DPH (Hons.) NUI 1949, DPM 1949. Prev: Ho. Phys. & Ho. Surg. Roy. City of Dub. Hosp.
CROUCH, Andrew Douglas Kenneth Hardwicke House Surgery, Hardwicke House, Stour Street, Sudbury CO10 2AY Tel: 01787 370011 Fax: 01787 376521 — MB BS 1988 Lond.
CROUCH, Eric Christopher Barnsley District General Hospital, Barnsley S75 2EP Tel: 01226 786599 Fax: 01226 289330 Email: eric.crouch@bcps-tr.trent.nhs.uk; 1 Intake Gardens, Pogmoor, Barnsley S75 2DP Tel: 01226 786599 Email: eric-crouch@lineone.net — BM BCh 1975 Oxf.; BA Oxf. 1969; MRCS Eng. LRCP Lond. 1974; FRCPsych 1993, M 1978. (Oxf. & St. Mary's) Cons.Psyciatric. Barnsley Community & Priority Serv.s NHS Trust, Barnsley, S, Yorks.; Asst. Med. Director BCPS NHS Trust. Prev: Cons. Psychiat. & Clinic Director S.Bucks NHS Trust; Cons. Psychiat. St. John's Hosp. Stone; Sen. Regist. Rotat. (Psychiat.) Oxf. RHA.
CROUCH, George Alan Dr Moss and Partners, 28-38 Kings Road, Harrogate HG1 5JP Tel: 01423 560261 Fax: 01423 501099; 18 Hollins Road, Harrogate HG1 2JF Tel: 01423 60261 — MB ChB 1967 Ed.; FRCGP 1983, M 1973; DObst RCOG 1972. Assoc. Regional Adviser (Gen. Pract.) Yorks; Hon. Lect. (Gen. Pract.) Univ. Leeds. Socs: Med. Protec. Soc. (Mem. Cases Comm. & Gen. Pract. Advis. Bd.). Prev: Mem. N. Yorks. FHSA; Mem. Yorks. RHA 1984-9; Course Organiser Harrogate VTS 1981-87.
CROUCH, Graeme Keith 37 Dorset Avenue, Norwood Green, Southall UB2 4HG — MB BS 1979 Lond.; MRCPsych 1984.
CROUCH, Henrietta Elizabeth (retired) Tyrella, Dr. Crouch's Road, Eastcombe, Stroud GL6 7EA Tel: 01452 770425 — MB BCh BAO 1942; MB BCh BAO Belf. 1942; MD Belf. 1974. Assoc. Specialist Gloucester Roy. Hosp. Prev: Resid. Med. Off. Belf. City Hosp.
CROUCH, Lawrence (retired) 33 Shirley Hills Road, Addington, Croydon CR0 5HQ — MB BS 1952 Lond.; DObst RCOG 1954. Prev: Ho. Surg., Ho. Phys. & Obst. Ho. Surg. Padd. Hosp.
CROUCH, Muriel (retired) 50 Clarence Road, Hunstanton PE36 6HQ Tel: 01485 533364 — MB BS Lond. 1940; FRCS Eng. 1946; MRCS Eng., LRCP Lond. 1940. Prev: Surg. Eliz. G. Anderson Hosp. Lond., Marie Curie Unit Mt. Vernon Hosp. N.wood & S. Lond. Hosp. Wom. & Childr.
CROUCH, Naomi Sarah 50 Adur Avenue, Worthing BN13 3LW; 16 Garth Court, Northwick Pk Road, Harrow HA1 2ER Tel: 020 8424 0973 — MB BS 1997 Lond.; BSc (Hons) 1994. (University College, London) SHO (O & G), Lond.
CROUCH, Peter Anthony Taw Hill Practice, Queen Elizabeth Drive, Swindon SN25 1WL — MB BS 1990 Lond. (Lond. Hosp. Med. Coll.)
CROUCH, Timothy Frithwood Surgery, 45 Tanglewood Way, Bussage, Stroud GL6 8DE Tel: 01453 884646 Fax: 01453 731302; The Triangle, Eastcombe, Stroud GL6 7EB — MB BCh BAO 1974 Belf.; DObst RCOG 1976. GP Stroud. Prev: Med. Off. N.W. River Hosp. Labrador Canada; Res. Ho. Off. Belf. City Hosp.
CROUCHER, Carolyn Anne 31 Blackwood Close, West Byfleet KT14 6PP Tel: 01932 341581 Email: cjcrouch1@aol.com — MB BS 1989 Lond.; MRCOG 1994. Specialist Regist. yr. 5 (O & G), ST.

Geo.'s Med. Sch., Lond. Prev: Lect. (Obst. & Gyn) St. Helier Hosp.; Research Fell. & Hon. Sen. Regist. Hammersmith IVF Unit; Regist. (O & G) St. Helier Hosp. Carshalton & Kingston Hosp.

CROUCHER, Claire Louise Weston General Hospital, Grange Road, Uphill, Weston Super Mare BS23 4TQ Tel: 01934 636363 — MB BS 1987 Lond.; MRCP (UK) 1990; FRCR 1995.

CROUCHER, Jeffrey John Benhill and Belmont GP Centre, 54 Benhill Avenue, Sutton SM1 4EB Tel: 01932 336933 Fax: 01932 355681 — MB BS 1989 Lond.; MRCGP 2000; DRCOG 1998; DFFP 1998; DCH 1998. (St. Geo. Hosp. Med.Sch.) GP Princip., Benhill and Belmont GP Partnership, Sutton. Prev: Trainee GP/SHO (Paediat.) St. Peters Hosp. Chertsey; GP Regist., W. Byfleet Health Centre; GP Trainee/SHO (Obstetros) St Peters Hosp., Chertsey.

CROUCHER, Lesley Caroline The Health Centre, Bowers Place, Crawley Down, Crawley RH10 4HY Tel: 01342 713031 Fax: 01342 718715 — MB BS 1977 Lond.; MRCS Eng. LRCP Lond. 1977; DRCOG 1981. (St. Mary's) Hon. Med. Off. Qu. Vict. Hosp. E. Grinstead.

CROUCHER, Martin Derek Vicarage Field Surgery, Vicarage Field, Hailsham BN27 1BE Tel: 01323 441155 Fax: 01323 847209 — MB BS 1983 Lond.

CROUCHER, Peta Elisabeth The Surgery, 31 Tunbridge Lane, Bottisham, Cambridge CB5 9DU Tel: 01223 811203 Fax: 01223 811853 — MB BS 1986 Lond.; MRCGP 1991.

CROUCHMAN, Marion Rose Paediatric Neurosciences Child Health, King's College Hospital, London SE5 9RS Tel: 020 7346 3892 Fax: 020 7346 3564; 53 Rowan Road, Brook Green, London W6 7DT Tel: 020 7603 5425 Fax: 020 7610 5553 — MB BS 1967 Lond.; FRCP Lond. 1992; MRCP (UK) 1970; DCH RCP Lond. 1970. Cons. Paediat. King's Coll. Hosp. Lond.; Hon. Cons. Paediat. Roy. Bethlem & Maudsley Hosp. Lond. Prev: Cons. Community Paediat. Wexham Pk. Hosp. Slough; Lect. (Child Health) St. Geo. Hosp. Lond.; Sen. Regist. (Cardiol.) Guy's Hosp. Lond.

CROUCHMAN, Paul William Francis 146 Riverside Mansions, Milk Yard, London E1W 3SU — MB BS 1998 Lond.; MB BS Lond 1998.

CROUDACE, John (retired) 59 Showell Lane, Penn, Wolverhampton WV4 4TZ Tel: 01902 893061 — MB BS 1959 Durh. Prev: Med. Dir. Compton Hall Hospice, Wolverhampton.

CROUSE, Mark William 5 Higher Cottages, Ladock, Truro TR2 4PP — MB BCh 1993 Wales.

CROW, Barbara Mary (retired) Windfall, Forder Lane, Bishopsteignton, Teignmouth TQ14 9RZ Tel: 01626 779836 — MB ChB Liverp. 1945; DCH Eng. 1949. Prev: Clin. Asst. Paediat. Dept. Torbay Hosp.

CROW, Gerda Jane (retired) Barnstable Cottage, West End, Kingham, Chipping Norton, Oxford OX7 6YL Tel: 01608 658111 — MB BS Lond. 1953; FRCS Ed. 1964; FRCOG 1975, M 1960. Prev: Cons. O & G S.end-on-Sea Hosp. Gp.

CROW, Ian Stewart Northwick Hall, Pilning, Bristol BS35 4HB — MB ChB 1978 Birm.

CROW, John 17 Serpentine Gardens, Hartlepool TS26 0HQ Tel: 01429 891058 — LRCP LRCS 1947 Ed.; LRCP LRCS Ed. LRFPS Glas. 1947. (School of Medicine of Royal Colleges) Sen. Hosp. Med. Off.

CROW, Julie Carol Department of Histopathology, Royal Free Hospital, Pond St., London NW3 2QG Tel: 020 7830 2227 Fax: 020 7830 2529 Email: jcrow@rfhsm.ac.uk; 16 Northwick Circle, Kenton, Harrow HA3 0EJ Email: julie@jcrow.demon.co.uk — MB BS 1966 Lond.; BSc Lond. 1963; FRCPath 1989, M 1977. (Lond. Hosp.) Sen. Lect. (Histopath.) Roy. Free Hosp. Sch. Med. Socs: Internat. Acad. Path. & Path. Soc. GB & Irel. Prev: Sen. Regist. (Histopath.) N.wick Pk. Hosp.; Lect. (Path.) Univ. Aberd. Med. Sch.

CROW, Michael Anthony Bryan Fairhill Medical Practice, 81 Kingston Hill, Kingston upon Thames KT2 7PX Tel: 020 8546 1407 Fax: 020 8547 0075; 18 Cranleigh Road, Esher KT10 8DF Tel: 020 8873 8263 Email: michael.crow@btinternet.com — MB BS 1981 Lond.; MRCGP 1987; DRCOG 1986. (St. Bart.) Med. Manager & Dir. Thamesdoc GP Co-op.; Bd. Mem. Kingston PCG. Prev: SHO (O & G) St. Bart. Hosp. Lond.; SHO (ENT) Addenbrooke's Hosp. Camb.; SHO (A & E) Bristol Roy. Infirm.

CROW, Peter Gordon Radbrook Green Surgery, Bank Farm Road, Shrewsbury SY3 6DU Tel: 01743 231816 Fax: 01743 344099 — MB ChB 1981 Sheff.; MRCP (UK) 1986; MRCGP 1987. GP Shrewsbury; Shrops. VTS Course Organiser.

CROW, Robert Stewart (retired) Windfall, Forder Lane, Bishopsteignton, Teignmouth TQ14 9RZ Tel: 01626 779836 — MB ChB Aberd. 1945; MD Aberd. 1958; FRCP Lond. 1971, M 1952. Prev: Cons. Phys. Torbay Hosp. Torquay.

CROW, Professor Timothy John University Department of Psychiatry, Warneford Hospital, Oxford OX3 7JX Tel: 01865 226474 Fax: 01865 244990; 16 Northwick Circle, Kenton, Harrow HA3 0EJ — MB BS 1964 Lond.; PhD Aberd. 1970; FRCP Lond. 1978; MRCP (UK) 1972; FRCPsych 1981, M 1972; DPM Ed. & Glas. 1971. (Lond. Hosp.) MRC Extern. Scientif. Staff. Socs: Acad. of Med. Sci.; Soc. for Biological Psychiat.; Experim. Psychol. Soc. Prev: Head Div. Psychiat. MRC Clin. Research Centre N.wick Pk. Hosp.; Dep. Dir. Clin. Research Centre N.wick Pk. Hosp.; Sen. Lect. (Psych.) Univ. Manch.

CROW, Yanick Joseph Killoch, Ramoyle, Dunblane FK15 0BA — MB BS 1991 Newc.; MRCP (UK) 1994.

CROWCROFT, Andrew 7 Parkhill Walk, Tasker Road, London NW3 2YU Tel: 020 7267 0698 — MB BS Lond. 1956; BSc (Psychol.) Lond. 1950; MRCS Eng. LRCP Lond. 1956; FRCPsych 1973, M 1971; DPM Eng. 1960. (Roy. Free) Emerit. Cons. Guy's Hosp. Lond. Socs: Fell. Roy. Coll. Psychiat.; BMA. Prev: Assoc. Prof. Fac. Med. Univ. Toronto, Canada; Sen. Staff Psychiat. Hosp. Sick Childr. Toronto, Canada; Exec. Dir. W. End Creche Child & Family Clinic Toronto, Canada.

CROWCROFT, Natasha Sarah 20 Beauval Road, London SE22 8UQ — MB BS 1987 Lond.; MA Camb. 1988; MSc Lond. 1994; MRCP (UK) 1990; MFPHM RCP (UK) (1995). Prev: Fell. Europ. Progr. for Interven. Epidemiol. Train., Scientif. Inst. Pub. Health, Brussels, Belgium; Sen. Regist. (Pub. Health Med.) S. Thames (W.) RHA; Regist. (Microbiol.) Roy. Free Hosp. Lond.

CROWDER, Ann Mary (retired) 2 Rosemarkie Crescent, Broughty Ferry, Dundee DD5 2RQ Tel: 01382 78050 — MB ChB 1957 Glas.; FRCOG 1975, M 1962. Cons. O & G Ninewells Hosp. & Med. Sch. Dundee. Prev: Sen. Regist. Dundee Teach. Hosps.

CROWDER, Linda Elizabeth Four Lane Ends, Horsley Woodhouse, Derby DE7 6AX.

CROWDER, Rachel Elizabeth 46 Welbeck Road, Sheffield S6 5AY — MB ChB 1997 Sheff.

CROWDER, Stephen William 16 Bellefield Avenue, Liverpool L12 1LS — MB ChB 1976 Liverp.; FRCS Ed. 1992; MRCS Eng. LRCP Lond. 1976; FFAEM 1996. Cons. A & E Warrington Hosp. Socs: Brit. Assn. Accid. & Emerg. Med. Prev: Sen. Regist. (A & E) NW RHA; Regist. (A & E) Mersey RHA; Staff Grade (A & E) Roy. Liverp. Univ. Hosp.

CROWDY, Joseph Porter, CB, Maj.-Gen. late RAMC (retired) Pepperdon Mine, Lustleigh, Newton Abbot TQ13 9SN Tel: 01647 277419 Fax: 01647 277419 Email: crowdy@btinternet.com — MB ChB 1947 Ed.; MFOM 1981; FFPHM RCP (UK) 1974; DPH Lond. 1957; DIH Eng. 1957; DTM & H Eng. 1956. Prev: Hon. Cons. to Army in Nutrit.

CROWE, Alexander Vincent — MB BS 1989 Lond.; MRCP (UK) 1992. (St. Thomas' Hospital) Cons. Nephrologist Arrowe Pk. Hosp. and Countess of Chester Hosp.; ATLS Instruc./Roy. Coll. Surg.s; ALS Instruc.; Represen. Jt. Specialist Comm. for Renal Med./ Roy. Coll. of Phisicians. Socs: Roy. Coll. of Phys.s; Europ. Renal Assn. Prev: Sen. Regist., Roy. Liverp. Univ. Hosp.

CROWE, Andrew Michael The Wallace Medical Centre, 254 Thornhill Road, Falkirk FK2 7AZ Tel: 01324 622826 Fax: 01324 633447; 9 Greenhorn's Well Avenue, Falkirk FK1 5HL — BSc (Hons.) Ed. 1985, MB ChB (Hons.) 1987; MRCGP 1992; DCH RCPS Glas. 1989; DRCOG 1989. Prev: Trainee GP StenHo.muir; SHO (Psychiat.) Bellsdyke Hosp.; SHO (O & G, Med. & Paediat.) Falkirk & Dist. Roy. Infirm.

CROWE, Caitriona Alicia Shiobhaun 3 Hoopern Avenue, Exeter EX4 6DN — MB BCh BAO 1984 NUI.

CROWE, Daniel James Well House, Tolehurst Farm, Frittenden, Cranbrook TN17 2BN — MB BS 1996 Newc.

CROWE, Gail Hunter Department of Sexual Health, Herts. & Essex Hospital, Haymeads Lane, Bishop's Stortford CM23 5JH Tel: 01279 651320; 30 Albany Court, Epping CM16 5ED — MB ChB 1987 Ed.; MRCP (UK) 1991; Dip. GU Med. Soc. Apoth. Lond. 1994; DRCOG 1994; DFFP 1994. Cons. (Sexual Health & Genitourin.

Med.) P.ss Alexandra Trust; Hon. Cons. (Genitourin. Med.) St. Bart. Hosp. Prev: Sen. Regist. (Genitourin. Med.) Roy. Lond. Hosp.

CROWE, Jayne Anne Cleland Park Surgery, 2 Cleland Park, Bangor BT20 3EB; Knockmohr House, 120 Old Carrickfergfus Road, Greenisland, Carrickfergus BT38 8RJ — MB BCh BAO 1984 Belf.; MB BCh Belf. l984; MRCGP 1988.

CROWE, John Brian (retired) Westfield, Ffordd Uchaf, Harlech LL46 2SS Tel: 01766 780269 — MB BChir 1956 Camb.; MA Camb., MB 1956, BChir 1955; FFR 1965; DMRD Eng. 1959. Prev: Cons. Radiol. N. Staffs Hosp. Centre City Gen. Hosp. Stoke on Trent.

CROWE, Josephine Nancy The Rectory, Dorchester on Thames, Wallingford OX10 7HZ — MB BS 1998 Lond.; MB BS Lond 1998.

CROWE, Lisa Jane 62 Bridge Street, Llandaff, Cardiff CF5 2EN — MB BCh 1995 Wales.

CROWE, Martin Thomas Ian Queen Elizabeth Hospital, Gayton Road, King's Lynn PE30 4ET Tel: 01553 613613 Fax: 01553 613700 — MB ChB 1989 Leeds; MRCP (UK) 1992; FRCR 1995. (Univ. Leeds) Cons. Radiol. Qu. Eliz. Hosp. King's Lynn. Prev: Sen. Regist. (Radiol.) Roy. Hallamsh. Hosp. Sheff.

CROWE, Mary Bernadette Leyton Green Neighbourhood Health Service, 180 Essex Road, Leyton, London E10 6BT Tel: 020 7539 0756 Fax: 020 7556 6902; 77 Old Park Road, London N13 4RG Tel: 020 7886 4152 — MB BCh BAO 1977 NUI; MRCGP 1988; DCH RCPI 1979.

CROWE, Michael 46 Ainsdale Road, Royston, Barnsley S71 4HX — MB ChB 1994 Leic. Gen. Practitioner, Nottm. Prev: GP Regist. Nottm. VTS.

CROWE, Michael George Francis Syston Health Centre, Melton Road, Syston, Leicester LE7 2EQ Tel: 0116 260 9161 Fax: 01535 698388; Millstream Cottage, 40 Main St, Cossington, Leicester LE7 4UU Tel: 0150 981 2932 — MB BChir Camb. 1963; MRCS Eng. LRCP Lond. 1962; FRCGP 1981, M 1972. (Camb. & Guy's) Clin. Tutor (Community Health) Univ. Leic. Med. Sch.; Mem. (Ex-Chairm.) Leic. LMC; Mem. (Ex-Chairm.) Leic. Fac. RCGP. Socs: Fell. (Press Sec.) BMA; (Ex-Pres.) Leic. Med. Soc.; Dep. Chairm. Leics. Dist. Med. Advis. Comm. Prev: SHO (O & G) St. Lukes Hosp. Guildford; SHO (Cas.) Roy. Surrey Co. Hosp.; Ho. Surg. & Ho. Phys. St. Luke's Hosp. Guildford.

CROWE, Michael John 66 Palace View, Shirley, Croydon CR0 8QN — BM BCh 1963 Oxf.; MPhil (Psychiat.) Lond. 1970; DM Oxf. 1977, BM BCh 1963; FRCP Lond. 1992, M 1967; FRCPsych 1984, M 1971. (Lond. Hosp.) Cons. Psychiat. Bethlem Roy. & Maudsley Hosps. Lond. Prev: Sen. Lect. Inst. Psychiat. Lond.; SHO (Neurol. & Neurosurg.) Addenbrooke's Hosp. Camb.; Ho. Phys. Lond. Hosp.

CROWE, Natalie Asha (Desai) Highwood House, Broughton Crossroads, Scawby, Brigg DN20 9LZ — MB BS 1996 Lond. (St. Mary's Hospital Medical School, London) GP Princip.

CROWE, Patricia Margaret Oakengrove, Department of Child Health, Shrubbery Road, High Wycombe HP13 6PS Tel: 01494 426205; 90 Chestnut Lane, Amersham HP6 6EE — MB ChB 1980 Manch.; DRCOG 1983. Staff Grade Pract. (Community Paediat.) S. Bucks. NHS Trust.

CROWE, Paul Matthew Radiology Department, Birmingham Heartlands Hospital, Bordesley Green E., Birmingham B9 5SS Tel: 0121 424 0287 Fax: 0121 766 6919; Fax: 0121 680 5487 Email: paul_crowe@compuserve.com — MB BCh BAO 1988 Dub.; FFR RCSI 1996; FRCR 1997. Cons. Radiol. Birm. Heartlands Hosp. Socs: Brit. Soc. of Internat. Radiol.; Cardiovasc. & Internat. Radiol. Soc. of Europe; Brit. Inst. of Radiol. Prev: Sen. Regist. (Radiol.) W. Midl. RHA.

CROWE, Ruth Lyle Springfield, Comeytrowe Road, Trull, Taunton TA3 7NE — MB ChB 1990 Ed.; MRCGP 1994.

CROWE, Stuart Paul Brook Cottage, Long Road, Paignton TQ4 7PQ — MB ChB 1991 Bristol.

CROWELL, Eileen Marguerite Logan, Capt. RAMC 27 Orchard Grove, Orpington BR6 0RX Tel: 01689 890128 — BA (Hons.), MB BCh BAO Belf. 1941; FFA RCS Eng. 1957; DA Eng. 1946. (Qu. Univ. Belf.) Hon. Cons. (Anaesth.) Bexley & Lewisham Health Dists. Socs: BMA.

CROWFOOT, Jill Arden Medical Centre, Albany Road, Stratford-upon-Avon CV376AG Tel: 01789 414942 Fax: 01789 296427; Thistle Green, 6 Bearley Grange, Bearley, Stratford-upon-Avon CV37 0SR — MB ChB 1993 Birm.; ChB Birm. 1993; DRCOG 1995; MRCGP 1998. (Birmingham University)

CROWHURST, Edward Charles 12 Thurnton Mews, 65 Queens park Parade, Kingthorpe, Northampton NN2 6LP Tel: 01604 710611 Fax: MOB: 07957 564554 Email: eddiecrowh@aol.com — MB BChir 1993 Camb.; BA (Hons.) Oxf. 1990. (Univ. Camb.) Clin. Research Fell. (A & E) Leicester Gen. Hosp. Prev: SHO (Paediat. Surg.) Leicester Roy. Infirm.; SHO (Gen. Surg.) Good Hope Hosp. Sutton Coldfield; SHO (Orthop.) Nuneaton & N.ampton Gen. Hosp.

CROWHURST, John Anthony Department of Anaesthesia, Royal Postgraduate Medical School, Queen Charlotte's & Chelsea Hospital, Goldhawk Road, London W6 0XG Tel: 020 8383 3991 Fax: 020 8383 5373 Email: j.crowhurst@rpms.ac.uk — MB BS Adelaide 1974; BPharm Adelaide 1965; FANZCA 1992; FFA RACS 1980; DObst RCOG 1976. (University of Adelaide) Reader (Obst. Anaesth.) RPMS Univ. Lond. Hammersmith Hosp. Lond.; Hon. Cons. Anaesth. Hammersmith Hosp. NHS Trust. Socs: Austral. Soc. Anaesth.; Obst. Anaesth. Assn.; BMA. Prev: Sen. Lect. (Anaesth. Obst. & Gyn) Univ. Adelaide; Dir. Anaesth. (Wom.) Wom. & Childr. Hosp. Adelaide; Vis. Prof. Anaesth. Univ. Malaya.

CROWLE, Peter Michael 3 Claremont Road, Norwich NR4 6SH Tel: 01603 461412 — MB BS 1966 Lond.; FRCP Lond. 1983; MRCP (UK) 1970; MRCS Eng. LRCP Lond. 1965. (Univ. Coll. Hosp.) Cons. Paediat. Norwich HA. Prev: Regist. (Paediat.) Birm. Childr. Hosp.; Lect. (Child Health) Univ. Bristol.

CROWLE, Victoria Jane 3 Claremont Road, Norwich NR4 6SH — MB ChB 1994 Bristol.

CROWLESMITH, John Derek (retired) 28 The Four Tubs, Bushey WD23 4SJ Tel: 020 8950 2218 Email: j@ginbal.demon.co.uk — MB BS Lond. 1949; MRCS Eng. LRCP Lond. 1950; FFCM 1983, M 1973; DCH Eng. 1962. Prev: Sen. Med. Adviser Brit. Counc.

CROWLEY, Brian 5 Finsbury Place, Blackburn BB2 4JS — MB ChB 1989 Manch.

CROWLEY, Cornelius Joseph The Surgery, 6 Queens Walk, Ealing, London W5 1TP Tel: 020 8997 3041 Fax: 020 8566 9100 — MB BCh BAO 1976 NUI. (Cork) Socs: BMA. Prev: Cas. Off. W.m. Hosp. Lond.; Intern (Med.) & Intern (Surg.) Bon Secours Hosp. Cork.

CROWLEY, Daniel Joseph (retired) 7 Queen's Crescent, Southsea PO5 3HD Tel: 023 92 820560 — MB BCh BAO 1945 Dub. Prev: Ho. Surg. & Resid. Surg. Dr. Steevens' Hosp. Dub.

CROWLEY, David John Medical Centre, Rattray's Lane, Tomintoul, Ballindalloch AB37 9HF Tel: 01807 580219 — MB BS 1977 Lond.; MRCGP 1983; T(GP) 1991; DCH RCP Lond. 1981. Princip. GP Tomintoul. Prev: Trainee GP Aberystwyth VTS.

CROWLEY, Gail Elizabeth The Village Surgery, 24-26 Laughton Road, Thurcroft, Rotherham S66 9LP Tel: 01 709 542216; 10 W. Bank Drive, Anston, Sheffield S25 5HT Email: gec@anston.demon.co.uk — MB BS 1987 Lond.; MRCGP 1993. GP Princip.

CROWLEY, Gerald Patrick Hendford Lodge Medical Centre, Yeovil BA20 1UJ Tel: 01935 470200 Fax: 01935 470202; Hew Hill Cottage, East Coker, Yeovil BA22 9NF — MB BS 1968 Lond.; DObst RCOG 1970. (Roy. Lond. Hosp.) Socs: BMA. Prev: SHO (Paediat.) Good Hope Hosp. Sutton Coldfield; SHO (Obst.) Orsett Hosp. Grays; SHO (Med.) Torbay Hosp. Torquay.

CROWLEY, Gregory Simon The Arthur Medical Centre, Four Lane Ends, Horsley Woodhouse, Ilkeston DE7 6AX Tel: 01332 880249 — MB BS 1991 Lond.; BSc Lond. 1988; MRCGP 1995; DRCOG 1993.

CROWLEY, Joanna Mary North Road Surgery, 77 North Road, Richmond TW9 4HQ Tel: 020 8876 4442 Fax: 020 8392 2311 — MB BS 1978 Lond.; MRCS Eng. LRCP Lond. 1978; MRCGP 1983. Gen. Practitioner.

CROWLEY, Jonathan Mark Golland 25 Foxfield Avenue, Bradley Stoke, Bristol BS32 0BN Tel: 01454 619430 — MB ChB 1987 Birm.; MRCP (UK) 1992; DRCOG 1994.

CROWLEY, Margaret Clare Richmond (retired) 9 Holmesdale Road, Kew, Richmond TW9 3JZ Tel: 020 8948 4910 — MB BS 1950 Lond.; MRCS Eng. LRCP Lond. 1950. GP Richmond. Prev: Sen. Ho. Off. Bethlem. Roy. & Maudsley Hosps.

CROWLEY, Mark Patrick 14 Lordsmead Road, London N17 6EY — MB BS 1998 Lond.; MB BS Lond 1998.

CROWLEY, Matthew (retired) 11 Park Lane, Fareham PO16 7LF Tel: 01329 234653 — MB BCh BAO 1936 NUI; MFPHM RCP (UK) 1989; MFCM 1974; DPH Lond. 1947. Prev: MOH Fareham UD.

CROWLEY, Nicola Louise Hill Flat C4, Calthorpe Mansions, Frederick Road, Edgbaston, Birmingham B15 1JN Tel: 0121 455 9731; 25 Linkway, Edgcumbe Park, Crowthorne RG45 6ES Tel: 01344 774296 — MB ChB 1993 Birm.; ChB Birm. 1993. (Univ. Birm.) SHO (Psychiat.) Qu. Eliz. Psychiat. Hosp. Birm. Prev: Ho. Off. (Med.) Good Hope Hosp. Sutton Coldfield.

CROWLEY, Sophie Elizabeth The Old Bakehouse, 7 Rushton Road, Wilbarston, Market Harborough LE16 8QL — MB BS 1991 Newc. Socs: Roy. Coll. Gen. Pract.

CROWLEY, Suzanne 177 Shirland Road, London W9 2EU Tel: 020 7289 5292 — BM 1980 Soton.; MRCP (UK) 1988; DRCOG 1985; DM 1997. Specialist Regist. (Paediat. IC Unit & Respirat. Med.) Roy. Brompton & Harefield Trust. Prev: Sen. Regist. (Paediat. Respirat. Med.) Roy. Brompton Hosp. Lond.; Research Fell. (Paediat. Endocrinol.) The Middlx. Hosp.

CROWLEY, Theresa Clinic One, Bristol Royal Infirmary, Bristol Tel: 0117 928 3010 — MB BS 1976 Lond.

CROWN, Anna Louise Dept. Diabetes and Metabolism, Medical School University, Southmead Hospital, Bristol BS10 5NB Tel: 0117 9159 5337 Fax: 0117 959 5336 Email: a.l.crown@bris.ac.uk; 11 Marlborough Hill Place, Kingsdown, Bristol BS2 8HA Tel: 0117 927 2448 — MB BChir 1991 Camb.; MA Camb. 1991; MRCP (UK) 1994; PHD. Uni.Brist. 1998. p/t Lect. in Med. Socs: Soc. Endocrinol. Prev: Research Regist. (Endocrinol.) Bristol Roy. Infirm.; SHO (Med.) Bristol Roy Infirm.; SHO Middlx. Hosp. Lond.

CROWN, Isidore Wolfe 37 Reid House, Bampton Road, London SE23 2BJ Tel: 020 8291 4428; 14 Leslie Gardens, Sutton SM2 6QU Tel: 020 8643 5141 Fax: 020 8291 4428 Email: isidore_wolfe.crown@virgin.net — MRCS Eng. LRCP Lond. 1947. (King's Coll. Hosp.) Prev: Ho. Surg. Vict. Hosp. Blackpool; RAMC.

CROWN, June Madge, CBE (retired) 118 Whitfield St, London W1T 5EG Tel: 0207 387 6787 Fax: 0207 387 6787 Email: junecrown@aol.com — MB BChir 1962 Camb.; MSc (Social Med.) Lond. 1974; MA Camb. 1962; FRCP Lond. 1992; FFPHM 1981, M 1975. Prev: Past Pres., Fac. Pub. Health Med.

CROWN, Maureen Patricia 23 King's Avenue, Buckhurst Hill IG9 5LP Tel: 020 8504 0122; 43 Frederica Road, Chingford, London E4 7AL — MB BS 1974 Lond. (Roy. Free) p/t Asst. GP Buckhurst Hill; Health Screening and GP work at Holly Huse Hosp., High Rd., Buckhurst Hill, Essex, IG9 5HX.

CROWN, Sidney 14 Devonshire Place, London W1G 6HX Tel: 020 7935 0640 Fax: 020 7224 6256; 118 Whitfield Street, London W1P 5RZ Tel: 020 7387 6787 Fax: 020 7387 6787 Email: sidneycrown@aol.com — MRCS Eng. LRCP Lond. 1959; PhD Lond. 1949; FRCP Lond. 1975, M 1965; FRCPsych 1973; DPM Eng. 1964. (Middlx.) Cons. Psychiat. Lond. Hosp. Socs: Experim. Psychol. Soc.; Brit. Psychol. Soc. Prev: Sen. Regist. (Psychiat.) Nat. Hosp. Qu. Sq. Lond.; Regist. Acad. Psychiat. Unit & Ho. Surg. Middlx. Hosp. Lond.

CROWNE, Elizabeth Clare Bristol Royal Hospital For Children, Upper Maudlin Street, Bristol BS2 8BJ — FRCPCH 1997; MB ChB Manch. 1984; BSc (Hons.) Manch. 1981, MD 1994; MRCP (UK) 1988. Cons. Paediat. (Endocrinol. & Diabetes) Bristol Roy. Childr. Hosp. Socs: Brit. Soc. Paediat. Endocrinol.; Eur. Soc. Paediat. Endocrinol.; Brit. Soc. Ad. Of Gyn. Prev: Research Fell. Paediat. Endocrinol. Bristol; Clin. Lect (Paediat. Endocrinol.) John Radcliffe Hosp. Oxf.

CROWNSHAW, Tina Louise Plot 2 Phase II, The Retreat, Isaf Hendy, Miskin, Pontyclun CF72 8QS — MB BCh 1989 Wales.

CROWSON, Jonathan Brian 133 Ash Road, Leeds LS6 3HD — MB ChB 1993 Ed.

CROWSON, Jonathan David Regay, North End Crescent, Tetney, Grimsby DN36 5LZ — MB ChB 1994 Leeds.

CROWSON, Richard Alastair 25 Beckett House, Becket St., London SE1 4XY — MB BS 1996 Lond.

CROWSTON, Jonathan Guy Department of Ophthalmology, Royal Free Hospital, London NW3 Tel: 020 7794 2500; 56B Hornsey Lane, Highgate, London N6 5LU Tel: 020 7281 7046 Fax: 020 7281 7046 — MB BS 1990 Lond.; BSc Immunopath. Lond. 1987; FRCOphth 1994. SHO (Ophth.) Roy. Surrey Hosp. Guildford. Prev: SHO (Ophth.) St. Helier Trust Sutton Surrey; Ho. Off. (A & E) St. Richards Chichester; Ho. Surg. Watford Gen. Hosp.

CROWTHER, Alan Pendleside Medical Practice, Clitheroe Health Centre, Railway View Road, Clitheroe BB7 2JG Tel: 01200 421888 Fax: 01200 421887; 37 Langshaw Drive, Clitheroe BB7 1EY Tel: 01200 423058 — MB BS 1984 Lond.; BSc (Hons.) Lond. 1981; MRCGP (Distinc.) 1988; DRCOG 1987. (King's Coll. Hosp.) Prev: Trainee GP Gt. Yarmouth VTS.

CROWTHER, Andrew Nicholas Church Street Surgery, 77 Church Street, Tewkesbury GL20 5RY Tel: 01684 292343 Fax: 01684 274305; Green Farm, Bushley, Tewkesbury GL20 6HY Tel: 01684 294177 — BM BCh 1966 Oxf.; MA Oxf. 1966; MRCGP 1976; DA Eng. 1971; DObst RCOG 1970. (Oxf. & St. Bart.) Clin. Asst. (Anaesth.) Tewkesbury Gen. Hosp. Socs: BMA; (Hon. Treas) Community Hosps. Assn. Prev: Ho. Surg. (Obst.) Rochford Gen. Hosp.; Ho. Surg. Roy. Berks. Hosp. Reading; Ho. Phys. St. Bart. Hosp. Lond.

CROWTHER, Anthony George Oliver, SBStJ (retired) St. Luke's Hospice, Little Common Lane, Sheffield S11 9NE Tel: 0114 236 9911 Fax: 0114 262 1242 — MB BChir 1962 Camb.; Hon. Duniv. (Italian University) 2001; MA Camb. 1961; DObst RCOG 1963. Med. Dir. St. Luke's Hospice Sheff.; Hon. Cons. Palliat. Med. W.one Pk. Hosp. Sheff.; Hon. Lect. (Gen. Pract.) Sheff. Univ. Med. Sch.; Hon. Clin. Adviser Trent Region Palliat. Care Centre Sheff.; Hon. Cons. Adviser St. Peter's Hospice Barnsley; Specialist (Palliat. Med.) Barnsley HA. Prev: Ho. Off. (Radiother.) & Ho. Surg. (Plastic & Orthop. Surg.) Middlx. Hosp. Lond.

CROWTHER, Caroline Anne Wyle-Cop, Camel St., Marston Magna, Yeovil BA22 8DB — MB ChB 1975 Birm.; MRCOG 1980.

CROWTHER, Caroline Elizabeth 18 Leyfield Road, Dore, Sheffield S17 3EE Email: caroline@familydownes.freeserve.co.uk — MB ChB 1995 Sheff.; MRCGP; DFFP. GP Non Princip.

CROWTHER, Christine Asya Sandwell Healthcare Trust, Lyndon, West Bromwich — MB ChB 1981 Bristol; MA (Med. Ethics) Keele 1991; MRCP (UK) 1986. Cons. Phys. (Elderly Care) Sandwell Health Care Trust Lyndon, W. Bromwich. Prev: Sen. Regist. (c/o the Elderly) New Cross Hosp. Wolverhampton; Clin. Research Fell. (Clin. Pharmacol.) Qu. Eliz. Hosp. Birm.; Regist. (Gen. Med.) Sandwell Dist. Gen. Hosp. W. Bromwich.

CROWTHER, Christopher Hugh (retired) Barlow Medical Centre, 8 Barlow Moor Road, Didsbury, Manchester M20 6TR Tel: 0161 445 2101 Fax: 0161 445 9560 — MB ChB 1964 Manch.; MRCGP 1974; DObst RCOG 1966. Med. Adviser Newbury Resid. Ther. for Chronic Alcoholism; Med. Adviser Mary & Joseph Hse. Prev: Lect. Div. Family Med. Univ. W. Ont., Lond., Canada.

CROWTHER, Derek Christie Hospital NHS Trust, Wilmslow Road, Manchester M20 4BX Tel: 0161 445 8123 Fax: 0161 434 7728; 52 Barlowmoor Road, Didsbury, Manchester M20 2TR Tel: 0161 434 6685 — MB BChir 1963 Camb.; MSc Manch. 1977; PhD Lond. 1968; MA Camb. 1963; FRCP Lond. 1976, M 1966; FRCR 1992. (St. Bart.) Prof. Med. Oncol. Christie Hosp. & Holt Radium Inst. Manch. & Univ. Manch.; Mem. Scientif. Comm. Cancer Research Campaign. Socs: Europ. Organisation for Research on Treatm. of Cancer; Amer. Soc. Clin. Oncol. & Cancer Research. Prev: Sen. Lect. (Med. Oncol.) St. Bart. Hosp. Lond.; Regist. Roy. Marsden Hosp. & Chester Beatty Research Inst.; Ho. Surg. (Radiother.) Hammersmith Hosp.

CROWTHER, Dorothy Linda Corner Croft, Lonstries, Keswick CA12 4TD Tel: 017687 74689 — MB ChB 1965 Sheff.; Dip. Therapeut. Cardiff 1995; MSc (Gen. Pract.) Lond. 1991; FRCGP 1986, M 1975; DObst RCOG 1967. (Sheff.) Socs: BMA; GP Writers Assn.; Fell. Roy. Coll. GPs. Prev: Med. Adviser Brent & Harrow FHSA; Med. Dir. Herts. Family Health Hertford; GP Potters Bar & Maghull, Lancs.

CROWTHER, Geoffrey Raymond 39 Kensington Road, Belfast BT5 6NJ — MB BCh BAO 1978 Belf.

CROWTHER, Ian Alexander (retired) Gannochy, Dunblane FK15 0DP Tel: 01786 824006 — MB BS 1957 Durh.; MRCGP 1976; DCH RCPS Glas. 1962. Prev: GP DunbLa.

CROWTHER, Mr John Alexander Department of Otolaryngology, Victoria Infirmary, Langside, Glasgow G46 Tel: 0141 201 5289 Fax: 0141 201 5093; 6 Lynton Avenue, Whitecraigs, Glasgow G46 7JP — MB ChB 1979 Dundee; FRCS Glas. 1994; FRCS Eng. 1984; T(S) 1991. Cons. ENT Surg. Vict. Infirm. Glas.; Cons. Neurolotol. Inst. Neurol. Sci. S. Gen. Hosp. Glas. Prev: Research Fell. Univ. Michigan; Regist. (ENT) Radcliffe Infirm. Oxf.

CROWTHER, John Watson (retired) Ostlers, North Meadow, Offham, West Malling ME19 5NU — MB ChB 1938 Liverp.

CROWTHER, Kathryn Amanda Lampard Brook Farm, Lampard Brook, Framlingham, Woodbridge IP13 9SB — MB ChB 1978 Manch.

CROWTHER, Mr Mark Andrew Austen Green Farm, Bushley, Tewkesbury GL20 6HY Tel: 01684 294177 — MB BS 1993 Lond.; FRCS (Eng.) 1997. (St. Mary's Hospital Medical School) Specialist Regist., Orthop./Trauma, S. W. N.ern Rotat.

CROWTHER, Martin Francis St Peters Surgery, 51 Leckie Road, Walsall WS2 8DA Tel: 01922 23755 Fax: 01922 746477 — MB ChB 1989 Birm.; MRCGP 1994; DCH RCP Lond. 1993.

CROWTHER, Paul Stephen Tennyson Avenue Medical Centre, 1 Tennyson Avenue, Chesterfield S40 4SN Tel: 01246 232339 Fax: 01246 209097 — MB ChB 1976 Sheff. Examr. St. John's Ambul.

CROWTHER, Rachel Louise Oxfordshire Health Authority, Old Road, Headington, Oxford OX3 7LF Tel: 01753 741841 Email: rachel.crowther@oxon-ha.anglox.nhs.uk; 281 Woodstock Road, Oxford OX2 7NY Tel: 01865 556005 Email: rachel@raku.demon.co.uk — MB BChir 1989 Camb. (Cambridge/St. Bartholomews) Specialist Regist. (Pub. Health Med.) Oxf.shire HA. Prev: SHO (Paediat.) Whipps Cross Hosp. Lond.; CMO (Paediat.) S. Bucks. NHS Trust.

CROWTHER, Sean Michael 42 Shandon Drive, Bangor BT20 5HR — MB BCh BAO 1994 Belf.; MB BCh Belf. 1994.

CROWTHER, Simon David Department of Thoracic Medicine, King's College Hospital, Denmark Hill, Camberwell, London SE5 9RJ Tel: 020 7737 4000 Fax: 020 7346 3589; 112 Court Road, Orpington BR6 0PZ Tel: 01689 815547 — MB BS 1989 Lond.; MRCP (UK) 1993. Research Fell. (Thoracic Med.) King's Coll. Hosp. Lond. Socs: BMA & Med. Defence Union. Prev: Regist. (Med.) Bromley Hosp. & King's Coll. Hosp. Lond.; SHO (Med.) FarnBoro. Hosp.

CROXFORD, Vivienne Alice, MBE (retired) Grazeley, Waters Green, Brockenhurst SO42 7RG Tel: 01590 623613 — MB ChB 1945 St. And.; BSc St. And. 1942; FRCOG 1982, M 1954. Prev: Obst. i/c Wendover Matern. Hosp. ChristCh., NZ.

CROXSON, Richard Selwyn 61 Wimpole Street, London W1G 8AH Tel: 020 7935 2617 Fax: 020 7224 1680 Email: medcent.london@dial.pipex.com; 13 Ripplevale Grove, London N1 1HS Tel: 020 7607 1694 Email: richard@croxson.net — MB ChB NZ 1960; FRACP 1972, M 1965. (Otago) p/t Chief Med. Off. Swiss Re Life & Health UK & Lincoln Assur. Company; Pres. Assur. Med. Soc. Socs: Brit. Cardiac Soc.; Med. Soc. of Lond. Prev: Cons. Cardiol. & Med. Tutor Auckland Hosp., NZ; Cons. Cardiol. S. (Manch.) Health Dist. (T).

CROXSON, Simon Christopher Martin Bristol General Hospital, Bristol BS1 6SY Tel: 0117 928 6288 Fax: 0117 928 6245 Email: simon.croxson@virgin.net — BM 1981 Soton.; MD Leicester 1995; MRCP (UK) 1984; FRCP (Lond) 1999. Cons. Phys. United Bristol Healthcare NHS Trust; Hon. Sen. Clin. Lect. (Med.) Univ. Bristol. Socs: Brit. Diabetic Assn. & Brit. Geriat. Soc. Prev: Sen. Regist. (Gen. & Geriat. Med.) N.. Gen. Hosp. Sheff.

CROXSON, Susan Anne Currie (retired) Hope Cottage, 13 Ripplevale Grove, London N1 1HS Tel: 020 7607 1694 Email: croxson@scroxson.freeserve.co.uk — MB ChB Glas. 1961.

CROY, Melanie Frances Ashworth Hospital, Parkbourne, Maghull, Liverpool L31 5HW Tel: 0151 473 0303; 5 Bracken Way, Bridgend CF31 1YQ — MB ChB 1988 Dundee; BMSc (Pharmacol.) Dund 1985; MRCPsych 1993. Sen. Regist. Forens. Psychiat. Ashworth Hosp. Liverp. Socs: Roy. Coll. Psychiat. Prev: Regist. (Psychiat.) Roy. Edin. Hosp.; SHO Rotat. (Psychiat.) Del La Pole Hosp. Hull; SHO (Psychiat.) Grimsby Dist. Gen. Hosp.

CROYDON, Edgar Austin Peter Paradise House, Church Lane, Yealmpton, Plymouth PL8 2HG Tel: 01752 881561 Fax: 01752 881561 — MB BS Lond. 1955; MRCS Eng. LRCP Lond. 1955; FFPM 1990; Dip. Pharm. Med. RCP (UK) 1977. (St. Geo.) Indep. GP & Pharmaceut. Cons. Devon. Socs: Fell. Roy. Soc. Med.; Plymouth Med. Soc. Prev: Med. Dir. Europ. Div. Beecham Pharmaceut., Brussels.

CROZIER, Catherine Lesley 8 Broomhill Park, Belfast BT9 5JB Tel: 028 90 666940 Fax: 028 90 666940 — MB BCh BAO 1966 Belf. GP Med. Off. Purdysburn Hosp. Prev: Regist. N. Irel. Hosps. Auth.; SHO Purdysburn Hosp. Gp.; Ho. Off. Roy. Vict. Hosp. Belf.

CRUICKSHANK, Alan Hamilton (retired) The Old House, 28 North Road, Grassendale Park, Liverpool L19 0LR Tel: 0151 427 1738 — MB ChB 1936 Aberd.; PhD Liverp. 1953; MD Aberd. 1942; MCPath 1964. Prev: Reader (Path.) Univ. Liverp.

CRUICKSHANK, Alexander Neil (retired) The Old Vicarage, Tuddenham St Martin, Ipswich IP6 9BZ Tel: 01473 85415 — MRCS Eng. LRCP Lond. 1958; FFA RCS Eng. 1965. Cons. i/c Intens. Ther. Unit Ipswich Hosp.; Clin. Teach. Fac. Clin. Med. Univ. Camb. Prev: Sen. Regist. & Clin. Tutor Univ. Dept. Anaesth. Roy. Infirm. Edin.

CRUICKSHANK, Anne McDonald Department of Biochemistry, Southern General Hospital NHS Trust, 1345 Govan Road, Glasgow G51 4TF Tel: 0141 445 2466 Fax: 0141 445 3670; 10 Craigmillar Avenue, Milngavie, Glasgow G62 8AU Tel: 0141 956 6532 — MB ChB 1982 Glas.; MD (hons.) Glas. 1993; MRCPath. 1991. Cons. Clin. Biochem. S.ern Gen. Hosp. NHS Trust; Hon. Clin. Sen. Lect. (Path. Biochem.) Glas. Univ.

CRUICKSHANK, Annette Health Centre, Bank Street, Cupar KY15 4JN Tel: 01334 653478 Fax: 01334 657305; Vantage House, Cupar KY15 4RT — MB ChB 1977 Aberd.

CRUICKSHANK, Charles Ian Thomas (retired) 83 Dunbar Street, Burghead, Elgin IV30 5XQ — MB ChB Aberd. 1953; FRCGP 1984, M 1961. Prev: Gen. Phys. Inverurie Hosp.

CRUICKSHANK, Clive Alexander The Aberford Centre, Fieldhead Hospital, Wakefield — MB ChB 1979 Leeds; MRCPsych 1983; FRCPsych 1999. Cons. Psychiat. Fieldhead Hosp. Wakefield.

CRUICKSHANK, Derek James South Cleveland Hospital, Marton Road, Middlesbrough TS4 3BW Tel: 01642 854858; North Park House, Green Lane, Yarm TS15 9EH Tel: 01642 782682 — MB ChB 1980 Aberd.; MRCOG 1987. Cons. Gyn. S. Cleveland Hosp. Middlesbrough. Socs: Brit. Gyn. Cancer Soc. & Brit. Soc. for Colposcopy & Cerv. Path.; Internat. Gyn. Cancer Soc.

CRUICKSHANK, Donald McDonald 110 St Andrew's Drive, Glasgow G41 4RB Tel: 0141 427 1355 — LRCP LRCS 1950 Ed.; LRCP LRCS Ed. LRFPS Glas. 1950. (Glas.)

CRUICKSHANK, Donald Murray Braemar Health Clinic, St. Andrews Terrace, Braemar, Ballater AB35 5WR Tel: 01339 741202 Fax: 01339 741450 — MB ChB 1985 Glas. (University of Glasgow) Socs: BMA; CMF. Prev: Trainee GP Lanarksh. HB VTS; Ho. Surg. Gartnavel Gen. Hosp. & W.. Infirm. Glas.; Ho. Phys. Raigmore Hosp. Inverness & Belford Hosp. Fort William.

CRUICKSHANK, Professor Eric Kennedy, OBE Parsonage House, Oare, Marlborough SN8 4JA Tel: 01672 63547 — MD (Hons.) Aberd. 1948, MB ChB (Hons.) 1937; FRCP Lond. 1955, M 1948; Hon. FACP 1970. (Aberd.) Socs: Assn. Phys. & BMA. Prev: Emerit. Prof. Univ. Glas.; Prof. Postgrad. Med. Educat. & Dean Postgrad. Med. Univ. Glas.; Prof. & Dean of Med. Univ. of the W. Indies.

CRUICKSHANK, Frances Regina Tyrel (retired) 18 Ashcombe Avenue, Handsworth Wood, Birmingham B20 1AT Tel: 0121 554 1059 — MB ChB 1943 St. And. Prev: Gen. Practitioner Birm.

CRUICKSHANK, George Watt (retired) Caprice, Send Marsh Road, Ripley, Woking GU23 6JB — MB ChB 1951 Aberd. Prev: Med. Off. Burin Cott. Hosp. Newfld.

CRUICKSHANK, Gillian Ruth (retired) Strathy Cottage, Kidrochit Drive, Braemar, Ballater AB35 5YW Tel: 013397 41202 Fax: 013397 41450 — MB ChB 1982 Glas. Prev: Trainee GP E.erHo. Health Centre Glas.

CRUICKSHANK, Gordon Stuart Path House, 7 Nether St., Kirkcaldy KY1 2PG Tel: 01592 644533; 22 Ben Ledi Road, Kirkcaldy KY2 5RP Tel: 01592 643769 — MB ChB Ed. 1966; DObst RCOG 1970. (Ed.)

CRUICKSHANK, Mrs Helen Elizabeth ENT Department, Pinderfields and Pontefract NHS Trust, Aberford Road, Wakefield WF1 4DG Tel: 01924 212138 Fax: 01924 213601; 7 Harrowby Crescent, Leeds LS16 5HP — MB ChB 1980 Leeds; BSc Psychol. Leeds 1977; FRCS (Orl.) 1997; DLO RCS Eng. 1983. Cons. (Otolaryngologist) Pinderfields & Pontefract NHS Trust. Prev: Clin. Asst. (ENT) Harrogate Gen. Hosp; Regist. (ENT) Ninewells Hosp. Dundee & Yorks. RHA; Sen. Regist. Rotat. ENT Yorks. Deanery.

CRUICKSHANK, Iain David Old Coulsdon Medical Practice, 2A Court Avenue, Old Coulsdon, Coulsdon CR5 1HF Tel: 01737 553393 Fax: 01737 550267; 9 Egmont Road, Sutton SM2 5JR — MB BS 1986 Lond.; DCH RCP Lond. 1989.

CRUICKSHANK, Iain Nicolson Leven Health Centre, Victoria Road, Leven KY8 4ET Tel: 01333 425656 Fax: 01333 422249 — MB ChB 1981 Glas.; MRCGP 1993. (Univ. Glas.)

CRUICKSHANK, John Alexander St Peters Hill Surgery, 15 St. Peters Hill, Grantham NG31 6QA Tel: 01476 590009 Fax: 01476 570898; The Barn, School Lane, Pickworth, Sleaford NG34 0TF — MB ChB 1984 Manch.; MB ChB Manch. l984; MRCGP 1993; FCAnaesth. 1989.

CRUICKSHANK, John Gladstone (retired) Coombe Farm, Knowle, Cullompton EX15 1PT Tel: 01884 33533 — MB BS Lond. 1956; MA Camb. 1957; MD (Hons.) Birm. 1968; MRCS Eng. LRCP Lond. 1956; FRCPath 1977, M 1965. Microbiol. Pub. Health Laborat. Exeter. Prev: Dean Godfrey Huggins Sch. Med. Salisbury, Rhodesia.

CRUICKSHANK, John Kennedy Clinical Epidemiology Unit (& Manchester Diabetes Centre), University of Manchester Medical School, Manchester M13 9PT Tel: 0161 275 5199 Fax: 0161 275 5208 Email: clinep@man.ac.uk; 16 King's Drive, Heaton Moor, Stockport SK4 4DZ Tel: 0161 432 2429 — MB ChB 1975 Birm.; BSc Birm. 1972, MD 1986; MRCP (UK) 1978; MSc Lond. 1986; FRCP 1999. Sen. Lect. (Clin. Epidemiol.) & Cons. Phys. (Diabetes) Univ. Manch. Med. Sch. & Roy. Infirm. Socs: Brit. & Internat. Diabetes Federat.; Brit. Hypertens. Soc.; Internat. Diabetes Federat. Prev: Sen. Regist. Diabetic & MRC Epidemiol. Units N.wick Pk. Hosp. Harrow & Centr. Middlx. Hosp. Lond.; Research Fell. Hammersmith Hosp. Lond.; Lect (Med.) Univ. W. Indies Kingston, Jamaica.

CRUICKSHANK, Mr John Louis Department of Orthopaedics, St James Hospital, Beckett Street, Leeds LS9 7TF Tel: 0113 243 3144; 7 Harrowby Crescent, Leeds LS16 5HP Tel: 0113 274 1430 — MB ChB Leeds 1980; BSc (Anat.) Leeds 1977; FRCS Ed. 1985; FMGEMS 1989. Cons. Orthop. Surg.Leeds Teachg. Hosp.s NHS Trust & Hon. Sen. Clin. Lect. Univ. Leeds. Socs: Brit. Orthop. Assn. & Brit. Scoliosis Soc.; Corr. Mem. Scoliosis Research Soc. USA. Prev: Sen. Lect. & Hon. Cons. Spinal Orthop. Surg. Univ. Leeds & St. Jas. Univ. Hosp. Trust; Leatherman Spine Fell. Louisville, USA; Action Research for Crippled Child Fell. Univ. Leeds.

CRUICKSHANK, John Malcolm 16 Laleham Green, Bramhall, Stockport SK7 3LJ — BM BCh 1965 Oxf.; MA, DM Oxf. 1970; FRCP Lond. 1985, M 1968. (Oxf. & St. Mary's) Indep. Cardiovasc. Cons.; Asst. (Cardiol.) Wythenshawe Hosp. Manch. Socs: Fell. Roy. Soc. Med.; BMA. Prev: Lect. (Cardiol.) Soton. Univ.; Regist. (Med.) Gen. Hosp. Birm.; Research Fell. Birm. RHB.

CRUICKSHANK, John McAra Heightside, Whins Lane, Read, Burnley BB12 7QY Tel: 01282 772737 — MB ChB 1972 St. And.; MRCOG 1977, DObst 1974; FRCOG 1997. Cons. O & G Burnley Gen. Hosp. Prev: Cons. O & G Selly Oak Hosp. & Sorrento Matern. Hosp. Birm.

CRUICKSHANK, John McRae Mowbray House, Malpas Road, Northallerton DL7 8FW Tel: 01609 775281 Fax: 01609 778029 — MB ChB 1966 Aberd.; DObst RCOG 1971. GP. Prev: Ho. Off. Aberd. Roy. Infirm.; Med. Regist. Perth Roy. Infirm.

CRUICKSHANK, Leslie Duffus (retired) Ardshona, 27 Arbroath Road, Forfar DD8 2JJ — MB ChB 1955 Aberd.

CRUICKSHANK, Leslie James William Bo'ness Road Medical Practice, 31-33 Bo'ness Road, Grangemouth FK3 8AN Tel: 01324 482653 — MB ChB 1981 Aberd.; MRCGP 1986; DRCOG 1986.

CRUICKSHANK, Margaret Eleanor Gynaecology Oncology Unit, Ward 43, Aberdeen Royal Infirmary, Aberdeen AB25 1LD Email: ogy095@abdn.ac.uk — MB ChB 1985 Aberd.; MRCOG 1991; MD 1999 Aberdeen. (University of Aberdeen)

CRUICKSHANK, Mary Calderwood Wilson 110 St Andrew's Drive, Glasgow G41 4RB — MB ChB 1950 Glas. (Glas.)

CRUICKSHANK, Neil Robert John 12 Elveley Drive, West Ella, Hull HU10 7RU Tel: 01482 657058 — MB ChB 1990 Dundee. SHO (Cardiothoracic) Sheff. Gen. Hosp. Prev: Ho. Off. (Gen. Med. & Plastic & Gen. Surg.) Ninewells Hosp. Dundee.

CRUICKSHANK, Robert Henry St. James's University Hospital, Beckett St., Leeds LS9 7TF — MB BS 1982 Newc.; FFA RCS Eng. 1987. Cons. Anaesth. St. Jas. Univ. Hosp. Trust. Prev: Sen. Regist. (Anaesth.) Yorks. RHA.

CRUICKSHANK, Roger John (retired) Wytham Cottage, 3 Acre End St., Eynsham, Witney OX29 4PE Tel: 01865 882187 — MB ChB Glas. 1948. Prev: Med. Off. HMP Grendon.

CRUICKSHANK, Rona Anne — MB ChB 1985 Glas.; MSc (Pub. Health & Epidemiol.) Manch. 1992; MFPHM RCP (UK) 1994. Cons. Pub. Health Med. Stockport Health Auth. Socs: Manch. Med. Soc. Prev: Sen. Regist. (Pub. Health Med.) NW Region.

CRUICKSHANK, Ruth Kineal, 1 East Drive, Upper Largo, Leven KY8 6EZ — MB ChB 1985 Ed. Regist. (Anaesth.) S.. Gen. Hosp. Glas.

CRUICKSHANK, Steven Gillies Heath Dept of Anaesthesia & ITU, Newcastle General Hospital, Westgate Road, Newcastle upon Tyne NE4 6BE Tel: 0191 256 3193 Fax: 01912563154 Email: scruick@aol.com; 3 North Road, Ponteland, Newcastle upon Tyne NE20 9UH Tel: 01661 825 5173 Email: sghcruickshank@gmx.co.uk — MB BS 1974 Newc.; BA Open 1988; MB BS (2nd cl. Hons.) Newc. 1974; FRCA Eng. 1979. (Newcastle upon Tyne) Cons. Anaesth.Newc. Hosp.s NHS Trust.

CRUICKSHANKS, Sarah Tracey 8 Upper Malone Crescent, Belfast BT9 6PR — MB BCh BAO 1990 Belf.

CRUIKSHANK, Anne Webb and Partners, Cox's Yard, West Street, Somerton TA11 7PR Tel: 01458 272473 Fax: 01458 274461 — MB ChB 1985 Bristol; MRCGP 1993.

CRUIKSHANK, David Alexander Toberargan Surgery, 27 Toberargan Road, Pitlochry PH16 5HG Tel: 01796 472558 Fax: 01796 473775; Kindrochet, 166 Atholl Road, Pitlochry PH16 5AR Tel: 01796 472776 — MB ChB 1973 Aberd.; MRCGP 1978; DRCOG 1976; Cert Family Plann. RCOG, RCGP & FPA 1977; FRCGP 1997. (Aberdeen) Prev: Community Phys. Tayside Primary Care Trust.

CRUIKSHANK, Graham Macdonald Station Road Surgery, Haworth, Keighley BD22 8NL — MB ChB 1979 Aberd.

CRUIKSHANK, John Graham Ford Ranken 33 Moray Place, Edinburgh EH3 6BX Tel: 0131 225 6931 — MB ChB 1961 Ed.; FRCP Ed. 1980, M 1965; FRCR 1975; FFR 1973; DMRD Ed. 1971; DCH Eng. 1963. (Ed.) Cons. (Radiol.) Lothian Health Bd. Socs: Scott. Radiol. Soc. & Edin. Radiol. Soc. Prev: SHO (Gen. Med.) & Sen. Regist. (Radiol.) Roy. Infirm. Edin.; SHO Qu. Eliz. Hosp. Childr. Lond.

CRUIKSHANKS, Penelope Jane 200 New Kings Road, London SW6 4NF — MB ChB 1992 Cape Town.

***CRUISE, Andrew Stanbury** 18 Beaumont Street, London W1G 6DG — BM 1997 Soton.; BSc Soton. 1996.

CRUM, Jacqueline Ellen Community Child Health, Cornhill Hospital, Berryden Road, Aberdeen AB25 3HG Tel: 01224 663131 Fax: 01224 840795 — MB ChB 1977 Glas.; MRCP (UK) 1980; DCH Eng. 1980. Cons. (Communitty Paediat.).

CRUMBLEHOLME, George Kunert Burnley Wood Medical Centre, 50 Parliament Street, Burnley BB11 3JX Tel: 01282 425521 Fax: 01282 832556; 30 Reedley Road, Reedley, Burnley BB10 2LU — MB ChB 1981 Manch.; DRCOG 1984. Prev: Trainee GP Stockport FPC.

CRUMLISH, Patrick 21 Kilnford Crescent, Dundonald, Kilmarnock KA2 9DW — MB ChB 1969 Glas.; FRCR 1976; DMRD Eng. 1973; DObst RCOG 1971. (Glas.) Cons. Radiol. CrossHo. Hosp., Kilmarnock. Socs: BMA (Treas. Ayrsh. & Arran Div.). Prev: Sen. Regist. (Radiol.) Glas. Roy. Infirm.; Sen. Regist. (Neuroradiol.) Inst. Neurol. Sc. Glas.

CRUMMIE, Arthur James McCracken Monkwearmouth Health Centre, Dundas Street, Sunderland SR6 0AB Tel: 0191 567 4293 Fax: 0191 514 7889; 17 Park Avenue, Roker, Sunderland SR6 9PU Tel: 0191 548 3658 — MB BCh BAO 1978 NUI; LRCPSI 1978; MRCGP 1985; DCH NUI 1982; DObst RCPI 1980; LM 1980. Club Doctor Sunderland AFC.

CRUMP, Ann Auriol St Claire Woodward 4 The Meadows, Hilderstone, Stone ST15 8XT — MB BS 1997 Lond. (St. Mary's) Basic Surgic. Trainee N. Staffs.

CRUMP, Bernard John Leicestershire HA, Gwendelen Road, Leicester LE5 4QG Tel: 0116 258 8552; 29 Hill Field, Oadby, Leicester LE2 4RW Tel: 0116 271 7196 Fax: 0116 271 7198 Email: bernard@dphm.demon.co.uk — MB ChB 1980 Birm.; MRCP (UK) 1983; MFCM RCP (UK) 1990. Dir. Pub. Health Leicester HA; Hon. Sen. Clin. Lect. Dept. Pub. Health & Epidemiol. Univ. Leicester. Prev: Dir. Pub. Health S. Birm. HA.

CRUMP, Martin Stuart Midlands Occupation Health Service Ltd., 83 Birmingham Road, West Bromwich B70 6PX — MB ChB 1984 Birm.; AFOM RCP Lond. 1996. Sen. Regist. Midl. Occupat. Health Serv. W. Bromwich. Prev: SHO Shrewsbury Eye, Ear & Throat Hosp.; SHO (Psychiat.) Shrewsbury Shelton Hosp.; SHO (Cas.) Roy. Shrewsbury Hosp.

CRUMPLIN, Elizabeth Ann Greenridges, 57 Wynnstay Lane, Marford, Wrexham LL12 8LH Tel: 01978 854701 — MB BS 1965

Lond.; MRCS Eng. LRCP Lond. 1965; MFFP 1993; DA Eng. 1975; DObst RCOG 1967. (Middlx.) Clin. Asst. (Gyn.) Maelor Gen. Hosp. Wrexham; Instruc. Doctor (Family Plann.) Wrexham. Prev: SHO (Obst.) Amersham Gen. Hosp.

CRUMPLIN, Mr Kenneth Hugh Greenridges, Wynnstay Lane, Marford, Wrexham LL12 8LH Tel: 01978 854701 — MB BS 1965 Lond.; FRCS Eng. 1969; MRCS Eng. LRCP Lond. 1965. (Middlx.) Cons. Surg. Wrexham Maelor Trust; Cons. Surg. Maelor Gen. Hosp. Wrexham; Examr. UEB & Intercollegiate Specialist Examr.; Ex-Chairm. Ct. of Examrs. RCS Eng. Socs: (Counc.) Assn. Surgs.; Welsh Surgic. Soc.; BASO. Prev: Sen. Regist. (Surg.) United Birm. Hosps.; Hon. Research Fell. Qu. Eliz. Med. Centr. Birm.; Regist. (Surg.) Middlx. Hosp. Lond.

CRUMPTON, Margaret Ingram, Back Lane, Skerne, Driffield YO25 9HP Tel: 01377 241786 — MB BS 1954 Durh. Psychother. N. Humberside.

CRUMPTON, Norman Edward (retired) Ingram, Back Lane, Skerne, Driffield YO25 9HP Tel: 01377 241786 Email: norecrum@tesco.net — MB BS Durh. 1953, DPM 1958; FRCPsych 1977, M 1971. Prev: Cons. Psychiat. BRd.gate Hosp. Beverley & De La Pole Hosp. Hull.

CRUNDWELL, Neil Barton 8 Wickor Way, Emsworth PO10 7RE — BChir 1989 Camb.

CRUSZ, Thomas Aquinas Marinus South London Blood Centre, 75 Cranmer Terrace, Tooting, London SW17 0RB Tel: 020 8258 8300 Fax: 020 8258 8453; 4 Grosvenor Gardens, Woodford Green IG8 0BE — MB BS 1971 Ceylon; MSc Med. Immunol. Lond. 1990; FRCPath 1988; T(Path) 1991. Assoc. Specialist Nat. Blood Serv. Lond. & S. E. Zone. Prev: Assoc. Specialist NE Thames Regional Transfus. Centre Brentwood; Regist. (Haemat.) Whipps Cross Hosp. & Chase Farm Hosp. Lond.

CRUTCHFIELD, Leigh Ann Keep Cottage, 108 St Leonards St., West Malling ME19 6PD — MB BS 1998 Lond.; MB BS Lond 1998.

CRUTCHLEY, Dennis George 1 The Gables, Hoe Road, Bishops Waltham, Southampton SO30 — MB BS 1974 Lond.; DCH Eng. 1979.

CRUTCHLEY, Elaine Buryfields Clinic, Buryfields, Guildford GU2 4AZ Tel: 01483 783330; 17 Fife Way, Bookham, Leatherhead KT23 3PH Tel: 01372 452845 — MB ChB Birm. 1971; MRCP (UK) 1974; MRCPsych 1984. Cons. Child & Adolesc. Psychiat. N. Downs Community Health in Child & Family Consult. Serv. Buryfields Clinic Guildford; Med. Dir. N. Downs Community NHS Trust Farnham. Prev: Cons. Child & Adolesc. Psychiat. Frimley Childr. Centre.

CRUTCHLOW, Emma Jane 30 Silver Birch Avenue, Bedworth, Nuneaton CV12 0AZ — MB BS 1996 Lond.

CRUTHERS, Jennifer Patricia 17 Mayes Close, Warlingham CR6 9LB Tel: 020 8657 0067 Fax: 020 8657 0037 — MB ChB 1959 Birm. (Birm.)

CRUTHERS, Robert (retired) 17 Mayes Place, Mayes Close, Warlingham CR6 9LB Tel: 01883 623441 — MB ChB Birm. 1960. Prev: GP Croydon.

CRUWYS, Michele Jane 51 Roxwell Road, Shepherds Bush, London W12 9QE Email: mcruwys@roxwell.demon.co.uk; Hillingdon Hospital, Pield Heath Road, Uxbridge UB8 3NN Tel: 01895 279519 Fax: 01895 279519 Email: mcruwys@maxwell.demon.co.uk — MB BS 1984 Lond.; FRCPCH; MRCP (UK) 1989; DRCOG 1988; DCH RCP Lond. 1986. Cons. Paediat. Hillingdon Hosp. Uxbridge. Prev: Ho. Phys. Profess. Unit King's Coll. Hosp. Lond.

CRUZ ARTEAGA, Jose Carlos 58 Trinity Court, Grays Inn Road, London WC1X 8JZ — LMS 1981 La Laguna.

CRYER, Katherine Jane St Brycedale Road Surgery, Kirkcaldy KY1 1ER — MB ChB 1990 Leic.

CRYER, Linda Margaret Fallsworth Health Centre, Ashton Road West, Fallsworth, Manchester M35 0HN Tel: 0161 682 6297 Fax: 0161 683 5861 — MB ChB 1977 Manch.; MRCGP 1981; DRCOG 1980.

CRYER, Peter Ivy Cottage, West Morton, Keighley BD20 5UP — MB ChB 1972 Leeds.

CRYER, Robert Jackson Thornycrft, 190 Bramhall Lane Sth., Bramhall, Stockport SK7 2PR Tel: 0161 439 2530 — MB BChir 1962 Camb.; MB Camb. 1962, BChir 1961; MRCP Lond. 1967; MRCS Eng. LRCP Lond. 1961. (St. Mary's) Cons. Phys. (Endocrinol.) Stockport & Buxton Gp. Hosps. Socs: Hosp. Consults. & Specialists Assn.; Fell. Roy. Soc. Med. Prev: Sen. Regist. Med. Unit St. Bart. Hosp. Lond.; Regist. Wexham Pk. Hosp. Slough; Regist. Metab. Unit St. Mary's Hosp. Lond.

CRYMBLE, Mr Barry Templeton (retired) 28 Golf Links Road, Newcastle BT33 0AN — MB BCh BAO 1945 Belf.; FRCS Eng. 1951. Prev: Cons. Orthop. Surg. N.. Irel. Hosps. Auth.

CRYSTAL, Mr Alan Maurice Royal Berkshire Hospital, London Road, Reading RG1 5AN; Eyotwood, Bolney Road, Lower Shiplake, Henley-on-Thames RG9 3NS — MB BS 1977 Lond.; FRCS Ed. 1983; FRCOG 1996, M 1983. (Westm.) Cons. Gyn. Roy. Berks. Hosp. Reading. Socs: BSCCP; BGGS. Prev: Sen. Regist. (O & G) St. Bart. Hosp. Lond.; Regist. (O & G) St. Thos. Hosp. & Ashford Hosp. Lond.

CRYSTAL, Boris Leonard 9 Sandmoor Close, Leeds LS17 7RP — M.B., B.Ch. Wales 1946.

CRYSTAL, Samuel Cyril, OBE (retired) 13A Hanover Gate Mansions, Park Road, London NW1 4SJ Tel: 020 7724 2646 — MB ChB Leeds 1935.

CUBBIN, Sally Ann Highlands, Wells Lane, Whitchurch RG28 7AT — MB ChB 1993 Bristol; DTM & H Liverp. 1995; DCH RCP Lond. 1996. SHO (Psychiat.) Cefn-Coed Hosp. Swansea. Prev: SHO (Psychiat.) Shelton Hosp. Shrewsbury; Staff Grade (Community Paediat.) Shrops. Community Health Trust; SHO (Paediat. & Neonat.) Roy. Shrewsbury Hosp.

CUBBON, David Henry The Burns Practice, 4 Albion Place, Bennetthorpe, Doncaster DN1 2EQ Tel: 01302 810888 Fax: 01302 812150 — MB ChB 1974 Liverp. Occupat. Health Adviser Doncaster Roy. & Mexboro Hosp. Trust.; Occupat.al Health Med. Off. Doncaster & Basset Law Hosp.s NHS Trust & Doncaster Healthcare Trust. Prev: Regist. (Psychiat.) Glenside Hosp. Bristol; SHO (Gyn.) Frenchay Hosp. & (Obst.) S.mead Hosp. Bristol.; SHO (Psychiat.) Bristol Gen. Hosp.

CUBES MONTORO, Josefa 1st Floor Flat, 20 Denning Road, London NW3 1ST — LMS 1987 Valencia.

CUBEY, Mr Robert Bevis (retired) — MB BChir 1962 Camb.; MA Camb. 1962; Dobst RCOG 1964; DCH Eng. 1965; FRCS Ed. 1966; FRCS Eng. 1967; DO Eng. 1973; FRCSI (Opth.) 1973; DObst RCOG 1964. Proprietor Tarn Lodge Eye Hosp. Carlisle. Prev: Indep.Cons. Opth. Tarn Lodge Eye Hopsital, Carlisle & Originator Lakeland Mobile Eye Clinic Cumbria.

CUBIE, Alexander (retired) 14 Mortonhall Road, Edinburgh EH9 2HW Tel: 0131 667 0776 — MB ChB 1932 Glas.; DPH 1936. Prev: Cons. Chest Phys, Vict. Hosp. Kirkcaldy.

CUBIE, George McNaught (retired) Oak View, Private Road, Ormesby, Great Yarmouth NR29 3LH — MB ChB 1941 Glas.; DPH Glas. 1947. Prev: GP Whitley Bay.

CUBISON, Miss Tania Clare Strange, Maj. Slipmill Hollow, Hawkhurst, Cranbrook TN18 5AB Tel: 01580 753123 — MB BS Newc. 1991; FRCS (Eng) 1997; Roy. Coll. Surg. Eng. (Newcastle upon Tyne) SHO (Hon.) Burns & Plastic Surg. Qu. Vict. Hosp. E. Grinstead. Socs: BMA; MDU.

CUBITT, Evelyn Diane Portglenone Health Centre, 17 Townhill Road, Portglenone, Ballymena BT44 8AD Tel: 028 2582 1551 Fax: 028 2582 2539 — MB BCh BAO 1987 Belf.; MRCGP 1991; DCH Dub. 1991; DRCOG 1990. Prev: SHO (Psychiat.) N.. HSSB.

CUBITT, George Terence Tel: 01420 84676 Fax: 01420 542975; Lodge Hill House, Lodge Hill Road, Farnham GU10 3RD — MB BChir 1974 Camb.; MA Camb. 1974; MRCP (UK) 1976; MRCGP 1978; DCH RCP Lond. 1977; MRCPCH 1997. (Camb./Univ. Coll. Lond.) Socs: Wessex Research Network; Sec. elect, Soc. for Research into Spina Bifida and Hydrocepholus. Prev: Trainee GP Kentish Town Health Centre; Resid. (Med.) King Edwd. Hosp. Bermuda; SHO (Obst.) St Mary's Hosp. Lond.

CUBITT, Kathleen Anne 24 Rydal Road, Harrogate HG1 4SQ — MB ChB 1976 Leeds; DCH Eng. 1980. Staff Grade (Paediat.) Harrogate Health Care Trust. Prev: SHO (Paediat.) Harrogate HA.

CUBUKCU, Arzu Ayse Aksungur 7 Grangeway, Wilmslow SK9 3HY — Tip Doktoru 1985 Istanbul.

CUCHEL, Marina Department of Pathological Biochemistry, 4th Floor, QEB, Glasgow Royal Infirmary, Glasgow G4 0SF — State Exam 1987 Milan; PhD Milan 1998. (Milan) Clin. Research Asst. (Path. Biochem.) Glas. Roy. Inifrm. Univ. NHS Trust Glas.

CUCKOW, Mr Peter Malcolm Department Paediatric Surgery, Leeds General Infirmary, Belmont Grove, Leeds LS2 9NS Tel: 0113 243 2799 — MB BS 1985 Lond.; FRCS Eng. 1988; LMSSA Lond.

1984. Career Regist. (Paediat. Surg.) Leeds Gen. Infirm. & St. Jas. Hosp. Leeds. Prev: Resid. Regist. Addenbrooke's Hosp. Camb.
CUCKSON, Alexandra Clare 268 Eaton Road, West Derby, Liverpool L12 2AN — BChir 1996 Camb.
CUDDEHAY, Catherine Maria 15 Harvest Ridge, Leybourne, Maidstone ME19 5LY — MB BS 1998 Lond.; MB BS Lond 1998.
CUDDIGAN, Astrid Siobhan Feidrfair Health Centre, Feidrfair, Cardigan SA43 1EB Tel: 01239 612021 Fax: 01239 613373; Manor Gwyn, Login, Whitland SA34 0XD Tel: 01994 419372 — MB BS 1988 Lond.; BSc York 1980; DRCOG 1993. (Univ. Coll. Hosp. Med. Sch.) Prev: Trainee GP Pembrokesh. VTS.
CUDDIGAN, Brian John (retired) 1 Kidbrooke Gardens, Blackheath, London SE3 0PD — MB BS 1956 Lond.; FRCPath 1977, M 1965. Prev: Cons. Haemat. Brook Gen. Hosp. Greenwich Heath Dist.
CUDDIGAN, Jeremy Hugh Patrick (retired) Eastcliffe, Bembridge PO35 5NH — MB BChir Camb. 1965; BA Camb. 1961; FRCP Lond. 1983, M 1969. Cons. Rheum. Frimley Pk. Hosp. NHS Trust. Prev: Regist. (Med.) St. Peter's Hosp. Chertsey.
CUDDIHY, Anastacia Margaret Department of Dermatology, Royal Alexandra Hospital, Corsebar Road, Paisley PA2 9PN Tel: 0141 887 9111; 58 Beechwood Drive, Broomhill, Glasgow G11 7HQ Tel: 0141 334 1709 — MB BCh BAO 1983 NUI. Staff Dermatol. Roy. Alexandra Hosp. Paisley.
CUDDIHY, Patrick John 67 Priorsfield Road, Woolton, Liverpool L25 8TL Tel: 0151 428 4050; 6 The Maltings, North Pentwyn, Cardiff CF23 8EP Tel: 01222 734384 — MB ChB 1992 Liverp. SHO (Cas.) Walton Hosp. Liverp.
CUDDIHY, Thomas Patrick Buckingham Terrace Surgery, 31 Buckingham Terrace, Glasgow G12 8ED Tel: 0141 221 6210 Fax: 0141 211 6232 — MB BCh BAO 1984 Dub.; MRCGP 1988; MICGP 1988; DCH RCPSI 1987; DObst RCPSI 1987. GP Glas.
CUDDIHY, Vincent Ashfield House Surgery, Ashfield House, 1 Ashfield Road, Milngavie, Glasgow G62 6BT Tel: 0141 956 1339 Fax: 0141 956 7098 — MB ChB 1972 Glas.; MRCGP 1977.
CUDLIP, Mr Simon Anthony 26 Honor Oak Road, London SE23 3SB Email: simonc@taoming.netkonect.co.uk — MB BS 1990 Lond.; BSc (Hons) 1987; FRCS Lond. 1994. (Kings College London School of Medicine & Dentistry) Specialist Regist. (Neurosurg.) Atkinson Marley Neurosci. Centre, St. Geo.'s Hosp. Med. Sch. Lond.; Hon. Lect. (Neurosurg.) St. Geo. Hosp. Med. Sch. Lond.
CUDMORE, Josephine Kate Grove House Surgery, West Shepton, Shepton Mallet BA4 5UH Tel: 01749 342314; Laurel Barn, 15 Carlingcott, Bath BA2 8AN — MB BS 1993 Lond.; DRCOG 1995. (Univ. Coll. Med.) GP Princip. Prev: GP/Regist. Hanham Surg. Bristol.
CUDMORE, Mr Roger Edward (retired) 15 Grange Drive, Eccleston Hill, St Helens WA10 3BG Tel: 01744 23596 — MB ChB 1959 Sheff.; FRCS Eng. 1967; DCH Eng. 1962; DObst RCOG 1961. Prev: Cons. Paediat. Surg. Alder Hey Childr. Hosp. Liverp.
CUFF, Barbara Elisabeth 62 Main Street, Pembroke SA71 4HH — MB BS 1991 Lond.
CUFF, Christopher Michael Nansmellion Road Health Centre, Nansmellion Road, Mullion, Helston TR12 7DQ Tel: 01326 240212 Fax: 01326 240420; Chy-Dowr, La Flouder Lane, Mullion, Helston TR12 7HT Tel: 01326 240997 — MB BS 1979 Lond.; MRCGP 1984. (Char. Cross) Prev: Trainee GP Boston VTS; SHO (Surg.) Char. Cross Hosp. Lond.
CUFF, Peter (retired) Eastgate House, Maidenwell Lane, North Kelsey, Market Rasen LN7 6EY Tel: 01652 678678 — MB ChB Manch. 1949. Prev: Hon. Med. Adviser Roy. Nat. Lifeboat Inst.
CUGNONI, Helen Leila Royal London Hospital, Whitechapel, London E1 1BB Tel: 020 7377 7000 Ext: 3008 Fax: 020 7377 7014; 43 Albion Drive, London E8 4LT — MB BS 1984 Lond.; MRCP (UK) 1987; FRCS Ed. 1990; FFAEM 1997. Cons. A & E Roy. Lond. Hosp. & Homerton Hosp. Lond. Prev: Sen. Regist. (A & E Med.) St. Bart. Hosp. Lond.; Regist. (A & E Med.) St. Mary's Hosp. Lond.
CULANK, Leslie Seymour Department of Clinical Biochemistry, Addenbrooke's Hospital, Box 232, Hills Road, Cambridge CB2 2QR Tel: 01223 217153 Fax: 01223 216862 Email: lsc1@cam.ac.uk; 15 Home End, Fulbourn, Cambridge CB1 5BS Tel: 01223 880371 Email: les.culank@virgin.net — MB ChB Birm. 1967; MA Camb. 1978; MSc Birm. 1974, BSc 1964; FRCPath 1986, M 1974; AMQ 1967. (Birm.) Cons. Chem. Path. Addenbrooke's Hosp. Camb.; Assoc. Lect. Univ. Camb. Socs: Assn. Clin. Biochems.; (Ex Pres.) Newmarket Med. Soc. Prev: Sen. Regist. (Clin. Chem.) Birm. AHA (T); Regist. (Clin. Chem.) Birm. RHB; Ho. Surg. (Neurosurg.) & Ho. Phys. (Nutrit.) United Birm. Hosps.
CULBERT, Brian David Department of Anaesthesia, Castle Hill Hospital, Castle Road, Cottingham HU16 5JQ Tel: 01482 875875; Highgate Cottage, 33 Highgate, Cherry Burton, Beverley HU17 7RR Email: bculb28807@aol.com — MB ChB 1985 Dundee; FRCA 1992; Dip IMC RCS Ed. 1991; DA (UK) 1989. Cons. Anaesth. Castle Hill Hosp. Cottingham. Prev: Regist. (Anaesth.) St. Jas. Univ. Hosp. Leeds.
CULBERT, Margaret Anne (retired) 23 King's Road, Belfast BT5 6JF Tel: 01232 651412 — MB BCh BAO 1969 Belf. Prev: GP Belf..
CULE, John Hedley Abereinon, Capel Dewi, Llandysul SA44 4PP Tel: 01559 362229 Fax: 01559 362238 Email: john@cule.demon.co.uk — MB BChir 1947 Camb.; FRCP Ed.; MA Camb. 1947, MD 1960; MRCS Eng. LRCP Lond. 1943; FRCGP 1977, M 1957. (Camb. & King's Coll. Hosp.) Head Med. Hist. Unit Univ. Wales Coll. of Med. Cardiff. Socs: Hon. Fell. Roy. Soc. of Med.; (Ex-Pres. Counc.) Hist. of Med. Soc. Wales; Fell.Soc. of Antiquaries. Prev: Former High Sheriff, Dyfed; Pres. Brit. Soc. Hist. of Med.; Capt. RAMC (Mentioned in Despatches).
CULL, Andrew David 3 Nepean Street, Roehampton, London SW15 5DW Tel: 020 8780 0792 Fax: 020 8780 9956 — MB ChB 1965 Birm.; FRCGP 1985, M 1974. (Birm.) Prev: GP Leicester Pract. Comm.
CULL, Frederick Ewart (retired) 'Highwood', 52 Filey Road, Scarborough YO11 2TU Tel: 01723 70792 Fax: 01723 370792 — MB, ChB Ed. 1945.
CULL, Margaret Anne Beech House, Wattlefield, Wymondham NR18 9LE — MB BS 1978 Lond.; DRCOG 1982. (Middlx.) Prev: GP Trainee Norwich VTS.
CULL, Mary Elizabeth 35 Ballymacormick Road, Dromore BT25 1QR — MB BCh BAO 1993 Belf.
CULL, Roger Ewart Department of Clinical Neurosciences, Western General Hospital, Crewe Road, Edinburgh EH4 2XU Tel: 0131 537 2097 Fax: 0131 537 2096 Email: rec@skull.dcn.ed.ac.uk — MB ChB 1971 Ed.; PhD Ed. 1976, BSc (Hons.) (Physiol.) 1968; FRCP Ed. 1984; MRCP (UK) 1974. (Ed.) Cons. Clin. Neurophysiol. W.. Gen. Hosp. Edin.; Hon. Sen. Lect. (Clin. Neurosci.) Univ. Edin. Socs: Assn. Brit. Neurol.; Scott. Assn. Neurol. Sci.; Founder Mem. Brit. Assn. for Study of Headache. Prev: Cons. Neurol. Roy. Infirm. Edin.; Lect. (Clin. Neurol.) Inst. Neurol. Nat. Hosp. Nerv. Dis. Lond.
CULL, Trevor William Boon (retired) The Elders, Wardington, Banbury OX17 1RY Tel: 01295 758353 — MB ChB Birm. 1938; MRCS Eng. LRCP Lond. 1938. Prev: Jun. Anaesth., Ho. Phys. & Ho. Surg. Qu.'s Hosp. Birm.
CULLEN, Adrian Kenneth Parkgrove Terrace Surgery, 22B Parkgrove Terrace, Edinburgh EH4 7NX Tel: 0131 312 6600 Fax: 0131 312 7798 — MB ChB 1989 Ed.
CULLEN, Archibald Skinnider (retired) 1 Beaconsfield Road, Kelvinside, Glasgow G12 0PJ Tel: 0141 339 3923 — MB ChB Glas. 1947. Prev: Res. Asst. Cas. & Orthop. Depts. & Sen. Resid. W.. Infirm. Glas.
CULLEN, Barbara Elisabeth Henriette Meierberg 12, 4934 Horn-Bad Meinberg, Germany; 5 Turnberry Green, Tandragee, Armagh BT61 2EG Tel: 01762 841868 — State Exam Med 1985 Munster. SHO Craigavon Area Hosp.
CULLEN, Barry Tel: 023 9237 7514 Fax: 023 9221 4236; 5 Ventnor Way, Fareham PO16 8RU — MB BCh BAO 1978 NUI; MRCGP 1984; DCH NUI 1982; DObst RCPI 1982. Socs: Portsmouth Med. Soc.; Fareham Med. Soc. Prev: SHO (Paediat.) Nat. Matern. Hosp. Dub.; SHO (ENT) Qu. Alexandra Hosp. Cosham; Regist. (Psychiat.) St. Ita's Hosp. Portrane, Dub.
CULLEN, Bernadette Marie Area Department Public Health Medicine, Eastern Health and Social Services Board, 12/22 Linen Hall St., Belfast BT2 8BS Tel: 01232 321313 — MB BCh BAO 1980 Belf.; MSc Ed. 1984; MFPHM 1990.
CULLEN, Cecilia Marie Royal Victoria Hospital, Broadway, Belfast BT12 1UB Tel: 01232 240503 Fax: 01232 312907; 3 Royal Lodge Mews, Purdysburn Road, Belfast BT8 7YT — MB BCh BAO 1986 Belf.; BSc (Hons.) Belf. 1983, MB BCh BAO 1986; MRCP (UK)

1990; MD Belf. 1995 (Cardiol.). (Qu. Univ. Belf.) Staff Cardiol. Roy. Vict. Hosp. Belf. Prev: SHO (Med.) Roy. Vict. Hosp. Belf.

CULLEN, Christopher Patrick 62 Fountainhall Road, Edinburgh EH9 2LP — MB BChir 1988 Camb.; MB 1988, BChir 1987 Camb.

CULLEN, Derek Redmond Park Hurst, 9 Endcliffe Grove Avenue, Sheffield S10 3EJ Tel: 0114 266 6545 Fax: 0114 268 3516 Email: derekrcullen@compuserve.com — MB BS 1960 Durh.; MD Newc. 1973; FRCP Glas. 1984, M 1965; FRCP Lond. 1979, M 1967. (Newc.) Cons. Phys. Roy. Hallamsh. Hosp. Sheff.; Hon. Lect. (Med.) Univ. Sheff. Prev: Sen. Regist. (Med.) Roy. Infirm. Edin.; Regist. Newc. Gen. Hosp.

CULLEN, Dorothy 3 School Lane, Shaldon, Teignmouth TQ14 0DG Tel: 01626 872388 — MB BS 1957 Lond.; MRCS Eng. LRCP Lond. 1957; MFCM 1972; DPH Bristol 1962. (Roy. Free) Indep. Cons. Pub. Health Med. Teignmouth. Prev: SCM (Epidemiol. & Informat. Servs.) Warks. HA & W. Midl. RHA; Dep. MOH Exeter Co. Boro.

CULLEN, Edwin Sinclair 22 Tremadoc Road, London SW4 7LL — MB ChB 1957 Ed.; LRCP LRCS Ed. LRFPS Glas. 1957. (Ed.)

CULLEN, Ian Donaldson (retired) Flat 88, The Majestic, Clifton Drive N., Lytham St Annes FY8 2PH — MB ChB Glas. 1949. Prev: Med. Off. DHSS Blackpool.

CULLEN, James Desmond Station Drive Surgery, Station Drive, Ludlow SY8 2AR Tel: 01584 872461 Fax: 01584 877971; Ashleigh, St. Julians Avenue, Ludlow SY8 1ET — MB BCh BAO 1975 Belf.; MRCGP 1982; DRCOG 1982.

CULLEN, James Finbarr (retired) 17 Lauder Road, Edinburgh EH9 2EN Tel: 0131 667 2251 Email: barrycullen@catcha.com — MB BCh BAO 1952 Dub.; 1954 DO Eng.; MD NUI 1969; MCh (Ophth.) NUI 1960; FRCS Ed. 1975; FRCS Eng. 1960; FRCOphth 1988; LM Coombe 1954. Prev: Cons. Ophth. Edin. Roy. Infirm.

CULLEN, James Henry Stuart 1 Wylam Close, Leicester LE3 9BW Tel: 01162 871772 Email: james.cullen@btinternet.com; 6 Orpen Road, Hove BN3 6NJ Tel: 01273 505718 Fax: 01273 505718 — MB BChir 1989 Camb.; MA Camb. 1991, BA 1986, MB BChir 1989; MRCP (UK) 1991. (Camb.) Specialist Regist (cardiol.) Glenfield Hosp. Leicester. Prev: SHO (Med.) Qus. Med. Centre Univ. Hosp. Nottm.; Regist. (Cardiol.) Trust Regional Rotat.

CULLEN, James Patrick 75 Main Road, Onchan, Douglas IM3 1AJ Tel: 01624 629714 Fax: 01624 614668; Troutbeck, Cronkbourne, Braddan, Douglas IM4 4QA Tel: 01624 623308 — MB BChir Camb. 1962; DObst RCOG 1964. (St. Mary's) Socs: BMA; Pres. Isle of Man Med. Soc. Prev: Assoc. Specialist (Obst.) Nobles Iom Hosp.; Specialist (O & G) RAF.

CULLEN, James Ronald 11 Zenda Park, Ballyskeagh Road, Drumbeg, Lairg IV27 9LW — MB BCh BAO 1979 Belf.

CULLEN, Jeffrey Graham Viewfield Lane Health Centre, Viewfield Lane, Selkirk TD7 4LJ Tel: 01750 21674 Fax: 01750 23176; Oaklea, 7 Viewfield Park, Selkirk TD7 4LH — MB ChB 1987 Aberd.

CULLEN, Mr Keith William The Queen Victoria Hospital, East Grinstead RH19 3DZ Tel: 01342 410210 Fax: 01342 317907 Email: queenvic@queenvic.demon.co.uk — MB ChB 1977 Ed.; FRCS Ed. 1981. Cons. Plastic Surg. Qu. Vict. Hosp. E. Grinstead; Cons. Plastic Surg. E.bourne Dist. Hosp. Socs: Brit. Assn. Plastic Surg.; Brit. Assn. Aesthetic Plastic Surgs.; Brit. Soc. Surg. Hand. Prev: Sen. Regist. (Plastic Surg.) Sheff.; Regist. (Plastic Surg.) NE Thames Regional Plastic Surg. Unit Billericay & Qu. Mary's Hosp. Lond.

CULLEN, Linda Parkview Clinic, 60 Queensbridge Road, Moseley, Birmingham B13 8QE Tel: 0121 243 2000 Fax: 01527 60121; 102 Northfield Road, Kings Norton, Birmingham B30 1JG — MB BS 1985 Lond.; MA Camb. 1982; MRCPsych 1989. (Camb. & Middlx. Hosp.) Cons. Adolesc. Psychait. Pk.view Clinic Birm. Prev: Cons. Child & Adolesc. Psychiat. Worcs. Community Trust.

CULLEN, Magda Gillian Lowesmoor Medical Centre, 93 Lowesmoor, Worcester WR1 2SA Tel: 01905 727874 Fax: 01905 724987; Lower Court Farm, Cotheridge, Worcester WR6 5LZ Tel: 01905 333642 — MB BS 1977 Lond.; DRCOG 1980. (Univ. Coll. Hosp. Lond.)

CULLEN, Margaret Jane 26 Inverleith Gardens, Edinburgh EH3 5PS — MB ChB 1982 Glas.; FRCA 1988. (Univ. Glas.) Cons. Anaesth. W.. Gen. NHS Trust Edin. Prev: Sen. Regist. (Anaesth.) Roy. Infirm. Edin.; Regist. & SHO (Anaesth.) & Ho. Off. (Med.) W.. Infirm. Glas.

CULLEN, Mark Simon Abbey Surgery, 28 Plymouth Road, Tavistock PL19 8BU Tel: 01822 612247 Fax: 01822 618771; The Dower House, Lewdown, Okehampton EX20 4PL — MB BChir 1982 Camb.; MA Camb. 1978; MRCGP 1985; DRCOG 1985; Cert. Family Plann. JCC 1985. (Camb. & St. Bart.)

CULLEN, Martha Pauline Department of Anaesthetics, Royal Hospital for Sick Children, Yorkhill, Glasgow G3 8SS — MB BCh BAO 1975 NUI; FFA RCS Eng. 1981; DRCOG 1977. Cons. Anaesth. Roy. Hosp. Sick Childr. Glas.

CULLEN, Maurice Enda Uillanova, Rossbeg, Dungannon — MB BCh BAO 1983 Belf.

CULLEN, Michael Cottage Pie, Higher Metcombe, Ottery St Mary EX11 1SR — MB ChB 1970 Birm.; MRCS Eng. LRCP Lond. 1970. (Birm.)

CULLEN, Michael Henry Queen Elizabeth Centre for the Treatment of Cancer, University Hospital Birmingham, NHS Trust, Birmingham B15 2TH Tel: 0121 627 2444 Fax: 0121 627 2496; 56 St. Agnes Road, Moseley, Birmingham B13 9PN — MB ChB 1971 Bristol; FRCR 2001; BSc (Anat. 1st cl. Hons.) Bristol 1968, MD 1979; FRCP Lond. 1988. Hon. Reader in Med. Oncol. Univ. Birm.; Cons. Med. Oncol. Qu. Eliz. Hosp. & Univ. Hosp Birm. NHS Trust. Prev: Clin. Dir. (Oncol. & Haematol.) Birm. Health Dist. Qu. Eliz. Hosp.; Clin. Research Fell. ICRF (Med. Oncol.) St. Bart. Hosp. Lond.; Sen. Regist. (Med.) Nottm. City Hosp. & Univ. Hosp.

CULLEN, Moira Wirral Health, St. Catherine's Hospital, Tranmere, Birkenhead Tel: 0151 611 0011; Carrwood, 11 Boundary Road, Birkenhead CH43 7PB Tel: 0151 652 4580 — MB BS 1984 Lond.; Dip. IMC RCS Ed. 1991. Regist. (Pub. Health) Grampian HB; Hon. Lect. Robt. Gordon Univ. Prev: Manager & Asst. Manager (Med. Serv.) RGIT Survival Centre Aberd.

CULLEN, Niall Michael Portland Hospital, 209 Great Portland St., London W1W 5AH Tel: 0207-580 4400 Fax: 0207 631 1170; 37 Costa Brava, Laguna Niguel CA 92677, USA Tel: (001) (949) 661 5867 Fax: (001) (949) 443 0375 — MB BCh BAO NUI 1955; FACOG 1970. Cons. Gyn. Portland Hosp. Lond. & Hosps. of St. John & St. Eliz.; Asst. Clin. Prof. Obst. & Gyn. Univ. Calif. USA; Dip. Amer. Bd. (Obst. & Gyn.). Socs: Fell. Roy. Soc. Med.; Founder Fell. Bellevue Obst. & Gyn. Soc. New York. Prev: Asst. Lect. (O & G) Univ. Hong Kong; Resid. O & G Bellevue Hosp. New York, USA; Ho. Phys. & Ho. Surg. Mater Hosp. Dub.

CULLEN, Paul Edmund Dudley Priority Health NHS Trust, Bushey Fields Hospital, Russells Hall, Dudley DY1 2LZ Tel: 01384 244960 Fax: 01384 244903 Email: paul.cullen@dudleyph-tr.wmids.nhs.uk — MB BCh BAO 1984 NUI; MRCPsych 1990. (University College, Dublin) Cons. Adult Psychiat. Socs: Birm. Med. Hist. Soc.; Birm. Med. Inst. Counc. mem. 1998-99, Vice Pres. 2000, Pres. 2001. Prev: Sen. Regist. W. Midl. Gen. Adult Psychiat. Rotat.; SHO & Regist. Coventry & Warks. Rotat.al Train. Scheme in Psychiat.

CULLEN, Mr Paul Thomas Queen Elizabeth Hospital, Gayton Road, King's Lynn PE30 4ET Tel: 01553 766266; Home Farm Lodge, Water Lane, Blackborough End, King's Lynn PE32 1SD Tel: 01553 840047 — MB BCh BAO 1980 NUI; MCh NUI 1992; FRCSI 1985; FRCS Ed. 1985. Cons. Surg. Qu. Eliz. & Wisbech Hosps. King's Lynn. Socs: Surg. Research Soc. & Assn. Surgs. Train.; BMA; Roy. Soc. Med. Prev: Sen. Regist. UCL Hosp. Gp. & E. Anglia RHA.

CULLEN, Richard James 23 Tasker Road, Sheffield S10 1UY — MB ChB 1995 Sheff.

CULLEN, Richard Michael 36 Eastleigh Avenue, Harrow HA2 0UG; 9 Richmond Street, Barnstaple EX32 7DP Tel: 01271 343367 Email: richard@cullen68.freeserve.co.uk — MB BS 1992 Lond. (Royal Free) Socs: BMA; RCGP.

CULLEN, Robert Francis Orgarswick Avenue Surgery, 9 Orgarswick Avenue, Dymchurch, Romney Marsh TN29 0NX Tel: 01303 872245 Fax: 01303 872616; The Elms, New Church, Romney Marsh TN29 0ED Tel: 01303 874300 Email: rfcullen@lineone.net — MB BS 1980 Lond.; MRCGP 1984. Med. Off. Folkestone Racecourse.

CULLEN, Mr Ronald John Nuffield Hospital, Wolverhampton; 137 Goldthorn Hill, Wolverhampton WV2 4PS Tel: 01902 30368 — MB ChB 1973 Aberd.; FRCS Eng. 1979. Cons. (ENT & Head & Neck Surg.) W. Midl. RHA. Prev: Regist. (ENT) Avon AHA (T); SHO (A & E) & SHO (Paediat.) Cumbld. Infirm. Carlisle.

CULLEN, Seamus 12 Townshend Terrace, Richmond TW9 1XL — MB BCh BAO 1981 NUI; MRCPI 1987.

CULLEN, Stephen Anthony, QHS, OStJ, Air Commodore RAF Med. Br. RAF Centre of Aviation Medicine, Henlow SG16 6DN Tel:

01462 851515 Ext: 8060 Fax: 01462 819996 Email: avpath@rafcam.org.uk; Tel: 01280 816355 — MB ChB 1962 Liverp.; FRCPath 1982, M 1970; DCP Lond 1970; FRAeS. (Liverp.) Cons. Path. (Aviat. Path.) RAF Centre of Aviat. Med.; Hon. Surg. HM the Qu. Socs: Brit. Assn. of Forens. Med. Prev: Cons. Adviser (Path.) to DGMS (RAF) IPTM, Halton; Cons. Path. RAF Hosp. Wegberg, Germany; Path. No. 4 RAAF Hosp. Butterworth, Malaysia.

CULLEN, Stephen Peter Gresford Medical Centre, Pilch Lane, Huyton, Liverpool L14 0JE Tel: 0151 489 2020 — MB ChB 1980 Liverp.; MRCGP 1984. GP Liverp.; Clin. Doctor (Crowd) Everton Football Club Liverp. Prev: Lect. (Anat.) Liverp. Univ.; Sen. Off. (Gen. Pract.) King Khalid Nat. Guard Hosp., Jedda, Saudi Arabia.

CULLEN, Susan Nicola 16 St Michael's Avenue, Hemel Hempstead HP3 8HF — MB BS 1991 Lond.; MRCP (Lond) 1994. Specialist Regist. (Gastroenterol. & Gen. Med.) John Radcliffe Hosp. Oxf.

CULLEN, Mr Thomas Henry, MBE (retired) The Bungalow, Halstead Road, Lexden Heath, Colchester CO3 5JU Tel: 01206 579123 — MB BS 1940 Lond.; FRCS Eng. 1946; MRCS Eng. LRCP Lond. 1939. Prev: Cons. Surg. Kettering & Dist. Gen. Hosp.

CULLEN, Thomas James Ranworth Surgery, 103 Pier Avenue, Clacton-on-Sea CO15 1NJ Tel: 01255 421344 Fax: 01255 473581; 48 Holland Road, Clacton-on-Sea CO15 6EL Tel: 01255 475900 — MB BS 1976 Lond.; FFA RCSI 1983; Dip. Pract. Dermat. Wales 1993.

CULLEN, Thomas Joseph O'Hea 1 Beaconsfield Road, Glasgow G12 0PJ — MB ChB 1993 Glas.

CULLIFORD, Larry Dirk Brighton Community Mental Health Centre, 79 Buckingham Road, Brighton BN1 3RJ Tel: 01273 749500 Fax: 01273 821365; 52 Penlands Vale, Steyning BN44 3PL — MB BChir 1975 Camb.; MRCPsych 1984. Cons. Gen. Adult Psychiat. & Rehabil. S. Downs Health NHS Trust. Prev: Hon. Sen. Regist. Brompton Hosp. Lond.; Sen. Regist. (Psychiat.) St. Geo. & Atkinson Morley's Hosps. Lond.

CULLIGAN, Dominic John Department of Haematology, Aberdeen Royal Infirmary, Foresterhill, Aberdeen AB25 2ZN Tel: 01224 681818; 24 Brighton Place, Aberdeen AB10 6RS — MB BS 1986 Lond.; BSc (1st cl. Hons.) Lond. 1983, MD 1994; MRCP (UK) 1989; MRCPath 1995, D 1994. Cons. Haemat. Aberd. Roy. Infirm. Socs: Brit. Soc. Haematol.; Fell. of the Roy. Coll. of Phys.s of Edin. Prev: Sen. Regist. (Haemat.) Univ. Hosp. Wales Cardiff; Hon. Regist. & Leukaemia Research Fund Fell. Univ. Wales Sch. of Med. Cardiff; Regist. (Med.) Basildon Hosp.

CULLIMORE, Mr John Edward Department of Obstetrics & Gynaecology, Princess Margaret Hospital, Swindon SN4 0AT Tel: 01793 536231; Email: john@cullimorey.fsnet.co.uk — MB BS 1978 Lond.; MD Lond. 1991; FRCS Ed. 1983; MRCOG 1986; FRCOG 1998. (Middlx.) Cons. O & G Swindon HA. Socs: Brit. Gyn. Cancer Soc.; Brit. Soc. Colpos. & Cerv. Path. (SW Regional Rep.). Prev: Lect. (O & G) Leicester Roy. Infirm.; Lect. (O & G) Bristol Univ. Matern. Hosp.; Research Fell. Birm. & Midl. Hosp. for Wom.

CULLINAN, Timothy Paul 138 Lauriston Road, London E9 7LH Tel: 020 8986 8648 — MB BS 1982 Lond.; MSc Lond. 1990; MD Lond. 1992; MRCP (UK) 1986. Sen. Lect. Nat. Heart & Lung Inst. Lond.; Hon. Cons. Phys. Roy. Brompton Hosp. Lond.

CULLINANE, Sharon Catherine 8 Breadalbane Terrace, Edinburgh EH11 2BW — MB ChB 1990 Leic.

CULLINEY, Paul 22 Kirkdale Crescent, Leeds LS12 6AS — MB ChB 1993 Manch.

CULLING, Janice Anne Bristol Royal Hospital for Sick Children, St Michaels Hill, Bristol BS2 8BJ Tel: 0117 928 5413 Fax: 0117 928 5457 — MB BS 1973 Lond.; MRCPsych 1977. Cons. Child & Adolesc. Psychiat. United Bristol Healthcare NHS Trust. Prev: Cons. Child & Adolesc. Psychiat. S.mead Health Servs. Trust.

***CULLING, John Paul** 64 Greystoke Road, Cambridge CB1 8DS — MB ChB 1997 Manch.

CULLING, Stephen Douglas (retired) 98 St Lukes Road, Old Windsor, Windsor SL4 2QJ Tel: 01753 855788 Email: steve.chairmat@virgin.net — MB BS 1964 Lond.; MRCS Eng. LRCP Lond. 1965; DObst RCOG 1970. Prev: Med. Off. RAMC.

CULLING, William 8 Ravenswood Court, Kingston Hill, Kingston upon Thames KT2 7JL Tel: 020 8546 4687 Fax: 020 8546 4687 — MB ChB 1976 Manch.; MD Manch. 1988; FRCP Lond. 1995; MRCP (UK) 1979. Cons. Phys. Kingston Hosp., Kingston upon Thames. Prev: Sen. Regist. (Cardiol.) Bristol Roy. Infirm.

CULLINGTON, Derek Edward (retired) Old School House, Little Wittenham, Abingdon OX14 4QU Tel: 01865 407903 — MA, MB BChir Camb. 1946; MRCS Eng. LRCP Lond. 1945; FFCM 1974; DPH Lond. 1951; DCH Eng. 1947. Prev: Chief Admin. Med. Off. Borders HB.

CULLINGTON, Stella Juliet Larne Health Centre, Gloucester Avenue, Larne BT40 1PB Tel: 028 2826 1921 Fax: 028 2826 1988; 113 Station Road, Greenisland, Carrickfergus BT38 8UW Tel: 01232 863852 — MB ChB 1963 Ed.; MFFP 1994; MRNZCGP 1979; DObst RCOG 1970. (Ed.) SCMO, Newtonabbey; Staff Grade (Paediat.), Newtonabbey. Socs: Brit. Med. Acupunct. Soc. Prev: Sch. Med. Off. Belf.

CULLINGWORTH, Thomas Mackison (retired) 17 Hintlesham Avenue, Birmingham B15 2PH Tel: 0121 454 9232 — MRCS Eng. LRCP Lond. 1945; BA (Hons.) Camb. 1942; MFOM RCP Lond. 1980.

CULLIS, Elizabeth Fowler (retired) Manor Lodge, Rickmansworth Road, Northwood HA6 2QT Tel: 01923 821085 — MRCS Eng. LRCP Lond. 1942. p/t Clin. Asst. (Obst.) Watford Gen. Hosp. Prev: Ho. Surg. King's Coll. Hosp.

CULLIS, Jeffrey Eaton (retired) 4 Bowling Green Lane, Swindon SN1 4EU Tel: 01793 521744 Fax: 01793 521744 — MB BS 1955 Lond.; BSc Lond. 1952; DObst RCOG 1963; DCH Eng. 1959. Prev: Regist. St. Peter's Hosp. Chertsey.

CULLIS, Jonathan Oliver Salisbury District Hospital, Salisbury SP2 8BJ Tel: 01722 429043 Fax: 01722 333933 Email: dr.j.cullis@shc-tr.swest.nhs.uk — MB BS 1985 Lond.; MA Camb. 1986; MD Lond. 1994; MRCP (UK) 1988; MRCPath 1996. Cons. (Haemat.) Salisbury Dist. Hosp. Socs: Brit. Soc. Haematol.; BMA; Assn. Clin. Path. Prev: Sen. Regist. King's Coll. Hosp.; Research Fell. Roy. Postgrad. Med. Sch. Lond.; Regist. (Haemat.) Soton. Gen. Hosp.

CULLIS, Susan Ann Quorn Medical Centre, 1 Station Road, Quorn, Loughborough LE12 8PB Tel: 01509 412232 Fax: 01509 620652; 1 Orchard View, Mountsorrel, Loughborough LE12 7HW — MB ChB 1981 Manch.; BSc St. And. 1978; MRCGP 1985; DRCOG 1985. Socs: BMA. Prev: Trainee GP Leicester VTS.

CULLOTY, Michael (retired) 85 Rowlands Avenue, Hatch End, Pinner HA5 4AW — MB BS 1960 Lond.; FFR 1967; DMRD Eng. 1965. Prev: Cons. Radiol. Barnet Gen. Hosp. & Watford Gen. Hosp.

CULLOTY, Sean Michael The Spinney Surgery, The Spinney, Ramsey Road, St. Ives, Huntingdon PE27 37P Tel: 01480 492501 Fax: 01480 356159 — MB BS 1986 Lond.

CULLUM, Angela Rosemary 118 Albert Street, London NW1 7NE Tel: 020 7267 4656 — MB BS 1965 Lond.; FFA RCS Eng. 1969. (Univ. Coll. Hosp.) Prev: Sen. Regist. (Anaesth.) W.m. & Brompton Hosps. Lond.; SHO Anaesth. Roy. Sussex Co. Hosp. Brighton.

CULLUM, Sarah-Jane Institute of Public Health, Forvie Site, Robinson Way, Cambridge CB2 2SR Tel: 01223 330300 — MB ChB 1986 Leeds; MSc 2001 London; BSc (Hons.) Leeds 1983; MRCPsych 1993; MPhil (Cantab) 1998. MRC Health Serv.s Research Train. Fell., Hon. Cons. Gen. Adult & Old Age Psych. Inst. of Pub. Health, Univ. Of Camb. Prev: Sen. Regist. Liaison Psychiat., Addenbrooke's Hosp. Camb.; Sen. Regist.Adult Psychiat. Addenbrooke's Hosp. Camb.; Sen. Regist. Old Age Psychiat. W. Suff. Hosp. Bury & St. Edmunds, Suff..

CULLUMBINE, Ann Tel: 0151 353 1061 — MB ChB 1992 Birm.; Cert. Prescribed Equiv. Exp. JCPTGP 1996; MRCGP 1996; DFFP 1995; DRCOG 1995. Prev: GP/Regist. Chester.

CULORA, Giuseppe Antonio University Pathology, Level E (813) Southblock, Southampton General Hospital, Tremonia Rd, Southampton SO16 6YD — BM 1991 Soton.; MRCPath 1999.

CULPITT, Sarah Varney 51B Mile End Road, Stepney, London E1 4TT Tel: 020 7790 2788 Fax: 020 7366 7212 Email: dr.sarah@virgin.net; The Old Black Swan, Water Lane, Bassingham, Lincoln LN5 9LA Tel: 01522 788793 — MB BS 1993 Lond.; MRCP (UK) 1996. (Lond. Hosp. Med. Coll.) Clin. Research Fell., Nat. Heart & Lung Inst. Prev: SHO (Gen. Med.) Roy. Lond. Hosp.; SHO (Respirat.) Roy. Brompton Hosp.; SHO (Gastroenterol. & Haemat.) Hammersmith Hosp. Lond.

CULSAN LORENZO, Juan Pedro 1 Valley Close, St Saviours Hospital, St Saviour, Jersey JE2 7UA — LMS 1986 Cadiz.

CULSHAW, Angela Jane Tel: 01945 464980 — MB ChB 1990 Manch.; MRCGP 1995; DRCOG 1994. (Manch.) GP Wisbech. Prev:

SHO GPVTS Qu. Eliz. Hosp. Kings Lynn.; Ho. Off. (Med.) Hope Hosp. & Salford Roy. Hosp.; Ho. Off. (Surg.) Bolton Gen. Hosp.

CULSHAW, Joseph Anthony Sherwood House, Sherwood Road, Tideswell, Buxton SK17 8LH Tel: 01298 871396 — MB ChB 1955 Liverp.; MRCGP 1968. (Liverp.) Chairm. & Founder Tideswell Med. Foundat. Socs: BMA. Prev: RAF Med. Br.; Cas. Off., Ho. Surg. & Ho. Phys. Whiston Hosp. Prescot.

CULSHAW, Martin Andrew 14 Portal Road, Glasgow G13 3XN — MB ChB 1993 Glas.

CULSHAW, Martin Christopher Sherwood House, Sherwood Road, Tideswell, Buxton SK17 8LH — MB ChB 1986 Leeds; MRCP (UK) 1994; T(GP) 1994; Dip. IMC RCS Ed. 1990. Specialist Regist. Rotat. (A & E) Yorks.

CULSHAW, Thomas Dunstan Chantry Lane Health Centre, 17 Chantry Lane, Grimsby DN31 2LP Tel: 01472 342063 Fax: 01472 242066 — MB ChB 1967 St. And.

CULSHAW, Valerie 24 Catherine Street, Motherwell ML1 2RN — MB ChB 1992 Glas.

CULVER, James McLean The Glen, Longhill Avenue, Alloway, Ayr KA7 Tel: 01292 41432 — MB ChB 1944 Glas. (Glas.) Prev: Surg. Ho. Off. Gartloch EMS Hosp. Glas.; Res. Med. Off. & Gynaecol. Wards, Roy. N.. Infirm. Inverness; Res. Asst. Phys. Mearnskirk Hosp. Glas.

CULVER-JAMES, Jeremy Waterfield 1 Sherfield, Winterbourne Dauntsey, Salisbury SP4 6HF — MRCS Eng. LRCP Lond. 1969; MA, BM BCh Oxf. 1969; MRCPath (Haemat.) 1986; LMCC Vancouver 1978; DAvMed. FOM RCP Lond. 1984. (Oxf. & St. Thos.) Prev: Wing Cdr. RAF Med. Br. (Sen. Specialist Path.); Flight Surg. Canad. Armed Forces; Regist. Treloar Haemophilia Centre Alton Hants.

CULVERWELL, Nigel John Charles The Health Centre, Midland St., Long Eaton, Nottingham NG10 1NY Tel: 0115 973 2370 — MB ChB 1979 Sheff.; MRCGP 1984; DRCOG 1984. (Sheff.)

CUMARASAMY, Kumaresh Fairfield General Hospital, Rochdale Old Road, Bury BL9 7TD — MB ChB 1996 Liverp.

CUMBER, Peter Michael West Wales General Hospital, Dolgwili Road, Carmarthen SA31 2AF — MB ChB 1982 Bristol; MRCP (UK) 1985; MRCPath 1991; T(Path) 1991. Cons. Haemat. W. Wales Gen. Hosp. Prev: Sen. Regist. (Haemat.) Univ. Hosp. Wales Cardiff.

CUMBERBATCH, Mr Gary Leonard 14 Chiswich Court, Moss Lane, Pinner HA5 3AP — MB BS 1988 W. Indies; FRCS Ed. 1993.

CUMBERBATCH, John Barrie (retired) 32A Ellerton Road, London SW18 3NN Tel: 0208 874 9556 — BSc (Physiol., Hons.) Lond. 1953, MB BS 1956; MRCS Eng. LRCP Lond. 1956; DObst RCOG 1959. Tutor Dept. Gen. Pract. St Geo. Hosp. Med. Sch. Lond.

CUMBERLAND, Alan Gilbert 67 Charlton Road, Blackheath, London SE3 8TJ Tel: 020 8858 8513 — MB BS 1963 Lond.; MRCS Eng. LRCP Lond. 1963; DObst RCOG 1968. (Guy's) Socs: BMA. Prev: Ho. Surg. Guy's Hosp. Lond.; Ho. Phys. & Ho. Surg. Roy. Hants. Co. Hosp. Winchester.

CUMBERLAND, Professor David Charles .118 Maida Vale, London W9 1PT Tel: 020 7604 3394 Fax: 020 7604 3394 Email: cumberlandarid@aol.com — MB ChB 1967 Ed.; FRCP Ed. 1986; FRCS 1994; FRCR 1975. Prof. Interven. Cardiol. Private Pract., Lond. Socs: Fell. Europ. Soc. Cardiol.; FACC; Brit. Cardiac Soc. Prev: Prof. Inetrventional Cardiol, Univ. of Sheff..

CUMBERLAND, Janet Elizabeth Accident & Emergency Department, Sheffield Childrens Hospital, Western Bank, Sheffield S10 2T Tel: 0114 271 7000; 59 Barholm Road, Sheffield S10 5RR — BM 1985 Soton.; BSc (Biochem. Pharmacol.) Soton. 1981; DCH RCP Lond. 1990. Staff Grade Paediat. (A & E) Sheff. Childr. Hosp.

CUMBERLAND, John Harry (retired) 34 Lubenham Hill, Market Harborough LE16 9DQ Tel: 01858 62716 — BM BCh 1943 Oxf.; MA Oxf. 1944, BM BCh 1943. Prev: Ho. Surg. & Res. Surg. Off. Worcester Roy. Infirm.

CUMBERLAND, Margaret Anne The Coach House, Herondale Avenue, London SW18 3JN — MB ChB 1988 Manch.

CUMBERLAND, Nigel Stewart Frimley Park Hospital NHS Trust, Portsmouth Road, Frimley, Camberley GU16 7UJ Tel: 01276 604604 Fax: 01276 21547 — MB ChB 1978 Liverp.; MRCPath 1986; MSc 1986 London; PhD 1976 Liverpool. (Liverpool Univ.) Cons. Microbiol. Frimley Pk. Hosp. NHS Trust. Prev: Cons. Path. Qu. Eliz. Milit. Hosp. Woolwich Lond.

CUMBERLIDGE, Duncan Frank Saville Medical Group, 7 Saville Place, Newcastle upon Tyne NE1 8DQ Tel: 0191 233 1050, 0191 234 4274 — MB BS 1984 Newc.; D Occ Med. Prev: Surg. Lt. Cdr. RN.

CUMBERWORTH, Mr Vincent Lee 14 Grafton Road, Harrow HA1 4QT — MB ChB 1981 Leeds; MB ChB Leeds 1984; BSc (Hons.) Med. Microbiol. Leeds 1981; FRCS Eng. 1991. Cons. Surg. (ENT) W. Middlx. Univ. Hosp. Lond. Socs: RCS Eng.; Fell. Roy. Soc. Med. Prev: Sen. Regist. (ENT) St. Bart. & Whipps Cross Hosps. Lond.; Regist. (ENT) Char. Cross Hosp. Lond.

CUMING, Kathleen Veronica c/o Royal Alexandra Children's Hospital, Dyke Road, Brighton BN1 Tel: 01273 328145; c/o 34 Savernake Road, London NW3 2JP Tel: 020 7428 0292 — MB ChB 1993 Bristol; DTM & H RCP Lond. 1994. SHO (Paediat.) Roy. Alexandra Childr. Hosp. Brighton. Socs: BMA; MDU. Prev: SHO (A & E) Preston; Ho. Off. (Med.) S.mead; Ho. Off. (Surg.) Exeter.

CUMING, Tamzin 60 Borstal Hill, Whitstable CT5 4NA — MB BS 1994 Lond.

CUMMIN, Andrew Richard Comyn Dept. of Respiratory Medicine, National Heart & Lung InStreet, Imperial College School of Medicine, 5th Floor, Charing Cross Hospital, Fulham Palace Road, London W6 8RP Tel: 020 8846 7178 Fax: 020 8846 7170 Email: a.cummin@ic.ac.uk; 68 Frensham Road, Lower Bourne, Farnham GU10 3QA Email: a.cummin@virgin.net — BM BCh 1975 Oxf.; MA Oxf. 1976, DM 1989, BM BCh 1975; MRCP (UK) 1979. (St. Thomas' Hospital Medical School London) Sen. Lect. (Respirat. Med.); Civil Cons. in Respirat. Physiol. to the RAF; Hon. Cons. in Respirat. Med. ;Hammersmith Hosps. NHS Trust. Prev: Sen. Med. Off. (Research) Min. of Defence; Sen. Med. Off. Meds. Control Agency; Lect. (Med.) St Geo.'s Hosp. Med. Sch. Lond.

CUMMIN, Anna Rosalind Elizabeth The Jarvis Screening Training & Diagnostic Centre, Stoughton Road, Guildford Tel: 01483 783200; 68 Frensham Road, Lower Bourne, Farnham GU10 3QA — MB BS 1977 Lond.; DRCOG 1981. (Westm.) SCMO Jarvis BrE. Screening Centre Guildford. Prev: GP Princip. Herne Hill Lond.; Trainee GP Kent & Canterbury VTS; SHO (A & E Unit) Kent & Canterbury Hosp.

CUMMIN, Annette Lesley Cornerways, 48 Park Road, Woking GU22 7DB — MB BS 1979 Lond.; DRCOG 1981. Clin. Asst. (Gyn.) N.W. Surrey HA. Prev: Med. Off. (Occupat. Health) N.W. Surrey HA.

CUMMIN, Crispin George Winchcombe Medical Practice, The Surgery, Abbey Terrace, Winchcombe, Cheltenham GL54 5LL Tel: 01242 602307 Fax: 01242 603689; Turnpike House, Greenway Lane, Charlton Kings, Cheltenham GL52 6PW — MB BChir 1972 Camb.; MA Camb. 1972; DA Eng. 1973. (Cambridge) Clin. Asst. Winchcombe Hosp.

CUMMIN, Olwen Joy (retired) 1 Courthope, Pembroke Road, Woking GU22 7DS Tel: 01483 764688 — MB ChB 1949 Bristol. Prev: SCMO S. Glam. HA.

CUMMIN, Philip John Comyn Cornerways, 48 Park Road, Woking GU22 7DB Tel: 01932 340484 — BM BCh 1977 Oxf.; MA Oxf. 1979; MRCP 1980; FRCP 1996. GP W. Byfleet; Hosp. Pract. Cardiol. St. Peter's Hosp. Chertsey. Socs: Assur. Med. Soc.

CUMMINE, Duncan Penny 132 Mount Castle Drive S., Edinburgh EH15 3LL Tel: 0131 669 6101; Oak Lea, East Mains, Ormiston, Tranent EH35 5NG Tel: 01875 610230 — MB ChB 1957 Aberd.; MRCGP 1976; DCH Eng. 1962; DObst RCOG 1961. Prev: Regist. Aberd. Gen. Hosp.; SHO Bristol Childr. Hosp.

CUMMINE, Rachel Elizabeth B9-2 Menara Bangsar, 297 Jalan Maarof, Kuala Lumpur 59000, Malaysia; Oaklea4/2 Liddesdale Place, Edinburgh EH3 5JW — MB ChB 1989 Ed.

CUMMING, Alexander (retired) 222 Colinton Road, Edinburgh EH14 1DL — MB ChB 1957 Glas.

CUMMING, Alister Knox (retired) Abergeldie Mains House, Crathie, Ballater AB35 5SY Tel: 013397 42427 — MRCS Eng. LRCP Lond. 1943; BA Camb. 1938.

CUMMING, Allan David Department of Renal Medicine, University of Edinburgh, Royal Infirmary, Edinburgh EH3 9YW Tel: 0131 536 2307 Fax: 0131 536 1541 Email: a.cumming@ed.ac.uk; 59 Morningside Drive, Edinburgh EH10 5NF Tel: 0131 447 5738 — MB ChB 1975 Ed.; BSc (Hons.) Ed. 1973, MD 1990; FRCP Ed. 1992; MRCP (UK) 1978. (Ed.) Sen. Lect. & Hon. Cons. Univ. Dept. Renal Med. Roy. Infirm. Edin.; Assoc. Dean (Teachg.) Fac. of Med. Univ. of Edin.; Dir. Med. Teachg. Organisation Univ. of Edin. Socs: Renal Assn.; Med. Res. Soc.; Eur. Renal Assn. Prev: Regist. (Med.)

Bangour Gen. Hosp. & Roy. Infirm. Edin.; Clin. Research Fell. Univ., W.. Ontario; Lect. (Med.) Roy. Infirm. Edin.

CUMMING, Amy Montgomery Haughton Vale Surgery, Tatton Road, Denton, Manchester M34 7PL Tel: 0161 336 3005 Fax: 0161 320 3884; 18 Highfield Park, Heaton Mersey, Stockport SK4 3HD Tel: 0161 432 7109 — MB ChB 1964 Manch.; MRCS Eng. LRCP Lond. 1964; MRCGP 1982. Socs: Roy. Coll. Gen. Pract.

CUMMING, Archibald (retired) Elder Cottage, Lochranza, Brodick KA27 8HL — MB ChB 1926 Glas.; BSc Glas. 1924, MB ChB 1926.

CUMMING, Craig Andrew 21 Greenmore Gardens, Aberdeen AB24 4JE — MB ChB 1995 Aberd.

CUMMING, Daniel Anthony Tel: 0141 531 8370 Fax: 0141 531 4431 — MB ChB 1986 Glas.; MRCGP 1990.

CUMMING, Douglas Mitchell 3 Clarence Drive, Hyndland, Glasgow G12 9QL — MB ChB 1983 Glas. Assoc. Specialist Dept. of Med.Hairmyres Hosp. E. Kilbride. Prev: Staff Grade Phys. Glas.

CUMMING, Enid Jane Clifton Road Surgery, 95 Clifton Road, Rugby CV21 3QQ Tel: 01788 578800/568810 Fax: 01788 541063 — MB ChB 1987 Glas. GP Rugby.

CUMMING, Eveline Mary (retired) 33 Oakwood Road, Horley RH6 7BZ — MRCS Eng. LRCP Lond. 1938; MFCM 1974; DPH Eng. 1947. Prev: Sen. Med. Off. Surrey AHA.

CUMMING, Frederick Gordon, MBE, Wing Cdr. RAF Med. Br. Retd. 45A Seaview Road, Hayling Island PO11 9PD Tel: 01705 462060 — MB ChB 1947 Ed. CEng. Socs: MRAeS. Prev: Head of Human Factors, Roy. Aircraft Estab. FarnBoro. (MoD); Wing Cdr. RAF Med. Br.

CUMMING, Grant Philip Sherwood, Fisher's Lane, Darnick, Melrose TD6 9QX — MB ChB 1988 Manch.; BSc (Hons.) St. And. 1983; MRCOG 1994.

CUMMING, Henry Allan (retired) Sherwood, Fishers Lane, Darnick, Melrose TD6 9AS Tel: 0189 682 2667 — MB ChB 1958 Ed.

CUMMING, Ian Robert 30 Fremont Street, London E9 7NQ — MB BS 1988 Lond.

CUMMING, Irma Mary Angus (retired) Kingarth, Wadeslea, Elie, Leven KY9 1EA Tel: 01333 330275 — MB ChB Glas. 1937. Prev: Ho. Surg. Glas. Roy. Infirm.

CUMMING, Jean Edith (retired) The Old Rectory, Poltimore, Exeter EX4 0AR Tel: 01392 61410 — MB ChB 1948 Birm. GP. Prev: Ho. Phys. Gen. Hosp. Birm. & Qu. Eliz. Hosp. Birm.

CUMMING, Mr John Chalybeate Hospital, Chalybeate Close, Tremona Road, Southampton SO16 6UY Tel: 02380 764357 Fax: 02380 764358 Email: 100030.451@compuserve.com; Newtown Cottage, Minstead, Lyndhurst SO43 7GH Tel: 02380 813535 — MB ChB 1972 Ed.; ChM Ed. 1984, MB ChB 1972; FRCS Ed. 1976. Cons. Urol. Soton. Univ. Hosp. Trust. Socs: Roy. Soc. Med.; Internat. Continence Soc.; Brit. Assn. Urol. Surg. Prev: Sen. Regist. (Urol.) Soton Gen. Hosp.; Rgist. Inst. of Urol. Lond.; Resid. Surg. Off. St. Mark's Hosp. Lond. & St. Peter's Hosp. Lond.

CUMMING, Mr John Anthony Cumberland Infirmary, Carlisle CA2 7HY Tel: 01228 23444; Farlam Ghyll, Hallbankgate, Brampton CA8 2NH — MB ChB 1980 Leeds; ChM 1990; FRCS (Urol.) 1992; FRCS Lond. 1984. Cons. Urol. Cumbld. Infirm. Carlisle.

CUMMING, Mr Joseph Gerard Richard 31 Cluny Gardens, Morningside, Edinburgh EH10 6BH Tel: 0131 447 1070 — MS Lond. 1983, MB BS 1976; BDS St. And. 1970; FRCS Ed. 1980; MRCS Eng. LRCP Lond. 1976. (St. Geo.) Socs: Assn. Surg. & Vasc. Surg.

CUMMING, Katherine Jean Homerton Hospital, Homerton Row, London E9 6SR Tel: 020 8510 5555; 18 Wynchgate, Southgate, London N14 6RR — BM 1988 Soton.; MRCP 1993. (Southampton) Cons. in Geriat. & Gen. Med., Homerton Hosp., Lond. Prev: Specialist Regist. (Geriat. Med.) Whittington Hosp. Lond.; Specialist Regist. (Geriat. Med.), UCH Lond.; Regist. (Palliat. Med.) Trinity Hospice Clapham Common Lond.

CUMMING, Robert Lamont Couper (retired) 1 Sandfield Avenue, Milngavie, Glasgow G62 8NR Tel: 0141 956 2004 — MB ChB 1959 Glas.; MD Glas. 1971; FRCP Glas. 1972, M 1964; FRCP Ed. 1974, M 1965; DObst RCOG 1961. Prev: Cons. Haemat. Glas. N. Hosp. Gp.

CUMMING, Robert Loudon St Ronans Health Centre, Buchan Place, Innerleithen EH44 6QE Tel: 01896 830203 Fax: 01896 831202; The Riggs of Traquair, Traquair, Innerleithen — MB ChB 1971 Glas.; LMCC 1975; MRCGP 1988.

CUMMING, Robert Pattison Aitken (retired) Wester Grange, Elie, Leven KY9 1AR Tel: 01333 330650 — MB ChB Ed. 1944; FRCP Ed. 1980, M 1949. Mem. Med. Bd. Dept. Health & Social Security. Prev: Clin. Asst. Roy. Infirm. Edin.

CUMMING, Mr Ronald Patrick (retired) 62 Hammerfield Avenue, Aberdeen AB10 7FJ Tel: 01224 313192 — MB ChB Aberd. 1945; FRCS Ed. 1952. JP. Prev: Hon. Sheriff Shetland Is.s.

CUMMING, Roy Langdon (retired) 1 Hodnett Ave, Flixton, Manchester M41 6LQ Tel: 0161 747 0648 — MB ChB 1953 Manch. Prev: Regist. Anaesth. Pk. Hosp. Davyhulme.

CUMMING, Stuart Allan Killearn Health Centre, Balfron Road, Killearn, Glasgow G63 9NA Tel: 01360 50339 Fax: 01360 550176; 4 The Oaks, Killearn, Glasgow G63 9SF — MB ChB 1983 Glas.; MRCGP 1987; DRCOG 1986.

CUMMING, William James Kenneth Neuro Science Department Unit, Alexandra Hospital, Mill Lane, Cheadle SK8 2PX Tel: 0161 428 1072 Fax: 0161 428 3421 Email: cumming@ukip.co.uk — MB BCh BAO 1971 Belf.; BSc (1st cl. Hons.) Belf. 1968, MD 1979; FRCP Eng. 1988; FRCPI 1984, M 1974. Cons. Neurol. Alexandra Hosp. Chesh.; Hon. Lect. (Med., Cell & Struct. Biol.) Univ. Manch. Socs: Assn. Brit. Neurols.; Brit. Neuropath. Soc. Prev: Hon. Cons. (Neurol.) Univ. Hosp. S. Manch. NHS Trust.

CUMMINGS, Andrea Jane Holywood Road Surgery, 54 Holywood Road, Belfast BT4 1NT Tel: 028 9065 4668; 30 Glenhugh Park, Saintfield Road, Belfast BT8 7PQ — MB BCh BAO 1986 Belf.; MRCGP 1991; DRCOG 1990; DCH Dub. 1990. GP Belf.; Clin. Med. Off. (Family Plann.) Belf.

CUMMINGS, Conrad Sean 16-17The Links, Shepherds Bush Centre, London W12 8PP Tel: 020 8749 1882 — MB BS 1986 Lond.; LLM Wales 1993; MRCGP 1990; DFFP 1993; DRCOG 1990.

CUMMINGS, Diane Heather Cornamuckla House, 60 Bush Road, Dungannon BT71 6QE — MB BCh BAO 1984 Dub.

CUMMINGS, George Christopher Brae View, Rix Hill, Tavistock PL19 9EB — MB ChB 1976 Glas.; FFA RCS Eng. 1980. Clin. Dir. Cons. (Cardiothoracic Anaesth.) S.W. Cardiothoracic Centre Derriford Hosp. Plymouth. Prev: Cons. Anaesth. N. Ayrsh. Dist. Gen. Hosp. CrossHo. Kilmarnock; Cons. Anaesth. W.. Infirm. Glas.; Vis. Asst. Prof. Univ. Texas Med. Sch. Dallas, USA.

CUMMINGS, Geraldine Elisabeth Community Child Health, Ida Darwin, Fulbourn, Cambridge CB1 5EE Tel: 01223 884160 Fax: 01223 884161; Beechwood, 197 Hinton Way, Great Shelford, Cambridge CB2 5AN Tel: 01223 842476 — MB ChB 1966 Sheff.; DCH Eng. 1969; DObst RCOG 1968. (Sheff.) SCMO (Community Child Health) Lifespan NHS Trust Camb.; Clin. Asst. (Urol.) Addenbrooke's Hosp. Camb. Socs: Roy. Coll. Paediat. & Child Health. Prev: GP N.olt Middlx.; SHO (Paediat.) Worcester Roy. Infirm.; Ho. Surg. & Ho. Phys. Sheff. Roy. Infirm.

CUMMINGS, Glenworth Everton 27 Parkhill Road, London NW3 2YH — MB BS 1992 Lond.; BSc Lond. 1988. SHO Profess. Dept. Orthop. Surg. Ealing & Hammersmith Hosps. Lond. Prev: SHO (Surg.) Char. Cross Hosp. Lond.; SHO Roy. Brompton Hosp. Lond.

CUMMINGS, Ian Gustavus 40 The Chase, London SW16 3AD — BM BCh 1996 Oxf.

CUMMINGS, Kathryn Elizabeth 16 Woodville Drive, Stalybridge SK15 3EA — MB ChB 1994 Leeds.

CUMMINGS, Michael Hunter Dept & Diabetes & Enterinology, Queen Alexandra Hospital, Portsmouth PO6 3LY Tel: 02392 286044 Fax: 02392 286791; 21 Leafy Lane, Whiteley, Fareham PO15 7HL Tel: 01489 880944 Fax: 01489 880933 Email: paddy01@globalnet.co.uk — MB BS Lond. 1987; MD Lond. 1995; MRCP (UK) 1991; FRCP 2000 UK. Cons. Phys. (Endocrinol. & Diabetes) Qu. Alexandra Hosp. Portsmouth; Hon. Sen. Lect. (Endocrinol. & Diabetes) UMDS St. Thos. Hosp. Lond.; Hon. Reader (Endocrinol. & Diabetes) UMDS St. Thos. Hosp. Lond. Prev: Lect. & Hon. Sen. Regist. (Endocrinol. & Diabetes) UMDS St. Thos. Hosp. Lond.; Research Fell. (Endocrinol. & Chem. Path.) UMDS St. Thos. Hosp. Lond.; Regist. Rotat. (Med.) Qu. Alexandra Hosp. Portsmouth & Soton. Gen. Hosp.

CUMMINGS, Paul St Helen's Medical Centre, 151 St. Helens Road, Swansea SA1 4DF Tel: 01792 476576 Fax: 01792 301136; Grove Cottages, Pk Road, Penclawdd, Swansea SA4 3LE — MB BCh 1975 Wales.

CUMMINGS, Relton Alexander Osborne Road Surgery, 17 Osborne Road, Newcastle upon Tyne NE2 2AH Tel: 0191 281 4588 Fax: 0191 212 0379; Rosemount, 4 West Avenue, Benton, Newcastle upon Tyne NE12 9PA Tel: 0191 215 0202 — MB BS 1975 Newc.; MRCGP 1979. (Newcastle) Prev: Clin. Asst. (Geriat.) Newc.AHA; Clin. Asst. (Anaesth.) N. Tyneside AHA.

CUMMINGS, Thomas Michael 5 Lime Terrace, Manor Court Road, Hanwell, London W7 3HE Tel: 020 8579 9607 Email: msjc@easynet.co.uk — MB ChB 1987 Leeds. Dir. of Educat. BMAS. Prev: RAF Med. Off.

CUMMINGS, Trevor Francis Hornby Grange Farm, Little Smeaton, Northallerton DL6 3HP Tel: 01609 81746 — MB ChB 1978 Sheff.; AFOM 1988; DA Eng. 1980. Area Med. off. ICI C&P Ltd. Cleveland. Prev: GP Hunstanton.

CUMMINGS, Tricia Ann 37 Brenthurst Road, London NW10 2DX — MB BS 1978 Lond.; MRCP (UK) 1982. (St. Bart.)

CUMMINS, Anthony 20 Burrell Close, Birkenhead CH42 8QE — MB BCh BAO 1979 NUI; MRCGP 1990.

CUMMINS, Barbara Daniela Coleford Health Centre, Railway Drive, Coleford GL16 8RH Tel: 01594 832117 — MB BCh 1987 Wales; MRCGP 1992; DFFP 1995. GP Princip. Prev: Clin. Med. Off. (Child Health) Gwent; SHO (Oncol.) Plymouth.

CUMMINS, Eithne Mary 16 Meadow Terrace, Sheffield S11 8QN — MB BCh BAO 1992 NUI.

CUMMINS, Mrs Eva Lore Field House, Dummer, Basingstoke RG25 2AJ — MB BS 1954 Lond.; MRCS Eng. LRCP Lond. 1954; FRCR 1972; DMRD Eng. 1969. Cons. Radiol. Frimley Pk. Hosp. Surrey.

CUMMINS, John Christopher (retired) — MB BS 1960 Lond.; MRCS Eng. LRCP Lond. 1960; FRCGP 1983, M 1973; DObst RCOG 1962. Prev: Ho. Surg. Univ. Coll. Hosp. Lond.

CUMMINS, Kate Teresa (Surgery), 149-151 Westoe Road, South Shields NE33 Tel: 0191 554621; (resid.), 16 Sinniside Terrace, Cleadon Village, Sunderland SR6 7XE Tel: 0191 536 2864 — MB BCh BAO 1947 NUI; LM Coombe 1948; MRCGP 1965. (Galw.) Prev: Ho. Surg. Gen. Hosp. Galway; Orthop. Regist. Roy. Infirm. Sunderland; Cas. Off. & Orthop. Ho. Surg. E. Ham Memor. Hosp.

CUMMINS, Mary Catherine Ealing Hospital NHS Trust, Uxbridge Road, Southall UB1 3HW Tel: 020 8967 5624 Fax: 020 967 5339 Email: mcummins@eht.org.uk — MB ChB 1970 Leeds; FRCP Lond. 1993; DCH Eng. 1972; FRCPCH 1997. Cons. Paediat. Ealing Hosp. S.all.

CUMMINS, Mary Cecilia Pen y Maes Health Centre, Beech Street, Summerhill, Wrexham LL11 4UF Tel: 01978 756370 Fax: 01978 751870 — MB BS 1979 Lond.

CUMMINS, Michelle Elizabeth Royal Free Hospital, Pond Street, London NW3; Tamarind, Little Houndbeare Farm, Aylesbeare, Exeter EX5 2DD Tel: 020 8995 8827 Email: michelle@cummins01.freeserve.co.uk — MB BS 1992 Lond.; MRCP Lond. 1996. (Charing Cross and Westminister) Specialist Regist. (Haemat.), N. Thames.

CUMMINS, Niel Lawson (retired) Clifton Lodge, Elwick Road, Hartlepool TS26 9NP Tel: 01429 266454 — LRCPI & LM, LRSCI & LM 1963; LRCPI & LM, LRCSI & LM (Hons.) 1963.

CUMMINS, Sebastian John George Lumley Farmhouse, Westbourne, Emsworth PO10 8RU — MB BS 1996 Lond.

CUMMINS, Siobhan Marie 69 St Pauls Av, Harrow HA3 9PR — MB BS 1997 Lond.

CUMMINS, Thomas Anthony Dickens Place Surgery, Dickens Place, Chelmsford CM1 4UU Tel: 01245 442628 Fax: 01245 443647 Email: thomas.cummins@gp-f81024.nhs.uk — MB BChir 1969 Camb.; MRCS Eng. LRCP Lond. 1969; MRCGP 1979; DObst RCOG 1971. (Camb. & Lond. Hosp.) Socs: BMA; Chelmsford Med. Soc. Prev: Research Regist. Chelmsford & Essex Hosp.; Receiv. Room Off. Lond. Hosp.

CUMPSTY, Claire Elizabeth Hillcrest Surgery, Wellow Lane, Peasedown St. John, Bath BA2 8JQ Tel: 01761 434469 Fax: 01761 432499 — MB BS 1991 Lond.

CUMPSTY, Donald Reginald (retired) Saundersfoot Medical Centre, Saundersfoot SA69 9JW Tel: 01834 812407 — MB ChB 1956 Birm. Prev: Ho. Surg. Qu. Eliz. Hosp. Birm.

CUMPSTY, Julian Richard Hope House Surgery, The Street, Radstock, Bath BA3 3PL Tel: 01761 433157 Fax: 01761 431880 — MB BS 1988 Lond.

CUNARD, Alan John Keith St Peter's Surgery, 6 Oaklands Avenue, Broadstairs CT10 2SQ Tel: 01843 860777 Fax: 01843 866647; The Lodge, 41 Kingsgate Avenue, Kingsgate, Broadstairs CT10 3QP Fax: 01843 603893 — MB ChB 1980 Cape Town; BSc Cape Town; DCH S Afr 1984. Clin. Asst. (Ophth. & Anaesth.) Thanet Dist. Hosp. Trust.

CUNARD, Malcolm Alexander Blossoms Inn Medical Centre, 21-26 Garlick Hill, London EC4V 2AU Tel: 020 7606 6159 Fax: 020 7489 1134; 32 South Grove House, South Grove, London N6 6LR — MB ChB 1973 Cape Town; DCH (S.A.Coll Medicine). Med. Off. to the Bank of Eng., Deutsche Bank, W. LB and other financial Inst.s.

CUNDALL, David Bolton Belmont House, 3-5 Belmont Grove, Leeds LS2 9NP Tel: 0113 392 6220 Fax: 0113 392 6219 Email: cundal@globalnet.co.uk — MB BS 1977 Newc.; MRCP (UK) 1980; DCH RCP Lond. 1980; FRCPCH. Cons. Community Paediat. Leeds Community & Ment. Health Servs. NHS Trust. Prev: Tutor (Paediat.) St. Jas. Univ. Hosp. Leeds; Med. Off. Maua Methodist Hosp. Kenya.

CUNDALL, Richard Leslie (retired) 24A Manor Road, Wendover, Aylesbury HP22 6HN — MB ChB 1963 Ed.; MSc Ed. 1972; FRCPsych 1981, M 1972; DPM Ed. 1967. Prev: Cons. Psychiat. Amersham Gen. Hosp.

CUNDALL, Mr Robert Davies (retired) 32 Woodside, Harrogate HG1 5NG — MB BChir Camb. 1949; FRCS Eng. 1953; DObst RCOG 1951.

CUNDILL, Joan Gwendoline (retired) 15 Linkway, Crowthorne RG45 6ES — MB BS Lond. 1967; MRCS Eng. LRCP Lond. 1967. Prev: Staff Grade (Community Paediat.) Roy. Berks. & Battle NHS Trust Reading.

CUNDILL, John Graham Department Anaesthetics, Hull Royal Infirmary, Hull; Muulberry House, 21 Towthorpe Road, Haxby, York YO32 3LZ — MB ChB 1977 Manch.; BSc (Hons.) Manch. 1974, MB ChB 1977; FFA RCS Lond. 1981. Cons. Anaesth. Hull & E. Yorks. HA.

CUNDY, Amanda Louise Wilton Farm, Trerulefoot, Saltash PL12 5BX — MB BS 1984 Lond.; DRCOG 1987.

CUNDY, Jeffrey Michael (retired) 31 Quernmore Close, Bromley BR1 4EL Tel: 020 8460 9556 — MB BS Lond. 1956; FFA RCS Eng. 1963; DA Eng. 1960. Prev: Cons. Anaesth. Lewisham Gp. Hosps.

CUNDY, Paul Robert The Surgery, 35A High Street, Wimbledon, London SW19 5BY Tel: 020 8946 4820 Fax: 020 8944 9794; 49 Hazlewell Road, Putney, London SW15 6UT — MB BS 1982 Lond.; BSc Lond. 1979; MRCGP 1986. (Westm.) Mem. Gen. Med. Servs. Comm.

CUNINGHAM, Penelope Michelle 10 Maitland Road, Reading RG1 6NL — MB ChB Bristol 1989.

CUNION, David Whitby Group Practice, Spring Vale Medical Centre, Whitby YO21 1SD Tel: 01947 820888 Fax: 01947 603194; Low Farm, Ugglebarnby, Whitby YO21 5HX — MB ChB Sheff. 1968; DObst RCOG 1970.

CUNLIFFE, Anthony Clegg Knipe Tarn, Crook, Kendal LA8 8LN Tel: 015395 68435 — MRCS Eng. LRCP Lond. 1937; MD Camb. 1946, MB BChir. 1937; FRCPath 1964. (St. Geo.) Emerit. Prof. Med. Microbiol. (Univ. Lond.) KCH. Socs: Fell. Roy. Soc. Med.; Med. Research Club. Prev: Bacteriol. King's Coll. Hosp.; Examr. Univs. Lond., Manch., Bristol & E. Africa & Primary FRCS Eng.; Dir. Studies Roy. Coll. Path.

CUNLIFFE, Clare Helen 50 Earlsway, Curzon Park, Chester CH4 8AZ — MB ChB 1992 Leeds.

CUNLIFFE, David Robert Department of Oral and Maxillofacial Surgery, Cheltenham General Hospital, Cheltenham GL53 7AN; Tilstock, 2 Ashdale Close, Aldsworth, Cheltenham GL54 3QT — MB BCh 1994 Wales; BDS Wales 1985; FRCS Eng. 1997; FDS RCS Ed. 1990. Specialist Regist. (Oral & Maxillofacial Surg.) Cheltenham Gen. Hosp. & Oxf. John Radcliffe. Socs: BMA; Brit. Assn. Oral & Maxillofacial Surg. Prev: SHO Rotat. (Surg.) Swansea; Lect. (Oral & Maxillofacial Surg.) Cardiff.

CUNLIFFE, Gordon 11 Georges Crescent, Grappenhall, Warrington WA4 2PP — MB ChB 1977 Manch.; MRCGP 1981.

CUNLIFFE, Mr Ian Andrew Department of Ophthalmology, Birmingham Heartlands Hospital, Bordesley Green E., Birmingham B9 5SS Tel: 0121 766 6611 Fax: 0121 773 6897 — MB ChB 1985 Sheff.; FRCS Glas. 1988; FCOphth 1989. (Univ. Sheff.) Cons. Ophth.

Birm. Heartlands Hosp. & Solihull NHS Trust (Teachg.) & Birm. & Midl. Eye Centre.

CUNLIFFE, Ian Foster Dapdune House Surgery, Wharf Road, Guildford GU1 4RP Tel: 01483 573336 Fax: 01483 306602 — MB BS 1982 Lond.; MA Oxf. 1982; MRCGP 1985; DRCOG 1985. (Oxf. & St. Thos.) Prev: Trainee GP S.W. Surrey HA VTS; Ho. Phys. Roy. Surrey Co. Hosp. Guildford; Ho. Surg. St. Thos. Hosp. Lond.

CUNLIFFE, Jamie Waterside Health Centre, Beaulieu Road, Hythe, Southampton SO45 5WX Tel: 02380 845955 — MB ChB 1969 Manch.; MRCP (UK) 1973. Prev: Regist. (Neurol.) Middlesbrough Gen. Hosp.; SHO (Gen. Med.) Roy. United Hosp. Bath; Ho. Off. & Res. Clin. Pathol. Manch. Roy. Infirm.

CUNLIFFE, Jayne Louise Oldland Surgery, 192 High Street, Oldland Common, Bristol BS30 9QQ Tel: 0117 932 4444 Fax: 0117 932 4101 — MB ChB 1993 Ed.; DRCOG 1996; MRCGP 1998. (Edin.) Socs: BMA. Prev: GP Regist. Edin.; SHO (Paediat.) Stirling Roy. Infirm.; SHO (Geriat. Gen. Med.) Borders Gen. Hosp.

CUNLIFFE, Lindsay Frances Bradley Shaw Health Centre, Crookesbroom Lane, Hatfield, Doncaster DN7 6JN Tel: 01302 841373 — MB ChB 1974 Leeds. Prev: Jun. Ho. Off. Beckett Hosp. Barnsley & Pinderfields Gen. Hosp.; Wakefield.

CUNLIFFE, Mary 42 Hornby Lane, Calderstones, Liverpool L18 3HH — MB BS 1976 Newc.; FFA RCS Eng. 1981. Cons. Anaesth. Roy. Liverp. Childr. Hosp.

CUNLIFFE, Nigel Andrew Department of Medical Microbiology & Genito-Urinary Medicine, University of Liverpool, Liverpool L69 3GA Tel: 0151 706 4381 Fax: 0151 706 5805 Email: n.a.cunliffe@liv.ac.uk; 9 Carlton Road, Ainsdale, Southport PR8 2PG — MB ChB 1988 Manch.; PhD 2001 (Univ. Liverpool); BSc (Hons.) Manch. 1985; MRCP (UK) 1991; DTM & H Liverp. 1991. (Manch.) Clin. Lect. Dept. of Med. MicoBiol. Gum Univ. of Liverp. Prev: Research Fell. (Viral Gastroenteritis) CDC Atlanta, USA; Regist. (Microbiol.) Univ. Edin. Med. Sch.; Wellcome Trust Research Train. Fell. Wellcome Trust Trop. Centre Univ. of Liverp. & Malawi.

CUNLIFFE, Peter Nicholson (retired) 25 Highlands Way, Whiteparish, Salisbury SP5 2SZ — MB BChir 1943 Camb.; MRCS Eng. LRCP Lond. 1943; DObst RCOG 1948; DA Eng. 1954. Prev: Anaesth. Watford Gen. Hosp.

CUNLIFFE, Philip Nicholas Alton Health Centre, Anstey Road, Alton GU34 2QX Tel: 01420 84676 Fax: 01420 542975 — MB ChB 1969 Birm.; MRCP (UK) 1972; DRCOG 1979; DA Eng. 1979.

CUNLIFFE, Robert Neil 7 Abberbury Road, Oxford OX4 4ET — BM BCh 1994 Oxf.; MRCP (UK) 1997. (Oxf.)

CUNLIFFE, Timothy Peter 58 Beechfield Rise, Coxhoe, Durham DH6 4SB Tel: 0191 377 9970 — MB BS 1993 Newc. SHO (Paediat.) Bishop Auckland Gen. Hosp. Prev: SHO (Med.) N. Tees Gen. Hosp. Stockton; SHO (Gen. Surg.) Sunderland Dist. Gen. Hosp.; SHO (Gen. Med.) Dryburn Hosp.

CUNLIFFE, Professor William James 47 Tredgold Avenue, Bramhope, Leeds LS16 9BS Tel: 0113 267 2326 — BSc Manch. 1960, MD 1970, MB ChB 1962; FRCP Lond. 1977, MRCP 1965; MRCS Eng. LRCP Lond. 1962. (Manch.) Prof. Dermat. Leeds Gen. Infirm. Socs: Eur. Soc. Dermat. Res.; Amer. Acad. Dermat.; Eur. Acad. Dermat. & Venereol. Prev: Sen. Regist. (Dermat.) Roy. Vict. Infirm. Newc.; Asst. Lect. (Path.) Univ. Manch.; SHO Manch. Roy. Infirm.

CUNLIFFE, Mr William James Queen Elizabeth Hospital, Sheriff Hill, Gateshead NE9 6SX Tel: 0191 482 0000 Fax: 0191 403 6187; 83 Jesmond Park W., Newcastle upon Tyne NE7 7BY Tel: 0191 487 2148 Fax: 0191 281 6731 — MB BS 1976 Newc.; MD Newc. 1989; FRCS Eng. 1981. (Newc.) Cons. (Gen. Surg.) Gateshead Hosps. NHS Trust. Socs: Assn. Coloproctol.; Brit. Assn. Surgic. Oncol.; Soc. Gastroenterol.

CUNNAH, David Trefor Edward Broomfield Hospital, Chelmsford CM1 7ET Tel: 01245 440761; The Chilterns, Cedar Avenue W., Chelmsford CM1 2QH — MB BS 1977 Lond.; BSc Lond. 1974; MD Lond. 1988; FRCP Lond. 1995; MRCP (UK) 1980. Cons. Broomfield Hosp. Chelmsford. Socs: Brit. Diabetic Assn.; Brit. Endocrine Soc. Prev: Sen. Regist. (Med.) St. Bart. Hosp. Lond.; MRC Train. Fell. St. Bart. Hosp. Lond.; Regist. St. Thos. Hosp. Lond.

CUNNANE, Joseph Gerard Chesterfield & North Derbyshire Royal Hospital, Calow, Chesterfield S44 5BL Tel: 01246 277271 Fax: 01246 552612 — MB ChB 1984 Leeds; MB ChB Leeds I984, MMedSci 1991; MRCPsych 1988. Cons. Psychiat. Chesterfield & N. Derbysh. Roy. Hosp. Prev: Sen. Regist. (Psychiat.) Warneford Hosp.; Regist. (Psychiat.) Leeds.

CUNNIFFE, Gerald Anthony Baddow Road Surgery, 115 Baddow Road, Chelmsford CM2 7PY Tel: 01245 351351 Fax: 01245 494192; 4 Fawkner Close, Chelmsford CM2 6UP — MB BS 1982 Lond.; MRCGP 1987; T(GP) 1991; Cert. Family Plann. JCC 1987; DRCOG 1986. (St. Barts.)

CUNNING, Brendan William Hunter Health Centre, Andrew Street, East Kilbride, Glasgow G74 1AD Tel: 01355 906622 Fax: 01355 906629 — MB ChB 1985 Glas.; MRCGP 1990; DRCOG 1990; DCH Glas. 1987. GP Hunter Health Centre E. Kilbride.

CUNNING, Clare Anne Riverview Medical Centre, 6 George Street, Johnstone PA5 8SL Tel: 01505 320208 Fax: 01505 322543; 18 Marchbank Gardens, Paisley PA1 3JD — MB ChB 1984 Glas.; MRCGP 1988; DRCOG 1987. Prev: Trainee GP Renfrewsh. Dist. VTS.

CUNNINGHAM, Alan Anderson 36 Kyleakin Road, Arden, Glasgow G46 8AF — MB ChB 1983 Dundee; DRCOG 1986.

CUNNINGHAM, Alison Sara 60 Sherdley Park Dr, St Helens WA9 3TW — MB ChB 1997 Manch.

CUNNINGHAM, Angela Rudland 50 Bathgate Road, London SW19 5PJ — MB BS 1970 Lond.; BSc (Hons.) Lond. 1967, MB BS 1970; FRCR 1977. (St. Geo.) Cons. Radiol. St. Helier Hosp. Carshalton.

CUNNINGHAM, Anne Marie 259 Moyadd Road, Kikleel, Newry BT34 4HP — MB BCh BAO 1996 Belf.

CUNNINGHAM, Astrid Coreen Elizabeth Grannary Cottage, Blacksmiths Lane, Beckford, Tewkesbury GL20 7AH; Warwick House, 26 High St, East Malling, Maidstone ME15 6AL Tel: 01732 84009 — MB BS 1987 Lond.; MRCGP 1991.

CUNNINGHAM, Mr Christopher 20 Bearside Road, Stirling FK7 9BX — MB ChB 1987 Ed.; BSc (Hons.) Ed. 1985, MB ChB 1987; FRCS Ed. 1991; MD 1997.

CUNNINGHAM, Ciara 62 Ballymageogh Road, Kilkeel, Newry BT34 4SX — MB BCh 1998 Belf.; MB BCh Belf 1998.

CUNNINGHAM, Colin Smart 804 Alaska, Grange Road, Tower Bridge Quarter, London SE1 3BG — MB ChB 1994 Manch.; BSc (Med. Sci.) St. And. 1991; BSc (Hons.) Immunol. & Cell Biol. Aberd. 1988. Ho. Off. (Surg.) Trafford.; Paedatrics; Sen. SHO. Kingston. Hosp.

CUNNINGHAM, David Department of Medicine, The Royal Marsden Hospital, Downs Road, Sutton SM2 5PT Tel: 020 8642 6011 Fax: 020 8643 9414 — MB ChB 1978 Glas.; MD Glas. 1987; FRCP Lond. 1995; FRCP Glas. 1991; MRCP (UK) 1981. Cons. Phys. Roy. Marsden Hosp. Lond. & Surrey. Socs: Assn. Cancer Phys. & Amer. Soc. Clin. Oncol. Prev: Sen. Lect. (Med.) Inst. Cancer Research Roy. Marsden Hosp.; Sen. Clin. Sci. Ludwig Inst. for Cancer Research St. Marys Hosp. Med. Sch. Lond.

CUNNINGHAM, David Frew Terrace Surgery, 9 Frew Terrace, Irvine KA12 9DZ Tel: 01294 272326 Fax: 01294 314614; Southview, 5 Lochend Road, Troon KA10 6EU Tel: 01292 318964 — MB ChB 1985 Ed.; BA 1988 (Hon. Open); MPhil 2000 Glasgow; MRCGP 1995; DFFP 2001. (University) Socs: Roy. Coll. Gen. Pract. Prev: SHO (A & E & Gen. Med.) CrossHo. Hosp. Kilmarnock; SHO (Infec. Dis.) Avrsh. Centr. Hosp. Irvine.

CUNNINGHAM, David Alexander Hafle, Pwllhobi, Llanbadarn Fawr, Aberystwyth SY23 3SX — MB BCh 1998 Wales.

CUNNINGHAM, David McLeod (retired) 44 Flax Bourton Road, Failand, Bristol BS8 3UN — MB ChB 1948 Bristol.

CUNNINGHAM, Deborah Alison Department of Radiology, St. Mary's Hospital, Praed St., London W2 1NG Tel: 020 7886 6275 Fax: 020 7886 6669; 14 Cholmeley Crescent, London N6 5HA Tel: 020 8348 3517 — BM BCh Oxf. 1973; FRCP Lond. 1996; MRCP (UK) 1975; FRCR 1981; DMRD Eng. 1979. (Undergraduate: Girton College, Cambridge; Postgraduate: Somerville College, Oxford.) Cons. Radiol. St. Mary's Hosp. Lond. Socs: Roy. Coll. Radiol. (Mem. Train. & Accreditation Comm.); (Hon. Sec. & Counc. Mem.) Brit. Inst. of Radiol.; Roy. Coll. Phys.s (Chairm. SAC in Nuclear Med.). Prev: Research Fell. Washington Univ. Sch. Med. St. Louis, USA; Sen. Regist. (Radiol.) Hammersmith Hosp. Lond.; Regist. (Med.) St. Mary's Hosp. Lond.

CUNNINGHAM, Deirdre Gillian Lambeth, Southwark & Lewisham Health Authority, 1 Lower Marsh, London SE1 7NT Tel: 020 7716 7060; 20 Greenend Road, London W4 1AJ — MRCS Eng. LRCP

Lond. 1969; MSc (Community Med.) Lond. 1982; FFPHM RCP (UK) 1990; MFCM 1985; DObst RCOG 1972. (Roy. Free) Dir. of Health Policy & Pub. Health Lambeth, S.wark & Lewisham HA; Hon. Sen. Lect. (Pub. Health Med.) UMDS Guy's & St. Thos. Lond. Prev: Regional Dir. of Pub. Health NE Thames RHA; Head of Pub. Health Div. NHS Managem. Exec.; Dir. Pub. Health Pk.side HA.

CUNNINGHAM, Donald Ian Alexander (retired) Westpark, Church St., Dufftown, Keith AB55 4AR Tel: 01340 820486 Email: diacun@globalnet.co.uk — MB ChB 1956 Aberd.; DObst RCOG 1963.

CUNNINGHAM, Edith Louise (retired) Ballytrim House, 10 Ballytrim Road, Killyleagh, Downpatrick BT30 9TH Tel: 0139 682210 — MB BCh BAO 1954 Belf.; MRCGP 1978. Prev: GP Killyleagh.

CUNNINGHAM, Elinor Betty (retired) 13 Riverside Walk, Yealmpton, Plymouth PL8 2LU Tel: 01752 880823 — MB ChB 1953 Birm.; DObst RCOG 1955. Prev: SCMO (Family Plann. & Cytol.) Plymouth HA.

CUNNINGHAM, Frances Louise Lonsdale Medical Centre, 24 Lonsdale Road, London NW6 6RR Tel: 020 7328 8331 Fax: 020 7328 8630; 5 Dundonald Road, London NW10 3HP — MB BS 1981 Lond.; MRCGP 1985; DRCOG 1985. (Middlx.)

CUNNINGHAM, Gail Kathleen Francis Street Archway Medical Practice, Stornoway HS1 2GX; 37A Eoropie, Ness, Isle of Lewis HS2 0XH Tel: 01851 810518 — MB ChB 1985 Glas.; MRCGP 1989; DRCOG 1989. (Glasgow) p/t Sessional GP; Sessional GP Borve Med. Pract. Isle of Lewis.

CUNNINGHAM, Geoffrey Allan Brockman 17 St Helen's Place, London EC3A 6DE Tel: 020 7588 6503 Fax: 020 7256 5295; 4 West Terrace, Cranbrook TN17 3LG Tel: 01580 712240 Fax: 01580 712240 Email: geoffrey.cunningham@which.net — MB BS 1955 Lond.; MFOM RCP Lond. 1982; FRCGP 1977, M 1964; DIH Eng. 1970; DObst RCOG 1964. (St. Bart.) Med. Adviser to City Med. Ltd., 17 St. Helens Pl., Lond.; Med. Advis. Shipping Cos. Kent.; Med. Adviser PCH Occupat.al Health Wenesford, Kent. Socs: Fell. Roy. Soc. Med.; Soc. Occupat. Med.; Fac. Occupat. Med. Prev: Sen. Med. Adviser (SE Asia) Unocal Ltd.; Sen. Med. Off. P & O SN Co. Lond.; Ho. Off. (Obst.) St. Helier Hosp. Carshalton.

CUNNINGHAM, George Leslie Whitton St. Regulus Cottage, St Andrews KY16 9PU — MB ChB 1952 Glas. (Glas.) Med. Off. Craigtown Geriat. Unit; Med. Off. Memor. Cott. Hosp. St. And. Socs: Glas. M.-C. Soc.; Roy. Coll. Gen. Pract. Prev: Ho. Phys. Roy. Matern. Hosp. Glas. & Stobhill Gen. Hosp. Glas.

CUNNINGHAM, Hazel Elizabeth 22 Annfield Gardens, Stirling FK8 2BJ — MB ChB 1966 Glas.; FRCR 1975; FFR 1973; DMRD Eng. 1971. Cons. (Radiol.) Stirling Roy. Infirm.

CUNNINGHAM, Jean Alexander Ashley Centre Surgery, Ashley Square, Epsom KT18 5DD Tel: 01372 723668 Fax: 01372 726796; Knowle House, Pleasure Pit Road, Ashtead KT21 1HR — MB BS 1968 Lond.; MRCS Eng. LRCP Lond. 1968; DCH Eng. 1970. (Char. Cross) Socs: BMA. Prev: Ho. Surg. Char. Cross Hosp. Lond.; SHO (Dermat. & Gen. Med.) St. Geo. Hosp. Lond.; Regist. (Med.) Lewisham Hosp.

CUNNINGHAM, Joan 73 Moneyscalp Road, Bryansford, Newcastle BT33 0PY — MB BCh BAO 1996 Belf.

CUNNINGHAM, John Royal London Hospital, London E1 1BB Tel: 020 7377 7366 Fax: 020 7377 7003; 31A King Henry's Road, London NW3 3QR Tel: 020 7722 3883 Fax: 020 7722 3883 — BM BCh 1973 Oxf.; BA Camb. 1970; DM Oxf. 1988; FRCP Lond. 1988; MRCP (UK) 1975. (Cambridge and Oxford) Cons. Nephrol. & Phys. Barts and the Lond. NHS Trust & Hon. Sen. Lect. (Med.) St Bartholomews & The Roy. Lond. Sch. of Med. & Dent. Lond.; Phys. Roy. Ho.hold; Phys. King Edwd. VII's Hosp. for Off. Socs: Amer. Soc. Bone & Mineral Research; Med. Res. Soc.; Amer. Soc. Nephrol. Prev: Fell. (Metab.) Washington Univ. Sch. Med. St. Louis, USA; Lect. (Med.) Lond. Hosp. Med. Coll.; Regist. (Med.) Centr. Middlx. Hosp. Lond.

CUNNINGHAM, John Allen Manor Park Surgery, Bell Mount Close, Leeds LS13 2UP Tel: 0113 257 9702 Fax: 0113 236 1537 — MB ChB 1979 Leeds.

CUNNINGHAM, Mr John Andrew Derek Joseph (retired) 5 Abbots Grange, Humberston Avenue, Humberston, Grimsby DN36 4TD Tel: 01472 812174 Email: abbots5@aol.com — LRCPI & LM, LRSCI & LM 1948; LRCPI & LM, LRCSI & LM 1948; FRCS Eng. 1966; FRCSI 1950. Prev: Cons. Surg. Grimsby HA.

CUNNINGHAM, John Leslie Bryn, Pine Walks, Prenton, Birkenhead CH42 8LG Tel: 0151 608 1674 — MB ChB 1966 Liverp.; FRCP Lond. 1982, M 1971. (Liverp.) Cons. Phys. Fairfield Indep. Hosp. Merseyside; Cons. Phys. Roy. Insur. Gp. Prev: Cons. Phys. Whiston Hosp.; Nat. Insts. Health Internat. Fell. Univ. Kansas Med. Center, Kansas; Wellcome Research Fell. Univ. Liverp.

CUNNINGHAM, Kenneth John Main East Inglewood, Houston Road, Langbank, Port Glasgow PA14 6XT Tel: 0147 554496 — MB ChB 1971 Glas.; BSc (Hons. Biochem.) Glas. 1966, MB ChB 1971; MRCPath 1981. (Glas.) Cons. Chem. Path. Monklands Dist. Gen. Hosp. Airdrie, Hairmyres Hosp. E. Kilbride & Matern. Hosp. Bellshill. Prev: Sen. Regist. (Biochem.) W.. Infirm. Glas.; Regist. (Biochem.) Glas. Roy. Infirm.; SHO (Obst.) S.. Gen. Hosp. Glas.

CUNNINGHAM, Lesley Marie Stoneham Lane Surgery, 6 Stoneham Lane, Swaythling, Southampton SO16 2AB Tel: 023 8055 5776 Fax: 023 8039 9723 — MB ChB 1978 Manch.; 1985 Lond.; MRCGP 1987; DCH RCP; MRCGP 1987; DCH RCP Lond. 1985. (Manch.) Adjudicating Med. Practitioner Sema/N.D.A.; Med. Mem. Tribunal Serv. part time Soton. Prev: Trainee GP Soton. VTS; SHO (Psychiat.) Wessex RHA; Clin. Med. Off. Blackburn Hyndburn & Ribble Valley HA.

CUNNINGHAM, Margaret (retired) 48 Murrayfields Gardens, Edinburgh EH12 6DF — MB ChB 1960 Aberd.; MRCOG 1968.

CUNNINGHAM, Maria Bernadette Brunswick Health Centre, Hartfield Close, Manchester M13 9YA Tel: 0161 273 4901 Fax: 0161 273 5952; 468 Wellington Road N., Heaton Chapel, Stockport SK4 5BA Tel: 0161 442 0593 — BM BCh 1981 Oxf.; MRCGP 1988; DRCOG 1986; DCH Lond. 1986. (Oxford) GP. Manch. Prev: Regt.. Med. Off. W. Berlin; SHO (Med.) Duchess of Kent's Milit. Hosp., Catterick, N. Yorks.; GP. Trainee Manch.

CUNNINGHAM, Marietta Majella Keenaghy, Lisnaskea, Enniskillen BT92 5GY — MB BCh BAO 1993 Belf.

CUNNINGHAM, Martin Jerome Joseph Kilkeel Health Centre, Knockchree Avenue, Kilkeel, Newry BT34 4BS Tel: 028 4176 2601 Fax: 028 4176 5485; Ferndale, 66 Manse Road, Kilkeel, Newry BT34 4BN Email: martin.kilkeel@virgin.net — MB BCh BAO 1985 Belf.; MRCGP 1990; Dip. Sports Med. Glas. 1996; DRCOG 1991; DCH RCPS Glas. 1988. (Qu. Univ. Belf.) Socs: BMA; Brit. Assn. Sport & Med. Prev: Trainee GP Armagh Health Centre; SHO (Paediat.) Belf. City Hosp.; SHO (Gen. Med.) Tyrone Co. Hosp.

CUNNINGHAM, Mary Eve (retired) Fairhaven, 29 Macdona Drive, West Kirby, Wirral CH48 3JH Tel: 0151 625 1040 — MB ChB Liverp. 1970; FRCR 1976; DMRD Liverp. 1973. Prev: Cons. (Radiol.) Mersey RHA.

CUNNINGHAM, Maureen Teresa (retired) 29 Moorside Court, Newcastle upon Tyne NE5 3AQ Tel: 0191 242 2596 — MB BS Durh. 1948. Prev: Sen. Med. Off. (Child Health) N.W. Durh. HA.

CUNNINGHAM, Michael Denis St James House Surgery, County Court Road, King's Lynn PE30 5SY Tel: 01553 774221 Fax: 01553 692181; 41 Extons Road, King's Lynn PE30 5NT Tel: 01553 761634 — MB BS 1972 Lond.; BA (Hons.) Dub. 1962.

CUNNINGHAM, Michael Jon Irving 86 Reservoir Road, Selly Oak, Birmingham B29 6TF — MB ChB 1992 Birm. SHO (Anaesth.) Univ. Birm. NHS Trust.

CUNNINGHAM, Nancy Elizabeth (retired) Pathology Department, Ayrshire & Arran Area Laboratory, Crosshouse Hospital, Kilmarnock KA2 0BE Tel: 01563 21133 — MB ChB 1965 Glas.; BSc (Hons.) Glas. 1962; FRCPath 1984, M 1972; DMJ Soc. Apoth. Lond. 1979. Prev: Cons. in Admin. Charge of Path. Servs. Ayrsh. HB.

CUNNINGHAM, Neil Woodlands Surgery, 1 Greenfarm Road, Ely, Cardiff CF5 4RG Tel: 029 2059 1444 Fax: 029 2059 9204; 18 Clos Llanfair, Wenvoe, Cardiff CF5 6DJ — MB BCh 1980 Wales; MRCGP 1984.

CUNNINGHAM, Neil 48 Woodsorrel Road, Liverpool L15 6UD — MB BS 1997 Newc.

CUNNINGHAM, Nicholas Joseph Birch Terrace Surgery, 25A Birch Terrace, Hanley, Stoke-on-Trent ST1 3JN Tel: 01782 212436; 1 Browning Close, Cheadle, Stoke-on-Trent ST10 1XD — BM BS 1985 Nottm.; MRCGP 1989; DRCOG 1988. GP. Prev: Trainee GP Derby VTS.

CUNNINGHAM, Penelope Jane Leigh Spring Wood Cottage, Dene Park, Tonbridge TN11 9NS Tel: 01732 353353 Fax: 01732

353353 — MB BS Lond. 1964. (St. Thos.) Prev: Ho. Off. (Med. & Surg.) St. Helier Hosp. Carshalton; Ho. Off. (Anaesth.) St. Thos. Hosp. Lond.

CUNNINGHAM, Peter Nisbet (retired) 12 Flint Meadow, Neston, South Wirral CH64 9XX — MB ChB 1941 Glas.; BSc 1938, MB ChB Glas. 1941, DPH 1943; DIH Eng. 1962. Prev: Med. Off. Min. of Defence.

CUNNINGHAM, Ralph Scott 6 Milngavie Road, Bearsden, Glasgow G61 2HX Tel: 0141 942 2702 — MB ChB 1991 Glas.; DA (UK) 1994.

CUNNINGHAM, Richard Plymouth PHL, Derriford Hospital, Derriford Road, Plymouth PL6 8DH Tel: 01752 792367 — MB BCh BAO 1987 Dub.; MRCPath 1994. Cons. Med. Microbiol. Derriford Hosp. Plymouth. Socs: Hosp. Infec. Soc.; Brit. Soc. Antimicrob. Chemother.; Assn. Clin. Path. Prev: Sen. Regist. (Med. Microbiol.) Qu. Med. Centre Nottm.

CUNNINGHAM, Robert Campbell (retired) 11 Pinewood Close, Ashton Road, Lancaster LA1 Tel: 01523 65440 — MB ChB 1938 Glas.; DPH 1940; FRCPsych 1971; DPA Leeds 1956; DPM Manch. 1947. Prev: Med. Supt. & Cons. Psychiat. Roy. Albert Hosp. Lancaster.

CUNNINGHAM, Robert John (retired) Urrard House, Hovingham, York YO62 4LQ Tel: 01653 628142 Fax: 01653 628024 — MB BS 1962 Lond.; MRCS Eng. LRCP Lond. 1962; AKC 1963; DObst RCOG 1967; MRCGP (Distinc.) 1970; DCH (Distinc.) RCPS Glas. 1970. Insur. Med. Off. Co-Op., Pruden., Crown Life & other Assur. Cos. Prev: Nuffield Trav. Fell. Child Health 1972 & Arthiritis & Rheum. Counc. Trav. Fell. 1979.

CUNNINGHAM, Ronan George Charles 126 Glenholm Park, Belfast BT8 6FP — MB BCh BAO 1994 Belf.

CUNNINGHAM, Ross Bruce c/o Tindal Oatts, 48 St Vincent St., Glasgow G2 5HS — MB ChB 1960 Glas.

CUNNINGHAM, Mrs Sally Ann Department of Cardiothoracic Surgery, Wynthenshane Hospital, Southmoor Road, Manchester M23 9LT Tel: 0161 998 7070; Clapton Farm House, Clapton, Berkeley GL13 9QX — MB BS Lond. 1986; FRCS Ed. 1993. Specialist. Regist. in Cardiothoracic Surg. Char. Cross & W.minster; Transpl. Fell. Cardiac Wing Gt. Ormond St. Hosp. Childr. Lond. Prev: Research Fell. (Transpl. Biol.) Inst. Child Health Lond.; Transpl. Fell. Cardiac Wing Gt. Ormond St. Hosp. Childr. Lond.; Regist. (Cardiothoracic Surg.) Bristol Roy. Infirm. & St. Geo. Hosp. Lond.

CUNNINGHAM, Sara Jane Ridgeview, 1st Floor, Plympton Clinic, Station Rd, Plympton, Plymouth PL7 2AU Tel: 01752 348676 — MB BS 1986 Lond.; MRCPsych 1992. (Westm.)

CUNNINGHAM, Sarah Frances The Surgery, 2 Church Lane, Merton Park, London SW19 3NY Tel: 020 8542 1174 Fax: 020 8544 1583 — MB BS 1982 Lond.; MRCGP (Distinc.) 1986.

CUNNINGHAM, Simon Lee 103 Stanley Street, Accrington BB5 6PQ — MB ChB 1994 Aberd.

CUNNINGHAM, Steven Royal Hospital for Sick Children, Sciences Road, Edinburgh EH9 1LF Tel: 0131 536 0641 Fax: 0131 5360052 Email: steve.cunninham@luht.scot.nhs.uk; 3 Lonsdale Terrace, Edinburgh EH3 9HN — MB ChB 1987 Dundee; PhD Ed. 1993; MRCP (UK) 1991. Cons. Respirat. Paediat. and Cons.Paediat. and Hon. Sen. Lect. Socs: Europ. Respirat. Soc.; Brit. Peadiatric Respirat. Soc.; Neonat Soc. Prev: Locum Cons. Respirat. Paediat., Mater Childr.s Hosp, Brisbane, Australia; Cystic Fibrosis Fell., Gt. Ormond St. Hosp; Lect. in Respirat. Paediat.

CUNNINGHAM, William Francis Corbridge Health Centre, Manor Court, Corbridge NE45 5JW Tel: 01434 632011 Fax: 01434 633878 — MB BS 1974 Lond.; MB BS (Hons. Med.) Lond. 1974; MRCP (UK) 1976; FRCGP 1990. (King's Coll. Hosp.) Course Organiser N.umbria VTS.; Chairm. Educat. Comm. Gen. Pract. Univ. Newc.

CUNNINGHAM, William Rattray (retired) St Clair, 18 Craigmore Road, Rothesay PA20 9LB Tel: 01700 2732 — MB ChB 1944 Glas.; BSc Glas. 1942, MB ChB 1944.

***CUNNINGHAM, Yvonne Catherine** 2 Whyte Walk, Dunfermline KY11 4UT; 18 Muirton Road, Dundee DD2 2JN Tel: 01382 646001 — MB ChB 1998 Dund.; MB ChB Dund 1998.

CUNNINGHAM-BURLEY, Rachel Anne 3F4, 26 Canaan Lane, Edinburgh EH10 4SY — MB ChB 1992 Ed.

CUNNINGHAM-DAVIS, Peter George Islay House, Capel Ed Lane, Penperlleni, Pontypool NP4 0AT Tel: 01873 880474 Fax: 01873 880474 — MB BCh Wales 1960; AFOM 1980; DObst RCOG 1962. Prev: SHO & Ho. Off. (O & G) Morriston Hosp. Swansea; Ho. Surg. Roy. Vict. Hosp. Boscombe.

CUNNINGTON, Alan Richard 4 Woodlands Avenue, Walsall WS5 3LN Tel: 0121 357 1750 — MB ChB Birm. 1970; BSc (Physiol.) Birm. 1967, MD 1979; FRCP Lond. 1988; MRCP (UK) 1973; DCH Eng. 1972. Cons. Phys. Walsall Hosps. NHS Trust. Socs: Brit. Cardiac Soc. Prev: Research Fell. (Med.) Qu. Eliz. Hosp. Birm.; Regist. (Med.) Nat. Heart Hosp. Lond.

CUNNINGTON, Alfred Joseph Park Gate Surgery, 28 St. Helens Road, Ormskirk L39 4QR Tel: 01695 72561 Fax: 01695 571709; Ivy House, 72 Holborn Hill, Ormskirk L39 3LJ Tel: 01695 573280 — MB ChB 1968 Liverp.; DObst RCOG 1970.

CUNNINGTON, Anne-Louise Glasgow Royal Infirmary, 84 Castle Street, Glasgow G4 0SF Tel: 0141 211 4000 — MB ChB 1993 Ed.; BSc Ed. 1991. (Edinburgh) Specialist Regist. (c/o Elderly & Gen. Med.) Glas. Roy. Infirm.

CUNNINGTON, Philip Mark David The Wardens Flat, Rootes Residences, University of Warwick, Gibbert Hill Road, Coventry CV4 7AL — MB BS 1993 Lond. SHO (Anaesth.) St. Geo. Hosp. Lond. Prev: SHO (A & E) Conquest Hosp. Hastings.

CUPIT, Diane Lesley (retired) East Kyloe, Berwick-upon-Tweed TD15 2PG Tel: 01289 381389 — MB ChB 1976 Manch.; MRCOG 1981. Prev: Clin. Asst. (O & G) Ashington Hosp. N.d.

CUPITT, Jason Mark 43 Bispham Road, Carleton, Poulton-le-Fylde FY6 7PE; 43 Bispham Road, Carleton, Poulton-le-Fylde FY6 7NU — MB ChB 1991 Manch.; FRCA 1998; BSc Manch. 1989. (Manch.) Cons. in Anaesth., Blackpool Vict. Hosp. Prev: SHO (Anaesth.) Vict. Hosp. Blackpool; SHO (A & E) Vict. Hosp. Blackpool; Ho. Off. (Med.) Manch. Roy. Infirm.

CUPPER, Gerald Arthur Gayton Road Health and Surgical Centre, Gayton Road, King's Lynn PE30 4DY Tel: 01553 762726 Fax: 01553 696819; The Old School,, Sutton Road,, Terrington St. Clement, King's Lynn PE34 4PJ. — MB ChB 1971 Manch.; MRCS Eng. LRCP Lond. 1971; DObst RCOG 1973. (Manch.) Med. Adviser to Porvair Plc. Prev: SHO (O & G) & Ho. Surg. (A & E) P'boro. Dist. Hosp.

CUPPER, Nicholas Christopher Chest Clinic, Ipswich Hospital, Heath Road, Ipswich IP4 5PD Tel: 01473 685070 Fax: 01473 688707; 7 Westerfield Road, Ipswich IP4 2UE Tel: 01473 422148 Email: n.cupper@ntlworld.com — MB BS 1988 Lond.; DRCOG 1991. (Roy. Free Hosp. Sch. of Med.) Clin. Asst. (Chest Med. & A & E) Ipswich Hosp.

CUPPLES, Anna Isobel 159 Newry Road, Banbridge BT32 3NB — MB BCh BAO 1946 Belf.

CUPPLES, Brian Barnett Main Street Surgery, 11 Main Street, Loughbrickland, Banbridge BT32 3NQ Tel: 028 4066 2692 Fax: 028 4066 9517; Harrybrook House, 49 Cloghoge Road, Tandragee, Craigavon BT62 2HB Tel: 01762 840605 — MB BCh BAO 1979 Belf.; MRCGP 1987; DRCOG 1981. (Queen's University Belfast)

CUPPLES, Margaret Elizabeth 10 Old Gilford Road, Tandragee, Craigavon BT62 2DW — MB BCh BAO 1977 Belf.; MD Belf. 1983, BSc 1974; FRCGP 1996, M 1981; DCH RCPSI 1980; DRCOG 1979. (Qu. Univ. Belf.) Sen. Lect. (Gen. Pract.) Qu. Univ. Belf.

CUPPLES, Pamela Anne 75 Langside Drive, Newlands, Glasgow G43 2ST Tel: 0141 423 0317 — MB ChB 1990 Glas.; FRCA 1995.

CUPPLES, Samuel Eric Little Yarnbury, Upton Lovell, Warminster BA12 0JW — MB BCh BAO 1941 Belf.; MFCM 1972; DPH Lond. 1957. Prev: Med. Off. Salisbury HA; MOH Warminster & W.bury UDs & RD; Wing Cdr. RAF Med. Br.

CUPPLES, Samuel John 18A Carnreagh Road, Hillsborough BT26 6LH — MB BCh BAO 1947 Belf.

CUPPLES, Wilma Annabel Morningside Medical Practice, 2 Morningside Place, Edinburgh EH10 5ER Tel: 0131 452 8406 Fax: 0131 447 3020 — MB ChB 1977 Glas.; MB ChB Glas.1977; MRCGP 1997; DRCOG 1995. GP.

CURATI-ALASONATTI, Professor Walter L Department of Imaging, Royal Postgraduate Medical School, Hammersmith Hospital, London W12 0HS Tel: 020 8383 3485 Fax: 020 8743 5409; Place Camoletti 4, Geneva CH-1207, Switzerland Tel: 00 41 22 7351861 — Diplome Federal 1970 Geneva; PhD Geneva 1980; MD 1973. Sen. Lect. Univ. Lond. Roy. Postgrad. Med. Sch.; Prof. Mainz Univ. 1987; Assoc. Prof. Geneva 1980. Socs: Fell. Roy. Soc.

Med.; Fell. Roy. Coll. Radiol.; Fell. Swiss Radiol. Soc. Prev: Cons. Univ. Hosp. Geneva.

CURBISHLEY, Peter George The Acorns Surgery, 85 Wheelock Street, Middlewich CW10 9AE Tel: 01606 837400; 79 Warmingham Road, Church Coppenhall, Crewe CW1 4PS — MB BS 1976 Lond. (St. Bart.) Princip. in Gen. Pract. Alorns Surg. Middlewich. Socs: Brit. Med. Assn. Prev: GP Oaklands, Middlewich; Regist. (Anaesth.) N. Staffs HA; Ho. Surg. St. Bart's Hosp. Lond.

CURE, Serge Maurice France 94 Forest Hill Road, London SE22 0RS Tel: 020 8693 4789 — M.R.C.S. Eng., L.R.C.P. Lond. 1943. (St. Bart.) Prev: Ho. Surg. E.M.S. Runwell Hosp.; Temp. Maj. R.A.M.C.

CURETON, Peter Charles Frimley Green Medical Centre, 1 Beech Road, Frimley Green, Camberley GU16 6QQ Tel: 01252 835016 Fax: 01252 837908; 3 Coleford Bridge Road, Mytchett, Camberley GU16 6DH Email: parcureton@aol.com — BM BS 1979 Nottm.; BMedSc Nottm. 1977; MRCGP 1988; DCH RCP Lond. 1983; DRCOG 1983. (Univ. Nottm. Med. Sch.)

CURETON, Ronald James Richard (retired) 35 Peaks Hill, Purley CR8 3JJ Tel: 020 8660 2594 — MRCS Eng. LRCP Lond. 1940; MD Camb. 1954, MB BChir 1942; FRCPath 1964. Prev: Sen. Lect. (Path.) St. Bart. Hosp. Med. Coll. Lond.

CURETON, Ruth Elizabeth 3 Coleford Bridge Road, Mytchett, Camberley GU16 6DH — BM BS 1981 Nottm.; BMedSci Nottm. 1979, BM BS 1981. (Nottm.) Asst. GP Retainer Scheme Camberley.

CURGENVEN, Amanda Butt Lane Medical Centre, 58 Butt Lane, Farnley, Leeds LS12 5AZ; 2 Priestley View, Pudsey LS28 9NG — MB BCh 1987 Wales; DFFP 1997. (Cardiff)

CURLE, James Michael 21 Woodview Drive, Airdrie ML6 9HJ — MB ChB 1980 Glas.

CURLESS, Eric Copperas Lodge, Copperas Lane, Haigh, Wigan WN2 1PA Tel: 01942 831052 — MB ChB Manch. 1961; FRCP Lond. 1991; MRCP (UK) 1979. (Manch) Hon. Cons. Phys. (Genitourin. Med.) Roy. Boltan Haf; Hon. Clin. Lect. (Med. of AIDS) Univ. Manch. Prev: Sen. Regist. (Venereol.) & Ho. Phys. & Ho. Surg. Manch. Roy. Infirm.; Asst. Lect. (Path.) Univ. Manch.

CURLESS, Richard Howard Department of Medicine for Elderly, North Tyneside District General Hospital, Rake Lane, North Shields NE29 8NH Tel: 0191 293 2793 Fax: 0191 293 2793 — MB BS 1985 Newc.; MRCP (UK) 1988; FRCP Lond. Cons. Phys. N.umbria Healthcare NHS Trust; Coordinator Stroke Assoc. Dist. Stroke Serv. 1996. Socs: Brit. Assn. Stroke Phys.; Brit. Geriat. Soc. Prev: Sen. Regist. (Med. & Geriat.) Freeman Hosp.; Research Fell. (Geriat.) Univ. Newc. u. Tyne.

CURLEY, (Eileen) Marguerite The Castle Medical Centre, 22 Bertie Road, Kenilworth CV8 1JP Tel: 01926 857331 Fax: 01926 851070 — MB ChB 1970 Birm.; MFHom 1988; DObst RCOG 1972. (Birm.) Socs: BMA; Fac. Homoeop. Prev: SHO (O & G) Good Hope Matern. Hosp. Sutton Coldfield; Ho. Phys. & Ho. Surg. Good Hope Hosp. Sutton Coldfield.

CURLEY, Jacqueline 41 Marlcroft Avenue, Stockport SK4 3LZ — MB BS 1993 Lond.

CURLEY, James 939 Green Lanes, London N21 Tel: 020 8360 2228 — MB BS 1954 Lond. Clin. Assit. Dermat. Roy. N. Hosp. Lond.

CURLEY, Jane Wallace Ainsworth Royal Preston Hospital, Sharoe Green Lane, Fulwood, Preston PR2 9HT Tel: 0772 710526 — MB ChB 1979 Bristol; FRCS Eng. 1984. Cons. Otolaryngol. Roy. Preston Hosp. Socs: Fell. (Paediat. Otolaryngol.) Roy. Alexandra Hosp. Childr. Sydney,; Austral.

CURLEY, Mr Paul Joseph Department of Surgery, Pinderfields Hospital, Aberford Road, Wakefield WF1 4DG Tel: 01924 213848; 14 Ridings Gardens, Wakefield WF3 3SN — MB BCh BAO 1986 Dub.; MCh NUI 1996; FRCSI (Gen.) 1995; FRCSI 1990; FRCS Eng. 1990; LRCPI & LM, LRCSI & LM 1986. (RCSI) Cons. Gen. & Vasc. Surg. Pinderfields Hosp. Wakefield. Socs: Assn. Surg.; Vasc. Surg. Soc.; RSM.

CURLEY, Regina Kathryn Whiston Hospital, Prescot L35 5DR Tel: 0151 426 1600; Whitegates, Firs Lane, Appleton, Warrington WA4 5LB Tel: 01925 263370 — MB ChB 1977 Liverp.; MD Liverp. 1988; FRCP Lond. 1995; MRCP (UK) 1980. Cons. Dermat. Whiston & St. Helens Hosps. Mersey RHA.

CURLING, Mary Elisabeth (retired) Foalhurst Close, Hadlow Stair, Tonbridge TN10 4HA Tel: 01732 355954 — MB BS 1948 Lond.; MRCP Ed. 1965; DCH Eng. 1951. Hon. Cons. Phys. Tunbridge Wells & Sevenoaks Health Dist.

CURLING, Olive Marigold The Rosary, Coleshill, Amersham HP7 0LB; The Rosary, Coleshill, Amersham HP7 0LB Tel: 01494 726431 — MB BS 1954 Lond.; MRCS Eng. LRCP Lond. 1954. (St. Bart.) Cons. Cytol. St. Bart. Hosp. Lond. Socs: Fell. Roy. Soc. Med. & Internat. Acad. Cytol. Prev: Sen. Lect. in Cytol. St. Bart. Hosp. Lond.; Asst. Lect. (Path.) St. Mary's Hosp. Lond.; Regist. (Cytol.) Hammersmith Hosp. & Postgrad. Med. Sch.

CURNIER, Alain Pierre Robert 4 Cranleigh Hill Crescent, Edinburgh EH4 2JE — MB ChB 1993 Ed.

CURNOCK, Amanda Louise The Matchbox Cottage, 2 Keysoe Road, Thurleigh, Bedford MK44 2DY Tel: 01234 771637 — MB BS 1992 Lond. Trainee GP E.bourne Dist. Hosp. VTS. Prev: Ho. Off. (Surg. & Med.) Newham Gen. Hosp.

CURNOCK, David Anthony Nottingham City Hospital, Hucknall Road, Nottingham NG5 1PB Tel: 0115 969 1169 Fax: 0115 962 7716 Email: dcurnock@ncht.trent.nhs.uk; 39 Sevenoaks Crescent, Bramcote Hills, Beeston, Nottingham NG9 3FP Tel: 0115 925 9116 — MB BChir 1971 Camb.; MB Camb. 1971, BChir 1970; MA Camb. 1971; FRCP Lond. 1989; MRCP (UK) 1974; MRCS Eng. LRCP Lond. 1970; FRCPCH 1997; DObst RCOG 1973; DCH Eng. 1972. (Camb. & Char. Cross) Cons. Paediat. Nottm. City Hosp. Prev: Sen. Regist. (Paediat.) Derbysh. Childr. Hosp. Derby; Regist. (Paediat.) Char. Cross Hosp. Lond.; Lect. (Child Health) Univ. Benin, Nigeria.

CURNOCK, George Henry Reginald (retired) 53 Arundel Drive, Bramcote Hills, Nottingham NG9 3FX Tel: 0115 922 6760 — MB BS 1942 Lond.; MRCS Eng. LRCP Lond. 1942; FRCGP 1983, M 1953; DCH Eng. 1948, CPH 1950; DObst RCOG 1947. Prev: Ho. Surg. & Ho. Phys. Char. Cross Hosp.

CURNOW, John Grampian Health Board, Summerfield House, 2 Eday Road, Aberdeen AB15 6RE; Chapel Croft, Arbuthnott, Laurencekirk AB30 1NA Tel: 01561 362335 — BM BS 1985 Nottm.; BMedSci Nottm. 1983, BM BS 1985. Cons. Communicable Dis. & Environm. Grampian HB; Sen. Clin. Lect. Aberd. Socs: Fell. Soc. Pub. Health. Prev: Cons. Pub. Health Med. Centr. Notts. HA.

CURPEN, N C Dovecot Health Centre, Longreach Road, Liverpool L14 0NL Tel: 0151 228 3336.

CURPHEY, Janet Mary Handbridge Medical Centre, Greenway St., Chester CH4 7JS Tel: 01244 680169 — MB ChB 1991 Manch.; JCPTGP 1996.

CURPHEY, Robert Norman (retired) Chy-An-Gwens, Moresk Road, Truro TR1 1BW Tel: 01872 277908 — MB BS Lond. 1966; MRCS Eng. LRCP Lond. 1966; FRCR 1975; DMRD Eng. 1973. Prev: Cons. Radiol. Roy. Cornw. Hosp. Treliske.

CURR, Elizabeth Anne 18 Ethiebeaton Terrace, Monifieth, Dundee DD5 4RL — MB ChB 1991 Aberd.

CURR, Ralph Donaldson, Surg. Cdr. RN Medical Director General, 2SL/CNH, HM Naval Base, Portsmouth PO1 3LS Tel: 023 92 22046 Fax: 023 92 25482 Email: ralphcurr@hotmail.com; Sea Garth, Pentewan, St Austell PL26 6DD Tel: 01726 843106 — MB BS 1967 Lond.; MRCS Eng. LRCP Lond. 1968; FRCGP 1992, M 1974; DObst RCOG 1975; AKC 1969. (King's Coll. Hosp.) Dir. Med. Operat.s, Med. Dir. Gen. (Naval) HM Naval Base, Portsmouth; Director of Primary Care. Socs: RN Med. Club; RCGP; BMA. Prev: Dir. of Med. Personnel Princip. Med. Off. HMS Drake.

CURRAN, Aine Mary 77 Warrenpoint Road, Newry BT34 2PS Tel: 02830 261370 — MB BCh BAO 1995 Belf.; MRCGP 1999; DRCOG 1998. GP Regist. Armagh Health Centre. Prev: SHO (Paediat., A & E, Med.) Daisy Hill Hosp. Newry.

CURRAN, Andrew John 6 Blackwood Avenue, Newton Mearns, Glasgow G77 5BA — MB ChB 1997 Manch.

CURRAN, Andrew Lancelot Myles Thursday Cottage, High St., Wrington, Bristol BS40 5QD — MB BCh BAO 1982 Belf. Research Regist., Paediatric Neurol., Frenchay Hosp. Bristol.

CURRAN, Angela, Col. late RAMC 2 Tregolls Drive, Avenue Road, Farnborough GU14 7BN — MB ChB 1966 Birm.; MRCGP 1976; DObst RCOG 1968; DCH Eng. 1969. (Birm.) Socs: BMA. Prev: Asst. Surg. SS 'Uganda'; SHO Child Psychiat. Guy's Hosp. Lond. SHO (Paediat.) St. Mary's Hosp.; Portsmouth.

CURRAN, Catherine Mary 3 Sir Charles Square, Duffryn, Newport NP10 8QP — MB BCh 1984 Wales; MB BCh Wales l984.

CURRAN, Cliona Anne 740 Antrim Road, Newtownabbey BT36 7PQ Email: cliona.curran@virgin.net — MB BCh BAO 1993 Belf.; MRCP (Paediatrics) 1999. Paediat.

CURRAN, David Patrick Mary Curran and Partners, Manor Health Centre, 86 Clapham Manor Street, London SW4 6EB Tel: 020 7411 6866 Fax: 020 7411 6857 — MB BCh BAO 1976 NUI. Socs: BMA.

CURRAN, Edward Francis 201 Albany Road, Cardiff CF24 3NU — MB BCh 1954 Wales.

CURRAN, Enid (retired) 44 Millbrook Road, Dinas Powys CF64 4DA Tel: 02920 3128 — MB BCh 1941 Wales; BSc 1938, MB BCh Wales 1941; DCH Eng. 1947. Prev: Asst. MOH Cardiff.

CURRAN, Mr Finlay James McConnachy 9 Highfield Road, Bramhall, Stockport SK7 3BE — MB ChB 1989 Glas.; FRCS Glas. 1993.

CURRAN, Florence Mary (retired) Tullybeg, 40 Tullyard Road, Drumbo, Lisburn BT27 5JN — MB BCh BAO Belf. 1954. Prev: Cas. Off. Belf. City Hosp.

CURRAN, Frances Mary The Surgery, 20-22 Westdale Lane, Carlton, Nottingham NG4 3JA Tel: 0115 961 9401 — MB ChB Manch. 1986; MRCGP 1991; DRCOG 1989.

CURRAN, Mr Francis Paul Accident & Emergency Department, Mater Hospital, Crumlin Road, Belfast BT14 6AB — MB BCh BAO 1986 Belf.; BSc (Hons.) Belf. 1981; FRCS Ed. 1994; MRCP (UK) 1993; MRCGP 1991; Dip. Ment. Health Belf. 1990; DRCOG 1990; FFAEM 1998. (Qu. Univ. Belf.) Cons. (Accid.&Emerg.)Med. Mater Hosp. Belf. Prev: Regist. (A & E) Ulster Hosp. Dundonald Belf.; Regist. (A & E) Mater Hosp. Dub.; Regist. (A&G) Roy. Vict. Hosp. Belf.

CURRAN, Mr Francis Thomas Department of Surgery, New Cross Hospital, Wolverhampton WV10 0QP Tel: 01902 643077 Fax: 01902 643020; 14 Maythorn Gardens, Wolverhampton WV6 8NP — MB ChB 1979 Birm.; MD Birm. 1989; FRCS Eng. 1986; FRCS Ed. 1984. Cons. Gen. Surg. New Cross Hosp. Wolverhampton. Socs: Assn. Surg.; Assn. Upper G.I. Surg. Prev: Sen. Regist. (Surg.) W. Midl. RHA; Chief Surg. Regist. Auckland Hosp., NZ; Research Regist. (Surgic.) Gen. Hosp. Birm.

CURRAN, Gary James Springhead Medical Centre, 376 Willerby Road, Hull HU5 5JT Tel: 01482 352263 Fax: 01482 352480; Pooghans, West Hill, Hessle HU13 0ER — MB ChB 1983 Liverp.; DRCOG 1987. Socs: Humberside Med. Soc.; Rugby League Med. Assn. Prev: Trainee GP E.ham & W. Kirby VTS; SHO (O & G) Arrowe Pk. Hosp. Wirral.

CURRAN, Hubert James Majella Dundonald Medical Centre, 1 St. Johns Wood Park, Dundonald, Belfast BT16 1RS Tel: 02890 482365 Fax: 024 419252 — MB BCh BAO 1976 NUI; FRCSI 1980. Chairm. S. & E. Belf. Primary Care Organisation.

CURRAN, Ian Edward 3 Rye View Maisonettes, The Gardens, London SE22 9QB — MB BS 1992 Lond.

CURRAN, Mr James Douglas Top Flat Left, 106 Deanston Drive, Shawlands, Glasgow G41 3LQ Tel: 0141 649 3839 — MB ChB 1988 Ed.; BSc (Bact.) Ed. 1985; FRCS Glas. 1994; FRCS Ed. 1994. (Univ. Ed.) Research Fell. Univ. Dept. Surg. W.. Infirm. Glas.

CURRAN, James Noel (retired) 3 Hereford Drive, Prestwich, Manchester M25 0JY Tel: 0161 773 2661 Email: noelcurren@compuserve.com — MB BCh BAO NUI 1939; DPM 1940; LM Coombe 1940. Prev: Cons. Psychiat. Regional Drug Treatm. Centre Prestwich Hosp.

CURRAN, John David Old Irvine Road Surgery, 4-6 Old Irvine Road, Kilmarnock KA1 2BD Tel: 01563 22413 — MB ChB 1988 Glas.

CURRAN, John Patrick James City Hospital, Hucknall Road, Nottingham NG5 1PJ; 9 Brookside, East Leake, Loughborough LE12 6PB — MB BS 1967 Lond.; PhD (NUI) 1983; FFA RCSI 1981; FFA RCS Eng. 1972. (Lond. Hosp.) Cons. Anaesth. Nottm. HA; Clin. Teach. Univ. Nottm. Socs: BMA & Assoc. Anaesth. Prev: Cons. Anaesth. Cork Regional Hosp. (S.. Health Bd. Cork) & N.ampton Gen. Hosp. (Oxf. HA).

CURRAN, Joy Edith The Queen Victoria Hospital, Holyte Road, East Grinstead RH19 3DZ; 8 Stuart way, East Grinstead RH19 4RS Email: curran@dircon.co.uk — MB BS 1987 Lond.; FRCA 1993. (St. Thos. Hosp. UMDS) Cons. (Anaesth.) The Qu. Vict. Hosp. E. Grinstead. Prev: Sen. Regist. (Anaesth.) King's Coll. Hosp. Lond.

CURRAN, Judith Corkland Road Surgery, 9 Corkland Road, Chorlton, Manchester M21 8UP Tel: 0161 881 6223 Fax: 0161 881 6223; 35 Westgate, Hale, Altrincham WA15 9AY — MB ChB 1980 Manch.; MRCGP 1984; Cert. Family Plann. JCC 1984. Prev: SHO (Gen. Med., Paediat. & O & G) Wythenshawe Hosp. Manch.

CURRAN, Julia Sheila Martina Auchindoune, 69 Bay Road, Wormit, Newport-on-Tay DD6 8LX — MB BCh BAO 1985 NUI; MRCPsych 1984.

CURRAN, Julie Elizabeth 47 Woodhead Crescent, Thornwood Grove, Uddingston, Glasgow G71 6LR Tel: 0141 817686; Nishaw Health Centre, Kenilworth Avenue, Wishaw Tel: 01698 372888 — MB ChB 1992 Glas.; MRCGP 1996. Trainee GP/SHO W.. & Gtr. Glas. HB; GP Princip. Wishaw. Prev: Locum Glas. Area; GP/Regist. W.. & Gtr. Glas. HB; SHO (Psychiat.) Gartnavel Gen. Hosp.

CURRAN, Kevin (retired) Kinawley, Enniskillen BT92 4BU Tel: 0138582 227 — MB BCh BAO 1946 NUI. Prev: Ho. Surg. St. Vincent's Hosp. Dub.

CURRAN, Lisa Ann Silver Birches, Nugents Park, Hatch End, Pinner HA5 4RA — BM BCh 1996 Oxf.

CURRAN, Maeve Patricia 14 Ashbourne Court, Omagh BT78 1NS — MB ChB 1998 Glas.; MB ChB Glas 1998.

CURRAN, Michael Gregory 110 Culmore Road, Londonderry BT48 8JF Tel: 01504 359128 Email: mgcurr@iol.ie — MB BCh BAO 1979 Belf.; MBA; MRCPsych 1987. Cons. Psychiat. Stradreagh Hosp. Lond.derry.

CURRAN, Natasha Clare Linden House, Royal Liverpool University Hospital, Prescot St., Liverpool L7 8XP — MB ChB 1998 Liverp.; MB ChB Liverp 1998.

CURRAN, Nora Christine 13 Lees Road, Bramhall, Stockport SK7 1BT — MB BCh 1971 Wales.

CURRAN, Paraic 26 Waverley Avenue, Appleton, Warrington WA4 3BN — MB BCh BAO 1989 NUI.

CURRAN, Peter Sylvester — MB BCh BAO Belf. 1969; FRCPsych 1996, M 1975. (Qu. Univ. Belf.) Cons. Psychiat. Mater Infirm. Hosp. Belf.; Mem. Sentence Review Commiss. 1998; Life Sentence Review Commiss.er (2001). Socs: Pres. N. Irel. Medico Legal Soc.1999-2000. Prev: Cons. Psychiat. & Lect. (Ment. Health) Qu. Univ. Belf.; Ho. Phys. & Ho. Surg. Roy. Vict. Hosp. Belf.; Mem. Ment. Health Commiss.

CURRAN, Philippa Mary Longrove Surgery, 70 Union Street, Barnet EN5 4HT Tel: 020 8441 9440/9563 Fax: 020 8441 4037; 14 Grimsdyke Crescent, Arkley, Barnet EN5 4AG Tel: 020 8440 7653 Email: pmc-doc@msn.com — MB BS (Hons.) (Distinc. Obst. & Gyn.) Lond. 1973; DCH Eng. 1976. (Guy's Hosp. Med. Sch. Univ. Lond.) Clin. Asst. (Palliat. Med.) N. Lond. Hospice & Clin. Asst. (Learning Disabil.) Winifred Hse. Barnet Healthcare Trust; Chairm. N. Barnet PCG.

CURRAN, Robert Crowe 34A Carpenter Road, Edgbaston, Birmingham B15 2JH Tel: 0121 440 0620 Fax: 0121 440 0620 Email: r.c.curran@bham.ac.uk — MD 1956 Glas.; MD (Hnrs. & Bellahouston Medal) Glas. 1956, MB ChB (Commend.) 1943; FRCP Lond. 1969, M 1959; FFPath RCPI 1983; FRCPath 1965. (Univ. Glas.) Emerit. Prof. Path. Univ. Birm. Socs: Hon. Med. Path. Soc. Gt. Brit. & Irel. Prev: Pres. Roy. Coll. Pathols.; Hon. Sec. Conf. Med. Roy. Coll.; Prof. Path. Univ. Lond. & Hon. Consult. St. Thos. Hosp. Lond.

CURRAN, Stephen Academic Unit of Psychiatry, Clinical Sciences Building, St James University Hospital, Leeds LS9 7TF — MB ChB 1986 Leeds; BSc (Hons.) Leeds 1983, MB ChB 1986. Human Psychopharmacol. Research Unit Univ. Leeds.

CURRANS, Janice Mary Cauldhame, Stewarton, Kilmarnock KA3 5HU — MB ChB 1995 Glas.

CURRANT, Paul Norman Corndene, Coreley, Ludlow SY8 3AW — MB ChB 1997 Glas.

CURRER, Bernadette Anne 180 Burton Road, Didsbury, Manchester M20 1LH — MB ChB 1992 Manch. Specialist Regist. (Anaesth.) N. W.ern Deanery. Socs: BMA; Train. Mem. Assn. AnE.h.; MRCAnaesth.

CURRER, Margaret 4 Manor Court, 8A Little Parkfield Road, Liverpool L17 8UD — MB ChB 1995 Dundee. SHO Critical Care Rotat. Whiston Hosp. Liverp. Socs: BMA; MPS.

CURREY, Jacqueline Herts & Essex Hospital, Bishop's Stortford CM23 5JH Tel: 01279 444455; The Heights, Galloway Road, Bishop's Stortford CM23 2HS Tel: 01279 654717 Email:

j.currey@talk21.com — MB BS Lond. 1964; FRCP Lond. 1990, M 1967. (Lond. Hosp.) p/t Cons. Rheum. Herts. & Essex Hosp. Bishop's Stortford, P.ss Alexandra Hosp. Harlow. Socs: BMA; Brit. Soc. Rheum. Prev: Sen. Regist. (Rheum.) & Ho. Phys. & Ho. Surg. Lond. Hosp.

CURRIE, Alan Newcastle City Health NHS Trust, Hadrian Clinic, Newcastle General Hospital, Westgate Road, Newcastle upon Tyne NE4 6BE Tel: 0191 273 6666 Fax: 0191 256 3088 — MB ChB 1987 Ed.; MRCPsych 1993; MPhil (Edin.) 1997. (Edinburgh) Cons., Hadrian clinic, Newc. Gen. Hosp., Newc.-upon-Tyne. Prev: Sen. Regist. (Psychiat.) Roy. Vict. Infirm. Newc.-upon-Tyne; Sen. Regist. (Psychiat.) N.ern & Yorks. RHA; Regist. (Psychiat.) Roy. Edin. Hosp.

CURRIE, Alison Dorothy McKay 6 The Perrings, Nailsea, Bristol BS48 4YD Tel: 01275 855926 Email: ali.currie4@virgin.net — MB BS 1993 Lond. SHO (Ophth.) Addenbrooke's Hosp. Camb. Prev: Anat. Demonst. St. Geo. Hosp. Tooting & Resid. Med. Off. Essex Nuffield Hosp. Brentwood; SHO (Ophth.) Hillingdon Hosp. Uxbridge.

CURRIE, Andrew (retired) 'Malin', Mansefield, Minard, Inveraray PA32 8YP Tel: 0154 66 267 — MB ChB 1941 Aberd.; MFCM 1972. Gp. Med. Supt. Inverness Hosp. Gp.; Hon. Capt. RAMC. Prev: Late. Community Med. Specialist Argyll & Clyde Health Bd.

CURRIE, Andrew Ewan Neonatal Unit, Kensington Building, Leicester Royal Infirmary, Leicester Square, Leicester LE1 5WW Tel: 0116 258 5522 Fax: 0116 258 5502 — BM 1986 Soton.; MRCP (UK) 1994; DCH RCPS Glas. 1990. (Soton.) Cons. Neonatologist Leicester Roy. Infirm.; Collegiate Mem. RCP Edin.; Coll. Tutor fro the Roy. Coll. of Paediat. and child health. Socs: Roy. Coll. Paediat. & Child Health; BMA; Brit. Assn. Perinatal Med. Prev: Clin. Research Fell. (Neonat.) Leicester Roy. Infirm.; Sen. Regist. (Paediat. Cardiol.) Glenfield Hosp. Leicester; Regist. (Neonat.) King Geo. V & Roy. Alexandra Hosp. Sydney, NSW.

CURRIE, Mr Andrew Thomas 5 Acorn Ridge, Matlock DE4 3TT — MB ChB 1992 Birm.; MB ChB (Hons.) Birm. 1992; FRCS Ed. 1996; FDS RCS Eng. 1987; BDS Lond. 1983. Specialist Regist. Rotat. (Oral & Maxillofacial Surg.) Trent. Prev: SHO Rotat. (Surg.) Nottm. & Derby; Ho. Phys. N. Staffs Hosp. Centre Stoke-on-Trent; Ho. Surg. Kings Mill Hosp. Mansfield.

CURRIE, Angela Pilkington The Surgery, 270 Hook Road, Chessington KT9 1PF Tel: 020 8397 3574; Hunters, Forest Lodge, Epsom Road, Ashtead KT21 1JX Tel: 01372 278707 — MB BS Lond. 1963; MRCGP 1976; DObst RCOG 1965. (Char. Cross) Prev: SHO (Obst.) Fulham Matern. Hosp.; Ho. Phys. & Ho. Surg. (Gyn.) Fulham Hosp.

CURRIE, Anne Elizabeth North East Wales NHS Trust, Catherine Gladstone House, Hawarden Way, Mablot, Deeside CH5 2EP Tel: 01244 538883 Fax: 01244 538884 — MB ChB 1982 Manch.; BSc (Hons.) Med. Sci. & Physiol. St. And. 1979. Assoc. Specialist (Community Paediat.), N. E. Wales NHS Trust. Socs: BMA; Brit. Assn. Community Child Health. Prev: Regist. & SHO (Psychiat.) Univ. Hosp. S. Manch.; Regist. Rotat. (Psychiat.) Mid-Kent Train. Scheme; Community Med. Off. (Developm. Paediat.) Medway HA.

CURRIE, Anne Louise Park Street Surgery, 3 Park Street, Dunster, Minehead TA24 6SR Tel: 01643 821244 Fax: 01643 821770 — MB BS 1973 Lond.; MRCS Eng. LRCP Lond. 1973; FFA RCS Eng. 1980; DA Eng. 1978; DObst RCOG 1976. (St. Bart.) Clin. Asst. (Anaesth.) Minehead Hosp.

CURRIE, Aoife Ann 48 Derryoghill Road, Dungannon BT71 7JJ — MB BCh 1998 Belf.; MB BCh Belf 1998.

CURRIE, Colin Thomas, RD Care of the Biferly Office, Balfour Bavition, Astley Ainslie Hospital, Grange Loan, Edinburgh EH9 2HL Tel: 0131 537 9017 Fax: 0131 537 9025; 17 Merchiston Gardens, Edinburgh EH10 5DD Tel: 0131 337 5581 — MB ChB Ed. 1970; BSc Ed. 1967; FRCP Ed. 1986; MRCP (UK) 1975. Hon. Cons. & Sen. Lect. (Geriat. Med.) Roy. Infirm. Edin. Socs: BMA; Brit. Geriat. Soc.

CURRIE, Crawford Linden Alexander Hillside, Gravel Path, Berkhamsted HP4 2PA; Hillside, Gravel Path, Berkhamsted HP4 2PJ — MB BS 1993 Lond.; BSc (Lond.) 1990; FRCS (Eng.) 1997. (London Hospital) Clin. Research Fell. (Cutaneous Laser Ther. & Plastic Surg.) Bedford Gen. Hosp.

CURRIE, David Cameron Dewsbury District Hospital, Healds Road, Dewsbury WF13 4HS Tel: 01924 512000 Fax: 01924 512059 — MD 1989 Camb.; MB BChir 1979 Camb.; MA 1981 Camb.; FRCP 1997; MRCP (UK) 1982. Cons. Phys. (Gen. & Respirat. Med.) Dewsbury Dist. Hosp. Socs: Brit. Thorac. Soc.; Yorks. Thoracic Soc. Prev: Sen. Regist. (Thoracic & Gen. Med.) W.m. & Brompton Hosps. Lond.; Regist. N. Staffs. Hosp. Centre.

CURRIE, F The Grange Surgery, 41 York Road, Southport PR8 2AD Tel: 01704 560506 Fax: 01704 563108.

CURRIE, Finlay Robert John Medical Centre, Caledonian Road, Perth PH2 8HH Tel: 01738 628234 Fax: 01738 624945 — MB ChB 1987 Aberd.; MRCGP 1992; DFFP 1992. (Aberdeen) GP.

CURRIE, Graeme Penman 116-118 Main Street, Muirkirk, Cumnock KA18 2AG Tel: 01290 661324 — MB ChB 1994 Glas.; DCH Glas. 1997; MRCP (UK) Glas. 1999. (University of Glasgow) SHO (Gen. Med.) Ayr Hosp. Prev: SHO (Paediat.) Ayr Hosp.; SHO (A & E) Cross Ho. Hosp.; Ho. Off. (Surg.) CrossHo. Hosp. Kilmarnock.

CURRIE, Heather Doreen Skewbridge Farm, Mouswald, Dumfries DG1 4LY Tel: 01387 830276 — MB BS 1982 Newc.; MFFP 1995; MRCOG 1991; MRCGP 1986; DRCOG 1986. Assoc. Specialist (O & G) Cressell Matern. Hosp. Dumfries. Prev: Staff Grade (O & G) Cresswell Matern. Hosp. Dumfries.

CURRIE, Ian 19 North Drive, Aylesbury HP21 9AN — MB ChB 1987 Leeds.

CURRIE, Mr Ian Cameron Allerton Ward, Level 7, Torbay General Hospital, Torquay TQ2 7AA Tel: 01803 654805 Email: iancurrie@sdevonhc-trswest.nhs.uk — MB ChB 1986 Bristol; MD Bristol 1995; FRCS Eng. 1990; FRCS (Gen.) 1998. (Bristol) Cons. Surg., Torbay Gen. Hosp. Prev: Sen. Regist. Derniford Hosp. Plymouth; Sen. Regist. Concord Hosp. Sydney; Sen. Regist. Bristol Roy. Infirm.

CURRIE, Ian David Campbell Bonnar and Partners, Sunnyside Surgery, Hawkins Road, Penzance TR18 4LT Tel: 01736 63340 Fax: 01736 332116 — MB BS 1983 Lond.

CURRIE, Ian Graham, Group Capt. RAF Med. Br. Retd. Culver Hey, 72 The Fiddle, Cricklade, Swindon SN6 6HN Tel: 01793 751717 — MB ChB 1953 Liverp. (Liverp.) Dept. Dir. Personnel Managem. (Med.) MoD RAF Innsworth Gloucester. Socs: Fell. Roy. Soc. Med. & Brit. Inst. Managem. Prev: CO RAF Hosp. Nocton Hall; Dep. Princip. Med. Off. RAF Support Command; Dep. Dir. Med. Personnel RAF.

CURRIE, Ian Hardie 8/8 Abercromby Place, Edinburgh EH3 6LB Tel: 0131 556 7504; 282 Cooden Drive, Cooden, Bexhill-on-Sea TN39 3AB Tel: 0142 434715 — MB ChB Ed. 1955. (Edinburgh) EMP Benefits Agency Med. Servs.

CURRIE, Ian Stewart 10 Howden Street, Edinburgh EH8 9HL — MB ChB 1996 Ed.; MB ChB (Hons.) Ed. 1996, PhD 1992; BSc (Hons.) Glas. 1988. (Ed.) SHO (Gen. Surg.) Edin. Socs: Fell. Foulkes Foundat. Lond. Prev: Transpl. Hepat.; A & E.

CURRIE, James Irvine (retired) The Old Rectory, Occupation Lane, Bramhope, Leeds LS16 9HS Tel: 0113 284 2850 — MB ChB 1950 Leeds; DObst RCOG 1951. Chairm. Ethics Cttee. Smith & Nepheew Gp. Research Centre York. Prev: GP Leeds.

CURRIE, Lady Jeanne Marion (retired) 42 Murrayfield Avenue, Edinburgh EH12 6AY Tel: 0131 337 3100 — MB ChB 1948 Glas. Prev: Clin. Lect. in Med. (p/t) & Med. Asst. (p/t) Diabetic.

CURRIE, Jessie Mitchell (retired) 14 Holm Park, Inverness IV2 4XT — MB ChB Glas. 1943; BSc Glas. 1940; DPH Glas. 1947. Prev: Sen. Resid. Med. Off. (Infec. Dis.) Hosp. Paisley.

CURRIE, Joanne Marion 71 Mile-End Avenue, Aberdeen AB15 5PS — MB ChB 1987 Aberd.

CURRIE, John (retired) 1 Balfour Crescent, Milnathort, Kinross KY13 9TA Tel: 01577 864104 — MB ChB Glas. 1947.

CURRIE, Mr John Campbell Miraumont, TD (retired) 152 Harley Street, London W1N 1HH Tel: 020 7935 1858 Fax: 020 7224 2574 — MB BChir 1951 Camb.; MA Camb. 1951, MChir 1965, MB BChir 1951; FRCS Eng. 1958. Mem. Ct. Examr. RCS Eng. Prev: Hon. Consg. Neurosurg. St. Bart. Hosp. Lond.

CURRIE, John Lennox (retired) 4 Otters Walk, New Milton BH25 5RR Tel: 01425 621974 Email: john.currie@btinternet.com — MB BS 1951 Lond.; DObst RCOG 1958. Prev: Obst. Regist. N. Herts. Hosp. Hitchin.

CURRIE, John Malcolm Stairwood House, Stair, Mauchline KA5 5HP — MB ChB 1975 Liverp.; FRCA 1982. Cons. Anaesth. Roy. Hosp. Sick Child. Glas. Socs: Assn. Anaesth. GB & Irel.; Assn. Paediat. Anaesth. Prev: Cons. Anaesth. Ayrsh. & Arran HB; Sen. Regist. (Anaesth.) Gt. Ormond St. Hosp. Sick Childr. Lond.; Vis. Asst. Prof. (Anaesth.) Univ. Texas SW Med. Sch. Dallas, USA.

CURRIE, John Norman Albertville Drive Surgery, 16 McCandless Street, Crumlin Road, Belfast BT13 1RU Tel: 028 9074 6308 Fax: 028 9074 9847 — MB BCh BAO 1992 Belf.; DCH RCPI 1995; DRCOG 1994; MRCGP 1997; DTM & H Liverp. 1997.

CURRIE, John Stewart Benoran, Scalasaig, Isle of Colonsay PA61 7YW Tel: 01951 200328 Fax: 01951 200328 — MB ChB 1974 Aberd.

CURRIE, Joyce 50 School Lane, Fulbourn, Cambridge CB1 5BH — MB ChB 1991 Glas.

CURRIE, Julie Ruth Malcolm 27 Meadowfield Terrace, Edinburgh EH8 7NR — MB ChB 1998 Ed.; MB ChB Ed 1998.

CURRIE, Lachlan James Flat 4, 62 Pembroke Road, Clifton, Bristol BS8 3DX — MB BS 1992 Lond.

CURRIE, Mr Michael Alastair Park Street Surgery, 3 Park Street, Dunster, Minehead TA24 6SR Tel: 01643 821244 Fax: 01643 821770 — MB BS 1974 Lond.; FRCS Eng. 1979; MRCGP 1987.

CURRIE, Peter Cardiovascular Department, Wirral Hospital, Arrowe Park Road, Upton, Wirral CH49 5PE Tel: 0151 678 5111 — MB ChB 1981 Liverp.; FRCP 1999; MD Liverp. 1993; MRCP (UK) 1984. (Liverp.) Cons. Cardiol. Phys. Wirral Hosp. Socs: Brit. Cardiac Soc.; Brit. Cardiovasc. Interven. Soc.; Collegiate Mem. Roy. Coll. Phys. Lond. Prev: Sen. Regist. (Cardiol.) Middlx. Hosp.; Regist. (Cardiol.) W.. Gen. Hosp. Edin.; Research Fell. (Cardiol.) Roy. Liverp. Hosp.

CURRIE, Peter Archibald (retired) Sunrise Assisted Housing, 13 Chestnut House, RRFrognal Avenue, Sidcup DA14 6LS — MRCS Eng. LRCP Lond. 1937; MFCM 1972. Prev: PMO Sch. Health Serv. Lond. Boro. Bromley.

CURRIE, Peter Fox 8 Balfleurs Street, Milngavie, Glasgow G62 8HW — MB ChB 1987 Aberd.; MRCP (UK) 1990.

CURRIE, Robert Alexander Charlotte Street Surgery, 1 Charlotte Street, Dumfries DG1 2AG Tel: 01387 267626 Fax: 01387 266824; 26 Ardwall Road, Dumfries DG1 3AQ — MB ChB 1982 Ed.; MRCGP 1986.

CURRIE, Robert Douglas (retired) Braeside, 345 Nantwich Road, Crewe CW2 6PD Tel: 01270 650484 — MB ChB 1949 Manch.; FRCGP 1990, M 1960. Prev: Sen. Med. Off. Rolls Royce Motors Ltd. Car & Mulliner-Pk. Ward Divs.

CURRIE, Rosemary Elizabeth Suzanne Health Centre, Neilsbrook Road, Randalstown, Antrim BT41 3AE Tel: 028 94 472575 — MB BCh BAO 1994 Belf.; MRCGP 1999; DMH Belf. 1997; DRCOG 1998. Full time GP, Randalstown Health Care. Socs: BMA. Prev: Trainee GP/SHO Antrim VTS; Ho. Off. Antrim Area Hosp.

CURRIE, Sarah Josepha The Health Centre, Alfred Squire Road, Wednesfield, Wolverhampton WV11 1XU Tel: 01902 731904; 9 Thistledown Drive, Featherstone, Wolverhampton WV10 7SX — MB ChB 1975 Birm.

CURRIE, Sheila Penlyn, 3 Church Close, Lelant, St Ives TR26 3JX — MB ChB 1964 Glas.; FFA RCS Eng. 1971; DA Eng. 1968. (Glas.) Cons. Anaesth. Roy. Cornw. Hosps. Truro. Socs: BMA; Assn. Dent. Anaesth. Prev: Cons. Anaesth. Qu. Eliz. Hosp. Barbados, W. Indies; Regist. (Anaesth.) Bristol Roy. Infirm.

CURRIE, Sian Louise 138 Hall Lane, Maghull, Liverpool L31 3EH — MB ChB 1998 Leeds.

CURRIE, Simon (retired) Flatts House, Leathley, Otley LS21 2JT Tel: 0113 284 2584 — MB BChir 1962 Camb.; MD Camb. 1971; FRCP Lond. 1979, M 1965. Prev: Cons. Neurol. St. Jas. Hosp. Leeds & Harrogate.

CURRIE, William Peter Shankhill Health Centre, 135 Shankill Parade, Belfast BT13 1SD Tel: 028 9024 7181 — MB BCh BAO 1982 Belf.; Dip. Occupational Medicine London 1999; MRCGP 1989; DMH Belf. 1989; DCH Dub. 1984. (Queen's University Belfast) Princip. GP; Hosp. Pract. Occupat. Health. Socs: BMA; Soc. Occupat. Med.

CURRIE, Zanna Isobel 13 Roslyn Road, Hathersage, Hope Valley S32 1BY Tel: 01433 651842 — MB ChB 1986 Dundee; MCOphth 1993. Regist. (Ophth.) Roy. Hallamsh. Hosp. Sheff. Prev: SHO (Ophth.) Barnsley HA; Anat. Prosector (Human Anat.) Oxf. Univ.; SHO (Neurosurg.) Walton Hosp. Liverp.

CURRIN, Simon Montgomery Medical Practice, Well Street, Montgomery SY15 6PF Tel: 01686 668217 Fax: 01686 668599 Email: simon@medex.org.uk; The Pinfold, Hyssington, Montgomery SY15 6AY Tel: 01588 620614 Fax: 01588 620160 Email: simon@medex.org.uk — MB BS 1984 Lond.; MRCGP 1992; DRCOG 1988; DCH RCPS Glas. 1987. (St Bartholomew's) Prev: Regist. (Paediat.) Shrewsbury.

CURRIVAN, Claude William (retired) Mandalay, 42 Pentire Crescent, Newquay TR7 1PU Tel: 01637 876205 — MRCS Eng. LRCP Lond. 1958.

CURRY, Mr Alan Rogers 5 Waverley Road, Kenilworth CV8 1JL Tel: 01926 59126 — MB BS 1963 Durh.; FRCS Ed. 1970.

CURRY, Andrew Watson Mayford House Surgery, East Road, Northallerton DL6 1NP Tel: 01609 772105 Fax: 01609 778553 — MB BS 1972 Newc.; MRCGP 1976; DCH Eng. 1976; DObst RCOG 1974. Prev: Trainee Gen. Pract. Newc. Vocational Trainee Scheme.

CURRY, Graham William 13 Loudon Terrace, Dowanhill, Glasgow G12 9AQ — MB ChB 1990 Ed.; MRCP (UK) 1993.

CURRY, Ian Peter 29 Hallsenna Road, Seascale CA20 1JL — BM BS 1988 Nottm.

CURRY, Mr Ignatius Joseph St George's Hospital, Blackshaw Road, Tooting, London SW17 0QT Tel: 020 8672 1255; 6 Poplar Crescent, Bradshaw, Halifax HX2 9RY Tel: 01422 247855 — MB BS 1989 Lond.; FRCS Eng. 1994. Specialist Regist. (Paediat. Surg.) St. Geo. Hosp. Socs: BMA; Brit. Assn. Paediat. Surg. Prev: Career Regist. (Paediat. Surg.) Soton. Gen. Hosp.; SHO (Gen. Surg.) Cheltenham Gen. Hosp.

CURRY, John Anthony 47 Uplands Avenue, Deeside CH5 4LF — MB ChB 1993 Sheff.

CURRY, Kathryn Margaret St. Stephens Vicarage, Clumber St., Newcastle upon Tyne NE4 7ST Tel: 0191 273 4680 — MB ChB 1976 Ed. Prev: GP N.umbria VTS.

CURRY, Kevin Mark Boehringer Ingelheim Ltd, Ellesfied Avenue, Bracknell RG12 8YS — BM BS 1988 Nottm.; MRCGP 1999; MRCP Lond. 1992; DRCOG 1997. (Nottingham) Sen. Med. Adviser, HIV Med. Socs: BMA. Prev: Clin. Scientist, Roche Products, Welwyn Garden City; Research Fell. in HIV Med., Roy. Sussex Co. Hosp., Brighton; Clin. Research Phys., Knoll Pharmaceut., Nottm.

CURRY, Michael John Montgomery House Surgery, Piggy Lane, Bicester OX26 6HT Tel: 01869 249222 — BM BCh 1972 Oxf.; DPhil, MA. (Oxf.) Princip., Dr. Curry and Partners; Clin. Governance Lead. ME Oxon PCT. Socs: BMA. Prev: Ho. Phys. Radcliffe Infirm. Oxf.; Ho. Surg. Roy. United Hosp. Bath; Ho. Off. (Obst.) John Radcliffe Hosp. Oxf.

CURRY, Nicola Jane 61 Halsey Drive, Hemel Hempstead HP1 3SE — MB ChB 1994 Bristol.

CURRY, Nicola Suzanne The Homerton Hospital, Homerton Row, London E9 6SR Tel: 020 8510 5555 Fax: 020 8985 6376; 33 Horndean Road, Emsworth PO10 7PU Tel: 01243 372312 Fax: 01243 370548 — BChir 1996 Camb.; MB BChir Camb. 1996, BA (Hons) 1994. (Camb. Univ.) SHO c/o the Elderly Homerton Hosp. Prev: PRHO Kings Lynn - Gen Surg. Orthop.; PRHO Addenbrockes - Gen. Med.

CURRY, Patricia Hilton Burley, 22 The Chase, Reigate RH2 7DH Tel: 01737 762141 — MB BChir 1961 Camb.; MB Camb. 1961, BChir 1960; MRCS Eng. LRCP Lond. 1960; DA Eng. 1962. Med. Jl.ist. Prev: Assoc. Specialist (Anaesth.) E. Surrey Health Dist.

CURRY, Patricia Margaret Lisburn Health Centre, Linenhall Street, Lisburn BT28 1LU — MB BCh BAO 1979 Belf.; MRCGP 1983; DCH Glas. 1982; DRCOG 1981; Cert. Family Plann. JCC 1982.

CURRY, Paul Vincent Langham Emblem House (Suite 205), London Bridge Hospital, 27 Tooley St., London SE1 2PR Tel: 020 7403 0824 Fax: 020 7403 2306 Email: drpcurry@aol.com — MRCS Eng. LRCP Lond. 1969; MD Lond. 1980, MB BS (Hons.) 1969; FRCP (Lond.) 1982 M 1971. (St. Bart.) Honarary Cons. Cardiol. Guy's & St Thomas's Hosp. Lond. Socs: Sec. Brit Cardiac Soc.; BMA. Prev: Ho. Phys. & Ho. Surg. St. Bart. Hosp. Lond.; SHO The Roy. Brompton Heart and Chest Hosp., Lond.; Lect. & Hon. Sen. Regist. Cardiovasc. Unit Roy. Postgrad. Med. Sch.

CURRY, Peter David Fife Acute Hospital NHS Trust, Whitefield Road, Dunfermline KY12 0SU Tel: 01383 623623 Fax: 01383 627039 Email: peter.ewry@faht.scot.nhs.uk — MB BS 1981 Lond.; BSc Lond. 1977; FFA RCSI 1990; DA RCS Eng. 1987. (St. geo.) Cons. Anaesth. & Trauma Managem. Qu. Margt. Hosp. Fife. Socs: Assn. Anaesth. & BASICS.; Intens. Care Soc.; Scott. Intens. Care Soc. Prev: Sen. Regist. (Anaesth.) Midl. Anaesth. Train. Scheme.

CURRY, Peter Sean 63 Vicarage Road, Eastbourne BN20 8AH — BM BS 1979 Nottm.

CURRY, Philip Alan 7 Drumcree, Cookstown BT80 8JB — MB ChB 1994 Bristol.

CURRY, Richard David The Faversham Health Centre, Bank Street, Faversham ME13 8QR Tel: 01795 532186 — MB BChir 1980 Camb.; MA Camb. 1981, MB BChir 1980; MRCGP 1985; DRCOG 1985.

CURRY, Mr Rodney Campbell Belfast City Hospital, Belfast BT9 7AB Tel: 01232 329241 — MB BChir Camb. 1952; FRCS Eng. 1961. Hon. Cons. Surg. Belf. City Hosp. Prev: Cons. Surg. & Dir. Surg. Belf. City Hosp.

CURRY, Ruth Christine 28 Worsall Road, Yarm TS15 9DF Tel: 01642 782308 — MB ChB 1965 Leeds. (Leeds) Med. Off. Billingham Family Plann. Clinics; Clin. Asst. (Gen. Med.) N. Tees Gen. Hosp. Stockton; Clin. Asst. (Diabetes) Hartlepool Gen. Hosp.; Health Screening Doctor Cleveland Nuffield Hosp. Socs: BMA. Prev: SHO Middlesbrough Matern. Hosp.; Ho. Phys. & Ho. Surg. Sedgefield Gen. Hosp.

CURRY, Sandra 8 Millfield Gardens, Nether Poppleton, York YO26 6NZ — MB ChB 1993 Leeds.

CURRY, Sean The Old Rectory, Croquet Gardens, Wivenhoe, Colchester CO7 9ES Tel: 01206 826160 Fax: 01206 826160 Email: kbc04@dial.pipex.com — MB BS 1992 Lond.; FRCS Eng. 1996. (Lond. Hosp. Med. Coll.) Specialist Regist. Rotat. Percivall Pott.

CURRY, Stanislaus (retired) The Victoria Club, Beresford St., St Helier, Jersey JE2 4WN Tel: 01534 23381 — MD 1933 Durh.; MB BS 1924. Prev: Clin. Asst. (Dermat.) Beckett Hosp. Barnsley.

CURRY, Stanley Henry 10 Riverine Lodge, Old Lodge Way, Stanmore HA7 3BE Tel: 020 8954 9972 — LRCP LRCS 1949 Ed.; MSc Lond. 1964; LRFPS 1949 Glas.; PhD 1966 Lond.; MRCGP 1957. (Ed.) Phys. Grosvenor Hosp. Hendon. Socs: BMA & Assur. Med. Soc. Prev: Hon. Med. Off. Wembley Hosp. & Harrow Hosp.; Resid. Med. Off. Surbiton Gen. Hosp.; Clin. Tutor Roy. Infirm. Edin.

CURSON, David Anthony The Roehampton Priory Hospital, Priory Lane, London SW15 5JJ Tel: 020 8392 4298 Fax: 020 8876 4015; 86 Rivermead Court, Ranelagh Gardens, London SW6 3SA Fax: 020 7384 1278 Email: davidcurson@cs.com — MB BS 1970 Lond.; MRCS Eng. LRCP Lond. 1970; FRCPsych 1996, M 1976; DPM Eng. 1976. (Guy's) Cons. (Psychiat.) Roehampton Priory Hosp., Lond.; Hon. Sen. Research Fell. Char. Cross & W.m. Med. Sch. Socs: Brit. Assn. Psychopharmacol.; Brit. Assn. Neuropsychiat.; Eur. Coll. Neuropsychopharm. Prev: Med. Dir. (Psychol. Med.) Roy. Masonic Hosp. Lond.; Med. Dir. Charter Clinic Chelsea; Cons. Psychiat. St. And. Hosp. N.ampton.

CURSON, Judith Anne MWRT, Wessex Deanery Postgraduate Medical & Dental Education, Highcroft, Romsey Rd, Winchester SO22 5DH Email: judy.curson@doh.gsi.gov.uk; Oak Perridge, Thornford Road, Crookham Common, Thatcham RG19 8EN Tel: 01635 269391 Email: intellegoj@aol.com — MB BChir 1982 Camb.; MSc 1986 (Community Med.) Lond; MA 1982 Camb; MFPHM 1989. (Camb.) Ass. Dean Wessex Deanery, Winchester; Asst. Med. Dir., Frimley Pk. Hosp., Camberley; Indep. Pub. Health Phys. Prev: Dir., Pub. Health, N. & Mid Hants HA; Cons. Pub. Health Med., S. Beds HA; Hon. Lect. Health Servs. Research Unit, Lond. Sch. of Hyg.

CURSON, Ruth Assisted Conception Unit, King's College Hospital, Denmark Hill, London SE5 9RS Tel: 020 7346 3049 Fax: 020 7346 4542 — MB BChir 1970 Camb.; MB BChir Camb. 1971; MA Camb. 1971. (Westm.) Assoc. Specialist Fertil. Clin. & Assisted Conception Unit King's Coll. Hosp. Lond.

CURSON, Steven Princess Street Group Practice, 2 Princess Street, London SE1 6JP Tel: 020 7928 0253 Fax: 020 7261 9804 — MB BChir 1971 Camb.; MA, MB Camb. 1971, BChir 1970; DObst RCOG 1972. (Univ. Coll. Hosp.) GP Trainer Lond.; Radio BRd.caster Lond. Talk Back Radio; Columnist Top Santé Magazine. Prev: Course Organiser St. Thos. Hosp. VTS; Project Team Mem. Lambeth Community Care Centre.

CURT, John Reginald Newstead, RD, OBE (retired) Moss Cottage, 1 Kenilworth Road, Sale M33 5DU Tel: 0161 973 9313 — MB ChB St. And. 1957; ChM Dund 1973; FRCS Eng. 1967; FRCS Ed. 1965. Prev: Cons. Gen. Surg. Salford AHA (T).

CURT, Nicholas Edwin Kirby Road Surgery, 58 Kirby Road, Dunstable LU6 3JH Tel: 01582 609121 Fax: 01582 472002; Sherwood, 82 Great Northern Road, Dunstable LU5 4BT Tel: 01582 696146 Fax: 01582 696146 Email: nkkdoc@aol.com — BM BS 1980 Nottm.; BMedSci (Hons.) Nottm. 1978; MRCGP 1984; DRCOG 1983. (Nottm.) GP Beds. FPC & Beds. HA; Chairm. Beds. LMC; GP Adviser to Beds. HA. Socs: BMA. Prev: Ho. Surg. W. Herts. Hemel Hempstead; Ho. Phys. Luton & Dunstable Hosp.

CURTICE, Martin John Redvers Spenicott, Pond St., Moretonhampstead, Newton Abbot TQ13 8NX — MB ChB 1992 Birm.

CURTIES, Richard Thomas Lees Leith Hill Practice, The Leith Hill Practice, Ockley, Dorking RH5 5TR Tel: 01306 711182 Fax: 01306 712751; Volvens Cottage, Mole St, Ockley, Dorking RH5 5PB Tel: 01306 621280 — MB BS 1968 Lond.; DObst RCOG 1971. (Middlx.) Med. Adviser Farm Pl. Treatm. Centre. Prev: Regist. (Med.) & Ho. Surg. Middlx. Hosp. Lond.; SHO (Paediat. & Obst.) St. Luke's Hosp. Guildford.

CURTIN, Brian Gerard 21 Cole Grove, Hertford SG14 2NL — LRCPI & LM, LRSCI & LM 1956; LRCPI & LM, LRCSI & LM 1956; LAH Dub. 1953.

CURTIN, David Michael Kirkstone House, Moat Hill, Totnes TQ9 5ER — MB BS 1975 Lond.

CURTIN, John Joseph Brunswick X-Ray Department, Norfolk & Norwich Hospital, Brunswick Road, Norwich NR1 3SR — MB BCh BAO 1985 NUI; MRCPI 1987; FRCR 1991. Trainee Regist. (Diag. Radiol.) N.wick Pk. Hosp. Harrow. Socs: Fell. Pulm. Radiol. Med. Coll. Wisconsin, USA.

CURTIN, Josephine Theresa 84 Higham Road, London N17 6NP — BM 1990 Soton.; DRCOG 1994. SHO (Paediat. Cardiol.) Soton. Gen. Hosp.

CURTIN, Mark John 17 St Josephs Close, Olney MK46 5HD — MB BS 1990 Lond.

CURTIN, Maurice Laurence Aloysius (retired) Wesley House, Church Hill, Bisley, Stroud GL6 7AB — MB BCh BAO 1952 NUI; LAH Dub. 1952. Prev: Capt. RAMC.

CURTIS, Alan Joseph 18 Tudor Rose Park, South Coast Road, Peacehaven BN10 8UR Tel: 01273 580264 — MB ChB 1970 Sheff.; DCH Eng. 1973. (Sheff.) Indep. Med. Pract. Lancer Med. Gp. Lond. Prev: GP Birm.; Regist. (Paediat.) Lanarksh. HB; SHO (Paediat.) Doncaster Roy. Infirm. & Chesterfield Roy. Hosp.

CURTIS, Alison Mary River Cottage, 39 Queens Drive, Thames Ditton KT7 0TJ Tel: 020 8398 1631; 39 Queens Drive, Thames Ditton KT7 0TJ — MB BS Lond. 1991; FRCA Lond. 1997. (St. Bartholomew's Hospital London) Specialist Regist. Anaesth.

CURTIS, Anne Parkgrove Terrace Surgery, 22B Parkgrove Terrace, Edinburgh EH4 7NX Tel: 0131 312 6600 Fax: 0131 312 7798; 22B Parkgrove Terrace, Edinburgh EH4 7HX — MB ChB 1980 Ed.; MRCGP 1983; DRCOG 1983. GP Edin.

CURTIS, Anthony Richard (retired) Heath Lodge, Boundary Drive, Wimborne BH21 2RE — MB ChB 1947 Sheff.; DLO Eng. 1950. Prev: Med. Off. DHSS (Basingstoke).

CURTIS, Arthur 96 Tongdean Lane, Brighton BN1 5JE Tel: 01273 553624 — MRCS Eng. LRCP Lond. 1945; MRCGP 1965. (Leeds) Socs: BMA. Prev: Squadron Ldr. RAFVR, Anaesth. RAF Hosp. Singapore; Ho. Surg. St. Luke's Hosp. Bradford; Cas. Off. Roy. Hosp. Wolverhampton.

CURTIS, Christopher John 69 Belsize Park Gardens, London NW3 4JP Fax: 020 7722 4387; Portland House, Salman Lane, Annesley Woodhaire, Nottingham NG17 9HB Tel: 01623 755465 — MB BS 1993 Lond. SHO (A & E) Edgware Gen. Hosp. Prev: Ho. Off. Brook Hosp.; Ho. Off. P.ss Roy. Hosp.

CURTIS, Claire Louise 27 Mayfair Gardens, Southampton SO15 2TW — BM 1997 Soton.

CURTIS, David Department Psychiatry, Royal London Hospital, Whitechapel, London E1 1BB Tel: 020 7377 729 Fax: 020 7377 7316 — MB BS 1985 Lond.; MA Camb. 1985; MD Lond. 1994; MRCPsych 1989; PhD Camb 1999. Cons. & Hon. Sen. Lect. Psychiat. Roy. Lond. Hosp. Prev: Sen. Lect. & Hon. Cons. Inst. Psychiat. & Maudsley Hosp. Lond.; Lect. St. Mary's Hosp. Lond.; Research Psychiat. Middlx. Hosp. Lond.

CURTIS, Edward Phillip Paul Department Obstetrics & Gynaecology, Royal Surrey County Hospital, Egerton, Guildford GU2 7XX Tel: 01483 571122 — MB ChB Bristol 1982; MRCOG 1988. Cons. O & G Roy. Surrey Co. Hosp. Guildford. Prev: Sen. Regist. Roy. Free Hosp. Lond.; Research Fell. Roy. Free Hosp. Lond.; Regist. (O & G) St. Bart. Hosp. Lond.

CURTIS, Edward William 41 South Canterbury Road, Canterbury CT1 3LH — MB BCh 1997 Wales.
CURTIS, Hazel Ann Dingley Childrens Centre, Battle Hospital, Oxford Rd, Reading Tel: 0118 636202; 6 Badgers Walk, Shiplake, Henley-on-Thames RG9 3JQ — MB BCh 1979 Wales; MD 1990; FRCP (UK) 1992; FRCPCH 1995. Cons. Paediat. Community Roy. Berks & Battle NHS Trust. Prev: Sen. Regist. (Child Health) Univ. Hosp. Wales Cardiff; Lect. Univ. Exeter.
CURTIS, Helen Jane Cardiopulmonary Transplant Unit, Freeman Hospital, Freeman Road, Newcastle upon Tyne NE7 7DN Tel: 0191 284 3111 — MB BS 1997 Newc. (Newcastle-Upon-Tyne) Sen. Ho. Off., Freeman Hosp., Newc. upon Tyne.
CURTIS, Howard Spencer 4 Stanhope Way, Staines TW19 7PJ — MB BS 1989 Lond.
CURTIS, James 8 Downsland Drive, Brentwood CM14 4JT — MB BS 1996 Lond.
CURTIS, Jillian Teresita Department of Anaesthetics, Royal Gwent Hospital, Newport Tel: 01633 234234 — MB BCh 1981 Wales; FRCA 1992. (Univ. Wales Coll. Med.) Cons. Anaesth., Roy. Gwent Hosp. Newport. Prev: Research Off. (Anaesth.) Univ. Wales Coll. Med. Cardiff; Regist. (Anaesth.) Univ. Hosp. Wales Cardiff.
CURTIS, Joan Marie 2 Ladybower Avenue, Cowersley, Huddersfield HD4 5XA Tel: 01484 59124 — MB ChB 1956 Manch.; DPH 1964. (Manch.)
CURTIS, Johanna Loraine 19 Sidney Square, London E1 2EY — MB BS 1994 Lond.
CURTIS, John Michael 17 Carrick Road, Curzon Park, Chester CH4 8AN — MB ChB 1987 Liverp.; MRCP (UK) 1991; FRCR 1995; DMRD Liverp. 1994. Cons. Radiol.Univ. Hosp., Aintree, Liverp. Prev: Lect. (Radiol.) Univ. Liverp. & Hon. Sen. Regist. (Radiol.) Roy. Liverp. Univ. Hosp.; Sen. Regist. (Radiol.) Mersey RHA; Regist. (Radiol. & Gen. Med.) Mersey RHA.
CURTIS, John Robert 96 Belmont Rise, Cheam, Sutton SM2 6EE Tel: 020 8643 1658 — MB BS 1956 Lond.; MD Lond. 1969; FRCP Lond. 1973, M 1958. (Char. Cross) Cons. Nephrol. & Sen. Lect. Dept. Med. New Char. Cross Hosp. Fulham. Socs: Renal Assn.; Med. Research Soc. Prev: Lect. in Med. Char. Cross Hosp. Med. Sch.; Sen. Med. Regist. Addenbrooke's Hosp. Camb.; Med. Regist. Nat. Heart Hosp. Lond.
CURTIS, Kathleen 66 Stonehouse Lane, Bath BA2 5DW — MRCS Eng. LRCP Lond. 1960.
CURTIS, Keith William Winchcombe Medical Practice, The Surgery, Abbey Terrace, Winchcombe, Cheltenham GL54 5LL Tel: 01242 602307 Fax: 01242 603689 — MB BS 1972 Lond.; BSc (Pharmacol.) Lond. 1969, MB BS 1972; MRCGP 1977; DObst RCOG 1976; DCH Eng. 1975. (St. Geo.)
CURTIS, Lloyd Douglas 2 Kelmore Villas, Kelmore Grove, London SE22 9BJ — BM BCh 1973 Oxf.; BM BCh Oxf. 1976; BA (Human Physiol.) (Hons.) Oxf. 1973; MRCP (UK) 1979.
CURTIS, Margaret Olive Brookside Clinic, Station Way, Aylesbury HP20 2SQ Tel: 01296 426228 Fax: 01296 398802; New Conkers, 176 Aylesbury Road, Bierton, Aylesbury HP22 5DT Tel: 01296 23950 — MB BS 1963 Lond.; MRCS Eng. LRCP Lond. 1963; MFFP 1993; DObst RCOG 1965. (Roy. Free) Cons. in Community Family Plann. Aylesbury Vale Community Health Care NHS Trust; Clin. Asst. (Obst. & Ultrasound) Stoke Mandeville Hosp.
CURTIS, Mark David 372 Burton Road, Lincoln LN1 3UP — MB BS 1991 Lond.; MRCP (UK) 1995. (Royal Free Hospital)
CURTIS, Mr Mark James Kingston Hospital, Galsworthy Road, Kingston upon Thames KT2 7QB Tel: 020 8546 7711 Fax: 020 8541 5613; New Victoria Hospital, 184 Coombe Lane W., Kingston upon Thames KT2 7EG Tel: 020 8949 9000 Fax: 020 8949 9099 — MB BS 1982 Lond.; FRCS Eng. 1987; FRCS Ed. 1986; T(S) 1992. (St. Geo.) Cons. Orthop. Surg. Kingston & New Vict. Hosps. Kingston upon Thames. Prev: Sen. Regist. (Orthop. Surg.) St. Geo. Hosp. Lond.; Research Fell. (Orthop. Surg.) Johns Hopkin's Hosp. Baltimore Maryland, USA.
CURTIS, Matthew Dominic 3 Crowton Avenue, Sale M33 4LY — BM BS 1998 Nottm.; BM BS Nottm 1998.
CURTIS, Michael 19 Strathmore Road, Hamilton ML3 6AQ — MB ChB 1977 Dundee; MRCPath 1985. Cons. Forens. Path. Univ. Glas.; Hon. Cons. Path. Gtr. Glas. HB. Prev: Sen. Lect. (Forens. Med.) Univ. Glas.; Cons. Path. N. Manch. Gen. Hosp.; Lect. (Path.) Univ. Newc. upon Tyne.
CURTIS, Michael 51 Craven Park, London NW10 8SR Tel: 020 8965 7494; 234 Chamberlayne Road, London NW10 Tel: 020 8459 4464 — MB ChB 1946 Leeds; MB ChB (Distinc. Foren. Med.) Leeds 1946. (Leeds) Med Examr. Brittanic Assur. Co.; Med. Adviser Television Internat. Prev: Res. Med. Off. Roy. Nat. Sanat. Bournemouth & Middleton-in-Wharfedale; Hosp. Ilkley; Orthop. Ho. Surg. Manch. Roy. Infirm.
CURTIS, Natalie Jane 10 Cragg Terrace, Rawdon, Leeds LS19 6LF — MB BS 1991 Lond.; MRCP (UK) 1994. SHO (Neurol.) Addenbrooke's Hosp. Camb. Prev: SHO (Med.) Kingston.
CURTIS, Nicholas Raymond La Route Du Fort Surgery, 2 La Route Du Fort, St Helier, Jersey JE2 4PA Tel: 01534 31421 Fax: 01534 280776 — MB BS 1990 Lond.; MSc Lond. 1985, BSc 1983; DRCOG 1994. (Middlx. Hosp. Lond.)
CURTIS, Peter Denis Victoria Hospital, Whinney Heys Road, Blackpool FY3 8NR Tel: 01253 300000 — MB BCh BAO 1982 NUI; LRCPI & LM, LRCSI & LM 1982; MRCPI 1990; DCH Dub. 1983. Cons. Paediat. Vict. Hosp. Blackpool. Socs: Brit. Paediat. Assn. Prev: Sen. Regist. (Paediat.) St. Lukes Hosp. Bradford Health Trust; Research Fell. (Child Health) Univ. Glas.; Regist. (Paediat.) Gen. Hosp. Jersey.
CURTIS, Peter Ronald Sandy Lane Surgery, Sandy Lane, Leyland, Preston PR25 2EB Tel: 01772 909915 Fax: 01772 909911 — MB ChB 1975 Manch.; MRCGP 1979.
CURTIS, Richard Nigel Mark 78 Essendine Mansions, Essendine Road, Maida Vale, London W9 2LY — MB BS 1985 Lond.; MA Camb. 1986, BA 1982; MRCP (UK) 1989; DTM & H 1990; DCH RCP Lond. 1988. (St. Mary's) MRC Train. Fell. (Paediat. & Immunol.) St. Mary's Hosp. Med. Sch. Lond.
CURTIS, Rodney Allan Parry Lime Grove Medical Centre, Lime Grove Walk, Matlock DE4 3FD Tel: 01629 582241; 168 Starkholmes Road, Matlock DE4 5JA — MB BChir 1963 Camb.; MRCS Eng. LRCP Lond. 1962; MRCGP 1976; DObst RCOG 1966; DCH RCP Lond. 1965; DA Eng. 1964. (St. Mary's Lond.) GP Trainer Derby VTS; Vis. Phys. Whitworth Hosp. Matlock; Bd. Mem. High Peak & Dales PCG. Socs: BMA; Roy. Coll. Gen. Pract. Prev: SHO (O & G) St. Luke's Hosp. Guildford; SHO (Anaesth.) St. Peter's Hosp. Chertsey.
CURTIS, Russell John 50 Winskell Road, South Shields NE34 9EQ — MB BS 1991 Newc.
CURTIS, Simon Philip Summertown Group Practice, 160 Banbury Road, Oxford OX2 7BS Tel: 01865 515552 Fax: 01865 311237 — MB BS 1988 Lond.; BSc Lond. 1985, MB BS 1988; MRCP (UK) 1992; MRCGP 1997. Prev: Sen. Regist. (Genitourin. Med.) Oxf.
CURTIS, Vivienne Amanda Department of Psychological Medicine, Institute of Psychiatry, De Crespigny Park Road, Denmark Hill, London SE5 8AF Email: v.curtis@iop.bpmt.ac.uk — MB BS 1991 Lond.; MRCPsych 1995. (St Thos. Hosp.) Clin. Lect. in Psychiat. Dept. of Psychol. Med. King's Coll. Sch. of Med. & Dent. Affil.d to the Inst. of Psychiat.; Hon. Sen. Regist. Maudsley Hosp.
CURTIS HAYWARD, Katherine Sarah May Lane Surgery, May Lane, Dursley GL11 4AA Tel: 01453 550555; 7 Old Town, Wotton-under-Edge GL12 7DH — BM 1980 Soton.; MRCGP 1992; DRCOG 1984. p/t GP.
CURTIS JENKINS, Graham Hugh Counselling in Primary Care Trust, Majestic House, High St., Staines TW18 4DG Tel: 01784 441782 Fax: 01784 442601 Email: 101450.3136@compuserve.com; 38 Richmond Road, Staines TW18 2AB Tel: 01784 455518 — MB Camb. 1960, BChir 1959; MA Camb. 1960; FRCGP 1989, M 1979; DObst RCOG 1961. (Camb. & St. Thos.) Dir. Counselling Primary Care Trust. Socs: Fell. Roy. Soc. Med. (Pres. Sect. Gen. Pract.); BMA. Prev: GP Ashford, Middlx.; Ho. Surg. (Obst.) Gen. Lying-in Hosp. Lond.; Ho. Surg. & Ho. Phys. Roy. Hosp. Wolverhampton.
CURTIS-RALEIGH, Jean Margaret Macdonald (retired) 5 St Peters Square, London W6 9AB Tel: 020 8748 8288 — MB BS Lond. 1959; FRCPsych 1996, M 1973; DPM Eng. 1965. Med. Mem. Ment. Health Review Tribunals. Prev: Cons. Psychiat. Qu. Mary's Hosp. Roehampton.
CURWEN, Ian Havelock Moncrieff (retired) 6 Beaulieu House, 93 Holders Hill Road, London NW4 1JY Tel: 020 8346 2626 — MB ChB 1943 Cape Town; DPhysMed. Eng. 1948. Prev: Cons. Phys. (Rheum. & Rehabil.) Richmond, Twickenham & Roehampton HA.

CURWEN, Joanna Lucy 6 Meadway Gate, London NW11 7LB — MB ChB 1997 Manch.

CURWEN, Montague (retired) 22 Kimberley Court, Sea Road, Westgate-on-Sea CT8 8SD Tel: 01843 833724 — MB BS 1942 Lond.; MRCS Eng. LRCP Lond. 1936; FRCGP 1970. Prev: Temp. Surg. Lt.-Cdr. RNVR.

CURWOOD, Victoria Louise 67 Barkby Road, Leicester LE4 9LG — MB ChB 1998 Leeds.

CURZEN, Nicholas Peter Department of Cardiology, Manchester Heart Centre, Manchester Royal Infirmary, Manchester M13 9WL Tel: 0161 276 4295 Fax: 0161 276 4772 Email: nc@mhc.cmht.nwest.nhs.uk — BM 1987 Soton.; BM (Hons.) Soton. 1987; MRCP (UK) 1990; PhD Lond. 1996. Cons. (Cardiol.) Manch. Roy. Infirm. Socs: Brit. Cardiac Soc.; BCIS (Elected Mem. of Counc.). Prev: MRC Train. Fell. & Hon. Regist. (Cardiol. & ITU) Roy. Brompton Hosp. Lond.; Regist. (Cardiol.) Roy. Brompton Hosp. Lond.; Specialist Regist. (Cardiol.) Lond. Chesh.

CURZEN, Professor Peter (retired) 2 Bishops Drive, Harnham Wood, Salisbury SP2 8NZ Tel: 01722 412713 — MRCS Eng. LRCP Lond. 1955; BSc (Hons.) Lond. 1952, MD 1966, MB BS 1955; FRCOG 1970, M 1962, DObst 1959. Prev: Regist. Postgrad. Dean & Prof. Med. Educat. Univ. Soton.

CURZON, Ian Lewis The Orchard, Stanmore Drive, Lancaster LA1 5BL — MB BS 1989 Newc.

CURZON, Robert Neil Derbe Road Surgery, 43 Derbe Road, Lytham St Annes FY8 1NJ Tel: 01253 720001, 01253 725811 — MB ChB 1979 Manch. Prev: SHO (Med.) W.morland Co. Hosp.; SHO (Anaesth.) Hope Hosp. Salford; SHO (O & G) Bolton Gen. Hosp.

CUSACK, Claire Frances 34 Carlyon Court, Rectory Road, Farnborough GU14 7BY — MB BCh BAO 1983 NUI.

CUSACK, Michael Robert 65 Review Road, Dagenham RM10 9DJ — MB ChB 1992 Manch.; BSc (Hons.) Physiol. Manch. Univ.; MRCP (UK) 1995. Regist. Rotat. (Cardiol. & Gen. Med.) Guy's Hosp. Lond.

CUSACK, Nora Mary 23 York Road, Weybridge KT13 9DY — MB BCh BAO 1946 NUI. (Univ. Coll. Dub.)

CUSACK, Paula Siew Yin 37 Collinswood Dr, St Leonards-on-Sea TN38 0NU — MB ChB 1997 Leic.

CUSACK, Rebecca Jane 31 Lime Grove, Leicester LE9 2DF — BM 1991 Soton.

CUSANO, Carmela 17 Macroom Road, London W9 3HY — State Exam Catholic U Rome 1992.

CUSCHIERI, Sir Alfred Denbrae Mill, Stratkiness Low Road, St Andrews KY16 9LT Tel: 01334 75046 Fax: 01382 641795 Email: acushieri@dundee.ac.uk — MD Malta 1961; ChM Liverp. 1968; FRCS Eng. 1967; FRCS Ed. 1965; Hon FRCS Glas 1994; Hon FRCS Ire 1996; FIBiol. 1988; Hon MD Liverp. (Hon) 1997. (Malta) Prof. Surg. Univ. Dundee. Socs: Surg. Research Soc. & Assn. Surgs. Prev: Reader (Surg.) Univ. Liverp.

CUSCHIERI, Marguerite Pamela (retired) Denbrae Mill, Strathkinness Low Road, St Andrews KY16 9TY Tel: 01334 475046 — MB ChB Liverp. 1959; MD Liverp. 1964; FRCPath 1983, M 1969. Prev: Hon. Sen. Lect. Path. Univ. Dundee Cons. Histopath., Tayside Health Bd.

CUSCHIERI, Mr Raymond Joseph Doncaster Royal Infirmary, Armthorpe Road, Doncaster DN2 5LT Tel: 01302 366666; 12 Drewery Lane, West Woodside, Doncaster DN9 2RE — MD 1975 Malta; ChM Liverp. 1985; FRCS Eng. 1980; FRCS Ed. 1979. Cons. Gen. & Vasc. Surg. Doncaster Roy. Infirm. Socs: Vasc. Surg. Soc. Prev: Regist. Liverp. Surg. Train. Scheme Walton Hosp.; Research Fell. Univ. Dept. Surg. Roy. Infirm. Glas.; Sen. Regist. (Gen. & Vasc. Surg.) Roy. Infirm. Glas.

CUSHEN, Michael Joseph St. Elizabeth Hospice, 565 Foxhall Road, Ipswich IP3 8LX Tel: 01473 727776 Fax: 01473 274717 Email: medical@stelizabethhospice.org.uk — MB BCh BAO 1982 NUI; MRCPI 1985; T(M) 1994; DCH NUI 1985. Med. Dir. St. Eliz. Hospice Ipswich; Hon. Cons. Palliat. Med. Ipswich Hosp. NHS Trust. Socs: Assn. Palliat. Med.; Brit. Med. Acupunct. Soc. Prev: Regist. (Palliat. Med.) St. Josephs Hospice Hackney Lond.; Research Regist. (Cardiol.) Edgware Gen. Hosp. Lond.; Regist. (Med.) Roy. Perth Hosp., W.. Austral.

CUSHING, Katherine Elizabeth Pine Lodge, Pilson Green, South Walsham, Norwich NR13 6EA — MB ChB 1993 Liverp.

CUSHING, Mark Charles Tel: 01704 226973 Fax: 01704 505758; 20 Preston Road, Southport PR9 9EG Tel: 01704 533863 — MB ChB 1981 Liverp.

CUSHING, Stephen North Shore Surgery, 95 Holmfield Road, Blackpool FY2 9RS Tel: 01253 593971 Fax: 01253 596039 Email: steve.cushing@gp-p81681.nhs.uk — MB ChB 1973 Birm.; MRCP (UK) 1977. (Birm.) Gen. Practitioner; Chairm. Blackpool Primary Care Gp. Socs: NHS Alliance. Prev: Gordon Hamilton Clin. Research; Fell. Med. Oncol.

CUSHION, Jane Elizabeth Louise 13 The Rise, Elstree, Borehamwood WD6 3JR — MB BS 1988 Lond.; BA (Hons.) Oxf. 1985; DCH RCP Lond. 1991. Library Clerk Ho. of Commons Lond.

CUSHLEY, Michael John Birds Barn Cottage, Sheepwash Lane, Upper Wolverley, Kidderminster DY11 5SB — MB BS 1974 Lond.; DM Soton. 1987; FRCP Lond. 1994; MRCP (UK) 1976. Cons. Phys. Corbett & Wordsley Hosps. Stourbridge.

CUSHNAGHAN, Barbara Campbell (retired) River Court, Waters Edge, Union Mills, Douglas IM4 4NN Tel: 01624 851581 Fax: 01624 852283 Email: cushnaghan@manxnet.com — MB ChB 1951 Leeds; MFPM RCP (UK) 1990; DA Eng. 1956; DObst RCOG 1953. Prev: Clin. Research Phys. Bioman CTS.

CUSHNIR, Morris Norman (retired) Orchard Rising, Herrings Lane, Burnham Market, King's Lynn PE31 8DW — MRCS Eng. LRCP Lond. 1951; MA Camb. 1951. Prev: Clin. Asst. Paediat. Dept., Roy. Caroline Med. Sch. Stockholm.

CUSICK, Eleri Lorna 21 Hillhead Road, Bieldside, Aberdeen AB15 9EJ — MB ChB 1983 Aberd.; BMedBiol Aberd. 1980, MB ChB 1983.

CUSICK, Peter Bernard Abbotts Cross Medical Practice, Doagh Road, Whiteabbey, Antrim BT41 Tel: 028 9076 4048; 86 North Parade, Ormeau Road, Belfast BT7 2GJ Tel: 01232 281323 Email: peter.cusick@ntlworld.com — MB BCh BAO 1993 Belf.; DCH 1998 (Dublin); MRCGP 1998 (Belfast/Edinburgh); DRCOG 1997. (Queens Univ.) GP Princip.; Med. Ref. Socs: Assoc. Mem. RCGP; BMA; MRCGP.

CUSSEN, William Damian The Surgery, 227 Lodge Causeway, Fishponds, Bristol BS16 3QW Tel: 0117 965 3102; 76 Quarry Way, Emersons Green, Bristol BS16 7BN — MB BS 1981 Lond.; MRCGP 1988; DRCOG 1985. (London hospital)

CUSSONS, Mr Paul David Mount Vernon Hospital, Rickmansworth Road, Northwood HA6 2RN — MB BS 1981 Lond.; MA, DPhil Oxf. 1979; FRCS (Plast.) 1993; FRCS Eng. 1987. Cons. Plastic Surg. Mt. Vernon Hosp. N.wood. Prev: Sen. Regist. (Plastic Surg.) Mt. Vernon Hosp. N.wood; Regist. (Plastic Surg.) Frenchay HA Bristol.

CUST, George (retired) 1 Gouthwaite Close, Clifton Moor, York YO30 4UJ — MB ChB Leeds 1952; FFCM 1979, M 1974; DTM & H Eng. 1967; DPH Leeds 1957. Prev: Regional Cons. Pub. Health Yorks. RHA.

CUST, Mr Michael Pury Derby City General Hospital, Uttoxeter Road, Derby DE22 3NE Tel: 01332 340131 Email: mike.cust@sdah-tr.trent.nhs.uk; Sturston Hall, Ashbourne DE6 1LN — MB BS Lond. 1980; MRCOG 1986. Cons. O & G Derby City Gen. Hosp. Prev: Sen. Regist. Rotat. (O & G) Derby City Hosp. Nottm.; Lect. (O & G) Univ. Hosp. Nottm.; Research Fell. (Gyn.) King's Coll. Hosp. Lond.

CUSWORTH, Charles James Broadgait Green, Broadgait Green, Gullane EH31 2DW Tel: 01620 842171 Fax: 01620 843020; 5 Dairy Cottages, Fenton Barns, North Berwick EH39 5AQ Tel: 01620 850583 — MB ChB 1986 Ed.; MRCGP 1991. (Ed.)

CUSWORTH, Elizabeth Jane Department of Child and Adolescent Psychiatry, The Manoc, Brown Street, Camelon, Falkirk FK1 4PX Tel: 01324 610846 Fax: 01324 610847 — MB BS 1980 Newc.; MRCPsych 1990. Cons. (Child & Adolesc. Psychiat.) Cent. Scot. Healthcare Trust. Prev: Cons. Child & Adolesc. Psychiat. N. Tyneside Healthcare Trust.; Sen. Regist. (Child & Adolesc. Psychiat.) N.. RHA; Regist. (Psychiat.) Lothian HB.

CUSWORTH, Rebekah Jayne 93 Borden Lane, Sittingbourne ME10 1BU — MB BCh 1998 Wales.

CUTAJAR, Abraham Peter Trent Road Surgery, Trent Road, Grantham NG31 7XQ Tel: 01476 571166 Fax: 01476 570397.

CUTAJAR, Peter Department of Learning Disabilities, Highbury Hospital, Highbury Road, Nottingham NG6 9DR — MD 1986 Malta; MRCPsych 1995. Sen. Regist. (Learning Disabil.) Qu. Med. Centre Nottm.

CUTHBERT, Alan Martonside Medical Centre, 1a Martonside Way, Middlesbrough TS4 3BY Tel: 01642 812266 Fax: 01642 828722 — BM BS 1975 Nottm.; BMedSci 1973. (Nottingham) Private GP.

CUTHBERT, Alison Joy Four Oaks Medical Centre, Carlton House, Mere Green Road, Sutton Coldfield B75 5BS Tel: 0121 308 2080 Fax: 0121 323 4694; 1 Boswell Road, Sutton Coldfield B74 2NB Tel: 0121 354 6571 — MB BCh BAO 1978 Belf.; DRCOG 1980; Cert. Family Plann. JCC 1982.

CUTHBERT, Ann Christine Department of Haematology, Airedale General Hospital, Skipton Road, Keighley BD20 6TD Tel: 01535 652511 Fax: 01535 657362 Email: ann.cuthbert@group.airedale.northy.nhs.uk — MB ChB 1979 Manch.; FRCP Lond. 1996; FRCPath 1998. (Manch.) Cons. Haemat. Airedale Gen. Hosp.

CUTHBERT, Christopher John 36 Parkstone Road, Poole BH15 2PG Tel: 01202 672532 Fax: 01202 660718; Lytchett Cottage, 3 Marsh Lane, Upton, Poole BH16 5NH Tel: 01202 622743 — MB ChB 1972 Bristol; DCH Eng. 1975; DObst RCOG 1974.

CUTHBERT, Colin Robert Barnard Castle Surgery, Victoria Road, Barnard Castle DL12 8HT Tel: 01833 690707 — MB ChB 1983 Sheff.; PhD Soton 1980; MA Oxf. 1977; MRCP (UK) 1987; MRCGP 1987; DRCOG 1985. Princip. GP Barnard Castle.

CUTHBERT, David Allan 77 Milverton Avenue, Bearsden, Glasgow G61 4BG — MB ChB 1998 Ed.; MB ChB Ed 1998.

CUTHBERT, James Anthony 124 Edge Lane Drive, Liverpool L13 4AF — MB ChB 1997 Liverp.

CUTHBERT, Jean Wilson (retired) 8 Riverview Place, Glasgow G5 8EB Tel: 0141 429 8106 — MB ChB 1941 Glas.; DPH 1950; FFOM RCP Lond. 1986, MFOM 1979; DHMSA Lond. 1970. Prev: Regist. (Obst.) Stobhill Hosp. Glas.

CUTHBERT, Mary Margaret Westcliffe Medical Centre, Westcliffe Road, Shipley BD18 3EE Tel: 01274 580787 Fax: 01274 532210; Holme Garth, 3 Nab Wood Drive, Shipley BD18 4HP Tel: 01274 597215 — MB ChB 1979 Manch.; MRCGP 1983; DRCOG 1982.

CUTHBERT, Maurice Frederick (retired) 24 Parkside, Grammar School Walk, Huntingdon PE29 3LF Tel: 01480 382431 — MB BS 1960 Lond.; PhD Lond. 1969; FFPM RCP (UK) 1991. Med. Assessor Advis. Comm. NHS Drugs DoH Lond.; Hon. Sen. Lect. (Med.) KCH Med. Sch.; Hon. Lect. (Pharmacol. & Therap.) Lond. Hosp. Med. Coll.; Hon. Med. Adviser Roy. Life Saving Soc. Prev: Med. & Scientif. Dir. Huntingdon Research Centre.

CUTHBERT, Naomi Dale The Garden Flat, 24 Kenilworth Avenue, London SW19 7LW — MB BS 1989 Lond.; BSc Lond. 1986, MB BS 1989; FRCS Eng. 1994. Prev: Hon. Research Fell. Roy. Free Hosp. Lond.

CUTHBERT, Olaf David (retired) Vishabreck, Evie, Orkney KW17 2PF Tel: 01856 751349 Email: olaf@orkney.com — MB BS 1945 Lond.; MD Lond. 1980. Prev: Regist. (Med.) Luton & Dunstable Hosp.

CUTHBERT, Robert James Gordon Belfast City Hospital, Lisburn Road, Belfast BT9 7AB Tel: .028 90 263733 Fax: 028 90 263870 Email: robert.cuthbert@bll.n-i.nhs.uk; .57 WOODROW Gardens, Saintfield, Ballynahinch BT24 7WG Tel: 028 97 519277 — MB BCh BAO 1982 Belf.; MD Belf. 1989; MRCP (UK) 1985; MRCPath 1991; T(M) 1991; T(Path) 1991. (Qu. Univ. Belf.) Cons. Haemat. Belf. City Hosp., Belf. Socs: Brit. Soc. Haematol. Prev: Cons. Haemat, Altnacelvin Hosp., Lodonderry; Leukaemia BMT Fell.sh. Vancouver Gen. Hosp. BC, Canada; Sen. Regist. (Haemat.) City Hosp. Nottm.

CUTHBERTSON, Daniel James Robert Byeways, Dell Lane, Gayton, Wirral CH60 2TS — MB ChB 1996 Liverp.

CUTHBERTSON, Fiona Mary 52 Barnhey Crescent, Wirral CH47 9RP — BM BCh 1998 Oxf.; BM BCh Oxf 1998.

CUTHBERTSON, Joanne Elise 2 Beech Hill, Hexham NE46 3AG — MB ChB 1994 Ed.

CUTHBERTSON, Paul James Randle Greasby Surgery, Greasby Health Centre, Greasby Road, Greasby, Wirral CH49 3NH Tel: 0151 678 3000 Fax: 0151 604 1813; Tanglewod, Dale Gardens, Heswall, Wirral CH60 6TQ Tel: 0151 342 1195 — MRCS Eng. LRCP Lond. 1965; Dip. Palliat. Med. Wales 1994. (Liverp.) Med. Off. St. John's Hosp. Wirral. Socs: Assn. Palliat. Med.; BMA. Prev: Regist. (Med.) Clatterbrige Hosp.

CUTHBERTSON, William Archibald (retired) Little Newlands, Corse, Staunton, Gloucester GL19 3RB Tel: 01452 840246 — MB BS 1957 Lond.

CUTHILL, Allan Robertson Cardiff Road Medical Centre, Cardiff Road, Taffs Well, Cardiff CF15 7YG Tel: 029 2081 0260 Fax: 029 2081 3002; 5 Maes y Wennol, Cardiff CF23 6NH Tel: 029 2073 2873 Email: allan.cuthall@virgin.net — MB BCh 1974 Wales; MRCGP 1980. Med. Adviser Bro Taf HA; Chair. Rhondda Cynon Inf. LHG prescribing subGp. Socs: Rhondda Med. Soc.; Cardiff Med. Soc.

CUTHILL, Ian Marson (retired) Ganilly, Church Lane, Guilden Sutton, Chester CH3 7EW Tel: 01244 300410 — MB ChB Ed. 1943; FRCP Ed. 1971, M 1955. Prev: Cons. Phys. Chester HA.

CUTHILL, James Macrae Kelvin Court, Penyfai, Bridgend CF31 4LS Tel: 01656 655824 — MB ChB 1948 Glas.; FRCP Glas. 1976, M 1962; FRFPS Glas. 1957; FRCPsych 1974, M 1971; DPM Lond. 1952. (Toronto & Glas.) Hon. Cons. Psychiat. M. Glam. HA. Socs: Fell. BMA; Mem., The Brit. Soc. for Clin. NeuroPhysiol.; Internat. Coll. Psychosomatic Med. Fell.. Prev: Asst. Psychiat. Whittingham Hosp.; Sen. Regist. (Psychiat.) Tone Vale Hosp. Taunton; Specialist Neuropsychiat. RAF.

CUTHILL, John Lyndene, Middlewich Road, Wistaston, Nantwich CW5 6PB — MB ChB 1989 Ed.

CUTHILL, Judith Jennifer (retired) 6 Westwood Avenue, Ipswich IP1 4EQ Tel: 01473 252249 — MB BCh BAO 1959 Dub.; MA Dub. 1959; MRCPsych 1972; DPM Eng. 1964. Prev: Cons. Family Psychiat. Inst. Family Psychiat. & High Trees Adolesc. Unit Ipswich.

CUTLER, Bernard 5 Larchfield Court, Larchfield Avenue, Glasgow G77 5PL — LRCP LRCS 1945 Ed.; LRCP LRCS Ed. LRFPS Glas. 1945.

CUTLER, Brian David (retired) 21 Barrowfield, Cuckfield, Haywards Heath RH17 5ER Tel: 01444 412790 Fax: 0870 125 7643 Email: bcutler@globalnet.co.uk — MB BChir Camb. 1969; MRCP (UK) 1971; MRCPsych 1974; MIHSM 1986. Prev: Assoc. Cons. Centre for Ment. Health Servs. Developm. Kings Coll. Lond.

CUTLER, Derek Hingley Shenlea, Leasowes Lane, Halesowen B62 8QE Tel: 0121 421 7803 — MB ChB 1941 Birm.; MB ChB (Hons.) Birm. 1941. SBStJ; Div. Surg. St. John Ambul. Brig. Socs: BMA.

CUTLER, Fiona Jane 31 Pitmedden Terrace, Aberdeen AB10 7HR Tel: 01224 323777 — MB ChB 1992 Aberd.; MRCP (UK) 1996. SHO (Haemat.) Glas. Roy. Infirm. Prev: Specialist Regist. (Haemat.) W.ern Gen. Hosp. Edin.; SHO (Haemat.) Glas. Roy. Infirm.; SHO (Gen. Med.) Aberd. Roy. Infirm.

CUTLER, Gillian Margaret 58 Green End, Comberton, Cambridge CB3 7DY Tel: 01223 262500 — MB ChB 1979 Manch.

CUTLER, Lucy Rachel Clare 1 Fairfield Gardens, Stockton Heath, Warrington WA4 2BX Email: luce270894@aol.com — MB BS 1993 Newc.; FRCS Ed. 1997. Specialist Regist. Mersey Deanery.(Orthop & Trauma.). Prev: Sen. SHO (Orthop. Surg.) N. Staffs. Hosps. Stoke-on-Trent.

CUTLER, Nicola Ann Louise South Norwood Hill Medical Centre, 103 South Norwood Hill, London SE25 6BY Tel: 020 8771 0742 — MB BS 1978 Lond.; DRCOG 1981.

CUTLER, Peter George Dept of Anaesthesia, Harrogate District Hospital, Lancaster park Road, Harrogate HG2 7SX Tel: 01423 553559; Straystones, St Winifred's Close, Harrogate HG2 8LZ Tel: 01423 887736 Email: cutler_peter@hotmail.com — MB BChir 1967 Camb.; MA, MB Camb. 1967, BChir 1966; FFA RCS Eng. 1971. (Westm.) Cons. (Anaesth.) Harrogate Health Dist.

CUTLER, Rebekah 70 Breinton Road, Hereford HR4 0JX — MB ChB 1996 Birm.; MRCGP MRCGP, 2000; DFFP DFFP, 2001. (University of Birmingham) Locum Gen. Practitioner, Hereford; G.P. Asst., The Surg., WylcwmSt. Surg., Knigmton; G.P. Assitant, The Surg., Kingstone, Heref. Prev: Ho. Off. (Med.) Roy. Shrewsbury Hosp.; Ho. Off. (Surg.) Co. Hosp. Hereford; SHO (GPVTS) Co. Hosp, Hereford.

CUTLER, Richard Charles (retired) 30 Dollis Hill Lane, London NW2 6JE Tel: 020 8450 7991 — MB BS Lond. 1968; MPhil Brunel 1992; MRCS Eng. LRCP Lond. 1967.

CUTLER, Robert Charles East Hill Surgery, 78 East Hill, Colchester CO1 2RW Tel: 01206 866133 Fax: 01206 869054 — MB BS 1970 Lond.

CUTLER, Timothy Patrick Ipswich Hospital NHS Trust, Heath Road, Ipswich IP4 5PD Tel: 01473 704043, 01473 704712; Bridge

House, Grundisburgh, Woodbridge IP13 6UF Tel: 01473 735796 Fax: 01473 735794 Email: tpcutler@uk-consultants.co.uk — MB BChir 1973 Camb.; 2000 F.L.S; MA Camb. 1973; FRCP Lond. 1994; MRCP (UK) 1976. (Guy's) Cons. Dermat. Ipswich Hosp.; RCP Represent. Advis. Comm. of Chelsea Physic Garden 1998. Socs: Fell. Amer. Acad. Dermat.; Fell. Roy. Soc. Med. (Mem. Sect. Dermat.); Fell. St. John's Hosp. Dermat. Soc. Prev: Sen. Regist. (Dermat.) Univ. Coll. Hosp. Lond.; Dunhill Dermat. Research Fell. Guy's Hosp. Lond.; Jun. Lect. (Med.) Guy's Hosp. Med. Sch. Lond.

CUTNER, Alfred Simon University College, London Hospitals, London Tel: 020 7387 2501 Email: alfred.cutler@uclh.org — MB BS 1985 Lond.; MD Lond. 1993; MRCOG 1993. Cons. (O & G) UCCH. Prev: Sen. Regist. Rotat. (O & G) St. Thos. & Guy's Hosp. Lond.

CUTRESS, Mark Lionel 1 Mill Close, Hemingford Grey, Huntingdon PE28 9DJ — MB BS 1998 Lond.; MB BS Lond 1998; BSc (Hons) London 1995. Med. Ho. Off. Gastroenterol. & Gen. Med. Derriford Hosp., Plymouth. Prev: Surgic. Ho. Off. Hepatobiliary Surg. & Urol. Roy. Free Hosp. Sch. of Med. Lond.

CUTRESS, Mr Ramsey Ian 1 Mill Close, Hemingford Grey, Huntingdon PE28 9DJ Tel: 01480 464742 — BM BCh 1994 Oxf.; BA (Hons.) Physiol. Scis. Oxf. Univ. 1991; FRCS (Ed.) 1998. (Oxf.) SHO Surg. Soton. Gen. Hosp. Prev: Demonst. (Anat.) Glas. Univ.; SHO Rotat. (Surg.) John Radcliffe Hosp. Oxf.; SHO Vasc. Surg. QAH, Portsmouth.

CUTTELL, Elizabeth Jane The Henry Moore Clinic, 26 Smawthorne Lane, Castleford WF10 4EN Tel: 01977 552007; The Vicarage, 140 High St, Normanton WF6 1NR Tel: 01924 893100 — MB ChB 1983 Birm.; DRCOG 1986. Prev: Trainee GP Wakefield.

CUTTELL, Philip John Charles Millway Medical Practice, Hartley Avenue, Mill Hill, London NW7 2HX Tel: 020 8959 0888 Fax: 020 8959 7050 — MB BS 1979 Lond.; MRCGP 1984; DRCOG 1983. (Roy. Free)

CUTTER, William Jonathan 16 Linom Road, Clapham N., London SW4 7PD — MB ChB 1995 Birm.; MB ChB (Birm.) 1995. SHO (Gen. Med.) Chertsey Hosp. Prev: SHO (A & E) Kingston-upon-Thames Hosp.; Ho. Off. (Gen. Med.) Sandwell Hosp.; Ho. Off. (Gen. Surg.) Dudley Rd. Hosp. Birm.

CUTTING, Mr Christopher James (retired) Taunton & Somerset Hospital, Musgrove Park, Taunton TA1 5DA Tel: 01823 333444 — MB ChB 1962 Ed.; FRCS Ed. 1965. Cons. Accid. Surg. (A & E) Taunton & Som. Hosp.

CUTTING, Mr Colin William Murray 14 Tamar House, Kennington Lane, London SE11 4XA — MB BS 1993 Lond.; FRCS Eng. 1997. (UMDS Guy's St. Thos. Hosp.) Research Fell. (Urol.) St. Geo.'s Hosp. Lond.

CUTTING, David Lennard Laurel House Surgery, 12 Albert Road, Tamworth B79 7JN Tel: 01827 69283 Fax: 01827 318029; School House, School Lane, Shuttington, Tamworth B79 0DX Tel: 01827 897125 — MB BS 1973 Lond.; MRCP (UK) 1977; Cert. JCC Lond. 1978. (King's Coll. Hosp.) Gen. Practitioner; Hosp. Practitioner,Sir Robt. Peel Hosp. Tamworth. Prev: Ho. Surg. King's Coll. Hosp. Lond.; SHO (Med.) Kent & Sussex Hosp. Tunbridge Wells; SHO (Paediat., O & G) Worcester Roy. Infirm.

CUTTING, Derrick Andrew Lower Addiscombe Road Surgery, 188 Lower Addiscombe Road, Croydon CR0 6AH Tel: 020 8654 1427 Fax: 020 8662 1272 — MB BS 1977 Lond.; BSc Lond. 1974; MRCGP 1988; DCH Eng. 1980; DRCOG 1980. (Univ. Coll. Hosp.)

CUTTING, Hazel Ann 14 Tamar House, Kennington Lane, London SE11 4XA — MB BS 1993 Lond.; BSc Hons. 1990. (United Med. and Dent. Schs. Guys and St. Thos.)

CUTTING, John Charles Wilbraham Place Practice, 9a Wilbraham Place, London SW1X 9AE Tel: 020 7823 5606; Mill Wood, Wall Hill, Forest Row RH18 5EG Tel: 0134 282 4408 Fax: 01342 282 4408 — MB BS 1969 Lond.; MPhil Lond. 1976, MD 1977; FRCP Lond. 1992; MRCP (UK) 1971; MRCS Eng. LRCP Lond. 1969; FRCPsych 1990, M 1975. (Guy's) Hon. Sen. Lect. Inst. Psychiat. Lond. & KCH. Socs: Fell. Roy. Soc. Med.; Assn. Brit. Neurol. Prev: Cons. Maudsley Hosp. & Bethlem Roy. Hosp. Lond.; SHO Nat. Hosp. Qu. Sq. Lond.

CUTTING, Pauline Ann c/o Risboro Lodge, Oldfield Road, Maidenhead SL6 1TX — MB ChB 1976 Liverp.; FRCS Eng. 1983.

CUTTING, Robert Ian Kelso Medical Group Practice, Health Centre, Inch Road, Kelso TD5 7JP Tel: 01573 224424 Fax: 01573 226388 — MB ChB 1990 Ed.; MB ChB (Hons.) Ed. 1990; BSc (Hons.) Ed. 1985; MRCGP 1994; DRCOG 1993; DCH RCP Lond. 1993. (Edinburgh) Princip. GP. Prev: SHO (A & E) Roy. Infirm. Edin.

CUTTING, Robert John 11 Beacon Road, Broadstairs CT10 3DD — MB ChB 1998 Liverp.; MB ChB Liverp 1998.

CUTTING, William Alexander Murray 5 Morningside Place, Edinburgh EH10 5ES Tel: 0131 447 1391 Email: william.cutting@ed.ac.uk — MB ChB 1958 Ed.; FRCP Ed. 1979, M 1968; MRCP Glas. 1968; DCH RCPS Glas. 1967; DObst RCOG 1961; FRCPCH 1997. (Ed.) Emerit. Reader (Child Health) Edin. Univ.; Cons. WHO. Socs: Fell. Roy. Soc. Trop. Med. & Hyg. Prev: Hon. Cons. (Paediat.) Gt. Ormond St. Hosp. Lond.; Ho. Phys. Roy. Hosp. Sick Childr. Edin.; Paediat. C.S.I. Hosp. Jammalamadugu, India.

CUTTS, Adam Mark Freshwell Health Centre, Wethersfield Road, Finchingfield, Braintree CM7 4BQ Tel: 01371 810328 Fax: 01371 811282; Oak House, Robin Hood End, Stambourne, Halstead CO9 4NN — MB BS 1989 Lond.; DRCOG 1992; DCH RCP Lond. 1992; MRCGP 1995. (St. Thomas Hosp. Univ. Lond.) GP Partner; Police Surg. Braintree Dist.; Civil Med. Examr. Chelmsford Territorial Army; GP Trainer; Research Lead for PCG. Socs: Colchester Med. Soc. Prev: Clin. Asst. (Paediat.) Colchester Gen. Hosp. Essex.

CUTTS, Felicity Tylden School of Hygiene & Tropical Medicine, Keppel St., London WC1E 7HT Tel: 020 7927 2209 Fax: 020 7436 4230 Email: fcutts@lshtm.ac.uk — MD 1989 Manch.; MSc Lond. 1983; MB ChB 1977; MRCP (UK) 1979; MFPHM RCP (UK) 1988; FFPHM 1996. Reader Infec. Dis.s Epidemiol. Unit. Prev: Sen. Lect. Communicable Dis.s Unit Lond. Sch. Hyg.; Vis. Sci. Immunisation Div. Centers for Dis. Control Atlanta, USA; Med. Epidemiol. MoH, Mozambique.

CUTTS, Mark William Julian 59 Greenway Road, Timperley, Altrincham WA15 6BD — MB ChB 1989 Manch.; BSc (Hons.) Manch. 1986, MB ChB 1989. SHO (Gen. Med.) Trafford Gen. Hosp.

CUTTS, Steven 3 Watchetts Green, Worcester WR4 0RT — MB BS 1993 Lond.

CVIJETIC, Mr Bosko Peter 'The Beeches', 55 London Road, Downham Market PE38 9AT Tel: 01366 383795 — MB BS 1967 Lond.; FRCS Eng. 1976; MRCS Eng. LRCP Lond. 1966. (Middlx.) Cons. (ENT) King's Lynn Health Dist. Prev: Ho. Phys., Ho. Surg. & Surg. Cas. Off. Middlx. Hosp. Lond.; Sen. Regist. (ENT) Leeds Gen. Infirm.

CWYNAR, Barbara Ursula Hypnotherapy Clinic, 101 Vernon Crescent, Ravenshead, Nottingham NG15 9BP Tel: 01623 796905 — MB BCh BAO NUI 1952; DPM Eng. 1960. (Univ. Coll. Dub.) Socs: Medico Chir. Soc. Nottm.; Medico-Legal Soc. Prev: Clin. Asst. Lond. Hosp., Sevenoaks Hosp. & W. Lond. Hosp.; Hon. Clin. Asst. St. Geo. Hosp.

CWYNARSKI, Katherine Louise 4 Mackeson Road, London NW3 2LT — MB BS 1992 Lond.; BSc (1st cl. Hons.) Pharmacol. Lond. 1989; MRCP (UK) 1995; Dip RCPath, 1997. BMT Coordinator/Specialist Regist. Haemat. Hammersmith Hosp. Prev: Regist. (Haemat.) Roy. Free Hosp. & N. Middlx. Hosps. Lond.; Regist. (Haemat.) P.ss Alexandra Hosp. Brisbane, Austral.; SHO (Med.) Hammersmith Hosp. Lond.

CWYNARSKI, Marek Tadeusz The Health Centre, Bank St., Faversham ME13 8QR Tel: 01795 533296; Wreights House, The Mall, Faversham ME13 8JL — MRCS Eng. LRCP Lond. 1962; MD Lond. 1971, MB BS 1962. (King's Coll. Lond. & King's Coll. Hosp.) Socs: BMA; Assoc. MRCGP. Prev: Lect. (Chem. Path. & Med.) Guy's Hosp. Med. Sch. Lond.; Fogarty Internat. Fell. Immunol. Br. Nat. Cancer Inst. Bethesda, USA.

CYBULSKA, Eva Thameslink NHS Trust, Stonehouse Hospital, Dartford DA2 6AU Tel: 01322 622222 — Lekarz 1972 Gdansk; Lekarz Gdansk Poland 1972; MRCPsych 1979; DPM 1978. Cons. Psychiat. Thameslink NHS Trust Dartford.

CYNK, Mr Marek Stefan 30 Pitreavie Drive, Knights Manor, Hailsham BN27 3XG Tel: 01323 442131 Fax: 01323 442131 Email: mark.cynk@btinternet.com — MB BS 1991 Lond.; BSc (Hons.) Lond. 1988; FRCS (Eng.) 1995. (Guys) Specialist Regist. (Urol.) S. E. Thames Rotat. Guys Hosp.

CYRIAC, Joseph Emmanuel Antony Department of Psychiatry, Bassetlaw Hospital & Community Services NHS Trust, Kilton, Worksop S81 0BD Tel: 01909 500990; 24 Alderson Road, Worksop S80 1XD Tel: 01909 501437 — MB BS 1975 Madras; DPM Eng.

1982. (Jawaharlal Inst. Post Grad. Med. Educat. & Research) Prev: Clin. Asst. Bassetlaw Dist. Gen. Hosp. Worksop.

CZAJKOWSKI, Marek Alexander 32 Ormsby Lodge, The Avenue, London W4 1HS — MB ChB 1994 Bristol.

CZAPLA, Krystyna Renal Unit, Wordsley Hospital, Stream Road, Stourbridge DY8 5QX — State Exam Med 1984 Hannover.

CZAUDERNA, Jack Maciej Darnall Community Health, 246 Darnall Road, Sheffield S9 5AN Tel: 0114 221 2600 Fax: 0114 221 2618; 185 Chippinghouse Road, Sheffield S7 1DQ Tel: 0114 258 2611 — MB ChB 1976 Bristol.

CZAYKOWSKI, Andrew Antoni Patrick Motto House Surgery, Lower Road, Sutton Valence, Maidstone ME17 3BJ Tel: 01622 842227 Fax: 01622 863030 — BM 1976 Soton.; MA (Hons.) Oxf. 1966; DRCOG 1979.

CZEPULKOWSKI, Edward Christopher Craven and Czepulkowski, 48 High Street, Royston, Barnsley S71 4RF Tel: 01226 722314; South Cottage, Back Lane, Wooley, Wakefield WF4 2JT — MA, MB BChir Camb. 1983. (St. Geo.) Prev: GP Denbigh; Gp Trainee Rawtenstall; Regist. (Gen. Med.) Pk. Hosp. Davy Hulme.

CZERNIEWSKI, Ian Wojciech David Dunchurch Surgery, Dunsmore Heath, Dunchurch, Rugby CV22 6AP Tel: 01788 522448 Fax: 01788 814609 — BM BCh 1987 Oxf.; MA Oxf. 1987; MRCS Eng. LRCP Lond. 1986; MRCGP 1990; DRCOG 1988. (Oxford)

D'AGAPEYEFF, Alexander Peter Laverton House, Laverton, Broadway WR12 7NA — MB BS 1998 Lond.; MB BS Lond 1998.

D'AGAPEYEFF, Katrina Elizabeth Rose Cottage, Wells Road, Eastcombe, Stroud GL6 7EE — MB BS 1992 Lond.

D'ALBA, Roberta Institute of Liver Studies, King's College Hospital, Bessemer Road, London SE5 8RX — State Exam 1991 Milan.

D'ALFONSO, Alfredo Arnoldus Leobinus Humares Ltd., Parmenter House, Tower Road, Winchester SO23 8TD — Artsexamen 1990 Rotterdam.

D'ALMADA REMEDIOS, Denis Joseph Department of Radiology, Northwick Park Hospital, Watford Road, Harrow HA1 3UJ; 39 Elmwood Avenue, Harrow HA3 8AJ — MB BS 1984 Lond.; MA Cantab.1985; MRCP (UK) 1988; FRCR 1994. Cons. (Radiol.) N.wick Pk. Hosp. Harrow. Prev: Sen. Regist. (Radiol.) N.wick Pk. Hosp. Harrow; Vis. Lect. & Hon. Sen. Med. Off. P. of Wales Hosp. & The Chinese Univ. of Hong Kong; Regist. (Med.) Mayday Hosp. Croydon.

D'ALTON-HARRISON, James John Fairacre, Church La, North Hayling, Hayling Island PO11 0SB Tel: 01705 467779 — LAH Dub. 1961; LRCPI & LM, LRCSI & LM 1961. Socs: BMA. Prev: Staff Grade Med. Off. (Community Child Health) Hants.

D'AMBROGIO, Margaret Susannah 19 Carthagena Avenue, Georgetown, Dumfries DG1 4XN — MB ChB 1989 Glas.

D'AMBROGIO, Victor Joseph 226 Wakefield Road, Halifax HX3 8TP — MB ChB 1994 Dundee.

D'AMBRUMENIL, Peter Lance Buckfurlong Farm, Catcott, Bridgwater TA7 9HT Tel: 01278 722761 Fax: 01278 723188 Email: airdoc@aeromedical.co.uk — MB BS 1975 Lond.; MRCS Eng. LRCP Lond. 1975. (St. Bart.) JP. Socs: Centre Med. Off. Brit. Red Cross Soc. Prev: SHO (O & G) Heatherwood Hosp. Ascot; SHO (Orthop. & Gen. Med.) Epsom Dist. Hosp.

D'AMORE, Angela 6 South Green Road, Cambridge CB3 9JP — MB ChB 1987 Ed.; MRCP (UK) 1995. Regist. (Paediat.) Addenbrooke's Hosp. Camb.

D'ANDRIA, Vivienne (retired) 122 Acomb Road, York YO24 4EY Tel: 01904 798790 — MB ChB 1950 Leeds; BA Open 1995; MRCS Eng. LRCP Lond. 1950.

D'ARCY, Anthony Hugh Edward Eastleigh Health Centre, Newtown Road, Eastleigh SO50 9AG Tel: 023 8061 2197 Fax: 023 8065 0786; Silver Birches, Green Lane, Chilworth, Southampton SO16 7JW Tel: 01703 766522 — MB BS 1974 Lond.; MRCS Eng. LRCP Lond. 1974; DObst RCOG 1976. (St. Mary's Lond.) Prev: SHO Soton. Gen. Hosp.; Ho. Surg. Battle Hosp. Reading; Ho. Phys. P'boro. Dist. Hosp.

D'ARCY, Brenda Lily The Malt House, Eddecross St., Ross-on-Wye HR9 7BZ — MRCS Eng. LRCP Lond. 1949.

D'ARCY, Catherine Ann 20 Manor Gardens, Larkhall Rise, Clapham, London SW4 6JZ — MB BS 1990 Lond.; BSc Lond. 1987; MRCGP 1994; T(GP) 1994. Prev: Trainee GP Lond.; Trainee GP Salisbury VTS.

D'ARCY, Catriona Mary Ross Merstow Green Medical Practice, Merstow Green, Evesham WR11 4BS Tel: 01386 765600 Fax: 01386 446807 — MB BCh BAO 1984 Belf.

D'ARCY, Mr Francis Gerard ENT Department, Royal Victoria Hospital, Belfast BT12 6BA Tel: 01232 240503 — MB BCh BAO 1965 NUI; MSc Manch. 1981; FRCS Ed. (Orl.) 1977; FRCSI 1970; FRCS Ed. (Gen. Surg.) 1969; DLO Eng. 1977. (Univ. Coll. Galway, Irel.) Cons. ENT Surg. E. Health & Social Servs. Bd. Socs: Brit. Assn. Otol.; Irish Otolaryngol. Soc.; BMA.

D'ARCY, Mr John Colman 5 Arlington Road, Eastbourne BN21 1DJ Tel: 01323 723857 — MB BCh BAO 1964 NUI; FRCS Eng. 1969. Cons. Orthop. Surg. E.bourne Dist. Hosp. Socs: Fell. BOA; BMA; Brit. Assn. Knee Surg. Prev: Sen. Regist. (Orthop.) Guy's Hosp. Lond.; Regist. (Surg.) Worthing, S.lands & Dist. Gp. Hosps.; SHO Roy. Nat. Orthop. Hosp. Lond.

D'ARCY, Jonathan Robert Ferguson Family Medical Practice, Berrymead Medical Centre, 140 Berrys Lane, Parr, St Helens WA9 3RP Tel: 01744 25533 Fax: 01744 734752; 92 Castle Green, Westbrook, Warrington WA5 7XA Tel: 01925 710153 — MB BS 1982 Newc. GP Merseyside. Socs: Pres. St. Helens Med. Soc. Prev: SHO (Geriat. Med.) Arrowe Pk. Hosp.; SHO (Psychiat.) Winwick Hosp.; Trainee GP Failsworth Gtr. Manch.

D'ARCY, Nicholas John School Road Health Centre, School Road, Kingskerwell, Newton Abbot TQ12 3HN Tel: 01803 873551 Fax: 01803 875774; St Andrews Medical Centre, Silver St, Ipplepen, Newton Abbot TQ12 5QA Tel: 01803 812621 Fax: 01803 813180 — MB; ChB; DRCOG; MRCGP. (Leeds Univ. Med. Sch.)

D'ARCY, Stuart Martin The Foxes, Highlands Close, High Salvington, Worthing BN13 3AH — MB BS 1992 Lond.; BSc Lond. 1992. (Char. Cross & Westm.) Med. Doctor for Brit. Antartic Survey Rothera Base Antarctica.

D'ARDENNE, Alison Jane 36 Sauncey Avenue, Harpenden AL5 4QJ — BM BCh 1974 Oxf.; DM Oxf. 1987, BM BCh 1974; MRCPath 1981.

D'ARIFAT, Philippe Francois Dominique Newtown Medical Centre, 205/207 Ormskirk Road, Newtown, Wigan WN5 9DP Tel: 01942 494711 Fax: 01942 826240 — MB BCh BAO 1983 NUI; LRCPI & LM, LRCSI & LM 1983; MRCGP 1988; DRCOG 1987.

D'ARRIGO, Corrado 8 Melville Terrace, Dundee DD2 1NT Tel: 01382 69033 — State DMS 1983 Catania; PHD St And. 1990.

D'ARRIGO, Wendy Louise Dept of Child Health, Hornsey Rise Health Centre, Hornsey Rise, London N19 3YU Tel: 020 7530 2480; 4 The Close, Southgate, London N19 3YU Tel: 020 8886 7586 — MB ChB 1987 Dundee; BSc St. And. 1984; MRCP (UK) 1991. Sen. Regist. Community Paediat., Camden and Islington Community Trust. Prev: Sen. Regist. (Neurol.) Neurodevelop.Gt. Ormond St Hosp.Lond; Clin. Research Fell. (Child Health) & Regist. (Paediat.) Ninewells Hosp. Med. Sch. Dundee.

D'ART, Yvonne Marie 59 Scholars Road, London SW12 0PF — MB BCh BAO 1989 Dub.; MRCGP 1994; DObst 1993; DCH Dub. 1991. Prev: Trainee GP Pewsey.

D'AURIA, Denis Andrew Primo Legge-Hunter Centre, Occupational Health Services, St Bartholomew's Hospital, West Smithfield, London EC1A 7BE Tel: 020 7601 8070 Fax: 020 7601 7017 Email: denis.dauria@excite.co.uk — MB BCh BAO 1970 Dub.; MA Dub. 1971, MD 1975; LLM Cardiff 1992; FFOM RCP Lond. 1991, M 1981, A 1979; Dip. Med. Educat. Dund 1989; DRCPath (Toxicol.) 1983; DIH Lond. 1981; CBiol. 1983; MIBiol. 1976. Cons. Occupat.al Phys. & Director, Occupat.al Health Serv.s Barts. and The Lond. NHS Trust; Hon. Sen. Lect. St. Geo. Hosp. Med. Sch. Lond.; Med. Dir. O'Heal Ltd.; Area Surg. St. John Ambul. Brig; Mem. Edit. Panel Occupat. Health Rev.; Chairm., Partner' Occupat.al Med. Gp.; Hon. Sen. Lect. St Bart. and The Roy. Lond. Sch. of Med. Socs: Brit. Occupat. Hyg. Soc. & Soc. Occupat. Med.; Brit. Acad. Forens. Sci.; Medico-Legal Soc. Prev: Chief Med. Adviser Midl. Bank plc; Cons. Occupat. Phys. SW Thames RHA; Cons. Phys. Lond. Ambul. Serv.

D'COSTA, Mr Andre Agnello 8 Luscome Close, Woodlands, Ivybridge PL21 9TT — MB ChB 1988 Glas.; FRCS Ed. 1994.

D'COSTA, Domnik Felix Royal Wolverhampton NHS Trust, Wolverhampton WV10 0QP Tel: 01902 643084 Fax: 01902 643084; 120 Wrottesley Road W., Tettenhall, Wolverhampton WV6 8UR — MB BS 1982 Bombay; MRCP (UK) 1987. Cons. Phys. (Care for the Elderly) Wolverhampton. Socs: BMA; BGS. Prev: Sen. Regist. (Gen. & Geriat. Med.) Addenbrooke's Hosp. Camb &

Hinchingbrooke Hosp. Huntingdon; Regist. (Med.) Leicester Gen. Hosps.; Regist. (Neurol.) Leicester Roy. Infirm.

D'COSTA, Mr Elias Francis 14 Spiers Way, Horley RH6 7NY Tel: 01293 822034 Fax: 01293 822034 Email: user337619@aol.com — Laurea Med. Chir. Padua 1965; FRCS Ed. 1975; FRCS Eng. 1975. (Padua) Socs: BMA.

D'COSTA, Horace Francis 8 Luscombe Close, Ivybridge PL21 9TT — MB ChB 1986 Dundee; BSc (Hons.) Lond. 1981; FRCPS Glas. 1991.

D'COSTA, Roque Anthony Francis John 57 Constable Gardens, Edgware HA8 5RX — MB BCh BAO 1982 NUI; LRCPI & LM, LRCSI & LM 1982.

D'CRUZ, David Pascal Lupus Unit, St Thomas' Hospital, Lambert Place Road, London SE1 7EH Tel: 0207 928 9292 Ext: 1512, 0207 928 9292 Ext: 2710 Fax: 0207 960 8698; 31 Mowbray Road, Edgware HA8 8JG — MB BS 1983 Lond.; MRCP (UK) 1986; MD Lond. 1998; FRCP 1999. (St. Mary's Hosp., Univ. Lond.) Sen. Lect. & Cons. Rheum. Roy. Hosps. NHS Trust & Qu. mary & W.field Coll. Prev: Sen. Regist. (Rheum. & Gen. Med.) St. Bart. Hosp. Lond.; Regist. (Rheum.) St. Thos. Hosp. Lond.; Regist. Rotat. (Gen. Med.) Newham Gen. Hosp. & The Lond. Hosp. Lond.

D'CRUZ, Gerard Lionel Alexandra Road Surgery, 31 Alexandra Road, Reading RG1 5PG Tel: 0118 935 2121 Fax: 0118 926 1562; 31 Alexandra Road, Reading RG1 5PG Tel: 01734 352121 — MB BS 1981 Lond.

D'CRUZ, Jude Egbert Maurice Alexandra Road Surgery, 31 Alexandra Road, Reading RG1 5PG Tel: 0118 935 2121 Fax: 0118 926 1562 — MB BS 1983 Lond. Clin. Asst. (Endoscopy) Battle Hosp. Reading.

D'CRUZ, Peter Agnelo 2 Greenroyd Croft, Birkby Hall Road, Birkby, Huddersfield HD2 2DQ Tel: 01484 516356 — MB BS 1973 Bombay.

D'MELLO, Benedict Joseph 3 Portland Gardens, Hucknall, Nottingham NG15 6RY — MB BS 1950 Bombay.

D'MELLO, Bernadette Marie Therese University Health Service, 2 Claremont Place, Sheffield S10 2TB Tel: 0114 222 2100 Fax: 0114 222 2123 — MB ChB 1982 Sheff. (Sheff.) GP Univ. Health Serv., Sheff.; Clin. Asst. (Dermat.) Roy. Hallamsh. Hosp. Sheff.

D'MELLO, Jeanne Marie Therese The Surgery, 63 Rowley Road, Orsett, Grays RM16 3ET Tel: 01375 892082 Fax: 01375 892487; The Thatched Cottage, High Road, North Stifford, Grays RM16 5UE — MB ChB 1980 Sheff.; MRCGP 1989; DRCOG 1983. Socs: BMA.

D'MELLO, Kevin Anthony D'Mello and Partners, The Health Centre, Curtis Street, Hucknall, Nottingham NG15 7JE Tel: 0115 963 2535 Fax: 0115 963 2885; 19 Villa Road, Nottingham NG3 4GG — MB ChB 1979 Sheff. GP.

D'MELLO, Martha Sebastian Albert Street Surgery, 63 Albert Street, Rugby CV21 2SN Tel: 01788 573366 Fax: 01788 573473; (Surgery), 63 Albert St, Rugby CV21 2SN Tel: 01788 573366 Fax: 01788 573473 — MB BS 1971 Poona.

D'MELLO, Myra Teresa D'Mello and Partners, The Health Centre, Curtis Street, Hucknall, Nottingham NG15 7JE Fax: 0115 963 2885; The Retreat, Linby Lane, Linby, Nottingham NG15 8AF Tel: 0115 963 0990 — MB BS 1976 Newc.

D'MELLO, Theresa Anna Maria 47 Longhill Rise, Hucknall, Nottingham NG15 6GL Tel: 0115 92373 — MB BS 1950 Bombay.

D'NETTO, Mr Douglas Cecil (retired) Ashtrees, 9 Dacre St., Morpeth NE61 1HW Tel: 01670 512319 — MB 1947 Calcutta; FRCS Ed. 1953; FRCS Eng. 1955. Hon. Cons. Orthop. Surg. N.ld. & N. Tyneside DHAs; Self-employed Cons. Orthopaedic Surg. undertaking medico-legal work. Prev: Cons Orthopaedic Surg to Wansbeck & N Tyneside Gp.s of Hosp.s N.umbria health care Trust).

D'NETTO, Marita Flat B McDougal House, Bellshill Maternity Hospital, Bellshill ML4 3JN Tel: 01698 747292 — MB BS 1983 Madras; DCH RCPS Glas. 1989.

D'NETTO, Phyllis Eleanor Beechwood Avenue, Kew Gardens, Richmond TW9 3DE — LRCP LRCS 1958 Ed.; FRCP Ed. 1989, M 1965; FRCP Glas. 1985, M 1964. Prev: Cons. Geriatr. Kingston & Esher HA.

D'OYLEY, Debbie Aretha 27 Colworth Road, London E11 1JA Tel: 020 8556 5709 — MB BS 1992 Lond. (St. Bartholomew's Hospital) SHO (Anaesth.) St. Thomas' Hosp. Socs: Train. Mem. Assn. AnE.h.; BMA. Prev: SHO (Anaesth.) Norf. & Norwich Hosp. Norwich, Lewisham Hosp. Lond. & Guy's Hosp. Lond.

D'SA, Shirley Patricia 47 Buckingham Gardens, Edgware HA8 6NB Tel: 020 8952 7883 Fax: 020 8952 7883 Email: shirley.dsa@talk21.com — MB BS 1990 Lond.; MRCP (UK) 1994; DRC Path 1997. (St. George's Hospital Medical School) Regist. (Haemat.) Mt. Vernon + Watford NHS trust. Socs: Brit. Soc. Haematol.; (Sec.) Jun. Haematol. Club. Prev: Regist. (Haemat.) Whittington Hosp. Lond.; Regist. (Haemat.) Univ. Coll. Hosp. Lond.; Regist. (Haemat.) Chase Farm Hosp. Enfield.

D'SILVA, Gustav Colin Joseph Wideopen Medical Centre, Great North Road, Newcastle upon Tyne NE13 6LN Tel: 0191 236 2115; 30 Greystoke Park, Gosforth, Newcastle upon Tyne NE3 2DZ Email: gustaved'silva@guss0.demon.co.uk — MB BS 1973 Newc. (Newcastle) City Police Surg. Newc. u. Tyne. Socs: Brit. Assn. Police Surg.; BMA.

D'SILVA, Karen 37 Higham Lane, Hyde SK14 5LX Tel: 0161 351 1377 — MB ChB 1994 Leeds. SHO (Psychiat.) St. Jas. Univ. Hosp. Leeds. Socs: BMA. Prev: Ho. Off. St. Jas. Univ. Hosp. & Huddersfield Roy. Infirm.

D'SILVA, Margaret Cynthia Bothwell Medical Centre, 3 Uddingston Road, Bothwell, Glasgow G71 8ET Tel: 01698 852299; Sweethope House, 6 Sweetfhope Gardens, Green St., Bothwell, Glasgow G71 8AB Tel: 01698 852860 — MB ChB 1976 Glas.; MRCGP 1980. (Glas.) Prev: Clin. Asst. (Dermat.) Lanarksh. Health Bd.; SHO (Gen. Med.) Stobhill Hosp. Glas. Sen. Med. Off. Minbank Clinic; Lusaka Zambia.

D'SILVA, Milbhor Roque 31 Tennal Road, Harborne, Birmingham B32 2JD — MB BS 1984 Bombay.

D'SILVA, Ronald Patrick 130 Harley Street, London W1G 7JU Tel: 020 7580 1336 Fax: 020 7730 0780 Email: rpds1@hotmail.com — MB BS Sind 1961; DTM & H Lond 1962. (Liaquat Med. Coll.)

D'SILVA, Roy Bothwell Medical Centre, 3 Uddingston Road, Bothwell, Glasgow G71 8ET Tel: 01698 852299; Sweethope House, 6 Sweethope Gardens, Green St. Bothwell, Glasgow G71 8BT Tel: 01698 852860 — MB ChB 1974 Glas.; MRCP (UK) 1977; MRCGP 1978. (Glas.) Prev: SHO (Med.) Stobhill Gen. Hosp. Glas.; SHO (O & G) Vale of Leven Hosp. Alexandria; Sen. Med. Off. Minibank Clinic, Lusaka.

D'SOUZA, Albert Socrates 35 Queens Anne's Grove, Bush Hill Park, Enfield Tel: 020 8360 5749 — MB BS 1949 Bombay. (G.S. Med. Coll.)

D'SOUZA, Atilla Carmen 188 Lower Addiscombe Road, Croydon CR0 5AH Tel: 020 8654 1427; The Old Manse, Lunghurst Road, Woldingham, Caterham SW16 4LW Tel: 01883 650143 — MB BS 1977 Bombay; MRCS Eng. LRCP Lond. 1980; DA (UK) 1982. GP Asst. Lond. Prev: GP Lond.; GP Retainer Scheme.

D'SOUZA, Benjamin Collier Row Lane Surgery, 250 Collier Row Lane, Romford RM5 3NJ Tel: 01708 764991 Fax: 01708 722377 — MB BS 1965 Karnatak.

D'SOUZA, Blanche (retired) 1 Raleigh Road, Southall UB2 5TP Tel: 0208 574 6416 — MB BS 1943 Bombay.

D'SOUZA, Brian Peter 10 Ayrefield Grove, Shevington, Wigan WN6 8DZ — MB ChB 1988 Manch. (Manch.)

D'SOUZA, David John 3 Northwick Terrace, London NW8 8JJ Tel: 0121 459 6742 Email: arthur@alvarez3.demon.co.uk, d.j.dsouza@amserve.net — MB ChB 1993 Birm.; MRCOG 2000; DFFP 1997. (Birmingham) Sen. Regist. (Obst. & Gyn.), Heartlands Hosp., Birm. Socs: MRCOG. Prev: SpR Birm. Wom.s 2000-01; Spr Heartlands, Birm. 1999-2000; Specialist Regist. (Obst & Gyn.) Walsgrave Hosp. 1998-99.

D'SOUZA, Eva Corporate Health Ltd, 30 Bradford Road, Slough SL1 4PG Tel: 01753 781618 — MB BS 1992 Lond.; Adv. Dip. Occupat Med. Manch. Univ. 1999. (Lond. Hosp. Med. Coll.) Specialist Regist., Occupat. Med. Corporate Health Ltd. Socs: Soc. Occupat. Med. Prev: SHO (Gen. Med.) Selly Oak Hosp.; SHO (Neurol.) MCNN; SHO (Gen. Med. & Diabetes) Sandwell Dist. Gen. Hosp.

D'SOUZA, Evelyn Rosalind 62 Curzon Avenue, Stanmore HA7 2AN — MB ChB 1988 Birm.; ChB Birm. 1988.

D'SOUZA, Gavin Richard Anthony 2 Spinney Close, Worcester Park KT4 7BS — BM 1983 Soton.; DRCOG 1988; Cert. Family Plann. JCC 1987. Police Surg. Gp. 22 Wimbledon, Wandsworth, Tooting & Sutton; Med. Adviser DSS; Local Med. Off. Civil Serv.; Mem. Young Forens. Med. Pract. Gp. Socs: BMA; Assn. Police Surg. Prev: Community Med. Off. (Child Developm.) Merton & Sutton HA;

Med. Off. St. Raphaels Hospice N. Cheam; Clin. Asst. (Cardiol.) Mayday Hosp. Croydon.

D'SOUZA, Jane Celia Hopton Berrylands Surgery, Howard Road, Surbiton KT5 8SA Tel: 020 8399 6362 Fax: 020 8339 5700; 28 Albany Park Road, Kingston upon Thames KT2 5SW Tel: 020 8546 7681 — MB BS 1968 Lond.; DA Eng. 1971. (Lond. Hosp.)

D'SOUZA, John Austin Gregory St Margaret's Hospital, Breast Screening Unit, The Plain, Epping CM2 8QQ Tel: 01253 781126, 01279 827046 — MB BS 1972 Bombay; DPM Eng. 1978; FRCPsych 1997. (G.S. Med. Coll.) Cons. Psychiat. Vict. Hosp. Blackpool. Prev: Sen. Regist. Clatterbridge Hosp. S. Wirral.

D'SOUZA, Jonathan Bernard 52 Parkway, Gidea Park, Romford RM2 5PA — MB ChB 1998 Ed.; MB ChB Ed 1998.

D'SOUZA, Judith Gerardine 159 Ambrose Rise, Dedridge, Livingston EH54 6JX — MB ChB 1986 Aberd.

D'SOUZA, Lynn Rebecca Oakwood Medical Centre, Malcolms Way, Reservoir Road, Southgate, London N14 4AQ Tel: 0208 886 1115 Fax: 0208 886 6166; 90 Whitehouse Way, Southgate, London N14 7LU Tel: 020 8368 2643 Email: lynnds@hotmail.com — MB BS 1987 Lond.; BA Oxf. 1984. Clin. Asst. (Diabetes) Chase Farm Hosp. Lond. Prev: Trainee GP Edmonton; SHO (Paediat., Obst & Gyn. & Psychiat.) N. Middlx. Hosp. Lond.; SHO (Med.) Chase Farm Hosp. Enfield.

***D'SOUZA, Melanie Jane** Tankerville, Kingston Hill, Kingston upon Thames KT2 7JH — MB BS 1994 Lond.; BSc (Hons.) Lond. 1991.

D'SOUZA, Michael Anthony James Vicarage Field Surgery, Vicarage Field, Hailsham BN27 1BE; 5 Vicarage Drive, Eastbourne BN20 8AR Email: mikedsouza@macace.net — MB BS 1989 Lond.; MRCGP 1994; DCH RCP Lond. 1993. (Char. Cross & Westm.)

D'SOUZA, Michael Francis Canbury Medical Centre, 1 Elm Road, Kingston upon Thames KT2 6HR Tel: 020 8549 8818 Fax: 020 8547 0058; 28 Albany Park Road, Kingston upon Thames KT2 5SW Tel: 020 8546 7681 — MB BS 1966 Lond.; MD Lond. 1979; MRCS Eng. LRCP Lond. 1966; FRCGP 1989, M 1977; FFPHM RCP (UK) 1989, M 1980. (Guy's) Hon. Sen. Lect. & Head Gen. Pract. Univ. Dept. Thoracic Med. Nat. Heart & Lung Inst Lond. of Imperial Coll. Lond. Univ.; Dist. Tutor (Gen. Pract.) Kingston; Course Trainer Kingston VTS. Socs: (Chairm.) Assn. Indep. Multifunds; Roy. Soc. Med.; Brit. Soc. Allergy & Clin. Immunol. Prev: Hon. Sen. Research Fell. (Community Med.) St. Thos. Hosp. Lond.; Hon. Clin. Research Fell. Kingston GP Research Gp. St. Geo. Hosp. Lond.; Mem. Kingston & Esher HA.

D'SOUZA, Rachel Elisabeth Margaret Pyke Centre, 73 Charlotte St., London W1T 4PL Tel: 020 7436 8391; 31 Umfreville Road, Haringey, London N4 1RY — MB BS 1991 Lond.; BSc 1988; MRCOG 1997. (UCMSM) Specialist Regist. (O & G) NE Thames.

D'SOUZA, Richard Joseph 188 Pennsylvania Road, Exeter EX4 6DZ — MB BS 1985 Lond.; MD Lond. 1995; MRCP (UK) 1988. (St. Geo. Hosp. Med. Sch.) Cons. Phys.

D'SOUZA, Rosemarie Celine Martha Radiology Department, Wansbeck General Hospital, Woodhorn Lane, Ashington NE63 9JJ Tel: 01670 521212; 6 Sycamore Close, Jesmond, Newcastle upon Tyne NE2 2TG — MB BCh 1984 Wales; BSc (Hons.) Wales 1981; MRCP (UK) 1988; FRCR 1992. Cons. Radiol. Wansbeck Gen. Hosp. N.d.

D'SOUZA, Shirley Anne 62 Curzon Avenue, Stanmore HA7 2AN — MB ChB 1990 Leeds.

D'SOUZA, Stephen Peter 4 Pendle Close, Saughall Massie Lane, Upton, Wirral CH49 6QN — MB ChB 1987 Liverp.; MRCP (UK) 1990. Regist. Rotat. (Radiol.) Mersey.

D'SOUZA, Stephen Walter Central Manchester and Childrens University Hospitals NHS Trust, University of Manchester, Academic Unit of Child Health, St.Marys Hospital, Hathersage Road, Manchester M13 0JH Tel: 0161 276 6600 Fax: 0161 224 1013 Email: sdesouza@man.ac.uk; 22 Moss Lane, Bramhall, Stockport SK7 1EH Tel: 0161 439 4164 — MB ChB E. Afr. 1964; PhD Manch. 1973; FRCP Lond. 1983; MRCP Lond. 1968; FRCPCH Lond. 1997. (University of East Africa: Makerere College Med. School & Univ. Manchester) Reader in Child Health, Acad. Unit of Child Health, Univ Manch.; Cons. Peadiatrician, St marys hosp, Manc. Socs: Eur. Soc. Paediat. Research; Brit. Paediat. Assn. & Brit. Paediat. Neurol. Assn.; Roy. Coll. of Paediat. and Child Health. Prev: Sen. Lect. (Child Health) Univ. Manch.; SHO (Paediat.) Hammersmith Hosp. Lond.; Regist. (Neurol.) Nat. Hosp. for Nerv. Dis.s, Lond.

D'SOUZA, Yvonne Bertram 3/158 Wigan Lane, Wigan WN1 2LA — MB BS 1989 Bombay.

D'URSO, Paul Joseph Lee Bank Group Practice, Colston Health Centre, 10 Bath Row, Lee Bank, Birmingham B15 1LZ Tel: 0121 622 4846 Fax: 0121 622 7105 — MB ChB 1989 Birm.; MRCGP 1994; T(GP) 1994; DCH RCP Lond. 1993; DRCOG 1991. Hon. Clin. Lect. (Gen. Pract.) Univ. Birm. Prev: Trainee GP S. Birm. VTS.

D'VAZ, George Anthony Wesley House, 10 Castlemere St., Rochdale OL11 3SW Tel: 01706 359137 — LM 1961 Dub.; LAH Dub. 1960. Prev: Med. Supt. St. Joseph's Hosp. Adazi, E. Nigeria.

DA COSTA, Aires Anthony 7 Beech Grove, Harrogate HG2 0EW Tel: 0113 206 5513 — MB BS Nagpur 1966; MD Nagpur 1968; FRCP Lond. 1993; FRCP Canada 1973. (Nagpur) Cons. Clin. Neurophysiol. St. Jas. Hosp. Leeds, Leeds Gen. Infirm., York Dist. Hosp. & Bootham Pk. Hosp. York; Sen. Lect. Univ. Leeds. Socs: Brit. Soc. & Assn. Clin. Neurophysiol. Prev: Sen. Regist. (Neurophysiol.) Hosp. Sick Childr. Gt. Ormond St. Lond.; SHO Leeds Gen. Infirm.; Resid. N.W.. Univ. Med. Sch. Chicago, USA.

DA COSTA, David Francis Northern General Hospital, Sheffield S5 7AU Tel: 0114 243 4343 Fax: 0114 256 0472 — MB BS 1979 Lond.; FRCP Lond. 1996; MRCP (UK) 1982. (St. Mary's) Cons. Phys. (Acute & Elderly Med.) N. Gen. Hosp. Sheff. Socs: BMA; Brit. Geriat. Soc.; Dep. Regional Adviser, Roy. Coll. Phys. Prev: Sen. Regist. (Geriat.) Durh. & Newc. Hosps.; Regist. (Med.) Portsmouth Hosps.; Research Regist. St. Mary's Hosp. Lond.

DA COSTA, Mr Gleado Ian Brougham (retired) 168 The Vale, London NW11 8SN Tel: 020 8209 0773 Fax: 020 8209 0773 — MB BS Madras 1946; FRCS Ed. 1956. Private medico-legal work for various solicitors (trauma and Orthop.) in Lond. Prev: Cons. Orthop. Surg. NW Durh. Health Dist.

DA COSTA, Indra Maria Victoria Nor 31 Moorcombe Drive, Preston, Weymouth DT3 6NP — MB ChB 1995 Glas.

DA COSTA, John Alric Graham c/o Reid, 16 Learmonth Terrace, Edinburgh EH4 1PG — MB ChB 1967 Ed.; MRCP (UK) 1971. Socs: Roy. Coll. Phys. & Surgs. Edin. Prev: Lect. (Therap.) Roy. Infirm. Edin.; Sen. Regist. Scott. Nat. Blood Transfus. Centre Roy. Infirm. Edin.

DA COSTA, Lourenco Jose Rosario The Vineyard Surgery, 35 The Vineyard, Richmond TW10 6PP Tel: 020 8948 0404 Fax: 020 8332 7598; 27 Hardwicke Road, Ham, Richmond TW10 7UB — MB BS 1981 Bombay; MRCS Eng. LRCP Lond. 1991; T(GP) 1994; DLO RCS Eng. 1984.

DA COSTA, Nancy Philomena 77 Greencourt Road, Petts Wood, Orpington BR5 1QN Tel: 01689 820501 — MB BS 1972 Mysore. (Govt. Med. Coll.) Clin. Med. Off. (Community Child Health) Oxleas NHS Trust Bexley. Socs: BMA. Prev: SHO (Surg.) Antonio Vincente DaCosta Memor. Clinic Goa, India; Ho. Off. (Geriat.) Oldham & Dist. Gen. Hosp.; Clin. Asst. (Gen. Med.) Joyce Green Hosp. Dartford.

DA COSTA, Mr Olaf (retired) Moorlands, 28 Whitehill Road, Kidderminster DY11 6JJ Tel: 01562 67541 — MB BS 1962 Bombay; FRCS Ed. 1967. Prev: Cons. Orthop. Surg. Kidderminster Health Dist.

DA COSTA, Philip Ernest Airedale General Hospital, Skipton Road, Steeton, Keighley BD20 6TD Tel: 01535 652511 — MB BS 1980 Lond.; MRCS Eng. LRCP Lond. 1980; FRCPath 1996, M 1986. Cons. Histopath. Airedale Gen. Hosp.

DA CRUZ, Mr Dilip Joseph Zeferino Accident Department, Torbay Hospital, Torquay TQ2 7AA Tel: 01803 654515 Fax: 01803 616331 Email: cruz.missile@virgin.net; 24 Parkhurst Road, Torquay TQ1 4EP Tel: 01803 328971 — MRCS Eng. LRCP Lond. 1978; FRCS Eng. 1983; FRCS Ed. 1983; FFAEM. Cons. Surg. in A & E Specialising in Soft Tissue & Hand Injury Torbay Hosp.; Examr. FRCS (A & E). Prev: Sen. Regist. (A & E) Leicester Roy. Infirm.

DA CUNHA, Francis Anthony Leopold (retired) The Coach House, Hill Carr Mews, St Margaret's Road, Bowdon, Altrincham WA14 2BE — MRCS Eng. LRCP Lond. 1943; MA Camb. 1945, MB BChir 1943; FRCOG 1962, M 1949. Cons. O & G Oldham Hosp. Gp. Prev: Surg. Lt. RNVR.

DA CUNHA, Janet (retired) Sycamore House, Front St., Churchill, Winscombe BS25 5NG — MB ChB 1950 Manch.

DA FONSECA, Jorge Manuel Gusmao 7A Crystal Palace Park Road, Sydenham, London SE26 6EG Email:

jorge@fonsdude.demon.co.uk — MB ChB 1991 Cape Town; FRCA 1997; DA (UK) 1995. Specialist Regist. King's Coll. Hosp. Lond. Socs: World Federat. Soc. Anaesth. (WFSA).

DA GAMA-ROSE, Bianca Maria 47 Cotebrook Drive, Chester CH2 1RB — MB ChB 1994 Liverp.; FRCS Pt 1 Dub 1996. SHO, Plastic Surg., St James Hosp. Leeds.

DA GRACA MENINO GLORIA, Maria Luisa Gastroenterology Unit, Guy's Tower 18th Floor, Guy's Hospital, London SE1 9RT — Lic Med Lisbon 1989.

DA'OOD, Mohanned Salih c/o Anaesthetic Secretary, The Maidstone Hospital, Hermitage Lane, Maidstone ME16 9NN — MB ChB 1972 Baghdad; DA Eng. 1982.

DA ROCHA-AFODU, Oladele 12 Washford Lane, Redditch B98 0HY — MB ChB 1958 Glas.; MSc Oxf. 1983; Dip. Bact. Lond 1964. Socs: Fell. W. Afr. Coll. Phys.; Fell. Nigerian Med. Counc. (Path.). Prev: Assoc. Lect. (Microbiol.) Univ. Lagos; Mem. Governing Counc. Univ. Ibadan, Nigeria; Chief Cons. Path. Federal MoH, Nigeria.

DA ROZA DAVIS, Jane Maree Fair Mile Hospital, Reading Road, Cholsey, Wallingford OX10 9HH Tel: 01491 651281 — MB BS 1984 Lond.; BSc Lond. 1979; MRCPsych 1988. (St. Geo.) Cons. Psychiat. Adult Gen. Psychiat. W. Berks. Prev: Sen. Regist. Oxf. Region; Clin. Asst. (Adult Psychiat.) Eldon Day Hosp. Reading & Wokingham Ment. Health Unit.; Research Asst. & Hon. Clin. Asst. (Psychiat.) MRC Clin. Pharmacol. Unit Littlemore Hosp. Oxf.

DA SILVA, Mr Antonio Eduardo Cortesao Figueira Wrexham Maelor Hospital, Croesnewydd Road, Wrexham LL13 7TD Tel: 01978 291100; 15 Jeffreys Road, Wrexham LL12 7PB — Lic Med 1979 Coimbra; FRCS Ed. 1987. Cons. Gen. & Vasc. Surg. Wrexham Maelor Hosp. Socs: Full Mem. Europ. Soc. Vasc. Surg.; Vasc. Surg. Soc. GB & Irel. Prev: Sen. Regist. (Surg.) Mersey RHA; Regist. Rotat. (Surg.) Liverp. HA; Research Fell. Vasc. Surgic. Soc.

DA SILVA, C K Hackenthorpe Medical Centre, Main Street, Hackenthorpe, Sheffield S12 4LA Fax: 0114 251 0539.

DABAS, Rajive 166 Carlton Avenue W., Wembley HA0 3QX; 32 Michael Drive, Edgbaston, Birmingham B15 2EL Email: radjabas1@hotmail.com — MB BS 1994 Lond. Specialist Regist. Anaesth. Q. E. Hosp. Birm.

DABAS, Vinod Kumar 25 Knowsley Avenue, Southall UB1 3AX — MB BS 1996 Lond.

DABB, Rosina Gwen, MBE (retired) 14/44 Ethel Terrace, Edinburgh EH10 5NA Tel: 0131 447 4692 — MB ChB Ed. 1941. Prev: Med. Off. i/c Miss. Hosp. Mulanje, Malawi.

DABBOUS, Mr Fadi Mohamad 5 Matthews Road, Taunton TA1 4NH — MB ChB 1978 Alexandria; FRCS Ed. 1991.

DABBS, Mr Timothy Reginald 8 Limetree Gardens, Boston Spa, Wetherby LS23 6DY — MB BS 1980 Newc.; FRCS Ed. 1985; FCOphth 1989. Cons. Ophth. St. Jas. Univ. Hosp. Leeds. Prev: Sen. Regist. (Ophth.) Birm. & Midl. Eye Hosp.

DABESTANI, Ebrahim Anchor Practice, Glascote Health Centre, Caledonia, Tamworth B77 2ED Tel: 01827 251251 Fax: 01827 261164 — MB BS 1972 Bombay; DTM & H Liverp. 1985. Police Surg. Tamworth Police. Prev: SHO (Dermat.) Hull Roy. Infirm.; SHO (Paediat.) W. Wales Hosp. Carmarthen; Clin. Med. Off. Gwent HA.

DABESTANI, Mehdi Walderslade Medical Centre, Princes Avenue, Chatham ME5 7PQ Tel: 01634 682611 — MB BS 1974 Bombay. (Grant)

DABIR, Zahid Mahmood Chapel Lodge, Hall St., Worsthorne, Burnley BB10 3NR — MB BS 1974 Punjab.

DABNER, Stuart 32 Audley Road, Newcastle upon Tyne NE3 1QX — MB BS 1993 Newc.

DABORN, Andrew Kim 11 Horder Road, Fulham, London SW6 5ED Tel: 020 7731 1703 — MB BS 1983 Lond.; FCAnaesth. 1989. Sen. Regist. Rotat. (Anaesth.) Char. Cross & W.m. Hosp. Prev: Research Regist. (Anaesth.) Nat. Heart Hosp. Lond.; Regist. (Anaesth.) St. Thos. Hosp. Lond.; Regist. (Anaesth.) Medway Hosp. Gillingham.

DABORN, Dale Kevin Russell, Squadron Ldr. RAF Med. Br. 7 Rivershill, Watton-at-Stone, Hertford SG14 3SD Tel: 01920 830449 Email: dale.daborn@virgin.net — MB BS 1992 Lond.; BSc (Physiol. & Basic Med. Sci.) Hons. Lond. 1989; MRCGP 1996; Dip. IMC RCS Ed. 1996; DRCOG 1995; DFFP 1998. (Roy. Free Hosp.) Med. Off. RAF Marham; Norf. Ambul. Rescue Serv. Socs: Founder Mem. Fac. Pre-Hosp. Care RCS; Assoc. Mem. RCS; Roy. Coll. Gen. Pract. Prev: Med. Off. RAF Akrotiri; Trainee GP RAF Akrotiri; SHO (Med. & O & G) RAF Wegberg.

DABORN, Louise Gladys Department of Cytology, Royal Surrey County Hospital, Egerton Road, Guildford GU2 7XX Tel: 01483 406613 Ext: 4373 Fax: 01483 453615 — MB ChB 1983 Birm.; FRCPath 1989. Cons. Cytopath. Roy. Surrey Co. Hosp. Guildford. Prev: Cons. CytoHistopath. Dorset Co. Hosp. Dorchester; Sen. Regist. (Histopath.) St. Geo. Hosp. Lond.; Regist. (Histopath.) Roy. Surrey Co. Hosp. Guildford.

DABORN, Paul Gordon Russell 7 Rivershill, Watton-at-Stone, Hertford SG14 3SD — MB BS 1989 Lond.

DABRERA, Marian Guy Anthony Victor Department of Rheumatology, King George's Hospital, Barley Lane, Goodmayes, Ilford IG3 8YB Tel: 020 8970 8188 Fax: 020 8970 8189; 2A Weigall Road, Lee, London SE12 8HE — MB BS 1975 Ceylon; MRCP (UK) 1986; DGM RCP Lond. 1985. Cons. Rheum. & Rehabil. King Geo. Hosp. Goodmayes. Prev: Cons. Rheum. Rotherham Dist. Gen. Hosp.; Sen. Regist. (Rheum. & Rehabil.) Qu. Eliz. II Milit. Hosp. Lond.; Regist. (Rheum. & Rehabil.) King's Coll. Hosp. Lond.

DABROWICKI, Emil 128 Liverpool Road, Newcastle ST5 9EQ Tel: 01782 614996 — MD 1937 Cracow; MB BCh 1933. (Cracow) Socs: BMA. Prev: Res. Surg. Off. Chorley Dist. Hosp.; Res. Med. Off. Birm. Chest Hosp.

DABROWSKA, Jadwiga (retired) Vistula, 3 Willowtree Avenue, Gilesgate Moor, Durham DH1 1EB — MB ChB 1949 Polish Sch. of Med.

DABROWSKA, Maria Wiktoria (retired) 364 Uxbridge Road, London W3 9SL Tel: 020 8992 9537 — MB ChB 1948 Ed.; DObst RCOG 1956. Prev: GP Princip Lond.

DABROWSKI, Maciej Tadeusi 50 Whinney Heys Road, Blackpool FY3 8NP — Lekarz 1983 Gdansk, Poland.

DABYDEEN, Lyvia 13 Parkgrove Terrace, Glasgow G3 7SD — MB ChB 1988 Glas.; MRCP (UK) 1994. Regist. (Paediat.) Newc. Teach. Hosps. Prev: Regist. (Paediat.) Kettering Gen. Hosp.; Trainee GP/SHO P.ss Margt. Hosp. Swindon VTS.; SHO Rotat. (Paediat.) Sheff. Teach. Hosps.

DABYDEEN, Sonya Wen Ying 13 Parkgrove Terrace, Glasgow G3 7SD — MB ChB 1993 Glas.

DACE, Helen Mary The Hungerford Surgery, The Croft, Hungerford RG17 0HY Tel: 01488 682507 Email: helen.dace@gp-k81057.nhs.uk; Firbank House, Post Office Road, Inkpen, Hungerford RG17 9PU Tel: 01488 668713 — MB BS 1987 Lond.; DCH RCP Lond. 1989. (St Bartholomews Hospital, London.) p/t GP Princip. Prev: Retainer Scheme, Lambourn; SHO (O & G) P.ss Margt. Hosp. Swindon; SHO (Psychiat. & Paediat.) Seymour Clinic Swindon.

DACE, Mr James Stephen 3 Sperrin Heights, Portglenone, Ballymena BT44 8BQ — MB BCh BAO 1990 Belf.; MB BCh (Distinc.) BAO Belf. 1990; FRCS Ed. 1994. Demonst. (Anat.) Qu. Univ. Belf.

DACE, Julian Martin Braybrooke Waldron Health Centre, Stanley Street, London SE8 4BG Tel: 020 8692 2314; 147 Jerningham Road, New Cross, London SE14 5NJ — BM BCh 1977 Oxf.; BA (Hons.) Oxf. 1974, MA 1980; MRCS Eng. LRCP Lond. 1977; DRCOG 1980. (Oxford University) Sen. Partner, Drs Dace, Singh, Irvine & Hassan. Prev: SHO (O & G) John Radcliffe Hosp. Oxf.; SHO (Paediat.) Hillingdon Hosp. Uxbridge; SHO (Geriat.) Middlx. Hosp. Lond.

DACIE, Janet Elizabeth 23 Canonbury Place, London N1 2NY Tel: 020 7359 0873 — MB BS 1962 Lond.; FRCP Lond. 1983, M 1966; MRCS Eng. LRCP Lond. 1962; FRCR 1975; FFR 1970; T(R) (CR) 1991; DMRD Eng. 1968; DCH Eng. 1964; DObst RCOG 1965. Hon. Cons. (Diag. Radiol.) St. Bart. Hosp. Lond.

DACIE, Sir John Vivian 10 Alan Road, Wimbledon, London SW19 7PT Tel: 020 8946 6086 — MB BS Lond. 1935; FRCPath 1962; FRCPath. Founder Fell.; FRS; MD Lond. 1952; Hon. MD Aix-Marseille 1977; Hon. MD Uppsala 1961; FRCP Lond. 1956, M 1936; Hon. FRCPS Glas. 1985; Hon. FRCPC 1977; MRCS Eng. LRCP Lond. 1935. (King's Coll. Hosp.) Emerit. Prof. Haemat. Roy. Postgrad. Med. Sch. Lond. Socs: Hon. Mem. Brit. Soc. Haematol.; Hon. Mem. Internat. Soc. Haematol.; Hon. Fell. Roy. Soc. Med. Prev: Ho. Phys., Resid. Path. & Will Edmunds Clin. Research Fell. 1938, King's Coll. Hosp.; Maj. RAMC 1943-46.

DACIE, Julian Melbourne Street Medical Centre, 56 Melbourne Street, Leicester LE2 0AS Tel: 0116 262 2721; 22 Station Road, Birstall, Leicester LE4 3BA — LMSSA 1973 Lond.; MB Camb. 1974, BChir 1973; MRCGP 1981; DCH Eng. 1979.

DACOMBE, Carole Mary St Peter's Hospice, St. Agnes Avenue, Bristol BS4 2DU Tel: 0117 977 4605 Fax: 0117 977 9676; 5 Glentworth Road, Redland, Bristol BS6 7EG Tel: 0117 942 8466 — MB ChB 1976 Bristol; Dip. Palliat. Med. Wales 1995; DCH RCP Lond. 1981; DRCOG 1979. Assoc. Specialist (Palliat. Med.) St. Peter's Hospice Bristol.

DACRE, Professor Jane Elizabeth CHIME, Whittington Hospital, Highgate Hill, London N19 5NF; 52 Cholmeley Crescent, Highgate, London N6 5HA Tel: 020 8341 2134 — MB BS 1980 Lond.; BSc (Hons.) Lond. 1977, MD 1992; MRCP (UK) 1983; FRCP Lond. 1994; FRCP Glas 1999. (Univ. Coll. Hosp.) Sen. Lect (Clin. Skills) & Hon. Cons. (Phys. & Rheum.) Univ. Coll. Lond. Prev: Sen. Regist. (Gen. Med. & Rheum.) St. Bart. Hosp. Lond.

DACRE, John Alfred (retired) 47 Linden Close, Briggswath, Sleights, Whitby YO21 1TA Tel: 01947 810973 — MB ChB Leeds 1959; DObst RCOG 1961.

DADA, David Nicholas 64 Boddens Hill Road, Heaton Mersey, Stockport SK4 2DG — MB ChB 1996 Manch.

DADA, Mahomed Ayob Department of Cellular Science, Room 5501, Level 5, John Radford Hospital, Oxford OX3 9DU — MB ChB 1980 Natal.

DADABHOY, Mohamed Ebrahim Chingford Mount Road Surgery, 107-109 Chingford Mount Road, Chingford, London E4 8LT Tel: 020 8524 1230/8529 8288 Fax: 020 8559 3004 — MB BS 1967 Calcutta; MB BS 1967 Calcutta.

DADABHOY, Shahid Mohamed Chingford Mount Road Surgery, 107-109 Chingford Mount Road, Chingford, London E4 8LT Tel: 020 8524 1230/8529 8288 Fax: 020 8559 3004 — MB ChB 1993 Dundee.

DADARKAR, Pushkar 1 Wilfred Owen Close, Wimbledon, London SW19 8SW — MB BS 1990 Lond.; MRCP (UK) 1993.

DADDOW, Justin Roger 4 Drury Road, Tenterden TN30 6QG Tel: 01580 766016 — BM 1994 Soton. SHO (A & E) Qu. Alexandra Hosp. Portsmouth. Prev: Ho. Off. (Gen. Med. & Cardiol.) St. Mary's Hosp. Portsmouth; Ho. Off. (Elderly Med.) Qu. Alexandra Hosp. Portsmouth; Ho. Off. (Surg.) Weymouth & Dist. Hosp.

DADDY, Suzanne The Shaftesbury Practice, Abbey View Medical Centre, Salisbury Road, Shaftesbury SP7 8DH Tel: 01747 856700 Fax: 01747 856701 — MB BS 1970 Lond.; MRCS Eng. LRCP Lond. 1970; DObst RCOG 1985. (Guy's) Prev: SCMO Wilts. HA; Ho. Phys. Hackney Hosp. Lond.; Ho. Surg. Paddington Green Childr. Hosp. Lond.

DADGE, Nigel Geoffrey Churchward and Partners, Croft Medical Centre, 2 Glen Road, Oadby, Leicester LE2 4PE Tel: 0116 271 2564 Fax: 0116 272 9000; 1-3 London Road, Oadby, Leicester LE2 5 Tel: 712564 — MB ChB 1978 Sheff.; DRCOG 1982.

DADHANIA, Mathurdas Ramji St Georges Road Surgery, 102 St. Georges Road, Coventry CV1 2DL Tel: 024 7655 2531 Fax: 024 7663 4813; 39 Ivybridge Road, Coventry CV3 5PF Tel: 024 76 413318 — MB BS 1976 Saurashtra. (M. P. Shah Jamnagar India)

DADHEECH, Hima Harendranath Limes Medical Centre, Cooksey Road, Small Heath, Birmingham B10 0BS Tel: 0121 772 0067; Mulberry House, 2a Farquhar Road, Edgbaston, Birmingham B15 3RB Tel: 0121 455 0031 — MB BS 1978 Bhopal; LMSSA Lond. 1980. (Birmingham)

DADHEECH, Vinod Kumar Limes Medical Centre, Cooksey Road, Small Heath, Birmingham B10 0BS Tel: 0121 772 0067; Mulberry House, 2A Farquhar Road, Edgbaston, Birmingham B15 3RB — MB BS 1973 Rajasthan; DPM RCPSI 1984. (S.P. Med. Coll. Bikaner) Princip. GP Birm. FPC.

DADIBHAI, Ebrahim Ismail West Park Surgery, 20 West Park Street, Dewsbury WF13 4LA Tel: 01924 461735; 20 West Park Street, Dewsbury WF13 4LA Tel: 01924 461735 — MB ChB 1981 Aberd. Socs: Overseas Doctors Assn.; Med. Insur. Agency Ltd.

DADSWELL, John Victor (retired) Pinewoods, Soke Road, Silchester, Reading RG7 2PD Tel: 0118 970 0479 — MB BS Lond. 1951; FRCPath 1977, M 1965. Prev: Dir. Pub. Health Laborat. Reading.

DADY, Ian Michael 35 Broadhead Road, Turton, Bolton BL7 0BN — MB BS 1987 Lond.

DADZIE, Ophelia Entsir 215 Lordship Lane, London N17 6AA — MB BS 1998 Lond.; MB BS Lond 1998.

DAENGSVANG, Paul Andrew Damian Chaiyavat Tel: 07710 273205 Fax: 0151 498 4261 Email: maria.poly@blueyonder.co.uk; Irelands Farm, Lower Road, Liverpool L26 3UA — MRCS Eng. LRCP Lond. 1966; Cert. Family Plann. JCC 1974. (Liverp.) Clin. Asst. (Renal Dialysis) Mossley Hill Hosp. Liverp.; Mem. Local Med. Comm. Liverp. Socs: A Fell. of the Roy. Soc. of Med. Prev: Ho. Surg. (O & G) & Cas. Off. Sefton Gen. Hosp. Liverp.; SHO (Surg.) Mossley Hill Hosp. Liverp.

DAFALLA, Badr El Din Ahmed 10 Masefield Road, Drowlsdew, Manchester M43 6RW — MB BS 1980 Khartoum; MRCP (UK) 1988.

DAFF, John Allen Varclin Farm, Varclin, St Martin's, Guernsey GY4 6AL Tel: 01481 238855 — MB BS 1949 Lond.; MRCS Eng. LRCP Lond. 1944; MRCGP 1960; DCH RCP Lond. 1989. (King's Coll. Hosp.) Prev: Ho. Surg. Leatherhead Emerg. Hosp.; Ho. Phys. Ballochmyle Emerg. Hosp. Mauchline & Harrow Hosp.

DAFFORN, Eleanor Mary Fleet House, Higher Tatham, Lancaster LA2 8PR — MB ChB 1969 Liverp.; MRCP (U.K.) 1975; DCH Eng. 1971. Cons. Paediat. Awali Hosp., Bahrain. Prev: Cons. Paediat. Salmaniya Med. Centre, Bahrain; Cons. Paediat. Lito Clin. Athens; Research Fell. (Paediat.) Inst. Child Health Athens.

DAFYDD, Ruth Eleri Yr Hen Doolgain, Bron Aber, Trawsfynydd, Blaenau Ffestiniog LL41 4UR — MB BCh 1997 Wales.

DAGG, John Hunter (retired) Ardvulan, Gartmore, Stirling FK8 3RJ Tel: 01877 382325 — MB ChB 1957 Glas.; MD (Hons.) Glas. 1969; FRCP Ed. 1973, M 1962; FRCP Glas. 1971, M 1962; FRFPS Glas. 1960. Cons. Phys. Haemat. W.. Infirm. Glas. Prev: Sen. Research Fell. Nat. Inst. of Health (Haemat.) Univ. Washington Seattle, USA.

DAGG, Kenneth David Flat 20, Traquair Court, 125 Wilton St., Glasgow G20 6RD — MB ChB 1988 Glas.; MRCP (UK) 1991. Research Fell. Brit. Lung Foundat. Fund Co. Respirat. Med. Glas. Prev: Specialist Regist. in Thoracic & Cen. Med.

DAGG-HESTON, Roger Dagg-Heston, Cleeve, Raleigh Way, Hanworth, Feltham TW13 7NX Tel: 020 8384 2062 Fax: 020 8384 2063; 45 Stoke Road, Walton-on-Thames KT12 3DD Tel: 01932 267544 Fax: 020 8384 2063 — MB ChB Baghdad 1966. GP Feltham, Middlx. Socs: Fell. Roy. Soc. Med.; BMA. Prev: Med. Off. Gulf Air Bahrain, Arabian Gulf; Regist. (Neurol.) Qu. Sq. Inst. Neurol. & Maida Vale Lond.; Sen. Med. Off. Qatar Petroleum Corpn., Arabian Gulf.

DAGGER, Thomas (retired) Flat 3, 104 Evesham Road, Cheltenham GL52 2AL Tel: 01242 22615 — MRCS Eng. LRCP Lond. 1928; LDS RCS Eng. 1929.

DAGGETT, Helen Rachel Wharfe House, Hartlington, Burnsall, Skipton BD23 6BY — MB ChB 1995 Birm. (Birm.)

DAGGETT, Peter Roger 114 Newport Road, Stafford ST16 1DA — MB BS 1971 Lond.; MB BS (Hons. & Gold Medal) Lond. 1971; FRCP Lond. 1990; MRCP (UK) 1973; MRCS Eng. LRCP Lond. 1971. (Westm.) Cons. Phys. Staffs. Gen. Infirm. Stafford. Socs: Brit. Diabetic Assn. & Thyroid Club. Prev: Sen. Med. Regist. Centr. Middlx. Hosp.; Med. Regist. Middlx. Hosp.; Med. Regist. St. Peter's Hosp. Gp.

DAGLISH, Mark Robert Crawford Psychopharmacology Unit, University of Bristol, University Walk, Bristol BS8 9TD — MB ChB 1991 Ed.

DAGUE, James Robert Stuart 36 Parkstone Road, Poole BH15 2PG Tel: 01202 674344 — BM 1988 Soton.; MRCGP 1995; DA (UK) 1994. (Univ. Soton. Med. Sch.) GP Poole. Socs: BMA; RCGP.

DAHABRA, Sylvia Department of Psychiatry, Royal Victoria Infirmary, Newcastle upon Tyne — MB BCh BAO 1982 NUI; MRCP (UK) 1985; LRCPI & LM, LRCSI & LM 1982; MRCPsych 1992. Cons. Psychiat., Eating Disorder Serv., Newc.-upon-Tyne. Prev: Regist. (Psychiat.) N.. RHA; Regist. (Gen. Med.) Newc. HA; SHO (Gen. Med.) Preston Hosp. N. Shields.

DAHANAYAKE, Srimathi Beatrice Mallika 4 High Alder Road, Bessacarr, Doncaster DN4 7BB; 237B Srimath Kuda Ratwatta, Mawatha, Kandy, Sri Lanka — MB BS 1978 Colombo; MRCS Eng. LRCP Lond. 1989.

DAHANAYAKE, Mr Wijayasena Dias 73 Armthorpe Road, Doncaster DN2 5LU — MB BS 1975 Sri Lanka; FRCS Ed. 1987; MRCS Eng. LRCP Lond. 1988.

DAHAR, Mr Nazeer Ahmed 15 Burn Drive, Broomridge, Stirling FK7 7RN — MB BS 1981 Karachi; FRCS Ed. 1988.

DAHDAL, Maher Tewfik Elias Flat A, 2 Argyll Road, High St., Kensington, London W8 7DB — MB BCh BAO 1984 NUI; LRCPI & LM, LRCSI & LM 1984.

DAHELE, Anna Verna Marie 24 Polwarth Gardens, Edinburgh EH11 1LW — MB ChB 1993 Ed.; MRCP (Ed.) 1996. (Ed.) Research Fell. W.. Gen. Hosp. NHS Trust. Socs: BMA. Prev: Gen. Med. Qu. Margt. Hosp. NHS Trust; Renal Unit, Roy. Infirm. Edin.; Med. Unit Roy. Infirm. Edin.

DAHELE, Max Rakesh Flat 3 F/1, 24 Polwarth Gardens, Edinburgh EH11 1LW — MB ChB 1994 Ed.

DAHILL, Stephen William Royal Alexandra Hospital, Corsebar Road, Paisley PA2 9P Tel: 0141 580 4164 Email: stephen.dahill@rah.scot.nhs.uk; 27 Kinnaird Crescent, Bearsden, Glasgow G61 2BN — MB ChB 1984 Glas.; MB ChB Glas. I984; MRCPath 1992. Cons. Histopath. Roy. Alexandra Hosp. Paisley.

DAHIYA, Sanjay 106 Carver Hill Road, High Wycombe HP11 2UD — MB ChB 1991 Bristol.

DAHL, Michael George Cameron 3 Adeline Gardens, Gosforth, Newcastle upon Tyne NE3 4JQ — MB 1966 Camb.; BChir 1965; FRCP Lond. 1981, M 1968. (Middlx.) Cons. Dermat. Roy. Vict. Infirm. Newc.; Sec. Brit. Dermat. Surg. Gp. Socs: Brit. Soc. Dermats. Prev: Sen. Res. Assoc. & MRC Res. Fell. (Dermat.) Roy. Vict. Infirm. Newc.; SHO St. John's Hosp. Dis. of Skin Lond.

DAHMASH, Fahmi Husai 39 Bawnmore Road, Bilton, Rugby CV22 7QJ — MB ChB 1972 Al-Azhar Cairo. Regist. (Orthop.) Worcester Roy. Infirm.

DAHS, Christina Ingrebourne Gardens Medical Centre, 143 Ingrebourne Gardens, Cranham, Upminster RM14 1BJ Tel: 01708 228888 Fax: 01708 641479.

DAI, Chao-Chun Annie St James's University Hospital, Beckett St., Leeds LS9 7TF; 88 Hetton Road, Leeds LS8 3AE — MB ChB 1997 Leeds.

DAILEY, Lynn 49 Pearson Road, Cleethorpes DN35 0DR — MB ChB 1992 Aberd.

DAILEY, Terence Joseph Flat 1, 54 Park Road, Southport PR9 9JB — MB ChB 1951 Liverp.; DPH Manch. 1964.

DAILY, Beverly Neil John (retired) Health Centre, Minniecroft Road, Burnham, Slough SL1 7DE Tel: 01628 605333 Fax: 01628 663743 — MB BS 1960 Lond. Prev: Ho Surg. (ENT) Char. Cross Hosp.

DAILY, Simon David John Burnham Health Centre, Minniecroft Road, Burnham, Slough SL1 7DE Tel: 01628 605333; 142 Lent Rise Road, Burnham, Slough SL1 7BH Tel: 01628 662632 Fax: 01628 662632 Email: docatail@aol.com — MB BS 1992 Lond.; MRCGP 1996. GP Partner Burnham Slough. Socs: Windsor and Dist. Med. Soc. Prev: SHO (Geriat.) Wexham Pk. Hosp. Slough; SHO (O & G & Paediat.) & Ho. Surg. Heatherwood Hosp. Ascot; Ho. Phys. Hillingdon Hosp.

DAILY - JONES, Haydn Ronald The Timbers, 57 Laurence Church Hall, Shephards Close, Cowley, Uxbridge UB8 2EZ Tel: 01895 234585 Fax: 01895 233659 Email: docdaily_uk@yahoo.co.uk; 47 Orchard Drive, Cowley, Uxbridge UB8 3AF Tel: 01895 234110 Fax: 01895 234110 — MB BS 1973 Lond. (King's Coll. Hosp.) Princip. Med. Off. Clare Hse. Uxbridge; Med. Adviser Abbeyfield Soc. Socs: Fell. Roy. Soc. Health; BMA & Assur. Med. Soc. Prev: GP Mem. Hillingdon FHSA & Dist. Managem. Comm. Hillingdon HA; GP Facilitator for Asthma; Mem. M. Glam. LMC & M. Glam. AHA Rev. Comm. on Non Accid. Injury to Childr.

DAIN, Alice Victoria Department of Medicine for the Elderly, Herts & Essex Hospital, Bishop's Stortford CM23 5JH — MB ChB 1980 Leeds; MRCP (UK) 1983.

DAIN, Caroline Jennifer Parkfield Medical Centre, The Walk, Potters Bar EN6 1QH Tel: 01707 651234 Fax: 01707 660452 — MB ChB 1986 Leic.; MRCGP 1990; DFFP 1993; DRCOG 1990; DCH RCP Lond. 1989. GP Potters Bar. Prev: GP P'boro.; Trainee GP P'boro VTS; Research Assoc. Camb. Univ.

DAINOW, Ivor Israel (retired) Pineways, 137 Old Woking Road, Pyrford, Woking GU22 8PD Tel: 01932 344981 — MB BS 1955 Lond.; MRCS Eng. LRCP Lond. 1955. Med. Cons. Pharmaceut. & Med. Device Industry. Prev: Med. Dir. Solco Basle (UK) Ltd. High Wycombe.

DAINTITH, Hilary Ann Marie Department of Radiology, Glenfield General Hospital, Leicester; The Old Vicarage, 25 Main St, Great Dalby, Melton Mowbray LE14 2ET — MB ChB 1977 Dundee; BSc (Hons.) (Pharmacol.) Dundee 1973, MB ChB 1977; FRCR 1987. Cons. Radiol. Glenfield Gen. Hosp. Leics.

DAINTON, Jeremy Nicholas Flat 17, Gabriels Wharf, Water Lane, Exeter EX2 8BG — MB ChB 1990 Birm. Anat. Prosector Univ. Oxf. Prev: Ho. Off. (Surg.) Birm. Accid. Hosp.; Ho. Off. Phys. N. Devon Dist. Hosp.

DAINTON, Mary Crawford Burnage Primary Care Resource Centre, 347 Burnage Lane, Manchester M19 1EW Tel: 0161 432 1404 Fax: 0161 442 7900 — MB BS 1976 Lond.

DAINTREE, Rosalind Anne Chapel St Surgery, Newhaven BN9 9PW Tel: 01273 517000 Fax: 01273 515845; 9 Buxton Road, Eastbourne — MB ChB 1981 Bristol; MRCGP 1985; DRCOG 1984; DCH RCP Lond. 1983. p/t GP Newhaven E. Sussex. Prev: Clin. Asst. (A & E) Kent & Sussex Hosp. Tunbridge Wells; Trainee GP/SHO S. Birm. HA VTS.

DAINTY, Anna Rosamond (retired) Sandown, Rosemary Lane, Bampton OX18 2NF Tel: 01993 850540 — MB ChB 1939 Birm. Prev: Clin. Med. Off. (Family Plann.) Beds. AHA (S. Dist.) & Herts. AHA.

DAINTY, Christine Lewisham Medical Centre, 158 Utting Avenue East, Liverpool L11 1DL Tel: 0151 256 9800 Fax: 0151 256 5765 — MB ChB 1989 Liverp.

DAISH, Peter Church Farmhouse, 33 Church St., Rothersthorpe, Northampton NN7 3JD — MB Camb. 1976, BChir 1975; MSc (Biochem.) Lond. 1984; MA Camb. 1974, MD 1993; FRCP Lond. 1995; MRCP (UK) 1980. Cons. Paediat. N.ampton Gen. Hosp.

DAISLEY, Susan Elizabeth 43 Dalveen Quad, Coatbridge ML5 4RN — MB ChB 1994 Glas.

DAITZ, Allan Richard Torrington Park Health Centre, 16 Torrington Park, North Finchley, London N12 9SS Tel: 020 8445 7622/4127; 63 Parkgate Crescent, Barnet EN4 0NW — MB ChB 1987 Leeds; MRCGP 1991; T(GP) 1991; DRCOG 1991. Prev: Trainee GP/SHO (Paediat.) Salford VTS.

DAITZ, Howard 4 Laneroost Gardens, Southgate, London N14 6QE Tel: 020 8882 4396 Fax: 020 8364 8822; Rochdale Surgery, Broomfield Avenue, London N13 4JJ Tel: 020 8886 3631 Fax: 020 8364 8822 — MB ChB 1990 Leeds; DFFP 1996; DCP RCP Lond. 1995; MRCGP 1997. (Leeds) GP Lond. Socs: Brit. Med. & Dent. Hypn. Soc.

DAJANI, Fayek Fouad 99 Abingdon Road, London W8 6QU — MRCS Eng. LRCP Lond. 1963.

DAJANI, Mr Isam Abdul Muhsen Taher (Surgery) 30A Wimpole Street, London W1M 7AE Tel: 020 7935 2901; 7B Robin Hood Lane, Sutton SM1 2RN Tel: 020 8642 2976 — MB BCh 1965 Cairo; BSc Amer. Univ. Beirut 1957; FRCS Ed. 1978. Hon. Clin. Asst. (Gen. Surg.) St. Helier Hosp. Carshalton. Prev: Managing Dir. Old Ct. Clinic Lond.; Regist. (Gen. Surg.) Nelson Hosp. Lond.; Regist. (Thoracic Surg.) St. Helier Hosp. Carshalton.

***DAJI, Lulu** 70 Thornton Avenue, Chiswick, London W4 1QQ Tel: 020 8994 8744 — MB BS 1951 Bombay.

DAKEYNE, Madelyn Ann St Andrews Surgery, 166 Market Street, Eastleigh SO50 5PT Tel: 023 8061 2472 Fax: 023 8061 1717; 11 Hill Lane, Colden Common, Winchester SO21 1RZ Tel: 01608 730301 — BM BCh 1982 Oxf.; BM BCh Oxf 1982; MA Oxf. 1983; MRCGP 1994; DRCOG 1984. (Oxf.) Prev: GP Moreton-in-Marsh Glos.; Trainee GP Bicester VTS; SHO Horton Hosp. Banbury VTS.

DAKIN, Elsie Margaret (retired) 7 Firs Road, Gatley, Cheadle SK8 4JT — MB ChB 1945 Manch. SCMO Centr. Manch. Health Dist. Prev: Research Worker Dept. of Child. Health Manch. Univ.

DAKIN, Gary Howard Regent Square Group Practice, 8-9 Regent Square, Doncaster DN1 2DS Tel: 01302 819999 Fax: 01302 369204; Rockcliffe, 10 Regent Square, Doncaster DN1 2DS Tel: 01302 739339 Fax: 01302 367548 Email: ghd@lineone.net — MB BS 1982 Lond.; MB BS (Hons.) Lond. 1982; MRCGP 1991; T(GP) 1991; DRCOG 1986. (Roy. Free) Civil. Med. Off. TA.; CME GP Tutor Doncaster VTS; Adviser in Gen. Pract. to Doncaster Roy. Infirm. NHS Trust. Socs: Brit. Thorac. Soc.; Nat. Assn. GP Tutors; GP Asthma Gp. Prev: Trainee GP N.ampton VTS; Ho. Surg. Roy. Free Hosp. Lond.; Ho. Phys. Basildon Hosp.

DAKIN, Hannah Elizabeth Ramornie Mill, Pitlessie, Cupar KY7 — MB ChB 1991 Glas.; DRCOG 1992; MRCGP 1996.

DAKIN, Lucy Emily The Old Post House, Hammond St, Mappowder, Sturminster Newton DT10 2EH Tel: 01258 817866 Email: ledakin@aol.com — MB ChB 1994 Leic.; DTM & H 2001 Liverpool Sch. Of Trop. Med.; MRCP 1998. (Leicester) SHO Intens. Care, Addenbrookes Hosp. Camb.; Volunteer with relief & Developm. organisation overseas (NGO). Socs: Roy. Coll. Phys. Prev: SpR Elderly/Gen.Med. Leicester Roy. Infirm.; SpR. Elderly/ Gen. Med. Leicester Gen. Hosp.; SpR Elderly/ Gen. Med, Kettering Gen. Hosp.

DAKIN, Matthew Charles Northwood Medical Centre, 10/12 Middleton Hall Road, Kings Norton, Birmingham B30 1BY Tel: 0121 458 5507; 35 Sandhills Lane, Barnt Green, Birmingham B45 8NU Tel: 0121 445 5578 — BM 1992 Soton.; MRCGP 1996; DFFP 1995; DRCOG 1995. (Soton.) GP N.wood Med. Centre. Kings Norton, Birm. Socs: Birm. Med. Soc. Prev: SHO York. Dist. Hosp. VTS; Ho. Off. (Med.) Norf. & Norwich Hosp.; Ho. Off. (Surg.) Ipswich Hosp.

DAKIN, Melanie Jane Chelsea & Westminster Hospital, Magill Department of Anaesthesia, 369 Fulham Road, London SW10 9NH Tel: 020 8746 8000 Fax: 020 8746 8801; 16 Princes Road, Richmond TW10 6DH Tel: 020 8948 3019 — MB BS 1988 Lond.; FRCA 1993. Cons. Anaesth. Chelsea & W.minster Hosp. Lond. Socs: Assn. Anaesth. GB & Irel.; Difficult Airway Soc.; Obst. Anaesth. Assn. Prev: Sen. Regist. Hammersmith Hosps. Rotat.; Post Fell. Regist. Gt. Ormond St. Hosp.; Regist. Rotat. Char. Cross Hosp.

DAKIN, Paul Kingsley Greenfinch Medical Practice, 54 Leopold Rd, London N2 8BG Tel: 0208 883 3301; 33 Pages Hill, Muswell Hill, London N10 1PX Tel: 020 8883 7571 Email: pdakin@compuserve.com — MB BS 1981 Lond.; BSc 1978 Lond.; MRCGP 1987. (Roy. Free) GP Princip.; Pract. Tutor. Socs: FRSM. Prev: Regist. (Psychiat.) Barnet Gen. Hosp.; SHO (Neurosurg.) Roy. free Hosp. Lond.

DAKIN, Robert The Surgery, High Street, Lowestoft NR32 1JE Tel: 01502 589151 Fax: 01502 566719; Silverwood, Gunton Cliff, Lowestoft NR32 4PF Tel: 01502 563907 — MB ChB 1967 Leeds; DObst RCOG 1970. (Leeds) Prev: Cas. Off. Leeds Gen. Infirm.; SHO (Paediat.) Bradford Childr. Hosp.; Ho. Off. (O & G) St. Luke's Hosp. Bradford.

DAKIN, Susan Margaret The Surgery, 274 Havant Road, Drayton, Portsmouth PO6 1PA Tel: 023 9237 0422 Fax: 023 9261 8383; The Myrtles, Prinsted Lane, Prinsted, Emsworth PO10 8HR Tel: 01243 372079 — MB ChB 1985 Sheff.

DAKKAK, Mounes Gastrointestinal Unit, Hull Royal Infirmary, Kingston-Upon-Hull, Hull HU3 2JZ Tel: 01482 674356 Fax: 01482 674791 Email: mounes_dakkak@doctors.org.uk; Cherry Top, 10 Greenstiles Lane, Swanland, North Ferriby HU14 3NH Tel: 01482 632352 — MD 1977 Aleppo; PhD Hull 1993; MRCP (UK) 1987; MRCPI 1986; DTCD Wales 1982; FRCP 1998. Cons. Phys. (Gastroenterol.) Hull Roy. Infirm.; Hon. Sen. Lect. Univ. Leeds; Hon. Sen. Lect. Univ. Hull. Socs: Brit. Soc. Gastroenterol.; BMA. Prev: Research Fell. Hon.S.R. Hull Roy. Infirm.; Regist. (Med.) Ashington Hosp. N.d.; SHO (Med.) Chesterfield Roy. Hosp.

DAKO, Mr Kofi Otenadu 32 Sunny Gardens Road, London NW4 1RX — MB ChB 1970 Ghana; FRCS Eng. 1984. Regist. (Gen. Surg.) Middlesbrough. Prev: Regist. (Gen. Surg.) Montagu Hosp. & Rotherham Dist. Gen. Hosp.

DAKSHINAMURTHI, Manoharan 361 Deane Road, Bolton BL3 5HL Tel: 01204 655319 — MB ChB 1978 Manch. Prev: GP Halifax; GP Elland, Yorks.

DALAH, Maysek 7 Heronslea Drive, Stanmore HA7 4QY — MB BS 1984 Lond. Trainee GP S. Harrow. Prev: SHO (O & G) Caerphilly Dist. Miners Hosp. S. Glam.; SHO (Paediat.) Univ. Hosp. of Wales Cardiff.; SHO (Gen. Med.) Roy. Gwent Hosp. Newport. Gwent.

DALAL, Ajay 57 The Oval, Wood St Village, Guildford GU3 3DL — BM 1992 Soton.

DALAL, Anand, TD Wigan & Leigh Health Services, NHS Trust, Royal Albert Edward Infirmary, Wigan Lane, Wigan WN1 2NN Tel: 01942 244 0000; 254 Glazebrook Lane, Glazebrook, Warrington WA3 5AX Tel: 0161 775 3494 — MB ChB 1963 Manch.; MRCS Eng. LRCP Lond. 1963; FFA RCS Eng. 1971; DRCOG 1978; DA Eng. 1965. (Manch.) Cons. Anaesth. Roy. Albert Edwd. Infirm.; Tutor Univ. Manch. Med. Sch.; Maj. RAMC (TA) Cons. Anaesth. (Retd.); Cons. AnE.h. Defence Secondary Care MOD. Socs: Eccles Med. Soc.; Manch. Med. Soc. Prev: Cons. Anaesth. Salford Gp. Hosps.; Sen. Regist. (Anaesth.) Manch. Roy. Infirm.; SHO (Anaesth.) Roy. Manch. Childr. Hosp. Pendlebury.

DALAL, Brian Martin Queen Elizabeth Psychiatric Hospital, Mindelsohn Way, Birmingham B15 2QZ — MB ChB Dundee 1985; MRCPsych 1995. Cons. Psychiat. Gen. Adult Psychiat. S. Birm. Ment. Health NHS Trust.

DALAL, Dinesh Kanubhai Great North Road Surgery, 164 Great North Road, Gosforth, Newcastle upon Tyne NE4 5AB Tel: 0191 285 2460; 45 Burnside Road, Gosforth, Newcastle upon Tyne NE3 2DU Tel: 0191 285 3676 — MB BS 1971 Gujarat; DObst. Dub. 1979. GP Princip.

DALAL, Hasnain Mohamed Lemon Street Surgery, 18 Lemon Street, Truro TR1 2LZ Tel: 01872 73133 Fax: 01872 260900; 2 Arundell Place, Truro TR1 2BQ Tel: 01872 271263 — MB ChB 1981 Sheff.; MRCS Eng. LRCP Lond. 1981; FRCGP 1995, M 1986; DRCOG 1984. (Sheff.) Princip. in Gen. Pract.; Research Asst. (Cardiol.) Roy. Cornw. Hosp. Truro; Pract. Head Research & Developm.: approved NHS Exec. Research & Developm. Pract. Prev: Trainee GP Cornw. VTS; Ho. Off. Roy. Hallamsh. Hosp. & Lodge Moor Hosp. Sheff.

DALAL, Mazher Mohsin 1 Borthwick Park, Orton Wistow, Peterborough PE2 6YY — MB BS 1976 Bombay. (Topiwala National Medical College) Cons. (Psychiat.) Naseberry Ct. (Forest Health Care) Ohingford Essex.

DALAL, Neha Department of Histopathology, Tameside General Hospital, Fountain St., Ashton-under-Lyne OL6 9RW Tel: 0161 331 6416 Email: nehadalal@hotmail.com — MB BS 1987 Bombay; MRCPath 1996; MD Bombay 1992. Cons. (Cellular Path.). Prev: Sen. Regist. Addenbrookes Hosp. Camb.; Regist. Roy. Berks. Hosp. Reading.

DALAL, Paraskumar Uttamchand 79 Friar Road, Petts Wood, Orpington BR5 2BP — MB BS 1996 Lond.

DALAL, Mr Rakesh Bhujangi Department of Histopathology, Tameside General Hospital, Fountain St., Ashton-under-Lyne OL6 9RW; 7 Fobbing Farm Close, Dry St, Nether Mayne, Basildon SS16 5NP Tel: 01268 533911 — MB BS 1986 Bombay; FRCS Ed. 1992.

DALAL, Roshan Rusi Dalal and Partners, 75 Brunswick Road, Ealing, London W5 1AQ Tel: 020 8810 5545 Fax: 020 8998 4880; 3 Carlton Gardens, Ealing, London W5 2AN Tel: 020 8997 2076 Fax: 020 8998 4362 — MB BS 1953 Punjab; MB BS Punjab (Pakistan) 1953; MRCOG 1963, DObst 1958. (King Edwd. Med. Coll. Lahore) Socs: BMA; Med. Wom. Federat. Prev: Asst. MOH Lond. Boro. Ealing & Roy. Boro. Chelsea & Kensington; Regist. (O & G) Boston Gen. Hosp.

DALAL, Sameer 34 Ratcliffe Road, Sheffield S11 8YA — MB ChB 1997 Sheff.

DALAL, Sohrab Rusi 3 Carlton Gardens, London W5 2AN — MB BS 1988 Lond.; MRCGP 1992; DRCOG 1992; DFFP 1992; DCH RCP Lond. 1991. Chief Med. Off. Raleigh Internat. Borneo, Malaysia & Siberia. Prev: Trainee GP Maidstone.

DALAL, Mr Vasant Devidas (retired) 'Oakenroode', Oakenrod Hill, Rochdale OL11 4ED Tel: 01706 43466 — MB BS 1952 Bombay; FRCS Eng. 1962. JP; Cons. Orthop. Surg. Rochdale & Dist. Gp. Hosps. Fell. Manch. Med. Soc. Prev: Regist. (Orthop.) Wexham Pk. Hosp. Slough & St. Geo. Hosp. & Med.

DALAMPYRAS, Panagiotis 32 Vellacott House, Du Cane Road, London W12 0UQ — Ptychio Iatrikes 1991 Thessalonika.

DALBY, John Edgar (retired) Orchard House, Gayton Lane, Gayton, Wirral CH60 3SJ Tel: 0151 342 4516 — MB BChir 1950 Camb.; FFR 1959; DMRT Eng. 1956. Hon. Clin. Lect. (Radiother.) Univ. Liverp. Prev: Cons. Radiotherap. Liverp. RHB & United Liverp. Hosps.

DALBY, Karen Vanessa 17 Osborne Road, Jesmond, Newcastle upon Tyne NE2 2AH Tel: 0191 281 4588; 4 The Grove, Forst Hall, Newcastle upon Tyne NE12 9PE Tel: 0191 266 2242 — MB BS 1990 Newc.; MRCGP 1996; DFFP 1997.

DALBY, Marjorie (retired) 20 Ferndown, Great Coates, Grimsby DN37 9PW Tel: 01472 599750 — MRCS Eng. LRCP Lond. 1972. Prev: GP Cleethorpes.

DALBY, Miles Charles Denholm 172 Chamberlayne Road, London NW10 3JT — MB BS 1990 Lond.

DALBY, Muriel Dorothy Orchard House, Gayton Lane, Gayton, Wirral CH60 3SJ Tel: 0151 342 4516 — MB ChB 1950 Manch.; DA Eng. 1954. Anaesth. Liverp. AHA. Prev: Clin. Asst. Anaesth. Ashton Dist. Infirm.

DALBY, Richard Julian 15 The Mount, Selby YO8 9BH — MB ChB 1992 Leic.

DALE, Andrew Roland 1 Coniston Avenue, Leicester LE2 7FJ — MB BS 1994 Lond.

DALE, Anisa (Sabrine) Princess Margaret Hospital, Okus Rd, Swindon SN1 4JU — MB BS 1991 Newc.; FRCA 1997. (Newc. u. Tyne) Cons. (Anaesth) P.ss Margt. Hosp., Swindon. Socs: Cons.Trainee Mem. Roy. Coll. Anaesth. GB & Irel.; Assn. Of Anaesth. Gt. Brit. Prev: Specialist Regist. Wrexham Pk. Hosp. Slough; Spr Roy. Berks Hosp. Reading; SpR Oxf. Radcliff Trust.

DALE, Anne Kathleen c/o 170A Worsley Road, Eccles, Manchester M30 8LT — MB ChB 1987 Leeds; MRCP (UK) 1990.

DALE, Barbara Joan Campbell Surgery, 2A Campbell Road, Southsea PO5 1RN Tel: 023 9281 1275 — BM BS 1976 Nottm.; MRCGP 1982; DCH RCP Lond. 1984; DObst RCOG 1981. (Nottm.)

DALE, Barry Arthur Stanley Area Department Bacteriology, Dumfries & Galloway Royal Infirmary, Dumfries DG1 4AP Tel: 01387 241532 Fax: 01387 241367; Cimbri Glimpse, Powfoot, Annan DG12 5PS Tel: 01461 700324 Email: barry.dale@btinternet.com — MB ChB 1973 Manch.; FRCPath 1992; Dip. Bact. Manch. 1978. Cons. Bact. Area Dept. Bact. Dumfries & Galloway Roy. Infirm.; Dumfries.

DALE, Brian Bozier (retired) Pinewood Lodge Nursing home, Didworthy, South Brent TQ10 9EF — MB ChB Aberd. 1953; MFHom 1976; MLCO 1969.

DALE, Mr Bryan Archibald Brownhill (retired) 19 Dreghorn Loan, Edinburgh EH13 0DF Tel: 0131 441 2570 — MB ChB 1962 Ed.; FRCS Ed. 1966. Cons. ENT Surg. Roy. Infirm. & City Hosp. Edin. Prev: Sen. Regist. St. Mary's Hosp. Lond.

DALE, Catherine Karingla, Corse Lawn, Gloucester GL19 4LZ Tel: 01452 780444 — MB BS 1973 Lond.; MRCP (UK) 1978; MRCS Eng. LRCP Lond. 1973; FRCR 1982. Cons. Radiol. BromsGr.. & Redditch & Hereford & Worcs. BrE. Screening Unit P.ss of Wales Hosp. BromsGr.

DALE, Catherine Philippa 11 Ash Cl, New Malden KT3 3EA — MB BS 1997 Lond.

DALE, Christina 32 Coldstream Gardens, Putney, London SW18 1LJ — MB BS 1997 Lond. (Charing & Westminster)

DALE, Flora Mary (retired) 23 Regent Terrace, Edinburgh EH7 5BS — LRCP LRCS Ed. LRFPS Glas. 1951.

DALE, George (retired) Four Winds, 266 Newton Drive, Blackpool FY3 8PZ — MB ChB 1945 Glas. Prev: Ho. Phys. W.. Dist. Hosp. Glas.

DALE, Gillian Christine 5 The Byeway, Rickmansworth WD3 1JW — MB ChB 1987 Glas.; MRCGP 1994; DFFP 1994; DA (UK) 1990. GP Princip. Harefield Health Centre. Socs: BMA; MRCGP; CMF (Christain Med. Fell.ship). Prev: Asst. GP Lond.; Trainee GP Kennington Lond.; SHO (Anaesth.) W.. Infirm. Glas.

DALE, Gordon 26 Holywell Avenue, Whitley Bay NE26 3AA Tel: 0191 253 2907 — MB BS 1960 Durh.; BSc (Chem.) (1st Cl. Hnrs.) Newc.1966, MD 1972. (Newc.) Cons. Chem. Path. Newc. Gen. Hosp.; Sen. Lect. (Paediat. Biochem.) Dept. Clin. Biochem. Univ. Newc. Socs: Brit. Paediat. Assn. & Soc. Study Inborn Errors of Metab. Prev: Ho. Phys. & Ho. Surg. Roy. Vict. Infirm. Newc.; Regist. Dept. Path. Dryburn Hosp. Durh.; Sen. Regist. Dept. Clin. Biochem. Roy. Vict. Infirm. Newc.

DALE, Jane Elizabeth 18 Stourbridge Road, Fairfield, Bromsgrove B61 9LS — MB ChB 1990 Birm.; MRCP (UK) 1993. Specialist Regist. Diabetes & Endocrinol., Qu. Eliz. Hosp. Birm. Prev: Specialist Regist. Diabetes & Endocrinolgy Heartlands & Soihull NHS Trust Birm.; SHO Rotat. Gen. Med. Dudley Grp.Hosp.

DALE, Professor Jeremy Roland Primary Care Unit, University of Warwick, Coventry CV4 7AL Tel: 024 76 524254 Fax: 024 76 524311 Email: jeremy.dale@warwick.ac.uk; Cranbrook Lodge, Holly Lane, Balsall Common, Coventry CV7 7EA Tel: 01676 534969 Email: jeremydale@compuserve.com — MB BS 1983 Lond.; MA Camb. 1984; MRCGP 1987; DRCOG 1988; DCH RCP Lond. 1986; PhD London 1998. Prof. (Primary Care) Univ. Warwick. Prev: Sen. Lect. & Hon. Cons. King's Coll. Hosp. Med. Sch. Lond.; Trainee GP Oxf. VTS.

DALE, John Hinton Millview Surgery, 1A Goldsmith Street, Mansfield NG18 5PF Tel: 01623 649528; 36 Alexandra Avenue, Mansfield NG18 5AB Tel: 01623 478018 — MB ChB 1976 Liverp.; MRCOG 1982. (Liverp.)

DALE, John William The Mount, Little London, Ardingly, Haywards Heath RH17 6TJ Tel: 01444 892252 Fax: 01444 892974 Email: jwdale@ardingly.demon.co.uk; The Mount, Little London, Ardingly, Haywards Heath RH17 6TJ Tel: 01444 892252 Fax: 01444 892635 — MA; MB Camb. 1962, BChir 1961; MFPHM 1991; MFCM 1973. (Camb. & St. Bart.) Hon Cons Epidemiol., Dept. of State for Health, Social Welf. and Wom.'s Affairs, The Gambia. Socs: Brit. Computer Soc. Prev: Cons. Pub. Health Med. SE Thames RHA; Dir. (Med. Research) Health Educat. Counc.; Sen. Lect. (Epidemiol.) St. Thos. Hosp. Lond.

DALE, Jonathan Isaac Harris 60 Sutton Hall Road, Bolsover, Chesterfield S44 6JL — BM BS 1977 Nottm.; AFOM RCP Lond. 1986. Occupat. Phys. Derbysh.

DALE, Judith Mary Dept of Palliative Care, Worcestershire community NHS Trust, Worcester royal infirmary castle street branch, Worcester WR1 3AS Tel: 01905 760182 Fax: 01905 760186; 5 Athelstan Road, Worcester WR5 2BW Tel: 01905 763965 — MB BS Lond. 1967; Dip. Palliat. Med. Wales 1992. (St. Thos.) Macmillan Cons.Palliat. Med.; Hon. Cons Worcester Roy. Infirm. NHS Trust; Hos. Cons. St Richard Hospice Worcester. Socs: BMA; Assn. Palliat. Med.; Fell. RSM. Prev: Med dir.St Richards Hospice Worcester; GP Pershore; Ho. Off. Worcester Roy. Infirm.

DALE, Louise Sandra Trent Lodge, Main St., North Muskham, Newark NG23 6HD — BM BS 1985 Nottm.; BMedSci Nottm. 1983. Asst. GP, Newark, Notts. Prev: Asst. GP Mansfield, Notts.; Trainee GP Stoke on Trent VTS.

DALE, Mark Christopher 147 Clifton Drive, Blackpool FY4 1RT — MB ChB 1985 Manch. Sen. Lect., Fleetwood Hosp., Fleetwood.

DALE, Maureen Gormal (retired) Kincarse, Kinnaird, Inchture, Perth PH14 9QY Tel: 01828 86020 Email: jockdale@globalnet.co.uk — MB ChB 1962 Glas.; FRCP Ed. 1997; FRCPCH 1997. Cons. Paediat. Community Child Health Tayside HB.; Hon. Sen. Lect. (Child Health) Univ. Dundee. Prev: SCMO Community Child Health Serv. Gtr. Glas. HB.

DALE, Michael Hague, OBE (retired) Squirrels, The Rope Walk, Penpol, Devoran, Truro TR3 6NS Tel: 01872 864177 — MRCS Eng. LRCP Lond. 1942; FRCGP 1972, M 1966; DObst RCOG 1948.

DALE, Michael John 14A West Beach, Lytham St Annes FY8 5QH — MB ChB 1979 Ed.; DA (UK) 1984. Staff Grade Anaesth. Preston Acute Hosps. NHS Trust.

DALE, Norman (retired) 15 Sneyd Avenue, Newcastle under Lyme, Newcastle ST5 2QA — MB ChB 1956 Liverp.

DALE, Peter Gordon Doctors Corner, The Abbey, Romsey SO51 8EN Tel: 01794 513429 — MB BS 1956 Lond.; DObst RCOG 1960. (Middlx.) Socs: Soton. Med. Soc.; BMA; Brit. Assn. Psychopharmacol. Prev: Assoc. Specialist Ment. Handicap ColdE. Hosp.; Regist. (Cas. Surg.) & Ho. Surg. (O & G) Middlx. Hosp. Lond.

DALE, Peter John Dept Paediatrics & Child health, Royal Gwent Hospital, Cardif Road, Newport NP20 2UB Tel: 01633 656125 — MB BS 1986 Newc.; MRCPCH; MRCP (I); MRCP (UK). Cons. Paediat.Gastroenter.Roy.Gwent.Hosp/Univ.Hosp.Wales.Cardiff; Cons.Paediat., Roy. Gwent Hosp. Socs: MRCPI; Welsh Paediat. Soc.; BSPGHN. Prev: Sen.Reg.Paediat.Gastroent.Roy.Liverp.Childr.s.Hosp; Sen.Reg.Paediat.Nephrol.Roy.Liverp.Childr.s.Hosp; Sen. Regist. (Paediat.) Glan Clwyd Hosp.

DALE, Raymond Frederick Joseph 17 Millcroft, off Chesterfield Road, Great Crosby, Liverpool L23 9XJ — MB ChB 1967 Liverp. (Liverp.) Prev: Ho. Phys. & Ho. Surg. Birkenhead Gen. Hosp.

DALE, Robert Henry 3 Carnoustie Drive, Tytherington Links, Macclesfield SK10 2TB Tel: 01625 427742 Fax: 01625 427742 Email: dr_bob@falk21.com — MRCS Eng. LRCP Lond. 1964; MD (Anaesth.) Leiden 1978; DA Eng. 1968. (Leeds) Cons. Anaesth. Freelance. Socs: Yoga for Health Foundat. (Trustee & Life Mem.); Life Mem. (Ex-Counc. Mem.) Soc. Advancem. Anaesth. in Dent.; Life Mem. Europ. Soc. Regional Anaesth. Prev: Cons. Anaesth. Stg. Craeyenburch Handicap. Centre Nootdorp, Netherlands; Clin. Tutor & Lect. (Anaesth.) Acad. Med. Centre Univ. Amsterdam & Dent. Inst., Netherlands; Cons. Anaesth. Med. Centre Esthetisch Chirurgie, The Hague, Netherlands.

DALE, Russell Clive Weatheroak Farm, Weatheroak Hill, Alvechurch, Birmingham B48 7EH — MB ChB 1992 Leeds.

DALE, Sheila Mary Broadwood, Heathersage, Hope Valley S32 1DA — MB ChB 1975 Sheff.

DALE, Sukhjeevan Singh 5 Woodcoates Close, Beverley HU17 9UU — BM BS 1992 Nottm.

DALE, Susan Patricia The Mill House, Mill Lane, Bishop Burton, Beverley HU17 8QT — MB ChB 1980 Leeds; MRCGP 1984; DRCOG 1983.

DALE, Thomas Lawrence Cooke (retired) 5 Chiltern Close, Lytham St Annes FY8 4TG Tel: 01253 730636 Email: t.l.c.d@btinternet.com — LLB Lond. 1969; LRCP LRCS Ed. LRFPS Glas. 1947. Prev: Med. Dir. Beecham Products.

DALE, Vivien Anne Waterside Health Centre, Glendermoit Road, Londonderry BT47 Tel: 01504 45191; 4 Fernbrae Gardens, Kilfennan, Londonderry BT47 5XS Tel: 01504 41384 — MB BCh BAO 1979 Belf.; MRCGP 1983; DCCH RCP Ed. 1986; DRCOG 1984. Clin. Med. Off. (Community Paediat.) W.. Health & Social Servs. Bd.; Clin. Med. Off. (Family Plann.) Lond.derry.

DALES, Carolyn Jayne 66 Rudyard Road, Sheffield S6 2LD — MB ChB 1993 Sheff.

DALES, Frances Audrey 29 Lyncombe Crescent, Higher Lincombe Road, Torquay TQ1 2HP Tel: 01803 293913 — MB BCh BAO 1949 Belf. Prev: Ho. Surg. Roy. Vict. Hosp. Belf.

DALES, Mr Herbert Calvert (retired) 29 Lyncombe Crescent, Higher Lincombe Road, Torquay TQ1 2HP Tel: 01803 293913 — MB BCh BAO 1942 Belf.; MB BCh BAO (Hons.) Belf. 1942; MD Belf. 1973, MCh 1951; FRCS Eng. 1948. Prev: Surg. Lt. RNVR.

DALEY, Alexandra Clare 6 Lower Bere Wood, Waterlooville PO7 7NQ — MB BS 1994 Lond.

DALEY, Andrea Jane 6 Salisbury Park, Liverpool L16 0JT — MB BS 1998 Newc.; MB BS Newc 1998.

DALEY, Andrew George Palliative Care Team, Daisy Bank, 109 Duckworth Lane, Bradford BD9 6RN Tel: 01274 363767 Fax: 01274 363770; 7 Greenhead Drive, Utley, Keighley BD20 6EZ Tel: 01535 603082 Email: daleys@lineone.net — BM 1984 Soton.; MRCGP 1988; DRCOG 1987. (Soton.) Cons. Palliat. Med. Bradford Community NHS Trust; Palliat. Med., Bradford Marie Curie Centre. Prev: Med. Dir. Manorlands Hospice Oxenhope; Lect. (Palliat. Med.) St. Bart. Hosp. Lond.; Regist. St. Joseph's Hospice Hackney.

DALEY, Angela Jane 19 Martinfield, Fulwood, Preston PR2 9RH — MB ChB 1998 Sheff.; MB ChB Sheff 1998.

DALEY, Anna Grace 9 The Avenue, Potters Bar EN6 1EG — MB ChB 1995 Birm. (Birm.)

DALEY, Denis, OBE (retired) 337 Gower Road, Killay, Swansea SA2 7AE — MB BCh 1956 Wales; FRCP Lond. 1976, M 1963. Cons. Phys. W. Glam. AHA. Prev: Sen. Regist. (Med.) Llandough Hosp. Cardiff.

DALEY, George Harper Charlton (retired) 8 Drumble Field, Chelmsford, Macclesfield SK11 9BT Tel: 01625 861474 — MB ChB Birm. 1952; MRCGP 1973; ATLS 1993; DObst RCOG 1957.

DALEY, Helen Mary 54 Llys Wylfa, Mynydd Isa, Mold CH7 6XB — MB BS 1990 Lond.

DALEY, Sarah Elizabeth c/o 2 New Cottages, Faccombe, Andover SP11 0DU — MB BS 1998 Newc.; MB BS Newc 1998.

DALEY, Timothy Patrick Daley and Partners, Lakenheath Surgery, 135 High Street, Lakenheath, Brandon IP27 9EP Tel: 01842 860400 Fax: 01842 862078 — MB ChB 1975 Liverp.; DTM & H Liverp. 1977. Prev: SHO (Ophth.) Ipswich Hosp.; SHO (O & G) Essex Co. Hosp.; SHO (Cas.) Clatterbridge Hosp. Merseyside.

DALGLEISH, Abigail Thompson (retired) 82 Mothecombe, Holbeton, Plymouth PL8 1LA Tel: 01752 830402 — BA, MB BCh BAO Dub. 1943; FFA RCS Eng. 1954; DA Eng. 1948. Prev: Mem. Assn. Anaesths. Gt. Brit.

DALGLEISH, Angus George St. George's Hospital Medical School, Division of Oncology, Cranmer Terrace, London SW17 0RE Tel: 020 8725 5815 Fax: 020 8725 0158 Email: a.dagleish@sghms.ac.uk — MB BS 1974 Lond.; BSc Lond. 1971; MD Lond. 1989; FRCP Lond. 1993; MRCP (UK) 1984; FRCPath 1995, M 1993; FRACP 1984. (Univ. Coll. Hosp.) Cons. Phys. (Oncol.) St. Geo. Hosp. Med. Sch. Lond.; Prof. Foundat. Oncol.; Vis. Prof. Inst. Cancer Research. Prev: Cons. Virol. Roy. Lond. Hosp.; Head Retrovirus Research Gp. MRC Clin. Research Centre Harrow & Cons. Phys. Gen. Med. & Oncol.; Clin. Research Fell. Inst. Cancer Research.

DALGLEISH, Antonia The Old Stable, Tregassick, Gerrans, Truro TR2 5ES Tel: 01872 580604 — Special BSc Physiol. (Upp. 2nd cl. Hons.) Lond 1951, MB BS 1954; MRCPsych 1971; DPM Eng. 1963. (Roy. Free) Prev: Cons. Psychiat. Hill End Hosp. St. Albans; Sen. Regist. Hill End Hosp. St. Albans; Sen. Psychiat. Middletown State Hosp. New York.

DALGLEISH, Mr Daniel Jonathan Jersey General Hospital, St Helier, Jersey JE1 3QS; 35 Jumpers Road, Christchurch BH23 2JR — MB BChir 1989 Camb.; MA Camb. 1990, BA 1986; FRCS Eng. 1994; FRCS Ed. 1994; FRCA 1998.

DALGLEISH, James (retired) Ashleigh, Kellfield Avenue, Low Fell, Gateshead NE9 5YP Tel: 0191 487 5706 — MB ChB 1954 St. And.

DALGLEISH, John Gordon The Old Vicarage, Church Lane, Barnham, Bognor Regis PO22 0DA — MB BS 1975 Lond.; BSc (Physiol.) Lond. 1972; FFA RCS Eng. 1981. (St. Bart.) Cons. Anaesth. St. Richards Hosp. Chichester. Socs: Fell. Roy. Soc. Med. (Anaesth. Sect.); Obst. Anaesth. Assn. Prev: Sen. Regist. (Anaesth.) Bristol HA; Regist. (Anaesth.) Soton. HA.

DALGLEISH, Juli 71 Broomieknowe Gardens, Bonnyrigg EH19 2JD; 22 Union Street, Broughty Ferry, Dundee DD5 2AW — MB ChB 1992 Ed.; MRCGP 1996; DRCOG 1995; DFFP 1994. (Edinburgh) Locum GP. Prev: GP/Regist. Edin.; SHO (Paediat., O & G & A & E) Edin.

DALGLEISH, William Armstrong (retired) Lyndhurst, 3 Sea Road South, Bridport DT6 3XA Tel: 01308 422485 — LRCP LRCS Ed. LRFPS Glas. 1952; FRCPsych 1984, M 1974; DPM Eng. 1974; DTM & H Eng. 1966. Prev: Cons. Psychiat. Qu. Eliz. Milit. Hosp. Lond.

DALGLIESH, David Geoffrey, LVO, OStJ, Surg. Capt. RN Retd. (retired) Farmstone, Halwell, Totnes TQ9 7JF Tel: 01803 712224 — MRCS Eng. LRCP Lond. 1946; MFCM 1973; DPH Lond. 1964. Prev: Med. Off. HM Yacht Britannia.

DALGLIESH, Diana 21 St Francis Road, East Dulwich, London SE22 8DE — MB ChB 1989 Cape Town.

DALKIN, Timothy John Royal Edinburgh Hospital, Morningside Place, Edinburgh EH10 5HF Email: tim.dakin@lpct.scot.nhs.uk — MB BS 1985 Newc.; MRCPsych 1990. Cons. Gen. Adult Psychiat. Roy. Edin. Hosp. Prev: Cons. Gen. Adult Psychiat. Littlemore Hosp. Oxf.; Regist. (Psychiat.) Qu. Med. Centre Nottm.

DALL, Barbara Janet Gibson 2 Parkwood Avenue, Roundhay, Leeds LS8 1JW Tel: 0113 266 6397 — MB ChB 1980 Glas.; FRCR 1987.

DALL, Graham Fraser 1F2 69 Inverleith Row, Edinburgh EH3 5LT — MB ChB 1998 Ed.; MB ChB Ed 1998.

DALL, John Lamont Cameron, OBE, OStJ (retired) 6G Golf Court, Strathview Park, Nertherlee, Glasgow G44 3LD Tel: 0141 585 7585 Fax: 0141 585 7065 — MD 1962 Glas.; MB ChB 1953; DU (Hon.) Ottawa 1986; FRCP Ed. 1991, FRCP Glas. 1970, M 1962; FRFPS Glas. 1960. Prev: Cons. Phys. Vict. Geriat. Unit. Glas.

DALL, Lilian Margaret 6G Golf Court, Strathview Park, Netherlee, Glasgow G44 3LD Tel: 0141 637 0316 — MB ChB 1953 Glas. (Glas.) Assoc. Specialist (Anaesth.) S. E. (Glas.) Health Dist.; Sen. Clin. Med. Off. (Family Plann.) Clarkston Clinic Glas. Prev: SHO (Anaesth.) Vict. Infirm. Glas.

DALL'ARA, Roberto Giuseppe Woodside Surgery, High Street, Loftus, Saltburn-by-the-Sea TS13 4HW Tel: 01287 640385 Fax: 01287 644071 — MB ChB 1983 Leicester; MB ChB 1983 Leicester. Occupat.al Health Phys. Cleveland Potash Mine Boulby Cleveland.

DALLA VALLE, Giovanni Michele 5 Aston Close, Stevenage SG1 4TT — State Exam 1989 Padua.

DALLACHY, Russell (retired) 7 Orr Square, Paisley PA1 2DL Tel: 0141 889 2338 — MB ChB 1943 Glas.; FRCPath 1973, M 1963. Prev: Cons. Path. Whittington Hosp. Lond.

DALLAL, Helen Jane 31 Finchdene Grove, Finchfield, Wolverhampton WV3 8BG — MB ChB 1992 Bristol. SHO (Gen. Med.) New Cross Hosp. Wolverhampton.

DALLAS, Angela Jean 5 Cranmore Avenue, Belfast BT9 6JH — MB BCh BAO 1988 Belf.; MB BCh Belf. 1988; DRCOG 1991; DGM RCP Lond. 1990. Clin. Med. Off. (Community Child Health) Home1st Trust.

DALLAS, Fiona 12 Winchester Road, Lodge Moor, Sheffield S10 4EE — MB ChB 1993 Sheff.; MB ChB (Hons.) Sheff. 1993, BMedSci 1992; MRCP 1997.

DALLAS, Jayson Donald Alexander Roche Products Ltd., PO Box 8, Welwyn Garden City AL7 3AY Tel: 01707 365741 Fax: 01707 365782 Email: jayson.dallas@roche.com; Flat 2, 13 Fawley Road, West Hampstead, London NW6 1ST Tel: 020 7419 1173 Fax: 020 7410 1173 — MB BCh 1991 Witwatersrand. Pharmaceut. Phys. Roche Products Ltd. Socs: BMA; Brit. Soc. Pharmaceut. Phys. Prev: Pharmaceut. Phys. Procter & Gamble Pharmaceut. Staines; Research Phys. Guys Drug Research Unit Lond.

DALLAS, Mr Neil Lessels, TD (retired) Stonebeck, North Road, Bath BA2 6HY — MB BChir 1951 Camb.; MA Camb. 1947; FRCS Ed. 1961; FRCOphth 1987. Cons. Ophth. Bristol Eye Hosp. Prev: Cons. Ophth. SW Middlx. Hosp. Gp.

DALLAS-CHAPMAN, Glynis Dianne 14 Vaughan Court, Parsons Way, Wells BA5 2FT — MB BS 1978 Lond.; MRCS Eng. LRCP Lond. 1978; Cert. Prescribed Equiv. Exp. JCPTGP 1981. (Char. Cross) Prev: SHO (Psychiat.) St. Mary Abbots Hosp. Lond.; Ho. Surg. St. Stephen's Hosp. Lond.; Ho. Phys. Char. Cross Hosp. Lond.

DALLAS ROSS, William Peter (retired) Strathview, Emma Terrace, Blairgowrie PH10 6JA Tel: 01250 872762 Email: pdallasross@freenet.co.uk — MB BChir 1945 Camb.; MA Camb. 1945. Prev: Admin. Dean Fac. Med. & Dent. & Dir. Dept. Med. Educat. Univ. Dundee.

DALLAWAY, Catherine Mary Priory Medical Centre, Cape Road, Warwick CV8 1JP Tel: 01926 494411 — MB BS 1989 Lond.; MRCGP 1994; DRCOG 1992; DGM RCP Lond. 1991. (St. George's Hospital Medical School) p/t Gen. Practitioner Princip.

DALLEY, Christopher Dean 80 Coningham Road, London W12 8BH — MB BS 1990 Lond.

DALLEY, Vera Margaret (retired) 12 Pembroke Square, Kensington, London W8 6PA Tel: 020 7937 2122 Fax: 020 7938 1638 Email: 106622.165@compuserve.com — MB BS 1946 Lond.; MRCS Eng. LRCP Lond. 1945; FRCR 1975; DMRT Lond 1948; Hon. FFR RCSI 1964. Hon. Cons. King's Coll. Hosp.; Hon. Cons. Radiother. Chelsea Hosp. Wom., Memor. Hosp. Woolwich & St. Stephen's Hosp. Prev: Cons. Radiotherap. Roy. Marsden Hosp. & Roy. Nat. Throat, Nose & Ear Hosp.

DALLIMORE, John Sydenham 33 Lichfield Avenue, Hereford HR1 2RJ — MB ChB 1962 Liverp.; FFA RCS Eng. 1968. (Liverp.) Cons. Anaesth. Heref. Gp. Hosps.

DALLIMORE, Jonathan Nash Newhall, Pwllmeyric, Chepstow NP16 6LF Email: jondallimore@doctors.org.uk — MB BS 1984 Lond.; MSc (Medical Science) Glasgow 1998; MRCGP 1994; DCH RCP Lond 1991; Cert Prescribed Equiv Exp JCPTGP 1989; DRCOG 1987. (St. Mary's Hospital Medical School) p/t Locum, Gen. Practitioner, Mon.; Staff Grade (A & E) Bristol Roy. Infirm.; Med. Director, Wilderness Med. Train. Socs: Brit. Travel Health Assn.; Internationa; Soc. of Mt.ain Med.; Wilderness Med. Soc. Prev: GP Cowbridge S. Glam.; Regist. (Paediat.) Neath Gen. Hosp.; Trainee GP Old Windsor Berks VTS.

DALLIN, Valerie Jean 'Hellas', Crete Road W., Folkestone CT18 7AA Tel: 0130 389 2444 — MB ChB 1959 Bristol; FFA RCS Eng. 1982; DA Eng. 1966. (Bristol) Assoc. Specialist (Anaesth.) Maidstone Health Dist. Prev: SHO Anaesth. W. Kent Gen. Hosp. Maidstone; Ho. Surg. Canad. Red Cross Memor. Hosp. Taplow; Ho. Phys. S.mead Hosp. Bristol.

DALLING, Mr Robert 287 Southbrae Drive, Glasgow G13 1TR — MB ChB 1967 Glas.; FRCS Ed. 1972. Sen. Surg. Regist. W.. Infirm. Glas. Socs: Roy. M-C Soc. Glas. & W. Scotl. Surg. Assn.

DALLIWALL, Mr Kenneth, TD (retired) Hawthorne Cottage, The Staithe, Thurne, Great Yarmouth NR29 3BU Tel: 01692 670595 — MRCS Eng. LRCP Lond. 1938; BA (Hons. Nat. Sc.) Camb. 1934, MA 1944; FRCS Eng. 1943. Prev: Cons. Orthop. Surg. Wanstead, Chingford & Whipps Cross Hosps. Lond.

DALLOW, Peter Charles Kidsgrove Medical Centre, Mount Road, Kidsgrove, Stoke-on-Trent ST7 4AY Tel: 01782 784221 Fax: 01782 781703 — MB ChB 1981 Liverp.

DALLY, Ann Gwendolen (retired) Wellcome Trust Centre for the History of Medicine at University College,, Euston House, 24 eversholt Street, London NW1 1AD Tel: 0207 6790 8151 Email: a.dally@wellcome.ac.uk — MB BS Lond. 1953; MA Oxf. 1950; MD Lond. 1993; DObst RCOG 1955. Prev: Hon. Clin. Asst. (Psychol. Med.) W.m. Hosp. Lond.

DALLY, Helen Linda 19 Canisp Crescent, Dundee DD2 4TP Tel: 01382 645258 — MB ChB 1967 St. And.; DObst RCOG 1969. (St. And.) SCMO Family Plann. Clinics Dundee & Tayside HB.

DALLY, Peter John Montpellier Cottage, Brinksole, Petworth GU28 0HF — MB BS 1953 Lond.; FRCP Lond. 1966, M 1958; FRCPsych 1973; DPM Eng. 1956; T(Psych) 1991. (St. Thos.) Phys. in Psychol. Med. W.m. Hosp. Lond. Socs: Fell. Roy. Soc. Med. Prev: Lt. R.N.; Sen. Regist. St. Thos. Hosp. Lond.; Cons. Dept. Psychol. Med. W.m. Lond.

DALMAU CARRE, Jordi The Highland Islamic Clinic, Briton Lodge, 37 Telford St., Inverness IV3 5LD — LMS 1980 Barcelona.

DALPADADO, Mr Lakshman Sarath Galagoda 9 The Mews, Gatley, Cheadle SK8 4PS Tel: 0161 428 0524 — MB BS 1976 Sri Lanka; FRCS Glas. 1984; FRCS Ed. 1984.

DALRYMPLE, Andrew 21 Northumberland Avenue, London E12 5HD — MB BS 1996 Lond.; Dip. Obst & Gyn 1999. (Charing Cross Hospital London) SHO Gen. Manquzi Hosp. Kwazulu. Prev: SHO Obst &Gyn Oroote Schuur Cape town; SHO Addington Hosp.Durban; HS W. Middlx. Hosp.

DALRYMPLE, Mr James Oxenham 36 Weymouth Street, London W1G 6NJ Tel: 020 7224 3646 Fax: 020 7486 3828; 21 Northumberland Avenue, Wanstead, London E12 5HD Tel: 020 8989 3114 — MB BS 1955 Lond.; FRCSC 1969; FRCS Eng. 1964. (Char. Cross Hosp.) Private Pract. Socs: Fell. Roy. Soc. Med.; Fell. Coll. Internat. Surgs. Prev: Cons. Surg. Char. Cross Hosp. Lond.; Specialist (Surg.) Inuvik Gen. Hosp. NWT, Canada; Princip. Surg. Specialist Umtata Gen. Hosp. Transkei, S. Afr.

DALRYMPLE, James Samuel Oxenham Manor Farm Close Surgery, 8 Manor Farm Close, Drayton, Norwich NR8 6DN Tel: 01603 867532; 20 Norwich Road, Horsham St. Faiths, Norwich NR10 3LB Tel: 01603 898235 — MB BS 1980 Lond.; DRCOG 1985; Cert. Av Med. 1986. Clin. Asst. (Gastroenterol.) W. Norwich Hosp.

DALRYMPLE, Jean Grace Mary (retired) Summerfield House, Alde Lane, Aldeburgh IP15 5DZ Tel: 01728 453669 — MB BS 1955 Lond. Assoc. Specialist (Cytopath.) St. Margt. Hosp. Epping. Prev: Ho. Phys. & Cas. Off., Sen. Med. Cas. Off. & Resid. Pathol. St. Thos. Hosp.

DALRYMPLE, John Graham Craig Muir, Johnshill, Lochwinnoch PA12 4EL — MB ChB 1986 Glas.; MRCGP 1993; DRCOG 1993; DA (UK) 1993. Socs: BMA; MDDUS; MRCAnaesth.

DALRYMPLE, Paul Anthony, Maj. RAMC The Cottage, Court Hill, Frettenham, Norwich NR12 7NL Tel: 01603 890001; c/o M.R.S. Berakas, Royal Brunei Armed Forces BFPO 605 Tel: 00673 239 4906 — MB BS 1990 Lond.; DCCH RCP Ed. 1995; DRCOG 1993; DFFP 1993; MRCGP 197. (Charing Cross and Westminster) Sen. Med. Off. RAMC & Field Off. Brunei.

DALRYMPLE, Philip Martin, Flight Lt. RAF Med. Br. 34 Welland Road, Wittering, Peterborough PE8 6BN Tel: 01780 783891 — MB ChB 1995 Glas. SHO (Anaesth.) PeterBoro. Dist. Hosp.

DALRYMPLE, Samuel Desmond Gender Identity Clinic, Charing Cross Hospital, Fulham Palace Road, London W6 8RF; Richmond House, 59 Oathnall Road, Haywards Heath RH16 3EL Tel: 01444 455534 — MD 1976 West. Ontario; PhD Alberta 1968. Lead Clin. Gender Identity Clinic Char. Cross Hosp.; Hon. Cons. St. Lukes Hosp. Lond. Prev: Cons. & Dir. Research Lond. Psychiat. Hosp., Lond., Ontario; Lect. (Psychopath.) Huron Coll. Affil. to Univ. W. Ontario, Lond., Ontario.

DALRYMPLE-HAY, Mr Malcolm John Robert Department Caldiothalacic Surgery, Derriford Hospital, Plymouth PL6 8DH Tel: 01752 763833 — MB BS 1990 Lond.; FECTS 1999; FRCS 1999; BSc Lond. 1988; FRCS Ed. 1994; PhD Lond. 1997. Regist. (Cardiothoracic Surg.) Soton. Gen. Hosp. Prev: Transpl. Fell. (Intrathoracic Transpl.); SHO (Cardiothoracic Surg.).

DALRYMPLE-SMITH, David (retired) Ashenfell House, Church Lane, Baslow, Bakewell DE45 1SP Tel: 01902 754842, 01246 582199 Email: david@ashenfell_freeserve.co.uk, rufus@fernando.f9.co.uk — MB ChB 1960 Ed.; DObst RCOG 1962; DA Eng. 1966. Prev: Gen. Med. Practitioner.

DALSANIA, Mr Anil Velji Crest Medical Centre, 157 Crest Road, London NW2 7NA Tel: 020 8452 5155 Fax: 020 8452 4570 — MB BS 1973 Saurashtra; FRCS Glas. 1983. (M.P. Shah Med. Coll. Jamnagar) Socs: Soc. Orthop. Med. Prev: Assoc. Specialist (Orthop. Surg.) Manor Ho. Hosp. Lond.

***DALSANIA, Rajan Anil** 114 Preston Hill, Harrow HA3 9SJ — MB BS 1998 Lond.; MB BS Lond 1998; BSc 1995.

DALTON, Adrian John Christopher (retired) Pembury Hospital, Tunbridge Wells TN2 4QJ Tel: 01892 823535 Fax: 01892 825557 — MB BS 1969 Lond.; MRCPsych 1980. Cons. Psychiat. Pembury Hosp. Tunbridge Wells, Kent. Prev: Sen. Regist. (Psychiat.) Univ. Coll. Hosp. Lond. & Shenley Hosp.

DALTON, Mr Adrian Mark 35 Marlborough Park, Kempston, Bedford MK42 8AN Email: daltonmark@yahoo.com — MB BS 1980 Lond.; FRCS Ed. (A&E) 1988; FFAEM 1997. (The Lond. Hosp.) Cons. A & E Hemel Hempstead Hosp. Herts. Prev: Sen. Regist. Rotat. (A & E) St. Geo. Hosp. Lond.; Regist. Helicopter Emerg. Med. Serv. (HEMS) Lond. Hosp.

DALTON, Adrian Neil Randolph Medical Centre, 4 Green Lane, Datchet, Slough SL3 9EX Tel: 01753 541268 Fax: 01753 582324; 45 Montagu Road, Datchet, Slough SL3 9DR — MB BChir 1977 Camb.; MA Camb. 1981, MB BChir 1977; DRCOG 1981.

DALTON, Andrew David Anthony Department of Histopathology, Glan Clwyd Hospital, Bodelwyddan, Rhyl LL18 5UJ Tel: 01745 583910 — MB ChB 1980 Liverp.; MRCPath. 1988. Cons. Histopath. Glan Clwyd Hosp. Socs: Assn. Clin. Path.; Fell. Roy. Coll. Path.; Brit. Divison Internat. Acad. of Pathologists. Prev: Sen. Regist. (Histopath.) W.m. Hosp. Lond.; Regist. (Histopath.) N.ampton Gen. Hosp.; Ho. Off. Walton Hosp. Liverp.

DALTON, Brian Lauris Palmer (retired) Hollydown, Hindon Lane, Tisbury, Salisbury SP3 6QG Tel: 01747 870517 Email: briandalton@compuserve.co.uk — MB BS 1953 Lond. Prev: GP Salisbury.

DALTON, Christopher Michael 3A Park Valley, The Park, Nottingham NG7 1BS — BM BS 1994 Nottm.; BMedSci Nottm. 1991. SHO (Surg.) Qu.'s Med. Centre Nottm.; SHO (Surg.) Med. Centre Nottm. Prev: Resid. Med. Off. Convent Hosp. Nottm.

DALTON, Christopher Russell Darwen Health Centre, Union Street, Darwen BB3 0DA — MB ChB 1983 Manch.; DRCOG 1988. GP Darwen Lancs. Prev: SHO (ENT) Blackburn Roy. Infirm.; SHO (Paediat.) Burnley Gen. Hosp.; SHO (O & G) Leighton Hosp. Crewe.

DALTON, David James Neale 111 Teignmouth Road, Birmingham B29 7AX — MB ChB 1989 Birm.

DALTON, Davina Chiltern International Ltd., Chiltern House, Bells Hill, Stoke Poges, Slough SL2 4EG — MB ChB 1987 Leeds; DCH RCP Lond. 1989. Clin. Research Phys. Chiltern Internat. Ltd.

DALTON, Deirdre Mary Friargate Surgery, Agard St., Derby DE1 1DZ — LRCPI & LM, LRSCI & LM 1959; LRCPI & LM, LRCSI & LM 1959.

DALTON, Esther Mary 34 Hastings Road, Thorngumbald, Hull HU12 9PG — MB BS 1993 Lond.; DRCOG 1997. (UCC Med. Sch.) Trainee GP Hull.

DALTON, Geoffrey Richard 20 Queen Victoria Road, Bristol BS6 7PE — MB ChB 1986 Bristol; BSc (Psychol.) Bristol 1983, MB ChB 1986; MRCP (UK) 1990. Regist. (Med.) Exeter. Prev: SHO (Cardiol.) Britol Roy. Infirm.; SHO (Endocrinol. & Neurol.) Glos. Roy. Infirm.; SHO (Renal. Med.) S.mead Hosp. Bristol.

DALTON, George (retired) 51B Turnberry Drive, Wilmslow SK9 2QW Tel: 01625 520084 — MB ChB 1950 Sheff.; MRCGP 1960; MFOM RCP Lond. 1978; DIH Soc. Apoth. Lond. 1967. Prev: Cons. Occupat. Phys. Stockport.

DALTON, Mr George Allen (retired) 5 Birnam, 56 Harborne Road, Edgbaston, Birmingham B15 3HE Tel: 0121 454 4953 — MB ChB Birm. 1947; DLO Eng. 1949; FRCS Eng. 1956; FRCS Ed. 1956. Prev: Cons. ENT Surg. United Birm. Hosps.

DALTON, Harry Richard Royal Cornwall Hospital Trust, Penventinnie Lane, Truro TR1 3LJ Tel: 01872 252749 — MB BS 1983 Lond.; DPhil Oxf. 1992; BSc Lond. 1980; MRCP (UK) 1986; Dip. Med. Educat. Wales 1994; FRCP 1998. (Charing Cross Hospital Medical School London) Cons. Phys. Gastroenterol. Roy. Cornw. Hosp. Trust; Hon. Sen. Lect. Univ. of Plymouth. Socs: Med. Res. Soc. & Brit. Soc. Gastroenterol. Prev: Lect. (Med.) St. Jas. Univ. Hosp. Leeds; Research Fell. (Gastroenterol.) Radcliffe Infirm. Oxf.; Regist. (Med.) St. Geo. Hosp. Lond.

DALTON, Israel Sholame 12 Bancroft Avenue, London N2 0AS Tel: 020 8340 1364 — MRCS Eng. LRCP Lond. 1942; MD Lond. 1947, MB BS 1942; MRCP Lond. 1946. (St. Bart.) Prev: Res. Med. Off. Lond. Jewish Hosp.; Capt. IMS/IAMC; Clin. Asst. E. Ham Chest Clinic.

DALTON, Jacqueline Rebecca 430 Liverpool Road, Ainsdale, Southport PR8 3BA — MB ChB 1971 Liverp.; FFA RCS Eng. 1975. Cons. (Anaesth.) Aintree Hosps. Trust. Prev: Sen. Regist. (Anaesth.) Liverp. AHA (T); Regist. (Anaesth.) United Liverp. Hosps.

DALTON, James Edward 52 Banovallum Gardens, Horncastle LN9 6PN Tel: 01507 523020 — MB ChB 1994 Birm.; BSc Durham. 1984. SHO Rotat. Lincoln Hosps. VTS. Prev: Ho. Off. (Gen. Surg.) Pilgrim Hosp. Boston; Ho. Off. (Gen. Med.) St. Geo. Hosp. Lincoln.

DALTON, Jeffrey David 4 Plover Close, Bishopton Lane, Stratford-upon-Avon CV37 9EN — MB ChB 1986 Leic.

DALTON, Joan Isobel Francis The Dell, Wilton Lane, Jordans, Beaconsfield HP9 2RF — MB BCh 1959 Wales; FRCR 1975; FFR 1971; DMRT Eng. 1969. Prev: Cons. Radiother. N.ampton & Kettering; Cons. Radiother. Roy. Free & Roy. N.ern Hosps.; Cons. Radiol. Oncol. St. John New Brunswick, Canada.

DALTON, John Rollo Tisbury Surgery, Park Road, Tisbury, Salisbury SP3 6LF Tel: 01747 870204 Fax: 01747 871023 — MB BS 1980 Lond.; MRCGP 1985; DRCOG 1984. (St. Thos.) Prev: Trainee GP N. Devon Dist. Hosp. VTS; SHO (O & G) Canad. Red Cross Memor. Hosp.; SHO (A & E) Salisbury Gen. Infirm.

DALTON, Joy The Waterlow Unit, Highgate Hill, London N19 5NX Tel: 020 7530 2287 — MB BS 1971 Lond.; FRCPsych 1998; MRCS Eng. LRCP Lond. 1971; DPM Eng. 1976. Cons. Psychiat. & Head Med. Servs. Camden and Islington Ment. Health NHS Trust. Prev: Cons. Psychiat. Whittington & Friern Hosp. Lond.; Research Sen. Regist. (Psychiat.) Roy. Free Hosp. Lond.; Regist. (Psychiat.) Friern Hosp. & Roy. Free Hosp. Lond.

DALTON, Katharina Dorothea (retired) 102 Dorset House, Gloucester Place, London NW1 5AG Tel: 020 7486 3645 — MRCS Eng. LRCP Lond. 1948; FRCGP 1982, M 1959. Prev: Clin. Asst. (Psych. Med.) Univ. Coll. Hosp. Lond. PMS Clinic.

DALTON, Kevin John Department of Obstetrics & Gynaecology, University of Cambridge, Addenbrooke's Hospital (Box 223), Cambridge CB2 2SW Tel: 01223 410250 Fax: 01223 336873 Email: kjd5@cam.ac.uk — MB BS 1971 Lond.; PhD Camb. 1987; DPhil Oxf. 1978; BSc (Hons.) Lond. 1968; FRCOG 1991, M 1979; LLM (Distinction) Herts. 1998. (Middlx.) Cons. O & G Addenbrooke's Hosp. & Rosie Matern. Hosp. Camb.; Univ. Lect. (Obst. & Gyn.) Univ. Camb.; Fell. St Catharine's Coll. Camb. Socs: Fell.ship Roy. Soc. of Med.; Amer. Coll. Legal Med.; Medico-Legal Soc. Prev: Regist. (O & G) Simpson Memor. Matern. Pavil. Roy. Infirm. Edin.; Resid. Med. Off. (Obst.) Qu. Charlotte's Matern. Hosp. Lond.; MRC Research Fell. Nuffield Inst. Med. Research Univ. Oxf.

DALTON, Maria Elizabeth 3 Grainger Road, Isleworth TW7 6PQ — MB BS 1993 Lond.

DALTON, Martin James The Surgery, 59 Mansfield Road, Blidworth, Mansfield NG21 0RB Tel: 01623 795461 Fax: 01623 490514; 10 Bourne Drive, Ravenshead, Nottingham NG15 9FN — MB ChB 1985 Manch.; MRCGP 1993; DRCOG 1989. Socs: Mansfield Med. Soc.

DALTON, Mary Bernadette The Health Centre, Rydal Road, Ambleside Tel: 0153 94 32693; Swallowhowe, Gale Howe, Ambleside LA22 0BG Tel: 0153 94 32222 — MB ChB 1973 Manch.; BSc (Hons. Anat.) Manch. 1971; Cert. Family Plann. JCC 1977. (manch) Sen. Med. Off. (Occupat. Health) W.morland Co. Hosp. Kendal; Sen. Med. Off. (Occupat.al Health) Roy. Lancaster Infirm., Lancaster. Socs: Soc. Occupat. Med. & Med. Wom. Federat.; Fac.Fam.Plann.Reproduc.health.care; Brit. Menopause Soc. Prev: Research Regist. (Med.) Roy. Lancaster Infirm.; SHO (Paediat.) Duchess of York Hosp. Babies Manch.; Ho. Off. (Gen. Surg.) Manch. Roy. Infirm.

DALTON, Maureen Elizabeth Hillside Lodge, Tunstall Hill, Sunderland SR3 1AA Tel: 0191 528 9259 — MB BS 1975 Lond.; MRCS Eng. LRCP Lond. 1975 Lond.; FRCOG 1994; M 1981; MRCS Eng. LRCP Lond. 1975; FRCOG 1994, M 1981. (Roy. Free) Cons. O & G Sunderland DHA. Prev: Lect. (O & G) St. Jas. Univ. Hosp. Leeds; Regist. (O & G) Lond. Hosp.; SHO (Obst.) Qu. Charlotte's Matern. Hosp. Lond.

DALTON, Maurice (Surgery), 163 Beverley Road, Hull HU3 1UB Tel: 01482 28861; West Croft, 7 Sands Lane, Elloughton, Brough HU15 1JH Tel: 01482 667354 — MB ChB 1959 St. And. (St. And.) Med. Off. Reckitt & Colman Ltd. Hull.

DALTON, Michael Harry (retired) Chetton Grange, Chetton, Bridgnorth WV16 6UE Tel: 01746 789499 — MB ChB 1963 St.

And.; DCH Eng. 1968. Ex-Sec. Dudley Local Med. Comm. Prev: Sen. Med. Off. Sierra Leone Milit. Forces & OC Milit. Hosp. Freetown, Sierra Leone.

DALTON, Michael John Thomson Abbey House Medical Centre, 2 Defoe Road, London N16 0EF Tel: 020 7254 6820; 16 Old Park Road, London N13 Tel: 020 8886 4025 — MSc (Microelectronics) CNAA 1984; MRCS Eng. LRCP Lond. 1966; MRCGP 1977. (Roy. Free) Socs: Roy. Soc. Med. (Sect. Gen. Pract.). Prev: Hon. Clin. Asst. (Weight Reduction) Hackney Hosp.; Ho. Surg. St. Leonard's Hosp. Lond.; Ho. Phys. Lond. Jewish Hosp.

DALTON, Patrick Kevin Willows Medical Centre, Osbourne Drive, Queensbury, Bradford BD13 2GD Tel: 01274 882008 Fax: 01274 818447 — MB ChB 1980 Leeds.

DALTON, Richard Stuart John Ash Riding, Gatesdene Cl, Little Gaddesden, Berkhamsted HP4 1PB — MB ChB 1997 Leic.; DTM & H 1999.

DALTON, Rosemary Jean St George's Surgery, St Pauls Medical Centre, 121 Swindon Road, Cheltenham GL50 4DP Tel: 01242 707755 Fax: 01242 707749; Lindens, 11 Battledown Drive, Cheltenham GL52 6RX Tel: 01242 233680 — MB ChB 1981 Bristol; MRCGP 1996; DCH RCP Lond. 1985; DRCOG 1984; BSc (Hons.) (Med. Microbiol.) Bristol 1978. Prev: Trainee GP Gosbury Hill Health Centre Chessington; Clin. Med. Off. (Child Health) W. Lambeth HA; Trainee GP Coventry VTS.

DALTON, Ms Ruth 23 Grange Road, Kingston upon Thames KT1 2QU Email: ruth_dalton@bigfoot.com — MB BS 1985 Lond.; FRCOphth 1991. (St mary's Hospital Medical School, London) Cons. Ophth., Ashford & St. Peters NHS Trust, Ashford Hopsital, Ashford TW15 3AA.

DALTON, Sarah Jane Mr Kay Gordon Centre, Royal Manchester Childern's Hospital, Pedlebury, Manchester — MB BChir 1991 Camb.; MD 1999 Manch.; MA Camb. 1992; MRCPI 1998. Specialist Regist. Paediat., N. W. Region, Manch. Prev: Clin. Research Fell. (Atopic Eczema) Univ. Dept. Paediat. Booth Hall Childr. Hosp. Manch.; SHO (Paediat.) Kings Coll. Hosp. Lond., St. Jas. Univ. Hosp. Leeds.

DALTON, Stephen John 11 Glenthorn Road, West Jesmond, Newcastle upon Tyne NE2 3HL — MB BS 1996 Lond.

DALTON, Timothy Mark 11 Moisty Lane, Marchington, Uttoxeter ST14 8JY — MB BChir 1994 Camb.; BSc (Hons) City 1991; DRCOG 1998.

DALTON, Toby, Surg. Lt.-Cdr. RN Retd. Tel: 01720 422628 Fax: 01720 423160; Thorgils, Ram's Valley, St Mary's TR21 0JX Tel: 01720 423207 — MB BS 1980 Lond.; DA (UK) 1986. (St. Bart. Hosp. Lond.) Princip. Gen. Pract.; H.M.A. St. Marys Lifeboat. Prev: DPMD HMS Invincible.

DALTON, William Thomas Garfield Coastal Villages Practice, Pippin Close, Ormesby St. Margaret, Great Yarmouth NR29 3RW Tel: 01493 730205 Fax: 01493 733120; Brambles, Barn Lane, Runham, Great Yarmouth NR29 3EF — MB BCh BAO 1988 Belf.; MRCGP 1992; DMH Belf. 1993; DRCOG 1992; T(GP) 1992; Cert. Prescribed Equiv. Exp JCPTGP 1992; Cert. Family Plann. JCC 1992; DGM RCP Lond. 1990. (Qu. Univ. Belf.) Socs: E.Norf. Primary Care Audit Gp. Prev: Asst. GP Norwich; Trainee GP/SHO Erne Hosp. Enniskillen VTS; Trainee GP Peterhead, Aberd.sh.

DALTREY, Mr Ian Robert Royal Cornwall Hospital (Treliske), Truro TR1 3LJ Tel: 01872 274242; 4 Radnor Close, Bodmin PL31 2BZ Tel: 01208 78470 Fax: 01208 78470 Email: 101567.1721@compuserve.com — MB BS 1990 Lond.; FRCS Eng. 1995. (Roy. Free Hosp. Sch. Med. Lond.) Specialist Regist. Bristol & W.. Rotat. - Roy. Cornw. Hosp. (Tresliske), Truro. Socs: Brit. Assn. Surgic. Oncol. Prev: RCS Eng. Juniper Trust Research Regist. Roy. Surrey Co. Hosp. Guildford; Sen. SHO (Surg.) Poole Gen. Hosp.; SHO (Surg.) Soton. Gen. Hosp.

DALY, Anthony James 7 Victoria Park Road, Exeter EX2 4NT Tel: 01392 73696 — MB BChir 1938 Camb.; MA, MD Camb. 1944, MB BChir 1938; FRCP Lond. 1966, M 1946; MRCS Eng. LRCP Lond. 1938. (Camb. & Lond. Hosp.) Phys. Roy. Devon & Exeter Hosp.; Maj. RAMC TARO. Socs: Fell. Roy. Soc. Med. Prev: Ho. Surg., Path. Asst. & Med. Regist. Lond. Hosp.

DALY, Anthony St John The Surgery, Selcroft Avenue, Quinton, Birmingham B32 2BX Tel: 0121 428 2880 — MB ChB 1986 Leeds.

DALY, Brigid Martina Dermatology Unit, Burnley General Hospital, Burnley BB12 7ST Tel: 01282 474816; 10 Westmister Close, Simonstone, Burnley BB12 7ST — MB BCh BAO 1975 NUI; FRCPI 1996; MRCPI 1978. (Cork) Cons. Dermat. Burnley Gen. Hosp. & Blackburn Roy. Infirm. Prev: Sen. Regist. (Dermat.) Roy. Vict. Infirm. Newc.; Regist. (Dermat.) Aberd. Roy. Infirm.; Regist. (Neurol.) Regional Hosp. Cork.

DALY, Caroline Ann Patricia Waterside Health Centre, Glendermolt Road, Londonderry BT47 6AU Tel: 028 7132 0100 Email: enquiries@drconnolly.com — MB BCh BAO 1991 Belf.; MRCGP 1996; DFFP 1996. p/t Gen. Practitioner, Glendermot Rd., Lond.derry BT47 6AU. Socs: BMA; Roy. Coll. Gen. Pract.; Fac. of Family Plann. and Reproductive Health c/o the Roy. Coll. of Obst.s and Gynaecologists (Diplomate). Prev: Clin. Med. Off. WHSSB, N. Irel.; Trainee GP/SHO Altnagelvin Area Hosp.

DALY, Catherine 2 Crieve Court, Newry BT34 2PE — MB BCh 1998 Belf.; MB BCh Belf 1998.

DALY, Conal David 6 View Terrace, Aberdeen AB25 2RR — MB BCh BAO 1987 NUI.

DALY, Mr David William (retired) Rigg Cottage, Oswaldkirk, York YO62 5XZ Tel: 01439 788678 — ChM Leeds 1966, MB ChB 1955; FRCS Eng. 1959; MRCS Eng. LRCP Lond. 1955. Prev: Cons. Surg. Univ. Hosp. Nottm.

DALY, Dorothy Millicent (retired) 135 Blacker Lane, Netherton, Wakefield WF4 4EZ Tel: 01924 272884 — MB ChB Liverp. 1963. Prev: SCMO Pontefract Health Auth.

DALY, Elizabeth Lynne Adolescent Forensic Service, Mental Health Services of Salford, Prestwich, Manchester M25 3BL Tel: 0161 772 3668 Fax: 0161 772 3443 — MB BChir 1980 Camb.; MRCPsych 1984. (Cambridge University and Guy's Hospital) Cons. Adolesc. Forens. Psychiat. Ment. Health Serv. Salford NHS Trust. Prev: Sen. Regist. (Forens. Psychiat.) Wakefield.; Sen. Regist. (Old Age Psychiat.) St. Jas. Univ. Hosp. Leeds; Sen. Regist. (Psychiat.) Fulbourn Hosp. Camb.

DALY, Flora Mary (retired) Rigg Cottage, Oswaldkirk, York YO62 5XZ Tel: 01439 788678 — BM BCh 1955 Oxf.; MA, BM BCh Oxf. 1955. Prev: Clin. Asst. Dept. Genitourin. Med. Gen. Hosp. Nottm.

DALY, Francis William Marie Hurt (retired) 8 St Leonards, Tickhill, Doncaster DN11 9HX Tel: 01302 742080 — MB ChB Birm. 1948.

DALY, Gillian Anne The Wooda Surgery, Clarence Wharf, Barnstaple Street, Bideford EX39 4AU Tel: 01237 471071 Fax: 01237 471059; The Red House, 17 Pilton St, Barnstaple EX31 1PJ Tel: 01271 45569 — MB BS 1979 Lond.; DRCOG 1983. (St. Bart.) Prev: Trainee GP/SHO N. Devon Dist. Hosp. Barnstaple VTS; Ho. Surg. Roy. Berks. Hosp. Reading; Ho. Off. (Med.) Rochford Gen. Hosp. Rochford.

DALY, Helen Clare Siobhan 54 Oakwood Avenue, Beckenham BR3 6PJ — MB ChB 1993 Leeds; FRCA 1999 London. Specialist Regist. (Anaesth.) Frimley Pk. Hosp.; SpR (Anaesth.), Guys and St Thomas NHS Trust, Lond. Prev: SpR (Anaesth.) Univ. Hosp. Lewisham; SpR (Anaesth.) Qu. Vict. Hosp. E. Grinstead; SHO (Anaesth.) Univ. Hosp. Lewisham.

DALY, Jerome Joseph (retired) — MB BChir 1951 Camb.; MA, MD Camb. 1962, MB BChir 1951; FRCP Lond. 1972, M 1954. Hon. Clin. Lect. Univ. Sheff.; Examr. RCP Lond. (Med.). Prev: Cons. Phys. Sheff. DHA (T).

DALY, Joanne Elizabeth Karis Medical Centre, Waterworks Road, Edgbaston, Birmingham B16 9AL — MB ChB 1990 Sheff.; FRCS Ed. 1995.

DALY, Mr John Crawford Plastic Surgery Unit, Nottingham City Hospital, Hucknall Road, Nottingham NG5 1PB Tel: 0115 969 1169 Ext: 45773 — MB ChB 1980 Glas.; FRCS (Plast) 1996; FRCS Glas. 1984. Cons. Plastic Surg. Nottm. City Hosp. Prev: SR (Plastic Surg.) Nottm. City Hosp.; Regist. (Plastic Surg.) Shotley Bridge Gen. Hosp. Consett; SHO (Plastic Surg.) Sheff. & Billericay.

DALY, John Gerard 21 Main Street, Randalstown, Antrim BT41 3AB — MB BCh BAO 1974 Belf.; MRCP (UK) 1977.

DALY, Joseph 136 Dinting Road, Glossop SK13 7UU — MB ChB 1998 Glas.; MB ChB Glas 1998.

DALY, Karen Elizabeth Kingston Hospital, Galsworthy Road, Kingston upon Thames KT2 7QB Tel: 020 8546 7711 Fax: 020 8934 3267 — BM 1982 Soton.; FRCS Eng. 1986; FRCS (Orth.) 1994. Cons. Trauma & Orthop. Kingston Hosp. Surrey; Hon. Cons.

Qu. Mary's Univ. Hosp. Lond. Socs: Brit. Orthopaedic Assn.; Brit. Sociey Childr.'s Orthopaedic Surg.

DALY, Margaret Mary Department of Clinical Oncology, Addenbrookes Hospital, Kills Road, Cambridge; 107 Lynn Road, Grimston, King's Lynn PE32 1AG — MB BCh BAO 1984 NUI; MRCPI 1987; DCO 1991; FRCR 1992. Cons. (Clin. Oncol.) Addenbrookes Hosp. & Qu. Eliz. Hosp., Kings Lynn. Socs: Roy. Coll. Radiol.; MRCP (Irel.). Prev: Sen. Regist. (Oncol.) Beatsen Oncol. Centre W.ern Infirm. Glas.; Regist. (Radiat.Oncol.) W.. Gen. Hosp. Edin.

DALY, Mark Elliot Department Of Medicine, Wansbeck General Hospital, Ashington NE63 9JJ — MB BS 1991 Newc.

DALY, Martin Hugh, QHS, Brigadier late RAMC Longhope House, 47A Bridge St., Chepstow NP16 5EY; Longhope House, 47A Bridge St, Chepstow NP16 5EY Tel: 01291 627273 — MB ChB Birm. 1960; FFA RCSI 1970; DA Eng. 1963. (Birm.) Hon. Col. 204 (NI) Field Hosp. (V); Civil. Cons. Anaes. MOD. Socs: Sands Cox Med. Soc.; Airborne Med. Soc.; Assn. Anaesths. Prev: Col. Commandant RAMC; Cons. Adviser (Anaesth.) to the Army; Hon. Cons. Anaesth. Univ. Newc. Hosps.

DALY, Professor Michael de Burgh (retired) Department of Physiology, Royal Free and University College Medical School, Royal Free Campus, Rowland Hill St., London NW3 2PF Tel: 020 7830 2603 Fax: 020 7433 1921 Email: fleitao@rfhsm.ac.uk — MB BChir Camb. 1947; ScD Camb. 1960, MA 1948, BA 1944, MD 1963; FRCP Lond. 1978, M 1972. Distinguished Vis. Physiol. Roy. Free and Univ. Coll. Med. Sch.s, Roy. Free Campus. Prev: Prof. Physiol. (Univ. Lond.) St. Bart. Hosp. Med. Coll. 1958-1984.

DALY, Oscar Eunan Department of Psychiatry, Lagan Valley Hospital, Lisburn BT28 1JP Tel: 01846 665141 Fax: 01846 603899; Downshire Hospital, Ardglass Road, Drakes Broughton, Pershore BT30 6RA Tel: 01396 613311 — MB BCh BAO 1982 NUI; MRCPsych 1987. Cons. Community Psychiat. Lagan Valley Hosp. Lisburn. Socs: Eur. Soc. Traum. Stress Studies; Internat. Soc. Traum. Stress Studies. Prev: Sen. Regist. & Sen. Tutor Qu. Univ. Belf.

DALY, Pamela Evelyn Department of Anaesthesia, Royal National Throat, Nose & Ear Hospital, Grays Inn Road, London WC1X 8DA Tel: 020 7837 8855 Fax: 020 7278 3015; 54 Oakwood Avenue, Beckenham BR3 6PJ Tel: 020 8650 1856 Fax: 020 8650 1856 — MB BS 1957 Lond.; FFA RCS Eng. 1965; DA Eng. 1959. (Middlx.) Socs: Assn. Anaesths.; Roy. Soc. Med.; BMA. Prev: Cons. Anaesth. Greenwich HA & Roy. Nat. Throat, Nose & Ear Hosp. Lond.; Sen. Regist. (Anaesth.) Char. Cross Hosp. Lond.; Regist. (Anaesth.) Barnet Gen. Hosp.

DALY, Paul Gabriel The Central Hove Surgery, 3 Ventnor Villas, Hove BN3 3DD Tel: 01273 744911 Fax: 01273 744919 — MB BCh BAO 1975 NUI; DCH 1980. GP Hove. Prev: GP Trainee Bedford VTS; Rotating SHO (Surg.) Basingstoke Dist. Hosp.; SHO (Surg.) St. Luke's Hosp. Rathgar Dub.

DALY, Paul John 17 Salisbury Road, Moseley, Birmingham B13 8JS — LRCPI & LM, LRSCI & LM 1957; LRCPI & LM, LRCSI & LM 1957.

DALY, Rachel Mary 86 Woodman Road, Warley, Brentwood CM14 5AZ; 120 Coleraine Road, Blackheath, London SE3 7NU Tel: 020 8853 1669 Fax: 020 8333 3402 — MB BCh BAO 1988 NUI; MRCPsych 1992. (University College Cork, Ireland) Community Forens. Psychiat. Guys & Lewisham Ment. Health Trust.

DALY, Richard Charles 19 Edge View Road, Congleton CW12 3JQ — MB BS 1998 Newc.; MB BS Newc 1998.

DALY, Richard Francis Swallownest Health Centre, Aston, Sheffield S26 2BG Tel: 0114 287 2486; 1 Clifton Crescent N., Rotherham S65 2AS — MRCS Eng. LRCP Lond. 1981; DRCOG 1984. Prev: Dist. Med. Off. Kawambwa, Zambia.

DALY, Richard Simon Department of Pathology & Microbiology, Faculty of Medicine, University of Bristol, Tyndall Avenue, Bristol BS8 1TH Tel: 0117 928 2585 Fax: 0117 929 2440 Email: richard.s.daly@bris.ac.uk; Hall Floor Flat, 10 Cotham Gardens, Bristol BS6 6HD Tel: 0117 970 6188 Email: richard.s.daly@doctors.org.uk — MB ChB 1995 Birm.; BSc Birm. 1994. (Univ. Birm.) Lect. (Histopath.) Univ. Bristol. Socs: Assn. of Clin. Pathologists. Prev: Demonst.Histopath.Univ.Bristol; SHO (Histopath.) United Bristol Healthcare NHS Trust; Ho. Phys. (Nephrol. & Gen. Med.) & Ho. Surg. (Gen. Surg. & Otorhinolaryng.) Univ. Hosp. Birm. NHS Trust.

DALY, Rosemarie Joy 9 Mildenhall Road, London E5 0RT — MB BS 1994 Lond.; BSc (Biol.) Lond. 1985; MSc (Med. Parasitology) Lond. 1986. (St. Bart.) SHO (O & G) Lond. Hosp.

DALY, Rosemary Robin Lane Medical Centre, Robin Lane, Pudsey LS28 7DEBR — MB BCh BAO 1988 Belf.; MRCGP 1995; DRCOG 1994. (Qu. Univ. Belf.) p/t GP Leeds. Prev: SHO (O & G) Leeds Gen. Infirm.

DALY, Timothy Patrick (retired) 3 Mulroy Road, Sutton Coldfield B74 2QA Tel: 0121 354 2775 — MB ChB 1953 Birm.

DALZELL, Anita Jane Camm Moston Lodge Children's Centre, Countess of Chester Health Park, Liverpool Road, Chester CH2 1UL Tel: 01244 365000; Medhurst, St. Bridget's Lane, West Kirby, Wirral CH48 3JT Tel: 0151 625 0742 — MRCS Eng. LRCP Lond. 1979; BSc (Hons.) Biochem. Lond. 1976; MB BS Lond. 1979. (Char. Cross) Clin. Med. Off. Wirral HA.; Staff Grade (Paediat. Audiol.) Countess of Chester Hosp. Chester.

DALZELL, Anthony (retired) Broughton Park, Threapwood, Malpas SY14 7AN Tel: 01948 770653 — MB ChB 1948 Liverp. Prev: GP Chesh.

DALZELL, Anthony Mark Royal Liverpool Children's NHS Trust, Alder Hey, Eaton Road, Liverpool L12 2AP Tel: 0151 252 5373 Fax: 0151 252 5928 — MB BS 1980 Lond.; BSc (Hons.) (Biochem.) Lond. 1976; MRCP (UK) 1984; MRCS Eng. LRCP Lond. 1979; FRCPCH 1997. (Char. Cross) Cons. Paediat. Gastroenterol. Roy. Liverp. Childr. NHS Trust. Prev: Lect. (Child Health) Roy. Belf. Hosp. for Sick Childr.; Regist. (Paediat. Gastroenterol.) Roy. Childr. Hosp., Brisbane, Austral.; Research Fell. (Cystic Fibrosis) Roy. Liverp. Childr. NHS Trust Alder Hey.

DALZELL, Gavin William Noel 17 Royal Lodge Road, Belfast BT8 7UL — MD 1987 Belf.; MB BCh BAO 1981; MRCP (UK) 1984. Cons. Cardiol. Roy. Vict. Hosp. Belf. Prev: Cons. Cardiol. Altnagelvin Hosp. Lond.derry.

DALZELL, John Langley Medical Practice, Oak Hill Health Centre, Oak Hill Road, Surbiton KT6 6EN Tel: 020 8390 9996 Fax: 020 8390 4057 — MB BS 1980 Lond.; DRCOG 1983; DA Eng. 1982.

DALZELL, Kathleen (retired) Broughton Park, Threapwood, Malpas SY14 7AN Tel: 01948 770653 — MB ChB (Hnrs.) Liverp. 1950. JP. Prev: Princip. Clin. Med. Off. (Child Health) Clwyd HA.

DALZELL, Margaret Carol Urbal Road Surgery, 67 Urbal Road, Coagh, Cookstown BT80 0DP Tel: 028 7973 7243 Fax: 028 7973 7602 — MB BCh BAO 1984 Belf.; MB BCh BAO Belf. l984; MRCGP 1989; DRCOG 1988.

DALZIEL, Alison (retired) 12 Greyfriars Gardens, St Andrews KY16 9HG Tel: 01334 477035 — MB ChB 1947 Glas. Prev: SCMO Derbysh. AHA.

DALZIEL, Elizabeth Alison Brantwood, 13 Reedley Drive, Reedley, Burnley BB10 2QZ — MB ChB 1981 Manch.; BSc (Med. Sci) St. And. 1978.

DALZIEL, John Alexander Hereford Hospitals NHS Trust, Hereford General Hospital, Nelson St., Hereford HR1 2PA Tel: 01432 355444 Fax: 01432 274039; Tanhouse Barn, Tarrington, Hereford HR1 4HR Tel: 01432 890359 Fax: 01432 890359 — MB 1972 Camb.; BChir 1971; FRCP Lond. 1991; MRCP (UK) 1975. (Guy's) Cons. Phys. (Geriat. & Gen. Med.) Hereford Gen. Hosp. Socs: Brit. Geriat. Soc. Prev: Cons. Phys. (Geriat. Med.) Leicester Gen. Hosp.; Sen. Regist. (Gen. & Geriat. Med.) Radcliffe Infirm. & Cowley Rd.; Hosp. Oxf.; Regist. (Gen. Med.) St. And. Hosp. Bow.

DALZIEL, Katharine Lesley Department of Dermatology, Queen's Medical Centre, University Hospital NHS Trust, Nottingham NG7 2UH Tel: 0115 924 9924 — MB BS 1977 Lond.; MD Lond. 1989; FRCP Lond. 1995; MRCP (UK) 1980. Cons. Dermat. Qu.'s Med. Centre Univ. Hosp. Nottm. Prev: Sen. Regist. (Dermat.) Slade Hosp. Oxf.; MRC Train. Fell. Dermat. Univ. Hosp. Wales.

DALZIEL, Malcolm Lane Cottage, Claughton, Lancaster LA2 9LA — MB ChB 1967 Liverp.; FRCR 1975; DMRD Liverp. 1971. Cons. Radiol. Roy. Lancaster Infirm.

DALZIEL, Norman Ian Little Anniegrove, Kingston Road, Shalbourne, Marlborough SN8 3QH — MRCS Eng. LRCP Lond. 1966.

DAMAN WILLEMS, Charlotte Elizabeth University Hospital Lewisham, Lewisham High St., London SE13 6LA Tel: 020 8333 3000 Email: charlotte.daman@uhl.nhs.uk; 5 Aldebert Terrrace, Stockwell, London SW8 1BH Email: charlotte.daman@uhl.nhs.uk — BM 1977 Soton.; MRCP (UK) 1981; FRCP (UK) 1989; FRCPCH

1997. Cons. (Paediat.) Univ. Hosp. Lewisham Lond. Prev: Regist. (Paediat.) Hosp. for Sick Childr. Gt. Ormond St. Lond.

DAMANI, Nizamuddin Noordin Craigavon Laboratory, Craigavon Hospital, 68 Lurgan Road, Craigavon BT63 5QQ Tel: 02838334444 Fax: 0238 344582; 9 Drumclougher Park, Ballyhannon Lane, Portadown, Craigavon BT63 5TW Tel: 0238 338496 Fax: 0238 334451 — MB BS 1979 Karachi; MSc Lond. 1986; MRCPath 1988; FRCPath 1997; FRCPI 1998. Cons. Med. Microbiol. Craigavon Area Hosp. Co. Armagh; Clin. Director, Path. & Laborat. Serv.s, S.ern Helath and Social Serv. Bd., N.Irel. Socs: Founder Mem.: Infec. Control Soc. of Pakisatan; Mem. Internat. Comm. Assn. Professionals in Infec. Control (USA). Prev: SHO (Path.) Ashford Hosp. Middlx.; Regist. (Microbiol.) St. Helier Hosp. Carshalton; Sen. Regist. (Microbiol.) Roy. Vict. Hosp. & Belf. City Hosp.

DAMANI, Zaherali Bandali 16 Church Road, Wilmslow SK9 6HH — LRCP LRCS 1982 Ed.; LRCP LRCS Ed. LRCPS Glas. 1982.

DAMANIA, Achla 5 Connaght Close, Wellington College, Crowthorne RG11 Tel: 01344 778601 — MB ChB 1986 Manch. Prev: GP Partnership.

DAMANT, Harry Guybon 13 Westbourne Terrace, London W2 3UL Tel: 020 7723 1311 — MB BS 1949 Lond.; LMSSA Lond. 1949. (St. Mary's)

DAMANY, Mr Devendra Shashikant 40 Meynell walk, Netherton, Peterborough PE3 9RR Tel: 01733 874000 Fax: 01733 875172 — MB BS 1987 Gujarat, India; MS Orthop. Gujarat, India 1990; FRCS 1999. (Smt. N.H.L. Med. Coll. Ahmedabad, India) Staff Surg. (Trauma & Orthop.) P'boro. Hosp. NHS Trust. Socs: Indian Orthop. Assn.; Ahmedabad Orthop. Soc.; Ahmedabad Med. Assn. Prev: Clin. Fell. (Paediat. Orthop.) Roy. Hosp. Sick Childr. Glas.; Regist. (Trauma & Orthop.) Neath Gen. Hosp. & W. Wales Gen. Hosp. Carmarthen.

DAMAS MORA, Jorge Manuel Ribeiro Department of Psychiatry, Eaves Lane Hospital, Eaves Lane, Chorley PR6 0TT — Lic. Med. Oporto, Portgal 1967.

DAMASKINIDOU, Katina Prudence Skynner Family Therapy Clinic, Springfield Hospital, 61 Glenburnie Road, London SW17 7DJ — Ptychio Iatrikes 1985 Athens.

DAMATO, Professor Bertil Eric St. Paul's Eye Unit, Royal Liverpool University Hospital, Prescot St., Liverpool L7 8XP Tel: 0151 706 3973 Fax: 0151 706 5436; Curlews, Cottage Lane, Gayton, Wirral CH60 8PA Tel: 0151 342 2360 — MRCS Eng. LRCP Lond. 1977; MD Malta 1989; PhD Glas. 1988; FRCS Glas. 1990; FRCS Ed. 1982; FRCOphth 1989. Cons. Ophth. St. Paul's Eye Unit Liverp. Socs: BMA; French Ophth. Soc.; Amer. Acad. of Ophth. Prev: Reader (Ophth.) Glas. Univ.; Sen. Regist. (Ophth.) Tennent Inst. W. Infirm. Glas.; SHO (Path.) & Ho. Surg. & Ho. Phys. Glas. Roy. Infirm.

DAMBAWINNA, (Kankanige Pemasiri) Ranjith Grays Health Centre, Brooke Road, Grays RM17 5BY Tel: 01375 394439 Fax: 01375 394685; Woodlands, Warren Lane, North Stifford, Grays RM16 6YG Tel: 01375 480056 Fax: 01375 480056 — MB BS 1968 Ceylon. (Colombo) Socs: LMC; Coll. Gen. Pract., Sri Lanka. Prev: Clin. Asst. Varicose Vein Clinic Orsett Hosp.; Clin. Asst. (Dermat.) Basildon Hosp.

DAMBO, Karina Una 47 Turnbridge House, Spa-Green Est., Roseberry St., London EC1R 4TT — MB BS 1986 Benin.

DAMERAU, Nikolai Boris Leo Emil Good Hope Hospital, Rectory Road, Sutton Coldfield B75 7RR — State Exam Med 1988 Freiburg.

DAMES, Gillian 122 Braid Road, Edinburgh EH10 6AS — MB ChB 1990 Glas.

DAMJANOVIC, Vladimir (retired) 2 Keswick Road, Liverpool L18 9UH Tel: 0151 724 1786 — PhD Lond. 1973; MD Belgrade 1958; FRCPath 1987, M 1975. Hon. Lect. (Med. Microbiol.) Univ. Liverp. Prev: Cons. Med. Microbiol. Roy. Liverp. Univ. Hosp. Trust.

DAMLE, Anita Dileep St. Andrews Hospital, Billing Road, Northampton NN1 5DG Tel: 01604 616305 Fax: 01604 616306 Email: damle@doctors.org.uk — MB BS 1974 Gujarat; MRC Pysch 1981; Dip BA 1998. (B J Med Sch) Cons. Psych. In private Pract. & medico-legal Pract.; JP. Socs: RCPsych; Brit. Indian Psychiat.s Assn. Prev: Clin.dir.&Cons.Psychiat.St Crispins Hosp.N.ampton; Clin. Tutor, St. Cripsin's Hosp., N.ampton.

DAMMERS, Felicity Jane Hounsell The Wells Park Practice, 1 Wells Park Road, London SE26 6JQ Tel: 020 8699 2840; 6 Knatchbull Road, London SE5 9QS Tel: 020 7274 5502 — BM BS 1975 Nottm.; MRCGP 1989; DCH RCP Lond. 1981. Prev: Lect. (Gen. Pract. Studies) King's Coll. Sch. Med. & Dent. Lond.

DAMMS, Jean Catherine 15 Tamella Road, Botley, Southampton SO30 2NY — MB ChB 1980 Liverp.; MRCPsych 1990. Staff Psychiat. (Old Age Psychiat.) Cedar Wood Day Hosp. & St. Christopher's Hosp. Fareham. Prev: Regist. (Child Psychiat.) Glas.; Regist. (Psychiat.) Sheff.

DAMMS, Mary Malcolm (retired) 14 The Crescent, Farnborough GU14 7AS — MRCS Eng. LRCP Lond. 1946.

DAMOA-SIAKWAN, Stephanie Amma 35 Lennox Street, Birmingham B19 2PB — MB BS 1993 Lond.; BSc Lond. 1990. SHO (Med.) Heartlands Hosp. Birm. Prev: Ho. Off. (Med.) P.ss Roy. Hosp. Telford; Ho. Off. (Surg.) Guy's Hosp. Lond.

DAMRI, Michele 202 Lonsdale Drive, Gillingham ME8 9JN; 8 Thorleigh Road, Didsbury, Manchester M20 2DF Tel: 0161 445 1995 — MB ChB 1989 Manch.; MRCGP. (Manchester)

DANA, Ali 7 Elm Court, Nether St., London N3 1RH — MB BS 1992 Lond.; MRCP (UK) 1995. (Univ. Coll. & Middlx. Sch. Med.) Clin. Research Fell. Hatter Inst. Acad. & Clin. Cardiol. Univ. Coll. Lond. Hosps. Prev: SHO Rotat. (Med.) Char. Cross & W. Middlx. Hosps.

DANA, Emily Catherine 118 Hemingford Road, London N1 1DE — BM BCh 1997 Oxf.

DANAHER, James Gerald 33 Ashby Road, Ravenstone, Coalville, Leicester LE67 2AA Tel: 01530 836122 — BM BCh 1950 Oxf.; MA, BM BCh Oxf. 1950. (Oxf.)

DANAHER, Paul John Groby Road Medical Centre, 9 Groby Road, Leicester LE3 9ED — MB ChB 1992 Leic.; BSc (Hons.) ARCS Lond. 1987; DRCOG 1995; MRCGP 1997. (Leicester) GP Princip. Prev: SHO Leicester VTS.

DANBURY, Robert 55 Croham Road, South Croydon CR2 7HE Tel: 020 8688 6317 — MB BS 1953 Lond.; MRCS Eng. LRCP Lond. 1953; LMSSA Lond. 1952; DPhysMed. Eng. 1958. (Roy. Free) Socs: Brit. Assn. Physical Med. & Brit. Assn. Manip. Med. Prev: Dir. of Studies Brit. Assn. Manip. Med.; Cons. Brit. Rheum. & Arthritis Assn.; Regist. (Physical Med. & Rheum.) St. Stephen's Hosp. Chelsea.

DANBY, Gladys Anyan, MBE (retired) 6 Walford House, Walford Cross, Taunton TA2 8QW Tel: 01823 412047 — LMSSA 1927 Lond. Hosp. Ophth. Prev: Regist. (Psychiat.) Bromham Hosp. Bedford.

DANBY, Judith Ashwell Medical Centre, Ashwell Road, Manningham, Bradford BD8 9DP Tel: 01274 490409 Fax: 01274 499112; Pundles Farm, Pavement Lane, Bradshaw, Halifax HX2 9NW Tel: 01422 248842 — MB BS 1981 Lond.; MRCGP 1985; DRCOG 1984; DCH RCP Lond. 1985.

DANBY, Patrick Richard Fenton and Partners, Medical Centre, Burgage Green, Southwell NG25 0EW Tel: 01636 813561 Fax: 01636 816453; 33 Westgate, Southwell NG25 0JN Tel: 01636 812500 — BM BCh 1965 Oxf.; MA, BM BCh Oxf. 1965; MRCP Lond. 1969.

DANCE, Barbara Margaret (retired) The Acre, Ellastone, Ashbourne DE6 2HD Tel: 0133 532 4256 — MB ChB Ed. 1945. Prev: Res. Med. Off. Pk. Hosp. (EMS) Wellingboro.

DANCE, David Allan Brett Public Health Laboratory, Derriford Hospital, Plymouth PL6 8DH Tel: 01752 792366 Fax: 01752 517 725 Email: david.dance@phnt.swest.nhs.uk — MB ChB 1979 Bristol; MSc Med. Microbiol. Lond. 1984; MRCPath 1986; T(Path) 1991; FRCPath 1995. (University of Bristol) Dir. & Cons. Med. Microbiol. Plymouth Pub. Health Laborat.; Clin. Dir. Pathol., Plymouth Hosp. NHS Trust. Socs: Fell. Roy. Soc. Trop. Med. & Hyg.; Assn. Med. Microbiol.; BMA. Prev: Sen. Lect. (Clin. Sci.) Lond. Sch. Hyg. & Trop. Med.; Asst. Med. Microbiol. Pub. Health Laborat. Dulwich & Soton.; Sen. Lect. Wellcome-Mahidol Univ. Oxf. Trop. Med. Research Progr.

DANCE, Janet Christina Department of Community Child Health, Strathmartine Hospital, Dundee; 412 Perth Road, Dundee DD2 1JQ — MB ChB 1988 Dundee. Staff Grade (Community Health) Strathmartine Hosp. Dundee. Prev: Trainee GP Dundee.

DANCE, Jean Mary (retired) 6 Churchfield Road, Upton-St-Leonards, Gloucester GL4 8AN Tel: 01452 619191 — MB ChB Ed. 1947, DCH 1950. Prev: Med. Regist. Gloucester Roy. Infirm.

DANCE, Paul Jasper Flat 2, Oldthorpe, Esher Green, Esher KT10 8AD — MB BS 1992 Lond.

DANCER, Stephanie Jane Department of Microbiology, Vale of Leven District General Hospital, Alexandria G83 0UA Tel: 01389 754121 — MB BS 1983 Lond.; FRCPath 2001; BSc Lond. 1980, MD 1991; MSc (Clin. Microbiol.) Lond. 1992; MRCPath 1993; DTM & H RCP Lond. 1993. (St. Bart. Hosp. Univ. Lond.) Cons. Microbiol. Vale of Leven Dist. Gen. Hosp. Alexandria; Control of Infec. Off. Argyll; Asst. Edr. Jl. Hosp. Infec.; Nat. Panelist for MicroBiol., Scotl.; UnderGrad. Sub Dean, Glas. Univ. Socs: Path. Soc.; Hosp. Infec. Soc.; Brit. Infec. Soc. Prev: Lect. (Microbiol.) Univ. Edin.; Research Assoc. (Trop. Med.) Mahidol Univ. Bangkok, Thailand; Sen. Regist. (Microbiol.) St. Barts. Hosp. Lond.

DANCEY, Elizabeth-Jane 55 Wimpole Street, London W1M 7DF Tel: 020 7224 1330 Fax: 020 7486 1210; Deepwell House, Quemerford, Calne SN11 8JY — BM 1983 Soton. GP Antwerp, Belgium. Socs: Admin. Comm. Fondat. Pour Preven. Des Allergies Belgium; Internat. Soc. Mesother.; French & Belgium Socs. Mesother. Prev: Resid. Med. Off. Clare Pk. Clinic Farnham; Ho. Phys. St. Mary's Hosp. Newport; Ho. Surg. Salisbury Gen. Infirm.

DANCEY, Frances Madeleine Louise 32 The Green, Steeple Morden, Royston SG8 0NB — MB BS 1994 Lond.

DANCEY, Gairin Sara 32 The Green, Steeple Morden, Royston SG8 0NB — MB BS 1998 Lond.; MB BS Lond 1998.

DANCKWERTS, Richard Evelyn (retired) Thatched Cottage, The Row, Hartest, Bury St Edmunds IP29 4DJ Tel: 01284 830779 — MRCS Eng. LRCP Lond. 1942; MA Camb. 1980, MB BCh 1942. Prev: Dep. Exec. Dir. Med. Counc. on Alcoholism.

DANCOCKS, Angela Carolyn The Lodge, 27 Orchard St., Oughtibridge, Hope Valley S33 9HL — BM BS 1984 Nottm.; BM BS Nottm. l984.

DANCY, Christopher Mark North West London Hospitals NHS Trust, Acton Lane, London NW10 7NS Tel: 020 8453 2151 Fax: 020 8965 1837 Email: mark.dancy@nwlh.nhs.uk; 41 Berwyn Road, Richmond on Thames, Richmond TW10 5BU Tel: 020 8876 1931 — BM BCh 1973 Oxf.; FRCP Lond. 1994; MRCP (UK) 1976. Cons. Cardiol. N. W. Lond. Hosp.s NHs Trust & St. Mary's Hosp. Lond.; Nat. Clin. Chair, Coronary Heart Dis. Collaborative. Prev: Sen. Regist. (Med.) St. Geo Hosp. Lond.

DANCYGER, Anthony Michael 18 Osidge Lane, Southgate, London N14 5JE — MB ChB 1973 Dundee.

DANCZAK, Avril Franciszka Alexandra Practice, 365 Wilbraham Road, Manchester M16 8NG Tel: 0161 860 4400 Fax: 0161 860 7324 — MB BS 1979 Lond.; BSc 1976 Lond.; FRCP 2001 UK; MRCP (UK) 1982; MRCGP 1987. GP Princip.

DANCZAK, Edward Marian 50 Quarry Lane, Christleton, Chester CH3 7AY — MB BS 1975 Lond.; BSc (Hons.) Pharmacol. Lond. 1972, MB BS 1975; Dip Occ H 1998; Dip Med Acupunc 1998. (Univ. Coll. Hosp.) GP Chester. Socs: BMA.

DAND, John Alexander (retired) 94 Aldsworth Avenue, Goring-by-Sea, Worthing BN12 4XE Tel: 01903 244669 Email: john.dand@virgin.net — MB ChB Glas. 1954; DObst RCOG 1955. Prev: GP Worthing.

DAND, Pauline Anne 102 Reginald Street, Luton LU2 7RB — MB ChB 1992 Leic.

DANDAPAT, Raja White City Health Centre, Australian Road, Shepherds Bush, London W12 7PH; 78 Long Lane, Ickenham, Uxbridge UB10 8SY — MB BS 1968 Calcutta; DRCOG 1982.

DANDEKAR, Samantha Sujata 142 Manor Road, Chigwell IG7 5PR Tel: 020 8500 2113; Flat 4 Beauchamp Building, Brookes Market, London EC1N 7SX Tel: 020 7419 0468 Email: sam.@hitbits.co.uk — MB BS 1996 Lond.; BSc Lond. 1993. (St Bartholomew's London) SHO Ophth. Qu. marys Hosp. Sidcup; SHO Ophth. St Thomas Lond. Prev: SHO Opthalmology Greenwich Hosp; SHO (Neurosurg.) King's Coll. Hosp. Lond.; SHO (Cas.) Guy's Hosp. Lond.

DANDIE, Christine Elizabeth Jean 2 Rossett Park Road, Harrogate HG2 9NP Tel: 01423 872931 — MB ChB 1959 Ed. Sen. Clin. Med. Off. (Family Plann) & Clin. Asst. (Gyn.) Harrogate Dist. Hosp. Prev: GP Harrogate; SHO Bradford Childr. Hosp.; Asst. MOH & Sch. Med. Off. Doncaster Co. Boro.

DANDO, Patrick Burke The Medical Defence Union, 192 Altrincham Road, Sharston, Manchester M22 4RZ Tel: 0161 428 1234 Fax: 0161 491 3301; Hob y Deri, 1 Gleggs Close, Great Boughton, Chester CH3 5RE Tel: 01244 342845 — MB BS 1969 Lond.; MRCGP 1974; DA Eng. 1971; DObst RCOG 1971. (Univ. Coll. Hosp.) Head of MDU Advis. Serv. Prev: GP Lichfield Staffs.

***DANDO, Simon Burke** 1 Gleggs Close, Chester CH3 5RE Tel: 04325 127686 — MB BS 1998 Lond.; MB BS Lond 1998; PHD 1995; BSc 1992.

DANDY, Mr David James Orthopaedic Department, Addenbrooke's Hospital, Hills Road, Cambridge CB2 2QQ Tel: 01223 216103; The Old Vicarage, Great Wilbraham, Cambridge CB1 5JF Tel: 01223 880006 Fax: 01223 881779 — MB BChir Camb. 1965; MA Camb. 1965, MD 1990, MChir 1994; FRCS Eng. 1969. (Camb. & Lond. Hosp.) Cons. Orthop. Surg. Addenbrooke's Hosp. Camb.; Hon. Civil Cons. Adviser (Orthop. Surg.) RAF & RN. Socs: Fell. (Ex-Pres.) BOA; (Elect.) Counc. RCS of Eng.; (Ex-Pres.) Internat. Arthroscopy Assn. Prev: Sen. Regist. (Orthop.) St. Bart. Hosp. Lond.; Sen. Fell. Surg. Toronto Gen. Hosp.; Regist. (Orthop.) Roy. Nat. Orthop. Hosp.

DANE, David Maurice Surrey Murtmoor, Puttenham, Guildford GU3 1BQ Tel: 01483 810348 — MB BChir 1955 Camb.; FRCP Lond. 1980, M 1964; MRCS Eng. LRCP Lond. 1951; FRCPath 1972, M 1964. (St. Thos.)

DANE, Mr Thomas Edward Brian Ashlea, 52 Mountsandel Road, Coleraine BT52 1JF Tel: 028703 54404 Fax: 028703 328440 Email: brian@tebdane.demon.co.uk — MB BCh BAO Dub 1967; MB BCh BAO Dub. 1967; MD Dub. 1970; FRCSI 1972; FRCS Eng. 1973. (T.C. Dub.) Cons. Gen. Surg. NW Indep. Clinic Ch.ill Hse. Ballykelly. Socs: Fell. Roy. Acad. Med. Irel.; BMA. Prev: Cons. Gen. Surg. Coleraine Gen. Hosp.; Sen. Regist. (Surg.) Craigavon Area Hosp. & Adelaide Hosp. Dub.; Chief Resid. (Intens. Care) Univ. Alberta Edmonton, Canada.

DANE, Vanessa Julie 84 Valley Road, Rickmansworth WD3 4BJ — MB ChB 1993 Bristol.

DANEE, Asha 4 Portland Heights, 39 Batchworth Lane, Northwood HA6 3HE Tel: 01923 840380 Fax: 01923 826949 — MB BS 1959 Punjab; DCH RCPS Glas. 1965. (Med. Coll. Amritsar) Clin. Med. Off. E. Berks. NHS Trust. Socs: Brit. Assn. Community Drs in Audiol.

DANEE, Punam Kamari 4 Portland Heights, Batchworth Lane, Northwood HA6 3HE — MB BS 1992 Lond.

DANESH, Booth John Department of Medicine, North Glasgow University Hospital NHS Trust, Stobhill Hospital; 3 Ledcameroh Road, Bearsden, Glasgow G61 4AA — MB ChB 1963 Baghdad; PhD Dundee 1972; FRCP Glas. 1989; FRCP Lond. 1988; LAH Dub. 1969; DCH RCPS Glas. 1967. (Baghdad Med. Sch.) Cons. Phys. & Gastroenterol. Stobhill Gen. Hosp. NHS Trust; Hon. Sen. Lect. Univ.Glas. Socs: Coun of Roy. Coll. of Phys.s and Surg.s, Glas.; Brit. Soc. Gastroenterol.; Amer. Soc. Gastroenterol.

DANESHMAND, Loghman Southlands Hospital, Upper Shoreham Road, Shoreham-by-Sea BN43 6TQ — MD 1962 Tehran; MRCPsych 1973; DPM Eng. 1968. Cons. Psychiat. S.lands Hosp. Shoreham-by-Sea, W. Sussex.

DANESHMEND, Tawfique Khan Department of Medicine, Royal Devon & Exeter Hospital (Wonford), Barrack Road, Exeter EX2 5DW Tel: 01392 402803 Fax: 01392 402810; 419 Topsham Road, Countess Wear, Exeter EX2 7AB — MB ChB 1976 Bristol; MB ChB (Distinc. Path.) Bristol 1976; MD Bristol 1985; FRCP Lond. 1994; MRCP (UK) 1979. (Bristol) Cons. Phys. & Gastroenterol. Roy. Devon & Exeter Healthcare NHS Trust. Socs: Fell. Roy. Soc. Med.; Brit. Pharm. Soc.; Roy. Coll. Phys. (Advis. Comm. on Clin. Audit). Prev: Lect. & Hon. Sen. Regist. (Med. & Gastroenterol.) Qu. Med. Centre Univ. Hosp. Nottm.; Lect. (Med.) Bristol Roy Infirm.; Regist. (Gen. Med.) Plymouth Gen. Hosp.

DANFORD, Mr Martin Henry Royal Surrey County Hospital, Egerton Road, Guildford GU2 7XX Tel: 01483 555845 Fax: 01483 555846; 7 Woodlands Close, Claygate, Esher KT10 0JF Tel: 01372 467454 Fax: 01372 462170 — MB BS 1983 Lond.; BDS Lond. 1975; FRCS Glas. 1987; FFD RCSI 1991; LDS RCS Eng. 1975. (Guy's and King's) Cons. Maxillofacial Surg. Roy. Surrey Co. Hosp. Guildford. Prev: Cons. Kings Coll. & St. Geo.'s Hosps.; Sen. Regist. Roy. Surrey Hosp. Guildford; Regist. (Oral Surg.) Soton. Gen. Hosp.

DANG, Raymond Kai Bong Dept of Haematology, Dumfries & Galloway Royal Infirmary, Bankend Rd, Dumfries DG1 4AP Tel: 01387 241441 Fax: 01387 241344 Email: r.dang@dgri.scot.nhs.uk — MB BS 1987 Lond.; MD 1999 Edin.; MRCP (UK) 1992; 2000 MRCPath. Cons. Haematologist, Dumfries & Galloway Roy. Infirm., Dumfries. Socs: BMA; MPS. Prev: Regist. (Haemat.) Edin. Hosps.;

Research Fell. (Haemat.) Roy. Infirm. Edin.; SPR (Haemat) Edin. Hosp.

DANGARE, Nandkumar Dnyaneshwar Dr Hewish, Dangare and Partners, The Health Centre, Bartholomew Avenue, Goole DN14 6AW Tel: 01405 767711 Fax: 01405 768212; Madhuvan, 71 Hook Road, Goole DN14 5JN Tel: 01405 763774 — MB BS 1968 Poona. (B.J. Med. Coll.)

DANGERFIELD, Peter Hugh Department Human Anatomy, Cell Biology & Orthopaedic Surgery, University of Liverpool, PO Box 147, Liverpool L69 3BX Tel: 0151 794 5502; Robert Jones Unit. D1, Alder Hey Childrens Hospital, Eaton Road, Liverpool L12 2AP Tel: 0151 228 4811 — MD 1985 Dundee; MB ChB St. And. 1969. (St. And.) Lect. Human Anat. & Clin. Lect. Dept. Orthop. Surg. Liverp. Univ. & Roy. Liverp. Hosp. Socs: Treas. Brit. Assn. Clin. Anat.; Acting Sec. Internat. Research Soc. Spinal Deformities.

DANGOOR, Adam 3 Clydesdale Gardens, Richmond TW10 5EG Tel: 020 8241 3815 Email: adamd@doctors.org.uk; 3 Clydesdale Gardens, Richmond TW10 5EG Tel: 020 8241 3815 — BM BS 1993 Nottm.; BMedSci Nottm. 1991; MRCP 1999. (Notts) SHO Gen. Med. Grimley Pk. Hosp. Prev: SHO (Paediat.) Qu.s Med. Centre Nottm.; SHO (Neonatology) City Hosp. Nottm.; SHO (Paediat.) Kings Mill Hosp. Mansfield.

DANGOOR, Amira Masouda 47 Leven Walk, Bedford MK41 7XF — MB ChB 1992 Bristol.

DANGOOR, Eric Crouch End Health Centre, 45 Middle Lane, London N8 8PH Tel: 020 8348 7711 — MB BS 1985 Lond.; MRCGP 1993; DCH RCP Lond. 1989. Prev: Trainee GP Roy. Free Hosp. VTS.

DANGOOR, Helene Elisabeth Lilli Southcote Clinic, Southcote Rise, Ruislip HA4 7LJ Tel: 01895 635857 Fax: 01895 625044; 51 Dene Road, Northwood HA6 2DD Tel: 27205 — State Exam Med. Berlin 1963. (Berlin)

DANHER, Joseph Nobles Hospital, Douglas IM3 2JF Tel: 01624 642525 Email: radiol@dhss.gov.im — MB ChB 1980 Liverp.; MRCS Eng. LRCP Lond. 1980; FRCR 1986; DMRD Liverp. 1984. Cons. Radiol. Socs: Founder Mem. Liverp. Radiol. Soc. Prev: Clin. Dir. of Radiol., Aintree Hosps.; Sen. Regist. (Radiol.) Merseyside Hosps.; Sen. Regist. (Neuroradiol.) Walton Hosp. Liverp.

DANIEL, Aidan Charles Austin (retired) Lime Tree House, North Leverton, Retford DN22 0AB Tel: 01427 880645 — MB BS 1957 Lond. Prev: Ho. Phys. (Childr. & Radiother.) Lond. Hosp.

DANIEL, Alison Clare 9 Hazelwood Court, Wakefield WF1 3HP — MB ChB 1985 Ed.

DANIEL, Anthony Charles Mervyn Little Common, 8 Barnfield Rd, Sevenoaks TN13 2AY Tel: 01732 456 771 Email: anthony@anthonydaniel.com; 8 Barnfield Road, Riverhead, Sevenoaks TN13 2AY Email: acmd_ma@barnfield57.freeserve.co.uk — 1966 MB BS Lond. (Lond. Hosp.) p/t GP Locum (Semi Retd.). Prev: Ho. Surg. (ENT) Lond. Hosp.; SHO Qu. Eliz. Hosp. Childr. Lond.; Clin. Asst. (Gen. Med.) Sevenoaks Hosp. Sevenoaks.

DANIEL, Carol Ann Holly House Clinic, High Road, Buckhurst Hill IG9 5HX Tel: 020 8505 3311; 11 Stanmore Way, Goldings Manor Estate, Loughton IG10 2SA Tel: 020 8508 2042 Fax: 0182 502 0728 — MB BS Lond. 1967; MRCS Eng. LRCP Lond. 1966. (Roy. Free) Med. Screening Phys. Holly Ho. Clinic Buckhurst Hill. Socs: MRCOphth. Prev: PPP Med. Off. Lond. Bridge Hosp.; Asst. MOH Lond. Boro. Redbridge; Ho. Phys. Nat. Temp. Hosp. Lond.

DANIEL, Caryl Eirwen Clwydian Community Care, Royal Alexandra Hospital, Marine Drive, Rhyl LL18 3AS Tel: 01745 343188; Brignant, Halkyn Road, Holywell CH8 7SJ Tel: 01352 713207 — MB BCh 1982 Wales; MRCGP 1987; DCCH RCP Ed. 1994; DRCOG 1986. (Welsh Nat. Sch. Med.) Assoc. Specialist (Community Paediat.) Clwydian Community Care Trust. Socs: Welsh Paediat. Soc. Prev: Princip. GP Lichfield & Burntwood.

DANIEL, Christopher John 20 Pen yr Yrfa, Morriston, Swansea SA6 6BA — MB ChB 1998 Birm. (Birm.)

DANIEL, Mr Christy 3 St Paul's Close, Ashington NE63 9BZ — MB BS 1987 West Indies; FRCS Glas. 1994. Specialist Regist. (Urol.) Cumbld. Infirm. Carlisle.

DANIEL, Claire Suzanne 11 Stanmore Way, Loughton IG10 2SA Tel: 020 8508 2042 Fax: 020 8502 0728 — MB BS 1994 Lond.; BSc (Hons.) Lond. 1991. SHO Moorfields Eye Hosp. Lond. Prev: SHO (A & E) Lewisham Hosp. Lond.; Ho. Surg. Cardiothoracic Surgic. Unit Guy's Hosp. Lond.; Ho. Phys. Gen. Med. Unit. Greenwich Hosp. Lond.

DANIEL, David Gwyn Royal Gwent Hospital, Newport NP20 2UB Tel: 01633 52244 — MB BS 1961 Lond.; MRCS Eng. LRCP Lond. 1961; FRCOG 1979, M 1967, DObst 1964; DCH Eng. 1964. (Guy's) Cons. O & G Gwent AHA. Socs: Blair Bell Research Soc. Prev: SHO Paediat. Pembury Hosp.; SHO Gyn. Addenbrooke's Hosp. Camb.; Regist. O & G United Cardiff Hosps.

DANIEL, Diane Sherwood, Stanley Road, Bulphan, Upminster RM14 3RX — MB BCh 1992 Wales; BSc (Hons.) Physiol.) Wales 1989; DFFP 1995; DCH RCP Lond. 1994. Trainee GP N.ampton HA. Prev: SHO (O & G) Bedford & (Geriat. & Paediat.) N.ampton.

DANIEL, Francis Nan Francis Department of Clinical Oncology, Plymouth Hospitals NHS Trust, Derriford Hospital, Plymouth PL6 8DH Tel: 01752 777111 Fax: 01752 763992 Email: francis.daniel@phnt.swest.nhs — MB BCh 1978 Ain Shams; FFRCSI 1986. Cons. Clin. Oncol. PlymouthOncol.Centre Derriford Hosp. Plymouth. Socs: Radiother. Vis. Soc. Prev: Sen. Regist. (Radiother. & Clin. Oncol.) Freedom Fields Hosp.; Regist. (Radiother.) St. Luke's Hosp. Dub.; Research Regist. (Radiother.) Freedom Fields Hosp. Plymouth.

DANIEL, John Robert 26 New End, London NW3 1JA — MRCS Eng. LRCP Lond. 1968; MRCS Eng. LRCP Lond. 1968, MRCPsych. 1981; DTM & H Liverp. 1970. Sen. Phys. City Univ. Health Servs. Socs: Assn Jungian Analysts.

DANIEL, Johnson Herbert Dorairaja (retired) No. 2 The Spinney, West Park, Hartlepool TS26 0AW Tel: 01429 422841 Email: danspinneytop@bigfoot.com — MB BS 1959 Madras; DA 1969 London; BSc 1952 Madras. Prev: Cons. Anaesth. Hartlepool Health Dist.

DANIEL, Jonathan Romel 128 Minster Court, Liverpool L7 3QE — MB BS 1985 W. Indies.

DANIEL, Katharine Jane Chapel Row, Bendish, Hitchin SG4 8JH Email: t.arulampalam@virgin.net; 3 Riverside Close, Clapton, London E5 9SP — MB BS 1994 Lond.; DCH RCP Lond. 1998. (St Barts) GP Reg Hackney Lond. Prev: SHO (Paediat.) Whipps Cross Hosp. Lond.; Ho. Surg. N.ampton Gen. Hosp.; Ho. Phys. Gen. Hosp. St Helier Jersey.

DANIEL, Malcolm Kennedy F9 Clarendon Court, 9 Clarendon Place, St Georges Cross, Glasgow G20 7PZ Tel: 0141 333 9503 Fax: 0141 211 4622 Email: md23s@udcf.gla.ac.uk — MB ChB 1986 Aberd.; MRCP (UK) 1989; FRCA 1992. Cons. Anaesth. & IC Glas. Roy. Infirm. Prev: Vis. Asst. Prof. Anaesth. Univ. Calif., San Francisco; Regist. (Anaesth.) Glas. Roy. Infirm.; SHO (Gen. Med. & Anaesth.) Aberd. Teach. Hosp.

DANIEL, Mignonne Ann Marie Ingledene, Llandilo Road, 11 Cross Hands Road, Llanelli SA14 6RR — MB BS 1965 Lond.; MRCS Eng. LRCP Lond. 1965.

DANIEL, Mr Owen Clos Farm, Meidrim, Carmarthen SA33 2QZ Tel: 01994 230311 — MRCS Eng. LRCP Lond. 1942; MS Lond. 1960, MB BS 1942; FRCS Eng. 1948. (Univ. Coll. Hosp.) Hon. Cons. Surg. Clwyd Health Auth. Socs: Fell. Assn. Surgs. Gt. Brit.; Surg. Research Soc. Prev: Sen. Lect. in Surg. Univ. Sheff.; Lect. Surg. Postgrad Med. Sch. Lond.; Brit. Emp. Cancer Campaign, Amer. Cancer Soc. Exchange Fell. Johns.

DANIEL, Paul The Laurels Surgery, 73 Church Street, Flint CH6 5AF Tel: 01352 732349; Brignant, Halkyn Road, Holywell CH8 7SJ Tel: 01352 713207 — MB ChB 1982 Manch.; MRCGP.

DANIEL, Paul Gavin Heatherly Cottage, Ladbrook Lane, Corsham SN13 9PE — MB BS 1998 Lond.; MB BS Lond 1998.

DANIEL, Mr Reginald 152 Harley Street, London W1G 7LH Tel: 020 7935 3834 Fax: 020 7224 2574; London Bridge Hospital, London SE1 2PR Tel: 020 7403 4884 Fax: 020 7407 3162 — MB BS Lond. 1964; FRCS Eng. 1970; MRCS Eng. LRCP Lond. 1964; FRCOphth 1988; DO Eng. 1968; AKC. (Westm.) Cons. Ophth. Guy's & St. Thos. Hosps. Lond.; Chief Clin. Asst. Moorfields Eye Hosp. Lond.; Teach. Univ. Lond. Socs: Ophth. Soc. UK & Intraocular Implant Soc. UK; Moorfields Hosp. Surgs. Assn.; Amer. Acad. Ophth. Prev: Sen. Regist. Moorfields Eye Hosp. Lond.; Lect. (Ophth.) Inst. Ophth. Lond.; Ho. Surg. Profess. Gen. Surgic. Unit W.m. Hosp. Lond.

DANIEL, Mr Rhodri David Moorfields Eye Hospital NHS Trust, City Road, London EC1V 2PD Tel: 020 7566 2604 Fax: 020 7566 2603 Email: rhod.daniel@moorfldeye-tr.nthames.nhs.uk; Highgate

Private Hospital, 17-19 View Road, London N6 4DJ Tel: 020 8341 5163 Fax: 020 8342 8347 Email: highgate.privatehospital@lineone.net — MB BS 1979 Lond.; BSc Lond. 1976; FRCS Ed. (Ophth.) 1992; MRCOphth 1989; DO RCS Eng. 1983. (Univ. Coll. Hosp.) Cons. Ophth. Moorfields Eye Hosp. Lond. Socs: Chairm. BMA LNC Moorfields Eye Hosp. NHST; NE Thames Represen. BMA (Opthalmol. Gp. Comm.). Prev: Fell. Primary Care Clinic Moorfields Eye Hosp. Lond.; Hon. Sen. Regist. Moorfields Eye Hosp.

DANIEL, Richard John Earnshaw 26 London Road, Cowplain, Portsmouth PO2 0LN — MB ChB 1968 Sheff.; DObst RCOG 1970. (Sheff.)

DANIEL, Rosemary Anne The Surgery, Station Road, Knebworth SG3 6AP Tel: 01438 812494 Fax: 01438 816497; 135 Parkway, Welwyn Garden City AL8 6JB — MB BS 1972 Lond.; MRCP (UK) 1976.

DANIEL, Rosemary Marguerite 77a Alma Road, Clifton, Bristol BS8 2DP Tel: 0117 949 3366 Email: rdaniel@btinternet.com — MB BCh 1983 Wales; BSc (1st cl. Hons.) Wales 1980. (Univ. Hosp. of Wales) p/t Holistic Med. Cons. Onol. Dept. The Harley St. Clinic; Holistic Cons. Avon. Socs: Brit. Holistic Med. Assn. Prev: Doctor Brit. Cancer Help Centre; Med. Dir. Pulse Alternative Ther. Centre Cardiff & The Observatory Bristol; Med. Dir. Bristol Cancer Help Centre.

DANIEL, Sriharan Aranvas, 9A Radnor Place, Exeter EX2 4EH Tel: 01392 422115 — MB ChB Dundee 1993; DRCOG 1997. SHO (Med.) Redruth Hosp.; GP VTS Exeter. Prev: SHO (Accid & Emerg.) Treliske Hosp. Truro.

DANIEL, Susan Elaine Parkinsons Disease Society Brain Research Centre, Institute of Neurology, 1 Wakefield St., London WC1N 1PJ Tel: 020 7837 8370 Fax: 020 7278 4993 Email: s.daniel@ion.ucl.ac.uk — MB BS 1979 Lond.; BSc (Hons.) Lond. 1976, MD 1987; FRCPath 1997. (Univ. Coll. Hosp.) Sen. Lect. (Neuropath.) & Hon. Cons. Inst. Neurol. & Nat. Hosp. Neurol. & Neurosurg. Lond. Socs: Brit. Neuropathol. Soc.; Amer. Acad. Neuropath.; Fell.Roy. Coll. Pathologists. Prev: Asst. Lect. & Lect. (Histopath.) St. Thos. Hosp. Lond.; Lect. & Hon. Sen. Regist. (Neuropath.) Inst. Neurol. Nat. Hosp. Neurol. & Neurosurg. Lond.

DANIEL, Mr Thomas 7 Eglintoun Drive, Dunfermline KY12 9YL — MB BS 1973 Kerala; FRCS Glas. 1988.

DANIEL, Vasumathy Aranvas, 9A Radnor Place, St Leonard, Exeter EX2 4EH — MB ChB 1995 Dundee; BMSc (Hons.) Pharmacol.

DANIELIAN, Peter James Aberdeen Maternity Hospital, Cornhill Road, Aberdeen AB25 2ZL Tel: 01224 681818 Fax: 01224 840706 Email: peter.danielian@arh.grampian.scot.nhs.uk — MB BS 1982 Lond.; MA Camb. 1983; MD Lond. 1994; MRCOG 1988. (Cambridge/Guy's Hospital) Cons. (Obst.).

DANIELL, Philippa Ann Wake Green Surgery, 7 Wake Green Road, Moseley, Birmingham B13 9HD Tel: 0121 449 0300; Watendlath, Copcut Lane, Salwarpe, Droitwich WR9 7JB — MB ChB 1985 Birm.; MRCGP 1989; DRCOG 1988. Trainee GP/SHO S. Birm. HA VTS.

DANIELL, Simon John Newman Bromley Hospitals NHS Trust, Department of Diagnostic Imaging, Farnborough Hospital, Farnborough Common, Orpington BR6 8ND Tel: 01689 814145 Fax: 01689 814173; 24 Forest Drive, Keston BR2 6EF — MB BChir 1975 Camb.; MA, MB Camb. 1976, BChir 1975; FRCS Eng. 1980; FRCR 1989; DMRD 1986. (Downing College Cambridge and Guy's Hospital London) Cons. Radiol. Bromley Hosp. NHS Trust. Prev: Sen. Regist. (Diag. Radiol.) St. Bart. Hosp. Lond.; Lect. (Surg.) Char. Cross Hosp. Lond.; Regist. (Surg.) S.end Hosps.

DANIELLS, James John Wilson Street Surgery, 11 Wilson Street, Derby DE1 1PG Tel: 01332 344366 Fax: 01332 348813 — MB ChB 1985 Birm.; DCH RCP Lond. 1989.

DANIELS, Anthony Malcolm 44 Hartledon Road, Birmingham B17 0AD — MB ChB 1974 Birm.

DANIELS, Armon Wyn Rumney Medical Practice, 840-842 Newport Road, Rumney, Cardiff CF3 4LH Tel: 029 2079 7751 Fax: 029 2036 1971 — MB BS 1985 Lond.; MRCGP 1989; DRCOG 1989.

DANIELS, Barry John F.I.H., Grampian House, Marsh Wall, London E14 9YT Tel: 020 7308 0800 Fax: 020 7308 0832; 5 St. Pauls Courtyard, London SE8 3DR — MB BS 1984 Lond.; BSc (Psychol.) Lond. 1980. Chief. Med. Off. 1st Internat. Health Lond. Socs: BMA.

DANIELS, Charles Conrad Medical Director, St Lukes Kenton Grange Hospice, Kenton Road, Harrow HA3 08G Tel: 020 8382 8001 Fax: 020 8382 8080 Email: charles@stlukes-hospice.freeserve.uk — MB ChB 1988 Manch.; BSc (Hons.) Manch. 1985; MRCGP 1992; DRCOG 1991; Cert. Family Plann. JCC 1990. (Manch.) Med. Dir., St Lukes Hospice, Harrow; Cons. Palliat. Med., N.wick Pk. Hosp.; Cons. Palliat. Med., Harrow and Hillingdon Community NHS Trust. Socs: Assn. Palliat. Med. Prev: Sen. Regist. (Palliat. Med.) St. Josephs Hospice Lond.; Asst. Med. Dir. (Palliat. Med.) N. Lond. Hospice; Cons. W. Middlx. Hosp., Isleworth.

DANIELS, Charles Henry Lee The Dewerstone Surgery, Hampton Avenue, St Marychurch, Torquay TQ1 3LA Tel: 01803 323123/314240 Fax: 01803 322001; Two Gates, Teignmouth Road, Torquay TQ1 4SQ Tel: 01803 328779 Fax: 01803 328779 — MB ChB 1981 Birm.; MRCGP 1986; DRCOG 1987. Prev: Trainee GP Torbay Hosp. VTS; Ho. Phys. Stratford-upon-Avon Hosp.; Ho. Surg. Birm. Accid. Hosp.

DANIELS, Christopher Kevin 11 Prospect Street, Aberystwyth SY23 1JJ — MB BCh 1984 Wales; DRCOG 1988.

DANIELS, Colin James The Windsor Road Surgery, Windsor Road, Garstang, Preston PR3 1ED Tel: 01995 603350 Fax: 01995 601301; Highfield, Stones Lane, Catterall, Preston PR3 0HA Tel: 01995 603919 — MB ChB 1972 Sheff.; DObst RCOG 1974. Prev: SHO Cas., O & G & Paediat. Preston Roy. Infirm.

DANIELS, Darren Frazer 22 Kirby Lane, Leicester Forest E., Leicester LE3 3JG — MB ChB 1994 Birm. (Birm.)

DANIELS, David Graham West Middlesex University Hospital Trust, Twickenham Road, Isleworth TW7 6AF Tel: 0208 565 5718; 30 Black Lion Lane, London W6 9BE — MB BS 1986 Lond.; BA (Hons. Med. Sc.) Camb. 1983; FRCP 1999; MRCP (UK) 1989. (Cambridge, Charing Cross) Cons. Phys. W. Middlx. Hosp. Lond.; Hon. Cons. Chelsea & W.m.; Hon. Cons. Ealing Hosp.

DANIELS, David Gwilym 245 Kimbolton Road, Bedford MK41 8AE Tel: 01234 62418 — MB BCh 1960 Wales; MRCS Eng. LRCP Lond. 1962; MFPHM RCP (UK) 1989; MFCM 1973; DPH Wales 1969. (Cardiff) Sen. Med. Off. Beds. AHA. Socs: FRSH. Prev: Ho. Surg. Cardiff Roy. Infirm.; SHO (Psychiat.) St. David's Hosp. Carmarthen; Asst. MOH Mon. CC.

DANIELS, David William c/o Dr Kristen Randall, Anaesthetic Department, Worthing Hospital, Lyndhurst Road, Worthing BN11 2DH — MB BS 1991 Melbourne.

DANIELS, Edwin Philip 14 Priory Road, Halesowen B62 0BZ Tel: 0121 422 4001 — MB BS 1952 Durh.

DANIELS, Elizabeth (retired) 12 Stafford Road, Eccleshall, Stafford ST21 6JP Tel: 01785 850028 — MB BS 1949 Durh. Prev: Clin. Med. Off. (Community Med.) Mid.-Staffs HA.

DANIELS, Gordon Mark (retired) 383 Beverley Road, Anlaby, Hull HU10 7BQ Tel: 01482 656205 Email: gordon@vero.karoo.co.uk — MB ChB 1955 Ed. Prev: GP Hull.

DANIELS, Heledd Ffion 19 Llanishen Street, Cardiff CF14 3QB — MB BCh 1988 Wales.

DANIELS, Mr Henry Aeroux 7 The Drive, Kilner Park, Ulverston LA12 0DT — MB BCh BAO 1936 Dub.; BA, MB BCh BAO Dub. 1936, MC 1946; FRCS Eng. 1946; FRCSI 1946. (Dub.) Prev: Cons. Surg. Barrow & Furness Hosps. Gp.; Chief Asst. N. Middlx. Co. Hosp.

DANIELS, Ian Richard 24 Boverton Street, Cardiff CF23 5ES — MB BCh 1993 Wales.

DANIELS, Ian Samuel City Walls Medical Centre, St. Martin's Way, Chester CH1 2NR Tel: 01244 357800 — MB BS 1968 Lond.; MRCS Eng. LRCP Lond. 1968; MRCGP 1979; DObst RCOG 1971; DA Eng. 1970.

DANIELS, John Keith Palatine Group Practice, Murray's Road, Douglas IM2 3TD — MB ChB 1985 Sheff.; MRCGP 1990; DRCOG 1990; DCH RCP Lond. 1989. Prev: Trainee GP/SHO Sheff. VTS; Ho. Off. Roy. Hallamsh. & Lodge Moor Hosps. Sheff.

DANIELS, Jonathan Perrior 10 Coleman Drive, Staddiscombe, Plymouth PL9 9UN Tel: 01752 265538; 44 Sutherland Road, Plymouth PL4 6BN Tel: 01752 662992 Fax: 01752 265538 — BM BS 1985 Nottm.; BMedSci Nottm. 1983; MRCP (UK) 1989; T(GP) 1993; MRCGP 1993. Clin. Asst. (Chest Med.) Plymouth.

DANIELS, Justin Gerard 94 Leathermarket Street, London SE1 3HT Tel: 020 7787 4442 — BM BS 1994 Nottm.; BMedSci Nottm. 1992. (Nottm.) SHO (Paediat.) Lewisham & Guy's Hosp. Lond.

DANIELS, Kim Robert Benefits Agency Medical Services (SEMA), Bristol MSC, Spur R, Government Buildings, Flowers Hill, Brislington, Bristol BS4 5LA Tel: 0117 971 8406 Fax: 0117 971 8482; Ivy Park House, Rowden Hill, Chippenham SN15 2AF Tel: 01249 650224 Email: kimdaniels@lineone.net — MB BChir 1973 Camb.; MSc Lond. 1994; MA Camb. 1973; MRCGP 1979; T(GP) 1991; DAvMed. FOM RCP Lond. 1983; DRCOG 1978; DCH Eng. 1975. (Guy's) Med. Adviser Benefits Agency Med. Servs. (SEMA) Bristol. Socs: Roy. Coll. Gen. Pract. (Bd. Wessex Fac.); Clin. Soc. of Bath; Bristol Medico-Legal Soc. Prev: Commanding Off. No. 1 Aeromed. Evacuation Squadron; Sen. Med. Off RAF Lyneham; Assoc. Adviser (Gen. Pract.) RAF Germany.

DANIELS, Mark Steven 16 Grovemount, Davenham, Northwich CW9 8LY — BChir 1997 Camb.

DANIELS, Mary Victoria Department of Anaesthesia, Royal Cornwall Hospitals Trust, Treliske Hospital, Truro TR1 3LJ Tel: 01872 74242; Kennal Vale House, Ponsanooth, Truro TR3 7HJ — MB ChB 1980 Manch.; FFA RCS Eng. 1985. Cons. Anaesth. Roy. Cornw. Hosps. Trust.

DANIELS, Maurice Hunter (retired) Queen's House Crick, Northampton NN6 7TJ Tel: 01788 823268 — MB BCh BAO 1947 Dub. Prev: R.A.M.C. 1948-9.

DANIELS, Myrtle Priscilla 1 Harvey Croft, Trowell, Nottingham NG9 3QW — MB BS 1959 Madras; DObst RCOG 1967. (Christian Med. Coll.) Med. Off. Derbysh. AHA.

DANIELS, Nesta Lynne Silverdale Surgery, 4 Silverdale Road, Burgess Hill RH15 0EF Tel: 01444 233450; Tallinn, North Bank, Hassocks BN6 8JG Tel: 01273 845589 — MB BS 1982 Lond.; MA Camb. 1983; MRCGP 1986; DRCOG 1983. (King's Coll. Hosp.) Prev: GP Lond.; Trainee GP/SHO King's Coll. Hosp. VTS.

DANIELS, Paul Stephen Lime Tree Surgery, Lime Tree Avenue, Findon Valley, Worthing BN14 0DL Tel: 01903 264101 Fax: 01903 695494 — MB BS 1987 Lond.; BPharm. Nottm. 1980; FRACGP 1993; DRCOG 1988; MRPharm.S 1981. (Charing Cross and Westminster)

DANIELS, Robert James 12 Stafford Road, Eccleshall, Stafford ST21 6JP Tel: 01785 850028 — MB BS 1959 Madras; FRCOG 1987. (Christian Med. Coll. Vellore) Cons. (O & G) Mid Staffs. Gp. Hosps. Prev: Med. Asst. (O & G) Groundslow Hosp. & Stafford Gen. Infirm.; Regist. (O & G) Romford Hosps. Gp.

***DANIELS, Robert John** 9 Mile End Road, Norwich NR4 7QY Tel: 01603 452236 — BChir 1995 Camb.; MBCamb. 1995; MA (Cantol.) 1997.

DANIELS, Sarah SmithKline Beecham Pharmaceuticals, New Frontiers Science Park (South), Third Avenue, Harlow CM19 5AW Tel: 01279 646615 Fax: 01279 646099; 157 Marshalswick Lane, St Albans AL1 4UX Tel: 01727 764347 — MB ChB 1983 Ghana; MB ChB U. Ghana 1983; Dip. Pharm. Med. RCP (UK) 1992; DA (UK) 1988. Dir. Centr. Med. Affairs (Neurosci.s) SB Pharmaceut. Harlow Essex. Socs: Brit. Assn. Pharmaceut. Phys.; Fac. Pharmaceut. Med. Prev: Regist. (Anaesth.) Univ. Coll. Hosp. Lond.; Regist. (Anaesth.) Watford Gen. Hosp.

DANIELS, Simon Peter Gateshead Health Centre, Prince Consort Road, Gateshead NE8 1NR Tel: 0191 478 6728; 5 Saxilby Drive, Whitebridge Park, Gosforth, Newcastle upon Tyne NE3 5LS — MB ChB 1988 Leeds; Cert. Family Plann. JCC 1991; DRCOG 1991. Prev: Trainee GP Bradford VTS; Ho. Surg. Leeds Gen. Infirm.; Ho. Phys. Chapel Allerton Hosp. Leeds.

DANIELS, Stacey Myles 28 Weston Road, Aston-on-Trent, Derby DE72 2AS Tel: 01332 792355 — MB ChB 1957 Bristol; BDS Sheff. 1961. (Bristol) Prev: Ho. Surg. (ENT) Bristol Gen. Hosp.; Ho. Phys. Bristol Roy. Hosp.; Ho. Surg. (Dent.) Chas. Clifford Dent. Hosp. Sheff.

DANIELS, Thomas William Vaisey Flat D, 2 Lakeside Road, London W14 0DU — MB BS 1998 Lond.; MB BS Lond 1998. (CXWMS)

DANIELSEN, Mark Simon 60 Smithies Avenue, Sully, Penarth CF64 5SS; Chest Clinic, Derriford Hospital, Plymouth Tel: 01752 777111 — BM 1992 Soton.; BSc Soton. 1990; MRCP (UK) 1996. Regist. (Respirat.) Derriford Hosp. Plymouth. Socs: BMA; BTS. Prev: (IC) Qu. Alexandra Hosp. Portsmouth.

DANILLOWICZ, Anna 14 Ealing Village, Hanger Lane, London W5 2LY — LMSSA 1954 Lond.

DANIN, Joanna Claire Hillside, Exminster Hill, Exminster, Exeter EX6 8DW — MB BS 1987 Lond.; MRCP (UK) 1990.

DANINO, Charles Elwyn Cwmfelin Medical Centre, 298 Carmarthen Road, Swansea SA1 1HW Tel: 01792 653941 — MB BCh 1985 Wales; BPharm 1979; MRCGP 1990.

DANINO, Emmanuel Andrew, CBE Maesy Gwernen Court, Heol Maes, Eglwys, Morriston, Swansea SA6 6NN Tel: 01792 71590 — MRCS Eng. LRCP Lond. 1934; MD Lond., 1937 MB BS 1934; FRCP Lond. 1968, M 1937; DA Eng. 1938. (St. Bart.) Cons. Phys. Morriston Hosp. & Singleton Hosps. Socs: BMA.; Assn. Phys. Wales. Prev: Ho. Phys. St. Bart. Hosp.; Resid. Med. Off. Cardiff Roy. Infirm.; Lt.-Col. RAMC.

DANINO, Susannah Meresi 14 Rushwind Close, West Cross, Swansea SA3 5RF — MB BCh 1985 Wales.

DANJOUX, Gerard Regis 21 Davenport Drive, Newcastle upon Tyne NE3 5AE — MB BS 1989 Newc.

DANJOUX, Mr Jean-Pierre Sunderland Eye Infirmary, Queen Alexandra Road, Sunderland SR2 9HP Tel: 0191 528 3616 Fax: 0191 569 9165; 12 Roundstone Close, Newcastle upon Tyne NE7 7GH Tel: 0191 215 9292 Email: j.danjoux@virgin.net — MB BS 1985 Newc.; FRCOphth 1992. (Newcastle upon Tyne) Cons. Ophth. Sunderland Eye Infirm.

DANKER, Knud Ole (retired) The Surgery, 9 Ebdon Road, Worle, Weston Super Mare BS22 6UB Tel: 01934 514145 Fax: 01934 521345 — MRCS Eng. LRCP Lond. 1976; Cand. Med. et Chir. Copenhagen 1961; Leg. Lek Stockholm 1968; Cert. Family Plann. RCOG West. Austral. 1978.

DANKS, Jonathan Francis Danks, Smith, Sykes and Farrell, 134 Beeston Road, Beeston Hill, Leeds LS11 8BS Tel: 0113 276 0717 Fax: 0113 270 3727 — MB ChB 1974 Leeds; DA Eng. 1977.

DANN, Christopher Frank Rivermead Gate Medical Centre, 123 Rectory Lane, Chelmsford CM1 1TR Tel: 01245 348688 Fax: 01245 458800; 25 Tufted Close, Black Notley, Braintree CM7 8YE — MB BS 1977 Lond. (Roy. Free)

DANN, Nancy Hollies Farmhouse, Stanton by Bridge, Nr. Melbourne, Derby DE73 1HU Tel: 01332 862602 Email: dann@netcomuk.co.uk; X-Ray Department, Derbyshire Royal Infirmary, London Road, Derby DE1 2QY Tel: 01332 347140 — MB ChB 1972 Aberd.; FRCP Canada (Diag Radiol.) 1977 LMCC 1975; FRCR 1980. (Aberd.) p/t Cons. Radiol. Derby Roy. Infirm. Socs: BIR; RCR; Derby Med. Soc. Prev: Staff Radiol. Qu.sway-Carleton Hosp. Ottawa, Canada.

DANN, Thomas Charles 37 Balsall Street E., Balsall Common, Coventry CV7 7FQ Tel: 01676 532784 — MB BChir 1958 Camb.; MD Camb. 1963, MA 1958; MRCS Eng. LRCP Lond. 1957; DObst RCOG 1959; Cert Av Med MoD (Air) & CAA; Aviat. Auth. 1977. (Univ. Coll. Hosp.) Authorised Med. Examr. Civil Aviat. Auth. Socs: BMA & Brit. Assn. Health Servs. in Higher Educat. Prev: Med. Off. Univ. Warwick; Ho. Phys. Highlands Gen. Hosp.; Ho. Surg. (Obst.) Whittington Hosp. Lond.

DANN, William Lewis (retired) Hollies Farmhouse, Stanton By Bridge, Nr. Melbourne, Derby DE73 1HU Tel: 01332 862602 Email: dann@netcomm.co.uk — MB ChB 1964 Sheff.; FRCS Eng. 1970. Clin. Dir. & Cons. Anaesth. Derby HA. Prev: Cons. Anaesth. Derby Roy. Infirm.

DANSIE, Anthony Redgewell Trumpington Street Medical Practice, 56 Trumpington Street, Cambridge CB2 1RG Tel: 01223 361611 Fax: 01223 356837; The Cottage, Church Lane, Comberton, Cambridge CB3 7ED Tel: 01223 262337 — MB BS 1967 Lond.; MRCGP 1975; DObst RCOG 1970. (King's Coll. Hosp.) Prev: Capt. RAMC; Ho. Surg. & Ho. Phys. Staffs. Gen. Infirm.

DANSIE, Brandon Queen Anne's, 47 West St., Oundle, Peterborough PE8 4EJ Tel: 01832 272595 — MB BChir 1941 Camb.; MA Camb., MB BChir 1941; DIH Eng. 1970. (Univ. Coll. Hosp.) Socs: BMA & Soc. Occupat. Health. Prev: Chief Med. Off. Gallaher Ltd.; Capt. RAMC 1942-46; Med. Regist. Med. Unit Univ. Coll. Hosp. Lond.

DANSIE, Charles (retired) The Chequers, 116 Harmer Green Lane, Burnham Green, Welwyn AL6 0ET Tel: 01438 798707 — MB BS 1949 Lond.; DLO Eng. 1955; DObst RCOG 1954. Prev: GP Welwyn.

DANSIE, Nicholas Brandon Bridge Cottage Surgery, 41 High Street, Welwyn AL6 9EF Tel: 01438 715044 Fax: 01438 714013; The Vineyards, 15A Codicote Road, Welwyn AL6 9NE Tel: 0143871 6838 Email: nickdansie@compuserve.com — MB 1981 Camb.; MA Camb. 1981, MB 1981, BChir 1980; MRCGP 1984; DRCOG 1982. (Camb. & Middlx.) Hosp. Practitioner in Rehabil. Med., Danesbury Hosp. Socs: BMA & Middlx. Hosp. Club. Prev: Trainee GP Qu. Eliz. II Hosp. VTS. Welwyn Garden City; Ho. Surg. (Gen. Surg. & Orthop.) St. Albans City Hosp.; Ho. Phys. St. Albans City Hosp.

DANSIE, Oliver Bridge Cottage, 41 High St., Welwyn AL6 9EF — MB BS 1952 Lond.; MB BS (Distinc. Midw. & Gyn.) Lond. 1952. (Middlx.) Med. Off. Qu. Vict. Memor. Hosp. Welwyn; Med. Off. Danesbury Welwyn; Maj. AER. Prev: Regtl. Med. Off. 21 S.A.S. (Artists) T.A. & 2nd Bn. Parachute Regt.; Ho. Phys. & Ho. Phys. Paediat. Dept. Middlx. Hosp.

DANSKIN, Jane Mary 68 Millhouses Lane, Sheffield S7 2HB — MB ChB 1984 Sheff. Clin. Research Assoc. (Clin. Oncol.) W.on Pk. Hosp. Sheff. Prev: Trainee GP Swindon.

DANSKIN, Mary Joan (retired) 11 Westgate Close, Red House Farm, Whitley Bay NE25 9HT — MB BS 1953 Durh.; DPH 1960; DObst RCOG 1955. Prev: SCM N. Tyneside HA.

DANSO, Michael Anthony 12 Rona Road, London NW3 2JA — MB BS 1996 Lond.

DANSON, John Andrew 34 Waddington Close, Bury BL8 2JB — MB ChB 1993 Leeds.

***DANSON, Sarah Jean** 93 Bradshaw Meadows, Bradshaw, Bolton BL2 4NF — BM BS 1996 Nottm.; MRCP 1999.

DANSON, Simon Peter Prendeville c/o Parc Prison, Sarn, Bridgend; Golwg-y-Maes, Pen-y-Fai, Bridgend CF31 4LS — MB ChB 1979 Dundee; BDS 1973; MPhil (Law & Ethics) Glas. 1995; Dip. Forens. Med. Glas 1994; FDS RCS Eng. 1977. Sen. Med. Off. Parc Prison, Sarn, Bridgend. Socs: Coll. Prison Med.; Assoc. Mem. Brit. Assn. Oral & Maxillofacial Surg. Prev: Med. Off. Barlinnie Prison Glas.; Regist. (Maxillofacial Surg.) Canniesburn & Monklands Hosp. Glas.; Regist. (Oral Surg.) St. Geo. Hosp. Lond.

DANTON, Mark Henry Dunn 24 Bonds Glen Road, Killaloo, Londonderry BT47 3ST — MB BCh BAO 1987 Belf.

DANTON, Susan Jane Whitehill Surgery, Whitehill Lane, Oxford Road, Aylesbury HP19 3EN Tel: 01296 424488 Fax: 01296 398774 — MB BS 1993 Lond.; DRCOG 1997; DFFP 1998; MRCGP 1999. (Royal London)

DANZIGER, Arnold M, Flight Lt. RAF Med. Br. Retd. (retired) 34 Willow Court, Abbey Road, Macclesfield SK10 3PD — MRCS Eng. LRCP Lond. 1949; DA Eng. 1954. Prev: Cons. Anaesth. N. Manch. Hosps. & Booth Hall Childr. Hosp. Manch.

DAOUD, Janet Barbara St Christophers Hospital, 52 Wickham Road, Fareham PO16 7JD Tel: 01329 316410 — BM 1979 Soton.; MRCPsych. 1995. (Southampton) Cons. in Old Age Psychiat. Socs: Roy. Coll. Psych.

DAOUD, Mr Raouf Azmy 2 Damers Court, West Dorset Hospital, Dorchester DT1 2JY — MB BCh 1980 Ain Shams; FRCS Glas. 1987; FRCS Eng. 1987; FRCPS Glas. 1987.

DAOUD, Zaher Abdul-Salam Department of Anaesthetics, University Hospital of wales, Heath Park, Cardiff CF4 4XU Tel: 029 2074 3107; 25 Fford Rhiannon, Llanfairpwllgwyngyll LL61 5QB Tel: 01248 712407 Fax: 01256 333280 Email: zadshaya@cs.com — MB ChB 1982 Baghdad; FCAnaesth 1991; DA (UK) 1990. Specialist Regist. (Anaesth.) UHW Cardiff. Socs: BMA; Obst. Anaesth. Analgesic Assn. Prev: Regist. (Anaesth.) S.. Gen. Hosp. Glas.; LAT (Anaesth.) Kingston Hops. Surrey.

DAPAAH, Victor Stafford District General Hospital, Weston Road, Stafford ST16 3SA Tel: 01785 257731; Woodcroft, Leese Lane, Acton Trussell, Stafford ST17 0RG — Medic 1972 Bucharest, Roumania; FRCOG 1995, M 1978; MFFP 1994. Cons. O & G Mid. Staffs. Gen. Hosps. NHS Trust.

DAPLING, Mr Robert Brian Royal Shrewsbury Hospital NHS Trust, Mytton Oak Road, Shrewsbury SY3 8XQ Tel: 01743 261000 Fax: 01743 261006; The Poplars, Argoed, Kinnerlay, Oswestry SY10 8DJ Tel: 01691 682073 Fax: 01691 682074 Email: robert@dapling.demon.co.uk — MB BS 1982 Lond.; FRCPS Glas. 1992; FRCS Ed. 1987. Cons. Ophth. Surg. Roy. Shrewsbury Hosp. NHS Trust. Socs: Eur. Soc. Oculoplastic & Reconstruc. Surg.; Amer. Acad. of Ophthalmolohy. Prev: Fell. (Ophth., Plastic & Reconstruc. Surg.) Univ. Hosp. Nottm.; Sen. Regist. (Ophth.) Roy. Hallamsh. Hosp. Sheff.

DAPLYN, Ian Richard Bron Meirion Surgery, Castle Street, Penrhyndeudraeth LL48 6AL Tel: 01766 779304 Fax: 01766 770705 — MB BCh 1976 Wales; MB BCh 1976 Wales.

DAPRES, Paule Parexel International Ltd., Craven House, 40 Uxbridge Road, London W5 2BS — MD 1976 Paris.

DAR, Ambrin 45 Banstead Road, Carshalton SM5 3NS — MB BS 1998 Lond.; MB BS Lond 1998.

DAR, Mohamad Ashraf Walton Breck Road Practice, 291 Walton Breck Road, Liverpool L4 0SX Tel: 0151 260 2760.

DAR, Sadaf 45 Banstead Road, Carshalton SM5 3NS — MB BS 1997 Lond.

DAR, Sohail Ahmed 6 Haley Street, Cheetham Hill, Manchester M8 0PR — MB BS 1996 Lond.

DAR, Sumra Public Health/Occupational Health, Sandwell Health Authority, West Bromwich B70 9LD; 26 Woodfield Avenue, Oldbury B69 4TB — MB ChB 1993 Birm.

DAR, Vijay Kumar 1 Broadgates Avenue, Hadley Wood, Barnet EN4 0NU — MB BS 1962 Calcutta; MRCP (UK) 1975.

DARABSHAW, Gul Sarah Dinas Lane Medical Centre, 149 Dinas Lane, Huyton, Liverpool L36 2NW Tel: 0151 489 2298 — MRCS Eng. LRCP Lond. 1980; MS Jabalpur 1973, MB BS 1970; MRCOG 1978; MObstG Liverp. 1984. Prev: Regist. (O & G) Roy. Liverp. Hosp. & Fazakerley & Walton Gp. Hosps. Liverp.; Regist. & SHO (O & G) W. Middlx. Hosp.

***DARAKHSHAN, Amir Alborz** Northwick Park Hospital, Watford Road, Harrow HA1 3UJ; 226 Harrow Road, Wembley HA9 6QL — MB BS 1994 Lond.

DARASZ, Krystyna Halina Department of Cardiology, Hemel Hempstead General Hospital, Hillfield Road, Hemel Hempstead HP2 4AD Tel: 01442 213141; 57 Cline Road, Guildford GU1 3ND — MB BCh 1983 Oxf.; MA Camb. 1987, BA (Hons.) 1980; MA Oxf. 1987; MRCP (UK) 1986. Staff Grade (Cardiol.) Hemel Hempstead Hosp. Prev: Research Fell. Nat. Heart & Lung Inst. Lond.; Regist. (Cardiol.) Nat. Heart Hosp. Lond.; Regist. (Med. & Cardiol.) Hillingdon Hosp. Lond.

DARBISHIRE, William Duncan Bright Tel: 01229 582588; Copse Bottom, Pennington, Ulverston LA12 7NT Tel: 01229 582912 — MB ChB 1970 Liverp.; MRCGP 1977.

DARBY, Alan John Department of Pathology, Robert Jones & Agnes Hunt Orthopaedic Hospital, Oswestry SY10 7AG Tel: 01691 404148 Fax: 01691 404170 — MB BS 1965 Lond.; MRCS Eng. LRCP Lond. 1965; FRCPath 1984, M 1972. (Westm.) Cons. Histopath. Robt. Jones & Agnes Hunt Orthop. Hosp. OsW.ry. Socs: Internat. Skeletal Soc.; Bone & Tooth Soc.; Skeletal Dysplasia Gp. (Mem. Comm.). Prev: Cons. Histopath. King's Coll. Hosp. Lond.; Lect. (Path.) Radcliffe Infirm. Univ. Oxf.; Sen. Regist. (Histopath.) N.wick Pk. Hosp. Harrow.

***DARBY, Anthony Charles** 26 Rosa Road, Sheffield S10 1LZ — MB ChB 1998 Sheff.; MB ChB Sheff 1998.

DARBY, Brian James Kensington Medical Centre, 15A Donegall Road, Belfast BT12 5JJ Tel: 028 9032 5679 Fax: 028 9024 4267 — MB BCh BAO 1970 Belf.; MRCGP 1977; DObst RCOG 1972; LMCC 1974.

DARBY, Carl Terence Stoneleigh Surgery, Police Square, Milnthorpe LA7 7PW Tel: 015395 63307; Poppyfields, 2 Old Myse Storth, Milnthorpe LA7 7HQ — MB ChB 1984 Liverp.; MB ChB Liverp. l984; MRCP (UK) 1989.

DARBY, Caryl Walford Department of Paediatrics, Farnborough Hospital, Orpington BR6 8ND Tel: 01689 814 186, 01689 814185 Fax: 01689 814038 Email: caryl.darby@bromleyhospitals.nhs.uk; 8 Bullers Wood Drive, Chislehurst BR7 5LS — MB BS Lond. 1965; FRCP Lond. 1989; MRCP Lond. 1968; MRCS Eng. LRCP Lond. 1965; FRCPCH 1997. (Westm.) p/t Cons. Paediat. FarnBoro. Hosp. Kent Coll. Tutor Paediat.; Coll. Tutor (Paediat.); Cons. Paediat., Sloane Hosp. Beckenham, BR3 5HS. Socs: Roy. Coll. Paediat. & Child Health; UKCCSG; RCP Lond. Prev: Sen. Regist. Hosp. Sick Childr. Gt. Ormond St. Lond.; Teach. Fell. (Paediat.) Univ. Brit. Columbia Vancouver, Canada.; Cons. Paediat. (Sydenham Childr.'s Hospital, Lond.).

DARBY, Christopher Richard Nuffield Department of Surgery, John Radcliffe Hospital, Headington, Oxford OX3 9DU Tel: 01865 741166; Ash Cottage, Barton Lodge, Nr Bicester, Oxford OX25 5QH

Tel: 01869 340861 Email: crdarby@hotmail.com — MB BS 1981 Lond.; MD 1991; FRCS 1986. Cons. Surg. John Radcliffe and Ch.ill Hosp.s, Oxf..

DARBY, David Charles Barnsley District General Hospital, Gawber Rd, Barnsley S75 2EP Tel: 01226 791471 — MB BS 1980 Lond.; MRCP (UK) 1983; FRCR 1989. (Westm.) Cons. Radiologist, X-Ray Dept., Barnsley Dist. Gen. Hosp., Barnsley.

DARBY, David James William (retired) 73 Harley Street, London W1N 1DE Tel: 020 7487 4025 Fax: 020 7224 6381 — MB BS 1960 Lond.; MRCS Eng. LRCP Lond. 1960; MRCOphth 1988; DO Eng. 1962. Chief. Clin. Asst. Moorfields Eye Hosp.; Dir. Soc. Relief of Widows & Orphans Med. Men. Prev: Ho. Surg. (Ophth.) Lond. Hosp.

DARBY, Denise 57 Ashfield Road, Hemsworth, Pontefract WF9 4RR — MB ChB 1995 Manch.

DARBY, Dominique Odette Danielle Abbey Medical Centre, 42 Station, Kenilworth, Warwick CV35 8PH Tel: 01926 853142; The Stables, Frogmore Lane, Fen End, Kenilworth CV8 1NT — MB ChB 1983 Cape Town; MRCGP 1989; DRCOG 1989; Cert. Family Plann. JCC 1988. (University of Cape Town Medical School S. Afr.) p/t GP Kenilworth Warks. Retainer Scheme. Socs: MDU. Prev: Med. Adviser Wellcome Foundat. Ltd.; Sen. Med. Adviser for antivirals, The wellcome Foundat. Ltd.

DARBY, Jonathan Henry Halesowen Medical Practice, 14 Birmingham Street, Halesowen B63 3HN Tel: 0121 550 1185 Fax: 0121 585 0699; 10 Church Street, Hagley, Stourbridge DY9 0NA — MB ChB 1984 Birm.; DA (UK) 1988; Cert. Family Plann. JCC. SHO (Anaesth.) Qu. Eliz. Hosp. Birm. Prev: Cas. Off. Selly Oak Hosp. Birm.; Ho. Phys. Kidderminster Hosp.; Ho. Surg. Qu. Eliz. Hosp. Birm.

DARBY, Michael 28 Claremont Avenue, Bristol BS7 8JE — MB BS 1984 Lond.; BA Camb. 1981. Cons., Radiol., S.mead Hosp., Bristol. Prev: Sen. Ho. Off. (Neurol.) Nat. Hosp. Nerv. Dis. Lond.; Sen. Ho. Off. (Med.) St. Bart. Hosp. Lond.

DARBY, Michael James 10 School Hill, Kirkburton, Huddersfield HD8 0SG — MB ChB 1991 Leeds.

DARBY, Peter George (retired) 4 Hayne Park, Tipton St. John, Sidmouth EX10 0TA Tel: 01404 814002 — MB BS Lond. 1958; MRCS Eng. LRCP Lond. 1958; DMRD Liverp. 1972. Prev: Cons. Radiol. P.ss Margt. Hosp. Swindon.

DARBY, Philip Walter (retired) 8 Spinney Oak, Bickley, Bromley BR1 2NS Tel: 020 8467 0070 — MRCS Eng. LRCP Lond. 1946; MD Lond. 1959, MB BS 1946. Cons. Path. Bromley Health Dist. Prev: Ho. Phys. W.m. Hosp.

DARBY, Stephen Edward 52 Frederick Road, Sutton Coldfield B73 5QN — MB ChB 1974 Birm.; FRCR 1980. Cons. (Radiol.) Qu. Eliz. Hosp., Birm.

DARBYSHIRE, Ian Nance Rowan Hill, 55 Victoria Road, Fleet GU51 4DW — MB BChir 1942 Camb.; MRCS Eng. LRCP Lond. 1942; MFCM 1974. (St. Thos.) Prev: Cons. Med. Adviser United Med. Enterprises Ltd.; Regional Specialist (Community Med.) N.W. Thames RHA; Lt.-Col. RAMC.

DARBYSHIRE, Professor Janet Howard, OBE MRC Clinical Trials Unit, 222 Euston Road, London NW1 2DA Tel: 020 7670 4702 Fax: 020 7670 4815 Email: ctu.mrc.ac.uk; 300 Earlsfield Road, London SW18 3EH — MB ChB Manch. 1970; MSc Lond. 1990; FRCP Lond. 1988; MRCP (UK) 1973. Dir. MRC Clin. Trials Unit; Prof. Epidemiol. UCLMS; Hon. Cons. Phys. Roy. Brompton Nat. Heart & Lung Hosp.; Vis. Prof. Nat. Heart & Lung Inst.; Vis. Prof. Pharmacol. & Therap. Univ. Liverp.; Hon. Sen. Lect. (Epidemiol. & Populat. Sci.) Lond. Sch. Hyg. & Trop. Med.; Hon. Cons. & Clin. Epidemiol. Mortimer Market Centre & Islington Community Health Servs. NHS Trust. Prev: SHO (Chest Med.) Brompton Hosp.; SHO (Gen. Med.) Whittington Hosp.; Mem. Scientif. Staff MRC Tuberc. & Chest Dis. Unit.

DARBYSHIRE, Peter Gordon Shaftesbury Medical Centre, 480 Harehills Lane, Leeds LS9 6DE Tel: 0113 248 5631 Fax: 0113 235 0658; 25 Rossett Drive, Harrogate HG2 9NS — MB ChB 1978 Leeds; MRCGP 1985; MRCP Ed. 1981.

DARBYSHIRE, Philip John 5 Henglaze Terrace, Henleaze, Bristol — MB ChB 1975 Birm.; MRCP (UK) 1978. Leukaemia Research Fund Fell. Brist. Hosp. Sick Childr.

DARCH, Gillian Rosula Hatfield Place, Hatfield Road, Bath BA2 2BD — MB BS 1967 Lond.; MRCS Eng. LRCP Lond. 1967.

DARCH, Malcolm Henry The Health Centre, Testwood Lane, Totton, Southampton SO40 3ZN Tel: 023 8086 5051 Fax: 023 8086 5050 — MB BS 1974 Lond.; MRCS Eng. LRCP Lond. 1974; DRCOG 1977.

DARCY, Angela Elizabeth 45 Menlove Gardens W., Liverpool L18 2ET — MB ChB 1994 Liverp.

DARCY, Catharine Mary 45 Menlove Gardens W., Liverpool L18 2ET — MB ChB 1989 Liverp.; FRCS Ed. 1994; FRCS Glas. 1994.

DARCY, John Anthony 4 St John's Road, Epping CM16 5DN — MB ChB 1996 Dundee.

DARCY, John Francis The Surgery, St. Peters Close, Cowfold, Horsham RH13 8DN Tel: 01403 864204 Fax: 01403 864408 — MB BS 1982 Lond.; Dip. IMC RCS Ed. 1993; DRCOG 1987. Socs: (Vice-Chairm.) SIMCAS; BASICS.

DARCY, Michael Kevin Close Farm Surgery, 47 Victoria Road, Warmley, Bristol BS30 5JZ Tel: 0117 932 2108 Fax: 0117 987 3917; 8 Sion Hill Place, Bath BA1 5SJ — MB BS 1974 Lond.; MRCP (UK) 1978; MRCS Eng. LRCP Lond. 1974.

DARCY, Peter Francis 45 Menlove Gardens W., Liverpool L18 2ET — MB BS 1994 Lond.

DARCY, Yvonne Ann 45 Menlove Gardens W., Liverpool L18 2ET — MB ChB 1998 Liverp.; MB ChB Liverp 1998.

DARDAMISSIS, Evdokia Maelor General Hosptial, Croesnewydd Road, Wrexham LL13 7TD — State Exam Med. Hamburg 1990.

DARDIS, Philomena Mary Torrington Speedwell Practice, Torrington Park Health Centre, Torrington Park, North Finchley, London N12 9SS Tel: 020 8445 7261 Fax: 020 8343 9122; 1 The Garth, Holden Road, London N12 7DL Tel: 020 8445 5678 — MB BCh BAO 1981 NUI; MRCPI (Gen. Med.) 1983; MRCGP 1985; DRCOG 1985; DCH NUI 1984.

DARE, Christopher 30 Bellingham Road, London SE6 2PT — MB 1962 Camb.; BA Camb. 1958, MB 1962, BChir 1961; MRCP Lond. 1964; FRCPsych 1979, M 1971; DPM Lond. 1967. (Guy's) Cons. Psychiat. Bethlem Roy. & Maudsley Hosps.; Sen. Lect. Inst. Psychiat. Univ. Lond. Socs: Assoc. Mem. Brit. Psycho-Anal. Soc; Hon. Mem. Assn. Family Therap. Prev: Sen. Regist. (Child & Family Psychiat.) Tavistock Clinic Lond.; Regist. Maudsley Hosp. Lond.; Jun. Med. Regist. Guy's Hosp. Lond.

DARE, Douglas Rabindra Old Road Surgery, Old Road, Abersychan, Pontypool NP4 7BH Tel: 01495 772239 Fax: 01495 773786; Vicars Land Cottage, Penyrheol, Pontypool NP4 5XS — MB BS Madras 1964; FRCGP 1994, M 1985; DGM RCP Lond. 1985. (Madras) Course Organiser Postgrad. Dept. Roy. Gwent Hosp. Newport. Socs: Fell. Roy. Soc. Med.; Assn. Police Surg. Prev: SHO (Gen. Surg.) Co. Hosp. Griffithstown; SHO (Gen. Surg.) Medway & Gravesend Gp. Hosps.; SHO (A & E) Roy. Sussex Co. Hosp. Brighton.

DARE, Elaine Kathryn Regent House Surgery, 21 Regent Road, Chorley PR7 2DH Tel: 01257 264842 Fax: 01257 231387 — MB BS 1983 Lond.; BSc Lond. 1980, MB BS 1983; MRCGP 1988; DRCOG 1986. (Guy's) GP.

DARE, Jonathan Robert Belgrave Department Child & Family Psychiatry, King's College Hospital, Denmark Hill, London SE5 9RS Tel: 020 7346 3219 Fax: 020 7346 3221 — MB BS 1969 Lond.; MRCS Eng. LRCP Lond. 1968; MRCP (UK) 1973; MRCPsych 1975; FRCP Lond. 1995; FRCPsych 1997. (Guy's) Cons. Child & Family Psychiat. King's Coll. Hosp. Lond.; Hon. Fac. (Health) Brighton Univ. 1990; Vice Dean Inst. Psychiat. Lond. 1995-2000; Clin. Dir. Maudsley Childr. Dept. 1999-; Named Child Protec. Doctor Maudsley Hosp. 1996-; Hon. Sen. Lect. Instit. Psychiat.1998. Socs: Assn. Family Ther.; Assn. Child Psychol. & Psychiat.; NHS Conss. Assn. Prev: Cons. Child & Adolesc. Psychiat. Medway Health Dist.; Sen. Regist. (Child Psychiat.) Bethlem Roy. & Maudsley Hosp. Lond.; Ho. Phys. (Childr.) Guy's Hosp. Lond.

DARGAN, Christina Bridget 66 Bristow Park, Upper Malone Road, Belfast BT9 6TJ — MB BCh BAO 1973 NUI.

DARGAN, Paul Ivor National Poisons Information Centre, Guy's & St Thomas' Hospital Trust, London SE14 5ER Tel: 020 7771 5316 — MB BS 1993 Lond.

DARGIE, Hazel Emma 46 Ferryhill Road, Aberdeen AB11 6RR — MB ChB 1998 Ed.; MB ChB Ed 1998.

DARGIE, Henry John 7 Arnwood Drive, Glasgow G12 0XY — MB ChB 1968 Glas.; MRCP (U.K.) 1971. Cons. (Cardiol.) W.. Infirm. Glas.

DARGIE, Rosemary 7 Arnwood Drive, Glasgow G12 0XY — MB ChB 1972 Glas.

DARIGALA, Sreenivas 37 Parlington Villas, Aberford, Leeds LS25 3EP — MB BCh 1991 Wales; BSc Wales 1989. Specialist Regist. Neurol. Pinderfields Gen. Hosp. Wakefield.

DARJEE, Rajan Department of Psychiatry, Queen Margaret Hospital, Whitefield Road, Dunfermline KY12 0SU Tel: 01383 623623 — MB ChB 1994 Ed.; BSc Ed. 1992. SHO (Psychiat.) Qu. Margt. Hosp. Dunfermline.

DARK, Allan Aberdeen Royal Infirmary, Forresterhill, Aberdeen AB25 2ZN Tel: 01224 681818 Fax: 01224 685307; 2 Mile End Place, Aberdeen AB15 5PZ Tel: 01224 631870 — MB ChB 1987 Aberd.; FRCA 1996. Regist. Aberd. Roy. Hosps. NHS Trust.

DARK, Christopher Hedley 13 St Albans Avenue, London W4 5LL — MB ChB 1976 Cape Town; FFARCS 1981. (Cape Town) Head Clin. Serv. BUPA Hosp. Prev: Cons. Anaesth. Hillingdon Hosp.; Sen. Regist. (Anaesth.) Middlx. Hosp.; Regist. (Anaesth.) St. Geo. Hosp. Gp. Lond.

DARK, Graham Geoffrey Department of Medicine, Royal Marsden Hospital, Downs Road, Sutton SM2 5PT Tel: 020 8642 6011 Fax: 020 8643 0873 Email: dark@www.graylab.ac.uk; 14 The Dell, Tadworth KT20 5TQ — MB BS 1988 Lond.; MRCP (UK) 1992. (Roy. Free Hosp. Med. Sch.) Sen. Regist. (Med. Oncol.) Roy. Marsden Hosp.; Lect. (Med. Oncol.) & Research Fell. Mt. Vernon Hosp. N.wood. Socs: (Chairm.) Cancer Phys. in Train.; (Sec.) Jun. Oncol. Club. Prev: Lect. (Med. Oncol.) Char. Cross Hosp. Lond.; Regist. (Gen. Med. & Oncol.) Lister Hosp. Stevenage; SHO (Paediat. Oncol.) Roy. Marsden Hosp. Sutton.

DARK, Mr John Fairman (retired) 2 Richmond Hill, Richmond Road, Bowdon, Altrincham WA14 2TS Email: john.dark@btinternet.com — MB ChB 1945 Manch.; MB ChB (Distinc. Surg.) Manch. 1945; BSc Manch. 1942; FRCS Eng. 1949. Prev: cons.Cardiothoracic.Surg.S.Manch AHA & Roy.Manch.Childr.s Hosp.

DARK, Professor John Henry Regional Cardiothoracic Centre, Freeman Hospital, Freeman Road, Newcastle upon Tyne NE7 7DN Tel: 0191 284 3111 Fax: 0191 223 1152 Email: j.h.dark@ncl.ac.uk — MB BS 1976 Newc.; FRCS Ed. 1980; FRCS Eng. 1980; FRCP Ed. 1995. Cons. Cardiothoracic Surg. & Dir. (Cardiopulm. Transpl.) Freeman Hosp. Newc.; Prof. (Cardiothoracic Surg.) Univ. Newc. Socs: Pres. Europ. Soc. Organ Transpl.; (Counc.) Brit. Transpl. Soc. Prev: Cons. Cardiothoracic Surg. Roy. Infirm. Edin.; Sen. Regist. (Cardiothoracic Surg.) Harefield Hosp. & Middlx. Hosp. Lond.; Regist. (Cardiothoracic Surg.) Gtr. Glas. HB.

DARK, Mr Paul Michael 19 Pot Green, Holcombe Brook, Ramsbottom, Bury BL0 9RG — MB ChB 1989 Manch.; BSc (Hons.) Salford 1983; FRCS Ed. 1995. MRC (Clin. Research Fell.) critical care; Hon. Clin. Lect. (Emerg. Med.) Univ. Manch. Socs: Fell. Roy. Coll. Surg. Edin.; Fac. Accid. & Emerg. Med.; Intens. Care Soc. Prev: Tutor (Emerg. Med.) Univ. Manch.; Visit. Prof. (Emerg. Med.) Univ. Leuven, Belgium.

DARKE, Geoffrey (retired) The White House, 5 Grenfell Road, Leicester LE2 2PA Tel: 0116 709656 — MB BS 1934 Durh.

DARKE, Mr Geoffrey Harold (retired) 1 King's Acre, Crowcombe Heathfield, Taunton TA4 4BX Tel: 01984 618215 — MB BS Lond. 1937; FRCS Eng. 1978; FRCS Ed. 1939; MRCS Eng. LRCP Lond. 1937. Prev: Cons. Surg. (Urol.) Taunton & Som. Hosp., W. Som. Hosp. Minehead.

DARKE, Katrina Frances 46A Quicks Road, London SW19 1EY — MB BS 1997 Lond.; MA 1987; PGdip RNCM 1988. (UMDS)

DARKE, Mr Simon Geoffrey Oaks, 6 Leicester Road, Branksome Park, Poole BH13 6BZ Tel: 01202 761870 Fax: 01202 752353 Email: sgd@rbh.ong.uk — MRCS Eng. LRCP Lond. 1965; MB BS Lond. 1965; MS Lond. 1977; FRCS Eng. 1970. (Lond. Hosp.) Cons. Surg. Roy. Vict. Hosps. Bournemouth & Poole Gen. Hosp.; Pres. Vasc. Surg. Soc. GB & Irel. 1996. Socs: Vasc. Surg. Soc.; Europ. Soc. Vasc. Surg.; Fell. Roy. Soc. Med. Prev: Sen. Regist. Lond. Hosp. & Whipps Cross Hosp.; Ho. Surg. Lond. Hosp.; Treas. Europ. Soc. Vasc. Surg. 1987-1990.

DARKINS, Mr Adam William Flat 5, 76 Hamilton Terrace, London NW8 9UL — MD 1987 Manch.; MD 1987 Manch., MB ChB 1979; FRCS Eng. 1983. Sen. Regist. (Neurosurg.) Brook Gen. & Maudsley Hosps. Lond. Prev: Former Vis. Asst. Prof. Ucla Sch. Med. Los Angeles, USA.

DARKO, Daniel Asare 59 Limes Road, Croydon CR0 2HF — MB BS 1993 Lond.

DARKO, Kwadwo 42 Blackhorse Road, Walthamstow, London E17 7BE Tel: 020 8521 1822 — MB ChB 1976 Ghana.

DARKWAH, Jennifer Afra 343 Grove Green Road, Leytonstone, London E11 4AQ — MB BS 1997 Lond.

DARLA, S R Edge Lane Medical Centre, 1-5 Marmaduke Street, Liverpool L7 1PA Tel: 0151 260 5335.

DARLASTON, Laurie McLean 38 Sydenham Road, Cotham, Bristol BS6 5SJ — MB BS 1990 Lond.

DARLASTON, Patrick James (retired) 11 Park House Gates, Lucknow Drive, Nottingham NG3 5LX Tel: 0115 9662 1946 — MB BS 1951 Lond.; MRCS Eng. LRCP Lond. 1951.

DARLEY, Charles Russell Sussex Nuffield Hospital, Warren Road, Woodingdean, Brighton BN2 6DX Tel: 01273 627084 Fax: 01273 627085; Little Norlington Barn, Norlington Lane, Ringmer, Lewes BN8 5SG Tel: 01273 814575 Fax: 01273 814020 — MB BS 1972 Lond.; MD Lond. 1984; FRCP Lond. 1981; MRCP (UK) 1976. (St. Thos.) Cons. Dermat. Brighton Health Care Trust. Socs: Fell. Roy. Soc. Med. (Mem. Dermat. Sect.); Fell. (Ex-Pres.) St. John's Hosp. Dermat. Soc. Prev: Sen. Regist. (Dermat.) Lond. Hosp.; Regist. (Dermat.) & Aylwen Bursar St. Bart. Hosp. Lond.

DARLEY, Elizabeth Susan Rachel Dept medical microbiology, Southmead Hospital, Westbury on Trym, Bristol BS10 5NB Tel: 0117 959 5651 — MB ChB 1992 Dundee; MRCP (UK) 1996; Dip RCPath 1998. Specialist Regist. (Med. Microbiol.)N. Bristol NHS Trust. Socs: BMA; Brit. Soc. Antimicro. Chemo; Hosp. Infec. Soc. Prev: SHO (Med. Microbiol. & Infec. Dis.) S.mead Health Servs. NHS Trust; SHO (Microbiol.) Wycombe Gen. Hosp. High Wycombe; SHO (Infec. Dis.) Kings Cross Hosp. Dundee.

DARLEY, Jonathan Stephen Wedgwood Unit, West Suffolk Hospital, Hardwick Lane, Bury St Edmunds IP33 2QZ Tel: 01284 713118 Fax: 01284 712586 — MB ChB 1985 Birm.; MA Keele 1995; MRCPsych 1989. Cons. Old Age Psychiat. Local Health Partnerships, NHS Trust, Bury St Edmunds. Prev: Sen. Regist. (Old Age Psychiat.) W. Midl. RHA; Regist. Rotat. (Psychiat.) N. Worcs.

DARLEY, Malcolm Patrick 10A Lambton Road, London N19 3QH — MB BS 1990 Lond. Ho. Off. King. Geo. Hosp. Ilford. Prev: Ho. Off. Basildon Hosp.

DARLEY, Margaret Beatrice (retired) 57 Littledown Avenue, Queen's Park, Bournemouth BH7 7AX Tel: 01202 394522 — MB BCh BAO 1960 Dub. Prev: GP Bournemouth.

DARLEY, Simon Nicolas Rose Allod Surgery, 21 Knowsley Road, Ormskirk L39 4RB Tel: 01695 577215 Fax: 01695 572886 — MB ChB 1982 Liverp. GP Rose Allod Surg.

DARLEY, Timothy Andrew NHS Chemical Pathology, South Lab. & Path. Block, Southampton General Hospital, Tremona Road, Southampton SO16 6YD — BM 1980 Soton.

DARLING, Archibald Hunter (retired) 57 Roman Way, Bourton-on-the-Water, Cheltenham GL54 2EW Tel: 01451 20941 — MB ChB 1950 Ed.; MRCGP 1963. Prev: Med. Off. & Clin. Asst. (Cas.) Moore Cott. Hosp. Bourton-on-the-Water.

DARLING, Averell Shillington (retired) Le Foyer, Park Estate,La Route Des, St Brelade, Jersey JE3 8EQ Tel: 01534 742793 Fax: 01534 742796 — MB BCh BAO 1939 Belf.; DPH Eng. 1947. Prev: SCM (Environm. Health) Stockport AHA.

DARLING, Brian Martindale (Surgery), The Medical Group, Millyard House, Ushaw Moor, Durham DH7 7QH; Braeside, Acton Road, Esh Winning, Durham DH7 9PL Tel: 01385 734268 — MB BS 1961 Durh. (Durh.) Socs: BMA. Prev: Demonst. Anat. Dept. Univ. Newc.; Surg. Regist. Sunderland Hosp. Gp.; SHO P.ss Mary Matern. Hosp. Newc. upon Tyne.

DARLING, Christopher Harry Osborne Road Surgery, 200 Osborne Road, Jesmond, Newcastle upon Tyne NE2 3LD Tel: 0191 281 4777 Fax: 0191 281 4309; 20 Mitchell Avenue, Newcastle upon Tyne NE2 3LA — MB BS 1978 Newc.; MRCGP 1983; DRCOG 1981.

DARLING, Claire Horbury Health Centre, 2A Westfield Road, Wakefield WF4 6LL Tel: 01924 327721 — MB ChB 1975 Ed.; MRCPsych. 1984; DRCOG 1977. Cons. Psychother. Wakefield.

DARLING, Janet Mary Tel: 01865 730911 Fax: 01865 327759; 19 Lady Place, Sutton Courtenay OX14 4FB Tel: 01235 847903 — MB BS Lond. 1966; MRCS Eng. LRCP Lond. 1966; MFFP 1994; DObst RCOG 1969. (St. Thos.) GP. Socs: Mem.Ox Comm. Med. Wom. Federat. (Pres.-Oxf. Div.); BMA; Oxf. Med. Soc. Prev: SHO (Obst.), Ho. Phys. & Ho. Surg. St. Mary's Hosp. Portsmouth.

DARLING, Janie Christine East Street Surgery, South Molton EX36 3QX Tel: 01769 573811 Fax: 01769 574088 Email: eaststreet@cix.co.uk; Garliford, Bish Mill, South Molton EX36 3QX Tel: 01769 550242 Email: jdarling@clara.net — MB ChB 1976 Bristol; MRCGP 1982; DFFP 1993. (Bristol) Prev: Trainee GP Wellington VTS; SHO (Med.) MusGr. Pk. Hosp. Taunton.

DARLING, John Robert Killymacken, Aghalane P.O., Enniskillen BT92 9BP — MB BCh BAO 1987 Belf.; BSc (Hons.) Belf. 1984; MD Belf. 1994; FFA RCSI 1991. Cons. Anaesth. Ulster Hosp. Belf.

DARLING, Mr John Singleton, OBE (retired) Ashbourne, 14A Gore Tree Road, Hemingford Grey, Huntingdon PE28 9BP Tel: 01480 462593 — MB BCh BAO 1934 Belf.; FRCS Eng. 1940. Prev: Cons. Gen. Surg. Co. Hosp. Huntingdon.

DARLING, Jonathan Charles Academic Unit of Paediatrics & Child Health, St James's University Hospital, Leeds LS9 7TF Tel: 0113 206 5657 Fax: 0113 206 5661 Email: j.c.darling@leeds.ac.uk; 7 Adel Towers Close, Leeds LS16 8ES Tel: 0113 261 1679 — MB ChB 1986 Manch.; MD Manch. 1997, MB ChB 1986; MRCP (UK) 1990. (Manchester) Sen.Lect.Hon.cons. Paediat.St jas univ Hosp. Socs: Assoc. for Stud. Of Med. Educat. (ASME). Prev: Clin. Med. Off. St. Bart. NHS Gp.; Clin. Research Fell. Inst. Child Health Lond.; Lect. & Hon. Sen. Regist. (Paediat.) St. Jas. Univ. Hosp.

***DARLING, Katharine Elizabeth Anna** Drumearn, 16 Hermitage Drive, Edinburgh EH10 6BZ — MB BS 1994 Lond.; BSc Lond. 1991; MRCP (UK) 1997.

DARLING, Richard Mark Worle Health Centre, 125 High St, Worle, Weston Super Mare BS22 6HB Tel: 01934 510510 Fax: 01934 522088; Jessamine Farm, The Causeway, Mark, Highbridge TA9 4QD — MB BS 1972 Lond.; BSc Lond. 1969; MRCP (UK) 1974; MRCS Eng. LRCP Lond. 1972; DCH RCP Lond. 1977; DRCOG 1976.

DARLING, Rodney Andrew York Road Group Practice Surgery, York Road, Ellesmere Port, South Wirral CH65 0DB Tel: 0151 355 2112 Fax: 0151 356 5512; 8 Sutton Hall Gardens, Little Sutton, South Wirral CH66 4QH — MB ChB 1978 Liverp. Socs: BMA. Prev: Regist. Rotat. (Anaesth.) Liverp. HA(T); SHO (Anaesth.) Roy. Lancaster Infirm.; Ho. Off. BRd.green Hosp. Liverp.

DARLING, Scot Peter Baslow Road Surgery, 148-150 Baslow Road, Totley, Sheffield S17 4DR Tel: 0114 236 9957 Fax: 0114 262 0756; Shoreham Street Surgery, 251 Shoreham St, Sheffield S1 4SS Tel: 0114 272 1717 — MB ChB 1989 Sheff.; BSc Sheff. 1984; MRCGP 1994; DRCOG 1992.

DARLING, Stanley Gleason Monkspath Surgery, 27 Farmhouse Way, Monkspath, Shirley, Solihull B90 4EH Tel: 0121 711 1414 Fax: 0121 711 3753 — MB ChB 1969 Birm.; BSc Birm. 1966, MB ChB 1969.

DARLING, Trevor Walter (retired) The Old Pound, 7 Barrack Lane, Bognor Regis PO21 4BY Tel: 01243 824522 — MB BS 1962 Lond.; MRCS Eng. LRCP Lond. 1960.

DARLING, William John Egerton 15 Clipstone Avenue, Mapperley, Nottingham NG3 5JZ Tel: 0115 920 4508 — MB ChB 1941 Ed.; AFOM RCP Lond. 1980; DPH Lond. 1960; DTM & H Ed. 1947. (Ed.) Socs: Fell. Roy. Soc. Trop. Med. & Hyg.; Fell. Roy. Med. Soc.; Soc. Occupat. Med. Prev: Dep. Med. Off. S. Notts. Area Nat. Coal Bd.; Asst. Chief Med. Off. Luanshya Div. Roan Consolidated Mines Ltd., Zambia; DMS Zambia Defence Forces.

DARLINGTON, Barry Guy 29 Meynell Road, Leicester LE5 3NE — MB ChB 1994 Leic.

DARLINGTON, Deryk (retired) Melbourne Cottage, Main Road, Milfield, Wooler NE71 6HS Tel: 0166 216514 — MB ChB 1947 Birm. Prev: Exec. Dean Fac. Med. & Dent. Univ. Birm.

DARLINGTON, Jennifer Mary Department of Psychiatry, Rossendale Hospital, Haslingden Road Tel: 01706 233284; 7 Stainton Drive, Burnley BB12 0TS — MB ChB 1984 Manch.; BSc (Hons. Pharmacol.) Manch. 1981. (Manch.) Cons. Psychiat. Of Elderly (long term locum) Rossendale Hosp., rawthenstall, Lancs. Socs: Affil. of Roy. Coll. of Psychiat.s; Guild of Catholic Doctors Brit. Med. Assoc. Med. Defence Union. Prev: Regist. Rotat (Psyxhiatric) N. Worcs.; Regist.Rotat (Psychiatric) N. Worcs; SCMO (Psychiat. of Elderly) N. Manch. Gen. Hosp.

DARLINGTON, Lynda Gail Epsom General Hospital, Dorking Road, Epsom KT18 7EG Tel: 01372 735120 Fax: 01372 735261 Email: gdarlington@sthelier.sghms.ac.uk; The Garden House, Eyhurst Close, Kingswood, Tadworth KT20 6NR Tel: 01737 832678 — MB BS Lond. 1968; MD Lond. 1978; MRCS Eng. LRCP Lond. 1968; FRCP (Lond.) 1988; MRCP (UK) 1973. (Char. Cross) p/t Cons. Phys. (Gen. Med. & Rheum.) Epsom Gen. Hosp.; Hon. Clin. Tutor (Med.) Char. Cross Hosp. Lond.; Lead Clinician In-Patient Services, Epsom General Hospital; Hon. Snr. Research Fellowship, Division Of Neuroscience and Biomedical Systems, University Of Glasgow. Socs: Brit. Soc. Rheum.; Internat. & Europ. Soc. Study Purine & Pyrimidine Metab. Man. Prev: Vis. Med. Fell. Jesus Coll. Camb.; Trustees' Research Fell. Char. Cross Hosp. Lond.; Sen. Regist. (Gen. Med. & Rheum.) Char. Cross Hosp. Lond.

DARLINGTON, Silke 3 Beaumont Square, Pudsey LS28 8PT — State Exam Med 1992 Munster; MD Bochum 1992. (Westfaelische Wilhelms - Univ. Muenster, FRG) SHO III (Dermat.) Glas. Roy. Infirm. Prev: SHO (Dermat.) Centr. Sheff. Univ. Hosps.; SHO Inst. fuer Experimentelle Dermat. Witten, FRG; Ho. Off. (Dermat.) Klinikum Lippe Lemgo GmbH, FRG.

DARLISON, Michael Tatlow The Surgery, Emmview Close, Woosehill, Wokingham RG41 3DA Tel: 01189 788689 Fax: 01734 793661; St. Columba's, 6 Westward Road, Wokingham RG41 3HU Tel: 01189 783202 Email: miketat2@excite.comm — MB ChB 1970 Cape Town; MFGP S. Afr. 1976; Dip. Pract. Dermat. Wales 1992; DRCOG 1979; DTM & H Witwatersrand 1977. (Cape Town) Dep. Police Surg. Woodley & Wokingham; Capt. RAMC TA, Med. Off. 392 MRS (V). Socs: BMA. Prev: Sessional Med. Off. Family Plann. Clinic Egham; GP Anaesth. Baragwaneth Hosp. Johannesburg, S. Afr.; Med. Off. Goldfields W. Hosp. Libanon, S. Afr.

DARLOW, Henry Mark, Surg. Cdr. RN Retd. 'Cuckoo Pen', Porton, Salisbury SP4 0LF — MRCS Eng. LRCP Lond. 1940; BA Camb. (Middlx. & Camb.) Prev: Sen. Princip. Scientif. Off. War Dept.; Ho. Surg. Min. of Health Emerg. Hosp. Aylesbury.

DARLOW, John Michael Department of Immunology, Western Infirmary, Glasgow G11 6NT Tel: 0141 211 2152 Fax: 0141 337 3217 Email: john.m.darlow@clinmed.gla.ac.uk; Cuckoo Pen, Porton, Salisbury SP4 0LF Tel: 01980 610223 Email: jmdarlow@yahoo.com — MB ChB 1975 Dundee; PhD 1999 Molecular Genetics, Edin; MSc (Biochem. Genetics) New Foundland 1991; BMSc (Hons.) Human Genetics Dund 1972. Research Asst., Dept. of Immunol., Univ. of Glassgow, Glassgow. Socs: Clin. Genetics Soc.; Overseas Trainee Mem. Amer. Soc. Human Genetics. Prev: Regist. (Chem. Path. & Metab. Med.) Roy. Liverp. Hosp.; Research Asst. (Molecular Genetics). Health Sci. Centre St John's New Foundland, Canada; MRC PhD Stud.ship (Human Genome Mapping Project) Univ. Edin.

***DARLOW, Nadine Evelyn** 5 Cecil Road, Hertford SG13 8HP — MB BS 1996 Lond.

DARLOW, Simon John 34 Darlington Road, Southsea PO4 0NF — BM 1988 Soton.

DARMADY, Judith Mary (retired) Meadowview, 26 Vyne Road, Sherborne St. John, Basingstoke RG24 9HX Tel: 01256 850029 — MB BS 1961 Lond.; FRCP Lond. 1979, M 1968; MRCS Eng. LRCP Lond. 1961; DCH Eng. 1966. Prev: Cons. Paediat. Basingstoke Dist. Hosp.

DARMANI, Aziz Ahmad 16 Torrens Drive, Lakeside, Cardiff CF23 6DW Tel: 029 2076 6174; Flat 1/1, 31 Kelvindale Gardens, Glasgow G20 8DW Tel: 0141 946 1429 — MD 1964 Kabul; MD Kabul, Afghanistan 1964. Trust Doctor (Gen. Psychiat.) Scotl.

DARNBOROUGH, Alan 33 West End Rise, Horsforth, nr., Leeds LS18 5JL Tel: 0113 258 5177 — MB ChB 1957 Leeds; FFR 1967; DMRD Eng. 1964; DObst RCOG 1958. (Leeds) Cons. Radiol. Airedale Dist. Gen. Hosp. & Skipton Gen. Hosp.; Hon. Cons. Radiol. United Leeds Hosps.; Hon. Lect. (Radiol.) Univ. Leeds. Socs: BMA. Prev: Regist. (Diag. Radiol.) Gen. Infirm. Leeds; Ho. Surg. (Obst.) Leeds Matern. Hosp.; Ho. Phys. Leeds Gen. Infirm.

DARNBOROUGH, Dorothy Catherine Health Centre, Mulberry St., Pudsey; 33 West End Rise, Horsforth, Leeds LS18 5JL Tel: 0113 25177 — MB ChB 1957 Leeds; DObst RCOG 1958. (Leeds) Prev: SHO Bradford Childr. Hosp.; Ho. Surg. St. Mary's Matern. Hosp. Leeds; Ho. Phys. Leeds Gen. Infirm.

DARNBOROUGH, Jack (retired) 51 Gough Way, Cambridge CB3 9LN Tel: 01223 353288 — MB ChB 1948 Ed.; FRCPath 1971, M 1963. Prev: Dir. Regional Transfus. & Immuno-Haematol. Centre Camb.

DARNBOROUGH, Kathryn 33 West End Rise, Horsforth, Leeds LS18 5JL; The Mount, High St, Tattenhall, Chester CH3 9PX — MB ChB 1986 Liverp.; MRCGP 1994.

DARNBOROUGH, Sally 33 West End Rise, Horsforth, Leeds LS18 5JL — MB ChB 1988 Bristol.

DARNELL, Royce (retired) 23 Hillcross Drive, Littleover, Derby DE23 7BW Tel: 01332 766332 — MB ChB 1962 Sheff.; MD Sheff. 1976; Dip. Bact. Lond 1973. Prev: Cons. Asthma & Atopic Illness Midl. Asthma & Allergy Research Assn. Derby.

DARNLEY, Brian Jospeh Manuel 117 Ridley Road, Raised Ground Floor Flat, London E8 2NH — MB BS 1996 Newc.

DAROUGAR, Sohrab 2 Digby Place, Croydon CR0 5QR Tel: 020 8686 4711; 2 Digby Place, Croydon CR0 5QR Tel: 020 8686 4711 — MD 1953 Teheran; DSc 1990; FRCPath 1982, M 1972; DTM & H Lond 1961; Cert. Ophth. Teheran 1955. (Teheran) Emerit. Prof. Pub. Health Ophth. Inst. Ophth. Lond. Socs: Amer. Soc. Microbiol.

DAROWSKI, Adam 81 Thurleigh Road, London SW12 8TY — MB BS 1981 Lond.

DAROWSKI, Mark Janusz 1 Weetwood Avenue, Leeds LS16 5NG — MB ChB 1978 Leeds.

DARR, Anjum Javed 39 Alexandra Road, Wimbledon, London SW19 7JZ — MB BS 1983 Punjab; BSc Punjab 1978; LRCP LRCS Ed. LRCPS Glas. 1986; DA (UK) 1991. Prev: Trainee GP Surbiton; SHO (O & G) St. Helier Hosp. Carshalton; Regist. (Anaesth.) Poole Gen. Hosp.

DARRAGH, John Herdman Templemore Avenue Health Centre, 98A Templemore Avenue, Belfast BT5 4GR Tel: 028 9045 4321; 8 Cleland Park S., Bangor — MB BCh BAO 1964 Belf. (Qu. Univ. Belf.) Anaesth. Roy. Vict. Hosp. Belf. Socs: Assn. Anaesth. Gt. Brit. & Irel. Prev: Ho. Off. Belf. City Hosp.; Ho. Off. Jubilee Matern. Hosp. Belf.; SHO (Anaesth.) Belf. City Hosp.

DARRAGH, Paul Gerard 16 Springfield Park, Springfield Road, Belfast BT13 3PY — MB BCh BAO 1984 NUI; DCH RCPSI 1991; DRCOG 1991; MRCGP 1992; DGM RCP Lond. 1992. (University College Dublin) Staff Grade Phys. (Gen. Med.) Mid Ulster Hosp. N. Irel. Prev: GP Yorks.; GP Locum N. Irel.

DARRAGH, Paul Mervyn, TD 7 Donegall Avenue, Whitehead, Carrickfergus BT38 9NB — MB BCh BAO 1971 Belf.; PhD Belf. 1988; MSc (Human Genetics.) Ed. 1976; MD Belf. 1978; FRCPI 1975; FFCM 1980; Dip. Community. Med. Ed. 1978; DCH RCPSI 1973; Lic. FOM RCPI 1980. Lect. & Cons. E. Health & Social Servs. Bd. Qu. Univ. Belf. Prev: GP Whitehead Co. Antrim; Asst. Chief Admin. Med. Off. E.. Health & Social Servs. Bd.

DARRAH, Adrian James Jackson Whiteabbey Health Centre, 95 Doagh Road, Newtownabbey BT37 9QN Tel: 028 9086 4341 Fax: 028 9086 0443; 22 Glenariff Park, Jordanstown, Newtownabbey BT37 0RT Tel: 01232 861842 — MB BCh BAO 1975 Belf.; DRCOG 1977.

DARRAH, Alexander Coulter (retired) 9 Toberdowney Valley, Ballynure, Ballyclare BT39 9TS — MB BCh BAO Belf. 1946; FRCGP 1978; DPH Belf. 1951.

DARRAH, Elizabeth Rachel Allinson Dept of Radiology, West Suffolk Hospital, Hardwick Lane, Bury St Edmunds IP33 2QZ Tel: 01284 713376 Fax: 01284 713108 — MB BS 1989 Lond.; MRCP (UK) 1992; FRCR 1996. (St. Bart. Hosp.) Cons.Radiol.W. Sufolk Hosp.Bury St Edmunds. Socs: Fell. Roy. Coll. Radiol. Prev: Sp Regist. (Radiol.) John Radcliffe Hosp. Oxf.; SHO (Med.) Roy. Sussex Hosp. & Bromley Hosp.

DARRAH, Ronald Anthony Russell House Surgery, Bakers Way, Codsall, Wolverhampton WV8 1HD Tel: 01902 842488; 120 Codsall Road, Tettenhall, Wolverhampton WV6 9QJ Tel: 01902 752801 — MB ChB 1964 St. And. (St. And.)

DARROCH, Campbell James 20 Heswall Avenue, Higher Bebington, Wirral CH63 5QD — MB ChB 1985 Ed.; BSc (Hons.) Ed. 1983, MB ChB 1985; MRCP (UK) 1989. Regist. (Immunol.) Univ. Liverp. & Roy. Liverp. Hosps. Prev: Regist. (Med.) Roy. Liverp. Hosp.

DARROCH, Joseph Neil Airdrie Health Centre, Monkscourt Avenue, Airdrie ML6 0JU Tel: 01236 769333; Belhaven, Blairlinn View, Luggiebank, Cumbernauld, Glasgow G67 4AD — MB ChB 1978 Glas.; MRCGP 1982. GP Airdrie Health Centre.

DARROCH, Rachel Clare Westerton Lodge, 112 Old Woking Road, Woking GU22 8PB — MB BS 1986 Newc.; MRCGP 1990; DRCOG 1991.

DARROCH, Ross Archibald 73 East Avenue, Heald Green, Cheadle SK8 3BR — MB ChB 1987 Ed.

DART, David Embling (retired) Oldfield House, 48 Oldfield Crescent, Southwick, Brighton BN42 4FZ Tel: 01273 592135 — MB BS 1955 Lond.; MRCS Eng. LRCP Lond. 1955. Prev: Ho. Phys. Roy. Sussex Co. Hosp. Brighton.

DART, Mr John Kenneth George Moorfields Eye Hospital, City Road, London EC1V 2PD Tel: 020 7253 3411 Fax: 020 7253 4696 Email: jdart@dial.pipex.com; 8 Upper Wimpole Street, London W1M 7TD Tel: 020 7486 2257 Fax: 020 7487 3764 — BM BCh 1976 Oxf.; DM Oxf. 1992; BA Camb. 1973; MA Oxf. 1975; FRCS Ophth. Eng. 1982; FRCOphth 1988; DO RCS Eng. 1979. (Oxford) Cons. Moorfields Eye Hosp. Lond.; Hon. Sen. Research Fell. Dept. of Clin. Ophth. Inst. of Ophth. UCL. Socs: BMA & Assn. Research & Vision in Ophth.; Roy. Soc. Med.; (Counc.) Oxf. Ophth. Congr. Prev: Lect. (Clin. Ophth.) Inst. Ophth. Univ. Lond.; Hon. Cons. Moorfields Eye Hosp. Lond.

DARTEY, Phanuel Komla Wolanyo Suite 5, 22 Harley St., London W1N 1AA Tel: 020 8523 4947 Fax: 020 8503 3427 Email: phan-dartey@msn.com; 27 Forest Drive, Woodford Green IG8 9NG Tel: 020 8503 3427 Fax: 020 8503 3427 Email: phandartey@hotmail.com — MD 1969 Kalinin; MD (1st cl. Hons.) Kalinin 1969; MRCOG 1982; FRCOG 1999; MFFP 1982; DIP. Lang. 1970. Private Cons. Gyn.; Cons. Gyn. Marie Stopes Fairfield Clinic; Cons. Gyn. Brit. Pregn. Advis. Serv.; Vis. Cons. Humana Hosp. Wellington & Lond. Bridge Hosp. Lond.; RCOG Accredit. Indep. Specialist Portland Hosp. 1990; Mem. Minimal Access Gyn. & Laser Ther. Socs: BMA; Med. Protec. Soc.; EAGO. Prev: O & G & IVF Research Fell. Lond. Hosp.; Med. Dir. Blessings Private Clinic & IVF Unit; Regist. (O & G) Whipps Cross Hosp. Lond.

DARUWALA, Mr Pallon Dadi 4 Meadow View Cottages, Chatham Green, Little Waltham, Chelmsford CM3 3LF; 19 Fair a Far Cottages, Whitehouse Road, Edinburgh EH4 6PQ Tel: 0131 312 6595 — MB BS 1979 Bombay; MS Bombay 1983, MB BS 1979; FRCS Eng. 1985; FRCS Ed. 1984; FRCS (Urol.) 1998. Regist. (Urol.) W.ern Gen. Hosp. Edin. Prev: Regist. (Urol.) Whipps Cross Hosp. Lond.; Regist. (Urol.) Guy's Hosp. Lond.; Regist. (Gen./Vasc. Surg.) Broomfield Hosp. Chelmsford.

DARUWALLA, Neville Kersy 1 Birchwood Close, Horley RH6 9TX — MB BS 1998 Lond.; MB BS Lond 1998.

DARVELL, Francesca Jane Mytton Oak Surgery, Racecourse Lane, Shrewsbury SY3 5LZ — MB BChir 1990 Camb.; MRCGP 1993.

DARVELL, Mr Robin Harold John Charles Hicks Centre, 75, Ermine Street, Huntingdon PE29 3EZ Tel: 01480 457275 — MB BS 1963 Lond.; FRCS Eng. 1972; MRCS Eng. LRCP Lond. 1963; FCOphth 1988; DO Eng. 1970. (Westm.) Cons. Ophth. Surg. Kent & Canterbury Hosp. & I. of Thanet Dist. Hosp.; Fell. Ophth. Coll. Socs: B.M.A.; S.. Ophth. Soc. Gt. Brit. (Mem. Counc. & Treas.); BRd.stairs Med. Soc. Prev: Sen. Regist. W.. Ophth. Hosp. Lond.; Resid. Surgic. Off. Moorfields Eye Hosp. Lond.; Regist. (Plastic Surg.) Stoke Mandeville Hosp. Aylesbury.

DARVILL, Dougal Robert Hartcliffe Health Centre, Hareclive Road, Bristol BS13 0JP Tel: 0117 964 2839 Fax: 0117 964 9628 — MB ChB 1984 Bristol; MRCGP 1989; DCH RCP Lond. 1988; DRCOG 1987.

DARVILL, Simon Paul 16 Glenside, Appley Bridge, Wigan WN6 9EF — MB ChB 1987 Manch.

DARWENT, Anna Oakdene, Hailsham Road, Stonecross, Pevensey BN24 5AS — MB BS 1976 Lond.; MRCS Eng. LRCP Lond. 1976; Dip. Pract. Dermat. Wales 1994.

DARWENT, Jeffrey Paul The Medical Centre, 10 Richmond Road, Pevensey Bay, Pevensey BN24 6AQ Tel: 01323 762054 Fax: 01323 461180; Oakdene, Hailsham Road, Stone Cross, Pevensey BN24 5AS — MRCS Eng. LRCP Lond. 1976; BSc (Hons.) Lond. 1973, MB BS 1976.

DARWENT, Melanie South West Region Rotation, Bristol Royal Infirmary, Bristol; Heaven Cottage, Rectory Lane, Great Rissington, Cheltenham GL54 2LL Tel: 0185 682 1262 Email: firthfirm@aol.com — BM BCh 1990 Oxf.; MA 1986 Oxon; FRCS Eng. 1994. p/t Regist. Rotat. (A & E) S. W. Region.

DARWIN, Carol Ann 20 Gilkes Crescent, London SE21 7BS — MB BChir 1972 Camb.; MA Camb. 1973; MRCGP (Distinc.) 1976; DObst RCOG 1975. (St. Thos.) Prev: GP Lond.; Trainee GP Ipswich VTS; Hon. Research Fell. St. Geo. Hosp. Med. Sch. Lond.

DARWISH, Ahmed Kasem Child & Family Centre, Merthyr Road, Pontypridd CF37 4DD Tel: 01443 480541 Fax: 01443 480535; 26 Heol St. Denys, Lisvane, Cardiff CF14 0RU Tel: 01222 759682 Fax: 01222 765003 Email: adarwish@aol.com — MB ChB Alexandria 1975; MRCPsych 1984. Cons. Child & Adolesc. Psychiat. Rhondda NHS Trust. Prev: Cons. Psychiat. King Faisal Milit. Hosp., Saudi Arabia; Sen. Regist. (Child & Adolesc. Psychiat.) Wessex RHA; SHO & Regist. Leics. HA.

DARWISH, Darwish Hassan Hortiack, King's Drive, Caldy, Wirral CH48 2JH — MB ChB 1968 Alexandria; PhD Liverp. 1979; MRCOG 1975. (Alexandria) William Blair-Bell Lect. RCOG; Cons. (Obst. & Gyn.) Wirral AHA; Clin. Lect. (Obst. & Gyn.) Liverp. Univ. Socs: N. Eng. Soc. Obst. & Gyn. & Brit. Soc. Med. & Dent. Hypn. Prev: Lect. (O & G) Univ. Liverp.; Regist. (O & G) Liverp. AHA (T); Med. Off. Khartoum Civil Hosp. Sudan.

DARWOOD, Eileen Mary (retired) Flat 11, Blisworth Mill, Blisworth, Northampton NN7 3RZ Tel: 01604 879301 — MB BS 1955 Lond.; MRCS Eng. LRCP Lond. 1955; FFA RCS Eng. 1963; DA Eng. 1959. Prev: Cons. Anaesth. N.ampton Gen. Hosp.

DARYANANI, Renuka Mohandas Department of Child Psychiatry, Lanesborough Wing, St George's Hospital, Tooting, London SW17 — MB BS 1988 Lond.; MRCP (UK) 1992; MRCPsych 1996; DCH RCP Lond. 1991. Specialist Regist. Rotat. (Psychiat.) St. Geo. Hosp. Lond. Prev: Regist. & SHO (Psychiat.) St. Geo. Hosp. Lond.; SHO (Paediat.) Roy. Free Hosp. & Whittington Hosp. Lond.; SHO (A & E) Univ. Hosp. Lond.

DARZI, Ara Warkes 63 Kingstone House S., Ennismore Gardens, London SW7 1NH — MB BCh BAO 1984 NUI; LRCPI & LM, LRCSI & LM 1984.

DAS, Abhijit 6 Fairways Close, Liverpool L25 7AB — MB BS 1988 Calcutta, India.

DAS, Amarendra Nath Heene and Goring Practice, 145 Heene Road, Worthing BN12 4PY Tel: 01903 235344 Fax: 01903 247099 — MB BS 1976 Utkal; DRCOG 1989; LMSSA 1985.

DAS, Animesh Chandra Shettleston Health Centre, Shettleston Health Centre, 420 Old Shettleston Road, Glasgow G32 7JZ Tel: 0141 531 6250 Fax: 0141 531 6216 — MB BS 1959 Gauhati; DTM & H Liverp. 1962. (Assam Med. Coll. Dibrugarh)

DAS, Anita 10 Summerhouse Avenue, Heston, Hounslow TW5 9DA — MB ChB 1985 Leeds.

DAS, Ankur 24 Daylesford Road, Cheadle SK8 1LF — MB ChB 1992 Manch.

DAS, Anuka Boyatt Wood Surgery, Boyatt Wood Shopping Centre, Shakespeare Road, Boyatt Wood, Eastleigh SO50 4QP Tel: 023 8061 2051 Fax: 023 8062 0679; Koilash, 135 Bassett Avenue, Bassett, Southampton SO16 7EP Tel: 01703 767711 — MB BS Calcutta 1965; DCH Calcutta 1967. Prev: Trainee GP Soton. VTS; SHO (Gen. Med.) Grantham & Kesteven Hosp.

DAS, Arthita 147 Western Road, Sheffield S10 1LD — MB ChB 1998 Sheff.; MB ChB Sheff 1998.

DAS, Arun Kumar 30 Shackleton Way, Shrewsbury SY3 8SW; prativa Rohaban, 30 Shackleton way, Shrewsbury SY3 8SW Tel: 01743 341395 — MB BS 1967 Gauhati; MRCOG 1983; DObst RCPI 1981; FROCG. Staff Grade (O & G) Stirling Roy. Infirm.; Staff Grade Obst & Gyn . Roy. Shrewsbury Hosp. Socs: Med. & Dent. Defence Union Scotl.; Brit. Fertil. Soc.; Obst. & Gyn. Glas. Prev: Cons. O & G Taif Matern. Hosp., Saudi Arabia; Regist. (O & G) Stirling Roy. Infirm.

DAS, Asheesh Kumar 19 Edgerton Road, Huddersfield HD3 3AD Tel: 01484 425290; 139 Laburnum Court, Woolaston Avenue, Cardiff CF23 6EW Tel: 01222 752052 — MB BCh 1990 Wales. Prev: Ho. Off. (Gen. Med.) Withybush Hosp. HaverfordW.; Ho. Off. (Gen. Surg.) Llandough Hosp. Cardiff; Ho. Off. (Vasc./Gen. Surg.) Univ. Hosp. Wales.

DAS, Asutosh Fordbridge Medical Centre, 4 Fordbridge Road, Ashford TW15 2SG Tel: 01784 242251 — MB BS 1967 Calcutta. (Calcutta Nat. Med. Coll)

DAS, B 4-6 Kenley Parade, Sheil Road, Liverpool L6 3BP.

DAS, Bhagabat Charan, MBE (retired) 67 Half Edge Lane, Eccles, Manchester M30 9AZ Tel: 0161 789 6642 — MB BS 1954 Utkal; DTM & H Lond. 1961. Prev: Assoc. Specialist Geriat. Manch.

DAS, Mr Bichitra Nanda The Alexandra Hospital, Woodrow Drive, Redditch B98 7UB Tel: 01527 503030; 337 Pershore Road, Edgbaston, Birmingham B5 7RY Tel: 0121 472 0542 — MB BS 1976 Utkal; MS (Ophth.) All India Med. Scs. 1980; FRCS Ed. 1985; FRCOphth 1988; DO RCS Eng. 1983. Cons. Ophth. Surg. Alexandra Hosp. Redditch, P.ss of Wales Hosp. BromsGr. & Droitwich Private Hosp. Prev: Sen. Regist. Birm. Eye Hosp. & Wolverhampton Eye Infirm.; Sen. Research Fell. Leics. Univ. & Leics. Roy. Infirm.; Regist. S.. Gen. Hosp. Glas.

DAS, Bipad Taran Ashton Street Surgery, 34 Ashton Street, Ashton-on-Ribble, Preston PR2 2PP Tel: 01772 726588 Fax: 01772 760788 — MB BS 1967 Calcutta. (R.G. Kar Med. Coll.)

DAS, Mr Chaitanyananda Ruby Villa, 35 Taff Vale, Edwardsville, Treharris CF46 5NR Tel: 01443 412583 — MB BS 1958 Calcutta; BSc Calcutta 1951, MB BS 1958; FRCS Ed. 1964; FICS 1975. (Nilratan Sircar Med. Coll.) Cons. Orthop. Surg. P. Chs. Hosp. Merthyr Tydfil.

DAS, Chanchal Kumar 28 Whitehall Lodge, Pages Lane, London N10 1NY Tel: 020 8444 3756 — MB BS 1960 Calcutta; FRCOG 1982, M 1967; FICS USA 1983; DGO Calcutta 1962. (Calcutta) Sen. Lect. O & G Ahmadu Bello Univ. Zaria, Nigeria. Socs: BMA. Prev: Regist. (O & G) St. Helier Gp. Hosps. & St. And. Hosp. Bow; Consult. (O & G) W. Suff. Hosp. Bury St. Edmunds.

DAS, Chandan Kanti 144 Kings Avenue, Woodford Green IG8 0JQ — MB BS 1972 Calcutta.

DAS, Debajit 35 Taff Vale, Edwardsville, Treharris CF46 5NR — MB BCh 1996 Wales.

DAS, Debasis 24 Kinloch Drive, Bolton BL1 4LZ — MD 1986 Calcutta; MB BS 1981; MRCP (UK) 1988. Specialist Regist. (Gastroenterol.). Prev: Regist. (Med. & Gastroenterol.) Stepping Hill Hosp. Stockport.

DAS, Dhirendra Nath 1 Byrom Street, Salford M5 2UH — MB BS 1971 Calcutta.

DAS, Ghanashyam (retired) 160 Meadway, Birmingham B33 8NA Tel: 0121 783 3017 — MB 1927 Calcutta; MRCP Ed. 1930 LRCP LRCS Ed. LRFPS Glas. 1929.

DAS, Ilarani 8 Belgrave Close, Abergavenny NP7 7AP — MB BS Calcutta 1967; DA Calcutta (Gold Medallist) 1970. (Calcutta Nat. Med. Inst.) Clin. Asst. (Anaesth.) Nevill Hall Hosp. Abergavenny. Socs: Med. Protec. Soc. Prev: Cons. Anaesth. Ramkrishna Mission Seva, India; Regist. (Anaesth.) Staffs. Gp. Hosps.

DAS, Ira Dept. of Microbiology, Queen Elizabeth Hospital, Edgbaston Tel: 0121 472 3311 — MB BS 1978 Utkal; MD Aiims New Delhi 1981; MRCPath 1993. Cons. Microbiologist, Univ. Hosp. Birm. Socs: Brit. Soc. of Antimicrobial Agents of Chemotherp.; Hosp. Infec. Soc.; Assn. Med. Microbiol. Prev: Locom Cons. Microbiologist, Birm. Heartlands Hosp. Birm.; Locom Cons. Microbiologist, Good Hope Hosp. Sutton Coldfield, W. Midl.s.

DAS, Karuna Kanta Tel: 01274 636434 Fax: 01274 776522 — MB BS 1969 Gauhati. (Gauhati) GP Bradford, W. Yorks.

DAS, Kumar Shiv Vinayak 312 Falstones, Basildon SS15 5DT — MB ChB 1994 Manch.

DAS, Kumarendra Friarage Hospital, Northallerton DL6 1JG Tel: 01609 779911 — MB BS 1972 Dibrugarh; ATLS RCS Eng. 1997. (Assam Med. Coll.) Assoc. Specialist (Trauma & Orthop. Surg.) N.allerton; Prison Med. Off. N.allerton. Socs: Med. Protec. Soc.

DAS, Luna Pitshanger Family Practice, 209 Pitshanger Lane, Ealing, London W5 1RQ Tel: 020 8997 4747 Fax: 020 8566 7422 — MB BS 1994 Lond.; DROCG 1997; MRCOG 1998; DFFP 1997. (Charing Cross/Westminster) GP. Socs: BMA; MDU; MRCGP. Prev: GP VTS.

DAS, Nishebita South Street Surgery, South Street, Bargoed CF8 8ST Tel: 01443 821255 Fax: 01443 875409 — MB BS 1976 Utkal; MRCS Eng. LRCP Lond. 1982 London; MB BS 1976 Utkal.

DAS, Paul Kumar 11 Crossway, Didsbury, Manchester M20 6TU — BM BCh 1993 Oxf.; BA Oxf. 1990; MRCP (UK) 1996. Specialist Regist. (Cardiol.) Wythenshawe Hosp. Manch.

DAS, Peter West End Surgery, Moorgreen Road, West End, Southampton SO30 3PY Tel: 023 8047 2126/8039 9200 Fax: 023 8039 9201 — BM 1982 Soton.; DM-S MED (Society of Apothecaries of London) 1999; MLCOM 1998; MRCGP 1989. (Southampton)

DAS, Philip Ashoke Department of Anaesthesia, Edith Cavell Hospital, Bretton Gate, Peterborough PE3 9GZ Tel: 01733 874000; 3 Westhawe, Bretton, Peterborough PE3 8BA Email: philipdas@flashmail.com — MB ChB 1981 Bristol; FRCA 1992. (Bristol) Cons. Anaesth., PeterBoro. Hosp.s. Prev: Sen. Regist. Rotat. Hammersmith Hosp. Lond.

DAS, Philip Dev 4 Farcliff, Sprotborough, Doncaster DN5 7RE — MB ChB 1990 Leic.

DAS, Prasanta Kumar 454 Lea Bridge Road, Leyton, London E10 7DY Tel: 020 8539 1710 — MB BS 1968 Calcutta; PhD Calcutta 1980; MD Delhi 1974; Dip. Clin. Neurol. 1983. GP Princip. Socs: Brit. Neurol. Assn.; Life Mem. Neurol. Soc. India; Amer. Acad. Neurol. Prev: Neurol. Princ. Alex. Trust; Cons. Calcutta Med. Research Inst.; Regist. (Neurol.) Nat. Hosps. Qu. Sq. & Char. Cross Hosp. Lond.

DAS, Priyatosh The Surgery, 83 Priory Road, Hastings TN34 3JJ Tel: 01424 430800 Fax: 01424 465555 — MB BS 1969 Panjab; MB BS 1969 Panjab. (Panjab) GP Hastings, E. Sussex.

DAS, Purnendu Kumar Kenton Medical Centre, 7 Northwick Avenue, Harrow HA3 0AA Tel: 020 8907 6105 Fax: 020 8907 8259 — MB BS 1963 Calcutta; MD Delhi 1967; MRCP (UK) 1973. (Calcutta Nat. Med. Coll.) Clin. Asst. (Thoracic & Gen. Med.) Mt. Vernon Hosp. N.wood, Middlx.; Clin. Asst. (Thoracic Med.) Edgware Gen. Hosp. Edgware, Middlx. Prev: Lect. & Cons. Med. Univ. of Benghazi, Benghazi; Regist. (Thoracic Med.) Plaistow Hosp. Lond.

DAS, Mr Purnendu Kumar Kent & Canterbury Hospital, Ethelbert Road, Canterbury CT1 3NG — MB BS 1973 Utkal; FRCS Ed. 1988. Assoc. Specialist (ENT) Kent & Canterbury Hosp. Prev: Regist. (ENT) P. Chas. Hosp. Merthyr Tydfil.

DAS, Pushpa Woodhouse Hill Surgery, 71A Woodhouse Hill, Fartown, Huddersfield HD2 1DH Tel: 01484 533833 — MB BS 1962 Agra. (S.N. Med. Coll.) GP Huddersfield. Prev: Med. Off. (Clin.) Barnsley HA.

DAS, Rajiv 9 Roby Grove, Great Sankey, Warrington WA5 1RW Tel: 01925 725870 — BM BS 1985 Nottm.; MRCP (UK) 1993; DA (UK) 1992. Pharmaceut. Phys. Zeneca Pharma Wilmslow.

DAS, Rajiv 15 Reedley Drive, Burnley BB10 2QZ — MB ChB 1998 Leeds.

DAS, Ratan Kumar 9 Owl End, Great Stukeley, Great Stukeley, Huntingdon PE28 4AQ Tel: 01480 433265 Fax: 01480 416052; 9 Owl End, Great Stukeley, Great Stukeley, Huntingdon PE28 4AQ Tel: 01480 433265 Fax: 01480 416052 Email: ratan.das@hbhc-tr.anglox.nhs.uk — MB BS 1970 Mysore; FFAEM 1994; FRCS (Ed.) 1981; MS (New Delhi) 1977. (Kasturba Medical College) Cons. A & E Hichingbrooke Hosp. Socs: BMA; Brit. Assn. of Accid. and Emerg. Med.; FFAEM (Founding Fell.of Accid.and Emerg. Med.

DAS, Ratna Lea Bridge Road Surgery, 454 Lea Bridge Road, Leyton, London E10 7DY Tel: 020 8539 3246 Fax: 020 8556 9082 — MB BS 1968 Calcutta; PhD Calcutta 1981; MD Delhi 1972. (Calcutta) GP Princip. Socs: Life Mem. Federat. Obst. & Gyn. Soc. India. Prev: Cons. Calcutta Med. Research Inst., India.

DAS, Rhonaa 19 South Erskine Park, Bearsden, Glasgow G61 4NA — MB ChB 1996 Ed.

***DAS, Rita** 38 High Road, Stevenston KA20 3DR Tel: 01294 604450; 38 High Road, Stevenston KA20 3DR — MB BS 1997 Lond.; BSc Med. Sociology (Hons.) 1994.

DAS, Robert Peter Department of Genitourinary Medicine, Royal Gwent Hospital, Newport NP20 2UB Tel: 01633 234555 — MB BS 1974 Bangalor; MPhil Bradford 1985; MB BS Bangalore 1974; FRCP (UK) 1988; LMSSA Lond. 1986. Cons. Genitourin. Med. Glan Hafren NHS Trust Newport.

DAS, Sachinandan Ninewells Hospital & Medical School, Dundee DD2 1UB Tel: 01382 660111 Ext: 32850 — MB BS 1968 Utkal; FRCR 1977; DMRT Eng. 1971; ECFMG Cert 1970. (S.C.B. Med. Coll. Cuttack) Cons. Radiotherapist & Oncol. Ninewells Hosp. & Med. Sch. Dundee; Hon. Sen. Lect. & Head Dept. (Radiother.) Dundee Univ. Socs: BMA; Scott. Radiol. Soc.; Exec. & Therap. Working Party & Area Sec. Scotl. and Newc. Lymphoma Gp. Prev: Clin. Dir. (Radiother. & Oncol.) Ninewells Hosp. & Med. Sch. Dundee; Sen. Regist. & Regist. (Radiother. & Oncol.) Mersey Regional Centre; Radiother. & Oncol. Clatterbridge Hosp. Bebington.

DAS, Mr Samarendra Nath (cons. rooms), 139 Stoke Road, Guildford GU1 1EY Tel: 01483 533179 Fax: 01483 505737; 11 Levylsdene, Guildford GU1 2RS Tel: 01483 533179 Fax: 01483 505737 — MB BS 1960 Calcutta; 1966 (D.O.) London; FRCS Eng. 1968; FRCOphth 1988. (Med. Coll. Calcutta) Cons. Ophth. Surg. Mt. Alvernia Hosps. Guildford; Hon. Cons. Ophth. Roy. Surrey Co. Hosp. Prev: Sen. Regist. W.. Ophth. Hosp. Lond.; Regist. Addenbrooke's Hosp. Camb.; Clin. Asst. Moorfields Eye Hosp. Lond.

DAS, Sankar New Tynewydd Surgery, William Street, Tynewydd, Treherbert, Treorchy, Cardiff CF42 5LW Tel: 01443 771557 Fax: 01443 775780; Richfield, 57 Llandaff, Cardiff CF5 2PU Tel: 02920 563356 Email: sankdas@aol.com — MB BS 1974 Dibrugarh. (Assam Medical College) Socs: BMA; Rhondda Med. Soc.

DAS, Sankar Kumar St Helier Hospital, Wrythe Lane, Carshalton SM5 1AA Tel: 020 8644 4343; 62 Rose Hill, Sutton SM1 3EX Tel: 020 8644 1639 — MB BS Calcutta 1956; FRCP Glas. 1981, M 1966; FCCP 1974; FRCP Lond. 1998. (Med. Coll. Calcutta) Cons. Phys. Geriat. Med. St. Helier NHS Trust Hosp. Gp. Carshalton; Hon. Sen. Lect. Univ. Lond. St. Geo. Hosp. Tooting; Mem. (Adviser) Local Auth. Lond. Boro. Sutton, Selec. Comm. Homes & Hosp. Based Primary Care Team. Socs: FRSH; Brit. Geriat. Soc. & Roy. Inst. GB; NY Acad. Sci. Prev: Cons. Phys. Geriat. Med. Manor Hosp. Derby; Sen. Regist. (Geriat. Med.) King's Coll. Hosp. Lond.; Fell. (Internal Med. & Nuclear Med.) & Asst. Instruc. (Clin. Med.).

DAS, Mr Saroj Kumar The Hillingdon Hospital, Pield Heath Road, Uxbridge UB8 3NN Tel: 01895 279696 Fax: 01895 279890 Email: sarojdas@doctors.org.uk — MB BS 1978 Utkal; MS (Surg.) All India Inst. Med. Sc. 1980; FRCS Glas. 1986; MNAMS India 1982; MPhil Lond. 1996. (Orissa, India) Cons. in Surg. and Vasc. Surg., The Hillington Hosp.. Socs: A.S.G.B.I.; Roy. Soc. Med. (Fell.); Vasc. Surg. Soc. GB & Irel. Prev: Sen. Regist. (Vasc. Surg.) Roy. Brompton Nat. Heart & Lung Hosp. Lond.; Research Fell. (Surg.) Thrombosis Research Unit King's Coll. Sch. Med. & Dent. Lond.; Sen. Lect. & Cons. Vasc. Surg., Roy. Brompton Hosp., Nat. Heart & Lung Inst., Thrombosis Research Inst..

DAS, Satya Sundar Department of Medical Microbiology, St. Bartholomew's Hospital, West Smithfield, London EC1A 7BE Tel: 020 7601 8402 Fax: 020 7601 8409 Email: s.s.das@mds.qmw.ac.uk; 100 Pendennis Road, London SW16 2SP Tel: 020 8769 6281 — MB BS 1982 Lond.; BSc (Hons. Biochem.) Lond. 1979, MSc (Med. Microbiol.) 1989; MRCPath 1990; FRCPath 1998. (St. Bart.) Cons. Med. Microbiol. St. Bart. Hosp. Lond. Socs: Hosp. Infec. Soc.; Path. Soc.; Brit. Soc. Antimicrob. Chemother. Prev: Sen. Regist. (Microbiol.) Dulwich Hosp. Pub. Health Laborat. Lond. & St. Geo. Hosp. Lond.; Regist. (Bacteriol.) St. Mary's Hosp. Lond.; SHO (Path.) Hope Hosp. Salford.

DAS, Sean 19 South Erskine Park, Bearsden, Glasgow G61 4NA — MB ChB 1990 Glas.; DRCOG 1995; DFFP 1995; MRCGP 1996. Clin. Asst. Cardiol. Vict. Infirm.NHS Trust Glas.; Locum GP.

DAS, Sharmila 15 Reedley Drive, Burnley BB10 2QZ — MB BS 1994 Newc.; MRCP (UK) 1997. (Newcastle) SHO Rotat. (Gen. Med.).

DAS, Subhalaxmi Terra Nova House Medical Practice, 43 Dura Street, Dundee DD4 6SW Tel: 01382 451100 Fax: 01382 453679 — MB BS 1968 Utkal; FRCOG 1999; DFFP 1996; MD (Obst. & Gyn.) Sambalpur 1972; MRCOG 1979; DObst RCOG 1972. GP Dundee; Family Plann. Med. Off., Fife HCT. Socs: Brit. Soc. Clin. Cytol.; Fac. of Family Plann. Prev: Regist. O & G Clatterbridge Hosp. Bebington.; Clin. Cytologist, Roy. Infirm. Dundee.

DAS, Subhas 7 Lakeside Gardens, Merthyr Tydfil CF48 1EN. GP Merthyr Tydfil.

DAS, Sumit 41 Blakesley Road, Wigston, Leicester LE18 3WD — MB BS 1996 Lond.

DAS, Swadesranjan Gilfach Goch Health Centre, Gilfach Goch, Porth CF39 8TD Tel: 01443 672622 Fax: 01443 672622.

DAS, Vinay Kumar 56 Cranmoor Green, Pilning, Bristol BS35 4QF — MB BS 1975 India.

DAS GUPTA, Amareswar Parkfield Road Surgery, 287 Parkfield Road, Wolverhampton WV4 6EB Tel: 01902 333051; 1 Muchall Road, Penn, Wolverhampton WV4 5SE Tel: 01902 331895 — MB BS 1961 Calcutta. (Calcutta Med. Coll.) Mem. LMC (Wolverhampton Div.). Socs: BMA (Chairm. Wolverhampton Div.). Prev: SHO (Med.) Crossley Hosp. Frodsham; Ho. Phys. Guest Hosp. Dudley; Ho. Surg. Kidderminster Gen. Hosp.

DAS GUPTA, Ananda Lal Queens Park Surgery, 24 The Pantilles, Billericay CM12 0SP Tel: 01277 626446 Fax: 01277 630623 —

MBBS. (RG Kar) GP, Partner, Qu.s Pk. Surg., Billericay; Clin. Asst. in Diabetes, Orsett Hosp. Orsett.

DAS-GUPTA, Mr Ashis 1 Onslow Street, Guildford GU1 4YS Tel: 01483 554295 Fax: 01483 554818 — MB BS 1990 Lond.; BSc (Hons.) Lond. 1987; FRCS Eng. 1995. (The Lond. Hosp.) Med. Manager,Oncol.Sanofi; Dale Fund (Physiol.) 1987; Clin. Asst. Hon. Oncol. Roy. Surrey. Co. Hosp.Guildford. Socs: BMA; Roy. Soc. Med.; Med. Protec. Soc. Prev: SHO (Urol.) Roy. Hants. Co. Hosp. Winchester; SHO Rotat. (Surg.) Chelsea & W.m. Hosp. Lond.; SHO Rotat. (Surg.) St. Geo. Hosp. Lond.

DAS-GUPTA, Manoranjan (Surgery), 38 Cann Hall, Leytonstone, London E11 3HZ Tel: 020 8519 9914; 57 Bute Road, 38 Cann Hall Road, Ilford IG6 1AG Tel: 020 8554 9970 — MB BS 1949 Calcutta. (Carmichael Med. Coll.) Med. Off. Family Plann. Clinic Barking HA; Fell. Roy. Soc. Med. Prev: Regist. (Surg. & Orthop.) St. And. Hosp. Lond.; Regist. (Surg. & Gyn.) Sevenoaks & Orpington Gp. Hosp.; Clin. Asst. Ilford Matern. Hosps.

DAS GUPTA, Prabir Department of Cardiology, Queen Mary's Hospital, Sidcup DA14 6LT — MB BS 1976 Calcutta; LRCP LRCS Ed. LRCPS Glas. 1986.

DAS GUPTA, Ramaprasad Kingsfold Medical Centre, Woodcroft Close, Penwortham, Preston PR1 9BX Tel: 01772 746492 Fax: 01772 909141; Denholme, 182 Liverpool Road, Longton, Preston PR4 5ZE Tel: 01772 615539 — MB BS 1968 Calcutta. (Calcutta Nat. Med. Coll.)

DAS-GUPTA, Mr Rana 47 Cleveland Street, London W1P 5PL Tel: 020 7636 8333; 57 Bute Road, Gants Hill, Ilford IG6 1AG — MB BS 1985 Lond.; FRCS Eng. 1991. (Roy. Lond. Hosp.) Sen. Regist. (Plastic Surg.) Mt. Vernon Hosp. Middlx.; Lect. & Research Fell. Lond. Hosp. Med. Coll. Socs: Fell. Roy. Soc. Med.; Eur. Tissue Repair Soc. Prev: Regist. (Plastic Surg.) Univ. Coll. Hosp. Lond.; Regist. (Surg.) & SHO (Orthop.) Brook Hosp. Lond.; Cas. Off. & Demonst. (Anat.) St Mary's Hosp. Lond.

DAS GUPTA, Rita Queens Park Surgery, 24 The Pantiles, Billericay CM12 0SP Tel: 01277 626446 Fax: 01277 630623; 49 Tye Common Road, Billericay CM12 9NR — MRCS Eng. LRCP Lond. 1986; MB BS Calcutta 1975, DGO 1976.

DAS GUPTA, Saradindu (retired) Ex Drug Dependency Centre, St. Mary's Hospital, Praed St., London W2 1NY Tel: 020 7725 6486 — MB BS 1956 Calcutta; FRCPsych 1988; DPM Eng. 1964.

DAS-GUPTA, Satyajit The Surgery, 13 Westway, London W12 0PT Tel: 020 8743 3704 Fax: 020 8742 9500; 5 Kenelm Close, Harrow HA1 3TE Tel: 020 8904 9464 Fax: 020 8908 3554 Email: 100573.1340@compuserve.com — MB BS 1968 Vikram; MA (Sociol.) Bhopal 1973. (Gandhi Med. Coll.) Prev: Demonst. (Forens. Med. & Toxicol.) Gandhi Med. Coll. Bhopal, India; Gen. Duty Med. Off. Bharat Heavy Elec.s (India) Ltd. Bhopal, India.

DAS GUPTA, Mr Subhendu Eagelstone Health Centre, Standing Way, Eaglestone, Milton Keynes MK6 5AZ; 6 Haithwaite, Two Mile Ash, Milton Keynes MK8 8LJ — MB BS 1958 Calcutta; MS 1968.

DAS GUPTA, Subir Repose, 25 Belvidere Road, Walsall WS1 3AU — MB BS 1971 Gauhati.

DASAN, Ravi 7B Elmwood Road, London SE24 9NU — MB BS 1994 Lond.

DASAN, Mr Sunil 47 Tawney Road, Thamesmead, London SE28 8EF Tel: 020 8311 1836 — MB BS 1993 Lond.; BSc Lond. 1990; FRCS Eng. 1998. (UMDS St. Thos. Campus) Specialist Regist. Rotat. (Emerg. Med.) S. W. Thames Train. Progr.

DASGUPTA, Asim Kumar Flat 13, York House, Queen Alexandra Hospital, Cosham, Portsmouth PO6 3LY — MB BS 1967 Calcutta.

DASGUPTA, Bhaskar Southend General Hospital, Prittlewell Chase, Westcliff on Sea SS0 Tel: 01702 221048 Fax: 01702 221049 Email: dr.dasgupta@hospital.southend.nhs.uk; 89 Kings Road, Westcliff on Sea SS0 8PH — MD 1982 Med.; MD (Gen. Med.) Al India Inst. Med. Sc. 1982; MB BS Madras 1979; FRCP 1997. Cons. Rheum. S.end Health Care Trust Essex; Clin. Dir. R&D & Audit. Socs: Brit. Soc. Rheum. Prev: Sen. Regist. (Rheum. & Gen. Med.) Guy's Hosp. Lond.

DASGUPTA, Jayant 36 Coltsfoot, Welwyn Garden City AL7 3HZ — MB BS 1984 Magadh, India; MD 1984; DA 1993; FRCA 1997. Staff Grade Anaesth QEII Welwyn Garden City. Socs: RCA; AAGBI.

DASGUPTA, Ranan 4 Kensington Drive, Woodford Green IG8 8LR — BChir 1996 Camb.

DASGUPTA, Ranjit Kumar 50 Covertside, Wirral CH48 9UL — MB ChB 1993 Sheff.

DASGUPTA, Suhas Ranjan Selly Oak Hospital, Raddlebarn Road, Selly Oak, Birmingham B29 6JD Tel: 0121 627 1627; 31 Weoley Avenue, Birmingham B29 6PP — MB BS 1967 Calcutta; MRCP (UK) 1979.

DASH, Anjali 29 Nottingham Road, London SW17 7EA — MB BS 1983 Lond.; FCAnaesth 1990. Sen. Regist. (Anaesth.) Middlx. Hosp. Lond. Prev: Research Fell. (Anaesth.) Kings Coll. Hosp. Lond.

DASH, Clive Harry 8 Bluebird Way, Bricket Wood, St Albans AL2 3UH Tel: 01923 676225 — MB ChB 1963 Birm.; FFPM RCP (UK) 1989; Dip Pharm Med. RCP (UK) 1976; DObst RCOG 1965. Cons. Pharmaceut. Med. St Albans; Clin. Asst. (Thoracic Med.) Centr. Middlx. Hosp. Lond. Socs: Fell. Roy. Soc. Med.; Brit. Thorac. Soc.; Amer. Soc. of MicroBiol. Prev: Vice-Pres. Med. Affairs Bristol-Myers Squibb Pharmaceuts. N. Europe Region; Med. Dir. Glaxo Gp. Research; Clin. Asst. N.wick Pk. Hosp. Harrow.

DASH, Michael Glenmark (retired) The Mannamead Surgery, 22 Eggbuckland Road, Plymouth PL3 5HE Tel: 01752 223652 Fax: 01752 253875 — MB ChB 1960 Bristol; DObst RCOG 1965. Prev: Med. Off. (Occupat. Health) Plymouth Gen. Hosp.

DASH, Prasanna Kumar Shepperton Health Centre, Laleham Road, Shepperton TW17 8EJ Tel: 01932 245649 Fax: 01932 222922 — MB BS 1973 Utkal; LRCP LRCS Ed. LRFPS Glas. 1982 Edinburgh & Glasgow; MB BS 1973 Utkal.

DASHFIELD, Adrian Kenneth Directorate of Anaesthesia, Level 4, Derriford Hospital, Derriford Road, Plymouth PL6 8DH Tel: 01752 777111, 01752 792690 Fax: 01752 763287 Email: anaesthetics@phnt.swest.nhs.uk; Covert House, Yelverton PL20 6DF — MB ChB 1988 Birmingham; MD 2001 Birmingham; FRCA 1995. (Brimingham University) Cons. (Anaesth.) Derriford Hosp. Plymouth; Cons. in Anaesth. and Pain Managem. Socs: Soc. of Naval Anaesth.; Plymouth Med. Soc. Prev: Specialist Regist. Gt. Ormond St. Hosp.; Specialist Roy. Brompton Hosp.

DASHORE, Jagdish Prasad High Street Surgery, 108 High Street North, Dunstable LU6 1LN Tel: 01582 608420 — MB BS 1969 Indore; MB BS 1969 Indore.

DASHTI, Hassan 25 Fir Lodge, 3 Gypsy Lane, London SW15 5SA — MB ChB 1991 Dundee.

DASHWOOD, Caroline Sarah Mental Health Department, St. Georges Hospital, Blackshaw Road, London SW17 0RE Tel: 020 8725 5499 — MB BS 1989 Lond.; MRCPsych 1995.

DASOJU, Ramulu Grosvenor House, 147 Broadway, London W13 9BE Tel: 020 8567 0165 — MB BS 1974 Osmania. (Osmania Medical College, Hyderabad)

DASS, Badal Krishna Higher Broughton Health Centre, Bevendon Square, Salford M7 4TP Tel: 0161 792 5111 Fax: 0161 708 8944 — MB BS Calcutta 1962, DCH 1965; DPhysMed. 1974. Hosp. Pract. (Rheum.) Salford HA. Socs: BMA; BMA.; Bd mem.Salford/trafford med.Comm.

DASS, Joshua Muneer Habel 21 Linton House, St. Pauls Way, London E3 4AH — MB BCh BAO 1992 NUI; LRCPSI 1992.

DASS, Lakshman Alexandra Park Health Centre, 2 Whitswood Close, Manchester M16 7AW Tel: 0161 226 4616 — MB BS 1985 Newc.

DASS, Meenakshi Jessop Hospital for Women, Leavygreave Road, Sheffield S3 7RE — MB BS 1980 Punjab; MRCOG 1992. Staff Grade (O & G) Jessop Hosp. Sheff. Socs: Brit. Soc. Colpos. & Cerv. Path.; Brit. Med. Ultrasound Soc. Prev: Staff Grade Sheff.; Regist. Leicester Gen. Hosp.; Acting Regist. Lincoln Co. Hosp.

DASS, Shouvik 50 Brooklands Road, Prestwich, Manchester M25 0ED — BChir 1998 Camb.; BChir Camb 1998.

DASTGIR, Mary Bernadette Holly House, Old Town, Moreton-in-Marsh GL56 0LW — MB ChB 1957 Birm.; DPH Eng. 1968. (Birm.) Sen. Med. Off. DHSS Lond.

DASTIDAR, Bimalbhushan Ghosh St Philips Drive Surgery, 82 St. Philips Drive, Hasland, Chesterfield S41 0RG Tel: 01246 278008 Fax: 01246 278008 — MB BS 1966 Calcutta.

DASTUR, Neville Behram 34 Cedar Drive, Pinner HA5 4DE — MB BS 1997 Lond.

DATHAN, John Rodney Ellis Ewerby Farm, Off St Johns Road, Bashey, New Milton BH25 5SA Tel: 01425 611391 — MRCS Eng. LRCP Lond. 1964; MD Lond. 1974, MB BS 1964; FRCP Lond. 1980, M 1967. (Lond. Hosp.) Cons. Phys. Soton. & SW Hants. Health Dist.

Socs: Renal Assn.; Brit. Assn. Sport & Med. Prev: Sen. Regist. & Lect. (Med.) Lond. Hosp.; Cons. Phys. & Sen. Lect. (Gen. Med. & Nephrol.) Soton. Univ.

DATHI, Hamid Hussain Mohamadali The Golborne Medical Centre, 12-16 Golborne Road, London W10 5NT Tel: 020 8964 4801 Fax: 020 8964 5702; 26 Albert Road, Ealing, London W5 1RR Tel: 020 8998 4541 Email: hidathi@aol.com — MB BS 1980 Karnatak; DRCOG 1990; DFFM 1996. GP Lond.; Clin. Asst. (Ultra Sound) Redbridge HA.; Clin. Asst. (A & E Primary Care) St. Mary's NHS Trust. Prev: Regist. (O & G) Barking Hosp.

DATNOW, Arthur David 46 Shawfield Street, London SW3 4BD — MB ChB 1965 Liverp.; PhD Liverp. 1973, MB ChB 1965. Prev: Ho. Phys. & Ho. Surg. Roy. S.. Hosp. Liverp.; Lect. (Histochem. & Cell Biol.) Univ. Liverp.

DATNOW, Mr Edward Leyland 16 Notting Hill Gate, London W11 3JE Tel: 020 7243 2416 Fax: 020 7792 0461 Email: edwarddatnow@compuserve.com — MB BChir 1963 Camb.; MA Camb. 1963; FRCS Eng. 1967; FRCS Ed. 1966; MRCS Eng. LRCP Lond. 1962. (Camb. & Liverp.) Governor Nat. Soc. Epilepsy; Trustee Nat. Hosp. Neurol. & Neurosurg. Developm. Foundat. Socs: BMA; Liverp. Med. Inst. Prev: Regist. (Surg.) BRd.green Hosp. Liverp.; Regist. NW Regional Thoracic Surg. Unit Liverp.; Ho. Phys. & Ho. Surg. Liverp. Roy. Infirm.

DATOO, Munir Mohsin Abdulrasul Staverton Road Surgery, 51 Staverton Road, London NW2 5HA Tel: 0208 459 1359 Fax: 020 7459 6897 Email: datoo@dircon.co.uk; 71 Corbins Lane, Harrow HA2 8EN Tel: 248 5136 — MB BS 1986 Karachi; DLO RCS Eng. 1994. (Dow Med. Coll.) GP Princip. GP; Clin. Asst. ENT Centr. Middlx. Hosp. Socs: M.D.U.

DATOO, Safder Ali Lalji Watford Way Surgery, 278 Watford Way, London NW4 4UR Tel: 020 8203 1166/7 Fax: 020 8203 0430; 278 Watford Way, London NW4 4UR Tel: 020 8203 1166 — MB BS Bombay 1965; DRCOG 1973. Clin. Asst. (Cardiol.) Roy. Brompton & Nat. Heart Hosp. Lond. Socs: BMA; Med. Insur. Agency; Overseas Doctors Assn.

***DATTA, Amitava** 19 Selkirk Road, London SW17 0ER — MB BS 1992 Lond.; MB BS Lond 1992.

DATTA, Mr Asok Kumar 16 Buttermere Close, Kettering NN16 8LZ — MB BS 1972 Calcutta; FRCS Glas. 1982.

DATTA, Barindra Nath (retired) Pant Street Health Clinic, Pant Street, Aberbargoed, Bargoed CF81 9BB Tel: 01443 831185 Fax: 01443 839146 — MB BS 1955 Calcutta. Prev: Regist. (Med.) Staffs. Gen. Infirm. Stafford.

DATTA, Borunendra Nath Gellihaf House, Gellihaf, Blackwood NP12 2QE Tel: 01443 820847 — MB BCh 1997 Wales. Sen. Med. Ho. Off. P.ss of Wales Hosp. Bridgend. Prev: Med. Ho. Off. Llandough Hosp. Penarth; Surg. Ho. Off.W. Wales Gen. Hosp. Carmarthen.

DATTA, Cynthia Flat 5, 100 Drayton Park, London N5 1NF — BM BCh 1996 Oxf.

DATTA, Mr Debi Charan (retired) 18 Stanmore Court, Canterbury CT1 3DS Tel: 01227 760508 — MB BS 1949 Calcutta; FRCOG 1983; DGO 1954.

DATTA, Dibyendu c/o Royal College of Obstetricians & Gynaecologists, 27 Sussex Place, Regents Park, London NW1 4RG — MB BS 1988 Calcutta; MRCOG 1994.

DATTA, Mr Dipak Mobility and Specialised Rehabilitation Centre, Northern General Hospital, Herries Road, Sheffield S5 7AT Tel: 0114 256 1571 Fax: 0114 243 1646; 109 Bushey Wood Road, Dore, Sheffield S17 3QD Tel: 0114 236973 — MB BS Calcutta 1967; FRCS Ed. 1977; FRCS RCPS Glas. 1977; FRCP (Lond.) 1998. Cons. Rehabil. Med. N. Gen. Hosp. Sheff.; Hon.Sen. Clin. Lect., Med. Fac., Univ. of Sheff. Socs: Soc. Rehabil. Med. & Internat. Soc. Prosth.s & Orthotics.; Brit. Soc. of Rehabil. Med. - Past Hon. Sec..; Internat. Soc. of Prosth.s & Obst. (V.-Chair UK). Prev: Sen. Med. Off. Disabil. Servs. Auth.

DATTA, Dipankar (retired) 9 Kirkvale Crescent, Newton Mearns, Glasgow G77 5HB Tel: 0141 585 7764 Fax: 0141 639 2156 — MB BS 1958 Calcutta; FRCP Glas. 1981; MRCP (UK) 1970; FRCP (Lond.) 1998. Prev: Cons. Phys. & Gastroenterol. Hairmyres Hosp. E. Kilbride.

DATTA, Dwipaj 10 Burghley Road, London N8 0QE — MB BS 1994 Lond.

DATTA, Harish Kumar Department of Clinical Biochemistry, The Medical School, University Newcastle, Newcastle upon Tyne NE2 4HH; 15 Ottershaw, Newcastle upon Tyne NE15 7XP — MB BS 1985 Newc. Sen. Lect. Newc. u. Tyne. Prev: Sen. Regist. Newc.

DATTA, Jayatu 14 Framingham Road, Sale M33 3SH Tel: 0161 976 2440 — MB BS 1977 Calcutta; DGO 1978; MRCOG 1991.

DATTA, Jean Bronwen 9 Kirkvale Crescent, Newton Mearns, Glasgow G77 5HB Tel: 0141 639 1515 — MB ChB Glas. 1956; MRCP Glas. 1968; DObst RCOG 1958; DCH Eng. 1959. Socs: Brit. Soc. Study of Infec. Dis.; BMA. Prev: Hon. Sen. Lect. & Assoc. Specialist (Infec. Dis.) Ruchill Hosp. Glas.; Med. Asst. (Infec. Dis.) Belvedere Hosp. Glas.; Regist. Roy. Matern. Hosp. Glas., Childr. Hosp. Sheff. & Ruchill Hosp. Glas.

DATTA, Kalpita Jane 35 Willow Way, Ponteland, Newcastle upon Tyne NE20 9RF — MB ChB 1992 Aberd.

DATTA, Mridul Kumar Audley Health Centre, Longton Close, Blackburn BB1 1XA Tel: 01254 264016 Fax: 01254 696402 Email: smtpmridildata@gp-p81167.nhs.uk; 'Ellora', 8 Whinney Lane, Langho, Blackburn BB6 8DQ Tel: 01254 240788 Fax: 01254 247032 Email: mdatta2000@hotmail.com — MB BS 1963 Calcutta; DGO 1964; MRCOG 1967; FRCOG 1992. Med. Off., Family Plann., for Blackburn with Darwen Primary Care Trust; Med. Off., Family Plann. for Chorley & S. Ribble Primary Care Trust. Socs: Brit. Med. Assn.; Overseas Doctors Assn.

DATTA, Mrs Naomi 9 Dukes Avenue, London W4 2AA Tel: 020 8995 7562 Email: spdatta@easynet.co.uk — MB BS Lond. 1946; MD Lond. 1951; FRCPath 1973, M 1963; Dip. Bact. Lond 1950. (W. Lond.) Socs: Soc. for Gen. Microbiol. (Hon. Mem.); Path. Soc. GB (Hon. Mem.). Prev: Emerit. Prof. Microbiol. Genetics Univ. Lond.; Prof. Roy. Postgrad. Med. Sch. & Hon. Cons. Hammersmith Hosp. Lond.; Sen. Bact. Pub. Health Laborat. Serv.

DATTA, Mr Pradip Kumar Consultant Surgeon, Caithness General Hospital, Wick KW1 5NS Tel: 01955 605050; Garvyk, 17 Newton Avenue, Wick KW1 5LJ Tel: 01955 5739 — MB BS 1964 Andhra; MS (Gen. Surg.) Andhra 1967; FRCS Glas. 1990; FRCS Eng. 1970; FRCSI 1970; FRCS Ed. 1969. Cons. Gen. Surg. Caithness Gen. Hosp. Wick; Coll. Tutor RCS Edin.; Vis. Lect. (Surg.) USM Malaysia; Overseas Course Tutor RCS Edin.; Vis. Lect. (Surg.) Nat. Univ. Singapore. Socs: Roy. Coll. Surg. Edin. (Counc. Mem.). Prev: Sen. Regist. (Surg.) Whittington Hosp. Lond.; Regist. (Surg.) Roy. Cornw. Hosp.; Regist. (Gen. Surg.) Poole Gen. Hosp. Poole.

DATTA, Priti Sadhan Deerness Park Medical Centre, Suffolk Street, Sunderland SR2 8AD Tel: 0191 567 0961 — MB BS 1956 Calcutta.

DATTA, Protiva 14 Framingham Road, Sale, Manchester M33 3SH — MB BS 1978 Bangalore; MRCOG 1985.

DATTA, Ruplekha 2 Rosse Field House, Park Drive, Bradford BD9 4EF Tel: 01274 494796 — MB BS 1957 Patna; DObst RCOG 1965. (P. of Wales Med. Coll.) Clin. Asst. (Geintourin. Med.) Bradford. Socs: BMA. Prev: Clin. Med. Off. (Community Health) Bradford Health Dist.

DATTA, Mr Salil Kumar Eye Department, Hull Royal Infirmary, Anlaby Road, Hull HU3 2JZ Tel: 01482 674824; 43 Green Lane, Cottingham HU16 5JJ — MB BS 1965 Calcutta; FRCS Ed. 1977; FCOphth 1990; DO RCS Eng. 1968. Cons. Ophth. Hull Roy. Infirm. Socs: UK Interocular Implant Soc.; N. Eng. Ophth. Soc.; Hull Med. Soc. Prev: Sen. Regist. Leeds Gen. Infirm.; Sen. Regist. & Regist. Roy. Hallamsh. Hosp. Sheff.; Regist. Hull Roy. Infirm.

DATTA, Samyadev 68 Briars Meads, Oadby, Leicester LE2 5WD Tel: 0116 271 6566 — MB BS 1979 Mysore; FFA RCS Eng. 1987; DA (UK) 1986.

DATTA, Doctor (Mrs.) Saroj Audley Health Centre, Longton Close, Blackburn BB1 1XA Tel: 01254 264016 — FRCOG 1992 (Roy. Coll. of Obstetricians & Gynaecologists); MB BS 1962 Calutta; MB BS 1962 calcutta. Gen. Practitioner; Clin. Asst., Obst. and Gyn., Chesley NHS Trust; Clin. Asst., Child & Adolesc. Psychol., Blackburn.

DATTA, Professor Satya Prakash 9 Dukes Avenue, London W4 2AA Tel: 020 8995 7562 Email: spdatta@easynet.co.uk — MB BS Lond. 1947; BSc Lond. 1940. (Univ. Coll. Hosp.) Socs: Fell. Inst. Biol.; Biochem Soc.; Fell. RSM. Prev: Emerit. Prof. Med. Biochem. Univ. Lond.; Prof. Med. Biochem. Univ. Lond. At Univ. Coll. Lond.

DATTA, Satyendra Nath Datta, 64 Churchfield Road, Acton, London W3 6DL Tel: 020 8992 3854; 2C Sudbury Hill Close,

Wembley HA0 2QR Tel: 020 8908 2613 — FRCOG - 1998; MB BS Calcutta 1969; MRCOG 1981; FICS 1987; DRCOG 1980; Cert. Family Plann. JCC 1975; DGO 1970. (Bankura Medical College, India) Socs: Fell. Internat. Coll. Surg. Chicago Ill., USA. Prev: Clin. Asst. (Gyn.) Mt. Vernon Hosp. Middlx.

DATTA, Shantanu 2 Rosse Field House, Park Drive, Bradford BD9 4EF Email: s.datta@zen.co.uk — MB ChB 1989 Manch.; MRCGP 1993; MRCPsych 1997; DRCOG 1992; Cert. Family Plann. JCC 1992. (Manch.) Specialist Regist. Rotat. Old Age Psych. NW Eng. Socs: BMA (Hon. Sec. & Treas. Manch. & Salford Div.); Community Car Comm.; Jun. Doctors Comm. Prev: Regist. Rotat. (Psychiat.) Gtr. Manch.; SHO Rotat. (Psych.) Salford; Specialist Regist. Rotat. (Gen. Adult Psychiat.) NW Eng.

DATTA, Mr Shibendra Nath University Hospital of Wales, Cardiff CF14 4XW Tel: 029 2074 5115 Fax: 029 2074 5510; 36 Guenever Close, Thornmill, Cardiff CF14 9AH Tel: 029 2052 2790 Email: sndatta@dial.pipex.com — MB BCh 1990 Wales; FRCS (UROL) 2000; FRCS Eng. 1994; MD 1999. (Univ. wales Coll. Med.) Cons., Urol., Univ. Hosp. Of Wales, Cardiff; Specialist Regist., (UROL), Wales. Prev: Research Regist. (Urol.) Univ. Hosp. Cardiff; Specialist Regist. (Urol.) Wales.

DATTA, Shouren 9 Kirkvale Crescent, Newton Mearns, Glasgow G77 5HB — MB ChB 1998 Glas.; MB ChB Glas 1998.

DATTA, Mr Subimal Choppington House, 119 Horncastle Road, Boston PE21 9HX Tel: 01205 61618 — MB BS 1959 Calcutta; FRCS Ed. 1975. (Nat. Med. Coll. Calcutta) Assoc. Specialist (Orthop. A & E Dept.) Pilgrim Hosp. Boston. Socs: BMA. Prev: Ho. Surg. & Ho. Phys. Willingdon Hosp. New-Delhi; SHO Cumbld. Infirm. Carlisle; Regist. Orthop. Law Hosp. Carluke.

DATTA, Sudhir Ranjan (retired) Kingston General Hospital, Beverley Road, Hull HU3 1UR Tel: 01482 28631 — MB BS 1960 Calcutta; FRCP Ed. 1984, M 1968. Prev: Cons. Geriat. Serv. Hull Health Dist.

DATTA, Mrs Swastika 70 Westfield Road, Edgbaston, Birmingham B15 3QQ — MB BS 1962 Calcutta.

DATTA, Vipan Department of Paediatrics, George Elliot Hospital NHS Trust, Nuneaton CV10 7DJ Tel: 01203 865269 Fax: 01203 865279; 27 Lichen Green, Cannon Park, Coventry CV4 7DH — MB BS 1981 Delhi; MRCP (UK) 1993; MRCPCH 1997. Cons. Paediat. Geo. Elliot Hosp. Nuneaton. Socs: Brit. Soc. Paediat. Endocrinol.; Brit. Diabetic Assn.; B.M.A. Prev: Sen. Regist. Leicester Roy. Infirm. & P'boro Dist. Hosp.

DATTA, Vivek 4 Prince Consort Drive, Chislehurst BR7 5SB — MB BS 1993 Lond.

DATTA GUPTA, Rina 63 Broadway, Walsall WS1 3EZ — MB BS 1972 Calcutta.

DATTANI, Mehul Tulsidas Biochemistry, Endocrinology & Metabolism Unit, Institute of Child Health, London WC1N 1EH Tel: 020 7242 9789 Fax: 020 7831 1481 Email: m.dattani@ich.ucl.ac.uk; 63 Woodhall Gate, Pinner HA5 4TZ Fax: 01781 428 6954 — MB BS 1984 Lond.; MD Lond. 1995; MRCP (UK) 1988; DCH RCP Lond. 1987; FRCPCH 1998; FRCP (UK) 2000. (Middx Hosp) Sen.Lect./Hon Cons. Paediat.Endocrinol., Instit.Child Health & Gt. ormond St hosp.lond. Socs: Soc. of Endocrinol.; Eur. Soc. Paediat. Endocrinol.; Amer. Endocrine Soc. Prev: Research Fell. (Paediat. Endocrinol.) Middlx. Hosp. Lond.; Lect. (Paediat. Endocrinol.) Inst. Child Health Lond.

DATTANI, Minaxi 192 Kenton Lane, Harrow HA3 8SX — BM BS 1998 Nottm.; BM BS Nottm 1998.

DATTANI, Ramniklal Tribhovandas 22 Nicholas Road, Elstree, Borehamwood WD6 3JY Tel: 020 8953 8024; 414 Kingsland Road, London E8 4AA Tel: 020 7249 8732 — MB BS 1975 Kanpur. (G.S.V.M. Med. Coll.) Forens. Med. Examr. Metrop. Police. Socs: Police Surg. UK; Brit. Med. Assoc.; Roy. Soc. Med. Prev: GP Borehamwood; Trainee GP Lond.; Regist. (Haemat.) Qu. Charlotte's Matern. Hosp. Lond.

DATTNER, Rene 9 Vane Court, Dorothy Sayers Drive, Witham CM8 2LN — MB ChB 1955 St. And.; DA Eng. 1964.

DAU, Harjinder Singh 47 Birch Lane, Oldbury, Oldbury B68 0NZ — MB BS 1992 Lond.

DAUBENEY, Piers Edward Francis Royal Brompton Hospiital, Sydney St, London SW3 6NP Tel: 0207 351 8430 Fax: 0207 351 8547 Email: p.daubeney@rbh.nthames.nhs.uk — MB BS 1988 Lond.; MRCPCH 1998; DCH RCP 1992 Lond.; MRCP 1991 UK; BA 1985; MA 1985 Oxf.; MA Oxf. 1985, BA 1985; MRCP (UK) 1991; DCH RCP Lond. 1992. (Oxford and St. Thomas' Hospital London) Cons. Paediatric and Fetal Cariologist Roy. Brompton Hosp.; Also Chelsea & W.minster Hosp. Socs: BPCA; BMA. Prev: Sen. Regist. (Paediat. Cardiol.) Wessex Cardiothoracic Unit. Soton. Gen. Hosp.; Wessex Cardiac Trust Research Fell. Soton. Gen. Hosp.; Sen. Fell. (Cardiol.) Roy. Childr. Hosp. Melbourne, Austral.

DAUD, Mr Amer Salman Mina House, 7 Dalegarth Avenue, Lostock, Bolton BL1 5DW Tel: 01204 842695 — MB BCh 1975 Cairo; FRCS Ed. 1988; intercoll.Bd.Exam.Otolary. 1998. Assoc. Specialist (ENT) Fairfield Hosp. Bury & Birch Hill Hosp. Rochdale. Socs: Assoc. Mem. Brit. Assn. Otolaryngol. Prev: Sen. Specialist Regist. LAT Q.E. Hosp. Birm. Childr. Hosp.; Regist. (ENT) Fairfield Hosp. Bury; SHO (ENT) Hope Hosp. Univ. Manch.

DAUD, Laila Raouf Child Mental Health Unit, The Royal Oldham Hospital, Rochdale Road, Oldham OL1 2JH Tel: 0161 627 8080 Fax: 0161 627 8057; Mina House, 7 Dalegarth Avenue, Lostock, Bolton BL1 5DW Tel: 01204 842695 — MB BCh 1975 Cairo; MRCPsych 1989. Cons. Child & Adolesc. Psychiat. Roy. Oldham Hosp. Socs: Manch. Med. Soc.; Assn. Child Psychol. & Psychiat.; Assn. Behavioural & Cognitive Psychother. Prev: Sen. Regist. (Child Psychiat.) N. W.. RHA; Research Regist. (Psychiat.) Booth Hall Childr. Hosp. Manch.; Regist. (Psychiat.) S. Manch. Train. Scheme.

DAUD, Suleman Child Development Centre, Princess Alexandra Hospital, Hamstel Road, Harlow CM20 1RB Tel: 01279 444455; 11 Edens Close, Bishop's Stortford CM23 5AT Tel: 01279 651078 — MB BS 1979 Peshawar; MSc Lond. 1989; DCH RCP Lond. 1984. Assoc. Specialist (Paediat. & Child Health) P.ss Alexandra Hosp. Harlow. Socs: Brit. Paediat. Assn. & Europ. Acad. Childh. Disabil. Prev: Project Off. (Child Health) UNICEF. Pakistan.

DAUD, Sumiati Mohd Flat 1/2, 18 Cornwall St., Glasgow G41 1AQ — MB ChB 1995 Glas.

DAUDI, Mr Muhammed Irfan Terence Millett, 34 Sumner Place, South Kensington, London SW7 — MB BS 1977 Karachi; FRCS Ed. 1982; MRCS Eng. LRCP Lond. 1979. Asst. Prof. Surg. Aga Khan Univ. Hosp. Karachi. Prev: Regist. (Gen. Surg.) Yeovil Dist. Hosp.; SHO (Gen. Surg.) Rotat. Char. Cross Hosp. Lond. & W. Middlx. Hosp.; Lond.; Regist (Surg.) Roy. Masonic Hosp. Lond.

DAUID, Loay Maryois 33 Shrublands Close, Chigwell IG7 5EA — MB ChB 1976 Mosul; MB ChB Mosul Iraq 1976; MRCP (UK) 1990.

DAULEH, Mr Mohammed Issa Mohammed 74 Simpson Street, Dundee DD2 1UT — MB BCh 1980 Ain Shams; FRCS Glas 1989.

DAULTON, Dominique Paul Henri The Surgery, The Street, Wonersh, Guildford GU5 0PE Tel: 01483 898123 Fax: 01483 893104; Annery Cottage, Wonersh Common, Wonersh, Guildford GU5 0PL Tel: 01483 893082 — MB ChB 1978 Birm.; BSc (Anat.) Birm. 1975; MRCGP 1982; DRCOG 1980; Cert. Family Plann. JCC 1980. (Birmingham) Socs: Guildford Med. Soc.; Comm. Mem. W. Surrey LMC. Prev: Trainee GP/SHO Kidderminster Gen. Hosp. Worcs. VTS; Ho. Off. (Gen. Med.) The Guest Hosp. Dudley; Ho. Off. (Surg.) Birm. Accid. Hosp.

DAUM, Robert Edward Oliphant c/o Anaesthetic Department, Yeovil District Hospital, Higher Kingston, Yeovil BA21 4AT; Lower Farm, Longford Road, Thornford, Sherborne DT9 6QQ Tel: 01935 873145 — MB BS 1977 Lond.; FFA RCS Eng. 1983. Cons. Anaesth. Yeovil Dist. Hosp. Som. Socs: Eur. Regional Anaesth.; Brit. Assn. of Day Surg.; S. W. Soc. of Anaethesia. Prev: Cons. Anaesth. P.ss Mary's RAF Hosp. Halton & P.ss Mary's RAF Hosp. Akrotiri.

DAUNCEY, Amanda Clare Chisholm Child Development Centre, Northampton General Hospital NHS Trust, Cliftonville, Northampton NN1 5BD Tel: 01604 545841 — MB BS 1974 Lond.; MRCP (UK) 1977; MRCPCH (UK) 1996; DCH Eng. 1979; AKC 1974. (King's Coll. Hosp.) Assoc. Specialist (Community Paediat.) N.ampton Gen. Hosp. NHS Trust. Socs: Brit. Assn. Community Child Health; BMA; MRCPCH. Prev: SCMO N.ampton HA; SHO (Gen. Med. & A & E & Obst.) Epsom Dist. Hosp.; Ho. Phys. (Paediat.) Belgrave Childr. Hosp. Lond.

DAUNCEY, John Kingsley 45 Rosary Gardens, London SW7 4NQ Tel: 020 7373 6557 Fax: 020 7373 6426 — MB BChir 1956 Camb.; MA Camb. 1957; MRCS Eng. LRCP Lond. 1956; DObst RCOG 1958. (King's Coll. Hosp.) Aviat. Med. Examr. Prev: Ho. Surg. Tite St. Hosp. Childr. Chelsea; Ho. Off. (O & G) MusGr. Pk. Hosp. Taunton.

DAUNCEY, Margaret Karen Department of Psychological Medicine, St. Bartholomew's Hospital, West Smithfield, London EC1A 7BE; Flat 7 York House, 14 Highbury Crescent, London N5 1RP — BM BS 1983 Nottm.; MRCPsych 1987. Lect. (Psychiat.) St. Barts. Hosp. Lond.

DAUNCEY, Sarah Margaret Bushloe End Surgery, 48 Bushloe End, Wigston LE18 2BA Tel: 0116 288 3477; Pine Garth, 6 Enderby Road, Blaby, Leicester LE8 4GD Tel: 0116 278 7978 — BM BS 1981 Nottm.; BMedSci. Nottm. 1979; MRCGP 1986; DRCOG 1984; Cert. Family Plann. JCC 1984.

DAUNCEY, Terence Moore (retired) Woodway, Trellech, Monmouth NP25 4PS Tel: 01600 860433 Email: tdauncey@cardiff.u-net.com — BSc Birm. 1947, MB ChB 1950; MRCP Lond. 1957; FRCPath 1975, M 1963. Prev: Cons. Path. E. Glam. Hosp. Pontypridd.

DAUNT, Francis O'Neill (retired) 27A King's Road, Sandy SG19 1EJ Tel: 80799 — BM BCh 1944 Oxf.; MA, BM BCh Oxf. 1944.

DAUNT, Simon O'Neill Colchester General Hospital, Turner Road, Colchester CO4 3JL Tel: 01206 832524; 27A Queen's Road, Lexden, Colchester CO3 3PD Tel: 01206 545952 — MB BS 1974 Lond.; FRCP Lond. 1994; MRCP (UK) 1979; DObst RCOG 1976; FRCP 1995. (Roy. Free) Cons. Rheum. & Rehabil. NE Essex DHA. Socs: Brit. Soc. Rheum. Prev: Sen. Regist. Rotat. (Rheum. & Rehabil.) E. Dorset & Salisbury DHAs; Regist. (Rheum. & Rehabil.) Roy. Free Hosp. Lond.

DAVARASHVILI, Tenqir Ilich 51 Vincent Court, Bell Lane, Hendon, London NW4 2AW; 7 Shirehall Gardens, London NW4 2QT — Vrach 1978 Tblisi Medical Institute.

DAVDA, Anila Narendra Springburn Health Centre, 200 Springburn Way, Glasgow G21 1TR Tel: 0141 531 9631 Fax: 0141 531 9543; Meadows, 29 Kirkintilloch Road, Lenzie, Glasgow G66 4RJ Tel: 0141 776 6410 — MB ChB 1974 Glas. Prev: SHO (Psychiat.) S.. Gen. Hosp. Glas.

DAVDA, Kantilal Govindji 182 Anerley Road, London SE20 8BL Tel: 020 8778 5753 — MB BS 1970 Baroda; DObst. RCOG 1976. (Med. Coll. Baroda)

DAVDA, Mitesh 9 Barbara Road, Rowley Fields, Leicester LE3 2EB Tel: 01162 891046 — MB BS 1996 Lond. SHO (Orthop.) Leicester Roy. Infirm. Socs: RCS (Eng.); BMA; MDU. Prev: SHO (A & E) Medway Gillingham Kent; Ho. Off. (Med.) Ashford Hosp. Middlx.; Ho. Off. (Surg.) St. Helier Hosp. Surrey.

DAVDA, Narendra Sunderji The Turret Medical Centre, Catherine Street, Kirkintilloch, Glasgow G66 1JB Tel: 0141 211 8260 Fax: 0141 211 8264; The Meadows, 29 Kirkintilloch Road, Lenzie, Glasgow G66 4RJ Tel: 0141 776 6410 Email: rdavda@thefree.net — MB ChB 1973 Glas.; MRCGP 1978; DCH RCPS Glas. 1975. Hosp. Pract. (Gastroenterol.) Stobhill Gen. Hosp. Glas. Prev: Regist. (Gen. Med.) Gateside Hosp. Greenock; SHO (Gen. Med.) Stobhill Gen. Hosp. Glas.; Ho. Off. (Paediat.) Roy. Hosp. Sick. Childr. Glas.

DAVE, Ashwini Kumar 160 St Helens Road, Bolton BL3 3PH Tel: 01204 61188 — MB BS 1963 Rajasthan. (S.M.S. Med. Coll. Jaipur) Princip GP Bolton.

DAVE, Bhasker-Rai Pravinchandra Burgess Road Surgery, 357a Burgess Road, Southampton SO16 3BD Tel: 023 8067 6233 Fax: 023 8067 2909; 28 Redhill Close, Bassett, Southampton SO16 7BT — BM 1983 Soton.; BM Soton 1983; MRCP (UK) 1988; DRCOG 1989; DCH RCP Lond. 1984. (Southampton) Police Surg. Hants. Constab. Hants.

DAVE, Devendra Vijay 103 Salmon Street, London NW9 8NG — MB BS 1996 Lond.

DAVE, Mr Dinesh Department of Ophthalmology, Chesterfield & North Derbyshire Royal Hospital, Chesterfield S44 5BL Tel: 01246 277271 — MD 1984 Delhi; MB BS 1981; FRCS Ed. 1987; FCOphth 1989; DO RCS Eng. 1987. Staff Grade (Ophth.) Chesterfield & N. Derbysh. Roy. Hosp. Prev: Regist. (Ophth.) Inverclyde Roy. Hosp. Greenock; SHO E. Surrey Hosp. Redhill; Resid. (Ophth.) All India Inst. Med. Sci. New Delhi.

DAVE, Jiten 26 Kerrison Road, London W5 5NW Email: jdave@compuserve.com — MB BS 1988 Lond.; BSc (Hons.) Lond. 1984, MB BS 1988; MRCGP 1993; Dip. Pharm. Med. RCP (UK) 1997; DCH RCP Lond. 1989. (Char. Cross & Westm.) Med. Dir. Nycomed Amersham plc. Prev: Med. Advisor, SmithKline Beecham Pharmaceuts.; Therapeutic Head Internat. SmithKline Beecham Pharmaceut.

DAVE, Mahendra Shantilal Stuart Crescent Health Centre, 8 Stuart Crescent, Wood Green, London N22 5NJ Tel: 020 8889 4311 Fax: 020 881 0117; 85 Burleigh Gardens, Southgate, London N14 5AJ Tel: 020 8368 1031 — MB BS 1972 Gujarat. (B.J. Med. Coll. Ahmedabad)

DAVE, Narendra Pranlal Girdharlal Station Medical Centre, RAF Henlow SG16 6DN Tel: 01462 851515 Ext: 7006 Fax: 01462 893029 — MB BS 1978 Lond.; MRCGP 1991; MFFP 1993; T(GP) 1991; DRCOG 1981. (Middlx.) Civil. Med. Pract. MoD; Maj. RAMC (V); Med. Adviser, Adoption & Fostering, SSAFA Forces Help; Hon. Sen. Lect. Family Plann.. Roy. Def. Med. Coll. Socs: Fell. Roy. Soc. Med.; Mem. Biochem. Soc.; Grad. Inst. of Biol. Prev: Sen. Med. Off. Anguilla, W. Indies; Med. Off. of Health Tristan Da Cunha; Ho. Surg. Middlx. Hosp.

DAVE, Pushpa Nalinkumar (retired) 76 Lawnswood Sudden, Rochdale OL11 3HB Tel: 01706 43311 — MB BS 1961 Baroda; DCH RCPS Glas. 1969; DGO Baroda 1962. Prev: Sen. GP Lancs.

DAVE, Rashmikant Jagannath The Surgery, 2 Erith Road, Belvedere DA17 6EZ Tel: 01322 432315 Fax: 01322 440948; 1 Leyton Cross Road, Dartford DA2 7AP — MB BS 1980 Bombay; LRCP LRCS Ed. LRCPS Glas. 1985; MRCGP 1989.

DAVE, Roopal 26 Kerrison Road, London W5 5NW — MB ChB 1990 Birm.; MRCGP 1995.

DAVE, Sameer Vasant 143 Hall Drive, Middlesbrough TS5 7HU — MB BS 1994 Lond.

DAVE, Sangeeta Shashikant 2 Waddon Court Road, Croydon CR0 4AG — MB BS 1993 Lond. Cas. Off. Gold Coast Hosp. Qu.sland, Austral. Prev: Ho. Off. (Med.) Basildon Hosp.; Ho. Off. (Surg.) Gloucester Roy. Hosp.

DAVE, Shashikant Ravishanker (retired) 2 Waddon Court Road, Croydon CR0 4AG Tel: 020 8688 7604 — MB BS Bombay 1963.

DAVE, Shilpa Dunita 88 Park Road, Hampton Hill, Hampton TW12 1HR — MB BS 1997 Lond.

DAVE, Shirin Rashmikant Dartford East Health Centre, Pilgrims Way, Dartford DA1 1QY Tel: 01322 279881; 1 Leyton Cross Road, Wilmington, Dartford DA2 7AP — MB BS 1980 Bombay; DRCOG 1996; DFFP (RCOG) 1996.

DAVE, Sujata 4 Pinetree Close, Oadby, Leicester LE2 5US — MB BS 1995 Lond.

DAVE, Sushilkumar Kundanlal Barclay Street Health Centre, 36 Barclay Street, Leicester LE3 0JA Tel: 0116 254 7684 — MB BS 1964 Bombay; MRCOG 1969; Cert. Family Plann. JCC 1981; Cert FPA 1974; DObst RCOG 1967. Socs: Overseas Doctors Assn.

DAVE, Vinay Kant 260 Manchester Road, Blackrod, Bolton BL6 5AZ Tel: 01204 691078 — MB BCh 1962 Wales; FRCP Lond. 1983; MRCP (UK) 1969. (Cardiff) Cons. Dermat. Hope Hosp. & Skin Hosp. Salford (Univ. Manch. Sch. Med.); Hon. Cons. Dermat. Hope Hosp. Salford.

DAVENPORT, Andrew Royal Free Hospital, Pond St., London NW3 2QG Tel: 020 7794 0500; 32 Downage, London NW4 1AH — MB BChir 1981 Camb.; MB.B Chir Camb. 1981. Cons. Nephrol. & Transpl. Roy. Free Hosp. Lond.

DAVENPORT, Anna 14 Bank Road, East Linton EH40 3AH — MB ChB 1997 Manch.

DAVENPORT, Clare Frances 1 Meadow Crest Cottages, Burdrop, Sibford Gower, Banbury OX15 5RQ Tel: 01865 226856 Fax: 01865 226894; Directorate of Public Health and Health Policy, Richards Building, Oxfordshire Health Authority, Old Road, Headington, Oxford OX3 7LG Tel: 01865 226856 Fax: 01865 226894 — MB ChB 1992 Leic.; MSc (Pub. Health) Lond. 1996; BSc (1st cl. Hons.) Leic. 1989. (Leic.) Regist. (Pub. Health Med.) Oxf. HA. Socs: Train. Mem. Fac. Pub. Health Med. Prev: Regist. (Pub. Health Med.) Oxf.; SHO (Psychiat.) Oxf. HA.

DAVENPORT, Elaine Justine Orchard House Surgery, St. Marys Road, Ferndown BH22 9HB Tel: 01202 897000 Fax: 01202 897888; 19 Furze Hill Drive, Lilliput, Poole BH14 8QL — MB BS 1987 Lond. G. P. At Orchid Ho. Surg. Ferndown. Prev: Trainee GP Winton; SHO (Cas.) Poole Gen. Hosp.; SHO (Geriat. Med.) William Harvey Hosp. Ashford.

DAVENPORT, George Albert Acrefield, 6 Wiswell Lane, Whalley nr., Blackburn BB7 9AF — MB ChB 1955 Manch.; DObst RCOG 1958. Med. Off. Special Med. Bds. (Respirat. Dis.) DHSS Manch.

Prev: Gen. Pract. Whalley; Ho. Off. Ancoats Hosp. Manch. & Roy. Manch. Childr. Hosp.; Ho. Off. O & G Crumpsall Hosp. Manch.

DAVENPORT, Graham John The Surgery, The Green, Nantwich Road, Wrenbury, Nantwich CW5 8EW Tel: 01270 780210 Fax: 01270 780658 — MB 1974 Camb.; BChir 1973; MRCGP 1978; DRCOG 1976. Prev: SHO (Obst.), SHO (Paediat.) & SHO (Rheum.) Qu. Mary's Hosp. Lond.

DAVENPORT, Gwenan Jane 41 Hill Drive, High Ackworth, Pontefract WF7 7LQ — MB ChB 1986 Sheff.

DAVENPORT, Harold Thomas (retired) West House, 23 Green Lane, Northwood HA6 2UZ Tel: 019238 21739 — MB ChB Liverp. 1944; FRCP Canada 1972; MRCS Eng. LRCP Lond. 1944; FFA RCS Eng. 1954. Hon. Cons. Anaesth. N.wick Pk. Hosp.; Edr. Jl. One Day Surg. Prev: Dir. of Anaesth. Montreal Childr. Hosp. & Vancouver Childr. Hosp. Canada.

DAVENPORT, John (retired) 4 Ramms Court, Wells-next-the-Sea NR23 1JN Tel: 01328 710087 — MB BChir Camb. 1943. Prev: GP Alfreton Derbysh.

DAVENPORT, John Allan Avenue Road Surgery, 3 Avenue Road, Dorridge, Solihull B93 8LH Tel: 01564 776262 Fax: 01564 779599; 40 Rodborough Road, Dorridge, Solihull B93 8EF — MB ChB 1984 Birm.; MRCGP 1989; DCH RCP Lond. 1988; DRCOG 1988. Prev: SHO (Paediat.) Worcester Roy. Infirm.; SHO (Med.) BromsGr. Gen. Hosp. Birm. & Roy. Shrewsbury Hosp.

DAVENPORT, Mr Mark Department of Paediatric Surgery, King's College Hospital, London SE5 9RS Tel: 020 7346 3350 Fax: 020 7346 3643 Email: mark.davenport@kingshc.nhs.uk, markdav2@cs.com — MB ChB Leeds 1981; ChM Leeds 1995; FRCS (Paediat.) 1994; FRCS Eng. 1986; FRCS Glas. 1985. (Univ. Leeds) Cons. Paediat. Surg. King's Coll. Hosp. Lond.; Hon. Sen. Lect., Guy's, King's, Thos. Med. Sch. Prev: Sen. Regist. (Paediat. Surg.) Hosp. Sick Childr. Gt. Ormond St. Lond.; Lect. (Surg.) Kings Coll. Hosp. Lond.; Tutor (Paediat. Surg.) Univ. Manch.

DAVENPORT, Paul Geoffrey Newbold Verdon Medical Practice, St Georges Close, Newbold Verdon, Leicester LE9 9PZ Tel: 01445 822171 Fax: 01445 824968; Willows, Shackerstone Walk, Carlton, Nuneaton CV13 0BY Tel: 01455 293239 — Dip Occ Med; MB BS Lond. 1979; MRCGP 1984; DCH RCP Lond. 1984.

DAVENPORT, Mr Peter James The Consulting Suite, BUPA Hospital, Russell Road, Manchester M16 8AJ Tel: 0161 862 9563; High Barn, Pexhill Road, Henbury, Macclesfield SK11 9PY Tel: 01625 424362 Fax: 01625 424603 — MB BS Lond. 1969; FRCS Eng. 1975; MRCS Eng. LRCP Lond. 1969. (Guy's) Cons. Plastic Surg. S. Manch. DHA & NW RHA. Socs: Brit. Assn. Plastic Surg.; Brit. Assn. Anaesth. Plastic Surgs. Prev: Sen. Regist. (Plastic Surg.) Qu. Vict. Hosp. E. Grinstead; SHO (Surg.) Guildford & Godalming Gp. Hosps.; Regist. (Surg.) Univ. Hosp. Wales Cardiff.

DAVENPORT, Rebecca Jane Flat 5, 40 Burdon Terrace, Newcastle upon Tyne NE2 3AE — MB BS 1993 Newc.

DAVENPORT, Richard John Dept. of Clinical Neurosciences, Western General Hospital, Crewe Road, Edinburgh EH4 2XU Tel: 0131 537 7072 Fax: 0131 537 1132 Email: rjd@skoll.den.ed.ac.uk — BM BS 1987 Nottm.; B.Med.Sci. 1985; DM (Nottm.) 1996; MRCP (UK) 1990. (Nottingham) Cons. NeUrol. Edin. W.. Gen. Hosp. & Roy. Infirm. of Edin. Socs: Assn. of Brit. NeUrol.s.

DAVENPORT, Richard William Dow Surgery, William Street, Redditch B97 4AJ Tel: 01527 62285 Fax: 01527 596260; 26 College Road, Bromsgrove B60 2NF — MB ChB 1981 Birm.; MRCP (UK) 1984; MRCGP 1988; DRCOG 1988.

DAVENPORT, Robert Anthony Hamilton Road Surgery, 201 Hamilton Road, Felixstowe IP11 7DT Tel: 01394 283197 Fax: 01394 270304 — MB BS 1968 Lond.; DObst RCOG 1972; DA Eng. 1974; D. Occ. Med. 1997. (Lond. Hosp.) Socs: SOM; RSM; AAME. Prev: SHO (Obst. & Anaesth.) Redhill Gen. Hosp.; SHO (Paediat.) All St.s Hosp. Chatham.

DAVENPORT, Robert Horace, MBE (Surgery), 65 Chorley Road, Swinton, Manchester M27 4AF Tel: 0161 794 6237; 3 Welbeck Road, Eccles, Manchester M30 9EH — MB ChB 1966 Manch.; DObst RCOG 1968. (Manch.) Prev: GP Mem. Salford Dist. Med. Team; Clin. Asst. (Med.) Salford Roy. Hosp.; Chairm. Salford LMC.

DAVENPORT, Rosemary 3 Welbeck Road, Ellesmere Park, Eccles, Manchester M30 9EH Tel: 0161 707 0611, 0161 789 1635 Email: robert.davenport1@virgin.net — MB ChB 1966 Manch.; DPM 1972 Eng.; MRCPsych 1973; MRCPsych 1973; DPM Eng. 1972. (Manch.) Now Retd. from Cons. Appt., Acting as Second Opinion Approved Doctor for Ment. Health Act Commiss.. Prev: Sen. Regist. (Psychiat.) Oldham & Dist. Gen. Hosp. & Manch. Roy.; Infirm.; Sen. Regist. (Psychiat.) Withington Hosp. Manch. Sen. Regist.

DAVENPORT, Sarah Anne Women's Services, East Administration Building, Ashworth Hospital, Parkbourn, Maghall, Liverpool L31 1HW Tel: 0151 473 0303 Email: coyle-k@ashworth.nwest.nhs.uk — MB BS 1971 Lond.; MSc Manch. 1990; MRCS Eng. LRCP Lond. 1971; FRCP 2000. (Guy's Hosp. Med. Sch.) Hon. Lect. (Psychiat.) Manch. Univ.; Vis. Cons. Psychiat. to HMP Styal Chesh. Socs: Exec. Comm. Mem. UK Chapter Internat. Soc. Psychother. Schizophrenia; Manch. Med. Soc.; Chair Sec. Soc. & Rehab. Psychiat. RCPsych. from July 2001. Prev: Sen. Regist. (Psychiat.) Univ. Hosp. S. Manch.; Regist. (Psychiat.) Univ. Hosp. S. Manch.; Sessional Med. Off. W. Sussex & Trafford HAs.

DAVENPORT, Susan Mary 8 Chestnut Grove, Penkridge, Stafford ST19 5LX — MB ChB 1990 Birm.; ChB Birm. 1990.

DAVENPORT, Mr Thomas John (retired) Ellisons, North Lane, South Harting, Petersfield GU31 5NN — MB 1958 Camb.; BChir 1957; FRCS Eng. 1965. Prev: Cons. Urol. NW Surrey Dist. HA.

DAVENPORT-JONES, Christopher Ivor Aylesbury Partnership, Aylesbury Medical Centre, Taplow House, Thurlow Street, London SE17 2XE Tel: 020 7703 2205; Cobden Place, 326 South Lambeth Road, London SW8 1UQ Tel: 020 7622 9793 — MB BS 1968 Lond. (Middlx.)

DAVEY, Alan Thomas (retired) Ferndale, 14 Wolsey Road, Hampton TW12 1QW Tel: 020 8979 8076 — MB BS Lond. 1957; FRCPath 1974. Prev: Cons. Histopath. Hillingdon Hosp. Uxbridge.

DAVEY, Andrew Francis 22 Park Town, Oxford OX2 6SH; Gwenmenhir, Boscawfin Noon Farm, St Buryan, Penzance TR!9 6EH Email: frankdavey@hotmail.com — MB ChB 1993 Birm.; DCOG 2000; DCH 1999. Locum GP W. Cornw. Area.

DAVEY, Andrew John Department of Anaesthesia, Royal Sussex County Hospital, Eastern Road, Brighton BN2 5BE Tel: 01273 609060; 160 Woodland Drive, Hove BN3 6DE Tel: 01273 881521 — LRCPI & LM, LRSCI & LM 1973; LRCPI & LM, LRCSI & LM 1973; FFA RCS Eng. 1978. Cons. Anaesth. Roy. Sussex Co. Hosp. Brighton. Prev: Sen. Regist. (Anaesth.) Char. Cross Hosp. Lond.; Regist. (Anaesth.) Char. Cross Hosp. Lond.; SHO (Anaesth.) Middlx. Hosp. Lond.

DAVEY, Miss Clare Constantine Royal Free Hospital, Pond Street, London NW3 2QG Tel: 020 7794 0500 Fax: 020 7830 2208; 38 Cranley Gardens, Muswell Hill, London N10 3AP Tel: 020 8444 8003 Fax: 020 7830 2208 — MB BS 1978 Lond.; BSc (Hons.) Lond. 1975; FRCS Ed. (Ophth.) 1982; FCOphth 1988; FRCOphth 1988. Cons. Ophth. Roy. Free & Whittington Hosps. Lond. Socs: RSM; Chair Special Train. Comm. Ophth. Lond. Deanery. Prev: Clin. Lect. (Ophth.) Oxf. Eye Hosp.; Regist. (Ophth.) Tennent Inst. W.. Infirm. Glas.; SHO (Ophth.) Manch. Roy. Eye Hosp.

DAVEY, Gail 2 Clarke's Mews, Marylebone, London W1G 6QN — MB BChir 1991 Camb.; MRCP (UK) 1993. Clin. Research Fell. Lond. Sch. Hyg. & Trop. Med.

DAVEY, Gwynneth June (retired) Ashley Croft, Box, Corsham SN13 8AQ — MB ChB 1947 Birm. Prev: Cas. Ho. Surg. Gen. Hosp. Birm.

DAVEY, Hilary Mary 11 Coombe Close, Yeovil BA21 3PA — MB BS 1972 Lond.; MRCPsych 1980.

DAVEY, Jane Bomford 26 Ormonde Gate, Chelsea, London SW3 4EX Tel: 020 7352 7152 — MB BS 1957 Lond.; DMRT Eng. 1961. (Middlx.) Research Asst. Dept. Clin. Research Roy. Marsden Hosp. Lond.; Assoc. Specialist BrE. Diag. Unit Roy. Marsden Hosp. Lond. Socs: Fac. Radiols. Prev: Sen. Regist. Radiother. Dept. Hammersmith Hosp. Lond.; Ho. Surg. & Ho. Phys. Mt. Vernon Hosp. N.wood.

DAVEY, Julian Warwick Winyates Health Centre, Winyates, Redditch B98 0NR Tel: 01527 525533 Fax: 01527 517969; The Field House, Allimore Lane, Alcester B49 5PR Tel: 01789 764640 — LRCPI & LM, LRCSI & LM 1970; DObst RCOG 1973; DCH RCPSI 1972. (RCSI)

DAVEY, Katrina Anna Maria Spa Well Medical Group, Denburn Health Centre, Rosemount Viaduct, Aberdeen AB25 1QB Tel: 01224 640952 Fax: 01224 404422 — MB ChB 1995 Aberd.

DAVEY, Mr Keith Graham Eye Department, Huddersfield Royal Infirmary, Huddersfield HD3 3EA Tel: 01484 482991 Fax: 01484

482184 Email: keithdavey@enterprise.net — MB BS 1988 Lond.; MB BS (Distinc.) Lond. 1988; BSc (Hons.) Manch. 1981; FCOphth 1992. (UMDS Guy's Hosp.) Cons. Ophth. Huddersfield Roy. Infirm. Prev: Sen. Regist. (Ophth.) Yorks, RHA; SHO St. Paul's Eye Hosp., Walton Hosp. Liverp. & Manch. Eye Hosp.; Demonst. (Anat.) Univ. Manch.

DAVEY, Lorna Faye 10 Preston Close, Twickenham TW2 5RU — MB BS 1994 Lond. SHO (Med.) St. Geo. Hosp. Lond. Prev: SHO (A & E) W. Middlx. Univ. Hosp. Isleworth; Ho. Phys. Worthing Hosp.; Ho. Surg. St. Helier Hosp. Carshalton.

DAVEY, Michael Edward St Peters Medical Centre, Colbeck Road, West Harrow, Harrow HA1 4BS Tel: 020 8864 4868 — MB BS 1992 Lond.; MRCGP 1997.

DAVEY, Nigel Peter Todmorden Health Centre, Rose Street, Todmorden OL14 5AT Tel: 01706 815126 Fax: 01706 812693 — MB ChB 1984 Leeds; MRCGP 1988; DRCOG 1987. Prev: Trainee GP Blackburn VTS; Ho. Phys. & Ho. Surg. Harrogate Dist. Hosp.

DAVEY, Norman Barraclough Springhill House, Mill Road, Steyning BN44 3LN Tel: 01903 816133; The Beach House, Shore Path, Gurnard, Cowes PO31 8LL Tel: 01983 298924 — MB BS 1957 Lond.; DA Eng. 1965. (St. Thos. Hosp. Lond.) Socs: S.. Soc. Anaesth. Prev: Bitr Överlakare, Sweden; RAMC Sultan Muscat & Oman's Armed Forces; Anaesth. Univ. Hong Kong.

DAVEY, Patrick Paul 4 Sydenham Terrace, Halifax Road, Cambridge CB4 3PZ Tel: 01223 68300 — BM BCh 1984 Oxf.; MRCP (UK) 1987. Regist. (Cardiol.) Papworth Hosp. Camb.; Regist. (Nephrol.) Addenbrookes Hosp. Camb. Prev: SHO Rotat. (Med.) Leicester Roy. Infirm.

DAVEY, Mr Paul Adrian 14 Marble Hill Gardens, Twickenham TW1 3AX — MB BS 1990 Lond.; FRCS 2000; BSc (Hons) Neurobiol. Sussex 1985; FRCS Ed. 1995. (Char. Cross & Westm. Med. Sch.) Specialist Regist. Trauma & Orthop. S. Thames W. Rotat. Socs: Fell. Roy. Soc. Med.; Assoc. Brit. Orthop. Assn.; Brit. Soc. for Surg. of the Hand.

DAVEY, Professor Peter Garnet MEMO, Department of Clinical Pharmacology, Minewells Hospital, Dundee DD1 9SY Tel: 01382 632575 Fax: 01382 642637 Email: peter@memo.dundee.ac.uk; The Tower, 1 North View Terrace, Wormit, Newport-on-Tay DD6 8PP Tel: 01382 541635 Email: passeo@aol.com — MD 1982 Lond.; MB BS 1975; FRCP Ed. 1991; MRCP (UK) 1977. Prof. in Pharmacoeconomics, Univ. of Dundee; Hon. Cons. Phys. Tayside HB. Socs: Brit. Soc. Antimicrobial Chemother. & Brit. Pharmacol. Soc.

DAVEY, Philip 94 Kenton Road, Newcastle upon Tyne NE3 4NP — MB ChB 1998 Dund.; MB ChB Dund 1998.

DAVEY, Richard James Cae Ffynnon, Bryn-Y-Bia Place, Llandudno LL30 3AT — MB ChB 1996 Ed.

DAVEY, Richard Scott 18 Meadow Drive, Tickhill, Doncaster DN11 9ET — MB BS 1994 Lond.

DAVEY, Ronald James The Vicarage, Church Lane, Mellor, Blackburn BB2 7JL — MB BS 1966 Newc.

DAVEY, Ronald William (retired) — LVO 2001; Minst D 2000; MB BS Lond. 1968; FFHom 1990; AKC 1968; MD 1997. Trustee Blackie Foundat. Trust. AKC. Prev: Phys. to HM The Qu.

DAVEY, Timothy John 51 Sloane Street, London SW1X 9SW — MB BS 1985 Lond.

DAVEY-QUINN, Alan Paul 88 Ingledew Court, Alwoodley, Leeds LS17 8TY — MB ChB 1989 Leeds; BA Lond. 1994; FRCA 1996. (Leeds)

DAVEY-SMITH, George Department of Social Medicine, Canynge Hall, Whiteladies Road, Bristol BS8 2PR Tel: 0117 928 7329 Fax: 0117 928 7325 Email: zetkin@bristol.ac.uk — MB BChir 1983 Camb.; DSc Oxf. 2001; MSc Epidemiol. Lond. 1988; MA Oxf. 1984, BA (Psychol. Physiol. & Philosophy) 1981; MD Camb. 1991; FFPHM RCP (UK) 1996. Prof. Clin. Epidemiol. Univ. Bristol. Prev: Sen. Lect. (Pub. Health) Univ. Glas.; Lect. (Epidemiol.) Lond. Sch. Hyg. & Trop. Med.; Clin. Resid. Fell. Welsh Heart Foundat.

DAVID, Alison Frances 2A Chadlington Road, Oxford OX2 6SY — MRCS Eng. LRCP Lond. 1977.

DAVID, Ann Clair Anaesthetic Dept, Basildon Hopsital, Basildon SS16 5NL Tel: 01268 533911 — MB ChB 1982 Dundee; FFA RCS Eng. 1986. Cons. Anaesth. Anaesthetic Dept. Basildon and Thirrock Gen. Hosp. Socs: Intens. Care Soc. & Assn. Anaesth. Prev: Sen. Regist. (Anaesth.) Roy. Infirm. Edin.; Cons. Anaesth. Russell Hall Hosp. Dudley.

DAVID, Anna Louise Marie Queen Charlottes Hospital, Goldhawk Road, London W6 0XG Tel: 020 8383 1111 — MB ChB 1992 Manch.; BSc (Hons.) St. And. 1989; DFFP 1994; MRCOG 1998. Specialist Regist. O & G Qu. Charlottes Hosp. Lond. Socs: BMA; RCOG. Prev: Specialist Regist. (O & G) Ealing Hosp. W. Lond.; Sen. SHO (O & G) St. Thomas Hosp. Lond.; Specialist Regist. (O & G) W. Middlx. Hosp. Twickenham Lond.

DAVID, Professor Anthony Sion Department of Psychological Medicine, Guy's King's & St Thomas Schools of Medicine and, Institute of Psychiatry, P.O>. Box 68, London SE5 8AF Tel: 020 7848 0138 Fax: 020 7848 0572 Email: a.david@iop.kcl.ac.uk — MB ChB 1980 Glas.; MSc Lond. 1990, MPhil Psychiat. 1987, MSc (Birkbeck College) 1991; MD Glas. 1993, MB ChB 1980; FRCP Glas. 1994; MRCP (UK) 1983; MRCPsych 1986; FRCPsych 1998. Prof. & Hon. Cons. Inst. Psychiat., Kings Coll. Hosp. & Bethlem & Maudsley Hosps. Lond. Prev: Research Worker & Hon. Sen. Regist. Inst. Psychiat. & Maudsley Hosp. Lond.; Regist. (Psychiat.) Bethlem Roy. & Maudsley Hosp. Lond.; Regist. (Neurol.) Inst. Neurol. Sc. S.. Gen. Hosp. Glas.

DAVID, Arthur Bernard Bacon Lane Surgery, 11 Bacon Lane, Edgware HA8 5AT Tel: 020 8952 5073; 1 Orchard Drive, Edgware HA8 7SE — MB BCh 1953 Wales; BSc Wales 1950, MB BCh 1953. (Cardiff) Prev: GP Edgware; Ho. Phys. Med. Unit Cardiff Roy. Infirm.; Ho. Phys. (Child Health) & Ho. Surg. (O & G) Welsh Nat. Sch. Med. Cardiff.

DAVID, Christopher 4 St Margaret's Place, Whitchurch, Cardiff CF14 7AD — BM BS 1995 Nottm.

DAVID, David Rhoderic Medical Centre, Winch Lane, Haverfordwest SA61 1RN Tel: 01437 762333; 53 Queensway, Haverfordwest SA61 2NU Tel: 01437 763290 — LMSSA 1961 Lond.; MA Camb. 1957; DObst RCOG 1967.

DAVID, Godil (retired) 48 Mayflower Lodge, Regents Park Road, London N3 3HX Tel: 020 8343 1090 — MRCS Eng. LRCP Lond. 1944. Prev: Sen. Med. Off. Wilson Hosp. Mitcham.

DAVID, Heddwyn David and Partners, Clee Medical Centre, 363 Grimsby Road, Cleethorpes DN35 7XE Tel: 01472 697257 Fax: 01472 690852; 1 Park Drive, Grimsby DN32 0EE — MB BCh 1972 Wales; BSc (Hons.) Wales 1967. Clin. Asst. (Obst.) Grimsby Dist. Gen. Hosp. Prev: Lect. (O & G) Univ. Sheff.; SHO (Obst.) John Radcliffe Hosp. Oxf.; MRC Research Fell. Univ. Hosp. Wales.

DAVID, Mr Huw Gruffydd Derriford Hospital, Derriford, Plymouth PL6 8DH Tel: 01752 763786 — MB BS 1982 Lond.; FRCS (Orth.) 1993; FRCS Eng. 1987. Cons. Orthop. & Trauma Surg. Plymouth Hosps.

DAVID, Joan Claudia Conyers Pinewood, Weare Gillard, Bideford EX39 4QN Tel: 0123 72 70574 — LRCP LRCS 1950 Ed.; LRCP LRCS Ed. LRFPS Glas. 1950; DCH Eng. 1953.

DAVID, Joel Bernard Nuffield Orthopaedic Centre, Windmill Road, Headington, Oxford OX3 7LD Tel: 01865 741155; 20 Hamilton Road, Summertown, Oxford OX2 7PZ Tel: 01865 557187 — MB BCh 1981 Witwatersrand; FRCP 1996, M (UK) 1984. Cons. Rheum. Nuffield Orthopaedic Centre, Oxf.. Socs: Brit. Soc. Rheum.; BPRG. Prev: Sen. Regist. (Rheum.) N.wick Pk. Hosp. Harrow; Sen. Regist. (Med. & Rheum.) Hammersmith Hosp. Lond.; Regist. (Med.) Hammersmith Hosp. Lond.

DAVID, Judith Flora Ewing (retired) 9 Orme Lane, London W2 4RR Tel: 020 7229 8104 — MB ChB St. And. 1957; MRCPsych 1972; DPM Eng. 1964. Med. Off. HM Prison Wormwood Scrubs. Prev: Med. Off. HM Remand Centre Ashford.

DAVID, Lee Anthony 10 Walden Street, London E1 2AN — MB BS 1995 Lond.

DAVID, Lee Samantha Redroof, East View, Barnet EN5 5TN — MB BS 1996 Lond.

DAVID, Levin Timon Lonsdale Medical Centre, 24 Lonsdale Road, London NW6 6RR Tel: 020 7328 0808 Fax: 020 7328 8630 — MB BS 1986 Lond.; BSc Lond. 1983; DFFP 1994. (St. Mary's Hosp. Med. Sch. Lond.) GP Princip.; Hon. Primary Care Practitioner St Mary's Hosp. A & E Dept. Prev: Regist. (A & E) Cairns Base Hosp. Qu.sland, Austral.; Sen. Regist. (Med. for Elderly) St. Chas. Hosp. Lond.; Regist. (Med.) St. Chas. Hosp. Lond.

DAVID, Michelle Yelana Roathwell Surgery, 116 Newport Road, Cardiff CF24 1YT Tel: 029 2049 4537 — MB BS 1993 Lond.; BSc 1990; DFFP 1997. (Univ.coll.Middx.Sch.Med)

DAVID, Miriam Gwawr Jones The Family Practice, Western College, Cotham Road, Bristol BS6 6DF Tel: 0117 946 6455 Fax: 0117 946 6210 — MRCS Eng. LRCP Lond. 1987; BDS (Hons.) Lond. 1981; MRCGP 1991; DGM RCP Lond. 1995; DRCOG 1991. (Univ. Coll. Hosp. Lond.) Princip., Gen. Pract., Bristol.

DAVID, Miruna Delia 6 Leeson Walk, Birmingham B17 0LU — LRCP LRCS Ed. LRCPS Glas. 1997.

DAVID, Myra Cowan Child & Adolescent Mental Health Services, Ayrshire Central Hospital, Irvine KA12 8SS Tel: 01294 323425 Fax: 01294 313798 — MB ChB 1978 Glas.; MRCGP 1982; MRCPsych 1985. (Glasgow) Cons. Child & Adolesc. Psychiat. Ayreshire & Arran Primary Care NHS Trust. Prev: Sen. Regist. (Child & Adoles. Psychiat.) W. Scot. Train. Scheme.

DAVID, Nicholas Ieuan The Surgery, 39 Oswald Road, Scunthorpe DN15 7PN Tel: 01724 863631 Fax: 01724 855331; Kilburn, 8 Messingham Lane, Scawby, Brigg DN20 9AZ Tel: 01652 652461 — MB ChB 1979 Sheff.; Cert. Family Plann. JCC 1983; DRCOG 1983. Prev: Clin. Asst. Subst. Misuse Servs. Scunthorpe Community Health Care NHS Trust.

DAVID, Owen John Coed Melin, Tremain, Cardigan SA43 1SJ — MB BCh 1995 Wales.

DAVID, Peter Johnson Kenton Clinic, 533a Kenton Road, Harrow HA3 0UQ Tel: 020 8204 2255 Fax: 020 8204 7589 — MB BS Punjab 1965.

DAVID, Priscilla Shanti 49 Whitby Road, Ipswich IP4 4AF — MB ChB 1983 Sheff.

DAVID, Rachael Elisabeth St. Thomas Surgery, St. Thomas Green, Haverfordwest SA61 1QX Tel: 01437 762162 — MRCS Eng. LRCP Lond. 1962. (W. Lond.) Clin. Asst. (Haemat.) Withybush Hosp. HaverfordW. Socs: Fam. Plann. Assn.

DAVID, Sam Thomas The Health Centre, Elm Grove, Mengham, Hayling Island PO11 9AP Tel: 023 9246 6224 Fax: 023 9246 6079 — MB BS 1986 Lagos; 1989 LRCP LRCS LRCPS Glas. Edinburgh & Glasgow.

DAVID, Professor Timothy Joseph Booth Hall Children's Hospital, Charlestown Road, Blackley, Manchester M9 7AA Tel: 0161 795 7000 Fax: 0161 220 5387 Email: tjd@netcomuk.co.uk — MB ChB Bristol 1970; PhD Bristol 1975; MD Bristol 1981; FRCP Lond. 1986; MRCP (UK) 1976; FRCPCH 1997; DCH Eng. 1976. Prof. Child Health & Paediat. Univ. Manch.; Hon. Cons. Paediat. Booth Hall Childr., Roy. Manch. & St. Mary's Hosps. Manch. Socs: Roy. Soc. Med.

DAVID, Mr Verghese Cheeran ENT Department, Stafford District General Hospital, Weston Road, Stafford ST16 3SA Tel: 01785 57731 — MB BS 1973 Madras; FRCS Ed. 1977 (ENT 1984); FRCS Eng. 1978. (Jawharlal Inst. Postgrad. Med. Pondicherry) Cons. ENT Surg. Mid Staffs. HA.

DAVIDS, Cinonie (Surgery), 20 Nelson Road, Leigh-on-Sea SS9 3HU; 21 St James Gardens, Westcliff on Sea SS0 0BU — MB ChB 1967 Cape Town. GP Leigh-on-Sea.

DAVIDS, Esther 28 Remburn Gardens, Warwick CV34 5BH — Artsexamen 1993 Nijmegen.

DAVIDS, Zaib-un-Nisa Sadiq Child & Family Department, Tavistock Clinic, 120 Belsize, London NW3 5BA Tel: 020 7435 7111 — MB BS 1985 Lond.; MRCPsych 1992. Sen. Regist. Rotat. (Child Psychiat.) Tavistock Clinic & Roy. Free Hosp. Socs: Roy. Coll. Psychiat. Prev: Regist. & SHO Rotat. (Psychiat.) Roy. Free & Friern Hosps.

DAVIDSON, Mr Alan Ingram (retired) 20 Hillview Road, Cults, Aberdeen AB15 9HB Tel: 01224 867347 — MB ChB 1959 Aberd.; ChM Aberd. 1973; FRCS Ed. 1968; DObst RCOG 1963. Cons. Surg. Aberd. Roy. Infirm.; Hon. Sen. Lect. (Surg.) Univ. Aberd. Prev: Regist. (Surg.) Aberd. Roy. Infirm.

DAVIDSON, Alan John Lawson Ferry Road Health Centre, Ferry Road, Dingwall IV15 9QS Tel: 01349 863034 Fax: 01349 862022 — MB ChB 1976 Aberd.; MRCGP 1980.

DAVIDSON, Alan John Webster Argyll & Bute Hospital, Lochgilphead PA31 8LD Tel: 01546 602323 — MB ChB 1987 Glas.; BSc (Hons.) Glas. 1984; MRCP (UK) 1994; MRCGP 1995; MRCPsych 1999. (Glas.) Staff Grade (Psychiat.) Argyll & Bute Hosp. Lochgilphead. Prev: Trainee GP Argyll & Bute VTS; Regist. (Med.) Qu. Eliz. Hosp. Barbados, W. Indies; SHO Rotat. (Med.) Treliske Hosp. Truro.

DAVIDSON, Alastair Mackenzie (retired) 3 Cherry Grove, Gauldry, Newport-on-Tay DD6 8SF — MB ChB 1951 St. And.; DPH 1967.

DAVIDSON, Mr Alastair Watt 43 Blackford Road, Edinburgh EH9 2DT; Flat 8, 143 Holland Pk Avenue, London W11 4UT Tel: 020 7602 7105 — MB ChB 1994 Glas.; FRCS Ed 1998. Specialist Regist. Trauma & Orthop. Percival pott Rotat. Socs: Med. Defence Union; BMA.

DAVIDSON, Alexander 39 Glasgow Road, Denny FK6 5DW Tel: 01324 823035 — MB ChB 1953 Glas. Prev: Ho. Surg. (Obst.) Robroyston Hosp. Glas.

DAVIDSON, Alexander Fraser, OBE, Surg. Capt. RN Retd. (retired) 7 Searle Road, Farnham GU9 8LJ Tel: 01252 715361 — MB ChB Glas. 1952; MFOM RCP Lond. 1979; DAvMed Eng. 1973. Prev: Command Med. Off. to Flag Off. Naval Air Command & PMO RN Air Stn. Yeovilton.

DAVIDSON, Alison Elizabeth (retired) 32 St George's Road, Twickenham TW1 1QR Tel: 020 8892 9812 — MB BS Lond. 1970; MRCS Eng. LRCP Lond. 1970; DObst RCOG 1972.

DAVIDSON, Alison Elizabeth 7A Boxall Road, Dulwich, London SE21 7JS Tel: 020 7737 1149 Email: alisonlams@aol.com — MB BS 1994 Lond.; BSc Lond. 1991; DFFP 1997; DRCOG 1997; DCH 1998. (St Barts) GP.

DAVIDSON, Andrew Graham Hunter Wimpole Road Surgery, 52 Wimpole Road, Colchester CO1 2DL Tel: 01206 794794 Fax: 01206 790403; Paynes Farm House, Salcott-cum-Virley, Maldon CM9 8HG — MB BS 1976 Lond.; MRCS Eng. LRCP Lond. 1976; DCH RCP Lond. 1983; DRCOG 1980. (Char. Cross)

DAVIDSON, Andrew James Department of Anaesthetics, C Floor Outpatients, Royal Hallamshire Hospital, Glossop Road, Sheffield S10 2JF Tel: 0114 271 1900 — MB BS 1987 Newc.; MA Camb. 1988; FRCA 1992. Cons. Anaesth. Prev: Sen. Regist. (Anaesth.) N. Trent; Research Fell. (Anaesth.) Newc. Gen. Hosp.; Regist. (Anaesth.) Newc. u. Tyne.

DAVIDSON, Andrew John South Cliff Surgery, 56 Esplanade Road, Scarborough YO11 2AU Tel: 01723 360451 Fax: 01723 353518 — MB ChB 1985 Birm.; DRCOG 1989. (Birmingham) Prev: Trainee SHO/GP ScarBoro. VTS.

DAVIDSON, Andrew Randall Fernleigh House, Caldecott, Market Harborough LE16 8RN — MB BS 1966 Lond.; FRCP Lond. 1983, M 1969; MRCS Eng. LRCP Lond. 1966. (Lond. Hosp.) Cons. Phys. Kettering HA. Prev: Sen. Regist. Lond. Hosp.; Regist. Liver Unit King's Coll. Hosp. Lond.

DAVIDSON, Andrew Stuart Goodacre and Partners, Swadlincote Surgery, Darklands Road, Swadlincote DE11 0PP Tel: 01283 551717 Fax: 01283 211905; 64 Ashby Road, Woodville, Swadlincote DE11 7BY — BM BS 1979 Nottm.; BSc (Metallurgy) Birm. 1973; BMedSci Nottm. 1977; DRCOG 1982.

DAVIDSON, Anne Department of Paediatrics, Kingston Hospital NHS Trust, Galsworthy Road, Kingston upon Thames KT2 7QB Tel: 020 8546 7711; 24 Dawson Road, Kingston upon Thames KT1 3AT — MB BS 1985 Newc.; MRCP (UK) 1988; DCH RCP Lond. 1992. Sen. Regist. (Paediat.) Kingston Hosp. Prev: SHO (Gen. Med.) Dryburn Hosp. Durh.; Ho. Off. (Gen. Med. & Surg.) Freeman Hosp. Newc.

DAVIDSON, Anne Veronica McDougall The Health Centre, 68 Pipeland Road, St Andrews KY16 8JZ Tel: 01334 473441 Fax: 01334 466508; Brooksby, Queens Terrace, St Andrews KY16 9ER Tel: 01334 476108 — MB ChB 1964 Ed.; MRCGP 1976. Prev: Regist. (Geriat. Med.) Tayside HB; GP Edin.; Ho. Phys. & Ho. Surg. Deaconess Hosp. Edin.

DAVIDSON, Anthony William 36 Milson Road, London W14 0LJ Tel: 0207 603 9960 Fax: 0207 603 9960; 36 Milson Road, London W14 0LJ Tel: 0207 603 9960 Fax: 0207 603 9960 — MB BS 1970 Lond. (St. Bart.)

DAVIDSON, Mr Arthur Ian Greenwood 5 Mackintosh Way, Perth PH1 1SL — MB ChB 1960 Aberd.; PhD Aberd. 1969, ChM (Hnrs.) 1965, MB ChB 1960; FRCS Ed. 1965. Socs: Surg. Research Soc. & Assn. Surgs. Prev: Cons. (Gen. Surg.) Perth Gen. Hosps.; Sen. Regist. (Gen. Surg.) Aberd. Roy. Infirm.; Research Fell. Dept. Cardiovasc. Surg. W.. Reserve Univ.

DAVIDSON, Arthur Pryn, RD (retired) 12 Burnham Rise, Emmer Green, Reading RG4 8XJ Tel: 0118 947 3567 Email:

davidsonap@aol.com — LRCP LRCS Ed. LRFPS Glas. 1950. Surg. Capt. RNR. Prev: Hon. Phys. to H.M. the Qu.

DAVIDSON, Mr Arthur Samuel (retired) 3 Beach Walk, West Kirby, Wirral CH48 3JJ Fax: 0151 625 7633 Email: davidsonsam@hotmail.com — MB ChB 1942 Liverp.; FRCS Ed. 1950; MRCS Eng. LRCP Lond. 1942; DLO Eng. 1944. Prev: Cons. Otol. Mersey RHA.

DAVIDSON, Audrey (retired) 19 Prebendal Court, Shipton-under-Wychwood, Chipping Norton OX7 6BB Tel: 01993 832187 — MB BS 1951 Lond.; MRCPsych 1971. Prev: Cons. Psychiat. Oxon. Family & Child Guid. Serv.

DAVIDSON, Brian Kenneth Smith 279 Southbrae Drive, Glasgow G13 1TR — MB ChB 1989 Glas.

DAVIDSON, Mr Brian Ritchie 36 Cedar Road, Cricklewood, London NW2 6SR — MD 1989 Glas.; MB ChB 1981; FRCS Glas. 1985. Cons. & Sen. Lect. (Surg.) Roy. Free Hosp. & Med. Sch. Lond.

DAVIDSON, Carol Beverly 1 Morar Place, Newton Mearns, Glasgow G77 6UA — MB ChB 1998 Glas.; MB ChB Glas 1998.

DAVIDSON, Christine Mary (retired) Stockham Farm, Southleigh, Colyton EX24 6JA Tel: 01297 680250 Fax: 01297 680250 — MB ChB Birm. 1954; DObst RCOG 1956. Police Surg. Devon & Cornw. Constab. Prev: Partner Blackmore Health Centre.

DAVIDSON, Christopher Department of Cardiology, Royal Sussex County Hospital, Brighton BN2 5BE Tel: 01273 696955 Fax: 01273 684554 Email: chris.davidson@brighton-healthcare.nhs.uk; 11 Royles Close, Rottingdean, Brighton BN2 7DQ Tel: 01273 304349 — MB BChir Camb. 1969; MA Camb. 1969; FRCP Lond. 1984; MRCP (UK) 1970; LMSSA Lond. 1968; T (M) 1991; FRSC (1992). (St. Bart.) Cons. Cardiol., Brighton NHS Healthcare Trust; Sec. Europ. Federat. Internal Med. Socs: Fell. Europ. Soc. Cardiol.; Brit. Cardiac Soc.; Sec. Europ. Fed. of Internal Med. Prev: Cons. Phys. Rochdale HA.

DAVIDSON, Christopher Lynton Lowfield Cottage, Beamsley, Skipton BD23 6HN — MB ChB 1936 Leeds; MD Leeds 1940, BChD 1933, LDS 1932; FRCP Lond. 1965, M 1941; DCH Eng. 1941. (Leeds) Prev: Cons. Phys. Bradford Roy. Infirm. & St. Luke's Hosp. Bradford; Lt.-Col. RAMC; Centenary & Hardwick Fell. Univ. Leeds.

DAVIDSON, Claire Margaret 16 Pipeland Road, St Andrews KY16 8AH — MB ChB 1995 Manch.

DAVIDSON, Mr Colin Mackenzie (retired) Ashburnham House, 69 Coombe Lane, Westbury-on-Trym, Bristol BS9 2AZ Tel: 0117 968 4541 — MB ChB Glas. 1951; ChM Glas. 1967; FRCS Eng. 1985; FRCS Glas. 1972; FRCS Ed. 1959. Prev: Cons. Surg. Frenchay & Cossham Hosp. Gp.

DAVIDSON, Colin Mark Pennys Lane Surgery, Pennys Lane, Cranborne, Wimborne BH21 5QE Tel: 01725 517272 Fax: 01725 517746; Old Down House, Horton, Wimborne BH21 7HL Tel: 01258 840969 Fax: 01258 840969 — MB BS 1981 Lond.; MRCP (UK) 1985; DRCOG 1986. (Middlx.) Hosp. Pract. (Thoracic Med.) Roy. Bournemouth Gen. Hosp.; Clin. Asst. (Endoscopy) Vict. Hosp. Wimborne; Mem. Dorset LMC. Prev: Regist. (Gen. Med.) Roy. Newc. Hosp. NSW, Austral.; Regist. (Gen. Med.) Roy. Vict. Hosp. Bournemouth; Ho. Off. Middlx. Hosp. Lond.

DAVIDSON, David Goodinge Health Centre, Goodinge Close, North Road, London N7 9EW; 85 South Hill Park, London NW3 2SP — MB BS 1964 Lond.; BSc Lond. 1961; MRCS Eng. LRCP Lond. 1964; MRCGP 1979. Prev: Course Organiser Whittington Hosp. VTS; Clin. Asst. (Psychiat.) MarlBoro. Hosp. Lond.; Receiv. Room Off. & Ho. Phys. Med. Unit Lond. Hosp.

DAVIDSON, David Campbell 11 Andrews Lane, Formby, Liverpool L37 2EN — MB ChB 1967 Glas.; FRCP Lond. 1984; MRCP (U.K.) 1971; DObst RCOG 1969.

DAVIDSON, David Cunningham The Consulting Rooms, 21 Neilston Road, Paisley PA2 6LW Tel: 0141 889 5277 Fax: 0141 848 5500 Email: david.davidson@gp87502.ac-ht.nhs.swt.uk; The Moorings, 14 Thornly Pk Avenue, Paisley PA2 7SD — MB ChB 1983 Glas.; MRCGP 1987. Princip. in Gen. Pract., The Consg. Rooms, Paisley.; Clin. Assist., c/o the elderly, Argyll & Clyde Acute Hosp. NHS Trust Paisley. Socs: BMA. Prev: Trainee GP Glas. SE VTS; Regist. (A & E Med.) Vict. Infirm. Glas.

DAVIDSON, Donald Georges (retired) 15 Abbey Gardens, Chertsey KT16 8RQ Tel: 01932 564502 — MB BChir Camb. 1946; MRCS Eng. LRCP Lond. 1945; MRCGP 1964. Prev: Ho. Phys. Roy. Portsmouth Hosp. & St. Peter's Hosp. Chertsey.

DAVIDSON, Donald Graham Dunlop 9 The Green, Cheadle Hulme, Cheadle SK8 6JB Tel: 0161 485 3687 — MB ChB 1961 Ed.; DObst RCOG 1964; FFA RCS Eng. 1968. (Ed.) Cons. Anaesth. United Manch. Hosps. Prev: Regist. (Anaesth.) Aberd. Roy. Infirm.

DAVIDSON, Donald John MRC Human Genetics Unit, Western General Hospital, Crewe Road, Edinburgh EH4 2XU Tel: 0131 332 2471 Fax: 0131 343 2620 Email: donald.davidson@hgu.mrc.ac.uk; 6 Perth Street, Edinburgh EH3 5DP Tel: 0131 556 3858 — MB ChB 1994 Ed. (Ed.) Clin. Sci. (Molecular Genetics Studying Cyctic Fibrosis) MRC Human Genetics Unit W.. Gen. Hosp. Edin.

DAVIDSON, Dudley Graeme Campbell (retired) 55 Murray Road, London SW19 4PF Tel: 020 8946 3363 — MB ChB 1958 Cape Town; MRCP (UK) 1967. Prev: Assoc. Specialist (Renal Med.) SW Thames Regional Renal Unit St. Helier Hosp. Carshalton.

DAVIDSON, Duncan Lewis Watt Dept of Neurology, Ninewell Hospital, medical School, Dundee DD1 9SY Tel: 01334 425720 Fax: 01382425730 Email: duncand@tuht.scot.nhs.uk; Brrooksby, Queens Terrace, St Andrews KY16 9ER Tel: 01334 476108 Email: docs.davidson@care4free.net — MB ChB Ed. 1966; BSc Ed. 1963; FRCP Ed. 1979; MRCP (UK) 1970. (Edin.) Cons. Neurol. Tayside HB & Hon. Sen. Lect. Univ. Dundee. Socs: Assn. Phys.; Assn. Brit. Neurol.; Scott. Assn. of the Neurol. Sci. Prev: Clin. Staff MRC Brain Metab. Unit Edin.; Sen. Regist. (Neurol.) N.. Gen. Hosp. Edin.; Peel Trav. Fell. Clin. Research Inst. Montreal.

DAVIDSON, Elaine Millar 18 Eslington Terrace, Newcastle upon Tyne NE2 4RL — MB ChB 1994 Manch.

DAVIDSON, Elisabeth Grace Princes Park Health Centre, Bentley Road, Liverpool L8 0SY Tel: 0151 728 8313 Fax: 0151 728 8417; Flat 34, Princes Park Mansions, Sefton Park Road, Liverpool L8 3SA — BM BS 1979 Nottm.; MRCGP 1984; DTM & H Liverp. 1982. (Nottingham) Cons. (Primary Care) N. Mersey Community Trust; Dir. Primary Care N. Mersey Community Trust. Socs: Roy. Coll. Gen. Pract.; BMA; Liverp. Med. Inst. Prev: Course Organiser UnderGrad. Communication Skills Course Liverp.

DAVIDSON, Elspeth Dione Lamont Muirhouse Medical Group, 1 Muirhouse Avenue, Edinburgh EH4 4PL Tel: 0131 332 2201; 15 Montpelier, Edinburgh EH10 4LZ Tel: 0131 229 5073 — MB ChB Dundee 1985; MRCGP 1990; DCCH RCP Ed. 1992; Cert. Family Plann. JCC 1992; DRCOG 1991. Prev: Trainee GP Tayside HB.

DAVIDSON, Elspeth Sutherland 7 Searle Road, Farnham GU9 8LJ Tel: 01252 715361 — MB ChB 1952 Glas. (Glas.)

DAVIDSON, Emma Jayne Flat 15, Seawalls, Sea Walls Rd, Bristol BS9 1PG — MB ChB 1997 Ed.

DAVIDSON, Emma Margaret 16 Merchiston Gardens, Edinburgh EH10 5DD — MB ChB 1998 Ed.; MB ChB Ed 1998.

DAVIDSON, Finlina Corney Place, Medical group, The health Centre, Bridge Lane, Penrith CA11 8HW Tel: 01768 245226 Fax: 01768 245229; Eastview, Newton Reigny, Penrith CA11 0AY Fax: 01768 863807 — MB ChB 1972 Glas.; MPhil (Law & Ethics Med.) Glas. 1994.

DAVIDSON, Fiona Anne Maryhill Road Surgery, 96 Napiershall Street, Maryhill, Glasgow G20 Tel: 0141 211 9597 Fax: 0141 331 0071; 14 Randolph Road, Broomhill, Glasgow G11 7LG Tel: 0141 339 5114 — MB ChB 1982 Dundee; MRCGP 1986; DRCOG 1984. Clin. Asst. (Dermat.) Glas. Roy. Infirm.

DAVIDSON, Frank Blair (retired) 6 Doune Terrace, Edinburgh EH3 6DY — MB ChB 1941 Ed.; MFCM 1982; FRCOG 1981, M 1949. Prev: PMO Scott. Home & Health Dept.

DAVIDSON, Frederick Stanley (retired) 8 Pyefleet View, Langenhoe, Colchester CO5 7LD Tel: 01206 735816 — MB BS 1963 Lond.; MRCS Eng. LRCP Lond. 1963; DIH Eng. 1974; DObst RCOG 1966.

DAVIDSON, George William 222 Hillington Road S., Glasgow G52 2BB — MB ChB 1971 Glas.; FFA RCS Eng. 1977.

DAVIDSON, Gillian Amanda Park Lane Surgery, 2 Park Lane, Allestree, Derby DE22 2LN — BM BS 1994 Nottm.

DAVIDSON, Gillian Elizabeth North Tees General Hospital, Stockton-on-Tees TS19 8TR; 53 Landseer Drive, Billingham TS23 3GF Tel: 01642 562991 — MB BS 1990 Lond. (UMDS (St. Thomas' Campus)) Flexible SHO (A & E) N. Tees Gen. Hosp. Stockton.

DAVIDSON, Gillian Mary Stanley Surgery, 1 East Brougham Street, Stanley, Perth PH1 4NJ Tel: 01738 828294 Fax: 01738 827770; The Orchard, Milton of Luncarty, Luncarty, Perth PH1 3ES

Tel: 01738 827120 — MB ChB 1985 Dundee; MRCGP 1990. (Dundee) GP Stanley Pract. Perth Job-Share. Prev: Trainee GP Dundee VTS; SHO (O & G & Paediat.) Dundee; SHO (Orthop./Cas.) Dundee.

DAVIDSON, Graeme Griffiths King Woodside, Main St., Gargunnock, Stirling FK8 3BP Tel: 01786 86633; Woodside, Main St, Gargummock, Stirling FK8 3BP Tel: 01786 86 633 — MB ChB 1956 Ed. (Ed.)

DAVIDSON, Graham MacGregor The Gables, Apperley Lane, Apperlay Bridge, Bradford BD10 0PH Tel: 0113 250 4627 — MB ChB 1949 Aberd.

DAVIDSON, Hazel Elizabeth 82 Somerset Place, Stoke, Plymouth PL3 4BG Tel: 01752 563808 — MB ChB Glas. 1950; DMRT Eng. 1955. (Univ. Glas.) Clin. Med. Off. (Community Health) Plymouth HA. Prev: Assoc. Specialist Radiother. & Oncol. Plymouth HA; Sen. Regist. Radiother. Dept. W.. Infirm. Glas.

DAVIDSON, Heather Rosemarie Duncan Guthrie Institute of Medical Genetics, Yorkhill, Glasgow G3 8SJ Tel: 0141 201 0365 Fax: 0141 357 4277 Email: h.r.davidson@clinmed.gla.ac.uk; Braedine, Johnshill, Lochwinnoch PA12 4EL — MB ChB 1983 Ed.; BSc (Med. Sci.) 1981; MRCP (UK) 1986. Cons. Med. Genetics Duncan Guthrie Inst. Glas. Prev: Sen. Regist. (Med. Genetics) Duncan Guthrie Inst. Glas.

DAVIDSON, Helen Alisoun 15 Ketrine Avenue, Broughty Ferry, Dundee DD5 3HD Tel: 01382 76885 — MB ChB 1954 Aberd.

DAVIDSON, Iain Archibald (retired) 4 Midmar Drive, Edinburgh EH10 6BT Tel: 0131 447 7032 Fax: 0131 447 7032 Email: iadavidson@aol.com — MB ChB 1958 Ed.; FRCP Ed. 1994; FFA RCS Eng. 1963. Prev: Lect. (Dent. Anaesth.) Univ. Edin.

DAVIDSON, Ian Gordon Central Surgery, Gordon St., South Shields NE33 4JP Tel: 0191 455 4621; 4 Goodwood Close, Shotley Bridge, Consett DH8 0UF Tel: 01207 591531 — MB ChB 1981 Sheff.; MRCGP 1986; DRCOG 1984.

DAVIDSON, Mr Ian Robert Radiology Department, University Hospital, Queens Medical Centre, Nottingham NG7 2UH Tel: 0115 942 1421; 3 Chapel Kerrial, Grantham NG32 1PU — MB BCh BAO 1987 NUI; FRCSI 1991.

DAVIDSON, Ian Thomas Southern General Hospital NHS Trust, Glasgow G51 4TF Tel: 0141 201 1658; 10 Eastwood Avenue, Glasgow G46 6LR — MB ChB 1982 Glas.; FFA RCSI 1991; FRCA 1991. Cons. (Anaesth.) S.. Gen. Hosp. Glas.

DAVIDSON, Ian Wallace Foxhill Medical Centre, 363 Halifax Road, Sheffield S6 1AF Tel: 0114 232 2055 Fax: 0114 285 5963 — MB ChB 1973 Sheff.

DAVIDSON, Ian Walton (retired) Vinniehill Gatehouse of Fleet, Castle Douglas DG7 2EQ Tel: 01557 814529 Email: indavidson@aol.com — MB ChB St. And. 1948; FFA RCS Eng. 1960; FFA RCSI 1961; DA RCPSI 1952. Prev: Cons. Anaesth. W. Cumbld. Hosp. Gp.

DAVIDSON, Jacob 9 Waterside Place, Regents Park, London NW1 8JT Tel: 020 7586 3718 — MB ChB Ed. 1941; FRCA 1990; FFA RCS Eng. 1954; DA Eng. 1948. Prev: Cons. Anaesth. BRd.green Hosp. Liverp.; Cons. Anaesth. Mill Rd. Matern. Hosp. Liverp.; Teach. (Clin. Anaesth.) Univ. Liverp.

DAVIDSON, Jacqueline Anne 10 Crosby Hill Drive, Camberley GU15 3TY — MB ChB 1993 Leeds.

DAVIDSON, James 29 Wilton Crescent, Alderley Edge SK9 7RE — BM BS 1998 Nottm.; BM BS Nottm 1998.

DAVIDSON, James Cross Morses Farm, Huntley Road, Tibberton, Gloucester GL19 3AB Tel: 01452 790205 Email: hamjcd@aol.com — MB ChB 1948 St. And.; MB ChB (With Commend.) St. And. 1948; FRCP Ed. 1968, M 1957. (St. And.) Socs: Fell. Roy. Soc. Med. & Roy. Soc. Trop. Med. & Hyg. Prev: Sen. Cons. Phys. & Chief Internal Med. Hamad Gen. Hosp., Qatar; Emerit. Cons. Phys. Hamad Med. Corpn. Doha, Qatar; Sen. Cons. Phys. Lusaka Centr. Hosp., Zambia.

DAVIDSON, James Edward French Weir Health Centre, French Weir Avenue, Taunton TA1 1NW Tel: 01823 331381 Fax: 01823 323689; Mill Corner, Kingston St. Mary, Taunton TA2 8HH Tel: 01823 451386 — MB ChB 1969 Bristol; DObst RCOG 1971. Med. Off. Taunton Sch. Taunton. Prev: Clin. Tutor Univ. Bristol.

DAVIDSON, James Mark 38 Silverstream Road, Bangor BT20 3LR — MB BCh BAO 1987 Belf.

DAVIDSON, James Mitchell (retired) Little Onslow, 8 Torfield Road, Eastbourne BN21 2HN Tel: 01323 734980 — MB ChB 1954 Ed.; MFOM RCP Lond. 1981; MRCGP 1972; DIH Eng. 1981. Prev: Occupat. Health Adviser E.bourne & Hastings HAs.

DAVIDSON, Jane Mary North Road Surgery, 77 North Road, Richmond TW9 4HQ Tel: 020 8876 4442 Fax: 020 8392 2311; 10 Avondale Road, Mortlake, London SW14 8PT Tel: 020 8878 5092 — MB ChB 1984 Leeds; MB ChB Leeds l984.

DAVIDSON, Joan Mary Marlow, Leintwardine, Craven Arms SY7 0JP Tel: 0154 540226 Fax: 0154 540226 — BM BCh Oxf. 1944; DCH Eng. 1947; DObst RCOG 1946. (Oxf.) Socs: Ludlow & Dist. Med. Soc.

DAVIDSON, John (retired) Little Meadow, 15 Lewes Road, Haywards Heath RH17 7SP — MB BS Durh. 1946; MLCOM 1959; MRCGP 1958; FRSH 1981; AMR AeS 1981. Osteop. Phys., Private Pract., Haywards Heath. Prev: Cons. Osteop. Phys. Lond. Coll. Osteop. Med.

DAVIDSON, John 2 West Grange Steadings, St. Andrews KY16 8LJ; Flat 5, 101 Ridgway, Wimbledon, London SW19 4SX Tel: 020 8879 7486 Email: kayteemoss@hotmail.com — MB ChB 1990 Glas.; MSc 1997 (Nuclear Medicine) UCL; BSc (Hons.) Biochem. Glas. 1988; MRCP (UK) 1994. Cons. Phys. in Nuclear Med., Neuwells Hosp. Dundee. Prev: Sen. Regist. (Gen. & Nuclear Med.) Glas. Roy. Infirm.

DAVIDSON, John Cunningham (retired) King Street Medical Practice, 144A King Street, Aberdeen AB24 5BD Tel: 01224 644463 Fax: 01224 630231 — MB ChB 1970 Aberd. Prev: SHO/Regist. (Anaesth.) Aberd. Roy. Infirm.

DAVIDSON, John Forsyth (retired) Craigiebank, 20 Roman Road, Bearsden, Glasgow G61 2SL Tel: 0141 942 3356 Email: jforsyth@aol.com — MB ChB 1957 Aberd.; FRCP Glas. 1994; FRCP Ed. 1974, M 1965; MRCP (UK) 1992; FRCPath 1981, M 1977. Prev: Cons. Haemat. Glas. Roy. Infirm.

DAVIDSON, John Knight, OBE 15 Beechlands Avenue, Netherlee, Glasgow G44 3YT Tel: 0141 637 0290 Email: jkdavidson@onetel.net.uk; 15 Beechlands Avenue, Netherlee, Glasgow G44 3YT — MB ChB Ed. 1948; MD Ed. 1964; FRCP Glas. 1978, M 1974; FRCP Ed. 1966, M 1960; FRCR 1975, FFR 1958; Hon. FACR 1992; Hon. FRACR 1979. (Univ. Ed.) Cons. Advisor (Diving & Compressed Air Med.) Glas.; Hon. Fell. Med. & Dent. Defence Union Scotl. Socs: Hon. FACR.; Hon. Fell. (Founder Mem.) Internat. Skeletal Soc. (Medallist); Hon. Fell. Scott. Radiol. Soc. Prev: Cons. Radiol. in Admin. Charge W.. Infirm. & Gartnavel Gen. Hosp. Glas.; MRC Decompression Sickness Panel; Chairm. Health Policy Comm. Scott. Conserv. & Unionist Assn.

DAVIDSON, John Lindsay 12 Highfield, Lapford, Crediton EX17 6PY Tel: 01363 83764 — LRCPI & LM, LRSCI & LM 1951; LRCPI & LM, LRCSI & LM 1951. (RCSI)

DAVIDSON, Mr John Somerville Countess of Chester Hospital, Department of Orthopaedics, Liverpool Road, Chester CH2 1UL Tel: 01244 365000; Carn Cottage, Montgomery Hill, Frankby, Wirral CH48 1NF — MB ChB 1989 Glas.; FRCS Ed. 1994. Specialist Regist. Socs: Assoc. Mem. BOA; BOTA; Liverp. Med. Inst.

DAVIDSON, Joyce Mary (retired) Talfryn, 23 Min-y-Coed, Radyr, Cardiff CF15 8AQ Tel: 01222 842733 — MB BS 1953 Durh.; FRCGP 1983, M 1977. Prev: GP Cardiff.

DAVIDSON, Judith Department of Paediatrics, Child Development Centre, North Staffordshire City General Hospital, Stoke-on-Trent Tel: 01782 553352; 72 Meaford Road, Barlaston, Stoke-on-Trent ST12 9EB Tel: 01782 351077 — MB ChB 1985 Liverp.; MRCP (UK) 1990. Cons. Paediat. (Community Child Health) N. Staffs Hosp. Stoke-on-Trent. Socs: RCPCH; Brit. Paediat. Assn.; BAAF. Prev: Sen. Regist. (Paediat.) W. Midl. RHA; Research Regist. (Infec.) Univ. Birm.

DAVIDSON, Julia Forgie (retired) 79 Angusfield Avenue, Aberdeen AB15 6AT Tel: 01224 313461 — MB ChB Aberd. 1946. Prev: Research Asst. (Community Med.) Univ. Aberd.

DAVIDSON, Karen Elizabeth — MB ChB 1994 Dundee; DFFP 1996; DRCOG 1996. (Dundee) GP LOCUM. Prev: Salaried GP Oxenward Surg. Kilwinning; GP Regist. Kilbimie; GP Regist. Kilwinning Med. Centre.

DAVIDSON, Katharine Elaine 16 Merchiston Gardens, Edinburgh EH10 5DD — MB ChB 1993 Ed.

DAVIDSON, Katherine Elizabeth 69 Drumsmittal Road, Kessok, Inverness IV1 3JU — MB ChB 1984 Manch.; MB ChB Manch. l984.

Staff Grade (Palliat. Med.) Highland Hospice Inverness. Prev: Clin. Asst. (Palliat. Med.) Roxburghe Hse. Dundee.

DAVIDSON, Kathryn Elizabeth 7 Holywood Road, Newtownards BT23 4TQ — MB BCh BAO 1994 Belf. SHO (Gen. Med.) Roy. Vict. Hosp. Belf.

DAVIDSON, Mr Kenneth Gordon 19 Blackwood Road, Milngavie, Glasgow G62 7LB Tel: 0141 956 3700 — MB ChB 1965 Ed.; FRCS Ed. 1969. (Ed.) Cons. (Cardio Thoracic Surg.) Roy. Infirm. Glas. Prev: Sen. Regist. (Cardio Thoracic Surg.) Roy. Infirm. Edin.; Surg. Regist. Roy. Infirm. Edin.

DAVIDSON, Kenneth William Hythe Medical Centre, Hythe, Southampton SO45 4ZD; March Cottage, Noads Way, Dibden Purlie, Hythe, Southampton SO45 4PD — MB BS 1975 Lond. (Middlx.)

DAVIDSON, Kerri Lyn 25/4 South Elixa Place, Edinburgh EH8 7PG — MB ChB 1998 Ed.; MB ChB Ed 1998.

DAVIDSON, Kim 104 Winston Road, London N16 9LR — MB BS 1981 Lond.; MRCPsych 1986.

DAVIDSON, Kirsti 20 East Barnton Avenue, Edinburgh EH4 6AQ — MB ChB 1991 Manch.

DAVIDSON, Leslie Alan 4 Byeway, Guiseley, Leeds LS20 8JP — MB ChB 1985 Sheff.

DAVIDSON, Leslie Lodge National Perinatial Epidemiology Unit, Institute of Health Sciences, Old Road, Oxford OX3 7LE Tel: 01865 226965 Fax: 01865 227004 Email: leslie.davidson@perinat.ox.ac.uk; 18 Red Post Hill, London SE24 9JQ Tel: 020 7733 7556 Fax: 020 7733 7556 Email: leslie.davidson@perinat.ox.ac.uk — MD 1978 Columbia Univ. USA; MD Columbia Univ. USA 1978 BA1970; MSc Lond. 1982; FRCP Lond. 1997; MRCP (UK) 1993; MFPHM RCP (UK) 1994; FRCPCH 1997; FFPHM 1998. (Univ. Columbia (USA)) Dir. Nat. Perinatial Epidemiol. Unit; Reader in Pub. Health Med., Univ. of Oxf..; Hon. Cons. in Pub. Health Med., Oxf.shire Health Auth. Socs: Internat. Epidemiol. Assn.; Brit. Assn. Community Child Health; Assn. Child Psychol. & Psychiat. Prev: Cons. Paediat. Epidemiol. King's Healthcare Lond.; Assoc. Prof. Pediat. & Pub. Health Columbia Univ., NY.; Cons.Pub.Health Med.Lond.

DAVIDSON, Linde Elise Ursula 4 Rolfe Place, Harberton Mead, Oxford OX3 0DS Tel: 01865 68362 — MB BCh BAO 1944 Belf.; MD Belf. 1948; DCH Eng. 1946.

DAVIDSON, Lindsay Alexander Gordon (retired) Y Coety, Golden Grove, Carmarthen SA32 8LT Tel: 01558 668437 — MB ChB Ed. 1948; T(M) 1991; T(PHM) 1991; MD Birm. 1962; FRCP Glas. 1983; FRCP Lond. 1970; FRCP Ed. 1962; FFPHM RCP (UK) 1989; FFCM 1983; FRACMA 1980; FRACP 1977. Prev: Dean & Prof. Sch. Pub. Health & Trop. Med. Univ. Sydney, Austral.

DAVIDSON, Margaret Isobel 2 Kepplestone Avenue, Aberdeen AB15 7XF Tel: 01224 30761 — MB ChB 1955 Aberd. SCMO (Pre-Sch. Childr.) Grampian Health Bd.

DAVIDSON, Margaret Joan 8 Tollgate Drive, College Road, London SE21 7LS — MB BS 1971 Lond.; MRCS Eng. LRCP Lond. 1971; MFFP 1993; DObst RCOG 1973. (King's Coll. Lond.)

DAVIDSON, Marie Clare Hunter Health Centre, Andrew Street, East Kilbride, Glasgow G74 1AD Tel: 01355 906655; 5 Sutherland Avenue, Pollokshields, Glasgow G41 4JJ Tel: 0141 419 9274 — MB ChB 1981 Glas.; MRCGP 1987; DRCOG 1986. (Glasgow University) Prev: Sen. Med. Off. RAF Leuchars & Coningsby.

DAVIDSON, Martin Ellison High Street Surgery, 60 High Street, Lurgan, Craigavon BT66 8BA Tel: 028 3832 4591; 12 Dunkirk Road, Waringstown, Craigavon BT66 7SW Tel: 01762 881126 — MB BCh BAO 1976 Belf.; MRCGP 1980; DRCOG 1979.

DAVIDSON, Martyn John Faulkner John Lewis Partnership, 171 Victoria St., London SW1E 5NN Tel: 020 7592 6112 Fax: 020 7592 6525 Email: martyn_davidson@johnlewis.co.uk; Trewithen, Broom Way, Weybridge KT13 9TG Tel: 01932 829340 Fax: 01932 829340 Email: drsdavidson@compuserve.com — MB ChB 1978 Ed.; FFOM RCP Lond 2002; LLM Cardiff 1993; MFOM RCP Lond. 1992, AFOM 1987; MRCGP 1984; DRCOG 1985; DCH RCP Lond. 1984. Chief Med Advis. John Lewis Partnership.

DAVIDSON, Mary Waddell Aitken (retired) Dunvegan, Hornshill Farm Road, Stepps, Glasgow G33 6DE Tel: 0141 779 2103 Fax: 0141 779 4513 — LRCP LRCS 1950 Ed.; LRCP LRCS Ed. LRFPS Glas. 1950. Prev: Ho. Off. Redlands Hosp. Wom. Glas.

DAVIDSON, Mr Michael John Coutts Department of Oral & Maxillofacial Surgery, Taunton & Somerset Hospital, Musgrove Park, Taunton TA1 5DA Tel: 01823 333444 Fax: 01823 336877 Email: mike.davidson@zetnet.co.uk — MB BS 1984 Lond.; BDS 1976; FRCS Ed. 1989; FDS RCS Eng. 1982, L 1977. (Lond. Hosp. Med. Coll.) Cons. Oral & Maxillofacial Surg. Taunton, Som. & Yeovil NHS Trusts. Socs: Fell. Roy. Soc. Med.; Brit. Assn. Oral & Maxillofacial Surg.; Eur. Assn. Cranio-Maxillo. Surg. Prev: Sen. Regist. (Oral & Maxillofacial Surg.) Yorks. RHA; Regist. Maxillofacial Unit Chichester.

DAVIDSON, Miles John Gomersal Lane Surgery, 2 Gomersal Lane, Dronfield S18 1RU Tel: 01246 290120 Fax: 01246 291737 — MB ChB 1987 Sheff.; Cert. Family Plann. JCC 1990.

DAVIDSON, Myra Gray 11 Learmonth Gardens, Edinburgh EH4 1HB — MB ChB 1961 Ed.; DO Eng. 1968.

DAVIDSON, Neil Campbell 11 Andrews Lane, Fornby, Liverpool L37 2EN — MB ChB 1997 Glas.

DAVIDSON, Neil Colin Department of Cardiology, Freeman Hospital, High Heaton, Newcastle upon Tyne NE7 7DN Tel: 0191 284 3111; 23 Rosebery Crescent, Jesmond Vale, Newcastle upon Tyne NE2 1EU Tel: 0191 281 2443 Email: n.c.davidson@ncl.au.uk — MB BS 1990 Newc.; MRCP (UK) 1993; MD Newc. 1998. Specialist Regist. (Cardiol.) Freemand Hosp. Newc. Socs: Brit. Pacing & Electrophysiol. Gp. Prev: Career Regist. (Cardiol.) Freeman Hosp. Newc.; Brit. Heart Foundat. Research Fell. Univ. Dundee; SHO Rotat. (Med.) City Hosp. Nottm.

DAVIDSON, Neil Jeremy 100 Meneage Street, Helston TR13 8RF; Tel: 01326 561652 — BM BS 1984 Nottm.; B Med Sci 1982; MRCGP 1996; DCH RCP Lond. 1992; DRCOG 1991; DA (UK) 1989. (Univ. Nottm. Med. Sch.) Prev: Trainee GP Mevagissey; SHO (Med., Anaesth., O & G & Paediat.) Roy. Cornw. Hosp. (Treliske) Truro; SHO (Psychiat.) St. Lawrences Hosp. Bodmin.

DAVIDSON, Neil McDonald Beijing United Family Hospital, PO Box 720, @ Jiang Tai Lu, Chaoyang District, Beijing 100016, China Tel: 00 86 10 6434 2393 Fax: 00 86 10 6434 2393 Email: neildavidson@hotmail.com; 43 Blackford Road, Grange, Edinburgh EH9 2DT Tel: 0131 667 3960 Fax: 0131 662 9320 Email: neildavidson@hotmail.com — BM BCh 1964 Oxf.; BA Oxf. 1961; MA Oxf. 1964, DM 1978; FRCP Lond. 1984, M 1968; FRCP Ed. 1982, M 1980. (Oxf. & St. Thos.) p/t Head of Internal Med. Beijing United Family Hosp. Peoples RePub. of China. Socs: Fell. Roy. Soc. Trop. Med. & Hyg.; Med. Res. Soc.; Assn. Study Med. Educat. Prev: Vis. Prof. & Chief Internal Med. NW Armed Forces Hosp. Tabuk, Saudi Arabia; Cons. Phys. E.. Gen. Hosp. Edin. & Roodlands Gen. Hosp. Haddington; Sen. Lect. (Med.) & Hon. Cons. Phys. Ahmadu Bello Univ. Hosp. Zaria, Nigeria.

DAVIDSON, Norman James Hunter (retired) Woodbury, Brightlingsea Road, Thorrington, Colchester CO7 8JJ Tel: 01206 304464 — MB ChB Aberd. 1938; DCP Lond 1951; FRCPath 1963. Prev: Cons. Pathol. Medway Health Dist.

DAVIDSON, Paul Edward 159 Headland Court, Aberdeen AB10 7HZ — MB ChB 1994 Aberd.

DAVIDSON, Peter Hugh Tudor House, West End Road, West End, Southampton SO30 3BH — MB BS 1979 Newc.; MSc 1999 London; MRCP (UK) 1983. (Newcastle upon Tyne) Specialist Regist. (Pub. Health Med.) Wessex Rotat. Prev: Princip. (Gen. Pract.) Bitterne Health Centre Soton.

DAVIDSON, Ranald Dunbar 20 Hillview Road, Cults, Aberdeen AB15 9HB Tel: 01224 867347 — MB ChB 1991 Ed.; LLB (Hons.) Lond. 1995.

DAVIDSON, Richard Ian Anaesthetic Department, Bradford Royal Infirmary, Duckworth Lane, Bradford BD9 6RJ Tel: 01274 542200 Fax: 01274 366548 Email: richard.davidson@bradfordhospitls.nhs.uk; 6 Swallow Close, Pool-in-Wharfedale, Otley LS21 1RR — MB BS 1988 Lond.; FRCA 1995. (Roy. Free Hosp. Sch. Med.) Cons. Intens. Care Med. & Anaesth., Bradford Roy. Infirm., Bradford. Prev: SpR Intens. Cae Med., Yorks. Region; Vis. Instruc., Univ. of Michigan, Ann Arbor, USA.

DAVIDSON, Robert (retired) 36 Garngaber Avenue, Lenzie, Glasgow G66 4LL Tel: 0141 578 4282 — MB ChB Aberd. 1951; FRCPsych 1979, M 1971; DPM Eng. 1956. Phys. Supt. Gartloch Hosp. & E. Dist. Psychiat. Serv. Glas. Prev: Cons. Psychiat. Woodilee Hosp. Glas.

DAVIDSON, Robert Alexander 65 Buckingham Avenue, London N20 9DG — MB BS 1998 Lond.; MB BS Lond 1998.

DAVIDSON, Robert Andrew 21 Reynolds Road, Hove BN3 5RJ Tel: 01273 730761 — MB BS Lond. 1950; LMSSA Lond. 1950; DA Eng. 1957. (St. Mary's) Socs: BMA. Prev: Vis. Anaesth. Mombasa Hosp., Kenya; Hon. Cons. (Anaesth.) Coast Province Gen. Hosp., Mombasa.

DAVIDSON, Robert Cameron The Health Centre, Coatham Road, Redcar TS10 1SX Tel: 01642 475157 Fax: 01642 470885; 1 Trafalgar Terrace, Redcar TS10 1QQ Tel: 01642 478568 — MB ChB 1965 Ed. (Ed.) Prev: SHO (Orthop.) N. Staffs. Roy. Infirm. Stoke-on-Trent; Ho. Surg. Roy. Infirm. Edin. & Preston.

DAVIDSON, Robert Nicolas Lister Unit, Northwick Park Hospital, Harrow HA1 3UJ Tel: 020 8869 2833 Fax: 020 8869 2836 Email: r.n.davidson@ic.ac.uk — MD 1987 Cape Town; MB ChB 1978; MRCP (UK) 1981; DTM & H 1988; FRCP (UK) 1995. (Cape Town) Cons. Phys. N.wick Pk. Hosp. Harrow. Socs: Roy. Soc. Trop. Med. Hyg.; Amer. Soc. Trop. Med. Hyg. Prev: Sen. Regist. (Med.) Hosp. for Trop. Dis. Lond.; Lect. (Med.) Univ. Zimbabwe; Regist. (Med.) St. Geo. Hosp. Lond.

DAVIDSON, Robin Guthrie St Augustines Medical Practice, 4 Station Road, Keynsham, Bristol BS31 2BN Tel: 0117 986 2343 Fax: 0117 986 1176 — MB ChB 1980 Ed.; BSc 1978; MRCGP 1984; DCH RCP Lond. 1984; DRCOG 1982. GP Avon FPC Keynsham; Clin. Asst. (c/o Elderly) United Bristol Hosp. Trust. Prev: Regional Primary Health Off. MoH Sultanate of Oman; Trainee GP Dumfries & Galloway VTS; Ho. Off. Roy. Infirm. Edin.

DAVIDSON, Sandra Gail Spa Well Medical Group, Denburn Health Centre, Rosemount Viaduct, Aberdeen AB25 1QB Tel: 01224 640952 Fax: 01224 404422 — MB ChB 1987 Aberd. Socs: N.E. Scotl. Fac. Bd. RCCR.

DAVIDSON, Sara Louise 353 Harborne Lane, Harborne, Birmingham B17 0NU — MB ChB 1998 Birm.; ChB Birm. 1998.

DAVIDSON, Sarah Louise Renfrew Health Centre, 103 Paisley Road, Renfrew PA4 8LL — MB ChB 1980 Sheff.; DRCOG 1983; DTM & H RCP Lond. 1988. (Sheff.) GP Renfrew Health Centre; Med. Off. (Family Plann.) Argyll & Clyde HB. Prev: Paediat. Nat. Paediat. Hosp. Phnom Penh, Cambodia; Trainee GP Stocksbridge Sheff. & Silloth Cumbria.

DAVIDSON, Scott Mitchell 68 Overnewton Street, Glasgow G3 8RZ — MB ChB 1994 Aberd.

DAVIDSON, Serena Prudence Lillie Du Bois 27 Halsey Street, London SW3 2PT — BM BCh Oxf. 1963; MRCP (UK) 1969; FRCPCH 1996; DCH Eng. 1966. (Oxf. & St. Thos.) Hon. Cons. Paediat. Dispensaire Français de Londres. Socs: Fell. Roy. Soc. Med.; Fell. Roy. Coll. of Paed. & Child Health; EACD Europ. Acad. of Childh. Disabil. Prev: Cons. Paediat. Newham Gen. Hosp. Lond.; Research Assoc. (Paediat.) Neurosurg. Unit Guy's, Maudsley & King's Coll. Hosps.; Regist. (Rheum.) St. Stephen's Hosp. Lond.

DAVIDSON, Sheelagh Patricia 34 Kendall Avenue, Beckenham BR3 4QB Tel: 020 8658 2083 — MRCS Eng. LRCP Lond. 1965; DObst RCOG 1968. (King's Coll. Hosp.) Sen. Med. Off. (Community Health) King's Coll. Hosp. Lond.

DAVIDSON, Mr Sidney Isaac (retired) 8 Delamare Way, Cumnor Hill, Oxford OX2 9HZ Tel: 01865 865172 Fax: 01865 865172 — MB ChB 1955 Glas.; FRCS Eng. 1964; FRCOphth 1989; DO Eng. 1959; Hon.FRCOphth 1999. Treas. Oxf. Eye Foundat. Prev: Treas. Roy. Coll. Ophth.

DAVIDSON, Stuart Leighton Birchwood Surgery, Park Lane, North Walsham NR28 0BQ Tel: 01692 402035 Fax: 01692 500367 — MB BS 1982 London; MB BS 1982 London.

DAVIDSON, Susan Elizabeth Department of Radiotherapy, Christie Hospital, Wilmslow Road, Withington, Manchester M20 4BX Tel: 0161 446 3000 Email: dr.sdavidson@christie-tr.nwest.nhs.uk — MB BS 1980 Lond.; MD Lond. 1991; FRCP Glas. 1994; MRCP (UK) 1984; FRCR 1987; T(R)(CO) 1991. Cons. Radiother. Christie Hosp. Manch.; Hon. Clin. Lect. (Oncol.) Univ. Manch. Prev: Research Regist. (Radiobiol.) Paterson Inst. for Cancer Research Manch.

DAVIDSON, Susan Margaret Trewithen, Broomway, Weybridge KT13 9TG Tel: 01932 829340 Fax: 01932 829340 Email: drsdavidson@compuserve.com — MB BS 1978 Lond.; MRCP (UK) 1980; MRCGP (Distinc.) 1986; DRCOG 1985. Freelance Med. Edr. Weybridge.

DAVIDSON, Susanna Mary Cedar House, Longcross Road, Longcross, Chertsey KT16 0DR — MB BS 1975 Lond.; MRCS Eng. LRCP Lond. 1975; FRCR 1983; DCH Eng. 1979; DRCOG 1977. (Roy. Free) Cons. Radiol. Ashford Hosp. Middlx. Prev: Sen. Regist. (Radiol.) King's Coll. Hosp. Lond.

DAVIDSON, Thomas Bendelow 123 Hammerfield Avenue, Aberdeen AB10 7FD Tel: 01224 319521 — MB ChB 1940 Aberd. (Aberd.)

DAVIDSON, Mr Timothy Ian University Department of Surgery, Royal Free Hospital, Pond St., London NW3 2QG Tel: 020 7830 2794 Fax: 0207 830 2194; Fax: 020 7935 0427 — MB ChB 1977 Cape Town; ChM 1988; FRCS Eng. 1983; MRCP (UK) 1979. Cons. Surg. Hon Sen. Lect. Roy. Free Hosp. Lond.; Hon. Cons. Surg. Univ. Coll. Lond. Med. Sch; Asst. Edr. Clin. Oncol.; Edit. Bd. Trends in Urol., Gyn. & Sexual Health; Med. Adviser BrE. Cancer Care; RCS BrE. Reconstruction Course (core Fac.); Hon. Cons. Surg. St. Luke's Hosp., KE VII Hosp., The Lond. Clinic; Br. Assn. Surg. Oncol. (Medico-Legal SubComm.). Socs: Brit. Assn. Surg. Oncol.; Eur. Soc. Mastol.; Brit. BrE. Gp. Prev: Cons. & Sen. Lect. (Gen. Surg.) Univ. Coll. Lond. Med. Sch.; Sen. Regist. (Gen. Surg.) W.m. & Roy. Marsden Hosp. Lond. & Kingston Hosp. Surrey; Lect. Roy. Marsden Hosp. Lond.

DAVIDSON, Valerie 39F Jute Street, Aberdeen AB24 3EX — MB ChB 1970 Glas.; MRCPsych 1982. Sen. Regist. (Child & Family Psychiat.) Roy. Aberd. Childr. Hosp.

DAVIDSON, William Cameron (retired) Allt-Mhor, Kirkhill, Inverness IV5 7PE Tel: 01463 831570 — MB ChB Glas. 1956. Prev: GP Manch.

DAVIDSON, William Keith, CBE (retired) Dunvegan Hornshill Farm Road, Stepps, Glasgow G33 6DE Tel: 0141 779 2103 Fax: 0141 779 4513 — LRCP LRCS 1949 Ed.; LRCP LRCS Ed. LRFPS Glas. 1949; FRCGP 1980, M 1962; DPA Glas. 1967. JP. Prev: Maj. RAMC AER.

DAVIDSON, Winifred Beatrice (retired) The Coach House, 1A Dark Lane N., Steeple Ashton, Trowbridge BA14 6EY Tel: 01380 870325 — MB ChB 1941 Ed.

DAVIDSON-LAMB, Nanette Jamieson 21 Cairn Gardens, Cults, Aberdeen AB15 9TE Tel: 01224 868835 — MB ChB 1968 Aberd.

DAVIDSON-LAMB, Richard William Tel: 01224 868835 — MB ChB 1968 Aberd.; FFA RCS Eng. 1975; DObst. RCOG 1972. (Aberd.) Cons. Anaesth. Grampian HB (Aberd.). Prev: Sen. Regist. (Anaesth.) Roy. Infirm. Edin.

DAVIDSON-LAMB, Victoria Claire 21 Cairn Gardens, Cults, Aberdeen AB15 9TE — MB ChB 1995 Aberd.

DAVIDSON PARKER, John Joseph Parkside Hospital, Parkside, London SW19 5NX Tel: 020 8971 8000 Fax: 020 8971 8002; 4 Coach House Lane, Somerset Road, London SW19 5JY Tel: 020 8947 3112 Fax: 020 8947 3112 — MB BChir Camb. 1958; MA Camb. 1957; MRCS Eng. LRCP Lond. 1957; Dip. GU Med. Soc. Apoth. Lond. 1974. (Camb. & St. Bart.) Cons. Genitourin. Med. Pk.side Hosp., Lond. Socs: Med. Soc. Study VD; Med. Protec. Soc.; Fell. Roy. Soc. Med. Prev: Cons. Genitourin. Med. Haringey Health Care NHS Trust; Regist. (Venereol.) St. Thos. Hosp. Lond.; Clin. Asst. St. John's Hosp. Dis. Skin Lond.

DAVIDSSON, Gudmundur Kjartan Health Centre, Llanfairpwllgwyngyll LL61 5YZ Tel: 01248 714388 Fax: 01248 715826; Carreg Boeth, Llanddaniel, Gaerwen LL60 6EP — MB BChir 1983 Camb.; BSc (Hons.) St. And. 1978; LMSSA Lond. 1983. Prev: Regist. (Geriat.) Birch Hill Hosp. Rochdale; Research Regist. (Med.) Birch Hill Hosp. Rochdale; SHO (Med.) Roy. Albert Edwd. Infirm. Wigan.

DAVIDSSON, Helen Jane Carreg Boeth, Llanddaniel, Gaerwen LL60 6EP Tel: 01248 421223 — MB ChB 1983 Manch.; BSc St And. 1980.

DAVIE, Andrew Peter 87/3 Lancefield Quay, Finnieston, Glasgow G3 8HA — MB ChB 1990 Ed.; MRCP (UK) 1993. (Ed.) Clin. Lect. (Cardiol.) Glas.

DAVIE, Anne Maureen Flat 10 Windsor Court, Station Road, Poulton-le-Fylde, Blackpool FY1 5DS — MB ChB 1975 Aberd.; MRCGP 1981.

DAVIE, Charles Anthony 4 Rubislaw Drive, Bearsden, Glasgow G61 1PR — MB ChB 1986 Glas.; MRCP (UK) 1990. SHO (Neurol.) Nat. Hosp. Neurol. & Neurosurg. Lond.

DAVIE, Elspeth Grant 140 Craigleith Road, Edinburgh EH4 2EQ — LRCP LRCS 1950 Ed.; LRCP LRCS Ed. LRFPS Glas. 1950. (Roy. Colls. Ed.) SCMO Lothian Health Bd. Prev: Asst. Co. Med. Off. Herts. CC.

DAVIE, Henry Paterson (retired) 14 Briar Close, Newbold, Chesterfield S41 7AD Tel: 01246 273997 — MB ChB 1954 Ed.; DObst RCOG 1957. Prev: Gen. Practioner, Sen. Partner, Davie, Smith, Langan & Young, Chesterfield.

DAVIE, Hugh Muir (retired) 101 Dene Road, Manchester M20 2GU Tel: 0161 445 4014 — MB ChB 1927 Glas.

DAVIE, Ivor Turnbull Department of Anaesthesia, Western General Hospital NHS Trust, Crewe Road, Edinburgh EH4 2XU Tel: 0131 537 1652 Fax: 0131 537 1025; 26 Kingsburgh Road, Edinburgh EH12 6DZ Tel: 0131 337 1117 — MB ChB Ed. 1961; FRCP Ed. 1996; FFA RCS Eng. 1967. (Ed.) Cons. Anaesth. W.. Gen. Hosp. Edin.; Regional Educat. Adviser SE Scotl. Roy. Coll. Anaesth.; Hon. Sen. Lect. Fac. Med. Univ. Edin.; Lect. Centr. Midw. Bd. Socs: Assn. Anaesths.; (Ex-Pres.) Edin. & E. Scotl. Soc. Anaesth.; Scott. Soc. Anaesth. Prev: Sen. Regist. (Anaesth.) Edin. Roy. Infirm.; Hon. Clin. Tutor Fac. Med. Edin. Univ.; Ho. Phys. Leicester Roy. Infirm.

DAVIE, James Wilmot Ward 11A, Stobhill NHS Trust, Balornock Road, Glasgow G21 3UW Tel: 0141 201 3217 Fax: 0141 201 3218; 6 Woodlands Park, Deans, Livingston EH54 8AT Tel: 01506 411074 — MB ChB Glas. 1966; FRCP Ed. 1997; FRCP Glas. 1983; MRCP (UK) 1973; DObst RCOG 1968. Cons. Phys. (Gen. & Geriat. Med.) Stobhill Hosp. Glas.; Chairm. W. of Scotl. Higher Med. Train. Comm. Prev: Vis. Asst. Prof. Psychogeriat. W.. Psychiat. Inst. & Clinic Univ. Pittsburgh, USA; Sen. Regist. (Geriat. Med.) Stobhill Hosp. Glas.; Postgrad. Tutor Stobhill NHS Trust.

DAVIE, Jane Elizabeth (retired) 26 Kingsburgh Road, Edinburgh EH12 6DZ Tel: 0131 337 1117 — MB ChB 1967 Ed.; MFFP 1993; DObst RCOG 1969. Prev: SCMO (Family Plann. Servs.) Edin. Healthcare NHS Trust.

DAVIE, Jean Mairi Linlithgow Health Centre, 288 High Street, Linlithgow EH49 7ER Tel: 01506 670027; 15 Springfield Court, Linlithgow EH49 7TH Tel: 01506 670682 — MB ChB 1983 Ed.; MRCGP 1988; DRCOG 1989. (Univ. Med. Sch. Ed.)

DAVIE, John Paterson (retired) 'Greenstiles', Greenstiles Lane, Swanland, North Ferriby HU14 3NH Tel: 01482 632151 — MB ChB 1954 Ed.; FFA RCS Eng. 1961; DA Eng. 1958. Prev: Cons. Anaesth. Hull & Beverley Health Dists.

DAVIE, Michael James (retired) 43 Evendine Close, Worcester WR5 2DB — MB BS 1960 Lond.; DObst RCOG 1962. Prev: Ho. Phys. & Ho. Surg. St. Mary's Hosp. E.bourne.

DAVIE, Michael William John The Hollies, West Felton, Oswestry SY11 4JU — MB BChir 1969 Camb.; MD Camb. 1981, MB 1969, BChir 1968; MRCP (UK) 1972; FRCP Lond. 1988. Cons. Phys. & Dir. Research Robt. Jones & Agnes Hunt Orthop.; Hosp. OsW.ry. Socs: Roy. Soc. Med.; Bone & Tooth Soc. Prev: Med. Regist. Addenbrooke's Hosp. Camb.; Roy. Soc. Research Fell. Dunn Nutrit. Laborat. Camb.; Sen. Lect. Metab. Unit St. Mary's Hosp. Lond. W2.

DAVIE, Robert Carmichael, Group Capt. RAF Med. Br. Retd. Langho, Frithwood, Brownshill, Stroud GL6 8AE — MB BS 1957 Lond.; AFOM RCP Lond. 1980; DAvMed Eng. 1972; DA Eng. 1959. (Lond. Hosp.)

DAVIE, Robert Duncan McCallum (retired) 28 Hamilton Place, Perth PH1 1BD Tel: 01738 623527 — MB ChB 1949 Ed.; FRCA 1988; FFA RCS Eng. 1960; DA Eng. 1956. Prev: Cons. Anaesth. Perth Area.

DAVIE, Ronald Munro Department of Pathology, St John's Hospital, Livingston EH54 6PP Email: rond@wlt.scot.nhs.uk — MB ChB 1973 St. And.; FRCPath 1980; MRCPath 1979. (St Andrews) Cons. Histopath. St. John's Hosp. Howden, W. Lothian. Prev: Lect. (Path.) Univ. Dundee.

DAVIE, Wendy Jean Alison Carsleigh, Church Road, Southborough, Tunbridge Wells TN4 0RT Tel: 01892 33144 — M.B., Ch.B. Aberd. 1948.

DAVIES, Adrian South Cleveland Hospital, Marton Road, Middlesbrough TS4 3BW Tel: 01642 850850 Fax: 01642 812672; Crompton, 40 The Grove, Marton-in-Cleveland, Middlesbrough TS7 8AG Tel: 01642 321097 — MB BCh 1972 Wales; BSc (Hons.) (Anat.) Wales 1969; FRCP Lond. 1990; MRCP (UK) 1974. Cons. Cardiol. Immediate past Chief of Serv. S. Cleveland Cardiothoracic Unit. Socs: Brit. Soc. of Ediocardiography; Brit. Cardiac Soc., EUR Card. Soc. Prev: Resid. Med. Off. Nat. Heart Hosp. Lond.; Clin. Research Fell. & Hon. Sen. Regist. St. Geo. Hosp. & Med. Sch. Lond.; Med. Regist., St Geo.'s Hosp. & Med. Sch.

DAVIES, Aeron Gwyn Eryri, Brynrodyn, Clarach Road, Borth SY24 5NR — MB ChB 1963 Bristol; FRCP Lond. 1982 M 1968. (Bristol) Cons. Phys. Bronglais Hosp. Aberystwyth. Prev: Sen. Med. Regist. (Nephrol. & Gen. Med.) Welsh Hosp. Bd.; Regist. Med. Profess. Unit Cardiff Roy. Infirm.; Ho. Off. Cossham Memor. Hosp. Bristol.

DAVIES, Alan, TD (retired) Broad Eaves, Llys Helig Drive, Gogarth, Llandudno LL30 2XB Tel: 01492 860386 — MB BS 1952 Lond.; DObst RCOG 1954. Med. Off. Brit. Red Cross (N. Wales Br.); Maj. RAMC TA. Prev: SHO (O & G) St. David's Hosp. Bangor.

DAVIES, Alan Benjamin Bingley Health Centre, Myrtle Place, Bingley BD16 2TL Tel: 01274 565144 Fax: 01274 772354 — MB BS 1979 Lond.

DAVIES, Alan Glyn Kendle Ltd, 38 Wellington Buisiness Park, Crowthorne RG45 6LS Tel: 01344 750225 Email: davies.alan.kendle.com; The Cedars, Maori Road, Guildford GU1 2EL Tel: 01483 567242 Email: familydavies@ukgateway.net — MB BS 1975 Lond.; MD Lond. 1988; MRCP (UK) 1979. (Lond. Hosp.) Therapeutic Director, Kendle, Crowthorne. Prev: Sen. Dir. (Operat.s) Clintrials Research Ltd. Maidenhead; Gen. Manager Fujisawa Ltd.; Head of Clin. Research Fujisawa, Germany.

DAVIES, Alan James East Somerset NHS Trust, Yeovil District Hospital, Higher Kingston, Yeovil BA21 4AT Tel: 01935 384286 Fax: 01935 384645; Park House, 1 Swallowcliffe Gardens, Yeovil BA20 1DQ Tel: 01935 424459 Fax: 01935 384645 — MB BCh 1969; FRCOG 1993, M 1976; DObst RCOG 1973. Cons. O & G Yeovil Dist. Hosp. Som.; Tutor Univ. Bristol. Socs: Fell. Roy. Coll. Obst. & Gyn.; Drew-Smythe Gyn. Soc.; SW Obst. & Gyn. Soc. Prev: Sen. Regist. Jessop Hosp. Wom. Sheff. & Hon. Clin. Tutor Univ. Sheff.; Nuffield Research Fell. (O & G) Univ. Oxf.; Hon. Sen. Regist. (O & G) John Radcliffe Hosp. Oxf.

DAVIES, Aldwyth Hilda (retired) Boxwood Cottage, Shaw Lane, Nether Kellet, Carnforth LA6 1HA Tel: 01524 732431 — MB BS 1950 Lond. Prev: Sen. Cas. Off. Lancaster Roy. Infirm.

DAVIES, Aled Wyn Llwyn Celyn, Rhydybont, Llanybydder SA40 9RR — MB BCh 1986 Wales.

DAVIES, Alexander Hugh Church House, St Arvans, Chepstow NP16 6EU Tel: 01291 622677 — MB BS Lond. 1958; MRCS Eng. LRCP Lond. 1958; DObst RCOG 1961. (Lond. Hosp.) Prev: Ho. Surg. Thoracic Surg. Unit Lond. Hosp.; Ho. Phys. & Ho. Surg. (O & G) Roy. United Hosp. Bath.

DAVIES, Alison Anne 10 Bishops Garth, St Albans AL4 9AZ — MB BS 1981 Lond.; DRCOG 1983. Clin. Asst. McMillan Runcie Day Hospice St. Albans; Asst. GP St Albans Retainer Scheme. Socs: BMA. Prev: GP Harpenden; Asst. GP Harpenden Retainer Scheme; Trainee GP N.wick Pk. Hosp. VTS Harrow.

DAVIES, Alison Elizabeth 165 South View Road, Sheffield S7 1DE — BM BCh 1992 Oxf.

DAVIES, Alison Jane 5 Bloomsbury Court, Gosforth, Newcastle upon Tyne NE3 4LW — MB ChB 1986 Leic.; MRCGP 1990.

DAVIES, Alison Jane 27 Northampton Road, Towcester NN12 7AH — BChir 1996 Camb.

DAVIES, Alistair Huw 24 Walton Heath Drive, Macclesfield SK10 2QN — MB ChB 1997 Birm.

DAVIES, Allison Jane Royal Bolton Hospital, Minerva Road, Bolton BL4 0JR Tel: 01204 390390; 3 Brixton Avenue, Manchester M20 1JF — MB ChB 1986 Manch.; MRCOG 1993; DRCOG 1990; MSc 1999. Sen. Clin. Fell. (O & G) Wythenshawe Hosp. Manch. Prev: Locum Con O+S StMarys Hosp. Manch; Specialist Regist. O+S St Marys Hosp Manch; Specialist Regist. O+S Sharoe Hosp preston.

DAVIES, Allison Mochrie Craig Na Tia, Connel, Oban Tel: 0163 171229 — MB ChB 1980 Ed.; MRCGP 1984; DRCOG 1983.

DAVIES, Alun Bennett (retired) 29 Harrytown, Romiley, Stockport SK6 3BT Tel: 0161 430 5683 — MB BCh 1955 Wales; FFCM 1981, M 1974; MFCMI 1978; DPH Leeds 1963. Prev: Cons. Communicable Dis. Control Tameside & Glossop HA.

DAVIES, Alun Goronwy 37 Sword Close, Glenfield, Leicester LE3 8SY — BM BCh 1997 Oxf.

DAVIES, Alun Grier Queens Park and Moredon Surgeries, 146 Drove Road, Swindon SN1 3AG Tel: 01793 487394 Fax: 01793 342011 — MB BCh 1979 Wales.

DAVIES, Mr Alun Huw Department of Surgery, Imperial college School of Medicine, Charing Cross, Fulham Palace Road, London W6 8RF Tel: 020 8846 7320 Fax: 020 8846 7330 Email: a.h.davies@k.ac.uk; 4 York Avenue, East Sheen, London SW14 7LG Tel: 020 8876 2502 — BM BCh 1984 Oxf.; MA Oxf. 1992; MA Camb. 1985; DM Oxf. 1993; FRCS Eng. 1988. (Camb. & Oxf.) Cons. Surg. Univ. Lond ICSM; Windsor Sch. Emmanuel Coll. Camb. Prev: Sen. Lect. & Cons. Surg. Univ. Lond. Char. Cross & W.m. Med. Sch.; Lect. & Hon. Sen. Regist. (Surg.) Univ. Bristol; Vasc. Research Fell. Bristol Roy. Infirm.

DAVIES, Alun John 47 Bittell Road, Barnt Green, Birmingham B45 8LU — MB BS 1975 Lond.; MRCS Eng. LRCP Lond. 1975; MRCPath 1982. Cons. Microbiol. Sandwell Hosp. Bromwich. Prev: Sen. Regist. (Microbiol.) Bristol Roy. Infirm.; Regist. (Microbiol.) St. Bart. Hosp. Lond.

DAVIES, Alun Owen (retired) 15 Berne Avenue, Westlands, Newcastle ST5 2QJ Tel: 01782 611711 — MB BChir 1961 Camb.; FFA RCS Eng. 1967; DA Eng. 1964. Prev: Cons. Anaesth. N. Staffs. Hosp. Centre.

DAVIES, Alun Stewart 8 Alexander Crescent, Rhyddings, Neath SA10 8EB — MB BS 1993 Lond.; DFFP 1997; BSc (Hons.) Leeds 1986. (St. Geo. Hosp. Med. Sch.) GP Regist. Castle Surg. Neath.

DAVIES, Alwyn Lloyd West Midlands Regional Health Authority, 146 Hagley Road, Birmingham B16 9NX Tel: 0121 456 1444; 1 Cornflower Close, Earlsmead Est., Featherstone, Wolverhampton WV10 7ST — MB ChB 1987 Manch.; MFPHM RCP (UK) 1994; MRCGP 1993. Sen. Regist. (Pub. Health Med.) W. Midl. RHA.

DAVIES, Amanda Charlotte c/o Prof. Cooke's Secretary, Jessop Hospital for Women, Sheffield; The Boat House, Oak Lane, Kerridge, Macclesfield SK10 5AP Tel: 01625 572401 — MB ChB 1994 Leeds; MRCOG (Pt. I) 1996. (Leeds) SHO (Infertil.) Jessop Hosp. for Wom. Sheff.

DAVIES, Amanda Mary Pear Tree Surgery, 4 West Road, South Ockendon RM15 6PP Tel: 01708 852318 Fax: 01708 853216; 33 Middleton Road, Shenfield, Brentwood CM15 8DJ — MB BS 1982 Lond.; BSc Lond. 1979; MRCGP 1987.

DAVIES, Andrew 147 Western Road, Sheffield S10 1LD — MB ChB 1998 Sheff.; MB ChB Sheff 1998.

DAVIES, Andrew Doig 1 North Cottage, Southfield Farm, Longniddry EH32 0PL Tel: 01875 53321 & profess. 0875 610697; Tranent Medical Practice, Medical Centre, Springty Drive, Ormiston, Tranent EH35 5LP Tel: 01875 610248 Fax: 01875 615045 — BSc (Med. Sci.) Ed. 1966, MB ChB 1969; DObst RCOG 1971. Socs: Brit. Soc. Med. & Dent. Hypn.

DAVIES, Mr Andrew John 33 Revelstoke Road, Wimbledon Park, London SW18 5NJ — MB ChB 1988 Manch.; FRCS Eng. 1992. Regist. Rotat. (Orthop.) Char. Cross, Chelsea & W.m. Hosps.

DAVIES, Andrew John Lynwood, Sea Lane, Sunderland SR6 8EE — MB BS 1990 Newc.

DAVIES, Andrew John Department of Medical of Medicial Oncology, St Bartholomew's Hospital, London Email: a.j.davies@icrf.icnet.uk; 6 Dairy Court, Holyport, Maidenhead SL6 2US — BM 1993 Soton.; BM (Hons.) Soton. 1993; BSc (Hons.) Soton. 1992; MRCP (UK) 1997. (Soton.) ICRF Clin. Research Fell., St Bart. Hosp. Lond. Socs: Fell.Roy.soc.Med. Prev: Specialist Regist., Med. Oncol., St Bart. Hosp., Lond.

DAVIES, Andrew John Pittard, OStJ 12 Maillards Haven, Penarth CF64 5RF — MB BCh 1986 Wales; BSc (Hons.) Wales 1981; MRCGP 1991; DCH RCP Lond. 1989. (University of Wales, College of Medicine)

DAVIES, Andrew Johnston 90 Hazeley Bottom, Hartley Wintney, Hook RG27 8LU — BM 1997 Soton.

DAVIES, Andrew Wallace The Surgery, 19 Amwell Street, Hoddesdon EN11 8TU Tel: 01992 464147 Fax: 01992 708698 — DCH 1986; DRCOG 1986; MA 1985 Cambridge; MB 1982 Cambridge; BChir 1981 Cambridge.

DAVIES, Angela Margaret 51 Shenfield Road, Brentwood CM15 8EN — MB BS 1987 Lond.

DAVIES, Angela Rosemary (retired) 15 Berne Avenue, Westlands, Newcastle ST5 2QJ — MB BS 1960 Lond.; FFPHM RCP (UK) 1994; MFCM RCP (UK) 1988. Prev: Cons. Pub. Health Med. N. Staffs. HA.

DAVIES, Angharad Elizabeth 69 Harley Street, London W1 8QW Tel: 020 7486 6206 Fax: 01580 240021 Email: adavies@benenden.star.co.uk; Little Loddenden, High St, Staplehurst, Tonbridge TN12 0AD Tel: 01580 891147/893887 Email: anghavaddavies@loddenden.freeserve.co.uk — MB ChB Liverp. 1969; FRCOG 1988, M 1975; T(OG) 1991; DA Eng. 1973; DObst RCOG 1971. (Univ. Liverp.) Cons. Gyn. Benenden Hosp. Kent. Socs: ICS and ICS UK; SE Gyn. Soc. (Treas. 1990-1998); Assn. BRd.casting Doctors. Prev: Cons. O & G Sunderland Health Dist. N.. RHA; Sen. Regist. (O & G) Univ. Coll. Hosp. Lond. & Whittington Hosp. Lond.; Regist. (O & G) Hackney Hosp. & St. Bart. Hosp. Lond.

DAVIES, Angharad Puw Fron Fawnog, Gwernymynydd, Mold CH7 5JS — MB BChir 1992 Camb.; MRCPath 2001; MRCP 1996. (Camb. Univ.) Clin. Research Train. Fell., Dept. of Med. Microbiol., Roy. Free Hosp., Lond. Prev: Specialist Regist. (Med. Microbiol.) Roy. Free Hosp. Lond.

DAVIES, Anita Elaine 1 Upper Wimpole Street, London W1G 6LA Tel: 020 7580 5489 Fax: 020 7224 1094; 21 Lushington Road, Eastbourne BN21 4LG Tel: 01323 410441 Fax: 01323 410978 — MB BS 1959 Lond.; MRCP Lond. 1968; FFHom 1977, M 1968; DCH Eng. 1964; DObst RCOG 1963. (Roy. Free Hosp. Med. Sch.) Trustee Blackie Foundat. Trust; Tutor Fac. Homoeop.; Trustee ROSAC, MSM. Socs: Roy. Soc. Med.; BMA; ISARP. Prev: Sen. Research Regist. (Geriat.) Univ. Coll. Hosp. Lond.; SHO (Rheum.) Canad. Red. Cross Memor. Hosp. Taplow.

DAVIES, Ann (retired) Lapley Cottage, Lothians Road, Stockwell End, Tettenhall, Wolverhampton WV6 9PN — MB BS Lond. 1959; MRCS Eng. LRCP Lond. 1959; DCH Eng. 1962. Prev: SCMO Wolverhampton AHA.

DAVIES, Ann Elizabeth Jane 29 Cwrt-y-Vil Road, Penarth CF64 3HP — MB ChB 1979 Manch. Clin. Med. Off. S. Glam. HA.

DAVIES, Ann Patricia 15 Hoods Wood Road, Chesham HP5 1SQ — MB BS 1986 Lond.; BSc Lond. 1980, MB BS 1986; DFFP 1993. Med. Researcher Hse. Commons Library W.m. Lond.; Family Plann. Harringey Healthcare.

DAVIES, Anna Llewela 38 Pentremeurig Road, Carmarthen SA31 3ES; 38 Danlan Road, Pembrey, Burry Port SA16 0UF — MB BCh 1955 Wales; BSc, MB BCh Wales 1955. (Cardiff) Prev: Clin. Asst. (Geriat. Med.) Bryntirion Hosp. LLa.lli; Postgrad. Schol. MRC Neuropsychiat. Research Unit WhitCh. Hosp. Cardiff; SHO (Neurosurg & Thoracic) Morriston Hosp. Swansea.

DAVIES, Anna Louise 84 Priorwood Gardens, Ingleby Barwick, Stockton-on-Tees TS17 0XH Tel: 01642 765206 — BM BCh 1987 Oxf.; MA Camb. 1988; DCCH RCP Ed. 1994.

DAVIES, Anne Caroline Barnet General Hospital, Wellhouse Lane, Barnet EN5 3DJ Tel: 020 8216 5092 — BM BCh 1975 Oxf.; MA, BM BCh Oxf. 1975; MRCP (UK) 1979; FRCR 1983. (King's Coll. Hosp.) Cons. Radiol. Barnet Gen. Hosp. Prev: Sen. Regist. (Radiol.) Kings Coll. Hosp. Lond.

DAVIES, Anne Christina Ley Mill Surgery, 228 Lichfield Road, Sutton Coldfield B74 2UE Tel: 0121 308 0359 Fax: 0121 323 2682; 29 Highcroft Drive, Sutton Coldfield B74 4SX Tel: 0121 308 0359 — MB BCh 1977 Wales; MRCGP 1982; DRCOG 1981. Gen. Med. Practitioner.

DAVIES, Anne Elizabeth 45 High Street, Bodicote, Banbury OX15 4BS Tel: 01295 262588 — MRCS Eng. LRCP Lond. 1931; DPH Wales 1933; DObst RCOG 1936.

DAVIES, Anne Elizabeth Health Services for Elderly People, Royal Free Hospital, Pond St., Hampstead, London NW3 2QG Tel: 020 7794 0500 Fax: 020 7830 2202; 89 Lauderdale Mansions, Lauderdale Road, London W9 1LX Tel: 0179 286 2356 — MB BCh BAO 1986 Belf.; MRCP (UK) 1991. Cons. Phys., Geriat. Med. Roy. Free Hosp. Lond. Socs: Fell. Roy. Soc. Med.; Brit. Geriat. Soc. Prev: Sen. Regist. Roy. Free & Barnet Hosps. Lond.; Regist. (Gen. & Geriat. Med.) Guy's & Lewisham Hosps. Lond.; SHO (Gen. Med., Cardiol. & Haemat.) Roy. Vict. Hosp. Belf.

DAVIES, Anne Elizabeth Mary 4 York Avenue, E. Sheen, London SW14 7LG — MB ChB 1986 Bristol; MRCP (UK) 1991. Sen. Regist. (Paediat.) Chelsea & W.m. Hosp. Sick Childr. Prev: Sen. Regist. (Paediat.) Bristol Hosp. Sick Childr.; Regist. (Paediat.) Cardiff Roy. Infirm. & Bristol Hosp. Sick Childr.; SHO (Paediat.) John Radcliffe Hosp. Oxf.

DAVIES, Anne-Marie 43 Rose Avenue, Horsforth, Leeds LS18 4QE — MB ChB 1992 Sheff.

DAVIES, Annette 131 Lavernock Road, Penarth CF64 3QG — MB BCh 1965 Wales.

DAVIES, Annwen Cilfan, Heol-Yr-Ysgol, Coety, Bridgend CF35 6BL — MB BS 1977 Lond.; MRCS Eng. LRCP Lond. 1977; MRCGP 1982; DRCOG 1982. GP Retainee. Prev: Trainee GP Bridgend VTS.

DAVIES, Anthony Kings College Hospital, Denmaits Hill, London SE22 8PT Tel: 0207 346 3629; Kerswell Cross, Chudleigh TQ13 0DW Tel: 0207 346 3629 — MB BChir 1989 Camb.; MA Camb. 1989; MRCOG 1994. Cons. (O & G) Kings Coll. Hosp. Lond. Prev: Clin. Research Fell. (O & G) Roy. Free Hosp. Lond.

DAVIES, Anthony Berlyn St. Joseph's Hospital, Harding Avenue, Malpas, Newport NP20 6ZE; 23 Windsor Road, Porthcawl CF36 CHL — MD 1983 Lond.; MB BS Lond. 1971; FRCP Lond. 1994; MRCP (UK) 1974; FESC 2000. (Middlx.) Cons. Cardiol. Nevill Hall Hosp. Abergavenny; Hon. Cons. of Cardiol. Undergrad. Lect. at the Univ. Hosp. of Wales, Cardiff.; Cons. Cardiol. St. Joseph's Hosp. Newport. Socs: Brit. Cardiac Soc.; Europ. Soc. Cardiol. Prev: Regist. (Cardiol.) Univ. Hosp. Cardiff & Nat. Heart Hosp. Lond.; Research Fell. & Hon. Sen. Regist. (Cardiol.) Clin. Research Centre N.wick Pk. Hosp.

DAVIES, Anthony Fitz-Donald 18 Bryngwili Road, Cross-Hands, Llanelli SA14 6LR — MB BS 1991 Lond.

DAVIES, Mr Anthony Geraint Sheffield Children's Hospital, western Bank, Sheffield — MB ChB 1979 Bristol; BSc Bristol 1976, MD 1989; FRCS Eng. 1983; MD Bristol 1989. Cons. Sheff. Childr.'s Hosp. & Chesterfield Roayal Hosp. Socs: Brit. Soc. Childr. Orthop. Surg.; Brit. Limb Reconstruction Soc.; Brit. Assoc. Surg. Knee. Prev: Clin. Fell. (Paediat. Orthop.) Hosp. for Sick Childr. Toronto, Canada.

DAVIES, Anthony Hugh Lodge Surgery, Normandy Road, St Albans AL3 5NP; 10 Bishops Garth, St Albans AL4 9AZ Tel: 01727 856267 — MB BS 1984 Lond.; BSc (Hons.) Lond. 1978; DRCOG 1989; DCH RCP Lond. 1988. Prev: Clin. Med. Off. N. Herts. HA; Trainee GP Bridgend VTS.

DAVIES, Anthony John 19 New Road, Brynamman, Ammanford SA18 1AF Tel: 01269 822985 — MB BCh 1988 Wales; MRCP (UK) 1992; FRCR 1997. (Univ. Wales Coll. Med.) Regist. (Diag. Radiol.) Univ. Hosp. Wales Cardiff. Prev: Regist. (Med.) Singleton & Morriston Hosps. Swansea; Gen. Med. Rotat. P. Chas. Hosp. Merthyr Tydfil.; SHO Rotat. (Cardiopulm.) Univ. Hosp. Wales Cardiff.

DAVIES, Anthony Phillips The Laurels, Albury, Guildford GU5 9AH — MB BS 1953 Lond.

DAVIES, Arfon Ieuan Heathbridge House, The Old Bridge, Kenfig Hill, Bridgend CF33 6BY Tel: 01656 740359 Fax: 01656 745400; Cilfan, Heol-Yr-Ysgol, Coity, Bridgend CF35 6BL — MB BCh 1977 Wales; MRCGP 1981; DA Eng. 1982; DRCOG 1980. Prev: Trainee GP Bridgend VTS; SHO (Anaesth.) Univ. Hosp. Wales Cardiff.

DAVIES, Arthur Gordon (retired) 3 Leinster Mansions, Langland Gardens, London NW3 6QB Tel: 020 7435 2403 — MB BS 1943 Lond.; MRCS Eng. LRCP Lond. 1943. Barrister-at-Law, Lincoln's Inn. Prev: Coroner Roy. Ho.hold & GLC (Inner S. Dist.).

DAVIES, Arthur Mark MRI Centre, Royal Orthopaedic Hospital, Birmingham B31 2AP; 41 Serpentine Road, Harborne, Birmingham B17 9RD — MB ChB 1978 Birm.; FRCR 1983; DMRD Eng. 1982. Cons. Radiol. Roy. Orthop. Hosp. Birm. & Birm. Gen. Hosp.

DAVIES, Arthur Roy Meddygfa Rhiannon, Northfield Road, Narberth SA67 7AA Tel: 01834 860237 Fax: 01834 861625; Caerhug, Llandissilio, Clynderwen Tel: 01437 563232 — MB BCh 1966 Wales; MRCGP 1973; DObst RCOG 1969; DCH Eng. 1974. (Cardiff)

DAVIES, Arwel Wyn Brynhyfryd Surgery, Llangyfelach Road, Brynhyfryd, Swansea SA5 9DS Tel: 01792 655083 — MB BS 1982 Lond. GP Swansea.

DAVIES, Ashley 64 High Street, Gargrave, Skipton BD23 3LX — MB BCh 1995 Wales.

DAVIES, Barbara Ann Brocklebank Health Centre, 249 Garratt Lane, London SW18 4UE Tel: 020 8870 1341/871 4448 — MB BS 1976 Lond.; BSc Lond. 1973; MRCGP 1982; DRCOG 1981; DCH RCP Lond. 1980. (Univ. Coll. Dub.)

DAVIES, Barbara Stephens (retired) 10 Haven Way, Abergavenny NP7 7BA Tel: 01873 853387 — MB BS Lond. 1944; FRCP Lond. 1978, M 1965; DCH Eng. 1946; MRCPCH 1997. Prev: Cons. Paediat. W. Bromwich & Sandwell Hosp. W. Bromwich.

DAVIES, Barrie Clare Richmond Group Practice, Crickets Lane Health Centre, Ashton-under-Lyne OL6 6NG Tel: 0161 339 9161; 12 Weymouth Road, Ashton-under-Lyne OL6 9EP — MB ChB 1960 St. And. Socs: BMA & Oldham Med. Soc. Prev: Ho. Phys. Ashton Gen. Hosp.; Ho. Surg. & SHO Geriat. Oldham Gen. Hosp.

DAVIES, Barrie Rosser Tregaron, Hospital Road, Pontypridd CF37 — MB BCh 1977 Wales.

DAVIES, Benjamin Rees Ty-Elli Group Practice, Ty Elli, Llanelli SA15 3BD Tel: 01554 772678 / 773747 Fax: 01554 774476; Bwlchyffin, Newcastle Emlyn SA38 9RL — MB BChir 1979 Camb.; MA Camb. 1977, MB Chir 1979.

DAVIES, Bethan (retired) Fair Oaks, Coombe Hill Road, Kingston upon Thames KT2 7DU Tel: 020 8949 6623 — MRCS Eng. LRCP Lond. 1952; MEd Manch. 1974; Hon. FRCPCH 1996. Prev: Cons. Audiol. Phys. Char. Cross Hosp. Lond.

DAVIES, Beverley Sue West Road Surgery, 12 West Road, Westcliff on Sea SS0 9DA Tel: 01702 344492 Fax: 01702 437051 — MB BS 1980 Lond.; MRCS Eng. LRCP Lond. 1980; DRCOG 1982; TGP (vocational training scheme 1981-4). (Char. Cross) p/t GP Princip., Kent, Cardess, Gurnani; Chiarman S. Essex LMC. Prev: Trainee GP S.end VTS; SHO (Paediat.) S.end Hosp.; SHO (Obst.) Rochford Hosp.

DAVIES, Bozena Zofia Kingthorpe Lodge, Chapel Lane, Ullenhall, Solihull B95 5RT — MB ChB 1959 Birm.

DAVIES, Brenda Tel: 979 725 9521 Fax: 979 725 9521 Email: justbeb@cvtv.net — MB ChB 1977 Lusaka; BSc Lusaka 1974; MRCS Eng. LRCP Lond. 1977; MRCPsych. 1983; MPS 1962. Socs: Internat. Healing and Psychother. Gp. Prev: Dir. of Clin. Developm., Bowden Ho. Clinic; Cons. Psychiat. Charter Nightingale Hosp. Lond. & Ticehurst Hse. Hosp.; Director of Serv.s fro Wom., Charter Nightingale Hosp., Lond.

DAVIES, Brenda Jose (retired) 8 Maes-y-Parc, Cwmafan, Port Talbot SA12 9PU — MB BChir 1956 Camb.

DAVIES, Brian Collin (retired) 3 Wylcwm Street, Knighton LD7 1AD Tel: 01547 528171 — BM BCh 1953 Oxf.; DObst RCOG 1955. Med. Off. Kt.on Hosp. Prev: Ho. Phys. (Paediat.) & Ho. Surg. (A & E) Radcliffe Infirm. Oxf.

DAVIES, Brian Hamilton Llandough Hospital Trust, Llandough, Penarth CF64 2XX Tel: 029 2071 6936 — MB BCh 1968 Wales; FRCP Lond. 1987; MRCP (UK) 1971. Cons. Phys. (Gen. Med. with interest in Allergy & Respirat. Med.) Cardiff and Vale NHS Trust. Socs: Brit. Thorac. Soc. & Europ. Allergy Soc. Prev: Cons. Phys. & Sen. Regist. (Thoracic Med.) Sully Hosp.; Vis. Fell. in Pulm. Dis. W. Virginia Univ. Med. Centre Morgantown; Regist. (Thoracic Med.) Hammersmith Hosp.

DAVIES, Mr Brian William Queen's Medical Centre, Nottingham NG7 2UH; 48 Moor Lane, Beeston, Nottingham NG9 3FH Email: brianwdavies@doctors.org.uk — MB ChB 1989 Sheff.; FRCS (Paed. Surg.) 1999; FRCS Eng. 1994. (Sheff.) Specialist Regist. (Paediat. Surg.) Leeds/Notts/Sheff. Prev: Locum Cons. (Paediatric Surg.) Roy. Hosp. for Sick Childr. Larkhill Glas.; SHO Rotat. (Gen. Surg.) Exeter 1993-1995.

DAVIES, Bridget Ann 14b Ladbroke Terrace, London W11 — BM BCh 1957 Oxf.; DPM Eng. 1964.

DAVIES, Bronwen Mair The Lodge, 4 Brincliffe Crescent, Sheffield S11 9AW — MB ChB 1990 Leic.; MRCP (UK) 1994.

DAVIES, Bruce Henry Eastside Surgery, 7-8 Eastside, Hutton Rudby, Yarm TS15 0DB Tel: 01642 700993 Fax: 01642 701857 — MB BS 1981 Lond.; MRCGP 1985. GP Hutton Rudby.

DAVIES, Camilla Louise Werfa House, Abernant, Aberdare CF44 0YS — MB BCh 1985 Wales.

DAVIES, Caroline Elizabeth 18 Chantry Rise, Penarth CF64 5RS — MB ChB 1984 Ed.

DAVIES, Caroline Jennifer Anaesthetic Dept 2nd floor New guys House, Guys Hospital, St Thomas St., London SE1 9RT Tel: 020 7955 5000 — MB BS 1984 Lond.; FRCA 1993; DRCOG 1989. (Lond. Hosp. Med. Coll.) Cons. Anaesth. Guys Hosp. Lond. Socs: Fell. Roy. Coll. Anaesth.; Assn. Anaesth. Prev: Sen. Reg. Anaesth. Gt. Ormond St. Hosp. Lond.; Sen. Regist. (Anaesth.) St. Bart. Hosp. Lond.; Regist. (Anaesh.) St Bart. Hosp. Lond.

DAVIES, Caroline Marianne Tudor Croft, Tanners Green La, Earlswood, Solihull B94 5JT — MB BS 1997 Lond.

DAVIES, Carolyn Diane Brecon Medical Group Practice, Ty Henry Vaughan, Bridge Street, Brecon LD3 8AH Tel: 01874 622121 Fax: 01874 623742 — MB BCh 1989 Wales; MRCGP 1993.

DAVIES, Carys Mair Cefntiresgob Farm, Talley Road, Llandeilo SA19 7HS — BM BCh 1998 Oxf.; BM BCh Oxf 1998.

DAVIES, Catherine 106 Splott Road, Splott, Cardiff CF24 2XY Tel: 029 2046 2848 Fax: 02920 462034; 177 Pencisely Road, Llandaff, Cardiff CF5 1DP — MB BCh 1990 Wales; MRCGP 1994; DFFP 1993. Prev: Trainee GP St. Mellons, Cardiff; SHO (ENT) Bridgend Gen. Hosp.; SHO (Psychiat.) E. Glam. Hosp.

DAVIES, Catherine June Forestside Medical Practice, Beaulieu Road, Dibden Purlieu, Southampton SO45 4JA Tel: 023 8087 7900 Fax: 023 8087 7909 — MB ChB 1986 Manch.; MRCGP 1996; DRCOG 1988. (Manch.) Prev: Regist. (Old Age Psychiat.) Knowle Hosp. Fareham; SHO (Accid. & Trauma) Poole Gen. Hosp.; SHO (O & G) P.ss Anne Hosp. Soton.

DAVIES, Catherine Mary Dallas 86 Harley Street, London W1 1AE Tel: 020 7486 0900 — LMSSA 1948 Lond. (Roy. Free)

DAVIES, Catriona Lesley 20 Sunningdale Avenue, Kenilworth CV8 2BZ — MB BS 1990 Lond.; FRCR (UK) 2001; MRCP (UK) 1995. (Roy. Free Hosp. Sch. Med.) Specialist Regist. Rotat. (Radiol.) Oxf.

DAVIES, Ceila Dyfodwg 19 Rosemont Road, London W3 9LU — MB BS 1975 Lond.; MRCGP 1979; DRCOG 1977. (Char. Cross)

DAVIES, Celia Marjorie 27 The Pryors, East Heath Road, London NW3 1BS Tel: 020 7794 4677 — MB BCh 1943 Wales; BSc Wales 1940; MRCS Eng. LRCP Lond. 1943; FFA RCS Eng. 1957; DA Eng. 1950. (Cardiff) Socs: Fac. Anaesth. RCS Eng.; BMA. Prev: Cons. Anaesth. S. Lond. Hosp. Wom. & Childr. Lond.; Cons. Anaesth. St. Jas. Hosp. Lond.; Capt. RAMC.

DAVIES, Ceri Mark Salisbury District Hospital, Salisbury SP2 8BJ Tel: 01722 336262; 37 Cefn Road, Glais, Swansea SA7 9EZ — MB BS 1993 Lond.; BSc Lond. 1990, MB BS 1993.

DAVIES, Charlotte Elizabeth 10 Glen View, Litchard Higher, Bridgend CF31 1QU — MB BS 1996 Lond.

DAVIES, Chinekwu Chinwoke Ayo William Harvey Hospital, Ashford TN24 0LZ Tel: 01233 633331; 291 Manels Lane, London SE12 9PT Fax: 0208 857 3847 Email: chindavies@aol.com — MB BS 1978 Lond.; MA 1975 (Ox.); MBA 1998 (Strategic Health Serv. Man.); FFA RCS 1987. (Somerville College, Oxford; St. Thomas's Hospital Meedical Hospital) Cons. William Harvey Hosp. Ashford. Socs: BMA; Roy. Soc. Med.; Brit. Assn. of Day Surg. (Counc. Mem.). Prev: Sen. Regist. S. Thames RHA; Regist. & SHO (Anaesth.) William Harvey Hosp. Ashford Kent; SHO (Obst.) Is. Matern. Hosp., Lagos.

***DAVIES, Christina** Clinical Trial Service Unit, Nuffield Department of Clinical Medicine, Radcliffe Infirmary, Oxford OX2 6HE Tel: 01865 57241 Fax: 01865 58817; 34 Lower Furney Close, High Wycombe HP13 6XQ Tel: 01494 538245 — MB ChB 1990 Manch.

DAVIES, Christine Elizabeth Downland Practice, East Lane, Chieveley, Newbury RG20 8UY Tel: 01635 248251 Fax: 01635 247261; Field House, Westbrook, Newbury RG20 8DN — MB BS 1982 Lond.; BSc (Hons.) Lond. 1979; MRCGP 1986; DFFP 1993; DRCOG 1986. (Roy. Free) Prev: MAAG GP Co-Ordinator Berks.; Ho. Surg. Roy. Free Hosp. Lond.; SHO (O & G) Canad. Red Cross Memor. Hosp. Taplow.

DAVIES, Christopher Donald Wilson Homeland, Teignmouth Road, Maidencombe, Torquay TQ1 4SZ Tel: 0803 327005 — MB BS Lond. 1956; MRCS Eng. LRCP Lond. 1956. (Guy's) Prev: SHO Foxhall Hosp. Ipswich & Torbay Hosp. Torquay; SHO (Obst.) Derby City Hosp.

DAVIES, Christopher John St Johns Medical Centre, St. Johns Road, Altrincham WA14 2NW Tel: 0161 928 8727 Fax: 0161 929 8550 — BM BS 1981 Nottm.; BSc Leeds 1976; BMedSci Nottm. 1979; MRCP (UK) 1984; MRCGP 1986; DRCOG 1986. (Nottingham) Princip. (Gen. Pract.) Altrincham Chesh. Prev: Trainee GP Cheadle Hulme & Handforth; SHO (A & E) Hope Hosp. Manch.; SHO (Gen. Med., O & G & Paediat.) Wythenshawe Hosp. Manch.

DAVIES, Mr Christopher John Glan Clwyd Hospital, Bodelwyddan, Rhyl LL18 5UJ Tel: 01745 583910 — BM BCh 1966 Oxf.; MA Oxf. 1966, DM MCh 1981, BM BCh 1966; FRCS Eng. 1971. (Oxf. & Guy's) Cons. Surg. Glan Clwyd Dist. Gen. Hosp.; Cons. Surg. NHS BrE. Screening Progr., Breat Test Wales, Conwy. Socs: Brit. Assn. Surgic. Oncol. & Brit. Assn. Endocrine Surgs. Prev: Sen. Regist. (Surgic.) W. Berks. HA (Reading) & Hammersmith Hosp. Lond.; Cancer Research Campaign Surg. Research Fell. Nottm. City Hosp.

DAVIES, Christopher Julian Waide 24 Scholars Way, Amersham HP6 6UW — MB BS 1996 Lond.; BSc (Hons.) Lond. 1993; DRCOG 1998. (St. Thos.)

DAVIES, Christopher Marc Eaton Wood Medical Centre, 1128 Tyburn Road, Erdington, Birmingham B24 0SY Tel: 0121 373 0959 Fax: 0121 350 2719; 38 The Boulevard, Wylde Green, Birmingham B26 2PY — MB ChB 1981 Birm. Prev: SHO (Paediat.) Good Hope Hosp. Sutton Coldfield W. Midl.; Trainee GP Kings Norton Birm.; SHO (Trauma/Orthop.) Manor Hosp. Nuneaton.

DAVIES, Christopher Paul Wern Surgery, Bon y Wern, Bagillt, Flint CH6 6BT Tel: 01352 761907 Fax: 01352 730265; Iron House Farm, Dodleston Lane, Pulford, Chester CH4 9DS — MB ChB 1977 Liverp.; FFA RCS Eng. 1982. GP Trainee Bolton. Socs: Liverp. Med. Inst. & Liverp. Soc. Anaesth. Prev: SHO (Anaesth.) Roy. Liverp. Teach. Hosp.; Regist. (Anaesth.) Walton Hosp. Liverp.; Regist. (Anaesth.) Liverp. HA.

DAVIES, Christopher Price Smithy Green Health Centre, Cheadle SK8 6LU Tel: 0161 485 7272 Fax: 0161 485 5567; 29 South Acre Drive, Macclesfield SK11 7EW Tel: 01625 611505 — MB ChB 1987 Manch.; MRCGP 1991; DRCOG 1991; DCH RCP Lond. 1989. Prev: Trainee GP Macclesfield.

DAVIES, Christopher Rowland Pentre Bach, Pentre, Llanrhaeadr, Denbigh LL16 4NR — MB BS 1997 Lond.

DAVIES, Christopher Stephen 8 The Barncroft, Greasby, Wirral CH49 2SW — MB ChB 1995 Dundee. SHO Rotat. (Med.) Arrowe Pk. Hosp. Wirral. Prev: Ho. Off. Arrowe Pk. Hosp. Wirral.

DAVIES, Christopher Stuart Wentloog Road Health Centre, 98 Wentloog Road, Rumney, Cardiff CF3 8EA Tel: 029 2079 7746 Fax: 029 2079 0231 — MB BCh 1971 Wales.

DAVIES, Christopher Warren Howard Department of Respiratory Medicine, Battle Hospital, Reading RG30 1AG Tel: 0118 963 6282 Fax: 0118 950 3486 Email: cwhdavies@doctors.org.uk — MB ChB 1990 Birm.; ChB Birm. 1990; MRCP (UK) 1994. (Birm) Cons. Phys. (Respirat. and GIM) Roy. Berks. and Battle NHS Trust, Reading. Socs: Stand. Comm. Mem. RCP. Prev: Regist. (Med.) Wycombe Gen. Hosp.; SHO (Med.) Oxf. Centr. Hosps.; Regist. (Thoracic Med.) Osler Chest Unit Ch.ill Hosp. Oxf.

DAVIES, Claire Elisabeth Stonecot Surgery, 115 Epsom Road, Sutton SM3 9EY Tel: 020 8644 5187 — MB BS 1985 Lond.; BSc (Hons.) (Anat.) Lond. 1982, MB BS 1985; MRCGP 1990; DRCOG 1990; DCH RCP Lond. 1989. (Univ. Coll. Hosp.)

DAVIES, Claire Elizabeth Fraser Staddle Stones, Priston, Bath BA2 9EE — MB BS 1997 Lond.

DAVIES, Clare Banks Medical Centre, 272 Wimborne Road, Bournemouth BH3 7AT Tel: 01202 593444 Fax: 01202 548534; 11 Surrey Road, Bournemouth BH2 6BP — MB BS 1986 Lond.; MRCGP 1995; DRCOG 1992. (Middlx. Hosp. Med. Sch.) GP Princip. PIT. Prev: SHO (O & G, Orthop., Paediat. & Geriat.) Odstock Hosp. Salisbury.

DAVIES, Clare Elizabeth 23 Cefn Carnau Road, Heath, Cardiff CF14 4LZ — BM 1987 Soton.; MRCP (UK) 1991; MRCGP 1995; DRCOG 1993.

DAVIES, Colin Fletcher 16 Creffield Road, Colchester CO3 3JA Tel: 01206 764612 — MB BS 1959 Lond.; DObst RCOG 1962. (Char. Cross.)

DAVIES, Colin James Dept of Radiology, Royal Glamorgan Hospital, Ynysmaerdy, Llantrisant CF72 8XR Tel: 01443 443373 Email: colin.davies@pr-tr.wales.nhs.uk; 22 Plas Pamir, Portway Marina, Penarth, Cardiff CF64 1BT Tel: 029 2035 0073 — MB ChB 1975 Bristol; FRCR 1982. Cons. (Radiol.) Roy. Glam. Hosp. Prev: Sen. Regist. (Radiol.) Univ. Hosp. Wales; Regist. (Radiol.) Univ. Hosp. Wales Cardiff; Regist. (Radiol.) John Radcliffe Hosp. Oxf..

DAVIES, Cyril, TD — MB BCh Wales 1957; FRCPsych. 1981, M 1971; DPM Ed. & Glas. 1964. (Cardiff) Mem. Ment. Health Act Commiss.; Mem. Ment. Health Review Tribunals; Cons. Psychiat. Roy. United Hosp. Bath. Socs: Clin. Soc. Bath; BMA. Prev: Sen. Regist. United Sheff. Hosps.; Regist. Roy. Edin. Hosp.

DAVIES, Dafydd Rhodri Department of Gastroenterology, Caerphilly Dist. Miners Hospital, St. Martin's Road, Caerphilly CF83 2WW Tel: 029 2080 7315 Fax: 029 2080 7269 Email: rhodri.davies@virgin.net; Chon Ji Bungalow, The Downs, St. Nicholas, Cardiff CF5 6SD Tel: 029 2059 9101 Email: rhodri.davies@virgin.net — MB BCh Wales 1986; MRCP (UK) 1990; MD Wales 1997. Cons. Gastroenterol. Caerphilly; Hon. Cons. Gastroenterol., Uni. Hosp. Of Wales. Prev: Sen. Regist. (Med. & Gastroenterol.) Roy. Hallamsh. Hosp. Manch.; Research Regist. (Genetics & Gastroenterol.) St. Mary's Hosp. Manch.

DAVIES, Dai Illtyd 89 Cumberland Road, Bristol BS1 6UG — BM BS 1998 Nottm.; BM BS Nottm 1998.

DAVIES, Daniel Benjamin Scurlock Allteryn, Somerset Lane, Cefncoed, Merthyr Tydfil CF48 2PA — MB BCh 1951 Wales.

DAVIES, Daniel Elihu (retired) 45 Gronant Road, Prestatyn LL19 9DT — MB ChB 1927 Liverp.

DAVIES, David St Julians Medical Centre, 13A Stafford Road, Newport NP19 7DQ Tel: 01633 251304 Fax: 01633 221977 — MB BS 1959 Lond.; MRCS Eng. LRCP Lond. 1959. (Guy's) Prev: Ho. Phys. Morriston Hosp. Swansea; Sen. Ho. Off. (O & G) Mt. Pleasant Hosp. Swansea; Sen. Ho. Off. (Obst.) St. Woolos Hosp. Newport.

DAVIES, David Anthony Meddygfa Tywi, Nantgaredig, Carmarthen SA32 7LG Tel: 01267 290240 Fax: 01267 290062; Cwmynys, Nantgaredig, Carmarthen SA32 7NG — MB BS 1984 Lond.; MRCGP 1989; DRCOG 1989.

DAVIES, David Brian Fishguard Health Centre, Ropewalk, Fishguard SA65 9BT Tel: 01348 873041 Fax: 01348 874916; 8 Hillside Close, Goodwick SA64 0AX — MB BCh 1970 Wales; MRCP (UK) 1978; DCH Eng. 1977.

DAVIES, David Brian Arthur Llewelyn, Air Vice-Marshal RAF Med. Br. Retd. (retired) 28 Boyne Hill Road, Maidenhead SL6 4HG — MB BS 1956 Lond.; BSc (Special) Physiol. Lond. 1953; MRCS Eng. LRCP Lond. 1956; FRCGP 1980, M 1975; MFOM 1980; MFCM 1974; DAvMed Eng. 1968; DObst RCOG 1958. Prev: Princip. Med. Off. HQ RAF Support Command.

DAVIES, David Denison Department of Anaesthesia, Central Middlesex Hospital, Acton Lane, London NW10 7NS Tel: 020 8453 2160; 10 Beaufort Place, Bray, Maidenhead SL6 2BS Tel: 01628 671003 — MRCS Eng. LRCP Lond. 1951; PhD Lond. 1975; FRCA 1962, DA Eng. 1955. (Leeds) Cons. Anaesth. Centr. Middlx. Hosp. Lond. Socs: Fell. Roy. Soc. Med. (Mem. Sects. Anaesth. & Measurem. in Med.); Pain Soc.; Anaesth. Res. Soc. Prev: Research Fell. (Anaesth.) RCS Eng.; Sen. Regist. In Anaesth. United Birm. Hosps., Birm.; Ho. Phys. St. Luke's Hosp. Bradford.

DAVIES, David Eiddon Sketty Surgery, De la Beche Road, Sketty, Swansea SA2 9EA Tel: 01792 206862; Bro-Dawel, 348 Gower Road, Killay, Swansea SA2 7AE — MB BS 1965 Lond.; MRCS Eng. LRCP Lond. 1965; DObst RCOG 1968.

DAVIES, David Eurig Yr Hafod, Pontiago, Goodwick SA64 0JD Tel: 01348 891678 — MB BChir 1962 Camb.; LLM Wales 1990; MA Camb. 1963; MRCGP 1971; DObst RCOG 1966. Socs: Y Gymdeithas Feddygol. Prev: Sen. Med. Off. Swyddfa Gymreig.

DAVIES, David Frederick (Surgery), 129 Newland St., Witham CM8 1BH; Wakeford Cottage, 55A The Avenue, Witham CM8 2DN — MB BS 1956 Lond.; DObst RCOG 1962. (Univ. Coll. Hosp.)

DAVIES, Mr David Garfield London Clinic, 149 Harley St., London W1G 6DE Tel: 020 7935 0400 Fax: 020 7333 0340 — MB BS 1959 Lond.; FRCS Eng. 1964. (St. Bart.) Cons. Otolayngol. Roy. Nat. Throat, Nose & Ear Hosp. Lond.; Hon. Sen. Lect. Inst. Larynology & Otol. UCH; Cons. Emerit. UCL & Middlx. Hosp. Lond.; Cons. Larynology Roy. Acad. Music Trinity Coll. Music, Roy. Nat. Theatre, Roy. Shakespeare Co., Roy. Opera Hse., English Nat. Opera & Roy. Soc. Med. Socs: (Ex-Pres.) Med. Soc. Lond.; Bd. Mem. World Voice Consortium; (Chairm.) Brit. Performing Arts Med. Trust. Prev: Cons. Otolaryngol. Middlx. & Univ. Coll. Hosps. Lond.; Cons. Roy. Nat. Throat, Nose & Ear Hosp. Lond.; MRC Fell. Otol. Harvard Med. Sch. & Mass. Eye & Ear Infirm., USA.

DAVIES, Mr David Graham Leighton, RD (retired) Llandremor, 23 Windsor Road, Radyr, Cardiff CF15 8BQ Tel: 029 2084 2479 — MB BS 1946 Lond.; BSc (Distinc. Anat.) Wales 1943; FRCS Eng. 1953. Prev: Cons. Gen. Surg. E. Glam. Gen. Hosp.

DAVIES, David Gwilym (retired) Town End Cottage, Sandale, Boltongate, Carlisle CA7 1DE — MD 1958 Bristol; MB ChB 1942; FCPath. 1963; Dip. Bact. Manch. 1950. Hon. Cons. Bacteriol. E. Cumbld. Hosp. Gp. Prev: Dir. P.H.L.S. Laborat. Cumbld. Infirm. Carlisle.

DAVIES, David Gwyn (retired) Linden, 6 Fairway Dr, Rowany, Port Erin IM6 2EY Tel: 01624 834515 Fax: 01624 834515 — LRCP LRCS 1949 Ed.; LRCP LRCS Ed. LRFPS Glas. 1949. Prev: Ho. Phys. & Ho. Surg. Walton Hosp. Liverp.

DAVIES, David Henry Cwmfelin Medical Centre, 298 Carmarthen Road, Swansea SA1 1HW Tel: 01792 653941 — MB BCh 1976 Wales; MRCGP 1980; DRCOG 1978.

DAVIES, David Huw Cwm Examination Centre, Llantwit Fardre, Pontypridd Tel: 01443 204221; 61 St. Martin's Road, Caerphilly CF83 1EG Tel: 01222 863510 — MB BCh 1970 Wales; AFOM RCP Lond. 1982. Area Med. Off. Brit. Coal S. Wales Area. Prev: Regist. (Anaesth.) Univ. Hosp. Wales Heath Cardiff.

DAVIES, David Huw Winch Lane Surgery, Winch Lane, Haverfordwest SA61 1RN Tel: 01437 762333 Fax: 01437 766912; High Gables, Portfield Gate, Haverfordwest SA62 3LS Tel: 01437 760331 Email: d.h.davies@tesco.net — MB BCh 1987 Wales; DPD 1998; MRCGP 1992; DRCOG 1992. (University of Wales College of Medicine)

DAVIES, David Hywel 53 Ormond Avenue, Hampton TW12 2RY — MB BS 1998 Lond.; MB BS Lond 1998.

DAVIES, David James Cedric (retired) 36 Talycae, Tregarth, Bangor LL57 4AE Tel: 01248 601184 — MB BS Lond. 1958; MRCS Eng. LRCP Lond. 1958; DPH Wales 1966; FFCM 1981, M 1972. Prev: Chief Admin. Med. Off. & Dir. Pub. Health Med. Gwynedd HA.

DAVIES, David John (retired) Tredarren, Boughmore Road, Sidmouth EX10 8SJ Tel: 01395 513636 — MRCS Eng. LRCP Lond. 1955; MRCGP 1966; DObst RCOG 1957. Prev: Ho. Off. (Surg.) Guy's Hosp. Lond.

DAVIES, David Kenneth Lewis, OBE (retired) 54 Palace Road, Llandaff, Cardiff CF5 2AH Tel: 01222 562039 — MB BCh 1946 Wales; BSc Wales 1946; FRCR 1975; DMRD Eng. 1957. Pres. Cancer Research Wales Velindre Hosp. Cardiff. Prev: Cons. Radiol. S. Glam. Health Dist.

DAVIES, David Lawrence 10 Forest Hill, Gilwern, Abergavenny NP7 0DY Tel: 01873 830536 — MB BS 1970 Lond.; MRCS Eng. LRCP Lond. 1970; DObst RCOG 1972. (Guy's) Prev: Ho. Off. (Med.) Nevill Hall Hosp. Abergavenny; Ho. Off. (Surg.) & SHO (O & G) Roy. Gwent Hosp. Newport.

DAVIES, David Lloyd Department of Medicine, Western Infirmary, Glasgow G11 6NT Tel: 0141 211 2561; Rosebud Cottage, 23 Main St, Killearn, Glasgow G63 9RJ Tel: 01360 550990 — MB BS Lond. 1961; MD Lond. 1972; FRCP Lond. 1977, M 1968; FRCP Glas. 1975, M 1967; MRCS Eng. LRCP Lond. 1961. (St. Mary's) Sen. Lect. (Med.) W.. Infirm. Glas.

DAVIES, Professor David Margerison 300 High Street, Boston Spa, Wetherby LS23 6AJ — MRCS Eng. LRCP Lond. 1949; FRCP Ed. 1986; FRCP Lond. 1969, M 1954. (Lond. Hosp.) Socs: Brit. Pharm. Soc. & Brit. Toxicol. Soc. Prev: Hon. Cons. Phys. Shotley Bridge Gen. Hosp. & N. Regional Clin. Parmacol. Unit. Newc. & Emerit. Cons. Phys. Newc. HA; Cons. Edr. Adverse Drug Reaction Bull.; Prof. Clin. Pharmacol. Chinese Univ. Hong Kong.

DAVIES, David Mark 34 Dan y Lan, Swiss Valley, Llanelli SA14 8BP — MB BCh 1998 Wales.

DAVIES, David Mervyn (retired) 16 Wilbury Avenue, Cheam, Sutton SM2 7DU Tel: 020 8661 9030 Fax: 020 8661 9030 Email: david.m.davies@amserve.net — MB BChir 1953 Camb.; MA Camb. 1953; MRCP Lond. 1969; FFA RCS Eng. 1960; Hon. FFA RACS 1976; DA Eng. 1958. Hon. Cons. Anaesth. St. Geo. Hosp. Lond. Prev: Vis. Prof. Anaesth. Austral. 1976.

DAVIES, David Michael The Surgery, Much Birch, Hereford HR2 8HT Tel: 01981 540310 Fax: 01981 540748 — MB ChB 1979 Bristol; MRCGP 1983; DRCOG 1982. GP Hereford. Prev: Ho. Phys. Bristol Gen. Hosp.; SHO (A & E) Roy. United Hosp. Bath; Trainee GP Som. VTS.

DAVIES, Mr David Michael 55 Harley Street, London W1N 1DD Tel: 0208 635 6060 Fax: 0208 635 6061 — MB BS 1970 Lond.; FRCS Eng. 1975; MRCS Eng. LRCP Lond. 1970. (St. Bart.) Director Inst. cosmetic and Reconstruc. surg Stomford Hosp Lond.; Cons. & Hon. Sen. Lect. (Plastic & Reconstruc. Surg.) Roy. PostGrad. Med. Hosp. Hammersmith Hosp. Lond. Socs: Fell.Roy. Soc. Med.; Brit. Assoc. Plastic Surgs.; Hand Soc. Prev: Sen. Regist. (Plastic Surg.) Frenchay Hosp. Bristol; Microvasc. Research Fell. Roy. Melbourne Hosp. Australia; Research Fell. (Burns) & Hon. Sen. Regist. Qu. Vict. Hosp. Grinstead.

DAVIES, David Michael, OBE Loscombe Cottage, Buckland Ripers - Tatton, Weymouth DT3 4BX Tel: 01305 812434 Fax: 01305 816351 Email: d.m.davies@tesco.net — MB BCh MB BCh Wales 1961; PhD Lond. 1978; MD Wales 1977; FRCP Lond. 1993; FFOM RCP Lond. 1983, M 1980; MFCM 1973; DIH Eng. 1967; DPH Eng. 1966. (Welsh National School of Medicine) Cons. In Occupat.al and Environm. Med.; Medico-legal Cons. - various organisations. Socs:

Acad.ian, Internat. Acad. of Aviat. & Space Med. (ex-director); Aerospace Med. Assn. (ex. Vice-Pres.).; Airline Med. Directors Assn. (ex Pres.). Prev: Dir. Health Servs. Brit. Airways plc Lond. Heathrow Airport; Head Gp. Environm. & Gen. Med. Servs. BP Internat. Lond.; Surg. Cdr. (Cons. Submarine & Nuclear Med.) RN.

DAVIES, David Morris Tel: 01639 635331; 8 Woodview Terrace, Bryncoch, Neath SA10 7EQ Tel: 01639 645260 — MB BS Lond. 1959; AFOM RCP Lond. 1988. (St. Mary's) Socs: BMA. Prev: Ho. Phys. & Ho. Surg. (Obst.) Neath Gen. Hosp.

DAVIES, David Nigel Illtyd Somerset Health Authority, Wellsprings Road, Taunton TA2 7PQ Tel: 01823 333491 Fax: 01823 272710 Email: david.davies@staff.com-ha.swest.nhs.uk — MB ChB 1989 Leicester; MFPHM 1999; 1989 MB ChB Leic.; 1995 DPH Camb. (Leicester) Cons. in Pub. Health Med., Pub. Health Med., Taunton. Socs: Mem. of Fac. of Pub. Health Med. Prev: Sen. Regist. (Pub. Health Med.) P'boro.

DAVIES, David Noel White Cottage, 51 Shenfield Road, Brentwood CM15 8EN — MB BS 1962 Lond.; FFA RCS Eng. 1967; DA Eng. 1965; DObst RCOG 1964. (Middlx.) Cons. Anaesth. S. Essex Gp. Hosps.

DAVIES, David Paul Department of Medicine for The Aldealy, Cumberland Infirmary, Carlisle CA2 7HY Tel: 01228 523444 Email: d.paul.davies@northcumbria-acute.nhs.uk — MB BCh 1987 Wales; MD (NCLE) 2001; BSc (Hons.) Wales 1984; MRCP (UK) 1991. Gen. & Geriat. Med., Cumbld. Infirm., Carlisle. Socs: Brit. Thorac. Soc.; Brit. Geriat. Soc.; Brit. Assn. of Stroke Phys.s. Prev: Regist. (Med.) Roy. Vict. Infirm. Newc.; Regist. (Med.) Cumbld. Infirm. Carlisle; Research Regist. Freeman Hosp. Newc. u. Tyne.

DAVIES, David Prydderch Lan Parc, Burrows Road, Skewen, Neath SA10 Tel: 01792 2316 — MB BCh 1948 Wales; BSc 1945, MB BCh Wales 1948. (Cardiff) Clin. Asst. ENT Dept. Neath Gen. Hosp. Socs: BMA & Coll. GP. Prev: Ho. Surg. Llandough Hosp. & O & G Dept. Cardiff Roy. Infirm.; Capt. RAMC.

DAVIES, David Raoul Lancelot Danes Dyke Surgery, 463A Scalby Road, Newby, Scarborough YO12 6UB Tel: 01723 375343 Fax: 01723 501582 — MB ChB 1968 Birm.; MRCP (UK) 1972; MRCGP 1978; DCH Eng. 1970. (Birm.) Course Organiser & Trainer ScarBoro. VTS. Prev: Regist. (Paediat.) Birm. Childr. Hosp.; Resid. Med. Off. Qu. Eliz. Hosp. Childr. Lond.; SHO (Med.) City Hosp. Nottm.

DAVIES, David Reed 39 Devonshire House, Devonshire Avenue, Sutton SM2 5JJ Tel: 020 8642 3426 — MB BCh 1953 Wales; DA Eng. 1965.

DAVIES, David Robert Department of Cellular Pathology, Level 1, John Radcliffe Hospital, Headington, Oxford OX3 9DU Tel: 01865 220521 Fax: 01865 220519 Email: david.davies@ndp.ox.ac.uk; 22 Mill Street, Islip, Kidlington OX5 2SY Tel: 01865 377492 — MB BS Lond. 1963; MRCS Eng. LRCP Lond. 1963; FRCPath 1981, M 1969. (King's Coll. Hosp.) Cons. Histopath. John Radcliffe Hosp. Oxf.; Hon. Sen. Clin. Lect. Univ. Oxf. Socs: Path. Soc.; Roy. Soc. Med.; Assn. Clin. Path. Prev: Reader (Histopath.) UMDS St. Thos. Lond.; Lect. (Surg. Path.) St. Thos. Hosp. Med. Sch. Lond.; Ho. Phys. & Demonst. (Path.) King's Coll. Hosp. Lond.

DAVIES, Mr David Robin Ainsworth 1 Grange Road, Urmston, Manchester M41 9GN — MD 1975 Manch.; MB ChB 1963; FRCS Ed. 1969. Cons. Orthop. Surg. Trafford AHA. Prev: Research Fell. (Orthop. Research) Mayo Clinic Rochester U.S.A.; Sen. Regist. Dept. Orthop. Surg. Manch. Roy. Infirm.

DAVIES, David Watkin 11 Terry Road, High Wycombe HP13 6QJ — MB BS Lond. 1957; MRCS Eng. LRCP Lond. 1957; DCH Eng. 1960; DObst RCOG 1959. (Westm.) Locum GP Bucks. Socs: BMA (Ex-Chairm. Bucks. Div.); (Ex-Pres.) Chiltern Med. Soc. Prev: GP High Wycombe; Squadron Ldr. RAF Med. Br.; SHO (O & G) Morriston Hosp. Swansea.

DAVIES, David William Lloyd 12 Ambler Road, Finsbury Park, London N4 2QU Tel: 020 7354 4322 — MB BS 1989 Lond.

DAVIES, David Wyn 66 Harley Street, London W1N 1AE Tel: 020 7636 6340 Fax: 020 7631 1306 — MB BS 1976 Lond.; MD Lond. 1986; FRCP Eng. 1994; MRCP (UK) 1979; MRCS Eng. LRCP Lond. 1976. Cons. Cardiol. St. Mary's Hosp. Lond. Prev: Hon. Sen. Regist. (Cardiol.) Guy's Hosp. Lond.; Sen. Regist. (Cardiol.) St. Bart. Hosp. Lond.

DAVIES, David Wyn Department of Obstetrics & Gynaecology, St. Mary's Hospital, Milton Road, Portsmouth PO3 6AD Tel: 023 92 822331 Ext: 3510 — MB BS 1982 Lond.; MRCOG 1988; FRCOG 2000. Cons. O & G Portsmouth Hosps. NHS Trust; Clin. Dir. Obstetric Med. Socs: Brit. Matern. & Fetal Med. Soc.; Brit. Assn. of Perinatal Med. Prev: Sen. Regist. Roy. Hants. Co. Hosp. Winchester; Clin. Research Fell. (Human Reproduc. & Obst.) Univ. Soton.; Regist. (Obst.) S.mead Hosp. Bristol.

DAVIES, David Wynne Lloyd UCL Hospitals Trust, c/o Anaesthetic Department, Middlesex Hospital, Mortimer St., London W1T 3AA Tel: 020 7380 9013 Fax: 020 7380 9604 Email: w.davies@uclh.org; 10 Thornbury Square, Hornsey Lane, Highgate, London N6 5YN Tel: 020 7263 7718 Fax: 020 7272 3521 Email: w.davies@uclhgas.demon.co.uk — MB BCh 1980 Wales; FRCA 1986; DCH RCP Lond. 1983; DRCOG 1982. (Welsh Nat. Sch. Med.) Cons. Anaesth. Univ. Coll. Lond. Hosps. Trust. Prev: Sen. Regist. (Anaesth.) Bloomsbury HA; Vis. Lect. (Anaesth.) Chinese Univ. Hong Kong; Regist. (Anaesth.) Char. Cross Hosp.

DAVIES, Deborah Leigh 24 Scholars Way, Amersham HP6 6UW — MB BS 1996 Lond. (Char. Cross. & Westm.)

DAVIES, Debra Ann Bryn Darland Surgery, Bryn Darland, High Street, Coedpoeth, Wrexham LL11 3SA Tel: 01978 720285 Fax: 01978 757871 — MB BCh 1982 Wales.

DAVIES, Delyth Wyn Treflan Surgery, Treflan, Lower Cardiff Road, Pwllheli LL53 5NF Tel: 01758 701457 Fax: 01758 701209; Gwen Haul, Llwyn Hudol, Pwllheli LL53 5YF Tel: 01758 701885 — MB BCh 1969 Wales; Dip. Palliat. Med. Cardiff 1992. p/t Clin. Asst. Psychiat., Gwynedd, Bangor. Socs: Assn. Palliat. Med.

DAVIES, Denise Victoria 50 George Crescent, Muswell Hill, London N10 1AN — MB BS 1981 Lond.; MRCP (UK) 1985; MRCGP 1988; DRCOG 1987.

DAVIES, Denzil Ravenscourt Surgery, Tynewydd Road, Barry CF62 8AZ Tel: 01446 734744; Yr Hendre, 9 Pk Road, Barry — MB BCh 1957 Wales; DObst RCOG 1960. (Cardiff)

DAVIES, Derek (retired) 32 Barrow Bridge Road, Smithills, Bolton BL1 7NJ Tel: 01204 847129 Fax: 01204 840895 Email: daviesbltndc@cs.com — MB BChir 1958 Camb.; MA Camb. 1959; FRCP Lond. 1975, M 1963. Hon. Cons. & Endocrinol. Manch. Roy. Infirm. Prev: Cons. Phys. & Endocrinol. Manch. Roy. Infirm.

DAVIES, Dewi The Park Hospital, Sherwood Lodge Drive, Arnold, Nottingham NG5 8RX Tel: 0115 967 0670; The Sandholes, Farnsfield, Newark NG22 8HQ Tel: 01623 882351 — MD 1950 Lond.; MB BS 1945; FRCP Lond. 1970, M 1949. (Guy's) Prev: Cons. Phys. City Hosp. Nottm.; Cons. Chest Phys. Mansfield Hosp. Gp.; Pres. Brit. Thoracic Assn.

DAVIES, Dewi Richard Wynne Bodewi, Glynceiriog, Llangollen LL20 7EH — MB BCh 1968 Wales.

DAVIES, Diana Joy Eastfield House Surgery, 6 St. Johns Road, Newbury RG14 7LW Tel: 01635 41495 Fax: 01635 522751 — MB BS 1981 Lond.; DRCOG 1984.

DAVIES, Diana Patricia Cartref, Stead St., Eckington, Sheffield S21 4FY — MB ChB 1963 Bristol. (Bristol)

DAVIES, Dilys Kathrine (retired) 84 Liverpool Road, Penwortham, Preston PR1 0HT Tel: 01772 749566 — MB BS 1954 Lond. Prev: Med. Adviser Lancs. FHSA Preston.

DAVIES, Doreen (retired) 14 Cefn Morfa, Cefnllys Lane, Llandrindod Wells LD1 5NP Tel: 01597 22263 — MB ChB Birm. 1939; FFA RCS Eng. 1954; DA Eng. 1947. Anaesth. Roy. Salop. Infirm. Shrewsbury & Shropsh. Orthop. Hosp. OsW.ry. Prev: Sen. Res. Anaesth. Regist. Qu. Eliz. Hosp. Birm.

DAVIES, Doreen May Grant (retired) Riverlands, 85 Bronwydd Road, Carmarthen SA31 2AP — MB BS 1947 Sydney; BSc (High Distinc.) Sydney 1941, MB BS 1947. Prev: SHO Anaesth. Wolverhampton Roy. Hosp.

DAVIES, Dorian Hughson Health Centre, Pricess St., Gorseinon, Swansea SA4 Tel: 01792 895681; Brynderi, Bolgoed Road, Pontardulais, Swansea SA4 1 Tel: 01792 882271 — MB ChB 1949 Birm. (Birm.) Clin. Asst. Gen. Surg. & Anaesth. Gorseinon Hosp. Swansea; Local Treasury Med. Off. Prev: Jun. Med. Regist. Chest Unit Morriston Hosp.; Ho. Pahs. Swansea Hosp.; Med. Off. RAMC.

DAVIES, Douglas Lloyd The Graig, Borth SY24 5LH — MRCS Eng. LRCP Lond. 1944. (Char. Cross) JP. Prev: Res. Surg. Off. & Ho. Surg. W. Herts. Hosp. Hemel Hempstead; Flight Lt. RAFVR; Ho. Surg. Ashridge EMS Hosp.

DAVIES, Duncan Dunn Ridge House, 5 Lambourne Avenue, Wimbledon, London SW19 7DW — MB ChB 1951 Manch.; DObst RCOG 1954. (Manch.) Prev: Ho. Surg. (O & G, & Gen. Surg.) Pk.

Hosp. Davyhulme; Capt. RAMC, Med. Off. Brig. Gurkhas Depot., Malaya.

DAVIES, Dyfrig Morris Bryn Darland Surgery, Bryn Darland, High Street, Coedpoeth, Wrexham LL11 3SA Tel: 01978 720285 Fax: 01978 757871; 16 Green Park, Erddig, Wrexham LL13 7YE — MB BCh 1982 Wales.

DAVIES, Edna Lynette (retired) 114 New Road, Llanelli SA15 3DT Tel: 01554 773053 — MB BCh 1955 Wales; BSc Wales 1952, MB BCh 1955; DObst RCOG 1957. Prev: SCMO Dyfed AHA.

DAVIES, Edward Harlech, Monmouth Road, Raglan NP15 2LA — MRCS Eng. LRCP Lond. 1952. (Cardiff) Prev: Med. Off. Adelina Patti Hosp. Swansea; Clin. Asst. Dept. Dermat. Cardiff Roy. Infirm.

DAVIES, Edward Graham 1 Alltmawr Road, Cyncoed, Cardiff CF23 6NQ — MB BChir 1977 Camb.; MA Camb. 1976; MRCP (UK) 1978. (Univ. Coll. Hosp.)

DAVIES, Edward Hart 61 Lister Road, Margate CT9 4AF — MB ChB 1967 Cape Town.

DAVIES, Edward John James, OBE, KStJ (retired) Llechwedd, Cerrigydrudion, Corwen LL21 9SU Tel: 01490 420314 Fax: 01490 420314 — MB ChB 1949 Liverp.; MRCGP 1961. Edr. Welsh Med. Soc. Jl. Prev: Cas. Off. Liverp. Stanley Hosp.

DAVIES, Edward Thomas Lincoln Fernleigh Consulting Centre, 77 Alderley Rd, Wilmslow SK9 1PA Tel: 01625 636488 Fax: 01625 548348; 13 Bower Road, Hale, Altrincham WA15 9DR Tel: 0161 928 3241 — MB BS 1959 Lond.; BSc (Hons.) Lond. 1955; FRCP Lond. 1979, M 1965; MRCS Eng. LRCP Lond. 1958. (St. Mary's) Socs: Fell. Manch. Med. Soc.; Brit. Cardiac Soc. Prev: Cardiol. Phys. E. Chesh. NHS Trust Macclesfield; Lect. (Cardiol.) Univ. Manch. & Manch. Roy. Infirm.; Sen. Regist. (Med.) Manch. Roy. Infirm.

DAVIES, Eileen, OBE (retired) Bryn y Glyn, Nantglyn, Colwyn Bay LL29 7RB — MB ChB 1936 Liverp.

DAVIES, Eirwen Joy Ceredigion Mental Health Unit, Ty Helyg, Caradoc Road, Aberystwyth SY23 2ER Tel: 01970 623131 — MB BCh 1982 Wales. (Welsh National School of Medicine) Clin. Asst. (Psychiat. of Old Age) Bronglais Hosp. Aberystwyth; Clin. Asst. (Learning Disabilities). Prev: Clin. Asst. (Med. & Psychiat.) Machynlleth Chest Hosp.

DAVIES, Elaine Gwenlas, Llanbadarnfynydd, Llandrindod Wells LD1 6YF — MB ChB 1990 Manch.

DAVIES, Eleri 60 Capel Road, Clydach, Swansea SA6 5PY; 114 Pontardawe Road, Clydach, Swansea SA6 5PA Tel: 01792 846425 — MB BCh 1993 Wales; MRCGP 1997; DFFP. (Cardiff)

DAVIES, Eleri Lloyd 60 Birchwood Gardens, Whitchurch, Cardiff CF14 1HY — MB BCh 1991 Wales. SHO (Gen. Surg.) E. Glam. Gen. Hosp. Prev: Demonst. (Anat. & Physiol.) Sheff. Univ.; Resid. Med. Off. BUPA Hosp. Murrayfield; Ho. Off. (Gen. Surg.) E. Glam. Hosp.

DAVIES, Elfreda Alice Milestones, Glasllwch Lane, Newport NP20 3PR Tel: 01633 254881 — MB BCh 1952 Wales; BSc (Distinc. Anat.) Wales 1949. (Cardiff) Clin. Med. Off. Gwent HA. Prev: Ho. Phys. Neath Gen. Hosp.; Ho. Off. (Paediat.) Morriston Gen. Hosp.; Sen. Med. Off i/c Ment. Health Mon. CC.

DAVIES, Elin Powys Health Care NHS Trust, Bronllys Hospital, Bronllys, Brecon LD3 0LY Tel: 01874 711661 Fax: 01874 711601; Tirmynach Farm House, Hay-on-Wye, Hereford HR3 5RS Tel: 01497 821798 — MB BS 1987 Lond.; FRCA 1994; MRC Psych 1998. (Middlx. Hosp. Lond.) Staff Community Psychiat. Prev: SHO Rotat. (Psychiat.) Char. Cross Hosp. Lond.; Sen. Regist. (Anaesth.) St. Thos. Hosp. Lond.

DAVIES, Elisabeth Rachel Gade Surgery Gade House, 99b Uxbridge Road, Rickmansworth WD3 Tel: 01923 775291 — MB BS 1991 Lond.; MRCGP 1997. (St. Geo.) Prev: SHO (O & G & Paediat.) Hillingdon Hosp. Uxbridge; SHO paeds Hillingdon Hosp.Uxbridge.

DAVIES, Elizabeth 71 Derby Road, Bramcote, Nottingham NG9 3GW Tel: 0115 925 3171 — MB ChB 1961 Birm. (Birm.) Indep. GP Nottm.

DAVIES, Elizabeth Anne Department of Microbiology, Causeway Laboratory, 2 Newbridge Road, Coleraine BT52 1HS Tel: 01265 321051 Fax: 01265 321052 — MB BCh BAO 1982 Belf.; MRCPath 1990. Cons. Microbiol. & Dir. Causeway Laborat. Coleraine. Socs: BMA. Prev: Sen. Regist. (Med. Microbiol.) Roy. Vict. Hosp. Belf.

DAVIES, Elizabeth Anne National Institute for Clinical Excellence, 11 Strand, London Tel: 0207 766 9191 Fax: 0207 766 9123 Email: elizabeth.davies@nice.nhs.uk; Email: elizabethdavies@doctors.org.uk — MB BS 1989 Lond.; 2001 MPFHM; MSc Lond. 1986, BSc (Hons.) 1985; Phd Med 1998. (Univ. Coll. Middlx. Sch. Med.) Specialist Regist. (Pub. Health Med.) Nat. Inst. for Clin. Excellence; Hon. Lect. Dep. Palliat. Care & Policy, Guys, King's & St. Thomas'. Socs: Fell Roy. Soc. Med.; Soc. Psychosomatic Research; Soc. Social Med. Prev: SHO (Psychiat.) Maudsley Hosp. Lond.; Clin. Research Fell. Research Unit, RCP; Clin. Research Fell. (Neurol. Sci.) St Bart. Hosp. Lond.

DAVIES, (Elizabeth) Esmee (retired) 8 Broadlands Close, London N6 4AF — MRCS Eng. LRCP Lond. 1945; BPharm Lond. 1938, MB BS 1945. Prev: Cons. Pathol. Eliz. G. Anderson Hosp. Lond. & Roy. Lond. Homoeop.

DAVIES, Elizabeth Jane 41 Conybeare Road, Glan Hafren, Sully, Penarth CF64 5TZ; (profess.) Ravenscourt, Tynewydd Road, Barry CF62 8 — MB BCh 1977 Wales.

DAVIES, Elizabeth June — MB BS 1991 Lond.; MRCOG 1997. (Char. Cross Westm.) SpR (O&G) S. Manc. Univ. Hosp. Prev: Research Fell.Gyn &Oncol. Christie Hosp. Manch.

DAVIES, Elizabeth Shan Wootton Medical Centre, 36-38 High Street, Wootton, Northampton NN4 6LW Tel: 01604 709933 Fax: 01604 709944; Orchard House, Great Brington, Northampton NN7 4JD — BSc (Hons.) Lond. 1979, MB BS 1982; MRCP (UK) Paediat. 1986; MRCGP 1990; DRCOG 1987.

DAVIES, Eluned Barnett 'Greenways', 7 Woodcote Lane, Purley CR8 3HB — MB BS 1950 Lond.; MRCS Eng. LRCP Lond. 1950; DMRD Eng. 1958. Cons. Radiol. St. Geo., Bolingbroke & Eliz. Garrett Anderson Hosps.; Lond.

DAVIES, Emrys John Lloyd (retired) The Old Vicarage, Tregaer, Raglan NP15 2LH Tel: 01291 690517 — MB ChB 1946 Birm.; MRCS Eng. LRCP Lond. 1945; DObst RCOG 1950.

DAVIES, Mr Emyr Geraint Eye Department, Singleton Hospital, Swansea SA2 8QA; Bryncelyn, High St, Pontardawe, Swansea SA8 4JN — MD 1992 Wales; MD Wales. 1992, MB BCh 1981; FRCS Ed. 1986; FCOphth 1989; DO RCS Eng. 1985.

DAVIES, Emyr James The Towers Surgery, 163 Holton Road, Barry CF63 4HP Tel: 01446 734131 Fax: 01446 420002; Hillcrest, 59 Cog Road, Sully, Penarth CF64 5TE Tel: 01222 530860 — MB BCh 1983 Wales. (Cardiff)

DAVIES, Eric Gwyn Lewis Richmond Clinic., 172 Caerleon Road, Newport NP19 7FY; St. Winifreds, White Hart Lane, Caerleon, Newport NP18 1AB Tel: 01633 591 — MB BCh 1958 Wales; MRCS Eng. LRCP Lond. 1959; DObst RCOG 1961.

DAVIES, Eric James 1 Keswick Close, Liverpool L31 9BS — MB ChB 1997 Manch.

DAVIES, Mr Ernest Walter Geoffrey (retired) 60 Manor Way, Beckenham BR3 3LJ — MA, MB BChir Camb. 1955; FRCS Eng. 1964; FCOphth 1988; DO Eng. 1960. Cons. Ophth. Surg. King's Coll. Hosp. Lond.; Recognised Teach. Ophth. Univ. Lond. Prev: Sen. Resid. Off. Moorfields Eye Hosp. Lond.

DAVIES, Evan Mark 10 Winstanley Road, Nursling, Southampton SO16 0TF — BM 1990 Soton.

DAVIES, Evan William (retired) Canolfan Gwili, West Wales Genneral Hospital, Glangwili, Carmarthen SA31 2AF — MB BCh 1955 Wales; MA Wales 1984; MRCP Lond. 1967; MRCPsych 1973; DPM Eng. 1959. Cons. Child Psychiat. Dyfed AHA.

DAVIES, Faith Elizabeth 19 Linton Grove, Leeds LS17 8PS — MB BCh 1992 Wales; MRCP (UK) 1995.

DAVIES, Ffion Catrin Wyn A&E, Royal London Hospital, Whitechapel, London E1 1BB Tel: 020 7377 7161 Fax: 020 7377 7014 — MB ChB 1990 Leic.; MRCP (Paediat.) (UK) 1994; FFAEM 1998. (Leicester) Cons. Accid & Emerg. Roy. Lond. Hosp. Socs: RCPCH; Brit. Assn. Emerg. Med.; Fell.Fac.accid & Emerg.Med. Prev: Specialist Regist. (A & E) Roy. Liverp. Univ. Hosp.

DAVIES, Finlay John Matheson Macdonald Group Practice Surgery, Green Street, Forfar DD8 3AR Tel: 01307 462316 Fax: 01307 463623 — MB ChB 1984 Aberd.

DAVIES, Frances Mary The Dorchester Road Surgery, 179 Dorchester Road, Weymouth DT4 7LE Tel: 01305 766472 Fax: 01305 766499; 17 Custom House Quay, Weymouth DT4 8BG Tel: 01305 766814 — MB BS 1977 Lond.; BA Oxf. 1974; DRCOG 1988. (Char. Cross Lond.)

DAVIES, Frederick William 34 Caldwell Road, West Kilbride KA23 9LF — MB ChB 1984 Glas.; MB ChB Glas. l984; FFA RCSI 1989.

DAVIES, Mr Frederick William Thomas New Lodge, Bretby Village, Burton-on-Trent DE15 0RD — MRCS Eng. LRCP 1939 Lond.; FRCS Ed. 1946; MRCS Eng, LRCP Lond. 1939. (Cardiff) Socs: Fell. Brit. Orthop. Assn. Prev: Sen. Cons. Orthop. Surg. Burton-on-Trent Hosp. Gp.; Sen. Orthop. Regist. Canterbury & I. of Thanet Gps. of Hosps.; Ho. Surg. Roy. Infirm. Cardiff.

DAVIES, Gail Elizabeth Ynysangharad Road Health Centre, 70 Ynysangharad Road, Pontypridd CF37 4DA Tel: 01443 480521 Fax: 01443 400260; High Mead, Upper Church Village, Pontypridd CF38 1EE — MB BCh 1975 Wales; DRCOG 1977. Prev: Hon. Med. Off. Univ. Glam.

DAVIES, Gail Susan 19/21 Portland Street, Aberystwyth SY23 2NQ Tel: 01970 612453; Carrog, Llanddeimol, Llanrhystyd, Aberystwyth SY23 5DG — MB BS 1980 Lond.; DA (UK) 1987; DCH RCP Lond. 1985; DRCOG 1983.

DAVIES, Gaius (cons. rooms), 21 Wimpole St., London W1M 7AD Tel: 020 7637 0303 Fax: 020 7637 0303; 88 Overbury Avenue, Beckenham BR3 6PY Tel: 020 8650 8764 Fax: 020 8650 0138 — MB BS Lond. 1953; MPhil (Psychiat.) Lond. 1972; FRCPsych 1978, M 1972; DPM Eng. 1972. (St. Bart.) Emerit. Cons. Psychiat. King's Coll., Bethlem Roy. & Maudsley Hosps. Lond. Socs: Fell. Roy. Soc. Med. Prev: Sen. Regist. Hammersmith Hosp. & Bethlem Roy. & Maudsley Hosps. Lond.

DAVIES, Gareth (retired) The Maltings, Horsell Rise, Woking GU21 4BG Tel: 01483 768391 Fax: 01483 751806 — MB BS Lond. 1960.

DAVIES, Mr Gareth 12 Gresham Avenue, Westbrook, Margate CT9 5EH — MRCS Eng. LRCP Lond. 1972; BSc (Hons.) Lond. 1969, MS 1983, MB BS 1972; FRCS Eng. 1978. (St. Bart.) Clin. Director of Day Serv.s The Qu. Eliz. the Qu. Mother Hosp. Margate; Mem. Ct. Examr. RCS Eng. Prev: Sen. Regist. (Surg.) St. Bart. Hosp. Lond.

DAVIES, Gareth Edward Department of Accident & Emergency Medicine, Royal Hospitals NHS Trust, Whitechapel, London E1 1BB Tel: 020 7377 7125 Email: gdavies@compuserve.com; 15 August End, George Green, Slough SL3 6RP — MB ChB 1988 Sheff.; MRCP (UK) 1991; FFAEM 1996. (Sheff.) Cons. (A & E Med. & Prehosp. Care) Roy. Lond. Hosp. Socs: Exec. Comm. Mem. Brit. Assn. Immediate Care; Brit. Assn. Accid. & Emerg. Med. Prev: Sen. Regist. (A & E Med.) Roy. Lond. Hosp.; Regist. (Helicopter Emerg. Med. Serv.) Roy. Lond. Hosp.; SHO Rotat. (Med.) S. Tees Health Auth.

DAVIES, Gareth Griffith 6 Victoria Court, Durdham Park, Bristol BS6 6XS Tel: 0117 973 1093 — MA Camb. 1969, MB 1968, BChir 1967; DObst RCOG 1970. (Camb. & St. Thos.) Socs: BMA. Prev: Asst. Chief Dept. Emerg. Med. & Primary Care Al Hada Hosp. Taif, Saudi Arabia; SHO A & E Centre St. Peter's Hosp. Chertsey; Ho. Surg. & Obst. Ho. Off. St. Thos. Hosp. Lond.

DAVIES, Gareth James 7 Blanche Close, Newport NP10 8QF Tel: 01633 816098 — MB BCh 1994 Wales. Regist. (Radiol.) Univ. Hosp. of Wales Cardiff. Prev: SHO (ITU & Plastic Surg.) Roy. Gwent Hosp. Newport; SHO (A & E) Cardiff Roy. Infirm.; SHO (Urol.) Univ. Hosp. Wales.

DAVIES, Gareth John Killearn Health Centre, Balfron Road, Killearn, Glasgow G63 9NA Tel: 01360 50339 Fax: 01360 550176; Byways, Drumbeg Loan, Killearn, Glasgow G63 9NG — MB ChB 1975 Glas.; MBA (Healthcare) University of Sterling 1999; DRCOG 1977. Med. Dir. Forth Valley Primary Care Trust.

DAVIES, Gareth John 226 Lovely Lane, Warrington WA5 1QF — MB ChB 1998 Manch.; MB ChB Manch 1998.

DAVIES, Gareth Robert 1 Falkland Crescent, Moortown, Leeds LS17 6JL — MB BS 1984 Lond.; BSc (Hons.) Lond. 1981; MRCP (UK) 1987. Cons. Phys. & Gastroenterol. Harrogate Dist. Hosp. & Leeds Gen. Infirm. Socs: Brit. Soc. Gastroenterol. Prev: Lect. & Hon. Sen. Regist. (Gastroenterol.) St. Jas. Hosp. Leeds; Research Regist. (Gastrointestinal Sci.) Lond. Hosp. Med. Coll.; Regist. Rotat. Lond. Hosp.

DAVIES, Gareth Walter Marsden Coach and Horses Surgery, The Car Park, St. Clears, Carmarthen SA33 4AA Tel: 01994 230379 Fax: 01994 231449; Penalltiwan, Meidrim, Carmarthen SA33 5QE Tel: 01994 230345 — MB BChir 1965 Camb.; MA Camb. 1966; MRCS Eng. LRCP Lond. 1965. (Middlx.) Prev: Regist. (Med.) St And. Hosp. Billericay.

DAVIES, Gary John 12 Beechwood Close, Western Road, London N2 9JA Tel: 020 8444 0833 — MB BS 1993 Lond. Prev: Ho. Off. (Med.) Mt. Vernon Hosp. Rickmansworth; Ho. Off. (Surg.) Edgware Gen. Hsop.

***DAVIES, Gary William** Department of Medicine, St Helier Hospital, Carshalton Tel: 020 8644 4343; 36 Upper Vernon Road, Sutton SM1 4NW — MB BS 1994 Lond.

DAVIES, Gawain Pennant Birley Health Centre, 120 Birley Lane, Sheffield S12 3BP Tel: 0114 239 2541 Fax: 0114 264 5814; 22 Slayleigh Avenue, Sheffield S10 3RB — MB ChB 1988 Sheff.; MRCGP 1994; DFFP 1994; Dip (Sports Med.) 1998. (Sheffield) Socs: BMA; Brit. Assn. Sport & Med.

DAVIES, Gaynor 12 Maillards Haven, Penarth CF64 5RF — MB BCh 1986 Wales; DRCOG 1989.

DAVIES, Geoffrey Francis High Street Family Practice, 37-39 High Street, Barry CF62 7EB Tel: 01446 733355 Fax: 01446 733489; 23 Millbrook Road, Dinas Powys CF64 4BZ Email: gfdavies@epulse.net — MB BCh 1986 Wales; MRCGP 1990; DRCOG 1988. Prev: Trainee GP S. Gwent VTS.

DAVIES, Geoffrey Paul High Street Medical Centre, 46-48 High Street, Newhall, Swadlincote DE11 0HU Tel: 01283 217092; 10 The Sandlands, Midway, Swadlincote DE11 7PY Tel: 01283 213538 Fax: 01283 213538 — MB ChB 1973 Birm.; DFFP 1993. (Birm.) Med. Ref. Bretby Crematorium.

DAVIES, Geoffrey Stanley Burvill House Surgery, 52 Dellfield Road, Hatfield AL10 8HP Tel: 01707 269091; Chiswell Green Farm, Chiswell Green Lane, St Albans AL2 3AJ Tel: 01727 855786 — MB BS 1987 Lond. (University College London) Occupat. Health Phys. Univ. of Herts. Prev: Trainee GP/SHO Qu. Eliz. II Hosp. Welwyn.

DAVIES, Geoffrey Thomas The Surgery, High St., Clive, Shrewsbury SY4 Tel: 01939 28295; 5 Eagle Farm Close, Myddle, Shrewsbury SY4 3RQ — MB ChB 1981 Birm.; MRCGP 1984; DRCOG 1984.

DAVIES, George John 71 Derby Road, Bramcote, Beeston, Nottingham NG9 3GW Tel: 0115 925 3171 — MB ChB 1961 Birm.; MRCS Eng. LRCP Lond. 1961; DObst RCOG 1964. (Birm.) Indep. GP Nottm.

DAVIES, George Rhys (retired) 1 Pen-yr-heol Drive, Sketty, Swansea SA2 9JT Tel: 01792 204538 — MB BS Lond. 1956; MRCS Eng. LRCP Lond. 1957. Prev: GP Swansea.

DAVIES, Geraint Alyn Barton Surgery, 1 Edmunds Close, Barton Court Avenue, Barton-on-Sea, New Milton BH25 7EH Tel: 01425 620830 Fax: 01425 629812; Orchard House, 19 Waterford Lane, Lymington SO41 3PT Tel: 01590 670629 — MB BCh 1986 Wales.

DAVIES, Geraint Rhys Yaffle Lodge, Bleasby Road, Thurgarton, Nottingham NG14 7FW — BM 1991 Soton.

DAVIES, Mr Gerald Courtenay The Garden Cottage, Woodhouselee, Easter Howgate, Penicuik EH26 0PF Tel: 0131 445 5147 — MB BS 1970 Lond.; MS Lond. 1981; FRCS Ed. 1982; FRCS Eng. 1974; MRCS Eng. LRCP Lond. 1970. (Westm.) Prev: Cons. Surg. St. John's Hosp. Livingstone; Sen. Lect. (Surg.) Roy. Infirm. Edin.

DAVIES, Gerald Leighton (retired) Hillcroft, Little Haven, Haverfordwest SA62 3UH Tel: 01437 781387 — MB BCh Wales 1957; DObst RCOG 1959; Assoc. Fac. Occupat. Med. RCP Lond. 1980. Prev: Med. Off. Gulf Oil Refining Ltd. Milford Haven.

DAVIES, Gerald Rees 2 Westview Avenue, Whyteleafe CR3 0EQ Tel: 01883 627302 — MRCS Eng. LRCP Lond. 1945. (St. Bart.) Prev: Ho. Surg. Chest Unit St. Bart. Hosp.

DAVIES, Geraldine Anne Marr Station House Surgery, Station Road, Kendal LA9 6SA Tel: 01539 722660 Fax: 01539 734845; Thorn Rigg, Garth Row, Kendal LA8 9AT Tel: 01539 823698 — MB ChB 1972 Liverp.; MRCGP 1976; DFFP 1994; DObst RCOG 1975; DCH Eng. 1974. (Liverpool) Trainer (Gen. Pract.) Kendal. Prev: Trainee GP Lancaster VTS; Ho. Phys. & Ho. Surg. Preston Roy. Infirm.

DAVIES, Gerard Robert Department of Medicine, Wexham Park Hospital, Wexham Street, Wexham, Slough SL2 4HL; 49A Rudloe Road, London SW12 0DR — MB BS 1997 Lond.

DAVIES, Ghislaine Susan Ross Tilecoies, Oxford Road, Marlow SL7 2WT — MB BS 1979 Lond.; MRCP (UK) 1982. Assoc. Specialist (Gastroenterol.) Wycombe Gen. Hosp.; Dep. Coroner for Reading Dist. Prev: Regist. (Gastroenterol.) High Wycombe; Regist. (Med.) Ashford Hosp. Middlx.; Ho. Phys. St. Bart. Hosp. Lond.

DAVIES, Gilda Nadine Looe Health Centre, Station Road, Looe PL13 1HA Tel: 01503 283195 — MB BCh 1984 Wales; DCH RCP

Lond. 1990; DRCOG 1997. GP Looe; Sessional Doctor in Family Plann. Prev: Clin. Med. Off. Community Child Health S. Lincs. & Grimsby HA's; Trainee GP Swindon VTS.

DAVIES, Giles Lake Stephen Woodside, Horkesley Rd, Boxted, Colchester CO4 5HS — MB BS 1997 Lond.

DAVIES, Gillian 122 Merthyr Mawr Road, Bridgend CF31 3NY — MB ChB 1979 Manch.; MRCPsych 1985.

DAVIES, Ms Gillian Mary 407 Cinnamon Wharf, 24 Shad Thames, London SE1 2YJ Tel: 020 7378 0395 — MB BS 1960 Lond.; MRCS Eng. LRCP Lond. 1960; FFA RCS Eng. 1967; DA Eng. 1964; DObst RCOG 1963. (King's Coll. Hosp.) Anaesth. Brit. Red Cross ICRC Hosps.; Med. Asst. for MERLIN. Prev: Cons. Anaesth. Chelmsford Health Dist.; Sen. Regist. Anaesth. W.m. Hosp. & S.end Gen. Hosp.; SHO Anaesth. Addenbrooke's Hosp. Camb.

DAVIES, Glanmor Rhys (retired) Glyneiddan, Nantgaredig, Carmarthen SA32 7LY Tel: 01267 290234 — MB BCh 1939 Wales; BSc Wales 1936, MD 1948; FRCP Lond. 1969, M 1947. Prev: Cons. Phys. SW Wales Hosp. Gp.

DAVIES, Glyn Iestyn Priory Hospital, Roehampton, London SW15 5JJ Tel: 020 8876 8261 Fax: 020 8392 2632; Robinwood Place, Kingston Vale, London SW15 3SE — BA (Psych. Hons.) Wales 1936; MRCS Eng. LRCP Lond. 1942; FRCPsych 1978, M 1972; DPM Eng. 1948. (Wales & Middlx.) Vis. Psychiat. Priory Hosp. Roehampton; Vis. Psychiat. New Vict. Hosp. Kingston upon Thames; Psychiat. Adviser Cunard SS Co.; Cons. Psychiatr. Brit. Transport Commiss. Socs: Fell. Roy. Soc. Med. Prev: Med. Dir. Bowden Ho. Clinic Harrow; Psychiat. Specialist HQ & RAF Bengal-Burma; Cons. Dept. Psychiat. W. Lond. Hosp. & Med. Sch. Hammersmith.

DAVIES, Gordon Carne 22 Clifton Street, Aberdare CF44 7PB Tel: 01685 873445 — MB BCh 1947 Wales; FFA RCS Eng. 1956. (Cardiff) Cons. Anaesth. E. Glam. Gen. Hosp. Prev: Cons. Anaesth. Merthyr & Aberdare Hosp. Gp.; Regist. Dept. Anaesth. Cardiff Roy. Infirm.; Surg. Regist. Morriston Hosp.

DAVIES, Gower 206 Norsey Road, Billericay CM11 1DB — MRCS Eng. LRCP Lond. 1949. (St. Mary's) Socs: MRCGP.

DAVIES, Graham Christopher Meadow View Cottage, Broad Road, Monxton, Andover SP11 8AT — MD 1994 Lond.; MB BS 1981; MRCOG 1988.

DAVIES, Gwilym Ysbyty Glan Clwyd, Sarn Lane, Bodelwyddan, Rhyl LL18 5UJ Tel: 01745 583910 Fax: 01745 583143; 7 The Paddock, St Asaph LL17 0AQ Tel: 01745 583981 — MB ChB 1973 Liverp.; BA (Hons.) Open 1993; FFA RCS Eng. 1977. Cons. & Clin. Dir. Anaesth. Glan Clwyd Hosp. NHS Trust. Prev: Sen. Regist. (Anaesth.) Sheff. AHA (T); Visit. Asst. Prof. Univ. Texas, S.W.. Med. Sch. Dallas; Regist. (Anaesth.) BRd.green Hosp. Liverp.

DAVIES, Gwilym Alban 2 Glebe Close, Bolton Percy, York YO23 7HB — MRCS Eng. LRCP Lond. 1976.

DAVIES, Gwilym Pritchard Morris and Partners, Ty Bryn Surgery, The Bryn, Trethomas, Newport CF83 8GL Tel: 029 2086 8011 Fax: 029 2086 9463; 24 Ffos-y-Fran, Bassaleg, Newport NP10 8LU — MB BCh 1982 Wales; MRCOG 1988; MFFP 1993; DRCOG 1984. Clin Assist. Gyn. Dept. Roy. Gwent Hosp. Newport.

DAVIES, Gwyneth Ann c/o Medical Personnel, University Hospital of Wales NHS Trust, Heath Park, Cardiff CF14 4XW — MB BCh 1996 Wales.

DAVIES, Gwynneston Leighton (retired) 2 Claremont Drive, Marton, Middlesbrough TS7 8ND Tel: 01642 316794 — MRCS Eng. LRCP Lond. 1949; FRCPsych 1975, M 1971; DPM Roy. Med.-Psych. Assn. 1952. Hon. Cons. N. & S. Tees Hosp. Prev: Cons. Psychiat. Dept. Child & Family Psychiat. N. Tees Gen. Hosp. Stockton.

DAVIES, Hazel Clare 4 Southridge Heights, Weston Super Mare BS24 9JH — MB BS 1956 Lond.; LMSSA Lond. 1956. (Guy's)

DAVIES, Heidi Jane 4 Gladeside Close, Hunter's Green, Thornhill, Cardiff CF14 9HU Tel: 029 2061 9165; Singleton Hospital NHS Trust, Sketty Lane, Swansea SA2 8QF Tel: 01792 205666 — MB BCh 1995 Wales; BMedSci Wales 1994. (University of Wales College of Medicine) SHO (Anaesth.) Singleton Hosp. Swansea. Prev: Resid. Med. Off. (IC) Wollongong Hosp. NSW 2500 Australia; Ho. Off. (IC).

DAVIES, Helen Elizabeth 106 Heol Isaf, Radyr, Cardiff CF15 8EA — MB BS 1992 Lond.

DAVIES, Helen Isabel (retired) South Hayes Home, 101 London Road, Worcester WR5 2DZ Tel: 01905 350339 — MB BS 1923 Lond. Prev: on Staff Univ. Clinic Neurol. & Psychiat. Cologne & Vienna.

DAVIES, Helen Jayne 163 Surrenden Road, Brighton BN1 6NN — BChir 1990 Camb.

DAVIES, Helen Louise Plas Iorwerth, Nefyn, Pwllheli LL53 6HB Tel: 01758 720339 — MB BCh 1970 Wales; Dip. Med. Ac. 1995; DObst RCOG 1973. (Welsh Nat. Sch. Med.) p/t Med. Acupunct. Socs: Brit. Med. Acupunct. Soc. Prev: SHO (Dermat.) Roy. Infirm. Dundee; Ho. Off. (Profess. Med. Unit & Gen. Surg.) Univ. Hosp. Wales Cardiff.

DAVIES, Helen Mary 2 Station Terrace, Station Road, Sutton Weaver, Runcorn WA7 3EP — MB ChB 1988 Liverp.

DAVIES, Helen Wyn 17 Queens Road, Richmond TW10 6JW — MB BS 1983 Lond.; MRCP (UK) 1986. Pharmaceut. Phys. Sandoz Ltd. Frimley.

DAVIES, Helen Wynne Brentford Group Practice, Boston Manor Road, Brentford TW8 8DS Tel: 020 8321 3844 Fax: 020 8321 3862; 41 Windmill Road, Chiswick, London W4 1RN Tel: 020 8994 5516 — MB BCh 1971 Wales; MRCGP 1982; DRCOG 1973. (Welsh Nat. Sch. Med.) Prev: GP Tawam Hosp. Abu Dhabi, United Arab Emirates.

DAVIES, Helena Anne Sheffield Children's Hospital, Western Bank, Sheffield S10 27H Tel: 0114 271 7108 Email: h.davies@sheffield.ac.uk; Station House, Finkle, Wortley, Sheffield S35 7DH — MB ChB 1986 Bristol; MB ChB (Hons.) Bristol 1986; MRCP (UK) 1989; MD 1996. Cons. (Paediat.) Sheff. HA.

DAVIES, Henry Leighton (retired) Pengelli, Bryn Gannock, Deganwy, Conwy LL31 9UG Tel: 01492 583923 — MB BCh 1959 Wales; FRCS Eng. 1969; FRCS Ed. 1969; MRCS Eng. LRCP Lond. 1959. Cons. Surg. Gwynedd HA. Prev: Cons. Surg. Caerns & Anglesey Hosp. Bangor.

DAVIES, Henry Richard Glasbrook Bryn-y-Glyn, Colwyn Bay LL29 7RB Tel: 01492 2980 — MB ChB 1935 Liverp.; DPH 1946. (Liverp.)

DAVIES, Henry William Cecil (retired) 14 Brookfield Road, Lymm WA13 0QJ Tel: 0192 575 3798 — MB ChB 1956 Liverp.; FRCOG 1977, M 1963. Prev: Cons. O & G Warrington Gen. Hosp.

DAVIES, Herbert Julian 39 Penshurst Gardens, Edgware HA8 9TN Tel: 020 8958 3141 — MRCS Eng. LRCP Lond. 1956; BA, MB Camb. 1957, BChir 1956; DA Eng. 1958. (Westm.) Clin. Asst. (Anaesth.) Hammersmith Hosp. Lond.; Clin. Asst. Walford Gen. Hosp. Prev: Res. Anaesth. Connaught Hosp. Walthamstow; Ho. Surg. Epsom Dist. Hosp.; Ho. Phys. High Wycombe & Dist. Gen. Hosp.

DAVIES, Howard Eaton Freeman (retired) Bryneithin, Llanfarian, Ceredigion, Aberystwyth SY23 4BY Tel: 01970 625115 — MB BS 1948 Lond.; BSc Wales 1945; MD Lond. 1952; FRCP Lond. 1975, M 1952. Hon. Cons. Geriat. Med. Gwent HA. Prev: Ho. Phys. Guy's Hosp., Hammersmith Hosp. & Hosp. Sick Childr. Gt. Ormond St. Lond.

DAVIES, Howard Frankcom Craig Afon, Island Farm Road, Merthyr Mawr, Bridgend CF31 3LG — MB ChB 1971 Manch.; FFA RCS Eng. 1976. Bro Morgannwa NHS Trust, Bridgend. Socs: Assn. Anaesth. Prev: Sen. Regist. & Regist Univ. Hosp. Wales Cardiff.; Ho. Off. Manch. Roy. Infirm.

DAVIES, Howard Lynn Simms 24 Whitcliffe Drive, Penarth CF64 5RY — MB BCh 1953 Wales.

DAVIES, Howel Lewis Walford 114 New Road, Llanelli SA15 3DT — MB BS 1993 Lond.; Dip. S.M. Lond. 1996. (Royal London Hospital)

DAVIES, Howell Duncan (retired) 15 Woodridge Court, Langland, Swansea SA3 4TH — MB BS 1940 Lond.; MRCS Eng. LRCP Lond. 1938; FRCPath 1972, M 1964. Prev: Med. Supt&Cons, Path Morriston Hosp.

DAVIES, Hubert Cecil Rees Hadleigh House Medical Centre, 20 Kirkway, Broadstone BH18 8EE Tel: 01202 692268 Fax: 01202 658954; The Larch, Rowe Hill, Holt, Wimborne BH21 7EB Tel: 01202 880743 — MB BCh 1958 Wales. (Cardiff) Prev: Ho. Surg. Cardiff Roy. Infirm.; Ho. Phys. St. David's Hosp. Cardiff; Med. Off. RAF.

DAVIES, Hugh de la Haye (retired) Creaton House, Creaton, Northampton NN6 8ND Tel: 01604 505722 Fax: 01604 505722 Email: hdela@hugh72.fsnet.co.uk — BM BCh Oxf. 1955; MA Oxf.

1955; DMJ Soc. Apoth. Lond. 1965. Forens. Phys. N.ants. Prev: Princip. Police Surg. N.ants.

DAVIES, Hugh Thomas Newtons Practice, The Health Centre, Heath Road, Haywards Heath RH16 3BB Tel: 01444 412280; Gravelye, Hanlye Lane, Cuckfield, Haywards Heath RH17 5HR Tel: 01444 450507 — MB BS 1952 Lond.; MB BS (Hnrs.) Lond. 1952. (St. Bart.) Prev: Regist. (Med. & Paediat.) St. Richard's Hosp. Chichester; Maj. RAMC (Nat. Serv.); Ho. Phys. & Ho. Surg. St. Bart. Hosp.

DAVIES, Hugh Trevor St Mary's Hospital, Paediatrics Department, Paddington, London W2 1NY — BA Oxf. 1973; MD Lond. 1990, MB BS Lond. 1976; FRCP Lond. 1994; MRCP (UK) 1982; DCH RCP Lond. 1982. Cons. & Sen. Lect. Paediat. St. Mary's Hosp. Lond.

DAVIES, Humphrey Owen The Surgery, Kinmel Avenue, Abergele LL22 7LP Tel: 01745 833158 Fax: 01745 822490; Plot 1D, Lon Glanfor, Maes-y-Mor, Belgrano, Abergele LL22 8DH — MB ChB 1972 Sheff.; MRCGP 1976; Cert JCC Lond. 1976; DCH RCPSI 1975; DObst RCOG 1974.

DAVIES, Huw Eilian Camarthen Road Health Centre, Carmarthen Road, Cross Hands, Llanelli SA14 6SU Tel: 01269 831091; 41 Heol Trefenty, Cross Hands, Llanelli SA14 6TE Tel: 01269 845242 — MB BS 1982 Lond. Prev: Trainee GP Gwynedd VTS; Ho. Surg. E. Sussex Hosp. Hastings; Ho. Phys. United Hosp. Bath.

DAVIES, Huw Eirig Saundersfoot Medical Centre, Westfield Road, Saundersfoot SA69 9JW Tel: 01834 812407 Fax: 01834 811131 — MB BS 1983 Lond.

DAVIES, Huw John Ty-Cmsur, Carmel St., Dukestown, Tredegar NP22 4RG — MB BS 1997 Lond.

DAVIES, Huw Jones Cwmafan Health Centre, Cwmavon, Port Talbot SA12 9BA Tel: 01639 871071; 3 Hawthorne Close, Ynysygwas, Cwmafan, Port Talbot SA12 9BY Tel: 01639 891092 — MB BCh 1982 Wales.

DAVIES, Huw Lloyd Town Gate Practice, Chepstow Community Hospital, Tempest Way, Chepstow NP16 5XP Tel: 01291 636444 Fax: 01291 636465; Coed-Yr-Awel, Devauden, Chepstow NP16 6NN Tel: 01291 625196 — MB BCh 1979 Wales; MRCGP 1989; DA Eng. 1982.

DAVIES, Huw Martyn Treflan Surgery, Treflan, Lower Cardiff Road, Pwllheli LL53 5NF Tel: 01758 701457 Fax: 01758 701209 — MB BCh 1969 Wales; MRCGP 1982. (Cardiff)

DAVIES, Mr Huw Teifion The Ipswich Hospital, Heath Road, Ipswich IP4 5PD Tel: 01473 703763 Fax: 01473 703158 Email: davies.sec@ipsh-tr.anglox.nhs.uk — MB BS 1982 Lond.; BDS Lond. 1976; FDS RCS Eng. 1979; FRCS Eng. 1987. Cons. Oral & Maxillofacial Surg. Ipswich Hosp. Suff. Socs: Brit. Assn. Oral & Maxillofacial Surg.; BMA; BANO.

DAVIES, Huw William Penylan Surgery, 74 Penylan Road, Cardiff CF23 5SY Tel: 029 2049 8181 Fax: 029 2049 1507 — BM 1987 Soton.

DAVIES, Hyman (retired) 19 Danesway, Prestwich, Manchester M25 0ET Tel: 0161 740 6571 — MB ChB 1943 Manch.; FRCGP 1979, M 1971. Prev: Capt. RAMC 1944-47.

DAVIES, Hywel Francis 'Temple Field', Temple Road, Dewsbury WF13 3QE Tel: 01924 461056 — MB BS 1953 Lond.; MRCS Eng. LRCP Lond. 1948; DMRD Liverp. 1959; DMRD Eng. 1959; DObst RCOG 1952. (St. Bart.) Cons. Radiol. Dewsbury Gen. Hosp., Staincliffe Gen. Hosp. & Batley; Hosp. Socs: Fac. Radiols. & Brit. Inst. Radiol. Prev: Sen. Regist. (Radiol.) Roy. S.. Hosp. Liverp.; Sen. Ho. Off. (Obst.) St. David's Hosp. Cardiff; Ho. Surg. St. Bart. Hosp.

DAVIES, Mr Hywel Gwyn Orthopaedic Department, Nevill Hall Hospital, Abergavenny NP7 7EG Tel: 01873 852091 Ext: 5206 Fax: 01873 859168 — MB BCh 1978 Wales; FRCS Eng. 1982; T(SN) 1991. Cons. Orthop. Surg. Nevill Hall Hosp. Abergavenny Gwent. Prev: Regist. (Orthop.) St. Geo. Hosp. Lond.; Regist. Rotat. (Surg.) Univ. Hosp. Wales Cardiff.

DAVIES, Hywel Ivan 38 Enville Road, Newport NP20 5AD — MB ChB 1961 Liverp.; MRCS Eng. LRCP Lond. 1961; DMRD Eng. 1979; DObst RCOG 1965. (Liverp.)

DAVIES, Hywel Richard Furn Rock Cottage, Bridge St., Holt, Wrexham LL13 9JG — MB BCh 1992 Wales.

DAVIES, Ian Tal-y-Bont Surgery, Station Road, Pontardulais, Swansea SA4 1TL Tel: 01792 882368; 63 Alltiago Road, Pontardulais, Swansea SA4 1HU Tel: 01792 884695 — MB BCh 1984 Wales; MB BCh Wales l984.

DAVIES, Ian Francis Health Centre, Newgate Street, Worksop S80 1HP; Millwood House, Belph, Worksop S80 3NH Tel: 01909 500266 — MB ChB Birm. 1969. (Birm.) Socs: Fell. Soc. Orthop. Med. Prev: Regist. (Anaesth.) United Sheff. Hosps.; SHO (Anaesth.) Mansfield Hosps.

DAVIES, Ian Mark 49 Alma Road, Clifton, Bristol BS8 2DE Tel: 0117 973 0675 — MB BCh 1981 Wales; FFA RCS Eng. 1987. Cons. Anaesth. Bristol Roy. Infirm.; Hon. Sen. Lect. Univ. Bristol. Socs: Assn. Anaesth.; Soc. Cardiovasc. Anaesth. Prev: Fell. Cardiothoracic Transpl. St. Vincents, Sydney; Sen. Regist. (Anaesth.) St. Geo. & W.m. Hosps.; Vis. Asst. Prof. Univ. Texas Houston, USA.

DAVIES, Ian William The Surgery, Faraday Avenue, Tuxford, Newark NG22 0HT Tel: 01777 870203 Fax: 01777 872221; Bramble Cottage, Church St, East Markham, Newark NG22 0SA Tel: 01777 871426 — MB ChB 1981 Liverp.; DRCOG 1985.

DAVIES, Ieuan Augustine (retired) Meddygfa Teilo, Llandeilo SA19 6HL Tel: 01558 823435 — MB BCh 1956 Wales; DObst RCOG 1958. Prev: Ho. Phys. St. David's Hosp. Cardiff.

DAVIES, Ieuan Bevan Suunycroft, 103 Usk Road, Pontypool NP4 8AF — MRCS Eng. LRCP Lond. 1949.

DAVIES, Ieuan Havard Department of Paediatrics, University Hospital Of Wales, Heath Park, Cardiff CF4 4XN Tel: 012920 747747; 68 Yaysddu, Pontyclun, Rhondda Cynon Taf CF72 9UA — MB BS 1993 Lond.; MA Camb. 1994; MRCP (UK) 1998; MRCPCh 1998. (St John's Coll.Cambs./Roy.Lond.Hosp) SpR in Paediatric Gastroeaterology UHN, Cardiff; SpR Wrexham Maelor Hosp.; SpR Ysbyty Glan Clwyd; SpR Ysbyty Singleton; SpR PICU (UHW). Socs: Welsh Paediatric Soc. Prev: Regist. (Paediat.) Cheltenham Gen.; SHO (Paediat.) Addenbrooke's Hosp. Camb. & Roy. Lond. Hosp. + Gt. Ormond St (SNO); Ho. Off. (Gen. Med. & Surg.) Harold Wood Hosp. Lond. Hosp.

DAVIES, Ieuan John Treharne North of Scotland Institute of Postgraduate Medical Education, Ragmore Hospital, Inverness IV2 3UJ Tel: 01463 704347 Fax: 01463 713454 Email: ieuandavies@doctors.org.uk; Rhinduie House, Lentran, Inverness IV3 8RJ Tel: 01463 831315 Fax: 01463 713454 Email: ieuandavies@doctors.org.uk — MB BS 1962 Lond.; FRCP Glas. 1992; FRCP Ed. 1977, M 1974; FRCP Lond. 1980, M 1965; MRCS Eng. LRCP Lond. 1962. (Lond. Hosp.) Cons. Phys. Raigmore Hosp. Inverness; Clin. Sen. Lect. Univ. Aberd.; Regional Dir. Postgrad. Med. Educat. N.. Scotl. (Highlands & W. Isles); Surg. Lt.-Cdr. RNR (Retd.). Socs: Fell. Roy. Soc. Med.; Osler Club Lond. Prev: Sen. Regist. Univ. Hosp. of Wales Cardiff; Regist. Univ. Coll. Hosp. Lond.; Ho. Phys. Med. Unit Lond. Hosp.

DAVIES, Ioan Bleddyn 6 Stag Green Avenue, The Ryde, Old Hatfield, Hatfield AL9 5EA — MRCS Eng. LRCP Lond. 1975; MB BS (Hons.) Lond. 1975; PhD Lond. 1982, BSc (Hons.) 1973; MRCP (UK) 1979; MIBiol 1979. (St. Mary's) Dep. Med. Dir. CharterHo. Clin. Research Unit Lond.; Hon. Lect. Dept. Clin. Pharmacol. St. Bart. Hosp. Lond. Socs: Brit. Pharmacol. Soc.; Med. Research Soc. Prev: Lect. (Clin. Pharmacol., Therap. & Med.) St. Mary's Hosp. Med. Sch.; Lond.; Research Fell. & Hon. Regist. Med. Unit St. Mary's Hosp. Med.; Sch. Lond.; SHO Dept. Neurol. & Dermat. St. Mary's Hosp. Lond.

DAVIES, Isaac Neville Dremddu-Hall, Pont Creuddyn, Llanbedr-pont-Steffan, Lampeter SA48 8BL — MRCS Eng. LRCP Lond. 1945. (St. Bart.)

DAVIES, Isobel Louise Abbey Surgery, 28 Plymouth Road, Tavistock PL19 8BU Tel: 01822 612247 Fax: 01822 618771 — MB BCh 1979 Wales; MRCGP 1985.

DAVIES, Izabela Zofia Sandhurst Group Practice, 72 Yorktown Road, Sandhurst GU47 9BT Tel: 01252 872455 Fax: 01252 872456 — MRCS Eng. LRCP Lond. 1986; T(GP) 1991. Prev: SHO (ENT) Wexham Pk. Hosp. Slough.

DAVIES, Jacqueline Fiona Barton Webb-Peploe Partnership, Webb-Peploe House, Church Lane, Lymington SO41 3RA Tel: 01590 674118 Fax: 01590 675946; Orchard House, 19 Waterford Lane, Lymington SO41 3PT Tel: 01590 670629 — MB BCh 1986 Wales.

DAVIES, Professor James Andrew Professorial Medical Unit, G Floor Martin Wing, the General Infirmary, Leeds LS1 3EX Tel: 0113 392 3470 Fax: 0113 242 3811 Email: medjad@medphysics.leeds.ac.uk; 10 Monkbridge Road, Headingley, Leeds LS6 4DX Tel: 0113 274 1741 — MB ChB Aber. 1966; MD Aberd. 1974; FRCP Lond. 1981; MRCP (UK) 1969. (Aberd.) Prof.

Clin. Educat. Univ. Leeds; Hon. Cons. Phys. Gen. Infirm. Leeds. Prev: Regist. (Therap.) Radcliffe Infirm. Oxf.; Research Fell. Dept. Path. McMaster Univ. Hamilton, Canada.

DAVIES, James Brian Meredith (retired) Tree Tops, Church Road, Thoughton Hough, Wirral CH63 1JN Tel: 0151 336 3435 — MB BS 1943 Lond.; MD Lond. 1949; FFPHM 1974, M 1972; DPH Bristol 1948. Lect. (Clin. Preven. Paediat.) Univ. Liverp. Prev: Dir. of Social Servs. City Liverp. & Dir. Personal Health & Social Servs. Liverp.

DAVIES, James Lawrence 94 Newton Road, Mumbles, Swansea SA3 4SW — MB BCh 1996 Wales.

DAVIES, James Seiriol (retired) 1 Long House Close, Lisvane, Cardiff CF14 0XR — MB BCh 1961 Wales; FFA RCS Eng. 1966; DObst RCOG 1963. Cons. Univ. Hosp. Wales.

DAVIES, Jane Anne Paediatric Dept., West Suffolk Hospital, Hardwick Lane, Bury St Edmunds IP33 2QZ; 20 Paddock Way, Chedburgh, Bury St Edmunds IP29 4UY — MB BS 1985 Lond.; DRCOG 1988; DCH 1996. (St Mary's Hosp.Med.Sch.Lond.) p/t Clin. Asst. (Paediat.) W. Suff. Hosp. Prev: Trainee GP/SHO Co. Hosp. Hereford VTS; SHO Rotat. (Paediat.) Birm. Childr. Hosp.

DAVIES, Jane Bethan 3 Sunden Road, Pinesprings Drive, Poole BH17 7NX — MB BS 1988 Lond.

DAVIES, Jane Victoria Eagle House Surgery, Eagle House, White Cliff Mill Street, Blandford Forum DT11 7DQ Tel: 01258 453171; The Tallet, Nutford, Blandford Forum DT11 0QJ Tel: 01258 459266 — MB BS 1984 Lond.; DRCOG 1987. (King's Coll. Hosp.)

DAVIES, Jason Alan Mill Bank Surgery, Water Street, Stafford ST16 2AG Tel: 01785 258348 Fax: 01785 227144 — MB ChB 1990 Birm.; ChB Birm. 1990.

DAVIES, Jason Hilling Department of Histopathology, North Devon District Hospital, Barnstaple EX31 4JB Tel: 01271 22341 Fax: 01271 22328 — MB BS 1987 Lond.; MRCPath 1994. Cons. Histopath. N. Devon Dist. Hosp. Barnstaple. Prev: Sen. Regist. (Histopath.) Mt. Vernon Hosp. N.wood; Regist. (Histopath.) Roy. Marsden & Hammersmith Hosps. Lond.

DAVIES, Jason Malcolm 120 Gorseinon Road, Penllergaer, Swansea SA4 1AA — MB ChB 1991 Dundee.

DAVIES, Jean Alexandra 3 Mount Olive, Ingestre Road, Oxton, Birkenhead CH43 5TT — MB ChB Liverp. 1962; Dip Ven Liverp. 1971.

DAVIES, Jean Margaret (retired) Flat 4, Avenue Hall, Avenue Road, Highgate, London N6 5DN Tel: 020 8348 4868 — MB BS 1956 Lond.; MFCM 1972; DPH Eng. 1960. Prev: PMO Lond. Boro. Hackney.

DAVIES, Jeffrey Keith 44 Tuskar Street, Greenwich, London SE10 9UR — BM BCh 1992 Oxf.; BA (Hons.) Oxf. 1989; MRCP (UK) 1996. (Oxf.) Specialist Regist. (Haemat.) Roy. Lond. Hosp. Trust. Socs: (Mem) Brit. Soc for Haematol.

DAVIES, Jennifer Ann 64 Mallards Reach, Marshfield, Cardiff CF3 2PR — MB BCh 1981 Wales.

DAVIES, Jennifer Anne Billinge Hospital, Upholland Road, Billinge, Wigan WN5 7ET Tel: 01695 626200 Fax: 01695 626523 Email: jennifer.davies@wiganlhs-tr.nhs.uk; 18 Ollerbarrow Road, Hale, Altrincham WA15 9PW Tel: 0161 941 1748 Email: emmerson_family@msn.com — MB ChB 1983 Bristol; MRCOG 1989; MD Bristol 1999. Cons. Obst. and Gynaecologist, Billinge Hosp. Wigan. Prev: Sen. Regist. St. Mary's Hosp. Manch.; Sen. Regist. Hope Hosp. Salford; Regist. (O & G) St. Geo. Hosp. Lond. & St. Peter's Hosp. Chertsey.

DAVIES, Jeremy Robert Flat 7, 35 Haringey park, London N8 9JD Tel: 020 8374 4618 — MB BS 1993 Lond.; BA Oxf. 1983; FRCA 1998. (St. Marys Hosp. Med. Sch.) Specialist Regist. (Anaesth.) Roy.Nat.Throat Nose Ear Lond. Socs: BMA. Prev: Specialist Regist. Anaesth Whiittington Hosp/Middx Hosp/Roy Free Hosp.

DAVIES, Jeremy Ronald Llewelyn Well House, 38 Brook St., Bampton, Tiverton EX16 9LY — MB BS 1979 Lond.; MRCGP 1988.

DAVIES, Jeremy Sion 3 Lyric Way, Thornhill, Cardiff CF14 9BP — MB BCh 1997 Wales.

DAVIES, Jeremy William Haydn New Milton Health Centre, Spencer Road, New Milton BH25 6EN Tel: 01425 621188 Fax: 01425 620646; Oaklands, 16 Barrs Avenue, New Milton BH25 5HJ — MB BChir 1963 Camb.; MA Camb. 1964; DObst RCOG 1966. (Westm.) p/t Gen. Pract. Prev: Nuffield Regist. Roy. Hants. Co. Hosp. Winchester; Ho. Off. (Orthop. Surg.), Ho. Phys. & Jun. Cas. Off. W.m. Hosp. Lond.

DAVIES, Jill Margaret 32 Corporation Road, Grangetown, Cardiff CF11 7XA Tel: 029 2022 6057 Fax: 029 20640 524 — MB BCh 1979 Wales; BSc (Hons.) Lond. 1972; MSc Illinois, USA 1973. Partner in Gen. Pract. (Job Share). Prev: Clin. Asst. (Transfus. Med.) Blood Transfus. Serv. Cardiff.

DAVIES, Joan Royal National Hospital for Rheumatic Diseases, Upper Borough Walls, Bath BA1 1RL Tel: 01225 465941 Fax: 01225 421202; Bradway, Entry Hill Drive, Bath BA2 5NL Tel: 01225 316254 Fax: 01225 316254 — MB BCh 1961 Wales; DPH Ed. 1963. (Cardiff) Cons. Rheum. Roy. Nat. Hosp. Bath.

DAVIES, Joan Elaine Tel: 0116 252 5839 Fax: 0116 252 3108 — MB BCh 1984 Wales; PhD Wales 1981, BSc (Hons.) 1978; MRCPI 1988; FRCP 1998. (Welsh National School Medicine) Cons. Phys. In Med. and Therap. Leicester Roy. Infirm.; Hon. Sen. Lect. (Med. & Therap.) Leicester Roy. Infirm. Socs: Brit. Soc. of Echocardiography. Prev: Lect. (Clin. Pharmacol.) Leicester Roy. Infirm.; Research Regist. (Diabetes) Radcliffe Infirm Oxf.; Regist. (Med.) Llandough Hosp. Cardiff.

DAVIES, Joan Russell (retired) Yew Tree End, The Street, Effingham, Leatherhead KT24 5LP — MRCS Eng. LRCP Lond. 1951; MD Lond. 1959, MB BS 1951; Dip. Bact. Lond 1955; FRCPath 1989. Cons. Bacteriol. Pub. Health Laborat. Serv. Prev: Ho. Phys. Roy. Free Hosp.

DAVIES, Joan Victoria (retired) The Old Bank House, Blandford Forum DT11 7AE Tel: 01258 53171 — MB BCh 1948 Wales; DObst RCOG 1954.

DAVIES, Joanna Mary Marridge Hill, Ramsbury, Marlborough SN8 2HG — MB BS 1991 Lond.

DAVIES, Joanna Oriel Conibeare 1 Pen-Yr-Heol Drive, Sketty, Swansea SA2 9JT — BM 1994 Soton.; MRCP (UK) 1997.

DAVIES, Joanne Elizabeth Bryn Celyn, Tremeirchion, St Asaph LL17 0US — MB ChB 1994 Liverp.

DAVIES, Joanne Elizabeth Duncan St. Primary Care Centre, Duncan St., Blackenhall, Wolverhampton WV2 3AN — BM BS Nottm. 1993; DRCOG 1997; MRCGP 1998; DFFP 1999. (Nottingham) p/t GP Princip. Wolverhampton; Forens. Med. Examr., W. Midl.s.

DAVIES, John 28 Station Road, Nailsea, Bristol BS48 4PD — MB BCh 1954 Wales; BSc, MB BCh Wales 1954.

DAVIES, John Linden Hall Surgery, Station Road, Newport TF10 7EN Tel: 01952 820400; September Cottage, Marsh Lane, Hinstock, Market Drayton TF9 2TG — MB ChB 1985 Birm. Prev: Ho. Surg. City Gen. Hosp. Stoke-on-Trent; Ho. Phys. Roy. Shrewsbury Hosp.; SHO (Anaesth.) Stafford Dist. Gen. Hosp.

DAVIES, John Glan Hafren NHS Trust, Department of Cardiology, Royal Gwent Hospital, Cardiff Road, Newport NP20 2UB Tel: 01633 234295 Fax: 01633 255448; The Laurels, Porthycarne St, Usk NP15 1RY Tel: 01291 672604 Fax: 01291 673934 Email: dr.john@jdavies.fs.business.co.uk — MB BS 1973 Lond.; FRCP Lond. 1993; MRCP (UK) 1975; FECC 1995; FACC 1988. Cons. Phys. & Cardiol. Roy. Gwent & St. Woolos Hosps. Newport.

DAVIES, John Alan Hugh (retired) 46 Serpentine Road, Birmingham B29 7HU Tel: 0121 472 3442 — MB ChB 1952 Birm.; FFA RCS Eng. 1961; DA Eng. 1958; DObst RCOG 1957. Cons. Anaesth. Selly Oak & Roy. Orthop. Hosps. Birm.

DAVIES, John Anthony Keith (retired) 133 Haven Road, Haverfordwest SA61 1DL Tel: 01437 760129 Email: j.davies@which.net — MB BCh 1966 Wales; FRCOG 1984, M 1971; DObst RCOG 1968. Cons. Withybush Gen. Hosp. HaverfordW. Prev: Sen. Regist. Liverp. AHA (T).

DAVIES, John Arwyn Jones Brecon Medical Group Practice, Ty Henry Vaughan, Bridge Street, Brecon LD3 8AH Tel: 01874 622121 Fax: 01874 623742; Weirwood, Llanfryndch, Brecon LD3 7BJ — MB BS 1972 Lond.; BSc (Pharmacol., Hons.) Lond.; FRCP Lond. 1996; DObst RCOG 1974. (The Royal London) Hosp. Pract. (Gastroenterol.) & Clin. Asst. (Cardiol.) Brecon War Memor. Hosp.; Vis. Prof. Fac. Family & Community Med. Columbia Missouri, USA. Prev: Regist. (Med.) Lond. Hosp.

DAVIES, John Ballard Berkshire Health Authority, 57-59 Bath Road, Reading RG30 2BA Tel: 01734 503094 Fax: 01734 594620; Three Jays, The Ridge, Cold Ash, Thatcham RG18 9HY Tel: 01635 867687 — MB BS Lond. 1964; MRCS Eng. LRCP Lond. 1964; DTM & H Liverp. 1970; DRCOG 1967; AKC 1964. (King's Coll. Hosp.) Med. Dir. (Primary Care) Berks. HA. Socs: Fell. Roy. Soc. Trop. Med.

& Hyg.; BMA. Prev: GP Malpas, Chesh.; Med. Supt. Mengo Hosp. & Kisiizi Hosp. Kigezi, Uganda.

DAVIES, Mr John Brinley 5 Bloomsbury Court, Newcastle upon Tyne NE3 4LW — MB BCh 1980 Wales; FRCS Ed. 1987.

DAVIES, John Colin St Clements Partnership, Tanner Street, Winchester SO23 8AD Tel: 01962 852211 Fax: 01962 856010; Waterside House, Headbourne Worthy, Winchester SO23 7JR Tel: 01962 882068 Fax: 01962 886671 — MB BChir 1972 Camb.; MA Camb. 1973; Cert. Family Plann. JCC 1977; DObst RCOG 1974; DCH Eng. 1974; FRSH 1983. (Camb. & Guy's) Med. Off. Winchester Coll.; Clin. Asst. (Med.) Winchester HA. Socs: Fell. Roy. Soc. Med. Prev: Regist (Med.), Resid. (Obst.) & Ho. Phys. Guy's Hosp. Lond.; SHO Evelina Childr. Hosp. Lond.

DAVIES, John Edwin Rowan Cottage, Pempol, Devoran, Truro TR3 6NW Tel: 01822 863201 Fax: 01209 313813 — MB ChB 1971 Liverp.; MSc 2001 Glas; DTM & H Liverp. 1994; DObst RCOG 1973.

DAVIES, Professor John Elfed The Devonshire Hospital, 29-31 Devonshire St., London W1G 6PU; Chapel Farm House, Bryngwyn, Raglan N15 2DA Tel: 01291 690055 Fax: 01291 690055 — MRCS Eng. LRCP Lond. 1966; DPhysMed Eng. 1970. (Guys) Cons. Phys.Guy's Hosp., Devonshire Hosp. & Sports Injury Clinic Lond.; Prof. Sports Med. Cardiff. Inst.; Cons. Phys. Med. & Rehabil., Bermuda; Chairm. Edit. Bd. Internat. Jl. Sports Med.; Hon. Phys. Welsh Rugby Union. Socs: (Chairm.) Internat. Soc. Clin. Isokinetics; Med. Commiss. Accid. Preven. (Chairm. Sports Comm.). Prev: Cons. Med. Advisor Montedison Pharmaceut. Ltd.; Regist. (Rheum. & Rehabil.) Guy's Hosp. Lond.; GP HaverfordW..

DAVIES, Mr John Elgan ENT Department, Leighton Hospital, Crewe CW1 4QJ — MB BCh 1981 Wales; FRCS Ed. 1986. Cons. Otolaryngologist Mid Chesshire and E. Cheschire Trusts, Crewe and Macclesfield. Socs: Brit. Assn. of Otolaryngologist, Head and Neck Surg.; Europ. Rhinological Soc.; Europ. Acad. of Facial Plastic Surg. Prev: Overseas Fell., Univ. Calif., San Francisco; Sen. Regist. (Otolaryngol.) Gtr. Glas. HB.; Tutor (Otolaryngol.) Univ. Leeds.

DAVIES, John Elwyn 3 Mount Olive, Oxton, Prenton CH43 5TT Tel: 0151 652 8497 Email: john.elwyn.davies@cwcom.net — MB ChB Liverp. 1962; FFOM RCP Lond. 1985, M 1979; DIH Eng. 1970. p/t Company Med. Adviser, BOCM Pauls Ltd Ipswich. Socs: Soc. Occ. Med. Prev: Sen. Med Off. Unilever Ltd.

DAVIES, John Gareth The Surgery, 11 Sheffield Road, Penistone, Sheffield S36 6HG Tel: 01226 765300 Fax: 01226 763753 — MB BS 1974 Lond.; MRCS Eng. LRCP Lond. 1974; DA 1980. (Westm.) Prev: Cas. Off. Birm. Accid. Hosp.; Ho. Surg. (Profess. Surg. Unit) W.m. Hosp. Lond.

DAVIES, Mr John Hugh Department of Urology, Royal Surrey County Hospital, Guildford GU2 7XX Tel: 01483 571122 Fax: 01483 454871 Email: jhdavies@malehealth.uk.com — MB BS 1979 Lond.; BSc (Hons.) Lond. 1976; MRCS Eng. LRCP Lond. 1979; FRCS Ed. 1985; FRCS (Urol.) 1993. (St. Bart. Hosp. Lond.) Cons. Urol. Surg. Roy. Surrey Co. Hosp. Cancer Centre, Guildford and St Lukes. Socs: Brit. Prostate Gp.; Brit. Assn. Urol. Surg.; Brit. Assn. Cancer Research. Prev: Sen. Regist. (Urol.) St. Geo. Hosp. Lond., Roy. Surrey Co. Hosp. Guildford & Inst. Urol. Lond.; Research Fell. (Urol.) Roy. Marsden Hosp. Sutton; Regist. (Surg.) St. Geo. Hosp. Lond.

DAVIES, John Huw Wozencroft Merrow Park Surgery, Kingfisher Drive, Guildford GU4 7EP Tel: 01483 503331 Fax: 01483 303457; 74 Charlock Way, Burpham, Guildford GU1 1XZ Tel: 01483 826321 — MRCS Eng. LRCP Lond. 1967. (Guy's)

DAVIES, John Hywel (retired) Brookside, 1A Willow Way, Baglan, Port Talbot SA12 8TP Tel: 01639 813917 — MA, BM BCh Oxf. 1954. Prev: Paediat. Ho. Phys. & ENT Ho. Surg. Radcliffe Infirm. Oxf.

DAVIES, John Ivor Wynne (retired) 24 Abington Park Crescent, Northampton NN3 3AD Tel: 01604 37783 — MB BChir 1952 Camb.; DObst RCOG 1954.

DAVIES, John Leslie The Health Centre, Rosehill, Great Ayton, Middlesbrough TS9 6BL Tel: 01642 723421 Fax: 01642 724575; Brackenway, Busby Lane, Kirkby-in-Cleveland, Middlesbrough TS9 7AW Tel: 01642 723421 Email: johnval.davies@lineone.net — MB BS Newc. 1968; DObst RCOG 1970.

DAVIES, John Lloyd Jailhouse, Salisbury Hall, St Albans AL2 1BU — MB BS 1986 Lond.

DAVIES, John Maelor Trevega, Cedarway, Gayton, Wirral CH60 3RH — MD 1985 Camb.; MB 1977, BChir 1976; MRCP (UK) 1978; MRCPath 1985. Sen. Lect. (Haemat.) Univ. Liverp.

DAVIES, John Malcolm Mill Street Health Centre, Mill Street, Crewe CW2 7AQ Tel: 01270 212725 Fax: 01270 216323 — MB ChB 1959 Liverp. (Liverp.) Socs: BMA. Prev: Ho. Surg. & Ho. Phys. St. Catherine's Hosp. Birkenhead; Ho. Surg. (O & G) Chester City Hosp.

DAVIES, John Martin Grimsby Maternity Hospital, Second Avenue, Grimsby DN33 1NW Tel: 01472 874111; 13 Pelham Avenue, Grimsby DN33 3NA Tel: 01472 870772 — MB BChir 1964 Camb.; MB BChir Camb. 1965; MA Camb. 1966; FRCP Lond. 1990, M 1968; MRCS Eng. LRCP Lond. 1964; DCH Eng. 1970. (Camb. & Lond. Hosp.) Cons. Paediat. Grimsby & Louth Hosps.; Hon. Lect. (Child Health) Univ. Leeds. Socs: Brit. Paediat. Assn.; Brit. Assn. Perinatal Med.; (Ex-Pres.) Yorks. Reg.l Paediat. Soc. Prev: Sen. Regist. (Paediat.) Leeds & Bradford Gps. Hosps.; Ho. Phys. Bristol Childr. Hosp.; Ho. Surg. Lond. Hosp.

DAVIES, John Michael Cecil Crawley Hospital, West Green Drive, Crawley RH11 7DH — MRCS Eng. LRCP Lond. 1962; MB Camb. 1965, BChir 1964; FRACR 1983; FRCR 1975; FFR 1969; DMRD Eng. 1967. (Camb. & St. Mary's) Cons. Radiol. Mid. Downs DHA. Socs: Brit. Med. Ultrasound Soc. Prev: Regist. (Radiol.) St. Mary's Hosp. Lond.; Sen. Regist. (Radiol.) Addenbrooke's Hosp. Camb.; Cons. Radiol. Canberra Hosps., Australia.

DAVIES, John Michael Prosser (retired) 22 Newport Road, Bedwas, Caerphilly CF83 8AA Tel: 02920 885287 — MB BS 1955 Lond.; MRCS Eng. LRCP Lond. 1955; DObst RCOG 1957. Prev: Gen. Practiner.

DAVIES, John Morley (retired) Spring Cottage, Eardisley, Hereford HR3 6LT Tel: 01544 328401 — BSc MB ChB Birm. 1954.

DAVIES, John Moullin (retired) Tichfield, Park Rd, Combe, Witney OX29 8NA — BM BCh Oxf. 1951; MA Oxf. 1951; DPH Lond. 1958; DIH Soc. Apoth. Lond. 1955. Prev: Emerg. Off. Radcliffe Infirm. & Oxf. United Hosps.

DAVIES, John Norman Rosemount, Stapley, Taunton TA3 7QA — BM Soton. 1985; MRCP UK) 1989; MRCGP 1992. Prev: Regist. (Gen. Med.) Soton. Gen. Hosp.; SHO (Ophth.) Eye, Ear & Throat Hosp. Shrewsbury; Trainee GP Shrewsbury.

DAVIES, John O'Connor (retired) 148 Penylan Road, Cardiff CF23 5RE Tel: 029 2048 4571 — MRCS Eng. LRCP Lond. 1940. Prev: Ho. Phys. & Ho. Surg. Llandough Hosp.

DAVIES, John Orrell William Harvey Hospital, Willesborough, Ashford TN24 0LZ Tel: 01233 633331 — MB ChB 1975 Ed.; FRCOG 1996; MD Ed. 1986; MRCOG 1983. (Edinburgh) Cons. O & G William Harvey Hosp. Ashford, Kent. Socs: Brit. Soc. Gyn. Endoscopy; Folkestone Med. Soc.; Brit. Fertil. Soc. Prev: Sen. Regist. Plymouth & S.mead Hosp. Bristol; Research Fell. Bristol Matern. Hosp.

DAVIES, John Owen Greenland Rotherfield Surgery, Rotherfield, Crowborough TN6 3QW Tel: 01892 852415/853288 Fax: 01892 853499; Sandy Cottage, The Warren, Mayfield TN20 6UB Tel: 0189 285 2415 — MRCS Eng. LRCP Lond. 1977; MA Camb. 1977, MB BChir 1978; MRCP (UK) 1981; DRCOG 1984.

DAVIES, John Paget Harry (retired) Juniper, Colley Way, Reigate RH2 9JH — MRCS Eng. LRCP Lond. 1951; MD Lond. 1962, MB BS 1951; FRCP Lond. 1974, M 1956. Prev: Cons. Phys. E. Surrey DHA.

DAVIES, John Rhys Adams Llangollen Health Centre, Regent Street, Llangollen LL20 8HL Tel: 01978 860625 Fax: 01978 860174; Pentrefelin House, Llangollen LL20 8EE Tel: 01978 860826 Email: johnrhys@epulse.net — MB ChB 1980 Liverp.; MRCS Eng. LRCP Lond. 1980; MRCGP 1989; DRCOG 1983; Cert. Family Plann. JCC 1983. (Liverpool) Trainer (Gen. Pract.) Clwyd. Prev: Trainee GP Wirral VTS.

DAVIES, John Richard Albert House, Haverbreaks, Lancaster LA1 5BN Tel: 01524 381584 — MRCS Eng. LRCP Lond. 1972; FFA RCS Eng. 1976; DA Eng. 1974. (St. Bart.) Cons. Anaesth. Roy. Lancaster Infirm. Socs: Computing in Anaesth. Soc. & Obst. Anaesths. Assn. Prev: Sen. Regist. (Anaesth.) S. W.. RHA & Bristol Roy. Infirm.; Regist. (Anaesth.) St. Bart. Hosp. Lond.

DAVIES, John Richard Eccles (retired) 24 Ravenscroft Park, Barnet EN5 4NH Tel: 020 8449 2747 — MB BS Lond. 1954. Prev: GP Barnet.

DAVIES, John Rodyn (retired) 172 Singlewell Road, Gravesend DA11 7RB — MRCS Eng. LRCP Lond. 1925; DTM & H Eng. 1925. Prev: Med. Off. E. Afr. Med. Serv.

DAVIES, John Russell Abbey Lane Surgery, 23 Abbey Lane, Sheffield S8 0BJ Tel: 0114 274 5360 — MB ChB 1973 Birm.; MRCP (UK) 1978; MRCGP 1985. (Birmingham) Partner. Prev: Regist. (Haemat.) Manch. Roy. Infirm.; Med. Regist. N. Manch. Gen. Hosp.; SHO (Paediat.) Roy. Alexandra Hosp. Childr. Brighton.

DAVIES, John Russell 39 Dickerage Road, Kingston upon Thames KT1 3SR — MB BS 1997 Lond.

DAVIES, John Sambrook Caradoc Surgery, Station Approach, Frinton-on-Sea CO13 9JT Tel: 01255 850101 Fax: 01255 851004; 18 Holmbrook Way, Frinton-on-Sea CO13 9LW Tel: 012 551 671509 — MB ChB 1956 Sheff.

DAVIES, John Stephen Department of Medicine, University of Wales College of Medicine, Heath Park, Cardiff CF14 5FA Tel: 029 2074 3780 Email: daviesjs@cardiff.ac.uk; 20 The Pines, Hirwaun, Aberdare CF44 9QW — MB BCh 1989 Wales; MRCP (UK) 1992. (University of Wales College of Medicine) Lect. (Med.) Univ. of Wales Coll. of Med. Socs: BMA; Brit. Endocrine Soc.

DAVIES, Mr John Stewart Yarringtons, Alfrick, Worcester WR6 5EX Tel: 01905 763333 — MB BChir 1970 Camb.; MA, MB Camb. 1970, BChir 1969; FRCS Eng. 1975. (St. Bart.) Cons. (Orthop. Surg.) Worcester Roy. Infirm. Prev: Sen. Regist. (Orthop.) Roy. Nat. Orthop. Hosp. Lond.

DAVIES, John Stuart Stradling 43 Rhyd y Defaid Drive, Derwen Fawr, Swansea SA2 8AL — MB BCh 1979 Wales; FFA RCS Eng. 1984. Cons. Anaesth. Singleton Hosp. Swansea. Prev: Cons. Anaesth. Neath Gen. Hosp.; Sen. Regist. (Anaesth.) Kings Coll. Hosp. Lond.; Regist. (Anaesth.) St. Mary's Hosp. Lond.

DAVIES, John Trevor Granton Surgery, 114 Middleton Hall Road, Kings Norton, Birmingham B30 1DH Tel: 0121 459 9117 Fax: 0121 486 2889 — MB ChB 1958 Birm.; DObst RCOG 1963. (Birm.)

DAVIES, John Victor Law Street Surgery, 51 Laws St., Pembroke Dock, Pembroke Tel: 01646 3113; Ty Ar y Bryn, Cosheston, Pembroke Dock SA72 4UW Tel: 01646 682746 — MB BCh 1968 Wales; MRCGP 1977; DObst RCOG 1968. (Cardiff)

DAVIES, John William, Surg. Capt. RN (retired) 86 Pierrefondes Avenue, Farnborough GU14 8PA Tel: 01252 549435 — MB ChB 1959 Bristol; MSc (Ergonomics) Lond. 1977; FFOM RCP Lond. 1990, M 1980; DAvMed Eng. 1968. Prev: Med. Off. i/c Inst. Naval Med. Alverstoke.

DAVIES, Jonathan Adams Tel: 01970 613500 Fax: 01970 613505 — MB BS 1979 Lond.; MRCS Eng. LRCP Lond. 1979.

DAVIES, Jonathan Andrew 24 Penn Lea Road, Bath BA1 3RA — BChir 1994 Camb.

DAVIES, Jonathan Huw Radiology Department, Morriston Hospital, Swansea SA6 6NL Tel: 01792 703664 Fax: 01792 703674 — MB BChir 1979 Camb.; MA, MB Camb. 1979, BChir 1978; FRCR 1984; DMRD Eng. 1982. Cons. Radiol. Morriston Hosp. Swansea. Prev: Fell. (Interven.al Radiol.) Mt. Sinai Hosp. Toronto; Sen. Regist. (Radiol.) Leic. Roy.Infirm.

DAVIES, Mr Jonathan Neil Department of Vascular Surgery, Treliske Royal Cornwall Hospital, Truro TR1 3LJ Tel: 01872 252718 Fax: 01872 252426 — MB BS 1982 Lond.; FRCS Ed. 1988; FRCS Eng. 1988. Cons. Surg. with interest in Vasc. Surg. Vasc. Surgic. Unit, Cornw. Socs: Eur. Soc. Vasc. Surg.; Vasc. Surg. Soc. Prev: Sen. Regist. Rotat. (Surg.) Soton. Univ. Hosps. & Roy. United Hosp. Bath; Regist. (Surg.) P.ss Margt. Hosp. Swindon; Research Fell. (Vasc. Surg.) Soton. Univ. Hosp.

DAVIES, Mr Jonathan Prydderch 57 Burrows Road, Skewen, Neath SA10 6AB — MB BCh 1988 Wales; FRCS Ed. 1993. Regist. (Trauma & Orthop.) Welsh Higher Surgic. Train. Scheme. Socs: Brit. Orthop. Assn. Prev: SHO Rotat. (Surg.) Cardiff PeriFell.sh.; SHO (A & E) Cardiff Roy. Infirm.; Prosector (Anat.) Univ. Wales Coll. Med.

DAVIES, Joseph Huw 36 Boden Road, Hall Green, Birmingham B28 9DJ — BM 1995 Soton.

DAVIES, Joy (retired) Kingsway Hospital, Derby DE22 3LZ — MB BS 1956 Lond.; MRCPsych 1976; DPM Eng. 1968; DCH Eng. 1959. Prev: Cons. Psychiat. (Psychogeriat.) Kingsway Hosp. Derby.

DAVIES, Joy Lesley Annandale Medical Centre, Mobberley Road, Knutsford WA16 8HR Tel: 01565 755222 Fax: 01565 652049; Bate Mill Cottage, Bate Mill Lane, Chelford, Macclesfield SK11 9BW Tel: 01477 571313 — MB ChB 1980 Manch.

DAVIES, Judith Patricia Oldcastle Surgery, South Street, Bridgend CF31 3ED Tel: 01656 657131 Fax: 01656 657134 — MB BCh 1985 Wales; MRCP (UK) 1991; MRCGP 1989; DRCOG 1990; DCH RCP Lond. 1989. GP Princip., Oldcastle Surg., Bridgend; GP Trainer, Oldcastle Surg. Bridgend. Prev: Regist. (Paediat.) Llandough Hosp. Penarth; SHO (Paediat.) P.ss of Wales Hosp. Bridgend; Trainee GP Bridgend VTS.

DAVIES, Julian Emrys Rose Cottage, Penstone, Colebrooke, Crediton EX17 5JR — MB BChir 1970 Camb.; MA, MB BChir Camb. 1970; T(GP) 1991. (Camb. & Westm.) Socs: BMA. Prev: SHO (Cas.) Cardiff Roy. Infirm.; Trainee Gen. Pract. Bridgend Vocational Train. Scheme.

DAVIES, Juliet Marian The Royal College of Anaesthetists, 48/49 Russell Square, London WC1B 4JY Tel: 020 7813 1900 Fax: 020 7813 1875 Email: jdavies@rcoa.ac.uk; Wood End House, Ridgeway Lane, Lymington SO41 8AA — MB BS 1977 Lond.; MB BS (Hons. Path.) Lond. 1977; MA Oxf. 1980; MRCP (UK) 1979; FFA RCS Eng. 1986. Regist. Roy. Coll. Anaesths. Lond. Prev: Medico-Legal Adviser Med. Protec. Soc.

DAVIES, Justin Blair 1 Albert Grove, Leeds LS6 4DA — MB ChB 1991 Leeds.

DAVIES, Justin Huw Silverstone, Newport Road, Cardiff CF3 2UN — MB BCh 1993 Wales.

DAVIES, Karen 243 Bath Road, Stroud GL5 3NP — MB BS 1991 Lond.

DAVIES, Karen Duffy The Elms Surgery, 7 Lower Road, Chorleywood, Rickmansworth WD3 5EA; 150 Stanstead Road, Forest Hill, London SE23 1BX — MB BS 1987 Lond.; MRCP (UK) 1990; MRCGP 1993. Prev: Trainee GP Croydon VTS; SHO (Geriat. Med.) St. Thos. Hosp. Lond.

DAVIES, Karen Irene Sketty Surgery, 16 Dillwyn Road, Sketty, Swansea SA2 9AE; 11 Pinetree Court, Sketty Pk Road, Sketty, Swansea SA2 9AF — MB BCh 1986 Wales.

DAVIES, Katharine Sian 4 Thornbury, Harpenden AL5 5SN — MB BS 1998 Lond.; MB BS Lond 1998.

DAVIES, Miss Katherine Rose 16 Pxwich Close, Cardiff CF5 3BE — MB BCh 1988 Wales.

DAVIES, Kathleen Joyce Royal Hampshire County Hospital, Romsey Road, Winchester SO22 5DG Tel: 01962 825042 Fax: 01962 825044 — MB BS Lond. 1965; MRCS Eng. LRCP Lond. 1965; FFA RCS Eng. 1968; DA Eng. 1967. (Roy. Free) Cons. Anaesth. Roy. Hants. Co. Hosp. Winchester. Prev: Rotating Anaesth. Sen. Regist. Soton. & Winchester Gps. Hosps.; Anaesth. Regist. Qu. Vict. Hosp. E. Grinstead; Regist. (Anaesth.) Roy. Free Hosp. Lond.

DAVIES, Kathryn Anne 96 Kingston Avenue, North Cheam, Sutton SM3 9UF — MB BCh 1998 Wales.

DAVIES, Kathryn Elizabeth 7 Mynchen Close, Beaconsfield HP9 2AU; sycamore House, Main Road, Exeter EX6 8BU Tel: 01392 833651 — MB BS 1993 Lond.; BSc Lond. 1991; FRCA (Primary) 1998. (University College London) Lat Anaesth. Plymouth. Socs: MDU; BMA. Prev: SHO (Anaesth.) Centr. Middlx. Hosp. Lond.; SHO (Anaesth.) Bristol.

DAVIES, Katrina Maria 8 Melton Drive, Bridgend CF31 3ET — MB BS 1994 Lond.; BSc Psychol. Lond. 1991. SHO (A & E) Dewsbury Hosp. Prev: Ho. Off. (Med. & Surg.) Ealing.

DAVIES, Keith (retired) 8 Soberton Towers, Soberton, Southampton SO32 3PS — MB ChB 1952 St. And.

DAVIES, Keith Reynallt (retired) 25 Galingale Way, Portishead, Bristol BS20 7LU Tel: 01275 845519 — MB ChB Bristol 1960; DObst RCOG 1962.

DAVIES, Kelvin Parry Kingthorpe Lodge, Chapel Lane, Ullenhall, Solihull B95 5RT — MB ChB 1959 Birm.

DAVIES, Kelvin Stewart Hill Crest Medical Centre, 86 Holt Road, Wrexham LL13 8RG Tel: 01978 262193 Fax: 01978 310193 (Call before faxing); Llwyn Celyn, 10 Overleigh Drive, Overleigh Park, Wrexham LL13 9RZ — MB BS 1979 Newc.; JCPTGP, Certificate of prescribed experience-the joint Committee on Postgraduate Training General Practice 1983; Cert. Family Plann. JCC 1982. (Newc. u. Tyne) GP.

DAVIES, Kenneth Hugh West Cumberland Hospital, Hensingham, Whitehaven CA28 8JG Tel: 01946 693181 Fax: 01946 523513; Low Hall, Brandingill, Cockermouth CA13 0RE — MB ChB Sheff. 1969; FFA RCS Eng. 1974. Cons. Anaesth. & Med. Dir. W. Cumbld. Hosp. Whitehaven; Med. Dir. Prev: Lect. (Anaesth.) Sheff. Univ.;

Clin. Fell. (Anaesth.) Montreal Gen. Hosp., Canada; Regist. (Anaesth.) United Sheff. Hosps.

DAVIES, Keren Nicola The Royal London Hospital Mile End, Bancroft Road, London E1 4DG Tel: 020 7377 7843 Fax: 377 7844 — MB ChB 1981 Leeds; MSc Lond. 1993; FRCP 1997; MRCP (UK) 1984. Cons. Phys. (Med. for Elderly) Roy. Lond. Mile End. Prev: Sen. Regist. Rotat. (Geriat. & Gen. Med.) Mersey RHA.

DAVIES, Kerry Thomas and Partners, 3 High Street, Pontypool NP4 6EY Tel: 01495 752444 Fax: 01495 767820; 1 Talbot Place, Bridge St, Crickhowell NP8 1AR — MB BS 1987 Lond.; MRCGP 1993; DCH RCP Lond. 1990. Clin. Asst. Memory Clinic Woolos Hosp.; Examr. Roy. Coll. GPs 1997.

DAVIES, Kevin Andrew Ashley Rheumatology Unit, Hammersmith Hospital, London W12 0NN Tel: 020 8740 3276 Fax: 020 8743 3109 Email: kdavies@rpms.ac.uk; 19 Devonshire Road, Hatch End, Pinner HA5 4LY — MB BS 1983 Lond.; MA Camb. 1984; MD Lond. 1994; FRCP Lond. 1997. (St. Thos. Hosp.') Chief Serv. Gen. Internal Med. Hammersmith Hosp.; Sen. Lect. (Rheumatol.) Imperial Coll. Sch. of Med. at Hammersmith Hosp. Prev: Regist. Rotat. (Med.) Hammersmith Hosp. Lond.

DAVIES, Leighton 10 Woodman Terrace, Ystalyfera, Swansea SA9 2LR Email: ld50@dircon.co.uk — MB BCh 1991 Wales; MSc 1999. Research.Fell.Dept of Immunol. Chelsea & W.minster Hosp. Lond. Prev: Reg.HIV/GU Meds.t Marys hosp.Lond.

DAVIES, Linda Ann J D Lansdowne and Partners, Helston Medical Centre, Trelawney Road, Helston TR13 8AU Tel: 01326 572637 Fax: 01326 565525 — MB ChB 1976 Leeds; MRCP (UK) 1982; MRCGP 1992; T (GP) 1992.

DAVIES, Lindsey Margaret NHS Executive Trust, Fulwood House, Old Fulwood Road, Sheffield S10 3TH Tel: 0114 263 0300 Fax: 0114 282 0347 — BM BS 1975 Nottm.; BMedSci Nottm. 1973; FFPHM RCP (UK) 1991; MFCM RCP (UK) 1985. (Nottingham) Regional Dir. of Pub. Health & Regional Med. Dir. NHS Exec. Trent; Special Lect. Nottm. Univ. Prev: Head Pub. Health Div. NHS Exec. HQs; Dir. Pub. Health Derby & Nottm.; Dist. Med. Off. Derby.

DAVIES, Lisa 3 Mount Olive, Ingestre Road, Birkenhead CH43 5TT; 9 Hope Place, Liverpool L1 9BG Tel: 0151 709 7126 — BM BCh 1988 Oxf.; BA Oxf. 1985; MRCP (UK) 1993. (Oxf. Med. Sch.) Clin. Lect. Aintree Chest Centre Univ. Hosp. Aintree Liverp. Socs: Brit. Thorac. Soc. Prev: Specialist Regist. Liverp.

DAVIES, Lisa Anne 9 Kingston Drive, Sale M33 2FS — MB ChB 1979 Birm.; MFPHM 1990; DRCOG 1982. Cons. Pub. Health Med. Salford & Trafford HA. Socs: BMA; Manch. Med. Soc. (Mem. Community Med. Sect.). Prev: Sen. Regist. (Community Med.) N. W. RHA.

DAVIES, Mr Llewellyn Alan Lewis Charlton Hill Surgery, Charlton Road, Andover SP10 3JY Tel: 01264 337979 Fax: 01264 334251 — MB BS 1980 Lond.; FRCS Ed. 1985; MRCGP 1988.

DAVIES, Llewellyn Picton (retired) 2 Old Town Mews, Stratford-upon-Avon CV37 6GP Tel: 01789 297306 — MRCS Eng. LRCP Lond. 1937; MRCGP 1953.

DAVIES, Lorna Carne 13 Windsor Road, Aylesbury HP21 7JG — MB BS 1949 Lond.; FRCP Lond. 1976, M 1962; MRCS Eng. LRCP Lond. 1949; DCH Eng. 1952. (Univ. Coll. Hosp.) Prev: Cons. Phys. Geriat. Med. Aylesbury Vale HA.

DAVIES, Louise Mary Claire Hulbert, Price, Hulbert and Davies, Laurel Bank Surgery, Old Hall Street, Malpas SY14 8PS Tel: 01948 860205 Fax: 01948 860142; 4 Long Lane, Larkton, Malpas SY14 8LP Tel: 01948 820366 — MB BS 1985 Lond. (St. Bartholomew's London) Clin. Asst. (Rheumatol.) P.ss Roy. Hosp. Telford; Bd. Mem. Chesh. Rural PCG.

DAVIES, Lynne Coralie The Ashlea Medical Practice, 30 Upper Fairfield Road, Leatherhead KT22 7HH Tel: 01372 375666 Fax: 01372 360117; Flint Cottage, Yarm Way, Leatherhead KT22 8RQ Tel: 01372 374967 — BM BS 1985 Nottm.; MRCP (UK) 1988; T(GP) 1991; DRCOG 1989; Cert. Family Plann. JCC 1989.

DAVIES, Mair Swansea NHS Trust, Morriston Hospital, Swansea SA6 6NL Tel: 01792 702222 — MB BS 1983 Lond.; FFA RCSI 1991; FRCA 1992. (Middlx. Hosp.) Cons. Anaesth. Morriston Hosp. Swansea NHS Trust. Prev: Sen. Regist. (Anaesth.) Univ. Coll. Lond. Hosps.; Regist. (Anaesth.) St. Mary's Hosp. Lond.

DAVIES, Malcolm Carr High Street Surgery, Rose Cottage, High Street, Staplehurst, Tonbridge TN12 0AP Tel: 01580 891220; St. Helier, Staplehurst, Tonbridge TN12 0BS Tel: 01580 891220 — MB BCh 1974 Wales.

DAVIES, Mansel Leigh 103 Corporation Av, Llanelli SA15 3NP — MB BCh 1997 Wales.

DAVIES, Margaret Cecilia Albany House Surgery, Albany Terrace, Barbourne, Worcester WR1 3DU Tel: 01905 26086 Fax: 01905 26888; 33 Kings End, Powick, Worcester WR2 4RB — MB BS 1969 Lond.; MRCS Eng. LRCP Lond. 1968; LF. Hom. 1999. (St. Mary's)

DAVIES, Margaret Eleanor Butler (retired) Lyndale House, 26 Blackwell Road, Barnt Green, Birmingham B45 8BU Tel: 0121 445 1963 — MB BCh 1947 Wales; BSc, MB BCh Wales 1947; FRCPsych 1975, M 1971; DPM Eng. 1966. Prev: Cons. Psychiat. Lea & Lea Castle Hosps. Kidderminster. Asst. Psychiat. Hensol Castle, Glam.

DAVIES, Margaret Eluned (retired) Silver How, Llanhennock, Caerleon, Newport NP18 1LT Tel: 01633 421170 — MB BCh 1947 Wales; DObst RCOG 1951. Prev: Assoc. Specialist (Cytol. Dept.) Gp. Path. Laborat. Roy. Gwent Hosp. Newport.

DAVIES, Mrs Margaret Hughes (retired) Holly House, 5 Ampthill Road, Silsoe, Bedford MK45 4DX Tel: 01525 60632 — MRCS Eng. LRCP Lond. 1925; MB BS Lond. 1927. Prev: Asst. Med. Off. Severalls Ment. Hosp. Colchester.

DAVIES, Margaret Mary Rosina Counselling, Bereavement & Training Service, Morriston Hospital Swansea NHS Trust, Swansea SA6 6NL Tel: 01792 703312; 98 Dulais Road, Seven Sisters, Neath SA10 9ES Tel: 01639 700429 Fax: 01639 701655 Email: tamros@globalnet.co.uk — MB ChB 1965 Liverp.; MA (Psychother. & Counselling) City Univ. 1995; DObst RCOG 1967. (Liverp.) Dir.Couns.Bereavement & Train.Serv. Morriston Hosps.Swansea NHS Trust; UKCP Accredit. Pyschotherapist; Dip. Fac. Family Plann. & Reproduc. Health Care RCOG. Socs: BMA; Psycho-social Oncol. Soc.; Welsh Language Med. Soc. Prev: Dep. Med. Dir. Ty Olwen Hospice Swansea; Regist. (Med.) Morriston Hosp. Swansea.

DAVIES, Margaret Ross (retired) 12 Stanhope Road, Croydon CR0 5NS Tel: 020 8681 2785 — MB BS Lond. 1962; MCOphth 1991; MRCS Eng. LRCP Lond. 1962; DO Eng. 1968. Prev: Assoc. Specialist (Ophth.) Bromley Hosps. NHS Trust.

DAVIES, Marianne Riverside Health Centre, Canton Court, Wellington Street, Cardiff CF11 9SH Tel: 029 2034 1209 Fax: 029 2034 1209; Branch Surgery Address, 31 Penhill Road, Llandaff, Cardiff CF11 9PR Tel: 029 2023 2874 Fax: 01222 231077 — MB BCh 1963 Wales. (Cardiff)

DAVIES, Marie-Louise Department of Radiology, Royal Alexandra Hospital, Paisley PA2 9PN Tel: 0141 580 4147 Fax: 0141 849 0241; 34 Caldwell Road, West Kilbride KA23 9LF Tel: 01294 823562 — MB ChB 1981 Glas.; FRCR 1989. Cons. Radiol. Roy. Alexandra Hosp. Paisley.

DAVIES, Mrs Marilyn Buxton (retired) Garth-y-Glyn, Llandre, Bow St., Borth SY24 5BZ Tel: 01970 828366 — MRCS Eng. LRCP Lond. 1962; DObst RCOG 1964. Clin. Asst. (A & E) & Med. Asst. (Geriat. Med.) Bronglais Hosp. Aberystwyth.

DAVIES, Marjorie Joan Ann (retired) Eirianfa, 10 Kingston Road, Sketty, Swansea SA2 0ST — BSc Wales 1944, MB BCh 1947. Prev: Med. Off. Dept. Pub. Health, W. Glam. CC.

DAVIES, Mark 89 Burland Avenue, Wolverhampton WV6 9JG — MB ChB 1991 Dundee.

DAVIES, Mr Mark Bowen 9 Little Wood Lane, Thorpe Salvin S80 3LB — BM 1993 Soton.; FRCS 1998. Specialist Regist. (Trauma + Orthop. Surg.) Rotherham Dis.Gen.Hosp. Socs: Assoc. Mem. BOA. Prev: SHO Plastic & Recons. Surg. Mt. Vernon Hosp.N.wood.

DAVIES, Mark Paul 22 Clifton Street, Aberdare CF44 7PB — MB BCh 1981 Wales.

DAVIES, Mark Richard Barnhurst 93 Park Road, Hampton Hill, Hampton TW12 1HU — MB BS 1991 Lond.

DAVIES, Mr Mark Stephen St Thomas's Hospital, London SE1 — MB BS 1987 Lond.; BA Oxf. 1984; FRCS Eng. 1992; FRCS (Orth 1996). Cons. Guys & St Thomas Hosp. Prev: SHO (Plastic Surg.) St. Geo. Hosp. Lond.; SHO (Neurosurg.) Nat. Hosp. Neurosurg. Lond.; SHO (Gen. Surg.& Orthop.) St. Peter's Hosp. Chertsey.

DAVIES, Mark Stephen 21 Lothair Road, London W5 4TA — MB BS 1996 Lond.

DAVIES, Mark Warren Department of Anaesthesia, Royal Liverpool University Hospital, Prescot St., Liverpool L7 8XP Tel: 0151 706 2000 — MB ChB 1982 Manch.; FFARCS 1988; DA Eng. 1984.

Cons. Anaesth. Roy. Liverp. Univ. Hosp.; Lect. (Dent. Anaesth.) Univ. Liverp.

DAVIES, Martha Esther Nora Heti (retired) The Old Cottage School, Cousland EH22 2NZ — MB BCh 1955 Wales; DPM Eng. 1961 DCH Eng. 1958. Prev: Cons. Psychiat. St. Joseph's Hosp. Midlothian.

DAVIES, Martin Brendan 10 Lynton Grove, Stoke-on-Trent ST3 7XQ Email: brendand@mcmail.com — MB BS Lond. 1990; MRCP (UK) 1993; BSc 1987. (Charing Cross/Westminster) Specialist Regist. Neurol. Qu. Eliz. Univ. Hosp. Birm. Socs: Assoc.Brit. Neurol; Euro.Neurol.Soc; Amer. Acad.Neurol. Prev: Specialist Regist. Neurol.city hosp.Birm.; Specialist Regist. Neurol. N. Staffs hosp. Stoke on trent.

DAVIES, Martin Hugh (retired) 45 Elvetham Road, Edgbaston, Birmingham B15 2LY Tel: 0121 246 1921 — MB BChir 1959 Camb.; MD Camb. 1967; FRCPsych 1981, M 1971; DPM Eng. 1962; DTM & H Eng. 1961. Med. Mem. Ment. Health Review Tribunal S.O.A.D. Ment. Health Act Commiss. Prev: Cons. Psychiat. Qu. Eliz. Psychiat. Hosp. Birm.

DAVIES, Martin Leonard Rees East Cowes Health Centre, Down House, York Avenue, East Cowes PO32 6RR Tel: 01983 295611 Fax: 01983 280815; 2 Connaught Road, East Cowes PO32 6DR — BM BCh 1966 Oxf.; MA Oxf. 1966; DObst RCOG 1968. (Oxf. & St. Thos.) Prev: SHO Obst. St. Mary's Hosp. Portsmouth; Ho. Off. Wessex Renal Unit & Qu. Alexandra Hosp. Cosham.

DAVIES, Martyn Crwys Road Surgery, 151 Crwys Road, Cathays, Cardiff CF24 4XT Tel: 029 2039 6987 Fax: 029 2064 0523; 11 South Rise, Llanishen, Cardiff CF14 0RF — MB BCh 1979 Wales; MA Oxf. 1976.

DAVIES, Martyn John Pontcae Surgery, Dynevor Street, Georgetown, Merthyr Tydfil CF48 1YE Tel: 01685 723931 Fax: 01685 377048; 18 Woodland Way, Heolgerrig, Merthyr Tydfil CF48 1SQ — MB BCh 1980 Wales.

DAVIES, Martyn Watkin East Street Surgery, 6-7 East Street, Ware SG12 9HJ Tel: 01920 468777 Fax: 01920 484892; 100 Ware Road, Hertford SG13 7HN — MB BS 1983 Lond.; MB BS (Hons. Path.) Lond. 1983; MRCGP 1988; DCH RCP Lond. 1988; DRCOG 1985. Prev: SHO (Psych.) St. John's Hosp. Stone; Trainee GP Cookham Rise; SHO (O & G) N. Middlx. Hosp. Lond.

DAVIES, Mary 51 Heol-y-Coed, Rhiwbina, Cardiff CF14 6HQ — MB BS 1989 Lond. Socs: BMA & Fac. Community Health.

DAVIES, Mary Caroline Riddock (retired) Archers Folly, Hale Purlieu, Fordingbridge SP6 2NN Tel: 01725 513741 Fax: 01725 513741 — MB ChB 1949 Ed. Prev: GP Greenock.

DAVIES, Mary Catherine 38 Brook Street, Bampton, Tiverton EX16 9LY — MB BS 1979 Lond.; DA (UK) 1984; Dip. Palliat. Med. Wales 1998. BrE. Phys./Clin. Asst. Roy. Derm & Exeter Hosp.

DAVIES, Matthew Graham Abbey House Surgery, Golding Close, Daventry NN11 5RA Tel: 01327 877770 Fax: 01327 310267 — MB BS 1987 Lond.; MRCGP (Hons.) 1993; DCH RCP Lond. 1991; DRACOG 1990.

DAVIES, Matthew Rhys 46 Mayfield Avenue, Cardiff CF5 1AN — MB BS 1991 Lond.; BSc Lond. 1990; MRCP (UK) 1995. Regist. (Nephrol.) Univ. Hosp. Wales Cardiff.

DAVIES, Matthew Stephen 6 Maycroft Court, Hulse Road, Southampton SO15 2LB — BM 1995 Soton.

DAVIES, Matthew Timothy Creekside, 1 Freshwater Lane, St Mawes, Truro TR2 5AY — MB ChB 1994 Manch.

DAVIES, Matthew William The Rectory, Llandyrnog, Denbigh LL16 4LT — MB ChB 1997 Sheff.

DAVIES, Megan Jane 26/2 York Road, Edinburgh EH5 3EH — MB ChB 1989 Sheff.

DAVIES, Melanie Clare Reproductive Medicine Unit, University College London Hospitals, The Obstetric Hospital, Huntley St., London WC1E 6AU Tel: 020 7380 9759 Fax: 020 7380 9600 — MB BS 1979 Lond.; MA Camb. 1979; MRCP (UK) 1985; MRCOG (Gold Medallist) 1986; DObst 1981. Cons. O & G Univ. Coll. Hosp. Lond.; Hon Sen. Lec. UCL. Socs: Roy. Soc. Med.; Brit. Fertil. Soc.; Brit. Soc for Paediac. & Adolesc. Gynacology. Prev: Lect. St. Thos. Hosp.; SHO St. Bart. Hosp. & St. Mary's Hosp. Lond.

DAVIES, Melanie Jane Cheney House, Chapel Lane, Gaddesby, Leicester LE7 4WB; Cockscombe Farm, Watley Lane, Twyford, Winchester SO21 1QX Tel: 01962 712115 — MB ChB 1985 Sheff.; MD Sheff. 1994; MRCP (UK) 1988. Cons. Phys. (Gen. Med., Diabetes & Endocrinol.) Leicester Roy. Infirm.; Hon. Clin. Teach. Leicester Univ. Socs: Brit. Diabetic Assn.; Eur. Assn. for Study Diabetes; Soc. Endocrinol. Prev: Sen. Regist. (Med., Diabetes & Endocrinol.) Leicester Roy. Infirm.; Research Regist. Ipswich; Regist. (Med.) Ipswich Hosp. Suff.

DAVIES, Melanie Jane 40 Dunholme Road, Newcastle upon Tyne NE4 6XE — MB BS 1998 Newc.; MB BS Newc 1998.

DAVIES, Melfyn (retired) Waunadlais, Medelfyw Road, Felinfoel, Llanelli SA14 8NX Tel: 01554 758326 — MB BS 1952 Lond. Prev: GP LLa.lli.

DAVIES, Mererid Jones Portardawe Health Centre, Industrial Est., Pontardawe, Swansea Tel: 01792 863103; 24 Millborough Road, Ystalyfera, Swansea SA9 2AB Tel: 01639 849792 — MB BCh 1982 Wales. Prev: Clin. Asst. (Genitourin. Med.) Child Psychiat. Swansea.

DAVIES, Mervyn Huw St. James's University Hospital, Beckett St., Leeds LS9 7TF Tel: 0113 283 7080 Fax: 0113 244 8182; Whitegates, Dowkell Lane, Thorp Arch, Wetherby LS23 7AH Tel: 01937 541976 — MB ChB 1985 Birm.; MD Birm. 1995; MRCP (UK) 1989; FRCP UK 2000. (Univ. Birm.) Cons. Phys. & Hepatol. & Hon. Sen. Lect. St. Jas. Univ. Hosp. Socs: Brit. Soc. Gastroenterol. Prev: Sen. Regist. Qu. Eliz. Hosp. Liver Unit Birm.; Regist. (Med.) E. Glam. Gen. Hosp.; SHO Univ. Hosp. Wales, Cardiff.

DAVIES, Michael 24 Walton Heath Drive, Tytherington, Macclesfield SK10 2QN — MB BS Durh. 1967; FRCP Lond. 1984; MRCP (UK) 1971. Cons. Phys. Roy. Infirm. Manch.; Hon. Sen. Lect. (Med.) Univ. Manch. Socs: Med. Res. Soc.; Assn. Phys.

DAVIES, Mr Michael The Boat House, Oak Lane, Kerridge, Bollington SK10 5AP Tel: 01625 572401 — MB ChB 1965 Manch.; BSc 1962 Manch.; FRCS Ed. 1970. (Manch.) Socs: Fell. Manch. Med. Soc. Prev: Asst. Lect. in Anat. Univ. Manch.; Regist. (Surg.) Manch. Roy. Infirm.; Sen. Regist. (Surg.) Preston Roy. Infirm.

DAVIES, Michael Barrie, SBStJ Grosvenor House, 420 Chester Road N., Kidderminster DY10 1TB Tel: 01562 630544 Fax: 01562 630551 Email: barrie@flyingdoc.demon.co.uk — MB ChB 1969 Liverp.; Cert JCC Lond. 1980. In flight Med. Off.; Med. Adviser Heartsart Wyre Forest; Chairm. Kidderminster Immediate Care Scheme; Sen. Aeromed. Ref. Alert Assistance. Socs: (Ex-Sec.) Sec. BASICS.

DAVIES, Michael Christopher Redlands Surgery, Redlands Road, Penarth CF64 3WX Tel: 029 2070 5013 Fax: 029 2071 2599 — BM BS 1983 Nottm.; BMedSci Nottm. 1981, BM BS 1983; MRCGP 1987; DRCOG 1987.

DAVIES, Michael Geraint 5 Canal Street, Long Eaton, Nottingham NG10 4HN — MB ChB 1985 Birm.

DAVIES, Michael Glanmor Summerleas, Crapstone Road, Yelverton PL20 6BT Tel: 01822 854700 — MB ChB 1970 Bristol; BSc (Hons.) Bristol 1967, MB ChB 1970; FRCP Lond. 1988; MRCP (UK) 1973. Cons. (Dermat.) Plymouth Gen. Hosp. Socs: BMA & Europ. Soc. Dermat. Research. Prev: Sen. Regist. & Tutor Dermat. St. John's Hosp. Dis. Skin Lond.; Regist. (Dermat.) Univ. Hosp. Wales Cardiff; Regist. (Gen. Med.) Univ. Hosp. Wales Cardiff.

DAVIES, Michael Glyn Twyford Health Centre, Loddon Hall Road, Twyford, Reading RG10 9JA Tel: 0118 934 0112 Fax: 0118 934 1048; 132 Victoria Road, Wargrave, Reading RG10 8AJ Tel: 0118 940 2630 — MB BS 1984 Lond.; MRCGP 1988; DRCOG 1987.

DAVIES, Michael Gordon 1 Hargrave Avenue, Birkenhead CH43 2NH — MB BS 1994 Newc.

DAVIES, Michael Howard 18 Byron Avenue, Camberley GU15 1DP Tel: 01276 681325 — BM BCh 1971 Oxf.; BA Oxf. 1968, BM BCh 1971; MRCP (UK) 1975; FFA RCS Eng. 1981. Cons. Anaesth. Frimley Pk. Hosp.

DAVIES, Mr Michael John Pfizer Central Research, C746 Ramsgate Road, Sandwich CT13 9NJ Tel: 01304 648813 Fax: 01304 658159 Email: michael_davies@sandwich.pfizer.com — MB ChB 1985 Ed.; FRCS Ed. 1991; FRCS Eng. 1990; FRCS Glas. 1990; Dip. IMC RCS Ed. 1989. (Ed.) Clin. Project Manager Experim. Med. Centr. Research (ECRG) Pfizer Ltd. Sandwich Kent; Hon. Lect. (A & E) Qu. Eliz. Qu. Mother Hosp. Ramsgate. Socs: Amer. Heart. Assn. (Counc. Cardiopulm. & Critical Care). Prev: Clin. Research Fell. (Cardiac Surg.) Gt. Ormond St. Hosp. for Childr. Lond.; Clin. Research Fell. (Cardiac. Surg.) Duke Univ. Med. Centre Durh., USA.

DAVIES, Michael John Central Surgery, Brooksby Drive, Oadby, Leicester LE2 5AA Tel: 0116 271 2175 Fax: 0116 271 4015 — MB ChB 1981 Bristol; MRCGP 1986; DRCOG 1984.

DAVIES, Professor Michael John BHF Cardiovascular Pathology Unit, St. Georges Hospital, Cranmer Terrace, London SW17 0RE Tel: 020 8672 9178; 26 Station Road, Thames Ditton KT7 0NR Tel: 020 8398 3745 — MD 1968 Lond.; MB BS 1961; FRCP Lond. 1993; FRCPath 1978; FACC 1989. (Middlx.) Prof. & Hon. Cons. Cardiovasc. Path. Brit. Heart Foundat. St. Geo. Hosp. Lond. Socs: Brit. Cardiac Soc. & Path. Soc. Prev: Wm. Shepherd Research Fell. St. Geo. Hosp. Lond.; Nat. Inst. Health Research Fell. N.W. Univ. Chicago, USA.

DAVIES, Michael Kevin 12 Mellish Road, Walsall WS4 2ED — MB BChir 1976 Camb.; MD Camb. 1983, MA, MB 1976, BChir 1975; FRCP Lond. 1993. Cons. Cardiol. Selly Oak Hosp. Birm. Socs: Med. Res. Soc. & Brit. Cardiac Soc. Prev: Sen. Lect. (Cardiovasc. Med.) Univ. Birm. & Hon. Cons. Cardiol. Qu. Eliz. Hosp.; Lect. (Cardiovasc. Med.) Univ. Birm. & Hon. Sen. Regist. Qu. Eliz. Hosp. & E. Birm. Hosp.; Sheldon Research Fell. (Cardiovasc. Med.) Univ. Birm. & E. Birm. Hosp.

DAVIES, Mr Michael Morgan Rosehedge, Crendon Road, Chearsley, Aylesbury HP18 0DL — MB BS 1990 Lond.; BSc Radiol. Sci. Lond. 1987; FRCS Eng. 1995.

DAVIES, Michael Osborne Yew Tree Cottage, Bridgemere, Nantwich CW5 7PY Tel: 01227 203 — MB ChB 1968 Liverp. (Liverp.) Regional Med. Off. N. W.ern Div. Socs: PeterBoro. Med. Soc. Prev: GP Madeley.; Ho. Off. (Med. & Geriat.), (Surg. & Orthop.) & (Cas.) Vict. Centr. Hosp. Wallasey.

DAVIES, Michael Philip Naunton The Maltings, Horsell Rise, Woking GU21 4BG Tel: 01483 768391 Fax: 01483 751806; Unit 11/111 Markeri Streeet, Mermaid Waters Qld 4218, Australia Tel: 55 785645 — MB BS 1996 Lond.; BSc (Hons.) 1993 Lond. (Roy. Lond. Hosp.) Resid. Emerg. Dept. Gold Coast Hosp. Socs: M.P.S. QLD. Prev: Paediat. Resid. Gold Coast Hosp.

DAVIES, Michael Robert Price Flat 14 NA, Bolton General Hospital, Farnworth, Bolton BL4 0JR; 44 Kingsmead, Upton, Chester CH2 1EF — MB ChB 1985 Manch.

DAVIES, Mr Michael Stuart (retired) The Forest, Nineveh Lane, Benenden, Cranbrook TN17 4LG Tel: 01580 240654 — MB BS Lond. 1962; FRCS Eng. 1968; MRCS Eng. LRCP Lond. 1962; FCOphth 1989; DO Eng. 1967. Prev: Cons. Ophth. Surg. Kent Co. Ophth. Hosp. Maidstone & St. Bart. Hosp. Rochester.

DAVIES, Morgan Ernest (retired) Glyn Garth Cottage, Glyn Garth, Menai Bridge LL59 5PD Tel: 01248 714116 — MRCS Eng. LRCP Lond. 1942; CPH Eng. 1947. Prev: PMO (Schs.) Tower Hamlets Health Dist. (T).

DAVIES, Morris St Peter's Surgery, 6 Oaklands Avenue, Broadstairs CT10 2SQ Tel: 01843 860777 Fax: 01843 866647; 35 Fitzroy Avenue, Broadstairs CT10 3LS Tel: 01843 866114 — MB BS 1979 Lond.; DRCOG 1983. (Guy's Hosp. Med. Sch. Lond.) Hosp. Pract. (Med.) Qu. Eliz. Qu. Mother Hosp. Thanet Healthcare Trust Margate.

DAVIES, Muriel Ann 1 Heath Mount, Halifax HX1 2YR Tel: 01422 52961 — MB BS 1958 Lond.; MRCS Eng. LRCP Lond. 1958; DO Eng. 1963.

DAVIES, Nadia Janine 332 Brixton Road, Brixton, London SW9 7AA — MB ChB 1988 Ed.; MRCPsych 1992. Cons. Psychiat. Lambeth Healthcare Trust. Prev: Lect. Bethlem & Maudsley Hosps.; SHO & Regist. Rotat. (Psychiat.) Univ. Coll. Hosp.

DAVIES, Nathaniel Marsden Station Approach Surgery, Frinton-on-Sea CO13 9JT Tel: 01255 850101 — MRCS Eng. LRCP Lond. 1963; BSc (Hons. Physiol.) Lond. 1959, MB BS 1962; DObst RCOG 1964. (St. Bart.)

DAVIES, Neil Frederick BNFL Magnox Generation, Berkeley Centre, Berkeley GL13 9PB Tel: 01453 813698 Fax: 01453 813893 Email: neilfdavies/magnox/berkley/bufl@bnfl; 29A Over Lane, Almondsbury, Bristol BS32 4BL Tel: 01454 615013 Email: neilfd@nixondavies.freeserve.co.uk — MB BChir 1976 Camb.; MB Camb. 1976, BChir 1975; MA Camb. 1976; MRCP (UK) 1978; FFOM RCP Lond. 1993, MFOM 1988, AFOM 1982. (St. Bart.) Chief Med. Off. (Occupat. Med.) BNFL Magnox Generation Berkeley. Socs: BMA; Soc. Occupat. Med. Prev: Chief Med. Off. Nuclear Electric; Area Med. Off. CEGB; Med. Adviser Mobil Oil Company Ltd.

DAVIES, Neil Hunter 16 Westbrook Road, London SE3 0NS — MB BS 1992 Lond.

DAVIES, Mr Neil Martin 2 Cambridge Road, Kew, Richmond TW9 3JB Tel: 020 819 5908 Fax: 020 8287 9801 Email: nmdavies@aol.com — MB BS 1991 Lond.; BSc (Clin. Med. Sci.) Lond. 1990; FRCS Eng. 1995. (St. Mary's Hosp. Lond.) Specialist Regist. St. Geo. Hosp. & St Heliers Hosp. Socs: Roy. Soc. Med.; BOA; BOTA. Prev: Specialist Regist. (Orthop.) Kingston Hosp.; SHO (Orthop.) Qu. Mary's Hosp. Lond.; SHO (Gen. Surg.) Addenbrooke's Hosp. Camb.

DAVIES, Neil Sandon Ysbyty Glan Clwyd, Bodelwyddan, Rhyl LL18 5UJ Tel: 01745 585484 Fax: 01745 534405; Hafryn, Old Highway, Colwyn Bay LL28 5UY — MB BChir 1972 Camb.; MB Camb. 1972, BChir 1971; MA Camb. 1971; FRCPsych 1993, M 1975; DPM Eng. 1974. Cons. Psychiat. Ysbyty Glan Clwyd Bodelwyddan. Prev: Lect. (Psychiat.) Univ. Newc.; Hon. Sen. Regist. Newc. Gen. Hosp.

DAVIES, Nesta Gwenllian 8 Hillside Close, Goodwick, Fishguard — MB BCh 1970 Wales.

DAVIES, Nicholas 28 Stoke Grove, Bristol BS9 3SB — MB ChB 1985 Birm.

DAVIES, Nicholas John Hawksley Wood End House, Ridgeway Lane, Lymington SO41 8AA — BM BCh 1970 Oxf.; DM Oxf. 1981; MRCP (UK) 1973; FRCA 1975. (St. Thos. Hosp.) Cons. Anaesth. Soton. Gen. Hosp. Socs: Mem. Of Counc., Med. Protec. Soc. Prev: Sen. Lect. (Anaesth.) Brompton Hosp. Lond.

DAVIES, Nicholas Peter 46 Longmeadow Drive, Dinas Powys CF64 4TB — MB BCh 1991 Wales.

DAVIES, Nicholas Peter Gavin Alison Lea Medical Centre, Calderwood, East Kilbride, Glasgow G74 3BE Tel: 01355 236444; 22 Southend Drive, Strathaven ML10 6QT Tel: 01357 529496 Fax: 01357 529127 Email: mpdavies@strathaven22.freeserve.co.uk — MB ChB 1989 Leeds; BSc Leeds 1986; MRCGP 1995. (Leeds) Prev: SHO (O & G) William Smellie Matern. Unit. Law Hosp. Carluke; Trainee GP Strathaven.

DAVIES, Nicholas William Saunders 67 Roper Road, Canterbury CT2 7RS Tel: 01227 457682 — MB BS 1996 Lond.; MB BS (Hons) Lond. 1996, BSc 1993. (St George's Hospital Medical School London) SHO Infect.Dis. Coppett Wood Hosp. Lond. Socs: Fell.Roy.Soc.Med. Prev: SHO (Neurol.) Nat. Hosp. Neurol. & Neurosurg. Lond.; Ho. Phys. St. Geos. Hosp. Lond.; SHO (Cardiol.) Hammersmith Hosp. Lond.

DAVIES, Nicholas Wynne Tel: 01446 734131 Fax: 01446 420002 — MB BCh 1985 Wales; MRCGP 1990; DCH RCP Lond. 1989; DRCOG 1988.

DAVIES, Nicola Anne The Surgery, School House Lane, Abbots Bramley, Rugeley WS15 3BT Tel: 01283 840228 Fax: 01283 840919; 22 Moor Croft, Colton, Rugeley WS15 3ND Tel: 01889 574454 — MB BCh 1989 Wales; DFFP 1994; DRCOG 1993; DCH RCP Lond. 1992; MRCGP 1998. (Univ. Wales Coll. Med.) Princip. in Gen. Pract. Prev: Community Med. Off. (Child Health) Glan Hafren NHS Trust; SHO (A & E) Cardiff Roy. Infirm.; SHO (O & G) E. Glam. Hosp.

DAVIES, Nigel John 18 Manor Gardens, Larkhall Rise, London SW4 6JZ — MB BS 1994 Lond.

DAVIES, Nigel John Department of Obstetrics, University Hospital Wales, Heath Park, Cardiff CF4 4XN Tel: 029 2074 7747 — MB BCh 1982 Wales; MRCOG 1988.

DAVIES, Mr Nigel Philip Moorfields Eye Hospital, City Rd, London EC1U 2PD Tel: 01923 824265; Fourwinds, 57 Green St, Chorleywood, Rickmansworth WD3 5QS — MB BS 1992 Lond.; PhD London, 2000; BA (Hons.) Physics Oxf. 1987; FRCOphth 1996. (Lond. Hosp. Med. Coll.) Specialist Regist. (Ophth.) N. Thames; Wellcome Fell. Imperial Coll. & W.. Eye Hosp. Imperial Coll. Sch. of Med. Socs: UK & Irel. Soc. Cataract & Refractive Surg. Prev: SHO (Ophth.) W.. Eye Hosp. & Qu. Eliz. II Hosp. Welwyn Garden City; SHO (A & E) Centr. Middlx. Hosp. Lond.

DAVIES, Norma Esther 38 Stone Road, Bromley BR2 9AU Tel: 020 8460 1061 — MB BS 1953 Adelaide; FFA RCS Eng 1967; DA Eng. 1964. (Adelaide) Cons. Anaesth. Moorfields Eye Hosp. Lond. Socs: Assn. Anaesths.& BMA.

DAVIES, Norman Paul 83 Union Road, Sheffield S11 9EH — MB BS 1982 Lond.

DAVIES, Owen Meredith 93 Goetre Fawr Road, Killay, Swansea SA2 7QT — MB BCh 1985 Wales.

DAVIES, Pamela Anne (retired) 22 Manor House Court, 11 Warrington Gardens, London W9 2PZ — MB ChB 1947 Glas.; MD Glas. 1967; FRCP Lond. 1971, M 1955; Hon. FRCPCH 1996; DCH

Eng. 1953. Prev: Reader Inst. Child Health & Hon. Cons. Childr. Phys. Hammersmith Hosp.Lond.

DAVIES, Pamela Joan Oakend, 34 Tabors Avenue, Great Baddow, Chelmsford CM2 7ET Tel: 01245 71799 Email: dicdic@ndirect.co.uk — MB ChB Bristol 1975; MRCGP 1995; Cert. Prescribed Equiv. Exp. JCPTGP 1981. (Bristol) Exam. Med. Off. DHSS.

DAVIES, Patrick Emmanuel 7 West Carnethy Av, Edinburgh EH13 0ED — BM BS 1997 Nottm.

DAVIES, Paul Freemen's Common Health Centre, 161 Welford Road, Leicester LE2 6BF — MB BCh 1983 Wales; MRCGP 1989; DRCOG 1989; DA (UK) 1985.

DAVIES, Paul Benjamin Main St, Melbourne, Derby DE73 1AD — MB ChB 1997 Birm.

DAVIES, Paul Gillard Rose Barn, The Street, Little Dunmow, Dunmow CM6 3HS — MB BS 1975 Lond.; BSc (Hons. Biochem.) Lond. 1972; FRCP Lond. 1994; MRCP (UK) 1977; MRCS Eng. LRCP Lond. 1975. (Guy's) Cons. Rheum. Broomfield Hosp. Chelmsford. Socs: Brit. Soc. Rheum.; BMA. Prev: Sen. Regist. (Rheum.) Lond. Hosp. Whitechapel; Regist. (Med.) Lewisham Hosp.; SHO Roy. Postgrad. Med. Sch. Hammersmith.

DAVIES, Paul John Ambleside Health Centre, Rydal Road, Ambleside LA22 9BP Tel: 015394 32693 Fax: 015394 32520 — MB ChB 1989 Liverp.; MRCGP 1995; DRCOG 1994; DCH RCP Lond. 1992. GP. Prev: Trainee GP Ambleside Health Centre; SHO (Dermat.) Qu. Vict. Hosp. Morecambe; SHO (Rheum. & Gen. Med.) Roy. Lancaster Infirm.

DAVIES, Paul Pearce 67 North Denes Road, Great Yarmouth NR30 4LU — MB BS 1968 Lond.; MRCS Eng. LRCP Lond. 1968; FRCGP 1990, M 1972; Cert. Family Plann. JCC 1972; DObst RCOG 1971. (St. Bart.) Socs: BMA. Prev: Trainee GP Ipswich VTS; Ho. Phys. P. of Wales Hosp. Lond.; SHO (Paediat.) W. Herts. Hosp. Hemel Hempstead.

DAVIES, Paul Randolph Croswell 24 Fairways, Llandudno LL30 2HZ Tel: 01492 878736 — MB BCh Wales 1961; MFPHM RCPI 1978; DPH Liverp. 1974. (Cardiff) Socs: Liverp. Med. Inst. & Brit. Assn. Community Doctors in Audiol.; BMA. Prev: SCMO Halton HA; GP Newport; Ho. Surg. & Ho. Phys. Morriston Hosp. Swansea.

DAVIES, Paul Robert Kent House Surgery, 36 Station Road, Longfield DA3 7QD Tel: 01474 703550 — MB BS 1978 Lond.; DRCOG 1980. (St. Mary's) Prev: Trainee GP Luton VTS; Ho. Phys. & Ho. Surg. Qu. Eliz. II Hosp. Welwyn Garden City.

DAVIES, Penelope 15 Caer Efail, Pencoed, Bridgend CF35 6RW Tel: 01656 862536 — MB BCh 1993 Wales; MRCGP 1998; DRCOG 1997; DFFP 1997; BSc (Hons.) Biochem. 1990. (UWCM Cardiff) Staff Grade Community Wom. & child health Bridgend. Socs: Full Mem. Roy. Coll. GPs; Fac. Fam. Plann.; BMA. Prev: Completed UTS 1998.

DAVIES, Peter (retired) Yaffle Lodge, Bleasby Road, Thurgarton, Nottingham NG14 7FW Tel: 01636 830479 — MB BS 1962 Lond.; DM Nottm. 1981; MRCS Eng. LRCP Lond. 1962; FFR 1971; FRCR 1975; DMRD Eng. 1968. Prev: Cons. Radiol. Dir. of Radiol. City Hosp. Nottm.

DAVIES, Peter Albert Old Road Surgery, Old Road, Abersychan, Pontypool NP4 7BH Tel: 01495 772239 Fax: 01495 773786; Typorth, Pencroesored, Llanover, Abergavenny NP7 9EL — MB BCh 1970 Wales.

DAVIES, Peter Charles Howgrave-Graham and Partners, The Surgery, Moot Lane, Downton, Salisbury SP5 3QD Tel: 01725 510296 Fax: 01725 513119; Grace House, The Common, Woodgreen, Fordingbridge SP6 2BQ — MRCS Eng. LRCP Lond. 1978; BSc Lond. 1975, MB BS 1978; MRCGP 1983; DRCOG 1982; DA Eng. 1981. (Barts.) Prev: Ho. Surg. St. Bart. Hosp. Lond.; SHO (Anaesth.) Univ. Coll. Hosp. Lond.; SHO (Obst./Gyn.) Univ. Coll. Hosp. Lond.

DAVIES, Peter David Owen Cardiothoracic Centre, Thomas Drive, Liverpool L14 3PE Tel: 0151 228 1616 Fax: 0151 228 7688; Conway, Croft Drive W., Caldy, Wirral CH48 2JQ — BM BCh 1973 Oxf.; MA Oxf. 1973, DM 1986; FRCP Lond. 1993; MRCP (UK) 1977. Cons. Respirat. Phys. Aintree Hosp. Trust & Cardiothoracic Centre (NHS) Trust. Socs: Brit. Thorac. Soc. & Amer. Thorac. Soc.; Eur. Resp. Soc. Prev: Sen. Regist. (Gen. & Thoracic Med.) Llandough Hosp. Cardiff; Scientif. Off. Med. (Tuberc. & Chest Dis.) Research Counc. Brompton Hosp. Lond.

DAVIES, Mr Peter Donald West Norwich Hospital, Norwich NR2 3TU Tel: 01603 288375 Fax: 01603 621338 — MB BS 1965 Lond.; FRCS Eng. 1973; MRCS Eng. LRCP Lond. 1965; FRCOphth 1989; DO Eng. 1969. (Guy's) Cons. Surg. Ophth. Norwich Health Dist.; Hon. Reader Biological Scis. Univ. E. Anglia. Prev: Sen. Regist. Middlx. Hosp. Lond.; Resid. Surg. Off. Moorfields Eye Hosp. Lond.; Lect. (Experim. Ophth.) Inst. Ophth. Lond.

DAVIES, Peter Huw Department of Medicine, Queen Elizabeth Hospital, Edgbaston, Birmingham B15 2TH Tel: 0121 472 1311 Fax: 0121 627 2384 Email: 106012.3117@compuserve.com; 65 Blenheim Road, Moseley, Birmingham B13 9TZ Tel: 0121 449 5180 — MB BCh 1988 Wales; MD Wales 1996; MRCP (UK) 1991. (Univ. Wales Coll. Med.) Lect. (Med., Endocrinol. & Diabetes) Univ. Birm. & Hon. Sen. Regist. Univ. Birm. Hosps. Trust. Socs: Thyroid Club; Roy. Soc. Med.; Soc. Endocrinol. Prev: MRC Train. Fell. (Med.) Univ. Birm.; Regist. (Metab. Med.) St. Mary's Hosp. Lond.; SHO (Gen. Med.) Qu. Eliz. Hosp. Birm.

DAVIES, Peter James Cwmfelin Medical Centre, 298 Carmarthen Road, Swansea SA1 1HW Tel: 01792 653941 — MB BCh 1983 Wales; PhD Wales 1975, BSc 1970, MB BCh 1983.

DAVIES, Peter Llewelyn Tudor Gate Surgery, Tudor Street, Abergavenny NP7 5DL Tel: 01873 855991 Fax: 01873 850162; 43 St. Helens Road, Abergavenny NP7 5YA — MB BCh 1981 Wales; BSc Bath 1976; MRCGP 1992.

DAVIES, Peter Llewelyn (retired) Emmett Carr Surgery, Abbey Place, Renishaw, Sheffield S21 3TY — MB ChB 1963 Bristol; DCH Eng. 1966.

DAVIES, Peter Robert Francis Department Anaesthetics, Derriford Hospital, Plymouth PL6 Email: prfdavies@burraton.demon.co.uk — MB ChB 1984 Leeds; MB ChB Leeds l984; FRCA 1991. Cons. Anaesth. Derriford Hosp. Plymouth.

DAVIES, Philip Huw Emergency Department, Cheltenham General Hospital, Sandford Road, Cheltenham GL53 5AN — MB BS 1989 Lond.; MRCP (UK) 1994; DA (UK) 1995. Cons. Emerg. Med., Cheltenham Gen. Hosp. Prev: Specialist Regist. (Emerg. Med.) Frenchay Hosp. Bristol.

DAVIES, Philip Ivor Medical Centre, High Street, Ruabon, Wrexham LL14 6NH Tel: 01978 823717 Fax: 01978 824142 — MB BCh 1979 Wales; DRCOG 1981; Cert. Family Plann. JCC 1982. Prev: SHO S. Clwyd VTS; Ho. Off. (Med.) Profess. Unit. Univ. Hosp. Wales Cardiff; Ho. Off. (Surg.) Univ. Hosp. Wales & Renal Transpl. Unit Cardiff.

DAVIES, Philip Lifton 29 Jordanstown Road, Newtownabbey BT37 0QD — MB BCh BAO 1990 Belf.

DAVIES, Philip Lloyd Pen Coed, 13 Parc Gwelfor, Dyserth, Rhyl LL18 6LN — BChir 1996 Camb.

DAVIES, Philip Seymour The Old School House, Church Road, Tideford, Saltash PL12 5HW — MB BCh 1973 Wales; MRCGP 1979.

DAVIES, Philip Sydney Royal Glamorgan Hospital, Llantrisant, Pontyclun CF72 8XR Email: phil.daviespr-tr-wales.nhs.uk; 106 Heol ISAF, Radyr, Cardiff CF15 8EA Tel: 029 2041 9680 Email: philbrendadavies@hotmail.com — MB BS Lond. 1966; FRCP Lond. 1991; MRCP (UK) 1971. (Lond. Hosp.) Cons. Phys. Roy. Glam. Hosp. Llantrissant. Socs: Brit. Soc. Gastroenterol. & Brit. Pharmacol. Soc.; Brit. Assn. of Med. Managers. Prev: Sen. Regist. (Med.) Univ. Hosp. Wales; Sen. Regist. (Clin. Pharmacol.) W. Middlex. & Univ. Coll. Hosps.

DAVIES, Polly Miriam 555 Warwick Road, Solihull B91 1AW Tel: 0121 705 3040; Mayden House, 5 Main St, Westbury, Brackley NN13 5JR Tel: 01280 701695 — MB ChB 1991 Bristol; FRCA 1999; DCH 1996; DA 1994. Specialist Regist. Anaesth.Oxf. Prev: PHO Anaesth.Nam Dour Gen Hosp.Australia; SHO Paediat.Derriford Hosp Plymouth; SHO Anaesth.Derriford Hosp. Plymouth.

DAVIES, Mr Quentin 61 Oxford Road, Moseley, Birmingham B13 9ES — MB BS 1984 Lond.; FRCS Ed. 1990; MRCOG 1993. Research Regist. (O & G) Qu. Med. Centre Nottm.

DAVIES, Rachel Caroline Sarah 21 Jordanstown Road, Newtownabbey BT37 0QD — MB ChB 1995 Leic.

DAVIES, Rachel Eirlys Crosswinds, The Drive, Old Road, Acle, Norwich NR13 3RF — LRCPI & LM, LRSCI & LM 1970; LRCPI & LM, LRCSI & LM 1970; FFA RCS Eng. 1975. Cons. Anaesth. James Paget Hosp. Gorleston. Prev: Sen. Regist. (Anaesth.) S. Glam. & Gwent AHAs; Regist. (Anaesth.) Univ. Hosp. Wales Cardiff.

***DAVIES, Rachel Jane** 5 Victory Road, Wanstead, London E11 1UL — MB BS 1994 Lond.; BSc (Hons.) Lond. 1992.

DAVIES, Rachel Louise 21 Clwyd Avenue, Prestatyn LL19 9NG — MB ChB 1990 Manch.

DAVIES, Raymond Malpas Brook Health Centre, 107 Malpas Road, Newport NP20 5PJ Tel: 01633 855808 Fax: 01633 859414; Barncroft, 3 Fields Pk Avenue, Newport NP20 5BG — MB BCh 1968 Wales.

DAVIES, Mr Raymond Arthur Charles (retired) Malvern House, 10 Alexandra Road, Gloucester GL1 3DR — BSc (Anat.) Lond. 1956, MB BS 1959; FRCS Eng. 1965; MRCS Eng. LRCP Lond. 1959. Prev: Cons. Orthop. & Traum. Surg. Gloucs. HA.

DAVIES, Raymond Kerry Hazeldene Private Orthopaedic Clinic, 11 Merley Park Road, Wimborne BH21 3DA Tel: 01202 885783 Fax: 01202 882669; 11 Merley Park Road, Wimborne BH21 3DA Tel: 01202 885946 Fax: 01202 882669 — MB BS 1963 Lond.; DObst RCOG 1968. (St. Bart.) Orthop. Phys. Poole Hosp. & ChristCh. Hosp. Socs: Fell. Roy. Soc. Med.; Brit. Inst. Musculoskel. Med.; BMA & Indep. Doctors Forum. Prev: Specialist (O & G) RAMC; SHO (Gyn.) St. Bart. Hosp. Lond.; Ho. Phys. St. Woolos Hosp. Newport.

DAVIES, Reginald Parker (retired) Carlton Croft, Langford Ride, Burley-in-Wharfedale, Ilkley LS29 7ES Tel: 01943 863921 — MRCS Eng. LRCP Lond. 1951.

DAVIES, Rhiannon Mary 4 Severn Close, Caerhowel, Montgomery SY15 6JE — MB ChB 1996 Liverp.

DAVIES, Rhodri Pennant Longford House Surgery, Longford Road, Holyhead LL65 1TR Tel: 01407 762341 Fax: 01407 761554; Tel: 01407 860160 — MB BCh 1984 Wales; MRCGP 1992. Prev: Gwynedd VTS Bangor.

DAVIES, Rhys Glyn Robin Hall, Llanbedr, Ruthin LL15 1SA Tel: 01824 2014 — MB BS 1950 Lond.; MRCS Eng. LRCP Lond. 1950; DObst RCOG 1956. (Lond. Hosp.) Prev: Ho. Surg. Hillingdon Hosp.

DAVIES, Richard Alan 34 Tabors Avenue, Great Baddow, Chelmsford CM2 7ET Tel: 01245 471799 Fax: 01245 471799 Email: dicdic@ndirect.co.uk — MB ChB 1973 Bristol. Prev: Clin. Asst. (Palliat. Med.) Farleigh Hospice Chelmsford; Princip. GP Chelmsford; SHO (Obst.) S.mead Hosp. W.bury-on-Trym.

DAVIES, Richard Alexander Health Centre Practice, Bromsgrove Street, Kidderminster DY10 1PG Tel: 01562 822077 Fax: 01562 823733 — MRCS Eng. LRCP Lond. 1974. (St. Bart.)

DAVIES, Richard Andrew The Hawthorn Drive Surgery, 206 Hawthorn Drive, Ipswich IP2 0QQ Tel: 01473 685070 Fax: 01473 688707; PO Box 205, Ipswich IP2 0QS Tel: 0585 080159 — MB BCh BAO 1988 Belf.; MA Oxf. 1981; MRCGP 1992. Clin. Asst. (Peritoneal Dialysis) Ipswich Hosp. Socs: Ipswich & Dist. Clin. Soc.; BMA.

DAVIES, Richard Anthony The Maudsley Hospital, Denmark Hill, London SE5 8AF — MB BS 1985 Lond.; MRCPsych 1991. Cons. Psychiat. Maudsley Hosp. Lond.

DAVIES, Richard Arthur North Street Health Centre, North Street, Ashby-de-la-Zouch LE65 1HU Tel: 01530 414131 — MB ChB 1973 Liverp. Clin. Asst. Ashby & Dist. Hosp. Leics.

DAVIES, Richard Goronwy Cornford House Surgery, 364 Cherry Hinton Road, Cambridge CB1 8BA Tel: 01223 247505 Fax: 01223 568187; 23 Peacock Drive, Bottisham, Cambridge CB5 9EF Email: richard@rgodi.demon.co.uk — BM BCh 1986 Oxf.; MA Camb. 1983; MRCP (UK) 1989; DFFP 1993; DCH RCP Lond. 1990. Socs: BMA; MDU.

DAVIES, Richard Gregory 14 Walnut Drive, Bishop's Stortford CM23 4JT — MB ChB 1994 Birm.; ChB Birm. 1994.

DAVIES, Richard Hugh Trevor 20 Scott Avenue, Weddington, Nuneaton CV10 0DP — MB BS 1996 Lond.; BSc Lond. 1993; AKC. (KCSMD)

DAVIES, Richard Huw Glanrhyd Hospital, Bridgend CF31 4LN — MB ChB 1982 Leic.; MRCPsych. 1988; T(Psych.) 1993; T(GP) 1991; DRCOG 1986. Cons. Gen. Adult Psychiat. with Special Responsibil. for Rehabil. Glanrhyd Hosp. Bridgend.; Hon. Lect. Univ. of Wales Coll. of Med. Prev: Sen. Regist. Rotat. S. Wales; Regist. (Psychiat.) Glanrhyd Hosp. Bridgend; Trainee GP Bridgend VTS.

DAVIES, Richard Nigel (retired) 43 The Whiteway, Cirencester GL7 2HH Tel: 01285 653076 — MB ChB 1954 Bristol; MRCGP 1976.

DAVIES, Richard Picton 29 Cwrt y Vil Road, Penarth CF64 3HP — MB ChB 1978 Manch.

DAVIES, Richard Rhys Ysbyty Gwynedd, Bangor LL57 2PW Tel: 01248 384384; Llannerch, Efailnewydd, Pwllheli LL53 5TH Tel: 01758 612564 — BM BCh 1996 Oxf. SHO (Gen. Med.

DAVIES, Richard Simon Department of Radiology, Morriston Hospital, Morriston, Swansea SA6 4XN Tel: 01792 703274 — MB BCh 1987 Wales; MRCP (UK) 1990; DMRD Liverp. 1992; FRCR 1993. Cons. Radiol., Morriston and Neath Hosp.s, W. Glam. Prev: Fell. Diagnostic Radiol. PA Hosp. Brisbane, Australia; Regist. (Radiol.) Mersey RHA; Sen. Regist. Roy. Liverp. Hosp.

DAVIES, Robert 3 Elm Grove Lane, Dinas Powys CF64 4AU — MB BCh 1981 Wales; FFA RCS Eng. 1987; FFA RCSI 1986. Cons. Anaesth. E. Glam. NHS Trust Ch. Village. Socs: Assn. Anaesth. & Soc. Computing & Technol. in Anaesth. Prev: Sen. Regist. (Anaesth.) S. Glam. HA.

DAVIES, Robert Bruce Wern Farm, Llanwrtyd Wells LD5 4SE — MB BS 1993 Lond. (St Georges Lond)

DAVIES, Robert Havard Bodwrdda, St. David Road, Caernarfon LL55 1EL Tel: 01286 684014 Fax: 01286 678552 — MB BChir 1966 Camb.; FRCP Lond. 1995; MRCP (UK) 1969. (Lond. Hosp.) Cons. Community Paediat. Caernarfon. Prev: Sen. Regist. Alder Hey Childr. Hosp.; Regist. Bristol Roy. Hosp. for Sick Childr.; Regist. (Paediat.) Plymouth Gen. Hosp.

DAVIES, Robert Hugh Chase Farm Hospital, The Ridgeway, Enfield EN2 8JL Tel: 020 8967 5906 Fax: 020 8967 5906 — MB BS 1983 Lond.; FRCP 1999; MD Lond. 1994; MRCP (UK) 1986; BSc Manch. 1974. Cons. Cardiol. Chase Farm Hosp. Enfield; Hon. Cons. (Cardiol.) N. Middlx. Hosp. Lond. Socs: Brit. Cardiovasc. Interven. Soc.; Brit. Cardiac Soc. Prev: Regist. (Cardiol.) Soton. Gen. Hosp.; Regist. (Med.) Lond. Hosp. Whitechapel & Chase Farm Hosp. Enfield.

DAVIES, Robert James 16 Armitage Court, Sunninghill, Ascot SL5 9TA — MB BS 1984 Lond.; BSc (Hons.) Lond. 1981, MB BS 1984; MRCP (UK) 1987; FRCR 1991. Cons. Radiol. Ashford Hosp. Middlx. Prev: Sen. Regist. (Radiol.) W.m. Hosp. Lond.; Regist. (Radiol.) St. Geo. Hosp. Lond.; SHO (Med.) Kingston Hosp. Surrey.

DAVIES, Robert John Bwlch-y-Domen, Isaf, Pant-y-Bwlch, Newcastle Emlyn SA38 9JF — MB BCh 1993 Wales.

DAVIES, Robert John Oriel Osler Chest Unit, Oxford Radcliffe Hospital, Headington, Oxford OX3 7LJ Tel: 01865 225230 Fax: 01865 225221; Bridge Cottage, Mill Lane, Lower Heyford, Bicester OX25 5PG Tel: 01869 347995 — BM 1985 Soton.; DM Soton. 1993; MRCP (UK) 1988; T(M) 1995; FRCP 1999. Cons. Respirat. Phys. Osler Chest Unit Oxf. Radcliffe Hosp.

DAVIES, Robert Neale Manselton Surgery, Elgin Street, Manselton, Swansea SA5 8QQ Tel: 01792 653643 / 642459 Fax: 01792 645257 — MB BCh 1986 Wales. GP Swansea.

DAVIES, Robert Paul Lloyd Cuffley Village Surgery, Maynards Place No.5, Cuffley, Potters Bar EN6 4JA Tel: 01707 875201 Fax: 01707 876756 — MB BS 1973 Lond.; DTM & H Liverp. 1980. (Roy. Free) Prev: SHO (Paediat.) Mayday Hosp. Thornton Heath; Ho. Off. (Trauma & Orthop.) Lister Hosp. Stevenage; Ho. Off. (O & G) Whipps Cross Hosp. Lond.

DAVIES, Mr Robert Price (retired) 4 Carrwood Road, Wilmslow SK9 5DL Tel: 01625 531166 — MD 1962 Manch.; BSc Manch. 1953, MD 1962, MB ChB 1958; FRCS Ed. 1964; FRCS Eng. 1966. Prev: Cons. Surg. Wythenshawe Hosp. Manch.

DAVIES, Robert Richard Manchester Diabetes Centre, 130 Hathersage Road, Manchester M13 0HZ Tel: 0161 276 6709 Fax: 0161 273 5181 Email: rdavies@dc.cmht.nwest.nhs.uk — MD 1991 Wales; MB BCh Wales 1978; FRCP Ed. 1996; FRCP (UK) 1997, MRCP 1981. (Wales) Cons. Phys. Manch. Roy. Infirm. Prev: Cons. Phys. Leighton Hosp. Crewe.

DAVIES, Robert William Malpas Brook Health Centre, 107 Malpas Road, Newport NP20 5PJ Tel: 01633 855808 Fax: 01633 859414; 3 Hawks Moor Close, Rogerstone, Newport NP10 0BX Tel: 01633 893160 — MB BS Lond. 1967. (St. Mary's) Socs: BMA.; Gwent Med.Soc. Prev: SHO Kingston Hosp.; Ho. Surg. S.lands Hosp. Shoreham; Ho. Phys. Putney Hosp. Lond.

DAVIES, Robin Cedar Ford, Withycombe, Minehead TA24 6QE — MB BCh 1974 Wales; MRCGP 1980.

DAVIES, Robin Maelor Northgate Village Surgery, Northgate Avenue, Chester CH2 2DX Tel: 01244 390396 Fax: 01244 370762

— MB BCh 1984 Wales; Dip Occ Med 2000; MRCP (UK) 1988; MRCGP 1991. Occupat.al Phys. to bank of Scotl. Socs: Mem. of Diabetes UK; Mem. of the Soc. of Occupat.al Med.
DAVIES, Robin Maredudd Hafod y Nant, Parc, Bala LL23 7YR Tel: 01678 520308 — MB ChB 1988 Liverp.
DAVIES, Robin Paul Peartree Lane Surgery, 110 Peartree Lane, Welwyn Garden City AL7 3XW Tel: 01707 329292 — MB BS 1982 Lond.; MRCGP 1986. Clin. Asst. (Ophth.) & GP Trainer Welwyn. Prev: Trainee GP Watford VTS.
DAVIES, Roger Carlisle Dept. of Oral Medicine, Eastman Dental Hospital, 256 Grays Inn Road, London WC1X 8LD Email: r.davies@eastman.ucl.ac.uk; Email: r.davies@eastman.ucl.ac.uk — MRCS Eng. LRCP Lond. 1984; BDS Lond. 1976; LRCP; RCS Ed; FDS. (Westminster Hospital) Cons. in Special Needs Dent. Socs: Brit. Assn. Oral & Maxillofacial Surg.; Internat. Assn. of Disabil. & Oral Health; Fareham Med. Soc. Prev: Assoc. Specialist in Oral Surg., Qu. Alexandria Hopital, Cosham.
DAVIES, Roger Donald Station Drive Surgery, Station Drive, Ludlow SY8 2AR Tel: 01584 872461 Fax: 01584 877971; Easter Bush, Richard's Castle, Ludlow SY8 4EU — MRCS Eng. LRCP Lond. 1980; BSc (Hons.) Med. Physics Lond. 1977, MB BS 1980; MRCGP 1986; DRCOG 1983. (Guy's)
DAVIES, Mr Roger Michael Maesywern, 20 Upper Heathfield Road, Pontardawe, Swansea SA8 4LE Tel: 01792 864098 Email: rmdavies@doctors.org.uk — BM BCh 1966 Oxf.; MA Oxf. 1966; FRCS Eng. 1974. (Oxf. & Univ. Coll. Hosp.) Hon Surgon Welshrugby Union 19 Gp.; Hon Med. Off. Neath RFC. Socs: Fell. BOA; BMA. Prev: Sen. Regist. (Orthop.) S. Glam. (Cardiff) HA (T) & Swansea Health Dist.; Regist. (Orthop.) Bristol. Roy. Hosps.; Cons. Orthop. Surg. Morriston Hosp. Swansea & Neath Gen. Hosp.
DAVIES, Roger Michael Watermill House, Trosserch Road, Llangenrech, Llanelli SA14 8AQ — MB BS 1978 Lond.
DAVIES, Roger Neil Abbey Medical Centre, 42 Station Road, Kenilworth CV8 1JD Tel: 01926 852576 — MB ChB 1974 Birm.; MRCP (UK) 1979; DCH Eng. 1979. (Birmingham (UK))
DAVIES, Rona Marie Eveleigh Pettitts Hall, Pudding La, Chigwell IG7 6BY — MB BS 1997 Lond.
DAVIES, Rosalyn Anne Department of Neuro-Otology, National Hospital for Neurol. & Neurosurg., Queen Square, London WC1N 3BG Tel: 020 7837 3611 Fax: 020 7829 8775 — MB BS 1979 Lond.; FRCP 1996; PhD Lond. 1989; BA Oxf. 1976; MRCP Ed. 1982. Cons. Neuro-Otol. Nat. Hosps. for Neurol. & Neurosurg. Lond.; Hon. Sen. Lect. Inst. Neurol. 1991; Hon. Sen. Lect. Inst. Child Health, 1999. Socs: Brit. Assn. Audiol. Phys.: Hon. Sec.; Specialist Advis. Comm. for Audiological Med. (RCP, Lond.), Sec.; Brit. Soc. of Audiol. Prev: Lect. (Clin. Neurochem.) Qu. Sq. Lond.
DAVIES, Rosemary (retired) The Leys, Church Lane, Gaydon, Warwick CV35 0EY Tel: 01926 640462 — MB BS Lond. 1945; MD Lond. 1950; FRCP Lond. 1980; FRCP Ed. 1971, M 1954; MRCS Eng. LRCP Lond. 1944; DCH Eng. 1946. Prev: Cons. Phys. (Gen. & Thoracic Med.) S. Warks. AHA.
DAVIES, Rosemary Anne Greenmeadow Surgery, Greenmeadow Way, Cwmbran NP44 3XQ — MB ChB 1977 Bristol.
DAVIES, Rowland Bullock (retired) Skinner House, Skinner Road, Lydd, Romney Marsh TN29 9DD Tel: 01797 321797 — MB ChB 1938 Liverp. Prev: Sen. Resid. Med. Off. Lake Hosp. Ashton-under-Lyne.
DAVIES, Roy James, Wing Cdr. RAF Med. Br. Retd. Gwelfor, The Links, Burry Port SA16 0HT — MB BCh 1958 Wales; FRCPsych 1982, M 1971; DPM Eng. 1964. (Cardiff) Socs: EEG Soc. Gt. Brit. & Internat. League Against Epilepsy. Prev: Cons. (Neuropsychiat.) RAF.
DAVIES, Roy Townley (retired) Station Road, Madeley, Crewe CW3 9PW Tel: 01782 750253 — MB ChB 1941 Liverp.
DAVIES, Royden 19 Wimpole Street, London W1M 7AD Tel: 020 7637 9933 Fax: 020 7323 0042; Flat 1, 84 Parkhill Road, London NW3 2YT Tel: 020 7424 9222 Fax: 020 7424 9222 — MB BS (Hons., Distinc. Med.) 1968; MD Lond. 1978; FRCP Lond. 1984; MRCP (UK) 1971; MRCS Eng. LRCP Lond. 1968. (Middlx.) Cons. Phys. & Cardiol. Whittington Hosp. Lond.; Hon. Sen. Lect. UCL. Socs: Brit. Card. Soc; Internat. Soc. Hypertens. & Med. Research Soc.; Director, Soc. for Widows and Orphans of Med. Men. Prev: Research Fell. Cardiovasc. Center New York Hosp. (Cornell Univ.) USA; Lect. & Sen. Regist. Middlx. Hosp. Lond.; SHO Hammersmith Hosp. Lond.
DAVIES, Russel James Evans 80 The High Street, Cranfield, Bedford MK43 0DG — MB BS 1995 Lond.
***DAVIES, Russell** 93 Outwood Road, Radcliffe, Manchester M26 1AY — MB ChB 1995 Leeds.
DAVIES, Russell John 4 Green Lane, Bayston Hill, Shrewsbury SY3 0NS — BM 1988 Soton. SHO (Psychiat.) Roy. S. Hants. Hosp. Soton. Prev: Ho. Off. (Med.) Roy. Oldham Hosp.
DAVIES, Russell Rupert 11 Rydal Way, Birmingham B28 9DA — MB BS 1992 Lond.
DAVIES, Ruth Eileen Woodview Medical Centre, 26 Holmecross Road, Thorplands, Northampton NN3 8AW Tel: 01604 670780 Fax: 01604 646208; The Red House, Creaton, Northampton NN6 8NH Tel: 0160 124484 — MB BS 1979 Lond.; DRCOG 1981. (Westm.) Prev: Trainee GP N.ampton VTS; SHO (Paediat. & O & G) N.ampton Gen. Hosp.
DAVIES, Ruth Margaret 8 Pearson Av, Leeds LS6 1JA — MB ChB 1997 Leeds.
DAVIES, Ruth Shirley (retired) Bramble Corner, 70 St Marys Road, Long Ditton, Surbiton KT6 5EY Tel: 0208 398 0353 Fax: 0208 398 0353 — BM BCh Oxf. 1957; MA Oxf. 1957. Clin. Med. Off. Richmond, Twickenham & Roehampton HA.
DAVIES, Sallie Lorraine 18 Deredun Close, Hursley, Winchester SO21 2JB — MB BS 1992 Lond.
DAVIES, Professor Sally Claire Department of Haematology, Central Middlesex Hospital, Acton Lane, London NW10 7NS Tel: 020 8453 2112 Fax: 020 8965 1115; 147 Hemingford Road, Islington, London N1 1BZ Tel: 020 8453 2112 Fax: 020 8965 1115 — MB ChB 1972 Manch.; MSc Lond. 1981; FRCP Lond. 1992; MRCP (UK) 1978; MRCPath 1982; FRCPCH 1997; FRCPath 1996; FFRPHM 1999. Dir. of Research & Developm. NHS Exec. Lond. region; Cons. Haemat. Centr. Middlx. Hosp. Lond.; Prof. Haemoglobinopathies 1997 Imperial Coll. Prev: Fell. Recombinant DWA Technol. & Hon. Lect. (Haemat.) Middlx. Hosp. Lond.; Lect. (Haemat.) & SHO (Paediat.) Middlx. Hosp. Lond.
DAVIES, Sally Louise The Portland Practice, St Paul's Medical Centre, 121 Swindon Road, Cheltenham GL50 4DP Tel: 01242 707792 — MB ChB 1988 Leic.; MRCGP 1995; DRCOG 1992. Clin. Asst. (Psychiat.) Tewkesbury; Community Med. Off. (Family Plann.) Cheltenham.
DAVIES, Sally Ruth 36 Boden Road, Birmingham B28 9DJ — MB ChB 1997 Liverp.
DAVIES, Samantha Denise Tonya Thornhill Park Road Surgery, 90 Thornhill Park Road, Thornhill, Southampton SO18 5TR Fax: 023 8047 0004 — BM 1991 Soton.; MRCGP 1998; BSc Soton. 1987; DRCOG 1997; DFFP 1997. (Soton.) p/t GP Princip. S.ampton; Clin. Asst. Rheum., S.ampton City PCT; Lead GP Teach. Univ. of S.ampton. Prev: SHO (Obst. & Gyn) Roy. Hants. Co. Hosp. Winchester; SHO (Med.) P.ss Margt. Hosp. Swindon.
DAVIES, Samuel Howard (retired) 31 Midmar Gardens, Edinburgh EH10 6DY Tel: 0131 447 5611 — MB ChB Ed. 1952; FRCP Ed. 1963, M 1961; FRCPath 1972. Prev: Cons. Haematol. S. E. Rhb (Scotl.).
DAVIES, Sandra Ruth Child & Adolescent Mental Health Service, Andrew Lang Unit, Viewfield Lane, Selkirk TD7 4LJ Tel: 01750 23392; 39 Ettrick Haugh Road, Selkirk TD7 5AX Tel: 01206 742158 — MB BS 1970 Lond.; MRCPsych 1975. (Kings College Hospital) Cons. Child & Adolesc. Psychiat. & Psychotherapist Borders Primary Care NHS Trust. Socs: Assn. Child Psychotherap.
DAVIES, Sara Joy 26/2 York Road, Edinburgh EH5 3EH Tel: 0131 551 1183 — MB ChB 1983 Ed.; MSc (Econ.) Lond. 1992; MRCGP 1989; DFFP 1996. Health Plann. Adviser Edin. Prev: Health Plann. Adviser, DFID, Zambia; Health Plann. Adviser ODA, Fiji; Dist. Med. Off. VSO, Zambia.
DAVIES, Sara Naomi Maudsley Hospital, Denmark Hill, London SE5 8AF Fax: 020 7277 1462 — MB ChB 1988 Manch.; MRCPsych 1992. Sen. Regist. (Psychiat.) Maudsley Hosp. Lond.
DAVIES, Sarah Elizabeth 78 Llantrisant Street, Cathays, Cardiff CF24 4JE Tel: 029 2037 3115 — MB BCh 1994 Wales. SHO (O & G) E. Glam. Gen. Hosp. Prev: SHO (Med.) P.ss of Wales Hosp. Bridgend.
DAVIES, Sarah Elizabeth 10 Biscay Road, London W6 8JN — MB BS 1996 Lond.
DAVIES, Sarah Jane 9 The Rise, Llanishen, Cardiff CF14 0RA — MB BChir 1978 Camb.; MB Camb. 1979, BChir 1978; MRCP (UK)

1981; MRCGP 1986. Cons. Med. Genetics Univ. Hosp. Wales Cardiff.

DAVIES, Sarah Jane 59 Chawn Hill, Stourbridge DY9 7JA — BM BS 1998 Nottm.; BM BS Nottm 1998.

DAVIES, Saroj 69 Ballbrook Court, Wilmslow Road, Manchester M20 3QT — MB BS 1961 Bombay.

DAVIES, Sheilagh 90 Liverpool Road, Islington, London N1 0RE Tel: 020 7359 2195 Fax: 020 7359 2195 — MB BS 1970 Lond.; MRCS Eng. LRCP Lond. 1969; FRCPsych 1990, M 1975; MBPS 1984; DObst RCOG 1972; DPM Eng. 1974. (Roy. Free) Cons. Psychother. Roy Free Hosp. Prev: Sen. Regist. (Psychiat.) Maudsley Hosp.; Lect. (Psychiat.) St. Bart. Hosp. Lond.; Regist. (Psych.) Univ. Coll. Hosp. Lond. & Nat. Hosp. Nerv. Dis.

DAVIES, Shirley Ann (retired) Underhill Barn, Putley, Ledbury HR8 2QR Tel: 01531 670787 — MB BS Lond. 1959. Prev: Ho. Phys. St. Mary's Hosp. Portsmouth.

DAVIES, Siân Angharad Department of Radiotherapy & Oncology, North Middlesex Hospital, Edmonton, London N18 1QX Tel: 020 8887 2284 Fax: 020 8887 4219 — MB BS 1973 Lond.; FRCP Lond. 1995; MRCP (UK) 1979; FRCR 1979. (St. Mary's) Med. Exec. Dir. & Cons. Radiother. & Oncol. N. Middlx. Hosp. NHS Trust. Prev: Sen. Regist. (Radiother. & Oncol.) Middlx. Hosp.; Regist. (Radiother. & Oncol.) Hammersmith Hosp. Lond.; SHO (Neurol. & Dermat.) St. Mary's Hosp. Lond.

DAVIES, Sian Anna Freer 56 Weeping Cross, Stafford ST17 0DL — MB BS 1979 Lond.; BSc Lond. 1976.

DAVIES, Sian Eleri Maes-y-Deri, 24 Glan-y-Mor Road, Loughor, Swansea SA4 6SA; 12 Gladstone Avenue, Twickenham TW2 7PR Tel: 020 8898 1352 Fax: 020 8898 1352 — MB BCh 1979 Wales.

DAVIES, Sian Mair Worth House, High St., Somerby, Melton Mowbray LE14 2PZ — MB BCh 1991 Wales; MRCGP 1996; DRCOG 1995.

DAVIES, Sian Wyn Glyn Ebwy Surgery, James Street, Ebbw Vale NP23 6JG Tel: 01495 302716 Fax: 01495 305166; Ty Estoril, 2 White House Gardens, Little Mill, Pontypool NP4 0HW — MB BS 1987 Lond.; MRCGP 1992; DRCOG 1990. Prev: Trainee GP/SHO Nevill Hall Hosp. Abergavenny VTS.

DAVIES, Simon James Flat 9, 5 Penleys Grove Street, York YO31 7PN — MB ChB 1997 Ed.

DAVIES, Simon John Renal Unit, North Staffs Hospital Trust, Hartshill, Stoke-on-Trent ST4 7LN Tel: 01782 554164 Fax: 01782 554745 Email: simondavies1@compuserve.com; 88 Basford Park Road, Newcastle ST5 0PP — MB BS 1981 Lond.; MD Lond. 1989, BSc 1978; MRCP (UK) 1984; FRCP 1997. (King's College Hospital London) Cons. Renal Med. N. Staffs. Hosp. Trust; Sen. Lect. Sch. Postgrad. Med. Univ. Keele. Socs: Renal Assn.; Eur. Renal Assn.; Corresp. Mem. Amer. Soc. Nephrol. Prev: Sen. Regist. (Renal Med.) N. Staffs. Roy. Infirm.

DAVIES, Simon Jonathan 42 Malden Road, London NW5 3HG — MB BS 1994 Lond.

DAVIES, Simon Jonathan Cheshire Cmar, Croft Drive, West Kirby, Wirral CH48 2JN — MB BS 1993 Lond.

DAVIES, Simon Vyvyan Department of Haematology, Taunton & Somerset Hospital, Musgrove Park, Taunton TA1 5DA Tel: 01823 333444 Fax: 01823 271023 Email: simon.davies@tauntonsom-tr.swest.nhs.uk — MB BS 1982 Lond.; BSc (Hons.) Anat. & Med. Lond. 1979, MD 1992; MRCPath 1992; MRCP (UK) 1985; FRCPath 2000. (Guy's) Cons. Haemat. Taunton & Som. Hosp. & Yeovil Dist. Hosp. Prev: Lect. (Haemat.) Univ. Wales Coll. Med.

DAVIES, Simon William Cardiac Department, The Royal Brompton Hospital, Sydney St., London SW3 6NP Tel: 020 7351 8610 Fax: 020 7351 8131; Cardiac Department, Chelsea & Westminster Hospital, 369 Fulham Road, London SW10 9NH Tel: 020 8746 8039 Fax: 020 8746 8040 — MB BS 1981 Lond.; MA Camb. 1981; FRCP 1998; MRCP (UK) 1984. Cons. Cardiol. Roy. Brompton Hosp. & Chelsea & W.m. Healthcare Trust; Co-Dir. Cardiac Catheterisation Laborat.; Lect. & Tutor Nat. Heart & Lung Inst. Socs: Fell. Roy. Soc. Med.; Med. Res. Soc.; Yeoman Soc. of Apoth. Prev: Sen. Regist. (Cardiol.) Lond. Chest Hosp.

DAVIES, Sioned Seaton Oak Street Surgery, Oak Street, Cwmbran NP44 3LT Tel: 01633 866719 Fax: 01633 838208 — MB BCh 1993 Wales; MRCGP 1997; DFFP. (UWCM) GP Princip. Oak St. Surg. Cwmbran. Prev: GP Regist. Abersychan Surg. Pontypool; SHO (A & E) Nevil Hall Hosp. Abergavenny; SHO (Psychiat.) Ty Sirhowy Ment. Health Unit Caerphilly.

DAVIES, Steffan Arnold Lodge, Cordelia Close, Leicester LE5 5UB Tel: 0116 225 6100 Email: drsteffand@aol.com — MB ChB 1989 Manch.; MRCPsych 1993; CCST Gen Psychiat (Rehabil) 1998. Sen. Regist. (Forens. Psychiat.) Leics. Ment. Health Servs. Prev: Regist. Rotat. (Psychiat.) Mid. Trent Train. Scheme; SHO Rotat. (Psychiat.) Nottm. Train. Scheme; Ho. Off. (c/o Elderly, Gen. Med. & Neurosurg.) Manch. Roy. Infirm.

DAVIES, Stephanie Ann Child Development Centre, Danestrete Centre, Southgate, Stevenage SG1 1HB Tel: 01438 314333; Cheyne End, 55 Orchard Road, Tewin, Welwyn AL6 0HL Tel: 01438 798231 — MB BS Lond. 1967; BSc (Physiol.) Lond. 1964; MRCS Eng. LRCP Lond. 1967; DA Eng. 1969. (Roy. Free) Cons. Community Paediat. N. Herts. NHS Trust. Socs: BMA; Fell. Roy. Coll. of Paediat. and Child Health; Brit. Assn. Community Child Health. Prev: SCMO N. Herts.; Clin. Med. Off. N. Herts.; Regist. Anaesth. Lister Hosp.

DAVIES, Stephen 32 Mildenhall Road, Slough SL1 3JE — MB BS 1982 Lond.

DAVIES, Stephen Carlton Larwood Health Centre, 56 Larwood, Worksop S81 0HH Tel: 01909 500233 Fax: 01909 479722 — MB BS 1987 Lond.

DAVIES, Mr Stephen Donald Lewis White House, Aberedw, Builth Wells LD2 3UW — MB BS 1994 Lond.; BSc Lond. 1991, MB BS 1994; FRCS 1999.

DAVIES, Stephen Griffith Royal Glamorgan Hospital, Llantrisantt, Cardiff CF72 8XR Tel: 01443 443563 Fax: 01443 443367 Email: stephen.davies@pr-tr.wales.nhs.uk — MB BChir 1981 Camb.; MA Camb. 1981; MRCP (UK) 1984; FRCR 1989; T(R) (CR) 1991. Cons. Radiol. Pontypridd & Rhondda NHS Trust. Socs: Brit. Soc. Skeletal Radiologists. Prev: Sen. Regist. (Radiol.) Roy. Lond. Hosp.; Ho. Phys. (Med. & Renal Units) Roy. Lond. Hosp.

DAVIES, Stephen James c/o The Royal Hospital, Calow, Chesterfield S44 5BL — MB BCh 1972 Wales; BDS Birm. 1962; FDS RCS Eng. 1966. Cons. (Oral Surg.) Chesterfield & N. Derbysh. Hosps. & Chas. Clifford; Dent. Hosp. Sheff.

DAVIES, Stephen John 175 Leigh Sinton Road, Malvern WR14 1LB — MB ChB 1997 Manch.

DAVIES, Stephen Lewis (retired) 37 Holly Avenue, Breaston, Derby DE72 3BG — MB BCh 1953 Wales; MRCPsych 1971; DPM Durham. 1958. Prev: Cons. Psychiat. Notts. AHA (T).

DAVIES, Stephen Paul 9 Beaufort Court, Atlantic Wharf, Schooner Way, Cardiff CF1 4AH — MB BCh 1991 Wales; DGM RCP Lond. 1994.

DAVIES, Stephen Peter Little Brym, Hope, Leighton, Welshpool SY21 8JD — BChir 1982 Camb.; MRCP (UK) 1985. Research Fell. Dept. Med. Char. Cross Hosp. Lond.

DAVIES, Mr Stuart James Mansell (cons. rooms) Clare Park Clinic, Crondall Lane, Crondall, Farnham GU10 5DT Tel: 01252 850216; Grasmere, 13 Abbotswood, Guildford GU1 1UX Tel: 01483 565541 — BM BCh 1971 Oxf.; MA Oxf. 1971; FRCS Eng. 1976; Spec. Accredit. Orthop. RCS Eng. 1987. Cons. Trauma & Orthop. Surg. Frimley Pk. Hosp. Prev: Sen. Regist. (Orthop.) St. Geo. Hosp. & SW Thames Region; Lect. (Orthop.) Univ. Witswaterand S. Afr.

DAVIES, Susan Elizabeth Department of Histopathology, Royal Free Hospital School of Medicine, Pond St., London NW3 2QG Tel: 020 7794 0500 — MB BS 1983 Lond.; MRCPath 1993. Prev: Cons. Path. Worthing Hosp.; Sen. Regist. St. Bart. Hosp. Lond.; Lect. King's Coll. Sch. Med. & Dent. Lond.

DAVIES, Susan Helen The Towers Surgery, 163 Holton Road, Barry CF63 4HP Tel: 01446 734131 Fax: 01446 420002 — MB BCh 1982 Wales; DRCOG 1986.

DAVIES, Susan Jane Tawstock Medical Centre, 7 High Street, Chard TA20 1QF Tel: 01460 67763 Fax: 01460 66044; The Thatch Cottage, Stony Knaps, Near Winsham, Chard TA20 4NY Tel: 01460 301 88 — MB BS 1987 Lond.; MRCGP 1997; Cert. Family Plann. JCC 1990; DRCOG 1990. (St Georges) GP. Prev: Trainee GP Gt. Bookham Surrey; SHO (O & G, Psychiat., Paediat. & Accid & Emerg.) Epsom Dist. Hosp.; GP Tadworth, Surrey.

DAVIES, Susan Lynn Tel: 01458 841122 Fax: 01458 840044; The Tree House, Mounsdon, Butleigh, Glastonbury BA6 8SN — MB ChB (Hons.) Liverp. 1977; BA (Hons.) Camb. 1974; MRCGP 1982; DRCOG 1981; DCH RCP Lond. 1981.

DAVIES, Sydney Walter Vivian (retired) 17 Trecobeas Road, Falmouth TR11 2JB Tel: 01326 212156 Fax: 01326 212156 — MB BCh 1944 Wales; BSc Wales 1941, MB BCh 1944; MRCGP 1970. Prev: Dir. Swansea Mass Min. X-Ray Unit.

DAVIES, Tara Denise 37 Old Cardiff Road, Llantrisant, Pontyclun CF72 8DG — MB BS 1993 Lond.; BSc (Immunol.) Lond. 1990, MB BS 1993. Trainee GP E. Glam. VTS.

DAVIES, Teifion Wynne United Medical & Dental Schools, Academic Unit of Psychiatry, Guys,Kings St. Thomas Campus, St Thomas' Hospital, London SE1 7EH Tel: 020 7928 9292 Fax: 020 7633 0061 Email: teifion.davies@kcl.ac.uk — MB BS 1976 Lond.; PhD Lond. 1983, BSc 1973; MRCPsych 1991; DPMSA (Distinc.) 1980. Sen. Lect. (Community Psychiat.) Div. Psychiat. GKTUniv. Lond.; Edit. Adviser Brit. Med. Jl. Lond. Prev: Lect. United Med. & Dent. Schs. Univ. Lond.; Regist. (Psychiat.) Guys Hosp. Lond.; Lect. (Physiol.) Guy's Hosp. Med. Sch. (UMDS).

DAVIES, Terence Rees Davies and Partners, Meddygfa Teilo, Crescent Road, Llandeilo SA19 6HL Tel: 01558 823435 Fax: 01558 824045 — MB BCh 1967 Wales; FRCGP 1991, M 1979; DObst RCOG 1968. (Cardiff) GP & CME Tutor Carmarthen. Prev: Ho. Phys. Llandough Hosp. Penarth; Ho. Surg. United Cardiff Hosps.; Ho. Surg. (O & G) Cardiff Roy. Infirm. & Matern. Hosp.

DAVIES, Terence Stanley (retired) Armco House, 204 Llantarnam Road, Cwmbran NP44 3BH Tel: 0163 333697 — MRCS Eng. LRCP Lond. 1936; FRCPsych 1972; DPM Eng. 1951. Prev: Phys. Supt. & Cons. Psychiat. Llanfrechfa Grange Hosp. Cwmbran.

DAVIES, Thomas Douglas Walton (retired) 23 Scotts Avenue, Shortlands, Bromley BR2 0LG Tel: 020 8460 9259 — BA (Hons.) Camb. 1948, MB BChir 1950; FFA RCS Eng. 1957; DA Eng. 1955. Cons. Anaesth. King's Coll. Hosp. Lond. Prev: Sen. Regist. (Anaesth.), Jun. Anaesth. & Cas. Off. King's Coll. Hosp.

DAVIES, Thomas Elwyn Cheddar Medical Centre, Roynon Way, Cheddar BS27 3NZ Tel: 01934 742061 Fax: 01934 744374 Email: elwyn.davies@chedmed.nhs.uk; Victoria House, Barrows Park, Cheddar BS27 3AZ Tel: 01934 743984 Email: elwyn@vichouse.fsnet.co.uk — MB BChir 1988 Camb.; MA Camb. 1986; MRCGP 1993; DRCOG 1992; DCH RCP Lond. 1992.

DAVIES, Thomas Gruffydd Cefn Coed Hospital, Swansea SA2 0GH — MD 1971 Wales; MB BCh 1960; FRCPsych 1980, M 1973; DPM Eng. 1965. (Cardiff) Cons. Psychiat. Cefn Coed Hosp. Swansea. Prev: Asst. Psychiat. Cefn Coed Hosp. Swansea; Ho. Phys. Llandough Hosp. Penarth; Ho. Surg. Cardiff Roy. Infirm.

DAVIES, Mr Thomas Gwilym George (retired) Roslyn, 25 Keats Avenue, Littleover, Derby DE23 7EE Tel: 01332 513449 — MB BS Lond. 1955; BA (Art Hist.) Nottm. 1995; FRCS Eng. 1965; MRCS Eng. LRCP Lond. 1955; FRCOphth 1988; DO Eng. 1963. Prev: Cons. Ophth. Surg. Derbysh. Roy. Infirm. Derby.

DAVIES, Thomas Gwynfor Century House, 52-54 Endless St., Salisbury SP1 3UH Tel: 01722 429430 Fax: 01722 429479 — MB ChB 1978 Birm.; BSc (Hons.) Birm. 1975; MRCPsych 1983. Cons. Psychiat. Old Manor Hosp. Salisbury.

DAVIES, Thomas James Wyndham Tel: 01895 234440 Fax: 01895 272885 — MB BS 1978 Lond. (Char. Cross Hosp.) Gen. Practitioner; Director Harmony GP Co-op.

DAVIES, Thomas Jeffrey Bradford Royal Infirmary, Duckworth Lane, Bradford BD9 6RJ Tel: 01272 364191 Fax: 01274 364232 Email: jeffrey.davies@bradfordhospitals.nhs.uk; Dial House, 18 Uppingham Road, Oakham LE15 6JD Tel: 0788 182 6843 Fax: 01572 771685 Email: drjeffdavies@bigfoot.com — MB BS Lond. 1966; FRCPath 1988, M 1975. (Westm.) Cons. Chem. Pathologist, The Leeds Teachg. Hosp.s & Bradford Hosp.s NHS Trust Dept. of Clin. Biochem.ry & Imunology Bradford Roy. Infirm. Socs: Fell. Roy. Soc. Med.; Assn. Clin. Biochem. Prev: Dir. Med. Servs. Pembrokesh. NHS Trust; Cons. Chem. Path. Burton Hosps.; Cons. Chem. Path. Riyadh Al Kharj Hosp. Progr.

DAVIES, Thomas Maldwyn 124 Derwen Fawr Road, Swansea SA2 8DP — MRCS Eng. LRCP Lond. 1943. (St. Bart.) Capt. RAMC. Socs: BMA. Prev: Cas. Ho. Surg. & Sen. Ho. Surg. St. Bart. Hosp.

DAVIES, Thomas Mark Hazlemere, Idole, Carmarthen SA32 8DG — MB ChB 1995 Leeds.

DAVIES, Thomas Meredith Yaxley Group Practice, Yaxley Health Centre, Landsdowne Road, Yaxley, Peterborough PE7 3JX Tel: 01733 240478 Fax: 01733 244645; The Coach House, Norman Cross, Peterborough PE7 3TB Tel: 01733 240178 Fax: 01733 243968 Email: 100102.1743@compuserve.com — MB BS 1973 Lond.; FRCGP 1988, M 1978. (St. Marys) Prev: Chairm. RCGP Computing Comm.; Dep. Vice-Chairm. Roy. Coll. Gen. Practs.; Course Organiser & Trainee GP P'boro. VTS.

DAVIES, Thomas Stephen Graham Biolab Medical Unit, The Stone House, 9 Weymouth St., London W1W 6DB Tel: 020 7636 5959 Fax: 020 7580 3910 — BM BCh 1973 Oxf.; MA, BM BCh Oxf. 1973; LMCC 1976; Licentiate Med. Counc. Canada 1976. (Westm.) Dir., Biolab Med. Unit, Lond.; Med. Adviser (Hyperactive Childr. Support Gp.) Foresight. Socs: Fell. Amer. Coll. Nutrit. & Roy. Soc. Med.; Founder Chairm. Brit. Soc. for Nutrit. Med.; BMA. Prev: Asst. Med. Off. Harbour Breton, Newfld., Canada.; Ho. Surg. Kingston Hosp., Kingston upon Thames; Ho. Phys. Hereford Co. Hosp.

DAVIES, Mr Thomas Tibbott Plas-y-Coed, Aberdovey LL35 0NA — MRCS Eng. LRCP Lond. 1938; FRCS Ed. 1947. (Guy's) Prev: Cons. Surg. Passmore Edwd.s Hosp. Liskeard; Ho. Surg. Roy. United Hosp. Bath.; Surg. Regist. Mt. Gold Orthop. Hosp. Plymouth.

DAVIES, Thomas Whitney c/o Department of Public Health & Primary Care, Institute of Public Health, University Forvie Site, Robinson Way, Cambridge CB2 2SR Tel: 01223 330318 Fax: 01223 330330 Email: twd10@medschl.cam.ac.uk; 85 Chesterton Road, Cambridge CB4 3AP — MB BChir 1964 Camb.; MD Camb. 1969; FFCM 1986, M 1979. (Camb.) Univ. Lect. (Pub. Health.) Univ. Camb.; Hon. Cons. Pub. Health Med. Camb. & Huntingdon HA; Lect. (Community Med.) Univ. Camb.; Gen. Dir. E. Anglian Cancer Registry. Socs: BMA & Soc. for Social Med. Prev: Regist. (Med.) King's Lynn Gen. Hosp.; Med. Off. Brit. Solomon Is.s Protec.

DAVIES, Timothy (retired) 80 Leybourne Avenue, Bournemouth BH10 6HE Tel: 01202 526077 — MB BS 1963 Lond.; MRCS Eng. LRCP Lond. 1963; DObst RCOG 1966. Prev: Gen. Practitoner, Bournemouth.

DAVIES, Timothy Arlingham East Street Medical Centre, 18-20 East Street, Littlehampton BN17 6AW Tel: 01903 731111 Fax: 01903 732295; 81 Sea Road, East Preston, Littlehampton BN16 1LN Tel: 01903 783846 Fax: 01903 859129 Email: tdaviesuk@aol.com — BM Soton. 1982; MSc Lond. Business Sch. 1970; MA Oxf. 1971, BA 1968; MRCGP 1987; DFF P 1996; DCH RCP Lond. 1985. (Soton.) Prev: Trainee GP Frimley Pk. VTS; Ho. Phys. Roy. S. Hants. Hosp.; Ho. Surg. Soton. Gen. Hosp.

DAVIES, Timothy Charles Tel: 01707 273338 Fax: 01707 263564; Skimpans Farm House, Bulls Lane, North Mymms, Hatfield AL9 7PE Tel: 01707 271503 — MRCS Eng. LRCP Lond. 1964. (Guy's) p/t Gen. Pract. Prev: Cardiac Regist. Lond. Hosp.; Res. Med. Off. Nat. Heart Hosp. Lond.; Ho. Phys. & Ho. Surg. Guy's Hosp. Lond.

DAVIES, Timothy Edward Pierce Worcestershire Health Authority, Isaac maddox House, Shrubb Hill Road, Worcester WR4 9RW Tel: 01905 760065; Marlcliff Farm House, The Bank, Marlcliff, Bidford-on-Avon, Alcester B50 4NT — MB BS 1985 Lond.; MFPHM RCP (UK) 1993. Cons. Pub. Health Med.Worcs. Health Auth.

DAVIES, Timothy James Maes-y-Deri House, 1 Heol Wastad Waun, Pencoed, Bridgend CF35 6UY — MB BCh 1986 Wales.

DAVIES, Timothy James 20 Lupin Drive, Huntingdon, Chester CH3 6SD — BM BS 1994 Nottm.; BMedSci. 1992. Ho. Off. (Gen. Surg.) Qu. Med. Centre Univ. Hosp. Nottm.

DAVIES, Tina Louise 28 Irk Vale Drive, Chadderton, Oldham OL1 2TW — MB ChB 1994 Ed.

DAVIES, Toby Morley Ludgershall Health Centre, Central St., Ludgershall, Andover SP11 9RA Tel: 01264 790356 — MB ChB 1985 Birm.; MRCGP 1993.

DAVIES, Mr Tony Wynne Surgical Dept, Queen Marys Hospital, Sidcup DA14 6LT Tel: 020 8308 3283 Fax: 020 8308 3219 — MB BCh 1975 Wales; FRCS Ed. 1981. Cons. Gen. Surg., Queeen Mary's Hosp., Sidcup, Kent.

DAVIES, Tudor Griffiths (retired) 84 Liverpool Road, Penwortham, Preston PR1 0HT Tel: 01772 749566 — MB BS 1955 Lond. Prev: GP Preston.

DAVIES, Ursula Mary Dept. of Rheumatology, East Surrey Hospital, Canada Avenue, Redhill RH1 5RH; Hurley House, 20 College Road, Epsom KT17 4EY — MB BS 1980 Lond.; MRCP (UK) 1984; FRCP 1999. (St Bartholomew's Hospital Medical College) Cons. Phys. & Rheumatol. E. Surrey Hosp. Redhill. Socs: Brit. Soc.

for Rheum.; BMA. Prev: Sen. Regist. (Rheum. & Gen. Med.) St Mary's, W.m., Char. Cross & Qu. Mary's Hosps. Lond.; Research Regist. MRC Clin. Research Centre Middlx.; Regist. (Rheum and Gn Med.) MRC Clin. Research Centre Middlx.

DAVIES, Valerie Gwynne Brookside, Willow Way, Baglan, Port Talbot SA12 8TP Tel: 01639 813917 — MB BCh 1955 Wales; BSc, MB BCh Wales 1955. (Cardiff) Prev: Ho. Off. E. Glam. Hosp., Swansea Gen. Hosp. & Bridgend Hosp.

DAVIES, Valerie Temple (retired) sharanam, 11 Nelson St, Thame OX9 2DP Tel: 01844 212506 Email: valtempledavies@aol.com — MB ChB 1961 Ed.; DObst RCOG 1963. Prev: GP Blackpool.

DAVIES, Vincent John Elliott (retired) 30 Woolacott Drive, Newton, Swansea SA3 4RR Tel: 01792 368851 — MRCS Eng. LRCP Lond. 1948; MA, BM BCh Oxon. 1949. Prev: Asst. Pathol. Oldham Hosp. Gp.

DAVIES, Vivian Buckley Maes-y-Coed Doctors Surgery, Maes-y-Coed, Glandwr Park, Builth Wells LD2 3DZ Tel: 01982 552207 Fax: 01982 553826 — MB BS 1970 Lond.; Dip. Pall. Med. Cardiff 1998; DObst RCOG 1972; DA Eng. 1978. (St. Thos.) Prev: Ho. Off. Barnet Gen. Hosp.; Govt. Med. Off. Zambia.; Princip. Gen. Pract., Builth Wells, Powys.

DAVIES, Vivian Mansel Davies and Lawson, Station Road, Congresbury, Bristol BS49 5DX Tel: 01934 832158 Fax: 01934 834165; 5 Durban Way, Yatton, Bristol BS49 4QZ Tel: 01934 833727 — MRCS Eng. LRCP Lond. 1969.

DAVIES, Vivien Jones (retired) Harlech, Monmouth Road, Raglan NP15 2LA — MB BCh 1947 Wales; BSc Wales 1944, MB BCh 1947. Prev: Ho. Phys. & Ho. Surg., & Ho. Surg. O & G Dept. Morriston Hosp.

DAVIES, Walford Farr Thomas Ty-Elli Surgery, Vauxhall, Llanelli SA15 3BD Tel: 01554 772040; Hillside, 114 New Road, Llanelli SA15 3DT Tel: 01554 773053 — MB BS 1953 Lond.; LMSSA Lond. 1953; DObst RCOG 1957. (Guy's) Clin. Asst. (Geriat.) Bryntirion Hosp. LLa.lli; Employm. Med. Adviser (Dyfed Area); Med. Off. LLa.lly Govt. Train. Centre. Brit. Leyland & Ina Needle Bearings, LLa.lli. Prev: SHO. (Surg.) & Med. Regist Swansea Gen. Hosp.; Obst. Ho. Off. Neath Gen. Hosp.

DAVIES, Warren Adrian Gethin, Davies and Knowles, Harris Memorial Surgery, Robartes Terrace, Illogan, Redruth TR16 4RX Tel: 01209 842515 Fax: 01209 842380 — MB ChB 1985 Bristol; DRCOG 1990; Dip. IMC RCS Ed. 1990; DCH RCP Lond 1988.

DAVIES, Wendy Gillian 2 Hole Lane, Bentley, Farnham GU10 5LP — MB BS 1992 Lond.; MRCP 1996; BSc 1989. (Roy.Free.Sch.Med)

DAVIES, William Alexander Douglas The Crown Surgery, 23 High Street, Eccleshall, Stafford ST21 6BW Tel: 01785 850226 — MB ChB 1991 Manch.

DAVIES, William Alun The Old Vicarage, Vicarage Terrace, Maesteg CF34 9PF Tel: 01656 733 3337 — MB BCh 1955 Wales. (Cardiff)

DAVIES, William Bernard 33 Hendy Close, Sketty, Swansea SA2 8BB Tel: 01792 206429 — MRCS Eng. LRCP Lond. 1955.

DAVIES, William Bryan, KStJ, OBE 15 Maindy Grove, Ton Pentre, Pontypridd CF41 7EY Tel: 01443 433650 — MB ChB Leeds 1956. (Leeds) Vice-Chairm. Pontypridd-Rhondda NHS Trust. Socs: (Pres.) Welsh Assn. LMC's. Prev: Regtl. Med. Off. 1st Bn. Roy. Irish Fusiliers; Cdr. St. John Ambul. Brig. (Wales); Ho. Off. (Gen. Med., Surg. & Paediat.) Leeds Gen. Infirm.

DAVIES, William Cynyw (retired) Wayside, Borth SY24 5LJ Tel: 01970 871383 — MRCS Eng. LRCP Lond. 1953. Prev: Ho. Phys. Maelor Gen. Hosp. Wrexham.

DAVIES, William Gwyn 2 High Street, Ruswarp, Whitby YO21 1NH Tel: 01947 603953 — MB BChir 1951 Camb.; MRCP Lond. 1954. (Camb. & Guy's)

DAVIES, Mr William Hugh Wye Valley Nuffield Hospital, Hereford HR1 1DF Tel: 01432 851179; Underhill Barn, Putley, Ledbury HR8 2QR — MRCS Eng. LRCP Lond. 1946; MA Camb. 1948, MChir 1971, MB BChir 1946; FRCS Eng. 1950. (Camb. & St. Thos.) Surg. & Urol. Hereford. Socs: Brit. Assn. Urol. Surgs.; Fell. Assn. Surgs. Gt. Brit. Prev: Cons. Surg. & Urol. Hereford Hosp. Gp.; Chief Asst. Dept. Urol. Newc-upon-Tyne Gen. Hosp.; Res. Asst. Surg. &c. St. Thos. Hosp.

DAVIES, William John Hollington Surgery, Blue Line Lane, Ashford TN24 8UN Tel: 01233 622361, 01233 624916 Fax: 01233 647621 Email: gp@g82049.nhs.uk; Knolly Cottage, Willesborough, Ashford TN24 0NJ Tel: 01233 623507 — MRCS Eng. LRCP Lond. 1967. (King's Coll. Hosp.) Prev: Ho. Off. (Surg.) Qu. Vict. Hosp. E. Grinstead; Ho. Off. (Med. & Anaesth.) Kent & Canterbury Hosp.; Ho. Off. (Obst.) Margate Gen. Hosp.

DAVIES, William Rhys Silverwood, North Rdad, Bath BA2 6HP — MB ChB 1998 Sheff.; MB ChB Sheff 1998.

DAVIES, William Ronald Arthur Hafryn, Old Highway, Colwyn Bay LL28 5UY — MB BS 1997 Lond.

DAVIES, Mr William Tudor (cons. rooms), Glamorgan House, BUPA Hospital, Cardiff CF23 8XL Tel: 029 2073 5825 Fax: 029 2073 5825; 1A Mill Road, Lisvane, Cardiff CF14 0XA Tel: 029 2076 2307 — MD Wales 1975, MB ChB 1963; FRCS Eng. 1967; FICAngiol. 1978. (Cardiff) Cons. (Gen. & Vasc. Surg.) S. Glam. AHA (T); Sen. Lect. & Hon. Cons. Welsh Nat. Sch. Med. Prev: Surg. Regist. Middlx. Hosp. Lond.; Sen. Regist. Univ. Hosp. Wales; Clin. Research Fell. Harvard Med. Sch. Univ. Hosp. Boston USA.

DAVIES, William Wood Mid Glamorgan County Council, Occupational Health Unit, Lanelay Hall, Pontyclun CF72 9XA Tel: 01443 238088 Fax: 01443 222319; Glebe House, Llanharry, Pontyclun CF72 9LH — MRCS Eng. LRCP Lond. 1976; MFOM 1991, A 1987; LLM 1991. (St. Mary's) Cons. Occupat. Med. Co. Occupat. Phys. Mid. Glam. Counc.; Dep. Regional Specialty Adviser (Wales) Fac. Occcupat. Med. Roy. Coll. Phys. Socs: Soc. Occupat. Med. & Assn. Local Auth. Med. Advisors. Prev: Dep. Area Med. Off. Brit. Coal S. Wales.

DAVIES, Winifred Mary Apple Glade, 18 Park Drive, Masham, Ripon HG4 4HY — MB ChB Leeds 1943; MRCS Eng. LRCP Lond. 1943. (Leeds) JP. Prev: Med. Off. (p/t) Regional Blood Transfus. Serv. Manch. Area.

DAVIES, Yvonne Mary Kent House Surgery, 36 Station Road, Longfield DA3 7QD Tel: 01474 703550; Pinetum, Fawkham Green Road, Fawkham, Longfield DA3 8NN Tel: 01474 874912 Email: davies@pinetum.demon.co.uk — MB BS 1978 Lond.; DRCOG 1980; DFFP 1993. (St. Mary's) Gen. Med. Practitioner; Occupat. Health Phys. John Lewis, Bluewater, Kent. Socs: Soc. Occupat. Med.; St Mary's Hosp. Soc.; Fac. of Family Plann. Prev: Trainee GP Luton VTS; Ho. Phys. & Ho. Surg. Qu. Eliz. II Hosp. Welwyn Garden City.

DAVIES-HUMPHREYS, Mr John Countess of Chester Hospital, Liverpool Road, Chester CH2 1UL Tel: 01244 366422 — MA, MB Camb. 1968, BChir 1967; FRCS Eng. 1972; FRCOG 1989, M 1974. (Middlx.) Cons. (O & G) Countess of Chester Hosp. Chester. Socs: Mem. of Brit. Gyn. cancer Soc. Prev: Sen. Regist. (O & G) King's Coll. Hosp. Lond.; Regist. (O & G) Lond. Hosp.; Regist. (O & G) Profess. Unit Univ. Hosp. of Wales Cardiff.

DAVIES-JONES, Gwilym Aelwyn Benjamin 695 Abbey Lane, Sheffield S11 9ND Tel: 0114 236 9702 Fax: 0114236 9702 Email: gabdavies-jones@ukgateway.net — MD 1968 Sheff.; MB ChB 1959 Sheff; FRCP Lond. 1978, M 1964. (Sheff.) Cons. (Neurol.) Roy. Hallamsh. Hosp. Sheff. Emerit. Socs: Assn. Brit. Neurol. Prev: Previously engaged in private Pract. and medico-legal Pract.and occasional NHS clinic locum; Sen. Regist. (Neurol.) United Oxf. Hosps.; Neurol. Regist. United Sheff. Hosps.

DAVIES-WRAGG, Caroline Braeside Surgery, Gorse Hill, Farningham, Dartford DA4 0JU Tel: 01322 862110 Fax: 01322 862991; The White House, Long Mill Lane, Dunks Green, Tonbridge TN11 9SD — MB BS 1983 Lond.; BSc Lond. 1977, MB BS 1983. (Charing Cross Hospital)

DAVIN, David William (retired) 3 Loughbrickland Road, Gilford, Craigavon BT63 6BH Tel: 01762 831373 — MB BCh BAO 1946 Belf. Prev: Ho. Surg. Roy. Devon & Exeter Hosp.

DAVIS, Mr Abram Albert 41 Chester Close N., London NW1 4JE — MD 1933 Manch.; ChM 1931, MB ChB 1925; FRCS Eng. 1931; FRCOG 1960.

DAVIS, Adrian John Gilbert The Health Centre, St. Mary's, I. of Scilly, Truro TR2 0LE Tel: 01720 22628 — MB BS 1961 Lond.; MRCS Eng. LRCP Lond. 1961; DObst RCOG 1964. (St. Mary's)

***DAVIS, Adrian Mark** 11 Middle Park Road, Birmingham B29 4BE — MB BCh 1997 Wales.

DAVIS, Alan Park Medical Centre, 19 Bridge Road, St Austell PL25 5HE Tel: 01726 73042 Fax: 01726 74349; 13 Carnsmerry Crescent, St Austell PL25 4NA Tel: 01726 75036 — MB ChB 1974 Bristol; FFA RCS Eng. 1980; MFHom Lond. 1987; DObst RCOG 1976. Clin. Asst. Cornw. Community Drugs Team.

DAVIS, Alan Jacob Norwood Road Surgery, 70a Norwood Road, Southall UB2 4EY Tel: 020 8574 1822 Fax: 020 8571 2175 — BM BCh 1976 Oxf.; BA Oxf. 1971, MSc 1974, MA 1975, BM BCh 1976; DCH Eng. 1980; DRCOG 1980. (Westm.) Socs: Asthma Soc. (Chairm. Ealing Br.); Med. Adviser to Nat. Assn. of Limbless Disabled.

DAVIS, Alan Kenneth BOC Group, 10 Priestley Road, Guildford GU2 7XY; Rookswood, Richmond Road, Godalming GU7 2ET — MBA 2001 Warwick; BA (Open) 1994; MB ChB St. And. 1970; MFOM RCP Lond. 1993, A 1979. (St. And.) Med. Adviser BOC Gp. Guildford. Prev: Sen. Occupat. Phys. BICC Gp.; GP Swindon.

DAVIS, Alexandra Psychiatric Unit, Lagan Valley Hospital, Lisburn BT28 1JP — MB BCh BAO 1984 Belf.; MRCPsych 1990; DGM RCP Lond. 1988.

DAVIS, Alicia 72 Colwith Road, London W6 9EY — MB BS 1998 Lond.; MB BS Lond 1998.

DAVIS, Alison Mary Department of Chemical Pathology, Warrington Hospital NHS Trust, Lovely Lane, Warrington WA5 1QG Tel: 01925 662132 Fax: 01925 662043; Tel: 01925 754672 — MB ChB 1984 Manch.; MRCPath 1994. (Manchester) Cons. Chem. Path. Warrington Hosp. Prev: Sen. Regist. (Chem. Path.) N. W.. RHA; Research Assoc. (Med.) Leicester Univ.; Regist. (Chem. Path.) Leicester HA.

DAVIS, Alison Ruth Eye Department, South Wing, St Thomas' Hospital, London SE1 7EH; 7 Bousfield Road, London SE14 5TP — BM 1989 Soton.; FRCOphth 1994. Regist. (Ophth.) St. Thos. Hosp. Lond. Prev: SHO (Ophth.) King's Coll. Hosp. Lond.; SHO (Ophth.) Mayday Hosp. Croydon.

DAVIS, Allan Raymond (retired) 21 Middlegate Court, Cowbridge CF71 7EF — LMSSA Lond. 1949; MRCS Eng. LRCP Lond. 1951; MFCM 1973; DPH Wales 1958. Prev: SCM Mid Glam. HA.

DAVIS, Amanda Veronica Heather Friarsgate Practice, Friarsgate Medical Centre, Friarsgate, Winchester SO23 8EF Tel: 01962 853599 Fax: 01962 849982; Trilleachan House, 13 Hinton Fields, Old Kings Worthy, Winchester SO23 7QB — MB ChB 1982 Leeds; MRCGP 1986; DRCOG 1986; Cert. Family Plann. JCC 1986. (Leeds) Prev: Trainee GP Airedale VTS; Ho. Off. (Med. & Surg.) Airedale Gen. Hosp.

DAVIS, Andrea Ellen 17 Clayton Croft Road, Wilmington, Dartford DA2 7AU — MB ChB 1995 Bristol.

DAVIS, Andrew John Macleod 4 Nursery Gardens, Romsey SO51 5UU — BM BCh 1993 Oxf.; MA Camb. 1994; MRCP 1996. Specialist Regist. Gastroenter. Soton. Gen. Hosp. Prev: Specialist Regist. Roy.bournemouth Hosp.; Specialist Regist. Jersey Gen.Hosp; Specialist Regist. Roy.United Hosp.Bath.

DAVIS, Angela 52 Bradley Avenue, Winterbourne, Bristol BS36 1HS Tel: 01454 778436 — MB ChB 1969 Leeds. Clin. Asst. (Psychiat.) Glenside Hosp. Bristol.

DAVIS, Anne Elise The Market Place Surgery, Cattle Market, Sandwich CT13 9ET Tel: 01304 613436/612589 Fax: 01304 613877; Chase Side, 44 Monkton Road, Minster, Ramsgate CT12 4EB Tel: 01843 822102 Fax: 01843 823321 Email: p.murray@mcmail.com — MB BS 1977 Lond.; MRCP (UK) 1981; MRCGP 1989. (University College Hospital, London.)

DAVIS, Annette Julia Margaret Dept. of Anaesthetics, Alder Hey Children's Hospital, Eaton Rd, Liverpool L12 2AP — MB ChB 1988 Ed.; FRCA 1994. Cons. Paediatric Anaesth.

DAVIS, Anthony Edward Avon Valley Practice, Fairfield, Upavon, Pewsey SN9 6DZ Tel: 01980 630221 Fax: 01980 630393; Paddock House, High St, Netheravon, Salisbury SP4 9QP Tel: 01980 670401 Fax: 01980 670401 — MB BS 1964 Lond.; MSc (Computer Sc.) Lond. 1971; MRCS Eng. LRCP Lond. 1964; FRACGP 1976. (Guy's)

DAVIS, Anthony Henry 55 Wellington Avenue, Wavertree, Liverpool L15 0EH — MB ChB 1996 Liverp.

DAVIS, Anthony John Antony Road Surgery, 16 Antony Road, Torpoint PL11 2JW Tel: 01752 813277 Fax: 01752 815733; Borough Farm House, Torpoint PL11 2PE — MB BS 1977 Lond.; BDS Lond. 1969; MRCS Eng. LRCP Lond. 1977; MRCGP 1993; FDS RCS Eng. 1973, LDS 1969. (Guy's)

DAVIS, Arthur George Kinnaird Steading, Pitlochry PH16 5JL Tel: 01796 470015 — MB ChB 1965 Glas.; FFA RCS Eng. 1969. (Glas.) p/t Cons. (Anaesth.) Tayside Univ. Hosp. NHS Trust. Socs: Scott. Soc. Anaesths. & Assn. Anaesths. Prev: Ho. Phys. Ruchill Hosp. Glas.; Ho. Surg. Vict. Infirm. Glas.; Sen. Regist. (Anaesth.) W.. Infirm. & S.. Gen. Hosp. Glas.

DAVIS, Barbara Lynne Cranfield, Gorsey Lane, Ashton-under-Lyne OL6 9BT — MB ChB 1966 Manch.; FFA RCS Eng. 1972; DObst RCOG 1968.

***DAVIS, Benjamin Jonathon** 1 Fir Close, Portal Park, Tarporley CW6 0TN Tel: 0780 390 7332 — MB BCh 1998 Wales.

DAVIS, Bernard Aisar 12 Magnolia Court, Blenkarne Road, London SW11 6JD — MB BS 1986 Ghana; MB BS U Ghana 1986; MRCP (UK) 1991.

DAVIS, Bramwell William The Limes Medical Centre, 5 Birmingham Road, Walsall WS1 2LX Tel: 01922 20303 Fax: 01922 649526; 5 Warren's Croft, Walsall WS5 3JX Tel: 0121 357 8708 — MB ChB 1956 Birm. (Birm.)

DAVIS, Mr Brian Clive Department of Otolaryngology, Wd 27, Ninewells Hospital, Dundee DD1 9SY Tel: 01382 566887 — MB ChB 1969 Glas.; FRCS Ed. 1975. Cons. ENT Ninewells Hosp. Dundee & Univ. Dundee Med. Sch. Prev: Sen. Regist. (ENT) Lothian HB; Regist. (ENT) Tayside HB; SHO (Surg.) Vict. Infirm. Glas.

DAVIS, Mr Brian Roger Blaencwm, Llangain, Carmarthen SA33 5AS Tel: 01267 241381 Fax: 01267 241381 — MB BS 1972 Lond.; BSc (Biochem.) Lond. 1969; FRCS Eng. 1979. (Univ. Coll. Lond. & Westm.) Cons. ENT Surg. E. Dyfed & Pembroke HA. Socs: Brit. Assn. Head & Neck Surg. Prev: Sen. Regist. (ENT) Univ. Hosp. Wales Cardiff; SHO (ENT) Bristol Gen. Hosp.; SHO (Cas.), Ho. Surg. & Ho. Phys. St. Stephen's Hosp. Lond.

DAVIS, Cecil James 27 Victoria Embankment, Nottingham NG2 2JY — MB BCh BAO 1948 Dub.; MA Dub. 1949, MB BCh BAO 1948; DObst RCOG 1952. (T.C. Dub.) Prev: Asst. Med. Off. Gen. Hosp. S. Shields; Res. Med. Off. Manor Hosp. Walsall; Res. Obst. Off. City Gen. Matern. Hosp. Sheff.

DAVIS, Mr Charles Harvey George Royal Preston Hospital, PO Box 66, Sharoe Green Lane, Preston PR2 4HT Tel: 01772 716565; Kilncroft, Bilsborrow Lane, Preston PR3 0RP — MB BS 1971 Lond.; FRCS Eng. 1978; MRCS Eng. LRCP Lond. 1971. (St. Bart.) Cons. Neurosurg. Roy. Preston Hosp. Socs: Soc. Brit. Neurol. Surgs.; Brit. Cervical Spine Soc. Prev: Sen. Regist. (Neurosurg.) Nat. Hosps. Lond.; Regist. (Neurosurg.) Guy's, King's Coll. & Maudsley Hosps. Lond.; Jun. Regist. (Neurosurg., Gen. & Plastic Surg.) St. Bart. Hosp. Lond.

DAVIS, Professor Christopher John, OBE, Surg. Cdr. RN Retd. Veridian Systems Division Inc, Suite 100, 1400 Key Boulevard, Arlington VA 22209, USA Tel: 703 516 6384 Fax: 703 524 2420 Email: christopher.davis1@virgin.net; 2 Spa Close, Brill, Aylesbury HP18 9RZ Tel: 01672 841418 Fax: 01672 841118 Email: christopherjohndavis@earthlink-net — MB BS 1976 Lond.; DPhil Oxf. 1989; BSc (Hons.) Lond. 1973; MFPM RCP (UK) 1995; FIBiol 1996, M 1995; CBiol 1995; AKC 1973. (King's Coll. Hosp.) Chief Scien. Adv & Dir of Office of Sci. & Technol. Info Scien. Sec. Veridian Systems Div. Inc Alexandria Virg. USA; Vistiing Prof of Med Cent for Biodefence Studied John Hopkins Univ Baltimore Maryland USA. Socs: BMA; Fell Roy. Soc. of Med. Prev: Dir the ORAQ consultancy Ltd; Naval Med. Off. (Liaison & Research) CBDE Porton Down; Cons. Applied Physiol. RN.

DAVIS, Christopher John Fursdon The Old Vicarage, 11 High St., Drayton, Abingdon OX14 4JL — MB ChB 1965 Bristol; PhD Bristol 1970, BSc 1962, MB ChB 1965; MRCP (U.K.) 1972. (Bristol) Cons. Neurol. & Clin. Lect. Radcliffe Infirm. Oxf. Prev: MRC Jun Research Fell. Physiol. Univ. Bristol; Clin. & Research Assoc., & Regist. (Neurol.) Regional Neurol. Inst.; Newc. upon Tyne.

DAVIS, Christopher Joseph Gleadless Medical Centre, 636 Gleadless Road, Sheffield S14 1PQ Tel: 0114 239 6475 Fax: 0114 264 2277; 27 Whiteley Wood Road, Sheffield S11 7FF — MB ChB 1975 Sheff.

DAVIS, Mr Colin John Tel: 020 7377 7160 Fax: 020 7943 1312; Tel: 01362 668913 — MB BS 1990 Lond.; MRCOG 1995; Cert. Family Plann. JCC 1992. Cons. (O & G) St Bartholomews and The Roy. Lond. Hosp. Socs: Med. Protec. Soc.; BMS. Prev: Hon. Regist. & Research Fell. IUF Unit Hammersmith Hosp. Lond.; Regist. (O & G) W. Middlx. Hosp. Isleworth; Regist. (O & G) St. Mary's Hosp. Lond.

DAVIS, Cristina Pilar Grovemead Health Partnership, 67 Elliot Road, Hendon, London NW4 3EB Tel: 020 8203 4466 Fax: 020 8203 1682; 67 Huntingdon Road, London N2 9DX Tel: 020 8883

3199 — MB BS 1978 Lond.; MRCS Eng. LRCP Lond. 1978; DRCOG 1983.

DAVIS, David Huw John 24 Pentwyn Isaf, Caerphilly CF83 2NR — MB BS 1998 Lond.; MB BS Lond 1998.

DAVIS, David William (retired) Grove, Elm Gate, Saltash PL12 4QY Tel: 01752 840272 — MB ChB 1949 Birm.; DObst RCOG 1955. Prev: Princip. GP Plymouth.

DAVIS, Diana Margaret West Middlesex Hospital, Twickenham Road, Isleworth TW7 6AF; 32 Harman Drive, London NW2 2EO — MB BS 1988 Lond.; MRCP 1991. (Royal Free) Regist. (Gen. Med. & Rheum.) Char. Cross Hosp. Lond.; Cons. in Rheum. and Gen. Med., W. Middlx. Hosp. and Char. Cross Hosp., Lond. Socs: Roy. Coll. of Phys.s; Brit. Soc. of Rheum.

DAVIS, Dominic 14 Lodge Road, Southampton SO14 6RN — BM 1994 Soton.

DAVIS, Dominique Marie Suzanne The Library Wing, Abbey St Bathans House, Duns TD11 3TX Tel: 01361 840340 — MD 1973 Paris. Socs: Nat. Inst. Med. Herbalist.

DAVIS, Edward Thomas Moreborough, Ledbury Road, Ross-on-Wye HR9 7BE — MB ChB 1996 Birm.

DAVIS, Elise Lesley (retired) 72 Spring Road, Abingdon OX14 1AN — MB ChB 1964 Bristol; DObst RCOG 1967.

DAVIS, Elizabeth Mary Polvean, Freshwater Lane, St Mawes, Truro TR2 5AR Tel: 01326 270304 — MB BS 1943 Lond.; MRCS Eng. LRCP Lond. 1943; MFCM 1973; DCH Eng. 1951. (Roy. Free) Prev: Sen. Community Med. Off. (Child Health) Mid Surrey Health Dist.; Asst. Path. Eliz. G. Anderson Hosp Lond.; Research Schol. Roy. Free Hosp.

DAVIS, Emma Jane 62 Rosebank, Holyport Rd, London SW6 6LJ — MB BS 1997 Lond.

DAVIS, Esther Mary, OBE (retired) Main Street Surgery, 52 Main Street, Moira, Craigavon BT67 0LQ Tel: 028 9261 1278 Fax: 028 9261 0909 — MB BCh BAO 1943 Belf.; DObst RCOG 1952.

DAVIS, Everard Inseal (retired) Homefield, The Common, Cranleigh GU6 8LR Tel: 01432 274131 — MRCS Eng. LRCP Lond. 1938; MA Camb. 1954, BA 1935. Prev: Ho. Surg. & Genito-Urin. Ho. Surg. Guy's Hosp.

DAVIS, Everard Peter Riverbank Medical Centre, Dodsley Lane, Midhurst GU29 9AW Tel: 01730 812121 Fax: 01730 811400 — MB BChir 1968 Camb.; BA Camb. 1968; MRCS Eng. LRCP Lond. 1967; DObst RCOG 1970. (Guy's) Prev: Ho. Surg. & Ho. Phys. Lewisham Hosp.; Cas. Off. Guy's Hosp. Lond.; SHO (O & G) FarnBoro. Hosp. Kent.

DAVIS, Fiona Charlotte Walderslade Village Surgery, 62a Robin Hood Lane, Walderslade, Chatham ME5 9LQ Tel: 01634 687252 Fax: 01634 687253; Kirkham House, 7 Watts Avenue, Rochester ME1 1RX — MB BS 1986 Lond.; MRCGP 1990; DRCOG 1989. Prev: Trainee GP/SHO Kingston & Esher HA VTS.

DAVIS, Fiona Isobel Moorfield House Surgery, 11 Wakefield Road, Garforth, Leeds LS25 1AN Tel: 0113 286 2214; 22 Fryston Common Lane, Selby Road, Monk Fryston, Leeds LS25 5ER — MB ChB 1983 Glas.

DAVIS, Fiona Jacqueline 3 The Croft, Sherburn Hill, Durham DH6 1QL — MB ChB 1993 Leic.; MRCP Paediat 1997. Staff Grade Community Paediat.N. Durh. NHS Trust Chester le St. Socs: RCPCH; BACCH.

DAVIS, Garry John Bristol Eye Hospital, Lower Maudlin St., Bristol BS1 2LX — MB BS 1985 Adelaide; FRACS 1993.

DAVIS, George William Trescobeas Surgery, Trescobeas Road, Falmouth TR11 2UN Tel: 01326 434888 Fax: 01326 434899 — MB ChB 1971 Manch.; BSc (Pharmacol.) Manch. 1988, MB ChB 1971. GP Falmouth.

DAVIS, Gordon Roger 97 Ribblesdale Road, Sherwood, Nottingham NG5 3HW — MB BS 1996 Lond.; MA Oxon 1997. (St. Bartholomew's) SHO (Psychiat.) Duncan Macmillan Ho. Nottm.

DAVIS, Heather Jane 19 Crowndale Court, Crowndale Road, London NW1 1TY; 78B Southgate Road, London N1 3JD — MB BS 1994 Lond. (Royal Free School of Medicine) GP Lond. Socs: MRCGP; Diplomate.Fac.Fam.Plann; Diplomate.Roy.Coll.Obs.Gynae.

DAVIS, Heather Mary Royston The Surgery, Finings Road, Lane End, High Wycombe HP14 3ES Tel: 01494 881209; 24 Hill Road, Watlington OX49 5AD — MB ChB 1968 Liverp.; DCH RCP Lond. 1971; MRCGP 1985; DRCOG 1970.

DAVIS, Henry Selly Park Surgery, 2 Reaview Drive, Pershore Road, Birmingham B29 7NT Tel: 0121 472 0187 Fax: 0121 472 0187 — MB ChB 1990 Birm.

DAVIS, Hilary High Street Surgery, Cumberland House, 8 High Street, Stone ST15 8AP Tel: 01785 813538 Fax: 01785 812208; The Health Centre, Barlaston, Stoke-on-Trent — MB BS 1971 Lond.; MRCS Eng. LRCP Lond. 1971. Prev: Clin. Asst. (Paediat.) Highlands Hosp. Lond.; SHO (Geriat. Med.) Roy. Free Hosp. Lond.

DAVIS, Hillel 11 Holmfield Avenue, London NW4 2LP — MB BS 1989 Lond.

DAVIS, Howard Paul QE II Hospital, Howlands, Welwyn Garden City AL7 4HQ Tel: 01707 328111 — MB BS 1976 Lond.; FRCP Lond. 1996; FRCPath 1994. Cons. Haemat. Qu. Eliz. II Hosp. Welwyn Garden City. Prev: Lect. (Haemat.) Char. Cross Hosp. Lond.

DAVIS, Ian Robert Meadow View, Upper Up, South Cerney, Cirencester GL7 5US — MB BCh 1995 Wales.

DAVIS, Jacqueline Carol 27 Patshull Road, London NW5 2JX — MB BS 1972 Lond.; FRCR 1979; DMRD Eng. 1977. Cons. (Radiol.) Whittington & Roy. N. Hosps. Lond. Prev: Sen. Regist. (Radiol.) Roy. Free Hosp. Lond.; Ho. Surg. & Ho. Phys. St. Mary's Hosp. Lond.

DAVIS, Jacqueline Mary 47 Long Street, Stoney Stanton, Leicester LE9 4DQ — MB BS 1992 Newc. Clin. Asst. In Psychiat. Alcohol & Subst. Misuse, Roy. Bolton Hosp, Farnworth.

DAVIS, James Collinson Trelan, Trengwainton, Penzance TR20 8RZ — MB ChB 1947 Liverp.; MD Liverp, 1953, MB ChB (Hons.) 1947; FRCPath 1971, M 1963. (Liverp.) Reader (Endocrine Path.) Univ. Liverp. Prev: Lect. (Path.) Univ. Liverp.; Research Fell. (Path.) Mass. Gen. Hosp. Boston, USA; Ho. Phys. Roy. S. Hosp. Liverp.

DAVIS, Mr James Rous 82 Wellesley Road, London W4 3AL — MB BS 1990 Lond.; FRCS Eng. 1994.

DAVIS, Jean Mary Elizabeth Stewardship Department, Zeneca Agrochemicals, Fernhurst, Haslemere GU27 3JE Tel: 01428 655750 Fax: 01428 655758; 3 The Old School House, South Harting, Petersfield GU31 5QD Tel: 01730 825812 — MB ChB 1978 Manch.; AFOM RCP Lond. 1986; MRCGP 1984. Manager (Occupat. Health) Zeneca AgroChem.s Surrey. Socs: Soc. Occupat. Med. Prev: Manager (Occupat. Health) Nobels Explosives Co. Ltd. Ardeer Ayrsh.; Sen. Regist. (Occupat. Med.) NW RHA; Regist. (Med.) Roy. Preston Hosp.

DAVIS, Jean Stewart (retired) Tigh Na Gaoithe, Carnbee, Anstruther KY10 2RU Tel: 01333 720352 — MB ChB St. And. 1962; FRCP Ed. 1994; MRCP Ed. 1967; FRCPCH 1997. Prev: Cons. Comm. Paediat. W. Herts. Community NHS Health Trust.

DAVIS, Jeffrey 36 Rockbourne Avenue, Woolton, Liverpool L25 4TW Tel: 0151 428 2252 — MB BCh BAO 1946 Dub.

DAVIS, Jennifer Ann Greensboro, Weston-under-Redcastle, Shrewsbury SY4 5UX — BM BCh 1990 Oxf.; MRCGP 1994.

DAVIS, Jeremy Peter The Mount Surgery, George Street, Pontypool NP4 6YL Tel: 01495 763141 Fax: 01495 767895; Sunnybank, The Beeches, Lower Leigh Road, Pontypool NP4 8LG Tel: 01495 758602 — MB BCh 1980 Wales; MRCGP 1984; DRCOG 1982. (Cardiff)

DAVIS, Mr Jeremy Peter Medway Maritime Hospital, Windmill Road, Gillingham ME7 5NY Tel: 01634 825051 Email: jrd@kirkham house.freeserve.co.uk; Kirkham House, 7 Watts Avenue, Rochester ME1 1RX Tel: 01634 847993 Fax: 01634 819078 Email: jrd@entinfo.co.uk — MB BS 1985 Lond.; BSc Lond. 1982; FRCS Eng. 1991; FRCS Ed. 1990; FRCS (ORL-HNS) 1995. (St. Thomas's) Cons. Otolaryngologist Head & Neck Surg. Medway Maritime NHS Trust; Hon.Cons., Qu. Vict. Hosp., E. Grinstead. Socs: BMA; BAOL - HNS; BAHNO.

DAVIS, John Alan (retired) Briarcroft, 41 Drakes Avenue, Exmouth EX8 4AF Tel: 01395 272881 — MB BS 1957 Lond.; DObst RCOG 1960. Prev: Ho. Surg. (ENT) St. Thos. Hosp.

DAVIS, John Alfred Sinclair North Staffordshire Hospital, Stoke-on-Trent ST4 6QG Tel: 01782 718345 Fax: 01782 713071; Chebsey House, Chebsey, Stafford ST21 6JU Tel: 01785 760285 — MB BS 1971 Lond.; FRCP 1990; MRCS Eng. LRCP Lond. 1971. Cons. Cardiol. N. Staffs. Hosp. Socs: Brit. Pacing & Electrophysiol. Gp.; Brit. Cardiovasc. Interven. Soc.; Brit. Cardiac Soc. Prev: Sen. Regist. (Med. & Cardiol.) Harefield & Roy. Free Hosp.; Research Fell. & Hon. Sen. Regist. (Cardiol. & Clin. Pharmacol.) Roy. Free Hosp. Lond.

DAVIS, John Allen 1 Cambridge Road, Great Shelford, Cambridge CB2 5JE Tel: 01223 843316 — MB BS 1946 Lond.; MD Camb. 1988; MSc Manch. 1971 MB BS (Hons. & Gold Medal) Lond. 1946; FRCP Lond. 1967, M 1955. (St. Mary's) Prof. Emerit. Paediat. Univ. Camb.; Patron Child Psychother. Trust & Arts for Health. Socs: Fell. Emerit. PeterHo.; Fell. (Ex-Vice-Pres.) RCP; Neonat. Soc. & (Ex-Pres.) Europ. Soc. for Paediat. Research. Prev: Prof. Paediat. & Child Health Vict. Univ. Manch.; Reader (Paediat.) Inst. Child Health Hammersmith Hosp.; Research Fell. (Neonat. Physiol.) Nuffield Inst. Experim. Med.

DAVIS, John Benjamin HM Prison/ YOI Exeter, New North Road, Exeter EX4 4EX Tel: 01392 278321 Email: healix.hmexeter; Rosehill Cottage, Rosehill Road, Torquay TQ1 1RJ Tel: 01803 293540 Email: davis@grizebek.freeserve.co.uk — MB ChB 1977 Manch.; MRCGP 1982; DRCOG 1981; Dip Prison Med 1998; RCPsych, RCGP & RCP. Clin. Dir. Devon Prisons Cluster. Prev: Managing Med. Off. HM Prison Haveregg-Millom Cumbria; GP WoodCh., Wirral.

DAVIS, John Blair (retired) Chalet du Pre, Grange Lane, Roydon, Harlow CM19 5HG Tel: 01279 793293 — MB BS 1958 Lond.; MD Lond. 1975; MRCS Eng. LRCP Lond. 1958; MRCGP 1975; DObst RCOG 1960. Prev: GP Harlow.

DAVIS, John Lydford The Nook, Wigston Road, Oadby, Leicester LE2 5QE — MB BS 1954 Lond.; DObst RCOG 1956. (Lond. Hosp.) Prev: Ho. Surg. Lond. Hosp.; Ho. Phys. St. Martin's Hosp. Bath; Ho. Surg. (Obst.) Forest Gate Hosp. Lond.

DAVIS, Mr John Marshall 5 Kitchen Close, Barham, Canterbury CT4 6QN Tel: 01227 831527 — MRCS Eng. LRCP Lond. 1944; BA Camb. 1941, MChir 1956, MB BChir 1945; FRCS Eng. 1948. (St. Thos.) Cons. Surg. Whittington Hosp. Socs: Fell. Roy. Soc. Med. Prev: Sen. Regist. Addenbrooke's Hosp. Camb.; Research Fell. in Surg. Peter Bent Brigham Hosp. Boston, U.S.A.; Sen. Regist. St. Mark's Hosp. Lond.

DAVIS, John Michael 5 Bishbury Close, Edgbaston, Birmingham B15 3NU Tel: 0121 454 6811 — MB ChB 1964 Birm.; BDS 1955; FFA RCS Eng. 1970; LDS RCS Eng. 1955. (Birm.) Cons. (Anaesth.) Childr. & Gen. Hosps. Birm.; Hon. Sen. Lect. (Dept. Anaesth.) Univ. Birm. Prev: Ho. Phys. & Ho. Surg. Selly Oak Hosp. Birm.

DAVIS, Jonathan Andrew Stobhill Hospital, Glasgow G21 3UW; 5A Killermont View, Glasgow G20 0TZ — MB BChir 1971 Camb.; FRCOG 1989, M 1977; FRCS Glas. Cons. Gyn. Oncol. Stobhill Gen. Hosp. Glas.; Lead Clinician, W. of Scotl., Managed Clin. Network for Gyn. Cancer.

DAVIS, Jonathan Daniel 7 Edward Street, Sale M33 3HL — MB ChB 1997 Manch.; BSc 1994. (St Andrews/Manchester) SHO Surg.Train Rotat./Hope Hosp. Salford; SHO (Neurosurg). Socs: BMA Mem.; MDU. Prev: SHO orthop.

DAVIS, Jonathan Neil 16 Francis Street, Stornoway HS1 2XB Tel: 01851 703588 Fax: 01851 706338 — MB BS 1976 Lond.; DFFP 1997; FRCGP 1996; MRCGP 1983. (Middlx. Hosp.) Gen. Med. Practitioner; Assoc. Adviser (Gen. Pract.) Stornoway, N. of Scotl. Region. Socs: Roy. Med. Soc. Prev: Regist. (Med.) Aberd. Teach. Hosps.; Regist. (Med.) King's Coll. Hosp. Lond.; SHO Middlx. Hosp. Lond.

DAVIS, Judith Anne 105 Malvern Road, London NW6 5PU Tel: 020 7328 3625 — BM 1983 Soton.; MRCGP 1987; DRCOG 1987.

DAVIS, Julia Elizabeth Bromley-by-Bow Health Centre, St Leonards Street, London E3 3BT — MB BS 1986 Lond.; MRCGP 1991.

DAVIS, Professor Julian Richard Edgley Department of Endocrinology, Manchester Royal Infirmary, Manchester M13 9WL Tel: 0161 276 8750 Fax: 0161 276 8019 Email: julian.davies@man.ac.uk — MB ChB 1978 Ed.; PhD Birm. 1986; BSc (Hons.) Ed. 1975; MD Ed. 1991; FRCP Lond. 1993; MRCP (UK) 1981. (Edinburgh) Prof. Med. & Cons. Phys. Manch. Roy. Infirm. Socs: (Counc.) Soc. Endocrinol.; Assn. Phys.; Endocrine Soc. USA. Prev: Lect. & Hon. Sen. Regist. (Med.) Qu. Eliz. Hosp. Birm.; MRC Research Fell. (Med.) Univ. Birm.; Regist. (Med.) City Hosp. Nottm.

DAVIS, Julie Elizabeth 56 Stanklyn Lane, Summerfield, Kidderminster DY10 4HS — MB BCh 1995 Wales.

DAVIS, Kadicheeni Jacob Deepcar Medical Centre, 241-245 Manchester Road, Deepcar, Sheffield S36 2QZ Tel: 0114 288 2146; Leek House, Manchester Road, Deepcar, Sheffield S36 2QZ Tel: 0114 288 2146 — MB BS 1970 Kerala; MRCGP 1977; DCH RCPS Glas. 1974. (Calicut)

DAVIS, Karl Robert 43 Larch House, Kingsmill Hospital, Mansfield Road, Sutton-in-Ashfield NG17 4JL Tel: 01623 22515 Fax: 01623 21770; 7 Applefields, Leyland, Preston PR25 3AZ Tel: 01772 453706 — MB BS 1993 Newc.

DAVIS, Keri Everard 45 Albyfield, Bickley, Bromley BR1 2HY — MB BS 1962 Lond.; FFA RCS Eng. 1969; DA Eng. 1965.

DAVIS, Kieran James Room 44, Pointer Court, Ashton Road, Lancaster LA1 4RP — MB ChB 1991 Leeds.

DAVIS, Laurie Russell 15 Hicks Common Road, Winterbourne, Bristol BS36 1EH — MB ChB 1989 Oxf.; MA Camb. 1990. Trainee GP Oxf. VTS.

DAVIS, Leila Anne Brixton Hill Group Practice, 22 Raleigh Gardens, London SW2 1AE Tel: 020 8674 6376 Fax: 020 8671 0283 — MB BS 1987 Queensland.

DAVIS, Leon Malcolm St Mary's Medical Centre, Wharf Road, Stamford PE9 2DH Tel: 01780 64121 & 64234; The Gable House, Ketton, Stamford PE9 3TA Tel: 01780 720282 — MB BS 1952 Lond.; MRCS Eng. LRCP Lond. 1952; MRCGP 1965; DObst RCOG 1960. (Guy's) Prev: Orthop. Ho. Surg. Guy's Hosp.; O & G Ho. Surg. Ipswich & E. Suff. Hosp.; Surg. Lt. RN.

DAVIS, Leslie Russell, TD Dulcanter, Chapel Stile, Ambleside LA22 9JH Tel: 015394 37406 — MRCS Eng. LRCP Lond. 1948; MD Lond. 1952, MB BS 1948; FRCPath 1969. (King's Coll. Hosp.) Hon. Cons. King's Coll. Hosp & Emerit. Lect. King's Coll. Sch. Med. & Dent. Prev: Cons. Haemat. King's Coll. Hosp. Lond.; Lect. (Haemat.) Roy. Free Hosp. Med. Sch. Lond.; Maj. RAMC TA.

DAVIS, Linda Ann Cedar Pools, 3 Myton Crescent, Warwick CV34 6QA Tel: 01296 490942 — MB ChB 1969 Birm.; Cert. Community Paediat. Warwick 1988; DObst RCOG 1971.

DAVIS, Linda Joyce (retired) — MB BS Lond. 1967; MRCS Eng. LRCP Lond. 1967; T(GP) 1991. Prev: GP Milton Keynes.

DAVIS, Lionel 166 Fordwych Road, London NW2 3NY — MB BS 1987 Lond.

DAVIS, Louise Charlotte 42 Rowhill Avenue, Aldershot GU11 3LS — MB ChB 1997 Liverp.

DAVIS, Malin Sofia Karin Peel Medical Practice, 2 Aldergate, Tamworth B79 7DJ Tel: 01827 50575 Fax: 01827 318911 — MB BS 1986 Lond.; Dip. IMC RCS Ed. 1991; DRCOG 1990. Socs: BASICS & City & E. Lond. LMC. Prev: Med. Off. (Family Plann.) Newham HA; Trainee GP Lond. VTS.

DAVIS, Margery Helen Centre for Medical Education, Tay Park House, 484 Perth Road, Dundee DD2 1LR Tel: 01382 631968 Fax: 01382 645748 Email: m.h.davis@dundee.ac.uk; 20 Rockfield Street, Dundee DD2 1LD Tel: 01382 566887 Fax: 01382 642578 — MB ChB 1971 Glas.; MRCP (UK) 1975. (Glas.) Sen. Lect. Centre for Med. Educat. Ninewells Hosp. & Med. Sch. Dundee & Univ. Dundee. Socs: (Counc.) Assn. Study Med. Educat.; Assn. Med. Educat. Europ.; BMA. Prev: Sen. Regist. (Clin. & Laborat. Haemat.) W.. Gen. Hosp. Edin.

DAVIS, Marian The Croase Orchard Surgery, Kingsland, Leominster HR6 9QL Tel: 01568 708214 Fax: 01568 708188; Great Oaks, Eyton, Leominster HR6 0AQ — MB ChB 1978 Birm.; MRCGP 1984; DCH RCP Lond. 1983; DObst 1981.

DAVIS, Mark Ian Malcolm Station Road Surgery, 69 Station Road, Sidcup DA15 7DS Tel: 020 8309 0201 Fax: 020 8309 9040 — MB BChir 1981 Camb.; BA Camb. 1976. (Camb. & St. Thos. Hosp.)

DAVIS, Mark Jeremy Thorneloe Lodge Surgery, 29 Barbourne Road, Worcester WR1 1RU Tel: 01905 22445 Fax: 01905 610963 — MB ChB 1991 Birm.; ChB Birm. 1991.

DAVIS, Martin 22 Grampian Drive, Warren Wood Park, Arnold, Nottingham NG5 9PR — BM BS 1979 Nottm.; BMedSci Nottm. 1977, BM BS 1979; DRCOG 1983; Cert. Fam. Plann. JCC 1983. GP Trainee Nottm. Prev: SHO (Orthop.) Harlow Wood Orthop. Hosp. Mansfield; SHO (A & E) Univ. Hosp. Nottm.; Temp. Lect. Anat. Vict. Med. Sch. Univ. Manch.

DAVIS, Martin Esmond 13 Milligans Chase, Galleywood, Chelmsford CM2 8QD — MB BS 1979 Lond.; FFA RCS Eng.1985. Cons. Anaesth. Broomfield Hosp. Chelmsford.

DAVIS, Martin John 5 Gawsworth Close, Alsager, Stoke-on-Trent ST7 2XB — MB ChB 1981 Manch.; MRCP (UK) 1985. Sen. Regist. (Rheum.) Staffs. Rheum. Centre. Prev: Tutor Rheum. Manch. Univ.

DAVIS, Mary Elizabeth Loveband Square Medical Practice, High Street, Godalming GU7 1AZ Tel: 01483 415141 Fax: 01483

414881; Hill Cottage, Oakdene Road, Godalming GU7 1QF Tel: 01483 422895 Fax: 01483 422166 — BM BCh 1973 Oxf.; FRCGP 1990, M 1978; DRCOG 1976. Course Organiser Developm. Avisor, KSS Deanery. Socs: Med. Off.s for Sch.s Assn.; Assn. of Course Organisers.

DAVIS, Matthew Charles Pennells and Partners, Gosport Health Centre, Bury Road, Gosport PO12 3PN Tel: 023 9258 3344 Fax: 023 9260 2704 — BM 1984 Soton.; DRCOG 1988; Cert. Family Plann. JCC 1988. Prev: Trainee GP Portsmouth & SE Hants. VTS; A & E Off. Roy. Hants. Co. Hosp. Winchester.

DAVIS, Matthew Paul Pen Den Har, Garrett St., Cawsand, Torpoint PL10 1PD — MB ChB 1998 Birm. (Birm.)

DAVIS, Mr Mechery Davis House No. 4, Fobbing Farm Close, Dey St., Basildon SS16 5NP — MB BS 1981 Bangalor; MB BS Bangalore 1981; FRCS Glas. 1991.

DAVIS, Meryl Elaine 19 Milton Street, Nottingham NG1 3EN Tel: 0115 941 2567 — MB BS 1989 Lond.

DAVIS, Michael Longwood House, The Bath Clinic, Claverton Down Road, Combe Down, Bath BA2 7BR Tel: 01225 835555 Fax: 01225 835289; Chulmleigh Cottage, Marksbury, Bath BA2 9HP — MB BS 1967 Lond.; MD Lond. 1976; FRCP Lond. 1984; MRCP (UK) 1969. (St. Thos.) Cons. Phys. Roy. United. Hosp. Bath. Socs: Brit. Soc. Gastroenterol. & Brit. Assn. Study Liver. Prev: Cons. Phys. Dudley Rd. Hosp. Birm.; Sen. Lect. Liver Unit Kings Coll. Hosp. Lond.; Ho. Phys. St. Thos. Hosp. Lond.

DAVIS, Michael Kevin (retired) Bay Cottage, Birchwood Road, Cock Clarks, Chelmsford CM3 6RF Tel: 01621 828240 — MB BS 1954 Lond. Prev: O & G Ho. Surg. & Ho. Phys. Chase Farm Hosp. Enfield.

DAVIS, Michelle 81 Edgehill, Ponteland, Newcastle upon Tyne NE20 9RR — MB BS 1983 Lond.; BSc (Hons.) Lond. 1980.

DAVIS, Miss Naomi 6 Cambridge Close, Sale M33 4YJ Tel: 0161 972 0360 Email: naomi@cloud9.demon.co.uk — BM BS 1988 Nottm.; BMedSci Nottm. 1986; FRCS Ed. 1994. (Nottm.) Specialist Regist. (Orthop. Surg.) Manch.

DAVIS, Nathan Wexham Park Hospital, Slough SL2 4HL Tel: 01753 634019; 21 Kings Keep, Beaufort Road, Kingston upon Thames KT1 2HP Tel: 020 8546 4232 — MB BS 1996 Lond.; BSc (Hons) Lond. 1994. (Charing Cross and Westminster) SHO A & E Wexham Pk. Hosp. Slough.

DAVIS, Neil Colin 7 Boverton Street, Cardiff CF23 5ES — MB BCh 1990 Wales.

DAVIS, Neville, MBE Redroofs, Windmill Lane, Arkley, Barnet EN5 3HX Tel: 020 8449 4490 Fax: 020 8447 0004 Email: dr_no@totalise.co.uk — LMSSA Lond. 1948; FFOM RCP Lond. 1990, MFOM 1982, AFOM 1978; FRCGP 1979, M 1959. (Guy's) p/t Occupat. Phys. Lond.Boro. of Barnet; S.E.A.L. Train. Cources in Forens. Med. Partner; Sen. Forens. Med. Examr. Metrop. Police; Hon. Sec. Educat. & Traing. Comm. Expert Witness Inst. Socs: Hon. Med. Sec. And Vice-Pres., Medico Lagal Soc.; Fell. of Roy. Soc. of Med. (Vice-Pres. 1997-1999). Prev: Mem. (Comm.) Legal Aspects of Med. RCP; Chief Med. Off. Brit. Gas plc (E..); Occupat. Health Advisor Nat. Inst. Med. Research (MRC).

DAVIS, Nichola Jane 62 Dalkeith Road, Harpenden AL5 5PW — MB BChir 1986 Camb.; MA Camb. 1987; MRCGP 1990; DRCOG 1988.

DAVIS, Mr Patrick William (retired) 17 Northcliffe Drive, Totteridge, London N20 8JX — MB ChB Birm. 1958; FRCS Eng. 1963; MRCS Eng. LRCP Lond. 1959. Cons. Surg. Barnet Gen. Hosp.; Lect. in Surg. Profess. Surg. Unit Roy. Free Hosp. Lond. Prev: Sen. Surg. Regist. & Sen. Tutor in Surg. Univ. Hosp. of Wales Cardiff.

DAVIS, Paul Anthony The Old Church Surgery, 99 Chingford Avenue, Chingford, London E4 6RG Tel: 020 8529 5543 Fax: 020 8559 4149; 28 Oakland Place, Whitehall Lane, Buckhurst Hill IG9 5JZ Tel: 020 8559 1808 — MB BS 1979 Lond.; BA Open 1975; MSc Lond. 1992; FRCGP 1991, M 1983; DRCOG 1981. (Roy. Free) Cons. Primary Care Whipps Cross Hosp. Lond.; Hon. Sen. Lect. St. Bart. Med. Sch.

DAVIS, Paul Anthony Davis and Partners, 274 Manchester Road, Warrington WA1 4PS Tel: 01925 631132 Fax: 01925 630079 — MB ChB 1969 Liverp.

DAVIS, Paul Jeremy Manor View Practice, Bushey Health Centre, London Road, Bushey, Watford WD23 2NN Tel: 01923 225224 Fax: 01923 213270 — MB BS 1987 Lond.; MB BS (Distinc.) Lond. 1990; BSc Intercalated Pharmacol. Lond. 1987; MRCGP 1995; DCH RCP Lond. 1994. Prev: Trainee GP Watford VTS; SHO (Gen. Med.) St. Bart. Hosp. Lond.; Ho. Surg. Broomfield Hosp. Chelmsford.

DAVIS, Paul Magnus Felindre, Aberath, Aberaeron SA46 0LP — MB BCh 1984 Wales; MRCGP 1988. SHO (Paediat.) P.ss of Wales Hosp. Bridgend. Prev: Trainee GP Bridgend VTS.

DAVIS, Paul Richard Posterngate Surgery, Portholme Road, Selby YO8 4QH Tel: 01757 700561 Fax: 01757 213295 — MB ChB 1981 Leic.; MRCGP 1985.

DAVIS, Paul Stewart Falcon Square Surgery, 9-10 Falcon Square, Castle Hedingham, Halstead CO9 3BY Tel: 01787 460436 Fax: 01787 462829 — MRCS Eng. LRCP Lond. 1977. Socs: Med. Art Soc.

DAVIS, Paula Bridget Mary 1 Upton Park, Chester CH2 1DF — MB ChB 1987 Bristol; MRCGP 1993; T(GP) 1993; DRCOG 1991.

DAVIS, Penelope Jane Charlotte 68 shrubbery Avenue, Barbourne, Worcester WR1 1QP Tel: 01905 731365 — MB ChB 1994 Birm.; DRCOG 1996; MRCPCH 1999. (Birm) SHO Paediat. City Hosp. Birm. Prev: SHO (Neonatology) City Hosp. Birm.; SHO (GP VTS) Dudley Gp. of Hosps.; SHO (Paediat.) Birm. Childr.'s Hosp.

DAVIS, Peter Albert 171 London Road, Ewell, Epsom KT17 2BT — MB BS 1998 Lond.; MB BS Lond 1998.

DAVIS, Mr Peter Alexander 56 Thames Avenue, Guisborough TS14 8AF Email: peteralexanderdavis@yahoo.com — MB BChir 1989 Camb.; MA Camb. 1990; FRCS Eng. 1993; MChir 1999; FRCS Gen. Surg 1999. (Cambridge Univ) Specialist Regist. Rotat. (Gen. Surg.) N. W. Thames; S. Regist. Thoracic Surg., Harefield Hosp., Middlx. Prev: SHO Rotat. (Surg.) Char. Cross Hosp. Lond.; Cholmeley Research Fell. RCS Eng.; Research Fell. Imp. Coll. Sch. Med. Lond.

DAVIS, Peter Brian Mackintosh (retired) Hammerfield, Lowertown, Helston TR13 0BU Tel: 0132 65 572092 — MB BS 1960 Lond.; DObst RCOG 1963. Asst. Med. Off. Helston Cott. Hosp. & Meneage Hosp. Helston. Prev: Ho. Off. Obst. Unit & Ho. Surg. St. Mary's Hosp.

DAVIS, Peter John 54 Four Acre Road, Downend, Bristol BS16 6PH — MB ChB 1992 Birm.; MRCP (UK) 1995; MRCPCH 1996. Paediatric Intens. Care Fell. Gt. ormond St. Hosp. Lond. Socs: Paediat. Intens. Care Soc.; Paediatric Research Soc. Prev: Fell. Paediatric Intens. Care BC Childr.'s Hosp., Vancouver, Canada; Fell. Echo Glenfield Hosp. Leicester; Specialist Regist. Paediatric Intens. Care Birm. Childr.'s Hosp.

DAVIS, Peter John Montague Whitmish Medical Centre, 110 Coppice Road, Whitnash, Leamington Spa CV31 2LT Tel: 01926 316711 Fax: 01926 427260; 63 Golf Lane, Whitnash, Leamington Spa CV31 2QB Tel: 01926 336660 — MB BS 1977 Lond.; MA Oxf. 1987, BA 1974; MRCGP 1981; DRCOG 1980; DCH Eng. 1979. (King's Coll. Hosp.) Med. Adviser, Christian Outreach Relief & Dev. Leamington SPA. Socs: Christian Med. Fell.; BMA. Prev: SHO (Paediat.) Warwick Hosp.; Ho. Phys. St. Helen's Hosp. Hastings; Ho. Surg. (ENT & Gen. Surg.) King's Coll. Hosp. Lond.

DAVIS, Mr Peter Kerrich Byng The New Victoria Hospital, 184 Coombe Lane W., Kingston upon Thames KT2 7EG Tel: 020 8949 1111 Fax: 020 8949 0044; Tel: 020 8549 2691 — MB BS 1959 Lond.; MS Lond. 1968; FRCS Eng. 1964; T(S) 1991. (St. Thos.) Emerit. Cons. Plastic Surg. St. Thomas's Hosp. Socs: Brit. Assn. Aesthetic Plastic Surgs.; Brit. Assn. Plastic Surg.; Internat. Soc. Aesthetic Plastic Surg. Prev: Cons. Qu. Mary's Univ. Hosp. & Kingston Hosp.; Sen. Regist. (Plastic Surg.) United Oxf. Hosps.; Ex-Pres. Brit. Assn. Aesthetic Plastic Surgs.

DAVIS, Mr Peter Reginald Polvean, Freshwater Lane, St Mawes, Truro TR2 5AR Tel: 01326 270304 — MRCS Eng. LRCP Lond. 1946; PhD Lond. 1958, MB BS 1946; FRCS Eng. 1973. (St. Bart.) Emerit. Prof. Univ. Surrey. Socs: Anat. Soc.; FIBiol. Prev: Prof. (Human Biol.) Univ Surrey; Reader in Anat. Roy. Free Hosp. Sch. Med. Lond.; Res. Surg. Off. & Orthop. Asst. Highlands Hosp. Winchmore Hill.

DAVIS, Peter Richard, Surg. Lt.-Cdr. RN Retd. c/o 43 Malpas Drive, Higher Bebington, Wirral CH63 8LS Tel: 0151 608 4698; 26 Cascade Place, Sumner, Christchurch 8008, New Zealand Tel: 00 64 326 5768 Fax: 0064 326 5728 Email: alexpete@netaccess.co.nz — MRCS Eng. LRCP Lond. 1987; MRCGP 1994. Regist. (Emerg. Med.) Christchruch Hosp. ChristCh., NZ; Regist. (Emerg. Med.) St. Mary's

Hosp. Lond. Prev: Commando Med. Off., 45 Commando Roy. Marines, Arbroath.

DAVIS, Peter St John Church View Surgery, 5 Market Hill, Hedon, Hull HU12 8JE Tel: 01482 899348; 16 Holbeck Avenue, Scarborough YO11 2XQ Tel: 01723 369064 — MB BS 1977 Lond.; MRCP (UK) 1981; MRCGP 1982, FRCGP 1996. (King's Coll. Hosp.) Fac. Represen. Humberside RCGP; Mem. E. Riding MAAG; Course Organiser E. Yorks. VTS; Course Organiser Hull VTS. Prev: Trainee GP E. Cumbria VTS; SHO (Gen. Med.) Bromley Hosp.; Ho. Surg. (Gen. Surg. & Urol.) King's Coll. Hosp. Lond.

DAVIS, Phillip Lionel Pontardawe Health Centre, Pontardawe, Swansea SA8 4JU Tel: 01792 863103 Fax: 01792 865400; 7 Primrose Lane, Rhos, Pontardawe, Swansea SA8 3ES Tel: 01792 862053 — MB BCh 1970 Wales.

DAVIS, Rachel Elizabeth 11 Milestone Drive, Hagley, Stourbridge DY9 0LP Tel: 01562 884623 — BM BS 1990 Nottm.; BMedSci Nottm. 1987; MRCPsych 1996. (Nottm.) Specialist Regist. Rotat. (Old Age Psychiat.) Black Country Ment. Health NHS Trust. Prev: Regist. (Psychiat.) Bushey Fields Hosp. Dudley; Regist. (Learning Disabil.) Lea Castle Hosp. Kidderminster; Regist. (Psychiat.) Worcester Roy. Infirm.

DAVIS, Rachel Jane Nesbitt Royal Liverpool Children's NHS Trust, Alder Hay Hospital, Eaton Road, Liverpool L2 2AP Tel: 0151 228 4811; 10 The Sandhills, Wirral CH46 3ST — MB BCh BAO 1987 NUI; MRCPSych 1992. (Univ. Coll. Cork) Lect. Child & Adolesc. Psychiat. Roy. Liverp. Childr. Hosp. Socs: BMA; MDU; ACPP. Prev: Sen. Regist. M. Glam., S. Glam. & W. Glam.

DAVIS, Raymond (retired) 7 Dunedin Drive, Twatling Road, Barnt Green, Birmingham B45 8HZ — MB ChB 1953 Birm.; MRCGP 1967; DObst RCOG 1954. Hon. Research Fell. (Path.) Univ. Birm. Prev: Clin. Asst. Diabetic Clinic Selly Oak Hosp. Birm.

DAVIS, Renate Marie Ernesta 41 Chester Close N., Regent's Park, London NW1 4JE Tel: 020 7935 3848 — MB BS 1947 Lond.; MRCS Eng. LRCP Lond. 1943. (Lond. Sch. Med. Wom.) Clin. Asst. & Research Fell. in Cytol. Roy. Free Hosp. Lond. & Univ.; Coll. Hosp. Lond. Prev: Asst. Pathol. S. Lond. Hosp. Wom. & Roy. Hosp. Wolverhampton; Blood Transfus. Off. Radcliffe Infirm. Oxf.

DAVIS, Richard Dexter 4 Fieldfare, Aylesbury HP19 0FZ — MB BS 1956 Lond.; LDS RCS Eng. 1964. (St. Geo.)

DAVIS, Richard Ian 22 Ormiston Crescent, Belfast BT4 3JP — MB BCh BAO 1984 Belf.; MB BCh Belf. l984.

DAVIS, Richard James Lance (retired) The Lodestone, 150 Lower Road, River, Dover CT17 0RW Tel: 01304 822810 — MB BChir 1952 Camb.; MRCGP 1976; DA Eng. 1968; DObst RCOG 1961. Prev: Ho. Phys. Burton-on-Trent Infirm.

DAVIS, Richard John 3 Pine Close, East Leake, Loughborough LE12 6PN; 13 Hartside Gardens, Jesmond, Newcastle upon Tyne NE2 2JR Tel: 0191 281 0109 — MB BS 1993 Newc.; RCP Lond. 1996; DFFP 1998. GP Regist.

DAVIS, Richard Mark William 11 Leckey Road, Upper Ballinderry, Lisburn BT28 2QA Tel: 01846 619590 — MB BCh BAO 1984 Belf.; MB BCh BAO Belf. l984; MRCGP 1989; DRCOG 1988; DCH RCPSI 1987.

DAVIS, Robert Stephen — MB ChB 1976 Ed.

DAVIS, Robert William Church Street Surgery, 77 Church Street, Tewkesbury GL20 5RY Tel: 01684 292343 Fax: 01684 274305 — MB BS 1980 Lond.; LMSSA 1980; MRCGP 1985; DRCOG 1985. (Guy's)

DAVIS, Rosemary Anne Church Street Partnership, 30A Church Street, Bishop's Stortford CM23 2LY — MB BS 1987 Lond.; DCH RCP Lond. 1991. Prev: Clin. Med. Off. (Paediat.) P.ss Alexandra Hosp. Harlow.

DAVIS, Russell Collinson 11 Milestone Drive, Hagley, Stourbridge DY9 0LP Tel: 01562 884623 — MB BChir 1989 Camb.; MA Camb. 1990, BA 1986; MRCP (UK) 1991. (Camb.) Clin. Research Fell. (Cardiol.) Univ. Birm.; Hon. Regist. (Cardiol.) Selly Oak Hosp. Birm. Prev: Regist. (Cardiol. & Gen. Med.) Roy. Shrewsbury Hosp.; SHO (Gen. Med.) Russells Hall Hosp. Dudley; Ho. Off. (Med.) Addenbrooke's Hosp. Camb.

DAVIS, Sally Valerie Bramblehaies Surgery, College Road, Cullompton EX15 1TZ Tel: 01884 33536 Fax: 01884 35401; Oakleigh House, Brithem Bottom, Cullompton EX15 1NB Tel: 01884 34646 — MB ChB 1965 Birm.; DObst RCOG 1967. (Birm.)

DAVIS, Samuel 14 Windsor Avenue, Edgware HA8 8SR Tel: 020 8958 6141 — MB BCh BAO Dub. 1947. (Trinity College Dublin) Socs: Med. Defence Union.

DAVIS, Simon Glyn The Coach House Surgery, 27 Canterbury Road, Herne Bay CT6 5DQ Tel: 01227 374040 — MB BS 1983 Lond.; BSc (Hons) Lond. 1980; MRCP (UK) 1988; MRCPath 1994. (Westm.) GP Princip. Prev: Sen. Regist. (Haemat.) N. Staffs. Hosp. Centre Stoke-on-Trent; Ho. Off. Roy. Surrey Co. Hosp. & Watford Gen. Hosp.

DAVIS, Simon John Thompsons Close Surgery, 3 Thompsons Close, Harpenden AL5 4ES Tel: 01582 765266 Fax: 01582 765202; Lea Cottage, 132 Station Road, Harpenden AL5 4RH Tel: 01582 622717 Email: c.s.davis@mailexcite.com — MB BChir 1980 Camb.; MA Camb. 1980. GP Harpenden; Clin. Asst. (Gen. Surg.) St. Albans; Clin. Asst. (Orthop.) St. Albans.

DAVIS, Sonia (retired) 35 Meadowbank, Primrose Hill Road, London NW3 3AY Tel: 020 7483 0420 — MRCS Eng. LRCP Lond. 1954. Prev: GP Manch.

DAVIS, Stanley (retired) 12 Wildwood Road, London NW11 6TB — MB BS 1945 Lond.; FRCP Lond. 1976, M 1948; MRCS Eng. LRCP Lond. 1945; FRCR 1975; FFR 1955; DMRD Eng. 1949. Prev: Sen. Regist. X-ray Diag. Dept. Univ. Coll. Hosp.

DAVIS, Stuart Mark Moorfield House Surgery, 11 Wakefield Road, Garforth, Leeds LS25 1AN Tel: 0113 286 2214 Fax: 0113 287 4371; 22 Fryston Common Lane, Selby Road, Monk Fryston, Leeds LS25 5ER — MB ChB 1978 Dundee; MRCGP 1983; DRCOG 1982.

DAVIS, Tania Sarah Budleigh Salterton Medical Centre, 1 The Lawn, Budleigh Salterton EX9 6LS Tel: 01395 441212 Fax: 01395 441244; Armadale, 96 Honiton Road, Exeter EX1 3EE — MB BS 1988 Newc.; DRCOG 1996; DFFP 1996; MRCGP 1992. Mem. Clin. Exec. E. Deveon; 1996-8 Clin. Asst. Geriat.s Whipton Hosp. Exeter. Prev: Regist. (Palliat. Med.) Waikato Hosp.; Staff Grade Phys. (Palliat. Med.) Pontypridd Cottage Hosp.; Trainee GP Exeter VTS.

DAVIS, Timothy Paul Queen Mary's Hospital, Sidcup DA14 6LT Tel: 020 8302 2678 Fax: 020 8308 3171; 21 The Spinneys, Bromley BR1 2NT — MRCS Eng. LRCP Lond. 1967; MA Camb. 1984; FRCA Eng. 1980. (Univ. Coll. Hosp.) Cons. Anaesth. & Intens. Care Qu. Mary's Hosp. Sidcup Kent. Socs: Intens. Care Soc.; Eur. Soc. Intens. Care Med.; Assn. Anaesth. Prev: Cons. Anaesth. & Intens. Care Bromley Hosp. Kent.

DAVIS, Professor Timothy Ralph Carless Orthopaedic Department, Queens Medical Centre, University Hospital, Nottingham NG7 2UP Tel: 0115 970 9448 Fax: 0115 942 3656 — MB ChB 1980 Bristol; BSc Bristol 1977; ChM Bristol 1992; FRCS Eng. 1984. Cons. Orthop. Qu. Med. Centre Nottm.; Special Prof., Div. of Surg., Nottm. Univ., Nottm. Socs: Brit. Soc. for Surgey of the Hand; Edr., Jl. of Hand Surg. Prev: Sen. Regist. (Orthop.) Newc. HA.

DAVIS, Tracey Claire Child Development Centre, Northampton General Hsopital, Billing Road, Northampton NN1 5BD — BM Soton. 1987; MSc (Community Paediat.) Warwick 1996; MRCP (UK) 1990; DCH RCP Lond. 1990. p/t Cons. Community Paediat. N.ampton Gen. Hosp. Trust. Socs: MRCPH; BAACH; Brit. Burns Assn. Prev: Sen. Regist. (Community Paediat.) N.ampton Gen. Hosp. Trust; Regist. Rotating (Paediat.) N.ampton Gen. Hosp. & John Radcliffe Hosp. Oxf.; SHO (Paediat.) Gt. Ormond St. Lond.

DAVIS, Walter Samuel 4 Knocksilla Park, Omagh BT79 0AR — MB BCh BAO 1943 NUI.

DAVIS, Wayne Sefton Leicester Road Surgery, 53 Leicester Road, Salford M7 0LZ Tel: 0161 708 9992 Fax: 0161 792 9800 — MB ChB 1980 Liverp.

DAVIS-REYNOLDS, Loretta Marilyn Roma Barnsley District General Hospital, Gawber Road, Barnsley S75 2EP Tel: 01226 777745; The Perch, High Hoyland, Barnsley S75 4BA — MB BS 1973 Lond.; FRCP Lond. 1994; MRCP (UK) 1978; FRCPCH 1997. (Char. Cross) Cons. Paediat. Barnsley Dist. Gen. Hosp. Prev: Sen. Regist. (Paediat.) Nottm. & Derby; Research Regist. (Paediat.) St. Thos. Hosp. Lond.; SHO Hosp. for Sick Childr. Lond.

DAVISON, Alan Martin (retired) Cartington Terrace Medical Group, Heaton, Newcastle upon Tyne NE6 5RS Tel: 0191 265 5755 — MB BS Durh. 1956. Prev: GP Adviser to Nat. Counselling Serv. for Sick Doctors.

DAVISON, Professor Alexander Meikle, RD 9 Lidgett Park Road, Leeds LS8 1EE Tel: 0113 266 1042 Fax: 0113 236 9905 — MB ChB Ed. 1966; BSc Ed. 1964, MD 1978; FRCP Lond. 1982;

FRCP Ed. 1980; MRCP (UK) 1970; MD Marseille 1997. (Ed.) Prof. Renal Med. Univ. Leeds; Cons. Phys. (Renal Dis.) Regional Renal Unit St. Jas. Hosp. Leeds; Hon. Phys. St. Gemmas Hospice Leeds; Surg. Lt.-Cdr. RNR Rtd; Civil. Cons. Adviser in Renal Med. to the Roy. Navy. Socs: Fell. (Ex-Pres). Roy. Med. Soc. Edin.; Pres. Europ. Dial. & Transpl. Assn.; Ex-Pres. Internat. Soc. Artific. Organs. Prev: Sen. Clin. Lect. Univ. Leeds; Sen. Regist. (Med.) Roy. Infirm. Edin.; Research Fell. (Path.) Univ. Edin.

DAVISON, Andrew John Gatley Group Practice, Old Hall Road, Gatley, Cheadle SK8 4DG Tel: 0161 428 8484 Fax: 0161 428 6333; 27 Grange Park Avenue, Wilmslow SK9 4AJ — MB ChB 1986 Manch.; BSc (Med. Sci.) St. And. 1983; MRCGP 1990; DRCOG 1990.

DAVISON, Andrew Meikle The Wates Institute of Forensic Medicine, Cardiff Royal Infirmary, Cardiff CF24 0SZ Tel: 029 204484358 — MB ChB 1985 Leeds; BSc Leeds 1982; MRCPath 1994; DMJ(Path) Soc. Apoth. Lond. 1996. Sen. Lect. Univ. Wales Coll. Med. Prev: Sen. Regist. (Histopath.) Newc. & Sunderland Hosps.; Demonst. (Anat.) Univ. Leeds; Regist. (Histopath.) Leeds Gen. Infirm.

DAVISON, Anthony Graham 47 Tyrone Road, Thorpe Bay, Southend-on-Sea SS1 3HE — MB BS 1975 Lond.; BSc (Hons.) Kent 1969; MRCP (UK) 1978; DCH Eng. 1977. Cons. Phys. Gen & Thoracic Med. S.end Hosp. W.cliff on Sea Essex. Prev: Sen. Regist. Brompton Hosp. & Roy. Free Hosp. Lond.; Lect. Cardiothoracic Inst. Brompton Hosp. Lond.; Regist. (Gen. Med.) Lond. Hosp.

DAVISON, Brigid Catherine Clare 15 High Street, Trumpington, Cambridge CB2 2HA Tel: 01223 843891 — MB BCh BAO Belf. 1958; MD Belf. 1969; DPH Belf. 1962; DObst RCOG 1960. (Queen's University Belfast) Emerit. Cons. Addenbrooke's NHS Trust Camb. Socs: BMA; MWF. Prev: Cons. Genetic Counselling Addenbrooke's NHS Trust Camb.

DAVISON, Caroline Elizabeth Ferry House, Thornton Avenue, Warsash, Southampton SO31 9FJ — MB BCh 1991 Wales; FRCA 1999. (Cardiff) Specialist Regist. (Anaesth.) Leicester.

DAVISON, Charles Paul Parkgate Health Centre, Park Place, Darlington DL1 5LW — MB BS 1975 Lond.; MRCS Eng. LRCP Lond. 1975; MRCGP 1979; DRCOG 1977. Police Surg.

DAVISON, Mr Charles Richard Norris Royal Bournemouth Hospital, Castle Lane East, Bournemouth BH7 7DW — MB BChir 1982 Camb.; MA Camb. 1979; FRCS Eng. (Ophth.) 1989; MRCP (UK) 1986; DO RCS Eng. 1988. Cons. (Ophth.) Roy. Bournemouth Hosp. Prev: Regist. (Ophth.) Moorfields Eye Hosp. Lond.

DAVISON, Christine Ellen East Cheshire NHS Trust, Victoria Road, Macclesfield SK10 3BL Tel: 01625 663097 — MB BS 1982 Newc.; BMedSc Newc. 1979; MRCP (UK) 1986; FRCP 2000. Cons. Phys. Gen. Med. & Rehabil. E. Chesh. NHS Trust Macclesfield. Prev: Sen. Regist. (Geriat. & Gen. Med.) Hope Hosp. Salford; Regist. (Med.) Dryburn Hosp. Durh.; SHO (Neurol.) Roy. Vict. Infirm. Newc.

DAVISON, Clare Meriel Market Street Health Group, 52 Market Street, East Ham, London E6 2RA Tel: 020 8548 2200 Fax: 020 8548 2288; 26 Meynell Road, London E9 7AP — MB BS 1986 Lond.; DCH RCP Lond. 1990.

DAVISON, David Charles Infirmary Drive Medical Group, Consulting Rooms, Infirmary Drive, Alnwick NE66 2NR Tel: 01665 602388 Fax: 01665 604712; Greenacres, Steppey Lane, Lesbury, Alnwick NE66 3PU — MB ChB 1986 Manch.; BSc (Med Sci) St. And. 1983; MRCGP 1991; DRCOG 1990. Prev: Ho. Surg. Leighton Hosp. Crewe; Ho. Phys. Manch. Roy. Infirm.

DAVISON, Debra Ann Rushwyck, Old Road, Herstmonceux, Hailsham BN27 1PU — MB BS 1988 Lond.

DAVISON, Derek William, TD, RD 17 Tarnside Close, Offerton, Stockport SK2 5JB Tel: 0161 483 7874 — MB BCh BAO 1953 Belf. Prev: Surg. Cdr. RNR; Ho. Phys. Walton Hosp. Liverp.; Ho. Off. (Obst.) Preston Roy. Infirm.

DAVISON, Dermott Nigel Whitehead Health Centre, 17B Edward Road, Whitehead, Carrickfergus BT38 9RU Tel: 028 9335 3454 Fax: 028 9337 2625 — MB BCh BAO 1986 Belf.; MB BCh Belf. 1986; MRCGP 1990; DCH RCPSI 1989; Dip. Palliat. Med. Wales 1992.

DAVISON, Mrs Eleanor Pamela Shincliffe, Station Road, Cramlington NE23 1EW Tel: 01670 712234 — MB BS 1961 Lond.; MRCS Eng. LRCP Lond. 1961; DCH Eng. 1966; DObst RCOG 1964. (Westm.) Clin. Med. Off. Newc. AHA (T) & N.ld. AHA. Socs: N. Eng. Paediat. Soc. Prev: Ho. Phys. Gordon Hosp. (W.m. Hosp.) Lond.; Paediat. Ho. Phys. Newc. Gen. Hosp.; Obst. Ho. Off. Radcliffe Infirm. Oxf.

DAVISON, Elizabeth Ann (retired) Sunnybank, Fernwood Road, Newcastle upon Tyne NE2 1TJ Tel: 0191 281 0694 — MB BCh BAO Dub. 1954; DA Eng. 1957. Prev: Assoc. Specialist (Anaesth.) Newc. HA.

DAVISON, Harold Kenneth 16 Dalby Avenue, Bushby, Leicester LE7 9RD Tel: 0116 241 2061 — MB BS 1943 Durh.

DAVISON, Heather Wilma Holly Hill House, 10 Holly Hill, London NW3 6SE — MB ChB 1990 Glas.; 2000 Dip. OCC Medicine; MRCGP 1995; DRCOG 1995. Gen. Practitioner Rood La. Med. Gp., 164 Bishopsgate Lond. EC27 4LZ.

DAVISON, Ingrid Susan Leics. Child & Adolescent Mental Service, Westcotes House, Westcotes Drive, Leicester LE3 0QU Tel: 0116 225 2900 Fax: 0116 225 2899; 26 Spring Lane, Swannington, Leicester LE67 8QQ — MB ChB 1977 Ed.; MRCPsych 1981. Cons. Child Psychiat. Leics. & Rutland Healthcare Trust. Prev: Sen. Regist. (Child Psychiat.) N.. RHA.

DAVISON, Joan Ainsley (retired) 147 Birchwood Road, Marton-in-Cleveland, Middlesbrough TS7 8DF Tel: 01642 314181 — MB BS Durh. 1954; MFCM 1974; DPH Newc. 1966. Prev: Sen. Med. Off. S. Tees HA.

DAVISON, John Cardiovascular Investigaion Unit, Ward 15 Offices, Royal Victoria Infirmary, Newcastle upon Tyne NE1 4LP — MB BS 1992 Newc.

DAVISON, John Anthony Plastic Surgery Department, Bradford Royal Infirmary, Duckworth Lane, Bradford BD9 6RJ — MB ChB 1988 Cape Town.

DAVISON, Professor John Malcolm 27 Graham Park Road, Newcastle upon Tyne NE3 4BH — MD (Comm.) Newc. 1982; MSc Wales 1964; BSc Durham. 1962; MB BS Newc. 1966; FRCOG 1984, M 1971. Cons. O & G Newc. U Tyne Hosps. NHS Trust; Prof. Obst. Med. Univ. Newc. u. Tyne. Prev: Vis. Research Fell. Chicago Lying-In Hosp. Univ. Chicago Illinois, USA; Wellcome Research Fell. & Hon. Sen. Regist. Newc. HA.

DAVISON, Mr John Nicholas Sutton — MB BS 1986 Lond.; FRCS Eng. 1991; FRCS Ed. 1990; FRCS 1999 T, Osts. Prev: Cons. (Trauma & Orthop. Surg.), Leicester Gen. Hosp. & Leicester Roy. Infirm.

DAVISON, Kenneth (retired) 10 Grange Road, Fenham, Newcastle upon Tyne NE4 9LD Tel: 0191 274 4475 Fax: 0191 274 4475 Email: kennethdavison@hotmail.com — MB BS 1952 Durh.; FRCP Lond. 1973, M 1959; FRCP Ed. 1971, M 1959; FRCPsych 1971; DPM Durham. 1960. Prev: Cons. Psychiat. Newc. Gen. Hosp.

DAVISON, Leanne Breige Sinead 83 Gortnageeragh Road, Martinstown, Ballymena BT43 7NA — MB BCh BAO 1995 Belf.

DAVISON, Lorna Mary (retired) Hampton House, The High St., Hampton TW12 2ST — MB BChir 1954 Camb.; MA Camb. 1959; FRCR 1965; DMRD Eng. 1962; T(R) (CR). Prev: Cons. Radiol. Roy. Nat. Throat, Nose & Ear Hosp. Lond., Qu. Mary's Hosp. Roehampton & Putney Hosps.

DAVISON, Marc 60B Queens Crescent, London NW5 4EE — MB BS 1997 Lond.

DAVISON, Margaret Carol (retired) The Park Medical Centre, 434 Altrincham Road, Wythenshawe, Manchester M23 9AB Tel: 0161 998 5538 — MB BS 1967 Newc.; MRCGP 1974; DA Eng. 1969. Prev: Mem. Manch. LMC.

DAVISON, Mark John 25 Huddersfield Road, Mirfield WF14 8AE — MB ChB 1993 Leeds.

DAVISON, Michael Andrew 135 Inverness Road, Jarrow NE32 4JG — MB ChB 1998 Dund.; MB ChB Dund 1998.

DAVISON, Michele Mary North End Medical Centre, 211 North End Road, West Kensington, London W14 9NP Tel: 020 7385 7777 Fax: 020 7386 9612; 176 Sutherland Grove, London SW18 5QX — MB BS 1986 Lond.; DRCOG 1990. (St. Bart.)

DAVISON, Mr Owen William Woodland Hospital, Kettering NN16 8XF Tel: 01536 414515; Woodhollow, Church St, Cottingham, Market Harborough LE16 8XG Tel: 01536 771333 Fax: 0153 772311 Email: davidson@aol.com — MB BS Lond. 1969; FRCS Eng. 1973. Cons. Urol. Kettering Health Dist. Socs: BMA; BAUS; EUA. Prev: Sen. Regist. (Urol.) Guy's Health Dist.; Sen. Regist. (Gen. Surg.) Guy's Health Dist. (T); Regist. (Gen. Surg.) Guy's Hosp. Lond.

DAVISON, Paul Mental Health Services of Salford, Bury New Road, Prestwich, Manchester M25 3BL Tel: 0161 772 3427 Fax: 0161 798 5853 — MB ChB 1984 Manch.; MRCPsych 1989. (Manchester) Cons. Psychiat. Prev: Sen. Regist. Rotat. (Psychiat.) Manch.

DAVISON, Paul Anthony 27 Wright Way, Stapleton, Bristol BS16 1WE — MB ChB 1990 Sheff.; BSc Sheff. 1985; FRCS Eng. 1997.

DAVISON, Paul Matthew 2C Howitt Road, London NW3 4LL Email: paul.davison@ndirect.co.uk — MB BS 1997 Lond. SHO (A & E) Basildon Hosp. Essex.

DAVISON, Mr Paul Michael c/o Department Plastic Surgery, City General Hospital, Newcastle Road, Stoke-on-Trent ST4 6QG Tel: 01782 552680 Fax: 01782 552012 — MB BS 1975 Newc.; FRCS (Plast Surg.) Eng. 1990; FRCS Eng. 1981. Cons. Plastic Surg. N. & Mid. Staffs. Dist. Socs: Brit. Assn. Plastic. Surg.; Brit. Assn. of Aesthetic Plastic Surg.s. Prev: Sen. Regist. (Plastic Surg.) Lothian HB; Regist. (Plastic Surg.) Nottm.; SHO (Plastic Surg.) Preston Lancs.

DAVISON, Paula Marie Rosehall Surgery, 2 Mallusk Road, Newtownabbey BT36 4PP Tel: 028 9083 2188 Fax: 028 9083 8820; 77 Greenview, Parkgate, Ballyclare BT39 0JP Tel: 01849 433735 — MB BCh BAO 1990 Belf.; MRCGP 1994; DRCOG 1993.

DAVISON, Peter Herbert White House Surgery, Horsefair, Chipping Norton OX7 5AL Tel: 01608 642742 Fax: 01608 642794; Westhill House, Worcester Road, Chipping Norton OX7 5YF — MB BS 1968 Lond.; MRCS Eng. LRCP Lond. 1968; FFA RCS Eng. 1973. (St. Bart.)

DAVISON, Philip Stephen Haleacre Unit, Amersham Hospital, Amersham HP7 0JW Tel: 01494 734548; 46 Foxdown Close, Kidlington OX5 2YE Tel: 01865 842587 — MB ChB 1985 Ed.; BSc (Physiol.) St. And. 1982; MRCPsych 1990; T(GP) 1991. (St. And. & Ed.) Cons. Psychiat. Haleacre Unit, Amersham Hosp. Prev: Trainee GP Edin.; SHO & Regist. (Psychiat.) Roy. Edin. Hosp.; SHO (Gen. Med.) Bangour Gen. Hosp. Broxburn.

DAVISON, Rina Madhurima 8 Hamilton Way, Finchley, London N3 1AN Email: rina.davison@ucl.ac.uk — MB BChir 1992 Camb.; MA 1993; MRCP (UK) 1995. Specialist Regist. (Diabetes & Endocrinol.) N. Thames Region. Socs: Brit. Endocrine Soc.; Brit. Diabetes Assn. Prev: SHO Rotat. (Med.) Lond. Hosp.; Ho. Off. (Med.) Guy's Hosp. Lond.; Ho. Surg. Lewisham Hosp.

DAVISON, Robert Collinson 36 Melvinia Crescent, Barnsley S75 1DZ — MRCS Eng. LRCP Lond. 1946; DA Eng. 1956. (Leeds) Prev: Cons. (Anaesth.) Barnsley Dist. Gen. Hosp.; Regist. (Anaesth.) Clatterbridge Gen. Hosp.; Regist. (Anaesth.) Newc. upon Tyne Gen. Hosp.

DAVISON, Sarah 27 Graham Park Road, Newcastle upon Tyne NE3 4BH — MB BS 1998 Newc.; MB BS Newc 1998; BSc Leeds 1993.

DAVISON, Simon Charles 33 Leyland Road, Lee, London SE12 8DT — MB BS 1992 Lond.

DAVISON, Sophie Eleanor Department of Forensic Psychiatry, Institute of Psychiatry, De Crespigny Park, London SE5 8AF Tel: 020 7848 0123 Fax: 020 7848 0754 Email: s.davison@iopkcl.ac.uk — MB BChir 1990 Camb.; MPhil (Criminol.) Camb. 1996; MA Camb. 1990; MRCPsych 1993; Dip. Forens. Psychiat. 1997. Hon.Cons.Forens.Psychiat.BRd.moor Hosp & Clin Lect. Inst.of Psychiat.; Hon. Cons., Forens. Psychiat., S. Lond. and Maudsley Trust.

DAVISON, Stuart David Kelsey Ventnor, Trevanion Road, Wadebridge PL27 7PA; 15 Tintagel Terrace, Port Isaac PL29 3SE Tel: 01208 880222 — MB BS 1972 Lond.; BSc Lond. 1969, MB BS 1972; MRCP (UK) 1978. (St. Bart.)

DAVISON, Susan Carol Psychotherapy Unit, South London & Maudsley NHS Trust, Denmark Hill, London SE5 8AZ Tel: 020 7703 6333; 43 Rosendale Road, West Dulwich, London SE21 8DY Tel: 020 8670 5023 — MB BS 1975 Lond.; PhD Lond. 1973, BSc (1st cl. Hons.) 1969; MRCP (UK) 1978; MRCPsych 1981. (St. Bart.) Cons. Psychother. S. Lond. & Maudsley Hosp. Lond. Prev: Cons. & Sen. Lect. Psychother. St. Geo. Hosp. Lond.; Sen. Regist. (Psychother.) Tavistock Clinic Lond.

DAVISON, Suzanne Marie Department Paediatric Hepatology, St James University Hospital, Beckett Street, Leeds LS9 7TF — MB ChB 1986 Manch.; MRCP (UK) 1990. Cons. in Paediatric Hepat., St James Univ. Hosp., Leeds. Prev: Cons., Booth Hall Childr.s Hosp., Manch.

DAVITT, Michael Cahir 6 Whalley Road, Hale, Altrincham WA15 9DF — MB BCh BAO 1950 NUI.

DAVLOUROS, Periklis Flat 153a, O'Driscoll House, Du Cane Road, London W12 0UB — Ptychio Iatrikes 1992 Patras.

DAVOODBHOY, Saifu Caderbhoy Abdulhussan Little Court, Watling St, Strood, Rochester ME2 3UQ Tel: 01634 717972 Email: pat@littlecourt75.freeserve.co.uk — MB BS Lond. 1967; MRCS Eng. LRCP Lond. 1967. (Guy's) Aprroved Med. Practitioner, Maritime and Coastguard Agency. Prev: Resid. Med. Off. & SHO (Obst.) Guy's Hosp. Lond.; Ho. Surg. St. Olave's Hosp. Lond.; Ho. Phys. Lewisham Hosp.

***DAVY, Anthea Rebecca** 16 Graham Avenue, Patcham, Brighton BN1 8HA Tel: 01273 553224 — MB ChB 1995 Bristol; BSc (Anat Sci.) Bristol 1992.

DAVY, Brenda Louisa (retired) 9 Tredour Road, Newquay TR7 2EY Tel: 01637 872241 — MB ChB 1955 Birm.; DObst RCOG 1958. Prev: GP Newquay.

DAVY, Dorothy Maule (retired) Flat 56, Gretton Court, Girton, Cambridge CB3 0QN Tel: 01223 277149 — MB ChB Bristol 1939. Prev: Sen. Med. Off. Camb. Health Dist.(T), Family Plann. Serv.

DAVY, John Trevor (retired) Little Down, 17 Ninhams Wood, Orpington BR6 8NJ — MB BS 1955 Lond. Prev: Ho. Phys. Warneford Hosp. Leamington Spa.

DAVY, Karen Joanna 9 Eisenhower Road, Shefford SG17 5UP — MB BS 1992 Lond.

DAVY, Peter Humphrey (retired) Juglans, 17 Baldslow Road, Hastings TN34 2EZ Tel: 01424 425337 — MB BS 1947 Lond. Med. Ref. Hastings Crematorium. Prev: Capt. RAMC.

DAVY, Robin Adrian Altrincham Medical Practice, Normans Place, Altrincham WA14 2AB Tel: 0161 928 2424 — MB BS 1984 Lond.; BSc (Hons.) Lond. 1981, MB BS 1984; MRCGP 1992; DFFP 1997. (Lond. Hosp. Med. Coll.)

DAVYS, Michael G Douglas, VRD 14 Henniker Mews, Callo Street, Chelsea, London SW3 6BL Tel: 020 7352 4679 Fax: 020 7376 5494 Email: michaeldavys@doctors.org.uk — BM BCh Oxf. 1956; MA Oxf. 1956; MRCPsych 1971; International Fell. Amer. Psychiat. Assn. Washington. (Guy's) Indep. Cons. Lond. Gen. Psychiat..; Panel Psychiat. US Embassy Lond. Socs: Fell. Roy. Soc. Lond.; Anglo-Amer. Med. Soc.; Amer. Psychiatric Assn. (Fell.). Prev: Med. Dir. Bowden Ho. Clinic Harrow on the Hill; Cons. Psychiat. Brighton & Lewes & Mid-Sussex Hosp. Gps.; Regist. & Sir A. Fripp Research Fell. Guy's Hosp. Lond.

DAW, Edward George (retired) Tempest Barn, Tempest Court, Lock Lane, Lostock, Bolton BL6 4HQ — MB ChB 1964 Sheff.; FRCOG 1981, M 1969; DObst RCOG 1966. Prev: Cons. O & G N. Manch. Health Dist.

DAW, Nigel Selden (retired) Rowan House, 8 Belton Road, Epworth, Doncaster DN9 1JL Tel: 01427 873036 — MB ChB Leeds 1940; DLO Eng. 1948. Prev: Hon. ENT. Surg. Scunthorpe War Memor. Hosp. & Clanford Hosp. Brigg.

DAWAS, Mr Khalid 46b Munster Road, London SW6 4EP Email: kdawas@aol.com — MB BChir 1994 Camb.; F.R.C.S. (eng.) 1998. Clin. Research Fell. Surg. Oncol. Dept Surg. Roy. Free & Univ. Coll. Med Sch. Lond.

DAWBER, Emma Elizabeth 104 Front Street, Lockington, Driffield YO25 9SH Tel: 01430 810201 — MB ChB 1989 Sheff.; MRCGP 1996; DFFP 1995; DRCOG 1995. CMO Family Plann.; Clin. Asst. (Psychiat.).

DAWBER, Rodney Peter Richard Department of Dermatology, The Churchill Hospital, Headington, Oxford OX3 7LJ Tel: 01865 228265 Fax: 01865 228260; High Corner House, Beckley, Oxford OX3 9US Tel: 01865 351498 — MB ChB 1964 Sheff.; MA Oxf. 1977; FRCP Lond. 1978, M 1968. (Sheff.) Cons. Dermat. Oxf. Radcliffe Hosp. Trust; Clin. Sen. Lect. Univ. Oxf. Socs: Fell. Roy. Soc. Med. (Pres. Dermat. Sect.); St. John's Hosp. Dermat. Soc.; BMA. Prev: Cons. Dermat. N. Staffs. Hosp. Centre Stoke-on-Trent; Sen. Regist. & Clin. Tutor St. John's Hosp. & Inst. Dermat. Lond.; Regist. (Dermat.) Roy. Vict. Infirm. Newc.

DAWDA, Paresh 26 High Street, Wanstead, London E11 2AQ Fax: 020 8989 0407; 23 Drovers Way, Bishop's Stortford CM23 4GF Tel: 01279 833095 Fax: 01279 833098 Email: paresh@dawda.demon.co.uk — MB BS 1992 Lond.; DRCOG 1996;

DFFP 1996. (Lond. Hosp. Med. Coll.) GP Regist. Wanstead Lond. Prev: SHO (Paediat.) Whipps Cross Hosp. Lond.; SHO (O & G & c/o Elderly) Whipps Cross Hosp. Lond.

DAWDA, Mr Vinodkumar Gopaldas Paybody Eye Unit, Coventry & Warwickshire Hospital, Stoney Stanton Road, Coventry CV1 4FH Tel: 024 76 224055 Fax: 024 76 226280; 158 Winsford Avenue, Allesley Park, Coventry CV5 9NH Tel: 024 76 672265 — MB BS 1981 Bihar; FRCS Ed. 1990; FCOphth 1991; DO RCS Eng. 1989. SCMO Coventry & Warks. Hosp.

DAWE, Barry Christopher Edwin Priestthorpe Medical Centre, 2 Priestthorpe Lane, Bingley BD16 4ED Tel: 01274 568383 Fax: 01274 510788; Oak Cottage, 61 Manor Drive, Bingley BD16 1PN — MB ChB 1971 St. And.

DAWE, John Gordon (retired) 32 Bracklesham Road, Hayling Island PO11 9SJ Tel: 01705 464143 — MB BS 1950 Lond.; FFCM 1980, M 1974; DPH Eng. 1969.

DAWE, Margaret Sheila (retired) St Katharines House, Ormond Road, Wantage OX12 8EA — MB ChB Ed. 1947; DTM & H Eng. 1955; DObst RCOG 1949.

DAWE, Robert Stewart 1 FR, 12 Fergus Drive, North Kelvinside, Glasgow G20 6AG Tel: 0141 946 6047 — MB ChB 1989 Glas.; MRCP (UK) 1993. (Glasgow) Specialist Regist. (Dermat.) Glas.

DAWE, Simon Armitage Unit A2, Lloyds Wharf, Mill St., London SE1 2BD — MB BS 1994 Lond.

DAWES, Alfred Joseph Albert (retired) Durtshot, Thorncross Lane, Newport PO30 4PW Tel: 01983 741145 — MB BS 1946 Lond.; MRCS Eng. LRCP Lond. 1946. Prev: Assoc. Specialist (Psychiat.) Whitecroft Hosp., GainsBoro. Ho. & Buccleugh Hse. Newport & The Cedars Ryde.

DAWES, Belinda Jane Hurstwood Place, Hurstwood Lane, Haywards Heath RH17 7QY Tel: 01444 443845 — BM BS 1981 Flinders. Indep. Pract. Nutrit., Allergy & Homoeop.; Trustee United Response; Patron Suzy Lamplugh Trust. Socs: Brit. Soc. Allergy, Environm. & Nutrit. Med. Prev: Clin. Asst. Roy. Lond. Homoeop. Hosp.; Med. Adviser ME Action Camp & Myalgic Encephalomylitis Assn.; Radio Presenter BBC.

DAWES, David Laurence Engleton House, 2 Villa Road, Radford, Coventry CV6 3HZ Tel: 024 7659 2012 Fax: 024 7660 1913 — MB BS 1980 Lond. (Middlx.) Forens. Med. Examr., Healtheall Rd., Coventry. Prev: Regist. (Anaesth.) E. Birm. Hosp.; SHO (O & G) Marston Green Hosp. Birm.; SHO (Anaesth.) Walsgrave Hosp. Coventry.

DAWES, Judith Ann Prospect Road Surgery, 174 Prospect Road, Scarborough YO12 7LB — MB ChB 1980 Leeds.

DAWES, Kenneth Sheridan (retired) Jesmond, Town Lane, Chartham Hatch, Canterbury CT4 7NN Tel: 01227 730144 Email: dawes.jesmond@care4free.net — MB BS 1952 Durh.; FRCGP 1977, M 1968. Prev: Gen. Pract. Univ. Med. Serv.

DAWES, Kevin Richard Ladywell House, 76 Orton Lane, Lower Penn, Wolverhampton WV4 4XB — MB BCh 1984 Wales; MB BCh Wales l984.

DAWES, Luke 78 Sandling Lane, Maidstone ME14 2EA — MB BCh 1995 Wales.

DAWES, Martin Geoffrey Hollow Way Medical Centre, 58 Hollow Way, Cowley, Oxford OX4 2NJ Tel: 01865 777495 Fax: 01865 771472; 8 Belbroughton Road, Oxford OX2 6UZ — MD 1992 Lond.; MB BS 1978; MRCGP 1982; DRCOG 1982.

DAWES, Matthew 78 Sandling Lane, Maidstone ME14 2EA — MB BS 1991 Lond.

DAWES, Nicholas John 15 Heaton Road, Withington, Manchester M20 4PX — MB ChB 1972 Manch.; BSc (Hons. Physiol.) Manch. 1969, MB ChB 1972. SHO Rotat. Booth Hall Childr. Hosp. Prev: Ho. Surg. (Surg.) & Ho. Phys. (Med.) Withington Hosp.

DAWES, Norman Charles Bridge Surgery, 8 Evesham Road, Redditch B97 4LA — MB ChB 1984 Birm.; 1997 DOccMed; MRCGP 1990; DCH RCP Lond. 1988; Dmed 1997. (Birm) Prev: Trainee GP BromsGr. & Redditch VTS.

DAWES, Peter 113 The Portway, Kingswinford DY6 8HW — BM 1983 Soton.; PhD (Pharmacol.) Bath 1977; BSc (Pharmacol.) Bath 1974. Prev: SHO (O & G) St. Marys Hosp. I. of Wight; SHO (Orthop.) Roy. United Hosp. Bath; Research Phys. Pfizer Centr. Research UK.

DAWES, Peter Frederick Hume Northcote Surgery, 2 Victoria Circus, Glasgow G12 9LD Tel: 0141 339 3211 Fax: 0141 357 4480 — MB ChB 1986 Dundee.

DAWES, Peter Joseph Desmond Kneipp Northern Centre for Cancer Treatment, Newcastle General Hospital, Newcastle upon Tyne Tel: 0191 219 4227 — MB BS 1970 Newc.; FRCR 1975. Cons. Clin. Oncol. N. Centre for Cancer Treatm. Socs: Brit. Inst. Radiol.; Brit. Oncol. Assn.; Eur. Soc. Radiat. Oncol. Prev: Clin. Dir. N.. Centre for Cancer Treatm.; Lect. Radiother. Inst. Cancer Research & Sen. Regist. (Radiother.); Roy. Marsden Hosp. Lond.

DAWES, Peter Terence Staffordshire Rheumatology Centre, Haywood Hospital, High Lane, Burslem, Stoke-on-Trent ST6 7AG Tel: 01782 835721 Fax: 01782 813419; Grange Farm House, Whitegreave Lane, Whitegreave, Stafford ST18 9SP Tel: 01785 226570 — MB ChB 1976 Liverp.; FRCP Lond. 1994; MRCP (UK) 1980. Cons. Rheum. Staffs. Rheum. Centre. Stoke-on-Trent; Head of Div. Locomoter Directorate N.S.H.T. Stoke-on-Trent; Sen. Clin. Lect. Univ. of Keele. Socs: Brit. Soc. Rheum. (Chairm. Educ. Comm.); Amer. Coll. Rheum.; Brit. Soc. Immunol.

DAWES, Mr Raymond Frank Hay 19B Church Road, Longlevens, Gloucester GL2 0AJ Tel: 01452 525547; 23 Maidenhall, Highnam, Gloucester GL2 8DJ Tel: 01452 411448 — BM BCh 1978 Oxf.; MA Oxf. 1984, BA (Physiol.) 1975; MS Soton. 1988; FRCS Eng. 1982; MRCGP 1990; Cert. Av. Med. 1992; DRCOG 1980. (Oxf.) Assoc. Specialist (Gen. Surg.) Gloucester Roy. NHS Trust; Med. Panel Roy. Yachting Assoc. Socs: Fell. Roy. Soc. Med.; BMA; Assoc. Mem. GB & Irel. Prev: Trainee GP Gloucester; Regist. (Surg.) Glos. Roy. Hosp.; Research Fell. (Surg.) Univ. Soton.

DAWES, Susan Anne The Dawes Family Practice, 83 Spotland Road, Rochdale OL12 6RX Tel: 01706 644040; Newhouse Farm, Birch Road, Wardle, Rochdale OL12 9LH Tel: 01706 371368 — MB ChB 1977 Leeds; MRCGP 1981; DRCOG 1980; DCH RCP Lond. 1979. GP Princip.; Colposcopist, Dawes Family Pract.

DAWID, Fatemeh Elahe 9 Hillway, London N6 6QB Tel: 020 8340 1969 — MB BS 1961 Lond.; MRCP (UK) 1966. (Roy. Free) Socs: BMA. Prev: Regist. (Med.) Roy. Free Hosp. Lond.; Sen. Med. Off. Islington Health Dist.

DAWIDEK, Mr Gervase Milne Bain Whipps Cross Hospital, Leytonstone, London E11 1NR — MB BChir 1981 Camb.; BChir 1980; MB Camb. 1981; FRCS Eng. 1998; FRCS Glas. 1988; MRCP (UK) 1984; FRCOphth 1993; DO RCS Eng. 1988. (St. Thos.) Cons. Ophth. Surg. Harold Wood Hosp. & Whipps Cross Hosp. Socs: Fell.Roy. Soc. Med.; Fell.Med. Soc. Lond. Prev: Cons. Ophth. Wolverhampton & Midl. Cos. Eye Infirm.; Sen. Regist. (Ophth.) W. Midl. RHA; Regist. (Gen. Med.) E. Surrey Hosp. Redhill.

DAWKINS, Catherine Jayne Accident & Emergency Department, Morriston Hospital, Swansea SA16 6NLL Tel: 01656 654123; The Old School House, Hoel-yr-Ysgol, Coity, Bridgend SA6 6NL Tel: 01656 654123 — MB BCh 1988 Wales; MRCP (UK) 1992. (Univ. of Wales Coll. of Med.) Assoc. Specialist (Accid & Emerg.) Morriston Hosp. Swansea. Prev: SHO (Gen. Med.) P.ss Wales Hosp. Bridgend.

DAWKINS, Ceridwen Elizabeth Department of Chemical Pathology, Frenchay Hospital, Bristol BS16 1LE Tel: 01179 702043 Fax: 01179 571866 Email: cdawkins@compuserve.com; Jameson Lodge, 1 Bryants Close, Riverwood, Frenchay, Bristol BS16 1PA Tel: 0117 957 3743 — MB ChB 1976 Bristol; BSc Bristol 1973; FRCPath 1996, M 1984. Cons. Chem. Path. Frenchay Hosp. Bristol; Sen. Clin. Lect. (Path.) Univ. Bristol; Clin. Tutor Frenchay Hosp.; Dep. Director Med. Educat., N. Bristol Trust. Socs: Assn. Clin. Path. (Mem. Counc.).

DAWKINS, Christopher John 17 Austwick Close, Woodloes Park, Warwick CV34 5XA — BM 1986 Soton.

DAWKINS, Denise Margaret 29A Twatling Road, Barnt Green, Birmingham B45 8HY Tel: 0121 445 3323 — MB ChB 1976 Birm.; FRCR 1981; DMRD 1981. Cons. Radiol. Dudley Rd. Hosp. Birm.

DAWKINS, Mr Guy Peter Cranfield Bromley Hospitals, NHS Trust, Bromley BR2 9AJ Tel: 020 8289 7233 Fax: 020 8289 7234; Fax: 020 8464 1393 Email: guydawkins@hotmail.com — MB BS 1984 Lond.; BSc (Physiol.) Lond. 1981; FRCS Ed. 1989; FRCS (Urol.) 1997. Cons. Urol. Bromley NHS Trust. Socs: Assoc. Mem. BAUS.

DAWKINS, Judith Louise Baker and Duncan Family Consultancy, Ashwood Centre, Stonemasons Court, Cemetry Pales, Brookwood, Woking GU24 0BL Tel: 020 8725 2618 — MB BS 1985 Lond.; BSc (Hons.) Psychol. Lond. 1982; MRCPsych 1991; CCST Child and

Adolescent Psychiatry 1997. Cons. in Child and Adolesc. Psychiat. Prev: Sen. Lect. (Child & Adolesc. Psychiat.) St. Geo.'s Hosp. Med. Sch. & Cons. Child & Adolesc. Psychiat. Surrey Hants. Borders NHS Trust; Sen. Regist. & Hon. Lect. (Child & Adolesc. Psychiat.) St. Geo.'s Hosp. Lond.

DAWKINS, Justine Colette Maes-Yr-Haf, Penylan Road, St Brides Major, Bridgend CF32 0SB; 50 Rushfield Gardens, Bridgend CF31 1DF Tel: 01656 659355 Fax: 01656 769007 Email: 106422.1075@compuserve.com — MB ChB 1993 Bristol; MRCGP 1997. Probationary Partner Redlands Surg. Penarth Vale of Glam. Socs: BMA. Prev: SHO (Paediat.) P.ss of Wales Hosp. Bridgend; Bridgend GP VTS.

DAWKINS, Keith Dobson Danes Garden House, Danes Road, Awbridge, Romsey SO51 0GF Tel: 01794 342234 Fax: 01794 342244 Email: lzdd@cardiology.co.uk; Wessex Cardiac Unit, Southampton University Hospital, Southampton SO16 6YD Tel: 01703 796242 Fax: 01703 796352 Email: lzdd@heartbeat.org.uk — MB BS 1975 Lond.; BSc (1st cl. Hons. Path.) Lond. 1972, MD 1985; FRCP Lond. 1990; MRCP (UK) 1977; MRCS Eng. LRCP Lond. 1975; FACC 1991. (Guy's) Cons. Cardiol. Wessex Cardiothoracic Centre Soton. Gen. Hosp. Socs: Counc. Mem. Brit. Cardiovasc. Interven. Soc.; Brit. Cardiac Soc. Prev: Regist. (Med.) Radcliffe Infirm. Oxf.; Sen. Regist. (Cardiac.) Brompton & St. Geo. Hosp. Lond.; Post-Doctoral Research Fell. Stanford Univ. Med. Centre, USA.

DAWKINS, Paul Anthony — MB ChB 1993 Bristol; BSc (1st cl. Hons.) Microbiol. Bristol 1990; MRCP (UK) 1996. Specialist Regist. Resp. Med. W. Midl. Rotat. Socs: Brit. Thorac.Soc; Europ. Respirat. Soc.; Amer. Thoracic Soc.

DAWKINS, Robert Samuel 17 Lower Bury Lane, Epping CM16 5HA Tel: 01992 571685 Fax: 01992 571685 — MRCS Eng. LRCP Lond. 1960; BSc (Hons.) Lond. 1957, MB BS 1960; FRCS Eng. 1967; DObst RCOG 1962. (Lond. Hosp.) Socs: Lond. Hosp. Med. Club. Prev: Cons. ENT Surg. Waltham Forest HA; Sen. Regist. (ENT) Lond. Hosp.; Geoffrey Duveen Research Fell. (Otol.) Lond. Hosp.

DAWKINS, Ruth (retired) 36 Chantry Court, New Park St., Devizes SN10 1BH Tel: 01380 728486 — MB BS Lond. 1956; LMSSA Lond. 1955.

DAWNAY, Nicholas Alan Howard 24 Almond Grove, Bar Hill, Cambridge CB3 8DU Tel: 01954 781480 — BM BCh 1973 Oxf.; BA (1st cl. Hons. Nat. Sc.) Oxf. 1969, DPhil 1981; MA Oxf. 1973; LMSSA Lond. 1973. (Oxf. & St. Geo.) Lect. (Anat) Univ. Camb. Socs: BMA (Chairm. Camb., Huntingdon & Ely Div. & Hon. Sec. E. Anglian Regional Counc.); Med. Acad. Staff Comm. BMA; Anat. Soc. Prev: Demonst. (Anat.) Univ. Camb.; MRC Research Fell. (Human Anat.) Univ. Oxf.; Ho. Surg. Roy. E. Sussex Hosp.

DAWNAY, Peter Frederick Howard (retired) Westholme, 71 Cumberland St., Woodbridge IP12 4AG Tel: 01394 382530 — MRCS Eng. LRCP Lond. 1939. Prev: Mem. Counc. Med. Offs. Schs. Assn.

DAWOOD, Riadh Botrous Hatch End Medical Centre, 577 Uxbridge Road, Hatch End, Pinner HA5 4RD Tel: 020 8428 0272 Fax: 020 8421 4109; 81 Oxhey Lane, Hatch End, Pinner HA5 4AY Tel: 020 8421 1000 Email: rbdawoo@aol.com — MB ChB 1973 Baghdad; MRCP (UK) 1983; MRCGP 1990; DGM RCP Lond. 1988. GP Princip. Prev: Regist. (Gen. Med.) The Lond. Hosp. & Newham Gen. Hosp.; Regist. (Geriat.) Arrowe Pk. Hosp. Liverp.

DAWOOD, Richard Meir The Fleet Street Clinic, 29 Fleet St., London EC4Y 1AA Tel: 020 7353 5678 Fax: 020 7353 5500 Email: rmd@fleetstreetclinic. Com; Tel: 020 7581 8444 Fax: 020 7581 8445 — MB BS 1978 Lond.; BSc (Hons.) Lond. 1975, MD 1991; FRCR 1984; DRCOG 1982; DTM & H Liverp. 1979. (Univ. Coll. Lond.) Med. Dir. Fleet St. Clinic Lond.; Hon. Sen. Lect. Acad. Dept. Travel Med. & Vaccines, Roy. Free Hosp. Sch. Med. Socs: Fell. Roy. Soc. Trop. Med. & Hyg.; Amer. Soc. Trop. Med. & Hyg.; Internat. Soc. Travel (Founder Mem.).

DAWOUD, Mr Ramsis Aziz Orthopaedic Department, Hairmyres Hosptal, East Kilbride, Glasgow G75 8GR Tel: 0141 552 20292; 124 Glasgow Road, Strathaven ML10 6NF — MB ChB 1976 Alexandria; FRCS Ed. 1989. Regist. (Orthop.) Hairmyres Hosp. Glas. Prev: Regist. (Orthop.) Law Hosp. Carluke.

DAWRANT, John Michael 80 Heavitree Road, Exeter EX1 2LP Tel: 01392 77183 — MRCS Eng. LRCP Lond. 1959; MRCOphth 1988; DO Eng. 1964. (Leeds) Socs: SW Ophth. Soc.; BMA (Ophth.). Prev: Asst. Ophth. W. Eng. Eye Infirm. Exeter; Regist. Glas. Eye Infirm.; Outpat. Off. Moorfields Eye Hosp. Lond.

DAWRANT, Mary Lindsay 80 Heavitree Road, Exeter EX1 2LP Tel: 01392 77183 — MB ChB 1960 Glas.; MRCOphth 1988; DO Eng. 1963. (Glas.) Socs: BMA (Mem. Ophth. Gp.). Prev: Clin. Asst. W. Eng. Eye Infirm. Exeter; Regist. & SHO Glas. Eye Infirm.; Resid. Ho. Surg. & Resid. Ho. Phys. Hairmyres Hosp.

DAWRANT, Michael Jonathan 27 Bourne End Road, Northwood HA6 3BP — MB ChB 1998 Dund.; MB ChB Dund 1998.

DAWS, Mr Reginald Alex (retired) 22 Egerton Road, Ashton, Preston PR2 1AL Tel: 01772 728133 — MRCS Eng. LRCP Lond. 1946; FRCS Eng. 1953; FRCS Ed. 1953. Prev: Cons. Neurosurg. Roy. Preston Hosp.

DAWSON, Adelle 87 Newburgh Cr, Bridge of Don, Aberdeen AB22 8SU — MB ChB 1997 Aberd.

DAWSON, Adrian John 2 Candys Lane, Corfe Mullen, Wimborne BH21 3EF — MB ChB 1975 Leeds.

DAWSON, Adrian Michael Leyburn Medical Practice, The Nurseries, Leyburn DL8 5AU Tel: 01969 622391 Fax: 01969 624446 — MB ChB 1990 Liverp.; DA (UK) 1993; DRCOG 1994; MRCGP 1995. (Liverpool)

DAWSON, Alan James Hawkhill Medical Centre, Hawkhill, Dundee DD1 5LA Tel: 01382 669589 Fax: 01382 645526; 616 Perth Road, Dundee DD2 1QB Tel: 01382 562412 Email: alan@redroofs616.freeserve.co.uk — MB ChB 1978 Dundee; MRCGP 1984.

DAWSON, Alan Terence Tel: 028 9057 132 — MB BCh BAO 1983 Belf.

DAWSON, Mr Alexander Skeath (retired) Summerfield, Harmer Green Lane, Digswell, Welwyn AL6 0AT Tel: 0143871 4754 — MB ChB Glas. 1939; FRCS Eng. 1954. Hon. Cons. Qu. Eliz. II Hosp. Welwyn Garden City. Prev: Cons. Orthop. Surg. Qu. Eliz. II Hosp. Welwyn Garden City.

DAWSON, Allan Department of Pathology, Morrison Hospital, Swansea SA6 6NL Tel: 01792 703016 — MB ChB 1984 Bristol; MRCPath 1990; BSc Bristol 1981; FRCPath 2000. Cons. Histopath. & Cytopath. Morriston Hosp. Swansea.

DAWSON, Amanda Jane Guidepost Health Centre, North Parade, Choppington NE62 5RA Tel: 01670 822071 Fax: 01670 531066; The Manor House, Ulgham, Morpeth NE61 3AT — MB BS 1986 Newc.; MRCGP 1991. GP Choppington, N.umberland. Prev: GP Co. Durh.; Trainee GP N.umberland VTS.

DAWSON, Andrew David Grisdale Department of Anaesthesia, Bradford Royal Infirmary, Duckworth Lane, Bradford BD9 6RJ Tel: 01274 364066 Fax: 01274 364641 Email: david_dawson@healthcheck.demon.co.uk; 43 Fern Hill Road, Shipley BD18 4SL — MB ChB 1978 Liverp.; MRCS Eng. LRCP Lond. 1978; FFA RCS Eng. 1983. Cons. Anaesth. Bradford Dist. Hosps.; Head Serv. for Operating Theatres; Assoc. Sub-Dean for Admissions Leeds Univ. Med. Sch. Prev: Sen. Regist. (Anaesth.) Oxf. HA & Dunedin, New Zealand; Regist. (Anaesth.) Liverp. AHA (T).

DAWSON, Andrew Julian Nevill Hall Hospital, Brecon Road, Abergavenny NP7 7EG Tel: 01873 732141 — MB BS 1976 Lond.; MD Lond. 1988; MRCS Eng. LRCP Lond. 1976; FRCOG 1994, M 1981. (Guy's) Cons. O & G Nevill Hall Gwent Health Care NHS Trust; Vis. Prof. Univ. Washington Sch. of Med. Seattle, USA; Assoc., Welsh Instit. for Health & Social Care Univ. of Glam., Pontypridd, S. Wales. Socs: Brit. Matern. & Fetal Med. Soc.; BSCCP. Prev: Sen. Lect. & Hon. Cons. O & G Univ. Wales Coll. Med.

DAWSON, Ann 28 Grace Mews, London SE5 8JF — LRCPI & LM, LRSCI & LM 1968; Dip. Genealogy & Family History; MSc Lond. 1978; MRCP (UK) 1975; BA Hons 1988. (RCSI) Director/ Head WHO office for Quality in Non-Communicable Dis. & Cond. Socs: Fell. Roy. Soc. of Med. Prev: Sen. Med. Off. Dept. Health Lond.; Sen. Med. Regist. Dept. Gen. Med. St. Bart. Hosp. Lond.; Wellcome Research Fell. Renal Dept. King's Coll. Hosp. Lond.

DAWSON, Anthony 18 Frederick Avenue, Carlton, Nottingham NG4 1HP — MB ChB 1998 Aberd.; MB ChB Aberd 1998.

DAWSON, Audrey Anne, OBE (retired) 30 Raeden Park Road, Aberdeen AB15 5LQ Tel: 01224 317384 — MD 1966 Aberd.; MD (Hnrs.) Aberd. 1966, MB ChB (Hnrs.) 1956; FRCP Ed. 1971, M 1959; FRCPath 1979, M 1972. Cons. Clin. Haemat. Aberd. Gp. Hosps. Prev: Cons. Clin. Haemat. Roy. Albert Hosp. Trust.

DAWSON, Benjamin George 395 Unthank Road, Norwich NR4 7QG — BM BS 1994 Nottm. GP VTS Rotat. Derriford Hosp. Plymouth, Devon.
DAWSON, Blanche Mary (retired) Trakeir, Skene AB32 6YA Tel: 01224 743300 Email: banche.dawson@tinyworld.co.uk — MB ChB 1948 Ed.; DCH Eng. 1950; FRCPCH; BA 1991. Prev: Assoc. Paediat. Neonat. Paediat. Grampian Health Bd.
DAWSON, Catherine Jane 25 Bridlington Av, Gateshead NE9 6XJ — MB ChB 1997 Leeds.
DAWSON, Celia Jane 45 Rylett Road W12 9ST Tel: 020 8749 7863 — MB BS 1988 Lond.; MRCGP 1993; DRCOG 1992. Prev: Primary Care Pract. (A & E) Chelsea & W.m. Hosp. Lond.
DAWSON, Charles Conrad 11 Connaught Gardens W., Clacton-on-Sea CO15 6HX — MRCS Eng. LRCP Lond. 1944. (King's Coll. Lond. & St. Geo.) Prev: Ho. Phys. & Ho. Surg. St. Geo. Hosp.; Ho. Off. E.M.S. Slough; RAF.
DAWSON, Charles Richard 22 Ribchester Road, Wilpshire, Blackburn BB1 9JH — BM 1995 Soton.
DAWSON, Christopher Department of Urology, Edith Cavell Hospital, Bretton Gate, Peterborough PE3 9GZ Tel: 01733 875273 Fax: 01733 875726 Email: c.dawson@easynet.co.uk; 11 Sutton Road, Oundle, Peterborough PE8 4HT — MB BS 1986 Lond.; MS Lond. 1996; BSc Lond. 1983; FRCS Eng. 1990. (Univ. Coll. Hosp.) Cons. Urol. Edith Cavell Hosp. P'boro.
DAWSON, Claire Alexandra 45 Kilbride Road, Doagh, Ballyclare BT39 0SA; 1 Station Road, lambeg, Belfast BT9 4QD — MB BCh BAO 1997 Belf.
DAWSON, Claire Angela 16 Corrie Court, Hamilton ML3 9XE; Kakadu, 1 Easter Cockairney, Cleish, Kinross KY13 0LH Tel: 01577 861797 — MB ChB 1990 Glas.; DRCOG 1996. (Glasgow University) GP Partner.
DAWSON, David John Northern General Hospital NHS Trust, Herries Road, Sheffield S5 7AU Tel: 0114 243 4343; 4 Millhouses Glen, Sheffield S11 9HB Tel: 0114 235 2202 — MB ChB 1975 Bristol; BSc (Hons.) Bristol 1972, MD 1986; FRCP Lond. 1993; MRCP (UK) 1977. Cons. Phys. (Gastroenterol.) N. Gen. Hosp. Sheff. & Hon. Clin. Lect. Univ. Sheff. Socs: Brit. Soc. Gastroenterol. Prev: Sen. Regist. (Med.) Manch. Roy. Infirm.; Tutor (Med.) Univ. Manch.; Markland Research Schol. Brit. Digestive Foundat.
DAWSON, David Leslie Heaton Moor Medical Centre, 32 Heaton Moor Road, Stockport SK4 4NX Tel: 0161 432 0671; 7 Derby Road, Heaton Moor, Stockport SK4 4NE Tel: 0161 432 5776 — MB ChB 1980 Manch.; BSc St. And. 1977; MRCGP 1990. Clin. Asst. (A & E) Withington Hosp. Manch. Socs: Assn. Police Surg.
DAWSON, Dawn Elizabeth 145 Ryde Park Road, Rednal, Birmingham B45 8RQ — MB ChB 1993 Birm. Staff Grade A&E Solihull Hosp.
DAWSON, Derek William (retired) 5 Upton Close, Alkrington, Middleton, Manchester M24 1PG Tel: 0161 643 6566 — MB ChB Ed. 1947; FRCP Ed. 1970; FCPath 1969, M 1963. Prev: Cons. Path. N. Manch. HA.
DAWSON, Donald George Broadlands, Reading Road, Sherfield-on-Loddon, Hook RG27 0AA Tel: 01256 882379 Fax: 01256 880284 — MB ChB 1959 Aberd.; DObst RCOG 1963. (Univ. Aberd.) Managing Dir. Dawson Med. Consultancy Ltd. Hook, Hants. Prev: Manager Internat. Med.; Ho. Phys. & Ho. Surg. Aberd. Roy. Infirm.
DAWSON, Erin Mary c/o Department of Public Health, St. Leonards Hospital, Nuttall St., Hackney, London N1; 58 Winton Avenue, London N11 2AT — MB BCh BAO 1984 Dub. Community Med. Off. City & Hackney HA.
DAWSON, Esmond Colin, KStJ (retired) 109 Crofton Road, Orpington BR6 8HX Tel: 01689 829180 — MB BS 1952 Lond. JP.; Vice-Pres. Casualties Union. Prev: Ho. Phys. & Ho. Surg. Orpington Hosp.
DAWSON, George Andrew Watt Sillerton, Mayne Road, Elgin IV30 1PD — MB ChB 1989 Aberd.; MRCGP 1993.
DAWSON, Gerald Hilary Department of Psychiatry, Wexham Park Hospital, Wexham, Slough Tel: 01753 634670 Fax: 01753 634204 — MB ChB 1984 Manch.; MSc Manch. 1992; MRCPsych 1988. Cons. Old Age Psychiat. Heatherwood & Wexham Pk. Hosp. Trust. Prev: Cons. Old Age Psychiat. S. Durh. Healthcare NHS Trust; Sen. Regist. (Psychiat.) N. W.. RHA; SHO & Regist. Rotat. (Psychiat.) Salford & Prestwich.
DAWSON, Helen Louise 2 (4F2) South Oxford Street, Newington, Edinburgh EH8 9QF — MB ChB 1995 Ed.; BSc (Hons.) 1993. (Edin.) Trainee Psychiat. Edn.
DAWSON, Henrietta Elizabeth 142 Wingrove Road, Newcastle upon Tyne NE4 9BX — MB BS 1998 Newc.; MB BS Newc 1998.
DAWSON, Henry Arthur Robert (retired) 19A Trinity Crescent, London SW17 7AG Tel: 020 8672 0471 Email: h.dawson@virgin.net — MB BS 1965 Lond.; MPhil Lond. 1972, BSc (Physiol.) 1962, MB BS 1965; MRCP Lond. 1968; MRCPsych 1973. Volunteer Adviser Nat. Schizophrenia Fell.ship Kingston upon Thames.
DAWSON, Hugh, TD Savary, Barclay Park, Aboyne AB34 5JF Tel: 013398 87054 — MB ChB 1957 Manch.; DObst RCOG 1960. (Manchester) GP Locums. Prev: Ho. Off. (Obst.), Ho. Phys. & Ho. Surg. Crumpsall Hosp. Manch.
DAWSON, Ian Hugh Pudsey Lensfield Medical Practice, 48 Lensfield Road, Cambridge CB2 1EH Tel: 01223 352779 Fax: 01223 566930; 48 Lensfield Road, Cambridge CB2 1EG Tel: 01223 352779 — MB BS 1977 Lond.; MRCP (UK) 1981; MRCGP 1993.
DAWSON, Ian Malcolm, KStJ 21 The Meadows, Flackwell Heath, High Wycombe HP10 9LX Tel: 01628 523294 Fax: 01628 523294 Email: kstj@netscapeonline.co.uk — MB BS 1955 Lond.; MFOM RCP Lond. 1978; DIH Eng. 1966. (Middlx.) Company Med. Adviser (Occ Mdicine) I.C.L. Computers Windsor; Chairm. Civil Aviat. Centre of St. John Ambul., Feltham; Company Med. Adviser ICL Computers, Windsor. Socs: Soc. Occupat. Med. (Ex-Chairm. Lond. Gp.). Prev: Princip. Med. Off. (Ground) Brit. Airways Med. Serv.; Med. Off. Basrah Petroleum Co.; Med. Off. Slough Indust. Health Serv.
DAWSON, Jane Victoria Marmalade Cottage, East Bank, Winster, Matlock DE4 2DT — MRCS Eng. LRCP Lond. 1992.
DAWSON, Jeremy James 98 Clapham Road, Grond Floor Flat, London SW9 0JU — MB BS 1998 Lond.; MB BS Lond 1998.
DAWSON, Joan Denise Rhodes Farm, The Ridgeway, London NW7 1RH — MB BS 1989 Lond.
DAWSON, John 4 Eddisbury Road, West Kirby, Wirral CH48 5DS Tel: 0151 632 4165 — BM BCh 1973 Oxf.; DM Oxf. 1983, MA, BM BCh 1973; FRCP Lond. 1991; MRCP (UK) 1976. (Westm.) Cons. Phys. Wirral Hosp. Trust. Socs: Brit. Soc. Gastroenterol. & N. Eng. Gastroenterol. Soc. Prev: Sen. Regist. Qu. Eliz. Hosp. Birm.; Research Fell. Clin. Research Centre Harrow; Regist. Gastroenterol. Unit Hammersmith Hosp. Lond.
DAWSON, John (retired) Kinross, 5 Barnes Close, Winchester SO23 9QX Tel: 01962 52833 — MB ChB 1940 Leeds; MD (Distinc.) Leeds 1947, MB ChB 1940, BChD, LDS 1938; FRCR 1975; FFR 1951; DMR Lond 1947. Prev: Cons. Radiol. Roy. Hants. Co. Hosp. Winchester & War Memor. Hosp.
DAWSON, John Cameron Anaesthetic Department, Ashford Hospital, Ashford TW Tel: 01784 884530; 52 Ranelagh Road, Ealing, London W5 5RP — LRCP 1972 MRCS; LRCP MRCS 1972; FRCA Eng. 1981. (Westm.) Cons. Anaesth., Ashford and St. Peter's Hosp. Trust. Prev: Sen. Regist. Hammersmith Hosp. & Roy. Postgrad. Med. Sch. Lond.
DAWSON, John Michael Radiology Dept, Guys Maudsley Kings, Neurosurgical Unit, Maudsley Hospital, Denmark Hill, London SE5 8AZ Tel: 020 7703 6333; 15 Durham Avenue, Bromley BR2 0QE Tel: 020 8464 6736 — MRCS Eng. LRCP Lond. 1959; MA Camb. 1978, MB BChir 1959; FRCP Lond. 1978, M 1964; FRCR 1968. (Camb. & Guy's) Cons. (Radiol.) King's Coll. Hosp. Lond. & Guy's & Maudsley Neurosurg.; Unit. Lond.; Hon. Cons. Guy's Hosp. Lond. Prev: Sen. Regist. Hammersmith Hosp., Nat. Hosp. Nerv. Dis. Qu. Sq. & Hosp.; Sick Childr. Gt. Ormond St. Lond.
DAWSON, John Rex 149 Harley Street, London W1N 2DE Tel: 020 7935 6846 Fax: 020 7486 4578 — MB ChB 1975 Birm.; FRCP Lond. 1995; MRCP (UK) 1978. Cons. Cardiol. Roy. Hosps. Trust Lond. Socs: Brit. Cardiac Soc. Prev: Sen. Regist. (Cardiol.) Brompton & St. Geo. Hosps. Lond.; Regist. (Cardiol.) St. Thos. Hosp. Lond.
DAWSON, John Stewart 5 Padley Close, Allestree, Derby DE22 2TZ — MB ChB 1983 Sheff.
DAWSON, John Trevor Newtown Surgery, 147 Lawn Avenue, Great Yarmouth NR30 1QP Tel: 01493 853191 Fax: 01493 331861; The White House, Poplar Avenue, Gorleston-on-Sea, Great Yarmouth NR31 7PW Tel: 01493 662804 — MB ChB 1959 Liverp.; DObst RCOG 1961. Clin. Asst. (Genitourin. Med.) Gt. Yarmouth &

Waveney HA. Prev: Ho. Surg. Memor. Hosp. P'boro.; Ho. Phys. W. Norf. & King's Lynn Hosp.; Resid. Ho. Off. (Obst.) King's Lynn Gen. Hosp.

DAWSON, Mr Jonathan Wilfred Department of Surgery, Northampton General Hospital NHS Trust, Cliftonville, Northampton NN5 7AW Tel: 01604 545669 Email: jonathon.dawson@ngh-tr.anglox.nhs.uk — MB BS 1982 Lond.; MS Lond. 1991; FRCS Eng. 1988; FRCS Ed. 1988. Cons. Surg. Cliftonville, N.ampton. Prev: Vis. Fell. Colorectal Surg. Cleveland Clinic USA; Lect. (Surg.) Univ. Coll. Hosp. Lond.; Lect., P. of wales Hosp. Chinese Univ. of Hong Kong.

DAWSON, Joseph Allard Flat 18, Cranford House, Cranford Way, Southampton SO17 1UE — MB BS 1998 Lond.; MB BS Lond 1998.

DAWSON, Joseph Francis 38 Malone Meadows, Belfast BT9 5BG Tel: 02890 666036 Fax: 02890 666036 Email: jfdawso@doctors.org.uk — MB BCh BAO 1978 Belf.; FRCP Lond. 1996; FRCP Ed. 1993; MRCP (UK) 1981; FRCPI 1997. Cons. Dermat. Ulster Hosp. Belf. Socs: Brit. & Irish Assns. Dermats. Prev: Sen. Regist. Roy. Vict. Hosp. & City Hosps. Belf.

DAWSON, Joyce May (retired) Ashfield, Weeton Lane, Weeton, Leeds LS17 0AN — MB ChB 1943 Leeds.

DAWSON, Judith Patricia Lansdowne Road Surgery, 6 Lansdowne Road, Bedford MK40 2BU — MB BCh 1989 Oxf.; MA Camb. 1986; MRCGP (Distinc.) 1994; DFFP 1994; DCH RCP Lond. 1993; DRCOG 1993. Prev: SHO King's Coll. Hosp. Lond.; SHO (Med.) Hinchingbrooke Hosp. Huntingdon.

DAWSON, Julie Karen 2A Avon Road, Billinge, Wigan WN5 7QU — MB ChB 1989 Liverp. Regist. (Gen. Med.) Whiston Hosp. Prescot. Prev: SHO (Med.) Walton & Fazakerley Hosps.

DAWSON, Kenneth Department of Neurology, Royal United Hospital, Combe Park, Bath BA1 3NG Tel: 01225 316575 — MB BS 1987 Lond.; MRCP (UK) 1991. Cons. in Neurol. & Neurol. Rehabil. Roy. United Hosp. Bath.

DAWSON, Kenneth George The Medical Centre, Craig Croft, Chelmsley Wood, Birmingham B37 7TR Tel: 0121 770 5656 Fax: 0121 779 5619; Yew Tree Farm, Church Lane, Bickenhill, Solihull B92 0DN Tel: 01625 442069 — MB ChB 1969 Glas.; MRCGP 1975; DFFP 1994; DAvMed. FOM RCP Lond. 1994; DObst RCOG 1971; Cert. Av Med. (RAF Farnborough) 1984. Med. Insp. Port Health & Immigr. Birm. Airport; Contract Phys. Lufthansa German Airlines.

DAWSON, Kieran John Patrick Elm Cottage, Monument Hill, Weybridge KT13 8RH — MB BCh BAO 1982 Dub. Regist. (Surg.) Roy. Free Hosp. Lond.

DAWSON, Lesley Katherine 11 Braid Crescent, Edinburgh EH10 6AX — MB ChB 1991 Ed.; MRCP (UK) 1995. Specialist Regist. (Oncol.) W.. Gen. Hosp. Ed.

DAWSON, Leslie (retired) 33 Elms Road, Heaton Moor, Stockport SK4 4PS Tel: 0161 432 2619 — MB ChB Manch. 1947; BA Open 1994; MRCS Eng. LRCP Lond. 1947.

DAWSON, Leslie Robert The Surgery, Northfield, Aberdeen — MB ChB 1984 Aberd.; MA (Hons.) Aberd. 1978; MRCGP 1989; DRCOG 1988. Prev: GP Laurencekirk; Regist. (Psychiat.) Aberd.; SHO (Paediat.) Ashford Hosp. Middlx.

DAWSON, Lucy Katherine Accident and Emergency Department, Nevill Hall Hospital, Abergavenny NP7 7EG Tel: 01873 852091; 37 St. Thomas Road, Overmonnon, Monmouth NP25 5SB Tel: 01600 716615 — MB BCh 1988 Wales. Staff Grade (A & E) Nevill Hall Hosp. Abergavenny. Prev: GP Cwmbran; Trainee GP N. Gwent VTS; SHO (O & G & Paediat.) Nevill Hall Hosp. Abergavenny Gwent.

DAWSON, Margaret Fiona Kinning Park Medical Centre, 42 Admiral Street, Glasgow G41 1HU Tel: 0141 429 0913 Fax: 0141 429 8491; Ardfearn, 52 Mitre Road, Jordanhill, Glasgow G14 9LE Tel: 0141 959 7289 — MB ChB 1983 Aberd.; MRCGP 1992; DA (UK) 1989. Prev: Trainee GP Glas.; Regist. (Anaesth.) W.. Infirm. Glas.

DAWSON, Marjory Allan (retired) Summerfield, 48A Harmer Green Lane, Digswell, Welwyn AL6 0AT Tel: 01438 714754 — MB ChB Glas. 1939, DPH 1943; MFCM 1972. Prev: Med. Advis. W.m. City Counc. Dep. MOH City W.m.

DAWSON, Mary Jane Church House Surgery, Church Lane, Tonbridge TN9 1DA Tel: 01732 353225/352450 Fax: 01732 367977 — MB ChB 1975 Leeds.

DAWSON, Mr Matthew James Loaning Head Farmhouse, The Loaning, Alston CA9 3JZ Email: matnjo@dawsonresidnece.fsnet.co.uk; 17 Coquet Terrace, Heaton, Newcastle upon Tyne NE6 5LD — MB ChB 1987 Leic.; FRCS 1999 (Trand Orth); FRCS Glas. 1993. Cons. Trauma & Orthopaedic Surg. Cumbld. Infirm., Carlisle. Socs: Brit. Orthopasdic Assn.; Brit. Trauma Soc.; Brit. Med. Assn.

DAWSON, Michael John Stirchley Medical Practice, Stirchley Health Centre, Stirchley, Telford TF3 1FB Tel: 01952 660444 Fax: 01952 415139; The Old School, Upton Magna, Shrewsbury SY4 4TZ Tel: 01743 709577 — MB BChir 1974 Camb.; MA Camb. 1975; MMedSc Birm. 1994; MRCGP 1994; DRCOG 1976. (Westm.)

DAWSON, Moya Elena 26 Lansdowne Cr, London W11 2NS — MB ChB 1997 Bristol.

DAWSON, Nicola Jane 11 Rudgwick Drive, Bury BL8 1YA — MB ChB 1994 Liverp. Ho. Off. (Med.) Roy. Liverp. Univ. Hosp.

DAWSON, Nicola Jane 1 Kenn Moor Road, Yatton, Bristol BS49 4RN Tel: 01934 877324 — MB BChir 1993 Camb.; DCH RCP Lond. 1995; DA Roy. Coll. Anaesth. 1996.

DAWSON, Nuala Frances 1 Nottinghill Manor, Malone Road, Belfast BT9 5NS — MB ChB 1992 Dundee.

DAWSON, Paul Richard 132 Station Road, Fordingbridge SP6 1DG Tel: 01425 654386 Email: pdawson@nationwideisp.net — BM 1992 Soton.; BSc (Hons.) Bristol 1981; FRCA 1998. (Southampton) Specialist Regist. (Anaesth.) Roy. Bournemouth Hosp. Prev: SHO (Anaesth.) Soton. & Salisbury; Specialist Regist. (Anaesth.) Bournemouth; Specialist Regist. (Anaesth.) Soton.

DAWSON, Professor Peter Department of Radiology, UCL Hospitals, London W1N 8AA Tel: 0207 636 8333 Fax: 0207 380 9068 Email: Peter.Dawson@uchlh.org; Beechers, 18 Green Lane, Chesham Bois, Amersham HP6 5LQ Tel: 01494 728222 Fax: 01494 728222 Email: phd728222@aol.com — MB BS 1978 Lond.; PhD Lond. 1970, BSc (Hons.) 1967; FRCP Lond. 1993; FRCP Lond. 1994; MRCP (UK) 1980; FRCR 1984. (Westm.) Cons. Radiologist and Prof. of Radiol. UCL Hosp.s and UCL Med. Sch. Socs: Fell. Roy. Coll. Radiol.; Fell. Roy. Coll. Phys.; (Past Pres.) Brit. Inst. Radiol. Prev: Prof. Diagn. Radiol. Roy. Postgrad. Med. Sch. & Hon. Cons. (Radiol.) Hammersmith Hosp. Lond.; Sen. Regist. (Radiol.) Middlx. Hosp. Lond.; SHO (Med. Oncol.) Roy. Marsden Hosp. Lond.

DAWSON, Peter John Swineshead Medical Group, The Surgery, Church Lane, Swineshead, Boston PE20 3JA Tel: 01205 820204 Fax: 01205 821034; Northgate House, North End, Swineshead, Boston PE20 3LR Tel: 01205 820638 Fax: 01205 820638 Email: pjdawson@copmpuserve.com — MB BS 1973 Lond.; MRCS Eng. LRCP Lond. 1973; MRCGP 1979; DRCOG 1977. (Westm.) Prev: SHO (Med. Psychiat. & O & G) W. Suff. Hosp. Bury St Edmunds.

DAWSON, Mr Peter Martin West Middlesex University NHS Trust, Twickenham Road, Isleworth TW7 6AF Tel: 020 8565 5972 Fax: 01753 620971 — MB BS 1979 Lond.; MS Lond. 1988; FRCS Eng. 1983; MRCS Eng. LRCP Lond. 1979. (Char. Cross) Cons. Surg. (Coloproctol.) W. Middlx. Univ. NHS Trust. Socs: (Nat. Comm.) Brit. Assn. Surgic. Oncol.; Assn. Surg.; Assn Colopoct. GB & Irel. Prev: Sen. Regist. St. Mark's Hosp. & Char. Cross Hosp. Lond.; Research Fell. (Surg.) Roy. Postgrad. Med. Sch. Hammersmith Hosp. Lond.

DAWSON, Peter Pulsford The Surgery, 59 Mansfield Road, Blidworth, Mansfield NG21 0RB Tel: 01623 795461 — MB ChB 1964 Manch.; BSc (Hons. Physiol.) Manch. 1962; DCH Eng. 1967; DA Eng. 1967; DObst RCOG 1966. (Manch.) Prev: Govt. Med. Off. Kabwe, Zambia; SHO (Anaesth.) S. Manch. Hosp. Gp.

DAWSON, Philip John Northlands Wood Surgery, 7 Walnut Park, Haywards Heath RH16 3TG Tel: 01444 458022 Fax: 01444 415960; Fivestones, Little Blackhill, Lindfield, Haywards Heath RH16 2HE Tel: 01444 482078 Email: pjdfrcgp@aol.com — MB BS 1977 Lond.; FRCGP 1998; DFFP 1993; MRCGP 1981; DRCOG 1980; AKC 1977. (King's College Hospital) GP Tutor Postgrad. Med. Centre P.ss Roy. Hosp. Haywards Heath. Socs: BMA; GP Tutors Assn.; Old Carthusian Med. Soc.

DAWSON, Richard David Edward 5 Wakefield Croft, Ilkeston DE7 9LG Tel: 0115 932 4946; 5 Wakefield Croft, Ilkeston DE7 9LG Tel: 0115 932 4946 — MB ChB 1997 Leeds. SHO Huddersfield Roy. Infirmiary A & E Dept. Prev: PRHO Leeds Gen. Infirmiary Professional Surgic. Unit; PRHO Pinderfields Hosp. Diabetes & Endocrinol.

DAWSON, Richard Edward 13 Farnborough Road, Southport PR8 3DF — MB ChB 1952 Leeds. (Leeds) Prev: Squadron Ldr. RAF

Med. Br.; Ho. Phys. St. Jas. Hosp. Leeds; Cas. Off. Leeds Pub. Disp. & Hosp.

DAWSON, Richard James 18 Fairfields, Egerton, Bolton BL7 9EE — MB ChB 1998 Leeds.

DAWSON, Robert Thomas Medical Centre, The Grove, Rowlands Gill NE39 1PW Tel: 01207 542136 Fax: 01207 543340; Adderstone House, Dene Road, Rowlands Gill NE39 1DU Tel: 01207 545498 — MB ChB 1986 Ed.

DAWSON, Robin Derek 2 Sutherland Avenue, Glasgow G41 4JH Tel: 0141 427 1869 — MB ChB 1990 Aberd.; MRCGP 1994; DFFP 1994.

DAWSON, Rosemary Grace (retired) High Pines, 115 Chessetts Wood Road, Lapworth, Solihull B94 6EL Tel: 01564 779159 — MB ChB 1946 Birm. Prev: SCM Solihull HA.

DAWSON, Sarah Jane 34 Chatsworth Way, London SE27 9HN Tel: 020 8670 7739 — MB BS 1976 Lond.

DAWSON, Sheila Catherine Child & Family Consultation Service, Child Health Directorate, Northampton General Hospital, Northampton NN1 5BD Tel: 01604 604608; 87 Southernhay Road, Stoneygate, Leicester LE2 3TP — MB ChB 1987 Leic.; MRCPsych 1992. (Leicester Med. Sch.) Cons. Child & Adolesc. Psychiat. N.ampton.

DAWSON, Sheila Fay (retired) 1 Dunham Lawn, Bradgate Road, Altrincham WA14 4QJ Tel: 0161 928 8066 — MB ChB 1949 Leeds; DCH Eng. 1952. Clin. Med. Off. Manch. AHA. Prev: Clin. Asst. Manch. Roy. Infirm.

DAWSON, Sidney Patrick (retired) High Pines, 115 Chessetts Wood Road, Lapworth, Solihull B94 6EL Tel: 01564 779159 — MB ChB 1946 Birm. Prev: Mem. Dist. Managem. Team Solihull DHA.

DAWSON, Stephen Guy Department of Genitourinary Medicine, Upton Hospital, Slough SL1 2BJ Tel: 01753 635302 Fax: 01753 536938 — MB BS 1971 Lond.; MD Lond. 1986. Cons. Phys. Genitourin. Med. E. Berks. Community Health NHS Trust; Med. Dir. E. Berks. Community Trust. Socs: Med. Soc. Study VD; Internat. Soc. STD Research; Brit. HIV Assn. Prev: Sen. Regist. (Genitourin. Med.) Riverside HA; Regist. (Venereol.) St. Mary's Hosp. Lond.; Research Regist. (Microbiol. & Venereol.) St. Mary's Hosp. Med. Sch. Lond.

DAWSON, Susan Jane 3 Gray Place, Murray Road, Ottershaw, Chertsey KT16 0GB — MB ChB 1984 Manch. GP Chertsey Retainer Scheme. Prev: GP Darlington Retainer Scheme; GP Retainer Scheme Heywood; Trainee GP/SHO Birch Hill Hosp. Rochdale VTS.

DAWSON, Susan Jean c/o 3 Southwood Road, Trowbridge BA14 7BZ — MB BS 1984 Lond.; DA (UK) 1987.

DAWSON, Susannah Katharine Benbecula Medical Practice, Griminish Surgery, Griminish, Isle of Benbecula HS7 5QA Tel: 01870 602215 Fax: 01870 602630; The Old School, Iochdar, Lochboisdale HS8 5RQ Tel: 01870 610373 — MB ChB 1986 Ed.; DPD (Cardiff) 1999; MRCGP 1995; DFFP 1994; DRCOG 1993. (Ed.) Med. Off. Daliburgh Hosp. I. of S. Uist; Hosp. Practitioner Dermat. W.ern Isles Hosp. Prev: Med. Off. i/c Leprol. & Dermat. Molai Gen. Hosp. Maiduguri, Nigeria; Hon. Lect. Univ. Maiduguri, Nigeria; SHO (O & G) Inverness.

DAWSON, Suzanne Louise Glebe Croft, Higham-on-the-Hill, Nuneaton CV13 6AL — MB ChB 1991 Leic.; MRCP (UK) 1994. Cons. Phys. Integrateo Med., Leicester Gen. Hosp. Socs: Brit. Assn. of Stroke Phys.s; Brit. Geriat. Soc. Prev: Specialist Regist. (Med. For Elderly) Univ. Hosp. of Leiceter NHS Trust; Hon. Clin. Regist. (Integrated Med.) Glenfield Gen. Hosp. & Leicester Roy. Infirm.; Specialist Regist. Intergrated Med Glenfield Hosp.Leicester.

DAWSON, Thomas Andrew John (retired) 11 Ballyhannon Park, Portadown, Craigavon BT63 5SF Tel: 028 38 335455 — MB BCh BAO 1954 Belf.; MD Belf. 1964; FRCP Ed. 1978, M 1959; DPH 1964. Prev: Cons. Dermat. SHSSB N.. Irel.

DAWSON, Timothy Peter Royal Preston Hospital, PO Box 202, Sharoe Green Lane, Fulwood, Preston PR2 9HG Tel: 01772 522146 Email: timothy.dawson@patr.nhs.uk — MB BCh 1985 Wales; PhD Wales 1994, BSc (Hons.) 1982; DRCPath 1995; MRCPath 1997. (University of Wales College of Medicine) Prev: Lect. (Path.) Univ. Wales Coll. Med. Cardiff; Post Doctoral Research Fell. Univ. Basel, Switz..; Sen. Regist. (Neuropath.) Univ. Wales Coll. Med. Cardiff.

DAWSON, William Goodhugh 31 Manor Park Close, Tilehurst, Reading RG30 4PS Tel: 0118 945 1493 Fax: 0118 945 1493 Email: williamdawson@beeb.net — MB Bchir Camb. 1949; MA Camb. 1950; DA Eng 1955; D Obst 1956; FRCOG 1984, M 1970; MRCS Eng. LRCP 1945 Lond. (Camb. & St. Bart.) Locum Gen. Practitioner. Socs: Reading Path. Soc. Prev: Cons. O & G Cameron Hosp. Hartlepool; Cons. O & G RAF; Regist. (O & G) P.ss Margt. Hosp. Swindon.

DAWSON, Winifred Elizabeth (retired) 4 Rose Bank, Burley-in-Wharfedale, Ilkley LS29 7PQ Tel: 01943 862182 — MB ChB Manch. 1957.

DAWSON-BOWLING, Paul Richard Faversham Health Centre, Bank Street, Faversham ME13 8QR Tel: 01795 536621/533987/534150; 23 Court Street, Faversham ME13 7AT Tel: 01795 531372 — MB BS 1976 Lond.; MA Oxf. 1965.

DAWSON-EDWARDS, Mr Paul (retired) 12 Metchley Park Road, Edgbaston, Birmingham B15 2PG Tel: 0121 454 0242 — MB ChB Birm. 1943; FRCS Eng. 1951; MRCS Eng. LRCP Lond. 1943. Cons. Urol. & Dir. Transpl. United Birm. Hosps.; Lect. (Surg.) Univ. Birm. Prev: Sen. Regist. (Urol. Surg.) United Birm. Hosps.

DAWTON, Andrew Jeremy Humber Road Surgery, 27 Humber Road, Chelmsford CM1 7PE Tel: 01245 268635 Fax: 01245 344552 — MB BS 1981 Lond.; MRCGP 1986; Cert Family Plann. JCC 1984; DRCOG 1985.

DAY, Mr Adrian Conan Dept. Of Trauma & Orthopaedic Surgery, St George's Hospital, c/o 5th Floor St James' Wing, Blackshaw Rd, London SW17 0QT Tel: 020 8672 1255 Ext: 3229 — MB BChir 1987 Camb.; BMedBiol. Aberd. 1984; FRCS (Orth.) 1995; FRCS Eng. 1991. (Univ. Camb.) Cons. Ortho. Surg. St Geo.s's hosp. St Geo.s' Health Care NHS trust Lond.

DAY, Alan Joseph Children's Department, Cheltenham General Hospital, Sandford Road, Cheltenham GL53 7AN Tel: 01242 274239 Fax: 01242 273453 Email: alan.day@egnhst.org.uk — MB ChB 1974 Liverp.; BSc (Hons.) Liverp. 1971; FRCP Lond. 1996; FRCPCH 1997; DCH Eng. 1977. (Liverp.) Cons. Paediat. Gloucestershire Hosp. NHS Trust; Hon. Sen. Lect. Dept. of Child Health, Bristol Univ. Socs: SW Paediat.Club. Prev: Sen. Regist. (Paediat.) Univ. Hosp. Wales Cardiff; Clin. Research Fell. & Hon. Sen. Regist. (Paediat.) Univ. Birm. (Inst. Child Health); Regist. (Paediat.) Birm. AHA (T) & Burnley Gen. Hosp.

DAY, Albert Thomas Granary Wharf House, Leeds LS11 5PY Tel: 0113 243 6436 Fax: 0113 241 0500 — MB ChB 1965 Leeds; LLM 1994; FRCGP 1989, M 1971; DObst RCOG 1967. (Leeds) JP; Cons. Medico-Legal Adviser Med. Protec. Soc.; Adviser Med Protec. Soc. Prev: Hosp. Pract. (Rheum.) Harrogate HA; SCMO (Occupat. Health) Harrogate HA; Trainer (Gen. Pract.) Harrogate VTS.

DAY, Alexandra Helen Wallis House, 27 Broad St., Wokingham RG40 1AU Tel: 0118 977 1199 Fax: 0118 979 5561 — MB BS 1978 Lond.; MRCPsych 1983. Cons. Psychiat. Berks. Healthcare Trust. Prev: Sen. Regist. Oxf. Regional Higher Train. Scheme.

DAY, Alfred Charles Department of Anaesthetics, The County Hospital, Union Walk, Hereford HR1 2ER — MB ChB 1978 Auckland; FFA RCS Eng. 1982.

DAY, Andrew Philip Department of Chemical Pathology, Weston General Hospital, Uphill, Weston Super Mare BS23 4TQ Tel: 01934 636363 Fax: 01934 647051 — MB BS 1985 Lond.; MSc Lond. 1991; MA Camb. 1986; MRCPath 1994. Cons. Chem. Path. W.on Gen. Hosp.; Cons. Chem. Path. Bristol Roy. Infirm.; Hon. Clin. Sen. Lect. Univ. of Bristol. Prev: Sen. Regist. (Chem. Path.) Bristol Roy. Infirm.; Lect. (Chem. Path.) Char. Cross & W.m. Med. Sch.; Regist. (Chem. Path.) W.m. Hosp. Lond.

DAY, Anne 47 Henleaze Avenue, Bristol BS9 4EU Tel: 0117 962 3179 — MB ChB 1995 Bristol. (Bristol) SHO (A & E) Leicester Roy. Infirm. Prev: Ho. Phys. Frenchay Hosp. Bristol; Ho. Surg. W.on Gen. Hosp. W.ern-super-Mare.

DAY, Anne Mary Thanet House, 17 Montpelier Road, Ealing, London W5 2QP Tel: 020 8997 0338 — MB BS 1962 Lond.; MRCS Eng. LRCP Lond. 1962; FFA RCS Eng. 1967; DObst RCOG 1964. (Roy. Free) Prev: Cons. Anaesth. Mt. Vernon & Harefield Hosps.

DAY, Arnold George (retired) 5 Paxton Place, Norwich NR2 2JE — MB BS 1955 Lond.; LMSSA Lond. 1955; DObst RCOG 1959. Prev: Ho. Phys. Hosp. SS John & Eliz. Lond.

DAY, Arun Sekhar 564 Bury Road, Rochdale OL11 4DN Tel: 01706 33404 — MB BS 1955 Calcutta; FRCPath 1982, M 1970; DCP Lond 1966; DCH Eng. 1961. (R.G. Kar Med. Coll. Calcutta) Cons. Path. (Morbid Anat. & Histopath.) Tameside Gen. Hosp.; Ashton-under-Lyne. Prev: SHO (Path.) Bury Gen. Hosp.; Regist. Path.

St. Luke's Hosp. Guildford; Regist. (Morbid Anat. & Histopath.) Roy. Free Hosp. Lond.

DAY, Mr Brian Hanbury (retired) Iago, Grafton Road, Worcester Park KT4 7JN Tel: 020 8330 2361 — MB BS 1952 Lond.; FRCS Eng. 1959. Prev: Cons. Orthop. Surg. St. Helier Hosp. Carshalton, Nelson Hosp. Lond. & Wilson Hosp. Mitcham.

DAY, Brian Philip Tanglewood, Lovelands Lane, Tadworth KT20 6XG Tel: 0173 72 246365; 2 Richmond Close, Torquay TQ1 2PW Tel: 01803 298419 — MB BS 1956 Lond.; BSc (Hons.) Lond. 1945; MRCS Eng. LRCP Lond. 1956; DObst RCOG 1958. (Roy. Free) Assoc. Roy. Coll. Sci. (Hons.) 1945. Socs: BMA & Med. Defence Union. Prev: Resid. Med. Off. Gen. Hosp. Jersey; Nuclear Health & Safety Off. Centr. Electr. Generating Bd. Lond.; Ho. Surg. (Obst.) & SHO (Radiother.) Roy. Free Hosp.

DAY, Bryan Lynmore 40 Middleway, London NW11 6SG Tel: 020 8455 7894 — BM BCh 1948 Oxf.; BM BCh Oxon. 1948; FFA RCS Eng. 1955. (Univ. Coll. Hosp.) Cons. Anaesth. Roy. Nat. Orthop. Hosp., Thoracic Unit Brook Hosp.; Woolwich & Roy. Masonic Hosp.; Fell. Roy. Soc. Med. Socs: Assn. Anaesths. Prev: SHO Anaesth. & Regist. Anaesth. St. Geo. Hosp. Lond.; Sen. Regist. Anaesth. St. Geo. Hosp. & Soton. Gp. Hosps.

DAY, Carolyn Ann Ellesmere Medical Centre, 262 Stockport Road, Cheadle Heath, Stockport SK3 0RQ Tel: 0161 428 6729 Fax: 0161 428 0710 — MB ChB 1971 Manch.; DObst RCOG 1973.

DAY, Catherine Lousie 100B St Michaels Hill, Bristol BS2 8BQ — MB ChB 1994 Bristol.

DAY, Charlotte Isabel Flat 1, Grosslea, 90 Bishopsford Road, Morden SM4 6BE; 9 Dibdin Close, Sutton SM1 2PJ — MB BS 1993 Lond.; BSc (Hons.) Lond. 1990; DRCOG; DFFP. (St. Georges HMS) SHO (Paediat.) St. Helier Hosp. Carshalton; CMO (Family Plann.) Merton & Sutton Community Trust Sutton. Prev: SHO (A & E); SHO (Genitourin. Med.); SHO (Urol.).

DAY, Christopher Duncan Alghero, 44 Matlock Road, Walton, Chesterfield S42 7LE Tel: 01246 270942 — MB BS Durh. 1964; FFA RCS Eng. 1970. (University of Durham) Cons. Anaesth. Chesterfield & N. Derbysh. Roy. Hosp. NHS Trust. Socs: Assn. Anaesths. & Sheff. & E. Midl. Anaesth. Soc. Prev: Med. Director Chesterfield and N. Derbysh. NHS Trust.; Sen. Regist. & Regist. (Anaesth.) United Sheff. Hosps.; SHO (Anaesth.) Dudley Rd. Hosp. Birm.

DAY, Christopher James Edmund Royal Devon & exeter Hospital, Barrack Road, Exeter EX2 5DW Tel: 01392 411611 — MB ChB 1987 Bristol; MRCP 1990; FRCA 1993; MD 1997. Cons. Anaesth. IC Med.

DAY, Christopher John (retired) 40 Clay Hill, Enfield EN2 9AA Tel: 020 8366 8210 — MB BS 1966 Lond.; MRCS Eng. LRCP Lond. 1966; DObst RCOG 1970.

DAY, Christopher Paul Department of Medicine, Medical School, Newcastle University, Framlington Place, Newcastle upon Tyne NE2 4HH Tel: 0191 222 7043 Fax: 0191 222 0723 Email: c.p.day@ncl.ac.uk; 11 East Street, Priors House, North Shields NE30 4EB Tel: 0191 258 3590 — MB 1984 Camb.; BChir 1983; PhD Camb. 1994, MA 1985, MD 1994; MRCP (UK) 1986; FRCP 1998. (Addenbrooke's) Sen. Lect. (Hepat.) & Hon. Cons. Univ. Newc. & Freeman Hosp. Socs: Eur. Assn. for Study Liver; Brit. Assn. Study Liver; Amer. Assn. Study Liver Dis. Prev: MRC Clinicial Scientist Univ. Newc.; MRC Train. Fell. & Hon. Sen. Regist. Univ. Newc. u. Tyne; Brit. Heart Foundat. & Digestive Foundat. Personal Fell.sh.

DAY, Christopher Paul 35 Birchfield Road, Yeovil BA21 5RN — MB BCh 1997 Wales.

DAY, Christopher Peter Theodore Ryecroft Farm, Ryecroft Road, Glusburn, Keighley BD20 8RT — MB ChB 1980 Leeds; BSc Leeds 1977, MB ChB 1980; MRCP (UK) 1984.

DAY, Christopher William Cropredy Surgery, 18 Station Road, Cropredy, Banbury OX17 1PP Tel: 01295 758372 Fax: 01295 750435; Bryn Celyn, The Level, Shenington, Banbury OX15 6NA Tel: 01295 670358 — MB ChB 1977 Birm.; MRCGP 1982; DRCOG 1979.

DAY, David William Roborough House, Furzehill Road, Torquay TQ1 3JG Tel: 01803 214319 — MB BChir 1970 Camb.; FRCPath 1988, M 1975. (Camb. & King's Coll. Hosp.) Cons. Histopath. Torbay Hosp. Torquay. Socs: Path. Soc.; Assn. Clin. Path.; Brit. Soc. Gastroenterol. Prev: Sen. Lect. (Path.) Univ. Liverp.; Research Fell. (Histopath.) St. Mark's Hosp. Lond.; Lect. (Morbid Anat.) King's Coll. Hosp. Med. Sch. Lond.

DAY, Diana Ellen Mary Coolyermer House, Aughanaugh, Letterbreen, Enniskillen — MB BCh BAO 1981 Dub.; MRCPsych 1985.

DAY, Fiona Jane 6 Whitehaugh Park, Peebles EH45 9DA — MB ChB 1996 Ed.

DAY, Helen Clare Poundwell Meadow Health Centre, Poundwell Meadow, Modbury, Ivybridge PL21 0QL Tel: 01548 830666 Fax: 01548 831085; Walnut Tree House, Loddiswell, Kingsbridge TQ7 4EG — MB ChB 1984 Bristol; BSc Bristol 1979, MB ChB 1984; MRCGP 1988. Trainee GP Kingsbridge VTS. Prev: SHO (O & G) Freedom Fields Matern. Hosp. Plymouth.

DAY, Helen Elizabeth Oaklands Surgery, Birchfield Road, Yeovil BA21 5RL Tel: 01935 473068 Fax: 01935 412307; 88 Goldcroft, Yeovil BA21 4DF Tel: 01935 420973 Email: wickhamwoman@dial.pipex.com — MB BS 1990 Lond.; BSc Lond. 1987; MRCGP 1995; DFFP 1995. (St. Mary's Hosp. Med. Sch.) Socs: BMA; RCGP. Prev: Trainee GP Leicester VTS.

DAY, Herbert John Benjamin (retired) 26 Hitch Lowes, Chelford, Macclesfield SK11 9SR Tel: 01625 861474 — MRCS Eng. LRCP Lond. 1950. Prev: Sen. Med. Off. DHSS (Artific. Limb Appliance Centre).

DAY, Honor Marie Margaret Derby Childrens Hospital, North St., Derby DE1 3AZ Tel: 01332 340131; 10 Mona Street, Beeston, Nottingham NG9 2BY Tel: 0115 922 9848 — BM BS 1992 Nottm.; BMedSci 1990. SHO (Paediat.) Derby Childr. Hosp. & Derby City Hosp. Prev: Ho. Off. (Surg.) Kings Mill Hosp. Mansfield & (Med.) Qu. Med. Centre Nottm.

DAY, Ian Nicholas Monsarratt Human Genetics Research Division, Southampton University Hospital, Southampton SO16 6YD Email: inmd@soton.ac.uk — MB BChir 1983 Camb.; MA Oxf. 1984; PhD Camb. 1987; MRCPath 1992; FRCPath 2000. Lister Inst. Prof. Human Genetics, Univ. Soton. Prev: Lister Inst. Res. Fell.; Brit. Heart Foundat. Research Fell. Univ. Coll. Lond. Med. Sch.; MRC Train. Fell. Univ. Camb.

DAY, Janet Ruth 23 Woodlands Way, Middleton, Manchester M24 1WL — MB ChB 1990 Manch.

DAY, Jennifer May Cargill 31 Weiss Road, London SW15 1DH — MB ChB 1994 Leeds. SHO Rotat. (Psychiat.) Leeds Train. Scheme. Prev: Ho. Off. (Surg.) W. Cornw. Hosp.; Ho. Off. (Med.) Huddersfield Roy. Infirm.

DAY, Jeremy Noel Dept. of Infectious Diseases, North Manchester General Hospital, Delaugnays Road, Manchester BH13 7BP — MB BChir 1992 Camb.; DTM & H 2001 Liverpool; MA Camb. 1993; MRCP (UK) 1996. (Gonville & Caius Coll. Camb. & St Bart. Hosp.) Specialist Regist. Infect. Dis. Gen. Internal. Med. NW Higher Med Traing. Progr.. N. Manch. Gen Hosp.; Hon. Clin. Asst. Dept. of Infec. Dis.s, Univ. Hosp. Aintree Liverppol L9 7AL. Prev: SHO Trop.Med.Hosp.Trop.Dis.Lond; Reg.Infect.Dis.City & W.ern.Gen.Hosp.Edin.

DAY, Mr John Barry, RD Bon Air Consulting Rooms, Bon Air Lane, St Saviour, Jersey Tel: 01534 34014 Fax: 01534 70100; Fauvic Tower, Grouville JE3 9HG Tel: 01534 856431 — MB BS 1970 Lond.; FRCS Eng. 1973; MRCS Eng. LRCP Lond. 1969; FRCOG 1990, M 1977. (St. Geo.) Cons. O & G Jersey Gp. Hosps. Socs: BMA & Blair Bell Research Soc.; Brit. Colposcopy Soc.; Brit. Endoscopy Soc. Prev: Sen. Regist. & Regist. St. Thos. Hosp. Lond.; SHO Qu. Charlotte's Matern. Hosp. Lond. & Samarit. Hosp. Wom. Lond.

DAY, Mr John Branton, TD St. John's Court, 76 Gartside St., Manchester M3 3EL Tel: 0161 834 9349 Fax: 0161 839 1749 Email: john@johnbday.demon.co.uk — MB ChB Ed. 1969; FRCS Ed. 1974. (Ed.) Cons. Orthopaedic Surg., Centr. Manch. and Manch. Childr.'s Univ. Hosps. NHS Trust; Hon. Lect. (Orthop. Surg.) Univ. Manch. Socs: Fell. BOA; Brit. Orthop. Research Soc.; Brit. Limb Reconstruc. Soc.

DAY, John Chichester (retired) 15 Chyngton Road, Seaford BN25 4HH — MRCS Eng. LRCP Lond. 1940; DPH Eng. 1950; MFOM 1978. Prev: Med. Off. Brit. Petroleum.

DAY, John Francis The Health Centre, Smithy Green, Hulme, Cheadle Tel: 0161 485 7233 Fax: 0161 485 6567; Thornton, 65 Bramhall Pk Road, Bramhall, Stockport SK7 3NA Tel: 0161 485 2990 — MB ChB 1971 Manch.; DObst RCOG 1974.

DAY, John Howard HIV Medicine, The Middlesex Hospital, Mortimer St., London W1T 3AA; 2 Blyth Close, London E14 3DU Tel: 020 7538 1757 Email: drjday@aol.com — MB BS 1988 Lond.; MRCP (UK) 1993; DTM & H RCP Lond. 1994. (Lond. Hosp. Med. Coll.) Hon. Lect. Infec. Trop. Dis. Lond. Sch. Hyg. Socs: Christ. Med. Fell.sh.; Phys. Human Rights; Fell.Roy.Soc.Trop.med.Hyg. Prev: Sen. Regist. (Gen. Med.) Parirenyatwa Hosp., Harare, Zimbabwe; Regist. (Gen. Med.) Greenwich Dist. Hosp; Specialist Regist. (Infect. Dis. & Trop. Med.) N. Thames.

DAY, John Leigh The Diabetes Centre, Ipswich Hospital NHS Trust, Heath Road, Ipswich IP4 5PD Tel: 01473 704182 Fax: 01473 704197; Playford Grange, Great Bealings, Woodbridge IP13 6PH Tel: 01473 735444 — MD Lond. 1973, MB BS 1963; FRCP Lond. 1979, M 1966; DSc 2000. Cons. Phys. Ipswich Hosp. Socs: Brit. Diabetic Assn. Prev: Lect. (Med.) King's Coll. Hosp.; Regist. (Med.) King's Coll. Hosp. & Ipswich & E. Suff. Hosp.

DAY, Johnathan Rory The Surgery, PO Box 124, Kingstone Winslow, Swindon SN6 8PD Tel: 01381 634253 — MB BChir 1978 Camb.; MA Camb. 1971; MRCS Eng. LRCP Lond. 1978. (St. Bart.) Prev: GP N. Cornw.; Med. Off. P.ss Marina Coll. & Brunei Govt.

DAY, Jonathan James Luton & Dunstable Hospital, Lewsey Road, Luton LU4 0DZ Tel: 01582 491122 Fax: 01582 497359 Email: jonathan@postgrad.demon.co.uk — MB ChB 1981 Sheff.; BMedSci (Hons.) Sheff. 1980, MB ChB 1981; MRCP (UK) 1984; FRCP 1998. Cons. Phys. Med. Elderly Luton & Dunstable Hosp.; Clin. Tutor.

DAY, Jonathan Richard Stewart 30 Guthrie Court, Gleneagles Village, Auchterarder PH3 1SD — MB BS 1997 Lond.

DAY, Mrs Jose Ashton 97 Harley Street, London W1 Tel: 020 7935 1942; 26 Thurlow Road, Hampstead, London NW3 5PP Tel: 020 7435 0899 — MB BS 1953 Lond.; MRCS Eng. LRCP Lond. 1953; FRCGP 1982, M 1967. (Roy. Free) Med. Off. BUPA Med. Centre Lond. Socs: BMA & Med. Wom. Federat. Prev: Clin. Asst. (Rheum.) Roy. Free Hosp. Lond.; Clin. Asst. (VD) St. Thos. Hosp. Lond.; Mem. Comm. Rev. Med. & Safety Efficiency & Adverse Reactions Comm.

DAY, Julie Simone Family Medical Centre, 171 Carlton Road, Nottingham NG3 2FW Tel: 0115 504068 Fax: 0115 950 9844 — BM BS 1990 Nottm.

DAY, Kenneth Arthur Northgate & Prudhoe NHS Trust, Northgate Hospital, Morpeth NE61 3BP Tel: 01670 394070 Fax: 01670 394004 — MB ChB 1961 Bristol; FRCPsych 1978, M 1971; DPM Eng. 1964. Hon. Cons. Psychiat. Stot & Prudhoe NHS Trust Morpeth; Med. Mem. Ment. Health Review Tribunal, N.. & Yorks. Region; SOAD, Ment. Health Act Commiss.; Hon. Clin. Lect., Univ. of Newc.-upon-Tyne. Socs: Roy. Soc. of Med. - Fell. Worshipful Soc. of Apoth. of Lond. - Liveryman. Prev: Hon. Cons. Psychiat. Newc. Univ. Hosps.; Sen. Lect. Univ. Newc.

DAY, Lawrence Richard Arto University Health Service, University of Southampton, Building 48, Highfield, Southampton SO17 1BJ Tel: 023 8055 7531 Fax: 023 8059 3259; 86 Copperfield Road, Bassett, Southampton SO16 3NY Tel: 02380 676591 Email: lrday@tcp.co.uk — MB ChB 1982 Ed.; BSc (Hons. Bact) Ed. 1980; MRCGP 1994. (Univ. Ed.) Prev: Clin. Research Fell. Regional BrE. Path. Unit Bristol Univ.; Regist. (Histopath.) Frenchay Hosp. Bristol; Healthcare Cons. World Vision Israel & Egypt.

DAY, Lisa Maria 78 Beech Road, St Albans AL3 5AT — MB BS 1993 Lond.; DFFP 1996; DRCOG 1996. GP.

DAY, Louise Tina Thanet House, 17 Montpelier Road, Ealing, London W5 2QP — MB BS 1993 Lond.; MA Camb. 1993; DFFP 1998; MRCP 1997; MRCPCH 1997; MRCOG 1999. (Cambridge/London) LOCUMS. Prev: SHO (Paediat.) E. Lond. Rotat.; Acting Regist., King Geo. Hosp. (O & G) Goodmayes, Essex.

DAY, Professor Michael Herbert Department of Palaeontology, British Museum (Natural History), Cromwell Road, London SW7 5BD Tel: 020 7938 9314; 26 Thurlow Road, Hampstead, London NW3 5PP Tel: 020 7435 0899 Fax: 020 7794 4657 Email: m.day@mailbox.ulcc.ac.uk — MB BS Lond. 1954; DSc Lond. 1982; PhD Lond. 1962; MRCS Eng. LRCP Lond. 1954. (Roy. Free) Prof. Emerit. Lond Univ. Socs: Fell. (Ex-Pres.) Roy. Anthrop. Inst.; (Ex-Pres.) Primate Soc.; Anat. Soc. Prev: Prof. Anat. St. Thos. Hosp. Med. Sch. (Univ. Lond.); Reader (Phys. Anthrop.) Middlx. Hosp. Med. Sch. Lond.; Sen. Lect. (Anat.) Middlx. Hosp. Med. Sch.

DAY, Michael John Ingram Priory Gardens, Dunstable LU6 3SU — BM BCh 1970 Oxf. Socs: Brit. Menopause Soc.; Brit. Assn. Sport & Med.

DAY, Michelle Suzanne 10 Leadhall View, Rosset Green, Harrogate HG2 9PF — MB ChB 1991 Leeds.

DAY, Nicholas Joseph Bleak House, Church Road, Crowle, Worcester WR7 4AZ — MB ChB 1997 Manch.

DAY, Nicholas Philip John 16 Chiltern View, Little Milton, Oxford OX44 7QP — BM BCh 1986 Oxf.

DAY, Patrick John 6A Westfield Park, Bristol BS6 6LT — MB ChB 1971 Glas.

DAY, Paul Department of Paediatrics, Pembury Hospital, Tunbridge Wells TN2 4QJ Tel: 01892 823535; 66 Yew Tree Road, Southborough, Tunbridge Wells TN4 0BN — MB ChB Sheff. 1984; BSc (1st cl. Hons.) Human Biol. & Anat. Sheff. 1980; MRCP (UK) 1990; FRCPCH 1997. Cons. Paediat. Pembury Hosp. Tunbridge Wells. Socs: BMA; Brit. Diabetic Assn.; Brit. Soc. Paediatric Gastroenterol. Hepat. of Nutrit. Prev: Sen. Regist. (Paediat.) Roy. Alexandra Hosp. for Sick Childr. Brighton; Sen. Regist. (Child Health) King's Coll. Hosp. Lond.; Research Fell. Rayne Inst. St. Thos. Hosp. Lond.

DAY, Richard Carey Medway Hospital, Windmill Road, Gillingham ME7 5NY Tel: 01634 830000; Grove House, 54 Maidstone Road, Rochester ME1 1RJ — MB BChir 1966 Camb.; MA 1985; BA Camb. 1963; FRCP Ed. 1988; MRCP (UK) 1969; FRCP 1988. (Camb. & Guy's) Cons. Phys. & Gastroenterol. Medway Health Dist. Socs: Brit. Soc. Gastroenterol. Prev: Sen. Regist. Gastrointestinal Unit W.. Gen. Hosp. Edin.; Prophit Schol. & Hon. Lect. Dept. Med. Roy. Free Hosp. Lond.

DAY, Richard Kenneth Department of Psychiatry, University of Dundee, Ninewells Hospital, PO Box 120, Dundee DD1 9SY Tel: 01382 632121 Email: r.k.day@dundee.ac.uk — MB ChB 1993 Aberd. Clin. Lect. (Psychiat.) Ninewells Hosp. Dundee. Prev: Regist. (Psychiat.) Roy. Cornhill Hosp. Aberd.

DAY, Richard William Bradshaw Poole Hospital, Poole BH15 2JB Email: rday@poole-troswest.nhs.uk; 2 Brunstead Place, Branksome, Poole BH12 1EW — MB BS 1978 Lond.; FRCP Ed. 1995; FRCP Lond. 1994; MRCP (UK) 1983; MRCS Eng. LRCP Lond. 1978. (St. Mary's) Cons. Phys. Med. Elderly Poole Dorset. Socs: Brit. Geriat. Soc.; BMA. Prev: Sen. Regist. (Geriat.) Portsmouth & Soton. Hosps.

DAY, Ruth Elizabeth Fraser of Allander Unit, Royal Hospital for Sick Children, Yorkhill, Glasgow G3 8SJ Tel: 0141 201 0139 Fax: 0141 201 9270; 4 Stirling Drive, Bearsden, Glasgow G61 4NX Tel: 0141 942 5008 — MB ChB Bristol 1969; FRCP Glas. 1987; MRCP (UK) 1972. Cons. Paediat. (Developm. Paediat. & Neurol. Handicap) Roy. Hosp. Sick Childr. Glas.

DAY, Sara Jane c/o Headquarters, British Forces BFPO 52 — MB BS 1968 Lond.; MRCS Eng. LRCP Lond. 1968; DCH Eng. 1973. (Guy's)

DAY, Sara Louise 34 Highfield, Letchworth SG6 3PZ — MB ChB 1996 Birm.; ChB Birm. 1996.

DAY, Stephen William Cross Hills Health Centre, Holme Lane, Cross Hills, Keighley BD20 7LG — MB ChB 1993 Leeds.

DAY, Susan Patricia Shires Health Care, 18 Main Street, Shirebrook, Mansfield NG20 8DG Tel: 01623 742464 Fax: 01623 743921; Moorfield Farm House, Bishops Walk, Church Warsop, Mansfield NG20 0SN Tel: 01623 845019 — MB ChB 1987 Sheff. Prev: Trainee GP Mansfield VTS.

DAY, Sushama Medway Hospital, Windmill Road, Gillingham ME7 5NY Tel: 01634 830000; Grove House, 54 Maidstone Road, Rochester ME1 1RJ — MB BS 1966 All India Inst. Med. Scs.; FFA RCS Eng. 1972. Cons. Anaesth. Medway Hosp. Gillingham. Socs: Assn. Anaesth. GB & Irel.; Intens. Care Soc.; Roy. Soc. Med. Prev: Sen. Regist. (Anaesth.) King's Coll. Hosp. & Brook Gen. Hosp. Lond.

DAY, Mr Thomas Kevin North West Independent Clinic, Ballykelly, Limavady BT49 9HS Tel: 028 777 63090; 7 Queen Street, Londonderry BT48 7EF Tel: 02871 372694 Fax: 02871 372106 — MB BChir 1973 Camb.; MChir Camb. 1983, MA, MB 1973, BChir 1972; FRCS Eng. 1977; MRCP (UK) 1975; FICS 1992; Cert. Adv. Av. Med 1999. (Guy's) Cons. Surg. N. W. Indep.Hosp. Lond.derry; Squadron Ldr. Roy. Auxil. Air Force; Med. Examr. CAA; Surgic. Adviser, Medicins sans Frontiers, UK. Socs: Fell. Roy. Soc. Med.; Fell. Internat. Coll. Surgs. Prev: Sen. Regist. & Lect. (Surg.) Guy's

Hosp. Lond.; Jun. Research Fell. (Vasc. Surg.) King's Coll. Hosp. Lond.

DAY, Valerie NHS Modernisation Agency, Room 212, Eileen House, 80-94 Newington Causeway, London SE1 6EF Tel: 020 7972 2957 Fax: 020 7972 2794 Email: valerie.day@doh.gsi.gou.uk; Tel: 01564 730286 Email: vaday@yahoo.co.uk — MRCS Eng. LRCP Lond. 1979; MFPHM RCP (UK) 1989; MFCM 1989; MRCOG 1985; FFPHM 1996; FRCOG 2000. (Middlx.) Director of Progr.s, NHS Modernisation Agency. Prev: Sen. Med. Off.-NHS Exec.; Dir. of Pub. Health, N. Worcs. HA; Cons. Pub. Health Med., W. Midl. NHS Exec.

DAYA, Mr Hamid Flat 3, 17 Adamson Road, London NW3 3HU — MB ChB 1988 Manch.; BSc (Med. Sci.) St. And. 1985; FRCS (Otol.) 1993. Cons. (Ear, Nose & Throat) St. Geo.s Hosp. Lond. Prev: SHO (Gen. Surg.) Benenden Hosp. Kent; SHO (Plastic Surg.) Lister Hosp. Stevenage; SHO (ENT) Roy. Nat. Throat, Nose & Ear Hosp. Lond.

DAYA, Joan 11 Penrose Avenue, Carpenters Park, Watford WD19 5AE Tel: 020 8428 5134 — MB ChB 1959 Aberd.; DCH Eng. 1961. (Aberd.)

DAYA, Pravinchandra Group Practice Surgery, 33 Newton Road, Great Barr, Birmingham B43 6AA Tel: 0121 357 1690 Fax: 0121 357 4253; Maythorne, 31 Gorway Road, Walsall WS1 3BE — MB BCh 1967 Wales. Prev: Med. Off. Flying Doctor Serv. Zambia; SHO (O & G) & (Paediat.) Morriston Hosp. Swansea.

DAYA, Shamim 268C Kew Road, Richmond TW9 3EE — BM 1985 Soton.

DAYA, Mr Sheraz Mansoor 57 Harley Street, London W1G 8QS Tel: 020 7580 7660 Fax: 020 7580 7547 Email: sdaya@compuserve.com — MB BCh BAO 1984 NUI; MB BCh BAO (Hons.) NUI 1984; MD New York 1993; FACP 1995; FACS 1995; FRCS (Ed.) 1998. (Royal College of Surgeons in Ireland) Dir. & Cons. Ophth. Surg. Corneo Plastic Unit Qu. Vict. Hosp. E. Grinstead; Dip. Amer. Bd. Opthalmology & Amer. Bd. Internal Med. Socs: Fell. Roy. Soc. Med.; Fell. Amer. Acad. Ophthalmol.; Fell. Internat. Coll. Surg.s. Prev: Dir. & Cons. (Opthalmology Surg.) Cornea Servs. Catholic Med. Centre NY, USA; Fell. Specialist Univ. Minnesota & Phillips Eye Inst., USA; Resid. (Ophth.) Catholic Med. Center, USA.

DAYA, Suresh Govan Stanhope Parade Health Centre, Gordon Street, South Shields NE33 4HX Tel: 0191 451 6143 Fax: 0191 451 6146 — MB BS 1974 Newc.

DAYA, Vera Hilda Dept. of Anaesthetics, Sandwich District General Hospital, Lyndon, West Bromwich; Maythorne, 31 Gorway Road, Walsall WS1 3BE — MB BCh 1968 Wales; FFA RCS Eng. 1979; DA Eng. 1971. (Cardiff) Cons. Anaesth. Sandwell Healthcare Trust, W. Bromwich. Prev: Cons. Anaesth. Wordsley Hosp. Stourbridge & Russels Hall Hosp. Dudley; Sen. Regist. (Anaesth.) W. Midl. RHA; Regist. (Anaesth.) United Birm. Hosps.

DAYAH, Anantt Ramanlal Long Street Medical Centre, 24 Long Street, Wigston LE18 2AH Tel: 0116 288 3314 Fax: 0116 288 6711 — MB BS 1989 Lond.

DAYAH, Dipak Raman 2A Bruxby Street, Syston, Leicester LE7 1NB — MB ChB 1985 Dundee.

DAYAL, Mahendra Singh (retired) Woodbourne Clinic, 21 Woodbourne Road, Birmingham B17 8BZ Tel: 0121 434 4343 — MB BS Agra 1955; MRCPsych 1975; DPM Ed. 1971; DTM & H Calcutta 1957. Prev: Cons. Psychiat. Black Country Ment. Health Trust.

DAYAN, Professor Anthony David (retired) 21 Heathgate, London NW11 7AP — MB BS 1959 Lond.; MB BS (Hons.) Lond. 1959; BSc (Hons. Physiol.) Lond. 1956, MD 1968; FRCP Lond. 1986, M 1961; FFOM RCP Lond. 1995; FFPM RCP (UK) 1990; FRCPath 1977, M 1965; FIBiol. 1985. Prof. Toxicol. St. Bart. Hosp. Med. Coll. Univ. Lond.; Edr. in Chief Human & Experim. Toxicol. Prev: Cons. Neuropathol. Nat. Hosp. Nerv. Dis. & Hosp. Sick Childr. Lond.

DAYAN, Colin Mark University Department of Medicine, Bristol Royal Infirmary, Marlborough, Bristol BS2 8HW Tel: 0117 928 3525 Fax: 0117 928 3315 Email: colin.dayan@bris.ac.uk; Weston General Hospital, Weston Super Mare BS23 4TQ Tel: 01934 647174 — MB BS 1984 Lond.; PhD Lond. 1991; MA Oxf. 1981; MRCP (UK) 1987; FRCP 1998. Cons. Sen. Lect. (Med.) Univ. Bristol; Cons. Phys. (Diatetologist & Endocrinol.) W.on Gen. Hosp. Socs: Brit. Soc. Immunol.; Soc. Endocrinol.; Brit. Diabetic Assn. Prev: Lect. (Med.) Univ. Bristol; Fell. Endocrinol. Mass. Gen. Hosp.; Hon. Sen. Regist. (Endocrinol. & Gen. Med.) Char. Cross Hosp. Lond.

DAYAN, Mr Elia (retired) Woodside, 15 North Avenue, South Shields NE34 6BB Tel: 0191 456 0898 — MB BCh 1949 Cairo; FRCS Eng. 1954; LMSSA Lond. 1953. Prev: Cons. Surg. S. Shields Gp. Hosps.

DAYAN, Margaret Ruth Department of Ophthalmology, Royal Victoria Infirmary, Queen Victoria Road, Newcastle upon Tyne NE1 4LP Tel: 0191 232 5131 — BM BCh 1990 Oxf.; MA Physiol. Sci. Oxf. 1987; FRCOphth 1994. Cons. Ophthamologist, Roy. Vict. Infirm., Newc. upon Tyne.

DAYANANDA, Kota S S Riverside Health Centre, Wellington Street, Canton, Cardiff CF11 9SH Tel: 029 2034 2113 Fax: 029 2034 2686.

DAYANANDAN, Rejin Maudsley Hospital, Denmark Hill, London SE5 8AZ Tel: 020 7919 2193 Email: r.dayanandan@iop.kcl.ac.uk; 94 Ridge Lane, Watford WD17 4TA Tel: 01865 435869 Email: oxford@doctors.org.uk — MB BS 1993 Lond.; MRCPsych 1999; BA Physiol. Sci. Oxf. 1989; MA Oxf. 1998. (Univ. Oxf./Univ. Coll. & Middlx.) Specialist Regist. (Old Age Psychiat.) Maudsley Hosp., Lond. Socs: Oxf. Soc.; Roy. Coll. Psychiat. Prev: Regist. (Psychiat.) Warneford Hosp. Oxf.; Regist. (Psychiat.) Heatherwood Hosp. Ascot; SHO (Psychiat.) Fair Mile Hosp. Oxon.

DAYANI, Andrew Williton and Watchet Surgeries, Robert Street, Williton, Taunton TA4 4QE Tel: 01984 632701 Fax: 01984 633933; Orchard House, 15 Old Cleeve, Minehead TA24 6HJ Tel: 01984 632701 Email: 100450.3511@compuserve.com — MB ChB 1989 Leic.; MRCGP 1994. (Leic.) Locality Lead GP (Commiss.) Som. HA; Clin. Asst. Williton Hosp.

DAYANI, Lachman Naraindas Glebefields Health Centre, Saint Marks Road, Tipton DY4 0UB — MB BS 1963 Rajasthan.

DAYKIN, Andrew Philip Taunton and Somerset NHS Trust, Taunton TA1 5DA Tel: 01823 342114 Fax: 01823 342526 — MB BS 1975 Lond.; MA Oxf. 1972; MRCP (UK) 1978; FFA RCS Eng. 1980. Cons. Anaesth. & Dir. of Intens. Care Taunton & Som. Hosp. Taunton. Prev: Dir. Anaesth. & Theatres Taunton & Som. Hosp.(1994-1999); Sen. Regist. (Anaesth.) Soton. & Winchester Hosps.

DAYKIN, Stephen Michael Manor Farm Close Surgery, 8 Manor Farm Close, Drayton, Norwich NR8 6DN Tel: 01603 867532 — MB BS 1983 Lond.; MA Oxf. 1986, BA 1978; MRCGP 1990; DRCOG 1988. Socs: BMA (Sec. Norwich Div.).

DAYMOND, Patricia Winifred Rosemary (retired) 8 Phoenix Green, Norfolk Park, Edgbaston, Birmingham B15 3NR Tel: 0121 454 2554 — MB ChB Liverp. 1957; MRCS Eng. LRCP Lond. 1957; DCH Eng. 1960; FRCPCH 1997; FRIPHH 1998. Prev: SCMO Sandwell HA.

DAYMOND, Professor Terence John The Royal Hospital, Kayll Road, Sunderland SR4 7TP Tel: 0191 565 6256 Fax: 0191 569 9205 Email: terry.daymond@chs.northy.nhs.uk; 34 Eslington Terrace, Jesmond, Newcastle upon Tyne NE2 4RN Tel: 0191 212 1253 — MB ChB 1967 Ed.; FRCP Lond. 1987; MRCP (UK) 1974; DPhysMed Eng. 1975; DObst RCOG 1971; FRCP Ed. 1998. Cons. Rheum. & Rehabil. Sunderland City Hosps.; Lect. (Rheum.) Univ. Newc.; Hon. Phys. Sunderland SCOPE Soc.; Vis. Prof. Sunderland Univ. Socs: Fell. Roy. Soc. Med.; Nat. Osteoparosis Socicety; Brit. Soc. Rheum.

DAYNES, Graham Kenneth The Health Centre, Trenchard Avenue, Thornaby, Stockton-on-Tees TS17 0DD Tel: 01642 762921 Fax: 01642 760608; Three Steps, Crathorne, Yarm TS15 0BB Tel: 01642 701475 — MB BS 1978 Newc.; FRCGP 1997; DRCOG 1981.

DAYNES, Timothy John 1 Ullswater Road, London SE27 0AL — MB BS 1986 Lond.; MRCP (UK) 1995. Sen. Regist. (A & E) N. & Yorks. RHA. Prev: Regist. (A & E) Wolverhampton & Stoke-on-Trent; SHO (Med.) Stoke-on-Trent.

DAYSON, Carol Cameron Audley Mills Surgery, 57 Eastwood Road, Rayleigh SS6 7JF Tel: 01268 774981 — MB BCh 1970 Wales; DObst RCOG 1972; Cert. Family Plann. JCC 1983; Dip. Family Plann. 1996. (Wales)

DAYSON, David Frederick Central Locality, Community Mental Health Team, Bay Tree House, Graham Rd, Southampton SO14 0YH Tel: 02380 795300 — MB BS 1978 Lond.; MRCPsych 1986; MRCGP 1983; DCH RCP Lond. 1983; DRCOG 1982. (Guy's) W.

Hants. NHS Trust; Lead for UnderGrad. Med. Educat. Prev: Sen. Regist. (Psychiat.) Maudsley Hosp. Lond.; Research Regist. Assesm. Team Psychiat. Serv. Friern Hosp.; Regist. (Psychiat.) Hampstead HA.

DE, Mr Arun Kumar Shreea, Tan House Lane, Grat Harwood, Blackburn BB6 7UL — MB BS 1964 Calcutta; FRCS Glas. 1977.

DE, Barindra Kumar Royal Infirmary, Anlaby Road, Hull HU1 Tel: 01482 28541 — MB BS 1954 Calcutta; DOMS 1960. (Calcutta Med. Coll.)

DE, Debjani 22 Hood Street, Morpeth NE61 1JF — MB BS 1993 Newc.

DE, Dipa 10 Bulldog Lane, Lichfield WS13 7LN Tel: 01543 268120 Fax: 01543 417364 — MB BS 1963 Calcutta; FFA RCSI 1978; DA (UK) 1969. Assoc. Specialist (Anaesth.) Sandwell Dist. Hosp. Birm. Prev: Regist. Stoke on Trent & Blackpool.

DE, Mr Kshiti Ranjan 36 Mountbatten Avenue, Sandal, Wakefield WF2 6HD — MB BS 1953 Calcutta; DGO 1955; FRCS Eng. 1968; FRCS Ed. 1967; MRCOG 1963. (Calcutta Med. Coll.) Sen. Regist. (Gen. Surg.) Gen. Hosp. Jersey. Prev: Asst. Accid. Surg. United Leeds Hosps.; Regist. Gen. Surg. Clayton Hosp. Wakefield.

DE, Partha Pratim 10 Bulldog Lane, Lichfield WS13 7LN — MB BS 1990 Lond.; BSc Lond. 1987, MB BS 1990; DTM & H RCP Lond. 1993. Regist. (Bacteriol.) St. Mary's Hosp. Lond. Socs: Hosp. Infec. Soc.; Brit. Soc. Antimicrob. Chemother. Prev: SHO (Med. Microbiol.) Childr. Hosp., Gen. Hosp. & Qu. Eliz. Hosp. Birm.

DE, Mr Priti Ranjan 10 Bulldog Lane, Lichfield WS13 7LN Tel: 01543 268120 Fax: 01543 417364 — MB BS 1961 Calcutta; FRCS Ed. 1975; DLO Eng. 1970. (Nilratan Sircar Med. Coll. Calcutta) Cons. ENT Surg. SE Staffs. Health Dist. W. Midl. HA; Assoiate Med. Director (CPD) Buxton Hosp. NHS Trust. Socs: BMA & Roy. Soc. Med.; Brit. Asscoiation of OtoLaryngol.; Brit. Assn. of Head Neck Oncologists. Prev: Sen. Regist. (Otorlaryng.) Qu. Eliz. Hosp. Birm.

DE, Rabindra Nath 30 Marle Croft, Whitefield, Manchester M45 7NB — MB BS 1965 Calcutta. (R.G. Kar Med. Coll. Calcutta) Prev: Regist. Chest Dis. Canterbury Hosp.; SHO Geriat. St. Helen's Hosp. Hastings; SHO Geriat. Ryhope Hosp.

DE, Ranjit Kumar Gold Street Medical Centre, 106 Gold Street, Wellingborough NN8 4BT Tel: 01933 224678 Fax: 01933 229240 — MB BS 1965 Calcutta; DA Eng. 1974. (Nat. Med. Coll. Calcutta) Prev: Regist. Dept. Anaesth. Kettering & Dist. Gen. Hosp. & N.ampton Gen.; Hosp.

DE, Sabuj Kanti Alpha House Surgery, 32-34 Avenue Road, Coseley, Bilston WV14 9DL Tel: 01902 882070; 3 Springvale Avenue, Walsall WS5 3QB Tel: 01922 22250 — MB BS 1965 Dacca; DTM & H Liverp. 1974. (Sir Salimullah Med. Coll.) Prev: Regist. (Med.) Sandwell Dist. Gen. Hosp. W. Brom.; Regist. Dudley Rd. Hosp. Birm.; SHO N. Middlx. Hosp. Lond.

DE, Mr Santimoy (retired) 23 Viceroy Close, Bristol Road, Edgbaston, Birmingham B5 7UR Tel: 0121 440 2038 — MB BS 1961 Calcutta; FRCS Ed. 1972; FRCOphth 1988; DOMS Calcutta 1964. Prev: Cons. Ophth. H.M. Stanley Hosp. St. Asaph.

DE, Shashikala 30 Park Road, Walsall WS5 3JU — MB BS 1974 Bangalore.

DE, Subir Kanti 1 Fountains Crescent, London N14 6BG — MB BS 1975 Calcutta; DObst RCPI 1983; DA Eng. 1983.

DE, Mr Sujay Kumar (retired) 8 Snow Hill Rise, Wakefield WF1 2UA Tel: 01924 364276 — MB BS 1955 Calcutta; BSc (Physiol., Hons.) Calcutta 1948; FRCS Glas. 1976. Prev: Med. Off. DHSS Artific. Limb & Appliance Serv. Leeds.

DE ALMEIDA, Suresha Therese Lakmalie The Surgery, 142 Mitcham Lane, Streatham, London SW16 6NS Tel: 020 8769 0635; 29 Mount Ephraim Lane, London SW16 1JE — MB BS 1990 Lond.; MRCGP 1995; DRCOG 1992.

DE ALWIS, Chandrasena Department of Haematology, Royal Glamorgan Hospital, Ynys Maerdy, Pontyclun CF72 8XR Tel: 01443 443443 Fax: 01443 443335; Bryn Bedw, Birch Hill, Tongwynlais, Cardiff CF15 7LL Tel: 02920 810554 Fax: 029 2081 0554 — MB BS Ceylon 1968; FRCPath. 1991,M 1980; DPath Eng. 1977. (Faculty of Med. Univ. of Sri Lanka) Cons. Haemat. E. Roy. Glam. Hosp. Llantrisant. Socs: Brit. Soc. of Haemetology; Brit. Soc. of Transfus.; Assn. Clin. Path.

DE ALWIS, Mr Dilogen Valentine Croydon Eye Unit, Mayday University Hospital, London Road, Croydon CR7 7YE Tel: 020 8401 3477 Fax: 020 8401 3489 Email: dilogen.dealwis@mhc-tr.sthames.nhs.uk — MB BS 1979 Colombo; MPhil Sussex 1992; FRCS Ed. 1987; FRCOphth 1988; DO RCS Eng. 1984. Cons. Ophth. Croydon Eye Unit Mayday Univ. Hosp. Prev: Sen. Regist. (Ophth.) Bristol & Exeter; Regist. (Ophth.) Brighton & St. Thos.

DE ALWIS, Egodahage Don Mahindra Keerthiratne Haematology Department, Torbay Hospital, Lewton Bridge. Newton Road, Torquay TQ2 7AA — MB BS 1968 Ceylon; DPath Eng. 1978. (Colombo) SHO A & E Dept. E. Ham Memor. Hosp. Lond.

DE ALWIS, Erushani 7 Birch Hill, Tongwynlais, Cardiff CF15 7LL — MB BS 1997 Lond.

DE ALWIS, Kithsiri Hempala (retired) 14 Heideck Gardens, Hutton, Brentwood CM13 2UA Tel: 01277 232594 — MB BS 1966 Colombo; MRCPsych 1977; DPM Eng. 1977. Cons. Psychiat. Little Highwood Hosp. Brentwood.

DE ALWIS, Lasantha Chanaka The Surgery, 160 Haydons Road, Wimbledon, London SW19 8TR Tel: 020 8542 3105 Fax: 020 8544 1126 — MB BS 1984 Sri Lanka; MRCS Eng. LRCP Lond. 1988; DCH RCP Lond. 1994. GP Asst. S. Croydon. Prev: Trainee GP; SHO (Paediat.) Hammersmith Hosp.; SHO (Neonates) St. Geo. Hosp.

DE ARCE SEUBA, Cristina Daniela Basement Flat, 93 Norfolk St., Swansea SA1 6JE — LMS 1992 U Autonoma Barcelona.

DE BASS, Felix William John School Lane Surgery, School Lane, Thetford IP24 2AG Tel: 01842 753115; Hawthorns, Melville Road, Croxton, Thetford IP24 1NG Tel: 01842 752875 Fax: 01842 752875 — MB BS 1966 Lond.; MRCS Eng. LRCP Lond. 1966; DA Eng. 1970. (Univ. Coll. Hosp.) Prev: Maj. RAMC; Specialist (Anaesth.) BMH Rinteln; Ho. Phys. & Ho. Surg. Barnet Gen. Hosp.

DE BEAUX, Mr Andrew Charles 13 Cadogan Road, Edinburgh EH16 6LY Tel: 0131 664 3503 — MB ChB 1988 Aberd.; FRCS Ed. 1992.

DE BEAUX, Ishrat 13 Cadogan Road, Edinburgh EH16 6LY Tel: 0131 664 3503 — MB ChB 1991 Ed.; FRCA 1996.

DE BEAUX, Mr John Louis Marcus (retired) 21 Carnegie Crescent, Aberdeen AB15 4AU Tel: 01224 311236 — MB BS 1946 Madras; FRCS Eng. 1959; DTM & H Liverp. 1956. Hon. Cons. Surg. Dr. Gray's Hosp. Elgin. Prev: Sen. Cons. Surg. C.W.M. Hosp. Suva, Fiji.

DE BEER, Catharina Dorothea 33 Morgan le Fay Drive, Chandler's Ford, Eastleigh SO53 4JQ — MB ChB 1996 Stellenbosch.

DE BEER, David Anthony Houlton 4 Lymington Court, 48 Raymond Road, Wimbledon, London SW19 4AN Tel: 020 8946 8170 — MB ChB 1990 Cape Town; DA (UK) 1995; Dip Primary Emerg. Care (SA) 1993; Dip Obst. (S Afr) 1993; DCH (SA) 1992; FRCA 1998. (University of Cape Town, South Africa) Specialist Regist. Rotat. (Anaesth.) St. Geo. Hosp. Lond.

DE BELDER, Adam Julian The Cottage, Wilmington, Polegate BN26 5SJ — MB BS 1986 Lond.; BSc (Physiol.) Lond. 1983, MD 1994; MRCP (UK) 1990. (Lond. Hosp. Med. Coll.) Cons. Cardiol. Roy. Sussex Co. Hosp. Brighton.

DE BELDER, Mr Keith Roy John, Group Capt. RAF Med. Br. Retd. (retired) Cornerbrook, Kite Hill, Wootton Bridge, Ryde PO33 4LE Tel: 01983 882542 — MB BS 1950 Lond.; FRCS Eng. 1955; MRCS Eng. LRCP Lond. 1950. Prev: Cons. Orthop. Surg. I. of Wight Health Dist. & The Lord Mayor Treloar Orthop. Hosp. Alton.

DE BELDER, Mark Andrew James Cook University Hospital, Marton Road, Middlesbrough TS4 3BW Tel: 01642 854620 Fax: 01642 232408 Email: mdb.sch.heart.onyxnet.co.uk; Castle House Farm House, Little Broughton, Stokesley, Middlesbrough TS9 5JE Tel: 01642 712697 — MB BS 1980 Lond.; MA Camb. 1984, BA 1977; MD Lond. 1990; FRCP Lond. 1997. (Lond. Hosp. Med. Coll.) Cons. Cardiol. S. Tees Hosps. NHS Trust Middlesbrough. Socs: Brit. Cardiac Soc.; Brit. Soc. Echocardiogr.; (Counc.) Brit. Cardiovasc. Interven. Soc.(Nat. Audit Off.). Prev: Sen. Regist. (Cardiol.) St. Geo. Hosp., Roy. Brompton & Nat. Heart Hosp. Lond.; Clin. Research Fell. St. Geo. Hosp. Med. Sch. Lond.

DE BELDER, Matthew John Keith Upper Green Road Medical Centre, Upper Green Road, St. Helens, Ryde PO33 1UG Tel: 01983 872772 Fax: 01983 874800 Email: matthew.debelder@gp-j84dd7.nhs.uk; Langbridge Cottage, Newchurch, Sandown PO36 0NP Tel: 01983 867456 — MB BChir 1976 Camb.; MA, BChir 1975; MRCGP 1982; DAvMed FOM RCP Lond. 1984. (Lond. Hosp.) Gen. Practitioner, St. Helens Med. Centre, Isle of Wight; Clin. Dir. Isle of Wight Heart Care Club; CAA Authorised Med. Examr.; Company Doctor Britten Norman Aircraft Company Bembridge. Prev:

Sen. Med. Off. RAF Odiham; Gp. Flight Med. Off. RAF Aeromed. Evacuation Serv. HQ No. 1 Gp RAF Upavon; Sen. Med. Off. RAF Benson.

DE BERKER, David Adrian Roderick Bristol Dermatology Centre, Bristol Royal Infirmary, Bristol B52 8HW — MB BS 1985 Lond.; BA Oxf. 1981; MRCP (UK) 1989. Cons. Dermat. Bristol Ryl. Inf. Prev: Regist. (Dermat.) Slade Hosp. Oxf.

DE BOER, Mr Charles Henry Coniston, 9A Glebe Lane, Gnosall, Stafford ST20 0ER Tel: 01785 822628 — MB BChir 1945 Camb.; FRCS Eng. 1949; MRCS Eng. LRCP Lond. 1945; FRCOG 1965, M 1951. (Lond. Hosp.) O & G Liverp. HA.

DE BOER, Miss Frances Catherine Norfolk & Norwich Hospital, Brunswick Road, Norwich NR1 3SR Tel: 01603 286296 Fax: 01603 287532 Email: deboer@norfolk-norwich.thenns.com; Corporation Farm House, Wymondham Road, Hethel, Norwich NR14 8EU — MB BS 1978 Lond.; MRCOG 1984; FRCOG 1997. (Lond. Hosp.) Cons. O & G Norwich HA. Prev: Sen. Regist. (O & G) Nottm. Hosps.; Regist. (O & G) Lond. Hosp. Whitechapel.

DE BOER, Gillian Margaret Leeds Centre of Homoeopathy, 148 Harrogate Road, Leeds LS7 4NZ Tel: 0113 393 0113; 16 Helmsley Road, Leeds LS16 5JA Tel: 0113 278 3547 — MB ChB 1976 Leeds; MFHom 1993. Homoeop. Pract. Leeds & Harrogate.

DE BOER, Mr Peter Goffe York District Hospital, Wigginton Road, York YO31 8HE Tel: 01904 453626; Priory House, 2 Main St, Nether Poppleton, York YO26 6HS Tel: 01904 780506 — MB BChir 1972 Camb.; FRCS 1977. Cons. Orthop. Surg. York Dist. Hosp.; Assoc. Prof. St Geo. Med. Sch. Grenada; Trustee AO Foundat. Socs: Brit. Orthop. Assn.; York Med. Soc. Prev: Clin. Fell. Albert Einstein Coll. Med., New York; Regist. (Surg.) Bedford Gen. Hosp.; Demonst. (Anat.) Univ. Camb.

DE BOER, Richard Charles Royal Devon & Exeter Hospital, Exeter — MB BS 1987 Lond.; MRCP (Paediat.) (UK) 1991. Sen. Regist. Rotat. (Paediat.) S. W.. RHA. Prev: Regist. Rotat. (Paediat.) S. W.. RHA; SHO Rotat. (Paediat.) Char. Cross & W.m. Hosps.; SHO (Paediat.) Lond. Hosp. & St. John's Hosp. Chelmsford.

DE BOER, Rosemary Francesca Alice The Surgery, Balmuir Gardens, London SW15 6NG Tel: 020 8788 0818/659 2272 — MB BS 1974 Lond.

DE BOLLA, Mr Alan Robert Wrexham Maelor Hospital, Croesnewydd Road, Wrexham LL13 7TD Tel: 01978 291100 Fax: 01978 725418 — MB ChB 1975 Birm.; FEBU 1992; FRCS Eng. 1980; MD Birm. 1987; FRCS Ed. 1980. (Birmingham) Cons. Urol. Maelor Hosp. Wrexham. Socs: Brit. Assn. Urol. Surgs.; Internat. Continence Soc.; Oncol. Sect. of B.A.U.S. Prev: Sen. Regist. (Urol. Surg.) W. Midl. RHA; Research Fell. Qu. Eliz. Hosp. Birm.; Regist. (Surg.) Dudley Rd. Hosp. Birm.

DE BONO, Anne Mary Occupational Health Department, Gwendolen Road, Leicester General Hospital, Leicester LE5 4PW Tel: 0116 258 4930 Fax: 0116 249 0930; 75 Station Road, Cropston, Leicester LE7 7HG Tel: 0116 236 4140 — MB BChir 1972 Camb.; MA Camb. 1972; MFOM RCP Lond. 1996, AFOM 1994; MRCGP 1979; DObst RCOG 1973. (Camb. & St. Mary's) Cons. Occupat. Phys.Univ. Hosp.s of Leicester, NHS Trust. Prev: GP Leicester, Edin. & Oxf.; Ho. Surg. St. Mary's Hosp. Lond. & Camb. Matern. Hosp.; Ho. Phys. Addenbrooke's Hosp. Camb.

DE BONO, Edward Francis Charles Publius L2 Albany, Piccadilly, London W1V 9RR — MD 1955 Malta; DPhil, MA Oxf. 1961; PhD Camb. 1964; BSc Malta 1953. (Malta) Socs: Med. Res. Soc. Prev: Hon. Sen. Regist. Addenbrooke's Hosp. Camb. & Lect. Dept. Investig. Med. Univ. Camb.; Asst. Dir. Research Dept. Investig. Med. Univ. Camb.; Lect. (Med.) St. Thos. Hosp. Med. Sch. Lond.

DE BONO, Hazel Ann 10 Moncrieff Avenue, Lenzie, Kirkintilloch, Glasgow G66 4NL Tel: 0141 776 6042; 10 Moncrieff Avenue, Lenzie, Kirkintilloch, Glasgow G66 4NL Tel: 0141 776 6042 — MB ChB 1989 Glas.; MRCGP 1993; DRCOG 1992. (Glasgow) GP Retainee. Prev: Trainee GP Kirkintilloch.; GP Partner; Drs. Fallon & Reid.

DE BONO, Josephine Maria 6 Chaffinch Close, Horsham RH12 5HA — BM 1982 Soton.; MRCGP 1986; DRCOG 1985.

DE BRAUW, Daniel Frits Robert Queensview Medical Centre, Thornton Road, Northampton NN2 6LS Tel: 01604 713315 Fax: 01604 714378; Arkendale House, Rugby Road, Lower Harlestone, Northampton NN7 4ER — Artsexamen 1980 Utrecht. Princip. GP.

DE BRITO, Alexia Jane Frances 5 Kensington Place, London W8 7PT Tel: 020 7229 7111 — MB BS 1983 Lond.; DCH RCP Lond. 1991; DRCOG 1987; DA (UK) 1986. (St. Bart.) Asst. GP Lond. Prev: Trainee GP Harold Wood Hosp. VTS.

DE BRUYNE, Diana Merle Pauline Moor Hospital, Lancaster; 4 Norfolk Road, Lytham St Annes FY8 4JG Tel: 01253 730612 — MB ChB 1987 Dundee; DRCOG 1992. (Dundee) Regist. (Psychiat.) Moor Hosp. Lancaster. Prev: SHO (Paediat. & O & G) Geo. Eliot Hosp. Nuneaton; Ho. Off. (Gen. Med.) Ninewells Hosp. Dundee.

DE BRUYNE, Victoria St. Mark's Surgery, 47 St. Mark's Road, Teddington TW11 9DE Tel: 0208 943 3424 Fax: 0208 977 1855 Email: volebruyne@another.com — MB ChB. (Dundee Medical School)

DE BURCA, Diarmuid Iosaf Plot 20 Woodlee, Culmore Point, Londonderry BT48 8JW — MB BCh BAO 1990 NUI.

DE BURCA, Triona Treasa The Health Centre, Trenchard Avenue, Thornaby, Stockton-on-Tees TS17 0DD Tel: 01642 762921 Fax: 01642 760608; 5 Limpton Gate, Yarm TS15 9JA Tel: 01642 782779 — MB BCh BAO 1985 NUI; MRCGP 1991; DGM RCP Lond. 1991; DObst. RCPI 1990; DCH Dub. 1989. (Univ. Coll. Galway)

DE BURGH, Miranda Jennifer Anne 2/Fl, 2 Barony St., Edinburgh EH3 6PE — MB ChB 1996 Ed.

DE BURGH-THOMAS, Andrew George 50A Second Avenue, Mortlake, London SW14 8QE Tel: 020 8392 1513 — MB BS 1994 Lond.; BSc (Hons.) Lond. 1989; MRCP Lond. 1998. (Roy. Free Hosp. & Sch. Med.) SHO Dermat.St Johns Instit.Derm. Prev: SHO (Gastroenterol.) Qu. Mary Univ. Hosp. Roehampton.; SHO (Neurol./Respirator) Qu. Mary Univ. Hosp. Roehampton; SHO (Elderly Care) Qu. Mary Univ. Hosp. Roehampton.

DE CAESTECKER, James Peter Newingreen Farm, Stone St., Lympne, Hythe CT21 4JN; 128 Canterbury Road, Folkestone CT19 5SR Tel: 01303 43516 — MB BS 1985 Lond.; MRCGP 1989; DCH RCP Lond. 1987; DRCOG 1988.

DE CAESTECKER, John Simon Div. Biochemical Medicine, St. George's Hospital Medical School, Cramner Terrace, London SW17 0RE — MB BChir 1978 Camb.; MD Camb. 1990.

DE CAESTECKER, Linda Greater Glasgow Health Board, Department of Public Health Medicine, Dalian House, 350 St Vincent St., Glasgow G3 8YZ Tel: 0141 201 4545 Fax: 0141 201 4401; 269 Southbrae Drive, Glasgow G13 1TR — MB ChB 1979 Glas.; MFPHM RCP (UK) 1992; MRCOG 1984. Cons. Pub. Health Med. Gtr. Glas. HB; Hon. Sen. Lect. (Pub. Health Med.) Univ. Glas. Prev: Sen. Regist. (Pub. Health Research) Univ. Glas.; Regist. (Pub. Health) NE Thames RHA; Regist. (O & G) Simpson Memor. Matern. Pavil. Edin.

DE CAESTECKER, Peter Emile Anthony (retired) The Nestlings, Culvers Lane, Gillingham SP8 5DS Tel: 01747 822106 — MB BS 1946 Lond. Prev: GP Princip. Lond.

DE CALUWE, Diane Alder Hey Children's Hospital, Eaton Road, Liverpool L12 2AP — MD 1990 Antwerp.

DE CARTERET, Althea Margaret Springwoods, Thornhill, Bamford, Hope Valley S33 0BR Tel: 01433 651865; Family Planning and Women's Health Service, Saltergate Health Centre, Saltergate, Chesterfield S41 1SX Tel: 01246 233191 — MB 1972 Camb.; BChir 1971. SCMO N. Derbysh. Community Health Care Trust & Sheff. Community Health. Socs: BMA; Diplomate Fac. Family Plan. Reprod. Health; Brit. Menopause Soc.

DE CARTERET, John Raymond Cafts, Edmund Street Clinic, Chesterfield; Springwoods, Thornhill, Bamford, Hope Valley S33 0BR Tel: 01433 651865 — MB Camb. 1971, BChir 1970; MRCPsych 1976; DTM & H Eng. 1972. Cons. Child Adolesc. & Family Ther. Serv. Edmund St. Clinic Derbysh. Socs: Roy. Coll. Psychiat. (Child & Adolesc. Psychother. Sect.). Prev: Cons. Vale Dr. Clinic Barnet; Sen. Regist. & Regist. Tavistock Clinic.

DE CARTERET, Susan Louise 15 Howell Road, Exeter EX4 4LG — MB BS 1985 Lond.

DE CASSO MOXO, Maria del Carmen ENT Department, Victoria Infirmary, Langside Road, Glasgow G42 9HT — LMS 1984 U Complutense Madrid.

DE CASTELLA, Mr Hubert Cecil (retired) Cedar House, Newton Solney, Burton-on-Trent DE15 0SJ Tel: 01283 703358 Email: hdecas@cs.com — MB BS 1953 Melbourne; FRCS Eng. 1961; FACS 1974. Prev: Cons. Surg. Burton on Trent.

DE CATES, Caroline Rosanne Hinchingbrooke Heathcare Trust, Primrose Lane, Huntingdon PE29 1WG Tel: 01480 415211 Fax: 01480 415212; 45 Pilley's Lane, Boston PE21 9RA Tel: 01205 355477 — MB BS Lond. 1974; MSc Community Paediat. Lond. 1993, BSc (Physiol.) 1971; MRCP (UK) 1979. Cons. Community Paediat. Hinchingbrooke Healthcare, huntingdon; Med. Adviser to Adoption and Permanent Panel, Huntingdon. Prev: Sen. Regist. (Paediat.) Univ. Hosp. Qu. Med. Centre Nottm.; Cons. Community Paediat. Horsefair Clinic.

DE CHAZAL, Richard Charles Stewart Leicester Royal Infirmary Maternity Hospital, Infirmary Square, Leicester LE1 5WW Tel: 0116 254 1414; Coverack, Southmeads Road, Leicester LE2 2GS Tel: 0116 271 2302 — MD 1991 Lond.; MB BS Lond. 1976; MRCS Eng. LRCP Lond. 1976; MRCOG 1984; FRCOG 1997. (Char. Cross) Cons. O & G & Fetal Med. Leicester Roy. Infirm. Prev: Lect. (O & G) St. Geo. Hosp. Med. Sch. Lond.; Lect. (O & G) Char. Cross & W.m. Med. Sch. Lond.; Regist. (O & G) N.wick Pk. Hosp. Middlx.

DE CLEEN, Maarten Howard House Surgery, 62 Leopold Road, Felixstowe IP11 7NR Tel: 01394 282706 Fax: 01394 278955 — Artsexamen 1987 Free Uni. Amsterdam; Artsexamen 1987 Free Uni. Amsterdam.

DE CLERCQ, Sebastianus Maria Risedale House, Abbey Way, Barrow-in-Furness LA14 1BP — Artsexamen 1994 Amsterdam.

DE COCK, Mr Romain Kent & Canterbury Hospitals NHS Trust, Kent & Canterbury Hoispital, Ethelbert Road, Canterbury CT1 3NG — MB ChB 1980 Bristol; FRCS Eng. 1986; DO RCS Eng. 1985. (Bristol) Cons. Ophth. Kent & Canterbury Hosp.; Hon. Cons. Ophth. Qu. Vict. Hosp. E. Grinstead. Socs: Fell. Roy. Coll. Ophth.; Roy. Soc. Med.; Amer. Acad. Ophth. Prev: Surg. (Ophth.) St. John Ophth. Hosp. E. Jerusalem.

DE COCQ, Dirk Frederic Franciscus Custom House Surgery, 16 Freemasons Road, London E16 3NA Tel: 020 7476 2255 Fax: 020 7511 8980 — Artsexamen 1983 Rotterdam.

DE CORNET, Louise Claire Nook Cottage, Nook Lane, Dalston, Carlisle CA5 7JR — MB BS 1997 Lond.

DE COSSART, Linda Mary Little Barrow Hall, Station Lane, Barrow, Chester CH3 7JW Tel: 01244 301420 — MB ChB 1972 Liverp.; ChM 1983 Liverp.; FRCS Eng. 1977. Cons. Surg.; Cons. Gen. & Vasc. Surg. Countess of Chester NHS Trust. Socs: Vasc. Soc. GB & N. Irel.; Assn. Surg. GBI; RCA Eng. Prev: Mem. of Counc. RCA Eng.; Former Sec. VSSGBI; Pres. Assn. Surg. in Train.

DE COTHI, Anthony John Woodend View, New Inn Lane, Shrawley, Worcester WR6 6TE — MB ChB 1984 Birm.; MRCGP 1991. Socs: Internat. Med. Assn. Lourdes; BMA. Prev: SHO (Paediat.) Kidderminster Gen. Hosp.

DE COTHI, Elizabeth Mary Dysart House Surgery, 13 Ravensbourne Road, Bromley BR1 1HN Tel: 020 8464 0718; 24 Malmains Way, Beckenham BR3 6SA — MB ChB 1987 Birm.; MRCGP 1991; DRCOG 1991. Prev: Trainee GP Dulwich.

DE COTHI, Gabrielle Anne 45 Lawrence Grove, Henleaze, Bristol BS9 4EL Tel: 0117 962 4357 — MB ChB 1986 Birm.; ChB Birm. 1986; DRCOG 1991.

DE COURCY, Denis Louis Priestley (retired) The Cronk, Maughold, Ramsey IM7 1AL Tel: 01624 813344 — MA Oxf. 1939, BM BCh 1939; LMSSA Lond. 1938. Prev: Temp. Surg. Lt.-Cdr. R.N.V.R.

DE COURCY, James Gavin Department of Anaesthesia, Cheltenham General Hospital, Sandford Road, Cheltenham GL53 7AN Tel: 01242 274143 — MB BS 1984 Lond.; FRCA 1989; DA (UK) 1987; DCH RCP Lond. 1988. Cons. Anaesth. & Pain Managem. Cheltenham Gen. Hosp. Prev: Sen. Regist. (Anaesth.) Newc.; Regist. Wessex Regional Train. Scheme Anaesth. Poole & Soton.

DE COURCY, Richard Lennox 1 Kenmar Gardens, Caldebraes, Uddingston, Glasgow G71 6DY — MB ChB 1978 Glas.

DE COURCY, Sally Anne The Health Centre, Hermitage Road, St John's, Woking GU21 1TD Tel: 01483 723451 Fax: 01483 751879; Fishers Hill, Hook Heath Road, Woking GU22 0QF — MB BS 1985 Lond.; MRCGP 1989; DCH RCP Lond. 1987. Prev: Trainee GP Wonersh VTS; Trainee GP St. Stephens Hosp. Lond. VTS.

DE COURCY GRYLLS, Sara Catherine Brookside Cottage, Buxton Rd, Hazel Grove, Stockport SK7 6LU — MB ChB 1987 Sheff.

DE COURCY-WHEELER, Richard Horatio Beresford Tel: 028 3083 5000 Fax: 028 3026 8285 — MB BCh BAO 1984 NUI; LRCPSI 1984; MRCOG 1990; MD 1998. (RCSI) Cons. O & G Daisy Hill Hosp. Newry. Socs: Internat. Continence Soc.; Irish Perinatal Soc.; Ulster Obst. and Gyn. Soc. Prev: Sen. Regist. (O & G) Belf. City Hosp.; Research Fell. & Regist. UMDS St. Thos. Hosp. Lond.

DE COUTEAU, Martine Elizabeth 48 Cowdenbeath Path, London N1 0LG — MB BS 1997 Lond.

DE DOMBAL, Elizabeth 89 Hall Park Avenue, Horsforth, Leeds LS18 5LU — MB ChB 1990 Sheff.; MRCGP 1995; DRCOG 1995.

DE FERRARS, Richard James MacKenzie Frimley Green Medical Centre, 1 Beech Road, Frimley Green, Camberley GU16 6QQ Tel: 01252 835016 Fax: 01252 837908; Monastir, Green Lane E., Normany, Guildford GU3 2JL Tel: 01483 811405 — MB BS 1988 Lond.; MRCGP 1992; DRCOG 1991. (St. Bart.) Prev: Trainee GP Roy. Berks. Hosp. Reading VTS.

DE FONSEKA, Mr Chandra Pal (retired) 10 Glendevon Road, Whitchurch, Bristol BS14 0HT Tel: 01275 832661 — MB BS 1944 Ceylon; MS Ceylon 1957; FRCS Eng. 1949. Prev: Clin. Asst. (A & E) Roy. United Hosp. Bath.

DE FONSEKA, Sureshni Enoka 22 Cavendish Avenue, London NW8 9JE — MB ChB 1995 Bristol. (Univ. Bristol)

DE FREITAS, Alexis Joseph Stanislaus 181 Sopwith Crescent, Wimborne BH21 1SR — MRCS Eng. LRCP Lond. 1935; FFA RCS Eng. 1971; DA Eng. 1937. (St. Bart.)

DE FRIEND, Mr David Joshua Department of General Surgery, Torbay Hospital, Lawes Bridge, Torquay TQ2 7AA Tel: 01803 654845 — MB ChB 1984 Dundee.

DE GAY, Anne Collingham Health Centre, High Street, Collingham, Newark NG23 7LB Tel: 01636 892156 Fax: 01636 893391; Green Home, Bowbridge Road, Newark NG24 4BZ — BM BS 1976 Nottm.; BMedSci (Path.) Nottm. 1974; MRCGP 1980.

DE GAY, Nigel Robert de Gay and Partners, The Surgery, 50 Barnaby Gate, Newark NG24 1QD Tel: 01636 704225 Fax: 01636 613044 Email: ndegay@degay.fsnet.co.uk — BM BS 1976 Nottm.; BMedSci (Path.) Nottm. 1974; MRCGP 1980; DCH Eng. 1980. Prev: GP Tutor Nottm. Univ. Med. Sch.

DE GIORGI, Luisa SNBTS, Law Hospital, Carluke ML8 5ES Tel: 01698 373315 Fax: 01698 356770; 23 Midholm Close, London NW11 6EB — PhD Immunogenetics Univ. Lond. 1979; MD Padua 1969; MRCPath 1991; Dip. Haemat. Padua 1971; Dip. Clin. Path. Padua 1974. Sen. Scientist Scott. Nat. Blood Transf. Serv. Law Hosp. Carluke. Socs: Fell. RSM; Int. Transpl. Soc.; Brit. Soc. of Imm. Prev: Sen. Scientist (Immunol.) Rayne Inst. St. Thos. Hosp. Lond.; Mem. Internat. Transpl. Soc. & Brit. Soc. of Immunol.; Sen. Research Fell. (Immunol.) Roy. Lond. Hosp. Med. Sch.

DE GIOVANNI, Joseph V Birmingham Childrens Hospital NHS Trust, Steelhouse Lane, Birmingham B4 6NH Tel: 0121 333 9999 Fax: 0121 333 9441 Email: secretary.giovanni@bhamchildrens.wmids.nhs.uk; 9 Gillhurst Road, Harborne, Birmingham B17 8QS Tel: 0121 681 2442 Fax: 0121 440 0804 Email: degiovanni@cableinet.co.uk — MD 1973 Malta; MRCP (UK) 1976; FRCP Lond. 1991; MRCPCH 1997; FRCPCH 1998. (University of Malta) Cons. Cardiol. Childr. Hosp. Birm.; Hon. Cons. Cardiol. City Hosp. NHS Trust Birm.; Hon. Sen. Clin. Lect. Univ. Birm.; Hon. Cons. Cardiol. Univ. Hosp. NHS Trust Birm. Socs: BPCA. Counc Mem.; AEPC Treas. Working Gp. on Interven. Prev: Sen. Regist. (Cardiol.) Birm.

DE GLANVILLE, Hugh (retired) 45 Woodland Grove, Weybridge KT13 9EQ Email: hdg@bjhc.demon.co.uk — MB BChir 1950 Camb.; MRCS Eng. LRCP Lond. 1950; DIH Eng. 1967; DTM & H Liverp. 1956; FRCP Ed 1999. Publisher Drugs Quarterly Consg. Edr. Med. Digest; Publisher Brit. J. Healthcare Computing & Informat. Managem. Prev: Med. Cons. Afr. Med. Research Foundat., Kenya.

DE GLANVILLE, Philip Murray (retired) The Maltings, 3 Willow Vale, Frome BA11 1BG Tel: 01373 472997 — MB BChir 1975 Camb.; MA, MB Camb. 1975, BChir 1974; MRCGP 1979; DRCOG 1980.

DE GLANVILLE, Robert Geoffrey Launceston Medical Centre, Landlake Road, Launceston PL15 9HH Tel: 01566 772131 Fax: 01566 772223; Lower Bamham Farm House, Lawhitton, Launceston PL15 9QT Tel: 01566 773726 — MB BS 1970 Lond.; MRCS Eng. LRCP Lond. 1970; DObst RCOG 1973. (St. Thos.)

DE GLANVILLE, Timothy Brooks Richmond Surgery, Richmond Close, Fleet GU52 7US Tel: 01252 811466 Fax: 01252 815031; 1 Chestnut Grove, Fleet GU51 3LN — MB BS 1979 Lond.; BA (Hons.)

Kent 1969; MRCS Eng. LRCP Lond. 1979; MRCGP 1987; DRCOG 1984.

DE GORTER, Jean-Jacques c/o 16 Calverton Road, Stony Stratford, Milton Keynes MK11 1LE — MB BS 1993 Lond.

DE GRAEVE, John Henry (retired) 78 Ash Hill Drive, Shadwell, Leeds LS17 8JR Tel: 0113 265 7372 — MRCS Eng. LRCP Lond. 1950.

DE GRESSI, Susanna Dept. of Child Health, County Offices, St. George's Road, Cheltenham GL50 3EW Tel: 01242 516235 — State Exam 1988 (Hons.) Trieste; MRCP (UK) 1994. Cons. Community Paedatrician, Dept. of Child Health, Cheltenham. Prev: SHO (Paediat.) Leicester Roy. Infirm.

DE GROOT, Simon John St John's Group Practice, 1 Greenfield Lane, Balby, Doncaster DN4 0TH Tel: 01302 854521 Fax: 01302 310823 — MB BS Lond. 1985; MRCGP 1989.

DE GROOT, William Thys Flitwick Surgery, The Highlands, Flitwick, Bedford MK45 1DZ Tel: 01525 712171 Fax: 01525 718756 — MB BS 1975 Lond.

DE HAAR, Maria Gerarda Wilhelmina c/o Kostverloren 48, 1251 TR Laren (N-H) P, Netherlands — Artsexamen 1987 Amsterdam. (Univ. Amsterdam, Netherlands)

DE HAAS, Lara Nicole 6 Chapel Fold, Headingley, Leeds LS6 3RG — MB ChB 1995 Leeds.

DE HALPERT, Peter Alexander Carpenters Cottage, Froxfield, Petersfield GU32 1DH — MB BS 1998 Lond.; MB BS Lond 1998.

DE HEER, Nicholas Andrew Department of Public Health Medicine, Shropshire Health Authority HQ., Cross Houses, Shrewsbury SY3 9DF Tel: 01743 761242 Fax: 01743 761601; 62 Grange Road, Shrewsbury SY3 9DF Tel: 01743 233661 — MB BS 1958 Lond.; MRCS Eng. LRCP Lond. 1958; MFCM RCP (UK) 1985; MFPHM 1989; DPH Liverp. 1961. Sen. Med. Off. (Community Health) W. Berks. HA; Cons. Pub. Health Med. Adult Health & Statutory Servs. Socs: Soc. Pub. Health; Soc. Occupat. Med. Prev: Exec. Dir. W. African Health Community Lagos, Nigeria; Dep. Dir. Med. Servs. Ghana; Chief Med. Nutrit., Ghana.

DE HOXAR, Victoria Margaret The Jays, Noctorum Lane, Birkenhead CH43 9UB — MB ChB 1977 Sheff.

DE JODE, John Joseph (retired) Glenwood, Spinfield Lane, Marlow SL7 2JN — MB BS 1956 Lond.; MRCS Eng. LRCP Lond. 1956; DObst RCOG 1958.

DE JODE, Michael George 61 Antill Road, London E3 5BT — MB BS 1989 Lond.

DE JONG, Jolanda Camphill Community Glencraig, Seahill Road, Craigavad, Holywood BT18 0DB Tel: 01232 422907 — Artsexamen 1983 Groningen.

DE JONG, Nicolette Suzette 7 Bishops Walk, Rochester ME1 1JF — Artsexamen 1993 Utrecht.

DE JOUSSINEAU, Siegfried, KStJ The Research Institute, The Churchill Hospital, Headington, Oxford OX3 7LJ Tel: 01865 225825; c/o The Royal Bank of Scotland plc, London City Office, 62/63 Threadneedle St, London EC2R 8LA — Lakarexamen Stockholm 1977. Dip. Gen. Med. Social Stgrelsen Stockholm 1983.

DE KARE-SILVER, Nigel Stuart Gladstone Medical Centre, 5 Dollis Hill, London NW2 6JH Tel: 020 8452 1616 Fax: 020 8452 0446; 92 London Road, Stanmore HA7 4NS Tel: 020 8420 7578 Fax: 020 8385 7645 — MB BS 1983 Lond.; BSc (Hons.) Lond. 1980; MRCGP 1996; DRCOG 1989; MSc 1999. (St. Bart.) Princip. GP; Bd. Mem. Brent Centr. PCG. Socs: Fell. Roy. Soc. Med.; BMA. Prev: Resid. Med. Off. Lond. Clinic; Ho. Off. St. Bart. Hosp. Lond.

DE KEYSER, Paul David — MB BS 1996 Lond.; DCH 2000 Glasgow; DRCOG 2000; MRCGP 2001. (University College London)

DE KLERK, Christiaan Johannes The Princess Royal Hospital NHS Trust, Apley Castle, Grainger Drive, Telford TF1 6TF — MB ChB 1995 Pretoria.

DE KOCK, Marianna 45 Volsteedt Street, Strand 7140, South Africa Tel: 00 27 21 854 5640; Princess Royal Hospital, Apley Castle, Telford TF1 6TF Tel: 01952 641222 Fax: 01952 243405 — MB ChB 1996 Stellenbosch. (Tugerberg University of Stellenbosch) SHO Anaesth. Dept. P.ss Roy. Hosp. Telford Shrops. Prev: SHO (Accid. and Emerg. Dept.) P.ss Roy. Hosp.; Ho. Off. S. Africa Paarl Hosp. Paarl.

DE KRETSER, Anthony John Howard 33 Pines Road, Exmouth EX8 5NH Tel: 01395 270499 — MB BS 1952 Lond.; DIH Eng. 1962. (Westm.) Socs: BMA & Assn. Indust. Med. Offs. Prev: Sen. Med. Off. Vauxhall Motors Dunstable; Med. Regist. Clare Hall Hosp. S. Mimms; Ho. Phys. St. Stephen's Hosp. Lond.

DE KRETSER, Daneelo Mohan Harris 5 Danesbury Rise, Cheadle SK8 1JW — MB BS 1962 Durh.; MRCPath 1970. (Newc.) Cons. (Histopath.) N. Manch. Gen. Hosp. Prev: Sen. Regist. (Morbid Anat.) Manch. Roy. Infirm.

DE KRETSER, Jonathan Royal Crescent and Preston Road Practice, 25 Crescent Street, Weymouth DT4 7BY Tel: 01305 774466 Fax: 01305 760538; 11 Sutton Close, Sutton Poyntz, Weymouth DT3 6LJ Tel: 01305 832945 — MB BS 1988 Lond.; BSc (Psych.) Lond. 1985, MB BS 1988; MRCGP 1993; DRCOG 1992. Prev: Ho. Off. (Surg.) St. Albans City Hosp.; Ho. Off. (Med.) Qu. Alexandra Hosp. Portsmouth; Resid. Med. Off. Brisbane, Austral.

DE LA FUENTE PEREDA, Josu Department of Haematology, Faculty of Medecine, Imperial College of Science & Technology & Medicine, Hammersmith Hospital, Du Cane Road, London W12 0NN Tel: 0208 287 5226 Fax: 07069 950038 Email: jdelafuente@ic.ac.uk — LMS 1994 Basque Country; MRCP 1997 (UK Diploma); MRCPath 2000 (Part 1); LMS Basque Provinces 1994. (University of the Basque Country, Spain) MRC Research Fell. Dept. of Haemat. Imperial Coll. of Sci. Technol. & Med. Hammersmith Hosp. Lond.; SpR, Hammersmith NHS Trusts, Lond. Socs: Roy. Coll. of Phys.s; Roy. Coll. of Paediat. & Child health; Diplomate Roy. Coll. of Pathologists. Prev: SpR in Haemat., Hammersmith Hosp. Lond.; SpR in Haemat., St. Mary's Hosp. Lond.

DE LA HUNT, Mr Michael Norman Royal Victoria Infirmary, Queen Victoria Road, Newcastle upon Tyne NE1 4LP Tel: 0191 232 5131 Fax: 0191 227 5276 Email: mike.delahunt@nuth.northy.nhs.uk — MRCS Eng. LRCP Lond. 1976; MS Soton. 1986, MB BS 1976; FRCS Eng. 1980. (St. Mary's) Cons. Paediat. Surg. Roy. Vict. Infirm. Newc. u. Tyne. Prev: Sen. Regist. (Paediat. Surg.) Roy. Vict. Infirm. Newc.

DE LA MARE, Eric Anthony Pine Medical Centre, 5110-5 Avenue, Whitehorse YT Y1A 2B8, Canada Tel: (00 1) (867) 6683838 Fax: (00 1) (867) 6683899; Water Eaton Manor, Oxford OX2 8HE — MB ChB Glas. 1970; MSc (Occupat. Med.) Lond. 1977; MFOM RCP Lond. 1985; DAvMed Eng. 1980; DIH Eng. 1977. Chief Med. Staff Whitehorse Gen. Hosp. Yukon, Canada; Med. Adviser Canad. Internat. Airlines & Yukon Electric. Socs: Soc. Occupat. Phys.; Canad. Soc. Aviat. Med. Prev: Med. Off. Health Yukon, Canada; Resid. Phys. Cassiar Mining Corp. Brit. Columbia, Canada; Med. Off. Civil Aviat. Auth.

DE LA MOTA NICOLAS-CORREA, Maria del Pilar 5 Lancelot Close, Ifield, Crawley RH11 0PG — LMS 1989 U Complutense Madrid.

DE LACEY, Gerald John Northwick Park & St Marks Hospitals NHS Trust, North West London Hospitals NHS Trust, Harrow HA1 3UJ Tel: 020 8869 3895 Fax: 020 8869 3907; 34 Lansdowne Road, London W11 2LT Tel: 020 7229 8168 Fax: 020 7229 8168 — MB BChir 1966 Camb.; MA Camb. 1966; MRCS Eng. LRCP Lond. 1964; FRCR 1971; DMRD Eng. 1969. (Cambridge University and the Lond. Hosp.) Cons. Radiol. N.wick Pk. & St. Marks Hosps. Socs: Roy. Coll. Radiol.; Brit. Med. Assn.; Treas. Roy. Coll. Radiol. 1996-2000. Prev: Cons. Radiol. St. Geo. Hosp. Lond.; Sen. Lect. (Radiol.) Univ. Auckland Med. Sch., NZ; Staff Radiol. Univ. Miami Med. Sch., USA.

DE LACEY, Penelope Ann Willingham Surgery, 52 Long Lane, Willingham, Cambridge CB4 5LB Tel: 01954 260230 Fax: 01954 206204; 9 Woodlands Park, Girton, Cambridge CB3 0QB — MB BS 1971 Lond.; DObst RCOG 1974. (King's Coll. Hosp.) Prev: Clin. Med. Off. Camb. HA. & Bucks. HA; Asst. GP Camb. HA.

DE LACY, Susan Elizabeth 124a Grove Lane, Timperley, Altrincham WA15 6PL — MB BS 1988 Lond.; 2001 LFHom Glas.; MRCGP 1993. (St. Geo. Hosp. Med. Sch.) G.P. Retainer, Conwyay Rd Health Centre, Sale Moor, Chesh.

DE LAS HERAS GARCIA, Lucia 17 Harrow Fields Gardens, Harrow HA1 3SN — LMS 1980 Madrid; LMS U Complutense Madrid 1980.

DE LAUNAY, Leonard Desmond (retired) Willow Cottage, Henley Drive, Coombe Hill, Kingston upon Thames KT2 7EB Tel: 020 8942 7212 — MB BS 1941 Lond.; MRCS Eng. LRCP Lond. 1940. Hon. Mem. Med. Staff New Vict. Hosp. Kingston upon Thames; Surg. Metrop. Police; Div. Surg. (Crown Rank) St. John Ambul. Brig. Prev: Surg. Lt. RNVR.

DE LEVAL, Professor Marc Roger Hospital for Sick Children, Great Ormond St., London WC1N 3JH Tel: 020 7404 4383 Fax: 020 7831 4931; 32 Hamilton Terrace, London NW8 9UG Tel: 020 7266 3227 — MD 1966 Liege; FRCS Eng. 1989. (Belgium) Cons. Cardiothoracic Surg. Hosp. Sick Childr. Gt. Ormond St. Lond.; Prof. (Cardiothoracic Surg.) Inst. Child Health.

DE LIMA, Victor Robert Francis Riccarton Practice, Heriot Watt University Health Centre, The Avenue, Riccarton, Currie EH14 4AS Tel: 0131 451 3010 Fax: 0131 451 3503; 450 Lanark Road, Edinburgh EH14 5BB Tel: 0131 441 2330 Fax: 0131 441 2330 Email: vicdelima@aol.com — MB ChB 1975 Ed.; AFOM RCP Lond. 1986; MRCGP 1979; DRCOG 1978. (Edinburgh) Phys. i/c Univ Health Serv. Heriot-Watt Univ. Edin.; Occupat. Phys. Standard Life Assur. Company. Socs: Soc. Occupat. Med.; Med. Cell - Roy. Geograph. Soc.; Brit. Assn. Health Servs. in Higher Ed.

DE LLOYD, Lucy Jane Llwyn y Celyn, Old Mill Road, Lisvane, Cardiff CF14 0XP — MB BCh 1998 Wales.

DE LORD, Corinne Frances Mary Dept Haematology, Farnborough Hospital, Orpington BR6 8ND Tel: 01689 814233 Fax: 01689 814041 Email: corinne.delord@bromleyhospitals.nhs.uk — MB BS 1984 Lond.; MD 1994; MRCP 1988 (UK); MRCPath 1996; MRCP (UK) 1988; MRCPath 1996; MD 1994. (King's Coll.) Cons. Haemat. Bromley Hosp. NHS Trust.

DE LORD, Denise Anne 28 Selvage Lane, London NW7 3SP — MB BS 1990 Lond.; BSc Lond. 1987, MB BS 1990; MRCP (UK) 1993.

DE LORENZO, Ferruccio Francesco Clinical Trial Department, Thrombosis Research Inst., Emmanual Kaye Building, 1b Manresh Road, London SW3 6LR Email: dlorenzo@tri-london.ac.uk; Flat 12, 189 Old Brompton Road, Bladon Lodge, London SW5 0LQ — MD 1990 University of Naples; CCST Naples 1995; PhD London 2001. (II Medical School, University of Naples, Italy) Cons. Phys., Cardiovasc. Med., Thrombosis Research Inst. Socs: Brit. Med. Assn.-Mem. 7262959. Prev: Hon. Specialist Regist., Cardiol. Roy. Brompton Hosp. Lond.; Se. Ho. Off., Ashford Hosp. Middsx.

DE LUSIGNAN, Simon, TD Woodbridge Hill Surgery, 1 Deerbarn Road, Guildford GU2 8YB Tel: 01483 562230 Fax: 01483 452442 — MB BS 1982 Lond.; BSc Lond. 1979; MRCGP 1986; DFFP 1993; DRCOG 1985. (St. Bart.) Hon. Sen. Lect. St. Geo. Hosp. Med. Sch. Socs: Roy. Soc. Med. Prev: Trainee GP Reading VTS; Cas. Off. Univ. Coll. Hosp. Lond.; Ho. Surg. St. Bart. Hosp. Lond.

DE MARCO, Paolo Fakenham Medical Practice, The Fakenham Medical Centre, Greenway Lane, Fakenham NR21 8ET Tel: 01328 851321 Fax: 01328 851412 — MD 1982 Naples; MRCGP 1987; DRCOG 1986; DCH RCP Lond. 1986. PCG Bd. Mem. Prev: Chairm. Norf. Med. Audit Advis. Gp.; Sen. Research Assoc. (Gen. Pract.) Univ. Camb.

DE MARE, Patrick Baltzar 5 Holly Place, London NW3 6QU Tel: 020 7794 3171 — MRCS Eng. LRCP Lond. 1941; FRCPsych. 1982, M 1971; DPM Eng. 1947. (Camb. & St. Geo.) Prev: Cons. Psychotherap. Psychiat. Dept. St. Geo. Hosp. & Halliwick Hosp.; Maj. RAMC Command Psychiat. E. Afr.

DE MARS, Catherine Chineham Medical Practice, Reading Road, Basingstoke RG24 8ND Tel: 01256 479244 — MB ChB 1987 Birm.; DCH 1992; MRCGP 1992.

DE MATAS, Marcus 62 Princes Gardens, Highfield St., Liverpool L3 6LH — MB ChB 1994 Liverp.

DE MATTEIS, Francesco Luciano Antonio Istituto Di Farmcologia, Via P. Giuria 13, Torino 10125, Italy Tel: 00 39 11 6707792 Fax: 00 39 11 658606; 41 Downside Road, Sutton SM2 5HR Tel: 020 8 643 7382 — State DMS 1970 Bari; PhD Lond. 1965; Dip. Internal Med. Bari 1962. (Bari) Prof. Toxicol. Univ. Turin, Dept. Pharmacol. Turin, Italy. Prev: Dep. Director MRC Toxicol. Unit.

DE MEEUS, Jean-Baptiste Department of Obstetrics & Gynaecology, King's College School of Medicine, Denmark Hill, London SE5 8RX — MD 1989 Poitiers.

DE MELLO, Winston Fidelis Pain Clinic, Pontefract General Infirmary, Friarwood Lane, Pontefract WF8 1PL Tel: 01977 606546 Fax: 01977 606857; The Granary, Ackworth Grange, Rigg Lane, East Hardwick, Pontefract WF8 3EG Email: winston@apain.demon.co.uk — MB BS 1978 Lond.; BSc Lond. 1975; FCAnaesth 1989; Dip IMC RCS Ed. 1989; DA (UK) 1985; DRCOG 1982. (Guy's) Cons. Anaesth. and Pain Managem.; Med. Director, P. of Wales Hospice, Pontefract. Socs: Roy. Soc. Med.; BMA; Assn. Anaesth. GB & Irel. Prev: Cons. Anaesth & Dir. Intens. Care Camb. Milit. Hosp. Aldershot; Sen. Lect. (Anaesth. & Resusc.) Army; Sen. Regist. Guy's Hosp. Lond.

DE MENDONCA, Preston Maurice Simplicio Budshead Health Centre, 433 Budshead Road, Whitleigh, Plymouth PL5 4DU Tel: 01752 773492 Fax: 01752 775657; Church House, Cornwood, Ivybridge PL21 9QJ Tel: 01752 837657 — MB BS 1977 Lond.; DRCOG 1982. (St. Thos.)

DE MEY, Robert Douglas Ailsa Hospital, Dalmelllington Rd, Ayr KA6 6QB — MB ChB 1985 Ed.; MRCPsych 1994. Cons. (Psychiat. of Old Age) S.-E. Ayrsh.

DE MEZA, Peter Brook Hill Surgery, 30 Brook Hill, Little Waltham, Chelmsford CM3 3LL Tel: 01245 360253 Fax: 01245 361343 — MB BS 1974 Lond.; DRCOG 1977.

DE MIGUEL ARTAL, Mariano Burdon House, Flats 3-4, Hartlepool General Hospital, Holdforth Road, Hartlepool TS24 9AH; Flat 1 Rannoch House, 10 Lindisfarne Road, Newcastle upon Tyne NE2 2HE — LMS 1991 Saragossa.

DE MONTE, Joy Eleanor (retired) 12 Cranley Gardens, Wallington SM6 9PR Tel: 020 8395 5841 — MB Calcutta 1946; FPA 1981. Prev: SHO (Surg.) Eden Hosp. Calcutta & Dufferin Hosp. Calcutta.

DE MOOR, Michiel Maarten Anthony c/o Mrs R. Knight, 7 Greatfield Drive, Charlton Kings, Cheltenham GL53 9BT — MB BCh 1976 Witwatersrand.

DE MORTIMER-GRIFFIN, Claire Annabel Elizabeth 111 Cundy Street, Sheffield S6 2WJ — MB ChB 1998 Sheff.; MB ChB Sheff 1998.

DE MOWBRAY, John Marsh Miles (retired) 47 Church Lane, Lymington SO41 3RA — MB BS 1954 Lond. Prev: Clin. Asst. St. Thos. Hosp. Lond.

DE MOWBRAY, Michael Stuart (retired) 135c Holland Park Avenue, London W11 4UT Tel: 020 7602 4405 — BM BCh 1946 Oxf.; MRCPsych 1972; DPM Eng. 1956. Prev: Cons. Psychiat. St. Mary Abotts Hosp. Lond. & Banstead Hosp. Sutton.

DE MOWBRAY, Saskia Susan Parklands Medical Practice, The Medical Centre, 30 Buttershaw Lane, Bradford BD6 2DD — MB ChB 1988 Leeds. GP Princip., Bradford; Staff Grade, Accid. & Emerg., Bradford Roy. Infirm., Bradford.

DE MUINCK KEIZER, Jan Willem Flat 2 Grange Gardens, 8 Grange Road, Eastbourne BN20 7DA — Artsexamen 1991 Free U Amsterdam; Artsexamen Free Univ Amsterdam 1991.

DE MURTINHO-BRAGA OSSA, Jose Joaquin 40 Trenchard Avenue, Stafford ST16 3QB — MB BS 1996 Lond. (Univ. Coll. Lond.)

DE NETTO, Michelle-Ann Karen Romar, Rowtown, Addlestone KT15 1EZ — MB BS 1992 Lond.

DE NETTO, Noel Felix Oswald 1 Cavendish Road, Hull HU8 0JS Tel: 01482 74662 — MB BS 1953 Madras. (Madras) Socs: BMA. Prev: Chief Resid. in Surg. Fairview Pk. Hosp. Cleveland U.S.A.; Teach. Fell. Doctor's Hosp. Cleveland Heights U.S.A.; Paediat. Surg. Regist. Booth Hall Hosp. Manch.

DE NEWTOWN, Ruth Kathleen 400 Woodstock Road, Wolvercote, Oxford OX2 8JW — MB BS 1998 Lond.; MB BS Lond 1998.

DE NORONHA, Rebecca Jane 8 Newington Road, Huntess Bar, Sheffield S11 8RZ — MB ChB 1990 Sheff.; BMedSci Sheff. 1989; MRCP (UK) 1993. Sen. Regist. (Radiol.) Roy. Hallamsh. Hosp. Sheff.

DE NUNZIO, Mario Cosimo X-Ray Dept., Derbyshire Royal Infirmary, London Road, Derby DE1 2QY — BM BS 1986 Nottm.; MRCP (UK) 1990; FRCR 1994. Cons. Radiol. Derbysh. Roy. Infirm. Socs: BMA; BSIR. Prev: Sen. Regist. (Radiol.) Nottm. Hosps.

DE PASS, Jonathan Peter Crispin The Old Rectory, Little Cornard, Sudbury CO10 0PD — MB ChB 1979 Bristol.

DE PAUW, Karel Wilfried Department of Psychiatry, St. James University Hospital, Beckett St., Leeds LS9 7TF Tel: 0113 206 5519 Fax: 0113 206 5803 Email: kwdepauw@talk21.com — MB ChB 1979 Pretoria; MD Brussels 1980; MRCPsych. 1985. Cons. Psychiat. & Sen. Clin. Lect. St Jas. Univ. Hosp. Leeds. Socs: Internat. Mem. Amer. Psychiat. Assn.; Brit. Neuropsychiat. Assn.; Amer. Neuropsychiat. Assn. Prev: Cons. Psychiat. Doncaster Roy. Infirm.; Sen. Regist. (Psychiat.) Leicester.

DE PONT, Sunniva Anna Maria Theresia Norwood House Surgery, Belle Vue Street, Scarborough YO12 7EJ Tel: 01723

374485 Fax: 01723 501517 — Artsexamen 1989 Leiden; MRCGP 1995. GP Princip.

DE QUINCEY, Matthew Molteno Alton Health Centre, Anstey Road, Alton GU34 2QX Tel: 01420 542542 Fax: 01420 542975 Email: matt.dequincey@gp-j82136.nhs.uk — MB ChB 1989 Ed.; BA Camb. 1986; MRCGP 1993; DCCH RCP Ed. 1994; DRCOG 1992.

DE RAEVE, Peter Alan (retired) 5 Summerhill Road, Summertown, Oxford OX2 7JY Tel: 01865 512272 — MB BS Lond. 1952; DObst RCOG 1954.

DE RENZY-MARTIN, David Alfred Cadiot, St Amans de Pellagal, 82110 Lauzerte, France Tel: 00 33 05 6394 6815; Birchden Farm House, Groombridge, Tunbridge Wells TN3 9NR Tel: 01892 864424 — MB BS 1953 Lond.; MA Oxf. 1946; MFOM RCP Lond. 1978; DIH Soc. Apoth. Lond. 1964; DObst RCOG 1955. (St. Thos.) Socs: Soc. Occupat. Med. & Roy. Soc. Med. Prev: Resid. Phys. Khartoum Chervon Oil Company, Sudan; Med. Director Dubai Petroleum Comapny, UAE; Regional Med. Off. Lond. Postal Region Occupat. Health Serv.

DE RENZY-MARTIN, Nicolette Anne Tel: 01284 713000 — MB BS 1977 Lond.; FFA RCS Eng. 1982. (St. Thos.) p/t Trust Anaesth., W. Suff. Hosp., Bury St Edmonds. Socs: Anaesth. Res. Soc. Prev: Hon. Lect. (Anaesth. Lond.) Hosp.; Clin. Research Phys. Wellcome Foundat.; Regist. (Anaesth.) W.m. Hosp. Lond.

DE ROECK, Mr Nicholas John 96A Holland Road, London NW10 5AY — MB ChB 1994 Manch.; FRCS (Eng) 1998. Sir John Giarnloy Research Fell., E. Surrey Hosp.

DE ROOY, Laura Jean 42A Myddleton Road, London N22 8NR — MB ChB 1987 Cape Town; MRCP (UK) 1993.

DE ROSA, Dante Warstones Health Centre, Pinfold Grove, Wolverhampton WV4 4PS; 22 Wood Road, Wolverhampton WV6 8LS — BSc (Hons.) Physiol. Leeds 1981, MB ChB 1983; MRCGP (Distinc.) 1987; DCH RCPS Glas. 1986; DRCOG 1987.

DE ROSA, Sandro, Salvatore 5 Tudor Court, Gunnerbury Avenue, London W5 4HD Tel: 07092 069096 Fax: 07050 686206 Email: sandros-der-rosa@doctor.com; Email: sandros-der-rosa@doctor.com — State Exam Bologna 1994; M.D. Padua 1994. (University of Padua Faculty of Medicine and Surgery) Psychotherapist (+Med. Dir.), Medisan Assistance s.a.s., Padua (Italy); Analogic Psychol. Lect. from 11/98; Director of Psychother. Sci., The 1st Childr.'s Embassy in the world, Medjaslin - RePub. of Macedonia, Operat.al unuits in Padua (Italy). Socs: Roy. Soc. Med. (Overseas Mem.); Italian Med. Soc. of GB (Founding Mem.). Prev: Med. Watch - Spresiano (Treviso); Med. Watch - Dolo (Venice); A & E - Dolo (Venice).

DE RUITER, Annemarie Department of Genitourinary Medicine, St Thomas Hospital, London SE1 7EH — MB BS 1985 Lond.; FRCP 1999. p/t Cons. Genitourin. Med. St. Thos. Hosp. Lond. Prev: Sen. Regist. (Genitourin. Med.) St. Thos. Hosp. Lond.; Lect. & Regist. (Genitourin. Med.) Middlx. Hosp. Lond.; SHO (Renal Unit) St. Marys Hosp. Lond.

DE RUITER, Joost Matthys Flat 7, 5 Bassett Road, London W10 6LA — BChir 1990 Camb.

DE SICA, Anna Flat 2, 317 Grays Inn Road, London WC1X 8PX — LRCP LRCS Ed. LRCPS Glas. 1998; LRCP Ed LRCS Ed LRCPS Glas 1998.

DE SIENA, Paolo Maria 163 Cromwell Road, London SW5 0SQ — State Exam Naples 1988.

DE SILVA, Ambalang Odage K L Littleton Road Surgery, 29 Littleton Road, Salford M6 6ED Tel: 0161 736 7333 Fax: 0161 737 5199.

***DE SILVA, Aminda Niroshan** Shiralee, 5A Egmont Close, Avon Castle, Ringwood BH24 2DJ Email: aminda100@hotmail.com — MB BS 1998 Lond.; MB BS Lond 1998; BSc Lond 1995.

DE SILVA, Bimalka Yohan c/o Ms J. Draper, Personnel Manager, Stirling Royal Infirmary, Livilands Gate, Stirling FK8 2AU — MB BS 1980 Colombo; MRCOG 1987.

DE SILVA, Carpo The Surgery, Station Road, Shotton Colliery, Durham DH6 2JL Tel: 0191 526 5913; Wilton, Wellfield Road, Wingate TS28 5JX Tel: 01429 838395 — MB BS 1958 Bombay; BSc, MB BS Bombay 1958; DTM & H Eng. 1960. (Grant Med. Coll. Bombay) Socs: BMA. Prev: SHO Gen. Hosp. Bishop Auckland; Regist. Sunderland Gen. Hosp.; JHMO Leeholme Hosp. Easington.

DE SILVA, Chandra 23 East Causeway Vale, Adel, Leeds LS16 8LG Tel: 0113 613384 — MB BS 1970 Ceylon. (Ceylon) Clin. Med. Off. Leeds W.. HA.

DE SILVA, Deepthi Champika 22 Ashgrove Road W., Aberdeen AB16 5DY — MB ChB 1985 Aberd.; MRCP (UK) 1989. Regist. (Gen. Med.) Grampian Bd.

DE SILVA, Disentuwahandi Tilakasiri Department of Accident and Emergency, Russells Hall Hospital, Dudley DY1 2HQ — MB BS 1970 Ceylon; MRCOG 1981.

DE SILVA, Errajith Bertrand Ricardo 30 The Hollands, Worcester Park KT4 7LH — MB BS 1986 Lond.; BSc (Hons.) Lond. 1983, MB BS 1986.

DE SILVA, Erwin Stuart 4 Cavendish Place, Cavendish CrescentS., Nottingham NG7 1ED Tel: 01159 411961 Email: desilva@probeb.co.uk — BM BS Nottm. 1990. SHO (Psychiat.) Mill Brook Hosp. Mansfield. Prev: SHO Lincoln VTS.

DE SILVA, Gamini Ernest Highland House, 223 Beech Lane, Earley, Reading RG6 5UP Tel: 020 8986 1402 — MB BS Ceylon 1970; FFA RCS Eng. 1980.

DE SILVA, Gardiawasan Balage Don Neththananada Special Hospital Service Authority, Rampton Hospital, Retford DN22 0PD — MB BS 1966 Ceylon; MRCPsych 1984; DPM Eng. 1978. Sen. Med. Off. HM Prison Leicester. Prev: Clin. Asst. (Psychiat.) Hereford Gen. Hosp.; Regist. (Psychiat.) Airedale Gen. Hosp. Steeton; SHO & Regist. (Psychiat.) High Royds Hosp. Menston & Leeds Roy. Infirm.

DE SILVA, Gerard Edwin Francis Department of Radiotherapy & Oncology, Walsgrave Hospital, Clifford Bridge Road, Walsgrave, Coventry CV2 2DX Tel: 024 76 602020 Fax: 024 76 622197; 123 Wigston Road, Walsgrove Manor, Coventry CV2 2NG Tel: 024 76 619814 — MB BS 1966 Ceylon; DMRT Lond. 1976. Assoc. Specialist (Radiat. Oncol.) Walsgrave Hosp. Coventry. Socs: Roy. Coll. Radiol.; BMA; Brit. & W. Midl. Oncol. Assns. Prev: Staff Radiother. Walsgrave Hosp. Coventry; Cons. Radiat. Oncol. Govt. Cancer Inst. Maharagama, Sri Lanka; Regist. (Radiother. & Oncol.) Walsgrave Hosp. Coventry & W.on Pk. Hosp. Sheff.

DE SILVA, Gilbert Keith Christian 12 Tudor Rose Close, Stanway, Colchester CO3 5SD Tel: 01206 67013 — MB BS 1966 Ceylon; FFA RCS Eng. 1979.

DE SILVA, Gunamuni Udayi Yasoja 105 Exeter Road, Harrow HA2 9PQ — MB ChB 1998 Aberd.; MB ChB Aberd 1998.

DE SILVA, Hesha Archanie 639 Wilbraham Road, Chorlton, Manchester M21 9JT — MB ChB 1996 Manch.

DE SILVA, Jayangani Vasana 86 Manor Way, Mitcham CR4 1EE — MB BS 1990 Lond.

DE SILVA, Kanthi Padma Forston Clinic, Herrison, Dorchester DT2 9TB Tel: 01305 251812 — MB BS 1975 Sri Lanka.

DE SILVA, Kanthi Sri Mahavidane Queen Elizabeth Hospital, Gayton Road, King's Lynn PE30 4ET Tel: 01553 766266; 32 Elvington, Springwood, King's Lynn PE30 4TA Tel: 01553 760455 Email: gnksm@desilva.demon.co.uk — MB BS 1972 Sri Lanka; MD (Psychiat.) Sri Lanka 1983. Staff Psychiat. Qu. Eliz. Hosp. King's Lynn. Prev: Cons. Psychiat. Ment. Hosp. Angoda, Sri Lanka.

DE SILVA, Lanil Wimal Wesley Hall Surgery, Calcutt Street, Cricklade, Swindon SN6 6BA Tel: 01793 750645 Fax: 01793 752331; Dairy Farm, Purton Stoke, Swindon SN5 4JG Tel: 01793 772670 — MB BS 1984 Lond.; BSc (Hons.) Pharmacol. Lond. 1981; FRCS Ed. 1989; DFFP 1994; DCH RCP Lond. 1993. (King's Coll. Hosp.) Princip. GP Cricklade & Ashton Keynes Wilts.; Sec. Professional Advis. Comm. Swindon GP Co-op.; Lead GP, Gen. Surg., Ridgeway Downs and Swindon PCGs. Socs: BMA; (Ex-Pres.) Lond. Med. Gp. Prev: Trainee GP Tunbridge Wells & Brighton VTS; Regist. Roy. Lond. Hosp. Whitechapel; SHO (A & E) King's Coll. Hosp. Lond.

DE SILVA, Lilani Shamela 29 Gilbey Road, London SW17 0QQ — MB BS 1996 Lond.

DE SILVA, Mahamarakkala Sumanaseela Department of Obstetrics & Gynaecology, Wordsley Hospital, Stourbridge DY8 5QX Fax: 01384 244308; 3 Pedmore Court Road, Pedmore, Stourbridge DY8 2PH Fax: 01384 244445 Email: seela-de-silva@hotmail.com — MB BS 1978 Sri Lanka; MRCOG 1995. Clin. Asst. (Obst. & Gyn.) Wordsley Hosp.; Assoc. Specialist (Obst. & Gyn.) Wordsley Hosp. Dudley Gp. of Hosp.s NHS Trust; Assoc. Specialist (Obst. & Gyn.) Wordsley Hosp. Dudley Gp. of Hosps. NHS Trust. Prev: GP Cardiff; Regist. (O & G) P. Chas. Hosp. Merthyr Tydfil.

DE SILVA, Mahes National Blood Service North London, Colindale Avenue, London NW9 5BG Tel: 020 8258 2700 Fax: 020 8258 2970 Email: mahes.desilva@nbs.nhs.uk; 55 Selvage Lane, London NW7 3SS Tel: 020 8906 1419 — MB BS 1967 Ceylon; FRCPath. 1992, M 1981; DCH Eng. 1973. (Univ. Ceylon Peradeniya) Head Cons. (Red Cell Immunohaematol.) Lond. & S.E. Zone Natl. Blood Serv.; Hon. Sen. Lect. Imp. Coll. Sch. Of Med. Lond. Socs: Founder Mem. Brit. Blood Transfus. Soc. Prev: Cons. Haemat. N. Lond. Blood Transfus. Centre; Sen. Regist. N. Lond. Blood Transfus. Centre Edgware; Regist. (Haemat.) Watford Gen. Hosp.

DE SILVA, Malcolm Department of Rheumatology, Prince Charles Hospital, Merthyr Tydfil CF47 9DT; Spring Cottage, 20 Lake Road East, Cardiff CF23 5NN — MB BS (Hons.) Ceylon 1963; FRCP Lond. 1993, M 1977; DPhysMed Lond. 1976. (Colombo) Cons. Phys. Dept. Rheum. P. Chas. Hosp. Merthyr Tydfil; Hon. Clin. Teach. Welsh Nat. Sch. Med. Cardiff; Post Grad. Orgamsci (Climcal Tutor) N. Gamorgan N. H. S. Trust. Socs: Brit. Soc. Rheum. Prev: Sen. Regist. (Rheum. & Rehabil.) Addenbrooke's Hosp. Camb.; Regist. (Rheum. & Rehabil.) Norf. & Norwich Hosp. & St. Michael's Hosp. Aylsham.

DE SILVA, Meegahawattege Quintus Peter (retired) 6 Elton, Woughton Park, Milton Keynes MK6 3BJ Tel: 01908 607278 — MB BS 1956 Ceylon; MD Sri Lanka 1991; DCH Eng. 1966. Prev: Founder & Sen. Partner Eaglestone Health Centre Milton Keynes.

DE SILVA, Menaka Paediatric Department, Farnborough Hospital, Orpington BR6 8ND Tel: 01689 814184 Fax: 01689 814038; Fax: 020 8462 3159 Email: menaka.desilva@virgin.net — MB BS 1972 Sri Lanka; FRCP (UK) 2001; FRCPCH 1997; DCH Sri Lanka 1977. (Univ. Colombo, Sri Lanka) Cons. Paediat., Bromley Hosp.s NHS Trust.

DE SILVA, Nandin Ariyamithra 23 East Causeway Vale, Adel, Leeds LS16 8LG Tel: 0113 261 3384 — MB BS 1970 Ceylon.

DE SILVA, Nihal Tissa De Silva and Partners, 1 Morland Road, Croydon CR0 6HA Tel: 020 8688 0434 Fax: 020 8649 8477 — MB BS 1967 Ceylon. (Colombo) Vis. Med. Off. Stroud Green Lodge Croydon.

DE SILVA, Padmani Seneviratne 88 Shirland Road, Maida Vale, London W9 2EQ Tel: 020 7266 4298 — MB BS 1973 Ceylon; MRCP (UK) 1981.

DE SILVA, Mr Pinnaduwage Ariyaratne Dewsbury District Hospital, Healds Road, Dewsbury WF13 4JS Tel: 01924 816120 Fax: 01924 816040 Email: ariyaratne.desilva@dhc-tr.northy.nhs.uk; 46 Mountbatten Avenue, Sandal, Wakefield WF2 6HD Tel: 01924 251056 Email: ariyaratne@aol.com — MB BS 1969 Ceylon; FRCS Ed. 1978; FRCS Glas. 1978; MFFP 1993; FRCOG 1993, M 1977; Dip GU Med. Soc. Apoth. Lond. 1989; DObst RCOG 1976; 1996 FCLCOG. (Fac. of Med. Colombo, Sri Lanka) Cons. Phys. (Genitourin. Med.) Dewsbury Dist. Hosp.; Lead Clinician, Pat. Pub. Partnership (Consumer & Community Affairs) NHS, Modernisation task Gp. of the Dewsbury Health Care NHS Trust. Socs: BMA; Fell. Coll. Obst. & Gyn. Sri Lanka 1996; Med. Soc. Study VD. Prev: Cons. O & G Base Hosp. Matale Sri Lanka; Cons. O & G Base Hosp. Nuwara-Eliya Sri Lanka; Sen. Regist. (Genitourin. Med.) Gen. Infirm. Leeds.

DE SILVA, Pinnaduwage Chulanie 138 Hawton Road, Newark NG24 4QF — MB BS 1997 Lond.

DE SILVA, Pinnaduwage Vipula 6 Brockham Court, Bonchurch Close, Sutton SM2 6AZ — MB BS 1996 Lond.

DE SILVA, Prasanna Nemichandra 1 Larpool Mews, Whitby YO22 4NF Tel: 01947 820294 — MB ChB 1984 Aberd.; MB ChB Aberd. l984, BMed Biol. 1984; MRCPsych 1990. Cons. Neuropsychiat. ScarBoro. & S. Tees Ment. Health Trust. Prev: Sen. Lect. (NeuroPsychiat.) Univ. of Hull.

DE SILVA, Rajpal Kumar (retired) 48A Eversley Park Road, London N21 1JL Tel: 020 8360 2804 — MB BS 1957 Ceylon; DCH Eng. 1967. Hosp. Pract. (Paediat.) Enfield Dist. Hosp. Prev: GP Enfield.

DE SILVA, Ravi Joseph 12 Tuydor Rose Close, Stanway, Colchester CO3 5SD — MB BS 1996 Lond.

DE SILVA, Ruwanpura Derrwik Dharshana 20 Woodcock Dell Avenue, Kenton, Harrow HA3 0NS Tel: 020 8904 3208 — MB BS 1965 Ceylon; MRCS Eng. LRCP Lond. 1979; FRCR 1983; DMRD Eng. 1978; Cert JCC Lond. 1974. Sen. Regist. (Radiol.) St. Mary's Hosp. Lond. & Nat. Hosp. Nerv. Dis.; Maida Vale.

DE SILVA, Sajeeva Ramesh 40 St Andrews, Grantham NG31 9PE — MB ChB 1995 Leeds.

DE SILVA, Shanika Dineshi 40 St Andrews, Grantham NG31 9PE — MB ChB 1997 Leeds.

DE SILVA, Somitha Janassanda 6 Elton, Woughton Park, Milton Keynes MK6 3BJ — MB ChB 1992 Leeds. GP; SHO Huddersfield Roy. Infirm. Socs: BMA; MPS. Prev: Ho. Off. Leeds Gen. Infirm.

DE SILVA, Stephanie Gwendoline Fairmead, Worple Road, Staines TW18 1ED Tel: 01784 467295 Fax: 01784 46517; 12 Grove Road, Northwood HA6 2AP Tel: 01923 821356 — MB BS Ceylon 1966; FRCPsych 1992, M 1978; DPM Eng. 1977; DCH Eng. 1971. (Colombo) Cons. Psychiat. (Learning Disabil.) L.B. Spelthorne. Hounelow & Spelthorne Comm. & Ment. Health Trust. Prev: Cons. Psychiat. Leavesden Hosp. Abbots Langley Herts.; Cons. Phychiat. W.Middle. Hosp. Isleworth.

DE SILVA, Sumana Birch Hill Hospital, Rochdale OL12 9QB Tel: 01706 754056 Fax: 01706 754506 — MB BS 1972 Colombo; MRCP (UK) 1985; DCCH Ed. 1988; FRCPCH 1996. (Ceylon Colombo) Cons. (Paediat.) Community Child Health Rochdale. Socs: Fell.Roy. Coll. Paediat. & Child Health; Manch. Med. Soc.; Brit. Assn. Comm. Child Health.

DE SILVA, Thavamanidevi Department Anaesthesia, Pinderfield General Hospital, Aberford Road, Wakefield WF1 4DH Tel: 01924 375217; 46 Mountbatten Avenue, Sandal, Wakefield WF2 6HD Tel: 01924 251056 Email: 106352.1604@compuserve.com — MB BS 1968 Ceylon; DFFP 1994; DA (UK) 1982. Hosp. Med. Off. (Anaesth.) Pinderfield Gen. Hosp. Wakefield. Socs: BMA.

DE SILVA, Vimal Gunasiri 33 Capstan Drive, Littlehampton BN17 6SF Tel: 01903 725950 — MB BS 1974 Ceylon; MRCS Eng. LRCP Lond. 1988; DO RCPSI 1992. (Colombo, Sri Lanka) Med. Practit. (Ophth.); Clin. Asst. (Ophth.). Prev: SHO (Ophth.).

DE SILVA, Weerakondaratchige Sathischandra (retired) 26 First Avenue, Denvilles, Havant PO9 2QN Tel: 023 9245 5985 — MB BS Ceylon 1953; DPM Eng. 1979; DCH Eng. 1958. Prev: Assoc. Specialist St. Jas. Hosp. Portsmouth.

DE SILVA, Wickramaarachchige Kanishta Nimal (retired) 138 Brighton Road, Purley CR8 4HA Tel: 020 8660 6430 — MB BS Ceylon 1959.

DE SILVA, Winasi Mestrige Colvin Highlands, 42 Spareleaze Hill, Loughton IG10 1BT Tel: 020 8508 2471 — MB BS 1965 Ceylon; FRCPath 1989, M 1977. Cons. Haemat. Whipps Cross & Wanstead Hosps. Lond. Prev: Sen. Regist. (Haemat. & Blood Transfus.) St Mary's Hosp. Lond. & N.wick Pk. Hosp. Harrow; Sen. Regist. (Haemat. & Blood Transfus.) N. Lond. Blood Transfus. Centre Edgware.

DE SILVA NANAYAKKARA, Anupama Dyupathi Email: adesilva@btinternet.com — MB BS 1993 Lond.; MB BS (Hons.) Lond. 1993; MRCP (UK) 1996. (Univ. Coll. & Middlx.) Clin. Research Fell. Barts and the Lond. NHS Trust Lond. Prev: SpR (Gastro.) Roy. Free Hosp. NHS Trust Lond.; SpR (Gastro.) Barts and the Lond. NHS Trust Lond.; Specialist Regist. (Gastroenterol.) Havering Hosp. NHS Trust.

***DE SILVA NANYAKKARA, Thapthi Purnami Sashiprabha** 2 The Scholars, Lady's Close, Watford WD1 8RW — MB BS 1996 Lond.; MRCP part 1 1998.

DE SOUSA, Mr Bernard Alcuin Windsmoor House, Bass Lane, Summerseat, Bury BL9 5NS Tel: 0170682 3163 — MB BS 1966 Karachi; FRCS Eng. 1972. Cons. Gen. Surg. Bury HA. Socs: Manch. Med. Soc. & Assn. Surgs. Prev: Cons. Gen. Surg. Bury & Rossendale Hosps.

DE SOUSA, Beth (Savage) Honiton Medical Centre, Marlpits Road, Honiton; Tamarind, Little Houndbeare Farm, Aylesbeare, Exeter EX5 2DD Tel: 020 8995 8827 Email: michelle@cummins01.freeserve.co.uk — BM 1991 Soton.; DFFP; MRCGP; DRCOG. p/t Retained GP.

DE SOUSA, Carlos Miguel Candon Placido Department of Neurology, Great Ormond Street Hospital for Children, Great Ormond St., London WC1N 3JH Tel: 020 7405 9200 Fax: 020 7813 8279 Email: cdesousa@ich.ucl.ac.uk; 2 Bedford Villas, Wrythe Green Road, Carshalton SM5 2QT Tel: 020 8647 5990 — MB BS 1978 Lond.; BSc Lond. 1975, MD 1988; FRCP (UK) 1981; FRCPCH. (Guy's) Cons. Paediat. Neurol. Gt. Ormond St. Hosp. Lond. Prev: Cons. & Sen. Lect. (Paediat. Neurol.) St. Geo. Hosp. & Atkinson Morley's Hosp. Lond.; Lect. (Child Health) St. Geo. Hosp. Lond &

Qu. Mary's Hosp. Childr. Carshalton; Regist. (Neurol. & Psychiat.) Booth Hall & Roy. Manch. Childrs. Hosps.

DE SOUSA, Corinne Genevieve Highbury Hospital, Highbury Road, Bulwell, Nottingham NG6 9DR Tel: 0115 977 0000; 97 North Road, West Bridgford, Nottingham NG2 7NG Tel: 0115 914 5607 — MB BS 1991 Lond.; BSc (Hons.) Lond. 1988; MRCPsych 1995. (Char. Cross & Westm.)

DE SOUSA, Emma Louise Windsmoor House, Bass Lane, Summerseat, Bury BL9 5NS Tel: 01706 823163; Countess of Chester Hospital, Liverpool Road, Chester CH2 1UL Tel: 01244 365000 — BM BCh 1996 Oxf.; BA (Hons) Oxf. 1993. SHO (Gen. Surg.) Countess of Chester Hosp. Chester. Socs: BMA; MDU.

DE SOUSA, Luis Albert de Sousa Lillie Road Surgery, 139 Lillie Road, Fulham, London SW6 7SX Tel: 020 7385 7101; 5 Queen's Club Terrace, Normand Road, London W14 9TA Tel: 020 7385 8402 Fax: 020 7385 2785 — MB BS 1981 Lond.; MB BS Lond. 1980. (Charing Cross Hosp.) GP Princip.

DE SOUSA, Nigel Antoninus Coleridge Medical Centre, Canaan Way, Ottery St Mary EX11 1EQ Tel: 01404 814447 — MB BCh BAO 1990 Dub.; MRCGP 1996; DFFP 1996; DRCOG 1994.

DE SOUZA, Aldrin Tolentino 36 South Esk Road, London E7 8EY — MB BS 1998 Lond.; MB BS Lond 1998.

DE SOUZA, Mr Anthony Charles Royal Brompton Hospital, Sydney St., London SW3 6NP Tel: 020 7351 8566 Fax: 020 7351 8564 Email: t.desouza@rbh.nthames.nhs.uk; 70 Galveston Road, London SW15 2SA — BM BS 1985 Nottm.; BMedSci Nottm. 1983; FRCS (CTh) 1996; FRCS Ed. 1989; FRCS Eng. 1989. (Nottingham) Cons. Cardiac Surg. Roy. Brompton Hosp. Prev: Sen. Regist. Lond. Chest & Roy. Brompton Hosp.; Career Regist. Soton. Gen. Hosp.; Brit. Heart Foundat. Research Fell. Leicester Univ.

DE SOUZA, Beryl Antoinette 31 Fremont Street, London E9 7NQ — MB BS 1992 Lond.; MPhil Lond. 1988, BSc (Hons.) Biochem. 1985.

DE SOUZA, Dominic Savio Mark 2 Braithwaite Gardens, Stanmore HA7 2QH — MB ChB 1996 Leeds.

DE SOUZA, Emma Louise Gade House Surgery, 99B Uxbridge Road, Rickmansworth WD3 2DJ Tel: 01923 775291; 60 Hempstead Road, Watford WD17 4ER Tel: 01923 230325 — MB BS 1992 Lond.; DCH RCP Lond. 1995; MRCGP 1996; DRCOG 1996; DCH RCP Lond. 1995. (Univ. Coll. Hosp. & Middlx.) Trainee GP Rickmansworth.

DE SOUZA, John Martin Alexander 8 Bryce Avenue, Edinburgh EH7 6TX — MB ChB 1991 Ed.; BSc Glas. 1986; FRCS Ed. 1996. SHO (Surg.) Edin. Roy. Infirm.; Specialist Regist. (Urol.) Liverp. S.port & Formby Hosp. NHS Trust.

DE SOUZA, Mark Viren 20 Wildwood Road, London NW11 6TE — MB BS 1996 Lond.

DE SOUZA, Nandita Maria 53A Pelham Road, Wimbledon, London SW19 1SU — MB BS 1983 Newc.; BSc (Hons.) Physiol Newc. 1978, MB BS 1983; MRCP (UK) 1986; FRCR 1991. Sen. Regist. (Diag. Radiol.) Guy's & St. Thos. Hosps. Lond.

DE SOUZA, Philip Benjamin Crook Log Surgery, 19 Crook Log, Bexleyheath DA6 8DZ; 6 Heathdene Drive, Belvedere DA17 6HZ — BM 1983 Soton.; MRCGP 1988; DRCOG 1988. (Univ. Soton)

DE SOUZA, Richard Anthony 41 Maxwell Road, Welling DA16 2ES — MB ChB 1989 Leic.

DE SOUZA, Richard Frank Longfield Medical Centre, Princes Road, Maldon CM9 5DF Tel: 01621 856811 Fax: 01621 852627 — MRCS Eng. LRCP Lond. 1974; LMS Navarra 1971; MRCGP 1976. (Navarra) Prev: Trainee GP Dover Cinque Ports VTS; Ho. Off. (Med. & Surg.) Wigan Infirm.; SHO Rotat. Buckland Hosp. Dover VTS.

DE SOUZA, Richard George John The Surgery, 118/120 Stanford Avenue, Brighton BN1 6FE Tel: 01273 506361 Fax: 01273 552483; 115 Hythe Road, Brighton BN1 6JR — MB ChB 1985 Ed.; BSc (Hons.) Ed. 1982, MB ChB 1985.

DE SOUZA, Trevor Jude Forum Health Centre, 1A Farren Road, Wyken, Coventry CV2 5EP Tel: 024 7626 6370 Fax: 024 7663 6518 — MB BS 1976 Lond. GP Coventry.

DE SOUZA, Veena Carmen 20 Wildwood Road, London NW11 6TE — MB BChir 1992 Camb.

DE SOYSA, Digoarachchi Lalani Deepashika Wrexham Maelor Hospital, Croesnewyd Road, Wrexham LL13 7TX Tel: 01978 291100; 14 Rossett Park, Darland Lane, Rossett, Wrexham LL12 0FB Tel: 01244 571396 — MB BS 1986 Sri Lanka; MRCP (UK) 1993. (Peradeniya University (Sri Lanka)) Staff Grade Haematologist Wrexham Maelor Hosp. Wrexham.

DE SOYZA, Anthony Gerrard c/o Respiratory Medicine, Freeman Hospital, High Heaton, Newcastle upon Tyne NE7 7DN Tel: 0191 284 3111; 40 Windsor Terrace, South Gosforth, Newcastle upon Tyne NE3 1YL — MB ChB 1994 Dundee; BMSc (Hons.) Dund 1991. Hon. Regist. (Respirat.); Clin. Res. Fell.

DE SWIET, Professor Michael (cons. rooms) UCH Private Wing, Grafton Way, London WC1E 6AU Tel: 020 7383 7911 Fax: 020 7380 9816 Email: m.deswiet@ic.ac.uk; 60 Hornsey Lane, London N6 5LU Tel: 020 7272 3195 — MB BChir 1966 Camb.; MA Camb. 1966, MD 1976; FRCP Lond. 1981, M 1968; FRCOG 1992. (Univ. Coll. Hosp.) Cons. Phys. Qu. Charlotte's & Chelsea Hosp., Univ. Coll. & Whittington; Prof. of Obstetric Med., Imperial Coll. Sch. of Med.; Sen. Lect. Inst. Obst. & Gyn. & Univ. Coll. Med. Sch. Socs: Med. Res. Soc. & Neonat. Soc.; Internat.Soc.Study Hypertens. in Pregn. Prev: Sen. Regist. (Med.) Radcliffe Infirm. Oxf.; Research Fell. Cardiovasc. Research Inst. Univ. Calif., San Francisco, USA.

DE TAKATS, Dominic Laszlo Paul The Centre for Metabolic Bone Diseases at Sheffield, Ward G1, Royal Hallamshire Hospital, Glossop Road, Sheffield S10 2JF Tel: 0114 271 1725 Fax: 0114 271 2233 Email: p.l.detakats@sheffield.ac.uk; 309 Springrale Road, Crokes, Sheffield S10 1LL Tel: 0114 266 6931 Email: d.l.detakats@sheffield.ac.uk — BM BCh 1987 Oxf.; BA (Hons.) Oxf. 1986, MA 1993; MRCP (UK) 1992. Clin. Research Fell. Dept. Human Metab. & Clin. Biochem. Univ. Sheff. Prev: Regist. (Renal Med.) King's Healthcare NHS Trust; Regist. (Renal & Gen. Med.) Roy. Sussex Co. Hosp. Brighton.

DE TARANTO, Nicola Elisabeth North London Forensic Service, Camlet Lodge, Chase Farm Hospital, The Ridgeway, Enfield EN2 8JL Tel: 020 8967 1050 Fax: 020 8342 0806 Email: nikki.detaranto@enfieldcc-tr.nthames.nhs.uk — MB BCh 1986 Witwatersrand; MRCPsych 1993; LLM (University of Wales) 2000. (Witwatersrand) Cons. (Forens. Psychiat.) N. Lond. Forens. Serv. Prev: Sen. Regist. (Forens. Psychiat.) N. E. Lond. Higher Train. Scheme; Regist. Rotat. (Psychiat.) Roy. Free Hosp. Lond.

DE THIERRY, Albert Edward Lewis 2 The Spinney, Winchmore Hill, London N21 1LH Tel: 020 8360 5614 — MB 1955 Camb.; MA Camb. 1953, BA 1950, MB 1955, BChir 1954; DObst RCOG 1956; DPH Eng. 1970. (Camb. & Lond. Hosp.) Socs: BMA; Soc. Occupat. Med. Prev: SCMO S.E. Kent Health Dist.; Ho. Phys. Sheff. Childr. Hosp.; Lect. (Med.) Ships Masters 1st Aid Sch. of Navigation Minones Lond.

DE VEER, George Edzii 337 Dunchurch Road, Rugby CV22 6HT Tel: 01788 812687 — MB ChB 1987 Ghana. (Univ. Ghana Med. Sch.) Staff Grade Doctor (Community Child Health & Paediat.) Rugby NHS Trust. Prev: SHO (Paediat.) Dewsbury Dist. Hosp. & Wexham Pk. Hosp. Slough.

DE VERE, Mr Roger Duchene (retired) Durnsford Mill, Mildenhall, Marlborough SN8 2NG Tel: 01672 512673 — FRCS Eng. 1949; MRCS Eng. LRCP Lond. 1945; FRCOG 1962, M 1952. Prev: O & G Surg. W.m. Hosp.

DE VERTEUIL, John Arthur, Squadron Ldr. RAF Med. Br. Retd. Milestone Surgery, 208 Farnborough Road, Farnborough GU14 7JN Tel: 01252 545078 Fax: 01252 370751; Yew Tree Cottage, 5 Darby Green Lane, Darby Green, Camberley GU17 0DW Email: johndev1@btinternet.com — MB BS 1983 Lond.; MRCP (UK) 1991; MRCGP 1993. (Lond. Hosp. Med. Coll.)

DE VESSELITSKY MERRIMAN, Gabriel (retired) 22 Adair Road, Eastney, Portsmouth PO3 5HB Tel: 01705 814024 — MRCS Eng. LRCP Lond. 1943.

DE VIAL, Simon Richard Minden Medical Centre, 2 Barlow Street, Bury BL9 0QP Tel: 0161 764 2651 Fax: 0161 761 5967 — MB ChB 1987 Manch.

DE VILLE, Donald Crossley (retired) 89 Inham Road, Beeston, Nottingham NG9 4HW Tel: 0115 925 6717 — MRCS Eng. LRCP Lond. 1945. Prev: SHO Stamford & Rutland Hosp.

DE VILLE, Kathleen Mary (retired) Willow Tree Cottage, Main Road, Woodham Ferrers, Chelmsford CM3 8RN Tel: 01245 324931 — MRCS Eng. LRCP Lond. 1950. Prev: Clin. Asst. W.m. Hosp.

DE VILLIERS, Gerrit Stephanus Lower Flat, Deva House, Birmingham Road, Hatton, Warwick CV35 7JP — MB ChB 1991 Stellenbosch.

DE VILLIERS, Johanna Wilhelmina c/o Wonford House Hospital, Dryden Road, Exeter EX2 5AF — MB ChB 1996 Pretoria.

DE VIVO, Luigi New Heath Close, Firs Black No. 70, New Cross Hospital, Wolverhampton WV10 0QP — State Exam Naples 1990.

DE VOIL, Cedric Walter Benedict Abbey Health Centre, East Abbey Street, Arbroath DD11 1EN Tel: 01241 872692; 5 Albert Street, Arbroath DD11 1RA — MB ChB 1967 St. And.; MRCGP 1977; DObst RCOG 1969. (St. And.) Socs: BMA & Brit. Soc. for Clin. Ecology; McCarrison Soc. (Chairm. Scott. GP). Prev: Trainee GP Crieff Health Centre Perthsh.; SHO (O & G) St. John's Hosp. Keighley; Med. Off. (Volun. Serv. Overseas) Nixon Memor. Hosp. Sierra Leone.

DE VRIES, Hendrick 2 Boot Street, Earby, Colne BB18 6UX — Artsexamen 1992 Leiden.

DE VRIES, Petrus Johannes Section of Developmental Psychiatry, University of Cambridge, Douglas House, 18d Trumpington Road, Cambridge CB2 2AH Email: pd215@hermes.cam.ac.uk; 35 Causewayside, Cambridge CB3 9HD — MB ChB 1991 Stellenbosch; MRCPsych 1997. Research Fell. Sect. of Developm. Psychiat.; Hon. Specialist Regist. in Child & Adolesc. Psychiat. Socs: BMA; ACPP; CPRS. Prev: Trainee Psychiat. Univ Camb. Teach. Hosps. Rotat. Train. Scheme.

DE WAAL, Frances 79 Morvale Close, Belvedere DA17 5HT Tel: 0132 24 36375 — MB BS 1976 Lond.

DE WARDENER, Professor Hugh Edward, CBE, MBE (retired) Department Clinical Chemistry, Imperial College School of Medicine, Charing Cross Hospital, London W6 8RP Tel: 020 8846 7076 Fax: 020 8846 7007 Email: h.dewardener@ic.ac.uk — MB BS Lond. 1939; MD Lond. 1949; MD (Hon. Causa) Toulouse 1996; MD (Hon. Causa) Paris 1979; FRCP Lond. 1958, M 1946; MRCS Eng. LRCP Lond. 1939. p/t Emerit. Prof. (Med.) Univ. Lond. Prev: Prof. Med. Char. Cross Hosp. Med. Sch.

DE WEERD, Johannes Maarten 9 Morris Harp, Saffron Walden CB10 2EE — Artsexamen 1991 Free U. Amsterdam; Artsexamen Free Univ Amsterdam 1991.

DE WEEVER, Anthony Cyril Arthur The Health Centre, Central Road, Partington, Manchester M31 4FL Tel: 0161 775 7033 — MB ChB 1984 Dundee; T(GP) 1989.

DE WHALLEY, Philip Charles Stephen Queen Elizabeth Hospital, Gayton Road, King's Lynn PE30 4ET Tel: 01553 613613 — BM BCh 1989 Oxf.; MA Camb. 1990; MRCGP 1993; DCH RCP Lond. 1994; DRCOG 1992; MRCP (Paediat.) 1996. Staff Grade, Paediat., King's Lynn. Prev: PHO (Accid. & Emerg.) Toowoomba Base Hosp. Qu.sland, Austral.; Specialist Regist. (Paediat.) Kings Lynn; Trainee GP Gt. Yarmouth.

DE WILDE, Stephen James The Tod Practice, 12 Durham Road, Raynes Park, London SW20 0TW Tel: 020 8946 0069 Fax: 020 8944 2927; 50 Keswick Avenue, Kingston Vale, London SW15 3QJ — MB BS 1987 Lond.; BSc Psychol. Lond. 1984; MRCGP 1992; T(GP) 1992; DRCOG 1992. (Middlesex Hospital) GP Princip.; Clin. Research Fell. St. Geo. Hosp. Med. Sch. Prev: Trainee GP Reading VTS.

DE WILDT, Gilles Robert Jiggins Lane Medical Centre, 17 Jiggins Lane, Bartley Green, Birmingham B32 3LE Tel: 0121 477 7272 Fax: 0121 478 4319 — Artsexamen 1981 Groningen.

DE WINTER, Edith 49 Woodside House, Wimbledon, London SW19 7QN Tel: 020 8946 6787 — MD 1938 Prague; FFA RCS Eng. 1955; DA Eng. 1944. Socs: Assn. Anaesths. & Assoc. Fac. Gen. Pract. 1977. Prev: Maj. RAMC, Specialist Anaesth.; Res. Anaesth. Addenbrooke's Hosp. Camb.; Asst. Anaesth. Atkinson Morley's Hosp. Lond.

DE WINTER, Jan George (retired) 6 New Road, Brighton BN1 1UF Tel: 01273 727213 Fax: 01273 748915 — MD 1938 Prague; DSc (Hons.) Sussex 1996; FRCR 1982; FFR RCSI 1964; DMR Lond 1944. Dir. Clin. for Cancer Preven. Advice. Prev: Sen. Cons. Radiother. & Oncol. E. Sussex AHA.

DE WIT, Ansa Good Hope Hospital, Flat 6 Block 13, Rectory Redfield, Sutton Coldfield B75 7RR — MB ChB 1996 Pretoria.

DE ZEEUW, Fiona Jane 39 Taylors La, Dundee DD2 1AP — MB ChB 1997 Dundee.

DE ZOYSA, Himala Manjiri 126 St Dunstans Road, London W6 8RA — MB BS 1995 Lond.

DE ZOYSA, Nandrani Swarnamitta Mendis Regional Transfusion Centre, Wessex Region, Coxford Road, Southampton SO16 5AF Tel: 02380 776441 — MB BS 1961 Ceylon; DTM & H Colombo 1979.

DE ZOYSA, Sreema Department for the Elderly, East Surrey District Hospital, Redhill RH1 5RH Tel: 01737 768511 — MB BS 1967 Ceylon; FRCPsych. 1997; MRCPsych. 1979; DPM Eng. 1978. Cons. Psychogeriat. E. Surrey Dist. Hosp. Redhill.; Speciality Tutor (Psychiat. of Old Age). Socs: Fell. Roy. Col. Psychiat.; BMA. Prev: Sen. Regist. Psychiat. St. Nicholas Hosp. Gosforth; Regist. Psychiat. St. Mary Abbots Hosp. Lond.

DE ZOYSA, Walsinghe Sam Lilington 199 Willington Street, Maidstone ME15 8EE Tel: 01622 756184 Fax: 01622 662228 — MB BS 1966 Ceylon; FFA RCS Eng. 1975; DA Eng. 1973. (Fac. of Med. Univ. Ceylon) Cons. Anaesth. Mid. Kent Health Care Trust Maidstone. Socs: BMA; Assn. Anaesth. GB & Irel.; Internat. Assn. Study Pain (Brit. Chapter). Prev: Sen. Regist. (Rotat.) St. Geo. & W.m. Hosps. Lond.

DE ZULUETA, Felicity Ines Soledad Traumatic Stress Service, Maudsley Hospital, Denmark Hill, London SE5 8AZ Tel: 020 7919 2969 Fax: 020 7919 3573 Email: f.dezulet@iop.kcl.ac.uk; 17 Westhill Court, Millfield Lane, London N6 6JJ — MB ChB 1974 Sheff.; MA Camb. 1971; BSc E. Anglia 1969; MRCPsych 1978. (Cambridge-Sheffield) Hon. Cons. Psychiat./Psychotherapist Maudsley Hosp.; Clin. Lect. in Traum. Studies Inst. of Psychiat. Socs: BMA; Sen. Represent. L.N.C. (Char. Cross Hosp.). Prev: Cons. Psychotherapist at Char. Cross Hosp. (Lond.); Hon. Cons. Psychotherapist Cavel Hosp.; Hon. Sen. Lect. Char. Cross Hosp.

DE ZULUETA, Mavis Evelyn 602 Mountjoy House, Barbican, London EC2Y 8BP — MB BS Melbourne 1951; MPhil Lond. 1996, BA (Hons.) 1990; DPM Eng. 1972. (Melbourne) Socs: Liveryman Worshipful Soc. Apoth. Prev: Sen. Med. Off. Home Office; Resid. Med. Off. Qu. Vict. Hosp. Melbourne, Austral.; Med. Off. HM Overseas Civil Serv. Aden & Gibraltar.

DE ZULUETA, Paquita Carmen Boulan 9-14 Addison Court, 4 Brondesbury Road, London NW6 6AS Tel: 020 7328 1803; 27A Lansdowne Crescent, London W11 2NS — MB 1979 Camb.; BChir 1978; MRCP (UK) 1981; DRCOG 1983. Princip. GP Lond. Socs: BMA; Assoc. Mem. RCGP. Prev: Med. Regist. St. Bart. Hosp. Lond.

DEACOCK, Anthony Roy de Coq Cedar Lodge, 8a Sandringham Road, Fareham PO14 3DW Tel: 01329 845354 Email: ardeacock@ukgateway.net — MRCS Eng. LRCP Lond. 1950; FRCP Canada 1972; FFA RCS Eng. 1956; FACA 1959. (King's Coll. Hosp.) Socs: Fell. Roy. Soc. Med. (Mem. Sect. Anaesth.); Assn. Anaesth. Prev: Cons. Anaesth. Roy. Free Hosp., Roy. Nat. Orthop. Hosp. & Hosp. of St. John & St. Eliz.; Emerit. Cons. Hosp. of St. John & St. Eliz.; Sen. Regist. (Anaesth.) King's Coll. Hosp. & Thoracic & Neurosurg. Units Brook Hosp. Lond.

DEACOCK, Sarah Jane Department of Immunology, Royal Postgraduate Medical School, Hammersmith Hospital, Du Cane Road, London W12 0NN Tel: 020 8743 2030; Port House, St James St, Yarmouth, Isle of Wight PO41 0NU — BChir 1981 Camb.; PhD Lond. 1992; MA Camb. 1982, BChir 1981; MRCP (UK) 1984. Sen. Regist. (Clin. Immunol.) Hammersmith Hosp. Lond.

DEACOCK, Simon Jonathan de Coq Wychbury House, Quarry Road, Winchester SO23 0JG — MB BS 1984 Lond.; FRCA 1993. Cons. (Anaesth.)Roy.Hants.Co. hosp.Winchester. Socs: Assn. Anaesth. Prev: Sen. Regist. (Anaesth.) GreenLa.s Hosp. Auckland, NZ; Sen. Regist. Hammersmith Hosp. Lond.; Regist. Char. Cross. Hosp. Lond.

DEACON, Andrew Robert The Health Centre, Victoria Street, Marsden, Huddersfield HD7 6DF Tel: 01484 844332 Fax: 01484 845779; 17 Darnley Close, Meltham, Huddersfield HD9 4BT — MB BS 1981 Lond.; BSc Lond. 1978; MRCGP 1985; DRCOG 1984.

DEACON, Angela Dale 34 Thorn Drive, Bearsden, Glasgow G61 4LU Tel: 0141 942 3328 — MB ChB 1969 Otago; FFA RCS Eng. 1975. (Otago) Gen. Pract. Anaesth. Gtr. Glas. Health Bd.; Clin. Asst. Bone Metab. Research Unit. Socs: Glas. & W. Scotl. Soc. Anaesth. Prev: Regist. (Anaesth.) Lothian Health Bd.

DEACON, Caroline Susan Department of Radiology, The Royal Wolverhampton Hospitals, New Cross Hospital, Wolverhampton WV10 0QP Tel: 01902 307999 — MB ChB 1983 Sheff.; FRCR 1989. Cons. Radiol. The Roy. Wolverhamtpon Hosp.

DEACON, Ceridwen 37 Sandy Ridge, Chislehurst BR7 5DP — MB BCh 1971 Wales; MSc Audiol Med. Lond. 1995; DCH RCP Lond.

1974. Clin. Med. Off. (Audiol. & Community Health) Greenwich Healthcare. Socs: BACDA; BSA; BACCH.

DEACON, David Frank Clements (retired) 28 Hull Road, Hornsea HU18 1RL — MRCS Eng. LRCP Lond. 1950.

DEACON, David Jeremy Allington NHS Trust, Occupational Health Department, The Ipswich Hospital, Allington NHS Trust, Ipswich IP4 5PD Tel: 01473 704011 Fax: 01473 704241; Highdene, Northcliff, Kessingland, Lowestoft NR33 7RA Tel: 01502 742097 Email: daviddeacon@netmatters.co.uk — MB BChir 1974 Camb.; MA Camb. 1974; MRCS Eng. LRCP Lond. 1974; D.Occ.Med. RCP Lond. 1995. (Camb. & Westm.) Occupat. Ipswich Hosp. Socs: Assoc. Equinox Internat. Soc. Biophys. Med.; Brit. Soc. Med. & Dent. Hypn.; Brit. Med. Acupunct. Soc. Prev: GP LoW.oft; SHO (O & G) Bedford Gen. Hosp.; Med. Off. Lutheran Med. Foundat. Dundee, S. Afr.

DEACON, David Jonathan 58 Elgin Avenue, Harrow HA3 8QL — MB BS 1998 Lond.; MB BS Lond 1998.

DEACON, Mr Garth Peter 86 Rectory Road, Sutton Coldfield B75 7RP Tel: 0121 378 0624 — MB ChB 1979 Birm.; FRCS Ed. 1988.

DEACON, George Roger Clements 705 Beverley High Road, Hull Tel: 01482 853221 — MRCS Eng. LRCP Lond. 1950; DObst RCOG 1954.

DEACON, Janet Mabel Marcella 7 Magheralave Road, Lisburn BT28 3BE Tel: 01846 679073 — MB BCh BAO 1979 Belf.; MRCGP 1983; Cert. Family Plann. JCC 1983. Clin. Med. Off. Family Plann. Belf.

DEACON, Jill Frances 44 Salcombe Road, Plymouth PL4 7NF; 55 Queens Mead, Bedgrove, Aylesbury HP21 7AL Tel: 01296 580572 Fax: 01296 89358 — MB BS 1994 Lond.; BSc (Epidemiol. & Med. Statistics) Lond. 1991.

DEACON, Kenneth Robert 10 Ampton Road, Flat 5, Edgbaston, Birmingham B15 2UM Tel: 0121 456 5801 Email: kdeacon1@compuserve.com — MB ChB 1996 Birm; ChB Birm. 1996. SHO (Med.) Kidderminster Gen. Hosp. Prev: SHO (Orthop.) Birm. Heartlands Hosp.; SHO (A & E) Alexandra Hosp. Redditch.

DEACON, Max Bray 63 Rowan Road, Brook Green, London W6 7DT; 3 Cawley Road, Chichester PO19 1 Tel: s. 773292 & 782890 — MB BS 1963 Queensland; MFHom 1972.

DEACON, Mr Philip 7 Moor Allerton Way, Leeds LS17 6SA — MB ChB 1978 Leeds; BSc (Hons.) Anat. Leeds 1975, MB ChB (Hons.) 1978; FRCS Eng. 1982. Tutor Dept. Orthop. Surg. Leeds Univ.

DEACON, Richard Eliot 8 Moorhill Court, 494 Bury New Road, Salford M7 4WN Email: richard.deacon@virgin.net — MB ChB 1991 Leeds; MA (Health Care Ethics) Manch. 1994. GP Reg Prestwich. Prev: Gen. Med. SHO N. Manch. Gen; O & G SHO N. Manch. Gen; Reg. Psychiat. Gtr Manch. Ment. Health Trust.

DEACON, Robert Henry Swains Fold Farm, Cuerdale Lane, Walton de Dale, Preston PR5 4EP — MB ChB 1996 Leeds.

DEACON, Ronald Charles (retired) Acre Cottage, Clanville, Andover SP11 9HN Tel: 01264 773958 — MB ChB St. And. 1957; DTM & H Eng. 1973.

DEACON, Rosemary Jane Leigh 53 Longfleet Road, Poole BH15 2HW — MB BS 1974 Lond.; MRCS Eng. LRCP Lond. 1975; LMSSA Lond. 1974. (Guy's) GP Asst.

DEACON, Thomas Henry Kenneth (retired) Green Acre, 39A Cregg Road, Claudy, Londonderry BT47 4HX Tel: 02871 338655 — LRCPI & LM, LRCSI & LM 1947. Prev: Ho. Surg. Roy. City Dub. Hosp.

DEACON, Vivien Malham House Day Hospital, 25 Hyde Terrace, Leeds LS2 9LN — MB ChB 1978 Leeds; BSc (Hons.) Leeds 1975, MB ChB 1978; MRCPsych 1982. Cons. Psychiat. Malham Ho. Day Hosp. Leeds. Prev: Cons. Psychiat. Harrogate Dist. Hosp.

DEADY, Mr James Patrick Sunderland Eye Infirmary, Queen Alexandra Road, Sunderland SR2 9HP Tel: 0191 528 3616; 5 The Dene, Chester Moor, Chester-le-Street DH2 3TB Tel: 0191 388 4453 — MB BS 1975 Lond.; FRCS Ed. 1983; FCOphth 1988; DO Eng. 1980. (St. Bart.) Cons. Ophth. Sunderland Eye Infirm. & Dryburn Hosp. Durh. Prev: Sen. Regist. & Regist. Birm. & Midl. Eye Hosp.; Sen. Regist. Moorfields Eye Hosp. Lond.; SHO (Neurosurg) & Ho. Surg. Eye Dept. St. Bart. Hosp. Lond.

DEADY, Jane Mary Preston Park Surgery, 2a Florence Road, Brighton BN1 6DP Tel: 01273 559601/566033 Fax: 01273 507746 — MB BS 1979 Lond.

DEADY, Rosemary Nant Fawr, Corwen LL21 9AA — MB BCh 1998 Wales.

DEAHL, Martin Philip, TD, OStJ Department Psychological Medicine, St. Bartholomew's Hospital, London EC1A 7BE Tel: 020 7601 8108 Fax: 020 7601 7969; Department of Psychiatry, Homerton Hospital, Homerton Row, London E9 6SR Tel: 020 8919 8857 Fax: 020 8919 8716 — MB BS 1983 (Distinc. Med.) Lond.; MPhil Lond. 1989; MA Oxf. 1982, BA 1978; FRCPsych 1997, M 1988. (St. Bart.) Cons. E. Lond. & City Ment. Health NHS Trust; Lt. Col. 256 City Lond. Field Hosp. RAMC; Cons. Adviser St. John Ambul. Med. Bd.; Cons. Adviser Roy. Air Force; Vis. Prof. of Psychiat. &Ment. Health Studies , City Univ.; Reader St. Bart. & Roy. Lond. Sch. Med. & Dent. Prev: Sen. Regist. (Psychiat.) Maudsley Hosp. Lond.; Sen. Regist. (Neuropsychiat.) Nat. Hosps. Nerv. Dis. Lond.; Clin. & Research Fell. Johns Hopkins Univ. Baltimore, USA.

DEAKIN, David Paul 37 Daylesford Road, Cheadle SK8 1LE Tel: 0161 491 2476; Christie Hospital NHS Trust, Wilmslow Road, Manchester M20 4BX Tel: 0161 446 3000 — MB ChB Manch. 1967; FRCR 1975; FFR 1973; DMRT Eng. 1971. (Manchester) Cons. Radiother. Christie Hosp. & Holt Radium Inst. Manch. Socs: Fell. Manch. Med. Soc.

DEAKIN, David Philip Ward The Windsor Road Surgery, Windsor Road, Garstang, Preston PR3 1ED Tel: 01995 603350 Fax: 01995 601301 — MB BS 1984 Lond.; MRCGP 1988. (St. Mary's)

DEAKIN, Derek Thomas Francis (retired) Whitecroft, 83 Vale Road, Ash Vale, Aldershot GU12 5HR Tel: 01252 326308 — MB BS 1955 Lond.; MRCS Eng. LRCP Lond. 1955; DObst RCOG 1957. Prev: GP Ash Vale.

DEAKIN, Frederick John (retired) Budworth House, Southbank, Great Budworth, Northwich CW9 6HG — MB ChB 1951 Liverp. Prev: GP Warrington.

DEAKIN, Graham John Stoke Gifford Medical Centre, Ratcliffe Drive, Stoke Gifford, Bristol BS34 8UE Tel: 0117 979 9430 Fax: 0117 940 6999 — MB ChB 1978 Bristol. p/t GP Partner; Med. Director for NHS Direct (Avon, Glos, Wilts).

DEAKIN, Hannah Louise Rothay, Cannington, Bridgwater TA5 2ND — MB ChB 1997 Birm.

DEAKIN, Helen Minden Medical Centre, 2 Barlow Street, Bury BL9 0QP Tel: 0161 764 2652 Fax: 0161 761 5967 — MB BCh 1980 Wales; MRCGP 1986; DRCOG 1982. ((The then) Welsh National School of Medicine (Cardiff)) Gen. Med. Practitioner.

DEAKIN, Ian Paul Bishops Place Surgery, Bishops Place, Paignton TQ3 3DZ Tel: 01803 559421 Fax: 01803 663381 — MB ChB 1980 Leeds; DRCOG 1984.

DEAKIN, Professor John Francis William Neuroscience and Psychiatry Unit, Room G907, Stopford Building, Oxford Road, Manchester M13 9PT Tel: 0161 275 7427 Fax: 0161 275 7429 Email: b.deakin@man.ac.uk — MB ChB 1973 Lond.; BSc Leeds 1970; PhD Lond. 1981; FRCPsych 1991, M 1980. Prof. Psychiat. Univ. Manch.; Dir. Wellcome Trust Clin. Research Facility; Dir. Neurosci. & Psychiat. Unit. Prev: Mem. of Staff Nat. Inst. Med. Research Mill Hill; Hon. Sen. Regist. (Psychiat.) N.wick Pk. Hosp. Harrow; Sen. Lect. (Psychiat.) Univ. Hosp. S. Manch.

DEAKIN, Mr Mark University Department of Surgery, North Staffordshire Hospital, Thornburrow Drive, Stoke-on-Trent ST4 7QB Tel: 01782 716699 Fax: 01782 747319 — MB ChB 1978 Liverp.; ChM Liverp. 1988; FRCS Eng. 1983; FRCS Ed. 1982; T(S) 1991. Sen. Lect. (Surg.) Univ. Keele; Cons. Surg. N. Staffs. Hosp. Trust Stoke on Trent. Prev: Sen. Regist. (Surg.) Birm. HA; Post Doctoral Research Fell. Univ. Calif. San Diego, USA; Research Fell. Roy. Naval Hosp. Haslar.

DEAKIN, Michael Thomas Herefordshire Health Authority, Victoria House, Eign St., Hereford HR4 0AN Tel: 01432 262000 Fax: 01432 341958 Email: mike.deakin@hereford-ha.wmids.nhs.uk; Never More, Little Birch, Hereford HR2 8BB Tel: 0141 637 2587, 01981 540442 — MB ChB 1978 Sheff.; MFPHM RCP (UK) 1996. (Sheff.) Dir. Pub. Health Heref. Health Auth.; Pub. health Adviser to the Heref. PCT. Prev: Cons. Pub. Health Med. Heref. HA; Med. Dir. Solihull FHSA; GP Sheff.

DEAKIN, Philip John Derbyshire Lane Practice, 213 Derbyshire Lane, Sheffield S8 8SA Tel: 0114 255 0972 — MB ChB 1979 Sheff.; BSc (Hons.) Sheff. 1975, MB ChB 1979. GP Sheff.

DEAKIN, Susan Manchester Royal Infirmary, 2B Lorne St., Manchester M13 9WB; 24 Garner Avenue, Timperley, Altrincham

WA15 6AG — MB BS 1990 Newc. Prev: Ho. Off. (Med.) Qu. Eliz. Hosp. Gateshead; Ho. Off. (Surg.) Roy. Vict. Infirm. Newc. u. Tyne.

DEAKIN, Veronica Eileen Bishops Place Surgery, 1 Bishops Place, Paignton TQ3 3DZ Tel: 01803 559421 Fax: 01803 663381; Moorlands, 16 Western Road, Torquay TQ1 4RL — MB ChB 1980 Leeds. Examr. Benefits Agency Torquay.

DEAL, Jane Elizabeth Department of Paediatrics, St. Mary's Hospital, London W2 1NY Tel: 020 7886 6252 Fax: 020 7886 6341 Email: j.deal@ic.ac.uk — FRCP,(UK) 2001; MB BS Lond. 1978; MD Lond. 1995; MRCP (UK) 1982; MRCS Eng. LRCP Lond. 1978; DCH RCP Lond. 1980; FRCPCH 1997. (Char. Cross) Cons. Paediat. & Paediat. Nephrol. St. Mary's Hosp. Lond. Prev: Lect. (Paediat. Nephrol.) & Hon. Sen. Regist. Guy's Hosp. Lond.; Research Fell. (Paediat. Nephrol.) Inst. of Child Health Hosp. for Sick Childr. Gt. Ormond St. Lond.; Exchange Regist. Childr. Hosp. Philadelphia, USA.

DEALEY, Robert Anthony Sylvana, Beech Hill Road, Swanland, North Ferriby HU14 3QY — MB 1978 Camb.; MA Camb. 1978, MB 1978, BChir 1977; FRCR 1986. (Camb. & King's Coll. Hosp.) Cons. Radiother. & Oncol. P.ss Roy. Hosp. Hull. Prev: Sen. Regist. (Radiother. & Oncol.) Velindre Hosp. WhitCh.; Research Asst. Marie Curie Research Wing Mt. Vernon Hosp. N.wood; Regist. (Radiother. & Oncol.) Ipswich Hosp.

DEAN, Adrian John 26 Westwood Crescent, Cottingley, Bingley BD16 1NN Tel: 01274 567964 — MB ChB 1984 Manch.; MB ChB Manch. l984; DRCOG 1989; DA (UK) 1987. Prev: SHO (O & G, Geriat. & Anaesth.) Cottingley.

DEAN, Alan Derek EPIC, Regeneration House, York Way, Kings Cross, London N1 0BB Tel: 020 7713 1118 Fax: 020 7713 1119 Email: alan.dean@epic-uk.org; Smugglens Cottage, Smugglens Cove, Orsett TR16 4NS Tel: 01209 842209 Fax: 01209 844971 — MB BS Lond. 1960; FFPM. (Char. Cross Hosp.) Chairm. Gen. Pract. Database Research Company Ltd.; Med. Dir. Comasco Computer Serv. Ltd. Lond.; Chairm.. EPIC; Non-Exec. Dir. M. Pract. Lond. Prev: Med. Dir. Vamp Health Ltd. & Vamp Ltd.; Police Surg. Basildon Area Essex.

DEAN, Amal Talbot Court Medical Practice, 1 Talbot Court, Stretford, Manchester M32 0ZL Tel: 0161 865 1197 Fax: 0161 864 1966 — MB ChB 1982 Manch.; DRCOG 1986. Socs: BMA.

DEAN, Andrew David Peter CNS Clinical Research, Astra Zeneca, Bakewell Road, Loughborough LE11 5RH Tel: 01509 644128 Fax: 01509 645585 Email: andrew.dean@charnwood.gb.arta.com; 37 Main Road, Barleythorpe, Oakham LE15 7EE — MB BChir 1989 Camb.; PhD Camb. 1989; BSc Newc. 1981. Sen. Pharmaceut. Phys. CNS Clin. Research. Socs: Soc. for Endocrinol.; Brit. Assn. Pharmaceut. Phys.; Assn. Human Pharmacol. Pharmaceut. Industry. Prev: Clin. Pharmacol. Astro Charnwood & Halton; SHO (Med.) RAF Hosp. Wegberg; Med. Off. RAF Marham.

DEAN, Andrew Edward Calcot Medical Centre, Hampden Road, Chalfont St. Peter, Gerrards Cross SL9 9SA Tel: 01753 887311 — MB BS 1991 Lond.; BSc; MRCGP 1997 Lond. (St Mary's London) GP Prinicipal; Clin. Asst. Paediat.; Club doctor, Slough Town football club.

DEAN, Andrew Francis Department Pathology, St. Mary's Hospital, Praed St., London W2 — BM BCh 1987 Oxf. SHO (Path.) St. Mary's Hosp. Lond.

DEAN, Andrew John Philip Westgate Bay Avenue Surgery, 60 Westgate Bay Avenue, Westgate-on-Sea CT8 8SN Tel: 01843 831335 Fax: 01843 835279; 55 High Street, Minster, Ramsgate CT12 4BT Tel: 01843 821252 Email: andrew@domneva.freeserve.co.uk — MRCS Eng. LRCP Lond. 1976. (King's Coll. Hosp.) Prev: Trainee GP Thanet VTS.

DEAN, Anthony Frederick 2 Thorney Green Road, Stowupland, Stowmarket IP14 4BY — MB ChB 1998 Dund.; MB ChB Dund 1998.

DEAN, Arabelle Margaret Department of Radiology, General Hospital, Northampton NN1 5BD Tel: 016046 634700 — MB ChB Birm. 1967; FRCR 1976; DMRD Eng. 1970. (Birm.) Cons. Radiol. N.ampton Gen. Hosp. Prev: Sen. Regist. N.ampton Gen. Hosp.; Regist. (Radiol.) Middlx. Hosp. Lond.; Supernum. Regist. United Birm. Hosps. & Birm. RHB.

DEAN, Barbara Caithness (retired) 53 Whitecroft Way, Park Langley, Beckenham BR3 3AQ Tel: 020 8650 4767 — MB BS Lond. 1957; MRCS Eng. LRCP Lond. 1957.

DEAN, Bernard Charles AKOS Clinical Development Ltd, 47-49 High St., Redbourn, St Albans AL3 7LW Tel: 01582 793793 Fax: 01582 794396 Email: bernard_dean@akos.co.uk; 7 East Street, Kimbolton, Huntingdon PE28 0HJ Tel: 01480 860611 — MB BCh BAO Dub. 1970; BA Dub. 1968; FFPM RCP (UK) 1989. Med. Adviser AKOS Clin. Developm. Ltd. St. Albans. Prev: Med. Dir. Du Pont Pharmaceut. Ltd. Letchworth.

DEAN, Betty Katharine (retired) 1 Marshall Place, Perth PH2 8AH Tel: 01738 629216 — MB ChB 1952 St. And. Prev: Ho. Surg. Midw. & Gyn. Gen. Hosp. Bishop Auckland.

DEAN, Mr Brian Viewforth, 121 Rose St., Dunfermline KY12 0QT Tel: 01383 722488 — MB ChB Ed. 1961; MChOrth Liverp. 1969; FRCS Ed. 1967. (Ed.) Cons. Orthop. Surg. Prev: Cons. Orthop. Surg. Fife Orthop. Serv.

DEAN, Brian Edwin Ash Cottage, 77 Front Road, Drumbo, Lisburn BT27 5JX — MB BCh BAO 1972 Belf.; MRCGP 1977; DCH Dub. 1975; DRCOG 1974.

DEAN, Charles Richard Glendale Surgery, 19 Glendale Road, Wooler NE71 6DN Tel: 01668 281514 Fax: 01668 281514; Etterick Bank, 18 Queens Road, Wooler NE71 6DR — MB BS 1982 Lond.; BSc (Hons.) Lond. 1979, MB BS 1982; MRCGP 1988; DFFP. (St. Geo.) GP Wooler, N.d. Prev: Course Organiser Boston VTS; GP Alford Lincs.; SHO Rotat. (Med.) Freeman Hosp. Newc.

DEAN, Christine Department Psychiatry, Queen Elizabeth Hospital, Birmingham B15 Tel: 0121 627 2846 Fax: 0121 627 2832; 39 St. James Road, Birmingham B15 1JR Tel: 0121 440 0348 — MD 1984 Ed.; BA Open 1976; MB ChB 1964; MRCPsych 1978. Sen. Lect. Birm. Univ.

DEAN, Donald 13 Virginia Court, Station Parade, Virginia Water GU25 4AF Tel: 01344 844909 — MB ChB 1953 Manch.; FFOM RCP Lond. 1993, MFOM 1978; MFPHM 1989; MFCM 1973; DIH Soc. Apoth. Lond. 1967; DPH Lond. 1965; DTM & H Liverp. 1960. (Manch.) p/t Independant Cons. Occupat.al Phys. Socs: Soc. Occupat. Med. & BMA. Prev: Chief Med. Off. Chamber of Shipping Lond.; Head of Gen. Med. Servs. BP Internat. Ltd. Lond.; Chief Med. Off. Kuwait Oil Co. Ltd. Kuwait.

DEAN, Dora Charity 4 Belmont House, Belmont, Taunton TA1 4QB Tel: 01823 352664 — MB ChB Sheff. 1950. (Sheff.) Socs: BMA.

DEAN, Elizabeth Anne 20 Queens Road, Chislehurst BR7 5AZ Tel: 020 8467 8095 Fax: 020 8467 8095 — MB BS Lond. 1970; MSc Lond. 1982; MRCGP 1975; DObst RCOG 1973. (Univ. Coll. Hosp.) Indep. Cons. Pub. Health Kent. Prev: Dir. Pub. Health Bexley HA.

DEAN, Fiona Katherine The Firs, Ellesmere Road, Wem, Shrewsbury SY4 5TU — MB BS 1993 Lond.

DEAN, Miss Fiona Margaret Paybody Eye Unit, Coventry & Warwickshire Hospital, Stoney Stanton Road, Coventry CV1 4FH Tel: 02476 244055; Tel: 01926 814604 — MB BS 1986 Lond.; FRCOphth 1993. (St. Mary's Lond.) Cons. Ophth. & Paediatric Ophth. Coventry and Warks. Hosp., Coventry. Socs: Fell. Roy. Soc. Med.; BMA. Prev: Fell. Paediat. Ophth., Gt. Ormond St. Hosp.; SPR (Ophth) S. Thames Rotat.; REG (Ophth) NE Thames Rotat.

DEAN, Gerald Airethwaite House, 1 Airethwaite, Kendal LA9 4SP Tel: 01539 730435 — MB ChB 1964 Ed.; MRCGP 1977. (Ed.) p/t Benefits Agency Med. Servs. Prev: Upjohn Trav. Fell.sh.ip 1980.

DEAN, Gillian Louise 86 Old Lansdowne Road, Manchester M20 2WX — MB ChB 1991 Manch.; MRCP (UK) 1994.

DEAN, Gillian Shirley South Oxford Health Centre, Lake Street, Oxford OX1 4RP Tel: 01865 244428 Fax: 01865 200985; 6 The Shrubbery, Radley College, Abingdon OX14 2HU Tel: 01235 543086 — BM BCh 1976 Oxf.; BSc Hons Southampton 1971. (Oxford) GP Princip. Lake St. Oxf.; Asst. (Child Health) MalHo. Surg. Abingdon. Prev: Clin. Med. Off. (Child Health) Oxon. HA.

DEAN, Helen Muriel 'Fieldhead', Middleton Avenue, Ilkley LS29 Tel: 01943 4353 — MB ChB St. And. 1947; DPH Ed. 1957. (St. And.) Sen. Deptm. Med. Off. & Dep. MOH Div. I W. Riding CC. Prev: Med. Regist. & Paediat. Regist. Stoke Mandeville Hosp. Aylesbury; Ho. Surg. & Ho. Phys. Roy. Infirm. Bolton.

DEAN, Henrietta Charlotte 40 High Steet, Hemingford Grey, Huntingdon PE28 9BJ — MB BS 1996 Lond.

DEAN, Iona Mary (retired) 12 Porteshill Drive, Shirley, Solihull B90 4DS Tel: 0121 744 4572 — MB ChB 1952 Birm.; DObst

RCOG 1953. Prev: Ho. Phys. & O & G Ho. Surg. Manor Hosp. Walsall.

DEAN, Isabelle Anne Margaret Whiteparish Surgery, Common Road, Whiteparish, Salisbury SP5 2SU Tel: 01794 884269 Fax: 01794 884109 — BM 1980 Soton.; DCH RCP Lond. 1985; DRCOG 1985.

DEAN, Janet Helen Stewart 6 Grant Close, Westhill, Westhill AB32 6LH Tel: 01224 742653 — MB BChir 1984 Camb.; MA Camb. 1986, BA 1982. p/t GP Retainer, Spa Wall Pract., Denburn Health Centre, RoseMt. Viaduct, Aberd. Socs: Assoc. Mem. RCGP; BMA. Prev: Princip. GP Bracknell; Trainee GP Laindon Essex; Trainee GP Aberystwyth VTS.

DEAN, Jeremy Robertson Grailing House, North Cowton, Northallerton DL7 0HF Tel: 01325 378319 — MB BS 1986 Lond.; BSc Lond. 1983; MRCP (UK) 1989; FRCR 1993. (Roy. Free Hosp. Sch. Med.) Cons. Radiol. S. Cleveland Hosp. Middlesbrough. Prev: Sen. Regist. & Regist. (Radiol.) King's Coll. Hosp. Lond.; SHO Rotat. (Med.) Soton.

DEAN, Jill 118 Malden Road, London NW5 4BY Tel: 020 7813 1600 — MB BS 1960 Lond.; MRCS Eng. LRCP Lond. 1960; DObst RCOG 1962. (Univ. Coll. Hosp.)

DEAN, John Department of Clinical Genetics, Medical School, Foresterhill, Aberdeen AB25 2ZD Tel: 01224 552120 Fax: 01224 559390; Email: j.dean@abdn.ac.uk — MB ChB 1981 Ed.; MA Camb. 1993; BA Camb. 1978; FRCP Ed. 1993; MRCP (UK) 1986. (Camb. & Ed.) Cons. Clin. Genetics Grampian Univ. Hosp. NHS Trust; Clin. Sen. Lect. (Med. Genetics) Univ. Aberd. Socs: Amer. Soc. Human Genetics.; Eur. Soc. Human Genet.; Brit. Soc. Human Genetics. Prev: Sen. Regist. (Clin. Genetics) Grampian HB.

DEAN, John Daniel Salisbury Road Surgery, 43 Salisbury Road, Plymouth PL4 8QU Tel: 01752 665879; 15 Garfield Terrace, Stoke, Plymouth PL1 5NU — MB BS 1981 Lond.; MRCGP 1986. (Middlx. Hosp. Med. Sch.) Lect. (Gen. Pract.) Univ. Plymouth; Clin. Asst. (Urodynamics) Derriford Hosp. Plymouth; Dep. Serv. Liaison Off. Devon FHSA Plymouth; Clin. Tutor (Gen. Pract.) Univ. Bristol; RCGP Tutor Plymouth. Socs: Plymouth Med. Soc.; Internat. Continence Soc.

DEAN, John Duncan Royal Bolton Hospitals NHS Trust, Minerva Road, Bolton BL4 0JR Tel: 01204 390531 Fax: 01204 522821; 2 Steynton Close, Heaton, Bolton BL1 5FF Email: john_dd@lineone.net — MB ChB 1982 Leic.; MD Leic. 1993; MRCP (UK) 1985; FRCP 1999. Cons. Phys. with interest in Diabetes Bolton Hosps. NHS Trust.; Clin. Dir. of Med., Bolton Hosps. NHS Trust. Prev: Lect. (Med.) & Hon. Sen. Regist. Univ. Manch.; Regist. (Med.) Univ. Hosp. Wales; Clin. Research Off. Univ. Wales Coll. Med. Cardiff.

DEAN, John Henry, TD (retired) 48 Gretton Court, Girton, Cambridge CB3 0QN — MRCS Eng. LRCP Lond. 1939; MA, MD Camb. 1953, MB BChir 1939; FRCPath 1965. Prev: Cons. Pathol. Newmarket Gen. Hosp.

DEAN, John William Royal Devon & Exeter Hospital, Barrack Road, Exeter EX2 5DS Tel: 01392 402273 Fax: 01392 402273 — BM 1979 Soton.; DM Soton. 1989; MRCP (UK) 1982. Cons. Cardiol. Roy. Devon & Exeter Hosp. Socs: Brit. Cardiac Soc.; Brit. Pacing & Electrophysiol. Gp. Prev: Sen. Regist. Roy. Lond. Hosp.

DEAN, Karen Margaret Lesley Doctors Residence, St. Lukes Hospital, Bradford BD5 — MB ChB 1983 Leeds; DA (UK) 1985. SHO (Paediat.) Pontefract Roy. Infirm. Prev: SHO (Anaesth. & O & G) Bradford HA; Ho. Off. (Gen. Med.) Huddersfield HA.

DEAN, Kevin Malcolm Wright and Partners, Heald Green Medical Centre, Finney Lane, Heald Green, Cheadle SK8 3JD Tel: 0161 436 8448 Fax: 0161 493 9268; 7 Haddon Close, Alderley Grove SK9 7RD Tel: 01625 585480 — MB BCh 1981 Wales; MRCGP 1985.

DEAN, Leonard Charlton, MBE, MC (retired) Danesford, Streets Lane, Crow, Ringwood BH24 3EY Tel: 01425 473868 — MB BS Lond. 1952. Prev: Occupat. Health Phys. Odstock Hosp. Salisbury.

DEAN, Lindsay Anne The Medical Centre TN1 1JU Tel: 01892 529601; 20 St. Andrews Park Road, Southborough, Tunbridge Wells TN4 0NL Tel: 01892 517198 — MB BS 1988 Lond.; MRCGP 1993; DCH Lond. 1996. (St. Bart.) p/t GP on Retainer Scheme; Staff Grade Community Paediat. S. W. Kent Primary Care Trust. Child Health Dept. Homeopathic Hosp., Ch. Rd Tunbridge Wells, Kent. Socs: RCGP; BMA. Prev: Trainee GP Hemel Hempstead VTS.

DEAN, Lionel Jeremy Melrose Surgery, 73 London Road, Reading RG1 5BS Tel: 0118 959 5200 Fax: 0118 950 7726; 26 Grosvenor Road, Caversham, Reading RG4 5EN Tel: 01734 472513 — MB BS 1982 Lond.; DRCOG 1985. Prev: Trainee GP St. Alban's VTS.

DEAN, Lucy Joan (retired) 3 Glenside Cottages, High St., Bidborough, Tunbridge Wells TN3 0UP Tel: 01892 537761 — MRCS Eng. LRCP Lond. 1950.

DEAN, Lynda Helen Wards Medical Practice, 25 Dundonald Road, Kilmarnock KA1 1RU Tel: 01563 526514 Fax: 01563 573558; 139 Dundonald Road, Kilmarnock KA1 1UG — MB ChB 1981 Glas.; DRCOG 1983; DFFP 1997. (Glasgow) Instruc. Doctors in Family Plann.

DEAN, Michael Robin, Surg. Cdr. RN Institute of Naval Medicine, Alverstoke, Gosport PO12 2DL Tel: 023 92 768026 Fax: 023 92 504823 Email: mrdean@msn.com; 25 Ashburton Road, Alverstoke, Gosport PO12 2LH Tel: 023 95 582503 — MB BCh 1975 Wales; MFOM RCP Lond. 1995; MRCGP 1979; DRCOG 1978. (Cardiff) Cons. (Occupat. Phys.) Inst. Naval Med. Submarine & Radiat. Med. Div. Alverstoke, Gosport. Socs: BMA; Soc. Occupat. Med. Prev: Princip. Med. Off. FasLa. Naval Base Scotl.; Sen. Med. Off. (Submarine Med.) Undersea Med. Dept. Inst. Naval Med. Alverstoke, Gosport; Med. Off. (Occupat. Health) FasLa. Naval Base Scotl.

DEAN, Michael Ronald Elson 1 St Catherine's Drive, Radbrook, Shrewsbury SY3 6AR Tel: 01743 246142 — MB BChir 1961 Camb.; MB Camb. 1962, BChir 1961; BA Camb. 1962; FRCR 1992; DMRD Eng. 1965. (Westm.) Cons. Radiol. Roy. Shrewsbury Hosp.; Mem. (Counc.) Roy. Coll. Radiol. Socs: (Chairm.) Brit. Soc. Interven. Radiol. Prev: Sen. Regist., Ho. Surg. & Phys. X-Ray Dept. W.m. Hosp. Lond.

DEAN, Mohammed Rafy 2 Rushout Avenue, Kenton, Harrow HA3 0AR Tel: 020 8907 9341 Fax: 202 8909 9599 Mobile: 07831 273 888 Email: mrdean@pgen.net — MRCS Eng. LRCP Lond. 1971; FFA RCS Eng. 1979; DA Eng. 1978. (Kings Coll. Hosp.) Prev: Cons. Anaesth. Manor Hse. Hosp. Lond.

DEAN, Naeem 8 Godmond Hall Drive, Worsley, Manchester M28 1YF — MB BS 1985 Punjab.

DEAN, Nicola Ruth Department of Anatomy, Queen Mary & Westfield College, Mile End Road, London E1 4NS; 30B Thorn Lane, Leeds LS8 1NF — MB ChB 1993 Leeds.

DEAN, Paul Richard Victoria Surgery, Victoria Street, Bury St Edmunds IP33 3BD Tel: 01284 725550 Fax: 01284 725551 — MB BS 1974 Lond.; BSc Lond. 1971, MB BS 1974; MRCP (UK) 1979; MRCGP 1982; DRCOG 1982. (Lond. Hosp.) Prev: Regist. (Med.) Lond. Hosp.; Regist. (Chest Med. Unit) Papworth Hosp. Camb.

DEAN, Peter John 30 Longlands, Worthing BN14 9NN — MB BS 1990 Lond.

DEAN, Peter Joseph 81 Victoria Park Road, London E9 7NA Tel: 020 8986 2035 — MB BS 1982 Lond.; BDS (Hons.) Lond. 1975; LLM 1992; DRCOG 1985. HM Coroner Essex No. 2 Dist.; Forens. Med. Examr. Socs: Fell. Roy. Soc. Med. (Hon. Sec.) Sect. Clin. Forens. Med. Prev: SHO (Paediat.) Newham Gen. Hosp. Lond.; SHO (O & G) Whipps Cross Hosp. Lond.; SHO (A & E) St. Bart. Hosp. Lond.

DEAN, Raymond Thomas Wards Medical Practice, 25 Dundonald Road, Kilmarnock KA1 1RU Tel: 01563 526514 Fax: 01563 573558; The Wards, 25 Dundonald Road, Kilmarnock KA1 1RU — MB ChB 1981 Glas.; DCH RCP Glas. 1984.

DEAN, Richard 28 Endcliffe Avenue, Scunthorpe DN17 2RD — MB BS 1986 Lond.

DEAN, Richard Michael 5 Blacksmith's Hill, Sanderstead, South Croydon CR2 9AZ — MB BS 1988 Lond.

DEAN, Richard Paul Torridge Medical Services Ltd, Occupational Health Unit, Bidna Yard, Appledore, Bideford EX39 1LX Tel: 01237 425755 Fax: 01237 423911; Springdale, Daddon Hill, Northam, Bideford EX39 3PW Tel: 01237 476550 — MB BS 1971 Lond.; MRCP (UK) 1979; AFOM RCP Lond. 1992; DFFP 1993; DRCOG 1977; DCH Eng. 1975. (St. Geo.) Med. Dir. Torridge Occupat. Med. Servs. Ltd; Occupat. Phys. N.. Devon Healthcare Trust; Occupat. Phys. Devon Co. Counc. Socs: Brit. Occupat. Hyg. Soc.; Inst. Occupat. Safety & Health; Brit. Soc. of Allergy & Clin. Immunol. Prev: Regist. (Med.) Univ. Hosp. Wales Cardiff; SHO (Cardiol.) Papworth & Addenbrooke's Hosps. Camb.; Clin. Allergist N. Devon Dist. Hosp.

DEAN, Richard Simon (retired) The Health Centre, Woolpit, Bury St Edmunds IP30 9QU Tel: 01359 240298 Fax: 01359 241975 — MB Camb. 1961, BChir 1960. Prev: Gen. Practioner.

DEAN, Sandra 27 St Austell Road, Parkhall, Walsall WS5 3EF — MB ChB 1972 Glas.; BSc Glas. 1972; FRCP Lond. 1996; FRCP Glas. 1989. Cons. Phys. (Clin. Pharmacol.) Walsall Manor Hosp.

DEAN, Sheila Margaret (retired) 12 Mansionhouse Road, Edinburgh EH9 1TZ Tel: 0131 667 2504 — MB ChB 1949 Ed.; FRCGP 1984, M 1965; Cert. JCC Lond. 1977.

DEAN, Simon John Park Surgery, Albion Way, Horsham RH12 1BG Tel: 01403 217100; 8 Wimblehurst Road, Horsham RH12 2ED Tel: 01403 268166 — MB BS Lond. 1981; DCH RCP Lond. 1986.

DEAN, Sophie Caroline Tenterfield, Slip Mill Road, Hawkhurst, Cranbrook TN18 4JT — MB BS 1998 Lond.; MB BS Lond 1998.

DEAN, Stephanie Jane 1 Accentors Close, Alton GU34 2LH — BM 1998 Soton.

DEAN, Stephen George Little Court, 15 Manor Park, Leeds LS14 3BW — MB ChB 1981 Leeds; FRCA 1990; DA (UK) 1987. Cons. Anaesth. (Intens. Care) St. Jas. Univ. Hosp. NHS Trust Leeds.

DEAN, Susan 174 Longmeanygate, Midge Hall, Leyland, Preston PR26 6TD — MB ChB 1987 Liverp.; MRCOG 1993.

DEAN, Susan Elizabeth Dorset Cancer Centre, Poole Hopital NHS Trust, Poole BH15 2JB Tel: 01202 442491 Fax: 01202 448259; 21 Ashwood Drive, Broadstone, Poole BH18 8LN Tel: 01202 659980 Email: suedean@onchome.plus.com — MB BS 1972 Lond.; MRCS Eng. LRCP Lond. 1972; FRCR 1977. (Char. Cross) Cons. Clin. Oncologist Poole Hosp. NHS Trust. Prev: Sen. Regist. (Radiother.) St Lukes Hosp. Guildford; Regist. (Radiother.) St Lukes Hosp. Guildford & Char. Cross. Hosp.; Lond.

DEAN, Timothy Adrian Grosvenor 11 St Johns Mews, St Johns Chase, Wakefield WF1 2QY — MB ChB 1993 Leeds.

DEAN, Trevor Stephen 14 Biscay House, Mile End Road, London E1 4QU — MB BS 1981 Lond.; MRCGP 1985; DRCOG 1984.

DEAN, William Michael Forbes Beech Corner, Hemphill Road, Moscow, Galston KA4 8PS — MB ChB 1980 Dundee; FFR RCSI 1990. Cons. Radiol. CrossHo. Hosp. Kilmarnock.

DEAN, Yasmin 33 Corringham Road, London NW11 7BS Tel: 020 8381 4415 — MRCS Eng. LRCP Lond. 1984; FCAnaesth. 1990. (Sheff.) Prev: Locum Cons. (Anaesth) Guy's Hosp. Lond; Locum Cons. (Anaesth) Lewisham Hosp. Lond; Sen. Regist. (Anaesth.) Guy's Hosp. Lond.

DEAN, Zaka-Ud Malden Road Surgery, 118 Malden Road, London NW5 4BY Tel: 020 7813 1600 — MB BS 1955 Lond.; BSc Lond. 1950, MB BS 1955. (St. Geo.)

DEAN REVINGTON, Philippa Jane Honey Hall, Honey Hall Lane, Congresbury, Bristol BS49 5JX — MB BCh 1978 Wales.

DEANE, Alan George St. George's Hospital, Stafford ST16 3AG Tel: 01785 257888 Fax: 01785 246214 — MB ChB 1976 Birm.; MRCPsych 1983. Cons. Psychiat. St. Geo. Hosp. Stafford.

DEANE, Alexander Michael 36 Castlemaine Avenue, South Croydon CR2 7HR Tel: 020 8688 5603 — MB BS 1997 Lond. (UMDS)

DEANE, Anne Miriam 85 College Road, Norwich NR2 3JP — MB BCh BAO 1983 NUI; MRCP (UK) 1986.

DEANE, Mr Anthony Michael 24 Julian Road, Folkestone CT19 5HW Tel: 01303 220607 — MB BS 1974 Lond.; FRCS Eng. 1979; FRCS Ed. 1978; MRCS Eng. LRCP Lond. 1974. Cons. Urol. William Harvey Hosp. Ashford & Buckland Hosp. Dover. Prev: Sen. Regist. (Urol.) Addenbrooke's Hosp. Camb. & Norf. & Norwich Hosp.; Regist. (Urol.) Norf. & Norwich Hosp. & Inst. Urol. Lond.

DEANE, Caroline Jane The Medical Centre, Kingston Avenue, East Horsley, Leatherhead KT24 6QT Tel: 01483 284151 Fax: 01483 285814; Merlin House, Falconwood, East Horsley, Leatherhead KT24 5EG — MB BCh BAO 1987 Belf.

DEANE, Damien Michael Shantallow Health Centre, Racecourse Road, Londonderry BT48 8NL Tel: 028 7135 3054 — MB BCh BAO 1989 Belf.; MRCGP 1994; DRCOG 1993; DCH RCPSI 1992.

DEANE, Ernest William (retired) 17 Avon Run Road, Friars Cliff, Christchurch BH23 4DX Tel: 01425 275762 Email: bill.deane@tesco.net — MRCS Eng. LRCP Lond. 1943; MA, MB BChir Camb. 1946. JP. Prev: Ho. Surg. & Ho. Phys. Lond. Hosp.

DEANE, Mr Graham Heatherwood Hospital, Ascot SL5 7JL Tel: 01344 623333; The Lodge, Uplands Park, Sheringham NR26 8NE Tel: 01263 824672, 01344 622160 — MB BS 1962 Lond.; MSc (Biomechanics) Surrey 1970; FRCS Eng. 1967; MRCS Eng. LRCP Lond. 1962. (Westm.) Cons. Orthop. Heatherwood & Wexham Pk. Hosps. Trust; Vis. Lect. Dept. Mechanical Engin. Univ. Surrey, Guildford. Socs: Fell. BOA; Brit. Orthop. Research Soc.; Brit. Assn. of Surg. of the Knee (BASK). Prev: Cons. Orthop. Oxf. Orthop. Engin. Centre Nuffield Orthop. Centre Oxf.; Lect. (Orthop. Surg.) Nuffield Dept. Orthop. Surg. Univ. Oxf.

DEANE, Haydn John Harwood c/o P & O Medical Department, Richmond House, Terminus Terrace, Southampton SO14 3PN Tel: 02380 534208 Fax: 02380 534210; 33 Fort Road, Helen's Bay, Bangor BT19 1TR Tel: 01247 852569 Fax: 01247 852569 — MB BCh BAO 1975 Belf. (Qu. Univ. Belf.) P & O Lines Ships Doctor. Socs: BMA; SOM.

DEANE, Helen Lesley Eastcote 50 Brooklands Park, London SE3 9BL — BM BCh 1998 Oxf.; BM BCh Oxf 1998.

DEANE, Mr James Stuart 62 South Knighton Road, Leicester LE2 3LP Email: jd31@le.ac.uk — MB BS 1988 Lond.; FRCOphth 1993. (St. Geo. Hosp. Med. Sch.) Lect. Ophth. (Hon. Specialist Regist.) Leics. Socs: Midl. Ophth. Soc.; Ophth. Trainees Gp. RCOphth. Prev: SHO (Ophth.) Leicester Roy. Infirm.; SHO (Ophth.) Wolverhampton & Midl. Counties Eye Infirm.

DEANE, Judith Frances Oak Hall Surgery, 41-43 High Street, New Romney TN28 8BW Tel: 01797 362106 Fax: 01797 366495; 24 Julian Road, Folkestone CT19 5HW Tel: 01303 220607 — MB BS 1974 Lond.; MRCS Eng. LRCP Lond. 1974; MRCGP 1978; DCH Eng. 1977; DObst RCOG 1976.

DEANE, Lorraine Sylvia Breydon, 102 Bloomfield Road, Bath BA2 2AP Tel: 01225 29221 — MB BCh 1962 Wales. Clin. Asst. Ophth. Bath Health Dist. Prev: Asst. Lect. Path. Welsh Nat. Sch. Med. Cardiff.

DEANE, Mr Malcolm 2 Regent Street, Nottingham NG1 5BQ Tel: 0115 947 4755 Fax: 0115 958 7098; West Lodge, West Gate, Southwell NG25 0JN Tel: 01636 813363 Fax: 01636 813363 — MB BS 1957 Lond.; FRCS Eng. 1966; MRCS Eng. LRCP Lond. 1957. (Westm.) Emerit. Cons. Plastic & Jaw Surg. Nottm. City Hosp., Univ. Hosp. Nottm., Derbysh. Roy. Infirm. & Mansfield & Dist. Gen. Hsop.; Clin. Teach. Nottm. Univ. Med. Sch.; Vis. Prof. Plastic Surg. Univ. Miami, USA:. Socs: Brit. Assn. Plastic Surg. & Brit. Assn. Aesthetic Plastic; (Ex-Vice Pres.) Assn. Head & Neck Oncol. Gt. Brit.; Notts. M-C. Soc. Prev: Pres. Plastic Surg. Sect. Roy. Soc. Med.; Sen. Regist. (Reconstruc. & Jaw Surg.) United Bristol Hosps. & Frenchay Hosp. Bristol.; Vice pres Assn Head & neck Oncol. Gt Brit.

DEANE, Marie Elizabeth Florence 1 Birkdale Avenue, Lindley Park, Lindley, Huddersfield HD3 3WB; 16 Blackmoor Drive, West Derby, Liverpool L12 8RA — MB ChB 1988 Leeds; FRCA 1995.

DEANE, Martin Gerard Maphoner Surgery, Maphoner Road, Mullaghbawn, Newry BT35 9TR — MB BCh BAO 1988 Belf.

DEANE, Meryl Department of Radiology, Freeman Hospital, Newcastle upon Tyne — MB BS 1982 Lond.; MFPHM RCP (UK) 1992; DA (UK) 1984. Prev: Cons. Pub. Health Med. Tees Health Auth.; Lect. (Pub. Health Med.) Univ. Hull; Hon. Cons. E. Riding Health.

DEANE, Murray Hayden Knapp Croft, Knapp Lane, Romsey SO51 9BT — MB ChB 1961 Manch.

DEANE, Mr Robert Fletcher 27 Bellshaugh Lane, Glasgow G12 0PE Tel: 0141 334 8102 Fax: 0141 339 0489 Email: deane@bellshaugh.demon.co.uk — MB ChB 1962 Glas.; MSc Glas. 1965; FRCS Glas. 1984; FRCS Ed. 1967. (Glas.) Cons. Urol. W.. Infirm. Glas. & Gartnavel Gen. Hosp. Glas. Socs: Brit. Assn. Urol. Surgs. Presidenr 1998 -2000; Amer. Urological Soc. (Hon. Mem.). Prev: Sen. Regist. (Gen. Surg.) Bradford Roy. Infirm.; Regist. (Gen. Surg.) W.. Infirm. Glas.; SHO (Gen. Surg.) S.. Gen. Hosp. Glas.

DEANE, Shelley Elizabeth 3 Prudden Close, Elstow, Bedford MK42 9EB — MB ChB 1993 Cape Town.

DEANE, Terence Horton Walker The Surgery, 29 Thurloe Street, London SW7 2LQ Tel: 020 7584 6771 Fax: 020 7589 1591 — MRCS Eng. LRCP Lond. 1969; MB BCh BAO 1972; MFHom 1985. Tutor to Long Course Roy. Lond. Homoeop. Hosp. Lond.

DEANEY, Carl Nigel Western Grange, 12 Brent Av, Didcot OX11 7UD — MB BS 1997 Lond.

DEANFIELD, Professor John Eric Tel: 020 7404 5094 Fax: 020 7813 8263 Email: j.deanfield@ich.ucl.ac.uk — MB BChir 1975 Camb.; BA Camb. 1972; FRCP Lond. 1993; MRCP (UK) 1977. Cons. Cardiol. Hosp. for Sick Childr. Gt. Ormond St.; Prof. (Cardiol) UCL; Cons. Cardiol., Middlx. Hosp. Socs: Brit. Cardal Soc.; Assn. of Europ. Paediatric Cardiol.s; Europ. Soc. of Cardiol., Fell. Prev: Sen. Regist. Hosp. Sick Childr. Lond.; MRC Fell. Hammersmith Hosp. Lond.; SHO Hammersmith Hosp.

DEANS, Adrienne Kerri 2 Tollohill Crescent, Kincorth, Aberdeen AB12 5DS — MB BS 1994 Melbourne.

DEANS, Andrew Jonathan 11 Millfields, Nantwich CW5 5HS — MB BS 1993 Lond.

DEANS, Anne Catherine Vikings, Danes Hill, Woking GU22 7HQ — MB BS 1983 Lond.; MFFP 1993; MRCGP (Distinc.) 1987; MRCOG 1991; DCH RCP Lond. 1987. Cons. (O & G) Frimley Pk. Hosp., Surrey. Socs: Fell. Roy. Soc. Med. Prev: Sen. Regist. (O & G) Frimley Pk. Hosp. & Univ. Coll. Hosp. Lond.

DEANS, Charlotte Louise 6 Hill Farm Cottages, Huntington Rd, Lolworth, Cambridge CB3 8DW — MB BS 1996 Lond.

***DEANS, Derek Andrew Christopher** Langlee, Roadhead, Hawick TD9 7HR — MB ChB 1998 Ed.; MB ChB Ed 1998.

DEANS, Mr Gordon Taylor Stepping Hill Hospital, Poplar Grove, Stockport SK2 7JE Tel: 0161 483 1010; 71 Bramhall Lane S., Bramhall, Stockport SK7 2EG Tel: 0161 440 8820 — MB BCh 1982 Belf.; MD Belf. 1991; FRCS Eng. 1987; FRCS Ed. 1986; FRCSI 1986. (Qu. Univ. Belf.) Cons. Surg. Stepping Hill Hosp. Stockport.

DEANS, Heather Elizabeth 154 Hamilton Place, Aberdeen AB15 5BB Tel: 01224 641596; 154 Hamilton Place, Aberdeen AB15 5BB Tel: 01224 641596 — MB ChB 1977 Aberd.; FRCR 1985; DMRD Aberd. 1981. Cons. Radiol. Grampian Univ. Hosp.s Trust.

DEANS, James Craig Dunain Hospital, Inverness IV3 8JU Tel: 01463 242860; 29 West Heather Gardens, Inverness IV2 4DZ — MB ChB 1981 Aberd.; MPhil Ed. 1993; MRCPsych 1988. Assoc. Med. Dir. & Cons. Psychiat. Highland Comm. NHS Trust Inverness.

DEANS, James Pollock Orcadie, Dixonfield, Thurso KW14 8YN Tel: 01847 892666 — MB ChB Glas. 1955; AFOM RCP Lond. 1981; CIH Dund 1975. GP Thurso; Police Surg. Thurso. Prev: Ho. Phys. Lewis Hosp. Stornoway; Ho. Surg. Bridge of Earn Hosp. & Airthrey Castle Matern. Hosp.

DEANS, Joan Saidie 54 Beach Crescent, South Terrace, Littlehampton BN17 5NT — MB BCh BAO Belf. 1942. (Qu. Univ. Belf.) Socs: BMA. Prev: Flight Lt. Med. Off. RAF; Regist. (Anaesth.) W. Middlx. Hosp. Isleworth; Anaesth. Grad. Hosp. Univ. Penna. & Kings Co. Hosp. Univ. New York State.

DEANS, Mr Jonathan Andre James ENT Department, Leighton Hospital, Leighton, Crewe CW1 4QJ Tel: 01270 612084 — MB BS 1978 Lond.; FRCS Ed. 1987; MRCS Eng. LRCP Lond. 1977. (St. Mary's) Cons. ENT Surg. Mid Chesh. & E. Chesh. NHS Trust. Socs: Chairm. S. Chesh. Research and Ethics Comm..; Fell. Roy. Soc. Med.; Brit. Assn. Otol. Prev: Cons. ENT Surg. HM Armed Forces (Army); Sen. Regist. (Otolaryngol.) Freeman Hosp. Newc. u. Tyne.

DEANS, Mrs Madeline (retired) Helens Lodge, Inshes, Inverness IV2 5BG Tel: 01463 32304 — MB ChB 1951 Aberd.; DPH 1954. Prev: Asst. MOH Inverness-sh.

DEANS, Mandy Braidmhor, 7 Thistle Avenue, Grangemouth FK3 8YH — MB ChB 1998 Aberd.; MB ChB Aberd 1998.

DEANS, Nicola Jane Braidmhor, 7 Thistle Avenue, Grangemouth FK3 8YH — MB ChB 1996 Ed.

DEANS, Rachel Ann 1 Lonsdale Ter, Edinburgh EH3 9HN — MB ChB 1997 Ed.

DEANS, Robert Magnus (retired) 63 Thistlecroft, Ingol, Preston PR2 7BT Tel: 01772 732852 Email: rmdeans@supanet.com — MRCS Eng. LRCP Lond. 1963. Prev: Med. Off. i/c Dept. Audiometry Preston HA & Chorley & S. Ribble HA.

DEANS, Shona Patricia Calsayseat Medical Group, 2 Calsayseat Road, Aberdeen AB25 3UY Tel: 01224 634345 Fax: 01224 620210 Email: shona.deans@calsayseat.grampian.scot.nhs.uk — MB ChB 1986 Aberd.; MRCGP 1990. (Aberdeen) p/t Gen. Practitioner Calsayseat Med. Gp., Aberd. Prev: Trainee GP Aberd. VTS; SHO Roxburghe Hse. Aberd.; Ho. Off. (Orthop.) Raigmore Hosp.

DEANS, William James Douglas Skerryvore Practice, Health Centre, New Scapa Road, Kirkwall KW15 1BQ Tel: 01856 885440 Fax: 01856 870043 — MB ChB 1986 Glas.; BSc (Hons.) St. And. 1983. Socs: Roy. Coll. Gen. Pract. Prev: Med. Off. RN; Trainee GP Paisley VTS; Ho. Off. Glas. Roy. Infirm.

DEAR, Nicolas Paul Matheson Newmains Health Centre, 17 Manse Road, Newmains, Wishaw ML2 9AX Tel: 01698 384482 Fax: 01698 387456; 3 Conservation Place, Wishaw ML2 8EF Tel: 01698 355005 — MB ChB 1985 Dundee. Prev: Trainee GP StoneHo. VTS.

DEAR, Nigel John 175 Send Road, Send, Woking GU23 7ET Tel: 01483 223784 — MB BS 1987 Lond.

DEAR, Peter Robert Frederick 59 The Drive, Roundhay, Leeds LS8 1JQ Email: prfd@doctors.org.uk — MB BS 1968 Lond.; FRCPCH 1997; MD Lond. 1980; FRCP Lond. 1987, M 1975; DCH Eng. 1973. Cons. Neonat. Paediat. St. Jas. Univ. Hosp. Leeds.

DEARDEN, Andrew Richard c/o British Medical Association, BMA House, Tavistock Square, London WC1H 9JP; 23 Llwyd Coed, Cardiff CF14 7TT — MB BCh 1988 Wales. GP Roathwell Surg., Cardiff; Chair, BMA Community Care Comm.

DEARDEN, Anthony Martyn Aire Court Communitiy Unit, Lingwell Grove, Middleton, Leeds LS10 4BS Tel: 0113 277 4661 — MB ChB 1981 Leeds; MRCPsych 1986. Cons. Psychiat. Leeds Community & Ment. Health NHS Trust; Hon. Sen. Clin. Lect. Univ. Leeds.

DEARDEN, Christine Hazel 21 Rosetta Drive, Belfast BT7 3HL Tel: 028 640093 — MB BCh BAO 1973 Belf.; FRCS Ed. 1980. Cons. (A & E Med.) Roy. Vict. Hosp. Belf.

DEARDEN, Janet Camilla 100A Uplands Road, London N8 9NJ — MB BS 1995 Lond.

DEARDEN, Norman Mark Nan Tan House, Dixon Lane, Wortley, Leeds LS12 4AD Fax: 0113 279 8979 Email: richarddearden@aol.com — MB ChB 1977 Leeds; BSc Leeds 1974; BSc Leeds 1974; FFA RCS 1981. Cons. Anaesth. Leeds Gen. Infirm. Socs: Sec. Europ. Brian Injury Consortium. Prev: Cons. Neuroanaesth. & Sen. Lect. Univ. Edin.; Lect. (Anaesth.) Univ. Leeds.

DEARDEN, Vera Alice Brentwood, Hallroyd Road, Todmorden OL14 — M.B., Ch.B. Manch. 1946.

DEARDON, Mr David John Standerton, Seymour Drive, Plymouth PL3 5AT — BM 1984 Soton.; FRCS Ed. 1989; FRCS Eng. 1989.

DEARING, Janette 63 Manor Road, Worthing BN11 4SE — MB ChB 1982 Manch. Clin. Asst. (Anaesth.) Worthing & S.lands NHS Trust.

DEARING, Nicola Clare 314 Watford Road, St Albans AL2 3DW — BM BS 1995 Nottm.; BMedSci 1993; MRCP 1999.

DEARING, Ruth Millicent (retired) The Old Police House, Canonbie DG14 0UX Tel: 01387 371716 — MB BS Durh. 1943; MD Durh. 1953; DObst RCOG 1946.

DEARLOVE, John Charles Yeovil District Hospital, Higher Kingston, Yeovil BA21 4AT Tel: 01935 707540 Fax: 01935 707208 Email: morgw@msmail.esomerset-tr.swest.nhs.uk; Wynford Farm, Lower Halstock Leigh, Yeovil BA22 9QX Tel: 01935 891519 Fax: 01935 891880 Email: john.dearlove@virgin.net — MB BS 1971 Lond.; FRCP Canada 1977; MRCP (UK) 1980; MRCPCH 1997. (St. Bart.) Cons. Paediat. Yeovil Gen. Hosp. Socs: Neonat. Soc. Prev: Cons. Paediat. N. Sefton & W. Lancs. HA; Sen. Regist. (Paediat.) Char. Cross Hosp. Lond.

DEARLOVE, Oliver Raymond 146 The Green, Worsley, Manchester M28 2PA Tel: 0161 728 5685 Fax: 0161 794 0719 Email: o.dearlove@man.ac.uk — MB 1977 Camb.; MA Camb. 1977, BA 1973, MB 1977, BChir 1976; FFA RCS Eng. 1983; FFA RCSI 1982; DRCOG 1980; DA 1980. (Camb. & St. Bart.) Cons. Anaesth. & Hon. Lect. (Paediat. Anaesth.) Roy. Manch. Childr. Hosp.

DEARNALEY, David Paul Institute of Cancer Research, Royal Marsden Hospital, Downs Road, Sutton SM2 5PT Tel: 020 8642 6011 Fax: 020 8643 8809; 7 Hill Road, Carshalton Beeches, Carshalton SM5 3RA Tel: 020 8773 0153 — MD 1984 Camb.; MA MB 1976, BChir 1975; FRCP Lond. 1994; MRCP (UK) 1978; FRCR 1985. Reader in Prostate Cancer Studies & Hon. Cons. Inst. Cancer Research & Roy. Marsden Hosp. Surrey & Lond.; Head (Urol.) Roy. Marsden NHS Trust. Prev: Vice-Dean (Clin.) Inst. Cancer Research.; Clin. Scientist Ludwig Inst. Cancer Research (Lond. Br.); Regist. & Sen. Regist. (Radiother. & Oncol.) Roy. Marsden Hosps. Surrey & Lond.

DEARNALEY, Josephine Mary Margaret Sutton Child & Family Clinic, Robin Hood Lane Health Centre, Camden Road, Sutton

SM1 2SH Tel: 020 8770 6781; 7 Hill Road, Carshalton Beeches, Carshalton SM5 3RA Tel: 0208 773 0153 — MB ChB 1977 Dundee; MRCPsych 1983. Assoc. Specialist Child & Adolesc. Psychiat. Merton & Sutton Community Trust. Socs: BMA; MDU. Prev: Clin. Med. Off. (Child Health & Child Psychiat.) Merton & Sutton Community Trust; Clin. Asst. (Child Psychiat.) W. Middlx. Hosp. Isleworth; Regist. (Psychiat.) St. Geo. Hosp. Lond.

DEARY, Ian John Department of Psychology, University of Edinburgh, 7 George Square, Edinburgh EH8 9JZ Tel: 0131 650 3452 Fax: 0131 650 6512; 192 Craigleith Road, Edinburgh EH4 2EE Tel: 0131 332 6524 — MB ChB 1983 Ed.; PhD Ed. 1992; BSc Ed. 1980; MRCPsych 1990. Reader (Psychol.) Univ. Edin. Socs: Assoc. Fell. Brit. Psychol. Soc.; Brit. Assn. Psychopharmacol. Prev: Lect. (Psychol.) Univ. Edin.; SHO (Psychiat.) Maudsley Hosp. & Bethlem Roy. Hosp. Lond.; Regist. (Psychiat.) Roy. Edin. Hosp.

DEAS, Ewan David Hope Family Medical Centre, Hawarden Road, Hope, Wrexham LL12 9NL Tel: 01978 760468 Fax: 01978 760774 — MB ChB 1979 Birm.; MRCGP 1991; DRCOG 1983. GP Hope Clwyd. Prev: GP Trainee S. Clwyd VTS.

DEAS, Jill West Point Medical Centre, 167-169 Slade Lane, Levenshulme, Manchester M19 2AF Tel: 0161 248 5100; 5 Fog Lane, Didsbury, Manchester M20 6AX — MB ChB 1991 Manch.; BSc (Med. Sci.) St. And. 1989; DRCOG 1996; DFFP 1996; MRCGP 1998. (St. Andrews and Manchester) p/t GP Partner W. Point Med. entre Levenshulme Manch. Prev: Job-Share Research Phys. (Asthma & Allergy) N. W. Lung Centre Wythenshawe Hosp. Manch.; GP/Regist. Thornbrook Surg. Chapel-en-le-Frith; SHO (Dermat.) Qu. Vict. Hosp. Morecambe.

DEAS, Kenneth Steven (retired) Church Cottage, Dodleston, Chester CH4 9NG Tel: 01244 660304 — MB ChB 1949 Ed.; FFCM 1972; DPH Ed. 1954.

DEAS, Miles Courtenay Flat 5, Norton Court, Birmingham Women's Hospital, Metchley Park Road, Edgbaston, Birmingham B15 2TG — BM BCh 1996 Oxf.

DEAS, Stephen Cameron Mayfield Surgery, 246 Roehampton Lane, London SW15 4AA Tel: 020 8780 5770/5650 Fax: 020 8780 5649; 19 Enmore Road, Putney, London SW15 6LL Tel: 020 8788 8510 Email: sdeas19e@aol.com — MB BS 1977 Lond.; MA Oxf. 1978; MRCGP 1982; DRCOG 1980. GP Trainer, S. W. Thames Post Grad. Med. Fac.

DEASY, Denise Margaret University Health Service, 5 Lennoxvale, Belfast BT9 5BY Tel: 028 9033 5551 Fax: 028 9033 5540 — MB BCh BAO 1969 NUI. (Cork) Med. Off. Stud. Health Dept. Stranmillis Coll. Belf. Mem. Brit. Stud.; Health Assn. Prev: Resid. (Paediat.) McMaster Univ. Hamilton, Canada; SHO Drug Treatm. & Advis. Centre Jervis St. Hosp. Dub.

DEASY, Henrietta Caroline Angela 16 Red Post Hill, London SE24 9JQ — MB BS 1987 Lond.

DEASY, Jane Marie Longfield Medical Centre, Princes Road, Maldon CM9 5DF Tel: 01621 856811 Fax: 01621 852627 — MB BS 1989 Lond.; MRCGP 1994.

DEASY, Joseph Bartholomew (retired) Little Paddocks, 27 Maple Gardens, Bourne PE10 9DW Tel: 01778 421944 — MB BCh BAO NUI 1947; LM Coombe 1949. Prev: Consult. i/c Leeds & Bradford Mass Radiog. Servs.

DEASY, Neil Patrick King's College Hospital, Denmark Hill, London SE5 9RS — MB BS 1988 Lond.; BSc Lond. 1985; MRCP (UK) 1991.

DEAVALL, Tanya 35 Harberton Crescent, Summersdale, Chichester PO19 4NY — MB BS 1985 Lond.; MA Camb. 1988; MRCGP 1989; DRCOG 1989. Prev: Trainee GP Oxf. VTS.; GP Partner Farnham Surrey.

DEAVILLE, Alison Margaret 12 Melrose Avenue, Stone ST15 8SU — MB ChB 1990 Dundee.

DEB, Alok Kumar Hurrell's Farm, Boxford Lane, Boxford, Sudbury CO10 5JY — MB BS 1967 Calcutta; FRCP Lond. 1993; MRCP (UK) 1973; Dip. BMS Calcutta 1968. (Sir Nilratan Sircar Med. Coll.) Cons. Phys. Geriat. Med. Colchester Gen. Hosp. Socs: Brit. Geriat. Soc.; Roy. Coll. Phys. Lond. Prev: Regist. (Gen. Med.) Sharoe Green Hosp. Fulwood & Pk. Hosp. Daveyhulme; Sen. Regist. (Geriat. Med.) Lond. Hosp.

DEB, Kajal 25 East Butts Road, Etching Hill, Rugeley WS15 2LU — MB BS 1977 Calcutta.

DEB, Nripendra Krishna 19 Ashley Avenue, Ilford IG6 2JF Tel: 020 8551 8189 Fax: 020 8551 8189 — MB BS 1974 Calcutta; T(GP) 1991.

DEB, Saumitra Department of Psychological Medicine, University of Wales College of Medicine, Heath Park, Cardiff CF14 4XN Tel: 029 2056 2323 Fax: 029 20555 047 Email: deb@cardiff.ac.uk — MB BS 1979 Calcutta; MD Leic. 1993; MRCPsych 1986; FRCPsych. 1998. Clin. Sen. Lect. Univ. of Wales Coll. of Med. Prev: Cons. Psychiat. & Hon. Clin. Sen. Lect. Univ. Aberd.; Psychiat. Sen. Regist. Leicester HA; Regist. (Psychiat.) Char. Cross Hosp. Lond. & Univ. Wales.

DEB, Sekhar Horsefair Practice, Horse Fair, Rugeley WS15 2EL Tel: 01889 582244 Fax: 01899 582244 — MB BS 1972 Gauhati.

DEBEER, Philippe James House Flat 12, Residential Village, Bovemoors Lane, Exeter EX2 5DS — MD 1992 Louvain.

DEBELLE, Geoffrey David Birmingham Children's Hospital NHS Trust, Local Medical Services Directorate, Springfields, Raddlebarn Road, Birmingham B29 6JB Tel: 0121 627 1627 Fax: 0121 627 8202 Email: secretary.debelle@bhamchildrens.wmids.nhs.uk; 66 Cotton Lane, Moseley, Birmingham B13 9SE Tel: 0121 449 4564 Email: cotton.debelle@ic24.net — MB BS 1971 Adelaide; FRACP 1981; DObst RCOG 1974; FRCPCH 1997. (Adelaide) Cons. Community Paediat. Birm. Childr. Hosp. NHS Trust; Hon. Sen. Clin. Lect. Inst. Child Health Univ. Birm. Socs: Assn. Child Psychol. & Psychiat.; Roy. Coll. Paediat. & Child Health; Brit. Assn. for Study & Preven. of Child Abuse & Neglect. Prev: Cons. Paediat. Roy. Childr. Hosp. Melbourne; Cons. Paediat. Vict. Aboriginal Health Serv.; Cons. Paediat. Advis. Counc. for Childr. with Impaired Hearing, Vict.

DEBENHAM, Elizabeth Jane Rosann 29 Stourcroft Drive, Christchurch BH23 2PX — MB ChB 1981 Bristol.

DEBENHAM, Sir Gilbert, Bt (retired) Tonerspuddle Farm, Dorchester DT2 7JA — BChir 1935 Camb.; MRCPsych 1971; DPM Eng. 1946.

DEBENHAM, John Alan Robert (retired) Belgic House, White Street Green, Boxford, Sudbury CO10 5JP Tel: 01787 210540 — MB BChir 1945 Camb.; MRCS Eng. LRCP Lond. 1945; DObst RCOG 1949.

DEBENHAM, Matthew James 101 Wheatcroft Grove, Gillingham ME8 9JE — MB BS 1989 Lond.

DEBENHAM, Michael Robert Butchers Lane Surgery, Butchers Lane, Boxford, Sudbury CO10 5DZ Tel: 01787 211821 Fax: 01787 210145 — MB BS 1977 Lond.; MRCS Eng. LRCP Lond. 1977.

DEBENHAM, Phillip John 32C Coton House, Adrian Way, Cambridge CB2 2SD — MB BS 1996 Lond.; BSc (Hons.) Lond. 1993. (Royal Free Hospital School of Medicine London) SHO (Paediat.) Bedford Hosp. Bedford. Prev: Ho. Off. (Gen. Surg./Urol.) Lister Hosp. Stevenage; Ho. Off. Med. Unit Roy. Free Hosp. Hampstead Lond.

DEBENHAM, Susan Elizabeth Granton Medical Centre, 114 Middleton Hall Road, King's Norton, Birmingham B30 1DH Tel: 0121 459 9117 Fax: 0121 486 2889 — MB ChB 1981 Birm.; DRCOG 1984. Lect. Dept. of Gen. Pract. Univ. of Birm. 1996. Prev: Trainee GP Centr. Birm. VTS.

DEBENHAM, Thomas Robert Exmouth Health Centre, Claremont Grove, Exmouth EX8 2JF Tel: 01395 273001 Fax: 01395 273771; Heatherlands, Links Road, Budleigh Salterton EX9 6DG Tel: 01395 445138 — MB ChB 1981 Birm.; MRCGP 1987; DA Eng. 1984; DRCOG 1985. Trainee GP Torbay HA VTS.

DEBONO, Johann Sebastian the Beatson Oncology Centre, Western infirmary, Dumbarton Road, Glasgow G11 6UT Tel: 0141 211 2000 Email: gpmr08@udcf-gla.ac.uk; T/R 22 Polwarth Street, Hyndland, Glasgow G12 9TY Tel: 0141 334 1473 — MB ChB 1989 Glas.; MRCP (UK) 1992; MSc 1999; Phd 1999. (Glasgow) Specialist Regist. Med. Oncol. Clin. Research Fell. Prev: Regist. (Gen. Med. & Haemat.) W.. Infirm. Glas.; SHO Rotat. (Med., Diabetes & Endocrinol.) Monklands Dist. Gen. Hosp. Airdrie.

DEBONO, Martin Albert Calderdale Royal Hosp., Salterhebble, Halifax HX3 0PW Tel: 01422 357171 Fax: 01422 224691 Email: martin.debono@calderdale.nhs.uk; Forge House, Hollin Lane, Ripponden, Halifax HX6 4LH Tel: 01422 825067 — MB ChB 1984 Leeds; FRCOG 2001; MRCOG 1989. Cons. Calderdale Healthcare NHS Trust.

DEBOUTTE, Danielle 6 Highwood Avenue, London N12 8QP — MD 1977 Louvain.

DEBRAH, Kwasi Moses Frimely Park Hospital, Portsmouth Road, Frimley, Camberley GU16 7UJ Tel: 01276 604027 Fax: 01276 604862 — MB BS 1988 Lond.; MRCP (UK) 1992. (Guy's Hospital) Cons. Phys. with an interest in c/o the Elderly Frimley Pk. Hosp. Socs: BMA; BGS. Prev: Sen. Regist. (Gen. & Geriat. Med.) St Thomas' & Kent & Canterbury +Hosps.; Research Fell. Roy. Bournemouth & Soton. Hosp.

DEBRAY, Rajeeb 1 Daleside, Upton, Chester CH2 1EN — MB ChB 1998 Manch.; MB ChB Manch 1998.

DEBUSE, Madeleine Jane Flat 17, 44 Drury Lane, London WC2B 5RX — MB BS 1998 Lond.; MB BS Lond 1998.

DECALMER, Susan Ann Alliston Medical Centre, 28 Crofts Bank Road, Urmston, Manchester M41 0UH Tel: 0161 747 2411 Fax: 0161 747 8841; 10 Cornhill Avenue, Davyhulme, Manchester M41 5SY — MB ChB 1974 Manch.; BSc (Hons.) Anat. Manch. 1971, MB ChB 1974. GP.

DECATRIS, Marios Petrou Department of Clinical Oncology, Christie Hospital NHS Trust, Wilmslow Road, Withington, Manchester M20 4BX Tel: 0161 446 3000 Fax: 0161 446 3478 Email: mdecatris@picr.man.ac.uk — MB ChB 1991 Leic.; BSc (Hons.) Leics. 1988; MRCP (UK) 1995. Clin. Research Fell. (Clin. Oncol.) Christie Hosp. NHS Trust Manch. Socs: Fell.Roy.Soc.med. Prev: SHO (Clin. Med. Oncol.) Roy. Marsden Hosp. Surrey; SHO Rotat. (Med.) Leicester Roy. Infirm.

DECRUZE, Shandya Bridget 153 Oswald Road, Chorlton cum Hardy, Manchester M21 9AZ — MB ChB 1994 Sheff.

DEDICOAT, Martin John 1 Pettyfields Close, Solihull B93 9EG — MB BS 1992 Lond.

DEDMAN, Paul Anthony Priory Hospital Bristol, Heath House Lane, Off Bell Hill, Bristol BS16 1EQ Tel: 0117 952 5255 Fax: 0117 952 5552 Email: paul.dedman@bristol.ac.uk — MB BCh 1980 Wales; MRCGP 1987; MRCPsych 1985. Cons. Psychiat. Priory Hosp. Bristol; Hon. Clin. Teach., Univ. of Bristol. Socs: Brit. Assn. Behavioural & Cognitive Therapists; Bristol Medico-Legal Soc.; BMA. Prev: Cons. Psychiat. United Bristol Healthcare Trust; Cons. Psychiat. Roy. Pk. Hosp, Melbourne & Vis. Assoc. Roy. Melbourne Hosp., Austral.; Regist. Roy. Free Hosp. Lond.

DEDRICK, Simon Haywood New Cross Street Health Centre, New Cross Street, Bradford BD5 7AW Tel: 01274 733232 — BM BCh 1986 Oxf. GP Bradford.

DEE, Gareth 5 St Bartholomew's Gardens, Southsea PO5 1RD — MB BS 1992 Lond.

DEEBLE, Jennifer 52 Longlands Road, Carlisle CA3 9AE — MB BS 1969 Lond.; DMRD Eng. 1973; DObst RCOG 1971. (Roy. Free) Assoc. Specialist (Radiol.) Cumbld. Infirm. Carlisle. Prev: Sen. Regist. (Radiol.) Cumbld. Infirm. Carlisle & N. Staffs. Roy. Infirm. Stoke-on-Trent.

DEEBLE, Terence Jack Haematology Department, Arrowe Park Hospital, Upton, Wirral CH49 5PE Tel: 0151 678 5111 Ext: 2821 Fax: 0151 604 0370; 3 Devisdale Grove, Prenton, Wirral CH43 7NQ Tel: 0151 652 6296 — MB ChB Bristol 1964; FRCPath 1986, M 1973. Cons. Haemat. Wirral Hosp. Trust. Socs: Brit. Soc. Haematol.; Brit. Oncol. Assn.; Brit. Blood Transfus. Soc. Prev: Cons. Haemat. Cumbld. Infirm. Carlisle.

DEEGAN, John 5 Chapel House Road, Newcastle upon Tyne NE5 5AJ Tel: 0191 267 4088 — MB BS 1953 Durh.; DPH 1960. (Durh.) Prev: Sen. Sch. Med. Off. N.ld. CC.; Ho. Phys. Roy. Infirm. Sunderland; Obst. Ho. Off. & Gyn. Ho. Surg. Gen. Hosp. Sunderland.

DEEGAN, Katharine Mary 11 Convent Hill, London SE19 3QY — MB BS 1985 Lond.

DEEGAN, Stephen Paul 2 Barley Green, Barley, Burnley BB12 9JU — MB ChB 1983 Liverp.

DEEGAN, Timothy Francis Centre for Primary Health Care Studies, University of Warwick, Coventry CV4 7AL — MB BS 1992 Lond. Prev: SHO (Paediat.) N.. Gen. Hosp. NHS Trust Sheff.; Trainee GP/SHO Hereford Hosps. NHS Trust VTS.

DEEHAN, David John 19 Stoneywood Park, Londonderry — MB ChB 1989 Ed.

DEEHAN, Josephine Anne Omagh Health Centre, Mountjoy Road, Omagh BT79 7BA Tel: 028 8224 3521 — MB BCh 1987 Dublin; MB BCh Dub 1987. (Dublin) GP Omagh, Co. Tyrone.

DEEHAN, Simon Conor 11/5 Silvermills, Edinburgh EH3 5BF — MB ChB 1991 Ed. SHO (Anaesth.) Stepping Hill Hosp. Stockport. Prev: SHO (A & E) Roy. Vict. Infirm. Newc.

DEEKS, Amanda Jane 10 Sandringham Avenue, Wirral CH47 3BZ — BM 1993 Soton.

DEELEY, David Paul Leagrave Surgery, 37A Linden Road, Luton LU4 9QZ Tel: 01582 572817 — MB ChB 1984 Leic.; BSc Leic. 1981; DFFP. GP Luton. Prev: GP Regist. The Elms Md. Pract. Harpenden; SHO (O & G) Hemel Hempstead Gen. Hosp; SHO (Geriat. Med.) St. Albans City Hosp.

DEEMING, Kay Frances Fulham Road Surgery, 630 Fulham Road, London SW6 5RS Tel: 020 7736 4344 — MB BS 1991 Lond.; BSc (Hons.) Pharmacol. Lond. 1986; MRCGP 1995; DCH RCP Lond. 1993. Clin. Asst. (Rheum.) Char. Cross Hosp. Lond.

DEEN, Chitrakootam Veeraraghavan 9 Osbaldeston Gardens, Newcastle upon Tyne NE3 4JE — MB BS 1969 Madras; MRCP (UK) 1976.

DEENEY, Helena Noreen 1 Talbot Road, London N22 7UA — MB BS 1998 Lond.; MB BS Lond 1998.

DEENEY, Sheila 30 Waterloo Gardens, Belfast BT15 4EY — MB BCh BAO 1991 NUI.

DEENY, Anne Patricia The Green Surgery, 12 The Green, Irish Street, Downpatrick BT30 6BE — MB BCh BAO 1986 Belf.; MRCGP 1990; DRCOG 1990; DGM RCP Lond. 1989.

DEENY, Charles Kieran Mary Carrickmore Health Centre, Termon Road, Carrickmore, Omagh BT79 9JR Tel: 028 8076 1242 — MB BCh BAO 1980 NUI.

DEENY, Elizabeth Mount Alto, Newry Road, Banbridge BT32 — LRCPI & LM, LRSCI & LM 1948; LRCPI & LM, LRCSI & LM 1948.

DEENY, Eugene Dominick Martin Rathmore Clinic, Cliff Road, Belleek, Enniskillen BT93 3FY Tel: 028 6865 8382 Fax: 028 6865 8124; Finner, Belleek, Enniskillen BT93 3FJ Tel: 013656 58689 Fax: 013656 58124 — MB BCh BAO 1976 Dub.; BA Dub. 1976; MRCGP 1988; DRCOG 1980; DCH Dub. 1980. (TC Dub.) Prev: SHO (Obst. & Med.) Altnagelvin Hosp. Lond.derry; Intern Roy. City of Dub. Hosp.

DEENY, Jennifer Emile 12a Manor Court, Common Lane, Radlett WD7 8PU — MB BCh BAO 1971 NUI; MSc Lond. 1980; MFPHM RCP (UK) 1989; MFCM RCP (UK) 1986; FFA RCSI 1976. Cons. Pub. Health Med. Hertfondshire Health Auth.

DEENY, Miriam 15 Abbotsford Avenue, Rutherglen, Glasgow G73 3NX Tel: 0141 201 3682 Fax: 0141 201 3889 Email: miriam.deeny@northglasgow.scot.nhs.uk — MB ChB 1983 Glas.; BSc Glas. 1980; MRCOG 1989. Cons. Gyn. Stobhill Hosp. Glas. Socs: Glas. Obst. & Gyn. Soc. & Brit. Soc. Gyn. Endoscopy. Prev: Sen. Regist. (O & G) Glas. Roy. Infirm.

DEERE, Harriet Mary Rose 5 Beedingwood Drive, Forest Road, Colgate, Horsham RH12 4TE — MB BS 1994 Lond.

DEERE, Jonathan James The Forge, Epworth Road, Haxey, Doncaster DN9 2LF — MB BS 1998 Lond.; MB BS Lond 1998.

DEERING, Alistair Ravenscraig Hospital, Inverkip Road, Greenock PA16 9HA Tel: 01475 633777 Fax: 01475 721547; 99 Finnart Street, Greenock PA16 8HN — MB ChB 1985 Ed.; MRCPsych 1989. Cons. Psychiat. Ravenscraig Hosp. Greenock. Prev: Sen. Regist. Roy. Cornhill Hosp. Aberd.; Sen. Clin. Research Fell. (Psychiat.) & Regist. Roy. Edin. Hosp.

DEERING, Arnold Henri Cheltenham General Hospital, Sandford Road, Cheltenham GL53 7AN Tel: 01242 272046 Fax: 01242 272092 Email: arnold.deering@egnhst.org.uk — MB BCh BAO 1979 Belf.; BSc (Hons.) Physiol. Belf. 1976, MD 1987; FRCP Ed. 1998; FRCP Lond. 1996; MRCP (UK) 1984. p/t Cons. Phys. (Gen. & Geriat. Med.) Cheltenham Gen. & Delancey Hosps. & Moreton-in-Marsh Hosps. Socs: Fell. Ulster Med. Soc; Brit. Hypertens. Soc.; Brit. Geriat. Soc. Prev: Tutor RCP 1995-2000; Sen. Regist. (Geriat. & Gen. Med.) Addenbrooke's Hosp. Camb. & Hinchingbrooke Hosp. Huntingdon; DHSS Clin. Research Fell.

DEERING, Robert Basil Clayton Windmills, Hassocks BN6 9PG Tel: 01273 845732 Fax: 01273 845732 — MB BS 1956 Lond.; Cert. Av Med. MoD (Air) & Civil Av Auth. 1979; DCH Eng. 1961. (St. Bart.) Civil Serv. Med. Adviser; Civil Aviat. Auth. Med. Examr. Socs: Roy. Soc. Med. Prev: Ho. Surg. Padd. Green Childr. Hosp. & Cross Ho.s Hosp. Shrewsbury; Med. Off. RAF.

DEERY, Alastair Robin Stewart Department of Histopathology, Royal Free Hospital, Pond St., Hampstead, London NW3 2QG Tel:

020 7830 2944 Fax: 020 7830 2944 — MB BS 1978 Lond.; BSc Lond. 1975; FRCPath 1997, M 1987. Cons. Histopath. & Hon. Sen. Lect. Univ. Lond.; Dir. Cythopath. Unit Roy. Free Hosp. Lond. Socs: Path. Soc. Brit. & N.. Irel.; Brit. Soc. Clin. Cytol. Prev: Sen. Regist. (Histopath & Cytopath.) Char. Cross & St. Stephens Hosp.; Regist. (Histopath.) W.. Infirm. Glas.; SHO (Path.) Wythenshawe Hosp. Manch.

DEERY, Christopher Hugh DHSRU, Dental School, Park Place, Dundee DD1 4H Tel: 01382 26041 Fax: 01382 26550 — MSc Bristol 1988; BDS Ed. 1984, FDS 1995. (Ed.) Clin. Research Fell. Dundee Dent. Hosp.; Hon. Career Regist. Socs: Brit. Soc. Paediat. Dent.; Eur. Org. Caries Research; Brit. Dent. Research. Prev: Regist. Dund. Dent. Hosp.; Community Dent. Off. Grampian Health Bd.; Gen. Dent. Pract.

DEERY, Robert William The Surgery, 1 Arlington Road, Eastbourne BN21 1DH Tel: 01323 727531 Fax: 01323 417085 Email: robert.deery@gp-g81050.nhs.uk; The Copper Beeches, 289 Kings Drive, Eastbourne BN21 2YA Tel: 01323 502060 Fax: 01323 502060 — MB BS 1979 Lond.; MB BS 1979 Lond.; MRCGP 1984; DRCOG 1982. (St. Mary's) Prev: SHO (Gen. Med.) St. Mary's Hosp. E.bourne.

DEFRIEND, Diane Elizabeth Department of Radiology, Derriford Hosptial, Plymouth; Glebe House, Vicarage Road, Abbotskerswell, Newton Abbot TQ12 5PN — MB ChB 1991 Manch.; BSc (1st. cl. Hons.) Psychol. Lond. 1983; FRCR. Regist. (Radiol.) Plymouth. Prev: SHO (Cas.) N. Manch. Gen. Hosp.; Ho. Off. (Gen. Surg.) N. Manch. Gen. Hosp.; Ho. Off. (Gen. Med.) S. Manch. HA.

DEFRIEND, Kevin Paul Town End Surgery, 41 Town End, Caterham CR3 5UJ Tel: 01883 345613 Fax: 01883 330142; 10 Old School Place, Lingfield RH7 6AS — MB BS 1993 Lond.; BSc (Hons.) Lond. 1990, MB BS 1993; DRCOG 1996; MRCGP 1997. GP Princip. & Partner. Prev: Trainee GP Caterham Surrey.; Ho. Off. (Med.) E. Surrey Hosp.; Ho. Off. (Surg.) Roy. Surrey Co. Hosp.

DEGA, Mr Raman Kumar Consultant Trauma & Orthopaedics, Dept of Orthopaedics, Wexham Park Hospital, Slough Tel: 0175 363 3000; 28, Hillcroft Crescent, Watford WD19 4NY Tel: 01923 351318 Email: raman@nikhila.demon.co.uk — LMSSA 1991 Lond.; MB BS Kartanak 1986; LMSSA Soc. Apoth. Lond. 1991; FRCS (Orthop) 1997; FRCS Glas. 1991. Cons. Orthopaedic Heatherwood & Wrexham Pk. Hosp.s Trust. Socs: BOA; BMA; RCP (Glas.). Prev: Sen. Regist. Orthop. Roy. Lond. Hosp.

DEGAITAS, Panayotis Molebridge Practice, 3 Cannon Side, Fetcham, Leatherhead KT22 9LE Tel: 01372 379941 Fax: 01372 361178 — Ptychio Iatrikes 1966 Athens; Ptychio Iatrikes 1966 Athens.

DEGENAAR, Geraldina Dina Marisa 17 Dublin Road, Newry BT35 8DA — MB BCh BAO 1997 Belf.

DEGENS, Gillian Carolyn West Walk Surgery, 21 West Walk, Yate, Bristol BS37 4AX Tel: 01454 272200 — MB ChB 1982 Bristol; MRCGP 1990; DO Auckland 1988; DCH RCP Lond. 1986.

DEGNEN, Francis Howlett Princess Elizabeth Hospital, Le Vauquiedor, St Martin's, Guernsey GY4 6UU Tel: 01481 725241; Les Jehans, La Rue Des Jehans, Torteval, Guernsey GY8 0RE Tel: 01481 65899 — MB ChB 1966 Ed.; FRCP Ed. 1993; MRCP (UK) 1975; FRACGP 1977; MRCGP 1973; DObst RCOG 1970; FRCP Lond. 1997. (Ed.) Cons. Phys. P.ss Eliz. Hosp. Guernsey. Socs: Fell. Roy. Soc. Med.; Assur. Med. Soc. Prev: MOH Roebourne, W.. Austral.; Commonw. Med. Off. & Quarantine Med. Off. Govt. Austral.; Med. Adviser to Hamersley Iron Pty. Ltd. W.. Austral.

DEGORREQUER-GRIFFITH, Tamsin Beth Hunter 14 Bybrook Field, Sandgate, Folkestone CT20 3BQ — MB BS 1997 Lond.

DEGUN, Wynne Janine 9 Appleton Fields, Thorley, Bishop's Stortford CM23 4DP — MB BS 1982 Lond.

DEHADRAY, Mukund Gopal Hurst Cottage, Chapel Lane, Billingley, Little Houghton, Barnsley S72 0HZ — MB BS Nagpur 1968; DTM & H Liverp. 1972; DTD Nagpur 1969. (Nagpur) Socs: MPS.

DEHERAGODA, Percy (retired) 6 Maywater Close, South Croydon CR2 0RS Tel: 020 8651 4582 — MB BS Ceylon 1955; MD Ceylon 1966; FRCP Lond. 1994; MRCP (UK) 1969. Prev: Cons. Phys. (Genitourin. Med.) Mayday Univ. Hosp. Croydon and E. Surrey Hosp. Redhill.

DEHGHANI, Maryam 55 Tudor Gardens, London W3 0DU — MB BS 1995 Lond.

DEHN, Mr Thomas Clark Bruce Royal Berkshire Hospital, London Road, Reading RG1 5AN Tel: 01189 878623 Fax: 01189 877881 — MB BS 1973 Lond.; MS Lond. 1984; FRCS Eng. 1979; MRCS Eng. LRCP Lond. 1973; DObst RCOG 1975. (St. Bart.) Cons. Surg. Roy. Berks. Hosp. Reading. Socs: Fell. Roy. Soc. Med.; Brit. Soc. Gastroenterol.; Assn. Endoscopic Surgs. Prev: Clin. Lect. (Surg.) John Radcliffe Hosp. Oxf.; Lect. (Surg.) St. Bart. Hosp. Med. Coll. Lond.; Regist. (Surg.) Soton. Gen. Hosp.

DEIGHAN, Anne Jacqueline 14 Custance House, Provost St., London N1 7QU — MB BCh BAO 1976 Dub.

DEIGHAN, Margaret Patricia 1016 Great Western Road, Glasgow G12 0NP — MB ChB 1944 Glas.

DEIGHAN, Mary Jane 1/2, 79 Woodford Street, Shawlands, Glasgow G41 3HW — MB ChB 1991 Glas.

DEIGHAN, Michael James Spring Gardens Health Centre, Providence Street, Worcester WR1 2BS Tel: 01905 681781 Fax: 01905 681766; 32 Nunnery Lane, Worcester WR5 1RQ — MB ChB 1977 Manch.; BA Open 1992; MMedSc Birm. 1994; MRCGP 1982. (Manchester) Examr. MRCGP; VTS Course Organiser.

DEIGHTON, Christopher Michael Department of Rheumatology, City Hospital, Hucknall Road, Nottingham NG5 1PB Tel: 0115 969 1169 Fax: 0115 962 7709 — MB BS 1984 Newc.; MD Newc. 1992, BMed Sci (Hons.) 1988; MRCP (UK) 1987; FRCP (UK) 1997. Cons. Rheum. City Hosp. Nottm. Socs: BMA; Brit. Soc. Rheum.; (Pres.) Rheum. in Train. Soc. Prev: Sen. Regist. Rotat. (Rheum.) N.. RHA; Jun. Research Fell. Arthritis & Rheum. Counc. Roy. Vict. Infirm.; Regist. & SHO (Gen. Med.) Newc. VTS.

DEIGHTON, Frank William Gordon (retired) 4 Hatfield Drive, Glasgow G12 0YA — MB ChB 1949 Glas. Prev: Ho. Phys. Roy. Infirm. Glas.

DEIGHTON, John Graham Occupational Health,St Johns, Greater Manchester Police Training School, Sedgley Park Road, Prestwich, Manchester M25 0JT Tel: 0161 856 0546 Fax: 0161 856 0544; Larve end cottage, 275 congley Lane, gatley, Cheadle SK8 4EE Tel: 0161 491 5043 Email: johndeighton@doctors.org.uk — MB ChB Manch. 1969; AFOM RCP Lond. 1989. (Manch.) Sen. Occupat. Health Phys. Gtr. Manch. Police. Socs: ALAMA; SOM; Fac. Occupat. Med. Prev: Police Surg. Trafford.; Med. Adviser Trafford FHSA; GP Chesh.

DEIGNAN, Eithne Barbara 31 Hughenden Avenue, Belfast BT15 5DB — MB BCh BAO 1989 Belf.; MRCGP 1994; DCH RCPI 1995; DRCOG 1992.

DEIN, Simon Lawrence 76 Vancouver Road, London SE23 2AJ — MB BS 1983 Lond.

DEIRANIYA, Mr Abdulilah Haj Kheiro Beeches Consulting Centre, Mill Lane, Cheadle SK8 2YP Tel: 0161 491 2534 Fax: 0161 428 1692; 2 Allandale, Bradgate Road, Altrincham WA14 4PQ Tel: 0161 929 1479 Fax: 0161 928 1038 Email: adeiraniya@aol.com — MB ChB 1962 Sheff.; FRCS Eng. 1967; T(S) 1991; FETCS 1998; FESC 1999. Cons. Cardiothoracic Surg. Wythenshawe Hosp. Manch. Socs: Brit. Soc. Cardiovasc. Surgs.; Brit. Cardial. Soc.; Internat. Soc. Heart & Lung Transpl. Prev: Sen. Regist. (Cardiothoracic Surg.) Harefield Hosp. & Qu. Eliz. Hosp.

DEIRY, Abib Amin 262 Mary Street, Birmingham B12 9RJ Tel: 0121 440 1109 — MB BCh Cairo 1941. Gen. Med. Pract. Prev: Capt. RAMC.

DEJONG, Margaret Jean 7 Carson Road, London SE21 8HT — MD 1979 CM McGill U Canada. Cons. Child & Adolesc. Psychiat. Sutton Hosp. Surrey.

DEKANSKI, Jerzy Bazyli Biorex Laboratories Ltd., Biorex House, Canonbury Villas, London N1 — MD 1925 Warsaw; MPS; Mem. BMA.

DEKKER, Barrie James 2 Gimson Close, Witham CM8 2ER — MB BS 1993 Lond.

DEKKER, Mr Peter John Department ENT Surgery, City Hospital, Dudley Road, Birmingham B18 7QH Tel: 0121 507 5112 Fax: 0121 507 4557; 272 Station Road, Knowle, Solihull B93 0ES Fax: 0121 507 4557 — MB ChB 1980 Cape Town; FRCS Ed. 1990; FCS(SA) 1989; DCH (SA) 1984. (Univ. Cape Town) Cons. ENT Surg. City Hosp. Birm. Socs: Brit. Assn. Otol.; Midl. Inst. Otol. Prev: Regist. Rotat. Yorks. RHA; Regist. Groote Schuur Hosp. Cape Town, S. Afr.

DEL AMO VALERO, Julia Flat 1, 83 Granville Park, London SE13 7DW — LMS 1989 U Autonoma Madrid.

DEL BENE, Riccarda 205 Black Haynes Road, Selly Oak, Birmingham B29 4QZ — State Exam 1985 Florence.

DEL BIANCO, Guiseppina The Health Centre, Maison Diev Road, Dover Tel: 01304 202525; The Manse, Plain Hull, Smeeth, Ashford TN25 6QN Tel: 0130 381 2790 — State DMS 1979 Pisa.

DEL ESTAL HUERTAS, Dolores Maria 23 Kings Road, OxfordWhitley Bay, Whitley Bay NE26 3BD — LMS 1987 Cordoba.

DEL MAR, Alan Richard Ashdown Forest Health Centre, Lewes Road, Forest Row RH18 5AQ Tel: 01342 822131 Fax: 01342 826015; Mouse Hall, Ashurst Wood, East Grinstead RH19 3SA Tel: 01342 823196 — MB BS Lond. 1967; MRCS Eng. LRCP Lond. 1967; MRCGP 1974; DObst RCOG 1969. (St. Mary's) Mem. Gen. Pract. Staff Qu. Vict. Hosp. E. Grinstead. Prev: Ho. Surg. (ENT) St. Mary's Hosp. Lond.; Ho. Phys. (Med.) King Edwd. VII Hosp. Windsor; Ho. Surg. (Obst.) Kingston upon Thames Hosp.

DEL OLMO MANOSA, Jesus Flat 71, James Paget Hospital, Lowestoft Road, Great Yarmouth NR31 6LA — LMS 1979 Salamanca.

DEL RIO, Ana Isabel — MB ChB 1993 Leeds; MRCP Glas. 1997. SHO (Neonatology) Jessops Hosp. for Wom. Sheff.; SpR (Neonatology) Hope Hosp. Manch. Prev: Specialist Regist. (Paediat.) N. Manch. Rotat.; SHO (Paediat.) N.. Gen. Hosp. Sheff.

DEL RIO BASTERRECHEA, Ignacio 31 Hanover Road, Norwich NR2 2HD — LMS 1985 Basque Provinces.

DELAHOOKE, Toby Edward Stuart 25 Ladysmith Road, Edinburgh EH9 3EU — MB ChB 1993 Ed.

DELAHUNTY, Ann Margaret Department of Public Health, Iechyd Morgannwg Health, 41 High St., Swansea SA1 1LT Tel: 01792 458066 Fax: 01792 655364; 33 Dol-y-Dderwen, Llangain, Carmarthen SA33 5BE Tel: 01267 241849 — MB BCh 1976 Wales; BA (Hons.) Wales 1991; MRCGP 1982; MFPHM 1997. Primary Care Med. Advis.; Hon. Sen. Research Fell. Centre for Research into Environm. & Health Univ. Lampeter. Prev: Sen. Regist. (Pub. Health Med.) W. Glam. HA; GP Abertillery; Regist. (Pub. Health Med.) E. Dyfed HA.

DELAHUNTY, Caroline Beechmount, Gallowbank Road, Blairgowrie PH10 6EA — MB BS 1988 Lond.; MRCP Paediat. (UK) 1993. Regist. (Paediat.) Ninewells Hosp. Dundee. Prev: SHO Rotat. (Paediat.) Guy's Hosp. & King's Coll. Hosp. Lond.

DELAKI, Ekaterini County Hospital Residences, 10 St Anne's Close, Lincoln LN2 5RB — Ptychio Iatrikes 1985 Ioannina.

DELAMERE, John Peter Wordsley Hospital, Stream Road, Wordsley, Stourbridge DY8 5QX Tel: 01384 456111 Fax: 01384 244596; 33 Knighton Road, Birmingham B31 2EH Tel: 0121 477 0066 — MB BS 1971 Lond.; FRCP Lond. 1989; MRCP (UK) 1975; MRCS Eng. LRCP Lond. 1971; DObst RCOG 1973. (Kings College Hospital London) Cons. Phys. Wordsley Hosp. Dudley. Socs: Brit. Soc. Rheum.; Birm. Med. Res. Expeditionary Soc.; W Midl. Phys. Assn. Prev: Cons. Phys. Dudley Guest Hosp. Dudley.

DELAMORE, Irvine William (retired) Fisher House, Rivington, Bolton BL6 7SL Tel: 01204 696437 — MB ChB 1954 Ed.; PhD Ed. 1962, MB ChB (Hons.) 1954; FRCP Lond. 1982 M 1982; FRCP Ed. 1967, M 1958; FRCPath 1976, M 1963. Prev: Hon. Cons. Phys. Roy. Infirm. Manch.

DELAMORE, Jennifer Ann 18 Roberts Road, High Wycombe HP13 6XA Tel: 04022 43279 Email: jdelamore@hotmail.com — MB BS 1993 W. Indies; MB BS West Indies 1993; DCH 1996; MRCP 1997.

DELANEY, Brendan Clifford The Laurie Pike Health Centre, 95 Birchfield Road, Handsworth, Birmingham B19 1LH Tel: 0121 554 0621 Fax: 0121 554 6163 — BM BCh 1987 Oxf.; FRCP 2001; MRCP (UK) 1991; MRCGP 1992; DRCOG 1990; MD 1997. Reader, Primary Care & Gen. Pract., Univ. Birm. Prev: Lect. (Gen. Pract.) Univ. Birm.

DELANEY, Deirdre Mary Flat C, 20A Molyneux Park Road, Tunbridge Wells TN4 8DT — MB ChB 1996 Cape Town.

DELANEY, Elizabeth Kathleen 69 Largo Road, Lundin Links, Leven KY8 6DH — MB ChB 1998 Glas.; MB ChB Glas 1998.

DELANEY, Gillian Mary 25 High Street, Prestbury, Cheltenham GL52 3AR Tel: 01242 235974 — MB ChB 1964 St. And. Clin. Asst. (Oncol.) Cheltenham. Prev: Clin. Asst. (Dermat.) Gloucester; Clin. Asst. Younger Disabled Unit St. Francis' Hosp. Dulwich; Regist. (Dermat.) Liverp. Roy. Infirm.

DELANEY, Hannah Lucy 6 Latchford Road, Gayton, Wirral CH60 3RW — MB ChB 1997 Sheff.

DELANEY, James William Health Centre, 68 Pipeland Road, St Andrews KY16 8JZ Tel: 01334 476840 Fax: 01334 472295; 46 Lamond Drive, St Andrews KY16 8DD Tel: 01334 477085 — MB ChB 1959 Ed.; MRCGP 1974. (Ed.) GP St. And. Prev: Ho. Surg. Roodlands Gen. Hosp. Haddington & Matern. Hosp. Dunfermline; Ho. Phys. N.. Hosp. Dunfermline.

DELANEY, Jane Ann White Lodge, 60A Schools Hill, Cheadle SK8 1JD — MB ChB 1980 Dundee.

DELANEY, John Andrew 48 Roman Bank, Stamford PE9 2ST — MB BS 1997 Lond.

DELANEY, John Christopher Arrowe Park Hospital, Upton, Wirral CH49 5PE Tel: 0151 604 7046 Fax: 0151 604 7119; 1 Coral Ridge, Bidston, Prenton CH43 7XE Tel: 0151 652 1665 — MB ChB Liverp. 1965; FRCP Lond. 1984; MRCP (UK) 1971. (Liverpool) Cons. Phys. Repiratory and G/M Arrowe Pk. Hosp. Birkenhead. Socs: Brit. Thorac. Soc.& BMA; Merseyside & N. Wales Soc. Phys. Prev: Cons. Phys. Whiston Hosp. Prescot; Sen. Regist. (Med.) Walton Hosp. & David Lewis N.. Hosp. Liverp.

DELANEY, Mary Josephine Avila, 18 Beech Park. Avenue, Northenden, Manchester M22 4BL — MB ChB 1960 Glas.; DCH RCPS Glas. 1963. (Glas.) SHO (Path.) Booth Hall Childr. Hosp. Manch. Prev: Ho. Phys. S.. Gen. Hosp. Glas.; Ho. Surg. Stockport Infirm.; Sen. Ho. Off. (Paediat.) Booth Hall Hosp. Manch.

DELANEY, Michael Paul 73 Arnold Road, Shirley, Solihull B90 3JS Tel: 0121 733 6218 Fax: 0121 733 6218 Email: mike@arnoldrd.demon.co.uk — MB BS 1990 Lond.; BSc (Hons.) Lond. 1987; MRCP (UK) 1994. (St. Mary's Hosp. Med. Sch.) Specialist Regist. (Renal & Gen. Med.) Walsgrave Hosp. Coventry; Renal Transpl. Research, Univ. Warwick. Prev: Regist. (Renal) Birm. Heartlands Hosp.; SHO (Med.) Walsgrave Hosp. Coventry; Ho. Off. (Surg.) Acad. Surgic. Unit St. Mary's Hosp. Lond.

DELANEY, Russell James 64 Bourton Avenue, Patchway, Bristol BS34 6EE — MB ChB 1996 Birm.

DELANEY, Simon Gerard James 12 West Close, Birkenhead CH43 9RR Tel: 0151 677 2500; 169 Waterpark Road, Prenton, Birkenhead CH43 0TJ Tel: 0151 608 7244 — BM BS 1994 Nottm.; BMedSci (Hons.) Nottm. 1992. GP Regist. Lache Health Centre Chester. Prev: SHO (Orthop.) BRd.green Hosp. Liverp.

DELANEY, Thomas Joseph 25 High Street, Prestbury, Cheltenham GL52 3AR Tel: 01242 235974 — MB ChB 1964 Liverp.; FRCP Lond. 1982, M 1968; T (M) 1991; DCH Eng. 1968. (Liverp.) Cons. Dermat. Glos. & Cheltenham Health Dists. Socs: Sect. Dermat. Roy. Soc. Med.; BMA. Prev: Ho. Surg. & Ho. Phys. Roy. S.. Hosp. Liverp.; SHO Paediat. Roy. Liverp. Childr. Hosp. Sen. Regist. (Dermat.) St.; Geo. Hosp. Lond.

DELANEY, William Maurice Mary Health Centre, Newgate Street, Worksop S80 1HP Tel: 01909 500266 Fax: 01909 478014; Burnt Leys Farm, Steetley, Worksop S80 3DZ Tel: 01909 477236 Fax: 01909 477236 — MB BCh BAO 1977 NUI; MICGP 1985; MRCGP 1982. (Cork) Clin. Asst. (Ment. Handicap) Bassetlaw Dist. Gen. Hosp. Worksop. Socs: BMA. Prev: Trainee GP Worksop VTS; Ho. Phys. & Ho. Surg. Roy. Hosp. Wolverhampton.

DELANY, Brian Howard (retired) 4 Macclesfield Road, Congleton CW12 1NR Tel: 01260 276183 — MB ChB 1958 Manch. Prev: Mem. BMA.

DELANY, David John Department of Radiology, Southampton General Hospital, Shirley, Southampton SO16 6YD Tel: 02380 796833 Fax: 02380 796341; Oakvale Lodge, Crow Hill, Ringwood BH24 3DB Tel: 01425 479140 — MB BChir 1964 Camb.; MA Camb. 1964; FRCR 1970. Cons. Radiol. Soton. Univ. Hosp. & Wessex Cardiothoracic Centre. Socs: (Pres.) Soc. Thoracic Radiol.; (Sec.) Assn. Chest Radiol. Prev: Prof Radiol. Univ. N. Carolina Sch. Med., USA.

DELANY, Gwendolen Maria Balmore Park Surgery, 59A Hemdean Road, Caversham, Reading RG4 7SS Tel: 0118 947 1455 Fax: 0118 946 1766 — BM BCh 1973 Oxf.; MRCGP 1979.

DELANY, Michael Gerard Addison Road Medical Practice, 12-14 Addison Road, London E17 9LT Tel: 020 8520 4708 Fax: 020 8520 6266; 26 Osprey Close, Wanstead, London E11 1SY Tel: 020 8252 8297 — MB BS 1990 Lond. GP.

DELANY, Owen Joseph Silver Wood Centre, Northgate St., Great Yarmouth NR30 1BL Tel: 01493 337601; Winston Cottage, Rectory

Road, Gillingham NR34 0HH — MB BCh BAO 1971 Dub.; MRCPsych. Cons. Child & Adolesc. Psychiat. N.gate Hosp. Gt. Yarmouth. Socs: Roy. Coll. Psychiat.

DELAP, Peter, MC (retired) 53 Boroughgate, Appleby-in-Westmorland CA16 6XG — MB BCh BAO 1936 Dub.; MD Dub. 1945. Prev: Capt. RAMC, Att., Commandos.

DELAP, Mr Thomas Gerard ENT Department, Antrim Hospital, Antrim BT41 2RL — MB BCh BAO 1987 NUI. Cons. (ENT) Antrim Hosp.

DELARGY, Hugh James Market Harborough Medical Centre, 67 Coventry Road, Market Harborough LE16 9BX Tel: 01858 464242 Fax: 01858 462929 — MB ChB 1990 Sheff.; MRCP (UK) 1995; MRCGP 1996; DRCOG 1995. (Univ. Sheff.) GP Princip. Market HarBoro. Med. Centre. Prev: SHO (O & G) Jessop Hosp. for Wom. Sheff.; SHO (Paediat., A & E) Sheff. Childr. Hosp.; SHO Rotat. (Gen. Med.) Roy. Hallamsh. Hosp. Sheff.

DELARGY, Kevin Patrick 72 Ballyeamon Road, Cushendall, Ballymena BT44 0SW — MB BCh BAO 1993 Belf.

DELARGY-AZIZ, Yasmin Karen 37 Clarke Street, Market Harborough LE16 9AD — MB ChB 1990 Sheff.; DRCOG 1995. Trainee GP Sheff. Prev: SHO (Community Paediat. & Genitourin. Med.) Sheff.; SHO (O & G) Rotherham.

DELFAS, George The Surgery, 5 Albany Road, Coventry CV5 6JQ Tel: 024 76 228606; Arcadia, 38 Kenilworth Road, Leamington Spa CV32 6JE Tel: 01926 423082 — LMSSA 1974 Lond. Clin. Asst. (Rheum.) Co. & Warks. Hosp. Coventry. Prev: Regist. (Cardiol.) Walsgrave Hosp. Coventry; Regist. (Cardiol.) W.. Infirm. Glas.

DELFOSSE, John Brinley Woodlands Medical Centre, Woodland Road, Didcot OX11 0BB Tel: 01235 511355 Fax: 01235 512808; Holloway Thatch, The Holloway, Harwell, Didcot OX11 0LS — MB BS 1981 Lond.; MRCGP 1985; DRCOG 1984. Socs: Assur. Med. Soc.

DELGADO BELLOSO, Enrique U.T.S., Wolsey Hall, 66 Banbury Road, Oxford OX2 6PR — LMS 1994 Granda.

DELGADO MARTIN, Mario Bernardo 6/2 Myreside Court, Edinburgh EH10 5LX — LMS 1989 U Complutense Madrid.

DELHANTY, Michael Harry Vivian 24 Brookway Road, Charlton Kings, Cheltenham GL53 8HB Tel: 01242 571746 — MB ChB 1988 Bristol; MRCGP 1993; DRCOG 1992.

DELICATA, Mr Raymond John Department of Surgery, University of Wales College of Medicine, Heath Park, Cardiff CF14 4XN Tel: 029 2074 7747; 18 Tangmere Drive, Llandaff, Cardiff CF5 2PQ Tel: 029 2056 3446 — MD 1982 Malta; MRCS Eng. LRCP Lond. 1989; FRCS Ed. 1993. Research Fell. (Surg.) Univ. Wales Coll. Med. Cardiff. Prev: Regist. (Surg.) Barnsley Dist. Gen. Hosp.

DELIS, Konstantinos Appt. 1606, 2 Fann St., London EC2Y 8BR — Ptychio Iatrikes 1985 Athens.

DELISS, Mr Louis John Playford Mount, Great Bealings, Woodbridge IP13 6PH Tel: 01473 735600 Fax: 01473 735106 Email: louisjdeliss@cs.com — MB ChB 1968 Liverp.; FRCS Eng. 1973. (Liverp.) Chairm. of Brit. Palawan Trust; Mem. OSCE Panel of GMC. Socs: Fell.Brit. Orthopaedic Assoc.; Brit. Assn. Sports Med.; Brit. Soc. Surg. Hand. Prev: Cons. Trauma and Orthop., The Ipswich Hosp.; Rotating Sen. Reg. (Orthop), St Bart Hosp, Lond.; HO and SHO Liverp. and Norwich.

DELIYANNIS, Mr Savas Nicolas Hospital of St Cross, Barby Road, Rugby CV22 5PX Tel: 01788 572831; Hill Cottage, Woodbine Hill, Southam CV47 2DL Tel: 01926 812125 — MB ChB Alexandria 1962; FRCS Ed. 1975; LMSSA Lond. 1970; FRCS 1999. (Alexandria) Cons. Orthop. Surg. Hosp. St. Cross Rugby. Socs: Fell. BOA; Fell. RCS Edin.; BMA. Prev: Sen. Regist. (Orthop.) Nottm. Gen. Hosp.; Regist. (Orthop.) Harlow Wood Orthop. Hosp. Mansfield; Regist. (Orthop.) Coventry & Warks. Hosp.

DELL, Adrian Jules Stamford Hill Group Practice, 2 Egerton Road, Stamford Hill, London N16 6UA Tel: 020 8800 1000 Fax: 020 8880 2402; 45 Litchfield Way, London NW11 6NU Tel: 020 8455 8737 — MB 1958, BChir 1957; MA Camb. 1957; DCH Eng. 1960; FRCGP 1983, M 1969. (Westm.) Socs: BMA. Prev: Clin. Asst. (Neurol.) P. of Wales Hosp. Lond.; Ho. Off. (Paediat.) W. Middlx. Hosp. Isleworth; Ho. Surg. Chase Farm Hosp. Enfield.

DELL, Arthur Edward Victoria Infirmary, Langside, Glasgow G42 9TY Tel: 0141 201 5320 Fax: 0141 201 5318 — MB ChB 1975 Birm.; FCA RCSI 1985. Cons. Anaesth. Vict. Infirm. Glas. Socs: Assn. Anaesth. & Intens. Care Soc.; Soc. Computing & Technol. Anaesth.; BMA. Prev: Sen. Regist. Rotat. (Anaesth.) N.. RHA; Regist. (Anaesth.) Vict. Infirm. Glas.; Dist. Med. Off. Zimbabwe.

DELL, Mary Ethel 55 Laughton Road, Lubenham, Market Harborough LE16 9TE — MB ChB 1990 Leic.; DFFP 1996; DRCOG 1995. Prev: Trainee GP Kettering VTS.

DELL, Rebecca Emma 25 Grange Garth, York YO10 4BS — MB BS 1998 Newc.; MB BS Newc 1998.

DELL, Ross James 31 North Drive, Beaconsfield HP9 1TZ — MB BS 1990 Lond.

DELLAGRAMMATICAS, Demosthenes Doctors Mess, North Manchester General Hospital, Delaunays Road, Manchester M8 5RB; Flat 5, 25-27 Central Road, Manchester M20 4YE — MB ChB 1997 Manch.

DELLAL, Victor Meir (retired) 80 Brook Green, London W6 7BE Tel: 020 7603 6038 — MRCS Eng. LRCP Lond. 1930. Prev: Ho. Surg. & Ho. Phys. Rotherham Gen. Hosp. & LoW.oft Gen. Hosp.

DELLAPORTAS, Constantinos Cassidy Road Medical Centre, 651A Fulham Road, London SW6 5PX Tel: 020 7736 9988 Fax: 020 7736 5726 Email: c.dellaportas@ic.ac.uk; London Neurological Centre, 110 Harley St, London W1N 1DG Tel: 0191 935 3546 Fax: 0191 935 4172 — MD 1973 Athens. (Univ. Athens Med. Sch.) GP & Lect. (Neurol.) Imperial Coll. of Med. at Neurosci.s, Char. Cross Hosp. Socs: Fell. Roy. Soc. Med.; Int. League Against Epilepsy; Hon. Sec. BMA (W. Lond. Div.). Prev: Research Regist. (Neurol.) Inst. Psychiat. & King's Coll. Hosps. Lond.

DELLER, John Grover Winyates Health Centre, Winyates, Redditch B98 0NR Tel: 01527 25533 Fax: 01527 517969; The Old Smithy, Bradley Green, Redditch B96 6QU Tel: 01527 821374 — MRCS Eng. LRCP Lond. 1960; DObst RCOG 1961. (St. Mary's)

DELLIPIANI, Alexander William (retired) Lynton, 17 Maltby Road, Thornton-in-Cleveland, Stainton, Middlesbrough TS8 9BU Tel: 01642 590470 — MD 1968 Ed.; MB ChB 1959; FRCP Lond. 1980; FRCP Ed. 1970, M 1962. Cons. Phys. N. Tees Gen. Hosp.; Hon. Sen. Lect. Univ. Newc. Prev: Vis. WHO Sen. Lect. (Med.) Baroda Med. Coll. India.

DELLOW, Alan Charles Amersham Health Centre, Chiltern Avenue, Amersham HP6 5AY Tel: 01494 434344 — MB BS 1973 Lond.; FRCGP 1998; DCH 1982; DRCOG 1977. (King's Coll. Hosp.) Prev: Med. Off. Bandar Seri Begawan, Brunei & Sakaeo, Thailand.

DELLOW, Emma Louise 5 Lindfield Gardens, Guildford GU1 1TP — MB BS 1994 Lond.

DELORME, Mr Edmund Joseph (retired) 71 Harrington Gardens, London SW7 4JZ Tel: 020 7373 2861 — MD 1935 Toronto; FRCS Canada 1945. Prev: Nuffield Fell. in Med Research.

DELPORT, Barend Cilliers 44 Eynsford Rise, Eynsford, Dartford DA4 0HR Email: bennie@globalnet.com — MB ChB 1981 Pretoria; DRCOG 1996; DA (SA) 1984. GP Regist. Dartford.

DELUZ, Jacqueline Elisabeth Hawthorn House, Heartlands Hospital, Bordesley Green E., Birmingham B9 5SS; 44 Selly Oak Road, Bournville, Birmingham B30 1LS Tel: 0121 449 8814 — MB BS 1970 Lond. Staff Grade (Genitourin. Med.) Heartlands Hosp. Birm.

DELVAUX, Agnes 5 Cargil Terrace, Edinburgh EH5 3ND — MD 1988 Louvain.

DELVES, Caroline Elizabeth 94 Tolworth Park Road, Tolworth, Kingston upon Thames — MB BS 1997 Lond.

DELVES, George Henry, Capt. Vale Lodge, Kirk Hammerton Lane, Green Hammerton, York YO26 8BS — MB ChB 1996 Ed.; BSc (Hons) Ed. 1994.

DELVIN, David George c/o Gurney's Bank, PO Box 36, Bank Plain, Norwich NR2 4SP Tel: 07050 103270 — MB BS 1962 Lond.; MRCS Eng. LRCP Lond. 1962; MFFP 1992; MRCGP 1973; Dip. Ven. Soc. Apoth. Lond. 1977; Instruc. Doctor's Certif. 1975; Cert FPA 1972; DCH Eng. 1966; DObst RCOG 1965. (King's Coll. Hosp.) Columnist various UK nad overseas Pub.ations; Cons. to Net Doctor; Assoc. Edr. New English Encyc.; Med. Adviser various TV Progr.s; Mem. Edit. Bd. & Med. Cons. Brit. Jl. Family Plann.; Hon. Clin. Asst. Advis. Lond. Socs: Fell. Roy. Soc. Med.; (Exec. Comm.) Med. Jl.ists Assn.; Inst. Psycho-Sexual Med. Prev: Dir. Brit. Jl. Hosp. Med. Film Unit; Cons. Edr. Gen. Pract. Medeconomics & MIMS; Regist. Min. of Overseas Developm.

DELY, Caroline Jane Townhead Health Centre, 16 Alexandra Parade, Glasgow G31 2ES Tel: 0141 531 8940 Fax: 0141 531 8935 — MB ChB 1989 Ed.; BSc (Hons.) Ed. 1987; MRCGP 1993;

DRCOG 1992; DCH RCPS Glas. 1992. GP Glas. Prev: Trainee GP Univ. Health Serv. Edin.; Trainee GP Penicuik; SHO (O & G) E.. Gen. Hosp. Edin.

DEMADES, John Queens Avenue Surgery, 46 Queens Avenue, Muswell Hill, London N10 3BJ Tel: 020 8883 1846 Fax: 020 8365 2265 — MB ChB 1982 Liverp.; DCH RCP Lond. 1986. (Liverp.) p/t Exam. Med. Pract. DSS. Socs: (Pres. & Ex-Sec.) Hellenic Med. Soc. UK.

DEMAJUMDAR, Ranit 9 The Green, Oldbury, Oldbury B68 8DU Email: rrdm@lineone.net — MB ChB 1991 Birm.; FRCS Ed 1995; FRCS (Otol.) Lond. 1996. (Birmingham) Specialist Regist. (OtoLaryngol.) W. Midl. Deanery. Socs: BAO - HNS; AOT.

DEMAN, Elizabeth Joanna (practice), 134 Harley St., London W1N 1AH Tel: 020 7486 3846; 20 Beaumont Street, London W1G 6DG — MRCS Eng. LRCP Lond. 1961; DObst RCOG 1963. Clin. Asst. Roy. Free Hosp. Lond.

DEMETRIADI, Francesca Elena Heathfield, Heath Lane, Albury, Guildford GU5 9DD — MB BS 1993 Lond.

DEMETRIOU, Andrew Huntley Mount Medical Centre, Huntley Mount Road, Bury BL9 6JA Tel: 0161 761 6677 Fax: 0161 761 3283; Elton Grange, Elton Vale Road, Bury BL8 2RZ Tel: 0161 764 3823 — MB ChB 1974 Liverp.; MFHom 1988; MRCGP 1980; DCH Eng. 1978; DRCOG 1976. (Liverpool) Prev: Regist. (Communicable Dis.) Monsall Hosp. Manch.; SHO (Paediat.) Booth Hall Childr. Hosp. Manch.; SHO (O & G) Univ. Hosp. S. Manch.

DEMETRIOU, Maria Greenwich District Hospital NHS Trust, Vanbrugh Hill, Greenwich, London SE10 9HE Tel: 020 8858 8141; 38 North Park, Eltham, London SE9 5AP Tel: 020 8850 7659 — MB BS Durh. 1965; DA Eng. 1968. (King's Coll., Univ. Durh.) Clin. Asst. & Assoc. Specialist (Anaesth.) Greenwich Dist. Hosp. Lond. Socs: BMA. Prev: Regist. (Anaesth.) Dartford Gp. Hosps.; Ho. Surg. & Ho. Phys. St. Nicholas Hosp. Plumstead.

DEMETRIOU, Rhea Stavrou Parkside Clinic, 63 Lancaster Road, London W11 1QG Tel: 020 7221 4656; Flat 7, 55 Shepherds Hill, Highgate, London N6 5QP Tel: 020 8348 1710 — Ptychio Iatrikes 1971 Thessalonika; MRCPsych 1981. Indep. Med. Psychother. Lond.; Child Psychiat. Pk.side Clinic. Prev: Regist. (Child Adolesc. Psychiat.) Tavistock Clinic Lond.; Child & Adolesc. Psychiat. Roy. Hosp. Sick Childr. Glas.

DEMETROULIS, Constantinos 42 Vogans Mill, 17 Mill St., London SE1 2BZ — Ptychio Iatrikes 1993 Thessalonika.

DEMISSIE, Aklilu St. Mary's Hospital, Newport PO30 5TG Tel: 01983 524081 — MB BS 1975 Lond.; FRCP Lond. 1996; MRCP (UK) 1979; MRCS Eng. LRCP Lond. 1975. (Char. Cross) Cons. Phys. St. Mary's Hosp. Newport, I. of Wight. Prev: Sen. Regist. Rotat. (Geriat. Med.) Oxf. & Wessex RHAs; Regist. (Neurol.) Hurstwood Pk. Neurol. Centre Hayward's Heath; Regist. (Gen. Med.) SE Kent HA.

DEMNITZ, Ulf Hinrich 34 Gladstone Road, Chester CH1 4BY — BM BS 1984 Nottm.; BM BS Nottm. l984.

DEMOCRATIS, Jane Catherine 1 Nelson Avenue, St Albans AL1 5SE — MB ChB 1998 Liverp.; MB ChB Liverp 1998.

DEMPSEY, Brenda Mary (retired) Lyfords Meadow, 127 Locks Ride, Ascot SL5 8RX Tel: 01344 882129 — MB ChB 1950 Liverp.; FFA RCS Eng. 1955; DA Eng. 1954. Prev: Cons. Anaesth. Ashford Gen. Hosp., Ashford, Middlx..

DEMPSEY, Charlotte Marie 64 Hermitage Court, Woodford Road, Snaresbrook, London E18 2EP — MB BS 1996 Lond.

DEMPSEY, Emma Marie Limes Medical Centre, The Plain, Epping CM16 6TL Tel: 01992 566500; Nyali, Kingsmead Close, Roydon CM19 5JE — MB BS 1989 Lond.; MRCGP 1993; DRCOG 1993; DFFP 1993. Clin. Asst. Neurol., P.ss Alexander NHS Trust, Essex.

DEMPSEY, Helen Mary 6 Fullwood Drive, Golcar, Huddersfield HD7 4JH — MB BS 1986 Lond.; Cert. Family Plann. JCC 1991; T(GP) 1991; DCH RCP Lond. 1990.

DEMPSEY, Howard Francis Matthew St Annes Road East, 24 St. Annes Road East, Lytham St Annes FY8 1UR Tel: 01253 722121 Fax: 01253 781121 — MB ChB 1977 Manch.; BSc St. And. 1974. Gen. Practitioner; Clin. Asst. Surg.; Mem. of PCT.

DEMPSEY, Owen John Paul 89A Leslie Terrace, Aberdeen AB25 3XB — MB ChB 1992 Glas.

DEMPSEY, Owen Philip 9 Court Hill, Sanderstead, South Croydon CR2 9ND Tel: 020 8657 5953; 1 Victoria Lane, Golcar, Huddersfield HD7 4JG Tel: 01484 642984 — MB BS 1983 Lond.; BSc (Physiol.) Lond. 1981; DRCOG 1987. Mem. Huddersfield Gp. Commiss.ing Exec.; Mem. MAAG. Prev: Trainee GP Huddersfield VTS.

DEMPSEY, Stanley Ian Royal Belfast Hospital for Sick Children, Belfast BT12 Tel: 01232 240503; 4 Bristow Park, Belfast BT9 6TH Tel: 01232 665168 — MB BCh BAO 1970 Belf.; FRCP Lond. 1996; MRCP (U.K.) 1973; FRCPath 1991, M 1978. (Qu. Univ. Belf.) Cons. (Haemat.) Roy. Belf. Hosp. Sick Childr. & Roy. Vict. Hosp.

DEMPSEY, Vivien Jane Carleton Surgery, 9 Castle Gardens Crescent, Poulton-le-Fylde FY6 7NJ Tel: 01253 895545 Fax: 01253 899350 — MB ChB 1984 Manch.; MB ChB Manch. l984. Socs: BMA.

DEMPSTER, Mr David Walton Frimley Park Hospital, Portsmouth Road, Camberley GU16 7UJ Tel: 01276 692777; Lodge Hill Cottage, 47 Lodge Hill Road, Farnham GU10 3RD Tel: 01252 725201 — MB BS 1975 Lond.; FRCS Eng. 1980; MRCS Eng. LRCP Lond. 1975. Cons. Surg. Orthop. Frimley Pk. Hosp. Surrey. Prev: Sen. Regist. (Orthop.) Guy's & St. Thos. Hosps. Lond.; Clin. Fell. Albert Einstein Coll. Med. New York, USA; Orthop. Research Fell. Univ. Leeds.

DEMPSTER, Ian Anthony 12 Thornbridge Avenue, Litherland, Liverpool L21 5JX — MB ChB 1991 Glas.

DEMPSTER, Jane Crown House Surgery, Retford — MD 1988 Aberd.; MB ChB 1979; MRCOG 1984. Retainer Scheme (O & G) Lincoln Co. Hosp. VTS. Prev: Regist. (O & G) Ninewells Hosp. Dundee.

DEMPSTER, Jane Beaumont Farnham Health Centre, Brightwells, Farnham GU9 7SA Tel: 01252 723122; Lodge Hill Cottage, 47 Lodge Hill Road, Lower Bourne, Farnham GU10 3RD Tel: 01252 725201 Fax: 01252 725201 — MB BS 1978 Lond.; MRCGP 1985; DRCOG 1985. (St Thomas' Hospital London) Prev: SHO (Obst.) St. Thos. Hosp. Lond.; Clin. Fell. Albert Einstein Coll. Med. Bronx, NY, USA; Trainee GP Leeds VTS.

DEMPSTER, Janet Grace Parkside, 1 Little Meads, Romsey SO51 8HD Tel: 01794 518344 — MB ChB 1967 Glas. (Glas.) Assoc. Specialist (Dermat.) Roy. S. Hants. Hosp.

DEMPSTER, Mr John Hamilton 3 Park Court, Symington, Kilmarnock KA1 5QU — MB ChB 1980 Aberd.; FRCS (Orl.) Ed. 1986; FRCS Glas. 1984. Cons. Otolaryngol. Ayrsh. & Arran HB.

DEMPSTER, Richard Kenneth High Street Health Centre, High Street, Burton Latimer, Kettering NN15 5RH Tel: 01536 723566 Fax: 01536 420226; The Glebe House, West St, Geddington, Kettering NN14 1BD Tel: 01536 461003 — MB BS 1980 Lond.; MRCGP 1986; DRCOG 1986. (St. Thos.) Prev: Trainee GP Weymouth VTS.; SHO (Path.) W.m. Hosp. Lond.; SHO (Gen. Med.) Burton Gen. Hosp.

DEMPSTER, Shona Jacqueline 2 Lynchdown, Funtington, Chichester PO18 9LR Tel: 01243 575671 — MB ChB 1976 Ed.

DEMPSTER, Suzanne 3 Ardholm Place, Inverness IV2 4QG — MB ChB 1983 Aberd.; FCAnaesth 1990. Regist. (Anaesth.) Raigmore Hosp. Inverness.

DEMPSTER, William Hodge (retired) Arderyth, 98 Culduthel Park, Inverness IV2 4RZ — LRCP LRCS 1944 Ed.; LRCP LRCS Ed. LRFPS Glas. 1944; DMRD Eng. 1949. Prev: Cons. Radiol. Law Hosp. Carluke.

DEMPSTER, Mr William James Wavertree, Tytherley Road, Lockerley, Romsey SO51 0LW — LRCP LRCS 1941 Ed.; LRCP LRCS Ed. LRFPS Glas. 1941; FRCS Ed. 1948; FRCS Eng. 1961. (Roy. Colls. Ed.) Prev: Reader in Experim. Surg. Postgrad. Med. Sch. Lond.

DENBOW, Mark Leslie Royal United Hospital, Bath BA1 3NG — MB BS Lond. 1991. Specialist Regist. O & G S. W. Region.

DENBY, Peter 14 King's Close, Staining, Blackpool FY3 0EJ — BM BS 1979 Nottm.; BMedSci Nottm. 1977. (Nottm.) Med. Adviser Benefits Med. Servs.

DENCER, Mr Derrick Summerhill House, Primrose Hill, Oversley Green, Alcester B49 6LH Tel: 01789 762074 — MRCS Eng. LRCP Lond. 1944; FRCS Ed. 1947. (Birm.) Cons. Plastic Surg. Pk.way Hosp. Solihull. Socs: Brit. Assn. Plastic Surgs.; Rugby & Dist. Med. Soc. Prev: Cons. Plastic Surg. Coventry Hosps.; Sen. Surg. Regist. Regional Plastic Unit & United Birm. Hosps.; Surg. Specialist RAMC Milit. Hosp., Singapore.

DENCH, Deborah Mary Meadows Edge, Ashenhurst Road, Todmorden OL14 8DS — MB ChB 1980 Manch.

DENCH, Peter George Reginald, TD (retired) 4 Rawcliff Lane, York YO30 6NH Tel: 01904 55577 — MB BChir 1949 Camb.; BA Camb. Prev: Hon. Col. 250 Field Ambul. (V).

DENDY, Paul Richard 13 Five Mile Drive, Oxford OX2 8HT Tel: 01865 56525 — BM BCh 1966 Oxf.; Dphil; MA. (Oxf.)

DENDY, Richard Allan, TD Department of Maxillofacial Surgery, Royal Lancaster Infirmary, Lancaster LA1 4RP — MB BS 1970 Lond.; BDS Lond. 1962; MRCS Eng. LRCP Lond. 1970; FDS RCS Eng. 1967. (St. Geo.) Cons. Oral & Maxillofacial Surg. Roy. Lancaster Infirm., W.morland Co. Hosp. & Furness Gen. Hosp. Prev: Sen. Regist. Univ. Hosp. Wales & St. Lawrence Hosp. Chepstow.

DENFORD, John Douglas (retired) 25 Wood Lane, London N6 5UE Tel: 020 8883 9316 — MB ChB 1952 New Zealand; BSc New Zealand 1947; FRCPsych 1984, M 1971; DPM Eng. 1959. Prev: Cons. (Psychother.) Cassel Hosp. Func. Nerv. Disorders Richmond.

DENHAM, Alan The Surgery, 93 The Knares, Basildon SS16 5SB Tel: 01268 542866 Fax: 01268 491381; Little Burstead House, Little Burstead, Billericay CM12 9TN Tel: 01277 623623 — MB BS 1957 Durh. (Newc.) Med. Adviser Yardley Manufacturing Basildon, Tanquery Gordon, Basildon& Other Cos. Prev: Ho. Phys. & Ho. Surg. (Surg. & Gyn.) Maelor Gen. Hosp. Wrexham.

DENHAM, Maureen Milburn Little Burstead House, Little Burstead, Billericay CM12 9TN Tel: 01277 623623 — MB BS 1957 Durh.; DPM Eng. 1977; MRCPsych 1979. Cons. Psychiat. Basildon Hosp. & Suttons Manor Clinic Romford Essex. Socs: BMA; Brit. Soc. Med. & Dent. Hypn. Prev: Hon. Sen. Regist. Hosp. Sick Childr. Gt. Ormond St. Lond.

DENHAM, Michael John (retired) 21 Arnett Way, Rickmansworth WD3 4DA Tel: 01923 771860 — MB BChir Camb. 1961; MD Camb. 1976, MA 1961; FRCP Lond. 1979, M 1968, FRCP Edin. 1998; MRCS Eng. LRCP Lond. 1960; DCH Eng. 1964; DA Eng. 1964; DObst RCOG 1962. Censor Exam. RCP; Vis. Prof. Univ. of Herts. Prev: Cons. Geriat. N.wick Pk. Hosp.

DENHAM, Philippa Lesley Department of Histopathology, Frimley Park Hospital, Portsmouth Road, Frimley, Camberley GU16 7UJ Tel: 01276 604401 Fax: 01276 604150 — MB BS 1985 Lond.; MRCPath 1992. (Roy. Free Hosp. Sch. Med.) Cons. Histopath. Frimley Pk. Hosp. Prev: Sen. Regist. (Histopath.) N. Middlx. Hosp. Lond.

DENHAM, Robert Henry George Hector (retired) Orchardlea, The Avenue, Combe Down, Bath BA2 5EQ Tel: 01225 3384 — MD 1933 Aberd.; MB ChB 1923, DPH 1928; MFCM 1974. Prev: MOH Bathavon, Frome & Keynsham.

DENHAM, Mr Robin Arthur The Manor House, Droxford, Southampton SO32 3PA Tel: 01489 877450 Fax: 01489 878704 — MRCS Eng. LRCP Lond. 1945; FRCS Ed. 1951; FRCS Eng. 1951. (St. Thos.) Emerit. Cons. Orthop. Surg. Portsmouth Hosp. Gp. Socs: Fell. BOA. Prev: Pres. Brit. Assn. Surg. of Knee; Sen. Regist. Rowley Bristow Hosp. Pyrford & St. Peter's Hosp. Chertsey.

DENHOLM, James Lovell Brake Farm, St Andrews KY16 8LZ — MB ChB 1995 Aberd.

DENHOLM, Margaret Jack Roxburghe House, Tor Na Dee Hospital, Milltimber AB13 0HR Tel: 01224 681818; 22 Hillview Road, Cults, Aberdeen AB15 9HB Tel: 01224 868327 — MB ChB 1981 Glas.; MRCGP 1988; DRCOG 1986. Clin. Asst. (Palliat. Med.) Roxburghe Hse. Aberd. Prev: Clin. Med. Off. Norwich HA; SHO (Palliat. Med.) Norwich HA; Asst. GP Norwich.

DENHOLM, Rodney Bennett Department of Pathology, West Wales General Hospital, Carmarthen SA31 2AF Tel: 01267 227521 Fax: 01267 227790 — MB ChB 1977 Glas.; BSc Glas. 1974; MBA Keele 1996; FRCPath 1996, M 1985. Cons. Histopath. Carmarthenshire NHS Trust.; Q.A. Pathologist Cevical Screening Wales 18 Cathedral Rd Cardiff. Socs: BMA; ACP; BSCC. Prev: Med. Director, Camathen & Dist. NHS Trust.

DENHOLM, Mr Stuart Walker 4 Trinity Close, Mumbles, Swansea SA3 5SX — MB ChB 1983 Aberd.; FRCS Ed. 1991; FRCS Ed. 1987.

DENHOLM-YOUNG, Hilda Margaret The Nook, Farningham, Dartford DA4 0DT Tel: 01322 862297 — MB ChB 1932 Ed.; MA Ed. 1928, MB ChB 1932. (Univ. Ed.) Socs: BMA & Med. Wom. Federat. Prev: Res. Asst. Phys. Jordanburn Nerve Hosp. Edin.; Resid. Asst. Med. Off. Booth Hall Childr. Hosp. Manch. & Alder; Hey Childr. Hosp. Liverp.

DENIHAN, Cormac Lichfield Street Surgery, 19 Lichfield Street, Walsall WS1 1UG Tel: 01922 20532 Fax: 01922 616605 — MB BCh BAO 1986 Dub.; MRCGP 1992; DRCOG 1991. Prev: Trainee GP Centr. Birm. VTS.

DENING, Thomas Richard Fulbourn Hospital, Cambridge CB1 5EF Tel: 01223 218890 Fax: 01223 218992; 43 Gilmerton Court, Cambridge CB2 2HQ — MB BS 1980 Newc.; MA Camb. 1995; MD Newc. 1989; MRCPsych 1986. Cons. Old Age Psychiat. Addenbrooke's NHS Trust Camb.; Sen. Professional Adviser, Dept. of Health, Lond. Socs: Brit. Neuropsychiat. Assn.; Brit. Geriat. Soc.; Roy. Soc. Med. Prev: Sen. Regist. (Psychiat.) Oxf. RHA; Regional Research Fell. Dept. Psychiat. Univ. Camb.; Regist. (Psychiat.) Camb. HA.

DENING-SMITHERMAN, Peter St. Helens, East Farleigh, Maidstone ME15 0JT Tel: 01622 726219 — MB BS 1955 Lond.; MRCPsych 1971; DPM Eng. 1967. (St. Geo.) Vis. Psychiat. HM Prisons Servs. Prev: Med. Supt. St. Joseph's Hosp. Nguludi, Nyasaland.

DENIS, Raymond Basil 74 Cavendish Avenue, Ealing, London W13 0JN — MB BCh BAO 1976 Dub.; MA, MB BCh BAO Dub. 1976; BSc (Hons.) Open Univ. 1998. Staff Grade Haemat. & Oncol.Bristol Centre; Regist. (Path.) Harefield Hosp. Middlx. Prev: SHO (Path.) N.wick Pk. Hosp. Harrow; Regist.Path.harefield Hosp.Middx; Regist. (Haemat.) Mt. Vernon Hosp. Middlx.

DENIS LE SEVE, Patrick Thomas 91 Alric Avenue, New Malden KT3 4JP — MB ChB 1988 Manch.

DENIS LE SEVE, Philip Anthony The Health Centre, University of Sussex, Falmer, Brighton BN1 9RW Tel: 01273 679434 Fax: 01273 675689 — MB ChB 1984 Manch.; MB ChB Manch. l984; MRCGP 1989; DCH RCP Lond. 1987; DRCOG 1986.

DENIS-SMITH, Derek 37 Castle Street, Luton LU1 3AG Tel: 01582 726123 Fax: 01582 731150; 129 New Bedford Road, Luton LU3 1LF Tel: 01582 720170 — MB BChir Camb. 1959; MRCS Eng. LRCP Lond. 1959; DObst RCOG 1965.

DENISON, David Maurice Trelawney, Woburn Hill, Addlestone KT15 2QQ — MB BS 1961 Lond.; PhD Lond. 1968, BSc 1957, MB BS 1961; FRCP Lond. 1986, M 1979. (Westm.) Cons. (Respirat. Physiol.) Brompton Hosp. Lond.; Prof. Clin. Physiol. Cardiothoracic Inst. Univ. Lond. Socs: Med. Research Soc. & Brit. Thoracic Soc. Prev: Cons. Aviat. Physiol. RAF Inst. Aviat. Med. FarnBoro.; Sen. Research; Fell. & Hon. Sen. Regist. Roy. Postgrad. Med. Sch. Lond.; Assoc. Research Physiol. & Lect. Med. Univ. Calif. San Diego, USA.

DENISON, Fiona Charlotte 26 Braid Hills Road, Edinburgh EH10 6HY — MB ChB 1994 Ed.; BSc (Med. Sci.) Hons. Ed. 1992. SHO (O & G) SMMP & Roy. Infirm. Edin. Socs: MDDUS. Prev: Ho. Off. (Gen. Med.) Roy. Infirm. Edin.; Ho. Off. (Gen. Surg.) St. John's Hosp. Livingstone.

DENISON, Margaret Amelia Catherine Ivybank, 226 Union Grove, Aberdeen AB10 6SS — MB ChB 1996 Aberd.

DENISON, Richard Stephen Bruntsfield Medical Practice, 11 Forbes Road, Edinburgh EH10 4EY Tel: 0131 228 6081 Fax: 0131 229 4330; 26 Braid Hills Road, Edinburgh EH10 6HY Tel: 0131 447 3823 — MB ChB 1965 Ed.; FRCGP 1986, M 1972; DCH Eng. 1969; DObst RCOG 1967. (Ed.) Princip. Gen. Pract.; GP Trainer (Community Paediat.) Lothian HB; Sch. Med. Off. Geo. Heriots Trust. Socs: (Comm. Mem.) Edin. Medico-Chirurgical Soc. Prev: Occupat. Health Phys. City Hosp. Edin.; DHSS Examg. Doctor, Med. Bds. (Indust. & War Injuries) Edin.

DENKEMA, Jacobus Francois 3 St John's Road, Wrexham LL13 8PG — MB ChB 1991 Orange Free State.

DENLEY, Helen Elizabeth Department of Pathology, Nottingham City Hospital, Edwards Lane, Nottingham NG5 1PB; 51 Repton Road, Bulwell, Nottingham NG6 9GE — MB ChB 1992 Leic. Lect. (Histopath.) Nottm. City Hosp. NHS Trust. Prev: SHO (Histopath.) Roy. Liverp. Univ. Hosp. NHS Trust; Specialist Regist. (Histopath.) Univ. Hosp. Trust & Nottm. City Hosp. Trust.

DENMAN, Alan Michael Kingsley Unit, Northwick Park & St Marks NHS Trust, North Park Hospital, Harrow HA1 3UJ Tel: 020 8869 2621; Gaters, Old Shire Lane, Chorleywood, Rickmansworth WD3 5PW Tel: 01923 283959 Fax: 01923 283959 Email: amdenman@btinternet.com — MB BS 1958 Lond.; FRCP Lond. 1975, M 1961. (Char. Cross) Cons. Clin. Immunol.; Dir. Clin. Studies Harrow.

DENMAN, Mr Eric Edward (retired) The Old Barn, Madjeston, Gillingham SP8 5JH Tel: 01747 826131 — MRCS Eng. LRCP Lond. 1954; BA Camb. 1951, MB BChir 1954; FRCS Ed. 1960; FRCS Eng. 1960. Prev: Cons. Orthop. Surg. P.ss Margt. Hosp. Swindon.

DENMAN, Evelyn Joan Gaters, Old Shire Lane, Chorleywood, Rickmansworth WD3 5PW Tel: 01923 283959 Fax: 01923 283959 Email: amdenman@btinternet.com — MB BS 1964 Lond.; MRCS Eng. LRCP Lond. 1964. (Guy's)

DENMAN, Francesca Marie Carola dept Psychological treatment, Addenbrookes Hospital, Cambridge CB2 2QQ Tel: 01223 217958 — MB BS 1985 Lond.; MRCPsych 1989. Cons. Psychiat.Psychother.Addenbrookes Hosp; Assoc. Clin. Lect. Univ. Cambs. Prev: Sen. Regist. (Psychother.) Cassel Hosp. Richmond.

DENMAN, Geoffrey Highcot, Gwaenysgor, Rhyl LL18 6EP Tel: 01745 857118 Fax: 0871 056 8620 Email: doctor@pega.demon.co.uk — MRCS Eng. LRCP Lond. 1978; MRCGP 1984; MFOM RCP Lond. 1995, AFOM 1992. Cons. Occupat. Med. Glan Clwyd Hosp. Rhyl; Med. Adviser, Chesh. Co. Counc. Socs: Soc. Occupat. Med.; Asscoiation of NHS Occupat.al Physcians (ANHOPS); Assn. Local Auth. Med. Advisers (Alama. Prev: Med. Off. BR York; GP RAF Med. Br.; SHO (Cas. & Orthop. Surg.) Glan Clwyd Hosp. Bodelwyddan.

DENMAN, Margaret Susan Dr Margaret Denman, Marston Medical Centre, 24 Cherwell Drive, Oxford OX3 0LY Tel: 01865 744066 Fax: 01865 744066 — MB ChB 1972 Liverp.; DFFP 1993; DObst RCOG 1975. (Liverpool) Socs: Inst. Psychosexual Med. Prev: Clin. Asst. (Family Plann.) Alex Turnbull Clinic; GP Newc. & Oxf.; Clin. Asst. (Gyn.) John Radcliffe Hosp. Oxf.

DENMAN, Phyllis (retired) 41 Oakfield Road, Ashtead KT21 2RD — MRCS Eng. LRCP Lond. 1945.

DENMAN, Yvonne Louise Cornerways Medical Centre, Parkers Close, Gorley Road, Poulner, Ringwood BH24 1SD Tel: 01425 476688 Fax: 01425 470030 — BM BS Nottm. 1986; BMedSci Nottm. 1984; MRCGP 1990; DRCOG 1990; DCH RCP Lond. 1989. (Nottm.) Prev: SHO (Paediat.) Heatherwood Hosp. Ascot; SHO (Geriat. Med.) Worthing Hosp.; SHO (O & G) S.lands Hosp. Shoreham-by-Sea.

DENMAN-JOHNSON, Mark Melville Street Surgery, 17 Melville Street, Ryde PO33 2AF Tel: 01983 811431 Fax: 01983 817215 — MRCS Eng. LRCP Lond. 1973.

DENN, Mr Peter Gerald Pelyn Tor, Lostwithiel PL22 0JF Tel: 01208 872495 — MB BCh 1975 Wales; FRCS (Eng.) 1981. Assoc. Specialist (Orthop.) Roy. Cornw. Hosp. Truro. Prev: Staff Grade Surg. (Orthop.) Roy. Cornw. Hosp. Truro.; Regist. (Orthop.) Black Notley Hosp. Essex; Regist. (Surg.) Swansea Health Dist.

DENNARD, David Leslie The Pikes Lane Centre, Deane Road, Bolton BL3 5HP Tel: 01204 874300 Fax: 01204 874305 — MB ChB 1965 Manch. (Manch.) Socs: Bolton Med. Soc. Prev: Ho. Surg. & Ho. Phys. Bolton & Dist. Gen. Hosp.; Ho. Surg. Wythenshawe Matern. Hosp.

DENNEHY, Constance Marguerita Tel: 020 7935 0640; 18 Montpelier Grove, London NW5 2XD Tel: 020 7485 4210 Fax: 020 7485 4210 Email: dr.dennehy@medix-uk.xom — MB ChB 1955 NZ; FRCP Ed. 1979, M 1960; FRCPsych 1991, M 1971; DPM Eng. 1961. (Otago) Emerit. Cons. Qu. Eliz. Hosp. Lond.; Emerit. Sen. Lect. (Child Psychiat.) St. Bart. Hosp. Lond. Socs: Fell. Roy. Soc. Med. Prev: Med. Dir. Woodberry Down Child Guid. Clinic; Cons. Child Psychiat. Hosp. Childr. Lond.; Hon. Snr. Lect., St. Bartholomews Hosp., Child Psychiat., Lond.

DENNEHY, Harry Anthony (retired) 12 Park Way, Shenfield, Brentwood CM15 8LH Tel: 01277 224211 Fax: 01277 224211 — MB BCh BAO 1954 NUI; DCH NUI 1959; DPH NUI 1957. Prev: GP Upminster.

DENNELL, Miss Lucy Veronica Anne 18 Buxton Road, Archway, London N19 3XX Tel: 020 7281 5176 Fax: 020 7281 5176 Email: lucy@wilsonxxx.freeserve.co.uk — MB BS 1993 Lond.; BSc (Hons.) Hist. of Med. Lond. 1990; FRCS Eng 1999. (Roy. Free Hosp. Sch. Med.) SHO (Basic Surgic. Train.). Prev: SHO (Trauma) John Radcliffe Hosp. Oxf.; SHO (A & E) Norf. & Norwich Hosp.

DENNER, John Anthony (retired) Nutwood, 5 Selhurst Close, East Preston, Littlehampton BN16 2SR Tel: 01903 770338 — MB ChB 1971 St. And.; DObst RCOG 1976; DCH Eng. 1975; Cert. Family Plann. RCOG & RCGP & FPA 1975; DA Eng. 1973. Prev: GP Littlehampton.

DENNER, Paul James Tel: 01460 63071 Fax: 01460 66560 Email: paul.denner@essexhouse.nhs.uk; Willhayne Farm House, Wadeford, Chard TA20 3BA — MB ChB 1979 Birm.; MRCGP 1984; DCH RCP Lond. 1984; DRCOG 1983. Gen. Practitioner, Essex Ho. Med. Centre, Chard. Prev: SHO (A & E & Orthop.) Univ. Hosp. Nottm.; SHO (Thoracic Surg.) Frenchay Hosp. Bristol.; Trainee GP N. Devon VTS.

DENNES, William James Benedict 22 Dlae Street, Chiswick, London W4 2BL — MB BS 1989 Lond.; PhD Univ. of Canada 2001. (Univ. Lond. Roy. Free Hosp. Sch. Med.) Specialist Regist. (O & G) N. W. Thames Region. Socs: Fell. Roy. Soc. Med. Prev: Research Fell. (Hon. Regist.) Inst. O & G Roy. Postgrad. Med. Sch. Qu. Charlotte's & Chelsea Hosp. Lond.; SHO (O & G) Hammersmith Hosp. Lond.; Med. Off. MOD.

DENNESS, Mr Thomas (retired) 7 Hudshaw Gardens, Hexham NE46 1HY — MB BS 1936 Lond.; MChOrth Liverp. 1948; FRCS Eng. 1946; MRCS Eng. LRCP Lond. 1935. Prev: Cons. Orthop. Surg. E. Suff. & Boro. Gen. Hosps. Ipswich.

DENNEY, Meiling Christina The Stanground Surgery, Stanground, Peterborough PE2 8RB Tel: 01733 568569 Fax: 01733 892419; Field Farm House, Bullock Road, Washingley, Peterborough PE7 3SJ Tel: 01733 244780 Email: r.a.withers@lineone.net — MB BS 1983 Lond.; MRCGP 1988; DRCOG 1986; DCH RCP Lond. 1986. (Char. Cross Hosp. Lond.) Benefits Agency P'boro.; RCGP Examr. P'boro.

DENNEY, Robert William The Stables, Teagues Farm, Lewes Road, Scaynes Hill, Haywards Heath RH17 7NG — MB BS 1986 Lond.

DENNING, Anne Margaret PO Box 15, Chipping Campden GL55 6YQ — BM 1985 Soton.; FRCOphth. 1992; DO RCS Eng. 1989. Cons. Opthalmologist, Speciality Paediatric Opthalmology and Strabismus. Prev: Sen. Regist. (Ophth.) Manch.; Fell. in Paediatric Opthalmology (Vancouver); Regist. (Ophth.) Univ. Hosp. Wales Cardiff.

DENNING, David Wemyss Department of Infectious Diseases & Tropical Medicine, North Manchester General Hospital, Delaunays Road, Manchester M8 5RB Tel: 0161 720 2734 Fax: 0161 720 2732; 40 Crescent Road, Hale, Altrincham WA15 9NA Tel: 0161 928 3811 — MB BS 1980 Lond.; LMSSA Lond. 1980; FRCP Lond. 1995; MRCP (UK) 1983; MRCPath 1992; T(M) 1991; DCH RCP Lond. 1984; Cert. Family Plann. RCOG & RCGP 1982; FRCPath Lond. 1997. (Univ. Lond. & Guy's Hosp.) Sen. Lect. (Infec. Dis.) Univ. Manch. Hope. & N. Manch. Gen. Hosp. Socs: Liveryman Soc. Apoth. Lond.; Brit. Soc. Study of Infec.; Amer. Soc. Microbiol. Prev: Postdoctoral Fell. (Infect. Dis. & Diag. Microbiol.) Stanford Univ. Calif., USA; Sen. Regist. (Infec. Dis.) N.wick Pk. Hosp. Harrow; Regist. (Med.) Univ. Coll. & Roy. Masonic Hosps. Lond. & Stobhill Hosp. Glas.

DENNING, Miss Zyrieda Pontoppidan Abbotswood, Abbotswood Drive, Weybridge KT13 0LT — MB BS 1986 Lond.; FRCS Eng. 1990. Cons. Roy. Hants. Co. Hosp. Winchester. Socs: Brit. Assn. Accid. & Emerg. Med. Prev: Sen. Regist. Frimley Pk. Hosp.; Regist. (A & E) Frimley Pk. Hosp. Surrey; SHO Rotat. (Surg.) Char. Cross Hosp. Lond.

DENNIS, Andrew Richard 76 Whirlowdale Road, Sheffield S7 2NJ — MB BS 1986 Newc.; FRCA 1991; DA (UK) 1988. Cons. Anaesth. N. Gen. Hosp. Sheff. Prev: Sen. Regist. (Anaesth.) Sheff.; Research Fell. (Anaesth.) Nottm.; Regist. Nottm. & Mansfield.

DENNIS, Anne Sylvia 8A Thorn Grove, Bishop's Stortford CM23 5LD Tel: 01279 652485 — MRCS Eng. LRCP Lond. 1971; MFFP 1994; DObst RCOG 1973. (Middlx.) SCMO Essex & Herts. Community Trust. Socs: Brit. Paediat. Assn. Prev: Sen. Med. Off. Bexley Health Dist.; SHO (Paediat.) Sydenham Childr. Hosp.; SHO (O & G) St. Albans City Hosp.

DENNIS, Beatrice Irene (retired) Garthowen, The Ridge, Yatton, Bristol BS49 4DQ Tel: 01934 833265 — MB BS 1951 Lond. Prev: Clin. Med. Off. Avon AHA.

DENNIS, Beryl Yaxley Group Practice, Yaxley Health Centre, Landsdowne Road, Yaxley, Peterborough PE7 3JX Tel: 01733 240478 Fax: 01733 244645; 37 Westwood Park Road, Peterborough PE3 6JL Tel: 01733 564727 Fax: 01733 555920 Email: beryldennis@compuserve.com — MB ChB Birm. 1969; FRCGP 1995, M 1980; Dip. Pract. Dermat. Wales 1993; DTM & H Liverp. 1972; DObst RCOG 1971. (Birm.) Clin. Asst. (Dermat.) P'boro. Hosp. Trust; Med. Off. (Occupat. Health) P'boro. Hosp.

Trust. Socs: Primary Care Rheum. Soc.; Primary Care Dermat. Soc. Prev: Med. Off. Nairobi City Counc., Kenya; SHO (Anaesth) Hereford Gp. Hosps.; Ho. Off. (Paediat.) Birm. Childr. Hosp.

DENNIS, Brenda Josephine (retired) Boyne Cottage, Long Lane, Cann, Shaftesbury SP7 0BJ Tel: 01747 855882 — MB BS 1955 Lond.; MRCS Eng. LRCP Lond. 1955. Prev: Dir. Med. Affairs Johnson & Johnson Ltd. Slough.

DENNIS, Brian Dryhurst Red Hawthornes, Old Hill Crescent, Christchurch, Newport Tel: 01633 420330 — MB BCh 1960 Wales.

DENNIS, Cheryl Anne Rusholme, Llanvihangel Gobian, Abergavenny NP7 9UP — MB BCh 1975 Wales.

DENNIS, Christopher Mark c/o Dr T. W. Higenbottam, Regional Pulmonary Physiology Laboratory, Papworth Hospital, Papworth, Cambridge CB3 8RE; 129 Cambridge Road, Great Shelford, Cambridge CB2 5JJ — MB BS 1981 Sydney; FRACP 1988.

DENNIS, Clive Anthony Russell Dunallan, 24 Newbattle Road, Edbank, Dalkeith EH22 3AH — MB ChB 1956, DPH Ed. 1963.

DENNIS, Donna Louise Flat 2, 74A Lower Richmond Road, London SW15 1LL — MB BS 1994 Lond.

DENNIS, Elizabeth Anne 20 Walkworth Avenue, Worcester WR4 0DE — MB ChB 1994 Birm.; ChB Birm. 1994.

DENNIS, Gary Jon — MB ChB 1994 Leic.; BSc Leic 1992; MRCP 1997. (Leicester) Specialist Regist. Neurol., Roy. Hallamshire Hosp., Sheff. Prev: Gen. Med. SHO Rotat. Leicester.

DENNIS, Geraldine Anne Mary 8 Corslet Road, Currie EH14 5LY — MB BCh BAO 1988 NUI; MRCGO 1992.

DENNIS, Jennifer (retired) 8 Polstead Road, Oxford OX2 6TN — BM BCh 1962 Oxf.; MSc Oxf. 1983, MA 1962, DM 1983; MRCS Eng. LRCP Lond. 1963; DCH Eng. 1969. Hon. Assoc. Specialist. Pk. Hosp., Oxf.. Prev: Assoc. Specialist Childh. Ment. Handicap Pk. Hosp. Childr. Oxf.

DENNIS, Joanne Mary The Homestead, Manor Road, Edgmond, Newport TF10 8JS — MB ChB 1991 Manch.

DENNIS, Kevin Sidney Poverest Medical Centre, 42 Poverest Road, St Mary Cray, Orpington BR5 2DQ Tel: 01689 833643 Fax: 01689 891976 — MB ChB 1980 Leeds; MRCGP 1984; Cert. Family Plann. JCC 1984; DRCOG 1984; DCH RCP Lond. 1983. GP Orpington.

DENNIS, Mr Martin John Stewart Leicester General Hospital (Teaching), Gwendolen Road, Leicester LE5 4PW Tel: 0116 258 8164 Fax: 01162 588256; Fordyce, Gaulby, Leicester LE7 9LP Tel: 0116 259 6669 — BM BS 1983 Nottm.; BMedSci Nottm. 1981; DM Nottm. 1991; FRCS Eng. 1987. Cons. Vasc. Surg. Leicester. Prev: Sen. Regist. (Surg.) Bristol; Regist. Rotat. (Surg.) Nottm. HA; SHO Rotat. (Surg.) Camb. HA.

DENNIS, Martin Scott 3 Clark Road, Edinburgh EH5 3BD — MD 1988 Lond.; MB BS 1980; MRCP (UK) 1983. (St. Thos.) Sen. Lect. (Stroke Med.) & Hon. Cons. Phys. w. Special Responsibil. for Elderly Dept. Clin. Neurosci. W.. Gen. Hosp. Edin. Prev: Sen. Regist. (Gen. Med. & Geriat.) Oxf. & Amersham Hosp.; Acting Clin. Lect. Univ. Dept. Neurol. Oxf.; Regist. (Med.) St. Thos. Hosp. Lond.

DENNIS, Michael Stuart Department of Psychiatry for the Elderly, Leicester General Hospital, Gwendolen Road, Leicester LE5 4PW Tel: 0116 258 4597 Fax: 0116 273 1115 — MB BCh 1983 Wales; MRCPsych 1988. Hon. Cons. Psychiat. & Sen. Lect. (Psychiat. for the Elderly) Leicester Gen. Hosp. Prev: Sen. Regist. (Psychiat.) Univ. Hosp. Nottm.

DENNIS, Michael William Dennis and Partners, The Medical Centre, Folly Lane, Bewsey, Warrington WA5 0LU Tel: 01925 417247 Fax: 01925 444319 — MB ChB 1978 Sheff.

DENNIS, Michael William 8 North Road, West Kirby, Wirral CH48 4DF — MB ChB 1991 Dundee; MRCP (UK) 1996.

DENNIS, Nicholas Robert Wessex Clinical Genetics Service, The Princess Anne Hospital, Coxford Road, Southampton SO16 5YA Tel: 02380 796162 Fax: 02380 794346 Email: nrd1@soton.ac.uk — MB BChir Camb. 1969; BA Camb. 1965; FRCP Lond. 1987, M 1971; FRCPCH. (St. Thos.) Sen. Lect. & Hon. Cons. (Clin. Genetics) Univ. Soton. Hosp. Trust. Socs: Clin. Genetics Soc. & Soc. Study Inborn Errors of Metab.; Counc. Brit. Soc. for Human Genetics. Prev: Mem. Scientif. Staff MRC Clin. Genetics Unit Inst. Child Health Lond.; Asst. Prof. (Paediat. Research) & Buswell Fell. State Univ. New York Buffalo & Childr. Hosp. Buffalo, USA.

DENNIS, Nigel John 1 Danygraig Road, Graigfelin, Clydach, Swansea SA6 5DL — MB BCh 1983 Wales.

DENNIS, Paul David 10 Walton Street, Oxford OX1 2HG — BM BCh 1981 Oxf.

DENNIS, Peter John (retired) 5 Imeravale, Port Ellen PA42 7AL Tel: 01496 302440 — MB ChB 1955 St. And. Prev: GP Skipton.

DENNIS, Peter Julian Collingham Health Centre, High Street, Collingham, Newark NG23 7LB Tel: 01636 892156 Fax: 01636 893391; Greenfield Cottage, South Scarle, Newark NG23 7JH Tel: 01636 892847 Fax: 01636 893391 — MB BChir 1975 Camb.; MA Camb. 1974, MB BChir 1975; FRCGP 1989, M 1979; DRCOG 1978. (Camb. & Middlx.) Examr. Roy. Coll. Gen. Pract. Prev: SHO (Paediat.) MusGr. Pk. Hosp. Taunton; SHO (Med.) Frimley Pk. Hosp.; Ho. Surg. Middlx. Hosp. Lond.

DENNIS, Peter Michael 37 Westwood Park Road, Peterborough PE3 6JL Tel: 01733 64727 — MB ChB 1967 Birm.; BSc (Hons., 1st cl. Anat.) Birm. 1967, MB ChB 1970; MRCPath 1977; DMJ Soc. Apoth. Lond. 1980; DTM & H Liverp. 1972. (Birm.) Cons. (Path.) PeterBoro. Dist. Hosp. Socs: Assn. Clin. Paths. & Brit. Assn. Foren. Med. Prev: Sen. Regist. (Path.) PeterBoro. Dist. Hosp. & New Addenbrooke's; Hosp. Camb.; Lect. Human Path. Univ. Nairobi, Kenya.

DENNIS, Robert Tristan 54 Lochaline Street, London W6 9SH — MB BS 1993 Lond.

DENNIS, Robin Wayne Chimerique, Markington, Harrogate HG3 3NR — MB ChB 1995 Leeds.

DENNIS, Rosemary Elizabeth 3 Clark Road, Edinburgh EH5 3BD — MB BS 1984 Lond.; DRCOG 1988. Clin. Asst. (Haemat.) Haemophilia Centre Roy. Infirm. Edin.

DENNIS, Sarah Ellen Wesley The Surgery, 17 Church St., Ilchester, Yeovil BA22 8LN — MB BS 1983 Lond.; MRCGP 1989; Cert. Family Plann. JCC 1992. (St. Bart. Hosp. Med. Sch.) p/t GP Princip. The Surg. Ilchester Som.; Clin. Asst. Family Plann. Yeovil Dist. Hosp. Prev: Med. Off. Lata Hosp. Santa Cruz Temotu Province, Solomon Is.s; Ho. Phys. Whipps Cross Hosp.; Ho. Surg. Hackney Hosp.

DENNIS, Simon Charles Ralph 100 Whyke Lane, Chichester PO19 2AT — MB BS 1996 Lond.

DENNIS, Simon Timothy 12 Richmond Gardens, Southampton SO17 1RY — BM 1997 Soton.

DENNIS, Theresa Rothes Medical Centre, High St., Rothes, Aberlour AB38 7AU; Tom-na-Muiish, Abert Place, Dufftown, Keith AB55 4AY — MB ChB 1983 Liverp.; DA (UK) 1991; Dip. Obst. Otago 1989. Assoc. GP.

DENNIS, Victor 13 Bucknall Court, Wake Green Park, Birmingham B13 9XR Tel: 0121 449 3554; M. Burese 808, Policka 57201, Czech Republic Tel: 00 10 42 46322117 — MD 1943 Czechoslovakia; FRCGP 1995, M 1953. (Prague & Glas.) Chairm. & Mem. DHSS Med. Bds. Socs: Fell. Roy. Soc. Med.; BMA; Metchley Pk. Med. Soc. Prev: Capt. RAMC; Med. Off. St. Stephen's Hosp. Chelsea.

DENNISON, Mr Arthur James Nicholas (retired) Woodlands, 21 Lyndale Road, Hapton, Burnley BB11 5RD Tel: 01282 75497 — FRCS Ed. 1970; MRCS Eng. LRCP Lond. 1964. Cons. (Orthop.) Burnley Health Dist. Prev: Sen. Regist. (Orthop.) Leeds RHB.

DENNISON, Mr Ashley Robert 376 Helmshore Road, Haslington, Rossendale BB4 4JA — MB ChB 1977 Sheff.; FRCS 1982.

DENNISON, Elaine Margaret MRC Unit, Southampton General Hospital, Tremona Road, Southampton SU1E 64D Tel: 023 80777624 Email: emd@mrc.soton.ac.uk; 15 Hornbeam Gardens, West End, Southampton SO30 3RD Fax: 01703 777624 — MB BChir 1991 Camb.; PHD 2000; MSc Lond. 1997; MA Camb. 1992; MRCP (UK) 1994; MPhil. 1998. (Cambridge University) p/t Sen. Research Fell. MRC Unit Soton. Gen. Hosp.; Specialist Regist. Rheum. Qu. Alexandra Hosp., Wessex Roatation. Prev: Regist. & SHO (Med. for Elderly) Bournemouth Gen. Hosp.; SHO (Haemat.) Soton. Gen. Hosp.

DENNISON, Ernest James (retired) Wray Corner, 1 Raglan Close, Reigate RH2 0EU Tel: 01737 242934 — MB BS Lond. 1933; MRCS Eng. LRCP Lond. 1933; MRCGP 1958. JP E. Sussex (Supplem.); Hon. Med. Off. Qu. Vict. Hosp. E. Grinstead. Prev: Capt. RAMC.

DENNISON, Jacqueline Ann College Road Surgery, 50/52 College Road, Maidstone ME15 6SB Tel: 01622 752345 Fax: 01622 758133 — MB BS 1978 Lond.; DRCOG 1981. GP Maidstone.

DENNISON, James Conquest Hospital, The Ridge, St Leonards-on-Sea TN37 7RD Tel: 01424 755255; Meophams Bank, 307

Sedlescombe Road N., St Leonards-on-Sea TN37 7JL Tel: 01424 751362 — MB BS Lond. 1976; MRCS Eng. LRCP Lond. 1976; FRCP Lond. 1995; MRCP (UK) 1981. Cons. Phys. Conquest Hosp. St. Leonards-on-Sea. Prev: Sen. Regist. Guys Hosp. Lond.; Regist. (Neurol.) Brook Gen. Hosp.; Regist. (Med.) Roy. Hants. Co. Hosp. Winchester.

DENNISON, Janet Mary Adelaide Woodlands, 21 Lyndale Road, Hapton, Burnley BB11 5RD Tel: 01282 75497 — MB ChB 1968 Leeds.

DENNISON, Keith Christopher Victoria Road Health Centre, Victoria Road, Washington NE37 2PU Tel: 0191 417 3557; High Croft, Peareth Hall Road, Springwell, Gateshead NE9 7NT Tel: 0191 416 3182 — MB BS 1968 Newc. (Newc.) Socs: BMA. Prev: SHO Sunderland Eye Infirm.

DENNISON, Mark Lewis The Surgery, 51 Locks Load, Locks Heath, Southampton SO31 7ZL Tel: 01489 583777 Fax: 01489 571374; 15 Hornbeam Gardens, West End, Southampton SO30 3RD — MB BChir 1991 Camb.; MA Camb. 1992; DRCOG 1995; MRCGP 1995. (Cambridge) Prev: Trainee GP Ringwood, Hants.; SHO (Psychiat.) St. Anne's Hosp. Poole; SHO (O & G) Bournemouth & Poole.

DENNISON, Michael Monks Park Surgery, 24 Monks Park Avenue, Horfield, Bristol BS7 0UE Tel: 0117 796 9306, 0117 979 8011 — MB 1975 Camb.; BChir 1974; MA 1975 Camb. Princip. GP, Monks Pk. Surg.; Clin. Asst. Rheum., S.mead Hosp., Wot, Bristol. Socs: BMA; MPS.

DENNISON, Michael George The Old Barn, Guildford Road, Mayford, Woking GU22 9QT — MB BS 1988 Lond.

DENNISON, Peter Hendley 'Moss Bank', 621 Warwick Road, Solihull B91 1AP Tel: 0121 705 0805 — MRCS Eng. LRCP Lond. 1953; FFA RCS Eng. 1961; DA Eng. 1956. (St. Thos.) Cons. Anaesth. Solihull Hosp. & Roy. Orthop. Hosp. Birm. Socs: Assn. Anaesth. Prev: Sen. Regist. St. Geo. Hosp.; Regist. Lond. Chest Hosp.; Sen. Resid. Anaesth. St. Thos. Hosp.

DENNITTS, Paul James Boughton Medical Group, Boughton Health Centre, Hoole Lane, Chester CH2 3DP Tel: 01244 325421; 17 Eaton Road, Handbridge, Chester CH4 7EN — MB ChB 1972 Sheff.; MRCGP 1977.

DENNO, Hannah Mary Windle Grange, Rainford Road, St Helens WA10 6DB — MB ChB 1988 Sheff.; MA Camb. 1989; MRCGP 1992; T(GP) 1992; DRCOG 1991. GP Retainer Scheme Rainbow Med. Centre St Helens Merseyside. Prev: Trainee GP/SHO Ormskirk Hosp. Lancs. VTS.

DENNY, Catherine Marie 3 Rostron Crescent, Formby, Liverpool L37 2ET — MB ChB 1989 Sheff.

DENNY, Frank (retired) Revack Lodge, Comrie Road, Crieff PH7 4BP Tel: 01764 652003 Email: denny@revack.demon.co.uk — MD Lond. 1953, MB BS 1943; MRCS Eng. LRCP Lond. 1943; FRCOG 1962, M 1949. Prev: Cons. (O & G) Kensington, Chelsea & W.minster HA.

DENNY, Mark Richard Leslie Clarence Medical Centre, Vansittart Road, Windsor SL4 5AS Tel: 01753 865773 Fax: 01753 833694 — MB BS 1978 Lond. (Char. Cross Hosp.) Socs: Windsor & Dist. Med. Soc. Prev: SHO (O & G & ENT Surg.) Johannesburg Gen. Hosp.; Ho. (Orthop.) Char. Cross Hosp.

DENNY, Michael Frank Sheet Street Surgery, 21 Sheet Street, Windsor SL4 1BZ Tel: 01753 860334 Fax: 01753 833696; 5 Temple Road, Windsor SL4 1HP Tel: 01753 856798 — MB BChir 1975 Camb.; MA Camb. 1975. (St. Bart.)

DENNY, Nicholas Malcolm Birchdale, Market Lane, Crimplesham, King's Lynn PE33 9DZ — MB BS 1974 Lond.; FFA RCS Eng. 1983. (St. Thos.) Cons. Anaesth. Qu. Eliz. Hosp. King's Lynn. Socs: Assn. Anaesth. & Obst. Anaesth. Assn. Prev: Sen. Regist. (Anaesth.) Addenbrooke's Hosp. Camb.; Regist. Dept. Anaesth. St. Thos. Hosp.; Med. Off. Roy. Flying Doctor Serv. Kalgoorlie W. Australia.

DENNY, Paul Anthony The Health Centre, Midland St., Long Eaton, Nottingham NG10 1NY Tel: 0115 973 2157 Fax: 0115 946 5420 — MB BS 1976 Lond.; MRCS Eng. LRCP Lond. 1976; MRCGP 1981; DRCOG 1980. (Westm.) GP Trainer Nottm. VTS. Socs: Assur. Med. Soc.

DENNY, Roger Stephen Heaton St Martins Hospital, Milford Road, Bath BA2 5RP Tel: 01225 832383; 13 Pritchard Road, Oxford OX3 0DG Tel: 01865 721639 — MB ChB 1991 Bristol; BSc (Hons.) Psychol. Bristol 1988. SHO (c/o Elderly) St. Martins Hosp. Trust RHA. Prev: Ho. Off. Bath; Ho. Surg. Taunton.

DENNY, Simon John 235 Sternhold Avenue, Streatham Hill, London SW2 4PG — MB ChB 1993 Auckland.

DENNY, Susannah Radnor House Surgery, 25 London Road, Ascot — BM BCh 1992 Oxf.; LoC IUT 1999; BA (Hons.) Physiol. Sci. Oxf. 1989; DRCOG 1995; DFFP 1996; T (GP) 1997. (Oxford) p/t GP Non-Princip. Socs: Organiser, Berks. Non Princip. Gp. Prev: GP Princip., Binfield Surg., Berks.; SHO (Palliat. Med.) Derby; GP/Regist. N.ampton.

DENNY, Mr William Roy (retired) The Cottage, La Dimerie, St Mary, Jersey JE3 3DP — MRCS Eng. LRCP Lond. 1946; FRCS Eng. 1952; DLO Eng. 1949.

DENNYS, Elizabeth (retired) 38 Belsize Grove, London NW3 4TR — MB BS Lond. 1949; DObst RCOG 1952.

DENNYSON, Mr William George Springbank, High Cross Avenue, Melrose TD6 9SU — MB ChB 1966 Ed.; FRCS Ed. 1971. (Ed.) Cons. Orthop. Surg. Borders Gen. Hosp. Melrose. Prev: Cons. Orthop. Surg. Univ. Natal S. Africa; Sen. Regist. Dept. Orthop. Surg. Edin. Hosps.

DENOVAN, Eric Duncan Buchanan (retired) Old Mission House, North Erradale, Gairloch IV21 2DL — MB ChB Glas. 1947; MRCGP 1961.

DENOVAN, Jillian 23 Cecil Street, Stirling FK7 7PH — MB ChB 1998 Dund.; MB ChB Dund 1998.

DENSEM, Cameron George Wythenshawe Hospital, Southmoor Road, Wythemshawe, Manchester M23 9LT Tel: 0161 998 7070 — MB ChB 1993 Liverp.; BSc (Hons.) Liverp. 1990; MRCP (UK) 1996. (Liverp.) Research Regist. (Cardiol.) Wythenshawe Hosp. Manch. Prev: SHO (Cardiorespirat. Med.) Wythenshawe Hosp. Manch.; SHO (Med.) Macclesfield Dist. Gen. Hosp.

DENSHAM, Caroline Ann 14 Redcliffe Road, Torquay TQ1 4QG — MB ChB 1993 Bristol; Dip. Anaesth. (UK) 1997.

DENSHAM, Elizabeth Patricia St Quintins Health Centre, St. Quintin Avenue, London W10 6NX Tel: 020 8960 5677 Fax: 020 8968 5933 — BM 1983 Soton.; MRCGP 1990; DCH RCP Lond. 1990; Cert. Family Plann. JCC 1988; DRCOG 1987. (Southampton) Socs: Brit. Soc. Allergy Environm. and Nutrit. Med.; Nat. Sports Med. Inst. Prev: Trainee GP Brighton VTS; Clin. Med. Off. (Paediat.) St. Mary's Hosp. Lond.

DENSHAM, Lucy Jane 14 Redcliffe Road, Torquay TQ1 4QG — MB ChB 1994 Bristol.

DENSHAM, Peter Robert, RD The Medical Centre, St. Marychurch, Torquay TQ1 4QX Tel: 01803 325123 Email: pdensham@aol.com — MB ChB 1969 Bristol; MRCS Eng. LRCP Lond. 1968; MRCGP 1980; DMJ Soc. Apoth. Lond. 1984; DA Eng. 1971; DObst RCOG 1972. (Bristol)

DENT, Andrew John Fulford Surgery, 2 Fulford Park, Fulford, York YO10 4QE Tel: 01904 625566 Fax: 01904 671539; Fulford Surgery, 2 Fulford Park, Fulford, York YO10 4QE — MB ChB 1978 Glas.; MRCP (UK) 1982; MRCGP 1983. (Glas.) Prev: Trainee GP York; Regist. (Med.) York Dist. Hosp.; SHO (Geriat.) Gartnavel Gen. Hosp. Glas.

DENT, Andrew Robert Longfield Road Surgery, 1 Longfield Road, Harpfields, Stoke-on-Trent ST4 6QN Tel: 01782 616587 Fax: 01782 719108; 19 Sandon Avenue, Westlands, Newcastle ST5 3QB Tel: 01782 610035 — MB ChB 1980 Birm.; MRCGP 1990; Dip. Sports Med. (Scott. Roy. Coll.) 1991; DRCOG 1989. Med. Off. Stoke City Football Club.; Med. Off. Eng. Under 18 Football Team. Prev: SHO Rotat. (Plastic Surg. & Surg.) Train. Program. N. Staffs. Hosp. Centre Stoke-on-Trent; SHO (Orthop.) Roy. Orthop. Hosp. Birm.

DENT, Catherine Jane 9 Waverley Close, Odiham, Basingstoke RG29 1AT — MB ChB 1975 Dundee.

DENT, Christopher Charles Staff and Partners, Queensway Medical Centre, Olympic Way, Wellingborough NN8 3EP Tel: 01933 678767 Fax: 01933 676657 — MB BS 1986 Lond.

DENT, Mr Colin Michael Church Cottage, St. Hilary, Cowbridge CF71 7DP — MB BS 1984 Lond.; FRCS (Orth.) Eng. 1993; FRCS Eng. 1988. Hon. Cons. & Sen. Lect. (Orthop.) Univ. Wales Coll. Med. Cardiff.

DENT, Howard Gordon Raymond 29 Springfield Close, Burton-on-the-Wolds, Loughborough LE12 5AN — MB BS 1984 Lond.; BA Camb. 1981; FCAnaesth. 1989. Regist. (Anaesth.) Roy. Nat. Throat, Nose & Ear Hosp. Lond.

DENT, Joanna Tracey 63 Mallard Point, Rainhill Way, London E3 3JF — MB BS 1992 Lond.

DENT, John Aaron Ealing Hammersmith & Fulham NHS Trust, Uxbridge Road, Southall UB1 3EU Tel: 020 8574 2444 Email: johndent1@hotmail.com — MB BChir 1988 Camb.; MRCPsych 1992. Cons. (Psychiat.) W. Lond. Healthcare NHS Trust S.all. Prev: Research Regist. (Psychiat.) Char. Cross & W.m. Med. Sch. Lond.

DENT, Mr John Anthony University Department Orthopaedic Surgery, Royal Infirmary, Dundee DD1 9ND Tel: 01382 22803 Fax: 01382 202460 Email: j.a.dent@dundee.ac.uk; 12 Glamis Drive, Dundee DD2 1QL — MD 1991 Dundee; MB ChB 1977; FRCS Ed. 1983; MMed Educat. Dundee 1993. Sen. Lect. (Orthop. & Trauma Surg.) Univ. Dundee; Hon. Cons. Tayside HB; Sen. Lect. Univ. Dundee. Socs: Brit. Soc. Surg. Hand; Brit. Shoulder and Elbow Soc.; Assn. for Study of Med. Educat. Prev: Lect. (Orthop. & Trauma Surg.) Univ. Dundee; Kleinert Hand Fell. (Hand Surg.) Univ. Louisville Kentucky, USA; Hand Research Fell. Univ. Ed. & P.ss Margt. Rose Orthop. Hosp.

DENT, Mrs Kara Stephanie Slade Cottage, Stanton, Ashbourne DE6 2BY — MB BS 1992 Lond.; MRCOG 1998. (Lond.) Specialist Regist.

DENT, Kristina Jane 15 Honeywell Road, London SW11 6EQ — MB BS 1984 Lond.

DENT, Mervyn Terence 29 Springfield Close, Burton-on-the-Wolds, Loughborough LE12 5AN — MD 1992 Sheff.; BA Camb. 1979; MB ChB Bristol 1982; MRCP (UK) 1986. Career Regist. (Med., Diabetes & Endocrinol.) N. Gen. Hosp. Sheff. Prev: Research Regist Roy. Hallamsh. Hosp. Sheff.

DENT, Monica Ann Mill Barn Cottage, Mill Lane, Ecchinswell, Newbury RG20 4UD — MB ChB 1986 Birm.; MFPHM 1997; DPH 1992; DCH Otago, NZ 1990. Cons. Pub.health.med.Berks. HA. Prev: Regist. (Pub. Health Med.) Camb. HA.; Sen. Regist. (Pub. Health Med.) NW Anglia HA; Sen.Regist.Pub.health.Med W Surrey HA.

DENT, Philip 'Denville', 16 Dorset Lake Avenue, Lilliput, Poole BH14 8JD — MB ChB 1958 Bristol; DObst RCOG 1965. Prev: Surg. Lt.-Cdr. RN.

DENT, Richard Gordon White Cottage, 10 The Green, Datchworth, Knebworth SG3 6TL Tel: 01438 812156 Fax: 01438 817098 — MB BChir 1974 Camb.; MA 1974 Camb.; MD 1983 Camb.; BChir 1973 Camb.; MB 1974 Camb.; FRCP Lond. 1992; MRCP (UK) 1975. (Guy's) Cons. Phys. (Gen. Med. & Thoracic Med.) Qu. Eliz. II Hosp. Welwyn; Garden City & Hertford Co. Hosp. Prev: Sen. Med. Regist. (Thoracic Med.) Papworth Hosp. Camb.; Sen. Med. Regist. PeterBoro. Dist. Hosp.; Clin. Lect. Cardiothoracic Inst. Lond. Jun. Med. Regist. Guy's.

DENT, Thomas Francis Pinfold Health Centre, Field Road, Bloxwich, Walsall WS3 3JP — MB BS 1971 Lond.; MRCGP 1986; DCH RCP Lond. 1985. Princip. GP Pinfold Health Centre; PCG Comm. Mem. Prev: Regist. (Med.) Qu. Eliz. II Hosp. Welwyn Gdn. City.; Gen. Med. Off. Chililabombwe Hosp. Zambia.

DENT, Thomas Henry Stephen North & Mid Hampshire Health Authority, Harness House, Aldermaston Road, Basingstoke RG24 9NB — MB BS 1988 (Hons.) Lond.; MRCP (UK) 1991; MFPHM RCP (UK) 1994; DPH Camb. 1992. (Guy's Hosp. Med. Sch.) Cons. Pub. Health Med. N. & Mid Hants. HA; Vis. Sen. Lect., Nat.Co-ordinating Centre for Health Technol. Assessm. Univ. of S.ampton. Prev: Sen. Regist. (Pub. Health Med.) Camb. HA; SHO (Gen. Med.) Wolverhampton HA; Ho. Phys. Guy's Hosp. Lond.

DENTON, Allan 91 Lea Village, Birmingham B33 9SG — MB ChB 1957 Birm.

DENTON, Arshi Sulaiman Department of Oncology, Mount Vernon Hospital, Rickmansworth, Northwood HA6 2RN Tel: 01923 826111; 145, Pinner Road, Northwood HA6 1DB Tel: 01923 450695 Email: acdenton@compuserve.com — BSc (Hons.) Lond. 1987, MB BS 1990; MRCP (UK) 1994; FRCR 1998. (Royal Free Hospital) p/t Regist. Rotat. (Clin. Oncol.) Middlx. & Roy. Free Hosps. Lond. & Mt. Vernon Hosp.; Research Regist. Mt. Vernon Hosp. Prev: SHO (Clin. Oncol.) St. Bart. Hosp. Lond.

DENTON, Christopher Paul Department of Rheumatology, Royal Free Hospital, Pond Street, Hampstead, London NW3 2PF Tel: 020 7794 0500; 8 Parkgate Mews, Highgate, London N6 5NB Tel: 020 8342 9497 — PhD 1997; BSc (Hons.) Lond. 1983, MB BS 1986; MRCP (UK) 1990. Sen. Lect. in Rheum. (Hon. Cons.), Roy. Free Hosp., ondon; ARC Sen. Research Fell. Prev: Wellcome Advanced Fell. (Houston, USA); ARC Clin. Research Fell. & Hon. Sen. Regist. (Rheum.) Roy. Free Hosp. Lond.; Regist. Rotat. (Rheum. & Gen. Med.) Roy. Free Hosp. Lond.

DENTON, David Vaux 8 Holly Bank, Leeds LS6 4DJ Tel: 0113 278 5352 Fax: 0113 230 6174 — MB ChB 1956 Leeds.

DENTON, Elizabeth Mary Clare 111 Station Road, Glenfield, Leicester LE3 8GS Tel: 0116 287 3604; 10 Kingcup Close, Hunters Lodge, Leicester Forest E., Leicester LE3 3JU Tel: 0116 239 3066 — MB ChB 1985 Leic.; BSc MedSci (Hons.) Leic. 1982, MB ChB 1985; MRCGP 1989; DRCOG 1988. Socs: Fac. Bd. Leic. RCGP.

DENTON, Erika Ruth Elizabeth Dept. of Radiology, Norfolk and Norwich NHS Trust, Brunswick Road, Norwich NR1 3SR; St Margarets House, 1 Staithway Road, Wroxham, Norwich NR12 8TH Tel: 01603 781506 — MB BS 1989 Lond.; FRCR 1995; MRCP 1992 UK; MRCP (UK) 1992; FRCR 1995. (UMDS Lond.) Cons. Radiologist Norf. and Norwich NHS Trust; Clin. Director of BrE. Imaging Norf. and Norwich NHS Trust.

DENTON, Ernest Percival, MBE 10 Kimberley Drive, Sidcup DA14 4QF — MRCS Eng. LRCP Lond. 1952. (Lond. Hosp.)

DENTON, George Carlton Woodhouse Health Centre, Woodhouse St., Leeds LS6 2SF Tel: 0113 431281 & 452004 — MRCS Eng. LRCP Lond. 1956.

DENTON, Gregory Manor Street Surgery, Manor Street, Ruskington, Sleaford NG34 9EN Tel: 01526 832204 — MB BS 1981 Lond.; MRCGP 1987; DRCOG 1985.

DENTON, Mr John Stephen Whiston Hospital, Prescot L35 5DR; Fairfield Independent Hospital, Crank, St Helens WA11 7RS — MB ChB 1976 Sheff.; FRCS Eng. 1981; MChOrth. Liverp. 1984. Cons. Orthop. Surg. Whiston Hosp. Merseyside.

DENTON, Karin June Department of Cellular Pathology, Southmead Hospital, Bristol BS10 5NB Tel: 0117 959 5641 Fax: 0117 959 0087; Pound Farm, Lower Morton, Thornsbury, Bristol BS35 1LD — MB ChB 1987 Sheff.; MRCPath 1994. Cons. Histopath. (Cytol. Path.) S.mead Hosp. Bristol; Dir. S. W. Regional Cervical Screening Quality Assur. Team.

DENTON, Mark 13 Church Street, Bishop Middleham, Ferryhill DL17 9AF — MB BS 1977 Newc.; DRCOG 1986. Socs: BMA. Prev: Maj. RAMC.

DENTON, Melanie Jayne 39 Atherstone Avenue, Netherton, Peterborough PE3 9TU; the Old Bakery, 25 West St, Easton on the Hill, Stamford PE9 3LS Tel: 01780 753898 — MB ChB 1990 Leic.; BSc (Hons.) Leic. 1987. Retainee Oundle. Surg; Clin. Assist. Prev: Trainee GP P'boro. VTS.

DENTON, Mervyn Vyvyan Hulton (retired) 107 Harley Street, London W1 — MRCS Eng. LRCP Lond. 1938; FFA RCS Eng. 1954; DA Eng. 1944. Prev: Sen. Anaesth. Roy. Nat. Orthop. Hosp.

DENTON, Michael Beresford 11 The Willows, Station Road, Rustington, Littlehampton BN16 3BB — MB BS 1970 Lond.; MA Camb. 1955; MRCS Eng. LRCP Lond. 1970; DObst RCOG 1972. (St. Mary's) Socs: Fell. Roy. Soc. Trop. Med. & Hyg. Prev: Res. Obst. Asst. Qu. Mary's Hosp. Roehampton; Ho. Surg. St. Helier Hosp. Carshalton; Ho. Phys. St. Mary's Hosp. Lond.

DENTON, Miles The General Infirmary at Leeds, Great George St, Leeds LS1 3EX Tel: 0113 392 2922 Fax: 0113 233 5694 Email: milesd@patholoyg.leeds.ac.uk — BM BS 1988 Nottm.; DM Nottingham 1997; MRCPath Royal College of Pathologists 1997. Cons. (Microbiol.) The Gen. Infirm. at Leeds. Prev: Regist. (Microbiol.) Leeds Gen. Infirm.; SHO (Microbiol.) Walton Hosp. Liverp.

DENTON, Paul Henry (retired) Sissells, Purton, Swindon SN5 4BE Tel: 01793 770300 — MB BS 1937 Lond.; MD Lond. 1940; FRCP Lond. 1968, M 1941; LMSSA Lond. 1937. Prev: Princip. Med. Off. Allied Dunbar Assur. Swindon.

DENTON, Peter Francis George (retired) 30 Selsey Avenue, Sale M33 4RL Tel: 0161 973 1019 — MRCS Eng. LRCP Lond. 1943. Prev: Med. Off. GEC Power Engin. Ltd. Manch.

DENTON, Richard 27 winton Road, Bowdon, Altrincham WA14 2PE Tel: 0161 926 8556 Email: rdenton@cwcom.net — MB ChB 1989 Ed.; BSc (Med. Sci) Ed. 1987; MRCP (UK) 1992; FRCA 1994. (Edinburgh University) Cons. Anaesth. Warrington NHS Trust. Prev: Regist. Rotat. (Anaesth.) NW Region; SHO (Anaesth.) Manch. Roy. Infirm.; SHO (Med.) Hope Hosp. Salford.

DENTON, Roger Sinclair Portishead Health Centre, Victoria Square, Portishead, Bristol BS20 6AQ Tel: 01275 847474 Fax: 01275 818250 — MB ChB Sheff. 1987; MRCGP 1992.

DENTON, Susan Elizabeth The Surgery, 143 Park Rs, Camberley GU15 2NN Tel: 01276 26171 — MB ChB 1989 Cape Town; MRCGP 1995; DA (UK) 1994; DA S. Afr. 1992. (Univ. Cape Town) Gen. Practitioner. Socs: BMA.

DENTSCHUK, Anna 8 Millgate, Cuddington, Northwich CW8 2GX — BM BS 1998 Nottm.; BM BS Nottm 1998.

DENVER, Mark David, Maj. RAMC Retd. 26 Ladywell Drive, Fulwood, Preston PR2 9UX Tel: 01772 797629 — MB BS 1990 Lond.; Dip. IMC RCS Ed. 1996; DA (UK) 1995. (Char. Cross & Westm. Hosp.) Trainee (A & E Med.); Clin. Fell. (Accid. & Emegency) Blackpool Vict. Hosp. Socs: Brit. Assn. Immed. Care Schemes; MRCAnaesth.; Roy. Coll. Surg. Prev: Regist. (A & E) Frimley Pk. Hosp.; SHO (Anaesth., Trauma & Orthop.) Frimley Pk. Hosp.; SHO (Anaesth. & Intens. Care) Camb. Milit. Hosp.

DENVIR, Catherine Maire Orla The Surgery, 2 Causeway Place, Newcastle BT33 0DN Tel: 028 4372 2252 Fax: 028 4372 6731 — MB BCh BAO 1987 Belf.; MRCGP 1992; DMH Belf. 1993; DCH Dub. 1991. (Qu. Univ. Belf.)

DENVIR, Louise 33 Logs Hill, Chislehurst BR7 5LN — MB ChB 1992 Bristol. Ho. Off. Taunton & Som. Hosp.

DENVIR, Martin Anthony Cardiology, Western General Hospital, Crewe Road, Edinburgh EH4 2XU Tel: 0131 537 1733 — MB ChB 1987 Glas.; FRCPE 1999; PhD Glas. 1994, BSc (Hons.) 1984; MRCP (UK) 1990. (Glas.) Regist. (Cardiol.) Glas. Roy. Infirm.; Sen. Lect. (Hon. Cons.) (Cardiol.). Prev: Regist. (Cardiol.) Glas. Roy. Infirm.; BHF Jun. Research Fell. Glas.; Ho. Off. Rotat. (Gen. Med.) W.. Infirm. Glas.

DENYER, Mark Edward Seacroft Hospital, York Road, Leeds LS14 6UH Tel: 0113 206 3278 Fax: 0113 206 3736 — MB BS 1970 Lond.; FRCP Lond. 1990; MRCP (UK) 1973; MRCS Eng. LRCP Lond. 1970. Cons. Phys. Seacroft Hosp. Leeds & St. Jas. Univ. Hosp. Leeds. Socs: Brit. Soc. Gastroenterol. & Pancreatic Soc. GB & Irel. Prev: Sen. Regist. (Med.) Univ. Coll. Hosp. Lond.; Wellcome Research Fell. Middlx. Hosp. Lond.; Cons. Gastroenterol. Groote Schurr Hosp. Cape Town.

DEO, Harshad Dattatraya 66 Waltham Road, Woodford Bridge, Woodford Green IG8 8DW — MB BS 1996 Lond.

DEO, Manjit Kaur Department of Community Child Health, Westhulme Community Services, Royal Oldham Hospital NHS Trust, Westhulme, Oldham OL1 2JH Tel: 0161 627 8755; 6 Rookwood, Chadderton, Oldham OL1 2TU Tel: 0161 626 7899 — MB BS 1973 Panjab; MB BS Panjab (India) 1973; DCCH RCGP 1995; DObst RCOG 1976. (Christian Med. Coll. Ludhiana) Cons. Community Paediat. Oldham. Prev: SCMO Oldham HA; SHO (Med.) Middlx. Hosp. Lond.; SHO (Paediat.) Univ. Hosp. Wales.

DEO, Ripudaman Singh The Royal Oldham Hospital, Rochdale Road, Oldham OL1 2JH Tel: 0161 624 0420 Fax: 0161 627 8127; 6 Rookwood, Chadderton, Oldham OL1 2TU — MB BS 1973 Gura Nanak; MB BS Guru Nanak 1973; MRCPsych 1978. (Amritsar) Cons. Psychiat. Roy. Oldham Hosp.; Hon. Clin. Asst. Prof. Univ. Brit. Columbia Canada. Socs: Brit. Soc. Med. & Dent. Hypn. & Brit. Med. Acupunc. Soc.; BMA. Prev: Sen. Regist. W.m. Hosp. Med. Sch. & St. Mary Abbotts Hosp. Lond.; Regist. Char. Cross Hosp. Med. Sch. Lond.

DEO, Sandeep Dattatray Princess Margret Hospitalr, Okus Road, Swindon SN1 4JU Tel: 01793 426952; The corner, Sherbourne Street, Lechlade GL7 3AE Tel: 01793 426876 Email: deos5@hotmail.com — MB ChB 1989 Birm.; FRCS TR & ORTH 1999; FRCS Ed. 1993. Cons. Orthopaedic & Trauma Surg., P.ss Margt. Hosp. Swindon. Socs: BOA Mem.

DEO, Surendra Inder 10 Pretoria Road N., London N18 1EX — MB BS 1985 Lond.

DEODHAR, Atulya Achyut 145 Trevose House, Royal Cornwall Hospital, Treliske, Truro TR1 3LJ Tel: 01872 74242 — MD 1984 Poona; MB BS 1987; MRCP (UK) 1990. Socs: BMA; Brit. Soc. Rheum.

DEODHAR, Benjamin Gurusiddappa 261 Hainton Avenue, Grimsby DN32 9JX Tel: 01472 343071 Fax: 01472 250190 — MBAS; DORCS. GP Specialist in Ophth.; GP Clin. Assist. (Ophth.) Hosp.; GP Specialist (Ophth.) Community. Socs: Diploma from Roy. Coll. of Ophthal mology Lond.

DEODHAR, Hem Atulya 145 Trevose House, Royal Cornwall Hospital, Truro TR1 3LJ Tel: 01872 74242 — MD 1984 Poona; MB BS 1980; MRCP (UK) 1990.

DEOL, Harleen Kaur 5 Lampern Square, Nelson Gardens, London E2 7AQ — MB BS 1997 Lond.

DEPALA, Babalal Tulsidas 19 St Raphaels Way, Neasden, London NW10 0NU Tel: 020 8451 2946 — MB BS 1976 Sambalpur, India; MB BS Sambalpur India 1976; MRCS Eng. LRCP Lond. 1979. (V.S.S. Med. Coll.) Clin. Med. Off. (c/o the Elderly) Newham Healthcare NHS Trust. Prev: SHO (Gen. Med. & Gen. Surg.) Bideford Dist. Hosp.; Ho. Off. (Gen. Med.) Altrincham Gen. Hosp.

DEPANI, Ansuya Jayantilal Wexham House, Wexham Park Lane, Wexham, Slough SL3 6LX Tel: 01753 529794 Fax: 01753 512016 — MB BS 1977 Bombay; FFA RCSI 1986; DA (UK) 1979. (Topiwala Medical School Bombay, India) Staff Grade (Anaesth.) Wexham Pk. Hosp. Slough.

DEPANI, Mr Jayantilal Parsotam 1 Fulwood Close, Church Road, Hayes UB3 2NF Tel: 0208 573 2365 Fax: 573 5175; Wexham House, Wexham Park Lane, Wexham, Slough SL3 6LX Tel: 01753 529794 Fax: 01753 512016 — MB BS 1975 Gujarat; FRCS Glas. 1982. (B.J. Med. Coll. Ahmedabad) GP. Prev: SHO (Paediat. & O & G) Wexham Pk. Hosp. Slough; Trainee GP Narberth Health Centre, Dyfed.

DEPARES, John Alexandra Hospital, Consulting Suite, Mill Lane, Cheadle SK8 2PX Tel: 0161 428 3656 Fax: 0161 491 3867; 124 Knutsford Road, Wilmslow SK9 6JH Tel: 01625 582404 Email: john@depares.prestel.co.uk — MD 1975 Malta; FRCOG 1994, M 1981; T(OG) 1991. Cons. O & G Stepping Hill Hosp. Stockport; Hon. Lect. Univ. Manch. Socs: Brit. Soc. Colpos. & Cerv. Path.; N. Eng. Gynaecol. Soc.; Brit. Gyn. Endoscopy Soc. Prev: Sen. Regist. Rotat. (O & G) Leeds; Regist. (O & G) Univ. Hosp. Wales Cardiff & St. Mary's Hosp. Portsmouth.

DEPLA, Diana Naomi The Eye Department, Cumberland Infirmary, Carlisle CA2 7HY Tel: 01228 523444 — MB BS 1987 Lond.; FCOphth 1992; FRCOphth. Cons. Opthalmologist, Cumbld. Infirm. Prev: Fell. in Vitro-Retinal Surg., Roy. Vic Infirm.

DEPLA, Walter Mary Alphonse (retired) Applegarth, South Cary Lane, Castle Cary BA7 7ER Tel: 01963 350473 — MB BS Lond. 1952. Prev: Emerg. Off. & Ho. Phys. Lond. Hosp.

DERBYSHIRE, David Robert The Limes, Loxley Road, Stratford-upon-Avon CV37 7DP Tel: 01789 29943 — MB ChB 1975 Birm.; FFA RCS Eng. 1980. (Birm.) Cons. (Anaesth.) & Clin. Dir.y Warwick Hosp. Socs: Anaesth. Research Soc.; Midl. Soc. Anaesth. Prev: Lect. (Anaesth.) Univ. Leics. Hon. Sen. Regist. Leics. HA; Sen. Regist. Mersey HA; Regist. (Anaesth. & Intens. Ther.) Waikato Pub. Hosp. Hamilton NZ.

DERBYSHIRE, Emma 58 Elmshurst Gardens, Tonbridge TN10 3QX — MB BS 1997 Lond.

***DERBYSHIRE, Emma Victoria** Swan Surgery, Northgate St., Bury St Edmunds IP33 1AE — MB ChB 1994 Dundee.

DERBYSHIRE, Helen Ruth 200 Wellsway, Keynsham, Bristol BS31 1JL — MB BS 1981 Newc. SHO (Psychiat.) Coney Hill Hosp. Gloucester. Prev: SHO (Anaesth.) Roy. Berks. Hosp. Reading.

DERBYSHIRE, Judith Claire 15 Rectory Grove, Gosforth, Newcastle upon Tyne NE3 1AL — MB ChB 1987 Leeds; DCCH RCP Ed. 1992. p/t Disabil. Anal. Prev: Trainee GP Angus VTS; SHO (O & G) N. Tyneside Gen. Hosp.; SHO (A & E) Sunderland Dist. Gen. Hosp.

DERBYSHIRE, Michael John (retired) 6 Lingmell Close, Heaton, Bolton BL1 5EG Tel: 01204 841206 — MB ChB Manch. 1951. Prev: Ho. Surg. Surgic. Profess. Unit, Roy. Infirm. Manch.

DERBYSHIRE, Neil David James Department of Radiology, Royal Berkshire Hospital, London Road, Reading RG1 5AN; 'Hillside', Rectory Road, Streatley-on-Thames RG8 9BU Tel: 01491 872339 Mobile: 07768 054629 Email: neil.djd@virgin.net — BM BCh 1984 Oxf.; MA Oxf. 198; MRCP (UK) 1987; FRCR 1992. (Oxf.) Cons. Radiol. Roy. Berks. Hosp. Reading. Prev: Sen. Regist. (Radiol.) John Radcliffe Hosp. Oxf.; Regist. (Med.) Univ. Hosp. Wales & Llandough Hosp. Cardiff.

DERBYSHIRE, Nicola 30 Tulworth Road, Poynton, Stockport SK12 1BL — MB ChB 1997 Birm.

DERBYSHIRE, Mr Stephen Arthur A & E Department, North Manchester General Hospital, Crumpsall, Manchester M8 5RB Email: sderby@globalnet.co.uk — MB ChB 1989 Leeds; BSc (Hons.) Leeds

1986, MB ChB 1989; FRCS Ed. 1994. Cons. A & E Med. N. Manch. Healthcare NHS Trust, Manch.

DERGALUST, Robert 60 Daresbury Road, Eccleston, St Helens WA10 5DS — MB BCh BAO 1982 Dub.; MB BCh Dub. 1982.

DERHAM, Christopher John 14 Shakespeare Road, Widnes WA8 7DD — MB ChB 1984 Liverp. Prev: Ho. Off. (Med.) Halifax Gen. Hosp.; SHO (Psychiat.) Barnsley Hall Hosp. BromsGr..; Ho. Off. (Surg.) Ryhope Gen. Hosp. Sunderland.

DERHAM, Ian Alastair WheelerStreet HealthCare, Wheeler St., Hull HU3 5QE Tel: 01482 354933 Fax: 01482 355090; 233 Ganstead Lane E., Ganstead, Hull HU11 4BG — MB BCh BAO 1962 Dub.; DFFP 1994. (T.C. Dub.) Socs: (Ex-Pres.) Hull Med. Soc.; BMA (Ex-Pres. E. Yorks. Div.).

DERHAM, Roger Joseph Mary 14 Blagdon Court, Golden Manor, Hanwell, London W7 3EF — MB BCh BAO 1981 NUI; MRCOG 1988.

DERLIEN, James Anthony Leonard (retired) 10 Churchfields, Bowdon, Altrincham WA14 3PJ Tel: 0161 928 3821 — MB ChB Manch. 1948; MRCS Eng. LRCP Lond. 1948. Prev: Ho. Phys. Manch. Roy. Infirm.

DERODRA, Mr Jaswant Kumar Durlabh Mayday University Hospital, London Road, Croydon CR7 7YE Tel: 020 8401 3000; 17 Bushwood Drive, London SE1 5RE Tel: 020 7252 0570 — MB BS 1977 Lond.; FRCS Eng. 1983; MS Lond. 1992. Cons. Surg. (Vasc.) Mayday Univ. Hosp. Croydon.

DEROLA, Tadeusz 'Bangsang', Queen Hoo Lane, Tewin, Welwyn AL6 0LT — MB ChB 1946 Polish Sch. Med.; DTM & H Lond 1956. Med. Off. Min. of Health. Prev: Med. Off. Overseas Civil Serv. Gambia; Med. Supt. Govt. Hosp. Zanzibar.

DEROUNIAN, John Nubar Glenlivet Community Surgery, Drumin, Ballindalloch AB37 9AN Tel: 01807 590273 Fax: 01807 590411; Woodside of Drumin, Glenlivet, Ballindalloch AB37 9AN — MB BS 1975 Lond.; MRCS Eng. LRCP Lond. 1975; DRCOG 1978. (Char. Cross) Princip. GP Ballindalloch; Med. Off. Fleming Cottage GP Hosp. Aberlour. Prev: SHO (Paediat. & Obst.), Ho. Phys. (Geriat.) & Ho. Surg. (Orthop.) Char. Cross Hosp. Lond.

DEROUNIAN, Nubar Garabed Paylak 2 The Avenue, Hornsey, London N8 0JR — MD 1941 Beirut; DTM & H Eng. 1948. (Amer. Univ. Hosp. Beirut) Socs: Fell. Roy. Soc. Med.; BMA. Prev: Capt. RAMC 1941-7 (Graded Venereol. 1945-7).

DERRETT, Christopher John Barton House Health Centre, 233 Albion Road, London N16 9JT Tel: 020 7249 5511 Fax: 020 7254 8985; 17 Castleton Road, London E17 4AR Tel: 020 8531 3451 Fax: 020 8531 3451 Email: c.j.derrett@gmul.ac.uk — MB BS 1982 Lond.; BSc Durham. 1968; MPhil Lond. 1977; MRCGP 1986; Dip. Pract. Dermat. 1997; DCH RCP Lond. 1985; DRCOG 1984. (Roy. Free Hosp. Lond.) GP Tutor (Equip.) N. Essex; Head of GP Developm. City & Hackney. Socs: BMA; RCGP. Prev: GP Market St. Health Gp. E. Ham; SHO (O & G & Paediat.) Whipps Cross Hosp. Lond.; Ho. Surg. Roy. Free Hosp. Lond.

DERRETT, Jonathan Duncan — MB BS 1989 Lond.; MRCGP 1994; DRCOG 1991. GP Henfield.

DERRICK, Elizabeth Katharine Brighton General Hospital, Elm Grove, Brighton BN2 3EW — MB BS 1978 Lond.; FRCP 2001 UK; MRCP (UK) 1981; MRCGP 1984. Cons. Dermat. Brighton Gen. Hosp.

DERRICK, Gillian Margaret Anaesthetic Department, Birmingham Childrens Hospital, Steelhouse Lane, Birmingham B4 6NH Tel: 0121 333 9623 Fax: 0121 333 9621 Email: anaesthetic.secretary@bhamchildrens.wmids.nhs.uk; 1 Deeley Close, Edgbaston, Birmingham B15 2NR Tel: 0121 440 4857 — BM BS 1987 Nottm.; BMedSci Nottm. 1985; FRCA 1993. (notts) cons. Paediat. Anaesth.Birm Childr.s Hosp.

DERRICK, James Paddon Birtley Medical Group Practice, Birtley Medical Group, Durham Road, Birtley, Chester-le-Street DH3 2QT Tel: 0191 410 3421 Fax: 0191 410 9672; The Old Vicarage, Lamesley, Gateshead NE11 0EY Tel: 0191 487 4690 — MB BS 1961 Durh.; MRCGP 1981; FRCOG 1989, M 1971; DTM & H Liverp. 1964. (Newc.) Prev: Hosp. Pract. Dept. O & G Qu. Eliz. Hosp. Gateshead; Supt. Gahini Hosp. & Shyira Hosp. Rwanda; Regist. (O & G) Sunderland Matern. Hosp.

DERRICK, Mr John Charles Anthony Clifton Road Surgery, 22 Clifton Road, Rugby CV21 3QF Tel: 01788 544744/544718 Fax: 01788 553902 — MB ChB 1980 Manch.; FRCS Ed. 1989.

DERRICK, Shirley-Anne Lintonville Medical Group, Old Lane, Ashington NE63 9UT Tel: 01670 812772; King's Lodge, Cresswell Road, Cresswell, Morpeth NE61 5HT Tel: 01670 861375 — BM BS 1988 Nottm.; BMedSci 1986; MRCGP 1992; Dip. Thoracic Med. 1994; DRCOG 1991.

DERRINGER, Evelyn Winifred 9 Croxteth Road, Liverpool L8 3SE Tel: 0151 727 1220; Hylas Bach, Hylas Lane, Rhuddlan, Rhyl LL18 5AG Tel: 01745 591738 Fax: 01745 592162 Email: derringer@rapid.co.uk — LMSSA Lond. 1951. (Liverp.) Prev: Cas. Off. Roy. Liverp. Childr. Hosp. & Roy. S.. Hosp. Liverp.

DERRINGTON, Mary Clare Southern Derbyshire Health, Derwent Court, Stuart St., Derby DE1 2FZ Tel: 01332 626300 Fax: 01332 626350; 14 Woodland Avenue, Stoney Gate, Leicester LE2 3HG — MD 1990 Leic.; MB ChB Dundee 1976; FFA RCS Eng. 1981. Trainee (Pub. Health Med.) Trent Region. Prev: Cons. Anaesth. Leicester Roy. Infirm.; Asst. Co-ordinator NCEPOD Lincoln's Inn Fields Lond.

DERRINGTON, Petronella Maria c/o Mrs Derrington, 21 Sheldon Hall Avenue, Tile Cross, Birmingham B33 0ER Tel: 0121 624 8636; Huntworth Park House, Huntworth, Bridgwater TA7 0AH Tel: 01278 663581 Fax: 01278 661097 — MB ChB 1990 Cape Town. SHO Med UBHT. Prev: SHO (Med.) Vict. Hosp.; Regist. (Haemat.) Groote Schuur Hosp., S. Africa; Regist. (Path.) Red Cross Hosp.

DERRY, Charles Douglas Brockland, Sandling Road, Saltwood, Hythe CT21 4QJ Tel: 01303 269838 — MB BS Lond. 1964; FRCS Eng. 1968; MRCS Eng. LRCP Lond. 1964. (King's Coll. Hosp.) Cons. Surg. E. Kent Hosp. Trust. Prev: Sen. Regist. (Surg.) King's Coll. Hosp. Lond.; Research Fell. (Surg.) Harvard Univ., USA.

DERRY, Christopher Paul 9 Milford Close, Maidstone ME16 0EY — MB BS 1996 Lond.

DERRY, David Douglas Gaunts Cottage, Sandhills Green, Alvechurch, Birmingham B48 7BT — MB ChB 1994 Manch.

DERRY, Mr Fadel National Spinal Injuries Centre, Stoke Mandeville Hospital, Aylesbury HP21 8AL Tel: 01296 315000 Fax: 01296 315867 Email: derry@webstar.co.uk — MB ChB 1982 Baghdad; FRCS Eng. 1993; FRCS Glas. 1992. Cons. Surg. (Spinal Injuries) Nat. Spinal Injuries Centre Stoke Mandeville Hosp. Aylesbury. Socs: Internat. Med. Soc. Paraplegia; Internat. Continence Soc.; Assoc. Mem. BAUS. Prev: Sen. Regist. (Spinal Injuries) Stoke Mandeville Hosp.; Regist. (Urol. & Renal Transpl.) Med. City Teachg. Hosp. Baghdad, Iraq; SHO (Spinal Injuries) Ibn Al-Kuff Spinal Centre Baghdad Iraq.

DERRY, Jane Amanda 2 Wenlock Drive, Preston Grange, North Shields NE29 9HD — BM BS 1996 Nottm.; BMedSci. (Hons.) Nottm. 1994. (Nottingham)

DERRY, John Lawrence Nuffield Health Centre, Welch Way, Witney OX28 6JQ Tel: 01993 703641 — BM BCh 1979 Oxf.; FRCGP 1999; MA Oxf. 1980; MRCGP 1984; Cert. Family Plann. JCC 1984; Cert. Prescribed Equiv. Exp. JCPTGP 1984. Med. Adviser Oxon Health Auth. Gen. Practitioner Princip.; Audit Co-ordinator & Chairm. Oxon. Med. Audit Advis. Gp. Prev: GP Trainee Oxf. VTS.

DERRY THOMAS, James Peter (retired) Dan-y-Graig, St. Clears, Carmarthen SA33 4DY Tel: 01994 230504 — MB BS 1957 Lond. Prev: Ho. Surg. S.lands Hosp. Shoreham-by-Sea.

DERSO, Abraha Paediatric Department, New Cross Hospital, Wolverhampton WV10 0QR Tel: 01902 643082 Fax: 01902 444442 — MB ChB 1973 Birm.; MRCP (UK) 1978; FRCPCH 1997. (Univ. Birm. Sch. Med.) Cons. Community Paediat. Wolverhampton; Hon. Sen. Clin. Lect. (Child Health) Univ. Birm. Socs: BMA; FRCPCH. Prev: SCMO E. Birm. HA; Regist. (Paediat.) Alder Hey Childr. Hosp. Liverp.; Research Regist. (Clin. Paediat. & Virol.) E. Birm. Hosp.

DERVAN, Maire Frances Little Harwood Health Centre, Plane Tree Road, Blackburn BB1 6PH Tel: 01254 580931 Fax: 01254 695794; 65 Preston New Road, Blackburn BB2 6AY Tel: 01254 580931 — MB BCh BAO 1980 NUI; MRCGP 1986; DObst RCPI 1985; DCH RCPSI 1984. (Galway)

DERVISEVIC, Samir Westwards, Bickwell Valley, Sidmouth EX10 8RF — LRCP 1998 Ed.; LRCS 1998 Ed.; LRCS 1998 Glas.

***DERVISH, Hanife** 45 Drayton Park, London N5 1NT Tel: 020 7607 2500 — MB BS 1996; BSc (Pharmacol.) 1993; MB BS Lond. 1996.

DERVISH, Havva 45 Drayton Park, London N5 1NT — MB BS 1998 Lond.; MB BS Lond 1998.

DERVISH, Osman Oktay Twylands, Grange Hill, Halesowen B62 0JH Tel: 0121 429 1345 — LRCPI & LM, LRCSI & LM 1959. (RCSI) Socs: FRSM.

DERVISH, Sheila Dorrien (retired) Twylands, Grange Hill, Halesowen B62 0JH Tel: 0121 429 1345 — LRCPI & LM, LRCSI & LM 1960.

DERVOS, Herakles Demetrios Department of Anaesthetics, Guy's Hospital, St Thomas St., London SE1 9RT Tel: 020 7955 4051 Fax: 020 7955 8844; 46 Geoffrey Road, London SE4 1NT Tel: 020 8692 6755 Fax: 020 8691 7381 — MB BS Sydney 1965; FFA RCS Eng. 1971; DA Eng. 1971. (Univ. Sydney) Cons. Anaesth. Guy's Hosp. Lond. & Neurosurg. Unit King's Coll. Hosp. Lond. Socs: FRCA; Assn. Anaesths.; BMA. Prev: Sen. Regist. Middlx. Hosp. Lond.; Regist. (Anaesth.) Rachel Foster Hosp. Sydney, Austral.; Regist. St. Chas. Hosp. Lond.

DESAI, Anant 8 Cavendish Mansions, Mill Lane, London NW6 1TE — MB BS 1996 Lond.

DESAI, Mr Anil Jagdishchandra 130 Hever Avenue, West Kingsdown, Sevenoaks TN15 6DU Email: anil.desai@bromleigh-tr.sthames.nhs.uk — MB BS 1981 Baroda; FRCS Eng. 1991; MPhil (Lond.) 1997; FRCS Gen Surg 1999. Cons.Bromley Hosps. NHS Trust. Socs: BASO; ASGBI. Prev: Specialist Regist. W. Middlx. Univ. Hosp.; Specialist Regist. (Gen. Surg.) Bedford Hosp.; Specialist Regist. Char. Cross Hosp.

DESAI, Ashok Prathadrao c/o Mr S. Kulkarni, 1 Crescent Close, Stansted Abbotts, Ware SG12 8LL — MB BS 1978 Karnatak; DPM RCPSI 1986.

DESAI, Bhagwatprasad Narsinhbhai 363 Uppingham Road, Leicester LE5 4DP — MB BS 1952 Bombay. (Grant Med. Coll.)

DESAI, Bipin Ratilal 80 Hornsey Road, London N7 Tel: 020 7607 6475 — MB ChB 1974 Glas.; DRCOG 1983; Cert. JCPTGP 1983; Cert. Family Plann. JCC 1977. Mem. Roy. Soc. for Promotion of Health.

DESAI, Chittaranjan Dadubhai 7 Bray House, 4/5 Duke of York St., St James, London SW1 — MB BS 1946 Bombay; DTM & H Eng. 1949. (Grant Med. Coll.)

DESAI, Gita Postgraduate Centre, Sandwell District General Hospital, Lyndon, West Bromwich B71 4HJ — MB ChB 1998 Birm.

DESAI, Gladys 1/R, 17 Dalnair St., Yorkhill, Glasgow G3 8SD — MB ChB 1989 Glas.

DESAI, Harivadan Chhotabhai (retired) 64 School Road, Moseley, Birmingham B13 9SW Tel: 0121 449 0340 — MB BS 1959 Baroda; FRCS Ed. 1969; FRCS Eng. 1970; FFA RCS Eng. 1975; DA (UK) 1960. Med. Dir. John Taylor Hospice Birm. Prev: Cons. Anaesth. City Hosp. NHS Trust.

DESAI, Harsadroy Warkwick Hospital, Lakin Road, Warwick CV34 5BW Tel: 01926 495321 Fax: 01926 403715; Chintamini Dhama, 122 Lea Vale Road, Stourbridge DY8 2AU Tel: 01384 394314 — MB ChB 1968 Natal; PhD Lond. 1974; FRCP Lond. 1995; MRCP (UK) 1983. (Natal Medical School) Cons. Phys. & Dep. Dir. Med. Specialities Warwick Hosp.; Hon. Vis. Clin. Sen. Lect. Univ. Warwick; Chairm. Trust Drug & Therap. Comm.Warwick. Socs: Brit. Geriat. Soc.; Reg. & Local Counc. BMA; RCP (Lond.). Prev: Vis. Lect. to S. African Med. Schs. 1991 and 1996; Asst. Research Fell. Univ. Coll. Hosp. Lond.; Research Fell. (Immunol.) Univ. Natal.

DESAI, Hemlata 51 St Leonards Avenue, Lostock, Bolton BL6 4JE Tel: 01204 522042 — MB ChB 1989 Manch.; MRCGP 1993; DFFP 1993; DRCOG 1992. Socs: Bolton Med. Soc. Prev: Trainee GP Bolton; SHO (O & G & Med.) Leighton Hosp. Crewe; SHO (Paediat.) Tameside Hosp. Manch.

DESAI, Indravadan Thakorbhai Lower Addiscombe Road Surgery, 416 Lower Addiscombe Road, Croydon CR0 7AG Tel: 020 8654 1068 Fax: 020 8654 0487 — MB BS 1963 Calcutta. (Calcutta Nat. Med. Coll.)

DESAI, Mr Jatin Bhagwatprasad King's College Hospital, Denmark Hill, London SE5 9RS Tel: 020 7346 3191 Fax: 020 7346 3433 Email: jatin.desai@kcl.ac.uk; 121 Alleyn Park, Dulwich, London SE21 8AA Tel: 020 8693 4490 Fax: 693 5593 Email: jatin.desai@btinternet.com — MB ChB 1975 Glas.; FRCS (CTh) Ed. 1986; FRCS RCPS Glas. 1979; FRCS Eng. 1997. Cons. Cardiothoracic Surg. King's Coll. Hosp. Lond. Prev: Regist. (Cardiothoracic Surg.) Glas.; Hon. Sen. Regist. St. Mary's Hosp. Lond.; Sen. Regist. Rotat. (Cardiothoracic) Hammersmith, Harefield & Middlx. Hosps.

DESAI, Jayantilal Dahyabhai Belmont Road Surgery, 69 Belmont Road, Ilford IG1 1YW Tel: 020 8478 0555 Fax: 020 8220 3377; 67 Sunnymede Drive, Barkingside, Ilford IG6 1LD Tel: 020 8550 1186 — MB BS 1958 Bombay; DTM & H Liverp. 1971; DPH Eng. 1969; DIH Soc. Apoth. Lond. 1969; AFOM 1978; DFFP 1995. (Grant Med. Coll.) p/t Local Med. Off. Civil Serv. Med. Serv. (p/t); Med. Mem., Appeals Serv. Socs: BMA; Assoc. Fac. Occupat. Med; Indian Med. Assn. Prev: Pub. Health Advisor World Health Organisation; Specialist Community Med. (Environm. Health) Coventry AHA; Community Phys. Brent Health Dist. & Asst. Community Phys. W. Roding Health Dist.

DESAI, Jayesh 29-53 Himley Road, Dudley DY1 2QD Tel: 01384 254423 Fax: 01384 254424 — MB ChB 1987 Birm.; DOccMed 2000; MRCGP 1992; DFFP 1993; DCH RCP Lond. 1992; DRCOG 1991. (Birmingham) Occupat.al Health Adviser, W. Midl.s.

DESAI, Mr Kailash Balvantrai 50 Sutton Square, Urswick Road, London E9 6EQ Tel: 020 8985 5596 Fax: 020 8985 5596 — MB BS 1984 Lond.; FRCS Eng. 1988. Sen. Regist. (Orthop.) Hammersmith Hosp. Lond.

DESAI, Mr Kanaiyalal Maganlal University Hospitals Coventry and Warwickshire NHS Trust, 2 Clifford Bridge Rd, Walsgrave-on-Sowe, Coventry CV2 2DX Tel: 024 76 538747 Fax: 01203 604 4431; 20 Palmerston Road, Earlsdon, Coventry CV5 6FH Email: kdes1@compuserve.com — MB ChB 1975 Liverp.; ChM Bristol 1988; FRCS Eng. 1981; FRCS Ed. 1980. Cons. Urol. Univ. Hosps. Coventry and Warks. NHS Trust. Socs: Brit. Assn. Urol. Surg. & BMA; Eur. Assn. Urol.; Brit. Assn. Urol. Surg. Sec. of Oncol. Prev: Sen. Regist. (Urol.) S. W.. RHA; Regist. (Gen. Surg. & Renal Transpl.) S.mead Hosp. Bristol; Regist. (Gen. Surg.) Whiston & St. Helens Hosp. Merseyside RHA.

DESAI, Kripali 291 Loughborough Road, West Bridgford, Nottingham NG2 7EH — MB ChB 1998 Manch.; MB ChB Manch 1998.

DESAI, Manisha Mohan National Hospital for Neurology & Neurosurgery, Queen Square, London WC1N 3BG — MB BS 1989 Karnatak; MRCPsych 1994.

DESAI, Mr Manubhai Ishwerbhai Causeway Medical Centre, 166-170 Wilderspool Causeway, Warrington WA4 6QA — MB BS 1957 Bombay; FRCS Ed. 1972.

DESAI, Maya Department of C.F. & Respiratory Medicine, Birmingham Children's Hospital, Steelhouse Lane, Birmingham B4 6NH Tel: 0121 333 9999 Fax: 0121 333 8201; 99 Park Hill Road, Harborne, Birmingham B17 9HH Tel: 0121 427 2400 Email: m.desai@bham.ac.uk — BM BCh 1987 Oxf.; BA Camb. 1984; MRCP (UK) 1991. Specialist Regist. Paediat. Birm. Heartlands. Hosp. Socs: RCPCH; BTS. Prev: Regist. (Paediat.) Melbourne Roy. Childr. Hosp.; Lect. (Child Health) Childr.'s Hosp. Birm.

DESAI, Minaxi Sharad Penrhyn House, Woodlands Cottage, 12 Dorset Road, Altrincham WA14 4QN — MB BS 1974 Gujarat.

DESAI, Narsinh Krishnarao 130-131 St Mary's Road, Southampton SO14 0BB Tel: 02380 335151; 12 Butterfield Road, Bassett, Southampton SO16 7EE Tel: 02380 790813 — MB BS 1959 Bombay. (Grant Med. Coll. Bombay) Prev: Chest Regist. Broomfield Hosp.; Geriat. Regist. Amersham Gen. Hosp.

DESAI, Niranjan 7 Roche Road, London SW16 5PR — MB ChB 1985 Manch.

DESAI, Pankaj Manubhai 34 Cedars Road, Morden SM4 5AB Tel: 020 8540 7103 — MB BS 1982 Lond.; FFA RCS Eng. 1987. Regist. (Anaesth.) Guy's Hosp. Lond. Socs: Assn. Anaesth.

DESAI, Mr Paresh Moghabhai c/o Dr A. I. Rajpura, Chariton, 79 Track Road, Batley WF17 7AB — MB BS 1971 Poona; MS Bombay 1975; FRCS Eng. 1980; FRCS Ed. 1980.

DESAI, Parul High Corner, 7 Highwood Road, Appleton, Warrington WA4 5AJ — MB BCh BAO 1981 NUI; PhD Lond. 1996, MSc 1989; MSc Lond. 1989; FRCS Eng. 1989; FRCOphth. 1989; DO RCPSI 1986; MFPHM 1998.

DESAI, Prakashkumar Manubhai Whiteheath Clinic, Hartlebury Road, Oldbury, Warley B69 1BG Tel: 0121 552 2353 Fax: 0121 544 2232; 6 Ravenhurst Drive, Birmingham B43 7RS — MB ChB 1977 Birm.; DA Eng. 1979.

DESAI, Saida Spitalfields Practice, Spitalfields Health Centre, 9-11 Brick Lane, London E1 6PU Tel: 020 7247 7070 — MB BS 1988 Lond.

DESAI, Mr Sanmukhbhai Naranji The Long Barn, Drayton Beauchamp, Aylesbury HP22 5LS — MB BS 1958 Bombay; FRCS Eng. 1965. (Grant Med. Coll.) Sen. Cons. Plastic Surg. Regional Plastic Surg. & Jaw Injury Centre Stoke Mandeville Hosp. Aylesbury; Hunt. Prof. RCS Eng. Socs: Brit. Assn. Plastic Surgs.; Roy. Soc. Med. Prev: SHO (Surg.) City Hosp. Nottm.; Sen. Regist. (Plastic Surg.) Stoke Mandeville Hosp.; Regist. (Plastic Surg.) Wordsley Hosp. Stourbridge.

DESAI, Shaila Anil Histopathology Department, The Whittington Hospital, Highgate Hill, London N19 5NF Tel: 020 7288 3346; 80 St. Huberts Close, Gerrards Cross SL9 7ER Tel: 01753 890674 Fax: 01753 890674 — LRCP LRCS Ed. LRCPS Glas. 1984; MSc Lond. 1994; MRCPath 1994, D 1990. Cons. Histopath. Whittington Hosp. Lond.

DESAI, Sharad Chhabildas Penrhyn House, Woodlands Cottage, 12 Dorset Road, Altrincham WA14 4QN — MB BS 1974 Gujarat.

DESAI, Mr Shashank Rasiklal c/o Mr. K. J. Desai, 13 Kinloss Gardens, Finchley, London N3 3DU Tel: 020 8343 0888 — MB BS 1984 Bombay; FRCS Glas. 1992.

DESAI, Shrinivas Moreshwar Dryburn Hospital, Durham DH1 5TW Tel: 0191 333233 Ext: 2488; 6 Almoners Barn, Durham DH1 3TZ — MB BS 1975 Nagpur; MD (Radiodiagn.) Post Grad. Inst. Chandigarh 1978; FRCR 1983; FFR RCSI 1982; DMRD Aberd. 1981; DMRD Eng. 1980. Cons. Radiol. Gen. Hosp. Bishop Auckland.

DESAI, Mr Shrivatsa Pandurangrao 1 Burnham Close, Bessacarr, Doncaster DN4 7RE Tel: 01302 531215 — MB BS 1969 Karnatak; MS (Ophth.) Bombay 1974; FRCS Ed. 1978; FRCOphth 1994; DO Eng. 1975; DOMS Bombay 1970. (Karnatak Med. Coll.) Cons. Ophth. Doncaster Roy. Infirm. Prev: Sen. Regist. Wolverhampton & Midl. Co. Eye Infirm.

DESAI, Mr Sudhirbhai Prabhudas Narborough Health Centre, Narborough, Leicester LE9 5GX Tel: 0116 286 6859 — MB BS 1972 Gujarat; MS Gujarat 1975, MB BS 1972; DLO RCS Eng. 1978.

DESAI, Sujal 36 Acland Crescent, Denmark Hill, London SE5 8EQ — MB BS 1987 Lond.; MRCP (UK) 1990; FRCR 1994. (Middlx. Hosp. Med. Sch.) Clin. Research Fell. (Imaging) Roy. Brompton Hosp. Lond. Prev: Sen. Regist. & Regist. (Radiol.) King's Coll. Hosp.

DESAI, Sunil Jayantilal Sunderlal 1061A Finchley Road, Temple Fortune, London NW11 0PU — MB ChB 1976 Bristol; DCH Eng. 1980.

DESAI, Surendra Khodidas Langbank Medical Centre, Broad Lane, Liverpool L11 1AD Tel: 0151 226 1976 Fax: 0151 270 2873; Rajamee, 85 Lyndhurst Avenue, Mossley Hill, Liverpool L18 8AR Tel: 0151 724 3170 Fax: 0151 546 6864 — MB BS Gujarat 1968. (B.J. Med. Coll. Ahmedabad India) GP Liverp.

DESAI, Mr Suresh Bhimbhai Rambhai (retired) Scunthorpe General Hospital, Cliff Gardens, Scunthorpe DN15 7BH Tel: 01724 282282 — MRCS Eng. LRCP Lond. 1961; FRCS Eng. 1965. Cons. Gen. Surg. Scunthorpe Gen. Hosp. Prev: Pres. S. Humberside Dist. Div. BMA.

DESAI, Mrs Sushila 20 Delphian Crt., 188 Leigham Court Road, London SW16 Tel: 020 8769 1869 — MB BS 1965 Med.; MB BS Med. Inst. (I) Rangoon 1965. (Lady Hardinge Med. Coll. New Delhi) Prev: Ho. Off. Safdarjung Hosp. New Delhi.

DESAI, Vani Shrivatsa 1 Burnham Close, Bessacarr, Doncaster DN4 7RE — MB BS 1972 Karnatak; BSc Mysore 1965. (Karnatak Med. Coll. Hubli) Clin. Asst. (Psychiat.) Bassetlaw Dist. Gen. Hosp. Worksop, Notts. Prev: SHO (Psychiat.) Doncaster Roy. Infirm.

DESBOROUGH, Joan Portsmouth Department of Anaesthesia, Epsom General Hospital, Dorking Road, Epsom KT18 7EG Tel: 01372 735270 — MB ChB 1980 Leeds; MD Leeds 1995; FFA RCS Eng. 1985. (Leeds) Cons. Anaesth. Epsom Gen. Hosp. Prev: Sen. Lect. (Anaesth.) St. Geo. Hosp. Lond.; Sen. Regist. & Sen. Lect. (Anaesth.) Hammersmith Hosp. Lond.; Regist. (Anaesth.) Bradford Roy. Infirm.

DESBOROUGH, Richard Colin Risdons, Bradford-on-Tone, Taunton TA4 1HH — MRCS Eng. LRCP Lond. 1969; MB Camb. 1970, BChir 1969; FFA RCS Eng. 1974. Cons. (Anaesth.) MusGr. Pk. Hosp. Taunton. Socs: BMA & Assn. Anaesth. Prev: Anaesth. Regist. Hosp. Sick Childr. Gt. Ormond St. Lond.; Anaesth. Sen. Regist. Bristol Roy. Infirm.; Assoc. Prof. Anesthesiol. Univ. Oregon Med. Sch. Portland U.S.A.

DESBOROUGH, Stephen Howard Hastings House, Kineton Road, Wellesbourne, Warwick CV35 9NF Tel: 01789 840245 Fax: 01789 470993 — MB 1974 Camb.; BChir 1973 Camb.; MRCGP 1979; DRCOG 1980.

DESERT, Simon Andrew South Street Doctors Surgery, South Street, Cockermouth CA13 9QP Tel: 01900 324123 Fax: 01900 324122 — MB BS 1986 Newc.

DESHMUKH, Bhagawant Anandrao 77 Glenthorne Road, London N11 3HL — MB BS 1962 Poona.

DESHMUKH, Mr Rajiv Ganesh 12A Western Way, Kidderminster DY11 6JF — MB BS 1977 Bombay; FRCS Ed. 1991; FRCS Eng. 1990.

DESHMUKH, Sheela B The Medical Centre, 144-150 High Road, London NW10 2PT Tel: 020 8459 5550 Fax: 020 8451 7268 — MB BS 1966 Mysore.

DESHMUKH, Mr Subodh Chandrakant City Hospital NHS Trust, Dudley Road, Birmingham B18 7QH — MB BS 1986 Bombay; FRCS Glas. 1993.

DESHPANDE, Anant Hari Harikrupa, 24 Midgley Drive, Four Oaks, Sutton Coldfield B74 2TW — MB BS 1953 Poona. (B.J. Med. Coll. Poona) Med. Off. Adjucating Med. Pract. DHSS Birm.; Mem. Med. Bd.ing Panel. Prev: GP Sutton Coldfield; SHO (Thoracic Surg.) Milford Chest Hosp. Godalming; Regist. (Orthop.) W. Kent Gen. Hosp. Maidstone.

DESHPANDE, Arup Albert The Aldergate Medical Practice, The Mount, Salters Lane, Tamworth B79 8BH Tel: 01827 54775 Fax: 01827 62835 — MB ChB 1987 Manch.; MRCGP 1991.

DESHPANDE, Ashok Rangrao The Surgery, 39 Wood Lane, Elm Park, Hornchurch RM12 5HX Tel: 01708 450902 Fax: 01708 470875 — MB BS 1972 Poona; MB BS 1972 Poona.

DESHPANDE, Mr Hanumant Balakrishna 29 Clovelly Road, London NW9 6DT — MB BS 1971 Karnatak; FRCS Ed. 1983.

DESHPANDE, Hari Anant 24 Midgley Drive, Sutton Coldfield B74 2TW — MB ChB 1991 Leeds.

DESHPANDE, Madhusudan Kashirao c/o 2 Ashton Way, Sunderland SR3 3RX — MB BS 1972 Marathwada; DPM Eng. 1977. (Govt. Med. Coll. Aurangabad) Regist. (Psychol. Med.) Kidderminster Gen. Hosp.

DESHPANDE, Nalinee Prabhakar 26 Waterside Avenue, Newton Mearns, Glasgow G77 6TJ — MB BS 1976 Nagpur; MRCOG 1986.

DESHPANDE, Prabhakar Madhavrao 26 Waterside Avenue, Newton Mearns, Glasgow G77 6TJ — MB BS 1972 Poona.

DESHPANDE, Mr Prabhakar Vinayakrao (retired) White Rose, 3 Knoll Road, Abergavenny NP7 7AN Tel: 01873 854134 — MB BS 1954 Nagpur; FRCS Glas. 1966; FRCSI 1965. Prev: Cons. A & E Neville Hall Hosp. Abergavenny.

DESHPANDE, Sanjay Keshavrao Cumberland Infirmary, Carlisle CA2 7HY — MB BS 1982 Marathwada, India; FFA RCSI 1993.

DESHPANDE, Sanjeev Appajirao Neonatal Unit, Royal Shrewsbury Hospitals NHS Trust, Mytton Oak Road, Shrewsbury SY3 8XQ Tel: 01743 261000 Fax: 01743 261444 Email: deshpande@which.net; Bridge Bank Cottage, Yockleton, Shrewsbury SY5 9PU Tel: 01743 821261 Fax: 01743 821261 — MB BS 1984 Karnatak, India; MRCP (UK) 1995. (J.N. Med. Coll. Belgaum, India) Cons. Neonat. Roy. Shrewsbury Hosps. NHS Trust. Socs: BMA; Med. Res. Soc.; FRCPCh. Prev: Sen. Regist. (Neonat. & Paediat.) Roy. Vict. Infirm. Newc.; Clin. Research Assoc. Univ. Newc.

DESHPANDE, Sulbha Ashok 11 The Woodfines, Hornchurch RM11 3HR — MD 1977 Poona; MB BS 1974; MRCOG 1984; DGO Bombay 1976.

DESHPANDE, Suresh 119/121 High Street, Sevenoaks TN13 1UP — MB BS 1971 Osmania.

DESHPANDE, Vatsala Anant Harikrupa, 24 Midgley Drive, Four Oakes, Sutton Coldfield B74 2TW — MB BS 1961 Madras. (Stanley Med. Coll.) Med. Off. Adjucating Med. Pract. DHSS Birm.; Mem. Med. Bd.ing Panel. Prev: GP Sutton Coldfield; Clin. Asst. A & E Dept. Good Hope Gen. Hosp. Sutton Coldfield.

DESIRA, William Raphael 99 Park Road S., Middlesbrough TS5 6LF Tel: 01642 828380 & profess. 850 850 — MB BCh 1967 Cairo; FFA RCS Eng. 1979; DA Eng. 1974. (Cairo) Cons. Anaesth. & Obst. Analgesia S. Tees Health Auth. Prev: Sen. Regist. Anaesth. Grampian Health Bd. & Hon. Lect. Anaesth.; Aberd. Univ.; Regist. (Anaesth.) S.end AHA.

DESLANDES, Richard Charles 121 Forres Road, Sheffield S10 1WD — MB ChB 1990 Sheff.

DESMOND, Mr Anthony Dennis 88 Rodney Street, Liverpool L1 9AR Tel: 0151 709 0669 Fax: 0151 709 7279; 18 Knowsley Road, Cressington Park, Liverpool L19 0PG — MB BS 1968 Lond.; FRCS Eng. 1973. (Lond. Hosp.) Cons. Urol. Roy. Liverp.& BRd.green Univ. Hosps.; Cons. Male Infertil. Liverp. Wom. Hosp.; Lect. Clin. Surg. Liverp. Univ. Socs: Fell. Roy. Soc. Med.; Brit. Assn. Urol. Surgs.; Internat. Soc. Urol. Prev: Sen. Regist. (Urol.) Roy. Liverp. Hosp.; Regist. (Surg.) St. Thos. Hosp. Lond.; Ho. Surg. Surgic. Unit Lond. Hosp.

DESMOND, Harry Manor Park Medical Centre, High Street, Polegate BN26 5DJ Tel: 01323 482301 Fax: 01323 484848; 44 Kings Avenue, Eastbourne BN21 2PD — MB ChB 1970 Glas.; MRCGP 1978.

DESMOND, Joel Cardiothoracic Dept, Wythenshawe Hospital, Manchester M23 9LT; 44 Kings Avenue, Eastbourne BN21 2PD — BM BCh 1997 Oxf. SHO Wythenshawe Hosp., Manch.

DESMOND, John Michael Antony 31 St James Road, Rainhill, Prescot L35 0PB — MB ChB 1981 Liverp.; FRCR 1986; DMRD Liverp. 1985. Cons. Radiol. Warrington HA. Prev: Sen. Regist. (Radiol.) Mersey RHA.

DESMOND, Michael 55 Higher Parr Street, St Helens WA9 1BP — MB BCh BAO 1951 NUI; MB BCh, BAO NUI 1951. Prev: Med. Off. St. Helens Hosp. & Providence Hosp. St. Helens.

DESMOND, Michael Joseph The Cardiothoracic Centre, Thomas Drive, Broadgreen, Liverpool L14 3PE Fax: 0151220 8573; Woodlands, 7 Brooklands Drive, Maghull, Liverpool L31 3HN Tel: 0151 531 9774 — MB ChB 1978 Liverp.; MRCP (UK) 1983; FFA RCS Eng. 1985. Cons. Anaesth. Cardiothoracic Centre Liverp.

DESMOND, Noreen Mary New Nurses Home, Whittington Hospital, Highgate Hill, London N19 5NF — MB BCh BAO 1988 NUI.

DESOR, Deepak 75 Hanger Hill, Weybridge KT13 9YG — MB BS 1983 Lond.; MRCGP 1988.

DESOR, Maryse Ingrid Nilmini The Cobham Health Centre, 168 Portsmouth Road, Cobham KT11 1HT Tel: 01932 867231 Fax: 01932 866874 — MB BS 1986 Lond.; MRCGP 1990; DFFP 1993; DRCOG 1989. GP; Health Screening Phys. Ashstead Hosp. Surrey.

DESOR, Rakesh 6 Princess Drive, Oadby, Leicester LE2 4SB — MB ChB 1987 Manch.; MRCGP 1992.

DESSELBERGER, Ulrich Clinical Microbiology and Public Health Laboratory, Level 6, Addenbrooke's Hospital, Cambridge CB2 2QW Tel: 01223 216816 Fax: 01223 242775; 17 West End, Whittlesford, Cambridge CB2 4LX Tel: 01223 832359 — MD 1967 Berlin; State Exam Med. 1965; FRCP Glas. 1989; MRCP (UK) 1987; FRCPath 1991, M 1979. Cons. Virol. & Dir. Clin. Microbiol. & Pub. Health Laborat. Camb. Socs: Amer. Soc. Virol. New York Acad. Sc.; Soc. Gen. Microbiol. & Amer. Soc. Microbiol.; Germ. Soc. Virol. Prev: Cons. Virol. & Dir. Regional Virus Laborat. Birm.; Hon. Cons. Gtr. Glas. HB & Sen. Lect. Univ. Glas.; Cons. Hannover Med. Sch., Germany.

DESSOUKI, Mr Nazar Radwan Ragab Uist and Barra Hospital, Benbecula HS7 5LA Tel: 01870 603603 Fax: 01870 603636 Email: nazar.dessouki@btinternet.com; 7 Partridge Avenue, Chelmsford CM1 4JG Tel: 01245 349418 Email: nazar.dessouki@btinternet.com — MB ChB 1969 Cairo; FRCS Glas. 1978; MRCS Eng. LRCP Lond. 1981. (Cairo) Cons. Surg, Arrn War Memor. Hosp., Lamlash; Assoc. Edr. Emirates Med. Jl; Vis. Surg. to Gibraltar Health Auth. Socs: Counc. Biol. Edrs. USA; Consg. Edr., Emirates Med. Jl. Prev: Sen. Cons. Gen. Surg. MoH , UAE; SHO (Accid. & Emerg. & Orthop. Surg.) Frenchay Hosp. Bristol.; Regist. (Gen. & Neuro. Surg.) Essex AHA.

DESVEAUX, Jean-Claude Wychall Lane Surgery, 11 Wychall Lane, Kings Norton, Birmingham B38 8TE Tel: 0121 628 2345 Fax: 0121 628 8282; 32 All Saints Road, Kings Heath, Birmingham B14 7LL Tel: 0121 628 2345 — MB ChB 1983 Birm.; MRCGP 1988; DCCH RCP Ed. 1988; DA (UK) 1987; DRCOG 1985. Socs: BMA & Roy. Coll. GPs. Prev: Trainee GP/SHO (Anaesth.) Good Hope Hosp. Sutton Coldfield; Resid. Med. Off. Little Aston Hosp. Staffs.

DETHY, Martine 20 Burnside, Halebarns, Altrincham WA15 0SG — MD 1982 Louvain.

DETSIOS, Clare Louise Forest Gate Surgery, Hazel Farm Road, Totton, Southampton SO40 8WU Tel: 023 8066 3839 Fax: 023 8066 7090 — MB ChB 1981 Bristol; MRCGP 1985.

DETTORI, Helen Louise 20 Dene Mansions, Kingdon Road, West Hampstead, London NW6 1AY — MB BS 1991 Queensland.

DEUBEL, Eva Lieselotte Yorkhill NHS Trust, Royal Hospital for Sick Children, Yorkhill, Glasgow G3 8SJ — State Exam Med 1989 Marburg.

DEUCHAR, Andrew James Southfields Group Practice, 7 Revelstoke Road, London SW18 5NJ Tel: 020 8947 0061 Fax: 020 8944 8694; 14 Elsenham Street, London SW18 5NS Tel: 020 8874 5793 Fax: 020 8875 9729 — MB BS 1989 Lond.; Dip. Occ. Med. 1998. (St. Geo.) Gp. Med. Adviser to Lloyds TSB PLC; Assoc. Prac. Dr Kelly & Assoc. Lond. Socs: Roy. Soc. Med.; Soc. Occupat. Med. Prev: SHO (Paediat.) Epsom Gen. Hosp.; Cas. Off. Epsom Gen. Hosp.; Ho. Off. (Surg.) St. Geo. Hosp. Lond.

DEUCHAR, Neil John Ladywood Primary Care Liaison Team, 395 Ladywood Middleway, Birmingham B1 2TJ Tel: 0121 685 6900 Fax: 0121 454 0707 — MB BS 1984 Lond.; MRCPsych 1994; DRCOG 1993; MMedSc 1998. (Guy's) Cons. Psychiat. Primary Care Liaison, Ladywood, Birm. Prev: Sen. Regist. (Psychiat.) Qu. Eliz. Psychiat. Hosp. Birm.; Regist. Rotat. (Psychiat.) Qu. Eliz. Psychiat. Hosp. Birm.; Regist. (Psychiat.) Lond. Hosp.

DEUCHAR, Robert Andrew Dennycross Medical Centre, Duke Street, Denny FK6 6DB Tel: 01324 822330 Fax: 01324 824415 — MB ChB 1980 Glas.; BSc (Hons.) Glas. 1974, MB ChB 1980.

DEUCHARS, James Alastair (retired) Lauder Grange, 67/3 Grange Loan, Edinburgh EH9 2EG Tel: 0131 662 1272 — MB ChB 1941 Ed.; MRCGP 1952. Prev: Ho. Phys. & Clin. Asst. Roy. Infirm. Edin.

DEUTSCH, George Paul Hove Nuffield, 55 New Church Road, Hove BN3 4BG Tel: 01273 220919 Fax: 01273 220919; 23 Hill Drive, Hove BN3 6QN Tel: 01273 553556 — MB BS Lond. 1967; FRCP Lond. 1988; MRCP (UK) 1970; FRCR 1975; FFR 1973; DMRT Eng. 1972. (Middlx.) Cons. Clin. Oncologist Sussex Oncol. Centre Roy. Sussex Co. Hosp. Brighton. Socs: Assn. Head & Neck Oncol.; Brit. Oncol. Assn. Prev: Sen. Regist. Meyerstein Inst. Radiother. Middlx. Hosp.; Regist. (Med.) N. Middlx. Hosp.; Ho. Off. Middlx. Hosp. Lond.

DEUTSCH, Mr John 2 Lugg Vale Cottages, Broadlands Lane, Hereford HR1 1JB Tel: 01432 370874 Email: jscpae@lineone.net — MB ChB 1981 Liverp.; FRCS Glas. 1988; FRCOP 1988. Cons. Ophth. Vict. Eye Hosp. Hereford. Prev: Sen. Regist. (Ophth.) Birm. Eye Hosp.; Regist. (Ophth.) Birm. & Midl. Eye Hosp.; SHO (Ophth.) Roy. United. Hosp. Bath.

DEUTSCH, Katharina Ulrike Slieve Bloom, 15 Willowby Park, Yelverton PL20 6AN Tel: 01822 854903 Fax: 01822 854903 — MB ChB 1987 Liverp.; DRCOG 1992; DCH RCP Lond. 1992. CMO (Family Plann.).

DEV, Vikram Jeet The Old Vicarage, St Mary's Road, Riddlesden, Keighley BD20 5PA — MB BS 1978 Poona. Regist. (Community Med.). Prev: Regist. (Anaesth.).

DEVA, Ameya St James Health Centre, 47 St. Jame's Street, Walthamstow, London E17 7NH Tel: 020 85209 9308 — MB BS 1960 Lucknow; MB BS 1960 Lucknow.

DEVA, Samarendra Satyendra Chandra Flat 15, Church Court, 154 Snakes Lane E., Woodford Green IG8 7JB — MRCS Eng. LRCP Lond. 1989.

DEVADASON, Margaret Joanna Nesammal 20 Richmond Drive, Mapperley Park, Nottingham NG3 5EL Tel: 0115 606097 — MB BS 1967 Madras. (Stanley Med. Coll.) SCMO Nottm. HA. Prev: SHO Childr. Hosp. Nottm.; SHO (Obst.) Firs Matern. Hosp. Nottm.; Rotat. SHO Train. Scheme for Gen. Pract. Nottm.

DEVAKUMAR, Manikkarasa Hergest Unit, Ysbyty Gwynedd, Bangor LL57 2PW Tel: 01248 384074 Fax: 01248 371397 Email: deva@nww-tr.wales.nhs.uk — MB BS 1974 Sri Lanka; Dip Health Care Law 1998 (Swansea); FRCPsych 1998; MD (Psychiatry) Sri Lanka 1986; MRCPsych 1984. Cons. Psychiat. Gwynedd N. W. Wales NHS Trust; Hon. Sen. Lect. IMSCAR, Univ. of Wales, Bangor.

DEVAKUMAR, Vijayapura Chicknanjana (retired) 76 Ramsey Avenue, Bacup OL13 9PJ Tel: 01706 874991 — MB BS 1963 Mysore; MRCPsych 1978; DPM Eng. 1972.

***DEVAKUMAR, Vinodh Nanjanna** 76 Ramsey Avenue, Bacup OL13 9PJ Tel: 01706 874991 — MB ChB 1998 Manch.; MB ChB Manch 1998.

DEVAL, Sarah 25 Wroxall Road, Solihull B91 1DR — MB ChB 1990 Sheff.

DEVALIA, Vinodchandra Department of Haematology, Princess of Wales Hospital, Coity Road, Bridgend CF31 1RQ — MB ChB 1982 Glas.; BSc (Hons.) Biochem. Glas. 1980; MRCP (UK) 1985; MRCPath 1994. Cons. Haemat. P.ss of Wales Hosp. Bridgend. Prev: Sen. Regist. (Haemat.) Nottm. Hosps.; Clin. Lect. (Haemat.) Univ. Coll. & Hon. Sen. Regist. (Haemat.) Univ. Coll. Hosp. Lond.; Asst. Lect. & Hon. Regist. (Haemat.) Middlx. Hosp. Med. Sch. Lond. Univ.

DEVAN, Vivian Russell 46 Bathgate Road, London SW19 5PJ — LRCPI & LM, LRSCI & LM 1956; LRCPI & LM, LRCSI & LM 1956. (RCSI)

DEVANE, Leonard Stanislaus St. James House Surgery, County Court Road, King's Lynn PE30 5SY; 114 Gayton Road, King's Lynn PE30 4ER — MB BCh BAO 1951 NUI; DCH RCPSI 1954; LM Rotunda 1953. Prev: Ho. Phys. Bolton Gen. Hosp., Alder Hey Childr. Hosp. Liverp. & Chest; Hosp. Ham. Green Bristol.

DEVANE, Michael James Desmond Southampton General Hospital, Tremona Road, Southampton SO16 6YD — MB BS 1988 Lond. Regist. (Gen. Med.) Jersey Gen. Hosp. St. Helier.

DEVANE, Sean Proinnsias Department of Child Health, 4th Floor, Ruskin Wing, King's College Hospital, London SE5 9RS Tel: 020 7346 3573 Fax: 020 7924 9365 — MB BCh BAO 1980 NUI; MD NUI 1994; FRCPI 1995, M 1986; DCH NUI 1981. Cons. Paediat. King's Coll. Hosp. Lond. Prev: Lect. (Child Health) King's Coll. Sch. Med. & Dent.

DEVANEY, Jane Yvonne 12 Savon Hook, Liverpool L37 6DP — MB ChB 1989 Dundee.

DEVANEY, Noeleen Marie Lagan Valley Hospital, Lisburn BT28 1JP; 25 Tansy Road, Porter's Bridge, Ballinderry, Lisburn BT28 2PB — MB BCh BAO 1977 Belf.; MSc (Health & Social Sev. Managem.) Univ. Ulster 1996; MPhil (Med. Ethics & Law) Belf. 1993; BSc (Anat.) 1st. cl. Hons. Belf. 1974; MRCPsych 1982. (Queen's University, Belfast) Cons. Psychiat. of Old Age, Lagan Valley Hosp., Lisburn.; Jt. Med. Director, Down Lisburn HSS Trust. Socs: Inst. Health Serv. Managers; Fell. of the Roy. Coll. of Psychiat.s. Prev: Dir. N. Irel. Hosp. Advis. Serv.

DEVANNEY, Marie Catherine 84 Newlands Road, Glasgow G43 2JR — MB ChB 1984 Glas.; DRCOG 1987.

DEVAPAL, Damodaran Millfield Medical Centre, 63-83 Hylton Road, Sunderland SR4 7AF Tel: 0191 567 9179 Fax: 0191 514 7452 — MB BS 1967 Kerala.

DEVARAJ, Anand 43 Ormond Crescent, Hampton TW12 2TJ — MB BS 1998 Lond.; MB BS Lond 1998.

DEVARAJ, Kanakaratnam Samuel 2 Crescent View, Alwoodley, Leeds LS17 7QF — MB BS 1957 Madras.

DEVARAJ, Kiran Shashi Sri-Shyla, Ffordd Crwys, Bangor LL57 2NT — MB ChB 1993 Leeds.

DEVARAJ, Shalini Rebecca New Wortley Health Centre, 15 Green Lane, Tong Road, Leeds LS12 1JE — MB ChB 1984 Leeds; MRCGP 1999; DRCOG 1991. Gen. Practitioner.

DEVARAJ, Sivaramkrishnan 43 Ormond Crescent, Hampton TW12 2TJ — MB BS 1968 Mysore.

DEVARAJ, Mr Vikram Somasekhar The Royal Devon & Exeter NHS Trust, The Royal Devon & Exeter Hospital (Wonford), Barrack Road, Exeter EX2 5DW — MB ChB 1982 Leeds; FRCS (Plast Surg.) 1993; FRCS Eng. 1987. Cons. Plastic Reconstruc. & Hand Surg. Exeter. Prev: Sen. Regist. (Plastic Surg.) Radcliffe Infirm. Oxf.; Regist. (Plastic Surg.) St. Jas. Univ. Hosp. Leeds; SHO (Plastic Surg.) Frenchay HA.

DEVARAJ, Vimala 2 Crescent View, Alwoodley, Leeds LS17 7QF — MB BS 1954 Madras.

DEVARAJA, Gowrie 8 Pennyroyal Crescent, Witham CM8 2YN — MB BS 1981 Colombo; LMSSA Lond. 1992. (colombo.univ.Sri.Lanka)

DEVARAJA, Vadakklur Chidhambaram 11 Berkley Drive, Royton, Oldham OL2 5BB — MB BS 1974 Madras.

DEVARAJAN, Mr Raghuram 16 Wharton Avenue, Solihull B92 9LZ Tel: 0121 705 1465 Email: raghudevarajam@hotmail.com; City Hospital, Dudley Road, Birmingham B18 7Q Tel: 0121 554 3801 Ext: 4375 — MB BS 1982 Delhi; FRCS 1999 FRCS Urol.; FRCS Ed. 1989. Cons. Urol. City Hosp. NHS Trust Dudley Rd Birm.; Cons. Urol. Sandwell Gen. Hosp. Sandwell. Socs: Full Mem. of Urological Surg.s; Brit. Soc. for EndoUrol. Prev: Specialist Regist. Qu. E. Birm.; Specialst Regist. Stoke-on-Trent; Specialist Regist. Walsgrave Hosp. Coventry.

DEVAS, Professor Michael Bertrand Stamford House, Chipping Campden GL55 6AD Tel: 01386 840625 — MRCS Eng. LRCP Lond. 1943; MB BChir Camb. 1943; MChir Camb. 1976; FRCS Eng. 1950. (Lond. Hosp.) Socs: Fell. Roy. Soc. Med. Prev: Dir. Wishbone Appeal Brit. Orthop. Assn.; Prof. Orthop. Dept. Sch. Med. Sc. Univ. Sains, Malaysia; Hon. Cons. Orthop. Surg. Hastings Gp. Hosps.

DEVASIA, Neerampuzha Devasia 42 Newquay Road, Walsall WS5 3EW — MB BS 1978 Bangalor; MB BS Bangalore 1978; LRCP LRCS Ed. LRCPS Glas. 1983.

DEVCHAND, Divia Anaesthetic Department, Royal Marsden NHS Trust, Fulham Road, London SW3 6JJ Tel: 020 7352 8171 Fax: 020 7351 3785 Email: devchand@icr.ac.uk — MB ChB 1981 Zimbabwe; LRCP LRCS Ed. LRCPS Glas. 1983; FRCA 1992; FFA RCSI 1990; DA (UK) 1985. Cons. Anaesth. Roy. Marsden NHS Trust. Socs: BMA; Assn. Anaesth. GB & Irel.; Assn. Paediat. Anaesth. Prev: Sen. Regist. (Anaesth.) Hammersmith Hosp. Lond.; Regist. (Anaesth.) Middlx. Hosp. Lond.; Regist. Univ. Hosp. Wales Cardiff.

DEVENDRA, Devaselvan 3C Kingsbridge, Stranmillis Court, Belfast BT9 5EU — MB BCh 1997 Belf.

***DEVENEY, Gillian** 5 The Drums, Drums Terrace, Greenock PA16 7TX — MB ChB 1996 Glas.

DEVENNY, Anne Margaret — MB ChB 1991 Glas.; MRCP (UK) 1995. (Glasgow University) LOCUM Paediat. Cons. Socs: RCPCH; BMA; Roy. Coll. Phys. and Surg. Glasg. Prev: SHO (Paediat.) S.ern Gen. NHS Trust; SHO (Paediat.) Yorkhill NHS Trust & Glas. Roy. Matern. Hosp.

DEVENPORT, Catherine Eleanor 19 Weald View Road, Tonbridge TN9 2NG — MB BS 1992 Lond.

DEVERALL, Mr Philip Brook (retired) 3 Northfield Close, Bromley BR1 2WZ Tel: 020 8467 5418 Fax: 0870 131 9081 Email: phil@pdeverall.freeserve.co.uk — MB BS 1960 Lond.; FRCS Eng. 1964; MRCS Eng. LRCP Lond. 1960. Prev: Head (Cardiothoracic Surg.) Guy's Hosp. Lond.

DEVERELL, Mark Hamilton The Old Dispensary, 32 East Borough, Wimborne BH21 1PL Tel: 01202 880786 Fax: 01202 880736 — MB BS 1983 Lond.; BSc Lond. 1980, MB BS 1983. Lect. King's Coll. Hosp. Lond.

DEVEREUX, Barbara 13 Glebe Close, Gunton Church Lane, Lowestoft NR32 4NU Tel: 01502 572472 — MB BS Lond. 1952; Mem. Inst. Psychosexual Med. 1980; MFFP 1993. (St. Geo.) SCMO (Family Plann.) Norwich HA. Socs: Inst. Psychosexual Med.; Fac. Fam. Plann. & Reproduc. Health Care. Prev: Ho. Phys. Vict. Hosp. Childr. Lond.; Cas. Off. St. Geo. Hosp. Lond.; Ho. Phys.(Med.) Hove Gen. Hosp.

DEVEREUX, Emma-Jane 5 The Square, Woodford Green IG8 0UJ — MB BS 1992 Lond.; DCH RCP Lond. 1995. (UMDS)

DEVEREUX, Graham Stuart Department of Thoracic Medicine, Aberdeen Royal Infirmary, Foresterhill, Aberdeen AB25 2ZN Tel: 01224 681818 Fax: 01224 403051; Claymires Smithy House, Esslemont, Ellon AB41 8PL Tel: 01358 724079 — BM BCh 1988 Oxf.; BA Camb. 1985; MA Camb. 1989; MRCP (UK) 1991; MD Camb. 1995. (Oxf.) Sen. Regist. (Thoracic Med.) Aberd. Roy. Infirm. & Hon. Clin. Lect. Aberd. Univ. Prev: Regist. & Hon. Research Assoc. Chest Unit Newc.Gen. Hosp. Univ. of Newc.; SHO Rotat. (Med.) Newc. Health Auth.; Regist. (Respirat.) City Hosp. Nottm.

DEVEREUX, Helen Jane 15 Station Road, Verwood BH31 7PY Tel: 01202 825353 — MB BS 1986 Lond.; DRCOG 1991.

DEVEREUX, Joseph Guy John 1 Weston Way, Northampton NN3 3BL — MB BS 1991 Lond.; BSc Lond. 1990; FRCOphth 1996. (Royal Free School of Medicine)

DEVEREUX, Mr Malcolm Holt North London Nuffield Hospital, Cavell Drive, Enfield EN2 7PR Tel: 020 366 2122; Old Park, 4 Woodland Way, Woodford Wells, Woodford Green IG8 0QG Tel: 020 8504 6547 Fax: 020 8505 6517 — MRCS Eng. LRCP Lond. 1961; BSc Lond. 1958, MB BS (Hons.) 1961; FRCS Eng. 1966. (Guy's) Cons. Urol. Surg. N. Lond. Nuffield Hosp., Enfield EN2 7PR. Socs: Brit. Assn. Urol. Surgs.; Fell. Roy. Soc. Med. Prev: Sen. Urol. Regist. St. Peter's Gp. Hosps.; Surg. Regist. Char. Cross Hosp. Lond.; Cons. Urol. Surg. N. Middlx. Hosp. (1971-1997).

DEVEREUX, Sonia Linda Margaret Group Practice Surgery, Green Street, Forfar DD8 3AR Tel: 01307 462316; Rysland, Mount Tabor Rd, Perth PH2 7DE Email: devereux@ukonline.co.uk — MB

BS 1986 Lond.; MSc (Oncol.) Glas. 1995; MRCP (UK) 1990; MRCGP 1995; DRCOG 1995. Prev: Regist. (Clin. Oncol.) Beatson Oncol. Centre Glas.; SHO (Med.) Guy's Hosp. Lond. & Basle, Switz. Europ. Exchange Scheme.

DEVEREUX, Stephen Department of Haematological Medicine, Kings College Hospital, Denmark Hill, London SE5 9RS Tel: 0207 346 3709 Fax: 0207 346 3514 Email: stephen.devereux@kcl.ac.uk; 47 Beaumont Avenue, St Albans AL1 4TW — MB BS 1978 Lond.; MRCP UK 1980; MRCPath 1986; FRC Path 1996; FRCP 2000. Cons. Haematologist, Kings Coll. Hosp., Lond. Prev: Late Sen. Lect. Univ. Coll. Lond; Cons. Haemat. Kent & Canterbury Hosp.; Lect. (Haemat.) Middlx. Hosp. Lond.

DEVEREUX, Teresa Anne Hillfoot Surgery, 126 Owlcotes Road, Pudsey LS28 7QR Tel: 0113 257 4169 Fax: 0113 236 3380 — MB BS 1975 Lond.; BSc (Special Hons.) Lond. 1970; MRCGP 1980; DCH Eng. 1978; DRCOG 1977. (Univ. Coll. Lond. & Roy. Free) GP Trainer. Socs: BMA; Socialist Med. Assn.

DEVERS, Marion Claire 12 Kylepark Crescent, Uddingston, Glasgow G71 7DQ — MB ChB 1993 Glas.

DEVESHWAR, Sanjeev Kumar 69 Seymour Gardens, Ilford IG1 3LL — MB ChB 1979 Liverp.

DEVEY, George Frederick Swn-Y-Gwynt, 36 Preston Road, Preston, Weymouth DT3 6PZ — MB ChB 1952 Birm.; DPH Eng. 1958. Civil. Med. Off. Min. of Defence (N). Prev: Dep. MOH Flints.; Med. Adviser Fisons Pharmaceut. Ltd., Med. Adviser Roussel; Laborats. Ltd. Ho. Surg. Kidderminster & Dist. Gen. Hosp.

DEVEY, Luke Richard Royal Infirmary of Edinburgh, Lauriston Place, Edinburgh EH3 9YW — BM BCh 1998 Oxf.; BM BCh Oxf 1998.

DEVICHAND, Neena Community Health Department, West Glamorgan Health Authority, 21 Orchard St., Swansea; 5 Swallow Tree Close, Neath SA10 7EZ Tel: 01639 638037 — MB BS 1976 Delhi; LMSSA 1981; DRCOG 1988; DCH Delhi 1978. Clin. Med. Off. Community Paediat. (Community Child Health) E. Morgenwg Trust Neath & Port Talbot.

DEVICHAND, Prabodh Andrew Street Medical Centre, 22 Andrew Street, Llanelli SA15 3YP Tel: 01554 778017 Fax: 01554 778820 — MB BS Delhi.

DEVICHAND, Pramod Victoria Gardens Surgery, Victoria Gardens, Neath SA11 1HW Tel: 01639 643786 Fax: 01639 640018; Tel: 01639 638037 — MB BS 1973 Delhi; MD Delhi 1977. Princip. GP.

DEVILE, Catherine Josephine Great Ormond Street Hospital for Children NHS Trust, Great Ormond St., London WC1N 3JH Tel: 020 7405 9200; Oakleigh, Forsters Farm, Benover, Yalding, Maidstone ME18 6AX — MB BS 1986 Lond.; MA Camb. 1987, BA (Hons.) 1983; MRCP (UK) 1990; MRCPCH 1997. Sen. Regist. (Paediat. Neurol.) Gt. Ormond St. Hosp. Lond. Socs: Fell. Roy. Soc. Med.; Eur. soc. Paediat. Endocrinol. Prev: Research Fell. (Paediat.) Inst. Child Health Univ. Lond.

DEVILLIERS, Susan Hermien Flat 14, York House, Queen Alexandra Hospital, Southwick Hill Road, Cosham, Portsmouth PO6 3LY — MB ChB 1995 Stellenbosch.

DEVINE, Agnieszka Department of Anaesthesia, Royal Liverpool University Hospital, Prescot St., Liverpool L7 8XP Tel: 0151 706 3202; 5 Barkfield Lane, Formby, Liverpool L37 3JW — MB ChB 1987 Manch.; BSc Manch. 1984; FRCA 1992. Lect. & Cons. Anaesth. & Pain Managem. Univ. Liverp. Socs: Assn. Anaesth.; BMA. Prev: Lect. (Anaesth.) Univ. Manch.; Regist. Rotat. (Anaesth.) Mersey Region; SHO (Cardiothoracic Med.) Wythenshawe Hosp. Manch.

DEVINE, Alison 40 Rectory Park Road, Birmingham B26 3LJ — MB ChB 1993 Liverp.

DEVINE, Andrew Robert Yule Grave Park Surgery, 95 Burlington Lane, Chiswick, London W4 3ET Tel: 020 8747 1549 Fax: 020 8400 1092 — MB BS 1993 Lond.

DEVINE, Anna Josephine Patricia Stockings Farm, Little Berkhamsted, Hertford SG13 8LW Tel: 01992 583349 — MB BChir 1994 Camb.; BA (Hons.) Camb. 1991; BSc (Hons.) Lond. 1987. Trainee GP/SHO W. Suff. Hosp. NHS Trust Bury St Edmunds.

DEVINE, Anthony 14 Gainsthorpe Road, Kirton, Lindsey, Gainsborough DN21 4JH — MB ChB 1965 St. And.

DEVINE, Brendan Leo 16 Hamilton Drive, Cambuslang, Glasgow G72 8JG — MB ChB 1970 Glas.; MRCP (U.K.) 1974. Cons. Phys. (Geriat. Med.) Lightburn Hosp. Glas.

DEVINE, Elizabeth Anne Arran House, Newton Flotman, Norwich NR15 1QX — MB BS 1964 Lond.; MRCS Eng. LRCP Lond. 1964. (St. Geo.)

DEVINE, James Govan Health Centre, 295 Langlands Road, Glasgow G51 4BJ — LRCP LRCS 1949 Ed.; LRCP LRCS Ed. LRFPS Glas. 1949; MRCGP 1958. (St. Mungo's Coll. & Univ. Glas.) Prev: Ho. Off. (Paediat.) Stobhill Hosp. Glas.; Ho. Off. Matern. Hosp. Bellshill.

DEVINE, Jennifer Fiona 20 Southesk Avenue, Bishopbriggs, Glasgow G64 3AD — MB ChB 1985 Glas.

DEVINE, John, MC (retired) 1 Station Road, Thames Ditton KT7 0NU Tel: 020 8398 2122 — MB ChB 1936 Glas.

DEVINE, John Charles 35 Manor Avenue, Sale M33 5JQ — MB ChB 1993 Manch.

DEVINE, Marc Andrew 39 The Crescent, Watford WD18 0AD — MB BCh BAO 1984 Belf.; MB BCh l984 Belf.

DEVINE, Maureen Margaret 34 Southbrae Drive, Glasgow G13 1QA — LRCP LRCS 1947 Ed.; LRCP LRCS Ed. LRFPS Glas. 1947.

DEVINE, Michael Ellis 48 Radnor Road, Harrow HA1 1RZ — BM BCh 1996 Oxf.

DEVINE, Monica Bonner Flat 3/5, The Riggs, Milngavie, Glasgow G62 8LX Tel: 0141 956 1589 — LRCP LRCS Ed. LRFPS Glas. 1948. Prev: Adjudicating Med. Pract. DHSS Glas.; Clin. Med. Off. E.. Dist. Gtr. Glas. HB; GP Scotstown Glas. & Paisley.

DEVINE, Monica Denise Rees, Hoe, Rostron and James, Lister House Surgery, Bollams Mead, Wiveliscombe, Taunton TA4 2PH Tel: 01984 623471 Fax: 01984 624357 — MB ChB 1979 Glas.

DEVINE, Nicholas Joseph Bramhall Park Medical Centre, 235 Bramhall Lane South, Bramhall, Stockport SK7 3EP Tel: 0161 440 7669 Fax: 0161 440 7671 — MB ChB 1983 Manch.; MRCGP 1989; DRCOG 1987.

DEVINE, Paul Martin 52 Ashgrove Road, Newtownabbey BT36 6LJ — MB BCh BAO 1993 Belf.

DEVINE, Roy Arran House, Newton Flotman, Norwich NR15 1QX — MB ChB 1961 Sheff.; FRCPsych 1986, M 1971; DPM Eng. 1965. (Sheff.) Cons. Psychiat. InDepend. Sector. Prev: Lect. Univ. Dept. Psychiat. Sheff.; Cons. Psychiat. Holleton And Norf. And Norwich Hosp.

DEVINE, William Camillus 2 Croft Hey, Rufford, Ormskirk L40 1UX — MB BCh BAO 1970 NUI.

DEVITT, Hilary Jane Meanwood Group Practice, 548 Meanwood Road, Leeds LS6 4JN Tel: 0113 295 1737 Fax: 0113 295 1736; 3 West End Lane, Horsforth, Leeds LS18 5JP — MB ChB 1986 Liverp.; MRCGP 1990; DRCOG 1988. (Liverp.)

DEVITT, Nicola Mary Department of Rehabilitation, Weston General Hospital, Grange Road, Weston Super Mare BS23 4TQ Tel: 01934 636363; The Old Forge, Stoke St, Rodney Stoke, Cheddar BS27 3UP — BM 1976 Soton.; MRCP (UK) 1980. Staff Grade Phys. (Rehabil.) W.on Gen. Hosp. W.on Super Mare.

DEVITT, Pauline Mary 1 Dunbar Close, Gainsborough DN21 1YF — MB BCh BAO 1989 NUI.

DEVLIN, Anita May 4 Glen Terrace, Hexham NE46 3LA — MB BS 1988 Lond.; MRCP (Lond.) 1992. Cons. Paediatic Neurol., Newc.-upon-Tyne. Prev: Hon. Lect. Univ. of Aberd.; Sen. Regist. (Paediat. Neurol.).

DEVLIN, Barbara Ann Community Health Office, John Mitchel Place, Newry BT34 3BU Tel: 01693 67030; 14 Pine Valley, Rostrevor, Newry BT34 3DE — MB BCh BAO 1979 Belf.; DRCOG 1981; DCCH RCP Ed. 1987; DFFP 1992. (QUB) Assoc. Specialist Community Child health Newry & Mourne HSS Trust. Socs: Assoc. Mem. Inst. Psycho-Sexual Med.; BMA; BACCH.

DEVLIN, Barry Michael 316 Drumsurn Road, Limavady BT49 0PX — MB BCh 1998 Belf.; MB BCh Belf 1998.

DEVLIN, Beth 5 Biddick Close, Stockton-on-Tees TS19 0UJ — MB ChB 1998 Liverp.

DEVLIN, Brenda Joan Old Station House, Dunphail, Forres IV36 2QW — MB ChB 1970 Glas.; MRCGP 1977. Asst. GP Elgin Health Centre. Prev: Clin. Med. Off. Highland HB; Princip. GP Cornw. & Isles of Scilly; Squadron Ldr. RAF Med. Br.

DEVLIN, David Pollock Bovally Medical Centre, 2 Rossair Road, Limavady BT49 0TE Tel: 015047 66352 — MB BCh 1981 Belfast; MB BCh Belf. 1981. (Belfast) GP Limavady, Co. Lond.derry.

DEVLIN, Eamon Gerard 1 The Beeches, Altnagelvin Area Hospital, Londonderry BT47 6SB; Oakfern, 3 Woodbridge Hill, Londonderry BT47 2EE Tel: 01504 313494 — MB BCh BAO 1982 Dub.; FFA RCSI 1986. (Trinity Coll. Dub.) Cons. Anaesth. (Obst. Anaesth. & Intens. Care Med.) Altnagelvin Area Hosp. Lond.derry.

DEVLIN, Eileen Miriam Shantallow Health Centre, Racecourse Road, Londonderry BT48 8NL Tel: 028 7135 1323; 31 Mount Vernon, Londonderry BT48 8AG — MB BCh BAO 1986 Belf.; MRCGP 1992.

DEVLIN, Esther Margaret (retired) Rectory Stables, Mells, Frome BA11 3PT Tel: 01373 812951 — MB BCh BAO 1945 NUI; DPH Malaya 1961; LM Nat. Matern. Hosp. Dub. Prev: Asst. MOH Worcs. CC.

DEVLIN, James Scunthorpe General Hospital, Cliff Gardens, Scunthorpe DN15 7BH Tel: 01724 282282; 11 Avenue Fontenay, Skippingdale, Scunthorpe DN15 8EN Tel: 01724 874228 — MB ChB 1980 Ed.; DCH RCPS Glas. 1982; MRCP (UK) 1985. Cons. Paediat. Scunthorpe Gen. Hosp. Socs: Brit. Paediat. Assn. Prev: Research Fell. Booth Hall Childr. Hosp. Manch.; Regist. & Tutor (Paediat.) Univ. Manch.; Regist. (Paediat.) W.. Gen. Hosp. Edin.

DEVLIN, James Anthony Joseph 155 Blacker Lane, Netherton, Wakefield WF4 4EZ — MB BCh BAO 1988 NUI; MRCPI 1990. Research Fell. (Rheum.) Univ. Birm.

DEVLIN, John (retired) 2 Love Walk, Denmark Hill, London SE5 8AD — MRCS Eng. LRCP Lond. 1936.

DEVLIN, John Conor 622 Princes Avenue, West Kirby, Wirral CH48 7HJ Tel: 0151 625 5546 — MB BCh BAO 1983 Dub. Cons. Anaesth. Wirral Hosp. Trust.

DEVLIN, John Emmet 23 Cairnhill, Crieve Road, Newry BT34 2ST Tel: 01693 64865 — MB BCh BAO 1970 Belf.; FRCP Lond. 1992; MRCP (UK) 1974. Cons. Phys. Daisy Hill Hosp. Newry.

DEVLIN, Joseph (retired) Fofany, 4 Templemore Park, Londonderry BT48 0EQ Tel: 01504 266137 — LRCPI & LM, LRSCI & LM 1938; LRCPI & LM, LRCSI & LM 1938. Prev: Ho. Surg. & Ho. Phys. Jervis St. Hosp. Dub.

DEVLIN, Joseph Callistus 26 Cartmel Close, Sunnybank, Bury BL9 8JA Tel: 0161 766 3724 — MB BCh BAO 1954 Belf.; MRCPsych 1971; DPM Eng. 1960. Cons. Psychiat. N. Manch. Gen. Hosp. Prev: SHO St. Luke's Hosp. Armagh; Regist. Burnley Gen. Hosp.; Sen. Regist. Crumpsall Hosp. Manch.

DEVLIN, Kevin Francis Lurganboy Surgery, Lurganboy, Clones Road, Newtownbulter, Enniskillen BT92 6JT Tel: 028 6773 8203 — MB BCh BAO 1982 Belf.; MB Bch Belf. 1982; MRCGP 1986; DRCOG 1986. GP Newtown Butler. 1.

DEVLIN, Mark Francis Peter 1167 Pollokshaws Road, Shawlands, Glasgow G41 3NG — MB ChB 1995 Glas.

DEVLIN, Mark Lawrence — MB ChB 1990 Glas.; DRCOG 1996; 2001 DPCR Uni Bath; BSc (Hons.) Glas. 1987; MRCGP 1996.

DEVLIN, Michael Hart Lea, Sutton Road, Wigginton, York YO32 2RA — MB BS 1990 Lond.

DEVLIN, Michael Martin Anthony Health Centre, Great James Street, Londonderry BT48 7DH Tel: 028 7137 8522; Sorrento, 60 Culmore Road, Londonderry BT48 8JB Tel: 01504 351217 — MB BCh BAO 1975 NUI; DCH RCPI 1979. (Galway Irish Republic) Princip. GP Lond.derry. Prev: Intern. Altnagelvin Hosp. Lond.derry; SHO (Med., Paediat., Obst., Cas., ENT & Dermat.) Altnagelvin Hosp.; Lond.derry.

DEVLIN, Olive Paula The Mount Surgery, George Street, Pontypool NP4 6YL Tel: 01495 763141 Fax: 01495 767895; 19 Woodville Road, Newport NP20 4JB Tel: 01633 676242 — MB BCh 1979 Wales; MRCGP 1983; DRCOG 1981. (Welsh National School of Medicine)

DEVLIN, Patrick Brendan 103 Cow Hill Park, Londonderry BT47 6XX — MB BCh BAO 1979 Belf.

DEVLIN, Mr Peter (retired) Fallagh, 6 Fayre Oaks Drive, Hereford HR4 0QS Tel: 01432 273416 — LM 1941 Dub.; MCh NUI 1952, MB BCh BAO 1941. Prev: Cons. Obstetr. Hereford Hosp. Gp.

DEVLIN, Peter Nicholas Patrick Portslade Health Centre, Church Road, Portslade, Brighton BN41 1LX Tel: 01273 422525/418445 Fax: 01273 413510; 176 Tivoli Crescent N., Brighton BN1 5NA Email: peter.devlin@virgin.net — MB BS 1980 Lond.; MRCP (UK) 1984; DRCOG 1986. Med. Dir. Brightdoc Co-op. Brighton; Mem. LMC; GP Trainer.

DEVLIN, Siobhan Newcastle Surgery, Main St., Newcastle BT33 0AE — MB BCh BAO 1988 Belf.; MRCGP 1992; DRCOG 1993; DMH Belf. 1991; DGM RCP Lond. 1990. (Queens University Belfast) Full-time GP Partner in Doctors Gp. Pract., 56 Main St., Newc. BT33 0AG.

DEVLIN, Siobhán Bridin Anaesthetics Department, Altnagelvin Hospital, Londonderry BT47 1XX Tel: 01504 45171; 103 Caw Hill Park, Clooney Road, Londonderry BT47 6XX Tel: 01504 46704 — MB BCh BAO 1979 Belf.; DA Eng. 1981.

DEVLIN, Valery Bernadette (retired) — MB ChB 1994 Manch.; BSc Manch. 1991.

DEVNANI, Kishin Chand Station Medical Centre, RAF Henlow, Henlow SG16 6DN Tel: 01462 815016 — MB BS 1973 Dibrugarh. (Assam Med. Coll. Dibrugarh) Sen. Med. Off. RAF Henlow.

DEVONALD, Elizabeth Jane 21 Blind Lane, Coleby, Lincoln LN5 0AL Tel: 01522 810030 Fax: 01522 811415 Email: devonald@btinternet.com — MB BS 1971 Lond.; MRCS Eng. LRCP Lond. 1971; DFFP 1993; MRCGP 1976. (King's Coll. Hosp. Lond.) p/t Assoc. Specialist (Colposcopy Gyn.) Co. Hosp. Lincoln; Clin. Med. Off. (Family Plann.) Lincoln Dist. Health Unit; Non-Princip. G>P> Cliff Villages Med. Pract. Imere Rd. Waddington. Socs: Lincoln Med. Soc. (Ex-Pres.); (Community) Lincoln Med. Soc.

DEVONALD, Helen Clare 22 Alberta House, Blackwall Way, London E14 9QH — MB BS 1990 Lond.

DEVONALD, Mark Alexander John 7 Faringdon Close, Peterborough PE1 4RQ — MB ChB 1993 Ed.

DEVONALD, Rachel Claire 2 Llanerch Cottages, Llanerch, Llanelli SA15 3LY — MB BCh 1994 Wales.

DEVONPORT, Helen 10 Cliffewood Close, Heaton, Bradford BD9 5PD — BM 1991 Soton.

DEVONPORT, Neville John Saltash Health Centre, Callington Road, Saltash PL12 6DL Tel: 01752 842281 Fax: 01752 844651; Trematon Barton, Trematon, Saltash PL12 4RT Tel: 01752 842507 — MB BS 1980 Lond.; DRCOG 1986; DCH RCPS Glas. 1985.

DEVONSHIRE, Hilary Winnifred (retired) Park Surgery, 25 The Park, Yeovil BA20 1DG Tel: 01935 474196 Fax: 01935 411429 — MB BS Lond. 1980; MRCGP 1985; DRCOG 1983. Prev: Sen. Partner GP Aldershot.

DEVONSHIRE, Penny Irene 26 Wick Avenue, Wheathampstead, St Albans AL4 8QB — MB ChB 1987 Glas. Regist. (Bact.) W.. Infirm. Glas. Prev: Ho. Off. (Surg.) Vict. Infirm. Glas.; Ho. Off. (Med.) W.. Infirm. Glas.

DEVONSHIRE, Richard Edward Salisbury House, New Road, Acle, Norwich NR13 3BD — MB ChB 1966 Liverp.; PhD Lond. 1973; MSc Lond. 1969, MB ChB Liverp. 1966. (Liverp.) Prev: Lect. Dept. Physiol. Middlx. Hosp. Med. Sch.; Med. Supt. St. Lucy's Hosp. Tsolo Transkei, S. Africa.

DEVOS, Simon Edward 42 Southover, London N12 7ES — MB BS 1994 Lond.

DEVOY, Michael Alexander Bruce 26 Salisbury Road, Liverpool L19 0PJ — MB BS 1987 Lond.; MRCP (UK) 1990.

DEW, Anne Elizabeth Morley Street GP Surgery, Moreley Street, Brighton BN2 2RA — MB BS 1991 Newc.; MRCGP 1995; DTM & H Liverp. 1995; DRCOG 1995; DCH RCP Lond. 1994. GP Health Centre for Homeless, Morley St. Surg., Brighton. Prev: Volunteer Doctor Dharamsala, India; GP/Regist. N. Tyneside; SHO (O & G) N. Tyneside Gen. Hosp.

DEW, Anthony Brian (retired) Roseacre, Bospin Lane, South Woodchester, Gloucester GLS5 5EH — MB BCh 1960 Wales; FRCR 1975; FFR 1970; DMRD Eng. 1965. Prev: Sen. Regist. (Radiodiag.) Guy's Hosp. Lond.

DEW, John Alexander (retired) 7 Ashleigh Road, Horsham RH12 2LE Tel: 01403 262577 — MB BChir 1945 Camb.; MRCS Eng. LRCP Lond. 1945; DObst RCOG 1951. Prev: Ho. Phys. & Clin. Asst. Med. Unit & Res. Accouch. Lond. Hosp.

DEW, Michael John Prince Philip Hospital, Bryngwynmawr, Dafen, Llanelli SA14 8QF Tel: 01554 756567 Fax: 01554 772271 — MD 1980 Birm.; MB ChB 1973; FRCP Lond. 1991; MRCP (UK) 1976. Cons. Phys. LLa.lli Gen. Hosp. Dyfed.

DEW, Sara Elizabeth Village Surgery, 233 Village Street, Derby DE23 8DD Tel: 01332 766762 Fax: 01332 272084 — MB BS 1991 Lond.; MRCGP 1995; DCH RCP Lond. 1993. Prev: Asst. GP Ashby De La Zouch.

DEWADA, Chandrakanta Brickiln Street Surgery, 10 Brickiln Street, Brownhills, Walsall WS8 6AU Tel: 01543 372390 Fax: 01543 454583 — MB BS 1964 Nagpur.

DEWAN, Suresh Chand 6 Walnut Court, Orchard Road, Horsham RH13 5JH — MB BS 1965 Rajasthan.

DEWAN, Vini Garden Park Surgery, 225 Denbigh Street, Howdon, Wallsend NE28 0PW Tel: 0191 289 2525 Fax: 0191 289 2526 — MB BS 1982 Calcutta; MB BS 1982 Calcutta; LRCP Edin LRCS Edin LRCPS Glasg 1984. (Calcutta) GP Wallsend, Tyne & Wear.

DEWAR, Andrew Kinley (retired) Magpie Cottage, Wick Lane, Lower Apperley, Gloucester GL19 4DS Tel: 01452 780527 Fax: 01452 780527 Email: injwzakd@compuserve.com — MB ChB 1957 St. And.; FRCA 1965. Cons. Anaesth. Soton. Gen. Hosp.; Regional Educat. Adviser Wessex; Bernard Johnson Adviser RCA. Prev: Regist. Univ. Dept. Anaesth. Roy. Infirm. Sheff.

DEWAR, Ann Louise Poole Hospital NHS Trust, Longfleet Road, Poole BH15 2JB Tel: 01202 448379 Email: adewar@poole-tr.swest.nhs.uk; Email: e.crawley-boerey@doctors.org.uk, e.crawley-boevey@doctors.org.uk — BM 1988 Soton.; MRCP (UK) 1994. Cons. Paediat.Poole hosp. Socs: Roy. Coll. Paediat. & Child Health; Brit. Paediat. Assn.; Brit. Thorac. Soc. Prev: Specialist Regist. (Respirat. Paediat.) Poole Hosp. NHs Trust; Acad. Regist. (Paediat. Respirat. Med.) Soton. Gen. Hosp.; Regist. (Paediat.) St. Peters Hosp. Chertsey, St. Geo. Hosp. Lond. & St. Richard's Hosp. Chichester.

DEWAR, Colin McGregor 28 Cresttor Road, Liverpool L25 6DW — MB ChB 1991 Glas.

DEWAR, Colin Scott 27 Maxwelltown Drive, Dumfries DG2 9JH Tel: 01387 55974 — MB ChB 1988 Manch.; BSc (Hons.) St. And. 1985.

DEWAR, David Harold 7 Stepney Drive, Scarborough YO12 5DP — BChir 1995 Camb.

DEWAR, Derek Davidson Beacon Medical Practice, 40 Algitha Road, Skegness PE25 2AJ Tel: 01754 897000 Fax: 01754 761024 — MB ChB 1981 Glas.

DEWAR, Derick Athol Elmslie (retired) 27 Maxwelltown Drive, Dumfries DG2 9JH Tel: 01387 55974 — MB ChB 1943 St. And.; DMRD Ed. 1952; FFR 1958. Prev: Cons. Radiol. Dundee Teachg. Hosps. & Dumfries & Galloway Roy. Infirm.

DEWAR, Donald John 7 Stepney Drive, Scarborough YO12 5DP — MB BS 1997 Lond.; MA 1998. (UMDS) SHO Surg Kingston Hosp.

DEWAR, Elizabeth Frieda Harley 27 Maxwelltown Drive, Dumfries DG2 9JH Tel: 01387 55974 — MB ChB 1952 St. And.; DA Eng. 1956.

DEWAR, Mr Elliot Paxton, OBE Department of Surgery, Airedale General Hospital, Steeton, Keighley BD20 6TD Tel: 01535651301 Fax: 01535 295433 Email: paxton.dewear@aahst.nhs.uk — MRCS Eng. LRCP 1969; MB BS Lond. 1969; FRCS Eng. 1974; T(S) 1991. (King's Coll. Hosp.) p/t Cons. Gen. Surg. Airedale Gen. Hosp. Keighley. Socs: Fell. Roy. Soc. Med.; Brit. Soc. Gastroenterol.; Mem. Assn. Surgs. Prev: Cons. & Head Dept. Surg. RN Hosp. Haslar; Research Fell. Univ. Dept. Surg. Leeds Gen. Infirm.; Prof. Naval Surg. 1983-88.

DEWAR, Flora Margaret McKinnon (retired) Mulberry Lodge, 97A Anglesea Road, Ipswich IP1 3PJ — MB ChB 1961 Ed.; FFA RCS Eng. 1974; DA Eng. 1968. Cons. Anaesth. Ipswich Hosp.; Clin. Teach. Fac. Clin. Med. Univ. Camb. Prev: Sen. Regist. (Anaesth.) New Addenbrooke's Hosp. Camb.

DEWAR, Hewan Archdale (retired) Flat 2, Wylam Hall, Wylam NE41 8AS Tel: 01661 853390 — MB BS 1935 Durh.; MD Durh. 1938; FRCP Lond. 1954, M 1938. Prev: Med. Specialist RAMC.

DEWAR, Ian George Richmond, Deerness Road, Kirkwall KW15 1SN — MB ChB 1990 Ed.

DEWAR, Jane Caroline 46 Arnesby Road, Nottingham NG7 2EA — BM BS 1992 Nottm.

DEWAR, Jane Rosemary Dewar and Randerson, Meadows Health Centre, 1 Bridgeway Centre, Meadows, Nottingham NG2 2JG Tel: 0115 986 5410 — BM BS 1982 Nottm.; BMedSci Nottm. 1980; MRCGP 1987. Princip. in Gen. Pract.

DEWAR, Joanna Clare Royal Surrey County Hospital, Guildford GU2 7XX Tel: 01483 571122; Grove House, 19 Grove Road, Beaconsfield HP9 1UR Tel: 01494 673358 — BM 1995 Soton. SHO (Med.) Roy. Surrey Co. Hosp. Socs: Med. Defence Union; BMA.

DEWAR, John Anderson (retired) The White House, 7 Stepney Drive, Scarborough YO12 5DP Tel: 01723 367982 — MB ChB 1964 Ed.; FFA RCS Eng. 1968. Prev: Cons. Anaesth. ScarBoro. Hosp.

DEWAR, John Archdale Department Radiotherapy & Oncology, Ninewells Hospital, Dundee DD1 9SY Tel: 01382 660111 Fax: 01382 632885; Selbie Lodge, 12 Fairfield Road, Broughty Ferry, Dundee DD5 1PL — BM BCh 1975 Oxf.; MA Oxf. 1975; FRCP Ed. 1992; MRCP (UK) 1978; FRCR 1983; DMRT Ed. 1981. Cons. Radiother. & Oncol. Ninewells Hosp. Dundee. Prev: Sen. Regist. (Radiat. Oncol.) W.. Gen. Hosp. Edin.; Regist. (Med.) Roy. Vict. Infirm. Newc.

DEWAR, John Maxwell (retired) 3 Gladney Square, Kirkcaldy KY1 1QH — MB ChB 1929 St. And.

DEWAR, Kirsteen Margaret Shirra 3a Lennox Crt., 22 Stockiemuir Avenue, Bearsden, Glasgow G61 3JN Tel: 0141 942 8884 — MB ChB 1964 Glas.; DObst RCOG 1966; FFA RCS Eng. 1969. (Glas.) Cons. (Anaesth.) W.. Infirm. Glas. Prev: Sen. Regist. (Anaesth.) United Bristol Hosps. & S. W.. RHB; Research Asst. (Anaesth.) W.. Infirm. Glas. & Univ. Glas.

DEWAR, Margaret Elisabeth South Cliff Surgery, 56 Esplanade Road, Scarborough YO11 2AU Tel: 01723 360451 Fax: 01723 353518; The White House, 7 Stepney Drive, Scarborough YO12 5DP Tel: 01723 367982 — MB ChB 1965 St. And.; DA Eng. 1967. (St. And.)

DEWAR, Mary Elizabeth (retired) Garvock, Quarry Road, Elgin IV30 4NF — MB ChB 1959 Ed.; DPH 1964; MFPHM 1989; MFCM 1972; DObst RCOG 1961. Prev: Cons. Pub. Health Med. Grampian Health Bd.

DEWAR, Mervyn Ernest (retired) Pencoed, Garreglwyd, Benllech, Tyn-y-Gongl LL74 8RB Tel: 01248 853393 — MB BS Durh. 1940. Prev: GP Stanley, Durh.

DEWAR, Morna Shirra Wansbeck General Hospital, Woodhorn Lane, Ashington NE63 9JJ Tel: 01670 521212 Fax: 01670 529719 — MB ChB 1978 Glas.; FRCP 1999 Lond.; FRCPath 1997; FRCP 1993 Glas.; DObst 1980. Cons. Haemat. Wansbeck Gen. Hosp. N.d.

DEWAR, Nicholas 143 Turton Road, Tottington, Bury BL8 3QA — MB ChB 1997 Leic.

DEWAR, Richard Ian Royal Glamorgan Hospital, Llantrisant, Pontyclun CF72 8XR Tel: 01443 443443 Email: richard.dewar@pr-tr.wales.nhs.uk; Woodholme, 102 Heol Isaf, Radyr, Cardiff CF15 8EA Tel: 029 2084 2513 Email: richard.dewar@virgin.net — MB ChB 1978 Birm.; MD Birm. 1993; MRCP (UK) 1983. Cons. Phys., Roy. Glam. Hosp., Llantrisant. Socs: Brit. Geriat.s Soc., Sec. Welsh Br.. Prev: Sen. Regist. (Geriat. Med.) Cardiff Roy. Infirm.; Regist. (Gen. Med. & Cardiol.) Roy Sussex Hosp. & King's Coll. Hosp. Lond.

DEWAR, Ronald 24 Oaklands Road, Havant PO9 2RN — MB BS 1952 Lond.

DEWAR, Rosemary Helen Selbie Lodge, 12 Fairfield Road, Broughty Ferry, Dundee DD5 1PL — MB BS 1976 Newc.; MRCGP 1980; MFFP 1993; DRCOG 1981. SCMO (Family Plann. & Well Wom. Serv.) Dundee Healthcare NHS Trust. Prev: GP Edin.

DEWAR, Susan Patricia Stewart Hall, Main St, Longforgan, Dundee DD2 5EU — MB ChB 1982 Dundee. SCMO Dundee Healthcare NHS Trust. Socs: MRCPCH.

DEWAR, William Archibald, MC (retired) 1 Courtrai Avenue, Helensburgh G84 8EP Tel: 01436 677680 — MB ChB 1941 Glas.; MD Glas. 1952; FRCP Glas. 1970, M 1962; FRFPS Glas. 1955. Prev: Cons. Dermat. Grimsby, Louth & Scunthorpe Hosps. Gps.

DEWART, Paul James St. John's Hospital, Howden Road W., Livingston EH54 6PP Tel: 01506 419666 Email: dewart@wdgate.demon.co.uk; 8 Lidgate Shot, Ratho, Newbridge EH28 8TY Tel: 0131 335 3516 — MB ChB 1981 Aberd.; MD 1992; MRCOG 1989; MFFP 1992. (Aberdeen Univ) Cons. O & G St. John's Hosp. Livingstone. Socs: BMA & Edin. Obst. Soc.; Fac. Fam. Plann. & Reproduc. Health Care (Mem. Exam. Sub-Comm. of Fac.). Prev: Lect. (O & G) Withington & St. Marys Hosps. Univ. Manch.

DEWAST-GAGNERAUD, Chantal Cromwell Hospital, Cromwell Road, London SW5 0TU Tel: 0207 460 2000; 114 Coleherne Court, Old Brompton Road, London SW5 0EB Tel: 020 7460 5555 — MD 1978 Nantes; MFFP 1995. Socs: Coll. of Med. Gyn. Paris.

DEWBURY, Christine Elizabeth Chalk Ridge, Southdown Road, Shawford, Winchester SO21 2BY Tel: 01962 715788 Fax: 01962

715788 — MB BS 1970 Lond. (King's Coll. Hosp.) Med. Commiss. Edr. Euro Trans Med. Lond. Television Centre Lond. Prev: Phys. (Occupat. Health) Soton. Gen. Hosp.; Med. Dir. of Screening Wessex Nuffield Hosp.; GP Soton.

DEWBURY, Keith Charles Radiology Department, Southampton General Hospital, Tremona Road, Southampton SO16 6YD Tel: 02380 796327; Chalk Ridge, Southdown Road, Shawford, Winchester SO21 2BY Tel: 01962 712761 — MB BS 1969 Lond.; BSc Lond. 1966, MB BS 1969; FRCR 1975; DMRD Eng. 1973. (King's Coll. Hosp.) Cons. (Radiol.) Soton. Univ. Hosps.

DEWES, Jean Margaret (retired) 16 The Mount, Pontefract WF8 1ND Tel: 01977 706683 — MB ChB Leeds 1951; MRCS Eng. LRCP Lond 1951.

DEWHIRST, Carol Judith Shipley Health Centre, Alexandra Road, Shipley BD18 3EG Tel: 01274 595611; 5 Old Trough Way, Knox Lane, Harrogate HG1 3DE Tel: 01423 563573 — MB ChB 1973 Dundee; DCH Eng. 1977; DObst RCOG 1975. SCMO Bradford Hosp. NHS Trust. Socs: BMA; Assoc. Mem. Roy. Coll. Paediat. Child Health; Yorks. Regional Paediat. Soc. Prev: SHO Hosp. for Wom. Leeds.; SHO (O & G), Ho. Phys. & Ho. Surg. Airedale Gen. Hosp. Steeton.

DEWHIRST, David (retired) Little Plat, German St., Winchelsea TN36 4EN Tel: 01797 226336 — MB BS Lond. 1943. Prev: Regist. (Surg.) Nat. Temperance Hosp. & Roy. Masonic Hosp. Lond.

DEWHIRST, Kevin 19 Church Croft, Pooley Bridge, Penrith CA10 2NL — MB BS 1988 Lond.

DEWHIRST, Paul High Street Surgery, High Street, Normanton WF6 1AA Tel: 01924 893277 Fax: 01924 223535; North Wing, Hampole Priory, Hampole, Doncaster DN6 7ET — MB BS 1982 Lond.; MSc Sports Med. Nottm. 1994; MRCGP 1990. (St. Bart.) Prev: SHO (Anaesth.) N.wick Pk. Hosp. Lond.; SHO (Gyn.) St. Mary's Hosp. Manch.; Ho. Surg. St. Bart. Hosp. Lond.

DEWHURST, Alec Graeme St Richards Hospital, Spitalfield Lane, Chichester PO19 4SE Tel: 01243 788122; Cherry Tree Cottage, 5 Downview Road, Barnham, Bognor Regis PO22 0EE Tel: 01243 554256 — MB BChir 1981 Camb.; MA Camb. 1981, BA (1st. cl. Hons.) 1977; FRCP Lond. 1995; MRCP (UK) 1983. (Guy's) Cons. Phys. St. Richards Hosp. Chichester; Clin. Tutor St. Richards Hosp. Chichester. Socs: BMA & Brit. Geriat. Soc. Prev: Sen. Regist. (Gen. Med. & Geriat.) Roy. S. Hants. Hosp. Soton.; Regist. (Cardiol.) Freeman Hosp. Newc.; Regist. (Gen. Med.) St. Geo. Hosp. Lond.

DEWHURST, Alexander Timothy 123 Kyverdale Road, London N16 6PS — MB BS 1988 Lond.; DA (UK) 1995. (Roy. Free Hosp. Lond.)

DEWHURST, Alison 48 Rowley Lane, Lepton, Huddersfield HD8 0HN — MB ChB 1993 Liverp.

DEWHURST, Sir (Christopher) John 21 Jack's Lane, Harefield, Uxbridge UB9 6HE Tel: 01895 825403 — MB ChB 1943 Manch.; Hon. FRACOG; MRCS Eng. LRCP Lond. 1943; FRCS Ed. 1954; FRCOG 1969, M 1949; Hon. DSc Sheff.; Hon. MD (Uruguay); Hon. FRCSI; Hon. FRCOG (S. Afr.); Hon. FACOG. Prev: Prof. Emerit. O & G Univ. Lond. O & G Qu. Charlotte's; Hosp. Wom.; Reader Univ. Sheff.; Surg. Lt. RNVR.

***DEWHURST, Darren James** 15 Longstone Walk, Liverpool L7 3PP — MB ChB 1994 Liverp.; BSc (Hons.) Liverp. 1991.

DEWHURST, John Kesteven (retired) Til Occam Ltd., 50 Occam Road, Surrey Research Park, Guildford GU2 7YN Tel: 01483 505546 Fax: 01483 576078 — MB BChir 1957 Camb.; MA Camb. 1961; FFPM RCP (UK) 1993. Prev: Med. Dir. Til Occam Ltd.

DEWHURST, Neil Gordon Perth Royal Infirmary, Perth PH1 1NX Tel: 01738 623311 Fax: 01738 628502; Spruce Tree House, Seathaugh,, Blackford, Auchterarder PH4 1RG Tel: 01764 682525 Fax: 01764 682525 — MB ChB 1976 Ed.; BSc (1st cl. Hons. Bacteriol.) Ed. 1973; MD Ed. 1982; FRCP Lond. 1995; FRCP Ed. 1990; MRCP (UK) 1979. Cons. Cardiol. Perth Roy. Infirm.; Hon. Cons. Cardiol. W.. Gen. Hosp. Edin.; Hon. Sen. Lect. (Med.) Univ. Dundee. Socs: Scott. Cardiac Soc.; Scott. Soc. Phys.; Brit. Cardiac Soc. Prev: Lect. (Med.) Univ. Edin.; Sen. Regist. (Gen. Med. & Cardiol.) Lothian HB; Cons. Cardiol., Torbay Hosp.

DEWHURST, Peter Duncan Sitwell and Partners, Little Common Surgery, 82 Cooden Sea Road, Bexhill-on-Sea TN39 4SP Tel: 01424 845477 Fax: 01424 848225; 35 South Cliff, Bexhill-on-Sea TN39 3EH Email: pdewhurst@aol.com — MB ChB 1977 Leeds. GP Trainer Bexhill on Sea; Mem. E. Sussex LMC; Med. Manager, Seadoc; Chair of Exec. Comm. Bexhill & Ruther Primart Care Trust; Med. Manager Seadoc; Chair of Exec. Comm. Bexhill and Rother Primart Care Trust. Prev: Trainee GP St Peters Hosp. Chertsey VTS.

DEWING, Clive Richard Wish Valley Surgery, Talbot Road, Hawkhurst, Cranbrook TN18 4NB Tel: 01580 753211 Fax: 01580 754612; Tel: 01580 752688 — MB BS 1979 Lond.; BSc Lond. 1976; DRCOG 1982. (St Georges) p/t Clin. Asst. (Dermat.) Benenden Hosp. Kent; GP Tutor Tunbridge Wells PGMC; Asst. Specialist Cardiol., Kent & Sussex Hosp., Tunbridge Wells. Socs: Weald & Marsh Med. Soc. Prev: Clin. Asst. (Dermat.) Kent & Sussex Hosp. Tunbridge Wells.

DEWIS, Peter Benefits Agency, Warbeck Hill, Blackpool FY2 0UZ Tel: 01253 754257 — MB ChB 1977 Manch.; BSc Manch 1974; MRCP (UK) 1980. Princip. Med. Off. Benefits Agency Blackpool. Prev: Tutor in Med. Univ. Manch.

DEWJI, Hassanali During and Dewji, 306 Lordship Lane, London SE22 8LY Tel: 020 8693 4704 — MRCS Eng. LRCP Lond. 1978. (Bristol)

DEWJI, Mohamed Raza Merali Hilltops Medical Centre, Kensington Drive, Great Holm, Milton Keynes MK8 9HN Tel: 01908 568446 — MB BS 1987 Lond.

DEWLAND, Peter Maurice IBAM (UK) Ltd., Wessex Business Centre, Bumpers farm, Chippenham SN14 6NQ Tel: 01249 444212 Fax: 01249 444189 Email: dewlandp@ibam.com; Pentrecaeau Uchaf, Llandeilo Graban, Builth Wells LD2 3YX Fax: 01982 560733 Email: peterdewland@eggconnect.net — MB BS 1971 Lond.; MA Wales 1991; BSc Lond. 1968; Dip. Pharm. Med. RCP (UK) 1984; FFPM RCP (UK) 1993, M 1989. (St. Thomas's) Med. Dir., IBAM (UK) Ltd. Prev: Med. Dir. Simbec Research Merthyr Tydfil.

DEWS, Ian Mervyn Phoenix International GB Limited, Mildmay House, St Edwards Ct., London Road, Romford RM7 9QD Tel: 01708 735000 Fax: 01708 725413 Email: ian.dews@ibrd-rostrum-global.co.uk — MRCS Eng. LRCP Lond. 1975; MB BS Lond. 1975; MRCP (UK) 1986; MFPM RCP (UK) 1993.

DEWSBURY, Eric 298C Foleshill Road, Coventry CV6 5AH Tel: 024 76 688225; 189 Wall Hill Road, Allesley,, Coventry CV5 9EL Tel: 024 76 332635 — MB ChB Liverp. 1947. (Liverp.) Prev: Capt. RAMC.

DEWSBURY, Judith Angela 185 Russell Road, Moseley, Birmingham B13 8RR Tel: 0121 449 2498; 185 Russell Road, Moseley, Birmingham B13 8RR Tel: 0121 449 2498 — MB BS 1955 Lond.; MFFP 1993; DA Eng. 1957. (The Royal London Hospital) Specialist (Psychosexual Med.) City Hosp. Birm. Socs: Accred. Mem. Inst. Psychosexual Med.; Accredit. Mem. Brit. Soc. Med. & Dent. Hypn. Prev: Princip. GP Lewes; Sen. Clin. Med. Off. (Family Plann. & Psychosexual Med.) Birm. & Walsall HA; Research Assoc. Inst. Populat. Studies Univ. Exeter.

DEWSNAP, Claire Helen 57 Park Road, Stretford, Manchester M32 8FE — MB ChB 1997 Sheff.

DEWSNAP, Paul Allan East Mitcham CMHT, Wilson Hospital, Cranmer Rd, Mitcham CR4 4TP Tel: 020 8687 4714 Fax: 020 8687 4808 — MB BS 1982 Lond.; BSc Lond. 1979; MRCPsych 1986. (St. Bart.) Cons. Psychiat. E. Mitcham CMHT; Hon. Sen. Lect. St Geo. Hosp. Med. Sch. Lond. Prev: Cons. Psychiat. Springfield Unviersity Hosp.

DEX, Elizabeth Ann 31 Earlston Grove, London E9 7NE — MB ChB 1989 Leic.; FRCS Ed. 1996.

DEXTER, Andrea The Surgery, High Street, Epworth, Doncaster DN9 1EP Tel: 01427 872232 Fax: 01427 874944 — MB ChB 1984 Sheff.; DRCOG 1988; MRCGP 1988. GP Doncaster.

DEXTER, Andrew Malcolm The Emergency unit University hospital of Wales, Heath park, Cardiff CF14 4XW — MB ChB 1979 Sheff.

DEXTER, Brian Henry Gilbert and Partners, Cronehills Health Centre, Cronhills Walkway, West Bromwich B70 6TJ Tel: 0121 553 0287 Fax: 0121 580 1821 — MB BCh 1979 Wales; MRCGP 1983; DRCOG 1981.

DEXTER, Catherine Sarah 10 Deuchar Street, Jesmond, Newcastle upon Tyne NE2 1JX — MB BS 1996 Newc.

DEXTER, Colin Geoffrey Bridge Centre, Abertillery NP13 1BQ — 1999 (Dip. Therapeutics) Univ. of Wales College of Med.; MB BCh Wales 1982.

DEXTER, Denise, Wing Cdr. RAF Med. Br. OC Aviation Medicine Training Wing, RAF Centre of Aviation Medicine, RAF Henlow

SG16 6DN — MB ChB 1986 Leic.; BSc Lond. 1981; MRCGP 1993; DAvMed FOM RCP Lond. 1995; DRCOG 1992. RAF Centre of Aviat. Med., Henlow. Socs: Roy. Soc. of Med.

DEXTER, Derrick (retired) 13 Kings Mead, Ripon HG4 1EJ — MD 1953 Sheff.; MB ChB 1946; FRCPC 1968; FRCPath 1968. Prev: Prof. Univ. Saskatchewan, Canada.

DEXTER, Emma Louise Stephanie Wolverhampton Health Authority, Coniston House, Chapel Ash, Wolverhampton WV3 0XE Tel: 01902 444741 — BM BS 1985 Nottm.; MRCGP 1990; MFPHM 2000. Cons. in Pub. Health Med., Wolverhampton Health Auth.

DEXTER, Harvey (retired) Lyndhurst, 2 Warren Close, Meads, Eastbourne BN20 7TY Tel: 01323 736303 Fax: 01323 736303 Email: harbara@btinternet.com — MB BS 1959 Lond.; MRCS Eng. LRCP Lond. 1959; FRCR 1975; FFR 1966; DMRD Eng. 1964; DObst RCOG 1960. Prev: Cons. Radiol. E.bourne Hosp. NHS Trust.

DEXTER, Kathryn Elizabeth The Health Centre, High Street, Redbourn, St Albans AL3 7LZ Tel: 01582 792356; 24 Ox Lane, Harpenden AL5 4HE — MB ChB 1974 Birm.; MRCGP 1978; DObst RCOG 1976.

DEXTER, Penelope Jane Black and Partners, Sherwood Health Centre, Elmswood Gardens, Sherwood, Nottingham NG5 4AD Tel: 0115 960 7127 Fax: 0115 985 7899; 39 Grange Road, Woodthorpe, Nottingham NG5 4FU — BM BCh 1983 Oxf.; MRCGP 1987; DRCOG 1986.

DEXTER, Selwyn Leon The Surgery, 56 Maida Vale, London W9 1PP Tel: 020 7624 4433 — MRCS Eng. LRCP Lond. 1977; BSc (Hons.) (Pharmacol.) Liverp. 1972, MB ChB 1977. GP Lond.; Hon. Assoc. Specialist, City of Lond. Migraine Clinic. Socs: Brit. Headache Soc.; (Treas.) Internat. Headache Soc.

DEXTER, Mr Simon Patrick Laurence 4 The Woodlands, Farrer Lane, Oulton, Leeds LS26 8HW — BM 1987 Soton.; FRCS Eng. 1991. Research Fell. & Hon. Clin. Regist. (Surg.) Gen. Infirm. Leeds. Prev: Regist. (Surg.) Bournemouth & Soton.; SHO (Surg.) Nottm.

DEXTER, Sophia Ann Tel: 020 8669 3232/1717 Fax: 020 8773 2524; 28 Bushnell Road, London SW17 8QP — MB BS 1986 Lond.; MRCGP 1995; DRCOG 1990; DCH RCP Lond. 1989. (Lond. Hosp. Med. Sch.) GP Princip.

DEXTER, Timothy John Wycombe Hospital, High Wycombe HP11 2TT — MB ChB 1987 Bristol; FRCA 1992.

DEY, Abhijit 72 Holyrood Gardens, Edgware HA8 5LR — MB BCh 1995 Wales.

DEY, Ann Catherine East Street Medical Centre, 18-20 East Street, Littlehampton BN17 6AW Tel: 01903 731111 Email: ann@familydoctors.co.uk; Tel: 01273 416225 Email: ann@familydoctors.co.uk — MB BS 1994 Lond.; DFFP 1998; BSc Lond. 1992; DRCOG 1996. (St. Bartholomew's Hospital Medical School) GP Princip., E. St Med. Center, Littlehampton. Prev: SHO (Paediat.) St. Richard's Hosp. Chichester; SHO (Psychiat.) Brighton Gen. Hosp.; GP Regist. 17B Warmdene Rd. Brighton.

DEY, Biswa Nath (retired) Stafford Road Surgery, 214 Stafford Road, Wolverhampton WV10 6JT Tel: 01902 20954 — LLB Wolverhampton 1985; MB BS Calcutta 1961; DObst RCOG 1966. Prev: Clin. Asst. Matern. Dept. New Cross Hosp. Wolverhampton.

DEY, Chris 7 High Drive, New Malden KT3 3UJ Tel: 020 8942 5856 — MB BS 1998 Lond.; MB BS Lond 1998; BSc 1995. (Guys)

DEY, John Martin Moorhouse (retired) The Health Centre, Fieldway, Shepley, Huddersfield HD8 9DA Tel: 01484 602001 — MB ChB 1967 Ed.

DEY, Maria Paola 111 St John's Road, Lostock, Bolton BL6 4HB — MB BS 1985 Lond.

DEY, Nani Gopal Southport district General Hospital, Town Lane, Southport PR8 Tel: 01704 547471; 735 Liverpool Road, ainsdale, Southport PR8 3NS Tel: 01704 576795 — MB BS 1967 Karachi; FRCP Lond. 1996; FRCP Ed. 1996; MRCP (UK) 1979; FRCPS Glas. 1991. (Dow Med. Coll. Karachi, Pakistan) Cons. Phys. (Geriat. Med.) S.port Gen. Infirm. & S.port & Formby Dist. Gen. Hosp. Socs: Brit. Geriat. Soc. Prev: Sen. Regist. (Geriat. Med.) Univ. Hosp. S. Manch. & Leicester Gen. Hsop.; Regist. (Med.) Barnsley Dist. Gen. Hosp. & Macclesfield Dist. Gen.

DEY, Narayan Chandra Shakespeare Grove Surgery, 2-4 Shakespeare Grove, Worsley Mesnes, Wigan WN3 5YA Tel: 01942 241209 Fax: 01942 241209 — MB BS 1958 Calcutta; MB BS 1958 Calcutta.

DEY, Priyabrata c/o Department of Neurosurgery, University Hospital of Wales, Cardiff CF4 4XW — MB BS 1983 Calcutta.

DEY, Samir Kumar The Surgery, 4 Cross Street, Leicester LE4 5BA Tel: 0116 262 6969 — MB BS 1974 Calcutta.

DEY, Subir Kumar 21 Raby Street, Sheffield S9 1SQ — MB BS 1969 Calcutta.

DEYERMOND, Rachel Elizabeth 5 Royal Lodge Court, Belfast BT8 7YU; 5 Royal Lodge Court, Belfast BT8 7YU — MB BCh BAO 1993 Belf.; FFARCSI 1998. (QUB)

DEYS, Caroline Merula, SSStJ (retired) 20 Brookfield Park, London NW5 1ER Tel: 020 7485 3110 — MB BS 1962 Lond.; DO Eng. 1964.

DEYTRIKH, Margaret Susan Allerton Wood, Stanhope, Bishop Auckland DL13 2JP Email: msdeytrikh@doctors.org.uk — MB BS 1982 Newc.; DRCOG 1987.

DEYTRIKH, Nicholas Stanhope Health Centre, Dales Street, Stanhope, Bishop Auckland DL13 2XD Tel: 01388 528555 Fax: 01388 526122; Allerton Wood, Stanhope, Bishop Auckland DL13 2JP — MB BS 1977 Newc.; MRCGP 1984. GP Trainer N.d. VTS.

DEZATEUX, Carol Anne 54 Twyford Avenue, London N2 9NL — MB BS 1978 Newc.

DHABUWALA, Navnitlal Dahyabhai The Crossway Health Centre, 31 The Crossway, Farley Hill, Luton LU1 5LY — MB BS 1965 Med Inst Rangoon; MB BS 1965 Med Inst Rangoon.

***DHADDA, Amandeep Singh** 80 Pear Tree Crescent, Derby DE23 8RQ Tel: 01332 721334 — MB ChB 1998 Birm.; ChB Birm. 1998; BMedSci Neuroscience 1995.

DHADDA, Bukhtawar Singh 53 Callow Hill Way, Heatherton Village, Littleover, Derby DE23 7RJ — MB BS 1994 Lond.

DHADLI, Dhanwant Kaur (retired) Felmores Centre, Lanham Place, Basildon SS13 1PN Tel: 01268 728108 Fax: 01268 726870 — MB BS 1959 Punjab; DCH Eng. 1962. Prev: Ho. Surg. Lincoln Co. Hosp.

DHADLI, Mohneeta Kaur 32 Grange Road, Manchester M21 9NY — MB ChB 1993 Manch.

DHADLY, Mandeep Singh 234 BRoad Walk, Blackheath, London SE3 8NQ Tel: 020 8856 8412; 1 Longfellow Place, Apt. 2224, Boston MA 02114, USA Tel: 00 1 617 523 0672 Fax: 00 1 617 541 3600 Email: mdhadly@bidmc.harvard.edu — MB ChB 1984 Leic.; BSc (1st cl. Hons.) Leic. 1982, MB ChB 1984; Dip. Amer. Bd. Internal. Med. 1989; Dip. Amer. Bd. Haematology 1992; Dip. Amer. Bd. Cardiovasc. Med. 1995. Med. Dir. Roxbury Heart Center USA; Clin. Instruc. (Med.) Harvard Univ. Med. Sch. 1996-; Asst. Clin. Prof. (Med.) Boston Univ. Sch. of Med. 1996-. Socs: Amer. Soc. Internal Med.; Fell. Amer. Coll. Cardiol. Prev: Clin. Research Fell. Harvard Sch. Med. USA; Resid. (Med.) Geo.town Univ. USA; SHO Hammersmith Hosp.

DHADLY, Pritam Pal Singh Bromley Hospitals NHS Trust, Cromwell Avenue, Bromley BR2 9AJ Tel: 020 8289 7000; 19 Chetwode Roade, London SW17 1RF Tel: 020 8693 0970 Email: pdhadly@aol.com, shumanhussein@hotmail.com — MB ChB 1991 Leic.; FRCA 1996 (UK); BMedSci Leic. 1989; DA (UK) 1993. Cons., Anaesth. and Critical Care, Bromley Hosp., Bromley, Kent. Prev: Regist. (Anaesth.) Whipps Cross Hosp. Lond.; Specialist Regist., St. Bart. Hosp., Lond.

DHADWAL, Ajay Kapoor 68 Shelley Crescent, Hounslow TW5 9BJ — MB BS 1995 Lond.

DHADWAL, Kulwant Kaur 14 Beechcroft Road, Bushey, Watford WD23 2JU — BM 1994 Soton. (Univ. Soton.)

DHALIWAL, Jagdeesh Singh Adaes, 25a Beacon Road, Walsall WS5 3LF — MB ChB 1991 Leic.; MRCGP 1996; DFFP 1994; DRCOG 1994. Cons. Primary Care med.Walsall Community Health Trust; Primary Care Develop. Dir. WCHT. Prev: SHO Qu. Mary's Hosp. Sidcup VTS.

DHALIWAL, Jaswinder Kaur 139 Malefant Street, Cardiff CF24 4QF — MB BCh 1995 Wales.

DHALL, Pradeep 10 Bonaly Rise, Edinburgh EH13 0QX Tel: 0131 477 6222 Fax: 0131 477 1203 Email: pradeep.dhall@dial.pipex.com; 150 Halifax Road, Brierfield, Nelson BB9 5BQ — MB ChB 1997 Ed.; MA (Hons.) Oxon. 1994. SHO Psychiat. E. Anglian Rotat.

DHALLA, Nazirahmed Hassanali Kassam Grimble and Partners, 20 Pepys Road, Raynes Park, London SW20 8PF Tel: 020 8946

3074/8249 Fax: 020 8296 0145 — MB ChB 1974 Manch. SHO (Gen. & Cardiac Surg.) Univ. Hosp. Wales Cardiff. Prev: SHO Dept. Urol. Cardiff Roy. Infirm.; SHO (Orthop. & Traum.) & SHO A & E Dept. St. Stephen's; Hosp. Chelsea.

DHALLA, Parvin The Surgery, 71 Broad Lane, Hampton TW12 3AX Tel: 020 8979 5406 Fax: 020 8941 8838 — MB BCh 1978 Wales.

DHALLA, Parvin Nurmohamed Harold Road Surgery, 164 Harold Road, Hastings TN35 5NG Tel: 01424 720878; Kildare, Woodbury Road, Hawkhurst, Cranbrook TN18 4BY Tel: 01580 752071 Email: tricornleaches@compuserve.com — MB ChB 1973 Bristol; MRCP (UK) 1979. (Makerere, Uganda & Bristol) GP Hastings, E. Sussex. Socs: BMA. Prev: Clin. Asst. (Respirat. Med.) Conquest Hosp. Hastings; Clin. Asst. Lymington Day Hosp.; SHO (Med.) Bath Hosps.

DHALLU, Tajinder University Hospital of Wales, Heath park, Cardiff CF14 4XW Tel: 029 2074 7747 Fax: 029 2074 3838 — MB ChB 1984 Bristol; FRCA 1996; DA (UK) 1993. (Bristol) Cons. anaesth. Cardiff.

DHAMI, Davinder Singh Duke Street Surgery, 1328 Duke Street, Glasgow G31 5QG Tel: 0141 554 3587; 9 William Ure Place, Bishopbriggs, Glasgow G64 3BH Tel: 0141 946 7663 Email: davdhami@aol.com — MB ChB 1986 Aberd. Prev: SHO (Paediat.) Perth Roy. Infirm.; SHO (Homoeopath. & Gen. Med.) Glas. Homoeopath. Hosp.

DHAMIJA, Satish Kumar Lea Village Medical Centre, 98 Lea Village, Kitts Green, Birmingham B33 9SD Tel: 0121 789 9565 — MB BS 1974 Panjab.

DHAMRAIT, Rajvinder Singh 44 Great Hill Crescent, Maidenhead SL6 4RF Tel: 01628 25318 Fax: 01628 625318 — BM 1994 Soton.; BSc (Hons.) Soton. 1993. (Soton.)

DHANAWADE, Sudhaker Royton Medical Centre, Market Street, Royton, Oldham OL2 5QA Tel: 0161 652 6336 — MB BS 1968 Vikram; MB BS 1968 Vikram.

DHANAWADE, Vidya Belvedere House, Shaw Road, Milnrow, Rochdale OL16 4LX — MB BS 1968 Vikram.

DHANDEE, Indervir Singh 2 Hadley Gardens, Southall UB2 5SQ — MB BS 1994 Lond.

DHANJAL, Miss Mandish Kaur Queen Charlotte's and Chelsea Hospital, Ducane Road, London W12 0HS Tel: 020 8383 1000 — MB BS 1992 Lond.; BSc (Hons.) Lond. 1989; MRCP (UK) 1996; DFFP 1997; MRCOG 1999. (Guy's Hosp. Med. Sch.) Specialist Regist. (O & G), Qu. Charlotte's & Chelsea Hosp., Lond. Socs: BMA. Prev: Spr (O & G), N.wick Pk. Hosp., Harrow, Lond.; Spr (O & G), W. Middx. Hosp., Lond.; Spr (O & G), Centr. Middx. Hosp., Lond.

DHANJI, Al-Falah Abdul-Aziz Kings Medical Centre, 23 Kings Avenue, Buckhurst Hill IG9 5LP — MB BS 1995 Lond.; MRCGP 2000; BSc (Hons.) Physiol. as applied to Med. Lond. 1991; DRCOG 1998; DFFP 1998. (Lond. Hosp. Med. Coll.) Partner at Kings Avenue Surg.; Med. Adviser to Chigwell Sch.; Med. Adviser to Physical Fitness Club. Socs: BMA; Assoc. Mem RCGP; RCGP -Mem. Prev: SHO (O & G) Roy. Lond. Hosp.; SHO (Acute c/o Elderly) Newham Gen. Hosp.; SHO Paediat.Roy.Lond.Hosp.

***DHANJI, Al-Rehan Abdul-Aziz** 174 Court Road, Orpington BR6 0PY — MB BS 1996 Lond.; BSc (Physiol.) Lond. 1993.

DHANJI, Noorali Devji (retired) Beaufoy, 14 Downs Hill, Beckenham BR3 5HB Tel: 020 8650 3294 — MB BS Karachi 1953; LRCP LRCS Ed. LRFPS Glas. 1956; MRCGP 1964. Liveryman City of Lond. Prev: SCMO Margt. Pyke Centre Middlx. Hosp.

***DHANJJI, Fahreen Zulfikar** 12 Ketley Croft, Birmingham B12 0XG Email: drdharji@yahoo.com; P.O Box 14675, Nairobi, Kenya Tel: 2542 747187 Fax: 747187 — MB ChB 1998 Sheff.; MB ChB Sheff 1998.

DHANOA, Surinder Kaur 23 Holyrood, Great Holm, Milton Keynes MK8 9DR — MB BS 1982 Newc.; MRCOphth 1996; DRCOG 1986. (Univ. Newc. u. Tyne) Staff Ophth. Oxf. Region. Prev: Staff Ophth. Bucks. HA; Clin. Asst. (Ophth.) Maidstone HA.

DHANULSHAN, Paramathasan 13 Sandacre Road, Nine Elms, Swindon SN5 5UU — MB BS 1998 Lond.; MB BS Lond 1998.

DHAR, Ameet Flat 7, 15 Chesham Street, London SW1X 8ND — MB BS 1998 Lond.; MB BS Lond 1998.

DHAR, Rajeev 15 Rectory Green, West Boldon, East Boldon NE36 0QD — MB BS 1994 Lond.

DHAR, Roshan Lal Castletown Medical Centre, 6 The Broadway, Castletown, Sunderland SR5 3EX Tel: 0191 549 5113 — MB BS 1968 Jammus, Kashmir.

DHAR, Mr Sunil Department Orthopaedic Surgery, Queens Medical Centre, Nottingham University Hospital, Derby Road, Nottingham NG7 2UH Email: sdhari@aol.com — MB BS 1978 Kashmir; MS (Orthop.) Chandigarh, India 1981; MChOrth Liverp. 1988; FRCS Ed. 1991; FRCS Orth. 1992. Cons. (Orthop.) Qu.s Med. Centre Nottm.; Lect. Univ. of Nottm. Prev: Regist. (Orthop.) Chester Roy. Infirm.; Research Fell. (Orthop.) Roy. Liverp. Hosp.; Lect. (Orthop.) & Regist. Bone & Jt. Surg. Hosp. Kashmir India.

DHARIA, Ramesh Ramanlal Craven Park Medical Centre, 6 Craven Park, London NW10 8SY Tel: 020 8965 3396 Fax: 020 8965 7457 — MB BS 1965 Bombay.

DHARIWAL, Avtar Singh 36 Humphrey Middlemore Drive, Hardborne, Birmingham B17 0JN — MB ChB 1990 Leeds. Regist. Rotat. (Psychiat.) Birm. VTS.

***DHARIWAL, Daljit Kaur** 47 Clodien Avenue, Cardiff CF14 3NL Tel: 029 2052 2935 — MB BCh 1998 Wales; BDS FDS MB BCH.

DHARIWAL, Manjula 48 Mitchell Avenue, Jesmond, Newcastle upon Tyne NE2 3LA Tel: 0191 281 4523 — MB BS 1982 Rajasthan; MRCOG (UK) 1991. GP Regist., N.umbria UTS. Socs: Med. Protec. Soc. Prev: SHO (O & G) Ashington Gen. Hosp.; SHO (Geriat. Med.) S. Cleveland Hosp. Middlesbrough; SHO (O & G) Worcester Roy. Infirm.

DHARIWAL, Narendra Kumar Department of Anaesthesia, Sunderland District General Hospital, Kayll Road, Sunderland SR4 7UF Tel: 0191 565 6256; 48 Mitchell Avenue, Jesmond, Newcastle upon Tyne NE2 3LA Tel: 0191 281 4523 — MB BS 1979 Rajasthan; MRCPI 1983; MRCS Eng. LRCP Lond. 1982; FFA RCSI 1990; FRCA 1990; DA (UK) 1987. Cons. Anaesth. City Hosps. Sunderland. Socs: BMA; Med. Protec. Soc. Prev: Sen. Regist. (Anaesth.) N.. RHA; Regist. Rotat. (Anaesth.) Newc. HA; Regist. (Gen. Med.) Roy. Infirm. Sunderland.

DHARIWAL, Surendra Kumar The Surgery, 688 Romford Road, Manor Park, London E12 5AJ Tel: 020 8478 0757 Fax: 020 8478 2416 — MB BS 1963 Vikram.

DHARMA RAJAH, Shanmugam 1 Mayo Grove, Bradford BD5 8HX — MB BS 1994 Lond.

DHARMAPRIYA, Nelum Sujatha Kumari 17 Daylesford Drive, Newcastle upon Tyne NE3 1TW — MB ChB 1995 Aberd.

DHARMARAJ, Sharola Eye Department, Stoke Mandeville Hospital, Mandeville Road, Aylesbury HP21 8AL — MB BS 1986 Madras; FRCS Ed. 1993.

DHARMARATNAM, Radha 20 Southfields Road, Solihull B91 3PR — MB BS 1980 Peradeniya; MRCS Eng. LRCP Lond. 1986; FRCOphth 1991; DO RCS Eng. 1988. Staff Grade Med. Off. (Ophth.) Russells Hall Hosp. Dudley.

DHARMASENA, Alfred Douglas Ruwan, 59 Timothy Rees Close, Danescourt, Cardiff CF5 2AU Tel: 029 2081 0202 — MB BS 1975 Sri Lanka; MRCS Eng. LRCP Lond. 1978.

DHARMASENA, Helen Patricia 59 Timothy Rees Close, Danescourt, Cardiff CF5 2AU — MB ChB 1982 Sheff.; MSc Palliative Medicine (Bristol University 1999); MRCP (UK) 1990; MRCGP 1986; DRCOG 1985. Staff Grade (Palliat. Med.) P.ss of Wales Hosp. Bridgend. Prev: GP Cardiff.

DHARMASIRI, Akurange Herbert Christopher Oaklands Surgery, Oakland St., Bedlinog, Treharris CF46 6TE; 5 Ashgrove, Edwardsville, Treharris CF46 5PH Tel: 01443 410179 — MB BS 1958 Ceylon. (Colombo) Prev: SHO (Psychiat.) Hillend Hosp. St. Albans; Dist. Med. Off. Divulapitiya, Sri Lanka.

DHARMAWARDENE, Shyamali Bavani 63 Parfrey Street, London W6 9EW — MB BS 1993 Lond.

DHARMENDRA, Mysore Somoashekar Royal Cornhill Hospital, Aberdeen AB25 2ZH Tel: 01224 663131; 8 Belmont Gardens, Ashgrove Road, Aberdeen AB25 3GA Tel: 01224 627307 Email: mdharmendra@lineone.net — MB BS 1988 Bangalore. Sen. Regist. (Psychiat.) Roy. Cornhill Hosp.

DHARNI, Deepinder Singh 116 Sturdee Avenue, Gillingham ME7 2HL Tel: 01634 578309 — MB ChB 1996 Liverp. SHO Community Paediat. Gp. VTS. Prev: SHO Pub.Health.

DHASMANA, Divya Mount Vernon Hospital, Rickmansworth Road, Northwood HA6 2RN; 43 Upper Cranbrook, Redland, Bristol BS6 7UR — MB BS 1994 Lond. (St George's Hospital) SHO (Oncol.) Mt. Vernon Hosp. Watford.

DHATARIYA, Ketan Kumar 25 Broomfield Road, Bexleyheath DA6 7PD Tel: 01322 522272 Email: ket@netcomuk.co.uk — MB

BS 1991 Lond.; MRCP (UK) 1995. (Univ. Coll. & Middlx. Hosp. Med. Sch.) Specialist Med. Regist. Gen. Internal Med., Diabetes & Endocrinol., Medway Hosp. Prev: Regist. (Gen. Internal Med. Diabetes & Endocrinol.) Joyce Green Hosp. Dartford; Regist. (Gen. Med. & Diabetes) St Mary's Hosp. Newport Isle of Wight; SHO (ITU) & Research Fell. (Cardiol.) Whittington Hosp. Lond.

DHATARIYA, Ramesh Chandra Slade Green Medical Centre, 156 Bridge Road, Slade Green, Erith DA8 2HS Tel: 01322 334884 Fax: 01322 351510 — MB BS 1965 Rajasthan; MRCS Eng. 1974; MRCGP 1975.

DHATT, Madhuri Uxbridge Road Surgery, 337 Uxbridge Road, Acton, London W3 9RA Tel: 020 8993 0912 — MB BS 1990 Lond. (Univ. Soton.)

DHATT, Mohinder Singh Common Road, Slough SL3 8LE Tel: 01753 544288 Fax: 01753 592415 Email: mohinder.dhatt@gp-k81024.nhs.uk; Sun-Kosi, 1 Church Grove, Wexham, Slough SL3 6LF Tel: 01753 574778 Fax: 01753 574778 Email: drmsdhatt@telco4u.net — MB BS Punjab 1963; DTM & H RCP Lond. 1973. (Christian Med. Coll. Ludhiana, India) Princip. GP; Clin. Asst. (Haemat.) Wexham Pk. Hosp. Slough. Socs: BMA; Overseas Doctors Assn. (Berks. & Bucks. Div.); Past Chair Bd. Primary Care Gp. Slough. Prev: Resid. Regist. (Thoracic Med.) Harts Hosp. Woodford Green; Resid. Med. Off. (Thoracic Surg.) Madar Sanat., India; SHO Lodge Moor Hosp. Sheff.

DHAWAN, Jatinder Scunthorpe General Hospital, Cliff Gardens, Scunthorpe DN15 7BH Tel: 01724 290175 Fax: 01724 290406 — MB BS 1979 Delhi; PhD (Cardiol.) Manch. 1992; FRCP (1998); MBA (1998); T(M) 1994. Cons. Phys. Cardiol. Scunthorpe Gen. Hosp. Socs: Manch. Med. Soc. & Brit. Cardiovasc. Interven. Soc.; Brit. Cardiac Soc. Prev: Cons. Cardiol. Doctor S. Fakeeh Hosp., Jeddah.

DHEANSA, Mr Baljit Singh 58 Lloyds Way, Beckenham BR3 3QS — MB BS 1990 Lond.; FRCS Eng. 1994. (King's Coll. Sch. of Med. & Dent.) Specialist Regist. (Plastic Surg.) Pan Thames Train. Scheme. Socs: BMA; MDU; Fell. RCS. Prev: SHO (Plastic Surg.) Qu. Vict. Hosp. E. Grinstead; SHO (Plastic Surg.) Qu. Mary's Hosp. Roehampton; SHO (Plastic Surg.) Gt. Ormond St. Hosp. Childr. Lond.

DHEBAR, Mr Mahesh Ichchhashanker West Cumberland Hospital, Homewood, Henshingham, Whitehaven CA28 8JG Tel: 01946 693181 Fax: 01946 513513 — MB BS 1969 Gujarat; MS (Orthop.) Gujrat 1973; FRCS Ed. 1980. Cons. Orthop. Surg. W. Cumbld. Hosp. Prev: Sen. Regist. (Orthop.) Freeman Hosp. Newc.; Cons. & Sen. Regist. (Orthop. Surg.) King Khalid Univ. Hosp. Riyadh, Saudi Arabia.

DHENIN, Sir Geoffrey Howard, KBE, AFC, GM, CStJ, QHP, Air Marshal RAF Med. Br. Ruxbury Lodge, St. Ann's Hill Road,, Chertsey KT16 9NL Tel: 01932 563624 — MB BChir 1942 Camb.; MA, MD Camb. 1957; FFCM 1975, M 1972; DPH Lond. 1961. (Camb. & Guy's) Socs: Fell. Roy. Soc. Med. Prev: Med. Adviser Saudi Arabian Nat. Guard; Dir.-Gen. RAF Med. Servs.; Hon. Phys. to HM the Qu.

DHESI, Anoop Singh Staithe Surgery, Lower Staithe Road, Stalham, Norwich NR12 9BU Tel: 01692 582000 Fax: 01692 580428 — MB BChir 1988 Camb.; MRCGP 1992; T(GP) 1992.

DHESI, Gurjit Singh Calcot Medical Centre, Hampden Road, Chalfont St. Peter, Gerrards Cross SL9 9SA Tel: 01753 887311 Fax: 01753 891933; Email: gurjitdhesi@hotmail.com — MB BS 1988 Lond.; MA Oxf 1985; MRCGP 1993; Cert. Family Plann. JCC 1991; DRCOG 1991. (Guy's Hospital Medical School) Prev: Trainee GP Burnham; SHO (A & E) Ealing Hosp. Lond.; SHO (Gen. Surg.) Edgware Hosp. Lond.

DHESI, Iqbal Singh Department of Histopathology, Wigan Royal Albert Edward Infirmary, Wigan Lane, Wigan WN1 2NN Tel: 01942 244000 Fax: 01942 822042 Email: idhesi@wigan-hist.prestel.co.uk — MB ChB 1985 Manch.; BSc (Hons.) Path. Manch. 1983, MB ChB 1985; MRCPath 1994; MSc Lond. 1995. Prev: Sen. Regist. (Histopath.) Kings Coll. Hosp. Lond.; Regist. (Path.) Leeds Gen. Infirm.; Ho. Phys. Hope Hosp. Salford.

DHESI, Jugdeep Kaur 21 Thurlow Road, Leicester LE2 1YE — MB ChB 1994 Leic.

DHESI, Rosepal Kaur 39A Woodcote Valley Road, Purley CR8 3AN — MB ChB 1998 Manch.; MB ChB Manch 1998.

DHESI, Sukhpal Singh 47 Tudor Road, Southall UB1 1NY — MB ChB 1992 Manch.

DHILLO, Waljit Singh 8 Rowan Close, Ealing, London W5 4YL — MB BS 1994 Lond.; BSc Basic Med. Sci. & Biochem. (1st cl. Hons.) Lond. 1991; MRCP (UK) 1997. (St. Bart.) Specialist Regist. (Diabetes & Endocrinol.) N. W. Thames Rotat. Prev: SHO (Gen. Med.) Ealing Hosp. Lond.; SHO (Gen. Med.) Hammersmith Hosp. Lond.; SHO (A & E) St. Geo. Hosp. Lond.

DHILLON, Professor Amar Paul 121 Church Road, Hanwell, London W7 3BJ — MB BChir 1977 Camb.; MD Camb. 1988; FRCP Lond. 1996; MRCS Eng. LRCP Lond. 1976; FRCPath 1996. Prof. Roy. Free. Univ. Coll. Med. Sch. Lond. Prev: Lect. Bland-Sutton Inst. Middlx. Hosp.; Sen. Lect. Roy. Free Hosp. Lond.

DHILLON, Amritpal Singh 20 Woodbourne Road, Smethwick, Smethwick B67 5LY — MB ChB 1991 Leeds; MRCP (UK) 1996; MRCPCH 1996. Specialist Paediat. Regist. Rotat. W. Midl.

DHILLON, Mr Baljean Baljean Dhillon, Princess Alexandra Eye Pavilion, Chalmers St., Edinburgh EH3 9HA Tel: 0131 536 3900 Fax: 0131 536 3735; 55a Grange Road, Edinburgh EH9 1TX Tel: 0131 667 2686 — BM BS 1982 Nottm.; BMedSci (Hons.) Nottm. 1980; FRCS Ed. 1994; FRCS Glas. 1986; FCOphth 1988. Cons. Ophth. Surg. Edin.; Hon. Sen. Lect., Edin. Univ. Prev: Sen. Regist. (Ophth.) Edin.

DHILLON, Dharam Paul 3 Bilton Road, Rugby CV22 7AA Tel: 01788 540499 — MB BChir 1975 Camb.; BA Camb. 1971; MD Camb. 1983; FRCP Lond. 1995; FRCP Ed. 1993; MRCP (UK) 1977. Cons. Phys. Walsgrave Hosp. NHS Trust. Prev: Cons. Phys. Dundee Teach. Hosps. NHS Trust; Sen. Regist. Tayside HB; Resid. Med. Off. Brompton Hosp. Lond.

DHILLON, Gouri Argyle Surgery, 128 Argyle Road, Ealing, London W13 8ER Fax: 020 8991 2103; 121 Church Road, Hanwell, London W7 3BJ Tel: 020 8567 3260 Fax: 020 8567 3260 — MB BS 1978 Lond.; MRCGP 1996; DCH Eng. 1982; DRCOG 1981. (Middlx. Hosp. Lond.)

DHILLON, Gurpreet Singh 1 Hillcrest Avenue, Grays RM20 3DA — MB ChB 1990 Manch.

DHILLON, Gurwant Singh Grove Medical Centre, 175 Steel House Lane, Wolverhampton WV2 2AU Tel: 01902 455771 Fax: 01902 457594 — MB ChB 1976 Birm.; MRCS Eng. LRCP Lond. 1976.

DHILLON, Harvinder Singh 16 Francis Road, Hounslow TW4 7JX — MB ChB 1983 Dundee.

DHILLON, Joginder Singh Overton House, 46 The Broadway, Sheerness ME12 1TR Tel: 01795 663481; Svenska, 180 Sandyhurst Lane, Ashford TN25 4NX Tel: 01233 626809 Fax: 01233 626809 — LMSSA 1971 Lond. (St. Thos.) Socs: BMA. Prev: Ho. Surg. St. Mary's Hosp. Plaistow; Ho. Phys. Sevenoaks Hosp.; Ho. Surg. (Obst.) Weir Matern. Hosp. (St. Jas.) Balham.

DHILLON, Manpreet Singh 19 Sherbourne Crescent, Coundon, Coventry CV5 8LF — MB ChB 1995 Birm.; ChB Birm. 1995.

DHILLON, Narinder Singh 20 Woodbourne Road, Bearwood Warley, Warley B67 5LY — MB BS 1998 Lond.; MB BS Lond 1998.

DHILLON, Paramdeep Singh 122 Colchester Road, London E10 6HD — MB BS 1998 Lond.; MB BS Lond 1998.

DHILLON, Paul Jit 204 Hampton Road, Twickenham TW2 5NJ — MB BCh 1995 Wales.

DHILLON, Perminder Tony Singh 56 Blackamoor La, Maidenhead SL6 8RG Email: tdhi631920@gol.com — MB BS 1997 Lond.; BSc Lond 1994. (Univ.Coll.Lond) SHO Med. Rotat. Oxf. Hosp. Socs: BMA; Middx. Med. Soc. Prev: Ho. Off. UCL.

DHILLON, Ramanjit Singh 7 Sutherland House, 135 Queenstown Road, London SW8 3RJ — BM BS 1985 Nottm.; MRCP (UK) 1990.

DHILLON, Mr Ramindar Singh Northwick Park Hospital, Watford Road, Harrow HA1 3UJ Tel: 020 8869 2963; 34 York Street, London W1H 1FF Tel: 020 7935 7384 Fax: 020 7580 7166 — MB BS 1978 Lond.; FRCS Eng. 1984. Cons. ENT Surg. N.wick Pk. Hosp., Hillingdon Hosp. & Watford Gen. Hosp. Prev: Sen. Regist. Middlx. & Univ. Coll. Hosps.

DHILLON, Soniadeep 57 Oak Lodge Avenue, Chigwell IG7 5JA — MB ChB 1994 Birm.

DHILLON, Sukhvinder Singh Flat7 Edward Court, London Road, Harrow HA1 3NW Email: suki@dircon.co.uk — MB ChB 1990 Liverp.; MRCP (UK) 1995; FRCRI 1998. Specialist Regist. (Radiol.) N.wick Pk. Hosp. Middlx. Socs: BMA; Roy. Coll. Radiol.; Brit.Instit.Radiol. Prev: Specialist Regist. (Nephrol.) Univ. Hosp. Birm.; Specialist Regist. (Nephrol.) Birm. Heartlands Hosp.; Specialist Regist. (Nephrol.) Walsgrave Hosp. Coventry.

DHILLON, Sundeep, Capt. RAMC 38A Vineyard Hill Road, Wimbledon, London SW19 7JH Tel: 020 8947 6162 Fax: 020 8947 6162 — BM BCh 1994 Oxf.; MA Oxf. 1994. (Oxf.) Roy. Army Med. Corps. Socs: Fell. Roy. Soc. Trop. Med. & Hyg.; Wilderness Med. Soc. (USA). Prev: Ho. Off. (Gen. & Orthop. Surg.) Hereford Hosps. NHS Trust; Ho. Off. (Gen. Med.) Withington Hosp. Manch.

DHILLON, Surjit Kaur Pai and Dillon, Tile Hill Primary Health Care, Jardine Crescent, Coventry CV4 9PN Tel: 024 7646 0800 Fax: 024 7646 7512; 9 Canon Young Road, Whitnash, Leamington Spa CV31 2QU — MB BS 1990 Lond.; DFFP 1993; DRCOG 1993. (Saint Mary's Hospital Medical School)

DHILLON, Veena Bali Rheumatic Diseases Unit, Department of Medicine, University of Edinburgh, Western General Hospital, Edinburgh EH4 2XU — MB BS 1982 Lond.; MA Camb. 1983; MD Lond. 1993; MRCP (UK) 1986. (Girton College Cambridge; Kings College Hospital London) Cons. (Rheum.) Rhematic Dis. Unit, Lothian Univ.y Hosp.s NHS Trust, W.ern Gen. Hosp., Edin.. Prev: Sen. Regist. (Rheum.) W.. Gen. Hosp. Edin.; Sen. Regist. (Rheum.) Addenbrooke's Hosp. Camb.; Research Fell. (Wellcome Trust) Med. Molecular Biol. Unit Univ. Coll. Lond.

DHIMAN, Arun St George's Hospital NHS Trust, Blackshaw Road, London SW17 0QT Tel: 020 8672 1255; 22 Avalon Road, West Ealing, London W13 0BN Email: a.dhiman@sghms.ac.uk — MB BChir 1989 Camb.; BA Camb. 1986; MRCP (UK) 1992. Specialist Regist. (Gastroenterol. & Med.Epsom & St helier NHS Trust. Prev: Clin. Research Fell. St. Geo. Hosp. Med. Sch. Lond.; Regist. (Gastroenterol. & Med.) Centr. Middlx. Hosp. & St. Mary's Hosp. Lond.; SHO (Med.) John Radcliffe Hosp. Oxf.

DHINDSA, Amarjit Singh Rochester Health Centre, Delce Road, Rochester ME1 2EL Tel: 01634 401111 — MB BCh 1984 Wales; MB BCh Wales l984.

DHINGRA, Harpal Singh Tamar Medical Centre, Severn Drive, Perton, Wolverhampton WV6 7QL Tel: 01902 755053 Fax: 01902 751010 — MB BS 1974 Punjab.

DHINGRA, Mr Jagdish Kumar 160 Herne Hill Road, Herne Hill, London SE24 0AH Tel: 020 7733 4072 — MB BS 1985 Delhi; DLO RCS Eng. 1991; FRCS Ed. 1992; FRCS Eng. 1992.

***DHINGRA, Kavita** 60 Upton Court Road, Slough SL3 7LZ Tel: 01753 536780 — MB BS 1997 Lond.; BSc.

DHINGRA, Suresh Kumar 85 Hart Road, Thundersley, Benfleet SS7 3PR Tel: 01268 757981 — MB BS 1963 Rajasthan.

DHINGSA, Rajpal 4 Moorcroft Road, Birmingham B13 8LX — MB ChB 1990 Aberd.

DHIR, K S The Surgery, 1 Evesham Terrace, St Andrews Road, Surbiton KT6 4DS Tel: 020 8399 1837 Fax: 020 8399 5791.

DHIR, Kiran Pathology Laboratory, Warrington District General Hospital, Lovely Lane, Warrington WA5 1QG Tel: 01925 635911 Fax: 01925 234748; The Nook, Balmoral Road, Grappenhall, Warrington WA4 2EB Tel: 01925 261173 Fax: 01925 573113 — MB BS 1970 Poona. Cons. Haemat. Warrington Dist. Gen. Hosp. Socs: Assoc. Mem. Roy. Coll. Path.

DHIR, Susan Eightlands Surgery, Eightlands Road, Dewsbury WF13 2PA Tel: 01924 465929 Fax: 01924 488740 — MB ChB 1981 Leeds; BSc (Hons.) Leeds 1976; DRCOG 1984. Gen. Practitioner.

DHITAL, Achyut Prasad The Surgery, 73 Upper Wickham Lane, Welling DA16 3AF Tel: 020 8854 1910 Fax: 020 8317 3711 — MB BS 1972 Calcutta; MB BS 1972 Calcutta.

DHITAL, Kumud Kumar 12 Hansapel Drive, Brackley NN13 6HD — BM BCh 1991 Oxf.

DHITAL, Raghav Prasad Hurst Road Health Centre, Hurst Road, Walthamstow, London E17 3BL Tel: 020 8520 5571 Fax: 020 8509 1659; 48 Cheyne Avenue, London E18 2DR Tel: 020 8989 3211 — MB BS 1969 Dacca; LRCP LRCS Ed. LRCPS Glas. 1982.

DHITAL, Mr Sanjiv Kumar Plastic & Reconstructive Surgery Unit, Countess of Chester Hospital, Liverpool Road, Chester CH2 1UL Tel: 01244 366282 Fax: 01244 366277; Timbers, Moss Lane, Manley, Frodsham, Warrington WA6 9JN Tel: 01928 740312 Fax: 01928 740597 — MB BS 1980 Lond.; FRCS Ed. 1986. (The London Hospital Medical College) Cons. Plastic & Reconstruc. Surg. Countess Chester NHS Trust. Prev: Sen. Regist. (Plastic Surg.) Whiston Hosp. Liverp.; Regist. (Plastic Surg.) Wordsley Hosp. Stourbridge; Research Fell. (Surg.) Roy. Postgrad. Med. Sch. Lond.

DHIYA, Luway Hassan Westfield Surgery, Westfield, Graham Street, Johnstone PA5 8QY Tel: 01505 337888 Fax: 01505 337700 — MB ChB 1971 Mosul. (Mosul) GP Johnstone, Renfrewsh.

DHIYA, Saba 21 Huntly Gardens, Dowanhill, Glasgow G12 9AU — MB ChB 1997 Glas.

DHOAT, Jasjeet Singh South Norwood Medical Centre, 93 Whitehorse Lane, London SE25 6RA Tel: 020 8771 9779 Fax: 020 8771 3779 — MB BS 1992 Lond.; MRCGP 1996; DRCOG 1995. (St. Geo. Hosp. Med. Sch.)

DHOAT, Narinder South Norwood Medical Centre, 93 Whitehorse Lane, London SE25 6RA Tel: 020 8771 9779 Fax: 020 8771 3779 — MB BS 1963 Panjab; MB BS Panjab (India) 1963; Dip. Dermat. Lond 1968. Hosp. Pract. (Dermat.) Mayday Hosp. & Croydon Gen. Hosp. Socs: BMA.

DHOLAKIA, Rajendra Pushpakrai Eastcourt Lane Surgery, 52 Eastcourt Lane, Gillingham ME8 6EY Tel: 01634 232144 Fax: 01634 261811 — MB BS 1967 Gujarat. (M.P. Shah Med. Coll. Jamnagar) Princip.

DHOND, Girish Raghunath 20 Matlock Way, New Malden KT3 3AY — MB BS 1988 Lond.; MRCP (UK) 1991; FRCA 1994; DA (UK) 1992. Cons. Anaesth., Roy. Surrey Co. Hosp., Guildford. Prev: SHO (Anaesth.) Nottm.

DHOND, Milind Raghunath 20 Matlock Way, New Malden KT3 3AY — MB BS 1989 Lond.

DHORAJIWALA, Dina The Clock Tower Practice, 50-66 Park Road, Crouch End, London N8 8SU Tel: 020 8348 7711 — MB BS 1989 Lond.

DHORAJIWALA, Mr Jagdish Meghji 11 Acrefield Park, Church Road, Woolton, Liverpool L25 6JX — MB BS 1970 Newc.; FRCS Eng. 1975.

DHOTHER, Sukhjinder Singh 70 Cranbrook Road, Handsworth, Birmingham B21 8PG — MB ChB 1985 Leeds.

DHUMALE, Mr Rajendra Govind Gayton Road Health and Surgical Centre, Gayton Road, King's Lynn PE30 4DY Tel: 01553 762726 Fax: 01553 696819 — MB BS 1979 Bombay; MS (Gen. Surg.) Bombay 1979; FRCSI 1982. Prev: Sen. Regist. (Cardiothoracic Surg.) BRd.green Hosp. Liverp.

DHUNDEE, Jennifer Histopathology Department, Queen Alexandra Hospital, Cosham, Portsmouth PO6 3LY Tel: 023 92 286000 — MB BS 1986 Lond.; BSc (Hons.) Lond. 1983, MB BS 1986; MRCPath 1993; DRCPath. Cons. Histopath. & Cytopath. Qu. Alexandra Hosp. Portsmouth.

DHUNY, Abdool Rashid South View Surgery, 12 South View, Graghead, Stanley DH9 6AR Tel: 01207 290032; Hedley House, Hedley Lane, Nr. Sunniside, Newcastle upon Tyne NE16 5EQ — MB ChB 1977 Manch.; DCH Eng. 1980.

DHUPELIA, Ila Rashmi 24 Foxfield Close, Northwood HA6 3NU Tel: 01923 829310 — MB BS 1973 Gujarat; FFA RCSI 1990; DA (UK) 1977. Assoc. Specialist Edgware Gen. Hosp. Middlx.

DI BIASIO, Nicholas Highfield, 72 Island Road, Sturry, Canterbury CT2 0EE — MB ChB 1992 Manch.; BA (Hons.) Lond. 1983.

DI CEGLIE, Domenico 48 Pickwick Road, Dulwich Village, London SE21 7JW Tel: 020 7733 5811 — State DMS 1976 Perugia; Dip. Med Chir Perugia 1972; MRCPsych 1984. Cons. Child & Adolesc. Psychiat. Croydon Child Guid. Clinic. Prev: Sen. Regist. (Child & Adolesc. Psychiat.) Tavistock Clinic & Hill End Adolesc. Unit St. Albans; Regist. (Psychiat.) Centr. Middlx. Hosp. & N.gate Clinic Lond.

DI CEGLIE, Giovanna Rita 48 Pickwick Road, Dulwich Village, London SE21 7JW Tel: 020 7733 5811 — State DMS 1976 Perugia; Dip. Med Chir Perugia 1972; Dip. Psychiat. Perugia 1976. Psychiat. & Psychoanalyst in Private Pract.; Train. Psychotherapist, Lincoln Clinic & Centre for Psychother. & The BAP. Socs: Brit. Psychoanalytic Soc.; Italian Med. Soc. UK. Prev: Cons. Psychiat. Assessm. Serv. Haringey Social Serv.; Regist. (Psychiat.) & Clin. Asst. Child Guid. Train. Centre Tavistock Centre; Professional Comm. Chair Lincoln Clinic & Centre for Psychother.

DI DARIO, Domenico 12A Lancaster House, Whiston Hospital, Warrington Road, Prescot L35 5DR — State Exam 1993 Naples.

DI LUCA, Chiara 2nd Floor Flat, 67 Canfield Gardens, London NW6 3EA — State Exam Perugia 1985.

DI LUSTRO, Mary Jean Arnold Lodge, Cordelia Close, Leicester LE5 0LE Tel: 0116 225 6101 Email: maryh@aol.com — MB ChB

1989 Leeds; MRCPsych 1994; MSc 1998. Sen. Regist. (Psych Leics. Prev: Regist. Rotat. (Psychiat.) Leics.

DI MAMBRO, Alexandra Jane 22 Hill View, Henleaze, Bristol BS9 4PY — MB ChB 1998 Bristol.

DI MAMBRO, Sally Louise Maria The Old Bakery, 51 Castle St., Nether Stowey, Bridgwater TA5 1LW — MB BS 1993 Lond. SHO (Obstet. & Gyn.) MusGr. Pk. Hosp. Taunton.

DI MONACO, Mario The Ochards, Hogpits Bottom, Flaunden HP3 0QB Tel: 01442 831987 — MB BS 1982 Lond.; FRCGP 2000; MRCGP 1987; DCH RCP Lond. 1989; DRCOG 1986. (Univ. Coll. Hosp.) GP Tutor Mt. Vernon. Hosp. Middlx.; VTS Course Organiser Hillingdon Hosp. Prev: Trainee GP Hillingdon Hosp. VTS; Ho. Surg. Luton & Dunstable Hosp.; Ho. Phys. Univ. Coll. Hosp. Lond.

DI PAOLA, Mr Michael Pasquale Winton Lodge, 3 The Crescent, Skelmorlie PA17 5DX — MB ChB 1971 Glas.; FRCS Glas. 1976. (Glas.) Cons. (Orthop. Surg.) Inverclyde Roy. Hosp. Greenock. Prev: Sen. Regist. (Orthop. Surg.) W.. Infirm. Glas.; MRC Research Fell. (Spinal Surg.) W.. Infirm. Glas.; Regist. (Orthop. Surg.) Vict. Infirm. Glas.

DI PASQUALE, Alfonso Boris Department of Urology, Charing Cross Hospital, Fulham Palace Road, London W6 8RF — State Exam 1991 Aquila.

DI SALVO, Carmelo The London Chest Hospital, Bonner Road, London E2 9JX Tel: 020 8980 4433; 55 Princes Road, Buckhurst Hill IG9 5DZ Tel: 020 8559 0576 — State Exam Catania 1985. Hon. Sen. Regist. Lond. Chest Hosp.

DIAB, Mohamad Ali Walton Village Medical Centre, 172 Walton Village, Liverpool L4 6TW Tel: 0151 525 1700 Fax: 0151 525 6448 — LMSSA 1990 Lond.

DIACK, Alison Morag 4 Willow Green, Liverpool L25 4RR — MB ChB 1994 Liverp.

DIACK, Gordon Allan Maxwell 28 St Nicholas Drive, Richmond DL10 7DY Tel: 01748 850842 — MB ChB 1976 Aberd.; DRCOG 1978.

DIACK, Hilary Jane Kings Road, Horley RH6 7DG Tel: 01293 772686 Fax: 01293 823950 — MB ChB 1983 Manch.; MRCGP 1987; DRCOG 1986; DCH RCP Lond. 1985.

DIACK, James Ian Donald (retired) The Old Vicarage, Lyminster, Littlehampton BN17 7QF Tel: 01903 882476 — MB ChB 1951 Aberd. Hosp. Pract. (Orthop.) Bognor Regis War Memor. Hosp. & St. Richard's Hosp. Chichester. Prev: Hosp. Med. Off. (Orthop.) & SHO (Orthop.) Aberd. Roy. Infirm.

DIACK, Pauline Patricia 29 King Street, Inverbervie, Montrose DD10 0RQ — MB ChB 1991 Aberd.

DIACK, William George Hendry The Health Centre, Church St., Inverbervie, Montrose DD10 0RU Tel: 01561 61260; 29 King Street, Inverbervie, Montrose DD10 0RQ — MB ChB 1963 Aberd.

DIACON, Martin James Raddlebarn, High Cogges, Witney OX8 6VW — MB ChB 1998 Sheff.; MB ChB Sheff 1998.

DIAMANT-DESSER, Margaret (retired) 50 Werburgh Drive, Trentham, Stoke-on-Trent ST4 8JP Tel: 01782 657719 — MD 1931 Vienna.

DIAMENT, Morton Leonard Farafield, Stromness, Orkney — MD 1967 Aberd.; MB ChB 1964.

DIAMENT, Mr Robert Hugh Crosshouse Hospital, Kilmarnock Road, Kilmarnock KA2 0BE Tel: 01563 577322 Fax: 01563 577974 Email: robert.diament@aaaht.scot.nhs.uk — MB ChB 1981 Aberd.; FRCS Eng. 1986; FRCS Ed. 1986. Cons. Surg. CrossHo. Hosp. Kilmarnock. Socs: Assn. of Surg.s of GB & I; Assn. of Coloprouology (Scott. Chapter); Assn. of Endoscopic Surg.s of GB & I. Prev: Sen. Regist. & Regist. Yorks. Region; Research Fell. Univ. Leeds.

DIAMOND, Aisling Mary 32 Commedagh Drive, Belfast BT11 8GH — MB BCh BAO 1993 Belf.

DIAMOND, Alison Jane Northam Surgery, Bayview Road, Northam, Bideford EX39 1AZ Tel: 01237 474994 — MB BCh 1985 Wales.

DIAMOND, Andrew William (retired) 74 Fedden Village, Nove Road, Portishead, Bristol BS20 8EJ Tel: 01275 818753 Email: andrewdiamond@compuserve.co — MB BS 1961 Lond.; FFA RCS Eng. 1965; DA Eng. 1963. Cons. Anaesth. Frenchay Hosp. Bristol. Prev: Pres. Pain Soc.

DIAMOND, Mr Charles Pleasantry, 93 Kenton Road, Newcastle upon Tyne NE3 4NL Tel: 0191 285 1606 — MB ChB 1956 Glas.; FRCS Glas. 1964; DObst RCOG 1960. Emerit. Cons. ENT Surg. Freeman Hosp. Newc.; Hon. Clin. Lect. (ENT Studies) Univ. Newc. Socs: Hon. Life Mem. Brit. Assn. Otolaryngol. Head & Neck Surg.; Hon Life Mem. N. Eng. Otolaryngol. Soc.; Roy. Soc. Med. Prev: Regist. (ENT) W.. Infirm. Glas.; Fell. Alberta Foundat. of Otol.; Flight Lt. RAF Med. Br. (Nat. Serv.).

DIAMOND, Eva Marianne (retired) 10 Henderson Court, 88 Holden Road, London N12 7EL Tel: 020 8445 4266 — LRCP LRCS Ed. LRFPS Glas. 1949. Clin. Asst. (Child Psychiat.) N.wick Pk. Hosp. Prev: Clin. Asst. (Child Psychiat.) Brighton.

DIAMOND, Jeannette (retired) 14 Rookery Road, Southport PR9 7JQ Tel: 01704 226510 — MB ChB Liverp. 1951; FFCM 1980, M 1972; DPH Liverp. 1954; DObst RCOG 1953. Prev: SCM Social Servs. Lancs. AHA.

DIAMOND, Mr Jeremy Paul 2 Clifton Park, Clifton, Bristol BS8 3BS — MB ChB 1984 Bristol; PhD Bristol 1995; FRCS Eng. 1990; FCOphth 1990. (Bristol) Cons. Bristol Eye Hosp.; Mem. Oxf. Ophth. Congr..; Mem. UK Glaucoma Soc. Socs: Roy. Soc. Med. Prev: Fell. Lions Eye Inst. Perth, W. Austral.

DIAMOND, John Gerard The Mulberries, Keyston, Huntingdon PE28 0RD Tel: 01832 710494 Email: jgdiamond@clara.co.uk — MRCS Eng. LRCP Lond. 1962; FFA RCS Eng. 1968. (St. Bart.) Prev: Emerit. Cons. Guy's & St Thomas NHS Trust.

***DIAMOND, Laura Ann** 58A Gamekeeper's Road, Edinburgh EH4 6LS — MB ChB 1997 Ed.; BSc (Epidemiol.) (Hons.) Ed. 1995.

DIAMOND, Margaret Pauline (retired) The Ridge, 28 Fairlight Road, Hythe CT21 4AD Tel: 01303 264686 Fax: 01303 264686 — MB ChB Liverp. 1943; MCPath 1965. Prev: Cons. Haemat. Hackney Hosp. Lond.

DIAMOND, Mary Claire McDonnell and Partners, 139-141 Ormeau Road, Belfast BT7 1DA Tel: 028 9032 6030 — MB BCh BAO 1989 Belf.; MRCGP 1994.

DIAMOND, Patricia Ann Mary, OBE (retired) The Mulberries, Keyston, Huntingdon PE28 0RD Tel: 01832 710494 — MB ChB Birm. 1960; FRCP Lond 1989; FFOM 1988, MFOM 1980; DIH Eng. 1977; DObst RCOG 1963; DA Eng. 1963. Prev: Dir. of Med. Serv. Lond. Transport.

DIAMOND, Paul Stephen (Surgery), 301 Farnham Road, Slough SL2 1HA Tel: 01753 520917 Fax: 01753 550680; 40 Larchmoor Park, Gerrard Cross Road, Stoke Poges, Slough SL2 4EY Tel: 01753 663659 — MB BS 1962 Lond. (Middlx.)

DIAMOND, Pauline Mary 36 Melmount Gardens, Strabane BT82 9EB — MB ChB 1990 Ed.

DIAMOND, Philomena Josephine Falls Road Surgery, 186 Falls Road, Belfast BT12 6AG Tel: 028 9032 3062; 17 Maryville Park, Belfast BT9 6LN — MB BCh BAO 1978 Belf.; MRCGP 1982; DCH RCPSI 1981; DRCOG 1981. GP Belf.

DIAMOND, Robert Lindsay 58A Gamekeeper's Road, Cramond, Edinburgh EH4 6LS — MB ChB 1968 Glas.; BSc (Hons.) (Elec. Engin.) Strathclyde 1956; DCM Ed. 1982; CIH Dund 1980.

DIAMOND, Mr Thomas Mary Plunket 4 Tudor Grove, Circular Road, Jordanstown, Newtownabbey BT37 0UX — MB BCh BAO 1981 Belf.; BSc Belf. 1978, MD 1991; FRCS Dub. 1985; FRCS Ed. 1985. Cons. Surg. Mater Hosp. Belf.; Hon. Lect. (Surg.) Qu. Univ. Belf.; Ref. Brit. Jl. Surg. Prev: Sen. Lect. (Surg.) Qu. Univ. Belf.

DIAPER, Mr Charles John Mayhew South Glasgow University Hospital NHS Trust, 1345 Govan Road, Glasgow G51 4TF Tel: 0141 201 1100; Email: candc@georgen.u-net.com — MB ChB 1987 Birm.; FRCS Ed. 1993; FRCOphth 1993. Cons. Ophth. Glas. Prev: Specialist Regist. (Ophth.) Glas.; SHO Rotat. (Ophth.) Bradford & Leeds.

DIAPER, Elwyn David John, Group Capt. RAF Med. Br. (retired) Holt Rise, Holt Pound, Farnham GU10 4LA Tel: 01420 22186 — MB ChB 1956 Leeds; AFOM RCP Lond. 1982; DAvMed Eng. 1968.

DIAPER, Martyn David Friarsgate Practice, Friarsgate Medical Centre, Friarsgate, Winchester SO23 8EF Tel: 01962 853599 Fax: 01962 849982; 23 Edgar Road, Winchester SO23 9TW — MB BS 1989 Lond.; MRCGP 1994; DFFP 1994; T(GP) 1994.

DIAS, Anna Marie 43 The Marlinespike, Shoreham-by-Sea BN43 5RD — MB BS 1988 Lond.; MRCGP Lond. 1992; DRCOG Lond. 1991.

DIAS, Aruna Sanjeeva 4 Whitehall Road, Sittingbourne ME10 4HB — MB BS 1997 Lond.

DIAS, Bernard Francis Mayfield Medical Centre, Park Road, Jarrow NE32 5SE Tel: 0191 489 7183 Fax: 0191 483 2001 — MB ChB 1976 Manch.; BSc (Med. Sci.) St. And. 1973.

DIAS, Bernard Palandapatirage Burton Lodge Medical Centre, 86 Station Parade, Harrogate HG1 1HH Tel: 01423 503129 Fax: 01423 561820; 21 St. Leonards Road, Harrogate HG2 8NX Tel: 01423 884426 Fax: 01423 884426 Email: bdias@mcmail.com — MD 1974 2nd Moscow Med. Inst. Hosp. Pract. (Cardiol.) Harrogate Dist. Hosp. Prev: Regist. (Med.) Harrogate Dist. & Gen. Hosp.

DIAS, Bonaventure George (retired) White House, 3 Cromwell Road, Chesterfield S40 4TH — MB BS 1954 Nagpur; BSc Bombay 1948; DO Eng. 1957. Prev: SHO (Ophth.) N. Staffs. Roy. Infirm. Stoke-on-Trent.

DIAS, Catherine Jane Ponteland Health Centre, Thornhill Road, Ponteland, Newcastle upon Tyne NE20 9PZ Tel: 01661 825513; 8 Westfield Drive, Gosforth, Newcastle upon Tyne NE3 4XU Tel: 0191 284 4903 — MB BS 1985 Newc.; DFFP 1998; MRCGP 1990; DRCOG 1990. GP Newc. u. Tyne Retainer Scheme. Prev: Clin. Asst. (Dermat.) Newc.; GP Univ. Med. Centre Newc. u. Tyne.

DIAS, Dona Renuka Camelia 18 Theobalds Way, Frimley, Camberley GU16 9RF — MB BS 1986 Colombo; MRCP (UK) 1993.

DIAS, Elizabeth Mary 4 The Green, Brompton, Northallerton DL6 2QT Tel: 01609 3374 — MB BCh BAO 1954 NUI. (NUI) Clin. Asst. (A & E) Friarage Hosp. N.allerton.

DIAS, Jean-Pierre 2 Church Row, Beckwithshaw, Harrogate HG3 1QW — MB ChB 1992 Leeds.

DIAS, Mr Joseph Joaquim The White Hall, Brook Lane, Billesdon, Leicester LE7 9AB — MB BS 1981 Bombay; FRCS Ed. 1983.

DIAS, Mr Palitha Srilal Hillcote, 104 Lancaster Road, Newcastle ST5 1DS Tel: 01782 611874 — MB BS 1972 Ceylon; FRCS Ed. 1983; FRCS Eng. 1977. (Colombo) Cons. Neurosurg. N. Staffs. Hosp. Trust; in Surg. Neurol. 1983-84. Socs: Brit. Soc. Neurol. Surgs. Prev: Sen. Regist. (Neurosurg.) Sheff. Hosps.; Cons. Neurosurg. King Faisal Hosp. Taif, Saudi Arabia; Regist. (Neurosurg.) Atkinson Morley's Hosp. Lond.

DIAS, Paul James 16 Roedean Dr, Eaglescliffe, Stockton-on-Tees TS16 9HT — BM BS 1997 Nottm.

DIAS, Raul Cesar 16 Roedean Drive, Eaglescliffe, Stockton-on-Tees TS16 9HT — MB BCh BAO 1963 NUI; MRCP (U.K.) 1971; DCH Eng. 1965. Cons. Paediat. N. & S. Tees Health Dists. Prev: SHO (Paediat.) & Regist. (Paediat.) Childr. Hosp. Stockton-on-Tees.; Sen. Regist. Childr. Hosp. Nottm.

DIAS, Subaweerage Anusha Nayanthi Optimum Health Services NHS Trust, Elizabeth Brackwell House, Wardalls Grove, Avonley Road, New Cross, London SE14 5ER; 31 Meredith Close, Pinner HA5 4RP Tel: 020 8428 3182 — MB BS 1989 Lond.; DFFP 1995. Clin. Med. Off. Optimum Health Serv. NHS Trust; Clin. Med. Off. (Family Plann.) Pk.side NHS Trust. Prev: Clin. Med. Off. Waltham Forest HA & Lewisham & N. S.wark HA; SHO Middlx. Hosp. Lond.; Ho. Surg. Watford Gen. Hosp.

DIAS, Subaweerage George Ariyapala Inner Park Health Centre, 86-88 Inner Park Road, Wimbledon, London SW19 6DA Tel: 020 020 8788 3231 — MB BS 1959 Ceylon; DCH RCP Lond. 1968. Socs: BMA. Prev: SCMO (Paediat.) Riverside HA; Regist. (Gen. Med. & Rheum.) St. Jas. Hosp. Lond.

DIAS, Subaweerage Roshantha Chandima — MB BS 1993 Lond.; MRCP 1999. (Charing Cross & Westminster Medical School) Sen. Med. Adviser. Prev: Trust Regist. Gen. & Elderly Med. Qu. Mary's Hosp. Sidcup; SHO (Gen. & Elderly Med.) Qu. Mary's Hosp. Sidcup; SHO (A & E) St. Geo.'s Univ. Hosp. Lond.

DIAS, Thomas Francis (retired) Greylags, Boustead Hill, Burgh-by-Sands, Carlisle CA5 6AA Tel: 01228 576286 — MB BS 1953 Durh.; BA Open 1995. Prev: Ho. Phys. Cumbld. Infirm.

DIAS, Valerie Odette The Surgery, 112 Princedale Road, London W11 4NH Tel: 020 7727 2022 Fax: 020 7727 2022 — MB BS 1976 Lond.; MRCGP 1984; DCH RCP Lond. 1983. GP Lond.; Orthopaedic Med., Acupunc., Homoeopathy.

DIAS, Yves M (retired) The Old Vicarage, Topcliffe, Thirsk YO7 3RU Tel: 01845 577405 — MB BS 1954 Durh.; FRCGP 1972. Prev: Ho. Surg. & Ho. Phys. Hexham Gen. Hosp.

DIAS WEERASINHA, Rene Noeline (retired) 212 Lavender Hill, Enfield EN2 8NJ Tel: 020 8366 4350 Fax: 020 8366 4350 — MB BS 1951 Ceylon; MRCPsych 1972; DPM Eng. 1957. Prev: Cons. Psychiat. (Ment. Handicap) Bromham Hosp. Bedford.

DIAZ-GUIJARRO HAYES, Jesus 62 Watford Road, Croxley Green, Rickmansworth WD3 3BP — LMS 1983 U Complutense Madrid.

DIAZ OJEDA, Maria Hecate Flat 32, Lister House, Restell Close, London SE3 7UL — LMS 1990 Barcelona; LMS Autonoma Barcelona 1990.

DIBA, Ali Anaesthetic Dept., Queen Victoria Hospital, East Grinstead RH19 3DZ Tel: 01342 410210 Ext: 256 Email: ali.diba@qvh-tr.sthames.nhs.uk — BM 1986 Soton.; FRCA 1994; DA (UK) 1990. (Soton. Univ.) Cons. Anaesth., Qu. Vict. Hosp., E. Grinstead. Socs: Assn. Anaesth. UK & N. Irel.; Difficult Airway Soc.; Soc. for Intravenous Anaesth. (UK). Prev: Regist. Rotat. (Anaesth.) Guy's Hosp. Lond.; SHO (Anaesth.) Roy. United Hosp. Bath.; Sen. Regist. (Anaesth.) St. Thos. Hosp. Lond.

DIBA, Victoria Catherine 69 Idonia Road, Perton, Wolverhampton WV6 7NQ Tel: 01902 745864 — MB ChB 1995 Dundee. (Dundee) SHO (Med.) City Hosp. Birm. Prev: SHO (A & E) Birm. Heartlands Hosp.

DIBB, Ann 4 River Walk, St Austell PL25 5DJ — MB ChB 1971 Liverp.; DObst RCOG 1973. (Liverp.) Socs: Christians in Caring Professions. Prev: GP St. Austell; Clinic Doctor (Community Med.) Wirral AHA; SHO Alder Hey Childr. Hosp.

DIBB, Sheila 6 Selwood, Doncaster Road, Rotherham S65 2BW Tel: 01709 372981 — MB ChB 1950 Sheff.

DIBBEN, Claire Rebecca Mary 1 Royston Close, Highfield, Southampton SO17 1TB — MB BS 1996 Lond.; BSc Lond. 1993. (St. Bart. Med. College) SHO (c/o the Elderly) Poole Hosp. Poole. Prev: SHO (A & E) Salisbury; PRHO (Gen. Surg.) St. Mary's Hosp. Lond.; PRHO (Gen. Med.) Broomfield Hosp. Chelmsford.

DIBBLE, Antony Michael Borough Green Medical Practice, Quarry Hill Road, Borough Green, Sevenoaks TN15 8BE Tel: 01732 883161 Fax: 01732 886319; 1 Yaldham Cottages, Kemsing Road, Wrotham, Sevenoaks TN15 6NN — MB ChB 1984 Manch.; MB ChB Manch. l984; MRCGP 1989; DCH RCP Lond. 1990; Cert. Family Plann. JCC 1989; DRCOG 1988. (Manch.) Prev: Trainee GP Mayday Hosp. VTS; SHO (Paediat. & Community Paediat.) St. Helens & Knowsley HA.

DIBBLE, John Barnard Benenden Hospital, Cranbrook TN17 4AX Tel: 01580 240333 Fax: 01580 241877; Chimneys, Cranbrook Rd, Tenterden TN30 6UL — MB ChB 1971 Manch.; MRCP (UK) 1974; FRCP (Lond.) 1997; MD Manch. 1985; FRCP (UK) 1974. Cons. Phys. & Nephrol. Benenden Hosp. Kent; Med. Director Benenden Hosp. Socs: BMA; Renal Assn. & EDTA.; Brit. Thoracic Soc. Prev: Sen. Regist. (Med.) Yorks RHA; Regist. (Med.) St. Jas. Univ. Hosp. Leeds; SHO (Med.) Manch. Roy. Infirm.

DIBBLE, Laraine Dept Paediatrics,Torbay Hospital, Lawes Bridge Newton Road, Torbay, Paignton TQ2 7AA Tel: 01803 614567 Email: larained@doctors.org.uk — MB BS 1989 Lond.; MRCP (UK) 1994; DCH RCP Lond. 1992; MSc 1998. (CharingCross/Westminster) Cons. Paediat. Prev: Regist. (Paediat.) Whipps Cross Hosp. & Whittington Hosp. Lond.; Regist. (Paediat.) St Geo.s, Lond.

DIBBLE, Terence Frederick Charles Queensway Medical Centre, Olympic Way, Wellingborough NN8 3EP Tel: 01933 678777 Fax: 01933 676657; 428 St. John's Road, Kettering NN15 5HF Tel: 01536 513173 — MB BChir 1961 Camb.; BA Camb., MB 1961, BChir 1960; DObst RCOG 1963; Cert. Family Plann. JCC 1972. (W. Lond.) Socs: Assn. Occupat. Med. & Assn. Police Surgs. Prev: Ho. Surg. (O & G) St. Stephen's Hosp. Lond.; Ho. Surg. W. Lond. Hosp.; Ho. Phys. New End Hosp.

DIBBLE, Tracey Louise 3 Rupert Road, Sheffield S7 1RN — MB BS 1992 Lond.

DIBDIN, Emily Marianne Flat 4, 42 Prospect Road, Birmingham B13 9TD — MB ChB 1992 Sheff.

DIBDIN, Susan Joyce Gloucester Road Medical Centre, Tramway House, 1A Church Road, Bristol BS7 8SA Tel: 0117 949 7774 Fax: 0117 949 7730; 8 Woodstock Avenue, Bristol BS6 6EN Tel: 0117 974 1404 — MB BS 1964 Lond.; MRCS Eng. LRCP Lond. 1964; DObst RCOG 1966. (Roy. Free)

DICHMONT, Edward Victor c/o Department of Anaesthesia, Pilgrim Hospital, Sibsey Road, Boston PE21 9QS Email: tedmont1@aol.com — MB ChB 1981 Cape Town. (Univ. Cape Town) Cons. Anaesth. Pilgrim Hosp. Boston.

DICK, Alan Neil Bonnybridge Health Centre, Larbert Road, Bonnybridge FK4 1ED Tel: 01324 812613; 2 Rennie Street, Falkirk FK1 5QW Tel: 01324 626332 — MB ChB 1966 Ed. (Ed.)

DICK, Alan Robertson Gillan House Surgery, 457 Green Lanes, Palmers Green, London N13 4BS Tel: 020 8882 9393; Heathcrest, 117 Hatfield Road, Little Heath, Potters Bar EN6 1H — MRCS Eng. LRCP Lond. 1964; MA, MB Camb. 1965, BChir 1964; DObst RCOG 1970. (Camb. & St. Mary's) Med. Off. Post Office (Telecommunications) N. Lond. Area; Clin. Asst. (Neurol.) Qu. Eliz. II Hosp. Welwyn Garden City. Socs: BMA (Sec. Enfield Div.). Prev: Clin. Asst. City of Lond. Matern. Hosp.; Ho. Phys. St. Mary's Hosp.

DICK, Alison Elizabeth Corn Cottage, Ramsey Road, Kings Ripton, Huntingdon PE28 2NJ — MB BS 1974 Lond.; FFA Cape Town 1980; MRCS Eng. LRCP Lond. 1974.

DICK, Alison Marie Flat 4, 7 Wellington Square, Cheltenham GL50 4JU — MB BS 1991 Lond.

DICK, Mr Alistair Charles 20 Grangewood Road, Dundonald, Belfast BT16 1GW — MB BCh BAO 1990 Belf.; FRCS Ed.; FRCSI 1994. Regist. (Gen. Surg.) Daisy Hill Hosp. Newry.

DICK, Mr Andrew David c/o Department of Ophthalmology, Aberdeen University Medical School, Foresterhill, Aberdeen AB25 4WA Tel: 01224 681818 Fax: 01224 685158 Email: adick@abdn.ac.uk — MB BS 1985 Lond.; MD Aberd. 1993; FRCS Lond. 1990; MRCP (UK) 1988; FRCOphth 1990. (Char. Cross & Westm.) Sen. Lect. & Hon. Cons. (Ophth.) Univ. Aberd.; MRC Pigott-Wernher Fell.sh. Prev: Sen. Regist. (Ophth.) Aberd. Roy. Infirm.

DICK, Andrew Gordon Hill Medical Group, The Hill, 192 Kingsway, Dunmurry, Belfast BT17 9AL Tel: 028 9061 8211 — MB BCh BAO 1992 Belf.; MRCGP 2000; DRCOG 1995; DGM RCPS Glas. 1994. (Qus. Univ. Belf.)

DICK, Anthony Francis 5 Milton Close, Hampstead Garden Suburb, London N2 0QH — MB BS 1973 Sydney.

DICK, Catherine Laura The Topsham Surgery, The White House, Holman Way, Topsham, Exeter EX3 0EN Tel: 01392 874646 Fax: 01392 875261; 9 Elm Grove Road, Holman Way, Topsham, Exeter EX3 0EQ — MB ChB 1984 Bristol; MRCGP 1989; DCH 1987; DRCOG 1987. GP.

DICK, Charles John Hill Medical Group, The Hill, 192 Kingsway, Dunmurry, Belfast BT17 9AL Tel: 028 9061 8211 Fax: 028 9060 3911; Innisfree, 15 Church Avenue, Dunmurry, Belfast BT17 9RT — MB BCh BAO 1960 Belf.; DObst RCOG 1962; Mem. BMA.

DICK, Charles Mark Ballymena Health Centre, Cushendall Road, Ballymena BT43 6HQ Tel: 028 2564 2181 Fax: 028 2565 8919 — MB BCh BAO 1986 Belf.; MRCGP 1990; DRCOG 1988; DCH RCPSI 1989. (Queen's University Belfast)

DICK, Colin Robert Flat 4, Bearnville, Berne Road, Portstewart BT55 7PA Tel: 028 70836181 — MB BCh BAO 1988 Belf.; DTM & H 1995 Liv.; MRCGP 1992; DCCH RCP Ed. 1992; DRCOG 1991; T(GP) 1992. Socs: BMA. Prev: Med. Superintendent, Ekwendi Hosp., Malawi.

DICK, Craig Andrew St Mary's Hospital, Postgraduate Centre, Newport PO30 5TG; 5 Caesars Road, Newport PO30 5ED — LRCP LRCS Ed. LRCPS Glas. 1997.

DICK, Craig Peter Charles Flat 2nd Left, 49 Tassie St., Glasgow G41 3QG — MB ChB 1998 Glas.; MB ChB Glas 1998.

DICK, Darrell Gordon The Crossings, Earby, Colne BB8 6UF — MB BS 1951 Lond.; DPH Leeds 1967. (St. Bart.)

DICK, David Cunningham 4 Millbrae, Gargunnock, Stirling FK8 3BB Tel: 01786 718 — MB ChB 1972 Glas.; BSc Glas. 1968; MRCP (U.K.) 1974. Cons. Dermat. Forth Valley Health Bd.

DICK, David John The Old Rectory, Kirstead, Norwich NR15 1ER — MD 1984 Aberd.; MB ChB 1974; FRCP Lond. 1994; MRCP (UK) 1977; DObst RCOG 1976. Cons. Neurol. Norf. & Norwich Hosp. Socs: BMA; Assoc. Mem. Brit. Neuropath. Soc. Prev: Sen. Regist. (Neurol.) Regional Neurol. Centre Newc.; SHO (Neurol.) Nat. Hosp. Nerv. Dis. Lond.; Ho. Phys. St. Martins Hosp. Bath.

DICK, David Shaw (retired) Fife Lodge, Strathpeffer IV14 9AP Tel: 01997 21277 — MB ChB 1938 Ed.; BSc Ed. 1935, MB ChB 1938; DA Eng. 1956. Prev: Anaesth. Ross. Memor. Hosp. Dingwall.

DICK, Donald Hugh Brooklands, Charminster, Dorchester DT2 9QZ Tel: 01305 264467 Fax: 01305 264467 — MB BChir 1960 Camb.; MA, MB Camb. 1960, BChir 1959; FRCPsych 1981, M 1971; DPM Eng. 1963. (St. Bart.) Mem. Ment. Health Review Tribunal. Socs: (Ex-Vice Pres.) Roy. Coll. Psychiat. Prev: Cons. Psychiat. Herrison Hosp. Dorchester; Dir. Nat. Health Serv. Health Advis. Serv.; 1st Asst. Dept. Psychiat. St. Geo. Hosp. Lond.

DICK, Douglas Hamilton Kilsyth Medical Partnership, Kilsyth Health Centre, Burngreen Park, Kilsyth, Glasgow G65 0HU Tel: 01236 822081 Fax: 01236 826231 — MB ChB 1980 Ed.

DICK, Elaine Sylvia Top Left, 12 Colebrooke St., Glasgow G12 8HD — MB ChB 1998 Glas.; MB ChB Glas 1998.

DICK, Elizabeth Ann Royal Free Hospital, Pond St., London NW3 — MB BS 1993 Lond.; BSc Lond. 1990; MRCP (UK) 1996. (Univ. Coll. Lond. Sch. Med.) Specialist Regist. Roy. Free Hosp.

DICK, Finlay David University of Aberdeen, Department of Environmental and Occupational Medicine, University Medical School, Foresterhill, Aberdeen AB25 2ZD Tel: 01224 681818 Email: f.dick@abdn.ac.uk; 98 Desswood Place, Aberdeen AB15 4DQ Tel: 01224 630742 — MB ChB 1987 Aberd.; AFOM RCP Lond. 1995; MRCGP 1991; T(GP) 1991. (Aberdeen) Clin. Lect. (Occupat. Med.) Univ. of Aberd. Socs: Soc. Occup. Med. Prev: Med. Off. RGIT Ltd. Aberd.

DICK, Gillian Martine 33 St Marys Road, Wimbledon Village, London SW19 7BP Tel: 020 8947 0880 Fax: 020 8944 5611 — MRCS Eng. LRCP Lond. 1977; MB BS Lond. 1977; MA Lond. 1970, BA 1969. (Guy's) Prev: Med. Off. Goldsmith Coll. Univ. Lond.; SHO Greenwich Dist. Hosp.; Ho. Off. Guy's Hosp. Lond.

DICK, Heather Elizabeth Ruth 11 Woodburn Terrace, Edinburgh EH10 4SJ — MB BCh BAO 1992 Belf.; MB BCh Belf. 1992; MRCGP 1996; DRCOG 1995.

DICK, Professor Heather May, CBE (retired) 4 West Park Gardens, Dundee DD2 1NY Tel: 01382 644663 Email: gm0irz@compuserve.com — MB ChB St. And. 1957; FRSE 1985; MD Dundee 1981; FRCP Glas. 1981 M 1978; FRCPath 1983, M 1974. Prev: Prof. Med. Microbiol. Dundee.

DICK, Henry Paul (retired) Allt Romain, Crossaig, Skipness, Tarbert PA29 6YQ Tel: 01880 760242 — MB BChir Camb. 1940; BA Camb. 1940; MRCS Eng. LRCP Lond. 1939.

DICK, James Allan (retired) 6 Woodthorpe Park Drive, Sandal, Wakefield WF2 6HZ Tel: 01924 250544 — MB ChB 1943 Ed.; FFOM RCP Lond. 1979. Cons. Occupat. Med. Wakefield. Prev: Dep. Dir. Med. Servs. Nat. Coal Bd.

DICK, Mr James Fairweather Danebridge Medical Centre, Northwich CW9 5HR Tel: 01606 3781; 8 Edisbury Hill Park, Delamere, Northwich CW8 2HY — MB BCh BAO 1925 Dub.; BA Dub. 1924, MB BCh BAO 1925; FRCS Ed. 1930. (T.C. Dub.) Prev: Surg. Vict. Infirm. N.wich; Res. Surg. Off. S. Devon & E. Cornw. Hosp. Plymouth; Surg. Specialist RAMC.

DICK, James Forrest (retired) 1 Tummel Place, Comrie, Crieff PH6 2PG — MB ChB 1949 Glas.; MFCMI 1979; DPH Glas. 1973; DTM & H Liverp. 1953. Prev: SCM Highland Health Bd.

DICK, Jeremy Peter Rose Manchester Sinosciences Unit, Hope Hospital, Stott Lane, Salford M6 8HD Tel: 0161 276 4312 Fax: 0161 291 3682; Beech House, Elm Grove, Alderley Edge SK9 7PD — MB BChir 1977 Camb.; PhD Lond. 1987; MA Camb. 1978; FRCP Lond. 1996; MRCP (UK) 1979. (King's Coll. Hosp.) Cons. Neurol. Withington & Wythenshaw Hosp., and Hope Hosp. Prev: Cons. Neurol. Roy. Lond. & Newham Gen. Hosp.

DICK, Mr John Alexander Kingston Hospital, Galsworthy Road, Kingston upon Thames KT2 7QB Tel: 020 8934 2737 Fax: 020 8934 3269 Email: johndick@kh-trsthames.nhs.uk; 33 St. Marys Road, Wimbledon, London SW19 7BP Tel: 020 8947 0880 Fax: 020 8944 5611 Email: john@johndick.net — MB BChir 1973 Camb.; MA Camb. 1973, BA 1970; FRCS Eng. 1978; FRCS Ed. 1977; MRCP (UK) 1977. (Guy's) Cons. Urol. Kingston Hosp. Socs: Brit. Assn. Urol. Surgs. Prev: Astley Cooper Stud. Guy's Hosp. Lond.; Lect. & Hon. Sen. Regist. (Renal Stone Surg.) Inst. Urol. Lond.; Sen. Regist. (Surg. & Urol.) Guy's Hosp. Lond.

DICK, John Bruce Cameron Princeland House, Blairgowrie Road, Coupar Angus, Blairgowrie PH13 9AU — MB ChB 1981 Ed.; BSc (Hons.) (Biochem.) Ed. 1976; MRCP (UK) 1985. Cons. & Hon. Sen. Lect. Dept. Med. Ninewells Hosp. & Med. Sch. Dundee.

DICK, John Robert Francis Flat 3, 27-19 St Johns Wood, High St., London NW8 7NH — MB ChB 1995 Manch.

DICK, Kathleen (retired) 5 Hawthorn Court, Abbey Meadows, Morpeth NE61 2LF Tel: 01670 512647 — MB BS 1934 Durh.; BHy DPH 1937. Prev: MOH No. 2 Area N.ld. CC.

DICK, Keith Douglas 72 High View, Wallsend NE28 8SS Tel: 0191 262 2439 — MB BS 1961 Durh.; DObst RCOG 1963. Med. Off. Gen. Counc. Brit. Shipping S. Shields. Prev: Ho. Phys. Qu. Eliz.

Hosp. Gateshead; Ho. Surg. (O & G) Bensham Gen. Hosp. Gateshead; SHO (Obst.) Preston Hosp. N. Shields.

DICK, Keith Sloan The Surgery, 2 Heathcote Street, Newcastle ST5 7EB Tel: 01782 561057 Fax: 01782 563907; 68 Sneyd Avenue, Newcastle ST5 2PY Tel: 01782 633414 — MB ChB 1968 Glas. Socs: BMA & Brit. Soc. Med. & Dent. Hypn. Prev: SHO (Surg.) Glas. Roy. Infirm.; Ho. Off. Vict. Infirm. Glas.; Ho. Off. Glas. Roy. Infirm.

DICK, Michael James William Saltoun Surgery, 46 Saltoun Place, Fraserburgh AB43 9RY Tel: 01346 514154 Fax: 01346 517680; Rivendell, Muir Road, Mensie, Fraserburgh AB43 7AQ Tel: 01346 541407 — MB ChB 1983 Aberd.; MRCOG 1991. Prev: Staff (O & G) Sir Thos. Roddick Hosp. Stephenville, Newfld., Canada; Regist. (O & G) Aberd. Teachg. Hosps.; SHO (Anaesth.) N. Staffs. Hosps. & N. Staffs. Matern. Hosp. Stoke-on-Trent.

DICK, Moira Christine 12 Spenser Road, London SE24 0NR Tel: 020 7733 2662 — MB BChir 1974 Camb.; MB 1975, BChir 1974; BA Camb. 1971; MRCP (UK) 1981; DCH Eng. 1976; FRCP 1995; FRCPCH 1997. (Camb. & Guy's) Cons. Paediat. Lambeth Healthcare NHS Trust; King's Healthcare. Prev: SCMO City & Hackney HA; Research Regist. (Paediat.) Ropy. Post. Grad. Med. Sch.; Regist. (Paediat.) Belgrave Hosp. Childr. & All St.s Hosp. Chatham.

DICK, Ninian Cameron 7 Morton Hall Park Avenue, Edinburgh EH17 8BP; (Surgery), 107 Ferry Road, Edinburgh EH6 4ET Tel: 0131 554 3209 — MB ChB 1944 Glas.; BSc Glas. 1942, MB ChB 1944. (Univ. Glas.)

DICK, Peter Hunter Carseview Centre, 4 Tom McDonald Avenue, Medi Park, Dundee DD2 1NH Tel: 01382 423000 Email: peter.dick@tpct.scot.nhs.uk — MB ChB 1969 Glas.; FRCPsych 1988, M 1973; DPM Ed. & Glas. 1972. (Glas.) Cons. Psychiat. Carseview Centre, Dundee.

DICK, Peter Reid Lour Road Group Practice, 3 Lour Road, Forfar DD8 2AS Tel: 01307 463122 Fax: 01307 465278; 1 Turfbeg Road, Forfar DD8 3LT — MB ChB 1985 Dundee; MRCGP 1990. (Dundee University)

DICK, Peter Thomas Holmes Ballymena Health Centre, Cushendall Road, Ballymena BT43 6HQ Tel: 028 2564 2181 Fax: 028 2565 8919 — MB BCh BAO 1969 Belf.

DICK, Robert 14 Holly Mount, Hampstead, London NW3 6SG Tel: 0207 431 9331 — MB BS 1961 Sydney; BA (OU) 1997; FRACR 1984; FRCR 1967. Sen. Consulatant (Radiol.) St John's & St Eliz.'s Hsopitals Lond..; Emerit. Consulatant Radiologist, Roy. Free Hosp., Lond.. Socs: RSM Brit. Inst. Radiol.

DICK, Robert (retired) Crosshill Cottage, Auchterarder PH3 1LN Tel: 01764 681478 — MB ChB Glas. 1945.

DICK, Sheila Mary 6 Woodthorpe Park Drive, Sandal, Wakefield WF2 6HZ Tel: 01924 50544 — LRCPI & LM, LRSCI & LM 1945; LRCPI & LM, LRCSI & LM 1945. (RCSI) Asst. Co. Med. Off. W. Riding CC. Socs: BMA. Prev: Ho. Off. E. Surrey Hosp. Redhill; Orthop. Ho. Surg. Pinderfields Hosp. Wakefield; Ho. Phys. Roy. Bath Hosp. Harrogate.

DICK, Thomas Sturrock Buttars (retired) 17 Marchmont Road, Richmond TW10 6HQ Tel: 020 8940 4705 — MB ChB 1937 St. And. Prev: Ho. Surg. & Ho. Phys. Crumpsall Hosp. Manch.

DICKENS, Anthony John Gilmore (retired) 9 Avon Way, Stoke Bishop, Bristol BS9 1SJ Tel: 0117 968 1278 Fax: 0117 968 3638 — MB ChB 1963 Bristol; FFPHM RCP (UK) 1994, M 1989; FRCPath 1990; MFCM 1988; DPH Bristol 1966. Prev: Adviser Life Sci. & Technol. Commiss. Europ. Communities Research, Directorate-Gen. Brussels.

DICKENS, Christopher Mark 40 Massie Street, Cheadle SK8 1BP — MB BS 1986 Lond.; MRCP (UK) 1990.

DICKENS, David Andrew 2 Shelton Circle, Bilton Heath, Shrewsbury SY3 5AD — MB BS 1990 Lond.

DICKENS, Diana Margaret (retired) 9 Avon Way, Stoke Bishop, Bristol BS9 1SJ Tel: 0117 968 1278 Fax: 0117 968 3638 — MB ChB 1961 Bristol; FRCPsych 1984, M 1974; DPM Eng. 1973; DCH Eng. 1964. Prev: Cons. Learning Disabil. Bassetlaw NHS Trust Worksop.

DICKENS, Donna 17 Junction Road, Stockton-on-Tees TS20 1PH — MB BS 1991 Newc.

DICKENS, Emmy Louise 109 Red Lion Lane, London SE18 4LF — MB BS 1998 Lond.; MB BS Lond 1998.

DICKENS, Gerald (retired) 1 Grange Park, Welcombe Grange, Stratford-upon-Avon CV37 6XH Tel: 01789 267240 — MRCS Eng. LRCP Lond. 1962; LMSSA Lond. 1960; DPM Eng. 1965; FRCPsych 1982, M 1971. Hon. Cons. (Psychother.) S. Birm. M.H.T. Prev: Postgrad. Clin. Tutor Gp. Psychother. Birm. Univ.

DICKENS, Gordon Barry, Squadron Ldr. RAF Med. Br. Retd. Rosehill Surgery, 189 Manchester Road, Burnley BB11 4HP Tel: 01282 428200 Fax: 01282 838492; Forest Bank, Forest Lane, Barrowford, Nelson BB9 6QL Tel: 01282 614603 — MB ChB 1974 Liverp.; FRCGP 1996, M 1978; MFFP 1993; DRCOG 1976. GP Trainer (Family Plann.) & Course Organiser Burnley VTS. Prev: Sen. Med. Off. RAF Chivenor Barnstaple; Sen. Med. Off. RAF AlderGr. N. Irel.; Clin. Asst. (Paediat.) St. Geo. Hosp. Lond.

DICKENS, Jo-Anne Chester Court Hotel, 30 Cleveland Road, Torquay TQ2 5BE Tel: 01803 294565 — MB BS 1989 Lond.; DCH RCP Lond. 1993. SHO (Palliat. Care) Rowcroft Hospice Torquay. Prev: Trainee GP Totnes; SHO (Paediat.) Freedom Fields Hosp. Plymouth; SHO (O & G) Torbay Hosp. Devon.

DICKENS, Justin James 321 Ombersley Road, Worcester WR3 7BY Tel: 01905 453691 — MB ChB 1994 Birm. SHO (Anaesth.) Rotat. Worthing & Chichester.

DICKENS, Leonard Anthony Pall Mall Surgery, 178 Pall Mall, Leigh-on-Sea SS9 1RB Tel: 01702 478338 Fax: 01702 471294; 11 Parkside, Westcliff on Sea SS0 8PR — MB BS 1979 Lond.; DRCOG 1981.

DICKENS, Peter Robert Green Street Clinic, 118-122 Green Street, Eastbourne BN21 1RT Tel: 01323 722908 Fax: 01323 723136 — MB BCh 1982 Wales; MRCGP 1986. (University Hospital of Wales Cardiff) Med. Adviser to Ericsson UK. Prev: GP Hove.

DICKENSON, Mr Andrew John 195 Mansfield Road, Papplewick, Nottingham NG15 8FL — MB BS 1996 Newc. Specialist Regist. Oral-Maxillo-Facial. Surg. Trent Region.

DICKENSON, John Edward Woodlands, Maidstone Road, Warmlake, Sutton Valence, Maidstone ME17 3LR — MB BCh BAO 1974 Belf.; FFA RCS Eng. 1979. Cons. Anaesth. S.E. Thames RHA.

DICKER, Andrew Pearce The Cambridge Street Surgery, 93 Cambridge Street, London SW1V 4PY Tel: 020 7834 5502 Fax: 020 7834 2350 — MB BS 1978 Lond.; MSc (Gen. Pract.) Lond. 1994; BSc (Physiol.) Lond. 1973; LMSSA Lond. 1977; Dip. Addic. Behaviour Lond. 1992; MA (Ethics & Med. Law) Lond. 1997. (St. Thos.) Hon. Sen. Clin. Lect. Imperial Coll. Lond.; Liveryman Worshipful Soc. Apoth. Lond. Socs: Roy. Soc. Med.; Balint Soc.

DICKER, Brian John The Surgery, 65 Holloway, Northfield, Birmingham B31 1TR Tel: 0121 475 1422; 29 Selwyn Road, Edgbaston, Birmingham B16 0SJ Tel: 0121 455 0932 — MB BS 1974 Lond.; MA Camb. 1962. (St. Mary's) Prev: SHO (Paediat.) Good Hope Hosp. Sutton Coldfield; Med. Off. Donald Fraser Miss. Hosp. Sibasa, S. Africa; SHO Sorrento Matern. Hosp. Birm.

DICKERSON, Helen Elizabeth 133 Marlborough Crescent, Sevenoaks TN13 2HN — MB ChB 1998 Bristol.

DICKERSON, Robert Peter George, OStJ (retired) 75 Geffers Ride, Ascot SL5 7JZ — MB BS 1949 Lond.; MRCS Eng. LRCP Lond. 1949; MFOM RCP Lond. 1979. Prev: Chief Med. Off. Brit. Railways Bd.

DICKEY, John Michael (retired) Dove Cottage, Outwoods Lane, Anslow, Burton-on-Trent DE13 0AB Tel: 01283 815187 — MB ChB 1956 Manch. Prev: GP Burton-on-Trent.

DICKEY, William Altnagelvin Hospital, Londonderry BT47 6SB Tel: 02871 345171 Fax: 028 7161 1331 — MB BCh BAO 1983 Belf.; FRCPI 2001; BSc (Hons.) Belf. 1980, MD 1990; FRCP 1999 Edin.; FRCP 1999 Lond.; PhD 2000 Amsterdam; FACG 1999. Cons. Gastroenterol. Altnagelvin Hosp. Lond.derry; Hon. Clin. Lect., Qu.s's Univ. of Belf. Socs: Amer. Coll. Gastroenterol.; Irish Soc. of Gastroenterol. Prev: Sen. Regist. (Gastroenterol. & Gen. Med.) Antrim Hosp.; Sen. Regist. Tutor (Gastroenterol.) Qu. Univ. Belf.; Fell. (Endoscopy) Acad. Med. Center, Amsterdam.

DICKIE, Albert Wallace (retired) Shambley Green, 81 Mullahead Road, Tandragee, Craigavon BT62 2LB Tel: 028 3884 0577 — MB BCh BAO Belf. 1945; MD Belf. 1948; FRCP Glas. 1977 M 1967; DCH Eng. 1948. Prev: Cons. Phys. (Geriat.) S.. Health & Social Servs. Bd.

DICKIE, Andrew Hutton (retired) 28 Norton Grange, Lindsay Road, Branksome Park, Poole BH13 0BD — MB ChB 1932 Glas.

DICKIE, Andrew Robert The Orchard Medical Centre, Heath Road, Coxheath, Maidstone ME17 4PL Tel: 01622 744994 Fax: 01622 741162; Poundlands House, Frittenden, Cranbrook TN17 2EP Tel: 01580 852271 Email: poundlands@aol.com — MB ChB 1981 Manch.; MRCGP 1988; DRCOG 1988; DCH RCP Lond. 1987.

DICKIE, Anne Mackay Taynish, 11 Churchill Drive, Stornoway HS1 2NP Tel: 01851 705001 — MB ChB 1979 Aberd. Prev: SHO Aberd. Roy. Infirm.; Ho. Off. City Hosp. Aberd. & Roy. Aberd. Childr. Hosp.

DICKIE, Colin Henry Health Centre, Gordon Road, London N11 2PA — MB ChB 1967 Liverp. (Liverp.)

DICKIE, Ian Wallace Gorton Road Family Surgery, 306 Gorton Road, Reddish, Stockport SK5 6RN Tel: 0161 432 1235 Fax: 0161 442 2495; 43 South Parade, Bramhall, Stockport SK7 3BJ Tel: 0161 440 9010 — MB ChB 1981 Manch.; DRCOG 1984.

DICKIE, Robert Edward (retired) St. Oswalds Surgery, The Parade, Pembroke SA71 4LD Tel: 01646 682374 — MB ChB 1951 Glas.; DIH Dund 1971. Med. Off. S. Pembs. Hosp.; Med. Off. Texaco Oil Refinery Pembroke & Pembroke Power Sta. Prev: Ho. Phys. & Ho. Surg. Harrogate & Dist. Gen. Hosp.

DICKIE, Robert John The Group Practice, Health Centre, Springfield Road, Stornoway HS1 2PS Tel: 01851 703145 Fax: 01851 706138 — MB ChB 1978 Aberd.; Dip Pract Derm 2001; BMedBiol (Hons.) Aberd. 1975; FRCGP 1996, M 1985; DRCOG 1984. (Aberd.) Gen. Practitioner, The Pract. Gp., Stornoway; Assoc. Adviser (Gen. Pract.) W.. Is.; Hosp. Practitioner (Dermat.), W.. isles Hosp., Stornoway; Hon. Clin. Sen. Lect. (Gen. Pract.), Univ. of Aberd. Socs: BMA (Hon. Sec. & Treas. W.. Is. Div.); Mem. Assn. Police Surgs.; Fell. of RCGP (N. of Scotl. Fac. Represen. on UK Counc.). Prev: Lect. (Path.) Aberd. Univ. Med. Sch.; Trainee GP/SHO Aberd. VTS; Ho. Off. Woodend Gen. Hosp. Aberd. & W.. Infirm. Glas.

DICKIE, Susan Jacqueline Highgate Group Practice, 44 North Hill, London N6 4QA Tel: 020 8340 6628 Fax: 020 8342 8428 — MB BS 1991 Lond.; BA Oxf. 1988; MRCP (UK) 1995; MRCGP 1995; DCH RCP Lond. 1994; DRCOG 1993. Trainee (Primary Care) Univ. Coll. Lond. Acad. Scheme.

DICKIN, Paul Douglas 12 Saltwood Gardens, Cliftonville, Margate CT9 3HQ — MB ChB 1987 Sheff. SHO (Spinal Injuries) Odstock Hosp. Salisbury.

DICKINS, Philippa Jane Nicola Quarter Jack Surgery, Rodways Corner, Wimborne BH21 1AP Tel: 01202 882112 Fax: 01202 882368 — MB BS 1979 Lond.; MA Oxf. 1979; MRCGP 1987; DRCOG 1985; DCH RCP Lond. 1984. (Univ. Oxf.)

DICKINSON, Alan Michael (retired) 37 Brompton Square, London SW3 2AF Tel: 020 7589 2274 — MRCS Eng. LRCP Lond. 1947. Exam. Phys. Barclays Bank Internat. Ltd., Standard Chartered Bank Ltd., Sir Wm. Halcrow & Partners & other Cos.

DICKINSON, Alison Jane Royal Victoria Infirmary, Queen Victoria Road, Newcastle upon Tyne NE1 4LP; 182 Jesmond Dene Road, Jesmond, Newcastle upon Tyne NE2 2NL Tel: 0191 212 0664 — MB ChB 1981 Aberd.; FRCS (Ophth) Eng. 1988; MRCP (UK) 1985; FRCOphth 1989. Cons. Ophth. Roy. Vict. Infirm. Newc.; Hon. Lect. Univ. Newc. Prev: Sen. Fell. (Oculoplastic Surg.) Qu. Med. Centre Nottm.

DICKINSON, Alwyn Guy Wethered Royal Crescent and Preston Road Practice, 25 Crescent Street, Weymouth DT4 7BY Tel: 01305 774466 Fax: 01305 760538; 1 Beech Road, Broadwey, Weymouth DT3 5NP Tel: 01305 813508 — MB BS 1978 Lond.; BSc (Hons.) Reading 1971; MRCP (UK) 1981. (Char. Cross) Prev: SHO Guy's Hosp. Lond.; SHO W. Middlx. Hosp. Lond.; Ho. Phys. Char. Cross Hosp. Lond.

DICKINSON, Barbara Margaret 5 Links Way, Flackwell Heath, High Wycombe HP10 9LZ Tel: 01628 527617 — MB ChB 1970 Manch; MB ChB Manch. 1970; DO Eng. 1972. (Manch) Clin. Asst. (Ophth.) Roy. Berks. Hosp. Reading. Socs: Roy. Coll. Ophth. Prev: Clin. Asst. (Ophth.) Sunderland Eye Infirm.; Regist. (Ophth.) Wolverhampton & Midl. Cos. Eye Infirm.; Ho. Surg. Manor Hosp. Walsall.

DICKINSON, Beverley Jane 18 Barton Drive, Solihull B93 0PE — MB ChB 1992 Birm.; PHEC 2000; MRCGP 1996; DRCOG 1994; DFFP 1995. (Birmin.)

DICKINSON, Caroline Margaret Caversham Practice, 4 Peckwater Street, London NW5 2UP Tel: 020 7530 6500 Fax: 020 7530 6530; 31 Courthope Road, London NW3 2LE — MB BS 1981 Lond.; MRCGP 1986. Coure Organizer, Whittington Hosp. VTS Scheme.

DICKINSON, Catherine Jane 22 The Moorlands, Shadwell Lane, Leeds LS17 8AB — BM BCh 1987 Oxf.

DICKINSON, Professor Christopher John Wolfson Institute of Preventive Medicine, St. Bart. & Royal London School Med. & Dentistry, Charterhouse Square, London EC1M 6BQ Tel: 020 7882 6219 Fax: 020 7882 6270 Email: c.j.dickinson@qmul.ac.uk; Griffin Cottage, 57 Belsize Lane, London NW3 5AU Tel: 020 7431 1845 — BM BCh Oxf. 1952; MA Oxf. 1960, BA 1948, MSc 1950, DM 1960; FRCP Lond. 1968, M 1955. (Oxf. & Univ. Coll. Hosp.) Vis. Prof. Wolfson Inst. Preven. Med. Qu. Mary, Univ. Lond.; Emerit. Prof. Med. St. Bart. Hosp. Med. Coll. Lond. Socs: (Ex-Chairm.) Med. Research Soc.; Hon. Mem. (Ex-Sec.) Europ. Soc. Clin. Invest.; Former Mem. Med. Research Counc. Prev: Cons. Phys. Univ. Coll. Hosp. & Sen. Lect. Univ. Coll. Hosp. Med. Sch.; R. Samuel McLaughlin Vis. Prof. Med. McMaster Univ., Canada; Rockefeller Trav. Fell. (Med.) Cleveland Clinic, USA.

DICKINSON, David Frederick Yorkshire Heart Centre, Leeds General Infirmary, Great George St., Leeds LS1 3EX Tel: 0113 243 2799 Fax: 0113 392 8212 Email: dfdickinson@cwcom.net; 306 High Street, Boston Spa, Wetherby LS23 6AJ — MB ChB Manch. 1968; FRCP Lond. 1990; MRCP (UK) 1975; DCH Eng. 1970; FRCPCH. (Manch.) Cons. Paediat. Cardiol. Leeds Gen. Infirm. Prev: Sen. Regist. (Paediat. Cardiol.) Liverp. AHA; Tutor (Child Health) Manch. Univ.; Fell. (Paediat. Cardiol.) Hosp. Sick Childr. Toronto.

DICKINSON, Edward Justin 53 Addison Gardens, London W14 0DP Tel: 020 7603 2517 Fax: 020 7603 2565 Email: ejdickinson@hotmail.com — MB BChir 1981 Camb.; MBA Lond. 1995; MA Camb. 1981; FRCP Lond. 1995; MRCP (UK) 1984. (Camb. & St. Thos.) Prev: Acting Director Research Unit Roy. Coll. of Phys.s, Lond.; Sen. Clin. Research Fell. Roy. Coll. Phys. Lond.; Sen. Lect. Lond. Hosp. Med. Coll.

DICKINSON, Elsie Bain (retired) 16 Olive Grove, Blackpool FY3 9AS — MB ChB 1923 Glas.; DPH Ed. & Glas. 1925. Prev: Asst. Sch. Med. Off. Co. Boro. Blackpool.

DICKINSON, Fiona Louise 12A Clarendon Park Road, Clarendon Park, Leicester LE2 3AD — MB ChB 1990 Birm.; ChB Birm. 1990; MRCP Lond. 1993; FRCR 1997. Regist. (Radiol.) Leicester Roy. Infirm. Socs: Roy. Soc. Radiol. Prev: SHO (Paediat.) Birm. Childr. Hosp.; SHO Rotat. (Med.) Russells Hall Hosp. Dudley.

DICKINSON, Gary 14 Windlestone Drive, Park End, Middlesbrough TS3 0BQ Tel: 01642 319745 — BM BCh 1986 Oxf.; BA (Hons.) Oxf. 1983; FRCA 1995. Specialist Regist. (Anaesth.) Wessex Region.

DICKINSON, Gaye Melanie (Higham) Brockwell Medical Group, Northumbrian Road, Cramlington NE23 9XZ Tel: 01670 392700, 01670 392701 — MB BS 1984 Newc.; MB BS Newc. l984; MRCGP 1988; DRCOG 1988. p/t Salaried GP; Hosp.Practitioner Menopause Clinic Musculoskeletal Unit Freeman Hosp. Newc. u. Tyne.

DICKINSON, Geoffrey H Joseph (retired) Finney Farm, Kingswood, Frodsham, Warrington WA6 6JP — MB BChir 1950 Camb.; MA Camb. 1967, BA 1946, MB BChir 1950; MRCGP 1970; Cert. Av. Med. 1978. Prev: GP Warrington.

DICKINSON, George David (retired) — MB ChB 1966 St. And.

DICKINSON, Gerard Herne Hill Group Practice, 74 Herne Hill, London SE24 9QP Tel: 020 7274 3314 Fax: 020 7738 6025; Churchside, 125 Herne Hill, London SE24 9LY Tel: 020 7274 2617 Email: gerard@herne-hill.demon.co.uk — MB 1973 Camb.; MB BChir Camb. 1973; MA Camb. 1980, BA 1969; MRCGP 1980; DRCOG 1978; DA Eng. 1975. (Camb. & St. Thos.) Socs: BMA; RCGP. Prev: Trainee GP St. Thos. Hosp. VTS; Specialist Anaesth. State of Brunei, N. Borneo.

DICKINSON, Harry Andrew Fair Mile Hospital, Wallingford OX10 9HH Tel: 01491 651281; 12 Henwood, Boars Hill, Oxford OX1 5JX Tel: 01865 862177 — MB ChB 1970 St. And.; MRCPsych 1974; FRCPsych 1999. (St. And.) p/t Cons. Psychiat. Fair Mile Hosp. Wallingford. Prev: Sen. Regist. Warneford Hosp. Oxf.; Clin. Asst. Littlemore Hosp. Oxf.

DICKINSON, Mr Ian Keith Darent Valley Hospital, Darenth Wood Road, Dartford DA2 8DA Tel: 01322 428100 Fax: 01322 428654 Email: ian.dickinson@dag-tr.sthames.nhs.uk; Orchard House, The St,

Horton Kirby, Dartford DA1 5PL Email: ikdickinson@tinyworld.co.uk — MB BS 1977 Lond.; FRCS Ed. 1983. (St. Mary's) p/t Cons. Urol. Joyce Green Hosp. Dartford. & Androlgist Dept. of Urol. Darent Valley Hosp. Dartford. Prev: Sen. Regist. (Urol.) St. Peter's Gp. Hosps. Lond.; Regist. (Urol.) King's Coll. Hosp. Lond.; Lect. (Androl.) Inst. Urol. Lond.

DICKINSON, Jean Margaret Euphemie (retired) 51 Queens Court, Queens Road, Richmond TW10 6LB Tel: 020 8948 7551 — LRCPI & LM, LRSCI & LM 1950; LRCPI & LM, LRCSI & LM 1950; MRCPI 1973.

DICKINSON, Jennie Elizabeth Neston Medical Centre, 14-20 Liverpool Road, Neston, South Wirral CH64 3RA Tel: 0151 336 4121 Fax: 0151 353 0151 — MB ChB 1986 Liverp.

DICKINSON, John Alexander Central Surgery, King St., Barton-upon-Humber DN18 5ED Tel: 01652 632573 Fax: 01652 636122; New Hall, Newport St, Barton-upon-Humber DN18 5QJ Tel: 01625 632010 — MB BS 1963 Lond.; MRCS Eng. LRCP Lond. 1963; FRCGP 1996, M 1972; DObst RCOG 1965. (Guys)

DICKINSON, Mr John Charles Wexham Park Hospital, Wexham St., Slough SL2 4HL Tel: 01753 633000; Oak Knoll, 5 Furzefield Road, Beaconsfield HP9 1PQ Tel: 01494 676117 Fax: 01494 681021 — MB BS 1976 Newc.; FRCS Ed. 1981. Cons. Plastic Surg. Wexham Pk. Hosp. Slough. Prev: Cons. Plastic Surg. Stoke Mandeville Hosp. Aylesbury.

DICKINSON, John Graham, Col. L/RAMC United Mission to Nepal, PO box126, Kathmandu, Nepal; 7, Alvercliffe Drive, Alverstone, Gosport PO12 2NB — BM BCh 1965 Oxf.; DM Oxf. 1982; FRCP Lond. 1980, M 1968; T(M) 1991; DTM & H Liverp. 1974. (Oxf.) Dir HIV & TB program. Socs: Fell. Roy. Soc. Trop. Med. & Hyg. Prev: Med. Supt. & Phys. Patan Hosp. Kathmandu, Nepal; Prof. Clin. Physiol. Inst. Med. Tribhuwan Univ. Kathmandu, Nepal; Phys. Shanta Bhawan Hosp. Kathmandu, Nepal.

DICKINSON, John Robert Edward Swincar House, Walkers Row, Yeadon, Leeds LS19 7ES — BM 1998 Soton.

DICKINSON, Joy Priscilla Georg-Cantor Strasse 29, Halle D-06108, Germany Tel: 01684 299017 Email: ukor@bigfoot.com — MB BCh 1992 Wales; MRCPath 1999 (Haematology); MRCP 1996. Socs: Brit. Soc. Haematol.

DICKINSON, Katherine Anne Orchard House, The Street, Horton Kirby, Dartford DA4 9BY Tel: 01322 868596 Fax: 01322 868596 Email: ikdickinson@yahoo.com — MB BS 1984 Lond. Assoc. Specialist Community Paediat. Prev: Community Med. Off. Dartford; CommunityMed. Off. Fleet, Hants.; Trainee GP Fleet VTS.

DICKINSON, Kenneth Gordon (retired) 60 Hyde Lane, Kinver, Stourbridge DY7 6AF Tel: 01384 873434 — MB ChB 1951 Birm.; AFOM RCP Lond. 1981; FRCGP 1970; DIH Eng. 1981; DPM Eng. 1966; DObst RCOG 1956. Prev: GP Handsworth Birm.

DICKINSON, Mr Kenneth Montague (retired) Rob Ridding, Kaber, Kirkby Stephen CA17 4ER Tel: 017683 41473 Fax: 017683 41473 — MB ChB 1954 Manch.; FRCS Eng. 1960. Prev: Cons. Surg. Blackpool Health Dist.

DICKINSON, Lewis Kakad and Dickinson, 90 Wyndham Road, London SE5 0UD Tel: 020 7703 2046; 63 Pages Walk, London SE1 4HD — MB ChB 1979 Dundee.

DICKINSON, Linda Mary Syston Health Centre, Melton Road, Syston, Leicester LE7 2EQ Tel: 0116 260 9161 — MB ChB 1991 Leeds; MRCGP 1995. (Leeds) p/t GP, Syston Health Centre,Melton Rd., Syston; Clin. Asst., Dermat. Leicester Roy. Infirm., Leicester.

DICKINSON, Lisa 15 Wingate Drive, Cardiff CF14 5LR Tel: 029 2076 3104 — MB BCh 1993 Wales; BSc (Hons.) Anat. Sci. Bristol 1990. SHO (Surg.) Townsville Gen. Hosp. Qu.sland, Austral. Prev: SHO (A & E) Cardiff Roy. Infirm.; SHO (O & G) Singleton Hosp. Swansea; Ho. Off. (Gen. Surg.) P. Chas. Hosp. Merthyr Tydfil.

***DICKINSON, Lucy Jane** Medical Residence, Aberdeen Royal Infirmary, Aberdeen AB25 2ZN Tel: 01224 681818 — MB ChB 1998 Aberd.; MB ChB Aberd 1998.

DICKINSON, Mark Alexander James Danebridge Medical Centre, 29 London Road, Northwich CW9 5HR Tel: 01606 45786 Fax: 01606 331977 — MB ChB 1988 Manch.; BSc Manch. 1985, MB ChB 1988.

DICKINSON, Mark John St Anns Hospital, St Anns Road, Haringey, London N15 3TH Tel: 020 8442 6111 — MB BS 1981 Lond.; BSc Lond. 1977, MB BS 1981; MRCPsych 1986. Prev: Sen. Regist. (Ment. Handicap) Cell Barns Hosp. St. Albans.

DICKINSON, Matthew Charles 10 Longfields, Marden Ash, Ongar CM5 9BZ — MB BS 1998 Lond.; MB BS Lond 1998; BSc 1995. (St Barts)

DICKINSON, Nicola Ann (retired) 24 Grange Road, Abbotskerswell, Newton Abbot TQ12 5PJ — MB BS 1958 Lond.

DICKINSON, Paul Stanley Mossley House, Mossley Hill Hospital, Park Avenue, Liverpool L18 8BU Tel: 0151 250 6128 Fax: 0151 729 0457 — MB ChB 1976 Liverp.; MRCPsych. 1981. Hon. Clin. Lect. Univ. Liverp. Prev: Cons. Psychol. Med. Liverp. HA.

DICKINSON, Mr Peter Henry, MBE (retired) Leazes Cottage, Leazes Lane, Corbridge NE45 5QE Tel: 01434 632215 — MB BS 1945 Durh.; MB BS (Hons.) Durh. 1945; MSc Illinois 1955; FRCS Ed. 1983; FRCS Eng. 1951. Hon. Cons. Surg. Roy. Vict. Infirm. Newc. u. Tyne; Hon. Lect. (Clin. Surg.) Univ. Newc. Prev: Ho. Phys. & Ho. Surg. Roy. Vict. Infirm. Newc.

DICKINSON, Mr Peter John (retired) Norfolks, 29 Callis Street, Clare, Sudbury CO10 8PX Fax: 01787 278738, 01787 278738 — MB BS 1965 Lond.; MRCS Eng. LRCP Lond. 1964; FRCS Ed. 1973. Prev: Othopaedic Surrgeon, Private Pract., Hong Kong.

DICKINSON, Rashmi 53 Addison Gardens, London W14 0DP — MB BS 1979 Delhi; MFPM 1992. Manager Med. & Scientif. Affairs Merck, Sharpe & Dohme. Socs: BMA & Brit. Assn. Pharmaceut. Phys. Prev: Head Cardiovasc. Clin. Research Rhône Poulenc Rorer Dagenham; Cardiovasc. Med. Advisor Beecham Pharmaceut.; Clin. Asst. Whittington Hosp. Lond.

DICKINSON, Richard John Hinchingbrooke Hospital, Hinchingbrooke Park, Huntingdon PE29 6NT Tel: 01480 416367, 01480 416561; (resid.) Church Farm House, Comberton, Cambridge CB3 7EB Tel: 01223 262176 — MD 1983 Lond.; FRCP Lond. 1993; MRCP (UK) 1975. (St. Thos.) Cons. Phys. Huntingdon HA. Socs: Brit. Soc. Gastroenterol. Prev: Hon. Sen. Regist. Addenbrooke's Hosp. Camb.; Regist. (Med.) Gen. Infirm. Leeds.

DICKINSON, Timothy Robin Torbay Hospital, Torquay TQ2 7AA — MB ChB 1990 Sheff.; MRCPsych 1998; MRCGP 1995. Cons. Psych. , Torbay Hosp. Prev: GP/Regist. ScarBoro. VTS; Regist. Rotat. (Psychiat.) Oxf. Region Train Scheme.

DICKINSON, Winefride Mary 59 Claremont Avenue, West Denton, Newcastle upon Tyne NE15 7LE — MB ChB 1976 Birm.; DA Eng. 1979.

DICKS, Andrew Gordon 21 Sandalwood Drive, Gloucester GL2 5XD — BM BS 1991 Nottm.

DICKS, Julia Rachel 131 Rustlings Road, Sheffield S11 7AB — MB ChB 1995 Sheff.

DICKSON, Mr Alan Peden Booth Hall Children's Hospital, Charlestown Road, Blackley, Manchester M9 7AA Tel: 0161 220 5194 Fax: 0161 220 5609 — MB ChB 1977 Ed.; FRCS Ed. 1982. Cons. Paediat. Surg. Manch. Childr. Hosp. Socs: Brit. Assn. Paediat. Surg.; Brit. Assn. Urol. Surg.; BMA. Prev: Sen. Regist. (Paediat. Surg.) Roy. Hosp. Sick Childr. Edin.

DICKSON, Alan Robert Ardgowan Medical Practice, 2 Finnart Street, Greenock PA16 8HN Tel: 01475 888155 Fax: 01475 785060; 3 Overton Grove, Kilmacolm PA13 4DR Tel: 01505 874839 — MB ChB 1985 Glas.; MRCGP 1989; DRCOG 1988. (Glasgow) GP Partner. Prev: Trainee GP/SHO (Geriat.) Roy. Alexandra Hosp. Paisley VTS.

DICKSON, Alexander Lairg Health Centre, Main Street, Lairg IV27 4DD Tel: 01549 402007 Fax: 01549 402511 Email: alexander.dickson@gp55249.highland-hb.scot.nhs.uk; Muirlands, Lairg IV27 4ED — MB ChB 1969 Aberd.; DObst RCOG 1971. Socs: BMA. Prev: Ho. Phys. (Gen. Med.) Larkfield Hosp. Greenock; Ho. Off. (Obst.) Mat. Hosp. Brighton; Ho. Off. (Paediat.) Roy. Aberd. Childr. Hosp.

DICKSON, Brigadier Alexander Souter Barclay, TD, Brigadier late RAMC Retd. (retired) Port Nan Each, Shore Road, Cove, Helensburgh G84 0NX Tel: 01436 842848 Fax: 01436 842848 — MB ChB Glas. 1959. Prev: Cdr. HQ RaMS (TA) Keohg Barracks, Aldershot.

DICKSON, Alison Isobel Levenshulme Health Centre, Dunstable Street, Manchester M19 3BX Tel: 0161 225 4033 Fax: 0161 248 8020 — MB ChB 1990 Manch.; MRCGP 1997; DRCOG 1992. Socs: BMA.

DICKSON, Andrew Frederick Lambart Wanless Medical Services Overseas, Snow's Medical Building, Slad, Stroud GL6 7QE; Snow's Farm, Slad, Stroud GL6 7QE Tel: 01452 812043 — MB BS

1978 Lond.; AFOM RCP Lond. 1993; MRCGP 1986; DCH RCP Lond. 1986; DRCOG 1983; DA Eng. 1983; Cert. Family Plann. JCC 1983; DTM & H Liverp. 1980. (Westm.) Dir. of Med. Servs. Overseas Ltd.; GP (non Princip.); NHS Occupat. Phys. Newham, Lond. Socs: Soc. Occupat. Med.; Internat. Soc. Travel Med. Prev: Med. Off. Shell Internat.; Med. Off. Hunt Oil; Med. Off. AEA/SOS.

DICKSON, Arabel Alice 7 Montpelier Park, Edinburgh EH10 4LU — MB BS 1974 Bombay.

DICKSON, Catherine Jane 22 Primrosehill Road, Cults, Aberdeen AB15 9ND — MB ChB 1988 Dundee.

DICKSON, Christopher John Clayton Cottage, Sharoe Green Lane, Fulwood, Preston PR2 8EJ — MB BS 1983 Lond.

DICKSON, Christopher William The Castle Medical Centre, 22 Bertie Road, Kenilworth CV8 1JP Tel: 01926 857331 Fax: 01926 851070; 54 Malthouse Lane, Kenilworth CV8 1AD — MB ChB 1962 Birm.; DObst RCOG 1965. (Birm.)

DICKSON, David Edward The Surgery, 12 Wetmore Road, Burton-on-Trent DE14 1SL Tel: 01283 564848 Fax: 01283 569416 — MB BS 1978 Lond.; MRCS Eng. LRCP Lond. 1977; FRCGP 1996, M 1982; DFFP 1993; DRCOG 1979. (Guy's) Sec. S. Staffs. LMC. Socs: BMA. Prev: Trainee GP Medway VTS; Ho. Phys. & Ho. Surg. St. Bart. Hosp. Rochester.

DICKSON, David John Rheumatology Unit South Cleveland Hospital, Marton Road, Middlesbrough TS4 3BN Tel: 01642 854754 Fax: 01642 954661; The Warrens, Yafforth, Northallerton DL7 0LT Tel: 01609 772817 Fax: 01609 772817 Email: johndicksonpctsol@btinternet.com — MB ChB 1969 St. And.; FRCP Glas. 1990; MRCP (UK) 1977; MRCGP 1979; DA Eng. 1972; DObst RCOG 1971; FRCP 1999. Tutor & Examr. (Primary Care Rheum. Dipl.) Univ. Bath; Hosp. Pract. (Rheum.) S. Cleveland Hosp.; Business Manager Primary Care Rheum. Soc. Socs: Brit. Soc. Rheum.; Primary Care Rheum. Soc. Prev: Regist. (Gen. Med.) York City Hosp.; Amer. Heart Assn. Fell. (Cardiol.) Youngstown Hosp. Assoc., USA.

DICKSON, David Munroe Anaesthetic Department, Royal Bournemouth Hospital, Castle Lane E., Bournemouth BH7 7DW Tel: 01202 303626 — MB BS 1977 Lond.; FFA RCS 1981. Cons. Anaesth. Roy. Bournemouth Hosp.

DICKSON, Derek 92 Barnton Place, Glenrothes KY6 2PT — MB ChB 1992 Ed.

DICKSON, Derek Gordon 18 Rectory Lane, Byfleet, Weybridge Tel: 0193 23 43363 — MB BChir 1951 Camb. (St. Thos.) Prev: Ophth. Ho. Surg. St. Thos. Hosp. Lond.; Ho. Phys. St. Stephen's Hosp. Fulham; Obst. Ho. Surg. Lambeth Hosp. Lond.

DICKSON, Diana Elizabeth Leeds Teaching Hospital, Pain management Sevice, Chapel Allerton, Leeds Tel: 0113 292 4682; Manor Farm House, Tockwith Road, Long Marston, york YO26 7PJ Tel: 01904 738227 Email: dianadickson@aol.com — MB ChB 1967 Leeds; FFA RCS Eng. 1972. (Leeds) Cons. Anaesth. Leeds Teach. Hosps. Trust; Hon. Sen. Clin. Lect. Univ. Leeds. Socs: Assn. Anaesth Counc. Mem; Internat. Assn. Study of Pain; Chairm. Neuromodulation s/i Gp. Pain soc. Prev: Cons. Anaesth. Birch Hill Hosp. Rochdale; Lect. (Anaesth.) Univ. Leeds; Instruct. (Anaesth.) Harvard Med. Sch.

DICKSON, Dugald McDonald (retired) Redlands, 48 Bristol Road, Frenchay, Bristol BS16 1LQ Tel: 0117 956 6066 — MB ChB 1946 Aberd. Prev: GP BRistol.

DICKSON, Elizabeth Jane The Fairfield Centre, Fairfield Grove, Charlton, London SE7 8TX Tel: 020 8858 5738 Fax: 020 8305 3005 — MB BChir 1991 Camb.

DICKSON, Elizabeth Margaret Ann The Linhay, Slymeford Farm, Bere Alston, Yelverton PL20 7HW Tel: 01822 840807 — MB ChB St. And. 1964. (St. Andrew University Dundee) Locum in Gen. Pract. Socs: Assoc. Mem. Fac. Homoeop; Assoc. Mem. Brit. Med. Acupunc. Soc.; Primary Care Rheum. Soc. Prev: Partner in Gen. Pract. Wharfside Surg., Tavistock, Devon.

DICKSON, Emma Mary 7 Lygon Road, Edinburgh EH16 5QD — MB ChB 1995 Ed.

DICKSON, Euan John 28 Wellesley Road, East Kilbride, Glasgow G75 8TR — MB ChB 1995 Glas.

DICKSON, Fraser Guy 34 Compton Way, Olivers Battery, Winchester SO22 4HW — MB ChB 1987 Manch.

DICKSON, Garry Tel: 0141 959 2118 Fax: 0141 959 9851 — MB ChB 1981 Glas.

DICKSON, Mr George Haines Worthing Hospital, Worthing BN11 2DH Tel: 01903 205111; Skyring, 106 Warren Road, Worthing BN14 9QX Tel: 01903 265333 Fax: 01903 265333 — MB BS 1959 Lond.; MS Lond. 1971; FRCS Eng. 1964; FRCS Ed. 1964; MRCS Eng. LRCP Lond. 1959. (St. Mary's) Cons. Surg. Worthing & S.lands Hosp. Gp.; Tutor (Surg.) RCS Eng.; Head Clinician Cancer Unit. Socs: Assn. Surg.; Brit. Assn. Surg. Oncol. (Ex. Nat. Comm.); Assn. Upper G.I. Surg. Prev: Sen. Regist. (Surg.) St. Mary's Hosp. Lond.

DICKSON, Gillian Christine Bonnyrigg Health Centre, High Street, Bonnyrigg EH19 2DA Tel: 0131 536 8989 Fax: 0131 536 8909 — MB ChB 1977 Ed.; MRCGP 1981; DRCOG 1980. Gen. Practitioner; Managem./Lead GP for Ment. Health Progr. Midlothian Health Care CoOperat.

***DICKSON, Graeme Noel** 19 Abbotshall Road, Kirkcaldy KY2 5PH — MB BS 1994 Lond.; BSc (Hons.) Biomed. Sci. Lond. 1991.

DICKSON, Harriet Anne 95 Bullingdon Road, Oxford OX4 1QL — BM BCh 1988 Oxf.; MRCP (UK) 1991; DRCOG 1995; MRCGP 1996. (Oxford) GP Non-Princip., Oxf.

DICKSON, Mr James Alexander Scott (retired) 86 School Green Lane, Sheffield S10 4GR Tel: 0114 230 6049 Email: j.a.s.dickson@sheffield.ac.uk — MB ChB 1953 Glas.; FRCS Eng. 1961; FRCS Ed. 1960; FRCPCH 1997. Prev: Cons. Paediat. Surg. Childr. Hosp. Sheff.

DICKSON, James Dewar Thornbeck, 17 Mansion House Road, Paisley PA1 3RG Tel: 0141 889 2835 — MB ChB 1952 Glas.; DA Eng. 1954; Asst. Anaesth. Roy. Alexandra Infirm. Paisley. Prev: Regist. Anaesth. Vict. Infirm. Glas.

DICKSON, Mr James Russell (retired) Avoca, Les Fauconnaires, St Andrews GY6 8UE Tel: 01481 720261 — MB BS 1946 Lond.; FRCS Eng. 1954. Prev: Surg. P.ss Eliz. Hosp. Guernsey.

DICKSON, James William Leighton (retired) Stell House, Nunthorpe Village, Middlesbrough TS7 0NR — MB ChB 1928 St. And. Prev: Hon. Anaesth. N. Riding Infirm. Middlesbro.

DICKSON, Jane West Kennacott, Newton Tracey, Barnstaple EX31 3PW — MB BS 1980 Lond.

DICKSON, Janet Elizabeth Anne 13 South Gillsland Road, Edinburgh EH10 5DE — MB ChB 1977 Aberd.

DICKSON, Janet Mary Windermere Day Hospital, West Cumberland Hospital, Whitehaven Tel: 01946 693181; The Mount, Camp Road, Maryport CA15 6JN Tel: 01900 812244 — MB ChB 1980 Ed.; MRCGP 1985; DRCOG 1982. Clin. Asst. in Pychogeriats.

DICKSON, Jean Grierson (retired) 86 School Green Lane, Sheffield S10 4GR — MB ChB 1959 Ed. Prev: Princip.Clin. Med, Off Community Health Sheff.

DICKSON, Jeanette Experimental Radiation Oncology, Paterson Institute for Cancer Research, Manchester M20 4BX; 161 Carsaig Drive, Craigton, Glasgow G52 1AS Tel: 0141 810 4375 Email: jdickson@picr.man.ac.uk — MB ChB 1991 Glas.; Msc (Oncology) 1998; FRCR 1997; MRCP (UK) 1994. (Glas.) Clin. Research Fell. Paterson Inst. for Cancer Research Christle Hosps. NHS Trust Manch. Prev: Career Regist. (Clin. Oncol.) Beatson Oncol. Centre; SHO (Clin. Oncol.) Beatson Oncol. Centre Glas.

DICKSON, Jennifer Anne — MB ChB 1981 Manch.; MRCGP 1986. p/t Clin. Assist. Dermat. Dept., Burnley Gen. Hosp., Burnley, Lancs. Socs: BMA.

DICKSON, Joan (retired) 7 Lygon Road, Edinburgh EH16 5QD Tel: 0131 667 5148 — MB ChB Ed. 1959; DObst RCOG 1961.

DICKSON, John 23 Mansionhouse Road, Paisley PA1 3RG — MB ChB 1983 Glas.; FRCA 1990.

DICKSON, John George (retired) Culdeegeo, 51 Leathwaite, Whitehaven CA28 7UG Tel: 01946 3886 — MB ChB 1947 Ed. Prev: Med. Asst. (Cas.) Workington Infirm.

DICKSON, John Michael Hill (retired) Hall Farm, Wenhaston, Halesworth IP19 9HE Tel: 0150 478287 — MB BChir 1951 Camb.; BA, MB BChir Camb. 1951; FRCGP 1989, M 1962; DObst RCOG 1956. Prev: Ho. Phys. Hillingdon Hosp. Uxbridge.

DICKSON, John Patrick c/o National Westminster Bank plc, Lambeth North, 91 Westminster Bridge Road, London SE1 7ZB; BNH Medical Centre, 9 Convent Road, Bangkok 10500, Thailand Tel: 0662 637 0577 Fax: 0662 632 0579 — MB BChir 1954 Camb.; MD Thailand 1959. Examr. Civil Aviat. Auth. Prev: Med. Dir. BNH Hosp., Bangkok.

DICKSON, Jonathan Duncan St margarets Health Centre, St margarets Drive, Auchterarder PH2 7HH Tel: 01764 662275 — MB ChB 1991 Ed.; MRCGP; DFFP. (Edin) Clin. Asst. Rheum. Perth Roy. Infirm. Prev: SHO Rotat. (Gen. Med.) Hull Roy. Infirm.; SHO (Gen. Med.) Roy. Infirm. Edin.; Trainee GP Tayside VTS.

DICKSON, June (retired) 5 Bridge Street, Helmsley, York YO62 5BG Tel: 01439 770663 — MB BS 1948 Durh. Prev: Cons. in Electroencephalog. Severalls Hosp. Colchester.

DICKSON, Keith Rodwell 48 Leicester Road, Wigston, Leicester LE18 1DR Tel: 0116 288 2566 — MB BS 1969 Lond.; BSc Lond. 1967, MB BS (Hons.) 1969; MRCGP 1974. (Univ. Coll. Lond.)

DICKSON, Linda Scott Willow Tree House, Church Lane, Kingston, Cambridge CB3 7NG — MB ChB 1973 Aberd.; DCH RCPS Glas. 1975. Prev: SHO Aberd. Matern. Hosp. & Roy. Aberd. Childr. Hosp.

DICKSON, Malcolm John 99 Merchants Quay, Salford M5 2XQ — MB ChB 1990 Manch.; BSc St. And. 1988; MRCOG 1997.

DICKSON, Margaret Jean 4 Bridge Road, Balerno EH14 7AH — MB ChB 1985 Ed.; MRCGP 1990; DRCOG 1990. Gen. Pract.-Doctors Retainer Scheme. Prev: Trainee GP Newc. Newc. VTS.

DICKSON, Margot Herriot (retired) 102 Stoke Lane, Westbury-on-Trym, Bristol BS9 3RH — MRCS Eng. LRCP Lond. 1942; MRCGP 1959. Prev: GP W.bury-on-Trym.

DICKSON, Mark Jonathan 4 Nicholsons Place, Silsden, Keighley BD20 0AF — MB ChB 1992 Leeds.

DICKSON, Mary Anna Sibell 13 South Gillsland Road, Edinburgh EH10 5DE — MB ChB 1984 Manch.; MB ChB Manch. l984; FFA RCSI 1991. Sen. Regist. (Anaesth.) Edin.

DICKSON, Matthew Crawford (retired) 25 Lawhead Road E., St Andrews KY16 9ND Tel: 01334 473692 — MB ChB 1932 Glas. Prev: Apptd. Fact. Doctor, Glas. W..

DICKSON, Michael Crawford Moylinny Mill, 9 Nursery Park, Antrim BT41 1QR Tel: 01849 66033 — MB BCh BAO 1963 Belf.; DObst RCOG 1965; MRCGP 1968.

DICKSON, Mr Miles Gordon Lister Hospital, Corey's Mill Lane, Stevenage SG1 4AB Tel: 01438 314333 — MB BS 1975 Lond.; FRCS Eng. 1979. Cons. Plastic & Reconstruc. Surg. Lister Hosp. Stevenage.

DICKSON, Nigel Keith St Denys Surgery, 7 St Denys Road, Portswood, Southampton SO17 2GN Tel: 023 8055 4161 Fax: 023 8055 4853; 6 The Meadows, Romsey SO51 0GX Tel: 01794 517735 Email: nigeldicksonso510gx.uk@networkmed.com — MB BS 1980 Lond.; MRCS Eng. LRCP Lond. 1980; MRCGP 1985. (Guy's) Socs: Soton & SW Hants. LMC.; (Treas.) Wessex Gp. Educat. Trust; Assn. Univ. Teach. Gen. Pract. Prev: Clin. Dir. (Primary Care) Univ. Soton.; GP Derby; Clin. Tutor (Gen. Pract.) Univ. Nottm.

DICKSON, Penelope Jane Lesley (retired) The Surgery, 7-8 Park Street, Ripon HG4 2AX Tel: 01765 692337 Fax: 01765 601757 — MB ChB 1969 Leeds; MRCP (UK) 1974; DObst RCOG 1972; DCH Eng. 1971. Prev: Clin. Asst. (Diabetes) York Dist. Hosp.

DICKSON, Peter Ilkley Health Centre, Spring Lane, Ilkley LS29 8TQ; Moorlands, 1 Moor Lane, Addingham, Ilkley LS29 0PS — MB ChB 1974 Manch.; MRCGP 1980; DObst RCOG 1976. (Manch.) Med. Off. Ardenlea Marie Curie Centre Ilkley; CME Tutor Univ. of Leeds. Socs: Airedale Med. Soc. Prev: GP Doncaster; SHO (Obst. & Gen. Med.) Salford HA; SHO (Paediat.) Roy. Liverp. Childr. Hosp.

DICKSON, Richard John St. James' Hospital, Locksway Road, Milton, Portsmouth PO4 8LD Tel: 023 92 822444 Fax: 023 92 872710 — MB BChir 1974 Camb.; MRCPsych 1997. (St. George's Lond.) Staff-Grade Psychiat., Portsmouth Healthcare Trust. Prev: Specialist Regist. (Psychiat.) Portsmouth & SE Hants. HA.

DICKSON, Professor Robert Andrew Clinical Sciences Building, St. James's University Hospital, Leeds LS9 7TF Tel: 0113 243 3144 Fax: 0113 206 6791; 14A Park Avenue, Leeds LS8 2JH Tel: 0113 265 4491 — MB ChB Ed. 1967; MA Oxf. 1979; DSc Ed. 1991; ChM Ed. 1973; FRCS Eng. 1982; FRCS Ed. 1972. Prof. Traum. & Orthop Surg. Univ. Leeds; Mem. Gen. Med. Counc.; Cons. Surg. St. Jas. Univ. Hosp. Leeds & Leeds Gen. Infirm.; Exec. Edr. Curr. Orthop. Socs: (Exec. Comm.) Brit. Scol. Soc.; Fell. Brit. Orth. Assoc. Prev: Dean, Fac of Med. & Dent. Univ. Leeds; Clin. Reader Nuffield Dept. Orthop. Surg. Univ. Oxf.; Fell. Kosair Spine & Scoliosis Treatm. Centre Louisville, USA.

DICKSON, Robert Ian The Surgery, Springwell House, Ardmillan Terrace, Edinburgh EH11 2JL; 52 Hainburn Park, Edinburgh EH10 7HH — MB ChB 1983 Ed.; BSc (Hons.) Ed. 1980, MB ChB 1983; MRCP (UK) 1987; DRCOG 1986.

DICKSON, Robert Russell Bruin Wood, Warren Lane, Long Ashton, Bristol BS41 9DA Tel: 01275 392223 — MB BS Lond. 1941; MRCS Eng. LRCP Lond. 1940; DA Eng. 1941. (St. Bart.) Surg. Lt.-Cdr. RNVR. Prev: Anaesth. Regist. & Tutor in Anaesths. Bristol Roy. Infirm.; Ho. Phys. & Ho. Surg. St. Bart. Hosp.

DICKSON, Rodger Norman Norden House Surgery, Avenue Road, Winslow, Buckingham MK18 3DW Tel: 01296 713434; Yew Tree Cottage, 30 Sheep St, Winslow, Buckingham MK18 3HN Tel: 01296 74124 — MB BS 1982 Lond. (Guy's) Socs: Sec. Buckingham & Dist. Med. Soc.; Exec. Mem. Bucks. BMA. Prev: Trainee GP Ashford VTS; GP Brisbane, Austral.

DICKSON, Roger Donald 49 Ashley Drive, Bramhall, Stockport SK7 1EP Tel: 0161 439 0422 — MB ChB 1965 Manch.; MRCS Eng. LRCP Lond. 1965; DMRD Eng. 1971. Cons. Radiol. Stockport Acute Servs. NHS Trust. Socs: Roy. Coll. Radiol. Prev: Regist. (Radiol.) United Sheff. Hosps.; Resid. (Family Med.) McMaster Univ. Hamilton, Canada; Ho. Surg. Manch. Roy. Infirm.

DICKSON, Rona Elizabeth 8 Claremont Grove, Aberdeen AB10 6RF — MB ChB 1991 Aberd.

DICKSON, Stephen Richard Downlands Medical Centre, 77 High Street, Polegate BN26 6AE Tel: 01323 482323/486449 Fax: 01323 488497; 5 Badgers Brow, Eastbourne BN20 9EE Tel: 01323 504393 — MB BS 1979 Lond.; MRCS Eng. LRCP Lond. 1979; MRCGP 1983; DRCOG 1983. (St. Bart.) Prev: Trainee GP E. Cumbria (Carlisle) VTS.

DICKSON, Stuart James 112 Compton Avenue, Plymouth PL3 5DE — MB ChB 1994 Ed.

DICKSON, Susan Dorothy Ilkley Health Centre, Spring Lane, Ilkley LS29 8TQ; Moorlands, 1 Moor Lane, Addingham, Ilkley LS29 0PS — MB ChB 1975 Manch.; DGM RCP Lond. 1986; DCH Eng. 1982. (Manch.) Socs: Airedale Med. Soc. Prev: Trainee GP Airedale; SHO (Psychiat.) & Clin. Med. Off. Doncaster HA; SHO (Paediat.) Roy. Manch. Childr. Hosp.

DICKSON, Terrina Clare Strathesk Medical Practice, Sutherland House, 209 Mayburn Avenue, Loanhead EH20 9ER Tel: 0131 440 0149 Fax: 0131 449 2026 — MB ChB 1989 Ed.; DPD 2001; MRCGP 1993; DFFP 1995; DRCOG 1995. (Ed.)

DICKSON, Thankam 4 Nicholsons Place, Silsden, Keighley BD20 0AF — MB ChB 1992 Leeds.

DICKSON, Thomas Edward (retired) 7 Lygon Road, Edinburgh EH16 5QD Tel: 0131 667 5148 Email: thodickson@aol.com — MB ChB Ed. 1954; MRCGP 1970; DObst RCOG 1966.

DICKSON, Timothy David Spring Hill Medical Centre, Spring Hill, Arley, Coventry CV7 8FD Tel: 01676 540395 Fax: 01676 540760; Greens Farm, Nuneaton Road, Fillongley, Coventry CV7 8DN Tel: 01676 541987 — MB ChB 1986 Sheff.; MRCGP 1990; DRCOG 1993. GP Coventry.

DICKSON, Ursula Kristina Department of Anaesthetics, Cumberland Infirmary, Carlisle CA2 6HY; 4 Victoria Road, Poulton-Le-Fylde, Blackpool FY1 3JT — MB ChB 1990 Aberd. SHO (Anaesth.) E. Cumbria HA.

DICKSON, Walter The Gables, Kenyon, Warrington WA3 — MB ChB 1940 Manch.; FRCP Lond. 1971, M 1948; DCH Eng. 1946. (Manch.) Cons. Paediatr. Bolton & Dist. Gen. Hosp. Socs: Fell. Manch. Med. Soc.; Brit. Paediat. Soc. Prev: Asst. Lect. Dept. of Child Health, Manch.; Res. Off. Pendlebury Childr. Hosp.

DICKSON, Mr William Alexander 3 Deans Gardens, The Danes, Chepstow NP16 5SG — MB ChB 1974 Ed.; BSc Ed. 1971; FRCS Glas. 1982; FRCS Eng. 1998. Cons. Welsh Centre for Burns and Plastic & Maxillofacial Surg. Morriston Hosp. Swansea. Socs: Mem. Exec. Comm. Brit. Burn Assn.; Chairm., Serv. & Developm. Comm., Brit. Assn. of Plastic Surg.s 1998-2000. Prev: Sen. Regist. (Plastic Surg.) Gwent HA; Regist. (Plastic Surg.) Bradford HA.

DICKSON, William Elphinstone State Hospsitals Board for Schools, Carnwath, Lanark ML11 8RP Tel: 0155 840112, 0155 840293 — MB ChB 1975 Ed.; MPhil Ed. 1984; FRCPsych 1994, M 1981. Med. Dir. The State Hosp. Bd. for Scotl. Carstairs Lanarksh. Prev: Cons. Psychiat. Fife Psychiat. Servs.; Manager Ment. Health Servs. Fife HB; Vis. Psychiat., H.M. Prison Perth.

DICKSON MABON, Rt. Hon. Jesse, PC (retired) Royal London Homoeopathic Hospital, Great Ormond St., London WC1N 3HR Tel: 020 7713 7752 Fax: 020 8342 9583 — MB ChB Glas. 1954; DHMSA Lond. 1974; FFHom 1995, M 1984. Prev: Chairm. Roy. Lond. Homoeop. NHS Hosp. Trust.

DIDCOCK, Elizabeth Ann 45 Rothesay Avenue, Lenton, Nottingham NG7 1PU — BM BS 1984 Nottm.; BM BS Nottm. l984.

DIDDEE, Anjali Shekhar 59A Balmoral Road, Westcliff on Sea SS0 7DB — MB BS 1983 Nagpur; FFA RCSI 1992.

DIDDEE, Raman Kumar 14 North Terrace, Spital Tongues, Newcastle upon Tyne NE2 4AD — MB BS 1998 Newc.; MB BS Newc 1998.

DIDDEE, Shekhar Dev 59A Balmoral Road, Westcliff on Sea SS0 7DB — MB BS 1980 Nagpur; FRCA 1993.

DIDEHVAR, Roxana 6 Bourne Lodge Close, Blean, Canterbury CT2 9HD — MB BS 1997 Lond.

DIDI, Mohamed Ali Alder Hey Children's Hospital, Eaton Road, Liverpool L12 2AP Tel: 0151 228 4811; 21 Tunbridge Close, Great Sankey, Warrington WA5 3RF Tel: 01925 712585 — MRCS Eng. LRCP Lond. 1980. Cons. Paediat. Aldey Hey Childr.'s Hosp.

DIDIER, Haydn Paul 48 Park Avenue, Bedford MK40 2NF — MB BS 1967 Lond.; MRCOG 1972; DA Eng. 1969.

DIDSBURY, Catherine Leslie Carlgton Surgery, Oastle Gardens Crescent, Poulton-le-Fylde FY6 7NJ Tel: 01253 895545 Fax: 01253 899350; 34 Scotforth Road, Lancaster LA1 4SB Tel: 01524 37511 — BM BS 1993 Nottm.; MRCGP 1998; 1991 (Bmed Sci) Nottm.; DCH 1996; DRCOG 1996. (Nottingham) p/t GP Princip., Carleton Surg., Poulton-le-fylde.

DIEDERICKS, Ralph James Epsom General Hospital, Dorking Road, Epsom KT18 7EG Tel: 01372 735735; 11 Farriers Road, Epsom KT17 1LP Tel: 01372 749361 — MB ChB 1972 Cape Town. Cons. Paediat. Epsom Gen. Hosp.

DIEDRICKS, Heidi Liesl O'Grady Peyton, Centre Court 1301, Stratford Road, Hall Green, Birmingham B28 9HH — MB ChB 1996 Cape Town.

DIEH, Annabel Pui Tect 48 Hayfield Road, Salford M6 8QA — MB ChB 1997 Manch.

DIEKER, Andrea Ghlyle House, Abbey Way, Barrow-in-Furness LA14 1BP Tel: 01229 870870; Capernwray-Hall, Carnforth LA6 1AG Tel: 01524 734848 Fax: 01524 736681 — State Exam Med 1993 Hanover. GP/Regist. (O & G) Barrow-in-Furness VTS. Prev: GP Regist. (Eyes/Ear, Nose & Throat) Barrow-in-Furness VTS; GP Regist. (Paediat.) Barrow-in-Furness VTS; GP Regist (A & E) Barrow-in-Furness VTS.

DIEKERHOF, Carel 3 Gledhow Avenue, Roundhay, Leeds LS8 1NU — Artsexamen 1991 Utrecht.

DIEPPE, Clare Rachel 41 Middleton Road, Kings Heath, Birmingham B14 7HX — MB ChB 1998 Birm.

DIEPPE, Professor Paul Adrian Department Social Medicine, Canynge Hall, Whiteladies Road, Bristol BS8 2PR — MB BS 1970 Lond.; BSc (Special) (1st cl. Hons. Physiol.) Lond. 1967; MD Lond. 1985; MRCS Eng. LRCP Lond. 1970; MRCP (UK) 1973; FRCP Lond. 1983; FFPHM 1999. (St. Bart.) Dir., MRC Health Serv. Research Collaboration, Univ. Bristol, Dept. Social Med.; Hon. Cons. N. Bristol Hosp. NHS Trust; Hon. Prof. Health Serv. Research, Bristol Univ. Prev: Dean, fac. Med., Bristol Univ.

DIETCH, Daniel Marc 19 Cainsborough Gardens, London NW11 9BJ — MB ChB 1992 Manch.

DIETZEL, Thomas Aberdare General Hospital, Aberdare CF44 0RF — State Exam Med 1988 Munster.

DIEZ-RABAGO DEL BARRIO, Maria Victoria 4 Jellicoe Court, Atlantic Wharf, Cardiff CF10 4AJ Tel: 029 2045 0926; 22 Silver Hill Road, Sheffield S11 9JG Tel: 0114 236 6512 — LMS 1981 Santander. Research Regist. (Geriat. Med.) Cardiff. Socs: Brit. Geriat. Soc.

DIFFEY, Ronald Francis Church Walk Surgery, Drury St., Metheringham, Lincoln LN4 3EZ Tel: 01526 320522; The Old Vicarage, Nocton, Lincoln LN4 2BJ Tel: 01526 320296 — MB ChB 1985 Leeds.

DIFFLEY, Frances Sara The Surgery, 1 Richmond House, East Street, London SE17 2DU Tel: 020 7703 7393 Fax: 020 7708 3077; 8 Reservoir Road, Brockley, London SE4 2NU Tel: 020 7358 0959 — MB BCh BAO 1980 NUI; MRCGP 1986; DRCOG 1987.

DIFFORD, Caroline Elizabeth 36 Egerton Road, Bournemouth BH8 9AY Email: a.sopitt@virgin.net — MB ChB 1991 Birm.; ChB Birm. 1991; DRCOG.

DIFFORD, Frederick The Priory Surgery, 326 Wells Road, Bristol BS4 2QJ Tel: 0117 949 3988 Fax: 0117 778250; 7 Moreton Close, Whitchurch, Bristol BS14 9QN — MB ChB 1964 Sheff.; FRCGP 1988, M 1980. Assoc. Adviser Gen. Pract. S. W. Region. Prev: Course Organiser Avon GP VTS.

DIGBY, Ian Francis (retired) 54 Woodrush Road, Purdis Farm, Ipswich IP3 8RD Tel: 01473 718670 Email: iandigby@ukonline.co.uk — MB BS 1951 Lond.; DObst RCOG 1953. Prev: Gen. Practitioner, Ipswich.

DIGBY, Richard John Old School Surgery, Rectory Fields, Cranbrook TN17 3JB Tel: 01580 712476 — MB BCh 1985 Wales. (Welsh National School of Medicine)

DIGBY, Samantha Trevinia Claire 22 Holly La W., Banstead SM7 2BB — BM BS 1997 Nottm.

DIGGENS, David Northdown Surgery, St Anthony's Way, Cliftonville, Margate CT9 2TR Tel: 01843 296413 Fax: 01843 231231; Morningside, 5 Old Green Road, Northdown, Margate CT9 3LZ Tel: 01843 292239 Fax: 01843 231231 — MB BS 1965 Lond.; MRCS Eng. LRCP Lond. 1965; FRCGP 1993, M 1974; Cert. Family Plann. JCC 1979; DObst RCOG 1967. (Char. Cross) RCGP Tutor Thanet; GP Tutor Isle of Thanet PGMC; Mem. Fac. Bd. RCGP SE Thames. Socs: BMA. Prev: Surg. Lt.-Cdr. RNR; SHO (Med.) Unit Fulham Hosp.; SHO (Obst.) Char. Cross Hosp. Lond.

DIGGENS, Elizabeth Frances (retired) Northdown Surgery, St Anthony's Way, Cliftonville, Margate CT9 2TR Tel: 01843 296413 Fax: 01843 231231 — MB BS Lond. 1965; Cert. Family Plann. JCC 1985; DObst RCOG 1967. Prev: SHO (Obst.) Kingsbury Matern. Hosp. Lond.

DIGGENS, Samantha Elizabeth Highlands Medical Centre, 102 Highlands Rd, Fareham PO15 6JF Tel: 01329 842226; 22A Dairymoor, Wickham, Fareham PO17 5JR Email: sam@diggens30.freeserve.co.uk — MB BS 1993 Lond.; DFFP 2001; BSc (Med. Sci. with Biochem.) Lond. 1991; DRCOG 1996. (Char. Cross & Westm. Med. Sch.) p/t GP Princip., Fareham. Socs: BMA. Prev: SHO (O & G) Kent & Canterbury Hosp.; SHO (A & E) & Ho. Off. (Surg.) S.end Hosp. Essex; Ho. Off. (Med.) King Edwd. VII Hosp. Midhurst.

DIGGER, Timothy John The Firs, 31 Fir Grove, Wollaston, Stourbridge DY8 3PG — MB ChB 1975 Sheff.; FFA RCS Eng. 1979. Cons. Anaesth. Russells Hall Hosp. Dudley.

DIGGES, Charles Nigel O'Neill Tanglelands, Hill Crest, Dormans Park, East Grinstead RH19 2LX Tel: 01342 870239 Fax: 01342 870420 Email: nigedig@aol.com; X-Ray Department, Surrey & Sussex Trust, Canada Avenue, Redhill RH1 5RH Tel: 01737 768511 — MA MB BCh BAO Dub. 1967; FRCR 1976; DMRD Eng. 1975. (Trinity Coll. Dub.) Cons. Radiol. Surrey & Sussex Trust. Socs: BMA. Prev: Cons. Radiol. New E. Surrey Hosp. Redhill & Qu. Eliz. Milit. Hosp. Woolwich.; Clin. Dir. Diag. Imaging E. Surrey Trust.

DIGGLE, Douglas Phillip Health Centre, Little Lane, South Elmsall, Pontefract WF9 2NJ Tel: 01977 465331 Fax: 01977 645832 — MB BChir 1971 Camb.; MA Camb. 1971. (Oxford) Forens. Phys. W. Yorks. Police Auth.; BRd.caster BBC Radio Leeds & Yorks. TV. Socs: BMA.

DIGGLE, Geoffrey Edward 97 Bennetts Way, Shirley, Croydon CR0 8AG Tel: 020 8777 3871 Email: drgediggle@aol.com — MB BS 1970 Lond.; FFPM; Dip. Pharm. Med. RCP (UK) 1987; AKC. (King's Coll. Hosp.) Independant Cons.in Pharmaceutical Med.; Lect. Univs. Surrey & Wales. Socs: Fell. Fac. Pharmaceut. Med. Prev: Sen. Med. Off. & Med. Off. DoH; Princip. Regist. & SHO (Med.) King's Coll. Hosp. Lond.

DIGGLE, John Hamilton Isca General Practice Unit, Cadoc House, High Street, Caerleon, Newport NP18 1AZ Tel: 01633 423886 Fax: 01633 430153 — MB BCh 1980 Wales. GP Caerleon.

DIGGLE, John Harvey (retired) 11 Cliff Road, Sheringham NR26 8BJ Tel: 01263 825696 — MB ChB 1944 Manch.; BSc Manch. 1941, MB ChB (Hons.) 1944; FRCP Lond. 1974, M 1952; DCH Eng. 1946. Prev: Sen. Med. Regist. Paediat. Childr. Hosp. Sheff.

DIGGLE, Sybil B 97 Bennetts Way, Shirley, Croydon CR0 8AG — MB ChB 1961 Manch.; MSc Occupat. Med. Lond. 1986; MRCS Eng. LRCP Lond. 1960; MFOM RCP Lond. 1988, AFOM 1986. p/t

InDepend. Cons. Socs: Fell. Roy. Soc. Med.; Soc. Occupat. Med. Prev: Sen. Regional Med. Off. BT Lond.; Regional Med. Off. Brit. Telecom (HQ) & Lond. Region; Med. Off. Brit. Rail.

DIGGORY, Clive John Derwent Practice, Norton Road, Malton YO17 9RF Tel: 01653 600069 Fax: 01653 698014 — MB ChB 1982 Manch.; DCH RCP Lond. 1986; DRCOG 1985. GP Malton.

DIGGORY, Paul Mayday Hospital, Mayday Road, Thornton Heath, Croydon CR7 7TE Tel: 020 8401 3000 Fax: 020 8401 3620; 9 Maunsel Street, London SW1P 2QL Tel: 020 7828 8264 — BM Soton. 1982; BSc Physiol. Lond. 1977; MRCP (UK) 1985. Cons. Med. for Elderly Mayday Hosp. Croydon. Socs: Fell. Roy. Soc. Med.; Brit. Geriat. Soc. Prev: Research Fell. (Geriat. Med.) St. Jas. Hosp. Leeds; Sen. Regist. (Geriat.) Nat. Research Inst. & Mt. Roy. Hosp. Melbourne, Austral.; Sen. Regist. (Geriat.) St. Geo. Hosp. Lond.

DIGGORY, Mr Peter Lionel Carr The London Welbeck Hospital, 27 Welbeck St., London W1G 8EN Tel: 020 8876 4626; 10 Campden Hill Square, London W8 7LB Tel: 020 7727 6877 Fax: 020 7727 6877 — MRCS Eng. LRCP Lond. 1950; BSc Lond. 1942, MB BS 1950; FRCS Eng. 1958; FRCS Ed. 1957; FRCOG 1973, M 1961, DObst 1954. (Univ. Coll. Hosp.) Cons. Gyn. New Vict. Hosp. Kingston on THames; Cons. Gyn. Roy. Marsden Hosp. Surrey & Lond. Welbeck Hosp.; Chairm. Internat. Family Health Lond. Socs: Fell. Galton Inst.; Hosp. Cons. & Spec. Assn. Prev: WHO Cons. Matern. & Child Health, SE Asia.

DIGGORY, Mr Robert Trevor Princess Royal Hospital, Apley Castle, Telford TF6 6TF Tel: 01952 641222 — MD 1988 Dundee; MB ChB 1977; FRCS Eng. 1982; FRCS Ed. 1981. Cons. Gen. Surg. P.ss Roy. Hosp. NHS Trust, Telford; Cons. Gen. Surg. Roy. Shrewsbury Hosp. NHS Trust, Shrewsbury. Prev: Cons. Gen. Surg. Vict. Hosp., Kirkcaldy.

DIGGORY, Tina Mary 21 The Mount, Malton YO17 7ND — MB ChB 1982 Manch.; MRCP (UK) 1985; DRCOG 1987.

DIGHE, Adrian Mark Child Development Centre, Southlands Hospital, Upper Shoreham Road, Shoreham-by-Sea BN43 6TQ Tel: 01273 446017 Fax: 01273 446004 — MB BS 1980 Lond.; BSc (Hons.) Lond. 1976; MRCS Eng. LRCP Lond. 1979; MRCGP 1983. (Guy's) SCMO (Child Health & Paediat. Audiol.) S.lands Hosp. Shoreham-by-Sea.

DIGHE, Sonal Vijaykumar 21 Heron Road, Oakham LE15 6BN — MB ChB 1994 Aberd. SHO (O & G) Aberd. Roy. Infirm. Socs: BMA. Prev: Regist. (Med.) Qu.sland Health Bd.; SHO (Emerg. Med.) Qu.sland Health Bd.; SHO (Anaesth.) Qu.sland Health Bd.

DIGHE, Vilas Chintaman Maternity Unit, Grantham General Hospital, Manthorpe Road, Grantham NG31 8DG Tel: 01476 565232 Fax: 01476 565232; 15 Maplewood Close, Grantham NG31 8GY Tel: 01476 591308 Fax: 01476 590441 — MB BS 1974 Bombay; MD 1976; DRCOG 1981; DFFP 1981. Staff O & G Grantham & Dist. Hosp.; Med. Off. (Family Plann.) Grantham; GP Asst. Socs: MPS.

DIGHE-DEO, Deepa 3 Hanworth Road, Hampton TW12 3DH — MB BS 1989 Bombay.

DIGHTON, David Henry 115 High Road, Loughton IG10 4HJ Tel: 020 8508 7741 — MB BS 1966 Lond.; MRCP (UK) 1973. (Lond. Hosp.) Med. Dir. Loughton Clinic Essex. Socs: BMA; Roy. Soc. Med. Prev: Cardiol. Acad. Hosp. Free Univ. Amsterdam; Lect. (Cardiac Med.) Char. Cross Hosp. Lond.

DIGNAN, Mr Albert Patrick, CB, MBE, Maj.-Gen. late RAMC Retd. (retired) 182 Beckenham Hill Road, Beckenham BR3 1SZ Tel: 020 8658 7690 — MB BCh BAO 1943 Dub.; MA, MD Dub. 1968; FRCS Eng 1976; FRCSI 1947. Prev: Hon. Surg. to HM the Qu.

DIGNAN, Fergus Joseph Brentford Health Centre, Boston Manor Road, Brentford TW8 8DS Tel: 020 8321 3838 Fax: 020 8321 3814 — MB BS 1979 Lond.; MRCP (UK) 1984; MRCGP 1987; AKC 1979; Dip. Sports Med. 1998. (Westm.) Prev: Med. Off. Jane Furse Hosp. Lebowa, S. Africa; Regist. (Med.) Epsom Dist. Hosp.

DIGNAN, James Edward Patrick 32 Bell Lane, Broxbourne EN10 7HE Tel: 01992 66559; (Surgery), 171 Ordnance Road, Enfield EN3 6AD — LRCPI & LM, LRSCI & LM 1956; LRCPI & LM, LRCSI & LM 1956. (RCSI) Prev: Intern Mercer's Hosp. Dub.; SHO (Genito-Urin. Surg.) St. Kevin's Hosp. Du-.; Maj. RAMC, Regtl. Med. Off. 2nd Bn. Scots Guards.

DIGNEY, John Marion Gerard Clanrye Surgery, Newry Health Village, Monaghan Street, Newry BT35 6BW Tel: 028 3026 7639 Fax: 028 3025 7414 — MB BCh BAO 1980 NUI; MRCGP 1984; DRCOG 1982.

DIGNON, Neil Michael 9 Lansdown Grove, Chester CH4 8LD — MB ChB 1994 Manch.

DIGNUM, Helen Margaret Dept. of Haemat., Royal Victoria Infirmary, Newcastle upon Tyne NE1 4LP — BM BCh 1991 Oxf.; MA Camb. 1991, BA 1987; MRCP (UK) 1994; Dip RCPath 1996. Regist. Rotat. (Haemat.) Newc. Prev: SHO (Haemat.) Christie Hosp. Manch.; SHO (Gen. Med.) Freeman Hosp. Newc. u. Tyne; Ho. Off. (Med.) John Radcliffe Hosp. Oxf.

DIHMIS, Mr Walid Carlos The Cardiothoracic Centre, Liverpool NHS Trust, Thomas Drive, Liverpool L14 3PE Tel: 0151 228 1616 Email: wdihmis@ccl_tr.nwest.nhs.uk — MB BS 1985 Lond.; FRCS Ed. 1990; FRCS (Cth.) 1996. (The London Hospital Medical College) Cons. Cardiac Surg. The Cardiothoracic Centre Liverp. Prev: Sen. Regist. (Cardiothoracic Surg.) Bristol Roy. Infirm. & Frenchay Hosp. Bristol.; Regist. (Gen. Surg.) Harold Wood Hosp.

DIJKUIZEN, Roelf Soene 12 Blomville Road, Dagenham RM8 3DH Tel: 020 8517 1652 — Artsexamen 1987 Nijmegen.

DIKE, Angela Elizabeth National Blood Service, Oxford Centre, John Radcliffe Hospital, Oxford OX3 9DU Tel: 01865 741188 Fax: 01865 741343; Inverbroom, Manor Road, Towersey, Thame OX9 3QS Tel: 01844 215287 — MB BS 1962 Lond.; FRCPath 1981, M 1969. (St. Bart.) Assoc. Specialist Nat. Blood Serv. Oxf. Prev: Med. Asst. (Bact.) Stoke Mandeville Hosp. Aylesbury.

DIKIMLI, Aydin (retired) 93 The Knares, Lee Chapel S., Basildon SS16 5SB Tel: 01268 542866 Fax: 01268 491381 — State Exam Med 1985 Frankfurt; MD Frankfurt 1986; DFFP 1995.

DILAWARI, Professor Jang Bahadur Inverclyde Royal Hospital, Greenock PA16 0XN Tel: 01475 633777; 51 Esplanade, Greenock PA16 7SD Tel: 01475 656142 — MRCS Eng. LRCP Lond. 1971; FRCP 1985, M 1970; MD (Germany) 1966. (Munich) Cons. Phys. & Gastroenterol.; Sen. Lect. Glas. Univ. Socs: Brit. Soc. Gastroenterol.; Indian Soc. Gastroenterol.; Brit. Assn. for the Study of Liver. Prev: Prof. Gastroenterol. & Hepato.; Postgrad. Med. Inst. Chandigarh, India.

DILIP KUMAR, Mr R Eye Department, Coventry & Warwickshire Hospital, Stoney Stanton Road, Coventry CV1 4FH — MB BS 1975 Madras; FRCS Ed. 1981; DO Eng. 1978. (Madras Med. Coll.) Middle. Ophth. Soc. Prize for Best Original Work 1983; Cons. Ophth. Coventry & N. Warks. HAs. Prev: Sen. Ophth. Regist. Birm. & Midl. Eye Hosp.; Hon. Clin. Tutor Ophth. Birm. Med. Sch.; Regist. (Ophth.) & Hon. Clin.; Tutor Tennant Inst. Ophth. W.. Infirm. Glas.

DILKE, Timothy Fisher Wentworth 152 Harley Street, London W1N 1HH Tel: 020 7935 0444 Fax: 020 7224 2574; 15 Wemyss Road, Blackheath, London SE3 0TG Tel: 020 8852 9692 — MA, BM BCh Oxf. 1964; FRCP Lond. 1986, M 1969. (Guy's) Cons. Rheum. Qu. Mary's Hosp. Sidcup & Greenwich Dist. Hosp. Socs: Fell. Med. Soc. Lond. & Roy. Soc. Med. Prev: Sen. Regist. (Rheum.) Guy's Hosp. Lond.; Regist. (Med.) Willesden Gen. Hosp.; Regist. (Physical Med. & Rheum.) Roy. Free Hosp.

DILKE-WING, Gillian Mary 5 Woodside Park Avenue, Horsforth, Leeds LS18 4TF — MB ChB 1985 Sheff.; MRCP (UK) 1992.

DILKES, Mr Michael George ENT Department, St. Bartholomew's Hospital, West Smithfield, London EC1A 7BE Tel: 020 7601 7172; Dormers Lodge, Flaunden Lane, Borringdon, Hemel Hempstead HP3 0PA Tel: 01442 833058 — MB BS 1985 Lond.; FRCS Eng. 1991; FRCS Ed. 1990; FrCS (ORL) 1996; MS 2000 London. (St Mary's London) p/t Cons. (ENT/Head & Neck) St Bartholomews, Whipps Cross & Roy. Lond. Hosps.; Med. Direcgtor, The Lond. Laser Clinic. Socs: Roy. Soc. Med. & Brit. Assn. Otolaryngol.; Brit. Med. Laser Assn. Prev: Sen. Regist. (ENT) Roy. Lond. Hosp. & N.wick Pk. Hosp. Harrow; SHO (ENT) St. Mary's Hosp. Lond.; Lect. (ENT) Roy. Lond. Hopital.

DILL-RUSSELL, Patrick Colm Anaesthetic Dept., Chelsea and Westminster Hospital, 369 Fulham Road, London SW10 9NH Tel: 0208 746 8000; 78 Frankfurt Road, Herne Hill, London SE24 9NY Tel: 0207 274 0252 Fax: 0207 274 0252 Email: pditr@yahoo.co.uk — MB BS 1991 Lond.; MRCP (UK) 1994; FRCA 1999. (St Thomas' Hospital (UMDS)) Specialist Regist. (Anaesthetic) Chelsea and W.minster Hosp. Socs: Assn. Anaesth.; Obsteric Anaesthetics Assn.; Difficult Airway Soc. Prev: Specialist Regist (Anaesthetic) Kingston & St. Geo.s Hosp.

DILLEY, Christine Mary 38 Overton Way, Orton Waterville, Peterborough PE2 5HF Tel: 01733 441303 — MB ChB 1975 Ed.; MRCPath 1984.

DILLEY, Christopher John Coleridge Medical Centre, Canaan Way, Ottery St Mary EX11 1EQ Tel: 01404 814447; Malgré, Longdogs Lane, Ottery St Mary EX11 1HX Tel: 01404 813271 — MB BS 1984 Lond.; BSc (Hons.) Psychol. Lond. 1982; MRCGP 1988; DRCOG 1989; DCH RCP Lond. 1987.

DILLEY, John Charles Chilvester Hill House, Calne SN11 0LP Tel: 01249 813981 Fax: 01249 814217 Email: john.dilley@talk21.co.uk; Chilvester Hill House, Calne SN11 0LP — MB BS 1951 Lond.; MRCS Eng. LRCP Lond. 1950; MFOM RCP Lond. 1979; MRCGP 1968; DIH Eng. 1966; DObst RCOG 1952; Specialist. Accredit. (Occupat. Med.) JCHMT 1980. (Lond. Hosp.) Private Occupat.al Health Cons.; Local Med. Off. Civil Serv. Med. & Advis. Serv. Chippenham & Calne; Cons. Occupat. Phys. Brit. Computer Soc., Emerson Electric., Swindon; Sessional Physcian, Consignia, Bristol/Bath. Socs: Soc. Occupat. Med. & Balint Soc.; Roy. Soc. Med.; Fac. Occupat. Med. R.C.P. Prev: Company Med. Off. WH Smith Swindon; Sen. Med. Off. BP Trading Ltd. Lond.; Sen. Med. Off. BP Refinery Hosp. Little Aden.

DILLEY, Michael David Glenside, Honeysuckle Lane, Headley Down, Bordon GU35 8JA — MB BS 1998 Lond.; MB BS Lond 1998.

DILLEY, Richard James Addington Road Surgery, 33 Addington Road, West Wickham BR4 9BW Tel: 020 8462 5771 Fax: 020 8462 8526 — MB BS 1978 Lond.; BSc (Hons.) Lond. 1973; DRCOG 1981. (Charing Cross Hospital)

DILLEY, Sally Penelope Beauchamp House Surgery, 37 Baddow Road, Chelmsford CM2 0DB Tel: 01245 262255 Fax: 01245 262256 — BM 1984 Soton.; MRCGP 1988; DRCOG 1987. Partner. Prev: Trainee GP Portsmouth VTS.

DILLEY, Stephen Ernest Blue Dykes Surgery, Eldon Street, Clay Cross, Chesterfield S45 9NR Tel: 01246 862468 — MB ChB 1972 Sheff.; MRCGP 1976; DObst RCOG 1975. Prev: SHO (Paediat. & Gen. Med.) Roy. Hosp. Chesterfield; SHO (Obst. & Gyn). Scarsdale Hosp. Chesterfield.

DILLISTONE, Edward Beverley, 67 Castle Avenue, Dover CT16 1EZ Tel: 01304 201140 — MRCS Eng. LRCP Lond. 1946. (Lond. Hosp.) Socs: W Kent. M-C Soc. Prev: Receiv. Room Off. Poplar Hosp.; Squadron Ldr. RAFVR Med. Br.; Supernum. Med. Off. Lond. Hosp.

DILLIWAY, Gregory Dennis Ashton Health Centre, Pedders Lane, Preston PR2 1HR Tel: 01772401600 Fax: 01772 768110 — MB ChB 1988 Birm.; DCH RCPS Glas. 1997; DTM & H Liverp. 1989; DCCH RCP Ed. 1998. Stafe Grade (Paediat.) Preston. Socs: Fell. Roy. Soc. Trop. Med. & Hyg.; Internat. Soc. Travel Med.; Brit. Travel Health Assn.

DILLNER, Luisa Marie 21 Richmond Drive, Hayling Island PO11 0EP — MB ChB 1985 Bristol.

DILLON, Ann Theresa Maeve 9 Beaufort Close, Langland, Swansea SA3 4PA Tel: 01792 366815 — MB BCh BAO 1977 Dub.; BA Dub. 1977; MFFP 1993. Clin. Med. Off. (Family Plann.Swansea Trust.

DILLON, Brian Aloysius Kilkeel Health Centre, Knockchree Avenue, Kilkeel, Newry BT34 4BS Tel: 028 4176 2601 Fax: 028 4176 5485; 47 Manse Road, Kilkeel, Newry BT34 4BN — MB BCh BAO 1985 NUI; MRCGP 1991; DRCOG 1991; DCH RCPSI 1990.

DILLON, Mr Brian Patrick (retired) Boswell Farm, Sidford, Sidmouth EX10 DPP Tel: 01395 514162 Email: dillon@boswell-farm.co.uk — MB BS 1957 Lond.; FRCS Glas. 1971; FRCOG 1982, M 1966, DObst. 1959. Prev: Sen. Regist. (O & G) St. Geo. Hosp. Lond.

DILLON, Clare Geraldine Mary (retired) 37 Box Lane, Wrexham LL12 8BY Tel: 01978 357129 — MB BCh 1947 Wales. Prev: Clin. Med. Off. Clwyd S. Health Dist.

DILLON, David Anthony 2 Knockmoe Heights, Omagh BT79 7LX — MB ChB 1993 Manch.

DILLON, Elizabeth Radiology Department, The Memorial Hospital, Darlington DL3 6HX Tel: 01325 743507 Fax: 01325 743622 Email: elizabeth.dillon@smtp.sdhc-tr.northy.nhs.uk; Clowfield House, Monk End, Croft on Tees, Darlington DL2 2SW Tel: 01325 721114 Fax: 01325 722529 Email: elizabeth.dillon@virgin.net — MB ChB Leeds 1969; FRCR 1975; DMRD Eng. 1973; DCH Eng. 1971. Cons. Radiol. Darlington Memor. Hosp. Prev: Cons. Radiol. N. Tees Gen. Hosp. Stockton on Tees.

DILLON, Frances Clare The Mill House, Hasketon, Woodbridge IP13 6HQ Tel: 01473 735210 — MB BS 1984 Lond.; MA Camb. 1981.

DILLON, Geoffrey (retired) 61 Pinchbeck Road, Spalding PE11 1QF Tel: 01775 723721 — MB ChB Aberd. 1958. Prev: Ho. Phys. & Ho. Surg. Aberd. Gen. Hosps.

DILLON, Helen Ford Bayne 61 Pinchbeck Road, Spalding PE11 1QF Tel: 01775 3721 — MB ChB 1956 Aberd.

DILLON, Ivan James 18 Chiltern Road, The Mount, Birkenhead CH42 6SG — MB ChB 1991 Sheff.

DILLON, James Anthony Flat 16 Highbury, 52 Mauldeth Road, Heaton Mersey, Stockport SK4 3HA — MB BCh BAO 1988 NUI.

DILLON, Jane Kerr Sprott (retired) Applethwaite, Brooklyn, Stainton, Penrith CA11 0DZ — MB ChB Ed. 1960. Prev: Clin. Asst. Penrith Day Hosp. E. Cumbria.

DILLON, John Andrew New Frontiers Science Park, Third Avenue, Harlow CM19 5AW — MB BCh BAO 1988 NUI. (Faculty of Medicine, University College, Dublin) Sen. Director, Europ. Med. Affairs, Glaxosmithkline, Harlow. Prev: GP Hanworth Middlx.; Trainee GP/SHO St. Helier Hosp. VTS.

DILLON, John Blake (retired) 70 Carlton Road, Nottingham NG3 2AP Tel: 0115 958 0630 — MB BCh BAO 1941 NUI.

DILLON, John Francis Department of Clinical Pharmacology, Ninewells Hospital & Medical School, Dundee DD1 9SY Tel: 01382 660111 Email: johnd@oth.scot.nhs.uk; 26 Birkhill Avenue, Wormit, Newport-on-Tay DD6 8PW Tel: 01382 543452 — MB BS 1986 Lond.; FRCP Ed 1999; MRCP (UK) 1990; MD Lond. 1997. (St. Geo.) Cons. Phys. Gastroenterol. & Hepatol. Nivewell Hosp. Dundee; Hon. Sen. Lect. Clin. Pharmacol. Univ. of Dundee; Hon. Sen. Lect. Molecular & Cellular Path. Univ. of Dundee. Prev: Lect. (Gastroenterol. & Hepatol.) Univ. Edin.

DILLON, John Mclean 12 College Gate, Bearsden, Glasgow G61 4GG — MB ChB 1995 Aberd.

DILLON, Jonathan Martin Fortwilliam House, 39 Lurganville Rd, Moira, Craigavon BT67 0PL — MB BCh BAO 1997 Belf.

DILLON, Louise 58 Riverside Road, Wormit, Newport-on-Tay DD6 8LJ Tel: 01382 543452 — MB BS 1986 Lond.; MRCGP 1991; DCH RCP Lond. 1990; DGM RCP Lond. 1989.

DILLON, Marianne Doctors Res 6, Room4, Medway Hospital, Gillingham — MB BS 1997 Lond.

DILLON, Professor Michael John Great Ormond Street Hospital for Children NHS Trust, Great Ormond St., London WC1N 3JH Tel: 020 7405 9200 Fax: 020 7916 0011 Email: m.dillon@ich.ucl.ac.uk; 62 Elwill Way, Park Langley, Beckenham BR3 6RZ Tel: 020 8650 3497 — MB BS Lond. 1962; FRCP Lond. 1979, M 1967; FRCPCH (1997); MRCS Eng. LRCP Lond. 1962; DCH Eng. 1965; DObst RCOG 1964. (St. Mary's) Prof. Paediat. Nephrol., Inst. of Child Health Lond.; Cons. Phys. & Sen. Clin. Nephrologist Gt. Ormond St. Hosp. for Childr. Lond.; Civil. Cons. Adviser to the Army. Socs: Eur. Soc. Paediat. Nephrol.; Internat. Paediat. Nephrol. Assn.; Amer. Soc. Nephrol. Prev: Alan Moncrieff Research Fell. Inst. Child Health Lond.; Sen. Regist. (Med.) Hosp. Sick Childr. Gt. Ormond St.; Regist. (Paediat.) Guy's Hosp. Lond.

DILLON, Patrick John 19 Chestnut Gardens, Cliftonville Road, Belfast BT14 6EN — MB BCh BAO 1986 Dub.

DILLON, Philip Albert 43 Scott Street, Dundee DD2 2AP — MB ChB 1996 Dundee.

DILLON, Richard Dennis Stefan 77 Whitburn Road, Cleadon, Sunderland SR6 7RB — MB ChB 1969 Leeds; FRCPath 1990, M 1978. Cons. (Chem. Path.) Sunderland HA.

DILLON, Roger Morecambe Health Centre, Hanover Street, Morecambe LA4 5LY Tel: 01524 418418 Fax: 01524 832584; 3 The Shore, Bolton le Sands, Carnforth LA5 8JR — MB ChB 1971 Birm.; MRCGP 1975; DObst RCOG 1973; DCH RCPS Glas. 1973. Prev: Ho. Phys. & Surg. City Gen. Hosp. Stoke-On-Trent; SHO (Paediat.) Univ. Hosps. Newc.-on-Tyne; Trainee GP Newc.-on-Tyne VTS.

DILLON, Stanley (retired) 159 Cannock Road, Stafford ST17 0QN Tel: 01785 662312 — MB ChB 1940 Birm.; MB ChB (Hons.) Birm. 1940. Prev: Ho. Surg. Qu.'s Hosp. Birm.

DILLON, Sylvia New Medical Centre, Crossley Street, Wetherby LS22 6RT; Quarry House, 14 Quarry Hill Lane, Wetherby LS22 6RY — MB ChB 1987 Leeds; MRCGP 1991; DRCOG 1991.

DILLY, Peter Noel, GM 11 Westwood Park, Forest Hill, London SE23 3QB Tel: 020 8699 7876 — MB BS 1965 Lond.; MB BS (Hons. Distinc. Obst. & Gyn.) Lond. 1965; PhD Lond. 1962, BSc (1st cl. Hons.) 1958; MRCS Eng. LRCP Lond. 1965; FRCOphth. 1988; DO RCS Eng. 1988. (Univ. Coll. Hosp.) Chairm. & Prof. Anat. St. Geo. Hosp. Med. Sch. Lond.; Hon. Assoc. Specialist (Ophth.) St. Geo. Hosp. Lond. Prev: Sen. Lect. (Anat.) Univ. Coll. Lond.; SHO Eye Unit Mayday Hosp. Croydon; Ho. Surg. (Obst.) Univ. Coll. Hosp. Lond.

DILLY, Stephen George SmithKline Beecham, New Frontiers Science Park (South), Third Avenue, Harlow CM19 5AW Tel: 01279 644091 Fax: 01279 644100 — MB BS 1982 Lond.; PhD Lond. 1988, BSc 1979; MFPM RCP (UK) 1992. Vice Pres. Neurosci.s Clin. Research SmithKline Beecham. Prev: Research Fell. Brit. Heart Foundat.; Clin. Project Manager Pfizer Centr. Research.

DILLY, Professor Susan Ann Faculty of Health, Keele University, Newcastle ST5 5DY Tel: 01782 583901 Fax: 01782 583903 Email: s.a.dilly@keele.ac.uk — MB BS 1979 Lond.; BSc Lond. 1976, MB BS 1979; MRCPath 1985; FRCPath 1995. (University College London) Dean Fac. of Health & Head Med. Sch. Keele Univ.; Sen. Lect. Keele Univ.; Cons. Histopath. - N. Staffs. NHS Trust. Prev: Sen. Lect. & Cons. St. Geo. Hosp. Lond.; Sen. Regist. Roy. Marsden Hosp. Sutton; Regist. St. Geo. Hosp. Lond.

DILNOT, Peter (retired) 10 Fourth Avenue, Denvilles, Havant PO9 2QX — MB BS 1952 Lond.; DObst RCOG 1955. Prev: Cas. Off. & Ho. Phys. St. Thos. Hosp.

DILRAJ GOPAL, Mr Thayil Ram Burnley General Hospital, Casterton Avenue, Burnley BB10 2PQ Tel: 01282 425071 Fax: 01282 474124; 6 Pennine Grove, Padiham, Burnley BB12 9AB Tel: 01282 771559 — MB BS 1976 Kerala; FRCS Ed. 1981. Cons. Gen. Surg. Burnley Gen. Hosp. Socs: Fell. Of Assoc. Of Surg. Of GB & I; Fell. Of Brit. Assoc. Of Day Surg.; Fell. Of Ass. Of Endoscopic Surg. Of GB & I. Prev: Cons. Surg. Armed Forces Hosps. S.. Region, Min. Defense & Aviat. Khamis Mushayt Saudi Arabia; Sen Regist. (Surg.) NW Thames RHA; Regist (Surg.) Aberd. Teach Hosp. & Herefordsh. HA.

DILS, Ruth Catherine 47 Ramsbury Drive, Earley, Reading RG6 7RT Tel: 0118 926 4729; 11 Salcombe Road, Basford, Nottingham NG5 1JW Tel: 0115 978 5766 — BM BS 1994 Nottm.; MRCPI 1996. (Nottm.) SHO (Med.) Nottm. City Hosp.

DILWORTH, Andrew 104 Manor Road, Crosby, Liverpool L23 7UU — MB ChB 1980 Liverp.

DILWORTH, Mr George Raymond (retired) 32 Massey Crt., Belmont Road, Belfast BT4 3GJ Tel: 01232 760394 Fax: 01232 761705 — MB BCh BAO 1969 Belf.; FRCS Ed. 1973. Private consultancy work, Belf. Prev: Cons. Orthop. Surg. Ulster & Musgrave Pk. Hosps. Belf.

DILWORTH, Peter Anthony Central Surgery, 22 Cowley Hill Lane, St Helens WA10 2AE Tel: 01744 24849 Fax: 01744 456497 — MB ChB 1976 Liverp.; DRCOG 1981; DCH Dub. 1981.

DIMA-OKOJIE, Mr Sylvester Inegbenoise 65 Magnolia Way, Pilgrims Hatch, Brentwood CM15 9PP Tel: 01277 229374 — MB BS 1985 Benin, Nigeria; FRCSI 1992. Specialist Regist. A&E Old Ch. Hosp.

DIMASCIO, Rita Pasqua Rosa 58 Cairnhill Road, Airdrie ML6 9HD — MB ChB 1988 Aberd.

DIMECH, Julian 21 Hamilton Road, Oxford OX2 7PY — MB ChB 1998 Leeds.

DIMETRI, Assaad El Zikri c/o Burton District Hospital, Belvedere Road, Burton-on-Trent DE13 0RB Tel: 01283 66333 — MB BCh 1958 Cairo; MB BCh Cario 1958.

DIMIGEN, Marion Department of Obstetrics and Gynaecology, Memorial Maternity Pavilion, Royal Infirmary of Edinburgh, Lauriston Place, Edinburgh EH3; 1FR, 30 Lutton Place, Edinburgh EH8 9PG — MB ChB 1997 Ed.

DIMITRAKOS, Maria-Anastasia 52 The Limes Av, London N11 1RH — MB BS 1997 Lond.

DIMITRI, Paul John 44 Kenilworth Road, Coventry CV3 6PG — MB ChB 1997 Manch.

DIMITRI, Mr Wadih Raghib Walsgrave Hospital, Clifford Bridge Road, Coventry CV2 2DX Tel: 024 76 538936 Fax: 024 76 538829; 44 Kenilworth Road, Coventry CV3 6PG — MB ChB (Hons.) Alexandria 1968; FRCS Ed. 1974. Cons. Cardiothoracic Surg. & Sen. Lect. Walsgrave Hosp. NHS Trust Coventry. Socs: Soc. Cardiothoracic Surg. of GB & Irel.; Soc. Thoracic Surgs. (USA).; Hon. Fell. Indian Soc. of Thoracic & Cardiovasc. Surg. Prev: Sen. Lect. & Hon. Cons. Cardiothoracic Surg. Glas.

DIMITRIADIS, Ioannis 36 Leonard Court, Kensington High St., London W8 6NN — State Exam Rome 1989.

DIMITRIOU, Christos 5 Oak Hill House, Oak Hill Park, London NW3 7LP — Ptychio Iatrikes 1993 Thessalonika.

DIMITRIOU, Gabriel 61 East Dulwich Road, London SE22 9AP — Ptychio Iatrikes 1983 Athens.

DIMITRIU, Virgil-Nicolae Lyon Street, Dundee DD4 6RB; 30 Riverside Place, Dundee DD2 1QE — LRCP LRCS 1978 Ed.; MB Bucharest 1964; LRCPS Glas. 1978. (Bucharest) Socs: BMA. Prev: SHO (Paediat., Psychiat., Dermat. & ENT Ninewells Hosp. Dundee.

DIMITRY, Essam Shokry Department of Obstetrics & Gynaecology, Wexham Park Hospital, Wexham, Slough SL2 4HL Tel: 01753 633000 — MB BCh 1977 Ain Shams; MPhil Lond. 1993; FRCOG 1999. Cons. O & G Wexham Pk. Hosp. Slough. Prev: Sen. Regist. (O & G) John Radcliffe Hosp. Oxf.; Lect. (O & G) Roy. Free Hosp. Lond.; Clin. Research Fell. (IVF) Hammersmith Hosp. Roy. Postgrad. Med. Sch. Lond.

DIMMOCK, David Paul 25 Avenue Road, Wallington SM6 9QF — MB BS 1998 Lond.; MB BS Lond 1998.

DIMMOCK, Sandra Ann 59 Highbury Hill, London N5 1SX — MB BS 1975 Lond.; FRCR 1982; DMRD Lond. 1981. Cons. Radiol. P.ss Alexandra Hosp. Harlow & St. Margt. Hosp.; Epping.

DIMOND, Claire Wendy Community Adolescent Team, 32 York Road, Battersea, London SW11 3QJ — MB BS 1989 Lond.; BSc Lond. 1986; MRCPsych 1995. (St. Bart.) Sen. Regist. (Child & Adolesc. Psychiat.) SW Thames RHA.

DIMOND, John Patrick Flat 7, 1 Adelaide Mansions, Hove BN3 2FD Email: jaydee@mistral.co.uk — MB BS 1984 Lond.; FRCA 1992; FFA RCSI 1991. Sen. Regist. (Anaesth.) Guy's Hosp. Lond. Prev: Regist. King's Coll. Hosp. Lond.

DIMOND, Sarah Kathleen Caroline c/o WHO, No. 120 Street 228/51, Phnom Penh, Cambodia Tel: 00 855 23 26211 Fax: 00 855 23 26610; 6 Thurlestone Gardens, Dartmouth TQ6 9HG Tel: 01803 832693 — MB BS 1985 Lond.; BSc Lond. 1983; MSc (Econ.) Lond. 1995; MRCGP 1991; DRCOG 1987. Assoc. Profess. Overseas Developm. Admin. Off. Socs: WHO. Prev: Med. Co-ordinator Save the Childr. Fund (UK); Trainee GP King's Coll. Hosp. Lond.

DIMOPOULOS, Vassilios Flat 31, Dee House, Bushey Fields Road, Dudley DY1 2LT — State DMS 1989 Milan.

DIMPEL, Hans Lorenz Department of Anaesthetics, University Hospital of Wales, Heath Park, Cardiff CF14 4XW — MD 1989 Kiel; State Exam Med 1989.

DIMSON, Helen Patricia Medical Centre, Inglis Barracks, London NW7 1PX Tel: 020 8818 6320 Fax: 020 8818 6359; 2 Arlington, London N12 7JR Tel: 020 8445 9988 — MB BS Newc. 1969; DObst RCOG 1971; DFFP 1998. (New. u. Tyne) Civil. Med. Pract. Inglis Barracks Lond.; Med. Adviser for Benefits Agency. Socs: BMA & Assoc. Inst. Psychosexual Med.; Diplomate of the Fac. of Family. Prev: Ho. Off. (Paediat. Med.) Dudley Rd. Hosp. Birm.; Ho. Off. (O & G) Hillingdon Hosp.; Med. Off. Family Plann. Clinic Mill Hill.

DIMYAN, Mr Wafik Azer Brecon Medical Group Practice, Ty Henry Vaughan, Bridge Street, Brecon LD3 8AH Tel: 01874 622121 Fax: 01874 623742; The Laurels, Camden Road, Brecon LD3 7RY Tel: 01874 611171 — MB BCh 1963 Cairo; FRCS Eng. 1974; MRCS Eng. LRCP Lond. 1976; DRCOG 1985. GP Brecon; Clin. Asst. (Surg.) Brecon. Prev: Regist. (Surg.) W.. Infirm. Glas.

DIN, Khondaker Mohammed Anis Ud 19 Red Brook Road, Cavendish Park, Reedswood, Walsall WS2 7RB Tel: 01922 725192 — MB BS Dacca 1961. (Dacca Med. Coll. & Univ Dacca, Bangladesh) Fell. Age Concern. Socs: Fell. Roy. Soc. Med.; Assoc. Mem. Roy. Coll. Gen. Pract. Prev: Med. Off. 130th Station Hosp. US Army Heidelburg, Germany; Med. Off. 12 RSME Regement Chattenden Barracks Rochester.

DIN, Mr Nasimullah Asmatullah 1 High Buckstone, Edinburgh EH10 6XS Tel: 0131 445 5101 — MB ChB 1966 Ed.; FRCS Ed. 1970. (Ed.) Sen. Cons. Surg. Roy. Hosp. Muscat, Oman. Prev: Cons.

Surg. Univ. Teachg. Hosp. Lusaka, Zambia; Sen. Lect. (Surg.) Univ. Zambia, Lusaka; Sen. Regist. E.. Gen. Hosp. Lothian HB.

DIN, Robert Rafiq 11 Southcote Road, London N19 5BJ — MB ChB 1992 Manch.

DIN, Sajid Akhtar Flat 5, 549 Barlow Moor Road, Manchester M21 8AN — MB ChB 1994 Manch.

DINAH, Ahmed Feroz Oldchurch Hospital, Oldchurch Road, Romford RM7 0BE; 2 Lister Court, Stevenage SG1 4AQ — MB BS 1996 Lond.

DINAKARAN, Mr Subramanian Department of Ophthalmology, Doncaster Royal Infirmary, Doncaster DN2 5LT Tel: 01302 366666 Fax: 01302 320098; 39 Abingdon Road, Intake, Doncaster DN2 5JP Tel: 01302 369189 Email: dina@thefree.net — MB BS 1986 Madras; MD New Delhi 1990; FRCS Ed. 1991. Staff Ophth. Doncaster Roy. Infirm. Socs: MRCOphth.

DINAN, Professor Timothy Gerard Department of Psychological Medicine, St. Bartholomew's Hospital, London EC1A 7BE Tel: 020 7601 8138 Fax: 020 7601 7969 Email: t.g.dinan@mds.qmw.ac.uk — MB BCh BAO 1979 NUI; MB BCh BAO NUI 1986; DSc NUI 1996; PhD Lond. 1992; MD NUI 1986; FRCPI 1994; MRCPsych 1983. (Univ. Coll. Cork) Prof. Psychol. Med. St. Bart. at Roy. Lond. Sch. Med. & Dent. Prev: Sen. Lect. (Psychiat.) Trinity Coll. Dub.

DINANI, Shamim 10c Downfield Road, Clifton, Bristol BS8 2TJ — MB BCh 1980 Wales; MRCPsych 1984. Cons. Psychiat. Ment. Handicap Farleigh Hosp. Bristol.

DINAPALA, Prabhath Leslie 27 Bassett Green Road, Bassett, Southampton SO16 3DJ — BM 1995 Soton.

DINARDO, Lorraine Ruth Bathgate Tighness, Kirkhouse Road, Killearn, Glasgow G63 9ND — MB ChB 1997 Aberd.

DINEEN, Robert Andrew 8 Chestnut Avenue, Chesham HP5 3NA — BM BS 1998 Nottm.; BM BS Nottm 1998.

DINEEN, Simon Jonathan The Surgery, The Street, Holbrook, Ipswich IP9 2PZ Tel: 01473 328263 Fax: 01473 327185 — MB BS 1975 Lond. GP Ipswich; Med. Off. for Roy. Hosp. Sch.

DINERSTEIN, Isaac 51 Hillingdon Road, Whitefield, Manchester M45 7GL Tel: 0161 766 5353 — LAH Dub. 1952. (RCSI) Med. Off. Brit. Bd. of Boxing Control; Police Surg. Salford City Police. Prev: Ho. Surg. Promenade Hosp. S.port; Jun. Hosp. Med. Off. Ment. Hosp. Prestwich.

DINES, John Hilary (retired) Wainwood, Stevenage Road, St Ippolytts, Hitchin SG4 7PE Tel: 01462 459952 — MB BS 1954 Lond.; DObst RCOG 1967. Prev: HM Coroner Hitchin Dist.

DING, Col Daau 37 Hillside, Cromer NR27 0HY — MB BCh 1970 Cairo; DTCD Wales 1980.

DING, Grace Hsi Yen 47 Trinity Street, Oxford OX1 1TY — BM 1987 Soton.; MRCGP 1992; DRCOG 1991.

DINGLE, Miss Ann Frances Leighton Hospital, Middlewich Road, Crewe CW1 4QP Tel: 01270 612297 Fax: 01270 612085; Browns Bank, Whitchurch Road, Audlem, Crewe CW3 0EJ — MB ChB 1984 Birm.; FRCS (Gen.) Lond. 1989; FRCS (Orl.) 1995; FRCS (Ent.) Lond. 1990. (Birm.) Cons. (ENT) Leighton Hosp. Crewe. Prev: Sen. Regist. S. Wales Rotat.; Regist. Middlesbrough; SHO Selly Oak Hosp. Birm.

DINGLE, Donald Graham (retired) Linkinhorne, Balmoral Road, Grappenhall, Warrington WA4 2EB — MB 1954 Camb.; BChir 1953; DObst RCOG 1958. Prev: Flight-Lt. RAF Med. Br.

DINGLE, Hugh Reginald (retired) Abbotsbury, Vallee Des Vaux, St Helier, Jersey JE2 3GB Tel: 01534 26337 — BM BCh 1954 Oxf.; BA Oxf. 1951, MA 1957, BM BCh 1954; FFA RCS Eng. 1962; DA Eng. 1958. Prev: Cons. Anaesth. Jersey Gen. Hosp.

DINGLE, Michael Lewis Dorian 148 Harley Street, London W1N 1AH Tel: 020 7935 7362 — BM BCh 1966 Oxf.; BSc Lond. 1962; MRCP (U.K.) 1971; DObst RCOG 1974. (Univ. Coll. Lond. & Oxf.) Phys. Cavendish Med. Centre Lond. Socs: Fell. Roy. Soc. Med.; BMA. Prev: Specialist in Med. Qu. Alexandra's Milit. Hosp. Lond.; Ho. Phys. Univ. Coll. Hosp. Lond.; Ho. Surg. King Edwd. VII Hosp. Windsor.

DINGLE, Peter Robert Herrington Medical Centre, Philadelphia Lane, Houghton-le-Spring DH4 4LE Tel: 0191 584 2632; Kielder, 28 Biddick Lane, Fatfield 13, Washington NE38 8AE Tel: 0191 416 2287 — MB BS 1953 Durh. Prev: Clin. Asst. Psychiat. Durh. Hosp. Gp.

DINGLEY, Edward Richard, OBE Lotus House, The Street, Draycott, Cheddar BS27 3TH Tel: 01934 744215 Fax: 01934 744672 Email: dingleylotus@freecall-uk.co.uk — MB BS Lond. 1955; MRCS Eng. LRCP Lond. 1955; FCOphth. 1988; DO RCS Eng. 1960. (King's Coll. Hosp.) p/t OMP Med. Eye Centre, Cheltenham. Socs: SW Ophth. Soc.; Brit. Soc. Refractive Surg. Prev: Sen. Cons. Ophth. Sabah, Malaysia.; Surg., Optimax Laser Eye Clinics.

DINGLEY, John Cardiac Centre, Morriston Hospital, Swansea SA6 6NL Tel: 01792 703279 Email: john.dingley@mornhst_tr.wales.nhs.uk; 103A Swansea Road, Llandfelach, Swansea SA5 7HX — MB BCh 1987 Wales; FRCA 1993. Cons. Cardiothoracic Anaesth. Cardiac Centre Morriston Hosp. Swansea. Prev: Sen. Regist. (Anaesth.) Univ. Hosp. Wales Cardiff; Regist. (Anaesth.) Univ. Hosp. Wales.

DINGLEY, Leslie David Albany Road Medical Centre, 24 Albany Road, Roath, Cardiff CF24 3YY Tel: 029 2048 6561 Fax: 029 2045 1403; 1 St. Edeyrn's Close, Cyncoed, Cardiff CF23 6TH — MB BCh 1972 Wales; MRCGP 1978; DObst RCOG 1975.

DINGSDALE, Frances Charlotte Brooklands Cottage, Narrow Moss Lane, Ormskirk L40 8HY — MB ChB 1995 Leeds.

DINGWALL, Angela Mary Elizabeth 38 Mansionhouse Road, Paisley PA1 3RF — MB ChB 1974 Glas.

DINGWALL, Anne Elizabeth Royal Cornwall Hospital Trust, Truro TR1 3LJ Tel: 01872 74242 — MB ChB 1977 Manch.; FFA RCS Eng. 1981. Cons. Anaesth. Roy. Cornw. Hosps. Trust. Prev: Cons. Anaesth. Stepping Hill Hosp. Stockport.

DINGWALL, Douglas Watson Taeblair Smithy, Munlochy IV8 8NZ Tel: 01463 811380 — MB ChB 1963 Ed.; BSc Ed. 1960; FRCGP 1979, M 1972; DObst RCOG 1965; DCH RCPS Glas. 1965. (Ed.) Med. Adviser Benefits Agency Med. Servs. Inverness & Highlands & Is.s. Prev: GP Glenrothes Fife; SHO (Paediat.) & Ho. Off. (Surg.) Vict. Hosp. Kirkcaldy; Ho. Off. (Obst.) Forth Pk. Matern. Hosp. Kirkcaldy.

DINGWALL, Isobel Margaret Greenfield Surgery, 11 Greenfield Avenue, Stourbridge DY8 1SU Tel: 01384 442111 — MB ChB 1980 Aberd.; MRCGP 1985; DRCOG 1982. (Aberdeen Univ.)

DINLEY, Mr Roy Richard John 21 Ashwood Drive, Broadstone BH18 8LN Tel: 01202 760115 — MB BS 1965 Lond.; FRCS Eng. 1973; FRCS Ed. 1972; MRCS Eng. LRCP Lond. 1965; DObst RCOG 1967. (Westm.) Cons. Orthop. Surg. Roy. Bournemouth Hosp., ChristCh. Hosp. Trust & Poole Hosp. Trust. Socs: Fell. Roy. Soc. Med.; Fell. BOA; BMA. Prev: Sen. Regist. Nuffield Dept. Orthop. Surg. Nuffield Orthop. Centre Oxf.

DINMORE, Peter (retired) Camden, Biggin Hall Lane, Thurlaston, Rugby CV23 9LD — MRCS Eng. LRCP Lond. 1950; FFA RCS Eng. 1957. Cons. Anaesth. Rugby & Coventry DHA.

DINN, Arthur James (retired) Candlers, Harleston IP20 9HB Tel: 01379 852470 — MB BS 1946 Lond.; DObst RCOG 1951. Prev: Surg. Lt. RNVSR.

DINNEEN, Mr Michael Dominic Department of Urology, Chelsea & Westminster Hospital, 369 Fulham Road, London SW10 9NH Tel: 020 8746 8559 Fax: 020 8746 8846; 29 Hale Gardens, London W3 9SG — MB BCh BAO NUI 1983; MD NUI 1994; FRCS (Urol.) 1995; FRCSI 1986. (Univ. Coll. Cork) Cons. Urol. Chelsea & W.m. Hosp. & Char. Cross Hosp. Lond.

DINNEN, John Sheridan Pathology Department, County Hospital, Hereford HR1 2ER Tel: 01432 355444 — MB BS 1971 Lond.; BSc Lond. 1968, MB BS 1971; FRCPath 1978. (King's Coll. Hosp.) Cons. (Histopath.) Co. Hosp. Hereford. Socs: Assn. Clin. Path. & Internat. Acad. Path. Prev: Sen. Regist. (Histopath.) Univ. Hosp. Wales Cardiff; Demonst (Path.) King's Coll. Hosp. Lond.

DINNEN, Rodney Lewis Health Centre, Oakworth Road, Keighley BD21 1SA — MB BS 1973 Lond.

DINNEPATI, Sudarsana Reddy 1 Hazelwood Road, Wigan WN1 2PE Tel: 01942 824277 — MB BS 1969 Sri Venkateswara; MS (Ophth.) Osmania Univ. India 1972. Staff Grade (Ophth.) Wigan.

DINNER, Lila 8 Prospero Road, London N19 3RF — MB BS 1990 Lond.; BSc Lond. 1987; FRCA 1995. (St. Mary's Hosp. Med. Sch.) Specialist Regist. (Anaesth.) Univ. Coll. Lond. Hosp. Trust. Prev: Clin. Research Fell. (Surg.) Univ. Coll. Lond.; Regist. (Anaesth.) Univ. Coll. Hosp. Lond.

DINNETT, Eleanor Margaret 22 Avondale Drive, Paisley PA1 3TN — MB ChB 1978 Glas. Clin. Asst. (Cytol.) Vict. Infirm. Glas.

DINNICK, Susan Eleanor Cotwold House, Sutton Hospital, Cotswold Road, Sutton SM2 5NF Tel: 020 8652 7900 Fax: 0208 652 7909; 36 Gerard Road, Barnes, London SW13 9RG — MB BS 1971 Lond.; MRCPsych 1979; DObst RCOG 1976. Cons. Child & Adolesc. Psychiat. S. W. Lond. & St Geo.'s Ment. Health (NHS)

Trust. Prev: Sen. Regist. (Child Psychiat.) Guy's Hosp. Lond.; Sen. Regist. (Psychiat.) St. Geo. Hosp. Lond.

DINNING, Mr William John 9 Lascelles House, Harewood Avenue, London NW1 6NS Tel: 020 7724 6388 — MB BS (Hons.) Sydney 1965; FRCS Eng. 1972; MRCP (UK) 1972; DO Eng. 1968. (Sydney) p/t Indep. Cons. Ophth. Lond. Prev: Asst. Prof. Ophth. Washington Univ. Sch. Med. St. Louis, USA; Cons. Surg. (Ophth.) W. Middlx. Hosp. Isleworth; Hon. Cons. Ophth. Moorfields Eye Hosp.

DINNIS, George Andrew Newbury Street, Wantage OX12 7AY Tel: 01235 763451 Fax: 01235 771829 Email: dreudinnis@doctors.org.uk; Torbet House, Larkhill, Wantage OX12 8HW — MB BS 1973 Lond.; MRCGP 1979; DRCOG 1978. (St. Thos.) Prev: Trainee GP Tunbridge Wells VTS; Ho. Phys. Salisbury Gen. Hosp.; Ho. Surg. St. Thos. Hosp. Lond.

DINSDALE, Claire Louise Albert House, Albert Place, Mumbles, Swansea SA3 4LE — MB BS 1994 Lond.

DINSHAW, Daulat 52 Mersham Drive, Kingsbury, London NW9 9PN Tel: 020 8204 5819 — MB BS 1968 Bombay. (Bombay)

DINSMORE, Esther Amanda 26 Kensington Park, Bangor BT20 3RF — MB BCh BAO 1995 Belf.

DINSMORE, Judith Elizabeth 87, Woodside, Wimbledon, London SW19 7BA — MB BS 1986 Lond.; FCAnaesth 1992; DA (UK) 1989. Cons. Anaesth. with Specialist Interest in Neuroanaesth. St. Geo.'s & Atkinson Morleys Hosps. Lond.

DINSMORE, Wilbert Wallace Department of Genito Urinary Medicine, Royal Victoria Hospital, Grosvenor Road, Belfast BT12 6BA Tel: 01232 240503 Fax: 01232 322303; 1 Brackenwood Lane, Upper Malone, Belfast BT17 9JJ Tel: 01232 622530 Fax: 01232 600429 — MB BCh BAO 1978 Belf.; MD Belf. 1984; FRCP Ed. 1996; FRCP Lond. 1993, M 1981; FRCPI 1996, M 1995. Cons. Phys. (Genitourin. Med.) Roy. Vict. Hosp. Belf.; Edr. Internat. Jl. of STD & AIDS. Socs: Sec. Brit. Soc. For Sexual & Impotence Research; Sec. MSSD Sexual DysFunc. s/i Gp.; Fell.Roy. Soc. Med. Prev: DHSS Research Fell. Regist. Roy. Vict. Hosp.

DINTINGER, Emma Louise Shaftesbury Medical Centre, 480 Harehills Road, Leeds LS9; 20 Featherbank Terrace, Horsforth, Leeds LS18 4QW — MB ChB 1993 Manch. SHO (Anaesth.) Qu. Med. Centre Nottm.; SHO (GP VTS) Leeds Gen. Infirm.

DINWIDDIE, Janet Fiona Tel: 01797 252140 Fax: 01797 252077 Email: janetdinwiddie@gp-g81087.nhs.uk; Stonepit House, Stonepit Lane, Sandhurst, Cranbrook TN18 5PR Tel: 01580 850722 Fax: 01580 850722 — MB BS 1973 Lond.; MRCS Eng. LRCP Lond. 1973; DCH Eng. 1978; DObst RCOG 1975. (St. Bart.) GP Tutor. Prev: Med. Off. (Child Health) Tunbridge Wells Dist.; Clin. Med. Off. Kwun Tong Community Health Project, Hong Kong; Med. Off. United Christian Hosp., Hong Kong.

DINWIDDIE, Robert Great Ormond Street Hospital for Children NHS Trust, Great Ormond St., London WC1N 3JH Tel: 020 7405 9200 Fax: 020 7829 8634 — MB ChB Aberd. 1969; FRCP Lond. 1984; MRCP (UK) 1974; FRCPCH 1997; DCH Eng. 1971. (Aberd.) Cons. Respirat. Paediat. Hosp. Childr. Gt. Ormond St. Lond.; Hon. Sen. Lect. Inst. of Child Health Univ. Lond. Socs: Fell. Roy. Soc. Med.; Fell. Roy. Coll. Paediat. & Child Health; Brit. Paediat. Respirat. Soc. Prev: Ho. Phys. (Cardiothoracic) Hosp. Sick Childr. Gt. Ormond St.; Research Fell. (Child Health) Univ. Aberd.; Asst. Chief Resid. Phys. Childr. Hosp. Philadelphia, USA.

DINWOODIE, Doreen Laverock (retired) 75 East Trinity Road, Edinburgh EH5 3EL Tel: 0131 552 6891 — MB ChB Glas. 1952; DObst RCOG 1954. Prev: Genetic Register Clinician Dept. Human Genetics W.. Gen. Hosp. Edin.

DINWOODIE, Hugh Parker (retired) 75 East Trinity Road, Edinburgh EH5 3EL — MB ChB 1953 Glas.; FRCGP 1974, M 1965; DObst RCOG 1957. Prev: Ho. Surg. Glas. Roy. Infirm. & Glas. Roy. Matern. & Wom. Hosp.

DINWOODIE, John Mark Fairfield Park Health Centre, Tyning Lane, Camden Road, Bath BA1 6EA Tel: 01225 331616 Fax: 01225 485522 Email: mark.dinwoodie@gp_l81071.nhs.uk — MB BS 1987 Lond.; DFFP 1996; MA Camb. 1988; MRCGP 1991; DRCOG 1990; DCH RCP Lond. 1990; DGM RCP Lond. 1989; Cert. Family Plann. JCG 1989. (Camb. & Guy's Hosp.) Princip. GP Bath; Clin. Asst. Cardiol. Prev: Trainee GP Bath VTS; Ho. Phys. Lewisham Hosp., Lond.; Ho. Surg. Guy's Hosp. Lond.

DIONG, Kok-Leong 3 Rossdale Glen, Belfast BT8 6XQ — MB BCh BAO 1991 Belf.

DIOR, Alastair Roger Elgar House Surgery, Church Road, Redditch B97 4AB Tel: 01527 69261 Fax: 01527 596856 — MB ChB 1986 Birm.; BSc (Hons.) Birm. 1983; MRCGP 1992. (Birm.) Socs: MRCGP.

DIPPIE, Thomas Hall Purves (retired) 6 Driffold, Sutton Coldfield B73 6HE — MB ChB 1952 Glas. Prev: Ho. Surg. Vict. Infirm. Glas. & Glas. Roy. Matern. Hosp.

DIPPLE, Heather Claire 70 Thirlmere Road, Barrow-on-Soar, Loughborough LE12 8QQ — MB ChB 1982 Sheff.; MRCPsych 1987. Sen. Reg. (Psychiat.) Leicester.

DIPPLE, Rosemary Margaret (retired) 7 Church Mill Close, Market Rasen LN8 3JL Tel: 01673 842221 — MB ChB 1960 Cape Town; MFCM 1972; MFPHM 1989; DCH Eng. 1968; DPH Bristol 1967. Prev: SCM Brent DHA.

DIPPY, John Edward Rheumatology Department, Princess Margaret Hospital, Okus Road, Swindon SN4 0DA Tel: 01793 536231 — MB BS 1966 Lond.; BPharm. Lond. 1961; FRCP Lond. 1986; MRCP (UK) 1973. (Lond. Hosp.) p/t Cons. Phys. Rheum. P.ss Margt. Hosp. Swindon. Socs: Brit. Soc. Rheum. Prev: Sen. Regist. (Rheum.) Univ. Hosp. of Wales Cardiff; Regist. (Med.) Cardiff Roy. Infirm.; Jun. Lect. (Pharmacol.) Guy's Hosp. Lond.

DIPROSE, Jill The Health Centre, Hospital Hill, Dawlish EX7 9NS Tel: 01626 862227; Greystoke, Stockton Avenue, Dawlish EX7 9LU Tel: 01626 863970 — MB ChB 1968 Bristol. SCMO Torbay Health Care Trust.

DIPROSE, Paul Anaesthetic Department, Southampton University Hospital, Tremona Road, Southampton SO16 6YD — BM 1993 Soton.; FRCA 2000; FRCS A&E Ed 1998. Specialist Regist. Anaesth. Wessex Deanery.

DIPROSE, Ronald Henry Barton Surgery, Barton Terrace, Dawlish EX7 9QH Tel: 01626 888877 Fax: 01626 888360; Greystoke, Stockton Avenue, Dawlish EX7 9LU Tel: 01626 863970 — MB ChB 1968 Bristol; MRCGP 1978; FFA RCS Eng. 1973. Prev: Regist. (Anaesth.) Bristol Roy. Infirm.; SHO (Anaesth.) Frenchay Hosp. Bristol.

DIRCKZE, Jeremy Michael 33 Keswick Drive, Frodsham, Warrington WA6 7LT — MB ChB 1982 Leeds; MRCGP 1986.

DIRMEIK, Bernice Felicity 14 Fitzjohns Avenue, London NW3 5NA Tel: 0207 435 6229 Fax: 0208 458 5798 Email: fdirmeik@dirmeik.freeserve.co.uk; 7 Wycombe Gardens, London NW1 1 8AN Tel: 0208 458 5798 Fax: 0208 458 5798 Email: fdirmeik@dirmeik.freeserve.co.uk — MB ChB 1970 Cape Town; MRCPsych 1975. (Cape Town) Private Pract. Socs: Brit. Psychoanalyt. Soc.; Gp. Analyt. Soc. Prev: Sen. Lect. (Psychother.) Univ. Coll. & Middlx. Sch. Med. Lond.; Cons. (Psychother.) Lond. Hosp. (Whitechapel); Sen. Regist. (Psychother.) Tavistock Clinic Lond.

DIRMIKIS, Helen 10 Wilton Cres, Wimbledon, London SW19 3QZ Tel: 020 8540 2612 — MB ChB 1998 Sheff.; MB ChB Sheff 1998. (Univ of Sheffield) SHO. (A&E.) UCL. Lond. Prev: HO. (Med.) Chesterfield Dist Hosp. Chesterfield; HO. (Med.) Barnsley Dist Hosp. Barnsley.

DIRNHUBER, Mark James Clifton House, Gomeldon Road, Porton, Salisbury SP4 0JT — BM BCh 1983 Oxf.

DISCHE, Frederick Ephraim Farrer-Brown Histopathology Ltd, 80 Harley St., London W1A 1AE Tel: 0207 291 0291; 3 Holmden Court, High Street, Edenbridge TN8 5DP Tel: 01732 860075 — MD 1952 Lond.; MB BS 1947; FRCP Lond. 1977, M 1952; FRCPath 1970, M 1963. (Middlx.) Prev: Cons. Path. Dulwich Hosp. (King's Coll. Hosp.) Lond.

DISCHE, Professor Stanley, Air Marshal RAF Med. Br. Marie Curie Research Wing for Oncology, Mount Vernon Centre for Cancer Treatment, Mount Vernon Hospital, Northwood HA6 2RN Tel: 01923 844533 Fax: 01923 844167; Highbeech, 1 Green Lane, Northwood HA6 2UY Tel: 01923 825483 Fax: 01923 825483 Email: dische@mtvern.co.uk — MB BS 1950 Lond.; MD Lond. 1957; FACR 1994; FRCR 1963; DMRT Eng. 1957. (Middlx.) Hon. Cons. Radiother. & Oncol. Mt. Vernon Cancer Treatm. Centre; Vis Prof. Oncol. UCL Med. Sch. Prev: Clin. Dir. Mt. Vernon Centre for Cancer Treatm. N.wood; Dir. of Research & Developm. Mt. Vernon & Watford Hosps. NHS Trust.

DISCHE, Sylvia (retired) 3 Holmden Court, High Street, Edenbridge TN8 5DP Tel: 01732 860075 — MB BCh 1946 Witwatersrand; BSc

(Hons.) Witwatersrand 1945, MB BCh 1946; MRCP Ed. 1950. Prev: SCMO Camberwell HA.

DISCOMBE, Cynthia Joan (retired) Distant Hills, Chetnole, Sherborne DT9 6PE Tel: 01935 872448 — MB ChB Liverp. 1951; MD Liverp. 1956. Prev: Cons. Path. Ormskirk & Dist. Gen. Hosp.

DISHER, Alan Derek Rhodes (retired) 59 Putnoe Lane, Bedford MK41 9AE Tel: 01234 354325 — BM BCh 1962 Oxf.; MA Oxf. 1962; DObst RCOG 1965. Prev: Hosp. Pract. (A & E) Bedford Gen. Hosp.

DISKIN, Lynn 10 Bellevue, Bristol BS8 1DA — MB ChB 1997 Bristol.

DISLEY, Ann 19 Woodland Road, Weston Super Mare BS23 4HF — BM 1978 Soton.

DISLEY, Phyllis Jean (retired) 18 Whatley Court, Whatley Road, Clifton, Bristol BS8 2PS — MB ChB 1951 Glas.; DPH Liverp. 1955. Prev: Clin. Med. Off. Liverp. HA.

DISLEY, Rachel 10 Handley Court, Aigburgh, Liverpool L19 3QS — MB ChB 1996 Liverp.

DISMORR, Anthony Richard (retired) Noyan, Jack Straws Lane, Headington, Oxford OX3 0DN — MRCS Eng. LRCP Lond. 1944; BA 1942, BM BCh Oxf. 1944. Prev: Ho. Phys. Roy. United Hosp. Bath.

DISMORR, Henry James 21 Harmer Street, Gravesend DA12 2AP — LMSSA 1939 Lond.; MA, MB BCh Camb. 1944. (Camb. & St. Geo.) Fell. St. John's Hosp. Dermat. Soc. Prev: Asst. Skin & VD Depts. St. Geo. Hosp.; Jun. Med. Regist. Essex Co. Hosp. Colchester; Capt. RAMC.

DISMORR, Katharine Jane Rusthall Medical Centre, Nellington Road, Rusthall, Tunbridge Wells TN4 8UW Tel: 01892 515142 Fax: 01892 532256; 11 Hungershall Park, Tunbridge Wells TN4 8NE Tel: 01892 549260 — MB BS 1978 Lond.; DRCOG 1980. (Guy's) Prev: Trainee GP S.Boro.; SHO (Paediat.) Sydenham Hosp. Lond.; SHO (ENT) Kent & Sussex Hosp. Tunbridge Wells.

DISNEY, David James The Park Medical Centre, Maine Drive Clinic, Maine Drive, Chaddesden, Derby DE21 6LA Tel: 01332 665522 Fax: 01332 678210; The Park Medical Practice, 46 Derby Road, Borrowash, Derby DE72 3HA Tel: 01332 665511 Fax: 01332 669676 — MB ChB 1981 Sheff.; MRCGP 1986; Dip. Pract. Dermat. Wales 1995; DRCOG 1985. (Sheffield) Socs: Derby Med. Soc.

DISNEY, John Norton The Surgery, Fortey Road, Northleach, Cheltenham GL54 3EQ Tel: 01451860 247 Fax: 01451 860718 — MB BS 1973 Lond.; DRCOG 1979. (Char. Cross) Clin. Asst. (Gyn.) Moore Cottage Hosp. Bourton-on-the-Water & Cirencester Hosp. Prev: Cas. Surg. Off. Middlx. Hosp. Lond.; SHO (Gyn.) Qu. Mary's Hosp. Roehampton; Ho. Off. (Paediat.) Guy's Hosp. Lond.

DISNEY, Maurice Edmund (retired) Flat 2, 3 Dagmar Road, Exmouth EX8 2AN Tel: 01395 279778 — MD Lond. 1935, MB BS 1933; FRCP Lond. 1969, M 1935; MRCS Eng. LRCP Lond. 1933; FRCPCH 1988. Prev: Ho. Phys. Childr. Dept. Lond. Hosp.

DISON, Gerald, MC (retired) Sunny Mount, Hinckley Road, Burton Hastings, Nuneaton CV11 6RG Tel: 01455 220550 — LRCP LRCS Ed. LRFPS Glas. 1939; MFCM 1974; DPH Ed. 1950; DObst RCOG 1949. Prev: Dist. Community Phys. Nuneaton (N. Warks.) Health Dist. MOH Nuneaton.

DISON, Penelope Jane New Cross Hospital, Wednesfield Road, Wolverhampton WV10 0QP Tel: 01902 642882 Email: dr.dison@rwh-tr.wmids.nhs.uk — MB ChB 1980 Manch.; FRCPCH 1997; BSc St. And. 1977; FRCP 1997; MRCP (UK) 1984. Cons. Paediat., Roy. Wolverhampton NHS Trust. Socs: Fell. Roy. Coll. Phys.s; Fell. Roy. Coll. Paediat. & Child Health; BMA. Prev: SHO (Paediat.) Booth Hall Childr. Hosp. Manch.; SHO (Paediat. Cardiol.) Roy. Liverp. Childr. Hosp.; SHO (Neonat.) Univ. Hosp. Nottm.

DISSANAYAKA, Nuwan 50 The Fairway, Fixby, Huddersfield HD2 2HU — MB BS 1995 Newc.

DISSANAYAKE, Hettiarachchige Ranjith Marcus The Surgery, 11 Bincote Road, Enfield EN2 7RD Tel: 020 8367 7315 Fax: 020 8366 0623 — MB BS 1971 Ceylon.

DISSANAYAKE, Madhava Prasad 15 The Fairway, Gorleston, Great Yarmouth NR31 6JS — BM 1997 Soton.

DISSANAYAKE, Sanjeeva Bandara 20A Glenton Road, London SE13 5RS — MB BS 1993 Lond.

DISSEVELT, Anna Christina Elisabeth 3 Apsley Terrace, Braunton EX33 2EG; Lammenschansweg 5, Leiden 2313 DH, Netherlands Tel: 00 31 071 5125002 — Artsexamen 1992 Leiden; DTM & H Liverp. 1995. SHO (Genitourin. Med.) Roy. Hallamsh. Hosp. Sheff. Prev: SHO (Paediat.) Worcester; SHO (Gen. Surg. & Orthop.) Amersfourt, Netherlands.

DISSONT, Andre Damian 16 Albany Avenue, Eccleston Park, Prescot L34 2QW — MB ChB 1993 Liverp.

DISTON, Caroline Frances 188 High Street, Cottenham, Cambridge CB4 8RX — MB BChir 1987 Camb.; MRCGP 1991.

DITCHBURN, Christopher 41A Virginia Gardens, Middlesbrough TS5 8BX — MB ChB 1998 Manch.; MB ChB Manch 1998.

DITCHBURN, Janet Susan (retired) Lower Springfield, Walls, Shetland ZE2 9PF Tel: 01595 809227 — MB ChB 1963 Leeds; DObst RCOG 1965. Acupunc. Clinics, Shetland Health Bd. Prev: GP Danby, Whitby.

DITCHBURN, Robert Keith (retired) Lower Springfield, Walls, Shetland ZE2 9PF Email: robin.ditchburn@zetnet.co.uk — MB BS 1963 Durh.; MA Oxf. 1958; MD Newc. 1971; MRCP (UK) 1972; DCH Eng. 1966. Prev: GP Danby, Whitby.

DITCHFIELD, Adam Residence Block 3, Southampton General Hospital, Tremona Road, Southampton SO16 6YD — MB BS 1990 Lond.

DITRI, Anthony The Surgery, 121 Wrythe Lane, Carshalton SM5 2RT Tel: 020 8644 2727 Fax: 020 8641 7994 — MB BS 1990 Lond.; BSc (Hons.) Med. Statistics Lond. 1987; MRCGP 1995; DRCOG 1995; DFFP 1995. (Lond. Hosp. Med. Coll.) Socs: BMA & Med. Defence Union; Sutton Med. Soc.; BMA. Prev: GP Trainee Gosbury Hill Health Centre, Chessington; SHO (Paediat., Obst., Accid & Emerg. & Gen. Psychiat) Epsom Gen. Hosp.

DITTMAN, Robert (retired) 112 Market Street, Hindley, Wigan WN2 3AZ Tel: 01942 401144 — MB ChB 1957 Liverp. Prev: Hosp. Med. Off. Bootle Gen. Hosp.

DIU, Resham Singh New Hayesbank Surgery, Cemetery Lane, Kennington, Ashford TN24 9JZ Tel: 01233 624642 Fax: 01233 637304 — MB BS 1976 Newc.; MRCGP 1980. Socs: Soc. Orthop. Med.; Assoc. Mem. Brit. Assn. Manip. Med.

DIVAKARAN, Kutty 23 Brackley Square, Woodford Green IG8 7LJ — MB BS 1965 Rangoon; MB BS Med. Inst. (I) Rangoon 1965. (Univ. Rangoon) Cas. Off. Bethnal Green Hosp.; Assoc. Specialist (Genitourin. & Community Med.) Roy. Lond. Hosp. Prev: SHO (Orthop.) E. Ham Memor. Hosp. Lond.; Ho. Surg. & Cas. Off. Bethnal Green Hosp. Lond.

DIVALL, John Melvyn Hawthorns Surgery, 331 Birmingham Road, Sutton Coldfield B72 1DL Tel: 0121 373 2211 Fax: 0121 382 1274; 17 Mayfield Road, Sutton Coldfield B73 5QL — BM 1985 Soton.; MRCGP 1990; DRCOG 1988; Cert. Family Plann. JCC 1988. (Univ. Soton.) GP Princip.; GP Trainer. Prev: GP Sutton Coldfield; Trainee GP Good Hope Hosp. Sutton Coldfield VTS.

DIVALL, Paul Andrew William St Martins Hospital, Midford Road, Bath BA2 5RP Tel: 01225 831670 — MB BChir 1978 Camb.; MA Camb. 1978; MRCPsych 1982. (Camb. & St. Thos.) Cons. Old Age Psychiat. St. Martins Hosp. Bath; Psychiat. Adviser Inst. for Health and Social Policy, King's Coll., Lond.. Prev: Sen. Regist. (Psychiat.) Barrow Hosp. Bristol & Roy. United Hosp. Bath; Research Fell. Marriage Research Centre; Regist. (Psychiat.) Fulbourn Hosp. Camb.

DIVALL, Sarah Elizabeth Ferryview Health Centre, 25 John Wilson Street, Woolwich, London SE18 6PZ Tel: 020 8319 5400 Fax: 020 8319 5404; 23 Gilmore Road, Lewisham, London SE13 5AD Tel: 020 8852 9277 Fax: 020 8852 9277 — BM 1983 Soton.; MSc Lond. 1990; MRCGP 1987; DObst 1987; DGM RCP Lond. 1986. GP Tutor UMDS (UnderGrad.); GP Tutor (Postgrad.) Qu. Eliz. Hosp. Prev: Trainee GP Huntingdon VTS.

DIVAN, Ally Mohammed 10 Peel Avenue, Paddock Hill, Frimley, Camberley GU16 8YT — MB BS 1969 Karachi. (Dow Med. Coll.) Clin. Asst. (Med.) Frimley Pk. Hosp.

DIVEKAR, Mr Anand Bhalchandra 16 Canon Woods Way, Kennington, Ashford TN24 9QY — MB BS 1983 Bombay; MS (Orthop.) Bombay 1986; MCh (Orthop.) Liverp. 1992. Assoc. Specialist (Orthop.) William Harvey Hosp. Ashford. Prev: Staff Surg. (Orthop.) William Harvey Hosp. Ashford.

DIVER, Andrew Oliver 60 Central Hill, Upper Norwood, London SE19 1DT Tel: 020 8670 7117 — MB ChB 1969 Glas.; DPM Eng. 1973.

DIVER, Joseph Paul The Granary, Hurston Lane, Pulborough RH20 2EW; Room 11, Doctors Residence, Manchester Royal

Infirmary, Oxford Road, Manchester M13 9WL — MB ChB 1987 Leic.

DIVERS, Anthony Richard Department of Radiology, St. Albans & Hemel Hempstead NHS Trust, Hemel Hempstead General Hospital, Hillfield Road, Hemel Hempstead HP2 4AD Tel: 01442 287336 Fax: 01442 287351; 5 Penrith Way, Cumberland Park, Aylesbury HP21 7JZ Tel: 01296 21041 — MB BS 1975 Lond.; FRCR 1986. (Char. Cross Hosp.) Cons. Radiol. St. Albans & Hemel Hempstead NHS Trust; Mem. Edit. Bd. Curr. Topics in Radiol. Socs: Brit. Inst. Radiol.; BMA. Prev: Cons. Radiol. PM RAF Halton Aylesbury; SHO (Cas.), Ho. Surg. & Ho. Phys. Char. Cross Hosp. Lond.

DIVERS, Lloyd Sydney Peck (retired) Willow Croft, Horley Road, Charlwood, Horley RH6 0BJ Tel: 01293 862553 — MB ChB 1943 Leeds; MRCS Eng. LRCP Lond. 1942; MRCGP 1977. Prev: Dermat. Redhill Gen. Hosp.

DIVERS, Michael John 44 Carnew Road, Katesbridge, Banbridge BT32 5PS — MB ChB 1985 Leeds; BSc (Hons) Leeds 1982; MRCOG 1991. Cons. O & G Nobles Hosp. Douglas, I. of Man; Postgrad. Clin. Tutor, Isle of Man. Prev: Sen. Regist. (O & G) Simpson Memor. Matern. Pavil. Edin.; Research Fell. (O & G) Univ. Leeds.

DIWAKAR, Kethavandalu Narayanaswamy Department of Radiology, Medway Hospital, Gillingham ME7 5NY Tel: 01634 830000 — MB BS 1963 Mysore; DMRD Eng. 1970. (Bangalore Med. Coll.) Cons. Radiol. Medway Hosp. Gillingham.

DIWAKAR, Vinod Woodpeckers Cottage, Sway Road, Brockenhurst SO42 7RX — MB BS 1990 Lond. SHO (Paediat.) Dudley Rd. Hosp. Birm.

DIWAN, Shanti Parkash The Surgery, 71 Fellows Lane, Harborne, Birmingham B17 9TX Tel: 0121 427 1273 — MB BS 1961 Panjab; MRCP (UK) 1970.

DIX, Mr Francis Paul 5 Brook Vale Court, Sowerby Road, Sowerby, Preston PR3 0TT — MB BS 1992 Lond.; BSc (Anat.) Lond. 1989; FRCS Lond. 1997. (Middlesex/UCL) Specialist Regist. Gen. Surg. N. W. Region.

DIX, Janet Hazel 26 Heatherlands, Sunbury-on-Thames TW16 7QU Tel: 01932 765080 — MB ChB 1955 Bristol. (Bristol)

DIX, Margaret Ruth (retired) The Rectory, Badger, Wolverhampton WV7 3EP — MD 1957 Lond.; MB BS 1937; FRCS Eng. 1943. Hon. Phys. (Audiol.) Inst. Neurol. Lond.; Attached Worker MRC Neuro-Otol. Unit Nat. Hosp. Nerv. Dis. Qu. Sq. Lond. Prev: Ho. Surg. ENT Dept. Roy. Free Hosp.

DIX, Melanie Flat 10, 11 Hanover Square, Leeds LS3 1AP — MB ChB 1989 Leeds. SHO (A & E) Harrogate Dist. Hosp.

DIX, Philippa Jayne 83 Kennington Ave., Bishopston, Bristol BS7 9EX — BM BS 1989 Nottm. p/t Specialist Regist. (Anaesth.) Bristol.

DIXEY, John Maurice Duncan (retired) Inisfail House, Isleham, Ely CB7 5RY — MRCS Eng. LRCP Lond. 1956; MRCGP 1964. Mobility Allowance Med. Off. DHSS (Cambs.). Prev: Ho. Phys. (Paediat.) St. Albans City Hosp.

DIXEY, John Roger Bertram (retired) Elm Lodge, Streatley, Reading RG8 9JR Tel: 01491 872882 — BA 1943, MB BChir Camb. 1946; FRCGP 1980, M 1966. Prev: Hosp. Pract. (Med.) Roy. Berks. Hosp. Reading.

DIXEY, Josh Robert Jones & Agnes Hunt Orthopaedic Hospital, Oswestry SY10 7AG Tel: 01691 404384 Fax: 01691 404320 Email: josh.dixey@rjahoh-tr.wmids.nhs.uk — MD 1988 Lond.; MB BS Lond. 1978; FRCP Lond. 1994; MRCP (UK) 1980. Cons. Rheumat. Robt. Jones & Agnes Hunt Orthop. Hosp. OsW.ry & P.ss Roy. Hosp. Telford.; Med. Dir. Robt. Jones & Agnes Hunt Orthop. Hosp. OsW.ry. Prev: Sen. Regist. Char. Cross & W.m. Hosp. Lond.

DIXEY, Simon John Penn Hospital, Penn Road, Wolverhampton WV4 5HN Tel: 01902 444129 Fax: 01902 444127; 9 St. Marks Close, Great Wyrley, Walsall WS6 6PZ Email: simon.dixey@which.net — MB ChB 1985 Sheff.; BA (Physiol. Sc.) Oxf. 1982; MRCPsych 1991. Cons. Psychiat. Old Age Wolverhampton.

DIXIT, Bir Bala 36 Lloyd Park Avenue, Croydon CR0 5SB — MB BS 1968 Lucknow; MRCOG 1975, DObst 1971. (King Geo. Med. Coll. Lucknow) Regist. (O & G) Belf. City Hosp. & Down Hosp. Downpatrick.

DIXIT, Chandrashekhar Madhukar The Galleries Health Centre, Town Centre, Washington NE38 Tel: 0191 416 6084 — MB BS 1974 Poona. (Poona) GP Washington, Tyne & Wear.

DIXON, Professor Adrian Kendal University Department of Radiology, Box 219, Addenbrooke's Hospital, Hills Road, Cambridge CB2 2QQ Tel: 01233 336890 Fax: 01223 330915 Email: akd15@radiol.cam.ac.uk; 8 Alwyne Road, Cambridge CB1 8RR Tel: 01223 247048 — MB BChir 1972 Camb.; FRANZCP 2001 (Hon); MA Camb. 1973, MD 1988; F MED SCI 1998; FRCP Lond. 1991; FRCR 1978; DMRD Eng. 1977; MRCP (UK) 1974; (Hon) F.Med.Sci 1998; FFRRCSI 1999. (St Bartholomew's Medical College) Prof. & Hon. Cons. Radiol. Addenbrooke's Hosp. Camb.; Vis. Prof. Univ. Otago, NZ, 1992; Fell. PeterHo. Camb. Prev: SHO (Med.) Nottm. Gen. Hosp.; Ho. Off. & Sen. Regist. (Radiol.) St. Bart. Hosp. Lond.

DIXON, Allan St John, OBE Tregisky, Coverack, Helston TR12 6TQ Tel: 01326 280203 Fax: 01326 280693 Email: asdixon@sheffield.ac.uk — MB BS 1945 Lond.; MD Lond. 1948; FRCP Lond. 1968, M 1948; LMSSA Lond. 1945. (Guy's) Emerit. Cons. Phys. Roy. United Hosp. & Roy. Nat. Hosp. Rheum. Dis. Bath. Socs: Brit. Soc. Rheum.; Assn. Phys.; (Pres.) Nat. Osteoporosis Soc. Prev: Vis. Prof. Univ. Bath 1983-6; Cons. St. Stephen's & St. Mary Abbot's Hosps; Lect. (Rheum.) Postgrad. Med. Sch. Lond. & Univ. Manch.

DIXON, Andrew David 15 Hawkins Way, Wootton, Abingdon OX13 6LB — MB ChB 1998 Leic.; MB ChB Leic 1998; BSc 1992. (Leicester)

DIXON, Angela Woodroffe, Dixon and Raitt, Ravenswood Surgery, New Road, Forfar DD8 2AE Tel: 01307 463558 Fax: 01307 468900 — MB BS 1987 Lond.; MNIMH 1996; MRCGP 1991; DRCOG 1991. (St. Geo. Hosp. Med. Sch. Lond.) Socs: MNIMH 1996. Prev: Trainee GP Cleveland VTS.

DIXON, Anne Marjorie (retired) 51 Elizabeth Road, Henley-on-Thames RG9 1RA Tel: 01491 577024 — MB BS 1957 Lond.; DPH Eng. 1963, DA 1960 Eng. Prev: Clin. Med. Off. W. Berks. HA.

DIXON, Anthony Michael Birchwood Medical Centre, 15 Benson Road, Birchwood, Warrington WA3 7PJ Tel: 01925 823502 Fax: 01925 852422; 34 Kingsbury Close, Appleton, Warrington WA4 5FF Tel: 01925 213082 — MB ChB 1985 Leeds; MRCGP 1989; DRCOG 1988. (Leeds)

DIXON, Anthony Noel 40 Fassett Road, Kingston upon Thames KT1 2TF — BM 1995 Soton.

DIXON, Mr Anthony Richard The Glen, Redland Hill, Durdham Down, Bristol BS6 7UT Tel: 0117 973 2562 Fax: 0117 974 3203; Old Manor Farm, Ingst Hill, Olveston, Bristol BS35 4AP Fax: 01454 631410 — MB BS 1983 Lond.; DM Nottm. 1992; FRCS Ed. 1987. (St. Geo. Hosp. Med. Sch. Lond.) Hon. Sen. Lect. (Surg.)--Bristol Univ. Socs: Fell. Roy. Soc. Med. (Coloproctol.); Brit. Assn. Surgic. Oncol.; Assn. Coloproctol. Prev: Sen. Regist. (Surg.) Bristol Roy. Infirm.; Laparoscopic Fell. (Surg.) Brisbane Roy. Hosp. Qu.sland, Austral.; Research Fell. BrE. Unit City Hosp. Nottm.

DIXON, Antony Michael Yew Tree Cottage, 30 Worksop Road, Thorpe Salvin, Worksop S80 3JU Tel: 01909 770367 — MB ChB 1975 Sheff.; FFA RCS 1982. Cons. Anaesth. Bassetlaw HA; Squadron Ldr. Roy. Aux. Air Force Med. Br. Socs: BMA & Assn. Anaesths. Prev: Sen. Regist. (Anaesth.) Sheff. HA; Regist. (Anaesth.) Sheff. HA (T).

DIXON, Christopher George Gillies Health Centre, Sullivan Road, Basingstoke RG22 4EH Tel: 01256 479747 Fax: 01256 32 — MB BS 1972 Lond.; MRCGP 1978; DObst RCOG 1976. Hosp. Practiioner N. Hants. Hosp. Indpendent Review Panel.

DIXON, Christopher James 96 Whittington Close, Hythe, Southampton SO45 5NQ — BM BS 1996 Nottm.

DIXON, Ciaran Michael 201 Hills Road, Cambridge CB2 2RN — MB BS 1980 Lond.; MRCGP 1990; FRCS A&E 1996. (Westm.) Socs: BMA.

DIXON, David Charles (retired) 25 St Aubins Park, Hayling Island PO11 0HQ Tel: 01705 464555 — MB ChB 1962 St. And.

DIXON, David Michael Culmside, Uffculme, Cullompton EX15 3AT — MB BS 1979 Lond.

DIXON, Elizabeth Helen Marie Willow Bank, 7 Hunter Rise, Beckermet CA21 2YP — MB ChB 1989 Manch.

DIXON, Elizabeth Mary 'Hawkrigg', Egremont Road, Hensingham, Whitehaven CA28 8QW Tel: 01946 4226 — MB ChB Manch. 1958.

DIXON, Emma Clare 8 Marton Avenue, Middlesbrough TS4 3SQ — MB ChB 1998 Dund.; MB ChB Dund 1998.

DIXON, Enid Mary (retired) 12 Bellevue Road, Ayr KA7 2SA Tel: 01292 264933 — MB ChB 1924 Glas.; DPH 1929. Prev: Asst. Sch. & Child Welf. MOH Ayrsh. CC & Educat. Auth.

DIXON, Garth Leonard James 172 Leighton Road, London NW5 2RE — MB ChB 1992 Bristol.

DIXON, Geoffrey Thomas 6 Coppice Lane, Queniborough, Leicester LE7 3DR Tel: 0116 260 7559 — MB BS 1973 Lond.; PhD Lond. 1971, BSc 1967; FFPM RCP (UK) 1993; Dip. Pharm. Med. RCP (UK) 1981. (Westm.) Socs: Brit. Pharm. Soc. Prev: Head Clin. Pharm. Hoechst UK Ltd. Milton Keynes; Med. Adviser Glaxo Gp. Research Ltd.; dir. Pharmacol., Astra Charnwood LoughBoro.

DIXON, Gillian Wendy 20 Fir Park, Great Parndon, Harlow CM19 4JY Tel: 01279 435987 — MB ChB 1988 Aberd. Prev: SHO (Pub. Health Med.) Croydon Health Commiss. Agency Lond.; Clin. Med. Off. (Community Child Health) Centr. Clinic Colchester Essex Rivers Healthcare Trust; SHO (Psychiat.) Pastures Hosp. Mickleover Derby.

DIXON, Gladys Eileen 5 Hatherley Court Road, Cheltenham GL51 3AQ Tel: 01242 513036 — MB ChB 1960 Birm.; MFFP 1993; DObst RCOG 1962. (Birm.) Head of Family Plann. & Reproduc. Health E. Glos. NHS Trust.

DIXON, Glen Reginald Department of Cellular Pathology, Tameside & Glossop Acute Services NHS Trust, Tameside General Hospital, Fountain St., Ashton-under-Lyne OL6 9RW Tel: 0161 331 6417 Fax: 0161 331 6496 — MB ChB 1987 Liverp.; MRCPath 1993. Cons. Histopath. & Cytopath. Tameside & Glossop Acute Servs. NHS Trust. Socs: Roy. Coll. Path.; Assn. Clin. Path.; Amer. Soc. Clin. Path. Prev: Sen. Regist. (Histopath.) N. W.. RHA; Regist. (Histopath.) Mersey RHA; SHO (Path. & Histopath.) BRd.green Hosp. Liverp.

DIXON, Harold Hilton The Surgery, Denmark Street, Darlington DL3 0PD; 3 Ashcroft Road, Darlington DL3 8PD Tel: 01325 468988 — MB BS 1975 Newc.; BSc Newc. 1972; FRCGP 1998; MRCGP 1979; DRCOG 1977. Mem. of Panel of Examrs. Roy. Coll. of GPs; Educat. Research Fell., Univ. of Newc.-upon-Tyne Postgrad. Inst. for Med. and Dentristry. Prev: Ho. Surg. & Ho. Phys. Cumbld. Infirm. Cumbria; Trainee GP E. Cumbria VTS.; Course Organiser Cleveland VTS.

DIXON, Helen Margaret Ebenezer Cottage, Hollington, Ashbourne DE6 3GB — MB ChB 1985 Sheff.; MA Oxf. 1987. Assoc. Specialist (Learning Disabilities) Aston Hall Hosp. Derby. Prev: Regist. (Psychiat.) Kingsway & Pastures Hosps. Derby; Clin. Asst. & GP Asst. Aston Hall Hosp. Derby.

DIXON, Hilary 8 Holyrood Court, Sandringham Drive, Bramcote Hills, Nottingham NG9 3NG Tel: 0115 943 6631 — MB ChB 1988 Ed.; MRCP (UK) 1993. (Edinburgh) Sen. Regist. (Paediat.) Derebyshire Childr.'s Hosp. Derby. Prev: Sen. Regist. (Paaediatrics) Qu.s Med. Centre Nottm.; Sen. Regist. (Paediat.) City Hosp. Nottm.; Regist. Rotat. (Paediat.) Sheff./Barnsley.

DIXON, James Westholm', 52 Two Ball Lonnen, Newcastle upon Tyne NE4 9RQ Tel: 01632 742934 — MB BS 1951 Durh.

DIXON, James Charles Manor Farm, Caple Lane, Chew Stoke, Bristol BS40 8YE Tel: 01275 332085 Fax: 01275 332085 — MB ChB 1993 Bristol; BSc (Hons.) Bristol 1979.

DIXON, Mr James William Theodore (retired) Shorts Orchard, Broadhempston, Totnes TQ9 6BD Tel: 01803 813538 — MB BS Lond. 1944; FRCS Ed. (ad eund.) 1960; FRCS Eng. 1954; MRCS Eng. LRCP Lond. 1944; DLO Eng. 1952. Surg. i/c ENT Glas. Roy. Infirm. & Lanarksh. Hosps.; Hon. Clin. Lect. Univ. Glas.; Examr. Final FRCS, RCS Edin., Dubl. & Glas. Prev: Mem. Dist. Managem. Team Torbay.

DIXON, Jane Ann 2 Tarn Villas, Ilkley LS29 8RH — MB ChB 1991 Manch.

DIXON, Jenni Julie Department of Clinical Genetics, Ashley Wing, St James' University Hospital, Beckerr St., Leeds LS1 9TP Tel: 0113 206 5423; Manor Farm, Caple Lane, Chew Stoke, Bristol BS40 8YE Tel: 01275 332085 Fax: 01275 332085 — MB ChB Bristol 1992; MRCP (UK) 1995; BVetMed Lond 1985; Cert EP 1988. Specialist Regist. in Clin. Genetics.

DIXON, Jennifer Kings Fund Policy Institute, 11-13 Cavendish Square, London W1G 0AN Tel: 020 7307 2547 — MB ChB 1984 Bristol; MSc Lond. 1990; MFPHM RCP (UK) 1995; DCH RCP Lond. 1988. Fell. (Health Policy Anal.) Kings Fund Policy Inst.; Hon. Sen. Lect. Lond. Sch. Hyg. & Trop. Med.; Hon. Cons. Pub. Health Kensington, Chelsea & W.m. Health Agency.

DIXON, Jennifer Helen 64 Woodbine Road, Newcastle upon Tyne NE3 1DE — MB BCh 1993 Wales.

DIXON, Jessie Lingard (retired) Old Church House, Hett, Croxdale, Durham DH6 5LZ Tel: 01388 819670 — MB ChB 1924 Glas. Prev: Asst. Sch. Oculist Durh. CC.

DIXON, Jill Elizabeth Department of Obstetrics & Gynaecology, Stafford General Hospital, Stafford ST16 3SA Tel: 01785 257731; House on the Hill, Toothill Road, Uttoxeter ST14 8JT — MB BS 1979 Lond.; BSc Lond. 1976, MD 1997; MRCOG 1984; DRCOG 1982; DCH RCP Lond. 1981; M.D. (London) 1997. (Westm.) Cons. O & G Stafford Gen. Hosp.; Sen. Lect. Keele Univ. Prev: Sen. Regist. (O & G) Good Hope Hosp. Sutton Coldfield; Sen. Regist. (O & G) Newc. Gen. Hosp. & Roy. Vict. Infirm. Newc. u. Tyne; Research Regist. (Obst.) Guy's Hosp. Lond.

DIXON, Joanna Lucy 11 Buttercup Close, Liverpool L22 3YR — MB ChB 1986 Leeds; FRCA 1993. Regist. (Anaesth.) Gen. Infirm. Leeds; Clin. Fell. (Paediat. IC & Anaesth.) Gen. Infirm. Leeds. Prev: Regist. (Anaesth.) Huddersfield Roy. Infirm.; SHO (Neonat.) St. Jas. Univ. Hosp. Leeds; SHO (Anaesth.) Bradford HA.

DIXON, John Weston General Hospital, Grange Road, Uphill, Weston Super Mare BS23 4TQ; 12 St. Johns Close, Weston Super Mare BS23 2LP — MB BS 1975 Lond.; FRCA 1982. (Roy. Free) Cons. Anaesth. W.on Gen. Hosp. W.on Super Mare. Prev: Sen. Regist. (Anaesth.) S. W.. RHA; Regist. (Anaesth.) Hammersmith Hosp.

DIXON, Mr John Alexander Church Street Partnership, 30A Church Street, Bishop's Stortford CM23 2LY Tel: 01279 657636 Fax: 01279 505464 — MB BS 1982 Lond.; MA Oxf. 1986; FRCS Lond. 1988; FRCS Ed. 1986; MRCGP 1991; DRCOG 1991. (Guys Hospital) Hosp. Practitioner (Ear, Nose & Throat) Addenbrooke's Hosp. Camb.

DIXON, John Crispin 83 Queens Road, Caversham, Reading RG4 8DN — MB 1979 Camb.; BChir 1978.

DIXON, John Evelyn Ronald (retired) 1 Leylands, 8 Westbourne Terrace, Budleigh Salterton EX9 6BR — MB BS 1947 Lond.; MRCS Eng. LRCP Lond. 1947. Prev: GP Romford.

DIXON, John Howard, Maj. RAMC Retd. Myrtle House, 154 Blackburn Road, Accrington BB5 0AE Tel: 01254 233651 Fax: 01254 391965; Dove Syke Farm, Eaves Hall Lane, West Bradford, Clitheroe BB7 5JG Tel: 01200 427634 — MB ChB 1972 Liverp.; MRCGP 1977. (Liverp.) Med. Dir. Vasectomy Servs. Accrington Vict. Hosp.

DIXON, Mr John Hughes Nash House, Lower Langford, Bristol BS40 5BW Tel: 01934 862248 Fax: 01934 862248 — BM BCh 1971 Oxf.; MA Oxf. 1971; FRCS Ed. 1977; MCh (Orthop.) Liverp. 1980. (Middlx.) Cons. Orthop. Surg. W.on Area Health Auth.; Hon. Lect. Univ. Bristol. Socs: Fell. BOA & Roy. Soc. Med.; Brit. Orthop. Oncol. Soc.; BMA. Prev: Sen. Regist. Middlx. Hosp. Lond.; Regist. Harlow Wood Orthop. Hosp.

DIXON, John Maurice 1 Basin End Cottages, Chester Road, Acton, Nantwich CW5 8LA — MB ChB 1990 Manch.

DIXON, Mr John Michael Joseph Academic Office, Edinburgh Breast Unit, Western General Hospital, Edinburgh EH4 2XU Tel: 0131 537 2643 Fax: 0131 537 2653 Email: jmd@wght.demon.co.uk; 29 Dregton Loan, Colinton, Edinburgh EH13 0DF Tel: 0131 441 2493 Fax: 0131 441 2493 — MB ChB 1978 Ed.; BSc (Hons.) Ed. 1975; MD Ed. 1985; FRCS Ed. 1985; FRCS Lond. 1985. (University of Edinburgh) Cons. Surg. Edin. BrE. Unit W.ern Gen. Hosp.; Hon. Sen. Lect. (Surg.) Univ. of Edin. Socs: Mem. Europ. Soc. Mastology; Surgic. Research Soc.; Brit. BrE. Gp.

DIXON, John Thwaites (retired) 4 Moorfield Road, Exmouth EX8 3QU Tel: 01395 266039 — MB ChB Ed. 1952. Prev: Med. Off. Colombo Med. Scheme Ceylon.

DIXON, Jonathan Alan Burley Park Doctors, Burley Park Medical Centre, 273 Burley Road, Leeds LS4 2EL Tel: 0113 230 4111 — MB ChB Leeds 1993.

DIXON, Jonathan Mark 25 Tunwells Lane, Great Shelford, Cambridge CB2 5LJ — MB ChB 1990 Birm.; ChB Birm. 1990; FRCA 1996.

DIXON, Judith Ann St Pauls Road Medical Centre, 248 St Pauls Road, London N1 2LJ — MB BS Lond. 1969; MRCS Eng. LRCP Lond. 1969; DCH Eng. 1971. (St. Bart.) p/t Chairm. Camden &

Islington Med. Audit Advis. Gp. Prev: Ho. Surg. (Orthop.) & Ho. Phys. (Paediat.) St. Bart. Hosp. Lond.; Ho. Phys. Whipps Cross Hosp. Lond.

DIXON, Katherine Belvoir Vale Surgery, 17A Walford Close, Bottesford, Nottingham NG13 0AN Tel: 01949 842341; The Laurels, Harston, Grantham NG32 1PW Tel: 01476 870829 — MB ChB 1986 Bristol; MRCGP 1990; Cert. Prescribed Equiv. Exp. JCPTGP 1991; Cert. Family Plann. JCC 1990. Mem. Med. Wom. Federat. Socs: BMA. Prev: Trainee GP/SHO Avon VTS; Ho. Phys. S.mead Hosp. Bristol; Ho. Surg. Yeovil Dist. Hosp.

DIXON, Kathryn 8 Sydling Springs, Sydling St Nicholas, Dorchester DT2 9NU — MB BS 1989 Lond.

DIXON, Katie Elizabeth Fareham Health Centre, Osborn Road, Fareham PO16 7ER Tel: 01329 822111 Fax: 01329 286636 — BM 1991 Soton.; MRCGP 1995.

DIXON, Lana Jayne 36 Avonbrook Gardens, Coleraine BT52 1SS — MB BCh 1997 Belf.; MB BCh BAO Belf. 1997.

DIXON, Lawrence Andrew 8 Pullman Close, Wirral CH60 1YW — MB ChB 1985 Liverp.; MRCGP 1991; DCCH 1997.

DIXON, Mark Stephen c/o S.M. Dixon, 8 Montagu Road, Freshfield, Liverpool L37 1LA Tel: 01704 873536 — MB BS 1983 Lond.; MRCP (UK) 1988; DTM & H Liverp. 1995. Cons. Phys. Mpilo Hosp. Bulawayo, Zimbabwe.

DIXON, Mary Dixon (retired) Avon Cottage, Bantham, Kingsbridge TQ7 3AP Tel: 01548 560352 — MB ChB 1942 Bristol; DCH Eng. 1944.

DIXON, Professor Michael Frederick Academic Unit of Pathology, University of Leeds, Leeds LS2 9JT Tel: 0113 233 3379 Fax: 0113 233 3404 Email: miked@pathology.leeds.ac.uk; 2 Tarn Villas, Ilkley LS29 8RH Tel: 01943 601917 Fax: 01943 601709 Email: mike.dixon@btinternet.com — MB ChB 1965 Ed.; MD Ed. 1980; FRCPath 1972. (Ed.) Prof. Gastrointestinal Path. Univ. Leeds; Hon. Cons. Centre for Digestive Dis. Gen. Infirm. Leeds. Socs: Path. Soc.; Brit. Soc. Gastroenterol.; Assn. Clin. Path. Prev: Lect. (Path.) Univ. Edin.

DIXON, Mr Michael Hadley Nurrish Larkhill, 35 New Road, Esher KT10 9NU Tel: 01372 466191 Fax: 01372 470622 — MB BS 1944 Lond.; FRCS Eng. 1951; MRCS Eng. LRCP Lond. 1944; FRCGP 1978, M 1954. (St. Mary's) Prev: Surg. i/c Varicose Vein Clinic Thames Ditton Hosp.; Supernum. Regist. (Surg.) St. Mary's Hosp.; Sen. Ho. Surg. Centr. Middlx. Hosp.

DIXON, Naomi (retired) 15 Marldon Road, Northowram, Halifax HX3 7BP — MB 1969 Camb.; BChir 1968; MRCGP 1986.

DIXON, Nicholas John Heather Dene, Ribby Road, Kirkham, Preston PR4 2BE — MB ChB 1996 Liverp.

DIXON, Nicholas Thomas Creffield Road Surgery, 19 Creffield Road, Colchester CO3 3HZ Tel: 01206 570371 Fax: 01206 369908 — BM BCh 1976 Oxf.; PhD Indiana 1973; BA Oxf. 1968; MRCGP 1979; DCH Eng. 1979.

DIXON, Nicolette Mary Gloucester Road Medical Centre, Tramway House, 1A Church Road, Horfield, Bristol BS7 8SA Tel: 0117 949 7774 — MB BS 1983 Lond.; BSc Lond. 1980; MRCGP 1987; DRCOG 1987. p/t GP Princip.

DIXON, Nigel William Prestwich Health Centre, Fairfax Road, Prestwich, Manchester M25 1BT Tel: 0161 773 2483 Fax: 0161 773 9218; 4 Clothorn Road, Didsbury, Manchester M20 6BQ Tel: 0161 434 7394 — MB ChB 1977 Manch.; MRCGP 1986; Cert. Family Plann. JCC 1984.

DIXON, Norman David Old School Surgery, 54 Station Road, Greenisland, Carrickfergus BT38 8TP Tel: 028 9086 4455 Fax: 028 9036 5367; 3 Oldstone Close, Greenisland, Carrickfergus BT38 8YG Tel: 01232 853243 — MB BCh BAO 1976 Belf.; BSc Belf. 1968; DRCOG 1978.

DIXON, Patricia Joy 4 Empire Avenue, Edmonton, London N18 1AD — MB BS 1984 Lond.

DIXON, Patrick John Vibart Global Change Ltd, 1 Carlton Gardens, London W5 2AN Tel: 0208 567 9824; 1 Carlton Gardens, London W5 2AN — MB BS 1982 Lond.; MA Camb. 1982. (Char. Cross) Dir. Global Change LTD f/t. Socs: Christian Med. Fell.sh. (Advis. Counc.). Prev: Director ACET (AIDS Care Educat. and Train.).; Clin. Asst. Terminal Care Support Team Univ. Coll. Hosp. Lond.; SHO St. Joseph's Hospice Lond.

DIXON, Paul Edgar Appleby House, Locks Lane, Leavenheath, Colchester CO6 4PF — MB BS 1971 Lond.; BSc Lond. 1968, MB BS 1971; FRCP Lond. 1994; MRCP (UK) 1975. (St. Mary's) Cons. Phys. Geriat. Med. Colchester Hosps.

DIXON, Paul Kendall 64 Woodbine Road, Newcastle upon Tyne NE3 1DE — MB BCh 1992 Wales.

DIXON, Peter Anthony Wellfield Surgery, 53-55 Crescent Road, Crumpsall, Manchester M8 9JT Tel: 0161 740 2213 Fax: 0161 720 9311 — MB ChB 1984 Manch.; Cert. Family Plann. JCC 1988. (Manch.) Prev: Trainee GP St. Gabriels Med. Centre Prestwich Manch.; SHO (A & E) Bury Gen. Hosp.; SHO (Obst.) Manygates Hosp. Wakefield.

DIXON, Peter Frederick (retired) 121 The Street, Hougton St Giles, Walsingham NR22 6AQ — MB BChir 1953 Camb.; BA Camb. 1953. Prev: Cons. Path. Chem. Path. Bromley HA & FarnBoro. Hosp. Kent.

DIXON, Richard Xavier (retired) The Croft, 30 Forest Road, Hoylake, Wirral CH47 6AX Tel: 0151 632 2915 — MB BCh BAO 1952 NUI; MRCGP 1964; DObst RCOG 1961. Prev: SHO (O & G) Omagh Gen. Hosp.

DIXON, Richenda Jane 7 Milford Close, Narborough, Leicester LE9 5FG — MB 1983 Camb.; BChir 1982.

DIXON, Robert Terence c/o DHSS, Dundonald House, Belfast BT4 3SF Tel: 01232 524371 Fax: 01232 524810 — MB BCh BAO 1972 Belf. Sen. Med. Off. DHSS Belf. Socs: Ulster Med. Soc.

DIXON, Rosemary Elizabeth Julia Polwarth Surgery, 72 Polwarth Gardens, Edinburgh EH11 1LL Tel: 0131 229 5914 Fax: 0131 221 9897 — MB ChB 1978 Ed.; MRCP (UK) 1985; LMCC 1982; MRCGP 1990. (Edinburgh) Asst. GP Edin. Prev: Regist. (Med. Paediat.) W.ern Gen. Hosp. Edin.; Regist. (Paediat.) Adelaide Childr.s Hosp. Inc., Australia; Resid. Paediat. Hosp. for Sick Childr. Toronto, Canada.

DIXON, Ruth Marian Fairfield, High St., Little Chesterford, Saffron Walden CB10 1TS — MB ChB 1987 Leeds; BSc Leeds 1984; MRCP (UK) 1990.

DIXON, Sarah Frances 76 Conway Road, Pontcanna, Cardiff CF11 9NW — MB BS 1989 Newc.

DIXON, Sarah Jane Ryle & Partners, Suite C, Havant Health Centre, Civic Centre Road, Havant PO9 2AT — MB ChB 1990 Bristol; DGM RCP Lond. 1992; MRCGP Lond. 1996. (Bristol) p/t GP Princip. Prev: Regist. GP Bristol; SHO (Psychiat.) Wonford Hse. Hosp. Exeter; SHO Cheltenham VTS.

DIXON, Sarah Pauline 34 Kingsbury Close, Appleton, Warrington WA4 5FF Tel: 01925 213082 — MB ChB 1986 Leeds; DRCOG 1990.

DIXON, Sean Michael 66 Patshull Road, London NW5 2LD — MB BS 1998 Lond.; MB BS Lond 1998.

DIXON, Sharon Louise 5/2 Easter Dalry Wynd, Edinburgh EH11 2TB — MB ChB 1997 Dundee.

DIXON, Simon Alexander Stocks Meadow, Stocks Lane, Meonstoke, Southampton SO32 3NQ — MB BS 1998 Lond.; MB BS Lond 1998.

DIXON, Simon Jeremy Colchester General Hospital, Turner Road, Colchester Email: sjdixon@doctors.org.uk; Parsonage Farm, Boxted, Colchester CO4 5ST Tel: 01206 852927 — MB BS 1991 Lond.; BSc Lond. 1984; FRCA 1997. (St. Mary's Hosp. Med. Sch. Lond.) Cons. Anaesth. Prev: Fell. In Hepatobiliary Anaesth., Roy. Free Hosp. Lond.; Fell. In Cardiothoracic Anaesth., Harefield; Specialist Regist. N. Thames Rotat.

DIXON, Susan Elaine Sydney and Partners, St Mary's Medical Centre, Rock St, Oldham OL1 3UL Tel: 0161 620 6667 Fax: 0161 626 2499; Sykes Cottage, 4 Hollygrove, Dobcross, Oldham OL3 5JW — MB ChB 1988 Sheff.; MRCGP 1992. Prev: Trainee GP Oldham; SHO (O & G, Paediat. & Acute Geriat.) Roy. Oldham Hosp.

DIXON, Susan Margaret Appleby House, Locks Lane, Leavenheath, Colchester CO6 4PF — MB BS 1980 Lond.; DRCOG 1984.

DIXON, Thomas Paul Barton Health Centre, Short Lane, Barton-under-Needwood, Burton-on-Trent DE13 8LB Tel: 01283 712207 Fax: 01283 712116 — MB BS 1965 Lond. (Middlx.) Prev: Ho. Surg. Ipswich & E. Suff. Hosp.; Ho. Phys. Burton-on-T. Gen. Hosp.; SHO (Obst.) Derby City Hosp.

DIXON, Tina Ann 48 Birch Road, Oxton, Birkenhead CH43 5UA — MB ChB 1974 Liverp.; FRCP Lond. 1996; MRCP (UK) 1979. Cons. (Allergy & Clin. Immunol.) Roy. Liverp. & Roy. Liverp. Childr. Hosps.

DIXON, William Gregory Endwell Cottage, 33 Bondgate, Castle Donington, Derby DE74 2NS — MB BS 1997 Lond.

DIXON, William Morris (retired) Playford, Cokes Lane, Chalfont St Giles HP8 4TA Tel: 01494 762275 Fax: 01494 766909 Email: wmdixon@waitrose.com — MB BS 1947 Lond.; FRCP Lond. 1982, M 1952; FFOM RCP Lond. 1979, MFOM 1978; DIH Eng. 1962. Bd. Dir. Corporate Health plc Slough. Prev: Head Med. Servs. John Lewis Partnership Lond.

DJABATEY, Edwin Ameuda 14 Thorntree Close, Aigburth, Liverpool L17 7EP — MB ChB 1985 Ghana; MB ChB U Ghana 1985.

DJAN, Nathaniel Brooklands Parade Surgery, 2 Brooklands Parade, Wolverhampton WV1 2ND Tel: 01902 453345 Fax: 01902 452141; 6 Sidcup Close, Cherry Tree Estate, Bilston WV14 9YF Tel: 01902 880260 — MD Lekarz Krakow 1972. Asst. GP Wolverhampton. Socs: BMA (Wolverhampton Div.); Fell. Roy. Soc. Med.; ODA (Wolverhampton Div.). Prev: Clin. Asst. (Geriat. Med.) Walsall HA; Regist. (Geriat. Med.) New Cross Hosp. Wolverhampton; SHO & Acting Regist. (Psychiat.) New Cross Hosp. Wolverhampton.

DJAZAERI, Mr Behzad 4 White Court, Platts Lane, London NW3 7PL Tel: 020 7435 1101 — MB BCh 1975 Wales; MCh Wales 1985, MB BCh 1975; FRCS Eng. 1980.

DJAZAERI, Benham 4 White Court, Platt's Lane, London NW3 7PL — MB BS 1983 Lond.

DJERKOVIC, Gordana Sofija 169 Bedford Hill, London SW12 9HG; 7 Sutherland House, Marloes Road, London W8 5LG — BM 1998 Soton. PRHO Surg. Poole.Gen.Hosp. Socs: MDU; BMA; MPS.

DJUKANOVIC, Ratko Vojislav University Medicine, Level D, Centre Block, Southampton General Hospital, Southampton SO16 6YD Tel: 02380 794195 Fax: 02380 701771 Email: rdl@soton.ac.uk — MD 1978 Belgrade; MD Belgrade, Yugoslavia 1978. Sen. Lect. (Med.) & Hon. Cons. Phys. Univ. Med. Gen. Hosp. Soton. Socs: BMA; Brit. Thorac. Soc.; Brit. Soc. Allergy & Clin. Immunol. Prev: Hons. Cons. Phys. & MRC Sen. Clin. Research Fell. Univ. Med. Soton. Gen. Hosp.

DJUROVIC, Vesna Department of Forensic Medicine, Guy's Hospital, St Thomas St., London SE1 9RT — Lekarz 1987 Belgrade, Yugoslavia; Lekar Belgrade, Yugoslavia 1987; MRCPath 1993.

DLAMINI, Nomazulu 47 Angelica Drive, Beckton, London E6 6NS — MB BS 1996 Lond.

DO, Mai Kim 35 Holly Grove, London SE15 5DF Tel: 020 7701 7309 — MD 1967 Saigon. Clin. Med. Off. Optimum Health Trust. Prev: SHO Rosie Matern. Hosp. Camb.

DOA, Joanna Michelle 32 Frickley Road, Nethergreen, Sheffield S11 7EX — MB ChB 1994 Manch.; BSc Med. Sci. St. And. 1991. Ho. Off. (Med.) Hope Hosp. Salford. Prev: Ho. Off. (Surg. & Orthop.) Trafford Gen. Hosp.

DOA, William Norwood Surgery, 491 Norwood Road, London SE27 9NJ Tel: 020 8670 1000 Fax: 020 8766 7557; 84 Copers Cope Road, Beckenham BR3 1RJ Tel: 020 8650 1840 — MB BS 1959 Madras; DCH 1961. (Vellore) Socs: Brit. Med. Acupunct. Soc. & BMA. Prev: Regist. Hosp. Sick Childr. Gt. Ormond St. Lond.; SHO Qu. Eliz. Hosp. Childr. Lond.; Ho. Off. (Obst.) Kent & Canterbury Hosp.

DOAK, William Martin 105 Old Greenock Road, Bishopton PA7 5BB — MB ChB 1976 Glas.; MRCGP 1984; DObst RCPI 1979. Princip. GP Gt.er Glas. Health Bd.

DOB, Daryl Perdeep 1 Longfield Drive, London SW14 7AU — MB BS 1987 Lond. (St. Thos. Hosp.) Cons. Anaesth. Chelsea & W.m. Hosp. Socs: FRCA.

DOBBIE, Alison Elizabeth Biggar Health Centre, South Croft Road, Biggar ML12 6BE Tel: 01899 20383; 14A Smithycroft, Hamilton ML3 7UL — MB ChB 1982 Glas.; MRCGP 1986; Cert. Family Plann. JCC 1986.

DOBBIE, Calum McAllister 26 Firhill Avenue, Airdrie ML6 9DZ — MB ChB 1992 Glas.

DOBBIE, Catherine Rose 71 Harlescott Road, London SE15 3DA — MB ChB 1982 Otago; MRCGP 1990.

DOBBIE, David Thompson Portland Park Medical Centre, 51 Portland Park, Hamilton ML3 7JY Tel: 01698 284353 Fax: 01698 891101 — MB ChB 1977 Glas.; MRCGP 1988; DRCOG 1979. (Glasgow University) Assoc. Adviser (Gen. Pract.) Lanarksh.; Hon. Sen. Clin. Lect. Glas. Univ. Prev: GP Trainer Hamilton.

DOBBIE, Gordon Macgregor (retired) 61 Village Close, Kirby Cross, Frinton-on-Sea CO13 0PF Tel: 01255 672518 — MB ChB 1950 Ed. Prev: GP Biddulph.

DOBBIE, Hamish Scott 240 Howlands, Welwyn Garden City AL7 4HF — MB BChir 1992 Camb.; MRCP (UK) 1994.

DOBBIE, James Angus 1 Manor Farm Cottages, Patchway Common, Bristol BS34 6AZ — MB ChB 1991 Bristol.

DOBBIE, James Waugh Lister Research Laboratories, Department of Surgery, University of Edinburgh, Royal Infirmary, Lauriston Place, Edinburgh EH3 9YW Tel: 0131 536 3825 Fax: 0131 536 3837; 26 Firhill Avenue, Airdrie ML6 9DZ — MB ChB 1961 Glas.; MB ChB (Commend.) Glas. 1961; MD (Hons. & Gold Medal) Glas. 1968; FRCP Lond. 1982; MRCP (UK) 1972; FRCPath 1979, M 1969. (Glas.) Dir. Mesothelial & Peritoneal Research Centre, Lister Research Labs. Univ. Edin.; Sen. Med. Research Fell. Univ. Dept. Surg. Edin. Socs: Assn. Phys.; Path. Soc. Prev: Vice-Pres. Advanced Scientif. Developm. Baxter R & D Europe, Belgium; Med. Dir. Artific. Organs Div. Travenol Laboratories Ill, USA; Sen. Lect. (Med.) & Cons. Nephrol. Glas.

DOBBIE, Jennifer Joy Dalitso 240 Howlands, Welwyn Garden City AL7 4HF — MB BS 1994 Lond.

DOBBIE, Ronan Chilton 11 Blandford Avenue, Luton LU2 7AY Tel: 01582 508432 — MB Camb. 1958, BChir 1957; DObst RCOG 1963. (Lond. Hosp.)

DOBBIE, Sheila Wishaw Health Centre, Kenilworth Avenue, Wishaw ML2 7BQ Tel: 01698 373341 — MB ChB 1978 Glas.; MFFP 1993; Cert. Family Plann. JCC 1982. Clin. Med. Off. (Family Plann.) Lanarksh. HB.

DOBBIE, Sonia Noreen Lodge Cottage, Petersfield Road, Ropley, Alresford SO24 0EE — MB BS 1992 Lond.; BSc (Hons.) Path. Lond. 1990. (Lond.Hosp) GP. Prev: SHO (Psychiat.) Tower Hamlets Healthcare Trust; SHO (O & G) Roy. Lond. NHS Trust; SHO (Geriat. Med. & A & E) Roy. Lond. NHS Trust.

DOBBIN, Alistair Edward Brunton Place Surgery, 9 Brunton Place, Edinburgh EH7 5EG Tel: 0131 557 5545 — MB BS 1975 Lond.; DRCOG 1983.

DOBBING, Christopher John Island Health, 145 East Ferry Road, London E14 3BQ Tel: 020 7363 1111 Fax: 020 7363 1112 — MB BS 1973 Lond.; MRCGP 1986; DRCOG 1978; DCH Eng. 1977. Tutor (Gen. Pract.) Tower Hamlets.

DOBBING, Professor John Higher Cliff Farm, Birch Vale, High Peak SK22 1DL Tel: 01663 743220 Fax: 01663 743220 Email: john@nwpsu.u-net.com — MB BS Lond. 1953; DSc Manch. 1982; BSc (1st cl. Hons.) Lond. 1950; FRCP Lond. 1981, M 1974; FRCPath 1975, M 1963; FRCPCH 1997 (Hon). (St. Mary's Lond.) Emerit. Prof. Child Growth & Developm. Univ. Manch. Socs: Hon. Fell. Roy. Coll. Paediat. & Child Health. Prev: Hon. Cons. Neuropath. Manch. Roy. Infirm.; Hon. Cons. Hosp. Sick Childr. Gt. Ormond St. Lond.; Lect. (Path.) & Gull Stud. Guy's Hosp. Lond.

DOBBINS, Brian Mansell 29 East Causeway Vale, Leeds LS16 8LG — MB ChB 1990 Liverp.

DOBBINS, Stephen Terence 26 Cressington Avenue, Higher Tranmere, Birkenhead CH42 6QJ Tel: 0151 644 6757 — MB BS 1990 Lond.

DOBBS, Francis FitzGerald Department of Primary Healthcare & General Practice, ITTC, Tamar Science park, Derriford, Plymouth PL6 8BX Tel: 01752 764230 Fax: 01752 764230 Email: fdobbs@plym.ac.uk — MB BCh BAO 1979 Dub.; BA (Biochem.) Dub. 1973, MD 1993; FRCGP 1994, M 1985; MRCOG 1984; DCH Dub. 1981; Cert. Family Plann. JCC 1981. (Trinity Coll. Dub.) Sen. Lect. & Head Dept. Primary Health Care & Gen. Pract. Univ. Plymouth. Socs: Irish Coll. Gen. Pract.; BMA; Vice-Chairm. Europ. GP Research Workshop. Prev: GP Drumcliffe Co. Sligo; Regist. (Obst.) Birm. Matern. Hosp.; Basic Grade Biochem. St. Vincent's Hosp. Dub.

DOBBS, Frederick Brian 110 Shirley Drive, Hove BN3 6UP Tel: 01273 557929 — MB BS Lond. 1950; DObst RCOG 1952. (Univ. Coll. Hosp.)

DOBBS, (Helena) Jane Guy's King's & St Thomas' Cancer Centre, Guy's & St Thomas Hospital NHS Trust, Lambeth Palace Road, London SE1 7EH Tel: 020 7928 9292 ext. 2044 Fax: 020 7928 9968; Tel: 01689 860252 — MB BChir 1976 Camb.; MA Camb.

1975; FRCP Lond. 1994; FRCR 1980. Cons. Clin. Oncol. Guy's & St Thomas' Hosp. Trust. Prev: Cons. Radiother. & Oncol. King's Coll. Hosp. Lond.; Lect. & Hon. Sen. Regist. (Radiother. & Oncol.) Inst. Cancer Research Roy. Marsden Hosp. Lond.

DOBBS, Jeremy Francis Roland Cerne Abbas Surgery, 51 Long St., Cerne Abbas, Dorchester DT2 2JY Tel: 01300 341666 Fax: 01300 341090 — MB BS 1989 Lond.; BSc Lond. 1986; MRCGP 1994; DRCOG 1993. Princip. GP Cerne Abbas. Socs: BMA & MDU. Prev: Trainee GP Blandford Forum Dorset; SHO Dorset VTS; SHO (Psychiat. & Oncol.) Univ. Coll. Hosp. Lond.

DOBBS, Patrick 26 Bolehill Lane, Sheffield S10 1SB — MB ChB 1989 Sheff.

DOBBS, Phyllis Mary (retired) 55 Kingstown Street, London NW1 8JP Tel: 020 7586 2956 — MA, MB BChir Camb. 1936; MRCS Eng. LRCP Lond. 1932.

DOBBS, Richard John Clinical Research Centre, Northwick Park Hospital, Watford Road, Harrow HA1 3UJ; 2 Priory Gardens, Rectory Est., Berkhamsted HP4 2DR — MB ChB 1967 Manch.; MD Manch. 1982; MRCP (UK) 1973; DCH Eng. 1969. (Manch.) Clin. Sci. Worker (Therap. Elderly) Clin. Research Centre & Hon. Cons. N.wick Pk. Hosp. Harrow. Socs: Brit. Pharm. Soc. & Brit. Geriat. Soc. Prev: Sen. Regist. (Geriat. Med.) Roy. Free Hosp. Lond. & Barnet Gen Hosp.; Lect. (Clin. Pharmacol.) & Hon. Sen. Regist. St. Geo. Hosp. Med. Sch. Lond.; Research Fell. (Clin. Pharmacol.) Univ. Coll. Hosp. Med. Sch. Lond.

DOBBS, Stephen Peter Tel: 028 9026 3894 Fax: 02890 263953 Email: stephen.dobbs@bch.n-i.nhs.uk — MB BCh BAO 1987 Belf.; MRCOG 1993; MD 1999 (Nottingham). (Queens University Belfast) Cons. Gynacologist and Gyn. Oncologist, Belf. City Hosp. Belf.. Socs: Brit. Gyn. Cancer Soc. (BGCS); Brit. Soc. Colposcopy and Cevical Path. (BSCCP); Irish Gynaecol. Cancer Soc. (IGCS).

DOBER, Michael Howard The Health Centre, Granby Street, Littleport, Ely CB6 1NE Tel: 01353 860223 Fax: 01353 862198 — MB BS 1967 Lond.; MRCS Eng. LRCP Lond. 1967; DObst RCOG 1969. (St. Geo.)

DOBIE, Denise Ann 5 Goldthorn Crescent, Penn, Wolverhampton WV4 5TX — MB ChB 1993 Dundee; MRCGP 1997; DFFP 1996; DRCOG 1995.

DOBIE, Donald Kirkpatrick 5 Goldthorn Crescent, Penn, Wolverhampton WV4 5TX — MB ChB 1993 Dundee; BMSc (1st cl. Hons.) Med. Microbiol. Dund 1991. SHO (Med. Microbiol.) New Cross Hosp. Wolverhampton.

DOBIE, Frances Dorothy 81 Berkley Drive, Guisborough TS14 7LU — MB ChB 1990 Glas.

DOBIE, Neville (retired) 109 Main Street, Askham Bryan, York YO23 3QS Tel: 01904 707259 — MB BChir 1960 Camb.; MA, MB Camb. 1960, BChir 1959.

DOBIE, Victoria Jean Scott The Retreat, Blakerston, Duns TD11 3RY — MB ChB 1985 Ed.; MA Oxf. 1986; FRCS Ed. 1990. Assoc.Spec (Orthop. & Trauma) Borders Gen. Hosp. Prev: Clin. Asst. BrE. Unit W.. Gen. Hosp. Edin.; Regist. Rotat. (Surg.) Aberd. Teach. Hosp.

DOBLE, Nandika Shankari Perry Hill Surgery, 225 Perry Hill, London SE6 4HD Tel: 0208 699 1062 Fax: 0208 291 4421; 21 Burbage Road, London SE24 9HJ Tel: 0207 274 9008 Fax: 0207 207 9773 — MBBS; BSc; MRCP; MRCGP. (Royal Free Hosp. London) GP.

DOBLE, Rosemary Ann 17 Berkley Crescent, Moseley, Birmingham B13 9YD — MB ChB 1967 Birm. (Birm.) SCMO BromsGr. & Redditch HA. Socs: Fac. Community Health.

DOBNEY, George Henry (retired) 34 Hotson Road, Southwold IP18 6BS Tel: 01502 722489 — MB BS 1929 Lond.; MRCS Eng. LRCP Lond. 1928; DPhysMed. Eng. 1948. Hon. Cons. Physical Med. & Rheum. Roy. Free Hosp. Gp. & Whittington Hosp. Lond. Prev: Clin. Asst. Arthur Stanley Inst. & Ho. Surg. Middlx. Hosp.

DOBNEY, Sandra 90 Liverpool Road, Watford WD18 0DN Tel: 01923 34716 — MB BS 1988 Lond.

DOBRASHIAN, Richard David The Mount, Weston Rd, Baschurch, Shrewsbury SY4 2DE — MB ChB 1992 Manch.

DOBRASHIAN, Rowland Michael Prescott Surgery, Prescott Road, Prescott, Baschurch, Shrewsbury SY4 2DR Tel: 01939 260210 Fax: 01939 260752 — MB ChB 1964 Manch. (Manch.) Prev: Ho. Off. (Surg. & Med.) Hope Hosp. Salford; SHO Paediat. & SHO Path. Booth Hall Hosp. Manch.; Princip. GP Corris, M. Wales.

DOBREE, Charles Hatherley c/o National Westminster Bank, 25 High St., Colchester CO1 1DG — MB BS 1974 Lond.; MRCS Eng. LRCP Lond. 1974. (St. Bart.)

DOBSON, Adam Patrick John Derek 1 Newton Avenue, Withington, Manchester M20 1JJ — MB ChB 1986 Liverp.

DOBSON, Alan Herbert John 261 Hainton Ave, Grimsby DN32 9JX Tel: 01472 43071 — MB ChB 1954 Ed.; DCH Eng. 1957.

DOBSON, Christopher Martin Dept. of Dermatology, Link Unit 10 C, Royal Liverpool University Hospital, Prescot Street, Liverpool L7 — MB ChB 1981 Newc.; MRCP 1999; FRCPath 1997; MRCPath 1987. Specialist Regist. in Dermat., Roy. Liverp. Univ. Hosp.; Hon. Cons. Dermatopathologist, Dept. of Path., Roy. Liverp. Univ. Hosp.. Prev: LAT Specialist Regist. in Dermat., Hope Hosp. Salford.; SHO in Dermat. and Med.: Hope Hosp.; Locum Cons. Pathologist, Qu. Eliz. Hosp., Gateshead.

DOBSON, Craig Charles Department of Anatomy, University of Glasgow, Glasgow G12 — MB ChB 1991 Glas.; BSc (Hons.) Glas. 1988. Demonst. & Lect. (Anat.) Univ. Glas.

DOBSON, Elizabeth May 40 Bull Pasture, South Cave, Brough HU15 2HT — MB ChB 1989 Glas.; MRCGP 1993; DCH RCPS Glas. 1992.

DOBSON, Geoffrey Arthur Links Medical Centre, Restalrig Park Medical Centre, 40 Alemoor Crescent, Edinburgh EH7 6UJ Tel: 0131 554 2141 Fax: 0131 554 5363; 11 Coillesdene Avenue, Joppa, Edinburgh EH15 2JF — MB ChB 1978 Ed.; MRCGP 1983. Princip. GP Links Med. Centre Edin.

DOBSON, Giles 19 Bristow Park, Belfast BT9 6TF Tel: 01232 665281 — MB BCh BAO 1994 Belf. SHO (Anaesth.) Leicester Roy. Infirm. Prev: Ho. Off. Roy. Vict. Hosp. Belf.

DOBSON, Harold Sydney Brookland House, 501 Crewe Road, Wistaston, Crewe CW2 6QP Tel: 01270 567250 Fax: 01270 665829; Rope Grange, Rope Lane, Wistaston, Crewe CW2 5DA — MB BS 1969 Lond.; DObst RCOG 1972.

DOBSON, Harry Raymond 5 Blackthorne Close, Solihull B91 1PF Tel: 0121 705 6213 — MB ChB 1955 Birm.; FFA RCS Eng. 1965; DA Eng. 1961. (Birm.) Prev: Cons. Anaesth. Dudley Rd. Hosp. Birm; Med. Off. RN; Sen. Regist. United Leeds Hosps.

DOBSON, Hilary Margaret West of Scotland Breast Screening Service, Stock Exchange Court, Nelson Mandela Place, Glasgow G2 1QT Tel: 0141 572 5826 Fax: 0141 572 5863; 66 Monreith Road, Glasgow G43 2PE Tel: 0141 632 4417 — MB ChB 1979 Glas.; FRCP Glas. 1992; MRCP (UK) 1982; FRCR 1987. Cons. Radiol. & Clin. Dir. W. Scotl. BrE. Screening Serv. Socs: (Comm.) Roy. M-C Soc. Glas. Prev: Sen. Regist. (Radiol.) W.. Infirm. Glas.; Regist. (Radiol. & Gen. Med.) S.. Gen. Hosp. Glas.; Ho. Off. (Gen. Surg.) Vict. Infirm. Glas.

DOBSON, Jemma Annabel The University Hospital of North Tees and Hartlepool, Stockton-on-Tees TS19 8PE Tel: 01489 557160, 01642 617617 Fax: 01489 557158 Email: hetts@msn.com; Hook Park House, Hook Park Rd, Warsash, Southampton SO31 9LW Tel: 01489 557160, 01642 617617 Fax: 01489 557158 Email: hetts@msn.com — MB BS 1991 Lond. (Guy's Hosp. Med. Sch.) Cons. Gen. Paediat., Stockton on Tees. Socs: BMA. Prev: Ho. Off. Nambour Gen. Hosp. Nambour Qu.sland, Austral.; SHO (Paediat.) City Hosp. Nottm. & Norf. & Norwich Hosp.; Regist. (Paediat.) Roy. Vict. Infirm. Newc.

DOBSON, John Lindsay Catherall (retired) Priors Hatch Cottage, Priors Hatch Lane, Godalming GU7 2RJ — MB BS 1959 Lond.; MRCS Eng. LRCP Lond. 1959. Hosp. Pract. N. Downs Community Health Trust. Prev: Ho. Phys. & Ho. Surg. St. Bart. Hosp.

DOBSON, Julie Mary 122 Green La, Belle Vue, Carlisle CA2 7PU — BM BS 1997 Nottm.

DOBSON, Lee 1 Trym Road, Westbury-on-Trym, Bristol BS9 3EN Tel: 0117 950 2616 — MB ChB 1992 Bristol; BSc (Hons.) Anat. Bristol 1989, MB ChB 1992. SHO (Geriat. Med.) Cardiff Roy. Infirm.

DOBSON, Leslie Phillip The Health Centre, Bow Street, Guisborough TS14 7AA Tel: 01287 634171 Fax: 01287 630963 — MB BS 1966 Lond.; MRCS Eng. LRCP Lond. 1966; MRCGP 1974. (Lond. Hosp.)

DOBSON, Michael Buteux Nuffield Department of Anaesthetics, John Radcliffe Hospital, Oxford OX3 9DU Tel: 01865 221589 Fax: 01865 453266 Email: michael.dobson@ndm.ox.ac.uk; 1 Abberbury Avenue, Oxford OX4 4EU Tel: 01865 778513 Fax: 01865 453266

— MB ChB 1970 Ed.; MRCP (UK) 1974; FFA RCS Eng. 1976. (Ed.) Cons. Anaesth. Nuffield Dept. Anaesth. John Radcliffe Hosp. Oxf.; Hon. Clin. Lect. Univ. Oxf.; Acad. Europ. Acad. Anaesth. Socs: Fell. Roy. Soc. Med. Prev: Regist. Nuffield Dept. Anaesth. Radcliffe Infirm. Oxf.; Staff Anaesth. Shanta Bhawan Hosp. Kathmandu, Nepal; Sen. Regist. Bristol Roy. Infirm.

DOBSON, Michael Hunter Room 54, Block 11, Orsett Hospital, Rowley Road, Orsett, Grays RM16 3EU — MB BS 1997 Lond.

DOBSON, Nicola Ursula 171 Brownmoor Lane, Liverpool L23 9SF — MB ChB 1993 Liverp.

DOBSON, Philip Michael Stanley 99 Millhouses Lane, Millhouses, Sheffield S7 2HD — MB ChB 1984 Leeds; BSc (Hons.) Physiol. Leeds 1981; FCAnaesth 1990. Cons. Anaesth. N. Gen. Hosp. Sheff.

DOBSON, Mr Raymond (retired) Wildwoods, Orchard Road, Rowlands Gill NE39 1DN — MB BChir 1942 Camb.; MA, MB BChir Camb. 1942; FRCS Eng. 1950. Prev: Sen. Surg. Regist. S.E. Metrop. Regional Thoracic Unit.

DOBSON, Richard Brian (retired) The Health Centre, Bridge Street, Thorne, Doncaster DN8 5QH Tel: 01405 812121 Fax: 01405 741059 — MB ChB Leeds 1957. Prev: Ho. Surg. (Cas. & Orthop.) Bradford Roy. Infirm.

DOBSON, Simon John Clarence House Surgery, Russell Rd, Rhyl LL18 3BY Tel: 01745 390680 — MB ChB 1991 Manch.; MRCGP 1996. (Univ. Manch.) Partner, Clarence Ho. Surg., Rhyll.

DOBSON, Spencer Orrys Mount, Dark Lane, Ormskirk — MB ChB 1949 Manch.; DIH Soc. Apoth. Lond. 1961. (Manch.)

DOBSON, Susan (retired) 5 Blackthorne Close, Solihull B91 1PF Tel: 0121 705 6213 Email: dobsonsuedobson@aol.com — MB ChB 1960 Liverp. Prev: GP Solihull.

DOBSON, William Dobson, Gray and Troughton, The Health Centre, Tavanagh Avenue, Portadown, Craigavon BT62 3BU Tel: 028 3835 1393 — MB BCh BAO 1954 Dub.; LAH Dub. 1953. Socs: BMA.

DOCHERTY, Alan David The Surgery, Corse, Staunton, Gloucester GL19 3RB Tel: 01452 840228 — BSc Ed. 1976, MB ChB 1979; MRCP (UK) 1983; DCH RCP Lond. 1983.

DOCHERTY, Andrew James 24 Westfields, Bishopbriggs, Glasgow G64 3PL — MB ChB 1982 Dundee.

DOCHERTY, Bozena Helena Maria (retired) 439 Beechdale Road, Aspley, Nottingham NG8 3LF — LRCPI & LM, LRSCI & LM 1959; LRCPI & LM, LRCSI & LM 1959.

DOCHERTY, Caroline Scott Road Medical Centre, Scott Road, Selby YO8 4BL Tel: 01757 700231 Fax: 01757 213647 — MB ChB 1987 Birm.; MRCGP 1994; T(GP) 1994.

DOCHERTY, Daniel Joseph 1A Briar Gardens, Glasgow G43 2TF — LRCP LRCS 1949 Ed.; LRCP LRCS Ed. LRFPS Glas. 1949. (Glas.) Prev: Med. Ref. Glas. Corp. Transport Dept.

DOCHERTY, Elaine Marie Accident And Emergengy Department, Aberdeen Royal Infirmary, Foresthill, Aberdeen AB25 2ED Tel: 01224 681818 — MB ChB 1991 Glas.; FRCS (Glos) 1996. (Glasgow) Specialist Regist. (A&E) Aber. Roy. Infirm. Aber.

DOCHERTY, Mr James Gerrard GR, 113 Wilton Street, Glasgow G20 6RD — MB ChB 1985 Aberd.; FRCS Ed. 1989. Research Fell. (Surg. Gastroenterol.) Gartnavel Gen. Hosp. Glas.

DOCHERTY, James Norman (retired) 14 Canonbury Park N., London N1 2JT Tel: 020 7226 6420 — MB ChB 1952 Glas.; DPH Eng. 1960. Prev: GP 1955-1988.

DOCHERTY, John Val Coatbridge Health Centre, 1 Centre Park Court, Coatbridge ML5 3AP Tel: 01236 421468 — MB ChB 1989 Glas.; DRCOG 1992.

DOCHERTY, Marianne 6 Cedarwood, 49 Christchurch Road, Bournemouth BH1 3PA Email: mdocherty@doctors.org.uk — BM 1997 Soton; MRCP. (Southampton)

DOCHERTY, Paul Francis Scott Road Medical Centre, Scott Road, Selby YO8 4BL Tel: 01757 700231 Fax: 01757 213647 — MB BS 1987 Lond.; MRCGP 1992; T(GP) 1992.

DOCHERTY, Mr Peter Thomas Christopher Shamrock Lodge, 9 Farley Road, Derby DE23 6BY — LRCPI & LM, LRSCI & LM 1962; LRCPI & LM, LRCSI & LM 1962; FRCS Eng. 1974; FRCS Ed. 1972; FRCSI 1972; DO Eng. 1966; DOMS RCPSI 1966. Cons. Ophth. Surg. Derbysh. Roy. Infirm. Derby. Socs: Ophth. Soc. UK; Irish Fac. Ophth. Prev: Sen. Regist. Ophth. Woverhampton & Midl. Eye Infirm.

DOCHERTY, Peter Woodward Department Obstetric & Gynaecology, Salisbury District Hospital, Salisbury — MB ChB 1969 Ed.; FRCOG 1990, M 1978; DObst NZ 1974. Cons. O & G Salisbury Dist. Hosp. Prev: Cons. O & G Odstock Hosp. Salisbury; Sen. Regist. (O & G) St. Thos. Hosp. Lond.; Regist. (O & G) Nat. Wom. Hosp. Auckland, NZ & Pembury Hosp. Kent.

DOCHERTY, Rosaleen Clare Hunter Health Centre, Andrew Street, East Kilbride, Glasgow G74 1AD Tel: 01355 906622 Fax: 01355 906629; 86 Pitcairn Crescent, East Kilbride, Glasgow G75 8TP Tel: 01355 247438 — MB ChB 1970 Glas.; DPM Dub. 1974; DObst RCOG 1972; DObst RCPI 1972. Socs: BMA. Prev: Resid. Ho. Off. Roy. Hosp. Sick Childr. Glas.; Ho. Off. (O & G) Coombe Lying in Hosp. Dub.; Resid. Ho. Off. (Med.) W.. Infirm. Glas.

DOCHERTY, Suzanne Margaret 12 Sandringham Gardens, London N12 0NX — MB BS 1996 Lond.; BMedSci 1995. (St. Barths.) PhD Molecular Biol. of tumour markers; St Barths. Hosp. Lond.

DOCHERTY, Thomas Bernard, OBE Chastleton Surgery, Newton Drive, Framwellgate Moor, Durham DH1 5BH Tel: 0191 384 6171 Fax: 0191 386 3743; Relly Farm, Broom Lane, Broom Park, Durham DH7 7RJ Tel: 0191 384 8725 Email: t.b.docherty@virgin.net — MB ChB 1969 St. And. (St. And.)

DOCHERY, Andrew 19 Farm Court, Bothwell, Glasgow G71 8BU — MB ChB 1991 Glas.

DOCK, Valerie June Highbury New Park Surgery, 49 Highbury New Park, London N5 2ET Tel: 020 7354 1972; 2 Manse Road, Stoke Newington, London N16 7QD Tel: 020 7254 2504 Email: rjdock@aol.com — MB BS 1973 Lond.; DObst RCOG 1975. (Roy. Free)

DOCKER, Charles Walsgrave Hospital, Coventry CV2 2DX; 23 Braemar Road, Solihull B92 8BU Email: cdoc99@aol.com — MB ChB 1996 Liverp.

DOCKERTY, Julie Anne 2 The Park, Grasscroft, Oldham OL4 4ES — BChir 1990 Camb.; MB BChir Camb. 1991.

DOCKERY, Frances 387 Camden Road, London N7 0SH — MB BCh BAO 1992 NUI.

DOCKRELL, Jessica Claire 12 Meadow Park, Irwell Vale, Ramsbottom, Bury BL0 0QB — MB ChB 1997 Liverp.

DOCRAT, Feisal Arrazi Medical Centre, 1 Evington Lane, Leicester LE5 5PQ Tel: 0116 249 0000 Fax: 0116 249 0088 — MB BS 1981 Lond.; DLO RCS Eng.1987. (Univ. Coll. Hosp. Med. Sch. Lond.) Sen. Partner, Gen. Pract. Princip., Leicester.

DOCTON, Alex John Martin 322 Heaton Road, Newcastle upon Tyne NE6 5QH — MB BS 1992 Newc.

DOCTON, Roger Kenneth Edward 'Bridgecroft', The Shore, Bolton-le-Sands, Carnforth LA5 8JS — MRCS Eng. LRCP Lond. 1972.

DOCTOR, Noormohmed Haji Ahmed (retired) 4 The Larches, London N13 5AY Tel: 020 8886 6459 — MB BS 1954 Bombay; DA 1956; FRCA. Eng. 1960; DA Eng. 1960. Hon. Cons. Anaesth. St. Luke's Hosp. for Clergy Lond. Prev: Cons. Anaesth. St. Bart. Hosp. Lond. & City & Hackney HA (T).

DOCTOR, Ronald Samuel West Middlesex Hospital, Lakeside Mental Health Unit, Twickenham Road, Isleworth TW7 6AF Tel: 020 8321 6440 Fax: 020 8321 6412 — MB BCh 1977 Witwatersrand; MMed (Psych) Witwatersrand 1982; MRCPsych 1989. Cons. Psychiat. (Psychother.) W. Middlx. Univ. Hosp., Isleworth Ashford Hosp. Prev: Sen. Regist. (Psychother.) Portman Clinic Lond. Tavistock & Portman NHS Trust.

DODANWATAWANA, Honorable Kenneth Stephen — MB BS 1978 Sri Lanka; LMSSA Lond. 1989.

DODD, Abigail Florence Rosaline (retired) Beachfield, Trinity, Jersey JE3 5JU Tel: 01534 20270 — MB BCh BAO Belf. 1949. Prev: Family Welf. Clinic Jersey 1960-1982.

DODD, Alison Joan Askew Hill Farm, Littledale Road, Quernmore, Lancaster LA2 9HD — MB ChB 1991 Birm.; DCH RCP Lond. 1996; DFFP 1995; DRCOG 1994; MRCGP 1997. (Birmingham) GP Asst., Morecambe Bay.

DODD, Andrew Stuart Peterloo Medical Centre, 133 Manchester Old Road, Middleton, Manchester M24 4DZ Tel: 0161 643 5005 Fax: 0161 643 7264 — MB ChB 1985 Liverp.; MRCGP 1990.

DODD, Mr Christopher Alexander Ferrier Nuffield Orthopaedic Centre, Windmill Road, Headington, Oxford OX3 7LD — MB ChB 1979 Sheff.; FRCS Eng. 1983.

DODD, Mr Christopher Ledward 8 Old Hall Road, Whitefield, Manchester M45 7QW Tel: 0161 862 9564; Russell House, Russell Road, Whalley Range, Manchester M16 8AR — MB BS 1966 Lond.; FRCS Eng. (Ophth.) 1973; MRCS Eng. LRCP Lond. 1966; FRCOphth 1989; DO Eng. 1971. (St. Thos.) Cons. Manch. Roy. Eye Hosp. Prev: Sen. Regist. Manch. Roy. Eye Hosp.; Regist. Manch. Eye Hosp.; SHO (Ophth.) Soton. Eye Hosp.

DODD, Dorothy (retired) Ford View, Kippford, Dalbeattie DG5 4LJ Tel: 0155 662200 — MB BS 1937 Durh. Prev: Med. Off. Dumfries & Galloway HB.

DODD, Fiona Mary 12 Old Mill Close, Heatley, Lymm WA13 9RW — MB ChB 1983 Manch.; BSc St. And. 1980; FFA RCSI 1989; FCAnaesth. 1989; DA (UK) 1985. (Manchester) Cons. Anaesth. Wythenshawe Hosp. Manch. Prev: Sen. Regist. (Anaesth.) Manch.; Vis. Asst. Prof. Anaesth. Oregon Health Sci. Univ., USA; Regist. Rotat. (Anaesth.) Edin. Roy. Infirm.

DODD, Hifziye Princess Alexandra Hospital, Hamstel Road, Harlow CM20 1QX Tel: 01279 444455 Fax: 01279 827577; 35 Church Hill, Epping CM16 4RA — MB BCh 1973 Wales; FRCP Lond. 1995; MRCP (UK) 1977. Cons. Dermat. P.ss Alexandra NHS Trust Harlow. Socs: Fell. Roy. Soc. Med. & St. John's Hosp. Dermat. Soc.; Brit. Assn. Dermat. Prev: Sen. Regist. (Dermat.) Lond. Hosp. & Skin Hosp. Manch.; Regist. (Dermat.) Roy. Liverp. Hosp.

DODD, Hilary Julian Oldchurch Hospital, Romford RM7 0BE Tel: 01708 516046; 35 Church Hill, Epping CM16 4RA Tel: 01992 560381 Email: hilarydodd@hotmail.com — MB ChB 1976 Liverp.; FRCP Lond. 1995; MRCP (UK) 1979. Cons. Dermat. Havering Hosp. Romford Essex. Socs: Fell. Roy. Soc. Med.; Fell. St. John's Hosp. Dermat. Soc. Prev: Sen. Regist. (Dermat.) Roy. Free Hosp. Lond.; Regist. (Dermat.) St. Bart. Hosp. Lond.; Regist. (Gen. Med. & Nephrol.) Roy. Liverp. Hosp.

DODD, Hugh Sutherland, OStJ (retired) 19 The Terrace, Wokingham RG40 1BP — BM BCh Oxf. 1962; MA Oxf. 1958. Vis. Med. Off. Wokingham Hosp. Prev: GP Wokingham.

DODD, Ingrid Helena The Droveway, St Margaret's Bay, Dover CT15 6DE Tel: 01304 852291 Fax: 01304 853573; Steps Cottage, Bay Hill, St. Margaret's Bay, Dover CT15 6DU Tel: 01304 852371 — MB BS 1976 Lond.; MRCS 1975 Eng.; MA 1967 Aberd.; LRCP 1975 Lond. (Guy's Hosp. Med. Sch.) Indep. GP Kent. Prev: GP St. Margt.'s Dover; Asst. Surg. P & O Passenger Div.; Med. Off. Dept. Community Health Edendale Hosp. Kwazulu, Natal.

DODD, Keith Lumley Derbyshire Childrens Hospital, Uttoxeter Road, Derby DE22 3NE Tel: 01332 340131 Fax: 01332 200857 Email: keith@394hillside.fsnet.co.uk; 394 Duffield Road, Derby DE22 1ES — MB BS 1968 Lond.; BSc Lond. 1965, MB BS 1968; FRCP Lond. 1985; MRCP (UK) 1973; FRCPCH 1997; DCH Eng. 1971; DObst RCOG 1970. Cons. Paediat. Derbysh. Childr. Hosp. Derby. Socs: Off. for Health Serv.s. Roy. Coll. Paediat. and Child Health. Prev: Sen. Regist. (Child Health) Roy. Hosp. Sick Childr. Glas.

DODD, Keith William, DSC (retired) 24 Campbell Road, Edinburgh EH12 6DT Tel: 0131 337 1083 — MRCS Eng. LRCP Lond. 1943; FFA RCS Eng. 1960; DA Eng. 1953. Cons. Anaesth. E. Gen. Hosp. Edin. Prev: Cons. Anaesth. Edin. S.. Hosp. Gp.

DODD, Martin David 58 Osmaston Road, Birkenhead CH42 8LL — MB ChB 1998 Glas.; MB ChB Glas 1998.

DODD, Michael John Infirmary Drive Medical Group, Consulting Rooms, Infirmary Drive, Alnwick NE66 2NR Tel: 01665 602388 Fax: 01665 604712; Ashbrooke, Lesbury, Alnwick NE66 3AS Email: mjdodd@compuserve.com — MB BS 1976 Newc.; MB ChB (Hons.) Newc. 1976; BSc (Hons.) Newc. 1973; MRCP (UK) 1978; FRCGP 1994, M 1982; DRCOG 1982; FRCP Ed 1998. Hosp. Pract. (A & E & Geriat.) Alnwick Infirm.; Sen. Med. Off. (CMP) RAF Boulmer Alnwick; Course Organiser N.umbria VTS. Prev: Sen. Regist. (Rheum.) Newc. AHA; Regist. (Med.) Newc. AHA; Ho. Phys. & Ho. Surg. Roy. Vict. Infirm. Newc.

DODD, Nicholas Jonathan Department of Haematology, The Ipswich Hospital, Heath Road Wing, Ipswich IP4 5PD Tel: 01473 703718 Fax: 01473 703720 Email: doddn@ipsh-tr.angtox.nhs.uk — MB BS Lond. 1974; BSc (1st cl. Hons.) Lond. 1971; FRCP Lond. 1994; MRCP (UK) 1978; FRCPath 1996, M 1986. (St. Geo.) Cons. Haemat. Ipswich Hosp. Socs: Brit. Soc. Haematol. Prev: Sen. Regist. (Haemat.) King's Coll. Hosp. Lond.; Research Fell. (Renal Med.) King's Coll. Hosp. Lond.; Regist. (Haemat.) St. Bart. Hosp. Lond.

DODD, Patrick Paul 10 Oakland Place, Buckhurst Hill IG9 5JZ — MB BS 1979 Lond.; FFA RCSI 1985; T(Anaesth.) 1991. Cons. Anaesth. P.ss Alexandra Hosp. Harlow. Prev: Sen. Regist. (Anaesth.) Roy. Lond. Hosp.

DODD, Mr Peter Dominic Francis 15 Earle Road, Bramhall, Stockport SK7 3HE — MB ChB 1989 Manch.; FRCS Ed. 1994.

DODD, Richard John 33 South Barcombe Road, Liverpool L16 7QD Tel: 0151 722 5643 Email: rdodd@aol.com — MB ChB 1991 Liverp.; FRCA 1996. (Liverpool) Specialist Regist. (Anaesth.) Mersey Rotat.

DODD, Sarah Louise 24 Greenfield Street, Dunkirk, Nottingham NG7 2JN — BM BS 1995 Nottm.

DODD, Susan Jean Infirmary Drive Medical Group, Consulting Rooms, Infirmary Drive, Alnwick NE66 2NR Tel: 01665 602388 Fax: 01665 604712; Ashbrooke, Lesbury, Alnwick NE66 3AS — MB BS 1977 Newc.; DRCOG 1979; MRCGP 1981. Prev: GP Ponteland; Trainee GP N.umbria VTS; Ho. Surg. Newc. Gen. Hosp.

DODD, Susan Mary Department of Morbid Anatomy, The Royal London Hospital, London E1 1BB Tel: 020 7377 7370 Fax: 020 7377 7030 Email: s.m.dodd@mds.qmw.ac.uk; The Gate House, Shropsgate Road, Englefield Green, Egham TW20 0XY Tel: 01784 432485 — MB ChB 1981 Manch.; BSc (Med. Sci.) St. And. 1978; MRCPath 1988; FRCPath 1997. Sen. Lect. (Morbid Anat.) Lond. Hosp. Prev: Lect. (Morbid Anat.) Lond. Hosp.

DODD, William (retired) Gairn, Westmuir, Kirriemuir DD8 5LP Tel: 01575 572834 Email: bill.dodd@dial.pipex.com — MB ChB Ed. 1957.

DODDINGTON, Rosemary Ann South Molton Health Centre, 10 East Street, South Molton EX36 3BZ Tel: 01769 573101 Fax: 01769 574371; Bray Mill Cottage, Chittlehampton, Umberleigh EX37 9RE — MB ChB 1974 Bristol; DObst RCOG 1976.

DODDRELL, Andrew Ian Church Close Surgery, 3 Church Close, Boston PE21 6NB Tel: 01205 311133 Fax: 01205 358986 — MB BS 1988 Lond.; MMedSci (Primary Health Care) Nottm. 1996; MRCGP 1992; T(GP) 1992; DRCOG 1991. (Univ. Lond. Roy. Free Hosp. Sch. Med.)

DODDRIDGE, Marjorie Constance (retired) Marlowe, Back Edge Lane, Edge, Stroud GL6 6NS — MB BChir Camb. 1961; MA Camb. 1962; DObst RCOG 1962.

DODDRIDGE, Nicola Jane Flat 1B, Ainsley Court, Ainsley Road, Crookes, Sheffield S10 1EU — MB ChB 1997 Sheff.

DODDS, Allistair Duncan 9/5 Great King Street, Edinburgh EH3 6QW — MB ChB 1992 Ed.; FRCA 1998.

DODDS, Annabel Aileen East Lancashire Paediatric Audioloyg Service, Leeds Road, Nelson BB11 3E4 — MB ChB 1978 Manch.; MSc (Audiol. Med.) Manch. 1989; BSc (Med. Sci.) St. And. 1975; FRCPCH 1997. Cons. (Community Paediat. & Audiol.) E. Lancs. Paediat. Audiol. Serv. Burnley Health Care NHS Trust. Socs: Brit. Assn. Community Drs in Audiol.; Brit. Assn. Audiol. Phys.; Brit. Soc. Audiol. Prev: Cons. Community Paediat. (Audiol.) Tameside & Glossop NHS Trust & Salford Community NHS Trust.

DODDS, Christopher Orchard House, 25 Doctors Lane, Hutton Rudby, Yarm TS15 0EQ — MB BS 1974 Newc.; MRCGP 1982; FFA RCS Eng. 1985. Cons. Anaesth. S. Tees DHA. Prev: Lect. (Anaesth.) & Hon. Sen. Regist. Sir Humphry Davy Dept. Anaesth. Univ. Bristol, Bristol Roy. Infirm.

DODDS, David Hanbury Lee (retired) Shellsborough, The Esplanade, Woolacombe EX34 7DJ Tel: 01271 870739 — MB BS 1966 Lond.; MRCS Eng. LRCP Lond. 1966; DObst RCOG 1969. Hon Med. Off. RNLI - Ilfracombe Lifeboat. Prev: Gen. Practioner, Warwick Practise, Ilfracombe.

DODDS, David Harold Hainsworth The Surgery, Ivy Court, Tenterden TN30 6RB Tel: 01580 763666/764022 Fax: 01580 766199; Pittlesden Manor Farm, Tenterden TN30 6HG Tel: 01580 764061 Fax: 01580 766194 — MB BS 1983 Lond.; MBA Canterbury 1995; MA Camb. 1984, BA (Hons.) 1980; MRCGP 1988; DRCOG 1987; DCH RCP Lond. 1986. Prev: Trainee GP Epsom VTS; Ho. Surg. Epsom Dist. Hosp.; Ho. Phys. Lond. Hosp.

DODDS, David Owen 3 Oak Farm Drive, East Kilbride, Glasgow G74 4UF — MB ChB 1986 Glas.; MRCP (UK) 1989.

DODDS, Edgar John Archbold, SBStJ (retired) Holly Lodge, Cross St., Elmswell, Bury St Edmunds IP30 9DR Tel: 01359 242023 — MB BS Lond. 1954. Prev: JHMO Infec. Dis. & Tuberc. Honey La. Hosp.

DODDS, Elizabeth Ann Orchard House, 25 Doctors Lane, Hutton Rudby, Yarm TS15 0EQ — MB ChB 1976 Leeds; BA Open 1992.

DODDS, George Falkirk Royal Infirmary, Falkirk FK1 5QE Tel: 01324 624000 — MB ChB Ed. 1970; BSc (Hons. Physiol.) Ed. 1967; MRCPsych 1976; DPM Ed. & Glas. 1974. Cons. Psychiat. Prev: Med. Off. St. Barnabas Miss. Hosp. Ntlaza S. Afr.; Sen. Regist. (Psychiat. & Ment. Handicap.) Tayside & Fife HB.

DODDS, Gillian Wollaton Lodge, Crendell Lane, Damerham, Fordingbridge SP6 3HW Tel: 01725 518429; Community Child Health, Salisbury District Hospital, Salisbury SP2 8BJ Tel: 01722 336262 — MB BS 1971 Lond.; MRCS Eng. LRCP Lond. 1971; DCCH RCP Ed. RCGP & FCM 1984; DObst RCOG 1975. (Westm.) SCMO (Community Child Health) Salisbury Health Care NHS Trust. Prev: SHO (O & G) St. Mary's Hosp. Portsmouth; Ho. Phys. Qu. Mary's Hosp. Lond.; Resid. Med. Off. Roy. Alexandra Hosp. Childr. Sydney, Austral.

DODDS, Jean Mollie Raleigh Day Hospital, North Devon District Hospital, Barnstaple EX31 4JB Tel: 01271 22446; Shellsborough, The Esplanade, Woolacombe EX34 7DJ Tel: 01271 870739 — MB BS 1965 Lond.; MRCS Eng. LRCP Lond. 1965. (St. Mary's) Sen. Med. Off. (Geriat.) Day Hosp. N. Devon Dist. Hosp.; Assess. Doctor for HA & Social Serv. Socs: Med. Wom. Federat.; Brit. Geriat. Soc. Prev: Ho. Surg. & Ho. Phys. Chelmsford & Essex Hosp.; GP Ilfracombe.

DODDS, Judith Ann 32 Flockton Court, Rockingham St., Sheffield S1 4EB — BM 1984 Soton.; BSc Lond. 1979.

DODDS, Laura Margaret 107 South Beach, Troon KA10 6EQ Tel: 01292 311403 Fax: 01292 311403 — MB ChB 1959 Glas.; DA Eng. 1962.

DODDS, Mabel (retired) 9 Westdown House, Hartington Place, Eastbourne BN21 3BW Tel: 01323 23319 — MB BS 1926 Durh.; BHyg. DPH 1938. Prev: Sen. Asst. Med. Off. Middlx. CC (Harrow).

DODDS, Margaret 15 Langton Place, Newton Mearns, Glasgow G77 6QZ — MB ChB 1985 Aberd.; MRCGP 1989; Cert. Family Plann. JCC 1988.

DODDS, Paul Andrew Leighton Hospital, Middlewich Road, Crewe CW1 4QJ Tel: 01270 255141; 1 Pear Tree Cottages, Davenham Road, Billinge Green, Northwich CW9 7RY Tel: 01606 47060 — MB ChB 1985 Manch.; MRCP (UK) 1989. Cons. Phys. (Cardiol.) Leighton Hosp. Crewe. Prev: Research Fell. (Cardiol.) Cardiothoracic Centre NHS Trust Liverp.; Regist. (Gen. Med.) Walton Hosp. Liverp.

DODDS, Peter Aitchison The Grove Medical Group, 1 The Grove, Gosforth, Newcastle upon Tyne NE3 1NU; 10 Moor Place, Gosforth, Newcastle upon Tyne NE3 4AL Tel: 0191 285 6156 Fax: 0191 213 0715 — MB BS 1965 Newc.; DObst RCOG 1969. Clin. Tutor Family Med. Univ. Newc. Socs: BMA. Prev: Ho. Surg. & Ho. Phys. Roy. Vict. Infirm. Newc.; SHO (Paediat.) S. Shields Gen. Hosp.

DODDS, Mr Richard David Allan, OBE Orthopaedic Department, Royal Berkshire Hospital, Reading RG1 5AN Tel: 0118 975 2097 Fax: 0118 975 7790; Glebe Lodge, Thames St, Sonning, Reading RG4 6UR — MB BChir Camb. 1984; MA Camb. 1984; FRCS (Orth.) 1993; FRCS Eng. 1989. Cons. Orthop. Roy. Berks. Hosp. Reading. Socs: Fell.Brit. Orthopaedic Assoc. Prev: Sen. Regist. St. Mary's Hosp. Lond.; Regist. (Orthop.) Roy. Berks. Hosp. Reading & Nuffield Orthop. Centre Oxf.; Regist. (Gen. Surg. & Thoracic) King Edwd. VII, Midhurst & St. Richard's Hosp. Chichester.

DODDS, Sarah Rachel 9 Redruth Gardens, Gateshead NE9 6XW — MB ChB 1998 Dund.; MB ChB Dund 1998.

DODDS, Mr Simon Richard Dept of Surgery, Good Hope Hospital NHS Trust, Rectory Road, Sutton Coldfield B75 7RR Tel: 0121 378 2211 Email: simon.dodds@goodhot.wmids.nhs.uk; ChesterField hOuse, 15 Barnard Road, Sutton Coldfield B75 6AP Tel: 0121 378 0065 Email: mail@simondodds.com — MB BS 1985 Lond.; MA Camb. 1986, BA 1982; MS Soton. 1994; FRCS Eng. 1990; FRCS gen 1998. (St. Bart. Hosp. Lond.) Cons Surg. Good Hope Hosp. Sutton Coldfield. Socs: Fell. Roy. Soc. Med.; Euro.soc.Vasc..Surg; Vasc. Surgic. Soc. Prev: Research Regist. (Gen. Surg. & Vasc. Surg.) Roy. S. Hants. Hosp.; Sen. Regist. Roy. United Hosp. Bath; Sen. Regist. Roy. Hants. Co. Hosp., Winchester.

DODDS, Wendy Noelle Rheumatology Department, Medicine Unit 2, Royal Lancaster Infirmary, Ashton Road, Lancaster LA1 4RP Tel: 01524 583619 Fax: 01524 583977; Thistledown Cottage, 7 Lower Haverflatts, Milnthorpe LA7 7FB Tel: 015385 64747 — MB ChB 1972 Birm.; FRCP 2000 (Edin.); BSc (1st cl. Hons. Physiol.) Birm. 1972; BSc (1st cl. Hons. Physiol.) Birm. 1972; FRCP Lond. 1991; MRCP (UK) 1978; FRCPCH 1997; Dip. Sports Med. Scotl. 1997. (Birm.) Cons. Clin. Dir. (Rheum. & Med.) Morcambe Bay Hosps. NHS Trust; Hon. Med. Off. Brit. Olympic Assn. & Other Sporting Bodies. Socs: Brit. Soc. Rheum.; Brit. Assn. Sport & Med.; Roy. Coll. of Phys.s of Edin. Prev: Cons. (Rheum.) Bradford Hosp. Trusts; Tutor & Hon. Sen. Regist. (Rheum.) Univesity Manch.; Arthritis & Rheumatic Foundat. Train. Fell. Wellington Regional Centre for Rheum. Dis., NZ.

DODDS, William Ronald 47 Ridley Avenue, Blyth NE24 3BA Tel: 01670 352416 — MB BS 1946 Durh.; MD Durh. 1960. (Newc.) Clin. Asst. (Respirat. Dis. & Psychiat.) Blyth Hosp. Socs: (Ex-Pres.) Newc. & N.. Cos. Med. Soc. Prev: Med. Off. Shipping Federat. Blyth; Treasury Med. Off.; GP N.d.

DODDY, John Anthony Ryecroft Street Health Centre, Ryecroft Street, Stapleford, Nottingham NG9 8PN Tel: 0115 939 5555 Fax: 0115 939 5555; 268 Wollaton Road, Wollaton, Nottingham NG8 1GN Tel: 0115 928 4399 — MB BCh BAO 1985 NUI; MRCGP 1990. (Univ. Coll. Dub.) GP Single Handed; Private Complementary Med. Specialist. Socs: Brit. Med. Acupunct. Soc.; Brit. Soc. Med. & Dent. Hypn.

DODENHOFF, Ronald Martin 97 Atlantic Way, Porthowan, Truro TR4 8AH — MB BS 1989 Lond.

DODGE, Catherine Jane Beechlands Lodge, Maynards Green, Heathfield TN21 0BU — MB BS 1986 Lond.; BSc Lond. 1983, MB BS 1986; MRCGP 1990.

DODGE, Graham Stuart Department of Imaging, Royal Sussex County Hospital, Eastern Road, Brighton BN2 5GL Tel: 01273 696955 Ext: 4652 Fax: 01273 692887; The Ridge House, Jarvis Lane, Steyning BN44 3GL Tel: 01903 810015 Email: graham.dodge@brighton-healtcare.nhs.uk — MB BChir Camb. 1988; MA Camb. 1988, BA 1985; MRCP (UK) 1991; FRCR 1996. Cons. Radiologist, Roy. Sussex Co. Hosp., Brighton. Prev: Regist. (Radiol.) Roy. Free Hosp. Lond.; Regist. (Hepat., Gastro & Gen. Med.) Roy. Free Hosp.; Regist. (Gastroenterol. & Gen. Med.) Chase Farm Hosp.

DODGE, Professor John Ashton, CBE (retired) Department of Child Health, Singleton Hospital, Swansea SA2 8QA Tel: 01792 205666 Ext: 6130 Fax: 01792 285244 Email: john.dodge@swansea-tr.wales.nhs.uk — MB BCh 1956 Wales; MD Wales 1970; FRCPI 1987; FRCP Lond. 1984; FRCP Ed. 1973, M 1963; DCH Eng. 1961. Hon. Prof. Child Health. Univ. Swansea. Prev: Reader (Child Health) Welsh Nat. Sch. Med. Cardiff.

DODGE, Oliver Guy (retired) 28 Longton Avenue, Withington, Manchester M20 3JN — MD 1959 Manch.; MB ChB 1946; FRCPath 1972.

DODGEON, Louise Margaret 8 White Brook Lane, Uppermill, Oldham OL3 6ER — BM BS 1993 Nottm.; BMedSci (Hons) Nottm. 1991. GP Regist. Maryport Gp. Pract. Socs: BMA; RCGP. Prev: SHO (ENT, Dermat. & Gen. Med.) Cumbld. Infirm.

DODHIA, Hiten Lambeth, Southwark & Lewisham Health Authority, 1 Lower Marsh, London SE1 7NT Tel: 020 7716 7000 — MB ChB 1988 Leic.; MSc (Pub. Health Med.) Lond. 1995; DRCOG 1993; DCH RCP Lond. 1992; MFPHM 1998. Locum Cons. Pub. Health Med. Ealing, Hammersmith & Hounslow HA. Prev: Sen. Regist. Communicable Dis. Surveillance Centre PHLS Lond.; Pub. Health Regist. E. Kent HA Dover; Trainee GP Kettering VTS.

DODHY, Bashir Mohamed Azim, Wing Cdr. RAF Med. Br. Retd. Station Medical Centre, Royal Air Force, Uxbridge UB10 0RR Tel: 01895 237144 Email: bashir.dodhy@talk21.com; 86 Moorfield Road, Denham, Uxbridge UB9 5NF Tel: 01895 832481 Fax: 01895 832481 — MB ChB 1967 Glas.; DFFP 1993. (Glas.)

DODMAN, Barbara Angela Department of Dermatology, Pontefract General Infirmary, Friarwood Lane, Pontefract WF8 1PL; Grey Gable, 13 Creskeld Drive, Bramhope, Leeds LS16 9EJ Tel: 0113 261 9152 — MD Leeds 1978, MB ChB 1969. Cons. (Dermat.) Pontefract Gen. Infirm.; JP. Socs: Brit. Assn. Dermatol.; BMA.

***DODMAN, James David** Grey Cable, 13 Creskeld Drive, Bramhope, Leeds LS16 9EJ Tel: 0113 261 9152 — MB BS 1996 Newc.

DODMAN, Sally Rheumatology Department, Pembury Hospital, Tonbridge Rd, Pembury, Tunbridge Wells TN2 4QJ Tel: 01892 823535 Ext: 3365 Fax: 01892 673757; 8 Chipstead Lane, Riverhead, Sevenoaks TN13 2AG Tel: 01732 741721 — MB ChB Manch. 1969; FRCP (UK) 2001; FRACP 1977. p/t Cons. Rheum. Maidstone & Tunbridge Wells NHS Trust. Socs: BMA; Austral. Rheum. Assn.; BSR. Prev: Cons. Rheum. Roy. N. Shore Hosp. Sydney, Austral.; Sen. Regist. (Rheum. & Rehabil.) Middlx. Hosp. & Roy. Nat. Orthop. Hosp. Lond.; Regist. (Rheum. & Rehabil.) Middlx. Hosp. Lond.

DODOO, Edward Amanor Oxhey Drive Health Centre, South Oxhey, Watford WD1 6SF Tel: 020 8428 5577; 10 Arundel Close, Hemel Hempstead HP2 4QR Tel: 01442 217802 Fax: 01442217802 Email: edwarddoo@doctors.org.co.uk — MD 1971 Szeged. (Szeged Medical University, Hungary) Staff Grade (Paediat.) W. Herts.; Regist. (Paediat.) Hemel Hempstead Gen. Hosp. & St. Albans City Hosp. Socs: Fac. Community Health 1991. Prev: Regist. (Paediat.) Watford Gen. Hosp.

DODOO, John Buadoo The Park Surgery, 375 Chepstow Road, Newport NP19 8XR Tel: 01633 277333 Fax: 01633 279078; 44 Anthony Drive, Caerleon, Newport NP18 3DS — MB ChB 1968 Bristol; MRCS Eng. LRCP Lond. 1968; FRCOG 1992, M 1972; DObst 1970. Hosp. Pract. (Obst. & Gyn.) Roy. Gwent Hosp. Newport. Prev: Regist. (O & G) Roy. Gwent Hosp. Newport & Norf. & Norwich Hosp.; SHO (A & E) Bristol Roy. Infirm.

DODS, Alan Sydney (retired) 6 Blickling Court, Recorder Road, Norwich NR1 1NW — MB BS 1938 Lond.; MRCS Eng. LRCP Lond. 1938.

DODS, Iain McCraith 47 Brookside Glen, Chesterfield S40 3PG Email: imdods@bigfoot.com — MB ChB 1989 Liverp.; BSc (Hons.) Liverp. 1986; FRCA. Cons.Chesterfield & N. Derbys.Roy.Hosp. Socs: Intens. Care.Soc; Vasc. Anaesth. Soc. Prev: SHO (Anaesth.) Arrowe Pk. Hosp. Wirral.; Specialist Regist. (Anaesth.); Lect. (Anaesth.) Roy. Liverp. & BRd.green Hosps. Liverp.

DODSLEY, David Ronald (retired) 1 Ladycroft Paddock, Allestree, Derby DE22 2GA Tel: 01332 559687 — MB ChB 1952 Manch.; MRCS Eng. LRCP Lond. 1952.

DODSON, Helen Julie Marie Curie Centre, Caterham CR3 6YQ — MB ChB 1990 Leic.; MRCGP 1994; DRCOG 1993; Dip. Palliat Med.1998. (Leic.) Staff Grade Palliat. med.

DODSON, John Walter Blandfords Farmhouse, Fontmell Magna, Shaftesbury SP7 0PF — MB BS 1951 Lond. (St. Bart.) Socs: BMA. Prev: Ho. Phys. Lambeth Hosp.; Maj. RAMC.

DODSON, Malcolm John Circuit Lane Surgery, 53 Circuit Lane, Reading RG30 3AN Tel: 0118 958 2537 Fax: 0118 957 6115; Greenray Cottage, Sunnyside, Theale, Reading RG7 4BE — BM 1981 Soton.; MRCGP 1986; DRCOG 1983.

DODSON, Margaret Elizabeth (retired) 46 Chalfont Road, Liverpool L18 9UR — MB ChB Sheff. 1957; MD Sheff. 1969; FRCA 1962. Prev: Cons. Anaesth. Roy. Liverp. Univ. Hosp. Trust.

DODSON, Pamela Mary (retired) 4 Oakham Close, Tilehurst, Reading RG31 6LD Tel: 01734 21803 & profess. 582537 — MB ChB 1949 Ed.; DTM & H Eng. 1963; DObst RCOG 1957. Prev: GP Reading.

DODSON, Paul Manley Department of Diabetes, Birmingham Heartlands Hospital (Teaching Trust), Bordesley Green E., Birmingham B9 5SS Tel: 0121 424 2000 Fax: 0121 424 0593 Email: dodsonp@heartson.wmids.nhs.uk; 2 Hoyland Way, Bournville, Birmingham B30 1TS — MB BS 1975 Lond.; MD Lond. 1984; FRCP Lond. 1994; MRCP (UK) 1979; MRCS Eng. LRCP Lond. 1974; FRCOphth 1994. (St. Bart.) Cons. Phys. (Diabetes, Endocrinol., Med. & Ophth.) Birm. Heartlands Hosp.; Hon. Cons. Phys. Birm. & Midl. Eye Centre; Hon. Sen. Clin. Lect. Univ. Birm. Socs: Brit. Diabetic Assn. & Brit. Hypertens. Soc.; Hon. Sec. Med. Ophth. Soc. UK. Prev: Sen. Regist. (Diabetes & Med.) Dudley Rd. Hosp. Birm.; Hon. Regist. (Diabetes & Lipids) St. Bart. Hosp. Lond.; Regist. (Med.) Roy. Berksh. Hosp. Reading.

DODSWORTH, Helen (retired) 21 City Road, Cambridge CB1 1DP Tel: 01223 721209 Fax: 01223 721209 — MB BS Lond. 1964; BSc Lond. 1960; FRCP Lond. 1988; MRCP (UK) 1969; MRCS Eng. LRCP Lond. 1964; FRCPath 1984, M 1972. Prev: Hon. Cons. Phys. St. Mary's Hosp. Med. Sch. Lond.

DODU, Silas Rofino Amu (retired) c/o 15 Patterdale Close, Dronfield Woodhouse, Dronfield S18 8PW — MRCS Eng. LRCP Lond. 1951; MD Sheff. 1957, MB ChB 1951; FRCP Lond. 1969, M 1953. Prof. Med. Univ. Ghana, Accra. Prev: Chief. Cardiovasc. Dis. Unit WHO Geneva.

DODWELL, David John 1 Burn Bridge Road, Burn Bridge, Harrogate HG3 1NS Tel: 01423 873959 Fax: 01423 873959 Email: david.dodwell@leddsth.nhs.uk — MD 1991 Leeds; BSc (Hons.) Leeds 1980, MD 1991, MB ChB 1983; FRCP (UK) 1998; FRCR 1994. (Leeds) Cons. Clin. Oncol. Yorks. Regional Centre for Cancer Treatm. Cookridge Hosp. Leeds. Socs: Brit. BrE. Gp.

DODWELL, David John Francis Lucille van Geest Centre, Peterborough District Hospital, Thorpe Road, Peterborough PE3 6AN Tel: 01733 318159 Fax: 01733 318140 Email: ddodwell@nwahc-tr.anglox.nhs.uk — MB ChB 1978 Manch.; MSc Manch. 1983, MD 1986; MRCPsych 1982. Cons. Psychiat. Assertive Outreach Team, NWAHCT, P'boro.; Cons. Rehabil. Psychiat. St. Clement Hosp. Ipswich. Prev: Sen. Lect. (Psychiat. of Old Age) Birm. Univ.

DODWELL, Philip James Longlevens Surgery, 19b Church Road, Longlevens, Gloucester GL2 0AJ Tel: 01452 522695 Fax: 01452 525547; 16 Grafton Road, Gloucester GL2 0QW — MB 1970 Camb.; BChir 1969. (King's Coll. Hosp.)

DOE, Hilary Marian 1 Holehay Cottage, Lower Coombe, Brixton, Plymouth PL8 2BA — MB ChB 1986 Bristol.

DOE, Jon Christopher Department of Child & Family Psychiatry, Eversfield Hospital, West Hill Road, Hastings — BM 1981 Soton.; MRCPsych 1987. Cons. Child & Adolesc. Psychiat. Eversfield Hosp. Hastings.

DOEL, Stephen Robert William Tel: 01253 854321 Fax: 01253 862854 — MB ChB 1977 Manch.; MRCGP 1981; DRCOG 1981. GP Trainer Blackpool; Bd. Mem. & GP Clin. Governance Head, Wyre Primary Care Gp. Prev: Trainee GP Blackpool VTS.

DOEL, Vanessa Rita 23 Melton Road, Tollerton, Nottingham NG12 4EL — MB BS 1992 Lond.

DOERRY, Ursula Gabriele Sandwell Hospital, Lyndon, West Bromwich B71 4HJ — State Exam Med 1993 Heidelberg.

DOEY, Mr William David (retired) Llys Cariad, Ffairfach, Llandeilo SA19 6PE Tel: 01558 822600 — MB BChir Camb. 1938; MA Camb. 1973, BA 1934; FRCS Eng. 1946; MRCS Eng. LRCP Lond. 1937; DLO Eng. 1943. Prev: Surg. Roy. Nat. Throat, Nose & Ear Hosp. Gray's Inn Rd. & Golden Sq.

DOFFMAN, Sarah Rachel 18 Prestwich Pk Road S., Prestwich, Manchester M25 9PE — MB ChB 1997 Glas.

DOGGART, Elizabeth Ruth 5 Ravensdale, Newtownabbey BT36 6FA — MB BCh BAO 1990 Belf.; MRCGP 1995; DCH RCPSI 1994; DRCOG 1994; DMH Belf. 1991. (Qu. Univ. Belf.)

DOGGETT, John Mark West Midlands Police Occupational Health, Lloyd House, PO Box 52, Colmore Circus, Queensway, Birmingham B4 6NQ Tel: 0121 626 5078; 1 Darnick Road, Sutton Coldfield B73 6PE Tel: 0121 354 9298 — MB 1974 Camb.; BChir 1973; Dip. 2000. (Cambridge University/Charing Cross Hospital Medical School) Force Med. Adv., Occup. Health, W. Midl.s Police. Prev: Princip. GP Chorley, Lancs.; Regist. (Psychiat.) Univ. Hosp. S. Manch.

DOGGETT, Stephen Jeremy Grove House Surgery, 102 Albert Street, Ventnor PO38 1EU Tel: 01983 852427 Fax: 01983 852185 — MB BChir 1988 Camb.; MA Camb. 1992. (St. Bartholomews Hospital) Socs: I. of Wight LMC.

DOGRA, Karnail Singh 52 Margaret Drive, Boston PE21 9AL; Stuart House, 20 Main Ridge W., Boston PE21 6SS Tel: 01205 362173 Fax: 01205 359309 — MB ChB 1989 Glas.; BSc (Anat.) Glas. 1987, MB ChB 1989. Trainee GP W. Yorks. VTS.

DOGRA, Nisha Greenwood Institute, University of Leicester, Westcotes House, Westcotes Drive, Leicester LE3 0QU Tel: 0116 225 2880 Fax: 0116 225 2881 Email: nd13@leicester.ac.uk — BM 1986 Soton.; MA (Socio-legal Studies Childr.) Nottm. 1997; MRCPsych 1991; DCH RCP Lond. 1989. Sen. Lect. & Hon. Cons. Child Psychiat. Univ. Leicester. Prev: Lect. & Hon. Sen. Regist. (Child Psychiat.) Univ. Leicester.; Regist. (Psychiat.) Trent RHA.

DOGRA, Ranjit Singh River Street Surgery, 52 River Street, Rhyl LL18 1PT Tel: 01745 344680 Fax: 01745 344680; 20 Hardy Avenue, Rhyl LL18 3BG — MB BS 1969 Agra. (S.N. Med. Coll.)

DOGRA, Tara Singh (retired) 66 Spath Road, Manchester M20 2GT Tel: 0161 445 0671 — MB ChB Birm. 1955; FRCS (Otorhinolaryng.) Eng. 1970; Ed. 1967; FRCS MRCS Eng. LRCP Lond. 1956. Cons. ENT Surg. Univ. Hosp. S. Manch. & Wythenshawe & N. Chesh. Gp.

DOGRA, Virendra Kumar 9 Clements Close, Slough SL1 1NJ Tel: 01753 25506 — MB BS 1975 Lond.; BSc. (Hons) Lond. 1971, MB BS 1975. (Middlx.)

DOHERTY, Aileen Margaret Airthrey Park Medical Centre, Hermitage Road, Stirling University, Stirling FK9 4NJ Tel: 01786 463831 Fax: 01786 447482; 98 Henderson Street, Bridge of Allan, Stirling FK9 4HA — MB ChB 1987 Dundee; MRCGP 1992.

DOHERTY, Mr Alan Patrick The Royal Marsden Hospital, Fulham Road, London SW3 6JJ — MB BS 1988 Lond.; BSc Lond. 1985; FRCS Eng. 1992; MD 1998. (Lond.) Sp. Regist. Urol. Char. Cross Hosp.

DOHERTY, Alice Beatrix (retired) Primrose House, 29 Dalrymple Loan, Musselburgh EH21 7DJ Tel: 0131 665 3144 — MB ChB Ed. 1949.

DOHERTY, Andrew Joseph 22 Wellesley Drive, Crowthorne RG45 6AL — MB ChB 1994 Dundee.

DOHERTY, Anne Mary Health Centre, Great James Street, Londonderry BT48 7DH Tel: 02871 373248; 15 Benuarden Avenue, Londonderry BT47 2AS Tel: 02871 347474 — MB BCh BAO 1975 Belf.; MRCGP 1982.

DOHERTY, Arlene Maria 8 Croftwood, Bishopbriggs, Glasgow G64 3DX — MB ChB 1997 Glas.

DOHERTY, Austin Gerard Earnswood Medical Centre, 92 Victoria Street, Crewe CW1 2JR Tel: 01270 257255 Fax: 01270 501943; 1 Whitehall, Welsh Row, Nantwich CW5 5HA — MB ChB 1985 Manch.; MRCGP 1989.

DOHERTY, Bernadine Mary Hillview Surgery, 179 Bilton Road, Perivale, Greenford UB6 7HQ Tel: 020 8997 4661 Fax: 020 8810 8015; 16 Rosemount Road, London W13 0HJ — MB BS 1984 Newc.; MB BS Newc. l984; DRCOG 1988; Cert. Family Plann. JCC 1988; Cert. Prescribed Equiv. Exp. JCPTGP 1988.

DOHERTY, Bridget Michelle Marie Eastvale Resource Centre, 130A Stonelaw Road, Rutherglen, Glasgow G73 2PQ; 19 Kelvindale Gardens, Kelvindale, Glasgow G20 8DW — MB BCh BAO 1989 NUI.

DOHERTY, Caroline Anne (retired) — MB ChB 1986 Manch.; BSc (Med. Sci.) St. And. 1983. Prev: Trainee GP Unsworth Bury VTS.

DOHERTY, Catherine Heidi 32 Oakwood Avenue, Gatley, Cheadle SK8 4LR — MB ChB 1998 Manch.; MB ChB Manch 1998.

DOHERTY, Ciaran C Regional Nephrology Unit, Level 11, Belfast City Hospital Tower, Lisburn Road, Belfast BT9 7AB Tel: 01232 329241 Email: doherty@unite.net — MB ChB BAO 1972 Belf.; MD Belf. 1978, MB BCh BAO 1972; MRCP (UK) 1975; FRCP Edin. 1997; FRCP Lond. 1992; FRCPI 1992. (Qu. Univ. Belf.) Cons. Nephrologist Belf. City Hosp. Trust; Clin. Dir. Nephrol. Belf. City Hosp. Trust; Hon. Sen. Lect. Qu.'s Univ. Belf. Sch. of Med.; Censor Roy. Coll. Phys. Irel. Socs: Assn. Phys.; Internat. Soc. Nephrol.; .Amer.Soc.Nepurol. Prev: Clin. Instruc. (Nephrol.) Univ. S.. Calif., USA.; Postgrad. Tutor, Belf. City Hosp.

DOHERTY, Cora Brigid Paediatric Department, Addenbrooks Hospital, Hills Road, Cambridge Tel: 01223 245151 Email: cd209@cam.ac.uk — MB BCh BAO 1987 NUI; MRCPI 1992; DCH NUI 1990. (univ.coll.Galway) Research Regist. (Clin. Biochem.) Univ. Camb. Prev: Regist. (Paediat.) Camb. HA; SHO (Paediat.) Harrow & Camberwell HAs & Nat. Matern. Hosp. Dub.; MRC ClinTrain.Fell.Camb.

DOHERTY, David Arthur Frank (retired) 12 My Lords Lane, Hayling Island PO11 9PW — LRCPI & LM, LRSCI & LM 1958; LRCPI & LM, LRCSI & LM 1958. Prev: Princip. Med. Off. Home Office.

DOHERTY, Desmond James 21 Abingdon Drive, Preston PR2 1EY Tel: 01772 26822 — MB ChB 1938 Liverp.; DPH 1947. (Liverp.) Asst. Div. MOH Lancs. CC. Socs: Fell. Soc. MOH. Prev: RAMC; Sch. Med. Off. Liverp. Co. Boro.; Asst. MOH Preston Co. Boro.

DOHERTY, Diana Mary Waterfoot Health Centre, Cowpe Road, Waterfoot, Rossendale BB4 7DN Tel: 01706 215178; Meadowbank, 14 Meadow Way, Bacup OL13 8HU — MB ChB 1979 Manch.; Cert. Family Plann. JCC 1985; DRCOG 1983.

DOHERTY, Edward Frank Ravenscourt Surgery, 36-38 Tynewydd Road, Barry CF62 8AZ Tel: 01447 734744 — MB BCh 1973 Wales; BSc (Hons.) Wales 1970; MRCGP 1979; DObst RCOG 1976.

DOHERTY, Elizabeth Margot West Lodge, Corehouse, Lanark ML11 9TQ — MB ChB 1982 Glas.

DOHERTY, Gary Martin 11 Shrewsbury Gardens, Belfast BT9 6PJ — MB BCh 1998 Belf.; MB BCh Belf 1998.

DOHERTY, Jacqueline Emma Rowans, 3 Graycoates Drive, Crowborough TN6 2JT — MB ChB 1992 Birm.; MRCP (UK) 1995.

DOHERTY, Jennifer Anne 2 Lisdillon Road, Ardmore, Londonderry BT47 3RN — MB BCh 1998 Belf.; MB BCh Belf 1998.

DOHERTY, Jennifer Karen 22 Downview Av, Belfast BT15 4EZ — MB BCh BAO 1997 Belf.

DOHERTY, John 4 Racecourse View, Ayr KA7 2TS — MB ChB 1985 Glas.; MD Glas. 1993; MRCP (UK) 1990. Cons. Cardiol. CrossHo. Hosp. Kilmarnock Ayrsh. Socs: Brit. Soc. Echocardiogr.; Scott. Cardiac Soc. Prev: Regist. (Cardiol.) Roy. Brompton Nat. Heart Hosp. Lond.; Lect. (Med.) St. Bart. Med. Coll. Lond.; SHO Roy. Brompton & Nat. Heart Hosps. Lond.

DOHERTY, John Christopher Park Avenue Surgery, 13 Park Avenue, Redcar TS10 3LA Tel: 01642 470692 Fax: 01642 480163; 1 Atherstone Drive, Guisborough TS14 7BW Tel: 01287 635911 — MB BS 1970 Newc. Med. Adviser N. Machine Tools & Marsile Machine Co.; Chairm. LangBoro. Coast GP Commiss.ing Gp. Prev: Med. Off. United Biscuits (Tees) Ltd.

DOHERTY, John Dermot Hugh 136 Coleshill Road, Birmingham B36 8AD — LRCPI & LM, LRSCI & LM 1971; LRCPI & LM, LRCSI & LM 1971; DObst RCPI 1973; DCM NUI 1974; Dobst RCPI 1973; FAFOM 1994; FAFPHM 1990; FACOM 1984; MPH Sydney 1986; MFOM RCP Lond. 1985; DIH Dund 1981; DTM & H Liverp. 1976; DCH NUI 1974. (Roy. Coll. Surgs. Irel.) Chief. Med. Off. Internat. Atomic Energy Agency Vienna, Austria. Socs: Fell. Roy. Soc. Trop. Med. & Hyg.; Fell. Australasian Coll Trop. Med.; Fac. Comm. Health. Prev: Med. Off. FAO of United Nations, Rome, Italy; Med. Supt. Babinda Hosp. Austral.; Med. Off. Soc. Minière de Tenke-Fungurume Shaba Zaire.

DOHERTY, John Martin 65 The Greenway, Uxbridge UB8 2PL — MB BS 1997 Lond.

***DOHERTY, John Thomas** Ard Caoin, Prehen Park, Waterside, Londonderry BT47 2NY Email: jtdocherty@thefree.mail — MB BCh 1998 Belf.; MB BCh Belf 1998.

DOHERTY, Judith Frances 2A Rathmena Gardens, Ballyclare BT39 9HU — MB BCh BAO 1987 Belf.; MRCGP 1992; T(GP) 1992; DRCOG 1991. Med. Off. (Geriat. Med.).

DOHERTY, Julie Ann 4 Hughes Avenue, Warrington WA2 9EH — MB ChB 1987 Liverp.; BSc (Hons.) Liverp. 1984; MRCP (UK) 1993. Sen. Regist. (Paediat.) City Gen. Hosp. Stoke-on-Trent. Prev: Regist. (Paediat.) City Gen. Hosp. Stoke-on-Trent; Regist. (Paediat. & Neonatol.) Adelaide, S. Austral.; SHO (Paediat.) Booth Hall Childr. Hosp. Manch.

DOHERTY, Justin Francis Hospital for Tropical Diseases, 4 St Pancras Way, London NW1 0PE; 67 Chaucer Road, London SE24 0NY Tel: 020 7978 8125 — MB ChB 1982 Sheff.; MD Sheff. 1992; MRCP (UK) 1986; DTM & H Lond. 1993.

DOHERTY, Karen Ann 5 Laurel Wood, Belfast BT8 7RA — MB BCh 1998 Belf.

DOHERTY, Martin Joseph Russells Hall Hospital, Dudley DY1; 2 Sandhurst Drive, Pedmore, Stourbridge Tel: 01562 720367 — MB BS 1987 Lond.; MRCP 1991; MD 1999. (Roy.Free) Cons. Resp. Gen. Med, Dudley Gp. of Hosp.s, Dudley, W. Midl.s.

DOHERTY, Professor Michael Academic Rheumatology, Clinical Sciences Building, City Hospital, Nottingham NG5 1PB Tel: 0115 840 4733 Fax: 0115 840 4732 Email: michael.doherty@nottingham.ac.uk — MB BChir 1975 Middlesex; 2002 ILTM; MB B Chir 1975 Middlesex; MD Camb. 1988, MB 1976, BChir 1975; MRCP (UK) 1978; FRCP Lond. 1992. (Middlesex, London) Prof. Rheum. Univ. of Nottm. Med. Sch.; Cons. Rheum. City Hosp. Nottm. Prev: Cons. Reader Rheum. City Hosp. Nottm.

DOHERTY, Michael Brian 5 Station Cottages, Glazebrook, Warrington WA3 5BA — MB ChB 1991 Liverp.

DOHERTY, Michael Mary Department of Psychiatry, Windsor Hse, Belfast City Hospital, Lisburn Road, Belfast BT9 7AB — MB BCh BAO 1979 Belf.; MRCPsych 1984; MD 2000. (The Queen's

University of Belfast) Cons. Psychiat. Belf. City Hosp. Prev: Sen. Regist. (Psychiat.) Purdysburn Hosp. Belf.; Ho. Off. Belf. City Hosp.

DOHERTY, Michael Verran (retired) 7 Northfield, Braughing, Ware SG11 2QQ Tel: 01920 821739 — MRCS Eng. LRCP Lond. 1943; DAvMed Eng. 1968. Prev: Wing Cdr. RAF Med. Br. Surg. Lt. RNVR.

DOHERTY, Niall Patrick Winyates Health Centre, Winyates, Redditch B98 0NR Tel: 01527 525533 Fax: 01527 517969; Russet Lawns, Chamberlain Lane, Cookhill, Alcester B49 5LD Tel: 01527 892365 — LRCPI & LM, LRSCI & LM 1972; LRCPI & LM, LRCSI & LM 1972; MRCGP 1977; DObst RCOG 1974. (RCSI Dub.)

DOHERTY, Nicholas John 55 Midland Road, Birmingham B30 2ES — MB 1994 Birm.

DOHERTY, Pamela Anne 71 Limeside Av, Rutherglen, Glasgow G73 3TU — MB ChB 1997 Glas.

DOHERTY, Patricia Marie 3 Rosewell Park, Kingsgate, Aberdeen AB15 6HT; Royal Cornhill Hospital, 26 Cornhill Road, Aberdeen AB25 2ZH Tel: 01224 663131 — MB ChB 1991 Glas.; MRCGP 1995; DRCOG 1994. (Glasgow) SHO (Psychiat.) Roy. Cornhill Hosp. Aberd. Prev: SHO (Haemat. & Med.) Hairmyres Hosp. E. Kilbride Glas.; Trainee GP S.. Gen. Hosp. Glas.

DOHERTY, Patrick Columba 48 Dollymount Avenue, Dublin 3, Republic of Ireland; 37 Whitelow Road, Chorlton-cum-Hardy, Manchester M21 9HG — MB BCh BAO 1984 NUI; T(GP) 1991.

DOHERTY, Patrick James Clarendon Street Surgery, 17 Clarendon Street, Londonderry BT48 7EP Tel: 028 7126 1497 — MB BCh BAO 1983 NUI; DRCOG 1987.

DOHERTY, Patrick Joseph (retired) Blossomfield, Bidford-on-Avon, Alcester B50 4EN Tel: 01789 778804 — MB BCh BAO NUI 1944; DPH 1947; LM Nat. Matern. Hosp. 1945. Prev: GP Bidford-on-Avon.

DOHERTY, Peter Francis 60 Nassau Road, Barnes, London SW13 9QE Tel: 020 8741 5708 — MRCS Eng. LRCP Lond. 1948; DTM & H Eng. 1953; LM Rotunda 1959. (Dub. & Liverp.) Edr. Catholic Med. Quarterly. Prev: Sen. Med. Off. Charit. Hosp. Muscat, Oman; Med. Adviser to Political Resid., Persian Gulf; Regist. (Med.) Univ. Coll. Ibadan.

DOHERTY, Roger Worthington Lodge, Choley Road, Worthington, Wigan WN1 2XN — MB ChB 1970 Bristol; AFOM RCP Lond. 1987; DObst RCOG 1972. (Bristol) Prev: Ho. Phys. Ham Green Hosp. Bristol; Ho. Surg. Gloucester Roy. Infirm.; SHO Gloucester Matern. Hosp.

DOHERTY, Roger Patrick 8 Camber Place, Portsmouth PO1 2TZ Tel: 02392 861819 Fax: 02392 751887 — MB BS 1956 Lond.; FACS 1973; FRCOG 1977, M 1964. (St. Bart.) Medico-Legal Adviser Lond. Socs: Medico-Legal Soc.; Medico-Legal Soc. Irel. Prev: Dep. Sec. Med. Defence Union; Cons. O & G St. Bernards Hosp. & R.N. Hosp. Gibraltar; Ho. Phys. & Ho. Surg. St. Bart. Hosp. Lond.

DOHERTY, Sarah Jane Princess Street Group Practice, 2 Princess Street, London SE1 6JP Tel: 020 7928 0253 Fax: 020 7261 9804; 73 Hartham Road, London N7 9JJ Tel: 020 7607 7930 — MB BS 1987 Lond.; MRCGP 1991.

DOHERTY, Sean Paul 17 Colinvale, Dunmurry, Belfast BT17 0JN — MB BCh BAO 1994 Belf.

DOHERTY, Sharon Marie 40 Ardbeg Avenue, High Burnside, Rutherglen, Glasgow G73 5NF — MB ChB 1995 Glas. SHO (O & G) Law Hosp. Carluke. Socs: BMA. Prev: SHO (Psychiat.) CrossHo. Hosp.; SHO (Cas. Off. A & E) Monklands Dist. Gen. Hosp. Glas.

DOHERTY, Sheelagh Mary Hull Royal Infirmary, Anlaby Road, Hull HU3 2JZ Tel: 01482 674210 Fax: 01482 675234 — BM BCh 1972 Oxf.; MA Camb. 1972; BDS Sheff. 1969; FRCP Lond. 1988; MRCP (UK) 1976. (Girton Coll. Camb. & Somerville Coll. Oxf.) Cons. Phys. (Rheum. & Gen. Med.) Roy. Hull Hosps. Trust. Socs: NOS (Scientif. Sect.); BMA; Brit. Soc. Rheum. Prev: Sen. Regist. Rotat. (Rheum.) St. Thos. Hosp. Lond. & St. Peter's Hosp. Chertsey; Regist. (Rheum.) St. Thos. Hosp. Lond.

DOHERTY, Stephen Brendan Flat B, 25 Shepherds Loan, Dundee DD2 1AW — MB ChB 1998 Dund.; MB ChB Dund 1998.

DOHERTY, Stephen Thomas 39 Baddow Road, Chelmsford CM2 0HL Tel: 01245 284661 Fax: 01245 252633 — MB ChB 1979 Manch.; MSc Aberd. 1994; AFOM RCP Lond. 1993; DA (UK) 1983. Employm. Med. Adviser Health & Safety Exec. Chelmsford. Socs: SOM; Brit. Hyperbaric Assn.; Undersea & Hyperbaric Med. Soc. Prev: Regist. (Anaesth.) Ysbyty Glan Clwyd, N. Wales.

DOHERTY, Thomas Patrick The Health Centre, Linenhall St., Lisburn BT28 1LU Tel: 0184 62 665181; 32A Magheralave Road, Lisburn BT28 3BN — MB BCh BAO 1977 Belf.; MRCGP 1981; DRCOG 1980.

DOHERTY, Valerie Rose Royal Infirmary, Edinburgh EH3 9YW — MB ChB Glas.; MD Glas. 1993; FRCP Glas. 1994; FRCP Ed. 1993; MRCP (UK). (Glasgow) Cons. Dermat. Lothian Univ. Hosp. Prev: Sen. Regist. & Regist. (Dermat.) W.. Infirm. Glas.; Cons. Dermatol., Fife Health Bd.

DOHERTY, William Gerard Buckland House, Mill Road, Winchelsea TN36 4HJ — MB ChB 1974 Glas.; FFA RCSI 1980; T(Anaesth) 1991; DCH RCPS Glas. 1977; DRCOG 1976. Cons. Anaesth. Conquest Hosp. St Leonards on Sea. Prev: Cons. Anaesth. Stobhill Gen. Hosp. Glas.

DOHERTY, Yvonne Elizabeth Health Office, 44 King St., Magherafelt BT45 6AH Tel: 01648 31031 Ext: 3210 Fax: 01648 300401; 115 Ballyronan Road, Magherafelt BT45 6HP — MB BCh BAO 1977 Belf. SCMO Home1st Community Trust Magherafelt. Socs: BACCH; Fac. Community Health; BMA.

DOHNE, Silke Freia Reema, The Maultway, Camberley GU15 1QF Tel: 01276 675549; Orchard Lodge, Windermere Road, Lightwater GU18 5TH Tel: 01276 471801 Email: sdohne@reema.demon.co.uk — State Exam Med 1992 Kiel; MD Kiel 1997. SSHO (Paediat.) Roy. Surrey Co. Hosp. Guildford.

DOIDGE, Claire Louise Sheffield Teaching Hospital NHS Trust — MB ChB 1989 Sheff.; FRCA 2000. p/t Specialist Regist. Anaesth. N Trent Traing. Progr.. Sheff. Teachg. Hosp.

DOIDGE, Norman Harold Albany Surgery, Albany Street, Newton Abbot TQ12 2TX Tel: 01626 334411 Fax: 01626 335663; Oakyarde, 8 Bunting Close, Newton Abbot TQ12 6BU Tel: 01626 364333 — MB BS 1976 Lond.; BSc (Physiol.) Lond. 1973; MRCGP 1982; DRCOG 1982; DCH RCP Lond. 1980. (Univ. Coll. Hosp.) GP Trainer Devon. Socs: BMA. Prev: SHO Rotat. (Med. Paediat. & Infec. Dis.) St. Geo. Hosp.; SHO (O & G) Ashford Hosp.; Ho. Phys. (Paediat.) Univ. Coll. Hosp. Lond.

DOIDGE-HARRISON, Katharine Jane 19 Ingelow House, Kensington Church Walk, Holland St., London W8 4NF — MB BS 1996 Lond.

DOIG, Adrian Stuart 1 Brittany Mews, St Leonards-on-Sea TN38 0YU — MB ChB 1993 Leic.

DOIG, Alexander David 5 Farrers Place, Oaks Road, Croydon CR0 5HB — MB BS 1996 Lond.

DOIG, Andrew (retired) 13 Nile Grove, Edinburgh EH10 4RE Tel: 0131 447 4160 — MB ChB 1952 Ed.; FRCP Lond. 1974, M 1956; FRCP Ed. 1964, M 1956. Prev: Sen. Phys. Roy. Infirm. Edin.

DOIG, Anne Dumbarton Health Centre, Station Road, Dumbarton G82 1PW Tel: 01389 602633 Fax: 01389 602623 — MB ChB 1961 Glas.

DOIG, Miss Caroline May (retired) — MB ChB 1962 St. And.; ChM Dund 1970; FRCS Eng. 1970; FRCS Ed. 1967. Chairm. Of Assesment referal comm. GMC; Dir. Of Heritage, Roy. Coll. Surg. Ed. Prev: Sen. Regist. (Surg.) Hosp. Sick Childr. Gt. Ormond St.

DOIG, Charlotte Mary The Health Centre, Bath Road, Buxton SK17 6HL Tel: 01298 24105 Fax: 01298 73227; 15 Lismore Park, Buxton SK17 9AU — BM BS 1987 Nottm.; BMedSci Nottm. 1985; MRCGP 1991.

DOIG, Mr Graeme Joseph 19 Minerva Court, Elliot St., Finnieston, Glasgow G3 8EB — MB ChB 1986 Glas.; FRCS Glas. 1992.

DOIG, Henry Paul 100 Main Street, East Kilbride, Glasgow G74 4JY Tel: 0141 52 39111 — MB ChB 1956 Glas. (Glas.) Local Treasury Med. Off.; Police Surg.; Med. Off. E. Kilbride Dist. Counc. & E. Kilbride Developm. Corp. Socs: BMA. Prev: Ho. Surg. BE.on Memor. Hosp. Glas.; Ho. Phys. Hairmyres Hosp. E. Kilbride; O & G Ho. Surg. Matern. Dept. Stobhill Hosp. Glas.

DOIG, James Colin North Tyneside General Hospital, Rake Lane, North Shields NE29 8NH Tel: 0191 293 2597 Fax: 0191 293 2597 Email: j.c.doig@ncl.ac.uk; 79 North Road, Ponteland, Newcastle upon Tyne NE20 9UR Tel: 01661 820735 — MB ChB 1983 Glas.; FRCP 2000 Lond; MRCP (UK) 1986; FRCP (Glas.) 1996. ((Glasg.)) Cons. Phys. & Cardiol. N. Tyneside Gen. Hosp. N. Shields; Cons. Cardiol. Freeman Hosp. Newc. u. Tyne; Lect. (Clin. Med.) Newc. Univ. Socs: Brit. Soc. Echocardiogr; Brit. Cardiovasc. Interven. Soc.; Brit. Pacing & Electrophysiol. Gp. Prev: Sen. Regist. (Cardiol.)

Freeman Hosp. Newc.; Fell. (Electrophysiol. & Cardiol.) Toronto Gen. Hosp., Toronto, Canada; Regist. (Cardiol.) Freeman Hosp. Newc.

DOIG, John Kennedy 2 Platthorn Road, East Kilbride, Glasgow G74 1NW — MB ChB 1986 Glas.

DOIG, Keith Michael ChevronTexaco Ltd., 1 Westferry Circus, Canary Warf, London E14 4HA Tel: 0207 719 3386 Fax: 0207 719 5188 Email: mike.doig@chevrontexaco.com; Smithy Croft, Craigievar, Alford AB33 8JD Tel: 019755 81483 — MB BS 1977 Lond.; AFOM 1989 RCP, Lond.; 1985 Dip Adv Hyperbaric Med., Aberd.; MSc 1989 ((Occupat. Med.)) Lond.; MFOM 2000 RCP, Lond. Reg. Med. Dir. ChevronTexaco, Europe, Middle E. + Former Soviet Union. Socs: Soc. Occupat. Med.; Eur. Undersea Biomed. Soc.; Internat. Soc. Travel Med. Prev: Manager Med. Servs. RGIT Ltd. Aberd.; Sen. Occupat. Phys. Channel Tunnel Folkestone; Med. Off. Brit. Petroleum Adma Opco, Abu Dhabi.

DOIG, Martin Frank Dr McElhone and Partners, Townhead Surgery, 6-8 High St., Irvine KA12 0AY Tel: 01294 273131 Fax: 01294 312832; Emerald Bank, 38 Harbour St, Irvine KA12 8PY Tel: 01294 278870 — MB ChB 1977 Glas. Socs: Roy. Coll. Gen. Pract.

DOIG, Robert Jules 9 Court Lane, London SE21 7DH Tel: 020 8693 5563 — MD 1973 Aberd.; MRCPsych 1972; DPM Eng. 1964. Hon. Cons. Dispensaire Français. Prev: Cons. Psychiat. Hither Green & Guy's Hosps. Lond.; Interne Amer. Hosp., Paris; Cons. Psychiat. Cane Hill Hosp. Coulsdon.

DOIG, Mr Robertson Lindsay (cons. rooms), Nuffield Hospital, Horsforth, Leeds LS18 4HP Tel: 0113 258 8756; Strathleven, 439 Harrogate Road, Leeds LS17 7AB Tel: 0113 268 0053 — MB ChB 1961 St. And.; ChM Dund 1976; FRCS Ed. 1967; FRCS Eng. 1969. (St. And.) Cons. Surg. Leeds Gen. Infirm.; Hon. Sen. Lect. (Surg.) Univ. Leeds. Socs: Fell. Assn. Surgs.; Fell. Roy. Soc. Med.; Mem. Vasc. Surgic. Soc. Prev: Sen. Regist. (Surg.) St. Thos. Hosp. Lond.; Lect. (Surg.) St. Thos. Hosp. Med. Sch. Lond.; Regist. (Surg.) Dundee Roy. Infirm.

DOIG, Stuart Norman 18 Arnhall Drive, Dundee DD2 1LU — MB ChB 1992 Dundee.

DOIG, Wendy Jean Aon Occupational Health, Foresterhill Road, Aberdeen AB25 2ZP Tel: 01224 669000 Fax: 01224 669030 Email: wendy.doig@aers.aon.co.uk; Smithy Croft, Craigievar, Alford AB33 8JD Tel: 01975 581483 Email: drs.doig@virgin.net — MB ChB 1986 Aberd.; MFOM 1998; AFOM 1994 RCP, Lond.; MRCGP 1990. (Aberd.) Director Med. Servs. Scot.

DOIG, William Bradford Royal Hospital For Sick Children, Yorkhill, Glasgow G3 8SJ Tel: 0141 201 0000 — MB ChB 1962 Glas.; FRCPH 1998; FRCP Ed. 1981, M 1967; FRCP Glas. 1980, M 1967; DCH RCPS Glas. 1965. (Glas.) Cons. Paediat. Cardiol. Roy. Hosp. Sick Childr. Glas.

DOIG, Mr William Malcolm 10 Thorn Drive, Burnside, Rutherglen, Glasgow G73 4RH Tel: 0141 634 4888 — MB ChB Glas. 1959; FRCS Glas. 1964; FRCOphth 1988; DO Eng. 1963. (Glas.) Cons. Ophth. S.. Gen. Hosp. & Vict. Infirm. Glas. Socs: Pres. Scott. Ophth. Club.

DOKAL, Inderjeet Singh Department of Haematology, Hammersmith Hospital, Du Cane Road, London W12 0NN Tel: 020 8571 4334 — MB ChB 1983 Leic.; FRCPath 2001; MD Leic. 1994; MRCP (UK) 1986; MRCPath 1993; FRCPCH 1998; FRCP (UK) 1999. (Leicester) Cons. Haemat. Hammersmith Hosp. Lond.; Reader in Haematological Med., Imperial Coll. Sch. of Med. Socs: Brit. Soc. Haemat.; Amer. Soc. for Haemat.; 1942 Club. Prev: Sen. Regist. (Haemat.) N. Middlx. & Hammersmith Hosps. Lond.; Research Fell. (Haemat.) Roy. Postgrad. Med. Sch. & Hammersmith Hosp. Lond.; Regist. (Haemat.) Hammersmith Hosp. Lond.

DOLAN, Anne 'Carlowrie', 565 Queensferry Road, Barnton, Edinburgh EH4 8DU Tel: 0131 339 7100 — MB ChB 1955 Glas.

DOLAN, Anne Louise Addenbrooke's Hospital, Cambridge CB2 2; 81 St. Joseph's Vale, Blackheath, London SE3 0XG — MB BS 1985 Lond.; MA Camb. 1985.

DOLAN, Derval Mary Waterside Health Centre, Glendermolt Road, Londonderry BT47 6AU Tel: 028 7132 0100; 42 Bayswater, Limavady Road, Waterside, Derry City, Londonderry BT47 6JL — MB BCh BAO 1986 Belf.; MRCGP 1993; DRCOG 1993. Socs: BMA; RCGP; FPA. Prev: Trainee GP Waterside Health Centre Lond.derry; SHO (Haemat., Gastroenterol. & Gen. Med.) Belf. City Hosp.; SHO (Gen. Med. & Respirat.) Altnagelvin Hosp. Derry, NI.

DOLAN, Fiona Mary Derryargon, Enniskillen BT74 4RQ; 7 Woodside House, Woodside, Wimbledon, London SW19 7QN Tel: 020 8879 3871 — MB BCh BAO 1995 Belf.

DOLAN, Gerard Department of Haematology, University Hospital, Queen's Medical Centre, Derby Road, Nottingham NG7 2UH Tel: 0115 970 9187 Fax: 0115 970 9186 — MB ChB 1982 Glas.; MRCP (UK) 1986; MRCPath 1989; FRCP Ed. 1994; FRCP 1996; FRCPath 1998. Cons. Haemat. Univ. Hosp. Nottm. Socs: Brit. Soc. Haematol.; RCP Edin.; Roy. Coll. Path. Prev: Sen. Regist. (Haemat.) Sheff. Hosps.; Regist. (Haemat.) Glas. Roy. Infirm.

DOLAN, Gerard Patrick Antony, MBE Greenlaw Medical Centre, 27 Glasgow Road, Paisley PA1 3PA Tel: 0141 889 8465 Fax: 0141 889 8073; 3 High Calside, Paisley PA2 6BY — MB ChB 1965 Glas.; FRCGP 1981, M 1974. (Glas.) Hosp. Pract. (Urol.) S. Gen. Hosp. Glas. Socs: RCGP; Past Provost W. Scotl. Fac. RCGP. Prev: Mem. Scott. Health Servs. Advis. Counc.; Assoc. Adviser (Gen. Pract.) Renfrew Dist.

DOLAN, Mr James Joseph 19 Vauxhall Park, Belfast BT9 5GZ Tel: 01232 382261 — MB BCh BAO 1987 Belf.; BSc Microbiol. & Immunol. Belf. 1984; FRCS Eng. 1991. Regist. (Surg.) Belf. Gen. Train. Scheme.

DOLAN, John Charles The Health Centre, 20 Cleveland Square, Middlesbrough TS1 2NX Tel: 01642 246138 Fax: 01642 222291 — MB BCh BAO 1980 Dub.; MRCGP 1984; DRCOG 1983. Princip. GP Middlesbrough.

DOLAN, Kevin 11 Wood Sorrell Way, Lowton, Warrington WA3 2GX — MB ChB 1991 Manch.

DOLAN, Leo Joseph Wellfield Surgery, 53 Crescent Road, Manchester M8 9JT; 9 Nursery Road, Prestwich, Manchester M25 3EW Tel: 0161 773 4062 — MB ChB 1951 Manch.; MRCGP 1969; DObst RCOG 1957. Socs: Fell. Manch. Med. Soc. Prev: Ho. Phys. Crumpsall Hosp. Manch.; Ho. Surg. Eccles & Patricroft Hosp.; Ho. Surg. (O & G) Pk. Hosp. Davyhulme.

DOLAN, Lesley Catherine murray Royal Hospital, Perth PH2 7BH Tel: 01738 621151 Fax: 01738 440431 — MB ChB 1988 Dundee; MRCPsych 1993. Cons. Gen. Psych. Murray Roy. Hosp. Perth. Prev: Regist. Rotat. (Psychiat.) Roy. Edin. Hosp.; Sen. Regist. (Gen. Psychiat. & Cognitive Behavioural Ther.) Roy. Edin. Hosp.

DOLAN, Lucia Margaret Appt. 1, Malone Beeches, Belfast BT9 6UB Tel: 01232 664337 — MB BCh BAO 1989 Belf.; MRCOG 1997; MRCGP 1993.

DOLAN, Margaret Christine Edenfield Centre, Prestwich Hospital, Bury New Road, Prestwich, Manchester M25 3BL Tel: 0161 772 3619 Fax: 0161 772 3446 — MB BCh BAO 1985 NUI; MRC Pysch MSc Phd. (nat.univ.irel) Sen.Lec.Forens. Psychiat.

DOLAN, Olivia Mary Dermatology Department, The Royal Hospital, Level 5C, Grosvenor Road, Belfast BT12 6BA Tel: 01232 894635 Fax: 01232 312906; 20 Laganvale Manor, Stranmillis, Belfast BT9 5BE Tel: 01232 683564 — MB BCh BAO 1987 Belf.; MD Belf 1995, MB BCh BAO 1987; MRCP (UK) 1990. (Queens Univ. Belfast) Cons. Dermatol. The Roy. Hosps. Trust Belf. Socs: Brit. Assn. of Dermatol.; Brit. Soc. Dermat. Surg.; Europ. Soc. for Micrographic Surg.

DOLAN, Peter Robertson Health Centre, High Street, Alness IV17 0UN Tel: 01349 882229 Fax: 01349 884004; Culcairn House, Invergordon IV18 0LG — MB ChB 1970 Liverp.; DObst RCOG 1973.

DOLAN, Raymond Joseph The National Hospital for Neurology & Neurosurgery, Queen Square, London WC1N 3BG Tel: 020 7837 3611 Fax: 020 7209 0863 — MB BCh BAO 1977 NUI; MD NUI 1987. Prof. of NeuroPsychiat. Inst. of Neurol. Lond. Socs: F. Med. Sci.; FRC Psych (1995).

DOLAN, Sally-Ann Grove Medical Centre, 27 Grove Road, Wallasey, Wirral CH47 2DS — MB ChB 1985 Liverp. Socs: Med. Protec. Soc.

DOLAN, Susan Adrianne Shealagh 72 Wadsley Lane, Hillsborough, Sheffield S6 4EB Email: s.dolan@ic.ac.uk — MB ChB 1979 Sheff.; MSc De Montfort Univ. 1983. SHO (Psychiat.) Rotherham Priority Health NHS Trust Rotherham.

DOLAN, Mr Trevor George Newham General Hospital, Glen Road, Plaistow, London E13 8SL Tel: 020 7476 4000, 0207 363 8061 Fax: 020 7363 8064; Brunswick House, 108 Talfourd Road, Peckham, London SE15 5NZ Tel: 020 7708 0865 — MB BChir 1978 Camb.; MB Camb. 1979, BChir 1978; MA Camb. 1978; FRCS

Ed. 1984; FRCS Eng. 1984. (Univ. Camb. & St. Thos. Hosp.) Cons. Orthop. Surg. (Upper Limb & Revision Hip Surg.) Newham Gen. Hosp. Lond. Socs: Brit. Orthopaedic Assn.; Brit. Elbow and Shoulder Soc.

DOLBEN, John St James' Univ. Hospital, Leeds LS9 7TP — MB BCh 1980 Wales; BSc Wales 1977, MB BCh (Hons.) 1980; MRCP (UK) 1985. Cons. St James' Univ. Hosp. Leeds.

DOLBY, Alan Ernest 68 Celyn Avenue, Lakeside, Cardiff CF23 6EP — MD 1970 Wales; LDS RCS Eng. 1955; FDS RCS Eng. 1965; MB BCh 1964.

DOLDON, John Leonard David and Partners, Clee Medical Centre, 363 Grimsby Road, Cleethorpes DN35 7XE Tel: 01472 697257 Fax: 01472 690852 — MB ChB 1981 Leeds; MRCPsych 1985.

DOLL, Nicholas William Westwood Lodge, 57 Station Road N., Forest Hall, Newcastle upon Tyne NE12 7AS Tel: 0191 215 0305 — MB BS 1978 Newc.; MRCGP 1987.

DOLL, Sir (William) Richard (Shaboe), CH, OBE Imperial Cancer Research Fund Cancer Studies Unit, Radcliffe Infirmary, Oxford OX2 6HE Tel: 01865 557241 Fax: 01865 558817; 12 Rawlinson Road, Oxford OX2 6UE Tel: 01865 558887 — MB BS Lond. 1937; MRCS Eng. LRCP Lond. 1937; FFPHM 1974; Hon. FRCOG 1993; Hon. FRCR 1993; Hon. FFOM 1987; Hon. FRCGP 1979; FRS; DSc Lond. 1958, MD 1945; DM Oxf. 1969; Hon. DSc Newc. 1969, Belf. 1972, Reading 1973; Newfoundland 1973, Stonybrook 1988, Harvard 1988, Lond. 1988, Oxf. 1989; Brookes 1994, Kingston 1996; Hon. MD Tasmania 1976, Birm. 1994; FRCP Lond. 1957, M 1939. (St. Thos.) Hon. Cons. ICRF Cancer Studies Unit Oxf. Socs: Brit. Assn. Cancer Research; Soc. Social Med.; Amer. Assn. Cancer Research. Prev: Warden Green Coll. Oxf.; Regius Prof. Med. Oxf. Univ. & Hon. Phys. Radcliffe Infirm. Oxf.; Dir. MRC Statistical Research Unit.

DOLLERY, Clare Margaret The Middlesex Hospital, Cardiology Department, Mortimer St., London WC1E 6DB Tel: 020 7636 8333 Fax: 020 7380 9415 Email: c.dollery@ucl.ac.uk; 62B Ridgway Place, London SW19 4SW — MB BS 1988 Lond.; BSc (1st. cl. Hons.) Lond. 1985, MB BS 1988; MRCP (UK) 1991; PhD Lond. 1998. Specialist Regist. (Cardiol.). Prev: Med. Research Counc. Clin. Train. Fell. & Hon. Sen. Regist.; DMed Research & Counc. Clin. Train. Fell.; Regist. (Cardiol.) St. Geo. Hosp. Lond.

DOLLERY, Sir Colin Terence 101 Corringham Road, London NW11 7DL Tel: 020 8458 2616 Fax: 020 8458 5315; 101 Corringham Road, London NW11 7DL Tel: 020 8458 2616 Fax: 020 8458 5315 Email: colin_dollery-1@gsk.com — MB ChB 1956 Birm.; BSc Birm. 1953; FRCP Lond. 1968, M 1958. Senor Cons., Research and Developm., GlaxoSmithKline PLC, Harlow, Essex; Emerit. Prof. Univ. Lond. Socs: Med. Res. Soc.; Brit. Pharmacol. Soc.; Physiol. Soc. Prev: Pro Vice Chancellor for Med. Univ. of Lond.; Dean Roy. Postgrad. Med. Sch., Lond.; Chariman, Dept of Med., RPMS, Hammersmith Hosp., Lond.

DOLLERY, Wendy Carol 2 Highfield, Sale M33 3DN — MB ChB 1983 Aberd.

DOLLING, Matthew 5 Kestral Gardens, Great Hadham Road, Bishop's Stortford CM23 4LU — MB BS 1993 Lond.

DOLLING, Stuart Kirwan Hospital for Women, Townsville Qld, Australia; Ridgewood, Redhill, Buntingford SG9 0TQ — MB BS 1991 Lond. SHO (Neonat.) Kirwan Hosp. for Wom. Townsville, Austral.

DOLLOW, Stuart Clive Glaxo Wellcome Research & Development, Greenfold Rd, Greenford UB6 0HE Email: scd79061@glaxowellcome.co.uk; Chorley Gate, Colley Land, Chorleywood, Rickmansworth WD3 5NE — MB BS 1986 Lond.; BSc (Hons.) Lond. 1983; MFPM RCP (UK) 1996; T(GP) 1997; Dip. Pharm. Med. 1992; DRCOG 1990. (Lond. Hosp. Med. Coll.) Clin. Devel. Dir. (Cardiovasc. Critical Care Anaesth.) Glaxowellcome, Greenford. Prev: CNS Euro.Bus.Team.Ldr..Glaxo.Wellcome; Sen. Med. Advisor Roche Products Ltd. Welwyn Garden City.

DOLMAN, Jennifer Diane 30 Kingfishers, Shipton Bellinger, Tidworth SP9 7US — BM 1995 Soton. SHO (Psychiat.). Socs: RCP Inceptor.

DOLMAN, Lisa Jane The Surgery, Yeoman Lane, Bearsted, Maidstone ME14 4DS Tel: 01622 737326/738344 Fax: 01622 730745; Oak Apple Cottage, The St, Bearsted, Maidstone ME14 4EW — MB BS 1990 Lond.; DCH RCP Lond. 1993.

DOLMAN, Matthew John 53 Walsall Road, Sutton Coldfield B74 4NH — BM BS 1991 Nottm.

DOLMAN, William Frederick Gerrit Hornsey Coroner's Court, Myddelton Road, Hornsey, London N8 7PY Tel: 020 8348 4411 Fax: 020 8347 5229 Email: hmcwd@aol.com — MB BS 1965 Lond.; MRCS Eng. LRCP Lond. 1965; LLB Lond. 1987. (King's Coll. Hosp.) HM Coroner N. Lond.; JP; Assoc. Specialist (Dermat.) Sutton Hosp. Surrey; Med. Ref. Croydon Crematorium. Socs: BMA (Ex-Chairm. Jun. Mems. Forum) & Coroners Soc. Eng. & Wales.; Fell. Roy. Soc. Med. (Library Represen. Sect. of forens. & leg. med.). Prev: Med. Edr. Modern Med. of GB; Ho. Surg. (O & G) & Ho. Phys. (Neurol. & Dermat.) King's Coll. Hosp. Lond.

DOLPHIN, Mr Jeffrey Michael (retired) The Old Vicarage, 64 Highgate Road, Walsall WS1 3JE Tel: 01922 22100 — MB ChB 1952 Birm.; FRCS Eng. 1960; MRCS Eng. LRCP Lond. 1952. Cons. Surg. Walsall Hosp. Gp. Prev: Sen. Regist. Birm. RHB & United Birm. Hosps.

DOLS PERELLO, Salome Flat 1, 51 Earls Court Square, London SW5 9DG — MB BS 1996 Lond. Trainee GP/SHO Wexham Pk. Hosp. Slough VTS.

DOLTON, Vera Downstream, Bridge End, Old Hutton, Kendal LA8 0NH Tel: 01539 725519 — MB BS 1955 Lond. (King's Coll. Lond. & King's Coll. Hosp.) Prev: Lect. Chester Coll. Further Educat.; Sen. Tutor (Health Educat.) Carlett Pk. Coll. Wirral; Tutor (Health & Child Care) Halifax Coll. Further Educat.

DOLTON, Walter Duncan Downstream, Bridge End, Old Hutton, Kendal LA8 0NH Tel: 01539 725519 — MB BChir 1954 Camb.; MA Camb. 1954; MRCS Eng. LRCP Lond. 1954; FFPHM RCP (UK) 1990; FFCM 1979; DPH Lond. 1963. (King's Coll. Hosp.) Prev: Assoc. Prof. Riyadh Univ.; Area Med. Off. Liverp. AHA(T); Chairm. Child Health Computing Comm.

DOMAN, Laura Bethan 23 Standard View, Porth CF39 0HR — MB BCh 1997 Wales.

DOMAR, Alexander (retired) 9 Highlands Road, Wolverhampton WV3 8AH Tel: 01902 654071 — MB ChB 1943 Polish Sch. of Med.; MRCGP 1955. Prev: Adj. Med. Auth. DHSS.

DOMBROWE, Alexander John 5 Lowthes Close, Lowthes Road, Prestwich, Manchester — BM BCh 1998 Oxf.; BM BCh Oxf 1998; BA 1995. Prev: Ho. Phys.John Radcliffe Hosp.Oxf; Ho. Surg. Milton Keynes Gen.

DOMINEY, Jacqueline Ann The Surgery, 90 Church Road, Sheldon, Birmingham B26 3TP Tel: 0121 743 3409 — MB ChB 1985 Birm.; ChB Birm. 1985; DRCOG 1988. (Birm.) Clin. Asst. (Obst & Gyn.) Good Hope Hosp. NHS Trust.

DOMINGUEZ ALONSO, Carlos Javier Riding Edge, Scotland Lane, Horsforth, Leeds LS18 5SF — LMS 1993 U Autonoma Barcelona.

DOMINIAN, Jacobus, MBE Pefka, The Green, Croxley Green, Rickmansworth WD3 3JZ Tel: 01923 720972 — MB BChir Camb. 1955; Hon. DSc Lancaster 1977; FRCP Ed. 1977, M 1958; FRCPsych 1977, M 1971; DPM Lond. 1961. (Camb.) Hon. Cons. Psychiat. & Dir. One Plus One. Socs: BMA & Roy. Soc. Med. Prev: Cons. Psychiat. Centr. Middlx. Hosp.; Sen. Regist. Bethlem Roy. & Maudsley Hosps. Lond.; Resid. Med. Off. Ch.ill Hosp. Oxf.

DOMINIC, Michelle Adelanke Flat 3, 25 Onslow Road, Liverpool L6 3BA — MB ChB 1996 Liverp.

DOMINICZAK, Professor Anna Felicja University of Glasgow, Department of Medicine & Therapeutics, Gardiner Institute, Western Infirmary, Glasgow G11 6NT Tel: 0141 211 2688 Fax: 0141 211 1763 Email: anna.dominiczak@clinmed.gla.ac.uk; 27 Dunkeld Drive, Bearsden, Glasgow G61 2AR Tel: 0141 942 3742 — MD 1978 Gdansk; MD (Hons.) Gdansk 1978; MD Glas. 1989; FRCP Glas. 1995; MRCP (UK) 1986. (Med. Sch., Gdansk, Poland) Brit. Heart Foundat. Prof. of Cardiovasc. Med. Univ. of Glas.; Hon. Cons. Phys. & Endocrinol. Socs: BMA; Internat. Hypertens. Soc.; Fell. Amer. Heart Assn. Prev: Reader Univ. Glas.; Sen. Lect. Univ. Glas.; Lect. Univ. Glas.

DOMINICZAK, Marek Henryk Department of Pathological Biochemistry, Western Infirmary, Glasgow G11 6NT Tel: 0141 339 8822 Fax: 0141 339 4188; 27 Dunkeld Drive, Bearsden, Glasgow G61 2AR Tel: 0141 942 3742 — Lekarz 1975 Gdansk; PHD Gdansk 1979, Lekarz 1975; MRCPath 1985. Cons. Biochem. Dept. Path. Biochem.; Hon. Clin. Sen. Lect. Univ. Glas. Socs: Assn. Clin.

Biochem.; Amer. Assn. Clin. Chem. Prev: Regist. & Sen. Regist. (Biochem.) Glas. Roy. Infirm.

DOMINIQUE, Anna Vydha Flat 4, Block 3, Doctor's Residences, Royal Shrewsbury Hospital, Mytton Oak Road, Shrewsbury SY3 8XQ — MB BCh BAO 1993 NUI.

DOMIZIO, Paola Department of Histopathology, St. Bartholomews Hospital, West Smithfield, London EC1A 7BE Tel: 020 7601 8532 Email: p.domizio@qmul.ac.uk — MB BS 1984 Lond.; BSc (Anat.) Lond. 1981; MRCPath. 1992; FRC Path 2000. (Lond.) Sen. Lect. & Hon. Cons. Histopath. St. Bart. Hosp. Lond. Socs: Assn. Clin. Path.; Internat. Acad. Path.; Path. Soc. Prev: Lect. (Histopath.) St. Bart. Hosp. Lond.; SHO (A & E) St. Jas. Hosp. Lond.; SHO (Surg.) Hammersmith Hosp. Lond.

DOMIZIO, Sandra Anna Giulia 14 Paddocks Road, Guildford GU4 7LL — MB BS 1986 Lond.; Cert. in Underwater Med., Aberd. Univ. 2001; MRCGP 1990. (King's Coll. Hosp. Lond.) p/t Civil. Med. Practitioner (Gen. Pract.) Army Train. Regt. Pirbright Surrey.

DOMJAN, Janine Marie 60 The Crescent, West Wickham BR4 0HF Tel: 020 8777 2569 — MB BS 1986 Lond.; MRCP (UK) 1990. Regist. (Radiol.) St. Mary's Hosp. Lond. Prev: Regist. (Med.) FarnBoro. Hosp. Kent.

DOMMETT, Philip Granville Trescobeas Surgery, Trescobeas Road, Falmouth TR11 2UN Tel: 01326 434888 Fax: 01326 434899; West Hill, West End, Penryn TR10 8EX — BM BCh 1984 Camb.; BM BCh Oxf. 1984; BA Camb. 1981; MRCGP 1989; DRCOG 1988.

DOMMETT, Rachel Mary 7 Fluder Crescent, Kingskerswell, Newton Abbot TQ12 5JE — BM BS 1998 Nottm.; BM BS Nottm 1998.

DOMONEY, Claudine Lisa 79 Lucien Road, Tooting Bec, London SW17 8HS — MB BChir 1993 Camb.; MB BChir 1992; MA Camb. 1993.

DOMONEY, Mr Stewart Robin (retired) 74 Ditchling Road, Brighton BN1 4SG Tel: 01273 698657 Ext: 231746 Email: domoney@cwtv.net — MB BS Lond. 1966; FRCS Eng. 1973; FRCS Ed. 1972; MRCS Eng. LRCP Lond. 1966. Prev: GP Brighton.

DON, John Buchan Yorkhill, Perth Road, Crieff PH7 3EQ — MB ChB 1982 Dundee.

DONACHIE, Fergus Murray Doctor's Residence, Dumfries & Galloway Royal Infirmary, Bankend Road, Dumfries DG1 4AP; 14 Primrose Street, Dumfries DG2 7AU — MB ChB 1994 Aberd.

DONAGH, Andrea Christine 364 Cherry Hinton Road, Cambridge CB1 8BA Tel: 01223 247505; 56 Woollards Lane, Great Shelford, Cambridge CB2 5LZ Tel: 01223 843217 Fax: 01223 568187 — MB BS 1968 Lond.; MRCS Eng. LRCP Lond. 1968. (Middlx.)

DONAGH, Jerome Geoffrey Francis Oldcastle Surgery, South Street, Bridgend CF31 3ED Tel: 01656 657131 Fax: 01656 657134; Twyn Shippin, Heol Spencer, Coity, Bridgend CF35 6AU — MB BS 1988 Lond.; MRCGP 1992.

DONAGHY, Ceri Elizabeth Court Road Surgery, 29 Court Road, Barry CF63 4YD Tel: 01446 733181 Fax: 01446 420004; 1 Hensol Road, Miskin, Pontyclun CF72 8JT Tel: 01443 228148 — MB ChB 1986 Sheff. Socs: Rhondda Med. Soc. Prev: Trainee GP/SHO (O & G) S. Glam. HA VTS; Clin. Med. off. (Paediat.) Rhondda & Ely.

DONAGHY, Denis FitzGerald (retired) The Grange, 387 Malpas Road, Newport NP20 6WB Tel: 01633 858020 — MB BCh BAO Belf. 1948; MRCGP 1962. Prev: Ho. Surg. Roy. Vict. Hosp. Belf.

DONAGHY, Gerald Vincent 1 Adelaide Court, 17 Adelaide Crescent, Hove BN3 2JF Tel: 01273 732535 — MB BCh BAO 1957 Belf.; DObst RCOG 1959.

DONAGHY, John Brendan The Surgery, 39 Brunswick Street West, Hove BN3 1EL; 20 Lloyd Road, Hove BN3 6NL Tel: 01273 884100 — MB BCh BAO 1968 Dub.; BA, MB BCh BAO Dub. 1968.

DONAGHY, Joseph Fergus Ross Road Surgery, 21 Ross Road, Belfast BT12 4JR — MB BCh BAO (Commend.) 1983; MRCGP (Distinc.) 1987; DCH Dub. 1986; DRCOG 1985. GP Belf.

DONAGHY, Malcolm Charles (retired) The Homestead, 60 Ack Lane W., Cheadle Hulme, Cheadle SK8 7EL Tel: 0161 485 4089 — MB ChB Liverp. 1960. Prev: Med. Off. Cheadle Hulme Sch., BASF (UK) Cheadle Hulme & Chemix, Reddish.

DONAGHY, Michael John University Department of Clinical Neurology, Radcliffe Infirmary, Woodstock Road, Oxford OX2 6HE Tel: 01865 224698 Fax: 01865 790493 — MB BS 1978 Lond.; MB BS (Hons.) Lond. 1978; DPhil Oxf. 1991, MA 1987; PhD Camb. 1978; BSc Lond. 1972; FRCP Lond. 1993; MRCP (UK) 1981. (Univ. Coll. Hosp.) Reader (Clin. Neurol.) Univ. Oxf. & Hon. Cons. Neurol. Radcliffe Infirm. Oxf.; Mem., Comm. on the Safety of Med.s, Dept of Health.; Hon. Civil. Cons. in Neurol. to the Army. Socs: Assn Brit. Neurol.; Roy. Soc. Med.; Roy. Coll. Phys.s of Lond. (Counc. 2000 -). Prev: Sen. Regist. (Neurol.) St. Bart. Hosp. & Nat. Hosp. Nerv. Dis. Lond.; Regist. Nat. Hosp. Nerv. Dis. Lond.; Regist. (Neurol.) Middlx. Hosp. Lond.

DONAGHY, Philip Francis 45 Dillons Avenue, Shore Road, Newtownabbey BT37 0SU Tel: 01232 852671 — MB BCh BAO 1977 Belf.; MFCM RCP (UK) 1985.

DONAGHY, Siobhan Mary Hillcrest, Crosscavanagh Road, Dungannon BT70 3BJ — MB BCh BAO 1992 Belf.

DONAGHY, Una Maire 10 Barrhall Road, Portaferry, Newtownards BT22 1RQ — MB BCh BAO 1978 Belf.

DONALD, Alan Cary Malagan, Ferindonald, Sleat, Teangue, Isle of Skye IV44 8RF — MB BS 1972 Lond.; BSc Lond. 1969, MB BS 1972.

DONALD, Alastair Geoffrey, CBE 46 Ferry Road, Edinburgh EH6 4AE Tel: 0131 554 2958; 2 Northlawn Terrace, Easter Park, Edinburgh EH4 6SD Tel: 0131 554 2958 — MB ChB Ed. 1951; MA Camb. 1948; FRCP Glas. 1993; FRCP Ed. 1981; FRCGP 1972, M 1965. Chairm. Armed Serv. Gen. Pract. Approval Bd.; Chairm. Scott. Med. Advis. Comm. BBC. Socs: (Ex-Pres.) Roy. Coll. Gen. Pract.; (Vice-Chairm.) Med. & Dent. Defence Union Scotl. Prev: Chairm. JCPT; Pres. RCGP Lond.; Chairm. UK Regional Adviser in Gen. Pract.

DONALD, Angus High Street South Surgery, 47 High Street South, Dunstable LU6 3RZ Tel: 01582 663406; Rose Cottage, 173 Castle Hill Road, Totternoe, Dunstable LU6 1QQ Tel: 01525 222232 — BM BCh 1976 Oxf.; MA Oxf. 1978; MSc 1971; MRCGP 1984. GP Dunstable. Prev: Regist. (Gen. Med.) Stoke Mandeville Hosp. Aylesbury; SHO/Regist. (Gen. Med.) The Lond. Hosp. & St. And. & Mile End Hosp. Lond.; Ho. Surg./Ho. Phys. The Radcliffe Infirm. Ox.

DONALD, Anna Katherine Maple House, Flat 135, 40 Grafton Way, London WC1E 6DY — BM BCh 1992 Oxf.

DONALD, Carolyn Clare Health Centre, Victoria Sq, Portishead, Bristol BS20 6AQ Tel: 01275 847474 Fax: 01275 817516; Tafira, 62 Edward Road, Clevedon BS21 7DX — MB BS 1983 Lond.; MRCGP 1988; DRCOG 1987. (St. Thomas's) p/t Gen. Practitioner. Socs: BMA; BMAS. Prev: MacMillan Fell. St. Peter's Hospice Bristol.

DONALD, Charles Joseph Munro Padiham Group Practice, Padiham Medical Centre, Burnley Road, Padiham, Burnley BB12 8BP Tel: 01282 771298 Fax: 01282 777720; Brooklands, 60 Mitton Road, Whalley, Blackburn BB7 9RY Tel: 01254 822205 — MB ChB 1979 Liverp.; DRCOG 1981.

DONALD, Christobel (retired) Rheda, Frizington CA26 3TE Tel: 01946 810637 — MB ChB 1953 Aberd.; FRCGP 1994, M 1982.

DONALD, David Department of Pathology, Southend Hospital, Westcliff on Sea SS0 0RY Tel: 01702 348911; 148 Bishopsteignton, Shoeburyness, Southend-on-Sea SS3 8BQ — MB ChB 1965 Aberd.; PhD Aberd. 1973, MB ChB 1965; FRCPath 1987, M 1975. Cons. (Histopath.) S.end Gen. Hosp. Socs: Internat. Acad. Pathol. Prev: Sen. Lect. (Path.) Univ. Aberd.; Hon. Cons. (Path.) Grampian Health Bd.

DONALD, Ms Elizabeth Anne Everglades, Golf Lane, Church Brampton, Northampton NN6 8AY Tel: 01604 844066; Everglades, Golf Lane, Church Brampton, Northampton NN6 8AY Tel: 01604 844066 — MB BS 1999 London. (Imperial College)

DONALD, Fiona Alison Flat 4A, 28 Canynge Square, Bristol BS8 3LB — MB ChB 1985 Bristol. SHO (Anaesth.) John Radcliffe Hosp. Oxf.

DONALD, Fiona Elizabeth Public Health Laboratory, University Hospital, Queen's Medical Centre, Nottingham NG7 2UH Tel: 0115 970 9163 — BM BS 1981 Nottm.; BMedSci Nottm. 1979; MRCPath 1987. Cons. Microbiol. Pub. Health Laborat. Serv. Nottm.

DONALD, Ian Denburn Health Centre, Rosemount Viaduct, Aberdeen AB25 1QB Tel: 01224 644744; 278 Queens Road, Aberdeen AB15 8DR Tel: 01224 317320 — MB ChB 1954 Aberd. GP Clin. Asst. (Gen. Med.) Aberd. Roy. Infirm.

DONALD, Ian Pollok Gloucestershire Royal Hospital, Great Western Road, Gloucester GL1 3NN Tel: 01452 394112 Fax: 01452 394979; 8 Seabroke Road, Gloucester GL1 3JH Tel: 01452 394112 Email: ipd@ecare.worldonline.co.uk — MB ChB Ed. 1979; MA Camb. 1986, BA 1976; FRCP Lond. 1995; MRCP (UK) 1982; MD Cambridge, June 2000. Cons. Phys. (Gen. Med.) Glos. Roy. Hosp.;

Sen. Regist. (Health c/o Elderly) Qu. Med. Centre Nottm. Socs: Brit. Geriat. Soc.; Christ. Med. Fell.sh. Prev: Sen. Regist. Qu. Med. Centre Nottm.; Regist. Glos. Roy. Hosp.; Regist. Roy. Vict. Hosp. Edin.

DONALD, Isabelle Marie Marshall Place Surgery, 1 Marshall Place, Perth PH2 8AJ Tel: 01738 623463; 12 Kincarrathie Crescent, Perth PH2 7HH Tel: 01738 622425 — MB ChB 1958 Aberd. Socs: Scott. Soc. Hist. Med. Prev: Regist. (Psychogeriat.) Murray Roy. Hosp. Perth; Med. Asst. (Radiother.) Aberd. Roy. Infirm.; SHO (Paediat.) City Hosp. Aberd.

DONALD, Jack Lambert Medical Centre, 2 Chapel Street, Thirsk YO7 1LU Tel: 01845 523157 Fax: 01845 524508; 5 Croftheads, Sowerby, Thirsk YO7 1ND Tel: 01845 523193 — MB BS 1978 Newc.; MRCGP 1985; DRCOG 1980.

DONALD, James Frederick Weston Favell Health Centre, Weston Favell Centre, Northampton NN3 8DW; Everglades, Golf Lane, Church Brampton, Northampton NN6 8AY Tel: 01604 844066 — MB ChB 1955 Ed.

DONALD, Janet McKean 7 Invergowrie Drive, Dundee DD2 1RD Tel: 01382 668144 — MB ChB 1945 St. And.; DObst RCOG 1949. Prev: Regist. (Gyn.) Stanley Hosp. Liverp.; Regist. (Paediat. Neonatol.) Walton Hosp. Liverp.; Regist. (O & G) Sefton Gen. Hosp. Liverp.

DONALD, Jennifer 79 Berkley Close, Highwoods, Colchester CO4 4RZ — MB ChB 1988 Dundee. Med. Off RAMC.

DONALD, Jennifer Jane 78 Orakei Road, Remuera, Auckland, New Zealand Tel: 00649 522 6680 — MB BS 1982 Lond.; MRCP (UK) 1985; FRCR 1989. Cons. Radiologist Middlemore Hosp., Auckland, New Zealand. Prev: Cons. Radiol. Bromley Hosp. NHS Trust Kent.; Sen. Regist. (Radiol.) Middlx. Hosp. Lond.; Regist. Rotat. (Med.) Lond. Hosp.

DONALD, Jennifer Louise Eden Park Surgery, 194 Croydon Road, Beckenham BR3 4DQ Tel: 020 8650 9729 — MB BS 1987 Sydney.

DONALD, John Buchan Lothian Primary Caer Trust, Stevenson House, 555 Gorgie Road, Edinburgh EH11 3LE Tel: 0131 537 8503 Fax: 0131 537 8502 Email: j.donald@talk21.com; 11D Craigleith Hill Park, Edinburgh EH4 2NR Tel: 0131 343 3347 — MB ChB 1969 Ed.; BA Open 1987; FFA RCS Eng. 1976; FRCGP 1996, M 1978; DA Eng. 1972; DObst RCOG 1971. Referrals Adviser, Lothian Primary Care Trust; G.P. Blockhall Med. Centre, Edin. Prev: Hosp. Pract. (Anaesth.) St. Johns Hosp. Livingston.

DONALD, Sir John George, KBE Curzon House, Drews Park, Knotty Green, Beaconsfield HP9 2TT Tel: 0149 4 674621 — MB ChB 1951 Aberd.; FRCP Ed. 1986; FFCM 1984, M 1972; MFOM 1982; FRCGP 1977, M 1971; DTM & H Ed. 1964. Med. Adviser AMI Middle E. Servs. Ltd. Lond. Socs: Fell. Roy. Soc. Med. Prev: Hon. Surg. to H.M. the Qu.; Dir. Gen. RAF Med. Servs.; PMO HQ RAF Strike Command.

DONALD, John Gordon (retired) Todhall House, Cupar KY15 4RQ Tel: 01334 656344 Fax: 01334 656344 — MB ChB 1960 Aberd.; FRCOG 1980, M 1967.

DONALD, John Gordon Stuart (retired) The Little House, Coppice Way, Haywards Heath RH16 4NN — MB BS 1968 Lond.; MRCS Eng. LRCP Lond. 1968. Prev: Regist. (Surg.) & Ho. Off. Lond. Hosp.

DONALD, John Robin, TD 49 Cranworth Street, Glasgow G12 8AF Tel: 0141 576 7704 Email: donjon@ronald.gispnet.com — MB ChB 1952 Glas.; FFA RCS Eng. 1963; DA Eng. 1958. (Glas.) Prev: Cons. Anaesth. Inst. Neurol. Sci. Glas.

DONALD, Kathleen Jean Warren Wood House, Durris, Banchory AB31 6BD Tel: 01330 811392 — MB ChB 1981 Aberd.

DONALD, Kerr (retired) The Gables, Bitteswell Road, Lutterworth LE17 4EL Tel: 01455 552659 — MB ChB Glas. 1951. Prev: Ho. Surg. & Ho. Phys. Kilmarnock Infirm.

DONALD, Lesley Anne Department Anaesth., Strcathro Hospital, Brechin Tel: 01356 647291; Firwood, Inveriscandye Road, Edzell, Brechin DD9 7TN — MB ChB 1972 Aberd.; DA Eng. 1974. Assoc. Specialist (Anaesth.) Stracathro Hosp. Tayside.

DONALD, Marion Ramsay Haddow (retired) 103 Ardrossan Road, Seamill, West Kilbride KA23 9NF Tel: 01294 822505 — MB ChB 1954 Glas.; DObst RCOG 1957; DPH Glas. 1968. SCMO (Community Med.) Argyll & Clyde Health Bd.

DONALD, Michael John c/o Murray and Donald, Kingburn Castle, St Andrews KY16 9UA — MB ChB 1997 Manch.

DONALD, Patricia Mary Cramond Surgery, 2 Cramond Glere Rd, Edinburgh EH4 6NS; 26 York Road, Edinburgh EH5 3EH — MB ChB 1977 Ed.; FRCP (Edin.) 1999; FRCGP 1994, M 1981; DRCOG 1979. (Ed.) Primary Care Adviser to SIGN. Prev: GP Dept. Med. W.. Gen. Hosp. Edin.; Hon. Sec. Scott. Counc. RCGP (Clin. Guidelines Co-Ordinator for Scotl.).

DONALD, Robert Graham Exmouth Health Centre, Claremont Grove, Exmouth EX8 2JF — MB ChB 1967 Ed.; MRCGP 1989; DA Eng. 1972; DObst RCOG 1971. (Ed.)

DONALD, Robert Turner (retired) Bishop's Gate, 78 Don St., Old Aberdeen, Aberdeen AB24 1UU Tel: 01224 487256 Fax: 01224 484699 Email: rt.donald@btinternet.com — MB ChB 1951 Aberd.; MRCGP 1960; DPM Eng. 1979; DObst RCOG 1956. Prev: Assoc. Specialist (Psychiat.) Area Alcoholism Unit Sunnyside Roy. Hosp. Montrose.

DONALD, Shirley Ann Cockley Farm, Maryculter, Aberdeen AB12 5GP Tel: 01224 733938 — MB ChB 1984 Aberd. Med. Off. (Psychogeriat.) City Hosp. Aberd. Prev: Ho. Off. (Geriat. Med. & Urol.) Aberd. Roy. Infrim.

DONALD, Stewart Malcolm 147 Grange Loan, Edinburgh EH9 2HA — MB ChB 1985 Ed.; DRCOG 1988.

DONALDSON, Agnes Ditchburn (retired) Greenway, 3 Grange Court, Biddulph, Stoke-on-Trent ST8 6RX Tel: 01782 514820 — MB ChB 1938 Ed.; DPH Ed. 1940.

DONALDSON, Alan Clinical Genetics Department, Birmingham Women's Hospital, Edgbaston, Birmingham B15 2TG Tel: 0121 627 2630 Fax: 0121 627 2618 Email: adonald@hgmp.mrc.ac.uk — MB ChB 1986 Glas.; BSc (Hons.) Glas. 1983; MRCP (UK) 1991. (Glas.) Specialist Regist. (Clin. Genetics) Birm. Wom. Hosp. Socs: Brit. Soc. Human Genetics. Prev: Research Regist. Med. Research Counc. Sickle Cell Unit Kingston, Jamaica.

DONALDSON, Alan Eunson Ellon Group Practice, Health Centre, Schoolhill, Ellon AB41 9AH Tel: 01358 720333 Fax: 01358 721578 — MB ChB 1967 Aberd.; MRCGP 1973; DObst RCOG 1969. (Aberd.)

DONALDSON, Alan Malcolm (retired) 37 Kingsway, Nettleham, Lincoln LN2 2QA — MB ChB 1948 Aberd.; LLB (Hons.) 1985; FRCGP 1981, M 1968; DIH Soc. Apoth. Lond. 1972; DObst RCOG 1957. Prev: Sen. Med. Off. DHSS (Health).

DONALDSON, Alison Jane 1 Mayfair Drive, Thornhill, Cardiff CF14 9EN — MB BS 1997 Newc.

DONALDSON, Ann Kenya (retired) 1 High Mount, Shady Bower, Salisbury SP1 2RE Tel: 01722 330855 — MB BS Durh. 1948; DA Eng. 1968. Prev: Assoc. Specialist Newc. HA.

DONALDSON, Brian Blair Farm, Kilkerran Est., Crosshill, Maybole KA19 7QQ — MB ChB 1972 Glas.; FRCP Glas. 1994; MRCP (UK) 1978.

DONALDSON, Colin Alan The Mannamead Surgery, 22 Eggbuckland Road, Plymouth PL3 5HE — MB ChB 1981 Bristol; DCH RCP Lond. 1985; DRCOG 1984. Trainee GP Frampton Cotterell. Prev: SHO (O & G) & (Paediat.) Freedom Fields Hosp. Plymouth; SHO (Community Paediat.) W.m. Childr. Hosp. Lond.

DONALDSON, David (retired) 5 Woodfield Way, Redhill RH1 2DP Tel: 01737 764601 Fax: 01737 764601 — MB ChB 1959 Birmingham; Eur. ClinChem 2000; Cchem FRSC 2001; Cbiol. FI Biol. 2001; MRCP Lond. 1963; FRCPath 1981, M 1969; FRCP 1999. Cons. Chem. Path. Gatwick Pk. Hosp. Horley Surrey. Prev: Lect. & Hon. Sen. Regist. (Chem. Path.) Nat. Hosp. Nerv. Dis. Qu. Sq. Lond.

DONALDSON, David Bruce (retired) 24 Kinnear Road, Edinburgh EH3 5PE Tel: 0131 552 4314 Email: donaldson@waitrose.com — LRCP LRCS Ed. LRFPS Glas. 1942.

DONALDSON, David John Lisbarnet Road Surgery, 24 Lisbarnet Road, Lisbane, Newtownards BT23 6AW Tel: 028 9754 1466 Fax: 028 9754 2552 — MB BCh BAO 1973 Dub.

DONALDSON, Diane Pamela 3 Lindstrand Gardens, Limavady BT49 0TD — MB BCh BAO 1991 Belf.

DONALDSON, Dianne Elizabeth (retired) Whitewisp, Auchterarder PH3 1NB Tel: 01764 662662 Fax: 01764 662628 — MB BS Lond. 1960; MRCS Eng. LRCP Lond. 1960; DA Eng. 1962. Prev: SHO (Anaesth.) Middlx. Hosp. & Hillingdon Hosp.

DONALDSON, Mr Douglas Ramage St Peter's Hospital, Guildford Road, Chertsey KT16 0PZ Tel: 01932 872000 Fax: 01932 874757; Winchcombe,, Elmstead Road,, West Byfleet KT14 6JB Tel: 01932 401012 Fax: 01932 401015 Email: ddonal4010@aol.com — MD 1984 Dundee; BSc St. And. 1971; MB ChB 1974; FRCS Eng. 1979; FRCS Ed. 1979. Cons. Surg. N.W. Surrey Hosp. Gp.

Socs: Brit. Soc. Gastroenterol. & Assn. Coloproctol. Prev: Resid. Surgic. Off. St. Mark's Hosp. Lond.; Sen. Regist. (Gen. Surg.) S. Glam. HA; Regist. (Surg.) St. Jas. Univ. Hosp. Leeds.

DONALDSON, Gerald William (retired) Ardkeen, 61 Ashgrove Road, Newry BT34 1QN Tel: 028 3026 3373 — MB BCh BAO 1952 Belf.; DObst RCOG 1955. Asst. Med. Dir. Newry Hospice St John of God Hosp. Newry Co Down.

DONALDSON, Professor Iain Malcolm Lane Centre for Neuroscience, University of Edinburgh, Appleton Tower, 11 Crichton St., Edinburgh EH8 9LE Tel: 0131 650 3526 Fax: 0131 650 4579 Email: i.m.l.d@ed.ac.uk — MB ChB 1962 Ed.; MA Oxf. 1973; BSc Ed. 1959; FRCP Ed. 1981, M 1965; MRCP Lond. 1965. (Ed.) Prof. Neurophysiol. Univ. Edin.; Emerit. Fell. St. Edmund Hall Univ. Oxf. Socs: Physiol. Soc. & Internat. Brain Research Assn. Prev: Prof. Zool. Univ. Hull; Fell. & Tutor (Med.) St. Edmund Hall Univ. Oxf.; Hon. Lect. & Hon. Sen. Regist. Univ. Edin.

DONALDSON, Ian Craig c/o Royal Preston Hospital, Sharoe Green Lane, Fulwood, Preston PR2 9HT Email: ian.don@virgin.net — MB ChB 1989 Manch.; FRCA 1997. Cons. IC + Anaesth. Roy. Preston Hosp.

DONALDSON, Ian David Tranent Medical Practice, Loch Road, Tranent EH33 2JX Tel: 01875 610697 Fax: 01875 615046; 4 The Glebe, Pencaitland, Tranent EH34 5EZ Tel: 01875 340588 — MB ChB 1971 Ed.; MRCGP 1975; DObst RCOG 1975.

DONALDSON, Mr Ivor 131 Wentworth Road, Harborne, Birmingham B17 9SU — MB ChB 1970 Birm.; FRCS Eng. 1976. (Birm.) Cons. (Otolaryngol.) Selly Oak Hosp. Birm. Socs: Fell. Roy. Soc. Med.; Otorhinolaryng. Research Soc. Prev: Sen. Regist. (Otolaryng.) Manch. Roy. Infirm. & Christie Hosp. & Holt; Radium Inst. Manch.

DONALDSON, James Campbell (retired) 198 Belper Lane, Belper, Derby Tel: 01773 822390 — MB BCh BAO 1946 Belf.

DONALDSON, Janet Belmont, 7 Mottram Old Road, Stalybridge SK15 2TG — MB ChB 1984 Aberd.; MB ChB Aberd. l984. Clin. Asst. A & E Dept Tameside Gen Hosp. Ashton under Lyne.

DONALDSON, Janet Ann Brunswick Medical Centre, 53 Brunswick Centre, London WC1N 1BP Fax: 020 837 3811 — MB ChB 1986 Manch.; BSc (Hons.) Med. Biochem. 1983; MRCGP 1994; DCH RCP Lond. 1990. (Manchester) GP Asst. Socs: BMA; Med. Protec. Soc.; NANP. Prev: Clin. Research Asst. Nat. Hosp. Neurol. & Neurosurg. Lond.; Regist. (Palliat. Care) Perth, Austral.

DONALDSON, Jeane Bridon (retired) 18 Rosebery Road, Cheam, Sutton SM1 2BW Tel: 020 8642 5071 — MB BS 1951 Durh.; DObst RCOG 1960.

DONALDSON, John Gordon, Lt.-Col. RAMC Maidstone Hospital, Hermitage Lane, Maidstone ME16 9QQ Tel: 01622 729000; Willesley House, Waterloo Road, Cranbrook TN17 2EU Tel: 01580 715312 — MRCS Eng. LRCP Lond. 1978; MA Camb. 1982; FRCR 1993. Cons. Radiol. & Nuclear Med. Maidstone Hosp., Kent. Prev: Cons. Radiol. Qu. Eliz. Milit. Hosp. Woolwich; Command Cons. Radiol. BAOR, BMH Iserlohn; Cons. Radiol. Duchess of Kent's Milit. Hosp. Catterick.

DONALDSON, Judith Anne Ottershaw Surgery, 3 Bousley Rise, West Byfleet KT14 6JB Tel: 01932 875001 — MB ChB 1979 Leeds; DFFP 1993; T(GP) 1982. (Leeds) p/t GP Princip., Ottershaw Surg., Ottershaw.

DONALDSON, Katrina Isabella 39 Askrigg Avenue, Sunderland SR2 9SG — MB ChB 1992 Leeds.

DONALDSON, Keith Hermitage Terrace Surgery, 5 Hermitage Terrace, Edinburgh EH10 4RP Tel: 0131 447 3344 Fax: 0131 447 9866 Email: donaldson@70643.lothian-hb.scot.nhs.uk — MB ChB 1982 Ed.; FRCP Ed 1996; MRCP (UK) 1987; FRCGP 1993, M 1986; DRCOG 1986. (Edinburgh) GP Princip. Eddinburgh. Socs: RCGP (UK and Scot. Counc.); Vice-Chairm. RCGP Scott. Pat.s' Liaison Gp. Prev: Clin. Asst. Young Disabled Unit Liberton Hosp. Edin.; Clin. Asst., Gogarburn Hosp., Edin.

DONALDSON, Kenneth 388 Ormskirk Road, Pemberton, Wigan WN5 9DD Tel: 01942 222246 Fax: 01942 680125; Cuchullin, 17 St. Marys Avenue, Birchley, Billinge, Wigan WN5 7QL Tel: 01744 892459 Fax: 01744 895814 — MB ChB 1963 Glas.; DObst RCOG 1965.

DONALDSON, Kenneth James 98 Dalhousie Road, Broughty Ferry, Dundee DD5 2UB — MB ChB 1995 Dundee.

DONALDSON, Kirsteen Morag BIOS Ltd., Pinewood, College Ride, Bagshot GU19 5ER; 1 Forge Cottage, Romsey Road, Lockerley, Romsey SO51 0JF — BM BCh 1982 Oxf.; MA Oxf. 1983, BA (Hons.) Physiol. 1979; DM Soton. 1992; MRCP (UK) 1985; Dip. Pharm. Med. RCP (UK) 1993. Dir. Pharmacol. Unit, BIOS; Clin. Asst. Soton. & SW Hants. HA. Socs: Fac. Pharmaceut. Med.; Brit. Pharm. Soc.

DONALDSON, Mr Leslie Alexander Diana, Princess of Wales hospital, Scarth Rd, Grimsby DN3 2BA Tel: 01472 874111 Ext: 7457 Fax: 01472 875639 Email: l.a.donaldson@btinternet.com — MB ChB 1972 Glas.; FRCS Glas. 1976; FRCS Eng 1995. (Glasgow) Cons. BrE.. & Vasc. Surg. Grimsby Dist. Gen. Hosp.; Chairm. Mid Trent BrE. Network Examr. F.R.C.S. Glas.. Socs: B.A.S.O.; A.S.G.B.I. Prev: Sen. Regist. (Gen. Surg.) Welsh Nat. Sch. Med. Cardiff; Regist. (Gen. Surg.) Stobhill Gen. Hosp. Glas.; Buswell Research Fell. (Surg.) State Univ. Buffalo, USA.

DONALDSON, Professor Liam Joseph, QHP Richmond House, 79 Whitehall, London SW1A 2NL Tel: 0207 210 5150 Fax: 0207 210 2407 — MB ChB 1972 Bristol; FRCGP 1999; FRCP Ed 1999; F MWD SCI 1999; MD Leic. 1982; MSc (Anat.) Birm. 1976; FRCP Lond. 1997; FRCS Ed. 1977; FFPHM RCP (UK) 1990, M 1990; FFCM RCP (UK) 1987, M 1982; Hon DSc 1998; Hon Md 1999. (Univ. Bristol) Chief Med. Off. Dept of Health; Hon. Prof. Applied Epidemiol. Univ. Newc. Prev: Sen. Lect. (Epidemiol.) Univ. Leicester; Regist. (Surg.) Birm. AHA (T); Reg.dir. Pub.health NHS exe.

DONALDSON, Linda 8 Roman Road, Bearsden, Glasgow G61 2SW — MB ChB 1983 Glas.; DRCOG 1986. Staff Grade (Dermat.) Monklands Dist. Gen. Hosp. Airdrie. Prev: SHO (Dermat.) Monklands Dist. Gen. Hosp. Airdrie.

DONALDSON, Lindsay Department of Anaesthesia, Ninewells Hospital, Dundee; 7A Fairfield Road, West Ferry, Dundee DD5 1NX — MB ChB Aberd. 1992; FRCA 1997. Specialist Regist. Dept. of Anaesth. Ninewells Hosp. Dundee.

DONALDSON, Lorna Michelle Flat 1/1A West Crosscauseway, Edinburgh EH8 9JW — MB ChB 1997 Ed.

DONALDSON, Malcolm David Cairns Department of Child Health, Royal Hospital for Sick Children, Yorkhill, Glasgow G3 8SJ Tel: 0141 201 0241 Fax: 0141 201 0837 Email: mdcd1t@clinmed.gla.ac.uk; Rosemount, 2 Chapelton Avenue, Glasgow G61 2RE Tel: 0141 942 5770 — MB ChB 1973 Bristol; MRCP (UK) 1976; DCH Eng. 1976; MD Bristol 1996; FRCP Glas. 1996; FRCPCH 1996. (Bristol University) Sen. Lect. (Child Health) Univ. Glas. Socs: Eur. Soc. Paediat. Endocrinol.; Fell. Roy. Coll. Paediat. & Child Health; Brit. Soc. Paediat. Endocrinol. & Diabetes. Prev: Regist. (Paediat.) Brighton Hosp. & Guy's Hosp. Lond; Sen. Regist. (Paediat.) Bristol.

DONALDSON, Martin 22 Birch Rise, Hawarden, Deeside CH5 3DD — BM BCh 1975 Oxf.; MRCGP 1981.

DONALDSON, Michael Donald John Department of Anaesthesia, Hull Royal Infirmary, Anlaby Road, Hull HU3 2JZ; 20 Hall Walk, Cottingham HU16 4RL Tel: 01482 842027 — MB BChir 1980 Camb.; MRCP (UK) 1983; FFA RCS Eng. 1985. (St. Catherine's Coll. Camb. & St. Thos. Hosp. Lond.) Cons. Anaesth. Roy. Hull Hosps.

DONALDSON, Michael John 264 Andover Road, Newbury RG14 6PT — MB BChir 1975 Camb.; MB Camb. 1975, BChir 1974; DCH Eng. 1979; DObst RCOG 1976.

DONALDSON, Patricia Helen Peterhead Group Practice, The Health Centre, Peterhead AB42 2XA Tel: 01774 474841 Fax: 01774 474848; Ellon Castle, Ellon AB41 9QN — MB ChB 1982 Aberd.; MRCGP 1986; DRCOG 1986. Med. Off. Ugie Hosp. Peterhead. Socs: MRCGP.

DONALDSON, Paul Michael William Microbiology & Infection Control, Mid Sussex NHS Trust, The Princess Royal Hospital Lewes Road, Haywards Heath RH16 4EX Tel: 01444 441881 Ext: 4195 Email: paul.donaldson@mid-sussex.sthames.nhs.uk — MB BS 1981 Lond.; MRCS Eng. LRCP Lond. 1981; MRCPath 1997; MSc 1996 London. Cons. Med. microbiol. Infect. Control. Dr. Mid sussex NHS Trust. Prev: Regist. (Med. Microbiol.) Lothian HB; Regist. (Histopath.) Yorks. RHA; Sen. Regist. (Med. Microbiol.) Poole Hosp. NHS Trust.

DONALDSON, Mr Peter James Long Meadow, Gravel Pit Road, Wootton Bridge, Ryde PO33 4RB Tel: 01983 884161 — MB BS 1976 Lond.; FRCS Eng. 1980. (St. Bartholomew's Hospital) Cons. Urol. St. Mary's Hosp. Newport, I. of Wight & Hon. Cons. Urol. St.

Mary's Hosp. Portsmouth. Prev: Cons. Surg. St. Mary's Hosp. Newport, I. of Wight; Sen. Regist. (Gen. Surg.) Lond. Hosp.

DONALDSON, Raymond Joseph, OBE 11 Tower Rise, Kew Foot Road, Richmond TW9 Tel: 020 8940 5577 — MB BCh BAO 1943 Belf.; FFCM 1973; DPH Belf. 1948. Dir. S. E. Consortium Train. Pub. Health Med. St. Geo. Hosp. Hosp. Socs: Hon. Mem. Amer. Pub. Health Assn.; Hon. FRSH; BMA. Prev: Dir. of Studies, Centre Extension Train. Community Med. Lond. Sch.Hyg. & Trop. Med.; MOH, Princip. Sch. Med. Off. & Port Med. Off. Teeside Co. Boro.; MOH & Princip. Sch. Med. Off. Rotherham.

DONALDSON, Mr Richard Alexander, TD Misselthwaite, 4 The Cairns, Sydenham Avenue, Belfast BT4 2JQ Tel: 02890 654866 Fax: 02890 655857 — MB BCh BAO Belf. 1969; BSc Belf. 1966; FRCS Ed. 1973; MSSc (Org and Management) Bel. 1998. (Qu. Univ. Belf.) Cons. Surg. (Urol. & Renal Transpl.) Belf. City Hosp. Socs: Irish Soc. Urol.; Brit. Assn. Urol. Surgs.; Brit. Transpl. Soc.

DONALDSON, Robert Michael Royal Brompton & National Heart Hospital, London SW3 6HP Tel: 020 7352 8121; 25 Upper Wimpole Street, London W1G 6NF Tel: 020 7935 4855 Fax: 020 7935 3243 — LMSSA 1976 Lond.; FRCP Lond. 1988; MRCP (UK) 1976; FACC 1983. Cons. Cardiol. Roy. Brompton, Nat. Heart Hosp. & King Edwd. VII Hosp. for Offs. Lond.; Hon. Sen. Lect. Nat. Heart & Lung Inst. Lond. Socs: Brit. Cardiac Soc. Prev: Sen. Regist. (Cardiol.) Nat. Heart Hosp. Lond. & Middlx. Hosp. Lond.

DONALDSON, Robert Sanderson (retired) Troutbeck Nursing Home, Crossbeck Road, Ilkley LS29 9JP — MD 1933 Glas.; MB ChB 1924, DPH 1931; DTM Calcutta 1925. Prev: Med. Supt. Lady Willingdon Sanatoria, Chingleput, S. India.

DONALDSON, Roderick William Riversdale Surgery, 51 Woodcroft Road, Wylam NE41 8DH Tel: 01661 852208; 7 Meadow Park, Riding Mill NE44 6BT — MB ChB 1989 Glas.; MRCGP 1994; DRCOG 1992. Gen. Practioner. Prev: Trainee GP/SHO Glas. VTS.

DONALDSON, Samuel Noel (retired) 5 Rosepark, Dundonald, Belfast BT5 7RG Tel: 028 9048 6337 — MB BCh BAO Belf. 1952; MD Belf. 1966; FFCM 1979, M 1974; DPH Belf. 1956. Prev: Sen. Med. Off. Dept. Health & Social Servs. Belf.

DONALDSON, Shona Mairi 5 Old Church Lane, Edinburgh EH15 3PX — MB ChB 1993 Aberd.

DONALDSON, Stuart William Carronbank Medical Practice, Denny Health Centre, Carronbank House, Denny FK6 6GD Tel: 01324 822382 Fax: 01324 826675; 3 Loudens Walk, Dunipace, Denny FK6 6QH — MB ChB 1978 Dundee; DFFP 1998. Med. Off. RAF.

DONALDSON, Thomas (retired) Millbeck Farm, Millbeck, Keswick CA12 4PS Tel: 017687 72625 — MB ChB Glas. 1957.

DONALDSON, Thomas Horne (retired) Seton House, Wreay, Carlisle CA4 0RH Tel: 01228 521027 — MB ChB Ed. 1947. Prev: Res. Surg. Off. Gen. Hosp. Halifax.

DONALDSON, Thomas John 52 Towthorpe Road, Haxby, York YO32 3NA Tel: 01904 762873 — MB ChB 1973 Ed.; BSc Ed. 1970, MB ChB 1973; MRCGP 1979; DRCOG 1977. Prev: SHO (O & G) E. Gen. Hosp. Edin.; Ho. Off. W.. Gen. Hosp. Edin.

DONALDSON, William 11 Crawfurd Road, Edinburgh EH16 5PQ Tel: 0131 620 0092 — MB ChB 1938 Ed. (Univ. Ed.) Socs: BAFATT; BSMDH; Roy. Med. Soc. Edin. Prev: RAMC; Phys. Nakompaton Prisoner of War Hosp. Siam; GP Roslin, Midlothian.

DONALDSON, Mr William Blair MacGregor 45 Carlton Place, Aberdeen AB15 4BR Tel: 01224 641166 — MB ChB 1966 Ed.; FRCS Ed. 1977; FRCOphth 1989; DO Eng. 1973. Cons. Ophth. Surg. Aberd. Roy. Hosps. NHS Trust & Albyn Hosp. Aberd.; Sen. Lect. (Med.) Aberd. Univ.

DONALDSON-HUGH, Mrs Marcia Elizabeth Anne Leeds General Infirmary, Great George St., Leeds LS1 3EX Tel: 0113 392 3297; 36 Buckthorne Drive, East Ardsley, Wakefield WF3 2LP Tel: 01924 829989 — MB BS 1978 West Indies; FRCS Ed. 1991. (Univ. W. Indies, Mona Campus) Specialist Regist. (Neurosurg.) Leeds Gen. Infirm. Socs: Soc. Brit. Neurol. Surgs. Prev: Regist. (Neurosurg.) Pinderfields Gen. Hosp. Wakefield; SHO (Neurosurg.) Pinderfields Gen. Hosp. Wakefield; SHO (Gen. Surg. & Orthop.) Stracathro Hosp. Scotl.

DONAT, Mr Roland Department of Urology, Western General Hospital, Crewe Road, Edinburgh EH4 2XU Tel: 0131 537 1000 Fax: 0131 537 1019; 24 Polwarth Gardens, Edinburgh EH11 1LW — State Exam Med 1989 Hamburg; State Exam Med. Hamburg 1989; MD Hamburg 1992; FRCS Ed. 1994; FRCS Urol.1999. (Univ. Hamburg) Regist. (Urol.) W.. Gen. Hosp. Edin.

DONATI, Matthew Charles 80 Caraway Place, Wallington SM6 7AG — MB BS 1991 Lond.; BSc Lond. 1987. (Univ. Coll. Lond.) Specialist Regist. (Virol.) Pub. Health Laborat. & Med. Microbiol. King's Coll. Hosp., Lond. Prev: Wellcome Trust Train. Fell. Roy. Free Hosp. Lond.; SHO (Clin. Path.) Hosp. Neurol. Qu. Sq. Lond.; Ho. Off. (Med.) S.end Gen. Hosp. Essex.

DONE, Alan Roger Cater Street Surgery, 1 Cater Street, Kempston, Bedford MK42 8DR Tel: 01234 853461 Fax: 01234 840536; Wild Acre, Top End, Renhold, Bedford MK41 0LR — BSc (Med. Sci.) Ed. 1966, MB ChB 1969. Prev: Ho. Phys. Roy. Infirm. Edin.; Med. Regist. King Edwd. VIII Hosp. Durban, S. Africa & Radcliffe; Infirm. Oxf.

DONE, Brian Bertram Chestnut Cottage, Heapham, Gainsborough DN21 5PT Tel: 01427 838689 — MB ChB 1955 Manch. (Manch.) Prev: GP Gainsborogh; Clin. Med. Off. Scunthorpe Community Health Care NHS Trust.

DONE, Janet Margaret (retired) 468 Binley Road, Coventry CV3 2DL Tel: 01203 453130 — MB BS Lond. 1932; MD Lond. 1936; DObst RCOG 1946; DPH Lond. 1936. Prev: Sen. Asst. MOH Matern. & Child Welf. Coventry.

DONE, Katharine Lucy Chestnut Cottage, Heapham, Gainsborough DN21 5PT Tel: 01427 838689 — MB BS 1994 Lond.; DCH Lond. 1997; MA Oxf. 1995; DTM & H 1998. Prev: GP Regist. Goodinge Health Centre, Lond.

DONEGAN, Anne Mary 21 Providence Street, Earlsoon, Coventry CV5 6ED Tel: 024 76 673667 — MB ChB 1986 Sheff. GP Coventry Retainer Scheme. Prev: Trainee GP Hillfields Health Centre Coventry.

DONEGAN, Jayne Lavinia Mary (Surgery), 74 Herne Hill, London SE24 9QP Tel: 020 7274 3314 Fax: 020 7738 6025 — MB BS 1983 Lond.; MRCGP 1988; DCH RCP Lond. 1987; DRCOG 1986. GP S. Thames Region (E.) Retainer Scheme. Socs: Assoc. Mem. Fac. Homoeop; BMA. Prev: GP Lond.; Trainee GP Winchester VTS; SHO (Orthop. & A & E) Roy. Hants. Co. Hosp.

DONELL, Mr Simon Thomas Norfolk and Norwich Hospital, Brunswick, Norwich NR1 3SR Tel: 01603 287850 Email: simon.donell@norfolk-norwich.thenks.com; Tel: 01508 471307 Fax: 01508 471759 — MB BS 1980 Lond.; FRCS Eng. 1985; BSc (Hons.) Lond. 1977; FRCS (Orth) 1991. (University College London) Cons. (Orthop. Surg.) Norf. & Norwich Hosp.; Hon. Sen. Lect. Univ. of E. Anglia. Socs: Brit. Orthop. Assn.; Brit. Assn. Surg. Knee. Prev: Sen. Lect. Inst. Orthop. UCL; Hon. Cons. Roy. Nat. Orthop. Hosp. Stanmore.

DONEY, Alexander Surendra Fleetwood 11 Gladstone Road, Colchester CO1 2EB — MB ChB 1995 Aberd.

DONEY, Ivor Ernest 3 Wallcroft, Durdham Park, Bristol BS6 6XJ Tel: 0117 973 3110 — MB ChB Bristol 1957; DCH Eng. 1959; DObst RCOG 1959; DCH Eng 1959 Bristol; MRCS Eng. LRCP Lond. 1957; FFHom 1985, M 1968; MFOM RCP Lond. 1986, A 1979; MRCGP 1977; DMJ Soc. Apoth. Lond. 1973; DIH Soc. Apoth. Lond. 1972; DIH Eng. 1972; DObst RCOG 1959. (Bristol) Socs: Fell. BMA.

DONG, Bruce 2 Nursery Road, London N2 9RA — MB BCh 1993 Wales.

DONG, Yuet-Sun 23 Riverside Gardens, Peterborough PE3 6GE — MB ChB 1991 Aberd.

DONGRE, Anil Sadashivrao The Health Centre, Grasmere Street, Leigh WN7 1XB Tel: 01942 673831 Fax: 01942 680883 — LRCP LRCS 1976 Ed.; LRCPS 1976 Glas.; LRCP LRCS Ed. LRCPS Glas. 1976. Socs: Fell. Roy. Soc. Med. Prev: Research Fell. RCGP Leigh Clin. Research Unit Leigh Lancs.; Clin Asst.Cardio Leigh Infirm.

DONIACH, Israel 25 Alma Square, London NW8 9PY Tel: 020 7286 1617 — MB BS 1934 Lond.; MD (Path.) Lond. 1936; FRCPath 1963; FRCP Lond. 1968. (Univ. Coll. Hosp.) Hon. Lect. (Histopath.) St. Bart. Hosp. Lond.; Fell. Lond. Hosp. Med. Coll. Socs: Hon. Fell. Roy. Soc. Med.; Hon. Mem. Path. Soc. GB & Irel.; Hon. Mem. Soc. Endocrinol. Prev: Dir. Bernhard Baron Inst. Path. Lond. Hosp.; Emerit. Prof. Morbid Anat. Univ. Lond.; Reader (Morbid Anat.) Postgrad. Med. Sch. Lond.

DONKIN, Brian Force Medical Office, Lincolnshire Police HQ, Nettleham, Lincoln; 38 St. Mary's Park, Louth LN11 0EF Tel: 01507 605473 — MB ChB 1974 Leeds; BPharm Bradford 1968; DObst RCOG 1976.

DONKIN, Ian 124 Great Lime Road, Westmoor, Newcastle upon Tyne NE12 7DQ Tel: 0191 268 4931; 13 Everett Road, Withington, Manchester M20 3DW Tel: 0161 374 0530 — MB ChB 1989 Sheff.; DRCOG 1997. Prev: SHO (Psychiat.) Tameside Gen. Hosp.; SHO (O & G) Wythenshawe Hosp. Manch.; GP Regist. Gatley Health Centre Gatley Cheadle Chesh.

DONMALL, Richard Clinton Donmall and Partners, 87 Albion Street, London SE16 7JX Tel: 020 7237 2092 Fax: 020 7231 1435 — MB BS 1973 Lond.; BSc (Genetics) Lond. 1970, MB BS 1973; MRCP (UK) 1976; MRCPsych 1979. (Univ. Coll. Hosp.) Sen. Regist. Maudsley Hosp. Lond. Prev: SHO (Gen. Med. Rotat.) N.wick Pk. Hosp. Harrow.

DONNACHIE, Mr Nigel James Arrowe Park Hospital, Arrowe Park Road, Upton, Wirral CH49 5PE — MB ChB 1988 Liverp.; FRCSI 1992; Dip. IMC RCS Ed. 1994; FRCS (Orth)1997. Regist. Rotat. (Orthop.) Merseyside Region.

DONNAI, Professor Dian Department of Medical Genetics, St. Mary's Hospital, Hathersage Road, Manchester M13 0JH Tel: 0161 276 6264 Fax: 0161 276 6145 Email: ddonnai@central.cmht.nwest.nhs.uk; 24 Pine Road, Didsbury, Manchester M20 6UZ — MB BS Lond. 1968; MRCS Eng. LRCP Lond. 1968; FRCP Lond. 1984; MRCP (UK) 1971; FRCOG 1995; FRCPCH 1997. (St. Mary's) Cons. Med. Geneticist St. Mary's Hosp. Manch.; Prof. Med. Genetics Univ. Manch. Socs: Fell. Manch. Med. Soc.; Clin. Genetics Soc.; Brit. Soc. Human Genetics. Prev: Sen. Regist. (Med. Genetics) St. Mary's Hosp. Manch.

DONNAI, Paul St. Mary's Hospital, Manchester M13 0JH Tel: 0161 276 1234; 24 Pine Road, Didsbury, Manchester M20 6UZ Tel: 0161 445 3645 — MB BChir 1967 Camb.; MA, MB Camb. 1967, BChir 1966; FRCOG 1984, M 1971, DObst 1968. (St. Mary's) Cons. O & G St. Mary's Hosp. Manch. Socs: N. Eng. Obst. & Gyn. Soc.; Fell. Manch. Med. Soc. Prev: Sen. Lect. & Hon. Cons. (O & G) St. Mary's Hosp. Manch. Obst.; Regist. Jessop Hosp. Sheff.; Sen. Regist. (O & G) St. Mary's Hosp. Manch.

DONNAN, Alison Beryl 87 Lenton Manor, Nottingham NG7 2FP — BM BS 1995 Nottm.

DONNAN, Francis de Sales (retired) The Post Lodge, Kennel Lane, Windlesham GU20 6AA Tel: 01753 43212 — MB BS 1953 Lond.; DIH Soc. Apoth. Lond. 1958. Prev: Ho. Phys. & Ho. Surg. Middlx. Hosp.

DONNAN, Hilary Lorrain (retired) Willesden Nursing Home, 75 Church Road, Holywood BT18 9BX Tel: 0123 172135 — MB BCh BAO 1932 Belf.

DONNAN, Ian Grier Calder Bank, 107 The Crescent, Davenport, Stockport SK3 8SP Tel: 0161 456 0370; Calder Bank, 107 The Crescent, Davenport, Stockport SK3 8SP Tel: 0161 456 0370 Fax: 0161 292 2664 — MB ChB 1973 Manch.; DAvMed FOM RCP Lond. 1986. (Manchester University) Authorised Med. Exam. Civil Aviat. Auth. Dept. Transport; Div. Surg. & Air Attendant St. John Ambul. Brig. Socs: BMA; Assn. Aviat. Med. Examrs.; Brit. Med. Pilots Assn. Prev: Med. Off. Manch. Airport plc.; SHO (O & G) St. Mary's Hosp. Manch.; Ho. Phys. & Ho. Surg. Vict. Hosp. Blackpool.

DONNAN, James Stevenson Middlestown Health Centre, Ramsey Crescent, Middlestown, Wakefield WF4 4QQ Tel: 01924 272121 — MB ChB 1971 Ed.; BSc (Med. Sci.) Ed. 1968; MRCGP 1976; DObst RCOG 1975; Cert FPA 1975; DCH Eng. 1973.

DONNAN, Kenneth Edward, OBE (retired) Brena, 35 Shore Road, Killyleagh, Downpatrick BT30 9UE Tel: 01396 828355 — MD 1955 Belf.; MB BCh BAO 1947; FRCPsych 1975, M 1971; DPM RCPSI 1952. Prev: Cons. Psychiat. Downshire Hosp. Downpatrick.

DONNAN, Michael Stuart 1 Shirley Avenue, Southampton SO15 5RP Tel: 8077 1356 & 80773258 Fax: 8070 9978 — BM Soton. 1991; MRCGP 1996.

DONNAN, Roger Hugh Colm Beverley H.C., Manor Road, Beverley HU17 7BZ Fax: 01344 762753; 3 New Walk, Beverley HU17 7AE — MB BS 1981 Lond.; MRCGP 1985; DRCOG 1984.

DONNAN, Professor Stuart Paul Briot Lambeth, Southwark and Lewisham HA, London SE1 7NT Tel: 020 7716 7027 Fax: 020 7716 7018 Email: stuart.donnan@ob.lslha.sthames.nhs.uk — MB BS 1962 Sydney; MB BS Sydney. 1962; MPhil Soton. 1981; MSc (Social Med.) Lond. 1975; MA Health Care Ethics Manch. 1995; MD Sydney 1990; FRCP Lond. 1994; FRCS Eng. 1967; FFPHM 1983, M 1976. Visit. Prof. Pub. Health.guys.Kings & St Thomas med Schl Lond; Cons. Pub. Health Med. Lambeth S.wark & Lewisham HA; Regist. Fac. Pub. Health Med. Prev: Foundat. Prof. Community Med. Chinese Univ. Hong Kong; Sen. Lect. (Clin. Epidemiol.) Univ. Soton.; Prof.Epidemiol& Pub.Health Univ.Manch.

DONNE, Adam Jan 3 Rosewood Avenue, Newcastle upon Tyne NE3 5DD — MB ChB 1993 Manch.; BSc (Hons.) Manch. 1990, MB ChB 1993.

DONNE, Carol Anne Great Ayton Health Centre, Rose Hill, Great Ayton, Middlesbrough; Lingfield Cottage, Tofts Lane, Welbury, Northallerton DL6 2SH — MB BS 1984 Lond.; MRCGP 1988; DFFP 1997; DRCOG 1989.

DONNE, Rita Barrywood, Linden Close, Thornton Cleveleys, Blackpool Tel: 01253 868090 — MB ChB 1968 St. And.

DONNE, Rosemary Lucy High Cedar, The Avenue, Radlett WD7 7DQ Tel: 01923 857903; 3 Rosewood Avenue, Garden Village, Gosforth, Newcastle upon Tyne NE3 5DD Tel: 0191 285 8481 — BM BS 1993 Nottm.; BMedSci Nottm. 1991; MRCP 1996. (Nottm.) Renal Research Registr. Socs: RCP; Renal Assn. Prev: SHO Rotat. (Gen. Med.) Newc.

DONNELL, Armar John Henry (retired) 142 Westcotes Drive, Leicester LE3 0SP Tel: 0116 299 1745 — MB BCh BAO 1943 Dub.; BA, MB BCh BAO Dub. 1943. Prev: Ho. Surg. Sir P. Dun's Hosp. Dub.

DONNELL, Mr Stephen Charles 45 Glenmore Avenue, Liverpool L18 4QF — MB ChB 1983 Ed.; FRCS Ed. 1988; DCH RCP Lond. 1990. Sen. Regist. (Paediat. Surg. & Urol.) Roy. Liverp. Childr. Hosp. Liverp. Socs: Assoc. Mem. Brit. Assn. Paediat. Surgs.; Affil. Mem. Brit. Assn. Parenteral & Enteral Nutrit. Prev: Regist. (Paediat. Surg. & Urol.) Roy. Liverp. Childr. Hosp.; Regist. (Paediat., Cardiac & Gen. Surg.) Birm. Childr. Hosp.

DONNELLAN, Clare Fiona Oriel Lodge, Market Place, Easingwold, York YO61 3AL Tel: 01347 822445 — MB BS 1996 Lond.; BSc (Hons.) Lond. 1995; MRCP 1998. (St. Bartholomew's) SHO Med. Rotat. Torbay Hosp. Torquay. Prev: SHO (A & E) St. Mary's Paddington; Surg. Ho. Off. N.allerton N. Yorks.; Med. Ho. Off. St. Bart. & Homerton Hosps.

DONNELLAN, Ian Michael 6 Pasteur Drive, Leegomery, Telford TF1 6PQ — MB ChB 1989 Liverp.

DONNELLAN, Miss Imelda Mary Surrey & Sussex NHS Trust, Crawley Hospital, West Green Drive, Crawley RH11 7DH Tel: 01293 600300 Fax: 01293 600341; The Old House, Court Lodge, Rye TN31 6BB — MB ChB 1985 Liverp.; FRCS 1989; FRCS Ed. 1989. Cons. Surg. Crawley Hosp. Socs: FRCS; Assn. of ColoProctol. of GB & Irel.

DONNELLAN, John 5 Granville Road, Birkdale, Southport PR8 2HU — MD 1956 Liverp.; MB ChB 1941; FRCP Lond. 1973, M 1948. (Liverp.) Cons. Geriat. Phys. S.port Hosp. Gp. Prev: RAMC; Ho. Phys. Roy. S.. Hosp. Liverp.

DONNELLY, Ann Marie 109 St Dympnas Road, Dromore, Omagh BT78 3DJ — MB BCh BAO 1992 Belf.

DONNELLY, Anthony Barclay's Bank Chambers, Tudor Square, West Bridgford, Nottingham NG2 6BT Tel: 0115 981 1654 — LAH Dub. 1956. Prev: Ho. Surg. Orthop. & Ho. Phys. Roy. Portsmouth Hosp.; Ho. Surg. Obst. St. Mary's Hosp. Portsmouth.

DONNELLY, Caroline Sarah 32 Innisfayle Park, Belfast BT15 5HS — MB BCh 1998 Belf.; MB BCh Belf 1998.

DONNELLY, Catherine Marie 46 Turner Road, Colchester CO4 5LA — LRCPI & LM, LRSCI & LM 1970; LRCPI & LM, LRCSI & LM 1970.

DONNELLY, Catherine Mary 4 Maitland Terrace, Kildrochat, Stranraer DG9 9EX — MB BCh BAO 1984 Belf.

DONNELLY, Charles Vincent 77 Downhills Road, Liverpool L23 8SL Tel: 0151 924 1016 — MD 1949 Liverp.; BM ChB 1941. (Liverp.) Mem. Liverp. Med. Inst. & BMA. Prev: Ho. Surg. Chester Roy. Infirm.; Med. Regist. N.. Hosp. & Walton Hosp. Liverp.

DONNELLY, Columba Augustine 175 Ferry Road, Hockley SS5 6JH — MB BCh BAO 1972 Belf.

DONNELLY, David 3 Marbury Grove, Standish, Wigan WN6 0UF — MB ChB 1998 Manch.; MB ChB Manch 1998.

DONNELLY, Deirdre Elisabeth 28 Knockbracken Manor, Belfast BT8 6WQ — MB BCh BAO 1996 Belf.

DONNELLY, Deirdre Mary Foyleview House, 29 Lowertown Road, Ballymagorry, Strabane BT82 0LE — MB BCh BAO 1992 NUI.

DONNELLY, Ena Elizabeth 100 Strand Road, Portstewart BT55 7PG — MB BCh 1998 Belf.; MB BCh Belf 1998.

DONNELLY, Francis Martin Draperstown, Magherafelt BT45 7 — LRCPI & LM, LRSCI & LM 1940; LRCPI & LM, LRCSI & LM 1940. (Dub.) Prev: Ho. Surg. Jervis St. Hosp. Dub.

DONNELLY, Geraldine Mary (retired) 28 Old Coach Avenue, Belfast BT9 5PY Tel: 02890 604967 — MB BCh BAO 1964 Belf.; DO RCPSI 1976. GP Med. Off. (Ophth.) Eye & Ear Clinic Belf.; Clin. Med. Off. Community Eye Clinics. Prev: Clin. Med. Off. (Ophth.) E. Health & Soc. Servs. Bd.

DONNELLY, Heidi Marie 23 Underswood Road, Handsworth Wood, Birmingham B20 1JR — MB ChB 1996 Manch.

DONNELLY, Hubert Stephen 228 Dewsbury Road, Leeds LS11 6HQ — MRCS Eng. LRCP Lond. 1958.

DONNELLY, Jacqueline Ann 6 Monson Park, Skellingthorpe, Lincoln LN6 5UE — MB ChB 1985 Dundee; FRCA 1992.

DONNELLY, James Duncan 1 Atholl Gardens, Dunkeld PH8 0AY — MB ChB 1958 Ed.; MFCM 1973; FFCM 1984.

DONNELLY, Mr James Patrick Phillip 6 Medina Terrace, Hove BN3 2WL Tel: 01273 777613 — MB BS 1965 Lond.; FRCS Eng. 1972; MRCS Eng. LRCP Lond. 1965; DLO Eng. 1968. (St. Mary's) Cons. Surg. (ENT) P.ss Margt. Hosp. Swindon.

DONNELLY, Janet Mary The Sue Nicholls Centre, Manor House, Bierton Road, Aylesbury HP20 1EG Tel: 01296 489951 Fax: 01296 398802; 11 Meadow Park, Stoke Mandeville, Aylesbury HP22 5XH Tel: 01296 613009 — MB ChB 1973 Manch.; FRCPCH 1997; DCH RCP Lond. 1984; Cert. Prescribed Equiv. Exp. JCPTGP 1981; Cert Developm. Paediat. Ascertainm. (Salford) 1981; Cert Contracep. & Family Plann. JCC 1975; DObst RCOG 1975. Cons. Community Paediat. Aylesbury Vale NHS Healthcare Community Trust. Socs: MFCH 1989; Fac. Comm. Health; FRPCH 1998.

DONNELLY, Jill Sara 3 Galloway Close, Bishop's Stortford CM23 2HT — BM 1990 Soton.

DONNELLY, Joanne Marie Meadowside Medical Practice, 1-3 Meadowside, Lancaster LA1 3AQ Tel: 01524 32622 Fax: 01524 846353; Stane Brae, 23 Hall Park, Scotforth, Lancaster LA1 4SH Tel: 01524 380377 Fax: 01524 388958 Email: thesmyths@compuserve.com — MB ChB 1990 Liverp.; MRCGP 1994; Dip. Ven. Liverp. 1997; Dip. Pract. Dermat. Wales 1996; DRCOG 1992; DFFP 1992. (Liverp.) GP Princip.; Clin. Asst. (Dermat.) Roy. Lancaster Infirm.; CMO (Family Plann.) Bay Community Trust. Socs: BMA; Primary Care Dermat. Soc.; Soc. Advancem. Sexual Health.

DONNELLY, Johanna Elisabeth c/o Oakleigh House, Rectory Lane, Sidcup DA14 4QJ — MB BS 1986 Queensland.

DONNELLY, John Gerard Department of Anaesthesia, Royal Infirmary, Edinburgh Tel: 0131 536 1000; 32 Glendinning Way, Kirkliston, Edinburgh EH29 9HH Tel: 0131 333 5466 Fax: 0131 333 2552 Email: drjohndonnelly@hotmail.com — MB ChB 1988 Aberd.; FRCA 1994. Cons. Anaesth. Cardiothorcacic, Roy. Infirm. Edin. Prev: Specialist Regist. Glas. Sch. of Anaesth.

DONNELLY, John William Springburn Health Centre, 200 Springburn Way, Glasgow G21 1TR Tel: 0141 531 9631 Fax: 0141 531 9543; Townhead Health Centre, 16 Alexandra Parade, Glasgow G31 2ES Tel: 0141 552 3477 — MB ChB 1963 Glas. (Glas.) Police Cas. Surg. Glas. (E. Div.). Socs: BMA & Assn. Police Surgs. Prev: Ho. Off. (Surgic.) & Ho. Off. (Med.) Glas. Roy. Infirm.; Ho. Off. (O & G) Stobhill Hosp. Glas.

DONNELLY, Katherine Mary The Pines, 35 Windsor Hill, Newry BT34 1HS — MB BCh BAO 1970 Belf.

DONNELLY, Kevin Francis Cromwell Place Surgery, Cromwell Place, St. Ives, Huntingdon PE27 5JD Tel: 01480 462206 Fax: 01480 465313 — BM BCh Oxf. 1971; BM BCh Oxf. 1971; BA Oxf. 1968; BA Oxf. 1968; FRCGP 1996, M 1975; FRCGP 1996, M 1975; DObst RCOG 1974; DObst RCOG 1974. Prev: Trainee GP Reading VTS.

DONNELLY, Mark Gerard 5 Strand Avenue, Millisle, Newtownards BT22 2BU — MB BCh BAO 1992 Belf.

DONNELLY, Mark Thomas Dept of Gastroenterology, Northern General Hospital, Herries Road, Sheffield S5 7AU Tel: 0114 226 6955 Fax: 0114 226 6064; Tel: 0114 285 1325 — MB ChB 1989 Sheff.; MRCP (UK) 1992. (Sheff) Cons Phys. Gastroenter. N.ern. Gen. Hosp. Sheff; Hon. Sen. Lect., Univ. of Sheff. Med. Sch. Prev: Specialist Regist., Med. and Gastroenerology, Sheff.; Research Fell., Div. of Gastroenterol., Univ. Hosp., Nottm.; Regist., Med. and Gastroenterol., City Hosp., Nottm.

DONNELLY, Martin Joseph Clifton Street Surgery, 15-17 Clifton Street, Belfast BT13 1AD Tel: 028 9032 2330 Fax: 028 9043 9812 — MB BCh BAO 1975 Belf.

DONNELLY, Mary Asgard, 110 Dundrum Rd, Newcastle BT33 0LN — MB ChB 1996 Glas.

DONNELLY, Mary Claire 23 Taunton Avenue, Belfast BT15 4AD — MB BCh BAO 1992 Belf.

DONNELLY, Mary Eleanor Carmel Mental Health Resource Centre, Castle Rock Road, Coleraine Tel: 01265 42721; 4 Lir Court, Ballycastle BT54 6DH — MB BCh BAO 1967 Belf.; MRCPsych. 1984. Cons. Community Psychiat. Coleraine.

DONNELLY, Mary Philomena Edinburgh Homeless Practice, 22-24 Spittal St., Edinburgh EH3 9DY Tel: 0131 221 9805 Email: phil@gp70963.lothiam-hb.scot.nhs.uk; 21 Letham Mains, Haddington EH41 9DY Tel: 01620 822906 Email: phil.donnelly@virgin.net — MB ChB 1972 Glas. Lead Clinician Edin. Homeless Pract. Socs: BMA; MWF. Prev: GP Edin.

DONNELLY, Mary Rose Monica (retired) 38 Derrynoyd Road, Draperstown, Magherafelt BT45 7DN Tel: 01648 28225 — MB BCh BAO Belf. 1935. Disp. Doctor Draperstown; GP (Health Serv.) Draperstown. Prev: MoH Med. Off. Draperstown Disp. Dist.

DONNELLY, Mary Teresa 80 Russell Road, Mossley Hill, Liverpool L18 1EB — MB ChB 1991 Liverp.

DONNELLY, Michael Rosemount House, 58 Andersonstown Road, Belfast BT11 9AN — MB BCh BAO 1976 Belf.; DRCOG 1978. (Belf.) Socs: Ulster Med. Soc. & BMA; Assoc. Mem. Irish Cardiac Soc.

DONNELLY, Neil Patrick Clock House, Church St., Easton on the Hill, Stamford PE9 3LL — MB BS 1997 Lond.

DONNELLY, Patrick Francis 158A The Ridgeway, Enfield EN2 8AW — MB BCh BAO 1945 Belf. (Belf.)

DONNELLY, Patrick Martin Pinewood, Tamnabane Road, Newry BT34 3FH — MB BCh 1998 Belf.; MB BCh Belf 1998.

DONNELLY, Paul Xavier 53 Church Lane, Highfield, Southampton SO17 1SY — MB ChB 1985 Manch.

DONNELLY, Peter Gelligron, Gelligron Road, Pontardawe, Swansea SA8 4LU Tel: 01792 865696 Fax: 01792 863129 Email: gelligron@glan-y-mor.wales.nhs.uk; Broadelms, 36 Castle St, Loughor, Swansea SA4 6TU — MB BCh BAO 1983 NUI; MRCPsych 1988; BA 1996. Cons. Psychiat. Cefn Coed Hosp. Swansea. Prev: Sen. Regist. S. Wales Rotat. Scheme; Regist. Rotat. (Psychiat.) Sheff.

DONNELLY, Peter Duncan Iechyd Morgannwg Health, 41 High St., Swansea SA1 1LT Tel: 01792 458066 Fax: 01792 470743 Email: pddonn@aol.com; 4 Vale Court, Cowbridge CF71 7ES Tel: 01446 775274 Fax: 01446 775314 — MB ChB 1985 Ed.; MBA Stirling 1989; MPH Wales 1991; FFPHM RCP (UK) 1997; T(PHM) 1994; DA (UK) 1988. (Ed.) Dir. Pub. Health Iechyd Morgannwg Health; Hon. Sen. Lect. (Pub. Health Med.) Univ. Wales Coll. Med. (Centre for Applied Pub Health Med); Hon. Sen. Lect. (Pub. Health) Univ. Wales Swansea (Dept. of Psychol.). Socs: Resusc. Counc.; Eur. Resusc. Counc.; Treas. Elect Fac. Pub. Health Med. Prev: Sen. Lect. (Pub. Health Med.) Centre for Applied Pub. Health Med. Univ. Wales Coll. Med.; Dep. Dir. & Hon. Cons. Pub. Health Med. S. Glam. HA.

DONNELLY, Professor Richard Division of Vascular Medicine, University of Nottingham, Derbyshire Royal Infirmary, Derby DE1 2QY Tel: 01332 254966 Fax: 01332 254968 Email: richard.donnelly@nottingham.ac.uk; Gean Rise, Hob Hill, Hazelwood, Belper DE56 4AL Tel: 01332 840853 Fax: 01332 842656 Email: richard.donnelly@nottingham.ac.uk — MB ChB 1984 Birm.; MB ChB (Hons.) Birm. 1984; PhD Glas. 1988; MD Birm. 1994; FRCP Lond. 1998; FRCP (Glas.) 1999; FRACP 1995; T(M) 1993. Prof. Med. Univ. Nottm. Socs: Brit. Pharm. Soc.; Diabetes UK. Prev: Sen. Lect. (Med. & Pharmacol), Univ. Sydney, Australia; Lect. Univ. Glas. & Hon. Sen. Regist. (Med. & Therap.) W.. Infirm. Glas.; Research Fell. Univ. Dept. Mat. Med. Stobhill Hosp. Glas.

DONNELLY, Robert John 14 Oakdene, Beaconsfield HP9 2BZ — MB ChB 1977 Glas.; BSc (Hons.) Glas. 1975; MRCP (UK) 1979. Med. Dir. Janssen-Cilag Ltd. High Wycombe.

DONNELLY, Robin Patrick Shell Expro, 1 Altens Farm Road, Nigg, Aberdeen AB12 3AY; 13 Woodlands Park, Purris, Banchory

AB31 6BF Email: rob.donnelly@shell.com — MB ChB 1988 Ed.; MRCGP 1994; DRCOG 1993; AFOM RCP Lond. 1997; MFOM RCP Lond. 1999. (Univ Edin.) Sen. Med. Adviser, Shell Expro UK. Socs: Soc. Occupat. Med. Prev: RAMC Short Serv. Commiss.; GP Tidworth Garrison Wilts.; Chief Med. Off., Corus Gp.

DONNELLY, Roderick Siam Surgery, Sudbury CO10 1JH Tel: 01787 370444 Fax: 01787 880322; Trollbo, Rectory Lane, Newton, Sudbury CO10 0RA Tel: 01787 378162 — MB ChB Leeds 1966; CCFP Canada 1979. (Leeds) Princip. GP Sudbury. Socs: BMA; Sec. of Suff. Div. Prev: Med. Off. RAF Med. Br.; SHO (Obst.) W. Chesh. Hosp. Chester; Med. Staff Norway Ho. Hosp. Manitoba Canada.

DONNELLY, Ronan Peter 3 Mount Eden Park, Malone Rd, Belfast BT9 6RA — MB BCh BAO 1996 Belf.

DONNELLY, Seamus Ciaran Rayne Laboratory, University Medical School, Teviot Place, Edinburgh EH8 9AG — MB BCh BAO 1984 NUI; MRCPI 1988.

DONNELLY, Simon Peter Department of Rheumatology, Whipps Cross Hospital, Whipps Cross Road, London E11 1NR — MB BCh BAO NUI 1985; LRCPI & LM, LRCSI & LM 1985; MRCP (UK) 1990. Cons. Rheum. Whipps Cross Hosp. Lond. Socs: Roy. Soc. Med. Prev: Sen. Regist. (Rheum.) Whipps Cross Hosp. Lond.; Hon. Regist. (Rheum.) St. Bart. Hosp. Lond.

DONNELLY, Susan Janette 13 Kingfisher Drive, Redhill RH1 2AD — MB BS 1991 Lond.; DFFP 1994; DRCOG 1994; DGM RCP Lond. 1994. (Char. Cross & Westm. Hosp.) Socs: Roy. Coll. Gen. Pract.

DONNELLY, Thomas Brooks 7 Colley Rise, Lyddington, Upppingham, Oakham LE15 9LL — MB ChB 1968 Glas.; DObst RCOG 1971; DCH Eng. 1972.

DONNELLY, Thomas Peter 25 Newry Road, Banbridge BT32 3EA — MB BCh BAO 1987 NUI.

DONNELLY, Ursula Mary 9 Glenaan Avenue, Dunmurry, Belfast BT17 9AT — MB BCh BAO 1983 Belf.; DO RCPSI 1988. Clin. Med. Off. Daisy Hill Hosp. Newry; Staff Grade Mater Hosp. Belf. Socs: Roy. Acad. Med. Irel.; MRCOphth. (Irel.). Prev: Regist. (Ophth.) Roy. Vict. Hosp. Belf.

DONNELLY, William John c/o Oakleigh House, Rectory Lane, Sidcup DA14 4QJ — MB BS 1986 Queensland.

DONNELLY, William Joseph (retired) 332 Moorside Road, Davyhulme, Manchester M41 5SE Tel: 0161 746 8095 — LRCPI & LM, LRSCI & LM 1949; LRCPI & LM, LRCSI & LM 1949.

DONNER, Cathy Marie Chevet Chase, Chevet Lane, Wakefield WF2 6PT — BM BCh 1996 Oxf.

DONNISON, Aileen Barbara (retired) Yorkleigh, Blackpond Lane, Farnham Common, Slough SL2 3EG Tel: 01753 644050 — MB BCh Camb. 1952; MA Camb. 1953, BA 1949; FRCP Lond. 1976, M 1963; MRCS Eng. LRCP Lond. 1952; FRCPCH 1997; DCH Eng. 1956. Prev: Cons. Paediat. E. Berks. HA.

DONNISON, Philip Edward Innes 2 Ringwood Crescent, St Athan, Barry CF62 4LA — MB BS 1994 Lond.

DONOGHUE, Caroline Ann Tean Surgery, Old Road, Tean, Stoke-on-Trent ST11 SE4 Tel: 01538 722323 Fax: 01538 722215; 19 Shelley Drive, High Meadow, Cheadle, Stoke-on-Trent ST10 1XR Email: caroline@donoghue.demon.co.uk — MB BS 1993 Lond. GP. Prev: SHO (A & E) & Ho. Off. (Gen. Med.) Mayday Hosp. Croydon; Ho. Off. (Gen. Surg. & Orthop.) Qu. Mary's Hosp. Roehampton.

DONOGHUE, Cecilie (retired) 15 Cromarty Crescent, Bearsden, Glasgow G61 3LU Tel: 0141 943 1002 — MB ChB 1959 Glas.; FRCOphth 1990; DO Eng. 1966. Prev: Cons. Ophth. Lanarksh. HB.

DONOGHUE, Charles Norman (retired) 34 Camperdown Street, Broughty Ferry, Dundee DD5 3AB Tel: 01382 477970 Email: charles.donoghue@newscientist.net, cnd@cdonoghue.demon.co.uk — MB ChB 1957 Glas. Prev: Med. Pract. Broughty Ferry.

DONOGHUE, Ronald Edward Child & Family Unit, Sunderland District General Hospital, Kayll Road, Sunderland SR4 7TP Tel: 0191 569 9026 Fax: 0191 569 9247; Wooley Cottage, Low Wooley, Allendale, Hexham NE47 9AL Tel: 01434 683561 — MB BS 1969 Newc.; MRCPsych 1976. Cons. Child Psychiat. Sunderland Dist. Gen. Hosp.

DONOHOE, Mollie Eleanor Avonhayes, Buckerell, Honiton EX14 3EH Tel: 01404 850191 — MB BS 1976 Lond.; MRCP (UK) 1979; MRCGP 1981; DRCOG 1980. Specialist Regist. (Endocrinol. & Diabetes) Devon.

DONOHOE, Paul Thomas Flat 2, 17 Waterloo St., Hove BN3 1AQ — MB BCh BAO 1989 NUI.

DONOHUE, Eoin Patrick Gerard Department of Psychiatry, St Georges Hospital Medical School, Tooting, London SW17 0RE; 3 Meadside, Epsom KT18 7QF — MB BCh BAO 1985 NUI; DCH NUI 1990. (Univ. Coll. Dubl.) Regist. (Psychiat.) Geos. Hosp. Med. Sch. Prev: Regist. (Psychiat.) Mayday Hosp. Croydon; Ho. Phys. Adelaide Hosp. Dub.

DONOHUE, James Stephen (retired) Health Centre, Manor Road, Beverley HU17 7BZ Tel: 01482 862733 Fax: 01482 864958 — MB ChB Leeds 1967; DObst RCOG 1969. Clin. Asst. Dept. Anaesth. Hull & E. Yorks. HAs. Prev: Clin. Asst. Dept. Plastic Surg. Hull Roy. Infirm.

DONOHUE, Sarah Marie Newark Hospital, Boundary Road, Newark NG24 4DE Tel: 01636 685790 Fax: 01636 685973; Corner House, Rectory Lane, Barrowby, Grantham NG32 1BT — MB ChB 1979 Glas.; MRCP (UK) 1984; MRCPath 1989. Cons. Haemat. Newark Hosp.

DONOHUE, Sheila Mary 55 Talfourd Road, London SE15 5NN Tel: 020 7703 2522 — MB ChB 1967 Leeds; MSc (Mental Health Studies) UMDS Guy's and St. Thomas's. (Leeds) Staff Grade (Psychiat.) Lewin Rd. Community Health Centre Lond. Socs: Affil. Mem. Roy. Coll. Psychiat. Prev: Clin. Asst. (Psychiat.) Kingston Gen. Hosp. Hull; Resid. Med. Off. Ida & Robt. Arthington Hosp. Leeds; Ho. Phys. & Ho. Surg. Bishop Auckland Gen. Hosp.

DONOUGHMORE, Richard Michael John, (The Earl of) (retired) The Manor House, Bampton, Oxford OX18 2LQ Tel: 01993 850231 Fax: 01993 851334 — MA, BM BCh Oxf. 1952.

DONOVAN, Andrew David 6 Newland House, Landsdown, Bath BA1 5RE Tel: 01225 446465 — MB BS 1996 Lond.; BSc Lond. 1994.

DONOVAN, Mr Andrew George Batworth House, 18 Muston Road, Hunmanby, Filey YO14 0JY Tel: 01723 891112 — MB ChB 1962 Birm.; FRCS Eng. 1972. Cons. (Orthop.) ScarBoro. Hosp. Prev: Sen. Regist. Soton. & S.W. Hants. Health Dist. (T).

DONOVAN, Brian The Surgery, 4 Station Road, Frimley, Camberley GU16 5HF Tel: 01276 62622 Fax: 01276 683908 — MB BS 1964 Lond.; MRCS Eng. LRCP Lond. 1962. (Guy's) Socs: BMA. Prev: Dir. Clin. Research Crookes Laborats. Basingstoke; Jun. Specialist in Ophth. RAMC.

DONOVAN, Charles Fisher, OStJ (retired) Somerville, Burghill, Hereford HR4 7RN — MB BS 1946 Lond.; MRCS Eng. LRCP Lond. 1941. Prev: Ho. Surg. St. Bernard's Hosp. S.all.

DONOVAN, Christopher Ferrier Temple Fortune Health Centre, 23 Temple Fortune Lane, London NW11 7TE Tel: 020 8458 4431; 25 Middleway, Hampstead Garden Suburb, London NW11 6SH Tel: 020 8458 4526 — MB BS 1960 Lond.; MA Oxf. 1952; DObst RCOG 1962. (Univ. Coll. Hosp.) Course Organiser Bloomsbury & Roy. Free Hosps Lond. VTS; Chairm. N.E. Thames GP Postgrad. Comm.; Chairm. Omega Foundat.; Chairm. Hampstead & S. Barnet GP Forum; Mem. Regional Dir. Postgrad. Educat.; Mem. Med. Advis. Comm. Roy. Free Trust; Mem. RCGP Clin. Trials Ethical Comm. Socs: Assoc. RCGP. Prev: Lect. (Gen. Pract.) Edin. Univ.; Chairm. Educat. Comm. N. Lond. Fac. RCGP; Chairm. & Sen. Lect. (Gen. Pract. Teach.) Roy. Free Hosp. Lond.

DONOVAN, Daniel Thomas Village Medical Centre, 400-404 Linthorpe Road, Middlesbrough TS5 6HF Tel: 01642 851234 Fax: 01642 820821; 39 Cambridge Road, Linthorpe, Middlesbrough TS5 5NG Tel: 01642 281770 — MB BS 1984 Lond.; MRCGP 1988. (Char. Cross) Med. Off. Prison Serv.; Clin. Asst. Diabetic Servs.; Med. Adviser TFM Radio.

DONOVAN, David Hugh 3 Alwyne Road, Cambridge CB1 8RR — MB ChB 1992 Dundee; MA Ed. 1985; MRCGP 1996; DRCOG 1995. (Dundee)

DONOVAN, Elizabeth Wargrave House, 23 St Owen St., Hereford HR1 2JB Tel: 01432 272285; Lauristina House, Burghill, Hereford HR4 7RN — MB ChB 1969 Birm.; DObst RCOG 1972. (Birm.) Clin. Asst. (Gen. Pract. & Gyn.) Hereford Co. Hosp. Prev: Clin. Asst. Hereford Gen. Hosp.

DONOVAN, Mr Ian Alexander City Hospital NHS Trust, Birmingham B18 Tel: 0121 554 3801 — MB ChB 1968 Birm.; MD Birm. 1975; FRCS Eng. 1973. Cons. Surg. City Hosp. NHS Trust Birm. Socs: Assn. Surg.; Assn. Coloproct.; Assn. Upper G.I. Surg. Prev: Sen. Lect. (Surg.) Univ. Birm.; Lect. (Surg.) Qu. Eliz. Hosp. Birm. & Gen. Hosp. Birm.; Sen. Regist. (Surg.) Qu. Eliz. Hosp. Birm.

DONOVAN, James Francis (retired) 1 Bicton Place, Exeter EX1 2PF Tel: 01392 422239 — MRCS Eng. LRCP Lond. 1939; FRCPsych 1971; DPM Lond. 1946. Prev: Cons. Psychiat. Roy. Cornw. Hosp. Truro & St. Lawrence's Hosp. Bodmin.

DONOVAN, Judith Anne Gladstone House Surgery, Gladstone Street West, Ilkeston DE7 5QS Tel: 0115 932 0248 Fax: 0115 944 7347 Email: judith.donovan@gp_c81115.nhs.uk — MB ChB 1977 Leeds; BSc Leeds 1974; MRCGP 1982. Gen. Med. Practitioner; Exec. Comm. Chairm., Erewash PCT. Prev: Trainee GP Oldham; SHO (Med.) Manch. Roy. Infirm.; Ho. Surg. & Ho. Off. (Med.) Hull Roy. Infirm.

DONOVAN, Michael John Richard Edwards and Partners, Wargrave House, 23 St. Owen Street, Hereford HR1 2JB Tel: 01432 272285 Fax: 01432 344059 — MB ChB 1967 Birm.; DA Eng. 1970; DObst RCOG 1969. (Birm.)

DONOVAN, Rosamund Mary The Rowans, 57 Birmingham Road, Hagley, Stourbridge DY9 9JY Tel: 01562 884625 — MB ChB Birm. 1973; FRCR 1979; DMRD Eng. 1977. Cons. Radiol. Sandwell Dist. Gen. Hosp.

DONOVAN, Mr Rupert Furzehill, Yealmpton, Plymouth PL8 2LH Tel: 01752 880432 — MB 1963 Camb.; BChir 1962; FRCS Eng. 1967. (Camb. & Middlx.) Cons. ENT Surg. Plymouth Gp. Hosps. Prev: Sen. Regist. St. Thos. Hosp. Lond.; Regist. Roy. Nat. Throat, Nose & Ear Hosp. Lond.; Cas. Off. Middlx. Hosp. Lond.

DONOVAN, William Martin Butler Clinic, Langdon Hospital, Dawlish Tel: 01626 888371 — MB ChB 1968 Bristol; FRCPsych 1989, M 1973; DPM Eng. 1972. Cons. Forens. Psychiat. & Med. Dir. Butler Clinic Langdon Hosp. Dawlish. Prev: Cons. Forens. Psychiat. Midl. Centre Foren. Psychiat. Birm.; Sen. Clin. Lect. Univ. Birm.; Sen. Regist. Uffculme Clinic Birm.

DONOVAN, William Ross University Health Service, University of Edinburgh, Richard Verney Health Centre, 6 Bristo Square, Edinburgh EH8 9AL Tel: 0131 650 2777 Fax: 0131 662 1813 — MB BCh BAO 1985 NUI; MRCGP 1991; MCOphth 1989; DO RCS Eng. 1989; DObst RCPI 1988; DCH NUI 1987.

DOO, Alexander Kenneth 8 Carroll House, Craven Terrace, Lancaster Gate, London W2 3PP — MB ChB 1989 Glas.

DOODSON, Andrea Colette 33 Manor Leas Close, Lincoln LN6 8DE — BM BS 1996 Nottm. SHO (Gen. Med.) Derbys. Roy. Infirm. Derby.

DOODY, Patrick Failsworth Health Centre, Ashton Road W., Failsworth, Manchester M35 0HN Tel: 0161 682 6297; 12 Oakcroft, Mottram Rise, Stalybridge SK15 2UQ — MB ChB 1988 Manch.; MRCGP 1992; T(GP) 1992. (Manch.) Clin. Asst. (Drug & Alcohol Abuse) Roy. Manch. Hosp. Socs: BMA; NAFPD. Prev: Trainee GP/SHO (Med.) Tameside Gen. Hosp. Manch.

DOOHAN, John (retired) Park View, 162 Old Road, Blackley, Manchester M9 8BR Tel: 0161 795 5835 — MB BCh BAO NUI 1949; LM Dub. 1949. Prev: Capt. RAMC, Med. Off. Depot York & Lancaster Regt.

DOOLDENIYA PERERA, Dora 7 Borrowdale Close, Burnley BB10 2QN — MB BS 1978 Sri Lanka; MRCP (UK) 1989; MRCS Eng. LRCP Lond. 1986.

DOOLEY, Anne Patricia The Clinic, John Mitchel Place, Newry BT34 2BU Tel: 01693 67030; 16 Ballynalack Road, Camlough, Newry BT35 7HU — MB BCh BAO 1985 NUI. (Univ. Coll. Dub.) Clin. Med. Off. Newry & Mourne Trust; Staff Grade Community Paediat. N & Mourne HSS Trust. Socs: BMA; BACDA; Brit. Assn. Community Child Health.

DOOLEY, Brian Gerard (retired) 15 William Burt Close, Weston Turville, Aylesbury HP22 5QX Tel: 01296 612991 — MB BCh BAO 1950 NUI; MB BCh BAO (Hons.) NUI 1950; FRCGP 1979, M 1965; DObst RCOG 1957. Prev: Resid. Med. Off. & SHO (O & G) Gulson Hosp. Coventry.

DOOLEY, Mr Denis, OBE 7 Murray Road, Wimbledon, London SW19 4PD Tel: 020 8946 1020 — MRCS Eng. LRCP Lond. 1945; BA Lond. 1936; FRCS Eng. 1975. (St. Mary's) Arris & Gale Lect. RCS Eng. 1972. Socs: Sen. Fell. Brit. Assn. Clin. Anats. Prev: H.M. Insp. of Anat. for Eng., Wales & Scotl.; Sen. Med. Off. DHSS; Regist. Sir Alexander Fleming's Penicillin Unit St. Mary's Hosp. Lond.

DOOLEY, Henry James (retired) 30 Bowland Court, Lowergate, Clitheroe BB7 1AS Tel: 0120 444780 — MB ChB Sheff. 1943.

DOOLEY, James Selwyn Department of Medical, Royal Free Hospital, Pond St., London NW3 2QG Tel: 020 7830 2592 Fax: 020 7830 2960 — MB BS 1973 Lond.; BSc Lond. 1970, MD 1984; FRCP Lond. 1992; MRCP (UK) 1976. (Middlx.) Sen. Lect. (Med.) Roy. Free Hosp. Sch. Med. Lond.; Hon. Cons. Phys. & Gastroenterol. Roy. Free Hosp. Lond. Prev: Lect. (Med.) Roy. Free Hosp. Sch. Med. Lond.; Vis. Scientist Nat. Inst. Health Bethesda Maryland, USA; Regist. (Med. & Gastroenterol.) Roy. Free Hosp. Lond.

DOOLEY, Jennifer Margaret Rowan Villa, 127 Old Greencock Road, Bishopton PA7 5BB Tel: 01505 863727 Email: dooleygray@compuserve.com — MB ChB 1993 Aberd.; MRCGP 1997. GP.

DOOLEY, Mr John Frederick Rally Wood, Hascombe Road, Godalming GU8 4AA Tel: 01483 414999 Fax: 01483 423232; 14 Devereux Road, Windsor SL4 1JJ Tel: 01753 858113 — MB ChB 1974 Cape Town; BSc Cape Town 1969; FRCS Ed. 1980; FRCSC 1987. Cons. Orthop. Surg. Hillingdon & Mt. Vernon Hosp. Socs: Fell. BOA; Brit. Spinal Soc.; Brit. Orth. Foot Soc. Prev: Clin. Research Spinal Fell. (Toronto).

DOOLEY, Michael Matthew Patrick Department of Obstetrics & Gynaecology, West Dorset Hospital, Damers Road, Dorchester DT1 2JY Tel: 01305 251150 Fax: 01305 265424 Email: gynaecology2@hotmail.com; Four Winds, Broadmayne, Dorchester DT2 8LY Tel: 01305 854251 Fax: 01305 854551 Email: gynaecology2hotmail.com — MB BS 1980 Lond.; MFFP 1993; MRCOG 1986; DRCOG 1983; DObst RCPI 1983; MMs NUI 1985. (Char. Cross Med. Sch.) Cons. O & G W. Dorset Hosp.; Clin. Teach. (Obst. & Gyn.) Soton. Univ.; Liveryman Worshipful Soc. Apoth. 1986; Director of Sports Med. and Sci. to Brit. Equestrian Federat.; Med. Adviser to TAMBA. Socs: Fell. Roy. Soc. Med.; Brit. Fertil. Soc.; Amer. Fertil. Soc. Prev: Sen. Regist. (O & G) St. Thos. Hosp. Lond. & Poole Gen. Hosp.; Regist. (O & G) John Radcliffe Hosp. Oxf.; Research Regist. (Biochem.) Univ. Coll. Galway.

DOOLEY, Pauline Thelma (Surgery), Engleton House, 1A Engleton Road, Coventry CV6 1JF Tel: 024 76 592012 Fax: 024 76 601913; 60 Sunningdale Avenue, Kenilworth CV8 2BZ — MB BS 1960 Lond.; MRCS Eng. LRCP Lond. 1960. (St. Mary's) Prev: Ho. Surg. (O & G) St. Mary's Hosp. Lond.; Med. Off. N.ampton CC.

DOOLEY, Sylvia (retired) 15 William Burt Close, Weston Turville, Aylesbury HP22 5QX Tel: 01296 612991 — MB ChB 1952 Leeds. Prev: Paediat. Ho. Phys. Gulson Hosp. Coventry.

DOONAN, Justine Ferguson 41 Killymoon Road, Cookstown BT80 8TW — MB ChB 1993 Leeds. Trainee GP Skipton. Prev: Ho. Off. Gen. Infirm. Leeds; Ho. Off. (Med.) Pontefract Gen. Infirm.

DOORE, Janet Rosemary 85 Weetwood Lane, Leeds LS16 5NU — MB ChB 1986 Bristol. Trainee GP Leeds E. VTS. Prev: Regist. (Paediat. & A & E) Sheff. Childr. Hosp.; SHO (Gen. Med.) Trent HA.

DOORIS, John Brendan 2A Newby Road, Stockport SK4 2JJ — MB BS 1992 Lond.

DOOTSON, Gillian Margaret Queen Elizabeth Hospital, King's Lynn PE30 4ET — MB BS 1981 Lond.; FRCP Lond. 1999; MRCP Lond. 1984; BSc Lond. 1978. (Royal Free) p/t Cons. Dermat. Qu. Eliz. Hosp. King's Lynn. Prev: Sen. Regist. (Dermat.) Camb. & Kings Lynn; Regist. (Dermat.) Roy. Free Hosp. Lond.; Regist. (Med.) St. Mary's Hosp. Lond.

DOOTSON, Judith Claire Drs N S P Enevoldson & Dr J. H. Mountjoy, High Row Surgery, Scorton, Richmond DL10 6QD Tel: 01748 811320 — MB BS Lond. 1985; DRCOG 1987. (St. Mary's Hosp. Med. Sch. Lond.) p/t GP Retainee from 1998 & Dr. N S P Enevoldson & Partner. Prev: GP Welwyn Garden City.

DOOTSON, Peter Holt (retired) 20 Willow Road, Willersey, Broadway WR12 7QE Tel: 01386 852896 — MB ChB 1952 Ed.; MRCGP 1990; DObst RCOG 1955. Vocat. Train. Course Organizer (Postgrad. Med. Studies) Univ. Manch. Prev: GP Cheadle Hulme.

DOPFMER, Ulrich 19 Crossley Street, London N7 8PE — State Exam Med 1987 Berlin.

***DOR, Riaz** 138 Freer Road, Birmingham B6 6NB — MB ChB 1995 Leeds.

DORAISWAMY, Mr Nanjappachetty Velaswamychetty Royal Hospital for Sick Children, Yorkhill, Glasgow G3 8SJ Tel: 0141 201 0749 Fax: 0141 201 0839 Email: nanjappachelty.doraiswamy@yorkhill.slest.nhs.uk; 23 Drumbeg Terrace, Milngavie, Glasgow G62 7RH Tel: 0141 956 6321 — MB BS 1965 Madras; FRCPCH 1998; FFAEM 1994; MNAMS 1991; FRCS Ed. 1976; FRCS Glas. 2000; MS 1969. (Madurai Medical College) Cons. i/c A & E Roy. Hosp. Sick Childr. Glas.; Hon. Sen.

Clin. Lect. Univ. Glas. Socs: Brit. Assn. Paediat. Surg.; Brit. Assn. Accid. & Emerg. Med.; Brit. Paediat. Accid. & Emerg. Gp. Prev: Cons. Paediat. Surg. Ibn Sina Hosp., Kuwait.

DORAISWAMY, Wubayavedantapurum Seaforth Farm Surgery, Vicarage Lane, Hailsham BN27 1BH Tel: 01323 848494; Cheverton, 215 Eastbourne Road, Polegate BN26 5DU Tel: 0132 126225 — MB BS 1972 Madras. (Kilpauk Med. Coll.)

DORAN, Barry Reginald Harewood (retired) 11 Cotswold Avenue, Hazel Grove, Stockport SK7 5HJ Tel: 0161 483 4988 Fax: 0161 355 1022 Email: barry.doran@virgin.net — MB BS 1963 Lond.; FRCA; FFA RCS Eng. 1969. Cons. Anaesth. & Clin. Dir. Critical Care Unit Centr. Manch. HA (Trust); Lect. (Anaesth.) Vict. Univ. Manch. Prev: Wellcome Research Asst. RCS Eng.

DORAN, Catriona Anne Flat 1/2, 39 Henderson St., Kelvinbridge, Glasgow G20 6HP — MB ChB 1989 Glas.; DA (UK) 1995; DRCOG 1992; T(GP) 1993.

DORAN, Clare Louise Kingsway Surgery, 20-22 Kingsway, Waterloo, Liverpool L22 4RQ Tel: 0151 920 9000 Fax: 0151 928 2411; 2A Moorside Close, Crosby, Liverpool L23 2RL — MB ChB 1987 Liverp.; DCH RCP Lond. 1990; MRCGP 1991; DGM RCP Lond. 1991; DRCOG 1990. GP Liverp. Prev: Trainee GP/SHO Liverp. VTS; Ho. Off. Roy. Liverp. Hosp.

DORAN, Derek Malise Leslie (retired) Dell Farm, Vicarage Lane, Copythorne, Southampton SO40 2PA Tel: 01703 812502 — MRCS Eng. LRCP Lond. 1940; MA Oxon., BM BCh 1946; FRCP Lond. 1971, M 1953; DPhysMed. Eng. 1948. Hon. Cons. Phys. W. Middlx. Hosp. Prev: Cons. Phys. Dept. Rheum. & Rehabil. W. Middlx. Hosp. Isleworth.

DORAN, Geoffrey Robert Charing Cross & Westminster Medical School, The Reynolds Building, St Dunstans Road, London W6 8RP Tel: 020 7628 8502 Fax: 020 7628 8502; 520 Willoughby House, London EC2Y 8BN — MB BS 1964 Lond.; MD 1984 Lond.; FRCPath 1983, M 1971. (Char. Cross) Cons. In Clin. Path. for Clin. Pharmac. Trials. Socs: Fell. Roy. Soc. Med.; Europ. Undersea Biomed. Soc.; Assn. Clin. Path. Prev: Sen. Lect. In Chem. Path. Imperial Coll., Cons. Char. Cross Hosp.

DORAN, Grainne Bangor Health Centre, Newtownards Road, Bangor BT20 4LD Tel: 028 9146 9111; 34 Station Road, Carnalea, Bangor BT19 1HD — MB BCh BAO 1986 Belf.; MRCGP 1990; DCH Glas. 1989; DRCOG 1989; M.Phil (Med. Ethics & Law) 1993. (Queens University Belfast) GP Princip. Socs: Comm. Mem. R.C.G.P. (N.I. Fac.). Prev: Trainee GP Belf.; SHO (Paediat.) Roy. Belf. Hosp. for Sick Childr.; SHO (O & G) Roy. Matern. Hosp. Belf.

DORAN, Helen Elizabeth North Waestern Deanery -General Surgery Rotation, Dept. Postgraduate Medicine, Gateway House, Picadilly South, Manchester M60 7LP Tel: 01355 267821 ex directory, 0161 237 2298 — MB ChB 1991 Liverp.; FRCS Eng. 1995. Prev: SHO (Gen. Surg.) Roy. Liverp. Univ. Hosp.

DORAN, Helen Mary Department of Histopathology, Wythenshawe Hospital, Southmoor Road, Manchester M23 9LT — MB BS 1985 Lond.; MA Oxf. 1983; MRCPath 1992. Cons. Histopath. Wythenshawe Hosp. Manch. Prev: Sen. Regist. (Histopath.) Addenbrooke's & Papworth Hosps. Camb.

DORAN, Jane Rosemary 14 Rectory Road, Wokingham RG40 1DE Tel: 0118 978 4566; Treetops, 2A Glebelands Road, Wokingham RG40 1DR Tel: 0118 978 1458 — MB ChB 1975 Liverp.; DRCOG 1986. (Univ. Liverp.) GP Wokingham. Socs: Reading Path. Soc. Prev: SHO (Obst. & Cas.) Crawley Hosp.; Med. Off. Swaziland Irrigation Scheme; Ho. Surg. & Ho. Phys. BRd.green Hosp. Liverp.

DORAN, Mr John Elm House, Cropwell Road, Radcliffe-on-Trent, Nottingham NG13 9AE — MB BS 1970 Lond.; BSc Lond. 1967, MB BS 1970; DM Nottm. 1980; FRCS Ed. 1976. Cons. Surg. Univ. Hosp. Nottm. Prev: Lect. Surg. Univ. Nottm.

DORAN, John Francis 25 Westwood Park Road, Peterborough PE3 6JL — MB BCh 1976 Wales; BSc (Hons) Wales 1973; BDS Lond. 1969; MRCPath 1988; MRCP (UK) 1979. Cons. Chem. Path. P'boro. Prev: Sen. Regist. (Biochem. Med.) Ninewells Hosp. Dundee; Hon. Lect. (Biochem. Med.) Dundee.

DORAN, John Stephen Waterside Day Hospital, Waterside, Evesham WR11 6JT Tel: 01386 502512 — MB ChB 1980 Birm.; MSc (Psychother.) Warwick 1990; MRCPsych 1984. Cons. Psychiat. Worcs. Community NHS Trust. Prev: Cons. Psychiat. Hollymoor Hosp. E. Birm. HA.

DORAN, Keith Wilson St Johns Hospice, Balby, Doncaster DN4 8JS Tel: 01302 796666 Fax: 01302 796660 — MB ChB 1980 Manch.; BSc St. And. 1977; Dip. Palliat. Med. Wales 1995. Cons. In Palliat. Med. to Doncaster & Bassetlaw Dist. Socs: Assn. Palliat. Med. Prev: Med. Dir. & Cons. Palliat. Med. St. Johns Hospice Doncaster; GP Doncaster.

DORAN, Kenneth Michael St John's Surgery, Main Road, Terrington St. John, Wisbech PE14 7RR Tel: 01945 880471 Fax: 01945 880677 — MB BCh BAO 1969 Dub. Socs: BMA. Prev: Trainee Gen. Pract. King's Lynn Vocational Train. Scheme; Ho. Phys. & Ho. Surg. Sir Patrick Dun's Hosp. Dub.

DORAN, Mark The Walton Centre, Rice Lane, Liverpool L9 1AE Tel: 0151 529 4606; Coed Talwrn, Pentrecelyn, Ruthin LL15 2HT Tel: 01978 790366 — MB BS 1984 Lond.; PhD Manch. 1979; MD Lond. 1994; FRCP (UK) 2000. Cons. Neurol. Walton Centre Liverp. Prev: Lect. & Sen. Regist. (Neurol.) Addenbrooke's Hosp. Aylesbury; Regist. (Neurol.) Nat. Hosp. for Neurol. & Neurosurg. Lond.; Sen. Clin. Wellcome Fell. (Neurol.) Hammersmith Hosp. Lond.

DORAN, Niall Francis 22 Osborne Park, Belfast BT9 6JN Tel: 01232 660409 — MB BCh BAO 1986 NUI; MRCGP 1991; DRCOG 1990; DMH 1992 (Queens University Belfast). (University College Dublin) Primary Care Practitioner; Lect., Qu.s Univ., Belf. Med. Sch.

DORAN, Patricia Anne Ford Cottage, 2 Water St., Stamford PE9 2NJ — MB ChB 1957 Manch.; DCH Eng. 1959. Prev: GP Stamford; Ho. Off. Roy. Manch. Childr. Hosp.; Ho. Phys. & Ho. Surg. Manch. Roy. Infirm.

DORAN, Peter Seamus American Express Travel Service, Client's Mail, 6 Haymarket, London SW1Y 4BS.

DORAN, Mr Robert Malcolm Leslie Clarendon Wing, General Infirmary, Belmont Grove, Leeds LS2 9NS Tel: 0113 392 2531 Fax: 0113 292 6239 — MB BS 1971 Lond.; FRC Ophth. 1986; FRCS Ed. 1979. (St. Thos.) Cons. Ophth. Surg. Gen. Infirm. Leeds. Socs: Fell. Roy. Soc. Med. Prev: Cons. Sen. Lect. (Ophth.) Univ. Bristol & Bristol Eye Hosp.; Sen. Regist. (Ophth.) St. Mary's Hosp. Lond. & Moorfields Eye Hosp. Lond.

DORAN, Timothy Nigel Harewood 4 Thornton Drive, Handworth, Wilmslow SK9 3DA — MB ChB 1994 Ed.

DORANI, Mr Balaji Queen Elizabeth Hospital, Sheriff Hill, Gateshead NE9 6SX Tel: 0191 487 0000 Fax: 0191 403 2830 Email: dorani@mcmail.com — MB BS 1983 Osmania; FRCS Ed. 1990; FFAEM 1997. Cons. A & E Qu. Eliz. Hosp. Gateshead. Socs: BMA; BAEM. Prev: Sen. Regist. (A & E) Sunderland Gen. Hosp. & Newc. Gen. Hosp.; Sen. Regist. (A & E) Cumbld. Infirm.; Regist. (A & E) Roy. Vict. Infirm. Newc.

DORE, Alfred John Kenneth (retired) Evenlode Cottage, Itchen Stoke, Alresford SO24 0QZ Tel: 01962 779833 Email: kendore@aol.com — MB ChB 1958 Leeds. Prev: Princip. GP Watford.

DORE, Anne Marie 77 Southfield, Hessle HU13 0ET Tel: 01482 643269 — MB ChB 1977 Liverp.; BSc (Pharmacol.) Liverp. 1972, MB ChB 1977. Clin. Asst. Dept. Haemat. Kingston Gen. Hosp. Hull.

DORE, Philip Charles Immunology Department, Pathology Laboratory, Awlaby Rd, Hull HU3 2JZ Tel: 01482 607741 Fax: 01482 607739 Email: philipdore@rhh-tr.northy.nhs.uk — MB ChB 1977 Liverp.; MRCPath (Immunol.) 1984; Dip. HSM 1996. Cons. Immunol. Regional Immunol. Dept.Hull Roy. Infirm.,. Hull; Vis. Cons. Immunol., Lincs. Gen. Hosp.. Socs: Brit. Soc. Immunol.; Assn. Clin. Pathologists; Brit. Soc. of Allergy and Clin. Immunol. Prev: Clin. co-ordinator Path. Hull and E. Yorks. NHS Trust.

DORE-GREEN, Frances Jesmond House Practice, Chance Street, Tewkesbury GL20 5RF — MB ChB 1989 Leic.; MRCP (UK) 1992; MRCGP 1997. GP. Socs: MRCP (UK); MRCGP.

DORGAN, Mr John Christopher 72 Rodney Street, Liverpool L1 9AF Tel: 0151 709 2177; 23 Elton Avenue, Blundellsands, Liverpool L23 8UW Tel: 0151 924 1818 — MB ChB 1973 Liverp.; MChOrth 1979; FRCS Eng. 1977. Cons. Orthop. Surg. Roy. Liverp. Childr. Hosp. (Alder Hey). Socs: Brit. Soc. Childr. Orthop. Surg.; Fell. BOA; Hon. Sec. And Treas. Brit. Scoliosis Soc. Prev: Lect. Dept. Orthop. & Accid. Surg. Univ. Liverp.; Regist. (Orthop.) BRd.green Hosp. Liverp.; Research Fell. Dept. Orthop. Surg. Univ. Liverp.

DORING-BASSO, Silke 55 Eastgate Road, Holmes Chapel, Crewe CW4 7BN — State Exam Med 1987 Heidelberg.

DORIS, Alan Bruce 92/7 Craighouse Gardens, Edinburgh EH10 5LW — MB ChB 1989 Ed.

DORIS, Edward Joseph Vicarage Road Medical Centre, Vicarage Road, Mickleover, Derby DE3 5EB Tel: 01332 513283 Fax: 01332 518569; 82 Station Road, Mickleover, Derby DE3 5GL — MB ChB 1978 Leeds; MRCGP 1982; DRCOG 1981. Clin. Asst. A & E Dept. Derbysh. Roy. Infirm. Prev: Ho. Surg. (Orthop. & Gen. Surg.) & Ho. Phys. York Dist. Hosp.

DORIS, James Francis 18 Lancashire Road, Bristol BS7 9DL — MB ChB 1987 Birm.; ChB Birm. 1987; ECFMG Cert. 1992; DRCOG 1991; DCH RCP Lond. 1990. Family Pract. Resid. Healthplex Memphis, USA. Prev: SHO (Paediat.) MusGr. Pk. & Yeovil Hosps.; SHO (A & E) S.mead Hosp. Bristol; SHO (O & G) St. Michael's Hosp. Bristol.

DORIS, John Paul 35 The Meadows, Strangford Road, Downpatrick BT30 6LN — MB BCh 1998 Belf.; MB BCh Belf 1998.

DORKEN, Peter Roy Warwick Road Surgery, 65 Warwick Road, Carlisle CA1 1EB Tel: 01228 36303 — MB ChB 1965 Birm. (Birm.)

DORKIN, Trevor John 1st Floor Flat, 26 St Georges Terrace, Jesmond, Newcastle upon Tyne NE2 2SY Tel: 0191 281 4008 — MB BS 1991 Newc.; FRCS Eng. 1995. Clin. Research Assoc. (Surg.) Univ. Newc. u. Tyne. Prev: SHO (Gen. Surg.) Roy. Vict. Infirm. Newc.; SHO (Urol.) Freeman Hosp. Newc.

DORKINS, Catherine Eluned Butler Clinic, Langdon Hospital, Exeter, Dawlish EX7 0NR Tel: 01626 888371 Fax: 01626 865988 — BM BCh 1985 Oxf.; BA Oxf. 1982; MRCP (UK) 1988; MRCPsych 1992. (Oxf.) Cons. (Forens. Psychiat.) Langdon Hosp. Dawlish.

DORKINS, Huw Richard St. Peter's College, Oxford OX1 2DL Tel: 01865 278922 Fax: 01865 278855 Email: huw.dorkins@spc.ox.ac.uk — BM BCh 1983 Oxf.; MA Oxf. 1984, BM BCh 1983; DRCPath 1988; MRCPath 1996; MRCP (UK) 1997. (Oxford) Sen. Research Fell. & Tutor (Med.) St. Peter's Coll. Oxf. Prev: MRC Train. Fell. Nuffield Dept. (Med.) Univ. Oxf.; Ho. Phys. John Radcliffe Hosp. Oxf., Brompton Hosp. & Nat. Hosp. Qu. Sq. Lond.

DORLING, Anthony 28 Coldfall Avenue, Muswell Hill, London N10 1HS — MB BS 1987 Lond.; MRCP (UK) 1990.

DORLING, Bettina 26 Mitre Close, Bedford MK41 0SS — MB BS 1984 Lond. Trainee GP Knebworth.

DORLING, David Michael Temple Cowley Health Centre, Templar House, Temple Road, Oxford OX4 2HL Tel: 01865 777024 Fax: 01865 777548; 320 London Road, Headington, Oxford OX3 8DN Tel: 01865 65852 — BM BCh 1967 Oxf.; BA (Animal Physiol.) Oxf. 1963, BM BCh 1967. (Oxf.)

DORLING, James Steven Flat 2/2, 45 Commercial St., Dundee DD1 3DG — MB ChB 1995 Dundee.

DORLING, Robert Frank Plowright Surgery, Market Place, Swaffham PE37 7LQ Tel: 01760 722797 Fax: 01760 720025 — MB ChB 1974 Dundee; MB ChB 1974 Dundee.

DORMAN, Audrey Helen Liverpool Road Health Centre, 9 Mersey Place, Liverpool Road, Luton LU1 1HH Tel: 01582 722525; 33 Manor Farm Close, Barton-Le-Clay, Bedford MK45 4TB Email: helen@g6bjo.demon.co.uk — MB BCh BAO 1980 Belf.; MRCGP 1989. (Qu. Univ. Belf.) Clin. Asst. Dermat. Luton and Dustable Hosp., Luton.

DORMAN, David Eric Dorman, Dorman, Chambers, McCollum and Fearon, Willowbank Surgery, Crossmore Road, Keady, Armagh BT60 3RL Tel: 028 3753 1248 Fax: 028 3753 1404 — MB BCh BAO 1968 Dub.; FRCGP 1991; MRCGP 1974; DCH RCPSI 1972; DObst RCOG 1971. (T.C. Dub.) Trainer; Teach. of Med. Stud.s. Socs: BMA; Ulster Med. & Paediat. Soc.

DORMAN, Edgar Kennedy Homerton Hospital, London E9 6SR Tel: 020 8510 5555 Fax: 020 8510 7381 — MB BS 1984 Lond. Cons. Obstetrican & Gynaecologist.

DORMAN, Eric Steen (retired) Garden House, 4 Armagh Road, Armagh BT60 3RL Tel: 02837 531846 — MB BCh BAO 1935 Dub.

DORMAN, John Kennedy Addison (retired) Sketrick Island, Killinchy, Newtownards BT23 6QH Tel: 01238 541370 — MD 1940 Belf.; MD Belf. 1951. MB BCh BAO 1940; FFA RCS Eng. 1953; DA Eng. 1941. Hon. Cons. Anaesth. Belf. City Hosp., Musgrave Pk. Hosp., & Roy. Vict. Hosp. Belf. Prev: Cons. Anaesth. Benn Ulster ENT Hosp.

DORMAN, Laurence Alexander Willowbank, Armagh Road, Keady, Armagh BT60 3RL — MB BCh 1998 Belf.; MB BCh Belf 1998.

DORMAN, Paul Jacob 10 Wroxham Avenue, Urmston, Manchester M41 5TE — MB BS 1990 Newc.; MRCP (UK) 1993.

DORMAN, Richard Hobart Dorman, Dorman, Chambers, McCollum and Fearon, Willowbank Surgery, Crossmore Road, Keady, Armagh BT60 3RL Tel: 028 3753 1248 Fax: 028 3753 1404 — MB BCh BAO 1974 Dub.

DORMAN, Saskie 7 Lower Street, Rode, Bath BA11 6PU — MB BS 1997 Lond.

DORMAN, Teresa The Boskins, Royd Farm, Carr Road, Deepcar, Sheffield S30 5PR — MB ChB 1982 Leeds; FFARCS Eng. 1988.

DORMAND, George Scott (retired) Aviemore, Tilsmore Road, Heathfield TN21 0XU Tel: 01435 864941 — MRCS Eng. LRCP Lond. 1955. Prev: Ho. Off. (Gen. Surg. & Urol.) Unit Centr. Middlx. Hosp. Lond.

DORMANDY, Professor John Adam St George's Hospital, Blackshaw Road, Level 1, Inglebrook House, London SW17 0QT Tel: 020 8767 8346 Fax: 020 8682 2550 Email: dormandyjohn@aol.com; 82 East Hill, London SW18 2HG Tel: 020 8870 0910 Fax: 020 8870 1519 Email: dormandyjohn@aol.com — MB BS 1961 Lond.; DSc Lond. 1990; FRCS Eng. 1969; FRCS Ed. 1967; MRCS Eng. LRCP Lond. 1961. (Roy. Free) Prof. Vasc. Sci. St. Geo. Hosp. Med. Sch. Lond. M (Emerit.). Prev: Lect. (Physiol.) Inst. Basic Med. Scs. RCS Eng.; Sen. Regist. Roy. Free Hosp. Lond.; Cons. Surg. St. Geo. Hosp. Lond.

DORMANDY, Mr Thomas Louis 16 St Albans Road, London NW5 1RD Tel: 020 7485 8344 — LMSSA 1952 Lond.; DSc Lond. 1982; BesSc. Med. Geneva 1948; PhD Lond. 1965, MB BS 1952; FRCS Ed. 1956; FRCPath 1977, M 1965. (Geneva & Roy. Free) Cons. Chem. Pathol. Whittington Hosp. Lond.; Hon. Vis. Prof. Brunel Univ. Prev: Regist. (Clin. Path.) Centr. Middlx. Hosp.; Lect. (Chem. Path.) St. Geo. Hosp. Lond.; R. D. Lawrence Research Fell. Dept. Med. Guy's Hosp. Lond.

DORMER, Alwin Eric (retired) 20 Connaught Avenue, Loughton IG10 4DS Tel: 020 8508 3717 — MB BS 1951 Lond.; MB BS (Hons.) Lond. 1951; MD Lond. 1957; FRCP Lond. 1972, M 1953. Hon. Med. Advis. Roy. Brit. Legion; Hon. Cons. Phys. Whipps Cross Hosp. Lond.; Verderer, Epping Forest. Prev: Med. Off. UK Provid. Inst.

DORMER, Jonathan Keith Wayside Surgery, 12 Russells Crescent, Horley RH6 7DN Tel: 01293 782057 Fax: 01293 821809; 1 Knowle Manor, London Road, Cuckfield, Haywards Heath RH17 5ET — MB BS 1983 Lond.; MRCP (UK) 1988; DRCOG 1991. (St. Bar. Hosp. Lond.) Prev: Regist. (Med.) Roy. Sussex. Co. Hosp. Brighton; SHO (O & G) Cuckfield Hosp. W. Sussex VTS.

DORMER, Michaela Jane Spencer 1 Woodfield Cottages, Marlpit Lane, Oving, Chichester PO20 6BP — MB BS 1986 Lond.; MRCGP 1993; DCH RCP Lond. 1991; DRCOG 1990. (Charing Cross) GP Bognor Regis. Prev: GP Cranleigh Health Centre; Trainee GP Guildford; SHO (Paediat.)Roy. Surrey Co. Hosp. Guildford.

DORMON, Frances Mary 2 Spencer Road, Canford Cliffs, Poole BH13 7EU Email: drdormon@aol.com — MB BS 1978 Lond.; FFA RCS Eng. 1983. Cons. Anaesth. & Intens. Care Poole NHS Trust Dorset. Prev: Cons. Anaesth. & IC Lister Hospital Stevenage Herts.

DORNAN, Claudia Ceridwen Barlow Medical Centre, 8 Barlow Moor Road, Didsbury, Manchester M20 6TR Tel: 0161 445 2101 Fax: 0161 445 9560; 10 Raynham Avenue, Didsbury, Manchester M20 6BW Tel: 0161 434 2170 Email: ceridornan@cwcom.net — BM BCh 1975 Oxf.; MRCP (UK) 1977; DRCOG 1978; MRCGP 1980; FRCGP 1997. (Oxf.)

DORNAN, Harriet Gwendoline (retired) 71 Watson Road, Broom Hill, Sheffield S10 2SD — MB BCh BAO 1931 Belf.; DObst RCOG 1938. Prev: Ho. Surg. Roy. Samarit. Hosp. Glas. & Childr. Hosp. Derby.

DORNAN, James Connor Raneese, 8 Clanbrassil Road, Cultra, Holywood BT18 0AR Tel: 0123 175515 — MB BCh BAO 1973 Belf.; MD (Hons.) 1981; MRCOG 1978. Sen. Lect. Qu. Univ. Belf.; Cons. Obst. & Gyn. Roy. Vict. Hosp. & Roy. Matern. Hosp. Belf.

DORNAN, Janet Taylor Court View Surgery, Rosemary Street, Mansfield NG19 6AB Tel: 01623 623600 Fax: 01623 635460 — MB ChB 1984 Sheff. Prev: Trainee GP Chesterfield VTS.

DORNAN, Jessie Olivia Greig 346 Coast Road, Ballygally, Larne BT40 2QZ — MB BCh BAO 1982 Belf.; MB BCh Belf. 1982.

DORNAN, John Dunwoodie 20 Troutbeck Crescent, Bramcote, Nottingham NG9 3BP Tel: 0115 925 6297 — MB BCh BAO 1965

Dub.; FFOM RCP Lond. 1987, M 1980; DIH Eng. 1975. Cons. Occupat. Phys. Qu. Med. Centre Nottm. Socs: Soc. Occupat. Med. & BMA; Assn. NHS Occupat. Phys. Prev: Employm. Med. Adviser EMAS (Sheff.); Med. Off. Brit Steel Corp. Sheff.; Ho. Surg & Ho. Phys. Adelaide Hosp. Dub.

DORNAN, Michael George Holywell House Surgery, Holywell Street, Chesterfield S41 7SD Tel: 01246 273075 Fax: 01246 555711 — MB ChB 1970 Sheff.; FRCGP 1994, M 1974; DObst RCOG 1973; DCH Eng. 1972. (Sheff.)

DORNAN, Sean James 124 Broadway Tower, Broadway, Belfast BT12 6HG — MB ChB 1990 Dundee.

DORNAN, Timothy Lloyd Hope Hospital, Stott Lane, Salford M6 8HD Tel: 0161 787 5153 Fax: 0161 787 5989; 10 Raynham Avenue, Didsbury, Manchester M20 6BW — BM BCh 1975 Oxf.; BA Camb. 1972; DM Oxf. 1982; FRCP Lond. 1992; MRCP (UK) 1977. Cons. Phys. Hope Hosp. Salford; Sen. Lect. in Med. Educat., Manch. Univ.

DORNAN, Veronica Isabella Pauline 26 Glazbury Road, London W14 9AS — MB ChB 1986 Glas.

DORNHORST, Anne Department of Metabolic Medicine, Hammersmith Hospital, Du Cane Road, London W12 0NN Tel: 020 8383 3242 Fax: 020 8383 3142 Email: adornhorst@ic.ac.uk; 20 Vine Road, London SW13 0NE Tel: 020 8878 2381 Fax: 020 8878 9256 Email: anneritter@easynet.co.uk — BM BCh 1974 Oxf.; BSc Lond. 1972; DM Oxf. 1993, BM BCh 1974; MRCP (UK) 1976; FRCP 1998; MRC Path 2000. (Oxf.) Cons. Phys. & Hon. Sen. Lect. (Endocrin.) Char. Cross & Hammersmith Hosp. Imperial Coll. Sch. Med. Lond. Prev: Sen. Regist. (Med.) St. Mary's Hosp. Lond. W2.

DORNHORST, Antony Clifford, CBE 8 Albert Place, London W8 5PD Tel: 020 7937 8782 — MD Lond. 1939, MB BS 1937; FRCP Lond. 1955, M 1938. (St. Thos.) Prof. Med. Emerit. Univ. Lond.

DORNHORST, Helen Mary (retired) 8 Albert Place, London W8 5PD Tel: 020 7937 8782 — MB ChB 1940 Ed.; DMR 1943. Hon. Cons. Radiol. St. Mary's Hosp. Lond.; Hon. Cons. Radiol. Hosp. Sick Childr. Gt. Ormond St. Lond. Prev: Locum Cons. Radiologist, Harefield Hosp., Middlx.

DOROK, Anita Joyce Taransay, High St., Walton, Lutterworth LE17 5RG Tel: 014555 554585 — MB ChB 1973 Birm. (Birm.) GP Clin. Asst. (Psychogeriat.) Bennion Centre, Glenfield Hosp. Leicester.

DORR, Albert Arrowe Park Hospital, Upton, Wirral CH49 5PE Tel: 0151 678 5777; 10 Briar Drive, Wirral CH60 5RW — State Exam Med 1988 Mainz.

DORRAN, John Alfred (retired) 50 Overton Drive, Wanstead, London E11 2NJ Tel: 020 8989 0374 — LRCPI & LM, LRSCI & LM 1934; LRCPI & LM, LRCSI & LM 1934.

DORRANCE, Helen Reynard 32 St Adrians Place, Anstruther KY10 3DX — MB ChB 1990 Ed.

DORREEN, Mark Sinclair 23 Ashdell Road, Broomhill, Sheffield S10 3DA — MD 1990 Camb.; MB 1975, BChir 1974; MRCP (UK) 1979. Lect. (Clin. Oncol.) W.on Pk. Hosp. Univ. Sheff. Socs: Brit. Assn. Cancer Research (Mem. Exec.-Comm.); Assn. Cancer Phys.

DORRELL, Clare Elizabeth Ashwell Surgery, Gardiners Lane, Ashwell, Baldock SG7 5PY Tel: 01462 742230; Ringstead House, 18 Springhead, Ashwell, Baldock SG7 5LL Tel: 01462 743252 Fax: 01462 743058 — MB BS 1984 Lond.; BSc Manch. 1976; MSc Bath 1978. (St. Mary's) GP Retainer. Prev: SHO (Med.) Bedford Hosp.; SHO (Orthop./Accid.) Roy. Berks. Hosp. Reading; Ho. Surg. St. Mary's Hosp. Lond.

DORRELL, Mr Edmund David Royal Bournemouth Hospital, Castle Lane East, Bournemouth BH7 7DW Tel: 01202 704356 — MB BS 1965 Lond.; FRCS Eng. 1972; MRCS Eng. LRCP Lond. 1965. (St. Bart.) Cons. (Ophth.) The Roy. Bournemouth and ChristCh. Hosp.s NHS Trust, Bournemouth. Socs: FRCOphth; Oxf. Eye Congr.; Brit. Isles Neuro Ophtalmology Club. Prev: Sen. Regist. Moorfields Eye Hosp. Lond.; Regist. W.m. Hosp. Lond.; Ho. Surg. St. Bart. Hosp. Lond.

DORRELL, Mr John Hugh Lister Hospital, Corey's Mill Lane, Stevenage SG1 4AB Tel: 01438 314333 — BM BCh 1972 Oxf.; MA Oxf. 1986, BA Physiol. 1969; FRCS Eng. 1978. (Oxf. & St. Mary's) Cons. Orthop. Surg. Lister Hosp. Stevenage. Socs: Fell. BOA; Fell. Roy. Soc. Med. Prev: Sen. Regist. (Orthop.) St. Mary's & Roy. Nat. Orthop. Hosps. Lond.; Regist. (Surg.) St. Chas. Hosp. Lond.; Lect. (Anat.) Kings Coll. Lond.

DORRELL, Lucy Harrison Department, Radcliffe Infirmary/ John Radcliffe Hospital, Oxford OX2 6HE/ OX3; 24 Magdalen Road, Oxford OX4 1RP Tel: 01865 452507 — BM 1988 Soton.; MRCP (UK) 1991; DM Soton. 1998. Specialist Regist. Genito-Urin. Med.; MRC Clin. Scientist Fell. Socs: Brit. Soc. for Immunol. Prev: Research Regist. (Infec. Dis.) Newc. Gen. Hosp.; Regist. (Infec. Dis. & Genitourin. Med.) & Research Fell. (Genitourin. Med.) St. Mary's Hosp. Med. Sch. Lond.; MRC Clin. Train. Fell. Inst. Molecular Med. John Radcliffe Hosp. Oxf.

DORRELL, Mark George The Health Centre, Mullion, Helston TR12 7DQ Tel: 01326 240212 — MB BS 1988 Lond.; BSc Lond. 1985; FRCS Eng. 1992; DCH RCP Lond. 1997; DRCOG 1996. (Roy. Free Hosp. Lond.) Prev: GP/Regist. Mullion Health Centre, Cornw.; Dep. Princip. Med. Off. HMS Ark Roy.; Demonst. & Cas. Off. (Anat.) Roy. Free Hosp. Lond.

DORRELL, William 44 Lower Sloane Street, London SW1W 8BP Tel: 020 7352 2761; 127 Dovehouse Street, London SW3 6JZ Tel: 020 7352 2761 — MB BChir 1951 Camb.; MA Camb. 1951; MRCPsych 1974; DPM Lond. 1962. Hon. Sen. Lect. Stud. Counselling Serv. UCL. Socs: Fell. Roy. Soc. Med. Prev: Cons. Psychiat. Margt. Pyke Clinic Lond.; Asst. (Psychol. Med.) Middlx. Hosp.; Regist. Maudsley Hosp.

DORRETT, Stephen Quarry Ground Surgery, Broadway, Edington, Bridgwater TA7 9JB Tel: 01278 722077 Fax: 01278 722352; The Grove, Manor Road, Cossington, Bridgwater TA7 8JS Tel: 01278 722291 — MB BS 1968 Lond.; MRCP (UK) 1972; DObst RCOG 1974. (St. Bart) Prev: Regist. (Med.) St And. Hosp. Billericay; SHO (Paediat.) Orsett Gen. Hosp.; SHO (Obst.) Roy. United Hosp. Bath.

DORRIAN, Una Teresa Southbourne Surgery, 337 Main Road, Southbourne, Emsworth PO10 8JH; Bramley, Joys Croft, Chichester PO19 4NJ — MB BCh BAO 1981 NUI; LRCPI & LM, LRCSI & LM 1981.

DORRICOTT, Jacqueline Jane 24 Deerdale Way, Binley, Coventry CV3 2EQ — MB BS 1987 Lond. SHO (O & G) Frimley Pk. Hosp. Surrey. Prev: SHO (A & E) Frimley Pk. Hosp. Surrey.

DORRICOTT, Mr Norman John University Hospital Birmingham, Selly Oak Hospital, Birmingham B29 6JD Tel: 0121 627 1627 Fax: 0121 627 8275; 38 Frederick Road, Edgbaston, Birmingham B15 1JN Tel: 0121 454 6532 — MB ChB 1962 Birm.; ChM Birm. 1974; FRCS Eng. 1969. Cons. Surg. Univ. Hosp. Birm. Selly Oak Hosp.; Sen. Clin. Lect. (Surg.) Univ. Birm. Socs: Assn. Surg.; (Counc.) Assn. Endoscopic Surg.; Soc. Laparoendoscopic Surgs. USA. Prev: Sen. Regist. (Surg.) Birm. RHB; Surgic. Research Fell. Harvard Med. Sch. Boston, USA; Regist. (Surg.) Addenbrooke's Hosp. Camb.

DORRINGTON, Keith Leonard University College, High St., Oxford OX1 4BH — BM BCh 1982 Oxf.; MA DPhil. Oxf. 1977, DM 1990, BM BCh 1982; FCAnaesth. 1989; DA (UK) 1985. Univ. Lect. (Physiol.) Univ. Oxf.; Clin. Asst. Nuffield Dept. Anaesth. John Radcliffe Hosp. Oxf.

DORRINGTON, Roy Forshaw 3 Glenside, Castle Bytham, Grantham NG33 4SS Tel: 01780 410845 — MB BS Lond. 1957; MRCS Eng. LRCP Lond. 1957; DObst RCOG 1961. (King's Coll. Hosp.)

DORUDI, Mr Sina Royal London Hospital, Whitechapel, London E1 1BB Tel: 020 7377 7098 Fax: 020 7377 7283 Email: s.dorudi@mds.qmw.ac.uk — MB BS Lond. 1983; BSc Lond. 1980; FRCS (Eng.) 1987; PhD Lond. 1995; FRCS (Gen.) 1997. (St. Mary's Hospital Medical School, University of London) Cons. Colorectal Surg. Roy. Lond. & St Bart. Hosps. Lond.; Sen. Lect. in Srugery Univ. of Lond.

DORWARD, Alistair James Medical Unit, Royal Alexandra Hospital, Corsebar Road, Paisley PA2 9PN Tel: 0141 580 4363 Fax: 0141 889 5844; 64 Southbrae Drive, Glasgow G13 1QD Tel: 0141 954 7382 Email: alistair.clorward@rah.scot.nhs.uk — MB ChB 1976 (Commend.) Dundee; FRCP Ed. 1997; FRCP Glas. 1989; MRCP (UK) 1979. Cons. Phys. (Gen. & Respirat. Med.) Roy. Alexandra Hosp. Paisley.; Clin. Dir. Adult Med. RAH, Paisley. Socs: Scott. Thoracic Soc.; Brit. Thorac. Soc. Prev: Sen. Regist. W.. Infirm. & Kt.swood Hosp. Glas.; Regist. W.. Infirm. Glas.

DORWARD, Catriona Ruth The Health Centre, Queen Street, Jedburgh TD8 6EN Tel: 01835 863361 Fax: 01835 864273; Hundalee Mill Cottage, Hundalee, Jedburgh TD8 6PA Tel: 01835 864660 — MB ChB 1982 Ed.; DRCOG 1987.

DORWARD, David Watt Torrance West Gate Health Centre, Charleston Drive, Dundee DD2 4AD Tel: 01382 668189 Fax: 01382 665943; Fontstane, Loch of Liff Road, Liff, Dundee DD2 5NN Tel: 01382 580098 — MB ChB 1980 Dundee; MRCGP 1984; DRCOG 1983. GP.

DORWARD, Fiona Campbell Ravenswood Surgery, Thomson Avenue, Johnstone PA5 8SU Tel: 01505 331979 Fax: 01505 323444; 30 Hillside, Houston, Johnstone PA6 7NT — MB ChB 1987 Glas.; MRCGP Ed. 1991; T (GP) 1991; DCH RCPS Glas. 1990; DRCOG 1990. Socs: BMA. Prev: SHO (A & E) Glas. Roy. Infirm.; Trainee GP Dalry; SHO (Paediat.) Seafield Childr. Hosp. Ayr.

DORWARD, Ishbel Margaret Houndlaw Park Health Centre, Houndlaw Park, Eyemouth TD14 5DA Tel: 018907 50383 Fax: 018907 51749 Email: ishbel.dorward@eyemouthhc.borders.scot.nhs.uk — MB ChB 1975 Ed.; DRCOG 1978. (Edinburgh)

DORWARD, John Alexander Houndlaw Park Health Centre, Houndlaw Park, Eyemouth TD14 5DA; Tel: 018907 51732 — MB ChB 1975 Ed.; FRCGP 2000; MRCP (UK) 1978; MRCGP 1981; DRCOG 1979. (Edinburgh) GP Partner. Prev: Med. Off. Ekwendeni Hosp., Malawi; GP Jedburgh.

DORWARD, Mr Neil Lawrence Royal Free Hospital, Pond St., London NW3 2QG Tel: 0207 7830 2097 Fax: 0207 830 2560 Email: neil.dorward@nfh.n.thames.nhs.uk; Tel: 020 8449 8954 — MB BS 1989 Lond.; BSc Lond. 1985; FRCS Eng. 1993; FRCS SN 1998; MS 1999. (St. Mary's Hosp. Med. Sch. Lond.) Cons. Neurosurg. Hon. Sen. Lect. Roy. Free. Hosp. Socs: Brain Res. Assn.; Internat. Brain Research Org.; Brit. Cervical Spine Soc. Prev: Clin. Lect. (Neurosurg.) Nat. Hosp. for Neurol. & Neurosurg. Lond.; Regist. (Neurosurg.) Roy. Free Hosp. Lond.; SHO (Neurosurg.) W.. Gen. Hosp. Edin. & Nat. Hosp. Neurol. & Neurosurg. Lond.

DORWARD, Peter Stewart Imperial College Health Centre, Southside, Watt;s Way, London SW7 1LU Tel: 020 7584 6301 Fax: 020 7594 9390; 47 Onerstone Road, London W6 0AD Tel: 020 8741 5289 — MB ChB 1986 Manch.; MRCGP 1992; DRCOG 1990; DCH RCP Lond. 1989.

DORWARD, William Fyffe Morrison (retired) 5 Richmond Terrace, Dundee DD2 1BQ Tel: 01382 67229 Email: morrison.dorward@tesco.net — MB ChB 1951 Ed.; MA Ed. 1948, MB ChB 1951; Hon. LLD Dundee 1989; FRCGP 1975, M 1962. Prev: GP.

DOS REMEDIOS, Mr Ian Denis Michael Department of Orthopaedics, Avon Orthopaedic Centre, Southmead Hospital, Westbury on Trym, Bristol BS10 5NB; 20 Laurie Crescent, Henleaze, Bristol BS9 4TA Tel: 0117 942 4911 Email: ian@dosremedios.u_net.com — MB BS 1985 Bombay; FRCS Ed. 1992; FRCS Glas. 1992; FRCS (Orth). Specialist Regist. (Orthop.) Avon Orthop. Centre. Socs: Assoc. Mem. BOA; AO Alumni; BASK. Prev: Regist. (Orthop.) OsW.ry.

DOS SANTOS, Anabela Vieira Lopes 47 Chapel House Street, London E14 3AS — Lic Med 1977 Lisbon; Lic Med. Lisbon 1977.

DOSAJ, Ajay Kumar 40 Lyndhurst Road, Thornton Heath CR7 7PU — MB BS 1988 Lond.

DOSANI, Sabina Elmbray, Dene Close, Worcester Park KT4 7HQ — MB BS 1998 Lond.; MB BS Lond 1998.

DOSANJ, Rashpal Singh Daventry Road Surgery, 281 Daventry Road, Coventry CV3 5HJ Tel: 024 7650 3485 Fax: 024 7650 5730 — MB ChB 1992 Dundee. Trainee GP S. Warks. Hosp.

DOSANJH, Hergeven Singh Telfer Road, 190 Telfer Road, Coventry CV6 3DJ Tel: 024 7659 6060 Fax: 024 7660 1607 — MB BS 1992 Lond.

DOSHI, Anil Crawcrook Medical Centre, Back Chamberlain Street, Crawcrook, Ryton NE40 4TZ Tel: 0191 413 2243 Fax: 0191 413 8098; 8 Mayfield Road, Gosforth, Newcastle upon Tyne NE3 4HE Tel: 0191 284 2650 — MB BS 1989 Newc.; MRCGP 1993; DCH RCP Lond. 1994; DRCOG 1993; DFFP 1993. (Univ. Newc. u. Tyne) Socs: (Vice-Pres.) Newc. Med. Hockey Club.

DOSHI, Bhavesh 35 Greenfield Street, Nottingham NG7 2JN — BM BS 1997 Nottm.

DOSHI, Harish Vrajlal Fairway Medical Centre, 7 The Fairway, Leigh-on-Sea SS9 4QN Tel: 01702 421444 Fax: 01702 528300; 10 Woodside, Leigh-on-Sea SS9 4QU Tel: 01702 522282 — MB BS 1972 Bombay. (Topiwala Nat. Med. Coll.) Prev: Med. Asst. Moorefields Eye Hosp. Lond.

DOSHI, Miran Kantilal 11 Clifton Hill, Brighton BN1 3HQ — MB BCh 1986 Wales; MRCP (UK) 1989. Regist. (Med.) Bristol Roy. Infirm. & W.on Gen. Hosp. Bristol.

DOSHI, Mrudula Rajnikant 177 Broad Lane, Rochdale OL16 4PU — MB BS 1970 Gujarat; Cert Contracep. & Family Plann. RCOG, RCGP &; Cert FPA 1976. (B.J. Med. Coll. Ahmedabad) Family Plann. Doctor Oldham HA & Rochdale HA. Prev: Family Plann. Doctor Greenwich & Bexley AHA.

DOSHI, Rajnikant Motichand (retired) 177 Broad Lane, Rochdale OL16 4PU — MB BS 1959 Vikram; FFA RCS Eng. 1973; DA Eng. 1969. Prev: Cons. Anaesth. Oldham AHA.

DOSHI, Rasikbala 5 Bradbury Court, St John's Park, Blackheath, London SE3 7TP Tel: 020 8959 8976 — MB BS Delhi 1960; FRCPath 1983, M 1971; DPath Eng. 1967; DTM & H Liverp. 1967. (Lady Hardinge Med. Coll.) Cons. Neuropath. Inst. Psychiat. Lond. Socs: Brit. Neuropath. Soc.; Assn. Clin. Path. Prev: Cons. Neuropath. Brook Gen. Hosp. Lond.; Sen. Regist. (Neuropath.) Frenchay Hosp. Bristol; Regist. (Path.) Wythenshawe Hosp. Manch.

DOSHI, Sagar 3 Warren Road, London E11 2LX — MB BCh 1990 Wales.

DOSSETOR, Andrew Ernest (retired) Dittons, 1 Ditton Close, Newmarket CB8 8XE Tel: 01638 662852 — MB BS 1952 Lond.; MRCS Eng. LRCP Lond. 1947; MRCGP 1966. Prev: Med. Off. i/c ENT Dept. RAF Hosp. Aden.

DOSSETOR, Jonathan Francis Bryan The Queen Elizabeth Hospital, King's Lynn PE30 4ET Tel: 01553 766266 Fax: 01553 613090 Email: dosslynn@paston.co.uk; 63 Castle Rising Road, South Wootton, King's Lynn PE30 3JA Tel: 01553 671576 — MB BChir 1969 Camb.; MD Camb. 1979; FRCP Lond. 1987; MRCP (UK) 1972; DObst RCOG 1971; DCH Eng. 1970. (Univ. Coll. Hosp.) Cons. Paediat. Kings Lynn Health Dist. Norf. Socs: BMA. Prev: Lect. (Child Health) Roy. Hosp. Sick Childr. Glas.; Lect. (Child Health) Ahamadu Bello Univ. Teachg. Hosp. Zaria, Nigeria; SHO (Paediat.) St. Mary's Hosp. Portsmouth.

DOSSETOR, Roberts Simon 8 Orpen Road, Hove BN3 6NJ — BM BCh 1968 Oxf.; FRCR 1975; FFR 1974; DMRD Eng. 1972. (St. Bart.) Cons. Radiol. Roy. Sussex Co. Hosp. Brighton. Prev: Sen. Regist. Radiol. Radcliffe Infirm. Oxf.; Regist. Radiol. Radcliffe Infirm. Oxf.

DOSSETT, Alfred George Stonehaven Medical Group, Stonehaven Medical Centre, 32 Robert Street, Stonehaven AB39 2EL Tel: 01569 762945 Fax: 01569 766552; 36 Bernham Avenue, Stonehaven AB39 2WD — MB ChB 1987 Aberd.

DOSSETT, Andrew Christopher 53 Norbury Gardens, Romford RM6 5TR — MB ChB 1991 Dundee.

DOTT, Andrew Graham Kent House Surgery, 36 Station Road, Longfield DA3 7QD Tel: 01474 703550; Longview, Hartley Hill, Hartley, Longfield DA3 8LL — MB 1978 Camb.; BA Camb. 1974; BChir 1977; MA 1978; Dip Med Jurisp (Clin) Soc Apoth Lond 1998. (Cambridge University) Forens. Med. Examr. Socs: Brit. Acad. Forens. Sci.; Coun. Mem. Clin. Forens. & Legal Sect. Roy. Soc. Med.

DOUBLE, Duncan Brian 26 Christchurch Road, Norwich NR2 2AE — BChir 1984 Camb.; LMSSA Lond. 1984.

DOUBLE, Glynis 34 Sherborne Road, Petts Wood, Orpington BR5 1RF — MB ChB 1978 Liverp.; MSc Clin. Microbiol. Lond. 1986; MRCPath 1985.

DOUBLET-STEWART, Morris Patrick Hugh The Health Centre, Grasmere Street, Leigh WN7 1XB Tel: 01942 673017; Woodside, Old Hall Mill Lane, Atherton, Manchester M46 0RG Tel: 01942 678288 — MB ChB 1977 Manch.; DRCOG 1987; DCH RCP Lond. 1979. Socs: Anglo-French Med. Soc. Prev: Médecin Résident Étranger Hôpital Edouard Herriot Lyon, France; Regist. (Med.) Wellington Pub. Hosp., NZ; SHO (O & G) Nottm. City Hosp.

DOUCE, Gillian Elizabeth 11 Church Street, eccleshall, Stafford ST21 6BY — MB ChB 1986 Birm.

DOUCH, Geoffrey St. Lukes Hospital, 14 Fitzroy Square, London W1T 6AH Tel: 020 7388 4954 Fax: 020 7383 4812; Court Mead, Forest Row RH18 5HS Tel: 01342 822241 Fax: 01342 825766 Email: g.douch@doctors.org.uk — MB BS Lond. 1959; MFHom 1963. (Univ. Coll. Hosp.) Socs: (Counc.) Natural Med. Soc. Prev: Regist. (Med.) & Clin. Asst. Roy. Lond. Homoeop. Hosp.; Med. Dir. Raphael Med. Center HildenBoro.

DOUDS, Fergus Hugh Andrew 1 Craigmount Bank W., Edinburgh EH4 8HG — MB ChB 1991 Aberd.

DOUEK, Edward c/o Portland Consulting Room, 234 Gt Portland St., London W1W 5QT Tel: 020 7390 8310 Fax: 020 7390 8358 — MB BS 1982 Lond.; BSc Lond. 1979; MRCP (UK) 1985; DCH RCP Lond. 1984. (Univ. Coll. Hosp.) Cons. Paediat. Portland Hosp. Prev: Cons. Paediat. Watford Gen. Hosp.; Sen. Regist. & Lect. (Paediat. & Paediat. Oncol.) St. Bart. Hosp. Lond.; Regist. (Paediat.) St. Thos. Hosp. Lond. & Pembury Hosp. Kent.

DOUEK, Mr Ellis Elliot Consulting Rooms, Princess Grace Hospital, 42 Nottingham Place, London W1U 5NY Tel: 020 7908 2150/49; 24 Reynolds Close, London NW11 7EA Tel: 020 8455 6427 Fax: 020 8455 6047 Email: elgildouek@aol.com — MRCS Eng. LRCP Lond. 1958; FRCS Eng. 1967. (Westm.) Emerit. Cons. Otol. Guy's & St. Thomas' Hosp. Socs: Fell. Roy. Soc. Med.; BMA. Prev: Sen. Regist. (ENT) King's Coll. Hosp.; Regist. Roy. Free Hosp. Lond.; SHO Whittington Hosp. Lond.

DOUEK, Isabelle Francoise Division of Medicine, University of Bristol, Southend Hospital, Bristol BS10 5NZ; Top Floor Flat, 5 Hillside, Cotham, Bristol BS6 6JP — MB ChB 1994 Bristol. Clin. Research Fell., Div. of Med., Univ. Bristol.

DOUEK, Mr Michael Flat 86 Crown Lodge, 12Elystan St., London SW3 3PR Email: m.douekm.douek@ucl.ac.uk — MB ChB 1992 Dundee; FRCS Eng. 1996. Surgic. Research Fell. (Surg.) Univ. Coll. Lond. Socs: BMA; RSM; Brit. Assn. Surg. Oncol. Prev: SHO Rotat. (Transpl. & Gen. Surg.) Addenbrooke's Hosp. Camb.; SHO Rotat. (Surg.) Hammersmith Hosp. Lond.; Prosector (Anat.) Univ. Oxf.

DOUGALL, Angus James (retired) 27 Laurel Avenue, Kirkintilloch, Glasgow G66 4RT Tel: 0141 776 2876 — MB ChB Ed. 1959; FRCS Ed. 1963; FRCPath 1992, M 1980. Prev: Cons. Bact. Stobhill Gen. Hosp. Glas.

DOUGALL, Donald Ross (retired) 1 Rosemount Court, Rosemount Road, London W3 9LS Tel: 020 8752 1713 — MD 1953 Western Ontario; BA West Ontario 1955; LMCC 1954; Lic. Nova Scotia Med. Bd. 1957. Prev: Div. Surg. St. John Ambul. Brig.

DOUGALL, Hamish Thomson Armoury Cottage, Kenmore St., Aberfeldy PH15 2BL — MB ChB 1994 Aberd.; MSc (Clin. Pharmacol.) Aberd. 1989, MB ChB 1994; BSc (Hons.) Pharmacy Strathclyde 1988. (Aberdeen University)

DOUGALL, Helen Graham Gorman Hillview Day Unit, Stobhill Hospital, Balornock Road, Glasgow G21 3UW Tel: 0141 201 3919; 15 Baronald Drive, Glasgow G12 0JB Email: martin.waddell@cableol.co.uk — MB ChB 1978 Glas. Assoc. Specialist (Psychiat.) Stobhill Hosp. Glas. Prev: Clin. Asst. (Psychiat.) Stobhill Hosp. Glas.

DOUGALL, Helen Iona 27 Laurel Avenue, Kirkintilloch, Glasgow G66 4RT Tel: 0141 776 2876 — MB ChB 1989 Ed.; MRChP 2001; MRCOG 1995. (Ed.) Gen. Practitioner, Edin. Prev: SHO (O & G) Yorkhill Trust Glas.; Specialist Regist. W. of Scotl. Rotat. (O & G) Glas. Roy. Matern. Hosp. & Glas. Roy.; SPR Obs. & Gyane. Glas.

DOUGALL, Helen Kay 40/3 Bernard Street, Leith, Edinburgh EH6 6PR Tel: 0131 553 4742 Fax: 0131 553 5794 Email: hkdougall@msn.com — MB ChB 1984 Ed.; LLB Ed. 1990. (Ed.) Advocate Edin. Prev: SHO Roodlands Gen. Hosp. Haddington; SHO Roy. (Reg. Poisoning Treatm. Centre) Infirm. Edin.; Ho. Off. Roy. Infirm. Edin.

DOUGALL, James Robert Ian Ritchie 15 Earlspark Avenue, Newlands, Glasgow G43 2HN Tel: 0141 632 5500 — MB ChB 1974 Glas.; FFA RCSI 1980. Cons. Anaesth. W.. Infirm. Glas.

DOUGALL, Mr Timothy William 3 Blairadam Grove, Keltybridge, Kelty KY4 0JU Tel: 01383 839001 Email: timdougall@breathemail.net; 3 Blairadam Greove, Kelty Bridge, Kelty KY4 0JU — MB ChB 1987 Aberd.; FRCS (Orth.) 1996; FRCS Eng. 1992. Cons. Orthopaedic and Trauma Surg. Fife Acute Hosp.s NHS Trust; Hon Sen. Lect. Edin. Univ. Socs: Brit. Orthopaedic Assn. Prev: Regist. (Orthop.) Aberd. Roy. Infirm.; SHO (Surg.) N. Gen. Hosp. Sheff.; SHO (A & E) Soton. Gen. Hosp.

DOUGAN, Charlotte Frances Department of Neurology, Walton Hospital, Rice Lane, Liverpool L9 1AE; 10 Norwood Avenue, Heaton, Newcastle upon Tyne NE6 5RA — MB BS 1993 Newc.

DOUGAN, John Philip 33 Ethel Street, Belfast BT9 7FT — MB BCh BAO 1988 Belf.

DOUGAN, Michael Alexander 36 Airlie Street, Glasgow G12 9TP — MB ChB 1982 Glas.; FFA RCSI 1989; DA (UK) 1987.

DOUGHERTY, Shona Thomson Mount Vernon Hospital, Rickmansworth Road, Northwood HA6 2RN — MB ChB 1985 Ed.

DOUGHERTY, Simon Robert Charles, OStJ, Air Commodore Director Medical Personnel, Policy and Plans (RAF), HQ Personnel & Training Command, RAF Innsworth, Gloucester GL3 1EZ — MB BS 1972 Lond.; MSc (Occ Med) Lond. 1986; FFOM RCP Lond. 1993, MFOM 1985, AFOM 1980; DAvMed Eng. 1979 (Conjoint); DObst RCOG 1976; 1999 FRAeS. (Lond. Hosp.) Director Med. Personnel, Policy and Plans (RAF); Cons. Adviser in Occupat. Med. (RAF). Socs: Fell. Roy. Soc. Med.; Soc. Occupat. Med. Prev: Off. Commanding the The P.ss Mary's Hosp., RAF Akrotiri; Taylor Prof. Occupat. Med. (RAF); Dir. Health Servs. (RAF).

DOUGHMAN MARZOUK, Taher 18 Hospital Close, Leicester LE5 4PW — MB BCh 1982 Al Fateh, Libya.

DOUGHTY, Andrew Gerard (retired) Avondale, 10 River Avenue, Thames Ditton KT7 0RS Tel: 020 8398 3408 — MRCS Eng. LRCP Lond. 1941; MB BS Lond. 1941; DA Eng. 1946; FFA RCS Eng. 1953; FRCOG (ad eundem) 1980. Prev: Cons. Anaesth. Kingston & Richmond HA.

DOUGHTY, Bernard John (retired) Russell Court, Nursing Home, Russell Court, Longfield DA3 7RY — MB BS 1958 Lond.; MFOM RCP Lond. 1978; MFOM RCPI 1980; DIH Soc. Apoth. Lond. 1969. Prev: Sen. Occup. Phys. The Wellcome Foundat. Ltd. Dartford.

DOUGHTY, Charlotte 6 Redhouse Lane, Chapel Allerton, Leeds LS7 4RA Tel: 0113 236 9880 — MB BS 1991 Lond.; MRCP (Lond.) 1996. (University College London) Specialist Regist. (A & E Med.) Yorks. Rotat. Prev: Hull Roy. Infirm. (on Rotat.); SHO (Orthop.) Hope Hosp. Salford; SHO (A & E) Hope Hosp. Salford.

DOUGHTY, Heidi-Ann, TD National Blood Service, Birmingham Centre, Vincent Drive, Edgbaston, Birmingham B15 2SG Tel: 0121 253 4017 Fax: 0121 253 4032 — MB BChir 1985 Camb.; BSc (Hons.) Lond. 1983; MRCP (UK) 1989; MRCPath 1994; MBA (Open) 2001. (Charing Cross Hospital Medical School & Cambridge University Medical School) Cons. (Haemat. & Transfus. Med.) NBS Birm.; Hon. Sen. Clin. Lect. Univ. of Birm. 1999-; Cons. (Haemat.) Univ. Hosps. Trust Birm.; Cons. Armed Med. Serv.s. Socs: Liveryman Worshipful Soc. Apoth. Lond.; Brit. Blood Transfus. Soc.; Brit. Soc. Haematol. Prev: Sen. Regist. (Haemat.) St. Thos. Hosp. Lond.; Regist. (Haemat.) St. Bart. Hosp. Lond.; SHO (Haemat. & Gen. Med.) City Hosp. Nottm.

DOUGHTY, Joanne Marie 4 Peck Hill, Ropsley, Grantham NG33 4BL — MB ChB 1998 Manch.; MB ChB Manch 1998.

DOUGHTY, Jonathan 3 Brackenhill Walk, Seamer, Middlesbrough TS9 5NN — MB BS 1974 Newc.

DOUGHTY, Julie Claire Flat 6, 46 Addison Road, Glasgow G12 0TT — MB ChB 1987 Liverp.; FRCPS Glas. 1991.

DOUGHTY, Peter Raymond Mallows, Westby, Kirkham, Preston PR4 3PN — MRCS Eng. LRCP Lond. 1971; BSc (Hons.) Lond. 1968, MB BS 1971; DObst RCOG 1974. (St. Bart.) Med. Quality Manager Sema Gp. Med. Serv. Prev: Sen. Med. Off. DSS Norcross Blackpool.; Med.Qual.Manager. Benfits.Agy Meds.erv.

DOUGHTY, Victor Lamplough 9 Driffield Road, Beverley HU17 7LP — MB ChB 1965 Leeds; FRCPsyc 1996; MRCPsych 1973; DPM Leeds 1969. Cons. Psychiat. Adolesc. & Family Community Serv. Hull. Prev: Cons. Psychiat. (Childr. & Adolesc.) BRd.gate Hosp. Beverley; Sen. Regist. (Adolesc. Psychiat.) Hollymoor Hosp. Birm.; Sen. Regist. (Child Psychiat.) Chas. Burns Clinic Birm.

DOUGLAS, Adam Raoul Harvey Cestria Health Centre, Whitehill Way, Chester-le-Street DH2 3DJ Tel: 0191 388 7771 Fax: 0191 387 1803 — MB BS 1992 Newc.; MSc (Physiol.) Newc. 1988, BSc (Physiol.) 1985; MRCGP 1996. (Newc.)

DOUGLAS, Alan Jonathan Flat 2, 88 Craighouse Gardens, Edinburgh EH10 5LW — MB ChB 1994 Ed.; BSc (Hons.) Ed. 1992. (Univ. Ed.) SHO (O & G) E. Gen. Hosp. Edin. Prev: SHO (A & E) Monklands Hosp. Airdrie; SHO (Geriat. Med.) Liberton Hosp. Edin.

DOUGLAS, Alastair Macdonald Allander Street Surgery, 124 Allander Street, Glasgow G22 5JH Tel: 0141 336 8038 Fax: 0141 336 3440 — MB ChB 1987 Glas.

DOUGLAS, Alison Woodside Medical Group B, 80 Western Road, Woodside, Aberdeen AB24 4SU Tel: 01224 492828 Fax: 01224 276173; Rhicuillin, 9 Golfview Road, Bieldside, Aberdeen AB15 9AA Tel: 01224 861435 — MB ChB 1977 Ed.; BSc Ed. 1974, MB ChB 1977; MRCGP 1985. Prev: Research Fell. Depts. Med. & Thoracic Med. Univ. Aberd.; Clin Asst. (Geriat.) City Hosp. Aberd.

DOUGLAS, Andrew Chalmers and Partners, Cogges Surgery, Cogges Hill Road, Witney OX28 3FP Tel: 01993 700505 Fax: 01993 706610 — MB ChB 1989 Leeds.

DOUGLAS, Andrew Cairns (retired) 15/11 Craigend Park, Gilmerton Road, Edinburgh EH16 5XX Tel: 0131 664 9189 — MB ChB 1946 Ed.; FRCP Ed. 1965, M 1952. Reader (Respirat. Med.) Univ. Edin.; Cons. Phys. Roy. Infirm. & City Hosp. Edin. Prev: Lect. (Bact.) Univ. Edin.

DOUGLAS, Andrew Rutter Tel: 01730 267722/268585 Fax: 01730 233526; Durford Abbey Lodge, Rogate Road, Petersfield GU31 5AU Tel: 01730 821810 — MB BS 1978 Lond.; MRCP (UK) 1981; MRCGP 1988; DRCOG 1988. (St. Thos.) Hosp. Pract. Cardiol. Dept. St marys Hosp. Portsmouth.

DOUGLAS, Andrew Scott St Marys Surgery, 37 St. Mary's Street, Ely CB7 4HF Tel: 01353 665511 Fax: 01353 669532; Manor Farm House, 30 West End, Northwold, Thetford IP26 5LE — BM BS 1978 Nottm.; BMedSci Nottm. 1976, BM BS 1978; DRCOG 1982. Prev: SHO (Dermat.) Univ. Hosp. W. Indies, Kingston, Jamaica; SHO (Geriat.) Middlx. Hosp. Lond.; SHO (Paediat.) St. Mary's Hosp. Praed St. Lond.

DOUGLAS, Angela Margaret Fulford Way Surgery, Fulford Way, Woodbury, Exeter EX5 1NZ Tel: 01395 232509 Fax: 01395 232065; Exe View House, Exe View Road, Lympstone, Exmouth EX8 5AZ Tel: 01395 266921 — MB ChB 1975 Bristol; BSc Bristol 1972; MRCGP 1980; DCH Eng. 1978; DRCOG 1979. (Bristol) GP. Prev: Mem. of CSM; Bd. Mem. GMC.

DOUGLAS, Anna Margaret Rosemary Faringdon Health Centre, Coxwell Road, Faringdon SN7 7ED Tel: 01367 242388 Fax: 01367 243394; Bowling Green Cottage, Broadwell, Lechlade GL7 3QS Tel: 01367 860689 — MB ChB 1983 Birm.; MRCGP 1987. (Birmingham)

DOUGLAS, Anne Margaret Skinner Kinorth Medical Centre, 26 Abbotswell Crescent, Aberdeen AB12 5JW Tel: 01224 876000 Fax: 01224 899182; Kintore Cottage, Banchory Devenick, Aberdeen AB12 5XR — MB ChB 1974 Aberd.; DRCOG 1978; MFHom 1997.

DOUGLAS, Brian Christopher 35 Willingdon Road, London N22 6SG Tel: 020 8889 7832 — MB ChB 1988 Glas.; MRCPsych 1993. Sen. Regist. St. Bart. Hosp. Rotat. Scheme. Prev: Priory Lect. (Psychiat.) Univ. Coll. Lond.; Regist. (Psychiat.) Priory Hosp. & St. Bart & Hackney Hosp.; SHO (Psychiat.) United Med. Sch. Guy's & St. Thos. Hosp.

DOUGLAS, Charles Anthony 20 Concord Way, Dukinfield SK16 4DB Tel: 0161 343 6382 — MB ChB 1981 Manch.; BSc St. And. 1979. Princip. in Gen. Pract.; Clin. Lead, E. Lancs. Drug Serv.; Clin. Asst., Trafford Subst. Misuse Serv.; Managig Director, Go To Doc, Yates St., Oldham. Socs: Hon. Sec. Gtr Pennine Small Pract.s Assn.; Chairm. Hyde Physiother. Centre.

DOUGLAS, Christopher David 22 Argyll Street, Castlefields, Shrewsbury SY1 2SF; 46 Cowlishaw Road, Hunters Bar, Sheffield S11 8XF Tel: 01142 682569 — MB ChB 1996 Manch. SHO (Psychiat. Forens.), Wathwood Hosp., Rotherham, S. Yorks. Socs: BMA; MPS. Prev: SHO (Old Age Psychiat.), N.ern Gen. Hosp., Sheff.; SHO (Gen. adult Psychiat.), Doncaster Roy. Infirm., Doncaster; SHO (Community Psychiat.), N.ern Gen. Hosp., Sheff.

DOUGLAS, Clare Nicola Shere Surgery, Gomshall Lane, Shere, Guildford GU5 9DR; Pound House, Honeywood Lane, Okewood Hill, Dorking RH5 5PZ — MB ChB 1982 Bristol; MRCGP 1988.

DOUGLAS, Mr David Logan Department of Orthopaedics, Northern General Hospital, Hermes Road, Sheffield S5 7AU Tel: 0114 226 6921 — MD Sheff. 1984, MB ChB 1973; FRCS Ed. 1978. Cons. Orthop. Sheff. HA. Socs: Brit. Scoliosis Soc. Prev: Sen. Regist. (Orthop.) Sheff. HA; Regist. (Orthop.) Oxf. HA; Research Worker Univ. Sheff.

DOUGLAS, Dorothy Rachel (retired) Top of The Hill, Ashley Road, Battledown, Cheltenham GL52 6QE Tel: 01242 580055 — MB ChB 1951 Bristol.

DOUGLAS, Elma Patricia (retired) 47 Dowanhill Street, Glasgow G11 5HB — MB ChB 1967 Glas.; FRCS Ed. 1975; FCOphth 1988; DO Eng. 1969. Prev: Assoc. Specialist Eye Dept. Glas. Roy. Infirm.

DOUGLAS, Eric Murray (retired) 1 Foxdell, Northwood HA6 2BU Tel: 01923 824901 — MA, MB BChir Camb. 1952; MRCS Eng. LRCP Lond. 1952; MRCGP 1966; DObst RCOG 1959. Prev: Med. Regist. St. Francis Hosp. Trenton, U.S.A.

DOUGLAS, Evelyn Winifred Shirley (retired) 38 Ladhope Drive, Galashiels TD1 2BL — MB ChB 1958 Manch.; DCH Eng. 1962; DObst RCOG 1961. Prev: Assoc. Med. Specialist Borders Macmillan Palliat. Care Serv.

DOUGLAS, Ewen 38 Allan Park, Kirkliston EH29 9HA — MB ChB 1998 Ed.; MB ChB Ed 1998.

DOUGLAS, Geoffrey Andrew Anaesthetic Division, Vale of Leven Hospital, Alexandria G83 0UA Tel: 01389 754121 Fax: 01389 710452 — MB ChB 1971 Aberd.; FRCA 1978. Cons. Anaesth. Vale of Leven Dist. Gen. Hosp. Alexandria.; Hon. Clin. Sen. Lect. (Anaesth.) Glas. Univ. Prev: Cons. Anaesth. RAF Med. Br.

DOUGLAS, George 36 The Crest, Dinnington Green, Dinnington, Newcastle upon Tyne NE13 7LU Tel: 01661 5805 — MB BS 1964 Durh. Prev: Ho. Surg. & Ho. Phys. Roy. Vict. Infirm. Newc-upon-Tyne.

DOUGLAS, George Keith (retired) Glendale, 10 Park Way, Menston, Ilkley LS29 6LR Tel: 01943 872589 — MB ChB 1945 Ed.

DOUGLAS, Gwenth Jean Elizabeth 37 Warren Road, Banstead SM7 1LG Tel: 01737 357709 — MB ChB 1944 St. And.; MRCPsych 1971. Socs: Assoc. Mem. Brit. Inst. Psycho-Anal.. Prev: Psychiat. Clin. Asst. (O & G) Univ. Coll. Hosp. Lond.; Cons. Psychiat. Sutton Child Guid. Clinic; Asst. Psychiat. Cassel Hosp. Richmond.

DOUGLAS, Helen Margaret (retired) Lennox Lodge, 18 Village Road, Oxton, Birkenhead CH43 5SR — MB BS 1974 Lond.; FRCR 1986; DMRD Liverp. 1983. Prev: Cons. Radiol. BRd.green Hosp. Liverp.

DOUGLAS, Henry Guy Kennedy (retired) Les Grandes Rocquettes, St Andrews GY6 8SL Tel: 01481 38311 — MB ChB 1957 Bristol; FRCOG 1980, M 1966, DObst 1959. Prev: Mem. Staff P.ss Eliz. Hosp. St. Martins Guernsey.

DOUGLAS, Ian Alasdair Charles 42 Northbrook Street, Leeds LS7 4QH — MB ChB 1986 Ed.; MRCGP 1990.

DOUGLAS, Ian David Caithness Department of Haematology, Royal Surrey County Hospital, Egerton Road, Guildford GU2 7XX Tel: 01483 571122 — MB ChB 1966 Glas.; FRCPath 1985, M 1973. p/t Cons. Haemat. Roy. Surrey Co. & St. Luke's Hosp. Prev: Sen. Regist. (Haemat.) Roy. Mardsen Hosp.; Gordon Jacobs Research Fell. Roy. Marsden Hosp. & Inst. of Cancer Research.

DOUGLAS, James David MacDonald Tweeddale Medical Practice, High Street, Fort William PH33 6EU Tel: 01397 703136 Fax: 01397 700139 — MB ChB 1975 Aberd.; MD Aberd. 1995; FRCGP 1994, M 1980; Dip. Occ. Med. RCP Lond. 1996. Research Co-ordinator Highlands & Is.s Primary Care Research Network; Med. Ref. Brit. Sub Aqua Club; Hon. Med. Off. Scott. Sub Aqua Club; Assn. Adviser (Gen. Practitioner) Scotl.; Hon. Sen. Lect. Dept. of Gen. Pract., Univ. of Aberd. Socs: Eur. Undersea Biomed. Soc.; Undersea Med. Soc. USA; (Sec.) Lochaber Med. Soc.

DOUGLAS, James Frederick Belfast City Hospital, Lisburn Road, Belfast BT9 7AB Tel: 01232 329241 Fax: 01232 311917; Ballyrobert House, 5 Coyle's Lane, Ballyrobert, Bangor BT19 1UF Tel: 01247 853674 — MB BCh BAO Belf. 1969; BM BCh Oxf. 1969; FRCP Lond. 1986; MRCP (UK) 1972. Cons. Nephrol. Belf. City & Roy. Vict. Hosps. Belf. Socs: Renal Assn.; Brit. Transpl. Soc.; Internat. Soc. Nephrol. Prev: Sen. Nephrol. Belf. City Hosp.

DOUGLAS, Jean Macaulay (retired) 6 Kirkmay House, Crail, Anstruther KY10 3TH Tel: 01333 50556 — MB ChB 1923 St. And.; DPH 1929.

DOUGLAS, John (retired) Brentwood, Sandfield Park, West Derby, Liverpool L12 2AR Tel: 0151 228 1531 — MRCS Eng. LRCP Lond. 1943; MRCGP 1963; LM Rotunda 1947. Prev: Clin. Asst. (Gyn.) Providence Hosp. St. Helens.

DOUGLAS, John Graham Chest Clinic, Aberdeen Royal Infirmary, Aberdeen AB25 2ZN Tel: 01224 551212 Fax: 01224 840766 Email: j.g.douglas@arh.grampian.scot.nhs.uk — MB ChB 1974 Ed.; BSc (Hons.) Ed. 1972; FRCP Ed. 1988; MRCP (UK) 1977. (edinburgh) Cons. Phys. Respirat. med & Infec. Aberd. Teach. Hosp.; Clin. Sen. Lect. (Med.) Univ. Aberd. Socs: Brit. Thoracic Soc.; Scott. Thoracic Soc. (former Counc. Mem.); Brit. Infec. Soc. Prev: Sen. Regist. (Gen. Med.) Roy. Infirm. Edin.; Sen. Regist. (Respirat. Med.) N.. Gen. Hosp. & City Hosp. Edin.; Regist. (Gen. Med.) E.. Gen. Hosp. Edin.

DOUGLAS, John Henry Edward Bangor Health Centre, Newtownards Road, Bangor BT20 4LD Tel: 028 9146 9111; 8 Perry Road, Bangor BT19 6UA Tel: 01247 271053 — MB BCh BAO 1971 Belf.; DRCOG 1973.

DOUGLAS, John Kevin Sett Valley Medical Centre, Hyde Bank Road, New Mills, Stockport SK22 4BP Tel: 01663 743483; Hollins, Laneside Road, New Mills, High Peak SK22 4LU Tel: 01663 742899 — MB ChB 1981 Leeds; DRCOG 1983. GP Stockport.

DOUGLAS, Mr John Lindsay (retired) 74 Craighill Drive, Clarkston, Glasgow G76 7TD — MB ChB Glas. 1939; BSc. Glas. 1936; FRCS Ed. 1947.

DOUGLAS, Karen May Jane 5 Mullyloughran Heights, Armagh BT61 9HP — MB ChB 1994 Manch.; MRCP 1999.

DOUGLAS, Keith David Speedie Beccles Medical Centre, 7-9 St. Marys Road, St. Marys Road, Beccles NR34 9NQ Tel: 01502 712662 Fax: 01502 712906 — MB ChB 1977 Dundee.

DOUGLAS, Kenneth William 31 Villafield Drive, Bishopbriggs, Glasgow G64 3NW — MB ChB 1991 Glas.

DOUGLAS, Kevin Michael Tel: 01395 273001 Fax: 01395 273771; 4 South Parade, Budleigh Salterton EX9 6NR — BM BCh 1985 Oxf.; BA 1982 Oxf.; DRCOG 1987; MRCGP 1992; DA (UK) 1987. (Oxford) GP Claremont Med. Pract., Exmouth; Hosp. Practitioner (Anaesthetics). Prev: SHO (Paediat.) Roy. United Hosp. Bath; SHO (Anaesth.) Torbay HA.

DOUGLAS, Margaret Jean 32 Redford Road, Edinburgh EH13 0AA — MB ChB 1989 Ed.

DOUGLAS, Margaret Kathleen (retired) 190 Maidstone Road, Chatham ME4 6EW Tel: 01634 842216 — MB BS 1949 Lond.; DObst RCOG 1952.

DOUGLAS, Marlene Mary 155 Stanley Avenue, Gidea Park, Romford RM2 5DB — MB ChB 1986 Liverp.

DOUGLAS, Maureen The Surgery, Bunessan, Isle of Mull PA67 6DG Tel: 01681 700261 Fax: 01681 700261 — BM BCh 1974 Oxford; BM BCh Oxf. 1974. (Oxford) GP Isle of Mull.

DOUGLAS, Melanie Fiona The Grove Medical Practice, Shirley Health Centre, Grove Road, Shirley, Southampton SO15 3UA Tel: 023 8078 8500 Fax: 023 8078 3611 — MB BS 1987 Lond.; MRCGP 1992; T(GP) 1992; DCCH RCGP 1992; DCH RCP Lond. 1992; DRCOG 1991. (Char. Cross & Westm. Med. Sch.) p/t Gen. Practitioner on GP Retainer Scheme, The Gr. Med. Pract. Shirley Health Centre Soton..; Hospice Dr. In Childr.'s Palliat. Care (providing holiday cover on a long term basis) Naomi Ho., Sockbridge Rd, Sutton Scotney Winchester, Hamps, SO21 3JE. Prev: GP (Retainer) Soton.; Clin. Med. Off. (Community Paediat.) Soton. Community Health Servs. Trust; Staff Grade Community Paediat. (Audiol.) Soton. Community NHS Trust.

DOUGLAS, Michael Richard Flat 5, Charles Lamb Court, Gerrard Road, London N1 8AZ — MB ChB 1998 Birm.

DOUGLAS, Neil Alexander Island Health, 145 East Ferry Road, London E14 3BQ Tel: 020 7363 1111 Fax: 020 7363 1112 — MB BS 1983 Lond.; DCCH RCGP & FCM 1988; DCH RCP Lond. 1987. Clin. Med. Off. Tower Hamlets HA. Prev: Clin. Med. Off. Camberwell HA.

DOUGLAS, Professor Neil James Respiratory Medicine Unit, Department of Medicine, Royal Infirmary Edinburgh, Edinburgh EH3 9YW Tel: 0131 536 3252 Fax: 0131 536 3255 Email: n.j.douglas@ed.ac.uk; 42 Dick Place, Edinburgh EH9 2JB — MB ChB 1973 Ed.; MD Ed. 1983; FRCP Ed. 1985; MRCP (UK) 1975; FRCP Lond. 1998. Prof. of Respirat. & Sleep Med. Univ. Edin. & Dir. Scott. Nat. Sleep Laborat. Edin.; Dir. Scott. Nat. Sleep Centre Dean RCP Ed.; Vice Pres. RCPE. Socs: (Ex-Hon. Sec.) Brit. Thoracic Soc.; (Ex-Chairm.) Brit. Sleep Soc. Prev: Reader Med. & Respirat. Med. Univ. Edin.; Sen. Lect. (Respirat. Med. & Med.) & Lect. (Med.) Univ. Ed.; MRC Trav. Fell. Univ. Colorado.

DOUGLAS, Norman Thomas Edward Bradley Stoke Surgery, Brook Way, Bradley Stoke North, Bristol BS32 9DS Tel: 01454 616262 Fax: 01454 619161 — MB BCh BAO 1979 Belf.; LMCC 1085; MRCGP 1983; DRCOG 1981.

DOUGLAS, Pamela Margaret (retired) — MB BS 1956 Lond.; DObst. RCOG 1958. Prev: GP Settle.

DOUGLAS, Mr Peter Stewart Department of Maxillofacial Surgery, Torbay Hospital, Lawes Bridge, Torquay TQ2 7AA Tel: 01803 654834 Email: peter.douglas@sdevon-tr.swest.nhs.uk; Tall Trees, Old Mill Road, Torquay TQ2 6PP Tel: 01803 606224 Email: ps@douglas123.fsnet.co.uk — MRCS Eng. LRCP Lond. 1985; BDS Sheff. 1980; FRCS Ed. 1989; FDS RCS Eng 1988, LDS 1980. Cons. Oral & Maxillofacial Surg. Torbay Hosp. Socs: BMA & Brit. Assn. Oral & Maxillofacial Surg. Prev: Sen. Regist. (Oral & Maxillofacial Surg.) Glas.; Regist. (Oral & Maxillofacial Surg.) Burnley & Bury Gen. Hosps.; SHO (Oral Surg. & Otorhinolaryngol.) Leicester Roy. Infirm.

DOUGLAS, Raymond James Tams Brig Surgery, 107 New Road, Ayr KA8 8DD Tel: 01292 262697 Fax: 01292 265926 — MB ChB 1972 Aberd.; FRCGP 2000; MRCGP 1976. (Aberdeen)

DOUGLAS, Robin Grove Medical Group, 1 The Grove, Gosforth, Newcastle upon Tyne NE3 1NU Tel: 0191 210 6680 Fax: 0191 210 6682 — MB BS 1992 Newc.; MRCGP 1997; DCH RCP Lond. 1996. Princip. Socs: Med. Defence Union.

DOUGLAS, Ronald Neville Carfrae 22 Calderwood Road, Newlands, Glasgow G43 2RP Tel: 0141 571 0318 Email: r.douglas@ntlworld.com — MB ChB 1960 Glas.; BSc (Hons.) Glas. 1957; FRCGP 1986, M 1968; DObst RCOG 1962. (Glas.) Med. Mem. Social Security Appeal Tribunals (The Appeals Serv.). Socs: (Ex-Pres.) Glas. S.. Med. Soc. Prev: Princip. GP Gtr. Glas. HB & Chairm. Glas. LMC.

DOUGLAS, Steven 4 Langley Terrace, Stanley DH9 7TT — MB BS 1991 Lond.

DOUGLAS, Susan Fiona 125 Welbeck Crescent, Troon KA10 6AR — MB BS 1987 Lond.

DOUGLAS, Timothy Guy Charles Portchester Health Centre, West Street, Portchester, Fareham PO16 9TU Tel: 023 9237 6913 Fax: 023 9237 4265; 138A Castle Street, Portchester, Fareham PO16 9QH Tel: 01705 381606 — BM 1984 Soton.; MRCGP 1988; DRCOG 1986. Prev: Trainee GP Portsmouth VTS.

DOUGLAS, Timothy John 4 Meautys, St Albans AL3 4LU — MB ChB 1991 Sheff.; D.CH. RCP 1994; M.R.C.G.P. 1998. (Sheffield) Trainee GP Rotherham VTS.

DOUGLAS, Tonia Anne 6 Church Road, Coalbrookdale, Telford TF8 7NS — MB ChB 1994 Manch.

DOUGLAS, Mr William Keith (retired) Yew Trees, Warrington Road, Mere, Knutsford WA16 0TE — MRCS Eng. LRCP Lond. 1943; MA Camb. 1939, MChir 1958, MB BChir 1943; FRCS Eng. 1950. Prev: Cons. Cardoio-Thoracic Surg. Manch. AHA (T).

DOUGLAS, William Stewart Department of Dermatology, Monklands District General Hospital, Airdrie ML6 0JS; 102 Brownside Road, Cambuslang, Glasgow G72 8AF — MB ChB 1968 Glas.; FRCP Glas. 1983; MRCP (UK) 1972. Cons. Dermat. Monklands Dist. Gen. Hosp. Airdrie.; Clin. Dir. Med. Specialties Monklands Hosp. 1997-99. Socs: Scott. Dermatol. Soc. (Ex-Sec. & Pres. 2000-). Prev: Sen. Regist. (Dermat.) Aberd. Roy. Infirm.; Lect. (Dermat.) Univ. Nairobi, Kenya; Regist. (Dermat.) Glas. Roy. Infirm.

DOUGLAS, Yvonne Joan Birchwood Medical Centre, 15 Benson Road, Birchwood, Warrington WA3 7PJ Tel: 01925 823502 Fax: 01925 852422; Haslam Farm, 18 Hillock Lane, Woolston, Warrington WA1 4NF Tel: 01925 814369 — MB BS 1977 Lond.; DRCOG 1979; Cert. Family Plann. JCC 1979. (Lond. Hosp.)

DOUGLAS-JONES, Anthony Gordon Department of Pathology, University Hospital of Wales, Heath Park, Cardiff CF4 4XN Tel: 029 2074 2705 Fax: 029 2074 4276; 57 Heath Park Avenue, Cardiff CF14 3RF Tel: 029 2075 0721 — MB BChir 1976 Camb.; PhD Auckland 1986; MA Camb. 1976, BA 1972; FRCPA 1982. (St. Bart.) Sen. Lect. (Path.) Univ. Wales Coll. Med. Cardiff.

DOUGLAS-RILEY, Timothy Roger, Surg. Capt. RN ACOS (Med), rm2225 JHQ, Sandys Lane, Northwood HA6 3HP Tel: 01923 837334 Fax: 01923 837975; Smallack House, Smallack Drive, Plymouth PL6 5EB Tel: 01752 773148 — MB BS Lond. 1974; MRCS Eng. LRCP Lond. 1974; MRCGP 1983; Dip. Sports Med. Lond 1991; DA Eng. 1983. (Char. Cross Hosp.) Asst. Chief Staff (Med) cincfleet. Prev: PMO HMY Britannia; PMO RNSQ Drake; PMO Commando Train. Centre Roy. Marines.

DOUGLAS SMITH, Brian Joseph (retired) Hazeldene, 1 North St., North Petherton, Bridgwater TA6 6TE — MB BS 1946 Lond.; MRCS Eng. LRCP Lond. 1940. Prev: Chest Phys. S. Som. Clin. Area.

DOUGLAS-WILSON, Ian 10 Homan Court, 17 Friern Watch Avenue, London N12 9HW Tel: 020 8446 9047 — MB ChB 1936 Ed.; MD (Commend.) Ed. 1938; FRCP Ed. 1945, M 1939; Dr (hon. causa) Ed. 1974. (Univ. Ed. & Lond. Hosp.) Corr. Mem. Danish Soc. Internal Med. Prev: Edr. The Lancet; Ho. Phys. Roy. Infirm. Edin.; Maj. RAMC, Med. Specialist.

DOUGLASS, Andrew William Rowe Brent House Surgery, 14 King Street, Bridgwater TA6 3ND Tel: 01278 458551 Fax: 01278 431116 — MB BS 1972 Lond.; MRCS Eng. LRCP Lond. 1971;

MRCGP 1978; DObst RCOG 1974. (St. Bart.) Prev: SHO (Psychiat.) Barrow Hosp. Bristol; Med. Off. Berega Hosp. Tanzania.

DOUGLASS, Carolyn Ann (Stirrup) 23 Rutland Court, Queens Drive, West Acton, Ealing, London W3 0HL — BM BS 1993 Nottm.; BMedSci Nottm. 1991. Specialist Regist. Anaesth., NW Thames, N.wick Pk. Hosp. Lond. Prev: Specialist Regist. (anaesth.) Hemel Hampstead. Herts.; SHO (ITU) Roy. Brompton Hosp. Lond.; SHO (Anaesth.) Whittington Hosp. Lond.

DOUGLASS, Erica Jane Wells Homoeopathic Practice, Melbourne House, Chamberlain St., Wells BA5 2PJ Tel: 01749 676297 Fax: 01749 670315; Donegal Cottage, Kale St, Batcombe, Shepton Mallet BA4 6AD — MB BChir Camb. 1982; MA Camb. 1983; MFHom 1996; DRCOG 1984. (Camb.)

DOUGLASS, Richard Anthony Woodlands Medical Centre, 106 Yarm Lane, Stockton-on-Tees TS18 1YE Tel: 01642 607398 Fax: 01642 604603; Grindon Hall, Grindon, Thorpe Thewles, Stockton-on-Tees TS21 3HY — MB BChir 1975 Camb.; MA, MB Camb. 1975, BChir 1974; MRCGP 1978.

DOUGLASS, Simon Jonathan Hope House Surgery, The Street, Radstock, Bath BA3 3PL Tel: 01761 433157 Fax: 01761 431880; Laurel House, Fosse R, Stratton on The Fosse, Bath BA3 4QN Tel: 01761 232511 — MB BS 1988 Lond.; MRCGP 1993; DROG 1993.

DOUGLASS, Ursula Elizabeth Black Hedley Farm, Shotley Bridge, Consett DH8 Tel: 01207 280 — MB BS 1968 Newc.; MB BS Newc. 1968. Clin. Med. Off. Durh. HA. Prev: SHO (Dermat.) Roy. Vict. Infirm. Newc.

DOUGRAY, Thomas (retired) 9 Burnham Close, East Bridgford, Nottingham NG13 8NT Tel: 01949 20556 — MB ChB 1943 Glas.; FRCOG 1965, M 1949. Hon. Cons. O & G W. Midl. RHA.

DOULAH, Mohammed Assaf Ud 9 St Ilans Way, Caerphilly CF83 1EW — MB BS 1989 Lond.; BSc Immunol. Lond. 1985, MB BS 1989. lect. Paediat. Dept. Child. Health.Obst. Univ. Leeds.

DOULIA, Eleni 2 Grange Road, London W4 4DA Tel: 020 8995 6294 — Ptychio Iatrikes 1968 Thessalonika.

DOULL, Donald Henderson Whin Park Medical Centre, 6 Saughton Road, Edinburgh EH11 3RA Tel: 0131 455 7999 Fax: 0131 455 8800; 48 Spylawbank Road, Edinburgh EH13 0JG Tel: 0131 441 3015 Email: donald.doull@virgin.net — MB ChB Ed. 1970; BSc (Hons.) Ed. 1967. Prev: Trainee GP N. Lothian (W.. Gen.) VTS; Ho. Surg. & Ho. Phys. Roy. Infirm. Edin.

DOULL, Iolo John Manley 18 Heol Don, Cardiff CF14 2AU — BM 1984 Soton.; MRCP (UK) 1989. Cons., Univ. Hosp. Wales, Cardiff. Prev: Research Fell. (Med.) Univ. Soton.; Regist. (Paediat.) Soton. Gen. Hosp.

DOULTON, Timothy William Ronald 6 St Georges Road, Kingston upon Thames KT2 6DN — MB BS 1998 Lond.; MB BS Lond 1998.

DOURADO, Jose Roberto Dourado and Partners, Maybush Medical Centre, Belle Isle Health Park, Portobello Road, Wakefield WF1 5PN Tel: 01924 328132 Fax: 01924 328130; 13 Wingate Croft, Sandal, Wakefield WF2 6HB Tel: 01924 257601 — LRCPI & LM, LRCSI & LM 1967. (RCSI)

DOURISH, Mark Peter 119 Catharine Street, Cambridge CB1 3AP — MB BChir 1993 Camb.; BSc (Hons.) St. And. 1990. (Univ. St. And. & Univ. Camb.) Trainee GP/SHO Hinchingbrooke Hosp. Huntingdon VTS. Prev: SHO Rotat. (Med.) Stoke Mandeville Hosp. Aylesbury.

DOUSE, Frank Arras (retired) 161 Whalley Drive, Bletchley, Milton Keynes MK3 6JA Tel: 01908 375552 — MB BS 1963 Lond.; MRCS Eng. LRCP Lond. 1963; DObst RCOG 1966.

DOUSE, Helen Elizabeth Clifton Road Surgery, 26 Clifton Road, Rugby CV21 3QF Tel: 01788 543088 Fax: 01788 551496; 39 Acacia Grove, Rugby CV21 2QT — MB ChB 1990 Sheff.; DFFP. (Sheffield) GP Princip. Rugby. Socs: Roy. Coll. Gen. Pract. Prev: Trainee GP Doncaster VTS.

DOUSE, Joseph Edward Clifton Road Surgery, 26 Clifton Road, Rugby CV21 3QF Tel: 01788 543088 Fax: 01788 551496; 26 Clifton Road, Rugby CV21 3QF — MB ChB 1966 Sheff.; DObst RCOG 1968. (Sheff.) Prev: Ho. Surg. City Gen. Hosp. Sheff.; Ho. Phys. & SHO (O & G) N.. Gen. Hosp. Sheff.

DOUSE, Neil Andrew Stonedean Practice, Health Centre, Market Square, Stony Stratford, Milton Keynes MK11 1YA Tel: 01908 261155 — MB BS 1992 Lond. (St. Mary's Imperial)

DOUST, Philip James Moorfields Eye Hospital, City Road, London EC1V 2PD Tel: 020 7253 3411; 8 Ruskin Park House, Champion Hill, London SE5 8TQ — MB BS 1961 Lond.; MRCS Eng. LRCP Lond. 1961; DObst RCOG 1963. (Guy's) Chief Clin Asst. (Ophth.) Moorfields Eye Hosp. Lond. Socs: BMA. Prev: Regist. (Psychol. Med.) Guy's Hosp. Lond.; Sen. Resid. (Psychiat.) Univ. Alberta Hosp. Edmonton, Canada.

DOUZENIS, Athanassios 76 Redesdale Avenue, Coventry CV6 1BT; 3 Akamantos Street, Athens 10651, Greece Tel: 010 346 5528 Fax: 010 346 4047 Email: douzenis@compulink.gr — Ptychio Iatrikes 1985 Ioannina; MMedSci Sheff. 1989; MRCPsych 1991; PhD Athens 1995. Sen. Regist. (Psychiat.) Gordon Hosp. Lond.; Senor Lecutrer Univ. of Athens Med. Sch. Psychiat. Dep. Eginition Hosp. Prev: Regist. (Adult & Child Psychiat.) Char. Cross Hosp. Lond.

DOVE, Alan Peter Brockwell Centre, Brockwell Centre, Northumbrian Road, Cramlington NE23 1XZ Tel: 01670 733700 Fax: 01670 590606 — MB BS 1970 Newc. (Newc.) Prev: SHO (O & G) Bishop Auckland Gen. Hosp.; Ho. Surg. & Ho. Phys. Hexham Gen. Hosp.

DOVE, Andrew Frank University Hospital NHS Trust, Queens Medical Centre, Nottingham NG7 2UH Tel: 0115 970 9152 Fax: 0115 970 9281; 12 Stella Avenue, Tollerton, Nottingham NG12 4EX Email: ddoveaf@cs.com — MB ChB 1972 Bristol; MRCGP 1979; DObst RCOG 1976; FFAEM 1996. Cons. A & E Med. Univ. Hosp. Nottm.

DOVE, David Stephen 14 Foxbourne Road, London SW17 8EW — MB BS 1991 Lond.; BSc (Econ.) Lond. 1982; MRCP (UK) 1994.

DOVE, Geoffrey Arthur William (retired) Flat 5, West London Studios, 404 Fulham Road, London SW6 1HP Tel: 020 7381 1065 Fax: 020 7381 1547 — MB BS Lond. 1960; BSc (Hons.) Lond. 1946; MRCS Eng. LRCP Lond. 1958. Prev: Resid. Clin. Path. St. Geo. Hosp. Lond.

DOVE, Mr John 31 Quarry Avenue, Hartshill, Stoke-on-Trent ST4 7EW Tel: 01782 411517 Fax: 01782 747193 — MB BS 1968 Lond.; FRCS Eng. 1976; MRCS Eng. LRCP Lond. 1968. (St. Thos.) Cons. Orthop. Hartshill Orthop. Hosp. Stoke-on-Trent; Dir. Stoke-on-Trent Spinal Servs. Socs: Fell. BOA.

DOVE, John Roger Princess Street Surgery, Gorseinon, Swansea SA4 4US Tel: 01792 895681 — MB BCh 1956 Wales.

DOVE, Niall Allan Rider The Village Surgery, 5 Barrow Point Avenue, Pinner HA5 3HQ Tel: 020 8429 3777 Fax: 020 8429 4413; 8 Beech Hill Court, Berkhamsted HP4 2PR Tel: 0144 27 873936 — MB ChB 1978 Ed.

DOVE, Patricia Mary Kilsyth Medical Partnership, Kilsyth Health Centre, Burngreen Park, Kilsyth, Glasgow G65 0HU Tel: 01236 822081 Fax: 01236 826231 — MB ChB 1976 Glas.

DOVE, Peter Raymond 9 The Sycamores, Bishop's Stortford CM23 5JR — MB BS 1949 Lond.; MRCPsych 1972; DPM Eng. 1966. (Guy's) Hon. Cons. Psychiat. P.ss Alexandra Hosp. Harlow. Socs: BMA. Prev: Cons. Psychiat. P.ss Alexandra Hosp. Harlow; Asst. Psychiat. Long Gr. Hosp. Epsom; Clin. Asst. Maudsley Hosp. Lond.

DOVE, Philippa Jill Keele Practice, University of Keele, Keele, Newcastle ST5 5BG Tel: 01782 753550 Fax: 01782 753555; Park Hill, Pingle Lane, Stone ST15 8QT Tel: 01785 811775 — MB BS 1968 Lond.; MSc (Primary Health Care) Keele 1992; DCH Eng. 1973; DObst RCOG 1970. (St. Thos.) Asst. Med. Off. Keele Univ.

DOVE, Rosemary Ann 12 Stella Avenue, Tollerton, Nottingham NG12 4EX — MB ChB 1974 Bristol; DObst RCOG 1976; DCCH RCP Ed. 1985. SCMO (Community Child Health) Nottm.

DOVE, Samantha Elizabeth Moorlands, Burton End, Stansted CM24 8UE — MB BS 1998 Lond.; MB BS Lond 1998.

DOVE, Stuart James Willesborough Health Centre, Bentley Road, Willesborough, Ashford TN24 0HZ Tel: 01233 621626 Fax: 01233 622930; Cobblers Oak, Canterbury Road, Brabourne Lees, Ashford TN25 6QP Tel: 0130 381 3036 — MB BS 1969 Lond.; MRCGP 1988; DObst RCOG 1971. (St. Thos.)

DOVE, William Lionel 6 Woolton Hill Road, Liverpool L25 6HX Tel: 0151 428 1072 — MB ChB 1933 Liverp.; MRCS Eng. LRCP Lond. 1934. (Liverp.) Prev: Capt. RAMC; Ho. Surg. Liverp. Roy. Infirm.; Asst. Res. Med. Off. Walton Hosp. Liverp.

DOVE-EDWIN, Isis Abiodun Top Flat, 12 Crookham Road, London SW6 4EQ — MD CM 1990 McGill Univ. Canada; MD CM McGill Univ., Canada 1990; MRCP (UK) 1993.

DOVELL, Tamsin Mary 5 Templemere, Weybridge KT13 9PA — BM BS 1994 Nottm. SHO (Gen. Med. & IC) Gosford Dist. Hosp. Gosford City NSW, Austral. Prev: SHO (A & E) Roy. Perth Hosp. WA, Austral.; Ho. Off. (Gen. Med.) Torbay Dist. Hosp. Torquay Devon; Ho. Off. (Gen. Surg.) Qu. Med. Centre Nottm.

DOVER, Bertie The White House, 1B Carlton Road, Hale, Altrincham WA15 8RH Tel: 0161 980 4386 — MB ChB 1945 Liverp. (Liverp.) Socs: BMA. Prev: RAF Med. Br.; Ho. Phys. Birkenhead Gen. Hosp.; Resid. Med. Off. Port Sunlight Hosp.

DOVER, Clare Jane 5 Coneydale, Welwyn Garden City AL8 7RX — MB BS 1998 Newc.; MB BS Newc 1998.

DOVER, Juliet Rose 62 The Broadway, Oadby, Leicester LE2 2HE — MB ChB 1985 Leic.; MRCGP 1990; DRCOG 1988. (Leicester) GP Asst. Prev: GP Retainer Scheme Leicester.; Trainee GP Leicester VTS.

DOVER, Mr Michael Stephen Department of Maxillofacial Surgery, Queen Elizabeth Hospital, Edgbaston, Birmingham B15 2TH Tel: 0121 627 2301 Fax: 0121 627 2302 Email: dover@craniofacial.org.uk — MB ChB 1989 Birm.; BDS Birm. 1980; FRCS Eng. 1992; FDS RCS Eng. 1984. Cons. Oral & Maxillofacial Surg. Qu. Eliz. Hosp. Birm. Socs: Fell.ship Brit. Assoc. Oral & Maxillofacial Surg.; Internat. Assn. Maxillofacial Surg.; Internat. Team For Implantology. Prev: Research Fell. (Craniofacial) & Sen. Regist. (Maxillofacial Surg.) W. Midl. Rotat.; Regist. Rotat. (Gen. Surg.) Centr. Birm.; Regist. (Oral & Maxillofacial Surg.) BRd.green Hosp. Liverp., Wolverhampton & Wordsley Hosps.

DOVER, Oskar Edge Hill Health Centre, Crosfield Road, Liverpool L7 5QL Tel: 0151 260 2777; 153 Menlove Avenue, Liverpool L18 3EE Tel: 0151 722 1363 — MB ChB 1953 Liverp.; MRCGP 1970. (Liverp.) Mem. Liverp. Med. Inst. Socs: BMA. Prev: Vis. Med. Off. HM Prison Liverp. (Home Off.); Capt. RAMC; Ho. Phys. & Ho. Surg. BRd.green Hosp. Liverp.

DOVER, Richard William 44 Angelica Way, Whiteley, Fareham PO15 7HZ — BM 1988 Soton.; MRCOG 1993. Regist. (O & G) Qu. Med. Centre Nottm. Prev: SHO (O & G) P.ss Ann Hosp. Soton.

DOVER, Simon Bernard Department of Gastroenterology, Western Infirmary & Gartnavel General Hospital, 1053 Great Western Road, Glasgow G12 0YN Tel: 0141 211 3280 Fax: 0141 211 1006; 1 Glenpark Avenue, Rouken Glen, Glasgow G46 7JE Tel: 0141 638 2049 Fax: 0141 638 2049 — MB ChB 1982 Birm.; FRCP 2001 Glas.; MD Birm. 1995; MRCP (UK) 1988. Cons. Phys. & Gastroenterol. N. Glas. NHS Trust; Hon. Sen. Clin. Lect. Univ. of Glas.

DOVER, Stephen John Blurton & Newstead Health Centre, Ripon Road, Stoke-on-Trent ST3 3BS — BM BS 1985 Nottm.; MPhil Keele 1996; BMedSci Nottm. 1983; MRCPsych 1992. Cons. Child & Adolesc. Psychiat. Blurton Health Centre Stoke on Trent; Sen. Clin. Lect. (Child & Adolesc. Psychiat.) Univ. Keele. Prev: Lect. (Child & Adolesc. Psychiat.) Univ. Keele.

DOVERTY, Malcolm Ross The Health Centre, Kilbowie Road, Clydebank G81 2TQ Tel: 0141 531 6400 Fax: 0141 531 6490; 10 Munro Road, Jordanhill, Glasgow G13 1SF — MB ChB 1977 Glas.

DOVEY, Hugh (retired) 72 Rodney Street, Liverpool L1 9AF Tel: 0151 707 0086 Fax: 0151 708 5525 — MB BChir 1955 Camb.; MD Camb. 1963; MChOrth. Liverp. 1961; FRCSI 1961; FRCS Ed. 1958; MRCS Eng. LRCP Lond. 1954; MLCOM 1986. Prev: Lect. (Clin. Orthop.) Univ. Copenhagen.

DOVEY, Julie Karen The Old Hospital, Relands Lane, Edington, Bridgwater TA7 9JW — MB BS 1996 Lond.

DOVEY, Michael Sydney (retired) — MB ChB Bristol 1963. Hon. Med. Off. Keynsham Amateur Swimming Club. Prev: Sen. Resid. Ho. Surg. (Obst.) Bristol Matern. Hosp.

DOVEY, Peter X-Ray Department, Hillingdon Hospital, Uxbridge Tel: 01895 38282 — MB BCh 1962 Wales; FFR 1968; DMRD Eng. 1965. (Cardiff) Cons. Radiol. Hillingdon Hosp. Uxbridge. Socs: BMA. & Roy. Coll. Radiol. Prev: Sen. Regist. (Radiol. & Nulcear Med.) Roy. Marsden Hosp. Lond.; Sen. Regist. (Radiol.) Univ. W. Indies.; Sen. Regist. (Research Fell.) in Radiol. Cardiff Roy. Infirm.

DOVEY, Zachary Seth Flat 3, 125 Hammersmith Grove, London W6 0NJ — MB BS 1990 Lond.; BSc Lond. 1987, MB BS 1990.

DOW, Alan James 108 Long Lane, Charlesworth, Hyde SK13 5ES — MB ChB 1984 Aberd.; MB ChB Aberd. l984; MRCGP 1989; DA (UK) 1990; Dip. IMC RCS Ed. 1990.

DOW, Alexander Rattray (retired) East Lodge, Hylton Castle, Washington Road, Sunderland SR5 3JB Tel: 0191 516 8407 Email: sdow@globalnet.co.uk — MB ChB 1952 Aberd.; FFAEM 1993. Prev: Cons. (A & E Med.) Dist. Gen. Hosp. Sunderland.

DOW, Alison Margaret Dr Dow and Partners, 87-89 Prince of Wales Road, London NW5 3NT; 163 Tufnell Park Road, London N7 0PU Tel: 020 7609 1358 — MB ChB 1982 Aberd.; DFFP 1994; DRCOG 1988. (Univ. Aberd.)

DOW, Anne Brunton (retired) East Lodge, Hylton Castle, Washington Road, Sunderland SR5 3JB Tel: 0191 516 8407 — MB ChB 1951 Ed. Prev: Sen. Med. Off. Sunderland HA.

DOW, Carol Medical Advisers Office, Foreign & Commonwealth Office, Old Admiralty Building, London SW1A 2AF Tel: 020 7008 0595 Fax: 020 7008 0622 Email: carol.dow@flo.gov.uk; 146 Coleherne Court, Redcliffe Gardens, London SW5 0DY Tel: 020 7259 2445 — MB BS 1976 Lond.; MRCP (UK) 1981; AFOM RCP Lond. 1992; DTM & H RCP Lond. 1988. (St. Bart. Hosp. Lond.) Chief Med. Adviser Foreign & Commonw. Off. Lond.

DOW, (Cicely) Jean (retired) Dene Cottage, Privett, Alton GU34 3PW Tel: 01730 828211 — MB BS (Hons.) Lond. 1951; MRCP (UK) 1970; FFR 1970. Prev: Cons. Radiol. St. Geo. Hosp. Lond.

DOW, Eleanor Department of Biochemical Medicine, Ninewells Hospital, Dundee DD1 9SY Tel: 01382 632189 Fax: 01382 645333 Email: ellied@tuht.scot.nhs.uk — MRCS Eng. LRCP Lond. 1985; PhD Lond. 1994; BSc (Hons.) Glas. 1982; MRCPath 1996. (Middlx. Hosp. Lond.) Cons. Biochem. Med. Ninewells Hosp. Dundee; Hon. Sen. Lect. (Biochem. Med.) Univ. Dundee; Hon. Sen. Lect. (Biological Sci.) Univ. St. And. Prev: Sen. Regist. (Chem. Path.) St. Mary's Hosp. Lond.

DOW, George Robertson (retired) Donavourd, Cloan Drive, Auchterarder PH3 1BU Tel: 01764 664308 — MB ChB Glas. 1956; DA Eng. 1958. Prev: Cons. Anaesth. Stobhill Hosp. Glas.

DOW, Iain Alasdair McNeill Grange Street Surgery, 2 Grange Street, St Albans AL3 5NF Tel: 01727 851136 Fax: 01727 847961; 7 St. Peters Close, St Albans AL1 3ES Tel: 01727 856653 — MB ChB 1973 Glas.; MRCGP 1977. (Glas.)

DOW, Iain Campbell (retired) Rose Cottage, Cruise Hill, Ham Green, Redditch B97 5UA Tel: 01527 541587 — MB BChir 1952 Camb.; DObst RCOG 1957; DA Eng. 1958. Prev: Hosp. Pract. (Anaesth.) BromGr. Gen. & Smallwood Hosp. Redditch.

DOW, Jennifer Sandra Margaret Baillieston Health Centre, 20 Muirside Road, Baillieston, Glasgow G69 7AD Tel: 0141 531 8050 Fax: 0141 531 8067; 6 Albert Road, Lenzie, Glasgow G66 5AS Tel: 0141 776 1566 — MB ChB 1992 Glas.; MRCGP 1996; DRCOG 1995. (Univ. Glas.) Partner Baillieston Health Centre Glas. Prev: Asst. GP Baillieston Health Centre Glas.

DOW, John Dickson, MC 86 Harley Street, London W1N 1AE Tel: 020 7935 5811 — MD 1937 Glas.; BSc Glas. 1937, MD (Hons., Bellahouston Gold; Medal), MB ChB 1940; FRCP Ed. 1970, M 1967; DMRD Eng. 1946; FRCR 1975; FFR 1953. (Univ. Glas.) Socs: Fell. Roy. Soc. Med.; Brit. Inst. Radiol. Prev: Dir. X-Ray Dept. Guy's Hosp. Lond.; Cons. Radiol. W.. Infirm. Glas.; Maj. RAMC.

DOW, John Duncan Campbell Dow Surgery, William Street, Redditch B97 4AJ Tel: 01527 62285 Fax: 01527 596260 — BM BS 1987 Nottm.

DOW, Judith Mary GP Unit, St. Catherines Hospital, Church Road, Tranmere, Birkenhead CH42 0LQ Tel: 0151 647 6888; 6 Salem View, Birkenhead CH43 5UH Tel: 0151 647 6588 — MB ChB Liverp. 1959. (Liverp.) Socs: BMA. Prev: Cas. Off. Sefton Gen. Hosp. Liverp.; Ho. Off. (Surg.) Withington Hosp. Manch.; Ho. Off. (O & G) BRd.green Hosp. Liverp.

DOW, Lindsey 1 Daniel Street, Bath BA2 6NB — MB BS 1981 Lond.; DM Soton. 1991; MRCP (UK) 1983. Sen. Lect. & Cons. Med. Frenchay Hosp. Bristol & Univ. Bristol. Prev: Sen. Regist. (Gen. & Geriat. Med.) John Radcliffe Hosp. Oxf.; Research Fell. (Med.) Univ. Soton.; Regist. (Gen. & Chest Med.) Soton. & Salisbury HAs.

DOW, Robert James Dundarach, 1 Craig Lockhart Park, Colinton, Edinburgh EH14 1ER; Scotia Holdings Ltd., Scotia House, Castle Business Park, Stirling FK9 4TZ Tel: 01786 895279 Fax: 01786 895300 — MB ChB 1975 Dundee; BSc St. And. 1972; FRCP Ed. 1991; MRCP (UK) 1980; FFPM 1993. Chief Exec. Scotia Pharmaceut. Stirling. Socs: Brit. Pharm. Soc. (Clin. Sect.). Prev: Head Global Drug Developm., Hoffman La Roche, Switz.; Vice-Pres. Drug Developm., Syntex, USA; Sen. Regist. & Regist. Univ. Dept. Therap. Ninewells Hosp. Dundee.

DOW, Rosemary Catriona 5 Dunbar Avenue, Kirkcudbright DG6 4HD — MB ChB 1989 Manch.

DOW, Rosemary Ellen 56 Stonehouse Road, Strathaven ML10 6LF — MB ChB 1993 Glas.

DOW, Sally Catherine GP Unit, St. Catherines Hospital, Church Road, Tranmere, Birkenhead CH42 0LQ Tel: 0151 647 6888 — MB ChB 1989 Sheff.

DOW, Thomas Campbell, OStJ, TD (retired) 43 Crumpfields Lane, Redditch B97 5PN Tel: 01527 541458 — MB ChB 1947 Ed. Prev: Hon. Phys. to HM the Qu.

DOW, Thomas Gillespie Buchanan 53 Victoria Road, Lenzie, Kirkintilloch, Glasgow G66 5AP — MB ChB 1965 Glas.; FRCOG 1988, M 1969; DObst 1966. Cons. (O & G) Monklands Dist. Gen. Hosp. & Bellshill Matern. Hosp. Prev: Hall Tutorial Fell. Glas. Univ.; Sen. Regist. Glas. Roy. Matern. Hosp.; Sen. Lect. King Edwd. VIII Hosp. Durban Univ. S. Africa.

DOW, William Allister McGowan 2E Church Road, Alverstoke, Gosport PO12 2LB — MB ChB 1996 Birm.

DOW, William Ian McGowan (retired) Cwch House, Leep Lane, Alverstoke, Gosport PO12 2BE Tel: 01705 528122 — MB ChB St. And. 1962. Sessional Cons. Clin. NeuroPhysiol. The Roy. Hosp. Gosport. Prev: Med. Off. Gosport War Memor. Hosp.

***DOWARD, William Alastair** Pastoral, Ramble Close, Inkberrow, Worcester WR7 4EL — MB ChB 1998 Manch.; MB ChB Manch 1998.

DOWD, Ann Bernadette Department of Elderly Medicine, Queen Alexandra Hospital, Cosham, Portsmouth; 24 The Brow, Widley, Portsmouth — BM BS 1982 Nottm.; BMedSci Nottm. 1980; FRCP Lond. 1996; MRCP (UK) 1985. Cons. Geriat. Qu. Alexandra & St. Mary's Hosp. Portsmouth. Prev: Sen. Regist. (Med. Geriat.) Nether Edge Hosp. Sheff.; Regist. (Med.) Hope Hosp. Salford; SHO (Gen. Med.) Walsgrave Hosp. Coventry.

DOWD, Mr George Simon Edmund The Royal Free Hopsital, Pond Street, Hampstead, London NW3 2QG Tel: 020 7794 0500; Briery Hillsfield, Wayside, Cipperfield, Kings Langley WD4 9JJ — MD 1982 Liverp.; MB ChB 1971, MChOrth 1978; FRCS Eng. 1975. (Liverpool) Cons. Orthop. Surg. Roy. Free Hosp. Lond. Socs: Brit. Orthop. Res. Soc. & Brit. Orthop. Assn.; Brit. Assoc. Surg. Knee. I.S.A.K.O.S. Prev: Cons. Orthop. Surg. St. Bartholomews Hosp. Lond.; Sen. Lect. Inst. Orthop. Univ. Lond.; Hon. Cons. Roy. Nat. Orthop. Hosp. Lond.

DOWD, Hugo Denis Crossways, Chepstow Road, Langstone, Newport NP18 2LU — MB ChB BAO 1988 Belf.; FRCSI 1992.

DOWD, Mary Patricia 13B Pelham Crescent, The Park, Nottingham NG7 1AR — MB ChB 1990 Sheff. Sports Phys.GP Notts Forest FC & FA; Clin. Asst. (Rheum.). Socs: BASM; BMA; MRCGP.

DOWD, Professor Pauline Mary 152 Harley Street, London W1N 1HH Tel: 020 7935 0444 Fax: 020 7224 2574 — MB BS 1972 Lond.; MD Lond. 1984, BSc 1969; FRCP Lond. 1990; MRCP (UK) 1975; MRCS Eng. LRCP Lond. 1972. (Roy. Free) Cons. Dermat. Middlx. Hosp. Lond.; Prof (Dermat.) UCL Med. Sch. Socs: Fell. Roy. Soc. Med.; Fell. Amer. Acad. Dermat.; Brit. Assn. Dermat. Prev: Hon. Sen. Lect., Cons. & Sen. Regist. (Dermat.) St. John's Hosp. Dis. of Skin Lond.; Sen. Regist. Skin Dept. St. Bart. Hosp. Lond.

DOWD, Mr Timothy Clay North Riding Infirmary, Department of Ophthalmology, Newport Road, Middlesbrough TS1 5JE Tel: 01642 232323; Southend Cottage, Knayton, Thirsk YO7 4AS Tel: 01845 537002 Fax: 01845 537002 — MB BS 1979 Lond.; BSc (Hons.) Lond. 1976; FRCS Glas. 1985; MRCS Eng. LRCP Lond. 1979; FRCOphth 1989; DO Eng. 1985. (Guy's) Cons. Ophth. Surg. N. Riding Infirm. Middlesbrough. Socs: N. Eng. Ophth. Soc.; Amer. Acad. of Ophth.; Brit. Ophth. Anaesth. Soc. Prev: Sen. Regist. (Ophth.) N. RHA; Research Regist. Nuffield Laborat. Ophth. Oxf. Univ.; Ho. Off. (Ophth.) St. Bart. Hosp. Lond.

DOWDALL, James William — MB ChB 1969 Manch.; FFA RCS Eng. 1975. Cons. Anaesth. Stepping Hill Hosp. Stockport.

DOWDALL, Nigel Philip British Airways Health Services, Waterside (HMAG), PO Box 365, Harmondsworth UB7 0GB Tel: 020 8738 7707 Fax: 020 8738 7707 Email: nigel.1.dowdall@britishairways.com; Brambles, Cox Green, Rudgwick, Horsham RH12 3DE Tel: 01403 823713 Email: nigel.dowdall@quista.net — MB ChB 1981 Ed.; MSc (Occupat. Health) Aberd. 1994; MFOM RCP (UK) 1996, AFOM 1994; MRCGP 1987; DFFP 1993; DAvMed. FOM RCP Lond. 1990; DRCOG 1986. (Univ. Ed.) Sen. Cons. Occupat.al Phys. Socs: Soc. Occupat. Med.; Assn. Aviat. Med. Examrs. Hon. Sec.; Aerospace Med. Assn. Prev: Sen. Med. Off. RAF Kinloss.

DOWDALL, Thomas Gerard (retired) 20 Lisaclare Road, Stewartstown, Dungannon BT71 5AA Tel: 028 8773 8230 — MB BCh BAO NUI 1950.

DOWDELL, Mr John William Hallford House, Walton Lane, Shepperton TW17 8LQ Tel: 01932 243592 — MRCS Eng. LRCP Lond. 1966; FRCS Ed. 1980; MRCOG 1978. Cons. O & G Hillingdon & Mt. Vernon Hosps. NW Thames RHA; Hon. Cons. Hammersmith Hosp. Lond.

DOWDELL, Michael Pressley (retired) 42 Winsu Avenue, Paignton TQ3 1QF — MB BS 1957 Lond.; FFA RCS Eng. 1966; DA Eng. 1959.

DOWDEN, Neil c/o Applecross, 14 Eastern Way, Ponteland, Newcastle upon Tyne NE20 9PE — MB ChB 1985 Dundee; MRCGP 1991; DRCOG 1991; DGM RCP Lond. 1988; DCCH RCP Ed. 1988.

DOWDESWELL, Heather Janet The White House, Ridgeway Close, West Harptree, Bristol BS40 6EF — MB BS 1986 Lond.; BSc Lond. 1983. (St. Bart. Hosp. Med. Coll. Lond) GP Retainer Grange Rd. Surg. Bristol. Prev: Clin. Asst. (Psychiat.) Barrow Hosp. Bristol; Research Fell. (Psychol.) Univ. Exeter & (Neonat.) Heavitree Hosp. Exeter.

DOWDESWELL, Karen Ann, Surg. Lt.-Cdr. RN Renal Section, Imperial College School of Medicine, Hammersmith Hospital, Ducane Road, London W12 0HS Email: karen.dowdeswell@virgin.net; 467 Portswood Road, Southampton SO17 2TH — BM 1992 Soton.; MRCP(UK) 1998. (Soton.) Clin. Research. Regist. (Nephrol.) Hammersmith Hosp.

***DOWDING, Lynne** 15 Crosscombe Terrace, Cwm, Ebbw Vale NP23 7SP — MB BCh 1997 Wales.

DOWDLE, John Rhidian Harley, Llantwit Major Road, Cowbridge CF71 7JP — MB BChir 1970 Camb.; MA Camb. 1967; FRCP Lond. 1992. Cons. Phys. (Gen. Med. & Cardiol.) E. Glam. Gen. Hosp.

DOWELL, Anthony Charles Centre for Research in Primary Care, University of Leeds, 30/32 Hyde Terrace, Leeds LS2 9LN Tel: 0113 233 4835 Fax: 0113 233 4836; 4 Church Lane, Chapel Allerton, Leeds LS7 4LY — MB ChB 1975 Leeds; FRCGP 1993, M 1982; DTM & H Liverp. 1980. Dir. Centre for Research in Primary Care Leeds; GP Leeds; Sen. Lect. (Gen. Pract.) Leeds Univ. Prev: Med. Supt. Malosa Hosp., Malawi; GP Wainaiomata, New Zealand.

DOWELL, Christopher George Kilworth Road Health Centre, Kilworth Road, Husbands Bosworth, Lutterworth LE17 6JZ Tel: 01858 880522 Fax: 01858 575166; Audley End, Sulby, Northampton NN6 6EZ Tel: 01858 880364 — MRCS Eng. LRCP Lond. 1977; MA Oxf. 1977, MB BS Lond. 1977. (Oxf. & St. Bart.)

DOWELL, Ian Simon North Staffordshire Hospital, Obstetrics & Gynaecology Block, Stoke-on-Trent ST4 7PA — MB BS 1993 Lond.; BSc (Hons.) Lond. 1991. SHO (O & G) N. Staffs. Roy. Infirm. Prev: SHO (A & E) Jas. Paget Hosp. Gt. Yarmouth; Ho. Off. (Surg.) Middlx. Hosp.; Ho. Off. (Med.) Ipswich Hosp.

DOWELL, Jo David 18 Nairn Close, Arnold, Nottingham NG5 8QY Tel: 0115 967 1479; 13 Dartigton Way, Nuneaton CV11 4XL Tel: 01203 385202 — BM BS 1996 Nottm.; BMedSci Nottm. 1993. SHO Med. Geo. Elliot Hosp. NHS Trust. Socs: BMA. Prev: PRHO GenMed.) QMC, Nottm.; PRHO. Surg. & Orthop.) Wexham Pk. Hosp., Slough; SHO (A & E) Kings Mill Centre for Health Care, Mansfield.

DOWELL, Joanna Robson Hastings House, Kineton Road, Wellesbourne, Warwick CV35 9NF Tel: 01789 840245 Fax: 01789 470993; Hastings House, Wellesbourne, Warwick CV35 9NF Tel: 01789 840245 — MB ChB 1980 Birm.; MRCGP 1984; DRCOG 1983.

DOWELL, Mr John Keith Orthopaedic Department, King's College Hospital, Denmark Hill, London SE5 9RS Tel: 020 7326 3070 — MB BS 1977 Lond.; MB BS (Hons.) Lond. 1977; FRCS 1982. (Char. Cross) Sen. Regist. (Orthop.) King's Coll. Hosp. Lond. Prev: Regist. Ipswich Hosp.; SHO (Plastic Surg.) Qu. Vict. Hosp. E. Grinstead; Ho. Surg. & Ho. Phys. Char. Cross Hosp. Lond.

DOWELL, Jonathan Seymour Arnbathie Cottage, Pitroddie Road, Scone, Perth PH2 7PL — BM BS 1987 Nottm.; MRCGP 1992; DCH RCP Lond. 1991; DObst 1990. Clin. Research Fell. Univ. Dundee.

DOWELL, Mr Kenneth CARE at The Park, The Park hospital, Burnt Stump Country Park, Arnold, Nottingham Tel: 0115 967 1670 — MB ChB 1981 Leic.; DM Nottm. 1992; FRCS Ed. 1986; MRCOG 1988. Med. Dir. Care at the Pk. Arnold Nottm. (Centres for Assisted ReProduc.). Prev: Sen. Lect. & Hon. Cons. Asst. Gyn. QMC Nottm.f; Cons. Nurture IVF Unit & Clinic; Dir. NHS Fertil. Servs. QMC Nottm.

DOWELL, Ronald Craig Dalvennan Avenue Practice, 27 Dalvennan Avenue, Patna, Ayr KA6 7NA Tel: 01292 531367 Fax: 01292 531033; 41 Doonholm Road, Alloway, Ayr KA7 4QU Tel: 01292 442662 — MB ChB 1968 Glas.; BSc (Hons.) (Biochem.) Glas. 1965; MRCP (UK) 1972. (Glas.) GPS. Prev: Assoc. Adviser Ayrsh. & Wigtownship GP VTS.

DOWER, Frances Helen The Rothbury Practice, 3 Market Place, Rothbury, Morpeth NE65 7UW Tel: 01665 570388 Fax: 01669 620583 — MB BS 1969 Lond.; 1996 Dip. Counselling Scott. Inst. Human Relations Ed. (Westm.) p/t Princip. In Gen. Pract. Rothbury, N.umberland; Counsellor in Primary Care, Rothbury, N.d.. Prev: Clin. Asst. (Geriat.) Newc. Gen. Hosp.

DOWERS, Alexander David Townhead Health Centre, 16 Alexandra Parade, Glasgow G31 2ES Tel: 0141 531 8972 Fax: 0141 531 8980; 14 Kenmure Crescent, Bishopbriggs, Glasgow G64 2DN Tel: 0141 772 6872 — MB ChB 1982 Glas.; BSc Glas. 1979, MB ChB 1982; MRCGP 1986; DRCOG 1984. Prev: Trainee GP Glas. N. Dist. VTS.

DOWEY, Kathryn Elizabeth 6 Deramore Court, Belfast BT9 5JY — MB BCh BAO 1966 Belf.; MRCP (UK) 1976. (Belf.) Cons. A & E Dept. Belf. City Hosp.

DOWIE, Alexander Newton (retired) 6 Countess Gardens, Crieff PH7 3DP — MB ChB 1947 Glas. Prev: Ho. Phys. St. Mary Abbot's Hosp. Lond. & W.. Infirm. Glas.

DOWIE, Catherine Russell 11 Larch Place, Errol, Perth PH2 7UW — MB ChB 1949 Ed. (Ed.) Prev: Regist. Murray Roy. Hosp. Perth; Sen. Regist. Stratheden Hosp.; Regist. Bangour Village Hosp. Broxburn.

DOWLE, Alan Keith Doctor's House, Hillswick, Shetland — MRCS Eng. LRCP Lond. 1952. (Westm.)

DOWLE, Timothy Tel: 01243 837980 Fax: 01243 837982; 52 Victoria Drive, Bognor Regis PO21 2TF Tel: 01243 822648 — MB BS 1980 Lond. (St. Geo.) Hon. Med. Off. Bognor Rugby Football Club Hants. Avenue, Bognor Regis, W. Sussex. Prev: Clin. Asst. (c/o Elderly) Chichester HA.

DOWLER, Jean Bruce (retired) 12 The Grange, Hartford, Northwich CW8 1QJ Tel: 01606 74579 — MB ChB 1945 Manch. Prev: Mem. Pneumoconiosis Panel DHSS Manch.

DOWLER, Jenny Elizabeth 237 Winsley Road, Bradford-on-Avon BA15 1QS — BChir 1996 Camb.

DOWLER, Mr Jonathan George Frank Moorfields Eye Hospital, City Road, London EC1V 2PD Tel: 020 7566 2314 Fax: 020 7566 2972 — MB BS 1983 Lond.; FRCS Ed. 1989; FCOphth 1989; DO RCS Eng. 1987; MD (London) 2000. (St. Thos.) Cons. Ophth. Moorfields Eye Hosp. Socs: Macula Soc. Prev: Research Fell. (Retinal Diagn.) Moorfields Eye Hosp. Lond.; Cons. Ophth. Defence Med. Servs. Hosp. Haslar; Cons. Ophth. Camb. Milit. Hosp.

DOWLER, Sally Anne Morris House Surgery, Waltheof Gardens, Tottenham, London N17 7EB Tel: 020 8801 1277 Fax: 020 8801 8228 — MB ChB 1989 Stellenbosch.

***DOWLEY, Andrew Campbell** 5 Park Grove, Far Headingly, Leeds LS6 4BD — MB ChB 1995 Sheff.

DOWLEY, Sophia Penelope Marianne New Road Surgery, 46 New Road, Bromsgrove B60 2JS Tel: 01527 872027 Fax: 01527 574516 — MB ChB 1988 Birm.; MRCGP 1994; DFFP 1995; DRCOG 1991. Prev: Trainee GP BromsGr. & Redditch HA.

DOWLEY, William Giles Henry New Road Surgery, 46 New Road, Bromsgrove B60 2JS Tel: 01527 872027 Fax: 01527 574516 — MB ChB 1988 Birm.; MRCGP 1994; DRCOG 1993; DGM RCP Lond. 1991. (Birmingham) GP Princip.

DOWLING, Alexander (retired) Stafford House, 1 All Saints Road, Clifton, Bristol BS8 2JG — MB ChB 1945 Manch. Prev: Ho. Surg. Ho. Phys. & Gyn. Ho. Surg. Preston Roy. Infirm.

DOWLING, Mr Brian Leslie (retired) Box Cottage, Box, Stroud GL6 9HB — MB BS 1959 Lond.; MS Lond. 1970; FRCS Eng. 1964. Prev: Cons. Gen. Surg. N.ampton Gen. Hosp.

DOWLING, Christopher John 28 Robinson's Croft, Boughton Heath, Chester CH3 5YB — MB ChB 1980 Liverp.; FCAnaesth 1989; FRCA 1989. Cons. anaesth. Wrexham matelor hosp.

DOWLING, Clare Josephine 245 Brantingham Road, Manchester M21 0TP — MB ChB 1991 Manch.

DOWLING, Cornelius (retired) The Health Centre, Burnage Avenue, Clock Face, St Helens Tel: 01744 813425 — MB BCh BAO 1945 NUI. Prev: Ho. Surg. Providence Hosp. St. Helens.

DOWLING, Edmund John (retired) 2 St Cuthberts Court, 26 Church Road, Lytham, Lytham St Annes FY8 5LN — MRCS Eng. LRCP Lond. 1945; MA, MB BChir Camb. 1948. Prev: PMO DHSS.

DOWLING, Elizabeth 2 St Cuthberts Court, 26 Church Road, Lytham, Lytham St Annes FY8 5LN — MB ChB 1947 Liverp.

DOWLING, Fintan Mary 4 Elm Park, Gonalston Lane, Epperstone, Nottingham NG14 6BE — MB BCh BAO 1959 NUI.

DOWLING, Gracie Carmine Victoria The Surgery, Stock Hill, Biggin Hill, Westerham TN16 3TJ Tel: 01959 573352 Fax: 01959 570785; 7 Tower Road, Orpington BR6 0SG Tel: 01689 24823 — LRCPI & LM, LRSCI & LM 1962; LRCPI & LM, LRCSI & LM 1962; DA Eng. 1965.

DOWLING, Jonathan More The Surgery, Ivy Court, Tenterden TN30 6RB Tel: 01580 763666/764022 Fax: 01580 766199 — MB BS 1980 Lond.; MA Oxf. 1981; MSc Lond. 1985, MB BS Lond. 1980; MRCP (UK) 1983; MRCGP 1987; DRCOG 1988. Prev: Lect. (Med. Microbiol.) Lond. Hosp.; SHO (Gen. Med.) MusGr. Pk. Hosp. Taunton.

DOWLING, Karen Angela 24 New Street, Troon, Camborne TR14 9EW Tel: 01209 718541 — MB BCh 1995 Wales. (Wales) SHO (O & G) Salisbury; GP VTS Salisbury Dist. Hosp. Socs: BMA. Prev: SHO (Elderly Care) SDU; SHO (Ear, Nose & Throat & Opthalmology) SDH; SHO (A & E) Roy. Hants. Co. Hosp.

DOWLING, Marcella The Surgery, 10 Corfton Road, Ealing, London W5 2HS Tel: 020 8997 4215; 58 Cleveland Road, Ealing, London W13 8AJ Tel: 020 8991 2862 — MB BCh BAO 1974 Dub.; FFR RCSI Radiother. & Oncol. Dub. 1985. (Trinity College Dublin) p/t GP.

DOWLING, Maurice Adrian Furnace House Surgery, St. Andrews Road, Carmarthen SA31 1EX Tel: 01267 236616 Fax: 01267 222673; Dan y Cerrig, Peniel, Carmarthen SA32 7HX Tel: 01267 253411 Email: mdowlingwa@aol.com — MB BCh BAO 1988 NUI; MRCGP 1992; DCH RCP Lond. 1991. (Univ. Coll. Cork)

DOWLING, Michael Francis The New Surgery, River Street, Mevagissey, St Austell PL26 6UE Tel: 01726 843701 Fax: 01726 842565 — MB BS 1989 Lond. Trainee GP Oxf. John Radcliffe Scheme. Prev: Ho. Off. (Cardiol. & Chest Med.) St. Bart. Hosp. Lond.; Ho. Off. (ENT & Gen. Surg.) Wycombe Gen. Hosp.

DOWLING, Nicola Jane 4F1 28 Warrender Park Terrace, Marchmont, Edinburgh EH9 1EE; 164 Rudston Road, Childwall, Liverpool L16 4PJ Tel: 0151 722 1535 — MB ChB 1996 Ed.; BSc (Hons. Neurosci.) Ed. 1993. SHO (Paediat.) Stirling Roy. Infirm. Stirling. Prev: SHO (A & E) Glas. Roy. Infirm.

DOWLING, Olivia Mary Teresa 81B Bradbourne Park Road, Sevenoaks TN13 3LQ Tel: 01732 742201 — MB BCh 1950 Witwatersrand. Prev: Med. Off. Addington Hosp. & Union Health Dept.

DOWLING, Pauline 28 Robinson Croft, Caldy Valley Road, Boughton Heath, Chester CH3 5YB — MB ChB 1980 Liverp.

DOWLING, Professor Robert Hermon Gastroenterology Unit, GKT School of Med, 4th Floor N Wing, St Thomas's Hospitals, London SE1 7EH Tel: 020 7922 8008 Fax: 020 7928 4458 Email: h.dowling@umds.ac.uk; 16 Clarence Road, Kew Gardens, Richmond TW9 3NL Tel: 020 8940 3139 Email: h.dowling@talk21.com — MB BCh BAO 1959 Belfast; MD 1968 Belfast; FRCP 1974 London. (Queens Univ.Belfast) Emerit. Prof. Gastroenterol. GKT Sch. of Med.; Emerit. Cons. Phys. Sch. of Med., King's Coll. Lond., Guy's and St. Thomas' NHS Hosp. Trust. Socs: (Pres.) Digestive Disorders Foundat.; (Ex. Sec. & Pres.) Europ. Soc. Clin. Investig.; (Counc. & Past Pres.) Brit. Soc. Gastroenterol. Prev: Lect. (Med.) & Dep. Dir. MRC Intestinal Malabsorp Gp. Roy. Postgrad. Med. Sch. Lond.; Cons. Phys. Hammersmith Hosp.; MRC Research Fell. & Sen. Research Assoc. Boston Univ. Med. Centre, USA.

DOWLING, Robert Mitchell Brian Tidnor Mill, Lugwardine, Hereford HR1 4AS Tel: 01432 850359 — MB BS 1961 Lond.; DObst RCOG 1963; FFA RCS Eng. (Nuffield Prize) 1965. (Lond.

Hosp.) p/t Cons. Anaesth. Hereford Gp. Hosps. Prev: Sen. Regist. (Anaesth.) Whittington Hosp. Lond.; Regist. (Anaesth.) Hosp. Sick Childr. Gt. Ormond St.; Regist. (Anaesth.) Lond. Hosp. Whitechapel.

DOWLING, Sarah Elizabeth Maltings Surgery, 8 Victoria Street, St Albans AL1 3JB Tel: 01727 855500 Fax: 01727 845537 — MB ChB 1989 Leeds; BSc Chem. Path. Leeds 1986; MRCP (UK) 1993; MRCGP 1995. GP Princip., The Maltings Surg., St. Albans. Socs: The St. Albans Young Princip.'s Gp. Prev: Trainee GP Priory Med. Centre Liverp.

DOWLING, Susan Felicity Osmond Department of Postgraduate Medical Education, Academic Centre, Freeday Hospital, Bristol BS16 1LE Tel: 01179 757054 Fax: 01179 757060; 28 Kingsdown Parade, Bristol BS6 5UF — MB BS Lond. 1970; MSc (Soc. Med.) Lond. 1978, BSc 1967; MRCS Eng. LRCP Lond. 1970; MFCM 1978. (Guy's) Assoc. Med. Postgrad. Dean; Hon. Sen. Lect. Pub. Health Med. Univ. of Bristol. Prev: Cons. & Sen. Lect. (Pub. Health Med.) Univ. Bristol; Sen. Research Fell. Centre for Social Managem. SAUS Univ. Bristol; Lect. (Community Med.) Univ. Bristol.

DOWLING, Susan Philippa 17 Church Road, Longlevens, Gloucester GL2 0AJ — MB BS 1997 Lond.

DOWLING, Timothy Ian Davaar medical Centre, 20 Concord Way, Dukinfield SK16 4DB Tel: 0161 343 6382 Fax: 0161 330 7326 — MB ChB 1993 Manch.; MA Oxf. 1986. GP.

DOWMAN, Christopher George, RD Ballacoar, Eleanora Drive, Douglas IM2 3NN Tel: 01624 25971 — MB BS 1970 Lond.; MA Camb. 1965; MRCP (UK) 1974; MRCS Eng. LRCP Lond. 1970; AFOM RCP Lond. 1978.

DOWN, Andrew Gerald Tawstock Medical Centre, 7 High Street, Chard TA20 1QF Tel: 01460 67763 Fax: 01460 66044 — MB BS 1985 Lond.; MRCGP 1990; DRCOG 1989. Prev: Trainee GP N. Devon Dist. Hosp. Barnstaple; SHO (O & G) Hillingdon Hosp. Uxbridge; Ho. Off. (Surg.) N. Devon Dist. Hosp. Barnstaple.

DOWN, Eric Ronald Mid-Cheshire Homeopathic Group, 2 Watling Street, Northwich CW9 5EX Tel: 01606 42445; Tall Trees, 221 London Road, Leftwich, Northwich CW9 8AN Tel: 01606 43098 — MB ChB 1976 Manch.; MRCGP 1982; DRCOG 1982.

DOWN, James Fraser 21A Oval Road, London NW1 7EA — MB ChB 1994 Bristol.

DOWN, Mark William Fraser 62 Fentiman Road, London SW8 1LF — MB BS 1994 Lond.

DOWN, Nicholas Adrian Collett Oxshott Medical Centre, Holtwood Road, Oxshott, Leatherhead KT22 0QJ Tel: 01372 844000 — MB BS 1980 Lond.; MRCGP 1986; DRCOG 1984. (Lond. Hosp.)

DOWN, Peter Fraser Broadwey House, Watery Lane, Broadwey, Weymouth DT3 5QD Tel: 01305 812069; Dorset County Hospital, Williams Avenue, Dorchester DT1 1TS Tel: 01305 255574 — DHMSA 1997; MB BS Lond. 1963; FRCP Lond. 1980, M 1969. (St. Thos.) Cons. Phys. W. Dorset Gp. Hosps. Socs: Brit. Soc. Gastroenterol. & Med. Research Soc.; Hon. Archiv. Brit. Soc. Gastroenterol. Prev: Sen. Regist. Prof. Med. Unit Dundee Roy. Infirm.; Med. Regist. Wessex Regional Renal Unit Portsmouth; Res. Med. Off. Roy. Devon & Exeter Hosp.

DOWN, Ruth Clare Elisabeth Garden Flat 12 Caledonia Pl, Bristol BS8 4DJ — MB ChB 1997 Bristol.

DOWN, Sue Kim 355 Birmingham Road, Sutton Coldfield B72 1DL — MB ChB 1998 Manch.; MB ChB Manch 1998; BSc (Hons) Biomed Sci (1995) Manch. Sho Withington Hosp. Manch. Prev: PRHO Surg. Christie Hosp. Manch./Withenshawe Hosp. Manch.; PRHO Withington Hosp. Manch.

DOWNER, Janet Patricia 22 Mount Park Crescent, London W5 2RN — MB ChB 1974 Bristol; FFA RCS Eng. 1980; DRCOG 1977. Sen. Regist. (Anaesth.) Lond. Hosp. Whitechapel. Prev: Regist. (Anaesth.) Hosp. Sick Childr. Lond.; Regist. (Anaesth.) W.m. Hosp. Lond.

DOWNES, Alice Jane 3 Water Bag Bank, Knaresborough HG5 9AD — MB BS 1993 Newc.

DOWNES, Anthony James Spindlewood, Fron Bache, Llangollen LL20 7BW Email: tony.downes@virgin.net — MB ChB 1990 Birm.; ChB Birm. 1990; DRCOG 1993; DFFP 1993; MRCGP 1995; BDS Birm. 1982; LDSRCS 1982. (Birmingham) Non-Princip. Gen. Med. Practitioner, Dent. Practitioner; Non-Princip. Educat. Facilitator N. Wales. Socs: N. Wales CMC; Nat. Assn. Non-Princip. GP's; N. Wales Fac. RCGP.

DOWNES, Mrs Barbara Bolton Hospice, Queens Park St., off Chorley New Road, Bolton BL1 4QT Tel: 01204 364375 Fax: 01204 373163 Email: medic@boltonhospice.org; 1A Rydal Road, Heaton, Bolton BL1 5LQ Tel: 01204 841001 — MB BS 1981 Newc.; MA Camb. 1985, BA 1978; MRCGP 1985; Dip. Palliat. Med. Wales 1994; DCCH RCGP & FCM 1984; DRCOG 1983. Med. Dir. Bolton Hospice & Cons. Palliat. Care Bolton Hosps. Trust. Socs: Assn. for Palliat. Med. Prev: Clin. Asst. St. Oswalds Hospice Newc.; Med. Off. MRC Dunn Nutrit. Unit Keneba, The Gambia.

DOWNES, Catherine Mary 23 Eggbuckland Road, Plymouth PL3 5HF — MB ChB 1975 Birm.

DOWNES, Mr Edward Malcolm 128 Swansea Road, Pontlliw, Swansea SA4 4HQ — MB BCh 1967 Wales; FRCS Eng. 1972. (Cardiff) Cons. Orthop. Surg. Morriston Hosp. Socs: Fell. Brit. Orthop. Assn.; Hosp. Cons. & Specialists Assn.

DOWNES, Ellis George Robert Department of Obstetrics & Gynaecology, Chase Farm Hopsital, The Ridgeway, Enfield EN2 8JL Tel: 0208 366 6600 Ext: 5252 Fax: 0208 364 6331 Email: ellis@ellisd.demon.co.uk; Fax: 01707 655943 Email: ellis@ellisd.demon.co.uk — MB ChB 1989 Leic.; MRCOG 1994. Sen. Regist. & Lect. (O & G) Leeds Gen. Infirm. Socs: Brit. Gyn. Endoscopy Soc. (Trustee); Internat. Gyn. Endoscopy Soc.; Internat. Continence Soc. Prev: Regist. (O & G) City Hosp. Nottm.; Clin. Research Assoc. (O & G) Univ. Leics.; SHO (O & G) City Hosp. Nottm.

DOWNES, Gerald West (retired) 2 Upton Close, Norwich NR4 7PD Tel: 01603 458107 — MB BS 1947 Lond.; MRCS Eng. LRCP Lond. 1942. Prev: Ho. Phys. (Childr.) Guy's Hosp. Lond.

DOWNES, Joseph 228 Todmorden Road, Burnley BB11 3EZ Tel: 01282 24157 — MB BS 1954 Lond. (Westm.)

DOWNES, Mark Oliver The Treasury Farmhouse, The Street, Ickham, Canterbury CT3 1QN Tel: 01227 720107 — MB BS 1973 Lond.; MRCS Eng. LRCP Lond. 1973; FRCR 1978; DMRD Eng. 1977. (St. Mary's) Cons. Radiol. Kent & Canterbury Hosp. Prev: Sen. Regist. & Regist. W.m. Hosp. Lond.; Ho. Off. St. Mary's Hosp. Lond.

DOWNES, Michael Kevin The Surgery, Kingsmount Medical Centre, 444 Kingstanding Road, Kingstanding, Birmingham B44 9SA Tel: 0121 373 1734 Fax: 0121 377 8292 — MB ChB 1985 Birm.; DRCOG 1989. Prev: SHO (A & E) Selly Oak Hosp. Birm.; SHO (O & G & Geriat.) Dudley Rd. Hosp. Birm.; SHO (Paediat.) Wordsley Hosp. Dudley.

DOWNES, Nigel Malcolm Littlewick Medical Centre, 42 Nottingham Road, Ilkeston DE7 5PR Tel: 0115 932 5229 Fax: 0115 932 5413 — MB ChB 1983 Sheff. Med. Off. Ilkeston Community Hosp. Prev: SHO (Paediat.) Good Hope Hosp. Sutton Coldfield; SHO (O & G) Marston Green Hosp. Birm.; SHO (Orthop. Surg. & A & E) N.. Gen. Hosp. Sheff.

DOWNES, Peter William Edward (retired) 78 Hyatt's Wood Road, Backwell, Bristol BS48 3DB Tel: 01275 472305 — MB ChB Bristol 1953; DO Eng. 1960. Prev: GP Bristol.

DOWNES, Philip Gerard Cockburn Tyrrells Ride, Burley, Ringwood BH24 4DA — MB BS 1992 Lond.

DOWNES, Mr Richard Nicholas 66 Beeston Fields Drive, Bramcote, Nottingham NG9 3DD Tel: 0115 925 8095 — MB BS 1976 Lond.; BSc (Hons.) Lond. 1973, MB BS 1976; FRCS Ed. 1985; FCOphth 1988; DO RCS Eng. 1983. Cons. Ophth. Surg. Qu. Med. Centre Univ. Hosp. Nottm.

DOWNES, Robert Maxwell Mary Sheridan Centre, Leigh Infirmary, The Avenue, Leigh WN7 1HS Tel: 01942 264170 Fax: 01942 264176; 1A Rydal Road, Heaton, Bolton BL1 5LQ Tel: 01204 841001 — MB BS 1981 Newc.; MA Camb. 1985, BA 1977; FRCP Lond. 1997; MRCP (UK) 1985. Cons. Paediat. Community Child Health Wigan & Leigh Health Servs. NHS Trust. Prev: Sen. Regist. (Community Paediat.) N. Tyneside HA; Resid. Paediat. MRC Dunn Nutrit. Unit Keneba, The Gambia.

DOWNES, Susan Melissa 41 Skip Lane, Walsall WS5 3LW Email: susan.downes@opthalmology.oxford.ac.uk — MB ChB 1986 Bristol; FRCOphth 1991; MD 2000. (Bristol) Cons. Ophth. Surg. Oxf. Eye Hosp. Socs: BMA. Prev: Fell. Med.Retina. Moorfields Eye Hosp.

DOWNES, Thomas William 4 Cobden Terrace, Sheffield S10 1HN; 18 Leyfield Road, Dore, Sheffield S17 3EE Tel: 0114 236 1374 Email: tomdownes@bigfoot.com — MB BS 1993 Lond.; MRCP 1998. Specialist Regist., N.ern Gen. Hosp., Sheff. Socs: Brit.Geriat..Soc.

DOWNES, Veronica Bridget 39 Monkmoon Road, Shrewsbury SY2 5AH — MB BCh BAO 1991 NUI.

DOWNEY, Alison Christine 10 Moorfield, Banbridge BT32 4DE — MB ChB 1991 Manch.

DOWNEY, Anthony Woodland Surgery, Trelawney Road, Falmouth TR11 3GP Tel: 01326 312091 Fax: 01326 311260 — MB ChB 1989 Leeds; Dip. Ther. Newc. 1995; DRCOG 1991. (Leeds)

DOWNEY, Brendan Gerard Springfield Road Surgery, 26 Springfield Road, Belfast BT12 7AG — MB BCh BAO 1983 Belf.

DOWNEY, Damian Gerard 17 Townview Avenue, Omagh BT78 1HT — MB BCh BAO 1993 Belf.; MRCP 1997. Research Fell. (Resp. Med.) Belf. City Hosp.

DOWNEY, Katherine Sarah Woodland Surgery, Trelawney Road, Falmouth TR11 3GP Tel: 01326 312091 Fax: 01326 311260 — MB ChB 1989 Leeds; DFFP.

DOWNEY, Miss Louise Mary 178 Hull Road, York YO10 3LF — MB ChB 1993 Manch. Specialist Regist. Ophth. Socs: FRCOphth.

DOWNEY, Mr Martin Graham 15 Bellshaugh Lane, Kelvinside, Glasgow G12 0PE — MB ChB 1992 Glas.; FRCS Ed. 1996. (Glas.) Research Fell. (Gen. Surg.). Socs: Hon. Life Mem. Glas. Univ. M-C Soc. Prev: SHO III (Gen. Surg.) Law Hosp. Carluke; SHO III (Gen. Surg.) Glas. Roy. Infirm.

DOWNEY, Martin Paul c/o 1 Greenan Shaws Road, Belfast BT11 8LU — MB BCh BAO 1989 Belf.

DOWNEY, Michael Foster 42 Old School Close, Codicote, Hitchin SG4 8YJ — MB BChir 1951 Camb.; MA Camb. 1951. (Camb. & St. Bart.) Prev: O & G Ho. Surg. N. Herts. & S. Beds. Hosp.; Ho. Phys. & Ho. Surg. Lister Hosp. Hitchin; Flight Lt. RAF.

DOWNEY, Niall John 4 Belmont Drive, Derry, Londonderry BT48 7RP — MB BCh BAO 1993 Dub.

DOWNEY, Paul 12 Woodbridge close, Appleton, Warrington WA4 5RD Email: pd250262@aol.com — MB BCh BAO 1986 Belf.; FRCSI 1993; FRCS (urol) 2000; MD July 1999 (QUB). (Queen's Univ. Belf.) Cons. Socs: Assoc. Mem. Brit. Assn. Urol. Surgs.; BAGS Sect. of Endocrinol. Prev: Specialist Regist. (urological Surg.); Endocrinoloyg Fell.

DOWNEY, Paul Francis Pendeen Surgery, Kent Avenue, Ross-on-Wye HR9 5AL Tel: 01989 763535 Fax: 01989 768288; Orchard House, Fernbank Road, Ross-on-Wye HR9 5PP — MB ChB 1982 Liverp.; MRCGP 1986; DCH RCP Lond. 1986; DRCOG 1984. GP Tutor Hereford.

DOWNEY, Sarah Elizabeth Department of Surgery, Research & Teaching Building, Withington Hospital, Nell Lane, Manchester M20 2LR — BM BS 1989 Nottm.; FRCS Eng. 1994; FRCS Ed. 1994. Clin. Research Fell. Withington Hosp. Manch.

DOWNEY, William Raphael Hugh, OStJ Anvil Lodge, 37 High St., Waddesdon, Aylesbury HP18 0JB Tel: 01296 651601 — MB BCh BAO 1954 NUI; FRCP Lond. 1982, M 1969; DCH Eng. 1974. Clin. Asst. (Cardiol.) Middlx. Hosp. Lond. Prev: Ho. Phys. & Ho. Surg. Mater Miser. Hosp. Dub.; Resid. Rotat. St. Joseph's Hosp. Reading, USA.

DOWNHAM, Peter Andrew (retired) 11 Norwood Avenue, Southport PR9 7EG — MB ChB 1972 Manch.; DRCOG 1974. Hon. Sec. Qu.sCt. Hospice, S.port.

DOWNIE, (Agnes) Pauline 2 Cheadle Road, Cheadle SK8 1HR — MB ChB 1945 Glas.; TDD Wales 1947, CPH 1947; Assoc. Fac. Occupat. Med. RCP Lond. 1978. Socs: BMA. Prev: Asst. Chest Phys. Lanarksh. CC & NW Metrop. RHB; Asst. Phys. Stud. Health Serv. Univ. Manch.

DOWNIE, Aileen Jean 63 Binghill Road W., Milltimber AB13 0JB Tel: 01224 733406 — MB ChB 1966 Aberd. Cons. Venereol. Aberd. Roy. Infirm.

DOWNIE, Alan Robert The Consulting Rooms, 21 Neilston Road, Paisley PA2 6LW Tel: 0141 889 5277 Fax: 0141 848 5500 — MB ChB 1978 Glas.; MRCGP 1983; DRCOG 1980; Cert. Gen. Av. Med. 1983. Partner; Clin. Asst., Depart of Med. for the Elderly, S. Glas. Univ. Hosps. NHS Trust, Glas.; Aviat. Med. Examr., Civil Aviat. Auth., Paisley. Socs: Scott. Assn. Authorised Med. Examrs.

DOWNIE, Allan Watson (retired) Old Logie Cottage, Pitcaple, Inverurie AB51 5EE Tel: 0146 76 681 315 — MB ChB 1946 Aberd.; FRCP Lond. 1972. M 1951. Prev: Sen. Lect. (Med.) Med. Sch. Aberd.

DOWNIE, Andrew Campbell Department of Radiology, The Victoria Infirmary, Langside Road, Glasgow G42 9TY Tel: 0141 201 5550 Fax: 0141 201 5497 Email: andrew.downie@gvic.scot.nhs.uk; 52 Marywood Square, Strathbungo, Glasgow G41 2BJ Email: andrew@adownie.demon.co.uk — MB BS 1986 Lond.; BSc Lond. 1983; MRCP (UK) 1990; FRCR 1994. (Lond. Hosp. Med. Coll.) Cons. Interven.al Radiol. The Vict. Infirm. Glas. Prev: Sen. Regist. (Radiol.) Guy's & St. Thos. Hosp. Lond.; Clin. Fell. Vancouver Hosp. & Health Sci.s Centre, Canada.

DOWNIE, Anthea Catherine Family Planning Centre, 2 Claremont Terrace, Glasgow G3 7XR Tel: 0141 211 8130; 9 Riverview Drive, The Waterfront, Glasgow G5 8ER Tel: 0141 429 0747 — MB ChB Glas. 1964.

DOWNIE, Archibald Consultant Occupational Health, Cranley, 60 Albert Road, Dumfries DG2 9DC Tel: 01387 257478; Cranley, 60 Albert Road, Dumfries DG2 9DC Tel: 01387 257478 — MB ChB 1958 Glas.; MSc Lond. 1978; FFOM RCPI 1992; FFOM RCP Lond. 1991, M 1980; T(OM) 1991; DIH 1977. Hon. Clin. Sen. Lect. (Occupat. Health) Glas. Univ.; Hon. Med. Off. Qu. of the S. FC; Tutor Manch. Univ. Distance Learning Progr. Socs: Soc. Occupat. Med.; St. Andrews Ambul. Assn. Dumfries & Galloway Area - Vice Chairm. Prev: Corporate Med. Director N.. Telecom Ltd.; Phys. (Occupat. Health) Esso Petroleum Co. Ltd.; GP Drummore.

DOWNIE, Catherine Jean Langside Priory Hospital, 38 Mansion House Road, Glasgow G41 3DW Tel: 0141 636 6116 Fax: 0141 636 5151 — MB ChB 1977 Glas.; MRCPsych. Glas. 1983. Cons. (Psychiat.) & Dep. Med. Dir. Langside Priory Hosp. Glas. Prev: Cons. (Psychiat.) Pk.head Hosp. Glas.

DOWNIE, Cecilia Helen The Lomond Practice, Napier Road, Glenrothes KY6 1HL Tel: 01592 611000 Fax: 01592 611639 — MB ChB 1961 Aberd.; T(GP) 1991. (Aberd.) Socs: Fell. Roy. Soc. Med.; BMA.

DOWNIE, Colin James Campbell 138 Newbridge Road, Bath BA1 3LD — MB ChB 1981 Manch. Staff Grade (Paediat.) Roy. United Hosp. Bath. Prev: Staff Grade (Paediat.) Bone Marrow Transpl. Unit W.m. Childr. Hosp. Lond.; Resid. Med. Off. (Paediat.) Portland Hosp. for Wom. & Childr. Lond.; Regist. (Paediat.) Walsgrave Hosp. Coventry.

DOWNIE, Fiona Barbara Bishopton Health Centre, Greenock Road, Bishopton PA7 5AW Tel: 01505 863223 Fax: 01505 862798; 49 St. Andrews Drive, Bridge of Weir PA11 3HU — MB ChB 1979 Glas.; DRCOG 1981.

DOWNIE, Frank David Holmes 22 Parkneuk, Dunfermline KY12 9BD — MB ChB 1987 Dundee.

DOWNIE, Ian Peter 11 St Ann Street, Salisbury SP1 2DP — BM 1992 Soton.; BDS Liverp. 1983.

DOWNIE, Janet Fiona Mayfield, 1 Clydeview, Dumbarton G82 4AG — MB ChB 1979 Glas.; DRCOG 1982.

DOWNIE, Malcolm Campbell Pipers Meadow, Okehampton EX20 3JT; Grudgeworthy, Monkokehampton, Winkleigh EX19 8RY Tel: 01837 810774 Fax: 01837 810876 — MB BS 1981 Lond. (Lond. Hosp.)

DOWNIE, Paul Leonard Orchard House Surgery, Bleak Road, Lydd, Romney Marsh TN29 9AE Tel: 01797 320307 — MRCS Eng. LRCP Lond. 1978; MRCGP 1984; DRCOG 1982; Cert. Family Plann. JCC 1980. (King's Coll. Hosp.) Clin. Asst. (Gen. Med.) Roy. Vict. Hosp. Folkestone. Socs: Brit. Soc. Med. & Dent. Hypn. Prev: SHO (O & G) Ashford Hosp. Middlx.; SHO (Paediat. Surg.) Roy. Alexandra Hosp. Brighton; Ho. Off. Cuckfield Hosp.

DOWNIE, Paul Mackenzie 39 Savernake Road, London NW3 2JU — MB BS 1996 Lond.

DOWNIE, Robert Gavin Meadows Medical Practice, 9 Brougham Place, Edinburgh EH3 9HW Tel: 0131 229 7709; 8 Sylvan Place, Edinburgh EH9 1LH Tel: 0131 667 2138 — MB ChB 1983 Ed. Princip., Gen. Pract. Prev: Trainee GP Bonnyrigg Health Centre; Regist. Med. Off. ChristCh., NZ; SHO (Med. Paediat.) Roy. Hosp. for Sick Childr. Edin.

DOWNIE, Mr Robin John Gordon (retired) Redcot, 78 Warren Road, Blundellsands, Liverpool L23 6UG Tel: 0151 924 7663 — MB ChB 1954 Liverp.; FRCS Eng. 1961. Chairm. Woodlands Hospice Charitable Trust. Prev: Cons. Surg. Walton & Fazakerley Hosps.

DOWNIE, Roy Wilfrid (retired) 30 The Sanctuary, Green Lane, Morden SM4 5NX Tel: 020 8648 1800 — MB ChB 1950 Ed. Prev: Resid. Phys. Roy. Infirm. Edin.

DOWNIE, Sheila Elizabeth Morven, Union St., Coupar Angus, Blairgowrie PH13 9AE Tel: 01828 627217 — MB ChB 1974 Ed. Staff Grade Paediat. (Community) Drumhar Health Centre Perth; Clin. Asst. (Child & Family Psychiat.) Murray Roy. Hosp. Perth.

DOWNIE, Timothy John 19 Upper Crofts, Alloway, Ayr KA7 4QX Tel: 01292 443785 — MB ChB 1980 Aberd.; FFA RCS Eng. 1986. Prev: Regist. (Anaesth.) Nottm.; SHO (Anaesth.) Wycombe Gen. Hosp. High Wycombe; SHO (Anaesth.) S.mead Hosp. Bristol.

DOWNIE, Mr William Antony Longlands, 170 Swinston Hill Road, Dinnington, Sheffield S25 2SB — MB ChB 1954 Liverp.; FFAEM 1993; FRCS Ed. 1967. (Liverp.) Emerit. Cons. Surg. Gen. Surg. & A & E Bassetlaw Dist. Hosp. Worksop. Prev: Specialist Surg. MoH, Libya; Sen. Regist. (Gen. Surg.) Gen. Hosp. St. Helier, Jersey; Regist. (Gen. Surg.) Vict. Hosp. Swindon.

DOWNING, Christopher 6 Clipston Avenue, Leeds LS6 4AR — MB ChB 1995 Leeds; BSc (Hons.) Leeds 1992.

DOWNING, Helen Mary The Vine Medical Centre, 166 Tonbridge Road, Maidstone ME16 8SS Tel: 01622 754898 Fax: 01622 751611 — MB ChB 1979 Sheff.; MRCGP (Distinc.) 1983; DCH RCP Lond. 1985; DRCOG 1983. (Sheffield) GP Maidstone. Prev: Trainee GP Boston VTS; SHO (Paediat. & Accid.& Emerg.) Sheff. HA; Ho. Phys. & Ho. Surg. Sheff. AHA.

DOWNING, Hilary Ann 12 Glynhir Road, Pontardulais, Swansea SA4 1LY — MB BS 1984 Lond.; FRCA. 1991. Cons. Anaesth. King's Coll. Hosp. Lond. Prev: Sen. Regist., Lect. & Regist. (Anaesth.) King's Coll. Hosp. Lond.; SHO (Anaesth.) St. Bart. Hosp. Lond.

DOWNING, Jane Ann The Health Centre, Chepstow Road, Raglan NP15 2EN Tel: 01291 690222 Fax: 01291 690096; Holowun, Usk Road, Raglan NP15 2HJ — MB BCh Wales 1990; BSc (Anat.) Wales 1987; MRCGP 1995; DRCOG 1994; DCH RCP Lond. 1993. (University of Wales College of Medicine) Gen. Practitioner, Raglan Health centre.

DOWNING, Mark Peter Richard Rohais and Anns Place Medical Practice, Rohais, St Peter Port, Guernsey Tel: 01481 723322 Fax: 01481 725200; Les Vielles Saline, Rue De Bas, L' Islet, St Sampsons, Guernsey GY2 4FN — MB BS 1982 Lond.; DCH RCP Lond. 1986; Cert. Family Plann. JCC 1986; DRCOG 1985. (Westm.)

DOWNING, Michael Edward Nalder Hillfields Health Centre, 1 Howard Street, Coventry CV1 4GH Tel: 024 7622 0661 Fax: 024 7622 8300; The Old School House, 99 Birmingham Road, Allesley Village, Coventry CV5 9GT — MB ChB 1977 Birm.; Dip Occ Med 1998; DRCOG 1983. (Birmingham) GP Princip.; Occupat. Health Dr. Walsgrave NHS Trust Coventry. Prev: Maj. RAMC.

DOWNING, Mr Nicholas David 4 Oakfield Mews, Cyprus Road, Mapperley Park, Nottingham NG3 5EB Email: ndowning@doctors.org.uk; 51 Ferriby Road, Hessle, Hull HU13 OHS Tel: 0115 985 6553 — BM BCh 1989 Oxf.; FRCS (Tr. And Orth.) 1999; MA Camb. 1989; FRCS Eng. 1993. Career Regist. Rotat. (Orthop.) Mid Trent. Socs: Assoc. Mem., Brit. Soc. for Surg. of the Hand. Prev: Hand Fell., Roy. N. Shore Hosp., Sydney, Australia; Hand Fell., Qu.s Med. Centre, Nottm.

DOWNING, Nicholas Peter Damien Nutrition Associates, Galtres House, Lysander Close, Clifton Moor Gate, York YO30 4XB Tel: 01904 691591 Fax: 01904 690588 Email: ddowning@iname.com; Biolab Medical Unit, The Stone House, Weymouth St, London W1W 6DB Tel: 020 7636 5959 Fax: 020 7580 3910 — MB BS 1972 Lond. (Guy's) Med. Dir. Nutrit. Assoc. York; Sen. Edr Jl of Nutrit.al & Environment. Med. Socs: Brit. Soc. Allergy, Environm. & Nutrit. Med. Prev: Nutrit. Cons. TACIS (EU); Sen. Med. Off. Solomon Is.s; GP York.

DOWNING, Rena Carolyn — MB 1973 Camb.; DTM & H 2001 London; BA Camb. 1969, BChir 1972. (Camb. & Middlx.) Socs: LMC Vice Chairm. Prev: Ho. Surg. (O & G) Middlx. Hosp. Lond.; Ho. Phys. Med. St. Helier Hosp. Carshalton; SHO (Paediat.) Mayday Hosp. Croydon.

DOWNING, Mr Richard Worcester Royal Infirmary, Worcester WR5 1HN Tel: 01905 760725 Fax: 01905 760681; 46 Lark Hill, Worcester WR5 2EQ Tel: 01905 350808 — MB ChB 1975 Birm.; BSc Birm. 1972, MD 1983; FRCS Eng. 1980. p/t Cons. Vasc. Surg. Worcester Roy. Infirm. Socs: Vasc. Soc. GB & Irel.; Brit. Transpl. Soc.; Assn. Surg. Prev: Sen. Lect. (Surg.) & Hon. Cons. Qu. Eliz. Hosp. Birm.; Lect. (Surg.) Univ. Birm.; Research Assoc. (Surg.) Washington Univ. St. Louis, USA.

DOWNING, Robert Roderick Clarke 8 Schomberg Avenue, Belfast BT4 2JR — MB BCh BAO 1979 Belf.; MB BCh Belf. 1979; MRCGP 1985. Socs: BMA; Fac. of A & E Med. Prev: GP Belf.; Med. Off. DHSS Belf.; Med. Off. A & E Ulster Hosp. Belf.

DOWNING, Mr William Bennett Lawrence (retired) 16 Vicarage Park, Redlynch, Salisbury SP5 2JZ — MB ChB Birm. 1946; FRCS Ed. 1954; DLO Eng. 1953. Prev: Otolaryn. Catholic Med. Centre Manch. USA.

DOWNS, Andrew Peter Bank House Surgery, The Health Centre, Victoria Road, Hartlepool TS26 8DB Tel: 01429 274386 Fax: 01429 860811; 5 Endeavour Close, Seaton Carew, Hartlepool TS25 1EY — MB ChB 1984 Dundee; MRCGP 1989; DCCH RCP Ed. 1988; DRCOG 1989.

DOWNS, Anthony Magin Robert 25 Springfield, Wellmeadow Est., Bridgnorth WV15 6DN — MB BS 1991 Lond.

DOWNS, Christopher Thomas 5 Compton Grove, Bishop Auckland DL14 6LX — MB ChB 1992 Leic.

DOWNS, David John Crosby, Skene and Partners, College Way Surgery, Comeytrowe Centre, Taunton TA1 4TY Tel: 01823 259333 Fax: 01823 259336; Fairfield House, Blagdon Hill, Taunton TA3 7SG Tel: 01823 421869 — MB ChB 1986 Birm.; BSc Birm. 1981, MB ChB 1986; MRCGP 1991; DRCOG 1990.

DOWNS, Fiona Mary Strathcarron Hospice, Randolph Hill, Denny FK6 5HJ Tel: 01324 826222; 28 Griffiths Street, Falkirk FK1 5AJ Tel: 01324 631414 — MB ChB 1980 Glas.; BSc (Hons.) Glas. 1977. Cons. Palliat. Med. Strathcarron Hospice Denny; Cons. Palliat. Med., Stirling Roy. Infirm. Prev: Train. Fell. (Terminal Care) St. Columba's Hospice Edin.

DOWNS, Helen Elizabeth Azurdia and Partners, Bebington Health Centre, Civic Way, Bebington, Wirral CH63 7RX Tel: 0151 645 6936 Fax: 0151 643 1698 — MB ChB 1990 Birm.; ChB Birm. 1990; DRCOG 1994. Prev: Trainee GP Wirral VTS.

DOWNS, Mark Howard Munster Road Surgery, 292 Munster Road, Fulham, London SW6 6BQ Tel: 020 7385 1965 Fax: 020 7610 3765 — MB BS 1983 Lond.; MRCGP 1988. (Westminster)

DOWNS, Philip Andrew The Surgery, 155 Downing Drive, Evington, Leicester LE5 6LP Tel: 0116 241 3801; 70 Linden Drive, Leicester LE5 6AH Tel: 0116 273 4962 — MB ChB 1979 Sheff. GP Leicester.

DOWNS, Richard Edward 1 Water Lily, Watermead, Aylesbury HP19 0FJ — MB BS 1989 Lond. SHO (Anaesth.) St. Peter's Hosp. Chertsey. Prev: Ho. Off. (Med.) Amersham Gen. Hosp. Bucks.; Ho. Off. (Surg.) Stoke Madeville Hosp. Aylesbury.

DOWNS, Simon Muir Horning Road Surgery, Horning Road West, Hoveton, Norwich NR12 8QH Tel: 01603 782155 Fax: 01603 782189; Sylvan Lodge, Hall Road, Cromer NR27 9JQ Tel: 01263 514380 Email: downs@paston.co.uk — MB BS 1977 Lond.; MRCS Eng. LRCP Lond. 1977; MRCGP 1985; DRCOG 1980; DCH Lond. 1981; FRCGP 1998; Dip. Med. Dund. 1995. (Guy's) GP Princip. Wroxham; VTS Course Organiser Norf. & Norwich Hosp.; Hon. Sen. Lect. Sch. of Health Univ. of E. Anglian 1995. Prev: GP Tutor Norwich.

DOWNTON, Joanna Helen St Thomas' Hospital, Stockport SK3 8BL Tel: 0161 419 4321 Fax: 0161 419 4311 Email: jo.downton@stockport-tr.nwest.nhs.uk; 9 Kings Drive, Heaton Moor, Stockport SK4 4DZ — MB BS 1979 Newc.; MD Newc. 1990; MRCP (UK) 1982; FRCP 1996. (Newcastle Upon Tyne) Cons. Rehabil. Med. Stockport NHS Trust. Prev: Cons. Geriat.ian Stockport Acute Servs. NHS Trust; Lect. (Geriat. Med.) Univ. Manch.

DOWNWARD, David Charles Pine Lodge, 66 Caldy Road, Caldy, Wirral CH48 2HW — MB ChB 1975 Liverp.

DOWRICK, Christopher Frank The Orrell Park Surgery, 46 Moss Lane, Orrell Park, Liverpool L9 8AL Tel: 0151 525 2736 Fax: 0151 524 1037 — MB ChB 1987 Manch.; MSc Lond. 1977; BA Oxf. 1973; MRCGP 1991; DRCOG 1989. Sen. Lect. (Gen. Pract.) Univ. Liverp. Prev: SHO (O & G) Liverp. Matern. Hosp.; SHO (Geriat. & Pub. Health) Liverp.

DOWRICK, Sally Elizabeth Borough Green Medical Practice, Quarry Hill Road, Borough Green, Sevenoaks TN15 8BE — MB BS 1983 Lond.; DRCOG 1987.

DOWSE, Claire Teresa Marchwood, School Rd, Wrington, Bristol BS40 5NB — MB BCh 1997 Wales.

DOWSE, Mr John Leighton Anthony (retired) 1 The Retreat, Merthyrmawr Road, Bridgend CF31 3NU Tel: 01656 655396 — MB

BCh 1950 Wales; FRCS Eng. 1958. Prev: Cons. Surg. Bridgend Gen. Hosp.

DOWSE, Sarah Marion 17 Elmgrove, Scone, Perth PH2 6PA — MB ChB 1987 Aberd.

DOWSE, Simon Christopher Prim Farm, Bossingham Road, Stelling Minnis, Canterbury CT4 6BD — MB BS 1998 Lond.; MB BS Lond 1998.

DOWSETT, Angus Oldfield Wagstaffs, Iqwell Green, Biggleswade — MB BS 1980 Newc.

DOWSETT, Elizabeth Grace 47 Drewsteignton, Shoeburyness, Southend-on-Sea SS3 8BA Tel: 01702 584518 — MB ChB 1943 Ed.; Dip. Bact. Lond 1948. (Univ. Ed.) Hon. Cons. Microbiol., Basildon and Thurrock Gen. Hosps. NHS Trust; Med. Examr., Brit. Red Cross, Essex Br.; Mem. of the Chief Med. Off.'s Working Party on ME/CFS 1999-2001. Socs: Fell. Roy. Soc. Med.; Assn. Med. Microbiol. Prev: Cons. Microbiol. Basildon & Thurrock Health Auth.; Cons. Pathol. Tottenham Hosp. Gp.; Sen. Regist. (Bact.) St. Geo. Hosp. Lond.

DOWSETT, Lynette Mary (retired) Convent of St Lucy, Medstead Manor, High Street, Medstead, Alton GU34 5LL Tel: 01420 560049 — MD Lond. 1937, MB BS 1935; MRCS Eng. LRCP Lond. 1934; FRCPath 1964. Prev: Cons. Microbiol. Pub. Health Laborat. Serv.

DOWSETT, Mary Bridget 36 Monkhams Drive, Woodford Green IG8 0LE Tel: 020 8505 1311 — MB BS Lond. 1961; MRCS Eng. LRCP Lond. 1961; DCH Eng. 1964; DObst RCOG 1963. (Guy's) Socs: Mem. of Fac. Family Plann. & Reproduc. Health c/o RCOG. Prev: Cons.(Family Plann. & Reproductive Health Care) Forest Healthcare.

DOWSETT, Shirley Jane High Street Medical Centre, 19 High Street, Staveley, Chesterfield S43 3UU Tel: 01246 472296 Fax: 01246 471665 — MB ChB 1984 Sheff.; DPhil York 1977, BA (Hons.) 1973; MRCP (UK) 1988.

DOWSLAND, Michelle Helen Rutlands, The Towers, Lorton Road, Cockerton, Cockermouth CA13 9EB — MB BS 1994 Newc.

DOWSON, Andrew John Royal Surrey County Hospital, Egerton Road, Guildford GU2 7XX Tel: 01483 571122; Ludshott End, Headley Road, Grayshott, Hindhead GU26 6JH Tel: 01428 712546 Fax: 01428 712546 — MB BS 1984 Lond.; MRCGP 1991. (Guy's Hospital) Dir. of Kings Headache Serv. Lond.; Lect. Roy. & E. Surrey Neurol. Research Unit. Roy. Surrey Co. Hosp. Prev: GP Tadworth; SHO & Research Regist. (Neurol. & Med.) Roy. Surrey Co. Hosp. Guildford.

DOWSON, Caitlyn Margaret Cedars, South Lodge Court, Old Road, Chesterfield S40 3QG — MB ChB 1992 Leeds.

DOWSON, David Guy Garden Surgery, 78A Osmondthorpe Lane, Leeds LS9 9BL Tel: 0113 248 2291 Fax: 0113 240 5362; 5A Carlton Mount, Yeadon, Leeds LS19 7UZ Tel: 0113 250 6976 — MB ChB 1976 Leeds. Med. Represen. Healthcall Leeds.

DOWSON, David Ian Newbridge Surgery, Newbridge Hill, Bath BA1 3PT Tel: 01225 338171 Fax: 01225 338908 Email: 100256.2651@compuserve.com; The Old Ship, 548 Bath Road, Saltford, Bristol BS31 3JL Tel: 01225 874075 Fax: 01225 400227 — MB ChB 1969 Birm. Indep. Pract. Complementary Ther. Bath & Reading. Socs: Brit. Soc. Allergy & Environm. Med.; Brit. Med. Acupunct. Soc. Prev: Partner Centre for Study of Complementary Med. Soton.; GP Ferndown, Dorset; Clin. Research Asst. (Acupunc.) Univ. Soton.

DOWSON, Henry Malcolm Pollock 10 Queens Road, Colchester CO3 3NZ Tel: 01252 733265 — MB BS 1996 Lond.; BSc (Hons.) Lond. 1993. (Char. Cross and Westm. Med. Sch.) Basic Surg. Train. Scheme at Frimley Pk. Hosp. NHS Trust (SHO). Prev: SHO (A & E) Frimley Pk. Hosp.; Med. Ho. to Dr. R. Zeegan, Chelsea & W.m. Hosp. Lond.; Surg. Ho. to Mr. R. Booth, Qu. Mary's Univ. Hosp.

DOWSON, James Timothy Group Practice Surgery, Whitby, Ellesmere Port, South Wirral L65 6TG Tel: 0151 355 6144; 9 Old Hall Park, Guilden Sutton, Chester CH3 7ER Tel: 01244 300578 — MB ChB 1966 Liverp. (Liverp.) Socs: Chester & N. Wales Med. Soc. Prev: SHO (Paediat., O & G) St. Catharine's Hosp. Birkenhead; SHO (Psychiat.) W. Chesh. Hosp. Chester.

DOWSON, Jonathan Hudson Department of Psychiatry, Addenbrooke's Hospital, Hills Road, Cambridge CB2 2QQ — MB BChir 1967 Camb.; PhD Ed. 1974; MA Camb. 1967, MD 1985; FRCPsych 1981, M 1972; DPM Ed. 1969. (St. Thos.) Cons. Psychiat. & Univ. Lect. (Psychiat.) Camb. Univ. Prev: Cons. Psychiat. Wessex RHA; Lect. (Psychiat.) & Lect. (Anat.) Univ. Edin.

DOWSON, Lee John 37 Paddock Drive, Birmingham B26 1QP — MB ChB 1992 Leeds.

DOWSON, Simon Rodham The Old Ship, 548 Bath Rd, Saltford, Bristol BS31 3JL — MB ChB 1997 Birm.

DOWSON, Stephen North Durham, Healthcare NHS Trust, Dryburn Hospital, North Road, Durham DH1 5TW Tel: 0191 333 2333; Elm Park House, Shotley Bridge, Consett DH8 6SE — BM BS 1981 Nottm.; BMedSci (Hons.) Nottm. 1979, BM BS 1981; FFA RCS Eng. 1986. (Nottm.) Cons. Anaesth. N. Durh. Healthcare NHS Trust. Prev: Sen. Regist. (Anaesth.) Leeds; Regist. (Anaesth.) Leic.; SHO (Anaesth.) Nottm. Train. Scheme.

DOWSON, Timothy Teams Family Practice, Johnson St., Gateshead NE8 2PJ Tel: 0191 460 4239; 234 Jesmond Dene Road, Newcastle upon Tyne NE2 2JU Tel: 0191 281 1665 — MB ChB 1983 Sheff.; MRCGP 1988; DTM & H Liverp. 1988. (Sheffield) Staff Grade for Drug Unit Blyth; MAG Gateshead/S. Tyneside Teachg. Med. Stud. Prev: GP for Homeless Huddersfield; GP & Lect. Maputo, Mozambique.

DOWZER, John William (retired) Ash Lawn, 7 Half Edge Lane, Eccles, Manchester M30 9GJ — LRCPI & LM, LRSCI & LM 1925; LRCPI & LM, LRCSI & LM 1925. Capt. late RAMC (mentioned in despatches); Corps Surg. St. John Ambul. Brig. Prev: Ho. Surg. Lydney & Dist. Hosp.

DOYLE, Amanda Mary 162 Roby Road, Roby, Liverpool L36 4HQ — MB ChB 1988 Manch.

DOYLE, Andrew Patrick 30 Central Way, Carshalton Beeches, Carshalton SM5 3NF — MB BS 1989 Lond.

DOYLE, Anthony John Doyle and Falconer, The Surgery, Shore Road, Kilcreggan, Helensburgh G84 0JL Tel: 01436 842156 Fax: 01436 842259; Mount Pleasant, Shore Road, Kilcreggan, Helensburgh G84 0HN Tel: 0143 684 2409 — MB BCh BAO 1981 NUI; MRCGP 1985; DCH RCP Lond. 1984; DRCOG 1983. Prev: Trainee GP King's Lynn VTS.

DOYLE, Anthony Robert Ramblers Cottage, 7 Southover Farm, Southover, Frampton, Dorchester DT2 9NQ — MB BS 1985 Lond.

DOYLE, Arthur Shand Potter 35 Thorn Road, Bearsdesn, Glasgow G61 4BS — MB ChB 1997 Glas.

DOYLE, Catherine 48 St Isan Road, Cardiff CF14 4LY — MB BS 1992 Lond.

DOYLE, David, RD 35 Thorn Road, Bearsden, Glasgow G61 4BS — MB ChB 1961 Ed.; MD (Commend.) Ed. 1967; FRCP Ed. 1996; Dip. Forens. Med. Glas. 1992; Cert. Av. Med. 1987. (Ed.) Cons. Neuropath. Inst. Neurol. Sci. Glas. Socs: M.R.Ae.S.

DOYLE, David Vincent Whipps Cross University Hospital, Whipps Cross Road, London E11 1NR Tel: 020 8535 6723 Fax: 020 8535 6504 Email: david.doyle@whippsx.nhs.uk — MB BCh BAO 1972 NUI; MD NUI 1979; FRCP Lond. 1993; FRCPI 1984, M 1974. (Univ. Coll. Dub.) Chairm. Med. Advis. Comm. of Arthritis Care; Hon. Sen. Lect. King's Coll. Med. Sch.; Trustee Arthritis Care. Socs: Brit. Soc. Rheum - Mem. of Clin. Affair Comm.; Roy. Soc. Med- Mem. of Counc.; Secretayry of Jt. BSR/Roy. Coll. Phys. Rheum. Comm. Prev: Sen. Regist. (Gen. Med. & Rheum.) St. Bart. Hosp. Lond.; Copeman Research Fell. (Arthritis & Rheum. Counc.) St. Bart. Hosp. Lond.; Regist. (Gen. Med.) St. Vincent's Hosp. Dub.

DOYLE, Denis Cormac Ballymena Health Centre, Cushendall Road, Ballymena BT43 6HQ Tel: 028 2564 2181 Fax: 028 2565 8919; 96 Galgorm Road, Ballymena BT42 1AA — MB BCh BAO 1955 Belf.

DOYLE, Derek, OBE 7 Kaimes Road, Edinburgh EH12 6JR Tel: 0131 334 3168 Fax: 0131 334 2842 Email: derekdoyle@compuserve.com — MB ChB 1955 Ed.; FRCS Ed. 1987; FRCP Ed. 1985, M 1983; FRCGP 1981, M 1968; FRCS London 1998. (Ed.) Vice-Pres. Nat. Counc. Hospice & Specialist Palliat. Care Serv.; Hon. Vice-Pres. Scott. Partnership Agency. Palliat. Cancer Care; Vice-Chairm. Qu. Margt. Univ. Coll. Edin.; Pres. Emerit. Int. Assoc. Hospice Palliat. Care. Prev: Cons. Palliat. Med. Edin.

DOYLE, Mr Edmund Xavier Paul 2 Onslow Avenue, Sutton SM2 7EB — MB BS 1994 Lond.; FRCS 1999. (Roy.Free)

DOYLE, Edward Shand Potter Flat 2, 17 Brunswick Square, Hove BN3 1EH — MB ChB 1995 Glas.; MRCOphth 1&2. SHO Ophth. Brighton. Prev: SHO Ophth.Hasting; SHO Ashford.

DOYLE, Gerald Patrick Michael 5 Barns Road, Warkworth, Morpeth NE65 0TS — MB ChB 1986 Ed.; MRCGP 1992.

DOYLE, Gerard James Countess of Chester NHS Trust, Liverpool Road, Chester CH2 1UL Tel: 01928 366729 Fax: 01429 868830; Village Farm, 41 Chester Road, Sutton Weaver, Runcorn WA7 3EA Tel: 01928 713661 Email: gerry@quistanet.co.uk — MB ChB 1984 Manch.; BSc (Hons.) Manch. 1981; MRCP (UK) 1987; FRCR 1991; T(R) (CR) 1993. (Manchester) Cons. Diagnostic Radiol., Countess of Chester NHS Trust. Prev: Cons. Diagnostic Radiol. Hartlepool & E. Durh. NHS Trust.; Fell. (Diagnostic Radiol.) Univeristy Toronto; Sen. Regist. (Diagnostic Radiol.) Newc.

DOYLE, Harriet Elizabeth 1 Heather Cottages, Meavy, Yelverton PL20 6PL — MB BS 1994 Lond.

DOYLE, Jacqueline North Queen Street Surgery, 257 North Queen Street, Belfast BT15 1HS Tel: 028 9074 8317 Fax: 028 9075 4438 — MB BCh BAO 1987 Belf.; MRCGP 1992; DMH Belf. 1991. Socs: Ulster Med. Soc.; BMA.

DOYLE, Mr James Bury General Hospital, Walmersley Road, Bury BL9 6PG Tel: 0161 769 6081 Fax: 0161 705 3435 — MB BCh BAO 1977 NUI; MCh 1989; FRCSI 1982. Cons. Orthop. Surg. Bury HA. Socs: BMA & Brit. Orthop. Assn.

DOYLE, James Oliver (retired) 17 Willow Park, Poole BH14 0JB Tel: 01202 735663 — LM 1944 Dub.; MD NUI 1948, MB BCh BAO 1943; MRCP 1948. Prev: Cons. Genito-Urin. Med. Wessex RHA.

DOYLE, John Cornelius The Hawthorns, 1 Oxford Road, Redhill RH1 1DT Tel: 01737 762902 Fax: 01737 762902 — MB ChB 1981 Bristol; BSc (Hons.) Anat. Bristol 1978; MRCGP 1986; DRCOG 1986. (Bristol) GP; GP Trainer Surrey; Med. Off. MESSER UK Ltd., Reigate; Med. Off. Surrey Br. Brit. Red Cross Soc.; Chairm. E. Surrey LMC.

DOYLE, John Stephen Ashworth Street Surgery, 85 Spotland Road, Rochdale OL12 6RT Tel: 01706 44582 Fax: 01706 346767; 11 Tenterhill Lane, Norden, Rochdale OL11 5TY Email: steve.doyle@lineone.net — BM BS 1983 Nottm.; BMedSci (Hons.) Nottm. 1981; MRCGP 1988; DRCOG 1987. (Nottingham) Prev: SHO (A & E) Rochdale Infirm.; SHO (Med.) N.ampton Gen. Hosp.; SHO (O & G & Paediat.) Milton Keynes Gen. Hosp.

DOYLE, Julie Mary Pembridge Palliative Care Unit, St. Charles Hospital, London W10 6DZ Fax: 020 8962 4410; 20 Doyles's Road, Katesbridge, Banbridge BT32 5NL Email: jmdoyleos@hotmail.com — MB BCh BAO 1985 Belf.; MRCGP 1989; DRCOG 1989. Specialist Regist. in Palliat. Med.

DOYLE, Lesley Anne White Horse Hotel, Station Road, Leiston IP16 4HD — MB BS 1984 Lond.

DOYLE, Maire Fionnuala Moores Lane Surgery, 7 Moores Lane, Lurgan, Craigavon BT66 8DW Tel: 028 3832 7626 Fax: 028 3834 9950; Rockmore, Dromore Road, Banbridge BT32 4 — MB BCh BAO 1982 Belf.; MB BCh Belf. 1982; MRCGP 1988; DCCH RCP Lond. 1989.

DOYLE, Marguerite Ann 7 Willow Road, Bournville, Birmingham B30 2AT — MB BCh BAO 1977 NUI.

DOYLE, Micaela Elliott Hall Medical Centre, 165-167 Uxbridge Road, Hatch End, Pinner HA5 4EA Tel: 020 8428 4019 — MB ChB 1990 Sheff.; MRCGP 1994; DFFP 1994; DRCOG 1992. p/t GP Partner. Prev: GP Pinner Retainer Scheme.

DOYLE, Michael Brendan 32 Sperrin Drive, Magherafelt BT45 6DQ; 19 Watermeade Avenue, Greyabbey, Newtownards BT22 2XA Tel: 012477 88132 — MB BCh BAO 1986 Belf.; MRCGP 1991; DCH Dub. 1990; DMH Belf. 1990; DRCOG 1989. (Qu. Univ. Belf.) Prev: Cas. Med. Off. Ulster Hosp.

DOYLE, Michael John Lodgeside Surgery, 22 Lodgeside Avenue, Kingswood, Bristol BS15 1WW Tel: 0117 961 5666 Fax: 0117 947 6854 — MB ChB Sheff. 1970; MRCP (UK) 1974; DObst RCOG 1972. Prev: Regist. (Gen. Med.) Stoke Mandeville Hosp. Aylesbury.; SHO (Paediat.) Derbysh. Childr. Hosp.; SHO (Obst.) N.. Gen. Hosp. Sheff.

DOYLE, Minnie Katharine (retired) 6 Cranford Avenue, Exmouth EX8 2HT Tel: 01395 274601 — MB ChB St. And. 1944; Dip. Bact. Lond 1952; DPH Ed. 1948.

DOYLE, Nicola Jayne 2 Falcon Heights, Newtownards BT23 4GF; 36 Victoria Road, Holywood BT18 9BG — MB BCh BAO 1992 Belf.; DRCOG 1995; DCH RCP Lond. 1995; DGM RCP Lond. 1994. Socs: BMA.

DOYLE, Patrick Mark Wirral Womens Department, Arrowe Park Hospital, Upton, Wirral Tel: 0151 678 5111; Burnside, Closeburn Avenue, Heswall, Wirral CH60 4SP Tel: 0151 342 6788 — MB BS 1983 Lond.; BSc Lond. 1980; MRCOG 1989. (Univ. Coll. Lond.) Cons. O & G Wirral Wom. Hosp. Prev: Lect. Acad. Dept. O & G Keele Univ.

DOYLE, Patrick William 9 Kingston Street, Cambridge CB1 2NU — MB BCh 1988 Witwatersrand.

DOYLE, Peter 2 Hillview Close, Lickey End, Bromsgrove B60 1LA — MB ChB 1988 Birm.; FFAEM 2000; MRCP UK 1996; DRCOG 1992; (T)GP 1992. (Birm.) Specialist Regist. W. Midl. Accid. & Emerg. Rot. Scheme. Socs: BAEM; FAEM.

DOYLE, Peter Julian RM 322 Dept of Health, Wellington House, 135-155 Waterloo Road, London SE1 8UG Tel: 020 7972 4838 Fax: 020 7972 4852 Email: peter.doyle@gsi.gov.uk; Copper Beeches, 20 Rectory Close, Merrow, Guildford GU4 7AR Tel: 01483 564337 Fax: 01483 827042 Email: peterjdoyle@netscapeonline.co.uk — MB ChB Liverp. 1969; MSc Lond. 1989; FRCS Ed. 1976; DObst RCOG 1975; DCH Eng. 1973. (Liverp.) Sen. Med. Off. Health Servs. Directorate Dept. of Health. Prev: Cancer Research Campaign Surg. Research Fell. Univ. Nottm.; Regist. (Surg.) Glas. Roy. Infirm.; Med. Off. (Med. Miss.) Hosp. San Jose, Colombia.

***DOYLE, Peter Robb** 18 Braehead Crescent, Edinburgh EH4 6BP Tel: 0131 339 1822 — MB ChB 1994 Sheff.

DOYLE, Mr Peter Thomas Dept of Oral & Maxillofacial Surgery, Queens Hospital, Belvedere Road, Burton-on-Trent DE13 0RB — MB ChB 1990 Manch.; BDS Sheff. 1978; FRCS Eng. 1994; FDS RCS Eng. 1985; LDS RCS Eng. 1980; FRCS (Max. Fac.) 1998. (Univ. Manch.) Cons. Oral & Maxillofacial Surg.,Qu.s Hosp. Burton, Derbysh. Roy. Infirm.. Prev: Cons. Doncaster Roy. Infirm.; Sen. Regist.- Rotherham, Nottiongham, Derby; Regist. (Maxillofacial Surg.) Walton Hosp. Liverp.

DOYLE, Richard Barrow Hill House, 7 East Mersea Road, West Mersea, Colchester CO5 8SL — MB ChB 1978 Bristol; DO Eng. 1980. GP Vocational Trainee Basingstoke Dist. Hosp. Prev: Sen. Ho. Off. Roy. Eye Hosp. Surbiton; Ho. Surg. & Ho. Phys. St. Helier Hosp. Carshalton.

DOYLE, Ronald Franklin (retired) 7 y Gribin, Solva, Haverfordwest SA62 6UY Tel: 01437 720950 — MB BCh BAO 1948 Dub.; MA, MD Dub. 1958; FFPHM RCP (UK) 1981, M 1972; DPH NUI 1968. Prev: Dir. (Pub. Health Med.) & Chief. Admin.Med.Off. Pembrokesh. HA.

DOYLE, Siobhan Marie 22 College Park Avenue, Belfast BT7 1LR — MB BCh 1998 Belf.; MB BCh Belf 1998.

DOYLE, Stephen John Chorley New Road Surgery, 103 Chorley New Road, Horwich, Bolton BL6 5QF Tel: 01204 697696; 17 Dale View, Chorley PR7 3QJ Tel: 01257 279419 Email: sjdoyle@birkacre.presence.co.uk — MB BS 1973 Lond.; BSc (Biochem.) Lond. 1968; MRCS Eng. LRCP Lond. 1973; MRCOphth 1992. (Guy's) GP Horwich, Lancs.; Ophth. Optimax Laser Eye Clinic Manch.; Hosp. Pract. Manch. Roy. Eye Hosp. Socs: Fell. Manch. Med. Soc.; Eur. Soc. Cataract & Refractice Surgs.; Brit. Soc. Refractive Surg. Prev: Princip. GP Warrington; Regist. (Ophth.) Manch. Roy. Eye Hosp.; Lect. Guy's Hosp. Lond.

DOYLE, Timothy Neville X-Ray Department, Royal Sussex County Hospital, Brighton Tel: 01273 696955 Fax: 01273 692887 Email: tim@bhcnt2.demon.co.uk; 17 Princes Crescent, Hove BN3 4GS Tel: 01273 885197 — LRCPI & LM, LRSCI & LM 1976; LRCPI & LM, LRCSI & LM 1976; FFR RCSI 1984. Cons. (Radiol.) Roy. Sussex Co. Hosp. Brighton. Socs: RCR; Cardiovasc. & Interven.al Radiological Soc. of Europe; Brit. Soc. Internat. Radiologists.

DOYLE, Yvonne Gabrielle PPP Healthcare Group, Medical Division, PPP House, Vale Road, Tunbridge Wells TN1 1BJ Tel: 01892 512345 Fax: 01892 505678 Email: yvonne.doyle@pppgroup.co.uk; 21 Thorpewood Avenue, London SE26 4BU Tel: 020 8244 5835 — MB BCh BAO 1981 NUI; MRCPI 1983; FRCPI 1997; FFPHMI 1992; MFPHM RCP (UK) 1990; MFCMI 1988; MPH NUI 1985; DCH Dub. 1983. Dir. (Med. Policy) PPP Healthcare Gp. Tunbridge Wells; Sen. Lect. (Pub. Health Med.) UMDS Guy's & St. Thos. Hosps. Univ. Lond. Socs: BMA; Assur. Med. Soc. Prev: Sen. Lect. & Dir. Pub. Health S.E. Inst. Pub. Health Guy's & St. Thos. Hosps. Univ. Lond.; Cons. Pub. Health Med. &

Epidemiol. Camberwell HA; Hon. Sen. Lect. Kings Coll. Sch. Med. & Dent. Lond. (1990-1993).

DRABBLE, Eric Harold 46 High Street, Upwood, Ramsey, Huntingdon PE26 2QE — MB BS 1985 Lond.; MA (Hons.) Oxf. 1986, BA (Hons.) 1982; FRCS Eng. 1993; FRCS Ed. 1993; MS Univ. Lond. 1996; FRCS (Gen. Surg.) 1997. (Roy. Lond. Hosp.) Cons. Gen. Surg. Hinchinbrooke Hosp. Prev: Regist. (Gen. Surg.) Qu. Eliz. Hosp. Kings Lynn; Regist. (Surg.) John Hunter Hosp. Newc., Austral.; Clin. Lect. (Transpl. Surg.) Roy. Lond. Hosp.

DRABBLE, James Edwin (retired) 46 The Downs, Altrincham WA14 2QQ Tel: 0161 941 1633 — MB ChB 1945 Manch.; BSc Manch. 1942; DObst RCOG 1947. Barrister-at-Law (Eng.) 1969; JP. Prev: Resid. Obst. Off. & Ho. Surg. Roy. Infirm. Preston.

DRABU, Ghulam Jeelani Pine House, Park Hill Road, Hale, Altrincham WA15 9JX — MB BS 1949 Punjab; MB BS Punjab (Pakistan) 1949.

DRABU, Mr Khalid Jeelani East Surrey Hospital, Canada Avenue, Redhill RH1 5RH Tel: 01737 768511 Fax: 01737 782978; 25 Crabtree Drive, Givons Grove, Leatherhead KT22 8LG Tel: 01372 373129 — MB BS 1976 Lond.; FRCS Ed. 1980; MRCS Eng. LRCP Lond. 1976. (St Geo. Hosp.) Cons. Orthop. Surg. Redhill. Socs: Roy. Coll. Surg. Edin.; Brit. Orth. Assn.; Roy. Soc. Med.

DRABU, Reefat Khurshid Eastleigh Health Centre, Newtown Road, Eastleigh SO50 9AG Tel: 023 8061 2123 Fax: 023 8039 9032; Hillside, Main Road, Otterbourne, Winchester SO21 2HH Tel: 01703 262296 Fax: 01703 262471 — MB ChB 1973 Manch.

DRABU, Yasmin Jeelani Department of Microbiology, North Middlesex Hospital, London N18 1QX Tel: 020 8887 2000 Fax: 020 887 4227; 27 Alderton Hill, Loughton IG10 3JD Tel: 020 8502 1875 — MB ChB 1973 Manch.; MRCPath 1981; DCH Eng. 1977; FRCPath 1993. Med. Dir., N. Middlx. Hosp., Lond., 2000; Hon. Sen. Lect. Roy. Free Hosp. Lond. Prev: Cons. Microbiol. N. Middlx. Hosp. Lond.

DRACASS, John Frederick Testvale Surgery, 12 Salisbury Road, Totton, Southampton SO40 3PY Tel: 023 8086 6999/6990 Fax: 023 8066 3992; Glebe Moorings, Eling Hill, Totton, Southampton SO40 9HF Tel: 02380 865480 Email: dracsj@aol.com — MB BS 1971 Lond.; MB BS (Hons.) Lond. 1971; BSc Manch. 1966; FRCGP 1995, M 1982; MHM Lond. 1994; DCH RCPS Glas. 1974; DObst RCOG 1973; Cert FPA. 1973; DFFP 1998. (Univ. Coll. Hosp.) GP; Hon. Clin. Tutor Soton. Med. Sch.; Vice-Chairm. Soton. & SW Hants LMC; Clin. Assessor, GMC; Trainer in Gen. Pract. Socs: (Counc.) Roy. Coll. Gen. Pract.; Roy. Coll. Gen. Pract. (Wessex Fac.). Prev: Cons. Primary Med. Care Wessex RHA; Trainee GP N.ampton VTS; Chairm. Wessex Fac. Roy. Coll. Gen. Pract.

***DRAEGEBO, Morten** 83 Scott St, Dundee DD2 2BB; Lynghaugen 13, Bergen N-5035, Norway Tel: 00 47 55 258972 — MB ChB 1997 Dundee.

DRAGE, Martin William 20 Thirlmere Avenue, Nuneaton CV11 6HT — MB BChir 1994 Camb.; MA Camb. 1996; FRCS 1997. (Camb.) SHO (Gen. Surg.) Addenbroke's. Prev: SHO (Transpl.) Addenbrooke's; Demonst. (Anat.) Char. Cross & W.minster Med. Sch.; SHO (A & E) Addenbrooke's NHS Trust.

DRAGE, Sally Anne Carol Yew Tree House, Sand, Wedmore BS28 4XF Tel: 01934 712635 — BM 1981 Soton.; BSc Bristol 1975; MFFP 1993; Cert. Family Plann. JCC 1985. (Soton.)

DRAGE, Stephen Mark 6 Tucker Close, High Wycombe HP13 6QN Tel: 01494 452274 Email: drage@clara.net — MB ChB 1995 Leic.; BSc 1993. Specialist Regist. Wycombe Hosp. Prev: SHO Anaesth. Sheff.; SHO Anaesth. Plymouth; SHO A&E Plymouth.

DRAGE, Stewart Michael 75 Barn Hill, Wembley HA9 9LL Tel: 020 8904 3888 Email: stew@asylum.dircon.co.uk — MB BS 1980 Lond.; MRCGP 1986. (Middlx.) Med. Sec. Barnet, Brent & Harrow, Hillingdon, Ealing, Hammersmith & Hounslow, Enfield & Haringey LMCs. Prev: GP Lond.; Trainee GP Lond. VTS; Ho. Phys. Cardiol. N.wick Pk. Hosp. Harrow.

DRAGOWSKA, Ewa Monika (retired) 152 Wellsway, Bath BA2 4SE Tel: 01225 427355 — MB BS 1960 Lond.; MRCS Eng. LRCP Lond. 1960. Prev: Ho. Phys. Eliz. G. Anderson Hosp. Lond.

DRAH, Mohamed Abdussalam Prince Charles Hospital, Merthyr Tydfil CF47 9DT Tel: 01685 728357 Fax: 01685 721911; 31 Caer Wenallt, Rhiwbina, Cardiff CF14 7HP Tel: 01222 612059 Fax: 01222 612059 — MB BCh 1975 Cairo; MRCPI 1988; ECFMG Cert. 1981; FRCPI 1998. (Cairo, Egypt) Cons. Phys. (Gastroenterol.) P. Chas. Hosp. Merthyr Tydfil. Socs: BMA & Europ. Assn. Gastroenterol.; Brit. Soc. Gastroenterol.; Soc. Phys. Wales. Prev: Cons. Phys. Gastroenterol. (long term locum) Law Hosp. Carluke; Regist. (Med.) LLa.lli Gen. Hosp.; Regist. (Med. & Gastroenterol.) Singleton Hosp. Swansea.

DRAIN, Andrew John 7 Glencraig Park, Holywood BT18 0BZ — MB BCh 1998 Belf.; MB BCh Belf 1998.

DRAINER, Elaine Kennedy Flat 2/1, 101 Yorkhill St., Yorkhill, Glasgow G3 8NS — MB ChB 1990 Glas.

DRAINER, Mr Ian Kennedy (retired) 41 West Chapelton Crescent, Bearsden, Glasgow G61 2DE Tel: 0141 570 2832 — MB ChB Glas. 1962; FRCS Glas. 1968. Prev: Hon. Clin. Sen. Lect. Univ. Glas.

DRAISEY, Joanne Helen Half Acra, Aston Lane, Oker, Matlock DE4 2JP — MB ChB 1995 Leeds.

DRAISEY, Michael Harold, TD (retired) Trenchards, Piddinghoe, Newhaven BN9 9AT Tel: 01273 516242 Fax: 01273 612214 Email: mikfme@aol.uk — MB BS 1960 Lond.; MRCGP 1982; DMJ (Clin.) Soc. Apoth. Lond. 1989; DObst RCOG 1963. Princip Forens. Med. Examr. Sussex Police; Hon. Med. Adviser Newhaven RNLI; Med. Ref. RNLI. Prev: Asst. Med. Off. St. And. Hosp. N.ampton.

DRAKE, Amanda Jane Molecularendocrinology, Molecular Medicine Centre, Western General Hospital, Crewe Rd, Edinburgh EH4 2XU — MB BS 1991 Newc.; DCH RCP Lond. 1995; MRCPCH 1997. Research Fell. Edin. Prev: Specialist Regist. Paediat. Bristol.

DRAKE, Anne Teresa 2 Mossvale Terrace, Dromara, Dromore BT25 2DE — MB ChB 1992 Belf.

DRAKE, Anthony John Fairbrook Medical Centre, 4 Fairway Avenue, Borehamwood WD6 1PR Tel: 020 8953 7666; Walnut House, 29A Watford Road, Radlett WD7 8LG Tel: 01923 854291 — MB BS 1984 Lond.; MRCGP 1989; Dip. Sports Med. Ed. 1992; DCH RCP Lond. 1990. (St. Mary's) Prev: Trainee GP St. Albans VTS; SHO (O & G) Qu. Eliz. II Hosp.; SHO (A & E) Watford Gen. Hosp.

DRAKE, Beatrice Elizabeth Nollaig Tavistock Clinc, 120 Belsize Lane, London NW3 5BA Tel: 0207 435 7111 Ext: 2430 Email: nwhyte@tavi-port.org — MB BCh BAO 1976 NUI; BEd NUI 1968, BA Phil 1970; MRCPsych 1986. (Univ. Coll. Dub.) Cons. Psychother. Tavistock Clinic Lond.; Vice-Dean Tavistock Clinic Lond. Socs: Brit. Psychoanal. Soc.; Assn. for psychoanalytic psychotherapists in NHS. Prev: Sen. Regist. (Psychother.) Tavistock Clinic Lond.; Sen. Regist. (Adult Psychiat.) Roy. Free Hosp. Lond.

DRAKE, Brent Edgar 4 Whitchurch Av, Broadstone BH18 8LP — MB ChB 1997 Birm.

DRAKE, Brian John 45 Station Road, Histon, Cambridge CB4 9LQ Tel: 01223 232203; 45 Station Road, Histon, Cambridge CB4 9LQ Tel: 01223 232203 — BM BCh 1953 Oxf.; MA Camb. 1951; MA Oxf. 1951; DObst RCOG 1957. (Camb. & Oxf.) Emerit. Cons. Genitourin. Med. Bedford Hosp. Socs: Med. Soc. Study VD; Camb. Med. Soc. (Ex-Pres.). Prev: SHO (Accid. Serv.) Radcliffe Infirm Oxf.; Ho. Phys. Radcliffe Infirm. Oxf.; Ho. Surg. Addenbrooke's Hosp. Camb.

DRAKE, Claire Natalie 245 Bramhall Moor Lane, Hazel Grove, Stockport SK7 5JL — BM BS 1994 Nottm.; BMedSci Nottm. 1992. (Nottingham) SHO (Psychiat.) Wotton Lawn Hosp. Gloucester.

DRAKE, David Kings Head Hill Surgery, 178 Kings Head Hill, Chingford, London E4 7NX Tel: 020 8529 3501 Fax: 020 8559 4456 — MB BS 1982 Lond.; BSc Lond. 1979; DRCOG 1987. (Royal Free Hospital School of Medicine)

DRAKE, David John 31 Clarendon Road, Sale M33 2DU — MB ChB 1997 Manch.

DRAKE, Mr David Paul 14 College Gardens, Dulwich, London SE21 7BE Fax: 0207 813 8428 Email: david.drake@gosh-tr.nthames.nhs.uk — MB BChir 1970 Camb.; MA, MB Camb. 1970, BChir 1969; FRCS Eng. 1974; DCH Eng. 1975. (Camb. & Middlx.) Cons. Paediat. Surg. Hosps. for Sick Childr. Lond. Socs: Brit. Assn. Paediat. Surg.; BMA; FRCPCH. Prev: Cons. Paediat. Surg. Sydenham Childr. Hosp. & Guy's Hosp. Lond.; Sen. Regist. Wessex Centre Paediat. Surg. Soton. Gen. Hosp.; Regist. Qu. Mary's Hosp. Childr. Carshalton.

DRAKE, Delyth Anne Walnut House, 29A Watford Road, Radlett WD7 8LG Tel: 01923 854291 — MB BS 1984 Lond.; MFPHM RCP (UK) 1992.

DRAKE, Elizabeth Jane 17 Laniver Close, Earley, Reading RG6 5UD — BM 1998 Soton.; BM Soton 1998. A & E Warwick

Hosp. Prev: Ho. Off. Surg.Salisbury.Dis.Hosp; Ho. Off. Med. Worcester Roy Infirm.

DRAKE, Gillian Patricia White Medical Gp., Ponteland Medical Centre, Ponteland, Newcastle upon Tyne; 9 Stephenson Terrace, Wylam NE41 8DZ Tel: 01661 852160 — MB BS 1987 Newc.; MRCGP 1991; DRCOG 1991; DCM RCP Lond. 1990.

DRAKE, Helen Florence Department of Anaesthesia, Royal Sussex County Hospital, Eastern Road, Brighton BN2 5BE Tel: 01273 696955; Upper Burrells, Chiltington Lane, East Chiltington, Lewes BN7 3QT Tel: 01273 890703 Fax: 01273 891240 — MB BS 1980 Lond.; BSc Lond. 1980; FFA RCS Eng. 1984. (Charing Cross Hospital Medical School) Cons. Anaesth. Roy. Sussex Co. Hosp. Brighton. Prev: Cons. Anaesth. Roy. Sussex Co. Hosp. Brighton; Sen. Regist. (Anaesth.) St. Thos. Hosp. Lond.; Sir Jules Thorn Research Fell. Middlx. Hosp. Lond.

DRAKE, Humphrey Martyn Bridge Street Surgery, Bridge St., Louth LN11 0RD Tel: 01507 603121 — BM BCh 1959 Oxf.; DObst RCOG 1966; DA Eng. 1967. (Oxf.) Prev: Asst. Surg. P. & O. Orient S.N.Co.; Asst. Med. Off. Grand Bank Cott. Hosp. Newfld.; Med. Off. Med. Union Qu.stown, Tasmania.

DRAKE, Ian Michael Consultant Physician, Chorley & District Hospital, Preston Road, Chorley PR7 1PP — BM BS 1987 Nottm. SHO (Gen. Med.) Walton & Fazakerley Hosps. Liverp. Prev: Ho. Off. (Gen. Med.) City Hosp. Nottm.; Ho. Off. (Gen. Surg.) Halifax Gen. Hosp.

DRAKE, Ida Madelene (retired) Tudor Croft, North Road, Ponteland, Newcastle upon Tyne NE20 0AA Tel: 01661 22891 — MB BS 1948 Durh. Ref. DHSS. Prev: Ho. Surg. & Ho. Phys. Profess. Med. Unit. Roy. Vict. Infirm.

DRAKE, John 2 Deards Wood, Knebworth SG3 6PG — MB ChB 1975 Dundee. Gp. Med. Manager Roche Products Ltd. Socs: Fell. Roy. Soc. Med.; Med. Soc. Lond.; Fell. Fac. Pharmaceut. Med. Prev: Dir. Med. Operat. Boehringer Ingelheim UK; Med. Dir. Farmitalia Carlo Erba UK Ltd. St Albans; Assoc. Dir. Clin. Research Dupont UK.

DRAKE, Josephine Mary Norwood House Surgery, Belle Vue Street, Scarborough YO12 7EJ Tel: 01723 374485 Fax: 01723 501517; Lane End, Mount Pleasant, Scalby, Scarborough YO13 0RR Tel: 01723 360805 — MB BS 1970 Lond.; MRCS Eng. LRCP Lond. 1970; DA Eng. 1974.

DRAKE, Laurence Karsten Greensands Medical Practice, Brook End Surgery, Potton, Sandy SG19 2QS Tel: 01767 260260 Fax: 01767 261777 — MB BChir 1987 Camb.; MA Camb. 1989; DRCOG 1992. Socs: Med. Camb. Med. Soc. Prev: Trainee GP W. Suff. Hosp. VTS; Ho. Phys. Addenbrooke's Hosp. Camb.; Ho. Surg. W. Norwich Hosp.

DRAKE, Mr Marcus John Urology Department Churchill Hospital, Old Road, Headington, Oxford OX3 Tel: 01865 271876 Email: marcus.drake@pharm.ox.ac.uk — BM BCh 1991 Oxf.; MA Camb. 1992; FRCS Eng. 1996. (Oxf.) Specialist Regist. (Urol.) Ch.ill Hosp. Oxf.; Clin.Research.Fell.Oxf.Continence Gp. Univ.Oxf. Socs: Brit. Assn. Urol. Surg; Internat.Continence Soc.; Euro. Assn. Urol. Prev: SHO (Gen. Surg.) Hinchingbrooke Hosp. Huntingdon; SHO (Paediat. Urol.) Addenbrooke's Hosp. Camb.; SHO (Orthop.) Soton. Gen. Hosp.

DRAKE, Mark Roland Drake and Dalton, The Health Centre, King Edward Lane, St Mary's TR21 0HE Tel: 01720 422628 Fax: 01720 423160 — MB ChB 1983 Leic.; BSc (Med. Sci.) Leic. 1981. (Leicester) Prev: Trainee GP Redruth; SHO Treliske Hosp. Truro; SHO St. Lawrence's Hosp. Bodmin, Shotley Bridge Gen. Hosp.

DRAKE, Mary Brigid Geraldine 2 Mossvale Terrace, Ardtana Road, Dromara, Dromore BT25 2DE — MB BCh BAO 1989 Belf.

DRAKE, Michael John Bennetts End Surgery, Gatecroft, Hemel Hempstead HP3 9LY Tel: 01442 63511 Fax: 01442 235419; Fernside, Potten End, Berkhamsted HP4 2RD Tel: 01442 864816 — MB BChir 1968 Camb.; MA Camb. 1968; MRCP (UK) 1972; DCH Eng. 1971; DObst RCOG 1970. (St. Thos.) Prev: Ho. Surg. & Cas. Off. St. Thos. Hosp. Lond.; Ho. Phys. (Paediat.) Evelina Childr. Hosp. (Guy's Hosp.) Lond.; Resid. Med. Off. Qu. Eliz. Childr. Hosp. Lond.

DRAKE, Nicola Beverley 19 Upper Village Road, Sunninghill, Ascot SL5 7BA — MB ChB 1989 Liverp.; BSc (Hons.) Liverp. 1987, MB ChB 1989.

DRAKE, Peter Hawken (retired) 5 Manor Chase, Weybridge Park, Weybridge KT13 8SE — MB BS 1948 Lond.; MRCS Eng. LRCP Lond. 1948; FRCOG 1981, M 1958. Prev: Gp. Capt. RAF.

DRAKE, Richard James 13 Butley Lane, Prestbury, Macclesfield SK10 4HU — MB ChB 1992 Manch.

DRAKE, Shirley Rosemary Iona Cottage, 6 Honey Hill, Blean, Canterbury CT2 9JP Tel: 01227 471447 — MRCS Eng. LRCP Lond. 1948; FRCS Ed. 1964; FRCR 1975; FFR 1971; DMRT Eng. 1966. (Leeds) Cons. Radiother. Oncol. Kent & Canterbury Hosp. Socs: Fell. Roy. Soc. Med.; Fell. Brit. Inst. Radiol. Prev: Ho. Surg. Leeds Gen. Infirm.; Cas. Regist. Kingston Hosp.; Regist. Radiother. Dept. Roy. Marsden Hosp. Lond.

DRAKE, Simon Paul 10 Hulme Hall Crescent, Cheadle Hulme, Cheadle SK8 6LG Tel: 0161 485 8029 — MB BS 1989 Lond.; FRCA 1997. (St. George's London)

DRAKE, Susan Elizabeth Botesdale Health Centre, Back Hills, Botesdale, Diss IP22 1DW Tel: 01379 898295 — MB BChir 1983 Camb.; DRCOG 1988; DCH RCP Lond. 1986.

DRAKE, Susan Margaret Birmingham Heartlands Hospital, Bordesley Green E., Birmingham B9 5SS Tel: 0121 424 2000 Fax: 0121 766 8752 Email: sdrake@hawthorn.co.uk — MB BS Lond. 1972; FRCP Lond. 1994; MRCP (UK) 1978; MRCS Eng. LRCP Lond. 1972; Dip. Ven. Soc. Apoth. Lond. 1976. (Roy. Free Hosp. Sch. Med.) Cons. Genitourin. Med. Birm. Heartlands Hosp. Prev: Cons. Genitourin. Med. Coventry & Warks. Hosp. Geo. Eliot Hosp. Nuneaton & St. Cross Hosp. Rugby.

DRAKE, William Martyn Department of Endocrinology, St. Bartholomews Hospital, Smithfield, London EC1A 7BE — MB BS 1991 Lond.

DRAKE-LEE, Mr Adrian Brendan Queen Elizabeth Hospital, Birmingham B15 2TH Tel: 0121 697 8301 Fax: 0121 627 2291; 20 Vernon Road, Birmingham B16 9SH Tel: 0121 454 6343 — MB ChB 1973 Birm.; PhD Bath 1988; FRCS Eng. 1980. (Univ. Birm.) Cons. ENT Surg. Qu. Eliz. Hosp. & Birm. Childr. Hosp.; Hon. Sen. Lect. Univ. Birm. Prev: Cons. Surg. Roy. United Hosp. Bath.

DRAKE-LEE, John William Donnellan (retired) Cherrylands, New Mill Road, Finchampstead, Wokingham RG40 4QU Tel: 01189733159 Fax: 01189733159 Email: ducky-doc@supanet.com — MB BChir 1962 Camb.; MB Camb. 1962, BChir 1961; MA Camb. 1962; DObst RCOG 1964. Med. Off. i/c Wokingham Matern. Hosp.; Mem. Berks. LMC. Prev: GP Wokingham.

DRAKELEY, Andrew John 1 The Orchard, North Sudley Road, Liverpool L17 6BU Email: adrakeley@yahoo.com — MB ChB 1994 Liverp.; MRCOG 1999 Lond. (University of Liverpool) Regist. O & G Groote Schurr Hosp. Cape Town, S. Africa; Subspeciality Fell. Reproductive Med., Liverp. Wom.'s Hosp. Socs: Roy. Coll. Obst.s and Gynaecologists; Nat. Trainees Comm. Chairm. Prev: SHO (O & G) Liverp. Wom.s Hosp.; Research Fell. (Gyn.) Univ. of Liverp.; Hse. Off. Whiston Hosp.

DRAKELEY, Mr Michael John 1 The Orchard, North Sudley Road, Aigburth, Liverpool L17 6BT Tel: 0151 427 8427 — MRCS Eng. LRCP Lond. 1964; FRCS Ed. 1969. (Liverp.) Cons. Cardiothoracic Surg. BRd.green Hosp. Liverp. Socs: Soc. Cardiothoracic Surgs. Gt. Brit. & Irel. Prev: Fell. in Cardiothoracic & Vasc. Surg. Green La. Hosp. Auckland, N.Z.; Ho. Off. David Lewis N.. Hosp. Liverp.

DRAKES, Abigail Hannah 91 Outwoods Drive, Loughborough LE11 3LS — BM BS 1998 Nottm.; BM BS Nottm 1998.

DRANE, Nigel Rodney Field Lane Surgery, 42 Field Lane, Kessingland, Lowestoft NR33 7QA Tel: 01502 740203; 21 Southwold Road, Wrentham, Beccles NR34 7JE Tel: 01502 740203 Fax: 01502 742368 — MB BChir 1976 Camb.; BA, MB Camb. 1976, BChir 1975; MRCGP 1980; DCH Eng. 1978. GP Trainer Gt. Yarmouth VTS; Clin. Asst. Psychiat. St. Nicholas Hosp. Gt. Yarmouth.

DRANSFIELD, Philip (retired) 19A Longlands Road, Slaithwaite, Huddersfield HD7 5DN — MB BS Lond. 1943.

DRAPER, Adrian Godfrey 60 Abbotswood Road, E. Dulwich, London SE22 8DL — MB BS 1991 Lond.; MRCP (UK) 1996. (King's Coll. Lond.) Specialist Regist. (Respirat. Gen. Med.) SW Thames.

DRAPER, Carol Ann Ladywell, Grange Road, Buckfast, Buckfastleigh TQ11 0EH — MB ChB 1997 Manch.

DRAPER, Christopher Charles (retired) 29 High Street, Chipstead, Sevenoaks TN13 2RW Tel: 01732 452507 — BM BCh 1945 Oxf.; MA Oxf. 1945, DM 1963; DPH Lond. 1950; DTM & H Eng. 1949. Prev: Sen. Lect. & Cons. Trop. Hyg., Lond. Sch. Hyg. & Trop. Med.

DRAPER, Elizabeth-Louise 48 Luccombe Road, Upper Shirley, Southampton SO15 7RP Tel: 02380 392876 Fax: 02380 392876 — MB BS 1983 Lond.; MRCGP 1988; Cert. Family Plann. JCC 1987; DRCOG 1987.

DRAPER, Helen Lucy 34 Waldemar Avenue Mansions, Waldemar Avenue, Fulham, London SW6 5LT Tel: 020 7731 6593 — MB BS 1990 Lond.; MRCGP 1994.

DRAPER, Isabel Barbara Whitehall Medical Practice, Morton Gardens, Rugby CV21 3AQ Tel: 01788 544264 Fax: 01788 575783; 6 Hazelwood Close, Dunchurch, Rugby CV22 6QG — MB ChB 1980 Liverp.; MFFP 1993; MRCGP 1984; DRCOG 1983. (Liverpool)

DRAPER, Rev. Ivan Thomas (retired) 13/1 Whistlefield Court, 2 Canniesburn Road, Bearsden, Glasgow G61 1PX — MB ChB 1956 Aberd.; FRCP Glas. 1983; FRCP Ed. 1968, M 1960. Prev: Cons. Neurol. Inst. Neurol. Sci. S.. Gen. Hosp. Glas.

DRAPER, Juliet Newmarket Road Surgery, 125 Newmarket Road, Cambridge CB5 8HA Fax: 01233 366088; The Dumb Flea, Chiswick End, Meldreth, Royston SG8 6LZ Tel: 01763 60323 Fax: 01763 262599 — MB BChir 1968 Camb.; BA Camb. 1964, MD 1986; FRCGP 1995, M 1986; DCH Eng. 1971; DObst RCOG 1969. (Camb. & Lond. Hosp.) Reg. Comm. Skills, Faclitator Anglia Deaney. Socs: MITA. Prev: Regist. (Paediat.) Centr. Middlx. Hosp. Lond.; Research Fell. (Med.) Hughes Hall Camb.; Ho. Phys. Lond. Hosp.

DRAPER, Katharine Chance (retired) Stairfoot House, 29 High St., Chipstead, Sevenoaks TN13 2RW — MB BChir 1952 Camb.; MFFP 1993. Prev: Sen. Med. Off. Lewisham Health Dist.

DRAPER, Mark Richard 42 The Crescent, Farnborough GU14 7AS — MB BS 1992 Lond.

DRAPER, Mark Russell Wybourn Gables, 6 Avenue Road, Malvern WR14 3AG Tel: 01684 576657 Fax: 01684 576657; 107 Westgate, Chichester PO19 3HB Tel: 0243 773292 — MB BS Lond. 1979; BSc Zool. Lond. 1974; DRCOG 1985; DA Eng. 1983. Indep. Homoeop. Phys. Worcs. Prev: Med. Off. Turks & Caicos Is. Brit. W. Indies; GP Kings Lynn; Regist. (Anaesth.) Univ. Hosp. Wales, Cardiff.

DRAPER, Morrell Henry, OBE (retired) 10 West Mayfield, Edinburgh EH9 1TQ Tel: 0131 667 2431 — MB BS Adelaide 1944; FRSE; PhD Camb. 1955. Prev: Cons. WHO Geneva.

DRAPER, Nicola Elizabeth The Norfolk Hero 48 Station Street, Swaffham PE37 7HP — MB BCh 1997 Wales.

DRAPER, Paul Dudley Giffard Drive Surgery, 68 Giffard Drive, Farnborough GU14 8QB Tel: 01252 541282 Fax: 01252 372159 — MB BS 1963 Lond.; MRCS Eng. LRCP Lond. 1963; T(GP) 1991; DCH RCP Lond. 1965. (St. Georges)

DRAPER, Peter William Westmoor, George Green Road, George Green, Slough SL3 6BB — MB ChB 1978 Sheff.; MRCGP 1982; DA (Eng.) 1984; DRCOG 1981. GP Ashford Middlx.

DRAPER, Richard John Oxshott Medical Centre, Holtwood Road, Oxshott, Leatherhead KT22 0QJ Tel: 01372 844000 — MB ChB 1981 Birm.; MRCGP 1985; DA (UK) 1986; DRCOG 1985; DCH RCP Lond. 1983. Hon. Research Fell. Dept. Epidemiol. St. Geo. Hosp. Lond. Prev: GP Trainee King's Lynn VTS; Med. Off. Turks & Caicos Is. Brit. W. Indies; SHO (Anaesth.) W.m. Hosp. Lond.

DRAPER, Tracy Jayne Glenusk W ing, St.Cadocs Hospital, Newport Tel: 01633436700; Tysiriol, Mynyddislwyn, Blackwood NP12 2BG — MB ChB 1989 Ed.; MRCGP. Staff Grade Psychiat. of the elderly.

DRATCU, Luiz Guy's, King's & St Thomas' Sch. Med. Division of Psychiatry, Thomas Guy House, Guy's Hospital, 47 Weston St., London SE1 3RR Tel: 0207 955 4932 Fax: 0207 7403 6910 — Medico 1981 Brazil; Medico Escola Paulista De Medicina Brazil 1981; PhD Univ. Lond. 1996; MPhil Escola Paulista de Medicina Brazil 1986; MRCPsych 1989. Cons. Psychiat. Guy's Hosp. Lond.; Sen. Lect. GKT Div. Psychiat. Guy's Hosp. Lond. Socs: Brit. Assn. Psychopharmacol.; Assn. Europ. Psychiat.; CINP. Prev: Hon. Sen. Regist. Maudsley Hosp. & Clin. Researcher (Clin. Psychopharmacol.) Inst. Psychiat.; Locum Cons. in Liason Psychiat., St Thomas' Hosp. Lond.

DRATH, Matthias Christian Doctor's Residence 10A, Bishop Auckland Hospital, Bishop Auckland DL14 4AD — State Exam Med 1992 Munster.

DRAY, Noel Harrison (retired) 7 Colewood Drive, Rochester ME2 3UE — MRCS Eng. LRCP Lond. 1947. Prev: Resid. Med. Off. Beckenham Matern. Hosp.

DRAYCOTT, Timothy John Department of Obstetrics, Southmead Hospital, Bristol BS10 5NB Tel: 0117 959 5176 Fax: 0117 959 5178 Email: tdraycott@hotmail.com; 39 Lenaghan Park, Belfast BT8 7JB — MB BS 1989 Lond.; BSc Lond. 1986; MRCOG 1995; MD 1999 Bristol. Cons., Dept of Obst. and Gyn., S.mead Hosp., Bristol. Socs: MRCOG; Brit. Perinatal Assn.

DRAYER, Niessienus Marinus 12 Orchard Rise, Burford OX18 4SZ — L Newfoundland Med. Bd. 1965.

DRAYSON, Alan Michael Sunnyside Royal Hospital, Montrose DD10 9JP Tel: 01674 830361; Mansefield House, Kirkton of Kinnettles, Forfar DD8 1TQ Tel: 01307 820233 — MB ChB 1972 Ed.; MPhil Ed. 1979, BSc (Med. Sc.) 1969; FRCPsych 1997, M 1976. Cons. Psychiat. Sunnyside Roy. Hosp. Montrose. Prev: Sen. Regist. (Psychiat.) Roy. Edin. Hosp. & Univ. Edin.; Regist. (Psychiat.) Roy. Edin. Hosp.

DRAYSON, Mark Trehane Department of Immunology, The University of Birmingham Medical School, Edgbaston, Birmingham B15 2TT Tel: 0121 414 4069 Fax: 0121 414 3599 Email: m.t.drayson@bham.ac.uk — MB ChB Manch. 1980; BSc (1st cl. Hons.) Path. Manch. 1978, PhD (Immunol.) 1987; MRCPath (Immunol.) 1993. Sen. Clin. Lect. (Immunol.) Univ. Birm.; Hon. Cons. Univ. Birm. Hosp. Trust. Prev: Clin. Lect. (Immunol.) Univ. Birm.; Tutor (Haemat.) Manch. Roy. Infirm.; Rotat. (Gen. Med.) Manch. Roy. Infirm.

DRAYSON, Rachel Anne PO Box 306, Mpwapwa, Tanzania; 25 High Trees Road, Reigate RH2 7EH Tel: 01737 244574 Fax: 017343 244574 — MB ChB 1985 Ed.; MRCP (UK) 1990. Med. Coordinator St. Lukes Clinic Diocese of Mpwapwa Tanzania. Prev: Regist. (Haemat.) St. Mary's Hosp. Lond.; Regist. (Haemat.) Watford Gen. Hosp.; Regist. (Med.) Basildon HA.

DRAYSON, Richard William Church View Surgery, School La, Collingham, Wetherby LS22 5BQ Tel: 01937 573848 Fax: 01937 574754; 1 Langwith Terrace, Harewood Road, Collingham, Wetherby LS22 5DG Tel: 01937 572097 — MB ChB 1979 Bristol; MRCGP 1987; DCH RCP Lond. 1988.

DRAYTON, Mark Robert Charters, Druidstone Road, St Mellons, Cardiff CF3 6XD Tel: 029 2077 7537 — MB BChir 1976 Camb.; FRCPCH; MA Camb. 1987, BA 1972, MD 1987, BChir 1975; FRCP Eng. 1993. Cons. Neonat. Univ. Hosp. Wales Cardiff. Socs: Brit. Assn. for Perinatal Med.; Welsh Paediatric Soc. Prev: Sen. Regist. (Neonat. Med.) Bristol Matern. Hosp. & S.mead Gen. Hosp. Bristol; Regist. (Paediat.) Roy. Alexandra Hosp. Childr. Sydney, Austral.

DREAPER, Richard Edmund Friarsgate Medical Centre, Winchester SO23 8EF Tel: 01962 854091 Fax: 01902 854956; Willow House, Norlands Drive, Otterbourne, Winchester SO21 2DT — MB BS 1952 Lond.; DA Eng. 1973; DObst RCOG 1957; LLCO 1966. (St. Bart.) Clin. Asst. (Dermat.) Roy. Hants. Co. Hosp. Winchester. Prev: Clin. Asst. VD Dept. St. Bart. Hosp.; Clin. Asst. (Anaesth.) Roy. Hants. Co. Hosp. Winchester; Surg. Lt.-Cdr. RNR.

DREGHORN, Mr Clark Robertson 19 Thornhill Grove, Calverley, Pudsey LS28 5PB Tel: 0113 257 2227 — MB ChB 1977 Glas.; FRCS Orth. Ed. 1990; FRCS Glas. 1982. Sen. Regist. (Orthop.) Yorks. RHA.

DREGHORN, James Tigh an Darrach, Kinloch Rannoch, Pitlochry PH16 5PR — MB ChB 1969 Glas.; DObst RCOG 1971.

DREKE, Stephan Doctors' Mess, Norfolk & Norwich Hospital, Brunswick Road, Norwich NR1 3SR — State Exam Med 1991 Berlin.

DRENNAN, John Dudgeon 35 Braemar Avenue, Hull HU6 7UE Tel: 01482 850249 — LRCPI & LM, LRSCI & LM 1952; LRCPI & LM, LRCSI & LM 1952.

DRENNAN, Patrick Charles Director of Health Care, HMP Dartmoor, Princetown, Yelverton PL20 6RR Tel: 01822 890261 Fax: 01822 890745 — MB BS 1972 Lond.; DObst RCOG 1975. (St. Mary's) Socs: Fell.ship Roy. Soc. Med.; Medico-Legal Soc.; Assn. Police Surg. Prev: Med. Coordinator Continuing Care Unit, Sam Beare Ward Weybridge Hosp.; Sen. Police Surg. Surrey Police; Sen. Forens. Med. Examr. Metrop. Police.

DREPAUL, Lydia Rosemary Maria 44 Manor Road, London W13 0JA — MB BS 1993 Lond. SHO (O & G) St. Geo. Healthcare NHS Trust Lond.

DRESNER, Martin Richard Grove House W., North Lane, Leeds LS8 2QW Tel: 0113 232 9825 — MB BS 1983 Lond.; FCAnaesth. 1989; DA (UK) 1985. Cons. Anaesth. Leeds Gen. Infirm. Socs: Assn.

Anaesth.; Obst. Anaesth. Assn. Prev: Cons. Anaesth. St. Jas. Hosp. Leeds.; Sen. Regist. (Anaesth.) St. Jas. Hosp. Leeds; Regist. (Anaesth.) W.m. Hosp. Lond.

DRESNER, Mr Samuel Michael Northern Oesophago-gastric Cancer Unit, Royal Victoria Infirmary, Newcastle upon Tyne NE1 4LP Tel: 0191 282 0240 Fax: 0191 282 0237; 28 Linton Avenue, Leeds LS17 8PT — MB BS 1993 Newc.; FRCS Eng. 1997; FRCS Ed. 1997. (Newcastle) Research Regist. Prev: PeriFell.sh.ip SHO Rotat. (Surg.) Newc.

DRESSER, Iain George 23 Highbury Villas, Kingsdown, Bristol BS2 8BY Tel: 0117 923 9038 — BM BCh 1963 Oxf.; MPhil Lond. 1969; MA, BM BCh Oxf. 1963; FRCPsych 1984, M 1972. (Oxf.) Socs: Brit. Psycho-Analyt. Soc. Prev: Cons. Child Psychiat. St. Mary's Hosp. Lond.; Regist. Maudsley Hosp. Lond.; Sen. Regist. Child Guid. Clinic Belgrave Hosp. Lond.

DRESSER, Theresa Harriet General Practice Surgery, 55 St. Gabriels Road, London NW2 4DT; 145 Olive Road, London NW2 6XA Tel: 020 8452 0261 — MB BS 1964 Lond. (Univ. Coll. Lond. & Oxf.) GP Princip. Socs: Balint Soc.; BMA; LMC. Prev: Asst. Med. Edr. Update Pub.ats. Ltd. Lond.; Ho. Phys. (Paediat.) Radcliffe Infirm. Oxf.; Ho. Surg. Chest Unit Ch.ill Hosp. Oxf.

DREVER, Elizabeth Anne Staff Residence, Dumfries & Galloway Royal Infirmary, Bankend Road, Dumfries DG1 4AP — MB ChB 1993 Glas.

DREVER, George Franklyn 5 Frogston Gardens, Edinburgh EH10 7AF — MB ChB 1966 Ed.

DREVER, Ian Robert Surrey Hampshire Borders NHS Trust, The Ridgewood Centre, Old Bisley Road, Frimley, Camberley GU16 9QE Tel: 01276 692919 Fax: 01276 605366 — MB ChB 1991 Aberd.; MBA Ed. 1994. SHO (Psychiat.) Ridgewood Centre Frimley, Surrey. Prev: Psychiat. Resid. St. Paul's Hosp. Vancouver; Stagiere, Servier Pharmaceut. Co. Paris, France.

DREVER, John Charlton (retired) 5 Park Road, Eskbank, Dalkeith EH22 3DF Tel: 0131 663 1331 — MB ChB 1958 Glas.; FRCGP 1981, M 1972; DCCH RCP Ed. 1996; DCH RCPS Glas. 1966; DObst RCOG 1962. Prev: GP Dalkeith.

DREVER, John Henderson Brunton Place Surgery, 9 Brunton Place, Edinburgh EH7 5EG Tel: 0131 557 5545 — MB ChB 1978 Ed.

DREVER, William Mathew Henry 188 Addison Road, King's Heath, Birmingham B14 7ER — MB ChB 1993 Leeds.

DREW, Mr Alfred John (retired) Ridgeway, Barnes Lane, Milford-on-Sea, Lymington SO41 0RL Tel: 01590 642139 — MRCS Eng. LRCP Lond. 1939; FRCS Eng. 1941; MB BS Lond. 1939. Prev: Cons. Surg. Walsall Hosps.

DREW, Ann Bridge Cottage Surgery, 41 High Street, Welwyn AL6 9EF Tel: 01438 715044 Fax: 01438 714013; Bracken House, 7 Coltsfoot Lane, Bulls Green, Datchworth, Knebworth SG3 6SB Tel: 0143 879475 — MB BS 1971 Lond.; BSc Lond. 1968, MB BS 1971; MRCGP 1981.

DREW, Christopher Daking Macfarlane, CStJ 72 Mortlake Road, Kew, Richmond TW9 4AS Tel: 020 8876 5001 Fax: 020 8255 3731 — MB BChir Camb. 1960; MA Camb. 1961, BA 1957; FRCP Ed. 1989, M 1984; FRCP Lond. 2000, M 1964; MRCS Eng. LRCP Lond. 1960; FFPM RCP 1990. (Camb. & Middlx.) Socs: Fell. (ex-Pres) Fell.sh. Postgrad. Med.; Fell. (ex-Pres.) Med. Soc. Lond.; Fell. Roy. Soc. Med. Prev: Sen. Regist. (Med.) Lond. Hosp. Whitechapel; Regist. (Med.) St. Thos. Hosp. Lond.; Capt. RAMC (TAVR).

DREW, Colin Dodds (retired) Tor Hays, Cliff Road, Sidmouth EX10 8JN Tel: 01395 579224 — MB BChir 1944 Camb.; MRCS Eng. LRCP Lond. 1944; DObst RCOG 1948. Prev: Jun. Ho. Phys. (Obst.) & Med. Off. Special Depts St. Thos. Hosp.

DREW, David Walsall Manor Hospital, Moat Road, Walsall WS2 9PL Tel: 01922 721172 Fax: 01922 656742; 54 Anchorage Road, Sutton Coldfield B74 2PL Tel: 0121 355 0219 Email: daviddrew@doctors.net.uk — MB ChB 1972 Bristol; MRCP (UK) 1975; DTM & H Liverp. 1979; MRCPCH 1997. (Bristol University) Cons. Paediat. Walsall Manor Hosp.; Hon. Sen. Lect. (Paediat.) Univ. Birm. Prev: Sen. Lect. (Paediat.) Univ. Jos, Nigeria; Med. Off. N.. Refugee Camps, Thailand; Regist. Birm. Childr. Hosp.

DREW, Joanne Lesley Bangor Health Centre, Newtownards Road, Bangor BT20 4LD Tel: 02891 515222 Fax: 02891 515397; 100 Princetown Road, Bangor BT20 3TG Tel: 01247 271054 — MB BCh BAO 1983 Belf.; MRCGP 1987; MFHOM 1998. Socs: BMA.

DREW, Josephine Helen City Hospital, Nottingham NG5 1PB Tel: 0115 969 1169 — MB ChB 1988 Liverp.; MRCP (UK) 1997; DCH RCP Lond. 1991. Staff Grade (Paediat.) Notts.

DREW, Nicholas Charles QE II, Howlands, Welwyn Garden City AL7 4HQ Tel: 01707 365075; Bracken House, 7 Coltsfoot Lane, Bulls Green, Knebworth SG3 6SB Tel: 01438 798475 Fax: 01438 798099 — MB BS Lond. 1968; FRCOG 1994, M 1980; DRCOG 1976. (Univ. Coll. Hosp.) Cons. O & G Qu. Eliz. II & Hertford Co. Hosps.

DREW, Olivia Eleanor Tamarind, La Ruette de Patier, St Saviour, Jersey JE2 7LQ — BM BS 1998 Nottm.; BM BS Nottm 1998.

DREW, Mr Peter James Department of Plasitc Surgery, Morriston Hospital, Swansea SA6 6NL Tel: 01792 205678; 6 Dulverton Drive, Sully, Penarth CF64 5EW — MB BCh 1985 Wales; FRCS Eng. 1990; FRCS Ed. 1990. (Wales)

DREW, Peter John Timothy Park Place, High Park, Hawarden, Deeside CH5 3EF — MB BChir 1977 Camb.; BA (1st. cl. Hons.) Camb. 1974, MA, MB BChir 1977, MD 1986; FRCP Lond. 1994; MRCP (UK) 1979. (Camb. & Lond. Hosp.) Cons. Phys. & Nephrol. Wrexham Maelor Trust. Socs: Renal Assn. & Internat. Soc. Nephrol. Prev: Cons. Phys. & Nephrol. Clwyd HA; Sen. Regist. (Gen. Med. & Nephrol.) Lond. Hosp.; Lect. Med. Unit Lond. Hosp. Med. Coll.

DREW, Mr Philip James 29 West End, Walkington, Beverley HU17 8SX — MB BS 1990 Lond.; BSc (Hons.) Lond. 1987; FRCS Glas. 1995; FRCS Ed. 1995. Lect. Acad. Surgic. Unit Castle Hill Hosp. Hull Univ. Socs: BASO; Brit. Oncol. Soc.; Surgic. Research Soc. Prev: Research Regist. Acad. Surgic. Unit Hull Univ.

DREW, Stephen Colin High Street Surgery, 38 High Street, West Cornforth, Ferryhill DL17 9HR Tel: 01740 656578 Fax: 01740 653928; 6 St. Cuthbert's Way, West Cornforth, Ferryhill DL17 9ND Tel: 01740 654502 — MB ChB 1975 Sheff.; MRCGP 1979; DRCOG 1977; Cert. Contracep. & Family Plann. RCOG RCGP & FPA 1977. Prev: Trainee GP N.. RHA VTS; Ho. Off. (Cas.) & Ho. Off. (Med.) Sheff. Roy. Hosp.; Ho. Off. (Paediat.) Thornbury Annexe Sheff. Childr. Hosp.

DREW, Mr Stephen John Orthopaedic Department, University College Hospital, London SW10 Tel: 020 7387 9300 — MB BS 1988 Lond.; BSc (Hons.) Lond. 1985; FRCS Eng. 1992. Regist. Rotat. (Orthop.) Chelsea & W.m. Lond. Prev: Lect. (Anat.) Edin. Univ. Med. Sch.; SHO Rotat. (Gen. Surg.) St. Bart. Hosp. Lond.

DREW, Stuart Venn (retired) Old Postings, North St, Rogate, Petersfield GU31 5HG Tel: 01730 821307 Fax: 01730 821307 Email: s.drew@cw.com.net — MRCS Eng. LRCP Lond. 1969; MFFP 1994; DObst RCOG 1971. Phys Menopause Clinic, BUPA Hosp. Portsmouth; Cons. Pharm.Med. 1999-. Prev: SCMO Community Health (Family Plann.)Portsmouth & SE Hants Dist.

DREWE, Christopher David Cross Farm, Drewsteignton, Exeter EX6 6PA — MRCS Eng. LRCP Lond. 1968; MB Camb. 1970, BChir 1969. (Camb. & St. Mary's) Prev: GP Lond.; Ho. Phys. & Ho. Surg. Qu. Mary's Hosp. Lond.; Ho. Surg. (Obst. & Gyn) N. Middlx. Hosp. Lond.

DREWER, John Robert (retired) — MRCS Eng. LRCP Lond. 1975; BSc (Pharmacol.) Lond. 1972, MB BS 1975; DRCOG 1979. Prev: Trainee GP Swindon VTS.

DREWER, Robert William (retired) 46 Rockingham Road, Mannamead, Plymouth PL3 5BW — MB ChB 1945 Bristol; DObst RCOG 1949. Prev: GP Plymouth.

DREWERY, Helen Kay Dept. Anaesthesia, The Royal London Hospital, Whitechapel, London E1 1BB Tel: 0207 377 7793 — MB BS 1988 Lond.; FRCA 1994. (King's Coll. Lond.) Cons. Anaesth. Barts & The Lond. NHS Trust. Socs: Difficult Airway Soc.; Assn. Anaesth. Prev: Sen. Regist. (Anaesth.) Roy. Lond. Hosp.; Regist. (Anaesth.) Roy. Lond. Hosp.; SHO (Anaesth.) W.m. Hosp. Lond.

DREWETT, Kathlyn Anne Holts Health Centre, Watery Lane, Newent GL18 1BA Tel: 01531 820689 — MB ChB 1981 Manch.; BSc St. And. 1978; MRCGP 1986; DCH RCP Lond. 1985; DRCOG 1984.

DREWETT, Sharon Julia 8 Gayford Road, London W12 9BN — MB ChB 1990 Bristol.

DREWITT, Daniel James Nelson Wester Hailes Health Centre, 7 Murrayburn Gate, Edinburgh EH14 2SS Tel: 0131 537 7300 Fax: 0131 537 7337; 7 Craiglockhart Crescent, Edinburgh EH14 1EZ —

MB ChB 1983 Ed.; PhD Ed. 1978; BSc Bristol 1972. GP Edin. Prev: Regist. (Geriat. Med.) Longmore Hosp. Edin.

DREWITT, Helen Patricia Department of Dermatology, Royal Infirmiary, Lauriston Place, Edinburgh EH3 9HB; 7 Craiglockhart Crescent, Edinburgh EH14 1EZ — MB ChB 1977 Ed.; MRCGP 1981. Staff Grade Dermat. Roy. Infirmiary Edin. Prev: GP.

DREWRY, Henry Robert 40 Harley Street, London W1N 1AB Tel: 020 7436 2827; 18 Buck Lane, Kingsbury, London NW9 0AR Tel: 020 8205 3913 — MUDr 1971 Prague. Prev: Regist. (Orthop.) Ashford Hosp. Middlx.

DREYER, Clive Paul 2 Llandore Close, Connah's Quay, Deeside CH5 4GS — MB ChB 1988 Manch.; MRCP (UK) 1993; Dip. Sports Med. (Roy. Coll. Scotland) 1995; DA (UK) 1995; FRCS Ed. 1997. (Manchester University) Tutor (Emerg. Med.) Univ. Manch.

DRIEMEL, Stefan Janusz Department of Anaesthetics, Neath General Hospital, Neath SA11 2LQ — Lekarz 1964 Gdansk, Poland; FFA RCS Eng. 1972.

DRIFE, Diana Elizabeth Garforth Medical Centre, Church Lane, Garforth, Leeds LS25 1ER Tel: 0113 286 5311 Fax: 0113 281 2679 — BSc (Med. Sci.) Ed. 1969, MB ChB Ed. 1972; MRCGP 1984; DCH RCPS Glas. 1974. GP Leeds. Prev: GP Leicester; Clin. Asst. Bristol Roy. Hosp. Sick Childr.; Ho. Phys. (Paediat.) W.. Gen. Hosp. Edin.

DRIFE, Professor James Owen Department of Obst. & Gyn., D Floor, Clarendon Wing, Belmont Grove, Leeds LS2 9NS Tel: 0113 392 3888 Fax: 0113 392 6021 Email: j.o.drife@leeds.ac.uk — MB ChB 1971 Ed.; BSc (Hons.) Ed. 1968, MD 1982; FRCS Ed. 1981; FRCOG 1990, M 1978; FRCP 1998. (edinburgh) Prof. O & G Univ. Leeds; Edr. Contemporary Reviews in Obst. & Gyn.; UK Edr. Europ. Jl. Obst., Gyn. & Reproduc. Biol.; Non-Exec. Dir. United Leeds Teach. Hosp. NHS Trust; Mem. Edit. Bd. Brit. Jl. Obst. & Gyn. Socs: (Counc.) Roy. Coll. Obst. & Gyn.; Midw. Comm. UK Centr. Counc. for Nursing; Midw. & Health Vis. Prev: Cons. Sen. Lect. Univ. Leicester; Lect. (O & G) Univ. Bristol; MRC Clin. Research Fell. Edin.

DRILLIEN, Cecil Mary (retired) 6 Abbey Mews, North Berwick EH39 4BT Tel: 01620 895095 — MB ChB 1941 Bristol; MD Bristol 1948; FRCP Ed. 1974, M 1966; DCH Eng. 1943. Prev: Sen. Lect. (Child Health) Univ. Dundee.

DRING, Aileen Patricia Morvyth (retired) Spring Wold, Goodmanham, York YO43 3HX Tel: 01430 872350 — MB BS Lond. 1945; MRCS Eng. LRCP Lond. 1944; DPH Lond. 1957; DObst RCOG 1948. Prev: GP Market Weighton, E. Yorks.

DRING, Colin Martin (retired) 9 The Meadows, Worlington, Bury St Edmunds IP28 8SH Tel: 01638 713933 Email: colin@cdring.freeserve.co.uk — MB BS Lond. 1965; MRCS Eng. LRCP Lond. 1965.

DRING, Susan Margaret Sixways Clinic, London Road, Charlton Kings, Cheltenham GL52 6HS — MB ChB 1985 Birm.; MRCGP 1992; DGM RCP Lond. 1989; Dip Obst RACOG. Gen. Practitioner, Sixways Clinic, Cheltenham; Clin. Asst. Syncope Clinic Delancy Hosp. Cheltenham. Prev: Trainee GP Devon; SHO (Gen Med.) Dudley Rd. Hosp. Birm.; Clin. Med. Off. Child Health Torbay.

DRINKALL, John Newman Timberlea, The Street, Hitcham, Ipswich IP7 7NQ Tel: 01449 740718 — MRCS Eng. LRCP Lond. 1956. (Sheff.) Med. Assesor Benefits Agency Med. Serv. Socs: Soc. Back Pain Research. Prev: Med. Off. DSS; Regional Med. Off. DoH; Hosp. Pract. Doncaster Roy. Infirm.

DRINKWATER, Professor Christopher Kenneth, CBE Centre for Primary, Community Care Learning, University of Northumbria, Coach Lane Campus, Newcastle upon Tyne NE7 7XA Tel: 0191 215 6073 Email: chris.drinkwater@unn.ac.uk; Tel: 0191 285 5004 Email: chris.drinkwater@cableinet.co.uk — MB BChir 1970 Camb.; FFPHM 2000; MB Camb. 1970, BChir 1969; BA Camb. 1966; FRCGP 1990, M 1974; DObst RCOG 1973; DCH Eng. 1973. (Camb. & Middlx.) Prof. of Primary Care Developm. & Head of Course for Primary, Community Care Learning. Socs: BMA.; NHS Alliance - Exec. Comm. & Pub. Health Ldr. Prev: Lect. (Family Med.) Fac. Med. Memor. Univ. Newfld., Canada.; Sen. Lect. (Primary Health Care) Univ. Newc.

DRINKWATER, Jean Ann (retired) Stubblefield House, Brierfield, Nelson BB9 5JJ Tel: 01282 694600 — MB ChB 1949 Manch.; MB ChB (2nd cl. Hons. Distinc. Med. & Path.) Manch. 1949; DObst RCOG 1953. Prev: GP Brierfield.

DRINKWATER, Mr John Brian The Boat House, Aviemore PH22 1QP — MB ChB 1954 Sheff.; FRCS Eng. 1961. (Sheff.) Clin. Med. Off. (Community Child Health) Mid Argyll, Kintyre, Islay & Jura. Prev: Surg. Rear Admiral Operat. Med. Servs.; Dep. Med. Dir.-Gen. (Naval); Med. Off. i/c RN Hosp. Haslar.

DRINKWATER, Susan Lesley 27 Church Road, Longlevens, Gloucester GL2 0AB — MB BS 1994 Lond.

DRION, Mona (retired) 62 Eastfield Road, Messingham, Scunthorpe DN17 3PG — MB ChB 1963 Bristol; FFA RCS Eng. 1969; DA Eng. 1966. Prev: Cons. Anaesth. Scunthorpe Gen. Hosp.

DRIPPS, Kara 5 Grant Avenue, Randalstown, Antrim BT41 3AP — MB BCh 1998 Belf.; MB BCh Belf 1998.

DRISCOLL, Jonathan Mark Tel: 01643 703289 Fax: 01643 707921 — MB ChB 1986 Birm.; MRCGP 1993; DFFP 1995; DRCOG 1991. (Birmingham) Clin. Asst. Minehead Gp.

DRISCOLL, Paul Harry Heeley Green Surgery, 302 Gleadless Road, Sheffield S2 3AJ Tel: 0114 250 0309 Fax: 0114 250 7185 — BM BS 1990 Nottm.

DRISCOLL, Mr Peter Anthony 1 Sleningford Road, Nab Wood, Shipley BD18 4BL — MB ChB 1979 Leeds; BSc (Hons.) Leeds 1976; MD Leeds 1994; FRCS Ed. 1984; FFAEM 1993. (Leeds) Cons. (A&E) Hope Hosp, Salford. Socs: Brit. Assn. of Accid. & Emerg. Med.; Europ. Resusc. Counc.; Brit. Trauma Soc. Prev: Sen. Lect. (A & E Med.) Hope Hosp. Salford; Sen. Regist. (A & E) Whipps Cross Hosp., St. Bart. & Newham Hosp. & UCH; Regist. (A & E) Glas. W.. Infirm.

***DRISCOLL, Peter James** 2 West Byres Cottages, By Ormiston, Tranent EH35 5NJ Tel: 01875 340592 Fax: 01875 340592 — MB BS 1996 Lond.; BSc (Hons.) St. And. 1991.

DRISCOLL, Richard Charles Park House, Community Mental Health, Resource Centre, Park Road, Stroud GL5 2JG Tel: 01453 562096 Fax: 01453 562091 — MB ChB 1983 Liverp.; MRCPsych. 1988. Cons. Community & Gen. Adult Psychiat. Stroud. Prev: Sen. Regist. (Gen. Adult Psychiat.) W. Midl. RHA; Regist. Rotat. Char. Cross Train Scheme Lond.; Priory Research Fell. Char. Cross & W.m. Med. Sch.

DRISCOLL, William James (retired) 128 Cheam Common Road, Worcester Park KT4 8QR Tel: 020 8337 1217 — MB BCh BAO Belf. 1942; DObst RCOG 1947. Prev: Surg. Lt. RNVR.

DRIVER, Mr Christopher Philip 2 Highfield, Sale M33 3DN — MB ChB 1989 Aberd.; FRCS Ed. 1993; FRCS Paediat 1999. Socs: Brit. Assn. Paediat. Surg; Scott. Surg. Paediat. Soc.

DRIVER, Helen Elizabeth McKenna & Cameron, 160 Aldersgate St., London EC1A 4DD Tel: 020 7367 3000 Fax: 367 2000 Email: hed@cmck.com; 17 Barnsbury Street, London N1 1PW — MB BS 1978 Lond.; BSc Lond. 1975; MRCPath 1984; Dip. Toxicol. RCPath 1982. (University College London) Partner, Cameron & McKenna. Prev: Path. MRC Toxicology Unit Carshalton.

DRIVER, Mr Ian Kenneth Thorpe Cottage, Great Bealings, Woodbridge IP13 6NW — MB BS 1985 Lond.; FRCS Eng. 1990; FRCA 1994. (St. Thos. Med. Sch.) Cons. Anaesth. Ipswich Hosp. NHS Trust.

DRIVER, Marie (retired) 220 Denmark Hill, London SE5 8DX Tel: 020 7274 5226 — MB BS 1951 Lond.; FRCPath 1987, M 1975. Hon. Sen. Lect. (Morbid Anat.) KCH Med. Sch. Lond. Prev: Cons. Path. King's Coll. Hosp. Lond.

DRIVER, Maurice Venables 220 Denmark Hill, London SE5 8DX Tel: 020 7274 5226 — MB BS 1951 Lond.; PhD Lond. 1961; FRCPsych 1983, M 1971. (Char. Cross) Emerit. Phys. Bethlem Roy. & Maudsley Hosps. Lond. Prev: Cons. Neurophysiol. Bethlem Roy. & Maudsley Hosps. Lond.; Sen. Lect. (Experim. Neurol.) Inst. Psychiat. Univ. Lond.

DRIVER, Nicholas David Old Sea View Stables, Treleague, St Keverne, Helston, Helston TR12 6PQ — MB ChB Leeds 1971; T(GP) 1991. Ship's Doctor. Socs: BMA. Prev: Trainee GP Lerwick Shetland; SHO (O & G) St. Martin's Hosp. Bath; SHO (Paediat.) Bronglais Hosp. Aberystwyth.

DRIVER, Nicholas John Doctors Surgery, Newton Way, Baildon, Shipley BD17 5NH Tel: 01274 582506 Fax: 01274 532426; 37 Station Road, Baildon, Shipley BD17 6HS — MB BS 1985 Lond.; MRCGP 1991; DRCOG 1990. (Char. Cross & Westm.)

DRIVER, Nicholas Peter 45 The Tackleway, Hastings TN34 3BU — MB ChB 1992 Birm.; BSc (Anat) Birm. 1988; MRCP (UK) 1997. Socs: MRCPGH.

DRIVER, Nowshir Ratanshaw Lord Lister Health Centre, 121 Woodgrange Road, Forest Gate, London E7 0EP Tel: 020 8250 7510 Fax: 020 8250 7515 — MB BS 1971 Lucknow.

DRIVER, Ruth Katherine Church View Surgery, 5 Market Hill, Hedon, Hull HU12 8JE Tel: 01482 899348; Gilgal Cottage, Station Road, Ottringham, Hull HU12 0BJ — MB ChB 1987 Leeds; 2000 Dip. Ther. Newcastle. (Leeds)

DROBNIEWSKI, Francis Anthony Public Health Laboratory & Department Medical Microbiology, King's College School of Medicine & Dentistry, Dulwich Hospital, London SE22 8QF Tel: 020 8693 1312 Fax: 020 7346 6477 Email: francis.drobniewski@kcl.ac.uk; The Beeches, 123 Coleraine Road, London SE3 7NT Fax: 020 8858 0003 — MB BS 1991 Lond.; PhD Camb. 1988; MSc (Distinc.) Lond. 1993, MB BS 1991; MA Dub. 1986; DTM & H RCP Lond. 1993. (St. Barts. Med. Coll. Lond.) Cons. (Med. Microbiol.) Pub. Health Laborat. Serv. Dulwich Hosp. Lond.; Dir. Mycobacterium Refer. Unit 1996; Prof. of Tuberc. and Mycobacterial Dis.s, Guys, Kings and St thomas' Sch. of Med., Kings Coll. Lond.; Hon. Sen. Lect. Lond. Sch. Hyg. & Trop. Med.; Hon. Cons. King's Healthcare Trust. Socs: Fell. Roy. Soc. Med.; Fell. Linnean Soc. & Roy. Soc. Trop. Med. & Hyg.; Amer. Soc. Microbiol. & Soc. Gen. Microbiol. Prev: Hon. Clin. Lect. King's Coll. Sch. Med. & Dent. Lond.; Sen. Regist. Pub. Health Laborat. Serv.; Regist. Pub. Health Laborat. Serv.

DROLLER, Balbina (retired) 15 Holmwood Gardens, London N3 3NS Tel: 020 8346 8065 — LRCP LRCS 1935 Ed.; MD Berlin, 1933; LRCP LRCS Ed. LRFPS Glas. 1935. Prev: Med. Off. i/c Family Plann. Assn. Clinics Leeds.

DROMEY, John Finbarr The Surgery, Kinmel Avenue, Abergele LL22 7LP Tel: 01745 833158 Fax: 01745 822490; Gorllwyn, Alexandra Road, Abergele LL22 7LS Tel: 01745 825737 — MB BCh BAO NUI 1981.

DROMGOOLE, Jean Elizabeth (retired) 70 Meopham Road, Mitcham CR4 1BJ Tel: 020 8648 5550 — MB BChir Camb. 1956; MA Camb. 1957; MRCS Eng. LRCP Lond. 1956; DObst RCOG 1959; DA Eng. 1960. Assoc. Specialist (Anaesth.) Kingston Hosp. Kingston-upon-Thames.

DRONFIELD, Michael William West House, Melancholy Walk, Stamford PE9 2QN — MB ChB 1969 St. And.; DM Nottm. 1979; FRCP Lond. 1989; MRCP (U.K.) 1972. Cons. Phys. P'boro. Health Dist.

DROOGAN, Aidan Gerard Neurology Dept, Royal Victoria Hospital, Belfast BT12 6BA — MB BCh BAO 1987 Belf.; BSc (Hons.) Biochem. Belf. 1985, MD 1996; MRCP (UK) 1990; MD Belf. 1996. (The Queen's University of Belfast) Cons. (Neurol.) Roy. Vict. Hosp. Belf.

DROST, Frank 3 Whitegates, Whyteleafe, Caterham CR3 0BX — Artsexamen 1992 Amsterdam.

DROUET, Christopher John (retired) Overend, Greysouthen, Cockermouth CA13 0UA Tel: 01900 824455 Fax: 01900 824455 — MB BChir 1956 Camb.; MA Camb. 1960, BA 1956; MRCS Eng. LRCP Lond. 1956; DObst RCOG 1957. Prev: Ho. Off. (Surg.) St. Mary's Hosp. Lond.

DROUET, Felicity Halina c/o Bryn-y-Neuadd Hospital, Aber Road, Llanfairfechan LL33 0HH Tel: 01248 682682 Fax: 01248 682695 Email: vera.burns@nww.tr.wales.nhs.uk; Bryn Meddyg, Pentir, Bangor LL57 4UY Tel: 01248 364785 — MB ChB 1977 Leeds; MRCPsych 1988; BSc (Hons) Pharmacol. Leeds 1974. Cons. Psychiat. (Learning Disabil.) N. W. Wales NHS Trust. Socs: Welsh Psychiat. Assoc. Prev: Sen. Regist. (Psychiat. of Learning Disabil.) Nottm.

***DROUGHT, Judith Victoria** The Ipswich Hospital, Heath Road, Ipswich IP4 5PD — BM BCh 1997 Oxf.

DROUGHT, Lorna Hanson (retired) 140 Osborne Road, Sheffield S11 9BB Tel: 0114 255 0143 — MB ChB Ed. 1943; DPH Lond. 1947. Prev: Clin. Asst. (Geriat. Med.) Nether Edge Hosp. Sheff.

DROUGHT, Terence Kenneth Oakfield House Surgery, Low Westwood, Hamsterley Colliery, Newcastle upon Tyne NE17 7PT Tel: 01207 560206 Fax: 01207 560172 — MB BCh BAO 1972 Belf.; DObst RCOG 1974. (Queen's University Belfast) GP Newc. u. Tyne. Prev: GP Ruskington; Ho. Off. Mid-Ulster Hosp. Magherafelt; Squadron Ldr. RAF Med. Br.

DROUOT, Jane Elizabeth University Medical Centre, Giles Lane, Canterbury CT2 7LR Tel: 01227 765682; 1A Chapel Lane, Blean, Canterbury CT2 9HA Tel: 01227 471302 — MB BS 1978 Lond.

DROWN, Eva Margery Little Dene, 20 Brooklyn Avenue, Worthing BN11 5QJ Tel: 01903 48530 — MRCS Eng. LRCP Lond. 1937. (Lond. Sch. Med. Wom.) Prev: Res. Med. Off. Nether Edge Hosp. Sheff.; Res. Med. Off. Jenny Lind Hosp. Childr. Norwich; Ho. Surg. Eliz. G. Anderson Hosp.

DROWN, Geoffrey Keith Mervyn Netherthorpe House, Netherthorpe, Worksop S80 3JQ Tel: 01909 3513 — MB BS 1950 Lond. (St. Bart.) Prev: Ho. Surg. Lister Hosp. Hitchin; Ho. Phys. Selly Oak Hosp. Birm.; Capt. RAMC.

DRUCE, Jeanne Mary (retired) Hill House Farm, High Street, Wymington, Rushden NN10 9LS — MRCS Eng. LRCP Lond. 1946. Prev: Med. Off. Bedford Coll. Higher Educat.

DRUCKER, William Anthony Guy's Hospital, Department of Psychiatry, St Thomas St., London SE1 Tel: 020 7235 5743 Fax: 020 7245 6156; Vinnicombe Cottage, West Quantoxhead, Taunton TA4 4DS Tel: 01984 632356 — LMSSA 1984 Lond.; DRCOG 1988. (Oxf.) Regist. Guy's Hosp. Lond. Prev: SHO St. John's Hosp. Aylesbury & St. Geo. Hosp. Lond.; Ho. Off. Stoke Mandeville Hosp. & Roy. Surrey Co. Hosp.

DRUCQUER, John Kenneth (retired) Manesty, 5 Stoney Butts, Stainland Road, Barkisland, Halifax HX4 0EX Tel: 01422 823902 — MRCS Eng. LRCP Lond. 1939; BSc (1st cl. Hons. Physiol.) Leeds 1935, MB ChB; (2nd Cl. Hons.) 1938; MRCGP 1961. Clin. Asst. St Luke's Hosp. & Bradleywood Hosp. Huddersfield. Prev: Clin. Asst. Hosp. of St. Cross Rugby.

DRUMMOND, Alastair Wilson (retired) Valhalla, Unthank Square, Berwick-upon-Tweed TD15 2NG Tel: 01289 304788 — MB ChB 1955 Manch.; MRCPsych 1971; DPM Eng. 1959. Prev: Dir. Scott. Hosp. Advis. Serv.

DRUMMOND, Catherine Ruth Division of Psychiatry of Disability, Jenner Wing, St Georges Hospital Medical School, London SW17 0RE Tel: 020 8672 9944; Normansfield, Kingston Road, Teddington TW11 9JH Tel: 020 8977 7583 Fax: 020 8977 0697 — MB BS 1979 Lond.; MRCPsych 1987; MRCGP 1983. Sen. Lect. & Cons. St. Geo. Hosp. Lond. Prev: Lect. & Sen. Regist. Guys. Hosp. Lond.

DRUMMOND, David Clark 120 Braid Road, Edinburgh EH10 6AS Tel: 0131 447 6658 — LRCP LRCS 1947 Ed.; LRCP LRCS Ed. LRFPS Glas. 1947.

DRUMMOND, David Colin Department of Psychiatry of Addictive Behaviour, 6th Floor Hunter Wing, St George's Hospital Medical School, Cranmer Terrace, London SW17 0RE Tel: 020 8725 2780 Fax: 020 8725 2914 Email: sgju970@sghms.ac.uk; Ferndene, 9a Smitham Bottom Lane, Purley CR8 3DE Tel: 020 8668 5132 — MB ChB 1981 Glas.; MD Glas. 1991; MRCPsych 1985; FRCPsych 1998. Sen. Lect. (Addic. Behaviour) St. Geo. Hosp. Med. Sch. Lond.; Hon. Cons. Psychiat. S. W. Lond. St Geo. Ment. Health Care NHS Trust. Socs: Roy. Coll. Psychiat.; Soc. Study of Addic.; BMA. Prev: Sen. Lect. & Hon. Cons. Psychiat. Inst. Psychiat. Lond.; Lect. & Hon. Sen. Regist. Addic. Research Unit Inst. Psychiat. Lond.; Regist. (Psychiat.) S.. Gen. Hosp. Glas.

DRUMMOND, Garfield Anthony Dept of Clinical Pharmacology, Division of Medicine and Therapeutics, Leicester Royal Infirmary, Leicester LE2 7LX; 20 Hawthorn View, The Meadows, Nottingham NG2 1GA — BM BCh 1990 Oxf. Spec. Reg. Clin. Pharm. Leic. Roy. Inf.

DRUMMOND, Gordon Blair 73 Elveley Drive, West Ella, Hull HU10 7RX Tel: 01482 654197 — LRCP LRCS 1936 Ed.; LRCP LRCS Ed. LRFPS Glas. 1936. (Ed.)

DRUMMOND, Gordon Blair Department of Anaesthetics, Royal Infirmary, Edinburgh EH3 9YW Tel: 0131 536 3652 Fax: 0131 536 3672 Email: g.b.drummond@ed.ac.uk; 6 Millerfield Place, Edinburgh EH9 1LW Tel: 0131 662 4222 — MB ChB 1969 Ed.; MA Camb. 1970; FFA RCS Eng. 1973. Sen. Lect. (Anaesth.) Univ. Ed.; Sect. Ed. Brit. Jl. Anaesth. Prev: Professeur Associé Univ. Paris XII; Vis. Lect. McGill Univ., Montreal; Lect. & Regist. (Anaesth.) Roy. Infirm Edin.

DRUMMOND, James, VRD Loxwood Chase, Loxwood, Billingshurst RH14 0QW Tel: 01403 752253 — MB ChB Ed. 1948, DPH 1952; FFCM 1980, M 1972. Prev: Area Med. Off. Surrey AHA; Co. Med. Off. Surrey CC; Surg. Lt.-Cdr. RNR.

DRUMMOND, James Scott (retired) Abingdon, 16 Gallwey Avenue, Birchington CT7 9PA Tel: 01843 841831 — MB ChB 1941 Ed.

DRUMMOND, John Wilson Gatehead Road Surgery, Gatehead Road, Crosshouse, Kilmarnock KA2 0HU Tel: 01563 521506 Fax: 01563 573695 — MB ChB 1974 Dundee; MB ChB 1974 Dundee.

DRUMMOND, Lynne Marjorie Psychotherapy, Department of Psychiatry, St. George's Hospital Medical School, Cranmer Terrace, London SW17 0RE Tel: 020 8725 5561 Fax: 020 8725 1216 Email: ldrummond@sghm.ac.uk — MB ChB 1976 Glas.; MRCP (UK) 1979; FRCPsych 1996, M 1981. (Univ. Glas.) Cons. Psychiat. & Sen. Lect. (Behavioural Psychother.) St. Geo. Hosp. Med. Sch.; Clin. Tutor (Psychiat.) St. Geo. Hosp. Med. Sch. Prev: Sen. Regist. Rotat. Maudsley Hosp. Lond.

DRUMMOND, Margaret Blackwood 80/90 Kinfauns Drive, Drumchapel, Glasgow G15 7TS Tel: 0141 211 6150 — MB ChB 1963 Ed.; DCH RCPS Glas. 1966.

DRUMMOND, Mark William 42 Alexander Avenue, Eaglesham, Glasgow G76 0DW — MB ChB 1992 Glas.

DRUMMOND, Maurice Hugh 19 Riverbank Road, Heswall, Wirral CH60 4SQ — MB BCh BAO 1952 NUI.

DRUMMOND, Paula Margaret Child Health Centre, Jonh St., Ashington Email: paula2@doctors.org.uk; 1 Matthew Bank, High West Jesmond, Newcastle upon Tyne NE2 3QY Tel: 0191 284 9076 — MB ChB 1989 Glas.; MRCP (UK) 1993; DCH RCP Lond. 1993. p/t Specialist Regist. (Paediat.) Newc. u. Tyne. Prev: Regist. (Paediat.) Newc.

DRUMMOND, Paula Mildred Regents Park Road Surgery, 99 Regents Park Road, London NW1 8UR Tel: 020 7722 0038 Fax: 020 7722 9724 — MB BS 1972 Lond. Prev: Regist. (Radiother.) Univ. Coll. Hosp. Lond.; Regist. (Radiother.) Middlx. Hosp. Lond.; Ho. Phys. & Ho. Surg. Univ. Coll. Hosp. Lond.

DRUMMOND, Peter (retired) The Hollows, Stockbridge Road, Lopcombe, Salisbury SP5 1BW — MB BS Lond. 1954; MFOM RCP Lond. 1979; DIH Eng. 1967. Med. Off. Min. of Defence. Prev: Div. Med. Off. Fisons Ltd. Agrochem Div.

DRUMMOND, Mr Peter McGregor The Old Rectory, Lincoln Road, Boothby Graffoe, Lincoln LN5 0LB — MB ChB 1966 Ed.; FRCS Ed. 1972. (Ed.) Cons. Ophth. Lincoln Co. Hosp. Prev: Sen. Regist. Dept. Ophth. Roy. Vict. Infirm. Newc.; Regist. (Ophth.) P.ss Alexandra Eye Pavil. Edin.

DRUMMOND, Richard Charles Three Ways, Coney Weston, Bury St Edmunds IP31 1HG — MB ChB 1987 Bristol; MRCGP 1992; DRCOG 1991; DCH RCP Lond. 1991.

DRUMMOND, Robert Duff Woodlands Hospital, Cults, Aberdeen AB15 9PR Tel: 01224 551513 Fax: 01224 551607 — MB ChB 1969 St. And.; DPM Ed. & Glas. 1972; FRPsych 1973. Cons. Psychiat.; Clin. Sen. Lect. (Ment. Health) Univ. Aberd.; Hon. Lect. Robt. Gordon's Inst. Technol. Aberd. Prev: Psychiat. Internat. Grenfell Assn. St. Anthony, Newfld.; Sen. Regist. (Psychiat.) Roy. Cornhill Hosp. Aberd.

DRUMMOND, Robert Neil 22 Gower View, Llanelli SA15 3SN — MB BS 1997 Lond.

DRUMMOND, Roger Stuart Memorial Hospital, Hollyhurst Road, Darlington DL3 6HX Tel: 01325 380100 — MB ChB 1972 Ed.; FFA RCSI 1976; DA Eng. 1976. (Ed.) Cons. Anaesth. Memor. Hosp. Darlington.

DRUMMOND, Rupert Christopher Fraser (retired) Porch Surgery, Beechfield Road, Corsham SN13 9DL Tel: 01249 712232 Fax: 01249 701389 — MB BS 1966 Lond.; BSc Lond. 1962; MRCGP 1974; DObst RCOG 1970; DCH Eng. 1969. Prev: SHO (Obst.) Roy. Berks. Hosp. Reading.

DRUMMOND, Russell Sinclair Flat 1/R, 5 Havelock St., Glasgow G11 5JB — MB ChB 1997 Aberd.

DRUMMOND, Mr William, MBE (retired) Hazelbank, Westfield Road, Cupar KY15 5AR Tel: 01334 53013 — MB ChB 1936 Ed.; FRCS Ed. 1947. Prev: Cons. Surg. E. Fife Health Dist.

DRURY, Ann 3 Parkside Gardens, Wimbledon Common, London SW19 5EY — MB BS 1975 Lond.; MRCS Eng. LRCP Lond. 1974; FRCR 1981. (St. Geo.) Regional Cons. Med. Manpower SW Thames RHA; Hon. Cons. Clin. Oncol. Hammersmith Hosp. Lond. Prev: Sen. Regist. & Clin. Research Fell. (Radiother.) Roy. Marsden Hosp. Sutton; Sen. Regist. (Radiother.) W.m. Hosp. Lond.

DRURY, Arnold Eric Conrad 14 Oakey Lane, London SE1 7HL — MB BS 1987 Lond.; MRCP (UK) 1990.

DRURY, Christine Anne Eyre and Drury, Spring Terrace Health Centre, Spring Terrace, North Shields NE30 1PW Tel: 0191 296 1366 Fax: 0191 257 4050 — MB ChB 1989 Aberd. (Aberdeen)

DRURY, Denis Arthur Noel (retired) East Gate House, East End, Weedon, Aylesbury HP22 4NJ Tel: 01296 641480 — MB BCh BAO 1945 Dub.; BA, MB BCh BAO Dub. 1945; DMRD Eng. 1951. Prev: Cons. Radiol. Aylesbury & Romford Hosp. Gps.

DRURY, John James Cook University Hospital, Maryon Rd, Middlesbrough TS4 3BW — MB ChB 1975 Liverp.; MRCPath 1982; FRCPath 1992. (Liverpool) Cons. Chem. Path. S. Tees HA; Chief of Pathol. Prev: Med. Dir.

DRURY, John Howard 9 Cambridge Road, Bromborough, Wirral CH62 7HZ — MB BCh 1994 Wales.

DRURY, Mr John Kenneth South Glasgow University Hospitals NHS Trust, Department of Surgery, Victoria Infirmary NHS Trust, Glasgow G42 9TY Tel: 0141 201 6000; 10 Main Road, Castlehead, Paisley PA2 6AJ Tel: 0141 889 4512 Fax: 0141 889 4512 — MB ChB 1972 Glas.; PhD Glas. 1976; FRCS Glas. 1978. (Univ. Glas.) Cons. Gen. Surg. Vict. Infirm. NHS Trust Glas.; Clin. Dir. (Surg.) Vict. Infirm. NHS Trust; Hon. Clin. Sen. Lect. Fac. Med. Glas. Univ. Socs: Vasc. Soc. GB & Irel.; Eur. Soc. Vasc. & Endovasc. Surg.; BMA. Prev: Sen. Regist. (Gen. Surg.) Glas. Roy. Infirm.

DRURY, John Norman Girdwood Newark House, Blaby, Leicester LE8 4GB Tel: 0116 277 2707 — MA Dub. 1941, MB BCh BAO 1937; MRCGP 1961. (T.C. Dub.)

DRURY, Naomi Oxford Radcliffe Hospital, Headley Way, Headington, Oxford OX3 9DZ; 125 Bagley Close, Kennington, Oxford OX1 5LU — BM BCh 1997 Oxf.

DRURY, Peter Mary Edward (retired) 80 Green Lane, Liverpool L18 2ER Tel: 0151 722 4941 — MB Camb. 1958, BChir 1957; MRCS Eng. LRCP Lond. 1957; FFA RCS Eng 1965. Prev: Cons. Anaesth. Liverp. AHA (T).

DRURY, Ralph Eugene Frederick 192 Emlyn Road, London W12 9TB — MB BS 1992 Lond.

DRURY, Raymond Reginald 15A Hillcrest Road, Camberley GU15 1LF Tel: 01276 21772 Fax: 01276 21772 Email: raymonddrury@compuserve.com — MB ChB 1968 Sheff.; AFOM RCP Lond. 1989; DObst RCOG 1970. Occupat. Health Phys. Camberley; Co. Surg. (Surrey) St. John Ambul. Brig.

DRURY, Roger Anderson Brownsword South Hill, 69 Yealm Road, Newton Ferrers, Plymouth PL8 1BJ Tel: 01752 872662 — BM BCh 1945 Oxf.; DM Oxf. 1952, BM BCh 1945; FRCPath 1965. (Univ. Coll. Hosp.) Hon. Cons. Histopath. Derriford Hosp. Plymouth. Socs: Path. Soc. & Assn. Clin. Path. Prev: Cons. Path. Centr. Middlx. Hosp.; Prof. of Path. Makerere Univ. Kampala, Uganda; Sen. Lect. (Morbid Anat.) Univ. Coll. Hosp. Med. Sch.

DRURY, Mrs Sally Joanna Margaret Denbigh Royal Surrey County & St Lukes Hospital Trust, Egerton Road, Guildford GU2 7XX Tel: 01483 571122; Bracken House, 15A Hillcrest Road, Camberley GU15 1LF Tel: 01276 21772 — MB ChB Sheff. 1968. (Sheff.) Clin. Asst. (Cytol.) Roy. Surrey C. Hosp. Guildford. Socs: BMA Assoc. Mem. BSCC. Prev: Clin. Asst. (Cytol.) P.ss Margt. Hosp. Swindon; GP Swindon; SHO (Anaesth.) Doncaster Roy. Infirm.

DRURY, Victor Mark Wantage Health Centre, Church Street, Wantage OX12 Tel: 01235 770245 Fax: 01235 770727 — MB ChB 1975 Birm.; MRCGP 1979; DRCOG 1977.

DRURY, Professor Victor William Michael, OBE Rossall Cottage, 14 Church Hill, Belbroughton, Stourbridge DY9 0DT Tel: 01562 730229 Fax: 01562 730229 Email: mj7329@aol.com — MB ChB 1949 Birm.; MB ChB (Hnrs.) Birm. 1949; FRCP Lond. 1988; MRCS Eng. LRCP Lond. 1949; FRACGP 1988; FRCGP 1970. (Birm.) Emerit. Profess. Gen Pract. Univ. Birm.; Jephcott Vis. Prof. Char. Cross & W.m. Hosps. 1989. Socs: Fell. Roy. Soc. Med.; BMA. Prev: Nuffield Trav. Fell. Gen. Pract.; Ho. Surg. Gen. Hosp. Birm.; Capt. RAMC, Surg. Specialist.

DRY, David Stephen (retired) Barnard Castle Surgery, Victoria Road, Barnard Castle DL12 8HT Tel: 01833 690707 — MB BS 1967 Newcastle. GP Barnard Castle, Co. Durh.

DRY, Fiona Jane Salisbury House Surgery, Lake Street, Leighton Buzzard LU7 1RS Tel: 01525 373139 Fax: 01525 853006; Witsend, 5 Stanbridge Road Terrace, Leighton Buzzard LU7 4QU Email:

fiona@beds.demo.co.uk — MB BS 1983 Lond.; MRCGP 1988; Dip. Sports Med. Lond. 1991. Med. Off. Badminton Assn. of Eng.

DRYBALA, Gary 23 Hillcrest Road, Leicester LE2 6HG — MB ChB 1983 Leic.; MRCPsych. 1988. Regist. (Psychiat.) Leics. HA.

DRYBURGH, Elizabeth Henderson Department of Community Child Health, Peterborough District Hospital, Peterborough PE3 6DA Tel: 01733 874911 Fax: 01733 562187; 33 Chisenhale, Orton Waterville, Peterborough PE2 5FP — MB ChB Manch. 1970; FRCP Lond. 1992; MRCP (UK) 1973; FRCPCH 1997. Cons. Community Paediat. S. PeterBoro. Primary Care Trust.; Childr.'s Serv.s Represen. Exec. Comm., S. Peterboroough PCT; Designated Doctor-Child Protec. Camb.shire Helath Auth. Socs: Roy. Coll. Paediat. & Child Health. & Brit. Assn. Comm. Child Health. Prev: SCMO Community Health Servs. P'boro.; Cons. Paediat. P'boro. Dist. Hosp.; Sen. Regist. (Paediat.) Leeds AHA (T).

DRYBURGH, Frances Joan (retired) Biochemistry Department, Royal Infirmary, Castle St., Glasgow G4 0SF Tel: 0141 304 4630 Fax: 0141 553 1703 — MB ChB 1963 Glas.; BSc (Hons.) Glas. 1963; FRCP Glas. 1991; FRCPath 1992; MCB 1981. Prev: Sen. Regist. (Clin. Biochem.) Glas. Roy. Infirm.

DRYBURGH, Pamela Ann Kildonan House, Ramsbottom Road, Horwich, Bolton BL6 5NW Tel: 01204 468161 Fax: 01204 698186; 2 Salisbury Road, Horwich, Bolton BL6 6LN Tel: 01204 468708 — MB ChB Manch. 1970; DObst RCOG 1972.

DRYBURGH, Wilson Alexander 17 Weedling Gate, Stutton, Tadcaster LS24 9BS — LRCP LRCS Ed. LRFPS Glas. 1949; LRCP, LRCS Ed., LRFPS Glas. 1949.

DRYDEN, Colin Murdoch 170 Frew Terrace, Irvine KA12 9EH — MB ChB 1984 Dundee. SHO (Anaesth.) W.. Infirm. Glas. Prev: SHO (A & E) Pinderfields Hosp. Wakefield; SHO (Paediat.) Seafield Hosp. Ayr; Ho. Off. (Med.) Lewis Hosp. Stornoway.

DRYDEN, Fiona Anne The School House, Carrshield, Hexham NE47 8AA — MB ChB 1989 Ed.

DRYDEN, Magda Maria Tile House Surgery, 33 Shenfield Road, Brentwood CM15 8AQ Tel: 01277 227711 Fax: 01277 200649 — MRCS Eng. LRCP Lond. 1970. (Roy. Free) Prev: SHO (O & G) St. And. Hosp. Billericay; SHO (Paediat.) Basildon Hosp.

DRYDEN, Matthew Scott Royal Hampshire County Hospital, Winchester SO22 5DG Tel: 01962 824451 Fax: 01962 825431 Email: drydenm.@hotmail.com — MB BS 1983 Lond.; MA Oxf. 1980; MSc Lond. 1987, MD 1992; MRCPath 1990; FRCPath 1998. (Oxford University & St Thomas's) Cons. Clin. Microbiol. & CCDC Roy. Hants. Co. Hosp. Winchester. Prev: Lect. (Clin. Microbiol.) & Hon. Sen. Regist. St. Thos. Hosp. Lond.; Sen. Regist. (Clin. Microbiol.) W.mead Hosp. Sydney, Austral.; Regist. (Clin. Microbiol.) St. Stephen's Hosp. Lond.

DRYDEN, Norman Keith Barton Farm, Higher Odcombe, Yeovil BA22 8UP Tel: 0193 586 2695 — MB BChir 1946 Camb. (Middlx.)

DRYDEN, Patricia Rae Glynneath Surgery, Bodfeddyg, 102 High Street, Glynneath, Neath SA11 5AL Tel: 01639 720311; The Glere, Heol Eglwys, Coelbren SA10 9PF Tel: 01639 701059 Fax: 01639 700407 — MB ChB 1971 St. And.; FRCOG 1995. (University of St Andrews) Socs: Fell. Roy. Coll. Obst. & Gyn.

DRYDEN, Paul Wynne 1 Pepys Place, Manadon, Plymouth PL5 3DS — MB ChB 1984 Leeds; MRCGP 1993; T(GP) 1993; DA (UK) 1990.

DRYE, Elisabeth Ruth 25 Willow Cr, Oakham LE15 6EQ — MB BS 1997 Lond.

DRYE, Naomi Doreen 18 Wilmont Street, London E2 0BS — MB BS 1994 Lond.

DRYHURST, David James 27 Moor Road, Leeds LS6 4BG — MB BS 1989 Newc.

DRYHURST, Kay Marie 1 Prince Andrews Road, Norwich NR6 6XJ — MB BS 1992 Lond.; MRCP (UK) 1995; MSc 1998. Regist. (Paediat. Gastroenterol.) St Barts. Socs: BSPGN; MRCP. Prev: Regist. (Paediat. Gastroenterol.) Gt. Ormond St.; Regist. (Gen. Paediat.) Colchester Gen. Paediat.; SHO (Paediat. Infec. Dis.s) Gt. Ormond St. Hosp. Lond.

DRYSDALE, Mr Andrew James Taunton + Somerset Hospital, Musgrove Park, Taunton TA1 5DA — MB BCh BAO 1983 NUI; FRCS (Orl.) Eng. 1990; FRCS Ed. 1988; LRCPI & LM, LRCSI & LM 1983; FRCS (ORL) 1994. Cons. Otolaryngologist, Taunton & Som. Hosp. Prev: Regist. (Otolaryngol.) St. Geo. Hosp. Tooting & Roy. Surrey Co. Hosp. Guildford.; Sen. Regist. (Otolaryngol.) St. Mary's Hosp. Paddington & Roy. MarsdenHosp.

DRYSDALE, Constance Flockhart (retired) 69 Falcoln Court, Edinburgh EH10 4AG Tel: 0131 447 6701 — MB ChB 1943 St. And.; BSc (Hons.) St. And. 1937, MB ChB 1943; MFCM RCP (UK) 1971; DPH 1948. Prev: Community Health Specialist Scott. Health Servs.

DRYSDALE, Henry Campbell (retired) Tower View, South St., Totnes TQ9 5DZ — MB ChB 1961 Ed.; MSc Lond. 1985; BSc 1963, MB ChB 1961; MRCPath 1969, D 1968; DMJ Soc. Apoth. Lond. 1967.

DRYSDALE, Robert George Drymen Road Surgery, 96 Drymen Road, Bearsden, Glasgow G61 2SY Fax: 0141 931 5496 — MB ChB 1969 Ed.; MA Camb. 1970; MRCGP 1977; DGM RCP Glas. 1991; DObst RCOG 1972.

DRYSDALE, Stuart William Rendcomb Surgery, Rendcomb, Cirencester GL7 7BD Tel: 01285 831257; Manor House, Cowley, Cheltenham GL53 9NJ — MB ChB 1977 Aberd.

DRYSDALE, Susan Helen 16 Warlbeck, Kings Road, Ilkley LS29 9RH — MB ChB 1993 Manch.; MRCP (UK) 1997. (Manch.) Specialist Regist. Gen. Geriat. Med. Yorks. Deanery. Socs: Brit.Geriat.s soc. Prev: SHO (Med.) Blackburn, Hyndburn & Ribble Valley Health Care NHS Trust; Ho. Off. (Med.) Ormskirk & Dist. Gen. Hosp.; Ho. Off. (Surg. & Urol.) Roy. Lancaster Infirm.

DRYSDALE, William Ross, TD Amherst Medical Centre, Sevenoaks TN13 2JD; Old Well House, Rye Road, Sandhurst, Cranbrook TN18 5JG — MB ChB 1965 Glas.; MRCS Eng. LRCP Lond. 1965; DObst RCOG 1969. Sen. Med. Librarian & Dep. Chief Cas. Off. Sevenoaks Hosp.; Clin. Asst. Dept. Psychogeriat Sundridge Hosp. Socs: Brit. Med. Laser Assn.; Primary Care Dermat. Soc.; (Sec.) Pinnochio Med. Soc. Prev: Maj. RAMC, Med. Off. Dept. Dermat. Qu. Alexandra's Hosp. Millbank; Lond.

DRZYMALA, Maria Krystina 16 Westmead, London SW15 5BQ — MB BS 1987 Lond.

DU BOIS, Professor Roland Maclean Royal Brompton Hospital, Sydney St., London SW3 6NP Tel: 020 7351 8327 Fax: 020 7351 8336 Email: r.dubois@rbn.nthames.nhs.uk — MB BChir Camb. 1973; MD Camb. 1981; FRCP Lond. 1988; MRCP (UK) 1974. (Cambridge) Cons. Phys. Roy. Brompton Hosp. Lond.; Prof. Nat. Heart & Lung Inst. Imperial Coll. Lond.. Socs: Brit. Thoracic Soc.; Europ. Respiraritory Soc.; Amer. Thoracic Soc. Prev: Vis. Scientist Nat. Inst. Health Bethesda, USA; Cons. Phys. Roy. Free & Barnet Gen. Hosps.

DU BOULAY, Clair Evelyn Houssemayne Department of Histopathology, Level E, South Block, Southampton General Hospital, Southampton SO16 6YD Tel: 02380 796634 Fax: 02380 796603 Email: cedb@soton.ac.uk — BM 1976 Soton.; MSc (Med. Ed.) U.W.C.M 1997; DM Soton. 1985; FRCPath 1994, M 1982. (Southampton) p/t Cons. & Sen. Lect. (Path.) Soton. Univ. Hosps.; Director of Med. Educat., Sorton, Univ hosp; Director of professional standards, Roy. Coll. of Pathologsts. Socs: Path. Soc.; Int. Acad. Pathol.; Assn. Study Med. Educat. Prev: Cons. Histopath. Univ. Hosps.; Sen. Lect. & Clin. Sci. Soton. Univ. Hosp. & MRC Radiobiol. Unit Harwell, Oxf.

DU BOULAY, Philip Mark Houssemayne Dept. of Anaesthetics, Royal Hampshire County Hospital, Winchester SO22 5DG Tel: 01962 825042; Great Pecks, Blind Lane, Fareham PO17 5HD — MB BS 1975 Lond.; FFA RCS Eng. 1980. Cons. Anaesth., Roy. Hamps. Co. Hosp. Winchester.

DU FEU, Grant John Clement Fareham Health Centre, Osborn Road, Fareham PO16 7ER Tel: 01329 822111 Fax: 01329 286636; 44 Park Lane, Fareham PO16 7LB — BM 1981 Soton.; MRCGP 1985; DRCOG 1985.

DU FEU, Margaret Denmark House, Queen Elizabeth, Psychiatric Hospital, Vincent Drive, Birmingham B15 2QZ Tel: 0121 627 8283 Fax: 0121 627 2934 — MA Camb. 1979; MB BS Lond. 1978; MRCPsych 1987; DA Eng. 1982. Cons. Psychiat. W. Midl. Ment. Health Servs. for Deaf People Qu. Eliz. Psychiat. Hosp. Birm.

DU HEAUME, John Cabot The Surgery, Heywood, Lodway Gdns, Pill, Bristol BS20 0DN Tel: 01275 372105 Fax: 01275 373879; 10 Water Lane, Pill, Bristol BS20 0EQ Tel: 01275 373889 Fax: 01275 373879 — MB BS 1971 Lond. (Roy. Free) Clin. Asst. Psychogeriat. Dept. Som. Lodge. Prev: SHO (Paediat.) Copthorne Hosp. Shrewsbury; SHO (O & G) Co. Hosp. Griffithstown.

DU MELLO KENYON, Elizabeth Margaret 53 Winchester Street, London SW1V 4NY Tel: 020 7834 2780 — MB BS 1984 Lond.; MRCPsych 1990. Regist. (Psychiat.) St. Mary's Hosp. Lond. Socs: Conserv. Med. Soc.

DU PELOUX MENAGÉ, Hélène Giselle Department of Dermatoloy, University Hospital Lewisham, Lewisham High St., London SE13 6LH Tel: 020 8333 3000 Fax: 020 8333 3096; 71 Stradella Road, Herne Hill, London SE24 9HL — MB BS 1985 Lond.; FRCP 2001 UK; BSc Lond. 1982; MRCP (UK) 1988. (Guy's Hospital) Cons. Dermatol. Lewisham Univ. Hosp. Lond.; Cons. Dermatol. PhotoBiol. Dept. St. John's Inst. of Dermat. St. Thomas' Hosp. Lond. Prev: Sen. Regist. St. John's Inst. of Dermat. Lond.; SHO Brompton Hosp. & Hammersmith Hosp. Lond.; Ho. Phys. Guy's Hosp. Lond.

DU PLESSIS, Jacobus Meiring Room 9, Main Nurses' Home, Kingston Hospital, Galsworthy Road, Kingston upon Thames KT2 7QB — MB ChB 1988 Stellenbosch.

DU PLESSIS, Jan Van Breda 1 Cottesmore, West St., Oundle, Peterborough PE8 4EJ — MB ChB 1993 Stellenbosch.

DU TOIT, Jennifer Ann Hoyland House Surgery, Hoyland House, Gyde Road, Painswick, Stroud GL6 6RD Tel: 01452 812545 — MB BS 1982 Lond.; MRCP (UK) 1985; MRCGP 1988; DRCOG 1987.

DU TOIT, Johanna Elizabeth 60 Kennett Road, Oxford OX3 7BJ — MB ChB 1975 Pretoria.

DU VIVIER, Anthony Wilfred Paul 115A Harley Street, London W1N 1DG Tel: 020 7935 6465 Fax: 020 7935 5014 — MD Lond. 1977, MB BS 1968; FRCP Lond. 1985; MRCP (UK) 1971; MRCS Eng. LRCP Lond. 1968. (St. Bart.) Cons. Dermat. King's Coll. Hosp. Lond. Socs: Fell. Roy. Soc. Med. (Sect. Dermat. Ex-Pres.); Brit. Assn. Dermat.; St. John's Hosp. Dermat. Soc. Ex-Pres. Prev: Sen. Regist. (Dermat.) St. Mary's Hosp. Lond.; Jun. Regist. Med. Prof. Unit. St. Bart. Hosp. Lond.; Research Fell. Scripps Clinic La Jolla, USA.

DUA, Harminder Singh Department of Ophthalmology, B Floor, South Block, University Hospital, Queens Medical Centre, Nottingham NG7 2UH Tel: 0115 970 9796 Fax: 0115 970 9963; New Manor, 421 Mansfield Road, Redhill, Nottingham NG5 8PE Tel: 0115 920 4406 — MB BS 1975 Nagpur; PhD Nagpur 1984, MS 1977; MD Aberd. 1993; FRCS Ed. 1986; FRCOphth 1989; DO RCS Eng. 1985. (Govt. Med. Coll. & Hosp.) Chair & Prof. Ophth. Univ. Nottm.; Edr. CME Jl. in Ophth. Socs: (Counc.) Med. Contact Lens & Ocular Surface Assn.; (Counc.) Oxf. Ophth. Congr.; Amer. Acad. Ophth. Prev: Assoc. Prof. Thos. Jefferson Univ. Wills Eye Hosp. Philadelphia, USA; Sen. Regist. (Ophth.) Aberd.

DUA, Inderjeet Singh Rossington Practice, Grange Lane, New Rossington, Doncaster DN11 0LP Tel: 01302 868421 Fax: 01302 863622 — MB BS 1969 Jammu & Kashmir; MB BS 1969 Jammu & Kashmir.

DUA, Jasjeet Singh The Surgery, 32 Elsham Road, London W14 8HB Tel: 020 7603 5206 Fax: 020 7602 0417 — MB ChB 1984 Aberd.; MRCGP 1989; Cert. Family Plann. JCC 1989. (Univ. Aberd.) Socs: Brit. Med. Acupunct. Soc.

DUA, John Ashia 41 Holst Crescent, Old Farm Park, Milton Keynes MK7 8QN — MB ChB 1975 Ghana; BSc (Hons. Anat.) Ghana 1972; MRCOG 1984.

DUA, Lavanya Grace Selina Tadworth Farm Surgery, 1 Troy Close, Tadworth KT20 5JE Tel: 01737 362327; 75 Villiers Avenue, Surbiton KT5 8BE — MB BS 1983 Lond.; MRCGP 1992. Prev: SHO (Genitourin. Med.) Jas. Pringle Hse. Middlx. Hosp. Lond.; SHO (Obst.) Whittington Hosp. Lond.; SHO (O & G) Kingston Hosp. Kingston u. Thames.

DUA, Promila Rossington Practice, Grange Lane, New Rossington, Doncaster DN11 0LP Tel: 01302 868421 Fax: 01302 863622 — MB BS 1971 Jiwaji; MB BS 1971 Jiwaji.

DUA, Rita Department of Anaesthetics, Derby Royal Infirmary, London Road, Derby DE1 2QY Tel: 01332 347141; New Manor, 421 Mansfield Road, Redhill, Nottingham NG5 8PE — MB BS 1981 Nagpur; FFA RCSI 1988; DA (UK) 1987. Cons. Anaesth. DRI Derby. Socs: ASA; RCA. Prev: Cons. Anaesth. Thomas Jefferson Univ. Hosp. Philadalphina, USA.

DUA, Roopi Sascha 6 Grange Close, Doncaster DN4 6SE — MB BS 1998 Lond.; MB BS Lond 1998.

DUANE, Elizabeth (retired) 10 Lincoln Way, Rainhill, Prescot L35 6PJ — MB BCh BAO 1957 NUI; FFA RCS Eng. 1965; DA Eng. 1962; DCH Eng. 1961. Prev: Cons. Anaesth. Warrington Dist. Gen. Hosp.

DUANE, Mr Lorcan Peter 44 Cronington Close, Manchester M22 4ZQ — MB BCh BAO 1985 NUI; FRCSI 1989; LRCPSI 1985.

DUANE, Paul Daniel Morriston Hospital NHS Trust, Morriston, Swansea SA6 6NL Tel: 01792 703013 Fax: 01792 703283; 7 Mandinam Park, Gower Road, Sketty, Swansea SA2 7AW — MSc (Gen. Biochem.) Lond. 1986; MD Dub. 1991, MB BCh BAO 1978; MRCPI 1983. Cons. (Phys. Gastroenterol.) Morriston Hosp. NHS Trust Swansea. Socs: Brit. Soc. Gastroenterol. Prev: Cons. Phys. Gastroenterol. Withybush Gen. Hosp. Wales.; Tutor & Hon. Sen. Regist. (Med.) St. Jas. Univ. Hosp. Leeds; Regist. (Gastroenterol.) N.wick Pk. Hosp. Harrow.

DUARI, Mr Monoranjan (retired) Roundhay, 74 Castle Road, Colne BB8 7DS Tel: 01282 863342 — MB BS 1954 Calcutta; FRCS Eng. 1963; FRCS Ed. 1960. Prev: Cons. Gen. Surg. & Regist. (Gen. Surg.) Burnley Health Dist.

DUB, Isidor (retired) 20 Stanley Road, Leicester LE2 1RE Tel: 0116 270 8966 — MD 1934 Prague. Prev: Sen. Med. Off. Leics. AHA (T).

DUBAL, Pratap Rai The Surgery, 27 Burges Road, East Ham, London E6 2BJ Tel: 020 8472 0421 Fax: 020 8552 9912; 56 Bressey Grove, South Woodford, London E18 2HU Tel: 020 8989 4658 — MB BS 1965 Calcutta; MRCP (UK) 1973. (R.G. Kar Med. Coll.) Hosp. Pract. Diabetic Clin. Newham Gen. Hosp. Lond. Prev: Regist. (Med.) Qu. Mary's Hosp. for E. End Lond.; Regist. (Renal Med.) St. Mary's Hosp. Portsmouth; SHO (Med.) Doncaster Roy. Infirm.

DUBASH, Daraius Homi 8 Woodbourne Road, Edgbaston, Birmingham B15 3QH — MB BS 1972 Bombay.

DUBBERLEY, Jack (retired) Tan-yr-Allt Bach, Llanddona, Beaumaris LL58 8UN Tel: 01248 810591 — MB ChB Manch. 1947. Prev: Authorised Med. Examr. Civil Aviat. Auth.

DUBBERLEY, Jean Abell Court, Broxwood, Pembridge, Leominster HR6 9JJ Tel: 01544 340258 — MB ChB 1955 Manch. Community Paediat. Herefordsh. Community Health Trust; JP. Prev: Community Med. Off. Hereford & Worcs. HA; Med. Off. Family Plann. Assn.; Clin. Asst. (Gyn.) Darlington Memor. Hosp.

DUBBERLEY, Ralph Vincent Abell Court, Broxwood, Leominster HR6 9JJ — MB ChB 1954 Manch. Prev: Med. Asst. (Dermat.) Darlington Memor. Hosp.; Ho. Surg. & Ho. Phys. Salford Roy. Hosp.; Ho. Surg. (Obst.) Greenbank Matern. Hosp. Darlington.

DUBBINS, Paul Arthur Plymouth Hospitals NHS Trust, Derriford Hospital, Plymouth PL6 8DH Tel; 01752 763265 Fax: 01752 792853 Email: drdubbins@phnt.swest.nhs.uk; 10 the Crescent, Mount Batton, Plymouth PL9 9SJ Email: dubstruck@compuserve.com — MB BS 1973 Lond.; BSc Lond. 1970; FRCR 1978. (King's Coll. Hosp.) Cons. Radiol. Plymouth Gen. Hosp.; Hon. Assoc. Prof. Thos. Jefferson Hosp. Philadelphia, USA; Hon. Sen. Lect. Plymouth Univ. Socs: Brit. Med. Ultrasound Soc. Prev: Asst. Prof. Radiol. Thos. Jefferson Univ. Hosp. Philadelphia, USA.

DUBE, Asha Kumari 5 Rivelin Park Crescent, Sheffield S6 5GF — MB ChB 1991 Manch.; MRCP 2000; BSc (Hons.) Anat. Manch. 1988.

DUBE, Mr Purshottam (Surgery), 2 Bleakhey Road, Wythenshaw, Manchester M22 5ES Tel: 0161 437 2661; 7 Linden Road, Didsbury, Manchester M20 2QJ Tel: 0161 445 7132 — MB BS 1956 Nagpur; FRCS Eng. 1967. Trainer in Gen. Pract.; Lect. in Gen. Pract. Manch. Univ. Prev: Research Fell. Thoracic Surg. Univ. Toronto; Regist. (Gen. Surg.) Roy. Infirm. Oldham & Birch Hill Hosp. Rochdale.

DUBICKA, Bernadeta Walentina Royal Manchester Children's Hospital, Department of Child Psychiatry, Hospital Road, Pendlebury, Manchester M27 4HA — MB BS 1990 Lond.; BSc Lond. 1986; MRCPsych 1996. (Univ. Coll. & Middlx. Hosp.) Hon. Clin. Research Fell. Child Psychiat. Prev: Specialist Regist. Rotat. (Child Psychiat.) N. W.

DUBINSKI, John 21 The Summit, Loughton IG10 1SW Tel: 020 8502 1585 Fax: 020 8529 1461 — MB BCh 1965 Wales. (Cardiff) Prev: Ho. Off. (Urol.) Cardiff Roy. Infirm.; Ho. Off. Pontypool & Dist. Hosp.

DUBLON, George Peter Nicholas Outwood Surgery, 581A Leeds Road, Outwood, Wakefield WF1 2JL Tel: 01924 822626 Fax: 01924

870975; 25 Carr Lane, Sandal, Wakefield WF2 6HJ Tel: 01924 255522 — MRCS Eng. LRCP Lond. 1970. (Leeds) Tutor Dept. Gen. Pract. Univ. Leeds; Trainer GP Wakefield VTS; Mem. Regist. Cancer. Working.Grp. Prev: SHO (A & E) Gen. Infirm. Leeds; Demonst. Anat. Univ. Med. Sch. Leeds; Ho. Off. Gen. Med. St. James Hosp. Leeds.

DUBLON, Victoria Elisabeth 25 Carr La, Wakefield WF2 6HJ — MB ChB 1997 Leic.

DUBOIS, Jean Daniel Portsmouth Oncology Centre, St. Mary's Hospital, Milton, Portsmouth PO3 6AD Tel: 023 92 286 000 Fax: 023 92 866 882; Holmleigh, Solomons Lane, Shirrell Heath, Southampton SO32 2HU Tel: 01329 833073 — MB BS 1977 Lond.; MD Lond. 1988; FRCS Eng. 1981; MRCS Eng. LRCP Lond. 1977; FRCR 1991. (St. Bart.) Cons. St. Mary's Hosp. Portsmouth. Socs: Fell. Roy. Soc. Med.; Brit. Oncol. Assn. Prev: Sen. Regist. Mt. Vernon Hosp. N.wood; Regist. (Radiother.) Ch.ill Hosp. Oxf.; Regist. (Surg.) Roy. Marsden Hosp. Sutton & P'boro. Dist. Hosp.

DUBOIS, Stefan Victor 91 Foxhall Road, Ipswich IP3 8JX — Artsexamen 1990 Leiden.

DUBOURG, Gordon Osborne 11 Fairlawns, Mansfield NG18 3EP — MB ChB 1954 Liverpool; FRCPsych 19887, M 1971.

DUBOWITZ, David Julian 25 Middleton Road, London NW11 7NR — BM BCh 1988 Oxf.; MA Camb. 1989, BA 1985; MRCP (UK) 1991. Regist. (Diag. Radiol.) Addenbrooke's Hosp. Camb.

DUBOWITZ, Gerald 25 Middleton Road, London NW11 7NR — MB ChB 1991 Manch.; BSc Med. Sci. (Hons.) St And. 1988.

DUBOWITZ, Lilly Magdalena Suzanne 25 Middleton Road, London NW11 7NR Tel: 020 8455 9352 Fax: 020 8740 8281 — MB BS Melbourne 1956; MD Sheff. 1973; MRCP (UK) 1993, FRCP 1997, FRCPCH 1997; DCH Eng. 1962. Research Sen. Lect. Roy. Postgrad. Med. Sch.; Cons. Paediat. Hammersmith & Qu. Charlotte's Hosps. Lond. Socs: Brit. Paediat. Assn. & Neonat. Soc.

DUBOWITZ, Michael Nathan 19 Windmill Road, Oxford OX3 7BW — MB BS 1988 Lond.

DUBOWITZ, Victor Department of Paediatrics, Hammersmith Hospital, Ducane Road, London W12 Tel: 020 8383 3295 Fax: 020 8740 8281; 25 Middleton Road, London NW11 7NR Tel: 020 8455 9352 Fax: 020 8905 5922 — MB ChB Cape Town 1954; PhD Sheff. 1965; BSc Cape Town 1950, MD 1960; FRCP Lond. 1972, M 1962; DCH Eng. 1958. (Cape Town) Emerit. Prof. Paediat. Imperial Coll. Sch. of Med.; Hon. Cons. Paediat. Hammersmith Hosp. Lond. Socs: Fell. Roy. Soc. Med.; Brit. Paediat. Assn.; (Pres.) Europ. Paediat. Neurol. Soc. Prev: Reader (Child Health) Univ. Sheff.; Lect. (Clin. Path.) Inst. of Neurol. Qu. Sq. Lond.; Ho. Off. Groote Schuur Hosp., Cape Town, S. Afr.

DUBRAS, Louise Adele Alma Road Surgery, Alma Road, Romsey SO51 8ED Tel: 01794 513422; 142 Botley Road, North Baddesley, Southampton SO52 9EE Tel: 01703 732933 — MB BS 1985 Lond.; BSc Lond. 1982, MB BS 1985; MRCGP 1991; DRCOG 1990.

DUBREY, Simon William Moatfield Farm, Kent St., Cowfold, Horsham RH13 8BD Tel: 01403 864957 — MB BCh 1983 Wales; BSc (Hons. Physiol.) Wales 1978, MD 1993; MRCP (UK) 1987; DRCOG 1986; USMLE 1998. (Welsh Nat. Sch. Med.) Cons. Cardiol. Hilingdon. Hosp., Uxbridge.; Hon. Sen. Lect., Roy. Brompton and Harefield NHS Trust.; Hon. Sen. Lect. Imperial Coll. Sch. of Med.. Socs: Brit. Soc. Echocardiogr.; Europ. Soc. of Heart Failure. Prev: Fell. (Cardiol.) Boston Univ. Sch. Med.; Regist. (Cardivasc. Reseach) & Hon. Lect. (Cardiol.) Char. Cross & W.. Med. Sch. Lond.; Specialist Regist. (Cardiol.) Harefield Hosp. Lond.

DUCAT, William (retired) 31 Finnick Glen, Ayr KA7 4RF Tel: 01292 441855 — MB ChB 1958 Glas.; MFPHM RCP (UK) 1974; DPH Glas. 1961. Prev: Cons. Pub. Health Med. Ayrsh. & Arran HB & Gtr. Glas. HB.

DUCE, Carole Lynn Ribblesdale House Medical Centre, Market Street, Bury BL9 0BU Tel: 0161 764 7241 Fax: 0161 763 3557 — MB ChB 1970 Manch.

DUCE, Deborah Jacqueline Littlebury, 1 Longaford Way, Hutton, Brentwood CM13 2LT Email: deb@j-duce.demon.co.uk — MB BS 1992 Lond.; DA (UK) 1995; FRCA (UK) 1997. Specialist Regist. (Anaesth.) Roy. Lond. Hosp. Prev: SHO (Anaesth.) Broomfield Hosp. Chelmsford.

DUCE, Graham Martin 79 Ben Rhydding Road, Ilkley LS29 8RN Tel: 01943 609224; Flat 4, 403 Wilmslow Road, Withington, Manchester M20 4NB Tel: 0161 225 4736 — MB ChB 1994 Manch.; DCH RCP Lond. 1996; DFFP.RCOG 1999. (Manch.) GP reg Macclesfield. Prev: SHO (Neonates) St. Mary's Hosp. Manch.; SHO (Paediat.) Wythenshawe Hosp. Manch.; SHO (Paediat.) Roy. Manch. Childr.'s Hosp.

DUCHARME, Anna Louise The Surgery, School Street, Wolston, Rugby CV8 3HG Tel: 024 7654 2192 Fax: 024 7654 4075; Wheatfield, Smithy Lane, Church Lawford, Rugby CV23 9EQ — MB BS 1981 Lond.; MRCGP; DRCOG; Cert. Family Planning. GP Wolston.

DUCHARME, Wayne Albert The Surgery, School Street, Wolston, Rugby CV8 3HG Tel: 024 7654 2192 Fax: 024 7654 4075 — MB ChB 1982 Leic.; MRCGP 1986; DRCOG 1986; Cert. Family Plann. JCC 1986. GP Wolston. Socs: Rugby Med. Soc.

DUCHEN, Leo Wilfred (retired) 15B Greenaway Gardens, London NW3 7DH — MD 1969 Witwatersrand; DSc Lond. 1982, PhD 1963; MB BCh 1950; FRCP Lond. 1984, M 1979; DCP Lond 1955; FRCPath 1969, M 1964. Prev: Prof. Experim. Neuropath. Inst. Psychiat. Lond.

DUCHEN, Michael Roland Department of Physiology, University College London, Gower St., London WC1E 6BT Tel: 020 7380 7127 Fax: 020 7383 7005 Email: m.duchen@ucl.ac.uk — MB BS 1978 Lond.; PhD Lond. 1984; BA Oxf. 1975; MRCP (UK) 1980. Reader Cell Physiol. Dept. Physiol. Univ. Coll. Lond.; Lect. (Physiol.) UCL. Prev: Univ. Research Fell. Roy. Soc.

DUCHESNE, Gillian Mary Department of Radiotherapy & Oncology, Middlesex Hospital, Mortimer St., London W1T 3AA Tel: 020 7636 8333 Fax: 020 7436 0160 — MB ChB 1977 Bristol; BSc (1st cl. Hons.) Bristol 1974, MD 1986; FRCR 1984. Sen. Lect. & Hon. Cons. Radiother. & Oncol. Univ. Coll. Hosp. Lond. Prev: Lect. & Hon. Sen. Regist. Roy. Marsden Hosp.

DUCK, Bertram William (retired) Blackboys, 6 Norfolk Farm Road, Pyrford, Woking GU22 8LF Tel: 01483 715150 — MB BS Lond. 1953; MB BS Lond. 1953; FFOM RCP Lond. 1979; FFOM RCP Lond. 1979; DIH (Soc. Occupat. Med. Prize) Eng. 1967; DIH (Soc. Occupat. Med. Prize) Eng. 1967; DPH (Distinc., Chadwick & Newsholme Prizes) Univ; DPH (Distinc., Chadwick & Newsholme Prizes) Univ; Lond. 1966; Lond. 1966. Prev: Indep. Cons. Occupat. Med. Medico-Legal Expert: Indust. Dis.s & Hazardous Subst.s.

DUCK, Donald (retired) Winburg, Mallaig PH41 4RG Tel: 01687 462804 — LRCP LRCS Ed. LRCPS Glas. 1950. Prev: GP Mallaig.

DUCK, James Lechler 18 St Matthew's Road, Bristol BS6 5TS — MB ChB 1976 Ed.; BSc (Med. Sci.) Ed. 1973, MB ChB 1976.

DUCKENFIELD, Florence Mary Woodlands Surgery, Pilch Lane, Huyton, Liverpool L14 0JE Tel: 0151 489 1806 Fax: 0151 489 0920 — MB ChB Liverp. 1954; DObst RCOG 1957. (Liverp.) Socs: Liverp. Med. Inst.; BMA; Liverp. Med. Inst. Prev: Regist. (O & G) BRd. Green Hosp. Liverp.; Ho. Phys. & Ho. Surg. Liverp. Stanley Hosp.; Asst. Resid. Med. Off. St. Mary's Hosp. Leeds.

DUCKER, Christopher John The Surgery, 3 St. John Street, Whithorn, Newton Stewart DG8 7JA Tel: 01988 500218 Fax: 01988 500737 — MB ChB 1984 Bristol; MRCGP 1989; DRCOG 1988.

DUCKER, Daphne Mary (retired) Merrileas, Leatherhead Road, Oxshott, Leatherhead KT22 0EZ Tel: 01372 843670 — MB BS 1948 Lond. Clin. Med. Off. Kingston & Esher DHA. Prev: Cas. Off. Vict. Hosp. Childr. Lond.

DUCKER, David Anthony, TD Medway Hospital, Windmill Road, Gillingham ME7 5NY Tel: 01634825127 Fax: 01634 825128 Email: tony.@ducker.org.uk; Meadowbank, 265 London Road, Rainham Mark, Gillingham ME8 6YS Tel: 01634 372984 Fax: 01634 372984 Email: tony@ducker.org.uk — LRCPI & LM, LRSCI & LM 1970; LRCPI & LM, LRCSI & LM 1970; FRCP Lond. 1992; DCH Eng. 1972; FRCPCH 1997. Cons. Paediat. Neonatol. & Dir. Oliver Fisher Neonat. Unit Chatham. Socs: Brit. Assn. Perinatal Med.; Eur. Soc. Paediat. Research; Neonat. Soc. Prev: Lect. St. Geo. Hosp. Med. Sch. Lond.; Neonat. Research Fell. Univ. Leic. Med. Sch.

DUCKER, Gavin Michael The Gill Medical Centre, 5 Harriet St., Walkden, Manchester M28 3DR Tel: 0161 790 3033 Fax: 0161 702 9544; 15 East Lyn Drive, Walkden, Manchester M28 3WF Email: gavin.edwina@btinternet.com — BM 1985 Soton.; MRCGP 1990; Cert. Acupuncture Shanghai 1988.

DUCKERING, Jennifer The St Lawrence Surgery, 79 St. Lanewrence Avenue, Worthing BN14 7JL Tel: 01903 237346; 12 Robson Road, Goring-by-Sea, Worthing BN12 4EF — MB BS 1983

Lond.; MRCGP 1991. Prev: SHO (O & G) S.lands Hosp.; Trainee GP S.wick VTS.

DUCKETT, George Kenneth 23 Ridge Park, Bramhall, Stockport SK7 2BJ — MB ChB 1971 Manch.; MRCP (UK) 1976. Hon. Assoc. Lect. Univ. S. Manch.; Cons. (Geriat.) Stepping Hill Hosp. Stockport & St. Thos. Hosp. Stockport.

DUCKETT, Mr Jonathan Richard Alexander Medway Maritime Hospital, Windmill Road, Gillingham ME5 9PL Tel: 01634 830000 Fax: 01634 811250 Email: jonathan.duckett@medway-tr.sthames.nhs.uk — MB ChB 1988 Manch.; MRCOG 1993. Cons. Obst. & Gynaecologist, Medway Maritime Hosp., Gillingham.

DUCKETT, Stephen Paul 16 Thorn Side, Ingleby Barwick, Stockton-on-Tees TS17 0RT — MB ChB 1998 Liverp.; MB ChB Liverp 1998.

DUCKHAM, Christopher Michael John The Old Vicarage, Spilsby Road, Horncastle LN9 6AL Tel: 01507 522477 Fax: 01507 522997; Clapgate House, Ashby Puerorum, Horncastle LN9 6QU — MB ChB 1983 Leeds; DGM RCP Lond. 1986; DRCOG 1985. Princip. GP Horncastle. Socs: Lincoln Med. Soc.

DUCKHAM, Jennifer Margaret 7 Upper Park Road, Kingston upon Thames KT2 5LB Tel: 020 8546 4173 Fax: 020 8546 4173 Email: jennysevitt@ser_duckfsnet.co.uk — MB BS Lond. 1969; BSc (Hons. Anat.) Lond. 1966; MRCP (UK) 1972; MRCS Eng. LRCP Lond. 1969; Cert. Prescribed Equiv. Exp. Gen. Pract. JCPTGP 1981; MInstGA 1982; Professional Mem. Society of Analytical Psychology. (Univ. Coll. Hosp.) Indep. Psychoanalyt. Psychother. Kingston upon Thames (Jungian Analyst); Analyt. Psychol. Gp. Analyst Kingston upon Thames; Dir. C.G. Jung Clinic. Socs: Inst. Gp. Anal.; Internat. Assn. Anal. Psychol. Prev: Sen. Regist. (Med.) Portsmouth & SE Hants. Health Dist.

DUCKITT, Hilary Ann Heather Bank, Vicarage Lane, Birton, South Wirral CH64 5TJ — MB BChir 1984 Camb. Clin. Asst. Nightingale Hse. Hospice Wrexham.

DUCKITT, Kirsten 132 Cambridge Street, Rugby CV21 3NP Tel: 01788 573603 — MB BChir 1989 Camb.; MRCOG 1994. Clin. Research Fell. Roy. Coll. O & G. Prev: Regist. (O & G) Ipswich Hosp. & Addenbrooke's Hosp. Camb.; SHO (Obst.) Qu. Charlotte's & Chelsea Hosp. Lond.; SHO (Gyn.) Univ. Coll. Hosp. & Eliz. Garret Anderson Hosp. Lond.

DUCKSBURY, Christina Frances Joan 8 Princes Avenue, Didsbury, Manchester M20 6SE — MB ChB 1955 Ed.; MFCM 1974; DPH Bristol 1960. (Ed.) Socs: BMA. Prev: Area SCM Rochdale AHA; Asst. Sen. Med. Off. Manch. RHB; Sen. Med. Off. Nottm. City.

DUCKWORTH, Andrew John 237 Hempstead Road, Watford WD17 3HH — MB BS 1989 Lond.

DUCKWORTH, George Gilbert (retired) 4 Rose Bank, Burley-in-Wharfedale, Ilkley LS29 7PQ Tel: 01943 862182 — MB ChB Manch. 1958.

DUCKWORTH, Georgia Jacqueline CDSC London, Lower Ground Floor, 40 Eastbourne Terrace, London W2 3QR Tel: 020 7725 2603 Fax: 020 7725 2712 Email: g.duckworth@cdsc.nthames.nhs.uk; 148 Erlanger Road, London SE14 5TJ Tel: 020 7639 6074 — MB 1979 Camb.; MSc Lond. 1985; MA Camb. 1980, MB 1979, BChir 1978; FRCP 1997; MRCP (UK) 1982; FRCPath 1997, M 1987. (Camb. Univ.) Cons. Regional Epidemiologist, Lond.; CDSC Lond., PHLS. Prev: Cons. Communicable Dis. Control E. Lond. & the City HA; Sen. Lect (Med. Microbiol.) Lond. Hosp. Med. Coll.

DUCKWORTH, Gerald William (retired) 20 South Square, London NW11 7AJ Tel: 020 8458 4559 — MB BS 1953 Lond.; FFA RCS Eng. 1958; DA Eng. 1954. Prev: Cons. Anaesth. St. Geo. Hosp. & Roy. Nat. Orthop. Hosp.

DUCKWORTH, Judith J D Lansdowne and Partners, Helston Medical Centre, Trelawney Road, Helston TR13 8AU Tel: 01326 572637 Fax: 01326 565525 — MB ChB 1990 Sheff.; MRCGP 1995; DFFP 1994; DRCOG 1996.

DUCKWORTH, Louise Amanda 4 Rathgar Avenue, Ealing, London W13 9LP — MB ChB 1981 Liverp.

DUCKWORTH, Margaret Thirl (retired) 22 Lower Green, Westcott, Aylesbury HP18 0NS Tel: 01296 651441 — MB ChB 1958 Ed. Prev: Clin. Asst. The Skin Hosp. Birm.

DUCKWORTH, Marjorie Jean (retired) Hammonds Farm, Shelly Lane, Ower, Romsey SO51 6AS Tel: 01703 812585 — MB ChB 1953 Liverp.; MD Liverp. 1959; MFFP 1993; DObst RCOG 1954. Prev: SCMO Crawley & Horsham NHS Trust.

DUCKWORTH, Mary Jeanne 2 Barn Acre Drive, Parkgate, Wirral — MB ChB 1979 Dundee.

DUCKWORTH, Michael John Bowness Lovemead Group Practice, Roundstone Surgery, Polebarn Circus, Trowbridge BA14 7EH Tel: 01225 752752 Fax: 01225 776388; Redbridge Cottage, Rudge Road, Standerwick, Frome BA11 2PT Tel: 01373 831348 Email: michael.duckworth@virgin.net — BM 1982 Soton.; MRCGP 1988; DRCOG 1984. Princip. GP Trowbridge. Prev: Trainee GP Portsmouth VTS; SHO (Med.) St. Mary's Hosp. Portsmouth; SHO (A & E) Worthing Hosp.

DUCKWORTH, Paul Michelle 320 Buxton Road, Spixworth, Norwich NR10 3PN — MB BS 1975 Lond.; MRCS Eng. LRCP Lond. 1975.

DUCKWORTH, Professor Thomas Department of Orthopaedics, Royal Hallamshire Hospital, Glossop Road, Sheffield S10 2JF Tel: 0114 271 2933; White Lodge, 66 Church Lane, Dore, Sheffield S17 3GS Tel: 0114 236 4981 — MB ChB 1961 Manch.; BSc Manch. 1961; FRCS Eng. 1966. (Manch.) Prof. Orthop. Surg. & Head Univ. Dept. Orthop. Sheff. Univ.; Cons. Orthop. Surg. Sheff. AHA (T); Pres. Brit. Orthop. Research Soc. & Brit. Orthop. Foot Surg. Soc. Prev: Sen. Regist. Sheff. RHB & United Sheff. Hosps.; Surg. Regist. Sheff. Roy. Infirm.; SHO Surg. Manch. Roy. Infirm.

DUCKWORTH-SMITH, Helen Christine 20 South Square, London NW11 7AJ — BM BCh 1987 Oxf.; BA Oxf. 1984. SHO (A & E) Whipps Cross Hosp. Lond.

DUCROW, Mary (retired) 558 Warwick Road, Solihull B91 1AD Tel: 0121 704 3756 — MB ChB Birm. 1965; MRCS Eng. LRCP Lond. 1965; FFA RCS Eng. 1971. Prev: Cons. Anaesth. Solihull Hosp. Warks.

DUDANI, Pushpa Verhomal 75 Moorlands, Wickersley, Rotherham S66 1AS; 19 Dundee Drive, Blackburn BB1 1LR Tel: 01254 670977 — MB BS 1972 Bombay; MS (Gen. Surg.) Bombay 1976, MB BS 1972; FRCS Ed. 1984. Staff. Grade Surg. Rotherham Dist. Gen. Hosp. Prev: Regist. (Surg.) Arrowe Pk. Hosp. Upton Wirral; Regist. (Surg. & Urol.) Blackburn Roy. Infirm.; Lect. (Surg.) Grant Med. Coll.

DUDBRIDGE, Simon Bryan Cheriton Bishop Surgery, Cheriton Bishop, Exeter EX6 6JA Tel: 01647 242272 Fax: 01647 24038; Cotley House, Dunsford, Exeter EX6 7BH Tel: 01392 811647 — MB BS 1974 Lond.; MRCP (UK) 1977; MRCGP 1981; DRCOG 1981. (St. Thos.) GP Cheriton Bishop.

DUDDERIDGE, Tim John 8 Royal York Crescent, Clifton, Bristol BS8 4JZ — MB ChB 1998 Bristol.

DUDDING, Graham John Hadleigh House Medical Centre, 20 Kirkway, Broadstone BH18 8EE Tel: 01202 692268 Fax: 01202 658954 — MB ChB 1970 Birm.; DA Eng. 1972.

DUDDINGTON, Martha Pickering Medical Practice, South Gate, Pickering YO18 8BL Tel: 01751 472441 — MB ChB 1977 Liverp.; 1996 University Dipl. In Counselling; DRCOG 1979. Full Time Princip. Prev: Clin. Med. Off. (Family Plann.) ScarBoro.; Pract. Counsellor Pickering.

DUDDLE, Constance May (retired) Beach House, Shore Road, Silverdale, Carnforth LA5 0TP Tel: 01524 701547 — MB ChB 1944 Manch.; MB ChB (Hons.) Manch. 1944; FRCPsych 1977, M 1971; DPM Manch. 1960; DCH Eng. 1946. Prev: Cons. Psychiat. Univ. Hosp. S. Manch. & St. Mary's Hosp. Manch.

DUDDRIDGE, Michael Department of Immunology, University Hospitals of Leicester NHS Trust, Leicester Royal Infirmary, Leicester LE1 5WW Tel: 0116 258 6702 Fax: 0116 258 6704 Email: mduddridge@uhl-tr.trent.nhs.uk — BM BCh 1982 Oxf.; 2000 MRCPath (Immunology); MA Camb. 1983; MRCP (UK) 1985. Cons. Clin. Immunol., Dept of Immunol., Univ. Hosp.s of Leicester NHS Trust Leicester Roy. Infirm.; Clin. Teach., Fac. of Med. and Biological Sci., Univ. of Leicester (Hon. Position). Socs: Brit. Soc. for Clin. Immunol. & Allergy; Brit. Soc. for Immunol.; BMA. Prev: Speicalist Regist. in Immunol., Leciester Roy. Infirm.; Sen. Regist. in Gen. Med. & Clin. Immunol./ Allergy Univ. Hosp. , Nottm..; MRC Train. Fell., Hon. Sen. Regist. in Clin. Immunol. and Allergy, Addenbrookes Hopital, Camb..

DUDDY, James Ronald 1 Victoria Road, Worthing BN11 1XB — MB BS 1988 Lond.

DUDDY, Marcella Anne 29 Lairds Gate, Uddingston, Glasgow G71 7HR — MB ChB 1977 Glas.

DUDDY, Martin Edward 65 Royal Lodge Road, Belfast BT8 7UL Tel: 01232 793931 — MB BCh 1992 Belf.; MB BCh (Hons.) Belf. 1992; BSc (Hons.) Belf. 1989; MRCP (UK) 1995. Regist. (Neurol.) Roy. Vict. Hosp. Belf.

DUDDY, Martin John 25 Sycamore Drive, Hollywood, Birmingham B47 5QX — MB BCh 1981 Wales; FRCR 1987. Cons. Radiol. Selly Oak Hosp. Birm.; Hon. Sen. Clin. Lect. Univ. Birm. Prev: Sen. Regist. & Regist. (Radiol.) W. Midl. Train. Sch.; Regist. (Med.) WalsGr. Hosp. Coventry.

DUDDY, Olive Margaret St Gabriels Medical Centre, 4 Bishops Road, Prestwich, Manchester M25 0HT; 111 Bury Old Road, Prestwich, Manchester M25 0EQ Tel: 0161 737 2856 — MB ChB 1963 Manch.; MRCGP 1982. (Manch.) Asst. Lect. Gen. Pract. Manch. Univ.; Community Phys. Bury. Prev: Ho. Surg. Manch. Roy. Infirm.; Ho. Off. Oldham Dist. & Gen. Hosp.; Asst. Div. Med. Off. Lancs. CC (Div. 12).

DUDEK, Maria Krystyna Accident & Emergency Department, The Royal Berkshire Hospital, London Road, Reading RG1 5AN Tel: 0118 987 7014; 59 Frensham Close, Southall UB1 2YQ Tel: 020 8575 7152 — MB BS 1985 Lond.; FRCS Ed. 1989; FAEM 1997. (Charing Cross/Westminster Hosp.Lond) Cons(A & E Med.) The Roy. Berks. Hosp. Reading. Socs: MDU; BAEM; BMA.

DUDENEY, Terence Patrick The Bell Surgery, York Road, Henley-on-Thames RG9 2DR Tel: 01491 843250 Fax: 01491 411295; Silgrove House, Dog Lane, Rotherfield Greys, Henley-on-Thames RG9 4PY — MB BS 1968 Lond.; MRCS Eng. LRCP Lond. 1968; MRCGP 1974; DObst RCOG 1971. (St. Bart.) Socs: Reading Path. Soc. Prev: Ho. Surg. St. Bart. Hosp. Lond.; Ho. Phys. Brook Gen. Hosp. Lond.

DUDGEON, Ian de Vere The Cedars, Castor, Peterborough PE5 7AX Tel: 01733 380225 — LRCPI & LM, LRSCI & LM 1946; LRCPI & LM, LRCSI & LM 1946. (TC Dub. & RCSI) Prev: Med. Off. St. John's Hosp. PeterBoro.; Clin. Asst. Gloucester Centre PeterBoro.; Ship's Surg. Elder Dempster Lines.

DUDGEON, John Charles 75 Burhead Drive, Glasgow G51 4QH — MB ChB 1994 Glas.

DUDGEON, Timothy Alastair Moretonhampstead Health Centre, Embleford Crescent, Moretonhampstead, Newton Abbot TQ13 8LY Tel: 01647 440591 Fax: 01647 440089; Adley House, Adley Lane, Chagford, Newton Abbot TQ13 8JG Tel: 01647 433291 — MB BS 1976 Lond.; MRCGP 1983. GP Moreton-Hampstead; Research Fell. Dept. Gen. Pract. Univ. Exeter. Prev: Vocational Trainee Gen. Pract. Exeter; SHO (Intens. Ther. Unit.) St. Thos. Hosp. Lond.; SHO (Cardiol. & Respirat. Med.) Brompton Hosp. Lond.

DUDGEON, Valerie Elliott 13 Ingliston Drive, Bishopton PA7 5JS — MB ChB 1993 Glas.; MRCGP 1997; DCH RCPS Glas. 1995; DFFP RCOG 1997. (Glas.) GP Princip. Prev: SHO (Med.) Roy. Hosp. Sick Childr. Glas.; Ho. Off. (Surg.) Stobhill Hosp. Glas.; Ho. Off. (Med.) Roy. Alexandra Hosp. Paisley.

DUDLESTON, Keith Ernest Ridgeview, Station Road, Plympton, Plymouth PL7 2AU Tel: 01752 348676 — MB BS 1980 Lond.; MRCPsych 1985. Cons. Psychiat. Plymouth Community Servs. NHS Trust. Prev: Cons. Psychiat. Moorhaven Hosp.; Sen. Regist. (Psychiat.) Roy. S. Hants. Hosp. Soton; Lect. (Psychiat.) Soton Univ.

DUDLEY, Alan Edward (retired) 17 Augusta Road, Penarth CF64 5RH Tel: 029 2070 7324 Email: doc.dudley@virginnet.co.uk — MB BCh 1957 Wales. Prev: GP Penarth.

DUDLEY, Annabelle Frances 19 Ardwick Road, London NW2 2BX — MB BS 1984 Lond.

DUDLEY, Bernard (retired) 6 St Stephen's Close, Skipton BD23 1PF Tel: 01756 798483 — MB ChB Manch. 1952; DObst RCOG 1954. Prev: Assoc. Specialist (Gen. Med.) John Coupland Hosp. GainsBoro. & Diabetic Clinic Lincoln Co. Hosp.

DUDLEY, Brenda Moffat Alwoodley, 46 Amenbury Lane, Harpenden AL5 2DQ Tel: 015827 68389 — MB BS 1964 Lond.; MRCS Eng. LRCP Lond. 1964. (Roy. Free) JP; Clin. Asst. Respirat. Med. Watford Gen. Hosp. Prev: Ho. Phys. Brompton Hosp.; Ho. Phys. Med. Unit Roy. Free Hosp.

DUDLEY, Brian George Worcester Street Surgery, 24 Worcester St., Stourbridge DY8 1AW Tel: 01384 371616 Fax: 01384 444310 — MB ChB 1953 Birm.; DObst. RCOG 1958; Ref. Stourbridge Crematorium.

DUDLEY, Christopher Richard Knox The Richard Bright Renal Unit, Southmead Hospital, Westbury-on-Trym, Bristol BS10 5NB Tel: 0117 959 5433 Fax: 0117 950 8677 — MB BS 1982 Lond.; FRCP 1999; BSc (Biochem.) Lond. 1979, MD 1994; MRCP (UK) 1985. (St. Thos.) Cons. Phys. (Renal Med.) S.mead Hosp. Bristol; Sen. Clin. Lect. (Renal Med.) Univ. Bristol. Socs: Renal Assn.; Brit. Transpl. Soc.; Amer. Soc. of Nephrol. Prev: Clin. Lect. Nuffield Dept. Med. Univ. Oxf.; Jun. Fell. Brit. Heart Foundat.; Regist. John Radcliffe Hosp. Oxf.

DUDLEY, Derek Raymond (retired) Lovaine Place, Graiseley Lane, Wednesfield, Wolverhampton WV11 1PE Tel: 01902 31904 — MB ChB 1948 Birm.; DMJ (Clin.) Soc. Apoth. Lond. 1972. Prev: GP Wolverhampton.

DUDLEY, Esther Anne 12 Dun Park, Kirkintilloch, Glasgow G66 2DU — MB BCh BAO 1986 Belf.; MRCGP 1991; DRCOG 1990; DCH RCPSI 1990. Prev: Asst. GP Tyne & Wear.

DUDLEY, Frances Linda The Hurley Clinic, Ebenezer House, Kennington Lane, London SE11 4HJ Tel: 020 7735 7918 Fax: 020 7587 5296; 202 Peckham Rye, London SE22 0LU — MB BS 1975 Lond.; MRCGP 1983. (St. Georges Hospital) GP Princip.; Cons. GP to Lambeth, S.wark & Lewisham HA.

DUDLEY, Professor Hugh Arnold Freeman, CBE Broombrae, Glenbuchat, Strathdon AB36 8UA Tel: 01975 641341 Fax: 01975 641201 Email: hugh.dudley@btinternet.com — MB ChB 1947 Ed.; ChM (Gold Medal) Ed. 1958; FRCS Eng. 1974; FRCS Ed. 1951; FRACS 1965. (Univ. Ed.) Emerit. Prof. Surg. Univ. Lond. Prev: Prof. Surg. St. Mary's Hosp. Med. Sch.; Foundat. Prof. Surg. Monash Univ., Austral.; Sen. Lect. Univ. Aberd.

DUDLEY, James Mark Haematology Department, Lewisham Hospital, Lewisham High St., London SE13 6LH Tel: 020 8690 4311 — MB BS 1980 Lond.; MA Oxf. 1984; MD Lond. 1991; MRCP (UK) 1984; MRCPath. 1989. Cons. Haemat. Guy's & Lewisham Hosps. Lond.; Sen. Lect. Univ. Lond. Prev: Sen. Regist. St. Thos. Hosp. Lond.

DUDLEY, Janet Alison Children's Renal Unit, Southmead Hospital, Bristol BS10 5NB Tel: 0117 959 5318 Fax: 0117 959 5321 Email: dudley6789@yahoo.com; Manor Farm, Hollywood, Compton Greenfield, Bristol BS35 5RT — BM 1989 Soton.; MRCP (UK) 1992. Sen. Regist. (Paediat.) S.mead Hosp. Bristol. Socs: RCPCH; RCP; BAPN. Prev: CCA Hosp.Necker-Enfautsmaladen,Paris; Regist. S.mead Hosp. Bristol; SHO Gt. Ormond St. Hosp. Lond.

DUDLEY, Josephine The Health Centre, Stokenchurch, High Wycombe HP14 3TG Tel: 01494 483633 Fax: 01494 483690; 11A Green Lane, Radnage, High Wycombe HP14 4DJ Tel: 01494 483469 — MB ChB 1977 Sheff.; MRCGP 1981; DRCOG 1980; DCH Eng. 1979.

DUDLEY, Michael John Airedale General Hospital, Skipton Road, Steeton, Keighley BD20 6TD Tel: 01535 652511 — MB BS 1978 Lond.; FFA RCS Eng. 1986; Dip. IMC RCS Ed. 1991. (Roy. Lond. Hosp.) Cons. A & E Med.

DUDLEY, Mr Nicholas Eric Department of Surgery, John Radcliffe Hospital, Oxford OX3 9DU Tel: 01865 340464 Fax: 01865 341881 Email: nicholas.dudley@surgery.ox.ac.uk; Church House, Dorchester-on-Thames, Oxford OX10 7HR Tel: 01865 340464 — MB BS 1963 Lond.; FRCS Eng. 1968; FRCS Ed. 1968; MRCS Eng. LRCP Lond. 1963; MA Oxon. 1973. (St. Bart.) Hon. Cons. Surg. (Gen. & Paediat.) John Radcliffe Hosp. Oxf. Socs: Pres. Brit. Assn. Endocrine Surg.; Counc. Mem. Internat. Assn. of Endocrine Surgs.; Brit. Assn. of Paediat. Surg.s. Prev: Regional Advisor RCS Gen. & Paediat. Surg.; Chairm. Ct. of Examrs. RCS Eng.; Research Fell. Surg. Research Foundat. Roy. Childr. Hosp. Melbourne, Australia.

DUDLEY, Paul Maurice Dudley, 6 Dyas Road, Great Barr, Birmingham B44 8SF Tel: 0121 384 4848; 801 Chester Road, Wylde Green, Sutton Coldfield B73 5BA — MB ChB 1978 Birm.

DUDSON, Christina Mary Highfields, Heath Road, Whitmore, Newcastle ST5 5HB — MB BS 1973 Newc.

DUERDEN, Professor Brian Ion Department of Medical Microbiology & Public Health Laborator, University of Wales College of Medicine, Heath Park, Cardiff CF14 4XN Tel: 029 2074 2168 Fax: 029 2074 2169 Email: duerden@phls.nhs.uk; Pendle, Welsh St, Crossway Green, Chepstow NP16 5LU — MB ChB 1972 Ed.; BSc (Med. Sci., Hons. Bact.) Ed. 1970, MD 1979; FRCPath 1990, M 1978. (Edin. Univ.) Prof. Med. Microbiol. Univ. Wales Coll. Med.; Dep. Dir. Pub. Health Laborat. Serv. Bd.; Edr. in Chief Jl. Med. Microbiol.; Examr. Comm. Roy. Coll. Path. Socs: Fell. Infec. Dis. Soc. Amer.; (Comm.) Path. Soc. GB & Irel.; Soc. Anaerobic Microbiol

(Comm.). Prev: Cons. Med. Microbiol. Sheff. Childr. Hosp.; Prof. & Sen. Lect. (Med. Microbiol.) Sheff. Univ. Med. Sch.; Lect. (Bacteriol.) Edin. Univ. Med. Sch.

DUERDEN, John Wilson Neander (retired) 15 Carrick Avenue, Ayr KA7 2SN Tel: 01292 264118 — MB ChB 1938 Glas.

DUERDEN, Martin Gilbert National Prescribing Centre, 70 Pembroke Place, Liverpool L69 3GF Tel: 0151 794 8135 Fax: 0151 794 8139; 16 Melloncroft Drive, West Kirby, Wirral CH48 2JB Tel: 0151 625 3532 — MB BS 1982 Newc.; BMedSc (Hons.) Newc. 1979; MRCGP 1986; Dip. Ther. Newc. 1994; DRCOG 1986; DPH Camb. 1997. (Newc.) Med. Dir. Prev: GP Newc.; Med. Adviser E. Norf. Health Auth.

DUFF, Mr Alexander John Bahrain Defence Force Hospital, PO Box 28743, Riffa, Bahrain; Catslacknowe, Yarrow, Selkirk TD7 5NE Tel: 01750 82273 — MB ChB 1954 Ed.; FRCS Ed. 1961. (Univ. Ed.) Sen. Surg. Bahrain Defence Force Hosp. Bahrain. Prev: Chief Surg. Dhahran Med. Centre & milit. Med. Acad. Saudi Arabia; Cons. Surg. Roy. Infirm. Edin.; Director (Surg.) Armed Forces Hosp. Riyadh, Saudi Arabia.

DUFF, Angus Ross Brechin Health Centre, Infirmary Street, Brechin DD9 7AY Tel: 01356 624411 Fax: 01356 623259; Lothlorien, 5 Latch Gardens, Brechin DD9 6LN — MB ChB 1977 Aberd.; 2001 Dip. Primary Care Rheum. (DPCR) Univ. of Bath. S.P. Principle Brechin; Clin. Asst. / Rheum. / Angus (Tayside).

DUFF, Mrs Annabell Ultimo House, 70 Urbal Road, Coagh, Cookstown BT80 0DP Tel: 016487 37467 — MB BCh BAO 1967 Belf.; MFHom 1987. Pract. Homoeop. Coagh & Belf. Prev: SCMO Magherafelt & Cookstown Dists.; Clin. Asst. Mid-Ulster Hosp. Magherafelt.

DUFF, Caroline Stevenson (retired) 3 The Butchery, Sandwich CT13 9DL Tel: 01304 612783 — MB ChB 1951 Aberd. Prev: Med. Off. Dover Coll.

DUFF, Celia Helen NHS Eastern, Capital Park, Fulbourn, Cambridge CB1 5XB Tel: 01223 597649; 9 Ballard Close, Milton, Cambridge CB4 6DW Tel: 01223 440550 Email: celia.duff@dial.pipex.com — BM BCh 1978 Oxf.; MA Camb. 1991, BA 1975; FFPHM RCP (UK) 1996, M 1990. Dep. Regional Director of Pub. Health NHSE E.ern; Director of Studies for Clin. Med. and Fell. of Clare Coll., Camb.. Socs: Director of Train. (Visits) Fac. of Pub. Health Med. Prev: Cons. Pub. Health Med. Camb. HA.; GP Camb.

DUFF, Charlotte Jessie Stalker (retired) Norwood, Longforgan, Dundee DD2 5ET Tel: 01382 360377 — MB ChB 1946 St. And.; DPH St. And. 1949. Prev: Med. Off., H. M. Prison Castle Hantly, Scott. Prison Serv.

DUFF, Christopher Graham Whitefriars, Whittingham Lane, Grimsargh, Preston PR2 5LH — BM BCh 1993 Oxf.

DUFF, Deirdre Alison Whitefriars, Whittingham Lane, Grimsargh, Preston PR2 5LH — MB BS 1961 Lond.; DA Eng. 1965. (Middlx.)

DUFF, Derek Robertson (retired) Peterhouse, Newton Place, Lee-on-the Solent PO13 9JL Tel: 02392 550415 — MRCS Eng. LRCP Lond. 1944. Prev. Bd.ing Med. Off. DHSS.

DUFF, Eleanor Jane 9 Huntsmead Close, Thornhill, Cardiff CF14 9HY — MB BCh 1993 Wales.

DUFF, Gerard Conleth (retired) 93 Coombe Lane, Bristol BS9 2AR — MB ChB 1960 Bristol. Prev: Paediat. Ho. Phys. Roy. United Hosp. Bath.

DUFF, Gordon McGlashan 17 Falkland Avenue, Newton Mearns, Glasgow G77 5DR — MB ChB 1970 Glas.; DObst RCOG 1972; DA Eng. 1972.

DUFF, Professor Gordon William Section of Molecular Medicine, University Department of Medicine, Royal Hallamshire Hospital, Sheffield S10 2JF Tel: 0114 276 6222 Fax: 0114 278 0125 — BM BCh 1975 Oxf.; PhD Lond. 1980; MA Oxf. 1975, BA 1969; FRCP Ed. 1989; MRCP (UK) 1978. Prof. Molecular Med. Univ. Sheff.; Vis. Prof. (USA) Roy. Soc. Med. 1995; Hon. Cons. Phys. Trent RHA; Mem. SESC of Comm. Safety of Meds. Socs: Assn. Phys. Prev: Sen. Lect. & Lect. Univ. Edin.; Research Assoc. Yale Univ. Sch. Med.

DUFF, Mr Iain Stewart The Royal Masonic Hospital, Ravenscourt Park, London W6 0TN Tel: 020 8748 4611 Fax: 020 8748 3817; 62 Park Road, Hampton Hill, Hampton TW12 1HP Tel: 020 8979 1432 — MB BS 1960 Lond.; FRCS Eng. 1970; MRCS Eng. LRCP Lond. 1960. (Westm.) Cons. Surg. Orthop. W. Middlx. Hosp. Isleworth, Teddington Memor. Hosp. & Roy. Masonic Hosp. Lond. Socs: Fell. Roy. Soc. Med. & BOA. Prev: Sen. Regist. (Orthop.) King's Coll. Hosp. Lond.

DUFF, Margaret Catherine Gordon House Surgery, 78 Mattock Lane, Ealing, London W13 9NZ Tel: 020 8997 9564 Fax: 020 8840 0533 — MB BS 1985 Lond.; DCH RCP Lond. 1987; Cert. Family Plann. JCC 1987. Prev: Trainee GP Kent & Canterbury Hosp. VTS.

DUFF, Mhairi Catriona Noram Fry Research Centre, University of Bristol, Bristol BS8 1TX — MB ChB 1992 Bristol. Specialist Regist., Learning Difficulties, Univ. Bristol.

DUFF, Peter William Collings Park Medical Centre, 57 Eggbuckland Road, Hartley, Plymouth PL3 5JR Tel: 01752 771500 Fax: 01752 787183; 23 Eggbuckland Road, Plymouth PL3 5HF — MB ChB 1975 Birm.; DRCOG 1980. Socs: BMA.

DUFF, Sarah Elizabeth 140 Court Lane, London SE21 7EB — BM BCh 1994 Oxf.

DUFF, Mr Thomas Brian (retired) Whitefriars, Whittingham Lane, Grimsargh, Preston PR2 5LH — MB BChir Camb. 1959; FRCS Ed. 1968. Pension Appeal Tribunals The Ct. Serv. 48/49 Chancery La. WC2A IJF. Prev: Cons. Otolaryngol. Roy. Preston Hosp.

DUFF, William John Peter (retired) 48 St Johns Drive, Porthcawl CF36 5PW Tel: 01656 784142 — MB ChB 1952 Bristol. Prev: GP Porthcawl.

DUFF, Yvonne Ruth Anrim Area Hospital, 45 Bush Road, Antrim BT41 2RL Tel: 02894 424293 Fax: 02894 424852; 43 Glenbroome Park, Jordanstown, Newtownabbey BT37 0RL — MB BCh BAO 1980 Belf.; MRCGP 1984; DRCOG 1982; MSc (Palliative Medicine) Bristol 2000. Macmillan Cons. in Palliat. Med., N.ern Health and Social Serv.s Bd.; Regional Speciality Adviser for Palliat. Med.; N.Irel. Observer at Speciality Advisery Comm. of JCHMT. Socs: Assn. Palliat. Med.; Ulster Soc. Palliat. Med.; N. Irel. Forum Ethics in Med. & Health Care. Prev: Med. Dir./ Cons. N. Irel. Hospice Belf.; Clin. Research Fell. (Oncol.) Qu. Univ. Belf.

DUFF-MILLER, Donald Bruce Norbury Health Centre, 2B Pollards Hill N., London SW16 4NL Tel: 020 8679 1700; 60 Woodfield Avenue, Streatham, London SW16 1LD Tel: 020 8769 5226 — MB BS 1957 Lond.; MRCS Eng. LRCP Lond. 1963; MRCGP 1977; Cert JCC Lond. 1976. (Lond. Hosp.)

DUFF-MILLER, Malcolm Thomas 9 Gunnersbury Drive, London W5 4LL — MB BS Lond. 1964; FRCPsych 1984, M 1972; DPM Eng. 1970. (St. Thos.) Socs: BMA. Prev: Cons. Physiat. John Conolly Wing W. Lond. Healthcare NHS Trust; Cons. Psychiat. W. Lond. Healthcare NHS Trust; Sen. Regist. (Psychiat.) St. Thos. Hosp. Lond.

DUFFELL, Erika Frances Gloucestershire Health Authority, Victoria Warehouse, The Docks, Gloucester GL1 2EL Tel: 01452 300222; Top Floor Flat, 26 West Mall, Clifton, Bristol BS6 4BG Email: erika@yeoman.prestel.co.uk — MB ChB 1993 Manch.; BSc (Hons.) Manch. 1991. Specialist Regist. (Pub. Health Med.) S. W. Region. Prev: SHO (Infec. Dis.s) N. Manch. Gen. Hosp.; SHO (Med.) Macclesfield Dist. Gen. Hosp.; SHO (Med.) Nambour Hosp. Qu.sland, Austral.

DUFFELL, Jacqueline Clare Dwyer (retired) 11Landscape Road, Warlingham CR6 9JB — MB BS 1972 Lond.; BSc (Physiol., Hons.) Lond. 1969, MB BS 1972; FRCR 1978; DCH Eng. 1975.

DUFFETT, Jonathan Mark Moorfield House Surgery, 35 Edgar Street, Hereford HR4 9JP Tel: 01432 272175 Fax: 01432 341942 — MB BS 1989 Lond. GP Hereford.

DUFFETT, Richard Stephen Eastham memorial Hospital, Shrewsbury Road, London E7 8QR Tel: 020 8586 5000 Fax: 020 8586 5000; Email: r_duffett@compuserve.com — MB BS 1988 Lond.; MRCPsych 1994. Cons. Psychiat. Prev: Specialist Regist. Roy.Lond hosp.; Research.Fell.Roy.coll.Psychiat.Research.Unit.

DUFFEY, Philip Owen Frederick 7 Finneys Terrace, Claypath, Durham DH1 1RT — MB BS 1988 Newc.

DUFFIELD, David Patrick (retired) 42 Ballantrae Road, Allerton, Liverpool L18 6JQ — MRCS Eng. LRCP Lond. 1954; BSc (Hons.) Liverp. 1951, MD 1963, MB ChB 1954; FFOM RCP Lond. 1983; DIH Eng. 1962. Prev: Dep. PMO & Div. Med. Off. I.C.I. Ltd.

DUFFIELD, Jeremy Stuart 110 Beckett Road, Doncaster DN2 4AX; 21 Jeffrey Street, Old Town, Edinburgh EH1 1DR — BM BCh 1992 Oxf.; MA (Physiol. Sci.) Oxf. 1989; MRCP (UK) 1995.

DUFFIELD, John Elwes The Tithe House, Shurch St., Marcham, Abingdon OX13 6NP Tel: 01865 391357 — BM BCh 1939 Oxf.; BA (Hons. Zoology) Oxf. DM 1948, BM BCh 1939; DPM Eng. 1945. (Chicago, Oxf. & St. Mary's) Hon. Cons. Psychiat. Radcliffe Infirm.

Oxf., Oxf. RHB & Cowley Rd.; Geriat. Hosp. Oxf.; Vis. Cons. Psychiat. HM Prisons Oxf. & Reading. Socs: BMA. Prev: Mem. Parole Bd.; Commonw. Fund. Fell. Chicago Univ. 1931-4; Med. Off. Cane Hill Ment. Hosp. Coulsdon.

DUFFIELD, Michael William Staffa Health Centre, 3 Waverley Street, Tibshelf, Alfreton DE55 5PS Tel: 01773 872252; The Gables, 42 Station Road, Pilsley, Chesterfield S45 8BG — MB ChB 1970 Manch.; DCH Eng. 1974; DObst RCOG 1972. Prev: SHO Airedale Gen. Hosp. Keighley; Ho. Off. Univ. Hosp. Withington.

DUFFIELD, Mr Robert George Maxwell Princess Royal Hospital, Apley Castle, Telford TF1 6TF Tel: 01952 641222; Spring Hill, Sheinton, Cressage, Shrewsbury SY5 6DN Tel: 01952 510777 — MB BS 1970 Lond.; FRCS Eng. 1975. (St. Geo.) Cons. Surg. P.ss Roy. Hosp. Telford. Socs: Fell. Roy. Soc. Med.; BMA. Prev: Sen. Regist. (Gen. Surg.) St. Thos. Hosp. Lond.; Lect. (Gen. Surg.) Roy. Postgrad. Med. Sch. Lond.

DUFFILL, Mr Jonathan Wessex Neurological Centre, Southampton General Hospital, Tremona Road, Southampton SO9 4X7 Tel: 02380 777222 — MB ChB 1987 Manch.; FRCS (SN); FRCS Eng. 1992. Regist. (Neurosurg.) Wessex Neurol. Centre Soton./Cons. Neurosurg.

DUFFIN, David Neil Farndon Health Centre, Church Lane, Farndon, Chester CH3 6QD Tel: 01829 270206 Fax: 01829 270803; Rose Cottage, Caldecott Green, Farndon, Chester CH3 6PE — MB BS 1980 Lond.; DGM RCP 1985; MRCS LRCP 1980.

DUFFIN, Donal 67 Eglantine Park, Hillsborough BT26 6HL Tel: 01846 683563 — MB BCh BAO 1981 Belf.; MRCP (UK) 1985; MRCGP 1994.

DUFFIN, Linda Bettina Farndon Health Centre, Church Lane, Farndon, Chester CH3 6QD Tel: 01829 270206 Fax: 01829 270803 — MB ChB 1980 Manch.

DUFFIN, Marcia Sheila 5 Baronscourt Lane, Carryduff, Belfast BT8 8RR — MB BCh BAO 1984 Belf.; MB BCh BAO Belf. l984; MRCGP 1989; DRCOG 1988; DCH RCPSI 1987.

DUFFIN-JONES, Andrew Old School Surgery, School Street, Pontyclun CF72 9AA Tel: 01443 222567 Fax: 01443 229205; Graig House, Miskin, Pontyclun CF72 8JQ — MB BCh 1979 Wales; MRCGP 1983; Dip. Pract. Dermat. Wales 1992; DRCOG 1982; Cert. Family Plann. JCC 1983. Clin. Asst. (Dermat.) P.ss of Wales Hosp. Bridgend. Socs: (Sec.) Rhondda Med. Soc.

DUFFIN-JONES, Lucinda Parklane Surgery, Mill St, Tonyrefail CF39 8AJ Tel: 01443 670567 — MB BCh 1980 Wales; LF Hom (Med)1998; Cert. Family Plann. JCC 1983. p/t Gen. Practitioner. Prev: Clin. Med. Off. (Community Paediat.) Taff Ely & Rhondda, 1990-1996.

DUFFTON, Scot Nicolson 39 Everest Road, Cheltenham GL53 9LL — MB ChB 1986 Aberd.

DUFFTY, Jane Helen 13 Louisville Av, Aberdeen AB15 4TT — MB ChB 1997 Glas.

DUFFTY, Paul Neonatal Unit, Aberdeen Maternity Hospital, Cornhill Road, Aberdeen AB25 2ZL Tel: 01224 681818 Fax: 01224 404919; 13 Louisville Avenue, Aberdeen AB15 4TT — MB ChB 1970 Aberd.; FRCP Ed. 1995; FRCP Lond. 1993; MRCP (UK) 1976; T(M) (Paed) 1991. Cons. Paediat. Aberd. Matern. Hosp. Prev: Asst. Prof. Hosp. Sick Childr. Toronto, Canada.

DUFFUS, Elizabeth Catherine 2 Clinterty Close, Bucksburn, Aberdeen AB21 9TD — MB ChB 1947 Aberd. (Aberd.) Prev: Ho. Surg. Aberd. Roy. Infirm.; JHMO Sefton Gen. Hosp. Liverp.

DUFFUS, Peter James ThE Elizabeth Courtauld Surgery, Factory Lane West, Halstead CO9 1EX Tel: 01787 475944 Fax: 01787 474506 — MB ChB 1986 Aberd. Socs: BMA.

DUFFUS, Peter Ross Sinclair Albyn Medical Practice, 30 Albyn Place, Aberdeen AB10 1NW Tel: 01224 586829 Fax: 01224 213238; Thornlea, 14 Seafield Road, Aberdeen AB15 7YT Tel: 01224 312313 Email: peter.duffus@msm.com — MB ChB 1970 Aberd.; MRFRCGP 1974; DMJ Soc. Apoth. Lond. 1979; DObst RCOG 1973. Police Surg. Grampian Police; Med. Ref. Aberd. Crematorium; Med. Adviser Robt. Gordon Univ. Aberd. Prev: GP Trainig Advis.1981-1999.

DUFFY, Alice Margaret Farndon Green Medical Centre, 1 Farndon Green, Wollaton Park, Nottingham NG8 1DU Tel: 0115 928 8666 Fax: 0115 928 8343 — MB ChB 1987 Glas.; MRCGP 1991; DRCOG 1990. (Glas.)

DUFFY, Catherine Mary 38 Upper Malone Gardens, Belfast BT9 6LY — MB BCh BAO 1988 Belf.; FRCS Ed. 1992; FRCSI 1992.

DUFFY, Christopher John Argyle Street Surgery, 141 Argyle Street, Heywood OL10 3SD Tel: 01706 366135 Fax: 01706 627706 — MB ChB 1985 Manch.; DRCOG 1988. SHO Rotat. Grafton Base Hosp. VTS NSW, Australia. Socs: Roy. Coll. Gen. Pract. Prev: SHO (ENT) Morecombe; Trainee GP Birch Hill Hosp. VTS Rochdale.

DUFFY, David John 310 Moston Lane E., Manchester M40 3HZ — MB BS 1994 Newc.

DUFFY, Janet Elizabeth Health Centre, Pen y Bont, The Roe, St Asaph LL17 0LU Tel: 01745 583208 Fax: 01745 583748; Bwthyn-y-Wennol, Babell, Holywell CH8 8PR — MB ChB 1983 Manch.; DRCOG 1985. Prev: SHO (Paediat.) Roy. Childr. Liverp. Hosp.; SHO (Psychiat.) Fazakerley Hosp. Liverp.; SHO (O & G & Cas.) Ormskirk Hosp.

DUFFY, John Nicholas Walnote, 5 Bells Lane, Nether Wallop, Stockbridge SO20 8HA — MB ChB 1987 Liverp.; MRCP (UK) 1991.

DUFFY, John Peter Nottingham City Hospital, Department of Cardiothoracic Surgery, Hucknall Road, Nottingham NG5 1PB Fax: 0115 840 2605 — MB BS 1982 Lond.; BSc Lond. 1979, MS 1995; FRCS Eng. 1986; FRCS C-Th 1997. (Univ. Coll. Hosp.) Cons. Thoracic Surg. Prev: Sen. Regist. Rotat. (Cardiothoracic Surg.) Trent HA; Regist. Rotat. (Cardiothoracic Surg.) W. Midl.; Regist. (Cardiothoracic Surg.) Lond. Chest Hosp.

DUFFY, Lesley Jane Chalkers Cottage, Woolston, North Cadbury, Yeovil BA22 7BL — MB ChB 1983 Liverp. Prev: Asst. GP Thornbury Bristol; Clin. Med. Off. (Family Plann.) Bristol HA; Trainee GP S.port VTS.

DUFFY, Malachy Drumchapel Health Centre, 80-90 Kinfauns Drive, Glasgow G15 7TS Tel: 0141 211 6120 Fax: 0141 211 6128 — MB ChB 1984 Glas.; MB ChB Glas. l984.

DUFFY, Margaret Patricia 'Glengarriff', 68 Curly Hill Road, Strabane BT82 8LP — MB BCh BAO 1983 Belf. Staff Grade.Community.Paediat.

DUFFY, Maria Theresa Pollok Health Centre, 21 Cowglen Road, Glasgow G53 6EQ Tel: 0141 531 6860 Fax: 0141 531 6808 — MB ChB 1987 Glas.; Dip Therap. Wales 2000; MRCGP 1993; DRCOG 1994; DCH RCP Lond. 1991.

DUFFY, Martin Simon The Health Centre, Burgage Green, Southwell NG25 0EW Tel: 01636 813561; 10 Westgate, Southwell NG25 0JH Tel: 01636 813383 — MB BS 1959 Lond. (St. Thos.)

DUFFY, Mary 600 Liverpool Road, Platt Bridge, Wigan WN2 5BB Tel: 01942 866137; Everslie, 46 Hall Lane, Hindley, Wigan WN2 2SA Tel: 01942 56911 — LRCPI & LM, LRSCI & LM 1956; LRCPI & LM, LRCSI & LM 1956; LM Rotunda 1958.

DUFFY, Matthew (retired) Knights, Little Waltham, Chelmsford CM3 3NT Tel: 01245 360838 — LRCPI & LM, LRSCI & LM 1949; DPH NUI 1952. Cons. Chest. Phys. Chelmsford Health Dist. Prev: Med. Regist. in Tuberc. Ware Pk. Sanat.

DUFFY, Michael Crawford Park Avenue Medical Centre, Park Avenue, Dundee DD4 6PP Tel: 01382 462222 Fax: 01382 452866; 84 Blackness Avenue, Dundee DD2 1JL — MB ChB 1987 Dundee; MRCGP 1991; Dip. IMC RCS Ed. 1990. Socs: BMA. Prev: Trainee GP Moroysh.

DUFFY, Michael Richard 10 Westgate, Southwell NG25 0JH Tel: 01636 813383 — MB BS 1997 Lond.; BSc 1994. (London.Hosp) SHO Gen. Med. OldCh. Hosp. Romford.

DUFFY, Moya Frances Oak Vale Medical Centre, 158-160 Edge Lane Drive, Liverpool L13 4AQ Tel: 0151 259 1551 Fax: 0151 252 1121; Angorva, 6 Reservoir Road N., Prenton, Birkenhead CH42 8LU Tel: 0151 608 4306 — MB ChB 1972 Liverp.; MRCGP 1976; DObst RCOG 1974; FRCGP 1996. Socs: BMA. Prev: SHO (Dermat.) Newsham Gen. Hosp. Liverp.; SHO (Cas.) & SHO (Psychiat.) Sefton Gen. Hosp. Liverp.

DUFFY, Nicholas Charles 10 Westgate, Southwell NG25 0JH Tel: 01636 813383 — MB ChB 1992 Manch.; MRCP (UK) 1995. (Manch.)

DUFFY, Nicola Jane 22 Montague Street, Edinburgh EH8 9QX — MB ChB 1991 Ed.

DUFFY, Nicola Kathleen 32 Oakfield Road, Londonderry BT48 9BB — MB ChB 1994 Glas.

DUFFY, Mr Patrick Gregory Louise Ward, The Great Ormond Street Hospital for Children NHS Trust, London WC1N 3JH Tel: 020 7405 9200 Fax: 020 7813 8260; Old Willow Farm, The Green, Wickhambreaux, Canterbury CT3 1RQ — MB BCh BAO 1973 Belf.; FRCSI 1977. Cons. Paediat. Urol. Gt. Ormond St. Hosp. for Childr.

NHS Trust.; Hon. Cons. Paediat. Urol. Inst. Urol. Middlx. Hosp. Lond. Socs: BMA; BAUS; BAPU.

DUFFY, Patrick John 132 Tewkesbury Street, Cardiff CF24 4QS — MB BCh 1993 Wales.

DUFFY, Paul Hugh 19 Eastwood Avenue, Giffnock, Glasgow G46 6LS — MB ChB 1982 Glas.; MRCP (UK) 1986; FRCR 1990; T(R) (CR) 1992. Cons. S.. Gen. NHS Trust Glas.

DUFFY, Paul Samuel Flat 1/2, 404 Dumbarton Road, Clydebank G81 4DZ — MB ChB 1992 Aberd.

DUFFY, Mr Peter Martin Dept. Of Urological Surgery, Royal Lancaster Infirmary, Ashton Rd, Lancaster; Wyngarth, Brettargh Drive, Haverbreaks, Lancaster LA1 5BN Tel: 01524 581531 — MB BS 1988 Lond.; MD 2000 Southampton; 1999 FRCS Urol; BSc Lond. 1985; FRCS Glas. 1993; FRCS Eng. 1993. Cons. Urological Surg., Morecamce Bay NHS Trust; Specialist Regist. (Urol.) St Peter's Hosp., Chertsey; Specialist Regist (Urol.) St Geo.'s Hosp., Lond.; Specialist Regist (Urol.) Inst. Urol., Lond.; Specialist Regist. (Urol.) Epsom Gen. Hosp. Prev: Regist. (Urol.) St. Geo. Hosp. Lond.; Regist. (Gen. Surg.) Salisbury Dist. Hosp.

DUFFY, Mr Sean RG St James Hospital, Department Obstetrics & Gynaecology, Level 9, Gledhow Wing, Leeds LS9 7TF Tel: 0113 206 5872 Fax: 0113 234 3450 — MB BCh BAO 1993 NUI; FRCOG 2001; MD NUI 1993; FRCS Glas. 1987; MRCOG 1989. Cons. & Sen. Lect. Univ. Dept. O & G St. Jas. Hosp. Leeds. Socs: Internat. & Brit. Socs. Gyn. Endoscopy. Prev: Lect. & Sen. Regist. (O & G) N.. Gen. Hosp. Sheff.; Research Regist. & Regist. (O & G) N.. Gen. Hosp. Sheff.

DUFFY, Shiovaun Marian 16 Langham Place, Highwoods, Colchester CO4 4GB — MB BS 1983 Lond.

DUFFY, Susan Angela Barrow Health Centre, 27 High Street, Barrow on Soar, Loughborough LE12 8PY Tel: 01509 413525 Fax: 01509 620664 — MB BCh 1989 Wales; BSc Wales 1986, MB BCh 1989. Trainee GP Leicester VTS.

DUFFY, Mr Terence John Merry Tree, Baldwins Gate, Newcastle ST5 5ES Tel: 01782 680199 Fax: 01782 680199 Email: tjduffy@netcentral.co.uk — BM BCh 1972 Oxf.; MA Camb. 1973, BA 1969; FRCS Eng. 1977. (Oxf.) Cons. Surg. N. Staffs Hosp. Centre. Socs: Fell Assn. Surgs.; Roy. Soc. Med. Prev: Clin. Lect. (Surg.) & Sen. Regist. (Surg.) Addenbrooke's Hosp. Camb.; Fell. & Coll. Lect. Jesus Coll. Camb.; Wellcome Surg. Research Fell. Univ. Dept. Surg. Camb.

DUFFY, Thomas Maxwell c/o M O Q, Harold Wood Hospital, Gubbins Lane, Romford RM3 0BE — MB BS 1987 Queensland.

DUFFY, Una Mary Catherine 163 Dunstable Road, Luton LU1 1BW Tel: 01582 723553; Byways, Berry Grove Lane, Aldenham, Watford WD25 8AE — MB BS 1993 Lond.; DRCOG 1996.

DUFTON, Katharine Elizabeth A14 Archway Wing, Whittington Hospital, Highgate Hill, London N19 5NF Tel: 020 7530 2350 — MB BS 1980 Lond.; MA Camb 1977; MRCPsych 1985. (St. Geo. Hosp. Med. Sch. Lond.) Cons. Psychother. Camden & Islington NHS Trust. Prev: Sen. Regist. (Psychother.) Tavistock Clinic Lond.; Sen. Regist. (Psychiat.) Lond. Hosp.; SHO & Regist. (Psychiat.) Maudsley Hosp.

DUFTON, Michael (retired) 6 Cliff Road, Crigglestone, Wakefield WF4 3EQ — MB ChB 1961 Leeds.

DUFTON, Paul Albert BUPA Murrayfield Hospital, Holmwood Drive, Thingwall, Wirral CH61 1AU Tel: 0151 648 7000 Fax: 0151 648 7684; Pinewood, 39 Dawstone Road, Heswall, Wirral CH60 0BT Tel: 0151 342 6312 Fax: 0151 342 4228 Email: padufton@cybase.co.uk — MB ChB 1971 Liverp.; BA (Hons.) Open 1995; FRCP Lond. 1988, M 1976; MA 1998 Manch. (Liverp.) p/t Cons. Dermat. BUPA Murrayfield Hosp. Wirral; Cons. (Derm.) Grosvenor Nuffield Hosp.Chester. Socs: (Ex-Pres.) Wallasey Med. Soc.; (Treas.) Birkenhead Med. Soc.; Brit. Assn. Dermat. Prev: Cons. Mersey RHA; Clin. Tutor Clatterbridge Hosp. Bebington.

DUGAN, Joseph Patrick Hillhead Family Practice, 33 Stewartstown Road, Belfast BT11 9FZ Tel: 028 9028 6800 Fax: 028 9060 2944 — MB BCh BAO 1983 Belf.

DUGAN, Una Myrtle 27 Upper King's Drive, Willingdon, Eastbourne BN20 9AN — MB BS 1958 Lond.; MRCS Eng. LRCP Lond. 1958. (Guy's)

DUGAS, Matthew Norman Sycamore House Medical Centre, 111 Birmingham Road, Walsall WS1 2NL Tel: 01922 624320 Fax: 01922 646744 — MB ChB 1991 Birm.; BSc (Hons.) Med. Biochem. Studies Birm. 1988; DRCOG 1998. (Birmingham) GP. Prev: SHO (O & G) Sandwell Healthcare Trust Birm.; GP/Regist. Birm.; SHO (Orthop., Trauma & ENT) Birm. Heartlands Hosp.

DUGAS, Morag Jane Ashfurlong Health Centre, 233 Tamworth Road, Sutton Coldfield B75 6DX Tel: 0121 308 6311 — MB ChB 1992 Birm.; DRCOG 1995.

DUGDALE, Clodagh Mary Department of Public Health Medicine, North West Anglia Health Commission, Thorpe Road, Peterborough PE3 6; Street Farm, North St, Frechenham, Bury St Edmunds IP28 8HY — MB BS 1985 Lond.; MA Camb. 1986; DPH Camb. 1993. Sen. Regist. (Pub. Health Med.) NW Anglia Health Commiss. P'boro. Prev: Clin. Asst. (Anaesth.) Newmarket Gen. Hosp.

DUGDALE, Cyril John (retired) 1 Marguerite Avenue, Newcastle BT33 0PF Tel: 013967 23094 — MB BCh BAO 1944 Dub.; BDentSc. 1939.

DUGDALE, Robert Vivian (retired) 6 Oakfields Road, Knebworth SG3 6NS Tel: 01438 812784 — MB BS 1950 Lond.; DObst RCOG 1951. Prev: GP Bedwell.

DUGDALE-DEBNEY, Frank Warner The Malthouse Surgery, The Charter, Abingdon OX14 3JY Tel: 01235 524001 Fax: 01235 532197; 24 Norman Avenue, Abingdon OX14 2HQ Tel: 01235 531043 Email: frankdugdeb@doctors.org.uk — MB ChB 1970 St. And.; MRCGP 1977; DCH Eng. 1973; DObst RCOG 1972. (St. And.) Socs: (Pres '97-'98.) Oxf. Med. Soc. Prev: Regist. & SHO (Infec. Dis.) Kings Cross Hosp. Dundee; SHO (Child Health) Dundee Roy. Infirm.

DUGGAL, Ajay 28 Aintree Close, Colnbrook, Slough SL3 0QF Email: ajaydugga@hotmail.com — MB ChB 1992 Sheff.; MRCP (UK) 1996. Socs: Roy. Coll. Phys.

DUGGAL, Anita 37 Rue Claude Tiller, Paris 75012, France; 41 Thornlaw Road, West Norwood, London SE27 0SH Tel: 020 8 670 9272 — MB ChB 1985 Leeds; MRCPsych 1990.

DUGGAL, Balvinder Healy Medical Centre, 200 Upper Clapton Road, London E5 9DH Tel: 020 8806 1611; 50 Hillcrest, Winchmore Hill, London N21 1AT Tel: 020 8364 1355 — MB BS 1983 Ed.; LRCP LRCS Ed. LRCPS Glas. 1986. Prev: Trainee GP Wolverhampton.

DUGGAL, Harsh Vardhan Vidya Prakash South Staffordshire Health Authority, Mellor House, Corporation St., Stafford ST16 3SR Tel: 01785 252233 Fax: 01785 221131 Email: harsh.duggal@ssha.wmids.nhs.uk; 5 Epsom Close, The Chestnuts, Wildwood, Stafford ST17 4TY Tel: 01785 665359 — MB BS 1977 Poona; LMSSA Lond. 1983; FFPHM RCP (UK) 1997, M 1987. Cons. Pub. Health Med. S. Staffs HA. Socs: Pub. Health Med. Environm. Health Gp. Prev: Sen. Regist. (Community Med.) Mid Staffs. HA; SHO (Neurol.) Morriston Hosp. Swansea; SHO (Gen. Med.) Neath Gen. Hosp.

DUGGAL, Jennifer Anne 2 Castle Woods, Redlynch, Salisbury SP5 2PY Tel: 01725 513866 Fax: 01725 513866 — MB BCh 1984 Wales; BSc Wales 1981; DRCOG 1988. Prev: Trainee GP Newport VTS.; Ho. Phys. & Ho. Surg. Gwent HA.

DUGGAL, Kush Nath 27 Manor Way, Lee-on-the-Solent PO13 9JQ — MB BCh 1987 Wales; PhD Wales 1984, BSc 1981.

DUGGAL, Manjeet Singh Healy Medical Centre, 200 Upper Clapton Road, London E5 9DH Tel: 020 8806 1611; 43 Broad Walk, Winchmore Hill, London N21 3BL — MB BS 1970 Rajasthan.

DUGGAL, Monica 15 Granvill Street, Barnsley S75 2TQ — MB ChB 1986 Leeds.

DUGGAL, Rakesh 5 Priory Walk, Wylde Green, Sutton Coldfield B72 1XZ Email: r.duggal@virgin.net — MB ChB 1991 Manch.

DUGGAL, Royendra Prasad Hollyhurst Surgery, 8 Front Street, Winlaton, Blaydon-on-Tyne NE21 4RD Tel: 0191 499 0966 Fax: 0191 414 2891 — MB BS 1973 Dibrugarh. (Dibrugarh) GP Blaydon-on-Tyne, Tyne & Wear.

DUGGAL, Shallini 4 Hall Grove, Welwyn Garden City AL7 4PL Tel: 01707 328528; 13 High Oaks Road, Welwyn Garden City AL8 7BJ Tel: 01707 332023 — MB BChir 1988 Camb.; MA Camb. 1989, BA 1985, MB BChir 1988; MRCP (UK) 1992; MRCGP 1992.

DUGGAL, Vivak 29 Woodhill Crescent, Kenton, Harrow HA3 0LU — MB ChB 1996 Leeds.

DUGGAN, Anne Elizabeth Department of Gastroenterology, Queens Medical Centre, Nottingham NG7 2UH — BMed 1987 Austral.; BA (Hons.) Newc. Austral. 1981; FRACP 1994.

DUGGAN, Antony Joseph (retired) 58 Grosvenor Road, Wanstead, London E11 2ES Tel: 020 8989 2401 — MB BS Lond. 1943; MD Lond. 1948; FRCP Lond. 1978; DTM & H Eng. 1948. Prev: Dir. Wellcome Museum Med. Sc.

DUGGAN, Bernard James 7 Laghtfoggy Road, Castlederg BT81 7XD — MB BCh BAO 1994 Belf.; MB BCh Belf. 1994.

DUGGAN, Diane Rosemarie 28 Humber Drive, Bury BL9 6SJ — MB BS 1989 Newc.; Cert. Prescribed Equiv. Exp. JCPTGP 1995; DFFP 1994; DRCOG 1993. Trainee GP Bury.

DUGGAN, Elizabeth Joan 25 Oak Tree Road, Kendal LA9 6AN — MB ChB 1973 Ed.; FRCS Eng. 1978.

DUGGAN, Frances Elizabeth 8 Guilford Road, Leicester LE2 2RB — MB ChB 1980 Birm.; MRCGP 1984; Dip. Educat. Primary Health Care Lond. 1988; DRCOG 1984. Asst. GP Leicester. Prev: Gen. Pract. Retainer Scheme; Health Worker Brit. Volunteer Program in Peru; Trainee GP Leic. HA.

DUGGAN, Lorna Mary St Andrews Hospital, Billing Road, Northampton NN1 5DG Tel: 01604 616314 — MB ChB 1988 Leeds; BSc (Hons.) Physiol. Leeds 1985; MRCPsych 1993. Cons. (Forens. Psychiat.) in devlop. disabil. Prev: Sen. Regist. (Psychiat. Learning Disabil.) Oxf.

DUGGAN, Maureen Brigid Department of Community Health, College of Medicine, University of Malawi, Chichiri, Blantyre 3 PMB 360, Malawi; Springview Cottage, More Hall Lane, Bolsterstone, Sheffield S30 5ZL Tel: 0114 288 6308 — MB BS 1961 Lond.; MD Lond. 1985, MSc 1981; FRCP Lond. 1987, M 1968; MRCS Eng. LRCP Lond. 1961; DTM & H (Gold Medal Trop. Med.) Liverp. 1971; DCH RCPS Glas. 1964. (Roy. Free) Sen. Lect. (Paediat.) Univ. Sheff. & Hon. Cons. N.. Gen. Hosp. Socs: Brit. Paediat. Assn.; Gp.e d'Etudes et de Recherche sur la MalNutrit.. Prev: Reader (Paediat.) Ahmadu Bello Univ. Hosp. Zaria, Nigeria; Paediat. Wesley Guild Hosp. Ilesha, Nigeria; Regist. (Paediat.) St. Geo. Hosp. Lond. & Soton. Childr. Hosp.

DUGGAN, Michael Alan Kenneth West Wold, Talygarn Close, Talygarn, Pontyclun CF72 9DA — MB BS 1979 Lond.; MRCP (UK) 1986; MRCS Eng. LRCP Lond. 1979; LMSSA Lond. 1978. (St. Bart.) Socs: Fell. Roy. Soc. Med.; Biochem. Soc.

DUGGAN, Michael John Manor House Surgery, Emperors Gate, Chells Manor, Stevenage SG2 7QX Tel: 01438 742639 — MB BChir 1984 Camb.; LMSSA Lond. 1984; MRCS Eng. LRCP Lond. 1985.

DUGGAN, Philip James 34 Canonbury Road, London N1 2HS — MB BS 1992 Lond.

***DUGGAN, Therese Anita** 16 Overwood Drive, Glasgow G44 5SG Tel: 0141 637 7544 — MB ChB 1998 Glas.; MB ChB Glas 1998.

DUGGIE, John Grant Health Centre, Kersiebank Avenue, Grangemouth FK3 9EW Tel: 01324 471511 — MB ChB 1973 Aberd.; MRCGP 1977.

DUGGINS, Katrina Elizabeth Five Bats, 45 Hoe Lane, Abridge, Romford RM4 1AU — MB BS 1992 Lond.

DUGGINS, Richard Adrian Divison of Psychiatry, University of Nottingham, Duncan Macmillan House, Nottingham NG3 6AA — MB BS 1997 Newc.

DUGGLEBY, Jane Elizabeth The Lawns, Winterbrook, Wallingford OX10 9EF — MB BS 1982 Nottm.

DUGGLEBY, Mark Robert The Health Centre, North Road, Stokesley, Middlesbrough TS9 5DY Tel: 01642 710748 Fax: 01642 713037 — MB ChB 1987 Leeds. Trainee GP Friarage Hosp. N.allerton VTS.

DUGMORE, Mr Walter Neville 17 The Hazels, Wilpshire, Blackburn BB1 9HZ Tel: 01254 249150 — MB ChB 1955 Sheff.; FRCS Ed. 1962; DO Eng. 1960. (Sheff.) Cons. Ophth. Surg. Burnley & Dist. Hosp. Gp. Prev: Sen. Regist. Roy. Eye Hosp. Manch.; SHO (Ophth.) Roy. Infirm. Stoke-on-Trent; Cas. Off. Roy. Infirm. Sheff.

DUGUID, Barbara (retired) Walk Cottage, 3 St Martin's Road, Chatteris PE16 6JB Tel: 01354 695432 — MB BS Lond. 1951. Prev: Gen. Pract., Sutton, Ely, Camb.

DUGUID, Mr Ian Graham MacKenzie 30 Chester Close N., Regents Park, London NW1 4JE Tel: 020 7251 1541 Fax: 020 7251 1541 Email: grahamduguid@compuserve.com — MB ChB 1987 Aberd.; MD Aberd. 1993, BMedBiol. 1984; FRCS Glas. 1993. Locum Cons. Moorfields Eye Hosp., Lond.; Fell. (Vitroretinal Surg.) Moorfields Eye Hosp. Lond. Prev: Sen. Regist.(Opth) Moorfields Eye Hosp.; Vis. Schol. Walter & Eliza Hall Inst. Med. Research Melbourne, Austral.; Temp Lect. (Anat.) Univ. Glas.

DUGUID, Mr Ian McIver (retired) 2 Carlingnose View, North Queensferry, Inverkeithing KY11 1EZ Tel: 01383 413372 — MB ChB Aberd. 1948; PhD Lond. 1963; DSc Aberd. 1995; MD Aberd. 1959; FRCS Eng. 1961; FRCOphth 1989; DO Eng. 1951. Prev: Hon. Cons. Ophth. Surg. Moorfields Eye Hosp. & W.m. & Char. Cross Hosp. Lond.

DUGUID, James Paris, CBE Oaklands, Merlewood Road, Inverness IV2 4NL — BSc Ed. 1941, MD (Gold Medal) 1949, MB ChB (Hons.) 1942; FRCPath 1966. (Ed.) Prof. Emerit. Univ. Dundee. Socs: Hon. Mem. Path. Soc. Gt. Brit. & Irel. Prev: Prof. Bact. Univ. St And. & Univ. Dundee; Hon. Cons. Bact. Tayside HB; Reader Bact. & Crichton Research Schol. Bact. Univ. Edin.

DUGUID, Jennifer Karen Mary Wrexham Maelor Hospital, Croesnewydd Road, Wrexham LL13 7TD Tel: 01978 291100 Fax: 01978 366520 Email: jenny.duguid@new-tr.wales.nhs.uk; Galvia, 5 Beech Road, Barnston, Wirral CH60 2SR Tel: 0151 342 7205 Email: j.k.m.duguid@liverpool.ac.uk — MB ChB Liverp. 1970; FRCPath 1995, M 1983. (Liverp.) Cons. Haemat. Wrexham Maelor Hosp.; Hon. Lect. (Haemat.) Univ. Liverp.; Lead Clinican for Cancer Wrexham Maelor Hosp. Socs: Brit. Med. Soc.; Brit. Blood Transfus. Soc. (Counc.); Brit. Soc. Haematol. (Sec. BSCH Chaim.Transfus. Task Force). Prev: Sen. Regist. (Haemat.) Mersey RHA; Wellcome Research Fell. (Haemat.) Univ. Liverp.; Lead Clinician Nat. Blood Serv. Mersey & N. Wales.

DUGUID, Jill Constance Jane 4 Mclauchlan Rise, Aberdour, Burntisland KY3 0SS — MB ChB 1990 Ed.; FRCA 1995. Cons. Anaest.Victora.Hosp.Fife.

DUHRA, Parmjit 3 Newmans Close, Great Linford, Milton Keynes MK14 5AW — MB BS 1981 Lond.

DUIGNAN, Imelda Jacinta Catherine Mary Enfield Community Care Trust, Chase Farm Hospital, The Ridgeway, Enfield EN2 8JL — MB BCh BAO 1977 NUI; Diploma in Child Health, National University of Ireland 1981; MRCPsych 1985; Diploma in Obstetrics, Royal College of Physicians, 1980.

DUIGNAN, Maeve Rosslyn Villa, Park Gardens, Bath BA1 2XP — MB BCh BAO 1982 NUI; MRCGP 1989; DCH NUI 1986; DObst RCPI 1986.

DUKE, Alan Robert (Surgery) Ramsey Health Centre, Whytefield Road, Ramsey, Huntingdon PE17 2QE; Fleur-de-Lys, Church St., Wistow, Huntingdon PE28 2QE Tel: 01487 822828 — MB BS 1968 Lond.; MRCS Eng. LRCP Lond. 1968; DObst RCOG 1970; Assoc. Inst. Med. Laborat. Technicians 1972. (Univ. Coll. Hosp) Prev: Trainee GP Aylesbury VTS.

DUKE, Mrs Alexandra Mary The Surgery, Bridge End, Chester-le-Street DH3 3SL Tel: 0191 388 2038 — MB BS 1967 Newc. (Newc.)

DUKE, Mr Anthony Buhagiar — MD 1961 Malta; FRCS Ed. 1968; FRCOG 1980, M 1967; DRCOG 1964. p/t Cons. O & G Mid Staffs. Hosp. Gp.; Sen. Clin. Lect. Keele Univ. Socs: Birm. & Midl. Obst. & Gyn. Soc.; BMA. Prev: Lect. (O & G) Univ. Birm.; Sen. Regist. (O & G) United Birm. Hosps.; Regist. (O & G) Wolverhampton Hosp. Gp.

DUKE, Brian Olliver Lyndhurst, CBE (retired) 2 Hillside, Lancaster LA1 1YH Tel: 01524 66187 Fax: 01524 66187 Email: bold10@hotmail.com — MD 1962 Camb.; MB BChir 1951; ScD 1969; DTM & H RCP Lond. 1952; FRCP 1975. Prev: Distinguished Scientist Amer. Registry of Path.

DUKE, Christopher 6 Shanklin Avenue, Leicester LE2 3RE — MB ChB 1990 Liverp.

DUKE, Clive Jonathan Benedict 6 Manor Hall Avenue, London NW4 1NX — MB BS 1992 Lond.

DUKE, Diane Frances 22 Glenariff Park, Jordanstown, Newtownabbey BT37 0RT — MB BCh BAO (Commend. Obst. & Gyn.) 1983; DCH RCPS Glas. 1985; MRCGP 1987; DRCOG 1986. Asst. GP Randalstown.

DUKE, Eileen Margaret Cartner Grantley Street Surgery, 1 Grantley Street, Glasgow G41 3PT Tel: 0141 632 4698; 1 Abbey Drive, Glasgow G14 9JX Tel: 0141 954 7320 Email: kenwardrop@supanet.com — MB ChB 1971 Dundee; MRCP (U.K.) 1975; DRCOG 1977; DCH RCPS Glas. 1973. (Dundee) Prev: Sen. Regist. (Paediat.) Roy. Hosp. Sick Childr. Glas.

DUKE, Fiona Jane 120 Main St.d., Conlig, Newtownards BT23 7PT — MB BCh BAO 1985 NUI; MRCPsych Lond. 1989.

DUKE, Frances Carolyn Rai and Duke, Bingley Health Centre, Myrtle Place, Bingley BD16 2TL Tel: 01274 566617 Fax: 01274 772345; 95 Main Street, Menston, Ilkley LS29 6LQ Tel: 01943 872100 — MB ChB 1970 Glas.

DUKE, John Dempster High Street Health Centre, 45 High Street, Stewarton, Kilmarnock KA3 5BP; 90 Main Street, Dunlop, Kilmarnock KA3 4AG — MB ChB 1978 Glas.; DRCOG 1981. Clin. Asst. Eye Dept. Gartnavel Gen. Prev: Trainee GP Paisley VTS (Argyll & Clyde HB); SHO (Ophth.) Bristol Eye Hosp.

DUKE, Lesley Claire Sequoia House, Rownhall Hill, Leigh Woods, Bristol BS8 3PU — MB BS 1997 Lond.

DUKE, Nicola Catherine Sequoia House, Rownham Hill, Leigh Woods, Bristol BS8 3PU — MB BS 1998 Lond.; MB BS Lond 1998.

DUKE, Oliver Lyndhurst Department Rheumatology, St. Helier Hospital, Carshalton Tel: 020 8644 4343; 52 Lanercost Road, London SW2 3DN Tel: 020 8671 0577 — MB 1977 Camb.; BChir 1976; MD Camb. 1988; FRCP Lond. 1995; MRCP (UK) 1978. Cons. Rheum. St. Helier Hosp. Carshalton Surrey; Hon. Sen. Lect. St. Geos. Hosp. Med. Sch. Lond. Socs: Brit. Soc. Rheum. Prev: Lect. (Rheum.) Guy's Hosp. Lond.; Regist. (Med.) Guy's Hosp. Lond.

DUKE, Peter Jonathan Mental Health Unit, St. Charles Hospital, Exmoor St., London W10 6DZ Tel: 020 8962 4322 — MB BCh BAO 1982 Dub.; BA Dub. 1982; MRCPsych 1986. (Trinity Coll. Dub.) Cons. Psychiat. (Gen. & Community Psychiat.) St. Chas. Hosp. Lond. Prev: SHO Acad. Unit Psychiat. Lond. Hosp. St. Clements; Ho. Phys. Roy. City Dub. Hosp.

DUKE, Sandra Lesley Weemyss, Castle Road, Longforgan, Dundee DD2 5HA — MB BCh BAO 1984 Belf.

DUKE, Tina Gabrielle 64 South Knighton Road, Leicester LE2 3LP Tel: 0116 270 9682 Email: tinagduke@yahoo.co.uk — MB BS 1987 Lond.; FRCOphth. 1993. (St. Bart.) Specialist Regist. Leicester Roy. Infirm. Prev: Regist. (Ophth.) Bristol Eye Hosp.; SHO (Ophth.) Roy. Berks. Hosp. Reading, Oxf. Eye Hosp. Radcliffe Infirm & MusGr. Pk. Hosp. Taunton; SHO (Neurosurg.) Frenchay Hosp. Bristol.

DUKE, William Arthur The Surgery, Bridge End, Chester-le-Street DH3 3SL Tel: 0191 388 2038 — MB BS 1967 Newc. Prev: Ho. Phys. & Ho. Surg. Roy. Vict. Infirm. Newc.; Asst. Lect. (Anat.) Med. Sch. Newc.

DUKE-COX, Nicholas Mullis 110 Boutport Street, Barnstaple EX31 1TB — MB ChB 1974 Leeds; BSc (Chem.) Surrey 1969; DRCOG 1976.

DUKES, Alexander Fraser (retired) 2 Lytton Avenue, Penn, Wolverhampton WV4 4HL Tel: 01902 342800 — MB ChB 1950 Birm.

DUKES, Catherine Sarah The Bull House, Ampney St Mary, Cirencester GL7 5SN Tel: 01285 850650 — MB ChB 1983 Birm.; MRCPsych 1997. Specialist Regist. (Old Age Psychiat.); Regist. (Psychiat.) Coney Hill Hosp. Glos.; Research Fell. (Old Age Psychiat.) Vict. Hosp. Swindon. Prev: GP Trainer Cirencester; Trainee GP Dudley Rd. Hosp. VTS.

DUKES, Heather Margaret Holbrooks Health Team, 75-77 Wheelwright Lane, Coventry CV6 4HN — MB ChB 1965 Birm.; FRCS Eng. 1971; Dip. Community Paediat. Warwick 1982. (Birm.) p/t Princip. in GP (p/t). Socs: BMA. Prev: Princip. Med. Off. (Child Health) Coventry HA; Regist. Profess. Surg. Unit Univ., Rhodesia; Research Fell. (Surg.) Qu. Eliz. Hosp. Birm.

DUKES, Mr Ian Kerr Russells Hall Hospital, Dudley DY1 2HQ Tel: 01384 456111 Fax: 01384 244045 — MB BS 1982 Lond.; BSc (Hons.) Lond. 1979; FRCS Ed. 1987; FFAEM 1992. (Univ. Coll. Hosp. Med. Sch.) Cons. Emerg. Med. Russells Hall Hosp. Dudley W. Midl. RHA; W. Midl.s Regional ALS Represen. to Resusc. Counc. (UK); Chairm. Specialist Train. Comm. A&E Med. W. Midl.s Region. Socs: Brit. Assn. Accid. & Emerg. Med. Prev: Sen. Regist. (A & E) Good Hope & Selly Oak Hosps. Birm.; Regist. (A & E) Glos. Roy. Hosp.

DUKES, Ian Timothy March Hare House, Ryton, Shifnal TF11 9JJ Tel: 01952 750369 — MB ChB 1981 Birm.

DUKES, Stephen Miller Street Surgery, Miller Street, Off Kings Street, Newcastle ST5 1JD Tel: 01782 711618 Fax: 01782 713940; 60 Sutherland Drive, Westlands, Newcastle ST5 3NZ — MB 1973 Camb.; BChir 1972; MRCP (U.K.) 1976. Prev: Regist. Med. Profess. Unit St. Bart. Hosp. Lond. Ho. Off. Middlx.; Hosp. Lond.; SHO N. Staffs. Hosp. Centre Stoke-on-Trent.

DUKES, Susan Anne Highgate Group Practice, 44 North Hill, London N6 4QA Tel: 020 8340 6628 Fax: 020 8342 8428; 5 Bisham Gardens, Highgate Village, London N6 6DJ Tel: 020 8340 7408 Fax: 020 8340 7408 — MB BS Lond. 1968; MRCS Eng. LRCP Lond. 1968; DObst RCOG 1970. (Roy. Free) Prev: Ho. Surg. Hampstead Gen. Hosp.; Ho. Phys. Kent & Sussex Hosp. Tunbridge Wells.

DUKU, Ambrose Yaw Urology Department, Broomfield Hospital, Court Road, Broomfield, Chelmsford CM1 7ET Tel: 01245 440761 Fax: 01245 514399; 152 Glengall Road, London SE15 6RR Tel: 020 7732 1173 — MB ChB 1973 Ghana; BA (Biol.) Minnesota 1968. Clin. Asst. (Urol.) Broomfield Hosp. Chelmsford.

DUKU, Moses Dili Flat 32 Balmoral Court, 45 Clarence Parade, Southsea PO5 2ES — BM 1998 Soton.; BM Soton 1998.

DULAKE, Christopher, TD (retired) 2 Beckley Place, Stone St, Standford North, Ashford TN25 6DN Tel: 01303 812714 — BA Camb. 1954, MB 1958, BChir 1957; MRCS Eng. LRCP Lond. 1957; FRCPath 1976, M 1964; Dip. Bact. Lond 1967. Dir. Ashford Pub. Health Laborat. William Harvey Hosp. Ashford; Hon. Cons. Microbiol. SE Kent HA. Prev: Dir. Pub. Health Laborat. Dulwich.

DULAKE, Michael (retired) 12 Dover Park Drive, Roehampton, London SW15 5BG Tel: 020 8788 5396 — MB BChir Camb. 1952; MA Camb. 1953; FRCP Lond. 1973, M 1959; MRCS Eng. LRCP Lond. 1952. Prev: Cons. Phys. (Cardiol.) St. Jas. Hosp. Balham.

DULAY, Jasbir Singh 65 Hiltingbury Road, Eastleigh SO53 5NU — MB BS 1992 Lond.

DULEY, Lelia Mary Magda Resource Centre for Randomised Trials, Institute of Health Sciences, Oxford OX3 7LF; 33 Bartlemas Road, Oxford OX4 1XU — MB ChB 1981 Aberd.; MSc (Epidemiol.) Lond. Sch. Hyg. & Trop. Med. 1990; MRCOG 1987. Resource Centre for Randomised Trials, Inst. of Health Sci.s, Oxf.

DULLEA, Brian Charles Andrew Alloa Health Centre, Marshill, Alloa FK10 1AQ Tel: 01259 216476 — MB ChB 1988 Glas. SHO (A & E & Orthop.) S.. Gen. Hosp. Glas.

DULLEHAN, Rachel Mary Samantha 25 Wallace Road, Birmingham B29 7ND — MB ChB 1992 Birm.

DULLFORCE, Eivind James Coach House Surgery, 12 Park Avenue, Watford WD18 7LX Tel: 01923 223178 Fax: 01923 816464 — MB BS 1982 Lond.; MRCGP 1988; DRCOG 1987.

DULO, Agembo Moses Naaman The Cottage, Ellerton, York YO4 4NX — MB ChB 1968 East Africa; MRCOG 1983.

DULSON, Ernest Victor (retired) Haslemere, Woodville Road, Keighley BD20 6JA Tel: 01535 607549 — MB ChB 1954 Leeds; DObst RCOG 1959. Prev: Ho. Surg. Leeds Gen. Infirm.

DULSON, Kieran St Bede's Medical Centre, Lower Dundas Street, Sunderland SR6 0QQ Tel: 0191 567 5335; 10 Hawthorn Terrace, Eighton Banks, Low Banks, Gateshead NE9 7XY Tel: 0191 491 3306 — MB ChB 1987 Sheff.; MRCGP 1993; DCH RCP Lond. 1992; Dip. Obst. Auckland 1990. Prev: Trainee GP N.umbria VTS; SHO (A & E) Newc. Gen. Hosp.

DUMBELL, Margaret (retired) 1 Batten Court, Chipping Sodbury, Bristol BS37 6BL — MB ChB 1957 Bristol; DObst RCOG 1959. Prev: Ho. Surg. Bristol Roy. Infirm.

DUMBELTON, Ian Brian Cedar House Surgery, 14 Huntingdon Street, St. Neots, Huntingdon PE19 1BQ Tel: 01480 406677 Fax: 01480 475167; 20A Kings Road, St. Neots, Huntingdon PE19 1LD Tel: 01480 213976 — BM 1979 Soton. Chairm. LMC.

DUMBRECK, Alexander 175 Dunnikier Road, Kirkcaldy KY2 5AD — MB ChB 1959 Ed.; FRCR 1975; FFR 1972; DMRD Ed. 1968.

DUMBRECK, Lesley Ann 32 Ennismore Avenue, Guildford GU1 1SR — MB 1979 Camb.; MSc Lond. Univ. 1983; MA Camb. 1980, BChir 1978.

DUMMER, David Stewart The Surgery, Oxenfoord Avenue, Pathhead EH37 5QD Tel: 01875 320302 Fax: 01875 320494; Toll Cottage, Prestonmains, Pathhead EH37 5UN Tel: 01875 320656 — MB ChB 1967 Ed.; MRCGP 1975; DObst RCOG 1970. (Ed.) GP; Police Surg. Midlothian Div. Lothian & Borders Police Retd., Sports Med. Cons.; FASIC Clinic Edin. Univ. Prev: SHO (A & E) Roy. Infirm. Edin.; SHO (O & G) Raigmore Hosp. Inverness; Ho. Phys. Peel Hosp. Galashiels.

DUMMETT, Nicola Jane Gartnavel Royal Hospital, 1055 Great Western Road, Glasgow G12 0XH; 7 Queens Gardens, Dowanhill,

Glasgow G12 9DG — MB BChir 1990 Camb.; BA Hons. (Med. Sci.) Camb. 1986, MB BChir 1990. SHO Gartnavel Roy. Hosp. Prev: SHO (Paediat.) Roy. Lond. Hosp.

DUMONDE, Dudley Cohen Department Immunology, St. Georges Hospital, Medical School, Hunter Wing, London SW17 0RE — MB BChir 1957 Camb.; PhD Camb. 1974, MD 1977, MA, MB BChir 1957; FRCPath 1978, M 1966; FRIC 1973. (Middlx.) Prof. (Immunol.) St. Thos. Hosp. & Med. Sch. Lond. & Cons. Socs: Biochem. Soc. & Brit. Soc. Immunol. Prev: Head Div. Immunol. Kennedy Inst. Rheum. Hammersmith Lond. & Cons. Immunol. Char. Cross Hosps. Lond.; Sen. Lect. Immunol. St. Mary's Hosp. Med. Sch. & Cons. (Immunol.) St.

DUMONT, Stephen William Department of Anaesthetics, Royal Gwent Hospital, Newport NP20 2UB Tel: 01633 234167 Fax: 01633 234168 Email: sdumo1@gwent.nhs.gov.uk — MB BCh 1982 Wales; FFA RCS Eng. 1987. Cons. Anaesth. Roy. Gwent Hosp. Newport.

DUMOULIN, John Geoffrey, MBE (retired) 'Whitegate', Station Road, Ivybridge PL21 0AH Tel: 01752 892541 — MRCS Eng. LRCP Lond. 1942; MD Lond. 1950, MB BS 1943; FRCOG 1960, M 1949. Prev: Cons. (O & G) Plymouth Gen. Hosp.

DUMSKYJ, Martin John 41 St Albans Avenue, London W4 5LL — BM 1988 Soton.; MRCP (UK) 1992.

DUMUGHN, Catherine St. Michaels Hospital, St. Michaels Road, Warwick CV34 5QW Tel: 01926 406789; Home Farm, Ufton, Leamington Spa CV33 9PF — MB ChB 1988 Birm.; MRCPsych 1994. Assoc. Specialist (Gen. Psychiat.) St. Michaels Hosp. Warwick. Prev: Regist. (Psychiat.) Coventry & Warks.

DUMUGHN, Derek Barry Strathain, Ullapool IV26 2TL Tel: 01854 612842 — BM BCh 1961 Oxf.; DObst RCOG 1964. (St. Bart.)

DUN, Andrew Frederick Healthcall Group PLC, 401 South Row, Milton Keynes MK9 2PH Tel: 01908 691919; 2 Chestnut Corner, Station Road, Holt, Trowbridge BA14 6RB — MB BS 1984 Lond.; MRCGP 1989. Grp. Med. Dir. Socs: Med. Protec. Soc.

DUN, Mary Lyndale, Holt Road, North Elmham, Dereham NR20 5JS Tel: 01362 668073 Fax: 01362 668073 — MB ChB 1986 Aberd. Asst. GP N. Elmham. Socs: Represent. Local Med. Comm.; NANP.

DUNACHIE, Paul Alan St James's Practice, 138 Croydon Road, Beckenham BR3 4DG Tel: 020 8650 0568 Fax: 020 8650 4172 — MB ChB 1981 Glas.; MRCGP 1986; DRCOG 1986.

DUNACHIE, Susanna Jane 1 Campbell Drive, Bearsden, Glasgow G61 4NF — BM BCh 1998 Oxf.; BM BCh Oxf 1998.

DUNAWAY, Mr David James 55 Harley St, London W1G 8QR Tel: 0207 580 4111 Fax: 0207 6565 6417 Email: david.dunaway@doctors.org.uk — MB ChB 1989 Manch.; BDS Lond. 1980; LDS RCS Eng. 1981; FDS RCS Eng. 1988; FRCS Eng. 1992; FRCS (plast) 1997. Cons. Plastic and craniofacial Surg., Gt. Ormond St. Hosp. for Childr., Lond.. Socs: BMA; Brit. Asscociation of Plastic Surg.s; Brit. Assn. of Oral & Maxiofacial Surg.s. Prev: Cons. Plastic Surg., Canniesburn Hosp., Glas..

DUNBAR, Adrian Michael Health Centre, Holme Lane, Cross Hills, Keighley BD20 7LG Tel: 01535 632147 Fax: 01535 637576; Croft House, West Lane, Sutton-in-Craven, Keighley BD20 7AS Email: adriandunbar@compuserve.com — MB ChB 1979 Leeds; BSc Leeds 1976, MB ChB 1979; MRCGP 1984. Course Organiser Airedale VTS; Med. Off. Brit. Athletics. Socs: Brit. Assoc. Sports & Med.; Brit. Inst. Musculo-Skeletal Med.; Assoc. of Course Organisers. Prev: Trainee GP Airedale Hosp. VTS; Clin. Asst. (Disabil. & Rehabil.) Airedale Younger Disabled Unit.

DUNBAR, Allison Christina (retired) Rebhoan, 16 Culduthel Gardens, Inverness IV2 4AR — MB ChB 1958 Ed.; FRCS Ed. 1966; FRCOG 1977, M 1964, DObst 1961. Prev: Cons. O & G Croydon AHA.

DUNBAR, Ann Patricia Downfield Medical Practice, 325 Strathmartine Road, Dundee DD3 8NE Tel: 01382 812111 Fax: 01382 858315 — MB ChB 1971 St. And.; MB ChB (Commend.) St. And. 1971; MRCP (UK) 1973; Dip. Travel Med. 1996; FRCP Ed. 1998. Princip. Gen. Pract. Prev: Research Fell. (Med. Educat. & Therap.) Univ. Dundee.

DUNBAR, Mr Christopher Michael Tighnabruaich, Dinnet, Aboyne AB34 5LA — MB ChB 1982 Aberd.; FRCS Ed. 1994.

DUNBAR, Deirdre Ann 4 Meonside Court, Wickham, Fareham PO17 5AJ — MB ChB 1990 Sheff.

DUNBAR, Derek Scott 49 Lorne Crescent, Monifieth, Dundee DD5 4DY — MB ChB 1985 Dundee.

DUNBAR, Edward Milne 12 Rookwood, Irk Vale, Chadderton, Oldham OL1 2TU Tel: 0161 633 7233 — MRCS Eng. LRCP Lond. 1972; BSc Lond. 1969, MB BS 1972; MRCP (UK) 1977. (St. Geo.) Cons. Phys. (Infect. Dis.) Monsall Hosp. Manch. Prev: Sen. Regist. N. Manch. Gen. Hosp.; Regist. Slade Hosp. Oxf.; SHO St. Geo. Hosp. Tooting.

DUNBAR, Geoffrey Charles CNS Therapeutic Unit, Smithkline Beecham Pharmaceuticals, New Frontiers Science Park, Third Avenue, Harlow CM19 5AW Tel: 01279 644045 Fax: 01279 646147; 44 Carlton Green, Redhill RH1 2DA — MB BS 1972 Lond.; BSc Lond. 1969; MRCS Eng. LRCP Lond. 1972; FFPHM RCP Lond. 1995; FRCPsych 1995, M 1977. Dir. & Vice Pres. CNS Therap. Unit. Smithkline Beecham Pharmaceuts. Harlow. Prev: Dir. (Clin. Research) Wyeth Internat. Taplow.

DUNBAR, Graeme Dudley Lane Village Surgery, Dudley Lane, Cramlington NE23 6US Tel: 01670 712821 Fax: 01670 730837; 18 Green Close, Stannington, Morpeth NE61 6PE Tel: 01670 789562 — MB ChB 1985 Sheff.; MBA Durh. 1995; MRCGP 1989; DRCOG 1988. Med. Adviser Brit. Alcan; Clin. Asst. Newc. Ment. Health Trust. Prev: GP Newc.; Trainee GP N.umbria VTS; Ho. Off. (Surg.) Sheff. Childr. Hosp.

DUNBAR, Ian James Cameron (retired) 63 Wood Street, Gillingham ME7 5SD Tel: 01634 817769 — MB ChB 1961 Aberd. Prev: Staff Phys. Distant Early Warning Line, Canada.

DUNBAR, James Anthony, TD, Lt.-Col. RAMC Borders Primary Care, NHS Trust, Newstead, Melrose TD6 9DB Tel: 01896 828282 Fax: 01896 822887 Email: jdunbar99@hotmail.com; Morham, Gordon TD3 6JS Tel: 01573 410232 — MB ChB 1972 St. And.; MD Dundee 1990; FRCGP 1993, M 1976; DMJ (Clin.) Soc. Apoth. Lond. 1979; FRCP 1999. Med. Dir.Borders Primary Care NHS Trust; Hon Reader, Health Economics Policy & Managem. Univ. St. Andrews. Socs: Internat. Comm. Alcohol Drugs & Traffic Safety. Prev: Regist. (Path.) Ninewells Hosp. & Med. Sch. Dundee; GP Princip.; Hon. Lect. Forens. Med.

DUNBAR, James Mellis (retired) Hillspark, Brucefield Road, Rosemount, Blairgowrie PH10 6LA Tel: 01250 2923 — MB ChB 1946 St. And.; BSc St. And. 1943, MD (Hons. & Rutherford Gold; Medal) 1951, MB ChB 1946; FRCPath 1971, M 1963. Prev: Chief Clin. Bact. & Head Pub. Health Laborat. Univ. Leiden Netherlands.

DUNBAR, Kathleen Mary (retired) St Catherines, Kilbryde Crescent, Dunblane FK15 9BB — M.B., Ch.B. Aberd. 1949. Prev: Ho. Surg. Roy. Aberd. Hosp. Sick Childr.

DUNBAR, Keith Peter Lyon (retired) 20 The Street, Benacre, Beccles NR34 7LL Fax: 01502 741241 Email: keith_dunbar@care4free.net — MB ChB Ed. 1969. Prev: GP Sileby.

DUNBAR, Mark Robert 25 Walsh Drive, Sutton Coldfield B76 2NU — BM BCh 1998 Oxf.; BM BCh Oxf 1998.

DUNBAR, Olive Mable Jean (retired) Hillspark, Brucefield Road, Rosemount, Blairgowrie PH10 6LA — MB ChB 1946 St. And.; BSc, MB ChB St. And. 1946. Prev: Asst. Psychiat. Whiteabbey Hosp. Newtonabbey.

DUNBAR, Patricia Jane Ann 63 Ochiltree, Dunblane FK15 0DF Tel: 01786 822601 — MB ChB 1980 Manch.; BSc St. And. 1977; Dip. Sports Med. Scotl. 1994; DTM & H RCP Lond. 1986; DRCOG 1984. Med. Adviser to the Scott. Inst. of Sport, Centr. Region; Lect. (Sports Studies) Univ. Stirling. Socs: BASM (Scott. Exec. Comm.). Prev: GP Bridge of Allan; Sen. Med. Off. Operat. Raleigh (Round The World Expedition); Trainee GP Orkney VTS.

DUNBAR, Peter Alastair 1 Westdown Road, Seaford BN25 2LA — MRCS Eng. LRCP Lond. 1962; MA Camb. 1966. (Camb. & Leeds)

DUNBAR, Peter George Woodford House, Devizes SN10 5EU Tel: 01380 721414 — MB BS 1953 Lond.; MRCS Eng. LRCP Lond. 1953; DObst RCOG 1956; DA Eng. 1955. (Guy's) Prev: Phys. & Anaesth. Devizes Hosp.; Ho. Surg. & Out-pats. Off. Guy's Hosp.; Resid. Med. Off. Nuffield Hse. Guy's Hosp.

DUNBAR, Simon John The Grayshott Surgery, Boundary Road, Grayshott, Hindhead GU26 6TY Tel: 01428 604343; 78 Kingswood Firs, Hindhead GU26 6EX — MB BS 1984 Lond.; MRCGP 1988; Cert. Family Plann. JCC 1986; DRCOG 1985. (St. Bart.) GP Trainer; GP course organiser. Socs: RCGP.

DUNBAR-REES, Rupert James The Loft Apartment, 82 Slateford Road, Edinburgh EH11 1QU — MB BS 1996 Lond.

DUNBAVAND, Andrew City Walls Medical Centre, St. Martin's Way, Chester CH1 2NR Tel: 01244 357800; Westwards, Rowton Lane, Rowton, Chester CH3 6AT Email: andy.dunbavard@dial.pipex.com — MB BS 1985 Lond.; DRCOG 1988. Dir. Deva Emerg. Med. Serv. CoOperat. Chester. Prev: Trainee GP Chester VTS.

DUNCALF, Howard Albert 263 Wigan Road, Bolton BL3 5QX Tel: 01204 657878 Fax: 01204 658734; 141 Newbrook Road, Over Hulton, Bolton BL5 1EY Email: howardduncalf@msn.com — MB ChB 1972 Liverp.; MRCS Eng. LRCP Lond. 1972; DObst. RCOG 1976. Hon. Sec. Bolton & Dist. Med. Soc. Prev: SHO (A & E & O & G) Roy. Vict. Hosp. Bournemouth; Regist. (Med.) Greys Hosp. Pietermaritzburg, S. Africa.

DUNCAN, Alec Campbell Ironside (retired) 33 Church Street, Larkhall ML9 1EZ Tel: 01698 885247 — MB ChB 1959 Glas.; DObst 1967.

DUNCAN, Alexander Charles Weeks 37 Old Guildford Road, Broadbridge heath, Horsham RH12 3JY — MB BChir 1990 Camb. Prev: SHO (Paediat.) City Hosp. Birm.; SHO (O & G) Heartlands Hosp. Birm.

DUNCAN, Alexandra Anne 6 Monkbarns Drive, Arbroath DD11 2DS — MB BCh BAO 1984 NUI; MSc Lond. 1990. Prev: Sen. Regist. (Pub. Health Med.) Mersey RHA; Regist. (Community Med.) SW Thames RHA; Trainee GP/SHO (Community Med.) Stockport HA VTS.

DUNCAN, Alice Faith Stockton Hall Hospital, Stockton on the Forest, York YO3 9UN Tel: 01904 400500 Fax: 01904 400512; Duncan Field, Skates Lane, Sutton on the Forest, York YO61 1HB Tel: 01347 811715 — MB BS 1983 West Indies; BSc West Indies Univ. 1978; MRCPsych 1990. (University of the West Indies) Cons. Psychiat. (Gen. Adult Psychiat. & Forens. Pscyhiat.) Stockton Hall Hosp. York. Socs: BMA. Prev: Regist. Rotat. (Psychiat.) Manch. Train. Scheme.

DUNCAN, Alison Anne Walsgrave Hospital NHS Trust, Clifford Bridge Road, Walsgrave, Coventry CV2 2DX Tel: 024 76 602020 Fax: 024 76 622197 — MB ChB Manch. l984; MRCP (UK) 1988; FRCR 1992. (Manchester) p/t Cons. Radiol. Walsgrave Hosp. Coventry. Socs: Brit. Inst. Radiol.; Roy. Coll. Radiol. (BrE. Gp.); Roy. Coll. Radiol. Prev: Sen. Regist. (Radiol.) Birm.; Regist. (Radiol.) Birm.; SHO (Med.) Frenchay Hosp. Bristol.

DUNCAN, Mr Alistair Robert Northampton Trust Hospital, Billing Lane, Northampton NN1 5SB Tel: 01604 34700; Court House, Overstone Park, Northampton NN6 0AP Tel: 01604 646123 — MB BS 1981 Lond.; BSc Lond. 1979; FRCS Eng. 1987; FRCS Ed. 1986; MRCOG 1988. Cons. O & G N.ants. Gen. Hosp. Prev: Sen. Regist. (O & G) Simpson Memor. Hosp. Edin.; Regist. (O & G) Guy's Hosp. Lond.; SHO (Obst.) Qu. Charlotte Matern. Hosp. Lond.

DUNCAN, Andrew Douglas Graham St Brycedale Surgery, St. Brycedale Road, Kirkcaldy KY1 1ER Tel: 01592 640800 Fax: 01592 644944 — MB ChB 1976 Ed.; MRCGP 1980; DRCOG 1978.

DUNCAN, Mr Andrew John Department Cardiothoracic Surgery, Victoria Hospital, Whinney Heyes Road, Blackpool FY3 8NR Tel: 01253 303851; Spinney Cottage, Fairfield Road, Singleton, Blackpool FY3 8LD Tel: 01253 895882 — MB ChB 1983 Ed.; FRCS (C Th) 1995; FRCS Ed. 1987. Cons. (Cardiothoracic. Surg.) Vict. Hosp. Blackpool. Prev: Sen. Regist. (Cardiothoracic Surg.) Roy. Infirm. Edin.

DUNCAN, Andrew Winston Bristol Royal Hospital for Sick Children, Paul O'Gorman Building, Upper Maudlin Street, Bristol BS2 8BJ Tel: 0117 342 8463 Fax: 0117 342 8343 Email: andrewduncan@vbht.swest.nhs.uk; Orchard Cottage, The Street, Ubley, Bristol BS40 6PA Tel: 01761 462861 — American Board of Radiology 1976; MB BS Durh. 1966; FFR 1972; FRCR 1975; FRCPCH 1997; DMRD 1970. (Durh.) Cons. Paediat. Radiol. Bristol Roy. Hosp. for Childr.; Vis. Prof. San Paulo Univ., Brazil 1990; Clin. Sen. Lect. Bristol Univ. Socs: Eur. Soc. Paediat. Radiol.& Brit. Paediat. Assn.; Amer. Bd. Radiol.; BMA. Prev: Asst. Prof. Radiol. Harvard Univ. Boston, USA; Fell. Paediat. Radiol. Hosp. Sick Childr. Toronto, Canada; Sen. Regist. (Paediat. Radiol.) Hosp. Sick Childr. Lond.

DUNCAN, Ann Carolyn Flat 11/3, 10 Riverview Gardens, The Waterfront, Glasgow G5 8EL — MB ChB 1994 Glas.

DUNCAN, Anne Maria Rushden Medical Centre, Parklands, Wymington Road, Rushden NN10 9EB Tel: 01933 396000; Glebe Cottage Farm, Kelmarsh Road, Arthingworth, Market Harborough LE16 8JZ Tel: 01858 525108 Fax: 01858 525242 — MB ChB 1985 Leic.; MRCGP 1991; DCH RCP Lond. 1990; DRCOG 1988. (Leic.) Prev: Drs Anderson & Partners Repulse Bay Hong Kong; Civil. Med. Pract. Bielefeld, W. Germany; SHO (Community Paediat.) Sunderland.

DUNCAN, Barbara Bridget Alison Sylvan Lodge, 3 Sylvan Road, Wanstead, London E11 1QL Tel: 020 8530 3982 — MB BS 1974 Lond.; MRCP (UK) 1980; FFA RCS Eng. 1979.

DUNCAN, Barbara Cecile Omatimehin The Orchard, Arch Road, Great Wymondley, Hitchin SG4 7EP Tel: 01438 724291 Email: 106711.165@compuserve.com — MB BS Lond. 1991; BSc Lond. 1987; DA (UK) 1994; DRCOG 1996. (St. Mary's Hosp. Med. Sch.) GP Registr. Socs: Fell. Roy. Soc. Med. Prev: SHO (O & G) Lister Hosp. Stevenage; SHO (Psychiat.) Lister Hosp. Stevenage; SHO (Anaesth.) Addenbrooke's Hosp. Camb. & St. Mary's Hosp. Lond.

DUNCAN, Beryl Mary St. Clement Surgery, 24 Marshland Street, Terrington St Clement, King's Lynn PE34 4NE Tel: 01553 828475 Fax: 01553 827594 — MB ChB. (Aberdeen) Partner, St. Clements Surg.

DUNCAN, Bruce Anaesthetics Department, Raigmore Hospital, Inverness IV2 3UJ — MB ChB 1986 Cape Town.

DUNCAN, Caroline Jane 1 Broadmeadows, Darlington DL3 8SP — MB BS 1998 Newc.; MB BS Newc 1998.

DUNCAN, Catherine Helen Saffron Group Practice, 509 Saffron Lane, Leicester LE2 6UL Tel: 0116 244 0888 Fax: 01162 831405; Southcroft, 2 Meadowcourt Road, Oadby, Leicester LE2 2PB Tel: 0116 271 0340 Email: ronald.sawers@bt.com — MB ChB 1984 Leic.; MB ChB Leic. l984; BSc (Hons. Biol.) 1979; MRCGP 1989; DGM RCP Lond. 1987. (Leicester) Prev: Trainee GP Alton.

DUNCAN, Catriona 'Hazelbank', 15 West Albert Road, Kirkcaldy KY1 1DL — MB ChB 1976 Ed.

DUNCAN, Catriona Gail 48 Beechill Park W., Belfast BT8 6NW — MB BS 1994 Lond. SHO (Paediat.) Qu. Mary's Hosp. Sidcup. Prev: Ho. Off. (Surg.) Kent & Sussex Hosp. Tunbridge Wells; Ho. Off. (Med.) King's Healthcare Lond.

DUNCAN, Cecil Gibson (retired) Leprechaun House, Belmont, Durham DH1 2QW — LRCP LRCS Ed. LRFPS Glas. 1947.

DUNCAN, Charlotte Fiona Delapre Medical Centre, Gloucester Avenue, Northampton NN4 8QF Tel: 01604 761713 Fax: 01604 708589 — MB BS 1981 Lond.; MRCGP 1985; DRCOG 1985; Cert. Family Plann. JCC 1985. Prev: GP Lond. & Edin.

DUNCAN, Claire Lesley 15 Elm Bank, Lions Gate, Kirkintilloch, Glasgow G66 1PQ — MB ChB 1988 Glas.

DUNCAN, Craig Morrison 3 Anne Drive, Stenhousemuir, Larbert FK5 4JE — MB ChB 1980 Ed.

DUNCAN, Dale Ann 15 Newlands Avenue, Thames Ditton KT7 0HD — MB BS 1965 Sydney; DCH RCP Lond. 1970. GP. Prev: GP Thames Ditton; Regist. (Paediat.) Hillingdon HA; SHO (Paediat.) The Brook Hosp. Woolwich.

DUNCAN, David Avon Medical Centre, Academy Street, Larkhall ML9 2BJ Tel: 01698 882547 Fax: 01698 888138; 132 Lockhart Street, Stonehouse, Larkhall ML9 3PL — MB ChB 1974 Ed.; MRCGP 1986.

DUNCAN, David The Cardinal Clinic, Windsor SL4 5UL Tel: 01753 869755 Fax: 01753 869755; 7 Lockbridge Court, Ray Pk Road, Maidenhead SL6 8UP Tel: 01628 32842 — MB ChB 1954 Glas.; MRCPsych 1971; DPM Eng. 1958. (Glas.) Cons. Psychiat. Cardinal Clinic Windsor; Hon. Psychiat. Reading Indust. Ther. Organisat. Ltd.; Hon. Cons. Psychiat. Reading Marriage Guid. Counc. & Samarit.s. Prev: SHO (Med.) Shenley Hosp.; Sen. Regist. Napsbury Hosp. St. Albans; Asst. Phys. The Retreat, York.

DUNCAN, David McGechie, MBE (retired) The Cleuch, Twynholm, Kirkcudbright DG6 4SD Tel: 01557 860215 — MB ChB 1960 St. And. Prev: GP WellingBoro.

DUNCAN, Dennis Duffin Flat 2, 44 Fitzjohns Avenue, Hampstead, London NW3 5LX Tel: 020 7794 9307 — MB BCh BAO 1960 Dub.; MA Dub. 1967; FRCPsych 1987, M 1973; DPM NUI 1964. (T.C. Dub.) Socs: Brit. Psychoanal. Soc.

DUNCAN, Diana Felicity Jeyes (retired) 41 Christchurch Road, London SW14 7AQ — MB ChB 1950 Bristol; DA Eng. 1956; DCH Eng. 1953; DObst RCOG 1952.

DUNCAN, Douglas 83 Main Street, Aberdour, Burntisland KY3 0UQ — MB ChB 1993 Ed.

DUNCAN, Elizabeth Margaret The Surgery, John Street, Bellshill ML4 1RJ Tel: 01698 747195; 2 Creswell Terrace, Uddingston, Glasgow G71 7BZ — MB ChB 1978 Glas.; MRCGP 1994; DRCOG 1981. Chair Primary Care Audit Gp. Lanarksh. HB. Socs: BMA. Prev: Trainee GP Brighton; SHO (O & G) Roy. Sussex Co. Hosp. Brighton; SHO (Gen. Med.) Roy. Shrewsbury Hosp.

DUNCAN, Emma Letitia Radcliffe Infirmary, Woodstock Road, Oxford — MB BS 1992 Sydney; MB BS (Hons Class I) Syd. Univ.; MRCP (UK) 1995. (Sydney University) Specialist Regist. in Diabetes, Endocrinol. and Metab., Radcliffe Infirm., Oxf.; Research Fell., Wellcome Trust Centre for Human Genetics Oxf.

DUNCAN, Ernest Hugh 2 Highdaun Drive, Norbury, London SW16 4LY Tel: 020 8764 6561 — MB ChB 1951 St. And. Regional Med. Off. DHSS. Socs: BMA.

DUNCAN, Ernest Maurice (retired) Mount Lockwood, Lonsties, Keswick CA12 4TD Tel: 017687 75815 — MB ChB St. And. 1960; DObst RCOG 1962. Prev: SHO (Gyn. & Obst.) Gulson Hosp. Coventry.

DUNCAN, Esther Margaret 3A Allanvale Road, Bridge of Allan, Stirling FK9 4NU — MB ChB 1990 Ed.; DRCOG 1993.

DUNCAN, George 3 Balminnock Park, Ayr KA7 4EQ — MB ChB 1982 Glas.; MRCP (UK) 1986. Cons. Phys. (Geriat. Med.) Ayrsh. Centr. Hosp. Irvine.

DUNCAN, George Douglas (retired) 12 Storey's Way, Cambridge CB3 0DT Tel: 01223 363427 — MB ChB 1948 Aberd.; MA (Hon.) Camb. 1986; FFCM 1972; DPH Aberd. 1952. Prev: Qu.'s Hon. Phys.

DUNCAN, George Gordon (retired) Rannachy, 76 High St., Rothes, Aberlour AB38 7AY Tel: 01340 831268 Email: hjd224@aol.com — MB ChB 1950 Aberd.; DPH Aberd. 1955. Prev: Cas. Off. & Ho. Phys. (Obst.) Roy. Hants. Co. Hosp. Winchester.

DUNCAN, George Nicholas Tel: 01603 408275 Fax: 01603 401389; White House Farm, Edward Seago Place, Brookes, Norwich NR15 1HL — MB BChir 1988 Camb.; BSc (Hons.) St. And. 1983. (Cambridge)

DUNCAN, George Stewart (retired) Oakenshore, New Road, Wootton Bridge, Ryde PO33 4HY Tel: 01983 884117 — MRCS Eng. LRCP Lond. 1956; FRCGP 1980, M 1965; DObst RCOG 1960. Locum Med. Off., HM Prison Serv. Prev: Police Surg. I. of Wight.

DUNCAN, Gillian, OBE (retired) Westfield, Steeple Aston, Bicester OX25 4SS Tel: 01869 340277 — MB ChB 1947 St. And.; MFFP 1993. Prev: Princip. Clin. Med. Off. (Family Plann.) Oxf.

DUNCAN, Heather St Clair Balmerino House, Balmerino, Newport-on-Tay DD6 8RN — BM 1982 Soton. Trainee GP MusGr. Pk. Hosp. Taunton VTS.

DUNCAN, Iain Health Centre, University of East Anglia, Norwich NR4 7TJ Tel: 01603 592174 — MB ChB 1959 Glas.; BSc Glas. 1955; AFOM RCP Lond. 1981; MRCGP 1968; CIH Dund 1974; DObst RCOG 1963. (Glas.) Occupat. Health Phys. Univ. E. Anglia Norwich. Prev: Dir. Univ. Health Serv. Univ. E. Anglia.

DUNCAN, Ian Douglas Department Obstetrics & Gynaecology, Ninewells Hospital & Medical School, Dundee DD1 9SY Tel: 01382 632147 Fax: 01382 633847 Email: i.d.duncan@dundee.ac.uk; Thatched Cottage, 1 Main St, Glamis DD8 1RU Tel: 01307 840488 — MB ChB 1967 St. And.; MB ChB (Commend.) St. And. 1967; FRCOG 1984, M 1971. Reader & Hon. Cons. O & G Ninewells Hosp. Dundee. Socs: Bayard Carter Soc. Obst. & Gyn.; Ed. Obst. Soc. Prev: Pres. Internat. Federat. Cancer Path. & Colposcopy; Pres. Brit. Gyn. Cancer Soc.; Pres. Brit. Soc. Colposcopy & Cervical Path.

DUNCAN, Innes Douglas Armadale Group Practice, 18 North Street, Armadale, Bathgate EH48 3QD Tel: 01501 730432 — MB ChB 1980 Ed.

DUNCAN, Mr James George (retired) 1B Avon Road, Edinburgh EH4 6LA Tel: 0131 336 3774 — MB ChB Aberd. 1945; FRCP Glas. 1975, M 1971; FRCS Ed. 1967; FRCR 1975; FFR 1955; DMRD Ed. 1950. Prev: Cons. Radiol. in Admin. Charge Glas. Roy. Infirm. & Assoc. Hosps.

DUNCAN, James Newell Hawthorn Drive Surgery, 206 Hawthorn Drive, Ipswich IP2 0QQ Tel: 01473 685070 Fax: 01473 688707; 31 Park Road, Ipswich IP1 3SX Tel: 01473 685070 — MB BS 1971 Lond.; BSc (Anat.) Lond. 1968, MB BS 1971; LMCC 1974; Dip. Occ. Med. 1997. (St. Thomas' Hosp. Lond.) Occupat. Health Phys. Ipswich. Socs: BMA.

DUNCAN, Mr James Robert 11 Craigton Drive, Newton Mearns, Eastwood District, Glasgow G77 6UW — MB ChB 1987 Glas.; FRCS Glas 1992. SHO (Gen. Surg.) S.ern Gen. Hosp. Glas. Prev: SHO Rotat. (A & E/Orthop. & Gen. Surg.) Greenock VTS.

DUNCAN, Jane Elizabeth North Manchester NHS Trust, Central Drive, Crompsall, Manchester M8 5RL; c/o Duncan, 96a St. Andrews Drive, Pollokshields, Glasgow G41 4SF — MB ChB 1990 Ed.; MRCP (UK) 1997. Specialist Regist. (Paediat.).

DUNCAN, Janice Anne The Surgery, The Cannons, Fisher Street, Methil, Leven KY8 3HD Tel: 01333 426083 Fax: 01333 421833 — MB ChB 1984 Glas.; MB ChB Glas. l984; MRCGP 1991; T(GP) 1991; DCH RCP Lond. 1990. Prev: Trainee GP Kirkcaldy Health Centre; Surg. Lt. RN.

DUNCAN, Janice Margaret The State Hospital, Carstairs, Lanark ML11 5RP Tel: 01555 840293 — MB ChB 1969 Ed.; MD Gottingen 1977; MRCPsych 1984; FRCPsych 1997. (Ed.) Cons. Forens Psychiat. State Hosp. Carstairs.; Visitng Psychiat. HM Prison Polmont Y.O.I. Prev: Cons. Psychiat. Roy. Edin. Hosp.

DUNCAN, John (retired) 13/4 Whistlefield Court, 2 Canniesburn Road, Bearsden, Glasgow G61 1PX Tel: 0141 942 8955 — LRCP LRCS Ed. LRFPS Glas. 1946; MRCGP 1953. Prev: Local Treas. Med. Off.

DUNCAN, John Child & Family Clinic, 194 Quarry St, Hamilton ML3 6QR Tel: 01698 426753 — MB ChB 1974 Ed.; BSc (Med. Sci.) Ed. 1971, MB ChB 1974; MRCPsych 1981. (Edinburgh) Cons. Child & Adolesc. Psychiat. Lanarksh. HB.; Lead Clinician. Prev: Sen. Regist. (Child & Adolesc. Psychiat.) Lond. Hosp.; Regist. (Psychiat.) Roy. Edin. Hosp.; SHO (Geriat.) Leicester Gen. Hosp.

DUNCAN, John Austen Thomas (retired) 10 Inverleith Avenue, Edinburgh EH3 5PT Tel: 0131 551 2804 — MB ChB Ed. 1964; FFA RCS Eng. 1971; DObst RCOG 1970. Cons. Anaesth. Dunfermline & W. Fife Hosps. & Qu. Margt. Trust. Prev: Cons. Anaesth. Dunfermline & W. Fife Hosps. & Qu. Margt. Trust.

DUNCAN, John Kelly The Group Practise, Guy's and St Thomas's Hospital NHS Trust, Guy's Hospital, St Thomas St., London SE1 9RT Tel: 020 7955 5000 Fax: 020 7407 6112 Email: john.duncan@gstt.sthames.nhs.uk; Flat 215,, City View House, 463 Bethnal Green Road, London E2 9QY Tel: 020 7729 3832 — MB ChB 1984 Aberd.; MRCGP 1988; T(GP) 1991; DRCOG 1986; Cert Family Plann. JCC 1986; DFFP 1996. (Aberd.) PMS Practitioner. Socs: (GP Sect.) Roy. Soc. of Med.; BSMDH Scotl. Prev: Teachg. Fell. Dept. of Gen. Pract. Univ. of Aberd.; GP Trainer Aberd.; Trainee GP Falkirk Roy. Infirmiary VTS.

DUNCAN, Mr John Laing Raigmore Hospital, Inverness IV2 3UJ Tel: 01463 704000 Fax: 01463 711322; 47 Drummond Road, Inverness IV2 4NU Tel: 01463 230029 — MB ChB 1977 Aberd.; ChM Aberd. 1985; FRCS Glas. 1994; FRCS Ed. 1981; T(S) 1991. Cons. Surg. Raigmore Hosp. & Hon. Sen. Lect. Univ. Aberd. Prev: Sen. Regist. (Surg.) Sheff. Area Hosp.; Regist. (Surg.) Aberd. Teach. Hosp.; Research Fell. (Surg.) Harvard Med. Sch. Boston, USA.

DUNCAN, Mr John McKessar 138 Worcester Street, The Heath, Stourbridge DY8 1BA Tel: 01384 395681 — MB ChB 1941 Birm.; FRCS Eng. 1954. (Birm.) Prev: Cons. Surg. Guest Hosp. Dudley & Corbett Hosp. Stourbridge; Res. Surg. Off. Childr. Hosp. Birm.; Burns Off. MRC Burns Unit Birm. Accid. Hosp.

DUNCAN, John Reid 20 Surrenden Crescent, Brighton BN1 6WF — MB BChir 1977 Camb.; FRCP Lond. 1993; FRCPath 1995, M 1983. Cons. Haemat. Roy. Sussex Co. Hosp. Brighton. Prev: Research Fell. Duke Univ. Med. Center, Durh., N. Carolina, USA; Sen. Regist. (Haemat.) John Radcliffe Hosp. Oxf.; SHO (Med.) W.m. Hosp. Lond.

DUNCAN, Professor John Sidney National Hospital for Neurology & Neurosurgery, Queen Square, London WC1N 3BG Tel: 020 7837 3611 Fax: 020 7837 3941 Email: j.duncan@bigfoot.com — BM BCh 1979 Oxf.; MA Oxf. 1980, BA (Hons.) 1976, DM 1988; FRCP Lond. 1994; MRCP (UK) 1982. (Oxford) Prof. (Clin. Neurol.) Inst. Neurol. Nat. Hosp. Neurol. & Neurosurg. Lond.; Cons. Neurol. Nat. Hosps Neurol. & Neurosurg.; Med. Dir. Nat. Soc. Epilepsy. Socs: Fell. Roy. Soc. Med. Prev: Sen. Lect. & Reader Inst. Neurol. Lond.

DUNCAN, Jonathan Andrew Logan Castlehill Farm, Maybole KA19 8JT — MB ChB 1998 Manch.; MB ChB Manch 1998.

DUNCAN, Judith Anne Mosscroft, Logierieve, Udny, Ellon AB41 6PS Tel: 01651 842221 — MB ChB 1991 Aberd.

DUNCAN, Karen Ann In Patients X Ray Department, Aberdeen Royal Infirmary, Foresterhill, Aberdeen AB25 2ZN Tel: 01224 681818 Fax: 01224 840778 Email: k.o.duncan@abdn.ac.uk; 76 Desswood Place, Aberdeen AB15 4DQ Tel: 01224 635989 — MB ChB 1985 Aberd.; MRCP (UK) 1988; FRCR 1992; DMRD Aberd. 1991; DCH RCPS Glas. 1989. Cons. Radiol. Aberd. Roy. Hosps. Trust; Hon. Sen. Lect. Univ. Aberd. Socs: Scott. Radiol. Soc.; RCR BrE. Gp.; RCR BrE. Gp. Prev: Sen. Regist. & Regist. (Radiol.) Grampian HB; SHO Rotat. (Med.) Grampian HB; SHO (Med. & Paediat.) Glas. HB.

DUNCAN, Kathleen Mary 20 Windsor Road, St Annes, Lytham St Annes FY8 1ET Tel: 01253 723481 — MB ChB 1949 Manch. (Manch.) Prev: Clin. Pathol., Ho. Phys. & Ho. Surg. Manch. Roy. Infirm.

DUNCAN, Keith Robert Cobwold Centre, Southmead Hospital, Bristol BS10 5NB Tel: 0117 959 5178 Fax: 0117 959 5178 Email: keith.duncan@doctors.org.uk — MB ChB 1989 Leeds; DM Nottingham 2001; MRCOG 1994. Cons. Obst. & Gynae. S.mead Hosp. Bristol; Hon. Sen. Clin. Lect., Univ. of Bristol. Socs: Brit. Matern. & Fetal Med. Soc.; IFMSS; SWOGS. Prev: Feto-Matern. Fell. Qu. Charlotte's Hosp. Lond.; Regist. Rotat. (O & G) Merseyside; Lect. Sch. of Human Delelopment, Nottm. Univ.

DUNCAN, Kirsteen Jane — MB ChB 1991 Leeds; DF Planning. (Leeds) GP Locum, Wirral Health Auth.; Clin. Asst. A&E Dept., Wirral Hosps. NHS Trust Wirral; Clin. Asst. Dept. of Elderly Ment. Health, Wirral and W. Chesh. NHS Trust, Wirral. Socs: BMA & Med. Defence Union; Fac. of Family Plann. Diplomate. Prev: Trainee GP/SHO Wirral Hosp. VTS.

DUNCAN, Lesley Anne 11 Bankton Court, Murieston, Livingston EH54 9DL — MB ChB 1988 Ed.

DUNCAN, Lesley Elizabeth Inverkeithing Medical Group, 5 Friary Court, Inverkeithing KY11 1NU Tel: 01383 413234 Fax: 01383 410098 — MB ChB 1976 Glasgow; MB ChB Glas. 1976. (Glasgow) GP Inverkeithing, Fife.

DUNCAN, Leslie James Park (retired) 14 Moray Place, Edinburgh EH3 6DT Tel: 0131 225 8025 Fax: 0131 225 6749 — MB ChB 1951 Ed.; FRCP Ed. 1963, M 1954. Cons. Med. Off. PHI (Claims) Guardian Roy. Exchange. Prev: Cons. Phys. Roy. Infirm. Edin.

DUNCAN, Linda Elizabeth Howdenhall Surgery, 57 Howden Hall Road, Edinburgh EH16 6PL Tel: 0131 664 3766 Fax: 0131 672 2114; Tower Park, 7 Private Road, Gorebridge EH23 4HG Tel: 01875 20372 — MB ChB 1982 Ed.; DRCOG 1988; DCH RCPS Glas. 1984.

DUNCAN, Louise Elizabeth Marsden Road Health Centre, Marsden Rd, South Shields, South Shields NE34 6RE Tel: 0191 454 0457; 15 Noel Terrace, Winlaton Mill NE21 6SD Tel: 0191 414 3468 — MB BS 1991 Newc.; MRCGP 2000; DCH RCPS Glas. 1995. p/t GP Princip. Prev: GP Regist. Whickham Health Centre, Whickham.

DUNCAN, Malcolm Herbert 36A Russell Road, Northwood HA6 2LR — MB BS 1989 Lond.; BSc Lond. 1986, MB BS 1989. Prev: Ho. Off. Whittington & Roy. N.. Hosps. Lond.

DUNCAN, Margaret Elizabeth Ahlaine, Cardrona, Peebles EH45 9HX Tel: 01896 830681 Fax: 01896 830681 — MB ChB 1961 Ed.; MD (Gold Medal) Ed. 1983; FRCS Ed. 1970; FRCOG 1979, M 1967, DObst 1964. Research Gyn. Assoc. Research Worker (Med. Microbiol.) Univ. Med. Sch. Socs: Fell. Roy. Soc. Trop. Med. & Hyg.; Christ. Med. Fell.sh.; Internat. Leprosy Assn. Prev: Cons. O & G Al Qassimi Hosp. Sharjah, UAE; Research Obst. MRC Leprosy Project Addis Ababa, Ethiopia & Nat. Inst. Med. Research Lond.; Assoc. Prof. O & G Addis Ababa Univ., Ethiopia.

DUNCAN, Margaret Elizabeth 276 South Road, Sheffield S6 3TB — MB ChB 1992 Sheff.

DUNCAN, Margaret Jean Patricia Woodside, 4 Cumberland Road, Rhu, Helensburgh G84 8RX Tel: 01436 820366 — MB ChB 1960 Glas.

DUNCAN, Margaret Russell Southern General Hospital, 1345 Govan Road, Glasgow G51 4TF Tel: 0141 201 1100; 17 Dunlop Grove, Uddingston, Glasgow G71 5SE Tel: 01698 811579 — MB ChB (Hons.) Ed. 1992; MA Camb. 1993; MRCP (UK) 1995. (Ed.) Specialist Regist. (Gen. Med. & Rheum.) S.ern Gen. Hosp. Glas. Prev: SHO III (Rheum.) Gartnavel Gen. Hosp. Glas.; SHO (Med.) Glas. Roy. Infirm.

DUNCAN, Mary Elizabeth 33/8 Murrayfield Road, Edinburgh EH12 6EP — MB ChB 1953 Aberd. Socs: Fell. Roy. Soc. Med.; Assoc. Mem. RSC. Prev: Sen. Med. Off. Comm. Safety Meds.; Research Fell. (Microbiol. & Immunol.) Istituto Superiore di Sanita, Rome; Sen. Regist. (Bacteriol.) Guy's Hosp. Lond.

DUNCAN, Matthew Semple Flat B/1, 27 Lynedoch St., Glasgow G3 6AA — MB ChB 1960 Glas.

DUNCAN, Michael John Far Surgill Head Farm, Cowling, Keighley BD22 0LN — MB ChB 1970 Ed. (Ed.) Prev: SHO (O & G) & SHO (Anaesth.) Nottm. City Hosp.; Ho. Phys. & Ho. Surg. Nottm. Gen. Hosp.

DUNCAN, Michelle Rosalynd Princes Street Surgery, 155 Princes Street, Dundee DD4 6DG Tel: 01382 461090 Fax: 01382 461091; Balkemback Farm, Tealing, Dundee DD4 0RF Tel: 01382 380205 — MB ChB 1991 Dundee; MRCGP 1996; DFFP 1996; DRCOG 1995. (Dundee) Princip. GP P.ss St. Surg. Dundee. Prev: GP/Regist. Forfar, Angus; SHO (O & G) Perth Roy. Infirmiary; GP Asst. P.s St., Dundee.

DUNCAN, Morven Christine Lamont Annfield House, Kingskettle, Cupar KY15 7TN Tel: 01337 831888 — MB ChB Ed. 1970; BSc (Med. Sci.) 1967; Dip. of Faculty of Family Planning. (Edinburgh) Clin. Med. Off. Community Wom.'s Health Fife Health Bd. NHS Trust. Socs: BMA. Prev: GP 1976-1995.

DUNCAN, Neil Alexander (retired) Sapperton End, Maynards Green, Heathfield TN21 0DD Tel: 01435 812364 — MRCS Eng. LRCP Lond. 1944; DObst RCOG 1950. Chairm. & Hon. Field Dir. Flying Doctor Developm. Serv. of Afr. Prev: Flying Doctor, Cloncurry, Qu.sld.

DUNCAN, Pamela Scott 23 Radernie Place, St Andrews KY16 8QR — MB ChB 1991 Manch.

DUNCAN, Patricia Lesley Meeks Road Surgery, 10 Meeks Road, Falkirk FK2 7ES Tel: 01324 619930 Fax: 01324 627266 — MB ChB 1985 Ed.; MRCGP 1989; DRCOG 1988. Prev: SHO/Trainee GP Argyll & Clyde HB VTS; Ho. Off. (Med.) Inverclyde Roy. Hosp. Greenock; Ho. Off. (Surg.) Vict. Hosp. Kirkcaldy.

DUNCAN, Peter James Castlecroft Road Surgery, 104 Castlecroft Road, Castlecroft, Wolverhampton WV3 8LU Tel: 01902 761629 Fax: 01902 765660; 104 Castlecroft Road, Wolverhampton WV3 8LU Tel: 01902 761644 — MB BS 1970 Lond.; DObst RCOG 1974. (Roy. Free) Prev: Jun. Ho. Surg. New End Hosp. Lond.; Jun. Ho. Phys. (Paediat.) Hampstead Gen. Hosp. Lond.; Trainee Gen. Pract. Norwich Vocational Train. Scheme.

DUNCAN, Peter Reid (retired) 20 Windsor Road, St Annes, Lytham St Annes FY8 1ET Tel: 01253 723481 — MD 1952 Manch.; BSc Manch. 1940, MD (Commend.) 1952, MB ChB 1943; FRCP Lond. 1969, M 1948. Prev: Cons. Phys., Vict. Hosp., Blackpool.

DUNCAN, Peter Watson Royal Preston Hospital, Sharoe Green Lane, Preston PR2 9HT Tel: 01772 522555 Fax: 01772 522992 Email: peter.duncan@patr.nhs.uk; Tel: 01772 782856 — MB ChB 1977 Ed.; FRCA Eng. 1981. (Ed.) Cons. Anaesth. & ITU Roy. Preston Hosp. Socs: Assn. Anaesth.; Intens. Care Soc.; Eur. Soc. Regional Anaesth.

DUNCAN, Priscilla Ann New Place Farm, Pulborough RH20 2HZ Tel: 01798 872453 — MB BS 1956 Lond.

DUNCAN, Rhona Kathryn 18 Kilmorey Park Avenue, Chester CH2 3QU — MB ChB 1993 Birm.

DUNCAN, Robert Andrew Child Health Dept, Borders General Hospital, Melrose TD6 9BS Tel: 01896 826677 Fax: 01896 826689 — MB ChB 1987 Ed.; MRCP (UK) 1991; MRCPCH 1997. Cons. Paediat.Borders Gen Hosp. Socs: Scott. Paediat. Soc.; Assn. Research Infant & Child Developm. Prev: Career Regist. Roy. Liverp. Childr. Hosp.; Sen. Regist. (Respirat. Med.) Roy. Hosp. Sick Childr. Edin.

DUNCAN, Robert James 3 Wyteleaf Close, Ruislip HA4 7SP — MB BS 1990 Lond.

DUNCAN, Robert Wilson, Surg. Capt. RN Retd. (retired) Thatch End, Hill Road, Wangford, Beccles NR34 8AR — MA, MB BCh BAO Dub. 1937. Prev: Asst. Med. Dir. Gen. (Naval).

DUNCAN, Robin William New Park Medical Practice, 163 Robertson Road, Dunfermline KY12 0BL Tel: 01383 629200 Fax: 01383 629203; 11 Thimblehall Drive, Dunfermline KY12 7UG — MB ChB 1979 Dundee.

DUNCAN, Roderick Institute of Neurological Sciences, Southern General Hospital, Glasgow G51 4TF Tel: 0141 201 2517 Fax: 0141

201 2993 Email: r.duncan@clinmed.gla.ac.uk — MB ChB 1978 Aberd.; PhD Glas. 1993; MD Aberd. 1983; FRCP Glas. (Aberd.) Cons. Neurol. Inst. Neurol. Sci. S.. Gen. Hosp. Glas.; Sen. Lect. Univ. Glas.; Lead Clinician, W. of Scotl. Regional Epilepsy Serv. Socs: Assn. Brit. Neurol.; Internat. League Against Epilepsy. Prev: Charge De Recherche, Inserm CJF 90-12, Rennes, France; Med. Off. Brit. Antarctic Survey.

DUNCAN, Mr Roderick Douglas Dewar Department of Orthopaedics, Royal Hospital for Sick Children, Glasgow G3 8SJ Tel: 0141 201 0276 Fax: 0141 201 0275; 99 Rannoch Drive, Bearsden, Glasgow G61 2ER — MB ChB 1986 Dundee; FRCS (Orth.) 1996; FRCS Ed. 1991. Cons. Orthop. Surg. Roy Hosp. for Sick Childr. Glas.; Hon. Clin. Sen. Lect., Univ. of Glas. Prev: Sen. Regist. (Orthop.) N.. Region Orthop. Train. Scheme; Sen. Regist. (Paediat. Orthop.) Gt. Ormond St. Hosp. Lond. & Roy. Nat. Orthop. Hosp. Stanmore.

DUNCAN, Ronald Wallace Regent Road Surgery, 10/12 Regent Road, Lowestoft NR32 1PA Tel: 01502 565252; Kingsmead, 122 Yarmouth Road, Lowestoft NR32 4AQ Tel: 01502 563220 — MB ChB 1960 Aberd.; MRCOG 1970, DObst 1962. Socs: BMA. Prev: Ho. Surg. Gyn. & Ho. Surg. Aberd. Roy. Infirm.; Ho. Phys. City Hosp. Aberd.

DUNCAN, Russell Macpherson 10 London Road, Kilmarnock KA3 7AD Tel: 01563 23593 — MB ChB 1946 St. And. Prev: Capt. RAMC Ho. Surg. Ayr Co. Hosp.

DUNCAN, Sheila Longmuir Black (retired) 54 Quarry Lane, Sheffield S11 9EB Tel: 01142 554001 Fax: 01142 554001 — MB ChB (Commend.) Glas. 1955; MD Glas. 1968; FRCOG 1973, M 1960; DObst RCOG 1957; DHMSA 1999. Prev: Reader (O & G) Sheff. Univ.

DUNCAN, Stuart Henry Weir Tel: 01224 733535 Fax: 01224 735662; Kennerty House, Peterculter, Peterculter AB14 0LS Tel: 01224 733106 Fax: 01224 735566 — MB ChB 1965 Aberd.; MRCGP 1975; DObst RCOG 1968. Treas. Med. Off. Prev: Ho. Surg. & Ho. Phys. Aberd. Roy. Infirm.; Ho. Surg. Aberd. Matern. Hosp.

DUNCAN, Susan Elizabeth 7 Newhailes Avenue, Musselburgh EH21 6DW; Department Neurology, Hope Hospital, Scott Lane, Salford Tel: 0161 767 4626 Email: susanduncan@compuserve.com — MB ChB 1982 Ed.; BSc 1979; MRCPI 1988; MRCP (UK) 1988. (Edinburgh) Cons. Neurol. Dept. Clin. NNeurosci.s Hope Hosp. Salford. Prev: Sen. Regist. Dundee Roy. Infirm.

DUNCAN, Mr Thomas Four Winds, Sexhow, Stokesley, Middlesbrough TS9 7DX Tel: 01642 701025 — MB ChB 1955 St. And.; MB ChB (Commend.) St. And. 1955; FRCS Ed. 1961. Cons. Surg. S. Tees Health Dist. Prev: Sen. Regist. (Surg.) Aberd. Roy. Infirm., & Clin. Tutor in Surg.; Univ. Aberd.; MRC Research Fell. 1965-6.

DUNCAN, Timothy Jake 41 High Church Wynd, High St., Yarm TS15 9BQ — BM BS 1996 Nottm.

DUNCAN, Tracy Intensive Care Unit, Manchester Royal Infirmary, Oxford Road, Manchester Tel: 0161 276 1234 — MB ChB 1992 Manch.; MRCP Ed. Specialist Regist. (Respirat. Med.) N. W. Region. Socs: Brit. Thoracic Soc. (Full); Intens. Care Soc. (Full); Manch. Med. Soc. (Full).

DUNCAN, William 30A Inverleith Place, Edinburgh EH3 5QB Tel: 0131 552 2898 Fax: 0131 551 2224 — MB ChB 1954 Aberd.; FRCS Ed. 1977; FRCP Ed. 1972, M 1964; FRCPC 1985; Hon. FRACR 1992; Hon. FACR 1982; FRCR 1975; FFR 1962; DMRT Eng. 1960. (Aberd.) Special Adviser Christie Hosp. NHS Trust Manch.; Hon. Prof. Radiat. Oncol. Univ. Manch. Socs: Hon. Mem. Canad. Assn. Radiat. Oncol.; Hon. Mem. Scott. Radiol. Soc. Prev: Chief, Dept. Radiat. Oncol. P.ss Margt. Hosp. Toronto; Prof. Radiat. Oncol. Univ. Toronto; Prof. Radiat. Oncol. & Head (Clin. Oncol.) Univ. Edin.

DUNCAN, William Abbey Health Centre, East Abbey Street, Arbroath DD11 1EN Tel: 01241 872692; Annbank, 55 Keptie Road, Arbroath DD11 3EF Tel: 01241 872692 — MB ChB 1963 Glas.; MRCGP 1971; DObst RCOG 1965. (Glas.)

DUNCAN, William Colin Simpsons Memorial Maternity Pavillon, Royal Infirmary of Edinburgh, Lauriston Place, Edinburgh EH3 9 Tel: 0131 536 1000; Obst. and Gyn., Centre for Reproductive Biology, 37 Chalmers St, Edinburgh EH3 9EW Tel: 0131 229 2575 Fax: 0131 229 2408 — MB ChB 1990 Ed.; BSc (Path.) Ed. 1988; MD 1998; MRCOG 1998. Lect. Univ.Edin. Prev: Wellcome Trust Clin. Train. Fell.sh.; Specialist Regist. (O & G) Edin.

DUNCAN-WHYTE, Jean (retired) 8 Cornerways, Daylesford Avenue, London SW15 5QP Tel: 020 8876 8942 — MRCS Eng. LRCP Lond. 1935; DPH Lond. 1939. Prev: MO Family Plann. Assn. Clinics, Carshalton, Putney & Roehampton. Ho.

DUNCANSON, Karen Campbell 139 Ruthrieston Circle, Aberdeen AB10 7LB Tel: 01224 591939 — MB ChB 1995 Aberd.; DFFP 1997. CMO Family Plann. Centre, Aberd. Prev: SHO (O & G) Aberd. Roy. Infirm.; Jun. Ho. Off. Med. Ward 47, Aberd.; Jun. Ho. Off. Surg. Raigmore Hosp. Inverness.

DUNCKLEY, Harry George Eden Valley NHS.PCT, Central Clinic, 50 Victoria Place, Carlisle CA1 1HP Tel: 01228 603203 Fax: 01228 603201 Email: dr.dunckley@nlhc-tr.northy.nhs.uk — MB BS Lond. 1970; MRCS Eng. LRCP Lond. 1970; DObst RCOG 1973. (St. Bart) Macmillan Cons. in Palliat. Med. for E. Cumbria. Socs: Assn. Palliat. Med. Prev: Med. Dir. St. Michael's Hospice, Hereford; Staff Grade (Palliat. Med.) Derbysh. Roy. Infirm.; GP Kent.

DUNCKLEY, Paul David Flat 13, 15 Craven Road, Reading RG1 5LE — MB ChB 1995 Bristol.

DUNCOMBE, Andrew Stephen Department of Haematology, Southampton General Hospital, Tremona Road, Southampton SO16 6YD — MB BS 1981 Lond.; FRCP 1999 UK; FRCPath 2000 UK; MA Oxf. 1982, DM 1991; MRCP (UK) 1984; MRCPath 1992. Cons. Haemat. Soton. Univ. Hosps. Trust. Socs: Brit. Soc. Haematol.; Brit. Soc. for Blood and Marrow Transpl.ation; Brit. Soc. Immunol. Prev: Sen. Regist. Rotat. (Haemat.) St. Geo. Hosp. Lond.; Wellcome Research Train. Fell. & Hon. Lect. (Haemat.) Roy. Free Hosp. Lond.; Lect. (Haemat.) St. Thos. Hosp. Med. Sch. Lond.

DUNCOMBE, Catherine Louise 11 Suffolk Road, Potters Bar EN6 3EZ — MB ChB 1997 Birm.

DUNCUMB, Christine Elizabeth Trinity Mill, Bagendon, Cirencester GL7 7BH — MB ChB 1980 Bristol.

DUNCUMB, Rosemary Ethel Trinity Mill, Bagendon, Cirencester GL7 7BH Tel: 01285 654686 — MB BS 1949 Lond.; MRCS Eng. LRCP Lond. 1949. (Roy. Free) Clin. Asst. (A & E) P.ss Margt. Hosp. Swindon; Med. Off. (Family Plann.) Glos. & Wilts. AHAs. Prev: Ho. Surg. Roy. Free Hosp.; Res. Surg. Off. Tindal Gen. Hosp. Aylesbury; Med. Off. BCMS Hosp. Kachwa, India.

DUNDAS, Charles William Singleton Medical Centre, 10 Singleton Court, Ashford TN23 5GR Tel: 01233 646036/646037 Fax: 01233 663150 — MB ChB 1988 Ed.

DUNDAS, Derek Duncan St. James Wing X-Ray Department, St. George's Hospital, Blackshaw Road, London SW17 0QT Tel: 020 8725 1481 — MB ChB 1975 Dundee; FRCR 1980. Cons. Diag. Radiol. St. Geo. & Bolingbroke Hosps. Lond.; Hon. Sen. Lect. St. Geo. Hosp. Med. Sch. Lond.

DUNDAS, Kirsty Catherine 2F1, 7 Craigcrook Place, Edinburgh EH4 3NG — MB ChB 1991 Ed.; MRCOG 1996; DCH RCPS Glas. 1994. Specialist Regist. O & G Roy. Infirm. Edin. Prev: SHO (O & G) Roy. Infirm. & Simpson Memor. Matern. Pavil. Edin.

DUNDAS, Stephanie 27A Albany Street, Edinburgh EH1 3QN — MB ChB 1989 Glas.; MRCP (UK) 1993. Specialist Regist. (Med. & Infec. Dis.) City Hosp. Edin. Prev: SHO (Med.) Glas. Roy. Infirm.; SHO (Infec. Dis.) Ruchill Hosp. Glas.; SHO (Med.) Law Hosp. Carluke.

DUNDAS, Stephen Alan Craig Department of Cellular Pathology, Southport & Formby D.G.H., Town Lane, Southport PR8 6PN Tel: 01704 704682 — BM 1979 Soton.; MRCPath 1985. Cons. Cellular Path., S.port DGH; BMA Power; L.N.C. Chairm. Prev: Lect. (Path.) Sheff. Univ. Med. Sch.; SHO (Clin. Path.) Roy. Hallamsh. Hosp. Sheff.

DUNDEE, Joseph McKinney Sentry Hill, 40 Ballycraigy Road, Newtownabbey BT36 4SX — MB BCh BAO 1929 Belf.

DUNDEE, Ruth Crawford 191 Old Cullybackey Road, Cullybackey, Ballymena BT42 1BT — MB BCh BAO 1987 Belf.; MRCGP 1993; DRCOG 1991.

DUNDERDALE, Mark Alexander 73 Derby Road, Beeston, Nottingham NG9 2TB; Hop Gardens, Willingham, Gainsborough DN21 5JZ — BM BS 1991 Nottm.

DUNDON, Edward Anthony 185 Murray Road, Ealing, London W5 4DD Fax: 020 8932 3795 — MB BCh BAO 1974 NUI; DFFP 1993; DObst RCPI 1987. Regist. (O & G) Essex Co. & Colchester Matern. Hosp. Prev: SHO (O & G) Herts. & Essex Gen. Hosp. Bishops Stortford; SHO (O & G) Solihull Hosp.; SHO (Gyn.) Roy. Berks. Hosp. Reading.

DUNDROW, Jennifer Mary Meddygfa Minafon, Kidwelly SA17 4UL Tel: 01554 890234; The Croft, The Cliff, Ferryside SA17 5SP Tel: 0126 785273 — MB BCh 1982 Wales; DRCOG 1985.

DUNFIELD-PRAYERO, Andrew Charles 11 Montague Road, London SW19 1TB — MB ChB 1989 Manch.

DUNFORD, Andrew Peter Wapping Health Centre, 22 Wapping Lane, London E1W 2RL Tel: 020 7481 9376 — MB BS 1978 Lond.; MRCGP 1982; DRCOG 1982. (St. Thos.) Lect. (HIV Liaison Med.) Qu. Mary W.field Coll. Univ. Lond.; Mem. Nat. Inst. Med. Herbalists. Prev: GP Wapping Health Centre Lond.

DUNFORD, Carl Flat 4, 84 Cathedral Road, Cardiff CF11 9LN — BM 1986 Soton.

DUNFORD, Gordon Paul Ashcroft Surgery, Wing, Leighton Buzzard LU7 0NE Tel: 01296 688201 Fax: 01296 681421; Milebush Farm, 136 Soulbury Road, Linslade, Leighton Buzzard LU7 2RT Tel: 01525 851772 Fax: 01296 681421 — MB BCh 1979 Wales; MRCGP 1983; DRCOG 1985.

DUNGER, Gerald Thomas Southwood, 65 Hocombe Road, Chandlers Ford, Eastleigh SO53 5QA Tel: 01703 253921 — MB BS 1953 Lond.; MRCS Eng. LRCP Lond. 1956; DObst RCOG 1956. (St. Bart.)

DUNGU, Richard William Pathology Department, Harold Wood Hospital, Romford RM3 0BE Tel: 014023 45533; 24 Walsingham Way, Billericay CM12 0YE Tel: 01277 658674 — MB ChB 1969 Ed.; BA Columbia Univ. 1964; MMed (Path.) Makerere Univ. 1975; FRCPath 1987, M 1975. (Ed.) Cons. (Chem. Path.) Harold Wood Hosp. Prev: Sen. Regist. Dept. Chem. Path. Kingston Hosp.; Regist. Dept. Chem. Path. Roy. Postgrad. Med. Sch. Hammersmith Hosp. Lond.

DUNHAM, Angela Mary Maidstone Hospital, Hermitage Lane, Maidstone ME16 9QQ Tel: 01622 729000 Fax: 01622 720807; New House Farm, Otterden Road, Eastling, Faversham ME13 0BN Tel: 01795 890629 — MB Camb. 1967, BChir 1966; FRCS Ed. 1975; FRCOG 1998; DCH Eng. 1969. (Cambridge & Guys Hospital) InFertil. specialist, Kent Med. Imaging, Kent. Prev: Cons. O & G Maidstone Hosp; Sen. Regist. St. Thos. Hosp. Lond.; Resid. Med. Off. Qu. Charlottes Hosp. Lond.

DUNHAM, James Michael The Surgery, 7 Barmby Road, Pocklington, York YO42 2DL Tel: 01759 302500 Fax: 01759 305123 — MB ChB 1969 Manch.; DObst RCOG 1971. (Manch.)

DUNHAM, Richard John Charles Department of Radiology, Clarendon Wing, The General Infirmary at Leeds, Leeds; Kenilworth Lodge, 66 Main Street, Thorner, Leeds LS14 3BU — MB ChB 1983 Leeds; FRCR 1990. Cons. Radiol. The Gen. Infirm. at Leeds and Wharfedale Gen. Hosp. Prev: Sen. Regist. (Radiol.) Leeds Gen. Infirm., St. Jas. Univ. Hosp. Leeds & Bradford Teach. Hosps.

DUNHAM, William Robert Flat 5, Hornby Court, Bromborough, Wirral CH62 2EJ — MB BS 1968 Lond.; FRCPath 1991, M 1979. (Guy's) Socs: BMA. Prev: Cons. Med. Microbiol. N. Wirral Hosps.; Sen. Regist. Area Laborat. Exeter & W. Infirm. Glas.

DUNHILL, Zoë Mary Lothian.Univ.Hosp NHS Tust, Community Child Health Service, 10 Chalmers Crescent, Edinburgh EH9 1TS Tel: 0131 536 0486 Fax: 0131 536 0570 Email: scp@ed.ad.uk; Monkton House, Old Craighall, Musselburgh EH21 8SF Fax: 0131 665 2839 Email: fb58@dial.pipex.com — MB ChB 1973 Ed.; MBA Ed. 1995; FRCP Ed. 1990; MRCP (UK) 1980; FRCPCH 1997; DCH RCPS Glas. 1975. (Ed.) Cons. Paediat. Pat..Serv.Dir.Childr.s.Serv.; Hon. Sen. Lect. (Child Life & Health) Univ. Edin.; Dir. Sch. Community Paediat. Univ. Edin. Socs: Scott. Assn. Community Child Health; Brit. Assn. Paediat. Neurol.; Scott. Paediat. Soc.

DUNK, Arthur Albert Department of Medicine, Eastbourne District General Hospital, Kings Drive, Eastbourne BN21 2UD Tel: 01323 417400 Email: draadunk@aol.com — MB ChB 1978 Glas.; MRCP (UK) 1980; FRCP Lond. 1996; MD Glas. 1987; FRCPS Glas. 1991. (Glasgow) Cons. Phys. & Gastroenterol. E.bourne Dist. Gen. Hosp. Socs: Brit. Soc. Gastroenterol. Prev: Sen. Regist. & Hon. lect.; Aberd. Roy. Hosps. NHS Trust Univ. Aberd.; Regist. Acad. Dept. Med. Roy. Free Hosp. Lond.

DUNK, Rosemary Ann Tann Hills, Oxenholme Lane, Natland, Kendal LA9 7QH — MB ChB 1977 Sheff.

DUNKELMAN, Helen Margaret Alma Partnership, 31 Alma Road, Bournemouth BH9 1BP Tel: 01202 519311 Fax: 01202 548532 — MB BS 1985 Lond.; SRN 1977; MRCGP 1989; DCH RCP Lond. 1988; DRCOG 1987. (Univ. Coll. Hosp.) Clin. Asst. BrE. Clinic Roy. Bournemouth Hosp. Prev: Trainee GP N.wick Pk. VTS; Ho. Phys. Univ. Coll. Hosp. Lond.; Ho. Surg. N.wick Pk. Hosp. Middlx.

DUNKERLEY, Mr David Russell (retired) (cons. rooms) Longwood House, The Bath Clinic, Claverton Down Road, Bath BA2 7BR Tel: 01225 835555 — MB 1958 Camb.; BChir 1957; FRCS Eng. 1966. Prev: Cons. Orthop. & Hand Surg. Bath HA.

DUNKIN, Jonathan William St Peters Hill Surgery, 15 St. Peters Hill, Grantham NG31 6QA Tel: 01476 590009 Fax: 01476 570898; 3 Welby Gardens, Grantham NG31 8BN Tel: 01476 64536 Fax: 01476 564536 — MB ChB 1977 Manch. Socs: BMA. Prev: SHO (O & G) Univ. Hosp. S. Manch.; SHO (Paediat.) Booth Hall Childr. Hosp. Manch.; Ho. Phys. Stepping Hill Hosp. Stockport.

DUNKLEY, Mr Alan Bernard 26 Mount Avenue, London W5 2RD — BM 1987 Soton.; FRCS Eng. 1991; FRCS Orth 1997. Cons. Orthop. Surg. Taunton.

DUNKLEY, Alan Hastilow (retired) Tignals Farm, Frensham Lane, Headley, Bordon GU35 8TB — MB BS 1954 Lond. Prev: NHS Gen. Practitioner.

DUNKLEY, Brian Invicta Community Care NHS Trust, Woodside C.M.H.C., 89 London Road, Maidstone ME16 0EB Tel: 01622 757077 — MB ChB 1972 Bristol; MRCPath 1981. Clin. Med. Off. in Psychiat. Woodside Community Ment. Health Centre, Maidstone, Kent. Socs: Brit. Assn. Behavioural & Cognitive Psychotherapies. Prev: Dir., Drug Safety Eval.-Wellcome Research Labs; Hon. Cons. Neuropath. Inst. of Psychiat. Maudsley Hosp. Lond.

DUNKLEY, Christopher John 10 Highfield Drive, Wigston, Leicester LE18 1NN — BM BS 1988 Nottm.

DUNKLEY, Colin Peter 21A Darlington Road, Richmond DL10 7BE — MB ChB 1995 Leeds.

DUNKLEY, Martin Andrew 184 Canterbury Road, Davyhulme Urmston, Manchester M41 0QR — MB ChB 1984 Manch.; MB ChB Manch. l984.

DUNKLEY, Melanie Jane Bradgate Mental Health Unit, Glenfeid General Hospital, Leicester — MB ChB 1990 Leic.; MRCPsych 1996. SPR Leics., Rutland NHS Trust.

DUNKLEY, Miss Mercia Peta Surgical Skills Unit, Department of Surgery, Ninewells Hospital, Dundee DD1 9SY Tel: 01382 645857 Fax: 01382 646042 Email: m.p.dunkley@dundee.ac.uk; 30E Roseangle, Dundee DD1 4LY — MB BS 1974 Lond.; FRCS Eng. 1980; MRCS Eng. LRCP Lond. 1974; MBA Dundee 1998. (St. Mary's) Sen. Lect. (Surg.) Ninewells Hosp. Dundee.; Assoc. Dir. Surgial Skills Unit. Prev: Regist. (Plastic Surg.) Dundee Roy. Infirm.

DUNKLEY, Sarah Anne — MB BS 1991 Lond.; BSc Lond. 1988; MRCP (UK) 1994; DFFP; DRCOG. (St Marys)

DUNKOW, Paul David Flat 17, Langham Court, Mersey Road, Manchester M20 2PX — MB ChB 1994 Manch.

DUNLEAVY, Desmond Leo Francis 18 Graham Park Road, Gosforth, Newcastle upon Tyne NE3 4BH — MD 1972 NUI; MB BCh BAO 1964; FRCPsych 1981, M 1972; DPM Eng. 1968. Cons. Psychiat. Newc. Ment. Health Trust; Hon. Lect. (Psych.) Univ. Newc. Socs: Brit. Sleep Soc.; Inst. Psychosexual Med. Prev: Sen. Lect. (Psychol. Med.) Univ. Newc.; Lect. (Psychiat.) Nottm.; Research Fell. (Psychiat.) Univ. Edin.

DUNLEAVY, Moira Jean Bracadale, 29 Station Road, Killearn, Glasgow G63 9NZ Tel: 01360 550020 — MB ChB 1976 Glas.; DCCH RCP Ed. 1990. Staff Grade (Community Paediat.) Yorkhill NHS Trust, Glas. Prev: Clin. Med. Off. (Community Child Health) Chesterfield, W. Lothian & Nottm.

DUNLEAVY, Sarah Jane 34 Shelley Crescent, Heston, Hounslow TW5 9BJ — MB ChB 1998 Manch.; MB ChB Manch 1998.

DUNLOP, Alastair Valence (retired) Moffat, Cedar Road, Cobham KT11 2AA Tel: 01932 863210 — MB BChir 1952 Camb.; BA Camb. 1949; MRCS Eng. LRCP Lond. 1952.

DUNLOP, Andrew Leith Mount, 46 Ferry Road, Edinburgh EH6 4AE Tel: 0131 554 0558 Fax: 0131 555 6911; 14 House O'Hill Crescent, Edinburgh EH4 5DH Email: andrew.dunlop@cwcom.net — MB ChB 1980 Glas.; MRCGP 1985; DCH RCPS Glas. 1984; Dip. Pract. Dermatol. Wales 1997. (Glasgow)

DUNLOP, Angela Joan 5 Farm Close, West Wickham BR4 9JL — MB ChB 1979 Otago.

DUNLOP, Bruce Norman Burney Johnson and Partners, Langley House, 27 West Street, Chichester PO19 1RW Tel: 01243

782266/782955 Fax: 01243 779188; Church Cottage, Church Lane, Sidlesham, Chichester PO20 7RH Tel: 01243 641851 Fax: 01243 641851 Email: bndunlop@aol.com — MB BS 1981 Lond.; MRCGP 1986; DRCOG 1987. (St. Geo. Lond.) GP Trainer Chichester. Prev: Maj. RAMC.

DUNLOP, Charles Moir (retired) 35 Upland Road, Eastbourne BN20 8ER Tel: 01323 733240 Fax: 01323 733240 — MB ChB Aberd. 1946. Prev: Ho. Surg. (Obst.) Matern. Hosp. Aberd.

DUNLOP, Colin Charles Robert 64 The Beeches, Nantwich CW5 5YP — MB ChB 1996 Aberd.

DUNLOP, David Anthony Boyd Acacia Lodge, Kensington Place, London Road, Bath BA1 6AP Tel: 01225 428697 — MB BS 1971 Lond.; MA Camb. 1969; FRCR 1979. (Middlx.) Cons. Clin. Radiol. & Nuclear Med. Bath. Socs: (Sec.) SW Radiol. Assn. Prev: Sen. Regist. (Radiol.) Middlx., Brompton, St. Mark's, Roy. N. & Roy. Nat. Orthop. Hosps. Lond.

DUNLOP, David John 6 Piney Plateau, Belfast BT9 5QP — MB ChB 1989 Birm.

DUNLOP, Diana Clare Becket's Place, Marksbury, Bath BA2 9HP — MB BS 1987 Lond.; MD Bath 2000; MA Camb. 1988; MRCOG 1993.

DUNLOP, Mr Douglas Graham 18 Talygarn Street, Heath, Cardiff CF14 3PT — MB BCh 1990 Wales; FRCS Ed. 1994.

DUNLOP, Elspeth Marilyn Church Street Surgery, 77 Church Street, Tewkesbury GL20 5RY Tel: 01684 292343 Fax: 01684 274305 — MB BS 1975 Lond.; DA Eng. 1982; DRCOG 1979.

DUNLOP, Gertrude Forbes 8 Ness Gardens, Bishopbriggs, Glasgow G64 1BT; Flat 3, 23 Stirling Road, Drymen, Glasgow G63 0BW Tel: 01360 661060 — MB ChB 1940 Glas. (Glas.) Prev: Throat Hosp. Glas. & Stobhill Hosp.

DUNLOP, Helen Audrey, OBE (retired) Minster House, Castle Cary BA7 7PP — MB BCh BAO 1947 Belf.; DPH 1960; DCH Eng. 1959. Prev: Med. Off. Bruton Sch. Girls.

DUNLOP, Hester Jane 36 Knowl Road, Golcar, Huddersfield HD7 4AN — MB ChB 1981 Manch.; MRCGP 1989; DRCOG 1985.

DUNLOP, Hugh Richard Tel: 028 9040 1744 Fax: 028 9040 2069; 9 Stormont Park, Belfast BT4 3GW — MB BCh BAO Belf. 1965; DObst RCOG 1967. (Belf.)

DUNLOP, James (retired) 192 Kew Road, Richmond TW9 2AS Tel: 020 8940 1615 — MRCS Eng. LRCP Lond. 1961; FFOM RCP Lond. 1993, MFOM 1982; DPH Dundee 1969; DObst RCOG 1963. Prev: Princip. Med. Adviser Unilever Lond.

DUNLOP, James Montgomery Sungates, 136 Westella Road, Kirkella, Hull HU10 7RR Tel: 01482 655680 — MB BCh BAO 1959 Dub.; MA Dub. 1962; FRCP Lond. 1992; FFPHM 1989; FFCM 1978, M 1974; DPA Glas. 1966; DPH Glas. 1964; DObst RCOG 1962. (TC Dub.) Med. Ref. Hull Crematorium; Med. Off Kingston Communications, Hull Stagecoach. Socs: Fell. Roy. Med. Soc. Edin. & Roy Soc. Med. Lond.; Fell. RIPHH (Mem. Counc. & Smith Award Holder 1992).; Ex-Treas. Fac. Pub. Health Med. RCP. Prev: Dir. Pub. Health Hull HA & Port Med. Off. & Med. Insp. of Aliens & Commonw. Immigrants Hull & Goole Port HA; Dep. MOH Kingston Upon Hull; Chief Asst. Med. Off. N. Riding CC Yorks.

DUNLOP, Jane Louise 49 The Rise, Darras Hall, Ponteland, Newcastle upon Tyne NE20 9LQ Tel: 01661 23591 — MB ChB 1988 Bristol; BSc (Biochem.) Bristol 1985, MB ChB 1988. SHO (Paediat.) Roy. Devon & Exeter Hosp. Prev: Trainee GP Torquay; SHO (A & E) Torbay Hosp.; SHO & Ho. Off. (Med.) Roy. Devon & Exeter Hosp.

DUNLOP, John (retired) Sarala, 1 Ardnavalley Park, Comber, Newtownards BT23 5SH Tel: 01247 873346 — MB BCh BAO 1950 Belf.; DObst RCOG 1954. Prev: Ho. Off. (O & G) Roy. Infirm. Halifax.

DUNLOP, John Maurice 6 The Plateau, Piney Hills, Belfast BT9 5QP Tel: 01232 666387 — MB BCh BAO 1959 Belf.; DPM Eng. 1964; FRCOG 1981, M 1968, DObst 1965. (Qu. Univ. Belf.) Cons. O & G Ulster Hosp. Belf.; Clin. Dir., Wom. & Child Health Directorate, Ulster Community & Hosp. Trust Belf.; Chairm. BMA Counc. N.ern Irel. Socs: BMA; Ulster Obst. & Gyn. Soc.; N. Irel. Medico-Legal Soc. Prev: Sen. Lect. Midw. & Gyn. Qu. Univ. Belf.

DUNLOP, Josephine Birbeck Medical Group, Penrith Health Centre, Bridge Lane, Penrith CA11 8HW Tel: 01768 245200 Fax: 01768 245295; The Hollies, Wordsworth St, Penrith CA11 7QZ Tel: 01768 245384 — MB ChB 1976 Liverp.; MRCGP 1980; DRCOG 1979.

DUNLOP, Joyce Lilian Sungates, 136 Westella Road, Kirkella, Hull HU10 7RR Tel: 01482 655680 — MB BCh BAO 1957 Dub.; MA Dub. 1962; FRCPsych 1996, M 1976; DObst RCOG 1959. (TC Dub.) Cons. Psychiat. E. Riding Health. Socs: BMA (Ex-Pres. E. Yorks. Br.). Prev: Sen. Regist. De La Pole Hosp. Willerby & BRd.gate Hosp. Beverley; SHO (Anaesth.) Dumfries & Galloway Roy. Infirm.

DUNLOP, Kathryn Anne 7A Windsor Manor, Windsor Avenue, Belfast BT9 6EE; 17d Maxwell Road, Bangor BT20 3SQ Email: k.dunlop@mail.excite.com — MB ChB 1992 Ed.; MRCP (UK) 1995.

DUNLOP, Kenneth John, OBE (retired) Isca, New Pound Lane, Wisborough Green, Billingshurst RH14 0EG Tel: 01403 700373 — MB ChB 1939 Ed.; FRCP Ed. 1970, M 1948; MFOM RCP Lond. 1978; MRCGP 1968. Prev: Chief Med. Off. Thanai Med. Assn., Assam, India.

DUNLOP, Lorna Worthington Riverview Medical Centre, 6 George Street, Johnstone PA5 8SL Tel: 01505 320208 Fax: 01505 322543; Craigholm, Pk Road, Kilmacolm PA13 4EG — MB ChB 1982 Glas.; DFFP 1987; DCH RCP Glas. 1985; DRCOG 1984. Prev: Clin. Asst. (Colposcopy) Stobhill Hosp. Glas.

DUNLOP, Lucinda Jane Flat 1, 116 Gloucester Avenue, Primrose Hill, London NW1 8HX — MB BChir 1985 Camb.; MRCGP 1993; DCH RCP Lond. 1992; Dip. GU Med. Soc. Apoth. Lond. 1990; DRCOG 1989. Asst. GP Lond.

DUNLOP, Lyn Susan Ye Jolly Gardeners, Pleasant Place, West Hyde, Rickmansworth WD3 2XZ — MB BS 1983 Lond.; BSc Pharmacol. Manch. 1973; PhD Lond. 1979, MB BS 1983. Regist. (O & G) Luton & Dunstable Hosp. Luton. Prev: Research Regist. (Clin. Genetics) Kennedy Salton Centre; SHO (Neonat. Paediat.) Hammersmith & Qu. Charlottes Hosps.; SHO (O & G) Camberwell HA.

DUNLOP, Margaret Louise 1 Tramway Drive, Bushmills BT57 8YS Tel: 028 7035 1037 — MB BCh BAO 1995 Belf.; DRCOG 1999 UK; MRCGP 2000; DGM RCPS Glas. 1997; Dip. Ment Health Belf. 1998; Dip.Child Health.1998. (Qu. Univ. Belf.) GP. Socs: BMA; Ulster Med. Soc. Prev: Ho. Off. Coleraine Hosp.; SHO (Gen. Med.) Coleraine Hosp.; SHO (GP Train. Schme) Coleraine Hosp.

DUNLOP, Michael Stewart Birbeck Medical Group, Penrith Health Centre, Bridge Lane, Penrith CA11 8HW Tel: 01768 245200 Fax: 01768 245295; The Hollies, Wordsworth St, Penrith CA11 7QZ Tel: 01768 245384 — MB ChB 1974 Glas.; MRCGP 1978; DRCOG 1976; Dip. Palliat. Med. Wales. Prev: Clin. Asst. ENT Cumbid. Infirm. Carlisle; Ho. Surg. Belford Hosp. Fort William; Ho. Phys Gartnavel Gen. Hosp. Glas.

DUNLOP, Patricia Alison 8 Schomberg Park, Belfast BT4 2HH — MB ChB 1989 Ed.; BSc (Hons.) Ed. 1987, MB ChB 1989.

DUNLOP, Patricia Mary 25 Southdown Crescent, Cheadle Hulme, Cheadle SK8 6EQ — MB BS 1978 Lond.; MA; MB BS Lond. 1978; DRCOG 1980.

DUNLOP, Mr Paul 3 Birtley Close, Gosforth, Newcastle upon Tyne NE3 4RL Email: pauldunlop@compuserve.com — MB BS 1988 Newc.; MD Leic. 1996; FRCS Eng. 1992. Regist. Rotat. (Gen. Surg.) N. Region. Socs: Jun. Mem. Europ. Soc. Vasc. Surg.; Surgic. Research Soc.; Affil. Mem. Vasc. Surg. Soc. Prev: Research Fell. (Surg.) Leicester Univ.; SHO (Surg.) Newc. u. Tyne & Leicester; Demonst. (Anat.) Univ. Newc. u. Tyne.

DUNLOP, Paul Alistair 21 Kirkton Road, Fenwick, Kilmarnock KA3 6DJ — MB ChB 1998 Glas.; MB ChB Glas 1998.

DUNLOP, Peter David Moir Macclesfield District General Hospital, Victoria Road, Macclesfield SK10 3BL Tel: 01625 661167 — MRCS Eng. LRCP Lond. 1977; MA Camb. 1978, MB BChir 1978; MRCOG 1984; T(OG) 1988; CCST 1996. Cons. (O & G) Macclesfield Dist. Gen. Hosp. Prev: Sen. Regist. St. Mary's Hosp. Manch.; Regist. S.mead Hosp. Bristol.; Research Fell. Hammersmith Hosp. Lond.

DUNLOP, Peter Richard Chase Department of Radiotherapy & Oncology, South Cleveland Hospital, Marton, Middlesbrough TS4 3BW — MB BS 1974 Lond.; MD Lond. 1987; FRCR 1982. Cons. Radiother. & Oncol. S. Cleveland Hosp. Middlesbrough. Socs: Roy. Soc. Med. Prev: Sen. Regist. (Radiat. Oncol.) W.. Gen. Hosp. Edin.

DUNLOP, Robert John St. Christopher's Hospice, 51-59 Lawrie Park Road, London SE26 6DZ Tel: 020 8778 9252 Fax: 020 8659

8680 Email: rdunlop@dtchris.ftech.co.uk — MB ChB 1979 Otago; FRACP 1986. Med. Dir. St. Christopher's Hospice Lond.

DUNLOP, Mr Roger 2 Hampton Gardens, Sunnyside St., Belfast BT7 3DF Tel: 01232 645518 — MB BCh BAO 1982 Belf.; FRCSI 1986.

DUNLOP, Rosalyn Anne 5 Crusoe Gardens, Lower Largo, Leven KY8 6HT — MB ChB 1974 Glas.; DRCOG 1976.

DUNLOP, Timothy Dixon Woodside Cottage, Kirkbrae, Shandon, Helensburgh G84 8NP — MB ChB 1977 Dundee.

DUNLOP, Professor William Department of Obstetrics & Gynaecology, University of Newcastle upon Tyne, 4th Floor Leazes Wing, Royal Victoria Infirmary, Newcastle upon Tyne NE1 4LP Tel: 0191 232 5131 Fax: 0191 222 5066 Email: william.dunlop@ncl.ac.uk; 30 Eslington Terrace, Jesmond, Newcastle upon Tyne NE2 4RN Tel: 0191 281 4697 — PhD Newc. 1982; MB ChB Glas. 1967; FRCS Ed. 1971; FRCOG 1984, M 1971. (Glas.) Prof. O & G Univ. Newc.; Chairm. APOG; Pres., RCOG. Socs: (Ex-Chairm.) Blair Bell Research Soc. Prev: Hon. Sec. RCOG; Visit. Assoc. Prof. Med. Univ. S. Carolina, USA; Mem. Scientif. Staff MRC Reproduc. & Growth Unit Newc. u. Tyne.

DUNLOP, William Bennie 37 Braid Drive, Glenrothes KY7 4ES Tel: 01592 2100 — MB ChB 1961 Glas.; DObst RCOG 1966.

DUNMORE, Caroline Jane Penistan and Partners, Cordell Road, Long Melford, Sudbury CO10 9EP Tel: 01787 378226 Fax: 01787 311287; Yee Tree Cottage, Mill Lane, Combs, Stowmarket IP14 2NF — MB BS 1989 Lond.; MRCGP 1994. Prev: Trainee GP/SHO Heath Rd. Hosp. Ipswich; SHO (Orthop.) Soton. Gen. Hosp.; Ho. Off. (Gen. Med. & Endocrinol.) Mayday Hosp.

DUNN, Aidan Ronald Devon Square Surgery, Devon Square Surgery, Newton Abbot TQ12 2HH Tel: 01626 332182 — BM BCh 1974 Oxf.; MA, BM BCh Oxf. 1974. (Univ. Coll. Hosp.) Prev: Trainee GP Basingstoke VTS; Ho. Surg. Univ. Coll. Hosp. Lond.; Ho. Phys. Newmarket Hosp.

DUNN, Ailsa Margaret Bronllys Hospital, Brecon LD3 0LU Tel: 01874 711255 Fax: 01874 711971 Email: ailsadunn@pawys-tr.wales.nhs.uk — MB BS 1978 Lond.; FRCP Lond. 1995; MRCP (UK) 1981. (Roy. Free) Cons. Phys. Geriat. Med. Bronllys Hosp. Brecon. Socs: BMA & Brit. Geriat. Soc. Prev: Sen. Regist. (Gen. Med. & Geriat.) N. Staffs. HA & Sandwell HA; Regist. (Med.) Roy. Shrewsbury Hosp.; Ho. Surg. Roy. Free Hosp. Lond.

DUNN, Alastair Noel (retired) 48 High Street, Winterbourne, Bristol BS36 1JH Tel: 01454 778029 — MB BCh BAO Dub. 1960.

DUNN, Alison 58 Moss Side Road, Cowdenbeath KY4 9JP — MB ChB 1993 Manch.

DUNN, Alison Tamsin The Mount, 12 Longton Road, Barlaston, Stoke-on-Trent ST12 9AA — MB BS 1998 Lond.; MB BS Lond 1998.

DUNN, Andrew John 22 Clarks Lane, Wilburton, Ely CB6 3RH — MB BS 1992 Lond.; FRCS Eng. 1996. Specialist Regist. (Trauma & Orthop.) Camb. & E. Anglia. Prev: SHO Rotat. (Surg.) Chelsea & W.m. Hosp. Lond.

DUNN, Andrew John 48 High Street, Winterbourne, Bristol BS36 1JH — MB ChB 1995 Manch.

DUNN, Angela Justine Nithsdale Road Surgery, 162 Nithsdale Road, Glasgow G41 5RU Tel: 0141 424 1831 Fax: 0141 423 7422; 162 Nithsdale Road, Pollokshields, Glasgow G41 5RU Tel: 0141 424 1831 — MB ChB 1987 Glas.; MRCGP 1991; DRCOG 1991. Prev: Trainee GP Gtr. Glas. HB VTS.

DUNN, Mr Barry (retired) The Manor House, Graby, Sleaford NG34 0HS — MB BS 1955 Lond.; MRCS Eng. LRCP Lond. 1956; DLO Eng. 1966; DObst RCOG 1959. JP.; ENT Surg. Leicester Roy. Infirm. & LoughBoro. Gen. Hosp.; Capt. RCAMC (SR). Prev: Sen. Regist. (ENT) United Liverp. Hosps. & Liverp. RHB.

DUNN, Brian Philip Airdrie Health Centre, Monkscourt Avenue, Airdrie ML6 0JU Tel: 01236 768181 — MB ChB 1967 Glas.; MRCP (U.K.) 1971. (Glas.)

DUNN, Christian Keir Child & Family Consultation Centre, 161 Eccleshall Road, Stafford ST16 1PD Tel: 01785 222708 Fax: 01785 57609; 5 Green Lane, Bomere Heath, Shrewsbury SY4 3NG — MB ChB Manch. 1981; MRCPsych 1986. Cons. Child & Adolesc. Psychiat. Stafford.; Coll. Tutor at Foundat. NHS Trust; Serv. Dir., CAMH Serv. for the Foundat. NHS Trust. Prev: Regist. (Psychiat.) Moorhaven Hosp. Plymouth; Sen. Regist. Rotat. (Child & Adolesc. Psychiat.) W. Midl. Region.

DUNN, Christopher John 2 Eamont Court, Eamont St., London NW8 7DG — MB BS 1992 Lond.

DUNN, Christopher Michael (retired) Woodside Surgery, High Street, Loftus, Saltburn-by-the-Sea TS13 4HW Tel: 01287 640385 Fax: 01287 644071 — MB BS 1958 Durh. Med. Off. Cleveland Cott. Hosp. Brotton. Prev: Ho. Surg. (O & G) City Gen. Hosp. Carlisle.

DUNN, Courtney Hunter (retired) 7 Hill View Road, Twickenham TW1 1EB Tel: 020 8892 7272 — MRCS Eng. LRCP Lond. 1941; FFA RCS Eng. 1953; DA Eng. 1947. Prev: Sen. Anaesth. W. Middlx. Hosp.

DUNN, Donald Morton, MBE (retired) Gallery House, Glyn-Y-Mel Road, Lower Town, Fishguard SA65 9LY Tel: 01348 872005 — MB BS 1939 Lond.; MRCS Eng. LRCP Lond. 1938; DA Lond. 1941. Prev: Anaesth. Redhill Hosp. Gp.

DUNN, Edward Michael St. James's Hospital, Leeds; 4 Bear Meadow, Beyton, Bury St Edmunds IP30 9HS — MB BS 1994 Lond.; MRCP (UK) 1998. (Charing Cross & Westminster) SHO (Neurol.) St. Jas. Hosp. Leeds. Prev: Med. Rotat. Leeds Gen. Infirm.

DUNN, Elizabeth Caroline (retired) 70 Woodside Avenue, Muswell Hill, London N10 3HY Tel: 020 8883 2345 — MB BS Lond. 1957; FRCP Lond. 1988; MRCP (UK) 1976; MRCS Eng. LRCP Lond. 1957; DObst RCOG 1958. Prev: Cons. Rheum. & Rehabil. N. Middlx. Hosp. NHS Trust.

***DUNN, Emma Jane** 31 Trinity Road, Taunton TA1 3JJ Tel: 01823 353221 — MB ChB 1994 Bristol; MB ChB (Hons.) Bristol 1994.

DUNN, Fergal John 9 Newlands Crescent, Portstewart BT55 7JJ — MB ChB 1990 Leic.

DUNN, Fiona Janet The Surgery, 4 Old Irvine Road, Kilmarnock KA1 2BD; Little Underhills, By Craigie, Kilmarnock KA1 5NF — MB ChB 1993 Manch.; DRCOG 1999; MRCGP 1998; DFFP 1998. (Manchester) GP.

DUNN, Francis Gerard 14 Gadloch Avenue, Lenzie, Glasgow G66 5NP — MB ChB 1970 Glas.; FRCP Glas. 1985, M 1973.

DUNN, George Osborne Orsett Road Surgery, 86 Orsett Road, Grays RM17 5EL Tel: 01375 372505 Fax: 01375 394596; 9 St. Georges Avenue, Grays RM17 5XB — MRCS Eng. LRCP Lond. 1967. (St. Bart.) GP Surg. (Minor Surg.) Thameside HA; Hosp. Pract. (Orthop.) Basildon Hosp. & Orsett Hosp. Socs: Inst. Musculo Skeletal Med. Prev: Regist. (Orthop.) Orsett Hosp. Orsett; SHO (Radiother.) St. William's Hosp. Rochester; SHO (Gen. Surg.) St. Bart. Hosp. Rochester.

DUNN, Graham Richard 84 Beeston Fields Drive, Beeston, Nottingham NG9 3DD — MB ChB 1998 Ed.; MB ChB Ed 1998.

DUNN, Hazel Daphne Blacon Clinic, Church Way, Blacon, Chester CH1 5HS Tel: 01244 372677; 11 Hunts Close, Great Boughton, Chester CH3 5QH — MB BCh BAO 1982 Belf.; MB BCh Belf. 1982; DRCOG 1987. Clin. Med. Off. Chester.

DUNN, Heather Marion 15 Annetyard Drive, Skelmorlie PA17 5BN — MB ChB 1994 Aberd.

DUNN, Heather Mary Altnagelvin Area Hospital, Londonderry BT47 6SB Tel: 028 7134 5171 Email: hdunn@alt.n-i.nhs.uk — MB BCh BAO 1975 Belf.; MD Belf. 1983; FRCPI 1990, M 1982; FRCP Lond. 1996. (Queen's University Belfast) Cons. Phys. with Specialty in Cardiol. Altnagelvin Hosp. Lond.derry. Socs: Brit. Cardiac Soc.; Ulster Soc. Internal Med.; Brit. Soc. Echocardiogr.

DUNN, Helen Elizabeth Boglea House, Alyth, Blairgowrie PH11 8NU Tel: 0182 832442 — MB ChB 1975 Dundee; BSc St. And. 1973.

DUNN, Hilary Jane Saxmundham Health Group, Lambsale Meadow, Saxmundham IP17 1AS — MB BS 1982 Lond.; MRCGP 1986; DRCOG 1985.

DUNN, Ian Andrew Moir Medical Centre, Regent St., Long Eaton, Nottingham NG10 1QQ Tel: 0115 973 5820 Fax: 0115 946 0197 — MB BS 1978 Lond.; MA Oxf. 1979; DRCOG 1981. (King's Coll.) GP Tutor Nottm. Med. Sch. Prev: Trainee GP Aylesbury VTS.

DUNN, Ian Benedict 23 Cleveden Road, Glasgow G12 0PQ — MB ChB 1992 Glas.

DUNN, James Brian Inver Surgery, Moyle Medical Centre, Old Glenarm Road, Larne BT40 1XH Tel: 028 2826 1611 — MB BCh BAO 1976 Belf. Sec., N.. Local Med. Comm.

DUNN, James MacKinnon (retired) Duncrannaig, Glen Road, Lennoxtown, Glasgow G66 7JX Tel: 01360 311477 — MB ChB Glas. 1943; BSc Glas. 1939. Prev: Gen. Pract.

DUNN, Janine Ann M.H.H.U. BFHC Wegberg, JHQ BFPO 40 — MB ChB 1986 Aberd.; MRCGP 1990; MRCPsych 1993. Specialist (Psychiat.) BFPO 40. Prev: Trainee (Psychiat.) Brit. Forces, Germany.

DUNN, Jennifer Mary 71 Blairbeth Road, Rutherglen, Glasgow G73 4JD — MB ChB 1991 Glas.

DUNN, John Department of Psychiatry, Royal Free Hospital, Pond Street, London NW3 2CG Tel: 020 7794 0500 Fax: 020 7830 2808 — BM BS 1982 Nottm.; DM 1999 Sao Paulo, Brazil; BMedSci Nottm. 1980; MRCPsych 1987. Sen. Lect. and Hon. Cons. Psychiat., Roy. Free and Univ. Coll. Med. Sch., Lond. Prev: Sen. Regist. Hammersmith Hosp. Lond.; SHO & Regist. (Psychiat.) St. Thos. Hosp. Lond.; Sen. Regist. Maudsley & Bethlem Roy. Hosps. Lond.

DUNN, John James Bridgeton Health Centre, 210 Abercromby Street, Glasgow G40 2DA Fax: 0141 531 6639; 45 Queen Mary Avenue, Glasgow G42 8DS — MB ChB 1958 Glas. (Glas.) p/t Hon. Clin. Asst. (Matern. Family Plann.) Glas. Roy. Matern. Hosp. Socs: Glas. E. & S. Med. Soc.; BMA.

DUNN, John Leo Muirhouse Medical Group, 1 Muirhouse Avenue, Edinburgh EH4 4PL Tel: 0131 332 2201 — MB ChB 1985 Glas.; MRCGP 1989. Prev: Asst. GP Austral. Med. Serv.; Regist. (Paediat.) Memor. Hosp. Hawkes Bay, NZ.; Trainee GP Exeter VTS.

DUNN, John Malcolm Edwin Foster 12 Albert Road, Deal CT14 9RE Tel: 01304 368644 — MB BChir 1958 Camb.; MA, MB Camb. 1958, BChir 1957; MRCPsych 1972; DMP Eng. 1967. (Camb. & St. Thos.) Prev: Cons. Psychiat. S.E. Thames RHA.

DUNN, John William South Devon Healthcare trust, templer House Newton Abbot Hospital, East St., Newton Abbot TQ12 4PT Tel: 01626 354321 — BM 1989 Soton.; MRCPsych 1995. (Southampton) Cons. Ment. health Serv. Older people Teignbridge. Prev: Specialist Regist. UMDS/S.Thames Rotat.al Train.Scheme.

DUNN, Julia Anne 6 Boturich Drive, Balloch, Alexandria G83 8JP; The Health Centre, Station Road, Dumbarton G82 1PW Tel: 01389 602633 Fax: 01389 602623 — MB ChB 1991 Glas.

DUNN, Julie Mary Beacon House, Church Hill, Pinhoe, Exeter EX4 9JF — MB BS 1984 Newc.; MB BS Newc. l984; MD Bristol 1993; FRCS Eng. 1988. Cons. Gen. Surg. Roy. Devon & Exeter Hosp.

DUNN, Juliet Marie 14 Norman Avenue, Abingdon OX14 2HQ — BM BS 1996 Nottm.

DUNN, Kathleen Sylvia Weston Park Hospital, Whitham Road, Sheffield S10 2SJ Tel: 0114 226 5000; 14 Chorley Avenue, Sheffield S10 3RP Tel: 0114 230 4500 — MB BS 1978 Lond.; MRCP (UK) 1981; DCH RCP Lond. 1980; FRCR 1985; FRCP 1998. (Roy. Free) Cons. Radiother & Oncol. W.on Pk. Hosp. Sheff.

DUNN, Kathryn Ann Department of General Practice, Queens Medical Centre, Derby Road, Nottingham NG7 2UH Tel: 0115 970 9901; 3 Kings Road, Sandiacre, Nottingham NG10 5BY Tel: 0115 939 0750 — BM BS 1987 Nottm.; T(GP) 1995. Regist. Rotat. (Psychiat.) Qu. Med. Centre Nottm. Prev: GP Nottm.; Trainee GP Nottm. VTS; SHO (Gyn.) S. Derbysh. HA.

DUNN, Mr Kenneth William Department of Burns & Plastic Surgery, Withington Hospital, West Didsbury, Manchester M20 2LR Tel: 0161 291 4073 Fax: 0161 291 3785 Email: dunnkenin@aol.com — MB BS 1984 Lond.; BSc Lond. 1981, MB BS 1984; FRCS Eng. 1988; FRCS Lond. 1995. (Middlx., Univ. Coll. Hosp.) Cons. (Boms. & Plastic Surg.) Manch. Socs: Brit. Assn. Plastic. Surgs.; Exec. Comm. Mem. Brit. Burn Assn. Prev: Sen. Regist. (Plastic Surg.) Manch.; Regist. (Plastic Surg.) Odstock; Regist (Plastic Surg.) Birm.

DUNN, Kumud Rekha The Surgery, 287 Haslucks Green Road, Shirley, Solihull B9L Tel: 0121 744 6663 — MB BS 1991 Lond. (St Georges)

DUNN, Mr Laurence Thomas Dept. Of Neurosurgery, Institute of Neurological Sciences, 1345 Govan Road, Glasgow G51 4TF Tel: 0141 201 1100 Fax: 0141 201 2995 — MB ChB 1987 Ed.; MA, PhD Camb. 1984; FRCS (SN) 1995; FRCS Ed. 1991. (Edinburgh) Sen. Lect. & Hon. Cons. Neurosurg. Univ. Glas. Socs: Roy. Soc. Med.; Soc. Brit. Neurol. Surgs. Prev: Career Sen. Regist. & CAreer Regist. (Neurosurg.) Mersey RHA.

DUNN, Lawrence Edward Newlands Medical Centre, Borough Road, Middlesbrough TS1 3RX Tel: 01642 247401 Fax: 01642 223803 — MB BS 1958 Durh.

DUNN, Louise Ann 18 Greenmantle Way, Glenrothes KY6 3QG — MB ChB 1993 Glas. SHO (Paediat.) Bellshill Hosp.

DUNN, Maida Bowie 22 Glasgow Street, Hillhead, Glasgow G12 8JP Tel: 0141 334 2581 — MB ChB 1941 Glas. (Glas.)

DUNN, Margaret Joy (retired) 6 Warwick Grange, Solihull B91 1DD Tel: 0121 705 3336 — MB ChB 1945 Glas.

DUNN, Mark Julian Gerald 3 (2Fl) West Preston Street, Edinburgh EH8 9PX — MB ChB 1996 Ed.

DUNN, Mark William Wood End Health Centre, Hillmorton Road, Coventry CV2 1SG Tel: 024 7661 2929 Fax: 024 7661 8665 — MB ChB 1980 Manch.; BSc (Med. Sci.) St. And. 1977; AFOM RCP Lond. 1993; MRCGP 1984; DCH RCP Lond. 1983; DRCOG 1982. Med. Off. Several Midl. Companies.

DUNN, Mary Cecilia 51 Greenock Avenue, Glasgow G44 5TU Tel: 0141 637 2889 — MB ChB 1941 Glas. (Glas.)

DUNN, Mary Margaret (retired) Kirklee, 6A Abbotsford Grove, Darnick, Melrose TD6 9AE Tel: 01896 823479 Fax: 01896 823479 — MB ChB Glas. 1940; BSc Glas. 1938; FFPHM 1989; FFCM 1972. Prev: SCM Gtr. Glas. HB.

DUNN, Mr Michael The Nottingham Nhffield Hospital, 748 Mansfield Road, Woodthorpe, Nottingham NG5 3FZ — MB ChB 1966 Bristol; ChM Bristol 1976; FRCS Eng. 1971. (Bristol) Cons. Surg. (Urol.) Univ. Hosp. Nottm. & City Hosp. Nottm. Prev: Sen. Urol. Regist. Bristol Roy. Infirm.; Sen. Surg. Regist. S.mead Hosp. Bristol; Postgrad. Surg. Research Fell. Univ. Oxf.

DUNN, Nicholas George 16 Cairndow Avenue, Glasgow G44 3JQ — MB ChB 1994 Glas.

DUNN, Nicholas John 67 Chart Lane, Reigate RH2 7EA — MB BS 1986 Lond.; MRCPsych 1995; MRCGP 1990; DRCOG 1990. Regist. (Psychiat.) St. Geo. Hosp. Train. Scheme; Regist. Henderson Hosp. Sutton & Atkinson Morley Hosp. Wimbledon. Prev: Regist. (Child & Adult Gen. Psychiat.) Sutton Hosp.; Regist. (Psychiat.) Henderson Hosp.

DUNN, Nicholas Raymond Drug Safety Research Unit, Bursledon Hall, Southampton SO31 1AA Tel: 02380408605 Fax: 02380 408605 Email: ndunn@dsru.u-net.com; 17 Lower Golf Links Road, Broadstone BH18 8BQ Tel: 01202 693613 — BM 1977 Soton.; MA Camb. 1975; MRCGP 1981; DCH RCP Lond. 1980; DRCOG 1979; MSC.Lond. 1998; DLSHTM. Lond 1998; DM.Soton 1999. (Soton.) Sen. Res. Fell. Drug Safety Research Unit Soton. Socs: Internat. Soc. Pharmacoepidemiol. Prev: GP Poole; Trainee GP W. Dorset; Ho. Surg. Gloucester Roy. Infirm.

DUNN, Nigel Andrew The General Hospital, Holdforth Road, Hartlepool TS24 9AH Tel: 01429 266654; Garden Cottage, High Hesleden, Hartlepool TS27 4PZ Tel: 01429 836003 — MB BS 1976 Lond.; MA Oxf. 1980; FRCP Lond. 1995; FRCP Ed. 1995; MRCP (UK) 1980. (Oxf. & St. Bart.) Cons. Rheum. Hartlepool HA. Socs: Brit. Soc. Rheum. Prev: Sen. Regist. (Rheum. & Gen. Med.) Harlow Wood Orthop. Hosp. Mansfield, Nottm. City Hosp. & Univ. Hosp. Nottm.; Regist. (Med.) Profess. Unit Rheum. Univ. Edin. & N.. Gen. Hosp. Edin.; SHO (Gen. Med.) Roy. Shrewsbury Hosps.

DUNN, Mrs Pamela Mary 110 Brittains Lane, Sevenoaks TN13 2NE Tel: 01732 452824 — MB BS 1962 Lond.; DO Eng. 1965. (Middlx.) Assoc. Specialist Lewisham & Greenwich Dist. Hosps. Socs: Coll. Ophth. Prev: Clin. Asst. St. Thos., Lewisham & Greenwich Dist. Hosps.; Med. Asst. Manch. Roy. Eye Hosp.; Specialist (Ophth.) Trafford HA.

DUNN, Paul James Stanley Dept. of Histopathology, Worcester Royal Infirmary, Castle Street, Worcester WR1 3AS Email: doctorpauldunn@hotmail.com; 77 Church Road, Molesey, Birmingham B13 9EB Tel: 0121 449 6927 Fax: 0121 449 3737 Email: dayabora@hotmail.com — MB ChB 1978 Birm.; FRCPath 1994; MRCPath 1984. Cons. Path. Worcester Roy. Infirm.

DUNN, Professor Peter MacNaughton University of Bristol, Department of Child Health, Southmead Hospital, Bristol BS10 5NB Tel: 0117 950 5050 Email: p.m.dunn@bristol.ac.uk; Tramore, 173 Henbury Road, Henbury, Bristol BS10 7AD Tel: 0117 950 0682 — MB BChir Camb. 1953; MA Camb. 1955, MD 1969; FRCP Lond. 1979, M 1974; FRCOG ad endem 1983; Hon FRPCH 1996; DCH Eng. 1963; DObst RCOG 1958. (Camb. and Birm.) Emerit. Prof. Perinatal Med. & Child Health & Sen. Research Fell. Univ. Bristol Div. Child Health; Hon. Cons. Perinatal Paediat. S.mead Hosp., Roy. Hosp. Sick Childr., & St. Michael's Hosp. Bristol. Socs: Neonat. Soc.; (Ex-Pres.) Brit. Assn. for Perinatal Med.; Hon. Mem. Europ. Assoc. of Perinatal Med. Prev: Sen. Research Fell. Cardiovasc. Research Inst. Univ. Calif. San Francisco, USA; Neonat. Research Fell. United

Bristol Hosps.; De Snoo Foundat. Univ. Utrecht Prize & Medal 1983 & Gold Medal Brit. Orthop. Assn. 1986.

DUNN, Rachele Mary 89 Grange Lane, Stourbridge DY9 7HR — MB ChB 1988 Liverp.

DUNN, Rebecca Barton St Martin's Hospital, Midford Road, Bath BA2 5RP Tel: 01225 832383 Email: rebecca.dunn@ruh-bath.swest.nhs.uk — MB ChB 1976 Bristol; MB ChB (Hons.) Bristol 1976; BSc Bristol 1973; FRCP Lond. 1994; MRCP (UK) 1980. Cons. Phys. (Geriat. Med.) Roy. United Hosp. NHS Trust. Prev: Sen. Regist. (Geriat. Med.) Soton. & Portsmouth HAs; Lect. (Geriat. Med.) Univ. Hosp. Saskatoon Canada; Fell. (Geriat. Med.) Mt. Zion Hosp., San Francisco.

DUNN, Richard Michael Waldo Rivermeade, 124 Myton Road, Warwick CV34 6PR Tel: 01926 496691; 110 Coppice Road, Whitnash, Leamington Spa CV31 2LT Tel: 01926 316711 Fax: 01926 427260 Email: richarddunn@compuserve.com — MB ChB 1979 Birm.; MRCGP 1983; DRCOG 1982. (Birmingham)

DUNN, Richard Paul West Kingsdown Medical Centre, London Road, West Kingsdown, Sevenoaks TN15 6EJ Tel: 01474 855000 Fax: 01474 855001; Straightsmouth, 12 The Briars, West Kingsdown, Sevenoaks TN15 6EZ Tel: 01474 853890 Fax: 01474 855019 — MB BS 1981 Lond.; MRCS Eng. LRCP Lond. 1979; Dip. IMC RCS Ed. 1993; DA Eng. 1984. (Guy's Hosp. Lond.) Chief Med. Off. (Motorcycles) Brands Hatch Motor Racing Circuit; Pre-Hosp. Emerg. Care Instruc. Socs: BASICS.

DUNN, Robert Muiredge Surgery, Merlin Crescent, Buckhaven, Leven KY8 1HJ Tel: 01592 713299 Fax: 01592 715728 — MB ChB 1941 Glasgow; MB ChB Glas. 1941. (Glasgow) GP Leven, Fife.

DUNN, Robin Jeremy Sadlers, Sadlers Road, Inkpen, Newbury RG17 9EB Tel: 0148 84 310 — MB 1974 Camb.; BA Camb. 1970, MB 1974, BChir 1973; MRCGP 1980. (Camb, & St. Bart.) GP Hungerford. Socs: BMA. Prev: Trainee Gen. Pract. Oxf. Vocational Train. Scheme; Sen. Med. Off. Solomon Is.s.

DUNN, Mr Roderick Plastic Surgery Unit, Canniesburn Hospital, Bearsden, Glasgow G61 1QL Tel: 0141 211 5600 — MB BS 1989 Lond.; DMCC 1994; FRCS 1997. Specialist Regist. Plastic Surg.

DUNN, Roisin Angela 11 Queen Square, Glasgow G41 2BG — MB ChB 1985 Glas.

DUNN, Rosalie Therese Blantyre Health Centre, Victoria Street, Blantyre, Glasgow G72 0BS Tel: 01698 828868 Fax: 01698 823678 — MB ChB 1972 Glas.; MRCGP 1979; DObst RCOG 1974.

DUNN, Roy Albert Stanley 487 Loughbrough Road, Leicester LE4 Tel: 0116 258047 — MB BS 1953 Lond.; MRCS Eng. LRCP Lond. 1953. (Univ. Coll. Hosp.) Prev: Ho. Phys. Highland Hosp. Winchmore Hill; Ho. Surg. & Cas. Off. Redhill Co. Hosp.

DUNN, Sarah Mary Contraception & Sexual Health Service, Snow Hill Centre, 26A Snow Hill, Wolverhampton WV2 4AD Tel: 01902 444444 Fax: 01902 444449; Laburnum, Lansdowne Avenue, Codsall, Wolverhampton WV8 2EN Tel: 01902 844226 Fax: 01902 844226 — MB ChB 1976 Birm.; MRCGP 1981; MFFP 1993; DRCOG 1978; Dip. G-U Med 1998. (Birm.) Chief Clin. Off. (Reprod. Health Care) Contracep. & Sex. Health Servs. Snow Hill Centre, Wolverhampton; Locum GP. Socs: Brit. Menopause Soc.; Sec. W. Midl. Assn. of Family Plann. Doctors; Assoc. Inst. of Psychosexual Med. Prev: GP Wolverhampton; Clin. Asst. (Paediat.) New Cross Hosp. Wolverhampton.

DUNN, Sean Richard 20 Newland Park, Hull HU5 2DW Tel: 01482 444105 — MRCS Eng. LRCP Lond. 1968; BSc Lond. 1965, MB BS 1968; FFA RCS Eng. 1973. (Univ. Coll. Hosp.) Cons. Anaesth. N. Humberside HA. Prev: Sen. Regist. Anaesth. Univ. Coll. Hosp., Hosp. for Nerv. Dis. & Nat. Heart Hosp. Lond.; Ho. Phys. Univ. Coll. Hosp. Lond.

DUNN, Sheila Grace Maclean 78 Ormonde Drive, Muirend, Glasgow G44 3RG Tel: 0141 637 9687 — MB ChB 1977 Glas.; Dip. Palliative Medicine Wales 1998; DGM RCP Glas. 1991. (Glas.) Staff Phys. Vict. Geriat. Unit Glas. Socs: Brit. Geriat. Soc. Prev: Clin. Asst. Vict. Geriat. Unit Glas.

DUNN, Simon John St Annes Group Practice, 161 Station Road, Herne Bay CT6 5NF Tel: 01227 742226 Fax: 01227 741439 — BSc (Hons.) Lond. 1985, MB BS 1988; MRCGP 1992; DCH RCP Lond. 1992.

DUNN, Stephen 6 Boturich Drive, Balloch, Alexandria G83 8JP — MB ChB 1991 Glas.

DUNN, Susan Mary Royal Edinburgh Hospital, Morningside, Edinburgh EH10 5; 38 Craighouse Avenue, Edinburgh EH10 5LN — MB BCh BAO 1988 Dub.; MRCGP 1993; DRCOG 1992; DCH RCP Lond. 1990. SHO (Psychiat.) Roy. Edin. Hosp.

DUNN, Thomas Bryce (retired) 6 Rowans Way, Loughton IG10 1TZ — MB ChB 1942 Ed.; FRCP Lond. 1971, M 1949.

DUNN, Thomas Leslie (retired) 76 Northumberland Road, Leamington Spa CV32 6HG Tel: 01926 423434 — MB BCh BAO Belf. 1952; FRCP Lond. 1982; FRCP Glas. 1974; MRCP (UK) 1963; FRCPsych 1973, M 1971; DPM Eng. 1959. Prev: Vis. Schol. Green Coll. Oxf.

DUNN, Tracey Jane 73 Waverley Gardens, Glasgow G41 2DP — MB ChB 1988 Ed.; FRCA 1994; DRCOG 1990. Cons. Anaesth. Monklands NHS Trust. Socs: Anaesth. Scott. Soc. Anaesth.; Obst. Anaesth. Assn.; Assn. Study Med. Educat. Prev: Sen. Regist. & Career Regist. (Anaesth.) Vict. Infirm. NHS Trust Glas.; SHO (Anaesth.) Glas. Roy. Infirm.; SHO (A & E) St. Johns at Howden Livingston.

DUNN, Warren Thomas Pavely Brook Cottage, Witton, North Walsham NR28 9TU — MB BS 1994 Lond.

DUNN, William (retired) Nesacrag, The Tors, Kingskerswell, Newton Abbot TQ12 5DR Tel: 01803 873067 — MB ChB 1954 St. And.; DObst RCOG 1956; MRCPsych 1974; DPM Eng. 1967. Prev: Cons. Psychiat. Exeter & Devon Clin. Area.

DUNN, William Keith Nesacrag, The Tors, Kingskerswell, Newton Abbot TQ12 5DR — MB BS 1983 Newc.

DUNNE, Brendan John Racecourse Road Surgery, 3 Racecourse Road, Ayr KA7 2DF Tel: 01292 886622 Fax: 01292 614303; 3 Racecourse Road, Ayr KA7 2 — MB ChB 1977 Glas.; MRCGP 1981; DRCOG 1979.

DUNNE, Christine Lesley 10 Belgrave Mount, St. Johns, Wakefield WF1 3SB — MB ChB 1991 Liverp. Socs: Roy. Coll. Gen. Pract.

DUNNE, Crispin Thomas Pereira Swan Surgery, Northgate Street, Bury St Edmunds IP33 1AE Tel: 01284 750011 Fax: 01284 723565 — MB BS 1982 Lond.; MRCGP 1987; DRCOG 1986. (Charing Cross Hospital)

DUNNE, Fidelma Patricia Maria Department of Medicine, University Hospital Trust, Selly Oak, Raddlebum Road, Birmingham B29 6JD Tel: 0121 627 1627 Fax: 0121 627 8292; 26 Ravenhurst Road, Harborne, Birmingham B17 9SE Tel: 0121 427 4381 — MB BCh BAO 1984 NUI; PhD Birm. 1994; MD NUI 1990; MRCP (UK) 1989; MRCPI 1986; FRCPI 1997. Sen. Lect. (Med., Endocrinol. & Diabetes) Selly Oak Hosp. Univ. Birm. Socs: Soc. Endocrinol.; Irish Endocrine Soc.; EASD. Prev: Lect. & Sen. Regist. (Med. & Endocrinol.) Qu. Eliz. Hosp. Birm.

DUNNE, Francis James Warley Hospital, Warley Hill, Brentwood CM14 5HQ Tel: 01277 213241 — MB BCh BAO 1975 NUI; MRCPsych 1983. Cons. Psychiat. Warley Hosp. Brentwood. Prev: Sen. Regist. (Psychiat.) St. Barts. Hosp. Lond.

DUNNE, Mr James Anthony (cons. rooms), 219 Whitegate Drive, Blackpool FY3 9HW Tel: 01253 694485 Fax: 01253 792422 Email: mpjdunne@dunnes-mail.fsnet.co.uk; Victoria Hospital, Whinney Heys Road, Blackpool FY3 8NR Tel: 01253 303467 Fax: 01253 306743 — MB ChB 1972 Liverp.; FRCS Eng. 1977; MRCS Eng. LRCP Lond. 1972; FRCOphth 1992; DO Eng. 1976. Cons. Ophth. Surg. Blackpool & Fylde Dist. Socs: UK Intraocular Implant Soc.; N. Eng. Ophth. Soc.; Amer. Acad. of Ophth. Prev: Sen. Regist. (Ophth.) Manch. Roy. Eye Hosp.; Regist. & SHO (Ophth.) St. Paul's Eye Hosp. Liverp.

DUNNE, John Anthony 73 Kimberley Road, Penylan, Cardiff CF23 5DL — MB BCh BAO 1980 NUI; FFARCSI 1988; FFARCS Eng. 1988; MRCGP 1984; DRCOG 1988.

DUNNE, Julia Medicines Control Agency, 1 Nine Elms Lane, London SW8 9HQ — MB BS 1978 Lond.; BA Oxf. 1975; MRCP (UK) 1981. Sen. Med. Off. Med. Control Agency Dept. Health Lond.

DUNNE, Karen Michaela 153 Rowley Lane, Lepton, Huddersfield HD8 0HN — MB ChB 1991 Liverp.; DCCH; DRCOG. GP Regist.Ed.

DUNNE, Kieran Anthony Department of Rheumatology, Christchurch Hospital, Fairmile Road, Christchurch BH23 2JX — MB BCh BAO 1984 NUI; MRCPI 1990.

DUNNE, Nicholas Mark Anthony 56 High Street, Auchtermuchty, Cupar KY14 7AP — MB BCh BAO 1984 NUI.

DUNNE, Nuala Mary Department of Anaesthetics, University Hospital of Wales, Cardiff CF4 4XW Tel: 029 2074 3107; Valrosa, 29 Tydraw Road, Roath Park, Cardiff CF23 5HB Tel: 029 2045 1303 — MB ChB 1980 Bristol; FFA RCS Eng. 1985. Cons. Paediat. Cardiac Anaesth. Univ. Hosp. Wales Cardiff. Prev: Sen. Regist. (Anaesth.) Brompton Hosp. Lond.; Regist. (Anaesth.) Lond. Hosp.; SHO (Paediat. Cardiol.) Brompton Hosp. Lond.

DUNNE, Patrick James 32 Knole Wood, Devenish Road, Ascot SL5 9QR Tel: 01990 26419 — MB BCh BAO 1944 NUI. (Univ. Coll. Dub.) Socs: Windsor & Dist. Med. Soc. Prev: Ho. Surg. & Ho. Phys. St. Vincent's Hosp. Dub.; Res. Med. Off. A. Guinness. Son & Co. Dub.

DUNNE, Peter Andrew 25 Ashley Park, Bangor BT20 5RQ — MB ChB 1994 Liverp.

DUNNE, Rebecca Deborah Clare 6 West Drive, Brighton BN2 2GD — MB BS 1993 Lond.; BSc (1st cl. Hons.) Hist. Med. Lond. 1990; DFFP 1997; DRCOG 1996; DCH RCP Lond. 1995. (Roy. Free Hosp.) Asst. GP, Billingshurst, W. Sussex. Socs: Med. Defence Union; BMA. Prev: Regist., Billingshurst, W. Sussex; SHO (Paediat.) Kingston, Surrey; SHO (O & G) S.lands Hosp. W. Sussex.

DUNNE, William Thomas Martins Lane Surgery, 2 Martins Lane, Wallasey CH44 1BA Tel: 0151 630 4747 Fax: 0151 639 7395; Kingsford, The Royal, Hoylake, Wirral CH47 1HS — BM 1980 Soton.; PhD Aston 1976, BSc (Hons.) 1972.

DUNNET, Etienne Lucy Heroncroft, Southdown Road, Woldingham, Caterham CR3 7DP Tel: 0188 385 3332 — MB ChB 1948 Leeds; DPH Lond. 1968; DCH Eng. 1956. Clin. Med. Off. Surrey AHA. Socs: Fell. Roy. Soc. Med.; BMA. Prev: Ho. Surg. Hosp. Wom. Leeds & Matern. Hosp. Leeds; Ho. Phys. St. Jas. Hosp. Leeds.

DUNNET, Judith Margaret 11 Apsley Road, Clifton, Bristol BS8 2SH Tel: 0117 973 1411 — MB ChB 1978 Ed.; MRCP Ed. 1980; FFA RCS Eng. 1984. Cons. Anaesth. Frenchay Hosp. Bristol. Prev: Sen. Regist. (Anaesth.) Oxf. & Wessex RHA; SHO (Nephrol.) Roy. Infirm. Edin.; Ho. Phys. E.. Gen. Hosp. Edin.

DUNNET, Rosalyn Portland Medical Centre, 184 Portland Road, South Norwood, London SE25 4QB Tel: 020 8662 1233; The Garden Flat, 72 Beaconsfield Road, London SE3 7LQ Tel: 020 8305 1040 Email: 72132.415@compuserve.com — MB BS 1991 Lond. GP/Regist. Lond. Socs: BMA.

DUNNET, Samantha Catherine 4 Kelburne Close, Winnersh, Wokingham RG41 5JG — BM BS 1998 Nottm.; BM BS Nottm 1998.

DUNNET, William Albert (retired) Far Point, New Road, Blakeney, Holt NR25 7NZ Tel: 01263 740334 — MB ChB 1938 St. And. Prev: Res. Med. Off. Stamford, Rutland & Gen. Infirm.

DUNNET, Mr William James Sandford William Harvey Hospital, Kennington Road, Willesborugh, Ashford TN24 0LZ Tel: 01233 616280; Pinetrees, Chapel Road, Hothfield, Ashford TN25 4LN Tel: 01233 713445 Email: bill@dunnets.freeserve.co.uk — MB BChir 1987 Camb.; MA Camb. 1987; FRCS (Orth.) 1996; FRCS Eng. 1991. (Univ.Cambs/Guys Hosp) Cons. Orthop. Trauma William Harvey Hosp. Ashford. Socs: Assoc. Mem. BOA; BOA; BMA. Prev: Fell. hand surg. Qu. Vict. Hosp. E. Grinstead; Fell. Knee Surg, N. Sydney Orthop & Sports med Centre Australia; Sen.Reg.Kings Coll.Hosp.

DUNNET, William Nicholson (retired) Heroncroft, Southdown Road, Woldingham, Caterham CR3 7DP Tel: 0188 386 3332 — MB ChB Aberd. 1944; MD Aberd. 1961; FFCM 1978, M 1973; DPH Eng. 1957. Prev: PMO (Head Communicable Dis. Div.) DHSS.

DUNNETT, Iain Alastair Rowley Fordbank Cottage, Yate Rock, Chipping Sodbury, Bristol BS17 Tel: 01454 313110 — MB ChB 1964 Bristol; DA Eng. 1969; FFA RCS Eng. 1972; DObst RCOG 1967. Cons. Anaesth. S.mead Hosp. Bristol. Prev: Ho. Phys., Ho. Surg. &c S.mead Hosp. Bristol; Regist. (Anaesth.) Roy. Devon & Exeter Hosp.; Sen. Regist. (Anaesth.) Bristol Health Dist. (T).

DUNNETT, Keith Edward (retired) 12 Bilsby Road, Alford LN13 9EW Tel: 01507 466655 Email: keith.dunnett@which.net — MB BChir 1972 Camb.

DUNNETT, Susan Rosemary Chauvin Pharmaceuticals Limited, Ashton Road, Harold Hill, Romford RM3 8SL Tel: 01708 383838 Fax: 01708 379600; 10 Verdon Place, Barford, Warwick CV35 8BT Fax: 01926 624118 — MB ChB 1979 Birm.; BSc (Hons.) Soton. 1975; DA (SA) 1983.

DUNNIGAN, Matthew Gilmour 104 Beechwood Drive, Glasgow G11 7HH Tel: 0141 339 6479 Fax: 0141 339 6479 — MB ChB 1955 Glas.; MD (Hons.) Glas. 1968; FRCP Ed. 1971, M 1960; FRCP Glas. 1970, M 1962; FRFPS Glas. 1960. (Glas.) Sen. Research Fell. (Human Nutrit) Univ. Glasg. Roy. Infirm. Socs: Assn. Phys.; Hon. Assoc. Brit. Dietetic Assn. Prev: Cons. Phys. Stobhill Hosp. Glas.; Sen. Regist. (Med.) W.. Infirm. Glas.; Regist. (Med.) Glas. Roy. Infirm.

DUNNILL, Anthony (retired) East Oxford Health Centre, Cowley Road, Oxford OX4 1XD Tel: 01865 242109 — MB ChB Birm. 1958; MRCS Eng. LRCP Lond. 1958; MRCGP 1975; DObst RCOG 1961. Prev: Ho. Surg. & Ho. Phys. Gen. Hosp. Birm.

DUNNILL, Michael Giles Simpson Bristol Dermatology Centre, Bristol Royal Infirmary, Bristol BS2 8HW Tel: 0117 928 2785 Fax: 0117 928 2845 — MB BS 1987 Lond.; MD Lond. 1997; MRCP (UK) 1990. (St. Geo. Hosp. Lond.) Cons. Derm. Bristol Roy Infirm; Hon. Sen. Lect. Socs: Brit. Assn. Dermat.; St Johns Derm. Soc; Brit. Soc. of Dermatological Surg. Prev: Research Regist. (Cell. Path.) St. John's Inst. Dermat. St. Thos. Hosp. Lond.; Regist. (Cardiovasc. Med.) St. Geo. Hosp. Lond.; Sen. Regist. (Dermat.) Roy. Lond. Hosp.

DUNNILL, Michael Simpson (retired) 4 Oxford Road, Hampton Poyle, Kidlington OX5 2QE Tel: 01865 372055 Email: michael.dunmill@dial.appleinternet — MB ChB Bristol 1951; MA Oxf. 1965; MD Bristol 1961; FRCP Lond. 1971, M 1956; FRCPath 1973, M 1963. Fell. Merton Coll. Oxf. Prev: Lect. (Path.) Univ. Oxf.

DUNNILL, Richard Paul Hyde Dairy Farm House, Ringwood Road, Christchurch BH23 7BE Tel: 01425 673716 — MB BS 1969 Lond.; MRCS Eng. LRCP Lond. 1969; FFA RCS Eng. 1974. (Guy's) Cons. Intens. Care Anaesth. E. Dorset Health Dist. Socs: Assn. Anaesth.; Intens. Care Soc. Prev: Sen. Regist. Canterbury & Thanet Health Dist.; Sen. Regist. (Anaesth.) & Ho. Phys. Guy's Hosp. Lond.

DUNNING, Alan 4 Turnberry Drive, New Marske, Redcar TS11 8HR — MB BS 1971 Lond.

DUNNING, Barbara Helen Whiteladies Health Centre, Whatley Road, Clifton, Bristol BS8 2PU Tel: 0117 973 1201 Fax: 0117 946 7031; 4 Albemarle Row, Hotwells, Bristol BS8 4LY Tel: 0117 929 9781 — MB ChB 1979 Bristol; DRCOG 1988. (Bristol)

DUNNING, Helen Alexandra Sunnyside, Great Strickland, Penrith CA10 3DF — MB BS 1983 Newc.; MRCGP 1989; DRCOG 1986. Asst. GP E. Cumbria.

DUNNING, John Joseph Papworth Hospital, Papworth Everard, Cambridge CB3 8RE Tel: 01480 830541 Fax: 01480 831441 Email: jjd@doctors.org.uk — MB ChB Manch. 1984; BSc St. And. 1981; FRCS (Cth) 1994; FRCS Ed. 1989. Cons. Cardiothoracic Surg. Papworth Hosp. Socs: Internat. Soc. Heart & Lung Transpl.; Europ. Assn. for Cardio. Thoracic Surg.; Soc. of Cardio Thoracic Surg.s of GB & Irel. Prev: Sen. Regist. (Cardiothoracic Surg.) Papworth Hosp. Camb. & John Radcliffe Hosp. Oxf.

DUNNING, Mr Mervyn Walter Frank, VRD Belmont House, Shrewsbury SY1 1TE Tel: 01743 344625 — MRCS Eng. LRCP Lond. 1950; FRCS Eng. 1957; LDS RCS Eng. 1941. (Middlx.) Sen. Fell. Assn. Surgs. Gt. Brit. Socs: Fell. Roy. Soc. Med. Prev: Cons. Surg. Roy. Shrewsbury Hosp.; Sen. Surg. Regist. & Hon. Research; Fell. St. Mark's Hosp. Dis. of Rectum & Colon Lond.; Sen. Surg.; Regist. & Surg. Tutor United Liverp. Hosps. (Roy. S.. Hosp.).

DUNNING, Michael Timothy Sunnybank, Main Street, Grove, Wantage OX12 7JT — MB BS 1994 Lond.

DUNNING, Mr Paul Gordon 28 Lee Hill Court, Kings Norton, Lanchester, Durham DH7 0QE — MB ChB 1986 Birm.; FRCS Ed. 1991.

DUNNING, Richard Grove (retired) 6 Edith Road, Maidenhead SL6 5DY Tel: 01628 634595 — MB BS Lond. 1954; Master Business Admin. Univ. Chicago 1959. Prev: Sen. Tutor King Edwd. VII Hosp. Fund Lond. Coll. Hosp. Managem.

DUNNING, Tanya Louise Stannary House, Stainland Road, Stainland, Halifax HX4 9HA Tel: 01422 374109 — MB ChB 1987 Leeds. Clin. Asst. (Obst. & Gyn.) Huddersfield Roy. Infirm.

DUNNING, Vernon Ivor 23 Atherfold Road, London SW9 9LN — MB BS 1983 Lond.; MSc (Med. Anthropol.) Brunel 1993.

DUNNINGHAM, Mr Timothy Hugh 3 Oakfield Road, Manchester M20 6XA — MB ChB 1967 Manch.; FRCS Ed. (Orth.) 1981; FRCS Eng. 1972. Cons. Orthop. Surg. Tameside Gen. Hosp. Ashton-Under-Lyne. Socs: Fell. Manch. Med. Soc.

DUNPHY, Kilian Patrick Department of Palliative Care, West Herts. Community Health NHS Trust, 3 Old School House, George St., Hemel Hempstead HP2 5HJ Tel: 01442 240726 Fax: 01442 257383; 1 Eastcroft, Langdon St, Tring HP23 6BB Tel: 01442 825765 Email: kilian@btinternet.com — BM BS 1983 Nottm.; BMedSci Nottm. 1981; MRCGP 1987; MA 1997. (Univ. Nottm. Sch. Med.) Cons. Phys. (Palliat. Med.) W. Herts. Community Trust. Socs: Assn. for Palliat. Med. Prev: Med. Dir. St. Francis Hospice Berkhamsted; Sen. Regist. St. Josephs Hospice Hackney.

DUNPHY, Nicholas Wayne High Street Medical Centre, 19 High Street, Staveley, Chesterfield S43 3UU Tel: 01246 472296 Fax: 01246 471665; Westwood House, 42 Brooke Drive, Brimington Common, Chesterfield S43 1PD — MB ChB 1982 Leeds. GP Princip. Staveley Chesterfield. Prev: Trainee GP Chesterfield VTS.

DUNPHY, Patrick William Cuckmere Surgery, The Health Centre, Vicarage Field, Hailsham BN27 1BE Tel: 01323 449567 — MB BCh BAO 1977 Dub. (Trinity Coll. Dublin)

DUNPHY, Raymond Henry Pinfold Surgery, Pinfold Lane, Methley, Leeds LS26 9AB Tel: 01977 515203 Fax: 01977 551062; The Manor House, Carleton Road, Pontefract WF8 3NP — MB ChB 1974 Aberd.

DUNPHY, Richard Shane The Surgery, Sheep St., Burford, Oxford OX18 4LS Tel: 0199382 2176; 6 Parkhill Road, London NW3 2YN — MB ChB 1983 Otago; DObst 1986. Trainee GP Burford.

DUNPHY, Rosalind Anne The Manor House, Carleton Road, Pontefract WF8 3NP — MB ChB 1974 Aberd.

DUNSBY, Edward (retired) 16 Middlefield Road, Liverpool L18 3JR Tel: 0151 428 1939 — MRCS Eng. LRCP Lond. 1934; MSc Leeds 1927.

DUNSCOMBE, John Lewis (retired) Treneere Villa, 20 Tolver Place, Penzance TR18 2AD Tel: 01736 365864 — MB ChB 1947 Bristol; BA Open Univ. 1991; FRCPath 1973, M 1964; FRCPA 1971, M 1965; DCP Lond 1969; DPath Eng. 1969. Prev: Cons. Pathol. Cornw. Clin. Area.

DUNSEITH, Patrick Gavin Shane 39 Upper Ramone Park, Portadown, Craigavon BT63 5TD — MB BCh BAO 1989 Belf.

DUNSFORD, Melanie Louise 8 Sandringham Close, Chandlers Ford, Eastleigh SO53 4LE — BM 1992 Soton.; MRCP (UK) 1996. Specialist Regist. (Med. Oncol.) Roy. Hants. Hosp. Soton.

DUNSIRE, Magnus Fraser 31 Abbotsgrange Road, Grangemouth FK3 9JD — MB ChB 1991 Glas.; BSc (Hons.) Glas. 1989. SHO (A & E) Gold Coast Hosp. Qu.sland, Austral.

DUNSMORE, Hilda 5 Clifford Road, Stirling FK8 2AQ — MB ChB 1978 Glas. Clin. Asst. Dept. O & G S.. Gen. Hosp. Glas.

DUNSMORE, Miss Romola Diana 10 Kirkbie Green, Kendal LA9 7AJ — MB BS 1949 Lond.; FRCS Eng. 1962; MRCS Eng. LRCP Lond. 1946. (Lond. Sch. Med. Wom.) Emerit. Cons. ENT Surg. Doncaster Roy. Infirm. Prev: ENT Regist., Ho. Surg. & O & G Ho. Surg. Roy. Free Hosp.

DUNSMUIR, Mr Robert Allan 52 Lochlea Road, Rutherglen, Glasgow G73 4QH — MB ChB 1986 Glas.; FRCS Ed. 1991.

DUNSMUIR, Mr William Duncan Dept of Urology, St Georges Hospital, Blackshaw road Tooting, London SW17 0QT — MB BS 1988 Lond.; FRCS Eng. 1992.

DUNSTAN, Catherine Marguerite 72 Osmaston Road, Birmingham B17 0TN — MB ChB 1992 Birm.

DUNSTAN, Christopher John Douglas The Health Centre, Madeira Road, West Byfleet KT14 6DH Tel: 01932 336933 Fax: 01932 355681 — MB 1974 Camb.; BChir 1973.

DUNSTAN, Edmund James Selly Oak Hospital, Raddlebarn Road, Birmingham B29 6JD Tel: 0121 627 1627 Fax: 0121 627 8282 Email: edmund.dunstan@university_b.wmids.nhs.uk — MB BChir 1979 Camb.; FRCP Lond. 1995; MRCP (UK) 1980; T(M) 1991. (Middlx.) Socs: Brit. Geriat. Soc. Prev: Sen. Regist. (Geriat.) Soton. & E. Dorset HAs; Regist. (Med.) Roy. Preston Hosp.; SHO (Geriat.) Middlx. Hosp.

DUNSTAN, Edward Roy Rainier Hayford Hall, Buckfastleigh TQ11 0JQ — MB BS 1993 Lond.

DUNSTAN, Judith Ann Prudhoe Hospital, Prudhoe NE42 5NT — MB BS 1974 Newc.

DUNSTAN, Maurice Edward 5 Aldock, Welwyn Garden City AL7 4QF — MB BS 1985 Lond.

DUNSTAN, Richard James Rowley Surgery, Judges Close, East Grinstead RH19 3AE Tel: 01342 324628 Fax: 01342 318055; Shalesbrook, Forest Row RH18 5LS Tel: 01342 823079 — MB 1971 Camb.; BChir 1970.

DUNSTAN, Mr Simon Peter 61 Rutland Avenue, Beeston, Nottingham NG9 6EP — BM BS 1992 Nottm.; BDS Bristol 1984; BMedSci Nottm. 1990; FRCS Eng. 1996; FDS Eng. 1988. Specialist Regist. (Oral & Maxillofacial Surg.) Nottm. Socs: Jun. Fell. Brit. Assn. Oral & Maxillofacial Surg.; BMA. Prev: Regist. Rotat. (Oral & Maxillofacial Surg.) Derbysh. Roy. Infirm.

DUNSTER, Colin The Glenlyn Medical Centre, 115 Molesey Park Road, East Molesey KT8 0JX; 6 Hurst Road, East Molesey KT8 9AF — MB BS 1959 Lond.; DObst RCOG 1961. (St. Mary's) Socs: BMA. Prev: Ho. Off. Reading Accid. Serv. & E. Surrey Hosp. Redhill; Ho. Off. Obst. Co. Hosp. Redhill.

DUNSTER, Mr Geoffrey David Princess Anne wing, Royal United Hospital, Combe Park, Bath BA1 3NG; 16 Oldfield Road, Bath BA2 3ND — MB BCh 1966 Wales; FRCS Ed. 1972; FRCOG 1985, M 1971. (Cardiff) Cons. (O & G) Roy. United Hosp. Bath. Socs: BMA. Prev: Sen. Regist. Bristol Matern. Hosp.; SHO (O & G) United Liverp. Hosps.

DUNSTER, Robert John Peartree Lane Surgery, 110 Peartree Lane, Welwyn Garden City AL7 3XW Tel: 01707 329292; Gayton, Little Green, Ayot St Peter, Welwyn AL6 9BD Tel: 01707 325269 — MB BS 1968 Lond.; FRCS Eng. 1973; MRCS Eng. LRCP Lond. 1968; MRCGP 1988; DObst RCOG 1972. (Middlx.) Chairm. Wellwyn Hatfield PCG.

DUNSTONE, Mr George Hargreaves 218 Gilesgate, Durham DH1 1QN Tel: 0191 384 8181 — MB BS 1948 Durh.; FRCS Eng. 1958; FRCS Ed. 1958. (Newc.) Cons. Surg. Durh. Dist. Hosps. Socs: N. Eng. Surg. Soc. & Vasc. Surg. Soc. of GB&I. Prev: Sen. Surg. Regist. Roy. Vict. Infirm. Newc. Surg. Regist. Friarage; Hosp. N.allerton; Regtl. Med. Off. 1/7 Gurkha Rifles, Malaya.

DUNSTONE, Jane Hargreaves Hart Lodge Surgery, Jones Road, Hartlepool TS24 9BD Tel: 01429 267573 Fax: 01429 869027 — MB BS 1982 Lond.; MRCGP 1986; DRCOG 1985. Princip. GP Hartlepool.

DUNTON, Arthur Kenneth Naylor Great Abshot Farm, Titchfield, Fareham PO14 4NE Tel: 01489 576527 — MB ChB 1954 Manch.; DObst RCOG 1955. Prev: Ho. Phys. Manch. Roy. Infirm.; Capt. RAMC.

DUNTON, Margaret June Great Abshot Farm, Titchfield, Fareham PO14 4NE Tel: 014895 76527 & 75191 — MB ChB Manch. 1954. (Manch.) Socs: Fareham Med. Soc.; Farcham Med. Soc. Prev: Clin. Asst. (Dermat.) St. Mary's Hosp. Portsmouth; Ho. Surg. (ENT) Manch. Roy. Infirm.; Gen. Pract. Brook La. Surg. Packgate Hants.

DUNWELL, Michael Robin (retired) The Doctors House, Little Milton, Oxford OX44 7PU — MRCS Eng. LRCP Lond. 1973.

DUNWOODIE, William MacVicar Govan Health Centre, 5 Drumoyne Road, Govan, Glasgow G51 4BJ Tel: 0141 531 8470 Fax: 0141 531 8471; 142 Mugdock Road, Milngavie, Glasgow G62 8NP — MB ChB 1977 Glas.; MRCGP 1981.

DUNWOODY, Mr Gareth William 2 Hawthorne Grove, Wakefield WF2 0AU Tel: 01924 373532 Email: riam@globalnet.co.uk — MB BS 1980 Lond.; FRCS Ed. 1985.

DUNWOODY, John Elliott Orr, CBE The Surgery, 5-11 Stormont Road, Battersea, London SW11 5EQ Tel: 020 7978 5858; 9 Cautley Avenue, London SW4 9HX Tel: 020 8673 7471 — MB BS Lond. 1954; MRCS Eng. LRCP Lond. 1954. (Westm.) Vice-Chairm. Merton Sutton & Wandsworth LMC. Prev: Parliamentary Under Sec. DHSS; Chairm. Kensington, Chelsea & W.m. AHA; Chairm. FPA.

DUNWOODY, Michael William Orr 510 Fulham Palace Road, London SW6 6JD Tel: 020 7736 5334 Fax: 020 7371 0441 — MB BS Lond. 1960; MRCS Eng. LRCP Lond. 1960; DObst RCOG 1965. (Westm.) GP Princip. Prev: Ho. Surg. St. Stephen's Hosp. Chelsea; Ho. Phys. & Obst. Ho. Surg. St. Mary's Hosp. Newport, I. of Wight; Med. Off. Internat. Comm. of Red Cross Hosp. Uqd, Yemen.

DUNWOODY, William Orr 510 Fulham Palace Road, London SW6 — LRCPI & LM, LRSCI & LM 1924; LRCPI & LM, LRCSI & LM 1924. (Dub.) Prev: Res. Med. Off. Min. of Pens. Hosp. Blackrock.

DUONG, Thiet Van Pringle Street Surgery, 216-218 Pringle Street, Blackburn BB1 1SB Tel: 01254 56612 Fax: 01254 681630 — MRCS Eng. LRCP Lond. 1982; DRCOG 1985.

DUONG WUST, Ngoc Thuy Ha 55 Aldrich Road, Oxford OX2 7ST — MB ChB 1992 Birm.

DUPER, Balwinder 52 Atwood Road, Didsbury Village, Manchester M20 6GQ — MB ChB 1987 Manch.; MRCGP 1991; DRCOG 1990.

DUPONT, Michele Marie Brigitte Jasmine Cottage, Hadlow Road, Willaston, South Wirral CH64 2UW — MB ChB 1989 Cape Town.

DUPUCH, Leon Henry Bruce Taunton & Somerset NHS Trust, Musgrove Park Hospital, Taunton TA1 5DA — MB BS 1996 W. Indies.

DUQUESNAY, Renee Frances 19 Atlanta Street, London SW6 6TU — MB BS 1990 West Indies.

DURAISINGAM, Gunavathy 14 Ewelme Close, Dursley GL11 4NE — MB BS 1969 Ceylon.

DURANCE, Patricia Gladys School Health Service, Northgate Hospital, Northgate St., Great Yarmouth NR30 1BU Tel: 01493 856222; 33 Cotmer Road, Lowestoft NR33 9PL Tel: 01502 565209 — MB ChB 1969 Manch.; DObst RCOG 1971. (Manch.) Clin. Med. Off. Anglian Harbours NHS Trust. Prev: Clin. Med. Off. Gt. Yarmouth & Waveny HA; GP LoW.oft.

DURANCE, Robert Arthur (retired) Vine Farm House, Wivenhoe, Colchester CO7 9EU Tel: 01206822552 — MA, MB Camb. 1962, BChir 1961; FRCP Lond. 1984, M 1968; DObst RCOG 1964. Cons. Rheum. & Rehabil. Colchester Gen. Hosp. Prev: Sen. Regist. (Rheum. & Rehabil.) Kings Coll. Hosp. Lond.

DURAND, Anna Catherina Medical Services, The CADCAM Centre, Bighton, Alresford SO24 9RE Tel: 01962 734707 — MB BCh 1988 Witwatersrand.

DURAND, Michael Dominic Mary Quayside Medical Practice, 82-84 Strand Road, Londonderry BT48 7NN Tel: 028 7126 2790 Fax: 028 7137 3729 — MB BCh BAO 1978 NUI; MRCP (UK) 1984; MRCGP 1986; DCH RCPSI 1985.

DURANI, Shiban Krishen The Chinaar, 193 Norsey Road, Billericay CM11 1BZ — MB BS 1971 Kashmir; MRCPsych 1986.

DURBAN, Janet Cross Keys Practice, High Street, Princes Risborough HP27 0AX Tel: 01844 344488 Fax: 01844 274714; Romborough, Upper Icknield Way, Whiteleaf, Princes Risborough HP27 0LY Tel: 01844 345232 — MB BS 1969 Newc.; DObst RCOG 1971. (Newc.) Prev: SHO (O & G) Qu. Eliz. II Hosp. Welwyn Gdn. City; Ho. Phys. (Gen. Med.) & Ho. Surg. (Gen. Surg.) Dryburn Hosp. Durh.

DURBAN, Joanna Ruth 58 Bickersleth Road, London SW17 9SQ; 62 Eaton Road, Norwich NR4 6PR Tel: 01603 506688 Fax: 01603 506688 Email: jo@durban.co.uk — MB BS 1993 Lond.; BSc Lond. 1990; MRCP 1998. (St. Geo. Hosp. Med. Sch. Lond.) Specialist Regist. Palliat. Med. Socs: Christian Med. Fell.sh. (Jun. Doctors Comm.). Prev: Reg. Palliat. med Roy. Marsden. Hosp. Sutton; SHO (Palliat Med/Clin.Oncol. Roy.Marsden Hosp.Sutton; SHO (Med.) St. Peters Hosp. Chertsey.

DURBER, Cecil 1 Fairlawns, Newcastle ST5 9PX Tel: 01782 637716 — MB BS 1951 Lond.; MRCS Eng. LRCP Lond. 1951. (Univ. Coll. Hosp.)

DURBIN, Geoffrey Mottram 73 Cotton Lane, Mosley, Birmingham B13 9SE Tel: 0121 449 3372 Fax: 0121 449 3372 — BM BCh 1969 Oxf.; BA Oxf. 1966; MRCP (U.K.) 1974. (Univ. Coll. Hosp.) Cons. (Neonat. Paediat.) Birm. Wom.'s Hosp. & Birm. Childr. Hosp. Prev: Ho. Phys. (Med. Unit) Univ. Coll. Hosp. Lond.; Lect. (Paediat.) Dept. Paediat. Univ. Coll. Hosp. Med. Sch. Lond.; Lect. (Paediat. & Child Health) Univ. Birm.

DURBRIDGE, Jacqueline Anne Magill Department Of Anaesthesia, Chelsea & Westminister Hospital, 369 Fulham Road, London SW10 9NH Tel: 0208 746 8026; 178 Seaforth Gardens, Stoneleigh, Epsom KT19 0NW — MB BS 1990 Lond.; FRCA 1997. (St Georges Hosp. Med. Sch.) Cons. Anaesth. Chelsea & W.minister Hosp.

DURCAN, Giles Bernard (retired) 116 Bush Hill, London N21 2BS Tel: 020 8360 3422 — MB BCh BAO 1939 NUI.

DURCAN, John Joseph Department of Anaesthetics, Broomfield Hospital, Chelmsford CM1 7ET Tel: 01245 514080 Fax: 01245 514079 — MB BS 1980 Lond.; BSc Lond. 1977; FFA RCS Eng. 1986. Cons. Anaesth. & Intens. Care Broomfield Hosp. Chelmsford.

DURCAN, Sean Francis Trentham Lodge, 15 Castle St., Sneinton, Nottingham NG2 4AE — MB BCh BAO 1948 NUI; LAH Dub. 1948.

DURCAN, Thomas Gerard Queen Mary's Hospital NHS Trust, Sidcup DA14 6LT Tel: 020 8302 2678 Fax: 020 8308 3171 — MB BS 1987 Lond.; FRCA 1993. (Westm. Hosp. Med. Sch.) Cons. Anaesth. (Pain Relief) Qu. Mary's Hosp. Sidcup. Socs: Assn. Anaesth. GB & Irel.; BMA; Pain Soc./ IASP. Prev: Sen. Regist. Rotat. King's Coll. Hosp. Lond.; Research Fell. (Anaesth.) Pain Relief Unit King's Coll. Hosp. Lond.; Regist. Rotat. King Coll. Hosp. Lond.

DURDEN, Nicholas Peter Lichfield Grove Surgery, 64 Lichfield Grove, Finchley, London N3 2JP Tel: 020 8346 3123 Fax: 020 8343 4919; 54 Leopold Road, East Finchley, London N2 8BG Tel: 020 8883 3301 Fax: 020 8343 4919 — MB BS 1975 Lond.

DURDEY, Mr Paul Litfield House, Litfield Place, Bristol BS8 3LS; Litfield House, Litfield Place, Bristol BS8 3LS — MB BS 1977 Lond.; MS Lond. 1990; FRCS Eng. 1982. Cons. Surg. Bristol Roy. Infirm. Socs: Fell. Assn. Surgs.; Fell. Assn. Coloproctol.; Roy. Soc. Med. Prev: Cons. & Sen. Lect. Univ. Bristol; Lect. Roy. Lond. Hosp.; Fell. Dept. Colorectal Surg. Lahey Clinic Boston, USA.

DUREJA, Amita 64A Lawrence Road, London W5 4XH — BM 1993 Soton.

DURGE, Neal Narayan Flat 1, 305 Finchley Road, London NW3 6DT Tel: 020 7794 6324; 24 Goodshaw Avenue, Pleckgate, Blackburn BB1 8PF — MB BS 1996 Lond. (London) SHO (Med.) Hemel Hempstead Gen. Hosp. Prev: SHO (A & E) Joyce Green Hosp. Dartford.

DURHAM, Luke Harold Ranskill Mount, Blyth Road, Ranskill, Retford DN22 8LR — MB ChB 1981 Manch.

DURHAM, Mark Edward Restharrow, Longborough, Moreton-in-Marsh GL56 0QU — MB BS 1986 Lond.

DURHAM, Mr Michael Peter (retired) Tighnanros, Glen Caladh, Tighnabruaich PA21 2EH Tel: 01700 811264 — MRCS Eng. LRCP Lond. 1942; MA, MB BChir Camb. 1943; FRCS Eng. 1949; FRCOG 1962, M 1952. Prev: Cons. Gyn. & Obst. S.E. Kent Health Dist.

DURHAM, Michelle Glynis Huitt Square Surgery, Carmichael Close, Winstanley Estate, Battersea, London SW11 2DH Tel: 020 7228 8988 Fax: 020 7978 4550; 20 Granard Avenue, London SW15 6HJ — MB BS 1983 Lond.; MRCGP 1989; DRCOG 1989; DCH RCP Lond. 1988.

DURHAM, Nigel Philip 47 Heath Drive, Boston Spa, Wetherby LS23 6PB — BM BS 1993 Nottm.

DURHAM, Professor Stephen Reginald Upper Respiratory Medicine, Imperial College, School of Medicine, National Heart & Lung Institute, Royal Brompton Hospital, Fulham Road, London SW3 6NP Tel: 020 7351 8992 Fax: 020 7351 8949 Email: s.durham@rbh.nthames.nhs.uk; 37 West Hill Road, London SW18 1LL Tel: 020 8874 4927 — MB BChir 1976 Camb.; MA Camb. 1977, MD 1987; FRCP Lond. 1995; MRCP (UK) 1978. (Guy's) Prof. of allergy and Respirat. Med. Socs: Brit. Thorac. Soc.; Collegium Internat.e Allergologicum.; Hon. Sec. Brit. Soc. Allergy and Clin. Immunol. Prev: Sen. Regist. John Radcliffe & Ch.ill Hosp. Oxf.; Regist. (Med.) Adenbrooke's Hosp. Camb.

DURHAM, Stuart Thomas Grange Barn, Slyne Woods, Icellet Lane, Lancaster Tel: 01524 824447 Email: sdurham@msn.com — MB ChB 1987 Leic.; BSc (Hons.) Life Sci. Lond. 1982, MB ChB 1987; FFAEM 1997; FRCPS Glas. 1992. (Leic.) Cons. (A & E Med.) Roy. Lancaster Infirm. Socs: Brit. Assn. Accid. & Emerg. Med.; Fell. Fac. A&E Med.; Fac. Pre-Hosp. Care.

DURIE, Agnes Wallace Broadgait Green, Broadgait Green, Gullane EH31 2DW Tel: 01620 842171 Fax: 01620 843020; Mayfield, Drem, North Berwick EH39 5AY — MB ChB 1979 Ed.

DURIE, Thomas Bryson Mitchell (retired) 6 Bank Road, East Linton EH40 3AH Tel: 01620 860656 — MB ChB Ed. 1943; FRCP Ed. 1979, M 1976; FRCPath 1974, M 1963. Prev: Hon. Cons. Bacteriol. Roy. Infirm. Edin.

DURING, Mitford Emmanuel During and Dewji, 306 Lordship Lane, London SE22 8LY Tel: 020 8693 4704 — MB ChB 1964 Glas. (Glas.) Socs: Fell. Roy. Soc. Health.

DURKACZ, Kazimierz Piotr (retired) 26 Duddingston Mills, Edinburgh EH8 7NF Tel: 0131 657 2020 — MB ChB 1943 Polish Sch. of Med.; MD Polish Sch. of Med. 1946; LDS Ed. Prev: Dent. Surg.

DURKAN, Anne Maria 23 Bevan Crescent, Maltby, Rotherham S66 8AN — MB ChB 1992 Ed.

DURKAN, Ruth Mary Student Health Centre, De Montfort University, The Gateway, Leicester LE1 9BH Tel: 0116 257 7594

Fax: 0116 257 7614; The Old Lime Kilns, Cocks Lane, Wigston LE18 1JG Tel: 0116 281 1534 — MB ChB 1987 Leeds; MRCGP 1994; DCH RCP Lond. 1992. Prev: SHO (Psychiat.) Carlton Hayes Hosp. Leicester; SHO (Paediat.) S. Warks. Hosp. & Walsgrave Hosp. Coventry.

DURKAN, Victor John Richard Skegoneill Health Centre, 195 Skegoneill Avenue, Belfast BT15 3LL Tel: 028 9077 2471 Fax: 028 9077 2449; Chetwood, Notting Hill, Malone Road, Belfast BT9 5NS Email: drdurkan@iol.ie — MB BCh BAO 1984 Belf.; MB BCh BAO Belf. l984; MRCGP 1988, FRCGP 1996; DCH Dub. 1986; DRCOG Lond. 1989. (Belf.) Med. Off. Univ. Ulster.

DURKIN, Alison Potterells Medical Centre, Station Road, Welham Green, Hatfield AL9 7SN Tel: 01707 273338; 23 Stag Green Avenue, Hatfield AL9 5EB — MB ChB 1986 Leic.; BSc Leic. 1983, MB ChB 1986.

DURKIN, Carmel Ann Tavistock Clinic, 120 Belsize Lane, London NW3 5BA Tel: 020 7435 7111; Email: carmeldurkin@hotmail.com — MB BCh BAO 1986 NUI; MRCPsych 1997 London. (University College Dublin) Specialist Regist. Child Psychiat.

DURKIN, Catherine Maureen 10 Goldborne Road, Winwick, Warrington WA2 8SZ Tel: 01925 32175 — MB ChB 1949 Liverp.; BA Camb. 1946; DCH Eng. 1954. (Liverp.) Paediat. Regist. Sefton Gen. Hosp. & BRd.green Hosp. Liverp. Prev: Ho. Phys. Birkenhead Gen. Hosp. & Alder Hey Childr. Hosp.; Obst. Ho. Surg. Sefton Gen. Hosp.

DURKIN, Christopher John Bramble End, Seven Acres, Long Crendon, Aylesbury HP18 9DU — MB 1977 Camb.; MB BChir Camb. 1976; MA Cambridge 1977; FRCP Lond. 1992; MRCP (UK) 1978; T(M) 1991. Cons. Phys. Gen. & Geriat. Med. Stoke Mandeville Hosp. Aylesbury.; Clin. Dir. (Med.) Stoke Mandeville Hosp. Aylesbury. Socs: BMA & Brit. Geriat. Soc. Prev: Sen. Regist. (Gen. & Geriat. Med.) Oxf. RHA; Regist. (Med.) Good Hope Gen. Hosp. Sutton Coldfield; SHO Profess. Med. Unit Nottm. Gen. Hosp.

DURKIN, Mr Damien John 219 Warwards Lane, Birmingham B29 7QU; Flat 4 Horatio Place, 118 Kingston Road, Wimbledon, London SW19 1LY Tel: 020 8542 5998 Email: jasper01@msn.com — MB BS 1991 Lond.; BSc (Hons.) Lond. 1988; FRCS Eng. 1996. (St. Geo. Hosp. Med. Sch. Lond.) Specialist Regist. (Gen. Surg.) S. Thames (W.). Socs: Affil. Mem. Assn. Surg. GB & Irel. Prev: SHO (Surg.) St. Helier's Hosp. Carshalton; SHO Rotat. (Surg.) St. Geo. Hosp. Lond.; SHO (Orthop. Surg.) Rowley Bristow Unit St. Peter's Hosp. Chertsey.

DURKIN, Kenneth Paul (retired) Abenhall Lodge, Mitcheldean GL17 0DT Tel: 01594 54460 — MB ChB 1961 Ed. Prev: Ho. Surg. (Obst.) St. John's Hosp. Chelmsford.

DURKIN, Michael Anthony St Nicholas Health Centre, Saunder Bank, Burnley BB11 2EN Tel: 01282 422528 Fax: 01282 832834 — MRCS Eng. LRCP Lond. 1974.

DURKIN, Thomas Edward (retired) Coruisk, 82 Kingsholm Road, Gloucester GL1 3BB Tel: 01452 27932 — MB ChB 1956 St. And.; MRCGP 1964. Prev: Med. Examr. DHSS.

DURLING, Mark Edmund Wadsley Bridge Medical Centre, 103 Halifax Road, Sheffield S6 1LA Tel: 0114 234 5025 — MB ChB 1985 Sheff.

DURMAN, Linda Rosemary Jean Wrescombe Court, Yealmpton, Plymouth PL8 2NL Tel: 01752 881070 Fax: 01752 881070 Email: 100423.3470@compuserve.com — MRCS Eng. LRCP Lond. 1969; FFPHM RCP (UK) 1994; MFCM RCP (UK) 1985. Prev: Dir. of Pub. Health E. Surrey HA; Dir. of Pub. Health Riverside; GP Sheff.

DURNFORD, Simon Jeremy HQ DAAvn, Middle Wallop, Stockbridge SO20 8DY — MB BS 1974 Lond.; MSc Lond. 1986; MRCS Eng. LRCP Lond. 1973; MFOM RCP Lond. 1988; MRCGP 1979; DAvMed RCP Lond. 1982. Cons. Aviat. Med. UK Army. Socs: BMA & Soc. Occupat. Med.

DURNIN, Carol Anne 7 Private Road, Southwell NG25 0EJ — MB ChB 1989 Dundee. Staff Grade (Old. Age Psychiat.) City Hosp. Nottm. Prev: SHO (Psychiat.) Forth Valley HB & Countess of Chester Hosp.; SHO (A & E) Falkirk & Dist. Roy. Infirm.

DURNIN, John Valentine George Andrew Department of Human Nutrition, University of Glasgow, Yorkhill Hospitals, Glasgow G3 8SJ Tel: 0141 339 5113 Fax: 0141 357 3610 Email: gpaa02@udcf.gla.ac.uk; Dunairidh, Buchanan Castle, Drymen, Glasgow G63 0HX Tel: 01360 660677 — MB ChB 1946 Aberd.; MB ChB Aber. 1946; DSc Glas. 1961; MA Aberd. 1942; FRCP Glas. 1970, M 1963. Prof. Emerit. Univ. Glas. Socs: FIBiol; Physiol. Soc.. & Nutrit. Soc.; FRSE.

DURNING, Patricia 10 Cowley Road, Acklam, Middlesbrough TS5 7EU Tel: 01642 820002 Fax: 01642 817179 — MD 1983 Manch.; MB ChB 1973; FRCS Eng. 1977. Cons. Surg. S. Cleveland Gen. Hosp. Middlesbrough; Examr. & PostGrad. Tutor RCS. Socs: N. Eng. Surgic. Soc.; Brit. Assn. Surg. Oncol.; Endocrine Surg. Soc.

DURNO, Denis, MBE (retired) Olrig House, Portlethen, Aberdeen AB12 4QS Tel: 01224 781252 Fax: 01224 781252 — MB ChB Aberd. 1960; MD Aberd. 1972; FRCGP 1978, M 1968. Prev: GP Aberd.

DUROJAIYE, Olanrewaju Musibau 117 Dollis Road, Mill Hill, London NW7 1JX Tel: 020 8346 4617 Fax: 020 8349 4132 — MB BS 1980 Lagos; DFFP 1997; Dip. Cardiol. Lond. 1989.

DURR, Christine S Albany Road Surgery, 5 Albany Road, Earlsdon, Coventry CV5 6JQ Tel: 024 7622 8606 Fax: 024 7622 9985.

DURRANI, Mr Abdur-Rahman Ridgelands, 2 Upland Road, Eastbourne BN20 8EW Tel: 01323 733763 Fax: 01323 419230 Email: andy@ridgelands.demon.co.uk — MB BS 1964 Peshawar; FRCS Ed. 1972. (Khyber Med. Coll.) Cons. For the Trust, E.bourne Dist. Gen. Hosp. Socs: Fell. BOA. Prev: Regist. (Surg.) St. Mary's Hosp. E.bourne.

DURRANI, Mr Alamzeb 37 Furzehall Avenue, Fareham PO16 8UD — MB BS 1985 Peshawar; FRCS Glas. 1996.

DURRANI, Mr Amer James Ridgelands, Upland Road, Eastbourne BN20 8EW — MB BS 1994 Lond.; BSc (Hons.) Zool. Lond. 1989; FRCS (Eng.) 1998. (Middlesex)

DURRANI, Asghar Aurangzeb 70 Farringdon Road, North Shields NE30 3EU — MB BS 1980 Peshawar; MRCP (UK) 1989.

DURRANI, Mateen Linden Centre, Woodlandway, Broomfield, Chelmsford CM1 7LF Tel: 0245 318836 Fax: 01245 318801; GHAR, 101 Wivenhoe Road, Alresford, Colchester CO7 8AG Email: m.durrani@btinternet.com — MB BS 1980 Karachi; BCPsych 1994; DPM RCPSI 1991. (Sind Med. Coll. Karachi) Cons. Psychiat. N. Essex Ment. Health Partnership, NHS Trust Chelmsford; Jt. Med. Director, Mid Essex Community & Ment. Health NHS Trust, Chelmsford. Prev: Cons. Psychiat. Linden Centre Chelmsford; Regist. (Forens. Psychiat.) Hackney Hosp. Lond.; Regist. (Rehabil. Psychiat.) The Lakes Ment. Health Unit Colchester.

DURRANS, Mr David Stafford District Hospital, Weston Road, Stafford ST16 3SA Tel: 01785 257731 Fax: 01785 230822 Email: david@durrans.net; Hedgerow Cottage, Coppice Brook, Heather Hill, Stafford ST17 0TQ Tel: 01785 665973 — MB BS 1976 Lond.; MS 1987 Lond.; FRCS Eng. 1981. Cons. Surg. Mid Staffs. Gen. Hopital NHS Trust; Cliniacl Director, Surg., Mid Staffs. Gen. Hopitals NHS Trust. Socs: Assn. Surg. GB & Irel.; Vasc. Surg. Soc.; Europ. Soc. of Vasc. Surg. Prev: Sen. Regist. NW RHA.

DURRANT, Barry Warwick (retired) Marlcroft, Nyewood, Rogate, Petersfield GU31 5HY — MRCS Eng. LRCP Lond. 1949; FRCPsych. 1982, M 1971; DPM Eng. 1965; LDS RCS Eng. 1959. Prev: Cons. Psychiat. Maidstone & Medway HAs.

DURRANT, Charlotte Caroline Jill 12 Chatfield Road, Cuckfield, Haywards Heath RH17 5BB — MB BS 1994 Lond. (St Bartholomew's) GP Regist. Hassocks Health Centre Hassocks W. Sussex.

DURRANT, David Charles Sydney Histopathology Department, Pilgrim Hospital, Sibsey Road, Boston PE21 9QS Tel: 01205 364801 Fax: 01205 356548 — MB BS Lond. 1976; MRCPath 1984. Cons. Histopath. Pilgrim Hosp. Boston.

DURRANT, Deirdre Ann Elizabeth 57 West Street, Titchfield, Fareham PO14 4DG — MB ChB 1980 Bristol; MB ChB (Dist. Obst. & Gyn.) Bristol 1980; MRCGP 1984; DCH RCP Lond. 1984; DRCOG 1983.

DURRANT, Gavin Michael 6 Broadfield Road, Bristol BS4 2UQ — MB ChB 1994 Birm.

DURRANT, Hilary June 33 West Cross Lane, West Cross, Swansea SA3 5LS — MB ChB 1995 Bristol; PhD Wales 1992; MA Camb. 1987. (Bristol)

DURRANT, Irene Jill The Old Rectory, St. Michael's Lane, Begbroke, Kidlington OX5 1RT Tel: 0186 75 77927 Email: jilldurant@doctorsorg.uk — MB BS 1960 Lond.; MRCS Eng. LRCP Lond. 1960; FRCPath 1984, M 1972; DCH Eng. 1963. (St. Bart.) Mem. Adult & Childh. MRC Leukaemia Working Parties; Cons.

Haemat. CTSU MRC Trials Radcliffe Infirm. Oxf.; Co-ordinator MRC UKALL XII Trial. Socs: Fell. Roy. Soc. Med.; Brit. Soc. Haemat.

DURRANT, Joanna Mary 52 Salisbury Street, Beeston, Nottingham NG9 2EQ — BM BS 1997 Nottm.

DURRANT, Katherine Jane St Johns Way Medical Centre, 96 St. Johns Way, London N19 3RN Tel: 020 7272 1585 Fax: 020 7561 1237 — MB ChB 1978 Liverp.

DURRANT, Martin Andrew Kelsall Medical Centre, Church Street, Kelsall, Tarporley CW6 0QG Tel: 01829 751252 Fax: 01829 752593; Email: mad.tatt@virgin.net — MB ChB 1980 Liverp. Socs: Assur. Med. Soc.

DURRANT, Warren (retired) Argyle Health Centre, Conway Street, Birkenhead CH41 6PT Tel: 0151 647 8663 — MB ChB 1956 Liverp. Prev: Princip. GP Birkenhead & Wallasey.

DURRELL, Nicolas Gwyn 4 Edinburgh Drive, Rushall, Walsall WS4 1HW — MB ChB 1998 Birm.

DURRINGTON, Professor Paul Nelson Department of Medicine, Manchester Royal Infirmary, Oxford Road, Manchester M13 9WL Tel: 0161 276 4226 Fax: 0161 274 4833 — MB ChB 1972 Bristol; 2001 F.Med. Sci; BSc (Hons.) (Physiol.) Bristol 1969; MD Bristol 1978; FRCP Lond. 1987; MRCP (UK) 1975; FRCPath 1994. (Bristol) Prof. Med. Univ. Manch.; Hon. Cons. Phys. Manch. Roy. Infirm. Socs: Assn. Phys.; Brit. Atherosclerosis Soc.; Fell. Of the Arteriosclerosis Heart Assn. Prev: Dir. of Research & Developm. Centr. Manch. Healthcare NHS Trust; Reader (Med.) Univ. Manch. & Hon. Cons. Phys. Manch. Roy. Infirm.; Trav. Fell. Brit. Heart Foundat. & Amer. Heart Assn. 1979-80 Univ. Calif. San Diego, USA.

DURSTON, Glyn Wedmore The Surgery, 157-159 Reservoir Road, Erdington, Birmingham B23 6DN Tel: 0121 373 6902 Fax: 0121 373 3263 — MB BCh 1981 Wales; MRCGP 1987; DRCOG 1985. GP Birm.

DURSTON, Roger Stephen The Surgery, 13 Camberwell Green, London SE5 7AF Tel: 020 7703 3788 — MB BS 1978 Lond.

DURSTON-SMITH, Henry (retired) Holdridge Pastures, East St, North Molton, South Molton EX36 3JF Tel: 01598 740371 — MB BS 1939 Lond.; MRCS Eng. LRCP Lond. 1938.

DURVE, Dipalee Vijay 7 Chartwell Close, London SE9 3UQ — MB BS 1996 Lond.

DURWARD, Donald Fraser (retired) The Old Coach House, Landcross, Bideford EX39 5JA — MRCS Eng. LRCP Lond. 1924; MRCS Eng., LRCP Lond. 1924. Prev: Anaesth. & Dept. Surg. Chiswick Hosp.

DURWARD, Heather Diane Chesterfield & Derbyshire Royal Hospital, Chesterfield S44 5BL Tel: 01246 277271; Holly House, Wormhill, Buxton SK17 8SL — MB ChB 1985 Leeds. Staff. Paediat. Chesterfield & N. Derbysh. Roy. Hosp. Prev: Regist. (Paediat.) Nottm. City Hosp. & Chesterfield & N. Derbysh. Roy. Hosp.

DURWARD, William Farquharson Department of Neurology, Glasgow Royal Infirmary, Glasgow G4 0SF Tel: 0141 552 3535 Fax: 0141 339 1352; Overdale, 20 South Erskine Park, Bearsden, Glasgow G61 4NA Tel: 0141 942 3143 Fax: 0141 339 1352 — MB ChB 1968 Glas.; FRCP Ed. 1982; FRCP Glas. 1980; MRCP (UK) 1971. (Glas.) Cons. Neurol. Roy. Infirm. & Inst. Neurol. Scs. Glas. & Lanarksh. HB; Hon. Clin. Sen. Lect. (Neurol.) Glas. Univ. Socs: Assn. Brit. Neurol. & Scott. Soc. Experim. Med. & Medico-Legal Soc. Prev: Sen. Regist. (Neurol.) Inst. Neurol. Scs. Glas.; Regist. (Med.) W.. Infirm. Glas.; Fell. in Neurol. (Neurobehaviour) Boston Univ., USA.

DUS, Vince 46 Malford Grove, South Woodford, London E18 2DY Tel: 020 8989 0642 — MD Debrecen (Hungary) 1954; MRCP (U.K.) 1971; LRCP LRCS Ed. LRCPS Glas. 1968. Hon. Clin. Asst. St. Bart. Hosp. Lond. Socs: Assn. Brit. Clin. Neurophysiol. Prev: Sen. Regist. Clin. Neurophysiol. St. Bart. Hosp. Lond.; Regist. Killearn Hosp. Glas.; Lect. in Neurol. Precs Univ. Hungary.

DUSAD, Raj Kumar Adelaide Row Medical Centre, 1-2 Adelaide Row, Seaham SR7 7EF Tel: 0191 581 7661 Fax: 0191 513 0548 — MB BS 1975 Jiwaji; MRCGP 1982.

DUSHEIKO, Professor Geoffrey Mark Academic Department of Medicine, Royal Free Hospital, Pond St., London NW3 2QG Tel: 020 7830 2993 Fax: 020 7431 4581; 24 Colchester Drive, Pinner HA5 1DE Tel: 020 8868 8905 Fax: 020 8933 0175 — MB BCh 1972 Witwatersrand; FRCP Lond. 1991; FCP(SA) 1977. Prof. Med. & Hon. Cons. Roy. Free Hosp. & Sch. Med. Lond. Socs: Amer. Assn. Study Liver Dis.; Eur. Assn. for Study Liver; Internat. Assn. Study of Liver. Prev: Reader (Med.) & Sen. Lect. Roy. Free Hosp. Sch. Med.; Vis. Researcher Nat. Inst. Health.

DUSSEK, Mr Julian Eric The Cardiothoracic Unit, Guy's Hospital, London SE1 9RT Tel: 020 7955 4322 Fax: 020 7955 4858; Tebolds, The St, Plaxtol, Sevenoaks TN15 0QJ Tel: 01732 810489 — MB BS Lond. 1967; FRCS Eng. 1973; MRCS Eng. LRCP Lond. 1966. (Guy's) Cons. Thoracic Surg. Guy's & St. Thos. Hosps. Lond. & Brighton HA. Socs: Brit. Oesoph. Gp.; Eur. Assn. of Cardiothoracic Surgs.; Soc. Cardiothoracic Surgs. GB & Irel. Prev: Sen. Regist. (Cardiothoracic Surg.) Guy's Hosp., St. Thos. Hosp. & Brook Hosp. Lond.; Regist. (Cardiac. Surg.) Nat. Heart Hosp. Lond.

DUTCHMAN, David Andrew John Roebuck House, High Street, Hastings TN34 3EY Tel: 01424 420378/439988 Fax: 01424 719234 — MB BS 1978 Lond.; MRCGP 1983; DCH RCP Lond. 1983; DObst. RCOG 1982. GP Hastings. Prev: Med. Off. Solomon Is.s.

DUTHIE, A V Elizabeth (retired) Shepherds Hay, Brockhampton, Andoversford, Cheltenham GL54 5XJ Tel: 01242 820311 — MB ChB 1952 St. And. Prev: Med. Regist. City Gen. Hosp. Stoke-on-Trent.

DUTHIE, Alasdair Robert — MB ChB 1985 Liverp.; BSc Liverp. 1982; MRCGP 1990; DCH RCP Lond. 1990; DRCOG 1989. Socs: Reading Path. Soc.

DUTHIE, Ann 101 Arnold Road, Basford, Nottingham NG5 1NG — MB ChB 1979 Sheff.; MRCP (UK) 1982; Dip. Human & Clin. Genetics Lond. 1988. Lect. (Paediat.) Sheff. Prev: Research Regist. (Child Health) King's Coll. Hosp. Lond.

DUTHIE, Ashley Mackintosh (retired) Willow Cottage, 19 The Street, Felthorpe, Norwick NR10 4BU Tel: 01603 754424 Fax: 01603 754424 Email: duthrie.norfolk@amserve.net — MB ChB 1959 Aberd.; MD (Commend.) Aberd. 1976; FFA RCS Eng. 1966; DA Eng. 1962; DObst RCOG 1961. Prev: Cons. Anaesth. Norf. & Norwich Hosp.

DUTHIE, Birnie Winchester (retired) 126B Great Western Road, Aberdeen AB10 6QF Tel: 01224 588016 — MB ChB 1949 Aberd.; MRCGP 1973. Prev: GP Aberd.

DUTHIE, Brenda Alison McCaig Govan Health Centre, 5 Drumoyne Road, Glasgow G51 4BJ Tel: 0141 531 8400 Fax: 0141 531 8404 — MB ChB 1977 Glas.; MFFP 1990; MRCGP 1981; DRCOG 1981. p/t G.P., Gtr. Glas. Health Bd.; Locum CMO Primary Care Trust (Family Plann.). Prev: Govt. Med. Off. Cayman Is.s Brit. W. Indies.; Clin. Asst. (Family Plann.) Dept. Obst. Glas. Roy. Infirm.

DUTHIE, David James Ralph 1 Grange Lane, Thurnby, Leicester LE7 9PH — MB ChB 1979 Aberd.; FFA RCS Eng. 1983. Lect. (Anaesth.) Univ. Sheff. Prev: Research Fell. (Anaesth.) Univ. Sheff.; Regist. (Anaesth.) W.. Infirm. Glas.; Temp. Lect. Path. Univ. Aberd.

DUTHIE, Fraser Richard West of Scotland Histopathology Training Scheme, Dept og Pathology, Western infirmary, Glasgow Tel: 0141 211 2000 — MB ChB 1996 Glas.; BSc 1993. (Glasgow) Specialist Regist. Histopath.

DUTHIE, George McDonald Dr. Gray's Hospital, Elgin IV30 1SN Tel: 01343 543131 — MB ChB 1977 Aberd.; FFA RCS Eng. 1981. Cons. Anaesth. Dr Grays Hosp. Elgin.

DUTHIE, Mr Graeme Scott Academic Surgical Unit, Castle Hill Hospital, Cottingham HU16 5TQ Tel: 01482 875875 Fax: 01482 623274 — MD 1993 Aberd.; MB ChB Aberd. 1983; BMedBiol 1980; FRCS Ed. 1987. Reader & Hon. Cons. Surg. Acad. Surgic. Unit Castle Hill Hosp. N. Humberside. Prev: Sen. Regist. (Gen. Surg.) Roy. Infirm. Edin.

DUTHIE, Sir Herbert Livingston St Curig, 29 Windsor Road, Radyr, Cardiff CF15 8BQ Tel: 029 2084 3472 — MB ChB 1952 Glas.; MD (Hons.) Glas. 1962, ChM (Hons.) 1959, MB ChB 1952; Hon. LLD Sheff. 1990; FRCS Eng. 1957; FRCS Ed. 1956. Socs: (Ex-Pres.) Surg. Research Soc. & Brit. Soc. Gastroenterol.; (Ex-Pres.) Assn. Surgs. Prev: Provost Univ. Wales Coll. Med.; Prof. Surg. Univ. Sheff.; Cons. Surg. Hallamsh. Hosp. Sheff.

DUTHIE, Iain Queens Road Medical Group, 6 Queens Road, Aberdeen AB15 4NU Tel: 01224 641560 Fax: 01224 642773; 51 Anderson Drive, Aberdeen AB15 4UA Tel: 01224 325821 — MB ChB 1983 Aberd.; MRCGP 1987. Lect. (Gen. Pract.) Aberd. Med. Sch. Prev: Med. Off. Roxburghe Hse. Paliat. Care Centre Aberd.

DUTHIE, Ian Macdonald (retired) 7 South Headlands Crescent, Newtonhill, Stonehaven AB39 3TT Tel: 01569 730483 Fax: 01569 730483 Email: imutarb@globalnet.co.uk — MB ChB 1951 Ed.;

FRCOG 1971, M 1958, DObst 1954. Prev: Cons. O & G Fife Area Health Bd.

DUTHIE, James Alexander (retired) St Fillans, Alexander St., Airdrie ML6 Tel: 01236 769333 — MB ChB 1959 Aberd.

DUTHIE, Jane Carolyn Top Left Flat, 259 Gatrrioch Road, Glasgow G20 8QZ — MB ChB 1990 Glas.; BSc (Hons.) Glas. 1984. Regist. (Psychiat.) Glas.

DUTHIE, John 6 Ravenscourt Road, Mackworth, Derby DE22 4DL — MB ChB 1948 Aberd.; Dip. Audiol. Manch. 1972. Socs: Fac. Comm. Health.

DUTHIE, Mr John Scott 10 Millom Drive, Unsworth, Bury BL9 8NJ Tel: 0161 766 4875 — MB ChB 1962 Aberd.; ChM Aberd. 1973; FRCS Ed. 1968; FRCS Eng. 1969; DObst RCOG 1964. Cons. Gen. Surg. Roy. Oldham Health Trust.

DUTHIE, Katrina Evelyn Scott Health Centre, Balmellie Road, Turriff AB53 4DQ Tel: 01888 562323 Fax: 01888 568682 — MB ChB 1982 Aberd.

DUTHIE, Louis Herbert, Surg. Capt. RN Retd. 515 Burnley Lane, Chadderton, Oldham OL9 0BW Tel: 0161 624 2502 — MB ChB 1937 Aberd.; DPH Liverp. 1957. (Aberd.)

DUTHIE, Mark Livingston Email: markduthie@aol.com — MB BS 1983 Lond.; MRCPI 1997. (The Lond. Hosp.) Specialist Regist. (Paediat.) N.W. Region.

DUTHIE, Maureen 29 Windsor Road, Radyr, Cardiff CF15 8BQ — MB ChB 1957 Glas. (Glas.)

DUTHIE, Maureen Benton (retired) 2 Hawthorn Road, Gatley, Cheadle SK8 4LX — MB ChB 1954 Aberd.; BSc Aberd. 1949, MB ChB 1954; FRCR 1962; DMRT Eng. 1958. Prev: Cons. Radiother. Christie Hosp. & Holt Radium Inst. Manch.

DUTHIE, Neil John 6 Locksley Court, Cumbernauld, Glasgow G67 4BN — MB ChB 1991 Dundee; MFFP 1994; DCH RCPS Glas. 1993. Prev: Trainee GP Scotl.; SHO (Paediat.Perth & Dundee hosp.

DUTHIE, Pamela Irene 1 Wentworth Lane, Fairways Estate, St Mellons, Cardiff CF3 0LH Tel: 029 2077 8921 — MB BCh 1985 Wales; BSc (Hons) St. And. 1981; DCH RCP Lond. 1988.

DUTHIE, Philip Cameron Nethertown Surgery, Elliott Street, Dunfermline KY11 4TF Tel: 01383 623516 — MB ChB 1991 Glas.; DRCOG 1996; DFFP 1996; MRCGP 1999. GP Partner, Dunfermline.

DUTHIE, Mr Robert Andrew Orthopaedic Unit, Woodend Hospital, Eday Road, Aberdeen AB15 6XS Tel: 01224 681818 — MB ChB 1989 Aberd.; FRCS Ed. 1993; FRCS (Tr &Orth)1999. Cons. orthopaedic & Trauma Surg. Aberd.

DUTHIE, Professor Robert Buchan, CBE Barna Brow, 1 Harberton Mead, Headington, Oxford OX3 0DB Tel: 01865 762745 Fax: 01865 762745 Email: duth25@aol.com — MB ChB 1948 Ed.; DSc (Hons.) Univ. Rochester, USA; MA Oxf. 1966; ChM (Gold Medal) Ed. 1956; FRCS Eng. 1967; FRCS Ed. 1953; FACS (Hons.) 1987. (Univ. Ed.) Emerit. Prof. Univ. Oxf.; Cons. Civil. Adviser Orthop. Surg. RN; Emerit. Fell. Worcester Coll. Oxf.; SmithKline Vis. Prof. Roy. Soc. Med. Socs: (Ex-Pres.) Internat. Research Soc. Orthop. & Traum.; (Ex-Pres.) BOA; Orth. Soc. USA. Prev: Vice-Chairm. Roy. Berks. & Battle Hosp. Trust; Nuffield Prof. of Orthop. Surg. Univ. Oxf. & Hon. Surg. Nuffield Orthop. Centre & John Radcliffe Hosp. Oxf.; Prof. Orthop. Surg. Univ. Rochester Sch. Med. & Dent. USA.

DUTHIE, Robert McIntosh Finlayson Street Practice, 33 Finlayson Street, Fraserburgh AB43 9JW Tel: 01346 518088 Fax: 01346 510015; 8 Middleburgh Road, Fraserburgh AB43 9SG — MB ChB 1988 Aberd.; MRCGP 1992; T(GP) 1992. Socs: Roy. Coll. Gen. Pract.

DUTHIE, Mrs Ruth Blackpool Victoria Hospital NHS Trust, Whinney Heys Road, Blackpool FY3 8NR; 71 North Park Drive, Blackpool FY3 8NH — MB ChB 1983 Liverp.; MRCPath 1992. Cons. Microbiol. Blackpool Vict. NHS Trust. Prev: Sen. Regist. (Microbiol.) N. W.. RHA Manch.; Lect. Dept. Microbiol. Chinese Univ. of Hong Kong & Pr. of Wales Hosp.Shatin Hong Kong.

DUTHIE, Suresh John Blackpool Victoria Hospital NHS Trust, Blackpool FY3 8NR Tel: 01253 300000; 71 North Park Drive, Blackpool FY3 8NH — MB ChB 1980 Liverp.; MRCOG 1986; Dip. Ven. Liverp. 1984; FRCOG 1998. (Liverp.) Cons. O & G Blackpool Vict. Hosp. Socs: Brit. Menopause Soc.; Brit. Med. Ultrasound Soc. Prev: Sen. Regist. (O & G) Mersey RHA; Sen. Lect. Special Appt. (O & G) Univ. Liverp.; Lect. (O & G) Univ. Hong Kong.

DUTHIE, Virginia Jane 4 Hale Low Road, Hale, Altrincham WA15 8BD — MB BCh 1985 Witwatersrand.

DUTHIE, William Hume (retired) 2 Grey Gables, Southwood Road, Monkton, Prestwick KA9 1UR — MB ChB 1960 Ed.; FRCA 1995; FFA RCS Eng. 1965. Prev: Cons. Anaesth. Ayr Hosp.

DUTHIE, Yvonne Louise St James Medical Centre, St. James Street, Taunton TA20 1DB Email: yvonne.duthie@gp-l85023.nhs.uk; Roseneath, 16 High St, Bishops Lydeard, Taunton TA4 3AX — MB BS 1988 Lond.; 2001 (Hons) LF Lond.; MRCGP 1995; DCH RCP Lond. 1990. p/t Gen. Practioner; Clin. Asst. in A & E. Prev: Trainee GP Ealing Hosp. VTS; Ho. Off. St. Geo. Hosp. & Frimley Pk. Hosp. Lond.

DUTKA, David Paul 9 Carisbrooke Avenue, Burton Pastures, Gedling, Nottingham NG4 2RD — BM BS 1983 Nottm.; MRCP (UK) 1986. Research Fell. Hammersmith Hosp. Lond.

DUTSON, Max Edward John 1 High Way, Broadstone BH18 9NB — BM BS 1995 Nottm.

DUTT, Ganesh Chandra Bethnal Green Health Centre, 60 Florida Street, London E2 6LL Tel: 020 7739 4837 Fax: 020 7729 2190; 24 Summerlee Gardens, London N2 9QN Tel: 020 8444 9349 — MB BS 1957 Patna; BSc (Hons.) Patna 1952; MRCP (UK) 1974; MFHom 1975; DTM & H Ed. 1965. (P. of Wales Med. Coll.) Socs: BMA & Overseas Doctors Assn.; Brit. Med. Acupunct. Soc.; Fac. Homoeop. Prev: Regist. (Geriat.) Langthorne Hosp. Lond.; Regist. (Psychiat.) St. Nicholas Hosp. Newc.; Regist. (Med.) Gateshead Hosp.

DUTT, Kalyan Kumar 70 Westfield Road, Edgbaston, Birmingham B15 3QQ — MB BS 1961 Calcutta; FFA RCS Eng. 1971; DA Eng. 1965. (Calcutta) Cons. Anaesth. Dudley Rd. Hosp. Birm. Socs: BMA. Prev: Sen. Regist. Anaesth. Roy. Free Hosp. Lond. & Barnet Gp. Hosps.; Regist. (Anaesth.) St. Mark's Hosp. Lond. & Hammersmith Hosp. & Qu.; Charlotte's Matern. Hosp. Lond. & Chelsea Hosp. Wom.

DUTT, Sabita Bury General Hospital, Walmersley Road, Bury BL9 6PG Tel: 0161 705 3213 Fax: 0161 705 3410; 12 Gisburn Drive, Bury BL8 3DH — MB BS 1964 Utkal; FRCPath 1988, M 1976; ECFMG 1974. Cons. Histopath. & Morbid Anat. & Dir. Path. Bury Path. Servs. Bury Health Care NHS Trust; Chairm. Bury Postgrad. Med. Inst. Socs: MRCPath. & Internat. Acad. Path.; Assn. Clin. Path.

DUTT, Sheila 43 Dunstan Road, Golders Green, London NW11 8AE Tel: 020 8455 2570 — MB BS 1958 Punjab; MB BS Punjab (India) 1958; DA Eng. 1966; DObst RCOG 1963.

DUTT, Trevor Peter, RD 28 Weymouth Street, London W1N 3FA Tel: 020 7580 1723 Fax: 020 7436 6053 Email: trevor.dutt@easynet.co.uk; 129 Mount View Road, London N4 4JH Tel: 020 8348 7054 Fax: 020 8340 1352 Email: trevor.dutt@easynet.co.uk — MB BS 1965 Lond.; MRCS Eng. LRCP Lond. 1965; FRCOG 1988, M 1975; DObst 1967. (St. Bart.) Cons. (O & G), Whittington Hosp. Lond.; Surg. Cdr. RNR Princip. Med. Off. HMS Pres.; Hon. Cons. (Gyn. & Obst.) Hosp. of St. John & St. Eliz. Lond. Socs: Fell. Roy. Soc. Med.; BMA.; Brit. Soc. for Gyn. Endoscopy. Prev: Lect. & Hon. Sen. Regist. (O & G) Char. Cross Hosp. Lond.

DUTT-GUPTA, Jonathan Greenbriars, Limes Avenue, Nether Langwith, Mansfield NG20 9EU — MB ChB 1998 Birm.

DUTT-GUPTA, Rangit Kumar Health Centre, Main St., Shirebrook, Mansfield NG20 8AL Tel: 01623 742464 Fax: 01623 742558; Green Briars, Limes Avenue, Nether Langwith, Mansfield NG20 9EU Tel: 0162 385 2637 — MB BS 1963 Dacca; LMSSA Lond. 1970; Cert. Family Plann. JCC 1972; DObst RCOG 1972; DCH RCPSI 1968. Prev: SHO (O & G) St. Mary's Hosp. Newport & Newmarket Gen. Hosp. Newmarket; Ho. Phys. St. Mary's Hosp. Newport I. of Wight.

DUTTA, Amal Whiston Hospital, Prescot L35 5DR; 18 Elm Grove, Eccleston Park, Prescot L34 2RX — MB BS 1969 Calcutta; BSc Calcutta 1962, LLB 1966, MB BS 1969; MPsychMed Liverp. 1984; FRCPsych. 1992, M 1982; Dip. Psychother. Liverp. 1985; DPM Eng. 1979; TDD 1971. (R.G. Kar Med. Coll.) Cons. Psychiat. Whiston Hosp. Prescot. Prev: Cons. Psychiat. Rainhill Hosp. Liverp.; Sen. Regist. Sefton Gen. Hosp. Liverp.; Regist. Pk.side Hosp. Macclesfield.

DUTTA, Amitabha Whiston Hospital, Warrington Road, Prescot L35 5DR — MB BS 1982 Delhi; MRCPI 1990.

DUTTA, Amitava Department of Orthopaedics, Princess Alexandra Hospital, Raf Wroughton, Swindon SN4 0QJ — MB BS 1986 Madras, India.

DUTTA, Mr Anil ENT Department, Bradford Royal Infirmary, Duckworth, Bradford BD9 6RJ — MB BS 1973 Panjab; FRCS Eng 1992. Assoc. Specialist (ENT) Bradford Roy. Infirm. Prev: Regist. (ENT) Bradford Roy. Infirm.

DUTTA, Biman 39 Orsett Heath Crescent, Grays RM16 4UZ Tel: 01375 842019; 57 Calcutta Road, Tilbury RM18 7QZ Tel: 01375 859535 — MB BS 1962 Calcutta. (R.G. Kar Med. Coll.) Prev: SHO S. Lodge Hosp. Lond.; Ho. Phys. Highlands Gen. Hosp. Lond.; Ho. Surg. Wanstead Hosp. Lond.

DUTTA, Debanka Kumar Tranwell Unit, Gateshead Health NHS Trust, Gateshead NE10 9RW Tel: 0191 403 6313 Fax: 0191 403 6221; 32 Wilson Gardens, Gosforth, Newcastle upon Tyne NE3 4JA Tel: 0191 284 5784 Fax: 0191 242 1916 Email: d.dutta@blueyonder.co.uk — MB BS 1971 Dibrugarh; FRCPsych 1992, M 1977; DPM Eng. 1978. (Assam Med. Coll. Dibrugarh) Cons. Psychiat. Gateshead AHA; Hon. Clin. Lect. Univ. Newc. Prev: Sen. Regist. (Psychiat.) Newc. AHA (T); Regist. Rotat. Roy. Edin. Hosp.

DUTTA, Dipak Kumar (retired) Levitts Surgery, Levitts Road, Bugbrooke, Northampton NN7 3QN Tel: 01604 830348 Fax: 01604 832785 — MB BS 1964 Gauhati; Dip. Adv. Therapeutics (Keele Univ.).

DUTTA, James 251 Salmon Street, London NW9 8YA — MB BS 1940 Rangoon; DCH Eng. 1956. Prev: Civil Surg. Burma.

DUTTA, Jayasri Health Control Unit, Terminal 3 Arrival Heathrow Airport, Hounslow TW6 1NB Tel: 020 8745 7419 Fax: 020 8745 6181; 11 Burnham Avenue, Beaconsfield HP9 2JA Tel: 01494 676972 Fax: 01494 670915 — MB BS Calcutta 1967; DObst RCOG 1970. (Calculta Med. Coll. W. Bengal, India) SCMO Heathrow Airport; Acupunc. Specialist Beaconsfield & Heritage Health Care, Stoke Poges. Socs: Med. Protec. Soc.; Brit. Med. Acupunct. Soc.

DUTTA, Krishna Psychiatry Unit, Monklands Hospital, Monkscourt Avenue, Airdrie ML6 0JS Tel: 01236 748748 Fax: 01236 760015; 21 Mansewood Crescent, Whitburn, Bathgate EH47 8HA Tel: 01501 41871 — MB BS 1972 Dibrugarh. (Assam Med. Coll. & Hosp. Dibrugarh) Clin. Asst. (Psychiat.) Monklands Hosp. Airdrie, Lanarksh. Socs: Overseas Doctors Assn. (Comm. Mem. Scotl. Div.).

DUTTA, Nirendra Nath Ilford Lane Surgery, 165 Ilford Lane, Ilford IG1 2RS Tel: 020 8478 1366 Fax: 020 8491 9066; 29 Blakehall Road, Wanstead, London E11 2QQ — MB BS 1960 Assam; FRCOG 1989, M 1967; DGO Calcutta 1963. GP Ilford; Clin. Asst. Dept. Obst. & Gyn. Whipps Cross Hosp. Prev: SHO Derby City Hosp.; Regist. (Obst. & Gyn) Leicester Gen. Hosp.; GP. Newc.

DUTTA, Mr Raj Kumar Central Medical Centre, 42 St. Pauls Road, Coventry CV6 5DF Tel: 024 7668 1231 Fax: 024 7666 4935 — MB BS 1965 Agra; FRCS Ed. 1971; MRCS Eng. LRCP Lond. 1972. (S.N. Med. Coll.) Police Surg. W. Midl. Police Auth. Socs: Fell. Roy. Soc. Med.; BMA & Assn. Police Surgs. Prev: Regist. (Gen. Surg.) Roy. Vict. Hosp. Belf.; Regist. (Orthop.) Vict. Hosp. Burnley; Resid. Memor. Hosp. Halifax Nova Scotia, Canada.

DUTTA, Ranadhir Maerdy Surgery, North Terrace, Maerdy, Ferndale CF43 4DD Tel: 01443 733202 Fax: 01443 733730.

DUTTA, Ruma Louise 130 St Dunstan's Road, London W6 8RA — MB BS 1992 Lond.

DUTTA, Sambhu Nath 30 Bromley Road, Leyton, London E10 7AD Tel: 020 8539 1663 — MB BS 1951 Calcutta; DTM & H Eng. 1957. (R. G. Kar Med. Coll.) Socs: BMA. Prev: Ho. Phys. German Hosp. Lond.; Sen. Ho. Phys. E.. Hosp. Lond. Regist. Whipps Cross Hosp. Lond.

DUTTA, Shelah Southfield, Lennoxtown, Glasgow G66 7LQ — MB ChB 1982 Glas.

DUTTA, Soumitra c/o Dr C. R. Kundu Himaloy, 155A Soothill Lane, Batley WF17 6HW — MB BS 1987 Madras.

DUTTA, Sudeshna 8 Sterry Drive, Epsom KT19 0TG — MB BS 1986 Lond.

DUTTA, Sunil Kumar Prantik Harris Brow, Great Broughton, Cockermouth CA13 0XR Tel: 01900 824610 — MB BS 1953 Calcutta; DPM Eng. 1976; DCH Calcutta 1964; DTM & H 1960. Cons. Psychiat. Dovenby Hall Hosp. Cockermouth. Socs: Med. Protec. Soc. Prev: Sen. Regist. (Child Psychiat.) Aberd.

DUTTA, Swapan Kumar c/o Dr A. K. Ghosh, 56 The Avenue, Sunbury-on-Thames TW16 5ES — MB BS 1969 Calcutta.

DUTTA, Topan Lincoln House Surgery, Wolsey Road, Hemel Hempstead HP2 4TU Tel: 01442 254366; 9 The Horseshoe, Leverstock Green, Hemel Hempstead HP3 8QT — MB BS 1971 Lond.; BSc (Hons) Lond. 1968. (Guy's) Prev: Regist. (Med.) Hillingdon Hosp. Uxbridge.

DUTTON, Adam Charles Lawton House Surgery, Bromley Road, Congleton CW12 1QG Tel: 01260 275454 Fax: 01260 298412; Paddock House Farm, Back Lane, Congleton CW12 4RB Tel: 01260 280411 — MB BS 1973 Lond.; MRCP (UK) 1978.

DUTTON, Alan Jeffrey (retired) 42 Fleet Road, Holbeach, Spalding PE12 8LA Tel: 01406 425088 — MB ChB Manch. 1957; DA Eng. 1960. Clin. Asst. (Dermat.) Kings Lynn & Wisbech Hosps. Prev: Regist. (Anaesth.) Macclesfield Infirm.

DUTTON, Alasdair Hugh Whitefriars Surgery, Whitefriars Street, Perth PH1 1PP Tel: 01738 625842 Fax: 01738 445030; 5 Deer Park, Pitcairnfield, Perth PH1 3SP Tel: 01738 583261 — MB ChB 1982 Dundee; BMSc (Hons.) Dund 1979; MRCGP 1987. (Dundee) Civil Aviat. Auth. Approved Examr.; GP Trainer. Socs: Brit. Assn. Immed. Care Schemes. Prev: Regist. (Med.) Ninewells Hosp. Dundee; Cas. Off. Dunedin Pub. Hosp., NZ.

DUTTON, Claude Scott Rose Cottage, Stroud Road, Brookthorpe, Gloucester GL4 0UG Tel: 01452 813766 Fax: 01452 814474 Email: claudedutton@compuserve.com — MRCS Eng. LRCP Lond. 1959; FLCOM 1979; LLCO 1967; MRO 1967; DA Eng. 1961. (St. Thos.) Hon. Sen. Clin. Tutor Lond. Coll. Osteop. Med.; Hon. Clin. Supervisor Osteop. Assn. Clinic Lond.; Emerit. Prof. (Musculoskeletal Med.) Almaty Med. Univ. Kazakhstan. Socs: Brit. Inst. Musculoskel. Med.; (Ex-Vice Pres.) Brit. Osteop. Assn.; Inst. cl.ical Osteop. Prev: Cons. Orthop. & Osteop. Phys. Gloucester; SHO (Anaesth.) & Ho. Phys. St. Margt. Hosp. Epping; Sen. Resid. (Anaesth.) St. Thos. Hosp. Lond.

DUTTON, David Arthur Danisway, Queens Road, Colmworth, Bedford MK44 2LA — MB ChB 1975 Ed.; FFA RCS Eng. 1980; Dip. Palliat. Med. Wales 1995. Cons. Anaesth. Bedford Hosp. Prev: Cons. Anaesth. Vict. Infirm. Glas.

DUTTON, Diana 1 Barn Way, Wembley HA9 9LE Tel: 020 8904 3013 — MB BS 1960 Lond.; MRCS Eng. LRCP Lond. 1961; DMRD Eng. 1966; DObst RCOG 1962. (Lond. Hosp.) Cons. Radiol. Willesden Gen. Hosp. Socs: BMA; Brit. Inst. Radiol. Prev: Sen. Regist. X-Ray Dept. Centr. Middlx. Hosp. Lond.; Regist. X-Ray Dept. Radcliffe Infirm. Oxf.; Gyn. Ho. Surg. Lond. Hosp. Annexe.

DUTTON, Geoffrey Charles Downing 22A Brizlincote Lane, Burton-on-Trent DE15 0PR Tel: 01283 61020 — MRCS Eng. LRCP Lond. 1943; BA Camb. 1940. (Lond. Hosp.) Socs: BMA.

DUTTON, Mr Gordon Neale 3 Ledcameroch Crescent, Bearsden, Glasgow G61 4AD Tel: 0141 942 2739 — MD 1985 Bristol; MB ChB 1976; FRCS Glas. (Ophth.) 1989; FRCS Eng. (Ophth.) 1982; FRCOphth 1989. Cons. Ophth. Gartnavel Gen. Hosp., Glas..; Roy. Hosp. for Sick Childr. Glas. Prev: Sen. Lect. Glas. Univ.

DUTTON, Hilda Ray (retired) 1 Sunnyside Lane, Hambrook, Bristol BS16 1RX Tel: 0117 956 6801 — MRCS Eng. LRCP Lond. 1923.

DUTTON, Jane Arabella Elsworth 14A Highbury Place, London N5 1QP Tel: 01299 402255 — MB BS 1988 Lond.

DUTTON, John Edwin Martin (retired) The Hurst, Macclesfield Road, Alderley Edge SK9 7BN Tel: 01625 583421 — MB BS 1943 Durh.; FRCS Eng. 1950. Prev: Dir. Univ. Dept. Neurosurg. Manch. Roy. Infirm.

DUTTON, John Granville The Surgery, Clerk's Field, Headcorn, Ashford TN27 9QJ Tel: 01622 890294 Fax: 01622 891754 — MB BChir 1976 Camb.; DCH Eng. 1979; MRCGP 1984; DRCOG 1978. Prev: Trainee GP Medway VTS; Ho. Phys. OldCh. Hosp. Romford; Ho. Surg. Rush Green Hosp. Romford.

DUTTON, Joyce 2 Cresswell Way, Holmer Green, High Wycombe HP15 6TE — BM BCh 1956 Oxf.

DUTTON, Peter (retired) Flat 74, Solent Pines, 29 Manor Road, Bournemouth BH1 3HS Tel: 01202 555728 — MB ChB 1955 Manch.; MD Manch. 1959; FRCR 1989; DMRD Eng. 1961. Prev: Cons.Radiol.Bedford Hosp.GP.

DUTTON, Peter Michael Elsworth (retired) Wassell Top, Trimpley, Bewdley DY12 1NJ Tel: 01299 402255 — MB BChir 1953 Camb.; BA Camb. 1950, MB BChir 1953.

DUVAL, Christine Margaret North Tees and Hartlepool Health Trust, Department of Child Health, Lawson St., Stockton-on-Tees TS18 1HU Tel: 01642 672393 Fax: 01642 672545; Three Steps, Crathorne, Yarm TS15 0BB Tel: 01642 701475 — MB BS 1978 Newc.; MMed Sci 1996; MRCGP 1982; DRCOG 1981. Assoc. Specialist Community Child Health N. Tees & Hartlepool Health Trust, Stockton-on-Tees.

DUVALL, Edward Department of Pathology, University of Edinburgh, Medical School, Treviot Place, Edinburgh EH8 9AG Tel: 0131 650 2895 Fax: 0131 650 6528 Email: e.duval@ed.ac.uk — MB ChB 1978 Ed.; MA, DPhil Oxf. 1977; MRCPath 1984; FRCPath 1995. (Edinburgh) Sen. Lect. Dept. Path. Univ. Edin. Med. Sch.

DUVALL-YOUNG, Josephine Wycombe General Hospital, Queen Alexandra Road, High Wycombe HP11 2TT Tel: 01494 526161; 18 Magnolia Dene, Hazlemere, High Wycombe HP15 7QE Tel: 01494 452119 — MB ChB 1978 Ed.; BSc (Hons.) Ed. 1975, MD 1988; FRCS Ed. 1982; FRCOphth 1988. Cons. Ophth. Wycombe Gen. Hosp. Prev: Cons. Ophth. Walton Hosp. & St. Paul's Eye Hosp. Liverp.; Hon. Lect. Univ. Liverp.

DUX, Anthony Ernest Walter Department of Radiology, Leicester Royal Infirmary, Leicester LE1 5WW Tel: 0116 254 1414 Email: adux@uhl.trent.nhs.uk; Hay Cottage, Seaton Road, Morcott, Oakham LE15 9EB — MB BS 1976 Lond.; MRCS Eng. LRCP Lond. 1976.; FRCR 1984; DCH Eng. 1979; DMRD Eng. 1981. (Roy. Free) Cons. (paed radiol) Univeristy Hosp.s of Leicester N.H.S. Trust. Socs: BMA; Med. Equestrian Assn. (Chair.). Prev: Cons. (Radiol) PeterBoro. Hosp.; Sen. Regist. (Radiol.) Roy. Free Hosp. & Hosp. Sick Childr. Lond.; Regist. (Radiol.) W.m. Hosp. Lond.

DUX, Meike Susanne 5 Stanwell Avenue, Huddersfield HD2 2BY — State Exam Med 1984 Gottingen; MRCGP 1991.

DUXBURY, Brian John MacDougall (retired) Linchens, New Domewood, Copthorne, Crawley RH10 3HF Tel: 01342 716671 — MB BS 1953 Lond.; MRCS Eng. LRCP Lond. 1943; FRCPath 1971, M 1963. Hon. Cons. Haemat. Chase Farm Hosp. Enfield. Prev: Cons. Haematol. Chase Farm Hosp. Enfield.

DUXBURY, Fiona Ruth Caroline Gordon Blackbird Leys Health Centre, 63 Blackbird Leys Road, Oxford OX4 6HL Tel: 01865 778244 — MB BS 1979 Lond.; BSc Lond. 1976; MRCGP 1986; DCH RCP Lond. 1985; DRCOG 1984; Cert. Family Plann. JCC 1982. (Royal Free Hospital School of Medicine, London University)

DUXBURY, Michael John 74 Stoneygate Road, Leicester LE2 2BN — MB ChB 1986 Leic.; BSc (Hons.) E. Anglia 1980. Forens. Med. Off. Leics. Constab.

DUXBURY, Stephen Christopher Station House Surgery, Kendal LA9 6SA Tel: 01539 722660 — MB ChB 1988 Manch.; BSc St. And. 1986; MRCGP 1993. GP Asst. Station Ho. Surg. Kendal. Socs: BMA; RCGP.

DVORKIN, Lee Simon 1 Broughton Av, London N3 3ES — MB ChB 1997 Leeds.

DWARAKANATH, Anandapuram Deepak North Tees District General Hospital, Hardwick, Stockton-on-Tees TS19 8PE Tel: 01642 624571 Fax: 01642 624919; 29 Coal Lane, Wolviston, Billingham TS22 5LW — MB BCh 1986 Wales; FRCP Ed 1999; MRCP (UK) 1989; FRCP London 2000. (Univ. Wales, Coll. of Med.) Cons. Gen. Med. & Gastroenterol. N. Tees Dist. Gen. Hosp. Stockton-on-Tees. Socs: Brit. Soc. Gastroenterol. Prev: Sen. Regist. (Gen. Med. & Gastroenterol.) N.. Region; Sen. Research Fell. (Gastroenterol. Med.) Univ. Liverp.; Regist. (Gen. Med. & Gastroenterol.) Gen. Hosp. Birm. & Sandwell Dist. Gen. Hosp.

DWARAKANATH, Bhadravati Subbaraya Sastry 75 Rhydypenau Road, Cycoed, Cardiff CF23 6PZ Tel: 029 2075 2412 — MB BS 1971 Karnatak; MRCPI 1977. (Karnatak Med. Coll. Hosp.) Cons. Phys. in Geriat. Med. S. Glam. Health Auth.

DWARAKANATH, Linga Subbarama 14 High Brow, Harborne, Birmingham B17 9EN Email: dwarak@btinternet.com — MB BS 1986 Madras; MRCOG 1994. Sen. Regist. (O & G) Birm. Woms. Hosp. Birm.

DWARIKA, Wendell Michael Flat 95, Kendon Drive, Bristol BS10 5BU — MB BS 1987 West Indies.

DWERRYHOUSE, Mr Simon James 62 Alma Court, Clifton, Bristol BS8 2HJ — MB ChB 1990 Ed.; FRCS Eng. 1994.

DWIGHT, Jeremy Frank St John 11 St Albans Road, Bristol BS6 7SF — MB BS 1994 Lond.; BSc Lond. (1st. cl. Hons.) 1981, MB BS (Distinc.) Med. & Pathol. 1984; MRCP (UK) 1987. Research Fell. Brit. Heart Foundat. Nuffield Dept. Med. Oxf. Prev: Regist. (Renal Med.) St. Thos. Hosp. Lond.; SHO Nuffield Dept. Med. Oxf.; SHO (Intens. Care) St. Thos. Hosp. Lond.

DWIVEDI, Amitabh 49 Glenfield Drive, Great Doddington, Wellingborough NN29 7TE Tel: 01933 277945 — MB ChB 1993 Sheff.; BMedSci Sheff. 1990. SHO (Med.) Bristol Roy. Infirm. Prev: SHO (Cas.) Bath Roy. United Hosp.; SHO (ENT) P.ss Margt. Hosp. Swindon.

DWIVEDI, Kedar Nath Child & Adolescent Family Services, 8 Notre Dame Mews, Northampton NN1 2BG Tel: 01604 604608 Fax: 01604 604531 Email: kedar.dwivedi@ngh-tr.anglox.nhs.uk; Ken Stewart Family Centre, Sunnyside, Cliftonville, Northampton NN1 5BE — MB BS 1970 Banaras Hindu; MD (Preven. & Social Med.) Banaras Hindu 1972; FRCPsych 1992, M 1977; DPM Eng. 1977. (Inst. Med. Scs. Varanasi) Cons. Child & Family Psychiat. N.ampton Gen. Hosp. NHS Trust; Clin. Teach. Fac. Med. Leicester Univ.; Pres. Budhisam, Psychol. & Psychiat. Gp. Socs: Transcultural Psychiat. Soc. (UK); (Chairm.) Child & Adolesc. Gp. Work Assn.; Roy. Soc. Med. (Fell.). Prev: Asst. Prof. Preven. & Social Med. Simla, India.

DWIVEDI, Rahul The Pines 6 Stanley Avenue, Wirral CH63 5QF Email: rahul.dwivedi@virgin.net — MB ChB 1997 Liverp.

DWORKIN, Mr Michael Jonathan Department of Surgery, Southend Hospital, Prittlewell; Chase, Westcliff on Sea SS0 0RY — MB BS 1986 Lond.; MS Lond. 1996; FRCS (Gen.) 1997; FRCS Eng. 1990. (Middlesex Medical School) Cons. Surg., S.end Hosp..

DWYER, Amanda Susan Burley Park Doctors, Burley Park Medical Centre, 273 Burley Road, Leeds LS4 2EL Tel: 0113 230 4111; 32 Bankfield, Bardsey, Leeds LS17 9AP — MB ChB 1986 Leeds; DRCOG 1991; MBCUB (Hons) Leeds. 1986. Socs: BMA.

DWYER, Colmcille Michael Department of Dermatology, Crosshouse Hospital, Kilmarnock KA2 0BE Tel: 01563 577928 Fax: 01563 577978 — MB BCh BAO 1982 NUI; MMedSci NUI 1984; MRCP (UK) 1988; DCH NUI 1985. (Univ. Coll. Dub.) Cons. Dermat. CrossHo. Hosp. Kilmarnock. Prev: Sen. Regist. (Dermat.) Aberd. Roy. Infirm.

DWYER, Declan Michael Patrick (retired) North Road West Medical Centre, 167 North Road West, Plymouth PL1 5BZ Tel: 01752 662780 Fax: 01752 254541 — MB BS 1973 Lond.; FRCGP 1992, M 1978; FDS RCS Eng. 1971, LDS 1965. Assoc. Advis. SW. Prev: SHO Plymouth Gen. Hosp.

DWYER, James David Place Surgery, 361/2 David Place, St Helier, Jersey JE2 4TE Tel: 01534 619988; 68 Stoppard Road, St Helier, Jersey — MD 1992 Paris.

DWYER, Mr Jonathan St John Munro 31 Quarry Avenue, Hartshill, Stoke-on-Trent ST4 7EW Tel: 01782 417833 Fax: 01782 417844 Email: jonathan_s_m.dwyer@virgin.net — MB BS 1986 Lond.; BSc (Hons.) Lond. 1983; FRCS (Orth.) 1995; FRCS Eng. 1990. (The Lond. Hosp. Med. Coll.) Cons. Childr. Orthop. Surg. N. Staffs. Roy. Infirm. & Hartshill Orthop. Hosp.; Hon. Cons. Robt. Jones & Agnes Hung, Orthopaedic Hosp. OsW.ry; Hon. Cons. Manch. Roy. Infirm. Socs: BMA & RSM; BOA. Prev: Sen. Regist. Rotat. (Trauma & Orthop.) Robt. Jones & Agnes Hunt Hosp. OsW.ry; Train. Rotat. (Surg.) St. Bart. Hosp. Lond.; Regist. (Orthop.) St. Barts. Hosp.

DWYER, Martin John 3 Maple Close, Messingham, Scunthorpe DN17 3UQ — MB BS 1986 Lond.

DWYER, Michael John Adrian Bridge Street Surgery, Bridge Street, Louth LN11 0DR Tel: 01507 603121 Fax: 01507 605916; 33 Linden Walk, Louth LN11 9HT Tel: 01507 604802 Email: mickdwyer@usu.com — MB BS 1982 Lond.; MRCGP 1987; Dip. IMC RCS Ed. 1992; DCH RCP Lond. 1989; DGM RCP Lond. 1987; DRCOG 1986. (Westm.)

DWYER, Mr Nigel St John Pasfield (retired) 514 Streetsbrook Road, Solihull B91 1RH Tel: 0121 705 4544 — MB ChB 1960 Ed.; FRCS Ed. 1967; FRCS Eng. 1967. Prev: Cons. Orthop. Surg. E. Birm. Hosp.

DWYER, Noel Michael 32 Bankfield, Bardsey, Leeds LS17 9AP — MB ChB 1983 Leeds.

DWYER, Nuala Anne 52 Lower Redland Road, Bristol BS6 6ST Tel: 0117 973 1452 — MB BChir 1979 Camb.; MD Bristol 1992; BA (Nat. Sc.) Camb. 1976, MA; MRCOG 1988; MRCGP 1983. Cons. O & G W.on Gen. Hosp. Prev: Sen. Regist. (O & G) St. Michael's Hosp. Bristol; Regist. (O & G) John Radcliffe Hosp. Oxf.; SHO Hammersmith Hosp. Lond.

DWYER, Sean David Nigel 514 Streetsbrook Road, Solihull B91 1RH — MB BS 1987 Lond.

DYAR, Oliver James Nuffield Department of Anaesthetics, John Radcliffe Hospital, Headington, Oxford OX3 9DU Tel: 01865 221590 Email: oliver.dyar@nda.ox.ac.uk; Corner House, Bicester Road, Kidlington OX5 2LE — MB BCh BAO 1984 NUI; MRCPI 1986; FRCA 1989. (NUI) Cons. Anaesth. & Intens. Care Nuffield Dept. Anaesth. Oxf. Socs: BMA; Intens. Care Soc.; Assn. Anaesth. GB & Irel. Prev: Sen. Regist. Nuffield Dept. Anaesth. Oxf.

DYAS, Anne Celia Department of Microbiology, Solihull Hospital, Lode Lane, Solihull B91 2JL Tel: 0121 711 4455; Grange Lodge, 83 Grange Road, Dorridge, Solihull B93 8QU Email: dyas@grangelodge.demon.uk — MB ChB 1979 Birm.; MRCPath 1985.

DYBAS, Bozena 102 Brunswick Road, London W5 1AW — BA Dub. 1953, MB BCh BAO 1956. (T.C. Dub.)

DYCE, James Morrison 25 Gretton Court, Girton, Cambridge CB3 0QN Tel: 01223 276500 — LRCP LRCS Ed. LRFPS Glas. 1934; DDS Penna. 1935; LDS RFPS Glas. 1933. (Anderson College Medicine Glasgow & University Pennsylvania) Dir. Stress Pub.ats. Lavenham, Suff. Socs: Fell. Roy. Soc. Med.; Soc. Applicat. Research Camb.

DYCHE, Jacqueline Anne — MB ChB 1991 Bristol; DTM & H RCP Lond. 1993; MRCP (UK) 1996. (Bristol) Regist. Dermat. Roy. Lond. Hosp. Socs: Roy. Soc. Mem. Prev: Regist. Dermat. At St Mary's Hosp. Paddington, Chelsea & W.minister Hosp.; SHO Dermat. Ealing Hosp.

DYDE, Mr John Anthony (retired) Home Farm, Wormleighton, Fenny Compton, Leamington Spa CV47 2XG — MB BChir 1960 Camb.; FRCS Eng. 1963; MRCS Eng. LRCP Lond. 1959. Cons. Cardiac Surg. W. Midl. Regional Cardiothoracic Unit Walsgrave Hosp. Coventry. Prev: Regist. Thoracic Unit Guy's Hosp. Lond.

DYE, Derek John Royal Gwent Hospital, Newport NP20 2UB Tel: 01633 234234 — MB ChB 1970 Bristol; BSc Bristol 1967, MB ChB 1970; FFA RCS Eng. 1975. Cons. Anaesth. Gwent AHA. Prev: Cons. Anaesth. Welsh Regional Burns & Plastic Surgic. Unit.

DYE, Harry Kingsley 5 Stanmer House, Lypiatt Road, Cheltenham GL50 2QJ — MB ChB 1977 Otago; BA (Ancient Greek), MB ChB Otago 1977; MSc (Med. Genetics) Newc. 1992. MSc Stud. (Med. Genetics) Univ. Newc. u Tyne. Prev: Regist. (Obst.) Birm. Matern. Hosp.; Regist. (Gyn.) Birm. & Midl. Hosp. Wom.; SHO (O & G) Roy. Berks. Hosp. Reading.

DYE, Patricia Carol Cradley Surgery, malvern, Worcester Tel: 01886 880207 Fax: 01886 880630; The Old Rectory, Malvern Road, Stanford Bishop, Bringsty, Worcester WR6 5TT Tel: 01886 884058 — MB ChB 1982 Auckland; BHumanBiol 1979. (Auckland)

DYE, Rebecca Katherine 9 Dunsgreen, Ponteland, Newcastle upon Tyne NE20 9EH — MB ChB 1994 Ed.; DCH Glas. 1996; MRCGP 1998. (Edinburgh)

DYE, Stephen Michael Department of Psychiatry, Charing Cross Hospital, Fulham Palace Road, London W6 Tel: 020 8846 1234 Email: sdye@cu.rmps.ac.uk; 37A Fordhook Avenue, Ealing Common, London W5 3LS Email: sdye12345@aol.com — MB BS 1991 Lond. (St. Marys Hosp. Med. Sch.) Lect. (Psychiat.) Imp. Coll. Sc. Technol. & Med.

DYER, Aref Albert 125 Felstead Road, Orpington BR6 9AH — MB BS 1998 Lond.; MB BS Lond 1998.

DYER, Barry John 95 Clarence Crescent, London SW4 8LE — MB BS 1998 Lond.; MB BS Lond 1998.

DYER, Betty Barbara (retired) 1 Waltham Close, Bedford MK41 8DL Tel: 01234 365979 — MRCS Eng. LRCP Lond. 1949; MD Lond. 1953, MB BS 1949. Prev: Assoc. Specialist in Chest Dis. Bedford Gen. Hosp.

DYER, Catherine Frieda Bonnybridge Health Centre, Larbert Road, Bonnybridge FK4 1ED Tel: 01324 812315 Fax: 01324 814540; 41 Albert Road, Falkirk FK1 5LS Tel: 01324 638848 — MB ChB 1974 Zambia; MRCS Eng. LRCP Lond. 1977. Hon. Lect. Glas. Univ.; Macmillan GP Facilitator (Cancer & Palliat. Care) Forth Valley HB. Prev: Assoc. Specialist Strathcarron Hospice Denny.

DYER, Christopher Ashley Elmer 11 Metfield Croft, Birmingham B17 0NN — MB ChB 1989 Birm.; ChB Birm. 1989; MRCP (UK) 1993. Lect. (Geriat. Med.) Univ. Birm. Socs: Brit. Geriat. Soc.

DYER, David Frederick 9 Kinley Street, St. Thomas, Swansea SA1 8HE — MB BCh 1982 Wales.

DYER, Elizabeth Jane (retired) 15 Mayfield Close, Ramsbottom, Bury BL0 9TL Email: elizabethmikek.freeserve.co.uk — MB ChB 1983 Ed.; BSc (Med. Sci.) Ed. 1980; MRCPsych 1987. Prev: Cons. Child & Adolesc. Psychiat. Manch. Roy. Infirm.

DYER, Haydon Edwin George 113 Osborne Road, Jesmond, Newcastle upon Tyne NE2 2TA Tel: 0191 281 1497 — LMSSA 1949 Lond. (Guy's) Socs: Fell. Roy. Soc. Med. Prev: ENT Ho. Surg. Orpington Hosp. & Guy's Hosp.; Surg. Lt. RN 1950-54.

DYER, Helen Elizabeth Broadfields House, Leigh Sinton, Malvern WR13 Tel: 01886 32279; Flat 3, 25 Eardley Crescent, Earls Court, London SW5 9JS Tel: 020 7373 5278 — MB BS 1988 Lond.

DYER, Ian Richard 14 Digby Close, Lincoln LN6 3PZ — MB BS 1993 Newc.

DYER, James Archibald Thomson Mental Welfare Commission, Argyle House, 3 Lady Lawson St., Edinburgh EH3 9SH Tel: 0131 222 6160 Fax: 0131 222 6112 Email: jdyer@mwcscot.org.uk; 1 Frankscroft, Peebles EH45 9DX Tel: 01721 724729 — MB ChB 1970 (Hons.) Aberd.; FRCPsych 1992, M 1975. Dir. & HM Med. Commr. Ment. Welf. Commiss. Scotl.; Hon. Sen. Lect. Psychiat. Univ. Edin. Prev: Cons. Psychiat. Roy. Edin. Hosp.; Scientif. Staff MRC Unit Epidemiol. Studies Psychiat. Edin.; Regist. (Psychiat.) Roy. Edin. Hosp.

DYER, John Karl Queen Street Surgery, 13A Queen Street, Deal CT14 6ET Tel: 01304 363181 Fax: 01304 381996 — MB BS 1967 Lond.; MRCS Eng. LRCP Lond. 1967. (Lond. Hosp.)

DYER, John Melville Arthur (retired) 5 Cadogan Close, Holyport, Maidenhead SL6 2JS — MRCS Eng. LRCP Lond. 1959. Prev: Clin. Asst. (Rheum.) Maidenhead Gen. Hosp.

DYER, John Robert William Geoffrey 11 Africa Gardens, Cardiff CF14 3BT — MB BCh 1997 Wales.

DYER, John Vincent (retired) 2 Coastal Rise, Hest Bank, Lancaster LA2 6HJ — MB BS 1953 Lond.; BA Open 1983; MRCS Eng. LRCP Lond. 1953; FFCM RCP (UK) 1979, M 1974; DPH (Distinc.) Lond. 1957. Prev: Dir. (Pub. Health) Lancaster.

DYER, Julian David Scarborough Hospital, Scarborough YO12 6Q — MB ChB 1990 Leic.; BSc (Hons.) Leic. 1983; MRCP (UK) 1994; FRCR 1997 (on West Midlands Training Scheme). Cons. Radiol. ScarBoro. Socs: Brit. Soc. of Interven.al Radiologists; Roy. Coll. Radiol. Prev: Regist. Rotat. (Radiol.) W. Midls.; SHO Rotat. (Gen. Med.) New Cross Hosp. Wolverhampton; SHO (Cas.) Selly Oak Hosp. Birm.

DYER, Kate Elizabeth St James's Practice, 138 Croydon Road, Beckenham BR3 4DG Tel: 020 8650 0568 Fax: 020 8650 4172 — MB BChir 1988 Camb.; MA Camb. 1989; MRCGP 1992; DRCOG 1991. (Univ. Camb. & Char. Cross & Westm.) p/t G.P. Prev: Trainee GP Croydon HA.

DYER, Malcolm Wilson Ellers Lea, 5 South Broomage Avenue, Larbert FK5 3LD Tel: 01324 557892 — MB ChB 1993 Dundee. GP Regist. Prev: SHO Psychiat.Fulkirk & dis.Roy; SHO A&E Stirling Roy; SHO (Anaesth.) Ninewells Hosp. Dundee & Perth Roy. Infirm.

DYER, Marie Patricia Sheldon House, 2 Elmfield Park, Gosforth, Newcastle upon Tyne NE3 4UX Tel: 0191 285 2700; 170 West Road, Newcastle upon Tyne NE4 9BQ Tel: 0191 273 6364 — MB BS 1962 Durh. (Newc.) Prev: Ho. Phys. Roy. Vict. Infirm. Newc. & P.ss Mary Matern. Hosp.; Newc.

DYER, Marion Josephine Aldermoor Health Centre, Aldermoor Close, Southampton SO16 5ST Tel: 023 8079 7700 Fax: 023 8079 7767 — MB BCh BAO 1985 NUI.

DYER, Professor Martin John Swinnerton Leicester University, Dept. of Haematology, Robert Kilpatrick CSB, Leicester LE2 7ZX Email: mjsd1@le.ac.uk; Holdens, Shipton Lane, Itchenor, Chichester PO20 7BZ Fax: 01243 512375 — MB BChir 1983 Camb.; MA Oxf. 1983, DPhil. 1980; MB BChir. Camb. 1983; FRCP (UK) 1997, M 1985; FRCPath 1998. Prof. of Haemato. Oncol., Leciester Univ. Prev: Louise Buchanan Fulbright Schol. (Stanford Univ.); Meres Stud. for Med. Research St. John's Coll. Camb.

DYER, Michael John (retired) Mardens, Pancake Lane, Leverstock Green, Hemel Hempstead HP2 4NB Tel: 01442 219024 — MB BS 1957 Lond.; MRCS Eng. LRCP Lond. 1957. Prev: Hosp. Pract. Abbot's Langley Hosp.

DYER, Nicholas Henry (retired) Broadfields House, Leigh Sinton, Malvern WR13 5DQ — MB BChir 1962 Camb.; MD Camb. 1970, MA, MB 1962, BChir 1961; FRCP Lond. 1978, M 1964. Cons. Phys.

Worcester Roy. Infirm. (Ronkswood Br.). Prev: Regist. (Med.) Lond. Hosp.

DYER, Nora Christine 28 Church Crescent, London N20 0JP — BM BCh 1988 Oxf.; MA Oxf. 1989, BM BCh 1988.

DYER, Philip Henry Birmingham Heartlands Hospital, Bordesley Green East, Birmingham B9 5SS Tel: 0212 424 2103 Fax: 0121 424 3105 — MB BS 1991 Lond.; MD 2000; BSc Lond. 1988; MRCP 1994. (St Georges) Cons.(diabetes/Endocrinol./acute med.) Birm. heartlands Hosp. NHS Trust. Prev: Ho. Phys. (Med.) St. Geo. Hosp. Lond.; Ho. Off. (Surg.) Roy. Cornw. Hosp.; Specialist Regist. Diabetes & Endinocrology Univ. Hosp NHS Trust.Selly Oak Hosp.

DYER, Philip Mark 26 Toller Grove, Heaton, Bradford BD9 5NP — MB ChB 1983 Bristol.

DYER, Richard Stanbrook Bonnybridge Health Centre, Larbert Road, Bonnybridge FK4 1ED Tel: 01324 812315 Fax: 01324 814540; 41 Albert Road, Falkirk FK1 5LS — MB BS 1974 Lond.; MRCGP 1978; DRCOG 1976. (Lond. Hosp.) Prev: Med. Off. Mulanje Mission Hosp. Mulanje, Malawi.

DYER, Robert Geoffrey Department of Medicine, Torbay Hospital, Lawes Bridge, Torquay TQ2 7AA Tel: 07803 654823 — MB ChB 1985 Birm.; BSc (Hons.) Birm. 1982, MB ChB 1985; MRCP (UK) 1988; FRCP 1999. Cons. Phys. Torbay Hosp. Prev: Cons. (Phys.) Hexham N.umberland; Sen. Regist. (Med.) Newc.; SHO Rotat. (Med.) Dudley Rd. Hosp. Birm.

DYER, Stephanie Jane Vine Cottage, Fore St., Ipplepen, Newton Abbot TQ12 5RH — MB ChB 1988 Birm.; MRCGP 1992; DRCOG 1991.

DYER, Stephen John Willen Hospice, Manor Road, Willen Village, Milton Keynes MK15 9AB Tel: 01908 662265 Fax: 01908 695715; 7 Butlers Grove, Great Linford, Milton Keynes MK14 5DT Tel: 01908 662265 Email: dyerpasc@aol.com — MB BS 1975 Lond.; Dip. Palliat. Med. Wales 1993; DRCOG 1979. (Char. Cross) Cons. Palliat. Med. Willen Hospice Milton Keynes. Prev: GP Milton Keynes.

DYER, Timothy John Flintshire Child & Adolescent Mental Health Service, 9-13 Victoria Rd, Shotton, Deeside CH5 1EY Tel: 01244 831496 Fax: 01244 836052 — MB ChB 1974 Ed.; MRCPsych 1978. Cons. Child & Adolesc. Psychiat. N. E. Wales NHS Trust.

DYER-FANE, Matthew David (retired) 1 Warwick Gardens, Worthing BN11 1PE Tel: 01903 236867 — MB ChB St. And. 1942. Prev: Regist. (Surg.) Roy. Perth Hosp. W. Austral.

DYET, John Finlayson Alderson House, Hull Royal Infirmary, Anlaby Road, Hull HU3 2JZ Tel: 01482675245; 51 The Dales, Cottingham HU16 5JS Tel: 01482 844896 — MB ChB 1965 Glas.; FRCP Glas. 1995; FRCR 1972; DMRD Eng. 1969. (Glas.) Med.Dir. Hull & E.Yorks.Hosp.NHS Trust. Socs: Brit. Soc. Interven. Radiol.; Fell. Cardiovasc. & Interven. Radiol. Soc. Europe; Soc. Cardiovasc. & Interven. Radiol. (USA). Prev: Sen. Regist. & SHO (Radiol.) W.. Infirm. Glas.; Sen. Regist. (Radiol.) S.. Gen. Hosp. Glas.

DYET, Leigh Elizabeth Beechlands, 51 The Dales, Cottingham HU16 5JS Tel: 01482 844896 — MB BS 1996 Newc.; BMedSc Newc. 1995. SHO Paediat. Gt. Ormond St Hosp. Lond. Prev: SHO Neonat. Whittington hosp.Lond; SHO paediat.Whittington Hosp.Lond; SHO (A & E) Univ. Coll. Hosp. Lond.

DYKE, Garry Whitfield 46 Green Lane, Harrogate HG2 9LP — MB ChB 1981 Manch.; BSc St. And. 1978; MD Manch. 1992; FRCS (Gen.) 1996; FRCS Ed. 1988. Cons. Surg. Harrogate Dist. Hosp. Prev: Sen. Regist. Yorks. RHA & Flinders Med. Centre, Adelaide.

DYKE, Mark Peter Norfolk & Norwich University Hospital Trust, Colney Lane, Norwich NR4 7UY Tel: 01603 286337 Email: mark.dyke@norfolk-norwich.thenhs.com; Email: mark.dyke@btopenworld.com — MB ChB 1982 Bristol; MRCP (UK) 1986; DCH RCP Lond. 1986; FRCPCH 1997. Cons. Paediat. Norf. & Norwich Univ. Hosp. Trust; Hon. Sen. Lect. Univ. of E. Anglia. Socs: UK Childr.s Cancer Study Gp.; Brit. Assn. of Perinatal Med. Prev: Sen. Regist. (Paediat.) Addenbrooke's Hosp. Camb.; Sen. Regist. King Edwd. Memor. Hosp. Perth, W. Austral.; Lect. (Paediat.) Univ. Bristol.

DYKE, Robert Radcliffe (retired) Little Receven, Newbridge, Penzance TR20 8PJ Tel: 01736 366195 Fax: 0870 134 5647 Email: bob@steamcar.com — MRCS Eng. LRCP Lond. 1969; DObst RCOG 1971. Prev: GP Penzance.

DYKE, Tessa Nelia 4 Toronto Drive, Smallfield, Horley RH6 9RB — MB ChB 1958 Ed. (Ed.) J.P.

DYKE, Walter Robert (retired) The Granary, Talbot Lodge, North Road, Lifton PL16 0EH Tel: 01566 784108 — LMSSA Lond. 1939; MRCGP 1953. Prev: Gen. Pract. Rilla Mill.

DYKE, Wendy Anne — MB ChB 1981; MRCGP; DCH; DRCOG. (Birmingham)

DYKER, Alexander George 41 Kincardine Place, E. Kilbride, Glasgow G74 3DN — MB ChB 1991 Glas.; BSc (Hons.) Glas. 1989, MB ChB 1991; MRCP (UK) 1994.

DYKER, Elspeth Jean Chalmers Fax: 01355 906615 — MB ChB 1966 Glas. (Glas.) Socs: BMA.

DYKER, George Simpson Hunter Health Centre, Andrew Street, East Kilbride, Glasgow G74 1AD Tel: 01355 906611 Fax: 01355 906615; 4 Old Coach Road, East Kilbride, Glasgow G74 4DP Tel: 01355 220045 — MB ChB Glas. 1964; FRCP Glas. 1988; MRCP (UK) 1972; FRCGP 1987, M 1972. (Glas.) Dir. Hosp.Visit.RCGP Scotl. Socs: BMA; Roy. M-C Soc. Glas. Prev: Dep. Regional Adviser (Gen. Pract.) Univ. Glas.; Faulds Research Schol. Mat. Med. Dept. Stobhill Hosp. Glas.; Hon.sec.Scot.counc.RCGP 1997-1999.

DYKER, Karen Elizabeth Simpson 72 Lymekilns Road, East Kilbride, Glasgow G74 4TU — MB ChB 1994 Glas.; MRCP I 1996.

DYKES, Anne Cunningham 13 Ralston Road, Bearsden, Glasgow G61 3BA — MB ChB 1989 Glas.; MRCP (UK) 1992.

DYKES, Christopher James Brook House, Wychbold, Droitwich WR9 0BZ — MB ChB 1997 Manch.

DYKES, Miss Evelyn Hendry The Children's Hospital, University Hospital Lewisham, London SE13 6LH Tel: 020 8333 3136 Fax: 020 8690 1963; 5 Fairways, Kenley CR8 5HY — MB ChB 1978 Glas.; FRCS (Paediat.) 1989; FRCS Glas. 1982; FRCS Eng. 1997. (Univ. Glasgow) Sen. Lect. (Paediat. Surg.) Guys, Kings & St Thomas's Sch. of Med., King's Coll., Lond.; Assoc. Dean, Lond. Deanery. Prev: Cons. Paediat. Surg. King's Coll. Hosp. & Childr. Hosp. Lewisham; Sen. Regist. Hosp. for Sick Childr. Gt. Ormond St. Lond.; Fell. (Paediat. Surg. & Intens. Care) Hosp. Sick Childr. Toronto, Canada.

DYKES, Linda Kathleen 37 Conan Drive, Richmond DL10 4PQ Email: l.k.dykes@ncl.ac.uk — MB BS 1996 Newc.; MB BS (Hons.) Newc. 1996. (Newcastle upon Tyne)

DYKES, Paul Adrian The Old Granary, Forest Farm, Derby Road, Nottingham NG17 7QN — BM BS 1989 Nottm.

DYKES, Penelope Anne New Road Surgery, 46 New Road, Bromsgrove B60 2JS Tel: 01527 872027 Fax: 01527 574516 — MB ChB 1966 Birm.

DYKES, Peter William (retired) Chadwick Manor, Redhill Lane, Bromsgrove B61 0QF — MB ChB New Zealand 1951; MD Birm. 1964; FRCP Lond. 1972; MRCP (UK) 1955; FRACP 1968; FRCP 1972 London. Prev: Cons. Phys. United Birm. Hosp.

DYKES, Robert Malcolm 6 Overton Park Road, Cheltenham GL50 3BW — MB ChB 1932 Glas.; MA Glas. 1933, MD 1949, MB ChB 1932; DPH Wales 1938. (Univ. Glas.) Prev: Sen. Asst. MOH & Asst. Sch. Med. Off. Co. Boro. Smethwick; Maj. RAMC, DADH N. Assam.; MOH & Princip. Sch. Med. Off. Luton.

DYKES, Sheena Ritchie — MB ChB 1977 Glas.; MPhil Ed. 1988; MRCPsych 1986; MRCGP 1982; DObst. RCOG 1980. (Glasgow University) p/t Cons., Gen. Adult Psychiat. and Perinatal Psychiat., Bucks. Ment. Healthcare, NHS Trust, Aylesbury. Prev: Sen. Regist. (Gen. Psychiat.) Haleacre Unit.Amersham.Hosp; Sen. Regist. (Gen. Psychiat.) John Radcliffe Hosp. Oxf.; Sen.Reg.Gen.Psychiat.Warneford Hosp.

DYKINS, Roger James Corbridge Health Centre, Manor Court, Corbridge NE45 5JW Tel: 01434 632011 Fax: 01434 633878; White Cottage, Spoutwell Lane, Corbridge NE45 5LF — MB BS 1991 Newc.; MRCGP 1995; DRCOG 1994. (Newc. u. Tyne)

DYMOCK, Barbara Alice Roxburghe House, Royal Victoria Hospital, Dundee DD2 1SP Tel: 01382 423000 Fax: 01382423157 Email: bdymock281@aol.com; 49 Mains Loan, Dundee DD4 7AJ Tel: 01382 456184 — MB ChB 1978 Dundee. Assoc. Specialist (Palliat. Med.) Roxburghe Hse. Roy. Vict. Hosp. Dundee; Hon. Lect. Univ. Dundee.

DYMOCK, Iain William (cons. rooms), 87 Palatine Road, Manchester M20 8JQ Tel: 0161 434 3399; Ladythorn House, Ladythorn Grove, Bramhall, Stockport SK7 2HD Tel: 0161 440 9191 — MB ChB 1962 Glas.; FRCP Lond. 1984; FRCP Ed. 1974, M 1965; FRCP Glas. 1973, M 1965. (Glas.) Cons. Phys. Gastroenterol. Stepping Hill Hosp. Stockport. Socs: Fell. Manch. Med. Soc.; Brit. Soc. Gastroenterol. Prev: Sen. Lect. (Med.) Univ. Manch. & Hon.

Cons. Phys. Withington Hosp. Manch.; Lect. (Mat. Med. & Therap.) Univ. Glas.; Research Fell. MRC Liver Gp. King's Coll. Hosp. Lond.

DYMOCK, Sandra Mackenzie Ladythorn House, Ladythorn Grove, Bramhall, Stockport SK7 2HD Tel: 0161 440 9191 — MB ChB 1962 Aberd.; DA Eng. 1967; DCH RCPS Glas. 1964. (Aberd.) SCMO (Child Health) Manch. Community Health NHS Trust. Socs: Soc. Pub. Health. Prev: Regist. (Geriat. Med.) Stobhill Hosp. Glas.; Regist. (Anaesth.) Roy. Infirm. Edin.; SHO (Paediat.) Stobhill Hosp. Glas.

DYMOCK, Thomas Hillbank Health Centre, Flat 1A, 1 Constitution Street, Dundee DD3 6NF Tel: 01382 221976 Fax: 01382 201980; 49 Mains Loan, Dundee DD4 7AJ Tel: 01382 456179 — MB ChB 1979 Dundee; MRCGP 1985.

DYMOKE, James Patrick 16 Sycamore Avenue, Hatfield AL10 8LZ Tel: 017072 62509 — MRCS Eng. LRCP Lond. 1954. (Bristol) Med. Off. Welwyn Hatfield Dist. Counc. & Lee Valley Water Co. Prev: Ho. Surg. (ENT) Bristol Gen. Hosp.; Ho. Phys. (Med. & Paediat.) Pontypool Dist. Hosp.

DYMOND, Carmen Mary (retired) St David's, 11 Cyncoed Avenue, Cardiff CF23 6ST Tel: 01222 756154 — MA, BM BCh Oxf. 1952; MRCOG 1959, DObst 1954. Prev: Clin. Asst. to Prof. O & G Univ Hosp. of Wales Cardiff.

DYMOND, Donald Clive (retired) St David's, 11 Cyncoed Avenue, Cardiff CF23 6ST Tel: 01222 756154 — BSc Wales 1946, MB BCh 1949, DPH 1960; FRCGP 1979, M 1966; DObst RCOG 1951. Med. Off. (Occupat. Health) P. of Wales Hosp. Rhydlafar; Local Treasury Med. Off. Prev: Regist. O & G St. David's Hosp. Cardiff.

DYMOND, Duncan Simon 50 Wimpole Street, London W1M 7DG Tel: 020 7486 8963 Fax: 020 7486 7918 — MRCS Eng. LRCP Lond. 1972; MD Lond. 1980, MB BS 1972; FRCP Lond. 1992; MRCP (UK) 1974. (St. Bart.) Cons. Cardiol. St. Bart. Hosp. Lond.; Sen. Lect. to Barts & Roy. Lond. Hosp. Med. Sch. Socs: Fell. Amer. Coll. Cardiol.; Chairm. Europ. Soc. Cardiol. Working Gp. on Nuclear Cardiol. Prev: Sen. Regist. (Cardiol.) St. Bart. Hosp. Lond.; Asst. Prof. Med. (Cardiol. Sect.) Univ. Wisconsin Med. Sch., USA; Hon. Sec. Brit. Cardiac Soc.

DYMOND, Geoffrey Stuart 4 Bentinck Mansions, Bentinck St., London W1M 5RJ Tel: 020 7935 7678 Fax: 020 7935 6146 — MB BS 1959 Lond.; DIH Eng. 1965. (St. Bart.) Socs: Fell. Roy. Soc. Med.; BMA. Prev: Ho. Surg. (Obst.) Mile End Hosp. Lond.; Surg. Hillingdon Hosp. Uxbridge; Ho. Phys. W. Middlx. Hosp. Isleworth.

DYNAN, Caitriona Esther 29 Diamond Gardens, Belfast BT10 0HD — MB BCh BAO 1994 Belf.

DYNAN, Kevin Brendan 29 Diamond Gardens, Belfast BT10 0HD — MB BCh BAO 1993 Belf.

DYNAN, Yvonne M, Flight Lt. RAF Med. Br. 91 Broomfield Avenue, Newton Mearns, Glasgow G77 5JR Tel: 0141 639 6475 — MB ChB 1994 Manch.; BSc St. And. 1992. (Manch.) SHO (Surgic.) MDHU P'boro. Prev: Med. Off. RAF Leeming; Ho. Off. (Surg.) Manch. Roy. Infirm.; Ho. Off. (Med.) Glas. Roy. Infirm.

DYSART, John Gerald Govanhill Health Centre, 233 Calder Street, Glasgow G42 7DR Tel: 0141 531 8370 Fax: 0141 531 4431 — MB ChB 1976 Glas.; MRCGP 1980.

DYSON, Airlie Linda Macdonald Brooksbank Rickmansworth Road Surgery, 35 Rickmansworth Road, Watford WD18 7HL Tel: 01923 223232 Fax: 01923 243397 — MB BS 1975 Lond.; DFFP 1996; PhD Lond. 1972, BSc 1969; MRCGP 1980; Dip. Ven. Lond. 1984; DRCOG 1978.

DYSON, Andrew The Haven, Main St., Edingley, Newark NG22 8BG Tel: 01623 883260 — MB ChB 1981 Leeds; FFA RCS Eng. 1986. Cons. Anaesth. King's Mill Centre Mansfield. Prev: Cons. Anaesth. N.. Gen. Hosp. Sheff.; Sen. Regist. (Anaesth.) Sheff. HA; Regist. (Anaesth.) Cardiff Rotat. Train. Scheme.

DYSON, Anne Elizabeth The Surgery, Brickfields Road, South Woodham Ferrers, Chelmsford CM3 5JX Tel: 01245 328855 Fax: 01245 329849; Mayflower, Southview Road, Danbury, Chelmsford CM3 4DX — MB BS 1982 Lond.; MRCGP 1986; DRCOG 1985; Cert. Family Plann. JCC 1984. (Char. Cross) Prev: Trainee GP Redhill VTS.

DYSON, Anthony John Marley, Stubb Lane, Brede, Rye TN31 6EH Tel: 01424 883202 — BM BCh 1969 Oxf.; FRCP Lond. 1993; MRCP (UK) 1974; MRCS Eng. LRCP Lond. 1969; DCH Eng. 1972. Cons. Phys. Conquest. Hosp. St. Leonards-on-Sea. Prev: Regist. (Paediat.) Stoke Mandeville Hosp. Aylesbury; Research Fell. Brit. Thoracic & Tuberc. Assn.; Sen. Regist. St. Geo. Hosp. Sydney, Austral.

DYSON, Christopher Department of Microbiology, North Tees General Hospital, Hardwick, Stockton-on-Tees TS19 8PE Tel: 01642 617617; 13 Melingriffith Drive, Whitchurch, Cardiff CF14 2TS Tel: 02920 521162 — MB ChB 1982 Sheff.; MRCPath 1993. Cons., Med. MicroBiol., N. Tees Gen. Hosp. Prev: Sen. Regist. (Med. Microbiol.) S. Glam. HA.; Regist. (Med. Microbiol.) W. Midl. RHA.

DYSON, Edward Hugh RAF Institute of Aviation Med., Farnborough GU14 6SZ — MB BS 1977 Lond.; BA (Biochem.) Oxf. 1972, MA 1981; MRCP (UK) 1980. (Westm.) Med. Off. (Research) RAF Inst. Aviat. Med.

DYSON, Elsbeth Tegfan, Y Clogwyn, England Road S., Caernarfon LL55 1HY — BChir 1993 Camb.

DYSON, Ernest Darwent 77 Oxford Road, Abingdon OX14 2AB Tel: 01235 526021 — MB BChir 1945 Camb.; MA, MB BChir Camb. 1945. (Camb.) Radiat. &Nuclear Med. Adviser. Socs: MIEE; CEng.; Soc. Occupat. Med. & Brit. Occupat. Hyg. Soc. Prev: Research Med. Off. - Nat. Radiological Protec. Bd., Chilton; Med. Off. UKAEA Indust. Gp. HQ Risley; on Scientif. Staff Health Physics Div., AERE Harwell.

DYSON, Felicity Margaret Hay Bonnyrigg Health Centre, High Street, Bonnyrigg EH19 2DA Tel: 0131 663 7272 Fax: 0131 660 5636; 4 Midfield House, Lasswade EH18 1ED Tel: 0131 660 4456 — MB ChB 1986 Ed.; DRCOG 1991; DCH RCPS Glas. 1990; DA (UK) 1988. Partner.

DYSON, Gary David Elm Grove House, Far Common Road, Mirfield WF14 0DQ — MB ChB 1998 Manch.; MB ChB Manch 1998.

DYSON, James Anthony Park Attwood Clinic, Trimpley, Bewdley DY12 1RE Tel: 01299 861444 Fax: 01299 861375 Email: medsec.parkattwood@btinternet.com; 87 Osmaston Road, Norton, Stourbridge DY8 2AN Tel: 01384 373929 Fax: 01299 861375 — MRCS Eng. LRCP Lond. 1975. (Roy.Hosp.Sch.Med.) Assoc. Specialist (PT) Anthroposophic Med.Pk. Attwood Clinic. Nr Kidderminster. Prev: Med.Dir.Pk..Attwood Clin.

DYSON, Jennifer Lucille (retired) Flat 4, Manor Court, The Square, St Mawes, Truro TR2 5AG — MB BS 1963 Lond.; MA Oxf.; MD Lond. 1970; MRCS Eng. LRCP Lond. 1963; FRCPath 1982, M 1970. Prev: Cons. Histopath. Whittington Hosp. Lond.

DYSON, Jeremy Bentley (retired) Brook House, Adel Mill, Eccup Lane, Leeds LS16 8BF — MB ChB 1961 Leeds; FRCA Eng. 1967. Prev: Cons. Anaesth. Leeds (St. Jas.) Univ. Hosp.

DYSON, Keith c/o 1 Woodside, Shaw, Oldham OL2 8LN Tel: 01706 845682 — MB ChB 1991 Ed.; BSc (Med.) Ed. 1989. Socs: Roy. Coll. Phys.

DYSON, Lynne Lincoln House Surgery, Wolsey Road, Hemel Hempstead HP2 4TU Tel: 01442 254366 Fax: 01442 244554; Piccotts End House, 106 Piccotts End, Hemel Hempstead HP1 3AT Tel: 01442 254366 — MB BS 1975 Lond.

DYSON, Mary Downland Practice, East Lane, Chieveley, Newbury RG20 8UY Tel: 01635 248251 Fax: 01635 247261; 25 Papist Way, Cholsey, Wallingford OX10 9LL Tel: 01491 651284 Email: mary_dyson@hotmail.com — MB BS 1977 Newc.; MFFP 1993; DRCOG 1981; Cert. Prescribed Equiv. Exp. JCPTGP 1981; Cert. Family Plann. JCC 1979. (Univ. Newc. u. Tyne) GP Princip.; Family Plann. Instruc. Status 1988. Socs: Newbury Med. Soc.; Med. Grad. Soc. Univ. Newc.u. Tyne.

DYSON, Mary Pamela Lumsdaine (retired) Barton Brae, 21c South Way, Lewes BN7 1LX — MB BS Lond. 1943; MRCP Lond. 1951; MRCS Eng. LRCP Lond. 1943; DCH 1949.

DYSON, Michael Lister (retired) 172 Worcester Road, Hagley, Stourbridge DY9 0PS Tel: 01562 882198 — MRCS Eng. LRCP Lond. 1947; DMRD Eng. 1957; DMRT Eng. 1950. Prev: Radiol. Dudley AHA.

DYSON, Paul c/o Radiotherapy Department, Carlisle Infirmary, Carlisle CA2 7HY Tel: 01228 523444 Fax: 01228 814841 — MB BS 1980 Newc.; PhD Newc. 1973, BSc 1969; FRCR 1986; MRCP (UK) 1983; FRCP 2000. Cons. Radiother. & Oncol. Cumbld. Infirm. Prev: Sen. Regist. & Regist. (Radiother.) Newc. HA; SHO (Gen. Med.) Newc. Gen. & Freeman Hosps.

DYSON, Mr Peter Henry Philip 71 Park Street, London W1Y Tel: 0207 629 3763; 8 Molyneux Street, London W1H 5HP Email: dysonphp@yahoo.co.uk — MB BS 1975 Lond.; BSc Lond. 1972;

MCh (Orthop.) Liverp. 1986; FRCS Eng. 1980. (Univ. Coll. Hosp.) p/t Cons. Orthop. Surg. W. Herts. NHS Trust. Prev: Sen. Regist. Middlx. Hosp. Lond. & Roy. Nat. Orthop. Hosp.; Cons. Orthop. Surg. St Albans Hemel Hempstead & Luton & Dunstable Hosps.

DYSON, Philippa Ann (retired) 41 West Drive, Porthcawl CF36 3HS Tel: 01656 772004 Email: phillipdyson@tinyonline.co.uk — MB BChir Camb. 1946; MA Camb. 1968; MRCS Eng. LRCP Lond. 1946. JP. Prev: SCMO (Child Health) W. Dorset HA.

DYSON, Richard Paul (retired) 20 Outwoods Road, Loughborough LE11 3LY Tel: 01509 261450 — MB ChB Birm. 1951; DObst RCOG 1955. Med. Ref. LoughBoro. Crematorium. Prev: Ho. Surg. Qu. Eliz. Hosp. Birm.

DYSON, Robert Garth Bangholm Medical Centre, 21-25 Bangholm Loan, Edinburgh EH5 3AH Tel: 0131 552 7676 Fax: 0131 552 8145; 11 Inverleigh Row, Edinburgh EH3 5LS — MB ChB 1980 Ed.; FRCGP 1995, M 1984; DCCH RCP Ed. 1984; DRCOG 1983. Prev: Clin. Asst. (Geriat.) N.. Gen. Hosp. Edin.

DYSON, Simon Jan 136 Wakefield Road, Lightcliffe, Halifax HX3 8TH — MB ChB 1984 Birm.

DYSON, William Henry (retired) 38 Lochlibo Road, Lugton, Kilmarnock KA3 4DZ Tel: 01505 850663 — MB BS 1944 Lond.; MRCS Eng. LRCP Lond. 1943. Prev: Sen. Med. Off. DHSS.

DYTHAM, Annabelle Jane 24 Allingham Court, Haverstock Hill, London NW3 2AH — MB BS 1994 Lond.; BSc (Hons.) Anat. Lond. 1991.

DYTHAM, Neil Kevin Burvill House Surgery, 52 Dellfield Road, Hatfield AL10 8HP Tel: 01707 269091 — MB BS 1992 Lond.

DZENDROWSKYJ, Peter 55 Dorchester House, 228 Great Western Road, London W11 1BE — MB BS 1993 Lond.; BSc (Hons.) Lond. 1990; DA (UK) 1996. (St. Mary's Hosp. Med. Sch. Lond.) SHO (Intens. Care) Centr. Middlx. Hosp. Lond. Prev: SHO (Anaesth. & Intens. Care) Hillingdon Hosp. Uxbridge; SHO (A & E) St. Mary's Hosp. Lond.; Ho. Off. (Gen. Med. & Gen. Surg.) St. Mary's Hosp. Lond.

DZIEMIDKO, Helen Elizabeth 159 Doncaster Road, Rotherham S65 2DQ — MB BS 1977 Lond.; BA Oxf. 1974. (Middlx.) Socs: Brit. Soc. of Allergy & EnvironMent. Med; Assoc. Mem. Fac. Homoeopathy. Prev: Med. Adviser Dorling Kindersley Ltd.; Ho. Surg. City Gen. Hosp. Stoke-on-Trent; Ho. Phys. St. Geo. Hosp. Lincoln.

DZIEWANOWSKI, Roman Edward Anthony Stokes Drive Surgery, 11 Stokes Drive, Leicester LE3 9BR Tel: 0116 251 7700 Fax: 0116 253 9584; 15 Barnet Close, Oadby, Leicester LE2 5WA Tel: 0116 271 4530 — MB BS 1964 Lond. (Guy's) Socs: BMA.

DZIEWULSKI, Peter George 38 Elsley Road, Tilehurst, Reading RG31 6RP — MB BS 1984 Lond.

DZIK-JURASZ, Mr Andrzej Stanislaw Konrad 25 Wetherby Gardens, London SW5 0JR — MB BS Lond. 1987; FRCS Lond. 1991; FRCR 1995. (Westminster) Lect. Magnetic Resonance, Roy. Marsden Hosp., Sutton.

DZIKOWSKI, Wlodzimerz Kazimierz Flat nr. 1, Graylingwell House, College Lane, Chichester PO19 4PG Tel: 01243 787970 — Lekarz 1968 Gdansk; DPM Eng. 1981.

DZUMHUR, Sead 110 Grosvenor Road, Muswell Hill, London N10 2DT — Lekarz 1977 Sarajevo; Lekar Sarajevo 1977; MSc Newc. 1988. Cons. Gen. & Vasc. Surg. King Geo. Hosp. Ilford.

EABRY, Elizabeth Sara The Health Centre, Doctor Lane, Mirfield WF14 8DU Tel: 01924 495721 Fax: 01924 480605 — MB ChB 1981 Leeds; DRCOG 1986. (Leeds) GP, Mirfield, W. Yorks.; Clin. Med. Off. (Family Plann. & Child Health) Dewsbury HA. Socs: Hudds. Med. Soc.; BMA; Med. Protec. Soc. & Christian Med. Fell.sh. Prev: Trainee GP Huddersfield HA VTS; Ho. Off. (Med.) St. Jas. Hosp. Leeds; Ho. Off. (Surg.) Huddersfield Roy. Infirm.

EACOTT, Sandra Elaine (retired) 17 Vainor Road, Sheffield S6 4AP — MB ChB 1967 Sheff.; FRCPsych 1992, M 1973; DPM Eng. 1972; DObst RCOG 1969. Prev: Cons. Psychiat. Rotherham Dist. Gen. Hosp.

EAD, Russell Derek 40 Arkwright Road, Marple, Stockport SK6 7DB — MB ChB 1971 Manch.; FRCP Lond. 1988. Cons. Dermat. Salford Roy. Hosp. NHS Trust; Assoc. Lect. (Dermat.) Univ. Manch.

EADE, Oliver Edward Borders General Hospital, Melrose TD6 9BS Tel: 01896 754333 Fax: 01896 823476 — MB BS 1968 Lond.; DM Soton. 1980; FRCP Ed. 1986; MRCP (UK) 1971. Cons. Phys. Borders Gen. Hosp. Melrose; Head of Clin. Serv. Dept of Med Borders Gen Hosp Melrose. Socs: Brit. Soc. Gastroenterol. Prev: Ho. Phys. & Ho. Surg. Lond. Hosp.; Regist. (Med.) Roy. S. Hants. Hosp. Soton; Lect. (Med.) Univ. Soton.

EADE, Paul Francis West Wing, Dipple Medical Centre, Pitsea, Basildon SS13 3HQ Tel: 01268 555115; Cherry Acres, Ponds Road, Chelmsford CM2 8QP Tel: 01277 622393 — MB BS 1986 Lond.; BSc (Hons.) Lond. 1983, MB BS 1986.

EADEN, Jayne Alison Department of Medicine, Leicester Royal Infirmary, Infirmary Close, Leicester LE1 Tel: 0116 254 1414 Email: jayne.eaden@btinternet.com; Top Flat, 2 Uplands Road, Oadby, Leicester LE2 4NS Tel: 0116 271 5375 Email: jayne.eaden@btinternet.com — MB ChB 1992 Leic.; MD 2000 Leicester; MRCP (UK) 1995. (Leicester) Regist. (Gastroenterol. Med.) Leicester Roy. Infirm. NHS Trust. Prev: Regist. (Gastroenterol.med) Qu. Eliz. Hosp., Adelaide, Australia; Regist. (Gastroenterol.med) Gunfield Hosp., Leicester; Research Fell. (Gastroenterol.) Leicester Gen. Hosp., Leicester.

EADES, John Beadle (retired) Three Chimneys, 8 Peterborough Road, Castor, Peterborough PE5 7AX Tel: 01733 380220 — MRCS Eng. LRCP Lond. 1947. Prev: Ho. Surg. Co. Hosp. Orpington.

EADIE, Elizabeth Jane The Surgery, 118/120 Stanford Avenue, Brighton BN1 6FE Tel: 01273 506361 Fax: 01273 552483; Birnam, South Bank, Hassocks BN6 8JP Tel: 01273 845042 — MB BS 1972 Lond.; MRCS Eng. LRCP Lond. 1972. (Guy's) Prev: SHO (O & G) Roy. Sussex Co. Hosp. Brighton; Ho. Off. (Gyn.) Guy's Hosp. Lond.; Ho. Off. (Gen. Med.) St. Olave's Hosp. Lond.

EADIE, Mr Eric C (retired) Fairbrook, Chichele Road, Oxted RH8 0AG Tel: 01883 714022 — MB ChB 1941 Ed.; FRCS Ed. 1953. Prev: Surg. Oxted & Limpsfield Cott. Hosp.

EADIE, Gillian Briony Springhill, Coombe Lane, Kingsbridge TQ7 4AB — MB BS Lond. 1981.

EADIE, Jean Aileen 9 Garshake Road, Dumbarton G82 3LH — MB ChB 1945 Glas. (Glas.)

EADIE, Katharine Mary West Elloe House, 37 Cley Hall Drive, Spalding PE11 2EB; The Surgery, 9-11 Queen St, Whittlesey, Peterborough PE7 1AY Tel: 01733 204611 Fax: 01733 208926 — MB BS 1978 Lond.; MRCGP 1983.

EADIE, Miss Stella Paterson (retired) c/o Judge Baker, 2nd Floor N, 9 Old Square, Lincoln's Inn, London WC2A 3SR Tel: 020 7242 2633 Email: pub@global.co.uk — MB ChB 1947 Ed.; BSc 1946, MB ChB Ed. 1947; FRCS Ed. 1953; DO Eng. 1952. Prev: SHMO St. Geo. Hosp. Lond.

EADINGTON, David William Department of Renal Medicine, Hull Royal Infirmary, Anlaby Road, Hull HU3 2JZ Tel: 01482 675097 — MB ChB 1983 Ed.; FRCP 1998 London; BSc (Hons.) 1980, MD 1993; MRCP (UK) 1986; FRCP Ed. 1997. (Edinburgh) Cons. Phys. (Gen. Med. & Nephrol.) Hull Roy. Infirm.; Hon. Sen. Lect. Univ. of Hull. Socs: Eur. Dialysis & Transpl. Assn.; Scott. Renal Assn. Prev: Sen. Regist. (Gen. Med. & Nephrol.) Roy. Infirm. Edin.; Lect. (Med.) & Regist. (Nephrol.) Roy. Infirm. Edin.

EADSFORTH, Peter Moorcroft, 208 Bramhall Lane S., Bramhall, Stockport SK7 3AA — MB BS 1981 Lond.; FFA RCS Eng. 1986. Cons. Anaesth. N. Manch. Gen. Hosp.

EADY, Professor Robin Anthony Jeffery St. John's Institute of Dermatology, St. Thomas's Hospital, London SE1 7EH Tel: 020 7928 9292 Ext: 3318 Fax: 020 7922 8175 Email: r.eady@umds.ac.uk; 102 Englefield Road, London N1 3LQ — MB BS Lond. 1967; DSc (Med.) Lond. 1997; FRCP Lond. 1982, M 1970. (Guy's) Prof. Experim. Dermatopath. St. John's Inst. Dermat. Guy's, Kings & St. Thomas' Sch. of Med. Lond.; Cons. Dermat. Guy's & St. Thos. Hosp. Trust Lond.; Vice-Chairm. Div. Dermat. UMDS Guy's & St. Thos. Hosp. Lond. Socs: (Ex-Pres.) St. Johns Hosp. Dermat. Soc.; Eur. Soc. Dermat. Res.; (Ex-Pres. Sect. Dermat.) Roy. Soc. Med. Prev: Reader (Experiment. Path.) Inst. Dermat. UMDS Guy's & St. Thos. Hosp. Lond.; Sen. Fell. Biol. Struct. & Med. (Dermat.) Univ. Washington Sch. Med., USA; Regist. (Dermat.) & Ho. Phys. Guy's Hosp.

EAGGER, Sarah Anne Department of Mental Health of the Elderly, Communtiy Mental Health Unit, St Charles Hospital, Ladbroke Grove, London W10 6DZ Tel: 020 8969 2488; 19 Plympton Avenue, London NW6 7TL — MB BS 1979 Melbourne; MRCPsych 1987. Cons. Psychiat., BKCW Ment. Health NHS Trust, St. Chas. Hosp., Lond., W10; Hon. Sen. Lect. (PsychoGeriat.s), Imperial Coll. Sch. of Med. Socs: MRC Psych.; BMA; Chairpeson Brit. Holistic Med. Assn. Prev: Sen. Regist. & Research Worker

Maudsley & Bethlem Roy. Hosps. & Inst. Psychiat.; Clin. Research Fell. Inst. Neurol.

EAGLAND, Juliet Michelle The Chevin, Brafield Road, Horton, Northampton NN7 2AZ — MB ChB 1991 Birm.; MRCGP 1995; DRCOG 1994.

EAGLAND, Karen Grace Little Cliff Farm Road, Holmfirth, Huddersfield HD9 1QP — MB ChB 1992 Sheff.

EAGLE, Colin David Yardley Wood Health Centre, 401 Highfield Road, Yardley Wood, Birmingham B14 4DU Tel: 0121 474 5186 Fax: 0121 436 7648; 94 Tile House, Green Lane, Knowle, Solihull B93 9ER Tel: 01564 773832 — MB ChB 1980 Birm.; MRCGP 1986. GP; Clin. Asst. Diabetic Clinic Selly Oak Hosp. Birm.

EAGLES, Janette Isabel 41 Binghill Park, Milltimber AB13 0EE — MB ChB 1977 Aberd.; MRCPsych 1991. Staff Grade (Psychiat.) Roy. Cornhill Hosp. Aberd. Prev: SHO (Psychiat.) Kingseat Hosp. New Macher; Trainee GP Aberd.

EAGLES, John Bryan (retired) Springwood House, New Mill, Huddersfield — MB ChB 1949 Manch.; BSc (Hons. Physiol.) Manch. 1946, MB ChB 1949. Prev: Ho. Phys. Roy. Infirm. Manch.

EAGLES, John Mortimer Clerkseat Building, Royal Cornhill Hospital, Cornhill Road, Aberdeen AB25 2ZH Tel: 01224 663131 Fax: 01224 557433 Email: john.eagles@ghc.grampian.scot.nhs.uk; 41 Binghill Park, Milltimber AB13 0EE Tel: 01224 732434 — MB ChB 1977 Aberd.; MPhil Ed. 1984; FRCPsych 1995, M 1981. Cons. Psychiat. Roy. Cornhill Hosp. Aberd.; Hon.Reader (Ment. Health) Univ. Aberd. Prev: Regist. (Psychiat.) Roy. Edin. Hosp.; Lect. (Ment. Health) Univ. Aberd.

EAGLESON, Keith William Ferry Road Health Centre, Ferry Road, Dingwall IV15 9QS Tel: 01349 863034 Fax: 01349 862022; Nether Bogbain, Loch Ussie, Maryburgh, Dingwall IV7 8HJ — MB ChB 1979 Aberd.; MRCGP 1984; DRCOG 1981.

EAGLETON, Françoise Mariette Blanche 6 Hartham Close, Hartham Road, London N7 9JH Tel: 020 7607 3464 — MB BS 1970 Lond.; MRCS Eng. LRCP Lond. 1969. (Roy. Free) Clin. Asst. & Regist. (Orthop.) Hackney Hosp. Socs: Fell. Roy. Soc. Med. Prev: Ho. Surg. & Cas. Off. Roy. Free Hosp. Lond.

EAGLETON, Helen Jane John Radcliffe Hospital, Headley Way, Headingham, Oxford OX3 9DU — MB BS 1994 Newc.; MRCPath 2001; MRCP 1997. SPR Haemat., John Radcliffe Hosp.

EAGLETON, Terence Myles Flat 26, Byron Court, Mecklenburgh Square, London WC1N 2AF — MB BS 1995 Lond.

EAGLING, Miss Elizabeth Mary (retired) Punch Bowl, Dereham Road, Garvestone, Norwich NR9 4QU Tel: 01362 858580 — MB BS 1967 Lond.; FRCS Eng. (Ophth.) 1973; MRCS Eng. LRCP Lond. 1967; FCOphth 1988. Prev: Cons. Ophth. Surg. Birm. & Midl. Eye Hosp. & Selly Oak Hosp. Birm.

EAKIN, Helen Tel: 020 7622 2103 Fax: 020 7498 5206 Email: helen.eakin@gp-h58003.nhs.uk; 25 Melrose Road, Southfields, London SW18 1ND Tel: 020 8874 6239 — MB BCh BAO 1982 Belf.; DRCOG 1985. (Queen's University of Belfast) Gen. Practitioner, Battersea, Lond.

EAKIN, John Maurice High Street Surgery, 60 High Street, Lurgan, Craigavon BT66 8BA Tel: 028 3832 4591 — MB BCh BAO 1979 Belf.; DRCOG 1982.

EAKIN, Marshall David Leslie (retired) Cottage Grove Lane, 19 Bann Road, Kilrea, Coleraine BT51 5RU Tel: 02829 541326 Email: meakin65@aol.com — MB BCh BAO Belf. 1956; DObst RCOG 1958. Prev: Area Med. Off. Gen. Pract. N.. HSSB.

EAKIN, Ruth Louise 52 Upper Malone Gardens, Belfast BT9 6LY Tel: 01232 201263 Email: rleakin@compuserve.com; 19 Bann Road, Kilrea, Coleraine BT51 5RU Tel: 012665 41326 — MB ChB 1988 Bristol; MRCPI 1993; DCH RCSI 1992; FRCR 1997. (Bristol University) Regist. (Clin. Oncol.) N. Irel. Centre for Clin. Oncol. BelvoirPk. Hosp. Belf. Socs: Roy. Acad. Med. Irel.; Ulster Med. Soc. Prev: SHO (Paediat. & Med.) E. Health & Soc. Serv. Bd. NI.

EAKINS, Anna Theresa Moonfleet Cottage, East End, Lymington SO41 5SN Tel: 01590 626619 — MB BS 1987 Lond.; Dip. Obst. Auckland 1993.

EAKINS, Douglas (retired) Holly Lodge, Common Lane, North Runcton, King's Lynn PE33 0RD Tel: 01553 840744 — MB BCh BAO Belf. 1958; MD Belf. 1963; FRCPath 1978, M 1966; DObst RCOG 1960. Prev: Cons. Path. E. Anglian RHA.

EAKINS, Patrick Douglas Holly Lodge, Common Lane, North Runcton, King's Lynn PE33 0RD — MB BS 1993 Lond.

EAKINS, William Arthur, TD, CBE, KStJ (retired) 36A Malone Park, Belfast BT9 6NL Email: aeakins36a@hotmail.com — MB BCh BAO Belf. 1957; FFOM RCP Lond. 1991; FFOM RCPI 1989, M 1977; MRCGP 1968; FBIM 1981. Dean. Fac. Occ. Med. RCPI; Chairm. Somme Hosp Belf. Prev: Regional Med. Off. Post Office, BT NI.

EALAND, Winifred (retired) c/o Thorndale, Main St., Northiam, Rye TN31 6LS — MB BS 1923 Lond.; MRCS Eng. LRCP Lond. 1922. Prev: Asst. Med. Off. Rochford Hosp.

EALES, Graeme Church Lane Surgery, 1 Church Lane, Newsome, Huddersfield HD4 6JE Tel: 01484 514118 Fax: 01484 302698 — MB ChB 1982 Leeds.

EALES, Martin James Bracken House, Crewkerne Rd, Chard TA20 1YA Tel: 01460 67432 — MB BChir 1981 Camb.; PhD Lond. 1986; MA Camb. 1979; MRCPsych. 1988. Cons. Psychiat. Som. Partnership NHS & Social Care Trust; Hon. Sen. Lect. (Ment. Health) Univ. of Bristol. Prev: Sen. Regist. (Psychiat.) Maudsley Hosp. Lond.

EALES, Michael Clifford Alltwen Farm, Cae-Mansel Road, Gowerton, Swansea SA4 3HN — MB BS 1998 Lond.; MB BS Lond 1998.

EALES, Timothy David Victoria Avenue Health Centre, 36 Victoria Avenue, Porthcawl CF36 3HG Tel: 01656 783349 Fax: 01656 783899 — MB BS 1985 Lond.; MRCGP 1992; DCH RCP Lond. 1992. GP M. Glam.

EALING, John Edward Paul 9 Fulmar Court, Bicester OX26 4FG — MB BS 1994 Lond.; MB BS (Hons.) Lond. 1994; BSc Basic Med. Scs. & Biochem. (Hons.) Lond. 1991; MRCP (UK) 1997. (King's Coll. Med. & Dent. Sch.) SHO (Neurol.) Hammersmith Hosp. NHS Trust. Prev: SHO (Med.) Mayday NHS Trust; Ho. Off. (Surg.) Bromley Hosp. Kent; Ho. Phys. King's Coll. Hosp. Lond.

EALING, Katherine Mary 8 Fulmar Court, Bicester OX26 4FG — MB BS 1994 Lond.; BSc (Hons.) Lond. 1991. Trainee GP/SHO Bromley Hosps NHS Trust VTS. Socs: BMA; MDU; Med. Sickness Soc. Prev: Ho. Off. (Surg.) Mayday Hosp. Thornton Heath; Ho. Phys. Bromley & FarnBoro. Hosp. Kent.

EAMES, Amanda Mary Mowbray House Surgery, Malpus Rd, Northallerton DL7 8FW; 40 Thirsk Road, Northallerton DL6 1PH — MB BCh BAO 1984 Belf.; MRCGP 1989; DRCOG 1988; MRCP (UK) 1987. p/t GP N.allerton. Socs: LMC Represen.

EAMES, Geoffrey Michael (retired) Breton Barn, Layer Breton, Colchester CO2 0PW Tel: 01206 330273 — MB BChir 1962 Camb.; MA, MB Camb. 1962, BChir 1961; FFA RCS Eng. 1966. Cons. Anaesth. Colchester & Dist. Hosp. Gp. Prev: Sen. Regist. (Anaesth.) St. Thos. Hosp. Lond.

EAMES, Janet Kathleen Mansion House Surgery, Abbey Street, Stone ST15 8YE Tel: 01785 815555 Fax: 01785 815541 — MB BS 1982 Lond.; MRCGP 1989; DRCOG 1987.

EAMES, Jill Margaret 7 Pearman Drive, Dane End, Ware SG12 0LW Tel: 01920 438088 — MB BChir 1958 Camb.

EAMES, John Ransford Wallace House Surgery, 5-11 St. Andrew Street, Hertford SG14 1HZ Tel: 01992 550541; Ravenscroft, Heath Lane, Hertford SG13 7PT Tel: 01992 505840 — MB BChir 1961 Camb.; MB Camb. 1961, BChir 1960; MA Camb. 1961; MRCGP 1968; DPhysMed Eng. 1973; DObst RCOG 1963. (Camb. & Middlx.) Prev: Ho. Surg. Middlx. Hosp. Lond.

EAMES, Margaret Ruth Middleton, Combe Martin, Ilfracombe EX34 0LQ Tel: 01271 882427 — MB ChB Birm. 1950; MFHom RCP Lond. 1969. (Birm.) Prev: Clin. Asst. N. Devon Infirm.; SCMO & Instruc. Doctor (Family Plann.) N. Devon HA.

EAMES, Michael Harvey Alexander The See House, Cathedral Close, Armagh BT61 7EE — MB BCh BAO 1992 Belf.; MB BCh Belf. 1992.

EAMES, Michael Ronald Mill Road Surgery, Mill Road, Market Rasen LN8 3BP Tel: 01673 843556 Fax: 01673 844388 — MB BS 1974 Lond.; MRCGP 1978; DRCOG 1976.

EAMES, Niall William Adrian 3 Downshire Crescent, Hillsborough BT26 6DD — MB BCh BAO 1990 Belf.; FRCS Eng. 1994.

EAMES, Penelope Jean Victoria Leicester Royal Infirmary, Leicester LE2 7LX — MB ChB 1992 Leic.

EAMES, Peter George 45 Woodhill Road, Portishead, Bristol BS20 7EY Tel: 01275 842748 — MB BChir 1965 Camb.; MSc (Brain Studies) Brunel 1984; MA Camb. 1969; MRCP Lond. 1969; MRCPsych 1972; DPM Eng. 1970. (Camb. & Lond. Hosp.) Cons Neuropsychiat. Grafton Manor Brain Injury Rehabil. Unit N.ants.

Socs: Fell. Roy. Soc. Med.; Bristol M-C Soc.; Eur. Brain Injury Soc. Prev: Cons. Neuropsychiat. Burden Neurol. Hosp. Bristol & St. And. Hosp. N.ants; Cons. Neuropsychiat. St. Brendan's Hosp., Bermuda; Cons. Head Injury Ther. Unit Frenchay Hosp. Bristol.

EAMES, Ronald Arthur (retired) Middleton, Combe Martin, Ilfracombe EX34 0LQ Tel: 01271 882427 — MB ChB 1954 Birm.; DObst RCOG 1956.

EAMES, Rosemary Anne Department of Pathology, Queen Elizabeth Hospital, King's Lynn PE30 4ET Tel: 01553 613613; Hall House, Boughton, King's Lynn PE33 9AG Tel: 01366 500242 — MB BS 1968 Lond.; FRCP Lond. 1994; MRCP (UK) 1971; FRCPath 1991, M 1979. (St. Mary's) Cons. Histopath. Qu. Eliz. Hosp. King's Lynn. Socs: Assn. Clin. Path.; Assoc. Mem. Brit. Neuropath. Soc. Prev: Lect. (Path.) Inst. Neurol. Lond.; Regist. (Gen. Med.) Med. Unit St. Mary's Hosp. Lond.; Regist. (Neurol.) Roy. Free Hosp. Lond.

EAMES, Rosemary Sarah 3 Downshire Crescent, Hillsborough BT26 6DD — MB BCh BAO 1990 Belf.; MRCGP 1994; DRCOG 1993; DCH RCPSI 1992.

EAMES, Sara Ann 48 Honeyman Close, London NW6 7AZ Tel: 020 8830 0549 — MB ChB Bristol 1979; MFHom 1995; DGM RCP Glas. 1987. Homoeop. Specialist St. Annes Hosp. Lond.

EAMES, Stephanie Mary White Haven, Lower Frith Common, Eardiston, Tenbury Wells WR15 8JU — MB ChB 1982 Birm.; DO RCS Eng. 1987.

EAPEN, Elza Edward House, Consulting Rooms, Charter Nightingale Hospital, 7 Lisson Grove, London NW1 6SH Tel: 020 7535 7904 Fax: 020 7724 8115; Tel: 020 7935 0640 — MB BS 1978 Madras; MRCPsych. 1984. Cons. Psychiat.,Florence Nightingale Hosp.,Lond.; Cons. Psychiat., Lond. Socs: Fell. Roy. Soc. of Med.

EAPEN, Susan 11 Hillcote Close, Sheffield S10 3PT — MB BS 1988 Lond.

EAPEN, Valsamma 226 Colney Hatch Lane, Mangalam, St Georges Road, Bickley, Bromley BR1 2LD; UAE University, PO Box 17666, Al-Ain, United Arab Emirates — MB BS 1989 Kerala; PhD Lond. 1995; MRCPsych 1992. Prev: Lect. (Child Psychiat.) Univ. Coll. Lond. Med. Sch.

EARDLEY, Andrew John Nicholas 43 Cranbourne Drive, Harpenden AL5 1RJ — MB ChB 1966 Manch.; DA Eng. 1969. (Manch.)

EARDLEY, Gillian Ruth 166 Park Road, Kingston upon Thames KT2 5LP; 335 Kelvindale Road, Glasgow G12 0QU Tel: 0141 334 5573 — MB BS 1991 Lond.; MRCGP 1995; DRCOG 1993. Clin. Asst. (Drug Misuse) Glas. Drug Probl. Serv. Gtr. Glas. Community & Ment. Health Servs. Trust. Socs: BMA.

EARDLEY, Helen Louise 2 The Nurseries, Pant, Oswestry SY10 8JS — MB ChB 1990 Manch.

EARDLEY, Mr Ian Department of Urology, St James University Hospital, Baker St, Leeds LS27 Tel: 0113 206 6994 Fax: 0113 206 4920; 8 Wharfe Grove, Wetherby LS22 6HA Tel: 01937 582158 — MB BChir 1981 Camb.; MA Camb. 1983, MChir 1991; FRCS (Urol.) Eng. 1991; FRCS Eng. 1986; FEBU 1992. (Addenbrooke's Hosp.) Cons. Urol. Leeds Gen. Infirm. & St. Jas. Univ. Hosp. Leeds. Prev: Sen. Regist. (Urol.) Norf. & Norwich Hosp. Hosp.; Sen. Regist. (Urol.) Addenbrookes Hosp. Camb.; Clin. Research Fell. St. Bart. Hosp. Lond.

EARDLEY, Kevin Sean Queen Elizabeth Hospital, University Hospital Birmingham NHS Trust, Edgbaston, Birmingham B15 2T — MB ChB 1994 Birm.; MRCP (UK) 1997. Specialist Regist. (Renal & Gen. Med.).

EARDLEY, Marilyn 10 Woodbank Lane, Holywood BT18 0QA Tel: 01232 422655 — MB BCh BAO 1978 Belf.; MRCGP 1982; DCH Lond 1980; DRCOG London 1981. CMO Community Child Health N. & W. Belf. Community Trust Belf.

EARDLEY, Mary Louise Davenal House Surgery, 28 Birmingham Rd, Bromsgrove B61 0DD — MB ChB 1994 Birm.; MRCGP 2001; DFFP 1999; DRCOG 1997. p/t GP Retainer; Clin. Asst. in G.U. Med.

EARDLEY, Nicola Jayne 28 Hallville Road, Allerton, Liverpool L18 0HR — MB ChB 1998 Liverp.; MB ChB Liverp 1998. SHO Hersey Deanery Surgic. Rotat. Prev: PRHO Roy. Liverp. Univ. Hosp.

EARDLEY, Richard Clive Eardley and Partners, Biddulph Medical Centre, Well Street, Biddulph, Stoke-on-Trent ST8 6HD Tel: 01782 512822 Fax: 01782 510331; The Hollies, 108 West Road, Congleton CW12 4EU — MB ChB 1972 Leeds.

EARDLEY, Robin Arthur Anthony South Boduel Farm, Moorswater, Liskeard PL14 4JZ Tel: 01579 347702 — MRCS Eng. LRCP Lond. 1963. (Sheff.) Indep. Pract. Acupunc. Liskeard; Exam. Med. Pract. War Pens. Agency. Socs: Brit. Med. Acupunct. Soc.; Plymouth Med. Soc.; FRSM. Prev: Regional Med. Off. DoH; GP. Onchan I. of Man; GP Colne, Lancs.

EARDLEY, Ruth Elizabeth Market Harborough Medical Centre, Market Harborough LE16 9BX — MB ChB 1984 Leic.; MB ChB Leic. l984.

EARDLEY, William Grant Philip 76 Newmarket Road, Redcar TS10 2JA — MB ChB 1998 Aberd.; MB ChB Aberd 1998.

EARIS, John Edward Aintree Chest Centre, University Hospital Aintree, Longmoor Lane, Liverpool L9 7AL Tel: 0151 529 3654 Fax: 0151 529 2873 Email: earis@liverpool.ac.uk; 32 Brome Way, Bebington, Wirral CH63 9ND — MB BS 1970 Lond.; MD Lond. 1983; FRCP Lond. 1989; MRCP (UK) 1975. Cons. Phys. Univ. Hosp. Aintree & Aintree Chest Centre; Hon. Sen. Lect. Liverp. Univ. Prev: Sen. Regist. BRd.green Hosp. Liverp.; Clin. Tutor Hope Hosp. Manch. Univ.; Clin. Lect. Liverp. Univ.

EARL, Albert John (retired) 47 Beveridge Street, Barrow-upon-Soar, Loughborough LE12 8PL Tel: 01509 416494 — MB BChir Camb. 1958; MA Camb. 1958; MRCS Eng. LRCP Lond. 1958; MRCGP 1969; DA Eng. 1963. Prev: GP Barrow upon Soar.

EARL, Christopher Francis 15 Coniston Avenue, Whickham, Newcastle upon Tyne NE16 4ER — MB BS 1994 Lond.

EARL, Christopher Joseph 23 Audley Road, Ealing, London W5 3ES Tel: 020 8997 0380 — MB BS Lond. 1948; MD Lond. 1951; FRCP Lond. 1964, M 1950; FRCOpth. 1994. (Guy's) Hon. Cons. Phys. (Neurol.) Middlx. Hosp., Nat. Hosp. Qu. Sq. & Moorfields Eye Hosp. Lond.; Hon. Cons. Neurol. Hosp. St. John & Eliz. Socs: (Ex-Pres.) Assn. Brit. Neurol.; Corr. Mem. Amer. Neurol. Assn.; Fell. Roy. Soc. Med. (Ex.-Pres. Sect. of Neurol.). Prev: Phys. Neurol. Dept. Lond. Hosp.; Civil Cons. (Neurol.) RAF; Censor RCP.

EARL, David Frederick Highcroft Villas Medical Practice, 50 Highcroft Villas, Brighton BN1 5PT — MB BChir 1972 Camb.; MA Camb. 1972; MRCGP 1979; DObst RCOG 1974. Prev: Trainee GP Brighton VTS; Ho. Surg. (O & G) & Ho. Phys. (Cardiol. & Gen. Med.) Middlx. Hosp.

EARL, David Steven 26 Ingleside Road, North Shields NE29 9PB Email: earl@btinternet.com — MB ChB 1994 Bristol; 2001 FRCA; BSc Bristol 1991; MRCP (Uk) 1997. (Bristol) SHO in Anaesth. Roy. Lond. & St Bartholemews Hosp.; SPR in Anaesth., S. W. Rotat. Prev: Med. SHO Derriford Hosp., Plymouth; SHO in Anaesth, Derriford Hosp, Plym.

EARL, Helena Margaret Department of Oncology, University of Cambridge, Addenbrooke's Hospital Box 193 Hills Road, Cambridge CB2 2QQ Tel: 01223 274312 Fax: 01223 412213; 62 Marshall Road, Cambridge CB1 7TY Tel: 01223 411822 — MB BS 1977 Lond.; PhD Lond. 1988; FRCP (UK) 1997; MRCP (UK) 1979; MRCS Eng. LRCP Lond. 1977. (Guy's) Clin. Lect. (Med. Oncol.) Univ. Camb. & Hon. Cons. Med. Oncol. Addenbrooke's Hosp. Camb. Socs: Assn. Cancer Phys.; Eur. Soc. Med. Oncol. Prev: Sen. Lect. (Med. Oncol.) Univ. Birm. & Hon. Cons. Med. Oncol. City Hosp. Dudley Rd. & Qu. Eliz. Hosp. Birm.; Sen. Regist. (Oncol. & Gen. Med.) Univ. Coll. Lond. Med. Sch.; Clin. Scientist Ludwig Inst. Cancer Research (Lond. Br.).

EARL, Margaret Rosemary (retired) The Chestnuts, 47 Beveridge St., Barrow-upon-Soar, Loughborough LE12 8PL Tel: 01509 416494 — MB BChir 1958 Camb.; MA Camb. 1958; MRCS Eng. LRCP Lond. 1958. Prev: Gen. Med. Practit. LoughBoro.

EARL, Mr Philip David Oral and Facial Department, Worcester Royal Infirmary, Castle St., Worcester WR1 3AS Tel: 01905 760179 Fax: 01905 760213 Email: phillip.earl@worsacute.wmids.nhs.uk; 35 Showell Close, Droitwich WR9 8UQ Tel: 01905 797826 Fax: 01905 798520 Email: philearlfdsfrcs@aol.com — MB BS 1987 Newc.; 2000 FDS RCS Eng.; BDS Lond. 1977; FDS RCS Ed. 1982; FRCS Ed. 1991. (Newc. u. Tyne) Cons. Oral & Maxillofacial Surg. Worcs. Roy. Infirm.; Hon. Med. Off. Bedworth United Football Club; Examr. (Oral Surg.) for Fell.sh. in Dent. Surg. of RCS Edin. Socs: Fell. Brit. Assn. Oral & Maxillofacial Surg.; Eur. Assn. Cranio-Maxillo. Surg.; BMA. Prev: Sen. Regist. (Oral & Maxillofacial Surg.) NW Rotat.; Regist. (Oral & Maxillofacial Surg.) Bolton Gen. Hosp. & Sunderland Dist. Gen. Hosp.

EARL, Robert Charles 17 Gosforth Crescent, Dronfield S18 1PT — MB BS 1998 Lond.; MB BS Lond 1998.

EARL, Ursula Mary York House, 9 South Terrace, Skelton-in-Cleveland, Saltburn-by-the-Sea TS12 2EW — MB ChB 1981 Sheff.; BMedSci Sheff. 1979, MB ChB 1981; MRCPath 1988. (Sheff.) Cons. Histopath./Cytopath. Darlington Memor. Hosp.

EARLAM, Anthony David Plas-y-Bryn, Chapel St., Wrexham LL13 7DE Tel: 01978 351308 — MB ChB 1975 Manch.; DRCOG 1978. Med. Off. Clwyd Family Plann. Serv. & Mersey Regional Blood Transfus Serv. Socs: Assn. Police Surgs. Gt. Brit.; Fell. Roy. Soc. Med. Prev: Ho. Surg. Salford Roy. Infirm. Salford AHA (T); SHO (O & G) Pk. Hosp. Trafford AHA; SHO (Anaesth.) Univ. Unit Manch Roy. Infirm. Manch. Centr. AHA.

EARLAM, Christine Mary 12 Dean Drive, Wilmslow SK9 2EP — MB ChB 1971 Manch.; FFA RCS Eng. 1977.

EARLAM, Lawrence (retired) Lisroan, Fluin Lane, Frodsham, Warrington WA6 7QX Tel: 01928 32335 — MRCS Eng. LRCP Lond. 1925; MD Liverp. 1930, MB ChB 1925. Prev: Cas. Off. Roy. S. Hosp. Liverp.

EARLAM, Mr Richard John The Royal London Hospital, Whitechapel, London E1 1BB Tel: 020 7377 7439 Fax: 020 7377 7439; 4 Pembroke Gardens, London W8 6HS Tel: 020 7602 5255 Fax: 020 7602 5255 — MB BChir Camb. 1959; MA Camb. 1959, MChir 1970; FRCS Eng. 1964; MRCS Eng. LRCP Lond. 1958. (Camb. & Liverp.) Cons. Surg. Lond. Hosp. Socs: Examr. Surg. RCS Eng.; Brit. Soc. Gastroenterol. & Coll. Internat. Chir. Dig. Prev: Ho. Surg. Liverp. Roy. Infirm.; Research Asst. Mayo Clinic, USA; Asst. Chir. Klinik Munchen, Germany.

EARLE, Anne Mary 2 Woodcombe Cottages, Minehead TA24 8SE Tel: 0643 704825 — MB ChB Bristol 1949.

EARLE, Elspeth Margaret Orchard Dene, Hunton Road, Chainhurst, Marden, Tonbridge TN12 9SL — MB BS 1969 Lond.; MRCPsych 1973; DPM Eng. 1972. (Lond. Hosp.) Psychother. Oakwood Hosp. Maidstone Kent S.E. Thames RHA. Socs: Assoc. Mem. Brit. Psycho-Analyt. Soc. Prev: Cons. Psychiat. Qu. Charlotte's Matern. Hosp. Lond.; Child Psychiat. Middlx. Hosp. Lond.; Sen. Regist. Dept. Child Psychiat. Middlx. Hosp. & Child Guid.

EARLE, James Henry Oliver (retired) 18 Hillside, Wimbledon, London SW19 4NL Tel: 020 8946 3507 — MB BS 1946 Lond.; MD Lond. 1952; MRCS Eng. LRCP Lond. 1946; FRCPath 1964. Prev: Cons. Path. Qu. Mary's Hosp. Roehampton.

EARLE, John Vavasour (retired) Hailey Cottage, Hailey Lane, Hertford SG13 7NY Tel: 01992 462467 — MB BChir 1949 Camb.; 1949 MB BChir Camb.; 1975 MRCGP; 1972 MFCM; 1976 Dip Ven Soc. Apoth. Lond.; 1967 DPH Lond.; 1968 DIH Eng.

EARLE, Ruth Caroline 59 The Gables, Walton Road, Wisbech PE13 3EP — MB BS 1981 Lond.

EARLEY, Alison Rosemary Coyle Wycombe General Hospital, High Wycombe HP11 2TT Tel: 01494 562 6161; Northcott, Chiltern Road, Chesham Bois, Amersham HP6 5PH Tel: 01494 431652 — MB BS 1974 Lond.; FRCP Lond. 1995; MRCP (UK) 1976; MRCS Eng. LRCP Lond. 1974. (Roy. Free) Cons. Paediat. Wycombe Gen. Hosp. Bucks. Prev: Sen. Regist. (Paediat.) N.wick Pk. Hosp. Harrow; Research Fell. Cardiothoracic Unit Brompton Hosp. Lond.; Regist. (Paediat.) St. Mary's Hosp. Lond.

EARLEY, Mark Andrew Caerleon, Mont Sohier, St Brelade, Jersey JE3 8EA — MB ChB 1987 Manch.

EARLEY, Mark James 13 Rushmere Walk, Havant PO9 4LY — MB ChB 1993 Bristol.

***EARLEY, Michelle Anne** 13 Rushmere Walk, Warren Park, Havant PO9 4LY — MB ChB 1996 Birm.

EARLEY, Olivia Grangemore, Boyle, County Roscommon, Republic of Ireland; 1 Annadale Avenue, Apt. 4, Belfast BT7 3JH Tel: 01232 641403 — MB BCh BAO 1980 NUI; FCOphth 1987. Sen. Regist. (Ophth.) St. Thos. Hosp. Lond. Socs: Train. Acad. Ophth. Prev: Research Fell. Duke Univ. NC, USA; Sen. Regist. (Ophth.) Roy. Vict. Hosp. Belf.

EARLY, Alan Stephen X-Ray Department, Hull Royal Infirmary, Anlaby Road, Hull HU3 2JZ Tel: 01482 328541 Fax: 01482 674614 Email: ase@neutrino.demon.co.uk; 21 Westella Road, Kirkella, Hull HU10 7QD Tel: 01482 653280 — MB BS 1965 Lond.; FRCR 1975; FFR 1973; DMRD Eng. 1971. (Univ. Coll. Hosp.) Cons. Radiol. Hull Roy. Infirm. Prev: Sen. Regist. (Radiol.) Roy. Vict. Infirm. Newc.; SHO (Surg.) Doncaster Roy. Infirm.; Ho. Off. (Gen. Med. & Gen. Surg.) N. Ormesby Hosp. Middlesbrough.

EARLY, Ann Elisabeth Hermons Hill House, Haverfordwest SA61 1PT Tel: 01437 66546 — MB ChB 1972 Sheff.; MRCGP 1980.

EARLY, Donal Felix Mary The Old Rectory, Wapley Hill, Westerleigh, Bristol BS37 8RJ Tel: 01454 312929 — LRCPI & LM, LRSCI & LM 1941; LRCPI & LM, LRCSI & LM 1941; FRCPsych 1971; DPH NUI 1943; DPM RCPSI 1945; LM Rotunda 1942. Emerit. Cons. Psychiat. Bristol. Socs: BMA. Prev: Cons. Psychiat. Glenside Hosp. & S.mead Hosp. Bristol; SHO (Surg.) Vict. Hosp. Blackpool; Ho. Phys. Meath Hosp. Dub.

EARLY, Kay The Orrell Park Surgery, 46 Moss Lane, Orrell Park, Liverpool L9 8AL Tel: 0151 525 2736 Fax: 0151 524 1037; 29 Eshe Road N., Crosby, Liverpool L23 8UE Tel: 0151 924 5935 — MB ChB 1961 Sheff. (Sheff.) Socs: Liverp. Med. Comm.

EARLY, Nigel Edward Early, The New Surgery, Church Street, Ashover, Chesterfield S45 0ER Tel: 01246 590711 Fax: 01246 590738 — MB ChB Leeds 1962; DObst RCOG 1966. Socs: Disp. Doctors Assn.; BMA; NACGP. Prev: Clin. Asst. (Obst.) Doncaster Roy. Infirm.; Trainer Doncaster VTS; Indust. Med. Off. Hawker Siddeley.

EARLY, Mr Peter Francis (retired) 4 Wilkin Croft, Cheadle Hulme, Cheadle SK8 6SD Tel: 0161 485 2095 — MB BChir 1943 Camb.; FRCS Eng. 1954. Prev: Sen. Med. Off. DHSS Limb. Fitting Serv.

EARLY, Prudence Elizabeth (retired) The Old rectory, Wapley, Chipping Sodbury, Bristol BS37 8RJ — MB BCh BAO 1951 Dub. Prev: Med. Off. Day Centre Glenside Hosp. Stapleton.

EARNSHAW, Christopher John Wakefield and Partners, Lever Chambers Centre for Health, 1st Floor, Ashburner Street, Bolton BL1 1SQ Tel: 01204 360030/31 Fax: 01204 360033 — MB ChB 1993 Liverp.

EARNSHAW, Daniel Peter 27 The Spinney, Blackburn BB2 7BN — MB ChB 1997 Leeds.

EARNSHAW, David Anthony (retired) Hall Field House, Earl Shilton, Leicester LE9 7DH Tel: 01455 840050 — MRCS Eng. LRCP Lond. 1955; MA Camb. 1958, BA 1952, MB BChir 1955; FRCGP 1987, M 1969. Prev: GP Earl Shilton.

EARNSHAW, David Harold Ambleside Health Centre, Rydal Road, Ambleside LA22 9BP Tel: 015394 32693 Fax: 015394 32520 — MB ChB 1967 Liverp.

EARNSHAW, Geoffrey Lambeth Walk Group Practice, 5 Lambeth Walk, London SE11 6SP Tel: 020 7735 4412 Fax: 020 7820 1888; 4 Manor Court, Back Lane, Morcott, Oakham LE15 9DG — BM BS 1991 Nottm.; BMedSci Nottm. 1989; MRCP (UK) 1994; DTM & H Liverp. 1994; DFFP 1997; MRCGP 1998. Clin. Lect. Primary Care & Pub. Health; GP Regist. E. Surrey. Prev: GP Regist. E. Surrey; SHO Rotat. (Med.) Nottm. City Hosp.; Pub. Health Trainee.

EARNSHAW, Mrs Gillian Jane (retired) Hall Field House, Earl Shiton, Leicester LE9 7DH Tel: 01455 840050 — MB BChir 1955 Camb.; BA Camb. 1952, MB BChir 1955. Prev: GP Stoney Stanton.

EARNSHAW, Gregory 69 Whinlatter Drive, Barrow-in-Furness LA14 4NR — MB BS 1976 Lond.; MRCS Eng. LRCP Lond. 1976. (Guy's)

EARNSHAW, John Harold, TD (Surgery), 2 Church St., Sutton-on-Hull, Hull HU7 4TT Tel: 01482 826457 — MB ChB 1960 Manch. DL.

EARNSHAW, Mr Jonothan James Gloucestershire Royal Hospital, Great Western Road, Gloucester GL1 3NN Tel: 01452 394190 Fax: 01452 790100; Rudford House, Rudford, Gloucester GL2 8DT Tel: 01452 790651 Fax: 01452 790100 Email: earnshaw@rudford.demon.co.uk — MB BS 1979 Lond.; DM Nottm. 1988; FRCS Eng. 1984. Cons. Surg. Glos. Roy. Hosp.; Edr. Brit. Jl. Surg. Socs: Fell. Assn. Surgs.; Coun. Mem. Vasc. Surg. Soc. Prev: Sen. Regist. (Surg.) Bristol Roy. Infirm. & SW Region; Regist. Rotat. (Surg.) Nottm. & Mansfield; Regist. (Vasc. Research) Univ. Hosp. Nottm.

EARNSHAW, Mary Ann Greenridge, Farnley Mount, Durham DH1 4DZ — MB ChB 1976 Ed.; MRCGP 1990; DRCOG 1987.

EARNSHAW, Mr Peter Howard Department of Orthopaedic Surgery, Guy's Hospital, London Bridge, London SE1 9RT Tel: 020 7955 5000 — MB BS 1976 Lond.; FRCSC 1982; MRCS Eng LRCP Lond. 1976; FRCS (Eng.) 1998. (Guys Hosp.) Cons. Orthop. Surg.

Guy's & St. Thos. Trust Lond. Socs: Fell. Amer. Bd. Orthopedic Surg. 1988.

EARNSHAW, Philip Moxon — MB ChB 1974 Ed.; FRCP Lond. 1993; FRCP Ed. 1988; MRCP (UK) 1978; DRCOG 1976. (Edinburgh) Cons. Phys. Dryburn Hosp. Durh. Prev: Sen. Regist. (Geriat. & Med.) Freeman Hosp. Newc.

EARNSHAW, Phillip Ferrybridge Medical Centre, 8-10 High Street, Ferrybridge, Wakefield WF11 8NQ Tel: 01977 672109 Fax: 01977 671107; 4 Park Lane Close, Womersley, Doncaster DN6 9QB Tel: 01977 620680 Email: philearnshaw@compuserve.com — MB BS 1984 Lond.; DRCOG 1988. (St. Bartholomew's) Chairm. Wakefield & Pontefract Dist. GP's on call Ltd. (GP Co-op.).

EARNSHAW, Stephen Mark 2A Avon Road, Billinge, Wigan WN5 7QU — MB ChB 1989 Liverp. Regist. (Child Psychiat.) Warrington Dist. Gen. Hosp. Prev: Regist. (Psychogeriat.) Leighton Hosp.; SHO (Gen. Psychiat.) Whiston Hosp.

EARNSHAW, Mr Steven Andrew 75 Central Avenue, New Basford, Nottingham NG7 7AG Tel: 0115 962 5015 Email: s.earnshaw@dial.pipex.com; 9 Fir Heath Close, Foxwood Lane, York YO24 3JY Tel: 01904 792330 — MB ChB 1992 Sheff.; FRCS (Eng.) 1997; DM Nottm. 1997. (Sheff.) Specialist Regist. (Orthop.) Derbysh. Roy. Infirm. Derby. Socs: Nat. Osteoporosis Soc.; BMA. Prev: SHO (Orthop.) Qu.s Med. Centre Nottm.; Clin. Research Fell. (Orthop.) City Hosp. Nottm.; SHO (Neurosurg.) Walton Hosp. Liverp.

EARNSHAW, Thomas Gordon 23 Fern Bank, Scotforth, Lancaster LA1 4TT — MB ChB 1998 Sheff.; MB ChB Sheff 1998.

EARP, Annette Dominique Family Planning Clinic, Macclesfield District General Hospital, West Park Branch, Macclesfield SK10 3BL Tel: 01625 661169; 1 Bluebell Close, Macclesfield SK10 2JN Tel: 01625 611833 — MB ChB 1974 Manch.; MFFP 1993. Clin. Med. Off. E. Chesh. NHS Trust.

EARWICKER, Helen Margaret Radford Health Centre, 1 Ilkeston Road, Radford, Nottingham NG7 3GW — MB BS 1981 Lond.; MA Camb. 1977; MRCGP 1985; DRCOG 1985. (Univ. Coll.) Prev: Trainee GP Nottm. VTS; Ho. Phys. & Ho. Surg. Rochford Gen. Hosp. Essex.

EARWICKER, Stephen Charles Earwicker and Partners, The Health Centre, 97 Derby Road, Stapleford, Nottingham NG9 7AT Tel: 0115 939 2444 Fax: 0115 939 5625 — MB BS 1981 Lond.; BSc Lond. 1978; MPH Nottm. 1995; MRCGP 1985; DRCOG 1984. (Westm.) Chairm. Broxtowe & Hucknall PCG. Prev: Trainee GP Nottm. VTS; Ho. Surg. & Ho. Phys. Rochford Hosp. Essex.

EASBY, Barbara York Health Services Trust, Acomb Health Centre, 1 Beech Grove, Acomb, York YO26 5LD — MB BS 1983 Lond.; MRCPysch; M.Med.Sc.; M.psycho. Cons. Psych.

EASBY, Jason 12 Carlbury Avenue, Middlesbrough TS5 8SE — MB ChB 1994 Dundee.

EASMON, Charles John 101A Pimlico Road, London SW1W 8PH Tel: 0207 727508 Email: easmon@aol.com; Foreign and Commonwealth Office, 1 Palace St., London SW1E 5HE Tel: 020 7238 4774 — MB BS 1984 Lond.; MSc (Pub. Health Med.) Lond. 1994; MRCP (UK) 1990; DTM & H Liverp. 1995. (St. Geo. Hosp. Lond.) Med. Adviser Foreign & Commonw. Office; Pub. Health Adviser Lond. Health Economics Consortium. Socs: Roy. Soc. Trop. Med. & Hyg.; Fell. Roy. Inst. Pub. Health and Hyg. Prev: Med. Co-ordinator Merlin Rwanda.

EASMON, Charles Syrett Farrell British Postrgraduate Medical Federation, 33 Millman St., London WC1N 3EJ; 21 Cranes Park Avenue, Surbiton KT5 8BS — MRCS Eng. LRCP Lond. 1969; PhD Lond. 1975, MD 1981, MB BS 1969; MRCPath 1976. Prof. Med. Microbiol. St. Mary's Hosp. Med. Sch.

EASON, Alexander Robert Rankin (retired) Ellerlee, 39 Alexandra St., Kirkintilloch, Glasgow G66 1HE Tel: 0141 776 3838 — MB ChB 1955 St. And. Prev: Med. Supt. Broomhill Hosp. Kirkintilloch.

EASON, John Richard (retired) c/o Mr & Mrs Thorn, 41 Palace Road, Bromley BR1 3JU — MB BCh 1975 Camb.; MA Camb. 1976, MB BCh 1975; MRCP (UK) 1983; FFA RCS Eng. 1981. Sen. Lect. & Hon. Cons. (Anaesth. & Inten. Care) King's Coll. Hosp. Lond.

EASON, Jonathan Richard Mayday Healthcare NHS Trust, Croydon Eye Unit Manday Hospital, London Road, Croydon CR7 7YE; 9 Fryern Wood, Caterham CR3 5AR — MB BS 1981 Lond.; DO RCS Eng. 1989. Assoc. Specialist Croydon Eye Unit Mayday Healthcare NHS Trust Thornton Heath. Prev: Staff Grade Ophth. Croydon Eye Unit Thornton Heath.

EASON, Julian David Jenny Hind Childrens Department, Norfolk & Norwich Univ. Hosp, Colney Lane, Norwich NR4 7OZ Tel: 01603 287174 Fax: 01603 287584 Email: julian.eason@norfolk-norwich.thenhs.com; The River House, Skinners Lane, Wroxham, Norwich NR12 8SJ Tel: 01603 781466 Fax: 01603 781466 Email: julian@fisheas.freeserve.co.uk — MB BS 1986 Lond.; FRCPCH 1997; BSc (Hons.) Lond. 1983; MRCP (UK) 1990; FRCP Canada 1995; DCH RCP Lond. 1990. (Middlx. Hosp.) Cons. Paediat. & Neonatology Gen. Hosp. Norf. & Norwich Hosp.; Hon. Sen. Lect. Univ. of E. Anglia. Socs: Brit. Assn. of Peri-natal Med. Prev: Cons. Paediat. & Neonat. Gen. Hosp. St. Helier Jersey; Research Fell. BC's Childr.s's Hosp. Vancouver; Sen. Regist. (Nephrol., PICU) Guy's Hosp. Lond.

EASON, Scott MacDonald Flat 1/2, 3 Camphill Avenue, Glasgow G41 3AU — MB ChB 1994 Ed.

EASPARATHASAN, Vanathi Poorany 6 Cardinals Walk, Taplow, Maidenhead SL6 0LN — MB BS 1994 Lond.

EASSON, Mary Teresa Blackwoods Medical Centre, 8 Station Road, Muirhead, Glasgow G69 9EE Tel: 0141 779 2228 Fax: 0141 779 3225; 12 Coltmuir Drive, Bishopbriggs, Glasgow G64 2SU — MB ChB 1983 Glas.; MRCGP 1987; DCH RCP Lond. 1986; DRCOG 1986.

EASSON, William Thomas Tel: 0161 456 5205/2764 Fax: 0161 487 4472 — MB ChB Manch. 1965; FRCR 1975; FFR 1972; DMRD Eng. 1969. (Manch.) Hon. Cons. Socs: BMA. Prev: Hon. Clin. Teach. (Radiol.) Univ. Manch.; Cons radiol Stockport.

EAST, Anthony Michael Peter Queensway Medical Centre, Poulton-Le-Fylde, Blackpool FY4 7ST — MB BS 1980 Lond. SHO (Paediat.) Derby Childr. Hosp.

EAST, Brian Arthur (retired) 16 Fluder Hill, Kingskerswell, Newton Abbot TQ12 5JD Tel: 01803 872597 — MRCS Eng. LRCP Lond. 1952. Prev: Sen. Ho. Phys. St. Richard's Hosp. Chichester.

EAST, Mr Charles Anthony 150 Harley Street, London W1G 7LQ Tel: 020 7935 7435 Fax: 020 7935 3635; 17 Burlington Road, Chiswick, London W4 4BQ Tel: 020 8994 3514 — MB BS 1980 Lond.; FRCS Eng. 1986. (Char. Cross Hosp.) Cons. Surg. Roy. Nat. Throat, Nose & Ear Hosp. Lond. Roy. Free Hampstead NHS Trust. Prev: Sen. Fell. Univ. Washington, USA 1989; Sen. Regist. (ENT) Univ. Coll. & Middlx. Hosps. Lond. & Hon. Sen. Regist. Nat. Hosp. Nerv. Dis. Lond.

EAST, Mr David Murray 189 Green Lanes, Sutton Coldfield B73 5LX Tel: 0121 580 7406 Fax: 0121 686 5893 Email: dmeast@aol.com — MB 1971 Camb.; MA; BChir 1970; FRCS Eng. 1976. (Westm.) Cons. ENT Surg. Manor Hosp. Walsall. Socs: Found. Mem. Europ. Acad. Otol. & Neurol.; Midl. Inst. Otol.; Politzer Soc. Prev: Cons. ENT Surg. ScarBoro. Hosp.; Rotat. Sen. Regist. Newc. AHA (T); Regist. Eye, Ear & Throat Hosp. Shrewsbury.

EAST, John Anthony, MBE, Col. late RAMC Retd. Murray House, 5 Vandon Street, London SW1H 0AN Tel: 020 7593 5300 Fax: 020 7593 5301 Email: jeast@bmihs.co.uk; Bethesda, 33 St. Mark's Road, Salisbury SP1 3AY Tel: 01722 333572 — MB BCh BAO 1969 Belf.; MFOM 1983; DAMed. Eng. 1975. Dir of Occupat.al Health, BMI Health Serv.s Lond. Prev: Cons. Occup. Phys. PO. Employee. Health Serv. E.ern. Territories; Col. Army Med. Directorate MoD.

EAST, Kevin Richard St Albans Medical Centre, 26-28 St. Albans Crescent, Bournemouth BH8 9EW Tel: 01202 517333 Fax: 01202 517336 — MB BS 1976 Lond.; MRCS Eng. LRCP Lond. 1976. (St. Bart.) Med. Off. & Adviser AFC Bournemouth Football Club. Socs: Brit. Assn. Sport & Med. & Roy. Soc. Med. & Dent. Hypn. Prev: Regist. (O & G) & SHO Roy. Vict. Hosp. Bournemouth; SHO (Trauma & Orthop.) Bristol Roy. Infirm & Poole Gen. Hosp.; Ho. Surg. & Ho. Phys. St. Mary's Hosp. Newport.

EAST, Malcolm Richard Field House Medical Centre, 13 Dudley Street, Grimsby DN31 2AE Tel: 01472 350327; Westfield House, Main Road, Barnoldby le Beck, Grimsby DN37 0BG Tel: 01472 821837 — MB ChB 1973 Dundee; Dip. Occ. Med. RCP Lond. 1996. Fact. Med. Off. Ct.aulds plc Grimsby; Clin. Asst. (Dent. Anaesth. & Cardiol.) Grimsby Dist. Hosp.; Med. Adviser Reckitt & Coleman, Hull; Med. Adviser Occupat. Health St Hughs Hosp. Grimsby; Med. Adviser NE Lincs. Counc. Socs: Assoc. Mem. Assn. Anaesth. GB & Irel. Prev: Police Surg. Grimsby.

EAST, Michael O'Neill (retired) 2 Matthews Oast, Plough Lane, Upper Harbledown, Canterbury CT2 9AR Tel: 01227 463440 Fax: 01227 463440 Email: east@moneast.demon.co.uk — MB BS 1954 Lond.; DObst RCOG 1958. Cons. Clin. Quality Assur. & Data Audit. Prev: Dir. Europ. Clin. Research & Developm. Controller Clin. QA Pfizer Centr. Research.

EAST, Miranda Marion 19 High Street, Trumpington, Cambridge CB2 2HA — MB BS 1965 Lond.; MRCS Eng. LRCP Lond. 1965; DObst RCOG 1967. (Univ. Coll. Hosp.) SCMO (Community Child Health) Cambs. HA. Socs: BMA.

EAST, Rowena Mary Giffords Surgery, 28 Lowbourne, Melksham SN12 7EA Tel: 01225 703370; 2 Patney Weir, Chirton, Devizes SN10 3QU Tel: 01380 840761 — MB ChB 1975 Manch.

EAST, Samantha Jayne 56 Broome Grove, Wivenhoe, Colchester CO7 9QU — MB BS 1996 Lond.; DRCOG; DCH. GP Locum. Prev: Ho. Off. (Surg.) Colchester Gen. Hosp.; Ho. Off. (Med.) Qu. Mary's Hosp. Roehampton; SHO (A & E) Ashford Gen. Hosp. Middlx.

EAST, Sarah Kathryn Inverclyde Royal Hospital, Greenock PA16 0XN; Lower Ground Flat, 54 St Vincent Crescent, Finnieston, Glasgow G3 8NQ Tel: 0141 221 2772 — MB BCh 1994 Wales. SHO (Cas.) Inverclyde Roy. Hosp. Greenock. Prev: SHO (Geriat.) Vict. Geriat. Unit Glas.; Ho. Off. (Surg.) Inverclyde Roy. Hosp. Greenock; Ho. Off. (Med.) P. Chas. Hosp. Merthyr Tydfil.

EASTAUGH, Andrew Nathaniel Southwold Surgery, York Road, Southwold IP18 6AN Tel: 01502 722326 Fax: 01502 724708 — MB BS 1978 Lond.; FRCP 2001; MA (Univ. East Anglia) 1997; FRCGP 1996; MRCP (UK) 19811981; MRCS Eng. LRCP Lond. 1978; MRCGP 1983. (Char. Cross) GP Princip. E.augh Castle S.wold; GP Tutor S. Waveney. Prev: CRMF/RCGP Facilitator Palliat. Care. 1992-1994; SHO & Regist. Rotat. (Gen. Med.) United Norwich Hosps.

EASTAUGH-WARING, Mr Stephen John University Department Orthopaedic Surgery, Bristol Royal Infirmary, Bristol BS2 8HW Tel: 0117 928 2568 Fax: 0117 929 4217 Email: stewaring@hotmail.com; Overbridge Cottage, Back St, Chipping Sodbury, Bristol BS37 6A2 Tel: 01454 882712 — MB ChB 1992 Sheff.; FRCS Eng 1996. Specialist Regist. Orthop. & Trauma SW Rotat. Bristol Roy. Infirm. Bristol; Lect. Orthop. Surg. Socs: Brit. Orthop. Train. Assn.; BMA; Brit. Orthop. Assn. Prev: Sen. SHO, Orthop. Cheltenham DGH Surgic. Rotat. Frenchay Hosp. Bristol.

EASTAWAY, Anne Terry 1 Brookside, Cuddington, Northwich CW8 2QA — MB ChB 1981 Sheff.

EASTAWAY, James Andrew 13 Alcester Crescent, London E5 9PX — MB ChB 1989 Ed.

EASTCOTT, Mr Harry Hubert Grayson The Lindo wing, St Mary's Hospital, London W2 1NY; 47 Chiltern Court, Baker St, London NW1 5SP Tel: 0207 935 2020 Fax: 0207 486 4084 Email: hhgevasc@clara.net — MB BS (Hons.) Lond. 1941; MS Lond. 1951; FRCS Eng. 1946; MRCS Eng. LRCP Lond. 1941; Hon. FACS 1977; Hon. FRACS 1978; FRCOG 1981. (St. Mary's) Consg. Surg. St. Mary's Hosp. Lond.; Emerit. Cons. Surg. & Vasc. Surg. to RN. Socs: Fell. (Ex-Pres.) Assn. Surgs. GB & Irel.; Fell. Roy. Soc. Med. (Hon. Mem., Ex-Pres. & Edit. Represen. Sect.Surg., Ex-Pres. United Servs. Sect.); Fell. (Ex-Pres.) & Trustee Med. Soc. Lond. (Fothergill Gold Medal 1974). Prev: Cons. Surg. St. Mary's, Roy. Masonic Hosps & King Edwd. VII Hosp. Offs. Lond.; Mem. (Counc.) RCS Eng. 1971-83 & Vice Pres. 1981-93; Surgic Research Fell. Harvard Med. Sch. & Peter Bent Brigham Hosp.

EASTCOTT, Howard Robin Morello, Cherry Lane, Bolney, Haywards Heath RH17 5PR — MB ChB 1974 Otago.

EASTELL, Professor Richard Department of Human Metabolism & Clinical Biochemistry, Clinical Sciences Centre, Northern General Hospital, Herries Road, Sheffield S5 7AU Tel: 0114 271 4705 Fax: 0114 261 8775 Email: r.eastell@sheffield.ac.uk; 289 Ringinglow Road, Bents Green, Sheffield S11 7PZ — MB ChB 1977 Ed.; BSc (Hons.) Ed. 1974; MD Ed. 1984; FRCP 1996, M 1981. (Ed.) Prof. & Hon. Cons. Human Metab. & Clin. Biochem. Univ. Sheff. Socs: Sec. Bone & Tooth Soc.; (Progr. Comm.) Amer. Soc. Bone & Mineral Research.; (Organising Comm.) Europ. Soc. for Calcified Tissues. Prev: MRC Research Fell. Edin.; Regist. (Med.) Harrow; Research Assoc. Mayo Clinic Rochester.

EASTER, Mr Hedley John 2 Braehead Farm Court, Shotts Road, Fauldhouse, Bathgate EH47 9DN — MB ChB 1975 Ed.; FRCS (Orthop.) Ed. 1990; FRCS Ed. 1981. Cons. Orthop. Surg. Law Hosp. NHS Trust Carluke.

EASTER, Ronald Arthur The Alfred Salter Medical Centre, 6 Drummond Road, London SE16 4BU Tel: 020 7237 1857 — MRCS Eng. LRCP Lond. 1969. (Roy. Free) Med. Off. Rehabil. Centre for Former Drug Abusers Lond. Exam. Med. Off. 1st Aid Metrop Police; Med. Off. Canad. High Commiss.; Cons. Med. Adviser Roy. Lond. Gp. Mutual Provident & Insur. Socs.; Clin. Tutor (Gen. Pract.) Guy's & St. Thos. Med. & Dent. Sch. Lond.; Hon. Med. Adviser Lond. City Mission; Med. Off. Salvation Army Mens Hostel Lond. Prev: Ho. Surg. (Obst.) Roy. Free Hosp. Lond.; Ho. Phys. & Ho. Surg. Mildmay Mission Hosp. Lond.

EASTERBROOK, Professor Philippa Jane Kings College Hospital, Caldecot Centre, 15-22 Caldecot Road, London SE5 9RS Tel: 020 7346 4891; 7 Cyprus Terrace, St Peter's Road, Oxford OX2 8AT — MB 1983 Camb.; BChir 1982; MPH John Hopkins USA 1989; BSc (Hons.) Lond. 1980; MRCP (UK) 1985; DTM & H RCP Lond. 1994. Prof. (HIV Med.) Kings Coll. Sch. Med. Prev: Sen. Lect. & Cons. Phys. (Infec. Dis.) Chelsea & W.m. Hosp. Lond.; Sen. Regist. (Med.) Chelsea & W.m. Hosp. Lond.; Clin. Research Wellcome Trust Fell. (Med.) John Hopkins Univ. Sch. Med., USA.

EASTERBROOKE, Caroline Zoe Primrose Cottage, 6 The Culverhay, Wotton-under-Edge GL12 7LS — BM 1983 Soton.; FRCSI Ed. 1985; FRCA II Lond. 1997, I 1996; Dip. Sports Med. Lond 1991. (Soton.) Staff Grade (Anasth.) Frenchay Hosp. Bristol. Socs: Assn. Anaesth. GB & Irel.

EASTERBROOKE, Simon Jonathan Bramble Farm Cottage, French Mill Lane, Shaftesbury SP7 8EU — MB BS 1989 Lond.

EASTES, Mr Claude Neville d'Este (retired) Smugglers Hut, Greyfriars Lane, Storrington, Pulborough RH20 4HE Tel: 01903 745420 — MB BS 1948 Lond.; FRCS Eng. 1955; LMSSA Lond. 1942; DLO Eng. 1949. Hon. Cons. ENT Surg. Roy. Sussex Co. Hosp., Alexandra Hosp.; Childr. Brighton, Worthing Hosp. & S.lands Hosp. Shoreham-by-Sea. Prev: Chief Asst. Ear & Throat Dept. Guy's Hosp. Lond.

EASTES, Henry James (retired) Moons Close, Sheepfair Lane, Marshfield, Chippenham SN14 8NA Tel: 01225 891464 — MB BS 1937 Lond.; MRCS Eng. LRCP Lond. 1937; FRCGP 1973, M 1957. Prev: Ho. Phys., Obst. Ho. Surg. & Obst. Anaesth. Univ. Coll. Hosp.

EASTGATE, John William Marlborough House Adolescent Unit, Princess Margaret Hospital, Okus Road, Swindon SN1 4JU Tel: 01793 428800 Fax: 01793 428823; Baywards Ash Farm, Wootton Bassett, Swindon SN4 8DT — MB ChB 1973 Bristol; MRCPsych 1977; DCH Eng. 1975; FRCPsych 1998. Child & Adolesc. Psychiat. Swindon & MarlBoro. NHS Trust.

EASTHAM, David George 116 Otley Road, Leeds LS16 5JX — MB ChB 1962 Leeds; MRCGP 1972; DCH Eng. 1971. (Leeds)

EASTHAM, Edmund John Department Child Health, Royal Victoria Infirmary, Newcastle upon Tyne NE1 4LP Tel: 0191 232 5131 Fax: 0191 261 5881; 4 Bridge Park, Gosforth, Newcastle upon Tyne NE3 2DX Tel: 0191 285 4904 — MB BS Newc. 1969; FRCP Lond. 1987; FRCPCH 1997. Cons. Paediat. Gastroenterol. Newc. HA. Socs: Brit. Paediat. Assn. & Brit. Soc. Gastroenterol.; Eur. Soc. Paediat. Gastroenterol. & Nutrit. Prev: Clin. & Research Fell. Paediat. Gastrointestinal Unit Mass. Gen. Hosp. Boston, USA.

EASTHOPE, Mary Edith (retired) 4 Salterns Close, Hayling Island PO11 9PL Tel: 023 9246 4892 — MB ChB 1944 Ed.

EASTLEY, Jacqueline Rebecca Ann 5 Shakespeare Avenue, Bear Flat, Bath BA2 4RF — MB BS 1986 Lond.

EASTLEY, Roger James Department Anaesthesia, Royal Infirmary, Leicester LE1 5WW Tel: 0116 541414 — MB BCh 1977 Wales; FFA RCS (Eng.) 1982. (Cardiff) Cons. Anaesth. Univ. Hosp.s of Leicester NHS Trust; Hon. Clin. Teach. Univ. Leicester. Socs: Hist. Anaesth. Soc.; Soc. Burns & Plastic Surg. Anaesth.; Assn. of Anaesth.s. Prev: Lect. Anaesth. Univ. Calgary, Canada; Staff Anaesth. Foothills Hosp., Alberta Childr. Hosp. Calgary, Canada; Sen. Regist. (Anaesth.) Leicester Roy. Infirm.

EASTMAN, Frank Vincett 37 Shirehampton Road, Bristol BS9 1BL — MB ChB 1950 Bristol.

EASTMAN, Karen Elizabeth The Brow Surgery, The Brow, Burgess Hill RH15 9BS Tel: 01444 246123 Fax: 01444 232199 — MB BS 1992 Lond.; MRCGP 1997; DRCOG 1995; DFFP 1997. GP The Brow Surg. Prev: Trainee GP/SHO P.ss Roy. Hosp. Haywards Heath.

EASTMAN, Professor Nigel Lyons Gwynne Section of Forensic Psychiatry, St. George's Hospital Medical School, London SW17 0RE

Tel: 020 8725 5567 Fax: 020 8725 2475 Email: neastman@sghms.ac.uk — MB ChB 1979 Bristol; BSc (Econ) Lond. 1968; FRCPsych 1996; MRCPsych 1984; Barrister at Law Grays Inn 1976; MD Lond 2000. (Bristol) Sen. Lect. & Cons. Forens. Psychiat. St. Geo. Hosp. Med. Sch. Lond. Prev: Sen. Regist. (Forens. Psychiat.) Bethlem Roy. & Maudsley Hosps. Lond.; Regist. (Psychiat.) Warneford Hosp. Oxf.; SHO (Neurol. & Neurosurg.) Addenbrooke's Hosp. Camb.

EASTMAN, Stuart Vincett St Melor Surgery, St Melor House, Edwards Road, Amesbury, Salisbury SP4 7LT Tel: 01980 622474 Fax: 01980 622475; Browns Farm House, College Road, Durrington, Salisbury SP4 8AW Tel: 01980 654259 — MB ChB 1984 Birm.; DRCOG 1988. GP Amesbury; Med. Off. Holidays for Disabled People.

EASTMOND, Clifford John Department of Rheumatology, Aberdeen Royal Infirmary, Foresterhill, Aberdeen AB32 2ZN Tel: 01224 681818; The Rowans, Skene AB32 6YP — MB ChB 1969 Ed.; MD Ed. 1979; FRCP Lond. 1990; FRCP Ed. 1984; MRCP (UK) 1973. (Ed.) Cons. Rheum. Assoc.med.dir. Grampian Univ.Hosp.Trust; Hon. Sen. Lect. (Med.) Univ. Aberd. Socs: Fell (Ex-Pres.) Roy. Med. Soc. Edin.; Brit. Soc. Rheum. Prev: Sen. Regist. (Rheum. & Rehabil.) Gen. Infirm. Leeds; Research Fell. Rheum. Research Unit Leeds Med. Sch.; Research Fell. (Med.) Univ. Liverp.

EASTON, Alasdair Iain McLellan Carnoustie Medical Group, The Health Centre, Dundee Street, Carnoustie DD7 7RB Tel: 01241 859888 Fax: 01241 852080; Edenbank, 1 William St, Carnoustie DD7 6DG Tel: 01241 853445 — MB ChB 1979 Dundee; MRCGP 1983; DRCOG 1981.

EASTON, Mr Alfred Leonard Tytherleigh (retired) 612 Gilbert House, Barbican, London EC2Y 8BD Tel: 020 7638 0781 — MB BChir 1945 Camb.; MD Camb. 1958; FRCS Eng. 1954; MRCS Eng. LRCP Lond. 1945; FRCOG 1965, M 1954. Hon. Cons. O & G Surg. Roy. Lond. Hosp. Prev: Examr. Univ. Lond.

EASTON, Andrew Maurice Ekstein Roundhay Wing, St James's Hospital, Beckett St., Leeds LS9 7TF Tel: 0113 243 3144 Fax: 0113 234 7275 — MB BS 1983 Lond.; BSc Lond. 1980, MMedSc 1988; MRCPsych 1987; T(Psych) 1992. Cons. Psychiat. s/i Rehabil. St. Jas. Univ. Hosp. Leeds. Prev: Cons. Psychiat. Huddersfield NHS Trust; Regist. & SHO (Psychiat.) Leeds VTS; Ho. Phys. Middlx. Hosp. Lond.

EASTON, Caroline Susan 19 Fairmile, Henley-on-Thames RG9 2JR — MB BS 1992 Newc.

EASTON, Daphne Veronica Marjorie Grianan, 30 Hazeldean Avenue, Bo'ness EH51 0NS Tel: 01506 822302 Fax: 01506 822302 — MB ChB Ed. 1952.

EASTON, David Alan Halliday Huntly Health Centre, Jubilee Hospital, Bleachfield Street, Huntly AB54 8EX Tel: 01466 792116 Fax: 01466 794699; Cluny, Victoria Road, Huntly AB54 8AH Tel: 01466 792276 Email: david.easton@huntly.grampian.scot.nhs.uk — MB ChB 1982 Dundee; BSc (Hons.) Dund 1978, MB ChB 1982; DRCOG 1986. Hosp. Med. Dir. Jubilee Hosp. Huntly.

EASTON, David Morton Basildon Hospital, Basildon SS16 5NL Tel: 01268 593524 Fax: 01268 593194 — MB BS 1965 Lond.; FRCP Lond. 1994; MRCP (UK) 1969; MRCS Eng. LRCP Lond. 1965; FRCPCH 1997; FRACP 1980; DCH Eng. 1970. (Westm.) Cons. Paediat. Basildon & Thurrock NHS Trust. Socs: BMA. Prev: Cons. Paediat. Hawkes Bay Hosp. Bd. NZ; Sen. Regist. (Paediat.) Bristol Childr. Hosp.; Regist. (Paediat.) Hosp. Sick Childr. Lond.

EASTON, Euan Alexander 48 Park Mews, Roslin Place, Aberdeen AB24 5BL — MB ChB 1992 Glas.

EASTON, Graham Paul Tel: 0208 748 1065 — MB BS 1990 Lond.; MSc (Distinc.) Univ. Lond. 1995. (Lond. Hosp. Med. Coll.) Gen. Practioner; Sen. BRd.cast Jl.ist BBC Radio Sci. Socs: Fell. Roy. Soc. Med; GP Writers Assn. Prev: Trainee GP Oxf. VTS.

EASTON, Herbert Gordon (retired) Molendinar, Ferryfield Road, Connel, Oban PA37 1SR — MD 1954 Glas.; MB ChB 1939. Prev: Phys. Ruchill Fev. Hosp. Glas.

EASTON, Janet Christina (retired) 51 Aytoun Road, Pollokshields, Glasgow G41 5HW Tel: 0141 423 4305 — MB ChB 1952 Glas.; FFA RCS Eng. 1966; DA Eng. 1954. Prev: Cons. Anaesth. Inst. Neurol. Scs. S.. Gen. Hosp. Glas.

EASTON, Jeffrey Anthony Harcourt Medical Centre, Crane Bridge Road, Salisbury SP2 7TD Tel: 01722 333214 Fax: 01722 421643 — MB BS 1975 Lond.; BSc (Physiol.) Lond. 1972. (Univ. Coll. Lond. & Univ. Coll. Hosp.) GP Salisbury; Med. Off. Cathedral Sch. Salisbury; Med. Off Acting Company Salisbury PlayHo.; Prescribing Lead S. Wilts. PCT. Socs: Salisbury Med. Soc.; BMA. Prev: Regist. St. Thos. Hosp. Lond.; SHO (Phys.) Hammersmith Hosp. Lond.; Ho. Phys. Univ. Coll. Hosp. Lond.

EASTON, John Archibald (retired) Frenham, Old Beaconsfield Road, Farnham Common, Slough SL2 3LR Tel: 01753 643979 — MB BS 1956 Lond.; FRCPath 1976, M 1964; DPath Eng. 1964. Prev: Cons. Haemat. Wexham Pk. Hosp. Slough & E. Berks. Dist. Hosps.

EASTON, Lindsay James Crosbie The Rowans, High Street, Errol, Perth PH2 7QJ Tel: 01738 642248 Fax: 01738 642922 — MB ChB Dundee 1978.

EASTON, Paul Jake Weston General Hospital, Grange Road, Uphill, Weston Super Mare BS23 4TQ — MB BS 1993 Lond.; BSc (Hons.) Basic Med. Sci. & Pharmacol. Sci. Lond. 1990; MRCP. SHO Rotat. (Med.) Worcester Roy. Infirm.; Specialist Regist. (Geriat./Gen. Med.) S.-W. Region. Socs: Brit. Geriat. Soc.

EASTWOOD, Alan Stuart Yorkshire Street Surgery, 190 Yorkshire Street, Rochdale OL16 2DN Tel: 01706 644973/5 — MB ChB 1971 Manch.; MRCS Eng. LRCP Lond. 1971. (Manch.) Prev: Ho. Off. (Gen Surg.) Rochdale Infirm.; Ho. Off. (Gen. Med.) & SHO (O & G) Birch Hill Hosp. Rochdale.

EASTWOOD, Arthur Brian (retired) 12 Alton Grove, Heaton, Bradford BD9 5QL Tel: 01274 544621 — MRCS Eng. LRCP Lond. 1945; DA Eng. 1947; FFA RCS Eng. 1953.

EASTWOOD, Carolyn Jane 2 Orchard Lea, Sherfield-on-Loddon, Basingstoke RG27 0ES — MB ChB 1992 Birm.

EASTWOOD, Deborah Margaret Department of Orthopaedics, Royal Free Hospital, Pond St., London NW3 2QG Tel: 020 7794 0500 Fax: 020 7830 2947; 1 Julia Street, Oak Village, London NW5 4QJ Tel: 020 7267 9326 — MB ChB 1980 Birm.; FRCS Eng. 1984. (Birmingham) Cons. Orthop. Surg. Roy. Free Hosp., Roy. Nat. Orthop. Hosp. & Stanmore Hosp. Lond.; Edr.ialBooks JBJS INJURY. Prev: Sen. Regist. Bristol/SW RHA.

EASTWOOD, Derek Arrowe Park Hospital, Arrowe Park Road, Upton, Wirral CH49 5PE Tel: 0151 604 7056 Fax: 0151 604 7126; East Grange, 154 Caldy Road, Caldy, Wirral CH48 1LN Tel: 0151 625 2851 Fax: 0151 625 2851 Email: dreastwood@aol.com — MB ChB 1972 Liverp.; MRCS Eng. LRCP Lond. 1972; FFA RCSI 1977; FFA RCS Eng. 1977. (Liverp.) Cons. Pain Specialist & Anaesth. Arrowe Pk. Hosp.; Course Organiser & Lect. Nat. Symp. & Pain After Surg. 1990-98. Socs: Pain Soc.; BMA; Working Party for Acute Pain. Prev: Cons. Anaesth. Clatterbridge & Arrowe Pk. Hosps.; Sen. Regist. Mersey RHA; Regist. Liverp. AHA (T).

EASTWOOD, Mr Deryk Sandford 11 North Park Road, Leeds LS8 1JD Tel: 0113 661287 — MB BChir 1950 Camb.; FRCS Ed. 1959. Prev: Cons. Plastic Surg. Leeds (St. Jas.) Univ. Hosp. & United Leeds Hosps.

EASTWOOD, Gillian Louise Flat 6, Spath Holme, Holme Road, Manchester M20 2TX — MB ChB 1994 Manch.

EASTWOOD, Grace 262 Hardhorn Road, Poulton-le-Fylde FY6 8DW — MB ChB 1995 Manch.; DCH (London 1998). (Manchester)

EASTWOOD, Hugh Douglas Hurry (retired) 14 Brookvale Road, Southampton SO17 1QP — MB BS 1958 Lond.; FRCP Lond. 1980, M 1969; MRCP Ed. 1968. Prev: Cons. Geriat. Med. Soton. Gen. Hosp.

EASTWOOD, Ian Quarmby Temple Cowley Health Centre, Templar House, Temple Road, Oxford OX4 2HL Tel: 01865 777024 Fax: 01865 777548; High Bank, 71 Oxford Road, Garsington, Oxford OX44 9AD Tel: 01865 361205 — MB BS 1968 Lond.; MRCGP 1976; DObst RCOG 1973. (Middlx) Tutor (Gen. Pract.) Univ. Oxf. Med. Sch. Prev: Ho. Surg. Middlx. Hosp. Lond.; Ho. Phys. Lond. Chest Hosp.; SHO St. Mary's Hosp. Lond.

EASTWOOD, Jenny (retired) Hill House, North Queensferry, Inverkeithing KY11 1JJ Tel: 01383 417059 — MB ChB 1960 Ed.; FRCPsych 1990, M 1979; Dip. Soc. Med. Ed. 1970. Prev: Cons. Psychiat. Whytemans Brae Hosp. Kirkcaldy Fife.

EASTWOOD, Joanne Rachel 3 Meadowfield Road, Stocksfield NE43 7QX — BM BS 1992 Nottm.

EASTWOOD, John Bannister Department of Renal Medicine, St. George's Hospital, Blackshaw Road, London SW17 0QT Tel: 020 8725 1738 Fax: 020 8725 2068 Email: jbeastwood@compuserve.com — MB BS 1964 Lond.; MD Lond.

1975, MB BS 1964; FRCP Lond. 1982; M 1968; MRCS Eng. LRCP Lond. 1964; DObst RCOG 1966. (Char. Cross) Cons. Renal. & Sen. Lect. St. Geo. Hosp. & Med. Sch. Lond.; Dean Pre-regist. Studies St. Geos.Hosp. Med. Sch. Socs: Assn. of Phys.s of Gt. Britain & Irel.; Internat. Soc. Nephrol. Prev: Lect. (Med.) Char. Cross Hosp. Lond.; Sen. Regist. Univ. Ghana Med. Sch., Accra.

EASTWOOD, John Jamieson Hurry (retired) 1 Meadway, Rustington, Littlehampton BN16 2DD Tel: 01903 785998 — MB BS 1952 Lond.; DCH Eng. 1955. GP Staff Mem. Littlehampton Cott. Hosp. & Zachery Merton Community Hosp. Rustington. Prev: SHO Childr. Unit, Dryburn Hosp. Durh.

EASTWOOD, Jonathan Mark College Lane Surgery, Barnsley Road, Ackworth, Pontefract WF7 7HZ Tel: 01977 611023 Fax: 01977 612146; 33 Wenthill Close, Ashworth, Pontefract WF7 7LP Tel: 01977 602736 — MB ChB 1990 Birm.; BSc Birm. 1987; MRCGP 1994. Prev: Trainee GP Lancaster.

EASTWOOD, Louise Harriet 12 Royal Avenue, Great Yarmouth NR30 4EB — BSc (Physiol.) Leeds 1965, MB ChB 1968; DCH RCP Lond. 1989; DA Eng. 1970. Sen. Clin. Med. Off. Gt. Yarmouth & Waveney HA. Prev: Regist. (Paediat.) Sheff. Childr. Hosp.; Deptm. Med. Off. St. Helens & Knowsley AHA; Regist. Anaesth. Leeds Gen. Infirm.

EASTWOOD, Martin Anthony (retired) Hill House, North Queensferry KY11 1JJ — MB ChB Ed. 1960; MSc Ed. 1965; FRCP Ed. 1972, M 1966. Prev: Cons. Gastroenterol. W.. Gen. Hosp. Edin.

EASTWOOD, Nigel Barry Department of Anaesthesia, City General Hospital, Newcastle Road, Stoke-on-Trent ST4 6QG Tel: 01782 552883 Fax: 01782 552893 Email: nigel.eastwood@mailcity.com — MB BS 1986 Lond.; BSc (Hons.) Lond. 1983; FRCA 1992. (St. Bart.) Cons. Anaesth. N. Staffs Hosp. Stoke-on-Trent. Socs: Anaesth. Res. Soc.; Intens. Care Soc.; Soc. Critical Care Med. Prev: Vis. Assoc. Prof. Duke Univ. Med. Center Durh. NC, USA; Sen. Regist. Mersey Region; Research Fell (Clin.) Univ. Liverp.

EASTWOOD, Nigel John Bromley Forensic Department, St Lawrence Hospital, Bodmin PL31 2QT Tel: 01208 251349 — MB BChir 1985 Camb.; MA Camb. 1986; MRCGP 1994; MRCPsych 1992; DFFP 1994. (Cambridge) Cons. Psychiat.

EASTWOOD, Peter George Austhorpe Road Surgery, 15 Austhorpe Road, Cross Gates, Leeds LS15 8BA Tel: 0113 295 1820 Fax: 0113 295 1822 — MB ChB 1980 Leeds; MRCGP 1984; Cert. Family Plann. JCC 1983.

EASTWOOD, Philip Roger c/o Northgate Hospital, Northgate St., Great Yarmouth NR30 1BU Tel: 01493 330054 Fax: 01493 337648 — MB ChB 1968 Leeds; MB ChB Leeds. 1968; MRCPsych 1972; DPM Leeds 1971. Cons. Old Age Psychiat. Norf. Ment. Health Care NHS Trust. Prev: on Staff MRC Unit Dept. Psychiat. Univ. Sheff.; Sen. Regist. Liverp. RHB; Regist (Psychiat.) Univ. Leeds.

EASTY, Adrian Michael (retired) 11 Park Road, Pendleton, Salford M6 8HN Tel: 0161 789 5186 Fax: 0161 787 9684 — MB ChB Manch. 1956; DObst RCOG 1958; MRCGP 1968.

EASTY, Mr David Bristol Eye Hospital, Lower Maudlin St., Bristol BS1 2LX Tel: 0117 928 4827 Fax: 0117 925 1421; 42 Clifton Park Road, Bristol BS8 3HN — MB ChB 1959 Manch.; MD Manch. 1963; FRCS Eng. 1969; MRCS Eng. LRCP Lond. 1959; FCOphth 1989; DO Eng. 1966. (Manch.) Prof. & Head Dept. Ophth. Univ. Bristol; Hon. Cons. Bristol Eye Hosp.; Dir. CTS Eye Bank. Socs: BMA; Coll. Ophth. Roy. Soc. Med. Prev: Lect. (Clin. Ophth.) Moorfields Eye Hosp. Lond.; Med. Off. Brit. Antarctic Survey Expedit. Halley Bay 1961-2; Demonst. (Anat.) Univ. Witwatersrand, Johannesburg.

EASTY, Marina Jovanka 42 Clifton Park Road, Bristol BS8 3HN — MB BS 1990 Lond.

EASWAR, Meda Dasanna Mayfair Medical Centre, 8 Normanhurst Avenue, Bexleyheath DA7 4TT Tel: 020 8304 0786; 7 Dukes Orchard, Bexley DA5 2DU — MB BS Andhra 1965. Socs: Med. Protec. Soc.

EASY, Amanda Joyce 73 Mill Road, Ballyclare BT39 9DZ — MB BS 1997 Lond.

EASY, William Richard, Wing Cdr. RAF Med. Br. Retd. Department of Anaesthetics, Vale of Leven Hospital, Alexandria G83 0UA Tel: 01389 754121 Fax: 01389 603915; Easter Auchincarroch Farm, By Gartocharn, Alexandria G83 9LU Tel: 01389 751718 — MB ChB 1970 Ed.; BSc Ed. 1967; FFA RCS Eng. 1983; DA Eng. 1978; DCH Eng. 1975. (Ed.) Cons. Anaesth. Vale of Leven Hosp. Strathclyde.; Hon. Clin. Sen. Lect. Glas. Univ. Socs: (Counc.) Scott. Intens. Care Soc. Prev: Cons. P.ss Mary's RAF Hosp. Halton.; Sen. Regist. Nuffield Dept. Anaesth. Oxf.

EATOCK, Christopher Robert Department of Anaesthesia, Wishaw General Hospital, Wishaw M6 0DP Tel: 01698 361100 Email: christopher.eatock@laht.scot.nhs.uk — MB BS Lond. 1969; FRCA 1974; FFA RCSI 1974. (The Royal London Hospital) Cons. Anaesth. Wishaw Gen. Hosp., Wishaw. Socs: BMA; Assn. Anaesths. Prev: Ho. Surg. Poplar Hosp.; Ho. Phys. & Regist. (Anaesth.) St. Margt. Hosp. Epping; Sen. Regist. Nuffield Dept. Anaesth. Radcliffe Infirm. Oxf.

EATOCK, Elizabeth Mary Horton General Hospital NHS Trust, Oxford Road, Banbury OX16 9AL Tel: 01295 229223; Fernleigh, 11 Whittall St, Kings Sutton, Banbury OX17 3RD — BM BCh 1968 Oxf.; MA Oxf. 1994, BA 1965; MRCP (UK) 1979; DCH Eng. 1972. (Lond. Hosp.) Assoc. Specialist (Haemat.) Horton Hosp. NHS Trust Banbury; Research Off. (Med.) Childh. Cancer Research Gp. Oxf. Prev: Sen. Regist. John Radcliffe Hosp. Oxf.; SHO (Med.) Barking Hosp.; Ho. Phys. Lond. Hosp.

EATOCK, Fiona Campbell 12 Whithorn Crescent, Moodiesburn, Chryston, Glasgow G69 0HR — MB ChB 1992 Glas.; FRCS RCPS Glas. 1997. Research Fell. (Gen. Surg.) Univ. Dept. Surg. Glas. Roy. Infirm. Prev: SHO (Gen. Surg.) Falkirk & Distr. Roy. Infirm.; SHO (Gen. Surg.) Glas. Roy. Infirm.; SHO (Gen. Surg.) Vict. Hosp. Kirkcaldy.

EATON, Mr Alan Charles Department of Surgery, Queen Elizabeth Hospital, Gayton Road, King's Lynn PE30 4ET Tel: 01553 613692 — MRCS Eng. LRCP Lond. 1974; BSc (Biochem., 1st cl. Hons.) Lond. 1971, MB BS (Hons. Obst. & Gyn.) 1974; FRCS Eng. 1979. (St. Thos.) Bard Medal Brit. Assn. Urol. Surgs. 1981; Cons. Surg. Qu. Eliz. Hosp. King's Lynn & N. Camb. Hosp. Wisbech. Socs: Brit. Assn. Urol. Surgs. Prev: Sen. Regist. (Urol.) Norf. & Norwich Hosp. & Addenbrooke's Hosp.; Camb.; Regist. (Surg.) Univ. Hosp. Nottm.

EATON, Alison Helen Grange House Surgery, 22 Grange Road, Hartlepool TS26 8JB Tel: 01429 272679 Fax: 01429 861265 — MB ChB 1985 Aberd.; MRCGP 1989.

EATON, Andrew Thomas Church Street Surgery, Church Street, Martock TA12 6JL Tel: 01935 822541 Fax: 01935 826116 — MB BS 1994 Lond.; BSc (Anat. with Basic Med. Sci.) Lond. 1991; DCH Lond. 1997; DRCOG 1997; MRCGP 1998. (King's College Hospital London) GP Non Princip. Som. Prev: Ho. Off. (Gen. Surg.) Greenwich Dist. Hosp.; Ho. Off. (Gen. Med.) Brook Gen. Hosp. Lond.; Trainee GP/SHO (Gen. Pract.) Yeovil Dist. Hosp. VTS.

EATON, Christopher John Borough Lane Surgery, 2 Borough Lane, Saffron Walden CB11 4AF Tel: 01799 524224 Fax: 01799 524830; The Surgery, High St, Great Chesterford, Saffron Walden CB10 1PL Tel: 01799 530228 Fax: 01799 531218 — MB BS 1973 Lond.; MRCS Eng. LRCP Lond. 1972; Dip. IMC RCS Ed. 1989. (Roy. Free) Princip. GP; Med. Off. Bell Internat. Coll.; Fact. Doctor; Surg. St. John Ambul. Brig.; Chairm. Mid Essex Doctors' Immediate Care Scheme; Chairm. E. Anglian Gp of BASICs Schemes; Hon. Sec. BASICS (Mem. Research & Developm. Comm. & Educat. Comm.). Socs: Assur. Med. Soc.; Assoc. RCGP; Comm. Mem. UK Resusc. Counc. Prev: Surg. Lt. RN.

EATON, Deborah Joan Beechcrest, Leckhampton Hill, Cheltenham GL53 9QJ — MB ChB 1993 Manch.

EATON, Derek Anthony (retired) 15 Main Street, Cauldwell, Swadlincote DE12 6RR — MB ChB Manch. 1964; MRCS Eng. LRCP Lond. 1964. Prev: Clin. Assn. (Anaesth.) Burton Hosp.

EATON, Elizabeth Suzanne 10 Charnwood Drive, Markfield LE67 9RA Tel: 01530 244531 — BM BS 1980 Nottm.; BMedSci. 1978; MSc (ANU) 1972; BSc Hons. (Lond.) 1969. (Nottingham) p/t Locum GP; Clin. Asst. symptomatic brE. clinic, Glenfield Hosp., Groby Rd., Leicester. Socs: Assn. of Police Surg.s. Prev: Sen. Partner, Markfield Med. Centre, 24 Clutterman Way, Markfield, Leics. LE67 9WP.

EATON, Fiona Elizabeth Moncrieff Royal Condon Hospital, Whitechapel, London E1 Email: n.silver@ion.ucl.ac.uk; 33A Dollis Road, London N3 1RB Email: nicks@silverstar.swinteset.co.uk — MB ChB 1993 Manch.; MRCP 1996. (Manchester) Socs: RCPCH; BMA. Prev: Regist.(Paediat.) Booth Hall Childr. Hosp. Manch.

EATON, Jennifer Elizabeth 67 Longstomps Avenue, Chelmsford CM2 9BY — MB ChB 1995 Birm.

EATON, Jennifer Mary Department of Anaesthetics, Frenchay Hospital, Frenchay, Bristol BS16 1LE Tel: 0117 970 2020 Fax: 0117 957 4414; Foggam Barn, Box Hill, Corsham SN13 8ES Tel: 01225 742819 — MB ChB 1968 Leeds; FRCA 1977. Dep. PostGrad. Dean, SW Deanery Frenchay Hosp Bristol; Cons. Anaesth. Frenchay Hosp. Bristol. Prev: Sen. Regist. & Regist. (Anaesth.) Bristol & Bath; SHO (Anaesth.) Gen. Infirm. Leeds.

EATON, John Callard Robert The Surgery, 24 Albert Road, Bexhill-on-Sea TN40 1DG Tel: 01424 730456/734430 Fax: 01424 225615; 16 Oakfield Way, Little Common, Bexhill-on-Sea TN39 4EY — MB BS 1985 Lond.; MRCGP 1994; DRCOG 1991. Socs: Brit. Med. Acupunct. Soc. Prev: Trainee GP/SHO Hastings Hosps VTS.

EATON, John David 4 Racefield Road, Knutsford WA16 0BP — MB ChB 1993 Manch.; MRCP 1996. Regist. Christie Hosp. Manch. Socs: MRCP; BMA.

EATON, Margaret Joan (Megan) Paediatric Department, Yeovil District General Hospital, Higher Kingston, Yeovil BA21 4AT Tel: 01935 475122 Fax: 01935 707208; Applegarth, Middle Chinnock, Crewkerne TA18 7PW Tel: 01935 881436 — BM 1986 Soton.; MRCP (UK) Paediat. 1992. (Soton.) Cons. Paediat. Yeovil Dist. Gen. Hosp. Prev: Sen. Regist. (Paediat.) Plymouth & Bristol.

EATON, Michael David Church House Surgery, Church House, Shaw Street, Ruddington, Nottingham NG11 6HF Tel: 0115 984 7101 Fax: 0115 984 7404 — MB ChB 1988 Dundee; BMSc Dund 1986, MB ChB 1988; MRCGP 1994; DRCOG 1994; DFFP 1992.

EATON, Scott Miguel Fulbourn Hospital, Cambridge CB1 5EF Tel: 01223 245151 — MB ChB 1993 Manch. SHO (Rehabil. Psychiat.) Camb. Prev: SHO (Drug & Alcohol Serv.) Camb.; SHO (Child & Adolesc. Psychiat.) Camb.; SHO (Psychiat. Intens. Care Unit) Camb.

EATON, Simon Edwin Malcolm 10 Cresccent Road, Nether Edge, Sheffield S7 1HJ Tel: 0114 258 2262; Royal Hallamshire Hospital, Glossop Road, Sheffield S10 2JF Tel: 0114 271 1765 Fax: 0114 271 2912 Email: s.eaton@sheffield.ac.uk — BM BS 1993 Nottm.; BMedSci. Nottm. 1991; MRCP (UK) 1996. Specialist Regist. (Diabetes & Endocrinol.) Sheff.

EATON, Terence Joseph 5 Garlick Drive, Dalehouse Meadows, Dalehouse Lane, Kenilworth CV8 2TT — MB ChB 1984 Birm.

EAVES, David Laurence New Dover Road Surgery, 10 New Dover Road, Canterbury CT1 3AP Tel: 01227 462197 Fax: 01227 786041 — MB BS 1973 Lond.; MRCGP 1979; DCH Eng. 1978; DRCOG 1977. (Roy. Free)

EAVES, Michael Empingham Medical Centre, 37 Main Street, Empingham, Oakham LE15 8PR Tel: 01780 460202 Fax: 01780 460283; 1 Windsor Drive, Oakham LE15 6SN Tel: 01572 722819 Fax: 01572 722811 — MB ChB 1992 Leic.; BSc (Hons.) Liverp. 1987; DRCOG 1995; DFFP 1998. (Leicester)

EAVIS, Patrick Michael Oldfield Surgery, 45 Upper Oldfield Park, Bath BA2 3HT Tel: 01225 421137 Fax: 01225 337808 — MB BS 1994 Lond.; DRCOG 1997; MRCGP 2001. Trainee GP/SHO (c/o Elderly) Blackberry Hill Hosp., (A & E) W.on-super-Mare & (Psychiat.) Barrow Hosp. Bristol; GP Partner Bath; Clin. Asst. Oncol. Roy. United Hosp. Bath. Prev: Ho. Off. (O & G) S.mead Hosp. Bristol; Ho. Off. (Surg.) MusGr. Hosp. Taunton; Ho. Off. (Med.) Roy. United Hosp. Bath.

EAYRS, Patricia Jacqueline 94 Durban Road, Beckenham BR3 4EZ — MRCS Eng. LRCP Lond. 1970. (Roy. Free.)

EBAN, Raphael (retired) 2 Burlington House, Wedderburn Road, London NW3 5QS Tel: 020 7431 9151 Email: reban@aol.com — MB BChir Camb. 1950; MA Camb. 1950; FRCP Lond. 1974, M 1956; FRCR 1975; FFR 1958; DMRD Eng. 1955. Prev: Cons. Radiol. Ealing Hosp. S.all.

EBBAGE, Julia Cheryl 54 Grove Road, Burgess Hill RH15 8LF — MB BS 1991 Lond.

EBBETTS, John Hilary, OBE 3 Arundel Terrace, Brighton BN2 1GA Tel: 01273 603051 — MRCS Eng. LRCP Lond. 1942. (Westm. & W. Lond.) Socs: Fell. Roy. Soc. Med.; Brit. Inst. Musculoskel. Med.; (Pres.) Natural Therap. & Osteop. Soc. Prev: Cons. Brit. Assn. Manip. Med. Clinic; Med. Off. i/c Psychiat. Wards Milit. Hosp. Mombasa, Kenya; Osteopath i/c Rehabil. Dept. Pioneer Health Centre, Peckham.

EBBS, David Henry George 20 Queens Cottages, Toot Baldon, Oxford OX44 9NG — MB BS 1982 Lond.; BSc Lond. 1982, MB BS 1982. (Lond. Hosp.)

EBBS, Mr Stephen Robert Shirley Oaks Hospital, Poppy Lane, Croydon CR9 8AB Tel: 020 8655 2255 Fax: 020 8656 2868 — MB BS 1980 Lond.; MS Lond. 1990; FRCS Eng. 1984; T(S) 1991. (St. Bart.) Cons. Gen. Surg. Mayday Univ. Hosp. Croydon, Cons. Surg. Roy. Marsden Hosp.; Hon. Sen. Lect. Inst. Cancer Research. Prev: Lect. Kings Coll. Hosp. Lond.; SHO Bristol Roy. Infirm.; Ho. Surg. St. Bart. Hosp. Lond.

EBDEN, Philip Prince Philip Hospital, Llanelli SA18 8QF Tel: 01544 756567 — BM BCh 1977 Oxf.; PhD Lond. 1974; MA Oxf. 1982, BA 1969; FRCP Lond. 1994; MRCP (UK) 1981. (Oxf.) Cons. Phys. (Respirat. & Gen. Med.) P. Philip Hosp. LLa.lli; Sen. Lect. (Respirat. Med.) Univ. Swansea; RCP Specialty Adviser for Respirat. Med. in Wales; Mem. of Jt. Speciality Comm. for Respirat. Med.; Chairm. of Respirat. Train. Comm. Wales. Socs: (Sec.) Welsh Thoracic Soc.; Brit. Thorac. Soc.; Med. Res. Soc. Prev: Sen. Regist. (Gen. Med.) Leicester; Regist. (Thoracic Med.) Llandough Hosp. Penarth Wales; Regist. (Med.) Univ. Hosp. Wales.

EBDY, Michael John Health Centre, Gorse Lane, Tarleton, Preston PR4 6UJ Tel: 01772 812205 & 815441; The Coppice, 5 Douglas Avenue, Tarleton, Preston PR4 6RQ Tel: 01772 812400 — MB ChB 1979 Liverp.; MRCGP 1983; DRCOG 1981. Mem. (Vice-Chairm.) S. Lancs. LMC. Socs: (Pres.) W. Lancs. Med. Soc. Prev: GP Llanfyllin, Powys; SHO (Paediat.) Roy. Liverp. Childr. Hosp.; SHO (O & G) Ormskirk & Dist. Gen. Hosp.

EBEID, Suzanne 12 Green Road, Skelton-in-Cleveland, Saltburn-by-the-Sea TS12 2BQ — MB ChB 1990 Glas.

EBEN, Friederike 74 Kevan House, Wyndham Road, London SE5 0LR Tel: 020 7701 1499 — State Exam. Med. Mainz 1983.

EBER, Tania Rachel 6 Belsize Avenue, London NW3 4AU Tel: 020 7794 8385 — BM BS 1991 Nottm.

EBERLE, Sigrid Birmingham Heartlands Hospital, Bordesley Green E., Birmingham B9 5SS — State Exam Med 1993 Ulm.

EBERT, Frank Helmut Staff Accommodation Office, Dudley Road Hospital, Birmingham B18 7QH — State Exam Med 1992 Berlin.

EBIGBO, Mr Aloysius Patrick Mgbokwere 1 Tebworth Road, London N17 8AN — Vrach 1972 Volgograd Med. Inst. USSR; FRCS Glas. 1983; FRCSI 1982.

EBIZIE, Mr Anele Obioha 54 Birchwood, Firwood Park, Chadderton, Oldham OL9 9UJ Tel: 0161 633 4248 Fax: 0161 284 2864 Email: ani@ebiz.demon.co.uk — MB BS 1978 Nigeria; FRCS Ed. 1986; FRCS (Orth.) 1995. (University Nigeria, Enugu) Cons. Orthop. & Trauma Surg. Tameside Acute NHS Trust. Socs: Manch. Med. Soc. Prev: Regist. (Orthop.) Roy. Oldham Hosp.

EBMEIER, Professor Klaus Peter Department of Psychiatry, Royal Edinburgh Hospital, Morningside Park, Edinburgh EH10 5HF Tel: 0131 537 6000 Fax: 0131 537 6110 Email: klaus.ebmeier@ed.ac.uk — MD 1991 Aberd.; State Exam. Med. Bonn 1981; MRCPsych 1986. (Univ. Bonn.) Prof. Psychiat. Roy. Edin. Hosp.; Hon. Cons. Psychiat. Lothian HB. Prev: Clin. Sci. MRC Brain Metabol. Edin.; Lect. (Ment. Health) Aberd. Univ.

EBORALL, John Frederick Saywell Tel: 01636 704378/9 Fax: 01636 610875; Hampton Lodge, 3 Gray's Court, Main Street, Farndon, Newark NG24 3UD — MB ChB 1969 Sheff.; FFA RCS Eng. 1975. (Sheff.) Prev: Regist. (Anaesth.) N.. Gen. Hosp. Sheff.; Ho. Off. (Med.) Lodge Moor Hosp. Sheff.; Ho. Surg. Nottm. Gen. Hosp.

EBRAHIM, Abdul-Rahim 1 Lincoln Road, Luton LU4 8ND — MB ChB 1998 Dund.; MB ChB Dund 1998. Med. SHO Bedford Hosp. Prev: Med. Ho. Off. Goadhope Hosp. Sutton Coldfield; Surgic. Ho. Off. Milton Keynes Gen. Hosp.

EBRAHIM, Donald William 75 Kenilworth Road, Coventry CV4 7AF Tel: 024 76 418667 Fax: 024 76 693775 — MRCS Eng. LRCP Lond. 1952. (Sheff.) Prev: Cas. Off. Coventry & Warw. Hosp.; Ho. Surg. Childr. Hosp. Sheff.

EBRAHIM, Professor Gulamabbas Juma (retired) Institute of Child Health, 30 Guilford St., London WC1N 1EH Tel: 020 8670 7646 — MB BS 1957 Poona; FRCP Ed. 1971, M 1960; FRCP Glas. 1970, M 1960; MFPHM RCP (UK) 1995; DCH Eng. 1960; DCH Bombay 1958; FRCPCH 1996. Prof. Trop. Child Health Unit Inst. Child Health Lond.; Hon. Cons. Hosp. Childr. Gt. Ormond St.; Edr. Jl. Trop. Paediat. Prev: Cons. Paediat. MoH, Tanzania.

EBRAHIM, Irshaad Osman Flat 6, 15 Clanricarde Gardens, London W2 4JJ — MB ChB 1991 Natal.

EBRAHIM, Muhammad Ashraf Ysbyty Gwynedd, Bangor LL57 2PD Tel: 01248 370007 0492 860066 — MB BS 1985 Karachi; MRCPI 1992. Regist. Rotat. (Gen. & Geriat. Med.) Ysbyty Gwynedd Bangor.

EBRAHIM, Niloufer 5 Verge Walk, Aldershot GU11 3TG — MB BS 1992 Lond. Specialist Regist, Pub. Health Medic. S. Thames (W.).

EBRAHIM, Professor Shaheen Brian John Canynge Hall, Dept of Social Medicine, University of Bristol, Bristol BS8 2PR Tel: 0117 928 7350 Fax: 0117 928 7325 Email: Shah.ebrahim@bris.ac.uk — BM BS 1975 Nottm.; BMedSci 1973 Nottm; MSc (Epidemiol.) Univ. Lond. 1982, DM Nottm. 1985; FRCP Lond. 1993; MRCP (UK) 1980; FFPHM RCP (UK) 1993; MRCGP 1980; MFCM RCP UK 1983; DCH Eng. 1978. Prof. Epidemiol.of Ageing Univ. of Bristol. Socs: Brit. Geriat. soc. Memb.; Soc. Social Med. Prev: Prof. Clin. Epidemiol. Roy. Free Hosp. Sch. Med. Lond.; Prof. Geriat. Med. Lond. Hosp. Med. Coll. & St. Bart. Hosp. Med. Coll.Lond.; Cons. Phys. & Sen. Lect. Roy. Free Hosp. Lond.

EBRAHIM, Sundari Sydenham Green Health Centre, 26 Holmshaw Close, London SE26 Tel: 020 8676 8836 — MB BS 1957 Poona; DCH Bombay 1958; DCH Eng. 1960. (B.J. Med. Coll. Poona) Prev: MRC Research Fell. Dept. of Virol., Inst. of Child Health Lond.; Pediat. Resid. Grad. Hosp. Philadelphia; SHO O & G Whitehaven Hosp.

EBRILL, Charles Sidney Thomas Wells Health Centre, Bolts Close, Wells-next-the-Sea NR23 1JP Tel: 01328 710741 Fax: 01328 711825 — MB BS 1968 Lond.; MRCS Eng. LRCP Lond. 1968. (King's Coll. Lond. & St. Geo.) Socs: Fell. Roy. Soc. Med. Prev: Regist. Accid. Dept. Mayday Hosp. Thornton Heath; SHO (Surg.) Leicester Gen. Hosp.; Ho. Off. (Orthop.) Surg. St. Geo. Hosp. Lond.

EBRINGER, Alan King's College - Division of Life Sciences, 150 Stamford St., London SE1 8WA Tel: 0207 7836 4302 Fax: 0207 7836 4500 Email: alan.ebringer@kcl.ac.uk; 76 Gordon Road, Ealing, London W5 2AR Tel: 0208 997 1883 — MB BS 1962 Melbourne; BSc Melbourne 1961, MD 1969; FRCP Lond. 1987; MRCP (UK) 1970; FRACP 1973, M 1967; FRCPath 1997. Prof. (Immunol.) King's Coll. Lond.; Hon. Cons. (Rheum.) Middlx. Hosp. Lond. Prev: Drug Ho.s of Austral. Research Fell. Walter & Eliza Hall Research Inst. Roy. Melb. Hosp.; Berkeley Fell. Middlx. Hosp. Lond.

ECCERSLEY, Mr Alexander James Paul The Academic Surgical Unit, The Royal London Hospital, Whitechapel, London E1 1BB Email: a.j.eccersley@mds.qmw.ac.uk; 34 Saffron Road, Biggleswade SG18 8DJ — MB BChir 1991 Camb.; MA Camb. 1991; FRCS Eng. 1995. Specialist Regist. Gen. Surg. E. Anglian Rotat. Prev: Lect. & Hon. Regist. (Gen. Surg.) Roy. Lond. Hosp. Whitechapel.

ECCERSLEY, Peter Spencer (retired) 63 Canada Drive, Cottingham HU16 5EH Tel: 01482 843569 — MB ChB St. And. 1961; FFA RCS Eng. 1966. Cons. Anaesth. Roy. Hull Hosps. NHS Trust.

ECCLES, David Northgate Surgery, Northgate, Pontefract WF8 1NF Tel: 01977 703635 Fax: 01977 702562; 21 Hardwick Road, Pontefract WF8 3PQ — MB ChB 1980 Leeds; MRCGP 1985.

ECCLES, David Richard Eaton Road Surgery, 276 Eaton Road, West Derby, Liverpool L12 2AW Tel: 0151 228 3768 Fax: 0151; 23 Childwall Park Avenue, Liverpool L16 0JE Tel: 0151 722 2029 Fax: 0151 738 0403 Email: david@childwal.demon.co.uk — MB ChB 1980 Liverp.; DMJ Clin.) Soc. Apoth. Lond. 1994; DFFP 1994; DRCOG 1983. (Liverpool) Princip. Forens. Med. Examr. Merseyside Police; Hon. Lect. (Forens. Med.) Univ. Liverp. Socs: (Hon. Sec.) Merseyside Medico-Legal Soc.; (counc.) Assn. Police Surgs.; Brit. Acad. Forens. Sci. Prev: Trainee GP Ainsdale, S.port.; SHO (Paediat.) S.port Gen. Infirm.; SHO (O & G) Christiana Hartley Matern. Hosp. S.port.

ECCLES, Diana Margaret Department of Human Genetics, Level G, Princess Anne Hospital, Southampton SO16 5YA Tel: 02380 794172 Fax: 02380 794346 Email: de1@soton.ac.uk; Salterns Lodge, Salterns Lane, Old Bursledon, Southampton SO31 8DH — MB ChB 1983 Manch.; MB ChB Manch 1983; MD Manch. 1992; MRCP (UK) 1986; FRCP (UK) 1999. Cons. Clin. Genetics Dept. of Human Genetics Soton. Univ. Hosps. Trust; Sen. Lect. in Oncol., SUMT.; Brit. Soc. Human Genetics; UK Cancer Genetics Gp. Prev: Clin. Research Fell. (Genetics) CRC Genetic Epidemiol. Research Gp. Univ. Soton.; Research Fell. (Oncol.) Imperial Cancer Research Fund W.. Gen. Hosp. Edin.; Lect. (Oncol.) W.. Gen. Hosp. Edin.

ECCLES, Helen Michelle 131 Colliers Break, Emerssons Green, Bristol BS16 7EB — MB ChB 1990 Ed.

ECCLES, James Thomas St. James's University Hospital, Leeds LS9 7TF Tel: 0113 243 3144 — MB ChB 1975 Manch.; MA Health Care Ethics Leeds 1998; FRCP Lond. 1993; MRCP (UK) 1980. Cons. Phys. Elderly St. James Univ. Hosp. Leeds; Sen. Clin. Lect. Health Care Managem. Leeds Univ. Socs: Brit. Geriat. Soc.; Assoc. Mem. Soc. Research Rehab. Prev: Sen. Regist. (Geriat. Med.) St. Jas. Univ. Hosp. Leeds; Research Regist. (Geriat. Med.) Univ. Hosp. S. Manch.; Regist. (Med.) Derbysh. Roy. Infirm.

ECCLES, Jane Catherine 17 Forest Way, Fulwood, Preston PR2 8PR — MB ChB 1996 Manch. GP VTS.

ECCLES, Juliana Betty Felling Health Centre, Felling, Gateshead NE10; 16 The Drive, Gosforth, Newcastle upon Tyne NE3 4AH — MB BS 1978 Newc.; MRCGP 1982.

ECCLES, Lyall Mary Bitterne Park Surgery, Southampton SO18 1BW; The White House, 23 Holly Hill Lane, Sarisbury Green, Southampton SO31 7AB — MB BS 1966 Lond.; MRCS Eng. LRCP Lond. 1966. (Guy's)

ECCLES, Martin Paul Prospect House Medical Group, Prospect Place, Newcastle upon Tyne NE4 6QD Tel: 0191 273 4201; 16 The Drive, Gosforth, Newcastle upon Tyne NE3 4AH Tel: 0191 285 3483 — MB BS 1978 Newc.; MD Newc. 1988, MB BS 1978; MRCP (UK) 1981 DCH 1981.; MRCGP 1988.

ECCLES, Melanie Jane Flat 6, 9 Priory Road, Clifton, Bristol BS8 1TU — MB ChB 1998 Bristol.

ECCLES, Norman Christopher (retired) Northenden Health Centre, 489 Palatine Road, Northenden, Manchester M22 4DH Tel: 0161 998 3206 Fax: 0161 945 9173 — MB ChB 1959 Manch.; BSc (Hons. Anat.) Manch. 1957; DObst RCOG 1961.

ECCLES, Nyjon Karl 43 Effingham Road, London N8 0AA — MB BS 1992 Lond.

ECCLES, Mr Simon James 24 Querrin Street, Fulham, London SW6 2SJ Tel: 020 7731 7264 Email: simon.eccles@btinternet.com — MB BS 1992 Lond.; BDS Lond. 1985; FRCS Eng. 1996. Specialist Regist. (Plastic Surg.) Qu. Marys Hosp. Roehampton; Specialist Regist. St And.Centre for Plastic Surg. Chelmsford. Socs: Brit. Assn Plastic Surg.; BMA; Med. Protec. Soc. Prev: SHO (Plastic Surg.) Qu. Marys Hosp. Roehampton; SHO Plastic Surg. St. Geo. Hosp.; SHO (Gen. Surg.) St. Helier Hosp. Carshalton.

ECCLES, Simon John Arthur 17 Collingwood House, Darling Row, London E1 5RR; 42 Albion Yard, 331 Whitechapel Road, London E1 1BU — MB BS 1994 Lond.

ECCLES, Thomas Annesley (retired) Burn End Cottage, Carnousie, Turriff AB53 4LB Tel: 0188 822781 — MRCS Eng. LRCP Lond. 1921. Prev: Med. Off. Rathbone Convalesc. Home.

ECCLESHALL, Simon Charles 88 Grosvenor Road, Birmingham B17 9AN — MB ChB 1989 Birm.

ECCLESTON, Andrew David Hollybish Cottage, Kinnaird, Inchture, Perth PH14 9QY — MB ChB 1994 Dundee.

ECCLESTON, David Baron Handsworth Wood Medical Centre, 110 Church Lane, Handsworth Wood, Birmingham B20 2ES Tel: 0121 523 7117 Fax: 0121 554 2406; Weeford Lodge, St Mary's Barns, Weeford, Lichfield WS14 0PW Tel: 01543 483332 Fax: 01543 483332 — MB ChB 1987 Birm. (Birm. Univ.) GP; Consg. Doctor Lasercare Clinics Birm. Socs: BMA; Med. Protec. Soc.; Birm. Medico-Legal Soc.

ECCLESTON, David William 65 Beech Court, Darras Hall, Ponteland, Newcastle upon Tyne NE20 9NE — MB BS 1964 Durh.; MRCP (U.K.) 1970.

ECCLESTON, Donald Dept of Psychiatry, Royal Victoria Infirmary, Queen Victoria Road, Newcastle upon Tyne NE1 4LP — MB ChB 1957 Aberd.; DSc Ed. 1976, PhD 1966; FRCPsych 1978; DPM Eng. 1960. (Aberd.) Prof. Psychiat. Univ. Newc. Prev: Cons. Psychiat. & Asst. Dir. MRC Brain Metab. Unit Edin.

ECCLESTON, Elizabeth Clare Braeside Medical Group, Escomb Road, Bishop Auckland DL14 6AB Tel: 01388 663539 Fax: 01388 601847 — MB ChB 1986 Ed.

ECCLESTON, George Alexander 24 Legh Road, Prestbury, Macclesfield SK10 4HX Tel: 01625 820792 — MB ChB Manch. 1960; DFFP 1993; DObst RCOG 1962. (Univ. Manch.) Specialist Med. Off. (Menopause) Trafford Menopause Clinic Sale, Chesh.; Hosp. Pract. (Obst.& Gyn.) Wythenshawe Hosp. Manch.; Clin. Asst. (Endocrinol.) Hope Hosp. Salford. Socs: (Counc.) Brit. Menopause

Soc. Prev: GP Altrincham; Ho. Surg. (Neurosurg.) Manch. Roy. Infirm.; Ho. Surg. (Obst.) St. Mary's Hosps. Manch.

ECCLESTON, Ian Michael 50 Summerville Avenue, Blackpool FY3 0BP Tel: 01253 899842 — MB ChB 1986 Liverp.; MRCGP 1990; DRCOG 1991.

ECCLESTON, Susan Enid 2 Turners Wood, London NW11 6TD Tel: 020 8458 2189 — MB ChB 1978 Liverp.; MRCGP 1983; DRCOG 1980. GP Lond.

ECCOTT, John Nevill (retired) Bellsfield Hotel, 45 King St., Southport PR8 1LG — MRCS Eng. LRCP Lond. 1966; MB BChir Camb. 1968; MA Camb. 1967; DA (UK) 1970; DTM & H Liverp. 1968. Prev: Med. Off. S. Georgia, USA.

ECHEBARRIA ARTECHE, Juan Jose Anaesthetic Department, The Alexandra Hospital, Woodrow Drive, Redditch B98 7UB — LMS 1986 Basque Provinces.

ECHEBARRIETA, Jon Mikel 21 Mornington Road, Norwich NR2 3NA — LMS 1992 Navarre.

ECKERSALL, Ann Christine Corney Place Medical Group, The Health Centre, Bridge Lane, Penrith CA11 8HW Tel: 01768 245226 Fax: 01768 245229; 30 Wordsworth Street, Penrith CA11 7QY Tel: 01768 64728 — MB ChB 1977 Leeds; DRCOG 1980. GP Penrith Cumbria.

ECKERSALL, Stephen John c/o Anaesthetic Department, Queen Alexandra Hospital, Cosham, Portsmouth PO6 3LY — MB BS 1982 Lond.

ECKERSLEY, Eric The Old Curacy, Brome, Eye IP23 8AH — MB BS 1964 Lond.; MRCS Eng. LRCP Lond. 1964. (Guy's)

ECKERSLEY, Mr James Rupert Thomas St Mary's Hospital, Praed St., London W2 1NY Tel: 020 7886 1918 Fax: 020 7886 1766; 19 Twyford Avenue, London W3 9PY Tel: 020 8992 0881 Fax: 020 8992 0881 Email: rupert_e@msn.com — MB BS 1980 Lond.; FRCS Eng. 1985. Cons. Orthop. & Hand Surg. St. Mary's Hosp. & Chelsea & W.minster Hosp. Lond.

ECKERSLEY, Mr Jeremy Hyla (retired) Woodmans, Bosbury, Ledbury HR8 1JX — MB BChir 1956 Camb.; MA Camb. 1963, BA 1952; FRCS Eng. 1963. Hon. Cons. Orthop. Surg. Worcester Roy. Infirm. Prev: Sen. Regist. Nuffield Orthop. Centre.

ECKERSLEY, Neil Geoffrey 8 Dalton Square, Lancaster LA1 1PP Tel: 01524 842200 Fax: 01524 585411; 3 Orchard Lane, Lancaster LA1 5NJ Tel: 01524 382218 — MB ChB 1981 Leic.; DRCOG 1983; Cert Family Planning 1983; MRCGP 1985; MRCGP 1985; DRCOG 1983; Cert. Family Plann. JCC 1983. (Univ. Leic. Med. Sch.) Med. Off. Lancaster Roy. Grammar Sch.

ECKERSLEY, Patrick John Winyates Health Centre, Winyates, Redditch B98 0NR Tel: 01527 525533 Fax: 01527 517969; Springhill Farm, Foxlydiate Lane, Bentley, Redditch B97 5PB Tel: 01527 541207 — MB BS 1970 Lond.

ECKERT, Harold (retired) 3 Dinglewood Close, Westbury-on-Trym, Bristol BS9 2LL — MD (Commend.) Sheff. 1959, MB ChB 1955; DMRT Eng. 1962; FRCR 1975; FFR 1965. Cons. Clin. Oncol. United Bristol Healthcare NHS Trust; Clin. Lect. & Head (Clin. Oncol.) Univ. Bristol. Prev: Cons. Radiotherap. Sheff. Nat. Centre Radiother.

ECKFORD, Iain Baillie Craigen 86 Blackford Avenue, Edinburgh EH9 3ES — MB ChB 1954 Ed.; DPH 1957.

ECKFORD, Mr Seumas Douglas Dept. of Obstetrics & Gynaecology, North Devon District Hospital, Raleigh Park, Barnstaple EX31 4JB Tel: 01271 322602 Fax: 01271 322606 Email: seumaseckford@hotmail.com; Orchard House, Bellaire, Pilton, Barnstaple EX31 1QZ — MB BS 1987 Lond.; BSc Lond. 1984; FRCS Ed. 1997; MRCPI 1996; MRCOG 1994; MRACOG 1995; MRNZCOG 1995. (Roy. Lond. Hosp. Med. Coll.) Cons. O & G. Socs: ICS; BAUS; IUGA. Prev: Sen. Regist. Simpson Memor. Matern. Pavil. Edin.; Regist. Middlemore Hosp. Auckland, NZ; Regist. Bristol Matern. Hosp. & S.mead Hosp. Bristol.

ECKHARDT, Mr Sven Harald 23 Allerton Road, South Yardley, Birmingham B25 8NX — MB BCh BAO 1988 NUI; FRCS Ed. 1992; FRCSI 1992; LRCPSI 1988.

ECKLAND, David John Augustus Glaxo Wellcome Research & Development, Greenford Road, Greenford UB6 0HE; 17 Berceau Walk, Watford WD17 3BL — MB BS 1978 Lond.; PhD Lond. 1989; BSc Lond. (1st cl. Hons.) Biochem. 1975; MRCP (UK) 1981. (St. Bart.) Internat. Dir. Metabol. Dis. & Clin. Research Glaxo Wellcome Research & Developm. Greenford. Socs: Fell. Roy. Soc. Med. Prev: Lect. (Med.) & Hon. Sen. Regist. Char. Cross & W.m. Med. Sch. Lond; Ho. Phys. Med. Profess. Unit. St. Bart.; SHO Hammersmith Hosp. Lond.

ECKLE, Isolde 19 Compass Court, 39 Shad Thames, London SE1 2NJ — MD 1988 Berlin; State Exam Med 1987.

ECKSTEIN, Michael Bernard Sussex Eye Hospital, Eastern Road, Brighton BN2 5BF Tel: 01273 606126 — MB BS 1985 Lond.; FRCOphth 1990; DO RCS Eng. 1990; MD London 1997. Cons. Ophth. Moorfields Eye Hosp. Lond.

ECKSTEIN, Peter Arthur (retired) 48 George Street, Cambridge CB4 1AJ Tel: 01223 360023 — MB BChir 1955 Camb.; MA Camb. 1960; DA Eng. 1958. Prev: Diplomatic Serv. Med. Off., Warsaw.

ECLAIR-HEATH, Cynthia Melita Skeynes Park, Lingfield Road, Edenbridge TN8 5HN — MB BS 1973 Lond.; MRCS Eng. LRCP Lond. 1973. (St. Bart.)

ECOB, Colin Charles (retired) 17A Stoneleigh Road, Coventry CV4 7AB Tel: 01203 419664 — MB ChB 1951 Birm.

ECOB, Eleanor Ann (retired) 17A Stoneleigh Road, Coventry CV4 7AB Tel: 02476 419664 — MB ChB 1951 Birm.

ECONOMIDES, Demetrios Leonidas Royal Free Hospital, Pond Street, London NW3 2QG — MRCS Eng. LRCP Lond. 1981; MD Lond. 1990, MB BS 1980; MRCOG 1985. (Charing Cross) Cons. O & G Roy. Free Hosp. Lond. Prev: Lect. (O & G) John Radcliffe Hosp. Oxf.; Research Fell. King's Coll. Hosp. Lond.

ECONOMIDES, Vasos Andrea, Maj. RAMC (retired) 42 Colney Hatch Lane, Muswell Hill, London N10 1DY Tel: 020 8883 4908 — MRCS Eng. LRCP Lond. 1957; LMSSA Lond. 1957; DObst RCOG 1960. Prev: GP Lond.

ECONS, Apelles Ashley Medical Practice, 29 Hersham Road, Walton-on-Thames KT12 1LF Tel: 01932 252425 Fax: 01932 886912; The Woking Nuffield Hospital, Shores Road, Woking GU21 4BY Tel: 01483 763511 — MRCS Eng. LRCP Lond. 1976. (Middlx. Hosp. Med. Sch.) Mem. Med. Staff Walton Hosp. Walton-on-Thames; Hon. Med. Off. Brit. Volleyball Federat. Socs: Brit. Soc. Allergy & Environm. Med.; (Med. Comm.) Brit. Olympic Assn. Prev: SHO (Psychiat.) St. John's Hosp. Aylesbury; Ho. Surg. & Ho. Phys. Stoke Mandeville Hosp.

EDBROOKE, David Louis Highnoon, Hollinberry Lane, Howbrook, Sheffield S35 7EL Tel: 0114 284 8305 — MRCS Eng. LRCP Lond. 1970; FFA RCS Eng. 1976. Cons. (Anaesth.) Hallamshire Hosp. Sheff.

EDBROOKE, Donald Ralph (retired) Moorlands, Wrangaton, South Brent TQ10 9HJ Tel: 01364 72072 — MRCS Eng. LRCP Lond. 1958. Prev: Capt. RAMC.

EDBROOKE, Judith Anne 2 Constance Avenue, Lincoln LN6 8SN — MB ChB 1974 Leeds.

EDDIE, David Anthony Stirling (retired) 129 South Hey, Lytham St Annes FY8 4BE Tel: 01253 735640 — MB BS 1955 Lond.; FRCOG 1975, M 1959. Prev: Cons. O & G Blackpool, Wyre & Fylde HA.

EDDIE, George The Clinic, Ebanista, Braye Road, Vale, Guernsey GY3 5QN Tel: 01481 46965 — MB ChB Aberd. 1962; MLCOM 1988; DObst RCOG 1973; Dip Med Acupunc 1998 (B.M.A.S.). (Aberd.) Socs: Inst. Orthop. Med.; Brit. Med. Acupunct. Soc. Prev: Ho. Surg. Aberd. Roy. Infirm. & Bellshill Matern. Hosp.; Ho. Phys. Roy. Hosp. Sick Childr. Aberd.

EDDINGTON, Joseph The Central Surgery, 2 Surrey Gardens, Birchington CT7 9SB Tel: 01843 841384 Fax: 01843 848609; 30 Epple Bay Avenue, Birchington CT7 9HT — MRCS Eng. LRCP Lond. 1970; MRCGP 1977; DObst RCOG 1974. Prev: SHO (Psychiat.) Doncaster Roy. Infirm.; GP Trainee I. of Thanet Dist. Hosp. Ramsgate.

EDDINGTON, Michael Paul (Surgery) 204 Kings Road, South Harrow, Harrow HA2 9JH Tel: 020 8422 1667 & 2081; 104 Aldenham Road, Bushey, Watford WD23 2EX — MB BS 1978 Lond.; DRCOG 1984.

EDDINGTON, Wendy Alice 30 Epple Bay Avenue, Birchington CT7 9HT — MB ChB 1970 Sheff. (Sheff.) Prev: Ho. Phys. Roy. Infirm. Sheff.; Ho. Surg. (Cas. & Orthop.) Rotherham Hosp.

EDDISON, Dianne Mary Whiteladies Health Centre, Whatley Road, Clifton, Bristol BS8 2PU Tel: 0117 973 1201 Fax: 0117 946 7031 — MB ChB 1981 Newc.; MRCGP 1985; DRCOG 1984.

EDDISON, Paul Fearnley The Village Practice, Mere Lane, Armthorpe, Doncaster DN3 2DB Tel: 01302 300322 Fax: 01302 300737 — MB ChB 1978 Sheff.; DA Eng. 1981; DRCOG 1981.

Socs: BMA. Prev: SHO (Anaesth.) Sheff. AHA(T); SHO (O & G) Sheff. AHA(T).

EDDISON, Robert Mark St George Health Centre, Bellevue Road, St George, Bristol BS5 7FH — MB BS 1990 Lond.; MRCGP 1995; DTM & H RCP Lond. 1996; DFFP 1994; DRCOG 1994. (St. Bart. Hosp. Lond.) GP Princip. Prev: GP VSO Roy. Vict. Hosp. Banjul The Gambia.

EDDLESTON, Professor Adrian Leonard William Francis Guy's King's & St Thomas' School of Medicine, Weston Education Centre, Cutcombe Road, London SE5 9PJ Tel: 020 7312 5612 Fax: 020 7312 5613 — BM BCh Oxf. 1964; DM Oxf. 1972; FRCP Lond. 1979, M 1967. (Guy's) Dean Guy's King's & St Thomas' Sch. of Med.; Mem. Camberwell HA. Socs: Brit. Soc. Gastroenterol. & Assn. Phys. Prev: Prof. Liver Immunol. & Dean King's Coll. Sch. Med. & Dent. & Hon. Cons. Phys. King's Coll. Hosp. Lond.; Regist. (Med.) Kings Coll. Hosp. Gp.; Regist. (Med.) Guy's Hosp. Lond.

EDDLESTON, Brian (retired) Upalong, 61 Sandy Lane, Romiley, Stockport SK6 4NH Tel: 0161 430 4137 — MB ChB Manch. 1954; FRCR 1975; FFR 1965; DMRD Eng. 1961. Prev: Dir. Diag. Radiol. Christie Hosp. & Holt Radium Inst. Manch.

EDDLESTON, Michael Philip The Croft, Back Lane, Wiswell, Clitheroe BB7 9BU — BM BCh 1998 Oxf.; BM BCh Oxf 1998.

EDDOWES, Hilary Ann 22 Mosspark Avenue, Milngavie, Glasgow G62 8NL — MB ChB 1983 Bristol; MRCOG 1989; Cert. Family Plann. JCC 1985. Socs: BFS, BMUS & BMS. Prev: Clin. Asst. (Obst. Ultrasound) Qu. Mothers Hosp. Glas.; Clin. Research Fell. Bristol Univ.; Regist. Bristol Matern. Hosp.

EDDY, Benjamin Andrew 8 Henshaw Street, London SE17 1PD — MB BS 1996 Lond.

EDDY, John David West Mead, 3 The Driffold, Sutton Coldfield B73 6HE Tel: 0121 354 4846 — MB BS 1960 Lond.; FRCP Ed. 1979, M 1968. (St. Bart.) Cons. Phys. Good Hope Gen. Hosp. Sutton Coldfield. Socs: Brit. Cardiac Soc. Prev: Regist. Cardiol. Dudley RD. Hosp. Birm.; Med. Regist. Dreadnought Seamen's Hosp. Greenwich; Sen. Regist. (Cardiol.) United Birm. Hosps.

EDDY, Mr John Wellington Turner Rise Consulting Rooms, 55 Turner Road, Colchester CO4 5JY Tel: 01206 752444 Fax: 01206 752116; 23 Cambridge Road, Colchester CO3 3NS Tel: 01206 574668 — MB BS 1966 Lond.; FRCS Ed. 1973; MRCS Eng. LRCP Lond. 1968; FRCOG 1986, M 1972; DObst 1968. (Westm. Univ. Lond.) Regional Adviser Obst. & Gyn. RCOG N. Thames (E.) Region. Socs: BMA; Roy. Soc. Med.; Internat. Soc. Ultrasound in Obst. & Gyn. Prev: ons. O & G Essex Co. Hosp. Colchester Essex Rivers Health Trust; Sen. Regist. (O & G) Univ. Coll. Hosp. & Whittington Hosp. Lond.; Regist. (O & G) W.m. Hosp. Lond.

EDDY, Julia Heather Lantewey Farm, St. Neot, Liskeard PL14 6PH Tel: 01208 821613 — MB BS 1977 Lond.; MRCGP 1983; DRCOG 1981. (St. Geo.)

EDDY, Tracey 68 Fairfield Road, Winchester SO22 6SG — MB ChB 1985 Aberd.; MRCPsych 1990.

EDE, Jonathan Nigel 59/61 Addiscombe Road, Croydon CR0 6SD Tel: 020 8688 4822 Fax: 020 8686 5818 Email: jonede@compuserve.com — MB BS 1982 Lond.; MRCGP 1990; DRCOG 1984. Prev: Trainee GP Croydon VTS.

EDE, Robert James Frederick Saltoun Surgery, 46 Saltoun Place, Aberdeen AB23 9RY — BM 1989 Soton.

EDE, Roland Jarlath Darent Vallen Hospital, Darenth Wood, Dartford Tel: 01322 428100; 93 Marlborough Crescent, Riverhead, Sevenoaks TN13 2HL — MB BS 1976 Lond.; FRCP Lond. 1995; MRCP (UK) 1980; MRCS Eng. LRCP Lond. 1976. (Guy's) Cons. Phys. & Gastroenterol. Dartford HA & St. Thos. Hosp. Lond.; Subdean, Guys, king's & St. Thomas Sch. of Med. King's Coll. Lond. Socs: Brit. Soc. Gastroenterol.; Brit. Assn. Study Liver. Prev: Sen. Regist. (Gen. Med. & Gastroenterol.) Lond. Hosp.; MRC Fell. & Hon. Regist. Liver Unit King's Coll. Hosp. Lond.; SHO (A & E) Guy's Hosp. Lond.

EDEES, Susan 6 Padgbury Close, Astbury, Congleton CW12 4JU — MB BS 1982 Lond.; MRCP (UK) 1987. Regist. (Paediat.) Derbysh. Childr. Hosp.

EDEH, James Chukwu Thomas 45 Lings Coppice, Croxted Road, Dulwich, London SE21 8SX Tel: 020 8761 5337 — MB BS 1971 Ibadan; PhD Lond. 1984; MRCPsych 1976; DPM Eng. 1975. Sen. Lect. & Hon. Cons. Psychiat. St. Geo. Hosp. Med. Sch. Div. of Addictive Behaviour Lond.; Cons. Psychiat. Subst. Misuse Serv. Crawley Hosp., Horsham Hosp. & St. Francis Hosp. Haywards Heath.

EDELEANU, Ion-Dan (retired) Haydown, Great Buckland, Luddesdowne, Gravesend DA13 0XF Tel: 01474 814329 — MB BChir 1950 Camb.; MA Camb. 1951; MRCS Eng. LRCP Lond. 1950. Hypnother. Gravesend. Prev: GP Gravesend.

EDELMAN, Joy Beryl Department of Cardiology, King George Hospital, Barley Lane Goodmayes, Ilford Tel: 020 8970 8144 Fax: 020 8970 8191; 44 Kingsley Way, London N2 0EW Tel: 020 8455 5749 Fax: 020 8455 5749 — MB BS 1961 Lond.; FRCP Lond. 1980, M 1967; MRCS Eng. LRCP Lond. 1961; DObst RCOG 1963. (Lond. Hosp.) Cons. Gen. Phys. & Cardiol. King Geo. Hosp. Goodmayes; Mem. Jt. Cons. Comm.; Mem. Centr. Cons. Specialist Comm. Socs: Brit. Cardiac Soc.; BMA. Prev: Sen. Regist. (Med.) Brompton & Roy. Free Hosps.; Regist (Med.) Nat. Heart Hosp. & Lond. Hosp.

EDELSTEN, Anthony David James Paget Hospital NHS Trust, Gorleston, Great Yarmouth NR31 6LA Tel: 01493 452452; Church Farm House, The Green, Freethorpe, Norwich NR13 3AH Tel: 01493 701345 — MB BS 1966 Lond.; FRCP Lond. 1974; MRCS Eng. LRCP Lond. 1966; MRCPCH 1996; FCP(SA) (Paediat.) 1974. (St. Bart.) Cons. Paediat. Jas. Paget NHS Trust Gt. Yarmouth. Prev: Sen. Regist. (Paediat.) Bristol Childr. Hosp.; Regist. (Paediat.) Red Cross Childr. Hosp. Cape Town, S. Afr.; SHO (Paediat.) St. Bart. Hosp. Lond.

EDELSTEN, Mr Clive Department of Ophthalmology, Ipswich Hospital NHS Trust, Ipswich IP4 5PD Email: edelsten@easynet.co.uk — MB BChir 1984 Camb.; MA Camb. 1983; FRCS Glas. 1988; MRCP (UK) 1986; FRCOphth 1990. Cons. Ophth. Ipswich Hosps. NHS Trust; Cons. Med. Ophth. Gt. Ormond St. Hosp. Lond. Prev: Sen. Regist. (Ophth.) Windsor & Oxf.; MRC Train. Fell. Med. Eye Unit St. Thos. Hosp. Lond.

EDELSTEN, Mary Ann 34 Clifton Road, Winchester SO22 5BU — MB BS 1983 Lond.; 1990 JCPTGP; DRCOG 1988. (Middlx.) p/t Clin. Asst. (Med.) S.ampton Univ. Trust. Prev: SHO (ENT & O & G) Roy. Hants. Co. Hosp. Winchester; SHO (Paediat.) N.wick Pk. Hosp. Harrow; GP Trainee Winchester, Hants.

EDELSTEN, Miriam Baddow Road Surgery, 115 Baddow Road, Chelmsford CM2 7PY Tel: 01245 351351 Fax: 01245 494192; Eweland House, Main Road, Margaretting, Ingatestone CM4 9HU — MB ChB 1974 Liverp. Prev: SHO (Paediat.) Alder Hey Childr. Hosp. Liverp.; SHO (O & G) Fazakerley & Walton Hosps. Liverp.; Ho. Surg. Chest Unit BRd.green Gen. Hosp. Liverp.

EDELSTON, Ruth Hester Morris House Surgery, Waltheof Gardens, Tottenham, London N17 7EB Tel: 020 8801 1277 Fax: 020 8801 8228; 20 Brackendale, London N21 3DG Tel: 020 8886 3274 — MB BS 1962 Lond. (Lond. Hosp.) Socs: Brit. Menopause Soc.

EDEN, Ayed Ghalib Zuiable Southend Hospital NHS Trust, Westcliff on Sea SS0 0RY Tel: 01702 221062 Fax: 01702 221059; Witon Haw, Church End, Paglesham, Rochford SS4 2DP Tel: 01702 258152 — MB ChB 1978 Basrah; MRCPI 1994; FRCPath 1987. Cons. Haematologist S.end Hosp. W.cliff on Sea; Hon. Cons. Haemat. St. Bart. Hosp. Lond. Socs: BMA & Brit. Soc. Haemat. Prev: Lect. (Haemat.) St. Mary's Hosp. Med. Sch. Lond.; Sen. Regist. (Haemat.) Roy. Marsden Hosp. Sutton; SHO Ealing Hosp. Lond.

EDEN, Bruce William Radbrook Green Surgery, Bank Farm Road, Shrewsbury SY3 6DU Tel: 01743 231816 Fax: 01743 344099; Beech House, 5 Dovaston Court, West Felton, Oswestry SY11 4EQ Tel: 0169 188397 Email: eden@enta.net — MB ChB 1973 Birm.; MRCGP 1977.

EDEN, David John (retired) Balvenie, 167 Grampian Way, Thorne, Doncaster DN8 5YN — MB ChB 1974 Bristol.

EDEN, Helen Yasmin Flat 149, Russell Court, Woburn Place, London WC1H 0LR — MB BS 1994 Lond.

EDEN, Hiafa Hadi Aboud Southend Hospital, Westcliff on Sea SS0 0RY Tel: 01702 221062 Fax: 01702 221059; Winton Haw, Church End, Paglesham, Rochford SS4 2DP Tel: 01702 258152 — MB ChB 1978 Basrah; FRCPath. 1990; MRCPath 1990. Cons. Haemat. S.end Hosp. W.cliff-on-Sea. Prev: Cons. Haemat. Qu. Mary's Hosp. Lond.; Sen. Regist. Roy. Marsden Hosp. Sutton.

EDEN, Jane Elizabeth 6 Kirkland Avenue, Shrewsbury SY3 5LF Tel: 01743 358514 — MB ChB 1983 Birm.; MRCGP 1988; DRCOG 1986; DGM RCP Lond. 1985. (Birmingham) Prev: Clin. Asst. Risk Factor Clinic Glas. Roy. Infirm.

EDEN, Julian Christopher Paul 111 Mysore Road, Battersea, London SW11 5RZ — MB BS 1988 Lond.; MRCGP 1998; BSc (Psychol.) Lond. 1984, MB BS 1988. (Charing Cross & Westminster) SHO (A & E) Roy. I. of Wight Hosp.Ryde I. of Wight. Socs: BMA. Prev: Ho. Surg. St. Stephen's Hosp. Lond.; Ho. Phys. Roy. Cornw. Hosp. Truro.

EDEN, Professor Osborn Bryan Department of Paediatric Oncology, Christie Hospital, Wilmslow Road, Manchester M20 4BX Tel: 0161 446 3094 Fax: 0161 446 3092; 5 South Gillsland Road, Edinburgh EH10 5DE Tel: 0161 447 8749 — MB BS 1970 Lond.; FRCP Lond. 1992; FRCP Ed. 1983; MRCP (UK) 1974; FRCPCH 1997; FRCPath 1995; DObst RCOG 1972. (Univ. Coll. Hosp. Lond.) Prof. Paediat. Oncol. Univ. Manch.; Chairm. Med. Research Counc. Working Party for Childh. Leukaemia; Ex-Chairm. UK Childr. Cancer Study Gp. Socs: (Scientif. Comm.) Internat. Soc. Paediat. Oncol. (Chairm. Scientif. Comm.); (Comm.) Med. Aspects of Radiat. in Environm.; (Health Servs. Comm.) Brit. Paediat. Assn. (Ex Convener Haematol. & Oncol. Gp. Prev: Prof. Paediat. Oncol. St. Bart. Med. Sch. Lond.; Cons. Paediat. (Haemat. & Oncol.) Roy. Hosp. for Sick Childr. Edin.; Cons. Clin. Haemat. Bristol Childr. Hosp.

EDEN, Robert Ian Brooks Bar Medical Centre, 162-164 Chorlton Road, Old Trafford, Manchester M16 7WW Tel: 0161 226 7777 Fax: 0161 232 9963; 87 Park Road, Prestwich, Manchester M25 8DX — MB ChB 1973 Manch.; MSc Salford 1980.

EDEN, Sharon Beech House, 5 Dovaston Court, West Felton, Oswestry SY11 4EQ — MB ChB 1973 Birm.; DA Eng. 1976.

EDEN, Sidney 50 Bishops Road, Prestwich, Manchester M25 0AS Tel: 0161 773 3040 — MRCS Eng. LRCP Lond. 1946. (Manch.)

EDENBOROUGH, Frank Peter Adult Cystic Fibrosis Unit, Sorby Wing, Northern General Hospital, Herries Road, Sheffield S5 7AU Tel: 0114 271 4770 Fax: 0114 226 6280 Email: frank.edenborough@northngh-tr.trent.nhs.uk — BM BS 1988 Nottm.; BMedSci (Hons.) Nottm. 1986; MRCP Lond. 1991; DTM & H Lond. 1993; DM 1999 Nottm. (Nottingham University) Cons. Respirat. Phys. N.ern Gen. Hosp. Sheff. Socs: Brit. Thorac. Soc. & Midl. Thoracic Soc.; Roy. Coll. Phys. Prev: Specialist Regist. (Respirat. & Gen. Internal Med.); Clin. Fell. (Adult Cystic Fibrosis Med.) Birm. Heartlands NHS Hosp. Trust; Regist. Rotat. (Respirat. & Gen. Med.) Birm. Heartlands Hosp., Sandwell Hosp. & Qu. Eliz. Hosp. Birm.

EDESON, John Francis Bland (retired) 18 Glentilt Road, Sheffield S7 2EG — MB ChB 1942 Sheff.; BSc Lond. 1937; MD Sheff. 1954; DPH Liverp. 1965. Prev: Prof. Parasitol. & Trop. Health Amer. Univ. Beirut, Lebanon.

EDEY, Matthew Michael James Denbourne, Riverside Close, Oundle, Peterborough PE8 4DN — MB BS 1997 Newc.

EDGAR, Andrew John Brunswick House Medical Group, 1 Brunswick Street, Carlisle CA1 1ED Tel: 01228 515808 Fax: 01228 593048 — BM BS 1984 Nottm.; BM BS Nottm. l984.

EDGAR, Anthea Clare Drake The Beeches, Linton, Cambridge CB1 6JZ Tel: 01223 891205 — MB BS 1967 Lond.; MRCS Eng. LRCP Lond. 1967; DObst RCOG 1969. (Guy's) GP Saffron Walden; Clin. Asst. (Genitourin. Med.) Addenbrooke's Hosp. Camb. Prev: Ho. Surg., Ho. Phys. & SHO (O & G) P.ss Alexandra Hosp. Harlow.

EDGAR, Brian McCammon (retired) Orchard Farmhouse, High St., Stanton, Broadway WR12 7NE — MB BCh BAO 1948 Belf.

EDGAR, Claire Boag Flat 1/2, 102 Queensborough Gardens, Glasgow G12 9RU — MB ChB 1991 Glas.

EDGAR, F M The Surgery, 270 Hook Road, Chessington KT9 1PF Tel: 020 8397 3574.

EDGAR, Freda Elizabeth (retired) Nether Hall, Station Road, Baildon, Shipley BD17 6NW Tel: 01274 583013 Email: edgar@triom.net — MB BS 1952 Lond.; MRCS Eng. LRCP Lond. 1952; FFA RCS Eng. 1956; DA Eng. 1954. Prev: Cons. Anaesth. Bradford Gp. Hosps.

EDGAR, John David Moore Regional Immunology Service, Microbiology Building, Royal Victoria Hospital, Belfast BT12 6BN Tel: 01232 894670 Fax: 01232 263129 Email: david.edgar@bll.n-i.nhs.uk; 145B Millisle Road, Donaghadee BT21 0LA Tel: 01247 888748 Email: david.edgar@tinyonline.co.uk — MB BCh BAO 1985 Belf.; BSc (Hons.) Belf. 1982; MRCP (UK) 1989; MRCPath 1996; FRCP Ed. 1998. (Qu. Univ. Belf.) Cons. Immunol. Belf. City & Roy. Vict. Hosps. Socs: BSI; BSACI; ACP. Prev: Sen. Regist. (Immunol.) Univ. Hosp. Nottm. Qu. Med. Centre; Regist. (Immunol.) Belf.

EDGAR, John Gordon (retired) 23 Dolphin Court, St. Helens Parade, Southsea PO4 0QL Tel: 02392 738755 — MB ChB Leeds 1951; MRCGP 1963; DCH Eng. 1954. Prev: Examg. Med. Off. DHSS Lond.

EDGAR, Keith Joseph The Surgery, Barr Lane, Brinklow, Rugby CV23 0LU Tel: 01788 832994 Fax: 01788 833021; 1 Stocking Meadow, Monks Kirby, Rugby CV23 0RF Tel: 01788 832653 — MB BCh BAO 1982 Belf.; MRCGP 1990; DRCOG 1988. GP Brinklow; Course Organiser Coventry & Warks. VTS; Treas. Nat. Assn. Commiss.ing GPs; Indep. Med. Consg. Servs. Socs: BMA; Brit. Soc. Med. & Dent. Hypn.

EDGAR, Margaret Cockburn 5 West Fenton Gait, Gullane EH31 2HS Tel: 01620 843967 — MB BS Lond. 1969; DA Eng. 1973; DObst RCOG 1971.

EDGAR, Mark Anthony Trust Headquarters, Gipsy Lane, Humberstone, Leicester LE5 0TD Tel: 0116 246 0100 Fax: 0116 246 1222; Bridge House, Nether End, Great Dalby, Melton Mowbray LE14 2EY Tel: 01664 63574 — MB BS 1971 Newc.; MSc Manch. 1986; MFPHM RCP (UK) 1987; MFCM 1987. Med. Dir. Leics. & Rutland Healthcare NHS Trust. Prev: Regional Cons. Pub. Health Med. N.. W.. RHA; Cons. Pub. Health Med. Tameside & Glossop HA; Dir. Pub. Health W. Lancs. HA.

EDGAR, Mr Michael Alan 149 Harley Street, London W1N 2DE Tel: 020 7486 0027 Fax: 020 7487 5997 Email: mae@149harleystreet.co.uk; Fax: 020 7487 5997 — MB BChir Camb. 1964; MA Camb. 1965, MChir 1977; FRCS Eng. 1967. (Camb. & St. Thos.) Cons. Orthop. Surg. Middlx. Hosp. Lond., Roy. Nat. Orthop. Hosp. Lond. & King Edwd. V11 Hosp. Offs. Lond.; Hon. Cons. Nat. Hosp. Neurol. & Neurosurg. Qu. Sq. Lond.; Civil Cons. (Orthop.) RAF; Trustee Brit. Scoliosis Research Foundat. Socs: (Sec.) Brit. Orthop. Assn.; (Pres.) Brit. Scoliosis Soc.; (Counc.) Roy. Coll. Surgs. Eng. Prev: Sen. Regist. (Orthop.) Middlx. Hosp. Lond.; Regist. (Orthop.) Robt. Jones & Agnes Hunt Orthop. Hosp. OsW.ry; Ho. Surg. St. Thos. Hosp. Lond.

EDGAR, Paul Charles 114 Queens Road, Bury St Edmunds IP33 3ES — MB ChB 1993 Glas. SHO (Orthop.) Stracathro Hosp. Angus. Prev: SHO (A & E) Monklands Dist. Gen. Hosp. Airdrie; Ho. Off. (Gen. Surg.) Inverclyde Roy. Hosp. Greenock; Ho. Off. (Gen. Med.) Stobhill Hosp. Glas.

EDGAR, William, OBE (retired) Shepherds, Crowsley Road, Lower Shiplake, Henley-on-Thames RG9 3JU Tel: 0118 940 3232 — MB ChB Ed. 1943; FFCM 1972; DCH Eng. 1949; DPH 1948. Prev: Dist. Community Phys. W. Berks. Health Dist.

EDGAR, William Macreadie (retired) Nether Hall, Station Road, Baildon, Shipley BD17 6NW Tel: 01274 583013 — MRCS Eng. LRCP Lond. 1946; MA Camb. 1950, BA 1944, MD 1961, MB BChir 1946; FRCPath 1969, M 1963. Prev: Cons. Microbiol. Bradford HA.

EDGCUMBE, John Oliver Pearce (retired) 10 Cyprus Road, Exmouth EX8 2DZ Tel: 01395 264328 — MB BChir 1946 Camb.; MD Camb. 1952, MA, MB BChir 1946; MRCS Eng., LRCP Lond. 1946; FRCPath 1963. Prev: Cons. (Haemat.) Exeter HA.

EDGE, Mr Anthony John 31 Downview Road, Worthing BN11 4QP Tel: 01903 248673 Fax: 01903 248673; Kents Farm, Brookpit Lane, Climping, Littlehampton BN17 5QU Tel: 01903 721425 Fax: 01903 248673 Email: johnedge@kentsfarm.freeserve.co.uk — MB ChB 1968 St. And.; FRCS Eng. 1973. Cons. Surg. Orthop. Worthing Health Dist.; Regional Specialty Adviser (Orthop.) S. Thames W.; Chairm. Specialty Train. Comm. S. Thames W.; Hosp. Recognition Comm. Roy. Coll. of Surg.s. Socs: Fell RCS (Regional Specialty Adviser); Fell. BOA; Roy. Soc. Med. Prev: Orthop. Sen. Regist. Soton. & S.W. Hants. Health Dist. (T).

EDGE, Antony Norman Richmond Group Medical Centre, 1 Albion Street, Ashton-under-Lyne OL6 6HF Tel: 0161 339 9161 Fax: 0161 343 5131; Rivendell, 56C Manchester Road, Greenfield, Oldham OL3 7HJ Tel: 01457 870420 — MB ChB 1986 Manch.; MRCGP 1990; DRCOG 1990. Socs: BMA.

EDGE, Christopher John The Stone Barn, Gravel Lane, Drayton, Abingdon OX14 4HY Tel: 01235 529888 — MB BS 1984 Lond.; PhD Camb. 1979, MA 1980.

EDGE, Mr Colin James Maxillofacial Unit, Middlesborough General Hospital, Ayresome Green Lane, Middlesbrough TS5 5AZ — BM 1984 Soton.; BDS Lond. 1976; FDS RCS Eng. 1986, LDS 1977; FRCS Ed. 1988. Cons. (Oral & Maxillofacial Surg.) Middlesbrough

Gen. Hosp. Socs: BMA; Fell. Brit. Assn. Oral & Maxillo-Facial Surgs. Prev: Sen. Regist. (Oral & Maxillo-Facial Surg.) Qu. Vict. Hosp. E. Grinstead; Regist. (Oral & Maxillo-Facial Surg.) Kingston Hosp.; SHO (ENT) Soton. Gen. Hosp.

EDGE, Dawn Marie Longton Health Centre, Liverpool Road, Longton, Preston PR4 5HA Tel: 01772 615429 Fax: 01772 611094; 62 Church Lane, Charnock Richard, Chorley PR7 3RB Tel: 01257 263137 — MB ChB 1989 Liverp.; MRCGP 1994; DRCOG 1992; DCH RCP Lond. 1991. (Liverp.) Prev: Trainee GP Leyland, Lancs. VTS; Trainee GP/SHO Roy. Preston Hosp.; Ho. Off. (Med. & Surg.) S.port Dist. Gen. Hosp.

EDGE, James David (retired) 123 Carr Head Lane, Poulton-le-Fylde FY6 8EG Tel: 01253 890852 — BM BCh 1971 Oxf.; MA (Biochem.). Prev: Sports Phys. Blackpool.

EDGE, Jane Caroline Steels Lane Health Centre, 384-388 Commercial Road, London E1 0LR Tel: 020 7265 8655 Fax: 020 7702 8023; 31 Therapia Road, London SE22 0SF Tel: 020 8299 3785 — MB BS 1986 Lond.; MRCGP 1991; DRCOG 1991. Prev: GP Lond. Sch. Economics Health Centre; Trainee GP Leicester VTS.

EDGE, Janet Mary 59 Bryn Castell, Abergele LL22 8QA — MB ChB 1991 Ed.

EDGE, John Michael Harry Radiology Dept, Cumberland Infirmary, Carlisle CA4 7HY Tel: 01228 814589; Cairnbridge House, Heads Nook, Brampton CA8 9EH Tel: 01228 560350 — MB BS 1985 Lond.; MA Camb. 1986, BA 1982; MRCP (UK) 1989; FRCR 1993. (Kings' College Hospital London) Cons. Radiol. Cumbld. Infirm. Carlisle. Prev: Regist. & Sen. Regist. (Diag. Radiol.) Leicester Radiol. Train. Scheme.

EDGE, Julie Anne Department of Paediatrics, John Radcliffe Hospital, Oxford OX3 9DU Tel: 01865 221488 Fax: 01865 220479; 12 Conduit Road, Abingdon OX14 1DB Tel: 01235 550706 — MB ChB 1980 Bristol; MD Bristol 1992; MRCP (UK) 1983; FRCPCH 1997; DCH RCP Lond. 1982. Cons. Paediat. John Radcliffe Hosp. Oxf. Socs: Brit. Soc. Paediat. Endocrinol. & Diabetes; Brit. Diabetic Assn.

EDGE, Margaret (retired) Fernwood, 66 Alton Road, London SW15 4NJ Tel: 020 8788 9083 — MB ChB Liverp. 1939; DCH Eng. 1947; CPH Lond. 1946. Prev: SCMO Merton, Sutton & Wandsworth AHA (T).

EDGE, May Bulloch (retired) Southmeadow, 45 Greenhill Road, Otford, Sevenoaks TN14 5RR Tel: 01959 523158 — MB ChB Glas. 1943. DPH 1948; MFPHM 1972. Prev: Sen. Med. Off. Greenwich & Bexley AHA.

EDGE, P Geraldine Royal National Orthopaedic Hospital, Stanmore HA7 4LP Tel: 020 8954 2300; 65 Embry Way, Stanmore HA7 3AY — MB BS 1985 Lond.; PhD Lond. 1978; BSc Surrey 1972; FRCA 1993. (Charing Cross) Cons. (Anaesth.) Roy. Nat. Orthop. Hosp., Stanmore. Socs: AAGBI; Treas. Brit. Soc. Orthop. Anaesth. Prev: Sen. Regist. Rotat. Hammersmith Hosp. Lond.

***EDGE, Rosalind Mary** 30 Temple Street, Brill, Aylesbury HP18 9SX Tel: 01844 237151 — MB BS 1998 Newc.; MB BS Newc 1998; BSc Intercalated, London (UCL) 1997.

EDGE, Rosemary (retired) 27 Parkfield Road, Coleshill, Birmingham B46 3LD Tel: 01675 463165 Fax: 01675 466253 — MB BCh BAO Dub. 1956; DObst RCOG 1959.

EDGE, Vivien Mary 177 Congleton Road, Scholar Green, Stoke-on-Trent ST7 3HA; 162 Condell Avenue, Papanui, Christchurch 5, New Zealand Tel: 013 352 6877 — MB ChB 1983 Birm.; MRCGP 1991; DRCOG 1990; Cert. Family Plann. JCC 1990; DA (UK) 1986.

EDGE, William George (retired) Department of Anaesthetics, Stoke Mandeville Hospital, Aylesbury HP21 8AL Tel: 01296 315000 — MB ChB 1966 Ed.; FRCA 1976; DA (UK) 1973. Prev: Sen. Regist. (Anaesth.) Hammersmith Hosp. Lond.

EDGECOMBE, Jane Frances 35 Crosby Road, West Bridgeford, Nottingham NG2 5GG Tel: 0115 974 3859 Email: jane.dave@virgin.net — MB BS 1989 Lond.; MRCP (UK) 1993. (Lond. Hosp. Med. Coll.) Specialist Regist. Nottm. City Hosp.

EDGECOMBE, Philip Charles Egerton (retired) 9 Gloucester Road, Knutsford WA16 0EJ Tel: 01565 633933 Email: pce.edgecombe@virgin.net — MB BS 1955 Lond.; DObst RCOG 1961.

EDGECOMBE, Simon John Kiltearn Medical Centre, 33 Hospital Street, Nantwich CW5 5RN Tel: 01270 610200 Fax: 01270 610637; 29 Marsh Lane, Nantwich CW5 5HH Tel: 01270 610866 — MB BS 1986 Lond.; MRCGP 1990; DCH RCP Lond. 1989; Dip. Palliat. 1998. (Cardiff, University of Wales college of medicine) Clin. Asst. (Palliat. Care) Marie Curie Centre Liverp.

EDGELL, Alexandra Frances c/o Royal Lancaster Infirmary, Ashton Road, Lancaster LA1 4RP; 3 Bell Hill, Levens, Kendal LA8 8NQ — MB ChB 1984 Zimbabwe.

EDGELL, Mr Martin Selby Boxtree Crescent, Levens, Kendal LA8 8NZ — MB BS 1979 Lond.; FRCS Eng. 1983. (St. Geo.)

EDGER, Mr Michael John Holmeview, 14 Hensingham Road, Whitehaven CA28 8PS Email: medger@resed.ac.uk — MB BS 1993 Lond.; BSc (Hons.) Lond. 1990; FRCS Ed. 1998; FRCS Glas. 1998. (St. Geo. Hosp. Med. Sch.) SHO (Neurosurg.) Roy. Lond. Hosp., Whitechapel. Prev: SHO (Neurosurg) Inst. of Neurol. Sci.s Glas.; SHO (Neurosurg.) Nat. Hosp. Qu. Sq. Lond.; SHO (Surg.) Roy. Lancaster Infirm.

EDGERLEY, Robert Ian Nansmellion Road Health Centre, Nansmellion Road, Mullion, Helston TR12 7DQ Tel: 01326 240212 Fax: 01326 240420 — MB BChir 1981 Camb.; MB ChB Chir. Camb. 1981.

EDGHILL, Harold Byron 12 Darwin Crt., Green Acres, North Park, Eltham, London SE9 5BD — MB BS 1953 Lond.; DA Eng. 1960. (Westm.) Prev: Regist. Anaesth. Metrop. Hosp.; Ho. Phys. Gordon Hosp. Lond.; Ho. Surg. All St.'s (W.m. Hosp.) Lond.

EDGINGTON, John (retired) 7 Laurels Garth, Sheriff Hutton, York YO60 6SE — MB ChB Birm. 1952; MRCGP 1975; DTM & H Eng. 1962. Prev: Pres. Standing Med. Bd. York.

EDGINGTON, Kenneth (retired) Airport Medical Services, Forte Post House Hotel, Povey Cross Road, Horley RH6 0YR Tel: 01293 775336 Fax: 01293 775344 Email: amsgatwick@compuserve.com — MRCS Eng. LRCP Lond. 1965; FFOM RCP Lond. 1994, MFOM 1981; DAvMed Eng. 1972; FRCP 2000 Lond. Cons. Occup. Aviat. Med. Airport. Med. Serv. Gatwick Airport & Rood La. Med. Gp., City of Lond.; Authorised Med. Examr. Civil Aviat. Auth. & USFAA; Hon. Civil. Cons. Aviat. Med. RN & Army; Reader Civil Aviat. Med. RAF. Prev: Head UK Health Servs. Brit. Airways1988-1992.

***EDGINGTON, Penelope Jane** 1 Tynedale's Meadow, Dinton, Salisbury SP3 5HU — MB ChB 1977 Leeds.

EDGINTON, Sonya 50 Avondale Court, Liverpool Road, London E16 4LX — LMSSA 1995 Lond.

EDGLEY, John Neville Kingsmere, 12 The Avenue, Alsager, Stoke-on-Trent ST7 2AN Tel: 01270 875426 — MB ChB 1960 Ed.; DObst RCOG 1962. (Ed.) Prev: Ho. Surg. Birm. Matern. Hosp.

EDGLEY, Robert Steel 57 Holland Park, London W11 3RS — MB BS 1952 Sydney; MRACGP 1968. (Sydney) Commonw. Med. Off. (Austral. Dept. Health) & Med. Ref. Migration; Br., Austral. High Commiss. Lond.; Mem. Austral. War Pens. Assessm. Appeal Tribunals; Pens. Off. Lond. Br., Returned Servs. League of Austral.; Medico-Legal Adviser, Lond. Legacy; Austral. Mem. Commonw. Counc. Brit. Commonw. Ex-Servs. League. Socs: Fell. Roy. Soc. Med.; Soc. Psychosomatic Research. Prev: Capt. RAAMC; Med. Dir. Austral. Embassy Turkey.

EDHEM, Isa 49 Hillfield Park, Winchmore Hill, London N21 3QJ — MB BS 1989 Lond.; BSc (Hons.) Lond. 1986, MB BS 1989; FRCS 1996. Clin. Research Regist. Inst. of Urol. Lond. Socs: Brit. Assn. Urol. Surg.; Jun. Mem. Europ. Assn. Urol. Prev: SHO Rotat. (Gen. Surg.) Whipps Cross Hosp. Lond.; Demonst. (Anat.) Univ. Oxf.; SHO (Paediat. Surg.) Hosp. For Sick Childr. Gt. Ormond St. Lond.

EDHOUSE, Miss June Anne 43A Button Hill, Sheffield S11 9HF Tel: 0114 235 0426; Marlfield Cottage, 76 Coppice Rd, Poynton, Stockport SK12 1SN Tel: 01625 876789 — MB ChB 1986 Manch.; FRCS Ed. 1992; FFAEM 1999. (Vict. Univ. Manch.) Cons A & E Med., Steppinghill Hosp. Stockport. Prev: SHO (A & E) Stockport Infirm. Manch.; Ho. Off. (Gen. Surg.) Pk. Hosp. Davyhulme; Ho. Off. (Gen. Med.) Univ. Hosp. S. Manch.

EDINGTON, Francis Cameron (retired) The Beeches, Fell Lane, Penrith CA11 8AQ — MB ChB 1939 Ed. Prev: Res. Ho. Surg. & Res. Ho. Phys. Roy. Infirm. Edin.

EDINGTON, Jane Helen Rowand Morningside Medical Practice, 2 Morningside Place, Edinburgh EH10 5ER Tel: 0131 452 8406 Fax: 0131 447 3020; 8 Craiglockhart Bank, Edinburgh EH14 1JH — MB ChB 1982 Ed.; BSc (Biol. Sci.) Ed. 1977; DRCOG; MRCGP. Socs: BMA; Roy. Coll. Gen. Pract.

EDINGTON, Mr Paul Tellet (cons. rooms), 11 Regent St., Nottingham NG1 5BS Tel: 0115 947 5475 Fax: 0115 924 1606;

Baildon House, Baildon Close, Wollaton Park, Nottingham NG8 1BS Tel: 0115 978 6187 — MB BChir Camb. 1969; MA Camb. 1968; MRCS Eng. LRCP Lond. 1967; FRCOG 1990, M 1974. (Camb. & St. Mary's) Cons. O & G Univ. Hosp. Qu. Med. Centre Nottm. Socs: BMA; Gyn. Club. Prev: Sen. Regist. (O & G) Newc. HA; Regist. (O & G) St. Mary's Hosp. Lond.; Resid. Med. Off. Qu. Charlotte's Matern. Hosp. Lond.

EDIRISINGHE, Damitha Niromal Rowan House, Royal Liverpool University Hospital, Prescot St., Liverpool L7 8XP Tel: 07775 878402 Email: d.n.edirisinghe@liv.ac.uk; No.3 Sirigal Avenue, Kohuwala, Nugegoda, Sri Lanka Tel: 00 94 1 852807 — LRCP LRCS 1991 Ed.; LRCP LRCS Ed. LRCPS Glas. 1991; MBCHB Ed. 1992; MRCPI Irel. 1997. (Edinburgh) Clin. Asst. Roy. Liverp. Univ. Hosp. Prev: Research Fell. Univ. of Liverp.; SHO (Gastroenterol.) Gartnaval Geneal Hosp. Glas.; SHO Lincoln Co. Hosp.

EDIRISOORIYA, Ananda Wipulasena 38 Haddington Road, Whitley Bay NE25 9UY — MB BS 1973 Sri Lanka; FRCR 1981.

EDISON, Mini Mary 43 Parkstone Avenue, Emerson Park, Hornchurch RM11 3LN Tel: 014027 23132 — MRCS Eng. LRCP Lond. 1989; MB BS Kerala 1987.

EDKINS, Claire Louise 11 Keepers Close, Guildford GU4 7DB — BM 1992 Soton.; DA 1995; FRCA Lond. 1997. Regist. (Anaesth.) St Geo.s Hosp. Lond. Socs: Fell. Roy. Coll. Anaesths.; Anaesths. Assn.; Obst. Anaesth. Assn. Prev: Regist. (Anaesth.) Crawley Hosp. Lond.; Regist. (Anaesth.) Roy. Co. Surrey Guildford; SHO (Anaesth.) Frimley Pk. Hosp. Surrey.

EDMANDS, Deborah Frances Barn Acre, Juggs Road, Kingston, Lewes BN7 3JT — MB BS 1996 Lond.

EDMENDS, Shireen Directorate of Anaesthesia, City General, Newcastle Road, Stoke-on-Trent ST4 6QG Tel: 01782 552884 — MB BS 1987 Lond.; FRCA 1992; DA (UK) 1989; M Med Sci (Keele) 1997. Cons. Anaesth., N. Staffs. Hosp., Stoke on Trent. Socs: BMA; Assn. Anaesth. GB & Irel.; Assn. of Paediatric Anaesth.s. Prev: Sen. Regist. (Anaesth.) N. Staffs. Hosp. Stoke-on-Trent; Fell. Anaesth Monash Med. Centre Melbourne, Austral.; Regist. (Anaesth.) Addenbrooke's Hosp. Camb.

EDMISTON, David Ramsay 159 Pickering Road, Hull HU4 6TB Tel: 01482 508919 — MB ChB St. And. 1952; DPH Glas. 1959.

EDMOND, Helen Louise Lour Road Group Practice, 3 Lour Road, Forfar DD8 2AS Tel: 01307 463122 Fax: 01307 465278 — MB ChB 1992 Dundee.

EDMOND, Maurice Coull (retired) Field End, Shore Road, Bosham, Chichester PO18 8QL Tel: 01243 572355 — MRCS Eng. LRCP Lond. 1940; MA Camb. 1941, MB BChir 1947.

EDMOND, Neil Lennox Wellfield Surgery, 291 Oldham Road, Rochdale OL16 5HX Tel: 01706 355111; 30 Spencer Lane, Bamford, Rochdale OL11 5PE Tel: 01706 360701 — MB ChB 1953 Aberd.; DA Eng. 1958.

EDMOND, Mr Peter, CBE, TD National Spinal Injuries Centre, Southern General Hospital, 1345 Govan Road, Glasgow G51 4TF Tel: 0141 201 2555 Fax: 0141 201 2991; Flat 4/30 Mavisbank Gardens, Festival Park, Glasgow G51 1HG Tel: 0141 427 1299 — MB ChB 1958 Ed.; FRCS Glas. 1989; FRCS Ed. 1963; FRCP Ed. 1988. (Ed.) Dir. Nat. Spinal Unit Scotl. Prev: Cons. Urol. Surg. & Sen. Lect. Roy. Infirm. Edin.; Lect. (Clin. Surg.) Univ. Edin.; Hon. Surg. to HM the Qu. (TA).

EDMONDS, Cyril Michael Douglas 71 Lombard Street, London EC3P 3BS Tel: 020 7626 1500 — MB BS 1955 Lond.; DPH 1965; AFOM RCP Lond. 1979; DA Eng. 1958. (St. Bart.) Med. Adviser Lloyds Bank. Prev: Sen. Med. Off. Brit. Leyland Cars; Dep. Co. MOH Warks; Med. Off. Colon. Med. Serv. Kenya.

EDMONDS, Douglas Keith Queen Charlotte's & Chelsea Hospital, Goldhawk Road, London W6 0XG Tel: 020 8748 4666; 78 Harley Street, London W1N 1AE Tel: 020 7636 4797 Fax: 020 7323 0488 — MB ChB 1973 Sheff.; FRCOG 1990, M 1978; FRACOG 1980, M 1979. Cons. O & G Qu. Charlotte's & Chelsea Hosp. Lond. Prev: Sen. Regist. P.ss Anne Hosp. Soton; Regist. Soton. Gen. Hosp.; SHO Jessop Hosp. for Wom., Sheff.

EDMONDS, Duncan Alexander (retired) Leo House, The Green, Stalham, Norwich NR12 9PU Tel: 01692 580712 — MB BS Lond. 1962; DObst RCOG 1964. Prev: Ho. Surg. & Ho. Phys. St. Geo. Hosp. Lond.

EDMONDS, Emma Veronica Jane 64 Fielding Road, London W4 1HL — MB BS 1998 Lond.; MB BS Lond 1998.

EDMONDS, Ginette Marie Woodlands, 88 Westmoreland Road, Bromley BR2 0RZ Tel: 020 8464 7554; Woodlands, 88 Westmoreland Road, Bromley BR2 0RZ Tel: 020 8464 7554 — MB ChB 1951 Bristol; MRCS Eng. LRCP Lond. 1950. (Bristol) Indep. GP Bromley. Socs: BMA; Anglo-French Med. Soc. Prev: GP Beckenham; Ho. Surg. Bristol Roy. Infirm.; Med. Off. i/c Officials Kuala Lumpur.

EDMONDS, Jack Andre Thomas The Devonshire Clinic, Flat A, 21 Devonshire Place, London W1G 6HZ Tel: 020 7935 8666 Fax: 020 7935 6370 Email: devonshirecliniclondon@virgin.net; Little Crossways, 14 Amersham Road, Chesham Bois, Amersham HP6 5PE Tel: 01494 727831 Fax: 01494 727551 Email: dr.jackedmonds@virgin.net — MB BS 1978 Lond.; MRCGP 1983. (Royal Free Hospital London) GP Lond.; Med. Off. (Occupat. Health) Taylor Woodrow S.all. Socs: BMA; Soc. Occupat. Med.; Roy. Soc. Med. Prev: Clin. Tutor (Gen. Pract.) Univ. Coll. & Middlx. Hosps. Lond.; Clin. Asst. (Rheum.) Roy. N.. Hosp.; SHO (Gen. Med.) Lister Hosp. Stevenage & Orpington Hosp.

EDMONDS, Jean Cross Deep Surgery, 4 Cross Deep, Twickenham TW1 4QP Tel: 020 8892 8124 Fax: 020 8744 9801; Ave. House, Avenue Road, Teddington TW11 0BT Tel: 0208 977 9467 Fax: 0208 977 9467 — MB ChB 1973 Sheff.; DCH RCPS Glas. 1975.

EDMONDS, John Philip Foster Outwood Park Medical Centre, Potouens Lane, Wakefield WF1 2PE Tel: 01924 822626 Fax: 01924 786248; 14 Broomhall Avenue, Wakefield WF1 2AZ Tel: 01924 363889 — MB BS 1971 Lond.; MRCGP 1976; DObst RCOG 1975. (Roy. Free) Gen. Practitioner Wakefield; Med. Adviser. Polestar Chantry, Wakefield. Socs: Memeber of Soc. of Occupat.al Med. Prev: SHO (Paediat.) Seacroft Hosp. Leeds; Cas. Off. & 1st Ho. Surg. Roy. Free Hosp. Lond.

EDMONDS, Joy Elizabeth Underwood Surgery, Llanmartin, Newport — MB BCh 1979 Wales.

EDMONDS, Michael Edwin 226 Denmark Hill, Camberwell, London SE5 8DX Tel: 020 7274 7911 — MD 1985 Lond.; BSc 1969, MB BS 1972; FRCP Eng. 1991; MRCP (UK) 1977; AKC 1969. Sen. Lect. & Hon. Cons. Phys. (Diabetic Dept.) King's Coll. Hosp. Lond.; Hon. Cons. Phys. Dulwich Hosp. Socs: Assn. Phys. Prev: Cons. Phys. Qu. Vict. Hosp. E. Grinstead; Lect. & Hon. Sen. Regist. Diabetic Dept. Kings Coll. Hosp. Lond.; Regist. Prof. Unit Therap. St. Stephens Hosp. Chelsea.

EDMONDS, Neil Robertson Vickers Queen Elizabeth NHS Trust, Queen Elizabeth Hospital, Stadium Road, London SE18 4QH Tel: 020 8312 6029; 11 Hyde Vale, Greenwich, London SE10 8QQ Tel: 020 8691 4791 — MRCS Eng. LRCP Lond. 1967; FRCR 1978; DMRD Eng. 1972. (Sheff.) Cons. Radiol. Greenwich Healthcare Trust; Radiol. HMP Belmarsh; Hon. Cons. Kings Coll. Hosp. Socs: Brit. Inst. Radiol.; Blackheath Radiol. Soc. Prev: Cons. Radiol. Greenwich Dist. Hosp., Woolwich Memor. & Lond.; Sen. Regist. (Diag. Radiol.) Guy's Hosp. Lond.; Regist. (Radiol.) Sheff. HA.

EDMONDS, Oliver Philip (retired) 21 Gaddum Road, Bowdon, Altrincham WA14 3PD Tel: 0161 928 2152 — MB ChB 1945 Leeds; LLB Lond. 1957; MD Leeds 1958; FFOM RCP Lond. 1981; MFOM 1978; MFCM RCP (UK) 1973. Prev: Hon. Lect. (Occupat. Health) Manch.

EDMONDS, Paul Philip Foster 21 Gaddum Road, Bowdon, Altrincham WA14 3PD — MB BS 1991 Lond.; MRCP (UK) 1996. (Kings Coll. Lond.) Cons. Phys. & Geriat.ian, Hexham Gen. Hosp. N.umberland. Prev: Specialist Regist. (Gen. Med. & Geriat.) N. Region.

EDMONDS, Polly Palliative CareTeam, King's College Hospital, Denmark Hill, London SE5 9RS Tel: 020 7346 4060, 020 7346 4713 Email: polly.edmonds@kcl.ac.uk; 82 Eversleigh Road, London SW11 5XA — MB BS 1987 Lond.; MRCP (UK) 1990. (St. Mary's Hosp. Med. Sch.) Cons. (Palliat. Med.) King's Coll. Hosp. Prev: Sen. Regist. (Palliat. Med.) St. Geo. Hosp. & Trinity Hospice; Sen. Lect. (Palliat. Med.) GKTSM.

EDMONDS, Roger William (retired) Old Palace Farmhouse, Kings Somborne, Stockbridge SO20 6NJ Tel: 01794 389014 Fax: 01794 389018 — MB BS 1954 Lond.; MRCS Eng. LRCP Lond. 1954; DObst RCOG 1958; FRCGP 1976, M 1964. Clin. Teach. (Gen. Pract.) Soton. Univ. Med. Sch. Prev: Upjohn Fell. RCGP.

EDMONDS, Sally Elizabeth Stoke Mandeville Hospital NHS Trust, Aylesbury HP21 8AL Tel: 01296 316664; 5 Church Street, Brill, Aylesbury HP18 9RT — MB BS 1987 Lond.; MRCP (UK) 1991. (Univ. Coll. Hosp. Lond.) Cons. Rheum. Stoke Mandeville Hosp. &

Nuffield Orthop. Centre Oxf. Socs: Brit. Soc. Rheum.; Roy. Soc. of Med. Prev: Sen. Regist. (Rheum.) Wexham Pk. Hosp.; Clin. Research Fell. Bone & Jt. Research Unit Lond. Hosp. Med. Coll.

EDMONDS, Sally Margaret 15 Goring Lodge, Pegasus Grange, Whitehouse Road, Oxford OX1 4QE; Bethesda Hospital, P. Bog X602, Ubombo 3970, South Africa — MB ChB 1992 Birm.; BSc (Hons.) Hull 1987; DRCOG 1995; Dip. Trop. Med. & Hyg. (Liverp.) 1995. (Birm) SHO O & G.

EDMONDS, Mr Simon Edward Foster Royal Sussex County Hospital, Eastern Rd, Brighton BN2 5BE Tel: 01273 696955; Tel: 01273 738028 — MB BS 1993 Lond.; MRCOG 2001; DFFP 1998; BSc Lond 1990; 1999 FRCS Ed. (St Thomas' Hosp. Medical School. Lond.) SpR (O&G) Roy. Sussex Co. Hosp.; Med. Off. for Flight Retrieval Company, Europitssis, Sussex. Prev: Specialist Regist. O & G Ashford; Surgic. Regist. / Obst. Regist. Qu.sland Australia; SSHO St Thomas Hosp. O & G.

EDMONDS, Suzanne Mary University of East Anglia Health Centre, University of East Anglia, Earlham Road, Norwich NR4 7TJ Tel: 01603 592172 — MB BS 1980 Lond.; DRCOG 1983. (Royal Free Hospital London) Prev: Police Surg. Norf. Constab.

EDMONDS-SEAL, Rev. John (retired) Otway, Woodperry Road, Beckley, Oxford OX3 9UY — MB BS 1958 Lond.; MRCS Eng. LRCP Lond. 1960; FFA RCS Eng. (Nuffield Prize) 1963; DA Eng. 1960. Hon. Cons. Anaesth. Oxon. HA & Hon. Clin. Lect. Nuffield Dept. Anaesth. Univ. Oxf. Prev: Regional Educat. Adviser Anaesth. (Oxf.) Fac. Anaesth. RCS Eng.

EDMONDSON, Aline Nancy (retired) 33 Old Road, Mottram, Hyde SK14 6LW Tel: 01457 762098 — MB ChB 1945 Liverp. Asst. Co. Med. Off. Chesh. CC.

EDMONDSON, Charles Richard The Surgery, 10 Compayne Gardens, London NW6 3DH Tel: 020 7624 5883 Fax: 020 7328 8670; 79 Torbay Road, London NW6 7DU — MB BChir 1973 Camb.; MRCP (UK) 1976; MRCGP 1983.

EDMONDSON, Charlotte Lucy Stables Cottage, Builth Wells LD2 3NP — MB BCh 1998 Wales.

EDMONDSON, David Brayshay Victoria Gate Surgery, East Reach, Taunton TA1 3EX Tel: 01823 275656 Fax: 01823 321883; 5 Fons George Road, Taunton TA1 3JU Tel: 01823 272038 — MB BS 1971 Lond.; MRCP (UK) 1976; MRCS Eng. LRCP Lond. 1971; DObst RCOG 1976. (St. Bart.) Chairm. Taunton & Area PCG. Prev: SHO (O & G) Yeovil Dist. Hosp.; SHO (Med.) Leicester Roy. Infirm. & Groby Rd. Hosp. Leicester.

EDMONDSON, Diane Louise 4 Broadway, Sale M33 6NR — MB ChB 1993 Leic.

EDMONDSON, Edwin David 17 St John Street, Manchester M3 4DG Tel: 0161 834 9050 — MB ChB 1944 Liverp. (Liverp.)

EDMONDSON, Gill Micquetta Pye The Kaya Practice, Chorlton Health Centre, 1 Nicolas Road, Chorlton, Manchester M21 7PG Tel: 0161 581 6131 Fax: 0161 248 4580 — MB ChB 1990 Manch.; BSc (Hons.) Psychology Manch. 1987; MRCGP 1994; DRCOG 1994.

EDMONDSON, Professor Hugh Dunstan Huddington Court, Huddington, Droitwich WR9 7LJ Tel: 01905 391247 Fax: 01905 391447 Email: hugh.edmondson@universityb.wmids.nhsuk — MB ChB Birm. 1966; BDS Birm. 1959; DDS Birm. 1980; MRCS Eng. LRCP Lond. 1966; FDS RCS Eng. 1970, LDS 1960; DA Eng. 1969. (Birm.) Emerit. Prof. Univ. Birm.; Cons. Maxillofcial Surg. Selly Oak Hosp. Birm.; Serv. Lead Maxillofacial Surg. Socs: Fell. Brit. Assn. Oral Surgs.; Brit. Dent. Assn. Prev: Prof. Oral Surg. & Oral Med. Univ Birm. Dent.; Sen. Lect. & Head of Dept. (Oral Surg. & Oral Med.) Univ. Birm. Dent. Sch.; SHO (Anaesth.) & Ho. Phys. Worcester Roy. Infirm. (Ronkswood Br.).

EDMONDSON, Mr John Leonard (retired) 96 the Grove, Marton, Middlesbrough TS7 8AP Tel: 01642 315351 — MB ChB 1944 Liverp.; FRCS Eng. 1954. Prev: Cons. Surg. S. Tees HA.

EDMONDSON, John Stuart 11 Hawthorne Avenue, Louth LN11 0LD Tel: 01507 607334 Email: drjs@edmondson.mernet.co.uk — MB ChB Bristol 1958; MRCPsych 1971; DPM Eng. 1965; DObst RCOG 1961. Vis. Indep. Cons. Linkage Community Trust. Socs: Fell. Roy. Soc. Med. Prev: Cons. Child & Adolesc. Psychiat. S. Humberside Health Dist.

EDMONDSON, Kenneth William Commonwealth Secretarat, Marlborough House, Pall Mall, London SW1Y 5HX — MB ChB 1952 Bristol; DPH Sydney 1965. Asst. Dir. Health Progr. Commonw. Secretariat. Socs: Fell. Roy. Austral. Coll. Med. Admin.s; Fell. Fac. Community Med. Prev: Asst. Sec. Therap. Div. Austral. Dept. Health; Sec. Nat. Health & Med. Research Counc. Aust.

EDMONDSON, Leonard 22 Olympia Hill, Morpeth NE61 1JH — MB ChB 1978 Liverp.; FFA RCS Eng. 1984. Cons. Anaesth. Wansbeck Gen. Hosp. Ashington. Prev: Regist. (Anaesth.) Whipps Cross Hops. Lond.

EDMONDSON, Mary Ewins Steels Lane Health Centre, 384-388 Commercial Road, London E1 0LR Tel: 020 7265 8655 Fax: 020 7702 8023; 105 Ham Park Road, Stratford, London E15 4AD — MB ChB 1975 Manch.; MRCGP 1984.

EDMONDSON, Philip Charles 99 Harley Street, London W1N 1DF Tel: 020 7935 7501 Fax: 020 7935 2918; 18 Lennox Gardens, London SW1X 0DG Tel: 020 7584 5194 — MB BChir 1964 Camb.; MD Camb. 1972, MA 1964; MRCP Lond. 1967. (Camb. & St. Bart.) Phys. to W.m. Abbey & KLM & Other Indust. Companies; Vis. Med. Off. King. Edwd. VII Hosp. Offs. Lond.; Phys. Aust. High Comm. Socs: Fell. Roy. Soc. Med.; Fell. Med. Soc. Lond. Prev: Lect. (Physiol.) & Regist. (Med.) St. Bart. Hosp. Lond.; Regist. & Resid. Med. Off. Lond. Chest Hosp.

EDMONDSON, Philip Wallis, Surg. Capt. RN Retd. The Thatched Cottage, North St., Theale, Reading RG7 5EX Tel: 01734 302286 — MRCS Eng. LRCP Lond. 1937; DCP Lond 1959; FRCPath 1965, M 1964.

EDMONDSON, Richard John 194 Tamworth Road, Newcastle upon Tyne NE4 5AP — MB BS 1992 Newc.

EDMONDSON, Robert Anthony Norsted Manor, Norsted Lane, Orpington BR6 7PB Tel: 01959 534426 Fax: 01959 534426 — MB BS 1984 Lond.; MS Lond. 1994; FRCS Eng. 1988. (Kings Coll. Lond.) Cons. (Vasc. Surg.) Kings Coll. Hosp. Lond.

EDMONDSON, Robert Somerville (retired) Chalforde House, Hall Drive, Bramhope, Leeds LS16 9JE Tel: 0113 284 2478 — MB BS 1961 Lond.; FFA RCS Eng. 1966. Cons. Anaesth. Leeds Gen. Infirm.; Hon. Lect. (Anaesth.) Univ. Leeds.

EDMONDSON, Sarah Jane 2 Dorrit Way, Chislehurst BR7 6RX — MB ChB 1987 Bristol.

EDMONDSON, Stephen Gerald Cheltenham General Hospital, Sandford Road, Cheltenham GL53 7AN Tel: 01242 222222 Fax: 01242 274068 Email: stephen.edmondson@egulist.swest.nhs.uk — MB BS 1974 Lond.; BSc Lond. 1971; FRCPath. Cons. Microbiol. Cheltenham Gen. Hosp.

EDMONDSON, Mr Stephen John 50 Wimpole St, London W1M 7DG Tel: 020 7935 6375 Fax: 020 7224 3823 — MB BS 1974 Lond.; BSc (1st cl. Hons.) Lond. 1971, MB BS 1974; FRCS Eng. 1979; MRCP (UK) 1980. (Middlx.) Cons. Surg. Cardiothoracic Surg. St. Bart. Hosp. Lond. Socs: Europ. Assn. Cardiovasc. Surg. & NE Thames Thoracic Soc. Prev: Sen. Regist. (Cardiothoracic Surg.) St. Bart. Hosp. Lond.; Regist. (Cardiothoracic Surg.) Hammersmith Hosp. Lond.; Regist. (Surg.) Nat. Heart Hosp. Lond.

EDMONDSON, William Campbell Wrexham Maelor Hospital, Croesweutod Road, Wrexham LL13 7TD Tel: 01978 725955 Fax: 01978 725932 Email: w.edmondson@new-tr.wales.nhs.uk — MB ChB 1981 Glas.; FFARCSI 1987. Cons. in Anaesth., Wrexham Maelor Hosp., Wrexham. Socs: Assn. of Anaesth.s; Intens. Care Soc.; Nutrit. Soc. Prev: Specialist Anaesth. Green La. Hosp. Auckland NZ.; Sen. Regist. Anaesth., Sheff. Hosps.

EDMONDSON-JONES, Gwilym Frederick Edmondson (retired) Piper's Gate, Common Lane, Windermere LA23 1JQ Tel: 015394 88895 — MB ChB MB ChB St. And. 1948; FRCGP 1984, M 1968; DObst RCOG 1952. Prev: Chairm. Leicester FHSA & Jt. Chairm. Leics. Health.

EDMONDSON-JONES, John Paul, MBE, Col. late RAMC Portsmouth City Primary Care Trust, Finchdean House, Milton Road, Portsmouth PO3 6DP Tel: 02392 835136 Fax: 02392 835030 Email: paul.edmondson-jones@portsha.swest.nhs.uk; Meadow Bank, Bury Road, Bury Gate, Pulborough RH20 1NN Tel: 01789 839019 Fax: 01798 831277 Email: pauledmondsonjones@hotmail.com — MB ChB 1980 Dundee; MSc 1986 (Community Med.) Lond.; MFPHM RCP 1990 (UK); FFPHM RCP 2000 (UK). (Dundee) Cons. Pub. Health Med. Portsmouth City Primary Care Trust. Socs: Fell. Roy. Soc. Med. Prev: Commanding Off. 4th Fld. Ambul.; Commanding Off. Brit. Med. Batallion, Croatia; Chief of Staff Dir of Defence Med. Train., Defence Med. Train. Org, Gosport.

EDMONDSON-JONES, Michael Church Street Surgery, Church Street, Hibaldstow, Brigg DN20 9ED Tel: 01652 650580 — MB ChB 1966 St. And.; DObst RCOG 1970. (St. And.)

EDMONDSTONE, William Mark, Surg. Capt. RN Royal Hospital, Haslar, Gosport PO12 2AA Tel: 01705 584255; 124 Christchurch Road, Winchester SO23 9QY — MB BS 1973 Lond.; FRCP Lond. 1993; MRCP (UK) 1977; MRCS Eng. LRCP Lond. 1973; AFOM RCP Lond. 1979; DIH Soc. Apoth. Lond. 1977. Cons. Phys. Roy. Hosp. Haslar.

EDMONSTONE, Yvonne Grace New Caigs Hospital, Inverness IV3 6JU Tel: 01463 242860; Cradlehall Lodge, 1A Orchard Park, Inverness IV2 5TP Tel: 01463 794632 — MB ChB 1985 Aberd.; MRCPsych 1990. Cons. Psychiat. New Craigs Hosp Inverness. Prev: Sen. Regist. (Psychiat.) Roy. Edin. Hosp.; Sen. Research Fell. (Psychiat.) Edin. Univ.; Regist. (Psychiat.) Roy. Edin. Hosp.

EDMUND, June Vivienne McNally The Health Centre, Station Road, Sanquhar DG4 6BT; 31 Hillside Crescent, Stanmills, Belfast BT9 5EN — MB BCh BAO 1982 Belf.; MB BCh Belf. 1982; T(GP) 1991; DRCOG 1985. Clin. Med. Off. S.. Health & Social Servs. Bd. Prev: Trainee GP Annan.

EDMUNDS, Alun Trevor Royal Hospital for Sick Children, Sciennes Road, Edinburgh EH9 1LF; 13 Queens Crescent, Edinburgh EH9 2AZ — BM BCh 1969 Oxf.; MA; FRCP Lond. 1983; MRCP (U.K.) 1973. Cons. (Paediat.) & Sen. Lect. (Child Life & Health) Edin. Univ.

EDMUNDS, Catherine Jane 15 Choir Green, Knaphill, Woking GU21 2NQ Tel: 01483 488498 — MB BS 1986 Lond.; MRCP (UK) 1993; MRCGP 1990; DRCOG 1988. SHO (Paediat.) Guy's Hosp. Lond. Prev: SHO (Paediat.) Kent & Canterbury Hosp.; Trainee GP Addlestone; SHO (Med., Paediat., A & E & O & G) St. Peters Hosp. Chertsey.

EDMUNDS, Edwyn Carey Howell Meddygfa'r Sarn, Heol y Meinciau, Pontyates, Llanelli SA15 5TR Tel: 01269 860348 Fax: 01269 860120 — MB BCh 1978 Wales.

EDMUNDS, Edwyn Gwyn-Hefin Doerwendeg, Trimsaran, Kidwelly SA17 4RY — MB BCh 1957 Wales.

EDMUNDS, Eiry 19 Tyr Fran Avenue, Llanelli SA15 3LW — MB BS 1991 Lond.

EDMUNDS, Elaine Valerie 82 Murray Road, Rugby CV21 3JP — BM BCh 1980 Oxf.; MA, BM BCh Oxf. 1980; MRCPsych 1985. Cons. Psychiat. St. Cross Hosp. Rugby.

EDMUNDS, Elizabeth Marjorie (retired) 37 Orchard Grove, New Milton BH25 6NZ — MB BS Lond. 1957; FRCOG 1978, M 1963. Prev: Clin. Asst. Macmillan Unit. ChristCh. Hosp. Dorset.

EDMUNDS, Ian Gordon The Surgery, Station Road, Knebworth SG3 6AP Tel: 01438 812494 Fax: 01438 816497; Laurel End, Raffin Close, Datchworth, Knebworth SG3 6RP Tel: 01438 811082 — MB BS 1974 Lond.; MRCS Eng. LRCP Lond. 1974. (St. Mary's) Med. Off. Qu. Vict. Memor. Hosp. Welwyn Herts. Prev: Regist. (Gen. Med. & Neurol.) Edgware Gen. Hosp.; SHO (Emerg. Med.) St. Mary's Hosp. Lond.

EDMUNDS, Jacqueline Mae 15 Middleton Hall Road, Kings Norton, Birmingham B30 1AB — MB BS 1969 Lond.; MRCS Eng. LRCP Lond. 1969.

EDMUNDS, Mr James Pangbourne Cofton Medical Centre, 2 Robinsfield Drive, Off Longbridge Lane, West Heath, Birmingham B31 4TU Tel: 0121 693 4414; 15 Middleton Hall Road, Kings Norton, Birmingham B30 1AB Tel: 0121 458 4189 — MB BS 1969 Lond.; FRCS Eng. 1974; MRCS Eng. LRCP Lond. 1969. (St. Thos.) Prev: Regist. (Orthop.) Roy. Orthop. Hosp. Birm.; Regist. (Orthop.) Coventry & Warks. Hosp.; SHO Profess. Surg. Unit N.. Gen. Hosp. Sheff.

EDMUNDS, Miss Lorna Elizabeth Stella Royal College of Ophthalmologists, 17 Cornwall Terrace, London NW1 4QW Tel: 020 7935 0702 Email: beth@rcophthwin-net.uk; Flat 12, 134 Gloucester Place, London NW1 6DT — MB ChB 1989 Cape Town; FRCOphth 1994. Specialist Regist. (Ophth.). Prev: Research Fell. Audit Unit Roy. Coll. Opthalmols.

EDMUNDS, Mair Eluned Department of Renal Medicine, Walsgrave Hospital, Clifford Bridge Road, Coventry CV2 2DX — MD 1989 Leic.; BA Oxf. 1977, BM BCh 1980; MRCP (UK) 1983. Cons. Phys. Walsgrave NHS Trust Coventry.

EDMUNDS, Nicholas James Tillicoultry Medical Centre, Park Street, Tillicoultry FK13 6AG Tel: 01259 750531 Fax: 01259 752818; 36 Harviestoun Road, Dollar FK14 7HQ Tel: 01259 743766 — MB ChB 1982 Aberd. CEDOC: Clackmannansh. Emerg. Doctors on Call; Med. Dir. CEDOL Ltd; GP Partner, Tillicountry Med. Pract. Socs: Roy. Coll. Gen. Pract.; Brit. Soc. Med. & Dent. Hypn. (Scotl.). Prev: GP Aberd.

EDMUNDS, Richard Blair Osborne Road Surgery, 17 Osborne Road, Newcastle upon Tyne NE2 2AH Tel: 0191 281 4588 Fax: 0191 212 0379 — MB BS 1975 Newc.

EDMUNDS, Sally Elizabeth Southfield Medical Centre, 89 Southfield Road, Bedford Park, Chiswick, London W4 1BB Tel: 020 8994 4644 Fax: 020 8747 8968; 28 Newport, Portway, Warminster BA12 8RH Tel: 01985 217398 — MB BS 1978 Lond.; Dip. Sports Med. Lond 1986; DRCOG 1983; DCH RCP Lond. 1983; DA Eng. 1982. Socs: Austral. Coll. Phys.; Austral. Sports Med. Federat. Prev: SHO (Anaesth.) St. Thos. Hosp. Lond.; Ho. Surg. Roy. N.. Hosp. Lond.; Ho. Phys. Roy. Free Hosp. Lond.

EDMUNDS, Steven John Pontesbury Medical Practice, Hall Bank, Pontesbury, Shrewsbury SY5 0PS Tel: 01743 790325 Fax: 01743 792851 — MB BS 1981 Lond.; BSc (Hons.) Lond. 1978; MRCGP 1985; DRCOG 1984.

EDMUNDS, Thomas Charles Manor Surgery, Forth Noweth, Chapel Street, Redruth TR15 1BY Tel: 01209 313313 Fax: 01209 313813 — MB ChB 1987 Leeds.

EDMUNDS, Wendy Teresa Summerside Medical Centre, 29B Summerside Place, Edinburgh EH6 4NY Tel: 0131 554 3533 Fax: 0131 554 9722 — MB BS 1970 Lond.; MRCS Eng. LRCP Lond. 1970; DCH Eng. 1972.

EDMUNDSON, Heidi Fiona 63 Hopefield Avenue, Portrush BT56 8HE — MB ChB 1994 Dundee.

EDMUNDSON, Philip Arthur Edmund (retired) 8 Alders End Lane, Harpenden AL5 2HL Tel: 01582 760000 — MA Camb. 1942; MB ChB St. And. 1955; MRCGP 1965; DObst RCOG 1957. Prev: GP Herts. Assoc. Mem. Inst. Elec. Engin.

EDMUNDSON, William Lewis (retired) Dial Farm, Earl Soham, Woodbridge IP13 7SW Tel: 01728 685221 — MB BChir 1965 Camb.; MB Camb. 1965, BChir 1964. Prev: Ho. Surg. Hereford Gen. Hosp.

EDNEY, Patricia Pitsmoor Surgery, 151 Burngreave Road, Sheffield S3 9DL Tel: 0114 272 8228; 122 Brincliffe Edge Road, Sheffield S11 9BY — MB ChB 1977 Sheff. Vice Chairm. Sheff. LMC.; Med. Advis. Sheff. Area Health Auth. Prev: Trainee GP Sheff.; Regist. (Med.) Hallamsh. Hosp. Sheff.; SHO (Neurol.) Roy. Hosp. Sheff.

EDNEY, Roy James Mall House, Faversham ME13 8JJ Tel: 01795 532188 — MB BS 1947 Lond.; MRCS Eng. LRCP Lond. 1940. (St. Thos.) Admiralty Surg. & Agent; Treasury Med. Off.; Div. Surg. St. John Ambul. Brig; Hon. Med. Off. Faversham Cott. Hosp. Socs: B.M.A. Prev: Capt. R.A.M.C. (Graded Phys.) Ho. Surg. & Ho. Phys. Roy. Vict. Hosp.; Boscombe.

EDOMAN, Simon Holloway Road Surgery, 140 Holloway Road, London N7 8DD Tel: 020 7607 8259 Fax: 020 7609 8803; 43 St. James Avenue, Whetstone, London N20 0JS Tel: 020 7609 8803 — MD 1985 Brussels.

EDON, Peter James Mowbray House, 277 North End, Northallerton DL7 8DP Tel: 01609 775281 Fax: 01609 778029 — MB ChB 1980 Birm.; MRCGP 1985; DRCOG 1983. Socs: Dales Med. Soc. Prev: N.allerton VTS; SHO (Accid & Emerg.) Selly Oak Hosp. Birm.; Ho. Off. (Surg.) Birm. Gen. Hosp.

EDOZIEN, Leroy Chukwuma The Royal Oldham Hospital, Oldham OL1 2JH Tel: 0161 627 8162 Fax: 0161 627 8230; Kinders House, Kinders Lane, Greenfield, Oldham OL3 7BJ Email: leroy@edozien.com — MB BS 1984 Ibadan; MRCPI 1995; MSc Ibadan 1991; MRCOG 1993; MFFP 1993; LLB 1997; FWACS 1991. Cons. Obst. Gyn. Roy. Oldham Hosp. Socs: Brit. Menopause Soc.; Brit.Fertil..Soc; Roy. Soc. Med.

EDRICH, Cathryn Louise Flat 4, 62 Sinclair Road, West Kensington, London W14 0NH — MB BS 1994 Lond.; BSc Lond. 1988, MB BS 1994.

EDRICH, Penelope Jane St. Helen's & Knowsley NHS Trust, Whiston Hospital, Prescot L35 5DR Tel: 0151 426 1600 — MB ChB 1996 Liverp. Critical Care SHO Whiston Hosp. Prescot.

EDRIDGE, Anthony William (retired) Stella Maris, Brancaster Staithe, King's Lynn PE31 8BX Tel: 01485 210371 Fax: 01485 210371 — MRCS Eng. LRCP Lond. 1944; FFA RCS Eng. 1954; DA Eng. 1949. Prev: Cons. Anaesth. Plastic Surg. & Jaw Injury Centre Qu. Vict. Hosp. E. Grinstead.

EDRIDGE, Karen Anne Louise Old Barn Cottage, Sweeming Lane, Little Fenton, Sherburn in Elmet, Leeds LS25 6HF — MB ChB 1984 Leeds.

EDRIDGE, William Worthington 53 Shortridge Terrace, Jesmond, Newcastle upon Tyne NE2 2JE — MB BChir 1985 Camb.

EDRIS, Mohammed Attia Mohammed The Woottons Surgery, Priory Lane, North Wootton, King's Lynn PE30 3PT Tel: 01553 631550 Email: medris@doctors.org.uk; 2 Hall Lane, South Wootton, King's Lynn PE30 3LQ Tel: 01553 673985 — MB ChB; DRCOG 1999; MRCOG 1997; DFFP 2001. (Tanta, Egypt) GP; Family Plann. Practitioner, W. Norf. PCT; Clin. Asst., A&E, QEH, King's Lynn. Socs: Med. Protec. Soc.; Roy. Coll. of Gen. Practitioners (Assoc.).

EDSALL, Keith Christopher, Wing Cdr. RAF Med. Br. Croftlea, 129 Marlborough Road, Ryde PO33 1AR — MRCS Eng. LRCP Lond. 1975; MSc Lond. 1983, MB BS 1975.

EDSELL, Mark Edward George 26 Beach Road, Emsworth PO10 7JS — MB ChB 1997 Birm.

EDWARD, George Westbrook, MC (retired) Greystoke, Davey Lane, Alderley Edge SK9 7NZ Tel: 01625 583368 — MB BS 1951 Lond.

EDWARD, John Flat B, 2 Morningside Lane, Aberdeen AB10 7NB Tel: 01224 312154 — MB ChB Aberd. 1965. Med. Off. Grampian Health Care NHS Trust Ment. Health Servs. Prev: GP Aberd.; SHO (Anaesth.) & Ho. Off. Aberd. Gen. Gp. Hosps.; Med. Off. Grey's Hosp. Natal, S. Afr.

EDWARD, Malcolm Greig Lordswood House, 54 Lordswood Road, Harborne, Birmingham B17 9DB Tel: 0121 426 2030 Fax: 0121 428 2658 — MB ChB 1968 St. And. Hon. Sen. Clin. Lect. & Tutor (Gen. Pract.) Fac. Med. Univ. Birm.

EDWARD, Neil Brookwood, Northcote Road, Aberdeen AB15 7TB Tel: 01224 324321 — MB ChB 1961 Aberd.; FRCP Ed. 1978, M 1965. (Aberd.) Cons. Phys. & Nephrol. Roy. Hosps. NHS Trust Aberd.; Hon. Sen. Lect. (Med.) Univ. Aberd. Prev: Lect. (Med.) Univ. Aberd.; Sir Ashley Mackintosh Research Fell. Dept. Med. Univ. Aberd.; Instruct. (Med.) Temple Univ. Philadelphia, USA.

EDWARD, Mr Rex Hubert 10 Dale Walk, Dartford DA2 6JA Tel: 01322 27871 — MB BS 1973 Sri Lanka; FRCS Eng. 1981; FRCS Ed. 1980; MRCS Eng. LRCP Lond. 1981.

EDWARD, Vivien Evelyn Mark Brookwood, Northcote Road, Aberdeen AB15 7TB Tel: 01224 324321 — MB ChB 1962 Aberd.; DCH Eng. 1964. (Aberd.) Assoc. Specialist (Psychiat.) Roy. Cornhill Hosp. Aberd. Prev: Regist. Ross Clinic, Aberd.; SHO Qu. Eliz. Hosp. Childr. Lond.; Instruct. in Psychiat. Temple Univ. Philadelphia, U.S.A.

EDWARDES, Julie Ann The Riverside Surgery, Waterside, Evesham WR11 6JP Tel: 01386 40121 Fax: 01386 442615 — MB ChB 1979 Glasgow; MB ChB 1979 Glasgow.

EDWARDS, Adrian Gwyn Konrad 7 Somerton Court, Ouseburn Park, Gosforth, Newcastle upon Tyne NE3 2QZ — MB BS 1989 Newc.

EDWARDS, Adrienne Laura 2 Nantyglyn Road, Glanamman, Ammanford SA18 2YT — MB BCh 1997 Wales.

EDWARDS, Aileen Elizabeth (retired) Flat 2, Charlton Lawn, Charlton Kings, Cheltenham GL53 8AA Tel: 0242 516547 — MB ChB 1926 Ed.; DPH 1934.

EDWARDS, Alan Southwell House Surgery, Back Lane, Rochford SS4 1AY Tel: 01702 545241 Fax: 01702 546390; Windy Ridge, Rebels Lane, Barling Road, Southend-on-Sea SS3 0QE — MB BCh 1971 Wales.

EDWARDS, Alan David St Pauls Medical Centre, St. Pauls Square, Carlisle CA1 1DG Tel: 01228 524354 Fax: 01228 616660; Hill Top, Buckabank, Dalston, Carlisle CA5 7AA Tel: 01228 710524 — MB ChB 1985 Dundee; MRCGP 1993.

EDWARDS, Alan Martin 7 Fallowfield Close, Caversham, Reading RG4 8NQ Tel: 0118 947 6969 Fax: 0118 946 4778 Email: aedwards@vectiss-allergy.com — MB BChir 1962 Camb.; MA Camb. 1962; MRCGP 1968; Dip. Pharm. Med. RCP (UK) 1976. (Lond. Hosp.) Med. Dir. Vectis Allergy Ltd.; Hon. Clin. Asst., Univ. Med. Soton. Prev: Med. Adviser Fisons Pharmaceuts. LoughBoro.; Ho. Phys. Lond. Hosp.; Ho. Surg. St. Albans City Hosp.

EDWARDS, Alan Tawse (retired) Summercroft, Dryclough Lane, Halifax HX3 0LG Tel: 01422 367475 — MB ChB 1950 Aberd.; FRCPath 1973, M 1967. Prev: Cons. Path. Calderdale Healthcare Trust.

EDWARDS, Alexandra June (retired) 6 Westwood Gardens, Kenton, Newcastle upon Tyne NE3 3DA Tel: 0191 285 3803 — MB ChB 1948 Manch. Prev: Princip. Community Clinician (Child Health) Durh. HA.

EDWARDS, Alison Hayward (retired) Knowlands Cottage, Four Elms, Edenbridge TN8 6NA Tel: 0173 270481 — MB ChB 1952 Aberd. Prev: Med. Off. Family Plann. Clinics Kent AHA & Family Plann. Assn.

EDWARDS, Alison Jean (retired) 5 River View, Litton Mill, Buxton SK17 8SW Tel: 01298 872189 Fax: 01298 872189 Email: aliedw@aol.com — MB ChB Bristol 1963. Prev: Phys. Univ. Health Serv. Univ. Hong Kong.

EDWARDS, Alison Theresa Jane The Old Manor, Forest Road, Hartwell, Northampton NN7 2HE — BM BCh 1992 Oxf.

EDWARDS, Allen Thomas 38 Richards Street, Cathays, Cardiff CF24 4DA — MB BCh 1984 Wales; MB BCh Wales I984. Prosector Dept. Anat. Univ. Coll. Cardiff.

EDWARDS, Alun James Bryan (retired) 12 Ellerslie Road, Barnstaple EX31 2HT Tel: 01271 343324 — MB BS 1957 Lond.; FRCGP 1983, M 1965; DObst RCOG 1959.

EDWARDS, Andrea Pinn Medical Centre, 8 Eastcote Road, Pinner HA5 1HF Tel: 020 8866 5766 Fax: 020 8429 0251 — MB BS 1985 Lond.; MRCP (UK) 1988; MRCGP 1992; DRCOG 1991.

EDWARDS, Mr Andrew 37 Cambridge Road, Walton-on-Thames KT12 2DP Tel: 01932 220065 Email: andrew@rachel19.freeserve.co.uk — MB BS 1992 Lond.; FRCS Ed 1997; FRCS 1997. SHO (Orthop.) Frimley Pk. Hosp. Camberley; Specialist Regist. (Orthop) S. W. Thames Rotat. Socs: BOA; BOTA.

EDWARDS, Andrew Ian The Ling, Eassie by Glamis, Forfar DD8 1SE — MB ChB 1998 Aberd.; MB ChB Aberd 1998.

EDWARDS, Andrew John Barnside, Church Lane, Braishfield, Romsey SO51 0QH — MB BS 1994 Lond.

EDWARDS, Andrew John c/o Rev David Vail, 36 Silverthorne Drive, Caversham, Reading RG4 7NS — MB BS 1987 Lond.; BA Camb. 1984; MRCGP 1993; DRCOG 1992; DTM & H RCP Lond. 1991. Community Med. Off. Lalitpur Health & Developm. Project Kathmandu, Nepal. Prev: Trainee GP Lond.; SHO (Trop. Dis.) St. Pancras Hosp. Lond.; SHO (Paediat.) Qu. Mary's Hosp. Sidcup.

EDWARDS, Angelique 55 Coval Road, London SW14 7RW Tel: 020 8878 4648 — MB BS 1996 Lond.; DFFP 2001; DRCOG 1999; MRCGP 2001. SHO (Psychiat. VTS) Qu. Mary's Univ. Hosp. Roehampton; GP Locum. Socs: Roy. Coll. of Gen. Practitioners. Prev: Regist. (GP) Roehampton; Ho. Off. (Med.) Wexham Pk. Hosp.; Ho. Off. (Surg.) Char. Cross Hosp.

EDWARDS, Ann Eleri Arnon Cottage, Abbey Road, Llangollen LL20 8SL Tel: 01978 291100 — MB ChB (2nd cl. Hons., Distinc. Surg.) Liverp. 1960; FFA RCS Eng. 1963. (Liverp.) Cons. Anaesth. Clwyd HA; Examr. Part. III FCAnaesth.; Examr. Final FRCA. Socs: Ex. Pres. Welsh Soc. Anaesths.; Counc. Assn. Anaesth. GB & Irel. Prev: SHO (Anaesth.) United Liverp. Hosps.

EDWARDS, Ann Felicity (retired) 17 Pine Way Close, East Grinstead RH19 4JR Tel: 01342 322994 — MB BS Lond. 1963; MRCS Eng. LRCP Lond. 1963; MRCPCH 1996; MFCH 1989; DCCH RCP Ed. RCGP & FCM 1989; DA Eng. 1966. Prev: SCMO E.bourne & Co. Healthcare.

EDWARDS, Ann Jennifer Northbourne Surgery, 1368 Wimborne Road, Bournemouth BH10 7AR Tel: 01202 574100 Fax: 01202 590030; The Laurels, 136 Lonnen Road, Colehill, Wimborne BH21 7AZ Tel: 01202 885055 — MB BS Lond. 1971. (Char. Cross) Gen. Med. Practitioner, Bournemouth.

EDWARDS, Anne Genitourinary Medicine Department, Radcliffe Infirmary, Woodstock Road, Oxford OX2 6HE Tel: 01865 248040 Fax: 01865 224378 — BM BCh 1980 Oxf.; MA Oxf. 1980; FRCP Lond. 1995; MRCP (UK) 1985. Lead Clinician (Genitourin. Med.) Radcliffe Infirm. Oxf.; Fell. Brasenose Coll. Oxf.; Hon. Sen. Clin. Lect. in Genitourin. Med., Oxf. Univ. Socs: Assn. Genitourin. Med.; BMA; Med. Soc. Study VD. Prev: Cons. Genitourin. Med. Wycombe Gen. Hosp. & Radcliffe Infirm. Oxf.; Lect. & Hon. Sen. Regist. St. Thos. Hosp. Lond.

EDWARDS, Annette Susan Dept. Of Palliative Medicine, Pinderfields General Hospital, Aberford Rd, Wakefield WF1 4DG Tel: 01924 212290 Fax: 01924 212290 Email: annette.edwards@panp-tr.northy.nhs.uk; 36, Crimple Meadows, Pannal, Harrogate HG3 1EN Tel: 01423 873354 — MB ChB 1986 Leeds; MRCGP 1990; Dip.

Palliat. Med. Wales 1993; DRCOG 1989. p/t Macmillan Cons. in Palliat. Med., Pinderfields Gen. Hosp., Wakefield; Macmillan Cons. in Palliat. Med., Wakefield Hospice, Aberford Rd., Wakefield. Prev: Specialist Regist. (Palliat. Med.) Yorks.; Dep. Med. Dir. P. of Wales Hospice Pontefract; Trainee GP ScarBoro. VTS.

EDWARDS, Anthony Carter (retired) — MB ChB 1945 Bristol. Prev: Ho. Surg. & Cas. Off. Roy. Infirm. Bristol.

EDWARDS, Mr Anthony Norman Highmoor, Hill St., Cockermouth CA13 0AU — MB ChB 1970 Manch.; FRCS Eng. 1975. Cons. Orthop. Surg. Cumbld. Infirm. Carlisle. Socs: Fell. BOA. Prev: Cons. Orthop. Surg. W. Cumbld. Hosp. Whitehaven; Sen. Regist. (Orthop.) Birm. Accid. Hosp., Roy. Orthop. Hosp. Birm. & Wolverhampton Roy. Hosp.

EDWARDS, Anthony Richard St James Medical Centre, 11 Carlton Road, Tunbridge Wells TN1 2HW Tel: 01892 541634 Fax: 01892 545170 — MB BCh 1972 Wales; DObst RCOG 1974. (Welsh Nat. Sch. Med. Cardiff)

EDWARDS, Anusha Gillian 4 The Landway, St Paul's Cray, Orpington BR5 3LH — MB ChB 1998 Bristol.

EDWARDS, Arthur Gwilym (retired) The Croft, 489 Pensby Road, Thingwall, Wirral CH61 7UQ — MB ChB 1955 Liverp.; MRCS Eng. LRCP Lond. 1956; DObst RCOG 1959. Prev: GP Wirral.

EDWARDS, Ayliffe Mary Stonydelph Health Centre, Ellerbeck, Tamworth B77 4JA Tel: 01827 330980 Fax: 01827 330980; 40 Burton Road West, Lichfield WS13 6EN Tel: 0154 32 262720 — MB ChB 1975 Manch.; MRCGP 1983; DCH RCP Lond. 1984; DCCH RCP Ed. RCGP & FCM 1984; DRCOG 1979. p/t Cons. Community Paediat.; Hon. Clin. Fell. Paediat. Neurol. Dept. Childr.s Hosp. Socs: BMA; RCPCH; BPNA. Prev: SCMO S. E. Staffs.

EDWARDS, Barry Alan Brookland House, 501 Crewe Road, Wistaston, Crewe CW2 6QP Tel: 01270 567250 Fax: 01270 665829 — MB ChB 1992 Birm.; MRCGP (Distinc.) 1996; DRCOG 1996; DFFP 1995. (Birm.)

EDWARDS, Beverley Anne 8 Gadloch Avenue, Lenzie, Glasgow G66 5NP — MB BCh 1993 Witwatersrand.

EDWARDS, Bradley Montague Fitz-Arthur 29 Clapham Manor Street, London SW4 6DU — MB BS 1991 W. Indies. SHO (Gen. Surg.) P.ss of Wales Hosp. Bridgend; SHO (Thoracic Surg.) Frenchay Hosp. NHS Trust Bristol; SHO Rotat. Sandwell Healthcare NhS Trust W. Bromwich; SHO (Gen. Surg.) The P.ss of Wales Hosp. Bridgend. Socs: BMA. Prev: SHO (Paediat. Surg. & Orthop.) Soton. Gen. Hosp.

EDWARDS, Brenda Anne Pilcher (retired) 8 Bovisand Court, Bovisand, Plymouth PL9 0AD Tel: 01752 406543 — MB BS 1954 Lond.; MRCS Eng. LRCP Lond. 1954; DObst RCOG 1958; DCH Eng. 1956.

EDWARDS, Brian David Parexel International, River Court, 50 Oxford Road , Denham, Uxbridge UB9 4DL Tel: 01895 864522 Fax: 01895 231847 Email: brian.edwards@parexel.com; 105 Overdale, Ashtead KT21 1PX Tel: 01372 273789 Fax: 01372 276343 Email: brian.edwards@manutd.com — MB BS 1980 Lond.; BSc (1st cl. Hons.) Lond. 1977; MD Manch. 1994; MRCP (UK) 1984; MRCS Eng. LRCP Lond. 1980. Sen. Med. Dir., Med. Servs. Europe, Parexel. Prev: Sen. Med. Assessor Med. Control. Agency Lond.; Research Fell. & Lect. (Renal Med.) Manch. Roy. Infirm.; Regist. Rotat. (Gen. Med.) St. Geo. Hosp. Lond.

EDWARDS, Carl (retired) Tredayne, Braehead Road, Thorntonhall, Glasgow G74 5AQ Tel: 0141 644 3892 — MB ChB 1952 Glas.; DMJ Soc. Apoth. Lond. 1974.

EDWARDS, Catherine Ruth Albion House Suegery, Albion Street, Brierley Hill DY5 3EE Tel: 01384 70220 Fax: 01384 78284; 4 Park Road, Wollaston, Stourbridge DY8 3RS — MB ChB 1991 Birm.; MRCGP 1996; DRCOG 1995. (Birm.) Socs: BMA. Prev: Trainee GP Dudley & Stourbridge VTS.

EDWARDS, Catherine Sara Forde's Cottage, Oakshott, Hawkley, Liss GU33 6LS — BM BCh 1997 Oxf. SHO Rotat. (Med.) Guy's Hosp. Lond.

EDWARDS, Cathryn Mary Dept of Gastroenterology, University of Oxford, Radcliffe Infirmary Woodstock Road, Oxford OX9 5PT Email: cathryn.edwards@ndm.ox.ac.uk; Field House, 17 Stonor Green, Watlington OX49 5PT — MB BS 1989 Newc.; MRCP (UK) 1992; MA (Oxon) 1986. Regist. (Gastroenterol.) John Radcliffe Hosp. Oxf.; MRC Train. Fell.

EDWARDS, Charles John Albert, Surg. Cdr. RN Anaesthetic Department, RH Haslar, Gosport PO12 2AA Tel: 023 9258 4255 — MB BS 1984 Lond.; FRCA. (St. Bart. Hosp. Lond.) Cons. (Anaesth. & Chronic Pain) RH Haslar Gosport.

EDWARDS, Christine Haswell Lamb Hospital, PO Parbatipur, Dt Dinajpur 5250, Bangladesh Tel: 00 8802 889846 Fax: 00 8802 889846 Email: lamb@atechco.net; Savermake House, Lyme Road, Axminster EX13 5BE Tel: 01297 35310 Fax: 01297 35678 — MB BS 1985 Newc.; MRCOG 1991; DTM & H Liverp. 1992. Obst. Lamb Hosp. Parbatipur, Bangladesh.

EDWARDS, Christine Margaret Felin Bache, Llangollen LL20 8AW — MB ChB 1973 Birm.; MRCPsych 1977; DPM Eng. 1977. Cons. Psychiat. Llwyn-y-Groes Psychiatric Unit Wrexham Maelor Hosp. Wrexham.

EDWARDS, Christopher David Heathbridge House, The Old Bridge, Kenfig Hill, Bridgend CF33 6BY Tel: 01656 740359 Fax: 01656 745400; Pathways, 9 Celtic View, Bridgend CF31 1YG Tel: 01656 740359 — MB BCh 1988 Wales; MRCGP 1992.

EDWARDS, Christopher John 1 Aspenlea Road, London W6 8LH — MB BS 1990 Lond.; MRCP (UK) 1993.

EDWARDS, Christopher Mark Beresford 14 Cardigan Road, London E3 5HU — MB BS 1989 Lond.

EDWARDS, Professor Christopher Richard Watkin Imperial College School of Medicine, Principal's Suite, Sir Alexander Fleming Building, Imperial College Road, London SW7 2AZ Tel: 020 7594 8800 Fax: 020 7594 9833 Email: c.edwards@ic.ac.uk; 4 Thames Walk, Hester Road, London SW11 3BG Tel: 020 7223 6494 — MB BChir (Distinc. Phys.) Camb. 1967; FRSE 1990; MD Camb. 1974, MA 1967; FRCP Lond. 1979, M 1968; FRCP Ed. 1981. (St. Bart.) Princip. Imperial Coll. Sch. Med.; Prof. Med. Lond. Univ. Socs: Fell. Roy. Soc. Med.; Soc. Endocrinol. Prev: Prof. Clin. Med. Univ. Edin. & W.. Gen. Hosp. Edin.; Dean Fac. Med., Provost Fac. Gp. Med. & Veterin. Med. Univ. Edin.; Sen. Lect. (Med.) & Hon. Cons. Phys. St. Bart. Hosp. Lond.

EDWARDS, Christopher Worsley (retired) 30 Lovelace Avenue, Solihull B91 3JR — MD Liverp. 1971, MB ChB 1963; FRCPath 1981, M 1969. Prev: Cons. Path. Birm. Heartlands Hosp.

EDWARDS, Claire Victoria Sewell 70 Grasmere Road, Frodsham, Warrington WA6 7LQ — BM BCh 1996 Oxf. SHO Rotat. (Surgic.) Qu.'s Med. Centre Nottm.

***EDWARDS, Claudia Louise** 10 Throwley Drive, Herne Bay CT6 8LP — MB BS 1997 Lond.

EDWARDS, Clement David (retired) 'Gerlan', Rhydyfelin, Aberystwyth SY23 4QB Tel: 01970 612046 — MB BS 1948 Lond.; MRCS Eng. LRCP Lond. 1943; DPH Eng. 1949, DIH 1949. Prev: Ho. Surg. W.m. Hosp.

EDWARDS, David (retired) The Chestnuts, Broke Hall Park, Nacton, Ipswich IP10 0ET Tel: 01473 659599 — MB BS 1947 Lond.; FRCP Lond. 1969, M 1951; FFR 1958; DMRD Eng. 1955. Dir. Dept. Radiol. Univ. Coll. Hosp. Lond.; Dir. Dept. Computerised Tomogr. UCL. Prev: Sen. Regist. (X-Ray Diag.) Univ. Coll. Hosp.

EDWARDS, David Alan 3 Node Hill Close, Studley B80 7RN — MB ChB 1987 Leic.

EDWARDS, David Alun Bury Helath Care NHS Trust, Fairfield General Hospital, Rochdale Old Road, Bury BL9 7TD Tel: 0161 705 3210 Fax: 0161 705 3410 Email: alunella@hotmail.com — MB BCh 1995 Wales; MRCGP 2000; BSc 1994; DCH 1998. (Cardiff) GP, Caerphilly.

EDWARDS, David Arthur 117 Park Street, Tonypandy CF40 2BT — MB BS 1960 Lond.; MRCS Eng. LRCP Lond. 1959.

EDWARDS, David George (retired) 18 Swan Close, Moreton-in-Marsh GL56 0BE Tel: 01608 650525 — MB BCh 1952 Wales; BSc Wales 1949. Prev: GP Liverp.

EDWARDS, Mr David Henry (retired) (rooms) 540 Etruria Road, Basford, Newcastle ST5 0SX Tel: 01782 614419 Fax: 01782 630270 — BM BCh 1962 Oxf.; MA Oxf. 1962; FRCS Eng. 1968. Sen. Lect. (Orthop.) Univ. Keele. Prev: Cons. Orthop. Surg. N. Staffs. Hosp. NHS Trust.

EDWARDS, David Jason 29 Newry Street, Markethill, Armagh BT60 1TA — MB BCh BAO 1997 Belf.

EDWARDS, David Llewelyn Wern Deg, Talybont SY24 5DJ — MB BCh 1994 Wales.

EDWARDS, David Lynne Meadway Health Centre, Meadway, Sale M33 4PS Tel: 0161 905 2850; 38 Cranleigh Drive, Brooklands, Sale M33 3PW — MB ChB 1964 Manch.; DObst RCOG 1966. (Manch.)

EDWARDS, David Owen 10 Garside Avenue, Lowton, Warrington WA3 2RT — BM 1980 Soton.

EDWARDS, Mr David Peter 10 Corn Avill Close, Abingdon OX14 2ND — MB ChB 1988 Manch.; FRCS Ed. 1994; Dip. IMC RCS Ed. 1995; ChM Manchester 1998. Specialist Regist. (ColoProctol.) John Radcliffe Hosp. Oxf.; Lect. (Milit. Surg.) Surrey. Socs: Assoc. Mem. Assn. Coloproctol.; ASIT; Assoc. Mem. Assn. Surg. GB & Irel. Prev: Specialist Regist. (Gen. Surg.) Roy. Defence Med. Coll. Gosport; Specialist Regist. (Gen. Surg.) Frimley Pk. Hosp. Surrey; Specialist Regist. (Gen. Surg.) St. Peter's Hosp. Chertsey.

EDWARDS, David Ronald White House Surgery, Horsefair, Chipping Norton OX7 5AL Tel: 01608 642742 Fax: 01608 642794; Claridges Barn, Dean, Chipping Norton OX7 5XG — MB BS 1977 Lond.; DRCOG 1981. (Lond. Hosp.)

EDWARDS, David Rowland (retired) Ty Gwyn, Llanbadarn Road, Aberystwyth SY23 1HB Tel: 01970 624647 — MB BS 1946 Lond.; MRCS Eng. LRCP Lond. 1946; MRCGP 1967. Prev: Clin. Asst. (Cas.) Bronglais Hosp. Aberystwyth.

EDWARDS, David Walter 36 Pangbourne Close, Appleton, Warrington WA4 5HJ Tel: 01925 264049 — MB ChB 1966 Manch. (Manch.) S/E BAMS. Socs: Fell. Roy. Inst. Pub. Health & Hyg.; BMA; Inst. Health Serv. Managem. Prev: Med. Dir. Wigan FHSA; Regional Med. Off. DoH NW Div. Med. Off. Manch.; GP Runcorn.

EDWARDS, David William (Surgery), Posterngate Surgery, Selby YO8 4QH Tel: 01757 702561 Fax: 01757 213295; 33 Wistowgate, Cawood, Selby YO8 3SH Tel: 01757 268278 — MB 1973 Camb.; BChir 1972.

EDWARDS, Deborah Margaret 13 Brian Crescent, Southborough, Tunbridge Wells TN4 0AP — MB ChB 1989 Leeds; BSc (Hons.) Pharmacol. Leeds 1986, MB ChB 1989.

EDWARDS, Denis Meyrick Forge Road Surgery, Forge Road, Southsea, Wrexham LL11 5RR Tel: 01978 758311 Fax: 01978 752351 — MB BCh 1978 Wales.

EDWARDS, Mr Dennis John The Evelyn Hospital, 4 Trumpington Road, Cambridge CB2 2AF Tel: 01223 364830 Fax: 01223364830 Email: dennis.edwards@virgin.net — MB ChB 1983 Zimbabwe; MB ChB U Zimbabwe 1983; FRCS (Orth.) 1993; FRCS Ed. 1988; FRCS Eng. 1988; LRCP Ed. 1983; LRCS Ed. 1983; LRCPS Glas. 1983. Cons. Orthop. Surg. Addenbrooke's Hosp. Camb. Prev: Sen. Regist. (Orthop. Surg.) Addenbrooke's Hosp. Camb.; Regist. (Orthop.) Sheff.

EDWARDS, Denzil Robert Llewellyn 52 Edna Road, Raynes Park, London SW20 8BT — MB BS 1980 Lond.; MRCS Eng. LRCP Lond. 1979. (Char. Cross)

EDWARDS, Donna Jeanette Glasgow Royal Infirmary, 84 Castle St., Glasgow G4 0SF — MB BS 1992 Lond. SHO (c/o Elderly) Bolingbroke Hosp. Lond. Prev: SHO (Med.) FarnBoro. Hosp. Orpington.

EDWARDS, Dorcas 3 Beechfield Avenue, Torquay TQ2 8HU Tel: 01803 325062 — MB ChB 1953 Bristol. (Bristol)

EDWARDS, Dorothy Mildred White Lodge, 34 Paines Lane, Pinner HA5 3DB Tel: 020 8866 0762 — MB BS 1955 Lond.; MRCPsych 1979; DPH Eng. 1959. (Roy. Free) Cons. Psychother. Barnet Healthcare NHS Trust. Prev: Cons. Psychiat. Barnet, Lond.; Sen. Regist. (Adult Psychother.) Tavistock Clinic Lond.; Regist. (Psychiat.) N.wick Pk. Hosp. Harrow.

EDWARDS, Dyfrig Handel Edwards and Partners, Wargrave House, 23 St. Owen Street, Hereford HR1 2JB Tel: 01432 272285 Fax: 01432 344059; 60 Grandstand Road, Hereford HR4 9NF — BM BCh 1968 Oxf.; MA Oxf. 1968; DObst RCOG 1971. (Oxf. & St. Mary's)

EDWARDS, Edward Mylrea Hall Whetstone Medical Centre, 44 Whetstone Lane, Birkenhead CH41 2TF Tel: 0151 647 9613; Rannoch, 12 Eddisbury Road, West Kirby, Wirral CH48 5DS Tel: 0151 632 2346 — MB ChB Liverp. 1965; DPH Manch. 1972; DObst RCOG 1968. (Liverp.) Socs: Fell. Roy. Soc. Med. Prev: SCM Chesh. AHA; Dep. MOH Ellesmere Port Municip. Boro., Neston UD, Chester RD & Tarvin RD; Asst. Sen. Med. Liverp. RHB.

EDWARDS, Elaine Jillian 66 Swinburne Court, Basingdon Way, London SE5 8ER — MB BS 1993 Lond.

EDWARDS, Elias Wyn (retired) Castellfryn, Gaerwen LL60 6AS Tel: 01248 715100 Email: castellfryn@btinternet.com — LRCPI & LM, LRSCI & LM 1965. JP.; Local Med. Off. (Anglesey) Civil Serv. Occupat. Health Serv. Prev: Regist. (Traum. & Orthop. Surg.), SHO (Gen. Surg.) & SHO Accid.

EDWARDS, Elizabeth Ann Meadow House, 45 High Bannerdown, Batheaston, Bath BA1 7JZ — MB BS 1962 Lond.

EDWARDS, Elizabeth Anne 11 Pontfaen, Cyncoed, Cardiff CF23 7DU — MB BCh 1983 Wales.

EDWARDS, Elizabeth Anne Flat 2 Denham Lodge, Westbury Road, Ealing, London W5 2LF Tel: 020 8997 5853 Email: liz.edwards@bigfoot.com — MB ChB 1989 Leeds; DCH Otago New Zealand 1995. (Leeds Univ.) Paediat. Research Fell Roy. Brompton Hosp. NHLI Lond. Socs: Peadiat. Soc. New Zeeland; Am. Thoracic Soc.; Europ. Respirat. Soc. Prev: Paediat. Regist. Waikato Hosp. Hamilton, New Zealand; Paediat. Regist. ChristCh. Hosp. New Zealand; Paediat. Regist. Auckland Hosp., New Zealand.

EDWARDS, Elizabeth Dawn 22 New Road, Haverfordwest SA61 1TU — MB ChB 1988 Leic.

EDWARDS, Mr Eric Charlton 110 Dixon Drive, Chelford, Macclesfield SK11 9BX — MRCS Eng. LRCP Lond. 1948; MD Liverp. 1960, ChM 1958, MB ChB 1948; FRCS Ed. 1953; FRCS Eng. 1953. (Liverp.) Cons. Urol. Surg. Manch. Roy. Infirm. & Dialysis Unit Withington; Hosp.; Hon. Clin. Lect. in Urol. Univ. Manch. Socs: Brit. Assn. Urol Surgs. & Internat. Soc. Urol. Prev: Cons. Urol. Surg. Liverp. Regional Urol. Centre Sefton Gen. Hosp.; Liverp.; Linwood Keyser Fund Fell. in Surgic. Research, Mayo Foundat.

EDWARDS, Mr Errol Mendus (retired) Camden, 17 Hillcourt Road, Cheltenham GL52 3JJ Tel: 01242 582482 — MS Lond. 1960, MB BS 1948; FRCOG 1969, M 1953, DObst 1949; MRCS Eng. LRCP Lond. 1943. Prev: Cons. O & G Cheltenham.

EDWARDS, Ewa 2 Tanworth Lane, Shirley, Solihull B90 4 Tel: 0121 744 2025; Silverhow, 30 Lovelace Avenue, Solihull B91 3JR Tel: 0121 705 0709 — MB ChB 1963 Liverp. (Liverp.) Prev: Research Fell. Dept. Dermat. Univ. Liverp.; Ho. Surg. & Ho. Phys. BRd.green Hosp. Liverp.

EDWARDS, Ewan David 2 Chapel Row Lane, Old St Mellons, Cardiff CF3 5UB — MB BCh 1946 Wales; BSc, MB BCh Wales 1946. (Cardiff)

EDWARDS, Felicity Clare, OBE (retired) 78 Old Road, Headington, Oxford OX3 7LP Tel: 01865 760430 Fax: 01865 760430 — BM BCh 1952 Oxf.; DM Oxf. 1964; FRCP Lond. 1982, M 1955; FFOM RCP Lond. 1986, MFOM 1984, AFOM 1979. Mem. Internat. Commiss. Occupat. Health. Prev: Sen. Employm. Med. Adviser HSE Med. Div.

EDWARDS, Frances 4 Brynvale, Llanmill, Narberth SA67 8UE — MB ChB 1982 Leeds.

EDWARDS, Gareth Alun Pirbright House, West Cliff Gardens, Bournemouth BH2 5HL — MB BS 1994 Lond.

EDWARDS, Gareth John Nevill Hall Hospital, Abergavenny NP7 7EG; 41 Allt-Yr-Yn Heights, Newport NP20 5DX — BM BS 1990 Nottm.; MRCOG 1998; BMedSci 1988; Dip. Ven. Liverp. 1993. Specialist Regist. (Obs & Gynae.) Nevill Hall Hosp. Abergavenny.

EDWARDS, Geoffrey Peter Leslie Wadebridge and Camel Estuary Practice, Brooklyn, Wadebridge PL27 7BS Tel: 01208 812222 Fax: 01208 815907 — MB BS 1976 Lond.; 2001 (ILTM); FRCGP 2000; MRCGP 1982; DRCOG 1980. Course Organiser Cornw. VTS.; Clin. Tutor Gen. Pract., Cornw.

EDWARDS, George Morgan Department of Oral & Maxillofacial Surgery, Hull Royal Infirmary, Anlaby Road, Hull HU3 2JZ Tel: 01482 28541 — MRCS Eng. LRCP Lond. 1968; MB BS Lond. 1968, BDS 1959; FDS RCS Eng. 1966; LDS RCS Eng. 1959. (Guy's) Cons. Oral Surg. Hull Roy. Infirm. Socs: BMA; Brit. Assn. Oral & Maxillofacial Surg. Prev: Regist. Oral Surg. E.man Dent Hosp. Lond.; Sen. Regist. Roy. Dent. Hosp. Lond.

EDWARDS, George Philip Park Street Surgery, 6 Park Street, Falkirk FK1 1RE Tel: 01324 623577 Fax: 01324 633636 — MB ChB 1978 Ed.; BSc (Med. Sci.) Ed. 1975, MB ChB 1978. (Edinburgh University) Prev: SHO (Gen. Med.) Peel Hosp. Galashiels; SHO Elsie Inglis Memor. Hosp. Edin.; Med. Off. St. Luke's Hosp. Kaloleni, Kenya.

EDWARDS, Gerwyn James The Surgery, 90 Church Road, Sheldon, Birmingham B26 3TP Tel: 0121 743 3409; Tel: 0121 733 1701 — MB ChB 1986 Birm.; MRCGP 1993. (Birm.) Gen. Practitioner, Birm.; Clin. Asst. (Cardiol.) Heartlands Hosp. Birm. Socs: BMA; MDU; RCGP. Prev: Trainee GP Thornton-Cleveleys; SHO (Psychiat.) Vict. Hosp. Blackpool.

EDWARDS, Giles Felix St Leger Department of Microbiology, Stobhill NHS Trust, Balornock Road, Glasgow G21 3UW Tel: 0141 201 3015 Fax: 0141 558 5508; Flat Top Left, 166 Hyndland Road, Glasgow G12 9HZ Tel: 0141 334 0690 — MB BChir 1982 Camb.; PhD CNAA 1975; MA Camb. 1975; MRCPath 1990. (St. Bart.) Cons. Microbiol. Stobhill Hosp. Prev: Sen. Regist. (Microbiol.) Glas. Roy. Infirm.; Regist. (Microbiol.) Forth Valley HB; Ho. Phys. Glas. Roy. Infirm.

***EDWARDS, Gillian Avril** 25 Westcott Drive, Durham DH1 5AQ — MB ChB Manch. 1995.

EDWARDS, Gillian Mary 84 Irby Road, Heswall, Wirral CH61 6XG Tel: 0151 342 6994 — MB ChB 1965 Liverp.; DA Eng. 1968; FFA RCS Eng. 1980. Cons. Anaesth. Mersey RHA.

EDWARDS, Helen Elizabeth 59 Haywards Road, Charlton Kings, Cheltenham GL52 6RQ — MB BS 1989 Lond. Clin. Asst. (Palliat. Care) Cheltenham Gen. Hosp.

EDWARDS, Helen Gaynor Stockwell Group Practice, 107 Stockwell Road, London SW9 9TJ Tel: 020 7274 3225 Fax: 020 7738 3005 — MB BS 1986 Lond. (St. Bart. Hosp.)

EDWARDS, Henry Ashley Craig Menai, Menai Bridge LL59 5DT — MB ChB 1962 Liverp.; FFA RCS Eng. 1967; DObst RCOG 1965.

EDWARDS, Hilary Anne Mallett Godswell Lodge, Church Street, Bloxham, Banbury OX15 4ES Tel: 01295 720347; The Ranch, Moor Lane, South Newington, Banbury OX15 4JQ — MB ChB 1978 Liverp.; DRCOG 1980. (Liverpool) GP Partner.

EDWARDS, Hugh Garth Martin, Heol Henfwlch, Carmarthen SA33 5EG Tel: 01276 211318 Fax: 01267 211898 Email: huw.edwards2@btinternet.com — MB BS 1962 Lond.; MRCS Eng. LRCP Lond. 1962; FRCPsych 1986, M 1972; DPM Eng. 1966. (St. Bart.) Private Pract. Socs: Pres. (Ex-Chairm.) Welsh Med. Soc.; (Chairm.) Welsh Psychiat. Soc.; Hist. Med. Soc. Wales. Prev: Cons. Paediat., W. Wales Gen. Hosp., Carmarthen & Bronglais Hosp., Aberystwyth; Sen. Regist. (Psychol.) Med. Welsh Nat. Sch. Med. Cardiff; Regist. WhitCh. Hosp. Cardiff.

EDWARDS, Hugh Vincent East Wing, Ladywell Medical Centre, 26 Featherhall Avenue, Edinburgh EH12 7UN Tel: 0131 334 5000 Fax: 0131 334 8410 — MB ChB 1969 Ed.; BSc (Med. Sci.) Ed. 1966; FRCP Ed. 1994; MRCP (UK) 1974; FRCGP 1995, M 1978. (Ed.)

EDWARDS, Ifor Glyn 22 Fairways, Frodsham, Warrington WA6 7RU Email: ifor@mail.talk-101.com — MB ChB 1969 Liverp.; MSc Liverp. 1997; MRCGP 1975. Lead Clinician N. Chesh. Drugs Serv.

EDWARDS, Isobel Margaret Elizabeth Lime Tree Surgery, Lime Tree Avenue, Findon Valley, Worthing BN14 0DL Tel: 01903 264101 Fax: 01903 695494; Kingston House, Kingston Gorse, Littlehampton BN16 1SF Tel: 01903 770586 — MB ChB 1964 Ed.; MRCGP 1974; DObst RCOG 1966. (Ed.) GP. Socs: BMA & Scott. Thoracic Soc. Prev: Trainee GP Livingston VTS; Research Fell. Univ. Edin. (Respirat. Dis.) City Hosp. Edin.

EDWARDS, Jack (retired) 27 Elmsway, Bramhall, Stockport SK7 2AN Tel: 0161 439 3067 — MB ChB 1945 Sheff.; BSc (Physiol.), MB ChB Sheff. 1945; DCH Eng. 1953. Prev: Regional Med. Off. DHSS.

EDWARDS, Professor James Griffith, CBE National Addiction Centre, 4 Windsor Walk, London SE5 8AF Tel: 020 7252 5428 Fax: 020 7703 5787 Email: r.davies@ior.kcl.ac.uk; Sacrooms Hill, London SE10 8ER Tel: 020 8858 5631 — BM BCh Oxf. 1955; DM Oxf. 1966, MA 1955; DSc Lond. 1990; FRCP Lond. 1976, M 1971; FRCPsych 1976, M 1971; DPM Lond. 1962. (Oxf. & St. Bart.) Emerit. Prof. Addic. Behaviour Univ. Lond.; Hon. Prof. Univ. Chile; Edr.-in-Chief Jl. Addic.; Mem. WHO Expert Advisery Gp. on Drug Dependence. Socs: (Exec.) Soc. Study Addic.; Fell. Acad. Med. Sci.; Chairm. Pub.ations Comm. Soc. for the Study of Addic. Prev: Hon. Cons. Psychiat. Bethlem Roy. & Maudsley Hosp.; Regist. St. Bart. Hosp. Lond.; Ho. Phys. King Geo. Hosp. Ilford & Hammersmith Hosp.

EDWARDS, James Guy University of Southampton, Faculty of Medicine, Health & Biological Sciences, Department Psychiatry, Royal South Hampshire Hospital, Southampton SO14 0YG Tel: 02380 550118 Fax: 02380550118 Email: ge@soton.ac.uk; 30 Oakmount Avenue, Southampton SO17 1DR Tel: 02380550118 Fax: 02380 550118 Email: j_guy_ edwards@hotmail.com — MB BCh Wales 1958; MRCS Eng. LRCP Lond. 1958; FRCPsych 1976, M 1971; DPM Eng. 1964. (Cardiff) Cons. Psychiat.chalybeate Hosps.oton; Mem. Ment. Health. Review Trib.; Vis. Prof. Khon Kaen Univ & P. of Songla Univ. Thailand; Hon. Sen. Research Fell. Drug Safety Research Unit Soton. Socs: BMA. Prev: Cons. Psychiat. Soton. & SW Hants. HA; Hon.clin.sen.lect.univ.ston; Clin. Research Psychiat. Nathan S. Kline Inst. Psychiat. Research Orangeburg New York, USA.

EDWARDS, James Hendrik Reginald Tel: 01258 474500 Fax: 01258 471547; Bay Tree Cottage, Burton St, Marnhull, Sturminster Newton DT10 1PS Tel: 01258 820772 — MB BS 1987 Lond.; MRCGP 1992; DFFP 1994; DRCOG 1991. (Lond. Hosp.) Prev: Trainee GP Yotk VTS; Regist. (Paediat.) Auckland, NZ.

EDWARDS, Jane Margaret Department of Pathology, Royal Preston Hospital, Sharoc Green Lane North, Preston PR2 4HG Tel: 01772 710633; Willacy House, Willacy Lane, Catforth, Preston PR4 0JD Tel: 01772 690135 — MB ChB 1980 Manch.; MRCPath 1990. Cons. Histopath. Roy. Preston Hosp. Prev: Cons. Histopath. Vict. Hosp. Blackpool.

EDWARDS, Mr Jeffrey Alan Department of Obstetrics & Gynaecology, Glan Clywd District General Hospital, Bodelwyddan, Rhyl LL18 5UJ — MB BS 1969 Lond.; FRCS Eng. 1974; MRCS Eng. LRCP Lond. 1969; MRCOG 1977. (St. Thos.) Cons. (O & G) Clwyd AHA. Prev: Lect. (O & G) W.m. Med. Sch.; Resid. Surg. Off. Chelsea Hosp. Wom. Lond.; Resid. Med. Off. (Obst.) Qu. Charlotte's Matern. Hosp. Lond.

EDWARDS, Jennifer Jane Tel: 01568 614141 Fax: 01568 610293 — MB BS 1989 Newc.; MRCGP 1995; DRCOG 1997; DCH RCP Lond. 1995; DA (UK) 1991. Socs: DFFM. Prev: SHO (Psychiat.) Severn NHS Trust Gloucester; Trainee GP Hay on Wye; SHO (A & E) Roy. Infirm. Lancaster.

EDWARDS, Jennifer Mary 'Penrhyn', Stockwell, Silverton, Exeter EX5 4DF Tel: 0139 288307 — MB BS 1967 Lond.; MRCS Eng. LRCP Lond. 1967; FFA RCS Eng. 1971. (Westm.) SHO Anaesth. W.m. Hosp. Lond. Prev: Ho. Surg. Radiother. Dept. W.m. Hosp. Lond.; Ho. Phys. St. Stephen's Hosp. Lond.

EDWARDS, Jill Elizabeth White House Surgery, Horsefair, Chipping Norton OX7 5AL Tel: 01608 642742 Fax: 01608 642794; Claridges Barn, Dean, Chipping Norton OX7 5XG — MB BS 1978 Lond.; MRCGP 1984; DA (UK) 1982; DRCOG 1981.

EDWARDS, Joan Mary Bailey (retired) 18 Copthall Gardens, Mill Hill, London NW7 2NG — MB BS 1944 Lond.; MRCS Eng. LRCP Lond. 1944; FRCPath 1976, M 1964. Prev: Cons. Microbiol. Virus Ref. Laborat. Centr. Pub. Health Laborat. Colindale.

EDWARDS, Joan Maureen (retired) Avon Lodge, Bickton, Fordingbridge SP6 2HA Tel: 01425 652957 Email: mrsjoanedwards@aol.com — MB BS Lond. 1957; MRCS Eng. LRCP Lond. 1957; FRCPath 1978, M 1966; DObst RCOG 1959. Prev: Assoc. Specialist (Haemat.) Salisbury Dist. Hosp.

EDWARDS, Joan Worsley (retired) Bryn Afon, Llanarmon Road, Llanferres, Mold CH7 5TA — MRCS Eng. LRCP Lond. 1932. Prev: Ho. Surg. ENT Liverp. Roy. Infirm.

EDWARDS, John Clement (retired) Barnside, Church Lane, Braishfield, Romsey SO51 0QH — MB BS 1962 Lond.; FFA RCS Eng. 1968. Prev: Cons. Anaesth. Soton. Univ. Gp. Hosps.

EDWARDS, John David Elliott (retired) 128 Moorsholm Drive, Wollaton, Nottingham NG8 2EE Tel: 0115 985 4198 — MB ChB 1948 Liverp.; DOMS RCPSI 1951. Prev: Asst. Ophth. Surg. Arrowe Pk. Hosp. Upton.

EDWARDS, John Geoffrey South Dene Surgery, The Shrubberies, George Lane, London E18 1BD Tel: 020 8530 3731 Fax: 020 8518 8157 — MB BCh 1974 Wales; MRCGP 1982; DObst RCOG 1976; Dip. Thera. 1998. (Welsh National School of Medicine) Chairm. Redbridge & Waltham Forest Area Prescribing Comm.; Comm. Mem. of Prescribing Sub-Comm. to Chingford, Wanstead and Woodford PCT.

EDWARDS, Mr John Gurney 77 Jockey Road, Sutton Coldfield B73 5PH — MB ChB 1993 Birm.; FRCS Glas. 1997. (Birm.) Clin. Research Fell. Dept. Oncol.Univ. of Leicester. Socs: BMA. Prev: SHO (Thoracic Surg.) Fenchay Bristol; SHO (Cardiac Surg. & ITU) Qu. Eliz. Hosp. Birm.

EDWARDS, John Hilton 78 Old Road, Headington, Oxford OX3 7LP Tel: 01865 760430 Email: jhe@bioch.ox.ac.uk — MB BChir 1952 Camb.; FRS; FRCP Lond 1972, M 1956. (Middlx) Emerit. Prof. Genetics Univ. Oxf.; Hon. Lect. Biochem. Univ. Otago,

Dunedin, NZ; Hon. Prof. Dept. of Gen. Sci. Sydney Australia. Prev: Cons. Univ. Iceland; Cons. Clin. Genetics. Oxf. HA; Cons. Genetics WHO.

EDWARDS, John Innes Rhyd y Defaid, Rhosmeirch, Llangefni LL77 7NX Tel: 01248 722105 — MB ChB 1968 Liverp.; DA Eng. 1973. (Liverp.) Socs: BMA. Prev: SHO (Anaesth.) St. Mary's Hosp. Lond.; Res. Ho. Off. King Edwd. VII Memor. Hosp. Bermuda; Ho. Surg. (O & G) Sefton Gen. Hosp. Liverp.

EDWARDS, John James 25 Swarthmore Road, Selly Oak, Birmingham B29 4NQ — MB ChB 1990 Bristol. SHO (Med.) Walsall Hosp. NHS Trust. Prev: Ho. Off. (Gen. Surg. & Gen. Med.) Bristol Roy. Infirm.

EDWARDS, John Melfyn Talys, 34 Heol Newydd, Porthmadog LL49 4ED — MB BCh 1985 Wales.

EDWARDS, Mr John Morris St. Anthony's Hospital, North Cheam, Sutton SM3 9DW Tel: 020 8337 6691; 3 Dormy House, Deans Lane, Walton-on-the-Hill, Tadworth KT20 7TQ Tel: 0173 781 2216 — MS Lond. 1966, MB BS 1956; FRCS Eng. 1963. (St. Thos.) Cons. Surg. St Anthony Hosp. Surrey; Hon Cons. Surg. St. Helier Hosp. Carshalton. Socs: Intern. Soc. Lymphol.; Hon. Fell. Amer. Coll. Nuclear Med. 1977; Vasc. Soc. GB & I. Prev: Cons. Surg. Merton-Sutton HA; Sen. Lect. & Hon Cons. St Thos. Hosp. Lond.; Hon. Sen. Lect. St Geo. Hosp. Lond.

EDWARDS, Mr John Neill Thesen Sarum House, 29 Forest Road, Branksome Park, Poole BH13 6DQ Tel: 01202 751792 Fax: 01202 765287 Email: johnty@lds.co.uk — MB ChB 1972 Pretoria; FRCOG 1996; FRCS Ed. 1983; MRCOG 1980. Cons. O & G Poole Hosp. NHS Trust. Prev: Sen. Regist. Univ. Coll. Hosp. Lond.; Regist. John Radcliffe Hosp. Oxf.

EDWARDS, John Raymond (retired) Little Nettacott, Upton Pyne, Exeter EX5 5HX Tel: 01392 851307 — MB BChir Camb. 1952; DObst RCOG 1956. Prev: Ho. Surg. Roy. Waterloo Hosp. Lond.

EDWARDS, John Richard 96 Haslemere Avenue, Hanwell, London W7 2AU Tel: 020 8840 2974 Fax: 020 8840 2974 — MB BS 1986 Lond.; BSc (Hons.) Lond. 1983; MRCGP 1992; DCH RCP Lond. 1991; DRCOG 1991; MSc 1998. Prev: Trainee GP/SHO W. Middlx. Univ. Hosp. Lond. VTS; SHO (A & E) St. Helier Hosp. Carshalton.; GP Princip., Gen. Pract.

EDWARDS, John Wyn Lewis Blithe House, 79 Cottage Lane, Ormskirk L39 3NF Tel: 01695 572771 — MD 1950 Liverp.; MB ChB 1945; FRCP Lond. 1974, M 1950. (Liverp.) Cons. Phys. Allergy Roy. Liverp. Hosp. Prev: Cons. Phys. Ormskirk & Dist. Hosp.; Sen. Regist. (Med.) David Lewis N.. Hosp. & Roy. S.. Hosp. Liverp.; Surg. Lt. RNVR.

EDWARDS, Jonathan St Davids Medical Centre, Pentwyn Drive, Pentwyn, Cardiff CF23 7SD Tel: 029 2073 3032 Fax: 029 2054 1392; 11 Pantfaen, Cyncoed, Cardiff CF23 7DU — MB ChB 1983 Manch.; MRCGP 1987.

EDWARDS, Professor Jonathan Charles Wright UCL Rheumatology Centre, Arthur Stanley House, 40-50 Tottenham House, London W1T 4NJ Tel: 020 7380 9215 Fax: 020 7380 9278; 46 Park Drive, London NW11 7SP — MB BChir 1975 Camb.; MD Camb. 1983; BA Camb. 1971; FRCP Lond. 1992; MRCP (UK) 1976. Prof. Connective Tissue Med. Univ. Coll. Lond. Med. Sch. & Hon. Cons. Univ. Coll. Hosps. Prev: Sen. Regist. (Rheum.) Univ. Coll. Hosp. Lond.; Muir Hambro Fell. Rheum. St. Bart. Lond.; Regist. (Med.) & (Rheum.) Guy's Hosp. Lond.

EDWARDS, Jonathan Michael Oak Hill Health Centre, Oak Hill Road, Surbiton KT6 6EN Tel: 020 8399 6622 Fax: 020 8390 4470; Flat 3 Aranmor, Kingston Hill, Kingston upon Thames KT2 7LY Tel: 020 8546 4240 — MB ChB 1982 Bristol; MRCGP 1996; DRCOG 1986. (Univ. Bristol)

EDWARDS, Joseph Denis University Hospital of South Manchester, Withington, Manchester M20 2LR Tel: 0161 445 8111 — MB ChB 1971 Ed.; FRCP Lond. 1988. Cons. Phys. Univ. Hosp. S. Manch.; Dir. IC Unit Univ. Hosp. Manch.; Hon. Lect. Anaesth. Socs: IC Soc. (Mem. Counc.).

EDWARDS, Mr Joseph Rowland Goodman (retired) 8 Mitchell Avenue, Newcastle upon Tyne NE2 3LA Tel: 0191 281 1814 — BSc (Special) Lond. 1938, MB BS 1941; FRCS Eng. 1952; MRCS Eng. LRCP Lond. 1941. Hon. Cons. Plastic Surg. Newc. HA & N. RHA; Hon. Research Fell. Univ. Newc. 1980. Prev: Cons. Plastic Surg. Newc. HA (T) & N.. RHA.

EDWARDS, Judith Anne Department of Psychiatry, Epsom Hospital, Dorking Road, Epsom KT18 7EG Tel: 020 8873 4064 — MB BS 1978 Lond.; MRCPsych 1986; DRCOG 1981. (St. Mary's) Cons. Psychiat. Surrey Oaklands NHS Trust. Prev: Sen. Regist. (Psychother.) Cassell Hosp. Char. Cross; Regist. (Child Psychiat.) Slough Child Guid. Clinic & Pk. Hosp Oxf.; Specialist Regist. (Gen. Psychiat.) W. Lond. Healthcare Trust.

EDWARDS, Julia Malvern Health Centre, Victoria Park Road, Malvern Link, Malvern WR14 2JY Tel: 01684 612703 Fax: 01684 612779; 4 Sparrowhall Lane, Colletts Green, Powick, Worcester WR2 4SG Tel: 01905 830849 — MB ChB 1978 Birm.; DRCOG 1983.

EDWARDS, Juliet Jane Caer Ffynnon Surgery, Caer Ffynnon, Springfield Street, Dolgellau LL40 1LY Tel: 01341 422431 Fax: 01341 423717 — MB ChB 1986 Sheff.; MRCGP 1991. (Sheffield)

EDWARDS, Juliette Helen 10 Eachway Lane, Rednall, Birmingham B45 9LG Tel: 0961 342123 Email: julietteedwards@lickeyhills.freeserve.co.uk; 45 Winnie Road, Selly Oak, Birmingham B29 6JU Tel: 0961 342123 — MB ChB 1996 Birm.; MB ChB Birm. (Hons.) 1996. (Univ. Birm.) SHO Ophth., Sandwell DGH W. Midl. Socs: BMA; MDU. Prev: SHO (A & E Med.) Heartlands Hosp. Birm.; Lect. (Anat.) Univ. Birm.; Ho. Off. (Gen. Med. & Cardiol.) Univ. Hosp. Birm. NHS Trust.

EDWARDS, Justin Nathan 127 Upton Court Road, Slough SL3 7NG — MB BS 1998 Lond.; MB BS Lond 1998.

EDWARDS, Karen 23 Pinewood Cl, Walkford, Christchurch BH23 5RR — MB BS 1997 Lond.

EDWARDS, Katharine Meriel Rosina Pershore Health Centre, Priest Lane, Pershore WR10 1RD Tel: 01386 502030 Fax: 01386 502058 — MB BCh 1979 Wales; MRCGP 1984; DCH RCP Lond. 1983; DRCOG 1983.

EDWARDS, Kathleen Jennifer Burland 2 Cozens Close, Bedworth, Nuneaton CV12 8TS — MB BS 1960 Lond.; MRCS Eng. LRCP Lond. 1960; MRCPsych 1989; Dip. Psychother. 1987. (Roy. Free) Sen. Regist. (Child & Adolesc. Psychiat.) Mersey Regional Train. Scheme. Socs: Assn. Child Psychol. & Psychiat. & Assn. Family Ther.. Prev: Regist. (Psychiat.) Liverp. Univ. Train. Scheme & Burnley Gen. Hosp.; Regist. (Psychiat.) Lancaster Moor Hosp.; Clin. Asst. (Ment. Handicap) Roy. Albert Hosp. Lancaster.

EDWARDS, Kathryn Elizabeth Gap Cottage, 32 Kings Gap, Wirral CH47 1HF — MB ChB 1992 Liverp.

EDWARDS, Katie Jane Tamsin VSO Health Desk, 317 Putney Bridge Road, London SW15 2PN; 4 Queen Street, Henley-on-Thames RG9 1AP Tel: 01491 574357 — MB BS 1987 Lond.; MRCGP 1991; DCH RCP Lond. 1990; DRCOG 1989. Pub. Health Coordinator Addfood Project, Malawai. Prev: Dist. Health Off. Nkhotakota Dist. Hosp., Malawai.

EDWARDS, Kenneth Basil 170 Plymyard Avenue, Eastham, Wirral CH62 8EH Tel: 0151 327 1391 — MB ChB 1953 Liverp.; MRCS Eng. LRCP Lond. 1953. (Liverp.) MRCGP. Socs: Birkenhead Med. Soc. Prev: Squadron Ldr. RAF Med. Serv.; Ho. Surg. Liverp. Roy. Infirm.; Ho. Phys. Sefton Gen. Hosp.

EDWARDS, Kenneth George Toolerstone House, Off Norley Road, Sandiway, Northwich CW8 2JN Tel: 01606 883476 — MB ChB 1974 Manch.; PhD Manch. 1969, MSc 1967; FFPM RCP (UK) 1993, M 1989; DPharm. Med. RCP (UK) 1980. Med. Dir., Zeneca Pharma. Socs: FFPM; Fell. Roy. Soc. Med; Brit. Assn. Pharmaceut. Phys. Prev: Head Cardiovasc. Med. Research ICI Pharmaceuts. Macclesfield; Regist. (Gen. Med.) Leighton Hosp. Crewe; Research Off. (Experim. Chemother.) Christie Hosp. Manch.

EDWARDS, Kshanika Marini Josephine 64 Blandford Road, London W4 1EA — MB BChir 1985 Camb.

EDWARDS, Linda 461 Chelsea Cloisters, Sloane Avenue, London SW3 3EQ Tel: 020 7589 5100 Ext: 2461; 32 Estria Road, Edgbaston, Birmingham B15 2LQ Tel: 0121 440 5935 Fax: 0121 440 5935 — MB ChB 1993 Birm.; MRCP (Paeds) 1999. SHO (Paediat.) Birm. Childr. Hosp. (Haemat. / Oncol.); SHO (Neonatology) Birm. Wom. Hosp.; SHO (Paediat. Cardiol.) Birm. Childr. Hosp.

EDWARDS, Lukas Jon 2 Constable Close, Mile End, Colchester CO4 5EZ — MB BS 1991 Queensland.

EDWARDS, Madeleine Postal Cottage, Main St., Peatling Magna, Leicester LE8 5UQ — MB BS 1989 Lond.

EDWARDS, Marc Cadwgan Surgery, 11 Bodelwyddan Avenue, Old Colwyn, Colwyn Bay LL29 9NP Tel: 01492 515410 Fax: 01492

513270 — MB ChB 1991 Liverp.; MRCGP 1995; DCH RCP Lond. 1994. (Liverp.) GP Educat. Organiser N. Clwyd. Socs: Conf. Organizer Y Gymdeithas Feddygol. Prev: Trainee GP Gwynedd VTS; SHO (Paediat.) Glan Clwyd Hosp.

EDWARDS, Margaret (retired) Rose Cottage, Church Road, Llanblethian, Cowbridge CF71 7JF — MB BCh 1947 Wales; BSc Wales 1944, MB BCh 1947, CPH 1950. Prev: SCMO Waltham Forest DHA.

EDWARDS, Marian Searby (retired) 15 Winston Avenue, Ipswich IP4 3LS — MB BS 1954 Lond.; BSc Lond. 1947; FRCPath 1977, M 1965; DObst RCOG 1956. Prev: Cons. Haemat. Ipswich HA.

EDWARDS, Mark John James Flat 36, Park East Building, Fairfield Road, London E3 2UT — MB BS 1997 Lond.

EDWARDS, Mark Robert Clinical Development, Pfizer Ltd., Sandwich CT13 9NJ Tel: 01304 648797 Fax: 01304 655537 Email: mark_r_edwards@sandwich.pfizer.com — MB BS 1987 Lond.; BSc (Hons.) Lond. 1984; FRCA. 1992; DA (UK) 1990. Director, Clin. Devlopment Prof. Global R&D, Sandwich. Prev: Clin. Research Phys. Guy's Drug Research Unit Ltd. Lond.; Regist. (Anaesth.) Kent & Canterbury Hosp.; SHO (Anaesth.) Greenwich Dist. & Brook Gen. Hosps.

EDWARDS, Martin Christopher Highbridge Medical Centre, Pepperall Road, Highbridge TA9 3YA Tel: 01278 783220 Fax: 01278 795486; Ruscombe, Brent St, Brent Knoll, Highbridge TA9 4ED — MB ChB 1976 Birm.; MRCGP 1984; DRCOG 1984.

EDWARDS, Martin Varnam Jenner Health Centre, 201 Stanstead Road, London SE23 1HU Tel: 020 8690 2231; 127 Pepys Road, Telegraph Hill, London SE14 5SE Fax: 020 7277 5696 Email: martin@edwardes.freeserve.co.uk — MB BChir 1981 Camb.; MSc (Hist. Sci. & Med.) Lond. 1998; MRCGP 1984; DCH RCP Lond. 1983; DRCOG 1983; MA Camb. 1981. (Camb. Univ.)

EDWARDS, Matthew Dermot (retired) 9 Sheridan Drive, Helen's Bay, Bangor BT19 1LB Tel: 01247 853298 — LRCP LRCS Ed. LRFPS Glas. 1938; DPH Belf. 1955. Prev: Surg. Lt.-Cdr. RNVR.

EDWARDS, Matthew Kieron Ramsay Department of Accident and Emergency, Royal Sussex County Hospital, Eastern Road, Brighton BN2 5BE — MB BS 1998 Lond.; MB BS Lond 1998.

EDWARDS, Matthew Penry Royal Hallamshire H., Glussop Road, Sheffield S7 1RX; Tel: 01904 631313 — MB ChB 1991 Leeds; BSc 1988 (Pharm.) Leeds; FRCOphth 1996. (Leeds) Cons. (Ophth.) Roy. Hallamsh. Hosp. Sheff. Prev: SHO (Ophth.) Leeds Gen. Infirm.; SHO (Ophth.) Roy. Hallamsh. Hosp. Sheff.

EDWARDS, Michael Department Geriatric Medicine, Nevill Hall Hospital, Abergavenny — MB BS 1971 Lond.; MRCP (UK) 1976; MRCS Eng. LRCP Lond. 1971. (Lond. Hosp.) Cons. Phys. Geriat. Med. Gwent/Powys HAs. Prev: Sen. Regist. Dept. Geriat. Med. Cardiff; Regist. Dept. Histopath. Univ. Hosp. of Wales Cardiff.

EDWARDS, Michael Anthony Beechtree Road Surgery, 32 Beechtree Road, Walsall WS9 9LT Tel: 01543 375457; 7 Knighton Drive, Four Oaks, Sutton Coldfield B74 4QP Tel: 0121 308 5824 — MB ChB 1971 Birm.; MRCGP 1984; MRCOG 1977.

EDWARDS, Michael Bower (retired) Thie Gless, Ballakillowey, Colby, Castletown IM9 4BG Tel: 01624 833748 — MB ChB 1947 Manch.; MRCPsych 1971; DPM Manch. 1959. Prev: Cons. Psychiat. & Med. Supt. Cheadle Roy. Hosp.

EDWARDS, Mr Michael Harpur Friarage Hospital, Northallerton DL6 1JG Tel: 01609 779911 Fax: 01609 764631 Email: michaelhedwardsok@cs.com; Robingate, Lucy Cross Rd, Aldburgh St John, Richmond DL11 7TD Tel: 01325 374626 Fax: 01325 374626 Email: michaelhedwardsok@cs.com — MB ChB Liverp. 1964; FRCS Eng. 1970; Specialist Accredit. (Gen. Surg.) RCS Eng. 1976; FRCS 1969 (Ed). Cons. Surg. (Gen. Surg.) Friarage Hosp. N.allerton. Socs: Assn. Surg.; Assn. Endoscopic Surgs.; Roy. Soc. Med. Prev: Sen. Regist. Univ. Hosp. Wales Cardiff; Lect. King's Coll. Hosp. Lond.

EDWARDS, Michael Rex Fairbrook Medical Centre, 4 Fairway Avenue, Borehamwood WD6 1PR Tel: 020 8953 7666; 7 Bedford Avenue, Barnet EN5 2EP — MB BS 1985 Lond.; MRCGP 1990.

EDWARDS, Mr Michael Steven Delawar Woodland Barn, Oldfield Lane, Darley Bridge, Matlock DE4 2JY — MB ChB 1982 Sheff.; FRCS Ed. 1989; FRCS (Orth) 1997. Cons. Trauma & Orthop. Surg. Chesterfield & N.Derbysh. Socs: Brit. Soc. for Surg. of the Hand (Assoc. Mem.). Prev: Regist. Rotat. (Orthop.) Nuffield Orthop. Centre Oxf.; SHO (Gen. Surg.) E.bourne Dist. Gen. Hosp.; SHO (Neurosurg.) Hurstwood Pk. Neurol. Centre W. Sussex.

EDWARDS, Montague Dudley (retired) Whitewalls, Cilonen Rd, Three Crosses, Swansea SA4 3US Tel: 01792 872238 — MB BCh 1960 Wales. Clin. Asst. Gorseinon Cott. Hosp.

EDWARDS, Neal David University Department of Surgical, & Anaesthetic Sciences, Royal Hallamshire Hospital, Glossop Road, Sheffield S10 2JF; 8 Chorley Place, Fulwood, Sheffield S10 3RS — MB BS 1985 Lond.; FRCA 1990. Sen. Lect. (Anaesth.) Univ. Sheff. Socs: Chairm., Vasc. Anaesthetic Soc. of GB and Irel. Prev: Lect. (Anaesth.) Univ. Sheff.; Regist. (Anaesth.) Welsh Anaesth. Train. Scheme; SHO (Intens. Care) Roy. Cornw. Hosp. Truro.

EDWARDS, Nia Ilid Hycroft, Ffordd Menai, Penrhos, Bangor LL57 2LS — MB BS 1984 Lond.

EDWARDS, Nicholas John 7 Little St John Street, Woodbridge IP12 1EE — MB BCh 1985 Wales; MRCGP 1989; DRCOG 1988. GP Woodbridge. Prev: Trainee GP Gt. Yarmouth VTS.

EDWARDS, Mr Nigel (retired) Litfield House, Clifton Down, Bristol BS8 3LS Tel: 0117 973 1323 — MB BChir Camb. 1958; FRCS Eng. 1965; FRCS Ed. 1963; DObst RCOG 1959. Prev: Cons. ENT Surg. Frenchay & S.mead Hosps. Bristol.

EDWARDS, Norman Vernon Alderford Grange, Sible Hedingham, Halstead CO9 3RD Tel: 01787 460260 Fax: 01787 460816 — MB BS 1962 Lond.; LMSSA Lond. 1961; DObst RCOG 1965. (St. Mary's) Prev: SHO (ENT, Paediat. & Dermat.) Ashford Hosp. Middlx.; Resid. Obst. Off. St. Mary's Hosp. Lond.

EDWARDS, Owain Huw Pritchard 15 Frans Hals Court, 87 Amsterdam Road, London E14 3UX Tel: 020 7987 2823 — MB BS 1994 Lond.

EDWARDS, Owen Morris Dower House, 7 High St., Pampisford, Cambridge CB2 4ES Tel: 01223 834318 Fax: 01223 834318 Email: ome20@ac.cam.uk — MD Lond. 1974, MB BS (Hons. Med.) 1963; FRCP Lond. 1980, M 1967; MRCS Eng. LRCP Lond. 1963. (St. Mary's) Cons. Phys. Addenbrooke's Hosp. Camb. Prev: Univ. Sen. Asst. Phys. & Hon. Cons. Phys. Addenbrooke's Hosp. Camb.; Ho. Phys. St. Mary's Hosp. Lond.; Sen. Med. Regist. Addenbrooke's Hosp. Camb.

EDWARDS, Patricia Ann (retired) 18 Hall Drive, Sydenham, London SE26 6XB Tel: 020 8778 6853 — MB BS Lond. 1954; FFA RCS Eng. 1961; DObst RCOG 1957; DA Eng. 1957. Prev: Cons. Anaesth. St. Geo. Hosp. Tooting.

EDWARDS, Patrick Julian The Deganwy Medical Centre, York Road, Deganwy, Conwy LL31 9PX Tel: 01492 583304 Fax: 01492 572967; The Medical Centre, Plas Penrhyn, Penrhyn Bay, Llandudno LL30 3EU Tel: 01492 549368 Fax: 01492 548103 — MB BCh 1973 Wales; MRCGP 1978; DCH Eng. 1977; DObst RCOG 1976.

EDWARDS, Mr Paul Ronald 54 Mimosa Road, Liverpool L15 6UF — MB BChir 1978 Camb.; MB Camb. 1978, MA, BChir 1977; FRCS Eng. 1982; FRCS Ed. 1982. Sen. Research Asst. Dept. Surg. Univ. Liverp.

EDWARDS, Mr Peris Woodfine New Court Consulting Rooms, 21A Nevill St., Abergavenny NP7 5AA Tel: 01873 856071; West Wing, Llwyndu Court, Abergavenny NP7 7HG Tel: 01873 854896 Fax: 01873 854896 — MB BS 1957 Lond.; FRCS Eng. 1966; MRCS Eng. LRCP Lond. 1957. (Univ. Coll. Hosp.) Cons. Orthop. & Traum. Surg. Nevill Hall Hosp. Abergavenny. Socs: Fell. Roy. Soc. Med.; Fell. BOA; Welsh Orthop. Soc. Prev: Sen. Regist. Cardiff Roy. Infirm. & P. of Wales Orthop. Hosp. Cardiff.

EDWARDS, Peter Arthen Tal-y-Bont Surgery, Station Road, Pontardulais, Swansea SA4 1TL Tel: 01792 882368; Bry House, Bryn Road, Pontardulais, Swansea SA4 1TQ — MB BCh 1977 Wales.

EDWARDS, Peter Davey Buckfastleigh Medical Centre, 7 Bossell Road, Buckfastleigh TQ11 0DE Tel: 01364 42534 Fax: 01364 644057 — MB ChB 1970 Bristol; MRCGP 1974; DObst RCOG 1972.

EDWARDS, Peter Howell Ely Bridge Surgery, 23 Mill Road, Ely, Cardiff CF5 4AD Tel: 029 2056 1808 Fax: 029 2057 8871; 3 Dan-y-Bryn Avenue, Radyr, Cardiff CF15 8DB Tel: 029 2084 2024 — MB BCh 1977 Wales; MRCGP 1981. Sen. Lect. Dept. Post Grad. Studies Univ. Coll. Med. Wales. Prev: Course Organiser S. Glam. VTS; Lect Gen. Pract. Univ. Coll. Med. Wales, Cardiff.

EDWARDS, Peter John (retired) 104 Evington Lane, Leicester LE5 5PP Tel: 0116 273 6777 — MB BCh 1960 Wales; DObst RCOG 1962.

EDWARDS, Peter John Elmhurst Surgery, Aylesbury HP20 2AH Tel: 01296 84054 Fax: 01296 397016; Haddenham Low House, Dinton, Aylesbury HP17 8TT — MRCS Eng. LRCP Lond. 1957; MRCGP 1966. (St. Thos.) Med. Off. HM Prison Aylesbury. Prev: Hosp. Pract. (Accid.) Stoke Mandeville Hosp. Aylesbury; Ho. Phys. St. Luke's Hosp. Guildford; Ho. Surg. Tredegar Gen. Hosp.

EDWARDS, Peter Michael Patrick Queen Margaret Hospital, Whitefield Road, Dunfermline KY12 0SU Tel: 01383 623623; 40 Leamington Terrace, Edinburgh EH10 4JL Tel: 0131 229 6259 — MB ChB 1966 Cape Town; MRCPsych 1979. Cons. Psychiat. Qu. Margt. Hosp. Dunfermline. Prev: Sen. Regist. (Psychiat.) S.. Gen. Hosp. Glas.; Sen. Regist. (Psychiat.) Gartnavel Roy. Hosp. Glas.; Regist. (Psychiat.) Dingleton Hosp. Melrose.

EDWARDS, Peter Richard Bradford Health Authority, New Mill, Saltaire, Shipley BD18 3LD Tel: 01274 366007 Fax: 01274 366060; West Terrace, Burley in Wharfedale, Ilkley LS29 7HS Tel: 01943 863643 — BChir 1988 Camb.; BA Camb. 1985; MRCP (UK) 1992; MPH Leeds 1994. Sen. Regist. (Pub. Health Med.) Bradford HA; Trainee Mem. Fac. Pub. Health Med. Prev: Regist. (Respirat. Med.) Roy. Hallamsh. Hosp. Sheff.; SHO (Med.) OldCh. Hosp. Romford.; SHO (Oncol.) Middlx. Hosp. Lond.

EDWARDS, Philip Douglas 13 Malvern Drive, Bowdon, Altrincham WA14 4NQ — MB BChir 1990 Camb.

EDWARDS, Canon Doctor Philip John (retired) 21 Haywards Road, Haywards Heath RH16 4HX Tel: 01444 457880 — MRCS Eng. LRCP Lond. 1951. Prev: GP Ashtead Surrey.

EDWARDS, Philip John Highmoor, Hill St., Cockermouth CA13 0AU — MB ChB 1998 Manch.; MB ChB Manch 1998.

EDWARDS, Phillip David Llewelyn Department of Paediatrics, Princess of Wales Hospital, Bridgend Tel: 01656 752372; Mill House, Wick, Cowbridge CF71 7QD Tel: 01656 890505 — MB BCh 1968 Wales; FRCP Lond. 1994; FRCP Ed. 1989; MRCP (UK) 1975; MRCPCH 1996; DCH Eng. 1971; DObst RCOG 1971. (Cardiff) Cons. Paediat. P.ss of Wales Hosp. Bridgend; Hon. Clin. Teach. (Paediat.) Coll. Med. Cardiff. Socs: (Pres.) Welsh Paediat. Soc. Prev: Sen. Regist. (Paediat.) King's Coll. Hosp. Lond.; Regist. (Paediat.) Roy. Gwent Hosp. Newport; SHO (Paediat.) Dept. Child Health United Cardiff Hosps.

EDWARDS, Phoebe Alethea (retired) Burton Croft Surgery, 5 Burton Crescent, Leeds LS6 4DN Tel: 0113 274 4777 Fax: 0113 230 4219 — MB BS 1964 Lond.; MRCS Eng. LRCP Lond. 1964; DCH Eng. 1969; DObst RCOG 1966. Prev: Princip. GP, Burton Croft Surg., Leeds.

EDWARDS, Rachel 81 Longhurst Lane, Mellor, Stockport SK6 5AH — MB ChB 1995 Birm.; BSc (Hons) Pharmacology 1992. GP VTS Stockport.

EDWARDS, Ranjitham Shanthini 44 Turnfurlong La, Aylesbury HP21 7PQ — MB BS 1967 Ceylon. (Colombo) Clin. Med. Off. Community Health, Brookside Clinic, Aylesbury. Prev: SHO (ENT) Hillingdon Hosp. Uxbridge.

EDWARDS, Rhian Eleri 42 Underhill Road, London SE22 0QT — MB BS 1986 Lond.; FRCA 1991. (King's Coll. Hosp.) Cons. Anaesth. & Intens. Care St. Helier Hosp. Carshalton. Prev: Sen. Regist. (Anaesth.) St. Geo. Hosp. Lond.; Clin. Research Fell. Dept. Cardiol. Sci. St. Geo. Hosp. Med. Sch.; Regist. (Anaesth.) St. Geo. Hosp. Lond.

EDWARDS, Richard Bryn Llewelyn Meddygfa'r Llan, Church Surgery, Portland Street, Aberystwyth SY23 2DX Tel: 01970 624855 Fax: 01970 625824; Cilmeri, St. David's Road, Aberystwyth SY23 1EU Tel: 01970 623003 — MB BS 1974 Lond.; MRCS Eng. LRCP Lond. 1974; DRCOG 1976. (Westm.) Clin. Asst. (Cas.) Bronglais Hosp. Aberystwyth. Prev: Ho. Surg. W.m. Hosp. Lond.; Ho. Phys. Qu. Mary's Hosp. Roehampton.

EDWARDS, Richard David Department of Radiology, Gartnavel General Hospital, 1053 Great Western Road, Glasgow G12 0YN Tel: 0141 211 3113 Fax: 0141 211 3471; 8 North Gardner Street, Glasgow G11 5BT — MB ChB Ed. 1979; MCRP (UK) 1983; FRCR 1988. Cons. Radiol. Gartnavel Gen. Hosp.

EDWARDS, Professor Richard Humphrey Tudor (retired) Berthlwyd, Nantgwynant, Beddgelert, Caernarfon LL55 4NL Tel: 01766 890364 Fax: 01766 890613 Email: richardht@edwards.fsnet.co.uk — MB BS 1964 Lond.; PhD Lond. 1969, BSc (Hons.) 1961; FRCP Lond. 1976, M 1966; MRCS Eng. LRCP Lond. 1964. Prof. Research & Developm. Health & Social Care Univ. Wales Coll. Med. Cardiff. Prev: Dir. Research & Developm. Health & Social Care in Wales.

EDWARDS, Richard John Dryer House, Warley, Halifax HX2 7SH — MB BS 1994 Lond.; BSc Hons 1991. (UCLSM) Socs: MDU.

EDWARDS, Richard John 20 Gustard Wood, Wheathampstead, St Albans AL4 8RP — MB BS 1994 Lond.

EDWARDS, Richard Mark Eastleigh Surgery, Station Road, Westbury BA13 3JD Tel: 01373 822807 Fax: 01373 828904 — BM BS 1988 Nottm.; MRCGP 1992.

EDWARDS, Richard Nicholas 9 Lyme Park, Chinley, High Peak SK23 6AG — MB ChB 1998 Manch.; MB ChB Manch 1998.

EDWARDS, Richard Philip Brynderwen Surgery, Crickhowell Road, St. Mellons, Cardiff CF3 0EF Tel: 029 2079 9921 Fax: 029 2077 7740 — MB BCh 1972 Wales; DA Eng. 1979; DObst RCOG 1974.

EDWARDS, Mr Richard Stanley Kent & Canterbury Hospital, Etherlbert Road, Canterbury CT1 3NG Tel: 01227 766879; 22 South Canterbury Road, Canterbury CT1 3LJ — MB ChB 1972 Birm.; FRCS Eng. 1978; DO Eng. 1976. Cons. Ophth. Canterbury & Thanet & SE Kent HAs. Socs: Fell. Roy. Coll. of Ophth.; S.. Ophth. Soc. Prev: Sen. Regist. & Regist. (Ophth.) Birm. & Midl. Eye Hosp.; SHO (Neurosurg. & Neurol.) Midl. Centre for Neurosurg. & Neurol. Smethwick.

EDWARDS, Richard Thomas Martin 2 Ash Tree Close, Radyr, Cardiff CF15 8RX — MB BCh 1974 Wales; MRCP (UK) 1980. Cons. Phys. (Geriat. Med.) Mid Glam. HA.

EDWARDS, Mr Ridley Bryan 2 Cranborne Chase, Walsgrave, Coventry CV2 2JH — MB BS 1980 W. Indies; FRCS Ed. 1993; MSc Lond. 1997.

EDWARDS, Robert Wyn Vittoria Health Centre, Vittoria Street, Birkenhead CH41 3RH Tel: 0151 647 7321 Fax: 0151 650 0942; St. Andrews, 33 Meols Drive, Hoylake, Wirral CH47 4AE — MB ChB 1980 Liverp.; DRCOG 1984. (Liverpool) GP Birkenhead; Hosp. Practitioner, St. Catherine Hosp. Wirral Drugs Serv. Birkenhead. Socs: BMA. Prev: GP Manch.

EDWARDS, Robin Clive Tudor House Surgery, 43 Broad Street, Wokingham RG40 1BE Tel: 0118 978 3544 Fax: 0118 977 0420; Holly Tree House, 6 The Woodlands, Wokingham RG41 4UY — MB BS 1979 Lond.; MRCP (UK) 1984; DCH RCP Lond. 1987. (Univ. Coll. Hosp. Med. Sch.) Prev: Regist. (Med.) N. Staffs. Hosp. Centre Stoke-on-Trent.

EDWARDS, Robin Geoffrey 24 Great Meadow Road, Leicester LE4 0QA — MB BS 1978 Lond.; MRCS Eng. LRCP Lond. 1978. (Roy. Free) Socs: Jun. Mem. Assn. Anaesth.

EDWARDS, Roger c/o Worthing Hospital, Lyndhurst Road, Worthing BN11 2DH Tel: 01903 205111 — MB BS 1967 Lond.; FFA RCS Eng. 1971. (St. Thos.) Cons. Anaesth. Worthing Hosp. & S.lands Hosp. Socs: Assn. Anaesths. Prev: Cons. Anaesth. King Edwd. Memor. Hosp. Bermuda.

EDWARDS, Rosemary (retired) 46 Stumperlowe Park Road, Sheffield S10 3QP Tel: 0114 230 5512 — MB ChB 1954 Sheff.; MRCS Eng. LRCP Lond. 1954; DObst RCOG 1957; DCH Eng. 1958. Prev: SCMO Sheff. HA.

EDWARDS, Mr Roy Percy 'Merrilocks', 11 Granville Park, Aughton, Ormskirk L39 5DS Tel: 01695 421722 — MB ChB 1965 St. And.; FRCS Ed 1972; FRCOG 1984, M 1970, DObst 1969. (St. And.) Cons. O & G Ormskirk & Dist. Gen. Hosp. Socs: BMA. Mem. N. Eng. Med. Soc. Prev: Sen. Regist. (O & G) Mill Rd. Matern. & Wom. Hosps. Liverp.; Regist. (O & G) Pk. Hosp. Davyhulme St. Mary's Hosp. Manch.; Ho. Off. Obst. Matern. Hosp. Liverp.

EDWARDS, Ruth Barrie (retired) 28 Binscombe Lane, Oakwood, Derby DE21 2AZ — MB ChB 1961 Sheff.; FFA RCS Eng. 1975; DObst RCOG 1966; DCH Eng. 1963. Prev: Cons. Paediat. Anaesth. Derby.

EDWARDS, Ruthraj 145 Glenister Park Road, London SW16 5DY — MD 1977 Ceylon; MB BS 1969; MRCP (UK) 1980. (Colombo)

EDWARDS, Sarah Bridget Vibert 3 Simonside Close, Morpeth NE61 2XY Tel: 01670 514954 — MB BS 1965 Lond.; DO 1969.

EDWARDS, Sarah Jamison (retired) 24 Polmont House Gardens, Polmont, Falkirk FK2 0SH Tel: 01324 716988 — MB BCh BAO Belf. 1940. Prev: Ho. Surg. Belf. City Hosp.

EDWARDS, Sarah Jane Eira 22 The Chilterns, Hitchin SG4 9PP — MB BS 1998 Lond.; MB BS Lond 1998.

EDWARDS, Sarah Katharine Depart. of GU Medicine, West Suffolk Hospital, Hardwick Lane, Bury St Edmunds IP33 2QZ Tel:

01284 713243 Fax: 01284 713025; 10 Harcombe Road, Cherry Hinton, Cambridge CB1 9PD Tel: 01223 572189 — MB BS 1988 Newc.; FRCP Ed. 1999; DFFP 1995; MRCP (UK) 1991. Main Cons. Genitourin. Med. W. Suff. Hosp. Socs: Coun. Mem. Soc. Study VD; Assn. Genitourin. Med.; Brit. Soc. Colpos. & Cerv. Path. Prev: Sen. Regist. (Genitourin. Med.) Addenbrooke's Hosp. Camb.; Regist. Rotat. (Infec. Dis.) Newc. Gen. Hosp.; Regist. Rotat. (Gen. Med.) Shotley Bridge Dist. Gen. Hosp. Consett.

EDWARDS, Selwyn Crowther 'Crendon', Cruckmeole, Hanwood, Shrewsbury SY5 8JN Tel: 01743 660620 — MB ChB 1940 Birm. (Birm.) Prev: Pub. Health Administ. (Malaria) WHO E. Mediterranean Region.

EDWARDS, Sharon Louise Dept. of Pathology, Medical School, Grampian Univ. Hospital NHS Trust, Foresterhill, Aberdeen AB25 22D Tel: 01224 553781 — MB ChB 1994 Ed.; BSc Ed. 1991. (Edinburgh) Specialist Regist., Path., Aberd. Roy. Infirm. Prev: SHO (Med.) Aberd. Roy. Infirm.; Ho. Off. Falkirk Roy. Infirm. & Borders Gen. Hosp.

EDWARDS, Sheila 9 Lyme Park, Chinley, High Peak SK23 6AG Tel: 0166 32 64488 — MB ChB 1963 Sheff. (Sheff.)

EDWARDS, Sian Amanda 16 Kings Wood, Marlow SL7 2SD — MB ChB 1986 Liverp.

EDWARDS, Sian Angharad Station Road Surgery, 15-16 Station Road, Penarth CF64 3EP Tel: 029 2070 2301 Fax: 029 2071 2048; 88 Cardiff Road, Dinas Powys CF64 4JU Tel: 01222 513789 — MB BCh 1982 Wales; MRCGP 1987; DRCOG 1986. (Welsh Nat. Sch. of Med.) Prev: Trainee GP/SHO Bridgend VTS.

EDWARDS, Sian Elizabeth Royal Free Hospital, Pond St., Hampstead, London NW3 2QG; 46 Park Drive, London NW11 7SP — MB BS 1975 Lond.; BSc Lond. 1972; MRCP (UK) 1978; FRCR 1982; DMRD Eng. 1980. Cons. Radiol. Roy. Free Hosp. Lond. Prev: Sen. Regist. (Radiol.) St. Bart. Hosp. Lond.

EDWARDS, Sian Rosetta 151 Billy Lows Lane, Potters Bar EN6 1UY — MB BS 1994 Lond.

EDWARDS, Simon Charles Sands End Health Clinic, 120 Wandsworth Bridge Road, London SW6 2UQ Tel: 020 7371 8472 Fax: 020 7371 8473 Email: sehc@sehc.prestel.co.uk; Flat 2, 8 Keswick Road, London SW1S 2JN Tel: 020 8874 2267 Email: s.c.edwards@lineone.net — MB BS 1990 Lond.; MRCGP 1994. GP Sands End Health Centre.

EDWARDS, Simon George 8 Mill Street, Llandulas, Abergele LL22 8ES — MB ChB 1989 Manch.

EDWARDS, Simon Graeme Mylrea 32 St Margaret's Road, Girton, Cambridge CB3 0LT — MB BS 1990 Lond.; MRCP (UK) 1994.

EDWARDS, Sion Meirion North Cardiff Medical Centre, Excalibur Drive, Thornhill, Cardiff CF14 9BB Tel: 029 2075 0322 Fax: 029 2075 7705; 8 Kimberley Road, Penylan, Cardiff CF23 5DH Tel: 029 2046 1720 — MB BCh 1984 Wales.

EDWARDS, Sophie 7 The Spinney, Bradwell Village, Milton Keynes MK13 9BX — MB BS 1996 Lond.

EDWARDS, Stephen 30 Lovelace Avenue, Solihull B91 3JR — MB ChB 1990 Leeds.

EDWARDS, Stephen Black Country Mental Health NHS Trust, Edward Street Hospital, Edward St., West Bromwich B70 8NL Tel: 0121 607 3150 Fax: 0121 607 3576; 9 St. Mary's Road, Harborne, Birmingham B17 0EY — MB ChB 1977 Birm.; FRCPsych 2000. Cons. Old Age Psychiat. Edwd. St. Hosp.; Med. Dir. Black Country Ment. Health NHS Trust. Prev: Sen. Regist. (Forens. Psychiat.) Midl. Centre Forens. Psychiat. All St.s. Hosp. Birm.; Sen. Regist. (Community Psychiat. & Psychogeriat.) Worcester Roy. Infirm.

EDWARDS, Stephen The Surgery, 67 St. James Street, Wetherby LS22 6RS; 145 Moorside, Cleckheaton, Bradford BD19 6LE — MB BS 1974 Lond.; MMedSc Leeds 1984; MRCS Eng. LRCP Lond. 1973; DObst RCOG 1974. (Guy's) Prev: SHO (O & G) St. Luke's Hosp. Bradford; Ho. Phys. Bradford Roy. Infirm.; Ho. Surg. Lewisham Hosp. Lond.

EDWARDS, Stephen James Regent House Surgery, 21 Regent Road, Chorley PR7 2DH Tel: 01257 264842 Fax: 01257 231387 — MB ChB 1978 Manch.

EDWARDS, Stephen Mark Intensive Therapy Unit, Morriston Hospital, Morriston, Swansea SA6 6NL Tel: 01792 703470 Email: smedwards@doctors.org.uk — MB ChB 1994 Ed.; FRCA 1999. (Edinburgh) Advanced Trainee in Intens. Care Med., ICU Morriston Hosp., Swansea; Specialist Regist. Welsh Sch. of Anaesth. Socs: Welsh Intens. Care Soc. (Trainees Sect. Sec.); Intens. Care Soc.; Brit. Med. Assn. Prev: Specialist Regist. Anaesth., Llandovoh Hosp., Cardiff; Specialist Regist. Anaesth. & Intens. Care, Wrexham Maelor Hosp., Wrexham; Sen. Ho. Off., Anesthesia, Wrexham Maelor Hosp., Wrexham.

EDWARDS, Stuart Andrew 88 Beauchamp Avenue, Gosport PO13 0LQ — MB BS 1993 Lond.

EDWARDS, Stuart John Peelhouse Lane Surgery, 1 Peelhouse Lane, Widnes WA8 6TW Tel: 0151 424 6221 Fax: 0151 420 5436 — MB ChB 1972 Liverp.

EDWARDS, Susan Caryl The Surgery, 65 Holloway, Northfield, Birmingham B31 1TR Tel: 0121 475 1422; 14 Barlows Road, Edgbaston, Birmingham B15 2PL — MB ChB 1975 Bristol; DCH Eng. 1977. (Bristol) Prev: Princip. GP Lond.

EDWARDS, Thomas Brinsley (retired) 3 Dover Road, Lytham St Annes FY8 3HN Tel: 01253 725344 — MB ChB Manch. 1955. Prev: GP Blackpool.

EDWARDS, Thomas James The Laurels 136 Lonnen Road, Wimborne BH21 7AZ — MB BS 1997 Lond.

EDWARDS, Thomas John Town Gate Practice, Chepstow Community Hospital, Tempest Way, Chepstow NP16 5XP Tel: 01291 636444 Fax: 01291 636465 — MB BS 1973 Lond.; MRCS Eng. LRCP Lond. 1973; MRCGP 1977; DObst RCOG 1976. (Guy's)

EDWARDS, Thomas Peacock 4 Silverburn, 193 St Annes Road E., St Annes, Lytham St Annes FY8 3HQ — LRCP LRCS 1947 Ed.; LRCP LRCS Ed. LRFPS Glas. 1947. (Ed.) Med. Off. DHSS N. Fylde Centr. Off. Blackpool.

EDWARDS, Thomas Rhys 71 Hall Street, Stourbridge DY8 2JF — MB BCh 1992 Wales. SHO O & G Shrewsbury VTS. Prev: SHO (Psychiat.) Kidderminster Gen. Hosp.; Ho. Off. (Surg.) Torbay Hosp.; Ho. Off. (Med.) Roy. Devon & Exeter Hosp.

EDWARDS, Timothy Joseph Dorset County Hospital, Dorchester DT1 2JY Tel: 01305 251150 — MB BCh 1988 Wales; MRCP (UK) 1991. Cons. Cardiol. Prev: Regist. (Cardiol.) Soton.

EDWARDS, Trevor Graham The Health Centre, East Wittering, Chichester PO19 8BH Tel: 01243 670707 Fax: 01243 672808 Email: 113242.234@compuserve.com; ffolletts, Sidlesham Lane, Birdham, Chichester PO20 7QL Tel: 01243 672022 Fax: 01243 672808 — MB BS 1965 Lond.; MRCS Eng. LRCP Lond. 1965. (Univ. Coll. Hosp.)

EDWARDS, Victoria Anne Blackpool Victoria Hospitals NHS Trust, Whinney Heys Road, Blackpool FY3 8NR Tel: 01253 300000; 3 Cameron Toll Gardens, Edinburgh EH16 4TF — MB ChB 1995 Aberd. (Univ. Aberd.) SHO (Anaesth.) Blackpool Vict. Hosp. NHS Trust. Prev: SHO (Anaesth.) Chorley & S. Ribble Dist. Gen. Hosp.

EDWARDS, Vivian Byron John (retired) 8 Bankart Avenue, Leicester LE2 2DB Tel: 0116 270 6045 — MRCS Eng. LRCP Lond. 1944; LDS RCS Eng. 1951.

EDWARDS, Mrs Vivian Georgina (retired) 4 Fort Rise, Newhaven BN9 9DW Tel: 01273 513843 — MB BS Lond. 1956; DPH Lond. 1959; DObst RCOG 1959. Prev: Med. Off DHSS.

EDWARDS, Wayne John Flat 4D, The Sycamores, Cricket Field Grove, Crowthorne RG45 7ES — MB BS 1980 West Indies.

EDWARDS, Mr William Glyndwr (retired) 18 Hall Drive, Sydenham, London SE26 6XB Tel: 020 8778 6853 — BM BCh 1955 Oxf.; BA (Hons.) Oxf. 1952, MA 1955; FRCS Eng. 1960; DLO Eng. 1960. Prev: Sen. Cons. Surg. (ENT), King's Coll. Hosp.

EDWARDS, William Hugh The Vicarage, High St., Caerleon, Newport NP18 1AZ — MB BCh 1995 Wales.

EDWARDS, William John Flitwick Surgery, The Highlands, Flitwick, Bedford MK45 1DZ Tel: 01525 712171 Fax: 01525 718756 — MB BChir 1980 Camb.; AFOM 2000; BSc (Hons.) St. And. 1977; MRCGP 1985; DRCOG 1984; Dip. Occ. Med. 1996. (Camb.) Occupat.al Phys.

EDWARDS, William Maurice (Surgery), 276 Eaton Road, Liverpool L12 2AN Tel: 0151 228 3768; 4 Quickswood Green, Liverpool L25 4TS — MB ChB 1947 Liverp.; DObst RCOG 1948. (Liverp.) Prev: Res. Ho. Surg. N.. Hosp. Liverp.; Asst. Med. Off. BRd. Green Hosp. Liverp.; Res. Obst. Ho. Surg. Mill Rd. Infirm. Liverp.

EDWARDS, William Robert (retired) Apple Tree Cottage, 23 Rectory Lane, Woodstock OX20 1UF — MB 1964 Camb.; BChir 1963; DObst RCOG 1965. Prev: Ho. Phys. Lambeth Gen. Hosp.

EDWARDS-MOSS, David John Underwood Cottage, Turners Green, Upper Bucklesbury, Reading RG7 6RF — MB BS 1979 Lond.

EDWARDSON, Mr Kenneth Frank (retired) BUPA Murrayfield Hospital, Holmewood Drive, Thingwall, Wirral CH61 1AU Tel: 0151 648 7000 — MB ChB 1957 Liverp.; MB ChB (2nd cl. Hons.) Liverp. 1960; BSc (Anat. 1st. cl. Hons.) Liverp. 1957; FRCS Eng. 1964. Cons. Gen. Surg. Clatterbridge Hosp. Bebington & Arrowe Pk. Hosp.; Clin. Tutor RCS (Eng.); Clin. Lect. (Surg.) Univ. Liverp. Prev: Hon. Clin. Tutor (Surg.) Univ. Liverp.

EDWARDSON, Robert Stuart Yeadon Health Centre, 17 South View Road, Yeadon, Leeds LS19 7PS Tel: 0113 295 4040 Fax: 0113 295 4044 — BM BCh 1973 Oxf.; MA Oxf. 1974, BM BCh 1973; MRCP (UK) 1976; MRCGP 1978; DCH Eng. 1977.

EDWIN, Paul Julian (retired) Idlewild, 11 Forest Drive, Kinver, Stourbridge DY7 6DX Tel: 01384 873487 Email: pjedwin8109@aol.com — MB ChB 1957 Birm.; MFHom 1978. Prev: Mem. Med. Bd.ing Panel DHSS Birm. & Worcester.

EDYNBRY, Katharine Deborah 3 Lidderdale Road, Liverpool L15 3JG — MB BS 1991 Lond.

EDYVANE, Katherine Anne 16 Scott Street, Dulwich, London SE22 — BM BS 1993 Flinders.

EDYVEAN, Inderjit Kaur Derwent Medical Centre, 26 North Street, Derby DE1 3AZ Tel: 01332 292939 — MB BS 1975 Delhi; MB BS 1975 Delhi.

EDYVEAN, Richard John Flamank Derwent Medical Centre, 26 North Street, Derby DE1 3AZ Tel: 01332 292939 — MRCS Eng. LRCP Lond. 1970 London; MRCS Eng. LRCP Lond. 1970 London.

EE, Hock Leong 74 Blair Athol Road, Sheffield S11 7GB — MB ChB 1998 Sheff.; MB ChB Sheff 1998.

EECKELAERS, Eileen Anne Adswood Road Surgery, 270 Adswood Road, Adswood, Stockport SK3 8PN Tel: 0161 483 5155 Fax: 0161 419 9984 — MB ChB 1982 Manch.; MRCGP 1986; DRCOG 1986; DCH RCP Lond. 1986.

EECKELAERS, Michael Charles William West Gorton Medical Centre, 6A Wenlock Way, West Gorton, Manchester M12 5LH Tel: 0161 223 5226 Fax: 0161 230 6305; 2 St. Aldwyns Road, Didsbury, Manchester M20 3JF — MB ChB 1981 Manch.; FRCGP 1998; MRCGP 1989; DRCOG 1986; MRCP (UK) 1984. (Manch. Med. Sch.)

EEDLE, Emma Katherine Central Surgery, Corporation Street, Rugby CV21 3SP Tel: 01788 574335 Fax: 01788 547693; 116 Percival Road, Rugby CV22 5JU Tel: 01788 575341 — MB BS 1982 Lond.

EEDY, David John 77 Balmoral Avenue, Belfast BT9 6NY Tel: 01232 681830 Email: eedydj@aol.com — MB BCh BAO 1981 Belf.; MD Belf. 1990; FRCP 1995. Cons. Dermat. Craigavon Area Hosp. N. Irel. Prev: Sen. Regist. Roy. Vict. Hosp. Belf. & St. Thos. Hosp. Lond.

EELES, Angela Jane 2 Rayleigh Close, Cambridge CB2 2AZ Tel: 01223 362804 — MB BS 1985 Lond.; MRCGP 1997; T(GP) 1990; DCH RCP Lond. 1987. (St. Thos. Hosp.) GP & Clin. Asst. (Palliat. Med.) N.ants. Socs: BMA. Prev: Trainee GP Ashford VTS.

EELES, Eamonn Michael Paul 1 Fairfield Lane, Kidderminster DY11 5QH Tel: 01562 850567 — MB BS 1994 Lond.; MRCP 1998. (University College London) Sen. SHO (Gen. Med. & Diabetes) P.ss of Wales Hosp. Bridgend Mid Glam. Prev: SHO (Respirat. Med.) Conquest Hosp. St. Leonards-on-Sea; SHO A & E Dept. Wellington Hosp. New Zealand.

EELES, George Howard (retired) Dumbleton House, Fairfield Lane, Wolverley, Kidderminster DY11 5QH Tel: 01562 850567 — MB BS Durh. 1960; FRCPath 1981, M 1969. Prev: Cons. Histopath. & Cytol. Kiddeminster Health Care Trust & Alexandra Hosp. Redditch.

EELES, Rosalind Anne Institute of Cancer Research & Royal Marsden Hospital, Downs Road, Sutton SM2 5PT Tel: 020 8661 3642 Fax: 020 8770 1489 Email: ros@icr.ac.uk — MB BS 1984 Lond.; PhD 2000; MB BS (Hons. Surg. & Path.) Lond. 1984; MA Camb. 1984, BA 1981; MRCP (UK) 1987; FRCR 1990; FRCP 2000 London. (St.Thomas') Sen. Lect. & Hon. Cons. (Cancer Genetics & Clin. Oncol.) Roy. Marsden Hosp. Lond. & Sutton. Socs: UK Cancer Genetics Gp.; Amer. Soc. Human Genetics; Brit. Oncol. Assn. Prev: Vis. Asst. Prof. Univ. Utah, USA; Clin. Research Fell. & Sen. Regist. Inst. Cancer Research & Roy. Marsden Hosp. Surrey; Regist. (Clin. Oncol.) Roy. Marsden Lond. & Surrey.

EFFA, Nazir Nsor 85 Springwood Hall Gardens, Huddersfield HD1 4HA — MB ChB 1965 Aberd.

EFFINGHAM, Walden Howard 29 Gloucester Road, Wallasey CH45 3JS — BM BS 1994 Nottm.

EFFIONG, Paul 7 Tamarind House, Hereford Retreat, London SE15 6RL — MB ChB 1998 Liverp.; MB ChB Liverp 1998.

EFTHIMIOU, John 39 Five Mile Drive, Oxford OX2 8HT — MB BS 1977 Lond.; BSc (1st cl. Hons.) (Biochem.) Lond. 1974, MD 1990; MRCP (UK) 1980. (Guy's) Sen. Regist. (Gen. & Thoracic Med.) Oxf. RHA. Prev: Regist. (Med.) Univ. Coll. Hosp. Lond.; SHO Brompton Hosp. Lond.; Ho. Phys. & Surg. Guy's Hosp. Lond.

***EFTHYMIOU, Christopher** Leigh Lodge, Higher Drive, Banstead SM7 1PL — MB BS 1998 Lond.; MB BS Lond 1998; BSc Hons Lond 1995.

EFTHYMIOU, Evangelos Orthopaedic Department, Queen Marys Hospital, Frognal Avenue, Sidcup DA14 6LT — Ptychio Iatrikes 1990 Athens.

EGAN, Allyson Catherine 6 Morella Road, London SW12 8UH — MB BS 1998 Lond.; MB BS Lond 1998.

EGAN, Ann Castle Surgery, Kepwell Bank Top, Prudhoe NE42 5PW Tel: 01661 832209 Fax: 01661 836338; Old Barns, Corbridge, Corbridge NE45 5HF Tel: 01434 632243 — MB ChB 1983 Birm.; MRCGP 1987; DRCOG 1986. Prev: GP Whickham Newc. Whickham Newc.

EGAN, Anne Maria Bedford Hospital, Kempston Road, Bedford MK42 9DN; 11 Rothsay Gardens, Bedford MK40 3QA — BM BCh 1983 Oxf.; MRCP (UK) 1986; FRCR 1992. Cons. Radiol. Bedford Hosp. Prev: Sen. Regist. (Radiol.) Addenbrooke's Hosp. Camb.

EGAN, David John The Surgery, 20 Low Road, Debenham, Stowmarket IP14 6QU Tel: 01728 860248 Fax: 01728 861300; Yew Tree Farm House, Otley Road, Cretingham, Woodbridge IP13 7DP Tel: 01473 737490 — MB ChB 1981 Sheff.; MRCGP 1986; DCH RCP Lond. 1985. GP, Denham, Suff.; C. Suff. PCG Bd. Memb.

EGAN, Edward Oliver Royal Prince Alfred Hospital, Missenden Road, Camperdown, Sydney NSW 2090, Australia Tel: 0061 295156111; Flat 1, 11The Paragon, Blackheath, London SE3 0NZ Tel: 0208 297 0661 Fax: 0208 297 0661 Email: edwardegan@hotmail.com — BM BCh 1996 Oxf.; BA (Oxon.) 1992. (Oxford University) Anaesthetic Regist., Roy. P. Alfred Hosp. Sydney Australia.

EGAN, Elizabeth Ann The School House, Titkebarn Road, Knowsley Village, Prescot L34 0JA Tel: 0151 548 9707 Email: eganelizabeth@hotmail.com — MB BS 1993 Newc.; MRCGP 1997; DRCOG 1997. (University of Newcastle upon Tyne)

EGAN, Georg Patrick (retired) Woodland Thatch, 12 Hale Road, Hale, Liverpool L24 5RE Tel: 0151 425 4793 — MD 1950 NUI; MB BCh BAO 1940; FRCPsych 1972; DPM Lond. 1944. Prev: Cons. Psychiat. Roy. Liverp. Hosp.

EGAN, Hazel Mary (retired) 1/11 The Paragon, Blackheath, London SE3 0NZ Tel: 020 8297 0661 — MB BS 1956 Lond.; MRCS Eng. LRCP Lond. 1956; DA Eng. 1965; DCH Eng. 1962; DObst RCOG 1958. Prev: Clin. Asst. (Anaesth.) Greenwich Dist. Hosp.

EGAN, James John Gerard Francis North West Lung Centre, Wythenshawe Hospital, Southmoor Road, Manchester M23 9LT — MB BCh BAO 1985 NUI.

EGAN, John Medical Associates, 25 Derryvolgie Avenue, Belfast BT9 6FN Tel: 02890 382202 Fax: 02890 667488; 32 Deramore Park South, Belfast BT9 5JY Tel: 02990 682625 — MB BCh BAO 1961 Belf.; 1997 FRCPsych; MRCPsych 1972; DPM RCPSI 1965. Emerit. Cons. Psychiat., Purdysburn, Ulster & Belvoir Hosps., Belf. Socs: Fell. Ulster Med. Soc.; Ulster Neuropsychiatric Soc.; N. Irel. Medico-legal Soc. Prev: Cons. Psychiat. Tyrone & Fermanagh Hosp. Omagh; Res. Med. Off. Mater Infirm. Hosp. Belf.; Clin. Asst. Maudsley Hosp. Lond.

EGAN, John Anthony 6 Tennyson Avenue, Barrow-in-Furness LA13 9TX — MB ChB 1996 Sheff.

EGAN, Mr John Nicholas Terence Heron Water, Hensting Lane, Fishers Pond, Eastleigh SO50 7HH — MB BS 1966 Lond.; FRCS Eng. 1975; MRCS Eng. LRCP Lond. 1966; DObst RCOG 1969.

EGAN, Mark Joseph Old Barns, Corbridge NE45 5HF — MB ChB 1983 Birm.; MRCPath 1989.

EGAN, Sandra Anne 27 Danesdale Road, London E9 5DB Tel: 020 8533 2511 — MB BCh BAO 1982 NUI; MSc (Community

Paediat.) Lond. 1992; MRCPI 1985; DCH NUI 1985. Cons. Developm. Paediat. Donald Winnicott Centre Lond. Socs: FRCPCH; Fell. Brit. Assn. Community Child Health; BMA. Prev: Lect. (Child Health) St. Bart. & Lond. Med. Sch.; Regist. (Developm. Paediat.) Wolfson Centre Lond. & Gt. Ormond St. Lond.

EGAN, Sandra Mary 104 Hollows Close, Harnham, Salisbury SP2 8JX — MD 1973 Bristol; MB ChB 1968.

EGBASE, Patrick Ehimen 69 Great Dell, Welwyn Garden City AL8 7HP — MB BS 1981 Ibadan; MRCOG 1990.

EGDELL, Henry George 8 Stirtonber, Skipton BD23 1NH Tel: 01756 792236 — MB ChB 1956 Leeds; FRCP Ed. 1981 M 1967; FRCPsych 1985, M 1971; DPM Newc. 1964. (Leeds) Clin. Lect. Univ. Liverp. Prev: Cons. Psychiat. Airedale Gen. Hosp. Yorks.; 1st Asst. (Psychol. Med.) Roy. Vict. Infirm. Newc.; Sen. Lect. (Psychiat. Med.) Sch. Makerere Univ. Coll., Uganda.

EGDELL, John Duncan (retired) Gelli Gynan Lodge, Llanarmon-yn-lal, Mold CH7 4QX Tel: 01824 780345 — MB ChB 1961 Bristol; FFPHM 1979, M 1974; Dip. Soc. Med. Ed. 1967. Hon. Cons. Pub. Health Med. N. Wales HA. Prev: Regional Med. Off. Mersey RHA.

EGDELL, Linda Mary (retired) Gelli Gynan Lodge, Llanarmon-yn-lal, Mold CH7 4QX Tel: 01824 780345 Email: linda.egdell@doctors.org.uk — MB ChB 1962 Bristol; FFFP 2001; MFFP 1993; MFCH 1989. Prev: Cons. Family Plann. & Reproductive Health Care Conwy and Denbighsh. NHS Trust.

EGELSTAFF, Sarah Joanna The Old Coach House, Hillbrow Road, Hillbrow, Liss GU33 7PX — MB BS 1980 Lond.; DRCOG 1983; MRCGP 1984. (St. Bart.) p/t GP Drayton, Portsmouth. Prev: Clin. Med. Off. W. Surrey & N. E. Hants. HA.; GP Trainee Reading VTS; Ho. Off. (Med.) St. Barts. Hosp.

EGERTON, Dale Carlton Riverside Close Surgery, Liss GU33 7AD Tel: 01730 892412; Underwood Cottage, Langrish, Petersfield GU32 1QY Tel: 01730 263972 — MB ChB 1967 Liverp. (Liverp.) Prev: SHO (O & G) Roy. Hants. Co. Hosp. Winchester; Surg.-Lt. RN.

EGERTON, David Francis 57 High Street, Godstone RH9 8LT — MB ChB 1994 Bristol.

EGERTON, Florence 64 Blackisland Road, Annaghmore, Portadown, Craigavon BT62 1NH — MB BCh BAO 1939 Belf. (Qu. Univ. Belf.)

EGERTON, Pamela Joan Leven Health Centre, Victoria Road, Leven KY8 4ET; 78 Loughborough Road, Kirkcaldy KY1 3DD — MB BCh BAO 1989 Belf.; MRCGP 1993; DRCOG 1992; DGM RCP Lond. 1991. Prev: Trainee GP Belf.

EGERTON, Thomas James Anthony Priory Surgery, 26 High Street, Holywood BT18 9AD Tel: 028 9042 6991 Fax: 028 9042 3643 — MB BCh BAO 1984 Belf.; MB BCh Belf. l984; DCH Dub. 1988; DRCOG 1987.

EGGAR, Richard John 1 Deaconsfield, Hereford HR1 1XH — MB ChB 1993 Liverp.

EGGELING, Iain Terence Jenner House Surgery, 159 Cove Road, Farnborough GU14 0HH Tel: 01252 548141 Fax: 01252 371516; 2 Farley Court, Farley Hill, Reading RG7 1TT Tel: 01189 733340 — MB BS 1973 Lond.; DCH (SA) 1976. (St. Geo.)

EGGERS, Kathleen Ann — MB BS 1988 Lond.; FRCA 1993. (St. Bart. Hosp.) Cons. Anaesth., Bro Morgannyg NHS Trust Bridgend Wales.

EGGINGTON, William Robert Owen Benefits Agency, Warbreck House, Blackpool FY2 0YE; 65 Frobisher Drive, Lytham St Annes FY8 2RG Tel: 01253 726109 — MB BS Lond. 1955; MRCS Eng. LRCP Lond. 1955; MFCM RCP (UK) 1972; DTM & H Eng. 1960, DIH 1965; DPH Lond. 1965. (Guy's) Med. Adviser Med. Adviser Benefits Agency. Prev: Lt.-Col. RAMC.

EGGINTON, Anne Marie Southville Surgery, 67 Coronation Road, Southville, Bristol BS3 1AS Tel: 0117 966 9724 Fax: 0117 953 2604 — MB ChB 1988 Bristol; BSc Bristol 1982, MB ChB 1988; MRCGP 1992. (Bristol)

EGGINTON, Juliet Anne 20 Alanbrooke Grove, Stoke-on-Trent ST3 7ES — MB BCh 1962 Wales; FRCR 1975; FFR 1972; DMRD Eng. 1970; DCH Eng. 1966; DObst RCOG 1965.

EGGINTON, Michael John (retired) 29 Prory Road, West Bridgford, Nottingham NG2 5HU Tel: 0115 914 0914 — MB ChB 1950 Birm.; FFA RCS Eng. 1959. Prev: Cons. Anaesth. Nottm. Univ. Hosp.

EGGLEDEN, Joanne Clare 179 Quantock Drive, Ashford TN24 8QN — MB ChB 1992 Leic.; MRCGP 1996; DRCOG 1995. (Leicester)

EGGLESTON, Alan Courtyard Cottage, Coggers Cross, Horam, Heathfield TN21 0LG — BM BCh 1979 Oxf.; MA, BM BCh. Oxf. 1979.

EGGLESTON, Joan John Connolly Wing, Ealing, Hammersmith & Fulham NHS Trust, Uxbridge Road, Southall UB1 3EU Tel: 020 8967 5140 Fax: 020 8967 5798 — MB BS 1982 Lond.; MRCPsych 1987; T(Psych) 1994. (King's College) Cons. (Psychiat. for the Elderly) W. Lond. Prev: Sen. Regist. (Psychiat.) Soton. Scheme; Regist. (Psychiat.) St. Mary's Hosp., Lond.

EGGLESTON, Judith Margaret Marsden Road Surgery, The Health Centre, Marsden Road, South Shields NE34 6RE Tel: 0191 454 0457 Fax: 0191 427 1793; Tel: 0191 212 0177 — MB ChB 1977 Sheff.; MRCGP 1981; DRCOG 1981.

EGGLESTON, Madeleine Mary (retired) 3 Priors Walk, Priory Avenue, Taunton TA1 1JU Tel: 01823 289873 — MB ChB St. And. 1950; MFFP 1993. Prev: Clin. Asst. Geriat. Unit. Trinity Hosp. Taunton.

EGGLETON, Mrs Dorothy Anne, OBE Foreign & Commonwealth Office (Lilongwe), King Charles St., London SW1A 2AH Tel: 00265 782400 Fax: 00265 782657 Email: deggleton@malawi.net; King Charles Street, London SW1A 2AH — MB ChB 1964 Ed.; MRCGP 1979. Regional Med. Off.Foreign & Commonw. Off. Prev: Regional Med. Off New Delhi; GP Camb.; RMO.Moscow.

EGGLETON, John Derek Peter Delph House Surgery, 8 Pinhoe Road, Exeter EX4 7HL Tel: 01392 72304 Fax: 01392 423819; Taylor's Farm, Brampford Speke, Exeter EX5 5HN Tel: 01392 841193 — MB BS 1984 Lond.; BSc (Hons.) Lond. 1981; MRCGP 1990. (Univ. Lond.) Prev: Trainee GP Univ. Exeter Postgrad. Med. Sch. VTS; SHO (Med.) Roy. Free. Hosp. Lond.; SHO (Med.) Guy's Hosp. Lond.

EGGLETON, Mark Lloyd 6 Lower Penns Road, Paignton TQ3 1JE Tel: 01807 522445 — BM 1993 Soton.

EGGLETON, Stephen Peter Howard Rhone-Poulenc Rorer, 50 Kings Hill Avenue, West Malling ME19 4AH Tel: 01732 584407; 6 Alexandra Road, Burgess Hill RH15 0EW Tel: 01444 236127 — MB BS 1975 Lond.; MFPHM RCP (UK) 1993; DMRD Eng. 1982. (Middlx. Hosp.) Sen. Phys. Rhone Poulenc Rorer Oncol. W. Malling Kent. Prev: Research Dir. (Oncol.) Bristol-Myers Squibb.

EGGLETON, Susan Margaret Florey Unit, Royal Berkshire Hospital, Reading; The Little House, 65 High St, Wargrave, Reading RG10 8BU Tel: 017340 402028 — BM BCh 1985 Oxf.; BA Camb. 1982; MRCGP 1989; DCH RCP Lond. 1988; DRCOG 1987. Staff Phys. (Genitourin. Med.) Roy. Berks. Hosp. Reading. Prev: Trainee GP/SHO Co. Hosp. Hereford VTS.

EGLESFIELD, David Brian Mark 19 Courthouse Street, Otley LS21 3AN — MB ChB 1990 Leeds.

EGLESTON, Aidan Anthony Hill House, Pipers Lane, Edgmond, Newport TF10 8LE — MB ChB 1987 Birm.; DCH RCP Lond. 1993.

EGLESTON, Conor Vincent Department of Accident & Emergency, Southampton General Hospital, Tremona Road, Southampton SO16 6YD — MB BCh BAO 1987 NUI; FRCSI 1992; FRCS Ed 1995; FFAEM 1997; BSc Hons 1989.

EGLIN, Betty (retired) 11 Chestnut Park, Chestnut Hill, Keswick CA12 4LY Tel: 017687 71191 — MRCS Eng. LRCP Lond. 1942.

EGLINTON, David John 2F3, 13 Bruntsfield Place, Edinburgh EH10 4HN — MB ChB 1991 Ed.

EGLITIS, Helen Mara Orchard Surgery, Dragwell, Kegworth, Derby DE74 2EL Tel: 01509 672419 Fax: 01509 674196 — MB ChB 1987 Leic.; MRCGP 1991; DRCOG 1991.

EGNER, William Department of Immunlogy, PO Box 894, Northern General Hospital NHS Trust, Sheffield S5 7YS Tel: 0114 271 5700 Fax: 0114 261 9893 — MB ChB 1985 Bristol; BSc Bristol 1982; PhD Otago, NZ 1994; MRCP (UK) 1990; MRCPath 1996. (Bristol) Cons. Immunol. N. Gen. Hosp. NHS Trust Sheff.

EGUN, Anslem Asehosem 54 Melford Road, London SE22 0AQ — MB BS 1987 Lagos.

EHIGIE-OSIFO, Egbe 30 Ludlow Way, London N2 0LA — MB BS 1987 Ibadan; MBA Cranfield 1993; MSc Oxf. 1992; MRCP (UK) 1992.

EHLINGER, Eric Albert (retired) Brentwood Farm, 120 Glossop Road, Charlesworth, Glossop SK13 5HB Tel: 01457 869001 —

LRCP LRCS Ed. LRFPS Glas. 1952. Prev: Med. Off. Pennine View Nursing Home Glossop.

EHMANN, Jurg Frank 32 Bevan St. W., Lowestoft NR32 2AB — MB BChir 1991 Camb.; BA (Hons.) Camb. 1988.

EHRENSTEIN, Janine Sidonie 42 Fryent Way, London NW9 9SB — MB BS 1987 Lond.

EHRENSTEIN, Michael Randolph Fourth Floor Dept of Rheumatology, Arthur Stanley House, Tottenham Street, London W1P 9PG Tel: 0207 380 4281 Email: m.ehrensteinoucl.ac.uk — MB BS 1987 Lond.; PhD Lond. 1994, BSc 1984; MRCP (UK) 1990. (Middlesex) Sen Lec Univ coll Lond.; Hon cons Univ coll Lond. Hosps. Prev: Sen. Regist. (Rheum.) Univ. Coll. Hosp.; MRC Clinician Scientist Fell.sh. Univ. Camb.; Hon. Sen. Regist. (Rheum.) Addenbrooke's Hosp. Camb.

EHRHARDT, Peter Oskar George Higher Green End, Shore, Todmorden OL14 8SF Tel: 0170 681 3417 — MB ChB 1978 Manch.; MB ChB (Hons.) Manch. 1978; MRCP (UK) 1981.

EHSAN, Mohammed 65A Coventry Road, Ilford IG1 4QT — MB BS 1998 Lond.; MB BS Lond 1998.

EHSANULLAH, Muhammad 15 Heath Field Road, Bushey, Watford WD23 2LH — MB BS 1975 Punjab, Pakistan; MRCP (UK) 1977.

EHTESHAMI, Shahram Flat 6, 16 Grenville Place, London SW7 4RW Tel: 020 7373 1183 — MD 1974 Iran.

EHTISHAM, Javed 63 Morr Green Lane, Moseley, Birmingham B13 8NE — BChir 1996 Camb.

EHTISHAM, Mohammed City Hospital NHS Trust, Dudley Road, Birmingham B18 7QH Tel: 0121 554 3801; 63 Moor Green Lane, Birmingham B13 8NE Tel: 0121 449 2711 — MB BS 1958 Karachi; FRCP Lond. 1989, M 1968; DTM & H Lond 1959. (Dow Med. Coll.) Cons. Phys. Dudley Rd. Hosp. Birm.; Sen. Clin. Lect. Univ. Birm. Socs: Brit. Geriat. Soc. & BMA. Prev: Ho. Phys. Jinnah Hosp., Karachi; Regist. & Sen. Regist. (Med.) Selly Oak Hosp. Birm.

EHTISHAM, Mr Muhammad Flat 3, 42 North End, Durham DH1 4LW — MB BS 1985 Karachi; FRCS Ed. 1990.

EHTISHAM, Sarah Birmingham Childrens Hospital NHS Trust, Steelhouse Lane, Birmingham B4 6NH; 63 Moor Green Lane, Birmingham B13 8NE — BChir 1994 Camb.

EICKHOFF, Louise Frances Winifred (retired) Llidiart Wood, Laundry Lane, Moel-y-Garth, Welshpool SY21 9DA Tel: 01938 552798 — MB ChB 1937 Ed.; MD Ed. 1947; FRCPsych 1995, M 1971; T(Psychiat.) 1991; DPM Eng. 1944. Prev: Cons. Child Psychiat. Selly Oak Hosp. Birm.

EICKMANN, Carsten Thedford, Capel Llanilltern, Cardiff CF5 6JH — State Exam Med 1991 Marburg.

EID, Charles Samir 22 West Heath Gardens, London NW3 7TR Tel: 0208 671611 Email: 100626.2452@compuserve.com — MB BS 1989 Lond. (Roy. Free Hosp. Sch. Med.)

EID, Nagi Hussein 48 Eton Rise, Eton College Road, London NW3 2DQ — MB BCh 1981 Alexandria.

EID, Toufic Mamdouh 76 Chichester Road, Croydon CR0 5NB — MB BS 1985 Lond.

EIGENER, Katrin Fiona Eva 99 Mildmay Road, London N1 4PU — MB BS 1996 Lond. (St. Bartolomew's) SHO (Med.) OldCh. Hosp. Romford.

EILBECK, Susan Catherine Falkland House Surgery, 2a Falkland Road, Sheffield S11 7PL Tel: 0114 266 0285; 519 Fulwood Road, Fulwood, Sheffield S10 3QB — MB BS 1981 Lond.; MRCGP 1986; DRCOG 1987.

EINHORN, Benjamin 56 Fordhook Avenue, Ealing Common, London W5 3LR Tel: 020 8992 5040 — Med. Dipl. 1939 Krakow; Med. Dip. Krakow 1939.

EISEN, Mr Sandy Martin 13 Baxendale, London N20 0EG — MB BChir 1980 Camb.; BA (Hons.) Camb. 1977, MB BChir 1980; FRCS Eng. 1985; Dip. Pharm. Med. RCP Lond. 1991. Sen. Med. Off. Med. Control Agency Dept. Health Lond. Prev: Surg. Regist. Luton & Dunstable Hosp.; Regist. (Surg.) St. Bart. Hosp. Lond.; Ho. Surg. Prof. Unit St. Bart. Hosp. Lond.

EISEN, Timothy George Quentin 8 Rosecroft Avenue, Hampstead, London NW3 7QB — MB BChir 1987 Camb.; PhD Lond. 1996; BSc (Hons.) Lond. 1984; MRCP (UK) 1990. Sen. Lect. & Hon. Cous. Med. Oncol. Roy. Mausden Hosp. & Inst. of Cancer Research. Prev: Sen. Regist. Roy. Marsden Hosp.; Clin. Research Fell. Marie Curie Inst. Lond.; Regist. (Med.) Kent & Canterbury Hosp.

EISENBERG, John Norman Heathcote Macklin Street Surgery, 90 Macklin Street, Derby DE1 2JX Tel: 01332 340381 Fax: 01332 345387; 19 Chadfield Road, Duffield, Belper DE56 4DU Tel: 01332 841967 — MB BS 1978 Lond.; BSc Lond. 1975; MRCP Lond. 1981; MRCGP 1985. Prev: Regist. (Med.) N.. Gen. Hosp. Sheff.

EISENHANDLER, Seanna Jill 26 Luxborough Towers, Luxborough St., London W1U 5BP — MB BS 1997 Lond.

EISENSTEIN, Mr Stephen Michael Centre for Spinal Studies, The Robert Jones & Agnes Hunt Orthopaedic Hospital, Oswestry SY10 7AG Tel: 01691 404481 Fax: 01691 404054 Email: s.m.eisenstein@keele.ac.uk; Tel: 01691 655734 — MB BCh Witwatersrand 1968; PhD Witwatersrand 1980; FRCS Ed. 1973. Dir. (Spinal Disorders) & Cons. Spinal Surg. Robt. Jones & Agnes Hunt Orthop. Hosp.; Hon. Sen. Lect. Postgrad. Med. Fac. Univ. Keele. Socs: Internat. Soc. Study Lumbar Spine; Brit. Orthop. Assn.; Brit. Scoliosis Soc.

EISER, Noemi Milena Chest Clinic, Lewisham Hospital, Lewisham High St., London SE13 6LH Tel: 020 8333 3000 Fax: 020 8333 3092 — MB BS 1968 (Hons.) Lond.; MD Lond. 1983; FRCP Lond. 1986; MRCS Eng. LRCP Lond. 1968; MRCP (UK) 1973. (Lond. Hosp.) Cons. Lewisham Hosp. NHS Trust. Socs: Fell. RSM; Fell. RCP (Lond.); Thoracic Soc. Prev: Regist. Hammersmith Hosp. Lond.; Sen. Regist. Char. Cross Hosp. Lond.

EISINGER, Anthony John 54 Wimpole Street, London W1 Tel: 020 8644 1168; The Cop, Old Road, Buckland, Betchworth RH3 7DY — MB BChir 1965 Camb.; FRCP Lond. 1979, M 1966. (Camb. & Middlx.) Cons. Phys. & Nephrol. St. Helier Hosp. Carshalton; Dir. S.W. Thames Regional Renal Unit. Prev: Ho. Surg. Middlx. Hosp.; Ho. Phys. Brompton Hosp. Lond.; Med. Regist. St. Thos. Hosp. Lond.

EISNER, Margaret Claire Eisner, Goldman and Ship, Shipley Health Centre, Alexandra Road, Shipley BD18 3EG Tel: 01274 589153 Fax: 01274 770882 — BM BCh 1972 Oxf.; MA Oxf. 1972; MRCP (UK) 1974; MRCGP 1980; DRCOG 1977; DCH Eng. 1975; MSc 1996. (Univ. Coll. Hosp.) GP Trainer Bradford VTS; GP Tutor Univ. Leeds Med. Sch. Socs: N.ern & Yorks Multicentre Research Ethics Comm. Prev: SHO (Paediat.) Evelina Hosp. Lond.; SHO (Obst.) Univ. Coll. Hosp. Lond.; SHO (Med.) St. Stephen's Hosp. Lond.

EISNER-KISSMANN, Gisela (retired) 8 Wilmer Drive, Shipley BD18 3BB Tel: 01274 585039 — MD 1936 Prague; MFCM 1973; DCH Eng. 1948. Prev: Sen. Med. Off. Harlow Health Dist.

EJAZ, Sheeraza Glenburn Health Centre, Fairway Avenue, Paisley PA2 8DX Tel: 0141 884 7788 Fax: 0141 569 1090 — MB ChB 1981 Glas.; MRCGP 1993; DRCOG 1992. GP, Paisley.

EJAZ, Mr Tallat Beau Repaire Cottage, 2 National Terrace, Boston PE21 6QT — MB BS 1982 Punjab; FRCSI 1989.

EJIKEME, Ifeoma Felicia Vision Express, 9 Hale Leys, Aylesbury HP20 1TS Tel: 01296 338560 Fax: 01296 338561; 80 Ramsworth Way, Aylesbury HP21 7EY Tel: 01296 398047 — MB BCh 1977 Nigeria; LMSSA 1990; DO RCPSI 1982; MRCOphth 1991. Med. Pract. (Ophth.) Vision Express Aylesbury. Socs: Brit. Contact Lens Assn.; MCLOSA; Glamcome Assn. Prev: SHO (Ophth.) Oxf. RHA; SHO (Ophth.) Barnsley Dist. Gen. Hosp. & Stoke Mandeville Hosp.

EJSKJAER, Niels Department of Endocrinology and Diabetes, Aarhus University Hospital, Aarhus DK-8000C, Denmark; 331 Crystal Palace Road, East Dulwich, London SE22 9JL — MD Aarhus 1991. (Aarhùs Univ. Sch. of Med. and Dent.)

***EJUONEATSE, Michael Oritsetimeyin** Princes Park Health Centre, Bentley Road, Liverpool L8 0SY Tel: 0151 728 8313 Fax: 0151 728 8417 — MB ChB 1986 Liverp.

EKANAYAKE, Ariya Tilleke Warley Hospital, Warley Hill, Brentwood CM14 5HQ Tel: 01277 213241; 240 Warley Hill, Brentwood CM13 3AA Tel: 01277 217984 — MB BS 1968 Ceylon; DPH RIPHH 1980; Cert. Family Plann. JCC 1983. (Colombo) Assoc. Specialist (Psychiat.) Barking, Havering & Brentwood HA. Prev: Clin. Asst. (Ment. Illness) Barking, Havering & Brentwood HA; Regist. (Psychiat.) Barking & Havering AHA; SHO (Geriat.) Barnsley AHA & Leeds AHA (T).

EKBERY, David John The Park Surgery, 4 Alexandra Road, Great Yarmouth NR30 2HW Tel: 01493 855672; Tel: 01493 600359 — MB ChB 1986 Birm.; DCH RCP Lond. 1992; DRCOG 1992. p/t Gen. Practitioner; Assoc. Specialist in Rheum.

EKDAWI, Mounir (retired) Harwell, 7 Devon Road, Merstham, Redhill RH1 3EU — MB ChB 1952 Alexandria; LAH Dub. 1957; FRCPsych 1975, M 1972; DPM Eng. 1960. Prev: Cons. Psychiat. (Rehabil.) & Clin. Tutor (Psychiat.) Netherne Hosp. Coulsdon.

EKE, Allison Jane Employee Health Service, 9th Floor, Commercial Union House, 24 Martineau Square, Birmingham B2 4UU Tel: 07730 735052 Fax: 01252 328695 Email: allison.eke@postoffice.co.uk; 8 Stratford Road, Salisbury SP1 3JH Tel: 01722 336085 Fax: 01722 328695 Email: allisoneke@consignia.com — MB BS 1984 Lond.; MFOM RCP Lond. 1996; DIH Soc. Apoth. Lond. 1989; DAvMed RCP Lond. 1989. (King's Coll.) Cons. Occupat.al Phys. Consignia Employee Health Serv. W.. Territory; Cons. in Aviat. Med., 7 Regt. Army Air Corps (V) Neth; Cons. in Aviat. Med., 7 Regt. Army Air Corps (v) Netherawn, Salisbury, Wilts. Socs: Soc. Occupat. Med. & Aerospace Med. Assn.; Roy. Aeronaut. Soc. Prev: Cons. Aviat. Med. HQ LAND Command; Cons. Aviat. Med. DERA CHS FarnBoro.; SO1J1 AviatMed, Jt. Helicopter Command.

EKE, Mr Thomas Norfolk & Norwich University Hospitals, Norwich — MB BChir 1988 Camb.; MA Camb. 1990; FRCOphth 1995.

EKE, Zoe Sarah 8 St Leonard's Walk, Morpeth NE61 3SZ Tel: 01670 517164 Email: eke@st_leonards.freeserve.co.uk — BM 1993 Soton. SHO Rotat. (Anaesth.) Newc. SHO (Anaesth) Flexible Trainee N.ern Region. Socs: Train. Mem. Assn. Anaesth.; RCA. Prev: SHO (Med.) Wansbeck Gen. Ashington, N.d.; SHO Ratat. (Anaesth.) Newc.

EKEOWA, Ugochukwu Ifedi Flat 37, Ashbourne Court, 137 Daubeney Road, London E5 0EJ — MB BS 1998 Lond.; MB BS Lond 1998.

EKIN, Elizabeth Holland 17 Fairway Avenue, Upper Malone, Belfast BT9 5NL Tel: 01232 612166 — MB BCh BAO 1936 Belf. Prev: Ho. Surg. Waveney Hosp. Ballymena.

EKIN, Mr William Hugh 17 Fairway Avenue, Upper Malone, Belfast BT9 5NL Tel: 01232 612166 — MB BChir 1937 Camb.; BA (Nat. Sc. Trip.) Camb. 1931, MA, MB BChir 1937; FRCS Ed. 1947; LMSSA Lond. 1933; DPH Belf. 1939. (Camb. & Westm.) Hon. Cons. Surg. Belf. City Hosp. Prev: Ho. Surg. & Cas. Off. W.m. Hosp.; Asst. Med. Off. Route Dist. Hosp. Ballymoney.

EKPO, Enefiok Ben 24 Spring Shaw Road, Orpington BR5 2RH — MB BS 1978 Nigeria; MRCP (UK) 1983.

EKWURU, Michael Okechukwu 247 Hermitage Road, London N4 1NP — MB BS 1992 Lond.; BSc Lond. 1989; MRCP (UK) 1995.

EL ABBAR, Mr Mohammed Khalifa 316 Marston Road, Marston, Oxford OX3 0JA — MB BS 1977 Garyounis; MB BS Garyounis, Libya 1977; FRCS Ed. 1989.

EL AGNAF, Moulod Ramadan Department of Haematology, Ulster Hospital, Belfast BT16 1RH Tel: 01232 484511 — MB BS 1976 Garyounis; FRCP Ed. 1995; FRCPI 1989; FRCPath 1997; FRCP Lond. 1998. Cons. Haemat. Ulster Hosp. Belf. Prev: Cons. Haemat. Altnagelvin Hosp. Lond.derry.

EL ASHOURI, Abdel Rahma Fordbridge Medical Centre, 4 Fordbridge Road, Ashford TW15 2SG Tel: 01784 242251; Fordbridge Medical Centre, 4 Fordbridge Road, Ashford TW15 2SG Tel: 01784 253975 — MB BCh 1971 Ain Shams. Med. Regist. Maidstone Gen. Hosp. Prev: Med. Regist. Ashford Gen. Hosp. Middlx.; SHO (Gen. Med.) Preston Hall Hosp. Kent; Med. Off. UNRWA Jordan.

EL ASHRY, Ahmed Ahmed 17 Heathdene, Chase Side, Southgate, London N14 5HU Tel: 020 8886 4193; 169 Bowes Road, New Southgate, London N11 Tel: 020 8888 3201 — MD 1988 Leic.; MB BCh Cairo 1969. Clin. Res. Assoc. (Hypertens.) Dept. Med. Leics. Roy. Infirm.; Med. Regist. (Cardiol.) Enfield Dist. Hosp. (Highlands Wing).

EL ATTAR, Amir (retired) Department of Oral & Maxillo-Facial Surgery, Cannisburn Hospital, Bearsden, Glasgow G61 1QL Tel: 0141 211 5600 — MB BS Lond. 1963, BDS 1959; FDS RCPS Glas. 1971; FDS RCS Eng. 1971, LDS 1959. Locum Cons. Oral & Maxillo-Facial Surg. Altnagelvin Hosp., Lond.derry; Titular Prof. of Oral & Maxillo-Facial Surg. Univ. of Alexandria, Egypt. Prev: Cons. Oral & Maxillofacial Surg. Canniesburn Hosp. Glas.

EL AWAGE, Mr Abd El Salam Youssef 82 Hummersknott Avenue, Darlington DL3 8RS — MB ChB 1975 Alexandria; FRCS Ed. 1991.

EL AZAB, Ahmed El Syed Ahmed Barkerend Health Centre, Barkerend Road, Bradford BD3 8QH Tel: 01274 778400 Fax: 01274 770146; 15 Cricketers Green, Yeadon, Leeds LS19 7YS Tel: 0113 250 7690 — MB BCh 1971 Cairo; DObst RCPI 1986.

EL BADRI, Abubaker Mohamed Whiston Hospital, Prescot L35 5DR Tel: 0151 426 1600 — MB ChB 1983 Garyounis, Libya; MB ChB Garyounis Libya 1983; MRCP (UK) 1993; MRCPI 1993; DCH RCP Dub. 1987; DCH Tripoli 1987; MD 1999 Univ. of Manch. Paediatric Gastroenterol. Socs: Paediat. Research Soc.; Brit. Soc. Paediat. Gastroenterol.; RCPCH. Prev: Clin. Research Fell. (Child Health) Univ. Manch. Med. Sch. & Manch. Childr. Hosps.; Tutor (Child Health) Roy. Manch. Childr. Hosp.; Regist. (Paediat.) Bolton Gen. Hosp.

EL BADRI, Selim Mohamed Department of Psychiatry, School of Neurosciences, Leazes Wing, Royal Victoria Infirmary, Newcastle upon Tyne NE1 4LP Tel: 0191 232 5131 Fax: 0191 227 5108; c/o Dr A. Elbadri, 17 Silverline Gardens, St Helens WA9 5UN Tel: 0151 426 6414 — MB ChB 1982 Garyounis; DPM RCPSI 1991; BCPsych. Lond. 1992. Clin. Research Assoc. (Psychiat.) Univ. Newc. u. Tyne. Prev: Regist. (Gen. Psychiat.) Community, Rehabil. & Alcohol & Drug Depend. Clinic Our Lady's Hosp. & Limerick Regional Hosp. RePub. of Irel.

EL BARGHOUTY, Mr Nayef Mottasem Nayef Scarborough Hospital, Woodlands Drive, Scarborough YO12 6QL; Rhodelands, Main St, Allerston, Pickering YO18 7PG — MB BCh 1983 Ain Shams; FRCS Ed. 1988; MS Ain Shams 1987; PhD London 1996. Cons. Gen. & Vasc. Surg. ScarBoro. Hosp. Socs: BMA; ASGBI; USSGBI. Prev: Regist. (Surg.) P'boro. Dist. Gen. Hosp. & Yeovil Dist. Hosp.; Research Fell. Acad. Vasc. Unit St. Mary's Hosp. Med. Sch. Lond.; SR N.ern Region.

EL-BEREIR, Gaafer Mohamed Ali Flat 17, Heatherstones, Queens Gate, Halifax HX3 0DH — MB BCh 1976 Ain Shams.

EL BESHIR, Osama Ahmed Derriford Hospital, Derriford Road, Plymouth PL6 8BD Tel: 01752 357171 Fax: 01752 777111; Flat F3, Kingstor House, Derriford Road, Plymouth PL6 8BQ Tel: 01752 777111 — MB BS 1981 Khartoum; MRCPI 1991. Regist. (Gen. Med.) Derriford Hosp. Plymouth. Prev: Regist. (Gen.Med.) Scunthorpe Gen. Hosp.; SHO (Gen. Med.) Bolton Roy. Infirm.; SHO (Med.) Khrtoum Teach. Hosp. Sudan.

EL BESHTY, Mohamed Mahmud 16 Fitzjames Avenue, East Croydon, Croydon CR0 5DH — MB ChB 1963 Ed.; MD Ed. 1980; DCH Eng. 1968. Hon. Lect. Paediat. Dept. Guy's Hosp. Med. Sch. Socs: Fell. Roy. Soc. Med.; Paediat. Research Soc.

EL BEZE, Yves Simon 10A Thorney Crescent, London SW11 3TR — MD 1992 Marseilles.

EL BOGHDADLY, Mr Sami Abd El-Keriem Mohamed 'Hortiack', Kings Drive, Caldy, Wirral CH48 2JH — MRCS Eng. LRCP Lond. 1977; FRCS Eng. 1979.

EL BORAI, Claire Lisa The New Surgery, The Nap, Kings Langley WD4 8ET Tel: 01923 261035; Woodeaves, Pleasant Harbour, Bewdley DY12 1AD Tel: 01923 262306 Email: jon.stratton@ntlworld.com — MB BS 1993 Lond.; BSc Lond. 1990; DRCOG 1995; DCH 1996; MRCGP 1997. p/t GP Regist. Portsmouth Hosps.; Slaried GP Princip. The New Surg. The Nap Kings Langley Herts. Prev: GP Asst. at Theobald Centre Borehamwood, Herts.

EL BORAI, Mohamed Rimah El Borai, 32 Eardley Crescent, London SW5 9JZ Tel: 020 7373 0140 Fax: 020 7244 6617; Greentiles, Southfield Place, Weybridge KT13 0RQ Tel: 01932 857522 — MB BCh 1959 Cairo; LMSSA Lond. 1977; MRCS Eng. 1977; MFFP 1993. Princip. GP Kensington, Chelsea & W.m. FHSA; Tutor (Gen. Pract.)Imperial Coll.; Instruc. Doctor (Family Plann.) Riverside HA.

EL DABOUNI, Mr Mowafak Ahmed Mohammed 15 St Stephens Gardens, Manfred Road, Putney, London SW15 2RR Tel: 020 8874 7152 — MB BCh 1971 Ain Shams; FRCS Ed. 1982.

EL-DARS, Leila Dalia 10 East Avenue, Bournemouth BH3 7BY — MB BS 1997 Lond. (Guys and St Thomas')

EL DARS, Mostafa Kadry 10 East Avenue, Talbot Woods, Bournemouth BH3 7BY Tel: 01202 558017 — LMSSA 1965 Lond.; DM Cairo 1954, MB BCh 1949; FRCP Ed. 1981, M 1965. (Kasr El-Aini Med. Sch.) Cons. Phys. (Geriat.) Poole Gen. Hosp.; Lect. at Anglo-Europ. Coll. of Chiropractic, Bournemouth. Socs: Fell. Roy. Soc. Med. Prev: Consult. in Clin.-Neurophysiol. Birm. RHB; Sen. Regist. (Clin.-Neurophysiol.) Hosp. Sick Childr. Lond.

EL-DARS, Natasha 10 East Avenue, Bournemouth BH3 7BY Email: natashaeldars@hotmail.com — MB BS 1996 Lond.

EL DEEB, Batoul Badr El Deen Bellstone House, Haughton, West Felton, Oswestry SY11 4HF — MB BCh 1969 Cairo; MD Birm. 1985.

EL DERINI, Mohamed Sami (retired) Wynfield, Holme Lane, Bakewell DE45 1GF — LMSSA 1963 Lond.; DM Alexandria 1957, MB ChB 1952. Prev: Hon. Cons. Rheum. Sheff. HA.

EL-DOSOKY, Ahmed Mohamed Refaat Ahmed 58 Gainsborough Road, Epsom KT19 9DG — MB BCh 1983 Zagazig, Egypt; MRCPsych 1996.

EL DOSOKY, Mohamed Ebrahim 25 Towbury Close, Oakenshaw, South Redditch, Redditch B98 7YZ — MB BCh 1971 Cairo; MRCOG 1983.

EL ELIWI, Riad Aly 23 Ling Park Avenue, Wilsden, Bradford BD15 0NE — MB BCh 1972 Al-Azhar, Egypt.

EL-FAKHRY, Mr Tarek Tannous Stafford District General Hospital, Weston Road, Stafford ST16 3SA; The Mount, 13 Sutherland Drive, Westlands, Newcastle ST5 3NA — MD 1977 Amer. Univ. Beirut; FRCS Eng. 1987; FRCS Ed. 1987. Cons. Orthop. Surg. Stafford Dist. Gen. Hosp. Socs: Fell. BOA. Prev: Cons. Orthop. Surg. N. Staffs. Roy. Infirm. Stoke-on-Trent.

EL-FAKI, Mr Abd El Hamid Mohamed Ahmad c/o Mr. J. M. Buchanan, Sunderland District General Hospital, Kayll Road, Sunderland SR4 7TP; 126 Cleveland Road, Sunderland SR4 7JT Tel: 0191 528323 — MB BCh 1974 Ain Shams; FRCS Glas. 1985. Staff Orthop. Surg. Socs: Brit. Orthop. Assn. Prev: Staff Grade (Orthop.); Regist. (Orthpaedics); Cons. (Orthop.).

EL-FALLAH, Mr Mohammed El-Mahdi Royal Alexandra Hospital, Corsebar Road, Paisley PA2 9P Tel: 0141 580 4505 Fax: 0141 580 4135; 19 Newbold Avenue, Glasgow G21 1XB — MB BCh 1970 Ain Shams; FRCS Ed. 1984; FRCOphth 1993; FCOphth 1988; DOMS Cairo 1974. Ophth. Roy. Alexandra Hosp. Socs: Oxf. Ophth. Congr.; Scott. Ophth. Club; Scott. Medico-legal Soc.

EL-FARAMAWI, Medhat Abdel Aziz Danver Lodge, Pear Tree Lane, Shorne, Gravesend DA12 3JU — MB BCh 1971 Ain Shams; DRCOG 1976.

EL-FARHAN, Maissa Hamad Flat 4, 34 Hatherley Gr, London W2 5RB — MB BS 1997 Lond.

EL-FARHAN, Nadia Mohammed Mahdi 9 High Street, Bonsall, Matlock DE4 2AS — MB ChB 1997 Ed.

EL-FAROK, Mr Mohamed Omar 41 Kingstone Road, Broadesley, Birmingham B9 4DJ — MB BCh 1983 Ain Shams; FRCS Ed. 1993.

EL FIGHI, Mr Asaad Abdussalam Mohamed Health Care International, Beardmore St., Clydebank G81 4HX — MB BCh 1980 Cairo; FRCS Glas. 1991; FRCS Ed. 1990. Regist. (Gen. Surg.) N. Manch. Gen. Hosp. Prev: SHO & Regist. (Gen. Surg.) Rochdale HA.

EL-GADDAL, Ahmed Abdalla Hassan 26 Oakwood Park, Malone, Belfast BT9 6SE — MB BS 1986 Khartoum.

EL GADDAL, Mohammed El Hassan St Clement's Hospital, Foxhall Road, Ipswich IP3 8LS — MB BS 1971 Khartoum; MRCPsych 1980.

EL GADI, Ibrahim Abdulhakim 7 Statham Walk, Manchester M13 9YS — MB BS 1979 Garyounis; MRCP (UK) 1987.

EL-GADRA, Ahmed Hussen Awad 14 Ainslie Wood Road, London E4 9BY — MB ChB 1976 Alexandria; MRCPI 1985.

EL GAID, Idris Soleman 61 Delafield Road, Abergavenny NP7 7AW — MB ChB 1977 Alexandria; DCH RCPSI 1981; DTCD Wales 1984.

EL-GAMEL, Mr Ahmed Mohamed Hamed Mohamed The Cromwell Hospital, London Bridge Hospital, London SW5 0TU Tel: 0207 346 3247 Email: aelgamel@aol.com; 7 Great Splimons, Dulwich, London SE22 8SZ Tel: 020 8299 3863 Fax: 020 8299 3863 Email: aelgamel@aol.com — MB BCh 1982 Ain Shams; 1988 FRCS Eng.; MD Manchester; FRCS 1989 Ed.; FRCS 1997 (Eng) (CTn; MRCP 1986. (Ain Shams) Cons. Cardiothoracic Surg. King's Coll. Hosp; Cons. Cardiothoraic Surg., The Cromwell Hosp., Lond. Bridge Hosp. Socs: Roy. Soc. Med.; Amer. Soc. Cardiothoracic Surg.; Int. Soc. Heart and Lung Transpl.ation. Prev: SR Cardiothoraic Surg., Manch. Roy. Infirm.; Fell., Cardiothoracic Surg., Yale Univ., USA.

EL GAMMAL, Mr Mohsen Mohamed Youssef St Michaels Hospital, 2 Trelissick Road, Hayle TR27 4HY — MB BCh 1983 Cairo; FRCS Ed. 1993.

EL GARIB, Abd El Mawla Hassan 4 Maes Watford, Caerphilly CF83 1LP — MB BCh 1975 Ain Shams; MRCOG 1987.

EL-GASIM, Mohamed Hasim Abu Shortley Bridge General Hospital, Consett DH8 0NB — MB BS 1982 Khartoum, Sudan.

EL GAWLY, Raouf Michel Tewfik Billinge Hospital, Upholland Road, Billinge, Wigan WN5 7ET Tel: 01695 626295; Worthington House, 71 The Common, Parbold, Wigan WN8 7EA Email: elgawley@ukgateway.net — MB BCh 1980 Cairo; MRCOG 1987; FRCOG 1999. (Cairo Univ. Med. Sch.) Cons. O & G Billinge Hosp. Wigan. Socs: Brit. Med. Assoc'n; Soc. of Adolesc. Gynaecol. Prev: Regist. (O & G) Warrington Dist. Gen. Hosp. & All St.s Hosp. Chatham Kent.

EL-GAYLANI, Nadia Flat 33, Alexandra Court, The Esplanade, Penarth CF64 3LA — MB BCh BAO 1985 NUI; LRCPSI 1985; MRCPI 1988.

EL-GAZZAR, Yousry Abdel Shaffy Lanark Medical Centre, Ground Floor, 165 Lanark Road, London W9 1NZ Tel: 020 7328 1128 Fax: 020 7328 0605 — MB BCh 1972 Cairo; MB BCh 1972 Cairo.

EL-GHAZALI, Mr Ahmed Mohamed Shawki 5 Roman Bridge Close, Blackpill, Swansea SA3 5BE Tel: 01792 403156 — MB BCh 1972 Cairo; FRCS Glas. 1979; DLO RCS Eng. 1978.

EL GHAZALI, Mr Khaled Mohamed Shawki 5 Roman Bridge Close, Blackpill, Swansea SA3 5BE Tel: 01792 403156 — MB BCh 1976 Cairo; FRCS Ed. 1987; FCOphth 1988; DO RCPSI 1986. Cons. Ophth. Singleton Hosp. Swansea.

EL-GHAZAWY, Mr Mahmoud Abdel Latif Mohamed Abdo Trafford General Hospital, Moorside Road, Davyhulme, Urmston, Manchester M41 5SG; 16 Jakson Court, Urmston, Manchester M41 5SG Tel: 0161 747 1051 — MB BCh 1971 Ain Shams; MRCOG 1991. Staff O & G Trafford Gen. Hosp. Manch. Socs: Brit. Soc. Colposc. & Cervic. Pathol.; Eur. Assn. of Obst. & Gyn.; BMA.

EL-GINGIHY, Ali Sayed Ahmed 4 Davis Close, Beverley Hills, Leamington Spa CV32 6RT — MB BCh 1962 Cairo.

EL-GOHARY, Tarek Mahfouz Taher Edward Street Hospital, Edward St., West Bromwich B70 8NL Tel: 0121 553 7676 Fax: 0121 607 3576 Email: elgohary@hotmail.com; 21 Cofton Church Lane, Birmingham B45 8PS Tel: 0121 445 5760 — MB BCh 1972 Ain Shams; MRCPsych 1986. (Univ. Ain Shams Cairo, Egypt) Cons. Psychiat. Black Country Ment. Health NHS Trust W. Bromwich. Prev: Sen. Regist. W. Midl. Train. Scheme.

EL-GUINDI, Madeh El-Rasool Mostafa 6 Southall Drive, Hartlebury, Kidderminster DY11 7LD — MB BCh 1971 Cairo; MB BCh Cairo, Egypt 1971.

EL-HADI, Ali Abdel Razek Abd 18 Colworth Road, Leytonstone, London E11 1HY Tel: 020 8539 5496 Fax: 020 8539 5496; Brookside Unit, 107A Barley Lane, Goodmayes, Ilford IG3 8XQ Tel: 020 8924 6301 Fax: 020 8924 6302 — MB BCh 1972 Cairo; MSc Lond. 1996; MRCPsych 1979. (Kaser El-Elni, Univ. Cairo) Cons. Adolesc. Psychiat. Brookside Young People's Unit Redbridge; Hon. Sen. Lect. (Psychiat.) St. Bart. Hosp. Lond. Socs: Assn. Child Psychol. & Psychiat.; Assoc. Mem. Brit. Assn. Psychother. Prev: Sen. Regist. (Child & Adolesc. Psychiat.) Dept. Child Psychiat. Lond. Hosp.; Regist. (Psychiat.) Qu. Eliz. Midl. Nerve Hosp. Birm.; Regist. (Psychother.) Uffculme Clinic Birm.

EL HADIDI, Mr Maher Mohamed El Enam Redwood Lodge, 9 Ashby Park, Daventry NN11 5QW — MB BCh 1972 Cairo; FRCS Ed. 1981.

EL HAG, Omer Ahmed Omer Cardiology Department, Royal Infirmary of Edinburgh, 1 Lauriston Place, Edinburgh EH3 9YW — MB BS 1981 Sudan.

EL HAG, Mr Salaheldin Hassan Medical Flat No. 6, Bassetlaw District General Hospital, Kilton Hill, Worksop S81 0BD — MB BS 1983 Dacca; FRCS Glas. 1992.

EL HALHULI, Othman Abd El Rahman Shehde Adlington Medical Centre, 22-24 Babylon Lane, Anderton, Chorley PR6 9NW Tel: 01257 482076 Fax: 01257 474770; 4 Highfield Close, Adlington, Chorley PR6 9RL Tel: 01257 474803 — MB ChB 1972 Alexandria; MB ChB Alexandria, Egypt 1972; DObst RCPI 1986; DRCOG 1986.

EL-HALLAQ, Yehia Hassan Mohammed 9 St Annes Close, St. Annes Road, Lincoln LN2 5RB — MB ChB 1972 Cairo; MRCOG 1984.

EL-HARARI, Mohamed Basher Ahmed Ward 50, Royal Victoria Infirmary, Queen Victoria Road, Newcastle upon Tyne NE1 4LP Tel: 0191 232 5131; 9B North Terrace, Claremont Road, Newcastle upon Tyne NE2 4AD Tel: 0191 233 1218 Email: m.b.a.el-harari@ncl.ac.uk — MB BCh 1987 Al Fateh, Libya; MRCP (UK) 1993. Specialist Regist. Cardiol. R.V.I Newc. Prev: Regist. (Cardiol.) Roy. Vict. Infirm.; SHO (Med.) Dr Gray's Hosp. Elgin; Research Regist. (Cardiol.) Roy. Vict. Infirm. Newc. u. Tyne.

EL-HARIRY, Aiman Abdel Wahab Mohamed 24 Canada Drive, Redhill RH1 5AY — MB BCh 1983 Ain Shams; MRCP (UK) 1995.

EL-HIHI, Mohd Amin 35 Flora Gardens, Romford RM6 4BG — Laurea Bologna 1981.

EL-HILU, Saleh Hallam Street Hospital, West Bromwich B71 4NH Tel: 0121 607 3908 Fax: 0121 607 3914 Email: sel_hilu@bcmh-tr.wmids.nhs.uk; 16 Malvern Drive, Sutton Coldfield B76 1PZ Tel: 0121 313 1099 Email: drhilu@hotmail.com — Lekarz 1971 Stettin, Poland; MRCPsych 1977 (T Psych); DPM Eng. 1976; JBPsych 1990 - Jordanian Board of Psychiatry 1990. Cons. Psychiat. & Clin. Dir. (Adult Psychiat. Servs.) Sandwell. Socs: Roy. Coll. Psychiat.; World Psychiat. Assn.; World Federat. Ment. Health. Prev: Head Psychiat. Unit & Clin. Tutor Psychol. Med. Hosp., Kuwait.

EL HUSSEIN, Nahid Abdalla 23 Longwood Gardens, Ilford IG5 0EB — MUDr 1975 Prague; DTCD Wales 1980. Community Med. Off. Barking, Havering & Brentwood HA.

EL JABBOUR, Joseph Nabih Department of Cellular Pathology, Barnet General Hospital, Wellhouse Lane, Barnet EN5 3DJ Tel: 020 8216 4583 Fax: 020 8216 4842 Email: joseph.el-jabbour@barnet-chase-tr.nhs.uk; Email: joseph.eljabbour@btinternet.com — MD 1981 Damascus; FRCPath 1999. (Univ. Damascus Fac. of Med.) Cons. Cellular Path. (Cellular Path. & Histopath.) Barnet and Chase Farm Hosp.s NHS Trust Barnet; Clin. Prof. St. Geo. Univ. Sch. Med. Granada, W. Indies. Socs: Assn. Clin. Path; Internat. Acad. Path.; BMA. Prev: Sen. Regist. Mt. Vernon Hosp. & Char Cross Hosp. Lond.; Regist. Edin. Univ.; Resid. Amer. Univ. Beirut, Lebanon.

EL-JABRI, Mazen 30 Whinney Heys Road, Blackpool FY3 8NP — MB BCh 1978 Ain Shams; MRCPI 1989.

EL-JASSAR, Ra'ad Patrick 67 Crawford Avenue, Mossley Hill, Liverpool L18 1DP — MB ChB 1992 Liverp.

EL-KABIR, David Jamil, MBE The Surgery, 45A Pembridge Villas, London W11 3EP Tel: 020 7727 2222 Fax: 020 7266 1518; The Priory, Charlbury, Oxford OX7 3PX — DM Oxf. 1969, MA, BM BCh 1962; MA, MB BChir Camb. 1956; LMSSA Lond. 1955; FRCGP 1994, M 1989. (Camb. & Sheff.) Princip. Wytham Hall. Socs: Thyroid Club & Med. Research Soc. Prev: Fell. & Tutor St. Peter's Coll. Oxf.; Research Assoc. Inst. Psychiat. Maudsley Hosp. Lond.; Mem. Extern. Scientif. Staff Med. Research Counc.

EL-KABIR, Desiree Ruth The Priory, Charlbury, Oxford OX7 3PX Tel: 01608 870417; 181a Battersea Bridge Road, London SW11 3AS Tel: 020 7801 9658 — MB BChir Camb. 1991; MA Camb. 1992; MRCP (UK) 1994. (St. Mary's Hosp. Med. Sch. Lond.) SPR Gen. / Respirat. Med., Bromley Hosp., Kent. Prev: SPR Respirat. Med., St Thomas' Hosp., Lond.; Research Regist. La. Fox Unit, St. Thos. Hosp. Lond.; Regist. (Respirat., Geriat. & Gen. Med.) King's Coll. Hosp. Lond.

EL-KAFRAWY, Ula 41 High Elm Road, Hale Barns, Altrincham WA15 0HZ — MB BCh BAO 1985 NUI; MRCP (UK) 1994; LRCPI & LM, LRCSI & LM 1985; DRCOG 1988. Sen. Regist. (Paediat.) Roy. Manch. & Booth Hall Childr.'s Hosps. Manch. Socs: BMA. Prev: Sen. Regist. (Paediat.) Wythenshawe Hosp. Manch.

EL KARY, Sami Ibrahim 179 London Road, Gillingham ME8 7HH Tel: 01634 260602 — MB BCh 1975 Ain Shams.

EL KASHOTY, Mr Mohamed Abdel Moneim — MB BCh 1969 Cairo; MRCS Eng. LRCP Lond. 1981; FRCS Glas. 1981. GP Kenilworth.

EL-KATSHA, Erian Wilson 162 Plantation Hill, Kilton, Worksop S81 0DT — MB BCh 1952 Cairo; DA Cairo 1959. (Kasr El-Eini Med. Coll.) Socs: BMA & Assn. Anaesth. Prev: Regist. (Anaesth.) OldCh. Hosp. Romford; Regist. (Anaesth.) Redhill Gen. Hosp.

EL-KHANAGRY, Magdy Fouad Farag Department of Obst. Gyrae, Queen's Hospital, Belvedere Road, Burton-on-Trent DE13 0RB Tel: 01283 566 3333 Email: magdyfouad@hotmail.com; 22 Longbow Close, Stretton, Burton-on-Trent NG8 1FY Tel: 0115 913 9009 Email: magdyfouad@hotmail.com — MB BCh 1984 Ain Shams; MRCOG 1993. (Univ. Ain Shams) Cons. Obst. & Gyn. Palestine Hosp. Heliopolis, Egypt - Staff Grade Med. Off. at Qu.'s Hosp., Burthon upon Trent UK; Cons. Obst. & Gyn. Good Shepherd Hosp. Shoubra, Egypt; Cons. Obst. & Gyn.. Coptic Hosp. Ramsis St., Cairo. Prev: Regist. (Obst. & Gyn.) Neath Gen. Hosp. & Carlisle Gen. Hosp.; SHO City Hosp. Carlisle & Nottm. City Hosp.

EL-KHASHAB, Mr Tarek Ali Fahmy Manchester Royal Eye Hospital, Oxford Road, Manchester M13 9WH Tel: 0161 276 1234; 4 Fairacre Drive, Middlewich CW10 0RS — MB BCh 1982 Cairo; FRCS Ed. 1992; MRCOphth 1989; DO RCS Eng. 1988. Specialist Ophth. Manch. Eye Hosp. Socs: BMA; MDU; Amer Acad Ophth. Prev: SHO (Ophth.) Bolton Roy. Infirm. & Leighton Hosp.

EL-KHATIB, Abdul Rahman Ribhi Anaesthetic Department, Royal Infrimary Hospital, Edinburgh EH3 9YW — MB ChB 1984 Baghdad.

EL-KHATIEB, Moustafa Mohamed Hassan 10 Hollybush Heights, Cyncoed, Cardiff CF23 7HF — MB BCh 1984 Ain Shams; MRCPI 1994.

EL KHIDIR, Hisham Hassan 248 Woodland Gardens, Isleworth TW7 6LT — MB BS 1987 Khartoum.

EL KHOGIA, Abdulaziz Mahmoud 30 Limewood Close, St. Mellons, Cardiff CF3 0BU — MB BCh 1981 Al Fateh, Libya.

EL-KHOLY, Ahmed Abdel-Khabir Abel-Fattah 18 St Benet's Close, London SW17 7UB — MB BCh 1972 Ain Shams; MRCOG 1981. Cons. (Obst. & Gyn.) S. Mead G. Hosp. Bristol. Prev: Cons. (O. & G.) Moyle Hosp. Larne.

EL KOMY, Anwar Abdel Hakiem Ahmed The Manse, 13 Cornwall Road, Dorchester DT1 1RT Tel: 01305 257886; The Manse, 13 Cornwall Road, Dorchester DT1 1RT Tel: 01305 257886 — MB BCh 1969 Ain Shams; MRCPsych 1988; DPM 1985 RCS&P 1985; Master Neurol. 1975; Dip. Psych. Psych. Inst. Cons. Neuropsychiat. Socs: BMA; Roy. Coll. Psychiat.

EL-LAKANY, Mr Nasr El-Din Hashem Abd El-Hamed 16 St Peters Close, Swanscombe DA10 0BD Tel: 01322 382786 — MB ChB 1977 Alexandria; MRCOG 1990. Cons. (Obstet. & Gyn.) (long term Locum); Mem. Tutorial Systems Internat. Socs: BMA; MDU.

EL-LEMKI, Mohammed Abdallah Mohammed 125 Balmuildy Road, Bishopbriggs, Glasgow G64 3ER — MB BCh 1981 Ain Shams; MRCP (UK) 1994.

EL MABRUK, Farag Mahmud Department of Neurology, The Medical School, University of Newcastle upon Tyne, Framlington Place, Newcastle upon Tyne NE2 4HH — MB ChB 1984 Garyounis, Libya.

EL MAHALLAWY, Mona Hafez Ahmed Ahmed Frimley Park Hospital, Portsmouth Road, Frimley, Camberley GU16 7UJ; Rosetta, Yester Park, Chislehurst BR7 5DQ — MB BCh 1974 Cairo; MRCPath 1984; T(Path) 1991. Cons. Histopath. Frimley Pk. Hosp. Surrey. Prev: Sen. Regist. (Histopath.) St. Mary's Hosp. Lond.; Regist. & SHO (Path.) Stoke-on-Trent.

EL MAHAYNI, Nada Mohamad Rafik Plot 2, The Parklands, 3 Lucerne Drive, Cardiff CF14 9FA — MD 1977 Damascus.

EL MAHMOUDI, Bashir Krime Ahmed 135 Lancaster Road, Salford M6 8NB — MB BCh 1980 Cairo; MRCPI 1990.

EL-MALEK, Emad Aziz Abd 299 Whalley Road, Shuttleworth, Ramsbotton, Bury BL0 0ER Tel: 01706 827011; Bury General Hospital, Bury BL9 6PG Tel: 0161 705 3376 — MB ChB 1977 Alexandria. Staff Grade (Acc. & Emerg.) Bury Gen. Hosp.

EL-MALIK, Siddig Mohamed Osman Gastroenterology Department, Queen Alexandra Hospital, Southwick Hill Road, Cosham, Portsmouth PO6 3LY — MB BS 1977 Khartoum; MRCPI 1989.

EL MANKABADY, Samir Fayek 9 Burdons Close, Strechford, Birmingham B34 6ET Tel: 0121 784 1072 — MB BCh 1969 Cairo; FFA RCSI 1981.

EL-MASRY, Mr Wagih Shafik Midland Centre for Spinal Injuries, The Robert Jones & Agnes Hunt Orthopaedic Hospital, Oswestry SY10 7AG Tel: 01691 404363 Fax: 01691 404064 — MB BCh 1969 Cairo; FRCS Ed. 1978. (Kasr El Eini) Cons. Spinal Injuries & Dir. Midl. Centre for Spinal Injuries Robt. Jones & Agnes Hunt Orthop. Hosp. OsW.ry; Asst. Edr. Internat. Med. Soc. Paraplegia; Sen. Lect. Univ. Keele. Socs: Exec. Mem. Internat. Med. Soc. Paraplegla.

EL MEKKAWY, Emad El-Deen Abdel-Khalek Alderman Jack Cohen Health Centre, Springwell Road, Sunderland SR3 4HG Tel: 0191 522 9908 Fax: 0191 528 8294; 8 Brancepeth Chare, Castle Eden Dene, Peterlee SR8 1LU Tel: 0191 586 1808 Fax: 0191 518

4544 Email: emekkawy@aol.com — MB BCh 1973 Ain Shams; MRCOG 1987. (Ain Shams University) Socs: BMA (Chairm. Sunderland Br.); N. Eng. Soc. Obst. & Gyn. Prev: Regist. (O & G) Sunderland Dist. Gen. Hosp. & Bellshill Matern Hosp.

EL-MELIEGY, Dina Ahmed Nagib 8 Queens Gate, London SW7 5EL Tel: 0207 225 1354; Tel: 020 8451 2131 — MB BS 1981 Lond.; 1999 CCST; MRCP Paediat. (UK) 1991; DCH RCP Lond. 1988. Socs: BMA; Roy. Coll. of Paediat. and childhealth; RCPCH. Prev: SE Roy. Free until September 1998; Regist. (Paediat.) St. Mary's Hosp. Lond.; SHO (Paediat.) Qu. Eliz. Hosp. Lond.

EL MENABAWEY, Mohamed Abd-Alla Ahmed N. Tees & Hartlepool NHS Trust, Holdsworth Road, Hartlepool TS24 9AH Tel: 01429 266654 Fax: 01429 522770 Email: mmenabawey@aol.com; Oakridge, The Parade, Hartlepool TS26 0DS Tel: 01429 222367 Fax: 01429 423164 Email: mmenabawey@aol.com — MB BCh 1968 Cairo; MRCOG 1977. Cons. O & G N. Tees and Hartlepool NHS Trust; Dir. of Cameron IVF Clinic; Chair of Clin. Effective Comm. Socs: Fell. N. Eng. Obst. & Gyn. Soc.; Fell.Europ. Obst. & Gyn.; Eur. Soc. Human Reproduc. & Embryol. Prev: Lect. & Sen. Regist. (O & G) St. Bart. Hosp. Lond.; Rockefeller Foundat. Research Fell. Reproduc. Physiol Dept. St. Bart. Hosp. Lond.

EL-MENSHAWY, Hassan Mahmoud Mostafa Maidstone Hospital, Maidstone ME16 9QQ Tel: 01622 729000 Fax: 01622 224672; 3 Greyfriars Close, Maidstone ME16 0GS Tel: 01622 685988 Fax: 01622 685988 — MB BCh 1972 Cairo; MSc (Orthop.) Lond. 1994. Staff Orthop. Surg. Maidstone Hosp. Prev: Regist. (Orthop.) Maidstone Hosp. & E. Glam. Hosp.; Regist. (Orthop.) Riyadh Milit. Hosp. Saudi Arabia.

EL-MIKATTI, Nabil Anaesthetic Department, Wythenshawe Hospital, Manchester M20 2LR Tel: 0161 291 5710 Fax: 0161 291 4132 Email: n.el-mikatti@man.ac.uk; 25 Cheadle Road, Cheadle Hulme, Cheadle SK8 5HL Tel: 0161 485 4068 — MD Cairo 1972; MB BCh Cairo 1966; FFA RCS Eng. 1979. p/t Cons. Anaesth. Withington Hosp. Manch. Socs: Anaesth. Res. Soc.. & Acupunc. Soc. Prev: Hon. Clin. Lect. (Anaesth.) Manch. Univ.; Prof. Anaesth. Cairo Univ.

EL-MILIGY, Magdy Yahya Mahmoud Women's Clinic, Maternity Unit, Perth Royal Infirmary, Perth PH1 1NX Tel: 01738 23311 Fax: 01738 473212; Glen Bank, Glenfoot, Abernethy, Perth PH2 9LS Tel: 01738 850251 — MB ChB 1980 Cairo; MB ChB Cairo (Hons.) 1980; MRCOG 1991. (Univ. Cairo) Staff O & G Perth Roy. Infirm. Socs: Blair Bell Res. Soc.; N. Obst. & Gyn. Soc. Prev: Regist. (O & G) Milton Keynes Hosp.

EL MORSY, Mr Hesham Abd El-Hay Abd El-Hamid New Ayr Hospital, Dalmellington Road, Ayr KA6 6DX — MB ChB 1984 Cairo; FRCS Glas. 1995.

EL NAAMANI, Bilal 9 Clos Caradog, Meadow Farm, Llantwit Fardre, Pontypridd CF38 2DQ Tel: 01443 207306 — State Exam Bologna 1983. Prev: Regist. (Neurosurg.) Univ. Rome.

EL NAGGAR, Hany Mahmoud Ahmed West Herts Community NHS Trust, Hemel Hempstead General Hospital, Hillfield Road, Hemel Hempstead HP2 4AD Tel: 01442 287044 Fax: 01442 287590 Email: hnaggar@aol.com; 12 Crouch Hall Lane, Redbourn, St Albans AL3 7EQ Tel: 01582 626349 Fax: 01582 626346 Email: lnaggar@aol.com — MB BCh 1980 Ain Shams; MSc (Paediat.) Ain Shams 1984; MRCPI 1988; DCH RCP Lond. 1988; DCH RCPS Glas. 1988; FRCPCH Lond. 1997. Cons. Paediat. (Neonat.) Hemel Hempstead Gen. Hosp. Herts. Socs: Fell. Roy. Soc. Med. Prev: Cons. Paediat. Social Insur. Hosp., Riyadh; Regist. (Paediat.) Roy. Hosp. Sick Childr. & Qu. Mothers Hosp. Glas.

EL-NAGGAR, Mr Mamdouh Hussein Roushdi Amin North Riding Infirmary, Newport Road, Middlesbrough TS1 5JE Tel: 01642 232323; 193 Eagle Park, Middlesbrough TS8 9QU Tel: 01642 310495 — MB BCh 1976 Cairo; FRCS Ed. 1984; DO RCS Eng. 1983. Assoc. Specialist & Staff Grade (Ophth.) N. Riding Infirm. Middlesbrough. Prev: Regist. & Cons. Ophth., Saudi Arabia.

EL-NAGIEB, Omar Mohamed Panorama, The Horder Centre, St Johns Road, Crowborough TN6 1XP — MB BS 1978 Khartoum.

EL OAKLEY, Mr Reida Menshawe Department of Cardiac Surgery, Royal Brompton Hospital, Sydney St., London SW3 6NP Tel: 020 7352 8121 — MB BS 1983 Garyounis, Libya; FRCS Ed. 1989. Trainee Cardiothoracic Surg. Roy. Brompton Hosp. Lond. Prev: Tutor (Cardiothoracic Surg.) Manch. Univ.

EL-OMAR, Magdi Mounir Abdel Gabbar 8 Clos George Morgan, Morriston, Swansea SA6 6LZ — MB BS 1988 Lond.; BSc 1985; MRCP 1991. Specialist Regist. in Cardiol. Univ. of Wales, Cardiff. Prev: BHF Jun. research fell., Univ. of Wales; Clin. Research Fell. in Cardiol. John Radcliffe Hosp. Oxf.; Career Regist. Rotat. in Cardiol. W. Midl.

EL-OUSH, Mr Tarek Muhummad Munir 211 North Circular Road, Palmers Green, London N13 5JQ Tel: 020 8882 7907 — MB BCh 1969 Cairo; FRCS Ed. 1975.

EL-OUZI, El-Hadi Bashir 55 Hospital Close, Evington, Leicester LE5 4WQ — MB BCh 1985 Al Fateh; MRCPI 1990.

EL-RABAA, Mr Saleem Mohamed Ahmed 17 Friarwood Lane, Pontefract WF8 1DX Tel: 01977 600600 — MB BCh 1977 Cairo; FRCS Eng. 1989.

EL-RABIEY, Salah Salem Mohamed Hassan Department of Obstetrics & Gynaecology, St Mary's Hospital, Milton Road, Portsmouth PO3 6AD — MB BCh 1977 Ain Shams, Egypt; MRCOG 1993.

EL-RADHI, Abdul Sahib Queen Marys Hospital, Sidcup DA14 6LT Tel: 020 8302 2678 Fax: 020 8308 3069; 4 Denver Close, Orpington BR6 0SB Tel: 01689 607388 Fax: 020 8308 3069 Email: elradhi@hotmail.com — PhD Berlin 1971; State Exam Med. Berlin 1968; MRCP (UK) 1974; DCH Lond. 1971. (Berlin) Cons. (Paediat.) Qu. Mary's Hosp. Socs: BMA; MRCPCH. Prev: Kotka, Finland Regional Hosp.; Kuwat, Ahmadi Hosp.; Iraq, Al-Thawrah Hosp.

EL RAKSHY, Mohannad Mohamed Badr El Din Scunthorpe Hospital, Scunthorpe DN15 7BH Tel: 01724 282282 — MB BCh 1975 Cairo; FFA RCSI 1988.

EL-REFAEY, Hazem Ahmed Chelsea & Westminster Hospital, Academic Obstetrics & Gynaecology, Imperial College School of Medicine, 369 Fulham Road, London SW10 9NH Tel: 020 8846 7892 Email: h.elrefaey@ic.ac.uk; 63 Wavertree Road, Streatham, London SW2 3SL — MB BCh 1981 Cairo; MRCOG 1990; MD Aberd. 1994. Sen. Lect. (O & G) Chelsea & W.minster Hosp. Lond.; Hon. Cons. Prev: Sen. Regist. Univesity Coll. Hosp. Lond. 1994-1998; Regist. (O & G) Aberd. Roy. Infirm. 1990 - 1994.

EL-SADIG, Saad Eldin Ginawi 1106A Harrow Road, London NW10 5NL — MB BS 1983 Khartoum.

EL-SADIG, Siddig Ahmed B-Block, George Eliot Hospital, College St., Nuneaton CV10 7DJ — MB BS 1977 Khartoum; MRCOG 1991.

EL SAFADI, Noureddin 6 Ladysmith Drive, Ashton-under-Lyne OL6 9DL — LMS 1983 Santander.

EL SAFY, Ahmed Mohammad Ibrahim Eid Pallion Health Centre, Hylton Road, Sunderland SR4 7XF Tel: 0191 565 8598 — MB BCh 1978 Ain Shams. (Ain Shams) GP Sunderland.

EL-SAGHIER, Ashraf Ahmed Fouad 40 Silk House, Annesley Avenue, London NW9 5EE — MB ChB 1981 Alexandria.

EL-SAGHIR, Mohamed Aly 10 Broad Lane, Coventry CV5 7AB — MB BCh 1974 Ain Shams.

EL SAPAGH, Khaled Mahmoud Abouzeid 40 Grampian Road, Stirling FK7 9JP — MB BCh 1981 Zagazig; MRCOG 1995. Staff Grade (O & G) Stirling Roy. Infirm. Socs: Eur. Assn. Gyn. & Obst.; BSCCP; BHUS. Prev: Regist. (O & G) Liverp. Wom. Hosp.; SHO (O & G) P'boro. Dist. Hosp.

EL SARRAFF, Mustafa Riad Red Lea, 20 Liversedge Hall Lane, Liversedge WF15 7DB Tel: 01924 402176 — LRCP LRCS 1942 Ed.; LRCP LRCS Ed. LRFPS Glas. 1942; MRCGP 1952. SBStJ. Socs: Yorks. Soc. Anaesths. & BMA.

EL-SAYAD, Mr Ahmed Raouf Aly Hassan 7 Park Walk, Brierley Hill DY5 2HU — MB BCh 1978 Ain Shams; FRCS Ed. 1987.

EL-SAYED, F E H Abingdon Family Health Centre, 361-365 Queens Drive, Walton, Liverpool L4 8SJ Tel: 0151 226 1501 Fax: 0151 256 0593.

EL-SAYED, Mohammed Emadoddin Nasroddin Mohammed 55 St Catherine's Drive, Leeds LS13 2JY Tel: 0113 257 1424 — MB BCh 1975 Cairo; MRCPI 1984; FFR RCSI 1987; DMRT Eng. 1987.

EL SAYED, Tafida Fouad El Bahay 16 Avenue Lodge, Avenue Road, St Johns Wood, London NW8 6JA — MB BCh 1968 Ain Shams; FRCR 1977; DMRD Ain Shams 1971. (Ain Shams) Cons. Radiol. Watford Gen. Hosp.

EL-SAYEGH, Adil Yagoub Hussain 39 Birch Road, Rochdale OL12 9QB Tel: 01706 77777 — MB BS 1977 Khartoum; MRCOG 1988.

EL-SAYEH, Hany George Shehata Kalad 21 Gateside Road, London SW17 7NB — MB BS 1998 Lond.; MB BS Lond 1998.

EL-SERAFY, Nafisa Ibrahim 68 Union Road, Abergavenny NP7 7RH Tel: 01873 6139 — MB BCh 1964 Ain Shams; DGO 1969; MRCOG 1980.

EL-SERGANY, Mr Aly Yaser 7 Snowdrop Crescent, Beechwood, Runcorn WA7 4PL — MB BCh 1978 Ain Shams; FRCSI 1990.

EL-SHABOURY, Abdel-Hamid Mohamed Tower House, 1 Cefn Coed Road, Cardiff CF23 6AN Tel: 029 2075 2579; Hartlands, 18 The Grove, Merthyr Tydfil CF47 8YR Tel: 01685 722304 — MB BCh Wales 1958; MD Wales 1966; FRCP Lond. 1979; MRCP (UK) 1974; DCH Eng. 1961. (Cardiff) Cons. Phys. P. Chas. Hosp. Merthyr Tydfil; Hon. Clin. Teach. Univ. Wales Coll. Med. Cardiff. Socs: Med. Res. Soc.; Brit. Soc. Allergy & Clin. Immunol.; Brit. Diabetic Assn. Prev: Clin. Research Fell. Dept. Med. Univ. Wales Coll. Med. Cardiff; Sen. Regist. (Med.) Univ. Hosp. Wales Cardiff; Ho. Off. Roy. Infirm. Cardiff.

EL SHAFEI, Mr Hussein Mohammed Ali First Floor Flat, 7 Collingham Place, London SW5 0QE Tel: 020 7835 1250 — MB ChB 1983 Ain Shams; MB ChB Ain. Shams. 1978; MD Ain Shams 1988, MS 1983; FRCS (Cth) 1991; FRCS Ed. 1986; FRCS Glas. 1986.

EL-SHAMY, H Kamal (retired) Foxwood Lodge, Millington, York YO42 1UB — MB BCh Cairo 1954; FRCP Lond. 1993; FRCP Ed. 1976. M 1962; LMSSA Lond. 1963. Prev: Indep. Cons. Dermat. Purey Cust Nuffield Hosp., York & BUPA Belvedere Hosp. ScarBoro.

EL-SHARKAWI, Ahmed Mohamed Mostfa Singleton Hospital, Swansea SA2 8QA Tel: 01792 205666; 6 Northway Court, Bishopston, Swansea SA3 3JZ Tel: 0144 128 2289 — MB BCh 1969 Cairo; FRCR 1979. (Lond.) Cons. Radiother. & Oncol. Singleton Hosp. Swansea. Prev: SHO (Orthop. & Accid.) P.ss Margt. Hosp. Swindon; Regist. & Sen. Regist. (Radiother. & Oncol.) Cookridge Hosp. Leeds.

EL SHAZLY, Ahmed Hussein Ahmed Neath General Hospital, Penrhiwtyn, Neath SA11 2LQ — MB BCh 1977 Cairo; MRCOG 1991.

EL-SHAZLY, Mohamed Mohi El-Din Khaled Dept of Orthopaedics, University of Sheffield Clinical Sciences Centre, Northern General Hospital, Sheffield S5 7AU Tel: 0114 271 4478 Fax: 0114 261 9246 Email: m.shazly@sheffield.ac.uk; 64 School Green Lane, Fulwood, Sheffield S10 4GR Tel: 0114 230 1372 Fax: 0114 230 1372 Email: mes261285@aol.com — MB BCh 1979 Alexandria; BSc Alexandria 1975; MChOrth 1983. (Alexandria University) Sen. Lect. Sheff. Univ.; Hon. Cons. Orthop. Surg. N. Gen. Hosp. Sheff. Socs: Egyptian Orthop. Assn.; Fell. BOA; AO Alumni. Prev: Specialist Orthop. Surg. Alexandria Univ. Stud. Hosp.; Regist. (Orthop. Surg.) MusGr. Pk. Hosp. & Belf. City Hosp.; Sen. Regist. Ulster Hosp. Dundonald, Belf.

EL SHAZLY, Morad Abd El Megid Dorothy Pattison Hospital, Alumwell Close, Walsall WS2 9XH Tel: 01922 858000 Fax: 01922 858085 — MB ChB 1974 Alexandria; MRCS Eng. LRCP Lond. 1981; MRCPsych 1984; CEE 1995; FRCPsych 2000. (Alexandria Univ.) Cons. Adult Psychiat. Dorothy Pattison Hosp. Walsall; Hon. Clin. Sen. Lect., Univ. of Wolverhampton; Hon. Clin. Sen. Lect., Dept. of Neurosci.s, Univ. of Birm. Socs: MPS; BMA; BAP. Prev: Cons. Adult Psychiat. P.ss of Wales Hosp. Bridgend.; Cons. Psychiat. Bilbohall Hosp. Elgin.; Hon. Clin. Sen. Lect. (Ment. Health) Aberd. Univ.

EL-SHEIKH, Omar Abd-El Aziz Strensham Road Surgery, 4 Strensham Road, Balsall Heath, Birmingham B12 9RR Tel: 0121 440 3720 Fax: 0121 440 0591 — MB BCh 1975 Ain Shams; DRCOG 1988; DObst. RCPI 1988. (Ain Shams University Cairo Egypt)

EL-SHERBINI, Roushdy Mohammed 1 Northumberland Mansions, Luxborough St., London W1U 5BS Tel: 020 7486 8353 — MB ChB 1945 Cairo; DGO Cairo 1952; LMSSA Lond. 1973. (Cairo)

EL-SHERBINY, Samer Mohamed Flat 5, The Elms, 2 Church Lane, Chapel Allerton, Leeds LS7 4LY Tel: 0113 239 2274 Email: elsherbs@hotmail.com — MB ChB 1993 Sheff.; FRCS (Ed). Demonst. (Anat.) Sheff.; SHO (Ophth.) St. Jas. Hosp. Leeds. Prev: SHO (Neurol.) Roy. Hallamsh. Hosp. Sheff.; SHO (Ophth.) Glas. Roy. Infirm.

EL-SHESHTAWY NASR, Mohamed Hany Mohamed Prescot Medical Centre, 4 Atherton St., Prescot L34 5QN; Whiston Health Centre, Old Colliery Road, Whiston, Prescot L35 3SX Tel: 0151 430 6080 Fax: 0151 430 0470 — MB BCh 1972 Cairo; MRCOG 1982.

EL SHUNNAR, Mr Kassem Suliman Department of Neurosurgery, Derriford Hospital, Derriford Road, Plymouth PL6 8DH Tel: 01752 792542 Fax: 01752 784027; The Nuffield Hospital, Derriford Road, Plymouth PL6 8BG Tel: 01752 775861 Fax: 01752 768969 — MB BCh 1979 Ain Shams; FRCS Ed. (SN) 1990; FRCS Glas. 1987. Cons. Neurosurg. Derriford Hosp. Plymouth. Socs: Soc. Brit. Neurol. Surgs.; Plymouth Med. Soc. Prev: Sen. Regist. (Neurosurg.) OldCh. & St. Bart. Hosp. Lond.; Regist. (Neurosurg.) W.. Gen. Hosp. Edin. & Cork Regional Hosp.

EL SOBKY, Adel Barmoor Farm House, Barmoor, Morpeth NE61 6LB Tel: 01670 517445 — PhD Lond. 1979; MB BCh Cairo 1969; FRCPsych 1986, M 1974; DPM Eng. 1973. (Cairo) Cons. Psychiat. N. Tyneside Gen. Hosp. N. Shields. Prev: Cons. Psychiat. N. Tyneside Gen. Hosp. N. Shields.; Sen. Lect. Psychiat. Fac. Med. Univ. Leicester; Hon. Cons. Psychiat. Leicester Roy. Infirm.

EL TAHIR, Amin Mirghani Mohamed Department of Surgery, Medical School, Polwailh Building, Aberdeen AB9 2ZB Tel: 01224 685157 — MB BS 1988 Khartoum, Sudan; FRCS Glas. 1994. Research Fell. (Surg.) Med. Sch. Aberd.; Resid. Med. Off. Albyn Hosp. Aberd. Prev: SHO3 Aberd. Roy. Infirm.

EL TAHIR, Mr El Fatih Mirghani Mohammed Addenbrooke's NHS Trust, Hills Rd, Cambridge CB2 2QR Email: eltahir@hotmail.com; Email: eltahir@hotmail.com — MRCS Eng. LRCP Lond. 1987; FRCS (Gen. Surg.); MB BS Khartoum 1981; MSc (Med. Sci.); FRCS Glas. 1992. SPR (Gen. Surg.), Addinbrooke's NHS Trust, Hills Rd, Camb. Prev: SPR (Gen. Surg.) Stobhill Hosp., Glas.; SPR (Gen. Surg.) Roy. Infirm., Glas.; SPR (Gen. Surg.), Glas.

EL TAHIR, Mohamed Ali 1 Cherry Tree Avenue, Scarborough YO12 5DX — MB BS 1979 Khartoum; MB BS Khartoum Sudan 1979.

EL-TARANISSI, Mohamed Abdel Fattah Abdel Aziz University Hospital of Wales, Department of Obstetrics & Gynaecology, Heath Park, Cardiff CF14 4XW Tel: 029 20743376 & 0222 743235 — MB BCh 1976 Cairo; MRCGP 1986.

EL TAWIL, Helmy Mohamed Mohamed Gomaa 9 Keats Close, Barrow-in-Furness LA13 9TY — MB BCh 1967 Ain Shams.

EL TAYEB, Hassan Tohami Stepping Hill Hospital, Poplar Grove, Stockport SK2 Tel: 0161 483 1010; Green Meadows, 4 Clifton Drive, Marple, Stockport SK6 6PP Tel: 0161 427 7874 — MB ChB 1967 Cairo. Assoc. Specialist (Orthop.) N. W.. RHA. Socs: BMA; Manch. Med. Soc.

EL TERAIFI, Hassan Ali Ahmed Christie Hospital NHS Trust, Withington, Manchester M20 9BX Tel: 0161 446 3648 — MB ChB 1977 Baghdad; FRCPath 1997, MRCPath 1986; MIAC 1990. (Baghdad University Medical School) Cons. Path. & Hon. Clin. Teach. Univ. Manch. Socs: MRCPath.; BMA; Brit. Soc. Endocrinol. Prev: Sen. Regist. Gen. Hosp. & Midl. Centre for Neurosurg.

EL-TIGANI, Mohamed Abdel Hameed 429 Stanningley Road, Leeds LS13 4BL — MB BS 1979 Khartoum; MRCP (UK) 1990.

EL TREKI, Mr Rebhi Mohamed Hamad The Ipswich Hospital, Heath Road, Maternity Department, Ipswich IP4 5PD Tel: 01473 712233 Fax: 01473 703015 Email: v.m.e@ipsh-tr.anglox.nhs.uk; 7 Swinton Close, Ipswich IP2 9RL Tel: 01473 685555 Fax: 01473 703015 Email: rebhieltreki@btinternet.com — MB BCh 1974 Cairo; MRCOG 1983; FCOG 1998. (Univ. Cairo) Assoc. Specialist (O & G) Ipswich Hosp. Socs: Ipswich Clin. Soc.; OAA; E. Anglia Obst. & Gyn. Soc. Prev: Regist. (O & G) Ipswich Hosp.; SHO (O & G) William Harvey Hosp. Ashford & Mt. Vernon Hosp.

EL-ZEBDEH, Mr Mustafa Youssef Shabhan Royal Air Force Hospital, Wegberg BFPO 40 — MB BCh 1977 Ain Shams; FRCS Ed. 1989.

EL ZEINY, Hussein Mahmoud Sarwat 21 Cavendish Street, Coleridge Crescent, Colnbrook, Slough SL3 0QQ — MB BCh 1979 Ain Shams Egypt.

ELA, Mohamed Ahmed Aboul Pallion Health Centre, Hylton Road, Sunderland SR4 7XF Tel: 0191 565 8598 Fax: 0191 514 7467 — MB ChB 1965 Alexandria; LMSSA Lond. 1979; DLO Eng. 1976. (Alexandria)

ELAMIN, Mohd Elbagir Princess Alexandra Hospital, Hamstel Road, Harlow CM20 1QX — MB BS 1981 Kartoum; MB BS Kartoum, Sudan 1981; MRCP (UK) 1992.

ELANCHENNY, Nakanalini 109 St Benedicts Close, Tooting, London SW17 9NX Tel: 020 8767 8079 — MB BS 1989 Madras; MRCPsych 1995. Regist. (Psychiat. of Old Age) Char. Cross Hosp. Lond.

ELANCHENNY, Mr Ponniah 109 St Benedicts Close, Tooting, London SW17 9NX Tel: 020 8767 8079 — MB BS 1982 Colombo; FRCS Ed. 1991. Staff Grade (Ophth.) Whipps Cross Hosp. Lond.

ELASHA, Hassan Mohd Saeed c/o Dr Wallis Secretaruy, Pinderfieldds General Hosptial, Aberford Road, Wakefield WF1 4DG — MB BS 1986 Khartoum, Sudan; MB BS Khartoum 1986; MRCP (UK) 1992.

ELAZRAK, Senusi Mohamed Hussein 17 Rannock Avenue, London NW9 7JS — MB BCh 1980 Al-Fateh, Libya; MSc Lond. 1987; MRCP (UK) 1987.

ELBEIH, Nasser Mostafa Khairy Ibrahim 53 Ripley Avenue, Stockport SK2 7JS — MB BCh 1983 Ain Shams; MRCOG 1993.

ELBORN, Joseph Stuart Section of Respiratory Medicine, University of Wales College of Medicine, Llandough Hospital, Penarth CF64 2XX Tel: 01222 705187 Fax: 01222 708973 — MD 1989 Belf.; MB BCh BAO 1982; MRCP (UK) 1985. Lect. (Respirat. Med.) Univ. Wales Coll. Med. Llandough Hosp. Prev: Clin. Fell. (Respirat. Med.) City Hosp. Nottm.

ELBOROUGH, Aileen Yvonne The Health Centre, Queensway, Billingham TS23 2LA Tel: 01642 552700/552151 Fax: 01642 532908; 1 The Green, Elwick Village, Hartlepool TS27 3ED Tel: 01429 272382 — MB ChB 1987 Dundee; MRCGP 1992; DRCOG 1991.

ELCOCK, David Humphrey 50 Nevill Road, Rottingdean, Brighton BN2 7HG — MB BS 1987 Lond.; BA Camb. 1984; MRCP (UK) 1991.

ELCOCK, Martin The Cottage, Digbeth Lane, Claverly, Wolverhampton WV5 7BP — MB ChB 1992 Manch.

ELCOCK, Susan Kathryn Flat 60, Savoy Close, Harborne, Birmingham B32 2JA Tel: 0121 426 1985 — MB ChB 1998 Birm.; ChB Birm. 1998.

ELCOMB, Annie Margaret Nora Home Farm, Stoney Stoke, Wincanton BA9 8HY Tel: 0174 981 3204 — MB BS 1954 Lond. (Middlx.)

***ELCOMBE, Geraldine Mary** 10 Friar Close, Brighton BN1 6NR — MB ChB 1984 Bristol; MRCGP 1990.

ELDER, Alexander Gordon Salus Occupational Health & Safety Service, MacDougall House, Bellshill Hospital, Bellshill ML4 3JN Tel: 01698 845038 Fax: 01698 845687 Email: s.elder@salus.co.uk; 13 Craigbarnet Road, Milngavie, Glasgow G62 7RA — MB ChB 1985 Dundee; MFOM RCP Lond. 1996; MPH Glas. 1993; MRCGP 1989; DRCOG 1988. (Dundee) Cons. Occupat. Med. Lanarks. Occupat. Health & Safety Serv.; Hon. Sen. Clin. Lect. Univ. Glas. Socs: Soc. Occupat. Med. Prev: Cons. Occupat. Med. Gtr. Glas. Community & Ment. Health Servs. NHS Trust; Sen. Regist. (Occupat. Med.) Gtr. Glas. HB; Trainee GP Cleveland VTS.

ELDER, Andrew Hill Paddington Green Health Centre, 4 Princess Louise Close, London W2 1LQ Tel: 020 7887 1700 Fax: 020 7258 1943; 24 Muswell Road, London N10 2BG Tel: 020 8883 3399 Fax: 020 8883 8838 Email: aelder@claron.net — MB BS Lond. 1969; FRCGP 1992, M 1978; DObst RCOG 1971. (St. Mary's) Cons. GP & Primary Care Taristock Clinic; Hon. Sen. Lect. Roy. Free Hosp. Med. Sch. Socs: Balint Soc.; Assoc. Psychoanalytic Psychother. in NHS (APP); APP Mem. Primary Care Sect. Prev: Course Organiser St. Mary's & St. Chas. VTS 1985-93; Ho. Phys. St. Mary's Hosp. Lond.; Ho. Surg. (Obst.) Whittington Hosp. Lond.

ELDER, Andrew Murdoch Easter Calzeat House, Broughton, Biggar ML12 6HQ — MB BChir 1994 Camb.; MA Camb. 1992. (Univ. Camb.) SHO (Surg.) Lond. Prev: SHO (A & E) Qu. Mary's Univ. Hosp. Lond.; Ho. Off. (Surg.) Roy. Surrey Co. Hosp. Guildford; Ho. Off. (Med.) Roy. Free Hosp. Lond.

ELDER, Andrew Tyler Western General Hospital, Crewe Road, Edinburgh EH4 2XU Tel: 0131 537 2677; 8 Murrayfield Drive, Edinburgh EH12 6EB — MB ChB 1982 Ed.; BSc Ed. 1979, MB ChB 1982; FRCP Ed. 1994; MRCP (UK) 1986. Cons. Phys. & Hon. Sen. Lect. W.ern Gen. Hosp. Edin.

ELDER, Anne Margaret Walford Mill Medical Centre, Knobcrook Road, Wimborne BH21 1NL Tel: 01202 886999 Fax: 01202 840049; 41 Higher Blandford Road, Broadstone BH18 9AD — MB ChB Bristol 1988; DCH RCP Lond. 1990. Prev: Trainee GP Bournemouth FHSA.

ELDER, Catherine Tabor Bourn Hall Clinic, Bourn, Cambridge CB3 7TR Tel: 01954 717253 Fax: 01954 717274 Email: kayelder@compuserve.com — MB BChir 1981 Camb.; PhD (Experim. Path.) Colorado 1974; BSc (Hons.) Biochem. St. And. 1970. (St. And. & Camb.) Dir. of continuing ed Bourn Hall Clinic Camb.; Vis. Prof Danube Univ.of Krems Austria; Edr., Sec. & Admin. Alpha-Scientists in Reproductive Med.; Hon. Teachg. Fell. Univ. Leeds. Socs: Brit.Fertil..Soc; Fell of the Roy. Soc of Med. Prev: Research Fell. ICRF Lond.

ELDER, David Campbell Dudley Street Surgery, 11 Dudley Street, Grimsby DN31 2AW Tel: 01472 353303/4; 25 Fairway Court, Cleethorpes DN35 0NN Tel: 01472 812847 — MB ChB 1983 Leeds.

ELDER, Frederick Raymond Waterside Health Centre, Glendermolt Road, Londonderry BT47 6AU Tel: 028 7132 0100 — MB BCh BAO 1967 Belf.; MRCGP 1974.

ELDER, George Hill 37 Station Road, Llanishen, Cardiff CF14 5LS — MD Camb. 1973, MB 1963, BChir 1962; FRCP Lond. 1989; FRCPath 1980, M 1968. (St. Thos.) Prof. Med. Biochem. Univ. Wales Coll. Med. Cardiff; Hon. Cons. Med. Biochem. Univ. Hosp. Wales Cardiff. Prev: MRC Clin. Research Fell. Dept. Chem. Path. King's Coll. Hosp. Med. Sch. Lond.; Lect. (Chem. Path.) St. Geo. Hosp. Lond.

ELDER, Professor James Brown Room MO10, New Surgical Development, City General Hospital, London Road, Stoke-on-Trent ST4 6QG Tel: 01782 715444 Fax: 01782 747319; Sundown, Common Lane, Rough Close, Meir Heath, Stoke-on-Trent ST3 7ND Tel: 01782 388778 Email: pma14@keele.ac.uk — MB ChB Glas. 1962; FRCS Ed. 1966; FRCS Glas. 1983; FRCS Eng. 1966. (Glasgow) p/t Prof. Surg. Univ. Keele; Cons. Surg. N. Staffs. Hosp.Trust; Extern. Examr. Surg. Univ. of Birm.; Examr. Roy. Coll. of Phys.s & Surg.s of Glas.; Specialist in gastrointestinal Surg. & Surgic. Oncol. Socs: Brit. Soc. Gastroenterol. (Ex Counc.); Midl. Gastroenterol. Soc.; Surg. Research Soc. (Ex Counc.). Prev: Cons. Surg. & Reader (Surg.) Univ. Manch. Roy. Infirm. Manch.; Sen. Regist. (Gen. Surg.) W.. Infirm. Glas.

ELDER, John Balfour Market Cross Surgery, The Market Place, Corby Glen, Grantham NG33 4HN Tel: 01476 550056 Fax: 01476 550057 — MB ChB 1982 Liverp.; MRCGP 1987; DRCOG 1988; DCH RCP Lond. 1986. Socs: Assoc. Mem. Brit. Med. Acupunc. Soc. Prev: SHO (Paediat.) Odstock Hosp. Salisbury; SHO (ENT, Dermat. & O & G) Camb. Milit. Hosp. Aldershot.

ELDER, John William Hay, MBE (retired) Hillside, Annan DG12 6SA Tel: 01461 202222 — MB BChir 1950 Camb.; MRCGP 1959. Prev: Treasury Med. Off.

ELDER, Malcolm Robert Carradale Surgery, Carradale, Campbeltown PA28 6QG Tel: 01583 431376 Fax: 01583 431237; Ciaradh, Carradale, Campbeltown PA28 6SG Tel: 01583 431393 — MB ChB 1986 Dundee; MRCGP 1990. GP Princip. Carradale Surg. Prev: Assoc. GP Carradale & S.end Surgeries Argyll; Clin. Asst. (c/o the Elderly) Morningfield Hosp. Aberd.; Princip. GP, The Viaduct Med. Pract. Aberd.

ELDER, Mary Elizabeth (retired) 75 Montagu Court, Gosforth, Newcastle upon Tyne NE3 4JL Tel: 0191 285 1047 — MB BCh BAO 1951 Belf. Med. Off. DHSS. Prev: Clin. Asst. W. Chest Clinic Newc.

ELDER, Michael Lawrence Oakdene, 13 Thirsk Road, Yarm TS15 9HD — MB ChB 1975 Leeds; MRCGP 1979; DRCOG 1977.

ELDER, Professor Murdoch George (retired) Easter Calzeat House, Broughton, Biggar ML12 6HQ Tel: 01899 830359 Email: melder@eastercalzeat.fsnet.co.uk — DSc Lond. 1994; MD Ed. 1973, MB ChB 1961; FRCS Ed. 1968; FRCOG 1979, M 1968. Prev: Reader (O & G) Univ. Lond. at Char. Cross Hosp. Med. Sch. Lond.

ELDER, Olga Patricia Paula May 25 Glenavy Road, Lisburn BT28 3UT — MB BCh BAO 1978 Belf.; MFFP 1993; MRCGP 1983; DRCOG 1980. SCMO (Family Plann.) Lisburn.

ELDER, Peter McAllister (retired) Little Anchorage, Dervaig, Tobermory, Isle of Mull PA75 6QS Tel: 01688 400266 — MB BS 1939 Lond.; MRCS Eng. LRCP Lond. 1939. Prev: Med. Off. St. Eliz. Home & Sch. for Epileptics.

ELDER, Rachel Alison Hereward Group Practice, Exeter St., Bourne PE10 9XR Tel: 01778 393399 — BM 1982 Soton.; DFFP

1999; MRCGP 1987; DRCOG 1995. Clin. Asst. Dermat., Stamford and Rutland Hosp., Stamford, Lincs. Socs: Med. Equestrian Assn.

ELDER, Robert Lindsay (retired) 6 Chapelton Gardens, Bearsden, Glasgow G61 2DH Tel: 0141 942 6961 — MB ChB 1958 Glas. Prev: GP Glas.

ELDER, Rosemary Jane Highview Surgery, 20 Southgate Road, Potters Bar EN6 5DZ Tel: 01707 871980 Fax: 01707 871995 — MB ChB 1985 Dundee; MRCGP 1991; DCH RCP Lond. 1989.

ELDER, Sara Helen 37 Station Road, Llanishen, Cardiff CF14 5LS Tel: 029 2075 1876 — MB BS 1966 Lond. (Roy. Free) Prev: Ho. Surg. & Ho. Phys. Roy. Free Hosp. Lond.

ELDER, William Marriott, TD, CStJ (retired) 3 Stoneacre Gardens, Appleton, Warrington WA4 5ET Tel: 01925 267820 — MB ChB 1956 Glas.; MFOM RCP Lond. 1978. Area Med. Off. N. Nuclear Electric plc; ADC to HM the Qu. (TA); Hon. Phys. to HM the Qu.; DL; High Sheriff Gtr. Manch. Co. Prev: SHO (Metab. Dis.) Vict. Infirm. Glas.

ELDERKIN, Francis Michael (retired) Rose Barn, Rosley, Wigton CA7 8BZ Tel: 016973 42665 — MB BS (2nd cl. Hons.) Durh. 1956; FRCP Lond. 1975, M 1965; FRCP Ed. 1969, M 1959; FAAP (Hon.) 1989; DCH Eng. 1958. Prev: Cons. Paediat. Cumbld. Infirm. & City Matern. Hosp. Carlisle.

ELDERKIN, Rachel Ann Rose Barn, Rosley, Wigton CA7 8BZ — MB BS 1994 Lond.; BA Camb. 1991; MA Cantab 1994; DCH 1997. Prev: Paediat. Regist., Brisbane, Australia; Paediat. Regist. ChristCh., New Zealand; SHO (Paediat.) Derriford Hosp. Plymouth.

ELDERS, Mary Katherine 13 Lamplands Grange, Batley WF17 0LL — MB ChB 1991 Liverp.

ELDIN, Mr Ahmed Mahmood Ibrahim Sharat 3 Hyde House, Basing Road, Banstead SM7 2BR — MB BCh 1979 Cairo; FRCS Glas. 1988.

ELDON, Elizabeth Anne (retired) Skers Farm, Brook, Lyndhurst SO43 7HD — MB Camb. 1954, BChir 1953. Sen. Med. Off. (Community Med.) Soton. & S.W. Hants. Health Dist. (T). Prev: Ho. Surg. Eliz. G. Anderson Hosp.

ELDON, Helen Margaret Curzon Avenue Surgery, 74 Curzon Avenue, Ponders End, Enfield EN3 4UE Tel: 020 8364 7846 Fax: 020 8443 0503; 5 Gordon Hill, Enfield EN2 0QP — MB BS 1991 Lond.; MRCGP 1995; DFFP 1994; DCH RCP Lond. 1994. Prev: Trainee GP Carlton Hse. Surg. Enfield.

ELDON, Joseph (retired) 10 Old Church Lane, Aghalee, Craigavon BT67 0EB — MB BCh BAO 1931 Belf.

ELDRED, Anne Elizabeth Derwent House Surgery, Derwent House, Wakefield Road, Cockermouth CA13 0HZ; Westworth, Papcastle, Cockermouth CA13 0LB Tel: 01900 828636 — MB BChir 1982 Camb.; MA Camb. 1982; MRCP (UK) 1987; MRCGP (Dist.) 1986; DCH RCP Lond. 1985. Prev: Trainee GP Vict. VTS; SHO Freeman Hosp. Newc.

ELDRED, James Barry Strafford House, Gilroyd Lane, Stainborough, Barnsley S75 3EG — MB BS 1996 Lond.; BSc 1994. (St Barts) SHO Psych.

ELDRED, John Michael West Cumberland Hospital, Whitehaven CA28 8JG Tel: 01946 693181; Westworth, Papcastle, Cockermouth CA13 0LB Tel: 01900 828636 — MB BChir 1983 Camb.; MA Camb. 1982; MRCOG 1988; DRCOG 1984. Cons. O & G W.. Cumbld. Hosp. Prev: Sen. Regist. (O & G) N.. Region; Regist. (O & G) Newc. u. Tyne; SHO (Neonatol.) St. Thos. Hosp. Lond.

ELDRED, Kate Frances 20 Broadway Gardens, Peterborough PE1 4DU — MB BS 1991 Newc.

ELDRIDGE, Andrew George 33 Bronescombe Avenue, Bishopsteignton, Teignmouth TQ14 9SR — MB BS 1992 Lond.

ELDRIDGE, Andrew James The Anaesthetic Department, Queen Alexandra Hospital, Cosham, Portsmouth Tel: 023 92 286298 Fax: 023 92 286690 — MB BS 1986 Lond.; BSc 1983; FRCA 1992. (St Thomas' Hospital London) Cons. Anaesth. Qu. Alexandra Hosp. Cosham Portsmouth. Prev: Sen. Regist. (Anaesth.) Nuffield Dept. Anaesth. John Radcliffe Hosp. Oxf.

ELDRIDGE, Christopher Daniel 115 Wynchgate, London N14 6RJ — MB BS 1998 Lond.; MB BS Lond 1998.

ELDRIDGE, Harold Wilfred (retired) 33 Bronescombe Avenue, Bishopsteighton, Teignmouth TQ14 9SR Tel: 01626 775527 — MRCS Eng. LRCP Lond. 1942. Prev: Med. Off. Prisons Dept. (Home Office).

ELDRIDGE, Janice Ann Hollies Surgery, Elbow Lane, Liverpool L37 4AF Tel: 01704 877600 Fax: 01704 833811; 15 Spruce Way, Formby, Liverpool L37 2YF — MB ChB 1978 Glas.; FFA RCS Eng. 1986; MRCGP 1982; DCH RCP Lond. 1981; DRCOG 1980. Prev: Trainee GP Soton. VTS; Regist. (Anaesth.) Cardiff; Clin. Med. Off. Centr. Notts. HA.

ELDRIDGE, Mr Jonathan Douglas James 91 Sefton Park Road, Bristol BS7 9AW — MB ChB 1990 Bristol; FRCS Eng. 1994. (Bristol) Specialist Regist. & J. Lect. Rotat. SW. Orthop. & Trauma.

ELDRIDGE, Julian Raymond Littlerigg, Sweden Bridge Lane, Ambleside LA22 9EX Tel: 0153 94 32387 — MB ChB 1968 Liverp.

ELDRIDGE, Mary Graham (retired) 46 Chalfont Road, Colchester CO4 4NY Tel: 01206 841435 — MB BS 1950 Lond.; FRCOG 1974, M 1958.

ELDRIDGE, Michelle 31 The Wynd, Gosforth, Newcastle upon Tyne NE3 4LA — MB ChB 1996 Leeds. SHO Med. Rotat. York Dist. Hosp. Prev: Ho. Off. (Med.) Leeds Gen. Infimary; Ho. Off. (Surg.) Halifax Roy. Infirm.

ELDRIDGE, Mr Paul Richard Walton Centre for Neurology & Neurosurgery, Longmore Lane, Liverpool L9 7LJ Tel: 0151 525 3611 Fax: 0151 529 5509; 15 Spruce Way, Formby, Liverpool L37 2YF — MB BChir 1981 Camb.; MA Camb. 1981, MChir 1993; FRCS Eng. 1985. (Cambridge University and St Thomas's Hospital) Cons. Neurosurg. Walton Centre for Neurol. & Neurosurg. Liverp.; Hon. Sen. Lect. Liverp. Univ. Socs: Soc. Brit. Neurol. Surgs.; Intens. Care Soc.

ELDRIDGE, Sara Bridget Jane Warren cottage, The Warren, Ashtead KT21 2SP — MB BS 1989 Lond.

ELEFTHERIADIS, Haralabos Huddersfield Royal Infirmary, Staff Residence (N.H.), Acre St., Huddersfield HD3 3EA — Ptychio Iatrikes 1989 Thessalonika.

ELEMENT, Paul The Limes Medical Centre, 8-12 Hodge Road, Worsley, Manchester M28 3AT; 2 Simpson Grove, Boothstown, Worsley, Manchester M28 1LY Tel: 0161 799 7067 Fax: 0161 703 8670 — MB ChB 1967 Manch.; MF Hom. 1979. Socs: Fac. Homoeop. Lond. (Manch. Area Respresen.); Brit. Med. Acupunct. Soc.

ELEWA, Mr Akil Abdel-El-Hamid Mohamed 13 Cedar Avenue, St Leonards, Ringwood BH24 2QF Tel: 01202 872114 — MB BCh 1976 Ain Shams; MS (Urol.) Ain Shams 1980, MB BCh (Hons.) 1976; FRCS Ed. 1983. Staff Grade Surg. Roy. Bournemouth Hosp.

ELEY, Elizabeth Anne 5 Morgan Cl, Saltford, Bristol, Bristol BS31 3LN — MB BS 1997 Lond.

ELEY, Nicola Anne The Surgery, Finings Road, Lane End, High Wycombe HP14 3ES Tel: 01494 881209 — BM 1986 Soton.; MRCGP 1992. (Soton.) Socs: BMA. Prev: GP VTS Worcester; SHO (Ophth. & Emerg. Med.) Worcester.

ELFES, Christopher John Swanage Health Centre, Railway Station Approach, Station Road, Swanage BH19 1HB Tel: 01929 422231 — BM 1988 Soton.; MRCGP (Hons.) 1996; DCH RCP Lond. 1995; DFFP 1995; DRCOG 1993. (Soton.)

ELFORD, Julian Department of Radiology, Royal Hampshire County Hospital, Romsey Road, Winchester SO22 5DG Tel: 01962 825690 — MB BS 1990 Lond.; BSc (Hons.) Lond 1987; MRCP (UK) 1994; FRCR 1998. (St. Bart.) Cons. Radiologist. Socs: Med. Defence Union; BMA; BSIR.

ELFORD, Martin Terence 14 Halford Court, Green Lane, Chessington KT9 2EE Tel: 020 8397 8668 — MB BS 1974 Lond.; MRCS Eng. LRCP Lond. 1974; MRCGP 1978; DRCOG 1976. (Lond. Hosp.)

ELGADI, Saleh Mohamed Ahmed Department of Genitourinary Medicine, Cardiff Royal Infirmary, Newport Road, Cardiff CF24 0SZ — MB BCh 1982 Al Fateh; MRCPI 1990; Dip. GU Med. Soc. Apoth. Lond. 1992. Prev: Regist. (Chest. Med.) City Hosp. Edin.

ELGAMMAL, Suzanne Flat 0/2, 84 Stock St., Paisley PA2 6NH — MB ChB 1997 Glas.

ELGAR, Dennis Edward (retired) 102 Roseneath Road, London SW11 6AQ Tel: 020 924 7673 — MB BChir Camb. 1962; MChir Camb. 1967; FRCS Eng. 1967. Prev: Regist. (Surg.) W.m. Hosp.

ELGAR, Joseph Daniel 18 Park Ave, London NW11 7SJ Tel: 020 8458 9074 — State Exam Med 1964 Sofia. Clin. Asst. (Psychiat. & Psychother.) Roy. Free NHS Trust Hosp. & W. Hamstead Day Hosp. Lond. Prev: Staff Psychiat. Hadassah Med. Sch. & Talbieh Psychiat. Hosp. Jerusalem; Head. Dept. Kfar Shaul Psychiat. Hosp. Jerusalem.

ELGAR, Richard John 50 Kedleston Road, Derby DE22 1GW Tel: 01332 44895 — MB BS 1973 Lond.; MRCS Eng. LRCP Lond. 1973; MRCGP 1980; DObst RCOG 1976. Prev: Trainee Gen. Pract. Derby Vocational Train. Scheme; Ho. Surg. Genito-Urin. Surg. Unit & Ho. Phys. Geriat. Unit Char.; Cross Hosp. Lond.

ELGON, Jack Jeans Achiaobetia (Surgery), 29 Bunbury Road, Northfield, Birmingham B31 2DR Tel: 0121 477 3800; 209 Hole Lane, Birmingham B31 2DA — MB ChB 1974 Bristol.

ELGOOD, Frank Reginald Michael (retired) Castle Moat House, 18 Drury Lane, Lincoln LN1 3BN Tel: 01522 525892 — BM BCh 1944 Oxf.; MA, DM Oxf 1951; FRCP Ed. 1982; DCH Eng. 1945. Cons. Paediat. Lincoln Hosp. Gp. Prev: Cons. Paediat. Centr. Kent, Medway & Gravesend & Dartford Hosp. Gps.

ELHIBIR, Elwathig Idris Ashton House Hospital, Columbia Road, Oxton, Wirral; 25 Templemore Road, Birkenhead CH43 2HB — MB BCh 1980 Cairo; MB BCh Cairo, Egypt 1980.

ELIA, Mumtaz Hamid Department of Clinical Oncology, Raigmore Hospital, Old Perth Road, Inverness IV2 3UJ — MB ChB 1969 Baghdad; FRCR 1978; DMRT Eng. 1977. (Medical School Baghdad Univ Iraq) Cons. Clin. Oncol. Raigmore Hosp. Inverness; Dir. N. Scotl. Cancer Regist. Raigmore Hosp. Inverness; Hon. Sen. Lect. Aberd. Univ. Prev: Sen. Regist. (Radiother.) Newc. Gen. Hosp.; Regist. (Radiother.) Roy. Free Hosp. Lond.; Clin. Asst. Roy. Marsden Hosp. Lond. & Surrey.

ELIAD, Rami Albert Garston Medical Centre, 6a North Western Avenue, Watford WD25 9GP Tel: 01923 672086 Fax: 01923 681980 — MB ChB 1985 Sheff.

ELIADES, Anne-Marie 46 Stuart Way, Windsor SL4 5NT — MB BCh 1998 Wales. PRHO Gen. Med. & Nephrol., Wrexham Maelor Hosp. Prev: PRHO Gen. Surg. & Urol. Ysbyty Gwynedd, Bangor.

ELIAN, Marta Regional Centre for Neurology & Neurosurgery, Oldchurch Hospital, Romford Tel: 01708 46090 ext. 3106; 15 Chalcot Crescent, London NW1 Tel: 020 7722 5508 — MD 1958 Hebrew Univ. Jerusalem; MD Hebrew U. Jerusalem 1958. (Hadassa Med. Sch.) Cons. Clin. Neurophysiol. OldCh. Hosp. Romford. Socs: Assoc. Brit. Clin. Neurophysiols & ASMT; Assn. Brit. Neurol. Prev: Chief Phys. Dept. Neurol. & Seizure Clin. Beilinson Med. Center; Israel; Sen. Lect. (Neurol.) Tel-Aviv Med. Sch.

ELIAS, Ahmed Hamid St Peters Hospital, Guildford Road, Chertsey KT16 0PZ Tel: 01932 872000 Fax: 01932 874757; Amari House, Onslow Road, Sunningdale, Ascot SL5 0HW — MB BS 1980 Khartoum; FRCOG 2001 Lond.; MRCOG 1989. Cons. O & G Ashford & St. Peter's Hosps. NHS Trust. Socs: Brit. Soc. Colpos. & Cerv. Path.; Roy. Soc. Med. Prev: Sen. Regist. (O & G) Qu. Charlotte's & Chelsea Hosp. Lond.; Sen. Regist. (O & G) P.ss Anne Hosp. Soton.

ELIAS, David Andrew 12 South Lodge, Circus Road, London NW8 9ER — MB BS 1992 Lond.

ELIAS, Elwyn Queen Elizabeth Hospital, Edgbaston, Birmingham B15 2TH Tel: 0121 627 2416 Fax: 0121 627 2449 — MB BS 1968 Lond.; BSc (Physiol.) Lond. 1965, MD 1984; FRCP (UK) 1981, M 1970. (Guy's) Cons. Phys. Qu. Eliz. Hosp. Med. Centre Birm. Prev: Lect. (Med.) Roy. Free Hosp. Lond.; Regist. (Med.) Hammersmith Hosp. Lond.

ELIAS, Mr John Surgical Department, Neath General Hospital, Pant-Yr-Neol, Neath SA11 2LQ Tel: 01639 641161 — MB BS Lond. 1964; FRCS Eng. 1970; MRCS Eng. LRCP Lond. 1963. (St. Geo.) Cons. Surg. (Gen. Surg.) Neath Gen. Hosp.

ELIAS, Julian Albert 127 Harley Street, London W1N 1DJ Tel: 020 7935 9108 Fax: 020 7935 1427; Gallery House, 139 Burbage Road, London SE21 7AF Tel: 020 7274 1804 Fax: 020 7274 1804 — MRCS Eng. LRCP Lond. 1965; FRCOG 1983, M 1970; DObst 1966; MFFP 1993. (St. Mary's) Cons. O & G Greenwich Health Care Trust. Socs: Fell. Roy. Soc. Med.; Pres. S.E. Gyn. Soc.; Counc. Europ. Assn. Gyn. & Obst. Prev: Sen. Regist. (O & G) King's Coll. Hosp. Lond.; RCOG Research Fell. Kings Coll. Hosp. Lond.; Resid. Med. Off. Samarit. Hosp. Wom. Lond.

ELIAS, Mary McAlpine (retired) Westview, 55 Orchard Road, Seer Green, Beaconsfield HP9 2XH Tel: 01494 671984 Fax: 01494 671984 — MRCS Eng. LRCP Lond. 1948. Prev: Sen. Med. Off. (Child Health) Mid-Surrey.

ELIAS, Professor Peter Stefan (retired) 38 Fernhall Drive, Redbridge, Ilford IG4 5BW — MB BS 1952 Lond.; BSc (Hons.) Lond. 1945; MRCS Eng. LRCP Lond. 1952; MFPHM 1972; MRSC 1975; CChem 1975. Indep. Cons. Pub. Health & Toxicol. Germany; Vice-Chairm. EEC Scientif. Comm. for Food; Chairm. EEC Scientif. Comm. for Animal Nutrit. Prev: Hon. Prof. Univ. Hohenheim-Stuttgart Fac. Gen. & Appl. Nat. Scs. 1982.

ELIAS, Roger Garrett Sea Road Surgery, 39-41 Sea Road, Bexhill-on-Sea TN40 1JJ Tel: 01424 211616 Fax: 01424 733950; 64 Collington Avenue, Bexhill-on-Sea TN39 3RA — MB BS 1978 Lond.; BSc (Psychol.) Lond. 1975. (King's Coll. Hosp.)

ELIAS, Spiro André 3 Woodstock Gardens, Goodmayes, Ilford IG3 9SZ — MRCS Eng. LRCP Lond. 1970.

ELIAS, Trevor Hywel 9 Pine Court, Chaseville Park Road, Winchmore Hill, London N21 1PR Tel: 020 8360 3526 — MB BS 1946 Lond.; D.P.H. 1949; MCRS Eng., LRCP Lond. 1943. (Univ. Coll. Hosp.) Clin. Med. Off. Haringey, N. Lond. Prev: Asst. M.O.H. Middlx. No. 3 Area; Asst. M.O.H. Blackburn, Ipswich & Worcester.

ELIAS-JONES, Alun Cameron Childrens Hospital, Leicester Royal Infirmary, Havelock St., Leicester LE1 5WW Tel: 0116 585470; 11 Nursery End, Brook Lane, Nanpantan Road, Loughborough LE11 3RB Tel: 01509 211904 — MB ChB 1978 Bristol; LLM Cardiff 1996; BSc Bristol 1972; MBA Keele 1993; FRCP Lond. 1995; MRCP (UK) 1983; FRCPCH 1997; DCH RCP Lond. 1982; DRCOG 1980. (Univ. Bristol) Clin. Dir. Leicester Childr. Hosp.; Cons. Neonatologist Leicester Gen. Hosp. Socs: Neonat. Soc.; Paediat. Research Soc.; Paediat. Intens. Care Soc. Prev: Cons. Paediat. & Neonat. Leicester Gen. Hosp. & Leic. Roy. Infirm.; Sen. Regist. (Paediat.) City & Univ. Hosps. Nottm.; Regist. Hosp. for Sick Childr. Gt. Ormond St. Lond.

ELIAS-JONES, John Henry Alexandra Hospital, Woodrow, Redditch B98 4UB Tel: 01527 503030; Moorgreen Hall, Weatheroak, Alvechurch, Birmingham B48 7DZ Tel: 01564 824691 Fax: 01564 824691 — MB ChB 1973 Glas.; MRCOG 1981. (Glas.) Cons. O & G Alexandra Hosp. Redditch. Socs: (Ex-Treas.) Brit. Soc. Colposcopy & Cervial Path.; (Ex-Comm.) Brit. Assn. Day Surg.; Brit. Menopause Soc. Prev: Lect. & Sen. Regist. (O & G) Camb. Univ.

ELIAS-JONES, Margaret Cameron Blair (retired) 15C Mains Avenue, Giffnock, Glasgow G46 6QY Tel: 0141 638 8049 — 1129600. Prev: Med. Off. Glas. Family Plann. Assn.

ELIATAMBY, Samuel Ram-Kumar 14 Stanhope Road, London SW16 2DY — MB ChB 1981 Birm.

ELIOPOULOS, Fotios Basil Blundel Lodge, Blundel Lane, Stoke D'Abernon, Cobham KT11 2SP — Ptychio Iatrikes 1963 Athens.

ELIOT, Brian Wilford (retired) The Penthouse, Dallington Court, Dallington Park Road, Northampton NN5 7AA Fax: 01604 759366 — MB BS 1967 Lond.; MRCS Eng. LRCP Lond. 1967; FRCOG 1984, M 1971; DObst RCOG 1969. Prev: Cons. O & G N.ampton Gen. Hosp.

ELITHORN, Alick 71 Rose Hill, Oxford OX4 4JR Tel: 01865 777312 Fax: 01865 433050 Email: a.elithorn@ucl.ac.uk; 71 Rose Hill, Oxford OX4 4JR Tel: 01865 777317 Fax: 01865 433050 Email: a.elithorn@ntpworld.com — MB BChir 1946 Camb.; MA, MD Camb. 1956; FRCP Lond. 1973, M 1946; DPM Lond. 1950; FBPsS. (Univ. Coll. Hosp.) Hon. Cons. Psychiat. (Adult & Child Psychiat.) Roy. Free Hosp. Lond. & Nat. Hosp Dis. Maida Vale; Hon. Cons. Psychotherapist. Roy. Free Hosp. Lond.; Hon. Cons. Phys. Nat. Hosp. for Neurol. & Neurosurg.; Hon. Lect., Inst. of Neurol.; Hon Cons Phys. Nat. Hosp. for Neurol. and Neurosurg.; Hon Lec Inst. of Neurol. Socs: Fell. Brit. Psychol. Soc. (Mem. Occupat. Sect.); Experim. Psychol. Soc.; Brit. Computer Soc. Prev: Extern. Scientif. Staff Med. Research Counc.; Lect. (Psychopath.) Univ. Reading; Specialist Neuropsychiat. RAF.

ELIZABETH, Jimmy Eric 61 Weeping Cross, Stafford ST17 0DQ — MB ChB 1978 Liverp.; FRCP Lond. 1997; MRCP (UK) 1984; T(M) 1991. Cons. Phys. (Med. & c/o the Elderly) Staffs.

ELJAMEL, Mr Muftah Salem Tayside University Hospitals, Ninewell Hospital & Medical School, Dundee DD1 9SY Tel: 01382 660111 Fax: 01382 496202 Email: m.s.eljamel@dundee.ac.uk; 17 Terra Road, Plainville CT 06062, USA Tel: 00 1 860 7474697 Fax: 00 1 860 7474697 — MB BCh 1982 Al Fateh, Libya; MD Liverp. 1992; FRCS (SN) 1992; FRCSI 1986. Cons. Neurosurg. Tayside Univ. Hosp.; Hon. Sen. Lect. & Dept. Head Univ. Dundee. Socs: Internat. Assn. Study Pain; Scott. Assn. Neurol. & Neurosurg. (SANS); N. Amer. Skull Base Soc. Prev: Clin. Fell. Univ. Connecticut, USA; Sen. Regist. Dub.; Regist. Liverp.

ELKABIR, Mr Jeremy Joseph The Priory, Church Lane, Charlbury, Oxford OX7 3PX Tel: 01608 810417 — MB BS 1990 Lond.; FRCS

Eng. 1994. Regist. Rotat. (Urol.) Char. Cross Hosp. Lond. Prev: SHO Rotat. (Surg.) N.wick Pk. Hosp. & Clin. Research Centre Lond.; Demonst. (Anat.) Univ. Oxf.; SHO (A & E) W.m. Hosp. Lond.

ELKELES, Robert Samuel St. Mary's Hospital, Praed St., London W2 1NY Tel: 020 7886 6037 Fax: 020 7886 6037; The Consulting Rooms, Wellington Hospital, Wellington Place, London NW8 9LE Tel: 020 7586 3213 Fax: 020 7483 0297 — MB BS 1965 Lond.; MD Lond. 1974; FRCP Lond. 1981, M 1967; MRCS Eng. LRCP Lond. 1965. (Middlx) Cons. Phys. St. Mary's Hosp. Lond.; Cons. Phys. K. Edwd. VII Hosp. for Offs. Lond.; (Diabetes). Socs: Brit. Diabetic Assn. (Ex-Chairm. Nutrit. Sub-comm. & Mem. Comm. Med. & Scientif. Sect.); Brit. Hyperlipid. Assn. Prev: Cons. Phys. N.wick Pk. Hosp. & Clin Research Centre; Lect. (Med.) Univ. Hosp. Wales Cardiff; Regist. (Med.) Hammersmith Hosp. Lond.

ELKHOLY, Mmohamed El Shazly Mohamed 18 Beechwood, Uplands, Swansea SA2 0HL — MB BCh 1958 Cairo; FFARCSI 1975.

ELKIN, Albert Cecil (retired) 18 Hillside Road, Burnham-on-Crouch CM0 8EY Tel: 01621 782202 — MB BS 1929 Lond.; MRCS Eng. LRCP Lond. 1929. Prev: Cons. (Physical Med.) Finchley Memor. Hosp.

ELKIN, Sarah Louise North West Thames Rotation in Respiratory and General Medicine, London Email: s.elkin@doctors.org.uk — MB BS 1991 Lond.; MCSP 1986; MRCP (UK) 1995. Regist. (Respirat. & Gen. Med.) N. W. Thames.

ELKIN, Tristan 61 Strode Road, Street BA16 0DJ — MB ChB 1996 Liverp.

ELKINGTON, Andrew George Fiennes 67 Nassau Road, London SW13 9QG — MB BS 1997 Lond.

ELKINGTON, Professor Andrew Robert, CBE Little Court, Crawley, Winchester SO21 2PU Tel: 01962 776365 Fax: 01962 776842 — MB BChir Camb. 1961; MA Camb. 1970; FRCS Eng. 1969; FRCOphth 1988; DO Eng. 1968; DObst RCOG 1965. (Camb. & St. Thos.) Emerit. Prof. Ophth. Univ. Soton. Socs: Fell. Roy. Soc. Med. (Ex-Pres. Sect. Ophth.).; Fell. (Ex-Pres.) Roy. Coll. Ophth.; Oxf. Ophth. Congr. Prev: Prof. Ophth. Soton. Univ. & Cons. Ophth. Soton. Eye Unit Soton. Gen. Hosp.; RSM Europ. Trav. Profess. 1993; Sen. Lect. (Ophth.) Soton. Univ.

ELKINGTON, Helena Mary Guy's King's & St Thomas, Dept of General Practice & Primary Care, Cutcombe Road, London SE5 9RJ Tel: 0207 848 5683 Fax: 0207 848 5686 — BM BCh 1994 Oxf.; MRCGP 1999; DROG 1997; DCHR RCP Lond. 1996. Gp Asst., Walworth Rd. Surg., Lond. Prev: GP at Lond. Acad. Train. Scheme; GP Trainee Sonnig Community Health Centre, berks; GP Train. Scheme, Roy. Berks. Hosp., Reading.

ELKINGTON, John Richard Stephen 67 Nassau Road, London SW13 9QG Tel: 020 8748 5531 — MB ChB 1990 Aberd.

ELKINGTON, Mr Julian Scott BUPA Murrayfield Hospital, Thingwall, Wirral CH61 1AU Tel: 0151 648 7000; Sunningdale, Feather Lane, Heswall, Wirral CH60 4RL Tel: 0151 342 1490 — MB BChir 1958 Camb.; MA Camb. 1963; FRCS Ed. 1966; FRCS Eng. 1966. (Middlx) Cons. Surg. Arrowe Pk. Hosp. Wirral; Assoc. Med. Dir. Wirral Hosp. NHS Trust. Socs: Fell. Assn. Surg.; BMA (Ex-Mem. Counc.).; Assn. Endoscopic Surgs. Prev: RSO Brompton Hosp.; Ho. Surg. (Orthop.) Middlx. Hosp.

ELKINGTON, Nicholas Montague St. Thomas' Hospital, Lambeth Palace Road, London SE1 7EH Tel: 020 7928 9292; 15B Earlsfield Road, London SW18 3DB — MB BS 1992 Lond.; BSc (Hons.) Anat. Lond. 1989. (UMDS (St. Thos. Campus)) SHO (O & G) St. Thos. Hosp. Lond. Socs: Roy. Coll. Obst. & Gyn.; BMA. Prev: SHO (A & E) Soton. Gen. Hosp.; SHO (O & G) N. Hants. Hosp. Basingstoke.

***ELKINGTON, Paul Timothy George** Little Court, Crawley, Winchester SO21 2PU — BM BCh 1994 Oxf.; MRCP 1997.

ELKINGTON, Stephen George (retired) 67 Nassau Road, Barnes, London SW13 9QG Tel: 020 8748 5531 — MB BChir 1956 Camb.; MA Camb. 1961, BA (cl. 1 Pts. 1 & 2 Nat. Sc. Trip.) 1953; MD Camb. 1966; FRCP Lond. 1974, M 1958. Med. Chairm. Pens. Appeal Tribunals; Med. Panel Mem., The Appeals Serv. Prev: Cons. Phys. King's Coll. Hosp. Lond. & Brook Memor. Hosp. Woolwich.

ELKINS, Andrew Victor 38 Meadow Drive, Lindfield, Haywards Heath RH16 2RR — MB BS 1990 Lond.; MRCP (UK) 1994. Med. Regist. (Intens. Care) St. Thos. Hosp. Lond.

ELKOUBY, Karen c/o Mrs Lilli Gooch, 52 Roading Rd., London E5 0DW — State Exam Med 1992 Frankfurt; MD Frankfurt 1993.

***ELKS, Kevin Nigel** 30 Smithy Carr Avenue, Burncross, Sheffield S35 2ZQ — MB ChB 1986 Sheff.

ELL, Professor Peter Josef Institute of Nuclear Medicine, University College & Middlesex School of Medicine, Mortimer St., London W1N 8AA Tel: 020 7380 9424, 020 7631 1066 Fax: 020 7436 0603 Email: p.ell@ucmed.ucl.ac.uk; 39 Basing Hill, London NW11 8TG Tel: 020 8458 1384 — Med. Lic. Lisbon, Portugal 1969; MSc Lond. 1972; MD Lisbon 1986; FRCP Lond. 1990; MRCP (UK) 1983; FRCR 1984. (Lond.) Prof. & Hon. Cons., Univ. Coll. & Middlsex Sch. of Med.; Dir. Inst. Nuclear Med. Univ. Coll. & Middlx. Sch. Med.; Head Bloomsbury Dist. Nuclear Med. Estab. Chair Holder Univ. Lond. 1967. Socs: Pres. Europ. Assoc. Nuclear Med.; Corr. Mem. Finnish & Swiss Soc. Nuclear Med.; Founder Mem. Europ. Assn. Nucl. Med. Prev: Sen. Lect. Middlx. Hosp. Med. Sch. Lond.

ELL, Mr Stephen Robert Academic Department of Otolaryngology, Head & Neck Surgery, Hull Royal Infirmary, Anlaby Road, Hull HU3 2JZ Tel: 01482 674456 Fax: 01482 675539; 46 Manor Road, Swanland, North Ferriby HU14 3PB — MB BS 1985 Lond.; BSc (Hons.) Lond. 1982; FRCS (Orl.) 1995; FRCS Eng. 1990. (St. Bart.) Sen. Lect. (Otolaryngol.) Univ. Hull. Socs: Fell. Roy. Soc. Med. (Sect. Otol. & Laryngol.).

ELLA, Wendy Ann Southend General Hospital, Southend, Southend-on-Sea Tel: 01702 435555; 9 The Rowans, Billericay CM11 2PB — MB BS 1997 Lond.; BSc Hons 1989. SHO Med. Rotat.

ELLAHEE, Najab Flat 3K Portman Mansions, Chiltern St., London W1U 5AH — MB BS 1994 Lond.

ELLAHI, Rabia Tasneem Greenhills Health Centre, 20 Greenhills Square, E. Kilbride, Glasgow G75 8TT — MB ChB 1982 Glas.; MFFP 1993; MRCGP 1986; DCCH RCP Ed. 1991; DRCOG 1985. Community Child Health Off. Lanarksh. HB. Socs: Soc. Pub. Health; Assn. Child Psychol. & Psychiat.; Fac. Fam. Plann. Prev: Regist. (Child & Adolesc. Psychiat.) Child & Family Centre Hawkhead Hosp. Paisley.

ELLAHI, Tahira 6 Victoria Terrace, Halifax HX1 4DQ — MB BS 1997 Lond.; BSc 1995 UCL. SHO Gen. Adult Psychiat. Manch. Socs: BMA BMA, MDU.

ELLAM, Kenneth Stephen Woodview Medical Centre, 26 Holmecross Road, Thorplands, Northampton NN3 8AW Tel: 01604 670780 Fax: 01604 646208 — MB BS 1971 Lond.

ELLAM, Margaret St. John's Hospice, Lancaster Road, Slyne, Lancaster LA2 6AW Tel: 01524 382538 — MB ChB 1970 Leeds; FFA RCS Eng. 1974; DGM RCP Lond. 1991. Cons Palliat. med. St. John's Hospice Lancaster, roy.Lanc.infirm.

ELLAMUSHI, Mr Habib Elmabrouk Ibrahim 7 Lothian Court, 21 Lethington Place, Shawlands, Glasgow G41 3BJ Tel: 0141 632 5843 — MB BCh 1984 Libya; MB BCh Fateh Libya 1984; FRCS Ed. 1992.

ELLARD, Mr Michael Andrew 6 Woodland Park, Coleraine BT52 1JG — MB BCh BAO 1992 Belf.; MRCOG 1998. Research Fell. Bath Assisted Conception Clinic Roy. United Hosp. Combe Pk. Bath. Socs: Brit. Fertil. Soc.; ESHRE.

ELLEN, Amanda Jane (retired) Clappers, Private Road, Barton-le-Clay, Bedford MK45 4LE — MB ChB 1971 Ed.; BSc Ed. 1969.

ELLEN, Eunice (retired) Thornbury House, Week St Mary, Holsworthy EX22 6XN — MB ChB 1937 St. And.

ELLENBOGEN, Mr Simon Tameside General hospital, Fountain St, Ashton-under-Lyne OL6 9RW Tel: 0161 331 6723; Meerbrook, Alan Drive, Hale, Altrincham WA15 0LR Tel: 0161 980 6545 — MD 1991 Liverp.; MB ChB (Hons.) 1980; FRCS Eng. 1984. Cons. Gen. Surg. Tameside Gen. Hosp. Ashton-u-Lyne. Prev: Lect. (Clin. Surg.) Univ. Liverp.; Sen. Research Asst. (Surg.) Univ. Liverp.

ELLENGER, Krystyna The Health Centre, Sunningdale Drive, Eaglescliffe, Stockton-on-Tees TS16 9EA Tel: 01642 780113 Fax: 01642 791020; The White House, Church Road, Eaglescliffe, Stockton-on-Tees TS16 9DQ Tel: 01642 782668 — MB BS 1982 Newc.; MRCGP 1986; DRCOG 1985. Prev: Trainee GP Cleveland VTS.

ELLENGER, Paul Edward Tel: 01642 817166 Fax: 01642 824094; The White House, Church Road, Egglescliffe, Stockton-on-Tees TS16 9DQ Tel: 01642 782668 — MB BS 1982 Newc.; MRCGP 1986; DRCOG 1985. Prev: GP Trainee Cleveland VTS.

ELLERBY, Margaret Jean The Clock Tower Practice, 50-66 Park Road, Crouch End, London N8 8SU Tel: 020 8348 7711 — MB BS

1988 Lond.; Cert. Prescribed Equiv. Exp. JCPTGP 1992; DRCOG 1991; DCH RCP Lond. 1990. (Univ. Coll. & Middlx. Sch. Med.) Prev: Trainee GP St. Johns Way Med. Centre Lond.; Trainee GP/SHO Whittington Hosp. Lond. VTS; Ho. Surg. Amersham Gen. Hosp.

ELLERBY, Rosemary (Barnes) Dragon House, Broad Road, Kingswear, Dartmouth TQ6 0EE Tel: 01803 752500 — MB ChB 1960 Manch.; FRCPath 1996. (Manch.) Socs: Fell. Roy. Soc. Med.; Fell. Manch. Med. Soc. (Mem. Sects. Path. & Surg.); Mem. Internat. Acad. Path. (Brit. Div.). Prev: Lect. (Path.) Univ. Manch.; Scientif. Asst. MRC Working Party on Tuberc. of Spine in Developing Countries; Asst. Resid. Surgic. Off. Christie Hosp. & Holt Radium Inst. Manch.

ELLERBY, Susan Elizabeth South Cheshire Health Authority, 1829 Building, The Countess of Chester Hospital, Heath Park, Liverpool Road, Chester CH2 1UL Tel: 01244 650344 Fax: 01244 650341; 45B Appleton Road, Chester CH2 1JH — MB ChB 1985 Liverp.; MBA Manch. 1994, MSc 1991; MFPHM RCP (UK) 1994. Cons. Pub. Health Med. S. Chesh. HA; Hon. Lect. (Pub. Health) Liverp. Univ. Prev: Sen. Regist. (Pub. Health Med.) Mersey RHA; Regist. (Pub. Health Med.) Mersey RHA; SHO (Cardiol. & Thoracic Med.) BRd.green Hosp. Liverp.

ELLERINGTON, Michael Christopher 14 Cherry Close, Morden SM4 4HA Tel: 020 8542 3351 — MB BS 1980 Lond.; MRCOG 1987. (St. Geo.) Regist. (O & G) Redhill Hosp. Surrey; Research fell. & Regist. KCH Lond. Prev: SHO (Gyn.) Kingston Hosp. Kingston upon Thames; SHO (Obst.) Qu. Charlottes Matern. Hosp. Lond.; SHO (O & G) St. Geo. Hosp. Lond.

ELLERSHAW, John Edward Liverpool Marie Curie Centre, 1 Speke Road, Woolton, Liverpool L25 8QA — MB BCh 1984 Wales; MA Wales 1994, MB BCh l984; MRCP (UK) 1989. Med. Dir. Marie Curie Centre Liverp. & Cons. Roy. Liverp. Univ. Hosp. Prev: Sen. Regist. (Palliat. Med.) King's Coll. Hosp. & St. Christopher's Hospice.

ELLERTON, Miss Christine Rachel North Riding Infirmary, Newport Road, Middlesbrough TS1 5JE Tel: 01642 854058 — MB ChB 1984 Leeds; FRCS Eng. 1989; FRCOphth 1990. (Leeds.) Cons. Ophth., N. Riding Infirm., Middlesbrough. Prev: Sen. Regist. Rotat. (Ophth.) N.. Region; Regist. Rotat. (Ophth) N.ern region; SHO Rotat. (Ophth) Soton.

ELLERTON, Donald Arthur (retired) 42 Wiltshire Gardens, Bransgore, Christchurch BH23 8BJ Tel: 01425 673032 — MB BS Lond. 1949; AFOM RCP Lond. 1982. Regional Med. Off. Gen. Counc. Brit. Shipping; Lect. (Med.) Petro-Chem. Sect. Soton. Inst. Higher Educat. Prev: Ho. Surg. (Thoracic Surg.) Lond. Hosp.

ELLERTON, John Alexander Birbeck Medical Group, Penrith Health Centre, Bridge Lane, Penrith CA11 8HW Tel: 01768 245200 Fax: 01768 245295 — BM BCh 1984 Oxf.; MA Camb. 1985; MRCGP 1989; DRCOG 1988.

ELLERTON, John David Rowley (retired) Fairways, 60 High Bank Road, Burton-on-Trent DE15 0HX Tel: 01283 509474 — MB BS 1961 Durh. Prev: GP Burton-on-Trent.

ELLERY, Adam The Surgery, Dounby, Orkney KW17 2HT — MB BS 1991 Lond.; MSc Bristol 1986; BSc Nottm. 1983.

ELLERY, Susan Mary Lodge Cottage, Tarrant Keyneston, Blandford Forum DT11 9JE; 76 Chapelfields, Charterhouse Road, Godalming GU7 2AA Tel: 01483 423013 — MB BS 1997 Lond. SHO St Geo.'s Hosp.

ELLETT-BROWN, Harold (retired) Southfield, Little Weighton Road, Walkington, Beverley HU17 8SP Tel: 01482 881576 — BM BCh 1951 Oxf.; MA Oxf. 1947; FRCPsych 1979, M 1971; DPM Leeds 1955. Prev: Cons. Psychiat. & Dep. Phys. Supt. De la Pole Hosp. Willerby.

ELLEY, Clifford Mark King Street Surgery, 38 King Street, Lancaster LA1 1RE Tel: 01524 32294 Fax: 01524 848412; Middlefell, The Drive, Hest Bank, Lancaster LA2 6DQ Tel: 01524 823161 Email: elley@btinternet.com — MB BS 1983 Lond.; MRCP (UK) 1987; MRCGP 1990; DRCOG 1989; DCH RCP Lond. 1989. (Charing Cross Hospital Medical School) GP. Prev: Trainee GP Hampton Wick, Kingston Surrey; SHO (Gen. Med.) P.ss Margt. Hosp. Swindon; SHO (Paediat.) Ealing Hosp. Middlx.

ELLICE, Ross McAndrew London Lane Clinic, Kinnaird House, 37 London Lane, Bromley BR1 4HB Tel: 020 8460 2661 Fax: 020 8464 5041; 25 Avondale Road, Bromley BR1 4HS Tel: 020 8464 9636 — MB BChir 1972 Camb.; MA Camb. 1973; MRCOG 1978; DA Eng. 1975.

ELLIMAN, Alison Munro Flitwick Clinic, Highlands, Flitwick, Bedford MK45 1DZ Tel: 01525 719896 Fax: 01525 719897 Email: sbchts@business.ntl.com; 19 Alexandra Road, Kings Langley WD4 8DU Tel: 01923 260412 Fax: 01923 260412 Email: alison.elliman@lineone.net — BSc Glas. 1961, MB ChB 1964; FRCP Lond. 1989, M 1968; FRCPCH 1997. (Glas.) Cons. Community Paediat. Beds. and Luton Community NHS Trust. Socs: Eur. Soc. Paediat. Research; Roy. Soc. Med. Prev: Research Assoc. Hammersmith Hosp. & Qu. Charlottes Hosp. Lond.; Cons. Paediat. W. Middlx. Hosp. Isleworth; Clin. Dir. Child Health & Develop.

ELLIMAN, Alyson Jessica Croydon Community Health Trust, 12-18 Lennard Road, Croydon CR9 2RS Tel: 020 8680 2008; 2 South Rise, Carshalton Beeches, Carshalton SM5 4PD Tel: 020 8643 5022 — MB BS 1973 Lond.; BSc (Hons.) Lond. 1970; MFFP 1993; Cert. Family Plann. JCC 1982; DCH RCP Lond. 1976. (St. Geo.) SCMO Croydon Community Health Trust; Lead Clin. for Adult Med. Serv. Socs: Inst. Psychosexual Med.

ELLIMAN, David Anthony Cyril St. Georges Hospital, 2nd Floor, Clare House, Blackshaw Road, London SW17 0QT Tel: 020 8725 3737 Fax: 020 8725 0598; 2 South Rise, Carshalton Beeches, Carshalton SM5 4PD Tel: 020 8643 5022 Fax: 020 8643 5022 Email: davidelliman@compuserve.com — MB BS 1973 Lond.; BA Open 1989; FRCP Lond. 1994; MRCP (UK) 1976; DCH Eng. 1977. (St. Geo.) Cons. Community Child Health St. Geo. Healthcare NHS Trust; Hon. Sen. Lect. Inst. of Child Health Lond. Prev: Lect. (Community Child Health) St. Geo. Hosp. Med. Sch. Lond.

ELLIMAN, Jonathan Christopher Kingswood Surgery, Kingswood Avenue, Swindon SN3 2RJ Tel: 01793 534699 — BM 1983 Soton.; MRCGP 1987; DRCOG 1985.

ELLIN, Caroline Bridge Lane Health Centre, 20 Bridge Lane, Battersea, London SW11 3AD Tel: 020 7585 1499 Fax: 020 7978 4707 — MB ChB 1993 Bristol.

ELLINGER, Joan Walwyn (retired) 114 Avondale Road, Bromley BR1 4HA Tel: 020 8460 6573 — MB BS 1935 Lond. Prev: Med. Off. Brook La. Med. Miss. Downham. Ho. Phys. Co. Hosp. York.

ELLINGHAM, Jeremy Henry Mitford 10 Edelshain Grove, Wakefield WF2 6HG — MB ChB 1979 Sheff.; FRCR 1986. Cons. Radiol., Pinderfields and Pontefract (NHS) Trust. Prev: Sen. Regist. (Radiol.), Leicester Roy. Infirm.

ELLINGHAM, Katarzyna Ewa Directorate of Clinical Radiology, Bristol Royal Infirmary, Bristol BS2 8HW Tel: 0117 928 3267 — MB ChB 1992 Bristol; MRCP (UK) 1995. (Univ. Bristol) Specialist Regist. (Clin. Radiol.) Bristol Roy. Infirm. Prev: SHO (Gen. Med.) Glos. Roy. Hosp.

ELLINGHAM, Margaret Jennifer The Surgery, 3 Austin Road, Battersea, London SW11 5JP Tel: 020 7498 0232 Fax: 020 7498 0271; 114 Ritherdon Road, Upper Tooting, London SW17 8QQ — MB ChB 1987 Birm.; MRCP (UK) 1991; MRCGP (Distinc.) 1995; DRCOG 1992.

ELLINGHAM, Roger Bruce Bristol Eye Hospital, Lower Maudlin St., Bristol BS1 2LX Email: r.b.ellingham@bris.ac.uk; Top Floor Flat (4), 30 Apsley Road, Bristol BS8 2SS — MB BChir 1989 Camb.; BA Camb. 1986; FRCOphth 1994.

ELLINGSEN, Johan Didrik 2 Harley Street, London W1N 1AA — Lic Med Uppsala 1973.

ELLINGTON, Christine Anne 6 Hough Green, Ashley, Altrincham WA15 0QS Tel: 0161 928 2173 — MB BS 1964 Lond.; MRCS Eng. LRCP Lond. 1964. (Roy Free.) Prev: Clin. Med. Off. Chesh. AHA; Gen. Pract. Trafford Family Pract. Comm.; Clin. Asst. (Paediat.) Roy. Manch. Childr. Hosp. & Altrincham Gen.

ELLINGTON, Nicole Christine 47 Cator Road, London SE26 5DT — MB BS 1990 Lond.

ELLINGWORTH, Joanne Kate 16 Manor Lane Terrace, Lewisham, London SE13 5QL Tel: 020 8297 5113 — MB BS 1996 Lond. SHO in O & G Whipps Cross Hosp. Lond. Prev: SHO Anaesth. Greenwich Dist. Hosp.

ELLIOT, Catherine Anne The Old School Surgery, 2A Station Street, Kibworth, Leicester LE8 0LN Tel: 0116 241 3801 — MB ChB 1976 Bristol; MRCGP 1982.

ELLIOT, Charles Adam 23 Renshaw Road, Ecclesall, Sheffield S11 7PD — MB ChB 1995 Sheff. SHO (Med.) Chesterfield & N. Derbysh. Roy. Hosp. Chesterfield. Prev: SHO (Integrated Med. & A & E) Chesterfield.

ELLIOT, Mr David Woodlands, Cut-A-Thwart Lane, Woodham Walter, Maldon CM9 6LN Tel: 01621 857362 Fax: 01621 841127 Email: info@david-elliot.co.uk; Woodlands, Cut-A-Thwart Lane, Woodham Walter, Maldon CM9 6LN Tel: 01621 850576 Fax: 01621 841127 — BM BCh 1975 Oxf.; MA Oxf. 1975; FRCS Eng. 1980; T(SN) 1991. (St. Bartholomew's) Cons. Hand & Plastic Surg. St. And. Plastic Surg. Centre Broomfield & S.end Gen. Hosp. Socs: Brit. Assn. Plastic Surg.; Sec. Brit. Soc. Surg. Hand. Prev: Sen. Regist. (Plastic Surg.) Newc.

ELLIOT, Mrs Frances Mary (retired) Methilhaven Road Surgery, 361 Methilhaven Road, Methil, Leven KY8 3HR Tel: 01333 426913 Fax: 01333 422300 — MB ChB 1983 Glas.; MRCGP 1987; DCH RCPS Glas. 1986; DRCOG 1985.

ELLIOT, Ivan Robert Foden Street Surgery, 32 Foden Street, Stoke-on-Trent ST4 4BX Tel: 01782 411884; 2 Oakhill Hall, Oakhill Avenue, Stoke-on-Trent ST4 5NH — MB ChB 1979 Leeds; MRCGP 1983.

ELLIOT, James William Whinfield Surgery, Whinbush Way, Darlington DL1 3RT Tel: 01325 481321 Fax: 01325 380116 — MB BS 1985 Newc.; MRCGP 1993; DCH RCPS Glas. 1988. GP Tuto, Newc. Univ.; GP Traine, Cleveland UTS; Police Surg., Punham Constable. Prev: SHO (Accid & Emerg. & Paediat.) Shotley Bridge Hosp.

ELLIOT, John Michael Department of Anaesthesia, Good Hope Hospital, Rectory Road, Sutton Coldfield B75 7RR — MB BS 1985 Lond.; FRCA 1991; Dip. IMC RCS Ed. 1992.

ELLIOT, John Vincent 1 Keymer Gardens, Burgess Hill RH15 0AF — MB ChB 1978 Dundee.

***ELLIOT, Magda Christine** 48 Lawrie Park Gardens, London SE26 6XJ — MB ChB 1997 Ed.

ELLIOT, Rowland (retired) Rockville, Hillside Terrace, Selkirk TD7 4ND Tel: 01750 20551 — M.B., Ch.B. Ed. 1943. Prev: Gen. Practiitoner Selkirk.

ELLIOT, Steven Douglas Platt Lane Surgery, 204 Platt Lane, Manchester M14 7BS Tel: 0161 224 2468 Fax: 0161 256 4049 — MB BS 1980 Newc.; MRCGP 1984; DRCOG 1983.

ELLIOT-PYLE, Elizabeth Mary Oldwood Surgery, Station Road, Robertsbridge TN32 5DG Tel: 01580 880790 Fax: 01580 882192; Goodrooms, Salehurst, Robertsbridge TN32 5PJ Tel: 01580 880564 — MB BS Lond. 1965; MRCS Eng. LRCP Lond. 1965; DA Eng. 1967. (Lond. Hosp.) Med. Off. Hastings Family Plann. Assn. Clinic. Prev: SHO (Anaesth.) Whipps Cross Hosp. Lond.; Ho. Phys. (Skin & Plastic Surg.) & Receiv. Room Off. Lond. Hosp.; Ho. Surg. (Obst.) Forest Gate Hosp. Lond.

ELLIOT-SMITH, Adrian 14 Crooks Barn Lane, Norton, Stockton-on-Tees TS20 1LW — MB BS 1984 Lond.; MA Oxf. 1984; MRCGP 1988; DRCOG 1986.

ELLIOTT, Alison Mary Department of Infectous & Tropical Diseases, London School of Hygiene & Tropical Medicine, Keppel St., London WC1E 7HT Tel: 020 7927 2298 Fax: 020 7637 4314 Email: a.elliott@ishtm.ac.uk — MB BS 1984 Lond.; MA Camb. 1983, MD 1996; MRCP (UK) 1987; DTM & H RCP Lond. 1988. (Char. Cross Hosp. Med. Sch. Lond.) Sen. Lect. Lond. Sch. Hyg. & Trop. Med. Socs: Fell. Roy. Soc. Trop. Med. & Hyg. Prev: Fell. Infec. Dis. Univ. Colorado Denver, USA; Research Fell. Lond. Sch. Hyg. & Trop. Med. & Univ. Teachg. Lusaka, Zambia; SHO & Regist. (Med.) Aberd. Teachg. Hosp.

ELLIOTT, Amanda Jane Hollytree Surgery, 42 Boundstone Road, Wrecclesham, Farnham GU10 4TG Tel: 01252 793183 Fax: 01252 795437; Fordwych House, 4 Mavins Road, Farnham GU9 8JS — MB BS 1976 Lond.; MRCP (UK) 1979; DCH Eng. 1979. (Middlx.)

ELLIOTT, Mr Andrew John Fordwych House, 4 Mavins Road, Farnham GU9 8JS Tel: 01252 713731 Fax: 01252 713731 — MB BChir 1979 Camb.; MA Camb. 1979; FRCS Glas. 1985; FRCS Eng. 1985; MRCP (UK) 1982; T(Ophth) 1991; FRCOphth 1989. Cons. Ophth. Frimley Pk. Hosp. NHS Trust. Socs: Fell. Roy. Soc. Med. Prev: Sen. Regist. (Ophth.) Norwich & Camb. HAs; Regist. Bristol Eye Hosp.

ELLIOTT, Anthony James EMI Directorate, Shelton Hospital, Shrewsbury SY3 8DN Tel: 01743 261000 Fax: 01743 261279 Email: t.elliott@which.net — MB ChB 1985 Birm.; MRCPsych 1989; FRSH 1995; MSoc.Sci Birmingham 1996. (Birmingham) Clin. Dir. Shelton Hosp.; Cons. Ment. Health of Elderly Shelton Hosp. Shrewsbury. Prev: Regist. (Psychiat.) Newtown Hosp. & Worcester Roy. Infirm.

ELLIOTT, Arnold, OBE (retired) 26 Heathview Court, 20 Corringway, London NW11 7EF Tel: 020 8731 6302 Email: arnold@arnoldelliot.fsnet.co.uk — MB BCh BAO 1944 Belf.; FRCGP 1976, M 1953. Ex-Sec. Redbridge & Waltham Forest LMC; Ex-Examr. for Dip. Geriat. Med. RCP. Prev: Mem. Gen. Med. Servs. Comm.

ELLIOTT, Austen Ernest, MBE (retired) Waterside Lodge, Barrel Well Hill, Chester CH3 5BR — MB ChB 1950 Ed.; FRCGP 1972; DObst RCOG 1954.

ELLIOTT, Bernard Arthur 10 Prince Consort Drive, Ascot SL5 8AW Tel: 01990 21956 — MD 1962 NUI; MB BCh BAO 1957; FRCPath 1974, M 1965. Socs: Nuclear Med. Soc. Prev: SHO Path. Centr. Middlx. Hosp. Lond.; Regist. Path. W.m. Hosp. Lond.; Sen. Lect. Chem. Path. Univ. Coll. Hosp. Ibadan, Nigeria.

ELLIOTT, Mr Brian (cons. rooms), 24 West St., Chichester PO19 1QP Tel: 01243 789630 Fax: 01243 536591; Saffron House, 6 South Street, Emsworth PO10 7EH Tel: 01243 389744 — MB BS Lond. 1957; FRCS Eng. 1965; MRCS Eng. LRCP Lond. 1957. (Middlx.) Emerit. Cons. Orthop. Surg. Chichester HA. Socs: Fell. BOA; Fell. Roy. Soc. Med.; Brit. Assn. Surg. Knee. Prev: Sen. Regist. (Orthop.) Middlx. Hosp. Lond.; Regist. Roy. Nat. Orthop. Hosp.; Regist. (Accid.) Middlx. Hosp.

ELLIOTT, Carl Stephen South Tyrone Hospital, Carland Road, Dungannon BT71 4AU Tel: 01868 722821; 53 Sicily Park, Belfast BT10 0AL Tel: 01232 626634 — MB BCh BAO 1979 Belf.; FRCR 1990. Cons. Radiol. S. Tyrone Hosp. Socs: BMA & Ulster Radiol. Soc. Prev: Cons. Radiol. NHSSB.

ELLIOTT, Catherine Anne Walton and Partners, West Street Surgery, 12 West Street, Chipping Norton OX7 5AA Tel: 01608 642529 Fax: 01608 645066; 89 Burford Road, Chipping Norton OX7 5EE Tel: 01608 643811 — BM BCh 1979 Oxf.; MA Camb. 1976; MRCGP 1983; DRCOG 1982; Cert. Family Plann. JCC 1982. GP Chipping Norton. Prev: Trainee GP Horton Gen. Hosp. Oxon. VTS; Ho. Surg. & Ho. Phys. Horton Gen. Hosp. Banbury.

ELLIOTT, Catherine Elizabeth 123 Greenway Road, Timperley, Altrincham WA15 6BL — BM BS 1994 Nottm.

ELLIOTT, Catherine Lucy 37 Dancer Road, London SW6 4DU — MB ChB 1991 Ed. Research Fell. (O & G) Univ. Edin.

ELLIOTT, Catherine Mildred (retired) 158D Derby Road, Heanor DE75 7QL Tel: 01773 712682 — MB BS Lond. 1945; MRCGP 1960. Prev: Ho. Surg. (Orthop.) Manch. Roy. Infirm.

ELLIOTT, Catherine Shaw Cochran Rosalee, Rosalee Brae, Hawick TD9 7HH — MB ChB 1978 Glas. Clin. Asst. Dept. Med. for Elderly Borders Gen. Hosp. Melrose.

ELLIOTT, Cathleen Mary (retired) 93 Monument Lane, Rednal, Birmingham B45 9QH Tel: 0121 453 2622 — MB ChB 1950 Birm.; MRCS Eng. LRCP Lond. 1950; MRCGP 1966; DCH Eng. 1954; DObst RCOG 1954.

ELLIOTT, Charles Gavin (retired) The Old Post office, Cowbeech, Hailsham BN27 4JD Tel: 01323 832245 — BM BCh 1947 Oxf.; MA Oxf. 1947. Prev: Ho. Phys. (Paediat.) St. Bart. Hosp.

ELLIOTT, Christine (retired) Langford Cottage, Woollard, Pensford, Bristol BS39 4HT — BM Soton. 1981; DCH RCP Lond. 1984. Prev: SHO St. Richard's Hosp. Chichester.

ELLIOTT, Christine Sterndale Surgery, 74A Sterndale Road, London W14 0HX Tel: 020 7602 3797; 29 Bristol Gardens, London W9 2JQ Tel: 020 7289 7303 — MB BS 1980 Lond.; MRCS Eng. LRCP Lond. 1980; DRCOG 1986. GP Lond.

ELLIOTT, Christopher James The Surgery, 54 Benhill Avenue, Sutton SM1 4EB Tel: 020 8770 0587 Fax: 020 8770 0586; 138 Copse Hill, Wimbledon, London SW20 0NP Tel: 020 8879 1839 — MB BS 1977 Lond.; MRCS Eng. LRCP Lond. 1977; MRCGP 1985. (Charing Cross Hospital) Socs: Sutton Med. Soc.

ELLIOTT, Christopher John Richard (retired) 14 Aldridge Court, Baldock SG7 5TA — MB BS 1952 Lond.; FFA RCS Eng. 1960; DA Eng. 1955. Prev: Cons. Anaesth. Qu. Eliz. II Hosp. Welwyn Gdn. City & City Hosp. St.

ELLIOTT, Claire Alexandra Dental Centre, 3 Gower Place, London WC1E 6BN Tel: 020 7387 6306 Fax: 020 7387 3645 Email: gpp@gp-f83043.nhs.uk; 17 Rochester Terrace, London NW1 9JN Tel: 020 7267 7708 — MB BS 1982 Lond.; MRCGP 1986; DObst. RCOG 1985; MSC Lond. 1997; DFFP 1996. (Guy's) GP Princip.;

Hon. Stud. Health Phys. UCL. Socs: Med. Soc. Lond.; Roy. Soc. Med. (Edr.ial Asst., Mem. Canat Sedian Healthy of Med.).

ELLIOTT, Clare Mercote, Jordans, Beaconsfield HP9 2SW — MB BS 1975 Lond.

ELLIOTT, Clare Isabel 293 Dawlish Road, Birmingham B29 7AU — MB ChB 1991 Birm.; ChB Birm. 1991.

ELLIOTT, Daniel Henry 33 Hudson Close, Eastbourne BN23 5RB — BM 1998 Soton.; BM Soton 1998.

ELLIOTT, David Hallen, OBE 40 Petworth Road, Haslemere GU27 2HX — MB BS 1956 Lond.; MB BS (Hons.) Lond. 1956; DPhil Oxf. 1964; FRCP Lond. 1989; FRCP Ed. 1983; MRCP Lond. 1975; MFCM 1973; FFOM RCP Lond. 1983, M 1978; DObst RCOG 1958. (St. Bart.) Hon. Prof. Robens Inst. Health & Safety Univ. Surrey; Civil. Cons. Underwater Med. Roy. Navy. Prev: Pres. Undersea Med. Soc. Inc. & Europ. Undersea Biomed. Soc.; Chief Med. Off., Shell UK.

ELLIOTT, David Richard St Lukes Surgery, Warren Road, Guildford GU1 3JH Tel: 01483 572364 Fax: 01483 304379 — MB BS 1970 Lond.; MRCS Eng. LRCP Lond. 1970; DObst RCOG 1971. (Guy's)

ELLIOTT, Mr David Simon 38 Queens Road, Twickenham TW1 4EX Email: david.elliott@tesco.net.uk — MB BS 1981 Lond.; FRCS Eng. 1987; FRCS (Orth) 1994. Cons. Orthop. Surg. St Peter's Hosp. Chertsey Runnymede Hosp. Chertsey.

ELLIOTT, Delia Mary Little Chillaton Farm, Loddiswell, Kingsbridge TQ7 4EG — MB BS 1967 Lond.; MRCS Eng. LRCP Lond. 1967; DA Eng 1970; DObst RCOG 1970. (Roy. Free) Staff Grade Paediat. (Community Child Health) Plymouth Hosps. Trust. Socs: Med. Campaign Againt Nuclear Weapons; BMA. Prev: Regist. (Anaesth.) St. Helier Hosp. Carshalton; SHO (Anaesth.) Redhill & Netherne Hosp. Gp.; SHO (O & G) Mayday Hosp. Thornton Heath.

ELLIOTT, Edwin John Woolston Lodge Surgery, 66 Portsmouth Road, Woolston, Southampton SO19 9AL Tel: 023 8044 6733/6735 Fax: 023 8036 3568; Marchbank, Wangfield Lane, Curdridge, Southampton SO32 2DA Tel: 01489 786621 Email: ellojohn@epulse.net — MB ChB 1969 Ed.; BSc (Med. Sci.) Ed. 1966; MRCGP 1978; MRCPsych 1975; Cert. Family Plann. JCC 1981; DObst RCOG 1972. (Ed.) UKCP Registered NLP Psychotherapist. Socs: Brit. Soc. Experim. & Clin. Hypn.; Assoc. Mem. Brit. Med. Acupunc. Soc.; Nat. Counc. Hypnother. (Accred.). Prev: Sen. Regist. (Psychiat.) Portsmouth; Research Fell. (Psychiat.) Univ. Soton; SHO (O & G) & Ho. Surg. Roy. Infirm. Edin.

ELLIOTT, Elizabeth Margaret (retired) 'Cashelbawn', West Walton, Wisbech PE14 7EU Tel: 01945 780269 — MB BCh BAO 1945 Dub. Prev: Sen. Clin. Off. W. Norf. & Wisbech HA.

ELLIOTT, Eve Valerie 19 Mareham Road, Horncastle LN9 6HB — MB BS 1969 Lond.; MRCS Eng. LRCP Lond. 1969; DObst RCOG 1974; DA Eng. 1971. (St. Bart.)

ELLIOTT, Haydn Robert 1B Llanover Road, Culverhouse Cross, Cardiff CF5 6XJ — MB BCh 1969 Wales; DObst RCOG 1971. Prev: Ho. Phys. (Paediat.) Cardiff Roy. Infirm.

ELLIOTT, Heather 33 Maxwell Road, Bangor BT20 3SG Tel: 01247 451212 — MB BCh BAO 1979 Belf.; MRCPath 1986.

ELLIOTT, Heather Angela 15 Cliff Park Avenue, Paignton TQ4 6LT Tel: 01803 550244 — MB ChB 1983 Bristol; DRCOG 1990. Clin. Med. Off. (Family Plann.) Torquay. Prev: Trainee GP Torbay VTS.

ELLIOTT, Helen 9 Ridgewood Close, Baildon, Shipley BD17 6HE — MB ChB 1993 Leeds.

ELLIOTT, Henry Lamond University of Glasgow, Department of Medicine & Therapeutics, Western Infirmary, Glasgow G11 6NT; 4 Devonshire Terrace, Glasgow G12 0XE Tel: 0141 357 1623 — MD 1983 Glas.; MB ChB 1973; FRCP Glas. 1989; MRCP (U.K.) 1975. Sen. Lect. Univ. Glas. Dept. Med. & Therap.

ELLIOTT, Mr James Robert Martin Tel: 01232 669501 ext 2368 — MB BCh BAO 1975 Belf.; MD Belf. 1984; FRCS Ed. 1980. Cons. Orthop. Surg. Musgrave Pk. Hosp. & Roy. Vicoria Hosp.

ELLIOTT, Joan (retired) East Wing, Cramlington Hall, Cramlington NE23 6PZ Tel: 01670 713104 — MB BS 1960 Durh.; DPM Newc. 1969; DCH Eng. 1963. Prev: Cons. (Child Psychiat.) S. Shields Gen. Hosp.

ELLIOTT, John Amsden, GM (retired) Beaconhurst, Church Road, Crowborough TN6 1BN Tel: 01892 653526 — MB BChir 1946 Camb.; MRCS Eng. LRCP Lond. 1940; MRCGP 1953. Prev: Phys. i/c Burrswood Nurs. Home Groombridge.

ELLIOTT, John Arthur 5 Glen Truim View, Kilmarnock KA2 0LL — MB ChB 1974 Bristol; BSc Bristol 1971, MB ChB 1974; FRCP Glas. 1987; MRCP (UK) 1976. Cons. Phys. Heathfield & Ballochmyle Hosps. & Hon. Clin. Lect. Univ. Glas. Socs: Brit. Thoracic Soc. & Internat. Assn. for the Study of Lung Cancer. Prev: Sen. Regist. (Respirat./Gen. Med.) W.. Infirm. & Kt.swood Hosp.; Glas.; Research Fell. Dept. Chemother. Finsen Inst. Copenhagen.

ELLIOTT, John Charlton Consett Medical Centre, Station Yard, Consett DH8 5YA Tel: 01207 216116 Fax: 01207 216119; 58 The Grove, Gosforth, Newcastle upon Tyne NE3 1NJ — MB ChB 1986 Leeds; MRCGP 1995.

ELLIOTT, John Edwin, TD Flints, Hambleden, Henley-on-Thames RG9 6SL Tel: 01491 571514 Fax: 01491 411089; Cloondaragh, Askill, Ballyshannon, Donegal, Republic of Ireland — MB BS 1937 Lond.; MRCS Eng. LRCP Lond. 1935; MRCGP 1964; DObst RCOG 1939. (Guy's) Socs: Fell. Brit. Soc. Med. & Dent. Hypn.; Fell. Roy. Soc. Med.; Brit. Soc. Dowsers.

ELLIOTT, John Malcolm, MC (retired) 9 Lion House, 2 Carlton Hill, Exmouth EX8 2AH Tel: 01395 273177 Email: malcolm@lionhouse.freeserve.co.uk — MB ChB Birm. 1954; DMRD Eng. 1973. Prev: Cons. Radiol. Kidderminster & BromsGr. & Redditch HAs.

ELLIOTT, John Mark 11 Regents Wood, Magheralin, Craigavon BT67 0RX — MB BCh BAO 1989 Belf.; MB BCh BAO (Hons.) Belf. 1989. SHO (Med.) Craigavon Area Hosp. Prev: SHO (Med.) Roy. Vict. Hosp. Belf.; Ho. Off. Craigavon Area Hosp.

ELLIOTT, John Reginald Bank House, Abdon, Craven Arms SY7 9HY — MRCS Eng. LRCP Lond. 1943; MRCOG 1954; FFA RCS Eng. 1953; DA Eng. 1950. (Lond. Hosp.) Prev: Ho. Surg. S.end Gen. Hosp.

ELLIOTT, John Thomas West-Ville, Facit, Rochdale OL12 8LT Tel: 0170 685 3526 — MB ChB 1954 Leeds; DPM Eng. 1960. (Leeds) Cons. Psychiat. Rochdale & Dist. Hosp. Gp.

ELLIOTT, John Vincent The Grove Medical Centre, Church Road, Egham TW20 9QJ Tel: 01784 433159 Fax: 01784 477208; Rowans, Monks Road, Virginia Water GU25 4RR Tel: 01344 843643 — MB BS 1970 Lond.; FFA RCS Eng. 1977; DA Eng. 1972; Dip. Law City Univ. Lond. 1980. Barrister-at-Law Lincoln's Inn.

ELLIOTT, Kay Elizabeth Manor Road Surgery, 33 Manor Road, Caddington, Luton LU1 4EE Tel: 01582 25673 Fax: 01582 726672; 21 School Lane, Eaton Bray, Dunstable LU6 2DT Tel: 01525 222849 — MB BS 1981 Lond.; MRCGP 1986; DFFP 1993. (St. Mary's Hospital Medical School London.) Med. Off. (Family Plann.) Milton Keynes. Prev: GP High Wycombe.

ELLIOTT, Kenneth Clive The Croft, Ellertine Heath, Telford TF6 6R — MRCS Eng. LRCP Lond. 1970. (St. Mary's) Prev: Ho. Phys. City Gen. Hosp. Stoke-on-Trent; Ho. Surg. Poole Gen. Hosp.; Obst. Off. W. Chesh. Hosp. Chester.

ELLIOTT, Lee-Anne 15 Belfrey Court, Wakefield WF1 3TY — MB BS 1986 Newc.; MRCP (UK) 1990. Regist. (Diag. Radiol.) Leeds Gen. Infirm.

ELLIOTT, Lesley Cottingham Medical Centre, 17-19 South Street, Cottingham HU16 4AJ Tel: 01482 845078 Fax: 01482 845078; 7 Park Avenue, Princess Avenue, Hull HU5 3EN — MB ChB 1983 Glas.

ELLIOTT, Lindsay Mary (retired) Pells Farm, Pells Lane, West Kingsdown, Sevenoaks TN15 6AU — MB BS 1953 Lond.; FFPHM RCP (UK) 1990; FFCM 1983, M 1980. Prev: Med. Adviser Primary Care N. Kent Health Care Trust.

ELLIOTT, Lindsey Mary Ripley Medical Centre, Derby Road, Ripley DE5 3HR Tel: 01773 747486 Fax: 01773 513470 — MB BCh 1989 Wales; MRCGP 1994.

ELLIOTT, Margaret Elizabeth Lilian Irvinestown Health Centre, 20 Church Street, Irvinestown, Enniskillen BT94 1EH Tel: 028 6862 1212 Fax: 028 6862 8624; 60 Kesh Road, Moneykee, Irvinestown, Enniskillen BT94 1FZ Tel: 0136 56 21303 — MB BCh BAO 1967 Belf. Socs: BMA.

ELLIOTT, Margaret Louise The Surgery, 31 Tunbridge Lane, Bottisham, Cambridge CB5 9DU Tel: 01223 811203 Fax: 01223 811853 — MB ChB 1987 Bristol. SHO (Obst & Gyn.) S.mead Hosp. Bristol. Prev: Ho. Surg. Norf. & Norwich Hosp.; Ho. Phys. Bristol Roy. Infirm.

ELLIOTT, Maria Krisztina Crown Dale Medical Centre, 61 Crown Dale, London SE19 3NY Tel: 020 8670 2414 Fax: 020 8670 0277;

57 Baldry Gardens, London SW16 3DL Tel: 020 8679 6788 — MD 1970 Budapest; MRCS Eng. LRCP Lond. 1973; DObst RCOG 1975. Prev: Ho. Phys. Paddington Green Childr. Hosp. Lond.; Ho. Surg. Joyce Green Hosp. Dartford; SHO (Med.) Qu. Mary's Hosp. Sidcup.

ELLIOTT, Marian (retired) The old Coach House, 35 Barton Road, Hoylake, Wirral CH47 1HJ Tel: 0151 632 0241 — MB BS 1962 Lond.; MRCS Eng. LRCP Lond. 1962; MFCH 1989. Prev: SCMO Chester & Halton NHS Community Trust.

ELLIOTT, Mark Station House Surgery, Station Road, Kendal LA9 6SA Tel: 01539 722660 Fax: 01539 734845 — MB ChB 1974 Manch.; DCH Eng. 1978; DObst RCOG 1976.

ELLIOTT, Mark Donald 17 The Saplings, Newcastle ST5 4HW — MB ChB 1991 Liverp.

ELLIOTT, Mark William Tel: 0113 206 6037 Fax: 0113 2066042 Email: mark.elliott@lineone.net; 1 Oakwood Mount, Leeds LS8 2JG — MB BChir 1983 Camb.; MD Camb. 1993, MA; MRCP (UK) 1985; FRCP 1998. (Cambridge) Cons. Phys. St. Jas. Univ. Hosp. Socs: Brit. Thorac. Soc.; Amer. Thoracic Soc.; Chairm. ICU Assembly and Mem. of Exec. Comm. Europ. Respirat. Soc. Prev: Sen. Regist. (Thoracic Med.) Roy. Brompton Nat. Heart & Lung Hosp. Lond.; Sen. Regist. (Gen. & Thoracic Med.) King's Coll. Hosp. & Med. Sch. Lond.; Regist. (Med.) Brompton Hosp. Lond.

ELLIOTT, Martin 17 Navigation Wharf, Liverpool L3 4DP Tel: 0151 709 9291 — MB ChB 1990 Ed.; MRCP (UK) 1995. Specialist Regist. (Paediat.) Alder Hey Liverp. Prev: SHO (Paediat.) St. Jas. Hosp. Leeds & Leeds Gen. Infirm.

ELLIOTT, Mr Martin John Great Ormond Street Hospital for Children NHS Trust, Great Ormond St., London WC1N 3JH Tel: 020 7829 8853 Fax: 020 7813 8262 Email: martin.elliott@gosh_tronthames.nhs.uk; 13 Dalmore Road, Dulwich, London SE21 8HD Tel: 020 8488 2799 Fax: 020 8488 2772 — MD 1983 Newc.; MB BS Newc. 1973; FRCS Eng. 1978. Cons. Cardiothoracic Surg. Gt. Ormond St. Hosp. for Childr. NHS Trust Lond.; Sen. Lect. (Paediat. Cardiol.) Inst. Child Health Guildford St. Lond. Prev: Sen. Regist. (Cardiothoracic Surg.) Hosp. for Sick Childr. Gt. Ormond St. Lond.; 1st Asst. (Cardiothoracic Surg.) Regional Cardiothoracic Freeman Hosp. Newc.

ELLIOTT, Michael Edmund 11 Wallacefield Road, Troon KA10 6PL — MB ChB 1970 Glas.

ELLIOTT, Michael John The Surgery, Hambleden, Henley-on-Thames RG9 6RT Tel: 01491 571305; Pheasants Hill, Hambleden, Henley-on-Thames RG9 6SD Tel: 01491 571404 Fax: 01491 411089 — BM BCh 1965 Oxf.; MA, BM BCh Oxf. 1965. (Oxf. & Guy's) Prev: Ho. Phys. Guy's Hosp.

ELLIOTT, Niall William Andrew 19 Prospect Road, Portstewart BT55 7NF Email: niallwae@hotmail.com — MB ChB 1995 Dundee. SHO GP Rotat. Tayside Ninewells Hosp. Dundee. Prev: Princip. Ho. Off. Orthop. at Mackay Base Hosp., Qu.sland.

ELLIOTT, Nicholas Leigh View Medical Centre, Bradford Road, Tingley, Wakefield WF3 1RQ Tel: 0113 253 7629 Fax: 0113 238 1286; Grange View, The Runtlings, Ossett WF5 8JJ — MB BS 1982 Lond.; MRCGP 1986; DRCOG 1986.

ELLIOTT, Nicola Mary Corbett Medical Practice, 36 Corbett Avenue, Droitwich WR9 7BE Tel: 01905 795566 Fax: 01905 796984; Ivy Cottage, Dilmore Lane, Fernhill Heath, Worcester WR3 7TE Tel: 01905 53778 — MB BCh 1988 Wales; DRCOG 1994; MRCGP 1994. GP Princip.

ELLIOTT, Patricia Mary (retired) The Old Vicarage, Church End, Ashdon, Saffron Walden CB10 2HG Tel: 01799 584284 — MD 1948 Lond.; MB BS (Hnrs.) 1943, DPH 1948; MFOM 1982; DIH Eng. 1954; DObst RCOG 1947. Barrister-at-Law Inner Temple. Prev: Med. Dir. Harlow Indust. Health Serv.

ELLIOTT, Professor Paul Department of Epidemiology & Public Health, Faculty of Medicine, Imperial College, St Mary's Campus, Norfolk Place, London W2 1PG Tel: 020 7594 3328 Fax: 020 7262 1034 Email: p.elliott@ic.ac.uk — MB BS 1978 Lond.; PhD Lond. 1991, MSc 1983; MA Camb. 1978; MRCP (UK) 1981; FFPHM RCP (UK) 1995; MFCM 1989; FRCP 1998. (Univ. Coll. Hosp.) Prof. Epidemiol. & Pub. Health Med. Imperial Coll. Sch. of Med. Lond.; Hon. Cons. Med. Hammersmith Hosp. Lond.; Hon. Cons. Kensington, Chelsea & W.m. Health Agency; Hon. Cons. St. Mary's Hosp. Lond. Socs: Fell.Roy. Soc. of Med.; Fell.Acad. of Med. Sci.s; World Heart Foundat. (Mem. Scientif. Sect. Epidemiol. & Preven.). Prev: Reader (Environm. Epidemiol.) Lond. Sch. Hyg. & Trop. Med.; Wellcome Research Fell. (Med.) St. Mary's Hosp. Med. Sch. Lond.; Regist. (Med.) Edgware Gen. Hosp. Middlx.

ELLIOTT, Paul Anthony 44 Corporation Road, Redcar TS10 1PB — MB ChB 1993 Ed.; MRCP (Ed.) 1996; BSc (Physiol.) Ed. 1990. (Ed.) SHO Palliat. Care Med.; Specialist Regist. (Clin. Oncol.) W.ern Gen. Hosp. Edin.

ELLIOTT, Perry Mark 81A Erpingham Road, London SW15 1BJ — MB BS 1987 Lond.

ELLIOTT, Peter 18 Bristow Park, Belfast BT9 6TH Tel: 028 669358 — MD 1984 Belf.; MB BCh BAO 1977; FFA RCS Eng. 1981. Cons. Anaesth. Roy. Gp. Hosps. Belf.

ELLIOTT, Peter Richard Southdene Surgery, The Shrubberies, George Lane, South Woodford E18 1BD Tel: 0208 530 3731 Fax: 0208 481 1997 Email: peter.elliott@gp-f86066.nhs.uk — DFFP 2000; MRCS Eng. LRCP Lond. 1969; Cert. Family Plann. JCC 1979; DObst RCOG 1972. (Lond. Hosp.) GP; Med. Advisor, Barkiong & Dagenham PCT. Prev: Indep. Med. Adviser Ilford.; Med. Advisor, Redbridge & Waltham Forest HA.; GP Buntingford, Herts., March Cambs. & Meopham Kent.

ELLIOTT, Rachel 39 Brynhyfryd, Glynneath, Neath SA11 5BA Tel: 01639 720071 — MB BCh 1997 Wales. Med. SHO Rotat. at RUH, Bath; SHO in Clin. Pharmacol. Prev: Med. Ho. Off. Univ. of Wales Hosp., Cardiff; Surgic. Ho. Off. Singleton Swansea.

ELLIOTT, Rachel Mary 30 Wemyss Road, London SE3 0TG Tel: 020 8318 3712; 2 Keslake Road, Queens Park, London NW6 6DL Tel: 020 8969 1207 — MB BS 1993 Lond.; MA Camb. 1994; DCH 1996; DRCOG 1996. (Char. Cross and Westm. Med. Sch.) Prev: Trainee GP/SHO (Paediat.) St. Mary's Hosp. Lond. VTS; GP Reg Fernville Surg. Hemel Hempstead; SHO (A & E) St. Mary's Hosp. Lond.

ELLIOTT, Richard Hugh The White House, 100 Ewe Lamb Lane, Bramcote, Nottingham NG9 3JW Tel: 0115 939 2718 — MB BCh 1980 Wales; FFA RCS Eng. 1987. Cons. Anaesth. Derbysh. Roy. Infirm.

ELLIOTT, Robert John (retired) The Old Coach House, 35 Barton Road, Hoylake, Wirral CH47 1HJ Tel: 0151 632 0241 — MB BChir 1965 Camb.; MA Camb. 1965; MRCS Eng. LRCP Lond. 1962; MFCM 1974; DPH Liverp. 1970. Prev: Port Med. Off. Manch. Port HA.

ELLIOTT, Robert Walter (retired) 70 Darras Road, Darras Hall, Ponteland, Newcastle upon Tyne NE20 9PG Tel: 01661 820165 — MB BS 1954 Durh.; MD Durh. 1962; FRCP Lond. 1980; MRCP (UK) 1972. Prev: Cons. Phys. Newc. AHA (T).

ELLIOTT, Robert Wilfred (retired) Harlech House, 2 Isaacson Road, Burwell, Cambridge CB5 0AF Tel: 01638 741641 — MB BS Durh. 1939.

ELLIOTT, Ronald Witham, CBE (retired) Apartment 25, The Lawns, Skipton Road, Ilkley LS29 9EW Tel: 01943 607722 — MB ChB 1937 Sheff.; MB ChB (Hons.) Sheff. 1937; MSc Sheff. 1935, BSc (Hons.), MD 1947; FFCM 1972; DPH Lond. 1939. Hon. Maj. RAMC. Prev: MOH & Princip. Sch. Med. Off. Bolton Co. Boro.

ELLIOTT, Sarah Elizabeth 9 The Broadshoard, Cowbridge CF71 7DA — MB BCh 1992 Wales.

ELLIOTT, Sarah Jacqueline 62 High Street, Penistone, Sheffield S36 6BS Tel: 01226 764412 — MB BS 1988 Newc.; MRCPsych 1997. Regist. (Psychiat.) Community Health Sheff. Prev: SHO Manch. & Salford Health Auth.

ELLIOTT, Sean Michael 2 Keslake Road, London NW6 6DL — MB ChB 1990 Sheff. Socs: Pharmaceut. Soc. Prev: Ho. Off. (Gen. Med., Gen. Surg. & Neurosurg.) Roy. Hallamsh. Hosp. Sheff.

ELLIOTT, Shirley Ann The Portland Practice, St Paul's Medical Centre, 121 Swindon Road, Cheltenham GL50 4DP Tel: 01242 707794 Fax: 01242 707792 Email: shirley.elliott@gp-l84033.nhs.uk — MB BS 1973 Lond.; MRCGP 1978; DRCOG 1979. Clin. Governance Lead, Cheltenham & Tewksbury PCG.

ELLIOTT, Simon 9 Devonshire Avenue, Beeston, Nottingham NG9 1BS Tel: 0115 925 0330 — BM BS 1979 Nottm.; FRCR 1986. Cons. Radiol. Derby Hosps., Trent Region. HA.

ELLIOTT, Simon Denis Cotton Elliott, The Health Centre, Robin Hood Lane, Sutton SM1 2RJ Tel: 020 8642 2229/2220 — MB ChB 1974 Dundee.

ELLIOTT, Simon Timothy Dept. of Radiology, Freeman Hospital., Newcastle upon Tyne NE7 7DN — MB ChB 1978 Sheff.; FRCR

1985. Cons. Radiol. Freeman Hosp. NHS Trust Newc. Prev: Cons. Radiol. Sunderland HA; Sen. Regist. (Diag. Radiol.) N.. RHA.

ELLIOTT, Siobhan Colette Groveley Farm, Alvechurch, Birmingham B48 7AR Tel: 0121 445 1680 Fax: 0121 445 1680 — MB ChB 1989 Sheff.; MRCGP 1995; DRCOG 1994; DFFP 1995. (Sheff.) Clin. Asst. (GU Med.) Alexandra Hosp. Redditch; Clin. Med. Off. (Family Plann.) Worcester. Socs: BMA; MPS. Prev: SHO (Gen. & Geriat. Med.) Cheltenham Gen. Hosp.; Ho. Off. (Med.) Worcester Roy. Infirm.; Ho. Off. (Surg.) York Dist. Hosp.

ELLIOTT, Steven Andrew Old Hall Drive, Ulverston LA12 7DG — MB ChB 1994 Dundee.

ELLIOTT, Susan Carol Schopwick Surgery, Everett Court, Romeland, Elstree, Borehamwood WD6 3BJ Tel: 020 8953 1008 Fax: 020 8905 2196 — MB BS 1979 Lond.; DCH RCP Lond. 1983; MRCGP 1984; DRCOG 1982.

ELLIOTT, Thomas Paul Holywell Hospital, 60 Steeple Road, Antrim BT41 2RJ — MB BCh BAO 1979 Belf.; MRCPsych 1984.

ELLIOTT, Professor Thomas Stuart Jackson Department of Clinical Microbiology, Queen Elizabeth Hospital, Edgbaston, Birmingham B15 2TH Tel: 0121 627 2366 Fax: 0121 414 1682 Email: tom.elliott@university-b.wmids.nhs.uk — BM BS 1980 Nottm.; PhD Lond. 1975, BMed Sc. (Hons.) 1978, BTech (Hons.) 1972; FRCPath 1995, M 1984; FRMS 1974. (Nottingham) Cons. Microbiol. Qu. Eliz. Hosp. & Qu. Eliz. Med. Centre Edgbaston; Dir. Microbiol. Univ. Hosp. Birm. NHS Trust; Dir. Clin. Laborat. Servs. Univ. Hosp. Birm. NHS Trust. Socs: (Edit. Bd.) Hosp. Infec. Soc. Prev: Reader (Bact.) & Hon. Cons. (Microbiol. Med.) Sch. Univ. Newc.; Sen. Regist. (Med. Microbiol.) PHLS Laborat. Qu. Med. Centre Nottm.

ELLIOTT, Tom Kenneth (private), Dolcoath House, Coppenhall, Stafford ST18 9BL Tel: 01785 42814 — MB BS 1938 Lond.; MRCS Eng. LRCP Lond. 1939. (St. Mary's) CStJ; Mem. Pneumoconiosis Med. Panel Stoke-on-Trent; Assoc. Camborne Sch. Mines; Co. Commr. (R) St. John Ambul. Brig.; Mem. Cornish Inst. Engin. Prev: Mines Med. Off (Midl. Region) Min. of Fuel & Power; Ho. Surg. St. Mary's Hosp.; Asst. Phys. Moorcroft Ho. Hillingdon.

ELLIOTT, William Douglas (retired) East Wing, Cramlington Hall, Cramlington NE23 6PZ Tel: 01670 713104 — MB ChB 1948 Ed.; FRCP Ed. 1975, M 1957; DCH Eng. 1957. Prev: Cons. Paediat. N. Tyneside HA.

ELLIOTT-BINNS, Christopher Plunkett Elliott (retired) 31 Church Street, Cogenhoe, Northampton NN7 1LS Tel: 01604 890095 — MB BChir 1948 Camb.; MD Camb. 1974; FRCGP 1978, M 1963; DCH Eng. 1954; DObst RCOG 1954. Prev: GP N.ampton.

ELLIS, Alexander Walmsley Shiphay Manor, 37 Shiphay Lane, Torquay TQ2 7DU Tel: 01803 615059 Fax: 01803 614545; Hormead Bury, St. Katherine's Road, Torquay TQ1 4DE — MB BS 1974 Lond.; BSc Lond. 1971; MRCS Eng. LRCP Lond. 1974. (Guy's)

ELLIS, Amanda Jayne Pfizer Central Research, Sandwich CT13 9NJ Tel: 01304 616161 — MB BS 1989 Lond.; BSc Lond. 1986; MRCP (UK) 1992. Clin. Research Phys. Regulatory Affairs Gp. Pfizer Sandwich. Socs: Brain Res. Assn.; Brit. Neuropsychiat. Assn. Prev: Regist. (Psychiat.) Maudsley Hosp. Lond.; SHO (Cardiol.) Roy. Brompton Nat. Heat & Lung Hosp. Lond.; SHO (Med.) Whittington Hosp. Lond.

ELLIS, Andrée Georgina Church View Cottage, 51 High St. Chapeltown, Turton, Bolton BL7 0EW — MB ChB 1987 Manch.; BSc (Med. Sci.) St. And. 1984. SHO (Obst.) Stockport HA.

ELLIS, Andrew Michael Department of Elderly Mental Health, Clatterbridge Hospital, Bebington, Wirral CH63 4JY Tel: 0151 604 7467; Email: mail@andrewellis.co.uk — BM BS 1987 Nottm.; BMedSci Nottm. 1985; MMedSci Leeds 1994; MRCPsych 1993. Cons. Old Age Psychiat. Clatterbridge Hosp. Wirral & W. Chesh. Community NHS Trust. Prev: Sen. Regist. Rotat. (Old Age Psychiat.) Merseyside.; Regist. Rotat. (Psychiat.) Leeds; SHO Rotat. (Psychiat.) Humberside.

ELLIS, Anne Canolfan Iechyd, Village Road, Llanfairfechan LL33 0NH Tel: 01248 680021 Fax: 01248 681711; Tyddyn Ap Ifan, Penmaenmawr LL34 6ER — MB ChB 1978 Liverp. GP Princip.; CMO (Child Health & Learning Disabil.).

ELLIS, Anthony 5Z Link, Royal Liverpool University Hospital, Prescot St., Liverpool L7 8XP Tel: 0151 706 3414 Fax: 0151 706 5832 — MB ChB 1971 Liverp.; MD Liverp. 1980; FRCP Lond. 1989; MRCP (UK) 1975. Cons. Phys & Gastroenterol. Roy. Liverp. & BRd.green Univ. Hosps. NHS Trust. Socs: Brit. Soc. Gastroenterol.; Clin. Genetics Soc.

ELLIS, Anthony John Mesnes View Surgery, Mesnes Street, Wigan WN1 1ST Tel: 01942 242350 Fax: 01942 826431 — MB ChB 1978 Liverp. (Liverp.) Local Med. Off. Civil Serv.; Occupat. Phys. Remploy Centr. Lancs. Printers Wigan.

ELLIS, Antony John The Horton Hospital, John Radcliffe NHS Trust, Oxford Road, Banbury OX16 9AL Tel: 01295 229029 — MB BS 1987 Lond.; MRCP 1990. (St Thomas Hosp) Cons. Gestroenterologist/Hepatologist Horton Hosp. Banbury; Cons. Hepatologist John Radcliffe Hosp. Oxf. Prev: Sen.Reg.Instit.Liver.Studies kings.Coll..Hosp.Lond.

ELLIS, Arthur Glyndwr 13 Heol Peredur, Thornhill, Cardiff CF14 9HP — MB BCh 1961 Wales.

ELLIS, Basil Robert 1 Menlo Close, Oxton, Birkenhead CH43 9YD Tel: 0151 652 6829 — MRCS Eng. LRCP Lond. 1950; MFCM 1978; MFOM RCPI 1978; DPH Manch. 1958; DIH Eng. 1959. (Leeds) Occupat. Health Phys. Liverp. Univ. Socs: Soc. Occupat. Med. Prev: Med. Off. Vauxhall Motors, Ellesmere Port, Unilever Merseyside Ltd. & N. W.. Gas Bd.

ELLIS, Brian David Young, Ellis and Overton, 41 David Place, St Helier, Jersey JE2 4TE Tel: 01534 723318 Fax: 01534 611062; Le Grenier, Le Couvent, St Lawrence, Jersey JE3 1ND Tel: 01534 864488 Fax: 01534 866997 Email: bdellis@cinergy.uk — MB BS 1984 Lond.; BPharm (Hons.) Wales 1976; MRCGP 1988. (St. Thos. Hosp. Lond.) GP St Helier, Jersey. Prev: SHO/Trainee GP Bristol VTS.; Ho. Surg. Jersey Gen. Hosp.; Ho. Phys. ScarBoro. Hosp.

ELLIS, Brian Gareth Swan Surgery, Swan Street, Petersfield GU32 3AB Tel: 01730 264011 Fax: 01730 231093; 18 Heath Road, Petersfield GU31 4DU — MB BS 1978 Lond.; PhD Lond. 1973, BSc 1969, MB BS 1978; MRCP (UK) 1980. (St. Thos.)

ELLIS, Mr Brian William Ashford Hospital, London Road, Ashford TW15 3AA Tel: 01784 884429 Fax: 01784 884393; Graylands, 124 Brox Road, Ottershaw, Chertsey KT16 0LG Tel: 01932 873254 Fax: 01932 873254 Email: brian.ellis@dial.pipex.com — MB BS Lond. 1970; FRCS Eng. 1977. (St. Mary's) Cons. Urol. Surg. Ashford & St Peter's Hosps. NHS Trust; Hon. Sen. Clin. Research Fell. St. Mary's Hosp. Med. Sch. Lond.; Edr. Hamilton Bailey's Emerg. Surg. (Ed. 13). Socs: Brit. Assn. Urol. Surgs. Prev: Sen. Regist. (Surg.) St. Mary's Hosp. Lond.; Sen. Regist. (Surg.) N.wick Pk. Hosp. & Clin. Research Centre Harrow; Research Fell. (Surg. Unit) St. Mary's Hosp. Lond.

ELLIS, Carolyn Stoke Gifford Medical Centre, Ratcliffe Drive, Stoke Gifford, Bristol BS34 8UE Tel: 0117 979 9430 Fax: 0117 940 6999 — MB ChB 1982 Bristol; MB ChB 1982 Bristol.

ELLIS, Catherine Maria Department of Neurology, Institute of Psychiatry, De Crespigny Park, London SE5 8AF Tel: 0207 346 5172 Fax: 0207 346 5191 — MB BS 1991 Lond.; PhD 2001; BSc (Hons.) Lond. 1988; MRCP (UK) 1994. (UMDS) Research Fell. Specialist Regist. Neurol. S. E. Thames Inst. Psychiat. Lond. Prev: Regist. (Gen. Med.) King's Healthcare Lond.; Research Fell. (Neurol.) Inst. Psychiat. Lond.

ELLIS, Cathleen Margaret The Grange, Leigh, Sherborne DT9 6HL — MB BS 1974 Lond. (St. Bart.) Clin. Asst. (Anaesth.) Yeovil Dist. Hosp. Prev: Clin. Asst. (A & E) Yeovil Dist. Hosp.; Regist. (Anaesth.) Salisbury Gen. Hosp.; SHO (A & E) Roy. Hants. Co. Hosp. Winchester.

ELLIS, Cheryl Esme Gay Epsom General Hospital, Dorking Road, Epsom KT18 7EG Tel: 01372 735735 Fax: 01372 735290 — MB BS 1977 Lond.; MRCOG 1984; FRCOG 1997. (Royal Free) Cons. O & G Epsom Gen. Hosp. Prev: Sen. Regist. & Cons. O & G Roy. Postgrad. Med. Sch., Inst. O & G Qu. Charlotte's & Chelsea Hosp. for Wom. Lond.; Sen. Lect. & Cons. O & G Ealing Gen. Hosp.

ELLIS, Christine Vivian 109 Dorridge Road, Dorridge, Solihull B93 8BP — MB ChB Liverp. 1963.

ELLIS, Christopher David Winter Stopsley Group Practice, Wigmore Lane Health Centre, Luton LU2 8BG — MB BS 1982 Lond. Gen. Pract.

ELLIS, Christopher James Kirkham Heath Lodge, 28 Lower Golf Links Road, Broadstone BH18 8BH Tel: 01202 693311 — MD 1980 Lond.; BSc Lond. 1971, MD 1980, MB BS 1974; FRCP Lond. 1991; MRCP (UK) 1976. (Guy's) Cons. Neurol. Poole Gen. Hosp. & Wessex Neurol. Centre Soton. Prev: Sen. Regist. (Neurol.) Nat.

Hosp. Nerv. Dis. Lond.; Research Fell. (Neuro-ophth.) St. Thos. Hosp. Lond.

ELLIS, Christopher John Cults Medical Group, Cults Medical Centre, South Avenue, Cults, Aberdeen AB15 9LQ Tel: 01224 867740 Fax: 01224 861392 — MB BS 1983 Lond.; MRCGP 1995; DA (UK) 1993; DRCOG 1989; DLO RCS Eng. 1987. (Middlx. Hosp. Lond.)

ELLIS, Christopher John 27 Rosslyn Avenue, Mountsorrel, Loughborough LE12 7UQ — BM BS 1994 Nottm. SHO Rotat. (Med.) Lincoln Co. Hosp.

ELLIS, Christopher John Frome Medical Practice, Health Centre, Park Road, Frome BA11 1EZ Tel: 01373 301300 Fax: 01373 301313 — MB BS 1965 Lond.; MRCS Eng. LRCP Lond. 1965; DCH Eng. 1967; DObst RCOG 1968. (St. Mary's) Socs: BMA. Prev: SHO Soton. Childr. Hosp.; Ho. Phys. St. Mary's Hosp. Lond.; Ho. Surg. Chichester Hosp. Gp.

ELLIS, Christopher John Department of Infection and Tropical Medicine, Heartlands Hospital, Birmingham B9 5ST Tel: 0121 766 6611 Fax: 0121 766 8752; The White House, Tithe Barn Lane, Hockley Heath, Solihull B94 5DH Tel: 0156 470 2267 — MB BS 1971 Lond.; FRCP Lond. 1986; MRCP (UK) 1973; DTM & H Lond 1980. Cons. Phys. (Communicable & Trop. Dis.) Heartlands Hosp. Birm.; Sen. Clin. Lect. Univ. of Birm. Prev: Lect. Med. Unit Lond. Hosp. Med. Coll.; Sen. Regist. (Med.) Univ. Coll. Hosp. Ibadan Nigeria; Regist. (Med.) Bristol Roy. Infirm.

ELLIS, Colin D'Arcy (retired) The Gables, Lansdowne, Bourton-on-the-Water, Cheltenham GL54 2AR Tel: 01451 822208 Fax: 01451 82208 Email: cdaellis@aol.com — MB BS Lond. 1955; MRCS Eng. LRCP Lond. 1955; MRCGP 1966; DObst RCOG 1958. Prev: Mem. (Chairm.) St. Helens & Knowsley LMC.

ELLIS, Daniel Yitzhak 2 Thorburn Road, Northampton NN3 3DA — MB BS 1994 Lond. Resid. Med. Off. N. Lond. Nuffield Hosp.; Demonst. (Anat.) Char. Cross Hosp. Lond.; SHO (A & E) Lewisham Hosp. Prev: Ho. Off. (Gen. Surg.) Worthing Hosp.; Ho. Phys. N.ants. Gen. Hosp.

ELLIS, David Allen James Paget Hospital, Lowestoft Road, Gorleston, Great Yarmouth NR31 6LA; Woodside Barn, The Green, North Burlingham, Norwich NR13 4SZ — MB ChB 1971 Ed.; FRCP Lond. 1994; FRCP Ed. 1991. Cons. Phys. Chest Med. Jas. Paget Hosp. NHS Trust. Socs: Brit. Thorac. Soc. Prev: Sen. Regist. (Chest & Gen. Med.) Newc. AHA (T); Regist. (Respirat. Dis.) City Hosp. Edin.; Ho. Phys. Roy. Infirm. Edin.

ELLIS, David Baron (retired) 33 Winn Road, Lee, London SE12 9EX — MB BS 1958 Lond.; FFA RCS Eng. 1964; DA Eng. 1960. Prev: Cons. Anaesth. St. Peter's Hosp., Nat. Hosp. Nerv. Dis. & St. Luke's Hosp. for Clergy Lond.

ELLIS, David Graham Waterlow Unit, Whittington Hospital, Highgate Hill, London N19 5NX Tel: 020 7530 2216 Fax: 020 7530 2220; 37 Ashley road, London N19 3AG — MB BS 1987 Lond.; MA Oxf. 1979, DPhil 1979; MRCPsych 1991. Cons. Gen. Adult Psychiat. Camden & Islington Community Servs. NHS Trust. Prev: Sen. Regist. & Regist. (Psychiat.) Roy. Free Train. Scheme Lond.

ELLIS, David James Parr 6 Cliffton Terrace, Ilkley LS29 8ED — BM BCh 1961 Oxf.; MRCS Eng. LRCP Lond. 1961; DPM Eng. 1967.

ELLIS, David James Snow Amberleigh Farm, Chudleigh, Newton Abbot TQ13 0DH — MB ChB 1996 Ed.

ELLIS, Mr David John 32 Green Lane, Poynton, Stockport SK12 1TJ Tel: 01625 878666 — MB ChB 1987 Manch.; BSc (Hons.) St. And. 1984; FRCPS Glas. 1992. Specialist Regist. (Orthop.) Leeds.

ELLIS, Mr David John Sandwell General Hospital, Lyndon, West Bromwich B71 4HJ Tel: 0121 607 3459 Fax: 0121 607 3399; 35 Duncombe Street, Wollaston, Stourbridge DY8 3QY Tel: 01384 394408 Fax: 01384 828483 Email: djellis@doctors.org.uk — MB ChB 1970 St. And.; FRCS Eng. 1975. (St. And.) Cons. Gen. Surg. Sandwell Dist. Gen. Hosp. Sandwell Healthcare NHS Trust. Socs: Assn. Surg.; BASO. Prev: Sen. Regist. (Surg.) W. Midl. Train. Scheme; Regist. Rotat. (Surg.) United Birm. Hosps.; Ho. Surg. Profess. Surg. Unit Dundee Roy. Infirm.

ELLIS, David John 38 Kings Road, Minster on Sea, Sheerness ME12 2HL Tel: 0973 884915 Fax: 0973 884915 Email: djellis@baroque.co.uk — MB BS 1992 Lond. (Kings Coll. Sch. Med. & Dent.) Specialist Regist. Anaesth. Medway Hosp. Gillingham. Prev: SHO (Anaesth.) Brighton (RSCH); SHO (Anaesth.) E.bourne DGH; Locum Specialist Regist. Anaesth.E.bourne.DCH.

ELLIS, David Leslie Iain 3 Millbrook Green, Aylburton, Lydney GL15 6BY — MB ChB 1993 Bristol.

ELLIS, David Lionel Westlins, Langbank Drive, Kilmacolm PA13 4PL Tel: 01505 873139; Haematology Department, Inverclyde Royal Hospital, Larkfield Road, Greenock PA16 0RN Tel: 01475 656174 Fax: 01475 635486 — MB BS Lond. 1966; FRCPath 1987, M 1975. (St. Mary's) Cons. Haemat. Inverclyde Roy. Hosp. Greenock. Socs: Brit. Soc. Haematol. Prev: Sen. Regist. (Haemat.) W.. Infirm. Glas.; Regist. (Bact. & Haemat.) Vict. Infirm. Glas.; Ho. Surg. Qu. Eliz. II Hosp. Welwyn Gdn. City.

ELLIS, David Stuart London School of Hygiene & Tropical Medicine, Keppel St., London WC1E 7HT — BM BCh Oxf. 1957; DM Oxf. 1979. Hon. Sen. Research Fell. Lond. Sch. Hyg. & Trop. Med.; Hon. Cons. Microbiol. Pub. Health Laborat. Serv. Socs: Fell. Roy. Soc. Trop. Med. & Hyg. Prev: Sen. Lect. & Head. of Electron-Microscopy Laborat. Lond. Sch. Hyg. & Trop. Med.

ELLIS, Derick Davison (retired) Innisfree, Crescent Rise, Constantine Bay, Padstow PL28 8JE — MB BCh BAO 1948 Belf.; MRCPsych 1971; DPM RCPSI 1953. Prev: Cons. Psychiat. Cornw. & I. of Scilly HA.

ELLIS, Donald Henry (retired) Wentworth, The Street, Chilcompton, Bath BA3 4HG Tel: 01761 232877 — MB ChB 1949 Birm. Maj. RAMC T & AVR. Prev: Local Treasury Med. Off.

ELLIS, Donald Maxwell (retired) 23 Lansdowne Avenue, Mansfield NG18 4QJ Tel: 01623 653609 — MB BCh BAO 1953 Belf. Prev: Ho. Surg. & Ho. Phys., Ho. Obstetr. & Cas. Off. Banbridge Hosp.

ELLIS, Doreen Alice (retired) 46 St Margaret's Street, Bradford-on-Avon BA15 1DE Tel: 01225 863509 — MB ChB 1950 Bristol; DObst RCOG 1953. Prev: Asst. Resid. Med. Off. Childr. Hosp. Bristol.

ELLIS, Elin Mererid Glanrhyd Hospital, Tondu Road, Bridgend CF31 4LN Tel: 01656 752752 — MB BCh 1990 Wales; 1997 MRCPsych. (Cardiff) Specialist Regist. Glanrhyd Hosp. Socs: Welsh Med. Soc.; Welsh Psychiat. Soc.; Roy. Coll. Psychiat. Prev: Specialist Regist. (Psychiat.) Dany Bryn Unit, Ebbow Vale; Specialist Regist. (Psychiat.) St. Tydfils Hosp. Merthr Tydfil; Regist. (Psychiat.) Ysbyty Glan Clwyd.

ELLIS, Elizabeth 14 Bingham Terrace, Dundee DD4 7HH — MB ChB 1989 Glas.; MRCGP 1993.

ELLIS, Elizabeth Jane Bramblecombe, Newtown Common, Newbury RG20 9DD — MB ChB 1970 Liverp.; DObst RCOG 1972. Socs: Inst. Psychosexual Med. 1996.

ELLIS, Elizabeth Louise 27 Windsor Road, Renfrew PA4 0SS — MB ChB 1984 Glas.; MB ChB Glas. l984. SHO (Gyn.) W.. Infirm. Glas. Prev: SHO (Obst.) Qu. Mother's Hosp. Glas.; SHO (Gyn.) Roy. Samarit. Hosp. Glas.

ELLIS, Eric Leslie (retired) 2 Coach Hill, Titchfield, Fareham PO14 4EE Tel: 01329 843570 Email: ellis@leslie620-freeserve.co.uk — MA Camb.; MRCS Eng. LRCP Lond. 1939.

ELLIS, Eric William Walter (retired) Orchard Cottage, Chapel Lane, Kirby Cross, Frinton-on-Sea CO13 0NF Tel: 01255 677374 — MRCS Eng. LRCP Lond. 1944. Prev: Capt. RAMC.

ELLIS, Errington (retired) 10 Hawthorn Road W., Gosforth, Newcastle upon Tyne NE3 4DN Tel: 0191 285 3973 — MB BChir 1945 Camb.; MA, MD Camb. 1955; MRCS Eng. LRCP Lond. 1945, DCH Eng. 1950; FRCPCH 1997. Prev: Cons. Paediatr. Child Developm. Centre, Roy. Vict. Infirm. Newc.

ELLIS, Ervine Allingham Bognor Medical Practice, West Street, Bognor Regis PO21 1UT Tel: 01243 823864 Fax: 01243 623800; Holmwood House, Claypit Lane, Westhampnett, Chichester PO18 0NU Tel: 01243 776294 — MB ChB 1966 Liverp. Prev: SHO (Paediat.) Roy. W. Sussex Hosp. Chichester; Ho. Off. (O & G) & SHO (Psychiat.) Sefton Gen. Hosp. Liverp.

ELLIS, Professor Francis Richard Academic Unit of Anaesthesia, Clinical Sciences Building, St James' University Hospital, Leeds LS9 7TF Tel: 0113 206 5274 Fax: 0113 206 4140 Email: f.r.ellis@leed.ac.uk — MB ChB Manch. 1959; PhD Leeds 1971; FRCA 1964; DA Eng. 1962; DObst RCOG 1961. (Manch.) Prof. Anaesth. Univ. Leeds; Hon. Cons. Anaesth. Leeds HAs; Dir. Malig. Hyperthermia Unit St. Jas. Univ. Hosp. Socs: Assn. Anaesth.; Anaesth. Res. Soc.; Roy. Soc. Med. Prev: MRC Research Fell.

(Anaesth.) Univ. Leeds; Mem of Counc. & Sen. Vice Pres Roy. Coll of Anaesth.

ELLIS, Frank 2 Bladon Close, Woodstock Road, Oxford OX2 8AD Tel: 01865 59185 — MB ChB Sheff. 1929; MA Oxf. 1952; BSc Sheff. 1927, MSc 1928, MD 1944, MB ChB 1929; Hon. DSc Ohio State Univ. Columbus 1993; FRCP Lond. 1968, M 1959; FRCR 1938; DMR 1933; Hon. FACR 1977; Hon. FIPSM 1988. Socs: Brit. Inst. Radiol.; Fell. Roy. Soc. Med. Prev: Emerit. Cons. Dept. Radiat. Oncol. Oxf.; Cons. Radiother. Lond. Hosp.; Med. Dir. Sheff. Nat. Radium Centre.

ELLIS, Mr Frank The Cottage, Grammar School Lane, Northallerton DL6 1DA Tel: 01609 2492 — MB BS 1948 Durh.; FRCS Eng. 1955. (Durh.) Prev: Sen. Cons. Surg. Memor. Hosp. Darlington & Friarage Hosp. N.allerton; Sen. Regist. Univ. Coll. Hosp. Lond. & Roy. Vict. Infirm. Newc.; Cons. Mem. N. Yorks. HA & N.allerton Health Dist.

ELLIS, Mr Frank Groves 97 Harley Street, London W1N 1DF Tel: 020 7486 6220 Fax: 020 7403 2323 — MB BS 1950 Lond.; MS Lond. 1960; FRCS Eng. 1953; MRCS Eng. LRCP Lond. 1949. (Guy's) Emerit. Cons. Gen. & Vasc. Surg. Guy's Hosp.; Cons. Gen. & Vasc. Surg. Lond. Bridge Hosp. Socs: Assn. Surg.; (Ex-Pres.) Med. Soc. Lond. Prev: Cons. Surg. Roy. N.. Hosp. Lond.; Vis. Asst. Prof. Surg. Univ. Calif. Sch. Med. San Francisco, USA; Pres. Med. Soc. Lond.

ELLIS, George G Skene Medical Group, Westhill Drive, Westhill AB32 6FY Tel: 01224 742213 Fax: 01224 744664 — MB ChB 1979 Aberdeen; MB ChB 1979 Aberdeen.

ELLIS, Glenys Gwenhwyfar Isgaer, 21 Church St., Caernarfon LL55 1SW — LMSSA 1952 Lond.

ELLIS, Gordon Harcourt (retired) 152 St Peters Avenue, Caversham, Reading RG4 7DR Tel: 01118 947 5713 — MB BS 1955 Lond. Prev: Div. Med. Off., Dept. Health.

ELLIS, Graham 26 Lindsay Place, Glasgow G12 0HX — MB ChB 1995 Glas.

ELLIS, Graham Neil Pyenot House, Knowle Top Road, Lightcliffe, Halifax HX3 8SW — MB ChB 1995 Glas.

ELLIS, Gwyneth Nelian (retired) Brynfield Manor Nursing Home, Brynfield Road, Langland Bay, Swansea SA3 4SX — M.B., B.S. Lond. 1932.

ELLIS, Professor Harold, CBE 16 Bancroft Avenue, London N2 0AS Tel: 020 8348 2720 — BM BCh 1948 Oxf.; MA Oxf. 1951; DM Oxf. 1962, MCh 1956; FRCS Eng. 1951; Hon. FACS 1989; FRCOG 1987. (Oxf.) Emerit. Prof. Surg. Char. Cross & W.m. Hosp. Med. Sch.; Clin. Anat. Univ. Lond. Guy's Hosp. Socs: Hon. Fell. Roy. Soc. Med.; (Ex-Pres.) Brit. Assn. Clin. Anat. Prev: Clin. Anat. Univ. Camb.; Resid. Surg. Off. Roy. Infirm. Sheff.; Tutor (Surg.) Radcliffe Infirm. Oxf.

ELLIS, Ian Harold Department of Clinical Genetics, Alder Hey Children's Hospital, Eaton Road, Liverpool L12 2AP Tel: 0151 252 5905 Fax: 0151 252 5951 Email: Ian.Illis@vrcade.net; Tel: 0161 428 0546 Email: canelise@onetel.net.uk — MB BS 1983 Lond.; BSc (Hons.) Lond. 1980; MRCP (UK) 1987; FRCP 1999. (Middlx.) Sen. Lect. & Hon. Cons. Clin. Genetics Inst. Child Health Liverp. Socs: Clin. Genetics Soc.; Brit. Soc. of Human Genetics; Cancer Genentics Gp. Prev: Sen. Regist. (Clin. Genetics) Guy's Hosp. Lond.; SHO (Nephrol.) Hammersmith Hosp. Lond.; SHO (Neurol.) Nat. Hosp. Lond.

ELLIS, Ian Ogilvie Department of Histopathology, City Hospital, Hucknall Road, Nottingham NG5 1PB Tel: 0115 969 1169 Fax: 0115 962 7768 Email: ian.ellis@nottingham.ac.uk; Yew Tree House, 2 Kenilworth Road, The Park, Nottingham NG7 1DD Tel: 0115 947 2186 — BM BS 1978 Nottm.; MRCPath 1985. (Nottm.) Reader (Pathol.) Univ. Nottm.; Hon. Cons. Path. City Hosp. Nottm. Socs: (Treas. & Counc.lor) Brit. Soc. Clin. Cytol.; (Counc.lor) Europ. Soc. Analyt. Cellular Path.; (Counc.lor) Brit. Div. Internat. Acad. Path. Prev: Lect. (Path.) Univ. Nottm.

ELLIS, Isabelle Baird (retired) 38 Tyrone Road, Thorpe Bay, Southend-on-Sea SS1 3HF — MB ChB 1958 Glas.; MFCM 1974; DPH Glas. 1962; DObst RCOG 1960. Prev: Cons. Pub. Health Med. S.end HA.

ELLIS, Jacob 14 St Andrews Road, Heald Green, Cheadle SK8 3ES — MB ChB 1950 Manch. (Manch.) Prev: Asst. Gen. Pract. Darbishire Ho. Health Centre, Univ. Manch.

ELLIS, Mr James Douglas (retired) Upper Panshill Farm, Murcott, Kidlington OX5 2RQ Tel: 01869 253050 — MB BChir 1955 Camb.; FRCS Eng. 1961; FRCOG 1976, M 1964. Prev: Cons. O & G Oxf. Radcliffe Trust.

ELLIS, Mr James Stokes (retired) 3 Otterbourne House Gardens, Otterbourne, Winchester SO21 2ER Tel: 01962 713378 — MB BChir Camb. 1937; MA Camb. 1937, MChir 1941; FRCS Eng. 1939; MRCS Eng. LRCP Lond. 1937. Prev: Prof. Orthop. & Accid. Surg. Univ. Soton.

ELLIS, Jane Alison Health Centre, Midland St., Long Eaton, Nottingham NG10 1NY; 14 Middleston Crescent, Beeston, Nottingham NG9 2TH Tel: 0115 925 7796 — MB ChB 1988 Sheff.; MRCGP 1993. Prev: SHO (Geriat.) Netheredge Hosp. Sheff.; Trainee GP Doncaster VTS; Ho. Off. (Gen. Surg.) & Ho. Off. (Gen. Med.) Doncaster Roy. Infirm.

ELLIS, Jane Cathryn 7 North End Road, Hinxton, Saffron Walden CB10 1RE — MB ChB 1989 Sheff.; DTM & H 1997; MRCP (UK) 1994. Specialist Regist., Bradford Roy. Infirm. (Paediat.). Prev: Regist. (Paediat.) St. Jas. Hosp. Leeds; Regist. (Paediat.) York Dist. Hosp.

ELLIS, Janet Winifred Maude 102 Grove Park Terrace, London W4 3JD; 77 Elm Street, Apt 610, Toronto ON MSG 1H4, Canada Tel: 00 1 4162601418 — BChir 1990 Camb.

ELLIS, Jeffrey Princess Street Surgery, Princess St., Normanton WF6 1AB Tel: 01924 892132 Fax: 01924 898168; The Manse, Steep Lane, Sowerby Bridge HX6 1PE Tel: 01422 839958 — MB ChB Leeds 1961. (Leeds) CMS Tutor Pontefract VTS; Hon. GP Tutor Univ. Leeds. Prev: CMS Tutor Pontefract VTS; Hon. GP Tutor Univ. Leeds.; Ho. Surg. & Ho. Phys. (Clin. Med.) Gen. Infirm. Leeds.

ELLIS, Jill Mary 10 Willoughby Road, London NW3 1SA — MB BS 1990 Lond.

ELLIS, Jocelyn Charles 20 Worrall Road, Clifton, Bristol BS8 2UE — MB BS 1984 Lond.; MICGP 1996. (Middlx.)

ELLIS, John Anthony James Forest Cottage, 60 St Algars, West Woodlands, Frome BA11 5ER — MB ChB 1996 Ed.

ELLIS, John Anthony Thornley Morecambe Health Centre, Hanover St., Morecambe LA4 5LY Tel: 01524 418418; Windermere Lodge, 9 St. John's Grove, Morecambe LA3 1ET Tel: 01524 415974 — MB BChir 1960 Camb.; MA, MB Camb. 1960, BChir 1959; MRCGP 1968; DObst RCOG 1967.

ELLIS, John David 14 Bingham Terrace, Dundee DD4 7HH — MB ChB 1989 Glas.

ELLIS, John Emery Hollybank House, Hob Lane, Entwistle, Bolton BL7 0LP Tel: 01204 852606 — MB ChB Manch. 1966; FRCP Lond. 1985, M 1971; DCH Eng. 1968; FRCPCH 1997. (Manch.) Cons. Paediat. Roy. Bolton Hosp. Prev: Cons. (Paediat.) Scunthorpe Hosp.; Sen. Regist. Manch. AHA (T); Tutor Child Health Univ. Manch.

ELLIS, John Finbar Mark 90 Deyncourt Gardens, Upminster RM14 1DQ — MB ChB 1992 Bristol.

ELLIS, John Williams (retired) 18 Hammets Way, Taunton TA1 1JY — MB BS 1947 Lond.; MRCS Eng. LRCP Lond. 1943; MRCGP 1953.

ELLIS, Jonathan Russell Clifton 24 Regent Street, Horbury, Wakefield WF4 6EP — BM BCh 1994 Oxf.

ELLIS, Julia Peregrine (retired) Ridgeway Hospital, Moorhead Road, Wroughton SN4 9DD Tel: 01793 814848 Fax: 01793 480817 — MB BS 1959 Lond.; FRCP Lond. 1980, M 1963; DCH Eng. 1961. Prev: Sen. Regist. (Dermat.) United Oxf. Hosps. & St. Geo. Hosp. Lond.

***ELLIS, Karen Anne** Middleham House, 43 Woodditton Road, Newmarket CB8 9BQ Tel: 01638 662146 — BM BCh 1997 Oxf.

ELLIS, Mr Kenneth David, Lt.-Col. RAMC Retd. 70 Churchfield Road, Poole BH15 2QP — MB ChB 1954 Ed.; FRCS Eng. 1966; FRCS Ed. 1966.

ELLIS, Laurence Malcolm 55 West Street, Storrington, Pulborough RH20 4DZ Tel: 0190 663083 — MB ChB 1953 Liverp. Prev: Sen. Ho. Off. (Path.) Pk. Hosp. Manch.; Ho. Phys. (Paediat.) Warrington Gen. Hosp.; Ho. Surg. (Gen. Surg.) Walton Hosp. Liverp.

ELLIS, Lucy Malins (retired) 124 Holifast Road, Sutton Coldfield B72 1AF Tel: 0121 350 9122 — MB ChB 1952 Birm.; DCH Eng. 1956; DObst RCOG 1955. Prev: SCMO Solihull AHA.

ELLIS, Lynne Northgate Medical Centre, Anchor Meadow Health Centre, Aldridge, Walsall WS9 8AJ Tel: 01922 450900 Fax: 01922 450910 — MB ChB 1980 Liverp.; MRCGP 1985; DCH RCP Lond. 1984; DRCOG 1984.

ELLIS, Mr Marcus (retired) Willowbrake, Batherton Lane, Nantwich CW5 7QH Tel: 01270 626979 — MB BCh 1969 Wales; FRCS Eng. 1975.

ELLIS, Maria Yvette Three Arches, 24 Church St, Churchtown, Preston PR3 0HT — MB ChB 1990 Leeds. Prev: GP/Regist. Bradford VTS; GP/Regist. Preston.

ELLIS, Marie Louise Flat 4 Stable Yard, Church End, Bletchingdon, Kidlington OX5 3DN — MRCS Eng. LRCP Lond. 1959; MRCPsych 1982. (Guy's)

ELLIS, Mary (retired) Red Thorn, Foxholes Road, Horwich, Bolton BL6 6AS Tel: 01204 668900 — MB ChB 1956 Manch.; DCH RCPS Glas. 1975; DObst RCOG 1957. Prev: Clin. Asst. (Paediat.) Bolton Gen. Hosp.

ELLIS, Mary 4 Froxmere Close, Solihull B91 3XG Tel: 0121 705 4514 — MB BS 1960 Lond.; MRCS Eng. LRCP Lond. 1960; MFFP 1993. (Roy. Free) Assoc. Specialist O & G (Ultrasonics) Solihull Matern. Hosp.; Sen. Clin. Med. Off. Community Med. (Family Plann.). Socs: BMA. Prev: Resid. Med. Off. & Cas. Off. Eliz. G. Anderson Hosp. Lond.

ELLIS, Mary Marjorie Garngoch Hospital, Hospital Road, Gorseinon, Swansea SA4 4LH Tel: 01792 892921 — MB BS 1983 Lond.; MRCGP 1987; MRCPsych 1990. Cons. Psychiat. of Old Age Garngoch Hosp. Prev: Sen. Regist. (Psychiat. Old Age) Cefn Coed Hosp. Swansea.

ELLIS, Mary Richmond (retired) St. Michael Station Road, Yarmouth, Isle of Wight PO41 0QX Tel: 01983 760087 — MB BS 1942 Lond.; MRCS Eng. LRCP Lond. 1942; MRCOG 1951.

ELLIS, Matthew James Clifford Department of Medical Oncology, Vincent T Lombaerdi Cancer Center, 3800 Reservoir Road NW, Washington DC 20007, USA Tel: 202 687 2222 Fax: 202 687 7889; Orchard End, 13 Main St, Kibworth Harcourt, Leicester LE8 0NR Tel: 0116 279 2323 — MB BChir 1984 Camb.; PhD Lond. 1992; BSc Lond. 1981; MRCP (UK) 1986. Med. Oncol. Fell. Geo.town Univ. Hosp. Washington DC, USA. Prev: Research Fell. Imperial Cancer Research Fund Lond.; Hon. Regist. (Med. Oncol.) & Regist. (Gastroenterol.) Hammersmith Hosp. Lond.

ELLIS, Maura Pauline Judith Child & Adolescent Services, Fieldhead House, 2-8 St Martins Avenue, Listerhills, Bradford BD7 1LG Tel: 01274 770369 — MB BS 1977 Lond.; MRCPsych 1983. Cons. Child & Adolesc. Psychiat. BradfordCommunity NHS Trust. Socs: Roy. Coll. Psychiat.

ELLIS, Maureen Child, Adolescent & Family Service, 2 Dragon Parade, Harrogate HG1 2BY Tel: 01423 523076 Fax: 01423 508157 — MB ChB 1959 Manch.; FRCPsych 1995, M 1978; DPM Leeds 1974; DCH RCPS Glas. 1971. (Manch.) Cons. Child & Adolesc. Psychiat. Child Adolesc. & Family Serv. Harrogate Health Care Trust. Socs: Fell. (Co-Ordinator Regional Represen.) Roy. Coll. Psychiat.; Assn. for Child Psychiat. & Psychiat.; BMA. Prev: Cons. Child & Adolesc. Psychiat. Pindar Oaks Child & Family Unit Barnsley; Sen. Regist. (Child & Adolesc. Psychiat.) St. Jas. Univ. Hosp. Leeds.

ELLIS, Michael Charles Thorpe Health Centre, St William's Way, Norwich NR7 0AJ Tel: 01603 701010 — MB BS 1963 Lond. (Guy's) Socs: BMA. Prev: Trainee Bacteriol. Pub. Health Laborat. Serv. Norwich; SHO (O & G) Kettering & Dist. Hosp. Gp.; Cas. Off. & Ho. Phys. St. Anthony's Hosp. Cheam.

ELLIS, Michael Frederick The Penryn Surgery, Saracen Way, Penryn TR10 8HX Tel: 01326 372502 Fax: 01326 378126; Ringing Low, Treworthal Road, Perranarworthal, Truro TR3 7QB Tel: 01872 863627 — MB BS 1979 Lond.; MRCGP 1984; DRCOG 1983. Prev: Trainee GP/SHO Cornw. & Isles of Scilly HA VTS; Ho. Surg. King Geo. Hosp. Ilford; Ho. Phys. Joyce Green Hosp. Dartford.

ELLIS, Michael Frederick Sanders Royal Crescent Surgery, 11 Royal Crescent, Cheltenham GL50 3DA Tel: 01242 580248 Fax: 01242 253618; 121 Old Bath Road, Cheltenham GL53 7DH Tel: 01242 514286 Email: docellism@aol.com — MB BS 1976 Lond.; DA Eng. 1978. (Lond. Hosp.) Med. Off. Cheltenham Coll. Socs: Med. Off. Sch. Assn. & Brit. Assn. Sports. Med. Prev: Trainee GP Exeter VTS; SHO (Anaesth.) Cheltenham Gen. Hosp.

ELLIS, Michael Stead Cheltenham Road Surgery, 16 Cheltenham Road, Gloucester GL2 0LS Tel: 01452 522575 Fax: 01452 304321; The Ship House, Maisemore, Gloucester GL2 8EX — MB BS 1980 Lond.; LRCP 1980; MRCGP 1986; DCH RCP Lond. 1985; DTM & H 1985; DRCOG 1982. (St. Mary's) Prev: Med. Supt. Ekhombe Hosp. Kwa Zulu, S. Africa; SHO (Perinat.) St. Mary's Hosp. Lond.; Med. Off. Holy Cross, Transkei, S. Africa.

ELLIS, Nia Saint Francis Hospice, The Hall, Broxhill Road, Havering-Atte-Bower, Romford RM4 1QH Tel: 01708 753319 Fax: 01708 757957 Email: niaellis@stfrancishospice.co.uk; 33 Theydon Grove, Epping CM16 4PX Tel: 01992 572069 Email: nia.ellis@virgin.net — MB BS 1980 Lond.; MRCP (UK) 1984; FRCP 1998. (The Middlesex Hospital Medical School) Med. Dir. & Hon. Cons. Palliat. Med. St. Francis Hospice Romford. Socs: Assn. for Palliat. Med. Prev: Cons. Palliat. Med. St. Joseph's Hospice Lond.; Sen. Regist. (Palliat. Med.) St. Joseph's Hospice Lond.; Clin. Lect. (Chem. Path.) Middlx. Hosp. Med. Sch. Lond.

ELLIS, Paul Anthony Department of Medicine, Royal Marsden Hospital, London SW3 6JJ Tel: 020 7352 8171; 12 Crookham Road, London SW6 4EQ — MB ChB 1986 Otago.

ELLIS, Paul Charles 34 Purbeck Road, Hornchurch RM11 1NA — MB ChB 1991 Dundee.

ELLIS, Paul Martyn Bewley Drive Surgery, 79 Bewley Drive, Liverpool L32 9PD Tel: 0151 546 2480 Fax: 0151 548 3474 — MB ChB 1982 Liverp.; MRCGP 1986.

ELLIS, Peter Airey (retired) Fruit Farm Cottage, Little Laver Road, Moreton, Ongar CM5 0JE Tel: 01277 890316 — MB ChB 1949 Manch.; MRCP Ed. 1959. Prev: Cons. Path. OldCh. Hosp. Romford.

ELLIS, Mr Peter David Maitland Department of Otolaryngology, Addenbrooke's Hospital, Hills Road, Cambridge CB2 2QQ — MB 1968 Camb.; MA Camb. 1969, MB 1968, BChir 1967; FRCS Eng. 1972. Cons. Surg. (Otolaryngol.) Addenbrooke's Hosp. Camb. Socs: Roy. Soc. Med & Brit. Soc. Otolaryngol. Prev: Research Fell. Dept. Otolaryngol. Univ. Toronto, Canada; Sen. Regist. (ENT) Middlx. Hosp. Lond.; Regist. (ENT) Radcliffe Infirm. Oxf.

ELLIS, Peter Francis Medical Services, Olympic House, Olympic Way, Wembley HA9 0DL Tel: 0208 795 8400; Knightons, 24 Oakhill Avenue, Pinner HA5 3DN Tel: 020 8429 0006 Fax: 0208 868 9889 — MB BChir 1977 Camb.; MA Camb. 1976; MMed 1993; MRCGP 1981; DGM RCP Lond. 1986; DCH RCP Lond. 1980; DRCOG 1978. (Cambridge/UCH (London)) Med. Adviser, Benefits Agency Med. Servs.; Med. Adviser, Lond. Boro. of Harrow & Hillingdon; Ment. Health Practit. Sect. 12 Approved; Examr. DGM (RCP). Prev: GP Trainer & Course Organiser Harrow GP VTS; Examr. MRCGP; Med. Adviser Hillingdon FHSA.

ELLIS, Peter Jonathan Kildonan House, Ramsbottom Road, Horwich, Bolton BL6 5NW; Red Thorn, Foxholes Road, Horwich, Bolton BL6 6AS Tel: 01204 668900 — MB ChB 1955 Manch.; MRCGP 1966; DObst RCOG 1960. (Manch) Jt. Sec. Wigan & Bolton LMC; Under Sec. Bolston Practs. Comm. Socs: Fell. Manch. Med. Soc.; Bolton Med. Soc.; Orton Dyslexia Assn. of USA. Prev: SHO (Med.) Roy. Lancaster Infirm.; Capt. RAMC, BAOR; Ho. Surg. Manch. Roy. Infirm.

ELLIS, Peter Kenneth 15 Manor Hill, Carnesure, Comber, Newtownards BT23 5FN — MB BCh BAO 1989 Belf.; MB BCh BAO (Hons.) Belf. 1989; MRCP (UK) 1992; FRCR 1995. (Qu. Univ. Belf.) Cons. Radiol. Roy. Vict. Hosp. Belf. Prev: SHO (Radiol.) Roy. Vict. Hosp. Belf.; SHO (Rheum.) Musgrave Pk. Hosp. Belf.; SHO (Nephrol.) Belf. City Hosp.

ELLIS, Peter Simon Chambers of Bernard Pearl, 7 New Square, Lincoln's Inn, London WC2A 3QS Tel: 020 7430 1660 Fax: 020 7430 1531 Email: pellis1@compuserv.com; 6 Princes Drive, Wealdstone, Harrow HA1 1XH Tel: 020 8427 8122 Fax: 020 8427 8122 — MB BS 1984 Lond.; MRCP (UK) 1990; DHMSA 1982. (St. Mary's) Barrister; Called to the Bar (Middle Temple) 1997. Socs: Fell. Med. Hist. Fac. Lond. Soc. Apoth.; Soc. Doctors in Law. Prev: Med. Off. HMS Herald; Regist. (Med.) RN Hosp. Haslar; SHO (Med.) RN Hosp. Plymouth.

ELLIS, Richard Andrew Department of Anaesthesia, Birch House, Steppinghill Hospital, Stockport SK2 7JE Tel: 0161 419 5869 — MB ChB 1991 Sheff.; FRCA 1998. Cons. Anaesth. Dept. of Anaesth. Stepping Hill Hosp. Stockport. Prev: Specialist Regist. Rotat. (Anaesth) Sheff.; SHO Rotat. (Anaesth.) Sheff.; Specialist Regist. Rotat.al (Anaesth.) Manch.

ELLIS, Richard Andrew Department of Clinical Oncology, Western General Hospital, Crewe Road S., Edinburgh EH4 2XU; 8 Eyre Crescent, 2F1, Edinburgh EH3 5ET — MB ChB 1992 Ed.; FRCR 2001; BSc (Med. Sci.) Ed. 1990; MRCP (UK) 1995. (Edinburgh) Specialist Regist. (Clin. Oncol.) W.ern Gen. Hosp. NHS Trust Edin.

ELLIS, Richard David 31 Elthorne Avenue, London W7 2JY Tel: 020 8567 8327 Email: rellis@elthorne.demon.ac.uk — MB BS 1987 Lond.; MRCP (UK) 1991. (Charing Cross and Westminster) Regist. (Gen. Med. & Gastroenterol.) Centr. Middlx. Hosp. Lond. Prev: Regist. (Gen. Med. & Gastroenterol.) St Thomas' Hosp. Lond.

ELLIS, Mr Richard Mackay Department of Rheumatology, District Hospital, Salisbury SP2 8BJ Tel: 01722 336262 Fax: 01722 337912; 161 Bouverie Avenue S., Salisbury SP2 8EB Tel: 01722 334381 — MB BChir Camb. 1966; FRCP Lond. 1989; FRCS Eng. 1971. (St. Thomas's) Cons. Rheum. Salisbury Gen. Hosp.; Sen. Lect. (Rheum.) Soton Univ.; Edr. Jl. Orthop. Med. Socs: Brit. Inst. Musculoskeletal Med.; Pres, Soc. Orthopaedic Med. Prev: Asst. Prof. Orthop. Univ. Rochester, NY.

ELLIS, Robert Hayden (retired) Bartholomews Cottage, School Lane, Southam, Cheltenham GL52 3NS Tel: 01242 524434 — MB BChir Camb. 1945; MD Camb. 1952; FRCP Lond. 1973, M 1949; MRCS Eng. LRCP Lond. 1945. Prev: Cons. Phys. Glos. Roy. Hosp.

ELLIS, Mr Robert Paul Nuffield Hospital, Derriford Road, Plymouth PL6 8BG Tel: 01752 774146 Fax: 01752 774146; House on the Hill, Saltash PL12 4AX Tel: 01752 842601 — MA, BM BCh Oxf. 1959; FRCS Eng. 1967; FCOphth. 1988; DO Eng. 1963. (Oxf. & St. Bart.) Hon. Cons. Ophth. Surg. Plymouth Roy. Eye Infirm. Socs: Fell. Roy. Soc. Med.; (Ex-Pres.) Med. Contact Lens Assn. UK.; Hon. Life. Mem. Med. Contact Lens & Ocular Surface Assn. Prev: Cons. Surg. Roy. Eye Infirm. Plymouth; Civil. Cons. Ophth. Surg. Roy. Naval Hosp. Plymouth; 1st Asst. Ophth. Unit St. Geo. Hosp. Lond.

ELLIS, Robin Margaret Bowness Unit., Mental Health Services of Salford, Burynew Road, Manchester M25 3BL Tel: 0161 772 3664 — BM BS 1981 Nottm.; BMedSci Nottm. 1979; MRCPsych 1987; Dip. Family Ther. Manch. 1995. Cons Rehabil. Psychiat. Prev: Cons. Psychiat. Roy. Preston Hosp.

ELLIS, Roger Hugh (retired) 24 Head Street, Goldhanger, Maldon CM9 8AY Tel: 01621 788430 — BA Camb. 1954, MB 1958, BChir 1957; MRCOG 1974. Prev: Wing Cdr. RAF Med. Br., Specialist (O & G).

ELLIS, Ronald 8 St Mary's Road, Leicester LE2 1XA — MB ChB 1956 Sheff.; MRCOG 1966, DObst 1963.

ELLIS, S J Beighton Health Centre, Queens Road, Beighton, Sheffield S20 1BJ Tel: 0114 269 5061.

ELLIS, Sally Rachel 25 Burley Hill, Allestree, Derby DE22 2ET — MB ChB 1989 Leeds; BSc Leeds 1986; DCH Otago 1994; MRCP 1997. Specialist Paediat. Regist. Birm. Childr.'s Hosp.

ELLIS, Sarah Caroline 66 Culverden Park, Tunbridge Wells TN4 9QS Tel: 01892 536205 — BM 1998 Soton.; BM Soton 1998. SHO Paediat. B/ham Childr.s Hosp. Prev: PRHO Med. Salisbury Hosp. feb99-Aug99; PRHO Surg. Portsmouth QA Hosp. Aug 98 - Feb 99.

ELLIS, Simon Brian Auckland Northgate Medical Practice, 1 Northgate, Canterbury CT1 1WL Tel: 01227 463570 Fax: 01227 786147 — MB BS 1979 Lond.; MRCS Eng. LRCP Lond. 1979.

ELLIS, Mr Simon Charles Maidstone District Hospital, Hermitage Lane, Maidstone ME16 9QQ Tel: 01622 224966 Fax: 01622 224555; Tel: 01580 892984 — MB BS 1985 Lond.; MA Camb. 1988; FRCS (Orth.) 1996; FRCS Eng. 1990. (Char. Cross & Westm.) Cons. Orthop. Surg. Maidstone Dist. Hosp. Socs: Fell. Orthop. Assn.; Gauvain Soc.; SW Orthop. Soc. Prev: Sen. Regist. (Orthop.) Roy. United Hosp. Bath; Regist. (Orthop.) Lord Mayor Treloar Hosp. Alton & Qu. Alexandria Hosp. Cosham; SHO (Gen. Surg.) St. Margt. Hosp. Epping.

ELLIS, Simon Jonathan Department of Neurology, North Staffordshire Royal Infirmary, Princes Road, Stoke-on-Trent ST4 7LN Tel: 01782 554343 Fax: 01782 555091 — MB BChir 1983; MD 1994 Camb.; MRCP (UK) 1988; T(M) 1993; FRCP 1998. (Cambridge) Cons. Neurol. N. Staffs. Roy. Infirm.; Sen. Clin. Lect. Keele Univ.; Vis. Prof. In Neurosci., Staffs. Univ.. Socs: Chair N. Staffs. Local research ethics Comm. Prev: Clin. Lect. (Neurol.) Univ. Oxf.; Chief Resid. Neurol. Mt. Sinai Hosp., NY, USA.

ELLIS, Spencer Ian 19 Rusham Road, London SW12 8TJ — MB BS 1991 Lond.

ELLIS, Stephen Keith St Paul's Medical Centre, Dickson Road, Blackpool FY1 2HH Tel: 01253 623896 Fax: 01253 752818 — MB BCh BAO 1985 NUI; LRCPI & LM LRCSI & LM 1985.

ELLIS, Stephen Mark Kings Healthcare Trust, Department of Diagnostic Radiology, Denmark Hill, London SE22 0AQ Tel: 020 7346 3331 Fax: 020 7346 3157; 41B Melford Road, East Dulwich, London SE22 0AQ Tel: 020 8299 2180 — MB BChir Camb. 1992; MA Camb. 1992; MRCP (UK) 1995. Specialist Regist. (Diagn. Radiol.) Lond.

ELLIS, Susan Jacqueline Firhill, Mary Avenue, Aberlour AB38 9PL — MB ChB 1981 Aberd.

ELLIS, Sylvia Jane Chapel Street Clinic, Chapel St., Chichester PO19 1BX Tel: 01243 783325; 19 Montgomery Road, Havant PO9 2RH — MB BS 1978 Lond.; MRCS Eng. LRCP Lond. 1978; MFFP 1994; MRCGP 1982; DLO RCS Eng. 1985; DObst RCOG 1983. Cons. Family Plann. Chichester.

ELLIS, Thomas (retired) Angorta, Aberdesach, Caernarfon LL54 5EW Tel: 01286 660426 — MRCS Eng. LRCP Lond. 1945. Prev: Cas. Off. & Ho. Surg. St. Thos. Hosp. Lond.

***ELLIS, Vikki Alexandra** Cobblestones, 4 Well Lane, Heswall, Wirral CH60 8NE — MB ChB Manch. 1997.

ELLIS, William Herbert Baxter, AFC, KStJ, Surg. Cdr. RN (retired) Little Dalling, Rocks Lane, High Hurstwood, Uckfield TN22 4BN Tel: 01825 733139 Fax: 01825 733139 — MB BS Durh. 1944; MD Durh. 1954. Prev: Chief Cdr. St. John Ambul.

ELLIS, William Robert University Hospital of North Durham, Durham DH1 5TW Tel: 0191 333 2248 Fax: 0191 333 2747; Whitwell Grange, Durham DH1 2SJ Tel: 0191 372 0219 Fax: 0191 372 0219 Email: whitwell@lineone.net — MB BChir 1971 Camb.; DM Nottm. 1984; MA Camb. 1972, BA 1968, MB BChir 1971; FRCP Lond. 1991; MRCP (UK) 1973. (St. Thos.) Cons. Phys. Yair. Hosp. N.Durh. Socs: Med. Res. Soc. & Brit. Soc. Gastroenterol. Prev: Sen. Regist. (Med.) (Leeds/Bradford) Yorks. RHA; Res. Fell. & Hon. Sen. Regist. (Therap.) City Hosp. Nottm.; Regist. (Med.) Char. Cross Hosp. Lond.

ELLIS, Mr Wray (retired) Parkside, Durham Road, Sedgefield, Stockton-on-Tees TS21 3DW — MB ChB Liverp. 1949; MD Liverp. 1964, MCh Orth. 1962; FRCS Eng. 1984; FRCSI 1961. Prev: Hon. Cons. (Orthop. Surg.) N. & S. Tees HA.

ELLIS JONES, Edward (retired) 10 Harptree Close, Nailsea, Bristol BS48 4YT — MRCS Eng. LRCP Lond. 1940; BA Camb. 1937, MB BChir 1940; DObst RCOG 1945. Prev: Obst. Regist. St. Thos. Hosp.

ELLIS-JONES, Michael The Health Centre, Castleton Way, Eye IP23 7DD Tel: 01379 870689; The Old Rectory, Thrandeston, Diss IP21 4BX Tel: 01379 783491 — MB BS 1969 Lond.; FRCP 2000; MRCP (UK) 1972. (Middlx.) Prev: Ho. Phys. (Gastroentrol.) Centr. Middlx. Hosp. Lond.; SHO (Neurol.) Whittington Hosp. Lond.; Res. Med. Off. Nat. Heart Hosp.

ELLIS-JONES, William Benjamin Ellis 16 Fleetwood Road, Southport PR9 0JX Tel: 01704 500048 — MB ChB Liverp. 1942; MRCS Eng. LRCP Lond. 1942. (Liverp.) Socs: Hon. Life Mem. Liverp. Med. Inst. & BMA.

ELLIS-WILLIAMS, Gillian Wyn Meddygfa Penygroes, Bridge Street, Penygroes, Llanelli SA14 7RP Tel: 01269 831193 Fax: 01269 832116 — MB BCh 1988 Wales.

ELLISON, Allan James (retired) Boundary House, 462 Northenden Road, Sale M33 2RH Tel: 0161 962 4643 — MB ChB 1958 Manch.; DObst RCOG 1960. Prev: GP Chesh.

ELLISON, Anthony John Hubert (retired) Petit Four, Rue de La Blanche Pierre, St Lawrence, Jersey JE3 1EA Tel: 01534 723700 Fax: 01534 723700 Email: ellison@itl.net — MB BS 1958 Lond.; DObst RCOG 1960; DA Eng. 1961. Prev: SHO (Infec. Dis. & Poliomyelitis) St. Anne's Hosp. Tottenham.

ELLISON, Carice 123 Beaufort Street, Chelsea, London SW3 6BS Tel: 020 7352 0551; 4 The Ridge, North St, Pewsey SN9 5ER Tel: 01672 562710 — MB BS 1954 Lond.; MRCPsych 1971; DPM Eng. 1958; DObst RCOG 1956. (St. Bart.) Psychiat. Charter Clinic Chelsea. Socs: Life Fell Roy. Soc. Med.; Med. Wom. Federat.; Medico-Legal Soc. Prev: Med. Off. Psycho-sexual Clinic Maudsley Hosp. Lond.; Asst. Psychiat. The Priory, Roehampton; Regist. Maudsley Hosp. Lond.

ELLISON, Christopher Dixon Lane Medical Centre, 102 Dixon Lane, Lower Wortley, Leeds LS12 4AD Tel: 0113 279 7234 — MB ChB 1978 Leeds; DRCOG 1981. (Leeds) Med. Off. Benefits Agency, DHSS; Med. Adviser Pharmaceutical Packaging Ltd, Leeds; Tutor in UnderGrad. Gen. Pract. Univ. Leeds; Examr. St. John Ambul. Assn. Leeds Co. Socs: Soc. Occupat. Med. Prev: Research Clin. Asst (Dermat.) Leeds Gen. Infirm.; Clin. Asst (Accid. & Emerg.) St. Jas Hosp. Leeds.

ELLISON, David John (retired) Tall Trees, 34B Lowbourne, Melksham SN12 7DZ Tel: 01225 702049 — MB ChB 1945 Ed.; MD Ed. 1975; FRCP Ed. 1977, M 1950. Prev: GP Melksham.

ELLISON, David Peter Health Centre, Park Drive, Stenhousemuir, Larbert FK5 3BB Tel: 01324 554411 Fax: 01324 553629 — MB ChB 1984 Dundee.

ELLISON, David William c/o Department Neuropathology, Newcastle General Hospital, Newcastle upon Tyne NE4 6BE — MB BChir 1981 Camb.; PhD Soton. 1995; MSc Lond. 1984; MA Oxf. 1983; MD Camb. 1987; MRCP (UK) 1989; MRCPath 1993. Cons. Neuropathologist Newc. Gen. Hosp. and N.ern Region; Reader Neuro-oncological Path., Univ. of Newc. Socs: Amer. Assoc. Neuropaths.; Internat. Soc. Neuropath.; UK Childr.s Cancer Study Gp. Prev: Cons. Neuropath. Soton. Univ. Hosps. Trust & Wessex Region; Research Fell. Harvard Univ. & Mass. Gen. Hosp. Boston, Mass, USA; SHO (Histopath.) Oxf.

ELLISON, James Anthony 12 Avondale Road, Shipley BD18 4QX — MB BS 1989 Lond.

ELLISON, Joanne Oakbridge, Graham Road, Killearn, Glasgow G63 9RS — MB ChB 1993 Dundee.

ELLISON, Joseph The Elms, Cowley Hill Lane, St Helens WA10 2AW Tel: 01744 454868; Sandy Mount, 3 Hard lane, Dentons Green, St Helens WA10 6JP Tel: 01744 601434 — MB ChB 1976 Liverp.; MRCPsych. 1980; MPH Liverp. 1996. (Liverp. Univ.) Cons. Child & Adolesc. Psychiat. St. Helens & Knowsley Community NHS Trust. Prev: Tutor Child & Adolesc. Psychiat. Manch. Univ.; Lect. in Psychiat. Liverp. Univ.; Regist. Psychiat. Maudsley Hosp. Lond.

ELLISON, Julie Anne Paediatric Dept, Leighton Hospital, Middlewich Road, Crewe CW1 4QJ Tel: 01270 612185 Fax: 01270 612186 Email: julie.ellison@mcht.nhs.uk — MB ChB 1987 Manch.; BSc (Hons.) St. And. 1984; MRCP (UK) 1992; DCH RCP Lond. 1989. (Manchester) Cons. Paediat. Leighton Hosp. Prev: Clin. Lect. (Child Health) & Hon. Sen. Regist. Univ. Manch.

ELLISON, Julie Karen 19 Huntlyburn Terrace, Borders General Hospital, Melrose TD6 9BS Tel: 01896 754333; 17 Glenview Avenue, Holywood BT18 0PX Tel: 01232 427147 — MB ChB 1993 Ed. Trainee GP/SHO (Gen. Med.) Borders Gen. Hosp. VTS. Socs: BMA; Pharmaceut. Soc. Prev: Ho. Off. (Med.) St. John's Hosp. Livingston; Ho. Off. (Surg.) Falkirk & Dist. Roy. Infirm.

ELLISON, Lesley Evans Maryfield Medical Centre, 9 Morgan Street, Dundee DD4 6QE Tel: 01382 462292 Fax: 01382 461052 — MB ChB 1970 St. And.

ELLISON, Mairi Frances Ribblesdale House Medical Centre, Market Street, Bury BL9 0BU Tel: 0161 764 7241 Fax: 0161 763 3557 — MB ChB 1987 Manch.; BSc (Med. Sci.) St. And. 1984.

ELLISON, Martha Margaret Jezierski and Partners, The Health Centre, Sheen Lane, London SW14 8LP — MB BCh BAO 1991 NUI; MRCGP 1995. (Univ. Coll. Dub.)

ELLISON, Zoe Rebecca The Maudsley Hospital, Denmark Hill, London SE5 8AZ Tel: 020 7703 6333 Fax: 020 7919 2171 Email: spjuzre@iop.kcl.ac.uk — MB BS 1994 Lond.; MSc Lond 1998. (Kings college, London) Specialist Regist. (Child Psychiat.) Maudsley Hosp. Lond. Prev: Regist. (Psychiat) Maudsley; SHO (Psychiat.) Maudsley Hosp. Lond.; Ho. Off. (Med. & Surg.) Bromley Hosp.

ELLISTON, Paul Robert Albon Institute Medical & Social Care Research, Wheldon Building, University of Wales, Bangor LL57 2UW Tel: 01248 383970 Email: p.elliston@bangor.ac.uk — MB BS 1977 Lond.; 2001 PCME, UWCM; MFPHM RCP (UK) 1993; Cert. Health Serv. Managem. 1990; Cert. Av Med. 1986. (Lond. Hosp.) p/t Cons. Pub. Health Med. N. Wales HA; Vis. Clin. Reader Inst. for Med. & Social Care Research Univ. of Wales Bangor. Prev: Sen. Regist. & Regist. (Pub. Health Med.) Trent Region; GP Derby; Med. Off. Chas. Johnson Memor. Hosp. Kwazulu, S. Afr.

ELLMAN, Thomas Jethro 15 Vine Road, London SW13 0NE — MB ChB 1993 Ed.

ELLOR, Eunice Margaret 8 Lonsdale Road, Stamford PE9 2RW — BM BS 1983 Nottm.; MRCGP 1987; DRCOG 1986. Retainer GP Market Deeping.

ELLSBURY, Gillian Frances 59 Sunray Avenue, London SE24 9PX — MB BS 1994 Lond.

ELLSON, Carl Robert Corbett Medical Practice, 36 Corbett Avenue, Droitwich WR9 7BE Tel: 01905 795566 Fax: 01905 796984 — MB ChB 1982 Birm.; Cert. Family Plann. Birm. 1982. (Birm.)

ELLUL, John 11 Greylea, Delamer Road, Bowdon, Altrincham WA14 2NT Tel: 0161 928 5046 — State DMS 1987 Parma.

ELLUL, Mr Joseph Patrick Martin Department of Surgery, Bromley Hosp, Bromley DA15 4LT Tel: 0208 289 7158 Fax: 0208 289 7169 — MB BCh 1980 Wales; MCh Wales 1996; FRCS Eng. 1998; FRCS Gen. 1996; FRCS Ed. 1986. (Wales) Cons. Surg. Gen. Surg. Bromley Hosp Bromley Kent. Socs: Assn. Surg.of GB & Ire; Brit. Soc. Gastroenterol.; Brit. Assoc. Endoscopic Surgs. GB & Irel. Prev: Sen. Regist. (Surg.) Dept. Surg. Guy's Hosp. Lond.; Research Fell. (Gastroenterol.) United Med. Sch. Guy's & St. Thos. Hosp. Lond.

ELLUL, Norman 598 Rainham Road South, Dagenham RM10 8YP Tel: 020 8592 0049; 24, Hardwick Crescent, Brincliffe, Sheffield S11 8WB Tel: 01708 747267 — MRCS Eng. LRCP Lond. 1982. (Westm.) GP; Med. Off. for Harley Med. Clinic; Medico-Legal Expert. Socs: BMA. Prev: Ship's Phys. Carnival Cruise Lines.

ELLWOOD, David Stuart The Plane Trees Group Practice, 51 Sandbeds Road, Pellon, Halifax HX2 0QL Tel: 01422 330860 Fax: 01422 364830; Cock Hill, Sour Lane, Stirton, Skipton BD23 3LH Tel: 01756 797385 Fax: 01422 364830 — MB ChB 1980 Dundee. (Dundee)

ELLWOOD, Helen Louise 66 Humphrey Middlemore Drive, Harborne, Birmingham B17 0JN — MB BS 1993 Lond.; BA (Physiol. Sci.) Oxf. 1990.

ELLWOOD, Martin George Taunton & Somerset NHS Trust, Musgrove Park Hospital, Taunton TA19 0SB; Longcroft, Sea, Ilminster TA19 0SB — BChir 1964; MA Camb. 1964; FRCP Lond. 1981, M 1968. (Middlx.) Cons. (Gen. Med.) MusGr. Pk. Hosp. Taunton. Prev: Sen. Med. Regist. Bristol Roy. Infirm.

ELLWOOD, Neil Harvey The Surgery, High Street, Newnham GL14 1BE Tel: 01594 516241 — MB BS 1981 Lond.; MA Oxf. 1976; MRCGP 1985; DRCOG 1984.

ELLWOOD, Russell William Morrill Street Health Centre, Holderness Road, Hull HU9 2LJ Tel: 01482 320046 — MB ChB 1983 Leeds; BSc Leeds 1980, MB ChB 1983; Cert. Family Plann. 1988. GP Hull. Socs: BMA. & RCGP. Prev: Trainee GP Wakefield; SHO (Paediat.) Pinderfields Gen. Infirm. Wakefield; SHO (Obst.) Manygates Matern. Hosp. Wakefield.

ELLWOOD, Simon Timothy Fernbank Surgery, 18 Church Road, Lytham, Lytham St Annes FY8 5LL Tel: 01253 736453 — MB ChB 1983 Leeds; MRCGP 1988; DRCOG 1986; DCH RCP Lond. 1985. Prev: Trainee GP Pontefract VTS.

ELMAN, Hilda Annette M, Victoria St, Rochester ME1 Tel: 01634 43338; 42 Chester Close N., Regents Park, London NW1 4JE Tel: 020 7486 4660 Fax: 020 7486 4660 — MRCS Eng. LRCP Lond. 1946. (Lond. Sch. Med. Wom.) p/t JP. Prev: Cas. Off. Willesden Gen. Hosp.; Resid. Med. Off. Weir Hosp. Balham.

ELMARDI, Abubakr Amin Ahmed Good Hope General Hospital, Department of Obstetrics & Gynaecology, Rectory Road, Sutton Coldfield B75 7RR Tel: 0121 378 2211 — MB ChB 1977 Cairo; MRCOG 1991; DGO TC Dub. 1984. Staff Grade (O & G) Good Hope Hosp. Trust. Socs: Roy. Coll. Obst. & Gyn. & Internat. Coll. Surgs. USA.

ELMASRY, Karim Medhat c/o Cripps Postgraduate Medical Centre, Northampton General Hospital, Cliftonville, Northampton NN1 5BD; Flat 3, 7 Clumber Crescent, Nottingham NG7 1EH — BM BS 1993 Nottm.

ELMES, Euseby (retired) Mull Cottage, Denham Village, Uxbridge UB9 5BH — LRCPI & LM, LRSCI & LM 1935; LRCPI & LM, LRCSI & LM 1935. Prev: Surg. Lt.-Cdr. RNVR.

ELMES, Margaret Elizabeth (retired) Dawros House, St Andrews Road, Dinas Powys CF64 4HB Tel: 02920 512102 Fax: 029 2051 5975 — MB BS 1955 Lond.; PhD Belf. 1974. Prev: Assoc. Specialist (Path.) Univ. Hosp. Wales.

ELMES, Peter Cardwell (retired) Dawros House, St. Andrews Road, Dinas Powys CF64 4HB Tel: 02920 512102 Fax: 02920 515975 — BM BCh Oxf. 1945; MD West. Reserve Univ. Cleveland, Ohio 1947; FRCP Lond. 1967, M 1951; FFOM RCP Lond. 1981. Prev: Dir. MRC Pneumoconiosis Unit Llandough Hosp. Penarth.

ELMHIRST, Susanna Isaacs 1 Hollycroft Avenue, London NW3 7QG Tel: 020 7794 4160 — MD 1943 Chicago; MB BS Lond. 1944; FRCP Lond. 1970, M 1946; FRCPsych 1971; DCH Eng. 1945.

(Bristol & Chicago) Prev: Vice-Pres. Brit. Psycho-Analyt. Soc.; Cons. Child Psychiat. Child Guid. Train. Centre Tavistock Clinic Lond.; Phys. i/c Dept. Child Psychiat. St. Mary's Hosp. Lond.

ELMIYEH, Behrad 15 Cheviot Gardens, London NW2 1QP — MB BS 1998 Lond.; MB BS Lond 1998.

ELMORE, David Martin 3 Windermere Road, Newbold, Chesterfield S41 8QB Tel: 01246 877381 Fax: 01246 239828 — MB ChB 1968 Sheff.; DObst RCOG 1970. (Sheff.) Prev: Ho. Phys. Roy. Infirm. Sheff.; Ho. Off. (Obst.) Brighton Gen. Hosp.

ELMS, Stephen Thomas Killearn Health Centre, Balfron Road, Killearn, Glasgow G63 9NA Tel: 01360 50339 Fax: 01360 550176 — MB ChB 1975 Glas.

ELMSLIE, Andrew Gavin McIntosh Department of Liason Psychiatry, Leeds General Infirmary, Great George St., Leeds LS1 3EX — MB ChB 1991 Ed. Specialist Regist. Psychiat. Leeds.

ELMSLIE, Frances Veryan 99 Kelmscott Road, London SW11 6PU — MB ChB 1987 Bristol; MSc Lond. 1993; MRCP (UK) 1992; DCH RCP Lond. 1990. Sen. Regist. (Clin. Genetics) St. Geo.'s Hosp. Prev: Clin. Research Fell. (Paediat.) Univ. Coll. Lond.; Regist. (Paediat.) Plymouth Gen. Hosp.; SHO (Paediat. Neurol.) Hosp. Sick Childr. Gt. Ormond St. Lond.

ELMSLIE, Isabel Katherine Margaret (retired) Costards, Oaklands Lane, West Lavington, Midhurst GU29 0EL Tel: 01730 812524 — MB BS Lond. 1952. Prev: Clin. Asst. (Genitourin. Med.) Guildford.

ELMSLIE, John Alexander Grant (retired) 2 Alderdale Drive, Heaton Moor, Stockport SK4 4AS — MB ChB Aberd. 1951.

ELMUBARAK, Mr Mohammed Yousif 58/4 East Crosscauseway, Edinburgh EH8 9HD — MB BS 1978 Khartoum; FRCS Ed. 1993.

ELPHICK, Heather Elizabeth Sheffield Childrens Hospital, Western Bank, Sheffield S10 2TH Tel: 0114 271 7000 Email: h.elphick@shef.ac.uk; The Cottage, Cliffe Lane, Tudeswell, Buxton SK17 8NW — MB ChB 1993 Sheff.; MRCP (UK) 1997. Research Fell. (Respirat. Paediat.).

ELPHICK, Janet The Surgery, 15 West Town Road, Backwell, Bristol BS48 3HA Tel: 01275 850600 Fax: 01275 795609; 2 St. Margarets Close, Backwell, Bristol BS48 3JD Tel: 01275 463659 — MB ChB 1967 Manch.; MRCGP 1982; DCH RCP Lond. 1977. Prev: SCMO (Child Health) Bristol & W.on HA.; Clin. Asst. (Ophth.) Bristol Eye Hosp.

ELPHICK, Martin Elms Clinic, Oxford Road, Banbury OX16 9AL Tel: 01295 229280 Email: melphick@omhir.demon.co.uk — MB BS Lond. 1975; MD Lond. 1990; MRCPsych 1981. Cons. Psychiat. Oxf. Ment. Healthcare Trust; Clin. working Gp. Ldr., NHS info Auth. Winchester. Prev: Research Fell. Clin. Psychopharmacol.

ELPHICK, Peter Richard 17 Seaway Avenue, Friers Cliff, Christchurch BH23 4EU — MB BS 1962 Lond.; MRCS Eng. LRCP Lond. 1962; DCH RCP Lond. 1964; DA Lond. 1964; DObst RCOG 1965; LMCC Canada 1976. Family Pract. (Kitimat) Brit. Columbia, Canada; Clin. Assoc. Prof. Dept. Family Pract. Univ. Brit. Columbia, Vancouver; Pres. Med. Staff. Kitimat Hosp. Socs: Coll. Family Pract. Canada. Prev: Chief of Staff Kitimat Gen. Hosp. Kitimat B.C., Canada.

ELPHICK, Sally Jane Greystoke Surgery, Kings Avenue, Morpeth NE61 1JA Tel: 01670 511393 Fax: 01670 503282; 11 Westfield Grove, Gosforth, Newcastle upon Tyne NE3 4YA Tel: 0191 284 4712 — MB BS 1982 Newc.; MRCP (UK) 1985; MRCGP 1986; DRCOG 1986. Prev: Trainee GP Sheen VTS, Lond.; SHO (Med.) Freeman Hosp. Newc.; SHO (O & G) Roy. Vict. Infirm. Newc.

ELPHINSTONE, Catherine Dierdre Park Health Centre, 190 Duke Street, Sheffield S2 5QQ Tel: 0114 272 7768; 15 Rutland Park, Sheffield S10 2PB — MB BCh BAO 1975 Belf.; DRCOG 1977.

ELPHINSTONE, Lucy Helen, Wing Cdr. RAF Med. Br. Ministry of Defence, Surgeon General's Department, Main Building, Whitehall, London SW1A 2HW Tel: 020 7807 8762 Fax: 020 7807 8834 Email: phml.la@dial.pipex.com — MB ChB 1978 Glas.; MRCGP 1986; DFFP 1994; D Trav Med Glas 1997. (University of Glasgow) Staff Off. Surg. Gen.'s Dept. Socs: Internat. Soc. Travel Med.; Pub. Health Med. Environm. Gp.; Brit. Travel Health Assn. Prev: GP Glas.

ELPHINSTONE, Mary Georgiana, MBE 884 Wolseley Road, Plymouth PL5 1JY Tel: 01752 369117 — MB BS 1980 Lond.; BSc Lond. 1977, MB BS 1980; FFA RCS Eng. 1985; MRCGP 1995. (The London Hospital Medical College) Non Princip. GP; Clin. Asst. (Anaesth.). Socs: Fell. RSM; BMA.

ELPHINSTONE, Penelope Eugenie Ampthill Square Medical Centre, 219 Evershott Street, London NW1 1DE Tel: 020 7387 6161 Fax: 020 7387 0420; 42 Gibson Square, Islington, London N1 0RB Tel: 020 7700 6761 — MB ChB 1978 Manch.; MRCP (UK) 1982; MRCGP 1987; DRCOG 1985; Cert. Family Plann. JCC 1985; DCH RCP Lond. 1985. Prev: GP Shepherds Bush.

ELRAHMAN, Ibrahim Hassan Amin Abd 9 Horsley Close, Epsom KT19 8HB Tel: 01372 721233 Fax: 01372 722766 — MB BCh BAO 1991 NUI; BSc Lond. 1985; LRCPSI 1991. Lat. Regist. O & G E. Surrey Hosp. Socs: MDU; Irish Med. Counc. Prev: SHO (Pelvic Oncol. Surg.) Roy. Marsden Hosp. Lond.

ELRINGTON, Giles Maxwell Oaks Hospital, Colchester CO4 5XR Tel: 01206 753206 Fax: 01206 855125 — MB BS 1980 Lond.; MB BS (Hons. Surg. & Clin. Pharm.) Lond. 1980; MD Lond. 1990; MRCP (UK) 1983; FRCP 1998. Cons. Neurol. Colchester Gen. Hosp.; Hon. Cons. Neurol. Roy. Lond. Hosp. Socs: Assn. Brit. Neurol.; Internat. Headache Soc.; Roy. Soc. Med. Prev: Sen. Regist. (Neurol.) Radcliffe Infirm. Oxf.; Regist. (Neurol.) Nat. Hosp. Neurol. & Neurosurg. Lond.; Research Regist. (Neurol.) Inst. Molecular Med. John Radcliffe Hosp. Oxf.

ELSARRAG, Mohammed Elgawad 53A Hollybush Road, Cyncoed, Cardiff CF23 6TZ Tel: 029 2076 3610; 53A Hollybush Road, Cyncoed, Cardiff CF23 6TZ Tel: 029 2076 3610 — MRCP 1976 (Glas.); LMSSA Lond. 1966; FRCP Ed. 1994; FRCP Glas 1986, M 1986; MRCP Ed. 1968; MRCPsych 1971; DPM Ed. & Glas. 1963. (Kitchener Sch. of Med. Khartoum) Socs: Med. Sect. Amnesty Internat. Prev: Cons. Psychiat. WhitCh. & Ely Hosps. Cardiff; Hon. Clin. Teach. Univ. Hosp. Wales Med. Sch.; Med. Off Min. of Health Sudan.

ELSBY, Kevin Paul The Market Surgery, 26 Norwich Road, Aylsham, Norwich NR11 6BW Tel: 01263 733331 Fax: 01263 735829 — MB BS 1983 Lond.; MRCGP 1988; DRCOG 1987; DCH RCP Lond. 1986. Prev: Trainee GP Kings Lynn VTS; SHO (ENT) Kent & Canterbury Hosp.; Ho. Off. (Med.) St. Margt.s Hosp. Epping.

ELSDEN, William Allen Department of Anaesthesia, Perth Royal Infirmary, Perth PH1 1NX — MB BS 1976 Lond.; FFA RCS Eng. 1981. (St. Bart.) Sen. Regist. (Anaesth.) Newc. HA. Socs: N.E. Scotl. Soc. Anaesth. & Scotl. Soc. Anaesth. Prev: Regist. (Anaesth.) Tayside Area Health Bd.; SHO (A & E) Ho. Off. (Surg.) & Ho. Off. (Med.) Norf. & Norwich Hosp.

ELSDON, Cecil James Lindsay (retired) 36 Stockwell Street, Leek ST13 6DS Tel: 01538 383066 — MRCS Eng. LRCP Lond. 1942.

ELSDON, Simon James Stockwell Surgery, Park Medical Centre, Ball Haye Road, Leek ST13 6QP Tel: 01538 399398/384213 Fax: 01538 399523; Stockwell Surgery, Ball Haye Road, Leek ST13 6QP — MB ChB 1973 Aberd.; DA Eng. 1978.

ELSDON-DEW, Robin William March House, The Avenue, Tadworth KT20 5AT Tel: 01737 812781 Fax: 01737 814459 — MB BS 1958 Lond.; MRCS Eng. LRCP Lond. 1958; FFPM RCP (UK) 1989; DObst RCOG 1960. (Guy's) Prev: Dir. Internat. Med. Serv. Glaxo Gp. Research.

ELSE, Corinne Penelope Brimington Surgery, Church St, Brimington, Chesterfield S43 1JG Tel: 01246 273224 — MB BCh 1987 Wales; MRCGP 1995. p/t GP Princip., Chesterfield, Derbysh. Socs: BMA. Prev: GP/Regist. Sheff.; SHO (O & G) N.ern Gen. Hosp. Sheff.

ELSE, Oliver Francis Memorial Medical Centre, Bell Road, Sittingbourne ME10 4XX Tel: 01795 477764; 31 London Road, Sittingbourne Tel: 72534 — MB BS 1974 Lond.; MRCS Eng. LRCP Lond. 1974; DRCOG 1978. (St. Bart.)

ELSEY, Tamsin Ann Station Road Surgery, 69 Station Road, Sidcup DA15 7DS Tel: 020 8309 0201 Fax: 020 8309 9040; 17 Birchwood Avenue, Sidcup DA14 4JY — MB BS 1984 Lond.; BSc 1980; MRCGP 1988.

ELSHAZALI OSMAN, Gasim Mohamed 88 Scartho Road, Grimsby DN33 2BG — MD 1993 Leige.

ELSHERBINI, Mona Mahgoub Southern Derbyshire Mental Health Trust, The Mill, Lodge Lane, Derby DE1; 30 Westminster Road, Leicester LE2 2EG — MB ChB 1976 Cairo; MRCPsych 1982. Cons. Child Adolesc. Psychiat., Derby. Prev: Cons. Child & Adolesc. Psychiat. Leicester.

ELSMORE, Andrew John 17 Widecombe Avenue, Stafford ST17 0HX — BM BCh 1991 Oxf.

ELSMORE, Mr Steven St. Mary's Hospital, Newport PO30 5TG Tel: 01983 524081 — MB BS 1991 Lond.; FRCS (Gen.) 2000; MSC 2000; FRCS Eng. 1995. (Kings College) Cons. Gen. Colorectal Surg., St. Marys Hosp., Newport, Isle of Wight. Prev: Regist. (Surg.) SW Thames.

ELSOM, Joyce Fanny (retired) Westhaven Cottage, Pine Walk, Lyme Regis DT7 3LA Tel: 01297 442069 — BA Camb. 1943, MB BChir 1946; MRCS Eng. LRCP Lond. 1946; MA Camb. 1998. Prev: Med. Asst. Chest Dept. Staffs. Gen. Infirm. Stafford.

ELSON, Charles William Wickham Market Medical Centre, Chapel Lane, Wickham Market, Woodbridge IP13 0SB Tel: 01728 747101 Fax: 01728 747580 — MB ChB 1990 Ed.; MRCGP 1996; DRCOG 1994. Prev: Trainee GP W. Suff. HA VTS.

ELSON, Miss Claire Janine 5 Ladybridge Terrace, Turvey, Bedford MK43 8HB Email: mark.williams@easynet.co.uk — MB ChB 1993 Leic.; DFFP 1996; MRCOG 1998. Specialist Regist. (O & G) Luton & Dunstable Hosp. Socs: Roy. Coll. Obst. & Gyns.; Med. Wom. Fed. Prev: Regist. (O & G) N.ampton Hosp. Cliftonville N.ampton; Regist. (O & G) Kettering Gen.; Regist. (O & G) W. Suff.

ELSON, David Frank Lister House, The Common, Hatfield AL10 0NL Tel: 01707 268822; 40 Parkway Gardens, Welwyn Garden City AL8 6JW — MB BS 1961 Lond.; T(GP) 1991; DA Eng. 1964; DObst RCOG 1963. (Lond. Hosp.)

ELSON, Julia Gaye Hall Barn, Hungry Hall Lane, Long Melford, Sudbury CO10 9BB Tel: 01787 248306; 2 Ashburnham Gardens, Eastbourne BN21 2NA Tel: 01323 638877 — MB ChB 1990 Ed.; DRCOG 1995. Trainee GP W. Suff. VTS. Socs: BMA & MDDUS. Prev: Ho. Off. (Surg.) Dumfries & Galloway Roy. Infirm.; Ho. Off. (Med.) Edin. Roy. Infirm.

ELSON, Patricia Joan Woodsetts House, Woodsetts, Worksop S81 8RB Tel: 01909 2177; 4A Springview, More Hall Lane, Bolsterstone, Sheffield S36 3ST Tel: 0114 288 5796 — MB BS Lond. 1957. (Lond. Hosp.)

ELSON, Mr Reginald Arnold Woodsetts House, Woodsetts, Worksop S81 8RB Tel: 01909 2177 — MB 1958 Camb.; BChir 1957; FRCS Eng. 1962. (Lond. Hosp.) Cons. Orthop. Surg. N. Gen. Hosp. Sheff.; Hon. Lect. Mechanical Engin. Univ. Sheff. Prev: Sen. Orthop. Regist. Lond. Hosp. & Centre For Hip Surg. Wrightington; Regist. Robt. Jones & Agnes Hunt Orthop. Hosp. OsW.ry.

ELSTEIN, Professor Max (retired) — MB ChB Cape Town 1955; MSc Manch. 1978; MD Cape Town 1969; FRCOG 1980, M 1964; Hon. FFFP RCOG 1995. Prev: Reader (Human Reproduc. & Obst.) Univ. Soton.

ELSTON, Anne Christabel Rose Cottage, Fen St., Nayland, Colchester CO6 4HT — MB BS Lond. 1982; FFA RCSI 1989.

ELSTON, Professor Christopher William Department Pathology, City Hospital, Hucknall Road, Nottingham NG5 1PB Tel: 0115 969 1169 Fax: 0115 962 7768; Northfield Farm House, Widmerpool Road, Wysall, Nottingham NG12 5QW Tel: 01509 881252 Email: chris.elston@nottingham.ac.uk — MB BS 1961 Lond.; MD Lond. 1970; FRCPath 1980, M 1968. (Char. Cross) Cons. Path. City Hosp. Nottm.; Prof. Tumour Path. Nottm. Univ. Med. Sch. Socs: Brit. BrE. Gp.; Path. Soc.; Internat. Acad. Path. Prev: Sen. Lect. & Hon. Cons. Path. Kings Coll. Hosp. Med. Sch. Lond.; Regist. & Hon. Lect. (Path.) Char. Cross Hosp. Med. Sch.

ELSTON, Colin Charles Gayton Road Health and Surgical Centre, Gayton Road, King's Lynn PE30 4DY Tel: 01553 762726 Fax: 01553 696819; 368 Wootton Road, King's Lynn PE30 3EB Tel: 01553 762726 — MB BS 1973 Lond.; BSc (Hons. Physiol.) Lond. 1970; DRCOG 1977; DCH Eng. 1976. (Lond. Hosp.) Socs: W Norf. Clin. Soc. Prev: Trainee GP King's Lynn VTS; Ho. Phys. S.end Gen. Hosp.; Ho. Surg. Amersham Gen. Hosp.

ELSTON, Mr John Scorgie 66 Florence Park, London SE14 Tel: 020 8691 6433 — MB BS 1973 Lond.; BSc Lond. 1970, MB BS 1973; FRCS Eng. 1982. (St. Thos.) Lect. (Ophth.) Insts. Child Health & Ophth.

ELSTON, Richard Anthony Microbiology Laboratory, 214 Turner Road, Colchester CO4 5JR Tel: 01206 853535 — MB BS 1981 Lond.; BSc (Hons.) Lond. 1978, MB BS 1981; MRCP (UK) 1984; MRCPath 1991; Dip. Clin. Microbiol. Lond 1988; FRCPath 1999. (Kings. Coll. Hosp.) Cons. Microbiol. Colchester Hosp. Prev: Sen. Regist. (Microbiol.) Whipps Cross & St. Bart. Hosps. Lond.

ELSTON, William James 63 Dunstans Road, East Dulwich, London SE22 0HG Tel: 020 8693 6359 — MB BS 1991 Lond.; MRCP UK 1996. (Char. Cross & Westm.) Specialist Regist. (Respirat. Med.) N. E. Thames.

ELSTOW, Gillian Anne Grange Road Surgery, Grange Road, Bishopsworth, Bristol BS13 8LD Tel: 0117 964 4343 Fax: 0117 935 8422 — MB ChB 1981 Manch.

ELSTOW, Sonia Mary Harvey House Surgery, 13-15 Russell Avenue, St Albans AL3 5ES Tel: 01727 831888 Fax: 01727 845520 — MB ChB 1981 Manch.; MRCGP 1985; DCH RCP Lond. 1987; DRCOG 1984. GP St Albans.

ELSTUB, James 50 Marryat Road, London SW19 5BD Tel: 020 8947 4285 — MB BS 1947 Lond.; MD Lond. 1952; MRCS Eng. LRCP Lond. 1947; MRCOG 1952. (Univ. Coll. Hosp.) Prev: Lect. in O & G Radcliffe Infirm. Oxf.; Asst. Obst. Unit Univ. Coll. Hosp.; Regist. O & G W. Middlx. Hosp. Isleworth.

ELSWOOD, Robert Ladywell Medical Centre, Edinburgh EH12 7UN Tel: 0131 334 7696 Fax: 0131 334 8410 Email: rob.elswood@lineone.net; 30 Belgrave Road, Edinburgh EH12 6NF Tel: 0131 334 6949 — MB ChB 1978 Ed.; MA Oxf. 1979; FRCS Ed. 1983; MRCGP 1985; DRCOG 1980. Trainer (Gen. Pract.) Edin. Prev: Lect. (Surg.) Univ. Ghana.; Regist. (Surg.) Roy. Infirm. Edin.

ELSWORTH, Mr Christopher Francis 14 Marlowe Drive, Didsbury, Manchester M20 6DE Tel: 0161 445 3190 — MB BS 1975 Lond.; FRCS Eng. 1981; FRCS Ed. 1981. (St. Geo.) Cons. Orthop. Surg. Roy. Oldham Hosp. Prev: Sen. Regist. (Orthop. Surg.) Manch. & N.W. Region; Tutor in Orthop. Surg. Hope Hosp. Manch.; Regist. (Orthop.) St. Geo. Hosp. Lond.

ELSWORTH, Christopher Parry Riversong, Charlton Horethorne, Sherborne DT9 4PB Tel: 01963 220774 — MB ChB 1978 Cape Town; MMed (Anaesth.) Stellenbosch 1989; FFA S. Afr. 1989; DA S. Afr. 1986. Cons. Anaesth. Yeovil Dist. Hosp. Socs: Assn. Anaesth. GB. Prev: Cons. Anaesth. Tygerberg Hosp. Stellenbosch.

ELSWORTH, Elizabeth Anne c/o Dr, Fulong's Secretary, N.O. Block, St Ann's Hospital, St Ann's Road, Tottenham, London N15 Tel: 020 8442 6000 — MB BS 1985 Lond.; MRCPsych 1993. Sen. Regist. (Psychiat.) St. Ann's Hosp. Lond. Socs: BMA. Prev: Sen. Regist. (Psychiat.) Jt. Homelessness Team Lond.; Clin. Research Fell. Acad. Dept. Psychiat. Roy. Free Hosp. Lond.; Jun. Psychiat. Rotat. Roy. Free Hosp. Lond. Train. Scheme.

ELSWORTH, Geoffrey Harold (retired) 26 Welton Old Road, Welton, Brough HU15 1NU — MB ChB 1956 Leeds. Prev: Ho. Off. Gen. Hosp. Otley & St. Mary's Hosp. Leeds.

ELTIGANI, Mr Eltigani Abdel Hameed Department Plastic Surgery, Leicester Royal Infirmary, Leicester LE1 5WW Tel: 0116 254 1414 — MB BS 1977 Khartoum; FRCS 1998 (Plastic SurgerY); FRCSI 1983. Regist. (Plastic Surg.) Leics. Roy. Infirm.; Cons. Plastic and Reconstruc. Surg. Socs: Brit. Assn. of Aesthetic Plastic Surg.s; Brit. Assn. of Plastic Surg.s. Prev: Regist. (Plastic Surg.) St. And. Hosp. Billericay.

ELTOFT, Margaret Elizabeth Manor House, Cross Lane, Holcombe, Bury BL8 4LY — MB ChB 1973 Sheff.; FRCA Eng. 1978. Cons. Anaesth. Trafford Health Care NHS Trust.

ELTOM, Nisreen Khalid 17 Broughton Avenue, London N3 3ES — MB BS 1998 Lond.; MB BS Lond 1998.

ELTON, Sir Arnold, CBE The Consulting Rooms, Wellington Hospital, Wellington Place, London NW8 9LE Tel: 020 7935 4101 Fax: 020 7483 0297 — MB BS 1943 Lond.; MS Lond. 1950; FRCS Eng. 1946; MRCS Eng. LRCP Lond. 1943; FICS 1955. (Univ. Coll. Hosp.) Hon. Cons. Surg. N.wick Pk. Hosp. & Clin. Research Centre & Harrow Hosp.; Surgic. Tutor RCS, Eng..; Gosse Research Schol. Char. Cross Hosp. Lond.; Mem. Govt. Working Party on BrE. Screening; Mem. (Ex-Chairm.) Ct. Examrs. RCS Eng.; Mem. World Federat. Surgic. Oncol.; Examr. Surg. Gen. Nursing Counc.; Chairm. & Med. Adviser Internat. Healthcare (UK) & (Managem. Train.). Socs: Eur. Soc. Surg. Oncol.; Brit. Assn. Surgic. Oncol.; Internat. Advisor, World Fed. of Surg. Oncol. Socs. Prev: Sen. Regist. (Surg.) Char. Cross Hosp.; Clin. Asst. St. Peter's Hosp. For Stone; Ho. Surg., &c. Univ. Coll. Hosp.

ELTON, Christopher David 5 Barons Close, Kirby, Muxloe, Leicester LE9 2BW Email: cdel@leic.ac.uk — MB ChB 1988 Sheff.; BMedSci Sheff. 1986; FRCA 1994. Sen. Regist. (Anaesth.) S. Trent.

ELTON, Colin Elton Lodge, 7 Rathgar Close, London N3 1UA — MB BS 1989 Lond.

ELTON, Naomi Helen Brookside Family Consultation Clinic, 18d Trumpington Road, Cambridge CB2 2AH Tel: 01223 746001 Fax:

01223 746002 Email: naomi.elton@lifespan-tr.anglox.nhs.uk; Email: naomi@elton-levine.freeserve.co.uk — MB BS 1986 Lond.; 1983 BSc Lond.; MRCP 1991 (Psych); MB BS 1986 Lond. Cons. In child & Adolesc. Psychiat., lifespan healthcare NHS trust. Prev: Regist. (Psychiat.) Maudsley Hosp. Lond.; Sen. Regist. (Child & Adolesc. Psychiat.) Hosp. for Sick Childr. Gt. Ormond St. Lond.; Cons. in child and Adolesc. Psychiat. N. E. Essex Ment. Health NHS Trust.

ELTON, Peter Joseph Wigan & Bolton Health Authority, Bryan House, 61 Standishgate, Wigan WN1 1AH Tel: 01942 772842 Fax: 01942 772769 Email: wigbolha@aol.com; 172 Bury Old Road, Manchester M8 Tel: 0161 720 7169 Email: peter@delton.demon.co.uk — MB ChB 1975 Manch., MSc Manch. 1980; FFPHM RCP (UK) 1995; MFCM 1982. (Manchester) Dir. Pub. Health Wigan & Bolton HA. Prev: Cons. Pub. Health Med. Tameside HA, W. Pennie HA & N. Manch. HA.

ELTON, Richard John Department of Anaesthesia, Walsgrave Hospital, Coventry; 6 Brooke Road, Kenilworth CV8 2BD — MB ChB 1984 Birm.; FCAnaesth 1990. Cons. Anaesth. Walsgrave Hosp. Coventry; Trust Audit Adviser. Socs: Assn. Anaesth.; Obst. Anaesth. Assn. Prev: Sen. Regist. W. Midl.; Asst. Prof. Anaesth.Univ. Texas Houston, USA; Regist. (Anaesth.) Coventry HA.

ELTON, Samuel (retired) 44 Lloyd Park Avenue, Croydon CR0 5SB Tel: 020 8681 0988 — MRCS Eng. LRCP Lond. 1944. Prev: GP Thornton Heath.

ELTON, Susan Mary Manor Park Surgery, Bell Mount Close, Leeds LS13 2UP Tel: 0113 257 9702 Fax: 0113 236 1537 — MB BS 1984 Lond.; MRCGP 1991; T(GP) 1990; DRCOG 1988; Cert. Family Plann. JCC 1988; DGM RCP Lond. 1986; Cert Prescribed Exp Postgrad Law Huddersfield 1994. (Charing Cross Hospital) Socs: BMA. Prev: Trainee GP W. Middlx. Hosp. VTS; Clin. Asst. (BrE. Surg.) Leeds Gen. Infirm.

ELTRINGHAM, Ian 22 Waldemar Avenue, London SW6 5NA — MB BS 1990 Lond.

ELTRINGHAM, Mark Thomas 33 Shortridge Terrace, Jesmond, Newcastle upon Tyne NE2 2JE — MB BS 1992 Newc.

ELTRINGHAM, Roger James 289 Stroud Road, Gloucester GL1 5LB — MB ChB St. And. 1964; FFA RCS Eng. 1971. (St Andrews University) Cons. Anaesth. Roy. Hosp. Gloucester; Clin. Prof. Dept. Anaesth. Univ. Wisconsin; Chairm. Pub.ats. Comm. World Federat. Socs. Anaesthiesiol. Socs: SW Anaesth. Soc.; Assn. Anaesth. Prev: Lect. (Anaesth.) Univ. Colorado Med. Centre Denver, USA.

ELTRINGHAM, Mr William Keith (cons. rooms) Litfield House, Litfield Place, Clifton, Bristol BS8 3LS Tel: 0117 973 1323 Fax: 0117 973 3303; 2 Canynge Square, Clifton, Bristol BS8 3LA Tel: 0117 973 7078 — ChM Birm. 1972, MB ChB 1953; FRCS Eng. 1961; MRCS Eng. LRCP Lond. 1953. Cons. Gen. Surg. Bristol Roy. Infirm.; Clin. Lect. & Examr. (Surg.) Univ. Bristol. Socs: BMA & Assn. Surg. GB & Irel; Brit. Soc. Gastroenterol. Prev: Extern. Examr. (Surg.) Univ. Leeds & Univ. Birm.; Regist. & Sen. Regist. (Surg.) United Birm. Hosps.; Assoc. (Surg.) & Research Fell. (Surg.) Harvard Med. Sch. Boston.

ELVERSON, Hamilton James, MBE, Maj. RAMC Retd. 44 Hurlingham Court, Raneleagh Gardens, London SW6 3SQ — BM BCh 1942 Oxf.; BM BCh Oxon. 1942. (Oxf. & Middlx.) Sen. Med. Off. (Community Med.) SE Thames RHA. Prev: Res. Med. Off. St. And. Hosp. Dollis Hill; Admin. King Edwd. VII Memor. Hosp. Bermuda.

ELVES, Mr Andrew William Stuart 106 Rowley Street, Walsall WS1 2AY — MB ChB 1989 Birm.; FRCS Glas. 1994.

ELVIDGE, John Brian The Surgery, 17B Warmdene Road, Brighton BN1 8NL Tel: 01273 508811 Fax: 01273 559860; 14 Friar Road, Brighton BN1 6NG — MB BS 1969 Lond.; DObst RCOG 1971. (St. Geo.) Prev: SHO (O & G) St. Geo. Hosp. Lond.; Ho. Phys. Ashford Hosp. Middlx.; Ho. Surg. (Orthop.) St. Geo. Hosp. Lond.

ELVIN, Brian Charles Durrants, Fox's Lane, Kingsclere, Newbury RG20 5QE — MRCS Eng. LRCP Lond. 1961; MSc (Occupat. Med.) Lond. 1972; FFAEM 1994; DIH Eng. 1972. Cons. A & E Basingstoke Dist. Hosp.

ELVIN, Elizabeth Jane Top Floor Flat, 100 Saltram Crescent, London W9 3JX — MB ChB 1993 Manch.

ELVIN, Graeme Harvey The Triangle Medical Centre, 148 Rochford Way, Frinton-on-Sea CO13 0AZ Tel: 01255 851663 Fax: 01255 851074 — Artsexamen 1986 Utrecht. Socs: Essex Medico-Legal Soc.

ELVIN, Victoria 81 The Avenue, Sunbury-on-Thames TW16 5HZ Tel: 01932 782880 — MB BS 1991 Lond.; MRCGP 1997 BA Camb. 1954, MD 1966, MB 1958, BChir 1957; DRCOG 1996; DCH 1996; DFFP 1997. (Roy. Lond. Hosp.) GP Hampton Ct. Socs: BMA. Prev: SHO (Paediat.) Kingston Hosp. Surrey; SHO (Med. & Geriat.) Frimley Pk. Hosp. Surrey; SHO (Psychiat.) Springfield Hosp. Lond.

ELVY, Brian Leslie Oak Street Medical Practice, 1 Oak Street, Norwich NR3 3DL Tel: 01603 613431 Fax: 01603 767209; Pinewood, Town House Road, Old Costessey, Norwich NR8 5BX Tel: 01603 742053 Email: brian@elvy4.freeserve.co.uk — MB BS 1971 Lond.; BSc Lond. 1968; FRCGP 1996, M 1976; DObst RCOG 1974. (St. Mary's Hosp.) Hosp. Pract. (Dermat.) Jas. Paget Hosp. Gt. Yarmouth; Vasectomy Surg. Marie Stopes Organisation; Provider Vasectomy Servs. E. Norf. Health Commiss. & Fundholders; Provider Minor Surg. & Dermat. Surg. E. Norf. Socs: Brit. Soc. Dermat. Surg. Prev: Trainee GP Norwich VTS; Ho. Phys. Amersham Gen. Hosp.; Ho. Surg. St. Mary's Hosp. Lond.

ELVY, Mary Anne (retired) Pinewood, Town House Road, Old Costessey, Norwich NR8 5BX Tel: 01603 742053 — MB BS 1971 Lond. Prev: Ho. Phys. & Ho. Surg. Amersham Gen. Hosp.

ELWELL, Christine Mary The Coach House, Boycott Manor, Dadford Road, Stowe, Buckingham MK18 5JZ — MB ChB 1984 Leeds; MB ChB Leeds l984; MRCP (UK) 1988.

ELWELL, David 55 Brook Street, Woodsetton, Dudley DY3 1AG — MB BCh 1982 Wales; MA Oxf. 1991; BSc Wales 1979; MA Camb. 1989, BA 1986; MRCPsych 1991.

ELWERFALLI, Mr Mansour Muftah c/o Derek Sayers, Royal National Orthopaedic Hospital, Brockley Hill, Stanmore HA7 4LP — MB BCh 1981 Al Fateh, Libya; FRCS Glas. 1989.

ELWES, Robert Dudley Cary King's College Hospital, Denmark Hill, London SE5 9RS Tel: 020 7346 5309; 41 Hillier Road, London SW11 6AX Tel: 020 7738 1871 — MB ChB 1979 Ed.; BSc (Hons.) Ed. 1976, MD 1990; FRCP Ed. 1996; MRCP (UK) 1981. (Edin univ) Cons. Neurol. & Clin. Neurophysiol. King's Coll. Hosp. Lond.; Hon. Sen. Lect. (Neurol.) Inst. Psychiat. Lond. Socs: Assn. Brit. Neurol.; Brit. Soc. Clin. Neurophysiol.; Counc. Intnl. League against Epilepsy. Prev: Regist. Regional Neurol. Centre Newc.; Research Regist. (Neurol.) Inst. Psychiat. Lond.; Ho. Off. Roy. Infirm. Edin.

ELWIG, Nicholas Henry Long Furlong Medical Centre, 45 Loyd Close, Abingdon OX14 1XR Tel: 01235 522379 — MB BCh 1990 Wales; MRCGP 1995; DFFP 1995; DRCOG 1994.

ELWIN, Philip Michael (retired) The Larches, Four Forks, Spaxton, Bridgwater TA5 1BJ — MB BS Lond. 1955; MRCS Eng. LRCP Lond. 1955; DObst RCOG 1958. Prev: GP Bridgwater.

ELWOOD, Claire Mary 10 Liquorpond Street Surgery, Boston PE21 8UE Tel: 01205 362763 — MB BS 1985 Lond.; MA Camb. 1985, BA 1982; MRCGP 1989; DCH RCP Lond. 1990. Socs: BMA. Prev: GP Princip.; Trainee GP Boston VTS.

ELWOOD, James Stanley (retired) 34A Burnt Hill Road, Farnham GU10 3LZ Tel: 01252 710085 — MB BCh BAO 1943 Belf.; MB BCh BAO (2nd cl. Hons.) Belf. 1943; MD Belf. 1947; FRCPath 1966; DPath Eng. 1952; DCP Lond 1948. Prev: Civil. Cons. Path. Camb. Milit. Hosp. Aldershot.

ELWOOD, John Harold East Kent Health Authority, 7 Cambridge Terrace, Dover CT16 1JT Tel: 01304 227227 Fax: 01304 203846 — MB BCh BAO 1962 Belf.; PhD Belf. 1976, MD (Hons.) 1969; MRCS Eng. LRCP Lond. 1962; FFCM 1981, M 1972; FFCMI 1981; MFOM RCPI 1981; DIH Eng. 1967; DPH Belf. 1966. (Belf.) Commr. Health Serv. E. Kent; Specialist (Community Med.) & Hon. Cons. Health Servs. Studies Centre Univ. Kent. Socs: Soc. Social Med. Prev: Prof. Social & Preven. Med. & Head Dept. Community Med. Qu. Univ. Belf.; Cons. Community Med. E.. Health & Social Servs. Bd.; MRC Schol. Unit of Biometry Oxf. Univ.

ELWOOD, Nicholas Frazer East Glamorgan General Hospital, Church Village, Pontypridd CF38 1AB — MB BCh 1992 Wales.

ELWOOD, Peter Creighton 38 Beatty Avenue, Roath Park, Cardiff CF23 5QT — MB BCh BAO 1954 Belf.; MD (Hons.) Belf. 1963; FRCP Lond. 1981, M 1974; FFCM 1974; DPH Belf. 1960; DCH Eng. 1959. Hon. Prof. Univ. Wales Coll. Med. Cardiff. Prev: Dir. MRC Epidemiol. Research Unit Cardiff.

ELWOOD, Peter York 4 Laughton Way, Lincoln LN2 2JE — BM BS 1987 Nottm.; MRCPsych 1994.

ELWOOD, Philip Earle (retired) Bracken Lodge, 153 Church Road, Holywood BT18 9BZ Tel: 028 9042 3277 — MB BCh BAO Belf. 1955; DPH Belf. 1962; DObst RCOG 1957. Prev: GP Lincoln.

ELWOOD, Sharon Lesley Beech Farm, 35 Ballyknockan Road, Ballygowan, Newtownards BT23 6NR — BM 1986 Soton.

ELWYN, Glyn J Four Elms Medical Centre, 103 Newport Road, Cardiff CF24 0AF Tel: 029 2048 8025 Fax: 029 2048 2871; 103 Newport Road, Cardiff CF24 0AF Tel: 029 2048 5526 — MB BCh 1982 Wales; BA Wales 1976; MSc Medical Education Wales 1997; MRCGP 1987. Sen. Lect. Gen. Pract. Univ. Wales Coll. Med.; Primary Care Adviser, Clin. Effectiveness Support Unit; Mem. CEG (Outcomes) Clin. Effectiveness Gp. (Welsh Off.). Prev: CME Tutor Cardiff Postgrad.

ELY, Mrs Barbara Stewart 33 Bishopsgate Walk, Chichester PO19 4FG — MB BS Lond. 1956; MRCS Eng. LRCP Lond. 1956; AFOM RCP Lond. 1978; DHMSA 1979. (Lond. Hosp.) Socs: Fell. Fac. Hist. Med. Soc. Apoth.; Fell. Roy. Soc. Med.; Liveryman Soc. Apoth. Prev: Sen. Med. Off. DoH; Princip. Med. Off. Kensington & Chelsea & W.m. AHA.

ELY, Julia Christine Josephine Anaesthetic Dept, Queen Elizabeth Hospital, Birmingham B29 7DX; 81 Alton Road, Selly Oak, Birmingham B29 7DX — MB ChB 1995 Birm.; ChB Birm. 1995. Specialist Regist. Anaesth. Univ. Hosp. B/ham. Prev: SHO (Anaesth.) Univ. Hosp. Birm.

ELYAN, Sean Anthony Greensmith Department of Clinical Oncology, Cheltenham General Hospital, Sandford Road, Cheltenham GL53 7AN Tel: 01242 274016 — MD 1993 Bristol; MB ChB 1982; MRCP (UK) 1986; FRCR 1990; FRCP 1999. Cons. Clin. Oncol. Cheltenham Gen. Hosp. Prev: Sen. Regist. Roy. Marsden Hosp. Lond.; Research Regist. Christie Hosp. Manch.; Regist. (Radiother.) Addenbrooke's Hosp. Camb.

ELZIK, Cherif Sadek 22 St Leonards Road, Exeter EX2 4LA — MB ChB Alexandria, Egypt 1963. (Alexandria University Egypt) Med. Servs. Cons. Sonarco, Algeria; Clin. Asst. (ENT) Torbay Hosp.

EMAD, Farhad Churchfield Surgery, Iburndale Lane, Sleights, Whitby YO22 5DP Tel: 01947 810466 Fax: 01947 811375 — MB BS 1981 Lond.; BSc Lond. 1976; MRCGP 1987.

EMAM-SHOOSHTARI, Mehri 11 Wenlock Drive, Preston Grange, North Shields NE29 9HD — MD 1969 Tehran.

EMAMY, Hossein Forushani 57 Links Avenue, Whitley Bay NE26 1TF Tel: 0191 251 2720 — MD 1967 Isfahan; DPath Eng. 1972; DCP Lond 1971. Prof. Isfahon Univ. Iran. Socs: ACP & IAP. Prev: Hon. Regist. (Path.) Soton & Salisbury Gen. Hosp.; Dir. of Lab. Koshoni Hosp. Isfahon, Iran.

EMANUEL, John Arthur (retired) Pengelli Farm, Llanfabon, Nelson, Treharris CF46 6PG Tel: 01443 450256 — MB BCh 1948 Wales.

EMANUEL, Katherine Emma Vercoe 164b East Dulwich Grove, London SE22 8TB — MB BChir 1992 Camb.

EMANUEL, Martin Q Falls Road Practice, 181 Falls Road, Belfast BT12 6AF Tel: 028 9032 0547 Fax: 028 9024 9674 — MB BS 1984 Lagos; MB BS 1984 Lagos.

EMANUEL, Richard Wolff 6 Lansdowne Walk, London W11 3LN Tel: 020 7727 6688 Fax: 020 7221 3605 — BM BCh 1948 Oxf.; DM Oxf. 1954, MA; FRCP Lond. 1967, M 1952; FACC 1961. (Middlx.) Hon. Cons. Phys. (Cardiol.) Middlx. Hosp.; Hon. Cons. Phys. Nat. Heart Hosp.; Hon. Lect. Cardiothoracic Inst. Lond.; Hon. Fell. Philippine Coll. Cardiol. Socs: Brit. Cardiac Soc. (Asst. Sec., Sec., Counc. Mem.); Assn. Phys.; Hon. Mem. Heart Assn. Thailand. Prev: Civil Cons. Cardiol. RAF 1980-8; Asst. Dir. Cardiothoracic Inst. Lond. 1961-3; Research Fell. (Med.) Vanderbilt Univ. USA 1956-7.

EMANUEL, Wilhelm (retired) 14 Ridgway Road, Kettering NN15 5AH Tel: 01536 513170 — MD 1932 Munster; LRCP LRCS Ed., LRFPS Glas. 1935. Prev: GP Kettering.

EMARA, Medhat Mohamed Kamel 93 Howard Road, Woodside, London SE25 5BY — MB BCh 1980 Cairo.

EMBERSON, Christine 230 Cambridge Road, Great Shelford, Cambridge CB2 5JU — LRCPI & LM, LRSCI & LM 1959; LRCPI & LM, LRCSI & LM 1959; LAH Dub. 1958.

EMBERSON-BAIN, Dawn Ingrid 6 Ingate Terrace, 142 Queenstown Road, London SW8 3RR — MB BS 1986 West Indies.

EMBERTON, Anna Andrew House Surgery, 2 South Terrace, Camborne TR14 8ST Tel: 01209 714876 Fax: 01209 612334 — MB BS 1990 Lond.; BSc (Psychiat) Lond. 1987; DCH 1995; DRCOG 1995; MRCGP 1996; DFFP 1996. (St Marys Hospital Medical School London)

EMBERTON, Frederick Charles (retired) The Beeches, 2 Ballater Road, South Croydon CR2 7HS Tel: 020 8688 6858 Email: docemberton@msn.com — MRCS Eng. LRCP Lond. 1952; MCPS Alta. 1952; Cert. Av. Med. 1977. Prev: Mem. Off. & Aircrew Med. Selec. Bds. RAF Biggin Hill.

EMBERTON, Mr Mark Institute of Urology, 48 Riding House St., London W1P 7PN Tel: 020 7380 9328 Fax: 020 7637 7076; 55 Glengall Road, London NW6 7EL Tel: 020 7328 7144 — MB BS 1985 Lond.; BSc Lond. 1983; FRCS Eng. 1990; MD Lond. 1997. (St. Mary's Hospital Medical School) Sen. Lect. (Oncological Urol.) Inst. of Urol.; Dep. Dir. Surgic. Epidemiol. & Audit Unit RCS Eng.

EMBERTON, Paul c/o X-Ray Department, Leicester General Hospital, Gwendolen Road, Leicester LE5 4PW Tel: 0116 249 0490; 12 Byfield Drive, Wigston, Leicester LE18 3PY — MB ChB 1985 Leic.; BSc Leic. 1983; FRCR 1992. Cons. Radiol. Leicester Gen. Hosp. Socs: Skeletal Radiol. Soc.

EMBLETON, Davina Caroline (retired) 4 Firview Close, Marlow SL7 1SZ Tel: 01628 473089 — MB BS 1956 Lond.; MRCGP 1977; DCH Eng. 1960; DObst RCOG 1958. Prev: GP Beaconsfield.

EMBLETON, Mary Alison Waterloo Surgery, 191 Devonport Road, Stoke, Plymouth PL1 5RN Tel: 01752 563147 Fax: 01752 563304 — MB ChB 1991 Birm.; ChB Birm. 1991.

EMBLETON, Nicholas David 61 Jesmond Park W., Newcastle upon Tyne NE7 7BX Tel: 0191 281 9318 — MB BS 1990 Newc. SHO (Paediat.) P.ss Mary Matern. Hosp. c/o Roy. Vict. Infirm. Trust Newc. u. Tyne.

EMBLEY, Craig Partridge Barn, Shelfield, Alcester B49 6JN — MB BS 1997 Lond.

EMBLING, Kate Fiona 23 Brackendale Road, Camberley GU15 2JN — MB BS 1998 Lond.; MB BS Lond 1998.

EMEAGI, Chikeziri Ndubuisi 3 St Bartholomews Road, London E6 3AG — MB BS 1997 Lond.

EMENS, John Michael 14 Church Road, Edgbaston, Birmingham B15 3SR Tel: 0121 454 7576 Fax: 0121 414 1576; 14 Church Road, Edgbaston, Birmingham B15 3SR Tel: 0121 454 7576 Fax: 0121 454 7576 Email: m.emens@virgin.net — MB BS Durh. 1964; MD Birm. 1980; FRCOG 1991, M 1974; DObst RCOG 1966. (Newc.) p/t Cons. O & G Birm. Matern. Hosp. & Birm. & Midl. Hosp. Wom. Socs: HCSA & Counc.; BMA. Prev: Cons. O & G Solihull Hosp.; Squadron Ldr. RAF Med. Br., Jun. Specialist (Surg.) RAF Hosp. Wroughton.

EMENTON-SHAW, Louise Alicia 11 Petersfield Drive, Baguley, Manchester M23 9PS — MB ChB 1990 Ed.; BSc (Med. Sci.) Hon. St. And. 1987; MRCP (UK) 1994; DCH RCP Lond. 1994. (St. And. Univ. & Edin. Univ.) SHO (Psychiat.) Oxf. Prev: SHO (Psychiat.) Maudsley Hosp. Lond.; SHO (Paediat. Oncol.) Gt. Ormond St. Lond.; SHO (Paediat.) Whittington Hosp. Lond. & Rush Green Hosp. Romford.

EMERICK, Sydney Charles (retired) Springfield House, Hatfield Peverel, Chelmsford CM3 2HN Tel: 01245 380324 — MB BS 1951 Lond.; MRCS Eng. LRCP Lond. 1951. Prev: Hosp. Pract. (O & G) St. Johns Hosp. Chelmsford.

EMERSON, Alice Catherine The Surgery, 36 Waverley Road, Southsea PO5 2PW Tel: 023 9282 8281 Fax: 023 9282 2275; 3 The Square, Compton, Chichester PO18 9HA — BM BS 1985 Nottm.; DRCOG 1989; DCH RCP Lond. 1988.

EMERSON, Andrew Robert The Beeches, 67 Lower Olland Street, Bungay NR35 1BZ Tel: 01986 892055 Fax: 01986 895519; 9 Grange Road, Beccles NR34 9NR — MB BS 1983 Lond.; MRCGP 1989; DRCOG 1987. Prev: SHO (O & G & Paediat.) Qu. Eliz. II Hosp. Welwyn Garden City; SHO (Cas.) Guy's Hosp. Lond.

EMERSON, Bruce Martin 15 Nelson Road, Lexden, Colchester CO3 5AP — MB BS 1987 Lond.; FRCA 1995; T(GP) 1994; DRCOG 1991. (Char. Cross & Westm. Hosp. Lond.) Specialist Regist. (Anaesth.) St. And.Centre for Plastic Surg./Burns. Socs: RSM. Prev: Specialist Regist. (Anaesth.) St. Bart. Hosp. Lond.; Regist. & SHO (Anaesth.) Colchester Gen. Hosp.; SHO (O & G) Essex Co. Hosp.

EMERSON, Christine Victoria 135 Cherry Hinton Road, Cambridge CB1 7BX — MB BChir 1987 Camb.; BSc (Hons.) Aberd. 1983; DRCOG 1991; DPH 1995; MRCGP 1994. GP; Asst. Oakfield Surg. Newmarket. Socs: BMA; Med. Equestrian Soc. Prev: GP

Trainee Newham Walk Surg.; GP Asst. Echuca Vict. Australia; Sen. Regist. Pub. Health Med., Suff. Health.

***EMERSON, Claire Abigail** 78B Rydens Road, Walton-on-Thames KT12 3DR Tel: 01932 224644 — MB ChB 1998 Manch.; MB ChB Manch 1998.

EMERSON, Claire Elizabeth 45 Links View, Rochdale OL11 4DD — MB ChB 1997 Leic.

EMERSON, David 74 Cavendish Avenue, Cambridge CB1 7UT — MB BChir 1956 Camb.; MA, MB Camb. 1956, BChir 1955; DObst RCOG 1960. (Oxf.) Hosp. Pract. Drinking Problem Clin. Fulbourn Hosp. Socs: Camb. Med. Soc. Prev: Med. Off. Falkland Is.s; Ho. Surg. ENT Dept. Radcliffe Infirm. Oxf.; Res. Med. Off. Osler Pavil. Oxf.

EMERSON, Elizabeth Maureen Princes Road Surgery, 51 Princes Road, London SW19 8RA Tel: 020 8542 2827/2407 Fax: 020 8296 9505; 1 Hood Road, West Wimbledon, London SW20 0SR Tel: 020 8946 9218 Email: liz@davlizcr.demon.co.uk — MB BChir 1974 Camb.; MA Camb. 1974; MRCS Eng. LRCP Lond. 1973; MRCGP 1979; Cert. Travel Health Glasgow 1997. (Cambridge and Royal London Hospital)

EMERSON, Fiona-May Baldwin and Partners, Hucknall Road Medical Centre, off Kibworth Close, Nottingham NG5 1FX Tel: 0115 960 6652 Fax: 0115 969 1746 — MB ChB 1988 Leeds. Prev: Ho. Surg. Leeds Gen. Infirm.; Ho. Phys. W. Norwich Hosp.

EMERSON, Kim Marie Sonning Common Health Centre, Wood Lane, Reading RG4 9SW; 2 Red House Drive, Sonning Common, Reading RG4 9NT Tel: 01189 723885 — MB ChB 1991 Sheff.; DCH RCP Lond. 1993; DFFP RCOG 1994; MRCGP 1995. (Sheff.) GP Partner Soning Common Health Centre. Prev: SHO (Psychiat.) Fairmile Hosp. Reading.; SHO (O & G) Roy. Berks. Hosp. Reading; SHO (Paediat.) Battle Hosp. Reading.

EMERSON, Margaret Shirley 74 Cavendish Avenue, Cambridge CB1 7UT Tel: 01223 246166 Fax: 01223 515533 Email: mse1935@aol.com — MB BS Durh. 1958; Dip. Sports Med. RCP Ed. 1991. p/t Clin. Asst. Peter Wilson Sports Injuries Clinic Addenbrooke's Hosp. Camb.; Assoc. Specialist Sports Injury Clinic; BUPA Camb. Lea Hosp. Camb. Socs: Roy. Soc. Med.; BMA & Brit. Assn. Sports Med. Prev: GP Camb.; Ho. Phys. Friarage Hosp. N.allerton; Ho. Surg. War Memor. Hosp. High Wycombe.

EMERSON, Mrs Pauline Mildred (retired) Brightwell Manor, Wallingford OX10 0RT Tel: 01491 836138 — MB BS 1957 Lond.; MD Lond. 1965, MB BS (Hons.) 1957; Dip. Biochem; (Distinc.) 1967; MRCS Eng. LRCP Lond. 1957; FRCPath 1976. Prev: Cons. Haem. Oxf. Radcliffe Hosp.

EMERSON, Peter Albert Department of Information Systems, Chelsea and Westminster Hospital, 369 Fulham Road, London SW10 9NH Tel: 020 8746 8868 Fax: 020 8746 8285; 3 Halkin Street, London SW1X 7DJ Tel: 020 7235 8529 Fax: 020 7823 1009 Email: peter_ emerson@hotmail.com — MB BChir 1947 Camb.; BA Camb. 1943, MA 1948, MD 1954; FRCP Lond. 1964, M 1951; FACP 1970. (Camb. & St. Geo.) Clin. Cons. to Dept. Informat. & Systems Chelsea & W.m. Trust; Hon. Cons. Phys. Chelsea & W.m. Hosp. Lond. Socs: Soc. Med. Decision Making; Assn. Phys.; Amer. Med. Informatics Assn. Prev: Cons. Phys. W.m. Hosp. Lond.; Civil Cons. Dis. Chest to RN; Dean. W.m. Med. Sch.

EMERSON, Robert Graham, Brigadier late RAMC Retd. The Paddocks, 4 Lamberts Way, Ditchingham, Bungay NR35 2QB — MB BCh BAO Dub. 1946; MD Dub. 1963; FRCOG 1968, M 1959. (TC Dub.) Prev: Hon. Surg. to HM the Qu.; Cons. Adviser (O & G) MoD; Cons. Obstetr. & Gynaecol. Louise Margt. Hosp. Aldershot.

EMERSON, Russell Mark Dermatology Unit, University of Nottingham, Nottingham NG7 2UH — MB ChB 1988 Leeds.

EMERSON, Sandra The Health Care Surgery, 63 Palgrave Road, Sheffield S5 8GS — MB ChB 1980 Sheff.; MRCGP 1984; DRCOG 1982.

EMERSON, Susan Clare 14 Avon Close, The Bryn Estate, Pontllanfraith, Blackwood NP12 2GB — MB BCh 1983 Wales.

EMERSON, Thomas Richard (retired) 60 Thomas More House, Barbican, London EC2Y 8BT — MB BS 1973 Lond.; PhD Lond. 1960; BSc Lond. 1957; MRCPsych 1978. Prev: Cons. Psychiat. (Geriat.s) Chelsea W.minster Hosp. Lond.

EMERSON, Vanessa Jean 27 Clarendon Road, Sheffield S10 3TQ — MB BS 1973 Lond.; DRCOG 1975.

EMERTON, Mr David Glatton Charles Accident & Emergency Department, North Tees General Hospital, Hardwick, Stockton-on-Tees Tel: 01642 617617; 21 Grisedale Crescent, Egglescliffe, Stockton-on-Tees TS16 9DS Tel: 01642 788640 — MB ChB 1979 Leeds; FRCS Ed. 1992; FRCS Glas. 1988; DRCOG 1982. Cons. & Clin. Dir. A & E N. Tees Hosp. NHS Trust Stockton-on-Tees. Prev: Regist. (A & E) Morriston Hsop. Swansea; Asst. Med. Off. Murgwanza Hosp., Tanzania; SHO (A & E) Huddersfield Roy. Infirm.

EMERTON, Mr Mark Edward Orthopaedic Department, Leeds General Infirmary, Great George St., Leeds LS1 3EX Tel: 0113 392 2168 Fax: 0113 392 3770; Wodencroft, 16 Ancaster Road, West Park, Leeds LS16 5HH Tel: 0113 217 9559 — BM BCh 1988 Oxf.; BA 1985 Oxf.; FRCS Eng. 1993; FRCS (Orthop.) 1998. Cons. Orthopaedic Surg. Leeds Teachg. Hosp.s; Hon. Clin. Lect. Leeds Univ. Socs: Brit. Orthop. Assn.; Brit. Orthop. Research Soc.; Brit. Hip. Soc. Prev: Clin. Lect. in Orthop. Oxf. Univ.

EMERY, Professor Alan Eglin Heathcote Peninsula Medical School, Dept. Neurol., Royal Devon & Exeter Hospital EX2 5DW Tel: 01395 445847 Fax: 01395 443855 Email: enmc@euronet.nl; Ingleside, Upper West Terrace, Budleigh Salterton EX9 6NZ Tel: 01395 445847 Fax: 01395 443855 — MB ChB 1960 Manch.; MB ChB (Hons.) Manch. 1960; PhD Johns Hopkins Univ. 1964; DSc Manch. 1970, MSc 1953, BSc (1st Cl. Hons.) 1952, MD 1966; MD (hon causa) Würzburg 1995; MD (hon causa) Naples 1993; FRCP Ed. 1970, M 1967; FRCP 1985. (Manch.) Vis. Prof. (Peninsula Med. Sch.) - Chief Scientif. Adviser (Europ. Neuromuscular Centre, NL); Prof. Emerit. Human Genetics Hon. Fell. Univ. Edin. Med. Sch.; Advisery Bd., Asian Myology Centre, Tokyo; Exec. Comm. World Fed. Neurol.; Exec. Bd.. World Muscular; Hon. Vis. Fell. Green Coll. Oxf.; Emerit. Fell. Amer. Coll. Med. Genetics; Vice Pres. Muscular Dystrophy Cam. GB. Socs: Fell. Linnean Soc.; Roy. Soc. Lit; FRIPHH, MFCM, FRS (E). Prev: Fell. Med. Johns Hopkins Hosp. Baltimore, USA; Vis. Prof. Univ. Calif. & Duke Univ. N. Carolina, USA; Cons. Phys. & Prof. Human Genetics Edin.

EMERY, Alison Jane (retired) Meadow End, Rugby Road, Weston under Wetherley, Leamington Spa CV33 9BW — MB ChB 1978 Birm.; MRCPsych 1983. Prev: Sen. Regist. (Community Med.) W. Midl. RHA.

EMERY, Christine 39 Churchfield Lane, Rothwell, Leeds LS26 0NA — MB ChB 1980 Leeds.

EMERY, Mr David Frederick George 35 Charlecote Drive, North Millers Dale, Chandlers Ford, Eastleigh SO53 1SF Tel: 01703 251493 Fax: 01703 251493 Email: dfgemery@doctors.org.uk — MB BS 1989 Lond.; FRCS 1993 Eng. Specialist Regist. Wessex Region. Socs: Assoc. Mem. BOA.

EMERY, David Gordon Griffins Brook Medical Centre, Griffins Brook Lane, Bournville, Birmingham B30 1QN Tel: 0121 476 2441 — MB ChB 1958 Birm.; MRCGP 1967; DO Eng. 1967. (Birm.) Occupat. Health Med. Off. Off. Qu. Eliz. Hosp. Birm.; Civil Serv. Med. Off.; Med. Adviser Kalamazoo Business Sys. plc & Boxfoldia Ltd. Socs: BMA. Prev: Ho. Surg. & Ho. Phys. Birm. United Hosps.; RAF Med. Br.

EMERY, Edward Joseph (retired) 38 Homebriar House, Barns Park, Ayr KA7 2BA Tel: 01292 281697 — MB ChB 1933 Glas. Prev: Ho. Phys. Bradford Roy. Infirm.

EMERY, Eric Roy John 287 Sheen Lane, East Sheen, London SW14 8RN Tel: 020 8876 7520 — MB ChB 1953 Sheff.; FFA RCS Eng. 1960; DA Eng. 1958. (Sheff.) Hon. Cons. Anaesth. Char. Cross. Hosp. Lond.; Hon. Cons. Anaesth. Hosp. SS John & Eliz. Lond. Socs: Anaesth. Sect. Roy. Soc. Med. & Assn. Anaesths. Gt. Brit. Prev: Cons. Anaesth. Char. Cross Hosp.; Sen. Regist. (Anaesth.) Char. Cross Hosp. & W. End Hosp. Neurol. & Neurosurg.; Regist. (Anaesth.) Char. Cross Hosp. & W. Lond. Hosp.

EMERY, Frank Michael Whitehaven, Whitehaven Lane, Burland, Nantwich CW5 8NH Tel: 0127 074229 — MB BS 1962 Lond.; MRCS Eng. LRCP Lond. 1961; FFA RCS Eng. 1970; DA Eng. 1964. (St. Mary's) Cons. Anaesth. Leighton Hosp. Crewe. Prev: Sen. Regist. (Anaesth.) Roy. Free Hosp. Lond.

EMERY, Jacqueline Carol 25 Dartmouth Road, Wyken, Coventry CV2 3DP — MB ChB 1994 Leic. Prev: SHO (Neonatol.) Walsgrave Hosp. NHS Trust; SHO (Paediat.) Walsgrave Hosp. NHS Trust; SHO (Paediat.) Geo. Elliot Hosp. NHS Trust.

EMERY, John Christopher South Farm Surgery, 110 Coppice Road, Whitnash, Leamington Spa CV31 2LT Tel: 01926 316711

Fax: 01926 427260 — MB ChB 1978 Birm. GP Leamington Spa. Prev: Med. Off. DHSS Social Security Med. Div. Birm. Regional Office; Gen. Pract. Warwick & Leamington & Warks. Family Plann. Clinic.

EMERY, John Gerard Brian Dept of Anaesthesia, Queen's Medical Centre, Nottingham NG7 2UH — MB BS 1992 Lond.; FRCA 1997. Specialist Regist. (Anaesth.) Qu. Med. Centre Nottm.

EMERY, Jonathan David Department of Primary Health Care, University of Oxford, Institute of Health Sciences, Old Road, Headington, Oxford OX3 7LF Tel: 01865 227069 Email: jon.emery@dphpc.ox.ac.uk; 65 Langely Close, Oxford OX3 7BD Tel: 01865 764911 — BM BCh 1991 Oxf.; MA Camb. 1992; MRCGP 1995; DRCOG 1994. (Camb., Oxf.) Cancer Research Campaign Primary Care Oncol.Research Fell., Univ. of Oxf. Socs: BMA; AUD EP. Prev: Acad. GP Regist., Univ. of Soton, Bath EP VTS.

EMERY, Joseph George, OBE (retired) 6 Kilkenny Avenue, Taunton TA2 7PJ Tel: 01823 253113 Email: joe.emery@bakomi.demon.co.uk — MB BS Lond. 1955; DA Eng. 1957; Fell. Nat. Postgrad. Coll. Nigeria 1982; Founder Fell. W. Afr. Coll. Surgs. 1973; Hon. FMC (Anaesth.) Nigeria 1971. Prev: Assoc. Specialist (Anaesth.) Taunton & Som. NHS Trust.

EMERY, Leonard Leslie 32 Manor Rise, Whitchurch, Cardiff CF14 1QJ Tel: 029 2061 8105 — MB BS 1952 Lond.; MRCS Eng. LRCP Lond. 1952. (Guy's)

EMERY, Martin Charles Health Centre, Newgate Street, Worksop S80 1HP Tel: 01909 500288 Fax: 01909 479564; Camelot, Sparken Hill, Worksop S80 1AP Tel: 01909 500317 — MB ChB 1973 Sheff.

EMERY, Patricia Katherine East Berkshire NHS Community Health Trust, Children's Services, Skimped Hill Health Centre, Bracknell RG12 1LH Tel: 01344 458109 Fax: 01344 458124; 58 Sturges Road, Wokingham RG40 2HE — MB ChB 1974 Aberd.; MRCGP 1979; DCCH RCP Ed. 1988; MSc. Comm. Paed. UCL. (Aberdeen University) SCMO Bracknell & E. Berks. Community Health Trust. Socs: RCPCH. Prev: Clin. Med. Off. Berks. HA; Trainee GP Melton Mowbray Leic. FPC; SHO Rotat. (Med.) Soton. & SW Hants. Health Dist. (T).

EMERY, Professor Paul Rheumatology & Rehabilitation Research Unit, The University of Leeds, 36 Clarendon Road, Leeds LS2 9NZ Tel: 0113 233 4940 Fax: 0113 244 6066; Jameela House, 67 Kent Road, Harrogate HG1 2NH Tel: 01423 501414 Fax: 0121 414 6794 — MB BChir 1978 Camb.; BA Camb. 1974, MA Camb. 1976, MD 1985; MRCP (UK) 1979; Spec. Accredit. Rheum. JCHMT 1985. ARC Prof. of Rheum. Univ of Leeds; Lead Clinician The Leeds Teachg. Hosp NHS Trust. Socs: Brit. Soc. Rheum.; Amer. Coll. of Rheumatism; Europ. League Against Rheumatism. Prev: Asst. Phys. Roy. Melbourne Hosp. & Head Rheum. Unit Walter & Eliz. Hall Inst. Austral.; Sen. Regist. Rotat. (Rheum. & Gen. Med.) Guy's Hosp. Lond.; Hon. Sen. Regist. (Med.) Guy's Hosp. Lond.

EMERY, Pauline Jane Cross Church Cottages, The Street, Ardleigh, Colchester CO7 7LD — MB BS 1975 Lond.; FRCS Eng. 1980. (Univ. Coll. Hosp.) Cons. ENT Surg. Essex Co. Hosp. & Colchester Gen. Hosp. Prev: Sen. Regist. (ENT) Rotat. Norf. & Norwich Hosp., Gt. Ormond St. Hosp. Sick Childr. & St. Thos. Hosp. Lond.

EMERY, Mr Roger John Hart Hospital of St John and St Elizabeth, 60 Grove End Road, London NW8 9NH Tel: 020 7289 5951 Fax: 020 7289 5951; 41 Lansdowne Crescent, London W11 2NT Tel: 020 7221 7712 Fax: 020 7289 5951 — MB BS 1979 Lond.; MS Lond. 1988; FRCS Ed. 1984. (St. Thos.) Cons. Orthop. St. Mary's Hosp. Lond.; Wellcome Surgic. Fell.sh. 1986. Socs: (Ex-Sec.) Brit. Elbow & Shoulder Soc. Prev: Sen. Regist. (Orthop.) Addenbrookes Hosp. Camb.; Regist. (Orthop.) W.m. Hosp. Lond.; Ho. Surg. St. Thos. Hosp. Lond.

EMERY, Simon John Singleton Hospital, Sketty, Swansea SA2 8QA Tel: 01792 205666 Fax: 01792 285874; Greenlane Farm, Pennard, Swansea SA3 2AD Fax: 01792 232164 — MB ChB 1976 Sheff.; MRCOG 1982, D 1978. Cons. O & G Singleton Hosp. Swansea. Prev: Lect. Qu.'s Med. Centre Nottm; Regist. Jessop Hosp. Sheff.

EMERY-BARKER, John Arthur 3 Main Street, Newmills, Dunfermline KY12 8SR Tel: 01383 881917 — MB ChB 1975 Ed.; FFA RCS Eng. 1980.

EMILIANI, Orietta El Borai, 32 Eardley Crescent, London SW5 9JZ Tel: 020 7373 0140 Fax: 020 7244 6617 — State DMS 1980 Rome.

EMINSON, Basil Ian Franklin (retired) Chancel Barn, Church St., Messingham, Scunthorpe DN17 3SB Tel: 01724 763396 — MB BChir 1953 Camb.; MRCS Eng. LRCP Lond. 1953.

EMINSON, Dorothy Mary Royal Manchester Children's Hospital, Pendlebury, Manchester M27 4HA Tel: 0161 794 4696 — MB ChB 1976 Birm.; MA Camb. 1973; MRCPsych 1982. Tutor in Child Psychiat. Dept. Psychiat. Univ. Manch.

EMINSON, Paul Franklin (retired) 21 Ashlands, Ford, Salisbury SP4 6DY Tel: 01722 334034 — MB BS 1948 Lond.; FRCGP 1977, M 1954. Prev: Regional Med. Off. DHSS.

EMMANUEL, Anton Vignaraj 28 Medina Road, London N7 7JU — MB BS 1990 Lond.

EMMANUEL, Edward West Walk Surgery, 21 West Walk, Yate, Bristol BS37 4AA — MB ChB 1993 Bristol.

EMMANUEL, Elie Robert (retired) 16 Cheyne Walk, Hendon, London NW4 3QJ Tel: 020 8203 8608 — MB BS 1958 Lond.; MRCS Eng. LRCP Lond. 1958; FANZCA 1992; FFA RACS 1968; T(Anaes) 1991. Prev: Cons. Anaesth Neath Gen.Hosp. W. Glam.St. And.Hosp. Billericay & St Lawrence Burns & Plastic, Chepstow.

EMMANUEL, Francis Xavier Soosaipillai Department of Clinical Microbiology, University Medical School, Teviot Place, Edinburgh EH8 9AG Tel: 0131 650 6889 Fax: 0131 650 6515 Email: xavier.emmanuel@ed.ac.uk; 14 Polwarth Terrace, Edinburgh EH11 1ND Tel: 0131 228 4476 — MB BS 1972 Ceylon; PhD Immunol. Birm. 1982, MSc 1978; FRCPath 1995, M 1985. Cons. Microbiol. Roy. Infirm. Edin. NHS Trust; Hon. Sen. Lect. (Med. Microbiol.) Univ. Edin. Prev: Sen. Regist. (Clin. Microbiol.) Wycombe Gen. Hosp. & John Radcliffe Hosp. Oxf; Regist. (Clin. Microbiol.) W.. Gen. Hosp. Ed.; Research Stud. (Immunol.) Med. Sch. Univ. Birm.

EMMANUEL, Joanna Sian 28 Medina Road, London N7 7JU; 5 Lotus Road, Biggin Hill, Westerham TN16 3JL Tel: 01959 540696 — MB BChir 1991 Camb. Prev: Ho. Phys. Hemel Hempstead Hosp.; Ho. Surg. Roy. Free Hosp.

EMMANUEL, John Hubert The Surgery, 24 Albert Road, Bexhill-on-Sea TN40 1DG Tel: 01424 730456/734430 Fax: 01424 225615; 50 South Cliff, Bexhill-on-Sea TN39 3EE Tel: 01424 730456 Fax: 01424 225615 — MB BCh 1965 Wales; MRCP (UK) 1972; FRCGP 1985, M 1977.

EMMANUEL, Julian Jeramillo 58 Bruce Road, Mitcham CR4 2BG — MB ChB 1998 Liverp.; MB ChB Liverp 1998.

EMMANUEL, Kenneth Ross 39 Wroxham Road, Branksome, Poole BH12 1NJ — MB BS 1994 Lond.; BSc (Hons.) Lond. 1991. SHO (O & G) Poole Gen. Hosp. Prev: Ho. Off. (Plastic & Vasc. Surg.) Middlx. Hosp. Lond.

EMMANUEL, Sunil Solomon The Surgery, 20 Sackville Road, Hove BN3 3FF Tel: 01273 778585/736030 Fax: 01273 724648; Flat 4, 11 The Martlet, Hove BN3 6NT Tel: 01273 550297 — MB BS 1990 Punjab; BSc (Hons.) Wales 1982; MRCS Eng. LRCP Lond. 1992; MRCGP 1996.

EMMANUEL, Vedakan Owlescot, East End, Benenden, Cranbrook TN17 4BB Tel: 0158 082770 — MB BS 1953 Andhra; TDD Madras 1958. (Andhra Med. Coll. Vishakapatnam) Med. Asst. Benenden Chest Hosp. Prev: Med. Off. U.M.T. Sanat. Arogyavaram, India; SHO King Edwd. VII Sanat. Talgarth.

EMMERSON, Professor Alfred Michael Department of Microbiology, University Hospital, Queen's Medical Centre, Nottingham NG7 2UH Tel: 0115 970 9162 Fax: 0115 970 9233 Email: michael.emmerson@nottingham.ac.uk — MB BS 1965 Lond.; BSc (Hons Physiol.) Lond. 1962; FRCP Glas. 1988; MRCS Eng. LRCP Lond. 1965; FRCPath 1984, M 1972. (Univ. Coll. Hosp.) Prof. Microbiol. Univ. Nottm. Socs: Liveryman Soc. Apoth.; Fell. Zool. Soc. (Lond.). Prev: Prof. Clin. Bacteriol. Qu. Univ. Belf.; Cons. Microbiol. Whittington Hosp. Lond.; Ho. Surg. Radiother. Unit & Ho. Phys. Univ. Coll. Hosp. Lond.

EMMERSON, Anthony John Barrett Neonatal Medical Unit, St Mary's Hospital, Whitworth Park, Manchester M13 0JH Tel: 0161 276 6960 Fax: 0161 276 6536 Email: anthony.emmerson@man.ac.uk; 18 Ollerbarrow Road, Hale, Altrincham WA15 9PW Tel: 0161 941 1748 Email: emmerson_family@msn.com — MB ChB 1983 Bristol; BSc Bristol 1978, MD 1994; FRCP Lond. 1997; FRCPCH 1997; DCH RCP Lond.

1985. (Bristol) Cons. Paediat. St. Mary's Hosp. Socs: Paediat. Research Soc.; Neonat. Soc.; Brit. Assn. Perinatal Med. Prev: Lect. (Neonat.) Univ. Lond. & Hon. Sen. Regist. St. Thos. Hosp. Lond; Regist. (Paediat.) St. Thos. Hosp. Lond. & Pembury Hosp.

EMMERSON, Catherine Mary Hartlepool and East Durham NHS Trust, Holdforth Road, Hartlepool TS24 9AH Tel: 01429 266654; 2 Brookside Gardens, Ashbrooke, Sunderland SR2 7RJ Tel: 0191 565 9033 — MB BS 1986 Lond.; MFFP 1993; MRCOG 1992; Cert. Family Plann. JCC 1989. Cons. O & G Hartlepool & E. Durh. Trust. Prev: Sen. Regist. (O & G) N.. & Yorks. RHA; Regist. (O & G) Qu. Mary's Hosp. Sidcup, Greenwich Dist. Hosp. & King's Coll. Hosp. Lond.; Research Regist. (Obst.) King's Coll. Hosp. Lond.

EMMERSON, Christopher Irvin Heaton Road Surgery, 41 Heaton Road, Heaton, Newcastle upon Tyne NE6 1TP Tel: 0191 265 5509 Fax: 0191 224 1824 — MB BS 1963 Durh.; DObst RCOG 1967. (Durh.)

EMMERSON, Josephine Department of G.U. Medicine, Retford Hospital, North Road, Retford DN22 7XF Tel: 01777 705261 Ext: 442 Fax: 01777 869808; Sherwood House, Sparken Hill, Worksop S80 1AX — MB ChB 1971 Bristol; MFFP. Staff Phys. Dept. G.U. Med. Bassetlaw Trust.

EMMERSON, Judith Ann 13 Palmerston Road, London SW14 7QA — MB BS 1987 Lond.; BA (Hons.) Oxf. 1984; MRCP (UK) 1991. Lect. (Stroke Med.) St. Thos. Hosp. Lond. Prev: Regist. (Neurol.) Bristol United Bath Hosp. Trust.

EMMERSON, Kevin Peter 46 Waterloo Street, Newcastle upon Tyne NE1 4DG — MB BS 1986 Newc.

EMMERSON, Louise Frances 22 Granville Road, Chester CH1 4DD Tel: 01244 379025 — BM 1984 Soton. Clin. Asst. (Genetics) Wrexham Hosp.

EMMERSON, Ralph Colin Imperial Road Surgery, 8 Imperial Road, Matlock DE4 3NL Tel: 01629 583249 — BM BS 1986 Nottm.; MRCGP 1990; DRCOG 1990; DCH RCP Lond. 1989.

EMMERSON, Ronald William Marlowes, 5 Reading Road, Wokingham RG41 1EG — MB BS 1954 Lond.; FRCP Lond. 1977, M 1962; MRCS Eng. LRCP Lond. 1953. (King's Coll. Hosp.) Cons. Dermat. Reading Area. Socs: St. John's Hosp. Dermat. Soc.; BMA. Prev: Sen. Regist. St. John's Hosp. Dis. Skin Lond.; Regist. (Dermat.) St. Thos. Hosp. Lond.; Ho. Phys. King's Coll. Hosp. Lond.

EMMERSON, William Roger (retired) Garth Surgery, Westgate, Guisborough TS14 6AT Tel: 01287 632206 — MB BS 1965 Lond.; MRCS Eng. LRCP Lond. 1965. Prev: Ho. Off. Canad. Red Cross Memor. Hosp. Taplow. Ho. Off. King Edwd. VII Hosp. Windsor.

EMMETT, Christopher Patrick Bryn y Gwalia Hall, Llangedwyn, Oswestry SY10 9JW — MB BS 1977 Lond.; MRCS Eng. LRCP Lond. 1977; FFARCS Eng. 1984; DRCOG 1980. Cons. Anaesth. Shrops. AHA.

EMMETT, Paul Andrew South Parade Surgery, 7 South Parade, Llandudno LL30 2LN Tel: 01492 876907 Fax: 01492 871480; 4 Maes-y-Llan, Conwy LL32 8NB — MB ChB 1988 Liverp.; MRCGP 1993; DFFP 1993. Prev: Trainee GP Gwynedd VTS; SHO & Regist. (Geriat. Med.) Llandudo Gen. Hosp.

EMMETT, Vivienne Elizabeth The Surgery, 83 South St., Bishop's Stortford CM23 3AP Tel: 01279 653225; 11 Thorn Grove, Bishop's Stortford CM23 5LB — MB BCh 1979 Wales; DRCOG 1982. Prev: GP Trainee Mansfield; Ho. Off. (Med.) Derby City Hosp.; Ho. Off. (Surg.) Kings Mill Hosp. Sutton-in-Ashfield.

EMMITT, Kathryn Mary 29 Carlyle Road, Bournemouth BH6 5QN — MB BS 1994 Lond.

EMMOTT, Margaret Nancy Hillside House, Hillside Road, Huyton, Liverpool L36 8BJ Tel: 0151 489 4539 Fax: 0151 489 4409; (Surgery), Hillside House, Hillside Road, Huyton, Liverpool L25 5JT Tel: 0151 489 4539 — MB ChB 1966 Manch.; MRCGP 1981; DA Eng. 1969. (Manch.) Princip. in Gen. Pract. in St Helens and Knoosley. Socs: BMA. Prev: Regist. (Anaesth.) N. Manch. Hosp. Gp.; SHO Anaesth. Crumpsall Hosp. Manch.

EMMOTT, Raymond Anthony King's Arms Cottages, Heath, Wakefield WF1 5SL — MRCS Eng. LRCP Lond. 1966. (Leeds) Socs: Hull Med. Soc. Prev: SHO (Obst.) Hull Matern. Hosp.; Regist. Diag. Radiol. Gen. Infirm. Leeds; SHO Sedgefield Gen. Hosp.

EMMOTT, Rodney Simon Dept. Of Anaesthesia, Blackburn Royal Infirmary, Blackburn BB2 3LR; 254 Sharoe Green Lane N., Fulwood, Preston PR2 9HD — MB ChB 1980 Leeds; FFA RCS Eng. 1984. Cons. Anaesth. Blackburn, Hyndburn + Ribble Valley Health Care NHS Trust.

EMMOTT, Sean Michael Clifton House Medical Centre, 263-265 Beverley Road, Hull HU5 2ST Tel: 01482 341423 — BM BS 1992 Nottm.; MRCGP 1996.

EMMS, Janet Razia 9 Moorgate Avenue, Fagley, Bradford BD3 7LR Tel: 01274 632366; Brambly Cottage, 4 The Corner, Shroton, Blandford Forum DT11 Tel: 01258 861195 — MB ChB 1987 Birm. SHO (O & G) Plymouth Gen. Hosp. Prev: SHO (Orthop. & Trauma) & (Paediat.) Poole Gen. Hosp.

EMMS, Karen Joy Burton Lodge Medical Centre, 86 Station Parade, Harrogate HG1 1HH Tel. 01423 503129 Fax. 01423 561820; 12 The Crescent, Ripon HG4 2JB Tel: 01765 608689 — MB BS 1982 Newc.; MRCGP 1987. LMC Represen. N. Yorks. Area Child Protec. Comm. Prev: Clin. Med. Off. Harrogate HA.

EMMS, Nicholas Winston Blenheim, Ludwell Hill, Barnburgh, Doncaster DN5 7EE Tel: 01709 893167 Fax: 01709 893167 — MB ChB 1996 Liverp. Gen. Surg. SHO Glan Clwyd Hosp. Rhyl Denbighsh. N. Wales.

EMMS, Richard Joseph Abbey View Medical Centre, Shaftesbury SP7 8DH Tel: 01747 856700 Fax: 01747 856701; Tel: 01747 856700 — MB ChB 1984 Birm.; MRCGP 1997; DA (UK) 1988; DRCOG 1988. (Birm.) Gen. Med. Practitioner, Shaftesbury; Clin. Asst., Elderly Care, W.m. Memor. Hosp., Shaftesbury, Dorset. Prev: Trainee GP Dorchester VTS.

EMOND, Professor Alan Martin Professor of Community Child Health, Division of Child Health, 24 Tyndall Avenue, Bristol BS8 1TQ Tel: 0117 928 5753; 12 Rockwell Avenue, Kingsweston, Bristol BS11 0UF Tel: 0117 938 1465 — MB BChir 1978 Camb.; MB BChir Camb. 1977; MA Camb. 1978, MD 1987; MRCP (UK) 1980; FRCP Lond. 1994; FRCPCH 1997. (Cambridge) Cons. Community Paediat. Roy. Hosp. for Sick Childr. Bristol; Clin. Reader (Child Health) Univ. Bristol. Prev: Lect. (Child Health) Univ. Bristol.

EMOND, Marion Wendy 44 Ann Street, Edinburgh EH4 1PJ — MB ChB 1986 Ed.; MRCGP 1991; MRCOphth 1996; DRCOG 1992; DCH RCPS Glas. 1990. Clin. Asst. (Ophth.) Edin. Prev: Trainee GP Bonnyrigg; SHO Rotat. (Gen. Med.) Leeds Gen. Infirm.

EMOND, Richard Anthony The New Folly, Bellmead, Ingatestone CM4 0FA Tel: 01277 352224; The Wickett, Willow Green, Ingatestone CM4 0DQ — MB BS 1980 Lond. Prev: SHO/Trainee GP Mid-Essex HA VTS; Ho. Phys. (Gen. Med.) Roy. Free Hosp. Lond.; Ho. Surg. Qu. Eliz. Hosp. King's Lynn.

EMOND, Ronald Temple Duncan (retired) 18 Priory Close, Totteridge, London N20 8BB Tel: 020 8445 9105 — MB ChB 1945 St. And.; MB ChB (Commend.) St. And. 1945; FRCP Lond 1972, M 1956; DTM & H Eng. 1949. Cons. Phys. Roy. Free Hosp. Lond. Prev: Cons. Infec. Dis. Roy. Free & Roy. N.. Hosps. Lond.

EMPEY, Duncan William 18 Upper Wimpole Street, London W1G 6LX Tel: 020 7935 2977 Fax: 020 7935 2740 Email: doctorempey@email.com — MB BS 1969 Lond.; FRCP Lond. 1983; MRCP (UK) 1971; MRCS Eng. LRCP Lond. 1969. (Westm.) Cons. Phys. & Med. Dir. Roy. Hosps. Trust; Trust Unit Med. Dir., N. Thames Regional Off. NHSE; Hon. Cons. King Edwd. VII Hosp. Offs. Lond.; Hon. Sen. Lect. St. Bart. & Lond. Hosp. Med. Sch. Socs: BMA; Amer. Thoracic Soc.; Roy. Soc. Med. (Ex-Sec. Sect. Measurem. in Med.). Prev: USPHS Research Fell. Cardiovasc. Research Inst. Univ. Calif.; Cons. Phys. Roy. Brompton Nat. Heart & Lung Hosps.; Edr. Brit. Jl. Dis. Chest.

EMPSON, Benjamin David 104 Highgate Road, London NW5 1PB — MB ChB 1993 Sheff.

EMPSON, Katja 24 Robin Hood Lane, Birmingham B28 0LN — MB BCh 1998 Wales.

EMRYS-JONES, Gareth John Hughes The Surgery, St Columb TR9 6AA — MB BS 1968 Lond.; MRCS Eng. LRCP Lond. 1968; MRCGP 1978.

EMRYS-ROBERTS, Hugh Mervyn 15 Stafford Terrace, London W8 7BL Tel: 020 7937 2073 — MRCS Eng. LRCP Lond. 1944; MRCGP 1953. (Guy's) Prev: Regist. Dept. Anaesth. Roy. Vict. Infirm. Newc.; Ho. Surg. Accid. Serv. Radcliffe Infirm. Oxf.; Regist. (Child Health) Roy. Infirm. Cardiff.

EMRYS-ROBERTS, Ralph Meyrick (retired) Watersmead Cottage, Bittles Green, Motcombe, Shaftesbury SP7 9NX Tel: 01747 852365 Fax: 01747 850381 — MB BChir 1942 Camb.; MRCS Eng. LRCP

Lond. 1942; FRCGP 1980, M 1962. Prev: Med. Off. Walton-on-Thames Hosp.

EMSDEN, Alison Emma Mary 1 High Cedar Drive, Wimbledon, London SW20 0NU — MB BS 1985 Lond.; DRCOG 1988; DCH RCP Lond. 1988. (Westm.) GP Lond. Prev: SHO (Paediat.) Middlx. Hosp. Lond.; SHO (O & G) Univ. Coll. Hosp. Lond.; SHO (A & E) W.m. Hosp. Lond.

EMSLEY, Sally Patricia Close Farm, Bury Lane, Doynton, Bristol BS30 5SR — MB ChB 1983 Dundee; MB ChB Dundee I983.

EMSLIE, Alasdair John MIS House, Medical & Industrial Services Ltd., 23 St Leonards Road, Eastbourne BN21 3UT Tel: 01323 724889 Fax: 01323 721161; Green Lanes, Church Lane, Hellingly, Hailsham BN27 4HA Tel: 01323 844244 Fax: 01323 721161 Email: alasdair.elmslie@live.net — BM 1983 Soton.; AFOM RCP Lond. 1989; MRCGP 1987; DRCOG 1986; MFOM 1997; MIOSH 1997. Occupat. Phys. E.bourne Accredit. Specialist in Occupat. Med.; Dir. of Med. & Indust. Servs. Ltd. E.bourne. Socs: BMA & Soc. Occupat. Med. Prev: Med. Adviser Toyota (GB) Ltd., Pk.er Pens & CGU.

EMSLIE, Betty 5 Herman Avenue, Oldham OL8 1AG Tel: 0161 652 7112 — MB ChB Aberd. 1951. (Aberd.) Princip. GP Oldham. Prev: Asst. MOH Cos. Midlothian & Peebles.

EMSLIE, Carolyn Jane 17 Winchester Close, Worksop S81 0PW — MB ChB 1989 Aberd. GP Regist. N. Notts. Prev: Research Fell. (O & G) Univ. Aberd.; SHO (O & G) Aberd. Roy. Infirm.; SHO (O & G) St. Jas. Univ. Hosp. Leeds.

EMSLIE, Ellen Speers (retired) Corner Cottage, 5 lansdowne Road, Colwyn Bay LL29 7AY Tel: 01492 532041 — MB ChB 1952 Leeds; FRCP Lond. 1980; FRCP Ed. 1970, M 1958. Cons. Dermat. Clwyd N. & Gwynedd HA. Prev: Sen. Regist. (Dermat.) King's Coll. Hosp. Lond., & United Birm. Hosps. & Birm RHB.

EMSLIE, Linda Morag Royal Cornhill Hospital, Cornhill Road, Aberdeen AB25 2ZH Tel: 01224 557276 — MB ChB 1979 Glas.; MRCPsych 1984. Cons. Gen. Adult Psychiat. Roy. Cornhill Hosp. Aberd. Prev: Sen. Regist. (Psychiat.) Roy. Cornhill Hosp. Aberd.

EMSLIE, Michael John, SBStJ (retired) Blackford Farmhouse, Cinderford Lane, Hellingly, Hailsham BN27 4HL Tel: 01323 833156 Fax: 01323 833156 Email: m.emslie@talk21.com — MB ChB (Commend.) Aberd. 1954; AFOM RCP Lond. 1981; MRCGP 1965. Prev: Chairm. Med. & Indust. Servs. Ltd.

EMSLIE-SMITH, Alistair Mark Wallacetown Health Centre, Lyon Street, Dundee DD4 6RB Tel: 01382 457629 Fax: 01382 450365; 72 Seafield Road, Broughty Ferry, Dundee DD5 3AQ — MB ChB 1985 Manch.; BSc St. And. 1982; MRCGP 1989. Prev: Trainee GP Tayside VTS; Ho. Phys. Wythenshawe Hosp. Manch.; Ho. Surg. Ninewells Hosp. Dundee.

EMSLIE-SMITH, Donald, OStJ (retired) University Department of Medicine, Ninewells Hospital & Medical School, Dundee DD1 9SY — MB ChB 1945 Aberd.; MD (Hons) Aberd. 1957; FRCP Lond. 1968, M 1952; FRCP Ed. 1965, M 1962. Fell. Univ. Dundee. Prev: Reader (Med.) Univ. Dundee & Hon. Cons. Phys. (Cardiol.) Tayside HB.

EMSLIE-SMITH, Katherine Mary Blue Wing Medical Practice, Wallacetown Medical Centre, 3 Lyon Street, Dundee DD4 6RB Tel: 01382 458333 Fax: 01382 461833; 72 Seafield Road, Broughty Ferry, Dundee DD5 3AQ — MB ChB 1985 Manch.; BSc St. And. 1982; MRCGP 1989; DRCOG 1988. Prev: GP Tayside Doctors Retainer Scheme; Trainee GP/SHO Tayside VTS; Ho. Surg. Falkirk & Dist. Roy. Infirm.

EMTAGE, Mr Lawrence Aubrey Russells Hall Hosp, Pensett Road, Dudley DY1 2HQ Tel: 01384 244203 — MRCS Eng. LRCP Lond. 1978; MS Lond. 1991, MB BS 1978; FRCS Ed. 1982. (St. Bart.) Cons. Urol.Russells Hall Hosp Dudley W. Midl.s. Prev: Sen. Regist. (Urol.) W. Mid. RHA; Regist. (Urol.) Walsgrave Hosp., Coventry.; Research Fell. Univ. Birm.

ENCHILL-YAWSON, Mr Michael Kobina 8 Swale Road, Crayford, Dartford DA1 4PD — MB ChB 1989 Univ. Ghana; FRCS Ed. 1994.

ENDAF, Ap Ieuan Caeruni, Penrhyndeudraeth LL48 6RT — MB BCh 1991 Wales.

ENDBINDER, Harold Cecil (retired) 42 Winscombe Way, Stanmore HA7 3AU — MB ChB Liverp. 1947; MRCGP 1956; DObst RCOG 1952. Prev: Ho. Phys. Walton Hosp. Liverp.

ENDBINDER, Justin Solomon (retired) Flat 2, Regents Court, Stone Grove, Edgware HA8 8AD Tel: 020 8958 4797 — MB ChB Liverp. 1949. Prev: Ho. Phys. & Obst. Ho. Surg. Walton Hosp. Liverp.

ENDERBY, David Hale 21A Devonshire Close, London W1G 7BD Tel: 020 7580 0225 Fax: 020 7580 0225 — MB BChir 1966 Camb.; MA 1967 Camb.; FFA RCS Eng. 1972. (University College London) p/t Cons. Anaesth. Roy. Nat.Throat, Nose and Ear Hosp. Lond. Prev: Sen. Regist. & Lect. (Anaesth.) St. Thos. Hosp. Lond.

ENDERBY, George Edward Hale (retired) Furzefield, Dormans Park, East Grinstead RH19 3NU Tel: 01342 870255 Fax: 01342 870931 — MB BChir 1941 Camb.; MA Camb. 1941; LMSSA Lond. 1940; FRCA Eng. 1993; FFA RCS Eng. 1953; DA Eng. 1943. Hon. Cons. Anaesth. Qu. Vict. Hosp. E. Grinstead. Prev: Anaesth. Metrop. ENT Hosp.

ENDERSBY, Keith St Johns Road Surgery, 10 St. Johns Road, Newbury RG14 7LX Tel: 01635 40160; Glebe House, Enborne, Newbury RG20 0HD Tel: 01635 44779 — MB BS 1973 Lond.; BSc Lond. 1970, MB BS 1973; MRCGP 1977; DObst RCOG 1975. (St. Mary's)

ENELI, Alexander Chuma 85 Greencroft Gardens, London NW6 3LJ — MB ChB 1964 Birm.

ENEVOLDSON, Hilary Jane Mayford House Surgery, Boroughbridge Road, Northallerton DL7 8AW Tel: 01609 772105 Fax: 01609 778553; End House, Scorton, Richmond DL10 6DH Tel: 01748 818004 — MB BS 1977 Lond.; MRCS Eng. LRCP Lond. 1977.

ENEVOLDSON, Nigel Stuart Parker Scorton Surgery, High Row, Scorton, Richmond DL10 6QD Tel: 01748 811320 Fax: 01748 812004; End House, Scorton, Richmond DL10 6DG Tel: 01748 818004 — MB BS 1977 Lond.; DRCOG 1979.

ENEVOLDSON, Thyge Peter The Walton Centre for Neurology & Neurosurgery, Lower Lane, Liverpool L9 7LJ Tel: 0151 525 3611 Fax: 0151 529 5512 — MB BS 1984 Lond.; MA Oxf. 1982, DPhil 1982; FRCP (UK) 1998. Cons. Neurol. The Walton Centre for Neurol. & Neurosurg. Liverp. Prev: Sen. Regist. (Neurol.) Roy. Free Hosp. Lond.; Regist. (Neurol. & Neurosurg.) Nat. Hosp. for Neurol. & St. Thos. Hosp. Lond.

ENG, Mr Ji Bah Northern General Hospital, Herries Road, Sheffield S5 7AU; 52 Bannerdale Road, Sheffield S7 2DP — MB BChir 1984 Camb.; MA Camb. 1985; FRCS Ed. 1987. Transpl. Fell. (Cardiothoracic) N. Gen. Hosp. Sheff. Prev: Regist. (Cardiothoracic Surg.) Leeds Gen. Infirm.; Clin. Fell. (Cardiothoracic Surg.) Papworth Hosp.; Regist. (Surg.) Bradford Roy. Infirm.

ENG, Sunfei Theodore 1 Hillcroft Avenue, Rayners Lane, Pinner HA5 5AN Tel: 020 8868 7378 — MB BS 1956 Lond.; MRCS Eng. LRCP Lond. 1956; DObst RCOG 1961. (Univ. Coll. Hosp.) Socs: Chinese Acupunc. Sci. Research Foundat.; Brit. Med. Acupunct. Soc. Prev: Ho. Off. (Obst.) Whittington Hosp. Lond.; Ho. Phys. Univ. Coll. Hosp.; Resid. Med. Off. St. Pancras Hosp. (Univ. Coll. Hosp.).

ENGEL, Hans Oscar 58 Whitehouse Way, Southgate, London N14 7LT Tel: 020 8361 4643 — LRCP LRCS Ed. LRFPS Glas. 1941; FFOM RCP Lond. 1983, MFOM 1978; DIH . Ed. 1948. (Roy. Colls. Ed.) Socs: Fell. Roy. Soc. Med.; Soc. Occupat. Med. Prev: Sen. Med. Off. Ford Motor Company; Med. Off. Slough Indust. Health Serv.; Maj. RAMC.

ENGERT, David John 194 Woodseer Street, London E1 5HQ — MB BS 1994 Lond. (UCMSM) Socs: BMA.

ENGESET, Anne-Marie 5 Ilford Road, Jesmond, Newcastle upon Tyne NE2 3NX — MB ChB 1997 Aberd.

ENGESET, Mr Jetmund Pine Lodge, 315 North Deeside Road, Milltimber AB13 0DL Tel: 01224 733753 Email: jengeset@tesco.net; Aberdeen Royal Infirmary, Ward 36, Aberdeen AB25 2ZN Tel: 01224 681818 Fax: 01224 840519 Email: jetmund.engeset@arh.grampian.scot.nhs.uk — MB ChB 1964 Aberd.; ChM (Hons.) Aberd. 1970, MB ChB 1964; FRCS Glas. 1982; FRCS Ed. 1970. (Aberd.) Cons. Surg. Aberd. Roy. Infirm.; Hon. Sen. Lect. (Surg.) Univ. Aberd.; Surg. to Her Majesty in Scotl. Socs: Assn. Surg.; Euro.soc.Vasc. Surg.; Brit. Transpl. Soc. Prev: Sen. Lect. (Surg.) Univ. Aberd.; Head Dept. Surg. Univ. Aberd.

ENGINEER, Meher Pesi 199 Mortlake Road, Kew, Richmond TW9 4EN — MB BS 1990 Lond.; MRCGP 1994; DCH RCP Lond. 1993.

ENGINEER, Sohrab Rustom The Market Square Surgery, 4 Market Square, Waltham Abbey EN9 1DL Tel: 01992 704460 Fax: 01992 709461 Email: sohrab.engineer@gp-f81749.nhs.uk; 66

Honey Lane, Waltham Abbey EN9 3BS — MBBS 1971; MD Bombay 1974, MB BS 1971; DCH Bombay 1972. (Topiwala Nat. Med. Coll.) Socs: Roy. Soc. Med. Prev: Regist. (Community Med.) NE Thames RHA; Tutor (Paediat.) Topiwala Nat. Med. Coll. Bombay; Regist. (Paediat.) Roy. Hosp. Sick Childr. Edin.

ENGLAND, Alan Gordon Roselands, Croft Drive, Caldy, Wirral CH48 2JW — MB ChB 1967 Liverp. (Liverp.) Research Fell. Renal Unit Sefton Gen. Hosp. Liverp. Prev: Ho. Off. Liverp. Cardio-thoracic Surgic. Centre; Ho. Off. Gen. Surg. BRd.green Hosp. Liverp.; SHO Coronary IC Unit Sefton Gen. Hosp. Liverp.

ENGLAND, Ann Highland House, Aviemore Road, Crowborough TN6 1QX Tel: 01892 663650; 8 Ascot Close, Eastbourne BN20 7HL Tel: 01323 644680 — MB BCh 1959 Wales; MRCOG 1972. Clin. Med. Off. (Family Plann.) E.bourne & Co. Healthcare NHS Trust. Prev: Med. Miss. Overseas Miss. Fell.sh. Manorom Christian Hosp., Thailand.

ENGLAND, Catherine Mary New Court Surgery, 39 Boulevard, Weston Super Mare BS23 1PF Tel: 01934 624242 Fax: 01934 642608; 29 Frenchay Road, Weston Super Mare BS23 4JL — MB ChB 1981 Liverp. (Liverpool) Socs: Assoc. Mem. RCGP; BMA. Prev: Clin. Asst. (Gen. Pract.) Avon; Clin. Med. Off. (Community Child Health) W.on Health Trust; SHO (Psychiat.) W.on Gen. Hosp.

ENGLAND, Mr David William Lynthorpe, Battenhall Avenue, Worcester WR5 2HN — MB ChB Birm. 1978; BSc (Hons.) Birm. 1975, MD 1990; FRCS Eng. 1982. Cons. Gen. Surg. Qu. Eliz. Hosp. & Univ. Hosp. Birm.; Hon. Sen. Lect., Surg., Univ. of Birm. Socs: BASO. Prev: Sen. Regist. W. Midl. Train. Scheme.

ENGLAND, Elizabeth Jayne Ruth c/o England Stickland Solicitors, Bank Chambers, Six Ways, Erdington, Birmingham B24 6AA — MB BS 1998 Lond.; MB BS Lond 1998.

ENGLAND, Eric Gibson (retired) Rosemount, 33 Bells Hill, Limavady BT49 0DQ Tel: 028 777 62124 Email: eric_england@breathemail.net — MB BCh BAO 1949 Dub.; BA, MB BCh BAO Dub. 1949, DPA 1956; MRCGP 1963; DPH NUI 1955; DCH RCPSI 1956. Exam. Med. Off. Med. Ref. Serv.; Clin. Asst. Dub. Rheum. Clinic. Prev: Ho. Phys. Roy. City of Dub. Hosp.

ENGLAND, Mr James Patrick Sidney 73 Harley Street, London W1N 1DE Tel: 020 7487 4025 Fax: 020 7224 6381 — MB BS Lond. 1955; FRCS Eng. 1967; FRCS Ed. 1962. (Lond. Hosp.) Hon. Cons. Surg. (Orthop.) Char. Cross Hosp.; Sen. Lect. (Orthop.) Univ. Lond. Socs: Fell. BOA & Roy. Soc. Med.; Brit. Assn. for Surg. of the Knee; S.I.C.O.T. Prev: Cons. Orthop. Surg.Hammersmith Hosp.; Cons. Orthop. Surg. P. of Wales & St. Ann's Hosps. Lond.; Sen. Regist. (Orthop.) & Ho. Surg. Lond. Hosp.

ENGLAND, John Keith Kilmeny Surgery, 50 Ashbourne Road, Keighley BD21 1LA Tel: 01535 606415 Fax: 01535 669895 — MB ChB 1971 Leeds; MRCGP 1977; DCH Eng. 1974; DObst RCOG 1973. Clin. Asst. (Orthop.) Airedale Gen. Hosp.; Course Organiser Airedale Dist. VTS.

ENGLAND, John Michael Warders Medical Centre, 47 East Street, Tonbridge TN9 1LA Tel: 01732 770088 Fax: 01732 770033 — MB BS 1970 Lond.; DFFP 1994; Cert. Family Plann. RCOG 1976.

ENGLAND, Kaye Elizabeth Anne Highland Court Farm, Ash Priors, Taunton TA4 3NQ Tel: 01823 432328; 5 Towers Farm, Corfe Mullen, Wimborne BH21 3NY Tel: 01202 600937 — BM BCh 1991 Oxf. Regist. (Gen. Med. & Endocrinol.) Weymouth & Dist. Hosp. Prev: SHO (Chest Med. & Adult Intens. Care) Roy. Brompton Hosp.; SHO Manch. Roy. Infirm.

ENGLAND, Margaret Alison Kilmeny Surgery, 50 Ashbourne Road, Keighley BD21 1LA Tel: 01535 606415 Fax: 01535 669895; Airedale General Hospital, Eastburn, Keighley BD20 6TD Tel: 01535 606415 — MB ChB 1971 Leeds; DCH Eng. 1973. Clin. Asst. (Paediat.) Airedale Gen. Hosp.

ENGLAND, Michael The Trees, 97 Main St., Little Downham, Ely CB6 2SX — MB BS 1970 Lond.; MRCS Eng. LRCP Lond. 1970. (St. Mary's)

ENGLAND, Michael Harry, Maj. RAMC Heath Farm Cottage, Paston, North Walsham NR28 0SQ; Blacksmiths Cottage, Kings Thorn, Hereford HR2 8AW Email: michael.england@virgin.net — MB BS 1988 Lond.; MRCGP 1995; AFUM 1997. (St. Bart. Hosp.) Socs: Soc. Occupat. Health.

ENGLAND, Norman William James, OStJ, Brigadier late RAMC (retired) 93 Cromwell Tower, Barbican, London EC2Y 8DD Tel: 020 7638 5205 — MB ChB 1950 Birm.; BSc (Hons.) Birm. 1948, MB ChB 1950; FRCP Ed. 1971, M 1958; FRCPath 1973, M 1963. Prev: Dir. Army Path.

ENGLAND, Mr Peter Christopher High Trees, 266 Bramhall Lane S., Bramhall, Stockport SK7 3DG Tel: 0161 439 4877 — MD 1975 Manch.; MD (Gold Medal) Manch. 1975, MB ChB 1966; FRCS Eng. 1970. (Manch.) Cons. Surg. Stepping Hill Hosp. Stockport. Prev: Sen. Lect. Surg. Univ. Coll. Hosp. Med. Sch. Lond.; Lect. Surg. Univ. Hosp. S. Manch.; Surg. Regist. Stepping Hill Hosp. Stockport.

ENGLAND, Peter Gerard 6 Cedar Walk, 45 Romsey Road, Winchester SO22 5EU — MB BS 1986 Monash.

ENGLAND, Rachel Anne Kandahar, Barras Lane, Pleinheaume, Vale, Guernsey GY6 8EJ — BM BS 1995 Nottm.

ENGLAND, Rhiannon Statham Grove Surgery, Statham Grove, London N16 9DP Tel: 020 7254 4327 Fax: 020 7241 4098 — MB ChB 1983 Manch.

ENGLAND, Mr Rodney Martin (retired) 11 Russell Road, Moor Park, Northwood HA6 2LJ Tel: 01923 825020 — MB BCh BAO 1959 Belf.; BSc Belf. 1956, MB BCh BAO 1959; FRCS Ed. 1964. Prev: Cons. ENT Surg. N.wick Pk. Hosp. Harrow, Hillingdon Hosp., Mt. Vernon Hosp. & Watford Gen. Hosp.

ENGLAND, Mr Roland Crispin Damian 37 Manor Street, Heath, Cardiff CF14 3PW — MB BCh 1993 Wales.

ENGLAND, Ruth Elizabeth Radiology Department, South Manchester University Hospital, NHS Trust, Wythewshalse, Manchester Email: ruthengland@netscape.net; Craigmore, 9 Savile Park, Halifax HX13EA — MB BCh BAO 1985 Dub.; FRCPI 1998; MRCPI 1988; FRCR 1992. Cons. Radiologist, S. Manch. Univ. Hosp. NHS Trust.

ENGLAND, Simone Jane Uffculme Clinic, Birmingham B30 2TR; 133 Court Oak Road, Birmingham B17 9AA — MB ChB 1986 Leic.; MMedSci Leic. 1993, MB ChB 1986; MRCPsych 1992. Cons. Psychiat. St. Michaels Hosp. Warwick. Prev: Sen. Regist. (Psychiat.) W. Midl. RHA.

ENGLAND, Vanessa Mary, Maj. RAMC (retired) The Surgery, Much Birch, Hereford HR2 8HT — MB BS 1988 Lond.; 1999 DIPTHER; MRCGP 1995; DFFP 1993.

ENGLEBACK, Mary 42 Grosvenor Park, Tunbridge Wells TN1 2BD — MB BS 1988 Lond. Staff Grade (Anaesth.) Kent & Sussex Hosp. Tunbridge Wells. Prev: Regist. (Anaesth.) Kent & Sussex Hosp. Tunbridge Wells.

ENGLEDOW, Alec Harry 31 New Road, Water Orton, Birmingham B46 1QP — MB BS 1994 Lond.

ENGLEHART, Karin Margaret Omer Lodge, 9 St Omer Road, Guildford GU1 2DA — MB BS 1973 Lond.; MRCP (UK) 1978; DCH Lond. 1976.

ENGLER, Corina Feuer 9 Thorn Tree Court, 30 Park View Road, Ealing, London W5 2JB Tel: 020 8998 8201 — LRCP LRCS Ed. LRCPS Glas. 1964; MB Bucharest 1958; DA Eng. 1968. Prev: Regional Med. Dir. for Europe & Africa Syntex Internat.; Med. Dir. Syntex Pharmaceut. Ltd. Maidenhead; Regist. (Anaesth.) Stepping Hill Hosp. Stockport.

ENGLER, Jonathan Harry Winston 24 Valley Road, West Bridgford, Nottingham NG2 6HG — MB ChB 1988 Aberd. Med. Adviser Boots Pharmaceut. Nottm. Prev: SHO (Gen. Med.) Vict. Infirm. Glas.; Ho. Off. (Gen. Med.) York Dist. Hosp.; Ho. Off. (Gen. Surg.) Roy. Halifax Infirm.

ENGLERT, Linda Jane The Barn, Stacey Lane, Loxley, Sheffield S6 6SJ Tel: 0114 285 1075 — MB ChB 1988 Sheff.; FRCA 1995; DA (UK) 1990. Regist. Rotat. (Anaesth.) Roy. Hallamsh. Hosp. & Sheff. Univ. Hosps.

ENGLISH, Aitolia (retired) Bearhill House, Alvechurch, Birmingham B48 7JX Tel: 0121 445 2222 — MB BS Lond. 1940; MRCS Eng. LRCP Lond. 1940; DCH Eng. 1942. Prev: Princip. Phys. (Child Health) Heref. & Worcs. HA.

ENGLISH, Barbara South & East Belfast (H&SS) Trust, c/o Knockbracken Healthcare Park, Saintfield Road, Belfast BT8 8BH — MB ChB BAO 1992 Belf. Specialist Regist. Psychiat.

ENGLISH, Bryan Keith Northern General Hospital, Herries Road, Sheffield S5 7A Tel: 0114 226 6257 Fax: 0114 226 6225; 7A Moorcroft Close, Sheffield S10 4GU — MB ChB 1986 Sheff.; Dip. Sports Med. Lond 1993; DO MRO Eng. 1989; Dip Clin Gait Analysis Strathclyde . 1997. (Sheffield) Specialist (Orthop. & Sports Med.) N.ern Gen. Hosp. Sheff.; RMO Brit. Athletics Assoc. & Brit. Judo

Assoc.; Sec. Brit. Inst. Musculoskeletal Med. Socs: Brit. Assn. Sport & Med.; (Counc.) Brit. Inst. Musculoskeletal Med.

ENGLISH, Catherine Louise Ashton Cottage, Lower Pennance, Lanner, Redruth TR16 5TS — MB ChB 1988 Bristol. Staff Grade (Psychiat.) Cornw. Healthcare Trust. Socs: BMA; MPS.

ENGLISH, Christine Joy Dept of Occuptional Health, University Hospital of North Tees, Hardwick, Stockton-on-Tees TS19 8PE Tel: 01642 624189 Fax: 01642 624941 Email: nthocchealth@nth.northy.nhs.uk; 25 Cedar Drive, Durham DH1 3TF Tel: 0191 386 9522 — MB ChB 1974 Dundee; MFOM 1999; BSc (Med. Sci.) St. And. 1971. Cons. Occupat. Health N. Tees & Hartlepool NHS Health Trust Stockton-on-Tees. Socs: Soc. Occupat. Med. Prev: Sen. Regional Med. Off. Civil Serv. Occupat. Health Serv.; Med. Off. Inst. Ocupat. Med. Edin.; Phys. (Occupat. Health) Lothian HB.

ENGLISH, Elaine Margaret Community Health Services, Princess of Wales Hospital, Coity Road, Bridgend CF31 1RQ Tel: 01656 752528; 76 Park Street, Bridgend CF31 4BB Tel: 01656 650176 — MB BCh 1982 Wales. (Welsh Nat. Sch. Med.) SCMO Bro Morgannwg NHS Trust Community Paediat./Paediat. Audiol. Prev: Clin. Med. Off. Mid Glam. HA; SCMO Bridgend & Dist. NHS Trust.

ENGLISH, Frederick Campbell Level 7D, Royal Group of Hospitals Trust, Grosvenor Road, Belfast BT12 Tel: 01232 240503; 27 Carsons Road, Ballygowan, Newtownards BT23 5GB Tel: 01238 528633 — MB ChB 1982 Belf. Staff Surg. (ENT Surg.) Roy. Belf. Hosp. Sick Childr. & Belf. City Hosp. Prev: SHO (ENT Surg.) Roy. Vict. Hosp. Belf.

ENGLISH, Gillian Margaret 64 Alamein Avenue, Bedford MK42 0DF — MB BS 1968 Lond.

ENGLISH, Gillian Mary 2 St Albans Close, Flitwick, Bedford MK45 1UA — MB BCh BAO 1988 NUI.

ENGLISH, Howard Larmour Bwthyn Gwyn, Lôn Sant Ffraid, Trearddur Bay, Holyhead LL65 2UD Tel: 01407 860208 — MB BChir Camb. 1944; MRCP Lond. 1949; MRCS Eng. LRCP Lond. 1944; MRCPsych 1971; DPM Manch. 1955. (Camb. & Manch.) Socs: BMA; Welsh Psychiat. Soc. Prev: Cons. Psychiat. Morgannwg Hosp. Bridgend; Sen. Hosp. Med. Off. Deva Hosp. Chester; Sen. Regist. Winwick Hosp. Warrington.

ENGLISH, Ian Charles Woolrych (retired) 8 Riverside House, Williamson Close, Ripon HG4 1AZ Tel: 01765 692216 — MRCS Eng. LRCP Lond. 1943; FFA RCS Eng. 1953; DA Eng. 1947. Prev: Cons. Anaesth. Brompton Hosp.

ENGLISH, James Daniel Department of Obstetrics & Gynaecology, Worthing Hospital, Lyndhurst Road, Worthing BN11 2DH Tel: 01903 205111; Rock House, Washington RH20 3DA Tel: 01903 893867 Email: james.english@btinternet.com — MB BCh BAO NUI 1983; MD NUI 1996; LRCPSI 1983; MRCOG 1989. (RCSI) Cons. Worthing Hosp. Worthing; Cons. Goring Hall Hosp. Goring-by-Sea. Socs: BSGE; BSCCP; Soc. of Laparoendoscopic Surg. Prev: SR Chelsea & W.minster Lond.; Lect. Roy. Coll. of Surgs. in Irel.

ENGLISH, James Digby Forest Farm, Four Lanes, Redruth TR16 6LZ Tel: 01209 713441 — MB ChB 1995 Bristol. SHO (Gen. Med.) Treliske Hosp. Truro. Prev: SHO (A & E) Weymouth Dist. Hosp.

ENGLISH, Jason Spinney Brook Health Centre, 59 High Street, Irthlingborough, Wellingborough NN9 5GA Tel: 01933 650593 Fax: 01933 653641; 23 Berwick Way, Kettering NN15 5XF — MB ChB 1992 Leic.; MRCGP 1996. GP Princip.

ENGLISH, John Michael 87 Greencroft Street, Salisbury SP1 1JF Tel: 01722 321323 Fax: 01722 410417 Email: 100422.1664@compuserve.com — MB ChB Bristol 1957; FRCGP 1981, M 1973; FFHom 1987, M 1972; Dip Med Acupunc 1997. Indep. Homoeop. Salisbury; Lect. Fac. Homoeop. Socs: Brit. Med. Acupunct. Soc.; BMA. Prev: GP Hayes, Middlx.

ENGLISH, John Peter (retired) 1C Upton Close, Norwich NR4 7PD Tel: 01603 451751 — MB BChir 1954 Camb.; DObst RCOG 1956. Prev: Cas. Off. W.m. Hosp.

ENGLISH, John Simon Campbell Department of Dermatology, QMC, University Hospital, Nottingham NG7 2UH Tel: 0115 9249924 ext 43745 Fax: 0115 970 9003 — MB BS 1978 Lond.; FRCP Lond. 1996; MRCP (UK) 1981. (Westm.) Cons. Dermat. QMC Nottm. Socs: BMA; Brit. Assn. Dermat.; Fell. Roy. Soc. Mem. (Sect. Dermat.). Prev: Cons. Dermat. Staffs. Hosp.; Sen. Regist. St. John's Hosp. Dis. of Skin; Regist. (Dermat.) Glas. W.. Infirm.

ENGLISH, Judith Buchanan Dundee Healthcare NHS Trust, Royal Dundee Liff Hospital, Dundee DD2 5NF Tel: 01382 423000; 5 Madoch Road, St. Madoes, Perth PH2 7TT — MB ChB 1990 Aberd.; MRCGP 1995; MRCPsych 1998. (Aberd.) SHO Psychiat. Roayl Dundee Liff Hosp. Prev: GP Princip. Alva Med. Pract.; SHO (Med.) Roy. Liverp. Univ. Hosp.

ENGLISH, Marian Margaret The St Lawrence Surgery, 79 St. Lanewrence Avenue, Worthing BN14 7JL Tel: 01903 237346; 24 Belsize Road, Worthing BN11 4RE — MB ChB 1985 Dundee; MRCGP 1990; DCH RCP Lond. 1990.

ENGLISH, Martin William Oncology Department, Birmingham Children's Hospital, Steelhouse Lane, Birmingham B4 6NU Tel: 0121 333 8412 Fax: 0121 333 8413 — MB ChB 1986 Dundee; FRCP 2000 (Glas); BMSc Dund 1983; FRCPCH 2000; FRCP (hlas) 2000; MD Newcastle 1997. (Dundee) Cons. Paediat. Oncol. Univ. Hosp. of Wales & Llandough,Hosp. NHS Trust. Socs: Fell (Qua Phys.) RCP &S Glas.; Roy. Naval Med. Soc.; BMA. Prev: Sen. Regist. (Paediat. Oncol.) Birm. Childr. Hosp.; Clin. Research Asst. (Child Health) Univ. Newc. u. Tyne; Cons. (Paediat. Oncol.) Cardiff & Vale NHS Trust.

ENGLISH, Michael Charles 8 Thrifts Walk, Cambridge CB4 1NR — MB BChir 1988 Camb.; MRCP (UK) 1991.

ENGLISH, Patrick John Royal Shrewsbury Hospital, Mytton Oak Road, Shrewsbury SY3 8XQ Tel: 01743 261000; 18 Drawwell Street, Belle Vue, Shrewsbury SY3 7RF Tel: 01743 351572 — MB ChB 1991 Bristol; MRCP(UK) 1995. Regist. (Med.) Roy. Shrewsbury Hosp. Prev: SHO (Med.) Taunton & Som. Hosp.; SHO (c/o Elderly) Glos. Roy. Hosp.; SHO (A & E Med.) Gold Coast S.port Qu.sland, Austral.

ENGLISH, Peter Hedon Group Practice, 4 Market Hill, Hedon, Hull HU12 8JD Tel: 01482 899111 Fax: 01482 890967; 10 Main Street, Paull, Hull HU12 8AL — MB BS 1979 Lond.; BSc Lond. 1976, MB BS 1979.

ENGLISH, Mr Peter John North Durham Acute Hospitals, Dryburn Hospital, North Road, Durham DH1 5TW Tel: 0191 386 9522 — MB BS 1973 Lond.; BSc (Hons.) Lond. 1970; FRCS (Urol.) 1987; FRCS Ed. 1980; FRCS Eng. 1981. (Univ. Coll. Hosp.) Cons. Urol. Dryburn Hosp. Durh. Socs: Fell. Roy. Soc. Med.; Brit. Assn. Urol. Surgs.; Internat. Soc. Urol. Prev: Regist. (Urol.) St. Peter's Hosps. Lond.; Research Regist. (Urol.) Manch. Roy. Infirm.; Sen. Regist. (Urol.) Roy. Infirm. Edin.

ENGLISH, Peter Mark Bandele Surrey Communicable Disease Control Service, East Surrey Health Authority, West Park Road, Epsom KT19 8PH Tel: 0706 995 0467, 0706 9950 4673 Email: peter_english@bigfoot.com; 260 Chessington Road, Ewell, Epsom KT19 9XF Tel: 020 8873 7190 Fax: 0870 164 1219 Email: peter_english@iname.com — MB ChB 1984 Liverp.; MFPHM 1997; MPH Nottm. 1995; MRCGP 1989. Cons. Communicable Dis. Control for Surrey. Socs: Pub. Health Med. Environment Gp.; Thames & E.ern Region CCDC Audit Gp. - Chairm.; Roy, Inst. of Health. Prev: Regist. Pub. Health Med. Trent Regional Health Auth.; Clin. Fell. Teamcare Valleys Univ. Wales Coll. Med.; GP Leicester.

ENGLISH, Ruth Elizabeth Department of Radiology, John Radcliffe Oxford Radcliffe Hospital NHS Trust, Headley Way, Headington, Oxford OX3 Tel: 01865 225978; 3 Boults Close, Old Marston, Oxford OX3 0PP Tel: 01865 722914 — MB ChB 1974 Liverp.; MRCP (UK) 1978; FRCR 1985; DCH Eng. 1978. Cons. Radiol. Oxf. Radcliffe Hosp. NHS Trust; Hon. Sen. Clin. Lect. Univ. Oxf. Prev: Sen. Regist. (Radiol.) John Radcliffe Hosp. Oxf.; Regist. (Radiol.) Soton. Gen. Hosp.; Regist. (Gen. Med.) Liverp. HA.

ENGLISH, Samantha Penelope Jane Queens Road Surgery, Queens Road, Blackhill, Consett DH8 0TL Tel: 01207 216434 Fax: 01207 216426 — MB BS 1990 Lond.; MB BS (Hons.) Lond. 1990; BSc Durham. 1985; MRCGP 1995. (Char. Cross & Westm. Med. Sch.) GP Asst. Consett. Socs: MRCGP. Prev: SHO (O & G & Paediat.) Newc. Gen. Hosp.; SHO (Med.) Hexham Gen. Hosp.; SHO (Paediat. & Neonates) Newc. Gen. Hosp.

ENGLISH, Shirley Anne 3 Glenfield Road, Lurgan, Craigavon BT66 8EP — MB ChB 1997 Aberd.

ENGLISH, Sir Terence Alexander Hawthorne, KBE (retired) Master's Lodge, St. Catharine's College, Cambridge CB2 1RL Tel: 01223 368744 Fax: 01223 330809 — MB BS Lond. 1962; MA Camb. 1977; BSc (Eng.) Witwatersrand 1954; FRCP Lond. 1990; FRCS Ed. 1967; FRCS Eng. 1967; MRCP (UK) 1987; FACC 1986. Prev: Pres. BMA 1995/96.

ENGLISH, William Andrew 62 Wood Vale, Forrest Hill, London SE23 3ED — BM BS 1993 Nottm.; MRCP 1999. (Nottingham University)

ENGLISHBY, Veronica Lorna Abbott Laboratories, Abbott House, Norden Road, Maidenhead SL6 4XE Tel: 01628 644192 Fax: 01628 644185; Ash House, Milestone Avenue, Charvil, Reading RG10 9TN Tel: 0118 927 2773 — MB BCh BAO 1986 Belf.; MFPM RCP (UK) 1992; Dip. Pharm. Med. RCP (UK) 1990. (Queens University of Belfast) Med. Servs. Manager Abbott Laboratories Maidenhead. Prev: Sen. Med. Advisor Abbott; Med. Adviser Boechringer Inglehern.

ENI-OLOTU, Daniel Olaiya 7 Bay Road, Southampton SO19 8EZ — MB BS 1987 Ibadan; FRCS Glas. 1993. (Univ. Ibadan, Nigeria) Prev: Regist. (Orthop.) St. Mary's Hosp. Newport I. of Wight; SHO (Orthop.) Leeds Gen. Infirm.; SHO Rotat. (Surg.) Hull Roy. Infirm.

ENION, Mr David Stephen 4 Milton Road, West Kirby, Wirral CH48 5ES — MB ChB 1987 Liverp.; FRCS Glas. 1992.

ENNIS, Claire Julie 39 Oakdene Court, Culloden, Inverness IV2 7XL — MB ChB 1977 Glas.; MFFP 1993; MRCOG 1986.

ENNIS, Jack Eric 29 Mortonhall Park Avenue, Edinburgh EH17 8BP Tel: 0131 664 1315 — MB BS 1937 Lond.; MRCS Eng. LRCP Lond. 1937; FRCPath 1963. (St. Bart.) Socs: Brit. Assn. Forens. Med. & Assn. Clin. Pathols. Prev: Specialist Path. Broken Hill & Dist. Hosp. NSW, Casmarina Hosp. Darwin, NT,. Austral.; Cons. Path. Durh. Gp. Hosps.; Maj. Indian Med. Servs.

ENNIS, John Samuel Arthur 12 Leven Terrace (2FR), Edinburgh EH3 9LW — MB ChB 1990 Ed.

ENNIS, Mr Kieran Alwyn Bartholomew 85 Ashgate Road, Chesterfield S40 4AH Tel: 01246 38519 — MB ChB 1964 Liverp.; FRCS Eng. 1973. Cons. Orthop. Surg. Chesterfield Roy. Hosp.

ENNIS, Owain Wyn Llwyngwair Manor, Trefdraeth, Newport SA42 0LX — MB BCh 1998 Wales.

ENOCH, Barry Anthony (cons. rooms), 16 St John St., Manchester M3 4EA Tel: 0161 834 2554 Fax: 0161 835 1456 — MB ChB 1962 Liverp.; BSc (Hons. Physiol.) Liverp. 1959; FRCP Lond. 1980, M 1968. (Liverp.) Hon. Cons. Phys. (Gen. Med., Endocrinol. and Diabetes) N. Manch. HA; Hon. Lect. (Med.) Univ. Manch. Socs: Brit. Diabetic Assn. (Med. & Scientif. Sect.); Fell. Manch. Med. Soc. Prev: Sen. Regist. (Med.) Manch. Roy. Infirm.; Regist. Profess. Med. Unit Sheff. Roy. Hosp.; SHO Profess. Med. Unit Cardiff Roy. Infirm.

ENOCH, Bridget Elizabeth North Devon District Hospital, Raleigh Park, Barnstaple EX31 4JB Tel: 01271 22577 — MB BS 1971 Newc.; FRCS Eng. 1976; FRCOphth 1988; DO Eng. 1974. Cons. Ophth N. Devon Dist. Hosp. Barnstaple. Prev: Sen. Regist. (Ophth.) Manch. Roy. Eye Hosp.; Regist. (Ophth.) Univ. Hosp. Wales Cardiff; Clin. Lect. (Ophth.) Oxf. Eye Hosp.

ENOCH, David Andrew 32 Rivergarth, Darlington DL1 3SJ — MB BS 1998 Lond.; MB BS Lond 1998.

ENOCH, Lynne Ceris Surrey Lodge Group Practice, 11 Anson Road, Victoria Park, Manchester M14 5BY Tel: 0161 224 2471 Fax: 0161 257 2264; 6 Sevenoaks Avenue, Heaton Moor, Stockport SK4 4AW Tel: 0161 432 5147 — MB ChB 1978 Manch.; BSc St. And. 1975; MRCGP 1982. GP Trainer Manch. Prev: Trainee GP Moss Side; SHO (O & G) Wythenshawe Hosp. Manch.; SHO (Paediat.) Manch. (S.) Health Dist. (T).

ENOCH, Mary Anne Rushmere, Orley Farm Road, Harrow HA1 3PE — MB BS 1981 Lond.; MA Camb. 1975; MRCGP 1985; DCH RCP Lond. 1984. (Univ. Coll. Hosp.) GP Ealing. Prev: Fogarthy Fell.sh. Research in Genetics of Alcoholism Nat. Inst. on Alcohol Abuse & Alcoholism. Bethesda, MD, USA.; GP Harrow Middlx.; Trainee GP N.wick Pk. VTS.

ENOCH, Morgan David Cardiff consulting rooms, 128 Newport Rd, Cardiff CF24 IDH Tel: 02920 464499 Fax: 02920 470309; 120 Pencisely Road, Cardiff CF5 1DQ — MRCS Eng. LRCP Lond. 1954; FRCPsych 1974, M 1971; DPM Eng. 1958. (St. Thos.) Emerit. Cons. Psychiat. Roy. Liverp. Univ. Hosp. Socs: Expert Witness Inst.; Fell. Roy. Soc. Med.; BMA. Prev: Cons. Psychiat. Roy. Liverp. Univ. Hosp. & Sen. Clin. Lect. Univ. Liverp.; Cons. Psychiat. Shrewsbury Gp. Hosps. & Postgrad. Clin. Tutor Univ. Birm.; Sen. Regist. Lond. Hosp. & Runwell Hosp. Wickford.

ENOCH, Peter John, OBE (retired) Littlewick Medical Centre, Nottingham Road, Ilkeston DE7 5PR Tel: 0115 932 5229 Fax: 0115 932 5413 — MB BS 1957 Durh; MB BS Durh. 1957; FRCGP 1992, M 1970; DObst RCOG 1960. Hon. Phys. Ilkeston Community Hosp.; Authorised Med. Examr. Civil Aviat. Auth. Prev: Chairm. Standing Med. Advisory Comm. DoH.

ENRIGHT, Elsa Ruth (retired) 10 Milton Gardens, Princes Risborough, Aylesbury HP27 9DD — MB ChB 1942 St. And.; FFA RCS Eng. 1957.

ENRIGHT, Helen Madeleine Exmouth Health Centre, Claremont Grove, Exmouth EX8 2JF Tel: 01395 273001 Fax: 01395 273771; 4 Phillipps Ave, Exmouth EX8 3HY Tel: 01395 275409 — MB ChB 1976 Leeds.

ENRIGHT, Simon Michael 7 Berryfield Park, Amersham HP6 5QN — MB ChB 1989 Leeds.

ENRIQUEZ PUGA, Andres 28 Laburnum Road, Birmingham B30 2BA — LMS 1993 U Autonoma Madrid.

ENSAFF, Suzanne Treetops, Bryn Rhedyn, Llanfrechfa, Cwmbran NP44 8UB — MB BCh 1989 Wales.

ENSKAT, Anthony Richard Derek Surgery, Judges Close, East Grinstead RH19 3AE Tel: 01342 324628 Fax: 01342 318055 — MB BS 1975 Lond.; MRCS Eng. LRCP Lond. 1975; DRCOG 1980; DCH Eng. 1979. (St. Bart.) Prev: Ho. Phys. St. Bart. Hosp. Lond.; Ho. Surg. St. Leonards Hosp. Lond.; Ho. Phys. (Dermat.) St. Bart. Hosp. Lond.

ENSLIN, Renée Charlotte The Princess Grace Hospital, 42-52 Nottingham Place, London W1U 5NY Tel: 020 7486 1234 Fax: 020 7487 4476; Proverbs Green, High Roding, Dunmow CM6 1NQ Tel: 01245 231817 Fax: 01245 231636 — MB ChB 1977 Cape Town; MB ChB (Hons. Gen. Surg.) Cape Town 1977; FRCS Eng. 1982.

ENSOR, Geoffrey Francis (retired) 129 Cannons Close, Bishop's Stortford CM23 2BJ Tel: 01279 651329 — MRCS Eng. LRCP Lond. 1944; DOMS Eng. 1947. Prev: Asst. Ophth. Chase Farm Hosp. Enfield.

ENSOR, Jennifer Margaret 23 Farmoss Road, Blundellsands, Liverpool L23 8TG Tel: 0151 924 5937 — MB ChB 1967 Liverp. (Liverp.) Occupat. Phys. Liverp.; Adjudicating Med. Pract. For Benefits Agency. Socs: BMA & Soc. Occupat. Med. Prev: Ho. Surg. & Ho. Phys. David Lewis N.. Hosp. Liverp.; Clin. Asst. (A & E) BRd.green Hosp. Liverp.

ENTEKHABI-FARD, Omid 64 Elm Walk, London SW20 9EE — MB BS 1993 Lond.

ENTICKNAP, John Brandon (retired) 37 Bridewell Street, Clare, Sudbury CO10 8QD Tel: 01787 278403 — MB BS 1952 Lond.; MB BS Lond. 1945; MD Lond. 1952; FRCPath 1966; DCP Lond 1946; AKC 1990. Prev: Forens. Path. E. Dist. of Gtr. Lond.

ENTRESS, Anthony Hilmer c/o Department Anaesthetics, Killingbeck Hospital, York Road, Leeds LS14 6UQ — MB BS 1968 Lond.; FFA RCS Eng. 1972.

ENTRICAN, John Hamilton Courtside Surgery, Kennedy Way, Yate, Bristol BS37 4DQ Tel: 01454 313874 Fax: 01454 327110 — MB ChB 1974 Aberd.; MD Aberd. 1986; MRCP (UK) 1976; MRCGP 1987. Clin. Asst. (Gastroenterol.) Frenchay Hosp. Bristol. Prev: Research Fell. (Gastroenterol.) W.. Gen. Hosp. Edin.; Clin. Fell. (Immunol.) McMaster Univ. Hamilton Ontario Canada; Lect. (Med.) Univ. Aberd.

ENTWISLE, Ian David Thurlestone House, Maurys Lane, West Wellow, Romsey SO51 6DB — MRCS Eng. LRCP Lond. 1978; BSc Lond. 1975, MB BS 1978; MRCGP 1985; DRCOG 1981; DCH RCP Lond. 1982. (Guy's) Prev: SHO (Paediat.) Torbay Gen Hosp.; SHO (Obst.) Roy. Sussex Co. Hosp.; Cas. Off. Roy. Sussex Co. Hosp.

ENTWISLE, John James The Cot, 9 Park St., Market Bosworth, Nuneaton CV13 0LL Tel: 01455 290456 — MB BS 1990 Lond.; MRCP (UK) 1994; FRCR 1997. (St. Mary's Hospital Medical School London) Specialist Regist. Rotat. (Radiol.) Leicester. Prev: SHO (Med.) Roy. Hallamsh. Hosp. Sheff.; SHO Rotat. (Med.) Leicester; Ho. Phys. St. Mary's Hosp. Lond.

ENTWISLE, Katherine Gemma Radiology Department, Kent & Canterbury NHS Trust, Ethelbert Road, Canterbury CT1 Tel: 01227 766877; Tel: 01227 832007 — MB BS 1986 Lond.; MRCP (UK) 1989; FRCR 1993. (St. Thos.) Cons. Radiol. E. Kent Hosp.s NHS Trust Canterbury. Prev: Sen. Regist. (Radiol.) UMDS Lond.; Regist. (Radiol.) St. Thos. Hosp. Lond.

ENTWISTLE, Anthony John (retired) 113 Station Road, Delamere, Northwich CW8 2HZ — MB ChB 1952 Liverp.; DObst RCOG 1956. Prev: Ho. Surg. (O & G) Chester City Hosp.

ENTWISTLE, Anthony Neil Westway Medical Centre, Westway, Maghull, Liverpool L31 0DJ Tel: 0151 526 1121 Fax: 0151 531 2631 — MB ChB 1991 Liverp.; DRCOG 1998. GP Partner; Hosp. Practitioner Ashworth Hosp. Prev: GP Regist. N. Liverp. Mersey Surgic. Rotat.

ENTWISTLE, Charles (retired) Tall Trees, Lawn Farm, Tibberton, Droitwich WR9 7NW Tel: 0190 565651 — MB ChB 1954 Birm.; BSc, MB ChB Birm. 1954; DPM Eng. 1960. Prev: Capt. RAMC.

ENTWISTLE, Colin Carruthers (retired) 24 The Glebe, Cumnor, Oxford OX2 9QA — MB ChB 1958 Bristol; MA Status Oxf. 1980; FRCPath 1977, M 1965. Prev: Dir. Regional Blood Transfus. Centre Oxf.

ENTWISTLE, David Meredyth (retired) 34 Heol-y-Coed, Rhiwbina, Cardiff CF14 6HT Tel: 01222 616867 — MB BS Lond. 1956; DObst RCOG 1959.

ENTWISTLE, George David Cogshall Lane Farm, Cogshall Lane, Comberbach, Northwich CW9 6BW Tel: 01606 891363 Fax: 01606 891363 — MB ChB 1966 Liverp.; FRCOG 1986, M 1971. Cons. O & G Warrington Gen. Hosp.; Clin. Dir. (Obst. & Gyn.) Warrington NHS Trust. Socs: N. Eng. Obst. & Gyn. Soc.; Brit. Soc. Colpos. & Cerv. Path.

ENTWISTLE, Hilary Jane Perry Hill Surgery, 145 Perry Hill, London SE6 4LR Tel: 020 8699 1062; 68 Underhill Road, London SE22 0QT Tel: 020 8299 1604 — MB BChir 1979 Camb.; MRCP (UK) 1982; MRCGP 1987; DCH RCP Lond. 1983. (Cambridge and Kings College) Prev: Regist. & SHO (Med.) Rotat. Kings Coll. Hosp.; Med. Off. Jane Furse Hosp., Lebowa RSA.

ENTWISTLE, Ian Reid Consultation Suite, 42 Will Lane, Grayton, Wirral CH48 0RA Tel: 07050 261980 Fax: 0151 342 5135; Knollwood, Well Lane, Gayton, Wirral CH60 8NG Tel: 0151 342 2332 Fax: 0151 342 2332 Email: ianreidentwistle@amserve.com — MB ChB Liverp. 1956; FFOM RCP Lond. 1995, MFOM 1978; FFOM RCPI 1986, MFOM 1980; FRCGP 1980, M 1963; DFFP 1993; Specialist Accredit. (Occupat. Med.) RCP Lond. 1978. (Liverpool university) Accredit. Cons. Occ. Phys., Wiral, Merseyside.; Authorised Examr. Civil Aviat. Auth. Maritime & Coastguard Agency & Linpac Plastics.; Benefits Agency Med. Serv. Med. Dir. Berkeley Travel Clinic; Accredit. EEC Specialist in Occupat. Med; Cert. Gen. Aviat. Med. 1983 FarnBoro. (Hants.) MoD (Air) & Civil Aviat. Auth. (Re-validation, J.A.R. 1999); Med. Cons. Linpac Plastics, BMI Health Servs. & Nat. Med. Exam. Network; PREVIA. Occupat. Health, BHS plc, Amer. Colloid Company. Socs: Fell. Roy. Soc. Med.; Assoc. Fell. Aerospace Med. Assn. Washington; Roy. Aeronaut. Soc. Prev: Med. Supt. Cunard Steam Ship plc; Sen. Gp. Med. Cons. United Gas Industries; Cons. Occ. Phys. To Nuffield Hosp.s.

ENTWISTLE, Mr Martin Patrick Greenacre, Bridge End Lane, Prestbury, Macclesfield SK10 4DJ — MB ChB 1979 Birm.; FRCS Ed. 1985. Dir. Enigma Publishing Ltd. Socs: Fell. RSM; Fell. Med. Soc. Lond. Prev: Specialist (Surg.) Brit. Milit. Hosp. Hong Kong; Regist. (Trauma) Birm. Accid. Hosp.; SHO (Surg.) Camb. Milit. Hosp. Aldershot.

ENTWISTLE, Michael Arthur Teovil District Hospital, Higher Kingston, Yeovil BA21 4HT Tel: 01935 75188; 4 Tipcote Hill, Shepton Mallet BA4 5EQ Tel: 01749 344116 — MB BS 1994 Newc. Bath Rotat. SHO Anaesth.

ENTWISTLE, Michael David Department of Anaesthetics, Princess Margaret Hospital, Okus Road, Swindon SN1 4JU Tel: 01793 536231; 3 Barton Close, Bradenstoke, Chippenham SN15 4EZ Tel: 01249 890779 — MB ChB 1980 Birm.; T(Anaesth.) 1991; FFA RCSI 1987. Cons. Anaesth. P.ss Margt. Hosp. Swindon. Socs: Assn. Anaesth.; Intens. Care Soc.; Soc. Computing & Technol. Anaesth. Prev: Sen. Regist. (Anaesth.) Leeds Gen. Infirm.; Regist. (Anaesth.) Roy. Cornw. Hosp. & Dudley Rd. Hosp. Birm.

ENTWISTLE, Peter Brian The Corner Surgery, 180 Cambridge Road, Southport PR9 7LW Tel: 01704 506055 Fax: 01704 505818; 35 Hastings Road, Birkdale, Southport PR8 2LN — MB ChB 1986 Dundee; MRCGP 1990; Cert. Family Plann. JCC 1990. Prev: GP Auckland; Ho. Off. Ormskirk Lancs.; Trainee GP S.port VTS.

ENTWISTLE, William 9 Mainside, Redmarshall, Stockton-on-Tees TS21 1HY Tel: 01740 30155 — MB BS 1970 Newc.; DObst RCOG 1972. (Newc.)

ENVER, Mohamed Khalid 20 Cranbook Rise, Gants Hill, Ilford IG1 3QN — MB BS 1996 Lond. SHO (Surg.) Mayday Hosp. & King's Coll. Hosp.

EPENETOS, Professor Agamemnon Antoniou Department of Oncology, St. Mary's Hospital, Praed St., London W2 1RY; Flat 1, 6 Upper Pk Road, London NW3 2UP Tel: 020 7483 4104 — MB ChB 1973 Glas.; PhD Lond. 1983; FRCP Lond. 1992; FRCP Glas. 1992; MRCP (UK) 1977. Prof. & Cons. Clin. Oncol. St. Mary's Hosp. Lond. Socs: Med. Sickness Soc.; Amer. Assn. Cancer Research.

EPHSON, Pieter Martinus Johannes 12 Stone Park Avenue, Beckenham BR3 3LS — LMSSA 1961 Lond.

EPIE, Geoffrey Mboh 14 St Stephen's Crescent, Thornton Heath, Croydon CR7 7NP — MB BS 1972 Lond.

EPPEL, Bettina Jane 17 Grove Park Gardens, Chiswick, London W4 3RY — MB BS 1982 Lond.; FRCA 1989. (Middlx. Hosp. Med. Sch. Lond.) Cons. Anaesth. Socs: Assn. Anaesth. GB & Irel.; Obst. Anaesth. Assn.; Roy. Soc. Med. Prev: Cons. Anaesth., Wycomeb Gen. Hosp., High Wycombe, Bucks; Sen. Regist. (Anaesth.) Middlx. Hosp. Lond.; SHO (Anaesth.) N.wick Pk. Hosp. Harrow & Middlx. Hosp. Lond.

***EPPS, Henrietta** West End House, Didmarton, Badminton GL9 1DT — MB ChB 1996 Bristol.

EPPS, Marc Timothy Vern Cottage, Marden, Hereford HR1 3EX — MB ChB 1997 Bristol.

EPSOM, Michael The Strand Practice, 2 The Strand, Goring-by-Sea, Worthing BN12 6DN Tel: 01903 243351 Fax: 01903 705804 — MRCS Eng. LRCP Lond. 1972.

EPSTEIN, Andrew Charles Robert 185 Menlove Avenue, Calderstones, Liverpool L18 3JE Tel: 0151 428 3558 Email: andrew.epstein@ndm.ox.ac.uk; Institute of Molecular Medicine, John Radcliffe Hospital, Headington, Oxford OX3 9DS Tel: 01865 222381 Fax: 01865 222500 — BM BS 1994 Nottm.; BMedSci Nottm. 1992, BM BS 1994; MRCP (UK) 1997. (Nottingham)

***EPSTEIN, Elliot Fredrick** 45 Lynton Mead, London N20 8DG — MB ChB 1994 Birm.

EPSTEIN, Ellis Jacob 185 Menlove Avenue, Calderstones, Liverpool L18 3JE Tel: 0151 283 1203 — MD 1962 Manch.; MB ChB 1950; FRCP Lond. 1973, M 1956; FRCP Ed. 1971, M 1956. (Manch.) p/t Cons. Cardiol. Liverp. Cardio-Thoracic Centre. Socs: Brit. Cardiac Soc. & Assn. Phys. Prev: Surg. Lt. RNVR.

EPSTEIN, Gwendolen Ann 185 Menlove Avenue, Calderstones, Liverpool L18 3JE Tel: 0151 428 3558 — MB ChB 1965 Liverp. (Liverp.) Clin. Asst. Regional Cardio-Thoracic Centre BRd.green Hosp. Liverp. Prev: Ho. Phys., Ho. Surg. & SHO (Psychiat. & O & G) Sefton Gen. Hosp.

EPSTEIN, Jenny 26 St Petersburgh Pl, London W2 4LD — MB ChB 1997 Leeds.

EPSTEIN, Laura Jean Gill Street Health Centre, 11 Gill Street, London E14 8HQ Tel: 020 7515 2211; 218 East Ferry Road, London E14 3AY — BM 1988 Soton.; MRCGP 1992; DRCOG 1991. GP; Clin. Lect.

EPSTEIN, Madeleine Ray (retired) Pleasant, Barcombe Heights, Torbay, Paignton TQ3 1PT Tel: 01803 550156 — LRCPI & LM, LRSCI & LM 1944; LRCPI & LM, LRCSI & LM 1944; DCH RCSI 1946. Paediat. Attend. Child Developm. Clinics Co. Boro. Torbay; Lect. & Examr. Brit. Red Cross. Prev: Hon. Phys. Childr. Convent St. John Evangelist Dub.

EPSTEIN, Professor Sir (Michael) Anthony, CBE Nuffield Department of Clinical Medicine, University of Oxford John Radcliffe Hospital, Headington, Oxford OX3 9DU Tel: 01865 221334 Fax: 01865 222901 — MRCS Eng. LRCP Lond. 1944 Camb.; MB BChir Camb. 1949; FRCPath 1963; Hon. FRCPath 1995; Hon. FRCPA 1995; FRS 1979; Hon. FRSE 1991; DSc Lond. 1963, PhD 1952; DSc (hon. causa) Birm. 1996; MA Camb. 1949, MD 1951; MD (hon. causa) Ed. 1986; FRCP Lond. 1986. Emerit. Prof. Path. Univ. Bristol, & Nuffield Dept. Clin. Med., Univ. Oxf. John Radcliffe Hosp. Oxf.; Hon.Fell. Wolfson Coll. Oxf. Socs: Founder mem Acad. of Med. Sci.s 1998; Mem. d'Honneur Belgian Soc. Cancer research 1979; Hon Mem. Sect. of Pathol. Roy. Soc. of Med 1998. Prev: Prof. Path. & Head Dept. Univ. Bristol; Hon. Cons. Path. S. W.. RHA; Reader Experim. Path. Middlx. Hosp.; Med. Sch. & Hon. Cons. Virol. Middlx. Hosp. Lond.

EPSTEIN, Owen Division of Gastroenterology, Royal Free Hospital NHS Trust, Pond Street, Hampstead, London NW3 Tel: 020 7830 2683 Fax: 020 7794 6614; 1 Cyprus Gardens, Finchley, London N3 1SP — MB BCh 1972 Witwaterstrand; FRCP Lond. 1990; MRCP (UK) 1976. Cons. Phys. Gastroenterol. Socs: Brit. Soc. Gastroenterol.

& Brit. Assn. Study Liver. Prev: Div.al Med. Dir. Roy. Free Hosp. Sch. Med. Lond.; Clin. Tutor & Dir. Endoscopy Unit Roy. Free Hosp. Sch. Med. Lond.

EPSTEIN, Richard John Department of Metabolic Medicine, Hammersmith Hospital, Dulane Road, London W12 0NN Tel: 020 8383 3052; 54 Glebe Road, London SW13 0ED — MB BS 1979 Sydney; PhD Camb. 1988; MD Lond. 1995; FRACP 1987; FRCP 1997. (Univ. Sydney) Hon. Sen. Lect. Imperial Coll. Sch. of Med., Hammersmith Hosp.; Hon. Cons. W.m. Hosp. Lond. Prev: Instruc. Harvard Med. Sch. Boston, USA; Clin. Tutor Univ. Camb. Sch. Clin. Med.; CRC Sen. Clin. Sci. CRC Laborats. Lond. & Cons. Med. Oncol. Char. Cross Hosp. Lond.

EQBAL, Zehra Syed 1 Long Meadow, Moss Pit, Stafford ST17 9DP Tel: 01785 41265 — MB BS 1973 Osmania; ECFMG 1983; DPM Eng. 1980.

EQUI, Amanda Clare 28 Allanshaw Street, Hamilton ML3 6NJ — MB ChB 1992 Ed. (Ed.) Regist. (Paediat.) Hillingdon & Brompton Hosps. Socs: RCP.

EQUIZI, Fabrizio 27 Rufford Drive, Southport PR9 8AX — MB ChB 1988 Liverp.

ERANEVA, Kirsti Annikki British Airways Health services, Waterside, PO Box 365, Harmondsworth, West Drayton UB7 0GB Tel: 020 8738 7708 Fax: 020 8738 9754 — MB ChB 1988 Bristol; MRCGP 1993; DRCOG 1992; AFOM 1999; Cert Gam RAF 1996. Specialist Regist. (Occupat. Med.) Brit. Airways. Socs: BMA; Soc. Occupat. Med.; Assn. of Authorised Med. Examr.s. Prev: SHO (Genitourin. Med. & HIV Med.) Char. Cross Hosp. Lond.; Trainee GP Cheltenham; SHO (O & G.) Cheltenham Gen. Hosp.

ERASMUS, Theresa c/o Humares Ltd., Parmenter House, Tower Road, Winchester SO23 8TD — MB ChB 1992 Orange Free State.

ERAUT, Charles Dennis Southend Hospital, Prittlewell Chase, Westcliff on Sea SS0 0RY Tel: 01702 435555 Fax: 01702 221258 — MD Camb. 1976, MB 1967, BChir 1966; FRCP Lond. 1984; MRCP (UK) 1971; MRCS Eng. LRCP Lond. 1966. (Guy's) Phys. (Gen. Med. & Dis. Chest) S.end-on-Sea. Prev: Sen. Regist. (Med.) Lond. Chest Hosp.; Regist. (Med.) Guy's Hosp. Lond.; Regist. (Med.) Roy. Devon & Exeter Hosp.

ERCLEVE, Tor Nikolai Oyvin 47 Crossway, Manchester M20 6TU — MB ChB 1994 Manch.; BSc (Med. Sci.) St. And. 1992. (Univ. St. And. & Univ. Manch.) SHO (Surg.) Sheff. Prev: RMO Alexandra Hosp. Manch.; SHO (Orthop.) Derbysh. Roy. Infirm.; SHO (A & E) Roy. Hallamsh. Hosp. Sheff.

ERDMANN, Mr Matthias Walter Hans University Hospital of North Durham, Durham DH1 5TW Tel: 01207 214316 Email: matt@erdmann.fsnet.co.uk; 6 Aykley Green, Durham DH1 4LN — MB BCh 1980 Witwatersrand; FRCS (Plast) 1996; FRCS Eng. 1989. Cons. Plastic Surg. Shotley Bridge Hosp., Univeristy Hosp. of N. Durh., Sunderland Roy. Hosp. Sunderland. Socs: Brit. Assn. Plastic Surg.; Brit. Soc. For Surg. of the hand; Brit. Ass of Aesthetic Plastic Surg. Prev: Regist. (Plastic Surg.) St. Johns Hosp. Edin., Roy. Devon & Exeter Hosp. & Char. Cross Hosp. Lond.; Sen. Regist. (Plastic Surg.) Canniesburn Hosp. Glas.

EREN, Efrem 8 Princess Avenue, London N22 7SA — MB BS 1993 Lond.

ERENA MINGUEZ, Cesar Doctors Residence, Friarage Hospital, Northallerton DL6 1JG — LMS 1989 Basque Provinces.

ERHARDT, Carl Christopher Bromley Hospital, Cromwell Avenue, Bromley BR2 9AJ Tel: 020 8289 7076; 43 Homestead Road, Orpington BR6 6HN — MB BS 1972 Lond.; MD Lond. 1982, BSc 1969; MRCP (U.K.) 1975; FRCP 1997. (Char. Cross) Cons. Rheum. Bromley HA. Prev: Sen. Regist. Char. Cross Hosp. Lond.

ERIAM, Magdy Shawky Nevill Hall Hospital, Abergavenny NP7 7EG Tel: s. profess. 2091 & home 7139; West Hill Hospital, Dartford Tel: 01322 23223 — MB BCh 1974 Cairo; LRCP LRCS Ed. LRCPS Glas. 1983; MRCOG 1987; DObst RCPI 1982. W. Hill Hosp. Dartford.

ERIAN, Mr Anthony 10 Harley Street, London W1G Tel: 020 7580 5949 Fax: 01223 208251 Email: cosmeticplasticsurgeon@anthony.eriam.com; Orwell Grange, 43 Cambridge Road, Orwell, Royston SG8 5QD Tel: 01233 208249 Fax: 01223 208251 — FRCS Ed. 1976; FRCS Eng. 1976; MRCS Eng. LRCP Lond. 1979. (American Board certified) Cons. Cosmetic Surg. Harley St. Lond; Director of Cosmetic Surg. Camb. Private Hosp.; Conusltant Cosmetic Surg. Guy's Hosp. Nuffield Ho. Socs: Amer. Acad. of Cosmetic Surgs.; Pres. Europ. Acad. Cosmetic Surg.; Roy. Soc. Med. Prev: Regist. (Surg.) Qu. Mary's Hosp. Sidcup & Lewisham Gen. Hosp. (T) and Guy's; SHO Leicester Gen. Hosp. (T) & Greenbank Hosp. Plymouth; SHO Peace Memor. Hosp. Watford.

ERIKSEN, Mr Craig Alexander Department of Surgery, Perth Royal Infirmary, Perth PH1 1NX Tel: 01738 623311 Fax: 01738 473693 Email: ceriksen@pri.tuht.scot.nhs.uk; Seggiebank House, Milnathort, Kinross KY13 0RP Tel: 01577 862541 Email: craig.eriksen@btinternet.com — MB ChB 1978 Cape Town; MD Cape Town 1988; FRCS Ed. 1986. (University of Capetown) Cons. Surg. Perth Roy. Infirm. Socs: Brit. Assn. Surg. Oncol.; Assn. Surg.; Assn. Coloproct. Prev: Sen. Regist. (Surg.) Ninewells Hosp. Dundee; Career Regist. Ninewells Hosp. Dundee; Clin. Research Fell. Univ. Dundee.

ERIN, Edward Mark 5 Llandough Hill, Llandough, Penarth CF64 2NA — MB BCh 1993 Wales.

ERIN, Richard John Kennington Health Centre, 200 Kennington Road, Kennington, Oxford OX1 5PY Tel: 01865 730911 Fax: 01865 327759 — MB BCh 1987 Wales; MRCGP 1991; DRCOG 1992; DCH RCP Lond. 1991.

ERITH, Michael John The Lynher Surgery, St Germans, Saltash PL12 5LT Tel: 01503 230358 Fax: 01503 230133; Treverne, Budge's Shop, Trerulefoot, Saltash PL12 5DA Tel: 01752 851480 — MB BChir 1972 Camb.; BA Camb. 1969, MA 1973, MB BChir 1972; MRCP (UK) 1976; DCH Eng. 1975; DObst RCOG 1974; Dip. Sports Med. 1998. (Camb. & St. Bart.) GP; Lynher Sport & Exercise Clinic.

ERKELLER-YUKSEL, Melek Feza Department of Rheumatology & Orthopaedics, Barnet & Chase Farm Hospital NHS Trust, Enfield EN2 8JL Tel: 020 8366 9128 Fax: 020 8364 5289; 4 Asmuns Place, London NW11 7XG — Tip Doktoru 1980 Istanbul. Assoc. Specialist (Rheum. & Orthop.) Chase Farm Hosp. NHS Trust Enfield. Socs: BMA & BSR. Prev: Clin. Research Asst. (Rheum. & Immunol.) Univ. Coll. Lond. Hosp. & Bloomsbury Rheum. Unit Lond.

ERLAM, Anthony Robin Health & Safety Executive, 3 East Grinstead House, London Road, East Grinstead RH19 1RR Tel: 01342 334200 Fax: 01342 334222; 119 Fairfield Road, Burgess Hill RH15 8NP Tel: 01342 233496 — LMSSA Lond. 1967; MSc Lond. 1980; MRCS Eng. LRCP Lond. 1972; MFOM RCP Lond. 1984; DIH Eng. 1979; DObst RCOG 1972; FFOM RCP London 1997. (St. Mary's) Employm. Med. Advisor Health & Safety Exec. Socs: Fac. Occupat. Med.; Fell. Fac. Occupat. Med.; Soc. Occupat. Med. Prev: Hon. Lect. Univ. Coll.; Lond. & Roy. Free Med. Sch.

ERNAELSTEEN, Diana Ann Mary, CBE Department for Education & Skills, Sanctuary Buildings, 20 Great Smith St., London SW1P 3BT Tel: 020 7925 6300; 15 Valley Road, Welwyn Garden City AL8 7DG Tel: 01707 323178 — MB BS Lond. 1959; MRCS Eng. LRCP Lond. 1959; FRCPCH 1997; T(M) 1991. (Roy. Free Hosp.) p/t Cons. Med. Adviser DFES; Hon. Sen. Cons. Paediat. Tavistock Clinic Lond. Socs: Fell. Roy. Soc. Med.; BMA. Prev: Sen. Med. Off. DoH & Adviser DFE; Ho. Phys. & Ho. Surg. Hampstead Gen. Hosp. (Roy. Free).

ERNST, Dorothy May (retired) 70 Castellan Avenue, Gidea Park, Romford RM2 6EJ Tel: 01708 41228 — MRCS Eng. LRCP Lond. 1928. Prev: Ho. Phys. Lond. Temperance Hosp.

ERNST, Professor Edzard Department of Complementary Medicine, School ofsport & health sciences, University of Exeter, 25 Victoria Park Road, Exeter EX2 4NT Tel: 01392 430802 Fax: 01392 424989 Email: e.ernst@exeter.ac.uk — State Exam Med 1976 Munich; PhD Munich 1985; FRCP Ed. Prof. Complementary Med. Univ. Exeter. Prev: Prof. Med. Sch. Hannover, Germany; Prof. Univ. of Vienna, Austria.

ERNST, Eric Malcolm Conyers (retired) Brook Cottage, Marsh Lane, Stoke Mandeville, Aylesbury HP22 5UZ Tel: 0129 661 3502 — MB BS Lond. 1962; FFA RCS Eng. 1973. Anaesth. Cons. Stoke Mandeville & Aylesbury Gp. Hosps. Prev: Sen. Regist. (Anaesth.) Roy. Free Hosp. & Harefield Hosp.

ERNST, Mr Max Roslyn (retired) 70 Castellan Avenue, Gidea Park, Romford RM2 6EJ Tel: 01708 41228 — MB BS 1928 Lond.; FRCS Eng. 1930; MRCS Eng. LRCP Lond. 1927. Hon. Cons. Surg. Vict. Hosp. Romford & Rush Green Hosp. Romford. Prev: Ho. Surg. Roy. N.. Hosp. & St. Mark's Hosp. Dis. Rectum & Lond.

ERNST, Peter Russell Max (retired) Woodfield Cottage, Byng Hall Lane, Ufford, Woodbridge IP13 6EJ Tel: 01394 460250 — MB BS

Lond. 1962; MRCS Eng. LRCP Lond. 1960. Med. Adviser Essex CC Chelmsford. Prev: Med. Adviser Essex CC Chelmsford.

ERNSTING, John, CB, OBE, Air Vice-Marshal RAF Med. Br. Retd. Physiology Group, King's College London, Campden Hill Road, London W8 7AH Tel: 020 7333 4176 Fax: 020 7333 4008 Email: john.ernsting@kcl.ac.uk; White Gables, 2A Greenways, Fleet GU52 7UG Tel: 01252 621788 Fax: 01252 621788 — MB BS 1952 Lond.; MB BS (Hons.) Lond. 1952; PhD Lond. 1964, BSc (Hons. Physiol.) 1949; FRCP Lond. 1991; MRCP (UK) 1985; MRCS Eng. LRCP Lond. 1952; FFOM RCP Lond. 1993, MFOM 1980. (Guy's) Vis. Prof. King's Coll. Lond.; Civil Cons. Aviat. Med. (RAF); Vis. Prof. Physiol. King's Coll. Lond. Socs: Fell. Aerospace Med. Assn.; Physiol. Soc.; Past Pres. Internat. Acad. Aviat. & Space Med. Prev: Sen. Cons. RAF; Ho. Surg. & Ho. Phys. Guy's Hosp.; Ho. Surg. Guy's & Maudsley Neurosurg. Unit Maudsley Hosp.

EROOGA, Mark Akim (retired) 17 Foxbury Close, Luton LU2 7BQ Tel: 01582 507381 — MB BS Hong Kong 1939. Prev: Cons. (Chest Phys.) Hitchin Chest Clin. & Lister Hosp. Stevenage.

EROTOCRITOU, Petros Pavlou Liverpool Road Health Centre, Liverpool Road, Luton LU1 1HH; Birmingham Park, medical Centre, Lucas Gdns, Luton LU3 4BG — Ptychio Iatrikes 1973 Athens. Socs: MDU; GMC; BMA.

***ERRIDGE, Jane Frances** Dudley Lane Village Surgery, Dudley Lane, Cramlington NE23 6US Tel: 01670 712821 Fax: 01670 730837 — MB BS 1986 Lond.

ERRIDGE, Sara Catherine Department of Clinical Oncology, Western General Hospital, Edinburgh EM4 2XU — MB BS 1991 Lond.

ERRINGTON, Dominic Robert 353 Rawling Road, Gateshead NE8 4UH — BM BS 1994 Nottm.

ERRINGTON, Jacquelyn Ross Craiglockhart Surgery, 161 Colinton Road, Edinburgh EH14 1BE Tel: 0131 455 8494 Fax: 0131 444 0161 — MB ChB 1985 Ed.; MRCGP 1994; DFFP 1993. Clin. Asst. Migraine Clinic W.. Gen. Hosp. Edin. Socs: Brit. Med. Acupunct. Soc. Prev: SHO (O & G & Gen. Med.) Roy. Infirm. Edin.; SHO (Paediat.) Roy. Hosp. Sick Childr. Edin.

ERRINGTON, Mark Gregory 21 Co Operative Terrace, Gateshead NE10 9BT — MB ChB 1989 Leic.

ERRINGTON, Martin Lewis Western General Hospital, Crewe Road, Edinburgh EH4 2XU Tel: 0131 537 2056; 39 Woodhall Road, Edinburgh EH13 0DT — MB ChB 1984 Ed.; MA Oxf. 1986; MRCP (UK) 1987; FRCR 1993; DMRD Ed. 1992. (Oxford and Edinburgh) Cons. Radiol. & Dir. Radionuclide Imaging W.ern Gen. Hosp. Edin. Socs: FRCR; Brit. Medcial Ultrasound Soc.; Magnetic Resonance Radiol. Assn. Prev: Cons. Radiol. & Clin. Dir. of Radiological Servs. Qu. Margt. Hosp. Fife; Sen. Regist. (Radiol.) Roy. Infirm. Edin.; Regist. (Radiol.) W.ern Gen. Hosp. Edin.

ERRINGTON, Roger Douglas Clatterbridge Centre for Oncology, Wirral CH63 4JY Tel: 0151 334 4000 Fax: 0151 334 0882; 30 Beryl Road, Birkenhead CH43 9RT Tel: 0151 677 1534 — MB BS 1973 Lond.; BSc (Hons. Physiol.) Lond. 1970; MRCS Eng. LRCP Lond. 1973; FRCR 1980; DMRT Eng. 1980; DCH Eng. 1976. (St. Mary's) Cons. & Lect. (Radiother. & Oncol.) Univ. Liverp., Clatterbridge Centre for Oncol. & Douglas Cyclotron Centre. Prev: Sen. Regist. (Radiother. & Oncol.) MRC Cyclotron Unit Roy. Postgrad. Med. Sch. Lond.; Regist. (Radiother. & Oncol.) Hammersmith Hosp. Lond.; SHO (Paediat.) Hillingdon Hosp. Uxbridge.

ERSFELD, Elisabeth Wythenshawe Road Surgery, 216A Wythenshawe Road, Northern Moor, Manchester M23 0PH Tel: 0161 998 2503 Fax: 0161 945 0695; 25 Gateacre Walk, Brooklands, Manchester M23 9BA Tel: 0161 282 1952 — State Exam Med 1987 Bonn; DTM & H Liverp. 1991. Prev: Trainee GP Manch.; SHO (Gen. Surg.) Bad Hartburg. Germany; SHO (Orthop.) Göttingen, Germany.

ERSKINE, Archibald Walter Forbes 130 Walm Lane, London NW2 4RT Tel: 020 8452 9251 — BM BCh 1943 Oxf.; MA Oxf. 1943. (Oxf.) Socs: Fell. (Ex-Chairm.) Brit. Assn. Psychother. & Lond. Centre for Psychother. Prev: Clin. Asst. (Child & Family Psychiat.) Char. Cross Hosp. Lond.; Clin. Asst. (Psychiat.) St. Mary's Hosp. Lond.; Regist. Social Psychother. Centre & W. Lond. Hosp.

ERSKINE, David Orr The Surgery, 2 Gregson Avenue, Gosport PO13 0HR Tel: 01329 232446 Fax: 01329 282624 — MB BS 1973 Lond.; DObst RCOG 1975. (Middlx.)

ERSKINE, Fiona Margaret 22 Turfbeg Avenue, Forfar DD8 3LL — MB ChB 1993 Glas.

ERSKINE, Hugh Ralph (retired) 29 Braemar Gardens, Hereford HR1 1SJ Tel: 01432 350703 — MRCS Eng. LRCP Lond. 1947. Prev: Gen. Practitioner Melbourne Camb.shire.

ERSKINE, James Cobo Health Centre, Route De Carteret, Castel, Guernsey GY5 7HA Tel: 01481 56404; Les Raies De Haut, St. Pierre Du Bois, Guernsey GY7 9SF — MB BChir 1963 Camb.; MB Camb. 1963, BChir 1962; MA Camb. 1963. (Univ. Coll. Hosp.) Mem. Med. Staff P.ss Eliz. Hosp. Guernsey. Prev: Maj. RAMC; Ho. Surg. & Ho. Phys. Univ. Coll. Hosp. Lond.

ERSKINE, James Alexander 5 Manor Gardens, High Wycombe HP13 5HD; Box 86, Banjul, Gambia — MB BS 1983 Lond.; MRCGP 1994; DTM & H Liverp. 1992; DA (UK) 1988. (St. Bart.) Med. Off. Sibanor Clinic, The Gambia. Socs: Med. Protec. Soc. Prev: Trainee GP Stockport; Regist. (Anaesth.) & SHO (Paediat.) High Wycombe.

ERSKINE, James Gordon Haematology Department, Crosshouse Hospital, Kilmarnock KA2 0BE Tel: 01563 21133; 4 The Mote, Alloway, Ayr KA6 6BZ Tel: 01292 445226 — MB ChB 1971 Glas.; FRCP 1988, M 1976; FRCPath 1990, M 1978. Cons. Haemat. Ayrsh. & Arran HB; Hon. Clin. Sen. Lect. Univ. Glas. Socs: Brit. Soc. Haematol.; Scott. Soc. Phys. Prev: Sen. Regist. (Haemat.) Glas. Roy. Infirm.

ERSKINE, James Paton Orr (retired) The Garden Cottage, Buchanan Castle, Drymen, Glasgow G63 0HU Tel: 01360 660886 — MB ChB Glas. 1937; FRFPS Glas. 1939; FRCP Glas. 1972, M 1962; FRCOG 1957, M 1945. Prev: O & G Dunbarton Co. Area.

ERSKINE, John Francis 39 Westcombe Park Road, London SE3 7RE Tel: 020 8858 3060 — MB BChir 1939 Camb.; MRCS Eng. LRCP Lond. 1939; MFOM RCP Lond. 1978; DPH Lond. 1947. (Char. Cross) Mem. Internat. Forum for Organisational Health. Socs: Soc. Occupat. Med. Prev: Regional Med. Adviser Centr. Electr. Generat. Bd.; Area Med. Off. Nat. Coal Bd.; Res. Med. Off. Char. Cross Hosp. Lond.

ERSKINE, John Paton (retired) Leaflands, The Common, West Chiltington, Pulborough RH20 2PL Tel: 01798 812297 — MB ChB Glas. 1940; BSc Glas. 1937; FRCOG 1960, M 1944. Hon. Cons. O & G St. Mary's Hosp. & Samarit. Hosp. Wom. Lond. Prev: Tutor (O & G) Univ. Leeds.

ERSKINE, Katrina Jane The Homerton Hosp, Homerton Row, London E9 6SR Tel: 020 8510 7353 Fax: 020 8510 7787; St. Bartholomews Hospital, West Smithfield, London EC1A 7BE — MB BS 1980 Lond.; MD Lond. 1986; MRCP (UK) 1985; MRCOG 1987. Cons. O & G Homerton Hosps. Lond. Prev: Lect. & Hon. Sen. Regist. (O & G), Univ. Coll. Hosp. Lond.

ERSKINE, Keith Francis Charlotte Keel Health Centre, Seymour Road, Easton, Bristol BS5 0UA; Buxton Villa, 4 Richmond Pk Road, Clifton, Bristol BS8 3AT — MB BS 1985 Lond.; MRCGP 1990; DRCOG 1989.

ERSKINE, May Khin 61 Mortimer Road, London NW10 5QR Tel: 020 8964 0198 — MB BS 1971 Mandalay; MSc (Obst. & Gyn.) Mandalay 1978; MFFP 1992; MRCOG 1989. (Inst. Med. Mandalay, Burma) SCMO (Family Plann. & Reproduc. Health Care) Haringey NHS Trust Lond.; Sen. Clin. Med. Off. (Genitourin. Med.) Family Plann. & Sexual Health Clinic St. Bart. Hosp. Lond.; Assoc. Specialist (Colposcopy) Hammersmith Hosp. NHS Trust. Socs: Brit. Menopause Soc.; Eur. Assn. Gyn. & Obst.; Roy. Soc. Med. Prev: Clin. Asst. Colposcopy Clinic Whittington Hosp.; Dep. Dir. Margt. Pyke Centre Lond.; Sen. Regist. (O & G) Mandalay Gen. Hosp., Burma.

ERSKINE, Michael Edward Maldon Road Surgery, 35 Maldon Road, Wallington SM6 8BL Tel: 020 8647 4622 — MB BS 1977 Lond.; BA Oxf. 1972; MRCS Eng. LRCP Lond. 1977; DRCOG 1980.

ERSKINE, Richard Ian 51 Island Road, Ballycarry, Carrickfergus BT38 9JE — MB BCh BAO 1995 Belf.

ERSKINE, Robert, MBE (retired) Kawerau, 50 Caplethill Road, Paisley PA2 7TL — MB ChB 1949 Glas.; FRCGP 1981, M 1958. Though I am Retd. from Clin. Pract., I continue to act as Med. Ref. at Woodside Crematorium, Paisley.

ERSKINE, Robert John The Mount, Yeldersley, Ashbourne DE6 1LS Tel: 01335 342120 — MB BS 1984 Lond.; FRCA 1991. (Univ. Coll. Hosp.) Cons. Anaesth. Derbysh. Roy. Infirm. Prev: Sen Regist. Rotat. (Anaesth.) Nottm. & E. Midl.; Research Fell. (Anaesth.) Leicester Univ.; Regist. (Anaesth.) Leicester & Derbysh. Roy. Infirm.

ERSKINE, Robert Lawrence Alexander Tel: 02844 613311 — MB BCh BAO 1975 Dub.; MD 1988; MRCOG 1982, D 1978. Cons. O & G Downe Hosp., Downpatrick, Co. Down; Cons. Obst. & Gyn. Belf. City Hosp. Socs: Brit. Med. Assn.; Fell. Ulster Med. Soc.; Fell. of Roy. Soc. of Med. Prev: Sen. Regist. & Sen. Tutor Jubilee Matern. Hosp. & Belf. City Hosp. Belf.; Research Fell. Roy. Vict. Hosp. & Roy. Matern. Hosp. Belf.; Sen. Clin. Fell. Dept. Obst. Perinatol. Mt. Sinai Hosp. Toronto, Canada.

ERSKINE, Stephen Peter Ehrmann Benjy's Cottage, Uffington, Faringdon SN7 7RB Tel: 01367 820284 — MB BChir 1977 Camb.; DPhil Oxf. 1988; MA Camb. 1976; MRCP (UK) 1981. (Camb. & St. Thos.)

ERSKINE, William (retired) Colindale, Park Close, Sprotborough, Doncaster DN5 7LT Tel: 01302 850890 — MB BS 1958 Lond.; DObst. RCOG 1960. Prev: SHO (Obst.) W.. Hosp. Doncaster.

ERULKAR, Joseph Westholme, Westbourne Drive, Lancaster LA1 5EE — MB BS 1944 Durh.; FRCP Lond. 1973, M 1952; FRCPsych 1974; DCH Eng. 1951, DPM 1957. (Newc.) Cons. Child Psychiat. Roy. Manch. Childr. Hosp.; Hon. Cons. Child Psychiat. United Manch. Hosps.; Cons. Adolesc. Unit Prestwich Hosp. Manch.; Lect. (Child Psychiat.) Manch. Univ. Socs: Fell. Roy. Soc. Med.; Fell. Manch. Med. Soc. Prev: Ho. Phys. Battersea Gen. Hosp.; Sen. Regist. Maudsley & Bethlem Roy. Hosp; Cons. Child Psychiat. Stockport Child Guid. Clinic.

ERVINE, Ian Maxwell 115 Manor Road, Crosby, Liverpool L23 7UT — MB ChB 1987 Dundee.

ERWIN, Diana Clare 89 Hemingford Road, London N1 1BY — MB BS 1960 Lond.; MRCS Eng. LRCP Lond. 1960; FFA RCS Eng. 1978; DA Eng. 1962. Cons. Anaesth. Whipps Cross Hosp. Prev: Sen. Regist. Anaesth. Dept. Lond. Hosp; Anaesth. Regist. St. Bart. Hosp. Lond.

ERWIN, Lindsay 46 Dalhousie Road, Milliken Park, Kilbarchan, Johnstone PA10 2AT Email: lindsay@erwin.co.uk — MB ChB 1976 Glas.; FRCP Glas. 1990; MRCP (UK) 1980. Cons. Phys. (Gen. Med. & c/o Elderly) Stobhill Hosp. Glas.; Hon. Clin. Sen. Lect. Glas. Univ. Socs: Roy. M-C Soc. Glas.; Brit assoc of stroke Phys.s. Prev: Sen. Regist. (Geriat. Med.) Gtr. Glas. Health Bd.; Regist. (Gen. Med.) Renal Unit Glas. Roy. Infirm.; Ho. Off. Glas. Roy. Infirm.

ESAH, Mr Kithur Mohamed 9 Bengeworth Road, Harrow HA1 3SF Tel: 020 8904 5880 — MB BS 1958 Madras; FRCS Eng. 1966. (Stanley Med. Coll.) Cons. Orthop. Surg. Hillingdon Hosp., Mt. Vernon Hosp. N.wood & St. Vincent's Orthop. Hosp. Pinner. Prev: Sen. Regist. (Orthop.) St. Mary's Hosp. Lond.; SHO Roy. Nat. Orthop. Hosp. Stanmore; Regist. King's Coll. Hosp. Lond.

ESAN, Olukunle Oluwafemi 24 Wenlock Court, New North Road, London N1 7QR Email: kule@oesan.freeserve.co.uk — MB BS 1986 Benin. (Benin, Nigeria) Prev: GP Trainee.

ESBERGER, Mr Demas Alexander University Hospital Nottingham, Queens Medical Centre, Derby Road, Nottingham NG7 2UH Tel: 0115 924 9924; 9 Leigh Close, West Bridgford, Nottingham NG2 7TN — MB BS 1984 Lond.; FRCS Eng. 1989. (St Bartholomew's London) Cons. A & E Med. Univ. Hosp. Nottm.

***ESCHLE, Mark Robert** 16 Chapelfields, Harlow CM17 9EQ — MB BCh 1986 Wales; FRCS Ed. 1993.

ESCOBAR JIMENEZ, Ana Maria 24 Rectory Gardens, Worthing BN14 7TE — LMS 1992 Oviedo. SHO (Anaesth.) P.ss Roy. Hosp. Haywards Heath. Prev: SHO (Anaesth.) E. Surrey Hosp. Redhill; SHO (A & E) Worthing Hosp.

ESCOFET MARTINEZ DE ARENZANA, Xavier 83 Roman Way, Birmingham B15 2SL Tel: 0121 472 2378 — LMS 1991 Barcelona; LMS Autonoma Barcelona 1991. SHO (Orthop.) Alexandra Hosp. Redditch. Prev: SHO Rotat. Walsgrave Hosp. Coventry.

ESCOTT, Mr Trevor Ernest 2 Muirfield Road, Inverness IV2 4AY Tel: 01463 239746 — MB ChB 1960 Ed.; FRCS Ed. 1966; MRCGP 1984; DObst RCOG 1972. (Ed.) Exam. Med. Pract. Benefits Agency & Scott. Office Pens. Agency. Socs: Liverp. Med. Inst.; Brit. Burns Assn. Prev: GP Inverness; Regist. (Plastic Surg.) Whiston Hosp. Prescot; SHO (O & G) Raigmore Hosp. Inverness.

ESEN, Umo Ita 9 Crake Way, Washington NE38 0DR — MB BS 1983 Nigeria; MRCOG 1991. Staff Grade (Obst, & Gyn.) S. Tyneside Dist. Gen. Hosp. Prev: Regist. (O & G) Sunderland Dist. Gen. Hosp.; SHO Sunderland Dist. Gen. Hosp. & S. Tyneside Dist. Gen. Hosp.

ESEONU, Mr Onyebuchi Chikezie 50 Evistones Road, Low Fell, Gateshead NE9 5UA Tel: 0191 420 8069 — MB BS 1978 Ibadan; FRCS Ed. 1992; MRCOG 1988.

ESHIETT, Michael Udoh-Aka Wigan & Leigh NHS Trust, Whelley Hospital, Bradshaw St., Wigan WN1 3XD Tel: 01942 822620 Fax: 01942 822630; Email: m.eshiett@btinternet.com — BM BCh 1977 U. Nigeria; BM BCh Nigeria 1977; FRCPI 1999; MSc Clin. Neuro. Sci. Univ. Surrey 1996; Dip. Clin. Neurol. 1989; DTM & H RCP Lond. 1988; MRCPI 1987. (Univ. Nigeria) Cons. Neurol. Rehabil. Wigan & Leigh NHS Trust. Socs: Fell. Roy. Soc. Trop. Med.; BMA; BSRM, NW Regional Coordinator. Prev: Sen. Regist. (Neurol. Rehabil.) Qu. Mary's Univ. Hosp. & St. Geo. Healthcare; Regist. (Neurol.) Guy's Hosp. Lond.; Regist. (Gen. Med. & Geriat.) Bedford Gen. Hosp.

ESHUN, Mr Joseph Augustus 6 Blackthorn Place, Parc Llwynmawr, Tycoch, Swansea SA2 9JW; 98 St. Martin's Road, Caerphilly CF83 1EN Tel: 01222 851811 — MUDr 1981 Prague; FRCS Ed. 1991; FRCS Eng. 1990. Regist. (Gen. Surg.) Singleton Hosp. Swansea. Prev: Regist. (Orthop. & Neurosurg.) Morriston Hosp. Swansea.

ESHUN, Mr Joseph Erzuah 12B Central Park Road, London E6 3DY Email: erzuah@eshunj.freeserve.co.uk; 58 Woodland Avenue, Goole DN14 6RU — MB ChB 1983 Ghana; FRCS Eng. 1990. Staff Surg. (Gen. Surg. & Urol.) Goole & Dist. Hosp. N. Humberside. Prev: Regist. Manor Hse. Hosp. Lond. & Roy. Gwent Hosp. Newport; SHO Soton. Gen. Hosp.

ESHWARI, Colathor Gopal c/o 33 High Park Drive, Bradford BD9 6HX — MB BS 1969 Madras.

ESIRI, Frederick Obukowho Uruemuowho 70 Hamilton Road, Oxford OX2 7QA — BM BCh 1974 Oxf.; MRCS Eng. LRCP Lond. 1969.

ESIRI, Professor Margaret Miriam Department of Neuropathology, Radcliffe Infirmary, Oxford OX2 6HE Tel: 01865 224403 Fax: 01865 224508 Email: margaret.esiri@clneuro.ox.ac.uk; Clifford House, Charlton-on-Otmoor, Kidlington OX5 2UQ — BM BCh Oxf. 1967; DM Oxf. 1975; FRCPath 1988, M 1976. Prof. of Neuropath & Hon Cons. Neuropath. Radcliffe Infirm. Oxf. Prev: MRC Sen. Clin. Fell. (Neuropath.) Radcliffe Infirm. Oxf.; Sen. Regist. (Neuropath.) Radcliffe Infirm. Oxf.

ESKANDER, Mr Adel Aziz The Gynae Centre, 93 Harley St, London W1N 1DF Tel: 020 7935 7525 Fax: 020 7935 2989 Email: info@gynae_centre.co.uk; 28 Brocas Close, Fellows Road, Hampstead, London NW3 3LD Tel: 020 7586 8896 — MB ChB; MRCOG 1977; FRCOG 1997. (Alexandria University) Med. Dir. The Gynae Centre 93 Harley St Lond. Socs: Internat. Ultrasound Soc. of Obst. & Gynaecol.; Med. Soc. Of Lond. Prev: Cons. Obst. and Gyn. Mayday Univeristy Hosp.

ESKANDER, Rola Ismael 2 Lamacraft Drive, Honeylands, Exeter EX4 8QS Tel: 01392 439815 — MB ChB 1977 Baghdad; MRCOG 1992. Staff Grade (O & G) Roy. Devon & Exeter Healthcare NHS Trust. Prev: Regist. (Obst & Gyn.) Burnley Gen. Hosp. & Roy. Devon & Exeter Hosp.

ESKIN, Frada Sheffield Health, 5 Old Fulwood Road, Sheffield S10 3TG Tel: 01142 711246 Fax: 01142 711248; 62 The Glen, Endcliffe, Vale Road, Sheffield S10 3FN Tel: 01142 662210 — MB ChB Sheff. 1960; MEd Manch. 1979; FRCP Lond. 1988; FFPHM RCP (UK) 1992; FFCM 1979; DObst RCOG 1967; DPH Manch. 1966. (Sheff.) Dep. Dir. (Pub. Health) Sheff. HA. Socs: BMA; Soc. Social Med. Prev: Cons. Pub. Health Med. Yorks. RHA; Dir. Centre for Profess. Developm. Manch. Univ.; Specialist Community Med. (Social Servs. Liaison) Barnsley HA.

***ESKTEEN, Johannes Albertus** PO Box 95708, Waterkloof, Gauteng 0145, South Africa Email: drbertus@msn.com; 25 Bishops Road, Sutton Coldfield B73 6HX — MB ChB 1995 Pretoria.

ESLAH, Esmail 1 Thornleigh House, Clayton Road, Jesmond, Newcastle upon Tyne NE2 1TL — MB BS 1993 Newc.

ESLER, Mr Colin Neville Alfred University Hospitals of Leicester, Glenfield Hospital, Groby Road, Leicester LE3 9QP Tel: 0116 2563050 Fax: 0116 2321702; Tel: 001509 620806 — BM BS 1985 Nottm.; BMedSci (Hons.) Nottm. 1983; FRCS Ed. 1991; Dip. Biomechanics Strathclyde 1993; FRCS (Tr & Orth) 1998. (Univ. Nottm.) Sen. Lect./Hon. Cons., Trauma & Orthopaedic Surg. -Univ of Leci/Univ hosp of Leci NHS Trust. Socs: Past Pres. of Brit. Orthopaedic Trainees Assn. Prev: Sen. Regist. S. Trent Rotat.; Regist.

(Orthop. & Trauma) P.ss Eliz. Orthop. Hosp. Exeter & City Hosp. Truro; Arthroplasty Fell. UCLA Los Angeles.

ESLER, David James Woodside Health Centre, Barr Street, Glasgow G20 7LR Tel: 0141 531 9507 Fax: 0141 531 9509 — MB ChB 1983 Glas.; MRCGP 1988. Princip. GP Glas..

ESLER, James Ronald Davis Whitehead Health Centre, 17B Edward Road, Whitehead, Carrickfergus BT38 9RU Tel: 028 9335 3454 Fax: 028 9337 2625 — MB BCh BAO 1970 Belf.; MRCGP 1976.

ESLER, Mark David 3 Redan Street, Brook Green, London W14 0AD Tel: 020 7603 8544 Email: mark.esler@virgin.net — MB BS 1993 Lond.; BA Camb. 1990; FRCA 1998. (London) Specialist Regist. Imperial Sch. of Anaesth. Socs: Assn. of Anaesth.s of GB & I; Obst. Anaesth. Assn.

ESLER, Robert (retired) The Little Mythe, Julian Road, Sneyd Park, Bristol BS9 1LB Tel: 0117 968 3884 — MB BCh BAO 1946 Dub.; BA Dub. 1943, MB BCh BAO 1946. Prev: Med. Off. Ronkswood Hosp. (Min. of Pens.) Worcester.

ESLICK, Mr Michael Anthony Ropes, Col. L/RAMC (retired) Lindens, Mill Lane, Marnhull, Sturminster Newton DT10 1JT Tel: 01258 820619 Fax: 01258 820619 Email: michael.eslick@ntlworld.com — MB ChB 1953 Liverp.; FRCS Ed. 1972. Med. Mem. Appeals Tribunal Lond. Prev: Sen. Surg. & Dep. Med. Dir. King Khalid Nat. Guard Hosp. Jeddah, Saudi Arabia.

ESMAIL, Aneez Bahadurali Tel: 0161 226 3015 Fax: 0161 248 4580 Email: aneez.esmail@man.ac.uk — MFPHM 1990 Faculty of Public Health Medicine; DTM & H 1984 Liverpool University; PhD 1996 University of London; MRCS Eng. LRCP Lond. 1982 London. (Sheffield University)

ESMAIL, Mahdi Muhammad Ali 19 Ravens Court Close, Penylan, Cardiff CF23 9DJ — MB ChB 1980 Baghdad.

ESMAILJI, Esmail Anverali Stonehouse Health Clinic, High Street, Stonehouse GL10 2NG Tel: 01453 823144; Tara, Coronation Road, Stroud GL5 3SL Tel: 01453 764227 Fax: 01453 821393 Email: esmailji@aol.com — MB ChB 1978 Bristol; DRCOG 1983; Dip. Derm, 1997; Dip. Acupunc. 1997; DFFP 1998. (Bristol) GP StoneHo..; Clin. Asst. (Elderly Care Med.) Stroud Gen. Hosp. Gloucestershire. Socs: BMA; BMAS.

ESMOND, John Richard 25 Coley View, Northowram, Halifax HX3 7EB — MB BS 1990 Lond.

ESMONDE, Thomas Francis Grattan Department of Neurology, Royal Victoria Hospital, Belfast BT12 6BA — MB BCh BAO 1984 Dub.; MD Dub. 1995; MRCPI 1987; MRCP (UK) 1987. (Univ. Dub.) Cons. Neurol. Roy. Vict. Hosp. Belf. Socs: Irish Neurol. Assn.; Amer. Acad. Neurol.; Ulster Med. Soc. Prev: Sen. Regist. (Neurol.) Roy. Vict. Hosp. Belf.; Research Fell. (Clin. Neurosci.) W.. Gen. Hosp. Edin.; Regist. (Neurol.) Univ. Hosp. Wales Cardiff.

ESPARON, Mrs Janet Audrey Centre for Child Health, Dudhope Terrace, Dundee DD3 6 Tel: 01577 830523; Takamaxa, Drunlie, Glenfarg, Perth PH2 9PE Email: espo@btinternet.com — MB ChB 1981 Dundee; MRCPsych. 1992. Specialist Regist. (p/t) Centre for Child Health, Dudhope Dundee. Socs: Roy. Coll. Psychiat. Prev: Regist. Murray Roy. Hosp. Perth.

ESPIE, Jennifer Terry 9 Cloverhill, Chester-le-Street DH2 2LZ — MB ChB 1987 Ed. Trainee GP N.d. VTS. Prev: Ho. Off. (Gen. Med.) CrossHo. Hosp. Kilmarnock.

ESPIE, Paul James 9 Cloverhill, Chester-le-Street DH2 2LZ — MB ChB 1987 Ed.

ESPINER, Mr Harry John (retired) (cons. rooms), 2 Clifton Park, Bristol BS8 3BS Tel: 0117 906 4201 Fax: 0117 973 0887 Email: harry@espiner.com — MB ChB Otago 1955; ChM Bristol 1962; FRCS Eng. 1959. Emerit. Cons. Surg. United Bristol Hosps. Prev: Sen. Regist. (Surg.) United Bristol Hosps. & S. W.. RHB.

ESPIR, Michael Lucien Ernest 39 Hyde Park Gardens Mews, London W2 2NX Tel: 020 7262 7013 Fax: 020 7724 2315 Email: mpespir@compuserve.com — MB BChir Camb. 1950; MA Camb. 1950; FRCP Lond. 1971, M 1957; MRCS Eng. LRCP Lond. 1950; MFOM RCP Lond. 1985, A 1983. (Camb. & Middlx.) Cons. Neurol. Cromwell Hosp. Lond.; Hon. Cons. Neurol. Char. Cross Hosp. Lond. Socs: Fell. Roy. Soc. Med. (Mem. Sect. Neurol. & Occupat. Med.); (Ex-Pres.) Brit. Br. Internat. League Against Epilepsy; Assn. Brit. Neurols. Prev: Cons. Neurol. Trent Regional Dept. Neurosurg. & Neurol. Derbysh. Roy. Infirm., Nottm. Univ. & Leicester Hosps.; Princip. Med. Off. Civil Serv. Occupat. Health Serv. Lond.; Sen. Regist. (Neurol.) Nat. Hosp. Qu. Sq. & King's Coll. Hosp. Lond.

ESPIRIAN, Hayganoush Allway Health Centre, 18 Penkin Close, Alway, Newport NP19 9NT Tel: 01633 277882 Fax: 01633 290627 — Vrach 1966 Erevan Med Inst; Vrach 1966 Erevan Med Inst.

ESPITALIER-NOEL, Paul Joseph Francois (retired) South View Surgery, Guildford Road, Woking GU22 7RR Tel: 01483 63186 — MB BCh BAO 1957 NUI; DA Eng. 1963; LM Rotunda 1958. Prev: Regist. (Anaesth.) Salisbury Hosp. Gp.

ESPLEY, Mr Arthur James Orthopaedic Directorate, Perth Royal Infirmary, Perth PH1 1NX Tel: 01828 473696 — MB ChB 1968 Ed.; FRCS Ed. 1974; DObst 1971. Cons. Orthop. Surg. Perth Roy. Infirm.

ESSA, Najat Isaac Shamas 22A Delta Road, Chobham, Woking GU24 8PY Tel: 01483 6044 — MB ChB 1970 Mosul; MRCP (UK) 1981. Sen. Research Fell. (Cardiol.) Wexham Pk. Hosp. Slough. Prev: Regist. (Cardiol. of Elderly, Geriat. Med.) Qu. Eliz. Hosp. II Welwyn Gdn. City; Regist. (Med.) City Teach. Hosp. Baghdad, Iraq.

ESSAM, Marie Anne Sheepcot Medical Centre, 80 Sheepcot Lane, Garston, Watford WD25 0EA Tel: 01923 672451 Fax: 01923 681404 — MB BS 1984 Lond.; T(GP) 1990. GP Doctors Retainer Scheme Hemel Hempstead. Prev: Trainee GP/SHO (Orthop.) Hemel Hempstead VTS; Ho. Off. (Surg.) St. Albans City Hosp.

ESSAME, Robin Stephen Kennedy (retired) Oakmount, Dowell St., Honiton EX14 1NB Tel: 01404 42038 — MB BS 1952 Lond.; MRCS Eng. LRCP Lond. 1952; MRCGP 1962; DObst RCOG 1956. Prev: Med. Off. Honiton Hosp.

ESSANDOH, Richard Solomon c/o 430 Muskett Gardens, Carryduff, Belfast BT8 8QW — MB BCh BAO 1969 Belf.; DObst RCOG Lond. 1976.

ESSAPEN, Sharadah 7 Mill Place, Kingston upon Thames KT1 2RS — MB BS 1988 Lond.; MRCP (UK) 1992; FRCR 1998. (Lond. Hosp. Med. Coll.) Specialist Regist. (Clin. Oncol) Roy. Marsden NHS Trust; Specialist Regist. (Clin. Oncol.) Roy. Marsden Hosp. Sutton, Surrey. Prev: Regist. (Clin. Oncol.) Roy. Lond. Hosp. Trust; Regist. (Clin. Oncol.) Roy. Lond. Hosp. Trust.

ESSENHIGH, Mr David Malcolm (retired) Ravenoaks, Watermillock, Penrith CA11 0JH Tel: 01768 486928 — MB BChir 1957 Camb.; MA Camb. 1964, BA (1st cl. Hons.) 1953, MChir; 1964, MB 1957, BChir 1956; FRCS Eng. 1960. Prev: Cons. Surg. Dept. Urol. Freeman Hosp. Newc.

ESSER, Gerhard Doctor's Accommodation, The James Paget Hospital, Lowestoft Road, Great Yarmouth NR31 6LA — State Exam Med 1992 Berlin.

ESSEX, Benjamin John Sydenham Green Group Practice, 26 Holmshaw Close, London SE26 4TH Tel: 020 8676 8836 Fax: 020 7771 4710; 26 Terrapin Road, London SW17 8QN Tel: 0208 675 9990 — MB BS Lond. 1964; MSc (Social & Preven. Med.) Lond. 1972; MRCP Lond. 1969; MRCS Eng. LRCP Lond. 1964; FRCGP 1988, M 1976; FRCP 1999. (King's Coll. Hosp.) GP Cons. Lambeth, S.wark & Lewisham HA. Prev: Cons. WHO; Hon. Lect. (Community Med.) Univ. Nottm.; Sen. Lect. (Primary Care) Univ. Dar Es Salaam Tanzania.

ESSEX, Charles Child Development Unit, Gulson Hospital, Gulson Road, Coventry CV1 2HR — MB ChB 1978 Manch.

ESSEX-CATER, Alison Friarage Hospital, Northallerton DL6 1JG Tel: 01609 779911 — MB BCh 1975 Wales; MRCP (UK) 1983; DCH RCP Lond. 1982; FRCP (UK) 1997; FRCPCH 1997. Cons. Paediat. Friarage Hosp. N.allerton.

ESSEX-CATER, Antony John (retired) Honfleur, La Vallette, Mont Cambrai, St Lawrence, Jersey JE3 1JP Tel: 01534 872438 — MRCS Eng. LRCP Lond. 1948; AFOM RCP Lond. 1983; FFPH 1974; DIH Eng. 1955; DPH Lond. 1953; DCH RCP Lond. 1951. Prev: MOH States of Jersey.

ESSEX-LOPRESTI, Michael (retired) 14 Oakwood Park Road, London N14 6QG Tel: 020 8882 1337 Email: michael@sthgate.fsnet.co.uk — MRCS Eng. LRCP Lond. 1951; MFCM 1972; DA Eng. 1957. Prev: Dep. Sec. Counc. Postgrad. Med. Educat. in Eng. & Wales.

ESSIEN, Ani Ransome 312 Gloucester Avenue, Chelmsford CM2 9LJ — MB BS 1982 Lagos.

ESSIEN, Essien Utip 22 Curtis Road, Norwich NR6 6RB Tel: 01603 484725 — BM BCh 1979 Univ. Nigeria; MRCOG 1991.

Prev: Regist. (O & G) Jas. Paget Hosp. Gorleston; SHO (O & G) Norf. & Norwich Hosp.

ESSIGMAN, Martin Norbert — MB BS 1994 Lond.; MRCGP 2001; MRCGP 2000. GP Principle; Clin. Asst., Accid. & Emerg., Salisbury; GP Principle; Clin. Asst.; Clin. Asst., Accid. & Emerg., Salisbury. Socs: Roy. Coll. of GP; Roy. Coll. of GP.

ESSIGMAN, Wladyslaw (retired) 19 Barleycroft Road, Welwyn Garden City AL8 6JX Tel: 01707 335410 — MB BCh BAO 1953 Belf.; FRCP Lond. 1982, M 1968; MRCGP 1960. Prev: Lister Hosp. Stevenage Cons.

ESSLEMONT, Alison Maywood Surgery, Hawthorn Road, Bognor Regis PO21 9HL Tel: 01243 829141 — MB ChB 1990 Bristol; MRCGP 1994; DRCOG 1992. p/t GP Bognor Regis.

ESSMAILI SHAD, Jaleh 165 Moorgate Road, Rotherham S60 3AP; 3 Victoria Road, Broomhall, Sheffield S10 2DJ Tel: 0114 266 0908 — MB ChB 1982 Manch.

ESSOM, Joanne Marie The Lodge, Crooked Acres, 1 Spen Lane, Leeds LS5 3EJ Tel: 0113 295 3540; 8 Ridgeway, Leeds LS8 4DF — MB ChB 1986 Leeds; MRCPsych 1991. Staff Grade Psychiat. (Learning Disabil.) Crooked Acres, Leeds. Prev: Sen. Regist. (Psychiat. of Ment. Handicap) Meanwood Pk. Hosp. Leeds; Sen. Regist. (Psychiat. of Ment. Handicap) Halifax Gen. Hosp.; Regist. & SHO (Psychiat.) High Royds Hosp. Menston.

ESSON, Catherine Patricia Top Flat Left, 28 Partickhill Road, Glasgow G11 5BP Tel: 0141 338 8151 — MB ChB 1988 Glas.; MRCGP 1993; DRCOG 1994; DFFP 1994. Clin. Asst. Wom.'s Reproductive Health Serv. Glas. Roy. Matern. Hosp.; Clin. Med. Off. Family Plann. & Sexual Health Centre Glas. Socs: BMA; Glas. Obst. & Gyn. Soc.

ESSON, George Alexander Cockburn (retired) The Coach House, 14 Institution Road, Elgin IV30 1QX Tel: 01343 542291 — MB ChB 1936 Aberd. Prev: Graded Specialist Path. RAMC 1942.

ESSON, Walter Reid 7 Hatshill Farm Close, Bickleigh, Plymouth PL6 7JX Tel: 01752 839527 — BM BCh 1961 Oxf.; MA (Hons.) Oxf. 1961; MFOM RCP Lond. 1978; DPH Glas. 1970; DIH Eng. 1967; DObst RCOG 1964. (Oxf. & Guy's) Civil. Cons. & Naval Med. Off. of Health Devonport & W.. Area; Cons. Occupat. Med. Plymouth. Socs: Fell. Roy. Soc. Med.; Soc. Occupat. Med. Prev: Naval Med. Off. Health to Flag Off. Plymouth.

ESTCOURT, Peter Geoffrey Newick Health Centre, Marbles Road, Newick, Lewes BN8 4LR Tel: 01825 722272 Fax: 01825 724391; Peter House, Lewes Road, South Chailey, Lewes BN8 4AD Tel: 01273 400791 — MB BS Lond. 1967; MRCP (U.K.) 1972; DCH Eng. 1970; DObst RCOG 1969. (Middlx.) Med. Off. St. Peter & St. James Hospice, E. Sussex. Socs: BMA. Prev: Lect. (Paediat.) Univ. Baghdad; Regist. (Med.) Rochford Gen. Hosp.; Med. Off. CMCU Enugu, Nigeria.

ESTCOURT, Thomas 24 Grange Road, Bowdon, Altrincham WA14 3EE — MB ChB 1994 Bristol.

ESTELA-FERRERO, Catalina Maria Flat 13, Tuscany House, Durdham Park, Bristol BS6 6XA — LMS 1987 Barcelona. SHO (ENT) Countess of Chester Hosp.

ESTERLICH, Robert John 309 Milligan Road, Aylestone, Leicester LE2 8FH — MB BCh 1994 Wales; MRCP Lond. 1998. (Wales)

ESTERSON, Aaron 75 Harvard Court, Honeybourne Road, London NW6 1HW Tel: 020 7794 3273 — MB ChB Glas. 1951; DPM Eng. 1959. (Glas.)

ESTILL, Wendy Olive (retired) Broughton House, 10 Windsor Road, Chorley PR7 1LN Tel: 01257 266293 — MB ChB 1974 Manch.

ESTLIN, Edward John 21 Silverdale Close, Liverpool L36 5YJ — MB ChB 1987 Leeds.

ESTMENT, Paul Denton Westmore Centre, Wembley Hospital, Fairview Avenue, Wembley HA0 4UH — MB ChB 1988 Cape Town.

ESTRACH ROIG, Cristina Email: estrach@belloso.freeserve.co.uk — LMS 1990 U Autonoma Barcelona; MRCP (UK). Specialist Regist. Rheum., Merseyside Region -flexible Train. Prev: SHO (Med.) Vict. Hosp. Blackpool.; SHO Rheum. Nuffield Orthop. centre; SHO Wythenshawe Hosp. Manch.

ESTREICH, Loma 23 Kent Gardens, Ealing, London W13 8BU — MB BS 1983 Lond.; DRCOG 1987; Cert. Family Plann. JCC 1986.

ESTREICH, Steven Department of Genitourinary Medicine, St. Helier Hospital, Wrythe Lane, Carshalton SM5 1AA Tel: 020 8296 3189 Fax: 020 8641 4546 — MB BS 1983 Lond.; FRCP (UK) 1998; Dip. Genitourin. Med. 1989; Cert. Family Plann. JCC 1987; MRCP (UK) 1986; BSc (Hons.) Lond. 1980. Cons. Genitourin. Med. St. Helier Hosp. Carshalton. Socs: Med. Soc. Study VD. Prev: Sen. Regist. (Genitourin. Med.) Roy. Lond. Hosp.

ESTYN-JONES, Helen 3 Frinton House, Rushcroft Road, Brixton, London SW2 1JP; Church Park House, Diptford, Totnes TQ9 7NY — MB ChB 1991 Birm. Prev: Community Paediat. Haringey; Med. Off. MSF-Holland Sarajevo BH; SHO Rotat. (Paediat.) Guy's & Lewisham Hosps.

ESWARAPPA, Patre Rudrappa Hough Green Medical Centre, 158 Hough Green Road, Hough Green, Widnes WA8 4PG Tel: 0151 424 2920 Fax: 0151 424 3963 — MB BS 1965 Bangalore; MB BS 1965 Bangalore.

ETCHEGOYEN, Alicia Perinatal Service, Chelsea & Westminster Hospital, 369 Fulham Road, London SW10 9TI Tel: 020 8746 8646 Fax: 020 8237 5219; 51 Limerston Street, London SW10 0BL Tel: 020 7351 0398 Fax: 020 7351 0398 — Medico Buenos Aires 1971; FRCPsych 1996, M 1974; DPM Eng. 1974. Cons. Child & Adolesc. Psychiat. Chelsea & W.m. Hosp. Lond.; Child and Family Consultation Serv. Violet Melchett Lond. Prev: Cons. Psychother. W.m. Hosp. & W.m. Childr. Hosp.

ETCHELLS, Mr David Edward Bournemouth Eye Unit, Royal Bournemouth Hospital, Castle Lane East, Bournemouth BH7 7DW Tel: 01202 704361 Fax: 01202 740367; Sandhills, Coach Hill Lane, Burley St, Ringwood BH24 4HN Tel: 01425 402135 Email: davidetchells@redhotant.com — MB BChir 1977 Camb.; MA, MB Camb. 1977, BChir 1976; FRCS Eng. 1984; MRCS Eng. LRCP Lond. 1976; DO Eng. 1981. (Camb. & St. Thos.) Cons. Ophth. Bournemouth Eye Unit. Prev: Sen. Regist. (Ophth.) Leeds Gen. Infirm.; Regist. (Ophth.) Bristol Eye Hosp.

ETCHES, Frederick Guy Woodside, High St., Loftus, Saltburn-by-the-Sea TS13 — LRCPI & LM, LRSCI & LM 1965; LRCPI & LM, LRCSI & LM 1965. (RCSI)

ETHELL, Mark Edward 36 Clarence Road, Clarence Mews, London E12 5BB Tel: 020 8514 3132 — MB BChir 1990 Camb.; MA Camb. 1991; MRCP (UK) 1993; DRCPath 1996. (Camb.) Bone Marrow Transpl. Coordinator Roy. Free Hosp. Lond. Prev: Regist.Rotat (Haemat) N. Thames; Research Regist. (Haemat.) Univ. Camb.; Regist. Rotat. (Haemat.) Camb.

ETHERIDGE, Helen Elizabeth 93 City Way, Rochester ME1 2BA — MB BS 1992 Lond.

ETHERINGTON, Christine 1 Throstle Nest View, New Road Side, Horsforth, Leeds LS18 4LR — MB ChB 1990 Leeds.

ETHERINGTON, Clare Margaret Lakeview, Park Lane, Harefield, Uxbridge UB9 6HR — MB BS 1986 Lond.; BSc Lond. 1983, MB BS 1986; DRCOG 1990. Prev: Trainee GP Hillingdon VTS.

ETHERINGTON, Mr Ian James City Hospital NHS Trust, City Hospital, Dudley Road, Birmingham B18 7QH Tel: 0121 5074377 Fax: 0121 5075467 Email: ian.zoe@virgin.net; 83 Oxford Road, Mosely, Birmingham B13 9SG — MB ChB 1988 Bristol; MD Univ. Birmg. 2000; MRCOG 1993. (Bristol) Cons. Obst. & Gynaecologist and Hon. Sen. Lect., City Hosp. NHS Trust, Birm. Socs: Brit. Soc. Colpos. & Cerv. Path.; Exec. Comm. (2000-date); Chair website sub-Comm., chair IT Sub-Comm. Prev: Regist. Walsall Manor Hosp.; Research Fell. Univ. of Birm.; Regist. (O & G) S.mead Hosp. Bristol.

ETHERINGTON, James Derek (retired) 50 Elmtree Park, Yealmpton, Plymouth PL8 2ED Tel: 01752 881212 Email: dereketherington@doctors.org.uk — MB BS Durh. 1959; FRCGP 1985, M 1974.

ETHERINGTON, Joanne Gloria 14 Piethorne Close, Newhay, Rochdale OL16 3RH — MB ChB 1995 Dundee.

ETHERINGTON, John DSMRC, Headley Court, Epsom KT18 6JN Tel: 01372 378271 — MB ChB 1986 Birm.; MSc 1996 (Sports Medicine) Lond. Univ.; MRCP 1991. Cons. in Rheum.-Rehabil., DSMRC, Headley Ct.; Hon. Cons., Dept. of Rheum., St. Thomas' Hosp., Lond.; Cons. in Rheum. and Rehabil., Ashtead Hosp., Ashtead, Surrey. Socs: Brit. Soc. for Rheum.; Brit. Med. Assn.; Brit. Assn. for Sport and Exercise Med.

ETHERINGTON, Kenneth Agar (retired) 36 St Peters Road, West Mersea, Colchester CO5 8LJ Tel: 01206 384439 — MRCS Eng. LRCP Lond. 1949. Prev: SHO Oldham Roy. Infirm.

ETHERINGTON, Robert Henderson, Surg. Capt. RN Retd. (retired) London Drummonds, The Royal Bank of Scotland, 49 Charing Cross, London SW1A 2DX — MB BS 1945 Durh.

ETHERINGTON, Robert James Wyche House, Wyche Lane, Bunbury, Tarporley CW6 9PS Tel: 01829 261050; Department of Radiology, Countess of Chester Hospital, Liverpool Road, Chester CH2 1 Tel: 01244 366714 — MB ChB 1982 Bristol; FRCR 1987. Cons. Radiol. Chester Hosps. Prev: Sen. Regist. & Regist. (Diag. Radiol.) Univ. Hosp. Wales.

ETHERSON, John 123 Kylemore Park, Londonderry BT48 0RP — MB BCh BAO 1990 Belf.

ETHERTON, John Edward Meridian Surgery, Meridian Way, Peacehaven BN10 8NF Tel: 01273 581999 Fax: 01273 589025; 24 Gorham Avenue, Rottingdean, Brighton BN2 7DP Tel: 01273 300646 Fax: 01273 297507 Email: wol@cwcom.net — MB BChir 1979 Camb.; PhD CNAA 1977; MA Camb. 1980; DFFP 1993; DRCOG 1982. (Camb.) Socs: Christians in Caring Professions; Christ. Med. Fell.sh.; BMA. Prev: Ho. Surg. Newmarket Gen. Hosp.; Ho. Phys. Chesterton Hosp. Camb.

ETKIN, Herbert Ticehurst House Hospital, Ticehurst, Wadhurst TN5 7HU Tel: 01580 200391 Fax: 01580 201006; 2 de Warrenne Road, Lewes BN7 1BP Tel: 01273 471118 — MB BCh 1962 Witwatersrand; FRCPsych 1987, M 1972; DPM Witwatersrand 1970; T(Psych) 1991. (Witwatersrand) Med. Dir. & Cons. Psychiat. (Child & Adolesc.) Ticehurst Hse. Hosp.; Sch. Counsellor Eton Coll. Windsor Berks. Prev: Cons. Brighton Family Consultat. Centre, Colwood Adolesc. Unit., Ticehurst Hse. Hosp. E. Sussex; Clin. Tutor (Psychiat.) Brighton & Mid-Downs HA; Cons. Psychiat. Tara Hosp. Johannesburg & Univ. Witwatersrand Johannesburg, S. Afr.

ETON, Bruce (retired) Tower Lodge, 6 Gilbert Road, St Leonards-on-Sea TN38 0RH Tel: 01424 436551 — MB ChB 1943 Manch.; MD Manch. 1957; FRCOG 1966, M 1952. Prev: Cons. O & G Hastings Hosp. Gp.

ETTEH, Bassey Enobong Partington Health Centre, Central Road, Partington, Manchester M31 4FL Tel: 0161 775 7033 Fax: 0161 775 8411; 5 Rippenden Avenue, Chorlton-cum-Hardy, Manchester M21 9SS Tel: 0161 881 1030 — MB BS 1977 Ibadan; LMSSA Lond. 1990; DTCH Liverp. 1990; DTM & H Liverp. 1989. Prev: Trainee GP Brunswick Health Centre Manch.; SHO (Community & Hosp. Paediat.) Grimsby HA; SHO (A & E) Arrowe Pk. Hosp. Upton.

ETTI, Obi Roland 42 Lightwoods Hill, Smethwick, Smethwick B67 5EB — MB BS 1980 Ibadan; MRCP (UK) 1988; DTM & H RCP Lond. 1984. (Univ. Ibadan, Nigeria) Cons. Neurol. Dudley Gp. Hosps. & Qu. Eliz. Hosp. Birm. Socs: Brit. Soc. Rehabil. Med. Prev: Sen. Regist. (Rehabil. Med.) Regional Rehabil. Centre Selly Oaks; Regist. (Neurol.) Midl. Centre for Neurosurg. & Neurol.; Regist. (Neurol.) Qu. Eliz. Hosp. Psychiat. Hosp. Birm.

ETTLES, Duncan Forbes Radiology Department, Hull Royal Infirmary, Anlaby Road, Hull HU3 2JZ Email: ettles@compuserve.com; 78 Southfield, Hessle HU13 0EU — MB ChB 1982 Ed.; MB ChB (Hons.) Ed. 1982; MD Ed. 1994; MRCP (UK) 1985; FRCR 1992. Cons. Radiol. Hull Roy. Infirm. Socs: Brit. Cardiac Interven. Soc.; Soc. Interven. Radiol. Prev: Specialist Cardiac Radiol. (Cons.) Green La. Hosp. Auckland, NZ.

ETTLING, Thomas Michael St Thomas Road Health Centre, St. Thomas Road, Newquay TR7 1RU Tel: 01637 878599 — MB BCh 1978 Wales; MRCGP 1983; DRCOG 1982. GP Trainer & GP Cornw.

ETTLINGER, Nini Eleanor 120 Edith Road, London W14 9AP Tel: 020 7603 5091 — LMSSA Lond. 1948. (Roy. Coll. Ed.) Prev: Private Pract. Psychotherapist; Train. Therapist for Lond. Centre Psychother.; Med. Asst. Conolly Unit St. Barnard's Hosp. Middlx.

ETTLINGER, Paul Richard Albin The Devonshire Clinic, Flat A, 21 Devonshire Place, London W1G 6HZ Tel: 020 7935 8666 Fax: 020 7935 6370 Email: devonshireclinclondon@virgin.net; 14B Kensington Court Gardens, Kensington Court Place, London W8 5QE Tel: 020 7935 8666 Fax: 020 7935 6370 — BM 1981 Soton.; MRCGP 1986; DRCOG 1984. (Soton.) Clin. Asst. (Gen. Surg.) W.m. Hosp. Lond. Socs: BMA; Indep. Doctors Forum. Prev: Lect. (Gen. Pract.) St. Mary's Hosp. Med. Sch. & Lisson Gr. Heal th Centre Lond.; Trainee GP Char. Cross Hosp. VTS; Ho. Phys. Wexham Pk. Hosp. Slough.

EU, Tieng Yiing 1 Glenburn Mews, Dunmurry, Belfast BT17 — MB BCh BAO 1992 Belf.

EUDEN, Mark Pinfold Medical Practice, The Health Centre, Pinfold Gate, Loughborough LE11 1DQ Tel: 01509 263753 Fax: 01509 264124; 3 Compton Close, Nanpantan, Loughborough LE11 3SF — BM BS 1975 Nottm.; BMedSc (Hons.) Nottm. 1973, BM BS (Hons.) 1975; MRCP (UK) 1978; MRCGP 1984.

EUINTON, Hartley Andrew Department Diagnostic Radiology, Northern General Hospital, Herries Road, Sheffield S5 7AU Tel: 0114 243 4343; Pinch Mill Cottage, Royds Moor, Whiston, Rotherham S60 4NJ Tel: 01709 543982 — MB ChB 1976 Manch.; MB ChB Manch. l976; FRCR 1983; DMRD (Eng.) 1981. Cons. Radiol. Sheff. HA & Hon. Lect. Univ. Sheff.; Hon. Clin. Lect. Radiol. Univ. Sheff.

EUINTON, Leslie Edwin 47 Gunthorpe Road, Gedling, Nottingham NG4 4JR — MB ChB 1953 Leeds; DIH Eng. 1978; MFOM RCP Lond. 1980; Accredit. Specialist Occupat. Med. JCHMT 1978. Socs: FRSH; Soc. Occupat. Med. Prev: Sen. Advisor Occupat. Health JRB Assn. McLean USA; Dir. Occupat. Health Br. Govt. Saskatchewan Canada; HM Med. Inspect. Factories.

EUNSON, Graeme John Department of Paediatric Surgery, Royal Hospital for Sick Children, 9 Sciennes Road, Edinburgh EH9 1LF — MB ChB 1992 Ed.; MB ChB Ed 1992. Sen. Ho. Off., Roy. Hosp. for Sick Childr., Edin..

EUNSON, Paul David Bowstones, Hall Crescent, Gullane EH31 2HA; 13 Windsor Street, Dundee DD2 1BP — MB ChB 1981 Ed.; MSC Lond. 1989; MRCP (UK) 1988. Cons. Paediat. Zomba Gen. Hosp. Zomba, Malawi. Prev: Regist. (Paediat.) Ninewells Hosp. Dundee; Med. Off. Milo Hosp. Njombe, Tanzania; Med. Off. Makunduchi Hosp., Zanzibar.

EUSTACE, Damian Leonard Stuart Department of Obstetrics & Gynaecology, Queen Mary's Hospital, Frognal Avenue, Sidcup DA14 6LT Tel: 020 8302 2678 — MB BS 1983 Lond.; MD Lond. 1993; MRCOG 1989. Cons. O & G Qu. Mary's Hosp. Sidcup. Socs: Brit. Soc. Gyn. Endoscopy; Blair Bell Res. Soc.; Brit. Soc. Colpos. & Cerv. Path. Prev: Sen. Regist. (O & G) Qu. Mary's Hosp. Sidcup; Birthright Research Fell. (O & G) St. Thos. Hosp. Lond.; Research Regist. (Gyn.) St. Thos. Hosp. Lond.

EUSTACE, Jason Robert Coach and Horses Surgery, The Car Park, St. Clears, Carmarthen SA33 4AA Tel: 01994 230379 Fax: 01994 231449 — MB BCh 1993 Wales.

EUSTACE, Jean (retired) 47 Englishcombe Lane, Bath BA2 2EE — MB ChB 1950 Bristol; DObst RCOG 1951.

EUSTACE, John David Oakley and Overton Partnership, Overton Surgery, Station Road, Overton, Basingstoke RG25 3DU Tel: 01256 770212 Fax: 01256 771581 — MRCS Eng. LRCP Lond. 1960; DObst RCOG 1964; DA Eng. 1963. (Guy's) Prev: Ho. Surg. & Ho. Phys. Roy. Sussex Co. Hosp. Brighton; Res. Anaesth. Swindon Hosp. Gp.; Res. Med. Off. Swindon Matern. Home.

EUSTACE, Ruth Whiteside Royal Hospital, Chesterfield S44 5BL Tel: 01246 277271; 5 Harley Road, Sheffield S11 9SD — MB BCh BAO 1971 Dub.; BA Dub. 1969, MB BCh BAO 1971; FFA RCS Eng. 1976. (Trinity Coll. Dub.) Cons. Anaesth. Chesterfield & N. Derbysh. Roy. Hosp. Socs: Assn. Anaesth. Gt. Brit. & Irel.; Obst. Anaesth. Assn.; Med. Wom. Federat. Prev: Sen. Regist. Trent RHA; Head Asst. (Anaesth.) Academisch Ziekenhuis, Leiden, Holland; Ho. Surg. & Ho. Phys. Sir P. Dun's Hosp. Dub.

EVA, Lois Jane 7 Aldersleigh Drive, Stafford ST17 4RY — MB BS 1993 Lond. (Royal Free)

EVAN-WONG, Leslie Alexander Queen Margaret Hospital, Dunfermline KY12 0SU Tel: 01383 623623; Danmarick, 7 Saltpans, Charlestown, Dunfermline KY11 3EB — MB ChB 1973 Ed.; MD Aberd. 1987; MRCP (UK) 1976; MRCPath 1984. Cons. Haemat. Qu. Margt. Hosp. Dunfermline & Vict. Hosp. Kirkcaldy; Hon. Sen. Lect. Univ. Edin. Prev: Lect. (Haemat.) Univ. Aberd.

EVANGELOU, Litsa Victoria House Surgery, 228 Dewsbury Road, Leeds LS11 6HQ Tel: 0113 270 4754 Fax: 0113 272 0561 — MB ChB 1974 Leeds; DObst RCOG 1976. Prev: Clin. Asst. A & E Dept. St. Jas. Hosp. Leeds; SHO (Paediat.) Leeds Gen. Infirm.; SHO (O & G) St. Jas. Hosp. Leeds.

EVANS, Mr Adrian Allan Department of Obstetrics & Gynaecology, York District Hospital, Wiggington Rd, York YO31 8HE Tel: 01904 725547; 6 The Horseshoe, York YO24 1LX — MB ChB 1989 Manch.; 1986 BSc (Med.Sci.) St Andrews. Cons. Obst. & Gynaecologist, York Dist. Hosp. Prev: Seconded Pub. Health Dept. Nott. Health Auth.; Research Fell. (Obst. & Immunol.) City Hosp. & Qu. Med. Centre Nottm.; Specialist Regist. Obs. & Gynae., Qu.'s Med. Centre, Nottm.

EVANS, Adrienne Enid (House) Moonraker, North Lane, Weston-on-the-Green, Bicester OX25 3RG — MB ChB 1968 Liverp.; Dip. Occ. Health London 1996; Cert. Family Plann. JCC 1971; DObst RCOG 1970. Occupat. Health MOD. Socs: Soc. Occupat. Med.; Gp.s Comm. Prev: p/t Occupat.al Health Adviser, Oxf.shire Co. Counc.; Locum Occupat.al Health Adviser Culhamana Harwell.

EVANS, Ailsa Helena 9 Blakeway Hollow, Much Wenlock TF13 6AR — MB ChB 1987 Manch.

EVANS, Alan David Fronlas, Church Road, Penderyn, Aberdare CF44 9JP — MB ChB 1990 Manch.

EVANS, Alan John Brownlow Health Centre, 1 Legahory Centre, Legahory, Craigavon BT65 5BE — MB BCh BAO 1969 Dub.

EVANS, Alan Malcolm 87 Wychwood Avenue, Knowle, Solihull B93 9DJ — MB ChB 1956 Birm.; MRCGP 1977; Cert. JCC Lond. 1976. Med. Adviser BAMS (Midl.) Benefits Agency DSS Birm. Prev: GP Birm.; Regional Med. Off. Regional Med. Serv. (E. Midl. Div.) DHSS Nottm.

EVANS, Alan Roy Burncross Surgery, 1 Bevan Way, Chapeltown, Sheffield S35 1RN Tel: 0114 2848025 & 466052; 7 Wood End, Grenoside, Sheffield S35 8RR — MB ChB 1969 Sheff.; MRCGP 1975; DObst RCOG 1971. (Sheff.)

EVANS, Alan Stephen The Gables, 105 Plymouth Road, Penarth CF64 3DE — MB ChB 1973 Liverp.; MD Liverp. 1984, MB ChB 1973; MRCOG 1979. Dickson Carr Regional Prize 1983; Cons. Univ. Hosp. Wales Cardiff. Prev: Sen. Regist. N.. RHA; Research Fell. Gateshead Gyn. Oncol. Unit.

EVANS, Alan Thomas George Ivy House, Gill Road, Scotby, Carlisle CA4 8BT Tel: 01228 513376 — MRCS Eng. LRCP Lond. 1941; FCOphth. 1989; DOMS Eng. 1948. (Char. Cross) Socs: Ophth. Soc. UK. Prev: Cons. Ophth. Surg. Cumbld. Infirm. & Roy. Infirm. Dumfries; Asst. Ophth. Sunderland Eye Infirm.; Ho. Phys. Char. Cross Hosp.

EVANS, Alan Thomson Department of Histopathology, Ninewells Hospital & Medical School, PO BOX 120, Dundee DD1 9SY Tel: 01382 60111; 61 Albany Road, West Ferry, Dundee DD5 1JQ — MD 1993 Dundee; MB ChB Aberd. 1986, BMedBiol 1984; MRCPath 1993. Cons. Histopath. & Hon. Sen. Lect. Dundee Univ. Socs: Internat. Acad. Path.; Path. Soc. Prev: Sen. Regist. (Histopath.) & Hon. Lect. Dundee Univ.

EVANS, Mr Alastair Jeremy The Orchard, Salisbury Road, Winkton, Christchurch BH23 7AS — MB BS 1974 Lond.; MB BS (Hons.) (Obst. & Gyn.) Lond. 1974; FRCS Eng. 1980; MRCOG 1982; AKC 1974. Cons. (O & G) Roy. Vict. Hosp. Boscombe. Prev: Sen. Regist. (O & G) P.ss Anne Hosp. Soton.

EVANS, Aled 10 Cefn Melimdwr, Capel Bangor, Aberystwyth SY23 3LS — MB BCh 1992 Wales.

EVANS, Aled Barcham Aneuryn Abernant, Glan Conwy, Colwyn Bay LL28 5NT Tel: 0149 268277 — MB BS 1948 Lond.; MRCS Eng. LRCP Lond. 1944. (Middlx.) Prev: Cas. Off. Qu. Eliz. Hosp. Childr. Lond.; Ho. Phys. Mt. Vernon Hosp. N.wood; R.A.M.C. 1945-47.

EVANS, Aled Rhys 13 Canada Road, Cardiff CF14 3BW — MB BCh 1996 Wales.

EVANS, Alexander Robert Matheson X-Ray Department, Sandwell General Hospital, West Bromwich B71 4HJ Tel: 0121 607 3484 Fax: 0121 607 3403 Email: alex.evans@swellhot.wmids.nhs.uk; 97 Metchley Lane, Harborne, Birmingham B17 0JH Tel: 0121 427 4865 Fax: 0121 427 4865 Email: armevans97@cs.com — MB ChB Aberd. 1966; DMRD Eng. 1971. (Aberd.) Cons. Radiol. Sandwell HA. Socs: BMA; NHS Cons.s' Assoc. Prev: Cons. Radiol. N. Birm., NW Durh. & Durh. HA's; Sen. Regist. (Radiol.) Roy. Hosp. Wolverhampton & United Birm. Hosps.

EVANS, Alice The Cottage, Harpsden, Henley-on-Thames RG9 4HL — MB BS 1997 Newc.

EVANS, Alison 18 Bramshill Drive, Pontprennau, Cardiff CF23 8NX — MB BCh 1991 Wales; MRCP (UK) 1994; FRCR 1996. Specialist Regist. (Radiol.) UHW Cardiff.

EVANS, Alison Wakefield Health Authority, White Rose House, West Parade, Wakefield WF1 1LT Tel: 01924 214400 Fax: 01924 214401; 3 Netherton Hall Gardens, Netherton, Wakefield WF4 4JA — MB ChB 1973 Birm.; FFPHM RCP (UK) 1993; MFCM RCP (UK) 1984; MPH Leeds 1982. Dir. (Pub. Health) Wakefield HA.

EVANS, Alison Elizabeth 10 Beechwood Avenue, Pontefract WF8 4ED — MB ChB 1983 Leeds. SHO (Med.) Roy. Albert & Edwd. Infirm. Wigan. Prev: Ho. Off. (Med.) Halifax Gen. Hosp. W. Yorks.; Ho. Off. (Surg. & Urol.) Huddersfield Roy. Infirm. W. Yorks.

EVANS, Alison Jane 2 St Catherines Road, Blackwell, Bromsgrove B60 1BN — MB BCh 1990 Wales; MRCP (UK) 1994.

EVANS, Alison Jean The Surgery, Edward St., Earby, Barnoldswick BB18 6QT Tel: 01282 843407 Fax: 01282 844886; Springfield House, Salterforth Road, Earby, Barnoldswick BB18 6NE Tel: 01282 843070 Email: a.c.l.evans@btinternet.com — MB BChir 1976 Camb.; MSc (Gen. Pract.) Lond. 1990; FRCGP 1993, M 1980; DRCOG 1980; DCH Eng. 1979. (Cambridge) Sen. Lect. (Gen. Pract.) Leeds Univ.; Research & Developm. Fell. (Gen. Pract. Educat.) Yorks. Prev: Fell. Roy. Soc. Med.

EVANS, Allen Gwyn Russell Preston Grove Medical Centre, Preston Grove, Yeovil BA20 2BQ Tel: 01935 474353 Fax: 01935 425171 — MB BS 1975 Lond.; MRCP (UK) 1980; DRCOG 1982; Cert. Family Plann. JCC 1982. (St. Geo.) Prev: Med. Off. Govt. Anguilla.

EVANS, Professor Alun Estyn Division of Epidemiology, Mulhouse Building, Grosvenor Road, Belfast BT12 6BJ Tel: 01232 240503 Fax: 01232 236298 — MD 1984 Belf.; MB BCh BAO 1968; FRCPI 1989; MRCP (UK) 1971; FFPHM RCP (UK) 1992; FFCM 1987, M 1974; MFCMI 1987; Dip. Soc. Med. Ed. 1973. Prof. Epidemiol. & Head Dept. (Epidemiol.) & Pub. Health Qu. Univ. Belf.; Dir. Belf. Monica Project; Chairm. Monica Steering Comm.

EVANS, Mr Alun George Highlands, 73 Belper Road, Derby DE1 3ER Tel: 01332 341502 — MB BCh Wales 1956; FRCSI 1967; DLO Eng. 1965. (Cardiff) Emerit. Cons. ENT Surg. Roy. Infirm. Derby. Prev: Regist. (ENT) Roy. Infirm. Sheff.

EVANS, Mr Alun Gwynallt Llwyn Celyn, Craig Penllyne, Cowbridge CF71 7RT — MB BCh 1963 Wales; FRCS Ed. 1968; FRCS Eng. 1968. Cons. Surg. P.ss of Wales Hosp. Bridgend.

EVANS, Alun James (retired) Hampton Hill House, Hampton Hill, Swanmore, Southampton SO32 2QN Tel: 02380 890166 — MB BCh Wales 1944; BSc Wales 1941. Prev: Med. Pract. Rhymney, Gwent.

EVANS, Alun Vaughan St. John's Institute of Dermatology, St. Thomas' Hospital, Lambeth Palace Road, London SE1 7EH Tel: 0207 928 9292 Fax: 0207 922 8138 Email: alun@hotmail.com — MB BS 1994 Lond.; BSc (Biochem.) Lond. 1991; MRCP (UK) 1997. Specialist Regist., St. John's Inst. of Dermat., St. Thomas' Hosp. Lond.

EVANS, Alwyn Evan James (retired) 24 Longacres Road, Hale Barns, Altrincham WA15 0RS — MB ChB Liverp. 1957; MFOM RCP Lond. 1981; DCH Eng. 1960; DIH Soc. Apoth. Lond. 1972. Prev: Med. Off. UML Ltd. Warrington.

EVANS, Amanda Jane 102 Moorside N., Newcastle upon Tyne NE4 9DU — MB BS 1994 Lond.

EVANS, Amani Kamala Birchwood, Bonville Road, Altrincham WA14 4QR — MB ChB 1998 Manch.; MB ChB Manch 1998.

EVANS, Amlyn Llwyd 26 Lancaster Place, Wimbledon, London SW19 5DP — BChir 1995 Camb.; MB BChir Camb. 1995. (University of Cambridge)

EVANS, Andree 16 The Village, Clyst St George, Exeter EX5 1BQ — MB BCh BAO 1988 Belf.; MRCP (UK) 1994. Staff Grade (Emerg. Gen. Med.) Exeter.

EVANS, Andrew David 2 Woodland Avenue, West Cross, Swansea SA3 5LY — MB ChB 1998 Sheff.; MB ChB Sheff 1998.

EVANS, Andrew Gaylord 66 De Frene Road, Sydenham, London SE26 4AG — MB BS 1994 Lond.; MB BS (Hons.) Lond. 1994; BSc (Hons.) Lond. 1991; MRCP (UK) 1998. (St. Mary's Hosp. Lond.) Clin. Lect. (Stroke Med.). Prev: SHO (Med.) Hove Gen. Hosp.; SHO (Neurol.) Hurstwood Pk. Neurol. Centre Haywards Heath; SHO (Med.) Roy. Sussex Co. Hosp. Brighton.

EVANS, Andrew Jonathan Radiology Department, City Hospital, Hocknall Road, Nottingham NG5 1PB Tel: 0115 969 1689 Fax: 0115 962 7707; 23 Archer Crescent, Wollaton, Nottingham NG8 1HB — MB ChB 1984 Birm.; MRCP (UK) 1987; FRCR 1990. Cons. Radiol. (BrE. Imaging) City Hosp. Nottm. Prev: Sen. Regist. & Regist. (Radiol.) Qu. Med. Centre Nottm.; SHO (Gen. Med.) Mid Staffs. HA.

EVANS, Andrew Lloyd Department of Child Health, The Royal Free Hampstead NHS Trust, Pond St., Hampstead, London NW3 2QG Tel: 020 7830 2440 Fax: 020 7830 2003 Email: andrew.lloyd_evans@rfh.nthames.nhs.uk — BM BCh 1978 Oxf.;

MA Camb. 1979, BA 1975, MD 1993; FRCP Lond. 1994; MRCP (UK) 1980; FRCPCH 1997. (Camb. & Oxf.) Cons. Paediat. & Sen. Lect. (NeuroDevelopm.al Paediat.) Roy. Free Hosp. Lond. Socs: Brit. Paediat. Neurol. Assn.; Physiol. Soc.; Treas. Europ. Acad. Childh. Disabil. Prev: Sen. Regist. (Paediat.) Hammersmith Hosp. Lond.; Reasearch Fell. (Paediat.) Univ. Coll. & Middlx. Sch. Med.

EVANS, Andrew Neil Dimond Street Surgery, Dimond Street East, Pembroke Dock SA72 6HA Tel: 01646 682146 Fax: 01646 622414 — MB ChB 1975 Liverp.; DRCOG 1977.

EVANS, Andrew Nicholas William Department of Paediatrics, Greenwich District Hospital, Vanbrugh, London SE10 9HE Tel: 020 8312 6008 Fax: 020 8312 6174; 79 Kenwood Drive, Beckenham BR3 6QZ Tel: 020 8650 9701 — MB ChB Ed. 1970; MB ChB Ed. 1970; BSc (Med. Sci.) Ed. 1967; BSc (Med. Sci.) Ed. 1967; MRCP (UK) 1977; MRCP (UK) 1977. (Edinburgh) Cons. Paediat. Greenwich Dist. Hosp. Lond., Blackheath Hosp., Sloane Hosp. Beckenham, Chelsfield Pk. Hosp., Shirley Oaks Hosp. Socs: Brit. Paediat. Assn.; Roy. Soc. Med.; Med. Art Soc. Prev: Research Fell. (Paediat.) St. Geo. Hosp. Med. Sch. Lond.; Sen. Regist. (Paediat.) Qu. Mary's Hosp. Childr. Carshalton; Regist. Rotat. (Paediat.) Roy. Devon & Exeter & W.m. Childr. Hosps.

EVANS, Andrew Stewart Flat9 (3FL)/23 Lauriston Gardens, Edinburgh EH3 9HH — MB ChB 1997 Ed.

EVANS, Angela Grace Brockfield House, Villa Lane, Stanwick, Wellingborough NN9 6QQ Tel: 01933 625555 — MB BS 1964 Newc.; MRCPsych 1973; DPM Eng. 1969. Cons. Psychogeriat. St. Crispin's Hosp. N.ampton.

EVANS, Angela Mary The Health Office, Baron's Close, Fakenham NR21 8BE Tel: 01328 862751 Fax: 01328 864225; 56 Norwich Road, Horsham St. Faith, Norwich NR10 3AE Tel: 01603 891495 — MB ChB Ed. 1969; BSc (Med. Sci.) Ed. 1966; MRCGP 1979; DObst RCOG 1975; DCH Eng. 1972. (Ed.) Staff Grade Paediat., Norwich Comm. Health Partnership. Socs: Norwich M-C Soc.; BACDA; BMA. Prev: Med. Off. (Child Health) Norwich Community Health Partnership; GP Norwich; Regist. (Paediat.) Freedom Fields Hosp. Plymouth.

EVANS, Ann Ceinwen (retired) Bod Idris, 9 Chester St., Rhyl LL18 3ER — MB BCh 1927 Wales; BSc Wales 1927. Prev: Cons. Pathol. Welsh Hosp. Bd.

EVANS, Ann Christine 2 Heath Villas, Halifax HX3 0BB — MB ChB 1969 Manch.; BSc (Hons.) (Anat.) Manch. 1966, MB ChB 1969; MRCPsych 1973; DPM Eng. 1973; FRCPsych 1997. Cons. Psychiat. N.owram Hosp. & Halifax Gen. Hosp.

EVANS, Ann Dilys Llangollen Health Centre, Regent Street, Llangollen LL20 8HL Tel: 01978 860625 Fax: 01978 860174 — MB BCh 1980 Wales; MRCGP 1988; DRCOG 1988; DCH RCP Lond. 1986; DCCH RCP Ed. 1986. (Cardiff)

EVANS, Anne Elizabeth Contraception and Women's Health Service, The Leats Health Office, Truro TR1 3AH Tel: 01872 354393 Fax: 01872 354349 Email: evansan@cht.swest.nhs.uk; 24 Passage Hill, Mylor Bridge, Falmouth TR11 5SN — MB BChir 1983 Camb.; MA Camb. 1984; MFFP 1995. SCMO Cornw. Family Plann. Serv. Prev: Clin. Asst. (Diabetes) Cornw. Healthcare Trust; SHO (Gen. Med.) P'boro. HA; SHO (Cardiol.) Camb. HA.

EVANS, Anne Vaughan PowysHealthcare NHS Trust, Bronllys Hospital, Brecon LD3 0LU Tel: 01874 711661; Llwyn Celyn Fawr, Libanus, Brecon LD3 8NE Tel: 01874 624255 — MB BCh 1975 Wales; Dip. Palliat. Med. Wales 1993. Asst. Med. Dir. Powys NHS Healthcare Trust Nr Brecon. Prev: Clin. Asst. Bronllys Hosp. Brecon Powys HA.

EVANS, Anthony Donald Birkett Medical Division, Aviation House, Gatwick RH6 0YR Tel: 01293 573668 Fax: 01293 573995 — MB ChB 1984 Glas.; BSc CNAA 1978; MSc Lond. 1979; MFOM RCP Lond. 1996, AFOM 1992; DAvMed FOM RCP Lond. 1989; DGM RCP Lond. 1986. Dep. Chief Med. Off. Civil Aviat. Auth. Gatwick. Socs: Soc. Occupat. Med.; Roy. Aeronaut. Soc.; Aerospace Med. Assn.

EVANS, Anthony Francis 20 Westbourne Road, Birkdale, Southport PR8 2JA Tel: 01704 66409 — MB ChB 1968 Liverp.; FRCR 1974; DMRD Liverp. 1972. Cons. Radiol. Whiston Hosp. Liverp.; Clin. Lect. Radiodiag. Univ. Liverp.; Clin. Dir. Radiodiag. St. Helens & Knowsley HA. Prev: Sen. Lect. Radiodiag. Liverp. Univ.; Sen. Regist. United Liverp. Hosps.; Fell. in Radiodiag. Case W.. Univ. Cleveland USA.

EVANS, Mr Anthony Richard Queen Alexandra Hospital, Portsmouth PO6 3LY — MB BS 1982 Lond.; FRCS Ed. (Ophth.) 1988; FRCOpath 1989. (St Bartholomews Hosp) Cons. Ophth. Surg. Dept of Ophthamology Qu. Alexander Hosp. Portsmouth. Prev: Fell. Ophthamology Hosp. for sick Childr. Toronto Canada; Regist. Moorfield's Eye Hosp. Lond.; Regist. (Ophth.) Sir Chas. Gairdner Hosp. Perth, W. Austral.

EVANS, Anthony Victor Gwel-yr-Afon, Haulfryn, Llanfair Caereinion, Welshpool SY21 0BH Tel: 01938 810432 Email: antvevans@aol.com — MB BCh 1978 Wales; FRCGP 1995; MRCGP 1983; DRCOG 1981. (Welsh National School Medicine) Socs: Treas. Montg. Med. Soc.

EVANS, Antony Hugh Flat 5, 6 Chichester Place, Brighton BN2 1FE — MB BS 1988 Lond.

EVANS, Aoife Mary Fairfield Medical Centre, Lower Road, Bookham, Leatherhead KT23 4DB Tel: 01372 452755 Fax: 01372 451140; Tel: 01372 452141 Fax: 01372 450625 — MB BS 1978 Lond. (Charing Cross Hospital Medical School)

EVANS, Mr Arthur Briant (retired) Chilton House, Chilton, Aylesbury HP18 9LR — MB BChir Camb. 1937; BA Camb. 1930, MA 1937; FRCS Eng. 1937; MRCS Eng. LRCP Lond. 1933; FRCOG 1952. Cons. Surg. Chelsea Hosp. Wom.; Cons. Obst. Surg. Qu. Charlotte's Matern. Hosp. Prev: Cons. O & G Surg. W.m. Hosp.

EVANS, Arthur James (retired) 27 Deer Park Crescent, Tavistock PL19 9HQ Tel: 01822 613166 — MRCS Eng. LRCP Lond. 1940; MD Lond. 1965, MB BS 1952; DA Eng. 1942. Prev: Cons. VD Plymouth, Devon & Exeter Areas.

EVANS, Audrey Trevor 1001 Finchley Road, London NW11 7HB Tel: 020 8455 4320 — MRCS Eng. LRCP Lond. 1946; FFCM 1980, M 1972; DPH Eng. 1950. (Roy. Free) Socs: BMA; Fell. Soc. Community Med. Prev: PMO Lond. Boro. Camden; Area Specialist Community Med. (Social Serv.) Camden & Islington AHA; Intern Vassar Brothers Hosp. New York.

EVANS, Augusta Jane 22 Fitzharry's Road, Abingdon OX14 1EJ Tel: 01235 201990 — MB BCh 1948 Wales; BSc Wales 1945, MB BCh 1948. (Cardiff) Prev: Ho. Off. Cardiff United Hosps.; Med. Regist. Llandough Hosp.; Psychiat. Regist. WhitCh. Ment. Hosp. Cardiff.

EVANS, Mr Barrie Thomas Department of Oral and Maxillofacial Surgery, Southampton General Hospital, Southampton SO16 6YD Tel: 02380 796096 Fax: 02380 798640 — MB BCh 1981 Wales; FRCS 1985 Ed.; FRCS 2001 (UK); FFD RCSI 1983; BDS (Hons) 1971 Sydney; FDS RCS 1976 Eng.; BDS (Hons) Sydney 1971; FRCS Ed. 1985; FFD RCSI 1983; FDS RCS Eng. 1976. Cons. Oral & Maxillofacial Surg. Soton. Gen. Hosp. Socs: Fell. BMA & Brit. Assn. Oral Maxillofacial Surgs.; Brit. Assn. of Head & Neck Oncol. Prev: Sen. Regist. (Oral & Maxillofacial Surg.) Wessex Centre Plastic & Maxillofacial Surg. Soton. Gen. Hosp.; Regist. (Oral & Maxillofacial Surg.) Dent. Hosp. Welsh Nat. Sch. Med. Cardiff.

EVANS, Barry Graham Communicable Disease Surveillance Centre, 61 Colindale Avenue, London NW9 5EQ Tel: 020 8200 6868 Fax: 020 8200 7868 Email: bevans@phls.org.uk — BM BCh. Oxf. 1972; DM Oxf. 1996; MRCGP 1982; FFPHM RCP (UK) 1990; MFCM RCP (UK) 1985; DCH RCP Lond. 1977. Cons. Epidemiol. Communicable Dis. Surveillance Centre. Prev: Dir. (Pub. Health) Bexley & Greenwich HA.

EVANS, Barry John 36 Baskerville Gardens, Dog Lane, London NW10 1PF — MB ChB 1992 Glas.

EVANS, Beryl Mary (retired) 11 Gwydrin Road, Liverpool L18 3HA Tel: 0151 722 4909 — MB ChB 1950 Liverp. Prev: SCMO (Community Health) Liverp. HA.

EVANS, Betsy-Jane 8 Firs Close, Whirchurch, Aylesbury HP22 4LH — MB BS 1996 Lond.

EVANS, Bidi Mary Regional Department Clinical Neurophysiology, King's College Hospital, Denmark Hill, London SE5 9RS; The Orchard, Pollards Hill, Limpsfield, Oxted RH8 0QX — MA Camb. 1958, MB 1955, BChir 1954; FRCP Lond. 1980, M 1956. (Camb. & St. Thos.) Cons. (Clin. Neurophysiol.) Regional Neurosci. Centre Brook Gen. Hosp. Lond. & Neurophysiol Dept. Kent & Canterbury Hosp. Prev: Acad. Regist. Nat. Hosp. Qu. Sq.; Ho. Phys. Hosp. Sick Childr. Gt. Ormond St. & St. Thos. Hosp. Lond.; Pres. Assn. Brit. Clin. Neurophysiol.

EVANS, Brandon Thorpe The Health Centre, Hermitage Road, St John's, Woking GU21 1TD Tel: 01483 723451 Fax: 01483 751879;

3 Church Close, Horsell, Woking GU21 4QZ Tel: 01483 767801 — MB BS 1967 Lond.; MRCP (UK) 1973; MRCS Eng. LRCP Lond. 1967. (Roy. Free) Prev: Sen. Regist. (Gen. Med. & Infec. Dis.) Roy. Free & Roy. N.. Hosps. Lond.; Regist. (Gen. Med.) Roy Free Hosp. Lond.

EVANS, Brenda Kathleen 56 Green Pastures, Heaton Mersey, Stockport SK4 3RA Tel: 0161 432 3832; Seymour Grove Health Centre, 70 Seymour Grove, Old Trafford, Manchester M16 0LW Tel: 0161 872 5672 — MB ChB Leeds 1963. (Leeds) Princip. Clin. Med. Off. Trafford HA; Mem. Brit. Agencies for Adoption & Fostering (Mem. Med. Gp.). Socs: BMA (POWAR Trafford Community); Med. Gp. Brit. Agencies for Adoption and Fostering. Prev: Clin. Med. Off. Trafford HA.; Sch. Med. Off. Chesh. CC; SHO Roy. Manch. Childr. Hosp. Pendlebury.

EVANS, Brenda Mary 35 Willow Park, Willow Bank, Fallowfield, Manchester M14 6XT Tel: 0161 225 3725; Rockcliffe, Underbarrow, Kendal LA8 8HJ Tel: 0153 95 68409 — MB ChB 1955 Birm.; Cert. Family Plann. JCC 1962. Prev: SCMO Centr. Manch. HA.

EVANS, Brian Anthony (retired) Oak Cottage, 23 Green End, Granborough, Buckingham MK18 3NT Tel: 01296 670685 — MB BS Lond. 1959; FRCP Lond. 1986; MRCP (UK) 1971. Prev: Dir. (Genitourin. Med.) Char. Cross Hosp. Lond.

EVANS, Brian Rolt Wilson (retired) Whitson Lodge, Burnett, Keynsham, Bristol BS31 2TF Tel: 0117 9 862834 — MB ChB 1951 Bristol.

EVANS, Bronwen Elizabeth Knight 301 East Street, Walworth, London SE17 2SX Tel: 020 7703 1888; 23 Grandison Road, London SW11 6LS — MB ChB 1971 Leeds; MRCGP 1977; DObst RCOG 1973; DCH Eng. 1974. (Leeds & St. Mary's) Prev: SHO (Obst.) St. Helier Hosp. Carshalton; SHO (Paediat.) St. Stephens Hosp. Fulham; Ho. Phys. Harold Wood Hosp. Romford.

EVANS, Bruce (Surgery), 50 Church St., Shildon DL4 1DY Tel: 01388 777113 — MB ChB 1971 Leeds; MLCOM 1985; DObst RCOG 1976. Private Muscoskeletal Phys. Shildon.

EVANS, Carl Phillip Windrush Surgery, 21 West Bar Street, Banbury OX16 9SA Tel: 01295 251491; Badgers Sett, School Lane, North Newington, Banbury OX15 6AQ Tel: 01295 730835 — MB ChB 1990 Liverp.

EVANS, Carlton Anthony William 1 Brentwood Road, Brentwood CM13 3QH — MB BS 1990 Lond.; BSc (Hons.) Lond. 1988; MRCP (UK) 1993. MRC Clin. Train. Fell.sh. Univ. Camb.; Hon. Med. Regist. Addenbrooke's Hosp. Camb. Prev: Regist. (Infec. Dis. & Gen. Med.) Hammersmith Hosp. Lond.; SHO (Neurol.) Radcliffe Infirm. Oxf.; SHO Rotat. (Gen. Med.) Addenbrooke's Hosp. Camb.

EVANS, Carol Ann Sawston Medical Practice, Link Road, Sawston, Cambridge CB2 4LB; The Old Manse, 29 St Peters St, Duxford, Cambridge CB2 4RP — BM BCh 1972 Oxf.; MA Oxford 1969; DRCOG 1998. GP.

EVANS, Caroline Jane The Surgery, 31 Fitzroy Square, London W1T 5HG Tel: 020 7387 5798 Fax: 020 7387 2497 — MB BS 1984 Lond.; MRCGP 1988; Dip. Travel Med. and Health 1998 Lond. (Lond. Hosp. Med. Coll.) Gen. Practitioner; Med. Adviser, Nomad Travellers Clinic Lond. Socs: Brit. Travel Med. Assn.; Internat. Soc. of Travel Med. Prev: Trainee GP Camb. VTS; SHO (O & G) St. John's Hosp. Chelmsford; SHO (Geriat.) Broomfield Hosp. Chelmsford.

EVANS, Carolyn Ann Mill Stream Medical Centre, North Street, Storrington, Pulborough RH20 4DH Tel: 01903 743083 — MRCS Eng. LRCP Lond. 1968.

EVANS, Carolyn Sian Anaesthetic Department, Bradford Royal Infirmary, Duckworth Lane, Bradford BD9 6RJ Tel: 01274 364066 — MB BCh 1980 Wales; FRCA 1986 Eng.; DRCOG 1982. Cons. Anaesth. Bradford Roy. Infirm.

EVANS, Catherine Anne Penistone Group Practice, 19 High St., Penistone, Sheffield S36 6BR Email: cathy.evans@virgin.net; 74 Bradley Street, Sheffield S10 1PB — MB ChB 1993 Sheff.; DRCOG 1997; MRCGP 1997. (Sheffield) GP Sheff.

EVANS, Catherine Elizabeth Jane Cilgwyn, Greenfield Road, Ruthin LL15 1EW — MB BCh 1983 Wales.

EVANS, Ceri Elizabeth 4 Windsor Road, Radyr, Cardiff CF15 8BP — MB BCh 1988 Wales.

***EVANS, Ceri Gwynfryn** 15 Conway Road, Cardiff CF11 9NT — MB BS 1997 Lond.; BSc (Hons.) Lond. 1995.

EVANS, Ceri Lee Shaftesbury Clinic, Springfield Hospital, 61 Glenburnie Road, London SW17 7DJ — MB ChB 1987 Otago; BA (Hons.) Oxf. 1992; MRC Psych 1998; MSC Lond. 1998. Lect. & Hon. Specialist Regist. in Forens. Psychiat. @ St Geo.'s Hosp. Med. Sch., Lond. Prev: Regist. (Gen. Psychiat.) Maudsley Hosp. Lond.

EVANS, Charles Anthony Sydney, MBE Bognor Regis Health Centre, West St., Bognor Regis PO21 1UT Tel: 01243 826541; 5 Birch Close, Aldwick, Bognor Regis PO21 3BQ Tel: 01243 265714 — MB BS 1955 Lond. (King's Coll. Hosp.) Prev: Ho. Surg. & Ho. Phys. E. Surrey Hosp. Redhill; Sen. Ho. Off. (Obst.) Farnham Hosp.; Med. Off. RAF Med. Br.

EVANS, Charles William, Surg. Capt. RN Wayton House, Landulph, Saltash PL12 6QQ Tel: 01752 845297 — MB BS 1967 Lond.; MRCS Eng. LRCP Lond. 1967; MPH Dundee 1981; MFOM RCP Lond. 1982, AFOM 1979; DIH Dund 1977; DTM & H Eng. 1972. (St. Bart.) Prev: Ho. Surg. & Ho. Phys. RN Hosp. Plymouth.

EVANS, Christine Dawn 69 Station Road, Sidcup DA15 7DS Tel: 020 8309 0201; 5 Birkbeck Road, Sidcup DA14 4DB Tel: 020 8302 7390 — MB BS 1984 Lond.; BSc (Psychol.) Lond. 1981, MB BS 1984; MRCGP 1989; DRCOG 1988. Prev: SHO/Trainee GP Qu. Mary's Hosp. Sidcup VTS; Clin. Med. Off. (Child Health) Dartford & Gravesham HA; SHO (A & E) Medway Hosp. Gillingham.

EVANS, Christine Joan Argyll and Clyde Heath Road, Ross House, Hawkshead Road, Paisley PA2 7BN Tel: 0141 842 7200 Fax: 0141 848 1818; 2Fl, 6 Warrender Park Terrace, Edinburgh EH9 1JA Tel: 0131 229 3207 Email: evanscj@aol.com — MB ChB 1989 Ed. Specialist Regist. in Pub. Health Med. W. of Scotl. Train. Scheme. Socs: Soc. Social Med. Prev: Clin. Research Fell. Dept. Pub. Health Sci. Univ. Edin.; SHO (Med.) St. Johns Hosp. Livingston; SHO (A & E) W.. Gen. Hosp. Edin.

EVANS, Christine Lesley Mulberry Lodge, 3 Pencisely Road, Llandaff, Cardiff CF5 1DG Tel: 029 2022 6029 — MB BS Lond. 1966; MRCS Eng. LRCP Lond. 1966; MRCPsych 1982; DPM Eng. 1976. (St. Geo.) Indep. Pract. Individual & Family Psychother. Socs: Roy. Coll. Psychiatr. Prev: Cons. Child & Adolesc. Psychiat. Harvey Jones Adolesc. Unit WhitCh., Cardiff; Clin. Asst. (Psychiat.) Univ. Hosp. Wales Cardiff; Sen. Regist. (Child & Adolesc. Psychiat.) & Regist. Univ. Hosp. Wales Cardiff.

EVANS, Miss Christine Mary Glan Clwyd Hospital, Bodelwyddan, Rhyl LL18 5UJ Tel: 01745 583910 Fax: 01745 583143; Smithy Cottage, Llanarmon-yn-ial, Mold CH7 4QX Tel: 01824 780560 — MB ChB Ed. 1966; MD Ed. 1978; FRCS (ad eundem) 1995; FRCS Ed. 1972. Cons. Urol. Glan Clwyd Hosp. Bodelwyddan. Prev: Cons. Urol. Roy. Liverp. Hosp.; Lect. (Urol.) Flinders Univ., S. Austral.; Sen. Regist. (Urol.) Nottm. City Hosp.

EVANS, Christopher Charles Lagom, Glendyke Road, Liverpool L18 6JR Tel: 0151 724 5386 — MB ChB 1964 Liverp.; MD Liverp. 1973; FRCP Lond. 1979, M 1968; FRCPI 1997. (Liverp.) Cons. Phys. (Gen. & Respirat. Med.) Roy. Liverp. Univ. Hosp. & Cardiothoracic Centre Liverp.; Hon. Sen. Lect. Med. Univ.Liverp.; Censor & Examr. RCP Lond.; Cons. Med. Off. Roy. Life plc,.Beneden Health Care & Swiss Life. Socs: Brit. Thorac. Soc.; Assn. Phys.; Liverp. Med. Inst. Prev: Sen. Lect. (Med.) Univ. Liverp.; Wellcome-Swedish Trav. Fell. Univ. Uppsala, Sweden; Sen. Regist. (Med.) Cardiothoracic Unit BRd.green Hosp. Liverp.

EVANS, Christopher David Dermatology Department, Monklands District General Hospital, Airdrie ML6 0JS Tel: 01236 748748 — MB BS 1975 Lond.; FRCP Glas. 1992; MRCP (UK) 1980. Cons. Dermat. Monklands Dist. Gen. Hosp. Airdrie.

EVANS, Christopher David Morecambe Health Centre, Hanover Street, Morecambe LA4 5LY Tel: 01524 418418 Fax: 01524 832584; 28 Prospect Drive, Hest Bank, Lancaster LA2 6HZ — MB BS 1977 Lond.; BSc, MB BS Lond. 1977; MRCGP 1981. (Univ. Coll. Hosp.)

EVANS, Christopher David City Hospital, Truro TR1 2HZ; The Old Mill, Perranwell Station, Truro TR3 7JX Tel: 01872 863509 Fax: 01872 863509 Email: christopher.evans@btinternet.com — MB BS Lond. 1957; FRCP Lond. 1989; MRCP (UK) 1971; DPhysMed. Eng. 1962. (St. Thos.) Hon. Sen. Lect. Univ. of Plymouth; Hon. Cons. Roy. Cornw. Hosps. Trust. Socs: Brit. Soc. Rehabil. Med. Prev: Cons. Rheum. & Rehabil. Oxf. AHA (T); Wing Cdr. RAF Med. Br., Cons. Rheum. & Rehabil. Jt. Servs. Med. Rehabil. Unit RAF Chessington.

EVANS, Christopher David John 1 Netherby Road, Edinburgh EH5 3LW Tel: 0131 551 1013; Burnbrae House, 277 Milngavie

Road, Bearsden, Glasgow G61 3DG Tel: 0161 586 5473 Email: aveline.chris@ntlworld.com — MB ChB 1991 Manch.; BSc (Med. Sci.) St. And. 1988; MRCP (UK) 1995. Regist. (Gen. Med. & Gastroenterol.) Glas. W.ern Infirm. Prev: SHO (Gen. Med.) Edin. Roy. Infirm.; SHO (Gen. Med.) Falkirk & Dist. Roy. Infirm.; SHO (Cardiothoracic Med.) Wythenshawe Hosp. Manch.

EVANS, Christopher Graham St Paul's Medical Centre, Dickson Road, Blackpool FY1 2HH Tel: 01253 623896 Fax: 01253 752818 — MB BS 1980 Lond.; MRCGP 1984; DRCOG; DCH.

EVANS, Christopher John 4 Pen y Banc, Tanerdy, Carmarthen SA31 2HA — MB BCh 1978 Wales; MRCGP 1986; DRCOG 1981.

EVANS, Christopher Mark Children's Unit, Royal Surrey County Hospital, Egerton Road, Guildford GU2 7XX Tel: 01483 571122 Fax: 01483 450742 — MB BCh 1981 Wales; FRCP (UK) 1996; DCH RCP Lond. 1984; FRCPCH 1997. (Welsh National School of Medicine) Cons. Paediat. Roy. Surrey Co. Hosp. Guildford. Socs: Brit. Paediat. Soc.; Paediat. Research Soc. Prev: Regist. & Hon. Clin. Tutor (Child Health) S.mead Hosp. Bristol; CICRA Fell. (Paediat. Gastroenterol.) St. Bart. Hosp. Lond.; Sen. Regist. (Paediat.) Hosp. for Sick Childr. Lond.

EVANS, Christopher Paul Anthony Scrumpy House, Hatherleigh Road, Winkleigh EX19 8AP — MB BCh 1978 Wales; T(GP) 1991; DAvMed FOM RCP Lond. 1987. Dep. Dir. Med. Policy & Plans for Dir. Gen. Med. Servs. RAF. Prev: Desk Off. for Clin. Policy Surg. Gen.s Depart. Dec 96- June 99.

EVANS, Christopher Ronald Farnham Health Centre, Brightwells, Farnham GU9 7SA Tel: 01252 723122 — MB BS 1980 Lond.

EVANS, Mr Christopher Rupert The Laurels, 22Lyth Hill Road, Bayston Hill, Shrewsbury SY3 0EW — MB ChB 1991 Birm.; ChB Birm. 1991; FRCS Ed 1997; FRCS Glas.1997.

EVANS, Claire Elizabeth Diane 1 Rose Gardens, Tandragee, Craigavon BT62 2NJ — MB BCh BAO 1993 Belf.

EVANS, Claire Suzanne Tyghouse, Old Pottery Close, Reigate RH2 8AL — BM BS 1997 Nottm.

EVANS, Clare Helen The Surgery, Main Road, Sellindge, Ashford TN25 6JX Tel: 01303 812180 Fax: 01303 814069 — BM 1983 Soton.; BM Soton 1983; MRCGP 1988; DCH RCP Lond. 1986. (Soton.)

EVANS, Claudia Marie The Health Centre, Saffron Road, Biggleswade SG18 8DJ Tel: 01767 313647 Fax: 01767 312568 — BChir 1992 Camb.

EVANS, Clive Morris Whitehead (retired) Hilgarth, Church Lane, Worplesdon, Guildford GU3 3RU Tel: 01483 232458 — MRCS Eng. LRCP Lond. 1949. Lt.-Col. RAMC, TA. Prev: Capt. RAMC, Graded Clin. Off. in O & G.

EVANS, Colin The Rock, St. Fagans, Cardiff CF5 6DU — MB BCh 1971 Wales; FRCR 1977. Cons. Radiol. Univ. Hosp. Wales & Cardiff Roy. Infirm.

EVANS, Mr Colin Everson The Wallage, Welsh-St-Donats, Cowbridge CF71 7SS — MB ChB 1973 Aberd.; BDS Lond. 1959; FRCS Eng. 1977; FDS RCS Eng. 1968, L 1958. (Guy's) Cons. Surg. Head, Neck, Nose & Ear Clinic Mt. Eliz. Med. Centre; Singapore; Vis. Cons. Surg. Mt. Eliz. Hosp. & Amer. Hosp. Singapore. Socs: Assn. Head & Neck Oncol. Gt. Brit.; Brit. Assn. Oral & Maxillo-facial Surgs. Prev: Prof. ENT-Head & Neck Surg. Nat. Univ. Malaysia; Sen. Lect. Profess. Unit Inst. Laryng. & Otol. Lond.; Hon. Cons. Surg. Roy. Nat. ENT Hosp. Lond.

EVANS, Mrs Cynthia Mary (retired) 4A Stoneleigh Road, Coventry CV4 7AD Tel: 02476 419124 — MB ChB 1969 Manch.

EVANS, Dafydd Alun 12 Gorsto Road, Gwaun Cae Gurwen, Ammanford SA18 1UW — MB BCh 1997 Wales.

EVANS, Daniel Evan Norton Dept of Anaesthetists, Univ Hosp of Wales Cardiff & Vale NHS Trust, Heath Park, Cardiff CF5 1DG Tel: 029 2074 3107; Mulberry Lodge, 3 Pencisely Road, Llandaff, Cardiff CF5 1DG Tel: 029 2022 6029 — MB BS Lond. 1966; FFA RCS Eng. 1973. (Westm.) Cons. Anaesth. & Clin. Dir. Theatres, Day Surg. & Endoscopy Cardiff & Vale NHS Trust. Socs: (Counc.) Brit. Assn. Day Surg.; Assn. Anaesth.; Soc. Anaesth. Wales. Prev: Sen. Regist. (Anaesth.) Univ. Hosp. Wales Cardiff; Flight Lt. RAF Med. Br.; Ho. Surg. W.m. Hosp.

EVANS, Daniel Llywelyn Coed-y-Ffald, Pound Lane, Wenvoe, Cardiff CF5 6PL — MB BS 1994 Lond.

EVANS, Daniel Paul The New Surgery, 128 Canterbury Road, Folkestone CT19 5NR Tel: 01303 243516 Fax: 01303 244633; 14 Milestone Close, Folkestone CT19 5TE Tel: 01303 240716 — MRCS Eng. LRCP Lond. 1977. (St. Bart.) Prev: Med. Adviser (Occupat. Health) S.E. Kent HA.

EVANS, Darrell Marsh 5 St Peters Avenue, Caversham, Reading RG4 7DD Tel: 0118 947 3596 — MRCS Eng. LRCP Lond. 1943; MB BChir Camb. 1947; MA Camb. 1947; MFOM 1982; DIH Eng. 1956; Cert. Radiol. Protec. Battersea Coll. Technol. 1960. (Camb. & Westm.) Specialist Accredit. (Occupat. Med.) RCP Lond. 1978; Apptd. Fact. Doctor. Socs: BMA & Soc. Occupat. Med. Prev: Med. Off. Lond. Transport Exec.; Regist. (Surg.) Qu. Mary's Hosp. Carshalton & W.m. Hosp.

EVANS, Dason Edward William 1 Brentwood Road, Ingrave, Brentwood CM13 3QH — MB BS 1994 Lond.

EVANS, David Alan North Tyneside General Hospital, Rake Lane, North Shields NE29 8NH Tel: 0191 259 6660; 38 Kelso Drive, The Priory's, North Shields NE29 9NS — MB BS 1978 Newc.; FRCOG 1997, MR 1984. Cons. O & G N. Tyneside Dist. Gen. Hosp. Prev: Sen. Regist. (O & G) Roy. Infirm. Edin. & Simpson Memor. Matern. Pavilion.

EVANS, Professor David Alan Price Riyadh Armed Forces Hospital (RAFH), PO BOX 7897, Riyadh 11159, Saudi Arabia Tel: 479 1000 Ext: 0001 Email: <dapevans@kfshhub.kfshrc.edu.sa>; 28 Montclair Drive, Liverpool L18 0HA — MB ChB 1951 Liverpool; 1959 MD Univ. Liverp.; 1965 PhD Univ. Liverp.; 1981 DSc Univ. Liverp.; 1956 MRCP Roy. Coll. of Physicians Lond.; 1968 FRCP Roy. Coll. of Physicians of Lond.; 1951 MSc Univ. Liverp.; 1948 (1st Cl. Hons.) BSc Univ. Liverp. (University of Liverpool) Sen. Cons. Phys. Dept. of Med., Riyadh Armed Forces, Hosp. (Gen. Inter. Med.); Hon. Vis. Prof., Dept. of Med., Univ. of Liverp.; Life-Mem. Johns Hopkins Soc. of Schol.s. Socs: BMA; Assn. of Phys.s of Gt. Britain & Irel.; Johns Hopkins Med. & Surgic. Assn. Prev: Chairm. Dept. of Med., Univ. of Liverp.; Hon. Cons. Phys., Roy. Liverp. Hosp.

EVANS, Mr David Andrew Blackburn Royal Infirmary, Blackburn BB2 3LR Tel: 01254 263555; Holmes Farm Cottage, Higher Commons Lane, Balderstone, Blackburn BB2 7LR Tel: 01254 813594 — MB BS 1980 Lond.; MD Lond. 1990; FRCS Ed. 1985. (Middlesex Hospital Medical School) Cons. Surg. Blackburn Roy. Infirm.; Clin. Director for Surg. Prev: Sen. Regist. N. W. RHA.

EVANS, David Anthony Cherry Trees, Buckland Monachorum, Yelverton PL20 7NL — MB BCh 1985 Wales; BSc York 1980; MRCGP 1989; DRCOG 1989.

EVANS, David Anthony Stony Stratford Surgery, Market Square, Stony Stratford, Milton Keynes MK11 1YA Tel: 01908 565555; Oakfield House, Lower Weald, Calverton, Milton Keynes MK19 6EQ — MB ChB 1966 Bristol; BSc Bristol 1963, MB ChB 1966; MRCGP 1988; DObst RCOG 1969. (Bristol) Socs: BMA. Prev: Med. Off. S. Pacific Health Serv. Fiji.

EVANS, David Anthony, Lt.-Col. RAMC (retired) Gosport Health Centre, Bury Road, Gosport PO12 3PN Tel: 023 9258 3302 Fax: 023 9250 1421 — MB BS 1970 Lond.; AFOM RCP Lond. 1980; MRCGP 1979; DAvMed Eng. 1974; DRCOG 1982. GP Gosport Health Centre & Livingstone Ct. Surg. Prev: Surg. Cdr. RN. (1986).

EVANS, David Anthony Meadowcroft, Bankend Road, Dumfries DG1 4TP Tel: 01387 255503 Email: david.evans@talk21.com — MB ChB 1965 Ed.; BSc (Hons. Path.), MB ChB Ed. 1965. (Ed.) Prev: SHO Napier Hosp. Hawke's Bay, NZ; Ho. Phys. & Ho. Surg. Dumfries & Galloway Roy. Infirm.

EVANS, David Arthur (retired) Pilgrims Cottage, 9 Bowyer Crescent, Denham Green, Uxbridge UB9 5JE — MRCS Eng. LRCP Lond. 1948; MFOM RCP Lond. 1978; DIH Eng. 1969. Prev: Flight Lt. RAF.

EVANS, David Arthur Yeading Medical Centre, 18 Hughenden Gardens, Northolt UB5 6LD Tel: 020 8845 3434; 3 Chiltern Road, Pinner HA5 2TD Tel: 0208 866 5866 — MB BS 1961 Lond.; MRCS Eng. LRCP Lond. 1959. (Lond. Hosp.) Prev: Ho. Off. (Obst.), SHO (Med. & Paediat.) & Ho. Phys. St. And. Hosp. Billericay.

EVANS, David Charles Michael Florence Road Surgery, 26 Florence Road, Ealing, London W5 3TX Tel: 020 8567 2111; 41 Hillcroft Crescent, London W5 — MB ChB 1973 Glas.

EVANS, David Christopher Dr. Gray's Hospital, Elgin IV30 1SN Tel: 01343 543131 Fax: 01343 552612 Email: david.evans@mhs.grampian.scot.nhs.uk — MB ChB 1974 Ed.; FRCOG 1993, M 1980; T(OG) 1991. Cons. O & G Dr Gray's Hosp. Elgin.

EVANS, David Edward Dedworth Road Surgery, 300 Dedworth Road, Windsor SL4 4JR Tel: 01753 864545 Fax: 01753 620272 — MB ChB 1972 Sheff.

EVANS, David Frank 818 Alum Rock Road, Ward End, Birmingham B8 2TX Tel: 0121 327 6401 Fax: 0121 328 5697 — MB BCh 1965 Wales. (Cardiff) Socs: Sec. W. Midl. Soc. Hypnother. & Psychother.; Brit. Soc. Experim. & Clin. Hypn.

EVANS, David Gareth Richard Department of Medical Genetics, St. Mary's Hospital, Manchester M13 0JH Tel: 0161 276 6206 Fax: 0161 273 3806; Tycoch, Cilcain, Mold CH7 5NT Tel: 01352 741136 Fax: 01352 741136 — MD 1992 Lond.; MB BS 1983; MRCP (UK) 1988. Cons. Genetics St. Mary's Hosp. Manch. Socs: Bd. Mem. Clin. Genetics Soc.; Eur. Soc. Human Genet. Prev: Sen. Regist. (Genetics) St. Mary's Hosp. Manch.; Sen. Regist. (Paediat.) Brit. Milit. Hosp. Rinteln; SHO (Neonatol.) St. Geo. Hosp. Lond.

EVANS, Mr David Glyn, MBE 21 Devonshire Place, London W1G 6HZ Tel: 020 7487 4911 Fax: 020 7935 8071; 115 Cranley Gardens, Muswell Hill, London N10 3AE Tel: 020 8444 8078 — MB BCh 1965 Wales; FRCS Ed. 1971; FRCOG 1985; MRCOG 1973, DObst 1967. (Cardiff) Cons. O & G St. Bart. Hosp. Lond.; Asst. Dir. Clin. Acad. Unit. Lond.; Sen. Lect. Med. Coll. St. Bart. Hosp. Lond. Prev: Sen. Regist. (O & G) St. Bart. Hosp. Lond.; Obst. Resid. Qu. Charlotte's Matern. Hosp. Lond.; Regist. (Surg.) St. Bart. Hosp. Lond.

EVANS, David Grenville Llanishen Court Surgery, Llanishen Court, Llanishen, Cardiff CF14 5YU Tel: 029 2075 7025 Fax: 029 2074 7931 — MB BS 1985 Lond.

EVANS, David Gwyn St Saviour's Hospital, St Saviour, Jersey JE2 7UW — BM BCh 1960 Oxf.; MA, BM BCh Oxf. 1960; MRCPsych 1971; DPM Eng. 1965. (Oxf. & Middlx.) Cons. Psychiat. St. Saviour's Hosp. Jersey & Jersey Gen. Hosp. Prev: Sen. Regist. (Psychiat.) St. Geo. Hosp. & W. Pk. Hosp. Epsom; Psychiat. Regist. St. Geo. Hosp. Lond.; SHO Psychiat. & Neurol. Qu. Eliz. Hosp. Birm.

EVANS, David Howard Nicholl Street Medical Centre, Nicholl Street, Swansea SA1 6AY Tel: 01792 653548 Fax: 01792 653411 — BM BCh 1973 Oxf.; MA, BM BCh Oxf. 1973.

EVANS, David Howell Clee Flat 6, Crossways House, Cowbridge CF71 7LJ Tel: 01446 772210; Tydraw Farm, Ty Merchant, Pencoed, Bridgend CF35 6PN — MB BS 1970 Lond.; FFA RCS Eng. 1979; DObst RCOG 1975; DTM & H Eng. 1972. (Middlx.) Cons. Anaesth. P.ss of Wales Hosp.; Tutor (Anaesth.) Univ. Bristol 1977-79; Lect. (Anesth.) Univ. Hosp. Wales 1982. Socs: Fell. Roy. Soc. Trop. Med.; Assn. Anaesth. Prev: Dist. Med. Off. Mandera, Kenya; Sen. Regist. (Anaesth.) S. Glam. HA (T) & Swansea HA; Regist. Bristol Roy. Infirm.

EVANS, David Hugh (retired) 3 Llandennis Green, Cyncoed, Cardiff CF23 6JX Tel: 01222 758938 — MB BCh Wales 1956; MRCGP 1965. Prev: Med. Ref. Benefits Agency Med. Serv. DSS Cardiff.

EVANS, David Ivor Keith (retired) 4 The Green, East Hanney, Wantage OX12 0HH Tel: 01235 867456, 01902 644835 Fax: 01235 867456, 01902 644830 Email: rufus&fernando.f9.co.uk — MB BChir 1958 Camb.; DCH Eng. 1959; FRCP Ed. 1979, M 1964. Prev: Cons. Haemat. Booth Hall Childr. Hosp. Manch & Roy. Manch. Childr. Hosp.

EVANS, David James The John Kelso Practice, Park Medical Centre, Ball Haye Road, Leek ST13 6QR Tel: 01538 399007 Fax: 01538 370014 — MB BS 1984 Lond.; BSc Lond. 1981, MB BS 1984; MRCGP 1990.

EVANS, David John Kidlington Health Centre, Exeter Close, Oxford Road, Kidlington OX5 1AP Tel: 01865 841941; Three Horseshoes Cottage, Thrupp, Kidlington OX5 1JU — MB BCh 1975 Wales; BSc (Hons.) Wales 1972; MRCP (UK) 1977. GP Kidlington Health Centre. Prev: Hon Sen Reg John Radcliffe Hosp. Oxf.; Clin. Fell., Med. Coll. of Wisconsin; Lecture St. Mary's Hosp. (Paddington).

EVANS, David John New Court Surgery, 39 Boulevard, Weston Super Mare BS23 1PF Tel: 01934 624242 Fax: 01934 642608 — MB BS 1976 Lond.; DRCOG 1979; MRCGP 1980; Cert JCC Lond. 1979. (Roy. Free) Prev: Trainee Gen. Pract. Roehampton Vocational Train. Scheme.

EVANS, David John 5 Phoenix Terrace, Phoenix Green, Hartley Wintney, Hook RG27 8RU — MB BS 1987 Lond.; MRCP (UK) 1990; MD Lond. 1997. Cons. Phys. Prev: Sen. Regist. Roy. Brompton & St Geo.'s Hosps.

EVANS, David John 59 Back Lane, Hilton, Derby DE65 5GJ — BM BCh 1989 Oxf.

EVANS, Professor David John Department of Histopathology, St. Mary's Hospital Medical School, Norfolk Place, London W2 1PG Tel: 020 7594 3835 Fax: 020 7594 3835; 19 The Cross, Long Wittenham, Abingdon OX14 4QQ Tel: 0186 730 7178 — MB BChir 1961 Camb.; FRCPath 1981. (Lond. Hosp.) Prof. Histopath. Imperial Coll. Sci., Technol. & Med. Socs: Internat. Acad. Path. (Brit. Div.); Path. Soc. Prev: Prof. Tissue Path. Roy. Postgrad. Med. Sch. Lond.; Reader (Histopath.) Roy. Postgrad. Med. Sch. Lond.

EVANS, David John Evan The Surgery, 1 Onslow Road, Hove BN3 6TA Tel: 01273 502379 Fax: 01273 502379 — MB BChir 1965 Camb.; MA, MB Camb. 1965, BChir 1964; DObst RCOG 1970. (Camb. & St. Thos.) Indep. Pract. Hove. Socs: BMA; Roy. Soc. Med. Prev: Med. Off. Tarner Home Hospice Brighton; Regist. (Cardiac & Chest) & SHO (Intens. Ther. Unit) St. Thos. Hosp.Lond.

EVANS, David Kelk Otford Medical Practice, Leonard Avenue, Otford, Sevenoaks TN14 5RB Tel: 01959 524633 Fax: 01959 525086; 14 Tudor Crescent, Otford, Sevenoaks TN14 5QS Tel: 01959 523701 Email: david@evansotford.demon.co.uk — MB BS 1976 Lond.; MRCS Eng. LRCP Lond. 1975; DRCOG 1977. (Guy's) Med. Off. Sevenoaks Hosp.; Bd. Mem. Sevenoaks & Tonbridge PCG. Prev: Ho. Off. (Paediat.) FarnBoro. Hosp.; Ho. Off. (Obst.) Pembury Hosp.; Ho. Phys. Orpington Hosp.

EVANS, Mr David Kenneth (retired) Townhead House, Parwich, Ashbourne DE6 1QF Tel: 01335 390579 — MB BS Lond. 1948; FRCS Eng. 1956; MRCS Eng. LRCP Lond. 1948. Hon. Cons. Orthop. Roy. Hallamsh. Hosp., Childr. Hosp. & Lodge Moor Spinal Injuries Centre Sheff. Prev: Clin. Teach. (Orthop. Surg.) Univ. Sheff.

EVANS, Mr David Lawrence (retired) Lane End, 12 The Drive, Wimbledon, London SW20 8TG Tel: 020 8946 4016 Fax: 020 8947 7636 — MRCS Eng. LRCP Lond. 1942; MA Camb. 1949; FRCS Eng. 1949; Hon. FDS RCS Eng. 1993; FRCOG 1991; Hon. DGDP 1993. Cons. Orthop. Surg. Chelsea and W.minster Hosp. Lond. Prev: Vice-Pres. RCS Eng.

EVANS, David Lewis (retired) 49 Bishops Road, Whitchurch, Cardiff CF14 1LU Tel: 02920 693297 — BSc, MB BCh Wales 1952; MFOM RCP Lond. 1978; DObst RCOG 1954. Prev: Area Med. Off. Nat. Coal Bd. S. Wales Area, Cardiff.

EVANS, David MacLean Demetrius (retired) 19 Llwyn-y-Grant Road, Penylan, Cardiff CF23 9ET Tel: 029 2048 5709 — MB BS 1946 Lond.; MD Lond. 1953; FRCP Lond. 1979, M 1952; FRCPath 1968. Prev: Cons. Path. S. Glam. HA.

EVANS, David Martyn (retired) 3 Boucher Road, Budleigh Salterton EX9 6JF Tel: 01395 446410 Email: dm-mh.evans@virgin.net — MB 1965 Camb.; BChir 1964; DA Eng. 1966. Prev: GP Anaesth. Budleigh Salterton Hosp.

EVANS, Mr David Mervyn The Hand Clinic, Oakley Green, Windsor SL4 4LH Tel: 01753 831333 Fax: 01753 832109; Crossways, Hawthorn Lane, Farnham Common, Slough SL2 3SW Tel: 01753 645421 Fax: 01753 645190 — MB BS 1965 Lond.; FRCS Eng. 1970. (Middlx.) p/t Hon. Cons. Hand Surg. Roy. Nat. Orthop. Hosp., Lond. Socs: Fell. Roy. Soc. Med.; (Ex-Pres.) Brit. Soc. Surg. Hand. Prev: Cons. Plastic Surg. Wexham Pk. Hosp. Slough; Edr. Jl. Hand Surg. (Brit. & Europ.); Cons. Plastic Surg., Guy's and St. Thomas' Hosp. Lond.

EVANS, David Michael Bodnant Surgery, Menai Avenue, Bangor LL57 2HH Tel: 01248 364567 Fax: 01248 370654; 1 Coed Y Maes, Bangor LL57 2EJ — MB BCh 1973 Wales.

EVANS, David Michael St Lawrence Medical Centre, 4 Bocking End, Braintree CM7 9AA Tel: 01376 552474 Fax: 01376 552417 — MRCS Eng. LRCP Lond. 1969; DObst RCOG 1972. (Liverp.)

EVANS, David Michael Frederick Place Surgery, 11 Frederick Place, Weymouth DT4 8HQ Tel: 01305 774411 Fax: 01305 760417 — MB BS 1968 Lond.; MRCGP 1977. (St. Geo.) Prev: Ho. Off. Gen. Surg. St. Geo. Hosp. Lond.; SHO (Gyn.) St. Geo. Hosp. Lond.; SHO (Obst.) Kingston Hosp.

EVANS, David Norman St Thomas Court Surgery, St. Thomas Court, Church Street, Axminster EX13 5AG Tel: 01297 32126 Fax: 01297 35759 — MB BS 1972 Lond.; DA Eng. 1978; DObst RCOG 1975.

EVANS, David Owen Tanyfron Surgery, 7-9 Market Street, Aberaeron SA46 0AS Tel: 01545 570271 Fax: 01545 570136; Pentrefelin, Oakford, Llanarth SA47 0RP Tel: 01545 580418 Email: d.evans@doctorupdate.net — MB BS 1984 Lond.; BSc Lond. 1981; MRCGP 1994; DRCOG 1990; DGM RCP Lond. 1988. (St. Mary's Lond.) Prev: Trainee GP Newport Gwent.

EVANS, David Patrick (Surgery) John Evans House, 28 Court Yard, Eltham, London SE9 5PZ Tel: 020 8850 1300; Maplescombe Farm House, Maplescombe Lane, Farningham, Dartford DA4 0JY Tel: 01322 3211 — LRCPI & LM, LRSCI & LM 1961; LRCPI & LM, LRCSI & LM 1961. (RCSI) Prev: Ho. Phys. & Ho. Surg. Richmond Hosp. Dub.; Ho. Surg. Rotunda Hosp. Dub.

EVANS, David Perry Chugai Pharma Europe Ltd., Mulliner House, Flanders Road, Turnham Green, London W4 1NN Tel: 020 8987 5600 Fax: 020 8987 5660; Little Gaynes, School Lane, Hamble, Southampton SO31 4JD Tel: 01703 456023 — MB BS Lond. 1966; MSc (Biomechanics) Surrey 1968; MD Lond. 1976; MRCS Eng. LRCP Lond. 1966; FFPM RCP Lond. 1990. (Guy's) Head R&D Chugai Pharma. Europe Ltd. Lond. Prev: Hon. Research Asst. (Rheum.) Univ. Hosp. Wales Cardiff; Dir. Warner Lambert E.leigh.

EVANS, David Rhoderi 7 Eastby Close, Saffron Walden CB11 3BT — MB BS 1981 Lond.

***EVANS, David Richard** 110 Ellesmore Way, Morton, Carlisle CA2 6NA — MB BS 1996 Newc.

EVANS, David Rohan The Cottage, Lower Machen, Newport NP1 8UU Tel: 01633 440228; 353 Imperial Court, 225 Kennington Lane, London SE11 5QN — MB BS 1994 Lond.; FRCR 2001; BSc Lond. 1991. (St. Thos.) Specialist Regist. (Radiol.) Roy. Hosp. NHS Trust Lond. Prev: SHO (Cardiothoracic Surg.) King's Coll. Hosp. Lond.; SHO (Orthop.) E. Surrey Hosp. Redhill; SHO (A & E) Roy. Free Hosp. Lond.

EVANS, David Russell Sunnyrose Surgery, Sunnyrose, 75-77 Wheelwright Lane, Coventry CV6 4HN Tel: 024 7636 6775 Fax: 024 7636 5793 — MB BS 1980 Lond.; MRCGP 1984; DRCOG 1984. (St. Mary's)

EVANS, David Wainwright (retired) 27 Gough Way, Cambridge CB3 9LN Tel: 01223 356740 Email: dwevans@tinyworld.co.uk — MB BCh 1950 Wales; MA Camb. 1977; BSc Wales 1947, MD 1964; FRCP Lond. 1974, M 1958; DCH Eng. 1955. Prev: Cons. Cardiol. E. Anglian RHA.

EVANS, David William 18 Saxon Court, Tettenhall, Wolverhampton WV6 8SA Tel: 01902 754625 — MB BS 1974 Lond.; DCH Eng. 1978. (St. Mary's) Prev: Trainee GP Swansea VTS; Regist. (Paediat.) W.. Gen. Hosp. Edin.; Ho. Phys. & Ho. Surg. Roy. Gwent Hosp. Newport.

EVANS, David William Dudley, OStJ, Surg. Cdr. RN Retd. (retired) Riverbank, 11 Coombe Road, Saltash PL12 4ER Tel: 01752 847351 Fax: 01752 847351 — MB BCh BAO 1955 Dub.; MA Dub. 1964; FRCOG 1979, M 1964. Cons. O & G RNH Gibraltar. Prev: Cons. O & G St. Bernards Hosp. Gibraltar.

EVANS, David Wynne Brynawel, Heol Ddu, Trimsaran Road, Llanelli SA15 — MB BS 1977 Lond.

EVANS, Dean Llewellyn Willows, The Beacon, Rosemarket, Milford Haven SA73 1JX — MB ChB 1997 Birm.

EVANS, Denys Rhys, MC (retired) Withy Cottages, 20 Geeston, Ketton, Stamford PE9 3RH Tel: 01780 720407 — MRCS Eng. LRCP Lond. 1942. Prev: Supernum. Asst. (Dermat.) Lond. Hosp.

EVANS, Dewi Arwyn Oldcastle Surgery, Bridgend CF31 3ED Tel: 01656 657131 — MB BS 1954 Lond. (St. Mary's) Prev: Regist. (Med.) Bridgend Gen. Hosp.

EVANS, Dewi Richard Dept of Child Health, Singleton Hospital, Swansea SA2 8QA Tel: 01792 285045 Fax: 01792 285244 Email: dewievans@doctors.org.uk; Fax: 01792 869647 — MB BCh 1971 Wales; FRCP Lond. 1992; MRCP (UK) 1975; DObst RCOG 1973. (University of Wales College of Medicine Cardiff) Cons. Paediat. Singleton Hosp. Swansea. Prev: Regist. (Paediat.) Alder Hey Childr. Hosp. Liverp.; Lect. (Child Health) Univ. Hosp. Wales Cardiff; SHO (Obst. & Paediat.) Morriston Hosp.

EVANS, Diana Jane The Avenue Surgery, 1 The Avenue, Cirencester GL7 1EH Tel: 01285 653122 Fax: 01285 650098; 126 Old Vicarage Lane, Kemble, Cirencester GL7 6BB Tel: 01285 770986 — MB BS Lond. 1970; MRCS Eng. LRCP Lond. 1970. (St. Mary's)

EVANS, Diana Marguerite Orchard Surgery, Knypersley Road, Norton in the Moors, Stoke-on-Trent ST6 8HY Tel: 01782 534241; 52 Sneyd Avenue, Newcastle ST5 2PY Tel: 01782 628465 — MB ChB 1962 Birm.; BSc Birm. 1959. (Birm.) Prev: Asst. Med. Off. Univ. Keele.

EVANS, Donna Elizabeth 3 Keir Heights, Balmedie, Aberdeen AB23 8WJ — MB ChB 1990 Aberd.

EVANS, Douglas Glyn Breckside, 1A Tudor Avenue, Prestatyn LL19 9HN — MB ChB 1956 Liverp.

EVANS, Professor Edward Frank (retired) MacKay Institute of Communication & Neuroscience, University of Keele, Keele, Newcastle ST5 5BG Tel: 01782 583 057 Fax: 01782 583055 Email: coa18@keele.ac.uk — MB ChB 1960 Birm.; DSc Birm. 1988, PhD 1965, BSc 1957; FRCP Lond. 1989; MRCP (UK) 1985. Prof. Auditory Physiol. Dept. Communicat. Univ. Keele, Emerit.. Prev: Vis. Scientist Laborat. of Neurophysiol. Nat. Inst. Neurol. Dis. & Blindness, Nat. Insts. Health Maryland, USA.

EVANS, Elen Wyn Hafod y Coed, Abersoch, Pwllheli LL53 7EL — BM BCh 1992 Oxf.

EVANS, Elgan John Saer 18 Narrow Lane, Gresford, Wrexham LL12 8EH Tel: 0197 883 2347 — MRCS Eng. LRCP Lond. 1941; MA Camb. 1942, BA 1938, MB BChir 1942. (Camb. & Lond. Hosp.)

EVANS, Elisabeth Margaret 174 Tarbock Road, Huyton, Liverpool L36 0SE — MB ChB 1994 Liverp.

EVANS, Elizabeth Catherine Frizinghall Medical Centre, 274 Keighley Road, Frizinghall, Bradford BD9 4LH Tel: 01274 495577 — MB ChB 1993 Leeds; MRCGP 2000; DRCOG 1998; DFFP 1998. GP Princip. Prev: GP Regist. Bradford VTS.

EVANS, Elizabeth Cecily Ralphs Ride Practice, Ralphs Ride Surgery, Ralphs Ride, Bracknell RG12 9LH Tel: 01344 454626 Fax: 01344 303929; Crossways, Hawthorn Lane, Farnham Common, Slough SL2 3SW Tel: 01753 645421 Fax: 01753 645190 — MB BS 1968 Lond. Socs: GMC; BMA; Windsor Med. Soc. Prev: Clini. Asst. Rheum. Lect. to Social Workers.

EVANS, Elizabeth Claire Tudor Gate Surgery, Tudor Street, Abergavenny NP7 5DL Tel: 01873 855991 Fax: 01873 850162 — MB Camb. 1970, BChir 1969; MA Camb. 1970; MRCGP 1985; DA Eng. 1972; DCH Eng. 1972. (St. Mary's) Socs: Hon. Sec. BMA Gwent Div. Prev: Clin. Asst. (Child Psychiat.) S. Gwent Health Dist.

EVANS, Elizabeth Mary 7 Roxburgh House, Clifton Down, Bristol BS8 3HU Tel: 0117 973 5524; 7 Roxburgh House, Clifton Down, Bristol BS8 3HU — MB ChB 1992 Bristol; DTM & H Liverp. 1997; DRCOG 1994; DFFP 1994. GGP Locum, Bristol; Doctor, Medecins Sans Frontieres. Socs: BMA.

EVANS, Emrys (retired) Maelor, 43 The Rise, Trearddur Bay, Holyhead LL65 2UY Tel: 01407 860124 — MB BS Lond. 1948; MRCS Eng. LRCP Lond. 1947; MRCGP 1957; DObst RCOG 1951. Prev: Ho. Phys., Ho. Surg. & Receiv. Room Off. Lond. Hosp.

EVANS, Eustace (retired) 20 Gillylees, Scarborough YO12 5DR Tel: 01723 352975 — MB ChB 1948 Sheff.

EVANS, Fiona Margaret 42 The Copse, Calderstones, Liverpool L18 3NH — MB ChB 1991 Liverp.; MRCGP 1995. Prev: Retainee Gen. Pract.

EVANS, Miss Frances Alexandra The North Middlesex Hospital, Sterling Way, London N18 1QX Tel: 020 8887 2000; Tel: 020 7249 0848 — MB BS 1985 Lond.; FRCS Eng. 1990; MRCOG 1993. Cons. Gyn. & Obst. The N. Middlx. Hosp. Lond. Prev: Sen. Regist. (O & G) Kings Coll. Hosp. Lond.

EVANS, Mr Frank Ieuan, MBE, MC (retired) 11 Gwydrin Road, Liverpool L18 3HA Tel: 0151 722 4909 Email: FrankEvans2@compuserve.com — MRCS Eng. LRCP Lond. 1934; MB Camb. 1936; MA Camb. 1936; FRCS Eng. 1936; 1934 BChir Camb. Prev: Cons. Surg. United Liverp. Hosp.

EVANS, Frederick James Hile 33 Hill Road, Theydon Bois, Epping CM16 7LX Tel: 01992 812611 Fax: 01992 814096 — MB BCh 1971 Wales; BDS Lond. 1966; MRCS Eng. LRCP Lond. 1971; FDS RCS Eng. 1974, LDS 1966. Cons. Oral & Maxillofacial Surg. St. Margt. Hosp. Epping. Socs: Brit. Dent. Assn. & Brit. Assn. Oral & Maxillofacial Surg.; BMA. Prev: Sen. Regist. (Oral & Maxillofacial Surg.) King's Coll. Hosp. Lond. & John Radcliffe Hosp. Oxf.; Med. Resid. (Maxillofacial Surg. & Stomatol.) Hosp. de la Salpetriere.

EVANS, Gareth The Surgery, New Street, Stockbridge SO20 6HG Tel: 01264 810524 Fax: 01264 810591 — MB ChB 1974 Manch.; MRCGP 1980. Princip. Gen. Pract. Stockbridge. Socs: BMA. Prev:

SHO N.W. Neonat. Med. Unit St. Mary's Hosp. Manch.; SHO (Paediat.) Vict. Hosp. Blackpool; SHO Radcliffe Infirm. Oxf.

EVANS, Gareth Charles 16/2 Merchiston Park, Edinburgh EH10 4PN — MB ChB 1997 Leic.

EVANS, George (retired) 17 Chantry Lane, Grimsby DN31 2LP Tel: 01472 342063 — MB ChB 1957 Birm.; DA Eng. 1966. Prev: Ho. Phys. Qu. Eliz. Hosp. Birm.

EVANS, Mr George Herbert Charles Eastbourne District General Hospital, King's Drive, Eastbourne BN21 2UD Tel: 01323 417400; Beech Lawn, 4 Selwyn Road, Eastbourne BN21 2LE Tel: 01323 411424 — MB BChir 1977 Camb.; MA Camb. 1977; FRCS Eng. & Ed. 1981; MChir Camb. 1991. (Camb. & St. Bart.) Cons. Gen. & Vasc. Surg. E.bourne Dist. Gen. Hosp. Socs: Fell. Roy. Soc. Med.; Assn. Surg.; Vasc. Surg. Soc. GB & Irel. Prev: Sen. Regist. & Regist. (Gen. Surg.) Roy. Free Hosp. Lond.; Regist. (Gen. Surg. & Research) Barnet Gen. Hosp.

EVANS, Georgina Ann 15 Dorset Road, Westbury-on-Trym, Bristol BS9 4BJ — MB ChB 1990 Liverp.

EVANS, Geraint Brychan Peveril, Winchester Road, Bishops Waltham, Southampton SO32 1BD — MB BCh 1991 Wales.

EVANS, Mr Geraint William Lewis Accident & Emergency, Withybush General Hospital, Haverfordwest SA61 2PZ Tel: 01437 773448 Fax: 01437 773521 Email: gwlevans@rcsed.ac.uk — MB ChB 1979 Birm.; FRCS Ed. 1989; FFAEM 1994; T(GP) 1991. Cons. A & E Withybush Gen. Hosp. HaverfordW. - Hon. Clin. Tutor, Univ. of Wales Med. Sch., Cardiff; Clin. Director, Trauma & Orthop. Pembrokesh. & Derwen NHS Trust; Surg. Lt. Cdr., Roy. Naval Reserve; Advance Traume Life Support Instruc. Socs: Brit. Assn. Accid. & Emerg. Med.; Brit. Assn. Immed. Care Schemes; Milit. Surg. Soc. Prev: Clin. Dir. A & E Bromley Hosp. Kent,; Tutor (A & E) Univ. Leeds; Med. Off. RN.

EVANS, Gerald Vaughan 2 Stanley Road, Skewen, Neath SA10 6LN — MB BCh 1988 Wales.

EVANS, Gillian Addenbrookes Hospital, Hills Road, Cambridge CB2 2QQ Tel: 01223 245151 Email: gde10@yahoo.com — MB ChB 1991 Aberd.; MRCP 1994. Regist. Haemat. Addenbrookes NHS Trust Camb.

EVANS, Gillian Elizabeth Jenner Health Centre, Turners Lane, Whittlesey, Peterborough PE7 1EJ Tel: 01733 203601 Fax: 01733 206210; The Lindens, 4 Gracious St, Whittlesey, Peterborough PE7 1AP Tel: 01733 350782 — BM BCh 1978 Oxf.; MRCGP 1982; Cert. Family Plann. JCC 1982; DRCOG 1982. GP Princip. PeterBoro. Prev: GP Oxf. & Lond.

EVANS, Gillian Frances Derbyshire Dales & South Derbyshire Primary Care Group, Repton Health Centre, Askew Grove, Repton Tel: 01283 703407, 01285 760212 Fax: 01285 760885 Email: boothca@lineone.net; Lower Manor, Frampton Mansell, Stroud GL6 8JG Tel: 01283 703407, 01285 760212 Fax: 01285 760885 Email: boothca@lineone.net — BChir 1980 Camb.; MFPHM 1997; MRCGP 1985; DRCOG 1983. (St. Georges, Tooting) Cons. in Pub. Health Med., S.. Derbysh. Health Auth.

EVANS, Gillian Mary Gilbert House Surgery, 39 Woodfield Lane, Ashtead KT21 2BT Tel: 01372 276385 Fax: 01372 279530; 7 West Farm Close, Ashtead KT21 2LH Tel: 01372 276230 — MB BS 1979 Lond.; DRCOG 1980; MRCGP 1983. (Guy's Hosp.) p/t GP Princip. Ashtead Surrey. Socs: Fam. Plann. Assn.; Roy. Coll. Gen. Pract.

EVANS, Gillian Wynne Woodlands Surgery, Woodlands Terrace, Caerau, Bridgend CF34 0SR Tel: 01656 734203; Tairwaun House, 3 Tair Waun Place, Neath Road, Maesteg, Bridgend Tel: 01656 734955 Fax: 01656 734453 — MRCS Eng. LRCP Lond. 1957; DObst RCOG 1959; DA Eng. 1961.

EVANS, Mr Glyn The Orchard Hospital, Newport PO30 5BA Tel: 01983 531770 Fax: 01983528788; BUPA Chalybeate Hospital, Chalybeate Close, Tremona Road, Southampton SO16 6UY Tel: 01703 510836 Fax: 01703 510836 — MB BCh 1975 Wales; FRCS Ed. 1980; T(S) 1991. Cons. Orthop. St. Mary's Hosp. I. of Wight.; Cons. Orthop .Surg. BUPA Chalybeate. Hosps. Oton.; Dir. Isle of Wight Private. Hosp. Plc. Socs: BMA & Brit. Orthop. Assn.; Brit. Soc. Surg. Hand. Prev: Lect. (Orthop.) Univ. Soton.; Regist. (Orthop.) Harlow Wood Orthop. Hosp.; Regist. (Vasc. Surg.) Roy. Infirm. Edin.

EVANS, Glyn Richard 10 Sheraton Grange, Norton, Stourbridge DY8 2BE Tel: 01384 370036 — MB ChB 1981 Birm.; MRCP (UK) 1985. Regist. (Med.) Sandwell Dist. Gen. Hosp. Prev: SHO (Med.) E. Birm. Hosp.; SHO (Haemat.) Qu. Eliz. Hosp. Birm.

EVANS, Glynis Jacqueline Purton Surgery, High Street, Purton, Swindon SN5 4BD Tel: 01793 770207 Fax: 01793 772662; Lowfield Farm, Oaksey, Malmesbury SN16 9SB Tel: 01666 577259 — MB ChB 1974 Bristol; MRCGP 1978; DObst RCOG 1976. (Bristol Univ.) Prev: Trainee GP Reading VTS; SHO (Psychiat.) Fairmile Hosp. Wallingford; SHO (Paediat.) Roy. Berks. Hosp. Reading.

EVANS, Glynn Andrew, Maj. RAMC 7 Lubbington Road, Hampton Coppice, Solihull B92 9QH Fax: 0121 705 0533; 21 Hill Crest Farm Close, Warton, Tamworth B79 0JQ Fax: 01827 897 897079 Email: glynnevans@cwcom.net — MB BChir 1990 Camb.; MA Camb. 1991, BA 1987; FRCA 1995. (Camb.) Cons. in Trauma Anaesth. The Walsgrave Hosps. Socs: Founder Med. Fac. Pre-Hosp. Care RCS Edin.; Fell. Roy. Soc. Med.; Assn. Anaesth. Prev: Sen. Regist. (Anaesth.) Roy. Hosp. Haslar; Founder Med. Fac. Pre-Hosp. Care RCS Edin.; Hon. Sen. Regist. (Anaesth.) Soton.

EVANS, Gordon Madgewick Hylton (retired) 12 Springfield Park, Trowbridge BA14 7HT Tel: 01225 753447 — MRCS Eng. LRCP Lond. 1946. Prev: Asst. Cas. Off. Char. Cross Hosp.

EVANS, Graham Huw, Surg. Lt.-Cdr. RN Victoria Cottage, 32 Bury Road, Gosport PO12 3UD Tel: 01705 524497 — MB BS 1980 Lond.; MRCS Eng. LRCP Lond. 1980; FCAnaesth. Lond. 1989.

EVANS, Graham Lees (retired) Links Gate House, Beauclerk Road, St Annes-on-Sea, Lytham St Annes FY8 3LH Tel: 01253 711841 — MB BS 1951 Lond.; MRCS Eng. LRCP Lond. 1951; DObst RCOG 1958.

EVANS, Grant Robert Llewelyn Tredegain Farm, Penycoedcae Road, Pencoedcae, Pontypridd CF37 1PU Tel: 01443 202047 — MB BCh 1957 Wales; DObst RCOG 1960. Med. Off. (A & E) E. Glam. Health Trust Pontypridd. Socs: BMA; Rhondda Med. Soc. Prev: Sen. GP Ch. Village Pontypridd.

EVANS, Gruffydd Hailwood Medical Centre, 2 Hailwodd Court, Governors Hill, Douglas Tel: 01624 675444; 4 Tent Road, Laxey IM4 7DB — MB ChB 1984 Liverp.; DRCOG 1989.

EVANS, Gwenda Wynne (retired) Plas Heulog, 98 Lon Ceredigion, Pwllheli LL53 5RA Tel: 01758 612266 — MB BS 1952 Lond.; MRCS Eng. LRCP Lond. 1951; DObst RCOG 1955. Prev: Cas. Off. Roy. Free Hosp.

EVANS, Gwilym Miles Market Street Surgery, 3-5 Market Street, Caernarfon LL55 1RT Tel: 01286 673224 Fax: 01286 676405 — MB BCh 1986 Wales.

EVANS, Gwilym Morgan (retired) Stumbleberry, 7 Coombe Road, Otford, Sevenoaks TN14 5RJ Tel: 0195952 4357 — MD Lond. 1951, MB BS 1947; MRCS Eng. LRCP Lond. 1943; FRCOG 1963, M 1949. Hon. Cons. O & G FarnBoro. Hosp. & Bromley AHA; Hon. Tutor in Obst. Guy's Hosp. Med. Sch.; Examr. RCOG & Centr. Midw. Bd. Prev: Sen. Regist. (O & G) Guy's Hosp.

EVANS, Mr Gwyn Amman Children's Unit, Robert Jones & Agnes Hunt Orthopaedic Hospital, Oswestry SY10 7AG Tel: 01691 404376 Fax: 01691 404629 Email: nicola.pickles@rjahoh-tr.wimds.nhs.uk; Daywell Manor, Gobowen, Oswestry SY10 7EJ Tel: 01691 661250 — MB BS Lond. 1967; FRCS (Orthop.) Ed. 1979; FRCS Eng. 1972; MRCS Eng. LRCP Lond. 1967. (St. Bart.) Cons. Orthopaedic Surg. Childr.s's Unit Orthopaedic Hosp. OsW.ry; Hon. Cons. Orthopaedic Surg. N. Staffs. Hosp. Stoke-on-Trent, Maelor Hosp., Wrexham. Socs: Corr. Mem. Austral. Paediatric Orthopaedic Soc.; Hon. Mem. Jordanian Surgic. Soc.; Brit. Orthop. Assn. (Exec. Comm. Mem.). Prev: Regist. (Surg.) Univ. Hosp. Wales Cardiff; SHO Roy. Nat. Orthop. Hosp.; Ho. Surg. St. Bart. Hosp.

EVANS, Gwyn Hywel (retired) 102 Moorside N., Fenham, Newcastle upon Tyne NE4 9DU Tel: 0191 273 8266 Fax: 0191 273 8266 — MB BChir 1960 Camb.; MRCP (UK) 1964; FRCP Lond. 1978. Cons. Phys. (Gen. Med. & Cardiol.) N. Tyneside; Cons. Phys. Preston Hosp. N. Shields. Prev: Sen. Regist. (Med.) Roy. Vict. Infirm. Newc. u Tyne.

EVANS, Gwynneth (retired) The Hazards, 47 Drysgol Road, Radyr, Cardiff CF15 8BS Tel: 02920 842069 — MB BCh 1944 Wales; BSc 1941, MB BCh Wales 1944. Prev: Assoc. Specialist Nat. Blood Transfus. Serv.

EVANS, Heather 7 Nimrod Close, St Albans AL4 9XY — MB BCh 1990 Wales.

EVANS, Heather Aeronwen Meddygfa Tywi, Nantgaredig, Carmarthen SA32 7LG Tel: 01267 290240 Fax: 01267 290062; Cwmynys, Nantgaredig, Carmarthen SA32 7N6 Tel: 01994 231181

— MB BS 1983 Lond.; DRCOG 1986. GP St. Clears. Prev: Trainee GP/SHO W. Wales Gen. Hosp. Carmarthen VTS.

EVANS, Hefina Jane Meddygfa Pengorof, Gorof Road, Ystradgynlais, Swansea SA9 1DS Tel: 01639 843221 Fax: 01639 843790 — MB BCh 1993 Wales; BSc Med. Biochem. (1st cl. Hons.) Wales 1990. SHO Rotat. (Psychiat.) Cefn Coed Hosp. Swansea.

EVANS, Helen Maria City Hospital Trust, Dudley Road, Birmingham B18 7QH Tel: 0121 554 3801; 171 Metchley Lane, Harborne, Birmingham B17 0JL Tel: 0121 427 2647 Email: phewin@global.net.co.uk — MB ChB 1994 Birm.; BSc Birm. 1991; MRCP 1997; MRCPCH 1997. (Univ. Birm.) Specialist Regist. (Paediat.) City Hosp. Trust Birm. W. Midl. Deanery Rotat. Prev: SHO (Paediat.) Birm. Childr.'s NHS Trust; Ho. Surg. N. Staffs. Hosps. NHS Trust; Ho. Off. (Med.) S. Birm. Acute Unit.

EVANS, Helen Wynne Eynsham Medical Group, Conduit Lane, Eynsham, Witney OX29 4QB Tel: 01865 881206 Fax: 01865 881342; The Old Forge, Boot St, Stonesfield, Witney OX29 8PX Tel: 01993 881330 — MB BS 1981 Lond.; DRCOG 1986. (St. Bart.)

EVANS, Heulwen Pugh Page Hall Medical Centre, 101 Owler Lane, Sheffield S4 8GB Tel: 0114 261 7245 Fax: 0114 261 1643 — MB ChB 1989 Sheff.

EVANS, Hilary Anne 2 St Catherine's Road, Blackwell, Bromsgrove B60 1BN — MB ChB 1993 Sheff.

EVANS, Howard Conway (retired) 3 Lynwood Avenue, Epsom KT17 4LQ Tel: 01372 726066 — MB BS 1959 Lond.; MRCS Eng. LRCP Lond. 1958; DA Eng. 1960. Prev: Resid. (Anaesth.), Ho. Phys. & Ho. Surg. Guy's Hosp.

EVANS, Hugh Alexander North Sea Medical Centre, 3 Lowestoft Road, Gorleston, Great Yarmouth NR31 6SG Tel: 01493 663264 — BM BCh 1948 Oxf.; BM BCh Oxon. 1948; MRCGP 1967; AFOM RCP Lond. 1979; DObst RCOG 1953; MMSA Lond. 1955; DCH Eng. 1963. (St. Bart.) Staff Mem. N. Sea Med Centre Gt. Yarmouth. Socs: Europ. Undersea Bio-Med. Soc. Prev: Ho. Phys. & Childr. Ho. Phys. St. Bart. Hosp. Lond.; Res. Pathol. Hosp. Sick Childr. Gt. Ormond St.

EVANS, Hugh Christopher Doctors Surgery, 2 Maidavale Crescent, Coventry CV3 6FZ Tel: 024 7641 2372 Fax: 024 7641 1318; 4A Stoneleigh Road, Coventry CV4 7AD Tel: 02476 419124 — MB ChB 1969 Liverp.

EVANS, Mr Hugh James Royston Prince Philip Hospital, Llanelli SA14 8QF Tel: 01554 756567; Glan-yr-Afon, Ferryside SA17 5SP Tel: 01267 267387 — MB BS 1972 Lond.; BSc (Hons.) Lond. 1969, MS 1985; FRCS Eng. 1977; MRCS Eng. LRCP Lond. 1972. (St. Geo.) Cons. Gen. Surg. P. Philip Hosp. LLa.lli. Socs: Vas. Soc. GB; Brit. Soc. Gastroenterol.; BASO. Prev: Sen. Regist. (Surg.) St. Geo. Hosp. Lond.; Regist. (Surg.) St. Jas. Hosp. Lond.; Regist. (Surg.) Roy. Hosp. Wolverhampton.

EVANS, Huw Charles Llanfyllin Medical Centre, High Street, Llanfyllin SY22 5DG Tel: 01691 648054 Fax: 01691 648165 — MB BCh 1978 Wales; DRCOG 1981. GP Llanfyllin.

EVANS, Huw David Health Centre, Ropewalk, Fishguard SA65 9BQ — MB BS 1984 Lond.

EVANS, Huw Owain 26 Heol Don, Yr Eglwys Newydd, Caerdydd, Cardiff CF14 2AU — MB BCh 1983 Wales.

EVANS, Hywel Ifan Dolfach, Dinas, Newport SA42 0SD — MB BCh 1993 Wales.

EVANS, Hywel Selwyn New Chapel Street Surgery, Harold Street, Pontnewydd, Cwmbran NP44 1DU Tel: 01633 485155 Fax: 01633 484133; 38 Llyswen Road, Cardiff CF23 6NH — MB BCh 1980 Wales; BSc Nottm. 1973; MRCGP 1990; DRCOG 1984. Med. Off. Lucas. Indust. Cwmbran & Pontypool.

EVANS, Ian Evan Lloyd 8 Cardinal Close, Bury St Edmunds IP32 7LR — MB BCh 1988 Wales; MRCP (UK) 1993. Specialist Regist. Paediat. Ipswich Hosp. NHS Trust. Prev: SHO (Paediat.) Univ. Hosp. Wales Cardiff.

EVANS, Ian Llewellyn 2A Hyndland Court, 6 Sydenham Road, Glasgow G12 9NR — MB ChB 1962 Glas.; FRCP Glas. 1980, M 1965; MRCP Ed. 1966; FRCPath 1985, M 1973. (Glas.) Cons. Haemat. W.. Infirm. Glas. & Gartnavel Gen. Hosp. Prev: Sen. Haemat. Regist. W.. Infirm. Glas.; Clin. Research Asst. Roy. Marsden Hosp. Sutton; Med. Regist. Glas. Roy. Infirm.

EVANS, Ieuan Elfed Briarfields, 115 Fornham Road, Bury St Edmunds IP32 6AT Tel: 01284 753577 — MB BS 1949 Lond.; MB BS (Hons.) Lond. 1949; FRCP Lond. 1974, M 1954. (Guy's) Cons. Phys. W. Suff. Hosp. Gp. Prev: Sen. Regist. (Med.) Middlx. Hosp.; Regist. (Med.) & Ho. Phys. Guy's Hosp.

EVANS, Mr Ieuan Lynn (retired) 9 Poyntell Crescent, Chislehurst BR7 6PJ — MB BS Lond. 1949; FRCS Eng. 1954; MB BS 1949 London. Prev: Cons. Surg. Lewisham & Guy's Hosp.

EVANS, Ieuan Lynn Richard, MBE (retired) Terrace House, Rhymney NP22 5XJ Tel: 01685 840185 — MB BCh 1940 Wales; BSc Wales 1937, MB BCh 1940. JP. Prev: Clin. Asst. Redwood Hosp. Rhymney.

EVANS, Ieuan Morgan (retired) 16 Neath Abbey Road, Neath SA10 7BD Tel: 01639 768176 — MB BS 1956 Lond.; DObst RCOG 1958; DA Eng. 1961. Assoc. Specialist (Anaesth.) Neath Gen. Hosp. Prev: Regist. (Anaesth.) Neath Gen. Hosp.

EVANS, Imogen Margaret Angela Medical Research Council, 20 Park Crescent, London W1B 1AL Tel: 020 7637 6022 Fax: 020 7637 2856 Email: imogen.evans@headoffice.mrc.ac.uk; Little Orchard, Scotsford Road, Broad Oak, Heathfield TN21 8UD Tel: 01435 862588 Email: critchlowevans@compuserve.com — MD Ottawa 1969; PhD Lond. 1978; FRCPC 1974; Lic. Nova Scotia Med. Bd. 1973. (Ottawa) Research Strategy Manager, MRC. Prev: Exec. Edr. The Lancet; Hon. Cons. (Endocrinol.) Roy. Postgrad. Med. Sch. Lond. & Hammersmith Hosp. Lond.; Med. Edr. Med. Educat. (Internat.) Ltd.

EVANS, Irene Mary (retired) 83 Dowhills Road, Blundellsands, Liverpool L23 8SL — MB ChB Liverp. 1970; MRCP (UK) 1973; FRCP 1996. Prev: Cons. Phys. S.port Promenade Hosp.

EVANS, Mr Ivan Tom Gwenogfryn 21 Woodville Road, Newport NP20 4JB Tel: 01983 62734 — MB BCh 1962 Wales; FRCS Eng. 1969. (Cardiff) Cons. ENT Roy. Gwent Hosp. Newport. Prev: Fell. (Otol.) Providence Hosp. S.field, U.S.A.; Sen. Regist. ENT Univ. Hosp. Wales Cardiff; Surg. Regist. United Cardiff Hosps.

EVANS, Ivor Brynfab Towy (retired) Gors Hill, Gors Avenue, Holyhead LL65 1PB Tel: 01407 762414 — MB BS Lond. 1949. Prev: GP Holyhead.

EVANS, Jacqueline Ann 3 Green Lane Close, Chertsey KT16 9QW — MB BS 1976 Newc.; DO Eng. 1979.

EVANS, Jacqueline Ann Community S.london NHS Trust, Department of Family Planning & Reproductive Healthcare, St Giles Hospital, London SE5 7RN Tel: 020 7771 3330 — MB BS 1985 Lond.; BSc Lond. 1982; MRCGP 1989; DFFP 1994; DRCOG 1988; DCH RCP Lond. 1987; Dip. Genitourin Med. 1997. Staff Grade (Family Plann. & Reproduc. Healthcare) Community S.Lond. NHS Trust. Prev: GP, Felixstowe, Suff.

EVANS, James Edward Mortimer Highland Farm, St. Lawrence, St Lawrence, Jersey JE3 1FG Tel: 01534 861186 Fax: 01534 861186 — MB BS Lond. 1962; MRCS Eng. LRCP Lond. 1962; Cert. Av Med. 1988. Socs: Brit. Soc. Med. & Dent. Hypn..

EVANS, James Nicholas Bay View Cottage, 5 Liskey Hill Cottages, Perranporth TR6 0BB — MB ChB 1993 Birm.

EVANS, Mr James Roderick 6 Drumkeen Court, Upper Galwally Road, Belfast BT8 7TU — MB BCh BAO Dub. 1947; FRCSI 1951.

EVANS, Jane Madeleine Department of Health Care of the Elderly, King's College Hospital (Dulwich), East Dulwich Grove, London SE22 8PT Tel: 020 7346 6085 Fax: 020 7346 6476; 134 Dora Road, London SW19 7HJ — MB BS 1980 Lond.; MB BS (Distinc.) 1980; BSc (Hons.) Lond. 1977; MRCP (UK) 1984. (Lond. Hosp. Med. Coll.) Cons. Gen. Med. & Health Care for Elderly King's Health Care Lond. Prev: Lect. (Health c/o Elderly) Lond.

EVANS, Jane Phillipa Mary 17 Rees Street, London N1 7AR — MB BS 1978 Lond.; MB BS (Hons.) Lond. 1978; MRCP (UK) 1980; MRCPath 1985. Lect. Dept. Haemat. Roy. Free Hosp. Lond. Prev: Lect. Dept. Haemat. Inst. Child Health Lond.; Sen. Regist. Roy. Free Hosp. Lond.

EVANS, Janet Frances 20 Conigar Court, Usk NP15 1RX — MB BS 1989 Lond. Trainee GP/SHO (A & E) Nevill Hall Hosp. VTS.

EVANS, Janine 11 Redhouse Lane, Leeds LS7 4RA — MB ChB 1992 Dundee.

EVANS, Mrs Jean Margaret (retired) 49 Bishops Road, Whitchurch, Cardiff CF14 1LU Tel: 02920693297 01222 693297 — MB BCh 1952 Wales; BSc, MB BCh Wales 1952; DObst RCOG 1954; MFFP 1993. Prev: Clin. Med. Off. S. Glam. AHA (T).

EVANS, Jeanette Evelyn 110 Lake Avenue, Rainham RM13 9SQ — MB BS 1993 Lond.

EVANS, Jennifer Anne 6 Whitehall Gardens, London W3 9RD — MB BS 1986 Lond.; MRCP (UK) 1989. Lect. (Paediat.) St. Mary's Hosp. Med. Sch. Lond.

EVANS, Jeremy Andrew 5 Moor Crescent, Gosforth, Newcastle upon Tyne NE3 4AP Tel: 0191 256 3198 Fax: 0191 256 3154 Email: gasmen@dcotor.com; 5 Moor Crescent, Gosforth, Newcastle upon Tyne NE3 4AP Tel: 0191 285 7041 Email: jace.evans@virgin.net — MB BS 1981 Newc.; FRCA. 1990. Cons. Anaesth. Newc. Gen. Hosp. Socs: (Hon. Sec.) N. Eng. Soc. Anaesth. Prev: Sen. Regist. Rotat. (Anaesth.) N.. Region; Sen. Regist. (Anaesth.) Univ. Natal Durban, S. Afr.

EVANS, Jeremy Charles The Belford Medical Practice, Croft Field, Belford NE70 7ER Tel: 01668 213738 — MB BS 1984 Lond.; DCH RCP Lond. 1988; DRCOG 1987. Indep. GP (Acupunc.) Belford. Socs: BMA.

EVANS, Jeremy Edward Comber, Wing Cdr. RAF Med. Br. Retd. BUPA Occupational Health Care, 111 Piccadilly, Manchester M1 2HY Tel: 0161 228 8041 Fax: 0161 228 8040; 24 Park View Road, Lytham, Lytham St Annes FY8 4JE Tel: 01253 738580 — MB BCh 1974 Wales; AFOM RCP Lond. 1983; DAvMed Eng. 1980. (Welsh Nat. Sch. Med.) Sen. Occupat. Phys. Socs: BMA; SOM. Prev: Chief Med. Off. Brit. Aerospace (Milit. Aircraft Div.); Snr. Air Med. Specialist Brit. Aerospace Dhahran, Saudi Arabia; Cmd. Fl. Med. Off. (Aeromed) RAF High Wycombe.

EVANS, Jill Catherine Esher Green Surgery, Esher Green Drive, Esher KT10 8BX Tel: 01372 462726 Fax: 01372 471050 — MB ChB 1978 Ed. (Edin. Univ.)

EVANS, Joan Maray Westport Lodge, Cricket St Thomas, Chard TA20 4BY — MB BCh 1953 Wales; MRCP Lond. 1959; DPhysMed Eng. 1960; DObst RCOG 1955.

EVANS, Joanna Elizabeth Greystones, Long Ash Farm, Bishopston Road, Bishopston, Swansea SA3 3EW — BM 1995 Soton.

EVANS, Joanne 16 Flinn Close, Boley Park, Lichfield WS14 9YU — MB ChB 1987 Liverp.

EVANS, Joanne Kate The Grove Road Clinic, Norfolk & Norwich Hospital, Brunswick Road, Norwich NR1 3SR — MB BS 1986 London; MRCP 1989 UK; FRCP 2000 UK. Cons. Genitourin. Med. Norf. & Norwich Hosp. Socs: Soc. Study VD. Prev: Sen. Regist. (Genitourin. Med.) Roy. Lond. Hosp.; Regist. (Genitourin. Med.) Middlx. Hosp. Lond.

EVANS, John 26 Fordlea Way, West Derby, Liverpool L12 5HA — MB BCh 1991 Wales.

EVANS, John (retired) 35 Moray Place, Edinburgh EH3 6BX Tel: 0131 225 9506 — MB BCh 1950 Wales; BSc Wales 1947, MB BCh 1950; MRCP Lond. 1957; FRCPsych 1979, M 1971; DPM Eng. 1954. Hon. Sen. Lect. (Psychiat.) Univ. Edin.; Edr. Jl. of Adolesc. Prev: SHMO Adolesc. Unit Cassel Hosp.

EVANS, John 26 Merrow Chase, Guildford GU1 2RY — MB BS 1997 Lond.

EVANS, John Alastair Chilton, 93 Warren Road, Worthing BN14 9QU Tel: 01903 260086 Fax: 01903 260086 — MB BS Lond. 1966; BSc Lond 1962; FRCP Lond. 1987; MRCP (UK) 1970; MRCS Eng. LRCP Lond. 1966. (St. Thos.) Cons. Phys. Worthing Hosp. Socs: Brit. Thorac. Soc. Prev: Regist. (Med.) St. Thos. Hosp. Lond.; Sen. Regist. (Med.) Univ. Coll. Hosp. Lond.; Sen. Regist. (Thoracic Med.) Lond. Chest Hosp.

EVANS, John Anthony Fennell (retired) 7 St Margaret's Road, Hampton Park, Hereford HR1 1TS Tel: 01432273000 — MB BS Lond. 1958; DObst RCOG 1961. War Pens. Examr. Heref. Prev: Clin. Asst.St. Michael's Hospice Hereford.

EVANS, John Anthony Lodwick Abbey Surgery, 28 Plymouth Road, Tavistock PL19 8BU Tel: 01822 612247 Fax: 01822 618771; The Coppice, Brentor, Tavistock PL19 0LR — MB ChB 1981 Bristol; MRCP (UK) 1984; MRCGP 1987; DRCOG 1986.

EVANS, John Bryan Orchard Hill, Cross Oak Road, Berkhamsted HP4 3JB Tel: 01442 862458 — BM BCh 1958 Oxf.; MA, BM BCh Oxf. 1958; DObst RCOG 1961. (Oxf. & St. Mary's) Socs: Past Mem. Counc. Med. Protec. Soc. Prev: Ho. Surg. St. Mary's Hosp.; Ho. Phys. Harold Wood Hosp.; Ho. Surg. (Obst.) St. Albans City Hosp.

EVANS, Mr John Cecil Wyn The Penthouse Seawalls, Seawalls Road, Sneyd Park, Bristol BS9 1PG Tel: 0117 968 4637 — MB ChB 1964 Bristol; FRCS Ed. 1971; FRCS Eng. 1971. Sen. Surg. P & O Lines; Roy. Naval Med. Club. Prev: Sen. Lect. (Surg.) Univ. Qu.sld.; Lect. (Surg.) Univ. Bristol.; Research Surg. Univ. Texas.

EVANS, John David (retired) 28 The Court Yard, London SE9 5PZ Tel: Eltham 1300 — LMSSA 1927 Lond. Hon. Med. Off. Eltham & Mottingham Hosp. Prev: Ho. Surg. & Cas. Off. St. Mary's Hosp.

EVANS, John David Richards (retired) 102 Lavington Road, Worthing BN14 7SJ Tel: 01903 222900 — MB BS Lond. 1961. GP Trainer Worthing. Prev: Ho. Phys. Paddington Gen. Hosp.

EVANS, Mr John Dillwyn Green Bank, West Grove, Brooklands, Sale M33 — MB ChB 1950 Manch.; FRCS Ed. 1961; FRCS Eng. 1962. (Manch.) Cons. Orthop. Surg. Univ. Hosp. of S. Manch. & Wythenshawe & N.; Chesh. Gp. Hosps. Socs: Fell. Manch. Med. Soc. Prev: Sen. Regist. Manch. Roy. Infirm.; Orthop. Regist. Withington Hosp. Manch.; Surg. Regist. Crumpsall Hosp. Manch.

EVANS, John Earl 22 Radbrook Road, Shrewsbury SY3 9BE — MB ChB 1952 Birm.; MRCS Eng. LRCP Lond. 1953; DObst RCOG 1957; Approved Under Ment. Health Act 1959. Prev: GP Shrewsbury; Ho. Off. (O & G) Nottm. City Hosp.; Ho. Phys. Staffs. Gen. Infirm. & Ho. Surg. (Gyn.) Gen. Hosp. Birm.

EVANS, John Edward Church Villa, Cilybebyll, Pontardawe, Swansea SA8 3JP — MB ChB 1982 Leeds.

EVANS, John Graham Court Road Surgery, 29 Court Road, Barry CF63 4YD Tel: 01446 733181 Fax: 01446 420004 — MB BCh 1976 Wales.

EVANS, John Gwynfor Madoc Terrace Surgery, Meddyygfa Gyffin, Woodlands, Conwy LL32 8LT Fax: 01492 572708 Mobile: 0870 444 7744 — MB BS 1979 Lond.; LLB Newc. 1991; FRCS Eng. 1984; MRCGP 1986; DRCOG 1986. (St. Mary's) Socs: Welsh Med. Soc. Prev: Chairm., Conwy Local Health Gp.

EVANS, John Gwynfor Bron Seiont Surgery, Bron Seiont, Segontium Terrace, Caernarfon LL55 2PH Tel: 01286 672236 Fax: 01286 676404; Penlan, Rhosisaf, Caernarfon LL54 7NG Tel: 01286 831184 — MB BCh 1973 Wales; MRCGP 1977.

EVANS, John Howell (retired) 14 St John Street, Manchester M3 4DZ Email: nhoj@snave-freeserve.co.uk — MD 1957 Lond.; MB BS 1949; MRCPsych 1971; FRCP Lond. 1974, M 1953; DPM Eng. 1962. Prev: Cons. NeUrol. Hope Hosp. Salford.

EVANS, John Idwal 9 Bonaly Terrace, Edinburgh EH13 0EL — MD 1971 Ed.; MB ChB 1957; MRCPsych 1973; DPM Eng. 1961.

EVANS, John Llewelyn (retired) 40 Egerton Gardens, London NW4 4BA Tel: 0208 202 6621 — MB BS 1953 Lond.; MRCS Eng. LRCP Lond. 1953; DPH Leeds 1959; DObst RCOG 1956. Prev: Med. Off. DHSS.

EVANS, John Martin 23 Banbury Road, Oxford OX2 6NN Tel: 01865 559157 Fax: 01865 513091; Yew Tree Cottage, Eaton Road, Appleton, Abingdon OX13 5JH Tel: 01865 863822 Fax: 01865 864133 — MB BCh 1969 Wales; FFA RCS Eng. 1973. Cons. Anaesth. Nuffield Dept. Anaesth. John Radcliffe Hosp. Oxf.; Vis. Prof. Anaesth. Mt. Sinai Hosp., New York. Socs: Assn. Anaesth. & Anaesth. Research Soc.; Obst. Anaesth. Assn. Prev: Sen. Regist. (Anaesth.) Univ. Hosp. of Wales, Cardiff; Research Fell. Welsh Nat. Sch. Med. Cardiff.

EVANS, John Noel Gleave (retired) 55 Harley Street, London W1N 1DD Tel: 020 7580 1481 Fax: 020 7580 4163 — MB BS 1959 Lond.; FRCS (Hons.) Ed. 1987; FRCS Eng. 1965; DLO Eng. 1961. Cons. Surg. ENT King. Edwd. VII Hosp. for Off. Lond.; Hon. Cons. Otorhinolaryng. to the Army. Prev: Cons. Surg. Hosp. Sick Childr. Gt. Ormond St. Lond.

EVANS, John Rhodri Portway Surgery, 1 The Portway, Porthcawl CF36 3XB Tel: 01656 304204 Fax: 01656 772605; Kenilworth Apartments, Westgate St, Cardiff CF10 1DJ Tel: 01222 232213 — MB BCh 1988 Wales. SHO (Gen. Med.) Neville Hall Hosp. Abergavenny. Prev: Ho. Off. (Gen. Med.) Bronglais Gen. Hosp.; Ho. Off. (Gen. Surg.) Neville Hall Hosp.

EVANS, John Royden Tal-y-Bont Surgery, Station Road, Pontardulais, Swansea SA4 1TL Tel: 01792 882368; 15 Clos Glyndwr, Hendy, Pontardulais, Swansea SA4 1FW — MRCS Eng. LRCP Lond. 1952. (Guy's) Prev: Res. Clin. Pathol. Roy. Hosp. Sheff.

EVANS, John Vivian 35 Hoel-Y-Neuadd, Tumble, Llanelli SA14 6HR — MB BS 1996 Lond.

EVANS, Jonathan 10 Ty Gwyn Crescent, Cardiff CF23 5JL — MB BS 1991 Lond.

EVANS, Jonathan Charles Hedley The Surgery, 34 York Road, Acomb, York YO24 4LZ Tel: 01904 342999 Fax: 01904 342990; Manor Farm, Rufforth, York YO2 3QF Tel: 01904 738143 — MB BS 1981 Lond.; MRCGP 1985; DRCOG 1985. (Roy. Free) Socs: York

Med. Soc. Prev: Trainee GP York VTS; SHO (Cas.) Chelmsford & Essex Hosp.

EVANS, Jonathan Chasney 54 Grange Cross Lane, Wirral CH48 8BQ — MB ChB 1991 Liverp.

EVANS, Jonathan David Tile House Surgery, 33 Shenfield Road, Brentwood CM15 8AQ Tel: 01277 227711 Fax: 01277 200649 — MB BS 1980 Lond.

EVANS, Jonathan David Aneuryn Abernant, Glan Conwy, Colwyn Bay LL28 5NT — MB BCh 1978 Wales.

EVANS, Jonathan Gerwyn Penarth Health Centre, Stanwell Road, Penarth CF64 3XE Tel: 029 2070 0911 — MB BS 1987 Lond.; BSc Lond. 1984, MB BS Lond. 1987; MRCGP 1991.

EVANS, Jonathan Huw Charles Paediatric Renal Unit, Nottingham City Hospital NHS Trust, Nottingham NG5 1PB Tel: 0115 969 1169; 33 Blenheim Avenue, Lowdham, Nottingham NG14 7WD — MB BS 1983 Lond.; FRCP 1997; FRCPCH 1997. (Guy's) Cons. Paediat. Nephrol. Nottm. City Hosp. Socs: Roy. Coll. Phys.; NCPCH, BAPN,IPNA. Prev: Lect. (Child Health) Roy. Manch. Childr. Hosp.; Lect. (Paediat. & Child Health) St. Jas. Univ. Hosp. Leeds.

EVANS, Jonathan Lee Division of Psychiatry, University of Bristol, 41 St Michael's Hill, Bristol BS2 8DZ — MB ChB 1985 Birm.; MRCPsych. 1991. Cons. Sen.Lect. (Psychiat.) Bristol; Cons. Sen. Lect. (Psychiat.). Socs: MRCPsych. Prev: Regist. (Psychiat.) Horton Hosp. Epsom.; Lect. (Ment. Health) & Hon. Sen. Regist. (Psychiat.) Bristol.

EVANS, Jonathan Morgan The Surgery, White Cliff Mill Street, Blandford Forum DT11 7BH Tel: 01258 452501 Fax: 01258 455675; Bourneville, Shillingstone Lane, Okeford Fitzpaine, Blandford Forum DT11 0RB Tel: 01258 861176 Email: jmevansdoc@aol.com — MB BS 1976 Lond.; MRCS Eng. LRCP Lond. 1976; Cert. Av. Med. 1984; DA Eng. 1978. (Kings College Hospital, London) GP Practitioner; Clin. Asst. (Anaesth. & Elderly Care Med.) Blandford Hosp.; Authorized Med. Examr. Civil Aviat. Auth.; Med. Off. Dorset & Wilts. RFU; Clin. Governance Lead, Purbeck & Blandford PCG.

EVANS, Josephine Margaret 21 Frank Lane, Thornhill, Dewsbury WF12 0JW — MB BCh 1984 Wales.

EVANS, Judith The Nuffield Hospital, Plymouth PL6 8BG Tel: 01752 792110 Fax: 01752 763185 — MB BS 1980 Lond.; MA Oxf. 1977; MRCS Eng. LRCP Lond. 1977; FRCS (Plast Surg.) Ed. 1990; FRCS Ed. 1983; FRCS Lond. 1996. Cons. Plastic Surg. Nuffield Hosp. Plymouth. Socs: Brit. Assn. of Plastic Surgs.; Coun. Mem. Brit. Assn. Aesthetic Plastic Surg. Prev: Sen. Regist. (Plastic Surg.) Derriford Hosp. Plymouth; Regist. (Plastic Surg.) Leic. Roy. Infirm. & W. Norwich Hosp.; Lect. (Surg.) Univ. Hong Kong.

EVANS, Mr Julian Wynford Hugh Kent & Canterbury Hospital, Ethelbert Road, Canterbury CT1 3NG Tel: 01277 766877 Email: jwhevans@globalnet.co.uk; 11 Cossington Road, Canterbury CT1 3HU Tel: 01227 786865 Email: jwhevans@globalnet.co.uk — MB BS 1982 Lond.; MS Lond. 1992; FRCS Eng. 1987; FRCS 1995 UNOL. Cons. Urological Surg., E. Kent NHS Trust. Socs: Brit. Assn. of Urological Surg.s; Brit. Prostate Gp.; Baus. Sect. of Oncol. Prev: Sen. Regist. St. Thos. Hosp. Lond.; Regist. (Urol.) Middlx. Hosp. Lond.; Regist. (Gen. Surg.) Edgeware Hosp.

EVANS, Julie Anne 11 Paynters Way, Newick, Lewes BN8 4PH — MB ChB 1984 Liverp.

EVANS, Julienne Anaesthetic Dept, Barnet General Hosp, Wellhouse Lane, Barnet EN5 3DJ Tel: 01707 876915; 1 Tolmers Gardens, Cuffley, Potters Bar EN6 4JE — MB BS 1985 Lond.; BSc Pharmacol. Lond. 1982; FRCA 1995. (St Bart's) Cons Anaesth., Anaesthetic Dept Barnet Hosp Barnet.

EVANS, Karen Jane 54 Wicklow Road, Doncaster DN2 5JZ — MB ChB 1989 Ed.

EVANS, Kate Rebecca 18 Johns Avenue, London NW4 4EN — BM 1995 Soton.

EVANS, Katherine Ann 29 St Peters Street, Duxford, Cambridge CB2 4RP — MB ChB 1998 Sheff.; MB ChB Sheff 1998.

EVANS, Katherine Jane 65 Errol Street, Liverpool L17 7DH — MB ChB 1998 Sheff.; MB ChB Sheff 1998.

***EVANS, Katherine Margaret** Woodhall Barn, Woodhall Drive, Sutton, Woodbridge IP12 3EG — BM 1998 Soton.; BM Soton 1998.

EVANS, Kathryn Louise Brook Farm, Greenhouse Lane, Painswick, Stroud GL6 6SE — MB BS 1980 Lond.; FRCS Eng. 1985; MRCS Eng. LRCP Lond. 1979. Cons. ENT Surg. Gloucester Roy. Infirm.

EVANS, Keith St Matthew's Medical Centre, Prince Philip House, Malabar Road, Leicester LE1 2NZ Tel: 0116 224 4700; 22 Bankart Avenue, Oadby, Leicester LE2 2DB Tel: 0116 270 2246 — BM BCh 1975 Oxf.; MA Oxf. 1977, BA (Hons.) 1972; DGM RCP Lond. 1991; DCH Eng. 1978. (Oxf.) Socs: Roy. Coll. Gen. Practs. Prev: Sen. Med. Off. Solomon Is.s; SHO (Paediat.) Roy. Cornw. Hosp. Truro; SHO (Obst.) Norf. & Norwich Hosp.

EVANS, Keith Ellis Morriston Hospital, Morriston, Swansea SA6 6NL Tel: 01792 702222 Fax: 01792 703215 Email: keith.evans@morrnhst_tr.wales.nhs.uk; 15 Eden Avenue, Uplands, Swansea SA2 0PS Tel: 01792 418007 Fax: 01792 418007 — MB BS 1966 Lond.; FRCP Lond. 1990; MRCP (UK) 1974; MRCS Eng. LRCP Lond. 1966; DObst RCOG 1968. (Char. Cross) Cons. Phys. (Gen.Med. & Cardiol.) Morriston Hosp. Swansea Med. Dir. Morriston Hosp. NHS Trust. Socs: Brit. Cardiac Soc. & Welsh Thoracic Soc.; BMA. Prev: Lect. Univ. Coll. Med. Wales Cardiff; Regist. Llandough Hosp. Cardiff; Regist. (Med.) Kingston Hosp. Surrey.

EVANS, Keith James Forest House Surgery, 25 Leicester Road, Shepshed, Loughborough LE12 9DF Tel: 01509 508412; 69 Leicester Road, Shepshed, Loughborough LE12 9DF Tel: 01509 503525 — MB ChB 1973 Ed.; BSc (Med. Sci.) Ed. 1970, MB ChB 1973; FRCGP 1989, M 1977; DRCOG 1976. Clin. Teach. Leic. Univ. Med. Sch.; Hon. Sec. Leic. LMC. Prev: Ho. Surg. & Ho. Phys. Singleton Hosp. Swansea; Trainee GP Bridgend VTS.

EVANS, Keith Morton (retired) 11 Bell Lane, Frogmore, Camberley GU17 0NN — MB ChB 1956 Bristol; MRCS LRCP Eng. 1983; DObst RCOG 1961; MRCGP 1980.

EVANS, Keith Prosser Brynmeillion, Llanon SY23 5LA — MB BS 1977 Lond.

EVANS, Kenneth Gordon Cathcart The Hildenborough Medical Group, Tonbridge Road, Hildenborough, Tonbridge TN11 9HL Tel: 01732 838777 Fax: 01732 838297; Rochford, 110 Tonbridge Road, Hildenborough, Tonbridge TN11 9EJ Tel: 01732 834243 Fax: 01732 838626 Email: annkenev@cs.com — MB BS 1962 Lond.; MRCS Eng. LRCP Lond. 1962; MRCGP 1972; FRCGP 1988; DObst RCOG 1964; DCH Eng. 1964. (Guy's) Prev: Assoc. Adviser (Gen. Pract.) SE Thames RHA; Course Organiser Tunbridge Wells GP VTS.

EVANS, Kenneth Morgan Thornbury Close, Clwydyfagwr, Merthyr Tydfil CF48 1HP Tel: 01685 723931 — MB BCh Wales 1967; MRCGP 1984. Prev: Ho. Off. Gen. Surg. & Ho. Off. Gen. Med. E. Glam. Gen. Hosp.; Pontypridd.

EVANS, Kenneth Theodore The Meadows, Graig Road, Lisvane, Cardiff CF14 0UF Tel: 02920752215 — MB ChB 1948 Birm.; FRCP Lond. 1971, M 1952; FRCR 1975; FFR 1958; DMRD Eng. 1955; Hon. FFR RCSI 1976. Emerit. Prof. Diag. Radiol. Univ. Wales Coll. Med.; Hon. Cons. Radiol. S. Glam. HA. Socs: Brit. Inst. Radiol. Prev: Regist. Radiodiag. United Sheff. Hosps.; Sen. Regist. in Diag. Radiol. Hammersmith Hosp. & Postgrad. Med. Sch.; Cons. Radiol. United Bristol Hosps.

EVANS, Kevin Department of Clinical Chemistry, Staffordshire General Hospital, Stafford ST16 3SA Tel: 01785 230747 Fax: 01785 230740 Email: kevin.evans@msgh-tr.wmids.nhs.uk — MB BS 1987 Lond.; BSc Lond. 1983; MRC (Path) 1998. Cons. Chem. Path. Staffs. Gen. Hosp. Prev: Sen. Regist. & Clin. Lect. (Clin. Biochem.) John Radcliffe Hosp. Oxf.; MRC Train. Fell. & Hon. Sen. Regist. (Clin. Biochem. & Metab. Med.) Univ. Newc. & Roy. Vict. Infirm. Newc. u. Tyne; Regist. (Clin. Biochem. & Metab. Med.) Roy. Vict. Infirm. Newc.

EVANS, Kevin Robert Lapworth Solihull General Hospital, Solihull B91 2JL Tel: 0121 711 4455 — MB ChB 1971 Birm.; FFA RCS Eng. 1976. (Godfrey Huggins Sch. Med. Rhodesia) Cons. Anaesth. & Designated Obst. Cons. & Cons. i/c of Audit Solihull Gen. Hosp.; Roy. Coll. Tutor. Socs: Obst. Anaesth. Assn. Prev: Sen. Regist. (Anaesth.) Radcliffe Infirm. Oxf.; Regist. (Anaesth.) Qu. Eliz. Hosp. Birm.; SHO (Anaesth.) Mpilo Centr. Hosp. Bulawayo Zimbabwe.

EVANS, Laura Jane 11 Sandford Walk, Exeter EX1 2ES — MB BS 1993 Lond. Trainee GP Exeter VTS.

EVANS, Lesley Alison Margaret (retired) Brook House, Huntscott, Wootton Courtenay, Minehead TA24 8RR Tel: 01643

841426 — MB BS 1969 Lond.; MSc (Med. Parasitol.) Lond. 1971, BSc 1965; MRCP (UK) 1978; MRCS Eng LRCP Lond. 1969; ECFMG Cert. 1976; T(M) 1991. Prev: Cons. Geriat. Taunton Hosps.

EVANS, Lewis Timothy Iorwerth Shepley, Duffryn Road, Cyncoed, Cardiff CF23 6NP Tel: 029 2075 1170 — MB BCh 1953 Wales; BSc Wales 1950, MB BCh 1953; MRCGP 1984; DCH Eng. 1956; DObst RCOG 1966.

EVANS, Linda Michelle 15 Menzieshill Road, Dundee DD2 1PS — MB ChB 1998 Dund.; MB ChB Dund 1998.

EVANS, Linda Susan The Grange, Whittington Road, Gobowen, Oswestry SY11 3NE — MB ChB 1988 Liverp.; MRCP (UK) 1992. Cons. in Med.Oncol.: Preston & Blackpool. Prev: Regist. (Oncol.) Guy's Hosp. Lond.; CRC Clin. Fell./Lect. Med. Oncol. Christie Hosp. Manch.; Lect./Hon. Sen. Regist. W.on Pk. Hosp. Sheff.

EVANS, Louisa Jane 94 Coychurch Road, Pencoed, Bridgend CF35 5NA — MB BCh 1992 Wales; DRCOG; MRCGP.

EVANS, Louise Charlotte Worcester Road Surgery, 74A Worcester Road, West Hagley, Stourbridge DY9 0NH Tel: 01562 882474 Fax: 01562 887185 — MB ChB 1989 Sheff.; MRCGP 1993; DRCOG 1992.

EVANS, Louise Elisabeth Headmasters House, Dame Hannah Rogers School, Ivybridge PL21 9HE — MB ChB 1997 Manch.

EVANS, Lyndon Marc 2 Highlands Avenue, City Road, Haverfordwest SA61 2RS — MB BCh 1991 Wales.

EVANS, Mandie Greystones, Southmead, Cirencester GL7 1PA — MB BCh 1998 Wales.

EVANS, Margaret Anaesthetic Department, Queen Alexandra Hospital, Cosham, Portsmouth — MB BS 1963 Lond.; MRCS Eng. LRCP Lond. 1962; FFA RCS Eng. 1968; DA Eng. 1964. Cons. Anaesth. Portsmouth Hosps. Gp.

EVANS, Margaret (retired) 78 Boothroyd Lane, Dewsbury WF13 2LL Tel: 01924 465647 — MB ChB Leeds 1960; FFA RCS Eng. 1969; DA Eng. 1964; DObst RCOG 1962. Prev: Cons. Anaesth. Dewsbury Dist. Hosp.

EVANS, Margaret Ann The Medical Protection Society, Granary Wharf House, Leeds LS11 5PY Tel: 0113 243 6436; 27 Lakeside., Intake Lane, Acaster Malbis, York YO23 2TY Tel: 01904 708832 — MB ChB 1974 Sheff. (Sheff.) Asst. Sec. Med. Protec. Soc. Leeds. Prev: GP Sheff.; Regist. (Geriat.) N.. Gen. Hosp. Sheff.; SHO (Anaesth.) Trent RHA.

EVANS, Margaret Dorothea Elizabeth (retired) 6 Oakhurst Close, London E17 3PZ — MB BCh 1948 Witwatersrand; FRCPath 1973, M 1963. Cons. Morbid Anat. & Histol. Waltham Forest HA. Prev: Lect. (Path.) Univ. Witwatersrand.

EVANS, Margaret Ruth 1 Craigstewart Crescent, Doonbank, Ayr KA7 4DB Tel: 01292 445158 — MB ChB 1972 Glas.; Cert. Family Plann. JCC 1982. Clin. Med. Off. (Family Plann.) & SCMO (BrE. Screeing) Ayr.

EVANS, Margaret Wendy The Jorvik Medical Practice, 6 Peckitt Street, York YO1 9WF — MB ChB 1980 Sheff.; MRCGP 1986; DRCOG 1982. GP York.

EVANS, Marianne Lawrence 25 Glan.Yr.Afon Road, Sketty, Swansea SA2 9JA Tel: 01792 207706 — MB BCh Wales 1970; FFA RCS Eng. 1979. Cons. (Anaesth.) W. Glam. HA. Prev: Sen. Regist. (Anaesth.) S. Glam. AHA; Lect. Lond. Hosp. Whitechapel.

EVANS, Marilyn Ann 1 St Margaret's Road, Whitchurch, Cardiff CF14 7AA — MB BCh 1993 Wales. SHO (Child Health) Univ. Hosp. Wales. Socs: Med. Protec. Soc. Prev: Ho. Off. Morriston Hosp.

EVANS, Mark Lewis Flat 5, 52 Anson Road, London N7 0AA — MB BS 1988 Lond.; BSc Biochem. Lond. 1985, MB BS 1988; MRCP (UK) 1991.

EVANS, Mark Russell Wilmot Room 636B, Skipton House, Dept. Of Health, 80 London Rd, London SE1 6LH Tel: 020 7972 5672 Email: mrw.evans@lineone.net — MB ChB 1982 Liverp.; MRCP (UK) 1987; DCH RCP Lond. 1989; DTM & H RCP Lond. 1988; MD 1998. (Liverp.) Sen. Med. Off., Dept. of Health. Socs: Fell. Roy. Soc. of Trop. Med. & Hyg.; Brit. Infec. Soc. Prev: Lect. (Med.) UST, Kumasi, Ghana; Clin. Research Fell. St. Geo. Hosp. Med. Sch. Lond.; SHO & Ho. Off. Roy. Liverp. Hosp.

EVANS, Martin David 14 Rigby Road, Maghull, Sefton, Liverpool L31 8AZ — MB ChB 1983 Liverp.

EVANS, Martin James Hill View, Heol Dywyll, Clydach, Swansea SA6 5SR — MB BCh 1998 Wales.

EVANS, Martyn Huw Brynderwen Surgery, Crickhowell Road, St. Mellons, Cardiff CF3 0EF Tel: 029 2079 9921 Fax: 029 2077 7740; Overton, 73 Mallards Reach, Marshfield, Cardiff CF3 2NN — MB ChB 1988 Liverp.; MRCGP 1992. (Liverpool) GP Princip. Brynderwen & Minster Surgs. Cardiff. Prev: Trainee GP Swansea VTS; Ho. Off. Countess of Chester Hosp. Chester.

EVANS, Mary 6 Shaftesbury Avenue, Chesterfield S40 1HN — MB ChB 1981 Bristol; MRCPsych 1992.

EVANS, Mary Taunton & Somerset NHS Trust, Musgrove Park Hospital, Parkfield Drive, Taunton TA1 5DA Tel: 01823 343438 Fax: 01823 344747 — MB BS Lond. 1969; FRCP Lond. 1996; MRCP (UK) 1973; DObst RCOG 1971. (Roy. Free Hosp.) Cons. Geriat. MusGr. Pk. Hosp. Taunton.

EVANS, Mary (retired) Erw Nant, Llwyn Mawr, Llangollen LL20 7BG Tel: 01691 718340 — MB ChB Liverp. 1941. Prev: Med. Off. (Matern. Child Welf. & Schs.) Liverp.

EVANS, Mary Elizabeth (retired) 32 Folly Hill, Farnham GU9 0BH Tel: 01252 726938 — MB BCh BAO 1947 NUI. Prev: Civil. Med. Pract. MoD.

EVANS, Mary Glynwen (retired) 32 The Ridge, Derwenfawr, Swansea SA2 8AG — MB BCh Wales 1965.

EVANS, Mary Linklater 97 Metchley Lane, Harborne, Birmingham B17 0JH Tel: 0121 427 4865 — MB BS 1966 Lond.; MRCS Eng. LRCP Lond. 1966; DCH Eng. 1969. (Roy. Free) SCMO Birm. Centr. HA. Prev: Ho. Off. Roy. N.. Infirm. Inverness, Woodend Hosp. Aberd. & Hosp.; Sick Childr. Newc.

EVANS, Mavis Elizabeth Wirral Community Healthcare NHS Trust, Directorate of Elderly Mental Health, Clatterbridge Site, Bebington, Wirral CH63 4JY Tel: 0151 482 7851 Fax: 0151 482 7627 Email: mavis.evans@wwccnt.nhs.uk; 24 Paston Way, Thorpe St Andrew, Norwich NR7 9LT Fax: 01244 378337 Email: mavis.evans@virgin.net, p.burrows@dial.pipex.com — MB ChB 1977 Sheff.; MD Liverp. 1996; MRCS Eng. LRCP Lond. 1977; MRCPsych 1989; DTM & H Liverp. 1979. (Sheff.) Clin. Dir. (Elderly Ment. Health) & Cons. Psychogeriat Clatterbridge Hosp. Wirral; Hon Sen. Lect. (Psychiat.) Univ. Liverp.

EVANS, Meirion Rhys Temple of Peace and Health, Cathays Park, Cardiff CF10 3NW Tel: 029 2040 2478 Fax: 029 2040 2503 Email: meirion.evans@bro-taf-ha.wales.nhs.uk; Southerndown House, Southerndown, Bridgend CF32 0RN — MB BCh 1981 Wales; FRCP Lond. 1997; MRCP (UK) 1985; FFPHM RCP (UK) 1997, M 1989. Cons. Communicable Dis. Control, Bro Taf HA; Hon. Cons. Epidemiol. PHLS Communicable Dis. Surveillance Centre. Prev: Sen. Regist. (Pub. Health Med.) W. Midl. RHA.

EVANS, Mererid — MB BCh 1994 Wales; PhD 2001; BSc (Hons.) Wales 1993. (Univ. Hosp. Wales Cardiff) Specialist Regist. (Radiother.) Wales. Socs: Roy. Coll. of Radiologists. Prev: MRC Clin. Train. Fell. Univ. Hosp. Cardiff, Wales; SHO (Renal) Guy's Hosp. Lond.; SHO (Intens. Care) St Thos. Hosp. Lond.

EVANS, Meriel Sian Pantsais, Bwlch-y-Groes, Llandysul SA44 5JT — MB BCh 1995 Wales.

EVANS, Michael Adrian Lloyd Fulham Road Surgery, 630 Fulham Road, London SW6 5RS Tel: 020 7736 4344 Fax: 020 7736 4985 — MB BS 1975 Lond.; 1998 Dip. Occ. Med.; BSc (Hons.) Lond. 1971; MRCGP 1982; DRCOG 1981; DCH RCP Lond. 1981. Gen. Practitioner, Fulham, Lond.; Clin. Assitant, Dermat. Dept., Chelsea & W.minter Hosp., Lond.; Occupat.al Health Phys., Marks & Spencer, Lond. Prev: Lect. (Med. Microbiol.) Lond. Hosp. Med. Coll.; Dir. (Emerg.) Amer. Hosp., Paris.

EVANS, Michael John Queensway Medical Centre, Queensway, Poulton-le-Fylde FY6 7ST Tel: 01253 890219 Fax: 01253 894222; Fernknoll, Broadpool Lane, Hambleton, Poulton-le-Fylde FY6 9AG Tel: 01253 700415 — MB ChB 1978 Manch.; MRCGP 1982; DRCOG 1983. (Manch.) Expert Witness for AVMA; GP Represen. GP Advis. Gp. on Commiss. Care. Socs: Assoc. Mem. Brit. Med. Acupunc. Soc.; BMA. Prev: Mem. LMC; Chairm. BMA Local Br.

EVANS, Mr Michael John 144 Harley Street, London W1N 1AH Tel: 020 7935 0023 Fax: 020 8967 5609 Email: mike.evans@ic.ac.uk; White Lodge, Horton Road, Horton, Slough SL3 9NU Tel: 01753 685681 Fax: 01753 685681 Email: mje@evanorth.demon.co.uk — MB ChB Birm. 1962; FRCS Ed. 1969. Cons. Orthop. Surg. Hammersmith Hosp., Char. Cross Hosp. Lond. & New Ealing Hosp. S.all; Hon. Sen. Lect. (Orthop.) Roy. Postgrad. Med. Sch. Univ. Lond. Socs: Fell. Roy. Soc. Med.; Medico-

Legal Soc.; Brit. Orthop. Research Soc. Prev: Regist. (Orthop.) Roy. Free Hosp. Lond.; Sen. Regist. (Orthop.) Middlx. Hosp. & Roy. Nat. Orthop. Hosp.

EVANS, Michael Robert Elliott 95/97 Tabernacle Street, London EC2A 4BA Tel: 020 7253 2166 — MB BS 1945 Lond.; MRCP Lond. 1955. (Lond. Hosp.) Prev: Med. Resid. Roosevelt Hosp. New York; Supernum. Med. Regist. Lond. Hosp.; Res. Phys. Amer. Hosp. Paris.

EVANS, Michael Roland Witold Twyford Surgery, Hazeley Road, Twyford, Winchester SO21 1QY Tel: 01962 712202 Fax: 01962 715158; Downlands, Owslebury, Winchester SO21 1LU Tel: 01962 777275 — MB BS 1983 Lond.; BSc Lond. 1980; MRCP (UK) 1986; MRCGP 1989; DCH RCP Lond. 1987. (Guy's) Bd. Mem. Mid Hants PCG; Trainee GP Tutor Winchester. Prev: SHO (Obst.) Roy. Hants. Co. Hosp.; SHO Rotat. (Paediat. & Gen. Med.) Soton. Gen. Hosp.

EVANS, Michael Russell St Lukes Medical Centre, 53 Cainscross Road, Stroud GL5 4EX Tel: 01453 763755 Fax: 01453 756573; Rock cottage, Main Road, Whiteshal, Stroud GL6 6JS Tel: 01453 763755 Fax: 01453 756573 — MB ChB 1972 Bristol; T(GP) 1991. (Univ. Bristol) GP; Vis. Lect. Univ. Exeter Centre for Complimentary Med. Studies; Mem. Advis. Bd. Registration of Homoeop. Products; Med. Lect Hibernia Sch. of Aut.Ther. Socs: Hon. Sec. Med. Comm. Anthroposophical Med. Assn.; Med. Sect. Sch. Spiritual Sc. Goetheanum, Switz.. Prev: Med. Co-Dir. Pk. Attwood Clinic Trimpley Bewdley; SHO Acad. Dept. Psychiat. Middlx. Hosp. Lond.; Regist. Klinik Oeschelbronn D.7532 Niefern Oeschelbronn, W. Germany.

EVANS, Michelle Farnham Medical Centre, 435 Stanhope Road, South Shields NE33 4JE Tel: 0191 455 4748 Fax: 0191 455 8573; 4 Sand Grove, Sunderland SR6 7RL Tel: 0191 529 3234 — MB BS 1987 Lond.; MRCGP 1991; DRCOG 1991. Prev: Trainee GP N.umbria VTS.

EVANS, Moira Jones Whitelodge, 23 Wychwood Close, Langland, Swansea SA3 4PH Tel: 01792 360394; Singleton Hospital, Sketty Lane, Swansea SA2 8QA — MB BS 1985 Lond.; FCAnaesth 1991; DA (UK) 1988. (St. Mary's Hosp. Lond.) Cons. Anaesth. Singleton Hosp. NHS Trust Swansea. Prev: SHO (Anaesth.) Morriston & Singleton Hosps. Swansea; Regist. Cardiff Hosps. Gp.; Sen. Regist. (Anaesth.) Clwyd/Cardiff Hosps. Gp.

EVANS, Monica Margaret Mary (retired) 28 Court Yard, London SE9 5PZ Tel: Eltham 1300 — MRCS Eng. LRCP Lond. 1928. Prev: Ho. Surg. & Ho. Phys. W. Norf. & King's Lynn Gen. Hosp.

EVANS, Morton Eyre (retired) Doverhay, Ruthin Road, Denbigh LL16 4PT Tel: 01745 812277 — MB BS Lond. 1944; MRCS Eng. LRCP Lond. 1944. Prev: Regist. (Med.) Lewisham Gp. Hosps.

EVANS, Myrddin 1 Park View, Llanddew, Brecon LD3 9RL Tel: 01874 624484 — MB BCh 1945 Wales; BSc Wales 1945; FRCP Lond. 1971, M 1950; FRCPsych 1972; DPM Eng. 1956. Hon. Cons. Phys. Psychol. Med. S. Glam. HA. Socs: Brit. Psychol. Soc. & Biochem. Soc. Prev: Phys. Psychol. Med. Univ. Hosp. Wales & WhitCh. Hosp.; Clin. Teach. (Psychol. Med.) Welsh Nat. Sch. Med.; Sen. Regist. (Psychol. Med.) Middlx. Hosp.

EVANS, Nansi-Wynne Davies Forest Road Medical Centre, Forest Road, Hay-on-Wye, Hereford HR3 5DS Tel: 01497 822100 Fax: 01497 822110 — MB BCh 1980 Wales; DCH RCP 1983 Lond.; DPM 2000 Wales; MRCGP 1986.

EVANS, Nest Lloyd 36 Llanfair Road, Pontcanna, Cardiff CF11 9QB Tel: 01222 343113 Email: nestevans@hotmail.com — MB BS 1985 Lond.; MRCP (UK) 1989; FRCR 1997. (Royal Free Hospital Medical School) Cons. Radiol. Roy. Gwent Hosp. Newport. Prev: Sen. Regist. (Radiol.) Univ. Hosp. of Wales Cardiff.

EVANS, Mr Nicholas Aaron 4 Torrens Drive, Lakeside, Cardiff CF23 6DW — MB BS 1989 Lond.; BSc 1986; FRCS Ed. 1993. (St. Mary's Lond.) Sen. Regist. (Orthop.) Cardiff.

EVANS, Mr Nicholas David Whittington Hospital, St. Mary's Wing, Highgate Hill, London N19 5NF; 19 Woodberry Way, London N12 0HE Tel: 020 7272 3070 Fax: 020 7288 3451 Email: os@nixboxiz.demon.co.uk — MRCS Eng. LRCP Lond. 1976; MB BS Lond. 1977, BDS 1971; FRCS Ed. 1985; FDS RCS Eng. 1983, LDS 1970. Cons. Oral & Maxillofacial Surg. Whittington Hosp. & E.man Dent. Hosp. Lond.; UCLH.

EVANS, Nicholas John Richard Wotton Lawn, Horton Road, Gloucester GL1 3WL Tel: 01452 891500 Fax: 01452 891501 — BM BCh 1971 Oxf.; MA Oxf. 1971; FRCPsych 1995, M 1976. Cons. Psychiat. Severn NHS Trust; Vis. Psychiat. HM Prison Glos. Prev: Sen. Regist. Univ. Dept. Psychiat. Camb.; Regist. (Psychiat.) Warneford Hosp. Oxf.; Ho. Phys. Radcliffe Infirm. Oxf.

EVANS, Mr Nicholas Martin The Royal Eye Infirmary, Apsley Road, Plymouth PL4 6PL — MB BS 1976 Lond.; MA Oxf.; FRCS Ed. 1986; MRCS Eng. LRCP Lond. 1976; FRCOphth 1988; DO Eng. 1985. Cons. Ophth. Surg. Roy. Eye Infirm. Plymouth.

EVANS, Nicola Ann Aldous Bishops Waltham Surgery, Lower Lane, Bishops Waltham, Southampton SO32 1GR Tel: 01489 892288 Fax: 01489 894402; Downlands, Owslebury, Winchester SO21 1LU Tel: 01962 777275 — MB BS 1983 Lond.; MRCGP 1989; MRCGP 1989; DRCOG 1989; DCH RCP Lond. 1986. (Westm.) Prev: Trainee GP Alresford; SHO (Paediat., O & G & Med.) Basingstoke Dist. Gen. Hosp.

EVANS, Nicola Janet The Hildenborough Medical Group, Tonbridge Road, Hildenborough, Tonbridge TN11 9HL Tel: 01732 838777 Fax: 01732 838297; Middle Cottage, Egg Pie Lane, Hildenborough, Tonbridge TN11 8PE — MB BS 1981 Lond.; DRCOG 1984.

EVANS, Nigel Alwyn Pitt Royal Alexandra Hospital for Sick Children, Dyke Road, Brighton BN1 3JN Tel: 01273 328145 Fax: 01273 736685; Nevan House, 4 Varndean Road, Brighton BN1 6RL Tel: 01273 501241 — MB BS Lond. 1964; FRCP Lond. 1985; MRCP (UK) 1969; MRCS Eng. LRCP Lond. 1964; DCH Eng. 1967; DObst RCOG 1967; FRCPCH 1997. (St. Mary's) Cons. Paediat. Roy. Alex. Hosp. Sick Childr. Brighton. Socs: Brit. Soc. Gastroenterol. & Brit. Paediat. Assn. Prev: Sen. Regist. Birm. Childr. Hosp.; Ho. Phys. Hosp. Sick Childr. Gt. Ormond St.; Ho. Phys. Paediat. Unit St. Mary's Hosp. Lond.

EVANS, Noel John Bebbington, CB (retired) Providence House, Wyre Lane, Long Marston, Stratford-upon-Avon CV37 8RQ Tel: 01789 721509 — MB BChir 1958 Camb.; BA (1st cl. Hons. Nat. Sc. Trip.) Camb. 1954, MA 1959; FRCP Lond. 1977, M 1961; FFPHM 1973; DPH (Distinc.) Lond. 1965. Barrister-at-Law Gray's Inn; Mem. Counc. (Privy Counc. Appointee) Roy. Pharm. Soc. GB; Chairm. Nat. Biol. Standards Bd. Prev: Chairm. UK Transpl. Support Servs. SHA.

EVANS, Nora Deirdre Flat 1, 92 North Road, Belfast BT4 3DJ Tel: 01232 673574 — MB BCh BAO 1971 Belf.; DRCOG 1976; DCH RCPSI 1975. Prev: SHO (O & G) Craigavon Area Hosp.; Med. Off. Matern. Hosp. Fujairah, UAE; Clin. Med. Off. SHSSB, N. Irel.

EVANS, Noreen Marjorie Helen 2 Greycourt, Gledhow Lane, Leeds LS8 1NQ Tel: 0113 266 8078 — MB BCh BAO Dub. 1952; BA Dub. 1949; DObst RCOG 1954. (T.C. Dub.) Clin. Asst. BrE. Screening Serv. Seacroft Hosp. Leeds. Prev: Clin. Asst. (Gen. Surg.) Leeds Gen. Infirm.; Med. Off. Roy. Matern. Hosp. Belf. & Univ. Hosp. W. Indies Kingston, Jamaica; Med. Off. Wheatfields Hospice Leeds.

EVANS, Olwyn Proir Garth, Ewenny, Bridgend CF35 5AW Tel: 01656 3500 — MB BCh 1941 Wales; BSc, MB BCh Wales 1941. (Cardiff)

EVANS, Owen Gwynfor The Surgery, 30 Chartfield Avenue, London SW15 6HG Tel: 020 8788 6442; 5 Melville Avenue, Wimbledon, London SW20 0NS Tel: 020 8946 9870 — MB BS 1986 Lond.; BSc (Hons.) Wales 1980.

EVANS, Owen Walter Health Services Centre, Wynne Road, Blaenau Ffestiniog LL41 3DW Tel: 01766 830205 Fax: 01766 831121; Encil Wen, Ffestiniog, Blaenau Ffestiniog LL41 4PN Tel: 01766 762541 — MB BCh 1971 Wales. (Cardiff) GP Med. Staff Ffestinog Memor. Hosp. (Cymdeithas Feddygol Cymru). Prev: SHO (Cas. & Orthop.) Bridgend Gen. Hosp.; SHO (Psychiat.) Pen-y-Fai Hosp. Bridgend; Gen. Duties Med. Off. Nchanga Consolidated Copper Mines Ltd. Kitwe, Zambia.

EVANS, Pamela Mary 17 Foxcote, St Leonards-on-Sea TN37 7HJ Tel: 01424 754543 — MB BS 1973 Lond. (Lond. Hosp. Med. Coll.)

EVANS, Patrick Castle Hill Hospital, Cottingham HU16 5JQ — MB BS 1973 Lond.; FFA RCS Eng. 1978. (St. Geo.) Cons. Anaesth. Humberside Cardiothoracic Centre Castle Hill Hosp. N. Humberside. Prev: Sen. Regist. (Anaesth.) St. Geo. Hosp. Lond. & Hosp. Sick Childr. Lond.; Regist. & SHO (Anaesth.) St. Geo. Hosp. Lond.

EVANS, Paul Christopher The Surgery, 124 New Church Road, Hove BN3 4JB Tel: 01273 729194 Fax: 01273 881992; 2 Meadow Close, Tongdean Road, Hove BN3 6QQ — MB BS 1988 Lond.; MRCGP 1995; DFFP 1994; DRCOG 1994. (Guy's Hospital London)

EVANS, Mr Paul Ellison Lewis Erme House, Station Road, Plympton, Plymouth PL7 2AU; Erme House, Station Road, Plymouth PL7 2AU — MB BS 1971 Lond.; MSc (Biomechanics Distinc.) Surrey 1981; FRCS Eng. 1977. (St. Thos.) Cons. Orthop. Surg. Plymouth HA. Socs: BMA & Brit. Orthop. Assn. Prev: Lord Brock Memor. Trust Historical Essay Prize 'Developm. of Cerclage Fixation in Treatm. of Fracts.' 1984; Sen. Regist. (Orthop.) Soton Gen. Hosp.; Sen. Regist. (Orthop.) Guy's & St. Thos. Hosp. Lond.

EVANS, Paul Jeffrey 14 Stanley Road, Knutsford WA16 0DE — MB ChB 1992 Manch.

EVANS, Paula Antoinette Tel: 01904 342999; York Medical Group, 199 Acomb Road, 7 Sevens Avenue, Acomb, York YO2 — BM BS 1989 Nottm.; BMedSci (Hons.) Nottm. 1987; MRCGP 1996; DFFP 1996; DCH RCP Lond. 1992. (Nottm.) GP York; Clin. Asst. (Haemat.). Prev: Trainee GP Homerton, Lond. VTS.

EVANS, Peter Frederick Nobles Hospital, Westmoreland Road, Douglas Tel: 01624 642642 — MB BS 1976 Lond.; FRCS Eng. 1983; FRCR 1988. Cons. Radiol. Nobles Hosp. Isle of Man. Socs: Brit. Inst. Radiol. Prev: Cons. Radiol. Huddersfield Roy. Infirm.; Sen. Regist. (Diagnostic Radiol.) Char. Cross Hosp. Lond.; Regist. (Diagnostic Radiol.) Centr. Middlx. Hosp. Lond.

EVANS, Peter John 12 Great North Road, Milford Haven SA73 2LJ — MD 1987 Wales; MB BCh 1977; MRCP 1980. Cons. Phys. & Hon. Sen. Lect. (Med.) Ealing & Hammersmith Hosp. Prev: Research Fell. (Endocrinol.) Univ. Hosp. Cardiff; Sen. Regist. Guy's Hosp. Lond.

EVANS, Peter John Dudley Pan Management Centre, 2nd Floor South Wing, Charing Cross Hospital, Fulham Palace Road, London W6 8RF Tel: 020 8846 7016 Fax: 020 8846 7585 Email: pj.evans@ic.ac.uk; 15 Stott Close, Wandsworth, London SW18 2TG Tel: 0208 874 2710 Fax: 0208 874 2245 Email: peterjdevans@cs.com — MB BS 1970 Lond.; MRCS Eng. LRCP Lond. 1970; FFA RCS Eng. 1974; DMS Open 1994. (Guy's) Cons. Anaesth. Char. Cross Hosp.; Dep. Clin. Dir. (Anaesth. Surg.) Hammersmith Hosps. NHS Trust; Co-Founder PANG Gp. Socs: Fell. Med. Soc. Lond.; Assn. Anaesths.; Roy. Soc. Med. Prev: Research Fell. (Pain Relief) Nuffield Dept. Anaesth. & Univ. Oxf.; SHO (Anaesth.) Univ. Sheff.; Fell. (Cardiothoracic Anaesth.) Green La. Hosp. Auckland, NZ.

EVANS, Peter Mark 126 Old Vicarage La, Kemble, Cirencester GL7 6BB — MB BCh 1997 Wales.

EVANS, Peter Robert 21 Roxburgh Place, Newcastle upon Tyne NE6 5HU — MB BS 1991 Newc.

EVANS, Peter William George Hampton Hill House, Hampton Hill, Swanmore, Southampton SO32 2QN — MB BChir 1973 Camb.; FRCP 1998; MA; MRCP (UK) 1976; DCH Eng. 1975. GP Titchfield; Med. Director, Jusere Endoscopy Servs. Ltd. Socs: Primary Care Soc. Gastroenterol. Prev: Rotating Regist. (Paediat.) Roy. Alexandra Hosp. Sick Childr.; Brighton & Guy's Hosp. Lond.

EVANS, Philip Park Lodge, Gloucester Road, Boscombe, Bournemouth BH7 6JF Tel: 01202 397003 Fax: 01202 399649 — MB BS 1992 Lond.; DRCOG 1995; MRCGP 1998. (Charing Cross & Westminster Medical School) Staff Grade Addic. Serv. Dorset Healthcare NHS Trust Bournemouth. Prev: GP Regist. Bournemouth; SHO (O & G) Poole Hosp. Dorset; SHO (Psychiat.) St. Ann's Hosp. Poole, Dorset.

EVANS, Philip Anthony The Medical Centre, Love Lane, Burnham-on-Sea TA8 1EU Tel: 01278 782283 Fax: 01278 793024; Pilgrims, Gore Road, Burnham-on-Sea TA8 2HL Tel: 01278 782153 — MB BS 1958 Lond.; MRCS Eng. LRCP Lond. 1958; DObst RCOG 1962. (King's Coll. Hosp.) Med. Off. Burnham-on-Sea War. Memor. Hosp. Socs: BMA. Prev: Cas. Off. King's Coll. Hosp.; Demonst. Path. Univ. Bristol; Sen. Resid. Off. Bristol Matern. Hosp.

EVANS, Philip Hugh St Leonard's Medical Practice, 34 Denmark Road, Exeter EX1 1SF Tel: 01392 201790 Fax: 01392 201796 — MB BS 1983 Lond.; MPhil Exeter 1995; MRCGP (Distinc.) 1987; DRCOG 1986. GP, Exeter; Lect. (Gen. Pract.) Inst. Gen. Pract. Postgrad. Med. Sch. Univ. Exeter; Dir. Sandnet, Lead Researcher (St.Leonards Med. Pract.); Lect. in Gen. Pract. Exeter Univ. Prev: Trainee SHO/GP Plymouth VTS; Ho. Phys. Guy's Hosp. Lond.; Ho. Surg. Greenwich Dist. Hosp. Lond.

EVANS, Philip James A/E Dept, Norfolk & Norwich Hospital, Norwich NR1 3SR; Rookery Cottage, Tasburgh, Norwich NR15 1LP — MB BS 1963 Lond.; MRCS Eng. LRCP Lond. 1963. (Lond. Hosp.) Clin. Anat. & Clin. Asst. Norf. & Norwich Hosp.; Lect. Clin. Anat. Sch. Physiother. Univ. E. Anglia Norwich; Preceptor Anat. Corpus Christi Coll.Cambs. Socs: Fell. Brit. Assn. Clin. Anat. Prev: Lect. (Anat.) Harvard Med. Sch. Boston, USA & Middlx. Hosp. Med. Sch. Lond.

EVANS, Philip John 17 Coroners La, Widnes WA8 9JN — MB ChB 1997 Leeds.

EVANS, Philip Michael Scurlock 155 Pencisely Road, Llandaf, Cardiff CF5 1DN — MB BCh 1990 Wales; MRCP (UK) 1994.

EVANS, Philip Rhys Oliver and Partners, The Guildhall Surgery, Lower Baxter Street, Bury St Edmunds IP33 1ET Tel: 01284 701601 Fax: 01284 702943 — MB BS 1972 Lond.; BA (Hons.) Open 1987; MRCS Eng. LRCP Lond. 1971; FRCGP 1989, M 1976; DObst RCOG 1975. (Guy's) Princip. GP Bury St Edmunds; Mem. RCGP Counc.; Pres. Europ. Soc. Gen. Pract. & Family Med. (Wonca Region Europe). Socs: BMA; Direct Mem. WONCA. Prev: Chair. Europ. Forum; Chairm. Internat. Comm. RCGP; Edr. Europ. Jl. Gen. Pract.

EVANS, Philip Roland (retired) 7 Berks Hill, Chorleywood, Rickmansworth WD3 5AG Tel: 01923 282995 — MB BS Lond. 1960; MRCP (U.K.) 1970; MRCS Eng. LRCP Lond. 1960; FRCPsych 1990, M 1973; DPM Eng. 1964. Cons. Psychiat. Watford Gen. Hosp. Prev: Sen. Regist. (Psychiat.) Nat. Hosp. Nerv. Dis. Qu. Sq.

EVANS, Philippa Margaret Huntingdon Road Surgery, 1 Huntingdon Road, Cambridge CB3 0DB Tel: 01223 364127 — BM BCh 1977 Oxf.; MA Camb. 1978; MRCP (UK) 1981; MRCGP 1981; DRCOG 1980. Gen. Practitioner.

EVANS, Mr Phillip Adrian Department of Accident and Emergency, Leicester Royal Infirmary, Infirmary Square, Leicester LE1 5WW Tel: 0116 258 6320 Fax: 0116 258 6671; The Old Vicarage, 2 Melton Road, Ab Kettleby, Melton Mowbray LE14 3QX — MB BS 1983 Lond.; FRCS Ed. 1988; FFAEM. Cons. A & E Leicester Roy. Infirm. Socs: BMA; BAEM; FFAEM. Prev: Sen. Regist. Rotat. (A & E) St. Geo. Hosp. Lond.

EVANS, Prudence Anne Morton Kingston Hospital NHS Trust, Galsworthy Road, Kingston upon Thames KT2 7QB Tel: 020 8546 7711 Fax: 020 8547 2182; 35 St. Stephen's Road, Ealing, London W13 8HJ — MB BS 1979 Lond.; MRCP (UK) 1983; FRCR 1987. Cons. Radiol. Kingston Hosp.

EVANS, Rachael Andrea 42 Romway Road, Leicester LE5 5SA — MB ChB 1997 Leic.

EVANS, Rachel Elizabeth 24 Fairhaven Close, St. Mellons, Cardiff CF3 0LD Tel: 029 2025 9907 Email: r.evans3973@aol.com; Royal Gwent Hospital, Cardiff Road, Newport NP9 2YB Tel: 01633 234234 Fax: 01633 243047 — MB BCh 1991 Wales; MRCP (UK) 1994. (Univ. Wales Coll. Med.) Specialist Regist. (Paediat.) Roy. Gwent Hosp. Newport. Socs: MRCPCH; Welsh Paediatric Soc. Prev: Specialist Regist. (Community Paediat.) Glan-y-Môr NHS Trust; Specialist Regist. (Paediat.) Univ. Hosp. of Wales Cardiff.; Regist. (Paediat.) Singleton Hosp. Swansea.

EVANS, Rachel Georgina Lewisham Hospital, High St., Lewisham, London SE13 6LH Tel: 020 8690 4311; 16 Papillons Walk, Blackheath Park, London SE3 9SF Tel: 020 8852 3195 — MB BS Lond. 1956; FRCP Lond. 1978, M 1962; DCH Eng. 1961; FRCPCH 1997. (St. Bart.) Cons. Paediat. Childr. Hosp. Lewisham. Prev: Sen. Regist. (Paediat.) King's Coll. Hosp. Lond.; Regist. (Paediat.) Qu. Charlotte's Hosp.; Ho. Phys. Hosp. Sick Childr. Gt. Ormond St.

EVANS, Rachel Margaret 14 Deansfield Road, Brewood, Stafford ST19 9EQ — MB ChB 1997 Sheff.

EVANS, Ralph Charlton 30 Huntingdon Street, London N1 1BS Tel: 020 7607 3681; J. Sainsbury plc, Occupational Medical Department, Stamford St., London SE1 9LL Tel: 020 7921 7182 — MRCS Eng. LRCP Lond. 1958. Med. Off. J. Sainsbury plc. Prev: Med. Adviser Mercury Airfreight Internat. Ltd., Gordon Gotch Gp. of Cos. & Bourne & Hollingsworth Lond.

EVANS, Ralph Harvey (retired) Larches, The Croft, Old Costessey, Norwich NR8 5DS Tel: 01603 742197 Fax: 01603 742197 — MB BS Lond. 1966; MRCS Eng. LRCP Lond. 1956. Prev: GP Norwich.

EVANS, Mr Ramon James c/o Lloyds Bank, Queen St., Cardiff CF1 — MRCS Eng. LRCP Lond. 1958; CRCS Canada 1965; FRCS Canada 1973; LMCC 1966. (Cardiff) Assoc. Prof. (Anaesth., Med. & Surg.) Univ. Toronto; Dir. Smythe Pain Clinic Toronto Gen. Hosp.; Cons. Qu. Eliz., P.ss Margt. & Toronto Gen. Hosps. Socs: Canad. & Ont. Med. Assns. Prev: Med. Off. Col. Belcher Hosp. Calgary;

Orthop. Regist. Hammersmith Hosp. Lond.; SHO (Gen. Surg.) Frenchay Hosp. Bristol.

EVANS, Raymond Roker (retired) 10 St Peters Close, Goodworth Clatford, Andover SP11 7SF — MB BS Lond. 1952; MRCS Eng. LRCP Lond. 1952; MRCGP 1965; DObst RCOG 1958; DA Eng. 1957. Prev: GP Hartfield E Sussex.

EVANS, Rhian Janet 115 Trewyddfa Road, Morriston, Swansea SA6 8NY Tel: 01792 781643 — MB BS 1984 Lond.; MBA 1990; MRCGP 1989. (St. Bart.) GP. Prev: Sen. Research Fell. Wessex Inst. Pub. Health Med. Winchester.

EVANS, Rhodri Berwyn, 37 Cefn Esgair, Llanbadarn, Aberystwyth SY23 3JG — BM BCh 1996 Oxf.

EVANS, Rhodri Martin 84 Eaton Crescent, Swansea SA1 4QP — MB BCh 1983 Wales; FRCR 1989. Cons. Radiol. Morriston Hosp. Swansea. Prev: Vis. Lect. (Radiol.) Chinese Univ. Hong Kong.

EVANS, Rhys David The Old Forge, Boot St., Stonesfield, Oxford OX29 8PX — MD 1994 Lond., DPhil Oxf. 1989; BSc Lond. 1979, MD 1994, MB BS 1982; FFA RCS Eng. 1986.

EVANS, Richard Anthony Davies and Partners, Meddygfa Teilo, Crescent Road, Llandeilo SA19 6HL Tel: 01558 823435 Fax: 01558 824045; Pont Cennen, Derwydd, ammanford SA18 2LX Tel: 01269 850505 — MB BCh 1987 Wales; MRCGP 1994. (Univ. Wales Coll. Med.) Prev: Trainee GP Aberystwyth VTS; SHO (Cas., ENT & Orthop.) S.mead Hosp. Bristol; SHO (Radiother. & Oncol.) Bristol Radiother. Centre.

EVANS, Richard Ceiri Department of Medicine, University of Liverpool, Liverpool L69 3BX Tel: 0151 706 4070 Fax: 0151 706 5802 Email: revans@liv.ac.uk — MB BS 1986 Lond.; MRCP 1993. (Westm.) MRC Clin. Research Fell. (Gastroenterol). Socs: Amer. Assn. for Advancem. of Sci.; Med. Res. Soc.; Biochem Soc. Prev: Regist. Rotat. (Gen. Med. & Intens. Care) S.end Gen. Hosp. & St. Bart. Hosp. Lond.; SHO (Gastroenterol.) St. Marks Hosp.

EVANS, Richard Charles The Surgery, 90 Church Road, Sheldon, Birmingham B26 3TP Tel: 0121 743 3409; 47 Riddings Hill, Barsirc Common CV7 7RA — MB ChB 1984 Birm.; DRCOG 1987. Socs: DCOPD 1997 (NARTC).

EVANS, Richard Francis Marcham Road Surgery, Abingdon OX14 1BT Tel: 01235 543582 Fax: 01235 543844 Email: dr.who@tesco.net; Moonraker, North Lane, Weston on the Green, Bicester OX25 3RG Tel: 01869 350140 Fax: 01869 350675 Email: dr.who@tesco.net — MB ChB 1968 Liverp.; MRCGP 1978; Dip. Palliat. Med. Wales 1997; DCH Eng. 1979; DObst RCOG 1973. p/t Hosp. Pract. (Palliat. Med.) Michael Sobell Hse. Oxf. Prev: SHO Walton, Fazakerley & Alder Hey Childr. Hosps. Liverp.; Clin. Asst. (Palliat. Med.) Michael Sobell Ho. Oxf.

EVANS, Richard Gerwyn Tel: 01792 898844; 443 Gower Road, Killay, Swansea SA2 7AN — MB BCh 1981 Wales; MRCGP 1988. Socs: Roy. Soc. of Med. Prev: Regist. (Anaesth). Swansea; SHO (Psychiat.) Cefn Coed Swansea.

EVANS, Richard Graham Bertrand (retired) 67 Moorside N., Fenham, Newcastle upon Tyne NE4 9DU Tel: 0191 273 9574 — MB BS Lond. 1955; MRCS Eng. LRCP Lond. 1955; FRCR 1975; FFR 1962; DMRT Eng. 1959. Prev: Cons. Radiat. Oncol. Newc. HA.

EVANS, Richard Ivor The Avenue Surgery, 1 The Avenue, Cirencester GL7 1EH Tel: 01285 653122 Fax: 01285 650098 — MB BS 1970 Lond.; DObst RCOG 1972. (St. Mary's) Hosp. Pract. (Geriat.) Cirencester Hosp. Socs: BMA. Prev: Ho. Surg. Obst. Cheltenham Hosp. Gp.; Ho. Surg & Ho. Phys. Wexham Pk. Hosp. Slough.

EVANS, Richard John 20 Froghall Drive, Wokingham RG40 2LF — MB BS 1992 Lond.

EVANS, Mr Richard Llewellyn Redgate Medical Centre, Weston Zoyland Road, Bridgwater TA6 5BF Tel: 01278 444411 Fax: 01278 446816; 15 Steel Lane, Catcott, Bridgwater TA7 9HW Tel: 01278 722381 — MB BS 1965 Lond.; FRCS Ed. 1969; MRCS Eng. LRCP Lond. 1965; FRCOG 1984, M 1969; T(GP) 1991. (King's Coll. Hosp.) Socs: Fell. Roy. Soc. Med. Prev: Regist. (O & G) King's Coll. Hosp. Lond.; Govt. Surg. New Hebrides S.W. Pacific; Health Sector Coordinator Overseas Developm. Admin. (Tanzania).

EVANS, Richard Morgan 15 Clos Glyndwr, Pontardulais, Swansea SA4 1FW — MB BS 1987 Lond.

EVANS, Mr Richard Owen Norton 13 Amesbury Road, Penylan, Cardiff CF23 5DW — BM BS 1991 Nottm.; BMedSci Nottm. 1989; FRCS Eng. 1996. (Nottm.) Regist. (Orthop.) S. Wales.

EVANS, Richard Peter Hillview Medical Centre, 3 Heathside Road, Woking GU22 7QP Tel: 01483 760707 — MB BChir 1980 Camb.; MSc Lond. 1987; LMSSA Lond. 1980.

EVANS, Richard Philip 65 Sunny Bank Road, Meltham, Huddersfield HD9 5LL — MB BCh 1975 Wales; MRCGP 1981; MRCPsych 1990. (University of Wales Medical School) Sen. Med. Off. HM Prison Wakefield.

EVANS, Mr Robert (retired) 2 Beechcroft, St. George's Close, Birmingham B15 3TP Tel: 0121 454 2708 — MD 1929 Belf.; MB BCh BAO 1926; FRCS Ed. 1933; DLO Eng. 1933. Prev: Surg. Birm. & Midl. Ear & Throat Hosp.

EVANS, Mr Robert Anthony ENT Department, Princess of Wales Hospital, Coity Road, Bridgend CF31 1RQ Tel: 01656 752752 Fax: 01656 752186; The Croft, 81 Park St, Bridgend CF31 4AZ Tel: 01656 650484 — MB BS 1980 Lond.; FRCS Ed. 1984. (Middlx.) Cons. ENT Surg. P.ss of Wales Hosp. Bridgend. Socs: Brit. Cochlear Implant Gp. & Otorhinolaryngol. Research Soc. Prev: Sen. Regist. (ENT Surg.) Addenbrooke's Hosp. Camb. & Roy. Nat. Throat,Nose & Ear Hosp. Lond.

EVANS, Robert Byron Ty'r Felin Surgery, Cecil Road, Gorseinon, Swansea SA4 4BY Tel: 01792 898844 — MB BCh 1970 Wales.

EVANS, Sir (Robert) Charles (retired) Ardincaple, Capel Curig, Betws-y-Coed LL24 0EU Tel: 016904 273 — BM BCh 1943 Oxf.; MA, BM BCh Oxf. 1943; FRCS Eng. 1949; Hon. DSc Wales 1956. Prev: Sen. Surg. Regist. Neurosurgic. Unit, Liverp.

EVANS, Robert John (retired) Herons Hill, Guildford Road, Ottershaw, Chertsey KT16 0QW Tel: 01932 872422 — MB BS Lond. 1942; MD Lond. 1950; FCPath 1963. Prev: Dir. Path. Serv. & Cons. Path. NW Surrey Health Dist.

EVANS, Robert Morris (retired) Erw Nant, Llwynmawr, Llangollen LL20 7BG Tel: 01691 718340 — MB ChB (Hons.) Liverp. 1939; MB BChir Camb. 1941; MA Camb. 1941; FRCP Lond. 1968, M 1942. JP. Prev: Cons. Phys. Roy. S.. Hosp. Liverp. & Liverp. AHA.

EVANS, Robert Noel, CB, Maj.-Gen. late RAMC (retired) 32 Folly Hill, Farnham GU9 0BH Tel: 01252 726938 — MB BCh BAO 1947 NUI; MFCM 1979; FFA RCS Eng. 1963; DTM & H Eng. 1962. Prev: Commandmant & Postgrad. Dean Roy. Army Med. Coll.

EVANS, Roberta (retired) Bodwenan, 101 Maengwyn St., Machynlleth SY20 8EE Tel: 01654 702425 — MB BCh 1945 Wales; BSc Wales 1942; DObst RCOG 1947. Prev: Clin. Med. Off. E. Berks. Health Dist.

EVANS, Robin Ansdell 75 Grange Road, Cheam, Sutton SM2 6SW — MB BS 1980 Lond.; MRCP (UK) 1983; FRCR 1988. (Guy's) Cons. Radiol. Mayday Univ. Hosp. Croydon. Prev: Sen. Regist. & Regist. (Radiol.) Kings Coll. Hosp. Lond.; Regist. (Med.) W.m. Hosp. Lond.

EVANS, Robin Scott Swallownest Health Centre, Hepworth Drive, Aston, Sheffield S26 2BG Tel: 0114 287 2486 Fax: 0114 287 6045 — MB ChB 1983 Sheff. Prev: Trainee GP Rotherham Dist. Gen. Hosp. VTS.

EVANS, Robin Stedman 4A Links Court, Langland Bay, Swansea SA3 4QR — BA Camb. 1961, MB 1965, BChir 1964. (St. Thos.)

EVANS, Roger Curtis Emergency Unit, Univeristy Hospital of Wales, Heath Park, Cardiff CF14 4XW Tel: 029 2074 8090 Fax: 029 2074 8062 Email: rogers.evans@uhw-tr.wales.nhs.uk; The Cottage, Lower Machen, Newport NP10 8GU Tel: 01633 440228 — MB BS 1967 Lond.; FRCP Lond. 1986; MRCP (UK) 1975. (St. Mary's) Cons. Univ. Hosp. of Wales. Prev: Cons. Roy. Devon & Exeter Hosp.; SHO (Neurol.) Welsh Nat. Sch. Med.; Ho. Phys. (Cardiol.) St. Mary's Hosp. Lond.

EVANS, Roger Howard Wordsworth Surgery, 97 Newport Road, Cardiff CF24 0AG Tel: 029 2049 8000 Fax: 029 2045 5494 — MB BCh 1981 Wales.

EVANS, Roger Howard Wycombe General Hospital, Queen Alexandra Road, High Wycombe HP11 2TT Tel: 01494 526161; 24 Sycamore Crescent, Macclesfield SK11 8LW — MB ChB 1978 Sheff.; FRCR 1986. Cons. Radiol. S. Bucks. NHS Trust Wycombe. Prev: Sen. Regist. (Radiol.) N.wick Pk. Hosp. & Clin. Research Centre Harrow; SHO (Med.) Cheltenham Gen. Hosp.; Ho. Off. (Med.) N.. Gen. Hosp. Sheff.

EVANS, Mr Ronald Alexander 27 Rodney Street, Liverpool L1 9EH Fax: 0151 924 1131 — MB ChB 1975 Liverp.; MChOrth. Liverp. 1984; FRCS Ed. 1981. Cons. Hand Surg. Aintree Hosps. Liverp. Socs: Brit. Soc. Surg. Hand; Brit. Orthop. Assn. Prev: Dow

Corning Hand Surg. Research Fell. Wrightington Hosp.; Sen. Regist. (Orthop.) Mersey RHA; Lect. (Orthop. Surg.) Univ. Liverp.

EVANS, Mr Ronald Foster 19 Mimosa Close, Birmingham B29 4DA Tel: 0121 476 1384 — MB ChB 1958 Liverp.; MChOrth 1972; FRCS Eng. 1967. Cons. Surg. Birm. Accid. Hosp.; Sen. Clin. Lect. Univ. Birm. Socs: Inst. Accid. Surg. Prev: Sen. Regist. Accid. Unit Luton & Dunstable Hosp.; Orthop. Regist. Qu. Mary's Hosp. Roehampton; Ho. Phys. & Cas. Off. Liverp. Stanley Hosp.

EVANS, Rosemary Erica 8 Penlee Gardens, Plymouth PL3 4AN Tel: 01752 559366 Fax: 01752 606613 — MB BS Lond. 1969; MRCP (U.K.) 1972; DCH Eng. 1971; DObst RCOG 1971; FRCPCH 1997. (Roy. Free) Cons. Paediat. Community Child Health Dept. Scott Hosp. Plymouth. Socs: Brit. Paediat. Assn. Prev: Sen. Regist. (Paediat.) Freedom Fields Hosp. Plymouth; Research Asst. Dept. Child Health & Hon. Tutor (Child Health) Univ. Bristol; Ho. Phys. Hosp. Sick Childr. Gt. Ormond St. Lond..

EVANS, Rupert Jon 16 Perrin's Lane, London NW3 8TO — MB BCh 1983 Wales. Regist. (Gen. Med.) Jersey Gen. Hosp. Prev: SHO (Cas.) Cardiff Roy. Infirm.; SHO (Traum. & Orthop. Surg.) Welsh Nat. Sch. of Med. Cardiff; Regist. (Geriat.) Welsh Nat. Sch. Med. Cardiff.

EVANS, Ruth Linda Village Green Surgery, The Green, Wallsend NE28 6BB Tel: 0191 295 8500; 133 Benton Park Road, Newcastle upon Tyne NE7 7NB — MB BS 1988 Newc.; MRCGP 1994; DRCOG 1991. Prev: GP N.d.

EVANS, Sally Ann Civil Aviation Authority, Medical Division, Aviation House, Gatwick Airport S., Crawley RH6 0YR Tel: 01293 573669 Fax: 01293 573995 Email: sally.evans@srg.caa.co.uk — MB BS 1984 Lond.; MFOM 2000 London; AFOM RCP Lond. 1996; DAvMed FOM RCP Lond. 1995; Cert. Av. Med. 1992; DRCOG 1988; DCH RCP Lond. 1986. (St. Bart.) Head of Aeromed. Sect.. Civil Aviat. Auth. Gatwick.

EVANS, Sally Judith Willow Hill, Long St., Newport SA42 0TJ — MB ChB 1998 Bristol; BSc Hons Biochemistry Bristol 1995. BRI Med. Rotat. SHO Med., Bristol Roy. Infirm.

EVANS, Sally Teresa Barn 3, Upper Stanway, Rushbury, Church Stretton SY6 7GF — MB BS 1988 Lond.; MRCGP 1995. GP Retrainee Ironbridge Shrops.

EVANS, Sandra Eileen 14 Kirkland Avenue, Strathblane, Glasgow G63 9BZ — MB BCh 1969 Wales. (Cardiff) Clin. Med. Off. W.. Dist. Gtr. Glas. Health Bd. Prev: Ho. Phys. & Ho. Surg. Neath Gen. Hosp.

EVANS, Sandra Irene Rosemonde St. Bartholomews Hospital, West Smithfield, London EC1 Tel: 020 7601 8888 Email: sicvans@mds.qmw.ac.uk — MB BS 1983 Lond.; MRCPsych. 1988. (Lond. Hosp.) Cons. & Sen. Lect. Psychiat. for Elderly St. Bart. Hosp. City & Hackney HA. Socs: Inst. Gp. Anal. 1998. Prev: Sen. Regist. Rotat. (Psychiat.) St. Bart. Hosp. Lond.; Research Fell. Univ. Coll. & Middlx. Hosp. Lond.

EVANS, Sarah Ann 73 West Street, Titchfield, Fareham PO14 4DG — MB BS 1990 Lond.

EVANS, Sarah Anne 75 Grange Road, Cheam, Sutton SM2 6SW — MB BS 1980 Lond.; MRCP (UK) 1983; MRCGP 1986. (Roy. Free) Sen. Regist. (Radiol.) King's Coll. Hosp. Lond. Prev: GP Morden; Trainee GP Roehampton VTS; Regist. (Med.) Whittington Hosp. Lond.

EVANS, Sarah Cathcart Milton House Surgery, Doctors Commons Road, Berkhamsted HP4 3BY Tel: 01442 874784 Fax: 01442 877694; 78 Grove Road, Tring HP23 5PB — MB BS Lond. 1984; DRCOG Lond. 1987; MRCGP 1988; MSc Public Health Lond. 1992; MEPHM Lond. 1995; DFFP Lond. 1995. (Guys Hosp. Lond.) Princip, Gen. Pract, Berkhamsted. Prev: Princip Gen. Pract, Brix Hill GP Pract. S. Lond.

EVANS, Sarah Kathrine 13 Burrow Down, Eastbourne BN20 8ST — MB BS 1994 Lond.

EVANS, Sarah Louise 46 Graig y Coed, Penclawdd, Swansea SA4 3RN — BM 1994 Soton.

EVANS, Sarah Megan 3/2 22 Polwarth Street, Glasgow G12 9TY — MB ChB 1992 Glas.

EVANS, Sean Desmond 27 Grove Road, Lee-on-the-Solent PO13 9JA — MB ChB 1978 Dundee.

EVANS, Shân Ty Draw Farmhouse, Colwinstone, Cowbridge CF71 7NL — MB ChB 1983 Liverp.; DCH RCP Lond. 1989; DRCOG 1988; Cert. Family Plann. JCC 1988. Clin. Med. Off. S. W.. Hosp. Lond.

EVANS, Sharon Audrey Salisbury Hospice, Salisbury District Hospital, Salisbury SP2 8BJ Tel: 01722 336262 — MB BS 1969 Lond.; Dip. Palliat. Med. Wales 1995; DTM & H Liverp. 1971; DObst RCOG 1971. (King's Coll. Hosp. Med. Scu.) p/t Staff Grade Salisbury Hospice; GP.

EVANS, Sharon Edwina Department of Radiology, Morriston Hospital, Morriston, Swansea SA6 6NL Tel: 01792 703664 Fax: 01792 703674 Email: sharon.evans@mrrhst.tr.wales.nhs.uk — MB BCh 1981 Wales; BA Open 1993; FRCR 1987; DCH RCP Lond. 1984. Cons. Vasc. Radiol. Morriston Hosp. NHS Trust; Lead Clinician for AUDIT, Swansea NHS Trust. Prev: Sen. Regist. W. Midl. Radiol. Scheme Birm.

EVANS, Sian Amanda 5 Duffryn Road, Cyncoed, Cardiff CF23 6NP — BM BCh 1988 Oxf.; BA Oxf. 1985, BM BCh 1988. Clin. Asst. Hyperbaric Med. Unit Aberd.

***EVANS, Sian Claire** 26 Hill Village Road, Sutton Coldfield B75 5BA — MB ChB 1996 Birm.

EVANS, Sian Elizabeth Department of Medical Imaging, Leighton Hospital, Middlewich Road, Crewe CW1 4QJ Tel: 01270 612153; 83 Ravenscroft, Holmes Chapel, Crewe CW4 7HJ — MB ChB 1983 Liverp.; DMRD Liverp. 1988; FRCR 1989. Cons. Radiol. Leighton Hosp. Crewe Chesh.

EVANS, Simon Anthony 475 Manchester Road, Bury BL9 9SH — MB ChB 1985 Manch.; MRCP (UK) 1988. Research Regist. (Med.) Univ. Hosp. Nottm. Prev: Regist. (Gen. Med.) N. Manch. Gen. Hosp.

EVANS, Simon David 12 Luckley Wood, Wokingham RG41 2EW — MB ChB 1997 Bristol.

EVANS, Sion Prosser Y Fron, Lewis Terrace, New Quay SA45 9PG — MB BCh 1990 Wales.

EVANS, Sioned Elizabeth Royal Devon & Exeter Hospial, Barrack Road, Exeter; 6 Castle Cottages, Castle Lane, Woodbury, Exeter EX5 1HZ — BM 1993 Soton. (Soton.) Trainee GP Exeter VTS. Prev: SHO (Accid & Emerg.) & Ho. Off. (Med.) Qu. Alexandra Hosp. Portsmouth; SHO (Radiother. & Oncol.) Cookridge Hosp. Leeds; Ho. Off. (Surg.) Roy. Hants. Co. Hosp. Winchester.

EVANS, Siwan Gerallt Kings Road Surgery, 180 Kings Road, Canton, Cardiff CF11 9DQ Tel: 029 2034 1547 Fax: 029 2064 0499; 104 Pencisely Road, Cardiff CF5 1DQ — MB BS 1982 Lond.; MRCGP 1986; Cert. Family Plann. JCC 1986; DRCOG 1985; DCH RCP Lond. 1984. Clin. Asst. (Community Memory Project) Llandough Hosp. Prev: Trainee GP Wallingford Med. Centre Oxf. VTS; SHO (Psychiat.) Formile Hosp. Oxf.; SHO (Med. & Rheum.) Roy. Berks. Hosp. Reading.

EVANS, Stephanie Jayne 1 Kingscote Close, Shrewsbury SY2 6SE — MB ChB 1993 Bristol.

EVANS, Stephen Francis 39 Glasshouse Lane, Kenilworth CV8 2AH Tel: 01926 859966 — MB BS 1977 Lond.; MRCS Eng. LRCP Lond. 1977; FRCA 1981. (Guy's) Clin. Dir. (Specialist Servs.) & Cons. Anaesth. Walsgrace Hosp. Coventry. Socs: Intens. Care Soc. & Anaesth. Research Soc. Prev: Regist. Research Regist. & Sen. Regist. (IC & Anaesth.); St. Bart. Hosp. Lond.; Regist. (IC) Roy. Childr. Hosp. Melbourne Australia.

EVANS, Stephen John 17 Cornwallis Avenue, Clifton, Bristol BS8 4PP Tel: 0117 925 9118 Email: stephen.evans@bristol.ac.uk — MB ChB 1989 Bristol; PhD Bristol 1995; BSc Lond. 1983; MRCP (UK) 1992. (Bristol) Sen. Regist. (Cardiol.) Bristol Roy. Infirm. Socs: BMA; Med. Protec. Soc.

EVANS, Stephen Lawrence (retired) 23 Lake Road W., Roath Park, Cardiff CF23 5PG — MB BCh 1958 Wales. Prev: Ho. Surg. Accid. Unit St. David's Hosp. Cardiff.

EVANS, Stephen Mark 53 Longdales Avenue, New Carron Village, Falkirk FK2 7HZ Tel: 01324 613921; 9 Ash Grove, Bathgate EH48 1LS — MB ChB 1992 Ed.; BSc (Hons.) Ed. 1989, MB ChB 1992. Resid. Med. Off. & Demonst. (Anat.) BUPA Hosps. Edin.

EVANS, Stephen Mark 42 Ragstone Road, Slough SL1 2PX — MB BS 1996 Lond.

EVANS, Stephen Morda 88 Buckleigh Avenue, London SW20 9JZ; The Rayne Institute, St. Thomas' Hospital, Lambeth Palace Road, London SE1 7EH Tel: 0207 928 9292 Email: s.evans@unds.ac.uk — MB BS 1989 Lond.; BA (Hons.) Lond. 1979; MRCP (UK) 1994. (Univ. Coll. Lond.) Specialist Regist. (Gastroenterol.) St. Thomas' Hosp. Lond. Prev: Regist. (Gen. Med. & Gastroenterol.) Kent & Canterbury Hosp.; Regist. (Gen. Med.) Auckland Hosp. NZ; SHO (Gen. Med.) Kent & Canterbury Hosp.

EVANS, Stephen Nicholas The General Hospital, St Helier, Jersey Tel: 01534 79478; c/o Logwood, Frog Lane, Winford, Bristol BS40 8EX Tel: 01275 474164 — MB ChB 1988 Bristol; MRCP (UK) 1994. Regist. (Gen. Med. & Geriat.) Gen. Hosp. Jersey. Prev: SHO (Gen. Med.) E. Birm. Hosp.

EVANS, Steven Paul 22 Deva Lane, Upton, Chester CH2 1BW — BM 1987 Soton.

EVANS, Stuart Andrew 20 Knockview Road, Newtownabbey BT36 6TT — MB BCh BAO 1997 Belf.

EVANS, Mr Stuart Christopher Chelsea & Westminster Hospital, 369 Fulham Road, London SW10 9NH Tel: 020 8746 8349 — MB BS 1984 Lond.; BSc (Physiol.) Lond. 1981; FRCS (Orth.) 1995; FRCS Lond. 1988. p/t Cons. Trauma & Orthop. Chelsea & W.m. Hosp. Lond. Socs: Brit. Limb Reconstruction Soc.; Brit. Soc. Childr. Orthop. Surg. Prev: Sen. Regist. (Orthop.) Chelsea & W.m. & Univ. Coll. Hosps. Lond.; Regist. (Orthop.) Roy. Nat. Orthop. Hosp. Stanmore.

EVANS, Susan (retired) Lagom, Glendyke Road, Liverpool L18 6JR Tel: 0151 724 5386 — MB ChB 1964 Liverp.; MD Liverp. 1976; MRCP Lond. 1999. Cons. Dermat. St. Helens & Knowsley Hosps, Roy. Liverp. Univ. & BRd.green Hosp. Trust; Clin. Lect. (Dermat.) Univ. Liverp. Prev: Lect. & Research Fell. (Dermat.) Liverp. Univ.

EVANS, Susan Elisabeth Nantgarw Road Surgery, 9 Nantgarw Road, Caerphilly CF81 3FA Tel: 029 2088 3174 Fax: 029 2086 6753; 9 Nantgarw Road, Caerphilly CF83 3FA Tel: 029 2088 3174 — MB BCh 1980 Wales; DCH RCP Lond. 1984; DRCOG 1982.

EVANS, Susan Margaret 30 Fern Avenue, Jesmond, Newcastle upon Tyne NE2 2QT — MB BS 1996 Lond.

EVANS, Susan Rachel 13 Greenway, Harpenden AL5 1NQ Tel: 01582 715665 — MB BS 1996 Lond.

EVANS, Susanne Mary (retired) The Meadows, Graig Road, Lisvane, Cardiff CF14 0UF Tel: 029 2075 2215 — MB ChB 1947 Glas.; DObst RCOG 1951. Prev: Asst. GP Cardiff.

EVANS, Tamasin Kate Agard 7 Gibson Gardens, London N16 7HB — MB ChB 1994 Ed.

EVANS, Mr Thomas Arwyn, MBE Tawelan, Siliwen,, Bangor LL57 2BH Tel: 01248 364040 — MB BS Lond. 1955; FRCS Eng. 1964. (St. Bart.) Emerit. Cons. Orthop. Surg. Gwynedd HA & Robt. Jones & Agnes Hunt Orthop. Hosp. OsW.ry. Socs: Brit. Orthop. Assn. & HCSA.; Sen.Fell. BOA; HCSA. Prev: Sen. Regist. Roy. Nat. Orthop. Hosp.; Ho. Surg. Nat. Hosp. Nerv. Dis. Qu. Sq.; Ho. Off. Profess. Med. & Surg. Units St. Bart. Hosp.

EVANS, Thomas Charles Jameson (retired) Alvecote, Fleet, Aldershot Tel: 0125 144141 — MB BCh 1930 Camb.; MA Camb. MB BCh 1930; MRCS Eng. LRCP Lond. 1929. Prev: Anaesth. Farnham Hosp. Gp. & Lord Mayor Treloar's Hosp.

EVANS, Mr Thomas Goronwy, TD (retired) 55 Weigfach Lane, Cockett, Swansea SA5 5AD — MRCS Eng. LRCP Lond. 1943; FRCS Ed. 1950. Lt. Col. RAMC T & AVR Cons. Surg. Prev: Cons. Surg. Dyfed & W. Glam. AHA.

EVANS, Thomas Iorwerth 21 Anderson Lane, Southgate, Swansea SA3 2BX — MRCS Eng. LRCP Lond. 1967; MSc Lond. 1976; MFOM 1980; DIH Eng. 1976; DObst RCOG 1969. (St. Thos.) Regional Med. Off. The Welsh Office. Socs: Soc. Occupat. Med. Prev: Med. Adviser Brit. Petroleum; SHO (O & G) & Ho. Phys. Soton. Gen. Hosp.; Ho. Surg. St. Thos. Hosp. Lond.

EVANS, Thomas John 14 Kirkland Avenue, Strathblane, Glasgow G63 9BZ — MB BCh 1968 Wales; MRCP (UK) 1971. (Cardiff) Cons. Paediat. Roy. Hosp. for Sick Childr. Yorkhill & Stobhill Gen.; Hosps. Glas. Prev: Regist. (Paediat.) Roy. Hosp. Sick Childr. Edin.; Sen. Ho. Phys. Nuffield Neonat. Unit Hammersmith Hosp. Lond.; Sen. Ho. Phys. Hosp. Sick Childr. Gt. Ormond St. Lond.

EVANS, Thomas John Department Infectious Diseases, Faculty of Medicine, Imperial College, Hammersmith Hospital, Du Cane Road, London W12 0NN Tel: 020 8743 2030 Fax: 020 8740 3394 Email: tom.evans@ic.ac.uk; 137 Corbyn Street, London N4 3BX — MB BChir 1988 Camb.; MA Camb. 1986, PhD 1986; MRCP (UK) 1990; FRCP 2000 London. (Camb.) Cons. & Reader. (Infec. Dis.s) Fac. of Med., Imperial Coll.. Hammersmith Hosp. Socs: Clin. Infec. Soc. Prev: Cons. & Sen. Lect. (Infec. Dis. & Bacteriol.) Roy. Postgrad. Med. Sch. Lond.; MRC Clin. Scientist (Infec. Dis. & Bacteriol.) Hammersmith Hosp. Lond.; Regist. (Gen. Med. & Endocrinol.) Middlx. Hosp. Lond.

EVANS, Thomas Neal 21 Heol y Dre, Cefneithin, Llanelli SA14 7DR; 16 Bostock Road, Abingdon OX14 1DW Tel: 01235 538544 — MB BS 1992 Lond.; FRCA 1998. Specialist Regist. (Anaesth) Oxf. Radcliffe Hosps. Prev: SHO (Anaesth & IC) Addenbrookes Hosp. Camb; SHO (Anaesth) The Roy. Lond. Hosp.

EVANS, Thomas Robert, KStJ Royal Free Hospital, Pond St., Hampstead, London NW3 2QG Tel: 020 7794 0500 — MB ChB 1968 Liverp.; MB ChB (1st class Hons.) Liverp. 1968; FRCP Lond. 1982; FACC 1981; MRCP (UK) 1971. Cons. Cardiol. Roy. Free Hosp. Lond.; QHP(C); Dist. Surg. St. John Ambul. Lond. Dist.; Chairm. Emerg. Life Support Working Gp. Brit. Heart Foundat.; Chairm. Advanced Life Support Working Party, Resusc. Counc. (UK). Prev: Sen. Regist. (Cardiol.) Roy. Postgrad. Med. Sch.; Regist. (Med.) King's Coll. Hosp.; Ho. Phys. Liverp. Roy. Infirm.

EVANS, Thomas Ronald Jeffry CRC Department of Medical Oncology, University of Glasgow, Garscube Estate, Switchback Road, Bearsden, Glasgow G61 1BD; The Beatson Oncology Centre, Western Infirmary, Dumbarton Road, Glasgow G11 6NT — MB BS 1984 Lond.; FRCP 2000 (Lond.); MD Lond. 1993; FRCP Glas. 1998; MRCP (UK) 1988. (St. Bart. Hosp. Med. Sch.) Sen. Lect. (Med. Oncol.) Univ. Glas.; Hon. Cons. (Med. Oncol.) Beatson Oncol. Centre W.. Infirm. Glas. Socs: Brit. Assn. Cancer Research; Assn. Cancer Phys.; Eur. Soc. Med. Oncol. Prev: Lect. & Hon. Sen. Regist. (Med. Oncol.) St. Geo. Hosp. Med. Sch. Lond.; Research Regist. (Med. Oncol.) St. Geo. Hosp. Lond.; Regist. (Med.) St. Geo. Hosp. Lond.

EVANS, Thomas Wilson Viewfield Medical Centre, 3 Viewfield Place, Stirling FK8 1NJ Tel: 01786 472028 Fax: 01786 463388 — MB ChB 1976 Glas.; 1997 DOCC Med; DRCOG 1978; MRCGP 1980. Gen. Practitioner Stirling; Occasstional Phys. Fourth Valley PCT.

EVANS, Timothy Hugh David 25 Nothinggham Road, Wandsworth Common, Lond. SW17 7EA Tel: 020 8767 5661 — MB BS 1979 Lond.; MRCS Eng. LRCP Lond. 1979; MRCGP 1985; DA 1987; DRCOG 1984. Indep. Private GP Wandsworth; Dir. Med. Air Rescue Serv., Zimbabwe; Med. Dir. Blossom Ho. Sch.; Dir. Med. Baby List Co. Ltd. Socs: Chelsea Clin. Soc. Prev: RMO Portland Hosp. For Wom. & Childr. Lond.; Trainee GP Tewkesbury; Dist. Med. Off. Kariba Dist. Hosp. Zimbabwe.

EVANS, Timothy Richard 42 The Copse, Liverpool L18 3NH — MB ChB 1991 Liverp.

EVANS, Professor Timothy William Royal Brompton Hospital, Sydney St., London SW3 6NP Tel: 020 7351 8523 Fax: 020 7351 8524 — MB ChB 1979 Manch.; MB ChB (Hons.) Manch. 1979; PhD (Sheff.) 1985; BSc (Hons.) (Psychol.) Manch. 1976, MD 1990; FRCP Lond. 1993; MRCP (UK) 1982; MD Manch. 1990; DSc Sheff. 1997; Europ. Dip. Intens. Care Med. (1996). (Univ. Manch.) Prof. Intens. Care Med. Imperial Coll. Sch. Med.; Cons. IC & Thoracic Med. Roy. Brompton & W.m. Hosps. Lond.; Asst. Med. Dir. Roy. Brompton Hosp. Socs: Amer. Thoracic Soc.; Counc. Mem. Europ. Soc. of Intens. Care Med. Prev: Doverdale Fell & Sen. Regist. (ICU & Thoracic Med.) Brompton Hosp. Lond.; Dorothy Temple Cross Trav. Fell. (MRC) Univ. Calif. San Francisco, USA; Research Fell. (Med.) Univ. Sheff.

EVANS, Tom Norman Wain Department of Diagnostic Radiology, Prince Philip Hospital, Llanelli SA14 8QF Tel: 01554 756567 Fax: 01554 772271; Blaen Cwm Bychan, Tycroes, Ammanford SA18 3PP — MB BCh 1982 Wales; FRCR 1988. Cons. Radiol. P. Philip Hosp. & W. Wales Gen. Hosp. Carmarthen Dyfed. Socs: BMA. Prev: Sen. Regist. (Radiol.) Univ. Hosp. Wales Cardiff.

EVANS, Trevor Lawford 3 Denham Avenue, Llanelli SA15 4DB Tel: 01554 774864 — MRCS Eng. LRCP Lond. 1949. (St. Bart.)

EVANS, Tyrrell George John Robert Paxton Green Group Practice, Paxton Green Health Centre, 1 Alleyne Park, London SE21 8AU Tel: 020 8761 4532 Fax: 020 8766 7436 Email: tyrrell.evans@gp-g85039.nhs.uk — MB BChir 1974 Camb.; MA Camb. 1975; FRCP 1995; FRCGP 2000; DObst RCOG 1976. Gen. Practitioner. Prev: SHO (Cardiol.) Hammersmith Hosp.; SHO (Neurol.) Nat. Hosp. Qu. Sq.; SHO (Thoracic Med.) Brompton Hosp.

EVANS, Valerie Mary 17 Fields Park Road, Newport NP20 5BA Tel: 01983 65832 — MB BCh 1964 Wales; MRCPsych 1977. (Cardiff)

EVANS, Victoria Anne 20 Westbourne Road, Southport PR8 2JA — MB ChB 1998 Liverp.; MB ChB Liverp 1998.

EVANS, Victoria Judith Moor Beck, Moor Lane, Burley-in-Wharfdale, Ilkley LS29 7AF Tel: 01943 865552 Fax: 01943 865552;

Moor Beck, Moor Lane, Burley-in-Wharfdale, Ilkley LS29 7AF Tel: 01943 865552 Fax: 01943 865552 — MB BS 1977 Newc.; MRCGP 1981; DMJ(Clin) Soc. Apoth. Lond. 1993; LLM Univ Cardiff 1998. (Univ. Newc. u. Tyne) Forens. Phys., Leeds & Bradford; Clin. Asst. (Drug Dependence) Prestwich Hosp. Manch.; Hosp. Pract. (Paediat. Forens. Med.) St. Mary's Hosp. Manch.; Occupat. Phys. Craven Gilpin & Sons. Ltd. Leeds. Socs: Police Surgs. Assn. (Educat. Research Subcomm.); Roy. Soc. Med. (Treas. Clin. Forens. Med. Sect.); Brit. Acad. Forens. Sci. Prev: Police Surg. Gtr. Manch. Police Bolton & Manch.; Police Surg. W. Yorks. Police Leeds; GP Leeds.

EVANS, Victoria Lucy Stannary Surgery, Abbey Rise, Whitchurch Rd, Tavistock PL19 9BS Tel: 01822 613517 — MB BS 1989 Lond.; BSc Lond. 1986; MRCGP 1994; DFFP 1994; DRCOG 1993. (Char. Cross & Westm.)

EVANS, William Brian X Ray Department, Ipswich Hospital NHS Trust, Heath Road, Ipswich IP4 5PD Tel: 01473 712233 Fax: 01473 270655; Berner House, Hasketon, Woodbridge IP13 6JA Tel: 01394 382047 — MB BS Lond. 1962; FRCR 1975; FFR 1971; DMRD Eng. 1969. (Univ. Coll. Hosp.) Cons. Radiol. Ipswich & E. Suff. Hosp. Prev: Med. Regist. St. Chas. Hosp. Lond.; Regist. Radiol. St. Geo. Hosp. Lond.; Sen. Reg. Radiol. Univ. Coll. Hosp. & St. Mark's Hosp. Lond.

EVANS, William Emrys Tabernacle Street Surgery, 4 Tabernacle Street, Skewen, Neath SA10 6UF Tel: 01792 817009 / 817573 Fax: 01792 321029; Ty Gwyn, 33A Penywern Road, Neath SA10 7HN — MB BCh 1979 Wales; PhD Wales 1974, BSc 1971; MRCGP 1991; DRCOG 1984. GP. Prev: Force Med. Off. S. Wales Police Med. Centre M. Glam.

EVANS, William Henry Morris Prior Garth, Ewenny, Bridgend CF35 5AW Tel: 01656 3500 — MRCS Eng. LRCP Lond. 1941. (Cardiff & Middlx.) Cons. Chest Phys. Mid Glam. AHA. Prev: Asst. Med. Off. Welsh Nat. Memor. Assn.; Res. Med. Off. Llandough Hosp. Penarth.

EVANS, William Malcolm Isaac Langley Health Centre, Common Road, Slough SL3 8LE Tel: 01753 544288 Fax: 01753 592415 — BM BCh 1976 Oxf.; BA, BM BCh Oxf. 1976; MA Camb. 1980; MRCGP 1980; DRCOG 1979.

EVANS, Winifred Meadows 9 Blakeway Hollow, Much Wenlock TF13 6AR — MRCS Eng. LRCP Lond. 1956; DPH Liverp. 1960; DCH Eng. 1959.

EVANS, Wyn Vaughan Chest Clinic, Princes Charles Hospital, Merthyr Tydfil CF47 9DT Tel: 01685 721721 Email: wynevans@nglam-tr.wales.nhs.uk; Email: wynevans@attysoghotmail.com — MB ChB 1971 Sheff.; FRCP 1994; MRCP (UK) 1976. Cons. Phys. Mid Glam. HA. Prev: Sen. Regist. E. Anglian RHA; Regist. Llandough Hosp. Penarth.

EVANS-JONES, Frances Gillian Heath Lane Medical Centre, Heath Lane, Chester CH3 5UJ Tel: 01244 348844 Fax: 01244 351057; Windsor Cottage, Plough Lane, Christleton, Chester CH3 7PT Tel: 01244 335040 — MB ChB 1968 Liverp.; MFFP 1994. (Liverp.) Clin. Med. Off. Chesh. HA. Prev: Ho. Surg. & Ho. Phys. Sefton Gen. Hosp. Liverp.

EVANS-JONES, John Geraint Windsor Cottage, Plough Lane, Christleton, Chester CH3 7PT — MB ChB 1998 Sheff.; MB ChB Sheff 1998.

EVANS-JONES, Mr Jonathan Charles Department of Gynaecology, Constable Wing, Colchester General Hospital, Colchester CO4 5JL Tel: 01206 832979 Email: sandy.wright@exchange.erhc-tr.nthames.nhs.uk — MB BS 1975 Lond.; FRCOG 1994, M 1981. (Guy's Hosp. Med. Sch.) Cons. O & G Colchester Hosps. Essex. Prev: Sen. Regist. Univ. Coll. & Whittington Hosps. Lond.; Clin. Research Asst. Middlx. Hosp. Lond.; Regist. & SHO (O & G) St. Thos. Hosp. Lond.

EVANS-JONES, Lewis Gareth Women & Children's Directorate, Countess of Chester Hosp, Liverpool House, Chester CH2 1UL Tel: 01244 305059 Fax: 01244 305089 Email: secretary.dr.evansjones@coch-tr.nwest.nhs.uk; Windsor Cottage, Plough Lane, Christleton, Chester CH3 7BA — MB BS 1969 Lond.; FRCPCH 1997; FRCP (UK) 1987, M 1973; DCH Eng. 1971. (Middlx.) Cons. Paediat. Countess of Chester Hosp. Chester; Hon. Clin. Lect. Dept. Child Health Univ. Liverp. Socs: Chester & N. Wales Med. Soc.; Welsh Paediat. Soc. Prev: Sen. Regist. (Paediat.) Ahmadu Bello Univ. Hosp. Zaria, Nigeria; Regist. (Paediat.) Alder Hey Hosp. Liverp; Ho. Phys. Middlx. Hosp. Lond.

EVANS-JONES, Richard John Carnewater Practice, Dennison Road, Bodmin PL31 2LB Tel: 01208 72321 Fax: 01208 78478 — MB BS Lond. 1969; MRCS Eng. LRCP Lond. 1969; DObst RCOG 1971. (Char. Cross)

EVANS-PROSSER, Caryl Donough Geraint (retired) St Catherines, Paice Lane, Medstead, Alton GU34 5PT Tel: 01420 560271 Fax: 01420 560271 Email: caryl4ep@aol.com — BM BCh Oxf. 1957; MA Oxf. 1957; FFA RCS Eng. 1965; DA Eng. 1960; DObst RCOG 1960. Prev: Cons. Anaesth. Basingstoke Dist. Gen. Hosp.

EVANSON, Elizabeth Frances 4 Dunham House, Charcoal Road, Bowdon, Altrincham WA14 4RY Tel: 0161 941 6682 — MB BCh BAO 1953 NUI; DA Eng. 1957. (Univ. Coll. Dub.) SCMO Centr. Manch. HA. Prev: Regist. Anaesth. Withington Hosp. Manch.; Regist. (Anaesth.) & SHO (Anaesth.) Manch. Roy. Infirm.

EVANSON, Elizabeth Jane 12 Beckwith Road, London SE24 9LG — MB BS 1984 Lond.; BSc Lond. 1981, MB BS 1984; MRCP (UK) 1987; FRCR 1990. Cons. (Radiol) Roy. Lond. Hosp.

EVANSON, Professor John Malcolm (retired) High Trees, Reades Lane, Dane In Shaw, Congleton CW12 3LL Tel: 01260 272595 Email: evanson@btinternet.com — MSc Manch. 1955, BSc 1954, MB ChB 1957; FRCP Lond. 1970, M 1959. Emerit. Prof. Med. Univ. Manch. & Withington Hosp. Prev: Dean Fac. Med. Univ. Manch.

EVANSON, Rebecca Louise 17 Kenbury Mansions, Kenbury St., London SE5 9BU — MB BS 1987 Lond.; DCH RCP Lond. 1993.

EVASON, Arthur Rowland (retired) Pitfield, Gotherington Lane, Bishops Cleeve, Cheltenham GL52 8EN Tel: 01242 676337 — MRCS Eng. LRCP Lond. 1949. Prev: Ho. Surg. Connaught Hosp. Walthamstow.

EVASON, Mark Rowland The Surgery, 6 College Road, Eastbourne BN21 4HY Tel: 01323 735044 Fax: 01323 417705 — MB BS 1980 Lond.; MRCGP 1984; Cert. Family Plann. JCC 1984; DRCOG 1983. Prev: Clinic Doctor (Gen. Pract.) Mackay Hse. Dodoma, Tanzania.

EVASON, Suzanne Elizabeth 16 Kemp Place, Stockbridge, Edinburgh EH3 5HU — MB ChB 1992 Ed.

EVE, Joan Prust (retired) 23 Stradbroke Grove, Buckhurst Hill IG9 5PD Tel: 020 8504 6014 — MB BCh Wales 1947.

EVE, Judith Lynn Hebron, Bylchau, Denbigh LL16 5LT — MB BS 1975 Newc. SHO (Psychiat.) Ysbyty Gwynedd Bangor.

EVE, Julian Richard (retired) 58 Norwich Road, Horsham St Faiths, Norwich NR10 4EU Tel: 01603 898467 Email: evejulian@hotmail.com — MB BS Lond. 1950; DObst RCOG 1955. Prev: Ho. Phys., Ho. Surg. & Obst. Ho. Surg. Norf. & Norwich Hosp.

EVE, Linda Adrienne Boscombe Manor Medical Centre, 40 Florence Road, Boscombe, Bournemouth BH5 1HQ; 56 Harland Road, Southbourne, Bournemouth BH6 4DW Tel: 01202 432891 — MB BS 1982 Lond. (St. Mary's Medical School London)

EVE, Malcolm David c/o Pfizer Clinical Research Unit, Kent & Canterbury Hospital, Ethelbert Road, Canterbury CT1 3NG Tel: 01227 783160 Fax: 01227 783164 — MB ChB 1973 Leeds; BSc (Hons. Physiol.) Leeds 1970; MFPM RCP (UK) 1993. (Leeds) Med. Dir. Pfizer Clin. Research Unit Canterbury; Vis. Lect. Univ. Kent. Socs: Exec. Comm. Mem. AHPPI. Prev: Med. Dir. Leicester Clin. Research Centre; Med. Dir. Cardiff Clin. Trials Unit Univ. Wales Coll. Med. Cardiff; Cons. Burn Phys. NE Thames Regional Burn Unit St. And. Hosp. Billericay.

EVE, Richard Charles Clifton Lodge, 17 Cheddon Road, Taunton TA2 7BL Tel: 01823 282151 Fax: 01823 326755; 6 Mount Street, Bishop Lydyard, Taunton TA4 3LH Tel: 01823 432089 Email: eve97@msr.com — MB BS 1978 Lond.; MRCS Eng. LRCP Lond. 1978; DRCOG 1980.

***EVE, Richard Lloyd** 31 Burlington Road, Dore, Sheffield S17 3NQ Tel: 0114 235 1436 — MB ChB 1998 Bristol.

EVE, Roger Harry The Surgery, Torton Hill Road, Arundel BN18 9HG Tel: 01903 882517/882191 Fax: 01903 884326; Saiyang, 30 Torton Hill Road, Arundel BN18 9HL Tel: 01903 882517 Email: eveholme@ukgateway.net — MB BS 1968 Lond.; FRCGP 1991; DCH Eng. 1970. (Univ. Coll. Hosp.) Socs: BMA. Prev: SHO (Paediat.) & Ho. Phys. Roy. W. Sussex Hosp.; SHO (Obst.) Zachary Merton Hosp. Rustington.

EVELEIGH, David John (retired) 25 Glebe Avenue, Mauchline KA5 6AF — MRCS Eng. LRCP Lond. 1963; FFA RCS Eng. 1969.

Cons. Anaesth. S. Ayrsh. Hosps. Prev: Sen. Regist. (Anaesth.) Univ. Wales Hosp. Cardiff.

EVELY, Claire Lorraine 23 Drury Close, Thornhill, Cardiff CF14 9BJ — MB ChB 1984 Sheff.; MB ChB Sheff. l984. GP Cardiff. Socs: Roy. Coll. Gen. Practs.

EVELY, Roger Stephen 33 Barley Croft, Stoke Bishop, Bristol BS9 3TG Tel: 0117 968 4151 — MB ChB Sheff. 1981; MD Sheff. 1991; MRCPath 1993; MRCP (UK) 1985. Cons. Haemat. S.mead Hosp. Bristol. Prev: Sen. Regist. (Haemat.) Univ. Hosp. Wales.

EVELY, Tristan Keigwin William 49 New Century Road, Basildon SS15 6AG — MB BS 1985 Lond.

EVEMY, Keith Lionel Cardiology Office, Leazes Wing, Royal Victoria Infirmary, Queen Victoria Road, Newcastle upon Tyne NE1 4LP Tel: 0191 282 0168 Fax: 0191 227 5222 Email: keith.evemy@nuth.northy.nhs.uk; 23 Graham Park Road, Gosforth, Newcastle upon Tyne NE3 4BH Tel: 0191 284 2644 Fax: 0191 213 1551 Email: kevemy1970@aol.com — MB Camb. 1971, BChir 1970; FRCP Lond. 1988; MRCP (UK) 1973. (St. Geo. Hosp. Lond. & Univ. Camb.) Cons. Cardiol. Newc. Hosps. NHS Trust; Hon. Lect. Newc. Univ. Med. Sch. Socs: Brit. Soc. Echocardiogr.; Brit. Cardiac Soc.; Eur. Soc. Cardiol. Prev: Sen. Regist. (Cardiol.) Freeman Hosp. Newc. & Newc. Gen. Hosp.

EVENNETT, Andrew John Commons Surgery, Sandbach CW11 1HR Tel: 01270 764151 Fax: 01270 759944; 24 Main Road, Goostrey, Crewe CW4 8LL — MB ChB 1987 Bristol.

EVENNETT, Helen Clare 19 Belvedere Road, Leeds LS17 8BU Tel: 0113 268 1548 — MB ChB 1995 Leic.

EVENNETT, Jennifer 9 Orlando Road, Clarendon Park, Leicester LE2 1WN — MB ChB 1992 Leic.; MRCP (UK) 1996. Specialist Regist. (Paediat.) Qu.s Med. Centre Nottm. Prev: Specialist Regist. (Paediat.) Kings Mill Centre Mansfield; Regist. (Paediat.) W.mead Hosp. Sydney, Australia; Regist. (Transport Med.) NETS Sydney.

EVENNETT, Penelope Margaret The Old Orchard, 24 Main Road, Goostrey, Crewe CW4 8LL Tel: 01477 535412 — MB ChB 1988 Bristol. Clin. Asst. (Palliat. Med.) St Luke's (Chesh.) Hospice, Winsford.

EVENSON, Jillian 15 Highstone Court, New Wanstead, London E11 2SE — MB BS 1980 Lond.; BSc (Hons.) Pharmacol. Lond. 1977, MB BS 1980; MRCPsych 1991.

EVERALL, Ian Paul 15 Cedars Drive, Walton, Stone ST15 0BB; The Bethlem and Maudsley NHS Trust, Denmark Hill, London SE5 8AZ Tel: 020 7919 2773 Fax: 020 7740 5045 — MB ChB 1985 Leic.; BSc (Hons.) (1st cl. Med. Sc.) Leic. 1982; MB ChB (Hons.) Leic. 1985; PhD 1993; MRCPsych 1989. SHO/Regist. (Psychiat. Rotat.) Maudsley Hosp. & Inst. Psychiat. Lond.; Sen. Lect. IOP; Hon. Cons. (Psychiat.) B & M NHS Trust. Prev: MRC Clin. Train. Fell.; SHO & Regist. Maudsley Hosp.

EVERARD, Mark Lloyd Sheffield Children's Hospital, Western Bank, Sheffield S10 2TH Tel: 0114 271 7000 Fax: 0114 273 0522 Email: m.l.everard@sheffield.ac.uh — MB ChB 1981 Bristol; MRCP (UK) 1985; DM Nottm. 1997. Cons. Paediat. Sheff. Childr. Hosp.

EVERATT, Joseph Cecil Douglas Cole Department of Anaesthetics, Horton Hospital, Clifton, Banbury OX17 3DP; Garden Cottage, Charlton, Banbury Tel: 01295 810992 — MB BS 1987 Lond.; FRCA Lond. 1993. Prev: Regist. (Anaesth.) Univ. Hosp. Cardiff.

EVERATT, Silke Ashley House, Clifton, Banbury OX15 0PF — State Exam Med. Marburg 1989.

EVERDEN, Paul Ralph Birchwood Surgery, Park Lane, North Walsham NR28 0BQ Tel: 01692 402035 Fax: 01692 500367; Old Manor Farm House, The Hill, Swanton Abbott, Norwich NR10 5EA — MB BS 1982 Lond.; MRCGP 1989; DRCOG 1988; DCH RCP Lond. 1987. (St. Mary's Lond.) Chairm. PCAG; Vice Chairm. NPCAG.

EVERED, Christopher James Child Mental Health, Adcote House, Columbia Road, Oxton, Wirral — MB ChB 1978 Bristol; BSc Bristol 1975; MRCPsych 1984. Cons. Child Psychiat. Wirral.

EVERED, David Charles Whitehall Cottage, Whitehall Lane, Checkendon, Reading RG8 0TR Tel: 01491 682027 Fax: 01491 682047 — MB BS 1964 Lond.; BSc (Hons.) Lond. 1961, MD 1972; FRCP Lond. 1978, M 1967; MRCS Eng. LRCP Lond. 1964; FIBiol 1978. (Middlx.) Chair Nuffield Orthop Centre NHS Trust. Socs: Fell. Roy. Soc. Med. Prev: Second Sec. Med. Research Counc. Lond.; Dir. Ciba Foundat. Lond.; Cons. Phys. Roy. Vict. Infirm. Newc.

EVEREST, Matthew Patrick Doctors' Accommodation, Nevill Hall Hospital, Brecon Road, Abergavenny NP7 7EG — MB BCh 1998 Wales.

EVEREST, Michael Stanley 48 Warwick Park, Tunbridge Wells TN2 5EF Tel: 01892 30704 — MB BS 1958 Lond.; MB BS (Hons. Path. & Therap.) Lond. 1958; FRCP Lond. 1975, M 1960. (St. Mary's) Cons. Phys. Tunbridge Wells HA.; Hon. Cons. Phys. Tunbridge Wells HA; Med. Mem. Pens. Appeal Tribunals. Prev: Sen. Med. Regist. & Ho. Phys. Med. Unit St. Mary's Hosp. Lond.; Capt. RAMC, Med. Specialist.

EVEREST, Neil John 29 Canute Road, Faversham ME13 8SH — MB BS 1995 Lond.

EVEREST, Stephen Francis 7 Boverton Street, Roath, Cardiff CF23 5ES Tel: 029 2048 3729 — MB BCh 1990 Wales.

EVERETT, Annette Allen (retired) Lansmeade, 17A Chaucer Road, Cambridge CB2 2EB Tel: 01223 350337 Fax: 01223 357257 — MB BS Lond. 1959. Prev: Ho. Phys. (Paediat.) Middlx. Hosp. Lond.

EVERETT, Bernard James The Surgery, 1 Kimberworth Road, Rotherham S61 1AH Tel: 01709 561442/562319 Fax: 01709 740690; 17 Middle Drive, Moorgate, Rotherham S60 3DL Email: everettbj@lineone.net — BM 1980 Soton.; MRCGP 1987; DRCOG 1987. (Southampton Univ)

EVERETT, Bridget Dawn St Mary's Hospital, Greenhill Road, Leeds LS12 3QE — MB ChB 1984 Leeds. Assoc. Specialist (Psychiat.) Leeds Community & Ment. Health Servs. Trust. Socs: Roy. Coll. Psychiat. Prev: Staff Psychiat. High Royds Hosp. Menston; Regist. (Psychiat.) Stanley Royd Hosp. Wakefield.

EVERETT, Caroline Frances Badgers Quarry, Hockley La, Ashover, Chesterfield S45 0ER — BM BS 1997 Nottm.

EVERETT, Christopher Bruce Church Cottage, Holybourne, Alton GU34 4LL Tel: 01420 83304 Email: obdisk@aol.com — MB BS Lond. 1960; MRCS Eng. LRCP Lond. 1960; Cert. Av Med. (MOD) 1976; DA Eng. 1969; DObst RCOG 1965; DCH Eng. 1964. (Westm.) Vasectomy Surg. Lord Mayor Treloar Hosp. Alton; Research & Developm. WReN Wessex Assoc. RCGP. Socs: Assoc.Mem.Coll.GP. Prev: GP Alton Hants; Clin. Asst. (Anaesth.) Lord Mayor Treloar Hosp. Alton; SHO (Obst.) Univ. Coll. Hosp. Ibadan, Nigeria.

***EVERETT, Christopher Malcolm** 48 The Edison Building, 20 Westferry Road, London E14 8LU Tel: 020 7987 4041; 48 The Edison Building, 20 Westferry Road, London E14 8LU Tel: 020 7987 4041 — MB BS 1994 Lond.; MRCP 1997.

EVERETT, Janet Elizabeth (retired) Ainsty Lodge, 101 Hillcrest Rise, Cookridge, Leeds LS16 7DJ Tel: 0113 267 2605 — MB BS 1957 Lond.; MRCS Eng. LRCP Lond. 1957. Prev: Asst. Med. Off. Univ. Leeds Health Serv.

EVERETT, John Fallsworth Health Centre, Ashton Road West, Fallsworth, Manchester M35 0HN Tel: 0161 682 6297 Fax: 0161 683 5861 — MB ChB 1980 Manch.; MRCGP 1984; DRCOG 1983. Socs: Treas. Oldham Med. Soc. Prev: Med. Off. DSS Manch.; GP Dukinfield.

EVERETT, Marian Patricia University Department of Obstetrics & Gynaecology, Leeds General Infirmary, Leeds Tel: 0113 292 3668; 15 Vicarage Meadow, Pinfold Lane, Mirfield WF14 9JL Tel: 01924 492519 — MB ChB 1976 Liverp.; MFFP 1993. Clin. Asst. (Gyn.) Clarendon Wing Leeds; Clin. Asst. (Genitourin. Med.) Leeds Infirm.; Sen. Clin. Med. Off. (Family Plann. & Wom. Health) Leeds Community Trust; Mem. Family Plann. Dr's Gp. (N.. Inter Br.). Socs: (Sec.) N.. Menopause Soc.; Brit. Menopause Soc.

EVERETT, Mr Michael Thornton Highfield, 97 Hill Barton Road, Exeter EX1 3PW — MB BS 1956 Lond.; FRCS Eng. 1965; MRCS Eng. LRCP Lond. 1956. (Lond. Hosp.) p/t Med. Examr. Benefits Agency. Socs: BMA. Prev: GP Plymouth; Regist. (Surg.) United Cardiff Hosps.; Cas. Off. Radcliffe Infirm. Oxf.

EVERETT, Peter Stewart Shelton Hospital, Bicton Heath, Shrewsbury SY3 8DN Tel: 01743 492056 — MB ChB 1977 Leeds; MMedSci. Leeds 1982. Cons. Psychiat. Shelton Hosp. Shrewsbury. Prev: Cons. Psychiat. St. Mary's Hosp. ScarBoro.; Clin. Dir. Ment. Health Servs. ScarBoro. HA; Mem. Roy. Coll. Psychiat.

EVERETT, Simon Mark Centre for Digestive Diseases, Leeds General Infirmary, Leeds Email: severett@doctors.net.uk; Croft House, 3 Chestnut Grove, Calverley, Pudsey LS28 5TN — MB ChB 1991 Leeds; MD 2001; MRCP (UK) 1993. Locum Cons. Gastroenterol. Leeds Gen. Infirm. Socs: BSG, Trainee Mem. Prev:

Lect. In Med., St James' Hosp., Leeds; Specialist Regist. Bradford Roy. Infirm.; Specialist Regist. Friarage Hosp. N.allerton.

EVERETT, Suzanne Caroline The Surgery, Brickfields Road, South Woodham Ferrers, Chelmsford CM3 5JX Tel: 01245 328855 Fax: 01245 329849; The Wickett, 71 Willow Green, Ingatestone CM4 0DQ — MB BS 1980 Lond.; DRCOG 1982. (Roy. Free) Prev: Trainee GP N.ampton VTS; SHO (Psychiat.) Hill End Hosp. St. Albans; SHO (Rheum. Haem. & Gen. Med.) N.ampton Gen. Hosp.

EVERETT, Valerie Jill (retired) Barnstable Cottage, West End, Kingham, Chipping Norton OX7 6YL Tel: 01608 658111 — MB BS 1959 Lond.; MRCS Eng. LRCP Lond. 1959; FRCOG 1979, M 1968. Prev: Prof. O & G Univ. Papua, New Guinea.

EVERETT, Mr William George (retired) Lansmeade, 17A Chaucer Road, Cambridge CB2 2EB Tel: 01223 357257 — BM BCh 1958 Oxf.; MCh Oxf. 1970, MA, BM BCh 1958; FRCS Eng. 1964; FRCS Ed. 1963. Assoc. Lect. & Examr. Surg. Univ. Camb. Prev: Cons. Surg. Addenbrooke's Hosp. Camb.

EVERINGTON, Anthony Herbert (Sam) Bromley-by-Bow Health Centre, St Leonards Street, London E3 3BT — MB BS 1984 Lond.; MRCGP 1989. GP Stepney Lond.; Barrister-at-Law 1978. Socs: (Counc.) BMA.

EVERINGTON, Tamara Frances 19 Granville Road, Oxted RH8 0BX — MB BS 1993 Lond.

EVERISS, Janet Sandy Lane Surgery, Sandy Lane, Leyland, Preston PR25 2EB Tel: 01772 909915 Fax: 01772 909911; Sandiways, 10 Ewell Close, Chorley PR6 8TT Tel: 012572 61687 — MB ChB 1972 Manch.; MRCGP 1976; DObst RCOG 1976.

EVERITT, Alex Daniel Epilepsy Research Group, Institute of Neurology, Queen Square, London WC1N 3BG Tel: 020 7837 3611 Email: a.everitt@ion.ucl.ac.uk; Flat B, 8 Lancaster Grove, Belsize Park, London NW3 4NX Tel: 020 7722 8002 — MB BS 1990 Newc.; MRCP (UK) 1993. Specialist Regist. Neurol. SE Lond. Rotat. St Thomas. Hosp. Socs: BMA. Prev: Research Fell. & Regist. (Neurol.) Inst. Neurol. Qu. Sq. Lond. & MRI Unit Nat. Soc. Epilepsy Chalfont St. Peter.

EVERITT, Barbara Mary 128 High Street, Bentley, Doncaster DN5 0AT Tel: 01302 785541; Wrangbrook Grange, Wrangbrook Lane, Upton, Pontefract WF9 1LN Tel: 01977 40613 — MB ChB 1983 Liverp. Prev: GP Pontefract; Trainee GP Sheff. VTS; Ho. Off. Roy. Liverp. Hosp.

EVERITT, Elizabeth Florence (retired) 75 The Grove, Marton, Middlesbrough TS7 8AL Tel: 01642 316177 — MB BS 1947 Lond.; MRCS Eng. LRCP Lond. 1946; FFA RCS Eng. 1955; DA Eng. 1953; DA McGill 1951. Hon. Cons. Anaesth. S. Cleveland Hosp. Prev: Cons. Anaesth. S. Tees Gp. Hosps.

EVERITT, Hazel Anne Kings House, 14 New Road, Romsey SO51 7LN — MB ChB 1993 Bristol; DCH 1996; DRCOG 1997; DFFP 1997; MRCGP (with Distinction) 1998. (Bristol) Research Train. Fell. Primary Med. Care dept Univ. of Soton. Prev: GP Regist. Bath; SHSHO (O & G) RUH Bath; SHO (Psychiat.) Green La. Hosp. Devizes.

EVERITT, Margaret Teresa South Barn, Huccombe, Kingsbridge TQ7 2EP Tel: 01548 580733 — MB ChB BAO 1951 NUI; DA Eng. 1957. (Cork)

EVERITT, Michael William (retired) South Barn, Huccombe, Kingsbridge TQ7 2EP Tel: 01548 580733 — MB BS 1957 Lond.; MRCS Eng. LRCP Lond. 1957; DObst RCOG 1960. Ref. DSS.

EVERITT, Susanna Margaret Alice The Surgery, School Lane, Upton-upon-Severn, Worcester WR8 0LF Tel: 01684 592696 Fax: 01684 593122; Sapey Pitchard, Clifton-upon-Teme, Worcester WR6 6HE Tel: 01886 853593 — MB BS 1980 Lond.; MFHom. 2000; MRCGP 1985; DRCOG 1983. (St. Bart.)

EVERS, Abigail Mary Anne 2 Lea Bank, Marquis Lane, Harpenden AL5 5AE — MB BS 1991 Lond.; MRCGP 1996; DFFP 1996; DCH RCP Lond. 1995. (Univ. Lond., Char. Cross & Westm.)

EVERS, Jean-Anne Galbraith Cran, Gripper, Bolton and Evers, Health Centre, Chacewater, Truro TR4 8QS Tel: 01872 560346 Fax: 01872 561184; 5 Clifton Gardens, Truro TR1 3HL — MB ChB 1974 Ed.; BSc Ed. 1971, MB ChB 1974. (Ed.)

EVERS, John Alexander Camborne - Redruta Community Hospital, Illogan Highway, Redruth TR15 3ER Tel: 01209 881636 Fax: 01209 881714; 5 Clifton Gardens, Truro TR1 3HL Tel: 01872 263134 — BM BCh 1977 Oxf.; FRCP Lond. 1992; MRCP (UK) 1974; MRCS Eng. LRCP Lond. 1972. (Oxf. & St. Thos.) Cons. Phys. Special Responsibil. for Elderly Roy. Cornw. Hosp. Trust. Socs: Fell. RSM. Prev: Sen. Regist. (Gen. & Geriat. Med.) Oxf. AHA (T); Regist. (Med.) S.mead Hosp. Bristol; Sen. Resid. (Med. Oncol.) Cancer Control Agency of Brit. Columbia, Canada.

EVERSHED, Edward Zygmunt George Mentmore Road Surgery, 30 Mentmore Road, Leighton Buzzard LU7 2NZ Tel: 01525 383202 Fax: 01525 851740; 46 Chesterfield Crescent, Wing, Leighton Buzzard LU7 0TW Tel: 01296 688438 — MB BS 1975 Lond.; MRCGP 1979; DRCOG 1978. (Middlx.) Socs: BMA. Prev: Trainee Gen. Pract. ScarBoro. Vocational Train. Scheme.

EVERSHED, Marcus Charles, Surg. Lt.-Cdr. RN 62 Napier Road, Hamworthy, Poole BH15 4NB — MB ChB 1989 Leic.; DFFP 1995. GP Regist. Adam Pract. Poole; Sen. Med. Off. Roy. Marines Poole. Prev: SHO (A & E & O & G) Derriford Hosp. Plymouth; SHO (Surg.) Roy. Naval Hosp. Plymouth.

EVERSHED, Trevor Albury, Air Commodore RAF Med. Retd. (retired) 57 Hillsway, Littleover, Derby DE23 7DU Tel: 01773 771275 — MRCS Eng. LRCP Lond. 1945; BA Camb. 1943, MB BChir 1946; MFCM 1974; DPH Lond. 1956; DIH Eng. 1956; MFOM RCP Lond. 1981. Prev: Sen. Med. Off. Rolls-Royce Ltd. Derby.

EVERSON, Gary Scott Manor Park Medical Centre, 204 Harborough Avenue, Sheffield S2 1QU Tel: 0114 239 8602 Fax: 0114 265 8010 — MB ChB 1977 Sheff.

EVERSON, Mr Noel Williams The Leicester Royal Infirmary, Leicester LE1 5WW Tel: 0116 254 1414; 6 Meadowcourt Road, Oadby, Leicester LE2 2PB Tel: 0116 271 2512 — MS Lond. 1981, MB BS (Hons.) 1967; FRCS Eng. 1973. (The Middlesex Hospital Medical School) Cons. Gen. Surg. Leics. Roy. Infirm. Socs: Assn. Coloproctol.; Fell. Roy. Soc. Med.; Sect. Proct. Prev: Regist. (Surg.) Addenbrooke's Hosp. Camb.; SHO (Surg.) Norf. & Norwich Hosp.; Ho. Surg. Surg. Unit Middlx. Hosp. Lond.

EVERTON, Maurice John 31 Manor Close, Edwalton, Nottingham NG12 4BH — MB ChB 1950 Birm.

EVERY, Harriet Mary Cricketfield Surgery, Cricketfield Road, Newton Abbot TQ12 2AS Tel: 01626 208020 Fax: 01626 333356 — MB ChB 1980 Leeds; DRCOG. p/t GP Partner, Cricketfield Surg., Newton Abbot; Race Course Med. Officier, Newton Abbot Race Course, Devon & Exeter Race Course. Socs: BMA; BASEM.

EVERY, Mark 22 Home Close, Lower Oddington, Moreton-in-Marsh GL56 0XA — BM 1991 Soton.; BSc (Hons.) Biochem. Wales 1987; DFFP 1997.

EVES, Michael John Doclands Medical Centre, Blanche Street, Ashton-on-Ribble, Preston PR2 2RL Tel: 01772 723222 Fax: 01772 726619 — MB ChB 1974 Manch. Company Doctor for Thorn Lighting Ltd. Socs: Assoc. Mem. Brit. Med. Acupunc. Soc.

EVES, Sheila Christine 71 Woodside Drive, Waterfoot, Glasgow G76 0HD — MB ChB 1989 Ed.

EVESON, Jeannette Gaunt (retired) The Old Schoolhouse, Tuck Hill, Six Ashes, Bridgnorth WV15 6EW Tel: 01746 780237 — MB ChB 1946 Birm.; DObst RCOG 1954.

EVESON, Sarah Elizabeth 46 Manor Farm Meadow, East Leake, Loughborough LE12 6LL — MB BS 1994 Lond.

EVISON, Demetrius Manor Farm, Skelton, Goole DN14 7RH — MB ChB 1994 Liverp.

EVISON, Gordon (retired) Westfield Lodge, Weston Road, Bath BA1 2XT Tel: 01225 425898 — MB ChB 1957 Manch.; FRCR 1975; FFR 1967; DMRD Ed. 1965. Cons. Radiol. Roy. United Hosp. & Roy. Nat. Hosp. Rheum. Dis. Bath. Prev: Sen. Regist. Bristol Roy. Infirm.

EVISON, Jonathan Geoffrey Hall Grove Surgery, 4 Hall Grove, Welwyn Garden City AL7 4PL Tel: 01707 328528 Fax: 01707 373139 — MB BS 1987 Lond.; BSc Lond 1984, MB BS 1987; MRCGP 1991; DCH RCP Lond. 1990; DRCOG 1990. Prev: Trainee GP Welwyn Gdn. City VTS; Ho. Surg. N. Middlx. Hosp.; Ho. Phys. Univ. Coll. & Middlx. Hosps. Lond.

EVISON, Michelle Nicola 5 Kensington Road, Chorley PR7 1LU — MB ChB 1998 Manch.; MB ChB Manch 1998.

EVISON, Peter Raymond Holloway The Old Vicarage, Woodbastwick, Norwich NR13 6AL — MB BS 1961 Lond.; MRCS Eng. LRCP Lond. 1960. (St. Bart.)

EVISON, Roy Anthony Regent House Surgery, 21 Regent Road, Chorley PR7 2DH Tel: 01257 264842 Fax: 01257 231387; 6 King's Lea, Heath Charnock, Chorley PR7 4EN — MB ChB 1972 Manch.; MRCGP 1978; DObst RCOG 1975.

EVITT, John Alastair (retired) Upper Redhall, Stirling FK8 3AE Tel: 01786 860722 — MB ChB 1955 Glas. Prev: Ho. Surg. W.. Infirm. Glas.

EWAH, Bernadette Ngozi Epsom Healthcare NHS Trust, Dorking Road, Epsom KT18 7EG Tel: 01372 726100 Fax: 01372 743421; 18 Onslow Avenue, South Cheam, Sutton SM2 7EB Tel: 020 8642 6585 — MB BS 1976 Ibadan; MRCP (UK) 1981; FFA RCS (UK) 1988; DA (UK) 1986. Cons. Anaesth. Epsom Healthcare NHS Trust. Socs: Assn. Anaesth. Prev: Sen. Regist. Rotat. Roy. Free Hosp. Lond.; Regist. (Anaesth.) St. Mary's Hosp. Lond.

EWAH, Mr Peter Oifoghe Wrexham Maelor Hospital, Croesnewydd Road, Wrexham LL13 7TD Tel: 01978 291100; 18 Onslow Avenue, South Cheam, Sutton SM2 7EB — MB BS 1976 Benin; FRCS Ed. 1982. Cons. Urol. Basildon Hosp. Socs: Brit. Assn. Urol.

EWAN, Gavin Dysart Snaddon Oakfield Surgery, Oakfield Road, Aylesbury HP20 1LJ Tel: 01296 423797 Fax: 01296 399246; 45 Oving Road, Whitchurch, Aylesbury HP22 4JF Tel: 01296 641797 Fax: 01296 641797 — MB BS 1973 Lond.; MRCS Eng. LRCP Lond. 1973; Adv Dip Med 1998; AFOM 1999; Adv. Dip Occupat. Med 1999. (Roy. Free) GP Princip. Clin. Governance Lead Oakfield Surg., Aylesbury; Occupat. Health Phys. Aylesbury Vale Community Healthcare NHS Trust. Socs: Soc. Occupat. Med.

EWAN, Pamela Wilson Allergy & Clinical Immunology Clinic, Addenbrooke's Hospital, Hills Road, Cambridge CB2 2QQ Tel: 01223 217777 Fax: 01223 216953; 7 Chaucer Road, Cambridge CB2 2EB Tel: 01223 356117 Fax: 01223 512793 — MB BS 1969 Lond.; MA Camb. 1993; FRCP Lond. 1986; MRCP (UK) 1971; MRCS Eng. LRCP Lond. 1969; FRCPath 1997, M 1992; DObst RCOG 1971. (Roy. Free) Cons. Allergy & Clin. Immunol. Addenbrooke's Hosp. Camb.; Assoc. Lect. Univ. Camb. Clin. Sch. Socs: Assn. Phys.; Sub-comm. Mem. Europ. Acad. Allergy and Clin. Immunol.; Pres. Brit. Soc. For Allergy & Clin. Immunol. Prev: Sen. Lect. (Clin. Immunol.) St. Mary's Hosp. Med. Sch. Lond.; Sen. Regist. (Clin. Immunol.) Hammersmith Hosp. Lond.; Regist. (Med.) Hammersmith Hosp. Lond. & Guy's Hosp. Lond.

EWART, Colin Hamilton (retired) 20 Princes Way, Fleetwood FY7 8PG Tel: 01253 771336 — MRCS Eng. LRCP Lond. 1949. Prev: Ho. Surg. & Ho. Phys. Harold Wood Hosp.

EWART, David William Craigmillar Medical Group, 106 Niddrie Mains Road, Edinburgh EH16 4DT Tel: 0131 536 9500 Fax: 0131 536 9545 — MB ChB 1980 Ed.; MRCGP 1984.

EWART, Henrietta Southfield House, 67 High St., Braunston, Daventry NN11 7HS Tel: 01788 891217 Fax: 01788 891217 — MB BS 1983 Lond.; MA Oxf. 1986, BA 1980; MFPHM RCP (UK) 1990; DRCOG 1985. (Middlx.) Cons. Pub. Health Med. N.ampton HA.

EWART, Ian Alexander c/o Anaesthetic Department, Southend General Hospital, Prittlewell Chase, Westcliff on Sea SS0 0 — MB BS 1982 Lond.; BSc Lond. 1979, MB BS 1982; FFA RCS Eng. 1987. Cons. Anaesth. S.end Gen. Hosp. Prev: Sen. Regist. (Anaesth.) St. Mary's Hosp. & Nat. Hosp. Neurol. & Neurosurg. Lond.; Regist. (Anaesth.) Roy. Free Hosp. Lond.

EWART, Ian Charles Austen Road Surgery, 1 Austen Road, Guildford GU1 3NW Tel: 01483 564578 Fax: 01483 505368; 35 Orchard Road, Shalford, Guildford GU4 8ER Tel: 01483 572013 — MB BS 1982 Lond.; PhD Bristol 1975, BSc 1972; MRCGP 1993; Cert. Family Plann. JCC 1986; DRCOG 1986; DCH RCP Lond. 1985. (St. Bart.)

EWART, Janet Chessher 2 Haywood Park, Stewkley, Leighton Buzzard LU7 0HE — MB ChB 1969 Liverp.; DObst RCOG 1973.

EWART, Kathryn Elizabeth Stoneleigh, 125 Circular Rd, Newtownabbey BT37 0RE — MB ChB 1997 Dundee.

EWART, Margaret (retired) Darach Mor, 7 Barhill Drive, Dalbeattie DG5 4RG — MB BCh BAO 1948 Belf.; DPH Belf. 1956. Prev: SCMO Lewisham & N. S.wark HA.

EWART, Michael Colin Department of Anaesthetics and Intensive Care, Royal Berkshire Hospital, London Road, Reading RG1 5AN Tel: 0118 987 7065 Fax: 0118 987 7087 Email: mike.ewart@rbbh-tr.anglox.nhs.uk; Grange Farm, Islandstone Lane, Hurst, Reading RG10 0RJ Tel: 0118 934 0994 — MB BS 1979 Lond.; FRCA 1985; T(Anaes) 1991. (St. Mary's Hospital) Cons. Anaesth. Roy. Berks. Hosp. Reading. Prev: Sen. Regist. (Anaesth.) Hammersmith Hosp. Lond.; Regist. (Anaesth.) Hosps. for Sick Childr. Gt. Ormond St. Lond. & Char. Cross & Brompton Hosps. Lond.

EWART, Philip Albert Fulton Street Surgery, 94 Fulton Street, Glasgow G13 1JE Tel: 0141 959 3391 Fax: 0141 950 2692 — MB BCh BAO 1989 Belf.; MRCGP 1993.

EWBANK, George Stanley Alfred Huthwaite Health Centre, New Street, Huthwaite, Sutton-in-Ashfield NG17 2LR Tel: 01623 513147 Fax: 01623 515574 Email: george.ewbank@gp-c84077.nhs.uk; Tel: 01623 513147 Email: gewbank@genie.co.uk — BM BS 1978 Nottm.; BMedSci Nottm. 1976. (Nottm.) GP Principle; PCT Exec. Chair & Clin. Director, Ashfield Primary Care Trust, Sutton in Ashfield. Socs: Mansfield Med. Soc.

EWBANK, Jane Anna Flat 3, 17 The Paragon, Bath BA1 5LX — MB BS 1993 Lond.; MA Camb. 1995. Specialist Regist., Forens. Psychiat., Ravenswood Ho. Medium Secure Unit. Prev: SHO Rotat. (Psychiat.) Addenbrooke's NHS Trust; SHO Rotat. (Psychiat.) Mid-Anglia Community Health Trust W. Suff. Hosp. Bury St. Edmunds.

EWBANK, Josephine Alice 7 Castle Court, Castle St., Carlisle CA3 8TP Tel: 01228 810293 — MB ChB Ed. 1941; MD Ed. 1961; FRCOG 1959, M 1947. (Ed.) Socs: BMA; Emerit. Mem. Wom. Vis. Gyn. Club; (Ex-Pres.) Med. Wom. Federat. Prev: Sen. Cons. (O & G) Camb. Infirm.; SHO (O & G) Cumbld. Infirm. Carlisle & E. Cumbria HA; Regist. (O & G) Edin. Infirm.

EWELL, Ernest John, OBE, TD, OStJ The White House, Marks Corner, Newport PO30 5UD Tel: 01983 293750 — MRCS Eng. LRCP Lond. 1940; FRCGP 1975. (St. Mary's) Col. late RAMC; Hon. Surg. Roy. Yacht Squadron Cowes. Prev: ADMS 43 Wessex Inf. Div. (TA); Clin. Asst. Dermat. St. Mary's Hosp. Newport.

EWEN, Donna Mae Kyreen, Blackhall Road, Inverurie AB51 4JE — MB ChB 1995 Glas.

EWEN, George 3 Arthurlie Drive, Newton Mearns, Glasgow G77 5AF Tel: 01415770565 Email: geweng@netscape.net — MB ChB Aberd. 1973; BMedBiol (Hons.) Aberd. 1970. (Aberd.) Med. Adviser Benefits Agency Glas. Prev: Princip. GP Aberd.; Ltd. Specialist Anaesth. & Appts. Gen. Med. & Geriat. Shetland Health Bd.; Lect. (Path.) Univ. Edin.

EWEN, Jean Mercedes 19 Durban Road, London SE27 9RW; 80 Stoneham Road, Attadale 6156 WA, Australia Tel: 08 9 330 8342 — MB BCh BAO 1985 Dub.; DRCOG 1992. Clin. Asst. (Family Plann.) King's Coll. Hosp. Lond.; GP Austral. Med. Assn.

EWEN, Roderick Alistair Sharma and Ewen, Medical Centre, 13-15 Barmouth Road, London SW18 2DT Tel: 020 8874 4984 Fax: 020 8877 0732 — MB BS 1984 Lond. Prev: SHO (Geriat.) Farnham Hosp.; SHO (Paediat.) Lewisham Hosp.; SHO (Obst.) Kingston Hosp.

EWEN, Shona Jean 3 Arthurlie Drive, Newton Mearns, Glasgow G77 5AF — MB ChB 1998 Aberd.; MB ChB Aberd 1998.

EWEN, Mr Simon Pascoe Department of Obstetrics & Gynaecology, St Mary's Hospital, Milton Road, Portsmouth PO3 6AD Tel: 023 92 28 6000 Ext: 3510 Fax: 023 9286 6633 — MB ChB 1984 Otago; MRCOG 1991; DObst 1986. (Otago, Dunedin, New Zealand) Cons. O & G St Mary's Hosp. Portsmouth, BUPA Hosp. Havant & King Edwd. VII Hosp. Midhurst. Socs: Brit. Soc. Gyn. Endoscopy; Brit. Soc. Colpos. & Cerv. Path. Prev: Sen. Regist. St Peter's Hosp. Chertsey; Research Fell. (Gyn. Endoscopy) Roy. Surrey Co. Hosp. Guildford.

EWEN, Stanley William Barclay Pathology Department, Link Building, ForesterHill, Aberdeen AB25 2ZD Tel: 0133 022809 Email: s.w.b.ewen@abdn.ac.uk; Balanreich, Bridge of Cairn, Ballater AB35 5UD — MB ChB 1964 Aberd.; PhD Aberd. 1971; MRCPath 1972. (Aberd.) Cons.

EWER, Andrew Keith c/o Neonatal Unit, Birmingham Women's Hospital, Edgbaston, Birmingham B15 2TG Tel: 0121 472 1377 Fax: 0121 627 2689 Email: a.k.ewer@bham.ac.uk; 14 Kingshill Drive, Kings Norton, Birmingham B38 8SA — MB ChB 1985 Birm.; MRCP (UK) 1989; FRCPCH 1996; MD Univ of Birmingham 1998. (Birm.) Sen. Research Fell. & Hon. Cons. Neonat. Univ. Birm. Socs: Neonat. Soc.; Paediat. Research Soc. Prev: Sen. Fell. Neonat. Intens. Care Unit Monash Med. Centre Melbourne, Austral.; Sheldon Research Fell. Inst. Child Health Birm.; Regist. (Paediat.) Birm. Childr. Hosp.

EWER, Fritz (retired) 55 Military Road, Sandgate, Folkestone CT20 3BH Tel: 01303 48680 — MD 1932 Berlin; LRCP LRCS Ed. LRFPS Glas. 1934.

EWING, Archibald Yeats Orton Malborne Health Centre, Herlington, Peterborough PE2 5PH Tel: 01733 233016 Fax: 01733

232999 — MB ChB 1961 Ed.; FRCGP 1993, M 1974; DFFP 1993; DObst RCOG 1963. (Ed.) Prev: SHO Derbysh. Childr. Hosp.; Ho. Phys. Derby City Hosp.; Ho. Surg. O & G Chester City Hosp.
EWING, Carol Iris 8 High Lane, Chorlton-cum-Hardy, Manchester M21 9DF Tel: 0161 881 8783 Fax: 0161 741 5597 — MB ChB 1978 Manch.; BSc (Med. Sci.) Hons. St. And. 1975; MD Manch. 1993; MRCP (UK) 1983; DRCOG 1981; DCH RCP Lond. 1980. Cons. Paediat. Booth Hall Childr. Hosp. Manch. Socs: Manch. Med. Soc.; Med. Wom. Federat.; Brit. Paediat. Assn. Prev: Sen. Regist. (Paediat.) N. W.. RHA.; Tutor (Child Health) Univ. Manch.; Clin. Research Fell. Booth Hall Child. Manch. Hosp.
EWING, Conrad Gorlach 20 Aitken Street, Largs KA30 8A Tel: 01475 674545; 16 Cathcart Road, Largs KA30 8JB Tel: 01475 675496 — MB ChB 1964 Glas. GP Largs.
EWING, Conrad Paul Greenend, Spey St., Garmouth, Fochabers IV32 7NJ — MB ChB 1992 Ed.; MRCGP 1998; DTM & H 1997.
EWING, David John Scottish Executive health Dept, St. Andrews House, Edinburgh EH1 3DG Tel: 0131 244 2275 Fax: 0131 244 2069; 100 Redford Loan, Edinburgh EH13 0AT — MB BChir 1965 Camb.; MD Camb. 1977; FRCP Ed. 1983; MRCP (UK) 1970; MRCS Eng. LRCP Lond. 1965. (Camb. & Guy's) Sen. Med. Off Scott. Exec. health Dept. Prev: Wellcome Trust Sen. Lect. Univ. Edin. (Med.) Roy. Infirm. Edin.; Hon. Cons. Phys. Lothian HB; Lect. Roy. Infirm. Edin.
EWING, Donald Andrew (retired) 39 Shorncliffe Road, Folkestone CT20 2UD Tel: 01303 259964 — MB ChB Sheff. 1951; MRCS Eng. LRCP Lond. 1951; DCH Eng. 1962; DObst RCOG 1959. Prev: Ho. Phys. Sheff. Childr. Hosp. & Soton. Gen. Hosp.
EWING, Fiona Mary Elizabeth 10 Gransby Road, Edinburgh EH16 5NL — MB ChB 1991 Ed.; MSc Ed. 1999; FRCR 2001; MRCP (UK) 1994. Specialist Regist. (Radiol.) Roy. Infirm. Edin.
EWING, Greta The Health Centre, Orton Malborne, Peterborough PE2 Tel: 01733 233016; Olde Mullions, 23 Cherry Orton Road, Orton Waterville, Peterborough PE2 5EQ Tel: 01733 231860 — MB ChB 1959 Sheff.; DA Eng. 1965. (Sheff.) Socs: BMA. Prev: Clin. Asst. (Anaesth.) Hull 'A' Hosp. Gp.; Anaesth. Regist. Derby Hosp. Gp.; SHO Derbysh. Childr. Hosp.
EWING, Jane Mary Dale Farmhouse, Reepham Road, Bawdeswell, Dereham NR20 4RU Tel: 01362 688582 — MB ChB 1984 Bristol; DRCOG 1987; DCH RCP Lond. 1986. Clin. Asst. (Diabetes).
EWING, Joanne Claire Flat 2/5/3, St John's Court, Howden W., Livingston EH54 6PP — BM BCh 1991 Oxf.
EWING, Peter Anthony The Health Centre, King St., Crieff PH7 35A Tel: 01764 652456 Email: peter.ewing@zetnet.co.uk; Kildonan House, Caerlaverock, By Muthill, Crieff PH5 2BD Tel: 01764 681693 — MB ChB 1992 Aberd.; DRCOG 1995; MRCGP 1996; DFFP 1996. Partner GP, Savage Ewing & Kirkwood; Clin. Asst. Psychiat. Crieff Hosp. Socs: Brit. Assn. for Immed. Care. Prev: GP Regist. Oxf. VTS.
EWING, Mr Robert Aston House, Aston Lane, Aston, Runcorn WA7 3DG Tel: 01928 710222 — MB BS 1973 Lond.; FRCS Eng. 1978. Cons. Urol. Halton Gen. Hosp. Runcorn. Prev: Sen. Regist. (Urol.) Yorks. RHA.
EWING, Robert George Riemardon, Church Road, California, Falkirk FK1 2BD — MB ChB 1995 Aberd.
EWINGS, Sally Ann Barnfield Hill Surgery, 12 Barnfield Hill, Exeter EX1 1SR Tel: 01392 432761 Fax: 01392 422406 — MB BS 1985 Lond.; BSc Lond. 1982; MRCGP 1989.
EWINS, Anna Maria Department of Pathology, Glasgow Royal Infirmary, Glasgow G4 — MB ChB 1989 Glas. SHO (Path.) Glas. Roy. Infirm.
EWINS, Claire Marie 23 Tantallon Drive, Carron, Falkirk FK2 8DJ — MB ChB 1995 Glas.
EWINS, David Laurence Countess of Chester Hospital, Liverpool Road, Chester CH2 1UL Tel: 01244 366451 Fax: 01244 366455 Email: dr.ewins@coch-tr.nwest.nhs.uk — BM 1983 (Hons.) Southampton; DM 1993 Southampton; MRCP 1986 UK; FRCP 2000 UK. (Southampton) Cons. Gen. Med. Endocrinol. & Diabetes Countess of Chester NHS Trust Chester; Cons. Gen. Med., Endormal & Diabetes, Grosvenor Nuffield Hosp., Chester. Prev: Sen. Regist. (Gen. Med., Endocrinol. & Diabetes) Manch. Roy. Infirm.; MRC Research Fell. & Hon. Lect. Kings Coll. Sch. Med. Lond.; Regist. (Med.) Kings Coll. Lond.
EWINS, Debbie 11 Caledonia Place, First Floor Flat, Clifton, Bristol BS8 Tel: 0117 973 9340; 19 Downlands Court, Browning Road, Luton LU4 0LW Tel: 01582 508276 — MB ChB 1993 Bristol. SHO (Paediat.) Derby Childr. Hosp. Socs: BMA & Med. Defence Union. Prev: Ho. Off. (Surg.) Bristol Roy. Infirm.; Ho. Off. (Med.) Frenchay Hosp. Bristol.
EXADAKTILOS, Athanasios Plastic Surgery Department, Queen Victoria Department, East Grinstead RH19 3DZ Tel: 01342 410210 Fax: 01342 317907; 4 Anixeos Street, 55236 Panorama, Thessaloniki, Greece Tel: 00 031 342148 — Ptychio Iatrikes 1987 Thessalonika. Regist. (Plastic Surg.) Qu. Vict. Hosp. E. Grinstead. Prev: Vis. Fell. Regist. (Plastic Surg.) Whiston Hosp. Prescot.
EXELL, Clifford (retired) Alde Cottage, Hacheston, Woodbridge IP13 0DT Tel: 01728 746857 — BM BCh 1938 Oxf.; MA Oxf. 1947, BA 1935. Prev: Med. Off. Forest Hosp. Buckhurst Hill.
EXLEY, Andrew Robert Papworth Hospital, Papworth Everard, Cambridge CB3 8RE Tel: 01480 364117 Fax: 01480 364330 Email: andrew.exley@papworth-tr.anglox.nhs.uk — MB BS 1983 Lond.; MRCPath 1996; MA 1986 OXF; MRCP 1986 UK; BA 1980 (Hons Physiol. Sci.). (Oxford and The Royal London Hospital) Cons. Immunol. Socs: Chairm., Clin. Immunol. Affinity Gp., Brit. Soc. for Immunol.; BSACI. Prev: Sen. Regist. (Clin. Immunol. & Allergy) & Hon. Clin. Lect. Med. Sch. Birm.; Research Fell. (Infec. Dis.) Hammersmith Hosp. Lond.; Regist. (Med.) Leic. Roy. Infirm.
EXLEY, Anne 18 Talbot Avenue, Huddersfield HD3 3BH — MB ChB 1977 Leeds; MSc (Community Paediat.) Nottm. 1994; DCH RCP Lond. 1993. Assoc. Specialist (Community Paediat.) Huddersfield NHS Trust.
EXLEY, Diane Student Services Centre, 150 Mount Pleasant, Liverpool L69 3BX Tel: 0151 794 4720 — MB ChB 1989 Glas.
EXLEY, John (retired) 1 Elgar Close, Alverstoke, Gosport PO12 2LU — MB ChB 1944 Leeds.
EXLEY, Kenneth Alfred (retired) 48 Westminster Crescent, Burn Bridge, Harrogate HG3 1LY Tel: 01423 872207 — MD Leeds 1953, MB ChB 1947; DObst RCOG 1950. Prev: Cons. Clin Neurophysiologist Gen. Infirm. & St. Jas. Hosp. Leeds.
EXLEY, Margaret Dorothy (retired) 1 Elgar Close, Alverstoke, Gosport PO12 2LU — MB ChB 1944 Leeds. JP. Prev: Clin. Med. Off. Hants. AHA.
EXLEY, Penelope The Surgery, 29 Chesterfield Drive, Ipswich IP1 6DW Tel: 01473 741349; 31 Park Road, Ipswich IP1 3SX — MB ChB 1972 Leeds; LMCC 1974. Occupat. Health Phys. Brit. Sugar plc Ipswich. Socs: BMA & Med. Wom. Federat.
EXLEY, Peter Michael Church Street Medical Centre, 11B Church Street, Eastwood, Nottingham NG16 3BP Tel: 01773 712065 Fax: 01773 534295 — MB ChB 1987 Liverp.
EXON, Mr David Jonathan 19 Wilmington Road, Birmingham B32 1DY — MB BS 1990 Lond.; FRCS Ireland 1997.
EXON, Mary Elizabeth Edenmore, 142 Thwaite St., Cottingham HU16 4RF Tel: 01482 847203 — MB ChB 1956 St. And. (St. And.)
EXON, Peter Douglas (retired) 10a Duke Humphrey Road, London SE3 0TY Tel: 020 8297 2441 Fax: 020 8297 0306 Email: exonp@aol.com — MB ChB Birm. 1963; MRCP Lond. 1969. Prev: Sen. Med. Off. DoH.
EXON, Susan Mary Spokes and Partners, Phoenix Family Care, 35 Park Road, Coventry CV1 2LE Tel: 024 7622 7234 Fax: 024 7663 4816; 18 Whoberley Avenue, Coventry CV5 8EP — MB ChB 1983 Birm.; DRCOG 1987.
EXPOSITO COLL, Patricio 2 Briar Lea, Worksop S80 3QL — LMS 1991 Alicante.
EXTON, Geoffrey Lucas Spinney Cottage, Fairfield Road, Poulton-le-Fylde FY6 8LD — MB BS 1964 Newc. Med. Off. BDH Ltd. Poole; Apptd. Doctor Poole/Bournemouth Area, Control of Asbestos/Ionising; Radiat.s / Carcinogenic Subst.s Regs.
EXTON, Louise Christine 85 Milton Road, Portsmouth PO3 6AL — MB BS 1992 Lond.
EXTON, Wendy Rowena Sefton Lodge, 18 Leicester Road, Branksome Park, Poole BH13 6BZ Tel: 01202 762802 — MB BS 1967 Newc. (Newc.) Assoc. RCGP. Socs: Brit. Soc. Med. & Dent. Hypnotists.
EXWORTH, Desmond Brian 85 Whithamwood Road, Frinton-on-Sea CO13 9LD — MB ChB 1975 Birm. Prev: GP Frinton-on-Sea.
EXWORTHY, Timothy Paul Nicholas Redford Lodge Hospital, 15 Church St., Edmonton, London N9 9DY Tel: 020 8956 1234 Fax: 020 8956 1233 — MB BS 1985 Lond.; MRCPsych 1989; Dip. Forens. Psychiat. Lond. 1995. (Guy's Hosp. Med. Sch. Lond.) Cons.

Forens. Psychiat. Redford Lodge Hosp. Lond.; Hon. Sen. Lect. (Forens. Psychiat.) Inst. Psychiat. Lond. Prev: Cons. Forens. Psychiat. BRd.moor Hosp.; Lect. (Forens. Psychiat.) Inst. Psychiat. Lond.; Sen. Regist. (Forens. Psychiat.) BRd.moor Hosp.

EYEARS, Julian Mark Flat 3, 112B Brixton Hill, London SW2 1AH — MB BS 1992 Lond.; BSc Bristol 1982; PhD Bristol 1986.

EYEARS, Lewis William Sturt (retired) 104 Bromham Road, Biddenham, Bedford MK40 4AH — MB BS 1955 Lond.; MRCS Eng. LRCP Lond. 1955; DObst RCOG 1957.

EYERS, John Gilbert Upton Medical Partnership, 18 Sussex Place, Slough SL1 1NS Tel: 01753 522713 Fax: 01753 552790; St. Leonard's Dale, Windsor SL4 4AQ Tel: 01753 869859 — MB BCh BAO 1966 Dub.; MRCGP 1973. (T.C. Dub.) Civil Serv. Med. Off. Prev: Regist. (Med.) Luton & Dunstable Hosp.; SHO & Ho. Surg. Roy. City Hosp. Dub.

EYERS, Paul Simon Graham 8 Stanshalls Drive, Felton, Bristol BS40 9UW — MB BS 1987 Lond.

EYES, Brian Edward 36 Broadmead, Heswall, Wirral CH60 1XD — MB ChB 1973 Liverp.; FRCR 1978; DMRD Liverp. 1977.

EYKELBOSCH, Gerald 14 Highland Road, Northwood HA6 1JT — MB ChB 1970 Birm. Clin. Asst. Maj. Accid. Unit Whipps Cross Hosp. Lond. Prev: Surg. Regist. W. Scotl. Regional Rotat. Train. Scheme; Lect. Anat. Univ. Glas. Med. Sch.; Ho. Surg. Gen. Hosp. Birm.

EYKYN, Malcolm Lawrence Croft Medical Centre, Calder Walk, Leamington Spa CV31 1SA Tel: 01926 421153 Fax: 01926 832343; Lower Watchbury, Barford, Warwick — MB ChB 1972 Manch.

EYKYN, Professor Susannah Jane St. Thomas's Hospital, Lambeth Palace Road, London SE1 7EH — MB BS (Hons.) Lond. 1962; FRCP 1995; FRCS Eng. 1992; FRCPath 1987, M 1975; MRCP 1987. (St. Thos.) Prof. & Hon. Cons. Clin. Microbiol. St. Thos. Hosp. Lond.

EYLES, Nulece (retired) Jarna, 19 Honey Lane, Burley, Ringwood BH24 4EN Tel: 01425 402365 — MB ChB (Distinc. Forens. Med. & Pub. Health) Glas. 1946; DPH Eng. 1955. Prev: Fell. & Hon. Med. Adviser Learning Disabil. Unit Dept. Educat. Soton. Univ.

EYNON, Angharad Meleri Llwyn Deri, Llanddarog, Carmarthen SA32 8PD — MB BCh 1997 Wales.

EYNON, Colin Andrew 24 Monica Drive, Cheltenham GL50 4NQ — MB BS 1989 Lond.; BSc Lond. 1986, MB BS 1989; MRCP (UK) 1992.

EYNON, David Michael Station Medical Group, Gatacre Street, Blyth NE24 1HD Tel: 01670 396540 Fax: 01670 396517. GP Blyth, N.d.

EYNON, Sheila Mary Holme View, Deanscales, Cockermouth CA13 0SL — MB ChB 1966 Bristol.

EYNON, Theresa Elizabeth Perpetua Nottingham Psychotherapy Unit, St Ann's House, 114 Thorneywood Mount, Nottingham NG3 2PZ Tel: 0115 952 9452; 61 Melbourne Street, Coalville, Leicester LE67 3QU Email: alderoak@ntlworld.com — MB ChB 1985 Sheff.; MRCPsych 1993. Sen. Regist. (Flexible Train. in Psychother.) Nottm. PsycoTher. Unit. Socs: Soc. Psychother. Research; W Midls. Inst. Psychother. Prev: Regist. & SHO Rotat. (Psychiat.) W. Midl. RHA; Trainee GP Stafford VTS.

EYNON-LEWIS, Andrew John Clifton Surgery, Victoria Place, 35 Victoria Road, Dartmouth TQ6 9RT Tel: 01803 832212 Fax: 01803 837917; Camomile House, Strete, Dartmouth TQ6 0RH Tel: 01803 770417 — MB BS 1983 Lond.; BSc (Hons.) Lond. 1980; MRCGP 1988; DCH RCP Lond. 1987; DRCOG 1986; FRCGP 1997. (Char. Cross) Course Organiser, Plymouth; GP Vocational Train. Scheme. Socs: Hon. Sec. TAMAR Fac. RCGP. Prev: SHO Torbay VTS Torquay; Ho. Surg. Char. Cross Hosp. Lond.; Ho. Phys. Roy. United Hosp. Bath.

EYONG, Mr Effi Department of Obstetrics & Gynaecology, Stepping Hill Hospital, Poplar Grove, Stockport SK2 7JE Tel: 0161 419 5543 Fax: 0161 419 5297; 1 Pentland Close, Hazel Grove, Stockport SK7 5BS — MB BS 1978 Ibadan; ChM Manch. 1989; FMCOG Nigeria 1986; MRCOG 1984; FRCOG 1997. Cons. O & G Stepping Hill Hosp. Stockport.

EYRE, Adrian John King Street Surgery, 22A King Street, Hereford HR4 9DA Tel: 01432 272181 Fax: 01432 344725 — MB BS 1966 Lond.; DCH Eng. 1968; DObst RCOG 1968. (St. Thos.) Prev: Med. Off. Fiji Govt.; SHO (Psychiat.) Springfield Hosp. Tooting.

EYRE, David George 9 Victoria Park, Londonderry BT47 2AD Tel: 01504 348563 Email: davideyre@easynet.co.uk — MB BCh BAO 1974 Belf.; MRCPsych 1979. Cons. (Psychiat. Ment. Handicap.) Stradreagh Hosp. Lond.derry.

EYRE, David Herbert 22 Adderstone Crescent, Jesmond, Newcastle upon Tyne NE2 2HH — MB BS 1974 Newc.; PhD Leeds 1966; MRCGP 1978.

EYRE, Elizabeth Carol 1 The Oaks, Lisburn BT28 3AP — MB BCh BAO 1988 Belf.; DMH Belf. 1995; DRCOG 1991; DCH RCPS Glas. 1991. Socs: MRCGP.

EYRE, Francis John Harry 45 Rose Mount, Birkenhead CH43 5SQ — MB ChB 1994 Leeds.

EYRE, Professor Janet Ann 27 The Grove, Gosforth, Newcastle upon Tyne NE3 1NE — MB ChB 1979 Auckland; DPhil Oxf. 1983; BSc Auckland 1976, MB ChB 1979; FRCP Lond. 1993. (Auckland) Prof. Paediat. Neurosci. & Hon. Cons. Paediat. Neurol. Dept. Child Health Univ. Newc. u. Tyne. Prev: Wellcome Sen. Fell. (Clin. Sci.) & Hon. Cons. Paediat. Neurol. Dept. Child Health Univ. Newc. u Tyne; Hon. SHO John Radcliffe Hosp. Oxf.

EYRE, John (retired) 16 Beecot Lane, Walton-on-Thames KT12 3JW — MB BS 1968 Lond.; MRCS Eng. LRCP Lond. 1968; FDS RCS Eng. 1971; BDS (Hons.) Lond. 1965; LDS RCS Eng. 1965. Prev: Cons. Oral Surg. St. Mary's Hosp. Lond. & E.man Dent. Hosp. Lond.

EYRE, Judith Amanda 16 The Drive, Fulwood, Preston PR2 8FF — MB ChB 1986 Liverp.; MRCGP 1991; DRCOG 1990; DCH RCP Lond. 1989.

EYRE, Kathleen Elizabeth 22 Adderstone Crescent, Newcastle upon Tyne NE2 2HH — MB BS 1998 Lond.; MB BS Lond 1998.

EYRE, Olga Cumberland House, 58 Scarisbrick New Road, Southport PR8 6PG Tel: 01704 501500 Fax: 01704 549382; 27 Hesketh Road, Southport PR9 9PD Tel: 01704 31179 — MUDr 1980 Prague; LMSSA Lond. 1985; DRCOG 1986; MRCGP 1988; Dip. Prescribing Sci. Liverp 1997. (Charles Univ. Prague) Socs: BMA.

EYRE, Patricia Ann (retired) Beecot, 16 Beecot Lane, Walton-on-Thames KT12 3JW — MB BS 1967 Lond.; MRCS Eng. LRCP Lond. 1967. Prev: SCMO (Ment. Health) Mid Surrey HA.

EYRE, Rachel Mary (retired) 44 Woodbank Park, Prenton, Prenton CH43 9WN — MB ChB 1959 Liverp.; DObst RCOG 1961; DCH Eng. 1962.

EYRE, Rachel Mary 17 High Street, Rawcliffe, Goole DN14 8QQ — MB ChB 1991 Sheff.

EYRE, Richard Marlborough House, Princess Margaret Hospital, Swindon SN1 4JU Tel: 01793 428800 Fax: 01793 428823 — MB BS 1983 Lond.; BSc (Hons.) Lond. 1980; MRCPsych 1988. Cons. Child & Adolesc. Psychiat. Swindon & MarlBoro. NHS Trust. Prev: Sen. Regist. (Child Psychiat.) Kings Coll. Hosp. Lond.; Regist. (Psychiat.) Maudsley & Bethlem Roy. Hosps.

EYRE, Simon Jonathan Ian Gow Memorial Health Centre, Milfoil Drive, Eastbourne BN23 8BR Tel: 01323 766358 — BM BCh 1979 Oxf.; BA (Hons.) Camb. 1976; MRCP (UK) 1981; FRCGP 1994, M 1987. GP Course Organiser E.bourne VTS. Prev: Trainee GP Edenbridge; Regist. (Radiother. & Oncol.) St. Thos. Hosp. Lond.; Med. Off. Kapsowar Hosp. (Afr. Inland Ch.).

EYRE, Timothy Alexander Barrowgate, Sosgill Road, Mockerkin, Cockermouth CA13 0SJ — MB ChB 1977 Liverp.; FRCR 1985. Cons. Radiol. W. Cumbld. Hosp., Whitehaven. Prev: Sen. Regist. (Radiol.) Bristol Roy. Infirm.; Regist. (Radiol.) Kettering Dist. Gen. Hosp.; SHO (O & G) St. Catherine's Hosp. Birkenhead.

EYRE-BROOK, Anne 2 Meads Road, Guildford GU1 2NB — MB ChB 1975 Sheff.

EYRE-BROOK, Mr Arthur Lewis (retired) 8 Lodge Drive, Long Ashton, Bristol BS41 9JF Tel: 01275 393405 — MB ChB 1932 Bristol; MS Lond. 1934, MB BS (Hons.) 1933; MB ChB (Hons.) Bristol 1932; FRCS Eng. 1934; MRCS Eng. LRCP Lond. 1932. Prev: Lt.-Col. RAMC.

EYRE-BROOK, David George Dapdune House Surgery, Wharf Road, Guildford GU1 4RP Tel: 01483 573336 Fax: 01483 306602 — MB BS 1977 Lond.; MRCGP 1982; DRCOG 1979.

EYRE-BROOK, Edith Meriel (retired) 8 Lodge Drive, Long Ashton, Bristol BS41 9JF Tel: 01275 393405 — MB ChB 1939 Bristol; MCRS Eng. LRCP Lond. 1939. Prev: Asst. Surg. Winford Orthop. Hosp.

EYRE-BROOK, Mr Ian Arthur 16 Haines Hill, Taunton TA1 4HW — MD 1985 Sheff.; MB ChB Bristol 1976; FRCS Eng. 1980. Cons. Surg. Taunton & Som. Hosps.

EYRE-WALKER, Donald Wakefield (retired) Heath House, Offley Brook, Eccleshall, Stafford ST21 6HA Tel: 01785 280318 — MB ChB New Zealand 1952; FFA RCS Eng. 1959; DA Eng. 1957. Prev: Hon. Cons. Anaesth. Mid Staffs. DHA.

EYRES, Michael Gavin The Springhead, Springhead Road, Uplyme, Lyme Regis DT7 3RS Tel: 012974 43859 — MB BS Lond. 1989; MRCGP 1995.

EYTON, Sally Mary Anne 4 Island Cottages, High St., Ripley, Woking GU23 6AT; Cobham Health Centre, Portsmouth Road, Cobham KT11 1HT — MB BS 1987 Lond.; DRCOG 1992; DCH RCP Lond. 1990. (St. Thomas's) GP Partner Cobham Health Centre Cobham Job-share. Prev: Assoc. GP Old Cottage Hosp. Epsom; SHO (Radiother. & Oncol.) St. Mary's Hosp. Portsmouth; SHO (O & G) St. Richard's Hosp. Chichester.

EYTON-JONES, Mr Jack (retired) 228 Harden Road, Bingley BD16 1HT Tel: 01535 275717 — MB ChB 1948 St. And.; FRCS Ed. 1959; FRCOG 1971, M 1956, DObst 1952. Prev: Cons. (O & G) Bradford HA.

EZA, Dominique Elizabeth 38 Fleetwood Road, London NW10 1ND — MB ChB Ed. 1996; BSc Lond. 1994. (Edinburgh) SHO Histopath. The Roy. Vict. Infirm. Newc. Socs: Brit. Med. Assoc.; Assn. Clin. Path.

EZAD, Lubna 30 Valley Road, Chandlers Ford, Eastleigh SO53 1GP — MB BS 1985 Punjab; MRCP (UK) 1990.

EZAD, Muhammad Ashfaq 30 Valley Road, Chandlers Ford, Eastleigh SO53 1GP — MB BS 1981 Punjab; MRCP (UK) 1989.

EZEBUIRO, Uzoije Isaac 44 Lochinver Crescent, Paisley PA2 9HA — MB BS 1976 Lagos; MB BS Lagos, Nigeria 1976.

EZEH, Innocent Uchechukwu 32 Moyne Place, West Twyford, Ealing, London NW10 7EN — MB BS 1982 Nigeria; MRCOG 1993.

EZEKIEL, Garth Arnold Rajachandra The Vineyard Surgery, 35 The Vineyard, Richmond TW10 6PP Tel: 020 8948 0404 Fax: 020 8332 7598 — MB BS 1975 Bangalor; MB BS Bangalore 1975; MRCS Eng. LRCP Lond. 1976.

EZEKWE, Charles Kelechukwu Choice 7 Falcon Close, London W4 3XQ — LRCP LRCS Ed. LRCPS Glas. 1995.

EZEKWESILI, Raphael Afamefuna 38 Worsley Road, London E11 3JN — BM BCh 1977 Nsukka, Nigeria; MRCP (UK) 1983.

EZIKWA, Francis Ziggy 12 Farnol Road, Yardley, Birmingham B26 2AF — MB ChB 1990 Leeds.

EZQUERRO ADAN, Arturo 57 Hamlet Square, London NW2 1SR — MB ChB 1979 Navarra; T(Psych) 1991. Cons. Psychother. Kingston & Dist. Community NHS Trust. Socs: APP; M. Inst. GA Lond. 1994; BAGP.

EZRA, Helen (retired) 5 Bibsworth Lodge, Gravel Hill, London N3 3BJ Tel: 020 8346 6636 — MB Calcutta 1947; DObst RCOG 1955. Prev: GP Fortis Green.

ÉZSIÁS, Mr András Department of Oral & Maxillofacial Surgery, Prince Charles Hospital, Merthyr Tydfil CF47 9DT Tel: 01685 728814 Fax: 01685 728141; Tel: 029 2065 7201 Fax: 029 2065 7201 — 2000 European Bd. Cert. Oral & Maxillofacial Surg.; FRCS 1995 (Maxillofac.); 1995 Intercollegiate Bd. Cert. Oral & maxillofacial Surg. (UK); FRCS 1992 Ed.; FDS 1991 RCS; 1986 Specialist Cert. in Gen. Surg. Budapest; MD 1981 Semmelweis, Hungary; DMD 1977 Semmelweis, Hungary; 1996 CCST (UK). Cons. (Oral & Maxillofacial Surg.) P. Chas. Hosp., P.ss of Wales Hosp. & Roy. Glam. Hosp. S. Wales; Hon. Cons. Welsh Regional Burns & Plastic Surg. Centre, Morriston Hosp. Swansea. Socs: Europ. Acad. Sci.s & Arts; Fell. Brit. Assoc. Oral & Maxillofacial Surg.s; Fell. Internat. Assoc. Oral & Maxillofacial Surg.s. Prev: Regist. (Oral & Maxillofacial Surg.) St. Lawrence Hosp. Chepstow & Qu. Alexandra Hosp. Portsmouth; Sen. Regist. (Maxillofacial Surg.) John Radcliffe & Glos. & Cheltenham Hosps.; Regist. (Oral & Maxillofacial Surg.) Univ. Cardiff.

EZZAT, Ali Ahmed Spokes and Partners, Phoenix Family Care, 35 Park Road, Coventry CV1 2LE Tel: 024 7622 7234 Fax: 024 7663 4816; 221 Leamington Road, Styvechale, Coventry CV3 6JZ Tel: 024 76 411190 Fax: 01203 411190 — MB BCh 1970 Cairo; MFFP 1993; DRCOG 1980. (Lond.) Prev: Regist. (O & G) St. Cross Hosp. Rugby & (Venereol.) Coventry & Warwick Hosp.; SHO (Obst.) Doncaster Roy. Infirm.

EZZAT, Mohamad Hossni 68 Bray Bourne Drive, Osterley, Isleworth TW7 5DZ Tel: 020 8847 2045 — MB BCh 1970 Ain Shams; DA (UK) 1973.

EZZAT, Mostafa Aly Brookside, Coronation Road, Woodhall Spa LN10 6QD — MB BS 1954 Cairo; MRCPsych 1974; DPM Eng. 1970; DIH Eng. 1968; DPH Eng. 1965.

EZZAT, Vivienne Anne 47A Marlborough Road, Sheffield S10 1DA — MB ChB 1998 Sheff.; MB ChB Sheff 1998.

FAAL, Mamsallah Arit Flat 2, 2 Dartmouth Rd, London NW2 4EU — MB BS 1996 Lond.

FAARUP, Catherine Louise 32 Kitchener Road, Highfield, Southampton SO17 3SG — BM 1998 Soton.; BM Soton 1998.

FABBRONI, Gillon 7/7 St Marys Street, Edinburgh EH1 1TA — MB ChB 1997 Ed.

FABER, Mr Richard Grey Department of Surgery, Royal Berkshire Hospital, London Road, Reading RG1 5AN Tel: 0118 987 5111 Fax: 0118 987 8212; Church Gate House, Church Gate, Thatcham RG19 3PN Tel: 01635 864212 Fax: 01635 847869 Email: rgf_cgh@hotmail.com — MB BS 1964 Lond.; MS Lond. 1977; FRCS Eng. 1970; FRCS Ed. 1970; MRCS Eng. LRCP Lond. 1964. (St. Geo.) p/t Cons. Gen. Surg. Roy. Berks. & Battle Hosps. NHS Trust Reading, Berks; Chairm. Newbury Hosp. Cons.Comm.; Cons. Surg. Newbury Community Hosp., Newbury, Berks. Socs: Fell. Assn. Surgs.; Reading Path. Soc.; (Ex-Hon. Sec. & Counc. Mem.) Brit. Soc. Gastroenterol. Prev: Cons. Mem. Newbury Unit Managem. Gp.; Chairm. W. Berks. Hosps. Med. Advis. & Vis. Med. Staff Comm.; Roy. Coll. Surg. Tutor Reading Berks.

FABER, Vernon Charles The Old Rectory, Stanton St., Bernard, Marlborough SN8 4LP — MB BChir 1959 Camb.; MA, MB BChir Camb. 1959; DObst RCOG 1961. (St. Bart.) Clin. Med. Off. Frimley Childr. Centre Camberley; Med. Off. (Occupat. Health) Frimley Pk. Hosp. Prev: Clin. Asst. Dept. Anaesth. Frimley Pk. Hosp.; Ho. Surg. & Ho. Phys. Metrop. Hosp.; Obst. Ho. Off. Addenbrooke's Matern. Hosp. Camb.

FABISCH, Walter (retired) 470 Mansfield Road, Nottingham NG5 2EL Tel: 0115 960 6049 — MD 1927 Berlin; MD Palermo 1934; FRCP Lond. 1969, M 1948; FRCPsych 1971; DTM & H Eng. 1948; DPM Lond. 1950.

FABLING, Moira Surgery, 75 Bank Street, Alexandria G83 0NB Tel: 01389 752626 Fax: 01389 752169 — MB ChB 1982 Glas.; MRCGP 1986; DRCOG 1986. Princip. GP Glas.

FABRE, Clarissa Dorothy The Surgery, April Cottage, High Street, Buxted, Uckfield TN22 4LA Tel: 01825 732333 Fax: 01825 732072 — MB BS 1971 Sydney; MRCP 1974 Lond.; DCH 1973 Lond. (Sydney) GP Uckfield, E. Sussex.

FABRE, Professor John William Department of Clinical Sciences, Institute of Liver Studies, King's College Hospital, Bessemer Road, London SE5 9PJ Tel: 020 7346 3305 Fax: 020 7346 3700 Email: john.fabra@v.cl.ac.uk — MB BS Melbourne 1968; PhD Melbourne 1973, BMedSci (Hons.) 1971. (Melb.) Prof. of Clin. Sci.s, King's Coll. Lond. Sch. of Med.

FABRE, Robert Anthony (retired) Water Meadow Surgery, 31A Red Lion St., Chesham HP5 1ET Tel: 01494 782241 — MB BS 1963 Durh.; Cert. Contracep. & Family Plann. 1975. Phys. Chesham Hosp.; Med. Off. Coll. Chartridge Centre. Prev: SHO Sunderland Childr. Hosp.

FABRI, Mr Brian The Cardiothoracic Centre, Thomas Drive, Liverpool L14 3PE Tel: 0151 228 1616 Fax: 0151 220 8573 Email: bfabr@ccl-tr.nwest.nhs.uk; 16 Queens Drive, Mossley Hill, Liverpool L18 0HE — MD 1975 Malta; FRCS Ed. 1980. (Malta) Cons. Cardiac Surg. Liverp. HA. Socs: Soc. Cardiothoracic Surg. GB & Irel.; Eur. Assn. Cardioth. Surg.

FABRICIUS, John Michael Old Byeways, Upper Court Road, Woldingham, Caterham CR3 7BE Tel: 01883 653049 — MB BS 1944 Lond.; MRCS Eng. LRCP Lond. 1944. (Guy's) Prev: Anaesth. EMS; Ho. Phys. &c. Guy's Hosp.; RAMC.

FABRICIUS, Peter John, Col. late RAMC Frimley Park Hospital, Portsmouth Road, Frimley, Camberley GU16 7UJ Tel: 01276 604604 Fax: 01276 675660; 3 Rowhills Close, Farnham GU9 9EQ Tel: 01252 344491 Fax: 01252 350189 — MB BS 1976 Lond.; FRCP Lond. 1995; MRCP (UK) 1979. (St. Thos.) Cons. Phys. & Gastroenterol. MoD & Frimley Pk. NHS Trust; Cons. Adviser in Med. to the Army. Socs: Brit. Soc. Gastroenterol. Prev: Commanding Off. MoD Hosp. Unit Frimley Pk.; Cons. Phys. & Postgrad. Clin. Tutor

Brit. Milit. Hosp. Munster; Research Fell. & Regist. (Gastroenterol.) Gen. Hosp. Birm.

FACCENDA, Jacqueline Frances 31/7 Roseburn Terrace, Edinburgh EH12 5NQ Tel: 0131 337 6610 Fax: 0131 337 6610 Email: polar@globalnet.co.uk; Sleep Lab, Royal Infirmary Edinburgh, Lauriston Place, Edinburgh EH3 9YW Tel: 031 536 2362 Email: jfaccenda@ed.ac.uk — MB ChB 1990 Ed.; MRCP (UK) 1994. (Edinburgh) Regist. (Gen. Med. & Respirat.) Roy. Infirm. Edin.; Research Fell. Sleep Laborat. RIE. Socs: Brit. Thorac. Assn.; Collegiate Mem. RCPE; Scot. Thoracic Soc. Prev: Regist, Borders Gen. Hosp.; SHO III (Med. & Cardiol.) Stobhill Hosp. Glas.; SHO Rotat. (Med.) Roy. Infirm. & City Hosp. Edin.

FACER, Elspeth Kinnear Department of Anaesthesia, Hospital for Children NHS Trust, Great Ormond St., London WC1N 3JH; 7 Gilkes Crescent, Dulwich, London SE21 7BP — MB ChB 1968 St. And.; FFA RCS Eng. 1973. (St. And.) Cons. Anaesth. Hosp. Childr. Gt. Ormond St. Lond. Prev: Sen. Regist. (Anaesth.) St. Thos. Hosp. Lond.; Ho. Phys. Maryfield Hosp. Dundee; Ho. Surg. W. Cornw. Hosp. Penzance.

FACER, John Lovett, Group Capt. RAF Med. Br. Retd. (retired) Sack Hill Farm, Steplake Lane, Sherfield English, Romsey SO51 6FR — MB BS Lond. 1949; FRCP Ed. 1982, M 1965; MRCS Eng. LRCP Lond. 1949; MFCM 1974; DPH Lond. 1962; DIH Soc. Apoth. Lond. 1959.

FACTOR, Danielle Carrie 3 Warwick Road, Derwen Fawr, Swansea SA2 8DZ — MB BS 1998 Lond.; MB BS Lond 1998.

FADALY, Abdul-Haleem Ali 1 Left, 29 Arlington St., Glasgow G3 6DT — MB ChB 1998 Glas.; MB ChB Glas 1998.

FADDOUL, Elias 31 Dickens Close, Hartley, Longfield DA3 8DP — MD 1972 Damascus. (Damascus Univ.) Assoc. Orthop. Surg. SE Thames RHA.

FADE, Premila Zoya 32 Time Square, Colvestone Crescent, Dalston, London E8 2LT — MB BS 1992 Lond.; BSc Lond. 1989; MRCP (UK) 1995.

FADL, Omer El Farouk Mohamed Fair Mile Hospital, Wallingford OX10 9HH; 7 Albert Road, Caversham, Reading RG4 7AN — LMSSA 1967 Lond.; Dip. Med., Surg. & Obst. Univ. Khartoum 1957; MRCPsych 1973; DPM Eng. 1964. (Univ. Khartoum) Cons. (Psychiat.), Fairmite Hosp., Wallingford, Box, OX10 9HH; Hon. Clin. Teach. Univ. Soton. Socs: Fell. Roy. Soc. Med.; BMA. Prev: Clin. Asst. Inst. Psychiat. Bethlem Roy. & Maudsley Hosps. Lond.; Cons. (Psychiat.) Knowle Hosp., Fareham and Hon. Clin. Teach. Univ. Soton; Cons. (Psychiat.) Cherry Knowle Hosp. Sunderland.

FADRA, Shabbir Abdulkadar 28 King Edward Road, Thorne, Doncaster DN8 4BS; 4A Brooke Street, Thorne, Doncaster DN8 4AZ — MB BS 1972 Bombay.

FAERESTRAND, Harvey Ingvald East Lynne Medical Centre, 3-5 Wellesley Road, Clacton-on-Sea CO15 3PP Tel: 01255 220010 Fax: 01255 476350; Willow House, 173 London Road, Great Clacton, Clacton-on-Sea CO15 4DT Tel: 01255 222466 — MB ChB 1978 Aberd.

FAERESTRAND, Wendy Margaret St James Surgery, 89 Wash Lane, Clacton-on-Sea CO15 1DA Tel: 01255 222121; Willow House, 173 London Road, Clacton-on-Sea CO15 4DT — MB ChB 1979 Aberd.; MRCGP 1987; DRCOG 1982.

FAGAN, Brian Wexham Park Hospital, Slough SL2 4HL — MB BCh BAO 1988 NUI; LRCPSI 1988.

FAGAN, Charles 108 Rosslyn Avenue, Rutherglen, Glasgow G73 3EX — MB ChB 1986 Glas.

FAGAN, Daniel Four Elms Medical Centres, 103 Newport Road, Cardiff CF24 0AF Tel: 029 2048 5526 Fax: 029 2048 2871 — MB BS 1985 Lond.; BSc Lond. 1983, MB BS 1985.

FAGAN, David Godfrey Pathology Department, University Hospital, Clifton Boulevard, Nottingham NG7 2UH Tel: 0115 925 0969 — MB BChir 1963 Camb.; MD Camb. 1974, MA, MB BChir 1963; MRCS Eng. LRCP Lond. 1962; FRCPath 1985; FRCPCH 1997. (Camb & Guy's) Sen. Lect. (Paediat. Path.) Univ. Hosp. Nottm.; Hon. Cons. Trent RHA. Prev: Sen. Regist. Childr. Hosp. Sheff.; Lect. (Path.) Univ. Dundee; Sen. Staff Path. Hosp. for Sick Childr. Toronto, Canada.

FAGAN, John Melville Maxillofacial Unit, George Eliot Hospital, College St., Nuneaton CV10 7DJ Tel: 02476 865029 Email: john.fagan@geh-tr.wmids.nhs.uk; Tel: 01926 770418 Fax: 01926 770418 Email: maxillofacialfagan@hotmail.com — MB BChir 1976 Camb.; MA Camb. 1976; BDS Liverp. 1968; FDS RCS Eng. 1979. (Camb. & St. Geo.) Cons. Oral & Maxillofacial Surg. Geo. Eliot Hosp. Nuneaton & Coventry & Warks. Hosp. Coventry. Socs: Fell. Brit. Assn. Oral & Maxillofacial Surg. Prev: Sen. Regist. (Oral & Maxillofacial Surg.) St. Richards Hosp. Chichester; Regist. (Oral Med. & Surg.) Roy. Free & Whittington Hosps. Lond.; Ho. Surg. St. Geo. Hosp. Lond.

FAGAN, Josephine Mary 1 Amberley Grove, Whickham, Newcastle upon Tyne NE16 5JF — MB ChB 1986 Dundee.

FAGAN, Nigel Anthony Hill House, Sweffling, Saxmundham IP17 2BT — MB BS 1983 Lond.

FAGBEMI, Sunday Adebayo Olayinka Department of Paediatrics, Hammersmith Hospital, Du Cave Road, London W12 Tel: 020 8383 32006 Fax: 020 8383 2474 Email: afagbemi@rpms.ac.uk; 55 Ayr Way, Rise Park, Romford RM1 4UH Tel: 01708 742364 Fax: 01708 783286 — MB BS 1985 Ibadan; MRCP (UK) 1996, MRCPCH 1996; MRCPI 1996; DCH RCP Lond. (Univ. Ibadan) Specialist Regist., Research. Socs: Fell. Roy. Soc. Med. Prev: Neonat. research fell.

FAGBOHUN, Margaret 1 Brackley Close, Wallington SM6 9JR — MB BS 1996 Lond.; BSc (Hons. Physiol. & Blochem.) Lond. 1990. (King's College London) SHO (Med.) Orpington. Prev: SHO (A & E); Ho. Off. (Gen. Surg.); Ho. Off. (Gen. Med.).

FAGE, Virginia Ann Alexandra 15 Courtleigh Avenue, Barnet EN4 0HT — MB BS 1991 Lond.

FAGG, Christopher Grahame (retired) 33 Priory Way, Hitchin SG4 9BL Tel: 01462 434715 Fax: 01462 434715 Email: c-gf.hitchin@thefree.net — MB BS Lond. 1938; MD Lond. 1947; FRCP Lond. 1970, M 1947; MRCS Eng. LRCP Lond. 1938; FRCPCH 1997; DCH Eng. 1947. Prev: Paediat. Lister Hosp. Stevenage & Luton & Dunstable Hosp.

FAGG, Christopher Guy Coombs Station Road Health Centre, Station Road, East Looe, Liskeard PL13 1HA Tel: 01503 263195 Fax: 01502 265680 — MB BS 1968 Lond.; MRCS Eng. LRCP Lond. 1969. (St. Bart.)

FAGG, Nuala Louise Kelvena Department of Histopathology, Medical School, Guy's Hospital, London SE1 9RT Tel: 020 7955 4446; Marryat, 8A Kippington Road, Sevenoaks TN13 2LH — MB BS 1975 Lond.; MRCS Eng. LRCP Lond. 1975; MRCPath 1982. (Guy's) Sen. Lect. (Histopath.) United Med. & Dent. Sch. Guy's Hosp. Lond.

FAGG, Mr Phillip Stephen Doncaster Royal Infirmary, Armthorpe Road, Doncaster DN2 5LT Tel: 01302 366666 Fax: 01302 370997 Email: psfagg@thefarmpss.u-net.com; The Farm, Main St, Old Cantley, Doncaster DN3 3QH Tel: 01302 370997 — MB BS 1975 Lond.; FRCS Eng. 1980. (Westminster Hospital, Medical School) Cons. Orthop. Surg. Doncaster Roy. Infirm. & Montagu Hosp. Trust. Prev: Cons. RAF.

FAGG, Sara Louise Wingmore House, Withinlee House, Macclesfield SK10 4AT — MB BCh 1973 Wales; FRCS Eng. 1977. Indep. Surg. Chesh.

FAGHIHI NARAGHI, Ali Mohammad 107 Nottingham Terrace, London NW1 4QE — MB BS 1994 Lond.

FAGIN, Leonard Henry North East London Mental Health NHS Trust, South Forest Community Mental Health Care, 21 Thorne Close, Leytonstone, London E11 4HU Tel: 020 8535 6830 Fax: 020 8535 6822 Email: lfagin@mindsong.demon.co.uk; Hillview, 9 Womersley Road, Hornsey, London N8 9AE — Medico 1971 Buenos Aires; Médico Buenos Aires 1971; FRCPsych 1991, M 1975. (Fac. Med. Buenos Aires) Cons. Psychiat. & Clin. Dir. N. E. Lond. Ment. Health NHS Trust; Hon. Sen. Lect. UCL; Organiser, annual Gen. meetings of the Roy. Coll. of Psychiat. Prev: Sen. Regist. (Psychiat.) Lond. Hosp. (Whitechapel) & Claybury Hosp. Woodford Bridge; Regist. Napsbury Hosp.; Acad. Sec. (Rehabil. & Social Psychiat.) RCPsych.

FAHAL, Ibrahim Hassan Oldchurch Hospital, Romford RM7 0BE Tel: 01708 708236 Fax: 01708 708434 Email: ihf@webstar.co.uk; 14 Medlan Drive, Brandon Groves, South Ockendon RM15 6TS Tel: 01708 855895 Fax: 01708 8558 — MB BS 1981 Khartoum; FRCP 2001 Glasgow; FRCP 2000 London; MD 1997 Liverpool; MRCP (UK) 1990. Cons. Phys. & Nephrologist. Socs: Med. Res. Soc.; Eur. Renal Assn., Scott. Renal Assn. & Renal Assn. Prev: Lect. & Sen. Regist., Univ. of Liverp.

FAHEEM, Farooq Ghulam 14 Bolton Road, Newport NP20 4JX — MB ChB 1990 Bristol.

FAHEY, Cecily Ann 5 Keble Street, London SW17 0UH — BM 1987 Soton.

FAHEY, John Declan St Peters Street Medical Practice, 16 St Peters St., Islington, London N1 8JG Tel: 020 7226 7131 Fax: 020 7354 9120 — MB BCh BAO 1952 NUI; LM Rotunda 1954. (Galw.) Prev: Clin. Asst. Roy. Nat. Throat, Nose & Ear Hosp. Lond.; SHO Battersea Gen. Hosp.; RAMC.

FAHEY, Thomas Patrick Bernard Broadgate Surgery, Ardenton Walk, Brentry, Bristol BS10 6SP — MB BCh BAO 1986 NUI.

FAHMI, Fahmi Mohammed Rashad 3 Kenilworth Drive, Walton-on-Thames KT12 3JX — MB ChB 1971 Baghdad; FFA RCSI 1984; DA (UK) 1982.

FAHMY, Aida Issa 5 Ashleigh Mews, The Fairfield, Farnham GU9 8AH — MB BCh 1968 Cairo; MRCS Eng. LRCP Lond. 1980; Dip. Paediat. Cairo Univ. 1970. Clin. Med. Off. N.E. Hants./S.W. Surrey DHA.

FAHMY, Albert (retired) Wood Rising, Callow Hill, Virginia water GU25 4LD Tel: 01344 842475 — MRCS Eng. LRCP Lond. 1962; FRCP Ed. 1971; MRCP (UK) 1955. Prev: Cons. Phys. Harpur Memor. Hosp. Cairo, Egypt, Sudan Med. Servs. & Nigeria.

FAHMY, Fahmy Saad Royal Devon and Exeter Hospital, Barrack Road, Exeter EX2 5DW — MB BCh 1985 Ain Shams; MB BCh Ain Shams, Egypt 1985; MS Egypt 1992.

FAHMY, Mr Galal Eldin Ibrahim Fouad Central Surgery, Queens Avenue, Snodland ME6 5BP Tel: 01634 240295 Fax: 01634 245820 — MB BCh 1960 Cairo; FRCS Eng. 1971; FRCS Ed. 1970; LMSSA Lond. 1969. (Cairo) Prev: Regist. (Gen. Surg.) Medway Dist. Hosp. & St. Bart. Hosp. Rochester; Lect. Surg. Assiout Univ. Egypt.

FAHMY, Hind 5 Auriol Mansions, Edith Road, London W14 0ST — MB ChB 1990 Dundee.

FAHMY, Maurice Southlea Surgery, 276 Lower Farnham, Aldershot GU11 3RB Tel: 01252 344868 Fax: 01252 342596; Five Oaks, Sellars Hill, Godalming GU7 2QU Tel: 01483 424549 — MB BCh 1969 Cairo; MRCS Eng. LRCP Lond. 1979; MRCGP 1981; DRCOG 1980. Socs: Brit. Med. Acupunct. Soc.; BMA (Ex-Chairm. SW Thames Regional Counc.). Prev: Trainee GP Redbridge & Waltham Forest VTS; Regist. (Med.) Univ. Hosp. Benghazi, Libya; Company Phys. W.. Arabian Geophysical Company Cairo, Egypt.

FAHMY, Mohamed Ezz El-Din Saleh 25 Damers Road, Dorchester DT1 2JX — MB BCh 1981 Egypt.

FAHMY, Mohsen Mohamed El-Sayed High Street Surgery, 231-235 High Street, Sheerness ME12 1UR Tel: 01795 580909 Fax: 01795 665656; Rodmer Close, Minster-on-Sea, Isle of Sheppey, Sheerness ME12 2BS Tel: 01795 871499 — MB ChB 1971 Alexandria. (Univ. Alexandria Fac. Med.) Prev: Asst. All St.s Hosp.; Regist. (O & G) Birm.; Regist. (O & G) N.hamptonshire.

FAHMY, Mr Nabil Riad Mohamed Stockport Infirmary, Wellington Road S., Stockport SK1 3UJ Tel: 0161 419 4034; The White House, Billy's Lane, Cheadle Hulme, Cheadle SK8 6HT Tel: 0161 483 1010 — MB BCh 1964 Cairo; FRCS Ed. 1976. (Cairo) Cons. Orthop. Surg. Stockport HA. Socs: Brit. Orthop. Assn.; Brit. Soc. Surg. Hand. Prev: Sen. Regist. NW RHA; Tutor (Orthop. Surg.) Manch. Univ.

FAHMY, Mr Samih Woodclose, Chancellor's Road, Stevenage SG1 4AP Tel: 01438 351 3339 — MB BCh 1959 Cairo; FRCS Eng. 1971; LMSSA Lond. 1966. Private Cons. ENT Surg. Pinehill Hosp. Hitchin BUPA Hosp. Harpenden. Socs: Fell. Roy. Soc. Med.; Brit. Assn. Otolaryng. Prev: Cons. ENT Surg. Lister Hosp. Stevenage, Qu. Eliz. II Hosp. Welwyn Gdn. City & Hertford Co. Hosp.; ENT Sen. Regist. United Birm. Hosps. & Birm. RHB; ENT Regist. Centr. Middlx. Hosp. Lond. & Roy. Free Hosp. Lond.

FAHMY, Shafik Ibrahim 30 Corringham Road, London NW11 7BU Tel: 020 8455 1203 — MB ChB Cairo 1940; MRCS Eng. LRCP Lond. 1948; MRCPsych 1971. (Cairo) Cons. Child Psychiat. W.T. Child Guid. Unit Lond. Socs: Brit. Psychoanal Soc. Prev: Cons. Psychother. Cassel Hosp. Lond.; Cons. Child Psychiat. Harlow Child Guid. Clinic & St. Geo. Hosp. Lond.

FAHMY, Mr Tarek Mahmoud (cons. rooms), 14 Hunters Rise, Pogmoor, Barnsley S75 2JX — MB BCh 1970 Cairo; FRCS Glas. 1978.

FAHMY-GOBRIAL, Raouf Nashed 18 Billing Road, Northampton NN1 5RS Tel: 01604 38947 — MB BCh 1965 Cairo. (Cairo) Assoc. Specialist (Psychiat.) Oxf. RHA.

FAHY, Mr Damian Michael 238 Wandsworth Bridge Road, Fulham, London SW6 2UD — MB BS 1991 Lond.; BSc (Hons.) Lond. 1988; FRCS Ed. 1996. (Univ. Coll. Lond.) Specialist Regist. Rotat. (Orthop.) Chelsea & W.m. Hosp. Lond. Socs: Fell. Roy. Soc. Med.

FAHY, Mr Gerald Thomas Ophthalmology Department, Leicester Royal Infirmary, Infirmary Square, Leicester LE1 5WW — MD 1993 Bristol; MB BCh BAO NUI 1979; FRCS Ed. 1985; FRCOphth 1993; FCOphth 1988. Cons. Ophth. Leicester Roy. Infirm. Prev: Ocucoplastic & Orbital Fell. Vancouver, Canada; Cornea & Extern. Eye Fell. Bristol; Sen. Regist. Bristol.

FAHY, Haideh 39 Smoke Lane, Reigate RH2 7HJ — MB BS 1986 Lond.; DRCOG 1988; MRCGP 1992.

FAHY, Leonora Theresa The Cottage, 50 Graham Road, West Kirby, Wirral CH48 5DW Tel: 0151 632 1251 — MB BCh BAO 1980 NUI; FFA RCS Eng. 1986; FFA RCSI 1985. Cons. Anaesth. Roy. Liverp. Hosp. & Liverp. Matern. Hosp. Prev: Sen. Regist. (Anaesth.) Liverp. Matern. Hosp.

FAHY, Professor Thomas Augustine Maudsley Hospital, Denmark Hill, London SE5 8AZ Tel: 020 7740 5093 Fax: 020 7740 5092 Email: t.fahy@iop.kcl.ac.uk — MB BCh BAO 1984 NUI; MB BCh BAO NUI (Hons.) 1984; MPhil. Lond. 1990; MD NUI 1992; MRCPsych 1988. Prev: Cons. Psychiat. Maudsley Hosp. Lond.; Lect. Kings Coll. Hosp. & Inst. Psychiat. Lond.; Research Worker Inst. Psychiat. De Crespigny Pk. Lond.

FAICHNEY, Mr Alan West Glasgow Hospitals University NHS Trust, Dumbarton Road, Glasgow G11 6NT Tel: 0141 211 2578; 8 Humbie Lawns, Mearnskirk, Glasgow G77 5EA Tel: 0141 616 2334 — MB ChB 1973 Glas.; BSc (Hons.) Glas. 1971, MB ChB 1973; FRCS Glas. 1993; FRCS Ed. 1977. (Glas. Univ.) Cons. Cardiothoracic Surg. W.. & Roy. Infirm. Glas.; Hon. Sen. Lect. (Surg.) Univ. Glas. Prev: Sen. Regist. (Cardiothoracic Surg.) Lothian HB; Regist. (Surg.) Roy. Infirm. Glas.

FAIERS, Mary Christine 32A Pirton Road, Hitchin SG5 2BD — MB BS 1966 Lond.; MRCS Eng. LRCP Lond. 1966; MRCPath 1977; DObst RCOG 1968. (Roy. Free) Sen. Med. Microbiol. Pub. Health Laborat. Serv. Luton. Prev: Regist. (Path.) Edgware Gen. Hosp. & Kingston Hosp. Kingston upon; Thames; Lect. Dept. Med. Microbiol. St. Bart. Hosp. Lond.

FAIGAN, Mary Anne Yeovil District Hospital, Higher Kingston, Yeovil BA21 4AT — MB ChB 1988 Otago.

FAIL, Michael 22 Harnham Grove, Cramlington NE23 6AQ — MB ChB 1997 Glas.

FAINMAN, David 110 Huddleston Road, London N7 0EG — MB BCh 1983 Witwatersrand; MRCPsych 1990.

FAINT, Deborah Student Services Centre, 150 Mount Pleasant, Liverpool L69 3BX Tel: 0151 794 4720 — MB ChB 1990 Liverp.

FAIR, Barbara Elizabeth University Health Service, 5 Lennoxvale, Belfast BT9 5BY Tel: 028 9033 5551 Fax: 028 9033 5540; 28 Ballydrain Road, Comber, Newtownards BT23 5SR Tel: 01247 874171 — MB BCh BAO 1987 NUI; MRCGP 1991; Dip. Sports Med. RCS 1993; DCH Dub. 1991. (Univ. Coll. Dub.) Clin. Asst. (Sports Med.) Musgrave Pk. Hosp. Belf.; GP Practitioner Sports Injury Clinic Belf. City Hosp. Socs: Brit. Assn. Sport & Med. (NI Comm. Mem.). Prev: GP Priory Surg. Holywood.

FAIR, David Stuart 6 Peckitt Street, York YO1 9WF Tel: 01904 633881 Fax: 01904 633881; 2A Low Green, Copmanthorpe, York YO23 3SB Tel: 01904 704788 — MB BS 1987 Lond.; BA (Hons) Oxf. 1984; MRCGP 1991. (Charing Cross/Westminster) Clin. Asst. (Psychiat.) Bootham Pk. Hosp.; Forens. Med. Examr., N. Yorks. Police. Prev: Clin. Asst. (A & E) York Dist. Hosp.

FAIR, Elizabeth Anne Rosehall Surgery, 2 Mallusk Road, Newtownabbey BT36 4PP Tel: 028 9083 2188 Fax: 028 9083 8820 — MB BCh BAO 1986 Belf.; BSc (Hons) Belf. 1983; MRCGP 1991; DCH Dub. 1990; DRCOG 1988. Prev: SHO (A & E Med.) Roy. Vict. Hosp.; SHO (O & G) Roy. Matern. Hosp.

FAIR, James Frederick The Hermitages Medical Practice, 5 Hermitage Terrace, Edinburgh EH10 4RP Tel: 0131 447 6277 Fax: 0131 447 9866; The Old Birch, 46 Fountainhall Road, Edinburgh EH9 2LW Tel: 0131 667 1275 — MB ChB 1969 Ed.; BSc (Med. Sci.) 1966; FRCS Ed. 1974. (Ed.) Princip. GP. Socs: BMA; Vice-Pres

Med. Chi. Soc. Edin. (Counc. Mem.). Prev: Regist. Rotat. (Surg.) Lothian HB; Regist. (Surg.) Edin. S.. Hosps.; SHO Peripheral Vasc. Clinic Edin. Roy. Infirm.

FAIR, Janine Suzanne 15 Highland Road, Cradley Heath, Birmingham B64 5NB — MB ChB 1996 Birm.; ChB Birm. 1996; BSc (Hons.) Birm. 1992. (Birm.) Black Country VTS. Prev: GP Regist., N.umbria VTS.

FAIRBAIRN, Andrew Finlay 3 Killiebrigs, Heddon on the Wall, Newcastle upon Tyne NE15 0DD Tel: 01661 852686; Newcastle City Health NHS Trust, Newcastle General Hospital, Newcastle upon Tyne NE4 6BE Tel: 0191 273 6666 Fax: 0191 219 5053 — MB BS 1974 Newc.; FRCPsych 1993, M 1979. Cons. (Psychiat.) Newcastel, N. Tyneside and N.d. Ment. Health Trust; Clin. Lect. Univ. Newc. u Tyne. Prev: Policy Advisor NHS Exec. DH; Med. Dir. Newc. City Health.

FAIRBAIRN, David Trinity Medical Centre, New George St., South Shields NE33 5DU Tel: 0191 427 0338; 80 Whitburn Road, Cleadon, Sunderland SR6 7QX — MB BS 1966 Durh.; DObst RCOG 1968. (Newc.) Prev: Ho. Off. Paediat., Ho. Off. Surg. & SHO Obst. Dryburn Hosp. Durh.

FAIRBAIRN, George Kilpatrick Cairns 1 Broadstone Close, Rochdale OL12 7PH — MB ChB 1980 Ed.; MRCGP 1984.

FAIRBAIRN, Godfrey Roy Henderson The Surgery, Abbotswood Road, Brockworth, Gloucester GL3 4PE Tel: 01452 863200 Fax: 01452 864993; Holmwood, 2 Hatherley Court Road, Cheltenham GL51 3AQ Tel: 01242 696949 — MB BS 1973 Lond.; DRCOG 1979. (Westm.) Prev: SHO (A & E) Plymouth Gen. Hosp.; Clin. Med. Off. Nkonjeni Hosp. Kwazulu, S. Afr.; Ho. Off. (Paediat. Surg.) W.m. Childr. Hosp. Lond.

FAIRBAIRN, Ian Paul 13 Charnwood Close, Marske-by-the-Sea, Redcar TS11 6DS — MB ChB 1992 Manch.

FAIRBAIRN, Ida Marianne 37 Homewood Road, St Albans AL1 4BG — MB ChB 1975 Manch.; MRCGP 1981.

FAIRBAIRN, Karen Julia — MB BCh 1983 Wales; FRCS Ed. 1987; FRCR 1992. (Welsh Nat. Sch. Med.) Cons. Musculoskeletal Radiol. Nottm. City Hosp. NHS Trust. Socs: RSNA; Brit. Inst. Radiol.; Roy. Coll. Radiol. Prev: Fell. & Vis. Asst. Prof. Musculoskeletal Radiol. UMMS Baltimore, USA; Sen. Regist. Rotat. (Radiol.) Nottm., Derby & Mansfield; Regist. (Radiol.) Qu. Med. Centre. Nottm.

FAIRBAIRN, Marilyn Linda Department Anaesthetics, Gloucester Royal Hospital, Gloucester GL1 3NN Tel: 01452 528555; Holmwood, 2 Hatherley Court Road, Cheltenham GL51 3AQ Tel: 01242 696649 — BM BCh 1973 Oxf.; MA Oxf. 1973; FFA RCS Eng. 1984; DA Eng. 1978. (Westm.) Assoc. Specialist (Anaesth.) Gloucester Roy. Hosp. Prev: Ho. Off. (Gen. Med.) W.m. Hosp. Lond.; Clin. Med. Off. Nkonjeni Hosp. Kwazulu, S. Afr.; Regist. (Anaesth.) Gloucester Roy. Hosp.

FAIRBAIRN, Olive Jane Alexander House, 2 Salisbury Road, Farnborough GU14 7AW Tel: 01252 541155; High Oak, 16 The Crescent, Farnborough GU14 7AS Tel: 01252 545805 Email: odowdbooth@aol.com — MB BS 1979 Lond.; MRCGP 1986; DRCOG 1981.

FAIRBAIRN, Roderick John Stuart — MB BS Lond. 1969; MRCS Eng. LRCP Lond. 1969; DObst RCOG 1972. (Westm.) Prev: Ho. Surg. Gordon Hosp. Lond.; Ho. Off. (Med.) Roy. S. Hants. Hosp. Soton.; SHO (Obst.) Canad. Red Cross Memor. Hosp. Taplow.

FAIRBAIRN, Sara Elizabeth Anne Oakhill, 10 Pyles Thorne Road, Wellington TA21 8DX — MB BCh 1998 Wales.

FAIRBANK, Mr Adrian Christopher Department of Orthopaedics, St Georges Hospital, Blackshaw Road, London SW17 0QT Tel: 020 8725 1299 Fax: 020 8725 3610 — MB BChir 1986 Camb.; MA Camb. 1987; FRCS (Orth.) 1995; FRCS Eng. 1990. (St. Thos. Hosp.) Cons. Orthop. St. Geo. Hosp. Lond. Socs: Brit. Orthop. Assn.; Roy. Soc. Med.; Brit. Assn. Surg. Knee. Prev: Clin. Fell. Roy. Adelaide Hosp. S. Austral.; Post Doctor Fell. Johns Hopkins Univ., USA; Sen. Regist. SW Thames Orthop. Train. Rotat.

FAIRBANK, Mr Jeremy Charles Thomas Tel: 01865 741155 Fax: 01865 742348 — MB BChir 1972 Camb.; MD Camb. 1982, MA 1972; FRCS Eng. 1977. (St. Thos.) Cons. Orthop. Surg. Nuffield Orthop. Centre & John Radcliffe Hosp. Oxf.; Sen. Clin. Lect. (Orthop.) Univ. Oxf. Socs: Fell. BOA; Soc. Back Pain Research; Brit. Scoliosis Soc. Prev: Cons. Orthop. Surg. Birm. Hosp.; Sen. Regist. Rotat. (Orthop.) St. Bart. Lond.; Spinal Research Fell. Robt. Jones & Agnes Hunt Orthop. Hosp. OsW.ry.

FAIRBANK, John Wexham Park Hospital, Wexham, Slough SL2 4HL Tel: 01753 633000 — MB BChir 1982 Camb. Cons. O & G Wexham Pk. Hosp. Slough.

FAIRBRASS, Mark John Bradford Royal Infirmary, Duckworth Lane, Bradford BD9 6RJ; 4 Albion Fold, Wilsden, Bradford BD15 0AH — MB ChB 1981 Leeds; FFA RCS Eng. 1985.

FAIRBRASS, Simon Paul 66 Bishopsteignton, Shoeburyness, Southend-on-Sea SS3 8AR — MB ChB 1997 Bristol.

FAIRBROTHER, Mr Barry John King's Mill Centre for Health Care Services, Sutton-in-Ashfield NG17 4JL — MD 1984 Bristol; MD, MB ChB 1970; FRCS Eng. 1975. Cons. Surg. Gen. & Vasc. King's Mill Centre for Health Care Servs. Socs: BMA & Mem. Surgic. Research Soc.; Vasc. Surg. Soc.; Assn. of Surg.s of Gt. Britain & Irel. Prev: Sen. Regist. (Gen. Surg.) Roy. Hallamsh. Hosp. Sheff.; Clin. Lect. Nuffield Dept. Surg. Univ. Oxf. John Radcliffe Hosp.; Regist. (Gen. Surg.) N.. Gen. Hosp. Sheff.

FAIRBROTHER, Jennifer Mary 7 Sackville Road, Crookes, Sheffield S10 1GT — MB ChB 1998 Sheff.; MB ChB Sheff 1998.

FAIRBURN, Professor Christopher James Alfred Granville Department of Psychiatry, University of Oxford, Warneford Hospital, Oxford OX3 7JX Tel: 01865 226479 Fax: 01865 226244 — BM BCh 1974 Oxf.; MPhil Ed. 1980; MA Oxf. 1976, BA 1972, DM 1988; FRCPsych 1991, M 1979. (Oxf.) Wellcome Princip. Research Fell. & Prof. Psychiat. Univ. Oxf.; Hon. Cons. Psychiat. Oxf. HA. Prev: Wellcome Trust Sen. Lect. Univ. Oxf.; Research Psychiat. Univ. Oxf.; Lect. (Psychiat.) Univ. Edin. & Hon. Sen. Regist. Roy. Edin. Hosp.

FAIRBURN, Kevin Department of Medicine, Chesterfield & North Derbyshire Royal Hospital NHS Trust, Chesterfield S44 5BL Tel: 01246 277271 Fax: 01246 552663 — MB BS 1985 Lond.; FRCP 1999 UK; MRCP 1988 UK; BSc 1982 London. Cons. Rheum. Chesterfield & N. Derbysh. Roy. Hosp. Socs: Brit. Soc. Rheum.; Nat. Osteoporosis Soc.; Nat. Assn. Clin. Tutors. Prev: Hon. Lect. & Sen. Regist. Roy. Lond. Hosp.; Regist. (Neurol.) Qu.'s Med. Centre Nottm.; Regist. (Rheum.) Middlx. Hosp. Lond.

FAIRBURN, Richard Anthony 79 Hill Road, Pinner HA5 1LD — MB BS 1974 Lond.; BSc Lond. 1970, MB BS 1974. Med. Adviser Roussel Laborat. Prev: Ho. Phys. (Paediat.) Middlx. Hosp.; SHO (Cardiothoracic Surg.) Hosp. Sick Childr. Gt. Ormond St.; Surg. Regist. King's Coll. Hosp.

FAIRCLOTH, Howard Owen The Derrick, London Road, Clyst Honiton, Exeter EX5 2AN — MB ChB 1973 Bristol.

FAIRCLOUGH, Andrew Ayton Victoria Street Surgery, 1 Victoria Street, Norwich NR1 3XQ Tel: 01603 620872 — MB BS 1967 Lond.

FAIRCLOUGH, Ann Diana 14 Holly Mount, Hampstead, London NW3 6SG Tel: 020 7431 9331 — MB BS 1960 Lond.; MRCS Eng. LRCP Lond. 1960; DA Eng. 1965; DObst RCOG 1963. Prev: Med. Off. Marks & Spencer Ltd.

FAIRCLOUGH, Beverley Elizabeth West Redlands, 147 Woodhouse Lane, Bishop Auckland DL14 6JT — MB BS 1994 Lond.

FAIRCLOUGH, Mr John Arthur Fairoak Cottage, Cefn Mably, Cardiff CF3 6LP — BM BS 1976 Nottm.; FRCS Eng. 1981.

FAIRCLOUGH, Margaret (retired) Milburn House, 229 Garstang Road, Fulwood, Preston PR2 8XE — LAH Dub. 1955. Prev: Med. Off. Chorley & S. Ribble HA.

FAIRCLOUGH, Paul John 4 Rastell Avenue, London SW2 4XP Tel: 020 8674 3719 — MB BS 1971 Lond.; MRCS Eng. LRCP Lond. 1969; DObst RCOG 1971. (St. Bart.)

FAIRCLOUGH, Peter Donald Gastroenterology Department, St Bartholomew's and The London NHS Trust, London E1 1BB Tel: 020 7601 8516 Fax: 020 7601 8518; Endoscopy Unit, The London Clinic, 20 Devonshire Place, London W1G 6BW Tel: 020 7616 7781 Fax: 020 7616 7684 — MD 1978 Lond.; MB BS 1969; FRCP Lond. 1987; MRCP (UK) 1972. (St. Bart.) Cons. Phys. Bart's and The Lond. NHS Trust. Socs: Brit. Soc. Gastroenterol.; Amer. Soc. Gastrointestinal Endoscopy; Amer. Gastroenterol. Assn. Prev: MRC Trav. Research Fell.; Wellcome Sen. Clin. Research Fell.

FAIRE, Gabrielle Mary 28 Woodlea Road, London N16 0TH — MB ChB 1982 Auckland.

FAIREY, Anne Edwina Sanofi Winthrop Ltd, 1 Onslow St., Guildford GU1 4YS Tel: 01483 554089 Fax: 01483 554829 — BM 1985 Soton.; MRCP (UK) 1988. Dir. Med. Affairs, Sanofi Winthrop; Liveryman Worshipful Soc. Apoth. Lond. Prev: Med. Manager

(Oncol., Endocrinol. & Dermat.), Novartis Pharmaceut.; Med. Adviser (Oncol.) Asta Med. Ltd. Camb.; Hon. Sen. Regist. & Clin. Research Fell. (Med. Oncol.) Soton. Gen. Hosp.

FAIRFAX, Andrew John Staffordshire General Hospital, Weston Road, Stafford ST16 3SA Tel: 01785 257731 Fax: 01785 230980; Penn House, Radford Rise, Stafford ST17 4PS Tel: 01785 257634 Fax: 01785 606722 — MB BS 1971 Lond.; FRCP Lond. 1991; MRCP (UK) 1973. (Lond. Hosp.) Cons. Phys. Staffs. Gen. Hosp. & Cannock Chase Hosp. Socs: Brit. Thorac. Soc.; Brit. Cardiac Soc. Prev: Sen. Regist. Brompton & King's Coll. Hosps. Lond.; Ho. Phys. Hammersmith Hosp. Lond.

FAIRFAX, Charles Frederick Walker (retired) Heath Lawn, 334 Garstang Road, Fulwood, Preston PR2 9RY Tel: 01772 465179 Fax: 01772 517165 Email: efwfairfax@cable.net.co.uk — MB BS Lond. 1947; MFCM 1972; DPH Lond. 1955. Prev: Regional SCM Emerg. Plann. N W.. RHA.

FAIRFIELD, Gillian Evelyn Hillside House, Follifoot Lane, Kirby Overblow, Harrogate HG3 1EZ — MB ChB 1981 Birm.; MPH Leeds 1995; DCH RCP Lond. 1988; MFPHM 1998. Sen. Med. Off., Dept. of Health. Prev: Sen. Regist. (Pub. Health Med.) N.. & Yorks. Region.

FAIRFIELD, John Edward Department of Anaesthetics, St James's Hospital, Leeds LS9 7TF Tel: 0113 243 3144 Email: john.fairfield@leedsth.nhs.uk — MB ChB 1981 Birm.; FFA RCS Eng. 1987. Cons. Anaesth. St. Jas. Hosp. Leeds.

FAIRFIELD, Jonathan James Norden House Surgery, Avenue Road, Winslow, Buckingham MK18 3DW Tel: 01296 713434; 14 Kingfisher, Watermead, Aylesbury, Buckingham HP19 0FR — MB BS 1981 Lond.; BSc (1st. cl. Hons.) Lond. 1978; MRCGP (Distinc.) 1985; Cert. Av. Med. 1986. (Westm.)

FAIRFIELD, Michael Colin University Hospitals Leicester LGH, Gwendolen Road, Leicester LE5 4PW Tel: 0116 258 4661 Email: mfairfield@ntlworld.com — MB BS 1988 Lond.; BSc (Pharmacol.) Lond. 1985; FRCA 1994; DA (UK) 1991. (United Med. & Dent. Sch. Guy's & St. Thos. Hosp. Campus) Cons. Anaesth. Leicester Gen. Hosp. Prev: Sen. Regist. (Anaesth.) Leicester Roy. Infirm.; Regist. (Anaesth.) Nuneaton Hosp., Walsgrave Hosp. Coventry & E. Birm. Hosp.; SHO (Neonat. ITU) St. Geo. Hosp. Lond.

FAIRGRIEVE, Mr Brian David, OBE (retired) 19 Lyall Crescent, Millfield Estate, Polmont, Falkirk FK2 0PL Tel: 01324 715449 — MB ChB 1950 Glas.; FRCS Ed. 1982. Prev: Sen. Cas. Off. Falkirk & Dist. Roy. Infirm.

FAIRGRIEVE, Helen Steanbridge Mill, Slad, Stroud GL6 7QE — MB ChB 1998 Sheff.; MB ChB Sheff 1998.

FAIRGRIEVE, Mr John (retired) Steanbridge Mill, Slad, Stroud GL6 7QE Tel: 01452 814143 — MB BChir 1950 Camb.; MChir Camb. 1962, MB BChir 1950; FRCS Eng. 1957. Prev: Cons. Surg. Cheltenham Gen. Hosp. & Glos. HA.

FAIRGRIEVE, Ross 115 Earlspark Avenue, Glasgow G43 2HD Tel: 0141 637 9222 Email: rossf16@hotmail.com — MB ChB Glas. 1990; FRCA 1997. (Glas.) Specialist Regist. (Anaesth.) Vict. Infirm. Glas.

FAIRHALL, David William 10 Wellington Road, Maldon CM9 6HL — MB ChB 1990 Birm.; ChB Birm. 1990.

FAIRHAM, Stuart Allan Little Paddock, Essendine Road, Uffington, Stamford PE9 4SR Tel: 0136 782 53339 — MB ChB 1968 Bristol; MRCPath 1975. Cons. (Haemat.) PeterBoro. Dist. Hosp. Prev: Sen. Regist. (Haematol.) Nottm. Gp. Hosps.; Ho. Surg. Musgrave Pk. Hosp. Taunton; Ho. Phys. S.mead Hosp. Bristol.

FAIRHEAD, Isobel Anna 1 Baronsmere Road, London N2 9QD — MB BS 1993 Lond.

FAIRHEAD, Margaret Morgan Barrack Lane Medical Practice, 1 Barrack Lane, Ipswich IP1 3NQ Tel: 01473 252827 Fax: 01473 250463; 27 Cotswold Avenue, Ipswich IP1 4LJ — MB BS 1987 Lond.; MRCGP 1993; DRCOG 1992.

FAIRHEAD, Susan Broadway Medical Centre, 65-67 Broadway, Fleetwood FY7 7DG Tel: 01253 874222 Fax: 01253 874448 — MB BS 1985 Lond.; MRCGP 1989; DRCOG 1987.

FAIRHEAD, Susan Mary 113 Gloucester Avenue, London NW1 8LB — BM BCh 1971 Oxf.; BA (Hons.) Oxf. 1966, BM BCh 1971; FRCP Lond. 1994; MRCP (UK) 1974; FRCPath 1990, M 1978. (dyford univ) Cons. Haemat. Chase Farm Hosp. Socs: FRCPath; FRCPhys; Brit. Soc. Haematol. Prev: Sen. Regist. (Haemat.) Hammersmith & N. Middlx. Hosps. Lond.

FAIRHURST, Andrew Michael 25 Ham Close, Charlton Kings, Cheltenham GL52 6NP — MB BS 1991 Lond.

FAIRHURST, Bernard Joseph Carreg Boeth, Llanddaniel, Gaerwen LL60 6EP — MD 1958 Liverp.; MB ChB 1951; FRCP Lond. 1975, M 1957. (Liverp.) Phys. Roy. Albert Edwd. Infirm. Wigan. Socs: BMA. Prev: Sen. Buswell Fell. in Med. Univ. Rochester, U.S.A.; Sen. Regist. in Med. Roy. Infirm. Sheff.; Med. Regist. United Liverp. Hosps.

FAIRHURST, Colin Thomas Holderness Road Surgery, 445 Holderness Road, Hull HU8 8JS Tel: 01482 374255 Fax: 01482 790301 — MB ChB 1984 Leeds; DRCOG 1988; Cert. Family Plann. JCC 1988.

FAIRHURST, David Andrew 60 Southlands Avenue, Standish, Wigan WN6 0TT — MB ChB 1998 Manch.; MB ChB Manch 1998.

FAIRHURST, Helen Elizabeth 23 Cassel Avenue, Poole BH13 6JD — BM BCh 1983 Oxf.; 2000 DIPM; BA Oxf. 1980; MRCGP 1988; DRCOG 1986. SCMO Family Plann., Poole. Prev: Trainee GP Bristol VTS; Clin. Med. Off. (Child Health) Swindon; SHO (Psychogeriat.) Ham Green Hosp. Bristol.

FAIRHURST, Howard John 1 Hampshire Close, Wilpshire, Blackburn BB1 9LU — MB ChB 1989 Ed. SHO (O & G) Burnley Gen. Hosp.

FAIRHURST, Jean Antonia (retired) Foxes Wood, Shrub Lane, Burwash, Etchingham TN19 7ED — MB BS 1953 Lond.; DO Eng. 1956. Prev: Assoc. Specialist (Ophth.) King's Coll. Hosp. Lond.

FAIRHURST, Joanna Jadwiga Childrens X-Ray Department, Southampton General Hospital, Tremona Road, Shirley, Southampton SO16 6YD Tel: 02380 794016 Email: j.fairhurst@doctors.org.uk; 17 Hinton Fields, Kings Worthy, Winchester SO23 7QB — MB BS 1982 Lond.; MRCP (UK) 1985; FRCR 1988. Cons. Paediat. Radiol. Soton. Gen. Hosp. Prev: Sen. Regist. (Radiol.) Soton. Gen. Hosp.

FAIRHURST, Karen McKenzie Medical Centre, 20 West Richmond Street, Edinburgh EH8 9DX Tel: 0131 667 2955; 22 Park Road, Edinburgh EH6 4LD Tel: 0131 538 8490 — MB BS 1987 Lond.; MRCGP 1991; DRCOG 1990. Lect. (Gen. Pract.) Univ. Edin. Prev: Clin. Lect. (Gen. Pract.) Univ. Liverp.

FAIRHURST, Richard John NHS Direct, 449-51 Garstang Road, Broughton, Preston PR3 5LN Tel: 01772 773036 Fax: 01772 903927 Email: richard.fairhurst@las-tr.nwest.nhs.uk; Wiswell Eaves House, Wiswell, Clitheroe BB7 9BT Tel: 01254 823581 — MB BS 1969 Lond.; MRCS Eng. LRCP Lond. 1969; FFAEM 1995; Dip. IMC RCS Ed. 1995; DObst RCOG 1971. (Univ. Coll. Hosp.) Med. Dir. NHS Direct N. W. Coast; Examr. RCS Edin.; Med. Director Lancs. Ambul. Serv.; A & E Cons. Chorley and S. Pibble Dist. Gen. Hosp. Socs: Fell. Roy. Soc. Med.; (Ex-Chairm.) Brit. Assn. Immediate Care; Brit. Aeromed. Pract. Assn. Prev: Dir. Green Flag Trav. Med. Serv.; Hon. Clin. Asst. (A & E) Univ. Coll. Hosp. & Roy. Lond. Hosp.; SHO (O & G) & Accid. Off. Mid-Sussex Hosp. Gp.

FAIRHURST-WINSTANLEY, Allan John Fallon and Partners, 1 Houghton Lane, Shevington, Wigan WN6 8ET Tel: 01257 01257 Fax: 01257 251081 — MB ChB 1992 Manch.; MRCGP 1996; DRCOG 1995. (Manchester) Course Organiser for the N. Manch., Salford and Trafford Day Release Course for GP Regist.s.

FAIRLAMB, Professor Alan Hutchinson Department of Biochemistry, The Wellcome Trust Building, University of Dundee, Dundee DD1 5EH Tel: 01382 345155 Fax: 01382 345542 Email: ahfairlamb@dundee.ac.uk — MB ChB 1971 Ed.; PhD (Biochem.) Ed. 1975; BSc (Hons. Med. Sci.) Biochem. Ed. 1968. (Univ. Ed.) Prof. Molecular Parasitol. Univ. Dundee; Edr. Bd. Molecular & Biochem. Parasitology; Chairm. WHO/TDR Drug Discovery Research Steering Com. 1999-. Socs: Fell. Linn. Soc.; Roy. Soc. Trop. Med. & Hyg.; Biochem. Soc. Prev: Prof. Biochem.ry Lond. Sch. Hyg. & Trop. Med.; Asst. Prof. Laborat. Med. Biochem. Rockefeller Univ.; Research Fell. Lond. Sch. Hyg. Trop. Med.

FAIRLAMB, Christopher Paul Church Street Surgery, 4 Church Street, Wingate TS28 5AQ Tel: 01429 838217 — MB ChB 1977 Manchester; MB ChB Manch. 1977. (Manchester) GP Wingate, Co. Durh.

FAIRLAMB, Clare Agatha Walls 14 Church Hill Road, Tettenhall, Wolverhampton WV6 9AT Tel: 01902 751024 — MB BS 1975 Lond.; MRCP (UK) 1978; MRCS Eng. LRCP Lond. 1975. Clin. Asst. (Rheum.) Roy. Hosp. Wolverhampton. Prev: Regist. (Genitourin. Med.) The Roy. Hosp. Wolverhampton; Regist. (Gen. Med.) N.ampton Gen. Hosp.; SHO (Med.) Leicester Hosps.

FAIRLAMB, David John Department of Radiotherapy, Deanesly Centre, Royal Wolverhampton Hospitals, Wolverhampton WV10 0QP Tel: 01902 642975 Fax: 01902 642994; 14 Church Hill Road, Tettenhall, Wolverhampton WV6 9AT Tel: 01902 751024 — MB BS 1972 Lond.; FRCR 1980; DMRT Eng. 1980. Cons. Radiotherapist & Oncol. Roy. Hosp. Wolverhampton; Dir. Compton Hospice Wolverhampton; Hon. Sen. Lect. (Cancer Studies) Univ. Birm. Socs: BMA; Brit. Oncol. Assn.; Educat. Bd. Roy. Coll. Radiologist. Prev: Postgrad. Adviser W. Midl. (Radiother. & Oncol.) Roy. Coll. Radiols.; Sen. Regist. (Radiother.) Ch.ill Hosp. Oxf.; Regist. (Radiother.) Roy. Free Hosp. Lond.

FAIRLEY, Alexander Arthurton, Hardgate, Clydebank, Glasgow — MB ChB 1947 Glas.

FAIRLEY, Alison St Bartholomew's Medical Centre, Manzil Way, Cowley Road, Cowley, Oxford OX4 1XB Tel: 01865 242334 Fax: 01865 204018; 29 Croft Road, Thame OX9 3JF — MB BChir 1989 Camb. (Camb. & St. Bart.) Socs: Roy. Coll. Gen. Pract.

FAIRLEY, Andrew (retired) Garden Cottage, School Lane, North Mundham, Chichester PO20 6LA Tel: 01243 778328 — MB BChir 1952 Camb.; FRCP Ed. 1982, M 1966; MRCS Eng. LRCP Lond. 1952; DObst RCOG 1956. Prev: Cons. Phys. (Geriat. Med.) Chichester Health Dist.

FAIRLEY, Caroline Jane Dayton, The Green, Cheriton, Alresford SO24 0PY Tel: 01962 771370 — MB BS 1987 Lond.; FRCA 1991. Cons. Anaesth. Roy. Hants. Co. Hosp. Winchester. Prev: Sen. Regist. & Regist. Rotat. (Anaesth.) St. Geo. Hosp. Lond.

FAIRLEY, Eric William Rambaut, Group Capt. RAF Med. Br. Retd. c/o Lloyds Bank, 6 Pall Mall, London SW1Y 5NG — MRCS Eng. LRCP Lond. 1935; DTM & H Liverp. 1949. (St. Thos.) Prev: PMO Coastal Command RAF.

FAIRLEY, Ian Murray 25 Hilltop Crescent, Cosham, Portsmouth PO6 1BB — MB ChB 1976 Liverp.; FRCR 1985. Cons. Radiol. Portsmouth Hosp. NHS Trust.

FAIRLEY, Ian Robert 6 Kirkhills, Thorner, Leeds LS14 3EX — MB ChB 1987 Sheff.; MRCP (UK) 1991.

FAIRLEY, James Hamilton (retired) 51 Woodcote Road, Caversham, Reading RG4 7BB — BM BCh 1953 Oxf.; MA, BM BCh Oxf. 1953; MRCGP 1960; DCH Eng. 1958; DObst RCOG 1955. Prev: Ho. Surg. (O & G), Ho. Phys. (Paediat.) St. Bart. Hosp. Lond.

FAIRLEY, Mr James William ENT Department, William Harvey Hospital, Ashford TN24 0LZ Tel: 01233 633331 Fax: 01233 616132 Email: jwfairley@doctors.org.uk; Sandyhurst House, Sandyhurst Lane, Ashford TN25 4NX Tel: 01233 642244 Fax: 01233 662840 — MB BS 1981 Lond.; BSc Lond. 1978; MS Lond. 1996; FRCS Eng. 1988. (St. Thos.) Cons. ENT William Harvey Hosp. Ashford & Buckland Hosp. Dover. Socs: Fell. Roy. Soc. Med.; Otolaryngol. Research Soc.; (Treas.) Brit. Soc. Hist. ENT. Prev: Sen. Regist. (ENT) Roy. Hallamsh. Hosp. Sheff.; Regist. (ENT) Middlx. & Univ. Coll. Hosps. Lond. & Mt. Vernon Hosp. N.wood; SHO (ENT) Roy. Nat. Throat, Nose & Ear Hosp. Lond.

FAIRLEY, Louise Farrow Ercall Road, Brightons, Falkirk FK2 Tel: 01324 715753 — MB ChB 1960 Ed.; DObst. RCOG 1963. (Ed.)

FAIRLEY, Robert Bridge of Allan Health Centre, Fountain Road, Bridge of Allan, Stirling FK9 4EU Tel: 01786 833210; Ellenslea, St. Mary's Drive, Dunblane FK15 0HB — MB ChB 1970 Glas.; FRCGP 1989, M 1977; CIH Dund 1975; DObst RCOG 1973. (Glas.)

FAIRLIE, Andrew Blair Bothwell Medical Centre, 3 Uddingston Road, Bothwell, Glasgow G71 8ET; 57 Silverwells Crescent, Bothwell, Glasgow G71 8DP Tel: 01698 3290 — MB ChB 1963 Glas. (Glas.) Socs: Glas. Roy. M-C Soc. & BMA. Prev: Ho. Off. (Med.) & Ho. Off. (Surg.) Hairmyres Hosp. E. Kilbride; Ho. Off. (Obst.) Bellshill Matern. Hosp.

FAIRLIE, Edward John (retired) Cloverlea, Strathkinness High Road, St Andrews KY16 9UA — MB BS 1952 Lond.; MRCS Eng. LRCP Lond. 1947; FRCOG 1980, M 1962, DObst 1952. Prev: Cons. O & G E. Fife Hosps.

FAIRLIE, Fiona MacRae The Jessop Hospital For Women, Leavygreave Road, Sheffield S3 7RE Tel: 0114 276 6222 — MD 1989 Leeds; MB ChB Leeds 1978; MRCOG 1983. Cons. O & G Jessop Hosp. for Wom. Sheff. Prev: Sen. Regist. (O & G) Glas.

FAIRLIE, Henry (retired) 82 Norwood Park, Bearsden, Glasgow G61 2RZ Tel: 0141 942 8085 — MB ChB 1939 Glas.; FRCA 1954; DA Eng. 1947. Prev: Cons. Anaesth. W.. Infirm., Gartnavel Gen. Hosp., Roy. Samarit. & Matern. Hosp. Glas.

FAIRLIE, Hugh Hunter Grove Cottage, Penpol, Devoran, Truro TR3 6NW Tel: 01872 864609 — MB ChB 1982 Glas. SHO (Psychiat.) City Hosp. Truro. Prev: SHO (Obst.) Treliske Hosp. Truro; SHO (Orthop. & ENT) City Hosp. Truro.

FAIRLIE, Neil Cameron Department of Radiology, Northampton General Hospital, Northampton NN1 5BD; 20 Cottage Gardens, Northampton NN3 9YW — BM BCh 1982 Oxf.; MA Camb. 1982; MRCP (UK) 1985; FRCR 1989. Cons. Radiol. N.ampton Gen. Hosp.

FAIRLIE-CLARKE, Mr George Allan (retired) Northford House, 6 Northford Road, Dartmouth TQ6 9EP — MB BS Lond. 1938; MRCS Eng. LRCP Lond. 1937; FRCS Eng. 1941. Prev: Res. Surg. Off. Kent & Sussex Hosp. Tunbridge Wells.

FAIRMAN, Mr Hugh Douglas Polscatho, The Ropewalk, Penpol, Devoran, Truro TR3 6NP Tel: 01872 862105 — MB 1966 Camb.; MA Camb. 1965, BA 1962, MB 1966, BChir 1965; FRCS Ed. 1970; DLO Eng. 1970. (Lond. Hosp.) ENT Cons. Surg. Cornw. AHA. Prev: Sen. Regist. Univ. Hosp. Wales Cardiff; SHO (Cas.) Freedom Fields Hosp. Plymouth; SHO (Surg.) Poltimore Hosp. Exeter.

FAIRMAN, Martin John Pilgrim Hospital, Boston PE21 9QS Tel: 01205 364801; Skirbeck Grange, Sibsey Road, Boston PE21 9QX Tel: 01205 360743 — MB BS 1968 Lond.; FRCP Lond. 1987; MRCP (UK) 1972; MRCS Eng. LRCP Lond. 1968. (Lond. Hosp.) Cons. Phys. & Med. Dir. United Licolnshire, Hosp. NHS Trust. Socs: Brit. Soc. Gastroenterol. Prev: Sen. Regist. Leeds AHA (T); Fell. (Digestive Dis.) Cincinnati Med. Center, USA.

FAIRNEY, Angela Department of Metabolic Medicine, Imperial College School of Medicine at St Mary's, Paddington, London W2 1PG Tel: 020 7886 1097 Fax: 020 7886 1716 Email: a.fairney@ic.ac.uk; Kettlewell House, 33 New Road, Digswell, Welwyn AL6 0AQ Tel: 01438 714311 — MB BS; MB BS 1962 London; MD 1974 London; FRCP 1984 London; MRCP 1968 London; MRCS Eng. LRCP 1962 London; FRCPath 1992. (Westminster) Sen. Lect. & Hon. Cons. Chem. Path. Imperial Coll. Sch. of Med. (St Mary's) Lond.; Lead Clinician Osteoporosis Clinic St Mary's NHS Trust; Director Supna Regional Assay and Advis. Serv. for Bore Maekers St. Mary's NHS Trust. Socs: Europ. Calcified Tissure Soc.; Fell. Roy. Soc. Med.; Soc. Endocrinol. Prev: Lect. (Endocrine Chem.) & Hon. Sen. Regist. W.m. Med. Sch. Lond.; Williams Research Fell. Univ. Lond. & Hon. Sen. Regist. (Chem. Path.) Hosp. Sick Childr. Gt. Ormond St. Lond.

FAIRRIE, Anthony Johnston, VRD Gaddon House, Uffculme, Cullompton EX15 3DL Tel: 01884 40544 — MRCS Eng. LRCP Lond. 1942. (Westm.) Socs: Fell. Roy. Soc. Med.; BMA. Prev: Med. Off. Daily Express & Allied Newspapers; Ho. Surg. Post-grad. Med. Regist. W. Middlx. Hosp.; Ho. Phys. Hosp. SS. John & Eliz.

FAIRRIS, Geoffrey Michael Royal Hampshire County Hospital, Romsey Road, Winchester SO22 5DG Tel: 01962 863535 Fax: 01962 824826; Deneview, Stratton Road, Winchester SO23 0JQ Tel: 01962 879961 Fax: 01962 879961 — MB BS 1977 Lond.; DM Soton. 1988; MRCP (UK) 1980; MRCS Eng. LRCP Lond. 1977; T(M) 1991; FRCP 1997. Cons. Dermat. Roy. Hants. Co. Hosp. Winchester & Soton. Univ. Hosps. Trust. Socs: Fell. St. John's Dermat. Soc.; Fell. Roy. Soc. Med. (Mem. Sect. Dermat.). Prev: Sen. Regist. (Dermat.) Roy. S. Hants. Hosp.; Regist. (Dermat.) The Gen. Infirm. Leeds; Regist. (Med.) United Norwich Hosps.

FAIRS, Robert Gordon Fairview, Peareth Hall Road, Springwell, Gateshead NE9 7NT — MB BS 1969 Newc.

FAIRWEATHER, David Keith (retired) 13 Elm Lodge, Stevenage Road, London SW6 6NZ Tel: 020 7385 7490 Fax: 020 7385 7490 — MB BChir 1954 Camb.; MRCS Eng. LRCP Lond. 1954; MRCGP 1971; DObst RCOG 1958. Prev: GP Fulham Lond.

FAIRWEATHER, David Sebastian Armstead Department of Clinical Geratology, Radcliffe Infirmary, Oxford OX2 6HE Tel: 01865 224971 Fax: 01865 224815 Email: sebastian.fairweather@ccc.ox.ac.uk — MB BChir 1973 Camb.; PhD Birm. 1985; MA Oxf. 1987; FRCP Lond. 1991; MRCP (UK) 1976. Hon. Cons. Gen. & Geriat. Med. Oxf. Univ.; Lect. (Geriat. Med.) Oxf. Univ.; Fell. of Corpus Christi Coll. Oxf. Univ. Prev: Lect. (Geriat. Med.) Manch. Univ.; Regist. (Med.) Gen. Hosp. Birm.

FAIRWEATHER, Deborah Ann Little Red House, Hasketon, Woodbridge IP13 6JA — MB BS 1982 Lond.; DRCOG 1986; DA Eng. 1984.

FAIRWEATHER, Denys Vivian Ivor 37 Lyndhurst Avenue, Mill Hill, London NW7 2AD Tel: 0208 959 4466 Fax: 0208 959 4466

— MB ChB 1949 St. And.; MD St. And. 1966; FRCOG 1967, M 1958, DObst 1953. (St. And.) Emerit. Prof. Obst. & Gyn. Univ. Lond. UCL. Socs: Fell. Roy. Soc. Med.; Blair Bell Res. Soc. Prev: Sen. Lect. (Midw. & Gyn.) Univ. Newc u. Tyne; Pro. Vice Chancellor Med. Univ. Lond.; Squadron Ldr. RAF Med. Br., Surg. Div.

FAIRWEATHER, Frank Arthur (retired) Failran, Wayford, Stalham, Norwich NR12 9LH Tel: 01692 582588 — MB BS Lond. 1954; FRCPath 1975, M 1963; FIBiol 1972; FFOM (Hon.) 1991. Hon. Phys. to HM The Qu. Prev: Head of Clin. Studies BIBRA Internat. 1993.

FAIRWEATHER, Jane Ann Health Centre, High Street, Bildeston, Ipswich IP7 7EX Tel: 01449 740254 Fax: 01449 740903; Walnut Tree Cottage, The Causeway, Hitcham, Ipswich IP7 7NF — MB ChB 1980 Aberd.; BA (Hons.) Open 1994. Prev: Trainee GP Pontefract VTS.

FAIRWEATHER, Judith Elizabeth Green Lane Surgery, 2 Green Lane, Belper DE56 1BZ Tel: 01773 823521 Fax: 01773 821954; 11 Nether Close, Duffield, Belper DE56 4DR Tel: 01773 840070 Email: judithfairweather@compuserve.com — BM BS 1983 Nottm.; MRCGP (Distinc.) 1987. (Nottingham)

FAIRWEATHER, Nigel John Medical Centre, Adnitt Road, Rushden NN10 9TR Tel: 01933 412444 Fax: 01933 317666; 57 Fern Road, Rushden NN10 6AU Tel: 01933 58082 — MB ChB 1968 St. And.; DObst RCOG 1971. (Queen's Coll. Dundee) Clin. Asst. (Psychogeriat.) Rushden Hosp. Rockingham Forest NHS Trust. Socs: Kettering & Dist. Med. Soc.

FAIRWEATHER, Roger James (retired) Amberleigh, 24 Keyberry Park, Newton Abbot TQ12 1DF Tel: 01626 54345 — MB ChB 1963 Birm.; DObst RCOG 1965.

FAIRWEATHER, Ronald Alexander Dr MacBrayne and Partners, 19 Dinmont Road, Shawlands, Glasgow G41 3UJ Tel: 0141 632 8883 Fax: 0141 636 0654; 44 Cedarwood Avenue, Newton Mearns, Glasgow G77 5LP — MB ChB 1969 Glas. Hosp. Pract. (Dermat.) Vict. Infirm. Glas. Prev: Clin. Asst. (Dermat). Vict. Infirm. Glas.; SHO & Regist. (Dermat.) Vict. Infirm. Glas.

FAIRWEATHER, Sheila Helen Elizabeth (retired) Flat 2, Redcliff Court, Lower Park Road, Queens Park, Chester CH4 7BB — MB ChB 1950 Liverp.; DPH Eng. 1958, DCH 1956. Prev: Clin. Med. Off. Barnet AHA.

FAIRWEATHER, Susan Jeanette The Cross, Llanvair Kilgeddin, Abergavenny NP7 9DE — MB BCh 1980 Wales.

FAISAL, Katrel Nada Mohammad Ali 493 Brook Lane, Kings Heath, Birmingham B13 0BU Tel: 0121 777 6730 — Vrach 1969 Moscow; Vrach Peoples Friendship Univ, Moscow 1969.

FAISAL, Nuton Ahmed Bartley Green Health Centre, Romsley Road, Bartley Green, Birmingham B32 3PR Tel: 0121 477 4300; 16 Wynds Point, Birmingham B31 2EF Tel: 0121 472 4548 — MB ChB 1987 Leic.; BSc (Hons.) Med. Sci. Leicester 1984; MRCGP 1991. (Leicester) Princip. GP Birm. Univ.; Clin. Tutor Birm. Univ.

FAITH, Charles Norman (retired) 25 Greenacres, Hendon Lane, Finchley, London N3 3SF Tel: 020 8349 1509 — MB BS 1939 Lond.; MD Lond. 1941; MRCS Eng. LRCP Lond. 1936; DCH RCP Lond. 1953; DPH Lond. 1939. Prev: GP Lond.

FAITH, Lesley Stepping Hill Hospital, Stockport SK2 7JE; The Residence, Marple Dale Hall, Dale Road, Stockport SK6 6NL — MB ChB 1980 Manch.; BSc St. And. 1977; MRCPsych 1984. Cons. Psychiat. Stepping Hill Hosp. Stockport.

FAITHFULL-DAVIES, Donald Neil 1 Post Office Lane, Dummer, Basingstoke RG25 2AE Tel: 01256 397403 — MB BChir 1971 Lond.; MB BChir Camb. 1971; MSc Lond. 1979; FRCPath 1992, M 1980. Prev: Cons. Med. Microbiol. Camb. Milit. Hosp. Aldershot.

FAIYAZ, Farzana c/o Mr. M.H. Ahmad FRCS, General Hospital, Hartlepool TS24 9AH — MB BS 1971 Vikram. (Gandhi Med. Coll. Bhopal) Clin. Asst. (Anaesth.) Hartlepool. Prev: Regist. (Anaesth.) Hartlepool Gen. Hosp.; SHO (Anaesth.) Memor. Hosp. Darlington.

FAIZ, Ghulam Farouq Elysèe House, Petite Rue d'Elysèe, St Peter, Jersey JE3 7DT Tel: 01534 482525 — MB BS 1962 Punjab; MB BS Punjab (Pakistan) 1962; DPM RCPSI 1974. (King Edwd. Med. Coll. Lahore) Cons. Psychiat. Jersey Gp. Hosps. Socs: Jersey Med. Soc. Prev: Regist. Napsbury Hosp.; SHO Shenley Hosp.; Sen. Regist. St. Saviour's Hosp. Jersey.

FAIZ, Mr Mohamed Mazhar 486 Galle Road, Colombo 3, Sri Lanka; 12 Sutton Close, Milton, Cambridge CB4 6DU — MB BS 1982 Sri Lanka; FRCS Eng. 1994. Cons. Surg. Nawaloka Private Hosp., Asiri Private Hosp. & Delmon Private Hosp. Colombo. Socs: Life Mem. Coll. Surg. Sri Lanka. Prev: Regist. (Gen. Surg.) Milton Keynes Gen. Hosp. & Newmarket Gen. Hosp.

FAIZALLAH, Riyaz Arrowe park Hospital, Aeeowe Park Road, Upton L35 5DRCH49 Tel: 0151 604 7266; Winston, Prospect Road, Birkenhead CH42 8LE — FRCP 1994 London; MB ChB 1974 Baghdad; PhD Liverp. 1989; MRCP (UK) 1978. Cons. Phys. & Gastroenterologist, Arrowe Pk. Hosp., Upton. Socs: Brit. Soc. of Gastroenterol.; Brit. Assn. for the Study of the Liver. Prev: Cons. Phys. & Gastroenterol. Whiston Hosp. Prescot & St. Helens Hosp. Merseyside.

FAIZAN, Mr Ahmed 5 Logan Close, Wellington Road, North Hounslow, Hounslow TW4 7BP — MB BS 1986 Karachi; FRCS Glas. 1991.

FAJARDO PANDO, Pablo c/o Fitzroy College, Northdown House, Margate CT9 3TP — LMS 1993 Seville.

FAJEMIROKUN, Mrs Elizabeth Adetokunbo Queen Elizabeth The Queen Mother Hospital, St Peters Road, Margate CT9 4AN Tel: 01843 225544 Fax: 01843 220048; Flat 17, Frederick House, Pett St, Woolwich, London SE18 5PB Tel: 020 8855 1852 — MB ChB 1985 Ife, Nigeria; DA (UK) 1997. Staff Anaesth. Qu. Eliz. The Qu. Mother Hosp. Margate. Prev: Staff Anaesth. Thanet Gen. Hosp.; Regist. Mt. Vernon Hosp. N.wood, Middlx.; SHO Milton Keynes Gen. Hosp. & Mayday Univ. Hosp. Croydon.

FAJEMISIN, Babatunde Adetokunbo 310 Carterhatch Road, Enfield EN3 5ED — MB BS 1992 Lond.

FAJUMI, Anthony Oladiran 70 Golborne Avenue, Withington, Manchester M20 1EJ — MB ChB 1997 Manch.

FAKES, Diana Frances Royal Flying Doctor Service, PO Box 444, Kalgoorlie WA 6430, Australia Tel: 0190 912529; 107 Braeside Avenue, Patcham, Brighton BN1 8SQ Tel: 01273 504852 — MB BS 1988 Lond.; DA (UK) 1993.

FAKHOURY, Victoria Agnes Kildrum Health Centre, Afton Road, Cumbernauld, Glasgow G67 2EU Tel: 01236 721354 — MB ChB 1986 Glas. Prev: SHO (Community Paediat.) Edin.; SHO (Dermat.) S.. Gen. Hosp. Glas.; SHO (Geriat.) Harrmyers Hosp. E. Kilbride.

FAKHRY, Helmy Aziz Guirges 6 Walton Crescent, Blackburn BB2 3TQ Tel: 01254 51693 — MB BCh 1974 Ain Shams.

FAKIM, Mr Anwar 25 Compton Court, Victoria Crescent, Gipsy Hill, London SE19 1RF — MB BS 1979 Bombay; MB BS Bombay, India 1979; FRCS Ed. 1987.

FAKOYA, Adeniyi Oluwamoroti 39 Barville Close, St Norbert's Road, London SE4 2LL — MB BS 1988 Lond.

FALCON, Mr Michael Geoffrey 25 Wimpole Street, London W1G 8GL Tel: 020 7580 7199 Fax: 020 7580 6855 Email: falconeyes1@aol.com — MB 1968 Camb.; MA Camb. 1967, BChir 1967; FRCS Eng. 1973; MRCP (UK) 1971; FRCOphth 1990; DO Eng. 1970. (Camb. & Guy's) p/t Cons. Surg. Ophth. St. Thos. Hosp. Lond. Socs: Fell. Coll. Ophth; BMA. Prev: Lect. (Clin. Ophth.) & Sen. Resid. Surg. Off. Moorfields Eye; Hosp. Lond. (City Rd. Br.); Regist. (Ophth.) Guy's Hosp.

FALCONER, Mr Alan Scott (retired) The Old Granary, Back Lane, Sedbergh LA10 5AQ Tel: 0153 761 20863 — MRCS Eng. LRCP Lond. 1945; BA Camb. 1942; FRCS Eng. 1953; FRCOG 1974. Prev: Resid. Med. Off. Sedbergh Sch. Cumbria.

FALCONER, Alison Cancer Genetics Unit, Institute of Cancer Research, 15 Cotswold Rd, Sutton SM2 5NG — MB BChir 1991 Camb.; MA Cambridge 1991; BA (Hons) Cambridge 1998; MRCP (UK) 1994; FRCR 1999. Research Fell., Cancer Genetics Unit, Inst. of Cancer Research, Sutton. Prev: Specialist Regist. (Clin. Oncol.) St Lukes Cancer Centre Guildford.

FALCONER, Alistair Fleming The Taymount Surgery, 1 Taymount Terrace, Perth PH1 1NU Tel: 01738 627117 Fax: 01738 444713 — MB ChB 1979 Dundee. (Dundee) GP Perth.

FALCONER, Andrew Dean Kilcreggan Medical Centre, Kilcreggan, Helensburgh G84 0JL — MB ChB 1979 Aberd.; MRCGP 1985.

FALCONER, Ann Elizabeth 5 Hillview Drive, Cults, Aberdeen AB15 9HD Tel: 01224 868754 — MB ChB 1995 Aberd. SHO (Orthop.) Hartlepool. Prev: PRHO (Gen. Med.) Aberd.; PRHO (Orthop. & Gen. Surg.) Aberd.

FALCONER, Mr Denis Thomas Maxillofacial Department, Oldchurch Hospital, Wateroo Road, Romford RM7 0BE Tel: 01708 746090 — BCLD Leeds; MB ChB 1983; BChD Leeds 1976,; FRCS Ed. 1990; FDS RCS Eng. 1988. (Leeds) Cons. Oral & Maxilllofacial

Surg. OldCh. Hosp. Romford. Socs: BMA & Brit. Assn. Oral & Maxillofacial Surg.; BDA. Prev: Sen. Regist. (Oral & Maxillofacial Surg.) Glas. HA; Regist. (Oral & Maxillofacial Surg.) Roy. Free Hosp. Lond. & Ysbyty Glan Clwyd.; SHO (Plastic & Oral Surg.) St. Luke's Hosp. Bradford.

FALCONER, Dora Janet Burman (retired) Flat 3, Kingfisher Court, 77a Whitton Road, Hounslow TW3 2EG Tel: 020 8893 4967 — MRCS Eng. LRCP Lond. 1935; FRCS Ed. 1942. Prev: Regist. (Surg.) Roy. Free Hosp.

FALCONER, Gordon Francis — MRCS Eng. LRCP Lond. 1965; FRCOG 1984, M 1971. (Guy's) Cons. O & G Hope Hosp. Salford. Socs: N. Eng. Obst. & Gyn. Soc. & Manch. Medico-Legal Soc. Prev: Sen. Regist. (O & G) Hope Hosp. Salford, Oldham Gp. Hosps. & St. Lukes Hosp. Guildford.

FALCONER, Hugh Robert (retired) 28 Woodhill Terrace, Aberdeen AB15 5LE — MB ChB 1956 Aberd. Prev: Ho. Off. Gyn. Aberd. Roy. Infirm.

FALCONER, Ian Laing 49 Marine Avenue, Whitley Bay NE26 1NB Tel: 0191 252 4527; 98 Beach Road, Tynemouth, North Shields NE30 2QP — MB ChB 1976 Dundee.

FALCONER, Jane Angela Grace Shebburn Surgery, Main Street, New Abbey, Dumfries DG2 8BY Tel: 01387 850263 Fax: 01387 850468; Crofthill, 40 Dalbeattie Road, Dumfries DG2 7PL Tel: 01387 262488 Email: falconerjwre@cs.com — MB ChB 1975 Aberd.; MRCGP 1979; DObst RCOG 1979. (Aberdeen)

FALCONER, Jennifer Margaret (retired) 5 Cedor Court, Thorley Lane, Timperley, Altrincham WA15 7AH Tel: 0161 980 4015 — MB ChB 1954 Manch.; DObst RCOG 1955. Prev: Ho. Phys. Manch. Roy. Infirm.

FALCONER, Mr John Stuart Garden Flat, 5 Lauriston Gardens, Edinburgh EH3 9HH — MB ChB 1985 Dundee; FRCS Glas. 1989; FRCS (Gen) 1998. Cons. Gen. Surg. with a specialist interest in ColoProctol., Law Hosp. Socs: ACPGBI.

FALCONER, Lesley Mary 54 Claremount Road, Wallasey CH45 6UD Tel: 0151 639 3388 — MB ChB 1938 Ed. (Univ. Ed.) Prev: Clin. Med. Off. Wirral AHA; Med. Off. Child Welf. Clinic. Ed. Provid. Disp.; Ho. Phys. Roy. Liverp. Childr. Hosp.

FALCONER, Paul John (retired) Flat 1, Heald Mount, Heald Road, Altrincham WA14 2JD — MB ChB 1958 Manch.; DLO Eng. 1968. Prev: Clin. Asst. (Geriat.) Trafford AHA.

FALCONER, Robert James Tel: 01792 206446 Email: falconer@clara.co.uk — MB ChB 1981 Manch.; FFA RCS Lond. 1988. (Manch.) Cons. Anaesth. Singleton Hosp. Swansea. Prev: Regist. (Anaesth.) Univ. Hosp. Wales Cardiff.

FALCONER, Thomas Christie (retired) 23 Spoutwells Road, Scone, Perth PH2 6RW Tel: 01738 551884 — MB ChB St. And. 1951; DIH Dund 1973; DPH St. And. 1954. Prev: Wolfson Foundat. Trav. Fell. India, 1968.

FALCONER, William James (retired) 5 Cedar Court, Thorley Lane, Timperley, Altrincham WA15 7AH Tel: 0161 980 4015 — MB ChB 1954 Manch.; DObst RCOG 1955. Prev: Ho. Phys. Manch. Roy. Infirm.

FALCONER SMITH, James Francis The Department of Chemical Pathology, Leicester Royal Infirmary, Leicester LE1 5WW — BM BCh 1970 Oxf.; DM Oxf. 1982; MRCP (UK) 1975; FRCP (UK) 1992; FRCPath 1998. (Middlx.) Cons. Clin. Biochem. Leics. DHA. Socs: Assn. Clin. Biochem. Informat. Technol. Gp. Prev: Clin. Lect. Nuffield Dept. Clin. Biochem. Oxf.; SHO Wessex RHA Neurol. Centre; Ho. Phys. Middlx. Hosp. Lond.

FALDER, Linda Sian 3 Palm Street, Sheffield S6 2XF — MB BS 1992 Lond.; BSc Lond. 1989. SHO (Neurosurg.) Frenchay Hosp. Bristol.

FALDU, Vallabhdas Kingsley House Surgery, 184 Somerford Road, Somerford, Christchurch BH23 3QG Tel: 01202 480836 Fax: 01202 486399 — MB BS 1970 Rajasthan; MB BS 1970 Rajasthan.

FALE, Alistair Duncan 3 Edgerton Road, Leeds LS16 5JD Tel: 0113 216 8523 Email: afale@ulth.northy.nhs.uk; The General Infirmary at Leeds, Great George St, Leeds LS1 3EX Tel: 0113 392 6672 — MB BS 1985 Lond.; FRCA 1992. (King's Coll. Hosp.) cons. Anaesth. & Intens. Care Gen. Infirm. Leeds. Socs: BMA; ICS; NAS.

FALIAKOS, Stylianos Flat E, 95 Westbourne Terrace, London W2 6QT — Ptychio Iatrikes 1990 Athens.

FALK, Helen Charmian Royal National Orthopaedic Hospital, Brockley Hill, Stanmore HA7 4LP Tel: 020 8954 2300 Ext: 463; 6 Reed's Place, London NW1 9NA Tel: 020 7267 5435 — MB BChir 1975 Camb.; MA Camb. 1974; DA Eng. 1978. (Univ. Coll. Hosp.) Assoc. Specialist (Anaesth.) Roy. Nat. Orthop. Hosp. Lond. Socs: Brit. Soc. Orthopaedic Anaesth. Prev: SHO (Paediat.) Roy. United Hosp. Bath; SHO (O & G) Yeovil Dist. Hosp.; Ho. Phys. Univ. Coll. Hosp. Lond.

FALK, Richard Mark South Axholme Group Practice, 60-64 High St., Epworth, Doncaster DN9 1EP Tel: 01427 872232 Fax: 01427 874944; Sobraon Lodge, 89 Haxey Lane, Haxey, Doncaster DN9 2ND — MB ChB 1984 Leeds; MB ChB Leeds l984; MRCGP 1991; DRCOG 1987.

FALK, Samuel (retired) Old Falinge, Falinge Fold, Rochdale OL12 6LE Tel: 01706 44946 — MB ChB 1942 Manch.; MD Manch. 1951; FRCPsych 1972; DPM 1947. Prev: Cons. Psychiat. Rochdale & Dist. Hosp. Gp.

FALK, Stephen John Bristol Oncology Centre, Horfield Road, Bristol BS2 8ED Tel: 0117 928 2419 Fax: 0117 928 4409 Email: stephen.falk@ubht.swest.nhs.uk; Cider Farm, Backwell Common, Backwell, Bristol BS48 3AB Tel: 01275 857152 Fax: 0870 056 7340 Email: sjf@stephen-falk.demon.co.uk — MD 1994 Liverp.; MB ChB 1983; MRCP (UK) 1986; FRCR 1989; MD 1994 Liverp. Cons. Clin. Oncol. Bristol Oncol. Centre. Prev: MRC Clin. Scientist Coru MRC Centre Camb.; Regist. (Radiother. & Oncol.) Velindre Hosp. Cardiff; SHO (Med.) Walton Hosp. Liverp.

FALK VAN ROOYEN, Inge 20 Huntsmill, Fulbourn, Cambridge CB1 5RH — MB ChB 1992 Stellenbosch.

FALKNER, John David Tudor Gate Surgery, Tudor St., Abergavenny NP7 5DL Tel: 01873 5991 — MB BS 1965 Lond.; MRCS Eng. LRCP Lond. 1965. (St. Geo.) Prev: Med. Off. Busoga Miss. Hosp. Kamuli, Uganda.

FALKNER, Martin John The Upper Surgery, 27 Lemon Street, Truro TR1 2LS Tel: 01872 74931 Fax: 01872 260339 — MB BS 1981 Lond.; BSc Lond. 1978, MB BS 1981; MRCP (UK) 1984.

FALKNER-LEE, Michael John (retired) Crail, 8 Marianne Road, Talbot Vill., Poole BH12 5EF Tel: 01202 527824 — MB BS 1952 Lond. Prev: Hosp. Pract. (ENT) Roy. Vict. Hosp. Bournemouth.

FALKOV, Adrian Farrel William Geoffrey House, 35 Black Prince Road, Kennington, London SE11 6JJ Email: adfalk@globalnet.co.uk — MB BCh 1983 Witwatersrand; BSc (Med.) Witwatersrand 1980; MRCPsych 1989. (Univ. of the Witwatersrand, Johannesburg, S. Africa) Cons. (Child Psychiat.).

FALKOWSKI, Jan Patrick McManus The Royal London Hospital, 2A Bow Road, London E3 Tel: 020 7377 7960 Fax: 020 8981 4848; 9 York Court, Manor Crescent, Epsom KT19 7EY Tel: 01372 747949 — MB BS 1984 Lond.; BSc Lond. 1981; MRCPsych. 1989; MBA 1993. (St Georges) Cons. Psychiat. Roy. Lond. Hosp. Prev: Sen. Regist. Springfield Hosp. Lond.; Research Fell. St Geo. Hosp. Med. Sch.

FALKOWSKI, Witold Antoni Prema, 5 Eastbrook Way, Adeyfield, Hemel Hempstead HP2 5UQ Tel: 01442 235855 Fax: 01442 235855 — Lekarz Warsaw 1963. Assoc. Specialist (Trauma & Orthop.) Hemel Hempstead & St. Albans City Gen. Hosps. Socs: Companion Fell. BOA; BMA.

FALKOWSKI, Wojciech 25 Higher Green, Ewell, Epsom KT17 3BB Tel: 020 8393 7045 Fax: 020 8393 7045 — MB BCh BAO 1957 NUI; MPhil (Psychiat.) Lond. 1970; FRCPsych 1984, M 1972; DPM Eng. 1968; LM Rotunda 1958. (Univ. Coll. Dub.) Emerit. Cons. Psychiat. & Hon. Sen. Lect. Springfield & St. Geo. Hosp. Med. Sch.; Sen. Tutor Univ. Lond.; Prof. Polish Univ. Lond.; Chairm. Accept Research Foundat.; Founder Mem. Inst. Transactional Anal.. Prev: Pro Rector Polish Univ.; Chairm. Polish Med. Assn.; Vice-Pres. Centre for Analytic Psychother.

FALKUS, Garvin Kenneth James London Road Medical Practice, 97 London Road, Gloucester GL1 3HH Tel: 01452 522079 Fax: 01452 387884; 97 London Road, Gloucester GL1 3HH Tel: 22079 — MRCS Eng. LRCP Lond. 1969. Med. Off. Gloucester City Counc. Prev: Sen. Surg. P & O Shipping Lines; Civil. Med. Pract. RAOC Blackdown.

FALL, Caroline Hannah Dorothy MRC Environmental Epidemiology Unit, Southampton General Hospital, Southampton SO16 6YD Tel: 02380 777624 Fax: 02380 704021 Email: chdf@mrc.soton.ac.uk; Highcroft, Fairfield Road, Shawford, Winchester SO21 2DA Tel: 01962 713176 — MB ChB 1976 Bristol; MB ChB Bristol 1979; BSc (1st cl. Hons.) (Anat.) Bristol 1976;

MRCP (UK) 1983; DRCOG 1985; DCH RCP Lond. 1984; DM 1999 Southampton. Clin. Scientist & Hon. Cons. (Paediat. Epidemiol.) Med. Research Counc. Environm. Epidemiol. Unit Soton. Gen. Hosp. Socs: Fell.Roy. Coll. of Phys.s; Brit. Soc. for Paediatric Endocrinol. and Diabetes; Fell.Roy. Coll. of Paediat. and Child Health. Prev: Regist. (Paediat.) Roy. United Hosp. Bath; Trainee GP Hants VTS; SHO Rotat. (Med.) Soton.

FALLA, Henry Peter Laurens (retired) Les Issues, St John, Jersey JE3 4FA Tel: 01534 861628 — MB BS 1954 Lond.; MRCS Eng. LRCP Lond. 1954; DA Eng. 1957; DObst RCOG 1957. Prev: Regist. Anaesth. Bath Gp. Hosps.

FALLAW, Charles Rodney Fife Snowdrop Cottage, Wetheral, Carlisle CA4 8HD — MB BS 1970 Newc.

FALLER, Charlotte (retired) 2 Woodruff Avenue, Burpham, Guildford GU1 1XS Tel: 01483 440491 — MB BS Lond. 1944; DObst RCOG 1946. Prev: Clin. Med. Off. Community Health Serv. Surrey HA.

FALLER, Paul Frederick 2 Westfield Place, Wigginton, York YO32 2JQ — BM BCh 1979 Oxf.; MA Camb. 1978; MRCGP 1983; DRCOG 1982.

FALLON, Alison Margaret 320 Hykeham Road, Lincoln LN6 8BW — MB ChB 1979 Leeds.

FALLON, Christobel Wendy Balmore Road Surgery, 138-142 Balmore Road, Glasgow G22 6LJ Tel: 0141 531 9393 Fax: 0141 531 9389; 7 Branziert Road N., Killearn, Glasgow G63 9RE Tel: 01360 550519 — MB ChB 1967 Glas.; MRCGP 1983; Dip. Forens. Med. Glas 1995. GP Audit Facilitator; Dep. Police Surg. D Div. Glas. Socs: BMA; Assn. Police Surg.

FALLON, Helen Maura 7 Branziert Road N., Killearn, Glasgow G63 9RE Tel: 0141 550519 — MB ChB 1996 Manch.; BSc St And. 1993. SHO (Med.). Socs: BMA; Ex Chair. Med. Stud.s Comm. 1995-1996; MODUS.

FALLON, John Stephen Valentine House, 1079 Rochdale Road, Manchester M9 8AJ Tel: 0161 740 2524 Fax: 0161 795 2531 — MB BCh BAO 1979 NUI; MRCGP 1981; Cert. Family Plann. JCC 1988; DCH RCPSI 1988; DRCOG 1981.

FALLON, Katherine Mary Somerton House Surgery, 79A North Road, Midsomer Norton, Bath BA3 2QE Tel: 01761 412141 Fax: 01761 410944; Hill House, Pensford Hill, Pensford, Bristol BS39 4AF Tel: 01761 490008 — MB BS 1984 Lond.; MRCGP 1989. Prev: SHO (O & G) Swindon; Trainee GP Swindon & Cirencester VTS.

FALLON, Kathleen Janet Fallon and Partners, 1 Houghton Lane, Shevington, Wigan WN6 8ET Tel: 01257 253311 Fax: 01257 251081; 1 Green Vale, Shevington, Wigan WN6 8JE — MB BS 1978 Newc.; MA Oxf. 1982, BA 1975.

FALLON, Lisa Marianne 32 Redesmere Drive, Alderley Edge SK9 7UR — BChir 1992 Camb.

FALLON, Marie Therese Department of Oncology, Palliative Medicine, University of Edinburgh, Western General Hospital, Edinburgh Tel: 0131 537 1000; 17 Cadogan Road, Liberton, Edinburgh EH16 6LY Tel: 0131 672 2481 — MB ChB 1984 Glas.; DRCOG 1987; DCH Glas. 1991; MRCGP 1988; MD 1999; MRCP 1999. (Glasgow) Sen. Lect. in Palliat. Med., Univ. of Edin.; Hon. Cons., Dept. of Oncol., W.ern Gen. Hosp. Socs: APM; EAPM; IASP. Prev: Sen. Lect., Palliat. Med., Univ. of Glas.

FALLON, Mark Edward Swallowbeck Grange, 320 Hykeham Road, Lincoln LN6 8BW Tel: 01522 681400 — MB ChB 1979 Leeds; MRCGP 1983; DRCOG 1982; DCH RCP Lond. 1981.

FALLON, Matthew John Claremont Bank Surgery, Claremont Bank, Shrewsbury SY1 1RL — MB ChB 1987 Birm.

FALLON, Michael Paul Mary The Health Centre, High St., Winsford CW7 2AS — MB BCh BAO 1983 NUI; MRCGP 1988; DObst RCPI 1986; DCH RCP NUI 1985.

FALLON, Moira Yvonne 29 Netherhouse Avenue, Kirkintilloch, Glasgow G66 5NF — MB ChB 1988 Glas.

FALLON, Perween Kamal 26 Greenfield Drive, London N2 9AF — MB BS 1984 Lond.; MRCP (UK) 1989; DCH RCP Lond. 1987. Regist. (Paediat. Neurol.) Hosp. for Childr. Gt. Ormond St. NHS Trust. Prev: Clin. Research Fell. Paediat. Neurol. Inst. of Child Health.

FALLON, Peter Thomas Aberfoyle Health Centre, 120 Strand Road, Londonderry BT48 7PB Tel: 01504 264868 Fax: 01504 260919; San Michele, 30 Talbot Park, Londonderry BT48 7TA Tel: 01504 51387 — MB BCh BAO 1948 Belf.; FRCGP 1982, M 1972. (Belf.) Provost. N.I. RCGP. Prev: Ho. Surg. City & Co. Hosp. Lond.derry.

FALLON, Mr Timothy John — MB ChB 1975 Bristol; FRCS Ed. 1987; FRCOphth 1988; MD 1989 Bristol. Cons. Ophth. Centr. Middlx. Hosp.; Cons. Ophth. Edgware Gen. Hosp.

FALLOON, Andrew Thomas Stanley 51 Longbridge Road, Bramley, Tadley, Basingstoke RG26 5AN — MB ChB 1990 Otago; Cert Family Plann 1999; MRCGP 1997. (Otago, NZ) GP Basingstoke. Prev: SHO (Psychiat.) Loddon NHS Trust Basingstoke; SHO (Ophth.) Salisbury Dist. Hosp.; Staff Doctor (A & E) N. Hants. Hosp. NHS Trust.

FALLOW, Stephen Matthew Rehabilitation Service (Psychiatric), Sandringham Suite, Windsor House, Troon Way Business Centre, Humberstone Lane, Leicester LE4 9HA Tel: 0116 225 6870 Fax: 0116 225 6855; 29 High Street, Morcott, Oakham LE15 9DN Email: smfallow@aol.com — MB ChB 1978 Otago; MRCPsych 1984. (Otago) Cons. Psychiat. (Rehabil.) Leicester Healthcare NHS Trust. Prev: Cons. Psychiat. Acute & Rehabil. Towers Hosp. Leicester; Sen. Regist. (Psychiat.) Leicester Gen. Hosp.; SHO & Regist. (Psychiat.) N. Herts. DHA.

FALLOWFIELD, Jonathan Andrew 64 Wayland Av, Brighton BN1 5JN — BM 1997 Soton.

FALLOWFIELD, Joseph Michael 30 Thornway, Bramhall, Stockport SK7 2AF — MB ChB 1969 Manch.; MFPM 1991; Dip. Pharm. Med. 1989; DObst RCOG 1973.

FALLOWFIELD, Mary Elizabeth Chelmsford and Essex Centre, New Writtle Street, Chelmsford CM2 0PT Tel: 01245 513486 Fax: 01245 573464 — MB BS 1978 Lond.; FRCPath 2000; MD Lond. 1987; FRCS Eng. 1983; MRCPath 1992; MBA Stirling 1997. (Westm.) Cons. Histopath. Mid-Essex Hosp.s. Prev: Cons. Dermatopath. Glas.

FALLOWFIELD, Richard Edward (Surgery) 270 Woodchurch Road, Prenton, Birkenhead CH43 5UU Tel: 0151 608 3475 Fax: 0151 608 9535; 3 Vyner Road S., Bidston, Birkenhead CH43 7PN Tel: 0151 652 4223 — MCRS Eng. LRCP 1958 Lond.; MB ChB 1958 Liverp.; MB ChB Liverp. 1958; MRCS Eng. LRCP Lond. 1958. (Liverp.) Med. Adviser Pk. Food Gp. plc; Health & Safety Exec. Apptd. Doctor Asbestos & Ionising Radiat.s; Dept. Transport Apptd. Doctor Merchant Shipping Regulats. Socs: Birkenhead Med. Soc. Prev: Regist. (Med.) Gen. Hosp. Birkenhead; Regist. St. Paul's Eye Hosp. Liverp.; Ho. Phys. & Ho. Surg. David Lewis N.. Hosp. Liverp.

FALLOWFIELD, Thomas Leslie (retired) Ben Avon, Kindrochit Drive, Braemar, Ballater AB35 5YW Tel: 013397 41263 Fax: 013397 41263 Email: tfallowfield@compuserve.com — MB ChB 1955 Aberd.; MSc Birm. 1960; MFOM RCP Lond. 1980; Dip. DHM 1991. Prev: Cons. Hyperbaric Med. Armed Forces Hosp. Saudi Arabia.

FALLOWS, Ralph St Andrews, Dundonald, Kilmarnock Tel: 01563 850496 — LRCP LRCS 1951 Ed.; LRCP LRCS Ed. LRFPS Glas. 1951; MRCGP 1962; DFFP 1993; DFM Glas. 1993. (Belf.)

FALLOWS, Rosemary Florence 59 Dernaflaw Road, Dungiven, Londonderry BT47 4PR — MB ChB 1997 Liverp.

FALLOWS, Sarah Aileen Sharon Altnagelvin Area Hospital, Glenshane Road, Londonderry BT47 6SB; 11 bay View Park, Londonderry BT47 6TA Tel: 028 7134 4005 Email: sfollows@hotmail.com — MB BCh BAO 1989 Belf.; MD 1998 Belfast; MRCOG 1994. Cons. (O & G) Altnagelvin Area Hosp. Socs: BMA; Ulster Obst. & Gyn. Soc.

FALLS, Niall Brendan Terence 15 Belvedere Park, Belfast BT9 5GS — MB BCh BAO 1987 Belf.

FALOON, Keith Alyth Health Centre, New Alyth Road, Alyth, Blairgowrie PH11 8EQ Tel: 01828 632317 Fax: 01828 633272 — MB ChB 1993 Dundee.

FALOPE, Zacchaeus Folorunso 6 Carham Close, Gosforth, Newcastle upon Tyne NE3 5DX Tel: 0191 284 5084 Fax: 0191 284 5084 — MB BS 1981 Ibadan; MRCP (UK) 1996. (Ibadam) Specialist Regist. (Rehabil. Med.) Hunters Moor Regional NeuroRehabil. Centre Newc. Socs: Train. Mem. Brit. Soc. (Rehab. Med.); BMA; RCP. Prev: Specialist Regist. (Rehabil. Med.) Astley Ansley Hosp. Edin.; Regist. (Neurol.) HRI Hull.

FALSHAW, Rachel Louise Park Parade Surgery, 27-28 Park Parade, Harrogate HG1 5AG Tel: 01423 502776 Fax: 01423

568036; Stainley Mill, Burton Leonard, Harrogate HG3 3TE Tel: 01765 677590 — MB ChB 1984 Sheff.

FALWORTH, Mark Simon 12 Longbeach Road, London SW11 5ST — MB BS 1996 Lond.; BDS (Hons.) Lond. 1988; FDS RCS Eng. 1992; FDS RCS Ed. 1992. (King's Coll. Hosp.) SHO (Plastic Surg.) Chelsea & W.minster Hosp. Lond. Socs: Assoc. Mem. Brit. Assn. Oral & Maxillofacial Surg. Prev: SHO (Orthop.) Wexham Pk. Hosp. Slough Berks.; SHO (Gen. Surg.) Kings Coll. Hosp. Lond.; Regist. Oral & Maxillofacial Surg. Roy. Surrey Co. Hosp. Egerton Rd, Guildford, Surrey.

FALZON, Maria 2F2, 29 Comely Bank Road, Comely Bank, Edinburgh EH4 1DS Tel: 0131 315 2279 Email: maria.falzon@hamrun.demon.co.uk — MB ChB 1988 Dundee; MRCPsych 1993. Sen. Regist. (Psychiat.) Roy. Edin. Hosp. Prev: Regist. Roy. Dundee Liff Hosp.

FALZON, Mary Rose Ealing Hospital NHS Trust, Uxbridge Road, Southall UB1 3HW Tel: 020 8967 5486 Fax: 020 8967 5455; The Firs, 35 Watford Road, Radlett WD7 8LG Tel: 01923 855292 Email: mrfalzon@aol.com — MRCS Eng. LRCP Lond. 1981; FRCPath 1997, M 1989. (Middlx.) Cons. Histopath. Ealing Hosp.; Cons. (Histopathol. & Cytopathol.). Socs: (Chair) Thames Valley Cytol. Soc.; N. Thames Regional Quality Assur. Comm. Prev: Lect. & Hon. Sen. Regist. (Histopath.) Middlx. Hosp. Med. Sch. & Univ. Coll.

FAMILTON, Henry 1 Stoneleigh, Hepscott, Morpeth NE61 6NZ Tel: 01670 518410 — MB BS Durh. 1951.

FAMORIYO, Abidemi Adeyabo Akin 13 Burwell Reach, Peterborough PE2 7ZE — MB BS 1984 Lagos; MB BS Lagos, Nigeria 1984; MRCOG 1993.

FAN, Katherine 41D Osborne Place, Dundee DD2 1BE — MB ChB 1990 Dundee.

FAN, Siu Fai Fan and Partners, Great Western Surgery, Farriers Close, Swindon SN1 2QU Tel: 01793 421311 Fax: 01793 431412; 17 Beaufort Road, Wroughton, Swindon SN4 9HF — MB ChB 1983 Dundee; BSc Pharmacol. Dundee 1979; Dip Occ Med RCP Lond. 1995. Prev: Trainee GP Hollies Health Centre Merthyr Tydfil; Ho. Off. Ninewells Hosp. Dundee.

FAN, Victor Tai Weng 8 Coombe Croft, Pendeford, Wolverhampton WV9 5RS — MB BCh BAO 1994 Belf.; FDS RCS Eng. 1994; BDS 1985; FRCS 1998. (QUB) Specialist Regist. Oral & Maxillofacial. Surg. Socs: BMA; BAOMS.jun.Fell. Prev: Sen. Tutor Nat. Univ. Singapore.; HO.BRd.green.Hosp; BST Grey.Hosp.Birm.

FAN, Yen Shian Green Street Clinic, 120-122 Green St., Eastbourne BN21 1RT Tel: 01323 722908 — LMSSA 1971 Lond.

FANANAPAZIR, Mr Khazeh 24 Buckstone Dell, Edinburgh EH10 6PG — BM BCh 1973 Oxf.; FRCS Eng. 1977; MRCP (UK) 1975; LMSSA Lond. 1973.

FANANAS ESTEBAN, Ana Cristina c/o Regent Fitzroy, Northdown House, Margate CT9 3TP — LMS 1993 Cantabria.

FANCOURT, Graham John The Glenfield Hospital Trust, Groby Road, Leicester LE3 9QP Tel: 0116 287 1471; Weald House, Mowsley, Lutterworth LE17 6NY Tel: 0116 240 4088 — MB BS 1977 Lond.; FRCP Lond. 1994; MRCP (UK) 1980; MRCS Eng. LRCP Lond. 1977. (Char. Cross) Cons. Phys. Glenfield Hosp. Trust Leicester.

FANCOURT, Philip The Wall House, Yorke Road, Reigate RH2 9HG Tel: 01737 244325 Fax: 01737 244616; (resid.), 3 Caverswall Court, 22 Alders Road, Reigate RH2 0ED Tel: 01737 223387 — MB BS 1967 Lond.; DObst RCOG 1970. (St. Geo.) Prev: Ho. Phys. Croydon Gen. Hosp.; Ho. Surg. & Ho. Off. (O & G) Warneford Hosp., Leamington Spa.

FANCY, Nadege Elise 9 Antrim Mansions, Antrim Road, London NW3 4XT — MB BS 1994 Lond.

FANE, Sarah Katherine De La Beche Manor, Aldworth, Reading RG8 9SA Tel: 01635 578686 — MB ChB 1989 Bristol. Prev: Clin. Asst. (Geriat.) Meadowside Day Hosp. Basingstoke; SHO (O & G) Basingstoke Dist. Gen. Hosp.; Clin. Asst. (Oncol.) N. Hants. Hosp.

FANG, Carolyn Rosalie 96 Glenwood Gardens, Ilford IG2 6XX — MB ChB 1983 Bristol.

FANG, Christopher Sun Jor 3 Hornby Lane, Liverpool L18 3HH Tel: 0151 722 2138 Email: triode@aol.com; 3 Hornby Lane, Liverpool L18 3HH Tel: 0151 722 2138 Fax: 0151 722 2138 — BChir 1996 Camb.; BA 1994; MB 1997; MA 1998. (University of Cambridge) SHO.

FANG, Swee Hiang Homerton Hospital, Homerton Row, London E9 6SR Tel: 020 8510 5555; 1 Canonbury Park S., London N1 2JR — MB BS 1980 Malaya; MRCP (UK) 1985; FRCP. Cons Paediat. Whipps Cross Hosp. Lond.

FANIBUNDA, Hector 37 Kingsley Avenue, Melton Park, Gosforth, Newcastle upon Tyne NE3 5QN — BM BS 1996 Nottm.

FANIYAN, Adeniran 35 Greenfield Street, Dunkirk, Nottingham NG7 2JN Tel: 0115 978 8564 — MB BS 1979 Ibadan; MRCOG 1988. Regist. (O & G) Pilgrim Hosp. S. Lincs. HA.

FANNIN, Eileen Shauna Ballymoney Health Centre, Robinson Memorial Hospital, 21 Newal Road, Ballymoney BT53 6HB Tel: 028 2766 0303 Fax: 028 2766 0321; Lavin House, Knockahollet, Ballymena BT44 9BE Tel: 0126 56 41204 — MB BCh BAO 1984 Belf.; MRCP (UK) 1988; MRCGP (Distinc.) 1989; DCH Dub. 1986; DRCOG 1986.

FANNIN, Mr Thomas Francis (retired) Medical Associates, 25 Derry Volgie Avenue, Belfast BT9 6FN — MB BCh BAO Belf. 1962; MD Belf. 1967; FRCS Ed. 1969. Cons. Neurosurg. Roy. Vict. Hosp. Belf. Prev: Cons. Neurosurg. Roy. Hallamsh. Hosp. Sheff.

FANNING, Andrew Patrick Green Meadows Surgery, Winkfield Road, Ascot SL5 7LS Tel: 01344 21628 Fax: 01344 875136; Windy Ridge, Lovel Road, Winkfield, Windsor SL4 2EU — MB BS 1986 Lond.; MRCGP 1991; T(GP) 1992; DRCOG 1991; Cert. Family Plann. JCC 1989. Prev: Trainee GP Windsor; SHO (Paediat. & O & G) Wexham Pk. Hosp. Slough.

FANNING, Desmond Martin, OBE Derwent Villa, Fidlers Well, Bamford, Hope Valley S33 0AR Tel: 01433 659757 Email: dmfanning@aol.com — MB BS Lond. 1951; MRCS Eng. LRCP Lond. 1951; FFOM RCP Lond. 1983, M 1978; FFOM RCPI 1983; DPH Lond. 1967; DIH Soc. Apoth. Lond. 1968. (Westm.) p/t Cons. Occupat. Med. Socs: Soc. Occupat. Med. Prev: Gp. Med. Adviser Chloride Gp.; Chief Med. Off. Brit. Steel Corp.; Wing Cdr. RAF Med. Br.

FANNING, James (retired) 12 Oakhill Court, Edge Hill, London SW19 4NR — MRCS Eng. LRCP Lond. 1919; MD Lond. 1922, MB BS 1920; DPH Eng. 1927. Prev: Dep. MOH Surrey CC.

FANNING, John Kevin (retired) Beeches End, Nats Lane, Wendens Ambo, Saffron Walden CB11 4LQ Tel: 01799 541580 — MB BS 1953 Lond.; DObst. RCOG 1956. Prev: Ho.Phys.W.m.Childr.Hosp.

FANNING, Michael York Lodge, Hook End, Brentwood CM15 0HA Tel: 01277 821368 — MB BS 1952 Lond.; FFA RCS Eng. 1968; DA Eng. 1962. (King's Coll. Hosp.) Cons. (Anaesth.) Orsett Hosp. & Basildon Hosp. Prev: Wing Cdr., Cons. Anaesth. RAF; SHO (Anaesth.) King's Coll. Hosp.; Ho. Surg. & Ho. Phys. Metrop. Hosp. Lond.

FANNING, Patrick Philip Redwood House Surgery, Cannon Lane, Maidenhead SL6 3PH Tel: 01628 826227; Altwood Warren, Altwood, Maidenhead SL6 4PZ Tel: 01628 35435 Fax: 01628 829426 — MRCS Eng. LRCP Lond. 1964; LMSSA Lond. 1961. (Guy's) Socs: Med. Defence Soc.; BMA & Windsor Med. Soc. Prev: Ho. Surg. (bst. & Gyn.) Hillingdon Hosp. Uxbridge; Ho. Surg. Worthing Hosp.; Ho. Phys. Roy. I. of Wight Co. Hosp.

FANNON, Jane Kathryn 3 Coolers Farm, Broughton, Stockbridge SO20 8BG — MB BS 1983 Lond.

FANOUS, Mr Nabil Ishak James Paget Hospital, Lowestoft Road, Gorleston, Great Yarmouth NR31 6LA Tel: 01493 452452 Fax: 01493 452066 Email: fabousn@yahoo.com; La Perle, 6 Buxton Avenue, Gorleston, Great Yarmouth NR31 6HG Tel: 01493 664440 Email: fanoush@yahoo.com — MB BCh 1976 Ain Shams; FRCS Glas. 1988. Orthop. Surg. Jas. Paget Hosp. Gt. Yarmouth. Socs: Brit. Orthop. Assn.

FANOUS, Samir Fanous Victor Boulos c/o Drive S. Michael Soliman, Downsview Road, London SE19 3XD — MRCS Eng. LRCP Lond. 1980.

FANSA, Mr Moustafa Ahmed Chawki Lincoln County Hospital, Sewell Road, Lincoln LN2 5QY Tel: 01522 29921 — MB BCh 1973 Al Azhar; FRCS Glas. 1985. Prev: Regist. (Orthop.) Lincoln Co. Hosp.

FANTOM, Eileen Sheila Countess of Chester Hospital, Department of Accident & Emergency, Liverpool Road, Chester CH2 1UL Tel: 01244 365215; Countess of Chester Hospital, Department of Accident & Emergency, Liverpool Road, Chester CH2 1UL Tel: 01244 365215 — MB BChir 1990 Camb.; BSc (Hons.) St. And.

1987; DA (UK) 1994. (Univ. Camb.) Staff Grade Pract. (A & E) Countess of Chester Hosp., Chester.

FARAG, Mr Mounis Zakaria Mohamed Barnet & Chase Farm Hospitals NHS Trust, The Ridgeway, Enfield EN2 8JL Tel: 020 8967 5926 Fax: 020 8967 5926; 69 Mymms Drive, Brookmans Park, Hatfield AL9 7AA Tel: 01707 643683 Fax: 01707 664967 — MB BCh 1972 Cairo; FRCS Eng. 1978. (Cairo) Cons. ENT Surg. Barnet & Chase Farm Hosps. NHS Trust. Socs: Brit. Assn. of Otorhinolaryngol. Prev: Sen. Regist. (ENT Surg.) Gen. Infirm. Leeds; Regist. (ENT Surg.) Roy. Vict. Infirm. Newc. upon Tyne; SHO (ENT) Surg. Eye, Ear & Throat Hosp. Shrewsbury.

FARAG, Raafat Reda Department of Medicine for Elderly, Hemel Hempstead General Hospital Windsor Wing, Hillfield Road, Hemel Hempstead HP2 4AD Tel: 01442 213141 — MB BCh 1967 Ain Shams; FRCP Lond. 1992; MRCP (UK) 1979. Cons. Phys. Med. for the Elderly Hemel Hempstead Gen. Hosp. Prev: Sen. Regist. Dept. Clin. Gerontol. Univ. Wales; Regist. (Geriat. Med.) Walsgrave Hosp. Coventry; Regist. (Renal Med.) Kent & Canterbury Hosp.

FARAG, Shaheer Farag Selim c/o Dr K. T. Moussa, 16 Grandborough Drive, Solihull B91 3TS — MB ChB 1984 Tanta; MB ChB Med-Delta U, Tanta 1984; MRCP (UK) 1993.

FARAGO, Susan Anna Sarah 166 New Road, Croxley Green, Rickmansworth WD3 3BD Tel: 01923 778277; 6 Westbury Road, Watford WD18 0DL Tel: 01923 442652 — MB BS 1989 Newc. Asst. GP Rickmansworth. Prev: SHO (O & G) Sunderland Dist. Gen. Hosp.; SHO (Psychiat.) St. Mary's Stannington N.d.; SHO (Geriat.) St. Albans City Hosp.

FARAH, Abdel Ghanie 21 Llanrwst Road, Colwyn Bay LL29 7YT — MB BCh 1955 Cairo; FFA RCS Eng. 1969; DA Eng. 1959. (Cairo Univ.) Prev: Cons. (Anaesth.) Khartoum Civil Hosp.; Brigadier (Retd.) Head Dept. Anaesth. Sudan Army Med. Corps.

FARAH, Ahmed El Tayeb 104 Keslake Road, London NW6 6DG — Vrach 1972 Leningrad Inst. of Paediat.; MRCPsych 1986.

FARAH, Fawaz Lafi 55 Mayfield Road, North Chingford, London E4 7JB — MB ChB 1975 Baghdad; MB ChB Baghdad, Iraq 1975; MRCP (UK) 1982.

FARAH, Husam Hanna Department of Cardiology, The Royal Infirmary, Lauriston Place, Edinburgh EH3 9HB Tel: 0131 536 1000 — MD 1989 Damascus, Syria; MRCP (UK) 1993. Staff Grade (Cardiol.) Roy. Infirm. Edin. Prev: Regist. (Med.) Colchester Gen. Hosp.; Regist. (Chest & Gen. Med.) Univ. Coll. Hosp. Lond.; SHO (Med.) Doncaster Roy. Infirm.

FARAJ, Mr Adnan Abdil Magid Tel: 01535 292098; Email: adnanfaraj@hotmail.com — FRCS (Orth. & Tr.) 2000; MB ChB Mosul 1984; FRCS Ed. 1993; Mch(Orth) Liverp. 1997. (Mousl Medical School) Full time Cons. Orthopaedic Surg. Socs: Fell. Roy. Coll. Surg. of Edin.; Floow of Intercollegiate Orthopaedic Bd. Prev: Vis. Orthop. Regist. 1994-1997; Residency Orthop. Programms 1989-1992.

FARAJ, Karwan Saeed Radiology Department, The Royal Free Hospital, Pond Street, Hampstead, London NW3 2QG; Email: karwain@dctors.net.uk — MB ChB 1984 Iraq; FRCR (Lond.) 2001; MRCS Eng. LRCP Lond. 1991; MRCP (UK) 1995. (Charing Cross & Westminster) Specialist Regist. (Diagn. Radiol.) Roy. Free Hosp., Lond.

FARATIAN, Bahman 30 The Avenue, Mansfield NG18 4PD; 3rd Floor, 1045 Vali-Asr St, Tehran 15116, Iran Tel: 00 98 21 8721438 — MD Tabriz 1965; Nat. Dip. Obst. & Gyn. Tehran 1974. Progr. Dir. (Fertil. Servs.) Madaen Hosp., Tehran. Socs: Amer. Soc. Reproduc. Med. Prev: Med. Dir. Nurture Nottm. Univ. Hosp.; Clin. Lect. (O & G) Univ. Hosp. Nottm.; Asst. Med. Dir. Pk. Hosp. Nottm.

FARBOTKO, Teresa Alicja 143 Ashburnham Road, Luton LU1 1JW Tel: 01582 29639 — MB BCh BAO 1961 Dub.; DA Eng. 1965.

FARBRIDGE, Joseph Alan (retired) 20 Weetwood Avenue, Far Headingley, Leeds LS16 5NF Tel: 0113 275 8212 Fax: 0113 275 8212 — MB ChB 1965 Leeds; DObst RCOG 1967. Clin. Asst. (O & G) Leeds Infirm. Prev: Ho. Off. & Ho. Surg. St. Jas. Hosp. Leeds.

FARDELL, Sarah Josephine 66A Ridge Road, Kempston, Bedford MK43 9BS — MB BS 1998 Lond.; MB BS Lond 1998.

FARDON, Nicholas John Mark 26 Kingland Road, Poole BH15 1TP Tel: 01202 675609 Email: nick.fardon@btinternet.com; 36 Rothwell Road, Gosforth, Newcastle upon Tyne NE3 1UA Tel: 0191 213 2474 Fax: 0191 222 0723 Email: nick.fardon@ncl.ac.uk — MB BS 1989 Lond.; MRCPI 1993. Research Assoc. (Hypertens. & Diabetic Nephrol.) Univ. of Newc. Prev: Regist. Rotat. (Med. & Nephrol.) Weymouth Hosp. & St. Mary's Hosp. Portsmouth; SHO (Nephrol.) St. Helier Hosp. Carshalton; SHO Rotat. (Med.) MusGr. Pk. Hosp. Taunton.

FARDY, Catherine Helen Le Lechmere, Wick Road, Llandow, Cowbridge CF7 7YP — MB BCh 1989 Wales; MRCP (UK) 1992. Flexible Train. Sen. Regist. (Paediat.) Univ. Hosp. Wales Cardiff. Socs: BMA; Brit. Paediat. Assn. Prev: Sen. Regist. (Paediat.) Birm. Heartlands; Clin. Research Fell. Roy. Postgrad. Med. Sch. Hammersmith Hosp.; Regist. (Paediat. Intens. Care) Gt. Ormond St. Lond.

FARDY, Mr Michael John 23 Heol Dulais, Birchgrove, Swansea SA7 9LT — MB BS 1988 Lond.; FRCS Ed. 1992; FFD RCSI 1990.

FAREBROTHER, Lesley Ann Department of Public Health Medicine, East Kent Health Authority, Protea House, New Bridge, Marine Parade, Dover CT17 9HQ Tel: 01304 222293 Fax: 01304 203846 Email: ann.farebrother@ekentha.nhs.uk; 29 Audley Road, Folkestone CT20 3QB Tel: 01303 252306 Email: ann@annfarebrother.fsnet.uk — MB BChir 1968 Camb.; MB BChir Camb. 1967; MA Camb. 1968; FFPHM RCP (UK) 1996; MFCM RCP (UK) 1988; DObst RCOG 1969. (Camb. & St. Mary's) Cons. Pub. Health Med. E. Kent HA. Prev: Dir. Pub. Health Med. SE Kent HA; Cons. Pub. Health Med. Medway HA.

FAREBROTHER, Martin John Brice Cream House, 7 Church St., Burham, Rochester ME1 3SB Tel: 01634 660550 — MB BChir 1968 Camb.; MD Camb. 1977; FRCP Lond. 1983; MRCP (UK) 1969. (Camb. & Guy's) Socs: Brit. Thorac. Soc.; Eur. Respirat. Soc. Prev: Dir. of Med. King Fahd Armed Forces Hosp. Jeddah, Saudi Arabia; Cons. Phys. (Gen. & Thoracic Med.) Medway HA; Sen. Lect. (Med.) UMDS of Guy's & St. Thos. Hosp. Med. Sch. Lond.

FAREED, Mohammad Naziruddin Faizan, Beech Hill Road, Swanland, North Ferriby HU14 3QY — MB BS 1980 Peshawar; MRCP (UK) 1992.

FAREEDI, Mahey Alam Port Tennant Surgery, 125 Port Tennant Road, Port Tennant, Swansea SA1 8JN Tel: 01792 654470 — MB BS 1964 Calcutta.

FAREEDI, Sabena 53 Owls Lodge Lane, Mayals, Swansea SA3 5DP — MB BS 1994 Lond.

FAREWELL, Joan Gladys 27 Canons Close, Radlett WD7 7ER Tel: 01923 857388 — MB BS 1961 Sydney; MRC Psych. 1982; DPM Eng. 1966. (Sydney)

FAREY, Hilary Krystyna Brooklea Clinic, Wick Road, Bristol BS4 4HU Tel: 0117 971 1211; 59 Egerton Road, Bishopston, Bristol BS7 8HN Tel: 0117 940 9725 — MB ChB 1983 Bristol; MRCGP 1990; DRCOG 1990; Cert. JCPTGP 1989; Cert. Family Plann. JCC 1988. GP. Socs: BMA & Polish Med. Assn. Prev: Clin. Med. Off. Yellow Fever & BCG Clinic Bristol Roy. Infirm.; SHO (Obst.) S.mead Hosp. Bristol; SHO (Gyn.) Frenchay Hosp. Bristol.

FAREY, Mary Betty (retired) c/o 75 Brookbridge Lane, Datchworth, Knebworth SG3 6SZ — MB BS Lond. 1941; MRCS Eng. LRCP Lond. 1941. Prev: Retd. GP Barent Area.

FARFAN, Gerard Andrew 62A Savernake Road, London NW3 2JR; 9 Young Pow Avenue, La Seiva, Maraval,Trinidad, West Indies Tel: 00 809 6283659 — MB BS 1988 Lond.; MRCP (UK) 1992. Regist. (Gastroenterol.) S.end Health Care Trust. Prev: A & E Off. S.end HA.

FARGHER, Gillian The Thorndike Centre, Longley Road, Rochester ME1 2TH Tel: 01634 817217 — MB BS 1983 Lond. Prev: Ho. Surg. St. Barts./Medway Hosp. Gillingham Kent; Ho. Phys. St. Jas. Hosp. Lond.; Trainee GP VTS Medway.

FARHADIAN, Farhad 2 Dulwich Road, Kingstanding, Birmingham B44 0ER — MD 1984 Teheran.

FARHAN, Abdul-Karim 19 Laurel Close, Grimsby DN33 2BH — MB ChB 1983 Al-Mustansirya Univ. Iraq.

FARHAN, Mr Mahdi Moh'd 2 Beresford Drive, Stoneygate, Leicester LE2 3LA — MB ChB 1985 Sheff.; FRCS Eng. 1989; MRCGP 1993. Hon. Clin. Research Fell. Leicester Univ.

FARHAT, Mr Salem M. 27 North Drive, Aylesbury HP21 9AN Tel: 01296 315000 ext. 3142 — MB BCh 1988 Alfateh University, Libya; FRCS 1998 Royal college of Physicians & Surgeons of Glasgow; DLO 1994 Royal College of Surgeons, England; MSc 1997 University of Bristol. (Alfateh University, Tripoli, Libya)

FARHOUD, Jacquelyn Susan Lambart 273 Bedford Road, Kempston, Bedford MK42 8QD — MB BCh BAO 1986 Dub.; DRCOG 1990; DCH RCP Lond. 1989.

FARHOUMAND, Noushin Freshfield Mental Health Centre, Brighton General Hospital, Elm Grove, Brighton BN2 3EW Tel: 01273 696011 Fax: 01273 677126 — MB ChB 1968 East Africa; FRCPsych 1992, M 1973; DPM Eng. 1972. (Makerere Univ. Coll. Kampala) Cons. Psychiat. & Dir. Postgrad. Med. Educat. S. Downs Health NHS Trust Brighton; Med. Dir. E.bourne Clinic, Med. Dir. Sussex private clinic (St. Leonards-on-Sea); Clin. Tutor Brit. Postgrad. Med. Federat. Univ. Lond.; Psychiat. Tutor, Roy. Coll. Socs: Brighton and Sussex Medico-Chirurgical Soc. Prev: Research Fell., Hon. Sen. Regist. & Lect. (Psychopharmacol.) St. Bart. Hosp. Lond.; Sen. Regist. (Psychiat.) St. Bart. Hosp. Lond.; SHO (Psychiat.) St. Olave's Hosp. (Guy's Gp.) Lond.

FARID, Basem Tawfik 50 Leicester Road, Narborough, Leicester LE9 5DF Tel: 0116 286 3267; 30 Westminster Road, Leicester LE2 2EG — MB ChB 1976 Cairo; MMedSci Leeds 1983; MRCPsych 1982. Cons. Psychiat. Community Alcohol Team Leics.

FARIDI, Mr Salman Flat 3, Block 1, Grove Road, Solihull B91 2JL — MB BS 1978 Karachi; FRCS Ed. 1983.

FARIDIAN, Parviz 248 Earl's Court Road, London SW5 9AD; 7 1A Residence, 38A Marlborough Place, London NW8 0PS Tel: 020 7372 7201 — MB BS 1956 Lond.; MRCS Eng. LRCP Lond. 1956; DTM & H Eng. 1959; DObst RCOG 1964; MRCGP 1968; Cert Contracept. & Family Plann. RCOG RCGP &; Cert FPA 1975. (Univ. Coll. Hosp.) Socs: BMA. Prev: Hon. Clin. Asst. Profess. Unit (O & G) Univ. Coll. Hosp. & Med. Sch.

FARISH, Gillian 1 Ardoch Road, Bearsden, Glasgow G61 2BB — MB ChB 1993 Glas.

FARJAD AZAD, Fereshteh Abraham Cowley Unit, Holloway Hill, Lyne, Chertsey KT16 0AE Tel: 01932 872010; 81 Lynwood Road, Ealing, London W5 1JG Tel: 020 8998 3409 — MD 1973 Iran; PhD Lond. 1980. Assoc. Specialist Psychiat. Surrey.

FARJO, Bessam K P 130 Harley Street, London W1N 1AH Tel: 0161 237 3517 Fax: 0161 237 3279 Email: bessam@farjo.com; Arthur House, Chorlton St, Manchester M1 3FH Tel: 0161 237 3517 Fax: 0161 237 3279 — MB BCh BAO 1988 NUI; LRCPSI 1988; MiT 1997. (Roy. Coll. Surg. Irel.) Cons. Restorat. Hair Surg. Farjo Med. Centre Advanced Hair Techol. Lond. & Manch. Socs: Internat. Soc. Hair Restorat. Surg.; Founder Mem. (Sec.) Brit. Assn. Hair Restoration Surgs.; Eur. Soc. Hair Restoration Surg.

FARJO, Nilofer Parveen Fahmida 130 Harley Street, London W1N 1AH Tel: 0161 237 3517 Fax: 0161 237 3279 Email: info@farjo.com; Arthur House, Chorlton St, Manchester M1 3FH Tel: 0161 237 3517 Fax: 0161 237 3279 — MB BCh BAO 1988 NUI; LRCPSI 1988; MIT 1997. (Roy. Coll. Surg. Irel.) Cons. Hair Restoration Surg. Farjo Med. Centre of Advanced Hair Technol. Lond. & Manch. Socs: Internat. Soc. Hair Restorat. Surg.; Founder Mem. & Treas. Brit. Assn. Hair Restoration Surgs.; Eur. Soc. Hair Restoration Surg. Prev: SHO (Geriat. Med.) Lancaster Roy. Infirm.; SHO (A & E) Blackpool Vict. Hosp.; SHO (Haemat.) St. Jas. Hosp. Dub.

FARKAS, Mr Andrew George The Jessop Wing, TreeRoot Walk, Sheffield S10 2SF Tel: 0114 226 8167 Fax: 0114 226 8188 — MB BS 1981 Lond.; FRCS Eng. 1987; MRCOG 1991. (Lond. Hosp.) Cons. O & G The Jessop Wing,Regional Hallamshire Hosp. Prev: Sen. Lect. & Hon. Cons. O & G St. Bart. & Homerton Hosps. Lond.

FARLEY, Adrian James 67 Deneside Court, Newcastle upon Tyne NE2 1JW — MB BS 1996 Newc.

FARLEY, Miss Claire Alison 39 Vivian Road, Newport NP19 0ER — MB BCh 1992 Wales; BMedSci (Path.) Cardiff 1991; FRCS (Eng) 1996. (Univ. Wales Coll. Med.) SHO (Anaesth.) Morriston Hosp. Swansea.

FARLEY, Mr Desmond Laurence Bond (retired) 34 Little Minster Street, Winchester SO23 9HB Tel: 01962 868668 — MB BS Lond. 1944; FRCS Eng. 1948; MRCS Eng. LRCP Lond. 1944. Prev: Cons. Surg. Roy. N.. Hosp. Lond.

FARLEY, John Dashwood (retired) Bethcote Cottage, Holton Park, Holton, Oxford OX33 1QB — MB BS 1951 Lond.; MRCPsych 1971; DPM Eng. 1963. Prev: Hon. Cons. Psychiat. Fairfield Hosp. Hitchin.

FARLEY, Kathryn Lucy Ealing Park Health Centre, 195A South Ealing Road, Ealing, London W5 4RH Tel: 020 8758 0570 Fax: 020 8560 5182 — BM 1987 Soton.; MRCGP 1992; DRCOG 1990.

FARLEY, Keith Thomas James Manor House Surgery, Providence Place, Bridlington YO15 2QW Tel: 01262 602661 Fax: 01262 400891 — MB ChB 1976 Sheff.; MRCGP 1980; DRCOG 1979.

FARLEY, Malcolm David Hoods Place, The Street, Kingston, Canterbury CT4 6JQ Tel: 01227 766877 — MB BS 1969 Lond.; BA Manch. 1962; MRCS Eng. LRCP Lond. 1968; FRCPath 1989, M 1977. (Lond. Hosp.) Cons. Path. Kent & Canterbury Hosp. Canterbury. Prev: Regist. (Path.) Soton. Gen. Hosp.; Regist. (Path.) Univ. Hosp. W. Indies Kingston, Jamaica; Resid. Clin. Path. St. Geo. Hosp. Lond.

FARLEY, Paul Simon Worcester Street Surgery, 24 Worcester Street, Stourbridge DY8 1AW Tel: 01384 371616; 87 Worcester Road, Hagley, Stourbridge DY9 0NG — MB BS 1991 Lond.; BSc (Psychol.) Lond. 1988; MRCGP 1995; DFFP 1995; DRCOG 1994. Hon. Clin. Lect. Birm. Univ.; Mem. Local Med. Comm. Socs: BMA; Fac. Fam. Plann. & Reproduc. Health; AAG.

FARLEY, Stephen Edward Krishnan, Farley, McQuade and Stack, Ibstock House, 132 High Street, Ibstock LE67 6JP Tel: 01530 260216 Fax: 01530 261397 — MB BChir 1974 Camb.; MA, MB Camb. 1974, BChir 1973.

FARLEY, Thomas Matthew Churchtown Medical Centre, 137 Cambridge Road, Southport PR9 7LT Tel: 01704 24416; 10 Sandringham Road, Birkdale, Southport PR8 2JZ Tel: 01704 68165 — MRCS Eng. LRCP Lond. 1964; BSc (Anat. Hons.) Liverp. 1961, MB ChB 1964. (Liverp.) Socs: Liverp. Med. Inst.; S.port Med. Soc. Prev: Demonst. (Anat.) Univ. Liverp.; SHO Wom. Hosp. Liverp.; Ho. Surg. & Ho. Phys. BRd.green Hosp. Liverp.

FARLEY-HILLS, Edward Mark 109 Cathays Terrace, Cardiff CF24 4HU — MB BCh 1991 Wales.

FARLING, Peter Allen Department of Anaesthesia, Royal Victoria Hospital, Belfast BT12 6BA Tel: 01232 240503 Fax: 01232 325725 Email: peter.farling@dnet.co.uk — MB BCh BAO 1980 Belf.; FFA RCSI 1985. Cons. Neuroanaesth. Roy. Vict. Hosp. Belf. Socs: Assn. Anaesth. Gt. Brit. & Irel.; Hon. Sec. Neuroanaesth. Soc. GB & Irel.; N.. Irel. Soc. of Anaesth. Prev: Cons. Neuroanaesth. S.. Gen. Hosp. Glas.; Hon. Sen. Research Fell. Univ. Glas.

FARMAN, Robin David Christopher Centre for Occupational Health, Norfolk & Norwich Hospital, Norwich NR1 3SR Tel: 01603 287035 Fax: 01603 287026 Email: robin.farman@norfolk-norwich.thenhs.com — MB BS 1977 Lond.; MFOM RCP Lond. 1998; DA Eng. 1980. (St. Bart.) Cons. Occupat. Phys. Norf. & Norwich Univ. Hosp. Trust. Socs: Fac. Occupat. Med.; Assn. Nat. Health Occupat. Phys. (ANHOPS). Prev: GP Norwich; Trainer GP Norwich; Clin. Asst. (Anaesth.) Norf. & Norwich Hosp.

FARMER, Alan James 190 Adams Hill, Brtley Green, Birmingham B32 6PJ Tel: 0121 678 3700 — MB ChB 1988 Birm.

FARMER, Andrew John Thame Health Centre, East Street, Thame OX9 3JZ Tel: 01844 261066; 5 Town Farm Close, Thame OX9 2DA — BM BCh 1981 Oxf.; MA Oxf. 1983, BM BCh 1981; MRCGP 1985; DRCOG 1984; FRCGP 1996. Research Fell. Health Servs. Research Unit Oxf. Univ.; Harkness Fell.sh. Commonw. Fund, New York 1991-92. Prev: GP Oxf. VTS.

FARMER, Professor Anne Elizabeth Department of Postgraduate Education, University of Wales College of Medicine, Heath Park, Cardiff CF14 4XN Tel: 029 2074 3228 Fax: 029 2074 7839 Email: farmerae@cf.ac.uk — MB ChB 1972 Leeds; MD Leeds 1987; FRCPsych, 1993, M 1980; DPM Leeds 1976; Cert. JCC Lond. 1979. Prof. Psychol. Med. Cardiff; Adviser in Flexible Train. UWCM; Adviser in Postgrad Psychiatric Educat. UWCM. Prev: Lect. Inst. Psychiat. Lond.; Research Assoc. Washington Univ. St. Louis Missouri USA.

FARMER, Arthur Pring (retired) 152 Tonbridge Road, Maidstone ME16 8SP Tel: 01622 53419 — MB BS 1928 Lond.; MRCS Eng. LRCP Lond. 1927; DTM & H Eng. 1930. Prev: Med. Off. (Occupat. Health) Leybourne Grange Hosp. W.

FARMER, Charlotte Elizabeth The Old School House, Ashill, Cullompton EX15 3NH — MB BCh 1998 Wales.

FARMER, Christina Mary Parkview Clinic, 60 Queensbridge Road, Moseley, Birmingham B13 8QE Tel: 0121 243 2000 — MB ChB 1980 Birm. Clin. Asst. (Child Psychiat.) Pk.view Clinic. Birm.; Clin. Asst. (Adult Psychiat.) Highcroft Hosp. Birm.

FARMER, Christopher John La Couture, Belval Road, Vale, Guernsey GY3 5LW Tel: 01481 24 5334 Fax: 01481 24 5334 — BM BCh 1963 Oxf.; VKCP Reg. Psychotherapist & Trainer; MPhil

(Psychiat.) Lond. 1971; BA Oxf. 1960; MRCP Lond. 1968; FRCPsych 1991, M 1973; FRCP 1999. (Oxf. & St. Thos.) Cons. Psychiat. Castel Hosp. Guernsey. Socs: BMA. Prev: Research Regist. (ENT) Lond. Hosp.; Regist. (Gen. Med.) Metrop. Hosp. Lond.; Sen. Regist. Bethlem Roy. & Maudsley Hosps.

FARMER, Christopher Kenneth Trafford Renal Unit, 4th Floor Thomas Guy House, Guy's Hospital, London SE1 9RT Tel: 020 7955 5000 Fax: 020 7955 4909; 473 Tonbridge Road, Barming, Maidstone ME16 9LH — MB BS 1992 Lond.; MCRP Lond. 1995. Specialist Regist. (Nephrol.) Guy's Hosp.; SpR, Nephrol. & Gen. Med. Gen. Hosp. St. Helier, Jersey, CI. Prev: Regist. (Nephrol.) Brighton Healthcare NHS Trust; SpR, Nephrol. Guy's Hosp.; Research Regist. Nephrol. Guy's Hosp.

FARMER, David Charnwood Surgery, 5 Burton Road, Derby DE1 1TH Tel: 01332 737737 Fax: 01332 737738; Charnwood Surgery, 5 Burton Road, Derby DE1 1TH — MB BS 1979 Lond.

FARMER, George Raigmore Hospital, Inverness IV2 3UJ Tel: 01463 704000; 77 Old Edinburgh Road, Inverness IV2 3PG — MB ChB 1978 Aberd.; MD Aberd. 1989; MRCP (UK) 1985. Cons. Paediat. Raigmore Hosp. NHS Trust Inverness; Hon. Sen. Lect. Child Health Univ. Aberd. Socs: Fell.Roy. Coll. Paediat. & Child Health; Fell.Roy. Coll. Phys.s & Surg.s Glas. Prev: Cons. Paediat. Forth Valley HB; Lect. (Child Health) Univ. Aberd.

FARMER, Gerald Stanley Northbrook Health Centre, 93 Northbrook Road, Shirley, Solihull B90 3LX Tel: 0121 744 1872 Fax: 0121 733 6892; 17 Althorpe Drive, Dorridge, Solihull B93 8SG Tel: 01564 772825 — MB ChB Birm. 1956; MRCGP 1972. (Birm.) Prev: Ho. Surg. Gen. Hosp. Birm. & Qu. Eliz. Hosp. Birm.; Ho. Phys. Coventry & Warw. Hosp.

FARMER, Iain David Cill Chuimein Medical Centre, Fort Augustus PH32 4BH Tel: 01320 366216 Fax: 01320 366649; Cill Chumein Medical Centre, Fort Augustus PH32 4BH Tel: 01320 366216 Fax: 01320 366649 — MB ChB 1978 Manch.; BSc St. And. 1975; Dip IMC RCS (Ed) 1999.

FARMER, Ian Francis The Brownhill Surgery, 2 Brownhill Road, Chandlers Ford, Eastleigh SO53 2ZB Tel: 023 8025 2414 Fax: 023 8036 6604; 22 Kingsway Gardens, Chandlers Ford, Eastleigh SO53 1FE Tel: 01703 270979 — MB BS 1983 Lond.; BSc Lond. 1980; MRCGP 1988; DRCOG 1986. (Roy. Free) Socs: MDU. Prev: Trainee GP Chieveley; SHO (Geriat.) Arden Lodge E. Birm. Hosp.; SHO (Infec. Dis.) E. Birm. Hosp.

FARMER, Ian Stephen Stanwell Road Surgery, 95 Stanwell Road, Ashford TW15 3EA Tel: 01784 253565 Fax: 01784 244145 — MB ChB 1984 Liverp.; BSc (Hons.) Liverp. 1979, MB ChB l984. Prev: SHO (O & G & Geriat. Med.) Arrowe Pk. Hosp.; SHO (A & E) BRd. Green Hosp. Liverp.

FARMER, Jill Avril Melanie 53 Orpington Road, Winchmore Hill, London N21 3PL — MB BS 1991 Lond.; BA (Hons.) Exeter 1979.

FARMER, John (retired) 11 Barrington, Southacre Drive, Cambridge CB2 2TY Tel: 01223 464050 Fax: 01223 464050 Email: jfarm@home.cam.net.uk — MB BChir Camb. 1960; MA Camb. 1960; MRCS Eng. LRCP Lond. 1959; MRCOG 1967; DMRD Eng. 1977. Prev: Cons. Radiol. Wolverhampton AHA.

FARMER, Kim Denyse 11 Blackbrook Close, Walkhampton, Yelverton PL20 6JF — MB BS 1991 Lond.; MRCP (UK) 1995. (St. Bart. Hosp. Lond.)

FARMER, Kinley Dewar 70 (2FL) Findhorn Place, Edinburgh EH9 2NW — MB ChB 1994 Ed.

FARMER, Madge (retired) 8 Clarendon Drive, Thame OX9 3XP — MB ChB 1952 Liverp.; DPH 1959; MFCM 1979. Prev: Sen. Regist. (Venereol.) Radcliffe Infirm. Oxf.

FARMER, Martin 240 Ashenhurst Road, Dudley DY1 2JB — MB ChB 1990 Manch.

FARMER, Maureen (Surgery), 87-89 Prince of Wales Road, London NW5 3NT Tel: 020 7267 0067 Fax: 020 7485 8211; 28 Courthope Road, London NW3 2LD Tel: 020 7209 2637 — MB BS 1968 Lond.; MRCS Eng. LRCP Lond. 1968. (Roy. Free Hosp.)

FARMER, Miranda Alethea 14 Elmhurst Drive, Dorking RH4 2BA — MB ChB 1992 Manch.

FARMER, Paul Richard 17 Althorpe Drive, Dorridge, Solihull B93 8SG — MB ChB 1995 Sheff.

FARMER, Professor Richard Donald Trafford Department of Public Health & Primary Care, 4th Floor, Chelsea & Westminster Hospital, 369 Fulham Road, London SW10 9NH Tel: 020 8746 8160 Fax: 020 8746 8151; Sandtiles, 55 Leigh Hill Road, Cobham KT11 2HU Tel: 01932 862561 Fax: 01932 864833 — MB BS 1966 Lond.; PhD Leiden 1986; MRCS Eng. LRCP Lond. 1965; MRCGP 1971; FFPHM 1982. (King's Coll. Hosp.) Prof. Pub. Health Med. Char. Cross & W.m. Med. Sch.; Hon. Cons. Community Med. Riverside HA. Socs: Fell. Roy. Statistical Soc.; Fell. Roy. Soc. Med.; Internat. Soc. Pharmacoepidemiol. (Bd. Mem.). Prev: Lect. (Social Med.) Univ. Birm.; Ho. Phys., Ho. Surg. & SHO King's Coll. Hosp. Lond.

FARMER, Richard Edward Grey Friars, St Nicholas St., Hereford HR2 8QN Tel: 01432 65717 — MB BChir 1956 Camb.; BA, MB Camb. 1956, BChir 1955; DObst RCOG 1962. (Guy's) Prev: Ho. Phys. Guy's Hosp.; Asst. Ho. Surg. & Outpat. Off. Guys. Hosp.

FARMER, Robert Thomas 74 Bradley Street, Sheffield S10 1PB — MB ChB 1993 Sheff.

FARMER, Roger South West London and St George's Mental Health NHS Trust, Richmond Community Resource Centre, Kew Foot Rd, Richmond TW9 2TE Tel: 020 8940 3331 Fax: 020 8332 6114 — MB BCh BAO 1977 Belf.; MSc Manch. 1984; MD Belf. 1986; MRCP (UK) 1981; FRCPsych 1994, M 1982; T(Psych) 1991. Cons. Psychiat. Gen. Psychiat. S. W. Lond. & St Geo.'s Ment. Health NHS Trust Lon. Prev: Cons. Psychiat. Bloomsbury & Islington HA; Lect. (Psychiat.) St. Mary's Hosp. Med. Sch. Lond.; Sen. Lect. (Psychiat.) St. Geo.'s Hosp. Med. Sch. Lond.

FARMER, Sara Edwina Bradley Shaw Health Centre, Crookesbroom Lane, Hatfield, Doncaster DN7 6JN Tel: 01302 841373 — MB ChB 1978 Liverp.; MRCGP 1982; DCH NUI 1981.

FARMER, Simon Francis Department of Neurology, St Mary's Hospital, Praed St., London W2 1NY Tel: 020 7886 1387 Fax: 020 7886 1422 — MB ChB Bristol 1986; PhD Lond. 1991; BSc Bristol 1983; MRCP (UK) 1992; FRCP 2000 London. (Bristol) Cons. (Neurol.) St. Mary's Hosp. Lond. & Nat. Hosp. (Neurol. & Neurosurg.); Hon. Sen. Lect. Inst. Neurol. Lond. Socs: EEG Soc. & Physiol. Soc.; Assn. Brit. Neurols.; Fell. Roy. Soc. Med. Prev: Sen. Regist. (Neurol.) Nat. Hosp. Neurol. & Neurosurg. Lond. & St. Mary's; Regist. (Neurol.) Roy. Lond. Hosp. & Nat. Hosp. Neurol. & Neurosurg.; Wellcome Trust Research Train. Fell. Univ. Coll. Lond.

FARMERY, Andrew David Nuffield Department of Anaesthetics, University of Oxford, Radcliffe Infirmary, Oxford OX2 6HE Email: andrew.farmery@nda.ox.ac.uk — MB BS 1988 Lond. (United Med. & Dent. Sch. Guy's Hosp. Lond.) Cons. Anaesth., Oxf. Radcliffe Hosp.s, Oxf. Prev: Clin. Lect. Univ. of Oxf.; Sen. Regist. (Intens. Care) John Radcliffe Hosp. Oxf.; Regist. (Anaesth.) Addenbrooke's Hosp. Camb.

FARN, Kenneth Thomas (retired) 174 Watling Street, Grendon, Atherstone CV9 2PE — MRCS Eng. LRCP Lond. 1952. Treasury Med. Off. Prev: Jun. Res. Obst. Off., Ho. Phys. & Ho. Surg. Moorgate Gen. Hosp.

FARNALL, Elizabeth Ann The Surgery, 13 Fallodon Way, Henleaze, Bristol BS9 4HT Tel: 0117 962 0652 Fax: 0117 962 0839 — MB ChB 1982 Manch.; MRCGP 1987; DRCOG 1984.

FARNAN, Basil John The Group Surgery, 257 North Queen Street, Belfast BT15 1HS Tel: 028 9074 8317 Fax: 028 9075 4438; St Emilion, 779 Antrim Road, Belfast BT15 Tel: 776 7606 — MB BCh BAO 1979 Belf.; MICGP 1987; DRCOG Lond. 1981; MRCGP 1983.

FARNAN, Cormac Adrian 2 Lir Court, Clare Road, Ballycastle BT54 6DH Tel: 012657 69520 Email: camroc@ukgateway.net; Dalriada Health Centre, Coleraine Road, Ballycastle BT54 6BA Tel: 012657 62684 Fax: 012657 61501 — MB BCh BAO Belf. 1969. Med. Off. Dalriada Hosp. Ballycastle. Prev: Princip. GP Langton Med. Centre Melbourne, Vict.; Attend. Practitioner Dandenong & Dist. Hosp. Vict. 3175.

FARNAN, Edward Patrick 4 Upper Malone Crescent, Belfast BT9 6PR — MB BCh BAO 1995 Belf.

FARNAN, Niall Desmond 11 Foredown Close, Eastbourne BN20 8DD — MB BCh BAO 1954 Belf.; FRCPsych 1978, M 1971; DPM Eng. 1958. (Qu. Univ. Belf.)

FARNAN, Turlough Basil 41 Malone Meadows, Malone Road, Belfast BT9 5BG — MB BCh BAO 1996 Belf.

FARNDALE, John Anthony Harbottle Surgery, 9 Drakestone View, Harbottle, Morpeth NE65 7DF Tel: 01669 650280 Fax: 01669 650439; Ferniehaugh, Netherton, Morpeth NE65 7HD — MB BChir 1972 Camb.; 2001 DCM (Beijing); MA Camb. 1972; MRCGP 1976; DFFP 1994; DObst RCOG 1975; Cert. Contracep. & Family Plann.

RCOG & RCGP &; Cert FPA 1975; Dip. Ther. Newc 1995. (Camb. & Lond. Hosp.) Prev: Chairm. Cumbria Local Med. Comm.; GP Mem. S. Cumbria Dist. Managem. Team; Trainee GP Newc. VTS.

FARNDON, Professor John Richard Department of Surgery, Bristol Royal Infirmary, Bristol BS2 8HW Tel: 0117 926 0601 Fax: 0117 925 2736 Email: j.r.farndon@bristol.ac.uk; 5 Henleaze Avenue, Henleaze, Bristol BS9 4EU Tel: 0117 962 1554 — BSc Newc. 1967, MD 1986, MB BS 1970; BSc Newc. 1967, MD 1986, MB BS 1970; FRCS Eng. 1975; FRCS Eng. 1975; FRCS (Hons.) Edin. 1997; FRCS Ed (Hon.) 1997. (Newc.) Prof. Surg. Univ. Bristol; Cons. Surg. Bristol Roy. Infirm.; Edr. Brit. Jl. Surg. Socs: Assn. of Surg. of GB & Irel. - Comm. Mem.; Surg. Res. Soc.; Roy. Soc. Med. Prev: Sen. Lect. (Surg.) Univ. Newc. & Hon. Cons. Surg. Roy. Vict. Infirm. Newc.; Sen. Res. Assoc. Dept. Surg. Duke Univ. Med. Center, Durh. NC USA; Sen. Research Assoc. Dept. Surg. Univ. Newc.

FARNDON, Mark Andrew 5 Henleaze Avenue, Henleaze, Bristol BS9 4EU — MB BS 1998 Newc.; MB BS Newc 1998.

FARNDON, Professor Peter Anthony Clinical Genetics Unit, Birmingham Women's Hospital, Edgbaston, Birmingham B15 2TG Tel: 0121 627 2630 Fax: 0121 627 2618 — MB BS 1975 Lond.; MB BS Lond.; BSc Lond. 1972; MD Lond. 1995; FRCP Lond. 1992; MRCP (UK) 1979; DCH Eng. 1978. (King's Coll. Hosp.) Cons. Clin. Geneticist Birm. Wom.'s Hosp.; Prof. Clin. Genetics Univ. Birm. Socs: Clin. Genetics Soc.; (Treas.) Brit. Soc. Human Genetics; (Sec. Gen.) Europ. Soc. Human Genetics. Prev: Sen. Regist. (Clin. Genetics) St. Mary's Hosp. Manch.

FARNELL, Beverley Jane Fairfields, Lower Barns Road, Ludford, Ludlow SY8 4DS Tel: 01584 6549 — MB ChB 1981 Birm.; MRCGP 1985; DRCOG 1983. Asst. GP Ludlow.

FARNELL, Joanna Elaine Coles Lane Health Centre, Coles Lane, Linton, Cambridge CB1 6JS; 20 Church Lane, Abington, Cambridge CB1 6BQ Tel: 01223 892503 — MB ChB 1987 Birm.; MRCGP 1992; DCH RCP Lond. 1991; DRCOG 1990. (Birmingham) GP. Prev: Trainee GP Kidderminster Gen. Hosp. VTS.

FARNELL, Nicholas James Portcullis Surgery, Portcullis Lane, Ludlow SY8 1GT Tel: 01584 872939 Fax: 01584 876490; Portcullis Surgery, Portcullis Lane, Ludlow SY8 1GT Tel: 01584 872939 Fax: 01584 876490 — MB ChB 1981 Birm.; MRCGP 1986; DCH RCP Lond. 1984; DRCOG 1985. (Birmingham) GP Ludlow.

FARNELL, Mr Robert David — MB BS 1990 Lond.; FRCS 2001; FRCS Eng. 1995. (St. Geo. Hosp. Med. Sch.) Specialist Regist. (Orthop.) St. Jas. Univ. Hosp. Leeds.

FARNHAM, Barry Erle (retired) Uplands, 27 Airdale Road, Stone ST15 8DP Tel: 01785 813036 — MB BChir 1954 Camb.; MA Camb. 1955; DObst RCOG 1960. Prev: Gp. Med. Adviser Josiah Wedgwood & Sons Ltd. Stoke on Trent.

FARNHAM, Christopher William Erle 31 Mall Chambers, Kesington Mall, London W8 4DZ — MB BS 1992 Lond.

FARNHAM, Frank Read 56 Herongate Road, London E12 5EQ — MB BS 1990 Lond.

FARNHAM, Neil Godfrey James Kenrose, Whistley Down, Yelverton PL20 6EN — MB ChB 1987 Sheff.

FARNON, Catherine Mary 7 Ridgeway Park N., Portadown, Craigavon BT62 3DG — MB BCh BAO 1982 Belf.; MB BCh Belf. 1982.

FARNON, Desmond Lawrence Tralee General Hospital, Tralee, County Kerry, Republic of Ireland Tel: 0166 26222; 67 Anaverna Drive, Dundalk Tel: 0142 35103 — LRCPI & LM, LRSCI & LM 1962; LRCPI & LM, LRCSI & LM 1962; FFA RCSI 1978; DA Eng. 1977; DObst RCOG 1965. Cons. Anaesth. Tralee Gen. Hosp.

FARNSWORTH, Gillian Mary St Georges Healthcare, Blackshaw Road, London SW17 0QT Tel: 020 8672 1255 — MB Camb. 1970, BChir 1969; DObst RCOG 1971; FFA RCS Eng. 1974. Cons. Anaesth. St. Geo. Hosp. Lond.

FARNSWORTH, Thomas Alan Castle Hill Hospital, Cottingham HU16 5JQ Tel: 01482 875875; Damson Cottage, 12 Damson Garth, Lund, Driffield YO25 9TH Tel: 01377 217872 — BM 1982 Soton.; MSc Soton. 1978; BSc Reading 1976; FRCP Lond. 2000; MRCGP 1988. (Soton.) Cons. Phys. Castle Hill Hosp. Cottingham. Socs: Associatiote Edr., Europ. Jl. of Heart failure. Prev: Sen. Regist. (Geriat. & Gen. Med.) Leeds Gen. Infirm. & St. Jas. Hosp. Leeds; Regist. (Geriat. Med.) York Dist. Gen. Hosp.

FARNWORTH, Mr David 4 The Acorns, Thornhill, Cardiff CF14 9HZ — MB BS 1988 Lond.; MRCP (UK) 1991; FRCOphth 1994. (St. Georges) Clin. Fell. Uveitis Chelsea & W.minster Hosp. Lond.; Specialist Regist. Ophth. Univ. Hosp. Wales Cardiff. Socs: Oxf. Med. Soc. Prev: SHO Ophth. Leicester Roy. Infirm. Leicester.

FARNWORTH, Helen Elizabeth 8 Cohort Drive, Colchester CO2 9RP; 8 Cohort Drive, Roman Fields, Colchester CO2 9RP Tel: 01206 514683 — MB BS 1992 Newc.; MRCPsych 1999. (Newcastle Upon Tyne) SHO (Psychiat.) The Lakes Colchester. Prev: SHO (Psychiat.) Harrogate Dist. Hosp. Harrogate.

FAROOK, Mr Golam 2C St James Road, Stratford, London E15 1RL — MB BS 1988 Calcutta; FRCS Ed. 1995.

FAROOQ, Ahmed Room 3, Flat 22, Block 4, Phase III Residence, Walgrave Hospital, Coventry CV2 2DX — MB BS 1984 Punjab.

FAROOQ, Hussain Mohammed 73 Granville Road, Blackburn BB2 6JS — MB ChB 1998 Manch.; MB ChB Manch 1998.

FAROOQ, Najma 76 Dolphin Road, Slough SL1 1TA — MB BS 1996 Lond.

FAROOQ DAR, Mohammad Char Chimar, 7 Rosslyn Close, Ackworth, Pontefract WF7 7QQ Tel: 01226 725555 Fax: 01226 700051 — MB BS 1974 Kashmir; MRCP (UK) (Paediat.) 1984; MRCPCH 1997; DCH Eng. 1980; FRCP Ed. (Govt. Med. Coll. Srinagar) GP Havercroft; Clin. Asst. (Paediat.) Pinderfields Gen. Hosp. Wakefield. Socs: Med. Protec. Soc. Prev: Regist. (Paediat.) Marston Green Hosp. & E. Birm. Hosp.; SHO (Neonat. & Gen. Paediat.) Leicester Roy. Infirm.

FAROOQI, Ajaz Ahmed Argyle Health Centre, Conway Street, Birkenhead CH41 6PT Tel: 0151 647 8663; 9 Mere Farm Grove, Oxton, Birkenhead L43 9XQ Tel: 0151 653 4133 — MB BS 1968 Osmania; LMSSA Lond. 1978. Dep. Police Surg. Merseyside Police Force. Socs: Birkenhead Med. Soc. & Mem. Wallasey Med. Soc.

FAROOQI, Mr Anwar Uddin 5 Belsay Close, Elm Tree Farm, Stockton-on-Tees TS19 0UF — MB BS 1964 Sind; MB BS Sind Pakistan 1964; FRCS Ed. 1979. (Liaquat Med. Coll.) Assoc. Specialist (Orthop.) N. Tees Gen. Hosp. Stockton-on-Tees. Prev: Regist. (Orthop.) Greenwich Dist. Hosp. Lond.

***FAROOQI, Fahad Masood** Medical Protection Society, 10 Edgeborough Way, Bromley BR1 2UA Tel: 020 8466 6058 Email: fahadf@aol.com — MB BS 1997 Lond.

FAROOQI, Ismaa Sadaf 43 Four Oaks Road, Sutton Coldfield B74 2XU Email: ifaroqi@hgmp.mrc.ac.uk — MB ChB 1993 Birm.; MRCP 1996. (Birmingham) Wellcome Trust Train. Fell. in Med., Univ. of Camb. Prev: SHO (Med.) John Radcliffe Hosp., Oxf.

FAROOQI, Munira Rashad 217A Kingston Road, Ewell, Epsom KT19 0AB — MB BS 1985 Punjab; MRCGO 1995.

FAROOQI, Shah Masood Ahmed Roxbourne Medical Centre, 37 Rayners Lane, South Harrow, Harrow HA2 0UE Tel: 020 8422 5602 Fax: 020 8422 3911 — MB BS 1973 Sri Venkateswara; MB BS 1973 Sri Venkateswara.

FAROOQUE, Hafizuddin 56 Ridge View Drive, Birkby, Huddersfield HD2 2EX — MB BS 1973 Dacca. (Dakha Medical College) Med. Off. (Prison Med.) HMP.

FAROOQUE, Pervin Ghazala Bano 47 Courthouse Road, London N12 7PH — MB BS 1997 Lond.

FAROOQUI, Obaid Ahmed 43 Cecil Park, Pinner HA5 5HJ — MB BS 1986 Karachi.

FAROOQUI, Tariq Mahmood Warren Street Surgery, 37 Warren Street, Savile Town, Dewsbury WF12 9LX Tel: 01924 468686 — MB BS 1962 Sind.

FAROQUI, Muzaffar Hamid 32 Ellesboro Road, Harborne, Birmingham B17 8PT Tel: 0121 427 1182 — MB BS 1975 Kashmir; FFA RCSI 1981. Cons. (Anaesth & Intens. Care) Qu. Eliz. Hosp. Birm. Prev: Sen. Regist. S.W. Regional Rotat.; Clin. Fell. UCLA W.wood, Calif., USA; Regist. Cork Regional Hosp. Irel.

FAROUK, Mr Marwan Omar Department of Surgery, Royal Free Hospital, Pond St., London NW3 2QG Tel: 020 7749 0500; 54 Castlewood Road, London N16 6DW Tel: 020 8800 8621 — MD 1993 Bristol; MB ChB 1983; FRCS Ed. 1988; FRCS (Gen) 1998. Locum Cons. Surg. Socs: BMA; Transpl.ation Soc. Prev: Sen. Regist. Roy. Free Hosp.; Research Fell. Duke Univ. N. Carolina, USA; Regist. (Gen. Surg.) Roy. Edin. Infirm.

FARQUHAR, Alan Maxwell Kirriemuir Health Centre, Tannage Brae, Kirriemuir DD8 4DL Tel: 01575 573333 Fax: 01575 574230 — BM BS 1987 Nottm.; BMedSci 1985; MRCGP 1992.

FARQUHAR, Alison Jane Millbrook House, Castle Cary BA7 7BX — BM 1981 Soton.; MRCGP 1992; DA (UK) 1986. Prev: Asst. GP

Shrivenham; Trainee GP Surrey; SHO (Neonat. & Paediat.) St. Mary's Hosp. Lond.

FARQUHAR, Angela Diane The Medical Defence Union, 192 Altrincham Road, Manchester M22 4RZ Tel: 0161 428 1234 Fax: 07614913301; 83 York Street, Dunnington, York YO19 5QW — MB ChB 1987 Leic.; MRCGP 1994; DRCOG 1990. Medico-Legal Adviser Med. Defence Union Manch. Prev: Med. Off. Leics. Hospice.

FARQUHAR, Colin William Department of Chemical Pathology, Darent Valley Hospital, Darent Wood Road, Dartford DA2 8DA Tel: 01322 428481 Fax: 01322 428493 Email: colin.farquhar@dag-tr.sthames.nhs.uk — MB BS 1979 Lond.; MSc Lond. 1985; BA Oxf. 1975; MRCPath 1988; FRCPath 1997.

FARQUHAR, Donald Lyle St John's Hospital, Howden Road W., Livingston EH54 6PP Tel: 01506 419666 Fax: 01506 417493 Email: donald.farquhar@wlt.scot.nhs.uk; 35 Gillespie Road, Edinburgh EH13 0NW — MB ChB 1979 Ed.; BSc (Hons.) Ed. 1976; FRCP Ed. 1993. (University of Edinburgh) Cons. Phys. (c/o Elderly) W. Lothian NHS Trust; Hon. Sen. Lect. (Med. Educat. & c/o Elderly) Univ. Edin.; Clin. Dir. Med. Directorate St. Johns Hosp. Socs: Brit. Geriat. Soc. Asst. Sec. Scotl.; Scott. Soc. Phys.; Nat. Osteoporosis Soc. Prev: Lect. (Geriat. Med.) Univ. Edin.; Lect. (Med. Oncol.) Univ. Edin.

FARQUHAR, Fiona Jane 29 Welbeck Gardens, Beeston, Nottingham NG9 6JD — MB BCh 1990 Wales.

FARQUHAR, Garry South Road Health Centre, 19 South Road, Lerwick ZE1 0RB Tel: 01595 693201 Fax: 01595 697113; Tamauru, Quarff, Shetland ZE2 9EY Tel: 01950 477547 — MB ChB Dundee 1982.

FARQUHAR, Grant Neil Bryn Teg, Fachwen, Caernarfon LL55 3HD Tel: 01286 872108 Fax: +448700525578 Email: grant.farquhar@fachwen.demon.co.uk — MB ChB 1991 Dundee; BMSc (Hons) 1998; MRCPsych 1997.

FARQUHAR, Iain Kenneth Old Brookside Farm, Gypsy Lane, Bleasby, Nottingham NG14 7GG — BM BS 1979 Nottm.; FFA RCS Eng 1984.

FARQUHAR, Ian Harry (retired) Department of Obstetrics & Gynaecology, Caithness General Hospital, Wick KW1 5LA Tel: 01955 55050 — MB ChB Aberd. 1967; FRCOG 1990, M 1975; DObst 1972. p/t Hosp. Assoc. Specialist in Neonat. Paediat. Caithness. Prev: Cons. O & G Caithness Gen. Hosp. Wick.

FARQUHAR, James Keith (retired) Birch Grove, Lakeview Road, Felbridge, East Grinstead RH19 2QB Tel: 01342 712857 — MRCS Eng. LRCP Lond. 1942; FFA RCS Eng. 1954; DA Eng. 1948. Prev: Cons. Anaesth. Bexley AHA.

***FARQUHAR, Joanne Machell** Townend, Meikle Corsehill, Stewarton, Kilmarnock KA3 5JH — MB ChB 1997 Glas.

FARQUHAR-SMITH, William Paul Neonatal Intensve Care Unit, Box 226, Addenbrooke's Hospital, Cambridge CB2 2SW — BChir 1991 Camb.

FARQUHAR-THOMSON, Duncan Richard 4 Orchard Place, Arundel BN18 9BP Tel: 01903 885066 Email: 100613.366@compuserve.com; Garden Flat, 56 Ramsden Road, London SW12 8QZ Tel: 020 8673 8349 Email: duncanft@compuserve.com — MB BS 1989 Lond.; FRCA 1997. (St. Thos.) Specialist Regist. (Anaesth.) St Geo. Sch. Anaesth. Socs: Roy. Soc. Med.; Assn. Anaesth. Prev: SHO (Anaesth.) Soton. Univ.; SHO (Med.) Roy. Cornw. Hosp.; Ho. Phys. St. Mary's Hosp. Portsmouth.

FARQUHARSON, Archibald Douglas John (retired) Apothecary House, East St., Rye TN31 7JY Tel: 01797 227315 — BM BCh 1959 Oxf.; MRCS Eng. LRCP Lond. 1943; DTM & H Lond 1948; DA Eng. 1957. Prev: Sen. Specialist Anaesth. Min. of Defence.

FARQUHARSON, Colin Alexander Joseph 264A Blackness Road, Dundee DD2 1RU — MB ChB 1993 Dundee; MRCP (UK) 1996. Research Fell. (Cardiol./Clin. Pharmacol.) Dept. of Clin. Pharmacol. & Therap. Ninewells Hosp. Dundee. Prev: SHO (Med.) Perth Roy. Infirm.; SHO (Med.) Ninewells Hosp. & Med. Sch. Dundee.

FARQUHARSON, David Ian Malcolm Greenfield Lodge, Lasswade, Edinburgh EH18 1HE Tel: 0131 663 9338 — MB BS 1976 Lond.; FRCS Ed. 1982; MRCOG 1981; FRCOG 1993. (Middlx.) Cons. O & G E. & W.. Gen. Hosps. & Roy. Infirm. Edin. Socs: Brit. Soc. Colpos. & Cerv. Path.; Brit. Gyn. Cancer Soc. Prev: Cons. Bradford HA; Vis. Asst. Prof. Birm. Alabama; Sen. Regist. (O & G) E.. Gen. Hosp. Edin.

FARQUHARSON, Duncan 2 Up Left, 402 Byres Road, Glasgow G12 8AS — MB ChB 1983 Glas.

FARQUHARSON, Elizabeth Margaret Logan 6 Chamberlain Road, Edinburgh EH10 4DN Tel: 0131 447 1994 — MB ChB Ed. 1939. (Ed.) Prev: Ho. Surg. (Orthop.) Hosp. St. Cross, Rugby; Ho. Surg. N.. Staffs. Roy. Infirm. Stoke-on-Trent.

FARQUHARSON, Gillian Christine Borthwen Farm, Llandegfan, Anglesey, Menai Bridge LL59 5YD Tel: 01248 713635; Coed Y Glyn Surgery, Lon Las, Llangefni LL77 7DU Tel: 01248 722229 Fax: 01248 250551 — Med BSc St. Andrews 1975; MB ChB 1978 Manch. (Manchester)

FARQUHARSON, Gordon Booth (retired) Shuna, Culloden Road, Westhill, Inverness IV2 5BQ Tel: 01463 230930 — MB ChB Aberd. 1950; FRCGP 1981 M 1970. Prev: Mem. Highland Med. Soc.

FARQUHARSON, Iain Keatley Limavady Health Centre, Scroggy Road, Limavady BT49 0NA — MB BCh BAO 1974 Belf. GP Limavady.

FARQUHARSON, Judith Margaret Albyn Medical Practice, 30 Albyn Place, Aberdeen AB10 1NW Tel: 01224 586829 Fax: 01224 213238; 4 Cliff Park, Cults, Aberdeen AB15 9JT Tel: 01224 869934 — MB ChB 1982 Aberd.; MRCGP 1986; DRCOG 1984. Prev: SHO (O & G) Aberd. Matern. Hosp. & Aberd. Roy. Infirm.; SHO (Paediat.) Roy. Aberd. Childr. Hosp.; SHO (Geriat.) Woodend Gen. Hosp. Aberd.

FARQUHARSON, Malcolm James The Medical Centre, 32 London Road, Sittingbourne ME10 1ND Tel: 01795 472109/472100; 18 Jarrett's Court, Wykeham Road, Sittingbourne ME10 3NW Tel: 01795 478083 — MB ChB Aberd. 1968. (Aberdeen) Socs: BMA.

FARQUHARSON, Mary (retired) 23 Grey Ladies Gardens, Wat Tyler Road, Blackheath, London SE10 8AU Tel: 020 8692 5124 — MB BChir 1944 Camb.; MD Camb. 1950, MB, BChir 1944; FRCP Lond. 1972, M 1946; MRCS Eng., LRCP Lond. 1944; TDD Wales 1947. Prev: Tuberc. Regist. Middlx. CC.

FARQUHARSON, Myrtle (retired) 81B Countesswells Road, Aberdeen AB15 7YH Tel: 01224 326292 — MB ChB Aberd. 1954; DPH Glas. 1964; DObst. Prev: GP Milit. Hosp. Khamis Mushayt.

FARQUHARSON, Robin Grant (retired) Newcastle City Health NHS Trust, Milvain Building, Newcastle General Hospital, Newcastle upon Tyne NE4 6BE Tel: 0191 256 3007 Fax: 0191 219 5063 — MB BChir 1971 Camb.; MA Camb. 1971; FRCPsych 1987, M 1975. Cons. Psychiat. Newc. City Health NHS Trust; Clin. Lect. Univ. Newc. u. Tyne.

FARQUHARSON, Roy Gibb Liverpool Women's Hospital, Crown St., Liverpool L8 7SS Tel: 0151 702 4221 Fax: 0151 702 4137 Email: rgfarquharson@yahoo.com — MD 1986 Aberd.; MB ChB 1975; FRCOG 1993, M 1981. (Aberdeen) Cons. O & G Liverp Wom.'s Hosp. Prev: Regist. Aberd. Matern. Hosp. & Nat. Wom. Hosp. Auckland N.Z.; Lect./Sen. Regist. Univ. Hosp. Wales.

FARQUHARSON, Sheila Margaret The Merse, Baughurst, Tadley, Basingstoke RG26 5LP Tel: 0118 981 2976 — MB ChB 1969 St. And.; FRCS Ed. 1977; DCH RCPS Glas. 1973. Assoc. Specialist (Surg.) N. Hants. Hosp. Prev: Regist. (Surg.) Basingstoke Dist. Hosp.; SHO Hosp. Sick Childr. Gt. Ormond St. Lond. & Roy. Hosp. Sick Childr. Edin.

FARQUHARSON, Stewart 248 Unthank Road, Norwich NR2 2AH Tel: 01603 452190 — MB BS 1963 Lond.; FFA RCS Eng. 1969; DA Eng. 1966. (Middlx.) p/t Cons. Anaesth. Norf. & Norwich Hosps. Gp.

FARQUHARSON-ROBERTS, Mr Michael Atholl, CBE, QHS, Surg. Capt. RN Email: mfr@globalnet.co.uk; Fax: 023 9271 5641 Email: mfr@globalnet.co.uk — MB BS 1971 Lond.; FRCS Eng. 1976; MRCS Eng. LRCP Lond. 1971. (Westm.) Med. Quinquennial Review, Implementation Team Ldr., Defence Med. Train. Organisation. Socs: Fell. BOA; Girdlestone Orthop. Soc.; Mem. Roy. Coll. of Defence Studies. Prev: Cons. (Orthop. & Trauma) Gosport Hants.; Cons. Orthop. Surg. Roy. Hosp. Haslar; Defence Cons. Adviser (Orthop.).

FARR, Alison Patricia 9 James Road, Whitchurch, Tavistock PL19 9NJ Tel: 01822 614406 — MB BS 1990 Lond.; BSc (Med. with Anat.) Lond. 1987; MRCGP 1994; DRCOG 1995; DFFP 1993. GP Clin. Asst. Tavistock. Prev: Trainee GP Lister Hosp. Stevenage VTS & Devon.

FARR, Arthur Griffiths, MBE (retired) Amani, Tanfield Lane, Wickham, Fareham PO17 5NN Tel: 01329 833284 — MB BChir 1941 Lond.; MB BChir Camb. 1941; MA Camb. 1941; MRCS Eng.

LRCP Lond. 1940; MFCM 1974; DPH Lond. 1951; DTM & H Eng. 1942, DIH 1951. Prev: MOH Petersfield RD & UD & DrOxf. RD.

FARR, Claire Miranda 7 Salter Road, Poole BH13 7RQ — MB BS 1991 Lond. SHO (Med.) Lister Hosp. Stevenage.

FARR, David Robert 19 Western Road, Hednesford, Cannock WS12 4AS — MB ChB 1995 Leeds; BDS Liverp. 1985; FDS RCPS Glas. 1989; FDS RCS Ed. 1989. Specialist Regist. (Oral & Maxillofacial Surg.) W. Midl. Rotat. Prev: SHO (A & E) ScarBoro. Hosp.; SHO (Orthop.) ScarBoro. Hosp.; SHO (Gen. Surg.) ScarBoro. Hosp.

FARR, John (retired) Trelonydd, Penymorfa Lane, Carmarthen SA31 2NW Tel: 01267 237311 — MB BS Lond. 1937; MB BCh Wales 1937; FRCPsych 1981 M 1971; DPM Eng. 1946. Prev: Phys. Supt. St. David's Hosp. Carmarthen.

FARR, Julia Mary The Elms, Raglan NP15 2LQ Tel: 01291 690248 Email: juliafarr@doctors.org.uk; 8 Sens Close, St Martins Way, Chester CH1 2NF Tel: 01244 340053 — MB BS 1996 Lond.; BSc Lond. 1993; DFFP 2001. (Royal Free Hospital School of Medicine) GP Non-Princip. Socs: Med. Protec. Soc.; Brit. Med. Assn. Prev: Staff grade in Palliat. Med., Florence Nightingle Ho., Aylesbury; Salaried Princip. in Gen. Pract., BeoGr. Surg., Aylesbury.

FARR, Malcolm John Hull Royal Infirmary, Anlaby Road, Hull HU3 2JZ Tel: 01482 328541; 14 Hall Walk, Walkington, Beverley HU17 8TF — MB BS 1960 Lond.; FRCP Lond. 1982; MRCP (UK) 1972; MRCS Eng. LRCP Lond. 1960. Phys. Hull Roy. Infirm. Prev: GP Preston Lancs.

FARR, Margaret 35 West Drive, Heathfield Park, Handsworth, Birmingham B20 3ST Tel: 0121 554 0909 — MB ChB 1969 Birm.; MD Birm. 1985; BDS, LDS Manch. 1960. Assoc. Specialist (Rheum.) Birm.; Clin. Lect. (Rheum.) Univ. Birm. Socs: Brit. Soc. Rheum.; Anat. Soc. Prev: Research Fell. (Rheum.) Qu. Eliz. Hosp. Birm.; SHO (O & G) Birm.

FARR, Nigel Jeremy 4 Asquith Street, Griffithstown, Pontypool NP4 5HL — MB BS 1989 Lond.

FARR, Peter Michael Department Dermatology, Royal Victoria Infirmary, Newcastle upon Tyne NE1 4LP Tel: 0191 282 4548 — MD 1989 Birm.; MB ChB 1978; MRCP (UK) 1981.

FARR, S Mary (retired) 23 lagoon Road, Lilliput, Poole BH14 8JT Tel: 01202 700574 — MB ChB 1958 Bristol; MFFP 1993; AFOM RCP Lond. 1988. Prev: GP Bournemouth.

FARRAG, Mr Mohamed Zohni Abd El Rahim 50 Wimpole Street, London W1M 7DG Tel: 020 7935 4075 Fax: 020 7224 3549 Email: m.farrag@heart.org.uk; 44 Gunnersbury Avenue, Ealing, London W5 4HA Tel: 020 8992 3394 — MB BCh 1966 Ain Shams; DS Ain Shams 1969; FRCS Ed. 1974; FRCS Eng. 1974. (Ain Shams Egypt) Hon. Cons. Cardiothoracic Surg. Italian Hosp. Lond. Socs: Soc. Cardiothoracic Surgs. UK & Irel.; Eur. Assn. Cardiothoracic Surg. Prev: Sen. Regist. (Thoracic & Cardiovasc. Surg.) W.m. Hosp. Lond.; Regist. (Cardiothoracic Surg.) Hammersmith Hosp. & Lond. Heart Hosp.

FARRAJ, Dulair Abdul Aziz 19 Holman Street, Kidderminster DY11 6QY Tel: 01562 64258 — MB ChB 1966 Baghdad; DPM Eng. 1979. (Univ. Baghdad) Cons. Psychiat. E. Birm. HA (T). Prev: Sen. Regist. Birm. AHA (T).

FARRALL, David Lawson City Walls Medical Centre, St. Martin's Way, Chester CH1 2NR Tel: 01244 357800; The Old Vicarage, Shotwick, Chester CH1 6HX Tel: 01244 881239 — MB ChB 1973 Dundee.

FARRALL, Louise Ann Farracot, Station Road, Harbury, Leamington Spa CV33 9HQ — MD 1988 Manch.; MB ChB 1982; MRCOG 1988. Sen. Regist. (O & G) W. Midl. RHA.

FARRAND, David Anthony (retired) 187 Park Lane, Macclesfield SK11 6UD Tel: 01625 422893 — MB BS Lond. 1970.

FARRAND, David John Edmund 11 Copse Close, Burton Joyce, Nottingham NG14 5DD — MB ChB 1972 Bristol.

FARRAND, Roger John Royal Bolton Hospital, Bolton BL4 0JR Tel: 01204 390410 Fax: 01204 390464; 13 Chatsworth Road, Eccles, Manchester M30 9DZ Tel: 0161 789 2982 — MB BChir 1964 Camb.; MA, MB Camb. 1964, BChir 1963; MRCS Eng. LRCP Lond. 1963; FRCPath. 1981 M 1969. (Camb. & St. Mary's) Cons. Microbiol. Bolton HA. Socs: Path. Soc. & Assn. Clin. Path. Prev: Cons. Microbiol. Salford AHA (T); Sen. Regist. Centr. Microbiol. Laborat., W.. Gen. Hosp. Edin.; Regist. (Clin. Path.) United Sheff. Hosps.

FARRAND, Stephanie Ruth 50 Ferry Street, London E14 3DT Tel: 020 7515 7322 Fax: (20) 7537 3559 Email: farrandprs@aol.com; 58 Balmain Street, Dunedin Otago, New Zealand Tel: 034767772 — MB BS 1991 Lond.; FRACP 1999; BSc Immunopath. Lond. 1988; MRCP Lond. 1995. Gen. Med. Regist., Dunedin, NZ. Prev: Regist., WhippsCross, Lond.; SHO, Whipps Cross, Lond.

FARRANDS, Mr Paul Arthur Barn Place, Spatham Lane, Ditchling, Hassocks BN6 8XH Tel: 01273 844175 Fax: 01273 846493 — BM BS 1975 Nottm.; BM BS Nottm. 1973; BMedSci Nottm. (1st cl. Hons.) 1973; DM Nottm. 1983; FRCS Eng. 1979. Cons. Surg. Colorectal Dis. Roy. Sussex Co. Hosp. Brighton. Socs: BSG; Coloproctol. Div. Roy. Soc. Med.; Assn. Colorectal Surg. Prev: Lect. (Surg.) Soton. Univ.; RSO St. Marks Hosp. Lond.

FARRANT, Colin Frank Carrington Way Health Centre, 9 Carrington Way, Wincanton BA9 9JY Tel: 01963 32000 Fax: 01963 32146; Ashley, Hill Close, Wincanton BA9 9NF Tel: 01963 32336 Email: 101523.2132@compuserve.com — MB BS 1971 Lond.; BSc Lond. 1968; DObst RCOG 1974. (The Roy. Lond. Hosp.) Hosp. Pract. (Genitourin. Med.) Yeovil Hosp.

FARRANT, Colin Geoffrey Cameron Petersfield Medical Practice, Dr Farrant & Partners, 25 Mill Road, Cambridge CB1 2AB Tel: 01223 350647 Fax: 01223 576096; Holmfield, 13 Garden Fields, Little Shelford, Cambridge CB2 5HH — MB BS 1977 Lond.; MRCGP 1983. (St. Mary's) Prev: Trainee GP Swindon & Cirencester VTS; Ho. Surg. St. Mary's Hosp. Lond.; Ho. Phys. Amersham Gen. Hosp.

FARRANT, John Mark Royal United Hospital, Bath BA1 3NG Tel: 01225 824445 — MB BChir 1984 Camb.; MD Camb. 1992; MRCP (UK) 1986. (Cambridge and St. Thomas Hospital London) Cons. Phys. & Gastroenterol. Roy. United Hosp. Bath. Socs: Brit. Soc. Gastroenterol.; Brit. Assn. Study Liver. Prev: Sen. Regist. (Gastroenterol.) Battle Hosp. Reading & John Radcliffe Hosp. Oxf.; Wellcome Clinic Research Fell. Inst. Liver Studies Lond.

FARRANT, Philip Canning (retired) 8 Highview Road, Sidcup DA14 4EX Tel: 020 8300 5013 — MB ChB 1949 Bristol; MD Bristol 1959; FRCP Lond. 1971, M 1958; MRCS Eng. LRCP Lond. 1950. Prev: Cons. Phys. Dartford & Gravesham Health Dist.

FARRANT, Sarah Jane Pool Park, Eastcott, St Dominick, Saltash PL12 6TB Tel: 01579 350651 — MB BS 1981 Lond. Staff Grade (Community Child Health) Roy. Cornw. Hosp. Trust.

FARRANT, Terence 5 Westaway Court, Savile St., St Helier, Jersey JE2 3XF — MB BS 1992 Lond. SHO (Med.) Joyce Green Hosp. Dartford.

FARRAR, Cecil David Peel Croft Surgery, Lichfield Street, Burton-on-Trent DE14 3RH Tel: 01283 568405 Fax: 01283 515761; 1 Hamilton Road, Burton-on-Trent DE15 0LN Tel: 01283 535850 Fax: 01283 515761 Email: peel.croft@yahoo.com — MB BCh BAO 1976 Dub.; Dip. Occupat. Med. 1998; MRCGP 1980; DRCOG 1979. (TC Dub.) Socs: BMA.

FARRAR, Daniel 102 Monkton Lane, Monkton Village, Jarrow NE32 5NS Tel: 0191 421 2161 — MB BS 1994 Lond. (St. Geo. Hosp. Med. Sch.) SHO (Anaesth.) Frimley Pk. Hosp. Prev: SHO (Anaesth.) St. Peter's Hosp. Chertsey; SHO (Med.) P.ss Roy. Hosp. Haywards Heath; SHO (A & E) E. Surrey Hosp. Redhill.

FARRAR, David Ian Carnewater Practice, Dennison Road, Bodmin PL31 2LB Tel: 01208 72321 Fax: 01208 78478; Higher Fox Park, Lanhydrock, Bodmin PL30 5BE Tel: 01208 831750 — MB ChB 1983 Birm.; MRCGP 1989; DCH RCP Lond. 1988; DA (UK) 1986. Clin. Asst. (Child Psychiat.) Cornw.; Chain N. Conwall Primary Care Gp. Prev: SHO (Child Psychiat.) Child & Family Centre Roy. Cornw. Hosp. Treliske; Trainee GP Mullion; SHO (Paediat.& Obst.) Treliske Hosp.

FARRAR, Mr David James 38 Harborne Road, Edgbaston, Birmingham B15 3HE Tel: 0121 454 1390; 36 Mirfield Road, Solihull B91 1JD — MB BS Lond. 1966; MS Lond. 1979; FRCS Eng. 1971; MRCS Eng. LRCP Lond. 1966. (St. Thos.) Cons. Urol. Qu. Eliz. & Selly Oak Hosps. Birm. Socs: Brit. Assn. Urol. Surgs.; Roy. Soc. Med. (Sect. Urol.); Internat. Continence Soc. Prev: Sen. Regist. (Urol.) Withington Hosp. Manch. & Manch. Roy. Infirm.; Research Fell. Urodynamic Clinic Middlx. Hosp. Lond.

FARRAR, Edmund Brian (retired) 15 Old Glebe, Upper Tadmarton, Banbury OX15 5TH — MRCS Eng. LRCP Lond. 1949. Prev: Cas. Off. Sutton & Cheam Hosp.

FARRAR, Heather Eileen Wakefield Health Authority, West Parade, Wakefield WF1 1LT Tel: 01924 814400; 20 Lime Crescent,

Wakefield WF2 6RY — MB BCh BAO 1985 Belf.; MPH Leeds 1995; MRCGP 1989; DRCOG 1987. Trainee Regist. (Pub. Health Med.) N. & Yorks. RHA.

FARRAR, Jeremy James Wellcome Trust, Clinical Research Unit, 190 Ben Ham TV, Ho Chi Minh 5, Vietnam Fax: 00 848 8997279; Lansdowne Cottage, The Mews, Long St, Devizes SN10 1NJ Tel: 01380 722448 — MB BS 1987 Lond.; DPhil (Oxon) 1997; BSc Lond. 1984; MRCP (UK) 1990. (Westm.) Sen. Lect. Univ. Oxf. Centre Trop. Dis. Ho Chi Minh City, Vietnam. Prev: Research Regist. Inst. Molecular Med. Oxf.; Regist. (Neurol.) Austin Hosp. Melbourne, Austral.; Regist. (Med.) Roy. Infirm. Edin.

FARRAR, Mr Mark Jonathan 26 Greensleeves Avenue, Broadstone BH18 8DU Tel: 01202 600 071 Fax: 01202 600 942 Email: mark@twodox.freeserve.co.uk — MB BCh BAO 1986 Belf.; Dip Biomechanics 1996 Strathclyde; Dip IMC 1989 RCS, Ed.; FRCS 1998 ((Orth.)); FRCS 1992 Ed. (Queen's Belf.) Cons. Orthopaedic Surg., Poole Hosp. NHS Trust. Socs: Assoc. Mem. Brit. Trauma Soc.; Fell. BOA; Brit. Limb Reconstruction Soc. Prev: Clin. Fell. (Complex Trauma & Lower Limb Reconstruction) N.ern Gen. Hosp. Sheff.; Ch.ill Memor. Trav. Fell.sh. 1998; Career Regist. (Orthop. Surg.) St. Jas. Univ. Hosp. Leeds.

FARRAR, Mark William, Surg. Lt.-Cdr. RN 102 Monkton Lane, Monkton Village, Jarrow NE32 5NS Email: mark.farrar6@virgin.net — MB BS 1989 Newc.; FRCA 1996. Specialist Regist. RN.

FARRAR, Maureen Trumbull House, The Square, Hillsborough BT26 6AG — MB BCh BAO 1967 NUI.

FARRAR, Stephen William Clarendon House, Clarendon St., Hyde SK14 — MB ChB 1967 Leeds.

FARRAR, Susan Margaret The Surgery, 195 Queensferry Road, Rosyth, Dunfermline KY11 2LQ Tel: 01383 414874 Fax: 01383 410616; 3 Dovecot Park, Aberdour, Burntisland KY3 0TA Tel: 01383 860851 — MB ChB 1987 Ed.; MRCGP 1993; DRCOG 1992; DA (UK) 1990. Prev: SHO (Geriat.) Roy. Vict. Hosp. Edin.; Trainee GP S. Qu.sferry; SHO (Paediat.) Falkirk Dist. Infirm.

FARRAR, Suzanne Elizabeth The Redcliffe Surgery, 10 Redcliffe Street, London SW10 9DT Tel: 020 7460 2222 Fax: 020 7460 0116 — MB BS 1986 Lond.

FARRAWAY, Nicholas John Otford Medical Practice, Leonard Avenue, Otford, Sevenoaks TN14 5RB Tel: 01959 524633 Fax: 01959 525086; 9 Sutherland Way, Cuffley, Potters Bar EN6 4EG — MB ChB 1987 Sheff.; MRCGP 1991; DCH RCP Lond. 1993.

FARRELL, Adrian Jude Rheumatology Department, Leighton Hospital, Middlewich Road, Crewe CW1 4QJ — MB ChB 1981 Bristol; FRCP (Lond.); BSc (Hons.) Bristol 1978; MRCP (UK); MD Bristol. Cons. Rheum. Leighton Hosp. Chesh. & Haywood Hosp. Stoke-on-Trent; Hon. Sen. Lect., Keele Univ. Socs: Brit. Rheum. Soc.; Biochem. Soc.; Brit. Inflammation Research Assn. Prev: Sen. Regist. (Rheum.) Nottm. City Hosp. & Derbysh. Roy. Infirm.; Clin. Research Fell. (Bone & Jt. Research) Roy. Lond. Hosp.

FARRELL, Alan Alexander Iona, Back Dykes Road, Kinnesswood, Kinross KY13 9HJ — MB ChB 1976 Ed.; MRCGP 1982.

FARRELL, Alexander Murray Clinical Immunology & Tissue Typing, 5th Floor QEB, Glasgow Royal Infirmary, 10 Alexandra Parade, Glasgow G31 2ER — MB ChB 1982 Liverp. Cons. Immunol., N. Glas. Hosps. Univ.; Hon. Cons. Immunol., Glas. & W. Scotl. Blood Transfus. Centre; Hon. Sen. Lect. (Immunol.) Univ. Glas.

FARRELL, Andrew James 36 Meakin Avenue, Westbury Park, Clayton, Newcastle ST5 4EY — MB ChB 1986 Manch.

FARRELL, Angela Michelle 12 Captain Lees Road, Westhoughton, Bolton BL5 3UB — MB ChB 1998 Leeds.

FARRELL, Anne Marie Department of Dermatology, University Hospital, Cardiff CF14 4XW — BM BCh 1989 Oxf.; BA Oxf.; MRCP 1992 Lond.; DCH RCP 1993 Lond. Cons. (Dermatol.) Univ. Hosp., Cardiff. Prev: Sen. Regist. (Dermat.) Ch.ill Hosp. Oxf.; Regist. (Dermat.) Char. Cross & W.m. Med. Sch. Lond.; SHO (Dermat.) Chelsea & W.m. Hosp. Lond.

FARRELL, Arlene Anne 46 Alderman Road, Glasgow G13 3YE — MB ChB 1993 Aberd. GP Regist. (Inverness). Prev: SHO (Paediat.) Roy. Aberd. Childr.'s Hosp.

FARRELL, Danielle Maree McIlvride Medical Practice, 5 Chester Road, Poynton, Stockport SK12 1EU Tel: 01625 872134 Fax: 01625 859748; 10 Birchway, Bramhall, Stockport SK7 2AG — MB ChB 1991 Leeds; MRCGP 1995. (Leeds)

FARRELL, David Llewelyn Health Centre, Pier Road, Tywyn LL36 0AT Tel: 01654 710238 Fax: 01654 712143 — MB ChB 1984 Leeds; MB ChB Leeds l984.

FARRELL, Desmond Joseph Tel: 01803 655221 Fax: 01803 655209 — MB BCh BAO 1987 Dub.; BA Dub. 1987; MRCPath. 1994; DRCPath 1997. (Trinity Coll. Dub.) Cons. Histopath. Torbay Hosp. Torquay. Socs: Assn. Clin. Path; Brit. Soc. Clin. Cytol.; Brit. Div. of the Internat. Acad. of Path. Prev: Sen. Regist. Rotat. (Histopath.) N.. & Yorks. RHA.

FARRELL, James Peter Port Glasgow Health Centre, 2-4 Bay Street, Port Glasgow PA14 5ED Tel: 01475 74532; Cir Mhor, Law Brae, West Kilbride KA23 9DD — MB ChB 1986 Glas. Clin. Asst. (Anaesth.) Inverclyde Roy. Hosp. Prev: SHO (O & G, Anaesth. & Surg.) Inverclyde Roy. Hosp.

FARRELL, Joan Hynd Flat 6, 60 Roseangle, Dundee DD1 4NB — MB ChB 1988 Dundee.

FARRELL, John Gerard 102 Somerton Road, Belfast BT15 4DE — MD Belf. 1987, MB BCh BAO 1973; MRCGP 1982; MICGP 1987; DCCH RCP Ed. 1983; DCH Dub. 1975; DRCOG 1975. GP Newtownabbey.

FARRELL, Kyran Anthony Farrell and Partners, 4 Repton Road, Willington, Derby DE65 6BX Tel: 01283 703318 Fax: 01283 701457 — MB BS 1983 Lond.; BSc (Infec. & Immunity) Lond. 1980, MB BS 1983; DRCOG 1987. Prev: Trainee GP Redhill VTS.

FARRELL, Margaret Mary (retired) 157 All Saints Road, Birmingham B14 6AT Tel: 0121 444 2410 — MB BCh BAO NUI 1946, DCH 1952, DPH 1953; DObst RCOG 1951; BA (OU) 1997.

FARRELL, Margaret Rosemary (retired) 6 The Fairways, Newcastle BT33 0RX Tel: 028 4372 3296 — LRCP LRCS Ed. LRFPS Glas. 1950; DPH Glas. 1954. Mem. Fac. Community Med. Prev: Sen. Med. Off. Down Health Dist.

***FARRELL, Michael Brendan** 51 Raynald Road, Manor Park, Sheffield S2 1PR — MB ChB 1996 Birm.

FARRELL, Michael Conleth The Orchard, 9 The Village, Orton Longueville, Peterborough PE2 7DN Tel: 01733 235488 — MB BS 1969 Lond.; FFA RCS Eng. 1976; DObst RCOG 1971. (St. Mary's) Cons. (Anaesth.) PeterBoro. Dist. Hosp. Prev: Asst. Surg. SS Oriana; Sen. Regist. (Anaesth.) Sheff. AHA (T).

FARRELL, Michael Proinsias National Addiction Centre, Maudsley Hospital & Institute of Psychiatry, 36-65 Denmark Hill, London SE5 8AF Tel: 020 7405701 Fax: 020 7701 8454 Email: m.farrell@iop.kcl.ac.uk — MB BCh BAO 1979 NUI; LRCPI & LM, LRCSI & LM 1979; MRCP (UK) 1982; MRCPsych 1987. Sen. Lect. Inst. Psychiat. Nat. Addic. Centre. Socs: Exec. Soc. Study Addic.; (Exec.) Roy. Coll. Psychiat. (Mem. Subst. Misuse Sect.); Ex. Comm. Drug Dependence WHO. Prev: Research Sen. Regist. Addic. Research Unit Inst. Psychiat. Lond.; Sen. Regist. (Psychiat.) Maudsley Hosp. Lond.; Regist. (Med.) W.m. Hosp. Lond.

FARRELL, Patrick Jonathon Scott Townsend House, 49 Harepath Road, Seaton EX12 2RY Tel: 01297 20616 Fax: 01297 20810 — MB BS 1981 London; MB BS 1981 London.

FARRELL, Peter Danks, Smith, Sykes and Farrell, 134 Beeston Road, Beeston Hill, Leeds LS11 8BS Tel: 0113 276 0717 Fax: 0113 270 3727; 17 Gledhow Park Drive, Leeds LS7 4JT — MB ChB 1984 Leeds; MB ChB Leeds l984.

FARRELL, Mr Roy William Robert Wheat Hay, Shatton, Bamford, Hope Valley S33 0BG — MB BCh BAO 1983 Dub.; FRCS (Otol.) Eng. 1993; FRCSI 1988.

FARRELL, Stephen 31 Shanslieve Drive, Newcastle BT33 0HN — MB BCh 1998 Belf.; MB BCh Belf 1998.

FARRELL, Susan Helen 4 Golwg-y-fro, Brackla, Bridgend CF31 2HW — MB ChB 1993 Bristol.

FARRELL, Thomas Francis 545 Normanby Road, Normanby, Middlesbrough TS6 0DX — LRCPI & LM, LRSCI & LM 1945; LRCPI & LM, LRCSI & LM 1945; LM Coombe 1946. (RCSI) Prev: Ho. Surg. & Ho. Phys. Co. Hosp. Kilkenny; Clin. Clerk Coombe Matern. Hosp. Dub.; Res. Med. Off. PeaMt. Sanat. Newc.

FARRELL, Thomas Gerard 42B Holmbush Road, London SW15 3LE — MB ChB 1981 Leic.

FARRELL, William John Anthony Crossmaglen Health Centre, McCormick Place, Crossmaglen, Newry BT35 9HD Tel: 028 3086 1692 — MB BCh BAO 1982 NUI; MRCGP 1986; Dip. Palliat. Med. Wales 1992; DObst. 1985; DCH RCP Lond. 1984.

FARRELL-ROBERTS, Miss Maryanne Georgina Jessie William Harvey Hospital, A&E Department, Kennington Road, Willesborough, Ashford TN24 0LZ Tel: 01233 611113 — BM 1983 Soton.; FRCS Ed. 1989. Cons. (A&E), William Harvey Hosp., Ashford, Kent. Prev: Staff Grade (A & E) Roy. Preston Hosp.

FARRELLY, Colum Patrick 10 Glencoe Park, Newtownabbey BT36 7PT; 19 Altnagelvin Park, Derry City, Londonderry BT47 2LU Tel: 02871 44103 — MB BCh BAO 1980 Belf.

FARRELLY, George Allen The Surgery, 35 St Stephen's Road, London E3 5JD — MB BS 1984 Lond.

FARREN, John Edward (retired) Shangri La, Tresillian, Truro TR2 4BW — MB ChB 1936 Ed.; DPH Bristol 1965. Prev: Dep. Med. Supt. King Edwd. VIII Hosp. Durban, S. Africa.

FARRER, Christopher James, OStJ (retired) Ripplelodge, Ripple, Deal CT14 Tel: 01304 375077 — MB BChir 1957 Camb.; MB Camb. 1957, BChir 1956; MA Camb. 1957; DObst RCOG 1960. Area Surg. St. John Ambul. Brig. E. Kent. Prev: Cas. Off., Ho. Surg. & Jun. Hosp. Med. Off. Dept. VD St. Thos. Hosp.

FARRER, Claire Alison 22 First Avenue, Emsworth PO10 8HN — MB BS 1993 Lond.

FARRER, John Anson (retired) Hail Garth, Clapham, Lancaster LA2 8DR — MB BS 1945 Melbourne; DPH Leeds 1963. Prev: Clin. Asst. (Electromyogr., Orthop. & Cas.) Roy. Lancaster Infirm.

FARRER, Katharine Mary Neonatal Intensive Care Unit, St. George's Hospital, Blackshaw Rd, Tooting, London SW17 0QT; 3 Morden Cliff, Morden Hill, London SH3 7NR — MB ChB 1987 Manch.; MRCP (UK) 1996; MRCGP 1994; DRCOG 1991; DCH RCP Lond. 1991. (Manch.) Specialist Regist. (Neonatology & Paediat.) King's Coll. Hosp. & Cons. (Neonatology) St. Geo.'s Hosp. Prev: Regist. (Paediat.) Brighton; SPR Guys; SPR Kings.

FARRER, Victoria 2 Cedar Court, North Tyneside General Hospital, Rake Lane, North Shields NE29 8NH — MB BS 1988 Lond. SHO (Psychiat.) Warlingham Pk. Hosp. Surrey.

FARRER-BROWN, David Willow Green Surgery, Station Road, East Preston, Littlehampton BN16 3AH Tel: 01903 758152 Fax: 01903 859986; Sandfield House, Lyminster, Littlehampton BN17 7PG Tel: 01903 724129 Fax: 01903 71504 Email: farrersand@aol.com — MB BChir 1972 Camb.; BA Camb. 1969; MRCP (UK) 1975; DPD Wales 1998. (St. Thos.) GP Princip. Prev: Clin. Asst. (Dermat.) Worthing Hosp.; Clin. Asst. (Rheum.) S.lands Hosp. Shoreham by Sea.

FARRER-BROWN, Geoffrey (retired) Radnage Bottom Farm, Radnage Lane, Radnage, High Wycombe HP14 4DX — MB BChir 1960 Camb.; MD Camb. 1967, MA, MB 1960, BChir 1959; FRCPath 1980. Prev: Sen. Lect. (Path.) Bland Sutton Inst. Path.

FARRIER, Mr Christopher Donald Poole General Hospital, Longfleet Rd, Poole BH15 2JB Tel: 01202 442956 Fax: 01202 442826; Pinelands, Martello Road South, Poole BH13 7HF — MB BS 1954 Lond.; FRCS Eng. 1967; FRCS Ed. 1965; MRCS Eng. LRCP Lond. 1954. (King's Coll. Lond. & St. Geo.) Cons. Orthop. Surg. Poole Gen. Hosp. Socs: Fell. BOA & Roy. Soc. Med.; Sen. Fell. BOA. Prev: Cons. Qu. Eliz. Milit. Hosp.; Cons. A & E Wellington Hosp. NZ; Cons. P.A.R.A.F. Hosp. Wroughton.

FARRIER, Jeremy Nigel Flat 11, Fairoak Court, Lady Mary Rd, Cardiff CF23 5PD Tel: 029 2076 1062 — MB BCh 1997 Wales; BDS Wales 1982; FDS RCS Ed. 1993. (Wales)

FARRIER, Martin Philip The Old Vicarage, 25 Station Rd, New Longton, Preston PR4 4LN Tel: 01772 617833 Email: farrier@25stationroad.freeserve.co.uk — MB BS 1991 Lond.; DCH RCP 1994. (Charing Cross & Westminister) Regist. (Paediat.), Hope Hosp., Neonat. Unit, Manch. Socs: MRCGP; MRCP; MRCPCH.

FARRIES, John Stothart (retired) 31 Rogerley Close, Lytham St Annes FY8 4PL Tel: 01253 735641 — MRCS Eng. LRCP Lond. 1954; FFCM 1982, M 1972; DPH Manch. 1966; DObst RCOG 1963; DA Eng. 1962. Prev: Community Phys. (Environm. Health) Bolton DHA.

FARRIMOND, John Gordon 255 Walmer Road, London W11 4EW — MB BS 1973 Lond.; BSc (1st cl. Hons.) 1969; MRCP (UK) 1978; MRCS Eng. LRCP Lond. 1973; FFA RCS Eng. 1983. (St. Mary's)

FARRINGTON, Andrew 6 Millbank Close, Chelford, Macclesfield SK11 9SJ — MB BS 1991 Lond.

FARRINGTON, Anthony Gordon 11 Buckingham Road, Brighton BN1 3RA Tel: 01273 23395 — MB BS 1972 Lond.; MRCS Eng. LRCP Lond. 1972; MRCPsych 1978. (Univ. Coll. Hosp.) Cons. Psychiat. (Drug Dependency Clinic), Herbert Hone Clinic Brighton. Prev: Sen. Regist. (Psychiat.) St. Geo. Hosp. (Blackshaw Rd.) Lond.; Research Fell. & Hon. Sen. Regist. Acad. Dept. Psychiat. Roy. Free; Hosp. Lond.

FARRINGTON, Gillian Anne Gregson Clinic, Broadgreen Hospital, Thomas Drive, Liverpool L14 3LB Tel: 0151 282 6000; 39 The Beeches, Calderstones, Liverpool L18 3LT — MB ChB 1983 Liverp. Clin. Asst. (Dermat.) BRd.green Hosp. Liverp.; Clin. Asst. (Dermat.) Whistow Hosp. Prescot Merseyside. Prev: GP Liverp.; SHO (Dermat.) Liverp. HA; SHO (O & G & Paediat.) Milton Keynes HA.

FARRINGTON, Mr Graham Hugh (retired) 100 Sandbourne Avenue, Merton Park, London SW19 3EN — MB ChB Leeds 1958; MCh Leeds 1970; FRCS Eng. 1964. Prev: Cons. Surg. Kingston Hosp.

FARRINGTON, Jill Louise 12 Knot Acre, New Longton, Preston PR4 4JB — MB BS 1986 Lond.; MFPHM 1998; MPH Leeds 1994; MRCGP 1992; DCH RCP Lond. 1990; DGM RCP Lond. 1988. (Middlx. Hosp.) Dep. Head, Centre for Urban Health, WHO Regional Office for Europe, Copenhagen, Denmark. Prev: Sen. Regist. (Pub. Health Med.) Yorks. Region.

FARRINGTON, John (retired) (Surgery), 26 Clifton Road, Rugby CV21 3QF — MB ChB 1953 Birm.

FARRINGTON, Kenneth Lister Hospital, Stevenage SG1 4AB Tel: 01438 781230 Fax: 01438 781174 — MB BCh 1974 Wales; BSc (Hons.) Manch. 1968; MD Wales 1983; FRCP Lond. 1992; MRCP (UK) 1977. Cons. Nephrol. Lister Hosp. Stevenage; Hon. Cons. Nephrol. Hammersmith Hosp. Lond. Prev: Cons. Phys. King Geo. Hosp. Ilford & Barking Hosp.; Vis. Nephrol. St. Bart. Hosp. Lond.

FARRINGTON, Mark Clinical Microbiology & Public Health Laboratory, Box 236, Addenbrooke's NHS Trust, Cambridge CB2 2QW Tel: 01223 257036 Fax: 01223 242775 Email: mark.farrington@msexc.addenbrookes.anglox.nhs.uk — MB BChir 1980 Camb.; FRCPath 1996, M 1986. (Camb. & St. Thos.) Cons. Microbiol. Pub. Health Laborat. Serv. Camb.; Hon. Cons. Med. Microbiol. Addenbrooke's NHS Trust; Assoc. Lect. Camb. Univ. Socs: Counc. Hosp. Infec. Soc.; Brit. Soc. Antimicrob. Chemoth.; Amer. Soc. MicroBiol. Prev: Lect. (Med. Microbiol.) St. Thos. Hosp. Lond.; Lect. (Microbiol.) Chinese Univ., Hong Kong; SHO (Rheum.) St. Thos. Hosp. Lond.

FARRINGTON, Mark Richard 140 The Green, Worsley, Manchester M28 2PA — BM 1998 Soton.; BM Soton 1998.

FARRINGTON, Rebecca Louise Bla'Bheinn, Cruach, Bowmore PA43 7JQ Tel: 01496 810403 — MB ChB 1990 Dundee; DTM & H Liverp. 1995. Doctor Medecins Sans Frontiers Worldwide Pl.ments.

FARRINGTON, Reginald Merlyn (retired) Clydach House, Gilwern, Abergavenny NP7 0HB — MRCS Eng. LRCP Lond. 1934. Prev: Anaesth. Blaenavon Hosp.

FARRINGTON, Tara 19 Gillian Street, London SE13 7AH — MB BS 1993 Lond.

FARRINGTON, William James Bay Cottage, 150 Church Road, Wembury, Plymouth PL9 0HR Tel: 01752 862559 — MB BS 1992 Lond.

FARRINGTON, Mr William Trevor (cons. rooms) Elm House, 2 Mauldeth Road, Withington, Manchester M20 4ND Tel: 0161 434 9715 Fax: 0161 448 0310; Sandilands Farm, Crowley, Northwich CW9 6NX Tel: 01565 777462 Fax: 01565 777305 Email: trevorfarrington@man.ac.uk — MB BS Lond. 1966; FRCS Eng. 1972; MRCS Eng. LRCP Lond. 1966. (King's Coll. Hosp.) Cons. ENT, Head & Neck Surg. Manch. Roy. Infirm. & Christie Hosp. Nat. Health Trust; Hon. Clin. Lect. (Surg.) Vict. Univ. Manch.; Vis. Cons. Roy. Schs. for Deaf Chesh. Socs: Manch. Med. Soc. (Past Pres. 1995); Roy. Soc. Med. (Sects. Laryngol. & Otol.) (Past Pres. 1995). Prev: Lect. (Otolaryngol.) Vict. Univ. Manch.

***FARRIS, Claire Annabel** 72 Woodleigh Avenue, Birmingham B17 0NJ — MB ChB 1994 Birm.; ChB Birm. 1994.

FARROW, Amanda Karen 2 Westfield Drive, Great Bookham, Leatherhead KT23 3NU — MB BCh 1995 Wales.

FARROW, Catherine Ann 14 Maple Road, Harpenden AL5 2DU — MB ChB 1997 Sheff.

FARROW, Clifford Owen (retired) 21 Fitzwilliam Drive, Harlington, Doncaster DN5 7HY Tel: 01709 892241 — MB ChB 1955 Sheff.; MRCS Eng. LRCP Lond. 1955. Prev: Ho. Phys. & Asst. Cas. Off. Roy. Hosp. Sheff.

FARROW, David James Sandgate Road Surgery, 180 Sandgate Road, Folkestone CT20 2HN Tel: 01303 221133 Fax: 01303 261068; 2 Godwyn Gardens, Folkestone CT20 2JZ Tel: 01303 246492 — MB BS 1988 Lond.; MRCGP 1992; DRCOG 1991. (St. Bartholomew's) Prev: Trainee GP Gt. Yarmouth VTS.; Ho. Off. (Med.) St. Bart. Hosp. Lond.; Ho. Off. (Surg.) Hillingdon Hosp.

FARROW, David John Duncan (retired) East Sussex Local Medical Committee, 58A High St., Heathfield TN21 8JB Tel: 01435 867777 Fax: 01435 868886 Email: esimci@msn.com — MB BS Lond. 1962; MRCS Eng. LRCP Lond. 1962; DObst RCOG 1964. Med. Sec. E. Sussex LMC; Mem. Gen. Practitioners Comm.; Mem. (Counc.) Cameron Fund.; Indep. Med. Mem. of Appeal Bd. of the Code of Pract. Auth. (Prescription Meds.). Prev: Princip. GP Hawkhurst Kent.

FARROW, John 13 Bowmont Gardens, Glasgow G12 9LR — MB ChB 1995 Aberd.

FARROW, Mr John Sebastian Royal Shrewsbury Hospital, Myttan Oak Road, Shrewsbury SY3 8XQ Tel: 01743 261499; 10 Two Ashes, Bayston Hill, Shrewsbury SY3 0QF Email: famfarrow@aol.com — MB BChir 1978 Camb.; MA Camb. 1978; FRCS Eng. 1986. (Westm.) Staff Surg. (ENT) Roy. Shrewsbury Hosp. Socs: Assoc. Mem. Brit. Assn. Otolaryngol.; Assoc. Mem. Midl. Inst. Otol. Prev: Staff Surg. (ENT) Ear, Nose & Throat Hosp. Shrewsbury; Regist. (ENT) Ear, Nose & Throat Hosp. Shrewsbury & Odstock Hosp. Salisbury.

FARROW, Lewis Jesse Lindum Cottage, Scatterdells Lane, Chipperfield, Kings Langley WD4 9EZ — MD 1983 Lond.; MB BS (Hons). 1958; FRCP Lond. 1979, M 1964; DObst RCOG 1960. (St. Bart.) Cons. Phys. Watford Gen. Hosp. Socs: Fell. Roy. Soc. Med.; Brit. Soc. Gastroenterol. Prev: Sen. Regist. St. Mary's & W. Middlx. Hosps. Lond.; Regist. (Med.) Brompton Hosp. Lond. & Chase Farm Hosp. Enfield; Med. Off. RAF.

FARROW, Richard Fax: 01872 255314 — MB BS 1986 Lond.; 2001 PGCE; BSc Lond. 1983; MRCP (UK) 1989; FRCR 1993. (Char. Cross Hosp. Med. Sch.) Cons. Radiol. Roy. Cornw. Hosp. Hosp.; PBL Co-ordinator Peninsula Med. Sch. Socs: Radiol. Soc. N. America; Eur. Soc. Gastrointestinal & Abdom. Radiol.; Brit. Soc. Gastroenterol. Prev: Fell. (Diagn. Radiol.) McMaster Univ. Hamilton Ontario, Canada; Sen. Regist. (Diagn. Radiol.) Bristol Roy. Infirm.; Regist. (Diagn. Radiol.) Derriford Hosp. Plymouth.

FARROW, Richard James (retired) (Surgery) 17 North Road, Great Clacton, Clacton-on-Sea CO15 4DA Tel: 01255 423075 Fax: 01255 426215 — MB BS 1962 Lond.; DObst RCOG 1964. Police Surg. Clacton-on-Sea.

FARROW, Roger Edmund New Medical Centre, 264 Brentwood Road, Romford RM2 5SU Tel: 01708 478800 Fax: 01708 471422; Turret House, Ticknell Lane, Charlbury, Oxford OX7 3SJ — MB BS 1966 Lond.; MRCGP 1974; DObst RCOG 1968. (St. Bart.) Prev: SHO (Paediat.) Qu. Eliz. Hosp. Childr. Lond.; Ho. Phys. & Ho. Surg. Harold Wood Hosp.; Ho. Surg. Obst. Chase Farm Hosp. Enfield.

FARROW, Roslyn Joanne The Surgery, 4 Repton Rd, Willington, Derby DE65 6BX — BM BS 1993 Nottm.; MRCGP; DCH; DFFP.

FARROW, Sarah Jane 10 Wykeham Avenue, Hornchurch RM11 2LA Tel: 01708 478763 — MB ChB 1994 Liverp. (Univ. Liverp.) SHO (Med.) Whipps Cross Hosp. Lond.; SHO (Med.) Roy. Marsden Hosp. Fulham Lond. Socs: BMA. Prev: SHO (Med.) Chase Farm Hosp. Enfield; Ho. Off. Roy. Liverp. Univ. Hosp.

FARROW, Professor Stephen Charles 28 Muswell Avenue, London N10 2EG; Department of Public Health, Barnet Health Authority, Hyde House, The Hyde, Edgware Road, London NW9 6QQ Tel: 020 8201 4780 Fax: 020 8201 4702 — MA, MB Camb. 1969, BChir 1968; MD 1981; MRCP (UK) 1973; FFCM 1986, MFCM 1976; FFPHM 1989. (St. Bart.) Dir. of Pub. Health Barnet; Hon. Prof. Middlx. Univ. Prev: Sen. Lect. (Epidemiol. & Pub. Health Med.) Univ. Bristol; Sen. Lect. (Epidemiol. & Community Med.) Univ. Wales Coll. Med.

FARROW, Sydney Rydings Hall Surgery, Church Lane, Brighouse HD6 1AT Tel: 01484 715324 Fax: 01484 400847 — MB ChB 1973 Leeds.

FARRUGIA, David Carmel St Bartholomews Hospital, West Smithfield, London EC1A 7BE Tel: 020 7601 8522 Fax: 020 7601 7577 Email: dcfarrugia@mds.qmu.ac.uk; 56 Petersham Drive, St Paul's Cray, Orpington BR5 2QE Tel: 01689 837290 Email: farugia@clara.net — MD 1987 Malta; MRCP (UK) 1991; Phd (Univ. Lond.) 1998. Specialist Regist. (Med. Oncol.) Lond. Socs: Assoc. Mem. Amer. Soc. Clin. Oncol.; Assn. Cancer Phys.s (UK).

FARRUGIA, Joseph Francis de Pellegrino, TD (retired) Top Lodge, Broughton, Skipton BD23 3AE Tel: 01756 799585 Fax: 01756 796547 — MB ChB 1956 St. And. Princip. Clin. Asst. Roy. Infirm. Bradford; Maj. RAMC (RARO). Prev: GP Bingley.

FARRUGIA, Paul David Accident & Emergency Department, Royal Berkshire Hospital, London Road, Reading RG1 5AN — MB BS 1976 Lond.; FFA RCS Eng. 1982.

FARRUGIA, Philippa Flat 1, 41 Kellett Rd, London SW2 1EA — MB BS 1997 Lond.

FARRUKH, Abdul Aziz Rajabali (retired) Upton Lane Medical Centre, 75-77 Upton Lane, London E7 9PB Tel: 020 8471 6912/6045 — MCPS Bombay 1957.

***FARRUQUE, Syeeda Shanchita** 34 Atherton Road, London E7 9AJ — MB BS 1997 Lond.

FARTHING, Alan John 106 Harley Street, London W1G 7JE Email: a.farthing@ic.ac.uk — MB BS 1986 Lond.; MD Lond. 1996; MRCOG 1991. Cons. O & G St. Mary's Hosp. Lond.; Sen. Lect. Imperial Coll. of Sci. and Med. Socs: Brit. Soc. Gyn. Endoscopy; Roy. Soc. Med.; Coelio-Schanter Club. Prev: Sen. Regist. (O & G) St. Mary's Hosp. Lond.; Fell. (Gyn. Oncol.) King Edwd. Memor. Hosp. Perth, W. Austral.

FARTHING, Charles Peter 3 Childs Way, Wrotham, Sevenoaks TN15 7DR — MB BS 1953 Lond.; FRCPath 1975, M 1963. (King's Coll. Hosp.) Cons. Pathol. Microbiol. Bromley AHA. Prev: Demonst. (Path.) & Ho. Off. (Pathol.) King's Coll. Hosp; Ho. Surg. & Ho. Phys. Freedom Fields Hosp. Plymouth.

FARTHING, Professor Michael John Godfrey Digesture Diseases Research Centre, St Bartholomew's Hospital, London E1 2AD Tel: 0207 882 7190 Fax: 0207 882 7199 Email: m.j.g.farthing@mds.gmw.ac.uk — MD 1981 Lond.; BSc (Hons.) 1969, MB BS 1972; FRCP Lond. 1988, MRCP (UK) 1975; FAMS 1998; DHC Hungary 1999. Prof. Gastroenterol. & Hon. Cons. Phys. Dept. Gastroenterol. St. Bart. Hosp. Lond.; Hon. Cons. Gastroenterol. St. Mark's Hosp. Lond.; Hon. Cons. Gastroenterol. St Lukes Hosp; Hon. Cons. Gastroenterol. Army; Hon. Cons. Gastroenterol. Homerton. Hosp. Socs: Brit. & Amer. Socs. Gastroenterol.; Assn. Phys.; Roy. Soc. Med. & Amer. Soc. Trop. Med. & Hyg. Prev: Vis. Asst. Prof. Tufts Univ. Sch. Med., Div. Geogr. Med., Boston, USA; Regist. (Med. & Gastroenterol.) Addenbrooke's Hosp. Camb.; Dean Fac. Clin. Med. St. Barth. & Roy. Lond. Sch. Med. & Dent. 1995-1997.

FARUHAR, Mehrbanoo The Surgery, 71 Amhurst Park, London N16 5DL; Erskine Lodge, 50 Primrose Hill Road, London NW3 3AA Tel: 020 7722 9596 — MRCS Eng. LRCP Lond. 1963. (Guy's) Prev: Ho. Phys. Bolingbroke Hosp. Lond.; Ho. Surg. & SHO Putney Hosp.

FARUQ, Ashfaq 28 Oakwood Road E., Rotherham S60 3ER — MB BCh 1995 Wales.

FARUQI, Mohammad Tariq Holly Bush Lane Health Centre, Church Balk, Edenthorpe, Doncaster DN3 2PP — MB BS 1966 Dacca; MB BS 1966 Dacca.

FARUQUE, Syed Mohammad (retired) 2 Bluecoat Crescent, Newton, Preston PR4 3TJ Tel: 01772 685403 — MB BS 1957 Karachi; DTM & H Eng. 1959.

FARZANEH-FAR, Afshin 4 High Meadows, Chigwell IG7 5JX — MB ChB 1988 Ed.; BSc (1st cl. Hons. Physiol.) Ed. 1990, MB ChB (Distinc. Med.) 1992; MRCP (UK). Brit. Heart Foundat. Clin. PhD Fell. Univ. of Camb.; Specialist Regist. (Cardiol.) N. Thames Region. Socs: Roy. Coll. Phys. (UK). Prev: SHO Roy. Brompton Hosp. & Hammersmith Hosp. Lond. & Nat. Hosp. Neurol & Neurosurg. Lond.

FASEY, Christopher Nigel 11 Hillside Crescent, Leigh-on-Sea SS9 1EN — MB BS 1983 Lond.; LMSSA Lond. 1981; MRCPsych 1987. Cons. Psychiat. of Old Age Basildon Hosp.

FASHAKIN, Mr Emmanuel Olusegun 11 Fairfield Avenue, Pontefract WF8 4DY Tel: 01977 798974 — MB BS 1979 Ibadan; FRCS Ed. 1989.

FASLER, Julian James Alma Cottage, Stowmarket Road, Rattlesden, Bury St Edmunds IP30 0RS Email: 101352.3207@compuserve.com — MRCS Eng. LRCP Lond. 1974; MB BS Lond. 1974; BSc (Hons. Physiol.) Lond. 1971; MRCP (UK) 1977; FRCP Lond. 1996. (St. Geo.) Cons. Geriat. Med. W. Suff. Hosp. Bury St. Edmunds. Prev: Sen. Regist. (Geriat. Med.) St. Thos. Hosp. Lond.

FASNACHT, Michael 4 Norbury Grove, Astley bridge, Bolton BL1 8SH Tel: 01204 301484 — MB ChB Manch. 1948. (Manch.) Prev: Roman Catholic Chaplain N. Manch. Gen. Hosp.; Capt. RAMC; Ho. Surg. Roy. Infirm. Manch.

FASOLI, Lorella London House, Mecklenburgh Square, London WC1N 2AB — State Exam 1989 Verona.

FASSER, Ellis 113 Kenilworth Court, Lower Richmond Road, Putney, London SW15 1HA Tel: 020 8788 5265 — MB BCh 1937 Witwatersrand; MD Witwatersrand 1951, MB BCh 1937; DCH Witwatersrand 1948. (Witwatersrand) Prev: Sen. Lect. (Paediat.) H.F. Verwoerd Hosp. Pretoria; Cons. Paediat. S. Afr. Iron & Steel Corpn.; Cons. Paediat. Sch. Cerebral Palsied Pretoria.

FATAH, Mr Muhamad Fadhel Tayib Tel: 0121 627 8306 — MB ChB 1971 Baghdad; FRCS Ed. 1980. (Baghdad Univ. Coll. Med) Cons. Plastic & Reconstruc. Selly Oak & City Hosp. Birm. Socs: Brit. Assn. Plastic Surgs. & Brit. Soc. Surg. Hand.; Brit. Assn. Aesthetic Plastic Surgs.; BMA. Prev: Sen. Regist. (Plastic Surg.) Radcliffe Infirm. Oxf.; Regist. (Plastic Surg.) Wordsley Hosp. Stourbridge; Regist. (Plastic Surg.) N. Staffs. Roy. Infirm. Stoke-on-Trent.

FATEH, Mohammad The Surgery, 2 First Avenue, Dagenham RM10 9AT Tel: 020 8592 4082 Fax: 020 8592 8182 — MB BS 1968 Patna; MB BS 1968 Patna.

FATEMI LANGROUDI, Babak 20 Buckingham Mansions, West End Lane, London NW6 1LR — MB BS 1994 Lond.

FATHEAZAM, Shahin Avenue Surgery, 24 The Avenue, Alwoodley, Leeds LS17 7BE Tel: 0113 267 9703 — MB ChB 1966 Leeds.

FATHEAZAM, Shireen Louise 15 The Firs, Scarcroft, Leeds LS14 3JH Tel: 0113 289 2834 — BChir 1992 Camb.; MB 1992; MRCGP 1997; DRCOG 1996 DFFP 1995. (Camb.)

FATHERS, Edward Elliot Taunton & Somerset Hospital, Musgrove Park, Taunton TA1 5DA Tel: 01823 343822 Email: efathers@hotmail.com; Email: efathers@hotmail.com — BChir 1990 Camb.; MRCP (UK) 1993. (Cambridge 84-87, St. Bartholomews 87-90) Cons. NeUrol. Taunton & Som. Hosp.

FATHERS, Elizabeth Tamsin 22 Ashing Lane, Dunholme, Lincoln LN2 3NN Tel: 01673 860154 — MB BS 1996 Lond.

FATHULLA, Bahira Bashir 18 Albyfield, Bickley, Bromley BR1 2HZ — MB ChB 1966 Baghdad; MRCPI 1988.

FATNANI, Devi T 56C King Henry's Road, London NW3 3RP Tel: 020 7722 2466 — MB BS 1961 Bombay; MRCOG 1967, DObst 1964. GP Camden & Islington Family Plann. Centre; Clin. Asst. (Gyn.) Roy. N. Hosp. Lond. Prev: Regist. P.ss Alexandra Hosp. Harlow.

FATNANI, Sarla Tharumal 4 St Michaels Close, Worcester Park KT4 7NA — LRCP LRCS 1973 Ed.; LRCP LRCS Ed. LRCPS Glas. 1973; DA Eng. 1977.

FATTAH, Aseel Mouhammed Nouri 35 The Park, St Albans AL1 4RU — MB ChB 1971 Baghdad; MRCPath 1982.

FATTAH, Hasan Mahmood 68 Pentland Crescent, Fairholm View, Larkhall ML9 1UR Tel: 020 8658 0429; 39 Kane Place, Eastmains, Stonehouse, Larkhall ML9 3NR Tel: 01698 792158 Email: hasanmf@aol — MB ChB 1971 Mosul; MRCP (UK) 1980; MRCPI 1979; FRCP Glas. 1995. (Mosul, Iraq) Cons. Phys. Gen. Med./Gastroenterol. Caithness Gen. Hosp. Wick Caithness Highland and Hosp.s Trust; Cons. Phys. Socs: BMA. Prev: Locum Cons. Phys. Hairmyres Hosp. E. Kilbride.

FATTAH, Sabry Mohammad Ahmad Abdel Runwell Hospital, The Chase, Wickford SS11 7QE Tel: 01268 366000 Email: sabry.fattah@btinternet.com; 10c Ashingdon Road, Rochford SS4 1NJ Tel: 01702 541584 Email: sabry.fattah@hotmail.com — MB BCh 1975 Cairo; MSC (Neurosc.) Lond. 1994; MRCPsych 1994. (Cairo & Lond.) Cons. (Psychiat.) S.end Community Care NHS Trust. Socs: Roy. Coll. Psychiats.; BMA. Prev: Cons. (Psychiat.) Hartlepool & E. Durh. NHS Trust; Research Fell. (Psychiat.) Univ. Edin.; Regist. (Psychiat.) S.end NHS Trust.

FAUCON, Emmanuelle Marion Hoechstv Roussel, Broadwater Park, Denham, Uxbridge UB9 5HS — MD 1991 Paris.

FAULDING-BIRD, Helen Margaret 37 Argyle Place, Top Flat Left, Edinburgh EH9 1JT — MB ChB 1991 Ed.

FAULDS, Marion Murray Toberargan Surgery, Pitlochry — MB ChB 1967 Glas.; MB ChB St. And. 1967; BSc St. And. 1962; FRCP Ed. 1995; MRCP (UK) 1973; DCH RCPS Glas. 1969. (St. And.) Prev: Research Fell. Dept. Respirat. Dis. City Hosp. Edin.; Med. Regist. Perth Roy. Infirm.

FAULK, Malcolm (retired) 23 St John Street, Winchester SO23 0HF — MB BS 1962 Lond.; MPhil Lond. 1969, BSc 1959; FRCP Lond. 1982, M 1966; FRCPsych 1979. Med. Mem. Ment. Health Revue Tribunal. Prev: Med. Insp. HM Insp.ate of Prisons Lond.

FAULKES, Cyril Norman (retired) Health Centre, Nevells Road, Letchworth SG6 4TR Tel: 01462 684334 Fax: 01462 484876 — MB ChB 1954 Birm. Prev: Ho. Off. (Paediat. & O & G) Dudley Rd. Hosp. Birm.

FAULKNER, Amanda Jayne 105 Ffordd Penrhwylfa, Prestatyn LL19 8BS — MB BCh 1993 Wales.

FAULKNER, Anne-Marie 13 Ryecroft Close, Woodley, Reading RG5 3BP — MB BS 1997 Lond.

FAULKNER, Derek (retired) 54 Russell Grove, Westbury Park, Bristol BS6 7UF Tel: 0117 924 6717 — MB ChB 1957 Bristol; FFA RCS Eng. 1963; DA Eng. 1960. Prev: Cons. Anaesth. United Bristol Hosp.s.

FAULKNER, Edith Becket House, Pilgrims Way, Guildford GU4 8AB Tel: 01483 504827 — MB ChB 1949 Leeds. (Leeds)

FAULKNER, Gavin Stuart Tong Fold Health Centre, Hilton St., Bolton BL2 6DY Tel: 01204 521574 Fax: 01204 371571; 4 Ravenswood Drive, Heaton, Bolton BL1 5AJ — BM BS 1983 Nottm.; BMedSci Nottm. 1981; MRCGP 1987; DRCOG 1986.

FAULKNER, Geoffrey Edward (retired) 58 Morningside Road, Aberdeen AB10 7NT — MB ChB 1947 Birm.; MRCS Eng. LRCP Lond. 1947; MRCPsych 1971; DPM Eng. 1954. Prev: Cons. Psychiat. & Med. Admin. Kingseat Hosp. Newmachar.

FAULKNER, Joan Mary (retired) 12 Rawlinson Road, Oxford OX2 6UE Tel: 01865 58887 Fax: 01865 558817 — MB BS 1937 Lond.; MRCP Lond. 1969; FFCM 1975; DPH Eng. 1941. Prev: PMO Med. Research Counc.

FAULKNER, Margaret Ada Lane 3 Beverley Close, Barnes, London SW13 0EH — MB BChir 1963 Camb.; MPhil Lond. 1969; MA, MB Camb. 1963, BChir 1962; MRCS Eng. LRCP Lond. 1962. (St. Mary's) Prev: Cons. Child Psychiat. Qu. Mary's Hosp. Childr. Carshalton.

FAULKNER, Michael Huntley The Health Centre, North Road, Stokesley, Middlesbrough TS9 5DY Tel: 01642 710748 Fax: 01642 713037; 40 Riverslea, Stokesley, Middlesbrough TS9 5DE Tel: 01642 710815 — MB BS 1970 Lond.; BSc Lond. 1967; MRCS Eng. LRCP Lond. 1970; MRCGP 1974. (Guy's)

FAULKNER, Michele Anne The Health Centre, Ashton Road W., Failsworth, Oldham Tel: 0161 682 6297 — MB BS Newc. 1975.

FAULKNER, Paul c/o Medical Department, Watch Tower, The Ridgeway, London NW7 1RN — MB BS 1973 Lond. (St. Mary's)

FAULKNER, Paul Raymond 10 Casaeldona Park, Belfast BT6 9RB — MB BCh 1998 Belf.; MB BCh Belf 1998.

FAULKNER, Peter Owen Brecon Medical Group Practice, Ty Henry Vaughan, Bridge Street, Brecon LD3 8AH Tel: 01874 622121 Fax: 01874 623742; Stoneleigh, Cradoc, Brecon LD3 9PD — MB BCh 1973 Wales; MRCGP 1977; DCH RCP Lond. 1990; DCCH RCP Ed. 1990; DRCOG 1977. Prev: Trainee GP Bridgend VTS.

FAULKNER, Peter Patrick John Fieldhead Surgery, Fieldhead, Leymoor Road, Golcar, Huddersfield HD7 4QQ Tel: 01484 654504 Fax: 01484 460296; Stranraer House, 40 Longwood Gate, Longwood, Huddersfield HD3 4UP Tel: 01484 658978 Email: ppjf@ppjf.freeserve.co.uk — MB ChB 1980 Manch.; BSc St. And. 1977.

FAULKNER, Rebecca Louise c/o Cei Newydd, Talsarnau LL47 6YW Tel: 01766 770493; Flat 3, 21 Ladybridge Road, Cheadle Hulme, Cheadle SK8 5BL Tel: 0161 488 4836 Email: rebecca@cybase.co.uk — MB ChB 1991 Manch.; MB ChB (Hons.) Manch. 1991; FRCS Ed. 1996; MRCOG 1999. (Manch.) Specialist Regist. (O & G) N. W. Region.

FAULKNER, Ronald Ennis 16 Watton Road, Knebworth SG3 6AH Tel: 01438 237747 Email: ronald.faulkner@dtn.ntl.com — MB BS 1960 Lond.; MRCS Eng. LRCP Lond. 1960; DCH Eng. 1963; DObst RCOG 1962. (King's Coll. Hosp.) Prev: Princip. GP Stevenage.

FAULKS, Gerald Great Sutton Medical Centre, Old Chester Road, Great Sutton, Ellesmere Port CH66 3PB Tel: 0151 339 2424 Fax: 0151 339 9225; Bank Farm House, Sealand Road, Chester CH1 6BS Tel: 01244 390205 — MB ChB 1975 Liverp.

FAULL, Christina Mary 48 First Avenue, Selly Oak, Birmingham B29 7NS — MD 1993 Newc.; MB BS 1985, BMedSci (Hons.) 1982; MRCP (UK) 1988. Med. Dir. St. Mary's Hospice Birm. Prev: Sen.

Regist. (Palliat. Med.) Leics. Hospice; Research Fell. Univ. Newc.; SHO (Med.) Preston N. Shields.

FAUNCH, Edward Thomas (retired) Casares, Pollardrow Avenue, Bracknell RG42 1PS Tel: 01344 422360 — MB ChB 1952 Ed.

FAURE-WALKER, Sally Anne Vivienne Woodhill, Danbury, Chelmsford CM3 4AN Tel: 01245 222013 Fax: 01245 225354 — MB BChir 1976 Camb.; MB Camb. 1976, BChir 1975. (Univ. Coll. Hosp.)

FAUST, Guy Eric Samuel 22 Feilden Gr, Headington, Oxford OX3 0DU — BM BS 1997 Nottm.

FAUST, Saul Nicholas Academic Department of Paediatrics, Imperial College at St Mary's, Paddington, London W2 1PG Tel: 020 7886 6377 Fax: 020 7886 6284 Email: s.faust@ic.ac.uk; 22B Woodchurch Road, London NW6 3PN Email: s.faust@ic.ac.uk — MB BS 1993 Lond.; MA Camb. 1995, BA 1990; MRCP (UK) 1996. (Univ. Camb. & Univ. Coll. Lond.) Paediatric Specialist Regist., TheWluttington hos Nig. Prev: BPI Fell. St. Mary's Hosp. Lond.; SHO (Neonat. Med.) Hammersmith Hosp. Lond.; SHO (Paediat. Med.) Gt. Ormond St. Hosp. Childr. Lond.

FAUTLEY, Mandy Cornerways Medical Centre, Parkers Close, Gorley Road, Poulner, Ringwood BH24 1SD Tel: 01425 476688 Fax: 01425 470030; 12 Forestlake Av., Hightown, Ringwood BH24 1QU — MB ChB 1986 Liverp.; DRCOG 1988; MRCGP 1990. Prev: Trainee GP/SHO (O & G, Paediat. & Orthop.) Blandford Forum.

FAUVEL, Nicholas John 37 Yeldham Road, London W6 8JF Tel: 020 8748 3442 — MB BS 1981 Newc.; FRCA 1988. Cons. Magill Dept. Anaesth. Chelsea & W.m. Hosp. Lond. Prev: SIMS Fell. Magill Dept. Anaesth. Char. Cross & W.m. Med. Sch. Lond.; Fell. (Anaesth.) McGill Univ. Montreal, Canada; Regist. (Anaesth.) W.m. Hosp. Lond.

FAUX, Dominic Hilary Richard Albion House Suegery, Albion Street, Brierley Hill DY5 3EE Tel: 01384 70220 Fax: 01384 78284; 12 Red Hill, Stourbridge DY8 1ND Tel: 01384 376463 Email: 101334.3564@compuserve.com — MB ChB 1975 Birm.; FRCGP 1995; MMedSc Birm. 1994; MRCGP 1980; DRCOG 1980. (Birmingham) GP Brierley Hill; Course Organiser Dudley & Stourbridge GP VTS; Sen. Lect. (Med. Educat. & Primary Care) Univ. Wolverhampton; Hon. Treas. Midl Fac. Roy. Coll. GPs. Socs: Counc. RCGP; Finance Comm. Roy. Coll. GPs.

FAUX, Mr James Christopher 7 Moor Park Avenue, Preston PR1 6AS Tel: 01772 204710 Fax: 01772 558705; The Old Rectory, Whittington, Carnforth LA6 2NU Tel: 0152 42 72570 — MRCS Eng. LRCP Lond. 1968; FRCS Glas. 1973; FRCS 1997 England. (Liverpool) Cons. Orthop. Surg. Wrightington Hosp. Centre for Hip Surg. Appley Bridge Wigan; Mem. Liverp. Orthop. Circle. Socs: Fell. BOA; Chairm. Sir John Charnley Trust; Charnley Low Friction Soc. (Europ. Sec.). Prev: Sen. Regist. (Orthop.) Manch. AHA (T); Regist. (Orthop.) Wrightington Hosp. Wigan; Regist. Rotat. (Orthop. & Surg.) Whiston & St. Helens Hosp. Gp.

FAUX, James William Cardew Farm, Cardew, Dalston, Carlisle CA5 7JQ — MB ChB 1992 Birm.; BSc Applied Physics UMIST 1987. SHO (Gen. Surg.) Soton. Gen. Hosp. Prev: SHO (Gen. Surg.) Torbay; SHO (Neurosurg.) Radcliffe Inf. Oxf.; SHO (A & E & Trauma) John Radcliffe Hosp. Oxf.

FAUX, Patricia Anne Lyon Fylde Coast Hospital, St Walburga's Road, Blackpool Tel: 01253 394188; The Old Rectory, Whittington, Carnforth LA6 2NU Tel: 01524 272570 — MB ChB Liverp. 1967; DMRD Liverp. 1970. (Liverp.) Assoc. Specialist Radiol. Vict. Hosp. Blackpool. Prev: Clin. Asst. (Radiol.) Chesh. AHA & Clwyd S. Health Dist.; Sen. Regist. (Radiol.) Chester Hosp. Gp. & Whiston Hosp. Prescot.

FAVILL, Edward James 107 High Park Crescent, Sedgley, Dudley DY3 1QS — MB ChB 1996 Liverp.

FAVRE, Adrian 6 Harrow Road, Carshalton SM5 3QQ — MB BS 1998 Lond.; MB BS Lond 1998.

FAWCETT, Adrian 215 Tudor Drive, Kingston upon Thames KT2 5NU — MB BS 1989 Lond.; FRCS (Eng.) 1993. (Char. Cross & Westm.)

FAWCETT, Mr Alan Nigel (retired) Oakdene, 770 Wollaton Road, Wollaton Vill., Nottingham NG8 2AP Tel: 0115 928 3923 Fax: 0115 928 3923 — MB Camb. 1962, BChir 1961; MChir Camb. 1972; FRCS Eng. 1966. Cons. Surg. Nottm. Univ. Hosp. & Ilkeston & Heanor Hosps. Prev: Sen. Regist. Sheff. Roy. Infirm.

FAWCETT, Ann Isabel (retired) The Old Farmhouse, Easton-on-The-Hill, Stamford PE9 3LN Tel: 01780 762045 — MB ChB 1958 Birm.; FRCP Lond. 1987; MRCP (UK) 1978; Dip Ven Soc. Apoth. Lond. 1976. Prev: Cons. Genitourin. Med. P'boro. Dist. Hosp.

FAWCETT, Beatrice Kynaston (retired) Winterdown, Portsmouth Road, Esher KT10 9JN Tel: 01372 62341 — MRCS Eng. LRCP Lond. 1954.

FAWCETT, Caroline Elizabeth Portugal Place Health Centre, Portugal Place, Wallsend NE28 6RZ; 116 Moorside North, Fenham, Newcastle upon Tyne NE4 9DX Tel: 0191 273 5622 — BM BS 1986 Nottm.; MRCGP 1990; DRCOG 1990.

FAWCETT, Caroline Margaret 2 Bill Rickaby Drive, Newmarket CB8 0HQ — MB BS 1998 Lond.; MB BS Lond 1998.

FAWCETT, Christopher James The Dr S Fawcett, Hawicer & Alonso Surgery, 2 The Slieve, Handsworth Wood, Birmingham B20 2NR; 18 Somerville Drive, Sutton Coldfield B73 6JB Tel: 0121 354 2567 Fax: 0121 554 6830 — MB ChB 1980 Birm.; BSc (Hons.) Lanchester Polytech. 1973; MRCGP 1984; DRCOG 1984; DCH RCP Lond. 1983; AFOM 1998.

FAWCETT, Mr Derek Peter Department of Urology, Battle Hospital, Reading RG30 1AG Tel: 0118 970 1728 Email: djfawcett@msn.com — MB BS 1972 Lond.; FRCS Eng. 1976. Cons. Urol. Battle Hosp. Reading. Socs: Fell. Europ. Bd. Urol. Prev: Lect. & Sen. Regist. (Urol. & Transpl.) Char Cross Hosp. Lond.; Sen. Regist. (Urol.) Marsden Hosp. Lond.; Regist. (Surg.) St. Thos. Hosp. Lond.

FAWCETT, Gerald Edmond The Surgery, 113 Station Road, Ellesmere Port, South Wirral CH65 4BW Tel: 0151 339 3063; 511 Chester Road, Great Sutton, South Wirral CH66 3PX Tel: 0151 339 3063 — MB ChB 1960 Liverp. (Liverp.) Prev: Capt. RAMC (RAOR).

FAWCETT, Gillian Margaret 6 South Glebe, Lockington, Driffield YO25 9ST Tel: 01430 810200 — MB ChB 1968 Liverp.; FRCOG 1991, M 1974; DObst 1970. (Liverp.) Cons. O & G E. Yorks. HA.

FAWCETT, Helen Fiona Moorhill, 4 Highlands Road, Heath End, Farnham GU9 0LX — MB BS 1985 Lond.; DRCOG 1988.

FAWCETT, Hilary Ann Silchester Farm, Silchester, Reading RG7 2PS — MB BS 1973 Lond.; FRCP Lond. 1995; MRCP (UK) 1977. Cons. Dermat. Basingstoke Dist. Hosp. Socs: Roy. Soc. Med.; Brit. Assn. of Dermatol.s; Brit. Soc. for Paediatric Dermat. Prev: Sen. Regist. (Dermat.) Slade Hosp. Oxf.; Sen. Regist. St. John's Hosp. for Dis. of the Skin Lond.; Regist. (Dermat.) St. Geo. Hosp. Lond.

FAWCETT, Ian William Yeovil District Hospital, Higher Kingston, Yeovil BA21 4AT Tel: 01935 707470 — MB BChir 1968 Camb.; MA, MB Camb. 1968, BChir 1967; FRCP Lond. 1986; MRCP (UK) 1970. (Camb. & St. Thos.) Cons. Phys. Yeovil Dist. Hosp. Prev: Med. Regist. St. Thos. Hosp. Lond.; Lect. Clin. Immunol. Cardiothoracic Inst. Lond.; Sen. Med. Regist. St. Bart. Hosp. Lond.

FAWCETT, Mr Ivan Maxwell Herts and Essex Hospital, Haymeads Lane, Bishop's Stortford CM23 5JH Tel: 01279 444455 Email: ivan.fawcelt@btopenworld.com; Birchanger Hall, Birchanger, Bishop's Stortford CM23 5QH Tel: 01279 812260 Fax: 01279 812260 Email: ivan.fawcett@btinternet.com — MB BS 1981 Newc.; FRCS Glas. 1986; FRCOphth. 1989. Cons. Ophth. P.ss Alexandra Hosp. Trust. Socs: Fell. Roy. Soc. Med. Prev: Fell. (Retina Surg.) St. Paul's Eye Hosp. Liverp.; Sen. Regist. (Ophth.) Tennent Inst. of Ophth.

FAWCETT, Mr Jonathan 9 Mileway Gardens, Headington, Oxford OX3 7XH — MB BS 1983 Newc.; DPhil Oxf. 1994; FRCS Eng. 1988. Clin. Lect. & Sen. Regist. (Surg.) John Radcliffe Hosp. Oxf. Prev: Regist. (Surg.) Newc.

FAWCETT, Kenneth John Rhodes Hilltop, East Stour, Gillingham SP8 5JS Tel: 01634 838651 — MB ChB 1952 Bristol; BSc Lond. 1945. (Bristol) Prev: Med. Asst. A & E Dept. Salisbury Gen. Infirm.; Ho. Phys. Bristol Roy. Infirm.; Med. Off. Tristan da Cunha.

FAWCETT, Mark 79 Union Gr, Aberdeen AB10 6SJ — MB ChB 1997 Glas.

FAWCETT, Peter Godfrey Shirley Lodge, 12 Primrose Bank Road, Edinburgh EH5 3JH Tel: 0131 552 5067 — MB BS 1952 Durh.; FRCPsych 1980, M 1972; DPM Eng. 1958. (Durh.) Prev: Cons. Psychiat. Herdmanflat Hosp. Haddington & Roy. Infirm. Edin.; Cons. Psychiat. St. Mary's Hosp. Stannington & Angus Area; Lect. (Psychol. Med.) Univ. Edin.

FAWCETT, Peter Robert William Department of Clinical Neurophysiology, Regional Neurosciences Centre, Newcastle General Hospital, Westgate Road, Newcastle upon Tyne NE4 6BE Tel: 0191

273 8811 Fax: 0191 226 0775 Email: p.r.w.fawcett@ncl.ac.uk; 20 Graham Park Road, Gosforth, Newcastle upon Tyne NE3 4BH — MB BS 1971 Newc.; BSc Newc. 1967; FRCP Lond. 1987; MRCP (UK) 1974. (Newc. u. Tyne) Cons. Clin. Neurophys. Newc. Gen. Hosp. & Roy. Vict. Infirm. Newc. Socs: (Past Pres.) Assn. Brit. Clin. Neurophysiol.; Brit. Soc. Clin. Neurophysiol.; Assn. Brit. Neurols. Prev: Sen. Regist. Neurol. (Clin. & Applied Neurophysiol.) Newc. Gen. Hosp.

FAWCETT, Robert Lindsay Centre for Occupational Health, Antrim Hospital, 45 Bush Road, Antrim BT41 2RL Tel: 01849 424402; Site 15, Burandell Manor, Lisburn BT28 3AX Tel: 01846 604577 — MB BCh BAO 1979 Belf.; MRCGP 1988; MICGP 1988. Dir. N. Occupat. Health Serv. Antrim Hosp. Socs: Soc. Occupat. Med. & Mem. Medico-Legal Soc. N. Irel.; Assn. Police Surg.

FAWCETT, Stephen 43 North Street, Peterborough PE8 4AL — MB BS 1986 Newc.

FAWCETT, Venetia Anne Theresa 47 Amersham Hill Drive, High Wycombe HP13 6QX Tel: 01494 446387 — MB ChB 1981 Manch.; BSc St. And. 1978; MRCGP 1988; DRCOG 1986. Clin. Asst. (A & E) Wexham Pk. Hosp. Berks.

FAWCETT, William John Moorhill, 4 Highlands Road, Heath End, Farnham GU9 0LX — MB BS 1985 Lond.; FRCA 1989. Cons. Anaesth. Roy. Surrey Co. & St Lukes Hosp. Guildford Surrey. Socs: Ex-Pres. F. Boott Soc.; Hon. Sec. S.ern Soc. Anaesh. Prev: Lect. (Anaesth.) St. Geo. Hosp. Med. Sch. Lond.; Sen. Regist. (Anaesth.) W.m. Hosp. Lond.; Sen. Regist. & Regist. (Anaesth.) St. Geo. Hosp. Lond.

FAWCITT, Richard Andrew Beaulieu, 10 Ladythorn Crescent, Bramhall, Stockport SK7 2HA Tel: 0161 224 0006 — MB ChB 1967 Ed.; FRCR 1975; DMRD Eng. 1972. Cons. Radiol. Manch. Roy. Infirm. Prev: Sen. Lect. Dept. Diag. Radiol. Manch. Univ.

FAWDRY, Alison Jane 93 Tower Drive, Neath Hill, Milton Keynes MK14 6JX Tel: 01908 665806; 21 Temple Fortune Hill, Hampstead Garden Suburb, London NW11 7XL Tel: 020 8455 1837 — MB BS 1994 Lond.; BSc Sociol. & Basic Med. Scis. Lond. 1991. (St. Mary's Hosp. Med. Sch. Lond.) SHO (A & E) Univ. Coll. Hosp. Lond. Prev: SHO (O & G) Walsgrave Hosp. Coventry; Ho. Off. (Surg.) Wexham Pk. Hosp. Slough; Ho. Phys. High Wycombe.

FAWDRY, Mr Rupert David Shirehampton Milton Keynes General Hospital, Standing Way, Eaglestone, Milton Keynes MK6 5LD Tel: 01908 660033 Fax: 01908 243172; 41 St. Maryl Way, Leighton Buzzard LU7 2RX Tel: 01525 370137 Email: rupert@fawdry.demon.co.uk — MB BS 1964 Lond.; FRCS Ed. 1976; LMCC Canada 1968; FRCOG 1989, M 1977; DObst RCOG 1966. (Lond. Hosp.) Cons. O & G Milton Keynes HA; Hon. Sen. Lect. Inst. Child Health Univ. Lond. Socs: (Hon. Treas.) Action for Safe Motherhood (UK) Soc.; Christian Med. Fell.sh.; Brit. Matern. & Fetal Med. Soc. Prev: Sen. Regist. Yorks. Regional Train. Scheme; Specialist (O & G) The Christian Hosp. Isfahan Iran.

FAWIBE, Oladapo Omotayo 13 Niagara Court, Canada Est., Moodkee St., Rotherhithe, London SE16 7BA Tel: 020 7237 9284 — MB BS 1979 Nigeria; MRCP (UK) 1989; LRCP 1988.

***FAWKE, Joseph Anthony** 44 Robin Hood Lane, Winnersh, Wokingham RG41 5NQ — MB ChB 1995 Birm.

FAWKNER, Kirsten Jane The Hadleigh Practice, 20 Kirkway, Broadstone, Poole BH18 8EE — BM 1989 Soton.; MRCGP 1994; DRCOG 1994; DCH RCP Lond. 1992.

FAWKNER-CORBETT, David Plowden, Hawkins Lane, Rainon, Macclesfield SK10 5TL; Plowden, Hawkins Lane, Rainow, Macclesfield SK10 5TL — MB BS 1970 Lond.; BSc Lond. 1967, MB BS 1970; MRCGP 1974; DObst RCOG 1973. (St. Thos.) Prev: Gen. Pract. Trainee Roy. Berks. Hosp. Reading; Ho. Phys. St. Thos. Hosp. Lond.; Ho. Surg. St. Helier Hosp. Carshalton.

FAWKNER-CORBETT, Robin 18 High Street, Cranleigh GU6 8AE; 1 Tilehurst, Cranleigh GU6 8NR Tel: 01483 271344 Fax: 01483 275755 — MB BS 1971 Lond.; MRCGP 1976; DObst Auckland 1974; Cert. JCC Lond. 1976. (St. Thos.) Liveryman Soc. Apoth. Lond. Socs: (Counc.) Med. Off. Schs. Assn. (Ex-Pres.); Fell. Roy. Soc. Med. Prev: SHO Profess. Med. Unit Roy. S. Hants. Hosp. Soton.; SHO Auckland Hosp. Bd., NZ; Ho. Phys. (Med.) St. Thos. Hosp. Lond.

FAWTHROP, Fiona Wendy Rotherham DGH, Moorgate, Rotherham S60 3UD Tel: 01709 304275 — MB ChB 1985 Bristol; PhD Sheff. 1992; FRCP 2001; MRCP (UK) 1988. Cons. Rheum. Rotherham. Prev: Sen. Regist. (Rheum.) Nottm.

FAWZI, Hani Wahib 2 Coulton Drive, East Boldon NE36 0SZ Tel: 0191 536 1762 Fax: 0191 536 1762 Email: h.w.fawzi@ncl.ac.uk — MB BS 1986 Khartoum; MRCOG 1994; MPH Leeds 1990. (Khartoum Univ., Sudan) Sen. Regist. (O & G) (s/i Gyn. Oncol.) P.ss Anne Hosp. Soton. Socs: Brit. Soc. Colpos. & Cerv. Path.; Brit. Soc. Gyn. Endoscopy. Prev: Specialist Regist. (O & G) Sunderland Roy. Hosp; Regist. (Gyn. Oncol.) Qu. Eliz. Hosp. Gateshead.

FAWZI, Mr Hussein, Hussein Directorate of Ophthalmology, Stobhill NHS Trust, 133 Balornock Road, Glasgow G21 3UW Tel: 0141 201 3479 Fax: 0141 201 3887; 278 Nithsdale Road, Glasgow G41 5LP Tel: 0141 427 6314 — MB ChB 1966 Alexandria; FRCS Ed. 1976; FRCOphth 1988. (Alexandria Med. Coll.) Cons. Surg. Ophth. Stobhill NHS Trust; Hon. Sen. Clin. Lect. Univ. Glas. Socs: Scott. Ophth. Club.

FAWZI, Mohammed Faisal Mohammed North Glen Medical Practice, 1 Huntsmans Court, Glenrothes KY7 6SX Tel: 01592 620062 Fax: 01592 620465; Rosehill House, 14 Formonthills Lane, Glenrothes KY6 3EL Tel: 01892 745270 — MB ChB 1971 Alexandria; DAvMed FOM RCP Lond. 1976.

FAY, Anne Catherine Mary Immunology Department, Royal Victoria Infirmary, Queen Victoria Road, Newcastle upon Tyne NE1 4LP Tel: 0191 282 5517 Fax: 0191 227 5071 — MD 1987 Belf.; MB BCh BAO 1977; MRCPath 1984. Cons. Immunol. Newc. HA. Prev: Sen. Lect. & Cons. Immunol. The Qu. Univ. Belf.

FAY, Daniel Joseph Luton & Dunstable Hospital NHS Trust, Lewsey Road, Luton LU4 0DZ — MB BS 1996 Lond.

FAY, Elspeth Daphne June Gorland, Old Scapa Road, Kirkwall KW15 1BB — MB ChB 1985 Manch.; BSc (1st cl. Hons.) St. And. 1982. Prev: SHO (Gen. Med.) Tameside Gen. Hosp.; Ho. Phys. Tameside Gen. Hosp.; Ho. Surg. Pk. Hosp. Trafford.

FAY, Hugh Thomas (retired) 2 Cavendish Road, Heaton Mersey, Stockport SK4 3DW Tel: 0161 432 4837 — MB ChB 1953 Manch.; BSc Manch. 1947; MRCS Eng. LRCP Lond. 1953; MRCGP 1967; DObst RCOG 1955. Prev: GP Stockport.

FAY, Mary Patricia 35 Longdean Park, Hemel Hempstead HP3 8BZ — MB ChB 1962 Birm.

FAY, Matthew Robert Westcliffe Medical Centre, Westcliffe Rd, Shipley BD18 3EE Tel: 01274 580816 — MB ChB 1992 Leeds.

FAY, Peter John Skerryvore Practice, Health Centre, New Scapa Road, Kirkwall KW15 1BQ Tel: 01856 885440 Fax: 01856 870043; Gorland, Old Scapa Road, Kirkwall KW15 1BB Tel: 01856 875387 Email: faypj@globalnet.co.uk — MB ChB 1982 Manch.; BSc St. And. 1979; DCH RCPS Glas. 1988; DRCOG 1987; Cert. Family Plann. JCC 1987. Prev: SHO (Paediat. & Obst.) St. Mary's Hosp. Manch.; Trainee GP Annan.

FAY, Robert Andrew (retired) Yarley Cottage, Yarley, Wells BA5 1PA Tel: 01749 670814 — MB BS 1968 Lond.; MRCS Eng. LRCP Lond. 1968; MLCOM 1979; DObst RCOG 1971. Prev: GP Wells, Som. & Pewsey, Wilts.

FAYAZ, Mohammed GLan Clwyd Hospital, Rhuddlan Road, Bodelwyddan, Rhyl LL18 5UJ — MB BS 1970 Mysore.

FAYED, Mr Galaa Esmat Abdel Rahman 4 Eastridge Croft, Lichfield WS14 0LN — MB ChB 1976 Alexandria; FRCS Ed. 1989.

FAYERS, Katherine Eugune Boundary Cottage, Coxford Down, Micheldever, Winchester SO21 3BD — MB BS 1996 Lond.

FAYEYE, Michael Olabode 12 Homewood Drive, Hensingham, Whitehaven CA28 8JX Tel: 01946 3181 — MB BS 1978 Ibadan; MRCOG 1987.

FAYLE, Robert John Scarffe Nobles Hospital, Westmoreland Rd, Douglas IM1 4QA Tel: 01624 642125 Fax: 01624 642556 Email: robert.fayle@nobles.dhss.gov.im; 615 Gosford Place, Edinburgh EH6 4BJ Tel: 0131 530 1185 — BM BS 1981 Nottm.; BMedSci (Hon.) Nottm. 1979; FRCOG 2001; MObstG Liverp. 1990; MRCOG 1987. Cons. O & G Noble's Hosp. Douglas I. of Man. Prev: Sen. Regist. (O & G) Mersey RHA.

FAYYAZ, Imran 53 Sunnycroft Road, Hounslow TW3 4DS — MB BS 1987 Punjab; MRCP (UK) 1994.

FAZA, Hany Najib c/o Dr Lee, Flat 66 Thorne House, 279 Wilmslow Road, Manchester M14 6DW — MB ChB 1997 Manch.

FAZA, Miya Khan The Health Centre, Lulworth, Ashurst, Skelmersdale WN8 6TF Tel: 01695 32468; 7 Manor Grove,

Skelmersdale WN8 8NE — MB BS 1967 Nagpur. (Nagpur Med. Coll.)

FAZACKERLEY, Erica Janice Department of Anaesthesia, Warrington NHS Trust, Lovely Lane, Warrington WA5 Tel: 01925 635911; 1 Mill Bank, Lymm WA13 9DG — MB ChB 1979 Liverp.; FFA RCS Eng. 1983. Cons Anaesth. Warrington Hosp. NHS Trust. Prev: Cons. Anaesth. Wigan & Leigh NHS Trust; Sen. Regist. (Anaesth.) NW RHA; Ancienne Attachée Hôpital Bichat, Paris 1992.

FAZAKERLEY, Nicholas William Old Rectory, Oborne, Sherborne DT9 4LA — MB BCh BAO 1990 Belf.

FAZAL, Anjum Kidderminster General Hospital, Bewdley Road, Kidderminster DY11 6RJ — MRCS Eng. LRCP Lond. 1978.

***FAZEL, Mina Susan** Warneford Hospital, Oxford OX3 7JX — BM BCh Oxf. 1996.

FAZEL, Seena Babak University Department of Psychiatry, Warneford Hospital, Roosevelt Drive, Oxford OX3 7JX Tel: 01865 778911 Email: seena.fazel@psych.ox.ac.uk — MB ChB 1993 Ed.; BSc (Hons.) Ed. 1990. (Ed.) Research Fell., Hon. Specialist Regist. Socs: MRCPsych.

FAZLANI, Nadim Akhtar Edge Hill Health Centre, Crosfield Road, Liverpool L7 5QL Tel: 0151 260 2777; 36 Ewden Close, Childwall, Liverpool L16 5HF Tel: 0151 738 0991 Email: nadm@fazlani.demon.co.uk — MB BS 1981 Karachi; MRCPI 1986; MRCS Eng. LRCP Lond. 1984; MRCGP 1993; DMRT Liverp. 1990; DGM RCP Lond. 1986. Prev: Regist. (Oncol.) Mersey Centre for Oncol.; Regist. (Med.) York Dist. Hosp.; SHO (Med.) N. Manch. Gen. Hosp.

FAZLUDDIN, Chinnameeran Rowther Mohammad (retired) 21 Celandine Close, Marton, Middlesbrough TS7 8RX Tel: 01642 314184 — MB BS Kerala 1958; Dip. Ven. Soc. Apoth. Lond. 1976; DTM & H Eng. 1969. Prev: Cons. (Venereol.) Middlesbrough Gen. Hosp. & Gen. Hosp. Hartlepool.

FAZZI, Mr Umberto Giuseppe Western Infirmary, Dumbarton Road, Glasgow G11 6NT; 84 Mansionhouse Gardens, Langside, Glasgow G41 3DP — MB ChB 1985 Glas.; FRCS Ed. 1989; FRCS (Orth.) 1996. Cons. Orthop. Surg. W. Glas. Hosps. Univ. NHS Trust Glas.

FEAKINS, Martin John 161 Rayleigh Road, Hutton, Brentwood CM13 1LX; The Royal London Hospital, St Clement's, 2A Bow Road, London E3 4LL Tel: 020 7377 7960 — MB BCh BAO Dub. 1992; MRCPsych 1997. (Trinity College Dublin) Specialist Regist. Psychiat. Lond. Socs: MRC Psych 1997.

FEAKS, Richard Jeffrey 6 Greenfields Crescent, Wesham, Preston PR4 3EH — MB ChB 1986 Ed.; Dip. Palliat. Med. 1998; MRCGP 1994; DA (UK) 1994. Clin. Asst. Trinity Hosp. in the Fylde. Prev: Trainee GP Eccleston Health Centre; SHO (Anaesth.) Vict. Hosp. Blackpool.

FEALEY, Matthew John Lloyd Polbreen House, Polbreen Lane, St Agnes TR5 0UN — MB ChB 1998 Sheff.; MB ChB Sheff 1998.

FEAR, Carol Rosemary North Warwickshire NHS Trust, 5-7 Pool Bank St., Nuneaton CV11 5DB Tel: 01203 351333; 99 Pallett Drive, Nuneaton CV11 6JT — MB BS 1979 Lond.; MA Camb. 1978. Princip. Clin. Med. Off. N. Warks. NHS Trust Nuneaton.

FEAR, Christopher Frank Wotton Lawn Hospital, Horton Road, Gloucester GL1 3PX Tel: 01452 891500 Fax: 01452 891501 — MB ChB 1986 Liverp.; MD Liverp. 1995; MRCPsych 1992. Cons. Gen. Adult. Psychiat. Forest of Dean; Hon. Research Fell. Univ. Wales Coll. Med.; Hon. Clin. Teach. Univ. Bristol. Socs: Brit. Assn. Psychopharmacol.; Roy. Coll. Psychiat. Prev: Sen. Regist. Rotat. W. Midl.; Clin. Research Assoc. & Hon. Sen. Regist. N. Wales Hosp.; Regist. (Psychiat.) N. Wales Train. Scheme.

FEAR, Jonathan David Brae Fell, 13 Kings Road, Leeds LS16 9JN — MB ChB 1978 Leeds.

FEAR, Ruth Caroline 71 St Helen's Road, Solihull B91 2DB Tel: 0121 705 5146 — MB BChir 1975 Camb.; MB Chir Camb. 1975; MA Camb. 1976; MFFP 1992; MRCGP 1979; DRCOG 1977. (Camb. & St. Bart.) SCMO (Family Plann.) Solihull Healthcare; Clin. Asst. Menopause Clinic Solihull Hosp. Socs: Assn. Inst. Psychosexual Med.; BMA. Prev: Trainee GP Lond. (Hammersmith Hosp.) VTS; Ho. Surg. St. Bart. Hosp. Lond.; Ho. Phys. Hackney Hosp.

FEARBY, Simon 16 Clifton Gardens, Gateshead NE9 5DL — MB BS 1994 Lond. (United Med. & Dent. Sch.)

FEARFIELD, Louise Anne Holmire House, High lorton, Cockermouth CA13 9TX — MB BS 1992 Lond.; BA Oxf. 1989. Prev: Ho. Surg. (Urol.) Kingston Hosp.; Ho. Off. (Rheum. & Endocrinol.) St. Peter's Hosp. Chertsey.

FEARN, Mr Charles Barry D'Arcy, TD Colwell House, Lewes Road, Haywards Heath RH17 7TB Tel: 01444 454608 Fax: 01444 454608; 40 Wilbury Road, Hove BN3 3JP Tel: 01273 206206 Fax: 01273 721411 — MB Camb. 1959, BChir 1958; MA Camb. 1964, BA 1955; FRCS Ed. 1967; FRCS Eng. 1967. (Camb. & St. Mary's) Cons. Surg. Orthop. Sussex Nuffield Hosp. Brighton & Ashdown Hosp. Haywards Heath; Hon. Cons. Surg. Orthop. Roy. Sussex Co. Hosp. & P.ss Roy. Hosp. Haywards Heath; Dir. Sussex Osteoporosis Clinic Hove; Sen. Tutor SE. Thames Specialist Regist. Traing. Progr. for Orthop.; Clin.Teach. Guy's Kings St Thomas Med. Sch. 1999-2000. Socs: Girdlestone Orthop. Soc.; Assn. Med. Educat. Europ.; Brit. Orthop. Assn. Prev: Sen. Lect. & Hon. Cons. Orthop. Surg. Fac. Med. Univ. & Civil Hosp. Khartoum, Sudan; Capt. RAMC, RMO 1st Bn. Roy. Irish Fusiliers; Sen. Regist. Nuffield Orthop. Centre & Accid. Serv. Radcliffe Infirm. Oxf.

FEARN, Hazel Mary (retired) 5 The Paddock, Lound, Retford DN22 8RR Tel: 01777 817868 — MB ChB 1956 Manch.; MFCM 1982; DCH Eng. 1958. Prev: Cons. Pub. Health Med. Centr. Nottm. HA.

FEARN, Sarah Jane 5 Beechtree Avenue, Marlow SL7 3NH — MB ChB 1992 Birm.

FEARN, Shirley Jane Stepping Hill Hospital, Poplar Grove, Stockport SK2 7JE — MB ChB 1991 Birm.; FRCS Eng. 1995. Specialist Regist. (Gen. Surg.) Stepping Hill Hosp. Stockport. Socs: Surg. Research Soc. Prev: Research Fell. Hon. Clin. Lect. Brit. Heart Foundat. Univ. Hosp. S Manch.

FEARNHEAD, Miss Nicola Shan 7 School Lane, Turville, Henley-on-Thames RG9 6QX — BM BCh 1993 Oxf.; MA Camb. 1994; FRCS Eng. 1997. Specialist Regist. Rotat. (Gen. Surg.) Oxf. Region. Socs: BMA; MDU; FRCS. Prev: SHO Rotat. (Surg.) Frenchay Healthcare Trust Bristol; Demonst. (Anat.) Univ. Bristol; Ho. Off. (Med.) Roy. United Hosp. Bath.

FEARNLEY, Geoffrey 195 Thorpe Hall Avenue, Thorpe Bay, Southend-on-Sea SS1 3AP Tel: 01702 586028 — MB ChB 1954 Leeds; DObst RCOG 1958; Cert. Av Med. 1974.

FEARNLEY, Mr Ian Richard Department of Ophthalmology, Northampton General Hospital, Billing Road, Northampton NN1 5BD Tel: 01604 545482 Fax: 01604 545934 — MB BS 1982 Lond.; BSc Lond. 1979; FRCS (Ophth.) Lond. 1990; FCOphth 1990. (Westm. Med. Sch. Lond.) Cons. Ophth. N.ampton Gen. Hosp. Prev: Sen. Regist. (Ophth.) W. Norwich Hosp. & Addenbrooke's Hosp. Camb.; Regist. (Ophth.) Leicester Roy. Infirm.; Iris Fund Research Fell. (Ophth.) St. Thos. Hosp. Lond.

FEARNLEY, James David Oliver (retired) Bourton Green, Bishops Cannings, Devizes SN10 2LG Tel: 01380 860331 — MB BS 1936 Lond.

FEARNLEY, Julian Michael c/o Department of Neurology, Royal London Hospital, Whitechapel, London E1 1BB Tel: 020 7377 7421 Fax: 020 7377 7008 — MD 1990 Lond.; MB BS 1981; MRCP (UK) 1984. (St Thos. Hosp. Med. Sch.) Cons. Neurol. Roy. Lond. Hosp. Socs: Fell. Roy. Soc. Med.; Assn. Brit. Neurol.; Movem. Disorder Soc. Prev: Sen. Regist. & Regist. (Neurol.) Nat. Hosp. Neurol. Neurosurg.; NSE Chalfont Centre for Epilepsy; St Bart. Hosp. Lond.; Research Fell. Inst. Neurol. Lond.; Regist. (Med.) Qu. Eliz. Hosp. Birm.

FEARNLEY, Maurice Edward 44 Blake Hill Crescent, Poole BH14 8QS Tel: 01202 707454 — MB ChB 1954 Leeds; MRCP Lond. 1960; DTM & H. Eng. 1958. Prev: Lt-Col. RAMC.

FEARNLEY, Roger Haworth Park Hill Medical Practice, Park Hill Road, Torquay TQ1 2AL Tel: 01803 212489 Email: roger.fearnley@gp-i81310.nhs.uk — MB ChB 1986 Bristol; MRCGP 1991; DCH RCP Lond. 1990.

FEARNLEY, Sarah-Jane Department of Anaesthesia, Torbay Hospital, Lawes Bridge, Torquay Tel: 01803 614567; Rose Vine, Steep Hill, Maidencombe, Torquay TQ1 4TS — MB ChB 1986 Bristol; FCAnaesth 1990; DA (UK) 1988. Cons. Anaesth., Torbay Hosp. Socs: Assn. Anaesth.; BMA; Fell. Roy. Coll. AnE.hetists. Prev: Sen. Regist. (Anaesth.) SW RHA; Clin. Fell. (Cardiac Anaesth.) Soton. Gen. Hosp.; Regist. (Anaesth.) Roy. Devon & Exeter Hosp.

FEARNS, David Charles The Surgery, 25 St Mary's Road, Tickhill, Doncaster DN11 9NA Tel: 01302 742503; 11A Wilsic Road, Tickhill, Doncaster DN11 9JG — MB ChB 1979 Dundee; MRCGP 1983; DRCOG 1983.

FEARNS, Graeme Michael 46 Daneway, Ainsdale, Southport PR8 2QW — MB ChB 1995 Manch.

FEARNS, Judith Mary Carcroft Health Centre, Chestnut Avenue, Carcroft, Doncaster DN6 8AG Tel: 01302 723510; 29 Boswell Road, Bessacarr, Doncaster DN4 7BL Tel: 01302 539450 — MB ChB 1984 Dundee; DRCOG 1986.

FEARNS, Simon Nicholas Burns Practice, 4 Albion Place, Doncaster DN1 2EQ — MB ChB 1982 Dundee; MRCGP 1986; DRCOG 1984. GPLA (Learning Disabil.) St. Catherines Hosp. Doncaster. Socs: RCGP.

FEARNSIDE, John Eric St Ann's Medical Centre, Effingham Street, Rotherham S65 1BL Tel: 01709 379283/364437 — MB ChB 1974 Sheff.; BSc (Hons.) Sheff. 1968, MB ChB 1974. SHO (O & G) Moorgate Gen. Hosp. Rotherham. Prev: Ho. Off. (Gen. Surg.) Doncaster Roy. Infirm.; Ho. Off. (Gen. Med.) Rotherham Hosp.

FEARON, Eoghan Dwyer Dorman, Dorman, Chambers, McCollum and Fearon, Willowbank Surgery, Crossmore Road, Keady, Armagh BT60 3RL Tel: 028 3753 1248 Fax: 028 3753 1404 — MB BCh BAO 1990 Belf.; MRCGP 1994; DCH RCSI 1993; DRCOG 1992.

FEARON, Heather Penelope Weaver Vale Practice, Hallwood Health Centre, Hospital Way, Runcorn WA7 2UT Tel: 01928 711911 Fax: 01928 717368; 4 Dunham Court, Dunham Hill, Warrington WA6 0NH — MB ChB 1988 Liverp.

FEARON, Henrietta Clare 25 Meridian Pl, Bristol BS8 1JL — MB ChB 1997 Bristol.

FEARON, Joanne 5 Skardon Pl, Plymouth PL4 8HA — MB BS 1997 Lond.

FEARON, Julia Helen 97 Castle Green, Kingswood, Warrington WA5 7XB — MB ChB 1985 Liverp.

FEARON, Professor Kenneth Christopher Howard University Department of Surgery, Royal Infirmary, Lauriston Place, Edinburgh EH3 9YW Tel: 0131 536 3814 Fax: 0131 228 2661 Email: k.fearon@ed.ac.uk; 17 Cadogan Road, Liberton, Edinburgh EH16 6LY — MB ChB 1982 Glas.; MB ChB (Hons.) Glas. 1982; MD Glas. 1987; FRCS Ed. 1996; FRCS Glas. 1988; FRCS Eng. 1997. (Glasgow University) Prof. & Hon. Cons. Univ. Dept. Surg. Roy. Infirm. Edin. Prev: Reader & Hon. Cons. Univ. Dept. Surg. Roy. Infirm. Edin.; Sen. Lect. & Lect. (Surg.) Roy. Infirm. Edin.; Clin. Research Fell. (Oncol.) Glas. Univ.

FEARON, Michael Joseph Clanrye Surgery, Newry Health Village, Monaghan Street, Newry BT35 6BW Tel: 028 3026 7639 Fax: 028 3025 7414 — MB BCh BAO 1986 Belf.; MB BCh Belf. BAO 1986. Trainee GP Newry VTS. Socs: Assoc. Mem. RCGP.

FEARON, Paul Vincent Deep Eaves, 10 Victoria Square, Rostrevor, Newry BT34 3EU — MB BCh BAO 1996 Belf.; BSc (Hons.) Belf. 1993; MRCS Glasgow 1999. (Queen's University Belfast) Specialist Regist. (Trauma & Orthop. Surg.), Univ. of Newc.

FEAST, Martin James 39 Sharps Lane, Ruislip HA4 7JG — BChir 1992 Camb.

FEAST, Stephen Michael Biggleswade Health Centre, Saffron Road, Biggleswade SG18 8DJ Tel: 01767 313647 Fax: 01767 312568; Green Gables, 97 High St, Sandy SG19 1AL — MB ChB 1986 Bristol; BSc (Hons.) (Pharmacol.) Bristol 1982, MB ChB 1986; MRCGP 1990; MRCPsych 1992; DCH RCP Lond. 1989; DRCOG 1988. Prev: Regist. (Psychiat.) Univ. Camb.

FEATHER, Adam Flat 35, 86 Wapping Lane, London E1W 2RX — MB BS 1989 Lond. SHO (Med & Endocrinol.) Roy. Lond. Hosp.

FEATHER, Sally Anne Molecular Genetics Unit, Institute of Child Health, 30 Guildford St., London WC1N 1EQ — MB BChir 1989 Camb.

FEATHER, Sarah Diana Waddington Sexual Health Services, Sheopshire's Community & Mental Health Care Trust, Cross Hovses Site, Bayston Hill, Shrewsbury SY5 — DFFP 1993; MB ChB Sheff. 1987; MRCGP 1995; DRCOG 1993; DTM & H Liverp. 1993. (Sheff.) p/t Clin. Director, Shrops.'s Sexual Health Serv.

FEATHERBY, Elizabeth Anne Department of Child Health, Royal Devon & Exeter Hospital, Barrack Road, Exeter EX2 5DN Tel: 01392 411611; 6 Glenthorne Road, Duryard, Exeter EX4 4QU Tel: 01392 257640 — MB BS 1959 Lond.; MRCP Lond. 1965; MRCS Eng. LRCP Lond. 1959; DCH Eng. 1962; DObst RCOG 1961. (Roy. Free) SCMO (Child Health) Roy. Devon & Exeter Hosp.; Med. Advis. E. Devon Adoption Panel. Prev: Lect. in Child Health Univ. Bristol; Neonat. Paediat. Regist. Simpson Memor. Matern. Pavil. Edin. Roy.; Infirm.

FEATHERS, Luke Sebastian Brian 17 Buckthorne Grove, Huck Heaton, Newcastle upon Tyne NE7 7PS — MB BS 1996 Newc. SHO (Anaesth.) N. Tyneside Dist. Gen. Hosp.

FEATHERS, Mr Ronald Scott 10 Ferndown, Minnis Road, Birchington CT7 9QE Tel: 01843 847610 — MB BS Lond. 1967; FRCS Eng. 1972; MRCS Eng. LRCP Lond. 1967. (Roy. Free) Prev: Lect. (Anat. & Surg.) Roy. Free Hosp. Sch. Med. Lond.; Sen. Lect. (Surg.) Ahmadu Bello Univ. Hosp. Zaria, Nigeria; Regist. (Surg.) Roy. Free Hosp. Lond.

FEATHERSTONE, Carolyn Jane 19 Kensington Court, 20 Kensington Road, Glasgow G12 9NX — MB ChB 1992 Manch.; MRCP (UK) 1995. Specialist Regist. (Clin. Oncol.), BeatsonOncol.Centre Glas.

FEATHERSTONE, George Leonard, TD The Surgery, Front St., Great Lumley, Chester-le-Street DH3 4LE Tel: 0191 388 5600 Fax: 0191 388 3912; Castle View, Lumley Thicks, Chester-le-Street DH3 4HF Tel: 0191 385 7257 — MB BS 1957 Durh.; DObst RCOG 1961.

FEATHERSTONE, Jeffrey 14 Maybury Street, Tooting, London SW17 0SD — MB BS 1977 Lond.; DCH Eng. 1979.

FEATHERSTONE, John-James Sorwood House, Sheriff Hutton, York YO60 6SF — MB BS 1998 Lond.; MB BS Lond 1998.

FEATHERSTONE, Jonathan Mark 94 Longcroft Road, Devizes SN10 3AU — BM 1995 Soton.

FEATHERSTONE, Rosalind Mary Ashley, Eleanora Drive, Douglas IM2 3NN — MB ChB 1978 Zimbabwe; MB ChB U Zimbabwe 1978; LRCP LRCS Ed. LRCPS Glas. 1978. (Godfrey Higgins School of Medicine) Family Plann. Doctor, Isle of Man. Socs: Fac. Family Plann. & Reproductive Health Care, RCOG; Isle of Man Med. Soc.

FEATHERSTONE, Stephen Michael Department of Chemical Pathology, Leicester Royal Infirmary, Leicester LE1 5WW — MB ChB 1986 Liverp.; MSc Clin. Biochem. Surrey 1992. Regist. (Chem. Path.) Leicester Roy. Infirm.

FEATHERSTONE, Terence Department of Radiology, Sunderland Royal Hospital, Sunderland SR4 7TP Tel: 0191 565 6256 Fax: 0191 569 9226 Email: terry.featherstone@supanet.com; 6 Craven Court, Sunderland SR6 0RQ Tel: 0191 564 1715 Email: terry.featherstone@supanet.com — MB BS 1982 Newc.; FRCR 1989; DMRD Aberd. 1986. (Newc.) Cons. Radiol. Sunderland Roy. Hosp.; Med. Dir. Darlington MRI Centre. Socs: BMA; ISMRM; BIR. Prev: Cons. (Diag. Radiol.) Darlington Memor. Hosp.; Sen. Regist. Rotat. (Diag. Radiol.) St. Geo. Hosp. Lond.; Regist. (Diag. Radiol.) Aberd. Roy. Infirm.

FEAZEY, Angela Jane 27A Ondine Road, London SE15 4ED — MB BS 1990 Lond.

FEBBRARO, Salvatore 66 Upland Grove, Roundhay, Leeds LS8 2SY Tel: 0113 248 3617; Via Luigi Mercantini 23, Naples 80125, Italy Tel: 0103981 622650 — State Exam Naples 1989. Pharmaceut. Phys. (Clin. Pharmacol.) Besselaar Clin. Research Unit Leeds. Socs: BMA & Brit. Assn. Pharmaceut. Phys.

FEBRY, Gerald Norman (retired) 8 Woodland Close, Failand, Bristol BS8 3XB Tel: 01275 394424 — MB ChB Bristol 1954; DPH Bristol 1959. Prev: GP Bristol.

FEDDO, Mr Fuad Khellil Beauchamp House, 3 Beauchamp Road, Peverell, Plymouth PL2 3PZ Tel: 01752 709178 Fax: 01752 774107 Email: fuad@feddo.fonet.co.uk — MB ChB 1967 Baghdad; FRCS Ed. 1976; FCOphth 1991; DO RCPSI 1972. (Baghdad Univ. Med. Coll.) Cons. Ophth. Surg. Roy. Eye Infirm. Plymouth.

***FEDEE, Joanne Lisa** Birmingham Childrens Hospital NHS Tust, Steel House Lane, Birmingham B4 6NH Tel: 0121 3339999 Email: jofedee@hotmail.com; P.O Box 1512, Castries, St Lucia Tel: 001 7584523225 — MB BS 1996 W. Indies.

FEDER, Professor Gene Solomon Lower Clapton Health Centre, 36 Lower Clapton Road, London E5 0PQ Tel: 020 8986711 Fax: 020 89868140 — MB BS 1982 Lond.; BSc Sussex 1976; MD Lond. 1994; FRCGP 1994, M 1986; DRCOG 1985. (Guys Hospital) Prof. of Primary Care Research & Developm., Barts and the Lond. Qu. Mary's Sch. of Med. & denitistry. Socs: Brit. Hypertens. Soc. Mem. Prev: Research Fell. (Gen. Pract. & Primary Care) St. Bart. Hosp. Med. Coll. Lond.; Trainee GP Guy's Hosp. VTS.

FEE, John Gordon (retired) 92 Donaghadee Road, Bangor BT20 4QX Tel: 01247 465885 — MB BCh BAO Belf. 1939; DPH Belf. 1947. Prev: GP Bangor.

FEE, Professor John Patrick Howard Dept. of Anaesthetics and Intensive Care Medicine, Queen's University, Whitla Building, 97 Lisburn Road, Belfast BT9 7BL Tel: 028 9033 5785 Fax: 028 9032 9605 Email: h.fee@qub.ac.uk — MD 1980 Belf.; MB BCh BAO Belf. 1972; FFA RCSI 1976; PhD Belfast 1990; FRCA 1997. Prof. (Anaesth.) & Head of Depart. Qu.'s Univ. Belf.; Cons. (Anaesth.) Roy. Vict. & Musgrave Pk. Hosps. Belf.; Director, QUMED (Qu.'s Univ. Med. Devices); Director, Pat. Simulator Developm.s Ltd. Prev: Sen. Lect. (Anaesth.) Qu.'s Univ. Belf.

FEE, Mairi Catriona Diana Faculty of Medicine Office Level 10, Ninewells Hospital, PO Box 120, Dundee DD1 9SY — MB ChB 1997 Dundee.

FEE, Patrick Mary 28 Newry Road, Crossmaglen, Armagh BT60 1EN — MB BCh BAO 1986 NUI.

FEE, Samuel Rutherford, OBE (retired) 138 Sunnyside Avenue, Tunstall, Stoke-on-Trent ST6 6DZ Tel: 01782 837814 — MB ChB 1932 Glas.; FRCGP 1980 M 1963. Prev: Med. Off. W.cliffe Hosp. Stoke-on-Trent.

FEEGRADE, Mervyn Donald Ivydene, 42 Ragstone Road, Slough SL1 2PX — MB BS 1951 Agra. Prev: Regist. (Orthop.) St. Jas. Hosp. Balham; Cas. Off. (Orthop.) St. Helier Hosp. Carshalton; Cas. Off. Roy. S. Hants. Hosp. Soton.

FEEHALLY, Professor John Department of Nephrology, Leicester General Hospital, Gwendolen Road, Leicester LE5 4PW Tel: 0116 258 4132 Fax: 0116 258 4764 Email: jf27@le.ac.uk — MB BS 1975 Lond.; DM Oxf. 1986, MA 1977; FRCP Lond. 1991; MRCP (UK) 1978. (Westm.) Cons. Nephrol. Leic. Gen. Hosp. & Hon. Prof. of Renal Med. Socs: Renal Assn.; Assn. Phys.; Internat. Soc. Nephrol. Prev: Lect. (Med.) Univ. Leic.; Research Regist. (Renal Med.) Manch. Roy. Infirm.; Regist. (Renal & Gen. Med.) Leic. Gen. Hosp.

FEEHAN, Catherine Joan Child and Family Unit, Northbrook Health Centre, Northbrook Road, Solihull B90 3LX Tel: 0121 744 0449 — MB BCh BAO 1976 NUI; MMedSc (Psych.) Birm. 1994; MRCGP 1980; MRCPsych 1992; Dip. Community Paediat. Warwick 1986; DCH RCP Dub. 1979; DRCOG RCOG 1978. Cons. Child & Adolesc. Psychiat. Child and Fmaily Unit N.brook Health Centre. Prev: Sen. Regist. Rotat. (Child & Adolesc. Psychiat.) W. Midl. RHA.

FEELY, Morgan Patrick Department of Medicine, Martin Wing, General Infirmary, Leeds LS1 3EX Tel: 0113 243 2799 — MB BCh BAO 1969 NUI; MD NUI 1977; FRCPI 1985, M 1975. (Univ. Coll. Hosp.) Sen. Lect. (Clin. Pharmacol.) Dept. Med. Univ. Leeds.; Hon. Cons. Phys. Leeds Gen. Infirm. Prev: Fell. (Clin. Pharmacol.) Univ. Miami Sch. Med., USA; Regist. (Neurol.) St. Finbarr's Hosp. Cork; SHO (Med.) St. Vincent's Hosp. Dub.

FEENAN, Steven Dominic 37 Juniper Rise, Dunmurry, Belfast BT17 0BG — MB BS 1994 Lond.

FEENEY, Adrian James Woodlands, Moreton End Lane, Harpenden AL5 2HB — MB BS 1992 Lond.

FEENEY, Anne-Marie Rose Huddersfield Royal Infirmary, Lindley, Huddersfield HD3 3EA Tel: 01484 342507 Fax: 01484 342843 — MB BCh BAO NUI 1969; BSc (Med. Microbiol.) NUI 1971; MBA 1992; FRCPI 1982; FRCPath 1991, M 1978. Cons. Microbiol. Huddersfield Roy. Infirm.; Hon. Clin. Tutor (Microbiol.) Univ. Leeds. Socs: Assn. Med. Microbiol.; Eur. Soc. Clin. Microbiol. & Infec. Dis. Prev: Cons. Microbiol. Bradford Hosps. NHS Trust; Sen. Regist. Microbiol. Leeds AHA (T); Lect. (Med. Microbiol.) RCSI.

FEENEY, Denis Patrick Branch End Surgery, Stocksfield NE43 7LL Tel: 01661 842626 Fax: 01661 844392; Bixter, 34 Cade Hill Road, Stocksfield NE43 7PU — MB BS 1971 Newc.; MA 2000 (ED) Durham; MA 2000 (Ed) Durham Univ.; MRCGP 1975; DObst RCOG 1974. Clin. Asst. Prudhoe Hosp. N.d.; Clin. Asst. Hexham Gen. Hosp. Ophth. Socs: Mem. of Roy. Coll. of Gen. Pract.; Mem. of Roy. Coll. of Gen. Practicing. Prev: SHO (Gen. Med.) Shotley Bridge Gen. Hosp. Durh.; SHO (Paediat.) S. Shields Gen. Hosp.; SHO (O & G) Sunderland Gen. & Matern. Hosp.

FEENEY, Eamonn Colomban (retired) 7 Glenmore Close, Bamford, Rochdale OL11 5PF Tel: 01706 60844 — MB BCh BAO 1948 NUI.

FEENEY, Eamonn Columba (retired) 7 Glenmore Close, off Spencer Lane, Bamford, Rochdale OL11 5PF — MB BCh BAO 1948 NUI.

FEENEY, James 44A Lefroy Street, Coatbridge ML5 1NB — MB ChB 1987 Glas.

FEENEY, James Gerald Department of Obstetrics & Gynaecology, Royal Infirmary, Huddersfield HD3 3EA Tel: 01484 422191 — MB BCh BAO 1968 NUI; MAO 1979; FRCOG 1985, M 1973, DObst 1969. Cons. (O & G) Huddersfield Health Dist. Socs: Fell. Roy. Acad. Med. Irel. & N. Eng. Obst. & Gyn. Soc. Prev: Sen. Regist. (O & G) Leeds AHA (T) & Hon. Tutor (Obst.) Univ.; Leeds; Asst. to Master Coombe Lying-in Hosp. Dub.

FEENEY, John Thomas 110 Hazellville, London N19 3NA — MB BCh BAO 1978 NUI; DCH RCPI 1981. (Univ. Coll. Dub.) SHO (Psychiat.) St. Canice's Hosp. Kilkenny. Prev: SHO (Paediat.) Temple St. Childr. Hosp. Dub.; Med. Regist. Roy. Masonic Hosp. Lond.; SHO (A & E) Enfield Dist. Hosp. (Chace Wing).

FEENEY, Linda Anne Feeney and Partners, 29 Glasgow Road, Paisley PA1 3PA Tel: 0141 889 3356 Fax: 0141 887 5526 — MB ChB 1978 Glasgow; MB ChB Glas. 1978. (Glasgow) GP Paisley, Renfrewsh.

FEENEY, Mark Andrew Woodlands, Moreton End Lane, Harpenden AL5 2HB — MB BChir 1993 Camb.

FEENEY, Mary Teresa Chapeltown Health Centre, Spencer Place, Leeds LS7 4BB Tel: 0113 240 7000 Fax: 0113 240 8623 — MB BCh BAO 1983 NUI; MRCGP 1990; DObst RCPI 1989; DCH RCPSI 1988; Dip. Dermatol. 1998.

FEENEY, Meave Teresa (retired) Flat 9, Palmerston House, 126 Westminster Bridge Road, London SE1 7UW Tel: 020 7967 9750 — MB BCh BAO NUI 1951; LM Coombe 1952. Prev: GP Lond.

FEENEY, Patrick Joseph Lancing Health Centre, Penstone Park, Lancing BN15 9AG Tel: 01903 843333 Fax: 01903 843332; 107 Offington Avenue, Worthing BN14 9PR Tel: 01903 260945 — MB BCh BAO 1980 NUI.

FEEST, Professor Terry George Richard Bright Renal Unit, Southmead Hospital, Westbury-on-Trym, Bristol BS10 5NB Tel: 0117 959 5221 Fax: 0117 950 8677 Email: terry@feest.co.uk — MB BChir Camb. 1968; MA Camb. 1969, MD 1979; FRCP Lond. 1986; MRCP (UK) 1971; T(M) 1991. (Camb. & King's Coll. Hosp.) Cons. Nephrol. S.mead Hosp. Bristol; Prof. of Clin. Nephrol. Univ. Bristol. Socs: Renal Assn.; BMA; Eur. Renal Assn. Prev: Cons. Phys. & Nephrol. Roy. Devon & Exeter Hosp.; Lect. (Med.) Univ. Coll. Hosp. Lond.; Lect. (Med. & Nephrol.) Roy. Vict. Infirm. Newc.

FEETHAM, Mary Edith Gertrude (retired) 15 Juxon Close, Chichester PO19 2HA Tel: 01243 780774 — MB BS 1946 Lond.; MRCS Eng. LRCP Lond. 1946; DCH Eng. 1952; DObst RCOG 1948. Prev: Ho. Surg. (Gyn. & Obst.) Roy. Free Hosp.

FEGAN, Christopher Daniel 37 St Augustine's Road, Cardiff CF14 4BE — MB BS 1984 Newc.; MB BS Newc. l984.

FEGAN, Kathryn Jane 50 Wallasey Village, Wallasey, Wirral Tel: 0151 691 2088 — MB ChB 1983 Manch.; MRCGP 1987; DRCOG 1985. GP Wallasey. Socs: BMA. Prev: Trainee GP Manch. VTS; SHO (Geriat. Med.) Ladywell Hosp. Salford; SHO (O & G) & (A & E) Hope Hosp. Salford.

FEGAN, Kenneth George West Kilbride Surgery, 107B Main Street, West Kilbride KA23 9AR Tel: 01294 823607 Fax: 01294 829318 — MB ChB 1968 Glas.; MRCGP 1984; DObst RCOG 1970. (Glas.)

FEGAN, Mary 18 Bridge Road, Warrenpoint, Newry BT34 3QT Tel: 0169 37 73133 — MB BCh BAO 1989 Belf.; MRCGP 1995; DMH Belf. 1994. SHO (Psychiat.) Gransha Hosp. Derry. Socs: BMA.

FEGAN, Peter Gerard 3 Hairmyers Park, E. Kilbride, Glasgow G75 8SS — MB ChB 1993 Aberd.

FEGAN, Mr William George Carriere Bleu, Blue Stone Hill, Alderney GY9 3YE — MB BCh BAO 1945 Dub.; MCh Dub. 1952; FRCSI 1949.

FEGAN-EARL, Ashley William The Forensic Medicine Unit, St George's Hospital Medical School, Cranmer Terrace, London SW17 0RE Tel: 020 8725 0015 Fax: 020 8725 0017 — MB BS 1994 Lond.; BSc (Hons.) Lond. 1992. (Lond. Hosp. Med. Coll.) Specialist Regist. (Histopath.) St. Geo. Hosp. Tooting; Hon. Lect. (Forens. Med.) The Forens. Med. Unit St. Geo. Hosp. Med. Sch. Socs: Brit. Acad. Forens. Sci.; Brit. Assn. Forens. Med.; Roy. Soc. Med. Prev: Specialist Regist. (Hisotpath.) Roy. Lond. Hosp. & St. Bart. Hosp.; SHO (Histopath.) Wexham Pk. Hosp. Berks.

FEGENT, Julie Anne Cossington House Surgery, 51 Cossington Road, Canterbury CT1 3HX Tel: 01227 763377 Fax: 01227 786908 — MB BS 1977 Melbourne.

FEGGETTER, Graeme Stewart, TD Peterborough District Hospital, Thorpe Road, Peterborough PE3 6DA — MD 1986 Camb.; BA (Hons.) Open 1990; MA Camb. 1971, MD 1986, MB 1971, BChir 1970; MRCP (UK) 1973; MRCPsych 1976. (Camb. & Lond. Hosp.) Cons. (Psychiat.) PeterBoro. Dist. Gen. Hosp. Prev: Sen. Regist. (Psychiat.) Warneford Hosp. Oxf.; Regist. (Psychiat.) Newc. AHA (T); SHO (Gen. Med.) Newc. Gen. Hosp.

FEGGETTER, Mr Jeremy George Weightman, QHS, TD, OStJ Silksworth, Fernwood Road, Newcastle upon Tyne NE2 1TJ Tel: 0191 281 0444 Fax: 01670 529311 — MB BS 1966 Durh.; FRCS Eng. 1972. Cons. Urol. Wansbeck Hosp. & Freeman Hosp. Newc.; Hon. Clin. Lect. Univ. Newc. Socs: Fell. Roy. Soc. Med.; Brit. Med. Pilots Assn. Prev: Sen. Regist. (Urol.) St. Peter's Hosps. (St. Paul's Hosp.) Lond.; Sen. Regist. (Surg.) Roy. Vict. Infirm. Newc.; Hon. Sen. Research Assoc. Dept. Surg. Univ. Newc.

FEGHALI, Edmond 23 Brierley Hill Road, Wordsley, Stourbridge DY8 5SJ Tel: 01384 75064 — MD 1968 St. Joseph Univ. Beirut. Assoc. Specialist Orthop. Dudley HA.

FEHER, Michael David Beta Cell Diabetes Centre, Chelsea & Westminster Hospital, 369 Fulham Road, London SW10 9NH Tel: 020 8746 8134 Fax: 020 8237 2732 — MB BS 1977 Sydney; MRCP 1982 UK; MD 1994 London; FRCP 2000 UK. Cons. Phys. Diabetes, Clin. Pharmacol. and Gen. Med. Chelsea and W.minster Hosp. Lond. Prev: Sen. Lect. (Clin. Pharmacol.) & Hon. Cons. Diabetol. Imperial Coll. Sch. Med. Lond.; Lect. (Clin. Pharmacol. & Therap.) Char. Cross & W.minster Med. Sch. Lond.; Research Fell. (Clin. Pharmacol. & Therap.) St. Mary's Hosp. Lond.

FEHILLY, Bryan Sycamore House Medical Centre, 111 Birmingham Road, Walsall WS1 2NL Tel: 01922 624320 Fax: 01922 646744; 48 Buchanan Road, Walsall WS4 2EN Tel: 01922 638399 — MB ChB 1977 Glas.; MRCP (UK) 1982; Dip. Clin. Hypn. Sheff. 1991. (Glas.) Prev: Research Regist. (Gastroenterol.) St. Bart. Hosp. Lond; Regist. (Med.) Leicester Gen. Hosp; Regist. (Med.) P'boro. Dist. Hosp.

FEHLER, Boris Michael The Crouch Hall Surgery, 48 Crouch Hall Road, London N8 8HJ Tel: 020 8340 7736 Fax: 020 8455 0342; 78 Heath View, E. Finchley, London N2 0QB Tel: 020 8444 6480 — MB BCh 1949 Witwatersrand; FRCGP 1975; DCH Eng. 1959. GP Advisor & Tutor Univ. Witwatersrand; WONCA Counc.lor & Lect.; Boz-Fehler Fell. Socs: Hon. Mem. SA Acad. Family Pract.; Hon. Mem. SA Med. Assn.; (Counc.) Lond. Jewish Med. Soc. Prev: Pres. SA Acad. Family Med.; Counc. Mem. S.A. Coll. Med.; Federal Counc.lor S.A. Med. Assn.

FEILDEN, Elspeth Mary (retired) 10 Claremont Gardens, Gloucester GL1 3NY Tel: 01452 415454 — MB BS 1944 Durh.; (Durh.). Prev: Regist. (Psychiat.) All St.s' Hosp. Birm.

FEILDING, Emily Linnet 107 Hartfield Road, London SW19 3TJ — MB ChB 1997 Manch.

FEILERG, Karsten Axel Medical Vision Ltd, 108 Station Road, Hampton TW12 2AS Tel: 020 8941 6246 Fax: 020 8941 6399 Email: medical_vision@doctor.com — MD 1981 Copenhagen.

FEINMANN, Charlotte 11 Gardnor Road, London NW3 1HA Tel: 020 7431 2900 — MD 1983 Manch.; MSc Manch. 1981, MD 1983, MB ChB 1974; MRCPsych 1978. Cons. Psychiat. E.man Dent. Hosp. Lond.; Sen. Lect. (Psychiat.) Univ. Coll. & Middlx. Sch. Med. Lond. Prev: Research Fell. (Psychiat.) Inst. Psychiat. & King's Coll. Hosp. Lond.; Regist. (Psychiat.) Univ. Hosp. S. Manch.

FEINMANN, Richard 20 Winnington Road, Marple, Stockport SK6 6PD Tel: 0161 427 4804 — MB ChB 1970 Manch.; FRCP Lond. 1989; MRCP (UK) 1976; Dip. Med. Educat. Dund 1995; DObst RCOG 1972; MED 1999. Dep. Postgrad. Dean Univ. manch; Assoc. Dean Postgrad. Med. Univ. Manch; Hon. Cons. Phys. N.W.Lung Centre SMUHT. Socs: Manch. Med. Soc. & Brit. Thoracic Soc. Prev: Tutor (Med.) & Hon. Sen. Regist. Manch. Roy. Infirm.; Regist. (Med.) Leeds Gen. Infirm.

FEITELBERG, Michael John (retired) 82 Cornwall Road, Cheam, Sutton SM2 6DS Tel: 020 8642 3213 Fax: 020 8642 3213 — MB ChB 1957 Cape Town; DPhysMed Eng. 1976; DObst RCOG 1960. Prev: Hosp. Pract. (Rheum. & Rehabil.) St. Helier Hosp. Carshalton.

FEITELSON, Zalkind 22 Park Towers, Brick St., London W1Y 7DF — MB ChB 1946 Cape Town.

FEIZI, Ozgen 10 Craven Hill Mews, London W2 3DY Tel: 020 7402 6535; 1 Park Mews, Old Hertford Road, Hatfield AL9 5EP Tel: 01707 266569 — MB BS 1964 Lond.; MD 1980 London; FRCP 1995 London; MRCP 1970 UK; MRCS Eng. LRCP 1964 London. (Roy. Free) Cons. Phys. Qu. Eliz. II Hosp. Welwyn Gdn. City. Socs: Brit. Med. Soc.; Brit. Geriat. Soc. Prev: Regist. (Med.) Roy. Free Hosp. Lond.; Chas. Wolfson Fell. (Clin. Cardiol.) Middlx. Hosp. Lond.; Sen. Regist. (Geriat. Med.) Oxon. AHA (T).

FEIZI, Professor Ten Imperial College School of Medicine, Northwick Park Campus, Watford Road, Harrow HA1 3UJ Tel: 020 8869 3460 Fax: 020 8869 3455 Email: t.feizi@ic.ac; 94 Brunswick Road, Ealing, London W5 JAE Tel: 020 8997 3598 Fax: 020 8869 3455 — MD Lond. 1969, MB BS 1961; FRCP Lond. 1981, M 1964; FRCPath 1985, M 1978. (Roy. Free) Hon. Cons. Clin. Immunol. N.wick Pk. & Head The GlycoSci.s Imp. Coll. Sch. Med. N.wick Pk. Hosp.; Prof. Imp. Coll. Sch. Med. Socs: Brit. Soc. Immunol. & Biochem. Soc.; Amer. Soc. Immunols. Prev: Cons. Clin. Immunol. Clin. Research Centre & Head Sect. Glycoconjugate Research N.wick Pk.; Lect. (Med.) Roy. Free Hosp. Lond.; Asst. Prof. Rockefeller Univ. New York, USA.

FELCE, David William Fishponds Health Centre, Beechwood Road, Fishponds, Bristol BS16 3TD Tel: 0117 908 2365 Fax: 0117 908 2377; 25 Southfield Road, Westbury-on-Trym, Bristol BS9 3BG — MB ChB 1967 Bristol; MRCP (U.K.) 1972; DObst RCOG 1974. (Bristol) Socs: BMA & Cossham Med. Soc. Prev: SHO (Obst.) Bristol Matern. Hosp.; Regist. (Med.) Bristol Roy. Infirm.; SHO (Neurol.) Frenchay Hosp. Bristol.

FELCE, Jane Margaret Fairfield House, Selmeston, Polegate BN26 6UD — MB BS 1955 Lond. (Roy. Free)

FELD, Martin Stewart Gresford Medical Centre, Pilch Lane, Huyton, Liverpool L14 0JE Tel: 0151 489 2020; 8 Briars Close, Rainhill, Prescot L35 6DE Tel: 0151 430 7357 Fax: 0151 426 3433 Email: msfeldso@aol.com — MRCS Eng. LRCP Lond. 1973; LMSSA Lond. 1971. (Manch.) Prev: Regist. (O & G) Whiston Hosp.; SHO (Venereol.) Liverp. Roy. Infirm.; SHO (Obst.) Mill Rd. Matern. Hosp. Liverp.

FELDBERG, Miss Lore Elinor Jane Mersey Regional Plastic Surgery & Burns Centre, Prescot L35 5DR Tel: 0151 430 1262/2250 Fax: 0151 430 1855; Tel: 01925 756954 — MB BChir 1983 Camb.; BA (Natural Sc.) Camb. 1980; FRCS Eng 1988; FRCS (Plast.) 1996. (Lond. Hosp.) Cons. (Plastic & Hand Surg.) Whiston Hosp. Liverp. Socs: Brit. Soc. for Surg. of the Hand; Brit. Assn. of Plastic Surg.s. Prev: Regist. (Plastic Surg.) St. Jas. Univ. Hosp. Leeds & St. Luke's Hosp. Bradford; Fell. Hand Surg. Withington Hosp. Manch.; Fell. Hand Surg. Derby Roy. Infirm.

FELDERHOF, Jennifer Crawford Zuckerman, Felderhof and Ali, Northfield Health Centre, 15 St Heliers Road, Northfield, Birmingham B31 1QU Tel: 0121 478 0220 Fax: 0121 476 0931; 147 Oak Tree Lane, Bournville, Birmingham B30 1TT — MB ChB 1975 Dundee; BSc (Hons.) St. And. 1969; MSc (Biochem.) Dalhousie 1970.

FELDMAN, Mr Adam Yehudalev Department of Orthopaedic Surgery, Royal Lancaster Infirmary, Ashton Road, Lancaster LA1 4RD Tel: 01524 583506 Fax: 01524 583506; Lythe Brown Barn, Quernmore Road, Quernmore LA2 9LZ — MB ChB 1988 Bristol; FRCS Eng. 1993; FRCS Ed. 1993; FRCS (Tr. & Orth) 1999. (Univ. Bristol) Cons. Trauma & Orthopaedic Surg. at The Roy. Lancaster Infirm. and W.morland Gen. Hosp., Kendal, Cumbria; Orthopaedic Surg. to Morecambe Town Football Club. Socs: BOA (Full Mem.). Prev: Demonst. (Anat.) Univ. Bristol; Regist. (Orthop. & Traum. Surg.) P.ss Eliz. Orthop. Hosp. Exeter & Roy. Cornw. Hosp. Trust &Derriford & Mt. Gould Hosps. Plymouth & N. Devon Dist. Hosp.; Specialist Regist. Rotat. (Orthop. & Traum. Surg.) Cornw., Exeter & Plymouth Hosps.

FELDMAN, Albert (retired) 70 Petersfield Avenue, Harold Hill, Romford RM3 9PD Tel: 01708 343113 — MB BS 1946 Lond.; MRCS Eng. LRCP Lond. 1943. Prev: Vis. Med. Off. St. Leonard's Childr. Home HornCh.

FELDMAN, Charlotte (retired) 13 Burghley Road, Wimbledon Common, London SW19 5BG Tel: 020 8946 3138 Fax: 020 8947 8050 — MB ChB (2nd cl. Hons.) Leeds 1947; FRCP Lond. 1976, M 1948; DPhysMed Eng. 1957. Prev: Cons. Phys. (Rheum. & Rehabil.) Ealing Hosp. & Hon. Sen. Lect. (Rheum.) Roy. Postgrad. Postgrad. Med. Sch. Hammersmith Hosp. Lond.

FELDMAN, Eleanor Judith Department of Psychological Medicine, John Radcliffe Hospital, Oxford OX3 9DU — BM BCh 1981 Oxf.; MA Oxf. 1982, BA (Hons.) 1978, DM 1994; MRCPsych 1986.

(Oxford University Clinical Medical School) Cons. Psychol. Med. John Radcliffe Hosp. Oxf.; Hon. Sen. Clin. Lect. Univ. of Oxf. Clin. Med. Sch. Prev: Sen. Lect. & Hon. Cons. Psychiat. Univ. Nottm. Med. Sch.; Wellcome Fell. & Hon. Cons. Psychiat. Univ. Camb. Med. Sch.; Sen. Regist. Rotat. (Psychiat.) St. Geo. Hosp. Train. Scheme.

FELDMAN, Geoffrey Vivian (retired) Fairway, 59 Altrincham Road, Wilmslow SK9 5NH Tel: 01625 523748 — MB ChB 1944 Manch.; FRCP Ed. 1968, M 1954; FRCPCH 1997; DCH Eng. 1948. Hon. Cons. Paediat. S. Manch. HA. Prev: Cons. Paediat. Univ. Hosp. S. Manch. & Wythenshawe Hosp.

FELDMAN, Joan Dianne The Bungalow, St Clements Hospital, 2A Bow Road, London E3 4LL Tel: 020 880 6244 — MB ChB 1960 Witwatersrand; FRCPsych 1997; PhD Lond. 1978; MRCPsych 1983. Cons. Psychiat. Clin. Project Director E. Lond. and City Ment. Health NHS Trust. Prev: Regist. & Sen. Regist. (Psychiat.) Maudsley Hosp. Lond.

FELDMAN, Mark Roslyn Petersfield Surgery, 70 Petersfield Avenue, Harold Hill, Romford RM3 9PD Tel: 01708 343113 Fax: 01708 384672; Hoppits, Radley Green, Ingatestone CM4 0LU Tel: 01245 248125 Email: hoppits@compuserve.com — MB BS 1978 Lond.; MRCGP (Distinc.) 1982; D.Occ.Med RCP Lond. 1996; DFFP 1996. (Middlx. Hosp. Med. Sch.)

FELDMAN, Mr Maurice Avrom 90 Knightlow Road, Harborne, Birmingham B17 8QA Tel: 0121 429 3357 — MB ChB 1951 Bristol; FRCS Eng. 1964; FRCS Ed. 1963. (Bristol) Cons. Surg. Undertaking medicolegal Assessm.s and reports. (Gen. and Vasc. Surgic.); Emerit. Cons. Surg. Dudley Rd. Hosp. Birm. City Hosp. Trust; Sen. Clin. Lect. Univ. Birm.; Mem. Med. Appeal Tribunals Indep. Tribunal Serv.; Mem. Managem. Bd. W. Midl. Health Research Unit; Tutor, Surgic. workshops for G.P. Trainees, Birm. Med. Inst. Socs: Vasc. Surg. Soc. GB.; W Midl. Surgic. Soc.; Birm. Medico-Legal Soc. Prev: Capt. RAMC; Sen. Regist. (Surg.) Dudley Rd. Hosp. Birm.; Regist. (Surg.) City Hosp. Nottm.

FELDMAN, Michael Morris 32 Southwood Avenue, London N6 5RZ — MB BS 1966 Lond.; MPhil (Psychiat.) Lond. 1972, BA (Psychol., Hons.) 1960; MRCP Lond. 1968; MRCS Eng. LRCP Lond. 1966; FRCPsych 1978, M 1972; DPM Eng. 1971. (Univ. Coll. Hosp.) Cons. Private Pract. Prev: Cons. Psychotherap. Bethlem Roy. & Maudsley Hosps.; Sen. Regist. Maudsley Hosp.; SHO Lond. Hosp.

FELDMAN, Philippa Margaret Hoppits, Radley Green, Ingatestone CM4 0LU — MB BS 1979 Lond.; DRCOG 1983.

FELDMAN, Robert Graham Microscience Ltd., Imperial College of Medicine Hammersmith Campus, Du Cane Road, London W12 0NN Tel: 020 8383 3301 Fax: 020 8383 2074 Email: r.feldman@microscience.com; 91 Rusthall Avenue, London W4 1BN — MB BS 1978 Lond.; PhD Utrecht Univ. 1992; MSc Lond. 1989, BSc 1975; MRCPath 1985; T(Path) 1991. (Westm.) Chief Scientif. Off. MicroSci. Ltd.; Hon. Sen. Lect. & Cons. Lond. Prev: Sen. Lect. Fac. Med. Univ. Utrecht Netherlands; Clin. Lect. & Wellcome Train Fell. (Med.) Univ. Coll. Lond.; Hon. Sen. Regist. (Microbiol.) Univ. Coll. Hosp. Lond.

FELDMAN, Professor Roger Allen Emeritus Professor of Clinical Epidemiology, Royal London Hospital, Whitechapel Road, London E1 1BB Tel: 020 7377 7000 Ext: 3311 Fax: 020 7247 3410 Email: r.a.feldman@qmw.ac.uk; 11 Hermitage Meadow, Clare, Sudbury CO10 8QQ Tel: 01787 277637 Fax: 01787 277408 — MD Univ. Pennsylvania, USA 1957; FRCP Lond. 1993; FFPHM RCP (UK) 1991. Emerit. Prof. Clin. Epidemiol. St. Bartholomews & Roy. Lond. Sch. of Med. & Dent. Socs: Fell. Infec. Dis. Soc. Amer.; Fell. Amer. Epidemiol. Soc. Prev: Med. Epidemiol. WHO New Delhi; CHIPPS Cons. Padang W. Sumatra Indonesia; Dir. Div. Bacterial Dis. CDC Atlanta.

FELDMAN, Professor Stanley 28 Moore Street, Chelsea, London SW3 2QW Tel: 020 7584 4615 Email: ccarston@aol.com — MB BS 1955 Lond.; BSc Lond. 1950; FFA RCS Eng. 1959; DA Eng. 1957. (Westm.) Emerit. Prof. Anaesth. Imperial Coll. Sch. of Med. Lond.; Past Prof. Vis. Stanford. Univ. Calif. USA; Research Adviser Roy. Nat. Orthopaedic Hosp. Lond. Socs: Fell. Roy. Coll. Anaesth.; BMA; Assn. Anaesths. Prev: Cons. Anaesth. W.m. Hosp. Teachg. Gp. Hosps.; Sen. Lect. Roy. Postgrad. Med. Sch. Lond.; Research Fell. (Anaesthesiol.) Univ. Washington, USA.

FELDMAN, Stephen Mark The Dekeyser Group Practice, The Fountain Medical Centre, Little Fountain, Leeds LS27 9EN Tel: 0113 295 1600 Fax: 0113 238 1901; 2 Shadwell Park Court, Leeds LS17 8TS Tel: 0113 266 8266 — MB ChB 1985 Leeds; MRCGP 1989; DRCOG 1989; Cert. Family Plann. JCC 1988; Dip. Sports Med. 1994 (RCS Ed.). GP Partner.

FELDMANN, Professor Marc Kennedy Institute of Rheumatology, 1 Aspenlea Road, Hammersmith, London W6 8LH Tel: 020 8383 4444 Fax: 020 8563 0399 Email: m.feldmann@cxwms.ac.uk — MB BS Melbourne 1967; PhD Melbourne 1972, BSc (Med.) 1970; MRCP (UK) 1996; FRCPath 1984; FRCP (UK) 1998. (Melbourne) Head of Immunol. & Cytokine Div. Kennedy Inst. Rheumat.; Prof. Cellular Immunol. Univ. Lond. 1986; Hon. Cons. Immunol. Riverside Dist. HA. Prev: Sen. Research Scientist. Imperial Cancer Research Fund.

FELDMANN, Pia Jane 26 Winchester Road, London NW3 3NT — BM BS 1995 Nottm. SHO (Psychiat.) St. Bart. & Homerton Hosps. Lond.

FELDMAR, Graham Lewis Merrilees, 109 Frinton Road, Holland-on-Sea, Clacton-on-Sea CO15 5UN Tel: 01255 4266 — LMSSA 1953 Lond.; MB Camb. 1963, BChir 1962; DA Eng. 1957.

FELDSCHREIBER, Peter 21 Montague Road, Richmond TW10 6QW — MB BS 1974 Lond.

FELGATE, Michael John Department of Anaesthetics, Hull Royal Infirmary, Hull HU3 2JZ Tel: 01482 328541; 21 Bramley Lane, Handsworth, Sheffield S13 8TY Tel: 0114 269 3476 — MB ChB 1988 Sheff.; FRCA 1997. (Sheffield) Regist. (Anaesth.) Hull Roy. Infirm. Socs: (Trainee) Assoc. Anaesth. GB & N. Irel.; ICS; BMA.

FELGATE, Nicholas George Kent High Street Medical Centre, 46-48 High Street, Newhall, Swadlincote DE11 0HU Tel: 01283 217092; 385 Burton Road, Midway, Swadlincote DE11 7NA — MB ChB 1963 Sheff.

FELIX, David Henry Department of Oral Medicine, Glasgow Dental Hospital & School, 378 Sauchiehall St., Glasgow G2 3JZ Tel: 0141 211 9600 Fax: 0141 353 2899; 8 Birkhall Drive, Bearsden, Glasgow G61 1DB Tel: 0141 942 4845 — MB ChB 1988 Ed.; BDS Glas. 1978; FDS RCPS Glas. 1996; FDS RCS Eng. 1982; FDS RCS Ed. 1997. Cons. Oral Med. Gtr. Glas. HB; Postgrad. Coordinator W. Scotl. Centre for Postgrad. Dent. Educat. Socs: BMA; Brit. Dent. Assn.; (Hon. Sec.) Brit. Soc. Oral Med. Prev: MRC Research Fell. (Oral Med. & Oral Path.) Univ. Edin.; Ho. Off. (Med. & Surg.) Roy. Infirm. Edin.

FELIX, Robin Henry (cons. rooms), 4 Downing St., Farnham GU9 7NX Tel: 01252 716226; Tilewood, Seale Lane, Seale, Farnham GU10 1LE Tel: 01252 782509 Fax: 01252 782509 — MB BChir Camb. 1965; MA Camb. 1966; FRCP Lond. 1983; MRCP (UK) 1971; MRCS Eng. LRCP Lond. 1967; DObst RCOG 1967. (Westm.) Cons. Dermat. Frimley Pk. NHS Trust; Assoc. Dean of Postgrad. Med. S. Thames Dept. Postgrad. Med. & Dent. Educat; Non. Resid. Fell. Amer. Acad. Dermat. Socs: Fell. Roy. Soc. Med.; Brit. Assn. Dermat. Prev: Sen. Regist. (Dermat.) Roy. Vict. Infirm. & Univ. Newc.; Regist. (Med.) St. Luke's Hosp. Guildford; Ho. Surg. W.m. Hosp. Lond.

FELL, David Department Anaesthesia, Leicester Royal Infirmary, Leicester LE1 5WW Tel: 0116 258 6474 Fax: 0116 258 6174; 48 Avenue Road, Queniborough, Leicester LE7 3FA Tel: 0116 264 0551 — MB ChB 1974 Ed.; FFA RCS Eng. 1979. Cons. Anaesth. Leicester Roy. Infirm. Leicester. Prev: Sen. Lect. & Hon. Cons. Anaesth. Univ. Leicester & Leicester Roy. Infirm.; Sen. Regist. (Anaesth.) Leics. Roy. Infirm.; Med. Staff (Anaesth.) Chas. Janeway Hosp. St. Johns Newfld..

FELL, Elaine Dumbarton Road Surgery, 1398 Dumbarton Road, Glasgow G14 9DS Tel: 0141 959 1520 Fax: 0141 959 8463 — MB ChB 1963 Glas. (Glasgow University)

FELL, Henry William Ker (retired) The Elms, Gedding, Bury St Edmunds IP30 0QX Tel: 01449 736320 Email: hfell@doctors.org.uk — MB BChir Camb. 1965; Dip. Bact. Lond 1969. Prev: Cons. Microbiol. W. Suff. Gen. Hosp. Bury St. Edmunds.

FELL, John Michael Edgar Department of Paediatrics, Chelsea and Westminster Hospital, 369 Fulham Road, London SW10 9NH Tel: 020 8746 8628 Fax: 020 8746 8770; 41 Falkland Road, Hornsey, London N8 0NS — MB BS 1984 Lond.; MA Camb. 1986; MRCP (UK) 1987. (St Bartholomews Hospital) Cons. Paediat. Gastroeneterologist Chelsea & W.minster Hosp. Lond.

FELL, Lydia Frances Community Child Health Department, Spynie Hospital, Elgin IV30 5PW Tel: 01343 543131 Fax: 01343 552185; 45 Beech Brae, Elgin IV30 4NS — MB ChB 1971 Aberd. SCMO Grampian Primary Care NHS Trust.

FELL, Melville Robert (retired) The Poplars, Winterbourne Gunner, Salisbury SP4 6EG — MRCS Eng. LRCP Lond. 1946; FRCOG 1965, M 1952; MMSA Lond. 1956. Prev: Cons. O & G Salisbury Hosp. Gp.

FELL, Michael Burnard (retired) Willake, Goodameavy, Roborough, Plymouth PL6 7AP Tel: 01752 839322 — MB BS Lond. 1950. Prev: GP Yelverton.

FELL, Mr Nathaniel 11 Matherton Avenue, Newton Mearns, Glasgow G77 5EY Tel: 0141 616 2259 — MB ChB Glas. 1956; FRCS Ed. 1982; DO Eng. 1964.

FELL, Peter John The Health Centre, Deddington, Oxford Tel: 01869 338611 Fax: 01869 337009; Springfield, Milton Road, Bloxham, Banbury OX15 4HD Tel: 01295722976 Email: pjfell@tesco.net — MRCS Eng. LRCP Lond. 1965; MD Lond. 1973, MB BS 1965. (St. Mary's) Dir. Oxf. Allergy Centre. Prev: Dir. Med. Affairs Fisons; Clin. Pharmacol. Organon N.V.; Regist. & Research Asst. Steroid Unit St. Mary's Hosp. Lond.

FELL, Richard Hensman Lea Hurst, Farthing Green Lane, Stoke Poges, Slough SL2 4JQ Tel: 01753 643160 Fax: 01753 647282; Outwood, Haverthwaite, Ulverston LA12 8LY — MB BS 1961 Lond.; FFA RCS Eng. 1965; DA Eng. 1963. (St. Bart.) Cons. Anaesth. E. Berks. Health Dist. Socs: Anaesth. Res. Soc. Prev: Regist. (Anaesth.) Lond. Hosp.; Lect. (Anaesth.) Radcliffe Infirm. Oxf.; Tutor (Anaesth.) & Lect. (Physiol.) St. Bart. Hosp. Lond.

FELL, Sarah Jane — MB BS 1994 Newc.; MRCGP 1999; DCH RCP 1997; DFFP 1997. (Newcastle) GP Princip., Aberfeldy Pract., 50 Aberfeldy St., Poplar, Lond. E14 0NU. Prev: SHO (A & E) Univ. Coll. Hosp. Lond.; SHO O & G; SHO Paediat.

FELL, Susan Karen Punch Bowl, Dereham Road, Garvestone, Norwich NR9 4QU Tel: 01362 858580 — MB ChB 1987 Liverp.; DCH; BSc Lond. 1980; DRCOG. Prev: Trainee GP Warrington HA.

FELLER, Rolf CLDT, 18 Kilmersdon Rd, Hartcliffe, Bristol BS13 9JE Tel: 0117 902 0202 Fax: 0117 964 1114; The Old House, Chiverstone, Kenton, Exeter EX6 8NL Tel: 01626 890304 — State Exam Med 1988 Berlin; MRCPsych 1996. (Freie Universität Berlin, Germany) Specialist Regist. (Psychiat.&Learning Diff.), Community Psychiat. SW Bristol; Hon. Lect. (Ment. Health) Univ. Bristol 1996. Socs: BMA; MRCPsych. Prev: Regist. (Liaison Psychiat.), Truro; Regist. (Drug Misuse), Plymouth; Regist. (Gen. Adult Psychiat.) Wonford Ho. Hosp. Exeter.

FELLERMAN, Simon Morris Avenue Surgery, 24 The Avenue, Alwoodley, Leeds LS17 7BE Tel: 0113 267 9703; 4a Green Road, Leeds LS6 4JP Tel: 0113 295 3790 — MB ChB 1979 Leeds; DRCOG 1981. (Leeds)

FELLICK, Jeremy Mark 51 Market Street, Draycott, Derby DE72 3NB — BM BS 1989 Nottm.

FELLINGHAM, William Henry 8 Kingston Bay Road, Shoreham-by-Sea BN43 5HP — MB BS 1998 Lond.; MB BS Lond 1998.

FEATHERSTONE, Cornelia Juliane Fellner Laich Medical Centre, Clifton Road, Lossiemouth IV31 6DJ; Caledonia, Findhorn, Forres IV36 3TY Tel: 01309 690943 Fax: 01309 691301 — State Exam Med 1985 Ulm; T(GP). p/t GP. Prev: Med. Dir. Healthworks Forres Centre for Holistic Health Care; Med. Doctor in Private Pract.; Med. Dir. Hollistic Health Care.

FELLOW-SMITH, Elizabeth Anne Windmill Lodge, West London Mental Health Trust, Uxbridge Road, Southall UB1 3EU Tel: 020 8354 8509 Fax: 020 8354 8450 — MB BS 1981 Melbourne; MRCPsych 1988. Cons. Child & Adolesc. Psychiat. Child & Families Consultation Serv., Lond. Boro., Ealing; Med. Director, W. Lond. Ment. Health Trust. Prev: Clin. Director Child & Adolesc. Ment. Health.

FELLOWES, Edmund Christopher George Street Surgery, 99 George Street, Dumfries DG1 1DS Tel: 01387 253333 Fax: 01387 253301 — MB BS 1968 Lond.; MRCGP 1974; DGM RCP Lond. 1985; DObst RCOG 1973; DA Eng. 1971. (St. Thos.) Socs: BMA.

FELLOWES, Helena Mary (retired) South Warren, Waterworks Road, Old Hunstanton, Hunstanton PE36 6JE Tel: 01485 533629 — MB ChB 1945 Birm. Prev: Scientif. Off. MRC Reproduc. & Growth Unit. P.ss Mary Matern.

FELLOWES, Janet Lindsay Tayside Primary Care Trust, Royal Dundee Liff Hospital, Dundee — MB ChB 1979 Dundee; MRCGP 1988; MRCPsych 1984; Cert. Family Plann. JCC 1984. Locum Cons. Psych. Tayside Primary Care Trust Dundee. Prev: Cons. Psychiat. (Liason Psychiat.) Dundee Healthcare Trust.

FELLOWES, Mary Ann St Johns Surgery, 5 Kidderminster Road, Bromsgrove B61 7JJ Tel: 01527 871706 Fax: 01527 576022; 18 Marlborough Avenue, Bromsgrove B60 2PF Tel: 01527 76277 — MB ChB 1976 Birm.; MRCGP 1981.

FELLOWS, Andrew Howard James 57 Bradbourne Street, London SW6 3TF — MB BS 1987 Lond.

FELLOWS, Cecile Patricia (retired) 20 St Peters Road, West Mersea, Colchester CO5 8LJ Tel: 01206 382945 — MRCS Eng. LRCP Lond. 1938; DA Eng. 1944. Prev: Ho. Phys. Selly Oak Hosp. Birm.

FELLOWS, Elizabeth Jane The Surgery, 131 Goldsmith Avenue, Milton, Portsmouth PO4 8QZ — MB BS 1985 Lond. Resid. Med. Off. The Hants. Clinic Basingstoke. Prev: Ho. Phys. & Ho. Surg. Portsmouth HA.

FELLOWS, Eric William Honor Oak Health Centre, 20-21 Turnham Road, London SE4 2HH Tel: 020 7639 9797 — MB BS 1975 Lond.; DRCOG Lond. 1981; Cert. Prescribed Exp JCPTGP 1981.

FELLOWS, Gillian 6 Stanley Grove, Chorlton, Manchester M21 9DT — MB ChB 1989 Manch.; MRCGP 1993; DRCOG 1992.

FELLOWS, Mr Griffith John Tel: 01865 741841 Fax: 01865 226086; Dawsons Cottage, 65 Lower Radley, Abingdon OX14 3AY Tel: 01235 520479 Fax: 01235 520479 Email: gfellows@globalnet.co.uk — MB BS 1960 Lond.; MS Lond. 1972; FRCS Eng. 1964. (Univ. Coll. Hosp.) Socs: Fell. Roy. Soc. Med.; Internat. Soc. Urol.; Brit. Assn. Urol. Surgs. Prev: Sen. Regist. (Urol.) Gen. Infirm. Leeds; Sen. Regist. (Urol.) Roy. Hosp. Sheff.; Research Asst. (Cancer Research) Univ. Leeds.

FELLOWS, Ian Wilfred West Norwich Hospital, Bowthorpe Road, Norwich NR2 3TU Tel: 01603 286286 Fax: 01603 288368; Tamar House, Crows Hall Lane, Attleborough NR17 1AD — MB BChir 1978 Camb.; DM Nottm. 1985; FRCP Lond. 1995; MRCP (UK) 1979. Cons. Gastroenterol. Norf. & Norwich Healthcare Trust; Hon. Sen. Lect. Univ. E. Anglia.

FELLOWS, Kevin Peter Govanhill Health Centre, 233 Calder Street, Glasgow G42 7DR Tel: 0141 531 8361 Fax: 0141 531 8375 — MB ChB 1982 Ed.; BSc (Med. Sci.) Ed. 1979; MRCGP 1987; DRCOG 1987.

FELLOWS, Marcus John Carrington Way Health Centre, 9 Carrington Way, Wincanton BA9 9JY Tel: 01963 32000 Fax: 01963 32146; Tel: 01963 371215 — MB ChB 1977 Bristol; MRCGP 1981; DRCOG 1981. (Bristol)

FELLOWS, Peter Richard The Health Centre, Albert Street, Lydney GL15 5NQ Tel: 01594 845222 Fax: 01594 845637 — MB BS 1972 Lond.; MRCS Eng. LRCP Lond. 1972.

FELLS, Janette Frances Doctors Surgery, Pierce Street, Queensferry, Deeside CH5 1SY Tel: 01244 813340 Fax: 01244 822882 — MB ChB Manch. 1977.

FELLS, John Nicholas Hunters Way Medical Centre, Hunters Way, Kimbolton, Huntingdon PE18 0HY Tel: 01480 860205 Fax: 01480 861590; The Manor, Covington, Huntingdon PE28 0RU — MB BChir 1979 Camb.; MA Camb. 1983; MRCGP 1990; DRCOG 1983. Clin. Asst. (Gastroenterol.) Hinchingbrooke Hosp. Huntingdon. Prev: Trainee GP Camb. VTS.

FELLS, Mr Peter (retired) Moorfields Eye Hospital, Lower Corridor Suite, City Road, London EC1V 2PD Tel: 020 7566 2334 Fax: 020 7566 2334 — MB BChir Camb. 1959; MA Camb. 1959; FRCS 1966; FCOphth. 1988; DO Eng. 1962. Hon. Cons. Ophth. Moorfields Eye Hosp. Lond.; Mem. Ct. Examrs. RCS Eng. Prev: Hon. Cons. Ophth. Hammersmith Hosp. Lond.

FELMEDEN, Dirk Carsten 47 Beck Road, Madeley, Crewe CW3 9JF — State Exam Med. Marburg 1992.

FELMINGHAM, John Edward Cornerstones, 40 Park Drive, Wistaston, Crewe CW2 8EN — MB ChB 1972 Liverp.; FRCOG 1992, M 1977. Med. Dir. Mid Chesh. NHS Trust; Cons. Obst. & Gyn. Mid Chesh. NHS Trust; Sen. Clin. Lect. Dept. Obst. & Gyn. Univ. of Keele. Socs: BAMM; ATMD; Fell. RSM. Prev: Sen. Regist. (O & G) Liverp. AHA (T); Regist. Liverp. Matern. & Wom.'s Hosps. & Chesh. Matern. Hosp. Chester.

FELOY, Janet Mary Laidlaw Holmwood, Staverton, Totnes TQ9 6NX — MB ChB 1982 Manch.

FELSTEAD, Anne Baldwin and Partners, Hucknall Road Medical Centre, off Kibworth Close, Nottingham NG5 1FX Tel: 0115 960 6652 Fax: 0115 969 1746; 17 Sutton Passeys Crescent, Wollaton Park, Nottingham NG8 1BX — MB ChB 1981 Leic.; MRCGP 1985.

FELSTEAD, Margaret 93 Burfield Road, Old WIndsor, Windsor SL4 2LR — LRCP 1949 Irel.; LM, LRCSI & LM 1949.

FELSTEAD, Stephen John One Gable, Rectory Lane, Lyminge, Folkestone CT18 8EG — MB ChB 1982 Leeds.

FELSTEIN, Ivor Leslie (cons. rooms), 11 Chorley New Road, Bolton BL1 4QR Tel: 01204 384404 — MB ChB Glas. 1956. (Univ. Glas.) Private Therapist in Psychosexual Med. Socs: Brit. Geriat. Soc. & Inst. Psychosexual Med. Prev: Regist. (Med. & Geriat.) Kingston Gp. Hosps.; Sen. Hosp. Med. Off. (Geriat.) Bolton & Dist. Gp. Hosps.

FELTBOWER, Antony Richard Smith, Feltbower and Venn, 41 Westminster Road, Coventry CV1 3GB Tel: 024 7622 3565 Fax: 024 7623 0053; 27 Sunningdale Avenue, Kenilworth CV8 2BY Tel: 01926 864465 — MB BChir 1978 Camb.; MA Camb. 1979; MRCS Eng. LRCP Lond. 1978; AFOM RCP Lond. 1991; DRCOG 1982. (Westm.) GP Cons. Med. Defence Union; UK Register of Expert Witness; Med. Adviser Coventry City Counc. Prev: Chairm. Coventry LMC.

FELTHAM, Angela Mary 32 The Green Avenue, Porthcawl CF36 3AX — BM 1977 Soton.; MRCPsych 1983. Prev: SHO (Psychiat.) P.ss Margt.'s Hosp., Swindon, Wilts.; Regist. (Psychiat.) Dept. Psychiat. Roy. S. Hants. Hosp., Soton.

FELTHAM, Eleanor Rachel 8 Eastfield Road, Caerleon, Newport NP18 3EW — MB ChB 1997 Bristol.

FELTON, Anthony Edward Great Bainden Cottage, Piccadilly Lane, Mayfield TN20 6RH Tel: 01435 872149 Fax: 01435 873885 Email: tony.felton@btinternet.com — MB BS 1981 Lond.; MB BS (Hons.) Lond. 1981; MBA 1993; MRCGP 1987; DRCOG 1984. Asst. GP. & Managem. Cons. CrowBoro. Prev: GP E. Sussex; Trainee GP Brighton VTS; Resid. Psychiat. St. Brendans Hosp., Bermuda.

FELTON, Mr David John Christopher (retired) 4 Woburn Close, Peterborough PE3 6XP Tel: 01732 261971 — MB ChB 1955 Bristol; FRCOG 1976, M 1963. Prev: Cons. O & G P'boro. & Stamford Hosps.

FELTON, Hilary Megan 63 Savile Park Road, Halifax HX1 2EX Tel: 01422 354226 — MB BCh 1969 Wales; DObst RCOG 1972.

FELTON, Jessie Robinson Tremaine House, Tremaine, Launceston PL15 8SA — MB BS 1997 Lond.

FELTON, John Charles The Surgery, 54 Thorne Road, Doncaster DN1 2JP Tel: 01302 361222; The Oaks, 2 Shardlow Court, Bessacarr, Doncaster DN4 6FD — MB ChB 1976 Bristol; FRCGP 1994, M 1980; DRCOG 1980. Prev: SHO Doncaster Roy. Infirm.; Ho. Off. Frenchay Hosp. Bristol.

FELTON, John Mark Department of Infectious & Tropical Diseases, London School Hygiene & Tropical Medicine, Keppel St., London WC1E 7HT Email: m.felton@lshtm.ac.uk — MB ChB 1987 Sheff.; MRCP (UK) 1992; DTM & H Liverp. 1990; MSc Lond. 1997. Research Lond. Sch. Hyg. & Trop. Med.; Hon. Sen. Regist. Hosp. for Trop. Dis.; Clin. Lect. Lond. Sch. of Hyg. & Trop. Med. Socs: Fell. Roy. Soc. Trop. Med. & Hyg.; Fell. Brit. Infect. Soc. Prev: Regist. (Trop. Med.) Hosp. Trop. Dis. Lond.; Regist. (HIV Med.) Middlx. Hosp. Lond.

FELTON, Judith Rosemary University Health Centre, 9 Northcourt Avenue, Reading RG2 7HE Tel: 0118 987 4551; Maynard, 39A Bath Road, Reading RG1 6HL Tel: 0118 959 0978 — MB BS 1974 Lond.; MRCGP 1978; DRCOG 1977. (Univ. Coll. Hosp.) Asst. Phys. Univ. Reading; Clin. Coordinator Family Plann. Serv. Roy. Berks. & Battle Hosps. NHS Trust. Socs: Fac. Fam. Plann. & Reproduc. Health Care; Brit. Stud. Health Assn. Prev: Trainee GP Reading VTS; Ho. Surg. St. Chas. Hosp. Lond.; Ho. Phys. W. Suff. Hosp.

FELTON, William Fowler (retired) 63 Tongdean Avenue, Hove BN3 6TN Tel: 01273 881676 — MB BChir 1942 Camb.; MA Camb. 1942; MRCS Eng. LRCP Lond. 1942; DIH Soc. Apoth. Lond. 1951; DPH Lond. 1947. Hon. Cons. Venereol. Roy. Sussex Co. Hosp. Brighton. Prev: Med. Asst. (Venereol.) Sheff. RHB & St. Thos. Hosp. Lond.

FELTWELL, Stephen Robert James, Squadron Ldr. RAF Med. Br. Hamilton Road Surgery, 201 Hamilton Road, Felixstowe IP11 7DT Tel: 01394 283197 Fax: 01394 270304 Email: stephen.feltwell@gp-d83048.nhs.uk; The Manse, 3 Barton Road, Felixstowe IP11 7JH — MB BS 1983 Lond.; MRCGP 1987; DRCOG 1989; DCH RCP Lond. 1988. Gen. Med. Practitioner, Centr. Surg., Felixstowe; Aviat. Med. Examr.; Clin. Asst. Felixtowe Gen. Hosp. Socs: Brit. Soc. Med. & Dent. Hypn.; Assn. Aviat. Med. Examr.s; Christian Med. Fell.sh. Prev: SHO (Paediat.) St. Geo. Hosp. Lond.; Ho. Surg. St. Bart. Hosp. Lond.; Ho. Phys. Whipps Cross Hosp. Lond.

FENBY, Adrian Peter 28 Boyslade Road, Burbage, Hinckley LE10 2RG — MB ChB 1987 Manch.; 1999 D. OCC. Med. Socs: Soc. Occupat. Med. Prev: GP, Leicester; SHO (Paediat.) Geo. Eliot Hosp. Nuneaton; SHO (A & E) Manor Hosp. Nuneaton.

FENBY TAYLOR, Jeremy William The Old Forge Surgery, 14 Main Street, Market Overton, Oakham LE15 7PP Tel: 01572 767229; The Lodge, Church St, Hartshorne, Swadlincote DE11 7ER Tel: 01283 226668 — MB BS 1975 Lond.; BSc, MB BS Lond. 1975; MRCGP 1985; Dip. Occ. Med. RCP Lond. 1996. (Middlx. Hosp.)

FENDALL, Professor Neville Rex Edwards The Coach House, Mill St., Ludlow SY8 1BB Tel: 01584 877195; The Coach House, Mill St, Ludlow SY8 1BB Tel: 01584 877195 — MB BS Lond. 1943; BSc (Hons.) Lond. 1939, MD 1952; MRCS Eng. LRCP Lond. 1942; FFPHM 1989; FFCM 1974; DPH Lond. 1952. (Univ. Coll. Hosp.) Emerit. Prof. Internat. Community Health Sch. Trop. Med. Liverp.; Distinguished Fell. Boston Univ. Center for Internat. Health 1992-. Socs: Fell. Fac. Community Med.; Corr. Mem. Acad. Med. Phys. & Nat. Sci. Guatemala; BMA. Prev: Vis. Prof. Pub. Health Boston Univ., USA 1982-2001; Adjunct Prof. Community Health Scs. Univ. Calgary Canada 1983-88; Prof. Trop. Comm. Health, Univ. Liverp. 1971-81.

FENDER, David 21 Elmfield Gardens, Gosforth, Newcastle upon Tyne NE3 4XB — MB ChB 1990 Sheff.; FRCS Eng. 1994. Specialist Regist. Orthop. Surg. N. Rotat. Prev: PeriFell.sh. Rotat. (Surg.) Newc.; Research Fell. Dept. Orthop. Surg. Univ. Leic.

FENDER, Mrs Elisabeth (retired) St Phillips Health Centre, Houghton Street, London WC2A 2AE Tel: 020 7955 7016 Fax: 020 7955 6818 — BM BCh 1964 Oxf.; BSc Wales 1961; DPM Eng. 1968. Dir. Stud. Health Serv. Lond. Sch. Economics & Political Sci. Prev: Regist. (Psychiat.) Roy. Edin. Hosp.

FENDER, Guy Robert Keevney 66A Lonsdale Road, London SW13 9JS Tel: 020 7736 3495 — MB BS 1986 Lond.; MRCGP 1990. (St. Thos.) SHO (O & G) St. Thos. Hosp. Lond. Prev: Trainee GP Exeter VTS; Ho. Surg. (Urol. & Gen. Surg.) St. Thos. Hosp. Lond.; Ho. Phys. Roy. Devon & Exeter Hosp.

FENDER, Laura Jane 73 Manor Way, London SE3 9XG — BM BS 1995 Nottm.

FENDER, Royston Gray (retired) 69 Marlow Road, High Wycombe HP11 1TQ Tel: 01494 530825 — MB BS 1951 Lond. Prev: ENT Regist. Aylesbury & High Wycombe Hosps.

FENECK, Robert Owen High Bank, Melford Road, Sudbury CO10 1XU — MB BS 1974 Lond.; MRCS Eng. LRCP Lond. 1974; FFA RCS Eng. 1978.

FENELEY, Mr Mark Roger Department of Urology, Nottingham, Hucknall Road, Nottingham NG5 1PB; 18 Hawthorn Close, Bleasby, Nottingham NG14 7HW Tel: 01636 831178 — MB BChir 1987 Camb.; MA Camb. 1987, BA 1983, MD 1996; FRCS Eng. 1991; FRCS (Urol.) 1997; BA Camb 1983. (Camb. & Guy's) Cons. Urol., Nottm. City Hosp.; Clin. Teach., Univ. of Nottm. Socs: Fell. Roy. Soc. Med. (Mem. Sect. Urol.); Brit. Prostate Gp.; Full Mem. BAUS. Prev: Post Doctoral Fell. in Uro-Oncol., James Buchanan Brady Urological Inst., Johns Hopkins Hosp., Baltimore; Sen. Regist. (Urol.), St. Bart. Hosp., Lond.; Research Regist. (Urol.) St. Bart. Hosp. Lond.

FENELEY, Mr Roger Charles Leslie 51 Canynge Road, Clifton, Bristol BS8 3LH Tel: 0117 973 2858 Fax: 0117 973 0119 Email: rogerfenley@dial.pipex.com — MChir Camb. 1967, MB BChir 1958; FRCS Eng. 1962. (Guy's) Sen. Clin. Lect. Univ. Bristol.; Vis. Prof. of Health and Social Care Univ. of the W. of Eng.; Emerit. Cons. Urol. N. Bristol NHS Trust. Socs: Fell. Roy. Soc. Med.; BMA; Brit. Assn. Urol. Surg. Prev: Cons. Urol. Bristol & W.on Health Dist. (T) & S.mead Health Dist.; Sen. Clin. Lect. Univ. Bristol; Sen. Regist. (Urol.) Bristol Roy. Infirm.

FENERTY, Cecilia Helen Manchester Royal Eye Hospital, Oxford Road, Manchester M13 9WH Tel: 0161 276 5620 Fax: 0161 273 6354 — MB ChB 1988 Liverp.; FRCOphth 1995.

FENLON, Catherine Mary Greatwell, Duckpool Lane, West Chinnock, Crewkerne TA18 7QD — MB BCh BAO 1983 NUI; FRCSI 1988.

FENN, Mr Neil John 1 Amesbury Road, Penylan, Cardiff CF23 5DW Tel: 029 2048 0308 — MB BCh 1989 Wales; FRCS Ed. 1993. Specialist Regist. (Urol.) Morriston Hosp. Swansea.

FENN, Mr Peter John (retired) The Old Hall, Tonbridge Road, Barming, Maidstone ME16 9NH Tel: 01622 726330 — MB BS Lond. 1958; FRCS Eng. 1970; FRCS Ed. 1969. Cons. Surg. The Maidstone Hosp.

FENN, Sandra Elizabeth The Surgery, Madams Paddock, Chew Magna, Bristol BS40 8PP Tel: 01275 332420 Fax: 01275 333860 — BM BS 1989 Nottm.; BMedSci 1987. Trainee GP S.mead Hosp. VTS. Prev: SHO (A & E) MusGr. Pk. Hosp. Taunton.

FENNELL, Dean Anthony 63 Cedar Road, Oxford OX2 9ED Email: dfenn@zetnet.co.uk — MB BS 1993 Lond.; BSc (1st cl. Hons.) Lond. 1988; MRCP (UK) 1996. (Univ. Coll. Lond. Med. Sch.) Clin. Research Fell. (Antisense Pharmacol.) LRF Dept. Haemat. & Oncol. Univ. Coll. Lond. Inst. Child Health. Prev: SHO (Clin. Oncol.) Roy. Free Hosp. Lond.; SHO Hammersmith Hosp. & Roy. Brompton Hosp.; Ho. Off. (Med.) Univ. Coll. & Middlx. Hosps.

FENNELL, Jonathan Mark Barrington 6 Summefield, Ashtead KT12 2LF — BM 1989 Soton.; BSc Soton. 1984; MRCP (UK) 1993; FRCA 1996. Cons. in Anaesth. & Intens. Care Kingston Hosp. Galsworthy Rd Kingston Surrey. Socs: Intens. Care Soc.; Europ. Soc. of Intens. Care Mdicine; Soc. of Critical Care Med. (USA). Prev: SHO (Anaesth.) Soton. Gen. Hosp.; SHO (Intens. Care & Med.) Qu. Alexandra Hosp. Portsmouth.

FENNELLY, Elizabeth Deirdre Flat 4, 33 Russell Road, London W14 8HU — MB BS 1994 Lond.

FENNELLY, Mary Ellen Tangrin, 5 Heathfield Rd, Bushey WD23 2LH — MB BCh BAO 1982 NUI; LRCPI & LM, LRCSI & LM 1982; MRCPI 1985; FFARCSI 1988. Cons. Anaesth. Roy. Nat. Orthop. Hosp. Brockley Hill Stanmore. Socs: B. S. O. A.

FENNER, James Nicholas The Laurels Surgery, 73 Church Street, Flint CH6 5AF Tel: 01352 732349 Fax: 01352 730678; Moel View, Ruthin Road, Gwernymyndd, Mold CH7 5LQ — MB ChB 1978 Liverp.; MRCGP 1987.

FENNER, Michael Thomas Waterside Practice, St Brannocks Road, Ilfracombe EX34 8EG — MRCS Eng. LRCP Lond. 1972; MRCGP 1982; DObst RCOG 1976.

FENNER, Simon George Directorate of Anaesthesia, New Cross Hospital, Wolverhampton WV10 0QP Tel: 01902 644880 Fax: 01902 642859 — MB BS 1983 Lond.; BSc Lond. 1980; FCAnaesth. 1989. Cons. Anaesth., New Cross Hosp., Wolverhampton. Prev: Sen. Regist. (Anaesth.) Birm. Childr. Hosp.; Sen. Regist. Qu. Eliz. Hosp. Birm.; Regist. (Anaesth.) St. Geo. Hosp. Lond.

FENNERTY, Anthony Gerald c/o Harrogate District Hospital, Lancaster Park Road, Harrogate HG2 7SX Tel: 01423 885959 — MB ChB 1976 Liverp.; MD Liverp. 1987; FRCP Glas. 1993; MRCP (UK) 1980. Cons. Phys. Harrogate Dist. Hosp. Prev: Cons. Phys. S.ern Gen. Hosp. Glas.

FENNESSY, Patrick Alan Springhill, Braybrooke Road, Wargrave, Reading RG10 8D — MB BS 1964 Lond.

FENNING, Anne Helen The Health Centre, Chapel Road, Mendlesham, Stowmarket IP14 5SQ Tel: 01449 767722; White House, Mendlesham, Stowmarket IP14 5SL — MB BS 1976 Lond.

FENSKE, Mrs Mary 8 De Parys Avenue, Bedford MK40 2TW — MB BS 1992 Lond.; BSc (Hons.) Lond. 1989. (University College of London) GP Asst. Dr. Gray & Partners, Bedford.

FENTEM, Peter Harold Charlwood House, Carmen St, Great Chesterford, Saffron Walden CB10 1NR Tel: 01799 530401 Fax: 0870 0525 772 Email: phf@fentem.demon.co.uk — MB ChB (Hons.) Manch. 1959; MSc Manch. 1956, BSc (Hons.) 1955; FRCP Lond. 1989; MRCP (UK) 1985. (Manch.) Prof. Emerit. Univ. of Nottm.; Civil Cons. Aviat. Med. RAF.; Technical Adviser, Health Educat. Auth. Prev: Stroke Assn. Prof. Stroke Med. Nottm.; Dean Fac. Med. Univ. Nottm.; Prof. Physiol. Univ. Hosp. & Med. Sch. Univ. Nottm.

FENTIMAN, Graham John Crewe Medical Centre, 135 Boswall Parkway, Edinburgh EH5 2LY Tel: 0131 552 5544 Fax: 0131 551 5364 — MB BS 1970 Lond. (Westm.) Socs: BMA. Prev: Regist. (Anaesth.) St. Geo. Hosp. Lond.; SHO (Anaesth.) W.m. Hosp. Lond.; Princip. GP,Hounslow,Middlx.

FENTIMAN, Mr Ian Stuart ICRF Clinical Oncology Unit, Guy's Hospital, London SE1 9RT Tel: 020 7955 4540 Fax: 020 7403 8381 — MB BS 1968 Lond.; MD Lond. 1978; FRCS Eng. 1974; MRCS Eng. LRCP Lond. 1968. (King's Coll. Hosp.) Prof. Surgic. Oncol. & Cons. Surg. Guy's Hosp. Lond. Prev: Sen. Regist. (Surg.) Guy's Hosp. Lond.; Arris & Gale Lect. RCS Eng.; Lect. (Anat.) King's Coll. Univ. Lond.

FENTON, Alan Charles c/o Ward 35, Royal Victoria Infirmary, Queen Victoria Road, Newcastle upon Tyne NE1 4LP Tel: 0191 282 4346 Fax: 0191 282 5038 Email: a.c.fenton@ncl.ac.uk — MB BS 1982 Lond.; MD Leic. 1993; MRCP (UK) 1986. (King's Coll. Hosp.) Cons. Paediat. Roy. Vict. Infirm. Newc. u. Tyne. Prev: Lect. & Hon. Sen. Regist. (Child Health) Univ. Leicester.; Fell. Special Care Nursery Childr. Hosp. Vancouver, BC, Canada; Regist. (Paediat.) Leicester Hosps.

FENTON, Charles John Vincent Acton Lodge, Acton Burnell, Shrewsbury SY5 7PA — MB BS 1976 Lond.; MRCS Eng. LRCP Lond. 1975.

FENTON, Christopher Martin Highfield, Ballanard Road, Onchan, Douglas IM4 5AD — BM BS 1984 Nottm.; BM BS Nottm. l984.

FENTON, David The Gables, Mansfield Road, Farnsfield, Newark NG22 8HG — MB ChB 1974 Liverp.; DRCOG 1977.

FENTON, David Andrew 80 Harley Street, London W1G 7HL Tel: 020 7580 8356 Fax: 0207 637 0242; 1A Elm Tree Road, St. John's Wood, London NW8 9JY Tel: 020 7266 5575 — MB ChB 1977 Liverp.; MRCS Eng. LRCP Lond. 1977; MRCP (UK) 1981; T(M) 1991; FRCP 2000 UK. Cons. Dermat. (Hair, Scalp & Nail Dis.) St. John's Inst. Dermat. St. Thos. Hosp. Lond.; Cons. Dermat. (Hair, Scalp & Nail Dis. & Gen. Dermat.) St. And. Hosp.; Newham Gen. Hosp.; Med. Adviser to Brit. Red Cross (Cosmetic Camouflage Sect.), Vitiligo Soc. & Hairline Alopecia Areata Soc. Socs: Fell. Roy. Soc. Med.; Scientif. Fell. Zool. Soc. Lond.; Assn. BRd.casting Doctors. Prev: Sen. Regist. (Dermat.) St. Thos. Hosp. & St. John's Hosp. for Dis. of Skin Lond.; Regist. (Dermat. & Med.) Wycombe Gen. Hosp. High Wycombe; SHO (Gen. Med.) N. Manch. Gen. Hosp.

FENTON, David William Red Gables, Raven Field Lane, Hooton Roberts, Rotherham S65 4PQ — MB ChB 1973 Sheff.; FRCOG 1991, M 1979; DObst 1975. Cons. O & G Rotherham Dist. Gen. Hosp. Socs: Brit. Soc. Colposc. & Cervic. Pathol.; Gyn. Soc.

FENTON, Elizabeth Susan Noel (retired) Perrins House, Moorlands Road, Malvern WR14 2TZ Tel: 01684 576554 — MB ChB MB ChB Liverp. 1941; FFA RCS Eng. 1953; DA Eng. 1949. Prev: Cons. Anaesth. Liverp. Cardiothoracic Surg. Unit & BRd.green Hosp.

FENTON, Fiona Mary 21 Blacketts Wood Drive, Chorleywood, Rickmansworth WD3 5PY — MB BS 1996 Lond.

FENTON, George Reginald (retired) 54 Thorne Road, Doncaster DN1 2JP Tel: 01302 61222 — MB ChB 1957 Sheff.; MA Oxf. 1947; BSc Sheff. 1941, MB ChB 1957; DObst RCOG 1959.

FENTON, Ida Mary Kirk 54 Craiglockhart Terrace, Edinburgh EH14 1XH — MB ChB 1943 Ed.

FENTON, Isobel Stewart 12 Ravelston Heights, Edinburgh EH4 3LX — MB ChB 1946 Ed.; DPH Lond. 1949. (Ed.)

FENTON, Jennifer Ann Ridingleaze Medical Centre, Ridingleaze, Bristol BS11 0QE Tel: 0117 982 2693 Fax: 0117 938 1707 — MB ChB 1973 Bristol; DA Eng. 1977. SHO (Paediat.) Glos. Roy. Hosp.

FENTON, John Abinton Park Surgery, Christchurch Medical Centre, Ardington Road, Northampton NN1 5LT Tel: 01604 30291 Fax: 01604 603524; 379 Kettering Road, Spinney Hill, Northampton NN3 6QT Tel: 01604 643828 — MB ChB 1963 Leeds; MRCS Eng. LRCP Lond. 1963. (Leeds) Prev: Regist. Anaesth. United Leeds Hosps.

FENTON, John Chandos Bethel (retired) Y Berllan, 6 Rushbrook Close, Cardiff CF14 2BN — MB BChir 1952 Camb.; MA Camb. 1952; FRCPath 1973, M 1965; DCP Lond 1955. Prev: Sen. Lect. & Cons. Chem. Path. St. Bart. Hosp. Lond.

FENTON, John Charles (retired) 16 St Mary's Park, Bucklesham, Ipswich IP10 0DY — MB BS 1957 Lond.

FENTON, John Frederick Arthur (retired) 21 Blandy Road, Henley-on-Thames RG9 1QB — MRCS Eng. LRCP Lond. 1943.

FENTON, John Sinton Clifton Surgery, Victoria Place, 35 Victoria Road, Dartmouth TQ6 9RT Tel: 01803 832212 Fax: 01803 837917; Overstoke, Bidder Close, Stoke Fleming, Dartmouth TQ6 0NZ Tel: 01803 770761 Email: jsf.dart@lineone.net — MRCS Eng. LRCP 1967 Lond.; Dobst RCOG 1970; MB BS 1967 Lond.; DCH 1969 Eng. (Char. Cross) Liason GP Dartmouth Hosp. Prev: SHO (Paediat., Obst. & Cas.) Plymouth Gen. Hosp. (Freedom Fields Br.).

FENTON, Kevin Andrew 100A West Green Road, London N15 5AA — MB BS 1990 West Indies.

FENTON, Leonard Martin (retired) 15 Blossom Way, Hillingdon, Uxbridge UB10 9LL Tel: 01895 235915 Email: lenfenton2@cs.com — MRCS Eng. LRCP Lond. 1952. Prev: Capt. RAMC.

FENTON, Lesley Ann (retired) Goat Hill Farm, Briestfield Road, Dewsbury WF12 0NU Tel: 01924 840757 Fax: 01924 840757 — MB BS 1974 Lond.; MRCPath 1998. Prev: Cons. Histopath. & Cytopath. Dewsbury Dist. Hosp.

FENTON, Leslie Montague (retired) 5 Carlton Avenue, Prestwich, Manchester M25 0EB — LRCP LRCS Ed. LRFPS Glas. 1949; Medallist in Forensic Medicine, Edin. Univ.; MFOM RCP Lond. 1979; Cert. Av. Med. 1983; DIH Soc. Apoth. Lond. 1969; MRCGP 1966; BA (HONS) 1999. Phys. i/c Dept. Occupat. Med. City Manch.; Cons. Phys. (Occupat. Med.) Harrison & Jones Gp. Ltd.; Med. Adviser Thorn Brimar Gp.; Exam. Surg. St. John Ambul. Brig. (Manch.); Med. Ref. (Occupat. Med.) Dept. Health & Social Security & Civil Serv; Med. Off. Civil Aviat. Auth. Prev: Gp. Med. Adviser Brit. Aerospace PLC (Manch. Div.).

FENTON, Mark John 8 Rowlands Close, Wolvercote, Oxford OX2 8PW — MB BS 1992 Lond.

FENTON, Mr Oliver Michael Pinderfields General Hospital, Aberford Road, Wakefield WF1 4DG Tel: 01924 201688 — MB BS 1974 Lond.; FRCS Eng. 1978. Cons. Plastic Surg. Pinderfields Gen. Hosp. Wakefield. Prev: Cons. Plastic Surg. Aberd. Roy. Infirm. & Roy. Aberd. Childr. Hosp.; Sen. Regist. (Plastic Surg.) Hosp. for Sick Childr. Gt. Ormond St. & St. Thos. Hosp. Lond.

FENTON, Patricia Anne Microbiology Department, Doncaster Royal Infirmary, Doncaster DN2 5LT Tel: 01302 366666 Email: patricia.fenton@dbh.nhs.uk — MB BS 1978 Newc.; FRCPath 1996, M 1984. Cons. Microbiol. Doncaster Roy. Infirm.

FENTON, Mr Peter John Bere Farm House, North Boarhunt, Fareham PO17 6JL Tel: 01329 832169 — MB BS Lond. 1959; FRCS Eng. (Ophth.) 1969; DO Eng. 1964. (St. Thos.) Emerit. Cons. Ophth. Qu. Alexandra Hosp. Cosham. Prev: Sen. Regist. Eye Dept. St. Thos. Hosp. Lond.; Sen. Regist. Retinal Unit & Resid. Surg. Off. Moorfields Eye Hosp. (City Rd. Br.).

FENTON, Theodore Henry Michael Tel: 020 8401 3000 Fax: 020 8401 3372 Email: theo.fenton@mhc-tr.sthames.nhs.uk — MB BChir 1984 Camb.; MA Camb. 1985; MRCP (UK) 1989; FRCPCH 1997; DCH RCP Lond. 1988. Cons. Paediat. Mayday Univ. Hosp. Croydon. Prev: Sen. Regist. S.mead Hosp. Bristol; Sen. Resid. Hosp. Sick Childr. Toronto, Canada.

FENTON, Thomas William 79 May Lane, Hollywood, Birmingham B47 5PA Tel: 01564 822520 — MB ChB 1956 Ed.; FRCPsych 1984, M 1971; DPM Eng. 1961. (Ed.) Indep. Pract. Medico-Legal Birm.; Mem. W. Midl. Ment. Health Rev. Tribunal SOAD Ment. Health Act Commiss. Prev: Med. Dir. Hollymoor Hosp. Birm.; Cons. Psychiat. Solihull HA; Sen. Regist. (Psychiat.) Qu. Eliz. & Midl. Nerve Hosps. Birm.

FENTON, Timothy Roy 55 De Beauvoir Road, London N1 5AU Tel: 020 7249 6292 Email: tim.fenton@btinternet.com — MB BS 1971 Lond.; MD Lond. 1987, MSc 1981; FRCP Lond. 1994; MRCP (UK) 1975; FRCPCH 1996. (Medical College of St. Bartholomew's Hospital) Cons. Paediat. Greenwich Dist. Hosp. & Qu. Eliz. Hosp. Woolwich. Socs: Brit. Soc. Paediat. Gastroenterol. & Nutrit. Prev: Sen. Regist. St. Geo. Hosp. Lond. & Qu. Marys Hosp. for Childr. Carshalton; Research Fell. & Hon. Sen. Regist. Inst. Child Health, Hosp. for Sick Childr. Lond.

FENTON, William Stewart Rolleston (retired) 22 Amersham Road, High Wycombe HP13 6QU Tel: 01494 529054 — MRCS Eng. LRCP Lond. 1945; MA, MB BChir Camb. 1945; DObst RCOG 1946. Prev: GP High Wycombe.

FENTON-LEE, Carol Adele Flat 3, 176 Ingram St., Glasgow G1 1DN — MB ChB 1991 Glas.; MRCP (UK) 1994.

FENTON-MAY, Jane Mary Institute of Medical Genetics, University Hospital of Wales, Heath Park, Cardiff CF14 4XW Tel: 029 2074 4021 Fax: 029 2074 7603 Email: jfm@fenton_may.org — MB BCh 1975 Wales; BSc (Med. Sci.) St. And. 1972; Dip Palliat. Med. Wales 1999; MRCGP 1979; DRCOG 1978; Cert JCC Lond. 1978. Clin. Asst. (Med. Genetics) Inst. Med. Genetics Cardiff; Clin. Med. Off. (Genetics) Gwent NHS Trust; GP Locum. Socs: Fell. BMA. Prev: Clin. Asst. (Chronic Geriat.) Glan Ely Hosp. Cardiff; Trainee GP Newport VTS.; Clin. Med. Off. (Genetics) Mid. Glam. HA.

FENTY, Michael Alexander Houndlaw Park Health Centre, Houndlaw Park, Eyemouth TD14 5DA Tel: 018907 50383 Fax: 018907 51749; Grey Gables, Coldingham, Eyemouth TD14 5NH Tel: 018907 71495 — MB ChB 1971 Aberd.; MRCGP 1976; DObst RCOG 1974. (Aberd.) Hon. Med. Off. RNLI St. Abbs. Socs: BMA; Berwicksh. Med. Soc. Prev: Ho. Off. Lewis Hosp. Stornoway & Roy. Aberd. Childr. Hosp.; SHO Raigmore Hosp. Inverness.

FENUYI, Ifebdejo Adebola Akintola 3 Clipper Close, Kimburn St., Rotherhithe, London SE16 6DR — MB BS 1985 Ibadan; MRCOG 1994.

FENWICK, Craig David 40 Willow Crescent, Glenrothes KY6 1EY — MB ChB 1993 Ed.

FENWICK, Dale Kenneth Frederick 11A Beechgrove Terrace, Aberdeen AB15 5DR Tel: 01224 649233 — MB ChB 1988 Ed.; MRCOG 1996. (Edin.) Career Regist. (O & G) Aberd.

FENWICK, Gillian Mary Exwick Barton Cottage, St Andrews Road, Exeter EX4 2AF — MB BS 1972 Lond.

FENWICK, Hannah Jane 16 White House Gr, Elvington, York YO41 4AL — BM BS 1997 Nottm.

FENWICK, Helen Catherine 14 Cavendish Close, Doveridge, Ashbourne DE6 5LB — MB ChB 1998 Liverp.; MB ChB Liverp 1998.

FENWICK, Ian Ernest New Cross Street Health Centre, New Cross Street, Bradford BD5 7AW Tel: 01274 733232; 9 Glen Road, Bingley BD16 3EU — MB ChB 1974 Liverp.; MRCGP 1979; Dip. Palliat. Med. Wales 1992; DRCOG 1978.

FENWICK, Mr John Dalton The Leeds General Infirmary, Great George St., Leeds LS1 3EX — MB ChB 1967 Leeds; FRCS Eng. 1974; DLO Eng. 1971. (Leeds) Cons. ENT Surg. Leeds Gen. Infirm., Seacroft Hosp. & Wharfedale Gen.; Hosp. Otley. Socs: BMA. Prev: Rotating Sen. Regist. (ENT) Birm. AHA (T); Ho. Phys. Profess. Med. Unit. Leeds Gen. Infirm.; Demonst. Dept. Anat. Univ. Leeds.

FENWICK, Keith William Harry 6 Monkend Terrace, Croft-on-Tees, Darlington DL2 2SQ — MB BS 1952 Durh.; DPH RCPS Eng. 1961.

FENWICK, Michael John 5 Springfield Close, Ovington, Prudhoe NE42 6EL — MB BS 1992 Newc.

FENWICK, Peter Brooke Cadogan The Institute of Psychiatry, De Crespighy Park, London SE5 8AZ Tel: 020 7703 5411; 42 Herne Hill, London SE24 9QP Tel: 020 7274 3154 — MB BChir 1960 Camb.; BA Camb.1957; FRCPsych 1986; DPM Eng. 1966. Sen. Lect. Inst. Psychiat. Lond.; Hon. Cons. Clin. Research Neurophysiol. BRd.moor Hosp.; Cons. Clin. Neuropsychiat. Radccliffe Infirm. Oxf. Prev: Cons. Neuropsychiat. Bethlem Roy. & Maudsley Hosps. Lond.; Cons. Clin. Neurophysiol. St. Thos. Hosp. & W.m. Hosp. Lond.

FENWICK, Sean 4 Sledmere Close, Owington Farm, Billingham TS23 3LA — MB ChB 1993 Liverp. SHO Rotat. (Med.) S. Tees HA. Socs: BMA.

FENWICK, Stephen William Border Cottage, 32 Meadow St., Nottingham Lane, Ironville, Nottingham NG16 5NU — BM BS 1995 Nottm.

FENWICK, Mr Thomas (retired) Earldoms Lodge, Whiteparish, Salisbury SP5 2QW Tel: 01794 884228 — MB BChir 1939 Camb.; MChir Camb. 1952; FRCS Eng. 1948; MRCS Eng. LRCP Lond. 1938. Hon. Cons. Surg. Portsmouth & SE Hants. HA. Prev: Ho. Phys. (Obst.) St. Thos. Hosp.

FERDINAND, Mr Rupert David Department of Orthopaedics, Ninewells Hospital & Medical Shool, Dundee DD1 9SY Tel: 01382 660111; Hilaf House, Easter Bendochy, Blairgowrie PH13 9HU Tel: 01828 627051 Fax: 01828 627051 Email: rupert@ferdi.demon.co.uk — MB BS 1991 Newc.; BMedSc Newc. 1988; FRCS Eng. 1995; ECFMG 1998. (Newc. u. Tyne) Specialist Regist. (Orthop.) E. Scotl. Rotat. Prev: Peri-Fell.sh. Rotat. (Surg.) Newc.

FERDINANDUS, Edmond Leendert Cornelis Department of Ear, Nose & Throast, Whipps Cross Hospital, Whipps Cross Road, London E11 1NR — Artsexamen 1992 Rotterdam.

FERENTINOS, Athanassios Flat 7, Barker Mews, Victoria Rise, Clapham, London SW4 0NL — Ptychio Iatrikes 1981 Thessalonika.

FERGIE, Iain 15 Cameron Drive, Bearsden, Glasgow G61 2NH — MRCS Eng. LRCP Lond. 1991.

FERGIE, Neil 15 Cameron Drive, Bearsden, Glasgow G61 2NH — MB ChB 1991 Glas.; FRCS Glas. 1995.

FERGIE-WOODS, David Fergie 72 The Drive, Hove BN3 3PE Tel: 01273832546; The Cottage, 9 Trinity Road, Hurstpierpoint, Hassocks BN6 9UY Tel: 01273 832546 — MB BS Lond. 1959; LMSSA Lond. 1958; MFHom 1961. (Middlx.) Indep. GP E. Sussex & W. Sussex; Late Lt. RAMC RARO. Prev: NHS Princip. GP Burgess Hill; Assoc. Dir. Clin. Research Squibb Europe Ltd. Twickenham; Med. Adviser ICI Pharmaceuts. Div. Macclesfield.

FERGUS, Cameron James Yule 4D Reres Road, Broughty Ferry, Dundee DD5 2QA Tel: 01382 778021 — MB ChB 1987 Ed.; MRCGP 1991; DRCOG 1990. SHO (Radiother.) Ninewells Hosp. Dundee. Prev: Resid. Med. Off. Kempsey Hosp. NSW, Austral.; Clin. Med. Off. (Community Child Health) Stirling; Trainee GP Edin.

FERGUS, Gillian Catherine Flat 4/1 Canada Court, 63 Miller St., Merchant City, Glasgow G1 3EB — MB ChB 1996 Glas.

FERGUS, Mr John Naismith (retired) Cedar House, Yardley Hastings, Northampton NN7 1EX Tel: 01604 696230 Email: john@fegus.demon.co.uk — BM BCh Oxf. 1959; MA Oxf. 1959; FRCS Ed. 1965; FRCS Eng. 1965. Cons. Surg. (Urol.) N.ampton Gen. Hosp.; Anat. Demonst.: Univ. of Camb. Med. Sch. Prev: Sen. Regist. Inst. Urol. Lond.

FERGUS, Margaret Cecil (retired) Crispens Nursing Home, 43A Waverley Lane, Farnham GU9 8BH — MRCS Eng. LRCP Lond. 1927; DOMS Eng. 1932. Prev: Ophth. Ho. Surg. St. Mary's Hosp.

FERGUSON, Alastair Stuart St. Andrews Rectory, PO Box 21, Mvurwi, Zimbabwe Tel: 00 2 63 772401 Fax: 00 2 63 772561 Email: saintandrew@mango.zw; 7 Mill Street, North Petherton, Bridgwater TA6 6LX Tel: 01278 662357 — MB BS 1969 Lond.; MA Oxon. 1982, BA 1978; MRCS Eng. LRCP Lond. 1969. (Lond. Hosp.) Rector St. Andrews Ch. Mvurwi, Zimbabwe; GP Mvurwi, Zimbabwe. Prev: GP Burnham-on-Crouch; Regist. (Obst. & Gyn.) Univ. Cape Town, S. Afr.

FERGUSON, Alexander David Royal Devon & Exeter Hospital, Barrack Road, Exeter EX2 5DW Tel: 01392 402133 — BM BCh 1955 Oxf.; MA Oxf. 1956, BM BCh 1955; FRCP Lond. 1977; MRCP Ed. 1963. (St. Bart.) Phys. (Thoracic Med.) Devon AHA. Socs: Thoracic Soc. Prev: Head, Respirat. Clinic Groote Schuur Hosp. Cape Town; Assoc. Prof. Fac. Med. Univ. Cape Town.

FERGUSON, Alexandra Grace Alicia 92 Yew Tree Lane, Solihull B91 2RA — MB BS 1996 Lond.

FERGUSON, Alice Marjorie 134C Howth Drive, Glasgow G13 1RL — MB ChB 1997 Glas. SHO Psychiat. Hosp. Pract., Glas. Socs: BMA; MDDUS. Prev: Jun. Ho. Off. Med., Glas.; Jun. Ho. Off. Surg., Dumfries.

FERGUSON, Allison Elizabeth Royal Hospital for Sick Children, Yorkhill, Glasgow G3 8SJ Tel: 0141 201 0000 — MB ChB 1985 Glas.; MRCP (UK) 1991; MRCGP 1989; DCH Glas. 1988. Cons. Paediat. (Community) Yotkhill NHS Trust. Socs: Roy. Coll. Paediat. and Child Health; Brit. Assn. of Community Child Health. Prev: Sen. Regist. (Paediat.) Yorkhill NHS Trust.; Cons. Paediat. Dumfries and Galloway Community Trust Dumfries.

FERGUSON, Andrew Kingsgate Medical Practic, Bathgate Primary Care center, Wgitburn Road, Bathgate EH48 2SS Tel: 01506 653134 Fax: 01506 635943 — MB ChB 1986 Ed.; MRCGP 1990; DRCOG 1990; DGM RCP Lond. 1989; DCH RCPS Glas. 1988. Prev: Trainee GP Falkirk; SHO (Cas.) Stirling.

FERGUSON, Andrew George 75 Ringstead Crescent, Crosspool, Sheffield S10 5SH — MB ChB 1988 Sheff.; MRCGP 2000 UK; MPH Nottm. 1995; DTM & H Liverp. 1995; MFPHM RCP (UK) 1997. (Sheffield) Salaried GP Sheff.; Med. Coordinator for HMD Response (Charity Head Quarters, Lond.).

FERGUSON, Angela Elizabeth Woodlands Surgery, 5 Woodlands Road, Redhill RH1 6EY Tel: 01737 761343 Fax: 01737 770804; The Dove House, Wasp Green Lane, Outwood, Redhill RH1 5QE Tel: 01342 843716 — MB BS 1980 Lond.; MRCGP 1984.

FERGUSON, Miss Angela Mary North Manchester General Hospital, Delaney's Road, Manchester M8 5RB Tel: 0161 795 4567; Tel: 0161 226 0112 — MB BCh BAO 1972 Belf.; MD 1989; BSc (1st cl. Hons.) Belf. 1969, MD 1987; FRCOG 1993, M 1981; DCH RCP Lond. 1976. Cons. O & G N. Manch. Gen. Hosp.; Clin. Director. Socs: Brit. Colposcopy & Cervical Path. Soc.; Brit. Menopause Soc.; BMA. Prev: Dist. Tutor.

FERGUSON, Ann (retired) New Barn, 39A Grange Road, Broadstairs CT10 3ER Tel: 01843 867848 Fax: 01843 868537 — MB BS 1967 Lond.; MRCS Eng. LRCP Lond. 1967; FRCA 1971. Cons. Anaesth. Thanet Healthcare Trust. Prev: Regist. (Anaesth.) St. Bart. Hosp. Lond.

FERGUSON, Anne Gastrointestinal Unit, Weston General Hospital, Edinburgh EH4 2XU Tel: 0131 537 1731 Fax: 0131 537 1007 Email: anne.ferguson@ed.ac.uk; 204 Newhaven Road, Edinburgh EH6 4QE Tel: 0131 552 8810 — MB ChB 1964 Glas.; MB ChB Gls. 1964; PhD Glas. 1974, BSc (Hons.) 1961; FRCP Ed. 1981; FRCP Glas. 1975, M 1968; FRCP Lond. 1977, M 1967; FRCPath 1984, M 1973. (Glas.) Prof. Gastroenterol. Univ. Edin.; Cons. Phys. Gastrointestinal Unit W.. Gen. Hosp. Edin. Prev: Lect. (Bact. & Immunol.) Univ. Glas.; Lect. (Med.) & Hon. Regist. Roy. Infirm. Univ. Glas.; Reader (Med. & Gastroenterol.) Univ. Edin.

FERGUSON, Anne Elizabeth Dalmellington Health Centre, 33 Main Street, Dalmellington, Ayr KA6 7QL Tel: 01292 550238 Fax: 01292 551342; 29 Carsphairn Road, Dalmellington, Ayr KA6 7RE Tel: 01292 550325 — MB ChB 1971 Manch.

FERGUSON, Anne Gerardine Flat C, 15 Hughenden Gardens, Glasgow G12 9XW — MB ChB 1968 Glas.; DObst RCOG 1970. (Glas.)

FERGUSON, Anne Pamela Newton Heath Health Centre, 2 Old Church St., Newton Heath, Manchester M40 2JF Tel: 0161 684 9696 Fax: 0161 684 9264 Email: anne.ferguson@mchtr.nwest.nhs.uk — MB ChB 1981 Manch.; MRCP (Paediat.) (UK) 1985; FRCPCH 1997; DCCH RCP Ed. 1989. (Manchester) p/t Cons. Paediat. Community Child Health Manch.; Hon. Cons. Neurol. at N. Manch. Gen. Hosp.; Hon. Lect. Univ. Manch. Dept. of Child Health. Socs: Brit. Assn. Community Child Health; Founder Child Health; Fell. Roy. Coll. Paediat. Prev: Sen. Regist. & Regist. (Community Paediat.) NW RHA; SHO (Paediat.) Roy. Manch. Childr. Hosp.; Tutor (Child Health) & Hon. Regist. Univ. Manch.

FERGUSON, Anthony John Alexander (retired) 35 Cradock Villas, Bishop Auckland DL14 6HB Tel: 01388 602746 — MB BS 1944 Durh.; FRCGP 1978, M 1962. Prev: Chairm. Indust. Injuries Med. Bds. & War Pens. Med. Bds.

FERGUSON, Arthur James Woodlands Surgery, 5 Woodlands Road, Redhill RH1 6EY Tel: 01737 761343 Fax: 01737 770804; The Dove House, Wasp Green Lane, Outwood, Redhill RH1 5QE Tel: 01342 843716 — MB BS 1980 Lond.; MRCGP 1984.

FERGUSON, Arthur Wellwood (retired) 284 Kimbolton Road, Bedford MK41 8AG — MB BChir Camb. 1947; MA Camb. 1947; FRCP Lond. 1972, M 1951; DCH Eng. 1950; FRCPCH 1997. Hon. Cons. Paediat. Bedford Gen. Hosp. Prev: Cons. Paediat. Bedford Gen. Hosp.

FERGUSON, Audrey Lilian 62 West Sotckwell Street, Colchester CO1 1HE — MD 1950 Ed.; MB ChB 1944; DPM Eng. 1948. (Ed.)

FERGUSON, Barrie Margaret Wonford Green Surgery, Burnthouse Lane, Exeter EX2 6NF Tel: 01392 250135 Fax: 01392 498572 — MB BS 1989 Lond.

FERGUSON, Brian Gerard Stonebridge Research Unit, Stonebridge Centre, Cardiff St., Carlton Road, Nottingham NG3 2FH Tel: 0115 948 3268 Fax: 0115 985984 Email: brian@stoneresearch.com — MB BCh BAO 1977 NUI; MRCPsych 1984; MRCGP 1981; DCH Dub. 1981; DRCOG Lond. 1980. Cons. Psychiat. Nottm. HA; Dir. Clin. Research Dept. Stone Bridge Centre.

FERGUSON, Bridget Mary 17 Crawley Wood Close, Camberley GU15 2BX — MB ChB 1978 Dundee.

FERGUSON, Bruce James Mackenzie Y Graigwen, Station St., Maesteg CF34 9AL Tel: 01656 662166 — MB BS 1978 Lond.; BSc (Hons.) Lond. 1975, MB BS 1978; FFA RCS Eng. 1983. (St. Bart.) Cons. Anaesth. & Dir. Intens. Care P.ss Wales Hosp. Bridgend.

FERGUSON, Catherine Ann 82 Riverdale Road, Sheffield S10 3FD Tel: 0114 230 7334 — MB ChB Sheff. 1979; BSc (Hons.) Sheff. 1975; MRCGP 1994; DRCOG 1982. Clin. Asst. (A & E) Roy. Hallamsh. Hosp. Sheff.

FERGUSON, Catherine Eleanor (retired) Craigdarroch Lochdon, Lochdon, Isle of Mull PA64 6AP Tel: 01680 812451 — MB BCh BAO 1942 Dub. Prev: Asst. Co. Moh. Warw. CC. Dermatol. RAMC.

FERGUSON, Catherine Jane 75 Ringstead Crescent, Crosspool, Sheffield S10 5SH — MB ChB 1988 Sheff.; 2000 FRCR (Oncology); MRCP (UK) 1991. Regist. (Oncol. & Radiother.) W.on Pk. Hosp. Sheff. Prev: SHO Rotat. (Med.) Nether Edge Hosp. & Roy. Hallamsh. Sheff.; Regist. (Med.) Waikato Hosp. Hamilton, NZ.

FERGUSON, Catriona Nancy 1 Sharpleshall Street, London NW1 8YL — MB BS 1987 Lond.

FERGUSON, Charles Joseph Shaun Salisbury Medical Centre, 474 Antrim Road, Belfast BT15 5GF Tel: 01232 777905; 87 Downview Park W., Belfast BT15 5HZ Tel: 01232 778708 — MB BCh BAO 1979 Belf.; MRCGP 1988; DRCOG 1981.

FERGUSON, Colin John 139 Stanwell Road, Penarth CF64 3LL — MB ChB 1980 Dundee.

FERGUSON, Colin Nicol 20 Scholars Road, London SW12 0PG — BM BCh 1978 Oxf.; FFA RCS Eng. 1988. Cons. & Hon. Sen. Lect. Anaesth. & Intens. Care St. Bart. Hosp. Lond.; Europ. Dip. IC Med. 1993. Socs: Intens. Care Soc. & Europ. Shock Soc.

FERGUSON, Craig Andrew Upper Crichie, Stuartfield, Peterhead AB42 5DX Tel: 01771 624206 — MB ChB 1997 Aberd.; BSc 1995. (Aberdeen University) SHO Research Fell., Borders Gen. Hosp. Socs: BMA; MDDUS. Prev: SHO (Geriat. Med.), Borders Gen. Hosp.; Jun. Ho. Off. (Cardiol.) Infec. Dis. ARI & Chest Med.

FERGUSON, David (retired) 104 Shipston Road, Stratford-upon-Avon CV37 7LR — MB ChB 1934 Glas.

FERGUSON, Mr David George Royal Hallamshire Hospital, 8 Beech Hill Road, Sheffield S10 2SB Tel: 01142 712178 Fax: 01142 713765; Woodview, 226 Abbeydale Road S., Dore, Sheffield S17 3LA — MB BCh BAO Belf. 1970; FRCS Ed. 1974; FFAEM 1993. Dir. of Emerg. Servs. Roy. Hallamsh. Hosp. Sheff. & Med. Dir. Centr. Sheff. Univ. Hosps.

FERGUSON, David Ian (retired) 34 Malcolmson Close, Chad Hill, Edgbaston, Birmingham B15 3LS Tel: 0121 454 3774 — MB ChB 1952 Birm. Prev: Ho. Off. St. Chad's Hosp. Birm.

FERGUSON, David Muir Rectory Meadow Surgery, School Lane, Amersham HP7 0HG Tel: 01494 727711 Fax: 01494 431790 — MB ChB 1985 Ed.; MRCGP 1989; DCCH RCP Ed. 1989; DRCOG 1988; DGM RCP Lond. 1987.

FERGUSON, David Robert Nithsdale Road Surgery, 162 Nithsdale Road, Glasgow G41 5RU Tel: 0141 424 1831 Fax: 0141 423 7422; 162 Nithsdale Road, Glasgow G41 5RU Tel: 0141 424 1831 — MB ChB 1974 Glas.; BSc Glas. 1968, MB ChB 1974; MRCGP 1978; DRCOG 1977. (Glas.)

FERGUSON, David Whigham (Surgery) Merton Lodge, West St., Alford LN13 9DH Tel: 01507 463262 Fax: 01507 466447; The Elms, 36 East St., Alford LN13 9EH Tel: 01507 463426 — MB ChB 1959 Glas.; FRCGP 1995, M 1969; Cert. JCC Lond. 1978; DObst RCOG 1961. Prev: Ho. Surg. Midw. Robroyston Hosp. Glas.; Ho. Surg. W.. Infirm. Glas.; Ho. Phys. Roy. Infirm. Glas.

FERGUSON, Deborah Ann Whitefield Health Centre, Bury New Road, Whitefield, Manchester M45 8GH Tel: 0161 766 8221; 10 Park Hill Drive, Whitefield, Manchester M45 7PD — MB ChB 1984 Manch.; MRCGP 1988; DRCOG 1986. (Manchester) Prev: Clin. Asst. (Dermat.) Rochdale Infirm.; Trainee GP Bury; SHO (Paediat., O & G & Geriat.) Stepping Hill Hosp. Stockport.

FERGUSON, Diana Elizabeth Jane Beaumont Street Surgery, 28 Beaumont Street, Oxford OX1 2NT Tel: 01865 311811 Fax: 01865 310327; 13 Park Town, Oxford OX2 6SN — MB BChir 1976 Camb.; MA, MB Camb. 1976, BChir 1975; MFHom 1995; MRCGP 1980; DCH Eng. 1979; DRCOG 1977.

FERGUSON, Douglas James Longlane House, Forest Road, Wokingham RG40 5SD — MB BS 1993 Lond.; BSc (Hons.) Lond. 1990, MB BS 1993.

FERGUSON, Douglas Robertson 83 The Mall, Swindon SN1 4JE Tel: 01793 23894 — MD 1965 Bristol; MB ChB 1960. (Bristol) Lect. Dept. Pharmacol. Univ. Camb. Socs: Soc. Endocrinol. & Brit. Pharmacol. Soc. Prev: Lect. Dept. Pharmacol. Univ. Bristol; Ho. Phys. St. Margt.'s Hosp. Stratton St. Margt.; Ho. Surg. Surgic. Unit Bristol Roy. Infirm.

FERGUSON, Duncan James Munro (retired) 14 Cromarty Crescent, Bearsden, Glasgow G61 3LU Tel: 0141 942 1076 Fax: 0141 943 2445 Email: dochie.dph@ukgateway.net — MB ChB 1955 Glas.; FFA RCS Eng. 1962; DA Eng. 1959. Prev: Cons. Anaesth. Roy. Infirm. & Roy. Matern. Hosp. Glas.

FERGUSON, Eileen May (retired) c/o Mrs. Aquinkan, 78 Boundry Road, Woodgreen, London N22 6AB Tel: 020 8826 0636 — LRCPI & LM, LRSCI & LM 1938; LRCPI & LM, LRCSI & LM 1938. Prev: Clin. Med. Off. Rochdale AHA.

FERGUSON, Elaine 14 Scargie Road, Kilmarnock KA1 4UR — MB ChB 1991 Glas.

FERGUSON, Elizabeth 15C Hughenden Gardens, Hyndland, Glasgow G12 9XW — MB ChB 1998 Glas.; MB ChB Glas 1998.

FERGUSON, Elizabeth Mary Northumberland Community Health, The Health Centre, Civic Precinct, Forum Way, Cramlington NE23 6QN Tel: 01670 713021 Fax: 01670 735880 Email: elizabeth.ferguson@gp-84038.nhs.uk; The Vicarage, Kirkwhelpington, Newcastle upon Tyne NE19 2RT Tel: 01830 540260 — MB BS 1968 Newc. (Univ. Newc. u. Tyne) p/t Gen. Practitioner Cramlington, GP Diabetes Lead Blyth Valley PCG. Socs: BMA. Prev: GP Windsor, Berks. & N. Shields; SHO (Gen. Med.) Newc. Gen. Hosp.

FERGUSON, Evelyn Anne 15 Balgillo Road, Broughty Ferry, Dundee DD5 3LU — MB ChB 1984 Aberd.; DCCH RCP Ed. 1990.

FERGUSON, Evelyn Jean 17 Caltrop Place, Wallace Glen, Stirling FK7 7XS — MB ChB 1995 Glas.

FERGUSON, Frances Thornton (retired) Lingmell, 11 Selborne Drive, Douglas IM2 3LT Tel: 01624 621698 — MB ChB 1938 Manch.

FERGUSON, George Graham Cruden Medical Group, The Surgery, Main St Hatton, Peterhead AB42 0QQ Tel: 01779 841208 Fax: 01779 841239; Windyhill, Whinnyfold, Cruden Bay, Peterhead AB42 0QH Tel: 01779 812556 — MB ChB 1974 Aberd.; MRCGP 1978; DRCOG 1977.

FERGUSON, Gillon Caldwell 39 Vicarage Lane, Kingsthorpe, Northampton NN2 6QS — MB ChB 1960 St. And.; FRCP Ed. 1976, M 1966; FRCP Lond. 1980, M 1967. Cons. Phys. N.ampton Gen. Hosp. & Chest Clinic. Socs: Brit. Thoracic Assn. Prev: Phys. MRC Tuberc. & Chest Dis. Unit; Sen. Regist. (Med.) Dundee Roy. Infirm.; Regist. Chest. Serv. E.. Region (Scotl.).

FERGUSON, Ginette Eynhalllow, 26 Clinkerheel Drive, Birkhill, Dundee DD2 5RN — MB ChB 1989 Dundee.

FERGUSON, Gordon Bewick Crescent Surgery, 27 Bewick Crescent, Newton Aycliffe DL5 5LH Tel: 01325 313289 Fax: 01325 301428; 4 Highside Road, Heighington, Newton Aycliffe DL5 6PG Tel: 01325 320860 — MB ChB 1979 Leeds; MRCGP 1983; DRCOG 1983; MA (Med. Educ.) Durham 1998. (Leeds)

FERGUSON, Mr Graeme Henry Consultant Geral & Vascular Surgeon, Royal Bolton Hospital, Minerva Rd, Farnworth, Bolton BL4 0JR Tel: 01204 390544 — MB ChB 1981 Dundee; MD Dundee 1991; FRCS Ed. 1985. Cons. Surg. Bolton Hosps. NHS Trust. Prev: Sen. Regist. (Gen. Surg.) NW RHA.

FERGUSON, Heather Ruth General Medicine, Ulster Hospital, Dundonald, Belfast BT16 1RH — MB BCh 1998 Belf.; MB BCh Belf 1998. SHO Ulster Hosp.

FERGUSON, Helen Alexander c/o Drive R. M. Ainley, 49 Woodgrange Avenue, Kenton, Harrow HA3 0XG — MB ChB 1945 Glas.

FERGUSON, Helen Julann 17 The Abbey, Romsey SO51 8EN — MB BS 1992 Lond.; DRCOG 1996; MRCGP 1997. (Charing Cross and Westminster Medical School)

FERGUSON, Hugh Cameron, Col. late RAMC Retd. St Andrew's Hospital, Northampton NN1 5DG Tel: 01604 616 1000 — MB ChB Glas. 1953; FRCP Ed. 1977, M 1965; FRCPsych 1978, M 1972; DPM Eng. 1960. Vis. Cons. Psychiat. St. And.Hosp. N.ampton. Prev: Med. Dir. St And. Hosp. N.ampton; CO & Cons. Psychiat. Roy. Vict. Hosp. Netley Abbey.

FERGUSON, Iain Malcolm Station Road Surgery, 22 Station Road, Torphins, Banchory AB31 4JF Tel: 01339 882221 Fax: 01339 882699 — MB ChB 1972 Ed.; BSc 1969 Ed.; LMCC 1981; DA (UK) 1976. (Ed.) GP Torphins. Prev: Nanaimo Brit. Columbia.; Princip. Roblin Manitoba.

FERGUSON, Iain Tait 5 Apsley Road, Clifton, Bristol BS8 2SH Tel: 0117 973 4893 — MB ChB 1972 St. And.; MD (Commend.) Dundee 1982; FRCP Lond. 1990; FRCP Ed. 1986; MRCP (UK) 1976; T(M) 1991. Cons. Neurol. S.mead & Frenchay Hosp. Bristol; Hon. Clin. Sen. Lect. (Neurol.) Univ. Bristol. Socs: Assn. Brit. Neurol.; Brit. Soc. Clin. Neurophysiol. Prev: Cons. Lect. (Clin. Neurol.) Univ. Manch.

FERGUSON, Ian Gordon Station Road Surgeries, Station Road, Haworth, Keighley BD22 8NL — MB ChB 1977 Liverp.; MRCGP 1983. Princip. GP Haworth.

***FERGUSON, Ian Matthew Charles** c/o 20 Shaw Avenue, Kidderminster DY10 3YX — MB ChB 1998 Birm.

FERGUSON, Ian Robert 109 Poulters Lane, Worthing BN14 7SY — MB BS 1993 Lond.; DO RCS Eng. 1970.

FERGUSON, Ingrid Catherine Riverside Medical Practice, Ballifeary Lane, Inverness IV3 5PW Tel: 01463 715999 Fax: 01463 718763 — MB BCh 1989 Wales.

FERGUSON, Irene Elizabeth (retired) Windrush, Vicarage Lane, Longdown, Exeter EX6 7SW Tel: 01392 811330 — MB BChir 1954 Camb.; DCH RCP Lond. 1958; DRCOG 1957. Prev: Clin. Med. Off. Devon HA.

FERGUSON, Jacqueline Elizabeth Mudie Harlow House Day Hospital, Harlow Road, High Wycombe HP13 6AA Tel: 01494 425777; 5 Benson Place, Oxford OX2 6QH Tel: 01865 557960 — BM BCh 1968 Oxf.; MRCPsych 1983. (Oxf.) Cons. Psychiat. in Psychother.. Harlow Hse. Day Hosp. High Wycombe. Socs: Assoc. Mem. Brit. Assn. Psychother.; BMA; Assn. for Psychoanalytic Psychother. in the NHS. Prev: Cons. Psychiat. & Psychother. S. Bucks. NHS Trust; Sen. Regist. & Regist. (Psychiat.) Warneford Hosp. Oxf.; Trainee GP Oxf. VTS.

FERGUSON, Professor James Photodermatology Unit, Ninewells Hospital Medical School, Dundee DD1 9SY Tel: 01382 632240 Fax: 01382 646047 Email: j.ferguson@dundee.ac.uk; 56 South Street, St Andrews KY16 9JT Tel: 01334 473310 Fax: 01334 479342 — MB ChB 1977 Dundee; BMedSci 1974 St Andrews; FRCP 1995 Edinburgh; MRCP 1980 UK; MD 2000 Dundee. Cons. Dermat. Ninewells Hosp. Dundee.

FERGUSON, Mr James Accident & Emergency Department, Aberdeen Royal Infirmary, Foresterhill, Aberdeen AB25 2ZN Tel: 01224 550506 Fax: 01224 550718 Email: j.ferguson@arh.grampian.scot.nhs.uk; 142 Hamilton Place, Aberdeen AB15 5BB Tel: 01224 644359 — MB ChB 1983 Aberd.; FRCS (A&E) 1991; FRCS Ed. 1989; FFAEM 1994. (Aberdeen University) Cons. A & E Grampian Univ. Hosp.s NHS Trust; Sen. Lect. (A & E) Aberd. Univ. Socs: Roy. Coll. Surg. Edin.; RSM; (Hon. Vice-Pres.) Aberd. Med. Soc. Prev: Sen. Regist. (A & E) Aberd. Roy. Infirm.; Regist. Rotat. (A & E) S. Manch. Serv.; SHO Rotat. (Surg.) Aberd.

FERGUSON, James Andrew Joseph Intensive Care Unit, Antrim Hospital, Bush Road, Antrim BT14 2RL — MB BCh BAO 1991 Belf.; FRCA 1995; DICM, RCP&S (Ire.) 1998. Cons.Anaesth. & Intens. Care Med. Antrim Area Hosp. Antrim. Prev: Specialist Regist. (Anaesth.) Roy. Vict. Hosp. Belf.

FERGUSON, James B (retired) 33 Widey Lane, Crownhill, Plymouth PL6 5JS Tel: 01752 771991 — MB BCh BAO 1943 Belf.

FERGUSON, James Campbell (retired) Woodend, Failford, Mauchline KA5 5TF Tel: 01290 550318 Email: james.e.ferguson@talk21.com — MB ChB Glas. 1961; FRCP Ed. 1980, M 1965; FRCP Glas. 1976, M 1965; DObst RCOG 1962. Med. Dir. S. Ayrsh. Hosps. NHS Trust; Hon. Sen. Clin. Lect. Univ. Glas. Prev: Cons. Phys. Ballochmyle & Ayr Hosps.

FERGUSON, James Rodney Scotch Quarter Practice, Carrickfergus Health Centre, Carrickfergus BT38 7HT Tel: 028 9331 5800 Fax: 028 9331 5911; 12 Circular Road, Jordanstown, Newtownabbey BT37 0RF — MB BCh BAO 1971 Belf.; MICGP 1987; DCH RCPSI 1974; DObst RCOG 1973. (Queen's Belfast)

FERGUSON, James Stuart John Lambeth, Southwark and Lewisham Health Authority, 1 Lower Marsh, London SE1 7NT Tel: 020 7716 7000 Fax: 020 7716 7018 Email: jamie.ferguson@og.lslha.sthames.nhs.uk; Tel: 020 7716 700 Fax: 020 7716 7018 — MB BS Lond. 1985; MFPHM RCP (UK) 1995. Cons. Lambeth, S.wark & Lewisham HA.

FERGUSON, James Walker (retired) 20 Montrose Gardens, Milngavie, Glasgow G62 8NQ Tel: 0141 956 1980 — MB ChB (Hnrs.) Glas. 1936; FRFPS Glas. 1941; FRCP Glas. 1964, M 1962; FRCP Ed. 1957, M 1942. Prev: Cons. Phys. in Admin. Charge Glas. Roy. Infirm.

FERGUSON, James Walter 5 Apsley Road, Bristol BS8 2SH — MB ChB 1998 Dund.; MB ChB Dund 1998.

FERGUSON, James Wellwood Midway Surgery, 93 Watford Road, St Albans AL2 3JX Tel: 01727 832125 Fax: 01727 836384 — MB BChir 1977 Camb.; MB Camb. 1977, BChir 1976; MA Camb. 1977; MRCP (UK) 1980; MRCGP 1981; DRCOG 1982; DCH RCP Lond. 1981. (Camb. Univ. Med. Sch.)

FERGUSON, Jane Louise 36 Honey Cl, Chelmsford CM2 9SP — MB BS 1997 Lond.

***FERGUSON, Janice** 155 Seven Mile Straight, Muckamore, Antrim BT41 4QY — MB BCh 1998 Belf.; MB BCh Belf 1998.

FERGUSON, Janice Elizabeth The Dermatology Centre, Hope Hospital, Stutt Lane, Salford M6 8HD Tel: 0161 789 7373; 5 Park Road, Heaton Moor, Stockport SK4 4PY Tel: 0161 431 4414 — MB BCh BAO 1983 Belf.; PhD Manch. 1991; BSc Belf. 1980; MRCP (UK) 1986. (Qu. Univ. Belf.) Cons. Dermatol. Hope Hosp. Salford & Withington & Wythenshawe Hosps. Manch. Socs: Fell. Manch. Med. Soc.; BMA; Brit. Assn. Dermat. Prev: Sen. Regist. (Dermat.) Dermat. Centre Hope Hosp. Salford; Tutor (Med. Oncol.) Univ. Manch.; SHO (Path.) Univ. Hosp. S. Manch.

FERGUSON, Jean Baxter The Elms, Main St., Longforgan, Dundee DD2 5ET — MB ChB 1945 St. And. (Dundee)

FERGUSON, Jean Tait Pictfield, Nether Auchendrane, Ayr KA7 4EE — MB ChB 1960 Glas. (Glas.) Med. Off. Family Plann. Assn.; Clin. Med. Off. Arran Health Bd.

FERGUSON, Joan Mary Rosslyn Villa, 40 Windmill Road, Kirkcaldy KY1 3AQ Tel: 01592 651550; Rosslyn Villa, 40 Windmill Road, Kirkcaldy KY1 3AQ Tel: 01592 651550 — MRCS Eng. LRCP Lond. 1941. (Leeds)

FERGUSON, Mr John Medical Specialist Group, Alexandra House, Rue des Frieteaux, St Martin's, Guernsey GY2 4TH Tel: 0148 238565; Les Pequeries, Route des Pecqueries, St. Sampsons, Guernsey Tel: 01481 255546 Fax: 01481 252113 Email: johnferguson1@compuserve.com — MD 1971 Newc.; FRCSI 1995; MB BS Durh. 1966; FRCS Eng. 1974. (Newc.) Cons. Surg. Gen. Colorectal P.ss Eliz. Hosp. Guernsey. Socs: Founder Mem. Pancreatic Soc. GB & N. Irel.; Assn. Surg.; Assn. of Colo-Proctol. Prev: Sen. Research Assoc. Dept. Anat. Univ. Newc.; Wellcome Research Surg. Fell.; 1st Asst. (Surg.) & Ho. Phys. Roy. Vict. Infirm. Newc.

FERGUSON, John Bell Craigshill Health Centre, Craigshill Road, Livingston EH54 5DY Tel: 01506 432621 Fax: 01506 430431; Gorsemount, 34 Woodlands Park, Livingston EH54 8AT — MB ChB 1973 Ed.; MRCPsych 1979. Hosp. Pract. (Psychiat.) Bangour Village Hosp.

FERGUSON, Mr John Cameron The Lochans, Strathblane, Glasgow G63 9EX — MB ChB 1969 Glas.; FRCS Glas. 1974; FRCS Ed. 1974. Cons. Surg. S.. Gen. Hosp. Glas.; Hon. Clin. Lect. Glas. Univ. Socs: Brit. Soc. Gastroenterol.; Assn. Surg. Prev: Sen. Surg. Regist. S.. Gen. Hosp. Glas.; Surg. Regist. Glas. Roy. Infirm.; Research Instruc. State Univ. New York Buffalo, USA.

FERGUSON, John Dawes 137 Linwood Close, London SE5 8UY — MB ChB 1990 Cape Town; MRCP (UK) 1994.

FERGUSON, John Douglas Flat 16, Braehead House, Victoria Road, Kirkcaldy KY1 2SD — MB ChB 1984 Aberd.; MB ChB Aberd. l984.

FERGUSON, John Frank (retired) 10 Melton Avenue, Walton, Warrington WA4 6PQ — MB ChB 1943 Liverp. Jt. Med. Off. Laporte Chem.s Ltd.

FERGUSON, John Gibb The Elms, Main St., Longforgan, Dundee DD2 5ET Tel: 0138 234218 — MB ChB 1945 St. And. (Dundee)

FERGUSON, John Johnston, TD, Lt.-Col. RAMC Prescription Pricing Authority, Bridge House, 152 Pilgrim St., Newcastle upon Tyne NE1 6SN Tel: 0191 203 5352 Fax: 0191 203 5499 Email: john.ferguson@ppa.nhs.uk; 5 West Mains Road, Edinburgh EH9 3BQ Tel: 0131 667 1655 Fax: 0131 667 5076 — MB ChB Ed. 1964; BSc (Physiol.) St. And. 1961; MFFP 1993; FRCGP 1982; MHSM 1993; Dip. IMC RCS Ed. 1995; MICGP 1986; MIBiol 1971; FRSH 1997. (Ed.) Med. Dir. Prescrip. Pricing Auth. Newc. u Tyne; Examr. RCGP Lond. & RCS Edin.; Assessor Kings Fund Organisations Audit; Sec. UK Drug Utilisation Research Gp. & Vice Chairm., Eurodrug; Edr. PACT Centre Page Reports; Hon. Research Fell. DSRU Soton. Univ. Socs: Fell. Roy. Soc. Med. (Past Pres. Gen. Pract. Sect.); Pharmaceut. Med. & Research (Pres.); Fell. Roy. Soc. Health. Prev: Sen. Lect. (Gen. Pract.) Univ. Edin.; Assoc. Regional Adviser Edin. Postgrad. Bd. for Med.; Lect. (Physiol.) Univ. St. And.

FERGUSON, Mr John Scott 2 York Road, Northampton NN1 5QG Tel: 01604 32865 Fax: 01604 250159 Email: j.ferguson@compuserve.com; Blackthorn Lodge, Jarn Way, Boars Hill, Oxford OX1 5JF Tel: 01865 735212 — MB BS Lond. 1957; FRCS Eng. 1967; FRCS Ed. 1966; MRCS Eng. LRCP Lond. 1957. (Roy. Free) Hon. Cons. Orthop. Surg. Three Shires Hosp. N.ampton; Hon. Cons. Orthop. Surg. St. Mathews Private Hosp. N.ampton. Socs: Fell. BOA; Fell. Roy. Soc. Med.; BMA. Prev: Cons. Orthop.

Surg. N.ampton Gen Hosp.; Sen. Regist. Nuffield Orthop. Centre Oxf.; Sen. Lect. (Orthop.) Univ., Khartoum.

FERGUSON, John Wilkinson, MBE The Surgery, 23 Bolton Road, Salford M6 7HL Tel: 0161 736 1616; 4 Dentdale Close, Beaumont Road, Bolton BL1 5XD — MRCS Eng. LRCP Lond. 1945. (Manch.)

FERGUSON, Jonathan Irvine 4 Lisburn Road, Hillsborough BT26 6AA Tel: 01846 689203 — BM BCh 1994 Oxf.; MA Oxf. 1994. Demonst. (Anat.) Univ. Camb. Prev: Ho. Off. Roy. Vict. Hosp. Belf.

FERGUSON, Judith Katharine Donmall and Partners, 87 Albion Street, London SE16 7JX Tel: 020 7237 2092 Fax: 020 7231 1435 — MB BS 1967 Lond. (Lond. Hosp.)

FERGUSON, Kathleen (retired) 40 Shakespeare Road, Worthing BN11 4AS Tel: 01903 202920 — MB BChir 1942 Camb.; MRCS Eng. LRCP Lond. 1929.

FERGUSON, Kathleen 68 Fountainhall Road, Aberdeen AB15 4EH Tel: 01224 639248 — MB ChB 1983 Aberd.; FFA RCS 1988; DA 1986. Cons. Anaesth. Aberd. Roy. Infirm. Prev: Sen. Regist. (Anaesth.) Aberd. Roy. Infirm.

FERGUSON, Kathy 12 Marlborough Gardens, Belfast BT9 6SQ — MB BCh BAO 1993 Belf.; MRCGP 1997; DRCOG 1996; DCH Dub. 1996.

FERGUSON, Keith Duncan Nicol Street Surgery, 48 Nicol Street, Kirkcaldy KY1 1PH Tel: 01592 642969 Fax: 01592 643526 — MB ChB 1986 Dundee.

FERGUSON, Kenneth Malcolm 45 Castle Street, Dumfries DG1 1DU — MB ChB 1986 Glas.; MRCP (UK) 1991; MRCGP 1993; DRCOG 1993. Prev: Regist. (Gen. Med.) S.. Gen. Hosp. Glas.

FERGUSON, Lee Patrick 22 Wenlock Drive, North Shields NE29 9HD — MB ChB 1998 Ed.; MB ChB Ed 1998.

FERGUSON, Lesley Ann Nicol Street Surgery, 48 Nicol Street, Kirkcaldy KY1 1PH Tel: 01592 642969 Fax: 01592 643526; 14 Long Craig Walk, Kirkcaldy KY1 1SJ Tel: 01492 200408 — MB ChB 1985 Dundee; MRCGP 1989.

FERGUSON, Margaret The Health Centre, Springfield Road, Stornoway, Isle of Lewis HS1 2PS Tel: 01851 704888; 11 Braighe Road, Branahuie, Stornoway, Isle of Lewis HS2 0BQ — MB ChB 1984 Glas.; MRCGP 1988.

FERGUSON, Margaret McArthur Grove Medical Centre, 6 Uplands Terrace, Uplands, Swansea SA2 0GU Tel: 01792 643000 Fax: 01792 472800 — MB ChB 1980 Dundee; MB ChB 1980 Dundee.

FERGUSON, Mary Cowan (retired) 20 Drummond Road, Inverness IV2 4NB Tel: 01463 233987 — LRCP LRCS Ed. LRFPS Glas. 1947. Prev: Med. Off. Culduthel Hosp. & Raigmore Hosp.

FERGUSON, Mary Elizabeth Royal Oldham Hospital, Rochdale Road, Oldham OL1 2JH Tel: 0161 624 0420; Lane House, 46 Southgate, Honley, Huddersfield HD9 6NT Tel: 01484 665765 — MB BCh BAO 1981 NUI; MRCPsych 1990; Dip. Psychother. Liverp. 1994. (Univ. Coll. Dub.) Cons. Psychiat. Roy. Oldham Hosp. Socs: Liverp. Psychiat. Soc. Prev: Sen. Regist. (Ment. Handicap Psychiat.) NW Region HA.

FERGUSON, Maxine Claire 13 Queensborough Gardens, Glasgow G12 9PP — MB ChB 1995 Glas.

FERGUSON, Michael John Mayfield Road Surgery, 125 Mayfield Road, Edinburgh EH9 3AJ Tel: 0131 668 1095 Fax: 0131 662 1734 — MB ChB 1984 Aberd.; MB ChB Aberd. l984; MRCGP 1988.

FERGUSON, Michael Robert Rocklands, 31 Kingfisher Road, Mountsorrel, Loughborough LE12 7FG Tel: 01162 376094 Fax: 01162 376094 Email: mike.ferguson@uhl-tr.nhs.uk — MB ChB 1979 Ed.; FFA RCS Eng. 1984. Cons. Anaesth. Leics. HA. Socs: Jun. Mem. Assn. Anaesth.; Fell. Roy. Med. Soc. Edin.; Intens. Care Soc. Prev: Sen. Regist. Yorks. RHA; Regist. (Anaesth.) Leeds Gen. Infirm.; Regist. & SHO (Anaesth.) Norf. & Norwich Hosps.

FERGUSON, Michelle Jane 9 Marnie Park, Kirriemuir DD8 4TR — MB ChB 1994 Glas.

FERGUSON, Niall Robert Alexander House, 2 Salisbury Road, Farnborough GU14 7AW Tel: 01252 541155 — MB ChB 1976 Dundee; MRCGP 1981. GP FarnBoro..; Chairm. Blackwater Valley Locality Commiss.ing Gp.

FERGUSON, Nicola Joy Ferguson Family Medical Practice, Berrymead Medical Centre, 140 Berrys Lane, Parr, St Helens WA9 3RP Tel: 01744 25533 Fax: 01744 734752; Email: mparry@doctors.org.uk — MB ChB (Hons) Liverp. 1987. SHO (Cas.) Roy. Liverp. Hosp. Prev: Ho. Off. (Med.) & (Surg/Neurosurg.) Walton Hosp. Liverp.

FERGUSON, Norman James Postern Gate Surgery, Cinque Ports Street, Rye TN31 7AP Tel: 01797 223333/224924 Fax: 01797 226858; Grove Farm House, Grove Lane, Rye TN31 7PX Tel: 01797 280438 Email: normanferguson@compuserve.com — MB ChB Glas. 1972; MRCGP 1976; DObst RCOG 1974. GP Course Organiser Hastings VTS; GP Trainer. Prev: GP Vict., Austral.; Trainee GP Dumfries & Galloway VTS.

FERGUSON, Peter Whitelaw Halefield Family Medical Centre, 21 Halefield St., St Helens WA10 2DE Tel: 01744 22520; 13 Forest Grove, Eccleston Park, Prescot L34 2RY Tel: 01772 6744 — MB ChB 1955 Liverp. (Liverp.) Prev: SHO (O & G) Dorking Gen. Hosp.; Ho. Phys. Sefton Gen. Hosp.; Ho. Surg. Liverp. Roy. Infirm.

FERGUSON, Richard Watson Montalto Medical Centre, 2 Dromore Road, Ballynahinch BT24 8AY Tel: 028 9756 2929; 12 The Beeches Spa, Ballynahinch BT24 8RA Tel: 01238 563240 — MB BCh BAO 1973 Belf.; MRCGP 1978; DCH RCPSI 1977; DObst RCOG 1975. Asst. (Cardiol.) Ulster Hosp. Dundonald. Prev: SHO (Med. & Cardiol., O & G & Paediat.) Ulster Hosp. Dundonald.

FERGUSON, Robert Alexander The Health Centre, Thornton Dam Lane, Gilberdyke, Brough HU15 2UL Tel: 01430 440225 Fax: 01430 440646; 25 Westgate, North Cave, Brough HU15 2NG Tel: 01430 423821 — MB BS 1978 Lond.; MRCS Eng. LRCP Lond. 1976; MRCGP 1982; DRCOG 1982. (St. Bart.) Socs: BMA. Prev: Trainee GP Nottm. VTS; SHO (Obst. & Paediat.) City Hosp. Nottm.

FERGUSON, Robert James Arran, 40 Admiral Street, Glasgow G41 1HU Tel: 0141 429 2626 Fax: 0141 429 2331; 1 Kirkton Cottages, Drumcross Road, Bishopton PA7 5PX — MB ChB 1982 Glas.; MRCGP 1987; DCH RCPS Glas. 1986.

FERGUSON, Roger 89 Bidston Road, Prenton CH43 6TS Tel: 0151 652 3722 Fax: 0151 670 9536 Email: rferg10186@aol.com; 89 Bidston road, Prenton CH43 6TS Tel: 0151 652 3722 Fax: 0151 670 9536 Email: rferg10186@aol.com — MB ChB 1969 Birmingham; MRCP 1972 UK; MD 1977 Birm.; FRCP 1987 London. (Birm.) Cons. Phys. Arrowe Pk. Hosp. Birkenhead & Vict. Centr. Hosp. Wallasey. Socs: Brit. Soc. Gastroenterol. & N.. Gastroenterol. Soc. Prev: Sen. Regist. (Med.) Gen. Hosp. Nottm. & Derbysh. Roy. Infirm. Derby; Research Assoc. Nutrit. & Intestinal Unit Gen. Hosp. Birm.; Regist. (Med.) Worcester Roy. Infirm.

FERGUSON, Ruth 31 Abercorn Cl, South Croydon CR2 8TG — MB ChB 1997 Birm.

FERGUSON, Ruth Elizabeth 89 Bidston Road, Birkenhead CH43 6TS Tel: 0151 652 3722 — MB ChB 1972 Birm.; BMedBiol Aberd. 1969; Dip. Ven. Liverp. 1991. Clin. Asst. (Gastroenterol.) Arrowe Pk. Hosp. Upton Wirral. Prev: Staff Grade (Genitourin. Med.) Chester Roy. Infirm.; Sessional Screen. Doctor BUPA Murrayfield Med. Centre; Clin. Asst. (Ultrasound) Arrowe Pk. Hosp. Upton.

FERGUSON, Sally Kirsten Ann 5 Craignethan Road, Giffnock, Glasgow G46 6SQ — MB ChB 1998 Dund.; MB ChB Dund 1998.

FERGUSON, Sarah Anne Crawford 39 Charlton Park Keynsham, Bristol BS31 2NB Tel: 0196 442448 — MB ChB 1962 Ed.; DTM & H Liverp. 1971; DPH Liverp. 1970.

FERGUSON, Sarah Helen Oaklands, 8 Haslemere Rd, Long Eaton, Nottingham NG10 4AG — MB ChB 1997 Liverp.

FERGUSON, Scott Shepherd Dept of Anaesthesia, Level 4 Derriford Surgery, Plymouth Tel: 01752 792691 Email: scottferguson@phnt.swest.nhs.uk — MB ChB (Hons.) Dundee 1985, BMSc (Hons.) 1982; FCAnaesth 1991; DCH RCP Lond. 1989; DA (UK) 1987. Cons. in Anaesth. & IC, Derriford Hosp. Plymouth. Socs: Intens. Care Soc.; Paediat. Intens. Care Soc.; Assn. Anaesth. Prev: Sen. Regist. Univ of Soton Hosp; Fell. in Paediat. IC Childr.s Hosp. Sydney; Regist. (Anaesth.) Univ. of Soton. Hosp.

FERGUSON, Sharon Allison 21 Aviary Walk, Brickhill, Bedford MK41 7JD — MB BS 1990 Lond.

FERGUSON, Sheila Margaret 5 Chester Street, Edinburgh EH3 7RF — MB ChB 1988 Ed.

FERGUSON, Stanley David Ysgubor Fach, Crynant Farm, Rudry, Caerphilly CF83 3DD Tel: 029 2075 9391 — MB ChB 1975 Manch.; MA Camb. 1970; FRCP Lond. 1993; MRCP (UK) 1978. (Manch.) Cons. Paediat. Roy. Gwent Hosp. Newport; Lect. (Child Health) Welsh Nat. Sch. Med. (Univ. Hosp. Wales) Cardiff. Prev: Regist. (Paediat.) Roy. Gwent Hosp. Newport & Univ. Hosp. Wales Cardiff; SHO (Paediat.) Burnley Gen. Hosp.

FERGUSON, Stewart Craig 2nd Floor, 20 Spottiswoode Road, Edinburgh EH9 1BQ — MB ChB 1993 Ed.

FERGUSON, Susan Child Development Centre, Ross Road, Hereford HR2 7RL Tel: 01432 356438; Lower House, Westhope, Hereford HR4 8BT Tel: 01432 839529 — MB ChB 1971 Manch.; Msc (Univ Warwick) 1999. Community Paediat., Herefordsh. Community Health NHS Trust. Prev: SCMO Herefordsh. Community Health NHS Trust.; GP Cheadle.

FERGUSON, Susan Rose 3 Hunter Grove, Bathgate EH48 1NN — MB ChB 1986 Ed.; BSc Ed. 1984, MB ChB 1986.

FERGUSON, Theodore Arthur 14 Foxwell Street, Worcester WR5 2EP — MB BS 1988 W. Indies.

FERGUSON, Thomas Hume Broxburn Health Centre, 2 Holmes Road, Broxburn EH52 5JZ Tel: 01506 852678 Fax: 01506 858430; 37 Inch Crescent, Bathgate EH48 1EU Tel: 01506 652828 — MB ChB 1969 Ed.

FERGUSON, Timothy Gordon Cardiff Community Healthcare Trust, Lansdowne Hospital, Cardiff CF11 8PL Tel: 029 2037 2451 Fax: 029 2023 7378; 57 Cosmeston Street, Cathays, Cardiff CF24 4LQ Tel: 029 2023 6062 Email: timothy@ferguson.netkonect.co.uk — MB BCh 1979 Wales; MSc Wales 1994; DCH RCP Lond. 1989. Community Paediat. (Asst. Specialist) Lansdown Hosp. Cardiff.

FERGUSON, Mrs Veronica Mary Geneste Hammersmith Hospitals NHS Trust, Charing Cross Hospital, Fulham Palace Road, London W6 8RF Tel: 020 8846 1234 Fax: 020 8846 1911; 115A Harley Street, London W1N 1DG Tel: 020 7487 5581 Fax: 020 7486 0211 — MB BS 1983 Lond.; FRCS Glas. 1988; FRCOphth 1989. (United Medical and Dental School) Cons. Ophth. Surg. W.. Eye Hosp. & Char. Cross Hosp. Lond. Prev: Sen. Regist. (Ophth.) St. Geo. Hosp. & Moorfields Eye Hosp. Lond.

FERGUSON, Wendy Jane Pinrough, 14 Twatling Road, Barnt Green, Birmingham B45 8HT — MB ChB 1973 Bristol; Cert. Family Plann JCC 1976; DObst RCOG 1975. SCMO (Family Plann.) BromsGr. & Redditch HA.

FERGUSON, Mr William Jeremy Tricketts Cross Surgery, Corbin Avenue, Ferndown, Wimborne Tel: 01202 897989 — MB ChB 1979 Bristol; FRCS Ed. 1984; MRCP (UK) 1983.

FERGUSON, William John 58 Fonthill Road, Aberdeen AB11 6UJ — MB ChB 1998 Aberd.; MB ChB Aberd 1998.

FERGUSON, William Malcolm The Butts House, Leslie Road, Scotlandwell, Kinross KY13 9JE — MB ChB 1939 Ed. (Univ. Ed.) Med. Off. Remploy. Socs: BMA.

FERGUSON, William Percival 219 Scrabo Road, Newtownards BT23 4SJ — MB BCh BAO 1961 Belf.; FRCPath 1980, M 1968.

FERGUSON, William Robert Fergus Ball Tree Surgery, Western Road North, Sompting, Lancing BN15 9UX Tel: 01903 752200 Fax: 01903 536983; 109 Poulter's Lane, Worthing BN14 7SY Tel: 01903 260504 — MB Camb. 1962, BChir 1961; DO Eng. 1970. (King's Coll. Hosp.) Clin. Asst. Dept. Ophth. Worthing Hosp.

FERGUSON SMITH, John ICI Group Headquarters, 9 Millbank, London SW1P 3JF Tel: 020 7798 5065 Fax: 020 7798 5892; Talladale, 10 The Front, Middleton One Row, Darlington DL2 1AP Tel: 01325 332473 — MB ChB 1973 Glas.; AFOM RCP Lond. 1983; DObst RCOG 1976; CIH Dund 1980. Chief Med. Off. Imperial Chem. Industries PLC. Socs: Fell. Roy. Soc. Med.; Soc. Occupat. Med.

FERGUSON-SMITH, Professor Malcolm Andrew (retired) Cambridge University, Department of Clinical Veterinary Medicine, Madingley Road, Cambridge CB3 0ES Tel: 01223 766496 Fax: 01223 766496 Email: maf12@mole.bio.cam.ac.uk — MB ChB 1955 Glasgow; MB ChB Glas. 1955; FRS; FRSE; Hon. DSc Strathclyde 1992; FRCPath 1978, M 1966; FRCP Glas. 1974, M 1972; FRCOG 1993. Research Scientist; Edr. Prenatal Diag. Prev: Prof. Path. Univ. Camb.

FERGUSSON, Alison Jane 16 Brent Crescent, Houston, Johnstone PA6 7JE — MB ChB 1997 Ed.

FERGUSSON, Mr Colin Moore Yenton, Pearson Road, Sonning-on-Thames, Reading RG4 6UH — MB BS 1975 Lond.; MA Oxf. 1987; FRCS Lond. 1980. Cons. Orthop. Surg. Roy. Berks. Hosp. Reading. Socs: Fell. Brit. Orthop. Assn.; Brit. Assn. Surg. of Knee. Prev: Clin. Reader (Orthop. Surg.) Nuffield Dept. Orthop. Surg. Univ. Oxf.; Sen. Regist. Nuffield Orthop. Centre Oxf.; Regist. Rotat. (Surg.) Soton.

FERGUSSON, David Andrew Napier 47 Sandringham Road, Bromley BR1 5AR Tel: 020 8857 2234 Email: drandrewfergusson@tinyworld.co.uk — MB BS 1975 Lond.; MRCGP 1982. (St. Thomas's, University of London) Head of Policy, Centre for Bioethics and Pub. Policy, Lond.; Med. Adviser, Care (Christian Action Research & Educat.), Lond.; Chairm., Acorn Christian Foundat., Bordon. Socs: Christian Med. Fell.ship; Roy. Soc. of Med. (Fell.); Roy. Coll. of Gen. Practitioners. Prev: Gen. Sec. Christian Med. Fell.sh. Lond.; GP Brook La. Med. Mission.

FERGUSSON, Douglas Argyll Hawthornden, Wharf Lane, Bourne End SL8 5RX Tel: 01628 522864 Fax: 01628 533226; Kiln House, Pump Lane, Marlow SL7 3RD Tel: 01628 482103 Fax: 01628 533226 — MB BS 1964 Lond.; MRCS Eng. LRCP Lond. 1964; DObst RCOG 1966. (St. Thos.) Local Treas. Med. Off. Socs: Windsor Med. Soc. & Chiltern Med. Soc. Prev: Ho. Surg. St. Thos. Hosp. Hydestile; Chairm. & Sec. Bucks. LMC.

FERGUSSON, Grace Margaret Argyll & Bute Hospital, Lochgilphead PA31 8LD Tel: 01546 602323 Fax: 01546 606452; Castleton Harbour, Lochgilphead PA31 8RU — MB ChB 1977 Ed.; BSc Ed. 1974; MRCPsych 1993. Assoc. Specialist (Psychiat.) Argyll & Bute Hosp. Lochgilphead.

FERGUSSON, Graham Moore 12 Taunton Road Surgery, Bridgwater; Poole House, The Old Rectory, Enmore, Bridgwater TA5 2AN — MB BS 1978 Lond.; MRCGP Lond. 1982; DRCOG Lond. 1981; DCH Lond. 1981.

FERGUSSON, Ian Gordon Tudor Place, The Green, Richmond TW9 1NQ Tel: 020 8940 1926; 3 Lombard Street, London EC3V 9AL Tel: 020 7626 6985 — MB BS 1940 Lond.; MB BS (Hons.) Lond. 1940; MD Lond. 1948; MRCP Lond. 1945; MRCS Eng. LRCP Lond. 1940. (Westm.) Socs: Fell. Med. Soc. Lond.; Assur. Med. Soc. Prev: Ho. Phys. & Supernum. Regist. Nat. Hosp. Qu. Sq.; Sen. Regist. (Med.) & Chief Asst. W.m. Hosp.; Consg. Med. Off. Mercantile & Gen. Reinsur. Co.

FERGUSSON, Mr Ian Lewis Campbell Lister Hospital, Chelsea Bridge Road, London SW1W 8RH Tel: 020 7730 1273; 112 Fentiman Road, London SW8 1QA Tel: 020 7735 3867 — MB BChir 1967 Camb.; MA, MB Camb. 1967, BChir 1966; FRCS Eng. 1971; FRCS Ed. 1971; FRCOG 1986, M 1974, DObst 1968. (St. Thos.) Cons. (O & G) St. Thos. Hosp. Lond. & Chelsea Hosp. Wom. Lond.; Sen. Civil. Gyn. RN. Socs: RN Med. Club. Prev: Resid. Med. Off. Qu. Charlotte's Matern. Hosp. Lond.; Ho. Phys. & Ho. Off. (O & G) St. Thos. Hosp.; Ho. Surg. Addenbrooke's Hosp. Camb.

FERGUSSON, Josefa 20 Homefield Road, Wembley HA0 2NJ Tel: 020 8904 7525 — LRCPI & LM, LRSCI & LM 1942; LRCPI & LM, LRCSI & LM 1942. (RCPSI)

FERGUSSON, Keith Maxwell (retired) 2 Mallands Meadow, Abbotskerswell, Newton Abbot TQ12 5NL — MB BS 1947 Lond.; MRCS Eng., LRCP Lond. 1947. Prev: Clin. Asst. (Geriat.) Unit Newton Abbot Hosp.

FERGUSSON, Malcolm Lyon (retired) Hunters End, Keyser Road, Bodicote, Banbury OX15 4AN Tel: 01295 259065 — MB BChir 1963 Camb.; DObst RCOG 1966. Prev: GP Dartford.

FERGUSSON, Neil Vyvyan Dept. of Anaesthetics, Countess of Chester Hospital, Liverpool Road, Chester CH2 1UL Tel: 01244 365461 Fax: 01244 365435 Email: anaesthetic secretary a@coch; Long Green Farm, Long Green, Barrow, Chester CH3 7JU Email: neil.fergusson@btinternet.com — MB BS 1976 Lond.; MRCS Eng. LRCP Lond. 1976; MRCP (UK) 1980; FFA RCS Eng. 1982. Cons. (Anaesth.) Countess of Chester Hosp. Chester. Prev: SHO St. Thomas Hosp. Lond.; Regist. Soton. Gen. Hosp.; Sen. Regist. (Anaesth.) Radcliffe Hosp. Oxf.

FERGUSSON, Niall Stuart 9 Whitelea Crescent, Balerno EH14 7HF — MB ChB 1998 Ed.; MB ChB Ed 1998.

FERGUSSON, Robert Arthur 18 Peterburn Terrace, Gowrie Park, Dundee DD2 4TZ — MB 1979 Dundee; BMSc (1st cl. Hons. Gen. Path.) Dundee 1979, MB ChB 1982. SHO (Otolaryngol.) Ninewells Hosp. Dundee. Prev: SHO (Cas.) Dundee Roy. Infirm.; SHO (O & G & Anaesth.) Ninewells Hosp. Dundee.

FERGUSSON, Robert Somerled Cameron, MBE (retired) Delta Cottage, 3 Garden Place, Beauly IV4 7AW Tel: 01463 782132 — MB ChB 1947 Ed.; FRCGP 1978, M 1953; DFFP 1993; Cert. Contracep. & Family Plann. RCOG, RCGP & FPA 1976; DObst RCOG 1959. Med. Off. Civil Serv. & DHSS; Med. Examr. HQ (Army) Scotl. Prev: Hosp. Med. Off. N.. RHB Inverness.

FERGUSSON, Ronald John Respiratory Unit, Western General Hospital, Crewe Road, Edinburgh EH4 2XU Tel: 0131 537 1779 Fax: 0131 537 2675 Email: ronald.fergusson@ed.ac.uk; 5 Napier Road, Edinburgh EH10 5AZ Tel: 0131 229 2678 — MB ChB 1977 Ed.; BSc (Med. Sci.) Ed. 1974, MD 1990; FRCP Ed. 1996; MRCP (UK) 1981. Cons. Phys. W.ern Gen. Hosp. Edin.; Hon. Sen. Lect. (Med.) Univ. Edin. Prev: Cons. Phys. E.ern Gen. Hosp. Edin.; Sen. Regist. (Gen. & Respirat. Med.) Lothian HB; ICRF Research Fell. (Oncol. Unit) W. Gen. Hosp. Edin.

FERGUSSON, Thomas Edgar Syme (retired) 1 Edgehill Road, Bearsden, Glasgow G61 3AD Tel: 0141 942 0380 — MB ChB 1952 Glas.; MRCGP 1964; DRCOG 1962; Cert. Family Plann. JCC 1978. Prev: Med. Adviser BAMS.

FERMER, Frances Elizabeth Welbeck Road Surgery, 1A Welbeck Road, Bolsover, Chesterfield S44 6DF Tel: 01246 823742; 15 Shetland Road, Dronfield, Dronfield S18 1WB — MB ChB 1986 Sheff.; DRCOG 1990; DCH RCP Lond. 1989.

FERMIE, Peter Guy Rylett Road Surgery, 42A Rylett Road, Shepherds Bush, London W12 9ST Tel: 020 8749 7863 Fax: 020 8743 5161 — MB BS 1979 Lond.; MRCGP 1984; DCH RCP Lond. 1983; DRCOG 1984. (Westm.)

FERMONT, David Andre 114 Harley Street, London W1N 1AG; Sumnerhill, 16 Meadway, Esher KT10 9HF Tel: 01372 469009 — MB BS 1945 Lond.; MRCS Eng. LRCP Lond. 1943. (Middlx.) Mem. Gray's Inn; Med. Ref. Various Insur. Cos. Socs: Med.-Leg. Soc.; Fell. Roy. Soc. Med. Prev: Res. Med. Off. Beckenham Hosp.; Ho. Surg. Middlx. Hosp. Lond.; Clin. Asst. Roy. Nat. Throat, Nose & Ear Hosp.

FERMONT, Mr David Calvin Cancer Treatment Centre, Mount Vernon Hospital, Northwood HA6 2RN Tel: 019238 44231 Fax: 019238 44138; Great Sarratt Hall Cottage, Sarratt, Rickmansworth WD3 4PD — MB BS 1970 Lond.; FRCS Eng. 1975; FRCR 1981. (Middlx.) Cons. Clin. Oncol. Mt. Vernon, N.wick Pk. And St Marks Hosps. Socs: Fell. Roy. Soc. Med. Prev: Sen. Regist. Middlx. & Mt. Vernon Hosps.; Regist. (Clin. Oncol.) Middlx. Hosp. Lond.; Regist. (Surg.) Univ. Coll. Hosp.

FERN, Mr Alasdair Iain Eye Unit, Hairmyres Hospital, Eaglesham Rd, Glasgow G75 3RG Tel: 01355 585000 Fax: 01355 584473 — MB ChB 1981 Glas.; FRCS Glas. 1987; FCOphth. 1989; DO RCS Eng. 1986. Prev: Sen. Regist. (Ophth.) Tennent Inst. Ophth. W. Infirm. Glas.

FERN, Mr Edwin Darren Royal Cornwall Hospital, Trelliske, Truro TR1 3LJ — MB ChB 1984 Sheff.; FRCS 1988 Ed.; FRCS 1995 Ed. (Orth.). Cons. Orthopaedic Surg. (hip Surg., limb reconstruction), Roy. Cornw. Hosp.

FERNANDES, Agnelo Teles Parchmore Medical Centre, 97 Parchmore Road, Thornton Heath, Croydon CR7 8JY Tel: 020 8251 4200 Fax: 020 8251 0550; 63 Riddlesdown Road, Purley CR8 1DJ Tel: 020 8668 3967 Email: afern@globalnet.co.uk — MB BS 1987 Lond.; AKC 1987; BSc (Hons.) Pharmacol. Lond. 1982, MB BS 1987; MRCGP 1991; DCCH RCP Ed. 1991; T(GP) 1991; DRCOG 1990; Cert. Family Plann. JCC 1990. (Charing Cross & Westminster) GP Princip.; Asst. Med. Manager Croydon (GP Co-Op). Prev: Trainee GP Croydon VTS.

FERNANDES, Antonio Louis Caetano 35 Landseer Close, Edgware HA8 5SB — MB BS 1980 Lond.

FERNANDES, Cecilia Brierley Hill Health Centre, Albion St., Brierley Hill DY5 3EE Tel: 01384 77003 — MB BS 1959 Calcutta.

FERNANDES, Cheryl Frances 38 Whitefriars Drive, Harrow HA3 5HN — MB ChB 1994 Manch.; MRCP 1997. (Manchester University) Specialist Regist.

FERNANDES, Clifford Ryhope Health Centre, Ryhope, Sunderland SR2 0RY Tel: 0191 521 0559 Fax: 0191 521 3854 — MB BS 1973 Mysore. (Kasturba Med. Coll. Mangalore)

FERNANDES, Doreen Ann 255 High Road, London E10 5QE — MB BS 1996 Lond.; BSc Hons 1993; DRCOG 1998. (United Medical and Dental Schools of Guys & St Thomas's Hospitals) SHO GP VTS N. Middlx. Hosp. Lond. Prev: SHO Paediat. N. Middlx. Hosp.; SHO O & G N. Middlx. Hosp.; SHO Elderly Care N. Middlx. Hosp.

FERNANDES, Felix Joseph 12 St Albans, Westbury Park, Bristol BS6 7SJ Tel: 0117 942 3127 — MB ChB 1975 Bristol; FFA RCS Eng. 1980; DCH Eng. 1978.

FERNANDES, Helen Marie 12 The Drive, Gosforth, Newcastle upon Tyne NE3 4AH Tel: 0191 285 0525 — MB BS 1989 Newc.; FRCS 2000 (SN) Eng.; FRCS Eng. 1993. (Newcastle-upon-Tyne) Sen. Lect. and Hon. Cons. Neurosurg., Newc. Gen. Hosp. Prev: Demonst. (Anat.) Newc. Med. Sch.; Peri Fell.sh. Rotat. (Surg.) Newc.; SHO (ENT) Freeman Hosp. Newc.

FERNANDES, John Roy Department of Anaesthetics, Wexham Park Hospital, Wexham St., Slough SL2 4HL — MB BS 1985 Lond.

FERNANDES, Luke Royal Sussex County Hospital, Eastern Road, Brighton BN2 5BE Tel: 01273 696955 Fax: 01273 673466; 9 Dyke Close, Hove BN3 6DB — MB BS Bombay 1969; MPhil Lond. 1981; FRCP Lond. 1988; MRCP (UK) 1974. (Grant Med. Coll. Bombay) Cons. Phys. Rheum. Roy. Sussex Co. Hosp. Brighton; Hon. Clin. Teach. Univ. Brighton; Vis. Fell. Centre for Med. Research Univ. Sussex. Socs: Fell. Roy. Soc. Med.; Brit. Soc. Rheum.; Brighton & Sussex M-C Soc. (Ex-Pres.). Prev: Sen. Regist. (Rheum. & Rehabil.) King's Coll. Hosp. Lond.; Regist. (Med.) Metrop. Hosp. Lond.; Sen. Ho. Phys. St. Nicholas Hosp. Lond.

FERNANDES, Manuel Agnelo Andrew Mario Manor Road Surgery, 31 Manor Road, Folkestone CT20 2SE Tel: 01303 851122 Fax: 01303 220914 — MB BS Lond. 1983; BSc Lond. 1980; MRCGP 1987; AFOM RCP (UK) 1996; DRCOG 1988; DCH RCP Lond. 1987. (Westm. Med. Sch.) Princip. GP Folkestone. Socs: BMA. Prev: SHO (Anaesth.) SE Kent HA.

FERNANDES, Nicholas Bosco Horsman's Place Surgery, Instone Road, Dartford DA1 2JP Tel: 01322 228363/277444 — BM 1985 Soton.; DCH RCP Lond. 1991; DRCOG 1989; Cert. Family Plann. JCC 1989. SHO (Gen. Paediat. & Neonat.) Leeds Gen. Infirm. Prev: Trainee GP Portsmouth VTS.

FERNANDES, Nicholas Oswald Joseph 52 Den Park Crescent, Sheffield S10 5PD Tel: 0114 267 8325 Email: nickof@aol.com — MB BS 1989 Bangalor; MB BS Bangalore 1989; MRCP (UK) 1993. (St. Johns Med. Coll. Bangalore, India) Specialist Regist. (Anaesth.) Centr. Socs: Med. Defence Union; Assn. Anaesth.

FERNANDES, Paul 324 Parlaunt Road, Langley, Slough SL3 8AX — BM 1998 Soton.; BM Soton 1998.

FERNANDES, Paula Francesca Rosemarie Dental Surgery, 31 Bridge Avenue, Hammersmith, London W6 9JA Tel: 020 8748 5246 Fax: 020 8748 5248 — MB BS 1978 Lond.; BA (Hons.) Camb. 1975; MRCS Eng. LRCP Lond. 1978; MRCGP 1983; DRCOG 1982. GP Hammersmith.

FERNANDES, Mr Tennyson Joseph 11 Kneeton Park, Middleton Tyas, Richmond DL10 6SB Tel: 01325 377368 — MB BS Poona 1963; FRCS Eng. 1971; Specialist Accredit. (Orthop.) RCS Eng. 1976. (B.J. Med. Coll., Poona) Cons. Surg. (Orthop.) Memor. Hosp. Darlington. Socs: Fell. BOA. Prev: Cons. Surg. (Orthop.) Friarage Hosp. N.allerton; Sen. Regist. (Orthop.) Roy. Vict. Infirm. Newc.; Regist. (Orthop.) R. Jones & A. Hunt Orthop.Hosp., Oswetry.

FERNANDES, Trevor Don The Surgery, Parkwood Drive, Warners End, Hemel Hempstead HP1 2LD Tel: 01442 250117 Fax: 01442 256185 Email: trevor.fernandes@gp-e82091.nhs.uk — MB BS 1988 Lond.; BSc (Immunol.) Lond. 1985; MRCGP 1993. (St Thomas's Hospital) GP Princip.; Exec. Mem. Diacorum PCT, Hemel Hempstead; Assoc. Med. Director for Primary Care, Liaison, W. Herts. Hosp.s Trust, Hemel Hempstead; GP Trainer.

FERNANDES, Vasco Milton Keynes Primary Care Trust, Eaglestone, Milton Keynes MK6 5NG Tel: 01908 243084 Fax: 01908 243517; 2 Lufford Park, Gt Linford, Milton Keynes MK14 5ET Tel: 01908 661311 — MB BS 1975 Bombay; MRCGP 1980; MFCM 1985; DCH Eng. 1979. (G.S. Med. Coll.) Cons. Pub. Health Phys., Milton Keynes Primary Care Trust, Milton Keynes; Cons. Community Drug and alcohol Centre Milton Keynes PCT, Milton Keynes. Socs: BMA; Mem. Cent. Comm. For Pub. Health Med. and community Health; Chair, Oxf. regional Comm. for Pub. health Med. and community health. Prev: Sen. Regist. (Community Med.) Hillingdon HA.; Specialist in Community Med. Milton Keynes HA.

FERNANDEZ, Alexander (retired) Seathrift, Greenway, Lyme regis DT7 3EY Tel: 01297 443506 Fax: 01297 443506 Email: alexfernandez33@hotmail.com — MRCS Eng. LRCP Lond. 1945. Prev: Med. Off. Lyme Regis Hosp., Allhallows Sch. Rousdon & Woodroffe Sch. Lyme Regis.

FERNANDEZ, Brendan 89 Bramley Lane, Lightcliffe, Halifax HX3 8NS Tel: 01422 202898 — MB BS 1962 Karachi; DCH RCPS Glas. 1968. (Dow Med. Coll. Karachi)

FERNANDEZ, Cyril 3 Boyd Close, Crescent Road, Kingston upon Thames KT2 7RL — MD 1967 Lille; DTCD Wales 1970.

FERNANDEZ, Don Bosco Amberley, 21 High St., Edzell, Brechin DD9 7TE Tel: 01356 648209 Fax: 01356 648209; Amberley, 21 High St, Edzell, Brechin DD9 7TE — MB BS 1960 Madras. (Madras) Tutor (Gen. Pract.) Fac. Med. Univ. Dundee. Socs: Amer. Med. Soc. Vienna. Prev: Med. Asst. (Geriat. Med.) Stracathro Hosp. Brechin; Regist. (Med. & Geriat.) Stracathro Hosp. Brechin; Med. Off. Port Trust Hosp. Madras, India.

FERNANDEZ, Mr Graeme Nicholas Southbrook, Church St., Upwey, Weymouth DT3 5QB Tel: 01305 812018 — MB BS 1976 Lond.; FRCS Ed. (Orth.) 1989; FRCS Eng. 1982. Cons. Orthop. Surg. W. Dorset Gen. Hosp. NHS Trust. Prev: Sen. Regist. (Orthop. & Traum. Surg.) Soton. & SW Hants, Portsmouth, SE Hants., Basingstoke & N. Hants. HAs; Regist. (Orthop. & Traum. Surg.) Qu. Alexandra Hosp. Portsmouth & Lord Mayor Treloar Hosp. Alton; Regist. (Gen. Surg.) Poole Gen. Hosp.

FERNANDEZ, Helen Dawn Markfield Surgery, The Green, Markfield LE67 9WU Tel: 01530 242313 Fax: 01530 245668; The Mount, 2 High St, Barrow-upon-Soar, Loughborough LE12 8PY Tel: 01509 412791 Email: tribes@globalnet.co.uk — MB ChB 1982 Leic.; Cert. Family Plann. JCC 1990. (Leicester)

FERNANDEZ, Margaret Dorothy Sutton Hospital (Chiltern Wing), Cotswold Road, Sutton SM2 5NF Tel: 020 8296 2000; 8 Newbury Gardens, Stoneleigh, Epsom KT19 0NU Email: mdfernandez@supanet.com — Laurea Univ. Rome 1971; MRCPsych 1982; DTM & H Liverp. 1970. Cons. Psychiat., S.W. Lond. & St. Geaorge's Ment. Health Trust. Socs: BMA; MRC Psych; BACP. Prev: Cons. Psychiat. Sutton & St. Helier Hosps. Merton & Sutton HA; Sen. Regist. (Psychiat.) St. Mary Abbot's Hosp. Lond.; Sen. Regist. Qu. Mary's Hosp. Lond. (Char. Cross & W.m. Train. Scheme).

FERNANDEZ, Roma Supreme House, 300 Regents Park Road, Finchley, London N3 2JX Tel: 020 8346 3291/0446; 34 Glenloch Road, London NW3 4DN — MB BS 1978 Lond.; BSc Lond. 1975; MRCGP 1983; DRCOG 1980. (Lond. Hosp.)

FERNANDEZ, Ronald Herbert Peter, CStJ (retired) Carabine, Cross, Axbridge BS26 2EF Tel: 01934 732439 — MB ChB 1946 Leeds; MD Leeds 1960; MFOM RCP Lond. 1978; DIH Soc. Apoth. Lond. 1959. Prev: Sen. Med. Off. Centr. Elec. Generat. Bd. (SW Region).

FERNANDEZ, Sean Michael Bento 262 Eastcotte Lane, Harrow HA2 9AQ — MB BS 1996 Lond.

FERNANDEZ BONILLA, Eva Maria Flat 7, 22 Lyndhurst Road, Worthing BN11 2DF — LMS 1993 Granada.

FERNANDEZ-BRAVO ALVAREZ, Jose Maria UTS Oxford Centre, Wolsey Hall, 66 Banbury Road, Oxford OX2 6PR — LMS 1982 U Complutense Madrid.

FERNANDEZ DAIR, Nuria Edinburgh Sick Children's NHS Trust, Royal Hospital for Sick Children, Sciennes Road, Edinburgh EH9 1LF Tel: 0131 536 0000 Fax: 0131 536 0001; 10 Lochrin Buildings, (4F3) Gilmore Place, Edinburgh EH3 9NB Tel: 0131 229 0610 — LMS Barcelona 1982. (Barcelona) Staff Grade (Paediat./A & E) Sick Childrs. Hosp. Ed.

FERNANDEZ DE CASTILLO TORRAS, Bibiana Chalet 4, Frenchay Residences, Frenchay Hospital, Frenchay Park Road, Bristol BS16 1LE — LMS 1988 Navarre.

FERNANDEZ FIDALGO, Jose Luis York District Hospital, Wiggimton Road, York YO31 8HE; 53 George Street, Whitehaven CA28 7PH — LMS 1986 Oviedo. Princip. Lowther Med. Centre. Socs: BMA; Med. Sickness Soc.; MDU.

FERNANDEZ GONZALEZ, Francisco Eugenio Pontefract General Infirmary, 92 Southgate, Pontefract WF8 1PN; 32 Beechwood Avenue, Pontefract WF8 4ED — LMS 1987 U Complutense Madrid.

FERNANDEZ-MARTINEZ, Pablo Pharmanet Ltd, Oakley Court, Kingsmead business park, High Wycombe HP11 1JU Tel: 01494 510 610 Fax: 01494 510 611 Email: pfernandez@pharmanet.com; 8 Kingswood Close, Guildford GU1 2SD Tel: 01483 570911 Email: pablo_fernandez_martinez@hotmail.com — LMS 1979 Seville; MFPM RCP (UK) 1989. Sen. Vice Pres. Clin. Research, Pharmanet Ltd. Prev: Head (Biological Products) Bayer Europe Med. Affairs; Regional Dir. (Clin. Research) Wyeth-Ayerst Research; Head (Infec. Dis.) Wellcome Research Laborat.

FERNANDEZ MOYA, Eduardo Cardiothoracic Unit, The Hospital for Sick Children, Great Ormond St., London WC1N 3JH — LMS 1988 U Complutense Madrid.

FERNANDEZ PANOS, Marta Flat 2, 85 Kirkstall Road, London SW2 4HE — LMS 1994 Basque Provinces.

FERNANDEZ-SHAW ZULUETA, Sylvia Nuffield Department of Obstetrics & Gynaecology, John Radcliffe Hospital Maternity Department, Headington, Oxford OX3 9DU — LMS 1989 Autonoma Madrid.

FERNANDO, Andrew Michael Russell 1B Valley Road, London SW16 2XL Tel: 0709 207 3449, 07976 963985 Email: mikeef@lineone.net — MB ChB 1997 Ed. (Edin.) Reg. (Neonat.) Nat. Wom.'s Hosp. Aucklan, N. Zeeland. Socs: BMA; Med. Protec. Soc. Prev: SHO (Neonat.), St. Thomas' Hosp., Lond.; SHO (Paediat.) Maidstone Hosp.; Ho. Off. (Paediat. Surg.) Roy. Hosp. for Sick Childr. Edin.

FERNANDO, Andrew Ranjan National Blood Service, South Thames Centre, 75 Cranmer Terrace, Tooting, London SW17 0RB Tel: 020 8258 8300; c/o Barclays Bank, Dulwich Village Br., 117 Dulwich Village, London SE21 7BL — MD 1963 Kyushu, Japan; LAH Dub. 1968. (Kyushu, Japan) Assoc. Specialist Nat. Blood Serv. S. Thames Centre Lond. Socs: HCSA. Prev: Research Regist. (Urol. & Transpl.) St. Bart. Hosp. Lond.; SHO (Transpl. Surg.) Nuffield Transpl. Surg. Unit Edin.; Brit. Heart Foundat. Research Fell. & Freemasons Research Fell. Cardiac Surg. Dept. Surg. Sci. RCS Eng.

FERNANDO, Anthony Clement (retired) 38A Tebourba Drive, Alverstoke, Gosport PO12 2NT Tel: 02392 601881 — MB Camb. 1957, BChir 1956. Prev: Receiv. Room Off. Lond. Hosp.

FERNANDO, Anton Gabriel Roshan 2 Mallard Court, Swan Close, Rickmansworth WD3 1SB — MB BCh 1984 Wales; MB BCh Wales l984; FCAnaesth 1990; FFA RCSI 1989; DA (UK) 1986. Regist. (Anaesth.) Roy. Gwent Hosp. Newport. Prev: Regist. (Anaesth.) Univ. Hosp. Wales Cardiff.

FERNANDO, Asvini Dhammika 139 Jawatte Road, Colombo 5, Sri Lanka; 56 Golders Grove, Treboeth, Swansea SA5 9DG — MB BS 1981 Colombo; MRCP (UK) 1991.

FERNANDO, Bellana Vidanalage Esme Courtlands, Queens Avenue, Maidstone ME16 0EN — MB BS 1955 Ceylon; DPM Eng. 1981; DCH Ceylon 1972; DTM & H Ceylon 1967. (Colombo) Assoc. Specialist Leybourne Grange Hosp. W. Malling. Socs: BMA. Prev: Regist. Lynebank Hosp. Dunfermline.

FERNANDO, Bimbi Shiran 49 Donnage, London NW4 1HR — MB BS 1990 Lond.

FERNANDO, Dayantha Sunimal The Surgery, 143 Park Road, Camberley GU15 2NN Tel: 01276 26171 Email: themedico@hotmail.com — FRCP 2001 Lond.; MSc 2001 (Medical Ethics) Lond.; MB BS (Hons.) Ceylon 1971; MRCP (UK) 1975; MRCGP 1977.

FERNANDO, Emmanuel Christopher Kingsley 10 Croydon Road, Keston, Bromley BR2 6EB Tel: 020 8665 9410 — MB BS 1958 Ceylon. Prev: Sch. Med. Off. Kandy, Ceylon.

FERNANDO, Gyan Camillus Antony Scientific Support Unit, Devon and Cornwall Constabulary, Middlemoor, Exeter EX2 7HQ Tel: 01395 223139 Fax: 01395 223142 Email: gyan_f@ukgateway.net — MB BS 1973 Colombo; MRCPath 1984; DMJ(Path.) Soc. Apoth. Lond. 1986. Home Off. Path. Devon & Cornw. Constab. Socs: Fell. Brit. Assn. Forens. Med. Prev: Sen. Lect. (Forens. Med.) Univ. Edin.; Sen. Forens. Path. Univ. Dundee; Sen. Regist. (Histopath.) N. W.. RHA.

FERNANDO, H M Terence Courtlands, Queens Avenue, Maidstone ME16 0EN — MB BS 1955 Ceylon; DPH Sydney 1963; Cert. Nutrit. (Inst. Nutrit. Research Hydarabad) 1964; Cert. Populat. Plann. (Univ. Michigan) 1968; Cert JCC Lond. 1977. (Colombo) Sen. Med. Off. Maidstone Health Dist. Socs: FRIPHH; Ceylon Med. Assn. & Ceylon Pub. Health Assn. (Ex-Sec.). Prev: Clin. Med. Off. Fife HB; Asst. Supt. Health (Child Health & Family Plann.) Colombo Div. Ceylon.

FERNANDO, Harsha Gamini 73 Rayleigh Road, Hutton, Brentwood CM13 1AP — MB BS 1974 Sri Lanka; MRCPsych 1987.

FERNANDO, Illekuttigae Ashton Peter Nihal 31 Jacklins Approach, Bottesford, Scunthorpe DN16 3PF — MB ChB 1990 Ed.

FERNANDO, Indrajit Nalinika University Hospital Birmingham NHS Trust, Birmingham B29 6RQ — MB BS 1984 Lond.; BSc (Hons.) Lond. 1981; MRCP (UK) 1987; FRCR 1990; FRCP 2000. (Middlx. Hosp. Med. Sch.) Cons. Radiother. & Oncol. Univ. Hosp. Birm. NHS Trust. Prev: Sen. Regist. (Radiother.) Qu. Eliz. Hosp.

Birm.; Regist. (Radiother.) Roy. Marsden & Univ. Coll. Hosps. Lond.; Research Fell. Roy. Marsden (BrE. Unit).

FERNANDO, Joseph James Rufus Ashenfell House, Church Lane, Baslow, Bakewell DE45 1SP 4 The Green, East Hanney, Wantage OX12 0HH Tel: 01235 867456, 01246 582199, 01902 644835, 01902 754842, 01235 867456, 01902 644830 Email: david@ashenfell_freeserve.co.uk, rufus&fernando.f9.co.uk, rufus@fernando.f9.co.uk — MB BS; MRCOG 1981 UK; FRCOG 1997 UK; MFFP 1995 UK. (Univ. of Ceylon, Colombo) Cons. in Genito Urin. Med., New Cross Hosp., Wolverhampton; Cons. In Genito Urin. Med., St. Gisthlac Clinic, Co. Hosp., Hereford.

FERNANDO, Kryshani Therese Mallika 12 Upton Road, Chichester PO19 2QQ — BChir 1996 Camb.

FERNANDO, Mr Kumaragewatte Lakshman General Surgical Department, Maidstone Hospital, Hermitage Lane, Maidstone ME16 9QQ Tel: 01622 29000; 8 Cranleigh Gardens, Allington, Maidstone ME16 0TX Tel: 01622 686028 — MB BS 1979 Peradeniya; FRCS Ed. 1987. Regist. (Gen. Surg.) Maidstone Hosp.

FERNANDO, Lalinie Psychiatric Department, Ailsa Hospital, Dalmellington Road, Ayr KA6 6AB — MB BS 1971 Ceylon.

FERNANDO, Liyanage Roland Terrance Aloysius 17 Danebower Road, Stoke-on-Trent ST4 8TJ — MB BS 1968 Ceylon.

FERNANDO, Mahahettige Dona Ann Kumari Sharmalene 4 Jersey Road, London SW17 9RQ Tel: 020 8769 0883 — MRCS Eng. LRCP Lond. 1973. Ho. Phys. Lister Hosp. Stevenage. Prev: Ho. Surg. Lister Hosp. Stevenage.

FERNANDO, Marietta Yvonne Deborah 30 Toppesfield Ave, Wickford SS12 0PB — MB BS 1997 Lond.; BSc (Hons.) 1994. Ho. Off. (Med.) St. Helier Hosp. Carshalton.

FERNANDO, Medona Prasanthie 15 Lawrence Road, London E6 1JN — MB BS 1998 Lond.; MB BS Lond 1998.

FERNANDO, Merennage Lalinie Pushpa Bridge, Hatfield Road, Witham CM8 1EQ; 73 Rayleigh Road, Hutton, Brentwood CM13 1AP — MB BS 1974 Sri Lanka; Dip. Psychiat. 1989; MRCPsych. 1991. Socs: RCP.

FERNANDO, Mohanlal Ummega Maelor General Hospital, Wrexham LL13 7TD Tel: 01978 291100; 26 Green Park, Erddig Road, Wrexham LL13 7YE Tel: 01978 355019 — MB BS 1967 Ceylon; MRCP (UK) 1979; MRCS Eng. LRCP Lond. 1981. Cons. Phys. Med. for Elderly Maelor Gen. Hosp. Wrexham.

FERNANDO, Nellie Patricia (retired) 19 Wendover Court, Lyndale Avenue, London NW2 2PG Tel: 020 7794 9485 — MB BS Ceylon 1950; MRCP (UK) 1958; DCH RCP Lond. 1952.

FERNANDO, Mr Oswald Nihal Royal Free Hospital, Pond St, London NW3 2QG Tel: 020 7830 2882 Fax: 020 7830 2125; White Acres, 49 Downage, London NW4 1HR Fax: 020 8203 3360 — MB BS 1960 Ceylon; FRCS Eng. 1966; FRCS Ed. 1966; DA Eng. 1964. (Ceylon) Cons. Surg. Dept. Nephrol. & Renal Transpl. Roy. Free Hosp. Lond.; Hon. Sen. Lect. Roy. Free Hosp. Sch. Med.; Hon. Cons. Surg. Hosp. for Sick Childr. & St. John & St. Eliz. Hosp Lond. Socs: Brit. Transpl. Soc.; Transpl. Soc. Prev: Lect. (Surg.) Roy. Free Hosp. Lond.; Research Fell. Roy. Free Hosp. Lond.; Regist. (Surg.) Croydon Gen. Hosp.

FERNANDO, Panthiyage Henry Quintus 76 Brent Lane, Dartford DA1 1QS Tel: 01322 222436 — MD 1965 Ceylon; MB BS 1955; MRCP Lond. 1967; FRCP Ed. 1994, M 1967; MRCPsych 1971; DPM Eng. 1968. (Ceylon) Prev: Cons. Psychiat. Bexley Hosp.

FERNANDO, Payagalawaduge Mary Pushpa Damayanthi 12 Alban Road, North Woolton, King's Lynn PE30 3XF — MB BS 1980 Colombo; FFA RCSI 1987.

FERNANDO, Rashika Anne Marie 12 Crofton Lane, Orpington BR5 1HL — MB BS 1996 Lond. SHO Med. Rotat., King's Coll. Hosp., Lond. Socs: MDU. Prev: SHO (Elderly care), Roy. Sussex Co. Hosp.; SHO (A & E) Roy. Sussex Co. Hosp. Brighton; Ho. Off. (Gen. Surg.) Kings Coll. Hosp. Lond.

FERNANDO, Renuka Lilanthi College Road Surgery, 50/52 College Road, Maidstone ME15 6SB Tel: 01622 752345 Fax: 01622 758133 — MB BS 1982 Lond.; MRCGP 1990; MRCPsych 1987. GP Maidstone. Prev: Regist. (Psychiat.) St. Thos. Hosp. Lond.

FERNANDO, Sita Beatrice The Medical Centre, 100 Lavender Hill, London SW11 5RE Tel: 020 7738 0070 Fax: 020 7207 3302 — MBBS 1964; Dipl. Anaesth. (Roy. Coll. Surg.) UK. (University of Ceylon, Colombo, Sri Lanka)

FERNANDO, Sonali Marie 12 Upton Road, Chichester PO19 2QQ Tel: 01243 536128 — MB BS 1998 Lond.; MB BS Lond 1998. (United Medical and Dental Schools of Guy's and St. Thomas's) Ho. Phys. (Gen Med), St. Thomas's Hosp., Lond. Socs: Med. Protec. Soc.; Med. Defence Union. Prev: Ho. Surg. (Gen Surg & Orthop.), Greenwich Dist. Hosp., Greenwich.

FERNANDO, Subhas Chandra 59 Mornington Crescent, Hounslow TW5 9ST — MB BS 1970 Ceylon.

FERNANDO, Sumantra Jayanandana Mohandas Tel: 020 8366 6600; 20 Burghley Road, Kentish Town, London NW5 1UE Tel: 020 7485 9122 Fax: 020 7267 7405 Email: sumanfernando@compuserve.com — MB BChir 1957 Camb.; MA Camb. 1975. MD 1975; FRCPsych 1986, M 1971; DPM Eng. 1962. (Camb. & Univ. Coll. Hosp.) Hon. Cons. Psychiat. Enfield Community Care NHS Trust; Sen. Lect. (Ment. Health) Tizard Centre Univ. Kent, Canterbury; Vis. Prof. Univ. of N. Lond. Socs: Fell. Roy. Soc. Med. Prev: Cons. Psychiat. Claybury Hosp. & Chase Farm Hosp.; Ment. Health Act Commiss.er; Sen. Regist. (Psychiat.) Lond. Hosp.

FERNANDO, Warnakulasuriya Sudharman Bernard P The Surgery, 2 Thames Avenue, Rainham, Gillingham ME8 9BW Tel: 01634 360486 Fax: 01634 375159 — MB BS 1980 Colombo; MRCS Eng. LRCP Lond. 1988; DLO RCS Eng. 1987. Prev: Trainee GP Llandovery; SHO (Otolaryng.) W. Middlx. Univ. Hosp. Isleworth & Harrogate Gen. Hosp.

FERNELL, David Mark New House Farm Barn, Black Pitts Lane, Himbleton, Droitwich WR9 7LE — MB ChB 1977 Liverp.

FERNER, Robin Esmond City Hospital NHS Trust, Dudley Road, Birmingham B18 7QH Tel: 0121 554 3801 Fax: 0121 507 5820 Email: r.e.ferner@bham.ac.uk; 31 Moor Green Lane, Birmingham B13 8NE — MB BS 1978 Lond.; MSc Oxf. 1974; BSc Lond. 1971; MD Lond. 1988; FRCP Lond. 1995; MRCP (UK) 1980. (Univ. Coll. Hosp.) Cons. Phys. (Clin. Pharmacol.) City Hosp. Birm.; Dir. W. Midl. Centre for Adverse Drug Reactions Reporting; Hon. Sen. Lect. (Clin. Pharmacol.) Univ. Birm. Prev: Sen. Regist. (Gen. Med. & Clin. Pharmacol.) Roy. Vict. Infirm. Newc.; Ho. Phys. Univ. Coll. Hosp. Lond.; Ho. Surg. Stoke Mandeville Hosp. Aylesbury.

FERNER, Rosalie Elaine 3 Somerset Gardens, London N6 5EQ Email: r.ferner@umds.ac.uk — MB BS 1981 Newc.; MD Newc. 1995; MRCP (UK) 1984. (Newc. u. Tyne) Sen. Regist. (Neurol.) Guy's Hosp. Lond. Prev: Research Fell., Hon. Lect. & Regist. (Neurol.) Guy's Hosp. Lond.

FERNIE, Crawford George MacDougall The Medical & Dental Defence Union of Scotland, Mackintosh House, 120 Blythswood St., Glasgow G2 4EA Tel: 0141 221 5858 Fax: 0141 228 1208 Email: gf@mddus.com; Tel: 01505 610639 Email: cgmf@btinternet.com — MB ChB 1977 Glas.; MRCGP 1984; Dip. Forens. Med. Glas 1989; MPhil. Glas. 1996. Adviser; Police Surg.; Hon. Sen. Lect. Dep. Forens. Med. & Sci. Univ. Glas. Socs: Counc. Mem. Assn. Police Surg.; Coun. Mem.Scott.. Medico-Legal Soc.

FERNIE, Tracy Carol The Health Centre, Stock Road, Billericay CM12 0BJ Tel: 01277 658071 Fax: 01277 631892 — MB BS 1986 Lond.; MRCGP 1991; Cert. Prescribed Equiv. Exp. JCPTGP 1992; DRCOG 1990. (St Bartholomew's Hospital, London) GP Princip. Prev: Clin. Med. Off.

FERNLEY, Christine Ann Church Walk Surgery, Drury Street, Metheringham, Lincoln LN4 3EZ Tel: 01526 320522 Fax: 01526 322210; 1 Hall Lane, Branston, Lincoln LN4 1PZ Fax: 01522 793644 — MRCS Eng. LRCP Lond. 1983. (Manch.)

FERNS, Professor Gordon Ashly Anthony Clinical Laboratories, The Royal Surrey County Hospital, Egerton Road, Guildford GU2 7XX Tel: 01483 464121 Fax: 01483 464072; Division of Metabolic & Molecular Medicine, School of Biological Sciences, University of Surrey, Guildford GU2 7XH Tel: 01483 464121 Fax: 01483 464072 Email: g.ferns@surrey.ac.uk — MB BS 1980 Lond.; MSc (Clin. Biochem.) Lond. 1983, BSc (Hons.) 1976; MD Lond. 1986; MRCS Eng. LRCP Lond. 1979; MRCPath 1987; FRCPath 1997; Dip. Hlth. Mgt. Keele 1995. (St. Bart. Hosp. Med. Coll.) Prof. Metab. & Molecular Med. Univ. Surrey; Brit.-Amer. Research Fell. (Brit. Heart Foundat. - Amer. Heart Assn.) Univ Washingtonj, Seattle, USA. Socs: Fell. Roy. Soc. Med.; Assn. Clin. Biochem.; Brit. Atherosclerosis Soc. Prev: Sen. Lect. & Hon. Cons. (Chem. Path.) Univ. Leicester; Wellcome Path. Research Fell. (Chem. Path., Diabetes & Lipidol.) St. Bart. Hosp. Lond.; Hon. Sen. Regist. (Chem. Path.) & Clin. Asst. (Diabetes) St. Bart. Hosp. Lond.

FERNS, Millicent 38 Crosdaile Road, Stansted CM24 8DW — MB BS 1946 Lucknow.

FERNS, Robert Alan River Lodge Surgery, Malling Street, Lewes BN7 2RD Tel: 01273 472233 Fax: 01273 486879 — MB BChir 1979 Camb.; MRCS Eng. LRCP Lond. 1978.

FEROZE, Sir Rustam Moolan (retired) 9 Arbor Close, Beckenham BR3 6TW Tel: 020 8650 2972 Fax: 020 8650 9804 Email: rferoze@dial.pipex.com — MB BS Lond. 1946; MD (Obst. & Dis. Wom.) Lond. 1952; FRCSI (Hon.) 1984; FRCS Eng. 1952; MRCS Eng. LRCP Lond. 1943; FRCOG 1962, M 1948; FACOG (Hon.) 1986; FRACOG (Hon.) 1985. Prev: Pres. Roy. Coll. O & G 1981-4 & Europ. Assn. Gyn. & Obst. 1985-8.

FEROZE-DIN, Zakila (retired) 24 Bosworth Road, Cambridge CB1 8RG Tel: 01223 Ext: 245405 — MB ChB East Africa 1970; DA Eng. 1973. Prev: Regist. (Anaesth.) Qu. Charlottes Hosp., The Chelsea Hosp. for Wom. &.

FERRAN CABEZA, Jose Maria 4 Darnaway Close, Birchwood, Warrington WA3 6TR — LMS 1983 U Autonoma Barcelona; MRCPsych 1993.

FERRAND, Rashida 320 Chillingham Road, Heaton, Newcastle upon Tyne NE6 5SD — MB BS 1996 Newc.

FERRANDO, Anne Department of Community Paediatrics, Walsall Community Health Trust, Pheasey Clinic, Beacon Road, Great Barr, Birmingham B43 7BW; Pool Tail, 302 Skip Lane, Walsall WS5 3RA Tel: 01922 621373 — MB ChB Leeds 1965. (Leeds) SCMO Community Paediat. Wall CHT.

FERRANTE, Albert Michael Agius Blossoms Inn Medical Centre, 21 Garlic Hill, London EC4V 2AU Tel: 020 7606 6159 Fax: 020 7489 1134; Hill House, Albury, Ware SG11 2HT Tel: 01279 771217 — MB BS 1974 Lond.; MRCP (UK) 1977; MRCS Eng. LRCP Lond. 1974. (St. Bart.) Med. Adviser Victory ReInsur., Guardian Roy. Exchange Assur. Co., Aegon Life & Guardian Newspaper; Med. Adviser Lond. Internat. Finanical Futures, Clifford Chance & Various Banks & Ins. Cos.; Clin. Asst. Chelsea & W.m. Hosp.

FERRAR, John Michael (retired) Benington Old House, Benington, Stevenage SG2 7BT Tel: 01438 869281 — LMSSA 1963 Lond.; DObst RCOG 1966. Prev: SHO (Anaesth.) Roy. Sussex Co. Hosp. Brighton.

FERRAR, Roger John Burvill Street Health Centre, Burvill Street, Lynton EX35 6HA Tel: 01598 753226; The Cleeve, Lee Road, Lynton EX35 6HW — MB BS Lond. 1965; DObst RCOG 1967. (Char. Cross) Prev: Ho. Phys. (Psychiat.) Char. Cross Hosp. Lond.; SHO (O & G) St. Tydfil's Hosp. Merthyr Tydfil.

FERRARI, Miles Richard Newmarket Road Surgery, 7 Newmarket Road, Norwich NR2 2HL Tel: 01603 621006; 15 St. Stephens Square, Norwich NR1 3SS — MB BS 1986 Lond.; MRCGP 1991; DRCOG 1988.

FERRARIS, Gisella Maria Christina The Clarendon Surgery, 213 Burrage Road, London SE18 7JZ Tel: 020 8854 0356 Fax: 020 8855 5484 — MB BS 1962 Lond.; MRCS Eng. LRCP Lond. 1962; DObst RCOG 1965.

FERRARO, Alastair James 47 Copperkins Lane, Amersham HP6 5QP — BM BCh 1998 Oxf.; BM BCh Oxf 1998.

FERREIRA, Francis Geoffrey Cromwell Place Surgery, Cromwell Place, St. Ives, Huntingdon PE27 5JD Tel: 01480 462206 Fax: 01480 465313 — MB BS 1970 Lond.; MRCGP 1975; DObst RCOG 1974. (Lond. Hosp.)

FERREIRA, Ivor 28 Crawley Road, Guildford GU1 2JS — MB ChB 1975 Liverp.; DCH Eng. 1978. Regist. (Paediat.) Chelmsford Health Dist.

FERREIRA, Paula Tonnies Gil 34 Alwinton Terrace, Newcastle upon Tyne NE3 1UB Email: p.t.ferreira@incl.ac.uk — MB BS 1993 Newc.; BMedSc Newc. 1991; MScPHM 1997. SHO (A&E), Roy. Vict. Infirm., Newc. Socs: Assoc. Mem. RCGP; BMA. Prev: Hon. Regist. (Pub. Health) Newc.; GP Regist.; SHO (O & G), N. Tees.

FERRELL, William Russell Centre for Rheumatic Diseases, Department of Medicine, Queen Elizabeth Building Royal Infirmary, Glasgow G31 2ER Tel: 0141 211 4688 Fax: 0141 552 2953 Email: w.ferrell @bio.gla.ac.uk; 91 Balshagray Avenue, Jordanhill, Glasgow G11 7EQ — MB ChB 1973 Glas.; PhD Glas. 1977; FRCP Glas. 1996; MRCP (UK) 1994. (Glas.) Reader (Clin. Physiol.) Univ. Glas. Socs: Hon. Mem. Canad. Orthop. Research Soc.; Brit. Soc. Rheum.; Physiol. Soc. Prev: Vis. Prof. Univ. Calgary.

FERRER, Harold Peter (retired) 15 Oxford Road, Woodstock OX20 1UN Tel: 01993 812888 Fax: 01993 812888 Email: drpeter@drpeter.co.uk — MD 1982 Ed.; MB ChB Ed. 1959; FFCM 1977, M 1972; DPH (Distinc.) Liverp. 1966. Prev: Dist. Med. Off. Worcs. DHA.

FERRER, Ian Royston Allen, Moore, Jackson and Ferrer, Wellside Medical Centre, 3 Burton Road, Derby DE1 1TH Tel: 01332 737777 Fax: 01332 737778; 23 Avenue Road, Duffield, Belper DE56 4DW — BM BS 1983 Nottm.; BMedSci Nottm. 1981; MRCGP 1988; DRCOG 1986. (Nottingham)

FERRERO, Therese Marie Green Meadows Partnership, Winkfield Road, Ascot SL5 7LS; 12 Farm Close, Sunninghill, Ascot SL5 7AR Tel: 01344 625515 — MD 1991 Paris. p/t GP retainee. Prev: CO Instigator Paris, France; Med. Adviser MCRC (1993) and Med. Adviser, Procter & Gamble (1995); GP Regist. (1996).

FERRES, Christopher John Island House, Island Park, Greenisland, Carrickfergus BT38 8TW — MB BCh BAO 1977 Belf.; FFA RCS Dub. 1981. Sen. Regist. (Anaesth.) Roy. Vict. Hosp. Belf. Socs: Anaesth. Research Soc. Prev: Research Fell. Roy. Vict. Hosp.

FERRETT, Colin George European Scanning Clinic, 68 Harley Street, London W1G 7HE Tel: 0207 436 5755 Fax: 0207 436 5756 — MB BCh BAO 1988 Belf.; FRCR FRCR 1999; MRCPI 1993. (Queens University, Belfast) Specialist Regist. (Endocrine Med.) Roy. Vict. Hosp. Belf. Prev: Resid. Ho. Off. Roy. Vict. Hosp. Belf.; Cons. Radiologist Middlx. Hosp.. Lond.; Fell.. Diagnostic Radiol., UC Stanford, USA.

FERRIDAY, Charlotte Elizabeth Rosalind Trinity Surgery, Norwich Road, Wisbech PE13 3UZ Tel: 01945 476999 Fax: 01945 476900; 57 Pickards Way, Wisbech PE13 1SD — MB ChB 1992 Ed.; MRCGP 1996; DRCOG 1995; DFFP 1995; DCH RCP Lond. 1994. (Edinburgh University) GP Partner.

FERRIDAY, Ursula Teresa Unilever House, Blackfriars, London EC4P 4BQ Tel: 020 7822 6029 Fax: 020 7822 6334 Email: ursula.ferriday@unilever.com; Phoenix House, 22 School Close, High Wycombe HP11 1PH — MB BCh 1978 Wales; MFOM RCP (UK) 1996; MFFP 1993; MRCGP 1982; DRCOG 1981; MSc 1999. Sen. Med. Adviser Unilever UK.

FERRIE, Mr Bernard Gerard 1 Charlemont Close, Walsall WS5 3ND Tel: 01922 725392 Fax: 01922 725392 — MB ChB 1973 Glas.; FRCS Glas. 1978. Cons. Urol. Surg. Manor Hosp Walsall; Hon. Sen. Clin. Lect. (Surg.) Univ. Birm. Socs: Roy. Soc. Med. (Urol. Sect.); Brit. Assn. Urol. Surg. Prev: Sen. Regist. (Urol.) Salford Roy. Hosp.; Regist. (Urol.) Roy. Infirm. Glas.

FERRIE, Jennifer Isabel Post House, The Street, Washington, Pulborough RH20 1NG Tel: 01903 892334 Fax: 01903 892334 — MB BS 1982 Lond.; MRCGP 1990; T(GP) 1991; DCH RCP Lond. 1985. (Univ. Coll. Lond.)

FERRIE, Rosemary 33 Lorton Close, Fulwood, Preston PR2 8YS — MB ChB 1989 Ed.

FERRIER, Donald William The Pleasance, Golf Course Road, Blairgowrie PH10 6LQ — MB ChB 1974 Aberd.; DObst RCOG 1976.

FERRIER, Jonathan Francis (retired) The Gables, 36 Newland St, Eynsham, Oxford OX29 4LA Tel: 01865 881224 — MB BS 1968 Lond.; MRCS Eng. LRCP Lond. 1968; MRCGP 1978; DCH Eng. 1973; DObst RCOG 1970. Prev: Sen. Partner Gen. Pract. Witney Oxon.

FERRIER, Vivien 6 Hill Park, Darras Hall, Ponteland, Newcastle upon Tyne NE20 9RX — MB BS 1977 Lond.; MRCS Eng. LRCP Lond. 1977; MRCGP 1983.

FERRIES, John Henry (retired) Moonspinner, 6 Link Hill, Kithurst Park, Storrington, Pulborough RH20 4LS Tel: 01903 743979 — MB BS 1943 Lond.; MRCS Eng. LRCP Lond. 1943. Prev: Med. Off. Qu. Alexandra Hosp. Home Worthing.

FERRIMAN, Emma Louise 114 Bachelor Lane, Horsforth, Leeds LS18 5NF — MB ChB 1990 Liverp. Train.Fell.Feto-Matern.. Med. Leeds.Gen.Infirm.

FERRIMAN, John Hugh Monkseaton Medical Centre, Cauldwell Avenue, Whitley Bay NE25 9PH Tel: 0191 252 1616; 42 Reid Park Road, Jesmond, Newcastle upon Tyne NE2 2ES Tel: 0191 281 0370 Fax: 0191 281 0370 — MB BS 1979 Newc.; MRCGP 1983. (Newcastle)

FERRIN, Lynn Vera Birling Avenue Surgery, 3 Birling Avenue, Rainham, Gillingham ME8 7HB Tel: 01634 360390/361843 Fax:

01634 264061; Heatherbank, Woodgate Lane, Newington, Sittingbourne ME9 7QB Tel: 01795 842613 — MB ChB 1969 Leeds. (Leeds) Prev: Ho. Phys. (Dermat.) & Ho. Surg. (ENT) Leeds Gen. Infirm.; Deptm. Med. Off. Gillingham Municip. Boro.

FERRINGTON, Derek Forgham (retired) New Hall House, Betley Hall Gardens, Betley, Crewe CW3 9BB — MB ChB Birm. 1950; MA Keele 1991.

FERRIS, Alan Richard Parkfield Medical Centre, The Walk, Potters Bar EN6 1QH Tel: 01707 651234 Fax: 01707 660452; 3 St Vincents Way, Potters Bar EN6 2RG Tel: 01707 651801 Email: alan@thebloodycomputer.swinternet.co.uk — MB BS 1982 Lond.; MRCS Eng. LRCP Lond. 1982; MRCGP 1986; DGM RCP Lond. 1986. (Westm.) GP; Med. Off. Nat. Inst. Biol. Standards & Control S. Mimms; Assoc. Investigator U. S. Army Med. Research Inst. Infect. Dis. Maryland.

FERRIS, Anthony John (retired) Watersmeet, Chaffcombe, Chard TA20 4AP — BM BCh 1957 Oxf.; BA Oxf. 1953, BM BCh 1957; DObst RCOG 1959; DCH Eng. 1969; Cert JCC Lond. 1979. Prev: GP Chard.

FERRIS, Mr Barry David Department Orthopaedics, Barnet General Hospital, Wellhouse Lane, Barnet Tel: 0208 216 5433; 96 Bluebell Ave, Penistone, Sheffield S36 6LQ Tel: 01226 765644, 0208 958 2564 Email: barry@knee.demon.co.uk.(barry@knee.demon.co.uk — MB BS 1977 Lond.; MS Lond. 1986; FRCS Eng. 1980; MRCS Eng. LRCP Lond. 1977. (Westm.) Cons. Orthop. Surg. Barnet Gen. Hosp. Socs: Brit. Orthop. Assn.; Sec. Orthopaedic Sect.; Fell. Roy. Soc. Med. Prev: Sen. Regist. W.m. Univ. Coll. & Assoc. Hosps.; Wellcome Research Fell. CRC N.wick Pk. Hosp.; Regist. (Orthop.) W.m. & Assoc. Hosps. Lond.

FERRIS, Elizabeth Anne Esther Robey's Farmhouse, Brown Candover, Alresford SO24 9TN Tel: 01256 389352 Fax: 01256 389200 — MB BS 1965 Lond. (Middlx.) Med. Off. Modern Pentathlon Assn. GB. Socs: Fell. Roy. Soc. Med.

FERRIS, Janet Mary (retired) 97 Farndale Drive, Loughborough LE11 2RG — MB BS 1957 Lond.; FFA RCS Eng. 1973; FFA RCSI 1972; DA Eng. 1960. Prev: Cons. Anaesth. Leicester Gen. Hosp.

FERRIS, John Desmond 69 Springfield Road, Bristol BS6 5SW — MB ChB 1989 Bristol.

FERRIS, John Henry Nelson Danecroft, 13 Belfast Road, Newtownards BT23 4BJ Tel: 01247 3047 — MB BCh BAO 1955 Dub.; MAO 1960; FRCOG 1974, M 1961, DObst 1958. Cons. O & G N. Down., Downpatrick & Ulster Hosps.

FERRIS, Mr Keith Parham (retired) 39 Aspian Drive, Coxheath, Maidstone ME17 4JZ Email: kapeferris@hotmail.com — BM BCh 1955 Oxf.; MA Oxf. 1955; FRCS Eng. 1961; DLO Eng. 1960. Prev: Cons. ENT Surg. Kent Co. Ophth. & Aural Hosp. Maidstone & All St.s.

FERRIS, Manuel Maurice 4 Frobisher House, Dolphin Square, London SW1V 3LL Tel: 020 7828 1430 — LRCP LRCS Ed. LRFPS Glas. 1949; MRCGP 1971. (St. Mungo's Coll. & Univ. Glas.) Med. Adviser Spencer & Partners, Will Bros. (Overseas), Shaw & Hatton Internat. System Ford Ltd. Socs: BMA. Prev: Clin. Asst. Roy. Throat, Nose & Ear Hosp. Lond.; Resid. Phys. Stobhill Hosp. Glas.; Flight Lt. RAF Med. Br.

FERRIS, Mark Bennett 37 Brancaster Lane, Purley CR8 1HJ — MRCS Eng. LRCP Lond. 1976.

FERRIS, Matthew William The Old Malt House, High St., Broughton, Stockbridge SO20 8AE — BM 1993 Soton. SHO (Anaesth.) Soton. Gen. Hosp. Prev: SHO (Gen. Med.) P.ss Margt. Hosp. Swindon; SHO (A & E) & Ho. Off. (Gen. Surg.) P.ss Margt. Hosp. Swindon; Ho. Off. (Gen. Med.) Roy. S. Hants. Hosp.

FERRIS, Michelle Lane End Medical Group, 25 Edgwarebury Lane, Edgware HA8 8LJ Tel: 020 8958 4233 Fax: 020 8905 4657; 119 Green Lane, Edgware HA8 8EL Tel: 020 8958 2564 — MB BS 1981 Lond.; MRCGP 1985; DRCOG 1985; DCH RCP Lond. 1984. (Univ. Coll. Hosp.) Sch. Med. Off. N. Lond. Collegiate Sch. Prev: Trainee GP Ealing Hosp. VTS; Ho. Phys. Univ. Coll. Hosp. Lond.; Ho. Phys. Edgware Gen. Hosp.

***FERRIS, Paul Ieuan** 5 Scaliot Close, New Mills, High Peak SK22 3BX — MB ChB 1997 Liverp.

FERRIS, Rebecca Charlotte The Old Malt House, High St., Broughton, Stockbridge SO20 8AE Tel: 01794 301289 Email: rferris@dostors.org.uk — BM BS 1990 Nottm.; MRCP Lond. 1995. Specialist Rigist. (Community Paediat. & Neurol.), Soton. Socs: RCPCH. Prev: Specialist Regist. (Community Paediat.) Poole Hosp.; Neonat. Regist. Soton.; Paediat. Regist. Swindon.

FERRIS, Robert James The Oxford Clinic, Littlemore Mental Health Centre, Sandford Road, Littlemore, Oxford OX4 4XN Tel: 01865 223118 Fax: 01865 223348 — MB BS 1978 Adelaide; FRANZCPsych 1986, M 1984; T(Psych) 1991. Cons. Forens. Psychiat .Oxf. Clinic MSU, Littlemore Hosp. Oxf.; Clin. Director, Rehabil. & Forens. Dept.

FERRIS, Scott Tobias 13 Taylor Avenue, Kew, Richmond TW9 4EB — MB BS 1996 Lond.

FERRO, Albert Department of Clinical Pharmacology, St Thomas' Hospital, Lambeth Palace Road, London SE1 7EH Tel: 020 7928 9292 Fax: 020 7401 2242 Email: albert.ferro@kcl.ac.uk — MB BS 1984 Lond.; PhD Camb. 1994; BSc (Hons.) Lond. 1981; MRCP (UK) 1988; FRCP 1999. (King's Coll. Sch. Med. & Dent. Lond.) Sen. Lect. (Clin. Pharmacol.) & Hon. Cons. Phys. King's Coll. Lond., St. Thomas's Hosp. Lond. Socs: Med. Res. Soc.; Brit. Hypertens. Soc.; Brit. Pharm. Soc. Prev: Sen. Regist. (Clin. Pharmacol.) Hammersmith Hosp. Lond.; Regist. (Cardiol.) Bristol Roy. Infirm.; Hon. Sen. Regist. (Clin. Pharmacol.) Addenbrooke's Hosp. Camb.

FERRO, Mr Michael Huddersfield Royal Infirmary, Huddersfield HD3 3EA Tel: 01484 422191 Fax: 01484 482888; One Oak, Daisy Lea Lane, Lindley, Huddersfield HD3 3LP Tel: 01484 453965 Fax: 01484 421137 Email: mikeferro@btinternet.com — MD 1975 Malta; ChM (Bristol) 1988; FRCS Eng. 1982; FRCS Ed. 1981. Cons. Urol. Huddersfield Roy. Infirm. Socs: Brit. Assn. Urol. Surgs. Prev: Sen. Regist. Rotat. (Urol.) Leeds & Bradford Hosps.

FERRY, David Alexander Kilbirnie Medical Practice, 2 Kirkland Road, Kilbirnie KA25 6HP Tel: 01505 683333 Fax: 01505 683591 — MB ChB 1986 Aberd.

FERRY, David Raymond 22 Oak Leaf Drive, Moseley, Birmingham B13 9FE — MB ChB 1987 Leic.; BSc Leic. 1981; PhD Giessen 1984; MRCP (UK) 1990; FRCP 1999. (Leicester) Sen. Lect. (Med. Oncol.) Qu. Eliz. & Heartlands Trust Hosp. Birm. Socs: Amer. Assn. Cancer Research; Mem.BMA. Prev: Sen. Lect. (Med. Oncol.) Qu. Eliz. Hosp. Birm. & New Cross Hosp. Wolverhampton; Sen. Regist. (Med. Oncol.) Qu. Eliz. Hosp. Birm.; Regist. (Med. Oncol.) Qu. Eliz. & E. Birm. Hosps.

FERRY, Rose Marion Trethornas Health Centre, William St., Trethornas, Newport; Blaen Cwm Bychan, Tycroes, Ammanford SA18 3PP — MB BCh 1982 Wales; BSc Wales 1975, MB BCh 1982; MRCGP 1986. GP Taff's Well. Socs: BMA. Prev: SHO (O & G & Rheum.) E. Glam. Gen. Hosp. Pontypridd.

FERRYMAN, Stephen Robert Histopathology Department, Walsgrave Hospital, Coventry CV2 2DX Tel: 024 76 602020 — MB ChB 1983 Sheff.; MRCPath 1991. Cons. (Histopath. & Cytopath.) Walsgrave Hosp. Coventry. Prev: Cons. Gyn. Histopath. & Cytopath. Birm. Matern. Hosp. & Hon. Sen. Lect. Birm. Univ.; Sen. Regist. (Histopath.) W. Midl. RHA.

FERSHT, Naomi Lisa 2 Barrow Close, Cambridge CB2 2AT — MB BChir 1994 Camb.

FERTIG, Arnold Nuffield Road Medical Centre, Nuffield Road, Chesterton, Cambridge CB4 1GL Tel: 01223 423424 Fax: 01223 566450 Email: arnold.fertig@gp-d81044.anglox.nhs.uk; 13 Park Lane, Histon, Cambridge CB4 9JJ Tel: 01223 351447 — MB BChir Camb. 1974; MA (Med. Sc.) Camb. 1977; FRCGP 1993, M 1980; DRCOG 1980. (Westminster) Socs: BMA. Prev: Mem. Camb. LMC; Chairm. Camb. GP Forum; GP Tutor Camb.

FERTIG, Mrs Olga (retired) 35 Winchfield Drive, Harborne, Birmingham B17 8TG Tel: 0121 429 6651 — MD 1934 Prague.

FERTLEMAN, Caroline Renée Department of Paediatrics, The Rayne Institute, UCL, 5 University St., London WC1E 6JJ Tel: 020 7209 6663 Fax: 020 7209 6103 Email: c.fertleman@ucl.ac.uk; 5 Pond Square, Highgate, London N6 6BA Tel: 020 8341 9696 Fax: 020 8340 4565 — MB BChir 1990 Camb.; BA (Hons.) Camb. 1987; MRCP (UK) 1994; MSc (Lond) 1996. (Royal London and Cambridge) Clin. Lect. (Paediat.) Univ. Coll. Lond. Socs: Roy. Soc. Med.; MRCPCH; RCP. Prev: Regist. (Haemat. & Oncol.) Gt. Ormond St. Hosp. Lond.; Regist. (Paediat.) N. Middlx. Hosp.; SHO (Paediat.) Qu. Eliz. Hosp. For Chidr. Lond.

FERTLEMAN, Michael Barry Department of Medicine, Northwick Park Hospital, Watford Road, Watford; 17 Hogarth Hill, London NW11 6AY Tel: 020 8458 2742 Fax: 020 7631 5282 Email:

m.fertleman@hotmail.com — MB BS 1997 Lond.; BA (Law) Camb. 1994; MA Camb. 1998. (Imperial Coll. St. Mary's) SHO (Gen. Med.) N.wick Pk. Hosp. Socs: Roy. Soc. Med.; Med. Leg. Soc. Prev: Ho. Off. (Chest Med.) St Marys Lond.; Ho. Off. (Urol.) Centr. Middlx. Lond.

FESSEY, Barbara May (retired) 10 Ann Road, Wythall, Birmingham B47 6EP — MB BS 1957 Lond.; MRCS Eng. LRCP Lond. 1949. Prev: Med. Asst. (Clin. Path.) Gen. Hosp. Birm.

FESTA, Marino Salvatore Flat 2, 60 Chartfield Avenue, London SW15 6HQ — MB BS 1990 Lond.

FESTENSTEIN, Freda 14 Brackendale Grove, Harpenden AL5 3EJ — MRCS Eng. LRCP Lond. 1957. Hon. Sen. Lect. Nat. Heart & Lung Inst. Socs: Brit. Thoracic Soc.; Brit. Med. Assn.; Internat. Union Against Tuberc. and Lung Dis. Prev: Cons. Phys. Thoracic Med. Lond. Chest Hosp.; Regist. (Med.) Clare Hall Hosp. S. Mimms.

FESTENSTEIN, John Basil Edgware Community Hospital, Edgware HA8 0AD Tel: 020 8732 6204 Fax: 020 8732 6379 — MB BCh 1961 Witwatersrand; FRCR 1975; FFR 1973; Dip. Amer. Bd. Radiol. 1969. (Witwatersrand) Cons. (Radiol.) Barnet and Chase Farm NHS Trust. Socs: Brit. Inst. Radiol. Prev: Sen. Regist. St. Thos. Hosp. Lond.; Fell. in Cardiovasc. Radiol. Univ. Hosp. Boston, USA; Resid. (Radiol.) Beth Israel Hosp. Boston, USA.

FESTER, Julian Simon North Brink Surgery, 7 North Brink, Wisbech PE13 1JU Tel: 01945 585121; 5 Bowthorpe Road, Wisbech PE13 2DX — MB BS 1985 Lond.; BSc Lond. 1982, MB BS 1985; MRCGP 1989.

FETHERSTON, Helen Sinclair 12 Tara Wood, Farm Hill Road, Holywood BT18 0HS — MB BCh BAO 1939 Belf. (Qu. Univ. Belf.)

FETHERSTON, Mary Sinclair 26 Bristow Park, Belfast BT9 6TH Tel: 01232 666826 — MB BCh BAO 1971 Belf.; MB BCh BAO (Hons.) Belf. 1971; DCH RCPSI 1975. (Belf.) Med. Off. Health Clinics E. Health & Social Servs. Bd. N. Irel. Prev: Jun. Ho. Off. Roy. Vict. Hosp. Belf.; SHO Roy. Belf. Hosp. Sick Childr.; Regist. (Paediat.) Addington Hosp. Durban, S. Afr.

FETHERSTON, Mr Timothy Joseph Sunderland Eye Infirmary, Queen Alexandra Road, Sunderland SR2 9HP Tel: 0191 565 6256 — MB ChB 1975 Liverp.; FRCS Eng. 1980; FRCOphth 1988. Cons. Ophth. City Hosps. Sunderland NHS Trust. Prev: Cons. Ophth. S. Warks. & Coventry HAs.

FETTES, Colin David Brae Terrace Surgery, Brae Terrace, Munlochy IV8 8NG; 14 Cromwell Court, Shore St, Inverness IV1 1ND Tel: 01463 232150 — MB ChB 1978 Aberd. GP Munlochy & N. Kessock.

FETTES, Ian Fraser Albemarle Surgery, 27 Albemarle Crescent, Scarborough YO11 1XX Tel: 01723 360098 Fax: 01723 501546; 57 Scalby Road, Scarborough YO12 5QL Tel: 01723 501459 — MB ChB 1973 Ed.; DObst RCOG 1975.

FETTES, Mary Rose Howdenhall Surgery, 57 Howden Hall Road, Edinburgh EH16 6PL Tel: 0131 664 3766 Fax: 0131 672 2114; The Shieling, 21 Lasswade Road, Eskbank, Dalkeith EH22 3EE Tel: 0131 663 2430 — MB ChB 1967 Aberd.; DA Eng. 1969. (Aberd.) Prev: Regist. (Anaesth.) Falkirk & Dist. Roy. Infirm.; Research Fell. Dept. Therap. Univ. Edin.

FETTES, Paul Douglas William Torbay Hospital, Anaesthetic Office, Newton Road, Torquay TQ2 7AA; 2/1 27 Lacrosse Terrace, Kelvinbridge, Glasgow G12 8EX Email: paul.heidi@virgin.net — MB ChB 1995 Glas.; BSc (Hons.) Glas. 1992. SHO (Anaesth.) Torbay Hosp. Torbay. Prev: SHO (Emerg. Med.) 1996-1997.

FETTES, Peter Hugh The Surgery, Kirkfield Place, Arrochar G83 7AG Tel: 01301 702531; 21 Lasswade Road, Eskbank, Dalkeith EH22 3EE Tel: 0131 663 2430 — MB ChB 1968 Aberd.

FEUCHTWANG, Ann Cordelia Yatton Family Practice, The Surgery, 155 Mendip Road, Yatton, Bristol BS49 4ER Tel: 01934 832277 Fax: 01934 876085 Email: cordelia.feuchtwang@gp-l81074.nhs.uk — MB BS 1986 Lond.; BSc 1983 Lond.; MRCGP 1990; DCH RCP Lond. 1989; DRCOG 1988. (UCH & Middlx.) GP Principal. Prev: Asst. GP Retainer Scheme Telford; Trainee GP N.wick Pk. Hosp. Harrow & Pinner Middlx. VTS.; GP Retainer Scheme, N. Som.

FEUCHTWANG-FOY, Jeannette Nicola Hannah Child Health HQ, Edgware Community Hospital, Edgware HA8 0AD Tel: 020 8732 6566 Fax: 020 8732 6474; 46 Myddelton Park, Whetstone, London N20 0JL — MB BS 1979 Lond.; MSc (Community Paediat.) Lond. 1992; DCH RCP Lond. 1985. (Roy. Free) Cons. Community Paediat. Barnet & Chase Farm Hositals NHS Trust. Prev: SCMO (Child Health) Barnet HA.

FEUER, David Joseph 36 Howletts Lane, Ruislip HA4 7RS Tel: 01895 621400 — BM 1991 Soton.; BSc Soton. (1st cl. Hons.) 1990; MRCP (UK) 1995; DSR 1998 (Univ of London). (Soton.) Cons. in Palliat. Med. (Hon Sen. Lect.) Barts and the Lond. NHS Trust, St Bartholomews Hosp., Lond.; Hon Cons. in Pal Med. Homerton Hosp. Hackney. Socs: Roy. Soc. Med.; Assn. Palliat. Med. Prev: research fell., (Palliat. Med.) Roy. Marsden Hosp. Lond.; Regist. P.ss Alice Hospice Esher; SHO (Med.) Roy. Marsden Hosp. Sutton.

FEW, Andrew Stuart 15 Cage Lane, Stretham, Ely CB6 3LB — MB BS 1993 Lond.

FEWINGS, Paul Edward 53 Foxholes Hill, Exmouth EX8 2DH — MB BS 1989 Lond.; FRCS (Ed) 1994; FRCS (Glas.) 1994. Specialist Regist. (Neurosurg.) Sheff./Hull.

FEWINS, Hilary Elizabeth The Cardiothoracic Centre, Liverpool NHS Trust, Thomas Drive, Liverpool L14 3PE Tel: 0151 228 1616 Email: hfewins@ccl-tr.nwest.nhs.uk; Gale Moss Farm, Arley Road, Crowley, Northwich CW9 6NS Tel: 01565 777272 — MB BS 1976 Lond.; FRCR 1983; DRCOG 1979. (Guy's Hospital) Cons. radiologist The Cardiothoracic Centre, Liverp. NHS Trust; Hon. Lect. Dept. Radiodiag. Univ. Liverp.; Head of Train. Mersey Radiol. Train. Scheme. Socs: Liverp. Med. Inst. Prev: Cons. Radiol. Halton Hosp. Runcorn.

FEWSTER, Elizabeth Jane Hawthornden Surgery, Wharf Lane, Bourne End SL8 5RX Tel: 01628 522864; 36 Hambledon Walk, Maidenhead SL6 7UH Tel: 01628 37342 — MB BS 1984 Lond.; MA Camb. 1984; MRCGP 1988; DRCOG 1986.

FEWSTER, Helen Yew Tree Cottage, Pear Ash, Penselwood, Wincanton BA9 8LP Tel: 01747 841109 Fax: 01747 841260 — MB BS 1977 Lond.; MRCS Eng. LRCP Lond. 1977. (St. Bart.)

FEWSTER, Mr Stephen David Victoria Hospital, Whinney Heys Road, Blackpool FY3 8NR Tel: 01253 306991; 32 Longhouse Lane, Poulton-le-Fylde FY6 8DF — MB BS 1984 Lond.; MA Camb. 1985; FRCS (Orth.) 1994; FRCS Ed. 1989; FRCS Eng. 1989. (Camb. & Lond.) Cons. Orthop. Surg. Vict. Hosp. NHS Trust Blackpool. Socs: Fell. BOA; Brit. Orthop. Research Soc.; Brit. Assn. of Spinal Surg.s. Prev: Sen. Regist. Rotat. (Orthop.) Hammersmith Hosp. Lond.; Vis. Lect. (Orthop.) Chinese Univ., Hong Kong; Regist. Rotat. (Orthop.) Qu. Eliz. II Hosp. Welwyn Gdn. City, Hammersmith Hosp. & N. Middlx. Hosp. Lond.

FEWTRELL, Mary Scott Department of Paediatrics, Queens Medical Centre, Nottingham NG7 2UH Tel: 0115 9242 1421; 17 Barclay Court, Broad St, Banbury OX16 5BN Tel: 01295 53247 — BM BCh 1986 Oxf.; MA Camb. 1987.

FEY, Christina Mary Royal Hospital, Calow, Chesterfield S44 5BL Tel: 01246 277271; Ravensdale, Ashbourne DE6 5BS Tel: 01332 824148 — MB ChB 1972 Bristol; MRCGP 1977.

FEY, Royston Edward S Derbyshire Health Authority, Derwent Court, Stuart Street, Derby DE1 2FZ Tel: 01332 626300 Fax: 01332 203046 Email: roy.fey@mail.sderby-ha.trent.nhs.uk; Ravensdale, Ashbourne DE6 5BS Tel: 01332 824148 — MB ChB 1976 Bristol; MRCP (UK) 1979; MFPHM 1998. (Bristol) Cons. in Communicable Dis. Control, S.ern Derbysh. HA. Prev: Sen. Regist. (Pub. Health Med.) Gloucestershire HA.

FEYI-WABOSO, Mr Andrew Chima 184 King George V Drive, Heata, Cardiff CF14 4ED Tel: 029 2075 5496 Email: feyi-waboso@cf.ac.uk — MB BS 1986 Ibadan; FRCS Ed. 1993. (Ibapan, Nigeria) Specialist Regist. Univ. Hosp. of Wales Cardiff. Socs: MDU. Prev: Regist. Singleton Hosp. Swansea; Regist. HM Stanley Hosp. St. Asaph N. Wales; Regist. St. Woolos Hosp. Newport.

FFOOKS, Mr Oliver Owen Frazer (retired) Brimblecombes, Dunsford, Exeter EX6 7HA Tel: 01392 52103 — MRCS Eng. LRCP Lond. 1949; FRCS Eng. 1958; DO Eng. 1953. Prev: Cons. Ophth. St. Jas. Hosp. Leeds.

FFRENCH-CONSTANT, Charles Kenvyn Department of Medical Genetics, Cambridge University, Addenbrooke's Hospital, Cambridge CB2 2QQ; 420 Unthank Road, Norwich NR4 7QH — MB 1979 Camb.; MB BChir Camb. 1979; PhD Lond. 1986; MRCP (UK) 1982. Univ. Lect. & Hon. Cons. Camb.

FFRENCH-CONSTANT, Edward Paul Simon Bissoe Surgery, Bissoe Road, Carnon Downs, Truro TR3 6JD Tel: 01872 863221 Fax: 01872 864113; Tregew, Grenna Lane, Perranwell Station,

Truro TR3 7LL Tel: 01872 863221 — BA Oxf. 1979, BM BCh 1982; DCH RCP Lond. 1986.

FFRENCH-CONSTANT, Martin Charles (retired) Mylor Cottage, Droxford, Southampton SO32 3PT Tel: 01489 877462 — BM BCh 1953 Oxf.; BA, BM BCh Oxf. 1953. Prev: Wing Cdr. RAF Med. Br.

FFYTCHE, Dominic Hannes 1 Wellington Square, Chelsea, London SW3 4NJ — MB BS 1987 Lond.; BSc Lond. 1984, MB BS 1987; MRCP (UK) 1991; MRCPsych 1992.

FFYTCHE, Mr Timothy John, LVO 149 Harley Street, London W1G 6DE Tel: 020 7935 4444 Fax: 020 7224 2969 Email: t.ffytche@thelondonclinic.co.uk; 1 Wellington Square, Chelsea, London SW3 4NJ Tel: 020 7730 1410 — MB BS Lond. 1961; FRCS Eng. 1968; MRCS Eng. LRCP Lond. 1961; FRCOphth. 1989; DO Eng. 1966. (St. Geo.) Cons. Ophth. Surg, Moorfields Eye hosp.; Cons. Ophth. Surg. Moorfields Eye Hosp, King Edwd. VII Hosp. For Offs & Hosp for Trop Dis, Lond; Surg. Oculist to HM the Qu.; Chairm. IAPB Europe; Mem. Med. Advis. Bd. LEPRA; Mem. Advis. Comm. of Internat. Counc. of Ophth.; IFOS Coordinator Europe. Socs: Pres.-elect Med. Soc. Lond. Prev: Cons. Opthalmological Surg. St Thomas's Hosp. Lond.; Sen. Regist. (Ophth.) Middlx. Hosp. Lond.; Sen. Regist. Moorfields Eye Hosp. (High Holborn Br.) Lond.

FIAMANYA, William Kudjoe IVF & Fertility Centre, Cromwell Hospital, Cromwell Road, London SW5 0TU Tel: 020 7370 4233; 50 Hale End Road, London E17 4BQ — MD 1972 Bucharest; MRCOG 1980. Gyn. & IVF Specialist Cromwell Hosp IVF Unit Lond. Socs: Brit. Fertil. Soc.; Amer. Fertil. Soc. Prev: Regist. (O & G) N. Staffs. Hosp. Centre Stoke-on-Trent; Regist. Co. Hosp. Hereford; O & G IVF Unit Humana Hosp. Wellington Lond.

FIANDER, Alison Nina Department of Obstetrics & Gynaecology, Llandough Hospital, Penlan Road, Penarth CF64 2XX Tel: 029 2071 1711 Fax: 029 2071 6112 — BM 1981 Soton.; MSc (Med. Educat.) Wales 1995; MRCOG 1986; JCPTGP 1987; Cert. Family Plann. JCC 1985; DM Soton 1997. (Soton.) Cons. (O & G) Llandough Hosp. Cardiff; Hon. Cons. (Obst. & Gyn.) Univ. Cardiff. Socs: Brit. Soc. Colpos. & Cerv. Path.; Brit. Gyn. Cancer Soc.; Christ. Med. Fell.sh. Prev: Sen. Regist. (O & G) Rosie Matern. Hosp. Camb.; Sen. Regist. (O & G) Wales Univesity Hosp.; Obst. Bawku Hosp. N. Ghana, W. Africa.

FIBERESIMA, Sotonye Lanre 52 Express Drive, Ilford IG3 9QD; 72 Ashburn Road, Heaton Norris, Stockport SK4 2PU — MB BCh BAO 1979 NUI; LRCPI & LM, LRCSI & LM 1979; MRCOG 1988.

FICKER, Linda Anne Moorfields Eye Hospital, 162 City Road, London EC1V 2PD Tel: 020 7566 2018 Fax: 020 7566 2019 — MB BS 1977 Lond.; BSc (Hons.) Lond. 1974; FRCS Eng. 1983; FRCOphth 1988; Specialist Accredit. Ophth. RCS Eng. 1984; EBOD 1996. (Univ. Coll. Lond. & Westm.) Cons. Ophth. Moorfields Eye Hosp.; Lect. (Clin. Ophth.) Inst. Ophth. Univ. Lond.; Instruc. Amer. Acad. Ophth; Europ. Bd. Ophth. 1996. Socs: Assn. Research in Vision & Ophth.; Ocular Microbiol. & Immunol. Gp.; Oxf. Ophth. Congr. Prev: Sen. Regist. (Ophth.) Moorfields Eye Hosp. Lond.; Regist. (Neurosurg.) Nat. Hosp. Nerv. Dis. Lond.; Vis. Sci. (Ophth.) Emory Univ. Atlanta, Georgia, USA.

FICKLING, Mr Benjamin William, CBE (retired) 29 Maxwell Road, Northwood HA6 2YG Tel: 01923 822035 — MRCS Eng. LRCP Lond. 1934; FRCS Eng. 1938; MGDS RCS Eng. 1979; FDS RCS Eng. 1947, LDS 1932; DGDP 1992. Cons. Dent. Surg. Roy. Dent. Hosp., St. Geo. Hosp. & Mt. Vernon Hosp. Lond. Prev: Dir. Med. Sickness Insur. Soc. Permanent Insur. Company.

FICKLING, Kathryn Ann High Street Surgery, High Street, Willingham by Stow, Gainsborough DN21 5JZ Tel: 01427 788277 Fax: 01427 787630; Kilgarth, 27 Lodge Lane, Upton, Gainsborough DN21 5NW Tel: 01427 83731 — MB ChB 1981 Leic.; BSc Bristol 1976; MRCGP 1985; DRCOG 1984. GP Willingham By Stow; Clin. Asst. (Gastroenterol.) Lincoln Co. Hosp.

FICKLING, William Edward Royal United Hospital, Coombe Park, Bath BA1 1NH Tel: 01225 824547 — MB BChir 1990 Camb.; MRCP (UK) 1992. Regist. (Gastroenterol.) Chelsea & W.minster Hosp. Trust; Specialist Regist. (Gastroenterol.) Roy. United Hosp. Trust Bath. Prev: Regist. Rotat. (Gastroenterol.) Soton. Univ. & Portsmouth Hosps. Trusts.; SHO Rotat. (Med.) St. Richard's Hosp. Chichester.

FIDDES, William Frederick Gordon Viewfield Lane Health Centre, Viewfield Lane, Selkirk TD7 4LJ Tel: 01750 21674 Fax: 01750 23176; Ambleside, Goslawdales, Selkirk TD7 4EP — MB ChB 1971 Ed.; BSc Ed. 1968; DObst RCOG 1974. (Ed.)

FIDDIAN, Anthony Paul Sandiway, Milton Avenue, Chalfont St Peters, Gerrards Cross SL9 8QW Tel: 01753 887767 Fax: 01753 887767 Email: paul.fidian@which.net — MB BS 1975 Lond. (St. Bart.) Hon. Sen. Lect. (Clin. Virol.), Roy. Free & Univ. Med. Sch. Prev: Dir. (Viral Dis.) Glaxo-Wellcome Stockley Pk., Uxbridge; Head (Clin. Virol.) Wellcome Research Laborat. Beckenham Kent; Regist. (Microbiol.) St. Bart. Hosp. Lond.

FIDDIAN, Mr Nicholas James Old Ride Cottage, 4 Martello Road S., Poole BH13 7HF Tel: 01202 707375 Fax: 01202 707254 — MB BChir 1973 Camb.; MA Camb. 1974; FRCS Eng. 1978. Cons. Orthop. Surg. Poole and Roy. Bournemouth Hosps. Dorset. Socs: Fell. Mem. Counc. & Sec. Brit. Orthopaedic Assoc.; Brit. Assoc. Surg. to Knee; Brit. Hip Soc. Prev: Clin. Lect. Inst. Orthop. Roy. Nat. Orthop. Hosp. Lond.; Sen. Regist. Rotat. (Orthop.) St. Bart. Hosp. Lond.

FIDDLER, Garrick Ian 3 Laureldene, Widford Road, Much Hadham SG10 6AP Tel: 01279 843611 Fax: 01279 842349 — MB BCh Wales 1970; MRCP (UK) 1973; FFPM RCP (UK) 1994; DCH RCPS Glas. 1974; FRCP Lond. 1998. (Cardiff) Med. Dir. Medeva Pharma Ltd Leatherhead; Hon. Lect. (Pharmaceut. Med.) Univ. Wales & Surrey. Socs: Fell. Roy. Soc. Med.; Fell. Amer. Coll. Cardiol. Prev: Dir., Europ. C.N.S. Clin. Research, Glaxo Wellcome, Greenford; Sen. Regist. (Paediat. Cardiol.) Leeds HA; Mayo Foundat. Fell. (Paediat. Cardiol.) Mayo Clinic Rochester Minnesota, USA.

FIDLER, Harry (retired) Flat 3, 44 Bramhall Park Road, Bramhall, Stockport SK7 3NN Tel: 0161 485 8178 — BM BCh 1935 Oxf.; MA, BM BCh Oxf. 1935. Vice-Pres. BMA. Prev: Maj. RAMC.

FIDLER, Helen Margaret University Hospital, Lewisham, Lewisham High St, London SE13 6LH Tel: 020 8333 3000 Ext: 6182; 37 North Park, London SE9 5AW Email: m.fidler@btinternet.com — MB BS 1987 Lond.; BSc (1st cl. Hons.) Lond. 1984, MD 1994; MRCP (UK) 1990. Cons. Gastroenterol., Univ. Hosp. Lewisham (p/t). Socs: Roy. Soc. Med.; Brit. Soc. Gastroenterol. Prev: Sen. Regist. Middlx. Hosp.; Sen. Regist. (Gastroenterol.) Roy. Free Hosp. Lond.; Regist. (Gastroenterol.) Roy. Free Hosp. Lond.

FIDLER, Katherine Jane — MB BS 1992 Lond.; BSc UCL Lond. 1989; MRCP I & II. Research Fell., ICH.

FIDLER, Sarah Jane 37 St Peters Street, London N1 8JP — MB BS 1988 Lond.; BSc Immunol. Lond. 1985; MRCP (UK) 1992.

FIELD, Alice Barbara (retired) 22 Reading Court, Tiddington Road, Stratford-upon-Avon CV37 7SA — MB BChir 1934 Camb.; MRCS Eng. LRCP Lond. 1926; MMSA Lond. 1935; MRCOG 1940. Prev: Sen. Regist. (O & G) S. Warwick Gp.

FIELD, Allison Margaret St Martins Practice, 319 Chapeltown Road, Leeds LS7 3JT Tel: 0113 262 1013 Fax: 0113 237 4747; 10 Beaumont Avenue, Leeds LS8 1BU Email: allyfield@aol.com — MB ChB 1986 Leeds; MRCGP 1990; DRCOG 1990. (Leeds) GP. Socs: BMA; Brit. Med. Acupunc. Soc. Prev: GP Leeds Retainer Scheme; GP Meanwood Health Centre Leeds; Trainee GP Leeds VTS.

FIELD, Mr Andrew Francis 19 St Clements Grove, York YO23 1JZ — MB BS 1990 Lond.; BSc Lond. 1987, MB BS 1990; FRCS Eng. 1994.

FIELD, Angela Mary The Surgery, 2 Church Lane, Merton Park, London SW19 3NY Tel: 020 8542 1174 Fax: 020 8544 1583 — MB ChB 1967 Sheff.; DRCOG 1970. (Sheffield)

FIELD, Anthony Brendan Regional Rehabilitation Centre, Hunters Moor Hospital, Newcastle upon Tyne NE2 4NR; 1 Cross Terrace, Ryton NE40 3PZ — MB BS 1988 Newc.; MRCP (UK) 1992.

FIELD, Benjamin Christopher Thomas 121 Coleraine Road, London SE3 7NT — MB BS 1997 Lond.

FIELD, Catherine Mary 136 Trevelyan Road, London SW17 9LW — MB BS 1989 Lond.

FIELD, Claude Marcus Beresford (retired) 30 Osborne Gardens, Belfast BT9 6LF Tel: 01232 668354 — MB BCh BAO 1942 Belf.; MD Belf. 1946; FRCP Ed. 1963, M 1951; DCH Eng. 1948.

FIELD, Edward Crosby (retired) 27 Prideaux Road, Eastbourne BN21 2ND Tel: 01323 640383 — MB ChB 1941 Ed. Prev: Resid. Med. Off. City Hosp. Nottm. & S.. Gen. Hosp. Edin.

FIELD, Edwin Oscar (retired) Foxholes, Stokesheath Road, Oxshott, Leatherhead KT22 0PP Tel: 01372 842507 — BM BCh 1946 Oxf.; DM Oxf. 1953, BM BCh 1946; DMRD Eng. 1952. Prev: Chief Scientist Gallaher Ltd. Lond.

FIELD, Mr Ellis Simon The Blackheath Hospital, 40 Lee Terrace, Blackheath, London SE3 9UD Tel: 020 8318 7722; Craigallion, 34 North Park, Eltham, London SE9 5AP Tel: 020 8850 0696 — MB BChir 1962 Camb.; MA, MB Camb. 1962, BChir 1961; FRCS Eng. 1967. (Westm.) Cons. Surg. Brook Gen. Hosp. Lond. Socs: Fell. Roy. Soc. Med. Prev: Sen. Surg. Regist. Kings Coll. Hosp. & Brook Gen. Hosp. Lond.; Surg. Regist. St. Jas. Hosp. Balham.

FIELD, Mr Ephraim Joshua Beufort Nursing Home, 56 Kenilworth Road, Coventry CV4 7AH — PhD Bristol 1953; MD Durh. 1946, MS 1944, MB BS 1938; FRCP Lond. 1969, M 1964. (Durh.) Hon. Dir. Naomi Bramson Research Unit Univ. Warwick. Socs: Path. Soc. & NY Acad. Sci.; Hon. Mem. Brit. Soc. Immunol. Prev: Prof. Emerit. Experim. Neuropath. Univ. Newc.; Hon. Dir. Naomi Bramson Research Unit Univ. Warwick; Hon. Dir. MRC Demyelinating Dis. Gp. & Unit.

FIELD, Gary George 7 Granville Drive, Carnreagh, Hillsborough BT26 6DE — MB BCh BAO 1993 Belf.; DMH 1995; MRCGP 1997. Socs: BMA.

FIELD, Giles Edmund Woodbridge Hill Surgery, 1 Deerbarn Road, Guildford GU2 8YB Tel: 01483 562230 Fax: 01483 301132 Email: gfield@drs.desk.sthames.nhs; 10 Belmont Avenue, Guildford GU2 9UF Tel: 01483 572732 — MB BS 1987 Lond.; MRCGP 1993; DCH RCP Lond. 1992. Socs: Liveryman Soc. Apoth. Prev: Acad. Asst. (Gen. Pract. & Primary Care) St. Geo. Hosp. Med. Sch. Lond.; Med. Off. Vis. Rural Clinics Shiselweni Region, Swaziland; Trainee GP Roy. Surrey Co. Hosp. Guildford VTS.

FIELD, Graham John (retired) 37 Minster Road, Westgate-on-Sea CT8 8BP — MB BS Lond. 1965; MRCS Eng. LRCP Lond. 1965; DCH Eng. 1968; DObst RCOG 1967. Prev: VTS Course Organiser Thanet.

FIELD, Helen Avril 4 The Links, Oak Tree Lane, Mansfield NG18 5HW — MB ChB 1990 Birm.; ChB Birm. 1990. Trainee GP Centr. Notts. VTS. Socs: BMA. Prev: Ho. Off. (Surg.) Sandwell Dist. Gen. Hosp.; Ho. Off. (Med.) Dudley Rd. Hosp.

FIELD, Ian Trevor, CBE (retired) 10 Rockwells Gardens, London SE19 1HW Tel: 020 8670 5877 Fax: 020 8670 5877 — MB BS Lond. 1961; MRCS Eng. LRCP Lond. 1960; FFOM RCP Lond. 1991; FFPHM RCP (UK) 1979, M 1975. Prev: Sec. Gen. World Med. Assn.

FIELD, Jennifer Aldermoor Health Centre, Aldermoor Close, Southampton SO16 5ST Tel: 023 8079 7700 Fax: 023 8079 7767; 29 Middlebridge Street, Romsey SO51 8HJ Tel: 01794 517734 — BM BCh 1973 Oxf.; BA Camb. 1970; MRCP (UK) 1976; FRCGP 1997. Sen. Lect. (Primary Med. Care) Univ. Soton. Prev: Lect. (Primary Med. Care) Univ. Soton.

FIELD, Mr Jeremy Cheltenham General Hospital, Sandford Road, Cheltenham GL53 7AN Tel: 01242 273585 Fax: 01242 273468; Duntisbourne Leer Farm, Duntisbourne Leer, Cirencester GL7 7AS Tel: 01285 821508 Email: jeremy.field@egnhst.org.uk — MB BS 1983 Lond.; BSc (Biochem.) Lond. 1980; ChM Bristol 1993; FRCS (Orth.) 1995; FRCS Lond. 1989; FRCS Ed. 1988. (Char. Cross Hosp. Med. Sch.) Cons. Orthop.& Hand Surg. Cheltenham Gen. Hosp. Glos. Socs: Brit. Orthop. Assn.; Hand Soc. Prev: Sen. Regist. (Orthop.) Bristol Roy. Infirm.

FIELD, Jeremy Mark West Suffolk Hospital, Hardwick Lane, Bury St Edmunds IP33 2QZ Tel: 01284 713000 — MB BS 1983 Lond.; FFA RCSI 1993; DA (UK) 1988. (Charing Cross) Cons. Anaesth. W. Suff. Hosp. Bury St. Edmunds. Socs: Brit. Assn. Day Surg.; TriServ. Anaesthetic Soc.; Assn. of Anaesth.s of Gt. Brit. and Irel.

FIELD, Katherine Jane Kirkham Medical Practice, St Albans Road, Babbacombe, Torquay TQ1 3SL Tel: 01803 312233 Fax: 01803 313411; Widland Farm Cottage, Modbury, Ivybridge PL21 0SA — MB BS 1990 Lond.; MRCGP 1995; DCH RCP Lond. 1994. (Univ. Coll. Lond)

FIELD, Leopold Henry 152 Harley Street, London W1N 1HH Tel: 020 7935 0444 Fax: 020 7224 2574; 10 Thornton Way, London NW11 6RY Tel: 020 8458 3122 Fax: 020 8883 4033 — MB BS 1947 Durh.; FRCP Ed. 1975, M 1956; DPM Lond. 1951. (Newc.) Vis. Psychiat. Prison Dept. Home Office. Prev: Cons. Psychiat. Depts. Psychiat. Lond. Hosp. & St. Bart. Hosp. Lond.; 1st Asst. Lond. Hosp.; Regist. Univ. Coll. Hosp. Lond.

FIELD, Liliane Marthe 2 Lingfield Avenue, Kingston upon Thames KT1 2TN — MB BS 1984 Lond.; FRCA 1989. (Westminster) Socs: Intens. Care Soc. Prev: Cons. Anaesth.& IC W. Middlx. Univ. Hosp.; Sen. Regist. (Anaesth.) St. Geo.'s Hosp. & SW Thames RHA; Regist. (Anaesth.) Hosp. Sick Childr., King's Coll. Hosp., Greenwich Hosp. & Brook Gen. Hosp. Lond.

FIELD, Mark Leonard 33 Dagmar Grove, Beeston, Nottingham NG9 2BH — BM BS 1998 Nottm.; BM BS Nottm 1998.

FIELD, Mark William Rosser and Partners, Crewkerne Health Centre, Middle Path, Crewkerne TA18 8BX Tel: 01460 72435 Fax: 01460 77957 — MB BS 1989 Lond.; DRCOG 1992.

FIELD, Max Centre for Rheumatic Diseases, University Department of Medicine, Royal Infirmary, 10 Alexandra Parade, Glasgow G31 2ER Tel: 0141 211 4688 Fax: 0141 211 0414 Email: m.field@clinmail.gla.ac.uk; Killorn, 8 Baldernock Road, Milngavie, Glasgow G62 8DR — MD 1988 Lond.; BSc (Hons.) Lond. 1974, MB BS 1977; FRCP Glas. 1993; MRCP (UK) 1980; FRCP Lond. 1996. Sen. Lect. Centre Rheumat. Dis. Roy. Infirm. Glas. Prev: Lect. (Immunol. of Rheumat. Dis.) Char. Cross Hosp. Lond.

FIELD, Michael The Surgery, Darklands Road, Swadlincote, Swadlincote DE11 0PQ Tel: 01283 221604; Brook House Farm, Brook St., Hartshoring, Swadlincote DE11 7AH Tel: 01283 221653 — MB ChB 1965 Manch.; DObst RCOG 1971. (Manch.) Socs: BMA. Prev: Ho. Surg. & Ho. Phys. Withington Hosp. Manch.; Capt. RAMC, Ho. Surg. (Obst.) Brit. Milit. Hosp. Munster, Germany.

FIELD, Michael Alexander Sergiejewicz St Annes, St Andrews Road, Ceres, Cupar KY15 5NQ — MB ChB 1966 St. And.; MRCPsych 1972. Cons. Child Psychiat. Roy. Dundee Liff Hosp. Dundee & Murray Roy.; Hosp. Perth; Mem. Scott. Inst. Human Relat. Prev: Cons. Child Psychiat. Roy. Hosp. for Sick Childr. Edin.; Vis. Prof. Univ. Saskatchewan, Canada.

FIELD, Nicholas John Wincobank Medical Centre, 16 Chapman Street, Sheffield S9 1NG Tel: 0114 242 6411; 20 Chorley Drive, Fulwood, Sheffield S10 3RR — MB ChB 1983 Sheff.; MRCGP 1987; DGM RCP Lond. 1986; DRCOG 1986; Cert. FPA 1986. GP Tutor (CME).

FIELD, Patricia Mary Childrens Hospital, Dorchetster Royal Infirmary, Armthorpe Road, Doncaster DN2 5LT Tel: 01302 366666 Email: patricia.field@dbh.nhs.uk — MB BS 1980 Lond.; MRCP (UK) 1983. p/t Cons. Community Paediat. Doncaster.

FIELD, Pauline Margaret 70 Anson Road, London N7 0AA — MB BS 1972 Lond.; MRCS Eng. LRCP Lond. 1972; DObst RCOG 1975. (Roy. Free)

***FIELD, Rebecca** 34 North Park, Eltham, London SE9 5AP; 19 St Clement's Grove, York YO23 1JL Tel: 01904 670518 — MB BS 1994 Lond.

FIELD, Mr Richard Eddy Dept. Of Orthopaedics, St Hellier Hospital, Wrtha Lane, Carshalton SM1 5AA Tel: 01633 871177, 020 8296 2581 Fax: 01633 860234 — MRCS Eng. LRCP Lond. 1980; FRCS 2000 Eng. Ad Eundum.; PhD Camb. 1989; FRCS (Orth.) 1994; FRCS Ed. 1988. (Westminster) Cons. Orthop. Surg. Epsom & St. Helier NHS Trust Carshalton; Hon. Sen. Lect. St. Geo. Hosp. Lond. Socs: BMA; Brit. Orthop. Assn.; Brit. Hip Soc. Prev: Sen. Regist. Rotat. (Orthop. Surg.) Addenbrooke's & Black Notley; Regist. (Orthop. Surg.) W.m. Hosp. & Whittington Hosp. Lond.

FIELD, Rosemary 15B Collegiate Crescent, Sheffield S10 2BA Tel: 0114 268 7414 Fax: 0114 268 7414 Email: rosemary.field@dial.pipex.com — MB BS 1974 Lond.; MRCGP 1979; DRCOG 1979; DCH Eng. 1978. p/t Director of Primary Care, Nat. Clin. Assessm. Auth., Lond.; Salaried Gen. Practitioner. Prev: Sen. Med. Off. NHS Exec. HQ Leeds; GP Heeley, Sheff.

FIELD, Sarah Kathryn 57 Teignmouth Road, Birmingham B29 7BA — MB ChB 1997 Birm.

FIELD, Shirley Yendis The Surgery, Ivy Grove, Ripley, Derby DE5 3HN Tel: 01773 742286 Fax: 01773 749812; Cold Harbour, Ashover, Chesterfield S45 0JX — MB ChB 1964 Birm.; Cert. Family Plann. JCC 1976. (Birm.) Socs: Soc. Occupat. Med.; Nottm. M-C Soc. Prev: SCMO Nottm. HA; GP Huthwaite Nottm.

FIELD, Stephen John Bellevue Medical Group Practice, 6 Bellevue, Edgbaston, Birmingham B5 7LX Tel: 0121 446 2000 Fax: 0121 446 2015; 155 Russell Road, Moseley, Birmingham B13 8RR Tel: 0121 456 5600 Fax: 0121 455 6291 Email: s.field@pmde@hsrc.org.uk — MB ChB 1982 Birm.; MRCGP 1987; FRCGP 1997; Dip. Med. Educat. Dund 1994; DRCOG 1987; Cert. Family Plann. JCC 1986. (Birm.) Regional Adviser & Dir. Postgrad. Gen. Pract. Educat. W. Midl.; Examr. Roy. Coll. Gen. Practs.; Vice Chairm. Comm. Gen. Pract. Educat. Dirs. Socs: Assn. Course Organisers; RCGP (W. Midl.

Fac. Bd.); BMA. Prev: Dep. Regional Adviser W. Midl. Region; Course Organiser Worcester VTS.

FIELD, Professor Stuart Breast Screening Unit Kent + Canterbury Hospital, Ethelbert Road, Canterbury Hospital, Canterbury CT1 3NG Tel: 01227 766877 Fax: 01227 783041 Email: stuart.field@ekh-tr.sthames.nhs.uk — MB BChir Camb. 1970; BA (1st cl. Hons. Nat. Sc. Trip. Pt. 1) Camb. 1966; MA Camb. 1970; FRCR 1975; FFR 1974; DMRD Eng. 1972. (Camb. & King's Coll. Hosp.) Cons. Radiol. E. Kent Hosp. NHS Trust - Progr. Director, Kent BrE. Screening Assessm.; Clin. Dir. BrE. Screening Assessm. Centre Canterbury; Clin Dir. BrE. Screening Assessm. Canterbury. Socs: BMA. Prev: Clin. Tutor Kent Postgrad. Med. Centre Canterbury; Sen. Regist. (Diag. Radiol.) King's Coll. Hosp. Lond.; Ho. Phys. Med. Unit & Ho. Surg. Surg. Unit. King's Coll. Hosp.

FIELD, Susan Mary Queen Elizabeth Hospital, Sheriff Hill, Gateshead NE9 6SX Tel: 0191 482 0000 — MB BS 1982 Newc.; MRCOG 1988. Socs: Inst. Psychosexual Med.

FIELD, Vanessa Katherine Moor End House, New Lane, Oswaldtwistle, Accrington BB5 3NS — MB BS 1996 Newc.

FIELD, William Douglas 1 Imperial Crescent, Town Moor, Doncaster DN2 5BW Tel: 01302 323400 — MB BS 1969 Lond. SHO (Paediat.) Stoke-on-Trent City Hosp. Prev: Ho. Phys. & Ho. Surg. Gen. Hosp. Rochford.

FIELD-LUCAS, Adrian Stuart Practice A, Hill St., Hinckley LE10 1DS Tel: 01455 635362; Deane Cottage, 23 Main St, Cadeby, Nuneaton CV13 0AX Tel: 01455 292325 — MB BS 1977 Newc.; MRCP (UK) 1981. Socs: BMA. Prev: Regist. (Haemat.) Roy. Hallamsh. Hosp. Sheff.; Regist. (Med.) N. Manch. Gen. Hosp.; Trainee GP Torquay VTS.

FIELDEN, Alison Lydia Mary Norfolk & Norwich Hospital, Norwich NR1 3SR — MB BS 1982 Lond.; BSc Lond. 1979; MRCP (UK) 1987; FRCA. 1992. (Westm.) Assoc. Specialist (Anaesth.) Norf. & Norwich Hosp.

FIELDEN, Jonathan Mark Dept. Anaesthesia, Royal Berkshire Hospital, London rd, Reading RG1 5AN; 6 Water Road, Reading RG30 2NN Email: jonathan@j.fielden.demon.co.uk — MB ChB 1988 Bristol; BSc (Hons.) Pharmacol. Bristol 1985; MRCP (UK) 1991; FRCA 1994; DA (UK) 1992. (Bristol) Cons. (Anaesth. & Instensive care Med.). Socs: BMA; Intens. Care Soc.; (Counc.) Roy. Coll. Anaesth. Prev: Specialist Regist. Rotat. (Anaesth.) Soton.; Provisional Fell.sh. Year St. Vincents Hosp. Sydney, Austral.; Regist. (Anaesth.) Bristol Train. Scheme.

FIELDEN, Nicolas John Spencer 57 Prospect Road, St Albans AL1 2AT — MB ChB 1998 Leeds.

FIELDEN, Peter (retired) 23 The Brooklands, Wrea Green, Preston PR4 2NQ Tel: 01772 684269 — MB ChB Manch. 1963; MRCS Eng. LRCP Lond. 1963; FRCR 1975; FFR 1974; DMRD Eng. 1967. Prev: Cons. Radiol. Vict. Hosp. Blackpool.

FIELDER, Professor Alistair Richard Birmingham & Midland Eye Hospital, Church St., Birmingham B3 2NS Tel: 0121 236 4911 Fax: 0121 233 9213; 3 Bellemere Road, Hampton-in-Arden, Solihull B92 0AN Tel: 01675 442283 — MB BS 1966 Lond.; MRCP (UK) 1991; FRCS Eng. 1975; FCOphth 1988. (St. Geo.) Prof. Ophth. Univ. Birm. Socs: Fell. (Ex-Vice Pres. Sect. Ophth.) Roy. Soc. Med.; (Counc.) Profess. Supplm. Med. Orthoptists Bd. Prev: Reader (Ophth.) Univ. Leicester; Cons. Ophth. Derbysh. Roy. Infirm. Derby; Resid. Surg. Off. Moorfields Eye Hosp. High Holborn Lond.

FIELDER, Mr Colin Paul DDOL Farm, Dunvant, Swansea SA2 7UD — MB BS 1978 Lond.; FRCS Eng. 1982. Cons. ENT Surg. Singleton Hosp. Swansea. Prev: Sen. Regist. (ENT) S. Glam. HA.

FIELDER, Helen Claire 51 Hillside, Banstead SM7 1HG — MB BS 1998 Lond.; MB BS Lond 1998.

FIELDER, Hilary Margaret Pryce C/O Colin P. Fielder, ENT Department, Singleton Hospital, Swansea SA2 8QA; Ddol Farm, Ddol Road, Dunvant, Swansea SA2 7UD — MB BS 1978 Lond.; MB BS Lond. 1978.; MPH 1996; MFPHM RCP (UK) 1996; DRCOG 1982; DCH RCP Lond. 1980. Sen. Regist. (Pub. Health Med.) Iechyd Morgannwe Health.

FIELDER, John Patrick Seymour The Surgery, 20 Low Road, Debenham, Stowmarket IP14 6QU Tel: 01728 860248 Fax: 01728 861300; The Quaker House, Friday St, Brandeston, Woodbridge IP13 7BT Tel: 01728 685518 — MRCS Eng. LRCP Lond. 1975; MB BS Lond. 1976; BDS Lond. 1970; LDS RCS Eng. 1970; MRCGP 1980. Examr. Mobil. Attend. Allowance DSS.

FIELDER, Lawrence Vincent The Surgery, Clarks Hay, South Cerney, Cirencester GL7 5UA Tel: 01285 862112; 37 Berry Hill Crescent, Cirencester GL7 2HF Tel: 01285 640859 — MB BS 1986 Lond.; BSc (Hons.) Lond. 1982, MB BS 1986; DO RCS Eng. 1990. Indep. Orthop. Phys.; Lect. (Orthop.) Brit. Coll. Naturop. & Osteop. Lond. Socs: Reg. of Osteopath.

FIELDER, Michael Hugh Top Flat, 41 Buckland Crescent, London NW3 5DJ — MB BS 1976 Lond.; MRCPsych 1983.

FIELDHOUSE, David Christopher Bracken Hall, Denholme, Bradford BD13 4DX Tel: 01274 832759 — MB BS 1968 Durh. (Newc.) GP Bradford; Sen. Police Surg. W. Yorks. Police. Prev: Ho. Surg. Halifax Gen. Hosp.; Ho. Phys. Bradford Roy. Infirm.

FIELDHOUSE, Margaret Lesley Park Medical Practice, Maine Drive, Chaddesden, Derby DE21 6LA Tel: 01332 665522 Fax: 01332 678210 — MB BS 1981 Newc.; MRCGP 1986. (Newcastle upon Tyne) Prev: Clin. Med. Off. (Child Health) S.. Derbysh. Community Health Serv.

FIELDHOUSE, Richard Malcolm Anthony 6 Lawley Road, Chichester PO19 1UZ — MB BS 1989 Lond.; MRCGP 1995; DRCOG 1994. Chair, Nat. Ass. Of Non-Princip.s. Prev: Trainee GP/SHO Chichester VTS.

FIELDHOUSE, Rowena Diana 16 Carson Road, London SE21 8HU — MB ChB 1981 Bristol; MRCGP 1987; DCH RCP Lond. 1987; DRCOG 1985.

FIELDING, Andrew Paul Herbert (retired) Cara Domus, 24 Station Road, Dersingham, King's Lynn PE31 6PR Tel: 01485 540520 Fax: 01485 540520 Email: aphf@breathemail.net — MB BS 1967 Lond.; MRCS Eng. LRCP Lond. 1965; DObst RCOG 1967. Prev: Ho. Phys. Sevenoaks Hosp.

FIELDING, Anitra 2 Ribblesdale View, Langho, Blackburn BB6 8BZ — MB ChB 1992 Manch.

FIELDING, Anthony Steven The Surgery, 111 Pembroke Road, Clifton, Bristol BS8 3EU Tel: 0117 973 3790 — BM BCh 1983 Oxf.; MA Camb. 1984; MRCGP 1987; DRCOG 1984. (Camb. & Oxf.) GP Princip. Bristol; Chairm. W. Bristol PCG. Socs: Bristol. M-C Soc. Prev: SHO Bristol Childr. Hosp.; Ho. Surg. John Radcliffe Hosp. Oxf.; Ho. Phys. Bath Roy. United Hosp.

FIELDING, David William (retired) Springfield, 16 Tarvin Road, Littleton, Chester CH3 7DG Tel: 01244 336278 — MB ChB 1961 Liverpool; BSc (Hons. Anat.) Liverp. 1958; FRCP Lond. 1979, M 1967; DObst RCOG 1964; FRCPCH 1996 Lond. Cons. (Paediat.) Countess Chester Hosp.; Genetic Counsellor Mersey RHA; Clin. Lect. Dept. Child Health Liverp. Univ. Prev: Lect. Child Health Univ. Liverp. & Hon. Sen. Regist. (Paediat.).

FIELDING, Edith Irene (retired) 54 Ray House, Milton Road, Ickenham, Uxbridge UB10 8NJ — MRCS Eng. LRCP Lond. 1940.

FIELDING, Elizabeth Mary Pirie Ashmore Brook House, Cross in Hand Lane, Lichfield WS13 8DY — MB ChB 1971 Birm.

FIELDING, Jack 17 Bracknell Gardens, London NW3 7EE Tel: 020 7435 5853 Fax: 020 7435 5853 — MRCS Eng. LRCP Lond. 1939; FRCP Lond. 1973, M 1949; FRCPath 1963; DPH Eng. 1946. (Middlx.) Cons. Haemat. St. Mary's Hosp. Lond. Socs: Fell. Roy. Soc. Med.; Assn. Clin. Pathols. & Path. Soc. GB; Internat. Soc. Haematol. Prev: Bact. WHO, SE Asia; Asst. Path. Emerg. Pub. Health Laborat. St. Mary's Hosp.; Med. Dir. Padd. Gen. Hosp.

FIELDING, John Andrew Department of Radiology, Royal Shrewsbury Hospital, Mytton Oak Road, Shrewsbury SY3 8XQ Tel: 01743 261000; The Paddock, 156A Longden Road, Shrewsbury SY3 9ED Tel: 01743 245938 — MB ChB 1971 Liverp.; MD Liverp. 1993; FRCR 1978; DMRD Liverp. 1976; DObst RCOG 1973; FRCP 2000 Edinburgh. Cons. Radiol. Roy. Shrewsbury Hosp. Socs: Brit. Inst. Radiol. Prev: Regist. (Radiol.) Liverp. AHA (T); SHO (O & G) Fazakerley Hosp. Liverp.; SHO (Paediat.) Alder Hey Hosp. Liverp.

FIELDING, John David 18 Church Road, Lytham, Lytham St Annes FY8 5LL Tel: 01253 736453 — MRCS Eng. LRCP Lond. 1968; MB BS Lond. 1968; MRCP (U.K.) 1974; DObst RCOG 1971. (King's Coll. Hosp.) GP Med. Practitioner, DRS Fielding & Partners, Lytham, Lancs.; Clin. Specialist (Gastroenterol.) Vict. Hosp. Blackpool. Socs: Brit. Soc. Gastroenterol.; Fell. Manch. Med. Soc.; Brit. Assn. Performing Arts Med. Prev: Regist. (Med.) Vict. Hosp. Blackpool; Med. Off. Chas. Johnson Memor. Hosp. Nqutu, Zululand; Ho. Phys. (Gen. Med.) & Ho. Surg. (Urol. & Orthop.) King's Coll.

FIELDING, Mr John William Lewis Ashmore Brook House, Cross in Hand Lane, Lichfield WS13 8DY — MD 1982 Birm.; MB ChB Birm. 1971; FRCS Eng. 1976. Cons. Surg. Qu. Eliz. Hosp. Birm.
FIELDING, Michael Everett (retired) 12 Shirley Drive, Hove BN3 6UD — MB BS 1954 Lond.; BPharm 1947; FRCA 1962; MB BS 1954 London. Prev: Cons. Anaesth. Brighton HA.
FIELDING, Patrick Anthony University Hospital of Wales, Department of Clinical Radiology, Heath Park, Cardiff CF14 4XW Tel: 029 2074 7747; The Coach House, Llantilio Crossenny, Abergavenny NP7 8SU Tel: 01600780529 Email: pafielding@aol.com — BM 1994 Soton.; BM (Hons) Soton. 1994; BSc (Hons) Soton. 1993; MRCP of London, 1997. Specialist Regist.in Radiol., Univ. Hosp. of Wales, Cardiff. Socs: MDU; Roy. Coll. Phys.s Lond.; Roy. Coll. Radiol. Prev: Ho. Off. (Med.) Soton. Gen. Hosp.
FIELDING, Phillip Donald, Maj. RAMC Retd. The Royal Well Surgery, St Pauls Medical Centre, 121 Swindon Road, Cheltenham GL50 4DP Tel: 01242 707701 — BM 1985 Soton.; MRCGP 1991; DFFP 1993; DCH RCP Lond. 1989. Prev: SHO (ENT & O & G) Odstock Hosp. Salisbury; SHO (Paediat.) P.ss Margt. Hosp. Swindon; SHO (A & E) Camb. Milit. Hosp. Aldershot.
FIELDING, Richard Everett 12 Shirley Drive, Hove BN3 6UD — BM BS 1993 Nottm.; BMedSci 1991; MRCP 1996. (Nottingham) Specialist Regist. Nephrol., Hammersmith Hosp., Lond.
FIELDING, Sandra Frances 109 Mudeford, Christchurch BH23 4AE — MB ChB 1977 Manch.
FIELDING, Sian The Coach House, Llantilio Crossenny, Abergavenny NP7 8SU — BM 1993 Soton. SHO (Med. & Elderly Care) Roy. Hants. Co. Hosp. Winchester. Prev: SHO (A & E) Roy. Hants. Co. Hosp. Winchester.
FIELDING, William James Clifton Road Surgery, 26 Clifton Road, Rugby CV21 3QF Tel: 01788 543088 Fax: 01788 551496; 146 Bawnmore Road, Bilton, Rugby CV22 6JT Tel: 01788 810902 — MB BChir 1972 Camb.; MB Camb. 1972, BChir 1971; MRCP (UK) 1975; MRCGP 1980. (Cambridge and Middlesex Hospital)
FIELDMAN, Mr Nigel Roy Holly House Hospital, High Road, Buckhurst Hill IG9 5HX Tel: 020 8505 3311 — MB BChir 1971 Camb.; MA Camb. 1971; MChir (Distinc.) Camb. 1987; FRCS Eng. 1976; T(S) 1991. (Camb. & Guy's) Cons. Gen. Surg. Newham Healthcare Lond. Socs: Assn. of Surg.s of Gt. Britain & Irel.; Assn. of Endoscopic Surg.s of Gt. Britain & Irel.; Europ. Assn. for Endoscopic Surg. Prev: Lect. & Hon. Sen. Regist. (Surg.) Univ. Coll. & Middlx. Sch. Med. Lond.; Regist. Rotat. (Surg.) Middlx. Hosp. Lond.; Ho. Phys. (Gen. & Renal Med.) Guy's Hosp. Lond.
FIELDS, John Richard The Little Practice, 21 St. Mary Street, Stamford PE9 2DH Tel: 01780 763308 Fax: 01780 755878; Cowick Lodge, new Cross Road, Stamford PE9 1AJ Tel: 01780 766862 — MB BS 1980 Lond.; DRCOG 1982.
FIELDS, Paul Andrew 101 Sunnyfield, London NW7 4RE — MB ChB 1988 Liverp.; MRCP (UK) 1991. Regist. (Haemat.) Roy. Free Hosp. Lond. Prev: Regist. (Gen. Med. & Rheum.) Guy's Hosp. Lond.; Rotat. SHO (Med.) Qu. Eliz. Hosp. Birm.
FIELDS, Robert Kingswood Health Centre, Alma Road, Kingswood, Bristol BS15 4EJ Tel: 0117 961 1774 Fax: 0117 947 8969 — MB BS 1971 Lond.; BSc (Hons.) Lond. 1968, MB BS 1971; MRCGP 1977; DObst RCOG 1974.
FIELDSEND, Gerald Arthur Carter House, 112 Charnock Dale Road, Sheffield S12 3HR Tel: 0114 239 9202 — MB ChB 1952 Sheff.; FRCGP 1988, M 1968. Hon. Teach. (Gen. Pract.) Univ. Sheff.; Provost Sheff. Fac. Roy. Coll. Gen. Practs. Socs: Sheff. Med.-Chir. Soc.
FIELDSEND, Robert Charles Amersham General Hospital, Whielden St., Amersham HP7 0JD Tel: 01494 434411 Fax: 01494 734506 — MB BChir 1972 Camb.; MA 1971; MRCPsych 1976; DCH Eng. 1974; DObst RCOG 1973. (Cambridge & Guy's) Cons. Psychiat. Amersham Gen. Hosp. Socs: Fell. Roy. Coll. Psychiat. Prev: Sen. Regist. (Psychiat.) Warneford Hosp. Oxf.; Sen. Regist. (Psychiat.) St. John's Hosp. Stone; Regist. (Psychiat.) Warneford Hosp. Oxf.
FIELDSEND, Rosemary Lavinia Helen 112 Charnock Dale Road, Sheffield S12 3HR Tel: 0114 239 9202 — MB ChB 1992 Sheff. Specialist Regist. (Radiol.) Leicester.
FIFE, Amanda Jane Dept. of Medical Microbiology, Dulwich Public Healht Authority, GKT School of Medicine, Bessemer Road, London SE5 9PJ Email: amanda.fife@kcl.ac.uk — MB BS 1989 Newc.; BSc (Hons.) Microbiol. Newc. 1984, MB BS 1989; MRCP (UK) 1992; Dip RCPath 1994; MRCPath 1997. Cons. (Med Microbiol), Kings Coll. Hosp., Lond. Prev: Regist. (Med. Microbiol.) Roy. Berks. Hosp. Reading.; SHO (Infec. Dis. & Microbiol.) Newc. Gen. Hosp. & Roy. Vict. Infirm. Newc. u. Tyne.
FIFE, Mr David Gordon Thatched Cottage, Beredens Lane, Great Warley, Brentwood CM13 3JB Tel: 01277 224195 — MB BS Lond. 1963; FRCS Eng. 1969; MRCS Eng. LRCP Lond. 1963. (Lond. Hosp.) Cons. ENT Surg. Basildon & Thurrock Gen. Hosp.s Trust. Socs: Fell. Roy. Soc. Med. Prev: Ho. Surg. & Regist. (ENT) Lond. Hosp.; Sen. Surg. Off. Roy. Nat. Throat, Nose & Ear Hosp. Lond.
FIFE, James Gordon (retired) Summerhill, Alde House Drive, Aldeburgh IP15 5EE Tel: 01728 452127 — MB BS 1937 Lond.; MRCS Eng. LRCP Lond. 1937; DIH Soc. Apoth. Lond. 1961, DMJ (Clin.) 1964. Prev: Lt.-Col. IMS, ADMS GHQ India.
FIFE, John Commonhead Farm, Baillieston, Glasgow G69 6TY — MB ChB 1980 Glas.; LRCP LRCS Ed. LRCPS Glas. 1980.
FIFE, Kathryn Margaret 2 Kestrel House, Grant Road, London SW11 2NG; Thatched Cottage, Beredens Lane, Great Warley, Brentwood CM13 3JB — MB BS 1987 Lond.; MRCP (UK) 1990; FRCR (Oncol.) 1995; MD 1998. Specialist Regist. (Clin. Oncol.) Hammersmith Hosp., Lond. Prev: Regist. (Clin. Oncol.) Roy. Marsden Hosp. Lond.; SHO Rotat. (Med.) Stoke-on-Trent.
FIFE, Robert (retired) 8 Huntly Avenue, Giffnock, Glasgow G46 6LP Tel: 0141 638 5544 — MB ChB Glas. 1945; FRCP Lond. 1972; FRCP Glas. 1964; FRFPS Glas. 1949; MRCP (Lond.) 1962. Prev: Cons. Phys. Roy. Infirm. Glas.
FIFE, Robert John Arthur Meadowpark Street Surgery, 214 Meadowpark Street, Glasgow G31 2TE Tel: 0141 554 0464 — MB ChB 1979 Glas.
FIGA, Simon Adrian Millway Medical Practice, Hartley Avenue, Mill Hill, London NW7 2HX Tel: 020 8959 0888 Fax: 020 8959 7050 — MB BS 1988 Lond.
FIGGINS, Roger Newhaven Health Centre, Chapel Street, Newhaven BN9 9PW Tel: 01273 615000 Fax: 01273 611527 — MB ChB 1978 Manch.; PhD (Experim. Physics) Kent 1967; BSc (Hons.) (Physics) Lond. 1963; DRCOG 1981. p/t Med. Off. Vict. Hosp. Lewes. Prev: Trainee GP Brighton VTS; Ho. Off. Roy. Sussex Co. Hosp. Brighton.
FIGGIS, Morton Milnes (retired) 3 The Chippings, Linden Road, Aldeburgh IP15 5LB Tel: 01728 453281 — MRCS Eng. LRCP Lond. 1943.
FIKREE, Mohammad Amin 25 Hanover Gate Mansions, Park Road, London NW1 4SL — MB BCh 1968 Wales; MRCP (UK) 1978. Regist. (Cardiac) Char. Cross Hosp. Lond. Mem. BMA.
FILA, Christina Denmark Road Medical Centre, 37 Denmark Road, Winton, Bournemouth BH9 1PB Tel: 01202 521111 — MB ChB 1969 St. And.; MRCGP 1976.
FILBY, Harold James 14 Crimicar Avenue, Sheffield S10 4EQ — MB ChB 1988 Manch.; BDS 1979.
FILDES, George (retired) 12 Georges Lane, Horwich, Bolton BL6 6RT — MB ChB 1949 Manch.; MRCGP 1955. Prev: Ho. Surg. ENT Dept. Manch. Roy. Infirm.
FILDES, Nicholas Roby 30 Park Road, Prescot L34 3LR — MB ChB 1993 Liverp.
FILDES, Susan Lavinia 119 Church Street, West Houghton, Bolton BL5 3SF; 14 Georges Lane, Horwich, Bolton BL6 6RT Tel: 01204 692760 — MB ChB 1975 Manch.; DCH RCGP 1987.
FILER, Andrew David John 66 Broad Street, Bromsgrove B61 8LL — MB ChB 1995 Birm.; ChB Birm. 1995.
FILER, David Samuel (retired) 2 Hazelwood Close, Ealing, London W5 3JN — MA, MB BChir Camb. 1958; MRCS Eng. LRCP Lond. 1957; FRCGP 1980 M 1966. Prev: Police Surg. 'F' Div. Metrop. Police.
FILER, John Leslie The Arthur Medical Centre, Four Lane Ends, Main St., Horsley Woodhouse, Derby DE7 6AX Tel: 01332 880249; Lawn Cottage, 43A Marsh Lane, Belper DE56 1GS — MB ChB 1964 Sheff.; MRCGP 1979. (Sheff.) Prev: Regist. (Gen. Med. & Chest) Derwent Hosp. Derby; SHO (Neurol.) Roy. Infirm. Derby; Ho. Off. (Neurosurg. & Dermat.) Roy. Infirm. Sheff.
FILER COOPER, Roger Coham Bridge House, Black Torrington, Beaworthy EX21 5HW Tel: 01409 231244 Fax: 01409 231531 Email: wcls@cohambdg.demon.co.uk — MB BS 1966 Lond.; MRCS

Eng. LRCP Lond. 1966. (King's Coll. Hosp.) Med. Dir. W. Country Locum Servs.; Clin. Asst. (Psychiat.) Avalon Trust. Socs: Plymouth Med. Soc.

FILIK, Rachel Garden Flat, 6 College Fields, Bristol BS8 3HP — BM BS 1990 Nottm.

FILLENZ, Marianne 29 Upland Park Road, Oxford OX2 7RU Tel: 01865 58055 — MB ChB 1948 N.Z.; DPhil Oxf. 1952, MA 1959. (Otago) Socs: Physiol. Soc.

FILLETTI, Pierino Ormskirk Street Surgery, 51A Ormskirk Stret, St Helens WA10 2TB Tel: 01744 29209; Highfield, Joy Lane, Burtonwood, Warrington WA5 4DF Tel: 01925 445993 — MRCS Eng. LRCP Lond. 1981; DRCOG 1985. GP St. Helens.

FILLMORE, Emma Jane Strelley Health Centre, 116 Strelley Rd, Strelley KT16 0HU — MB BCh 1992 Wales.

FILOBBOS, Rafik 3 Vale Court, Dutton, Warrington WA4 4HA — MB ChB 1998 Manch.; MB ChB Manch 1998.

FILOSE, Myles Albert (retired) Furzy Corner, Boundway Hill, Sway, Lymington SO41 6EN Tel: 01590 682487 — MRCS Eng. LRCP Lond. 1943. Prev: GP Wallington Surrey.

FILOSE, Simon — MB BS 1980 Lond.; BSc 1977 (Hons.) Lond.; MRCGP 1987.

FILSHIE, Gilbert Marcus Department of Obstetrics & Gynaecology, University Hospital, Queen's Medical Centre, Nottingham NG7 2UH Tel: 01602 709236 Fax: 01602 709234; 2 Pembroke Drive, Mapperley Park, Nottingham NG3 5BG Tel: 0115 962 5632 — MB BS 1966 Lond.; DM Nottm. 1986; MRCS Eng. LRCP Lond. 1966; FRCOG 1984, M 1972; MFFP 1995. (King's Coll. Hosp.) Reader & Hon. Cons. Dept. O & G Nottm. Univ. Socs: Amer. Assn. Gyn. Laparoscopists; BMA. Prev: Lect. & Sen. Regist. (O & G) Nottm. Univ.; Sen. Lect. Makerere Univ. Kampala, Uganda; SHO Qu. Charlotte Matern. Hosp. Lond.

FILSHIE, Jacqueline Royal Marsden NHS Trust, Downs Road, Sutton SM2 5PT Tel: 020 8642 6011; 18 Dryburgh Road, Putney, London SW15 1BL Fax: 020 8789 9747 Email: jacqueline.filshie@btinternet.com — MB BS 1972 Lond.; FFA RCS Eng. 1976. (King's Coll. Hosp.) Cons. Anaesth. & Hon. Sen. Lect. Roy. Marsden Hosp. Sutton. Socs: (Sec.) Brit. Med. Acupunc. Soc.; Pres. Internat. Counc. for Med. Acupunc. & Related Techniques (ICMART).

FILSHIE, Sheila Ernestine The City Hospital Trust, Hucknall Road, Nottingham Tel: 0115 969 1169 ext 45582; 2 Pembroke Drive, Nottingham NG3 5BG Tel: 0115 962 5632 Fax: 0115 962 1748 Email: pemfill — MB BS 1966 Lond.; MRCS Eng. LRCP Lond. 1966. Assoc. Specialist (Psychosexual Med.) Nottm. City Hosp. Trust. Socs: Fac. Family Plann.; Inst. Psychosexual Med. Prev: SCMO Nottm. HA.

FINAN, Catherine Mary Acomb Health Centre, 1 Beech Grove, Acomb, York YO26 5LD Tel: 01904 791094; 104 Wetherby Road, Acomb, York YO26 5BY — MB ChB 1979 Liverp.; DRCOG 1981.

FINAN, Mr Paul John Leeds Genral infirmary., Leeds LS1 3EX Tel: 0113 392 3400 Fax: 0113 392 3598; 4 Lidgett Park Road, Roundhay, Leeds LS8 1EQ — MD 1983 Bristol; MB ChB 1974 Brist.; FRCS Eng. 1979. Cons. Surg. Leeds Gen. Infirm. & Chapel Allerton Hosp. Leeds; Hon. Clin. Sen. Lect. Univ. Leeds; Hon. Cons. ICRF. Socs: Fell. RSM (Hon. Sec. Sect. of ColoProctol. 1997/1998); Assn. Coloproctol.(Hon Treas. 1997-). Prev: Resid. Surg. Off. St. Mark's Hosp. Lond.; Lect. Surg. St. Jas. Univ. Hosp. Leeds; CRC Research Fell. MRC Clin. Oncol. & Radiother. Unit Camb.

FINBOW, Jillian Mary Riversmead, Blyth Hall, Blyth, Worksop S81 8HL — MB ChB 1960 Sheff.

FINBOW, John Ambrose Howard Riversmead, Blyth Hall, Blyth, Worksop S81 8HL — MRCS Eng. LRCP Lond. 1960; MRCPath 1972. (Sheff.) Cons. Morbid Anat. Dept. Path. Doncaster Roy. Infirm. Prev: Sen. Regist. Dept. Path. King's Coll. Hosp.; Research Asst., Dept. Med. Univ. Sheff.

FINCH, Alan Alastair 11 Dudley Street, Grimsby DN31 2AW — MB ChB 1980 Ed.; MRCGP 1996; DRCOG 1984. Mem. Liverp. LMC. Prev: SHO (O & G) Billinge Hosp.; SHO (Med.) Wigan Infirm. & Billinge Hosp.

FINCH, Ann Kinsey Fenwick Road Surgery, 261 Fenwick Road, Giffnock, Glasgow G46 6JX Tel: 0141 531 6993 Fax: 0141 531 6997; 11 Beverley Road, Newlands, Glasgow G43 2RT Tel: 0141 637 1370 Email: annandpete@supanet.com — MB ChB 1968 Sheff.; MFFP 1993; DObst RCOG 1970. (Sheffield) Princip. in Gen. Pract. Socs: Brit. Soc. Of Med. & Dent. Hypn., Scot.; Scot. Fam. Plan. Med. Soc.; Glas. S. Med. Soc. Prev: Sen. Med. Off. (Family Plann.) Gtr. Glas. HB; Instruc. Doctor Glas.; Research Asst. (O & G) Jessop Hosp. Wom. Sheff.

FINCH, Mr Daniel Robert Alexander Cues Farmhouse, Bishopstone, Swindon SN6 8PL Tel: 01793 790635; Department of Surgery, Princess Margaret Hospital, Okus Road, Swindon SN1 4JU Tel: 01793 536231 — MB BS Lond. 1968; MS Lond. 1977; FRCS Eng. 1973. (St. Bart.) Cons. Surg. Swindon & MarlBoro. NHS Trust. Socs: Assn. Surg. Prev: Ho. Surg. St. Bart. Hosp. Lond.; Research Fell. Nuffield Dept. Surg. Radcliffe Infirm. Oxf.; Clin. Lect. Nuffield Dept. Surg. John Radcliffe Hosp. Oxf.

FINCH, David Graham The Surgery, 3 Austin Road, Battersea, London SW11 5JP Tel: 020 7627 7100 — MB BS 1983 Lond.; MPhil 1999 City University; MRCGP 1987; DRCOG 1986. (St Thomas Hospital London) GP Battersea; Bd. Mem. Battersea PCG.

FINCH, Deborah Jane Cues Farmhouse, Bishopstowe, Swindon SN6 8PL — BM 1995 Soton.

FINCH, Eileen Anne Mary Cowes Health Centre, 8 Consort Road, Cowes PO31 7SH Tel: 01983 295251 Fax: 01983 280461 — MB BS 1977 Newc.; MFHom 2000; MRCGP 1982; DRCOG 1980.

FINCH, Elizabeth Anne 163 South Avenue, Abingdon OX14 1QX Tel: 01235 524781 — MB BS 1996 Lond. (St Mary Hosp.) GP Regist., P.ss Roy. Hosp., Haywards Heath. Prev: SHO (O & G) Hillingdon Hosp. Uxbridge; SHO (A & E) Centr. Middlx. Hosp.; Ho. Off. (Med.) Ealing Hosp.

FINCH, Elizabeth Louise 67 Heyes Lane, Alderley Edge SK9 7LL; Cumberland House, Jordangate, Macclesfield SK10 1EG Tel: 01625 428081 — BM 1986 Soton.; DRCOG 1990; Cert. Family Plann. JCC 1989. (Soton.) Prev: Trainee GP Macclesfield & Portsmouth VTS; SHO (A & E) Macclesfield Dist. Gen. Hosp.

FINCH, Emily Jane Lucy National Addition Centre, 4 Windsor Walk, London SE5 8AF Tel: 020 7919 3839 Email: spjeejf@iop.bpmf.ac.uk — MB BS 1986 Lond.; MRCPsych 1990. (University College London) Cons. Psychiat. Nat. Addic. Centre, Inst. of Psychiat. & Maudsley Hosp. Prev: Lect. Addic. Research Unit Inst. Psychiat. Lond.

FINCH, Gina 2 School Lane, Stanton-by-Dale, Ilkeston DE7 4QJ — MB ChB 1990 Leic.

FINCH, Jennifer Margaret Pond House, Ramsdell, Tadley RG26 5PR — MB BS 1974 Lond.; MRCPath 1980. Cons. Histopath. N. Hants. Hosp. Basingstoke. Prev: Sen. Regist. (Histopath.) King's Coll. Hosp. Med. Sch. Lond. & Kingston Hosp.; Regist. (Path.) St. Mary's Hosp. Lond. W2.

FINCH, John Alan Lewis (retired) 14 Hill Close, Purley CR8 1JR — MB ChB 1952 Glas.; DO RCS Eng. 1978.

FINCH, Mr Jonathan Guy 161 Howard Road, Leicester LE2 1XQ — MB ChB 1989 Sheff.; FRCS (Eng.) 1996. (Sheffield) Specialist Regist. (Gen. Surg.) Leicester. Socs: RSM; Assn. Surg. In Train.; Assn Of Upper Gastrointestinal Surg. Prev: SHO Rotat. (Gen. Surg.) Leicester.

FINCH, Judith 213 Regent Road, Tividale, Oldbury B69 1RZ Tel: 01384 252274 Fax: 01384 240088 — MB ChB Birm. 1959; DO Eng. 1966. (Birm.) Prev: Clin. Asst. (Ophth.) Birm. & Midl. Eye Hosp. & Dudley Guest Hosp.; Ho. Phys. & Ho. Surg. Walsall Gen. Hosp.

FINCH, Karen Rachel 31 Green Close, Stannington, Morpeth NE61 6PE — MB BS 1988 Newc. Trainee GP N.d. VTS. Prev: Ho. Off. (Med.) Roy. Vict. Infirm. Newc.; Ho. Off. (Surg.) Hexham Gen. Hosp.

FINCH, Kathleen Mary The Holdings, Moor House, Newark NG23 6DX — MB ChB 1970 Manch. Clin. Med. Off. Bassetlaw HA. Prev: SHO (Paediat.) Birch Hill Hosp. Rochdale; Ho. Off. (Med. & Surg.) Birch Hill Hosp.

FINCH, Mr Lawrence Donald 6 Calder Park Court, Calderstones Road, Liverpool L18 3HZ Tel: 0151 724 6573 — MB ChB Ed. 1961; BSc Liverp. 1950, BDS 1955; FRCS Ed. 1985; FDS RCS Ed. 1957. (Liverp. & Ed.) Emerit. Cons. Oral & Maxillofacial Surg. Roy. Liverp. Hosp. Socs: Fell. Brit. Assn. Oral & Maxillofacial Surg. (Down Surgic. Prize 1993). Prev: Emerit. Cons. Oral & Maxillofacial Surg. Roy. Liverp. Hosp.; Dean Fac. of Dent. Surg. Roy. Coll. Surgs. Edin.; Cons. Regional Oral & Maxillofacial Unit Roy. Liverp. Hosp. & Mersey HA.

FINCH, Malcolm Edwin The Surgery, Faraday Avenue, Tuxford, Newark NG22 0HT Tel: 01777 870203 Fax: 01777 872221 — MB

ChB Manch. 1968; MRCGP 1972; DObst RCOG 1970. (Manch.) Prev: Ho. Surg. & Ho. Phys. Ancoats Hosp. Manch.; SHO (O & G) Birch Hill Hosp. Rochdale.

FINCH, Michael Brendan 41 Belsize Road, Lisburn BT27 4BS — MB BCh BAO 1975; MD Belf. 1986; MRCP (UK) 1979. Cons. Rheum. Roy. Vict. & Musgrave Pk. Hosps. Belf. Socs: Fell. Ulster Med. Soc.; Brit. Soc. Rheum. Prev: Sen. Regist. (Rheum. Dis. & Rehabil.) Musgrave Pk. Hosp. Belf.

FINCH, Michael David Green Flag Medical, Green Flag House, Cote Lane, Pudsey LS28 5GF Tel: 0113 239 6919 Fax: 0113 239 6921; The Old Barn, King Lane Farm, King Lane, Leeds LS17 5PS Tel: 0113 261 4659 Fax: 0113 261 4659 — MB ChB 1985 Sheff.; DA (UK) 1992. (Univ. Sheff.) Chief Med. Off. (Med. Assistance & Aeromed. Transportation) Green Flag Ltd. Leeds.

FINCH, Peter John St Peter's Hospital, Guildford Road, Chertsey KT16 0PZ Tel: 01932 722229 Fax: 01932 722229 Email: peter.finhc@stph-tr.sthames.nhs.uk; West Hayes, Grange Road, Woking GU21 4DA Tel: 01483 721812 Fax: 0870 284 8782 Email: peter@finchpj.co.uk — MB BS 1980 Lond.; MD Lond. 1988; FRCP Lond. 1996; MRCP (UK) 1983. (St. Thos. Hosp. Lond.) Cons. Phys. St. Peter's Hosp. Chertsey. Socs: Brit. Soc. Gastroenterol. Prev: Sen. Regist. (Med.) St. Geo. Hosp. Lond.; Regist. (Gastroenterol.) Roy. Liverp. Hosp.; Research Fell. N.. Gen. Hosp. Sheff.

FINCH, Peter John Clement 35 Ludlow Close, Warminster BA12 8BJ — MB BS 1984 Lond.

FINCH, Robert Paediatric Department, Wycombe Hospital, Queen Alexandra Road, High Wycombe HP11 2TT Tel: 01494 426602 Fax: 01494 426227 Email: robert.finch@sbucks.nhs.uk; 3 Reynolds Close, Kettering NN15 5JT Tel: 01536 524974 — MB BS 1977 Lond.; MSc (Audiol. Med.) Lond. 1992; DCH Eng. 1980; FRCPCH 1996. (St. Bart.) Cons. Community Paediat. S. Bucks. NHS Trust High Wycombe. Socs: Brit. Soc. Audiol.; Brit. Assn. Community Drs in Audiol.; Brit. Assn. Community Child Health. Prev: SCMO Kettering Health Dist.; Clin. Med. Off. (Child Health) N.ants AHA; SHO (Paediat.) Burton Gen. Hosp.

FINCH, Robert Stanley Urbal Road Surgery, 67 Urbal Road, Coagh, Cookstown BT80 0DP Tel: 028 7973 7243 Fax: 028 7973 7602; The Mill House, Coagh, Cookstown BT80 — MB BCh BAO 1968 Belf.; MRCGP 1973 DRCOG 1972.

FINCH, Rodney John 101 Dukes Avenue, Muswell Hill, London N10 2QD — MB ChB 1970 Sheff.; MRCPsych 1976; DCH Eng. 1973. Cons. Psychiat. Watford Child & Family Psychiat. Clinic; Assoc. Mem. Brit. Psychoanalyt. Soc. Prev: Sen. Regist. Bristol Childr. Hosp. & Avon Child Guid.; Sen. Regist. (Child Psychiat.) Tavistock Clinic Lond. & St. Albans; Child & Family Psychiat. Clinic.

FINCH, Professor Roger Graham Department of Microbiology & Infectious Diseases, Nottingham City Hospital, Nottingham NG5 1PB — MB ChB 1969 Birm.; FRCP (Edin) 2001; FRCP Lond. 1985; MRCP (UK) 1972; FFPM RCP (UK) 1992; FRCPath 1991, M 1979. (Birm.) Prof. Infec. Dis. City Hosp. & Univ. Nottm.; Hon. Cons. Pub. Health Laborat. Serv.; Edr. Curr. Opinion in Infec. Dis. Socs: Fell. Infec. Dis. Soc. Amer.; Assn. Phys.; Pres. Europ. Soc. of Clin. microBiol. & Infec. Dis.s. Prev: Asst. Prof. (Med.) W. Virginia Univ. Med. Center Morgantown, USA; Lect. (Clin. Microbiol.) St. Thos. Hosp. Med. Sch. Lond.

FINCH, Sidney Albert Bruce Richardson Road Surgery, 56 Richardson Road, East Bergholt, Colchester CO7 6RR; Bedside Manor, Rectory Hill, East Bergholt, Colchester CO7 6TH Tel: 01206 298805 — LRCPI & LM, LRSCI & LM 1968; DObst RCOG 1970. (RCSI)

FINCH, Tracey Margaret Birmingham Heartlands and Solihull NHS Trust (Teaching), Solihull Hospital, Lode Lane, Solihull B91 2JL Tel: 0121 424 4540 Fax: 0121 424 5498 Email: fincht@heartsol.wmids.nhs.uk; Email: traceymfinch@hotmail.com — BM 1991 Soton.; MRCP (UK) 1994. (Soton. Univ. Med. Sch.) Cons. Dermatol. Birm. Heartlands and Solihull NHS Trust Solihull Hosp. Solihull. Socs: Brit. Assn. Dermatol.; Midl. Dermat. Soc.; Brit. Contact Dermatitis Gp. Prev: Sen. Regist. (Dermat.) Birm. Skin Centre City Hosp. NHS Trust; Regist. (Dermat.) Birm. Skin Centre City Hosp. NHS Trust; SHO (Dermat.) St. Mary's Hosp. Portsmouth.

FINCHAM, Anthony Clive The Surgery, Bower Mount, The Square, Yalding, Maidstone ME18 6HB Tel: 01622 814373 Fax: 01622 814549; High Weald, Ox Lane, St Michaels, Tenterden TN30 6NQ — MB BS 1976 Lond.; MRCS Eng. LRCP Lond. 1976; MRCGP 1981; DRCOG 1978. (Guy's)

FINCHAM, Colin Mark 3 The Thicket, Thorpe Marriott, Drayton, Norwich NR8 6AX Tel: 01603 262167 — MB BS 1992 Lond.

FINCHAM, Elizabeth (retired) The Maquis, Fairwarp, Uckfield TN22 3BL — MB BS Lond. 1952; MRCS Eng. LRCP Lond. 1952.

FINCHAM, Paul (retired) The Maquis, Fairwarp, Uckfield TN22 3BL Tel: 0182 571 2970 — MB BS 1952 Lond. Prev: Ho. Phys. Univ. Coll. Hosp.

FINDLATER, John (retired) 13 Lindeth Road, Silverdale, Carnforth LA5 0TT — MB ChB 1947 Ed.; BA (1st cl. Hons.) Open 1990; BA Open 1986.

FINDLAY, Alfred Graham (retired) Melrose, 1 Miller's Close, Warkworth, Morpeth NE65 0XN Tel: 01665 710316 — MB ChB 1950 Glas.; DObst RCOG 1954. Prev: GP Chesterfield.

FINDLAY, Alice Margaret Therese Accident & Emergency Department, St Richards Hospital, Chichester PO19 4SE Tel: 01243 788122 Fax: 01243 731260; 11 Fontwell Close, Fontwell, Arundel BN18 0SW — MB BS 1983 Lond.; FRCS Ed. 1992; FFAEM 1996; DA (UK) 1987. Cons. A & E St. Richards Hosp. Chichester. Prev: Sen. Regist. (A & E) Centr. Middlx. Hosp. Lond.; Regist. (A & E) Morriston Hosp. Swansea; SHO (Med. Elderly) Rochford Hosp. S.end.

FINDLAY, Alison Margaret 46 Church Road, Bishopsworth, Bristol BS13 8JW — MB ChB 1998 Bristol.

FINDLAY, Anne Fife Health Board, Springfield House, Cupar KY15 5UP Tel: 01334 656200; 17 Sunbury Place, Edinburgh EH4 3BY Tel: 0131 225 3274 — MB ChB 1981 Ed.; BSc Med. Sci. Ed. 1978; MRCP (UK) 1984; MFPHM RCP (UK) 1994; FRCP(E) 1999. Cons. in Pub. Health Med.; Hon. Sen. Lect. St. And. Univ. Prev: Med. Dir., Nat. Servs. Div.

FINDLAY, Catriona Mary Rumney Medical Practice, 840-842 Newport Road, Rumney, Cardiff CF3 4LH Tel: 029 2079 7751 Fax: 029 2036 1971 — MB ChB 1989 Glas. (Glasgow)

FINDLAY, Christine Anne 15 Holmhead Road, Cumnock KA18 1AQ; Flat 1 Up/Left, 7 Airlie St, Hyndland, Glasgow G12 9RJ — MB ChB 1991 Glas. Paediat. Specialist Regist. Roy. Hosp. for Sick Childr. Glas.

FINDLAY, Christopher David Crewe Mental Health Resource Centre, Eaton House, Eaton St., Crewe CW2 7EG Tel: 01270 506700 Fax: 01270 214744; 1 Artle Brook Cottage, Audlem Road, Hatherton, Nantwich CW5 7QT Tel: 01270 841643 Email: christopher@findlay.u-net.com — MB ChB 1978 Birm.; BSc (Hons.) Birm. 1975; MMedSci (Clin. Psychiat.) Leeds 1996; MRCP (UK) 1981; MRCPsych 1993; MRCGP 1984; DRCOG 1985. Cons. Psychiat. Crewe; Sen. Clin. Lect. Sch. PostGrad. Med. Keele Univ. Socs: Collegiate Mem. Roy. Coll. Phys. Edin. & Lond. Prev: Lect. (Psychiat.) Univ. Leeds; GP Trainee Edin.; SHO Rotating (Med.) Dudley Rd. Hosp. Birm.

FINDLAY, David John Brookroyd House Surgery, Cook Lane, Heckmondwike WF16 9JG Tel: 01924 403061; Pentland, High St, Burrelton, Blairgowrie PH13 9NX — MB ChB 1982 Glas.; BSc (Hons.) Glas. 1979; MRCGP 1987; DRCOG 1986.

FINDLAY, David John Royal Dundee Liff Hospital, Dundee DD2 5NF Tel: 01382 423000 Fax: 01382 423047 Email: dfindlay@liff.finix.org.uk; Lomondbank, 2 Oakley Place, Broughty Ferry, Dundee DD5 2HX Tel: 01382 730946 — MB ChB 1979 Glas.; BSc (1st cl. Hons.) Glas. 1976.; MRCPsych 1984. Cons. Gen. & Geriat. Psychiat. Roy. Dundee Liff Hosp.

FINDLAY, David White (retired) 7 Barncroft Way, St Albans AL1 5QZ Tel: 01727 858464 Fax: 01727 757512 Email: dfindlay@globalnet.co.uk — MB BS 1956 Lond.; BSc (Physiol., Hons.) Lond. 1953; DObst RCOG 1966; MRCGP 1965. Webmaster& Constr. Of the website of the Hunt. Soc.; Edr. & Constr. of the Collections of the Hunt. Soc. Prev: Chief Med. Adviser Electrolux plc.

FINDLAY, George Henry Sandgate Road Surgery, 180 Sandgate Road, Folkestone CT20 2HN Tel: 01303 221133 Fax: 01303 261068 Email: george.findlay@gp-g82121.nhs.uk — MB BS 1975 Lond.; MRCGP 1990. Prev: SHO (Med.) Kingston Hosp.; SHO (Neurol.) Brook Hosp. Lond.

FINDLAY, George Paxton Intensive Care Unit, B3, University Hospital of Wales, Heath Park, Cardiff CF14 4XW Tel: 029 2074 3084 Fax: 029 2074 3799 Email: findlay@cf.ac.uk; 4 Greenacre Drive, Cardiff CF23 8PA Tel: 029 2031 6531 Email:

findlay@macro.idps.co.uk — MB ChB 1989 Dundee; FRCA 1994. Cons. Intensivist Univ. Hosp. of Wales Cardiff. Socs: Intens. Care Soc.; Eur. Soc. Intens. Care; Welsh Intens. Care Soc. Prev: Sen. Regist. (Anaesth.) Univ. Hosp. of Wales; Sen. Regist. (IC) Univ. Hosp. of Wales; Clin. Research Fell. (IC) Univ. Hosp. of Wales.

FINDLAY, Graham (retired) 7 Hartshill Court, 104 Golf Links Road, Ferndown, Wimborne BH22 8DA Tel: 01202 871171 — MB ChB Aberd. 1953; DObst RCOG 1955.

FINDLAY, Henry Ritchie (retired) 202 Somerset Road, Almondbury, Huddersfield HD5 8LP Tel: 01484 421966 — MB ChB 1939 Aberd. Sen. Res. Med. Off. St. Luke's Hosp. Huddersfield. Prev: Demonst. Anat. King's Coll. Newc.

FINDLAY, Iain Nicolson Glenfarg, Kilbarchan Road, Bridge of Weir PA11 3EZ — MB ChB 1978 Dundee; MB ChB (Commend.) Dundee 1978; FRCPS Glas. 1992; MRCP Lond. 1980.

FINDLAY, James Black Rushden Medical Practice, Adnitt Road, Rushden NN10 9TU Tel: 01933 412666 Fax: 01933 317666; 2 The Barns, Duchess End, Mears Ashby, Northampton NN6 0EB Tel: 01933 412666 — MB BS 1982 Lond.; BSc (Hons.) Lond. 1979; DRCOG 1986. (Middlesex) Socs: Fell. Hunt. Soc.; Liveryman Soc. Apoth.

FINDLAY, James Scott 19 Sutherland Avenue, Glasgow G41 4HG Tel: 0141 440 1212 — MB ChB 1952 Glas. (Univ. Glas.)

FINDLAY, John Angus 178 Westbourne Road, Penarth CF64 5BR Tel: 01222 709285 — MB ChB 1955 Aberd.; MD Aberd. 1973.

FINDLAY, John Magill Beck House, Micklethwaite, Bingley BD16 1DD Tel: 01274 567181 Fax: 01274 518243 Email: jmfmadog@aol.com — MB ChB 1961 Liverp.; DMRD 1965; FRCP Lond. 1983, M 1969. Private Cons. Phys. (Gastroenterol.). Socs: Brit. Soc. Gastroenterol. Prev: Cons. Phys. (Gastroenterol.) Bradford Roy. Infirm. & St. Luke's Hosp.; Sen. Regist. W.. Gen. Hosp. Edin.; Sen. Regist. (Med.) Edin. Roy. Infirm.

FINDLAY, Katherine 66 Deanwood Avenue, Glasgow G44 3RQ — MB ChB 1990 Aberd.

FINDLAY, Linda 1B Briar Gardens, Newlands, Glasgow G43 2TF — MB ChB 1990 Glas.

FINDLAY, Martin James Rosegarth Surgery, Rothwell Mount, Halifax HX1 2XB Tel: 01422 353450/350420; Hillcrest, Stafford Road, Halifax HX3 0PF — MB ChB 1978 Aberd.

FINDLAY, Mary Graham Greenways, Windgates Road, Leven KY8 4DS — MB ChB 1943 Ed. (Ed.) Socs: BMA. Prev: Med. Supt. Rainy Hosp. Madras, S. India; Regist. Elsie Inglis Matern. Hosp. Edin.

FINDLAY, Nigel Graham West Farm Avenue Surgery, 381 West Farm Avenue, Longbenton, Newcastle upon Tyne NE12 8UT Tel: 0191 266 1728 Fax: 0191 270 1488 — MB ChB 1983 Sheff.; FRCGP 1996, M 1987; DCCH RCGP & FCM 1987; DRCOG 1985. Prev: SHO (Paediat.) Sunderland Gen. Hosp.; SHO (A & E) Roy. Vict. Infirm. Newc.; SHO (O & G) Hexham Gen. Hosp.

FINDLAY, Patricia Ann (retired) Beck House, Micklethwaite, Bingley BD16 3JN Tel: 01274 567181 — MB ChB Sheff. 1963. Prev: GP Bingley & Baildon.

FINDLAY, Paul Fraser Dr Grays Hospital, Elgin, Elgin; Craiglen, Sanquhar Road, Forres IV36 1DG — BM 1986 Soton.; BSc (Hons.) Aberd. 1982; MRCP (UK) 1995. (Soton.) Cons. Phys. & Geriat. Dr Grays Hosp. Elgin; Hon. Specialist Regist. for the Elderly Woodend Hosp. Aberd. Socs: BMA; Roy. Coll. Phys. & Surgs. Glas.; Brit. Geriat. Soc. Prev: Regist. (Med.) Borders Gen. Hosp. Melrose; SHO (Geriat. Med., Gen. Med. & Cardiol.) Raigmore Hosp. Inverness; SHO (Psychiat.) Roy. Cornhill Hosp. Aberd.

FINDLAY, Stewart Macpherson Bishopgate Medical Centre, 178 Newgate Street, Bishop Auckland DL14 7EJ Tel: 01388 603983 Fax: 01388 607782 — MB ChB 1979 Dundee; MRCGP 1983.

FINDLAY, Stuart 22 Torwood Brae, Hamilton ML3 9XB — MB ChB 1994 Aberd.

FINDLAY, Mr Stuart Charles The Surgery, The Green, Haddenham, Ely CB6 3TA Tel: 01353 740205 Fax: 01353 741364; 66 Aldreth Road, Haddenham, Ely CB6 3PW Tel: 01353 740039 Fax: 01353 741647 Email: stuart.findlay@dial.pipex.com — MB BS 1982 Lond.; FRCS (Ed.) 1986; MRCS Eng. LRCP Lond. 1981. (Char. Cross) Princip. GP, Haddenham; Bd. Mem. E. Cambs PCG (Clin. Gov.). Socs: MAGPAS. Prev: SHO (O & G) St Paul's Hosp. Cheltenham; Trainee GP Ch.down Glos.; RSO W.on Gen. Hosp.

FINDLAY, Stuart Robert Riverbank, Janet Street, Thurso KW14 7AR; 5 Grant Avenue, Thurso KW14 7LE Tel: 01847 894627 — MB ChB 1985 Aberd.; DRCOG 1990. GP Princip. Riverbank Pract. Thurso; Clin. Asst. Cas. Dunbar Hosp. Thurso. Prev: SHO (ENT) Bridgend Gen. Hosp.; SHO (Psychiat.) E. Glam. Hosp. Pontypridd; SHO (O & G) Morriston Hosp. Swansea.

FINDLAY-DOMES, Elisabeth Dermatology Outpatients, Leighton Hospital, Middlewich Rd, Crewe CW1 4QJ Tel: 01270 255141 — MD 1985 Graz, Austria; LRCP LRCS 1989; MRCGP 1991. (Glas.) Clin. Asst., Dermat., Crewe; GP Retainer Scheme Haslington Pract. Crewe. Socs: Primary Care Dermat. Soc.; Christian Med. Fell.ship. Prev: SHO (Paediat. & O & G) Vict. Hosp. Kirkcaldy; Ho. Off. (Dermat. & Gen. Med.) Roy. Infirm. Edin.; Trainee GP Edin.

FINDLEY, Inger Lilian 8 Alwyne Place, London N1 2NL — MB ChB 1971 Sheff.; FFA RCS Eng. 1976; DObst RCOG 1973. Cons. Anaesth. St. Geo. Hosp. Lond.

FINDLEY, John Richard Locks Farm, Institute Hill, Niton, Ventnor PO38 2BD — MRCS Eng. LRCP Lond. 1979; DRCOG 1983.

FINDLEY, Professor Leslie John, TD Ave. House, 27 Squirrels Heath Avenue, Gidea Park, Romford RM2 6AD Tel: 01708 722826 Fax: 01708 736323 Email: ljfindley@uk.consultants.co.uk; 8 Alwyne Place, London N1 2NL Tel: 020 7226 3409 Fax: 020 7704 0078 — MD 1988 Sheff.; MD Univ. Sheff. 1988; MB ChB Sheff. 1968; FRCP Lond. 1989; MRCS Eng. LRCP Lond. 1969; MRCP (UK) 1973; FACP 1994; DCH Eng. 1970; DObst RCOG 1970. Cons. Neurol. Regional Neurol. Centre OldCh. Hosp. Romford; Prof. Health Sci.s (Neurol.) S.bank Univ.; Hon. Cons. NeUrol. MRc Human Movement and Balance Unit. Inst. of Neurol. Lond.; Hon Conss Neurologis W. Lond. Neurosci.s Unit. Socs: Assn. Brit. Neurol. & EEG Soc.; (Chairm. 1994-1997) Pk.inson's Dis. Soc. (UK); Pres. Melvin Ramsay Soc. Prev: Cons. Neurol. Qu. Eliz. Milit. Hosp. Woolwich; Sen. Regist. (Neurol.) Nat. Hosps. Nerv. Dis. Lond. & St. Mary's Hosp.; Adjunct Prof. Univ. Kansas, USA 1991.

FINDLEY, Mark Health Centre, Marmaduke Street, Hessle Road, Hull HU3 3BH — MB ChB 1987 Dundee. Socs: Hull Med. Soc. Prev: Trainee GP Scunthorpe HA.

FINDLOW, David 8 Rochester Terrace, Edinburgh EH10 5AB Tel: 0131 221 1362 Email: davidfindlow@cs.com — MB ChB 1988 Manch.; FRCA 1994. Specialist Regist. (Anaesth.) Edin. Socs: Assn. Anaesth.; SE Scotl. Soc. Anaesth.; Scott. Intens. Care Soc.

FINE, Brian Paul Fax: 020 8678 5405; 6 Knatchbull Road, Camberwell SE5 9QS Tel: 020 7274 5502 — MB 1980 Camb.; MA Camb. 1976, MB 1980, BChir 1979; DRCOG Lond. 1981. (Camb. Univ. & King's Coll. Hosp. Med. Sch.) Sen. Lect. Gen. Pract. Dept. Gen. Pract. & Primary Care, Guy's King's & St. Thomas' Sch. Med. Socs: BMA; MEDACT.

FINE, David Roger Southampton General Hospital, Southampton SO16 6HD Tel: 02380 796872 Fax: 02380 794983; The Library House, Timsbury Manor, Timsbury, Romsey SO51 0NR Tel: 01794 367817 Fax: 01794 367817 — MB BS 1976 London; MRCP 1979 UK; FRCP 1996 London; MD 1987 Lond. (Guys Hospital Medical School) Cons. Gen. Med. & Gastroenterol. Soton. Univ. Hosps.; Hon. Sen. Lect. (Med.) Univ. of Soton. 1998. Socs: Brit. Soc. Gastroenterol.; Pancreatic Soc.; Eur. Pancreatic Club. Prev: Sen. Regist. (Gen. Med. & Gastroenterol.) Soton. Gen. Hosp.; Regist. (Med.) Soton. Gen. Hosp.; Clin. Research Fell. (Med.) St. Geo. Hosp. Lond.

FINE, Miss Esther 32 King Henry's Road, Lewes BN7 1BU Tel: 01273 480319; 53A The Grove, Ealing, London W5 5DX Tel: 020 8567 6299 — MB ChB 1994 Birm.; ChB Birm. 1994. Surg. SHO The Roy. Free Hosp. Prev: Resid. Med. Off. & Demonst. (Anat.) St. Geo. Hosp. Lond.

FINE, Jack (retired) Edenlea, Reynoldston, Gower, Swansea SA3 1AA Tel: 01792 390160 — MRCS Eng. LRCP Lond. 1948; MRCGP 1960; AFOM RCP Lond. 1978; DObst RCOG 1954. Ex-Sec. Hon. Advis. Panel for Driving & Disorders of the Nerv. System. Prev: Sen. Partner GP Brentwood.

FINE, Jeffrey Howard 68 Harley Street, London W1G 7HE Tel: 020 7935 3980 Fax: 020 7636 6262 — MB BS 1979 Lond.; MRCPsych 1984. (St. Bart. Hosp.) Cons. to Europ. Scanning Clinics Ltd. Socs: Fell. Roy. Soc. Med.; BMA; Indep. Doctors Forum. Prev: Clin. Research Phys. (Neuroendocrine) Lilly Research Centre; Regist. (Psychol. Med.) Nat. Hosp. Nerv. Dis. Lond.; SHO (O & G) St. Bart. Hosp. Lond.

FINE, Shirley Rhoda (retired) May Lodge, 30 Rickmansworth Road, Northwood HA6 1HA Tel: 0192 74 24446 — MB ChB 1953 Liverp.; MFCM 1972; DCH Eng. 1956, DPH 1957. Barrister-at-Law Middle Temple 1962. Prev: Sen. Med. Off. DHSS Lond.

FINE, Wilfred 21 Norrys Road, Barnet EN4 9JX Tel: 020 8440 8919 — MB BS Lond. 1939; MD Lond. 1947; FRCP Lond. 1969, M 1943; MRCS Eng. LRCP Lond. 1938. (Guy's) Emerit. Cons. Phys. Newsham Gen. Hosp.; Lect. (Geriat.) Dept. Med. Liverp. Univ. Socs: Brit. Geriat. Soc. Prev: Maj. RAMC, Specialist Phys.; Resid. Med. Off. Maida Vale Hosp. Nerv. Dis.; Chief Asst. Med. Unit Manch. Roy. Infirm.

FINEBERG, Naomi Anne Queen Elizabeth II Hospital, Howlands, Welwyn Garden City AL7 4HQ Tel: 01707 328111 — MB BS 1984 Lond.; MA Camb. 1981; MRCPsych. 1988. Cons. Psychiat. Qu. Eliz. II Hosp.; Hon. Clin. Sen. Lect. Imperial Coll. Sch. Med. Lond. Prev: Cons. Psychiat. St. Mary's Hosp. Lond.

FINEGAN, Niall Anthony Bolton Road Surgery, 23 Bolton Road, Salford M6 7HL Tel: 0161 736 1616 Fax: 0161 737 1878; Fuchsia Cottage, 15 Hough Lane, Wilmslow SK9 2LQ Tel: 01625 522718 — MB ChB 1970 Manch.; DA Eng. 1972. Med. Dir. Duty Doctor; Vice-Chairm. Salford LMC. Socs: Sec. & Treas. Federat. of Med. Servs.

FINEGAN, Wesley Clifford (retired) 555A Main Street, Stenhousemuir, Larbert FK5 4QB Tel: 01324 570383 Fax: 01324 570383 — MB BCh BAO 1978 Belf.; MRCGP 1982; Dip. Palliat. Med. Wales 1993; MICGP 1987; Cert. FPA 1981. Cons. (Med. Educat.), Univ. of Dundee. Prev: Lect. (Med. Educat.) Univ. Dundee.

FINER, David Isaac (retired) — MRCS Eng. LRCP Lond. 1934. Prev: SHO N. Riding Infirm. Middlesbrough.

FINER, Joseph Glenview, 63 Manor Road, Chigwell IG7 5PH Tel: 020 8500 3304 — MRCS Eng. LRCP Lond. 1931; MRCGP 1959. (Middlx.)

FINER, Nicholas Luton & Dunstable Hospital NHS Trust, Lewsey Road, Luton LU4 0DZ Tel: 01582 491122 Fax: 01582 564543 Email: nick.finer@ldh-tr.anglox.nhs.uk — MB BS 1973 Lond.; 1995 R.nutr; BSc (Hons.) Lond. 1970; FRCP Lond. 1994; MRCP (UK) 1977. (Univ. Coll. Hosp. Lond.) Cons. Phys. Endocrinol. Luton & Dunstable Hosp. NHS Trust; Vis. Specialist Addenbrooke's Hosp. Camb.; Vis. Prof. Inst. Health Serv. Research, Luton Univ.; Mem. Edit. Bd. Internat. Jl. Obesity. Socs: (Ex-Chairm.) Assn. Study Obesity; Brit. Diabetic Assn.; Clin. Comm. Mem., Brit. Soc. for Endocrinol. Prev: Hon.sen.lect.umds, guys campus; Med. Research Soc. Trav. Fell. (Mass. Inst. Technol.) Camb., USA; Hon. Sen. Regist. Guy's Hosp. Lond.

FINES, Daniel Peter 3 Evesham Avenue, Hadfield, Hyde SK13 1QP Tel: 01457 854317 — MB ChB 1991 Manch. SHO (A & E) N. Manch. Gen. Hosp.

FINGLAND, Ian Gordon Kelso Medical Group Practice, Health Centre, Inch Road, Kelso TD5 7JP Tel: 01573 224424 Fax: 01573 226388; 3 Berryhill Cottages, Kelso TD5 7SX — MB ChB 1983 Aberd.; DRCOG 1985. Prev: Trainee GP Dumfries & Galloway VTS.

FINGLAND, Ian William Wightman West House, Greenlaw, Duns TD10 6XF — MB ChB 1950 Glas.; FRFPS Glas. 1956; MRCP Glas. 1962; DCH Eng. 1955. Prev: Paediat. Regist. Stobhill Gen. Hosp. Glas.; Ho. Phys. Roy. Infirm. Glas.

FINGLETON, Patrick Gerard 66 Rock Road, Cambridge CB1 7UF — MB ChB 1997 Bristol.

FINGRET, Ann Lilian Mary Finsbury Healthcare, 2 Circus Place, London EC2M 5RS Tel: 020 7638 0909 Fax: 0207 638 9211 Email: enn_fingret@aers.aon.co.uk; Bunkers Hill Cottage, Swinbrook, Burford OX18 4EF Email: ann_fingret@msn.com — MB BS Lond. 1957; FFOM RCPI 1986, MFOM 1980; FFOM RCP Eng.1983, MFOM 1978; DIH Eng. 1967. (Roy. Free) Cons. Phys. (Occupat. Med.) AON Occupat.al Health; Law Soc. Working Party Pressure Managem.; Med. Adviser Brit. Performing Arts Med. Trust. Socs: (Ex-Pres.) Soc. Occupat. Med.; (Ex-Pres.) Internat. Med. Assn. Radio & Television; (Ex-Pres.) Internal Forum on Org. Health. Prev: Cons. Phys. (Occupat. Health) Roy. Marsden Hosp.; Chief Med. Off. BBC; Sen. Regional Med. Off. PO.

FINIGAN, Llary Mair (retired) Flat 4, Ringinglow Mews, 304 Ringinglow Road, Sheffield S11 7PX Tel: 0114 263 0617 — MB BCh Wales 1939; DPH Wales 1941; DCH Eng. 1946. Prev: Regist. W. Middlx. Hosp. Isleworth.

FINIGAN, Peter Alastair — MB ChB 1992 Liverp.; DRCOG 1996; MRCGP 1996. (Liverp.) GP.

FINK, Andrew Michael Goldschleger Eye Institute, Sheba Hospital, Tel Hashomer 52621, Israel Tel: 00 972 3 5302874; 19 Norris Road, Sale M33 3QW Tel: 0161 973 7397 — MB BS 1984 Newc.; MB BS l984 Newc.; MRCGP 1993; FRCOphth 1991; DRCOG 1987; DCH RCP Lond. 1987. Sen. Resid. (Ophth.) Sheba Hosp. Tel Hashomer, Israel. Prev: SHO (Ophth.) Stockport HA; SHO (Accid. & Emerg.) Gibraltar HA; SHO (Ophth.) Huddersfield HA.

FINK, Anne Michelle Kings College Hospital, Denmark Hill, London SE5; 43 Bateman Street, Cambridge CB2 1NA Tel: 01223 65383 — MB BChir 1982 Camb.; BSc Univ. E Anglia 1971; MRCP (UK) 1985.

FINK, Colin Graham Micropathology Ltd, University of Warwick Science Park, Barclays Venture Centre, Sir William Lyons Road, Coventry CV4 7EZ Tel: 024 76 323222 Fax: 024 76 323333 Email: colinfink@micropathology.com; 2 Elmdon Road, Selly Park, Birmingham B29 7LF — MB ChB 1979 Birm.; FRCPath 2000; BSc (Hons.) Birm. 1970, PhD 1974, MB ChB 1979; MRCPath 1993. Clin. Virol. & Phys. for Micropath. Ltd Univ. of Warwick Sci. Pk. Coventry. Prev: Sen. Regist. (Virol.) John Radcliffe Hosp. Oxf.; Clin. Research Fell. Depts. Virol. & Med. Microbiol. Univ. Birm.; Roy. Soc. Trav. Research Fell. 1974.

FINK, Professor George MRC Brain Metabolism Unit, University Department of Neuroscience, 1 George Square, Edinburgh EH8 9JZ Tel: 0131 650 3548 Fax: 0131 662 0240 Email: gfink@holyrood.ed.ae.uk — MB BS 1960 Melbourne; FRSE 1989 FRCP Ed. 1998; MA Oxf. 1976, DPhil 1968; MD Melbourne 1978. (Melb.) Dir. MRC Brain Metab. Unit, Univ. Dept. Neurosci. Edin.; Hon. Prof. Univ. Dep. Neurosci. Edin.; Hon. Prof. Univ. Edin. Socs: Physiol Soc. & Endocrine Soc.; (Ex-Pres.) Europ. Neuroendocrine Assn. Prev: Univ. Lect. & Tutor (Phys. & Med.) Univ. Oxf. & Brasenose Coll. Oxf.; Sen. Lect. (Anat.) Monash Univ. Austral.

FINK, Peter Robert The Maples Medical Centre, 2 Scout Drive, Newall Green, Manchester M23 2SY Tel: 0161 498 8484 Fax: 0161 428 9411; 37 Alton Road, Pownall Park, Wilmslow SK9 5DY — MB ChB 1982 Ed.; BSc (Hons.) Med. Sc. Ed. 1980, MB ChB 1982; MRCGP 1986; DRCOG 1986. Dir. Intermediate Care Project Manch. HA; Hon. Sec. Manch. LMC. Prev: Trainee GP N.enden Health Centre Manch.; SHO (O & G & A & E) Hope Hosp. Salford; SHO (Paediat.) Burnley Gen. Hosp.

FINKE, Arthur Samuel Wellfield Surgery, 53-55 Crescent Road, Crumpsall, Manchester M8 9JT Tel: 0161 740 2213 Fax: 0161 720 9311; 9 Wentworth Avenue, Whitefield, Manchester M45 7GQ — MB ChB 1985 Leeds; MRCGP 1990; DRCOG 1989; Cert. Family Plann. JCC 1988.

FINKLESTONE, Peter John Betts Avenue Medical Centre, 2 Betts Avenue, Benwell, Newcastle upon Tyne NE15 6TD Tel: 0191 274 2767/2842 Fax: 0191 274 0244; 35 The Riding, Newcastle upon Tyne NE3 4LQ — MB BS 1988 Newc.; MRCGP 1994. Prev: Trainee GP N.umbria VTS; SHO (Gen. Med.) Roy. Vict. Infirm. Newc.

FINLAISON, Bruce Harry William (retired) Le Petit Boulivot, Grouville JE3 9UH Tel: 01534 852888 Email: fin@super.net.uk — MB BS Lond. 1955; DObst. RCOG 1956. Prev: Ho. Surg. St. Thos. Hosp. Hydestile.

FINLAY, Alistair Munro Aspasia, 7 Undercliff Road, Kendal LA9 4PS — MB ChB Glas. 1966; DObst RCOG 1967. (Glas.) Prev: SHO Thornhill & Elderslie Hosps. Johnstone; Ho. Phys. Killearn Hosp. Glas.; Ho. Surg. W.. Infirm. Glas.

FINLAY, Professor Andrew Yule Department of Dermatology, University of Wales College of Medicine, Heath Park, Cardiff CF14 4XN Tel: 029 2074 2615 Fax: 029 2074 4312 Email: finlayay@cardiff.ac.uk; 19 The Cathedral Green, Llandaff, Cardiff CF5 2EB Tel: 029 2055 2740 — MB BS 1972 Lond.; FRCP Glas. 1992; FRCP Lond. 1991; MRCP (UK) 1975; MRCS Eng. LRCP Lond. 1972. (St. Mary's) Prof. of Dermat. Univ. Wales Coll. Med. Cardiff; Hon. Cons. Dermatol. Univ. Hosp. Wales Cardiff. Socs: Fell. Roy. Soc. Med.; Brit. Assn. Dermatol. Pres. 2000-2001. Prev: Sen. Lect. (Dermat.) Univ. Wales Coll. Med. Cardiff; Cons. Dermatol. S.ern Gen. Hosp. & W.ern Infirm. Glas.; Research Fell. (Dermat.) Mt. Sinai Med. Center Miami Beach, USA.

FINLAY, Bernard Richard 331 Church Lane, Kingsbury, London NW9 8JD Tel: 020 8205 6262 — MB BS 1946 Lond.; MRCGP

1958. (Univ. Coll. Hosp.) Prev: Capt. RAMC; Ho. Surg. & Ho. Phys. E. Ham Memor. Hosp.

FINLAY, Brigid Mary 3 The Hawthorns, Lancaster LA1 4PJ — MB ChB 1989 Manch. Trainee GP/SHO (O & G) Blackpool, Fylde & Wyre HA.

FINLAY, David Brian Lindsay 6 Knighton Grange Road, Stoneygate, Leicester LE2 2LE — MB ChB 1970 St. And.; FRCP Ed. 1991; MRCP (UK) 1974; FRCR 1977; DMRD Eng. 1976; DCH Eng. 1974. Cons. Radiol. Leicester Roy. Infirm.

FINLAY, David Thornton (retired) 45 Exe Vale Road, Countess Wear, Exeter EX2 6LF Tel: 01392 434402 — MB 1955 Camb.; BChir 1954; DObst RCOG 1958.

FINLAY, Eric Ritchie 40 Laigh Road, Newton Mearns, Glasgow G77 5EQ — MB ChB 1992 Manch.

FINLAY, Fiona Olwen Rashee, 34 Cadogan Park, Malone Road, Belfast BT9 6HH — MB BS 1985 Lond.

FINLAY, Hamish Hugh Maclean West Torrie, Callender FK17 8JL — MB ChB 1968 St. And.; DA Eng. 1973; FFA RCSI 1976.

FINLAY, Hazel Margaret (retired) 37 Kilraughts Road, Ballymoney BT53 7HL Tel: 0126 56 63712 — MB BCh BAO 1956 Dub. Prev: GP Co. Fermanagh.

FINLAY, Mr Ian Gardner Department of Surgery, Glasgow Royal Infirmary, Glasgow G4 0SF — MB ChB 1976 Manch.; BSc St. And. 1973; FRCS Ed. 1993; FRCS Glas. 1980. Cons. Surg. i/c Colorectal Disorders Roy. Infirm. Glas. Socs: (Counc.) Brit. Assn. Coloproctol.; (Counc. & Hon. Treas.) Roy. Coll. Phys. & Surgs. Glas.; Assn. Surg.

FINLAY, Ian Gerard 6 Oakham Drive, Liverpool L10 8LR — BM BS 1992 Nottm.

FINLAY, Professor Ilora Gillian Holme Tower Marie Curie Centre, Bridgeman Road, Penarth CF64 3YR Tel: 029 2070 0924 Fax: 029 2071 1070 Email: ilora.finlay@velindre-br.nhs.wales.uk; 19 The Cathedral Green, Llandaff, Cardiff CF5 2EB Tel: 02920 552740 Fax: 029 2057 6465 — MB BS 1972 Lond.; MRCS Eng. LRCP Lond. 1972; FRCGP 1992, M 1981; DCH Eng. 1975; DObst RCOG 1974; MRCP 1996; FRCP 1999. (St. Mary's) Med. Dir. Holme Tower Marie Curie Centre Cardiff & Cons. Palliat. Med. Velindre NHS Trust Cardiff; Hon. Prof. Univ. Wales; Edr. Palliat. Care Today; Profess. Assoc. Univ. Melbourne, Austral.; Non-Exec. Dir. Gwent HA. Socs: Assn. Palliat. Med. (Ex-Chair. Ethics Comm.); Chair. Roy.Soc.med.Palliat..Care.Forum. Prev: Postgrad. Adviser (Med.) Wom. Glas. Univ.; Assoc. Specialist Strathcarron Hospice Stirlingsh.

FINLAY, Karen Denise Rusthall Medical Centre, Nellington Road, Rusthall, Tunbridge Wells TN4 8UW Tel: 01892 515142 Fax: 01892 532256 — MB BS Lond. 1987; BSc (Cell Path.) Lond. 1984; MRCGP 1992; DRCOG 1992; DCH RCP Lond. 1991; DGM RCP Lond. 1989.

FINLAY, Kathleen Calder Kinloch Rannoch Medical Practice, Kinloch Rannoch, Pitlochry PH16 5PR Tel: 01882 632216 Fax: 01882 632772 — MB ChB 1972 Aberd. Socs: Scott. Family Plann. Med. Soc.

FINLAY, Lisa 34 Ballywillin Road, Portrush BT56 8JN; Blairhall House, Old Balkello, Auchterhouse, Dundee DD3 0QY — MB ChB 1994 Dundee; MRCP (UK) 1997. (Dundee) Clin. Lect. in Child Health, Univ. of Dundee. Socs: RCP Ed. Prev: ITU Clin. Fell. Roy. Hosp. for Sick Childr. Edin.; Overseas work in Tibetan Delek Hosp. India.

FINLAY, Mary Elizabeth Castle Hill Hospital, Department of Radiology, East Yorkshire Hospitals Trust, Cottingham HU16 5JQ Tel: 01482 875875 — MB BS 1979 Newc.; MRCP (UK) 1985; FRCR 1990. (Univ. of Newc. U. Tyne) Cons. Clin. Radiol. Castle Hill Hosp. Hull. Prev: Fell. (Radiol.) P.ss Alexandra Hosp. Brisbane Qu.sland, Australia; Sen. Regist. (Clin. Radiol.) Newc. Teach. Hosps.; Regist. (Med.) P.ss Margt. Hosp. Swindon.

FINLAY, Mary Nicol Ravensworth, 8 North Common Road, Uxbridge UB8 1PD Tel: 01895 234306 — MB ChB 1944 Ed. (Univ. Ed.) Prev: Med. Off. (Family Plann.) Hillingdon HA; Res. Ho. Surg. Matern. Sect. Ayrsh. Centr. Hosp.; Clin. Asst. Gyn. Dept. Eliz. G. Anderson Hosp. Lond.

FINLAY, Michael 14 Castleton Road, Broughton Park, Salford M7 4GU Tel: 0161 740 5495 — MB ChB 1975 Manch.; BSc (Hons.) Manch. 1972; FRCP Lond. 1993; MRCP (UK) 1978. Cons. Geriat. Birch Hill Hosp. Rochdale. Socs: Brit. Geriat. Soc. & Brit. Thoracic Soc.; Manch. Med. Soc. (Counc. Mem.). Prev: Sen. Regist. (Geriat.) St. Thos. & Stepping Hill Hosps. Stockport; Sen. Regist. (Geriat.) Withington Hosp. Manch.; Sen. Regist. (Gen. Med.) Stepping Hill Hosp. Stockport.

FINLAY, Robert (retired) 48 Chatsworth Street, Sunderland SR4 7TS Tel: 0191 522 7200 — MB ChB Glas. 1939. Prev: Res. Med. Off. Shotley Bridge Hosp.

FINLAY, Robert John 21 Gorteade Road, Upperlands, Maghera BT46 5SA — MB BCh BAO 1985 Belf.

FINLAY, Mr Robin Dundas (cons. rooms), Longwood House, The Bath Clinic, Claverton Down, Bath BA2 7BR Tel: 01225 835555 Ext 341 Fax: 01225 840708 Email: finlay@doctors.org.uk; The Old Vicarage, Norton St. Philip, Bath BA2 7LY Tel: 01373 834475 Fax: 01373 834475 Email: finlay@doctors.org.uk — BM BCh 1964 Oxf.; MA Oxf. 1964; FRCS Eng. 1971; FRCS Ed. 1971; FRCOphth 1988; DO Eng. 1969. (Oxford and King's College Hospital London) Hon. Cons. Ophth. Surg. Roy. United Hosp. Bath. Socs: BMA; UKISCRS. Prev: Sen. Exam. Dip. Exam. Roy. Coll. Ophth.

FINLAY, Samuel Raymond 34 Cadogan Park, Belfast BT9 6HH Tel: 01232 667595 — MB BCh BAO 1953 Belf.

FINLAY, Shaun Sidney Alexander 1 Moorfield Court, Comber, Newtownards BT23 5WD — MB BCh BAO 1990 Belf.; MRCGP 1994; DRCOG 1993; DCH Dub. 1992; TGP 1994.

FINLAY, Shielagh Curie Flat 3, 81 South Hill Park, Hampstead, London NW3 2SS Tel: 020 7431 0152 — MB ChB 1974 Aberd.; MRCGP 1985. Clin. Asst. (Psychother.) St. Ann's Hosp. Lond.; Supervisor Eating Disorder Team St. Ann's Hosp. Lond.; Jung. Analyst - Private Pract. Socs: Assoc. Mem. Inst. Psycho-Sexual Med.; Assoc. Mem. Soc. Analyt. Psychol. Prev: GP Lond.; Clin. Asst. (Psychother.) Humberstone Grange Clinic; Clin. Asst. (Psychosexual Med.) Leics. HA.

***FINLAY, Sian** 34 Ballywillin Road, Portrush BT56 8JN — MB ChB 1994 Dundee; BMSc (Med. Psychol.) 1991.

FINLAY, William Paul Bovally Medical Centre, 2 Rossair Road, Limavady BT49 0TE Tel: 028 7776 6352 — MB BCh BAO 1978 Belf.; MRCGP 1983; DRCOG 1982.

FINLAY, Winifred Elizabeth Irene (retired) 24 Laggan Road, Newlands, Glasgow G43 2SY Tel: 0141 633 1750 Fax: 0141 633 1750 — MB ChB 1960 Glas.; FRCP Glas. 1991, M 1989; FFA RCS Eng. 1966; DA Eng. 1962; FRCA 1992. Prev: Cons. Anaesth. W.. Infirm. & Assoc. Hosps. Glas.

FINLAYSON, Alexander James Kay (retired) Dalblair, 7 St Cuthberts Avenue, Dumfries DG2 7NZ Tel: 01387 254085 — LRCP LRCS Ed. LRFPS Glas. 1944. Prev: Ho. Surg. Cas. Dept. Roy. Infirm. Edin.

FINLAYSON, Anna Isabella (retired) 7 Abbotshall Road, Cults, Aberdeen AB15 9JX Tel: 01224 867856 — MB ChB 1955 Aberd.; DPH Aberd. 1972; DA Eng. 1958. Prev: Sen. Med. Off. Grampian HB.

***FINLAYSON, Brett Lindsay** Woodside medical Group, 80 Western Road, Aberdeen AB24 4SU Tel: 01224 492828 — MB ChB 1994 Aberd.; MRCGP 1998.

FINLAYSON, Bruce James Norfolk & Norwich Health Care NHS Trust, Brunswick Road, Norwich NR1 3SR Tel: 01603 286286 Email: bruce.finlayson@norfolk-norwich.thenhs.com — MB BS 1976 Lond.; MB BS (Hons. Med.) Lond. 1976; BSc Lond. 1973; FRCS Eng. 1984. (St. Bartholomew's) Cons. A & E Norf. & Norwich Hosp. Socs: Fell. Fac. Accid. & Emerg. Med.; Brit. Assn. Accid. & Emerg. Med.; BMA. Prev: Sen. Regist. (A & E Med.) Addenbrookes Hosp., Norf. & Norwich Hosp.; Regist. (A & E Med.) Qu. Univ. Hosp. Nottm.

FINLAYSON, Caroline Jane Department of Histopathology, St George's Hospital, Blackshaw Road, London SW17 0RE Tel: 020 8672 9944; Duns House, Hannington, Tadley RG26 5TX — MB BS 1980 Lond.; MRCS Eng. LRCP Lond. 1980; MRCPath 1988. Cons. & Sen. Lect. (Histopath.) St. Geo. Hosp. Lond.

FINLAYSON, Mr David Farquhar Department of Orthopaedic Surgery, Raigmore Hospital, Inverness IV2 3US Tel: 01463 704000 — MB ChB 1976 Aberd.; FRCS Glas. 1980; FRCS Ed. (Orth.) 1986. (Univ. Aberd.) Cons. Orthop. Surg. Raigmore Hosp. Inverness; Hon. Sen. Lect. (Orthop.) Univ. Aberd. Socs: Fell. BOA; Fell. BASK; BMA.

FINLAYSON, Elizabeth Anne (retired) 22 Breadalbane Terrace, Wick KW1 5AT Tel: 01955 602517 — MB ChB St. And. 1959. Prev: Clin. Med. Off. (Child Health) Highland HB.

FINLAYSON, James Alexander The Rowans, Broallan, Beauly IV4 7AH — MB ChB 1992 Glas.

FINLAYSON, James Alexander Donald Tarbert, Harris, Isle of Harris HS3 3BG Tel: 01854 2455 — MB ChB 1979 Aberd.; MRCGP 1988; MRCPsych 1984.

FINLAYSON, James Kerr (retired) 7 Abbotshall Road, Cults, Aberdeen AB15 9JX Tel: 01224 867856 Email: j.k.finlayson@talk21.com — MB ChB 1954 Aberd.; BSc Aberd. 1943, MB ChB 1954; FRCP Lond. 1973, M 1958. Prev: Cons. Phys. Aberd. Gen. Hosp. Gp.

FINLAYSON, Margaret Janet Wood (retired) 32 Calderwood Road, Rutherglen, Glasgow G73 3HE — MB ChB 1944 Glas.; MFCM 1972; DPH 1966; DCH Eng. 1950. Community Med. Specialist Gt.er Glas. Health Bd. (S. E. Dist.). Prev: PMO Matern. & Child Welf. Servs. Glas.

FINLAYSON, Niall Diarmid Campbell, OBE Centre for Liver & Digestive Disorders, Royal Infirmary, Lauriston Place, Edinburgh EH3 9YW Tel: 0131 536 2178 Fax: 0131 536 2197; 10 Queen's Crescent, Edinburgh EH9 2AZ Tel: 0131 667 9369 Fax: 0131 667 2174 Email: ndc.finlayson@which.net — MB ChB 1964 Ed.; PhD Ed. 1972, BSc (Hons.) 1962; FRCP Lond. 1982, M 1967; FRCP Ed. 1977, M 1967; FRCS Ed. 1999. (Ed.) Cons. Phys. Roy. Infirm. Edin.; Hon. Sen. Lect. (Med.) Edin. Univ. Socs: Amer. Assn. Study Liver Dis.; Brit. Soc. Gastroenterol.; Assn. Phys. Prev: Asst. Prof. Med. Cornell Univ. Med. Sch. New York, USA.

FINN, Professor Adam Hugh Roderick Institute of Child Health, Floor 3 Level 6, The Education Centre, United Bristol Healthcare Trust, Upper Maudlin Street, Bristol BS2 8DJ Email: Adam.Finn@bristol.ac.uk — BM BCh 1983 Oxf.; PhD Lond. 1994; MA Camb. 1984; FRCP 1996; FRCPCH 1997. Prof. Of Paediat. Div of Child Health Univ. of Bristol; Hon. Cons. Paediat. Immunol. Childr. Hosp. Sheff. Socs: Bd. Mem. Europ. soc. for Paediat. Infect. Dis. Prev: Lect. (Immunol.) Inst. Child Health Lond.; Hon. Sen. Regist. (Paediat.) Hosp. Sick Childr. Gt. Ormond St. Lond.; Fell. Paediat. (Infec. Dis.) Childr. Hosp. Philadelphia, USA.

FINN, Ann Margaret Occupational Health Department, GlaxoWellcome Research and Development, Greenford Road, Greenford UB6 0HE Tel: 020 8966 2202 Email: amf13093@glaxowellcome.co.uk; 26 Shortlands Road, Bromley BR2 0JD — MB BCh BAO 1981 NUI; MRCGP 1985; MFOM 1997, AFOM RCP (UK) 1993; LFOM RCPI 1990; Dip Occupat. Health NUI 1990; DObst RCPI 1984; DCH Dub. 1983. (Dublin) Head Occupat. Health, GlaxoWellcome Research & Developm. Greenford. Socs: Soc. Occupat. Med. Prev: Occupat. Phys. Wellcome Foundat. Ltd. Beckenham; SR (Occupat. Med.) SWTRHA; Princip. (Gen. Pract.) Dub.

FINN, Antony Peter Flat 3, 6 Ardberg Rd, London SE24 9JL — MB BS 1996 Lond.

FINN, Catherine Bernadette Good Hope Hospital, Rectory Road, Sutton Coldfield B75 7RR Tel: 0121 328 2211 — MB BCh BAO 1982 NUI; MRCOG 1987; DObst RCPI 1984. Cons. O & G Good Hope NHS Trust Sutton Coldfield. Socs: Brit. Colposcopy Soc. Prev: Sen. Regist. (O & G) Birm. Matern. Hosp. W. Midl. Train. Scheme; Regist. Rotat. (O & G) Dudley Rd. Hosp. Birm.; Sheldon Research Fell. (Gyn.) Univ. Birm.

FINN, Charles Isaac (retired) 7 Hare Crescent, Leavesden, Watford WD25 7EE Tel: 01923 672193 — MB BS 1954 Lond.; MRCPsych 1971; DPM Eng. 1959. Cons. Psychiat. Med. Legal Pract. Prev: Cons. Psychiat. Leavesden Hosp.

FINN, Deborah Louise Valley Surgery, 83 Bramcote Lane, Chilwell, Nottingham NG9 Tel: 0115 943 0530 — MB BS 1991 Lond.; BSc Lond. 1988; DGM RCP Lond. 1993; MRCGP 1996. Locum GP. Socs: BMA; Roy. Coll. Gen. Pract.

FINN, Gregory Peter John Eastwood Hospice, Mansfield Road, Sutton-in-Ashfield NG17 4HL; Rutland House, 23 West Bank Avenue, Mansfield NG19 7DJ — MB ChB 1977 Leeds; MRCGP 1988. (Univ. Leeds) Cons. Palliat. Med. & Med. Dir. John E.wood Hospice Notts. Socs: Assn. Palliat. Med.

FINN, Howard Peter 2 Woodgrove Road, Bristol BS10 7RE — MB ChB 1973 Leeds; FFA RCS Eng. 1979.

FINN, John Oliver Blenheim, 64 Junction Road, Deane, Bolton BL3 4NA — LRCPI & LM, LRSCI & LM 1944; LRCPI & LM, LRCSI & LM 1944.

FINN, Kevin Leo Flat 5, The Elms, Parker Avenue, Newcastle upon Tyne NE3 4BE — MB ChB 1991 Manch.

FINN, Melville (retired) Aulion, Coombe Park, Kingston upon Thames KT2 7JB Tel: 020 8549 6818 — BM BCh 1952 Oxf.; MA, BM BCh Oxf. 1952; DA Eng. 1954; DA RCPSI 1954. Prev: Chief Anaesth. Johannesburg Gen. Hosp.

FINN, Paul Jonathan Market Cross Surgery, 7 Market Place, Mildenhall, Bury St Edmunds IP28 7EG Tel: 01638 713109 Fax: 01638 718615; 10 Perse Way, Cambridge CB4 3SF — MB BS 1985 Lond.; MRCGP 1996. GP Mildenhall, Bury St. Edmunds, Suff. Prev: SHO (Med., ENT & O & G) W. Suff. HA.

FINN, Penelope Sandra West Suffolk Hospitals Trust, Hardwick Lane, Bury St Edmunds IP33 2QZ Tel: 01284 713000 Fax: 01284 701993; 39 Horringer Road, Bury St Edmunds IP33 2DQ Tel: 01284 769204 — MB BS 1985 Lond. Trainee SHO (Gen. Med.) W. Suff. Hosp. Prev: Clin. Asst. (A & E) Addenbrooke's NHS Trust; Clin. Asst. (D.S.C.) Addenbrooke's NHS Trust; Asst. GP NE Thames RHA Retainer Scheme.

FINN, Rachel Mary Flat 10, Coppice Oaks, 20 Coppice Road, Birmingham B13 9DP — MB ChB 1993 Birm.; ChB Birm. 1993. SHO (Histopath.) City Hosp. Birm.

FINN, Professor Ronald 45 Rodney Street, Liverpool L1 9EN Tel: 0151 708 0842 Fax: 0151 709 5679; 8 Prestwick Drive, Blundellsands, Liverpool L23 7XB Tel: 0151 924 6657 — MB ChB 1954 Liverp.; MD Liverp. 1961; FRCP Lond. 1972; MRCP (UK) 1958; Hon FRCPCH 1996. Emerit. Cons. Phys. Roy. Liverp. Univ. Hosp.; Vis. Prof. Dept. of Med. Univ. of Liverp. Socs: Assn. Phys.; (Ex-Pres.) Brit. Soc. Allergy & Environm. Med. Prev: Cons. Phys. Roy. Liverp. Univ. Hosp.; Research Fell. Johns Hopkins Hosp. Baltimore.

FINN, Ruth Caroline (retired) 40 North Road, Bourne PE10 — MB BS 1930 Lond.; MRCS Eng. LRCP Lond. 1929; DPH Eng. 1932. Prev: Asst. Sch. Med. Off. LCC.

FINN, Theresa Louise 3 Broadoaks, Stafford ST17 9DW — MB ChB 1991 Sheff. GP Asst. James Wigg Pract. Kentish Town Lond.

FINN, Thomas Joseph 51 Landcross Road, Fallowfield, Manchester M14 6LZ Tel: 0161 224 1670 — MB BCh BAO 1974 NUI; DObst RCPI 1976. (Galway) SHO (Anaesth.) Manch. Roy. Infirm. Prev: SHO (Med.) Regional Hosp. Galway; SHO (O & G) Portiuncula Hosp. Ballinasloe; SHO (Surg.) Co. Hosp. Wexford.

FINNAMORE, Vincent Preston The Medical Centre, Kingston Avenue, East Horsley, Leatherhead KT24 6QT Tel: 01483 284151 Fax: 01483 285814 — BM BCh 1973 Oxf.; MA Oxf. 1973; DRCOG 1976. Sen. Partner Gen. Pract.

FINNEGAN, Audrey Anne Drs Docherty & Partners, Hunter Health Centre, Andrew St, Glasgow G74 1AD Tel: 01224 906620; 12 Forres Avenue, Giffnock, Glasgow G46 6LJ Tel: 0141 621 0508 — MB ChB 1985 Glas.; MRCGP 1989; DRCOG 1990. Gen. Practitioner, Hunter Health Centre, E. Kilbride, Glas. G74 1AD.

FINNEGAN, Mr Brian Christopher 94 Stirling Crescent, St Helens WA9 3UA Tel: 01744 816987 Email: bfinne5689@aol.com — MB ChB 1991 Liverp.; FRCS Eng. 1996. Specialist Regist. (Orthop.) Firness Gen. Hosp. Barrow-in-Firness. Socs: BMA. Prev: Research Regist. (Orthop. Surg.) Roy. Preston Hosp.

FINNEGAN, Damian Peter 55 Cloughreagh Park, Bessbrook, Newry BT35 7EH — MB BCh BAO 1997 Belf.

FINNEGAN, David Michael Scott Clinic, Rainhill Road, Rainhill, St Helens WA9 5BD Tel: 0151 430 6300 Fax: 0151 430 8147 — MB ChB 1976 Liverp.; FRCPsych 1997, M 1982. Cons. Forens. Psychiat. St. Helens & Knowsley Hosps. Trust. Prev: Cons. Psychiat. Fazakerly Hosp. Liverp.

FINNEGAN, Gerard Francis Sherwood Rise Medical Centre, 31 Nottingham Road, Sherwood, Nottingham NG7 7AD Tel: 0115 962 2522 Fax: 0115 962 2989; 2 Goodwin Court, Farnsfield, Newark NG22 8LU Tel: 01623 882420 — MB BCh BAO 1979 NUI; DRCOG 1983. Socs: Irish Coll. GP's; Mansfield Med. Soc.

FINNEGAN, John Patrick 5 Cedar Court, New Road, Burbage, Hinckley LE10 2AW Tel: 01455 611491 — MB BCh BAO 1943 NUI; LM Nat. Matern. Hosp. Dub. (Univ. Coll. Dub.) Prev: Res. Med. Off. & Res. Med. Off. Dept. Path. St. Vincent's Hosp. Dub.

FINNEGAN, Joseph Anthony 36 Station Road, Blackwell, Bromsgrove B60 1PZ Tel: 0121 445 3708 & profess. 021 627 1627 — MB ChB Leeds 1967; FRCP Lond. 1992; MRCP (UK) 1978; FRCP 1992. (Leeds) Cons. Clin. Neurophysiol. Priory Hosptial, Birm.. Socs: EEG Soc. Prev: Sen. Regist. (Clin. Neurophysiol.) Gen. Infirm. Leeds; Regist. (Med.) St. Jas. (Univ.) Hosp. Leeds.; Cons. Ciin. Neurophysiologist, Qu. Eliz. Hosp. Birm..

FINNEGAN, Josephine Mary Belfast City Hospital, Belfast BT9 5AB Tel: 01232 329241; 2 Elmwood Park, Belsize Road, Lisburn BT27 4AX Tel: 01846 676526 — MB BCh BAO 1967 Belf.; FRCS Ed. 1971; DObst RCOG 1969. (Belf.) Staff Grade (Gen. Surg.) Belf. City Hosp. Socs: Assoc. Mem. Brit. Assn. Surg. Oncol. Prev: Sen. Regist. (Surg.) N. Irel. Hosps. Auth.

FINNEGAN, Mary Josephine 104 Mountsandel Road, Coleraine BT52 1TA — MB BCh BAO 1973 Belf.; MRCGP 1978; DObst RCOG 1975. (Queens University Belfast) p/t Med. Off., Med. Support Servs., Royston Ho., Belf. Prev: Med. Off. Stud. Health Serv. Univ. Bristol.; SHO (O & G) Craigavon Area Hosp.; SHO (Paediat.) Roy. Belf. Hosp. Sick Childr.

FINNEGAN, Michael James Bury General Hospital, Walmersley Road, Bury BL9 6PG Tel: 0161 705 3362 Fax: 0161 705 3383 Email: m.finnegan@bury-pgmc.nwest.nhs.uk; 10 Hale Road, Altrincham WA14 2EF Tel: 0161 928 1340 — MB ChB 1978 Liverp.; MD Liverp. 1986; MRCP (UK) 1981; Dip. Palliat. Med. Wales 1993; FRCP (UK) 1997. (Liverpool) Cons. Palliat. & Respirat. Med. Bury Health Care NHS Trust; Mem. Nat. Coun. Hospice & Specialist Palliat. Care Servs. Socs: Assn. Palliat. Med.; Palliat. Med. Rep. on Med. Specialities Subcomm. of CCSC of BMA. Prev: Med. Dir. Hospice of the Good Shepherd Chester; Hon. Cons. Palliat. Med. Countess of Chester Hosp.; Sen. Regist. (Gen. Med.) Roy. Free Hosp. Lond.

FINNEGAN, Owen Campbell Causeway Hospital, Coleraine BT52 1HS Tel: 0208 7032 7032 Email: owen.finnegan@lhsst.n-i.nhs.uk; 104 Mountsandel Road, Coleraine BT52 1TA Tel: 02870 354385 — MB BCh BAO 1971 Belf.; FRCP Ed. 1988; MRCP (UK) 1974. Cons. Phys. Causeway Hosp. Prev: Regist. (Med.) Mpilo Hosp. Bulawayo, Zimbabwe; Sen. Regist. (Med.) Brist. Roy. Infirm.; Ho. Off. Roy. Vict. Hosp. Belf.

FINNEGAN, Timothy Paul, Col. late RAMC DACOS Med. Land, HQ Land Command, Wilton, Salisbury SP2 0AG Tel: 01722 433770 — MB BS 1975 Lond.; BSc Lond. 1972; MSc Occupat. Med. Lond. 1983; FFOM RCP Lond. 1995, MFOM 1989, AFOM 1983; T(OM) 1991. (St. Bart.) Dep. Asst. Chief of Staff (Med.), HQ, Land Command. Socs: AMSUS; Internat. Assn. Phys. Overseas Servs.; Soc. Occupat. Med. Prev: Cdr. Med., HQ 1st (UK) Armoured Div.; Brit. Liaison Off. (Med.) to the US Army Surg. Gen.; Command. Off. 4 Armoured Fld. Ambul.

FINNEGAN, Vicki Lorraine Gum Clinic, Countess of Chester Hospital, Liverpool Road CH2 Tel: 01244 363091; 17 Highfield Drive, Monton, Eccles, Manchester M30 9PZ Tel: 0161 707 6157 Email: mfinnegan@bigwig.net — MB ChB 1978 Liverp.; 2001 Dip. Gum.; Cert. Family Plann. JCC 1981. p/t Staff Grade, Gum Clinic, Countess of Chester Hosp. Prev: GP Reading; Clin. Asst. Leic. Hospice; Asst. GP Chester.

FINNERAN, Nicola Kathryn 49 Barn Park Road, Teignmouth TQ14 8PJ — MB BS 1998 Lond.; MB BS Lond 1998.

FINNERTY, Gerald Thomas 6 The Old Yews, New Barn, Longfield DA3 7JS — MB BS 1984 Lond.; MA Camb. 1988; BA Camb. 1981; MRCP (UK) 1987.

FINNERTY, James Patrick Countess of Chester Hospital, Liverpool Road, Chester CH2 1BQ Tel: 01244 365000 Fax: 01244 366229 Email: jpfinnerty@christleton99.freeserve.co.uk — MB BS 1980 Newc.; DM 1992 Southampton; MRCP 1984 London; FRCP 1999 London. Cons. Respirat Phys. Countess of Chester Hosp. Prev: Sen. Regist. (Intens. Care) Alfred Hosp. Melbourne Australia; Sen. Regist. Soton. Gen. Hosp.

FINNERTY, Mark 20 Warren Hill, Newry BT34 2PH — MB BCh BAO 1997 Belf.

FINNERTY, Michael Joseph Gerard 38 St Philipps Road, London E8 3BP — MB BCh BAO 1985 NUI.

FINNERTY, Paul Anthony 73 Moorside N., Fenham, Newcastle upon Tyne NE4 9DU — MB BS 1983 Newc.

FINNEY, Alan Andrew William Struthers and Partners, 436 Mosspark Boulevard, Glasgow G52 1HX Tel: 0141 882 5494 Fax: 0141 883 1015 — MB ChB 1984 Glas.; MRCGP 1988; DRCOG 1986.

FINNEY, Elizabeth Jane 43 Clara Park, Belfast BT5 6FE — MB BCh BAO 1982 Belf.

FINNEY, John Michael Adelaide Street Health Centre, 19 Adelaide Street, Norwich NR2 4JL Tel: 01603 625015 Fax: 01603 766820; 36 St. David's Road, Hethersett, Norwich NR9 3DH — MB BS 1975 Lond.; MRCP (UK) 1979; MRCS Eng. LRCP Lond. 1975.

FINNEY, Keith (retired) Beech House, Holmfirth, Huddersfield HD9 3HX Tel: 01484 681535 — MRCS Eng. LRCP Lond. 1957.

FINNEY, Miranda Elizabeth 72 Emscote Road, Warwick CV34 5QG — MB BCh 1995 Wales. (Wales) SHO Basic Surgic. Train. Rotat. Cardiff S. E. Wales.

FINNEY, Roger David (retired) 5 Silton Grove, Hartburn, Stockton-on-Tees TS18 5AT Tel: 01642 580885 Fax: 01642 580885 — MB ChB 1964 Glas.; FRCP Ed. 1993; FRCPath 1983. Prev: Cons. Haemat. N. Tees Gen. Hosp. Stockton-on-Tees.

FINNEY, Sheila Margaret (retired) Beech House, Holmfirth, Huddersfield HD9 3HX Tel: 01484 681535 — MB ChB Manch. 1957; MRCGP 1979.

FINNEY, Simon Jonathan Adult Intensive Care Unit, Royal Brompton Hospital, Sydyney Street, London SW3 6LY Tel: 0207 351 8532 Fax: 0207 351 8524 Email: s.finney@ic.ac.uk; Email: s.finney@ic.ac.uk — MB ChB (Hons.) Manch. 1994; BSc St. And. 1991; MRCP (UK) 1997. Specialist Regist. (Anaesth.), Imperial Sch. of Anaesth., Lond. & Brit. Heart Foundat. Clin. Research Fell.; Hon. Regist., Adult Intens. Care, Roy. Brompton Hosp. Lond. Socs: Amer. Thoracic Soc.; Intens. Care Soc.; Soc. of Critical Care Med. Prev: Regist. (Anaesth.) Imperial Sch. Of Anaesth. Lond.; SHO (Anaesth.) Hammersmith Hosp. Lond.; SHO (Adult Intens. Care) Roy. Brompton Hosp. Lond.

FINNEY, Steven Mark 73 Kiln Lane, St Helens WA10 6AH — MB ChB 1998 Liverp.; MB ChB Liverp 1998.

FINNIE, Ian Alexander Glan Clwyd Hospital, Bodelwyddan, Rhyl LL18 5UJ — MB ChB 1983 Aberd.; FRCP (UK) 1999; MD Aberdeen 1997; MRCP (UK) 1988. Cons. Phys. & Gastroenterol. Glan Clywd Hosp. N. Wales. Prev: SHO (Med.) Whiston Hosp. Merseyside.

FINNIE, James Sadler (retired) Broompark, 29 Deeview Road S., Cults, Aberdeen AB15 9NA Tel: 01224 868610 — MD 1959 Aberd.; MB ChB 1946; FRCGP 1978. Prev: Assoc. Specialist Dept. Venereol. Aberd. Roy. Infirm.

FINNIE, Linda Ritchie Brown and Partners, 35 Saughton Crescent, Edinburgh EH12 5SS Tel: 0131 337 2166 Fax: 0131 313 5059 — MB ChB 1980 Ed.; MRCGP 1984; DCH Lond. 1983; DRCOG 1983. GP Edin.

FINNIE, Robert Marshall Dedridge Health Centre, Nigel Rise, Livingston EH54 6QQ Tel: 01506 414586 Fax: 01506 461806; 5 Howard Place, Edinburgh EH3 5JZ Tel: 0131 556 4830 — MB ChB 1974 Ed.; BSc Ed. 1971; FRCP Ed. 1989; MRCP (UK) 1976. (Ed.) Lect. (Gen. Pract.) Univ. Edin. Socs: Brit. Geriat. Soc. & Med. Assur. Soc.; Brit. Hyperlip. Assn. Prev: Ho. Off. (Med.) W.. Gen. Hosp. Edin.; Ho. Off. (Surg.) Roodlands Gen. Hosp. Haddington.

FINNIE, Sarah Marie Byrne, Langham, Apps, Finnie and McIlhinney, 186 Neasham Road, Darlington DL1 4YL Tel: 01325 461128 Fax: 01325 469123 — MB BS 1983 Lond.; MRCGP 1987; DRCOG 1986.

FINNIGAN, Anthony Edward Summertown Health Centre, 160 Banbury Road, Oxford OX2 7BS Tel: 01865 515552 Fax: 01865 311237; 33 Webbs Way, Kidlington OX5 2EW Tel: 01865 377101 — MB ChB 1958 Leeds; MRCS Eng. LRCP Lond. 1960; MRCGP 1984; DPM Eng. 1970; DObst RCOG 1968. Hosp. Pract. (Psychiat.) Littlemore Hosp. Oxf. Socs: BMA & Oxf. Assn. Coll. Doctors. Prev: SHO Horton Gen. Hosp. Banbury; Regist. Warneford Hosp. Oxf.; Med. Off. RAF.

FINNIGAN, Anthony Gerard Kenneth Yelverton Surgery, Westella Road, Yelverton PL20 6AS Tel: 01822 852202 Fax: 01822 852260 — BM BS 1978 Nottm.; BMedSci (Path.) (Hons.) Nottm. 1976, BM BS 1978; MRCGP 1982; DRCOG 1982; DCH RCP Lond. 1981. GP. Prev: Trainee GP Plymouth VTS; Ho. Off. (Surg.) & Ho. Off. (Med.) City Hosp. Nottm.

FINNIGAN, Diane May The Deepings, Hill Bottom, Whitchurch Hill, Reading RG8 7PT — MB BS 1973 Queensland; MRCP (UK) 1980.

FINNIGAN, Jean Pullar (retired) 3 Minto Place, Dundee DD2 1BR Tel: 01382 68810 — MB ChB 1923 St. And.; DPH 1936. Prev: Venereol. Wom.'s Clinics E. Regional Area.

FINNIGHAN, Ellen-Ann Charlton House, Rear High St., Ton Law, Bishop Auckland DL13 4DH Tel: 01388 730251 — MB BCh 1976 Dublin; MB BCh Dub. 1976. (Dublin) GP Bishop Auckland, Co. Durh.

FINNIS, Mr Derek Salisbury District Hospital, Salisbury SP2 8BJ Tel: 01722 336262; Fax: 01722 321789 — MB BS 1966 Lond.; FRCSC 1979; FRCS Eng. 1972; MRCS Eng. LRCP Lond. 1966. (King's Coll. Hosp.) p/t Cons. Surg. Salisbury Healthcare NHS Trust; Regional Speciality Adviser Gen. Surg. And Regional Adviser, Roy. Coll. of Surg.s of Eng.; Director, Cancer Servs., Salisbury Health Care NHS Trust. Socs: Fell.Roy. Soc. Med.; Fell.Assoc. Surg.s Gt. Britain & Irel.; Associaiton of ColoProctol. of Gt. Britain and Irel. Prev: Sen. Regist. (Gen. Surg.) Soton. & SW Hants. Health Dist. (T).

FINTER, Adrian Charles 9 Burntwood Road, Sevenoaks TN13 1PS — MB ChB 1989 Birm.

FINTER, Norman Boyne (retired) Tideswell, 9 Burntwood Road, Sevenoaks TN13 1PS — MB BChir 1947 Camb.; FRCP Lond. 1982, M 1948. Prev: Head Developm. Div. Wellcome Biotechnol. Ltd. Beckenham.

FINUCANE, Katherine Ann 13 Wigston Lane, Aylestone, Leicester LE2 8TH — MA Oxf. 1989, BM BCh 1986; MRCGP 1990; DCH RCP Lond. 1989; DRCOG 1988.

FINUCANE, Ursula Anne War Pensions Agency, Norcross, Blackpool — MB ChB 1977 Manch.; MRCPsych. 1981; T.Psychiat. Med. Off. War Pens. Agency Blackpool. Socs: Fell. Roy. Soc. Med.; Med. Wom. Federat. Prev: Sen. Regist. (Psychiat.) Whittingham Hosp. Preston.

FINZEL, Harry Francis Maurice (retired) Little Beeches, Torcross, Kingsbridge TQ7 2TJ Tel: 01548 580674 — MB ChB Bristol 1932; MD Bristol 1935; MD Lond. 1935, MB BS 1933; MRCS Eng. LRCP Lond. 1932. Prev: Squadron Ldr. RAFVR (Mentioned in Despatches).

FIORENTINI, Teresa c/o Clive Davies, 10 Earl Richards Road N., Exeter EX2 6AG — State Exam Bologna 1985.

FIREBRACE, David Aylmer John The Gratton Surgery, Sutton Scotney, Winchester SO21 3LE Tel: 01962 760267 Fax: 01962 761138 — MB BS 1970 Lond.; FRCGP 2000; DObst RCOG 1975. (Univ. Coll. Hosp. Med. Sch.) Chairm. Mid Hants. PCT Exec. Comm.; Chairm. Wessex GP Educat. Comm. Prev: Trainee GP Basingstoke VTS; Ho. Phys. Univ. Coll. Hosp. Lond.; Ho. Surg. Basingstoke Dist. Hosp.

FIREK, Sophie Clare Leicester Royal Infirmary, Leicester LE1 5WW Tel: 0116 254 1414; 74 Lorne Road, Clarendon Park, Leicester LE2 1YG Tel: 0116 270 1545 — MB ChB 1996 Leic. GP VTS Leic.

FIRKIN, Anthony David (retired) Hatcliffe House, Hatcliffe, Grimsby DN37 0TH Tel: 01472 371206 — MRCS Eng. LRCP Lond. 1964; DObst RCOG 1966. Prev: Ho. Surg., Ho. Phys. & SHO O & G City Hosp. Nottm.

FIRMAN, Mary Ann (Emma) 24 High Street, Marshfield, Chippenham SN14 8LP — MB BS 1984 Lond.; MSc Manch. 1993; BSc Lond. 1981; MRCGP 1989; DRCOG 1987. Occupat. Health Phys.

FIRMIN, Mr Richard Keith Glenfield Hospital NHS Trust, Leicester LE3 9QP; Home Farm House, Burley, Rutland, Oakham LE15 7SX — MB BS 1973 Lond.; FRCSI 1978; FRCS Eng. 1978; MRCS Eng. LRCP Lond. 1973. (St. Bart.) Cons. (Cardiothoracic Surg.) Glenfield Hosp. NHS Trust Leicester. Prev: Sen. Regist. (Cardiothor. Surg.) Nat. Heart & Chest Hosp. Lond.; Evarts Graham Trav. Fell. Amer. Assn. for Thoracic Surg.; Regist. Brompton Hosp. Lond.

FIRN, Shirley Department of Anaesthesia, Pinderfields General Hospital, Aberford Road, Wakefield WF1 4DG Tel: 01924 212348 Fax: 01924 814574; Oaklands House, 163 Netherton Lane, Netherton, Wakefield WF4 4HL Tel: 01924 274234 — MB BS 1965 Durh.; FFA RCS Eng. 1969; DA Eng. 1968. (King's Coll. Newc. u. Tyne) Cons. Anaesth. Pinderfields and Pontefract NHS Trust. Socs: Fell. Roy. Soc. Med.; Yorks. Soc. Anaesth. Prev: Chairm. Dept. of Anaesth. Pinderfields Hosp. NHS Trust; Med. Adviser to the Disaster Preven. and Limitation Unit Univ. oif Bradford; Hon. Clin. Tutor (Anaesth.) Univ. Sheff.

FIROOZAN, Soroosh 47 Trinity Street, Oxford OX1 1TY — BM 1987 Soton.; BM (Hons) Soton. 1987; MRCP (UK) 1990. Regist. John Radcliffe Hosp. Oxf. Prev: SHO (Gen. Med.) Qu. Alexandra Hosp. Portsmouth.

FIROZE, Azad Victoria Road Surgery, 122 Victoria Road, Stretford, Manchester M32 0AD Tel: 0161 865 1651 — MB BS 1963 Dacca. (Dacca) Socs: Stretford Med. Soc. & BMA. Prev: Ho. Surg. Ormskirk Gen. Hosp.; Ho. Phys. Burnley Gen. Hosp.; Ho. Phys. Childr. Hosp. Bradford.

FIROZE, Katherine Vivian Victoria Road Surgery, 122 Victoria Road, Stretford, Manchester M32 0AD Tel: 0161 865 1651 — MB ChB 1964 Liverp.; DObst RCOG 1966. (Liverp.) Socs: Stretford Med. Soc. & BMA.

FIRSTBROOK, Kim Janet Edenfield Road Surgery, Cutgate Shopping Precinct, Edenfield Road, Rochdale OL11 5AQ Tel: 01706 344044 Fax: 01706 526882 — MB BCh 1982 Wales.

FIRTH, Catherine Mary Forge Cottage, The Street, Horringer, Bury St Edmunds IP29 5RY 14 Station Road, Hest Bank, Lancaster LA2 6HP, 01524 824585, 01787 370011 — MB ChB 1995 Birm.; DFFP 2000. GP; GP Sudbury, Suff.

FIRTH, Colin Edward The Surgery, 195 Queensferry Road, Rosyth, Dunfermline KY11 2LQ Tel: 01383 414874 Fax: 01383 410616 — MB ChB 1979 Ed.; MRCGP 1983.

FIRTH, David Anthony, TD Child and Adolescent Mental Health Service, Homeopathic Hospital, 41 Church Road, Tunbridge Wells TN1 1JU Tel: 01892 522598 Email: dfirth@invictu-tr.sthames.nhs.uk; Owls Barn, 59 Sandown Park, Tunbridge Wells TN2 4RT Tel: 01892 822178 Email: dfirth@invicta-tr.sthames.nhs.uk — MB ChB 1982 Manch.; BSc St. And. 1979; MSc Manch. 1992; MRCPsych 1986; DCH RCP Lond. 1987. Cons. Child & Adolesc. Psychiat. Invicta Community Care Trust Roy. Tunbridge Wells. Prev: Sen. Regist. (Child Psychiat.) & Regist. (Paediat. Neurol., Child Psychiat.) N. W. RHA; Regist. (Psychiat.) Univ. Hosp. S. Manch.; Ho. Off. Nobles Hosp. Isle of Man.

FIRTH, David Cecil George Ashton View Medical Centre, 7 Ashton View, Leeds LS8 5BS Tel: 0113 295 3880 Fax: 0113 295 3881; Low Wood, The Avenue, Wetherby LS22 5BU — MB ChB 1964 Leeds; DObst RCOG 1966. Sen. Occupat. Phys. Leeds W.. HA; Clin. Asst. (Geriat., Psychiat. & Med. Rheum. & Rehabil.) Ida Hosp. Leeds.

FIRTH, David Richard (retired) 3 School Lane, Shaldon, Teignmouth TQ14 0DG — BM BCh 1957 Oxf.; MRCGP 1971; MRCS Eng. LRCP Lond. 1958; DObst RCOG 1959. Prev: GP Shaldon Devon.

FIRTH, Fiona Yolantha 14 West End, Long Clawson, Melton Mowbray LE14 4PE Tel: 01664 823618 Fax: 01664 823618 Email: fiona@firth.dircon.co.uk — MB BS 1981 Lond.; MSc Sports Med. Nottm. 1998; Dip. Med. Acupunc. 1995; MRCGP 1986; MRCS Eng. LRCP Lond. 1981. (Charing Cross) Med. Dir. GB Paralympic Equestrian Team; Accreditation Cert. Brit. Med. Acupunc. Soc. 1995; Team Doctor GB Paralympic Swimming Team; Doctor to Lawn Tennis Assoc.; Brit. Olympic Assn. Doctor. Socs: BMA; Brit. Acupunc. Soc.; Brit. Assn. Sport & Med. Prev: GP Swindon; Hon. Phys. Brit. Paralympic Team Atlanta 1996; Clin. Research Fell. (Pain) Ch.ill Hosp. Oxf.

FIRTH, Geoffrey Victor 8 The Rowans, Baildon, Shipley BD17 5DB — MB ChB 1950 Leeds. (Leeds) Prev: Ho. Phys. & Res. Med. Off. N. Ormesby Hosp. Middlesbrough.

FIRTH, Gregory Michael Churchtown Medical Centre, 137 Cambridge Road, Southport PR9 7LT Tel: 01704 224416 Fax: 01704 507168 — MB ChB 1981 Leeds; MB ChB Leeds. 1981; MRCGP 1985; DRCOG 1983.

FIRTH, Hedi Lucy (retired) 21 Heathgate, London NW11 7AP — MRCS Eng. LRCP Lond. 1961; BA Camb. 1958, MB BChir 1961. Prev: GP Lond.

FIRTH, Helen Valerie Department of Clinical Genetics, Box 134, Addenbrooke's Hospital, Hills Road, Cambridge CB2 2QQ Tel: 01223 216446 Fax: 01223 217054 Email: hfirth@hgmp.mrc.ac.uk; The White House, 1 Trumpington Road, Cambridge CB2 2AE Tel: 01223 364491 — BM BCh 1981 Oxf.; BA Oxf. 1978; MRCP (UK) 1984; MRCGP 1987; DRCOG 1987; DCH RCP Lond. 1984; DM 2000 Oxford. (Univ. Oxf.) p/t Cons. (clin. Genetics), Addenbroke's Hosp., Camb. Socs: Brit. Soc. Human Genetics. Prev: Sen. Regist. (Clin. Genetics) Addenbrooke's Hosp. Camb.; Regist. (Med. Genetics) Ch.ill Hosp. Oxf.; Sen. Regist. (Clin. Genetics) Ch.ill Hosp Oxf.

FIRTH, Jean Muriel (retired) Hurstwood House, Hurstwood Lane, Haywards Heath RH17 7QY — MB BS 1959 Lond.; MRCS Eng. LRCP Lond. 1959; MFFP 1993; DCH Eng. 1961. Prev: Med. Off. Mid. Downs Family Plann. Clinics & Clapham & Wimbledon Family Plann. Assn. Clinics.

FIRTH, John Meriden Avenue Surgery, 1 Meriden Avenue, Wollaston, Stourbridge DY8 4QL — MB ChB 1974 Birm. Clin. Asst.

(Urodynamics) Qu. Eliz. Hosp. Med. Centre Birm. Univ. Hosp. NHS Trust Edgbaston. Socs: Brit. Med. Acupunc. Soc.

FIRTH, John Barrie 144 Tilkey Road, Coggeshall, Colchester CO6 1QN — MB ChB 1978 Bristol.

FIRTH, John Clifford (retired) 'Cromar', 11 Hitchin Road, Letchworth SG6 3LT Tel: 01462 684669 — MB BS 1943 Lond.; MRCP Lond. 1951; MRCS Eng. LRCP Lond. 1941. JP. Prev: Cons. Gt. N. Herts Hosp GP.

FIRTH, John David Box 118, Addenbrooke's Hospital, Hills Road, Cambridge CB2 2QQ Tel: 01223 217180 Fax: 01223 586506 Email: john.firth@msexc.addenbrookes.anglox.nhs.uk — BM BCh 1981 Oxf.; BA Camb. 1978; DM Oxf. 1990; FRCP Lond. 1996. Cons. Phys. & Nephrol. Addenbrooke's Hosp. Camb. Prev: Wellcome Fell. & Hon. Cons. Phys. OXf.; Clin. Lect. (Clin. Med.) Oxf.

FIRTH, Mr John Lester 1 Clumber House, Park Drive, Thepark, Nottingham NG7 2UH Tel: 0115 941 9068, 0778 898 8687 Fax: 0115 941 9074 Email: firthfirm@aol.com; Heaven Cottage, Rectory Lane, Great Rissington, Cheltenham GL54 2LL Tel: 0185 682 1262 Email: firthfirm@aol.com — MB BS 1962 Lond.; FRCS Ed. 1967. (St. Thos.) Cons. Neurosurg. Emerit. Univ. Hosp. Qu. Med. Centre Nottm.; Clin. Teach. Univ. Nottm. & Univ. Leics. Med. Schs.; Hon. Pres. CIMP FAI Paris. Socs: BMA; Internat. Microsurg. Soc.; Soc. Brit. Neurol. Surgs. Prev: Lect. (Neurosurg. Stud.) Inst. Neurol. & Nat. Hosp. Nerv. Dis. Qu. Sq. Lond.; Regist. (Neurosurg.) King's Coll. Hosp. & Guy's Maudsley Neurosurg. Unit; Cas. Off. St. Thos. Hosp. Lond.

FIRTH, Joseph (retired) 15 Somerdale Avenue, Heaton, Bolton BL1 5HS Tel: 01204 40848 — MB ChB 1940 Leeds; FRCOG 1965, M 1951. Cons. O & G Bolton Roy. Infirm. & Bolton Dist. Gen. Hosp. Prev: Resid. Obst. Surg. & Sen. Regist. (O & G) St. Mary's Hosps. Manch.

FIRTH, Martin, Lt.-Col. RAMC Department of Radiology, The Royal Hospital Haslar, Gosport PO12 2AA Tel: 01705 584255 Fax: 01705 762400 — MB BS 1986 Lond.; FRCR 1994. (Middlx. Hosp.) Cons. Radiol. Roy. Hosp. Haslar Gosport.

FIRTH, Paul Nigel (retired) 10 Crabtree Avenue, Hale Barns, Altrincham WA15 0RZ Tel: 0161 980 5502 — MB ChB 1955 Sheff.; DObst RCOG 1959. Prev: Gen. Practitioner, Meadway Health Centre, Sale.

FIRTH, Mr Peter Stanley Hurstwood House, Hurstwood Lane, Haywards Heath RH17 7QY Tel: 01444 452990 — MB BS Lond. 1957; FRCS Ed. 1962; FRCS Eng. 1962; FRCOG 1979, M (Gold Medal) 1966. (Guy's) Indep. Gyn. Haywards Heath.; Sen. Racecourse Med. Off. Prev: Cons. O & G Mid-Sussex & Brighton & Lewes Gps. Hosps.; Regist. (Gen. & Genito-Urin. Surg.) W. Middlx. Hosp. Isleworth; SHO (O & G) Qu. Charlotte's Matern. Hosp. & Chelsea Hosp. Wom. Lond.

FIRTH, Rachel Jane Appleby Surgery, Hawkeys Lane, North Shields NE29 0SF Tel: 0191 296 1770 Fax: 0191 296 1770 — MB ChB 1988 Leeds; MRCGP 1992; T(GP) 1992; DRCOG 1992; Cert. Family Plann. JCC 1992.

FIRTH, Rachel Mary The New Surgery, Lindo Close, Chesham HP5 2JN Tel: 01494 782262 — MB BS Lond. 1986; MRCGP 1991.

FIRTH, Raymond Dixon Hawthorns, North Elkington, Louth LN11 0SF Tel: 01507 607513 — MRCS Eng. LRCP Lond. 1940. (St. Geo.) Med. Ref. Lond. Life Assn.; Hon. Maj. RAMC. Socs: Fell. Roy. Soc. Med.; Med. Leg. Soc. Prev: Phys. to The Late King Faisal II & Roy. Ct. of Iraq; Med. 1st Asst. St. Geo. Hosp.; Ho. Phys. King Edwd. VII Hosp. Windsor.

FIRTH, Richard Ainley Tudor House Surgery, 43 Broad Street, Wokingham RG40 1BE Tel: 0118 978 3544 Fax: 0118 977 0420; Bailiff's Cottage, Barkham, Wokingham RG41 4TG Tel: 0118 978 7400 Fax: 0118 978 1608 — MRCS Eng. LRCP Lond. 1962; DObst RCOG 1965. (St. Thos.) Prev: SHO (Cas.) St. Thos. Hosp. Lond.; Ho. Surg. & Ho. Phys. Worthing Hosp.

FIRTH, Sarah Helen Oakwood, 461 Newark Road, Lincoln LN6 8RT — MB ChB 1988 Leic.

FIRTH, Shaun Anthony Nuffield House Surgery, The Stow, Harlow CM20 3AX Tel: 01279 425661 Fax: 01279 427116 Email: shaun.firk@gp-f81120.nhs.uk — MB BS 1967 Lond.; DObst RCOG 1969. (St. Thos.) p/t Sen. Partner, Drs Firth, Chhibber, Swainsbury, Shalley, Ingham, Bansal & Hull, Harlow; Professional Adviser, Health Serv., Lond. Prev: SHO (Obst.) Doncaster Roy. Infirm.; Ho. Surg. & Ho. Phys. P.ss Alexandra Hosp. Harlow.

FIRTH, Sheila Margaret Park Crescent New Surgery, 1A Lewes Road, Brighton BN2 3JJ Tel: 01273 603531/680135 Fax: 01273 698863; Conifer House, Fulking, Henfield BN5 9LT Tel: 01273 857508 — MB BChir 1980 Camb.; MB Camb. 1980, BChir 1979; MRCGP 1983; DRCOG 1982.

FIRTH, Sian Helen 2 Stonelea Close, Silkstone, Barnsley S75 4JD — MB BS 1996 Newc.

FIRTH, Susan Roseberry Centre, St Lukes Hospital, Marton Road, Middlesbrough TS4 3AF Tel: 01642 854986; 34 The Holme, Great Broughton, Middlesbrough TS9 7HF — MB BS 1978 Newc.; MRCGP 1982; DRCOG 1981. (Newc. u. Tyne) Staff Grade (Child & Adolesc. Psychiat.) Roseberry Centre Middlesbrough. Prev: Regist. (Psychother.) Claremont Hse. Roy. Vict. Infirm. Newc. u Tyne.

FIRTH, Wilson Rayner Brandon Mental Health Unit, Leicester General Hospital, Gwendolen Road, Leicester LE5 4PW — MB ChB 1976 Glas.; BSc 1974 (Hon.) Glas.; MRCP (UK) 1979; MRCPsych 1982. Cons. (Psychiat.) Brandon Ment. Health Unit, Leicester Gen. Hosp. Prev: Sen. Regist. (Psychiat.) Warneford Hosp. Oxf.; Regist. (Med. Rotat.) W.. Infirm. Glas.; Regist. (Psychiat. Rotat.) Littlemore Hosp. Oxf.

FISCH, Ladislav (retired) 46 The Drive, Harrow HA2 7EJ Tel: 020 8866 3380 — MD 1939 Brno; DLO Eng. 1949. Hon. Cons. Otol. Nuffield Hearing & Speech Centre Roy. Nat. Ear, Nose & Throat Hosp.; Hon. Cons. Audiol. Phys. Hounslow Dist. Prev: Cons. Audiol. Phys. Hosps for Sick Childr. Gt. Ormomd St. Lond.

FISCHBACHER, Colin Murray Dept. of Epidemiology & Public Health, The Medical School, University of Newcastle, Newcastle upon Tyne NE2 4HH Tel: 0191 222 8752 Fax: 0191 222 6746 Email: c.m.fischbacher@ncl.ac.uk; 11 Berkeley Square, Newcastle upon Tyne NE3 2JB Tel: 0191 284 4488 Fax: 0191 284 4488 Email: colinfischbacher@compuserve.com — MB ChB 1979 Ed.; MSc Lond. 1993; MRCP (UK) 1982; Dip. Epidemiol. 1993. (Edinburgh) Lect. (Pub. Health Med.); Hon. Specialist Regist. (Pub. Health). Prev: Specialist Chogoria Hosp. Kenya.; Regist. (Med.) S.. Gen. & Ruchill Hosps. Glas.

FISCHBACHER, Eric (retired) 3 Greenvale Drive, Brightons, Falkirk FK2 0TQ Tel: 01324 715040 — MB ChB 1948 Glas.; MRCGP 1964. Prev: Assoc. Specialist (Ment. Handicap) Gogarburn Hosp. Edin.

FISCHEL, Jakob Daniel Opthalmology Outpatient Department, Royal Oldham Hospital, Rochdale Road, Oldham OL1 2JH — State Exam Med 1987 Giessen.

FISCHER, Cicely Margaret Gernos, St Dogmaels, Cardigan SA43 3LX Tel: 01293 612493 — MB BS 1962 Lond.; MRCS Eng. LRCP Lond. 1962. (St. Mary's) Prev: Ho. Phys. St. Mary's Hosp.; Ho. Surg. Paddington Gen. Hosp.

FISCHER, Huw Barrie James — MB ChB 1973 Bristol; FFA RCS Eng. 1977. Cons. Anaesth. Alexandra Hosp. Redditch.

FISCHER, Patricia Emily (retired) 35 St John Street, Oxford OX1 2LH — MB BCh Witwatersrand 1944; DCH RCP Lond. 1947. Prev: Sen. Research Asst. (Haemat.) Univ. Camb.

FISCHL, Elizabeth Ann The Finsbury Circus Medical Centre, 5 London Wall Buildings, Finsbury Circus, London EC2M 5NS Tel: 020 7638 0909 Fax: 020 7638 9211 Email: efischl@femc; 26 Warwick Avenue, Little Venice, London W9 2PT Tel: 020 7289 1172 Fax: 020 7286 1560 — MB BS Lond. 1976; MRCGP 1981; DCH Eng. 1980; DA (UK) 1979; DRCOG 1979. Indep. GP Lond.; Hon. Med. Adviser Lond. Philharmonic Orchestra. Socs: Chelsea Clin. Med. Soc. Lond. Prev: Ships Surg. P&O Cruises.

FISH, Mr. Andrew Nigel John The Royal Sussex County Hospital, Brighton BN2 5BE Tel: 01273 696955 Fax: 01273 664732 — MD BS 1981 Lond.; MB BS 1981; MD 1989 London; MRCOG 1989. (University College London) Cons. Gynaecologist & Obststrician. Brighton Health Care NHS Trust. Socs: Brit. Soc. Colpos. & Cerv. Path.; Brit. Gynaecol. Cancer Soc.; Brit. Soc. Gynaecol. Endoscopy. Prev: Sen. Regist. (O & G) Roy. Lond. Hosp.; Research Fell. Univ. Coll. Lond.; Regist. Rotat. Guy's Hosp. Lond.

FISH, Mr Brian Martin Walton Hospital, Rice Lane, Liverpool L9 1AE — MB ChB 1990 Birm.; FRCS 2000 (ORL - HNS); FRCS Eng. 1995, FRCS (Orl.) 1996. (Univ. Birm.) Specialist Regist. (ENT) Aintree Univ. Hosp. Liverp. Prev: Spr. Roy. Liverp. Univ. Hosp.; Spr. Alder Hay Childr.s Hosp.

FISH, Daniel Giles Henry 30A Overton Road, Sutton SM2 6QR — BChir 1996 Camb.

FISH, David Charles Henley Green Medical Centre, Henley Road, Coventry CV2 1AB Tel: 024 7661 4255 Fax: 024 7660 2699; Church Farm, Main St, Willey, Rugby CV23 0SH Tel: 024 76 614255 Fax: 01203 602699 Email: davidfishcf@email.msn.com — MB ChB 1979 Bristol; MRCPsych 1989; MRCGP 1985; DFFP 1994; DRCOG 1982. (Bristol) GP Coventry; Chairm. E. Coventry PCG. Prev: Ment. Health Educat. Fell. W. Midl.

FISH, David Elliott Department of Histopathology, East Surrey Hospital, Canada Avenue, Redhill RH1 5RH Tel: 01737 768511 ext. 6464 Fax: 01737 231839; High Rising, Quarry Road, Oxted RH8 9HE Email: david.fish1@virgin.net — MB BS 1982 Lond.; FRCPath (Histopath. & Cytopath.) 1999; MRCP (UK) 1985; BSc Lond. 1979. (Guy's Hospital Medical School) Cons. Histopath. & Cytopath. E. Surrey Hosp. Redhill. Socs: Internat. Acad. Path.; Assn. Clin. Path.; Brit. Soc. Clin. Cytol. Prev: Sen Regist. (Histopath.) St Mary's Hosp. Lond.

FISH, David Royden Department of Clinical Neurophysiology, National Hospital for Neurology & Neurosurgery, Queen Square, London WC1N 3BG Tel: 020 7837 3611 Fax: 020 7829 8720; Eastgate, The Rectory Drive, Gedling, Nottingham NG4 4BG — MB BS 1981 Lond.; MA Camb. 1982; MD Lond. 1989; FRCP Lond. 1994; MRCP (UK) 1984; T(M) 1992. Prof. of Epilepsy and Clin. NeuroPhysiol./Clin. Director of Clin. Neurosci.s Nat. Hosp. of Neurol. and Neurosurg. Inst. of Neurol. Lond. Socs: (Counc.) Internat. League Against Epilepsy (Brit. Br.). Prev: Sen. Lect. (Clin. Neurophysiol.) Nat. Hosp. Neurol. & Neurosurg. Inst. Neurol. Lond.; Vis. Prof. Cleveland Clinic, USA; Vis. Asst. Prof. Neurol. Dept. Neurol Neurosurg. Montreal Neurol. Inst.

FISH, George Henry (retired) Eastgate, The Rectory Drive, Gedling, Nottingham NG4 4BG — MB BS 1951 Lond.; LMSSA Lond. 1951; DCH Eng. 1954. Prev: RAMC.

FISH, Helen Louise 14 Southfield Road, Knottingley WF11 0JR — MB ChB 1998 Liverp.; MB ChB Liverp 1998.

FISH, Kevin Peter Francis Dundas Street West Surgery, 6 Dundas Street West, Saltburn-by-the-Sea TS12 1BL Tel: 01287 622207 Fax: 01287 623803 — MB ChB 1992 Dundee; MRCGP 1996.

FISH, Leslie Joseph (retired) Dor Chur, Kent's Lane, Standon, Ware SG11 1PJ — MB BS 1955 Lond.

FISH, Mark 2 Argyle Road, Finchley, London N12 7NU Tel: 020 8445 3448 — MB BS 1997 Lond.

FISH, Michael Jonathan Eckford House, Kelso TD5 8LE — MB ChB 1990 Leeds.

FISH, Peter David Westwood Surgery, 24 Westwood Lane, Welling DA16 2HE Tel: 020 8303 5353 Fax: 020 8298 0346; 3 Shortlands Grove, Bromley BR2 0LS Tel: 020 8466 6995 Email: peter.fish@lineone.net — MB BChir 1982 Camb.; MA Camb. 1982; MRCGP 1986; DRCOG 1985; Cert. Family Plann. JCC 1985. (St. Geo. Hosp. Lond.)

FISH, Rosemary Rebecca Josephine Ground Left Flat, 45 Clouston St., Glasgow G20 8QP — MB ChB 1997 Glas.

FISH, Steven John 77 Eastover, Langport TA10 9RY Tel: 01458 252724 Email: 106216.1301@compuserve.com — MB BS 1993 Lond.; BSc (Hons.) 1992. (Lond. Hosp. Med. Coll.) Regist., Gen. Pract., Langport, Som.; Brit. Cycling Team Doctor (Track Racing Squad). Prev: SHO (Anaesth) Frenchay Hosp. Bristol; SHO (Med.), Frenchay Hosp., Bristol; SHO (Anaesth.) Yeovil Hosp.

FISH, Susan Elizabeth The Surgery, High St., Borth SY24 5JE Tel: 01970 871475 Fax: 01970 871509; Y Gelli, Cae Melyn, Aberystwyth SY23 2HA Tel: 01970 617544 — MB BS 1987 Lond.; DCH RCP Lond. 1993; DRCOG 1992. Clin. Asst. Dermat. Bronglais Hosp. Aberystwyth.

FISH, William Harcourt Tel: 01865 376972 — MB BS 1990 Lond.; BSc (Biomed. Sci. & Biochem.) Lond. 1987; FRCA 1995; DA (UK) 1993. (St. George's Hospital) Cons. (Anaesth.) Roy. Cornw. Hosp. Truro Cornw. Socs: Assn. Anaesth.; Soc. Devon Intens. Therapists; Soc. SW Anaesth. Prev: Clin. Research Fell. in Paediatric Anaesth. Childerns Hosp. Brit. Columbia CANADA; Sen. Regist. GreenLa. Hosp. Auckland, New Zealand; Sen. Regist. Starship Childr.'s Hosp. Auckland, New Zealand.

FISHER, Mr Aeneas Mackay (retired) St Andrews, 4 The Fairway, Northwood HA6 3DY — MB BChir 1958 Camb.; BA 1954 (Camb), MA 1958; MD (Camb) 1967,; FRCOG 1973, M 1962; MChir1995 (Camb). Prev: Cons. O & G N.wick Pk. Hosp. & Clin. Research Centre.

FISHER, Alison Margaret (retired) 72 Station Road, Epworth, Doncaster DN9 1JZ Tel: 01427 875352 Fax: 01302 341525 — MB BS 1973 Lond.; MRCS Eng. LRCP Lond. 1973. Prev: GP Rotherham.

FISHER, Andrew John 15 Pershore Road, St Annes-on-Sea, Lytham St Annes FY8 1HA — BM BS 1993 Nottm.

FISHER, Andrew Scott 8 Heathfield Avenue, Stockport SK4 4QJ — MB ChB 1983 Manch.; MRCGP 1989; DRCOG 1988. GP Manch. Prev: SHO (O & G) St. Mary's Hosp. Manch.; SHO (Psychiat.) N. Manch. Gen. Hosp.; SHO (Paediat.) Duchess of York Hosp. Manch.

FISHER, Anna Friederike Arbury Road Surgery, 114 Arbury Road, Cambridge CB4 2JG Tel: 01223 364433 Fax: 01223 315728; 46 Gough Way, Cambridge CB3 9LN Tel: 01223 65857 — State Exam Med. Göttingen 1985; Dr. Med. Aachen 1986; MRCGP 1991; DCH RCP Lond. 1989; DLO RCS Eng. 1988.

FISHER, Anne Veronica (retired) Hill House, Great Bourton, Banbury OX17 1QH Tel: 01295 750625 — MB BS Lond. 1958.

FISHER, Anthony The Old Gloving House, Wooton, Woodstock, Oxford OX20 1DJ Tel: 01993 813521 — MB BCh 1957 Wales; FFA RCS Eng. 1962. (Cardiff) Cons. Anaesth. Radcliffe Infirm. Oxf. Prev: Sen. Regist. Nuffield Dept. Anaesth. Oxf. Ho. Phys. Med. Unit & Ho.; Surg. Cardiff Roy. Infirm.

FISHER, Antony Peter Department of Anaesthesia, King's Healthcare NHS Trust, Denmark Hill, London SE5 9RS Tel: 020 7346 3154; 22 Gleeson Drive, Orpington BR6 9LJ — MB BS 1981 Lond.; MA Oxf. 1981; FFA RCS Eng. 1985; T(Anaesth.) 1991. Cons. Anaesth. & Lead Paediat. Anaesth. King's Healthcare NHS Trust. Socs: Assn. Anaesth. GB & Irel. Prev: Lect. (Anaesth.) King's Coll. Hosp. Sch. Med. & Dent.

FISHER, Arthur Michael Harington (retired) 27 Third Avenue, Hove BN3 2PB Tel: 01273 772693 — MB BChir 1944 Camb.; MA Camb.; FRCR 1975; FFR 1957; DMRD Eng. 1951. Cons. (Radiol.) Roy. Sussex. Co. Hosp. Brighton. Prev: Sen. Regist. Middlx. Hosp. Lond., Radcliffe Infirm. Oxf. & United.

FISHER, Barbara Alice (retired) Ooty, 4 Blacksmith's Hill, Sanderstead, South Croydon CR2 9AY Tel: 020 8657 4491 — MB, BS Punjab 1946. Prev: Clin. Asst. (Eye Units) Sutton & Merton Health Dist. & Croydon AHA.

FISHER, Barrie Miles Glasgow Royal Infirmary, Castle Street, Glasgow G4 0SF Tel: 0141 211 4080 Fax: 0141 211 4080 Email: miles.fisher@northglasgow.scot.nhs.uk; 53 South Mains Road, Milngavie, Glasgow G62 6DE Tel: 0141 956 5915 — MB ChB 1979 Glas.; MD Glas. 1988; FRCP Glas. 1994; MRCP (UK) 1982; FrCP Ed 1999. Cons. Phys. (Med., Diabetes & Endocrinol.), Glas. Roy. Infirm., Glas. Socs: ABCD; ADA; Diabetes UK. Prev: Cons. Phys. (Med., Diabetes & Endocrinol.), Roy. Alexandra Hosp., Paisley; Sen. Regist. (Med.) Gtr. Glas. HB.

FISHER, Betty 226 Carlton Avenue E., Wembley HA9 8PZ Tel: 020 8904 4140 — MRCS Eng. LRCP Lond. 1951. (Roy. Free)

FISHER, Brian Henry Wells Park Practice, 1 Wells Park Road, London SE26 6JD Tel: 020 8699 2840 Fax: 020 8699 2552 — MB 1974 Camb.; BChir 1973; MSc Lond. 1990. Primary Care Developm. Practitioner Lambeth, S.wark & Lewisham Health Auth.; Hon. Research Worker (Gen. Pract.) Guy's Hosp. Lond.; Clin. Governance Lead S. Lewisham PCG. Prev: GP Tutor Guy's Hosp. Lond.; Vice-Chair Lambeth, S.wark & Lewisham MAAG.

FISHER, Carol Jane Machrie, Port Glasgow Road, Kilmacolm PA13 4QQ — MB ChB 1994 Manch.

FISHER, Carolyn Jane Whitby Group Practice, Springvale Medical Centre, Whitby YO22 1SD Tel: 01947 820888; 6 Martin's Row, Robin Hood's Bay, Whitby YO22 4SD Tel: 01947 880616 Email: carolyn@tinrow.demon.co.uk — MB ChB 1983 Manch.

FISHER, Charles Dalby, MBE, RD, Surg. Lt.-Cdr. RN Retd. 82 High Street, Saltney, Chester CH4 8SF; Greenmantle, 46 Rowcliffe Avenue, Lache Lane, Chester CH4 7PW Tel: 01244 676115 — MB ChB Liverp. 1953; MRCGP 1970; DObst RCOG 1957. Hon. Med. Off. Chester Br. Brit. Sub. Aqua Club. Prev: Med. Off. Roy. Flying Doctor Serv. Derby, W.. Australia.; Surg. CH Off. Roy. Fleet Auxil.; Med. Off. Roy. Marines Reserve Merseyside. Rank of Surg Lt Cdr RNR Med. Off.

FISHER, Charles Walter Stewart Department of Medicine, Milton Keynes General, Standing Way, Milton Keynes MK6 5LD Tel: 01908 243293; 10 Leckhampstead Road, Wicken, Milton Keynes MK19 6BY Tel: 01908 571245 — BChir Camb. 1968, MB 1969; FCRP Lond. 1989; MRCP (UK) 1972. Cons. Phys. (Gen. Thoracic

Med.) Milton Keynes Hosp. Prev: Cons. Phys. Nkana Hosp. Kitwe Zambia.

FISHER, Charlotte Jane Department of Pathology, Yeovil District Hospital, Higher Kingston, Yeovil BA21 4AT — MB ChB 1974 Birm.; MSc Lond. 1981; MRCPath 1992.

FISHER, Christopher James 5 Gladstone Street, Basford, Stoke-on-Trent ST4 6JG — MB ChB Birm. 1979; MRCP (UK) 1986. Sen. Regist. (Clin. Electrophysiol.) N. Staffs. Roy. Infirm. Socs: Fell. Roy. Soc. Med. Prev: Regist. (Neurol.) Morriston Hosp. Swansea; Regist. (Gen. Med.) Hereford Co. Hosp.; SHO (Neurol.) Midl. Centre for Neurol. Birm.

FISHER, Christopher John Earls House Hospital, Lanchester Road, Durham DH1 5RD Tel: 0191 333 6548 Fax: 0191 333 6363 Email: chris.fisher@cddps.northy.nhs.uk — MB BS 1979 Newc.; BMedSc Newc. 1976; FRCPsych 1984. Med. Dir. Co. Durh. & Darlington Priority Servs. NHS Trust. Prev: Cons. Psychiat. (Drug Dependence) Regional Drug Dependence Unit Prestwich Hosp. Manch.

FISHER, Constance Margaret Sherbrooke, Loch Carron, Strathcarron IV54 8YA — MB ChB 1959 Glas. (Glas.) Prev: Clin. Med. Off. Inverness; Families Med. Off. Milit. Hosp. Nairobi, Kenya.

FISHER, Crispin Allan Hans Marches Surgery, Westfield Walk, Leominster HR6 8HD Tel: 01568 614141 Fax: 01568 610293 — MB BS 1987 Lond.; BA Camb. 1984; MRCP (UK) 1990; MRCGP (Distinc.) 1994; DRCOG 1992. Socs: BMA. Prev: Med. Off. King Edwd. VII Memor. Hosp. Port Stanley, Falkland Is.s; Trainee GP Cleveland VTS & Much Birch, Hereford; SHO (Gen. Med.) S. Cleveland Hosp. & Middlesbrough Gen. Hosp.

FISHER, Cyril Department of Histopathology, Royal Marsden NHS Trust, Fulham Road, London SW3 6JJ Tel: 020 7808 2631 — BM BCh 1969 Oxf.; DSc (Med) 2001; MA Oxf. 1969, BA 1966; MD Lond. 1987; FRCPath 1988, M 1976; LMCC 1978; FLEX Lic. (USA) 1978. (Oxf. & Univ. Coll. Hosp.) Cons. Histopath. Roy. Marsden NHS Trust Lond.; Vis. Prof. Univ. Pennsylvania, 1992; Niels Dungal Lect. Univ. Iceland 1996. Socs: Arthur Purdy Stout Soc. of Surgic. Path.; Roy. Soc. Med. (Ex.-Pres. Sect. Oncol.); Amer. Soc. of Clin. Pathologists. Prev: Sen. Lect. (Morbid Anat.) Sch. Med. Univ. Coll. Lond.; Asst. Prof. Path. Dartmouth Med. Sch. New Hants., USA; Graham Schol. (Path.) Univ. Coll. Hosp. Med. Sch. Lond.

FISHER, David John Harvey University Hospital of Wales, Heath Park, Cardiff CF14 4XW Tel: 029 2074 4463 Fax: 029 2074 5148; 1 Main Avenue, Peterston-super-Ely, Cardiff CF5 6LQ — MB BS Lond. 1963; MD Lond. 1976; FRCP Lond. 1980, M 1967; MRCS Eng. LRCP Lond. 1963; DObst RCOG 1965. (Lond. Hosp.) Cons. Phys. Univ. Hosp. Wales Cardiff.; Med. Dir. Univ. Hosp. Wales Health Care Trust. Prev: Sen. Regist. Lond. Hosp.

FISHER, David Jonathan Roger (retired) Alveswood, 8 Hecklegirth, Annan DG12 2BG Tel: 01461 205139 — MB ChB 1979 Ed.

FISHER, David William Friary House Surgery, Friary House, 2a Beaumont Road, Plymouth PL4 9BH Tel: 01752 663138 Fax: 01752 675805 — BM 1984 Soton.; MRCGP 1988; Cert. Family Plann. JCC 1988. (Soton.) Prev: Trainee GP Exeter; Clin. Asst. (Cas.) Derriford Hosp. Plymouth.

FISHER, Diane Elizabeth The Surgery, Kirk Road, Johnstone PA6 7; Aldworth, Park Road, Kilmacolm PA13 4EJ — MB ChB 1988 Manch.; BSc St. And 1985; MRCGP 1992; DRCOG 1991. (Manchester) GP Retainer Houston. Prev: SHO (A & E) Inverclyde Roy. Hosp. Greenock.; GP Crawley.

FISHER, Mr Edward William ENT Department, Heartlands Hospital, Birmingham B9 5SS Tel: 0121 424 2000 Fax: 0121 424 1353 Email: ewfisher@doctors.org.uk; 59 Pilkington Avenue, Sutton Coldfield B72 1LG Email: ewfisher@doctors.org.uk — BM BCh 1983 Oxf.; MA Oxf. 1987, BA (Hons. Physiol. Sc.) 1980; DM Oxf. 1996; FRCS Ed. 1990; FRCS Eng. 1990. (Oxford) Cons. ENT Birm. Heartlands Hosp. & Good Hope Hosp. & Hon. Sen. Clin. Lect. Univ. Birm. Socs: Eur. Rhinol. Soc.; Pres. YCOHNS; Mid. Inst. Otorhinolaryngol. Prev: Sen. Regist. (ENT) Roy. Nat. Throat Nose & Ear Hosp. Lond. & Addenbrooke's Hosp. Camb.; Sen. Regist. & SHO (ENT) Addenbrooke's Hosp. Camb. & Gt. Ormond St.; Regist. & SHO (ENT) Roy. Nat. Throat, Nose & Ear Hosp. Lond.

FISHER, Elisa Jane 69 Avondale Road, Bromley BR1 4HS Tel: 0411 141755 — MB BS 1997 Lond. (Kings)

FISHER, Elizabeth Mary Pilfolds, Tower Hill, Horsham RH13 7JZ Tel: 01403 241724 Fax: 01403 241724 — MB BS 1985 Lond.; MRCGP 1989; DFFP 1988; DRCOG 1988; Dip Occ Med 1995. (Guy's) Occupat. Health Phys., Sussex & Surrey Healthcare (NHS Trust), Crawley Hosp. Socs: Soc. Occupat. Med.; Brit. Assn. Sport & Med.; Affil. mem. Fac. of Occupat.al Med. Prev: Area Occupat. Health Phys. Marks & Spencer; Trainee GP E.bourne HA VTS.

FISHER, Elizabeth Philipa Pomeroy, Chineham Lane, Sherborne St John, Basingstoke RG24 9LR — MB BS 1980 Lond.

FISHER, Mr ffolliott Francis Bedford Hospital NHS Trust, Kempston Road, Bedford MK42 9DJ Tel: 01234 355122; 4 Cross End, Thurleigh, Bedford MK44 2EE Tel: 01234 771856 — MB BS Lond. 1969; MRCS Eng. LRCP Lond. 1968; FRCS Eng. 1975. (Royal Free) Cons. Ophth. Bedford Gen. Hosp./Clin. Dir. Specialist Surg. Socs: Fell. Roy. Coll. Ophth.; BMA; Fell.RSM. Prev: Cons. Ophth. Zambia Consolidated Copper Mines; Regist. (Ophth.) W. Ophth. Hosp. Lond.

FISHER, Frances Muriel (retired) 2 Kenwood Drive, Burwood Park, Walton-on-Thames KT12 5AU Tel: 01932 221587 — MB BS 1953 Lond.; DPH 1957. Prev: Med. Off. City & E. Lond. AHA (T).

FISHER, Fred William New House, Church Walk, Rochford SS4 1NL — MB BS 1965 Lond.; MRCS Eng. LRCP Lond. 1965; DObst RCOG 1967. (Middlx.)

FISHER, Geoffrey Colin 17 Beech Close, Kinver, Stourbridge DY7 6LW — BM 1979 Soton.; FFA RCS Eng. 1985. Cons. Anaesth. Russells Hall Hosp. Dudley. Socs: Assn. Anaesth. & Intens. Care Soc. Prev: Sen. Regist. (Anaesth.) Midl. Train. Scheme; Regist. (Anaesth.) Leic. Roy. Infirm. & Qu. Eliz. Hosp. Adelaide, Austral.

FISHER, Geoffrey Herbert (retired) Marsh Leaze, Leonard Stanley, Stonehouse GL10 3LT Tel: 0145 382 4389 — MRCS Eng. LRCP Lond. 1946. Prev: Ho. Surg. Min. of Pens. Hosp. Stoke Mandeville.

FISHER, George Brian Rushton 49 Otley Street, Skipton BD23 1ET Tel: 01756 799622 Fax: 01756 796194; Garth House, Conon Ley, Keighley BD20 8LL Tel: 01535 633688 — MB BCh BAO 1961 Dub. Prev: Surg. P. & O.-Orient Line; Ho. Off. Preston Roy. Infirm.

FISHER, George Costa Humana Hospital Wellington, Wellington Place, London NW8 9LE — MB BS 1979 Lond.; MRCS Eng. LRCP Lond. 1979. Sen. Resid. Med. Off. Humana Hosp. Lond. Prev: SHO (Vasc. & Cardiac Surg.) & (Gen. Surg. & Urol.) St. Mary's Hosp.; Lond. W2.

FISHER, Gordon William Herbert (retired) 4 Wellswood Park, Torquay TQ1 2QB Tel: 01803 299783 — MB BS 1953 Durh.; FRCPsych 1987, M 1972; DPM 1963. Prev: Indep. Psychiat. Reports (Ment. Health Rev. Tribunals) Represent. Solicitors.

FISHER, Gwendoline Ruth (retired) 24 Green Court Gardens, Croydon CR0 7LH Tel: 020 8654 4081 — MB BS Lond. 1949; MRCS Eng. LRCP Lond. 1949. Prev: SCMO Croydon AHA.

FISHER, Haran 26 Belfast Road, London N16 6UH — MB BCh 1991 Witwatersrand.

FISHER, Henry (retired) 330 Musters Road, West Bridgford, Nottingham NG2 7DF — MD 1929 Berlin; LRCP LRCS Ed. LRFPS Glas. 1935; FRCPsych 1971; DPM Eng. 1937. Prev: Cons. Psychiat. & Dep. Phys. Supt. Mapperley Hosp. Nottm.

FISHER, Henry Michael (retired) Rakeshop House, Newtown Common, Newbury RG20 9DA Tel: 01635 40222 — MB BS 1960 Lond.; MRCS Eng. LRCP Lond. 1960; DA Eng. 1963; DObst RCOG 1962. Prev: GP Newbury.

FISHER, Jacqueline Anne Wisdom Hospice, St Williams Way, Rochester ME1 2NU Tel: 01634 830456 Fax: 01634 845890 Email: jackie.fisher@tgt.sthames.nhs.uk — MB BS 1982 Lond.; BSc Lond. 1979; MRCGP 1987; T(GP) 1991; DCH RCP Lond. 1986; DRCOG 1986. (Westm.) Cons. Palliat. Med. Thames Gateway NHS Trust; Wisdom Hospice, Rochester. Prev: Med. Dir. Ellenor Foundat. Hospice Care Team Dartford.

FISHER, James Alan Westbourne Medical Centre, Milburn Road, Bournemouth BH4 9HJ Tel: 01202 752550 Fax: 01202 769700 — MB BChir 1974 Camb.; MB Camb. 1974, BChir 1973; MA Camb. 1974; MRCP (UK) 1975.

FISHER, James Frederick (retired) Throop Mill Cottage, Throop Road, Bournemouth BH8 0DN Tel: 01202 515781 Fax: 01202 535678 — MA Camb. 1947, MB BChir 1945; FRCGP 1971; DPhilMed. Soc. Apoth. Lond. 1984. JP. Prev: Master Soc. Apoth.

FISHER, Mr James Robert Holdrich Manor Hospital, Moat Road, Walsall WS2 9PS Tel: 01922 721172; 38 Charlemont Road, Walsall WS5 3NQ Tel: 01922 38066 — MB 1961 Camb.; BChir 1960;

FRCS Eng. 1968. (St. Bart.) Cons. Orthop. Surg. Manor Hosp. Walsall. Socs: Fell. BOA. Prev: Orthop. Sen. Regist. Roy. Hosp. Wolverhampton; Regist. Birm. Accid. Hosp.; Surg. Regist. Guest Hosp. Dudley.

FISHER, Jean Philippa 84A Bocking Lane, Sheffield S8 7BL — MB ChB 1990 Ed.; BSc (Hons.) Ed. 1988; MRCGP 1996; DRCOG 1994; DFFP 1994. Med. Off. Volun. Servs. Overseas Zambia. Prev: Trainee GP/SHO (A & E) Sheff.

FISHER, John Allan Cranston Argyle House, Lady Lawson St., Edinburgh EH3 9SH Tel: 0131 222 5802; 24A Nelson Street, Edinburgh EH3 6LJ Tel: 0131 557 4767 — MB ChB 1958 Glas.; DObst RCOG 1960. (Glas.) Med.Business.Cons.Sema Med. Servs. Socs: BMA. Prev: Med. Off. Med. Clinic Uranium City, Canada; Med. Off. Cripps Health Centre Univ. Nottm.

FISHER, John Melvyn 18 Branksome Road, Norwich NR4 6SN — MB BCh BAO 1966 Dub.

FISHER, John Miles Hafod y Coed, Dolgellau LL40 2YP — MB BS 1998 Lond.; MB BS Lond 1998.

FISHER, Jonathan David 20 Maple Road, Thame OX9 2BH Tel: 01844 217572 Email: fisherjd@compuserve.com — MB BS 1992 Lond.; DTM & H Lond. 1997. (Univ. Coll. Middlx.) Socs: Christ. Med. Fell.sh. Prev: Delegate Internat. Comm. Red Cross (ICRC); Project Coordinator Medecins Sans Frontieres (MSF).

FISHER, Joyce Ingrid Ship Street, East Grinstead RH19 4EE Tel: 01342 325959 — MB ChB 1967 Sheff. (Sheff.) Prev: Ho. Phys. N.. Gen. Hosp. Sheff.; Ho. Surg. (Cas.) & SHO (Special Clinic) Roy. Hosp. Sheff.

FISHER, Judith Mary Essex Ambulance Service NHS, Broomfield, Chelmsford CM1 7WS Tel: 01245 444467 Fax: 01245 443619 Email: essexambuhq.demon.co.uk; The Fox Thatch, The St, Sheering, Bishop's Stortford CM22 7LN Tel: 01279 734084 Fax: 01279 734085 Email: drfisher@emaw.msn.com — MB BS 1963 Lond.; MRCS Eng. LRCP Lond. 1963; FRCGP 1990, M 1984; FFAEM 1999. (Roy. Free) Med. Dir. Essex Ambul.Serv. NHS Trust.; Examr. RCS Edin.; Mem. & Founder Chairm. Resusc. Counc. (UK); Mem. Jt. Roy. Coll. & Ambul. Liaison Comm. Socs: Fell. (Mem. Sect. Counc.) Roy. Soc. Med.; (Hon. Sec.) World Assn. for Emerg. & Disaster Med.; Brit. Assn. for Immediate Care. Prev: Chairm. BASICS; Chairm. Resusc. Counc. (UK); Hon. Sec. Jt. Roy. Coll. & Ambul. Liaison Cttee.

FISHER, Julia Clare 41 Northfield Road, Gosforth, Newcastle upon Tyne NE3 3UN — MB BS 1989 Newc.; MRCGP 1996. (Newc. u. Tyne) SHO (Dermat.) Sunderland Dist. Gen. Hosp. Prev: Trainee GP St. Redar Med. Centre.

FISHER, Katharine Margaret 8 Lancelot Drive, Watnall, Nottingham NG16 1JS Email: katefisher@doctors.org.uk — MB ChB 1993 Bristol; MRCPCH 1999; MRCP (UK) 1998. Specialist Regist. Rotat. W. Midl.s (Paediat.) Birm. Specialist Community Trust. Socs: Brit. Assn. for Community Child Health. Prev: Specialist Regist. Rotat. W.Midl. (Paediat.), Worcester Roy. Infirm.; SPR Gen. Paedat. Birm. Childr.'s Hosp.; SPR Neonat. Birm. Wom.'s Hosp.

FISHER, Keir Hall 3 Rowan Gardens, Dumbreck, Glasgow G41 5BT Tel: 0141 427 2185 — MB ChB 1960 Glas.; MRCGP 1977; DObst RCOG 1962. Socs: BMA. Prev: GP Ipswich; Ho. Surg. W.. Infirm. Glas.; Ho. Phys. Roy. Infirm. Glas.

FISHER, Linda Fleur Division of Ethics, Science & Information, BMA House, Tavistock Square, London WC1 9JP Tel: 020 7383 6112 Fax: 020 7388 2544 — MB BS 1960 Lond.; MRCS Eng. LRCP Lond. 1960; DObst RCOG 1967. (Roy. Free) Head Div. of Ethics Sci. & Informat. Brit. Med. Assn. Socs: Fell. Roy. Soc. Med.; Nat. Assn. Family Plann. Doctors. Prev: Unit Gen. Manager (Community & Ment. Handicap) Macclesfield HA; SCMO (Family Plann.) Macclesfield HA; Ho. Phys. Roy. Free Hosp. Lond.

FISHER, Lorna Ruth Department of Rehabilitation, Raigmore Hospital, Inverness IV2 3UJ Tel: 01463 704000; 1 Albert Gate, Nairn IV12 4JF Tel: 01667 452404 — MB BS 1974 Lond.; BSc (Hons.) Physiol. 1971; MRCP Lond. 1981. (University College Hospital London) Cons. Rehabil. Raigmore Hosp. Inverness. Socs: Brit. Soc. of Rheum.; Brit. Soc. of Rehabil. Med.; Scott. Seating and Wheelchair. Prev: Sen. Regist. (Rheum. & Rehabil.) Qu. Alexandra Hosp. Portsmouth.; Regist. (Rheumat.) Middlx. Hosp.

FISHER, Margaret Garden Flat, 524 Finchley Road, London NW11 8DD — MRCS Eng. LRCP Lond. 1952; BSc Lond. 1947, MB BS 1953; DPM Eng. 1972. (Char. Cross) Assoc. Specialist (Psychiat.) Warneford Hosp. Oxf. Prev: Clin. Asst. Warneford Hosp. Oxf. Med. Regist. St. And. Hosp. Billericay & Rheum. Research Unit, Sheff.; SHO Dorking Gen. Hosp.

FISHER, Margaret Louise (retired) Hartdale, Queensberry Avenue, Hartlepool TS26 9NW Tel: 01429 274397 — MB BCh BAO Belf. 1949. Prev: Ho. Phys. & Ho. Surg. Roy. Vict. Hosp. Belf.

FISHER, Marie Gwendoline (retired) 36 Westfield Road, Leicester LE3 6HS Tel: 0116 285 8393 — MB BS Lond. 1952; MRCS Eng. LRCP Lond. 1952. Prev: GP Leicester.

FISHER, Marlene Margaret The Old Gloving House, Wooton, Woodstock, Oxford OX20 1DJ Tel: 01993 813521 — MB BCh 1960 Wales. (Cardiff) Dep. Dir. Regional Blood Transfus. Serv. Oxf. Socs: BMA. Prev: Ho. Surg. & Ho. Phys. Cardiff Roy. Infirm.

FISHER, Martin (retired) 3 Snows Lane, Keyham, Leicester LE7 9JS Tel: 0116 259 5351 — MB BChir Camb. 1963; MRCS Eng. LRCP Lond. 1958; MRCGP 1975.

FISHER, Martin John 48 Harold EStreet, Pages Walk, London SE1 4HN Tel: 020 7232 1658 — MB BS 1988 Lond.; BSc (Hons.) Lond. 1985, MB BS 1988. SHO Rotat. (Gen. Med.) Dulwich & King's Coll.

FISHER, Michael Academic Department of Cardiology, University Hospital of Wales, Heath Park, Cardiff CF4 4XN Tel: 029 2074 2338 Fax: 029 2074 3500 Email: fisherm@cardiff.ac.uk; 20 Seymour Street, Splott, Cardiff CF24 2NR — MB ChB 1988 Manch.; BSc (Hons.) St. And. 1985; MRCP (UK) 1992. MRC Clin. Train. Fell. Prev: Regist. Rotat. (Cardiol.) N. W.. RHA; SHO (Cardiothoracic Med.) Wythenshawe Hosp. Manch.; SHO (Gen. Med.) Manch. Roy. Infirm.

FISHER, Michael Frank 86 Mackenzie Road, Beckenham BR3 4RZ Tel: 020 8659 2244 Fax: 020 8659 8457 Email: 100106.2433@compuserve.com — MB ChB 1964 Bristol; FFA RCS Eng . 1968. (Bristol) Cons. Anaesth. Qu. Mary's Sidcup NHS Trust. Prev: Cons. Anaesth. King's Coll. Hosp. Lond.

FISHER, Michael George Penton, Group Capt. RAF Med. Br. Retd. 9 Link Way, Camberley GU15 2NH Tel: 01276 62709 Email: micahel.fisher@aua.co.uk — MB BChir Camb. 1955; MA Camb. 1978, BA 1952; MFOM RCP Lond. 1980; DAvMed Eng. 1973; DCH Eng. 1969; DObst RCOG 1967. (Middlx.) p/t Authorised Med. Examr. CAA; Med. Adviser World Wide ReAssur. Socs: BMA; Soc. Occupat. Med. Prev: Head Clinics & Occupat. Health Servs. CAA; Commanding Off. P.ss Mary's RAF Hosp. Halton.

FISHER, Michael John (retired) 43 Tetcott Road, London SW10 0SB Tel: 020 7352 1167 — MB ChB 1956 Cape Town. Prev: Med. Off. Med. Research Counc.

FISHER, Michael John Yair Wolstanton Medical Centre, Palmerston Street, Newcastle ST5 8BN Tel: 01782 627488 Fax: 01782 662313; 10 Albert Road, Trentham, Stoke-on-Trent ST4 8HE Tel: 01782 644711 Fax: 01782 657801 Email: mikefisher@lipps.org.uk — MB ChB Birm. 1967; FRCGP 1983, M 1973; DCH Eng. 1971. (Birm.) Sen. Clin. Lect. Univ. Keele.; Area Dir. (Gen. Pract. Ed.) W. Midl.s Region. Prev: Regist. Profess. Unit. Dept. Psychiat. United Manch. Hosps.; Trainee GP N. Staffs. Gp. Hosps.

FISHER, Michael Litster, TD, OStJ (retired) 13 The Grove, Gosforth, Newcastle upon Tyne NE3 1NE — MB BS 1953 Durh.; MRCGP 1965; DObst RCOG 1957. Prev: GP Newc.

FISHER, Michael Stuart Chessel Surgery - Bitterne Branch, 4 Chessel Avenue, Bitterne, Southampton SO19 4AA Tel: 023 8044 7777 Fax: 023 8042 5429; 11 Hornbeam Gardens, West End, Southampton SO30 3RD Tel: 0703 361951 Email: msfimf@aol.com — MB ChB Ed. 1971. (Ed.) Prev: SHO (O & G) Bangour Gen. Hosp. Broxburn; SHO & Regist. Nazareth Hosp., Israel (Edin. Med. Miss. Soc.).

FISHER, Nancy Gillian Saville (retired) 27 Third Avenue, Hove BN3 2PB Tel: 01273 772693 — MB ChB 1950 Birm.; FFA RCS Eng. 1955; DA Eng. 1953. Cons. (Anaesth.) Brighton Health Dist.

FISHER, Neil Charles Russells Hall Hospital, Dudley DY1 2HQ Tel: 01384 244147 Email: neil.fisher@dudleygoh_tr.wmids.nhs.uk; The White House, Springhill Lane, Lower Penn, Wolverhampton WV4 4TJ — MB BS 1986 London; MRCP 1990 UK; MD 1999 London. (Roy. Free Hosp. Sch. Med.) Cons. Phys. & Gastroenterol., Dudley Gp. of Hosps. NHS Trust. Socs: Brit. Soc. of Gastroenterol.; Brit. Assn. for Study of the Liver; Brit. Assn. of Parenteral and

Enteral Nutrit. Prev: Specialist Regist. Rotat. (Gastroenterol.) W. Midl. Train. Scheme; Research Fell. Liver Unit Qu. Eliz. Hosp. Birm.

FISHER, Neil Duncan 47 Priory Orchard, Wantage OX12 9EL — MB ChB 1997 Liverp.

FISHER, Nicholas Barton Surgery, Lymington House, Barton Hill Way, Torquay TQ2 8JG Tel: 01803 323761 Fax: 01803 316920; Cleveland House, 1 Edginswell Lane, Kingskerswell, Newton Abbot TQ12 5LX Tel: 01803 872455 Fax: 01803 872455 — BM 1976 Soton.; MSc Soton. 1971; BPharm Bradford 1969; MRCGP 1981; DRCOG 1979; Cert. Family Plann. JCC 1978. (Soton University) GP Princip.; Forens. Med. Examr.; Sect. (12) approved Ment. Health Assessm. Examr. Socs: MRPS; Assn. Police Surg. Prev: SHO (O & G) Soton. Gen. Hosp.; SHO (Psychiat.) Exe Vale Hosp. Exeter; SHO (A & E) Torbay Hosp.

FISHER, Nicholas Gorden, Surg. Lt.-Cdr. RN 74 Sunnybanks, Hatt, Saltash PL12 6SA Tel: 01752 845123; Gorsanedd, Dinas, Pwllheli LL53 8UB Tel: 01758 87336 — MB BS 1991 Lond.; MRCP (Lond.) 1997. Specialist Regist. (Cardiol.) Derriford Hosp. Plymouth. Prev: SHO (Med.) Derriford Hosp. Plymouth.

FISHER, Nigel Jerome 43 Shortheath Crest, Farnham GU9 8SB — MB BS 1988 Lond.; DRCOG 1992.

FISHER, Nigel Raymond Springfield University Hospital, 61 Glenburnie Road, London SW17 7DJ Tel: 020 8682 4381 — MB BS 1984 Lond.; MPhil Lond. 1992; MA Camb. 1982; MRCPsych 1988. (Char. Cross) Cons. Psychiat. Springfield Univ. Hosp. & Hon. Sen. Lect. St. Geo. Hosp. Med. Sch. Lond.; Med. Dir. S. W. Lond. and St Geo.'s Ment. Health NHS Trust. Prev: Sen. Regist. Middlx. Hosp. Lond.; Regist. Bethlem Roy. & Maudsley Hosp. Lond.

FISHER, Pamela Mary (retired) Green Gables, 245 Barton Road, Comberton, Cambridge CB3 7BU Tel: 01223 262282 Fax: 01223 262282 — MB ChB Bristol 1955.

FISHER, Patricia Margaret 77 Hodge Lane, Hartford, Northwich CW8 3AG Tel: 01606 871077; 3 Coombe Road, Crookes, Sheffield S10 1FF Tel: 0114 268 1493 — MB ChB 1989 Manch.; MRCP (UK) 1992. Regist. (Clin. Oncol.) W.on Pk. Hosp. Sheff.

FISHER, Mr Paul William Caithness General Hospital, Wick KW1 5NS — MB BS 1980 Lond.; BSc (Hons.) Lond. 1977; FRCS Ed. 1984. Cons. Surg. Caithness Gen. Hosp. Wick; Clin. director. Prev: Chief Med. Off. Temotu Province, Solomon Is.; Surg. Turks & Caicos Is., W. Indies.

FISHER, Paula Clare 264 Wetsren Road, Sheffield S10 1LF — MB ChB 1995 Sheff.; Primary FRCA 1999. SHO/Regist. (Anaesth.) Rotat., Sheff.

FISHER, Peter Antony Goodwin Royal London Homoeopathic Hospital, Great Ormond St., London WC1N 3HR Tel: 020 7837 7223 Fax: 020 7833 7212 Email: pfisher@gn.apc.org; 146 Worlds End Lane, Orpington BR6 6AS Tel: 01689 856458 Fax: 01689 855997 — MB 1976 Camb.; BChir 1975; MRCP (UK) 1979; FFHom 1986, M 1976; FRCP 1998. Cons. Phys. & Clin. Director Roy. Lond. Homoeop. Hosp.; Hon. Edr. Brit. Homeop. Jl.; Hon. Cons. Rheumat. KCH Lond. Socs: FRSM; Vice-Pres. Fac. of Homeopathy. Prev: Vis. Rheum. St. Bart. Hosp. Lond.; Lect. (Rheum. & Complementary Med.) St. Bart. Hosp. Lond.; Research Fell. (Clin. Pharmacol.) St. Bart. Hosp. Lond.

FISHER, Peter McLaren Suvretta, 2 Murray Road, Newtonhill, Stonehaven AB39 3TP Tel: 01569 730456 Fax: 01569 731627 — MD 1976 Aberd.; MB ChB 1969; FRCOG 1989, M 1976; DObst 1971.

FISHER, Peter William (retired) Hill House, Great Bourton, Banbury OX17 1QH Tel: 01295 750407 Fax: 01295 750407 Email: nhsca@pop3.poptel.org.uk — MB 1958 Camb.; BChir 1957; FRCP Lond. 1976, M 1965; DObst RCOG 1959. Pres. NHS Cons. Assn. Prev: Cons. Phys. Horton Gen. Hosp. Banbury.

FISHER, Richard 12 The Mews, Watchfield, Swindon SN6 8TP — MB ChB 1989 Bristol.

FISHER, Richard Bennett 10 Park Lane Mews, Roundhay Park Lane, Leeds LS17 8SN — MB ChB 1984 Sheff.; MB ChB Sheff. l984; DPhil Oxf. 1992.

FISHER, Richard John Tranwell Unit, Queen Elizabeth Hospital, Sheriff Hill, Gateshead; 52 Cheviot Grange, Burradon, Cramlington NE23 7PN Email: dd@gwbs.demon.co.uk — MB BS 1991 Newc.; DFFP 1995; T(GP) 1996; MRCPsych 1998. Prev: SHO (Psychiat.) Prudhoe Hosp. Prudhoe, N.d.; SHO (Psychiat.) Tranwell Unit Qu. Eliz. Hosp. Gateshead; Trainee GP/SHO (Psychiat.) St. Mary's Hosp. Stannington.

FISHER, Richard Laurence Downing Street Surgery, 4 Downing Street, Farnham GU9 7NX Tel: 01252 716226 Fax: 01252 322338; 31 Echo Barn Lane, Wrecclesham, Farnham GU10 4NG Tel: 01252 714201 — MB BS Lond. 1968; BSc (Physiol.) Lond. 1965; MRCS Eng. LRCP Lond. 1968; DObst RCOG 1971. (King's Coll. Hosp.) Hosp. Pract. (Geriat.) Farnham Hosp. Prev: SHO (Paediat.) Farnham Hosp.; SHO (O & G) Farnham Hosp.; Ho. Off. (Surg.) Dulwich Hosp.

FISHER, Mr Robert Brian Belfast City Hospital, Belfast BT9 7AB Tel: 028 9032 9241 Fax: 028 9026 3768 Email: brian.fisher@bch.n-i.nhs.uk — MB BCh BAO 1978 Belf.; FFAEM 1992; FRCS Ed. 1982; DA (UK) 1985. Cons. A & E Belf. City Hosp. Trust. Socs: BMA; Brit. Assn. Accid. & Emerg. Med. Prev: Cons. A & E Ulster Hosp. Dundonald.

FISHER, Robert Holdrich Priory Medical Group, Cornlands Road, Acomb, York YO24 3WX Tel: 01904 781423 Fax: 01904 784886; 3 Park Grove, The Groves, York YO31 8LG — MB BS 1988 Lond.; MRCGP 1995; DRCOG 1995. (St. Bart.)

FISHER, Robert Kendall 21 Navigation Wharf, Liverpool L3 4DP — MB ChB 1993 Manch.

FISHER, Robin Brian Danzey c/o Episcopal Church of Sudan, Port Sudan Cathedral, Sudan; Iry Bank, Main Street, Taddington, Mr Bakewell SK17 9TU — MB ChB 1976 Bristol; 1997 DTM & H Liverpool; 1997 M. Phil. Bungsham Univ. Med. Cons. Episcopal Ch. of Sudan; Locum GP (Ocas.). Socs: BMA. Prev: GP Birm.

FISHER, Ronald Albert (retired) 6 Lagoon Road, Lilliput, Poole BH14 8JT Tel: 01202 708867 — MRCS Eng. LRCP Lond. 1943; MA Camb. 1943; FRCA 1954; DA Eng. 1947. Vice-Pres. Macmillan Cancer Relief. Prev: Cons. Phys. Palliat. Med. i/c Macmillan Unit & ChristCh. Hosp. Dorset AHA.

FISHER, Rosalind Rachel Contraception Service, Southbank Healthshop, 23-27 Middlesbrough Road, Middlesbrough TS6 6NW Tel: 01642 459583; Glenelg, Victoria Terrace, Saltburn-by-the-Sea TS12 1HN — MB ChB 1990 Dundee; MRCGP 1994; DFFP 1994. Staff Grade Contracep. & ReProduc. Health Serv. Middlesbrough. Prev: Chief Med. Off. (Child Health) W. La. Hosp. Middlesbrough; GP Princip. Skelton Health Centre; Trainee GP New Rd. Surg. Ayr.

FISHER, Mr Ross MacPherson Dept. Paediatric Surgery, University Hospital, Leicester LE1 5WW — MB ChB 1988 Sheff.; FRCS 1999 (Paediat. Surg.); MPhil 1999 Sheffield; FRCS Glas. 1993. Cons. Paediatric Surg., Univ. Hosp., Leicester; Hon. Cons. Paediatricf Surg. - PaterBoro., Nuneaton, Warwick, Coventry, Kettering. Socs: BMA; Christian Med. Fell.sh. Prev: Regist. & Research Fell. (Paediat. Surg.) Lewisham Hosp. Lond.; SHO (Neonat.) Jessop Hosp. for Wom. Sheff.; SHO Rotat. Roy. Hallamsh. Hosp. Sheff.

FISHER, Sheila Ann The Health Centre, 20 Duncan Street, Greenock PA15 4LY Tel: 01475 724477 Fax: 01475 727140; 1 Park Avenue, Greenock PA16 7QX — MB ChB 1972 Glas.

FISHER, Mrs Sheila Eunice Oral and Maxillofacial Unit, Leeds Dental Institute, Clarendon Way, Leeds LS2 9LU — MB ChB 1985 Birm.; MSc Birm. 1983; BDS Manch. 1974; FRCS Eng. 1989; FFD RCSI 1981; FDS RCS Eng. 1977. Sen. Lect. Hon. Cons. in Oral and Maxillofacial Surg. Univ. of Leeds; Cons. Maxillofacial Surg. Univ. Hosp. Qu. Med. Centre Nottm. Socs: Brit. Assn. of Oral and Maxillo Facial Surg.s, Counc. Number 2002-2005. Prev: Sen. Regist. (Oral & Maxillofacial Surg.) Walton & BRd.green Hosp.; Regist. (Oral & Maxillofacial Surg.) Middlesbrough Gen. Hosp.

FISHER, Simon 1 Wallace Street, Spital Tongues, Newcastle upon Tyne NE2 4AU Tel: 0191 261 2793 — MB BS 1996 Newc.; MB BS (Hons) Newc. 1996. SHO (Gen. Med.) Sunderland Roy. Hosp., Sunderland, Tyne & Wear. Prev: SHO (A & E) N. Tyneside Gen. Hosp., N. Shields, Tyne & Wear.

FISHER, Simon Richard Celandines, Chawleigh, Chulmleigh EX18 7HL — MB BS 1993 Lond.

FISHER, Stephen Robert Park Surgery, Albion Way, Horsham RH12 1BG Tel: 01403 217100; Pilfolds, Tower Hill, Horsham RH13 7JZ Tel: 01403 41724 — MB BS 1985 Lond.; MRCGP 1989; DRCOG 1988; DFFP 1988. (Guy's) GP Princip. Socs: BASM. Prev: Trainee GP E.bourne HA VTS.

FISHER, Steven Andrew 108 Station Road, Kegworth, Derby DE74 2FR — BM BS 1990 Nottm.

FISHER, Vanessa Mary The Hollies Medical Centre, 20 St. Andrews Road, Sheffield S11 9AL Tel: 0114 255 0094 Fax: 0114 258 2863 — MB ChB 1987 Sheff.; MRCGP 1993.
FISHER, Warren James 10 Cheselden Road, Guildford GU1 3SB — MB ChB 1989 Bristol.
FISHER, William George Fallin, Cowie and Airth Medical Practice, Stirling Road, Fallin, Stirling FK7 7JD Tel: 01786 812412 Fax: 01786 817496 — MB ChB 1979 Glas.
FISHLOCK, Douglas Joseph The Baird Health Centre, Gassiot House, St Thomas's Hospital, London SE1 7EH Tel: 020 7202 8300 Fax: 020 7202 8314; Outridge Cottage, College Hill Terrace, Haslemere GU27 2JJ — MB BS 1960 Lond.; MRCS Eng. 1960; LRCP Lond. 1960; DObst RCOG 1962; PhD (Med.) Lond. 1967; MA Camb. 1972; LMCC 1974; MCCFP 1977; MICGP 1987. (Guys Hospital) Sen. Med. Off. The Baird Health Centre St. Thomas,s Hosp. Lond. Prev: GP N.ern Med. Unit Univ. of Manitoba Winnipeg Canada; Surgic. Resid. Qu.s Univ. Kingston Ontario; Lect. (Anat.) Univ. of Lond., Lond. Hosp. Med. Coll.
FISHMAN, Daniel 26 Wakehams Hill, Pinner HA5 3BQ — MB BS 1988 Lond. SHO Rotat. (Med.) St. Mary's Hosp. Lond. Socs: BMA.
FISHMAN, Morris Fourth House, Beechwood Lane, Warlingham CR3 — LMSSA 1942 Lond. (St. Geo.) Prev: R.A.M.C. 1943-6.
FISHTAL, Alan The Park Group Practice, 113 Anerley Road, London SE20 8AJ Tel: 020 8778 8027 Fax: 020 8289 1418; 7 Hayes Way, Park Langley, Beckenham BR3 6RJ Tel: 020 8658 6097 — FRCGP 2001; MB ChB Bristol 1969; MRCGP 1981; DObst RCOG 1973; Cert FPA 1973. Trainer GP SE Thames RHA; Vice Chairm. Bromley LMC; Chairm.BromleyPCTPEc. Prev: Clin. Asst. (Ultrasonics) Lewisham Hosp. Lond.; SHO (Gen. Med.) Nevill Hall Hosp. Abergavenny; Ho. Surg. (O & G) Lewisham Hosp. Lond.
FISHWICK, David Respiratory Function Unit, Royal Hallamshire Hospital, Glossop Road, Sheffield S10 2JF Tel: 0114 271 1825 Email: fishies@enterprise.net; 10 Devonshire Road, Dore, Sheffield S17 3NT — MB ChB 1985 Manch.; MD Manch. 1991; MRCP (UK) 1988; AFOM RCP Lond. 1990. Sen. Lect. (Respirat. & Gen. Med.) Roy. Hallamsh. Hosp. Sheff.; Co-Dir. Sheff. Occupat. & Environment. Lung Injury Centre. Socs: BTS; Soc. Occupat. Med.; Thoracic Soc. Austral. & NZ. Prev: Sen. Regist. (Gen. & Respirat. Med.) Roy. Vict. Infirm. Newc.; Sen. Research Fell. Wellington Clin. Sch. Med. Wellington, NZ; Research Regist. (Chest Unit) Wythenshawe Hosp. Manch.
FISHWICK, John Lovett House, Fore St., Wylye, Warminster BA12 0RQ — MB BS 1979 Lond.; MRCP (UK) 1983; MRCGP 1986; DRCOG 1985. GP Warminster.
***FISHWICK, Kathryn Teresa** 3 Buttermere Road, Burnley BB10 4HU — MB ChB 1986 Liverp.
FISHWICK, Mr Nicholas Guy X-Ray Department, Leicester Royal Infirmary, Leicester LE1 5WW; 3 Byron Way, Melton Mowbray LE13 1NY — MB BChir 1981 Camb.; MA Camb. 1983; FRCS Ed. 1988; FRCR 1994. (Univ. Camb.) Cons. Vasc. Radiol. Leicester Roy. Infirm. Prev: Sen. Regist. & Regist. (Radiol.) Leicester Roy. Infirm.; Regist. (Gen. Surg.) Poole Gen. Hosp.
FISK, Geoffrey Gordon Department of Psychotherapy, 1 St Annes Road, Lincoln LN2 5RA Tel: 01522 512000 Fax: 01522 532445; Aberdeen House, Church Lane, Collingham, Newark NG23 7NQ Email: geoffrey.fisk@easynet.co.uk — MB ChB 1976 Birm.; MRCPsych 1980. Cons. Psychother. Lincs. Healthcare NHS Trust.
FISK, Mr Geoffrey Raymond (retired) 7 Manor Court, Pinehurst, Grange Road, Cambridge CB3 9BE Tel: 01223 323248 — MB BS 1939 Lond.; MB BS (Distinc. Chem.) Lond. 1939; MPhil Camb. 1991; FRCS Eng. 1949; FRCS Ed. 1943; MRCS Eng. LRCP Lond. 1939. Hon. Cons. Orthop. Surg. St. Margt. Hosp. Epping, P.ss Alexandra Hosp. Harlow & Harlow Indust. Health Serv.; Hon. Orthop. Surg. Regional Orthop. Centre Notley Hosp. Braintree. Prev: Hon. Chief Asst. (Orthop) Addenbrooke's Hosp. Camb.
FISK, Jonathan Airey Airedale General Hospital, Skipton Road, Steeton, Keighley BD20 6TD Tel: 01535 292246 Fax: 01535 655129; 35 Hallam's Yard, Skipton BD23 1JN Tel: 01756 794449 — MB BChir 1971 Camb.; MPhil Ed. 1979; MA Camb. 1972, BA 1968; MRCPsych 1976. Cons. Psychiat. Psychiat. Old Age Airedale Gen. Hosp. Prev: Lect. (Psychiat.) Univ. Manch.
FISK, Professor Nicholas Maxwell Imperial College School of Medicine, Inst. Obst. & Gyn., Queen Charlotte's & Chelsea Hospital, Goldhawk Road, London W6 0XG Tel: 0208 383 3190 Fax: 0208 748 6311 — MB BS 1980 Sydney; PhD Lond. 1992; FRACOG 1987; MRCOG 1986; T(OG) 1991; DDU 1987; FRCOG 1998. (Imperial College School of Medicine) Prof. O & G & Hons. Cons. Qu. Charlotte's & Chelsea Hosp. Lond. Socs: Pres. Elect Internat. Fetal Med. & Surg. Soc. Prev: Staff Specialist (Fetal Med.) Roy. P. Alfred Hosp. Sydney, Austral.; Hon. Sen. Regist. (O & G) Qu. Charlotte's & Chelsea Hosp.; Lect. & Hon. Sen. Regist. (O & G) Univ. Aberd. & Aberd. Roy. Infirm.
FISK, Peter Geoffrey 6 Holt Drive, Kirby Muxloe, Leicester LE9 2EX Tel: 0116 238 6057 — MB BS 1974 London; MB BS Lond. 1974; BSc Lond. 1968; FRCP Lond. 1993; MRCP (UK) 1980; MRCS Eng. LRCP Lond. 1974. (Lond. Hosp.) Cons. Genitourin. Med. Leicester Roy. Infirm. Socs: Fell. Roy. Coll. Phys. & Assur. Med. Soc.; MSSUD. Prev: Sen. Regist. (Genitourin. Med.) & Hon. Lect. Middlx. Hosp. Lond.; Regist. (Genitourin. Med.) St. Thos. Hosp. Lond.
FISKE, A P Lance Lane Medical Centre, 19 Lance Lane, Liverpool L15 6TS Tel: 0151 737 2882 Fax: 0151 737 2883.
FISKE, Suzannah Jane Wensum Valley Medical Practice, West Earlham Health Centre, 46 Earlham West, Norwich NR5 8HO Tel: 01603 250660 Fax: 01603 259202 Email: wvmp.we@aol.com — MB BS 1987 Lond.; DFFP. (King's Coll. Sch. Med. & Dent.) Mem. Norf. LMC; Mem. Norf. Area Child Protec. Comm.
FISKEN, Alastair Gordon 102 Little Sutton Road, Sutton Coldfield B75 6PS — MB ChB 1984 Ed.; MRCGP 1989.
FISKEN, James Union Brae Surgery, Union Brae, Tweedmouth, Berwick-upon-Tweed TD15 2HB Tel: 01289 330333 Fax: 01289 331075 — MB ChB 1969 Ed.; MRCGP 1975; DGM RCP Lond. 1986; DIH Eng. 1980; DObst RCOG 1973.
FISKEN, Jennifer Mary Rose Cottage, Church Wynd, Burneston, Bedale DL8 2JE — MB ChB 1975 Birm.; MA Oxf. 1975 MB ChB Birm. 1975; DCCH 1989; DRCOG 1977. (Oxf. & Birm.) Clin. Med. Off. N.allerton NHS Trust. Socs: Brit. Assoc. Comm. Child Health; Brit. Assoc. Community Doctors in Audiol. Prev: Clin. Med. Off. Liverp. HA.; Clin. Med. Off. City & Hackney Health Dist.; Clin. Med. Off.Birm. HA.
FISKEN, Murray Neil West Wing, Esk Medical Centre, Ladywell Way, Musselburgh EH21 6AB Tel: 0131 665 2594 Fax: 0131 665 2428; 39 Dalhousie Road, Eskbank, Dalkeith EH22 3AL — MB ChB 1982 Ed.; MRCGP 1986; DRCOG 1985. Prev: Trainee GP N. Lothian VTS.
FISKEN, Roger Anthony Friarage Hospital, Northallerton DL6 1JG Tel: 01609 779911 Fax: 01609 762053 Email: rfisken@nahs-tr.northy.nhs.uk; Rose Cottage, Church Wynd, Burneston, Bedale DL8 2JE — MB ChB 1975 Birm.; MA, DPhil Oxf. 1975; MD Birm. 1982; FRCP Lond. 1995; MRCP (UK) 1978. (Birm) Cons. Phys. Friarage Hosp. N.allerton. Socs: Brit. Diabetic Assn. (Mem. Med. & Scientif. Sect.); Roy. Soc. Med. (Endocrine Sect.). Prev: Sen. Regist. (Med., Diabetes & Endocrinol.) Mersey RHA; Regist. (Med. & Endocrinol.) St. Bart. Hosp. Gp.; MRC Research Fell. (Med.) Qu. Eliz. Hosp. Birm.
FISON, Mr Lorimer George (retired) 5 Clevedon Park, Sid Road, Sidmouth EX10 9YF Tel: 01395 577518 — MRCS Eng. LRCP Lond. 1944; MA Camb. 1946, BA (Nat. Sc. Trip.) 1941; FRCS Eng. 1953; FRCOphth 1990. Hon. Cons. Ophth. Surg. Moorfields Eye Hosp. Lond. Prev: Mem. Counc. RCS Eng.
FISON, Mr Peter Notley 21 Upper Wimpole Street, London W1G 6NA Tel: 020 7224 6175 Fax: 020 7935 2432 Email: peterfison@prestel.co.uk — MA Camb. 1976, BA (Nat. Sc. Trip.) 1969, MB BChir 1972; FRCS Eng. 1979; FRCOphth 1989. Cons. Ophth. Surg. St. Helier Trust Carshalton; Hon. Sen. Lect. St. Geo. Socs: Fell. Roy. Soc. Med. Prev: Sen. Regist. Eye Dept. St. Thos. Hosp. Lond.; Resid. Surg. Off. Moorfields Eye Hosp. (City Rd. Br.) Lond.; SHO (Neurosurg.) Inst. Neurol. Scs. Glas.
FISTEIN, Elizabeth Claire (retired) Suite 323, Parker's House, 48 Regent Street, Cambridge CB2 1FD Email: moonox@pobox.com — MB BS 1996 Lond.; BSc Lond. 1993.
FISTEIN, Jeanne 112 Claremont Road, Salford M6 8NL Tel: 0161 736 4036 — MB BCh BAO 1959 NUI; LAH Dub. 1958; DPH NUI 1963. (Univ. Coll. Dub.) Med. Off. Salford AHA (T).
FISTEIN, Jonathan Leo BMJ Publisihng Group, BMA House, Tavistock Square, London WC1H 9JR; Tel: 0973 753902 Fax: 07970 702049 Email: jlf@pobox.com — MB BChir 1997 Cambridge; BA Camb 1993; B Chir Camb 1996; MB Cambridge 1997; MA Cambridge 1997. (St Mary's Hospital, London & Cambridge

University) Knowledge Systems Manager, BMJ Knowledge. Socs: Fell. of Roy. Soc. of Med. Prev: Clin. research fell., Med. Informatics Gp., Manch. Univ.; Clin. Fell. in BioMed. Computing, Camb. Univ.; Director of Communications, Wax Info.. LTD.

FITCH, Christine Margaret 27 Pembridge Court, Belmont Road, Belfast BT4 2RW — MB BCh BAO 1991 Belf.

FITCH, Jane Angela 72 Hallam Grange Road, Fulwood, Sheffield S10 4BL — BM BS 1991 Nottm.

FITCH, (Jessie) Meuros 2 Lower Crescent, Belfast BT7 1NR Tel: 01232 320919 Fax: 01232 246357; 16 Royal Lodge Avenue, Belfast BT8 7YR Tel: 01232 797080 — MB BCh BAO 1966 Belf. (Qu. Univ. Belf.) Med. Adviser Ulster Orchestra; Mem. Adviser Brit. Orchestras; Mem. Forum EHSSB; Mem. Commiss. Gp. S. & E. Belf. Socs: BMA; Ulster Med. Soc.; Brit. Assn. Performing Arts Med. Prev: Hosp. Pract. (Paediat. & ENT) Roy. Vict. Hosp. Belf.

FITCH, Lorane Elizabeth Department of Microbiology, Bedford Hospital, Kempston Road, Bedford MK42 9DJ Tel: 01234 792097 Fax: 01234 795883 Email: lorane.fitch@bedhos.anglox.nhs.uk; Manor Lodge, Manor Close, Bromham, Bedford MK43 8JA — MB BS 1982 Lond.; MSc Lond. 1987; BSc (Psychol.) Leeds 1972; FRCPath. (St. Bart.) Cons. Microbiologist Bedford Hosp. Prev: Sen. Regist. Pub. Health Laborat. Serv. Dulwich Hosp., Lond.

FITCH, Matthew Craig 6 Sinclair Drive, Largs KA30 9BL Tel: 01475 674061 — LRCP LRCS 1943 Ed.; LRCP LRCS Ed. LRFPS Glas. 1943. Socs: Pharm. Soc.

***FITCH, Ruth Hannah** 21 Dunholme Avenue, Newark NG24 4AR — MB ChB 1996 Birm.

FITCH, Professor William Department of Anaesthesia, Royal Infirmary, 8-16 Alexandra Parade, Glasgow G31 2ER Tel: 0141 211 4625 Fax: 0141 211 1191 Email: w.fitch@clinmed.gla.ac.uk; 11 Craigenlay Avenue, Blanefield, Glasgow G63 9DR Tel: 01360 770022 — MB ChB 1962 Ed.; PhD Leeds 1975; BSc (Hons.) Ed. 1960; FRCP Glas. 1989, M 1987; FCAnaesth 1967; DObst RCOG 1964. (Univ. Ed.) Prof .Dept. Anaesth. Univ. Glas. Socs: (Ex-Pres.) Neuroanaesth. Soc. GB & Irel.; Europ. Acad. Anaesth.; Anaesth. Res. Soc. Prev: MRC Research Asst. Univ. Dept. Anaesth. Leeds; Head Univ. Dept. Anaesth. Univ. Glas.; Ho. Surg. & Ho. Phys. Falkirk Roy. Infirm.

FITCHET, Alan Manchester Heart Centre, Oxford Road, Manchester M13 9WL Tel: 0161 276 1234 Fax: 0161 276 8911 Email: alan@mhc.cmht.nwest.nhs.uk; 12 Old Oak Street, Disbury, Manchester M20 6RH Tel: 0161 448 0028 — BM 1988 Soton.; BM (Hons.) Soton. 1988; MRCP (UK) 1993. (Southampton) Specialist Regist. (Cardiol.) Manch. Roy. Infirm. Prev: Regist. (Cardiol. & Gen. Med.) Stepping Hill Hosp. Stockport; SHO (Gen. Med.) Roy. Naval Hosp. Haslar Gosport; RN Med. Off. HMS Hermione Lond. & RNAS Culdrose Helston.

FITCHET, Mr Martin Quinn 17 Clandon Drive, Eastleigh SO50 4QQ — BM BS 1991 Nottm.; BMedSci. Nottm. 1989; FRCS Eng. 1995. SHO (Otorhinolaryng.) Roy. Sussex Co. Hosp. Brighton. Socs: BMA; ASIT.

FITCHETT, Andrew Adam Grantley Street Surgery, 1 Grantley Street, Glasgow G41 3PT Tel: 0141 632 4698 Fax: 0141 649 6671 — MB ChB 1984 Glas.; MB ChB Glas. I984.

FITCHETT, Lynn Two Gates, Teignmouth Road, Torquay TQ1 4SQ Tel: 01803 328779 — MB BS 1981 Lond. Clin. Asst. Rowcroft Hospice Torquay.

FITCHETT, Michael John 35B Leazes Ter, Newcastle upon Tyne NE1 4LZ — MB BS 1997 Newc.

FITCHFORD, Reginald John The Surgery, Chestnut Walk, Stratford-upon-Avon CV37 6HQ Tel: 01789 292895 Fax: 01789 414721 — MB ChB 1962 Birm.; DObst RCOG 1964. (Birm.) Socs: BMA. Prev: Ho. Surg. Gen. Hosp. Birm. & Marston Green Matern. Hosp. Birm.; Ho. Phys. Dudley Rd. Hosp. Birm.

FITCHFORD, William James Park View, Church Road, Snitterfield, Stratford-upon-Avon CV37 0LE — MB ChB 1990 Birm.; ChB Birm. 1990.

FITNESS, Stuart John South Street Surgery, 83 South Street, Bishop's Stortford CM23 3AP Tel: 01279 710800 Fax: 01279 710801 — MB BS Lond. 1982.

FITT, Alan Walter David 29 Scargill Drive, Spennymoor DL16 6LY — MB BS 1990 Newc.

FITT, Catherine Sarah 1 Woodmere Way, Beckenham BR3 6SJ — MB ChB 1988 Leic.

FITT, Isabel Joan Kirwood 14 Raymer Close, St Albans AL1 3QH Tel: 01727 853139 — MB ChB Ed. 1946; DCH Eng. 1950. (Ed.)

FITTER, Alan Christopher The Dewerstone Surgery, Hampton Ave, Torquay TQ1 3LN Tel: 01803 316333 Fax: 01803 316393 Email: alan.fitter@gp-183111.nhs.uk; 2 Higher Elsford Cottages, Bovey Tracey, Newton Abbot TQ13 9NZ Tel: 01647 277582 — MB BS 1985 Lond.; MRCGP 1994. (Lond. Hosp.) Prev: Trainee GP Buckfastleigh; Regist. (Med.) Derriford Hosp. Plymouth; SHO (O & G) Plymouth.

FITTON, Antony Robert 58 Gowerton Road, Three Crosses, Swansea SA4 3PX Tel: 01792 874124; Brown House Farm, Bolton Road, Anaerton, Chorley PR6 9HJ — MB BS 1989 Lond.; FRCS (Plast.) 2001; FRCS Eng. 1993. (Roy. Lond. Hosp. Med. Sch.) Specialist Regist., The Welsh Centre for Burns & Plastic Surg. Socs: BMA; Brit. Burns Assn. Prev: Research Fell. (RCS Eng.) Univ. Wales, Swansea; SHO (Plastic Surg.) Welsh Regional Burns & Plastic Surg. Unit Morriston Hosp. Swansea; SHO (Plastic & Reconstruc. Surg.) Char. Cross Hosp. Lond.

FITTON, David Charles The Surgery, 1 Wheatley Street, Denaby Main, Doncaster DN12 4AT Tel: 01709 866175 — MB BS 1980 Lond.; DRCOG 1986; DGM 1989; DTM & H 1990. (King's College London)

FITTON, Janet Lesley Strathdon Medical Centre, Newe, Strathdon AB36 8XB Tel: 019756 51209 Fax: 019756 51476 — MB BChir 1989 Camb.; MA Camb. 1989; MRCGP 1992; T(GP) 1992.

FITTON, John Herbert Knowles Dryland Surgery, 1 Field Street, Kettering NN16 8JZ Tel: 01536 518951 Fax: 01536 486200; 26 Cranford Road, Barton Seagrave, Kettering NN15 5JH Tel: 01536 723409 — MB ChB 1972 Leeds; DObst RCOG 1975. Prev: Med. Off. Nat. Consolidated Copper Mines Ltd. Chingola, Zambia.

FITTON, Peter Holland Lepton Surgery, Highgate Lane, Lepton, Huddersfield HD8 0HH Tel: 01484 606161; 55 Barracks Fold, Hepworth, Huddersfield HD9 1TQ Tel: 01484 688451 — MB BS 1977 Lond.; BSc Lond. 1973; MRCS Eng. LRCP Lond. 1976; MRCGP 1980; DRCOG Eng. 1978. (Guy's) Prev: Med. Adviser Barnsley HA; GP Morden; Research Fell. (Gen. Pract.) St. Geo.'s Hosp. Med. Sch. Lond.

FITTON, Richard Peter Hadfield Medical Centre, 82 Brosscroft, Hadfield, Hyde SK13 1DS Tel: 01457 868686 Fax: 01457 857739; The Old Vicarage, Crowden, Hadfield, Hyde SK13 1HZ Tel: 01457 863030 — MB BS 1974 Lond.; MRCS Eng. LRCP Lond. 1974; MRCGP 1980; DCH Eng. 1979; DRCOG 1977. (Guy's Hosp. Med. Sch.) Socs: Manch. Med. Soc.; BMA. Prev: Clin. Tutor (Gen. Pract.) Centr. Manch. HA; Course Organiser Centr. Manch. VTS.

FITURI, Omar 4 Denford House, Kettering General Hospital, Rothwell Road, Kettering NN16 8UZ — MB BCh 1986 Al Fateh; MRCP (UK) 1991.

FITYAN, Zuhair (retired) — MD 1967 Damascus; LMSSA Lond. 1979; DRCOG 1980.

FITZ-CLARENCE, Halina 611 Howard House, Dolphin Square, London SW1V 3PG Tel: 020 7798 8849 — MB BS 1977 Lublin Poland; PhD (Inst. Rheum.) Warsaw 1995. Sen. Lect. & Hon. Cons. Rheum. Univ. Coll. Lond. Hosps. Socs: Brit. Soc. Rheum.; Roy. Soc. Med.; Nat. Osteoporosis Soc. Prev: Staff Grade Phys. Rotherham Dist. Gen. Hosp.; Research Fell. Arthritis & Rheum. Counc.

FITZ-HENRY, Joanne Keir 1 Esher Grove, Mapperley Park, Nottingham NG3 5DR Tel: 0115 960 6268 Email: jo@fitz-henry.demon.co.uk — BM 1988 Soton.; FRCA 1995. (Southampton) Regist. (Anaesth.) City & Qu. Hosps. Nottm.

FITZ-PATRICK, Joan Dianne (retired) 7 Aster Close, Attleborough, Gardens Est. Lutterworth Road, Nuneaton CV11 6PP — MB ChB 1960 Cape Town; MRCP Lond. 1969; FFR 1973; DCH Eng. 1965; DMRD Eng. 1971. Cons. Radiol. Coventry Gp. Hosps.

FITZGERALD, Mr Aidan Martin 40 Springfield Mount, Kingsbury, London NW9 0SG Tel: 01506 419666 — MB ChB 1988 Liverp.; FRCS Ed. 1993; FRCS Glas. 1993; MPhil 1998. Specialist Regist. (Plastic Surg.) St Johns Hosp. Livingston; Comp. Dir. Bradford Plastic Surg. & Burns Research Unit Ltd.

FITZGERALD, Alasdair John Linlithgow Health Centre, 288 High Street, Linlithgow EH49 7ER Tel: 01506 670027 — MB BCh BAO 1986 NUI; MRCGP 1992; MICGP 1992; DObst RCPI 1990; DCH RCSI 1989; DGM RCP Lond. 1988. Socs: Orthop. Med. Soc. Prev: Trainee GP Coldstream; Asst GP Peterhead & Tullamere.

FITZGERALD, Mr Andrew John 19 Windermere Road, Kingston Vale, London SW15 3QP — MB BS 1990 Lond.; FRCS Lond. 1994. (Charing Cross and Westminster Medical School)

FITZGERALD, Brian 565 Aigburth Road, Liverpool L19 0NU — MB BCh BAO 1989 NUI; MRCPsych 1995. Regist. Rotat. (Psychiat.) Liverp.

FITZGERALD, Christine Helen Thule, 3 Ledward Lane, Bowdon, Altrincham WA14 3AD Tel: 0161 928 8044 — MB ChB 1964 Manch. (Manch.) Assoc. Specialist Community Child Health Mancunian Community Health NHS Trust.

FITZGERALD, Christine Mary 53 Briarfield Road, Heaton Chapel, Stockport SK4 5HZ Tel: 0161 443 2107 — MB ChB 1955 Birm.; DTM & H Liverp. 1964. (Birm.) SCMO for Younger Disabled Unit Withington Hosp. & Mancunian Community Health NHS Trust. Socs: BMA. Prev: Clin. Med. Off. Community Geriat. Assessm. Unit Stockport HA; Clin. Asst. Stroke Rehabil. Unit Stockport HA; Med. Off. i/c Dareda, Makiungu & Namanyere Hosps. Tanzania.

FITZGERALD, David Andrew Dermatology Unit, Hope Hospital, Stott Lane, Salford M6 8HD; 10 Elm Road, Didsbury, Manchester M20 6XB Tel: 0161 434 2122 Fax: 0161 787 1018 Email: dfitzger@fsl.ho.man.ac.uk — MB ChB 1986 Manch.; BSc (Med. Sci.) St. And. 1983; MRCP (UK) 1989; DA (UK) 1991. Cons. (Dermat.) Hope Hosp. Salford & Bury Gen. Hosp. Prev: Fell. (Dermat. Surg.) Yale New Haven Hosp., USA; Sen. Regist. (Dermat.) Roy. Liverp. Univ. Hosp.; Regist. (Dermat.) N. Staffs. Hosp. Centre.

FITZGERALD, David Michael Walkley House Medical Centre, 23 Greenhow Street, Sheffield S6 3TN Tel: 0114 234 3716 — MB ChB 1985 Sheff.

FITZGERALD, Gearoid Specialist Psychotherapy Services, Brunswick House, 299 Glossop Road, Sheffield S10 2HL Tel: 0114 271 6890 Fax: 0114 271 6893; Flat 2, 23 Bainbridge Road, Headingley, Leeds LS6 3AD Tel: 0113 274 5335 — MB BCh BAO 1987 NUI; MRCPsych 1992; MPsychother. Leeds 1995. Cons. Psychiat. (Psychother.) Sheff. HA. Prev: Sen. Regist. (Psychiat) Sheff. HA.

FITZGERALD, Gerald Vincent (retired) 90 Sandy Lane, Hucknall, Nottingham NG15 7GP — MB BCh BAO NUI 1942. Prev: Ho. Surg. & Ho. Phys. Richmond Hosp. Dub.

FITZGERALD, Gillian Mary Red House Surgery, 124 Watling Street, Radlett WD7 7JQ Tel: 01923 855606; Greys, 7 The Drive, Radlett WD7 7BZ Tel: 01923 854905 — MB BChir 1978 Camb.; MA Camb. 1979; MRCGP 1983; DRCOG 1980.

FITZGERALD, Helen Mary Laurel House Surgery, 12 Albert Road, Tamworth B79 7JN Tel: 01827 69283 Fax: 01827 318029 — MB BCh BAO 1982 Dub.; MRCGP 1988; DRCOG 1987; DCH RCP Lond. 1987. Prev: Trainee GP Tamworth; SHO (O & G & Paediat.) Burton Gen Hosp.

FITZGERALD, Ita Maria (retired) 96 Filsham Road, St Leonards-on-Sea TN38 0PG Tel: 01424 436977 — MB BCh BAO 1945 NUI. Prev: Sen. Ho. Phys. Gen. & Childr. Hosp. Cheltenham.

FITZGERALD, Mr James Anthony Walden The Thatched Cottage, Dunbridge Lane, Awbridge, Romsey SO51 0GQ Tel: 01794 340260 — MB 1961 Camb.; MA Camb. 1962, BChir 1960; FRCS Eng. 1965. (St. Thos.) Cons. Orthop. Surg. Soton. Univ. Hosps. Socs: Fell. BOA; Brit. Soc. Surg. Hand. Prev: Sen. Regist. & Sen. Surg. Off. Roy. Nat. Orthop. Hosp.

FITZGERALD, James John 3 Ledward Lane, Bowdon, Altrincham WA14 3AD — BM BCh 1998 Oxf.; BM BCh Oxf 1998.

FITZGERALD, James Loman Launceston Medical Centre, Landlake Road, Launceston PL15 9HH Tel: 01566 772131 Fax: 01566 772223; Holly Bank Farm, Uphill, Bathpool, Launceston PL15 7NR Tel: 01579 63656 — MB ChB 1979 Bristol; MRCGP 1986; DGM RCP Lond. 1987; DRCOG 1985; DA (UK) 1984.

FITZGERALD, James Oswald Medical Centre, Portugal Place, Wallsend NE28 6RZ Tel: 0191 262 5252; 16 Woodbine Avenue, Gosforth, Newcastle upon Tyne NE3 4EU — MB BCh BAO 1955 NUI; LM Coombe 1955; MRCGP 1968. (Cork) GP Cas. Off. Sir G. B. Hunter Memor. Hosp. Wallsend; Life Assoc. Mem. Assn. Police Surgs. Prev: Regist. Wolsingham Chest Hosp.; SHO Childr. Hosp. Stockton-on-Tees; Ho. Surg. Gen. Hosp. Nottm.

FITZGERALD, Jane Mary 160 Weston Park, London N8 9PN — MB BS 1985 Lond.

FITZGERALD, Joan Maria Blood Transfusion Service, Holland Drive, Newcastle upon Tyne NE2 4NQ Tel: 0191 219 4400 Email: joan.loftus@pcpostal.com — MB BCh BAO 1986 NUI; BSc (Pharm) 1983; MRCPath 1994; MRCPI 1988. (NUI & UCG Ireland) Cons. Transfus. Med. Socs: Brit. Blood Transfus. Soc.

FITZGERALD, John Desmond Mere Croft, Chester Road, Mere, Knutsford WA16 6LG Tel: 01565 830082 Fax: 01565 830647 Email: jdf@materiamedica.fsnet.co.uk — MB BCh BAO 1954 NUI; BSc (Botany, Zool., Biochem.) NUI 1949; FRCP Ed. 1972, M 1961; FFPM RCP (UK) 1991. Cons. Pharmaceut. Med. Knutsford; Vis. Prof. Dept. Physiol. & Pharmacol. Univ. Strathclyde. Socs: Brit. Soc. for Gastroenterol.; Brit. Soc. Pharmacol.; ASPET. Prev: Gen. Manager Research Dept. & Internat. Med. Dir. ICI Pharmaceut. Div.; Prof. Med. McMaster Univ. Hamilton, Ontario.

FITZGERALD, John Joseph Anthony (retired) 32 Torkington Road, Gatley, Cheadle SK8 4PR Tel: 0161 428 2515 — MB BCh BAO 1948 NUI; CPH NUI 1951; DCH RCPSI 1951; LM Dub. 1950.

FITZGERALD, Julie Helen Springs Cottage, Freshford, Bath BA2 7TU Tel: 01225 723108 Fax: 01225 723335 — MB ChB 1987 Bristol; BSc Hons. (Physics) Bristol 1967, MB ChB 1987; MSc (Radiat. Physics) Lond. 1970. Prev: Physicist Roy. Marsden Hosp.

FITZGERALD, Mark Ritchie Taunton & Somerset Hospital, Musgrove Park, Taunton TA1 5DA Tel: 01823 333444 Fax: 01823 342622; Culm Davy House, Hemyock, Cullompton EX15 3UT Tel: 01823 680564 — MB BChir 1977 Camb.; MA Camb. 1977; FRCP Lond. 1994; MRCP (UK) 1980; MFFP 1995; DRCOG 1981. (Camb. & Lond. Hosp.) Cons. Genitourin. Med. Som. Hosps. Prev: Cons. & Assoc. Lect. Addenbrooke's Hosp. Camb.; Sen. Regist. Char. Cross Hosp. (W. Lond. Hosp.); Regist. Sheff. Roy. Infirm.

FITZGERALD, Maurice Alexis (retired) Blanchfield, 96 Filsham Road, St Leonards-on-Sea TN38 0PG Tel: 01424 436977 — MB BCh BAO 1941 NUI; FFR 1964; DMR Lond 1946; LM Nat. Matern. Hosp. Dub. 1941. Cons. Radiol. Benenden Chest Hosp. Cranbrook; Hon. Cons. Radiol. Hastings Health Dist. Prev: Asst. Radiol. Cheltenham Gen. Eye & Childr. Hosp.

FITZGERALD, Maurice Vincent John (retired) Linden Lodge, 223 Courthouse Road, Maidenhead SL6 6HP Tel: 01628 39032 Fax: 01628 633313 — MB BChir 1953 Camb.; MA Camb. 1970, MB BChir 1953; DObst RCOG 1956. Regional Med. Adviser Europe Lyondell Chem.; Med. Off. Ilex Lubricants Maidenhead. Prev: Ho. Surg., Ho. Phys. & Intern. St. Bart. Hosp. Lond.

FITZGERALD, Melissa Brigid Danish Perch, Lower Kelly, Calstock PL18 9RY Tel: 01822 833436 — MB BS 1983 Lond.; MB ChB Lond. 1983. Prev: Regist. (Cardiac Transpl. Unit) Hillingdon HA.

FITZGERALD, Michael Gerald (retired) Adamfield House, Fox Lane, Holmesfield, Dronfield S18 7WG Tel: 0114 289 0028 — MD 1956 Birm.; BSc Oxf. 1959; MB ChB (Hons.) 1947; FRCP Lond. 1968 M 1952. Prev: Cons. Phys. Gen. Hosp. Birm.

FITZGERALD, Peter Anthony 120 Woodlands Road, Barry CF62 8EE — MB BS 1986 Lond.

FITZGERALD, Richard 10 Mead Way, Silvermere Park, Shifnal TF11 9QB Email: richard.fitzgerald@talk21.com — MB BCh BAO 1979 NUI; FRCR 1985. (Cork, National University of Ireland) Cons. Radiol. New Cross. Hosp. Wolverhampton. Socs: Brit. Inst. Radiol.; BMA; RSNA. Prev: Sen. Regist. & Regist. Rotat. (Radiol.) W. Midl. Rotat. Train. Scheme.

FITZGERALD, Sheila Frances Bridge Lane Health Centre, 20 Bridge Lane, Battersea, London SW11 3AD Tel: 020 7585 1499 Fax: 020 7978 4707 — MB BS 1985 Lond.; MRCP (UK) 1988; MRCGP 1994; DCH RCP Lond. 1989. (Westm. Hosp. Med. Sch.)

FITZGERALD, Stephen Benedict Red House Surgery, 124 Watling Street, Radlett WD7 7JQ Tel: 01923 855606; Greys, 7 The Drive, Radlett WD7 7BZ Tel: 01923 854905 — MB BS 1977 Lond.; MRCP (UK) 1979; MRCGP 1983; DRCOG 1982. GP Radlett.

FITZGERALD, Thomas The Royal Infirmary of Edinburgh, Lavriston Place, Edinburgh EH3 9EW Tel: 0131 536 2935; 15 Lyefield Place, Livingston EH54 6TL Tel: 01506 415797 — MB ChB 1977 Glas.; FRCR 1986. Cons. Radiol. Lothian Univ. Hosp.s NHS Trust. Prev: Cons. Radiol. Kirkcaldy; Sen. Regist. (Radiodiag.) Manch. Hosps.; Regist. (Radiodiag.) Vict. Infirm. Glas.

FITZGERALD, Mr Thomas Benedict, DSC (retired) 23 Edward Street, Louth LN11 9LA — MB ChB 1939 Birm.; FRCS Ed. 1942; FRCOG 1961, M 1947. Prev: Cons. Gynaecol. St. Mary's Hosp. Manch.

FITZGERALD, Thomas James 69 Musard Road, London W6 8NR — MB BS 1993 Lond.

FITZGERALD, Tracey Alexandra The Old Vicarage, Laurel Mount, Leeds LS7 3JY — MB ChB 1990 Dundee.

FITZGERALD, Zachary c/o Dr Wieck's Secretary, Department of Psychiatry, Withington Hospital, Nell Lane, Manchester M20 2LR — MB ChB 1994 Liverp.

FITZGERALD-BARRON, Alexander William James St Clements Partnership, Tanner Street, Winchester SO23 8AD Tel: 01962 852211 Fax: 01962 856010; 48 St Cross Road, Winchester SO23 9PS Tel: 01962 856560 — MB BS 1985 Lond.; MRCGP 1993; DRCOG 1987.

FITZGERALD-FINCH, Otho Patrick (retired) — MB BS 1965 Lond.; MRCS Eng. LRCP Lond. 1966; FRCR 1975; FFR 1974; DMRD Eng. 1971. Prev: Cons. Radiol. Al-Qassimi Hosp. Sharjah, United Arab Emirates.

FITZGERALD FRAZER, Jonathan Simon Brockton House, Newport TF10 9EP — MRCS Eng. LRCP Lond. 1977; BSc Lond. 1974, MB BS 1977; MRCP (UK) 1980. (Guy's)

FITZGERALD O'CONNOR, Mr Alexander Francis 97 Harley Street, London W1N 7DF Tel: 020 7935 0646 Fax: 020 7935 1022; 36 Kidbrooke Grove, London SE3 0LG Tel: 020 7261 9848 Email: afoc@globalnet.uk — MB ChB 1971 Birm.; FRCS Eng. 1976. Clin. Dir. Otolaryngol. & Plastic Surg. Guy's & St. Thos. Trust Lond. Prev: Cons. Otolaryngol. St. Thos. Hosp. Lond.; Sen. Regist. Lond. Hosp.; Regist. Radcliffe Infirm. Oxf.

FITZGIBBON, Lettice Priscilla The Butts House, Wotton-under-Edge GL12 7DR Tel: 01453 842516 — MB BS 1930 Lond.; MRCS Eng. LRCP Lond. 1930. (Lond. Sch. Med. Wom.) Prev: JP.

FITZGIBBON, Shelagh Molyneux (retired) Barn Close Surgery, 38-40 High Street, Broadway WR12 7DT Tel: 01386 853651 Fax: 01386 853982 — MB BChir Camb. 1960; DObst RCOG 1965.

FITZHARRIS, Penelope Frances Allergy Clinic, St Mary's Hospital, Paddington, London W2 1NY; Flat 7, 10 Christchurch Road, Crouch End, London N8 9QL Tel: 020 8340 1677 — MB ChB Otago 1972; MD Otago 1983; FRACP 1986. (Univ. Otago) Hon. Cons. St. Mary's Hosp. Lond. Socs: Brit. Soc. Immunol. & Brit. Soc. Allergy & Clin. Immunol. Prev: Clin. Lect. Cardiothoracic Inst. Brompton Hosp. Lond.; Sen. Lect. (Immunol.) St. Mary's Hosp. Med. Sch. Lond.

FITZHERBERT JONES, Rosemary Constance 4 Grayling Court, De Montford Road, Reading RG1 8DL Tel: 01734 566684 — BM BCh 1984 Oxf.; MA, BM BCh Oxf. 1984. Prev: Trainee GP William Harvey Hosp. Ashford VTS; Ho. Surg. Battle Hosp. Reading; Ho. Phys. Roy. Cornw. Hosp. Truro.

FITZMAURICE, Brian 23 Woodburn Terrace, Edinburgh EH10 4SS — MB BCh BAO 1990 NUI.

FITZMAURICE, David Andrew Department of General Practice, The Medical School, University of Birmingham, Birmingham B15 2TT Tel: 0121 414 3352 Email: d.a.fitzmaurice@bham.ac.uk; 45 Northfield Road, King's Norton, Birmingham B30 1JD — MB ChB 1987 Birm.; MD 2000; MRCGP 1994. (Birmingham) Clin. Reader (Gen. Pract.) Med. Sch. Birm. Univ.; Sen. Clin. Fell. Bellevue Surg. Birm.

FITZMAURICE, David John (retired) 87a Lightfoot Lane, Fulwood, Preston PR2 3LU Tel: 01772 862236 — MB ChB 1952 Manch.; FRCOphth. 1988; DO Eng. 1962. Hon. Cons. Ophth. Roy. Preston Hosp. Prev: Cons. Ophth. Roy. Preston Hosp.

FITZMAURICE, Mojgan 140 Highlands Heath, Portsmouth Road, London SW15 3TZ Email: frankie.moj@virgin.net — MB ChB 1991 Manch. (Manchester)

FITZMAURICE, Richard John Department of Pathology, Clinical Sciences Building, Manchester Royal Infirmary M13 9WL Tel: 0161 2768812 Ext: 8813 Fax: 0161 2766348 Email: fitzmauricer@exchange.rhc-tr.nwest.nhs.uk — MB ChB 1981 Manch.; MD Manch. 1993; MRCPath 1988; T(Path) 1991. (Manchester) Cons. Histopath. Centr. Manch. Childr.s Univ. Hosp.s. Socs: Manch. Med. Soc. Prev: Cons. Histopath. Huddersfield Roy. Infirm.; Anatomic Path. Moncton Hosp. New Brunswick, Canad; Cons. Histopath. Birch Hill Hosp.

FITZMAURICE, Sanchia (retired) 166 Ebury Street, London SW1 8UP Tel: 020 7730 5832 — MB BS 1949 Lond.

FITZMAURICE-PETTY, Geraldine Leta (retired) 19 Midwood Avenue, Queens Park, Bournemouth BH8 9LX Tel: 01202 397998 — MB BS 1968 Lond.; MRCS Eng. LRCP Lond. 1968. Prev: GP Bournemouth.

FITZPATRICK, Adam Paul 239 West Blithedale Avenue, Mill Valley CA 94941, USA; Pony Patch, White Hart Lane, Cadnam, Southampton SO40 2NJ Tel: 01703 814049 — MD 1990 Lond.; BSc (Hons.) Lond. 1979, MD 1990, MB BS 1982; MRCP (UK) 1985. Sen. Regist. (Cardiol.) Wessex Reg. Cardiothoracic Centre. Socs: Brit. Pacing & Electrophysiol. Gp.; Brit. Cardiac Soc. & Brit. Cardiovasc. Interven. Soc. Prev: Regist. (Cardiol.) Roy. Brompton & Nat. Heart Hosp.; SHO Hammersmith Hosp. Lond.; Resid. Med. Off. Nat. Heart Hosp. Lond.

FITZPATRICK, Andrew Paul Peel View Medical Centre, 45-53 Union Street, Kirkintilloch, Glasgow G66 1DN Tel: 0141 211 8270 Fax: 0141 211 8279; Airedale, 52 Victoria Road, Lenzie, Glasgow G66 5AP — MB BCh BAO 1979 NUI; MICGP 1986; MRCGP 1984; DObst RCPI 1982; DCH NUI 1981. (Univ. Coll. Dub.)

FITZPATRICK, Anthony John Pearsonbrook, Glasson, Athlone, County Westmeath, Republic of Ireland; 6A Westbourne Avenue, Hessle HU13 0QH — MB BCh BAO 1985 NUI.

FITZPATRICK, Catherine Margaret 33 Countess Road, London NW5 2XH — MB BS 1995 Lond.

FITZPATRICK, Christina Department Child Health, The Barony Hospital, Nantwich Tel: 01270 415345; Elds Gorse, Willoughbridge, Market Drayton TF9 4EU Tel: 01630 647502 Email: byrnejph@msn.com — MB ChB Birm. 1968; MRCP (UK) 1974; MRCPCH 1996; DCH Eng. 1971; DObst RCOG 1970. (Birm.) Assoc. Specialist (Community Paediat.) Chesh. Community Health Care Trust; Locum Cons. (Community Paediat.) Community Healthcare Trust. Socs: Brit. Assn. Community Child Health. Prev: Sen. Regist. (Paediat.) N. Staffs. Hosp. Centre; SHO (Paediat.) Bristol Childr. Hosp.

FITZPATRICK, Colin Randall 116 Tullynakill Road, Ardmillan, Killinchy, Newtownards BT23 6QP — MB BCh BAO 1984 Belf.; MRCGP 1991; DCH NUI 1991; DMH Belf. 1991; DRCOG 1988.

FITZPATRICK, Daniel 101 Newtyle Road, Paisley PA1 3JY — MB ChB 1990 Glas.

FITZPATRICK, David Robert MRC Human Genetics Unit, WGH, Edinburgh EH4 2XU Tel: 0131 332 2471 Fax: 0131 343 2620 Email: david.fitzpatrick@hgu.mrc.ac.uk — MB ChB 1984 Ed.; MRCP (UK) 1987; MD Ed. 1992. MRC Sen. Clin. Scientist; Hon. Cons. in Paediatric Genetics. Socs: Brit. Soc. for Human Genetics; Europ. Soc. for Human Genetics; BSDB.

FITZPATRICK, Declan Gerard 4 North House, Monks Orchard Road, Beckenham BR3 3BW — MB BCh BAO 1980 Dub.; MRCPSych 1989.

FITZPATRICK, Emma Louise 9 Dunhaved Road, Launceston PL15 9JE; 61 Salisbury Road, Reading RG30 1BW — MB ChB 1994 Liverp.; DCHRCP 1997; DGMRCP 1996; DRCOG 1998; Dip. Family Plann. 1998. (Liverpool) GP Regist. Red Cross Rd. Surg. Goring-on-Thames. Socs: BMA; Full Mem. CMF. Prev: SHO (O & G, Med. & Paediat.).

FITZPATRICK, Geraldine Sarah Mary S.W.London & St Georges NHS Trust, CAMHS, Lanesborough Wing, St George's Hospital,, Blackshaw Road, London SW17 0QT Tel: 020 8725 1688 Fax: 020 8725 2246 Email: gfitzpatrick@swlstg-tr.nhs.uk — MB BCh BAO Belf. 1968; FRCPsych 1995, M 1972; DPM Eng. 1971. (Belf.) Hon. Cons. St. Geo. Hosp. Lond.; Cons. Psychiat. & Hon. Sen. Lect. St. Geo. Hosp. Lond.; Clin. Dir. S.W.Lond. & St Geo. CA NHS . Ment. Health Serv. Socs: Assn. Child Psychol. & Psychiat.; Assoc. Mem. Brit. Psychoanalyt. Soc.; Assoc. Mem. Lawyers for Childr. Prev: Sen. Regist. Child Guid. Train. Centre Lond.; Regist. Tavistock Clinic Lond.; Regist. (Ment. Health) Qu. Univ. Belf.

FITZPATRICK, Helen Josephine 67 Grange Avenue, Levenshulme, Manchester M19 2FZ; 47 Dee Banks, Chester CH3 5UU Tel: 01244 345548 — MB ChB 1990 Liverp. Specialist Regist. (Child & Adolesc. Psychiat.) Roy. Manch. Child. Hosp.

FITZPATRICK, James Joseph 10 Calderwood Road, Glasgow G43 2RP — MB ChB 1961 Glas.; FFA RCS Eng. 1970; DA Eng. 1966; DObst RCOG 1962. Cons. (Anaesth.) S.. Gen. Hosp. Glas.

FITZPATRICK, James Paul 103 Queensborough Gardens, Glasgow G12 9RS — MB ChB 1987 Glas.; BSc Glas. 1984; MRCGP 1995; DRCOG 1994. (Glas.) Prev: GP/Regist. Bishopbriggs Glas.; SHO (c/o Elderly & O & G) Stobhill Hosp. Glas.

FITZPATRICK, Kieran Thomas Joseph Department of Clinical Anaesthesia, Belfast City Hospital, 97 Lisburn Road, Belfast BT9 7AB Tel: 01232 329241 Email: kieran.fitzpatrick@bch.n-i.nhs.uk; 171 Killinchy Road, Comber, Newtownards BT23 5NE Tel: 028 9754 2357 Email: kieran.fitzpatrick@ukgateway.net — MB BCh BAO 1979 Belf.; FFA RCSI 1983. Cons. Anaesth. Belf. City Hosp.

FITZPATRICK, Margaret Mary Department of Paediatrics, Ward 11, St James University Hospital, Beckett St., Leeds LS9 7TF Tel: 0113 243 3144 Fax: 0113 242 6496 Email: medmmf@stjames.leeds.ac.uk; 36 The Drive, Roundhay, Leeds LS8 1JH Tel: 0113 266 1795 — MB BS 1979 London; BSc Lond. 1976; MRCP (UK) 1983; MD 1994 London; FRCP 1999 London. (Royal Free Hospital) Cons. Paediat. Nephrol. St. Jas. Hosp. Leeds. Socs: Fell. Roy. Coll. Paediat. and Clin. Health; Brit. Assn. Paediat. Nephrol. & Brit. Assn. Paediat. Nephrol.; Eur. Soc. Paediat. Nephrol. Prev: Lect. (Paediat. Nephrol.) Roy. Free Hosp. Lond. & Inst. Child Health Lond.

FITZPATRICK, Margaret Sinead 577 Donegall Road, Belfast BT12 6DX — BM BS 1988 Nottm.

FITZPATRICK, Michael John (retired) 57 Church Lane, Long Clawson, Melton Mowbray LE14 4ND Tel: 01664 822673 — MB ChB Leeds 1959; DObst RCOG 1963. Prev: GP Long Clawson Melton Mowbray.

FITZPATRICK, Michael John Barton House Health Centre, 233 Albion Road, London N16 9JT Tel: 020 7249 5511 Fax: 020 7254 8985 — MB BS 1976 Lond.; BA Oxf. 1972; DRCOG 1980.

FITZPATRICK, Mr Michael Owen 15 Troon Gardens, Westerwood, Glasgow G68 0JW Tel: 0141 732593 — MB ChB 1989 Glas.; BSc (Hons.) Glas. 1986, MD 1997; FRCS Glas. 1993; FRCS Ed. 1993. (Univ. Glas.) Regist. (Neurosurg.) Inst. Neurol. Sci. S.. Gen. Hosp. Glas. Prev: Research Fell. (Neurosurg. & Neurosci.) Univ. Glas.

FITZPATRICK, Owen John 44 Old Mill Heights, Hillsborough BT26 6RF — MB BCh BAO 1991 Belf.; DCH RCPSI 1996; DMH Belf. 1994; DRCOG Lond. 1996; MRCGP Lond. 1997.

FITZPATRICK, Rhona Catherine A & E Department, Weston General Hospital, Grange Rd, Weston Super Mare BS23 4TQ; Meynell, 14 Lowood Place, Revidge, Blackburn BB2 6JD Tel: 01254 667936 — MB ChB 1990 Aberd.; FFAEM 1999; FRCS Ed. 1994. (Aberdeen) Cons. (A & E) W.on Gen. Hosp. Socs: BMA; BAEM; FAEM. Prev: Regist. (A & E) Leics. Roy. Infirm.

FITZPATRICK, Robert George (retired) Rhadmorr, 33 Meadow View, Cumbernauld, Glasgow G67 2BZ — LRCP LRCS Ed. LRFPS Glas. 1956.

FITZPATRICK, Robert Henry Palmer, Maj. Retd. (retired) 2 Harton Close, Bromley BR1 2UD Tel: 020 8460 8044 — MRCS Eng., LRCP Lond. 1949; FFA RCS Eng. 1959; DA Eng. 1953. Prev: Cons. Anaesth. Bromley Gp. Hosps & Qu. Mary's Hosp. Sidcup.

FITZPATRICK, Sally Caroyln Brunton The Granary, Hurston Place Farm, Hurston Lane, Pulborough RH20 2EW — MB BS 1992 Lond.

FITZPATRICK, Sheila Anne Flat 4, 14 Kennington Park Place, London SE11 4AS — MB BS 1994 Lond.; BSc (Physiol.) Lond. 1990; BSc (Econ) Lond. 1979. SHO (Oncol.) Guy's Hosp. Lond. Prev: Ho. Off. (Med. & Surg.) St. Thos. Hosp. & Lewisham.

FITZPATRICK, William Joffre Francesco Darent Valley Hospital, Darenth Wood Road, Dartford DA2 8DA Tel: 01322 428100; 20 Rosewood Court, 35 Orchard Road, Bromley BR1 2TT Tel: 020 8460 8044 — MB BChir 1972 Camb.; MA Camb. 1973, MD 1987; MD Florence 1974; MRCP (UK) 1976; MRCS Eng. LRCP Lond. 1972; ECFMG Cert 1972. (Guy's & Camb.) Cons. Phys. In Elderly and Adult Med. Darent Valley Hosp. Dartford. Socs: MDU; Brit. Geriat. Soc.; BMA. Prev: Lect. & Hon. Sen. Regist. (Geriat. Med.) St. Bart. Hosp. Lond.; Hon. Sen. Regist. & Research Fell. (Gastroenterol.) St. Geo. Hosp. Lond.; SHO Nuffield Hse. Guy's Hosp. Lond.

FITZPATRICK, William John Stoneham Lane Surgery, 6 Stoneham Lane, Swaythling, Southampton SO16 2AB Tel: 023 8055 5776 Fax: 023 8039 9723; Orchard Cottage, Cranford Way, Highfield, Southampton SO17 1RN — MB BCh BAO 1974 NUI; MRCGP 1978; DRCOG 1976.

FITZPATRICK, William O'Carroll, Col. late RAMC Retd. 4 The Glebe, Creech St Michael, Taunton TA3 5PP Tel: 01823 442135 — LRCP LRCS Ed. LRFPS Glas. 1949; MFCM 1974; DIH St. And. 1966; DPH Lond. 1961; DTM & H Eng. 1960. (St. Mungo Coll. Glas.) Prev: DDAH HQ BAOR; ADAH 1 (BR) Corps Europe; Chief Med. Off. UN Force in Cyprus.

FITZSIMMONS, Christopher Richard The Cottage, Cliffe Lane, Tideswell, Buxton SK17 8NW — MB ChB 1993 Sheff.

FITZSIMMONS, Gail Margaret 011, 101 Marlborough Avenue, Broomhill, Glasgow G11 7LD Tel: 0141 334 2571 — MB ChB 1993 Glas. SHO (Anaesth.) S.. Gen. Hosp. Glas. Socs: BMA; MDU; Assn. Anaesth.s of GB & Irel. Prev: SHO (Anaesth.) Inverclyde Hosp. Greenock; SHO (A & E) CrossHo. Hosp. Kilmarnock; SHO (Thoracic Surg.) Hairmyers Hosp. E. Kilbride.

FITZSIMMONS, Ian Nicholas Paediatric Renal Unit, City Hospital, Hucknall Road, Nottingham NG5 1PB; 4 Harwood Close, Sandal, Wakefield WF2 6QY Tel: 01924 255318 — MB ChB 1989 Leeds; MB ChB Leeds. 1989; MRCP (UK) 1995. (Leeds) Sen. Regist. (Paediat.) City Hosp. Nottm. Prev: Sen. Regist. (Paediat.) Kings Mill Mansfield; Regist. (Paediat.) Huddersfield Roy. Infirm. & Leeds Gen. Infirm.; SHO (Paediat.) St. Jas. Hosp. Leeds.

FITZSIMONS, Brian James Assynt Medical Practice, The Health Centre, Lochinver, Lairg IV27 4JZ Tel: 01571 844226 Fax: 01571 844476; Assynt Medical Practice, Main St, Lochinver, Lairg IV27 4JB Tel: 01571 844226 Fax: 01577 844476 Email: assyntmedprac@msn.com — MB ChB 1987 Aberd.; MRCGP 1991. (Aberdeen) GP Assynt Med. Pract. Lochinver. Socs: Life Mem. Nat. Soc. Assn. GPs.

FITZSIMONS, Clare Patricia Royal Alexandra Hospital, Corsebar Drive, Paisley PA2; 14 Cairns Drive, Milngavie, Glasgow G62 8AJ — MB ChB 1978 Glas.; FRCP Glas. 1989; MRCP (UK) 1981. Cons. Dermat. Inverclyde Roy. Hosp. Greenock & Roy. Alexandra Hosp. Paisley.

***FITZSIMONS, Diane Elizabeth,** Surg. Lt. RN 91 Compton Avenue, Mannamead, Plymouth PL3 5DD Tel: 01752 662414 — MB ChB 1997 Leeds; BSc Pathological Sciences Leeds 1995.

FITZSIMONS, Edward Joseph 4 Kilmardinny Crescent, Bearsden, Glasgow G61 3NR — MD 1986 Glas.; BSc Glas. 1974, MD 1986, MB ChB 1976; MRCP (UK) 1978; MRCPath 1984. Cons. Haemat. Monklands Dist. Gen. Hosp. Airdrie. Prev: Lect. Haemat. Univ. Wales Coll. Med. Cardiff.

FITZSIMONS, Professor James Thomas Physiological Laboratory, Cambridge CB2 3EG Tel: 01223 333836 Fax: 01223 333840 Email: jtf10@cus.cam.ac.uk; Gonville & Caius College, Cambridge CB2 1TA — MB BChir Camb. 1954; FRS 1988; PhD Camb. 1960, MA 1954, ScD 1979, MD 1967; Hon. MD Lausanne 1978. Emerit. Prof. Med. Physiol. Univ. Camb.; Fell. Gonville & Caius Coll. Camb.; Pres. Gonville & Caius Coll. Camb. Socs: Physiol. Soc. Prev: Dir. Studies Med. Gonville & Caius Coll. Camb.; On Staff RAF Inst. Aviat. Med. FarnBoro.; Ho. Phys. Char. Cross Hosp. Lond.

FITZSIMONS, Orla 76 Drumconwell Road, Armagh BT60 2LT — MB ChB 1998 Manch.; MB ChB Manch 1998.

FITZSIMONS, Patricia Agnes Woodside Health Centre, Glasgow G20 7LR; 4 Kilmardinny Crescent, Bearsden, Glasgow G61 3NR — MB ChB 1978 Glas.; Cert Family Plann 1981; DRCOG 1981.

FITZSIMONS, Timothy James Medical Department, ICI Ltd., Pharmaceuticals Div., Mereside Alderley Park, Macclesfield SK10 4TG — MB ChB 1973 Bristol; MRCP (U.K.) 1976.

FITZWATER, Roger Edward Scarborough House, Pilgrams Way, Wouldham ME1 3RB Email: roger@rfitzwater.freeserve.co.uk — MB BCh 1970 Wales; MRCGP 1975.

FITZWATER, Trudy Ann Phoenix Surgery, 33 Bell Lane, Burham, Rochester ME1 3SX Tel: 01634 367982 Fax: 01634 864513 — MB ChB 1970 Sheff.; MRCGP 1975.

FITZWILLIAMS, Benjamin Charles Alan Lloyd Old Cilgwyn, Newcastle Emlyn SA38 9EW — MB BS 1996 Lond. (Guy's & St. Thomas' Lond.) SHO (Anaesth.) Frimley Pk. Hosp. Surrey.

FIXSEN, Mr John Andrew (retired) West Barn, Clamoak Farm Barns, Weir Quay, Bere Alston, Yelverton PL20 7BU Tel: 01822 841149 — MB BChir 1962 Camb.; MA Camb. 1962, MChir 1967; FRCS Eng. 1965. Prev: Cons. Orthop. Surg. Hosp. Childr. Gt. Ormond St. Lond.

***FLACK, Miss Emma** 2 Downlands, Royston SG8 5BY — BM 1997 Soton.

FLACK, Gerald Staunton (retired) Further Northfield, Bilting Lane, Bilting, Ashford TN25 4HD Tel: 01233 812391 — MB BS 1955 Lond.; MRCS Eng. LRCP Lond. 1956; DObst RCOG 1957. Prev: GP Ashford, Kent.

FLACK, Nicola Jane Finsbury Circus Medical Centre, 5 London Wall Buildings, Finsbury Circus, London EC2M 5NS Tel: 020 7638

0909 Fax: 020 7638 9211; 70 Alleyn Road, London SE21 8AH — MB BS 1984 Lond.; MRCGP 1995; MRCOG 1990. (St. Geo.) Hon. Regist. Harris Birthright Trust King's Coll. Lond. Socs: Fell. Roy. Soc. Med. Prev: Trainee GP Lond.; Research Regist. (Fetal Med.) Qu. Charlotte's Hosp. Lond.; Regist. (O & G) St. Geo. Hosp. Lond.

FLACK, Simon Thomas Talbot Medical Centre, 63 Kinson Road, Bournemouth BH10 4BX Tel: 01202 523059 Fax: 01202 533239; 6 Overbury Road, Lower Parkstone, Poole BH14 9JL Tel: 01202 722511 Email: stflack@aol.com — MB BS 1987 Lond.; BSc Lond. 1984; MRCP (UK) 1991; MRCGP 1991. GP; Clin. Asst. (Cardiac Pacing) Roy. Bournemouth Hosp. Castle La. E. Bournemouth.

FLACKETT, Luigi Keith University Hospital of Wales, Heath Park, Cardiff CF14 4XW Email: gx29@dial.pipex.com — BM BCh 1994 Oxf.; BSc (Hons.) St. And. 1991. SHO (Ophth.) Univ. Hosp. of Wales, Cardiff. Prev: SHO (Ophth.) Glos. Roy Hosp.; Ho. Off. (Med. & Surg.) N. Staffs. NHS Trust.

FLACKS, Robert Michael Manor Practice, James Preston Health Centre, 61 Holland Road, Sutton Coldfield B72 1RL Tel: 0121 354 2032 Fax: 0121 321 1779; 6 Mulroy Road, Sutton Coldfield B74 2PY Tel: 0121 355 1057 — MB ChB 1973 Birm.; DRCOG 1978. Hon. Clin. Lect., Div. Prim. Care, Pub. & Occupat. Health, Gen. Pract.

FLADEE, Hans Werner (retired) 3 Minton Rise, Taplow, Maidenhead SL6 0PD Tel: 01628 602345 — MB ChB 1953 Birm.; BSc Birm. 1950; MRCGP 1977; DObst RCOG 1960. Prev: GP Maidenhead.

FLAHERTY, Kevin Andrew (retired) 42 Netheroyd Hill Road, Fixby, Huddersfield HD2 2LS — MB BCh BAO 1938 NUI. Prev: Apptd. Fact. Doctor.

FLAHERTY, Thomas Anthony Haematology Department, Pathology Laboratory, Royal Preston Hospital, Sharoe Green Lane, Preston PR2 9HT Tel: 01772 710610 — MB BCh BAO 1972 NUI; FRCP Lond. 1990; MRCP (UK) 1975; FRCPath 1990, M 1979. Cons. Haemat. Roy. Preston Hosp. Socs: Fell. Roy. Soc. Med.; Fell. Manch. Med. Soc.; Brit. Soc. Haematol. Prev: Sen. Regist. (Haemat.) Manch. AHA (T); SHO Univ. Dept. Clin. Haemat. Manch. Roy. Infirm.; SHO (Med.) St. Finbarrs Hosp. Cork.

FLAHN, Mr George Ninneh Russells Hall Hospital, Pensnett Rd, Dudley DY1 2HQ Tel: 01384 456111; 24 Birchley Park Avenue, Oldbury B69 2JN Tel: 0121 552 0031 Fax: 0121 601 2417 Email: gn@flahn.freeserve.co.uk — MD 1981 Liberia; MD U. Liberia 1981; FRCS Ed. 1992. (A.M. Dogliotti College of Medicine) Socs: BMA.

FLAMBERT, Heather Margaret Broxtowe & NW Community Mental Health Team, b Floor South Block, Queens Medical Centre, Nottingham NG7 2 Tel: 0115 924 9924; 4 Carrfields Lane, Fisby on the Wreake, Melton Mowbray LE14 2NT Tel: 01664 434404 — MB BS 1987 Newc.; MRCPsych 1993. (Newcastle) Cons. Gen. Adult Pssychiatry. Prev: Regist. Rotat. (Psychiat.) Mid. Trent.

FLANAGAN, Adrienne Margaret Department of Histopathology, Div. of Investigative Science, Imperial College School of Medicine, St Mary's Campus, Norfolk Place, London W2 1PG Tel: 020 7594 3843 Fax: 020 7262 2947 Email: a.flanagan@ic.ac.uk; 46 Warrington Crescent, Maida Vale, London W9 1EP Tel: 020 7286 6616 — MB BCh BAO 1981 NUI; PhD Lond. 1990; LRCPI & LM, LRCSI & LM 1981; MRCPath 1988. (Iceland) Sen. Lect. & Hon. Cons. Histopath. ICSM at St Mary's Lond. Prev: MRC Research Fell. & Hon. Sen. Regist. (Histopath.) St. Geo. Hosp. Med. Sch. Lond.; Lect. St. Geo. Hosp. Med. Sch. Lond.; Regist. (Histopath.) Roy. Postgrad. Med. Sch. Lond.

FLANAGAN, Daniel Edward Henry 16 Copeland Drive, Poole BH14 8NW — MB BS 1989 Lond.; MRCP (UK) 1992.

FLANAGAN, David Joseph 18 Ardcaien, Culmore Road, Londonderry BT48 8AF — MB BCh BAO 1984 Belf.; MRCGP 1989; DGM RCP Lond. 1987.

FLANAGAN, David Michael Flanagan and Partners, 133 Liverpool Road, Crosby, Liverpool L23 5TE Tel: 0151 931 3197 Fax: 0151 931 4006; 5 Eshe Road, Liverpool L23 3AR — MRCS Eng. LRCP Lond. 1960. Prev: Ho. Surg. Liverp. Roy. Infirm.; Ho. Phys. Roy. S.. Hosp. Liverp.; Resid. Med. Off. King Edw. VII Memor. Hosp. Hamilton, Bermuda.

FLANAGAN, Mr Declan William 68 Common Lane, Hemingford Abbots, Huntingdon PE28 9AW Tel: 01480 469227 Fax: 01480 467268 Email: declan.flanagan@breathemail.net; 68 Common Lane, Hemingford Abbots, Huntingdon PE28 9AW Tel: 01480 469227 Fax: 01480 467268 — MB BCh BAO 1976 Dub.; FRCS (Ophth.) Eng. 1981; FRCOphth 1988. (Trinity Coll. Dub.) Cons. Ophth. Surg. Addenbrooke's & Hinchingbrooke Hosps. Camb.; Med. Director Hinchingbrooke Hosp. NHS Trust. Socs: Oxf. Ophth. Congr.; Europ. Soc. of Cataract and Refractive Surg.s. Prev: Resid. Surg. Off. Moorfields Eye Hosp. Lond.; SHO (Neurosurg.) Soton. Gen. Hosp.; SHO (Ophth.) Soton. Eye Hosp.

FLANAGAN, James Joseph 21 Blatchington Road, Tunbridge Wells TN2 5EG Tel: 01892 35226 — MB BCh BAO 1972 NUI; FFR 1982; DMRD 1978. Cons. Radiol. Pembury & Kent & Sussex Hosps. Tunbridge Wells. Prev: Sen. Regist. Addenbrooke's Hosp. Camb.

FLANAGAN, Kathleen Teresa (retired) Claytons, Station Road, Bourne End SL8 5QE Tel: 01628 23394 — MB BS 1951 Lond.; MRCS Eng. LRCP Lond. 1951; DObst RCOG 1955. Prev: Ho. Surg. Roy. Free Hosp.

FLANAGAN, Katie Louise 44 Museum House, Burnham St., London E2 0JA — MB BS 1992 Lond.; MRCP (UK) 1994; DTM & H Lond. 1994. Regist. (Infec. Dis. & Respirat. Med.) Hammersmith Hosp. Lond.

FLANAGAN, Margaret Siobhan 14 Bell Road, Strabane BT82 9RS — MB ChB 1993 Glas.

FLANAGAN, Mary Patricia Glebe House, Poyntzpass, Newry BT34 1EQ — MB BCh BAO 1980 NUI; DCH NUI 1985; DObst RCPI 1986.

FLANAGAN, Neil Gerard Department of Haematology, Victoria Hospital, Blackpool — MB ChB 1961 Ed.; FRCP Ed. 1987, M 1978; FRCPath 1986, M 1971; DMJ Path.) Soc. Apoth. Lond. 1975; DCP Lond 1969. (Ed.) Cons. Haemat. Vict. Hosp. Blackpool. Prev: Cons. in Path. RAF Hosp. Wegberg.

FLANAGAN, Nicole Jane Eastfields Lodge, Alrewas Road, Kings Bromley, Burton-on-Trent DE13 7HR — MB ChB 1989 Liverp.

FLANAGAN, Nuala Mary Department of Paediatrics, Royal Belfast Hospital for Sick Children, 180 Falls Road, Belfast BT12 6BE; 30 Armagh Road, Newry BT35 6DJ — MB BCh BAO 1996 Belf. SHO (Paediat.) Roy. Belf. Hosp. for Sick Childr.

FLANAGAN, Patricia Anne 17 Blaidwood Drive, Durham DH1 3TD — MB ChB 1979 Glas.; MSc (Community Health) Ed. 1986; MRCGP 1984; MFCM 1989; DRCOG 1983. Lect. (Community Med.) Univ. of Edin.

FLANAGAN, Patricia Mary Orchard Medical Centre, Macdonald Walk, Kingswood, Bristol BS15 8NJ Tel: 0117 980 5100 Fax: 0117 980 5104 — MB BCh BAO 1989 Dub.; MRCGP 1994; Cert. Family Plann. JCC 1995; DObst RCPI 1993; DCH RCPSI 1992.

FLANAGAN, Patrick Joseph (retired) 37 Cedar Avenue, Sutton Weaver, Runcorn WA7 3ET — MB BCh BAO 1955 NUI; DCH 1957.

FLANAGAN, Paul Gerard Public Health Laboratory, Poole General Hospital, Longfleet Road, Poole BH15 2JB — MB ChB 1988 Birm.; MRCPath 1997; MD Birmingham 1998. Cons. Microbiol., Poole Hosp. Socs: Welsh Microbiol. Assn. & Brit. Soc. Study Infec. Prev: Sen. Lect. (Med. MicroBiol.) Univ. Hosp. Wales, Cardiff; Lect. (Med. Microbiol.) Univ. Hosp. Wales Cardiff; Regist. (Med. Microbiol.) Univ. Hosp. Wales Cardiff.

FLANAGAN, Peter Regional Transfusion Centre, Bridle Path, Leeds LS15 7TW Tel: 0113 214 8647 — BM BS 1979 Nottm.; BMedSci Nottm. 1977, BM BS 1979; MRCP (UK) 1982; MRCPath 1987; FRCP 1996; FRCPath 1996. Clin. Dir. N&S N.ern Zone. Socs: Hon. Sec. BBTS; BSH ISBT. Prev: Dep. Dir. Yorks. Regional Transfus. Centre.

FLANAGAN, Peter Gerard Mary Braid Valley Hospital, Cushendall Road, Ballymena BT43 6HR Tel: 028 2563 5244 Fax: 028 2563 5237; 20 Broughshane Road, Ballymena BT43 7DX Tel: 028 2565 6783 Email: petergm@flanagan76.freeserve.co.uk — MB BCh BAO 1980 Belf.; MD Belf. 1989; FRCP 1997, M (UK) 1984. Cons. Geriat. Braid Valley Hosp. Ballymena. Socs: Brit. Geriat. Soc.; BMA. Prev: Regist. (Geriat. Med.) Belf. City Hosp. & Lurgan Hosp.; Regist. (Gen. Med.) Ulster Hosp. Dundonald.

FLANAGAN, Philip Michael Hilary Royal Lancaster Infirmary, Ashton Road, Lancaster LA1 4RP Tel: 01524 65944 Fax: 01524 583584; Brackenber, Brettargh Drive, Haverbreaks, Lancaster LA1 5BN — LRCPSI 1976; FRCR 1985; FFR RCSI 1985; DCH NUI 1979; DObst RCPI 1979. Cons. Radiol. Lancaster Acute Hosps. NHS Trust.; Sub-dean, Univ. of Liverp.

FLANAGAN, Sally-Ann 16 Copeland Drive, Parkstone, Poole BH14 8NW — MB BS 1989 Lond.

FLANAGAN, Sharon Maria Penketh Health Centre, Honiton Way, Penketh, Warrington WA5 2EY Tel: 0192 572 5644; 35 Lincoln Way, Rainhill, Prescot L35 6PH Tel: 0151 426 4334 — MB ChB 1983 Liverp.; DRCOG 1988. Prev: Trainee GP Birchwood VTS; SHO (O & G) Warrington Dist. Gen. Hosp.; SHO Rotat. (Med.) Roy. Liverp. Hosp.

FLANAGAN, William Lawrence (retired) Netherwood, Tullibardine, Auchterarder PH3 1JU — MB ChB 1950 Glas.; FRCPsych 1979, M 1971; DPM Eng. 1955. Prev: Cons. Psychiat. Gartnavel Roy. Hosp. Glas.

FLANIGAN, Ciara Marie Leverndale Hospital, 510 Crookston Road, Glasgow G53 7TU; 5 Courthill, Bearsden, Glasgow G61 3SN — MB BCh BAO 1983 Belf.; MS Med. Sci. Belf. 1994; MRCPsych 1990; DMH Belf. 1989. Sen. Regist. Rotat. W. of Scotl., Cons. Psychiat. Prev: Regist. (Gen. Psychiat.) N. Irel.

FLANIGAN, John Joseph North Park, 49 Blairhill St., Coatbridge ML5 1PH Tel: 01236 22950 — MB ChB 1947 Glas.; Med. Off. Alexander Hosp. Coatbridge.

FLANIGAN, Paul Damien Tel: 01236 422678 Fax: 01236 431411 — MB ChB 1976 Glas. (Glasgow University)

FLANIGAN, Paul Patrick Joseph Loy Medical Centre, 8 Loy Street, Cookstown BT80 8PE Tel: 028 8676 3030 Fax: 028 8676 1400; Garuda Lodge, 206 Drum Road, Cookstown BT80 9RU Tel: 016487 51933 — MB BCh BAO 1983 Dub.; BSc (Hons.) Aberd. 1978; MB BCh Dub. 1983; MRCGP 1987; DRCOG 1986. GP Cookstown.

FLANIGAN, Peter Gerard Parkhead Hospital, 81 Salamanca St., Glasgow G31 5ES — MB BCh BAO 1982 Belf.; MRCPsych 1987. Cons. Psychiat. Pk.head Hosp. Glas.; Hon. Sen. Lect. Univ. Glas.

FLANN, George Arnold 18 Rectory Road, Upton-on-Severn, Worcester WR8 0LX — MD 1938 Durh.; MB BS 1933. (Durh.) Socs: BMA. Prev: Sen. Accid. Room Ho. Surg. Roy. Vict. Infirm. Newc.; Res. Med. Off. P.ss Mary Matern. Hosp. Newc-on-Tyne; Maj. IMS.

FLANN, Peter-John Alexander 98 Commonside, Sheffield S10 1GG — MB ChB 1994 Sheff.; DRCOG; MRCGP; DFFP.

FLANNERY, Daniel John 18 Downview Park W., Belfast BT15 5HN Tel: 01232 778146 — MB BCh BAO 1979 Belf.; MD Belf. 1989, MB BCh BAO 1979; MRCP (UK) 1984.

FLANNERY, Dennis Paul 2 Broadgate Court, Horsforth, Leeds LS18 5TF — MB ChB 1970 Leeds; MRCPsych 1976; Dip. Psychother. Leeds 1976; DPM Leeds 1973. Cons. Psychother. Leeds; Sen. Clin. Lect. (Psychiat.) Leeds Univ. Prev: Cons. Psychiat. Calderdale HA; Unit Gen. Manager Community Servs. Calderdale HA.

FLANNERY, Kim Peter Tel: 0208 464 4138 Fax: 0208 466 9248 — MB BS 1976 Lond.; MRCS Eng. LRCP Lond. 1976; DRCOG 1980. (St. Mary's) GP Bromley. Prev: Trainee GP Carshalton Hosp. VTS.

FLANNERY, Mr Mark Christopher Royal Surrey County Hospital, Egerton Road, Guildford GU2 7XX Tel: 01483 406670; Marchfield, Crossways Road, Grayshott, Hindhead GU26 6LA Tel: 01428 605332 Fax: 01428 607593 Email: mark.flannery@talk21.com — MB BS Lond. 1980; FRCS Eng. 1986; FRCS Ed. 1985. (St. Mary's) Cons. Surg. Orthop. Roy. Surrey Co. Hosp. Trust Guildford. Socs: Fell. BOA; SICOT; BOSTA. Prev: Sen. Regist. Rotat. (Orthop.) St. Geo. Hosp. Lond.; Regist. Rotat. (Orthop.) St. Mary's Hosp. Lond.

FLANNERY, Michael Dominic Health Centre, Village Road, Llanfairfechan LL33 0NH Tel: 01248 680021 Fax: 01248 681711; Llys Meddyg, Paradise Road, Penmaenmawr LL34 6AS Tel: 01492 623191 Fax: 01492 622933 — BM BCh 1986 Oxf.; MRCGP 1990. (Oxf.) Prev: Trainee GP Aberystwyth VTS; Community Med. Off. (Community Paediat.) Roy. Alexandra Hosp. Rhyl.

FLANNIGAN, Claire Barbara St Jowes Hospital, Leeds — MB ChB 1985 Glas.; MRCPsych 1990. Cons. Psychiat. Riverside Ment. Health Trust Lond. Prev: Lect. & Hon. Sen. Regist. (Psychol. Med.) Med. Coll. St. Bart. Hosp. Lond.; Research Fell. & Hon. Sen. Regist. (Psychiat.) Char. Cross & W.m. Med. Sch. Lond.; Regist. (Psychiat.) St. Geo. Hosp. Lond.

FLANNIGAN, Mr George Michael Bradford Royal Infirmary, Duckworth Lane, Bradford BD9 6RJ Tel: 01274 364781 Fax: 01274 366944; West Point, 24 Nab Lane, Shipley BD18 4HJ Tel: 01274 824383 Email: mikeflannigan@aol.com — MB ChB 1975 Ed.; ChM Ed. 1987; FRCS Eng. 1979. Cons. Urol. Bradford Roy. Infirm. Socs: Corres. Mem. Amer. Urol. Assn.; Brit. Assn. Urol. Surgs. Prev: Sen. Regist. Leeds Gen. Infirm.

FLAPAN, Andrew Daniel Royal Infirmary Edinburgh, Edinburgh EH3 9YW — MD 1994 Lond.; MB BS 1980; MRCP (UK) 1985. Cons. Cardiol. Roy. Infirm. Edin.

FLASCHER, Stephen Michael Red Bank Group Practice, Red Bank Health Centre, Unsworth Street, Radcliffe, Manchester M26 3GH Tel: 0161 724 0777 Fax: 0161 724 8288 — MB BS 1981 Newc.; MRCGP 1985.

FLASHER, Maurice Cyril (retired) 21 Pinfold Court, Higher Lane, Whitefield, Manchester M45 7NZ Tel: 0161 766 2881 — MB ChB 1950 Manch. Clin. Asst. (Paediat.) Hull Roy. Infirm.; Adjudicating Med. Auth. DHSS. Prev: Ho. Surg. Hull Matern. Hosp. & Kingston Gen. Hosp. Hull.

FLASZ, Malcolm Hyam 36 Courtland Drive, Chigwell IG7 6PW — MB BCh 1981 Wales. Prev: Trainee GP N. Middlx. Hosp. VTS.

FLATHER, John Nicholas Squire and Partners, Market Place, Hadleigh, Ipswich IP7 5DN Tel: 01473 822961 Fax: 01473 824895 — MB BS 1978 Lond.; MRCS Eng. LRCP Lond. 1978; MRCGP 1984; DRCOG 1983; DCH RCP Lond. 1982. (St. Bart.) Socs: BMA. Prev: Trainee GP Winchester VTS; SHO (Anaesth.) Univ. Coll. Hosp. Lond.; SHO (Neurosurg.) St. Bart. Hosp. Lond.

FLATHER, Marcus Denis Director, Clinical Trials and Evaluation Unit, Royal Brompton Hospital, Sydney St., London SW3 6NP Tel: 020 7351 8867 Fax: 020 7351 8829 — MB BS 1982 Lond.; MRCP (UK) 1985. Dir. (Hon. Cons.) Clin. Trials & Eval. Unit Roy. Brompton Hosp. Lond. Prev: Sen. Research Fell. Div. Cardiol. McMaster Univ. Canada.

FLATLEY, Margaret Emma (retired) Little Newmans, 10 Bridge St., Witham CM8 1BT Tel: 01376 500072 — MB BS 1931 Lond. Prev: Ho. Surg. Roy. Free Hosp. & Nottm. Hosp. Wom.

FLATLEY, Martin Pendleside Medical Practice, Clitheroe Health Centre, Railway View Road, Clitheroe BB7 2JG Tel: 01200 422674 Fax: 01200 443652 — MB ChB 1980 Manch.

FLATMAN, Mr Gerald Edward (retired) Furzecroft, East Lennox Drive, Helensburgh G84 9JD Tel: 01436 672830 — MB BS 1945 Lond.; MD Lond. 1957; FRCS Eng. 1950; FRCS Glas. 1962; FRCR 1975; FFR 1956; DMRT Eng. 1954; Hon. FACR 1980. Prev: Dir. Glas. Inst. Radiother. & Oncol.

FLATMAN, Wendy Louise Westwoodhill, Station Road, Rhu, Helensburgh G84 8LW — MB ChB 1986 Glas.

FLATT, Nicholas Walter Royal Albert Edward Infirmary, Department of Anaesthesia, Wigan Lane, Wigan WN1 2NN Tel: 01942 822086 — MB ChB 1987 Dundee; BMSc (Hons.) Dund 1985; FRCS Ed. 1992; FRCA 1995. (Dundee) Cons. Anaesth., Dept. of Anaesth., Roy. Albeet Edwd. Infirm., Wigan.

FLATTERY, Harriet Brigid The Medical Centre, Old Chester Road, Great Sutton, South Wirral CH66 3PB Tel: 0151 339 2424 — MB BCh BAO 1982 NUI; DCH 1984; DRCOG 1987; Cert. Family Plann. 1988.

FLATTERY, Peter James 68 Devonfield Road, Liverpool L9 3BH Tel: 0151 523 6001; 63 High Road, Waterford, Hertford SG14 2PR Tel: 01992 552791 — MB ChB 1990 Liverp.; MRCGP 1996; DFFP 1994; DRCOG 1994; T(GP) 1994.

FLAVAHAN, Catherine Tay Court Surgery, 50 South Tay Street, Dundee DD1 1PF Tel: 01382 228228 Fax: 01382 202606 — MB ChB 1974 Glasgow; MB ChB Glas. 1974. (Glasgow) GP Dundee.

FLAVELL, Helen Louise Breydon Cottage, 16 Brook Lane, Billesdon, Leicester LE7 9AB Tel: 0116 259 6289 — MB ChB 1994 Leic. SHO (Integrated Med.) Leicester Roy. Infirm.

FLAXMAN, Penelope Ann Lutterworth Health Centre, Gilmorton Road, Lutterworth LE17 4EB Tel: 01455 553531; Elms Farm, Frolesworth Road, Leire, Lutterworth LE17 5HJ — MB BS 1981 Lond.

FLAYE, Deirdre Elizabeth Princess Alexandra Hospital NHS Trust, Hamstel Road, Harlow CM20 1QX Tel: 01279 444455 — BM BCh 1975 Oxf. (Oxf.) Cons. Ophth. P.ss Alexandra Hosp. Harlow. Socs: Fell. RCS; FRCOphth.

FLEAR, Margaret Elizabeth (retired) c/o Cross Cottage, Blackawton, Totnes TQ9 7BD — MB ChB 1951 Birm.

FLEAT, Gillian 2 Richardson Street, Rowntree Park, York YO23 1JU — BM 1994 Soton.; BSc (Hons.) Lond. 1990. GP Regist.

FLECK, Professor Adam Department of Chemical Pathology, Charing Cross Hospital, Fulham Palace Road, London W6 8RF Tel:

020 8846 7075 Fax: 020 8846 7007 — MB ChB 1958 Glas.; FRSE; PhD Glas. 1964, BSc (1st cl. Hons. Biochem.) 1955, MB ChB 1958; FRCP Glas. 1979, M 1977; FRCPath 1982, M 1971; FRSC 1971. (Glas.) Prof. (Chem. Path.) Char. Cross & W.m. Med. Sch. & Hon. Cons. (Chem.; Path. Char. Cross & W.m. Hosp. Socs: Fell. Roy. Soc. Med.; Assn. Clin. Biochem. & Assn. Clin. Path. Prev: Sen. Lect. (Path. Biochem.) & Hon. Cons. (Biochem.) Glas. W..; Infirm.; Cons. Biochem. Glas. Roy. Infirm.

FLECK, Mr Brian William Princess Alexandra Eye Pavilion, Chalmers St., Edinburgh EH3 9HA Tel: 0131 536 1000 Fax: 0131 536 3897 Email: bwfleck@srv2.med.ed.ac.uk; 8 Meadow Place, Edinburgh EH9 1JZ Tel: 0131 229 5856 — MB ChB 1980 Ed.; MD Ed. 1992, BSc (Hons.) 1977; FRCS Ed. 1984; FRCOphth 1988; T(Ophth) 1990. (Ed.) Cons. Ophth. Roy. Infirm. Edin. Socs: Amer. Acad. of Ophth. Prev: Vis. Specialist Nat. Univ. Hosp., Singapore; Sen. Regist. (Ophth.) Eye Pavil. Edin.

FLECK, Douglas George (retired) 22 Garrick Gardens, Hurst Park, East Molesey KT8 1SJ — MB BS Lond. 1948; MD Lond. 1961; FRCPath 1974, M 1962; Dip. Bact. 1956. Cons. Bacteriol. Pub. Health Laborat. Serv.; Sen. Lect. (Bact.) St. Geo. Hosp. Tooting Gr. Prev: Regist. (Path.) Ho. Surg. & Ho. Phys. Char. Cross Hosp.

***FLECK, Patrick David** 502A Upper Newtownards Road, Belfast BT4 3HB Tel: 01232 471136; 172 Kings Road, Belfast BT5 7EN — MB BCh BAO 1969 Belf.; BSc (Physiol.) Belf. 1961, MB BCh BAO 1969, BDS 1963.

FLEET, Helen Jane 71 Brighton Road, Sutton SM2 5BT — BM 1995 Soton.

FLEET, Jacqueline Clare Queens Avenue Surgery, 14 Queens Avenue, Dorchester DT1 2EW Tel: 01305 262886 Fax: 01305 250607 — MB ChB 1989 Leics.

FLEET, John David (retired) Pen Parc LLwyd, Henllan, Denbish, Conwy LL16 5DE Tel: 01745 812886 Fax: 01745 812886 Email: johnfleet@ukgateway.net — MB BS Lond. 1974 BDS Manch. 1964; MRCS Eng. LRCP Lond. 1974; FDS RCS Eng. 1969. Prev: Cons. Oral & Maxillo Facial Surg. Jersey.

FLEET, Mr Mahmud Salem Paediatric Surgery Department, Chelsea & Westminster Hospital, 369 Fulham Road, London SW10 9NH — MB BCh 1981 Al Fateh, Libya; FRCS Ed. 1987.

FLEET, Mustafa Salem Radiology Department, Queen Margaret Hospital, Dunfermline KY12 0SU Tel: 01383 623623 Fax: 01383 627072 Email: fleetms@aol.com; Email: fleetmu@hotmail.com — MB BCh 1989 Al Fateh; MRCP (UK) 1992; FRCR 1995. (Al Fateh Libya) Cons. Radiol. Qu. Margt. Hosp. Dunfermline. Socs: MRCRadiol.; Brit. Soc. Interven. Radiol.; Radiol. Soc. N. Amer. Prev: Sen. Regist. Glas. W.ern Infirm.; Regist. Gartnavel Gen. Hosp. Glas.; Regist. Yorkhill Hosp. Glas.

FLEET, Trevor Wilmot Accident & Emergency Department, Royal Lancaster Infirmary, Ashton Road, Lancaster LA1 4RP — MB ChB 1986 Liverp.

FLEETCROFT, Colin Thomas Square Medical Practice, High Street, Godalming GU7 1AZ Tel: 01483 415141 Fax: 01483 414881; Glebe Farm Cottage, 3 Peperharow Lane, Shackleford, Godalming GU8 6AN Tel: 01483 810860 — MB BChir 1973 Camb.; MA Camb. 1974; DObst RCOG 1974. (St. Geo.) Clin. Asst. Milford Hosp.; Med. Off. Aldro Sch. Godalming; Mem. W. Surrey LMC. Socs: BMA. Prev: Med. Off. Unsted Pk. Rehabil. Unit; SHO St. Geo. Hosp. Lond.; Ho. Phys. Ashford Gen. Hosp.

FLEETCROFT, Mr John Paul Medway Maritime Hospital, Gillingham ME7 5NY Tel: 01643 833988 — MB BS 1968 Lond.; FRCS Eng. 1975; DObst RCOG 1970. (Westm.) Cons. Orthop. Surg. Medway Maritime Hosp. Gillingham.; Cons. Knee Surg. BUPA Alexandra Hosp. Walderslade; Cons. Knee Surg. Somerfield Hosp. Maidstone. Socs: Eur. Soc. Sports Traumatol. Knee Surg. & Arthroscopy; Internat. Cartilage Research Soc.; Brit. Orthopaedic Assn. Prev: Sen. Regist. Roy. Nat. Orthop. Hosp. Lond.; SHO (Orthop.) Roy. Nat. Orthop. Hosp. Lond.; SHO (Accid. Serv.) Luton & Dunstable Hosp.

FLEETCROFT, Robert Charles Coastal Villages Practice, Pippin Close, Ormesby St. Margaret, Great Yarmouth NR29 3RW Tel: 01493 730205 Fax: 01493 733120 — MB ChB 1981 Sheff.; MRCP (UK) 1986; MRCGP 1988; DRCOG 1988. Tutor (Gen. Pract.) & Trainer Gt. Yarmouth. Prev: Regist. (Gen. Med.) Huddersfield Roy. Infirm.; Regist. (Therap.) Roy. Hallamsh. Hosp. Sheff.

FLEETWOOD, Alison Lesley Green Close Surgery, Kirkby, Lonsdale, Carnforth LA6 2BS — MB BS 1992 Newc.; DFFP 1996; MRCGP 1998. p/t GP Retainer, Kirkby, Lonsdale; CMO Family Plann., Bay Community NHS Trust. Prev: GP Regist. Cumbria; SHO (Geriat.) Newc. Gen. Hosp.; SHO (Paediat.) Gen. Hosp. Bishop Auckland.

FLEETWOOD, Marion Evelyn Prebend Street Surgery, 15 Prebend Street, London N1 8PG Tel: 020 7226 9090 Fax: 020 7354 3330 — MB BChir 1975 Camb.; MB Camb. 1975, BChir 1974; MA Camb. 1974. (King's Coll. Hosp. Lond.) Prev: Phys. Nursing & Resid. Staff St. Bart. Hosp. Lond.; SHO (Psychiat.) Bexley Hosp. & Friern Hosp. Lond.

FLEGG, Peter John Department of Medicine, Blackpool Victoria Hospital NHS Trust, Blackpool FY3 8NR Tel: 01253 30000 — MB ChB 1979 Rhodesia; MD Zimbabwe 1995; FRCP 2001 LONDON; LRCP LRCS Ed. LRCPS Glas. 1979; DTM & H Liverp. 1983. Cons. Phys. (Infec. Dis.) Blackpool Vict. Hosp. Socs: Brit. Infect. Soc.; Brit. HIV Assn. Prev: Sen. Regist. (Infec. Dis.) City Hosp. Edin.

FLEISCHER, Carl Christian 1A Pitcroft Av, Reading RG6 1NH — BM 1997 Soton.

FLEISCHER, Freda (retired) 8 River Court, Upper Ground, London SE1 9PE Tel: 020 7633 0634 — MB BS 1952 Lond.; MRCS Eng. LRCP Lond. 1952; DCH Eng. 1954. Prev: GP Lond.

FLEISCHMAN, Antony Peter 70 Belsize Lane, London NW3 5BJ — MB BCh 1989 Witwatersrand.

FLEISCHMANN, Charles William (retired) Wellwood House, 26 North Side, Hutton Rudby, Yarm TS15 0DA Tel: 01642 700522 — MB ChB 1940 Ed.; DA Eng. 1943. Prev: Cons. Anaesth. Newc. RHB.

FLEMING, Aikaterini Erifyli 12 Crosslands, Caddington, Luton LU1 4ER — MB BS 1984 Lond.

FLEMING, Alan Chalmers St Andrews Hospital, Billing Road, Northampton NN1 5DG Tel: 01604 629696 Fax: 01604 232525, 01604 616015 — MB BS 1944 Durh.; FRCPsych 1973, M 1972; DPM RCPSI 1954. (Durh.) Cons. Psychiat. St. And. Hosp. N.ampton / Vis. Cons. Psychiat. to Isham Ho. St Andrews Gp. of Hosps. Building Rd., N.ampton. Prev: Cons. Psychiat. Kneesworth Hse. Hosp. Royston; Med. Co-ordinator & Cons. Psychiat. Bromham Hosp. Bedford; Med. Supt. & Cons. Psychiat. Calderstones Hosp. Whalley.

FLEMING, Anthony Orpington Hospital, Sevenoaks Road, Orpington BR6 9JU Tel: 01689 815144 Fax: 01689 815127; 8 Chipstead Lane, Riverhead, Sevenoaks TN13 2AG Tel: 01732 741721 — MB BS 1962 Queensland; MD Queensland 1976; FRCP Lond. 1993; MRCP (UK) 1971; FRACP 1978, M 1976. Cons. Rheum. & Rehabil. Bromley Hosps. NHS Trust Orpington. Socs: Fell. Austral. Coll. Rehabil. Med.; Fell. Roy. Austral. Coll. Phys.; Brit. Soc. Rheum. Prev: Sen. Cons. Rheum. P. Henry & P. of Wales Hosps. Sydney, Austral.; Vis. Med. Off. Veterans Hosp. Conlord, Sydney, Austral.

FLEMING, Brenda 9 Middleton, Menstrie, Menstrie FK11 7HA Email: bf4@student.open.ac.uk — MB ChB 1976 Manch.; MBA Open 1998; FFAEM 1995; FRCS Ed. 1990; MSc Clin. Trop. Med. Lond. 1980. Socs: Assn. Trop. Med. & Hyg.; Brit. Assn. Emerg. Med.; BASICS. Prev: Cons. A & E Stirling Royayl Infirm.; Sen. Regist. (A & E) King's Coll. Hosp. Lond.

FLEMING, Brian Lagan Valley Hospital, Hillsborough Road, Lisburn BT28 1JP Tel: 01846 665141; Downshire Hospital, Ardglass Road, Downpatrick BT30 6RA — MB BCh BAO 1978 Belf.; MPhil Belf. 1994; FRCPsych 1999. Cons. (Psychiat.); Clin. Dir.

FLEMING, Charles, VRD (retired) Westering, Kilmany Road, Wormit, Newport-on-Tay DD6 8PG Tel: 01382 541540 — MB ChB 1944 St. And.; DPH St. And. 1948. Prev: SCM Fife HB.

FLEMING, Christine Georgina Kirkmailing, Denny Road, Larbert FK5 3NR — MB ChB 1958 Ed.

FLEMING, Christopher Francis Mental Welfare Commission for Scotland, Edinburgh; 27 Blacket Place, Edinburgh EH9 1RJ — MB ChB Leeds 1968; FRCP Ed. 1994; MRCPsych 1974; DPM Leeds 1972; DCH Eng. 1971. (Leeds) Ment. Welf. Commiss. for Scotl. Socs: Fell. Roy. Soc. Med. Prev: Princip. Med. Off. Scott. Office Home & Health Dept.; Cons. Psychiat. Lynfield Mt. Hosp. Bradford.

FLEMING, Colin John Friarsdale, Friarsbrae, Linlithgow EH49 6BH — MB ChB 1990 Glas.; BSc Glas. 1987; MRCP (UK) 1993. Cons. Dermatol., Ninewells Hosp. Dundee.

FLEMING, Cornel 8 Dartmouth Park Hill, London NW5 1HL Tel: 020 7272 1337 Fax: 020 7561 1494; 74 Hornsey Lane, London N6 5LU Tel: 020 7272 3439 — MB BS 1961 Sydney; DAvMed Eng. 1969. GP & Aviat. Med. Cons. Socs: BMA & AMA; Exec. Comm. Mem. Small Pract. Assn.

FLEMING, David Gerard Ground Floor Flat, 10 Eaton Crescent, Clifton, Bristol BS8 3EJ — BM 1992 Soton.

FLEMING, David Robert Murray Nelson Health Centre, Leeds Road, Nelson BB9 9TG Tel: 01282 698036 — MB ChB 1977 Birm.; DRCOG 1979.

FLEMING, Desmond Hugh 176 Burnage Lane, Burnage, Manchester M19 1EF — MB ChB 1975 Manch.

FLEMING, Diana Claire 48 Beltran Road, London SW6 3AJ — MB ChB 1997 Ed.

FLEMING, Douglas Ian Cannon Street Health Centre, Cannon Street, Oldham OL9 6EP Tel: 0161 909 8228 Fax: 0161 909 8226 — MB ChB 1974 Manch.; DRCOG 1979.

FLEMING, Douglas Munro, OBE Northfield Health Centre, 15 St. Heliers Road, Northfield, Birmingham B31 1QT Tel: 0121 478 1850 Fax: 0121 476 0931; 9 Dowles Close, off Corvedale Road, Birmingham B29 4LE Tel: 0121 475 6190 — MB ChB 1959 Birm.; FMedSci. 1999; PhD Maastricht 1993; FRCGP 1978; DObst RCOG 1963. (Birm.) Princip. in Gen. Pract.; Dir. Birm. Research Unit RCGP. Socs: BMA; Fell.Roy. Coll. of Gen. Practitioners; Fell.Acad. of Med. Sci.

FLEMING, Evelyn Mary 10 Hill Wootton Road, Leek Wooton, Warwick CV35 7QL Tel: 01926 55422 — MB ChB 1964 Leeds; Dip. Community Paediat. Warwick 1982. SCMO S. Warks. DHA; Tutor in Community Paediat. Warwick Univ.

FLEMING, Freda Williamson (retired) Carlin Craig, 15 Quadrant Road, Newlands, Glasgow G43 2QP — MB ChB Ed. 1954; FFA RCS Eng. 1963; DA Eng. 1958; DObst RCOG 1956. Prev: Cons. Anaesth. S.. Gen. Hosp. Glas.

FLEMING, Gail Aideen 20 Ravenhill Park, Belfast BT6 0DE — MB ChB 1995 Manch.

FLEMING, Gibson Paisley Road West Surgery, 1808 Paisley Road West, Glasgow G52 3TS Tel: 0141 211 6660 Fax: 0141 211 6662 — MB ChB 1970 Glas.

FLEMING, Harry (retired) The Oaks, Mobberley, Knutsford WA16 — LRCP LRCS 1934 Ed.; LRCP LRCS Ed. LRFPS Glas. 1934; MRCPsych 1971; DPM Eng. 1942. Prev: Cons. Psychiat. Winwick & Warrington Gen. Hosps.

FLEMING, Helen Catherine 14 Greystoke Close, Berkhamsted HP4 3JJ — MB ChB 1991 Liverp.; MRCGP 1995.

FLEMING, Hugh Alexander 12 Barrow Road, Cambridge CB2 2AS Tel: 01223 352587 Email: fleming_hugh@hotmail.com — MA Camb. 1970; MD New Zealand 1952, MB ChB 1947; FRCP Lond. 1967, M 1955. (Otago) Fell. Darwin Coll. Camb. Socs: Brit. Cardiac Soc. Prev: Emerit. Cons. Cardiol. Addenbrooke's Hosp. Camb. & E. Anglian RHA Cardiac Unit Papworth Hosp.

FLEMING, Hugh Alexander (retired) High House, Lamplugh, Workington CA14 4SQ Tel: 01946 861333 — MB ChB 1940 Glas. Prev: Surg. Lt. RNVR.

FLEMING, Ian Murray Geneste Culver Cottage, Langton Road, Tunbridge Wells TN4 8XA — MB ChB 1988 Birm. Specialist Regist. (Anaesth.) N. Staffs. Hosp. Stoke-on-Trent.

FLEMING, James Wilson (retired) Lower House, Bunch Lane, Haslemere GU27 1ET Tel: 01428 642480 — MB ChB 1939 Glas. Prev: Regional Med. Off. DHSS.

FLEMING, Jane Catherine Ormeau Road Practice, 485 Ormeau Road, Belfast BT7 3GR Tel: 028 9064 1506; 58 Lisnabreeny Road E., Belfast BT6 9SS — MB ChB 1974 Birm.

FLEMING, Jane Frances Pengelli Fach Farm, Vaynor, Merthyr Tydfil CF48 2TU — MB BS 1982 Lond.; DRCOG 1987; DCH RCP Lond. 1985.

FLEMING, Jane Kathryn Hillsborough Health Centre, Ballynahinch Street, Hillsborough BT26 6AW Tel: 028 9268 2216 Fax: 028 9268 9721; 12 Shrewsbury Park, Belfast BT9 6PN — MB BCh BAO 1984 Belf.; MB BCh Belf. l984.

FLEMING, Jane Sara Mary Wrexham Maelor Hospital, Wrexham LL13 7TD; Pen-y-Clawdd House, Pentredwr, Llangollen LL20 8DG — MB BCh BAO NUI 1982; MRCGP 1994; DCH NUI 1984. Cons. Palliat. Med. Wrexham Maelor Hosp.; Med. Dir. Nightingale Hse. Hospice Wrexham. Prev: Assoc. Specialist (Palliat. Med.) Myton Hamlet Hospice Warwick.

FLEMING, Mr John Anthony (retired) Mulberry House, Lugwardine, Hereford HR1 4DS Tel: 01432 851159 — MB BS 1952 Lond.; MS Lond. 1965; FRCS Eng. 1956; DObst RCOG 1953. Prev: Cons. Surg. W. Middlx. Hosp. Isleworth.

FLEMING, John Maclachlan (retired) Dunollie, 28 Stevenson St., Dalmuir, Clydebank G81 3LJ Tel: 0141 952 7665 — MB ChB 1945 Glas.; MRCGP 1966. Prev: Med. Ref. Regional Med. Off.

FLEMING, Josephine Olwen Charlotte Keel Health Centre, Seymour Road, Easton, Bristol BS5 0UA Tel: 0117 951 2244 Fax: 0117 951 2373; 14 Westbury Park, Durdham Downs, Bristol BS6 7JA Tel: 0117 973 5409 — MB ChB 1975 Bristol; MRCGP 1981; Cert. Family Plann. JCC 1980; DRCOG 1980; DCH Eng. 1979; DFFP. (Bristol) Partner in Gen. Pract. Prev: Med. Off. Stud. Health Serv. Bristol Univ.; Resid. (Paediat.) Hosp. for Sick Childr. Toronto; SHO (O & G) Bristol Matern. Hosp.

FLEMING, Kenneth Foresterhill, 65 Dunyeats Road, Broadstone BH18 8AE Tel: 01202 777435 — MB ChB 1962 Aberd.; DObst RCOG 1964.

FLEMING, Kenneth Anthony University of Oxford, Medical School Office Level 3 John Radcliffe Hospital, John Radcliffe Hospital, Oxford OX3 9DU Tel: 01865 817476; 2 The Winnyards, Cumnor, Oxford OX2 9RJ Tel: 01865 864793 — MB ChB 1968 Glas.; DPhil, MA Oxf. 1981; FRCPath 1988, M 1976. Dean. Med. Serv & Hon.Cons. Path; Fell. Green Coll. Oxf. Socs: Brit. Soc. Gastroenterol.; Eur. Assn. Study Liver; BMA & Path. Soc. Gt. Brit. Prev: Clin. Lect. in Path. Radcliffe Infirm. Oxf.; Wellcome Research Fell. in Path. Univ. Oxf.; MRC Trav. Fell.

FLEMING, Mr Leslie Brian (retired) 25 West Street, North Creake, Fakenham NR21 9LQ Tel: 01328 730197 — MB BS 1949 Durh.; MS Newc. 1965; FRCS Eng. 1956. Cons. Surg. Roy. Vict. Infirm. Newc.; Clin. Sub-Dean Univ. Newc. Med. Sch. Prev: Sen. Regist. (Surg.) Roy. Vict. Infirm. Newc.

FLEMING, Linda Jane 2A George Street, Chester CH1 3EQ; Laburnum Cottage, Church Road, Christleton, Chester CH3 7AG — BM BS 1978 Nottm.; BMedSci Nottm. 1976, BM BS 1978; MRCGP 1983; DRCOG 1982. (Nottm.) Prev: GP Trainee Melton Mowbray Leics.; SHO (Med. & Obst.) Univ. Hosp. Nottm.

FLEMING, Lorna Elisabeth Mary Masterton Health Centre, 74 Somerville Street, Burntisland KY3 9DF Tel: 01592 872761 — MB ChB 1980 Ed.; MRCGP 1984.

FLEMING, Mairi-Clare 60 Strathclyde Road, Motherwell ML1 3EE — MB ChB 1997 Glas.; BSc (Hons) 1994. (Galsgow) SHO (Med.) Rotat., W. Galsgow Hosps. NHS Univ. Trust, Glas.

FLEMING, Margaret Janet Primrose (retired) 17 Graham Park Road, Gosforth, Newcastle upon Tyne NE3 4BH Tel: 0191 285 1860 — MB ChB 1941 Ed.; MA Ed. 1938; MRCGP 1965. Prev: Resid. Surg. Off. (Surg.) & SHO (Phys.) Gogarburn EMS Hosp. Edin.

FLEMING, Mark Edward 1 Amethyst Road, London E15 2BE — MB BS 1997 Lond.

FLEMING, Mary Irene (retired) 22 Maple Close, Clarence Avenue, London SW4 Tel: 020 8674 5013 — MB BCh BAO 1942 Belf.; DCH Eng. 1948. Sen. Med. Off. GLC. Prev: Ho. Surg. Lurgan & Portadown Hosp. Ulster Hosp. Wom. & Childr. Belf. & Hither Green Fev. Hosp. Lond.

FLEMING, Maureen Chalmers (retired) Maxtyle, Milton Ernest, Bedford MK44 1RU — MB BCh BAO 1945 NUI. Prev: Clin. Asst. Bromham Hosp. Bedford.

FLEMING, Murray 8 Sycamore Avenue, Kirkintilloch, Glasgow G66 4NY — MB ChB 1993 Glas.

FLEMING, Otto (retired) 22 Whinfell Court, Sheffield S11 9QA Tel: 0114 262 0196 — MRCS Eng. LRCP Lond. 1949; FRCGP 1974. Prev: Clin. Asst. (Psychiat.) Roy. Hallam. Hosp. Sheff.

FLEMING, Pamela Ann Foresterhill, 65 Dunyeats Road, Broadstone BH18 8AE — MB ChB 1962 Aberd. Clin. Med. Off. Dorset HA.

FLEMING, Pauline Anne 2F2, 33 Mertoun Place, Edinburgh EH11 1JX — MB BCh BAO 1988 Dub.; MRCGP 1995; DCH Dub. 1991. (TC Dub.) Specialist Regist. (Occupat. Med.) Dept. Pub. Health Sci. Univ. Edin. Med. Sch. Socs: Soc. Occupat. Med.

FLEMING, Professor Peter John, CBE Institute of Child Health, UBHT Education Centre, Upper Maudlin St, Bristol BS2 8AE Tel: 0117 342 0172 Fax: 0117 342 0193 Email:

peter.fleming@bris.ac.uk — MB ChB 1972 Bristol; PhD Bristol 1993; FRCP Lond. 1988; FRCPC 1981; MRCP (UK) 1975; FRCPCH 1997. (Bristol University) Prof. Infant Health & Developm. Physiol. Inst. of Child Health Bristol; Head Div. Child Health Univ. Bristol; Cons. Paediat. Roy. Hosp. Sick childr. Bristol. Socs: Paediat. Intens. Care Soc.; Neonat. Soc.; Brit. Assn. Perinatal Med. Prev: Sen. Regist. (Paediat.) Bristol Matern. Hosp. & S.mead Hosp. Bristol; Fell. (Neonatology) & Sen. Resid. Hosp. Sick Childr. Toronto, Canada; Brit. Paediat. Assn. Guthrie Medal 1984.

FLEMING, Peter Robert (retired) 94 Grand Drive, London SW20 9DY Tel: 020 8540 1132 — MB BS 1948 London; FRCP 1968 London; DHMSA 1974; MD 1952 London; MRCP 1949 London. Sen. Lect. in Med. Char. Cross & W.m. Med. Sch.; Cons. Phys. W.m. Hosp.; Examr. to RCP Lond., Univ. Lond. & Univ. Newc. Prev: Sen. Med. Regist. W.m. Hosp.

FLEMING, Philip Morris Kingsway House, Portsmouth City Drugs and Alcohol Service, Kingsway House, 130 Elm Grove, Southsea PO5 1LR Tel: 023 9229 1607 Fax: 023 9229 1614; 21 Stafford Road, Petersfield GU32 2JF Tel: 01730 262489 Email: philipfleming@compuserve.com — BM BCh Oxf. 1966; BA (Hons.) Oxf. 1963, MA 1966; FRCPsych 1985, M 1972; DPM Eng. 1971. (Oxf. & Univ. Coll. Hosp.) p/t Cons. Psychiat. Portsmouth & SE Hants. Health Auth.; Clin. Teach. (Psychiat.) Soton. Univ. Med. Sch.; Vis. Cons. Psychiat. Stud. Servs. Univ. Portsmouth. Socs: BMA; Soc. for Study of Addic. Prev: Sen. Research Regist. Drug Dependence Clinic Univ. Coll. Hosp. Lond.; Sen. Regist. (Psychiat.) Univ. Coll. Hosp. Lond. & Shenley Hosp. St. Albans; Regist. (Psychiat.) Friern Hosp. & Univ. Coll. Hosp. Lond.

FLEMING, Robert (retired) 66 Rockingham Road, Bury St Edmunds IP33 2SE Tel: 01284 750563 — MRCS Eng. LRCP Lond. 1950.

FLEMING, Robert John Kennedy (retired) 4 Stonehouse Close, Combe Down, Bath BA2 5DP Tel: 01225 833261 — MB BS Lond. 1943 MRCS Eng. LRCP Lond. 1932.

FLEMING, Rodney Andrew Blue Wing Medical Practice, Wallacetown Medical Centre, 3 Lyon Street, Dundee DD4 6RB Tel: 01382 458333 Fax: 01382 461833 — MB ChB 1990 Manch.; MRCGP 1995; DRCOG 1994. (Univ. Manch.)

FLEMING, Simon Charles 46 Woodcroft Road, Wylam NE41 8DH — MB BS 1983 Lond.; MSc Lond. 1987, BSc 1980, MB BS 1983. Clin. Lect. (Clin. Biochem. & Metab. Med.) Univ. Newc. u. Tyne. Prev: MRC Clin. Research Fell. Div. Communicable Dis. & Regist. Chem. Path. St. Geo. Hosp. Lond.; SHO (Path.) S.mead Hosp. Bristol.

FLEMING, Mrs Stephanie Katharine (retired) Yew Tree Farm, Kixley Lane, Knowle, Solihull B93 0JF Tel: 01564 777633 — MB BCh BAO 1952 Cork; DCH Eng. 1954 London. Prev: Rotating Internship Memor. Hosp. Wilmington Delaware USA.

FLEMING, Stewart Department of Pathology, University of Edinburgh, Teviot Place, Edinburgh EH8 9AG Tel: 0131 650 2898 Fax: 0132 650 6528 Email: sf@srv4.med.ed.ac.uk — MB ChB 1980 Glas.; BSc (Hons.) Glas. 1978, MD (Hons.) 1989; FRCPath 1997, M 1987. Sen. Lect. (Path.) Univ. Edin.; Hon. Cons. Histopath. Roy. Infirm. of Edin. Socs: Path. Soc.; Renal Assn. Prev: Hon. Sen. Regist. (Histopath.) Wessex RHA; Lect. (Path.) Univ. Soton.; Regist. (Path.) W.. Infirm. Glas.

FLEMING, Victoria Anne Saundersfoot Medical Centre, Westfield Road, Saundersfoot SA69 9JW Tel: 01834 812407 Fax: 01834 811131; Cilrhiw Farm, Princes Gate, Narberth SA67 8TG — MB BS 1987 Lond.; MRCGP 1992; DCH RCP Lond. 1991; DRCOG 1989.

FLEMING, William Robert 77 High Street, Barrington, Cambridge CB2 5QX — MB BS 1982 Melbourne.

FLEMING, William Stuart 18 Chestnut Rise, Droxford, Southampton SO32 3NY — MB ChB 1967 Glas.

FLEMINGER, John Jack (retired) 59 Dulwich Village, London SE21 7BJ — MRCS Eng. LRCP Lond. 1943; MA Camb. 1945, MD 1954; FRCP Lond. 1965, M 1950; FRCPsych 1971; DPM Eng. 1947. Prev: Phys. Dept. Psych. Med. & Dir. York Clinic Guy's Hosp.

FLEMINGER, Martin Hollow Way Medical Centre, 58 Hollow Way, Cowley, Oxford OX4 2NJ Tel: 01865 777495 Fax: 01865 771472; 80 Hill Top Road, Oxford OX4 1PE — MB BS 1987 Lond.; MRCGP 1993; DRCOG 1991. Tutor (Primary Health Care) Oxf. Univ. Div. Pub. Health & Primary Health Care.

FLEMINGER, Ruth (retired) 59 Dulwich Village, London SE21 7BJ Tel: 020 8693 3143 — MB BS 1946 Lond.; MRCS Eng. LRCP Lond. 1945; FRCPsych 1985, M 1972; DPM Eng. 1968. Prev: Cons. (Psychiat.) St Bernard's Hosp. S.all and S. Lond. Hosp. for Wom.

FLEMINGER, Simon Maudsley Hospital, Denmark Hill, London SE5 8AF Tel: 020 7919 2092 Fax: 020 7919 2087 Email: s.fleminger@iop.kcl.ac.uk — MB BChir 1979 Camb.; PhD Lond. 1988; MA, MB Camb. 1979, BChir 1978; MRCP (UK) 1980; MRCPsych 1986. (St. Geo.) Cons. (Neuropsychiat.); Hon. Sen. Lect. Inst. of Psychiat. Socs: Fell. Roy. Soc. Med.; Brit. Neuropsychiat. Assn. Prev: Sen. Lect. Lond. Hosp. Med. Coll.; Regist. & Sen. Regist. Maudsley Hosp.; Ment. Health Foundat. Research Fell. Inst. Psychiat. Lond.

FLEMMING, Mr Adrian Frederick Stewart Hand Surgery Unit, St Andrews Centre for Plastic Surgery, East Wing, Broomfield Hospital, Court Road, Chelmsford CM1 7ET Tel: 01245 516125 Fax: 01245 516132; Tel: 01277 633230 Fax: 01277 633230 Email: stewart.fleming@virgin.net — MB BS 1975 Lond.; FRCS Eng. 1980; MRCS Eng. LRCP Lond. 1975. Cons. Hand & Plastic Surg. St. And. Centre for Plastic Surg. Mid Essex Hosps NHS Trust Chelmsford; Cons. Plastic & Hand Surg. Essex Rivers NHS Trust Colchester; Hon. Sen. Lect. St. Bart. Hosp. Med. Sch. Lond. Socs: Brit. Plastic Surg.; Brit. Soc. Surg. Hand; BMA. Prev: Pulvertaft Hand Surg. Fell. Wrightington Hosp. Appley Bridge Lancs.; Sen. Regist. (Plastic Surg.) Mersey RHA; Regist. (Plastic Surg.) Mt. Vernon & Univ. Coll. Hosps.

FLEMMING, Christopher John (retired) Skene House, Cedars Lane, Capel St Mary, Ipswich IP9 2JA — MB ChB 1968 Aberd. Prev: GP Ipswich.

FLENLEY, Colin Kerbotson Tel: 01922 450950 Fax: 01922 450960; 27 Branton Hill Lane, Aldridge, Walsall WS9 0NR Tel: 01922 55562 — MB ChB 1980 Birm.; DRCOG 1982.

FLETCHER, Adrian Michael 350 Willenhall Road, East Park, Wolverhampton WV1 2JB — MB BS 1996 Lond.

FLETCHER, Alan Kindersley, 8 Sunnycroft Road, Leicester LE3 6FT — MB ChB 1974 Aberd.; BMedBiol 1971; MRCPath 1982. Cons. Histopath. Leicester Roy. Infirm. Socs: Path. Soc.; Assn. Clin. Paths. Prev: Lect. Path. Leicester Univ.

FLETCHER, Alan Keith Norhtern General House, Herries Rd, Sheffield S5 7AN; 196 Psalter Lane, Sheffield S11 8UT — MB ChB 1992 Sheff.; BMedSci (Hons.) Sheff. 1991; MRCP (UK) 1995. Specialist Regist. N. Trent A&E Train. Scheme. Socs: Endocrine Soc. Prev: SHO (Anaesth.), N. Trust Train. Scheme; Clin. Lect. (Endocrinol. & Diabetes) Univ. Sheff. & N.. Gen. Hosp.; SHO (Med.) St. Jas. Univ. Hosp. Leeds.

FLETCHER, Alison Jane 6 (3FL) Brighton Street, Edinburgh EH1 1HD — MB ChB 1994 Ed.

FLETCHER, Amanda Louise 10 Woodside Grove, Larbert FK5 3HG — MB BS 1998 Lond.; MB BS Lond 1998.

***FLETCHER, Andrew David** 5 Penn Lea Court, Bath BA1 3RE Email: andifletcher@hotmail.com — MB ChB 1998 Aberd.; MB ChB Aberd 1998.

FLETCHER, Angela Rosemary 4 Myrtle Farm View, Croyde, Braunton EX33 1QH Tel: 01271 890128 Email: angela@doct21.freeserve.co.uk — BM BS 1993 Nottm. GP Regist., Cuen Med. Centre, Braunton. Prev: Ho. Off. P.ss Roy. Hosp. Telford & Kidderminster Gen. Hosp.; Ho. Off. Mater Miser. Adult Hosp. Brisbane & Mt. Isa, Austral.

FLETCHER, Anthony James Pearse Department of Anaesthesia, City Hospital NHS Trust, Hucknall Road, Nottingham NG5 1PF Tel: 0115 961169; 2 Hatchmere Close, Oakwood, Derby DE21 2HP — BM BS 1988 Nottm.; FRCA. Cons. Anaesth. City Hosp. Nottm.

FLETCHER, Anthony Travers Nethersole (retired) The Old Wheelwrights Brandeston, Woodbridge IP13 7AN Tel: 01728 685508 — BM BCh Oxf. 1952.

FLETCHER, Archibald Peter IMS International, 7 Harewood Avenue, Marylebone, London NW1 6JB Tel: 020 7393 5251 Fax: 020 7393 5279; Hall Corner Cottage, Little Maplestead, Halstead CO9 2RU — MB BS 1955 Lond.; PhD (Biochem.) Lond. 1965, MB BS 1955. (Lond. Hosp.) Med. Dir. IMS Internat.; Dir. PMS Internat. Ltd. Socs: Fell. Roy. Soc. Med.; Federat. Amer. Socs. Experim. Biol. Prev: Chief Scientif. Off. & Sen. PMO Med.-Scientif. Servs. DHSS; PMO Med. Div. DHSS; Sen. Lect. (Chem. Path.) St. Mary's Hosp. Lond.

FLETCHER, Bruce Rodney Glen (retired) Glebe House, 19 Firby Road, Bedale DL8 2AT Tel: 01677 422616 — MB ChB 1970 Ed.;

FRCP Ed. 1986; MRCP (UK) 1974; MRCGP 1976. Prev: Regist. & SHO Aberd. Roy. Infirm.

FLETCHER, Caroline Anne Wythenshaw Hospital, Manchester M23 9LT; Flat 4, 122 Palatine Road, West Didsbury, Manchester M20 3ZA — MB ChB 1997 Manch. SHO (Cas.) S. Manch. Hosps. Trust.

FLETCHER, Catherine Lorna Dunstan Medical Centre, 284 Bury Road, Bolton BL2 6AY Tel: 01204 531557 Fax: 01204 364407; Robin's Nest, 1 Oak Coppice, Heaton, Bolton BL1 5JD — MB ChB 1986 Sheff.; MRCGP 1990; DRCOG 1990; DCH RCP Lond. 1989. Prev: Trainee GP Kildonan Hse. Bolton; SHO (Paediat. & O & G) Bolton Gen. Hosp.

FLETCHER, Charles Henry The Surgery, 7-8 Park Street, Ripon HG4 2AX Tel: 01765 692337 Fax: 01765 601757; The Forge, Hutton Conyers, Ripon HG4 5EB — MB ChB 1978 Leeds; MRCGP 1982; DRCOG 1980. Prev: Ho. Off. Harrogate Dist. Hosps.; GP Wrexham VTS.

FLETCHER, Christopher David Marsden Department of Histopathology, Soft Tissue Tumour Unit, St Thomas's Hospital, London SE1 7EH Tel: 020 7928 9292 — MB BS 1981 Lond.; MD Lond. 1991; MRCPath 1988. (St. Thos.) Reader (Surg. Path.) & Hon. Cons. Histopath. St. Thos. Hosp. Lond.; Dir. Soft Tissue Tumour Unit St. Thos. Hosp. Lond.; Co-ordin. MRC Soft Tissue Sarcoma Registry. Socs: Histopath. Panel MRC Soft Tissue Sarcoma Registry.

FLETCHER, Christopher James Solihull Hospital, Lode Lane, Solihull B91 2JL Tel: 0121 424 4272 — MB ChB 1980 Birm.; BA Camb. 1977; FRCR 1986. Cons. Radiol. Birm. heartlands and Solihull NHS Trust. Prev: Sen. Regist. & Regist. (Radiodiag.) W. Midl. RHA; SHO (Gen. Med.) Sandwell HA.

FLETCHER, Christopher Paul Lisson Grove Medical Centre, 3-5 Lisson Grove, Mutley, Plymouth PL4 7DL Tel: 01752 205555 Fax: 01752 205558; Thornham House, Ermington, Ivybridge PL21 0LG Tel: 01752 892617 — MB BS 1974 Lond.; MRCGP 1988; DFFP 1994; DRCOG 1978. (St. Geo. Hosp. Med. Sch. Lond.) Area Med. Off. BT; Pract. (Occupat. Health) Plymouth. Socs: Brit. Soc. Sport & Med. & BMA. Prev: GP Trainer, W. Germany; Sen. Med. Off. & Civil. Med. Pract. Celle, Germany.

FLETCHER, Claire Louise 522 Willoughby House, London EC2Y 8BN — MB BS 1990 Lond.; MRCP (UK) 1995. (Kings College, London) Specialist Regist. (Dermat.), Guy's Hosp., Lond. Socs: Roy. Soc. Med.; Med. Protec. Soc.; Brit. Assoc. of Dermatol.s. Prev: Dermat. Research Assoc. UMDS, Guy's Hosp.

FLETCHER, Colin (retired) The Paddock, Hutton Buscel, Scarborough YO13 9LL Tel: 01723 862347 — MB BS 1965 Newc.

FLETCHER, David John Ribbleton Medical Centre, 243 Ribbleton Ave, Ribbleton, Preston PR2 6RD — MB ChB 1974 Manch.

FLETCHER, Denis Edward (retired) Greencote, The Green, Cark-in- Cartmel, Grange-over-Sands LA11 7NJ Tel: 015395 58389 — MB ChB Leeds 1945; MD Leeds 1971; FRCR 1975; FFR 1953. Prev: Cons. Radiol. Barrow & Furness Hosps.

FLETCHER, Derek Peter Minden Medical Centre, 2 Barlow Street, Bury BL9 0QP Tel: 0161 764 2651 Fax: 0161 761 5967; West Bank, Wood Road Lane, Summerseat, Bury BL9 5QA Tel: 01204 884934 Fax: 01204 884934 — MB ChB 1968 Manch.; FRCGP 1996, M 1978; DObst RCOG 1970. (Manch.) Mem. Bury LMC; Chairm. BARDOC (Bury & Rochdale doctors on call); Trainer (Gen. Pract.) Bury. Socs: BMA.

FLETCHER, Edward Walter Leslie (retired) Sandy Lodge, The Croft, Old Headington, Oxford OX3 9BT — MRCS Eng. LRCP Lond. 1959; MA Oxf. 1971; MA Camb. 1960, BA 1956, MB 1960, BChir 1959; FRCR 1967; DMRD Eng. 1965. Hancock Prize For Surg. RCS Eng. 1959. Prev: Cons. Radiol. John Radcliffe Hosp. & Ch.ill Hosp. Oxf.

***FLETCHER, Emily Claire** Forest Lodge, Frog Lane, Milton-under-Wychwood, Oxford OX7 6JZ Email: fetcheremily@hotmail.com — MB ChB 1998 Bristol.

FLETCHER, Frank 7 Home Street, Broughty Ferry, Dundee DD5 1DX — MB ChB 1955 Manch.; DMRD Eng. 1958.

FLETCHER, Freda Mary, SSStJ (retired) 1 Upper Nellington, Langton Green, Tunbridge Wells TN3 0AS Tel: 01892 863883 — MB BS 1955 Lond.; DObst RCOG 1959. Prev: Clin. Asst. & SHO ENT Kent & Sussex Hosp. Tunbridge Wells.

FLETCHER, Gavin Carmichael 29a Thorn Drive, Bearsden, Glasgow G61 4ND — MB ChB 1988 Ed.; FRCA 1993. Cons. (Anaesth.) Roy. Alexander Hosp. Paisley. Prev: Regist. Glas. Roy. Infirm.; Clin. Shock Team Study Gp. W.. Infirm. Glas.

FLETCHER, Gaynor Louise 32 Horderns Road, Chapel-en-le-Frith, High Peak SK23 9TB Tel: 01298 812080 — MB ChB 1997 Liverp. (Liverpool)

FLETCHER, Geoffrey Crompton (retired) 1 Westfield Drive, Mossley Road, Grasscroft, Oldham OL4 4HT Tel: 01457 872838 — MB ChB Manch. 1945; LRCP LRCS Ed. LRFPS Glas. 1945; MFOM RCP Lond. 1978. Prev: Occupat. Phys. The Guardian in Manch. Evening News Manch.

FLETCHER, George Herbert Perwick, 22 Lostock Hall Road, Poynton, Stockport SK12 1DP Tel: 01625 873679 — MD 1968 Liverp.; MB ChB 1949; FFOM RCP Lond. 1981, M 1978; TDD Wales 1956. (Liverp.) Occupat. Phys. Hon. Lect. Univ. Manch. Socs: BMA & Soc. Occupat. Med. Prev: Dep. Dir. Med. Serv. Health & Safety Exec.; Dir. Pneumoconiosis Med. Research Bureau Kitwe, Zambia.

FLETCHER, Gillian Mary OHSAS, Navy House, Stuart Way, Rosyth, Dunfermline KY11 2YD Tel: 01383 428400; 22 Braid Farm Road, Edinburgh EH10 6LF Tel: 0131 447 1048 Email: aflethcer@doctors.org.uk — MB ChB 1975 Birm.; MRCP (UK) 1980; DRCOG 1978; MFOM RCP Lond. 1996, AFOM 1992; FRCP 1999. Cons. Occupat. Health Fife Heathcare. Prev: Sen. Regist. (Occupat. Health) Roy. Infirm. Edin.; Phys. (Occupat Health) Lothian HB.

FLETCHER, Gordon 2 Church Street, Southport PR9 0QU Tel: 01704 547471 Fax: 01704 502004; West Winds, 4 Greenways, Tarleton, Preston PR4 6RN Tel: 01772 815850 — MB BCh BAO 1955 Dub.; MA Dub. 1973, BA 1953; DPH Manch. 1972. (TC Dub.) Cons. Pub. Health Med. S.port. Socs: S.port Med. Soc. Prev: Dir. (Pub. Health) & Dist. SCM S.port & Formby DHA; Area Specialist (Community Med.) & Dep. MOH S.port.

FLETCHER, Graeme Robert Lawrence The Simpson Health Centre, 70 Gregories Road, Beaconsfield HP9 1PS Tel: 01494 671571 Fax: 01494 680219; 5 Knottocks End, Beaconsfield HP9 2AN — MB BS 1984 Lond.; MRCGP 1988; DRCOG 1988. (St. Mary's Hosp. Med. Sch.)

FLETCHER, Harriet Connop 16 Mill Hill Road, Norwich NR2 3DP — MB BS 1998 Lond.; MB BS Lond 1998.

FLETCHER, Heather Jane Blyth Community Health Centre, Thoroton St., Blyth NE24 1DX Tel: 01670 396467 Fax: 01670 396457 Email: hjfletcher@hotmail.com; 15 Roseworth Crescent, Gosforth, Newcastle upon Tyne NE3 1NR Tel: 0191 285 8067 — MB ChB 1972 Aberd.; FRCP Lond. 1996; MRCP (UK) 1976; FRCPCH 1997; DCH (RCP) Lond. 1977. (Aberd.) Cons. Community Paediat. Blyth N.d. Socs: Brit. Assn. Community Child Health; Assn. Child Psychiat. & Psychol.; MRCPCH.

FLETCHER, Hugh Steel (retired) 3 Deveron Road, East Kilbride, Glasgow G74 2HS Tel: 01355 224340 — MB ChB 1957 Glas. Prev: GP E. Kilbride.

FLETCHER, Ian, KStJ (retired) 5 Lakeside, Ewell Court Avenue, Ewell, Epsom KT19 0ED Tel: 020 8393 3233 Email: elfan@mailbox.co.uk — MRCS Eng. LRCP Lond. 1946. Governor St. Dunstan's. Prev: Hon. Cons. Chailey Heritage Hosp. N. Chailey.

FLETCHER, Ian Harris The Surgery, 939 Green Lanes, Winchmore Hill, London N21 2PB Tel: 020 8360 2228 Fax: 020 9360 5702 — MB BS 1979 Lond.; MRCP (UK) 1983. (Univ. Coll. Hosp.)

FLETCHER, Ian Ronald Department of Anaesthesia, Royal Victoria Infirmary, Newcastle upon Tyne NE1 4LP Tel: 0191 232 5131 — MB BS 1971 Lond.; MRCP (UK) 1976; MRCS Eng. LRCP Lond. 1971; FFA RCS Eng. 1979; DA Eng. 1974; DObst RCOG 1973. (Roy. Free) Cons. (Anaesth.) Roy. Vict. Infirm. Newc.

FLETCHER, Ivor Maxwell (retired) Greenbank Cottage, Church St., Welford-on-Avon, Stratford-upon-Avon CV37 8EJ Tel: 01789 750991 — MB ChB Birm. 1956; MRCGP 1968; DObst RCOG 1960. Prev: GP Birm. & Nailsea.

FLETCHER, Janet Anne (retired) Lea Hall, The Lea, Ross-on-Wye HR9 7LQ Tel: 01989 750581 Fax: 01989 750581 — BM BCh Oxf. 1958; DObst RCOG 1960.

FLETCHER, Jeremy Allan Tel: 01245 515218 Fax: 01245 514677 — MB BS 1979 Lond.; MA Oxf. 1982; MD Lond. 1989; MRCP (UK) 1982. Cons. Phys. Broomfield Hosp. Chelmsford. Prev: Cons. Phys. P.ss Alexandra Hosp. Trust. Harlow; Sen. Regist. Birm.

FLETCHER, Jill Duncan Wilson Street Surgery, 11 Wilson Street, Derby DE1 1PG Tel: 01332 344366 Fax: 01332 348813; 2 Hatchmere Close, Oakwood, Derby DE21 2HP Tel: 01332 666635

— MB ChB 1988 Bristol; MRCP (UK) 1992; MRCGP 1994; DRCOG 1993; DFFP 1993. Prev: Trainee GP Wirksworth; SHO (O & G) Qu. Med. Centre; SHO (Paediat.) Derbysh. Childr. Hosp.

FLETCHER, Professor John 32 Regent Street, Nottingham NG1 5BT Tel: 0115 947 4126; Beck edge Cottage, 2 Main St, Caythorpe, Nottingham NG14 7ED Tel: 0115 966 3706 — MB BChir 1960 Camb.; MD Camb. 1969; FRCP Lond. 1975, M 1964. (Middlx.) Phys. Nottm. City Hosp.; Prof. Experim. Med. Nottm. Univ. Socs: Brit. Soc. Haematol.; Assn. Phys. Prev: Sen. Lect. (Clin. Haemat.) Univ. Coll. Hosp. Lond.; Watson Smith Research Fell. RCP Lond.; Regist. (Gastroenterol.) Centr. Middlx. Hosp. Lond.

FLETCHER, John Duncan Wallacetown Health Centre, 3 Lyon Street, Dundee DD4 6RF Tel: 01382 459519 Fax: 01382 453110 — MB ChB 1976 Aberd.; DRCOG 1979; MRCGP 1980.

FLETCHER, John Leslie Martin Lea Hall, The Lea, Ross-on-Wye HR9 7LQ — MB 1986 Camb.; MA Camb. 1986, MB 1986, BChir 1985; MRCGP 1992.

FLETCHER, John Robert (retired) 54 Saddleback Road, Shaw, Swindon SN5 5RN Tel: 01793 876107 — MRCS Eng. LRCP Lond. 1940. Prev: Capt. RAMC.

FLETCHER, John Williamson (retired) The Seckford Dispensary, 5 Seckford St., Woodbridge IP12 4LY Tel: 01394 385227 — MB ChB 1943 Manch.; MRCGP 1963; DCH Eng. 1944. Prev: Sen. Ho. Phys. Manch. Roy. Infirm.

FLETCHER, Joseph Sam Midlands Occupational Health Service Ltd., 83 Birmingham Road, West Bromwich B70 6PX Tel: 0121 553 7116; 13 Hilary Avenue, Mitcham CR4 2LA — MD 1971 Kharkov; MSc Occupat. Med. Lond. 1984; MD (Hons.) Kharkov 1971; MRCS Eng. LRCP Lond. 1982; MFOM RCP Lond. 1987, AFOM 1986; DIH Eng. 1979; DTM & H Liverp. 1976. Med. Dir. Midl. Occupat. Health Serv. W. Bromwich. Prev: Med. Off. W. Midl. Indust. Health Serv.

FLETCHER, Joy Valerie The Surgery, 7-8 Park Street, Ripon HG4 2AX; The Forge, Hutton Conyers, Ripon HG4 5EB — MB ChB 1978 Leeds; MRCGP (Distinc.) 1982; DRCOG 1981. Prev: GP Wrexham VTS; Ho. Off. Harrogate Dist. Hosps.; Clin. Asst. (Dermat.) Friarage Hosp. N.allerton.

FLETCHER, Julia Kate Park Avenue Medical Centre, 166-168 Park Avenue North, Northampton NN3 2HZ Tel: 01604 716500 Fax: 01604 721685; Measures House, Grafton Underwood, Kettering NN14 3AA — MB BS 1988 Lond.; MRCGP 1994.

FLETCHER, Kathryn Louise West Bank, Wood Rd. Lane, Summerseat, Bury BL9 5QA — MB ChB 1998 Manch.; MB ChB Manch 1998.

FLETCHER, Kathryn Mary St Bees Surgery, 34-36 St Bees Close, Moss Side, Manchester M14 4GG Tel: 0161 226 7615 Fax: 0161 226 0413; 7 Ballbrook Avenue, Manchester M20 6AB — MB ChB 1987 Manch.; MRCGP 1991; DRCOG 1990; DCH RCP Lond. 1989. Prev: Trainee GP Manch.

FLETCHER, Keron David New House Drug & Alcohol Unit, Shelton Hospital, Bicton Heath, Shrewsbury SY3 8DN Tel: 01743 492031 Fax: 01743 492299; 67 Underdale Road, Shrewsbury SY2 5EE — MB ChB 1981 Birm.; BSc Birm. 1977; MRCPsych 1988; MRCGP 1986; DFFP 1994; T(Psych) 1992. Cons. Psychiat. (Subst. Misuse) Shrops. Ment. Health NHS Trust; Regional Cons. Combat Stress Soc. Prev: Cons. Psychiat. RAF Hosp. Wroughton; Hon. Sen. Regist. (Psychogeriat.) Maudsley Hosp.; Hon. Sen. Regist. (Ment. Illness) Addenbrooke's Hosp. Camb.

FLETCHER, Leon Mark Westbank, 9 Park Crescent, Blackburn BB2 6DQ Email: lmf@holyrood.ed.ac.uk — MB ChB 1997 Ed. SHO (A&E), Cumbld. Infirm., Carlisle. Prev: SHO (A & E) Fazakerley Hosp. Liverp.; Ho. Off. (Gen. Med.) W.ern Gen. Hosp. Edin.; Ho. Off. (Gen. Surg.) Law Hosp. Carluke Lanarksh.

FLETCHER, Lorna Olive Adrienne Carnbroe Mains, Bellshill ML4 1RS Tel: 01698 748291 — MB BS 1954 Lond.; MRCS Eng. LRCP Lond. 1954.

FLETCHER, Louis (retired) 28 Argarmeols Road, Freshfield, Formby, Liverpool L37 7DA Tel: 0170 48 73303 — MB ChB 1940 Liverp.; DPH Leeds 1967; MFCM 1974. Prev: Sen. Asst. MOH Huddersfield Co. Boro. (Matern, Inf. & Child Welf.).

FLETCHER, Martin Furniss Birch Hill Hospital, Rochdale OL12 9QB Tel: 01706 377777 — MB BChir 1982 Camb.; MA Camb. 1982; MRCP (UK) 1984. Cons. Phys. (Integrated Med.) Rochdale Healthcare NHS Trust. Prev: Sen. Regist. (Geriat. & Gen. Med.) Manch. NW RHA.

FLETCHER, Martyn Steven Mandalay Medical Centre, 933 Blackburn Road, Bolton BL1 7LR Tel: 01204 302228 Fax: 01204 597949; 15 Great Stones Close, Egerton, Bolton BL7 9UY — MB ChB 1980 Manch.; DRCOG 1984.

FLETCHER, Mary (retired) Rowland Court Nursing Home, 21 Stocker Road, Bognor Regis PO21 1NY — MB ChB 1922 Manch.

FLETCHER, Mary Elizabeth Pasture Road Health Centre, Pasture Rd, Moreton, Wirral CH46 8SA — MB BS 1982 Lond.; BSc Lond. 1979; MRCGP 1986; DCH RCP Lond. 1986; DRCOG 1985. (Guy's) Socs: BMA & Family Plann. Assn. Prev: GP Greenwich, Lond.; Trainee GP Lewisham VTS.

FLETCHER, Matthew Douglas 67 Earlsmead Road, London NW10 5QD — MB BS 1996 Lond.

FLETCHER, Mr Matthew Shawcross The Hove Nuffield Hospital, 55 New Church Road, Hove BN3 4BG Tel: 01273 627057 Fax: 01273 220919; Sherwood, 32 Clermont Terrace, Preston Village, Brighton BN1 6SJ Tel: 01273 884436 — MB BS 1971 Lond.; MS Lond. 1986; FRCS Eng. 1977; MRCS Eng. LRCP Lond. 1971; DObst RCOG 1975. (King's Coll. Hosp.) Cons. Urol. Surg. Brighton Health Care NHS Trust. Socs: Fell. Roy. Soc. Med.; Soc. Minimally Invasive Ther.; BMA. Prev: St. Martins Lect. Stone Surg. Lond. Stone Clinic Lithotripter Centre & Inst. Urol. Lond.; Sen. Regist. (Urol.) King's Coll. Hosp. Lond.; Hon. Cons. Urol. Lithotripter Centre St. Thomas's Hosp. Lond.

FLETCHER, Maxine 6 Heathside Road, Northwood HA6 2EF — MB ChB 1987 Sheff. SHO (Anaesth.) Chesterfield Roy. & N. Derbysh. Hosp.

FLETCHER, Michael Antony Wallace and Partners, Blue Wing, Clydebank Health Centre, Kilbowie Road, Clydebank G81 2TQ Tel: 0141 531 6410 Fax: 0141 531 6413; 39 Woodend Drive, Jordanhill, Glasgow G13 1QJ — MB ChB 1976 Aberd.; MRCGP 1981.

FLETCHER, Michael Watford 2 Surrey Gardens, Birchington CT7 9SB Tel: 01843 841384 — MB BS 1964 Lond. (St. Bart.)

FLETCHER, Monica Mary Arnside Medical Practice, The Surgery, Orchard Road, Arnside, Carnforth LA5 0DP Tel: 01524 761311 Fax: 01524 762470; Ash House, Ball Lane, Caton, Lancaster LA2 9QN Tel: 01524 770476 — MB ChB 1971 Glas.

FLETCHER, Murray Harrison St Margarets Somerset Hospice, Heron Drive, Bishops Hull, Taunton TA1 5HA Tel: 01823 259394 Fax: 01823 345900 Email: mhf@st-marg-hospice.org — MB ChB 1985 Leic.; BSc (Hons.) E. Anglia 1980; MRCGP 1989; T (GP) 1991; DRCOG 1989. (Leicester University) Cons. Palliat. Med. St. Margt. Som. Hospice Taunton; Hon. Cons. Taunton & Som. NHS Trust, E. Som. NHS Trust & W.on Area Health Trust. Prev: Cons. Palliat. Med. W.on Hospicecare W.on Super Mare and W.on Area Health Trust; Regist. (Palliat. Med.) Marie Curie Centre Penarth; MacMillan Fell. (Palliat. Med.) St. Giles Hospice Lichfield.

***FLETCHER, Neil Edward** 21 Barr Crescent, Whitwick, Coalville LE67 5FF Tel: 01530 457622 Fax: 01530 457621 Email: nef1000@hotmail.com — BChir 1998 Camb.; BChir Camb 1998; BA (Hons.) Camb. 1995; MA Camb. 1999; MB Camb. 1999.

FLETCHER, Neville Hyman (retired) — MB BCh BAO 1955 Dub.; BA 1952. Prev: Full Time GP.

FLETCHER, Nicholas (retired) 55 Lawrence Gardens, Mill Hill, London NW7 4JU — MB ChB 1978 Birm.; BSc (Tech.) Manch. 1959; FFA RCSI 1978. Cons. (Anaesth.) Barnet Gen. Hosp. Prev: Sen. Regist. (Anaesth.) St. Mary's Hosp. Lond.

FLETCHER, Nicholas Anthony Walton Centre for Neurology & Neurosurgery, Liverpool L9 7LJ Tel: 0151 529 5701 — MB BS 1982 (Hons.) Lond.; MD Lond. 1990, BSc (Hons.) 1979; MRCP (UK) 1985; FRCP 1997. (Guy's) Cons. Neurol. Walton Centre for Neurol. & Neurosurg. Liverp.; Clin. Lect. (Neurol.) Univ. Liverp.; Cons. Neurol. Ysbyty Gwynedd Bangor & Countess of Chester Hosp. Socs: Movem. Disorder Soc.; Mem. Assn. Brit. Neurol.; Amer. Acad. of Neurol. Prev: Sen. Regist. (Neurol.) Nat. Hosp. Neurol. & Neurosurg. & St. Barts. Hosp. Lond.; Regist. (Neurol.) Nat. Hosp. Neurol. & Neurosurg. & Hammersmith Hosp. Lond.; MRC Clin. Research Fell. Inst. Neurol. Lond.

FLETCHER, Nicolas John Nene Valley Medical Centre, Clayton, Orton Goldhay, Peterborough PE2 5GP Tel: 01733 366600 Fax: 01733 370711 Email: admin@nenevalleysurgery.org.uk — MB ChB 1979 Sheff.; MRCGP 1985. Gen. Practitioner,Nene Valley Med. Pract.

FLETCHER, Norman John Penalverne Surgery, Penalverne Drive, Penzance TR18 2RE Tel: 01736 363361 Fax: 01736 332118; 22 Kings Road, Penzance TR18 4LG — MB BS 1980 Lond.; BSc (Hons.) Lond. 1977; DRCOG 1982. (St. Bart) Socs: W Penwith Med. Soc. Prev: Trainee GP/SHO Roy. Cornw. Hosp. Truro VTS; Ho. Phys. Greenbank Hosp. Plymouth; Ho. Surg. Gen. Hosp. St. Helier Jersey.

FLETCHER, Patricia Ann The Old Bakery, Burchetts Green, Maidenhead SL6 6QZ — MB ChB 1974 Liverp.; MRCGP 1988; AFOM RCP Lond. 1993. Sen. Occupat. Phys. BMI Health Serv. Lond. Prev: Occupat. Health Phys., OHC. Lond.; GP W. Berks.; SHO Paediat. Roy. Berks. Hosp. Reading.

FLETCHER, Patricia Duncan (retired) The Lantern, Kellacott, Launceston PL15 9SW Tel: 01566 784440 — MB ChB 1949 Birm.; DObst RCOG 1953; DCH Eng. 1951. Prev: Sen. Partner Gen. Pract. Lond.

FLETCHER, Patricia Florence Minden Medical Centre, 2 Barlow Street, Bury BL9 0QP Tel: 0161 764 2651 Fax: 0161 761 5967; West Bank, Wood Road Lane, Summerseat, Bury BL9 5QA Tel: 0120 488 4934 Fax: 01204 888 8411 — MB ChB 1968 Manch.; MRCGP 1979; FRCGP 1996. (Manch.) GP; Mem. LMC; Company Phys. Warner Lambeth (Radcliffe UK); Organiser VTS Scheme Bury and Course Organiser Bury (Barot); PCG Tutor, Bury N. PCGT. Socs: BMA.

FLETCHER, Paul Charles 11 Hunters Ridge, Bridgend CF31 2LH — MB BS 1987 Lond.

FLETCHER, Paul Thomas The Surgery, Front Street, Great Lumley, Chester-le-Street DH3 4LE Tel: 0191 388 5600 Fax: 0191 388 3912; 53 Longdean Park, Chester-le-Street DH3 4DG — MB BS 1980 Newc.; MRCGP 1985; DCH RCP Lond. 1983; DRCOG 1983; Cert. Family Plann. JCC 1982. Trainer (Gen. Pract.) N.umbria VTS.

FLETCHER, Peter Health Centre, Lawson St., Stockton-on-Tees TS18 1HU Tel: 01642 672351 Fax: 01642 618112; 540 Yarm Road, Eaglescliffe, Stockton-on-Tees TS16 0BH Tel: 01642 781215 — MB BS Durh. 1963. (Durham (now Newcastle)) Prev: SHO (Cas. & Orthop.) & SHO (Neurosurg.) Middlesbrough Gen. Hosp.; SHO (Obst.) Middlesbrough Matern. Hosp.

FLETCHER, Peter John Cheltenham General Hospital, Sandford Road, Cheltenham GL53 7AN Tel: 01242 272044 Fax: 01242 272092 Email: peter.fletcher@egnhst.org.uk; Black Horse Ridge, Stroud Road, Birdlip, Gloucester GL4 8JN Tel: 01452 864821 — MB ChB 1979 Birm.; MSc Wales 1998; FRCP Lond. 1995; MRCP (UK) 1985; T(M) 1991. Cons. Phys. (Gen. & Geriat. Med.) E. Glos. NHS Trust. Socs: Assn. Study Med. Educat.; Brit. Geriat. Soc.; Brit. Soc. Rehabil. Med. Prev: Sen. Regist. (Gen. & Geriat. Med.) Roy. Cornw. Hosp. Truro; Regist. (Med.) Taunton & Som. Hosp. & Yeovil Dist. Hosp.; SHO Guy's Hosp. Lond.

FLETCHER, Peter Richard Department of Anaesthetics, Hinchingbrooke Hospital, Hinchingbrooke Park, Huntingdon PE29 6NT Tel: 01480 416210 Fax: 01480 416698 Email: peter.fletcher@hghs-tr.anglox.nhs.uk; Email: pfletch@ntlworld.com — BM BCh Oxf. 1974; MA Oxf. 1974; MRCP (UK) 1977; Dip Amer Bd of Anaesthesiol 1981. (Univ. Oxf.) Cons. Anaesth. Hinchingbrooke Hosp. Huntingdon; Clin. Director Surgic. Serv.s Hinchingbrooke Hosp. Socs: BMA; Assn. Anaesth. GB & Irel.; Assoc. Mem. Amer. Soc. Anesthesiol. Prev: Attend. Anaesth. . & Dir. Dept. Anaesth. Delaware Co. Memor. Hosp. PA, USA; Asst. Prof. & Attend. Anesthesiol. Univ. Conn. Health Center, Farmington, CT, USA.

FLETCHER, Peter Ronald Hodson (retired) Summerfield, Stainburn Road, Workington CA14 1SL Tel: 01900 605288 — LRCPI & LM, LRSCI & LM 1959; LRCPI & LM, LRCSI & LM 1959.

FLETCHER, Richard Ian Lee Bank Group Practice, Colston Health Centre, 10 Bath Row, Lee Bank, Birmingham B15 1LZ Tel: 0121 622 4846 Fax: 0121 622 7105 — MB BS 1973 Lond.; BSc (Pharmacol.) Lond. 1969, MB BS 1973. (Univ. Coll. Hosp.) Hon. Sen. Clin. Lect. Birm. Univ. Med. Sch. Birm.

FLETCHER, Mr Robert David Michael Sunderland Royal Hospital, Kayll Road, Sunderland SR4 7TP; 7 Chester Crescent, Sandyford, Newcastle upon Tyne NE2 1DH — MB 1977 Camb.; MA Camb. 1974, MB 1977, BChir 1976. Assoc. Specialist (Orthop.), Sunderland Roy. Hosp. Prev: Staff Grade (Orthop.) Sunderland Roy. Hosp.; Regist. Rotat. (Surg.) Newc.; SHO Rotat. (Surg.) Nottm.

FLETCHER, Roger Hesketh (retired) 1 Henbury Lane, Cheadle Hulme, Cheadle SK8 6PS Tel: 0161 485 8288 — MB ChB Manch. 1967; MD Lund, Sweden 1980; FFA RCS Eng. 1972. Prev: Cons. Anaesth. Centr. Manch. Hosps. NHS Trust.

FLETCHER, Ronald Frank (retired) 11 St Mary's Road, Birmingham B17 0EY Tel: 0121 427 4043 — MB ChB MB ChB Birm. 1950; BSc (Hons. Physiol) Birm 1947; MD (Hons) Birm 1959; PhD Birm 1971; FRCP Lond. 1972 (M 1957). Hon. Cons. Phys. City Hosp. Birm.; Hon. Fell. Univ. Birm.

FLETCHER, Ruth Margaret EMAS Arden House, Regent Centre, Gosforth, Newcastle upon Tyne NE3 3JN Tel: 0191 202 6267 Fax: 0191 202 6300; 193 New Ridley Road, Stocksfield NE43 7QD Tel: 01661 842026 — MB BS 1975 Newc.; MA Camb. 1978, BA (Med. Sc.) 1972; MFOM RCP Lond. 1996, AFOM 1991; DRCOG 1978. Employm. Med. Adviser Health & Safety Exec. Socs: Soc. Occupat. Med.; Fac. Occupat. Med.; Brit. Assn. Sport & Med. Prev: Clin. Med. Off. (Ment. Handicap) N.d.; Community Med. Off. Family Plann.

FLETCHER, Sarah Elizabeth 25 East Budleigh Road, Budleigh Salterton EX9 6EJ Tel: 01395 443574 — MB ChB 1995 Leic. (Leic.) Resid. Med. Off. Rotat. Waneanui Hosp. N. Is., NZ. Prev: Ho. Off. (Surg.) Taunton & Som. Hosp.; Ho. Off. (Med.) Lincoln Co. Hosp.

FLETCHER, Sheila Mary Elizabeth (retired) Seckford Dispensary, 5 Seckford St., Woodbridge IP12 4LY Tel: 01394 385227 — MB ChB 1950 Manch.; MRCGP 1963; DObst RCOG 1952. Prev: GP Co-ordinator Kensington, Chelsea & W.m. FHSA DHSS.

FLETCHER, Simon Walsgrave Hospital, Clifford Bridge Road, Walsgrave, Coventry CV2 2DX Tel: 024 76 602020 Fax: 024 7653 8881 — MB BS 1987 London; BSc (Physiol.) Lond. 1984; MRCP 1989 UK; MD 2000 London. (St. Bartholomew's Hospital) Cons. Phys. Gen. and Renal Med. Walsgrave NHS Trust Coventry; Cons. Phys. (Gen. & Renal Med.). Socs: Renal Assn.; RCP. Prev: Regist. (Med. Nephrol.) Leeds Gen. Infirm.; Regist. (Med. Nephrol.) St. James' Teachg. Hosp. Leeds; Regist. (Nephrol.) Hull Roy. Infirm.

FLETCHER, Simon James 6 Christchurch Road, Norwich NR2 2AD Tel: 01603 250852 — MB BS 1983 Lond.; FRCA 1988. Cons. Anaesth. & Intens. Care Norf. & Norwich Hosp. Prev: Sen. Regist. (Anaesth.) Addenbrooke's Hosp. Camb.; SHO & Regist. (Anaesth.) St. Thos. Hosp. Lond.; Asst. Prof. Anaesth. Univ. Maryland, Baltimore, USA.

FLETCHER, Simon Nicholas 20 Monica Drive, Widnes WA8 9JP — MB BS 1989 Newc.

FLETCHER, Stephen Daniel Willesden Green Surgery, 125 High Road, Willesden, London NW10 2SR Tel: 020 8459 7755 Fax: 020 8459 7809; 22 Copthall Drive, Mill Hill, London NW7 2NB Tel: 020 8959 0352 — MB BS 1979 Lond.; MRCS Eng. LRCP Lond. 1979. (Char. Cross)

FLETCHER, Stephen John 47 Jenkin Roa, Horbury, Wakefield WF4 6DP — MB BS 1990 Newc. Regist. (Anaesth.) Leeds Gen. Infirm.

FLETCHER, Stewart Pathology Department, Al Zahra Hospital, Sharjah PO Box 3499, United Arab Emirates Tel: 00 971 65 675609 Fax: 00 971 65 624296; 56 Polwarth Terrace, Edinburgh EH11 1NJ Tel: 0131 337 5504 — MB ChB 1958 Glas.; BSc (1st cl. Hons. Bact.) Glas. 1956, MB ChB 1958; FRCS Ed. 1987; FRCPath 1977, M 1966. Cons. Pathologist Al Zahra Hosp. Sharjah UAE. Socs: Path. Soc. & Assn. Clin. Pathol. Prev: Sen. Lect. (Path.) Univ. Edin.

FLETCHER, Susan The Beeches, Elmslack Lane, Silverdale, Carnforth LA5 0RX — MB BS 1992 Lond.

FLETCHER, Mr Thomas (retired) Linden House, Papcastle, Cockermouth CA13 0LA Tel: 01900 823260 — MD (Commend.) Glas. 1939, MB ChB (Hons.) 1936; FRCS Glas. 1962; FRCS Ed. 1943; MRCGP 1962; DPH & BHyg. Durh. 1939. Prev: Chairm. Cumbld. Exec. Counc.

FLETCHER, Thomas Stanley The Health Centre, College Street, Leigh WN7 2RF Tel: 01942 678600 Fax: 01942 261179 — MB BS 1968 Lond.; MRCGP 1976; DObst RCOG 1975; Cert Contracep. & Family Plann. RCOG, RCGP &; Cert FPA 1975. (St. Mary's) Sport. Socs: Mem. Brit. Med. Acupunc. Soc. & Mem. Brit. Assn. of Trauma.

FLETCHER, Timothy George 24 Thorne Park Road, Chelston, Torquay TQ2 6RU — MB ChB 1980 Otago.

FLETCHER, Timothy John Good Hope Hospital, Rectory Road, Sutton Coldfield B75 7RR Tel: 0121 378 2211 Fax: 0121 378 6095 — MB BS 1986 Lond.; MA Oxf. 1981. Cons. Phys. Prev: Research Fell. Birm. Heartlands Hosp.; Regist. (Gen. Med.) King Edwd. VII Hosp. Windsor.

FLETCHER, Valerie Jane 29 Medstead Road, Beech, Alton GU34 4AD — BM 1993 Soton.

FLETCHER, Victoria Louise 22 Elmhurst, Egginton, Derby DE65 6HQ — BM BS 1997 Nottm.

FLETCHER, Wendy Lynne — BM BS 1986 Nottm.; BMedSci (Hons.) Nottm. 1984; MRCGP 1991; DRCOG 1990. p/t Clin. Asst. (Palliat. Care) W.on Hospice Care; GP Retainee Banwell Surg. W.on-Super-Mare. Prev: Clin. Asst. (Palliat. Care) Cossham Hosp.; Trainee GP Avon VTS; Trainee GP Derby VTS.

FLETCHER, William Donald (retired) 7 Tintern Gardens, Southgate, London N14 6AS Tel: 020 8886 3647 — MB ChB 1943 Leeds; DPhysMed Eng. 1951. Prev: Sen. Cons. Rheum. & Rehabil. Univ. Coll. Hosp. Lond.

FLETT, Mrs Aileen Elizabeth Easter Crichie Cottage, St Katherines, Inverurie AB51 8SR Tel: 01651 891620 — MB ChB Aberd. 1962. Clin. Asst. (p/t) Respirat. Med. Grampian Health Bd. Prev: Research Asst. in Genetics Aberd. Univ.; SHO (Orthop.) Woodend Hosp.; Research Asst. (Med.) Grampian Health Bd.

FLETT, Elizabeth Horne (retired) 1 Embankment, Putney, London SW15 1LB Tel: 020 8788 0370 — MRCS Eng. LRCP Lond. 1941; FFA RCS Eng. 1954; DA Eng. 1945. Prev: Cons. Anaesth. N.W. (St. Mary's) Health Dist. (T).

FLETT, Gillian Mary Melville Square 13, Centre for Reproductive Health, 13 Golden Square, Aberdeen AB10 1RH Fax: 01224 626359 — MB ChB 1980 Glas.; MFFP 1993; MRCOG 1986. Cons. Family Plann. & Reproduc. Healthcare, Grampian Univ. Hosp.s NHS Trust. Prev: Staff Doctor (O & G) Aberd. Roy. Hosps. NHS Trust; Regist. (Obst & Gyn.) Aberd. Roy. Infirm. & Matern. Hosp.

FLETT, Hilary Irene 6 Rye Grove, The Fairways, West Derby, Liverpool L12 9NF — MB ChB 1988 Liverp.

FLETT, Mr Martyn Esson 9 Berryden Road, Aberdeen AB25 3SB Tel: 01224 620077 Email: meflett@hotmail.com — MB ChB 1995 Aberd.; BSc (1st cl. Hons.) Med. Sci. Aberd. 1994; AFRCS (Ed) 1998 (RCSEd). (Aberdeen University) SHO (Paediat. Surg.), Yorkhill Hosp., Glas. Prev: SHO (Gen. Surg.) Basic Surgic. Train. Scheme Aberd.

FLETT, Rachel Hilary 51 Osborne Gardens, Belfast BT9 6LF Tel: 01232 665861 — MB BCh BAO 1967 Belf.; DObst RCOG 1971. (Belf.) Sen. Med. Off. DHSS. Belf. Prev: GP Dub.; SHO (Chest Med. & Tuberc.) PeaMt. Hosp. Newc., Dub.; Dept. Med. Off. Lond. Boro. Bromley.

FLETT, Sheila Russell Vale of Leven Hospital, Alexandria — MB ChB 1985 Aberd.; MSc 1990 Manch; MRCPsych 1990 Manch. p/t Sen. Regist. (Psychiat.) Withington Hosp. Manch. Prev: Regist. (Psychiat.) Withington Hosp. Manch.; Ho. Phys. & Ho. Surg. Aberd. Roy. Infirm.; Sen. Regist. (Psychiat.), Manch.

FLEURY, Renee Alice (retired) 1 Lime Close, Dorchester DT1 2HQ Tel: 01305 263988 — MB BCh BAO Dub. 1950; DA RCPSI 1956. Prev: Asst. Specialist (Anaesth.) W. Dorset Hosp. Gp.

FLEW, Jonathan Peter Priory Road Surgery, Priory Road, Park South, Swindon SN3 2EZ Tel: 01793 521154 Fax: 01793 512562; Elm Farm, Horpit, Lower Wanborough, Swindon SN4 0AT — MB BS 1973 Lond.; MRCGP 1980; DRCOG 1976; DA Eng. 1976. (St. Thos.) Prev: Cas. Off. St. Thos. Hosp. Lond.; SHO (Anaesth.) St. Thos. Lond.; SHO (O & G) Ashford Gen. Hosp. Middlx.

FLEW, Richard Claremont Surgery, Wilderness Medical Centre, 2 Cookham Road, Maidenhead SL6 8AN Tel: 01628 673033; Keeper's Cottage, Marlow Road, Maidenhead SL6 6PH Email: hu86@dial.pipex.com — MB BS 1968 Lond.; FRCGP 1988, M 1976; DCH Eng. 1971; DObst RCOG 1970. (Univ. Coll. Hosp.) Assoc. Regional Adviser Gen. Pract. Oxf. Prev: Ho. Phys. & Ho. Surg. Stoke Mandeville Hosp. Aylesbury; SHO (Obst.) Perivale Matern. Hosp. Greenford; SHO (Paediat.) Hillingdon Hosp. Uxbridge.

FLEW, Mr Timothy John (retired) Corners, Stone Allerton, Axbridge BS26 2NW Tel: 01934 712567 Email: timflew@compuserve.com — MB Camb. 1965, BChir 1964; FRCS Eng. 1969; MRCS Eng. LRCP Lond. 1964. Prev: Cons. Gen. Surg. W.on-super-Mare Gen. Hosp.

FLEWERS, Gillian Mary, Squadron Ldr. RAF Med. Br. (Avory) Email: gillavory@breathemail.net; 2 Southam Fields Farm, Bishops Cleeve, Cheltenham GL52 8ND Email: gillavory@breathemail.net — BM 1994 Soton.; MRCGP 1999; DCH 1996; DRCOG 1997; DFFP 1998. (Soton.) Unit Med. Off. Socs: BMA; MDU; Med. Sickness Soc. Prev: UMO, RMC, RAF Brize Norton; GP Regist. at RMC RAF Brize Norton; SHO (A&E) Peterboro Dist. Hosp.

FLEWETT, Thomas Henry (retired) 17 Sharmans Cross Road, Solihull B91 1RG Tel: 0121 705 0764 — MD 1948 Belf.; MD (High Commend.) Belf. 1948, MB BCh BAO (2nd Cl; Hnrs.) 1945; FRCP Lond. 1978, M 1974; FRCPath 1968. Prev: Dir. Birm. Regional Virus Laborat.

FLEWETT, Thomas Peter c/o Mr D. Flewett, 3 Warleigh Road, Brighton BN1 4NT — MB BS 1980 Lond.; MRCPsych 1985.

FLEWETT, William Edward Fox Hall, Marbury, Whitchurch SY13 4NB — MB BCh BAO 1948 Belf. (Belf.)

FLEWITT, Andrew Peter Sherrington Park Medical Practice, 402 Mansfield Road, Nottingham NG5 2EJ Tel: 0115 985 8552 Fax: 0115 985 8553; 161 Lichfield Lane, Berry Hill, Mansfield NG18 4RP Tel: 01623 622416 — MB BS 1983 Lond.; BSc Lond. 1980; DRCOG 1989; Cert. Family Plann. JCC 1989. (St. Mary's) GP; FEMO Roy. Navy & Marines Nottm. Prev: Trainee GP Lond. VTS.

FLEWITT, Pamela Constance (retired) 5 The Covert, Thorpe Road, Longthorpe, Peterborough PE3 6HT Tel: 01733 265898 — MB BCh BAO Dub. 1957; DA Eng. 1959. Prev: Regist. (Anaesth.) Roy. Vict. Hosp. Boscombe.

FLEWITT, Roger Malcolm (retired) 5 The Covert, Thorpe Road, Longthorpe, Peterborough PE3 6HT Tel: 01733 265898 Fax: 01733 265898 — MB BCh BAO Dub. 1956. Prev: GP P'boro.

FLIGELSTONE, Jonathan Sydney The Surgery, Heywood, Lodway Gdns, Pill, Bristol BS20 0DN Tel: 01275 372105 Fax: 01275 373879; 38 Lodway, Easton in Gordano, Bristol BS20 0JB Tel: 01275 375375 — MB ChB 1980 Manch.; DRCOG 1982.

FLIGELSTONE, Mr Louis John Department of Surgery, Morriston Hospital, Swansea SA6 6NL Tel: 01792 703584 Fax: 01792 704087 Email: fligelston@aol.com; 4 Channel View, Langland, Swansea SA3 4PL — MB BCh 1986 Wales; FRCS Eng. 1991; FRCS (Gen) 1997. (UWCM) Cons. Gen. & Vasc. Surg., Dept. Surg., Morriston Hosp., Swansea; Cons. Vasc. and Gen. Surg., Sancta Maria Hosp., Ffynone Rd., Swansea. Socs: Assn. Surg.; Eur. Soc. of Vasc. Surg.; Vasc. Surgic. Soc. GB & Irel. Prev: Sen. Regist., Regional Vasc. Unit, Char. Cross Hosp.; Research Fell. Cardiff Vasc. Unit; Regist. (Gen. & Vasc. Surg.) Univ. Hosp. Wales.

FLIGHT, Derek John Earleydene, Chesterfield Road, Eastbourne BN20 7NT Tel: 01323 730347 — MB BS 1952 Lond.; MRCS Eng. LRCP Lond. 1952. (St. Geo.) Prev: Hosp. Pract. (Genito-Urin. Med.) St. Helier Hosp. Carshalton; Ho. Surg. & Cas. Off. St. Geo. Hosp.

FLIGHT, Roy Julian c/o Iford Mill, Bradford-on-Avon BA15 2BB — MB BS 1952 Lond.

FLIND, Anthony Chisholm 75 Burnham Green Road, Welwyn AL6 0NH Tel: 01438 798077 Fax: 01438 798077 — BM BCh 1958 Oxf.; MA Oxf. 1958; FFPM RCP (UK) 1989; Dip. Pharm. Med. RCP (UK) 1976; DCH Eng. 1964. (Oxf. & St Geo.) Consg. Pharmaceut. Phys. Socs: Fell. Roy. Soc. Med.; Brit. Assn. Pharmaceut. Phys. Prev: Med. Dir. SmithKline & French Laborats. Ltd.; Regist. (Paediat.) Windsor Hosp. Gp.; Regist. (Med.) W. Lond. Hosp.

FLINDERS, Sharon Ann 5 Compton Avenue, Islington, London N1 2XD Tel: 020 7226 0951 Fax: 020 7226 0951 — MB BS 1987 Lond.; BSc.; MRCGP. (St. Thomas') Asst. In Gen. Pract.

FLINDT, Michael Leighton Huntley (retired) Lowridding, Cautley, Sedbergh LA10 5LU — MB BS 1946 Lond.; FFOM RCP Lond. 1980, MFOM 1978; MRCS Eng. LRCP Lond. 1945; DIH Eng. 1967. Prev: Hon. Fell. & Sen. Lect. (Occupat. Med.) Univ. Manch.

FLINN, Anthony John Huntingdon Road Surgery, 1 Huntingdon Road, Cambridge CB3 0DB Tel: 01223 364127 Fax: 01223 322541; 219 Hills Road, Cambridge CB2 2RN — BChir 1983 Camb.; BA Camb. 1980, BChir 1983, MB 1983; MRCGP 1988; DRCOG 1987; Dip. Occ. Med. 1995. (Cambridge) Prev: Trainee GP Aylesbury VTS; Ho. Phys. P'boro Dist. Hosp.; Ho. Surg. Addenbrookes Hosp. Camb.

FLINN, Janet Perth Royal Infirmary, Perth PH1 1NX; 21 Kincarrathie Crescent, Perth PH2 7HH — MB ChB 1984 Sheff.; MB ChB Sheff. l984; MRCP (UK) 1987; FRCR 1991; DMRD Ed. 1990. Cons. Radiol. Perth Roy. Infirm. Prev: Sen. Regist. (Radiol.) Edin. Roy. Infirm.

FLINN, Roger Martin 35 Medcroft Avenue, Handsworth Wood, Birmingham B20 1NB Tel: 0121 554 9582 — MB ChB 1958 Manch.; MSc Birm. 1963. (Manch.)

FLINT, E Jane Wordsley Hospital, Stream Road, Wordsley, Stourbridge DY8 5QX Tel: 01384 401401 Fax: 01384 244583; 8 The Woodlands, Pedmore, Stourbridge DY8 2RA — MB ChB Birm.

1975; BSc Birm. 1972, MD 1987; FRCP Lond. 1994; MRCP (UK) 1979. Cons. Phys. & Cardiol. Dudley Gp. Hosps. NHS Trust. Socs: (Past-Pres.) Brit. Nuclear Cardiol Soc.; Elected Rep. On Counc. of Brit. Cardiac Soc.; DGH Mem on Coll. Speciality Comm. Prev: Sen. Regist. (Cardiol.) United Birm. Hosp.; Regist. (Gen. Med. & Cardiol.) Gen. Hosp. Birm.; Sheldon Clin. Research Fell. (Nuclear Cardiol.) Walsgrave Hosp. Coventry.

FLINT, Mr Ewen Farquharson Dumfries & Galloway Royal Infirmary, Bankend Road, Dumfries DG1 4AP Tel: 01387 246246 Email: e.flint@dgri.scot.nhs.uk; Craigearn, 7 Kirkland Wynd, Calside, Dumfries DG1 4ES Tel: 01387 253697 Email: ewenflint@publiconline.co.uk — MB ChB 1976 Glas.; BSc (Hons.) Glas. 1974; FRCS Glas. 1980. (Glasgow) Cons. Surg. (ENT) Dumfries & Galloway Roy. Infirm. Socs: Scott. Otolaryg. Soc.; Brit. Assn. Otol. Prev: Sen. Regist. (ENT) Aberd. Roy. Infirm.; Regist. ENT Hosp. Glas.

FLINT, Frederic James (retired) 23 Sefton Road, Sheffield S10 3TP — BM BCh 1943 Oxf.; MA Oxf. 1953, BA (Physiol.) 1942, DM 1953; FRCP Lond. 1968, M 1946. Prev: Cons. Phys. N.. Gen. Hosp. Sheff.

FLINT, Gordon Douglas Ker Middle Deuglie, Glenfarg, Perth PH2 9QJ Tel: 01577 830250 Fax: 01577 830250 — MB ChB Ed. 1961; LRCP LRCS Ed. LRFPS Glas. 1961; DObst RCOG 1964. (Ed.) Founder Fell. Brit. Soc. Med. & Dent. Hypn. Socs: Fell. (Pres.) Inst. Psionic Med.; Founder Fell. Brit. Soc. Med. & Dent. Hypn.; Psonic Med. Soc. Dean Inst. Psionic Med. Prev: SHO Med. Astley Hosp.; SHO O & G Groundslow Hosp. Tittensor; Ho. Phys. Leigh Infirm.

FLINT, Mr Graham Arthur Department Neurosurgery, Queen Elizabeth Hospital, Edgbaston, Birmingham B15 2TH — MB ChB 1975 Birm.; BSc Birm. 1972, MB ChB 1975; FRCS Eng. 1980. Cons. Neurosurg. S. Birm. HA.

FLINT, Janet Elisabeth Huntingdon Road Surgery, 1 Huntingdon Road, Cambridge CB3 0DB Tel: 01223 364127 Fax: 01223 322541; 238 Queen Ediths Way, Cambridge CB1 8NL Tel: 01223 249921 — MB BS 1966 Lond.; MRCS Eng. LRCP Lond. 1966; DCH Eng. 1968; DObst RCOG 1968. (Westm.) Prev: Resid. Paediat. Yale New Haven Hosp. New Haven, USA; Ho. Phys. W.m. Hosp. Lond.

FLINT, Jonathan Institute of Molecular Medicine, John Radcliffe Hospital, Oxford OX3 9DU Tel: 01865 222631 Fax: 01865 222500 Email: jf@worf.molbiol.ox.ac.uk — BM BCh 1988 Oxf.; MRCPsych 1993. Wellcome Trust, Sen. Clin. Fell. Inst. Molecular Med. Oxf. Socs: Roy. Soc. Med. Prev: Regist. (Psychiat.) Maudsley Hosp. Lond.

FLINT, Neil James 142 Howard Road, Leicester LE2 1XJ — MB ChB 1998 Leic.; MB ChB Leic 1998.

FLINT, Peter John The New Surgery, Lindo Close, Chesham HP5 2JN Tel: 01494 782262 — MB ChB 1972 Leeds; MRCGP 1976; DObst RCOG 1975. (Leeds)

FLINT, Robert Peter 16 Amersham Road, High Wycombe HP13 6QU — MB ChB 1997 Leeds.

FLINT, Rupert Adam Saville Medical Group, 7 Saville Place, Newcastle upon Tyne NE1 8DQ Tel: 0191 232 4274 Fax: 0191 233 1050; 60 Elmfield Road, Gosforth, Newcastle upon Tyne NE3 4BD — MB BS 1986 Lond.; MRCGP 1990. Socs: BMA.

FLINT, Sarah Karen The New Orchard, School Hill, Wargrave, Reading RG10 8DY Tel: 01734 402328; 48 Oakbank Grove, Herne Hill, London SE24 0AJ — MB BS 1988 Lond.; BSc. Lond. 1985, MB BS 1988; MRCOG 1993. Hon. Regist. (O & G) Kings Coll. Hosp. Lond. Prev: Regist. (O & G) St. Geo. Hosp. Lond.; SHO (Urol.) Inst. Urol. Lond.; SHO (O & G) Greenwich Dist. & Kings Coll. Hosps. Lond.

FLINTAN, Bernadette Anne Bicester Health Centre, Coker Close, Bicester OX26 6AT Tel: 01869 249333 Fax: 01869 320314; Manor Farm, Wotton Underwood, Aylesbury HP18 0SB Tel: 01844 237551 — MB BS 1976 Lond.; MRCGP 1981; DRCOG 1981. (Middlx.)

FLINTAN, Kevin (retired) Woodside, 133 Boundary Road, Wallington SM6 0TE — MRCS Eng. LRCP Lond. 1957; DObst RCOG 1960. Phys. Carshalton War Memor. Hosp. Prev: Ho. Phys., Obst Ho. Surg. & Orthop. Sen. Ho. Off. St. Helier Hosp.

FLINTER, Frances Anne Genetics Centre, Division of Medical and Molecular Genetics, 8th Floor, Guy's Tower, Guy's Hospital, London SE1 9RT Tel: 020 7955 4648 Fax: 020 7955 2550 Email: f.flinter@umds.ac.uk; The Coach House, 29 Rowantree Road, Enfield EN2 8PY Tel: 020 8367 0931 Fax: 020 8364 4575 Email: frances.flinter@kcl.ac.uk — MB BS 1982 Lond.; MD Lond. 1989; FRCP Lond. 1997; FRCPCH 1997; DCH RCP Lond. 1984. (Guy's) Sen. Lect. & Hon. Cons. Clin. Genetics Guy's Hosp. Lond. Socs: Brit. Soc. Human Genetics; Fell. Brit. Paediat. Assn. Prev: Sen. Regist. (Clin. Genetics) Paediat. Research Unit Guy's Hosp. Lond.; SHO (Paediat.) Guy's Hosp. & W.minster Childr.s Hosp. Lond.

FLIPPANCE, Patrick Dennis Anthony Corporate Medical Management Ltd., The Courtyard, Hall Lane, Wincham, Northwich CW9 6DG Tel: 01606 354084 Fax: 01606 351330 Email: patrickflippance@cmn.uk.net; York House, 279 Stockport Road, Timperley, Altrincham WA15 7SP Tel: 0161 980 4624 — MB BS 1979 Lond.; AFOM RCP Lond. 1989; MRCGP 1986; DRCOG 1983. (St Thomas's) Occupat.al Phys., Corporate Med. Managem. Ltd. Prev: Sen. Med. Off. Corus Construction and Indust.; Sen. Med. Off., Corus plc (formerly Brit. Steel plc); Med. Off., BSC Stainless.

FLIS, Christine Margaret 21 Manchuria Road, London SW11 6AF Tel: 020 7738 1338 — MB BS 1996 Lond.; BSc Lond. 1993. (King's Coll.) SHO (A & E) Kingston Hosp. Surrey. Prev: SHO (Elderly Care Med.) Kingston Hosp.; Ho. Off. (Med.) King's Coll. Hosp. Lond.

FLITCROFT, Daniel Ian 2B Howley Place, London W2 1XA — MB BS 1991 Lond.; MA, DPhil Oxf. 1989.

FLOCKHART, David Rodger Greyfriars Medical Centre, 33-37 Castle Street, Dumfries DG1 1DL Tel: 01387 257752 Fax: 01387 257020 — MB ChB 1973 Glas.

FLOCKTON, Elizabeth Anne Hillcrest, Villa Road, Bingley BD16 4EY — MB ChB 1998 Ed.; MB ChB Ed 1998.

FLOHR, Carsten Freeman Hospital, Freeman Road, High Heaton, Newcastle upon Tyne NE7 7DN — BM BCh 1998 Oxf.; BM BCh Oxf 1998.

FLOOD, Ambrose Joseph 91 St Dunstans Road, London W6 8RE — MB BCh BAO 1969 NUI.

FLOOD, Andrew George 19 Rolph Close, Thorpe-le-Soken, Clacton-on-Sea CO16 0NS — MB BS 1996 Lond.

FLOOD, Anthony, MC (retired) 26 Kynance mews, London SW7 4QR Tel: 0207 937 5273 — MB ChB St. And. 1956; DPM Eng. 1961. Prev: Cons. Psychiat. Dorset.

FLOOD, Mr Brian Michael Haigh House, Raw End Road, Warley, Halifax HX2 7SR — MB BS 1975 Lond.; FRCS Eng. 1981; FRCS Ed. 1981; MRCS Eng. LRCP Lond. 1975. Cons. Orthop. Surg. Calderdale Healthcare NHS Trust.

FLOOD, Colin Patrick 29 Glantraeth, Bangor LL57 1HQ — MB BCh BAO 1986 Dub.; MB BCh Dubl. 1986.

FLOOD, Gerard Hall Green Surgery, 164 Ormskirk Road, Upholland, Skelmersdale WN8 0AB Tel: 01695 622268; 29 Tower Hill Road, Upholland, Skelmersdale WN8 0DU Tel: 01695 623044 — MB BCh BAO 1966 Dub.; MSc (Distinc.) Lond. 1988; MA Dub. 1974, BA 1963, MB BCh BAO 1966. (TC Dub.) GP Tutor Univ. Manch., Ormskirk & Dist. Gen. Hosps.; Course Organiser W. Lancs. VTS.

FLOOD, James Edward 80 High Street, Littleton Panell, Devizes SN10 4EX Tel: 01380 813300 Fax: 01380 818669 — MB ChB 1969 Manch.; MRCS Eng. LRCP Lond. 1969; MRCGP 1978. GP Devizes; Med. Off. H.M Prison Erlestoke; Police Surg. Devizes. Prev: SHO (O & G) Freedom Fields Hosp. Plymouth; Med. Off. RN.

FLOOD, Mr John Gerard 63 The Vinyard, Richmond TW10 6AS — MB BCh BAO 1977 NUI; FRCS RCPS Glas. 1985.

FLOOD, Mr Liam Martin North Riding Infirmary, Newport Road, Middlesbrough TS1 5JE Tel: 01642 854046 Fax: 01642 854064; The Forge, Kirby, Middlesbrough TS9 7AL Tel: 01642 710107 Fax: 01642 712971 — MB BS 1976 Lond.; FRCS Eng. 1980. (Univ. Coll. Hosp.) Cons. Otolaryngol. N. Riding Infirm Middlesbrough; Vis. Prof. UKM Malaysia 1991 & 1993.; Vis. Fell. Univ. Teesside. Socs: Fell. Roy. Soc. Med.; Otorhynolaryng. Soc. (Ex. Counc. Mem.); N. Eng. Soc. (Ex. Counc. Mem.). Prev: Clin. Research Fell. Univ. Michigan, USA; Regist. (ENT) Univ. Coll. Hosp. Lond.; SHO Roy. Nat. Throat, Nose & Ear Hosp. Lond.

FLOOD, Michael Kevin Falcon House Surgery, 17-19 Heaton Road, Newcastle upon Tyne NE6 1SA Tel: 0191 265 3361 — MRCS Eng. LRCP Lond. 1968. (Sheff.)

FLOOD, Richard Bertram Health Centre, John Mitchell Place, Newry BT34 3JD Tel: 01693 4811 — MB BCh BAO 1948 Dub.; BA Dub. 1948. (TC Dub.) Dep. Treasury Med. Off.; Med. Off. Govt. Train. Centre; Admiralty Surg. & Agent. Socs: MRCGP; N. Irel. Counc. Postgrad. Studies; BMA & Ulster Med. Soc.

FLOOD, Richard Derek Cornmarket Surgery, 6 Newry Health Village, Monaghan Street, Newry BT35 6BW Tel: 028 3026 5838

Fax: 028 3026 6727; 44 Seaview, Warrenpoint, Newry BT34 3NJ Tel: 016937 74272 — MB BCh BAO 1983 Dub.; MRCGP 1988; DCH RCSI NUI 1987; DRCOG 1985. (Trinity College Dublin)

FLOOD, Rosemarie Jane Flood and Partners, Essex House Surgery, Station Road, Barnes, London SW13 0LW Tel: 020 8876 1033 Fax: 020 8878 5894; 49 Hazlewell Road, Putney, London SW15 6UT Tel: 020 8788 8916 Fax: 020 8246 6728 — MB BS 1983 Lond.; MRCGP 1987; DCH RCP Lond. 1987. Prev: Trainee GP Qu. Mary's Hosp. Lond. & Barnes Lond. VTS; Ho. Surg. W.m. Hosp. Lond.; Ho. Phys. St. Stephen's Hosp. Fulham.

FLOOD, Mr Timothy Richard Odstock Centre for Plastic & Maxillofacial Surgery, Salisbury District Hospital, Salisbury SP2 8BJ Tel: 01722 336262 Fax: 01722 336262 Email: tim.flood@ukgateway.net; Brackens, Warren Copse, Woodgreen, Fordingbridge SP6 2QY — MB BS 1983 Lond.; BDS Birm. 1974; FRCS Ed. 1988; FDS RCS Eng. 1978. (Royal Free Hospital) Cons. Oral & Maxillofacial Surg. Odstock Centre for Plastic & Maxillofacial Surg. Salisbury Dist. Hosp.; Hon. Cons. S.ampton Gen. Hosp.; Hon. Cons. Roy. S. Hants Hosp. Winchester. Socs: Fell. Brit. Assn. Oral & Maxillofacial Surg.; Brit. Facial & Audiol. Implant Gp.; Assn. Head & Neck Oncol. Prev: Sen. Regist. W. Scotl. Regional Plastic & Oral Surgic. Unit Canniesburn Hosp. Glas.; Regist. (Oral & Maxillofacial Surg.) N. Staffs. Hosp. Centre Stoke-on-Trent.

FLOOD-PAGE, Joanna Jane The Manse, 18 Benlaw Grove, Felton, Morpeth NE65 9NG — MB ChB 1996 Leeds.

FLOOD-PAGE, Patrick Thomas The Manse, 18 Benlaw Grove, Felton, Morpeth NE65 9NG — MB ChB 1991 Ed.; MRCP (UK) 1994. (Ed.)

FLOOK, Mr David John Healey Dene, Healey Dell, Rochdale OL12 6BG — MB BCh 1977 Wales; MCh Wales 1986, MB BCh 1977; FRCS Eng. 1981. Cons. Gen. Surg. Roy. Oldham Hosp.

FLORA, Harsarn Kaur Guy's Hospital, St Thomas St., London SE1 9RT Tel: 020 7955 5000; 45 Shelley Gardens, North Wembley, Wembley HA0 3QF Tel: 020 8904 5964 — MB ChB 1975 Nairobi; MRCP (UK) 1985. Lect. & Hon. Sen. Regist. (Haemat.) UMDS Guy's & St. Thos. Hosp. Trust Lond. Socs: Roy. Coll. Path.; Brit. Soc. Haematol. Prev: Regist. (Haemat.) Hammersmith Hosp., N.wick Pk. Hosp. & King's Coll. Hosp. Lond.

FLORANCE, Robert Stewart Kenelm Accident & Emergency Department, Queen Elizabeth Hospital, Gayton Rd, Kings Lynn PE30 4ET — MB ChB 1992 Leic.; FFAEM 2000; BSc Leic. 1989; MRCP Edin. 1996. Cons. A & E, Kings Lynn and Wisbeck Hosps. NHS Trust. Prev: Specialist Regist. A & E E. Anglian Region.

FLORENCE, Anne McKenzie Broadgreen Hospital NHS Trust, Royal Liverpool & Broadgreen University, Hospitals NHS Trust, Liverpool L14 3LB Tel: 0151 706 3190; 49 Howey Lane, Frodsham, Warrington WA6 6DD Tel: 01928 731888 Fax: 01928 731888 — MB ChB 1962 Aberd.; FFA RCS Eng. 1966. (Aberd.) Cons. Anaesth. Cardiothoracic Centre Liverp. & Roy. Liverp. & BRd.green Univ. Hosps. NHS Trust; Hon. Sen. Research Fell. (Anaesth.) Univ. Liverp. Socs: Roy. Soc. of Med., Pres. of Sect. Anaesth. 2000-01; Liverp. Soc. of Anaesth.s, Pres. 2000-02. Prev: Hon. Sec. Anaesth. Sect. Roy. Soc. Med.; Hon. Sec. Liverp. Soc. Anaesth. & Liverp. Med. Inst.

FLORES, Frederick Richard Lincoln Road Practice, 63 Lincoln Road, Peterborough PE1 2SF Tel: 01733 565511 Fax: 01733 569230 — MD 1969 Malta.

FLORES, Mr Michael c/o Orthopaedic Department, James Paget Hospital, Lowestoft Road, Gorleston, Great Yarmouth NR31 6LA Tel: 01493 452452; Whimborne, Back Lane, Lound, Lowestoft NR32 5NE Tel: 01502 730913 — MB BS 1982 Poona; MS Orthop. 1984; MChOrth Liverp. 1988. Assoc. Specialist (Orthop.) Jas. Paget Hosp. Gt. Yarmouth. Socs: BOA. Prev: Regist. (Orthop.) N. Middlx., Hammersmith & Mayday Hosps. Lond.

FLORES DE LAURNAGA, Beatriz Flat 4, Saville House, 29 Hoop Lane, London NW11 8BS — LMS 1989 Basque Provinces.

FLOREY, Professor Charles du Ve Department Epidemiology & Public Health, Ninewells Hospital & Medical School, Dundee DD1 9SY Tel: 01382 632124 Fax: 01382 644197; Teesdale, Knowle Drive, Sidmouth EX10 8HW Tel: 01395 577142 Email: c.d.v.florey@doctors.org.uk — MB BChir 1960 Camb.; BA Camb. 1956; MD Camb. 1974; FRCP Ed. 1986; FFCM 1977, M 1974; MPH Yale Univ. 1963. (Univ. Coll. Hosp.) Emerit. Prof. Pub. Health Ninewells Hosp. & Med. Sch. Dundee. Prev: Prof. Community Med. St. Thos. Hosp. Med. Sch. Lond.; Sen. Lect. St. Thos. Hosp. Med. Sch. Lond.; Mem. Scientif. Staff MRC.

FLOREY, The Lady (retired) 4 Elsfield Road, Old Marston, Oxford OX3 0PR — BM BCh 1933 Oxf.; DM Oxf. 1950, BM BCh 1933. Prev: Univ. Lect. Sch. Path. Oxf.

FLORIN, Dominique Anne Hampstead Health Authority, Royal Free Hospital, Pond St., London NW3 2QG; 10 Hugo Road, London N19 5EU — MB BS 1986 Lond.; MSc Lond. 1992; MA Oxf. 1981; MRCGP 1990. Regist. (Pub. Health Med.) N. E. Thames RHA.

FLORIN, Liane Cécile (retired) Greenfield Medical Centre, 143-145 Cricklewood Lane, London NW2 1HS Tel: 020 8450 5454 — MD 1957 Paris; LRCP LRCS Ed. LRFPS Glas. 1960.

***FLOTO, Rodrigo Andres** 26 Montague Road, Cambridge CB4 1BX — BChir 1997 Camb.; MB Camb. 1998; MA Camb. 1995; Phd. Camb. 1997.

FLOWER, Audrey Julia Emmeline (retired) 15 Carisbrooke Avenue, Leicester LE2 3PA Tel: 0116 270 6678 — MB BS 1961 Lond.; MD Lond. 1979; Dip Bact . Lond. 1973; DCH Eng. 1963. Cons. Virol. Pub. Health Laborat. Leicester Roy. Infirm.

FLOWER, Christopher Dennis Robyn 11 Spinney Drive, Great Shelford, Cambridge CB2 5LY Tel: 01223 843914, 020 8788 6682 — MB BChir 1963 Camb.; MA Camb. 1960; FRCP Canada 1971; FRCR 1975; FFR 1972. (St. Bart.) Evelyn Hosp. Camb.; Cons. Radiologist. Prev: Cons. Radiol. Addenbrooke's & Papworth Hosp. Camb.

FLOWER, David John Colin British Airways PLC, Waterside (HMAG), P.O. Box 365, Harmondsworth, West Drayton UB7 0GB Tel: 020 8738 7709 Fax: 020 8738 9754 — MB BS 1982 Lond.; Dip Av Med 1999; BSc Lond. 1977; MD Lond. 1996; MFOM RCP Lond. 1996, AFOM 1993; MRCGP 1987; Cert. Av. Med. 1993; DRCOG 1986. (Univ. Coll. Lond.) Sen. Cons. Occupat.al Phys. Brit. Airways Health Serv.s Heathrow Airport Lond. Socs: Soc. Occupat Med.; Roy. Aeronautical Soc.; Internat. Acad. of Aviat. and Space Med. (Acadamician). Prev: Occupat. Phys. UK Atomic Energy Auth.; Princip. GP Wantage Oxon.; Ho. Surg. Profess. Surg. Unit Univ. Coll. Hosp. Lond.

FLOWER, Gillian Pat 34 Pickwick Road, London SE21 7JW Tel: 020 7733 2637 — MB BChir 1968 Camb; BA Camb. 1965; MRCP (UK) 1971. (St. Thos.) Psychoanalyst Lond. Socs: Assoc. Mem. Brit. Psychoanal. Soc. Prev: Cons. Dermat. FarnBoro. Hosp., Kent, Bromley Hosp. & Qu. Mary's Hosp. Sidcup; Sen. Regist. (Dermat.) St. Helier Hosp. Carshalton; Regist. (Dermat.) Guy's Hosp. Lond.

FLOWER, John Francis The Derby Medical centre, 8 The Derby Square, Epsom KT19 8AG Tel: 01372 726361; Gulmarg, 310 Firtree Road, Epsom Downs, Epsom KT17 3NW Tel: 01737 350580 — MB BS Lond. 1966; MRCS Eng. LRCP Lond. 1966; MRCGP 1979; DTM & H Liverp. 1972; DA Eng. 1970; DCH RCPSI 1969; DObst RCOG 1969. (Westm.) Socs: (Pres.) Epsom Med. Soc.

FLOWER, Kirsten Louise New Wortley Health Centre, Green Lane, Leeds LS12 1JE Tel: 0113 231 0585 Fax: 0113 231 0024 — MB ChB 1984 Leeds; MB ChB Leeds I984; MRCGP 1988. (Leeds)

FLOWER, Mr Nicholas Gwynne 30 Edgar Road, Winchester SO23 9TN Tel: 01962 864635 — MB BS 1984 Lond.; FRCS Eng. 1995.

FLOWER, Nicola Jane Balallan, 11 Penyfai Lane, Llanelli SA15 4EN — MB BCh 1985 Wales.

FLOWER, Stephen Paul Rhodes Farm Clinic, The Ridgeway, London NW7 1RH Tel: 020 8906 0885 Fax: 020 8906 3150 Email: spflower_1@aol.com — MB BS 1985 Lond.; MA Camb. 1982; MSc Lond. 1979; BA (Econ.) Essex 1970; MRCPsych 1991. Cons. Psychiat. Rhodes Farm Clinic. Socs: Hosp. Med. Soc.; Fell. Roy. Soc. of Med. Prev: Regist. Rotat. (Psychiat.) Roy. Free Hosp.; Sen. Regist. Rotat. (Child Psychiat.) Roy. Lond. Hosp.fa; Cons. (Child Psychiat.) Enfield Child Guidence Serv.

FLOWER, Teresa Dorothea 46 West Street, Oxford OX2 0BH — MB ChB 1992 Sheff.

FLOWERDEW, Mr Alistair Digby Stewart Dorset County Hospital, Williams Avenue, Dorchester DT1 2JY Tel: 01305 255491 Fax: 01305 255490; Limbury, Martinstown, Dorchester DT2 9JL Tel: 01305 889999 — MB BS 1975 Lond.; MS Soton. 1987; FRCS Ed. 1981. (St. Thos.) Cons. Gen. Surg. W. Dorset. Socs: Surg. Research Soc.; Vasc. Surg. Soc. Prev: Lect. & Hon. Sen. Regist. (Gen. Surg.) Soton. Univ. & Roy. United Hosp. Bath; Research Regist. (Surg.) Soton. HA; Regist. (Surg.) Co. Hosp. Hereford.

FLOWERDEW, Glyn David Knights Cross Cottage, Newstead Abbey Park, Nottingham NG15 8GE Tel: 01623 792812 — MB 1965 Camb.; BChir 1964; FFA RCS Eng. 1968; DA Eng. 1967; DObst RCOG 1966. (Camb. & St. Geo.) Cons. Anaesth. Nottm. Hosp. Gp. Prev: Sen. Regist. Dept. Anaesth. St. Geo. Hosp. & Hosp. Sick Childr. Gt.; Ormond St. Lond.

FLOWERDEW, James Alexander Ailsa Hospital, Ayr KA6 6AB Tel: 01292 610556 Fax: 01292 513044; The Craig, Turnberry, Girvan KA26 9LY Tel: 01655 331218 — MB ChB 1966 Ed.; MRCPsych 1973; DPM Eng. 1970. (Ed.) Cons. Psychiat. Ailsa Hosp. Ayr.; Mem. Scott. Psychiat. Rehabil. Interest Gp. Socs: BMA. Prev: Cons. Psychiat. Shelton Hosp. Shrewsbury.

FLOWERDEW, Robert James Glentaggart Farm House, Glentaggart, Glespin, Lanark ML11 0SH Tel: 01555 851330 — MB ChB 1988 Dundee; MRCGP 1997; DCH RCP Lond. 1993; DRCOG 1992. (Dundee) GP, Scott, Kane and Ferguson; Hon. Sen. Lec., Glas. Univ.

FLOWERDEW, Susan Mary Limbury, Martinstown, Dorchester DT2 9JL — MB ChB 1981 Birm.

FLOWERS, Anne-Marie Flat 1/R, 9 Grantley Gardens, Glasgow G41 3PY — MB ChB 1984 Ed.; DCH RCP Lond. 1989. Clin. Med. Off. Cumbernauld Centr. Health Centre.

FLOWERS, Christopher Ian Breast Test Wales, 24 Alexandra Road, Swansea SA1 5DY Tel: 01792 459988 Fax: 01792 650257 Email: c.flowers@dircon.co.uk; 30 Southerndown Avenue, Mayals, Swansea SA3 5EL Tel: 01792 414842 Email: cflowers@dircon.co.uk — MB BS 1981 Lond.; MRCS Eng. LRCP Lond. 1981; FRCR 1990. (Roy. Free) Cons. Radiol. BrE. Test Wales & Swansea NHS Trust; Hon. Cons. (Radiol.) Velindre NHS Trust Cardiff. Prev: Regist. & Sen. Regist. (Radiol.) Univ. Hosp. Nottm.; SHO (Gastroenterolgy, Gen. Medcine & A & E) Hull Roy. Infirm.

FLOWERS, Colin Seymour The Green, Swan Lane, Stoke Orchard, Cheltenham GL52 7RY — MB BS 1961 Lond. (Westm.) Indep. Cons. Medico-Legal (A & E & Personal Injury) Cheltenham. Socs: Fell. Fac. A & E Med.; BMA; BAE. Prev: Cons. A & E Gen. Hosp. Cheltenham; Med. Asst. (Cas.) E. Reach Hosp. Taunton; Regist. (Cas.) St. Mary Abbot's Hosp. Lond.

FLOWERS, Ian McLean (retired) Grinstead House, Needham Road, Barking, Ipswich IP6 8HG Tel: 01449 722484 — MB BChir Camb. 1955; MSc (Occupat. Med.) Lond. 1974; BA Camb. 1951; FRCGP 1985, M 1965; AFOM RCP Lond. 1978; DIH Eng. 1974. Prev: Med. Dir. Nottm. Univ. Health Serv.

FLOWERS, Joanna Mary 3 Shuteleigh, Wellington TA21 8PG — MB BS 1994 Lond.; BSc Lond. 1991; MRCP UK 1997. (Kings College VCH Medicine and Dentistry) Research Regist. (Neurol.) Kings Coll. Sch. of Med. & Dent. Lond. Prev: SHO (Med. Oncol.) Roy. Marsden Hosp. Sutton; SHO (Neurol.) Atlinson Moreley Hosp. Winisledge; SHO (Gen. Med.) Kingston Hosp. Surrey.

FLOWERS, Mr Mark Jonathan Orthopaedic Dept, Sheffield Children's Hospital, Western Bank, Sheffield S10 2TH Tel: 0114 271 7000 Fax: 0114 276 8419; Grange Court, 71 Ashland Road, Sheffield S7 1RH Tel: 0114 281 9818 Fax: 0114 281 9818 Email: m.j.flowers@sheffield.ac.uk — MB BS 1984 Lond.; FRCS (Orth.) 1995; FRCS Eng. 1989. (St. Mary's Hosp. Med. Sch.) Cons. Orthop. Surg. Sheff. Childr.'s Hosp. Socs: Brit. Orthop. Assn. Prev: Fell. Paediat. Orthop. HSC Toronto, Canada; Sen. Regist. Rotating (Trauma & Orthop. Surg.) Sheff.; Career Regist. Rotating N. Trent.

FLOWERS, Mr Michael Wilfred (retired) 7 The Crescent, Leeds LS16 6AA Tel: 0113 267 4321 Fax: 01132 216 6718 Email: michael.flowers@virgin.net — MB ChB Leeds 1958; FRCS Ed. 1972. Prev: Cons. A & E & Hand Surg. Gen. Infirm. Leeds.

FLOYD, Mr David Clifford 12 Monnery Road, London N19 5RZ — MB BChir 1989 Camb.; MSc Lond. 1995; MA Camb. 1989; FRCS Eng. 1993. SHO (Plastic Surg.) Qu. Vict. Hosp. E. Grinstead. Prev: SHO Rotat. (Surg.) St. Mary's Hosp. Lond.

FLOYD, Mary Jeannette Northbourne Medical Centre, Eastern Avenue, Shoreham-by-Sea BN43 6PE — MB BS 1985 Lond.; MRCGP 1990; DRCOG 1989; DCH RCP Lond. 1988.

FLOYER, Carole Elizabeth Sunnybanks, Chertsey Road, Shepperton TW17 9LA Tel: 01932 232190 Email: david4fear@aol.com — MB BS 1972 Lond.; BSc Lond. 1966, MB BS 1972; DObst RCOG 1975. (The Roy. London) Staff. Dermat. Surg. Amersham Hosp. S. Bucks. NHS Trust. Socs: Brit. Assn. Dermat.; Brit. Soc. Dermat. Surg.

FLUCK, David Simon St Peter's Hospital, Guildford Road, Chertsey KT16 0PZ Tel: 01932 872000 Fax: 01932 872011; Pyrford, Woking GU22 8TD Tel: 01932 336863 — MB BS 1986 Lond.; BSc (Biochem.) Lond. 1983, MB BS 1986; MD Lond. 1996; MRCP (UK) 1989. (St. Barts) Cons. (Cardiol.) St. Peter's Hosp., Chertsey & St Geo.'s Hosp. Socs: Brit. Cardiac Soc.

FLUCK, Nicholas Charles 616 Watford Way, London NW7 3JH — MB BS 1988 Lond.; BSc (Hons.) Lond. 1985; MRCP (UK) 1991. MRC Train. Fell. Lond. Socs: Brit. Transpl. Soc.; Brit. Soc. Immunol.; Renal Assn.

FLUCK, Richard James Brook Farm, 23 Main St., Milton, Derby DE65 6EF — MB BS 1985 Lond.; MA Camb. 1986; MRCP (UK) 1988. Research Fell. & Hon. Regist. (Nephrol.) St. Bart. Hosp. Lond. Prev: Regist. (Gastroenterol. & Gen. Med.) Lond. Hosp.; Regist. (Gen. Med.) Colchester Dist. Gen. Hosp.; SHO (Renal Unit.) Lond. Hosp.

FLUCK, Sarah Louise 616 Watford Way, London NW7 3JH — MB BS 1990 Lond.

FLUCKER, Christopher John Rendall Department of Anaesthesia, St James's Hospital, Leeds LS9 7TF — MB ChB 1992 Dundee; BSc (Hons.) Dund 1987; FRCA 1998. Hon. Locum Cons., Univ. Hosps. of Leicester. Socs: Intens. Care Surg.; Assoc. of Anaesth.s. Prev: Specialist Regist. (Anaesth.) PeterBoro. Dist. Hosp.

FLUDDER, Vanessa 24 Stallards Crescent, Frinton-on-Sea CO13 07N Tel: 01255 674037 — MB BS 1996 Lond. (UMDS) SHO (Anaesth.) E.bourne Gen. Hosp. Socs: Intens. Care Soc. Prev: SHO Rotat. (Anaesth.) Conquest Hosp. St. Leonards-on-Sea; SHO (Med.) Maidstone Hosp.; Ho. Off. (Surg.) Whipps Cross Lond.

FLUDE, Ian David Baldwins Lane Surgery, 266 Baldwins Lane, Croxley Green, Rickmansworth WD3 3LG Tel: 01923 774732 Fax: 01923 711933 — MB BS 1985 Lond.; MA Camb. 1985, BA 1982; DCH RCP Lond. 1988.

FLUKE, Raymond William BBC Occupational Health, Room 1414, BBC White City, 201 Wood Lane, London W12 7TS Tel: 020 8752 4877 Fax: 020 8752 4707 Email: raymond.fluke@bbc.co.uk; 3 Caple Road, Harlesden, London NW10 8AB — MB ChB 1973 Liverp.; MRCP (UK) 1977; AFOM RCP Lond. 1985; Mrgcp 1999; MRCGP 1999. (Liverpool) Sen. Med. Off. (Occupat. Health) BBC Lond. Prev: Regional Med. Off. (Occupat. Health) BT Manch.

FLURY, Joseph Roy (retired) 116 Church Road, Wheatley, Oxford OX33 1LU — MB BChir 1952 Camb.; BA Camb. 1949, MB BChir 1952; DObst RCOG 1956.

FLUTE, Deborah Frances Clanricarde House Surgery, Clanricarde Road, Tunbridge Wells TN1 1PJ Tel: 01892 546422 Fax: 01892 533987 — MB BS Lond. 1977; MRCP (UK) 1980; MRCGP 1984. (King's Coll. Hosp.)

FLUXMAN, Jonathan Derek Harrow Road Health Centre, 263-265 Harrow Road, London W2 5EZ Tel: 020 7286 1231 Fax: 020 7266 1253 — MRCS Eng. LRCP Lond. 1982; MRCGP 1992.

FLYNN, Adrian Joseph 5 Rowan Way, Lisvane, Cardiff CF14 0TB — MB BS 1991 Lond.

FLYNN, Andrew Gerard Flat 3, Kestrel House, 24 Mowbray Road, London SE19 2RN — MB BS 1992 Lond.

FLYNN, Ann Bernadette 25 Stafford Street, Edinburgh EH3 7BJ — MB BCh BAO 1987 NUI.

FLYNN, Ann Marie The Health Centre, Whyteman's Brae, Kirkcaldy KY1 2NA Tel: 01592 642178 Fax: 01592 644782; 3 Panha, Dysart, Kirkcaldy KY1 2TL Tel: 01592 654560 — LRCPI & LM, LRSCI & LM 1977; LRCPI & LM, LRCSI & LM 1977; DMJ (Clin.) Soc. Apoth. Lond. 1992; DRCOG 1980; DCH RCPSI 1979. (RCSI) Police Surg. Fife. Prev: Intern (Surg. & Med.) Jervis St. Hosp. Dub.; SHO (Med.) Ibn Al Bitar Hosp. Baghdad Iraq; SHO (Obst.) Al Corniche Hosp. Abu Dhabi, UAE.

FLYNN, Caroline Charlotte 43 St Catherines Way, Houghton-on-the-Hill, Leicester LE7 9HE — MB BS 1983 Lond.; MRCGP 1993; DCH RCP Lond. 1989; DRCOG 1988. (St. Thos.)

FLYNN, Catherine Ard-NA Greine, 63 Mountain Road, Kilkeel, Newry BT34 4AZ Tel: 016937 64794 Email: catherine flynn@hotmail.com — MB BCh BAO 1995 Belf.

FLYNN, Catherine Mary 4 Coverley Garth, Yeadon, Leeds LS19 7WD — MB ChB 1997 Leeds.

FLYNN, David Michael Royal Free Hospital, Pond Street, London NW3 2QG Tel: 020 7794 0500; 24 Foxes Dale, Blackheath, London SE3 9BQ Tel: 020 8852 6245 — MB ChB 1960 Ed.; MD 1966;

FRCP 1980 Lond.; DCH 1962 Eng. (Ed.) Cons. Paediat. Roy. Free Hosp. Lond.; Sen. Lect. Roy. Free Hosp. Med. Sch. Lond.; Examr. MB Lond. Socs: Neonat. Soc. & Brit. Paediat. Assn. Prev: Res. Asst. Phys. Hosp. Sick Childr. Gt. Ormond St. Lond.; Research Fell. Hosp. Sick Childr. Toronto, Canada; Regist. (Paediat.) Lond. Hosp.

FLYNN, Eileen Mary Kildrum Health Centre, Afton Road, Cumbernauld, Glasgow G67 2EU Tel: 01236 721354 Fax: 01236 727549 — MB ChB 1977 Glas.; MRCGP 1981; DObst RCOG 1979. (Univ. Glas.)

FLYNN, Ernest James Consett Medical Centre, Station Yard, Consett DH8 5YA Tel: 01207 216116 Fax: 01207 216119; The Coachman's Lodge, Greenwood, Shotley Bridge, Consett DH8 0SZ Tel: 01207 502266 — MB BCh BAO 1977 Dub.; BA Dub. 1977; MRCGP 1986; MRCOG 1985. (Trinity College Dublin) Police Surg. Durh. Constab. Prev: Trainee GP N.d. VTS; Regist. (Gyn. Oncol.) Qu. Eliz. Hosp. Gateshead; Regist. (O & G) Newc. VTS.

FLYNN, Frances Mary Dennycross Medical Centre, Duke Street, Denny FK6 6DB Tel: 01324 822330 Fax: 01324 824415 — MB ChB 1988 Ed.; MRCGP 1992.

FLYNN, Professor Frederick Valentine 20 Oakleigh Avenue, Oakleigh Park, London N20 9JH Tel: 020 8445 0882 — MB BS (Hons.) Lond. 1946; MD (Path.) Lond. 1951; FRCP Lond. 1973, M 1967; FRCPath 1971, M 1963. (Univ. Coll. Hosp.) Emerit. Prof. Chem. Path. Univ. Coll. & Middlx. Sch. Med. Socs: Fell. Roy. Soc. Med.; (Ex-Pres.) Assn. Clin. Path.; Assn. Clin. Biochem.s. Prev: Dir. Continuing Med. Educat. Roy. Coll. Path. Lond.; Civil Cons. Chem. Path. to RN; Hon. Cons. Chem. Path. Univ. Coll. Hosp.

FLYNN, Gordon Murray Flat 5, Rosemont, 80-81 Mount Ephraim, Tunbridge Wells TN4 8BS — MB BS 1996 Lond.

FLYNN, Ignacy Marian (retired) 24 Brockhurst Way, Northwich CW9 8AP Tel: 01606 42411 — MD 1935 Warsaw. Prev: GP N.wich.

FLYNN, James Francis St George's Surgery, St Pauls Medical Centre, 121 Swindon Road, Cheltenham GL50 4DP Tel: 01242 707755 Fax: 01242 707749; 22 Ham Close, Charlton Kings, Cheltenham GL52 6NP Tel: 01242 580468 — MB BS 1984 Lond.; BChD Leeds 1974. (Char. Cross. Lond.)

FLYNN, John Gaston Ballymoney Health Centre, Robinson Memorial Hospital, 21 Newal Road, Ballymoney BT53 6HB Tel: 028 2766 0300 Fax: 028 2766 0321; 130 Knock Road, Dervock, Ballymoney BT53 8AA Tel: 012657 41171 — MB BCh BAO 1979 Belf.; MRCGP 1983; DRCOG Lond. 1981; DCH NUI 1983.

FLYNN, Julian Robert 4 Fiveacres, Murcott, Kidlington OX5 2RP — MB BS 1990 Lond.; MA. Lond. 1993; FRCS Eng. 1994. (Oxf. Univ. St. Mary's Hosp. Med. Sch.) Specialist Regist. (Orthop.) Nuffield Orthop. Centre Oxf.

FLYNN, Margaret-Ann Medical Education Unit, University of Glasgow, University Avenue, Glasgow G12 8QQ Email: maf6b@clinmed.gla.ac.uk; 8 Darvel Crescent, Ralston, Paisley PA1 3EF — MB ChB 1989 Glas.; FRCA 1994. (University of Glasgow) Teachg. Facilitator.

FLYNN, Marina Elizabeth Szymanska Jessop Hospital for Women, Leavygrove Rd, Sheffield S2 Fax: 0114 226 8000 — MB ChB 1993 Sheff.; MRCOG 1999. Specialist Regist. (O & G), Jessop Hosp. for Wom., Sheff.

FLYNN, Mary Elizabeth Colette 2 Bayview Buildings, Dundrum, Newcastle BT33 — MB BCh BAO 1968 NUI.

FLYNN, Mary Gerardine 21 Cranmer Avenue, Hove BN3 7JP; Beacon House, Beacon Road, Ditchling, Hassocks BN6 8XB — MB ChB 1978 Bristol. Prev: GP Bristol.

FLYNN, Matthew John Tamborough Farmhouse, School Lane, Gaulby, Leicester LE7 9BE — BM 1998 Soton.; BM Soton 1998.

FLYNN, Michael Downing Department of Medicine, Kent and Canterbury Hospital, Ethelbert Road, Canterbury CT1 3NG Tel: 01227 766877 Fax: 01227 783018; 68 Station Road W., Canterbury CT2 8AN Tel: 01227 471387 Fax: 01227 471387 Email: michaelflynn@freenet.co.uk — MB BS 1979 London; FRCP 1999 UK; FRCP 1996 Edinburgh; MRCP 1982 UK; MD 1991 London. (St. Thos.) Cons. Phys. Gen. Med., Diabetes & Endocrinol. Kent & Canterbury Hosp., Canterbury. Socs: Roy. Coll. Phys.; Brit. Diabetic Assn. (Med. & Scientif. & Educat. Sect.). Prev: Sen. Regist. (Endocrinol.) Bristol Roy. Infirm. & Roy. Devon & Exeter Hosp.; Research Fell. & Hon. Regist. (Diabetic) King's Coll. Hosp. Lond. & (Physiol.) Char. Cross & W.m. Med. Sch. Lond.

FLYNN, Michael John Sinclair Pharmaceuticals, Borough Road, Godalming GU7 2AB Tel: 01483 426644 Fax: 01483 860927; Dinton, Hatherley Road, Richmond TW9 3LH Fax: 020 8832 9686 — MB BS 1965 Lond.; MRCS Eng. LRCP Lond. 1965. (King's Coll. Hosp.) CEO Sinclair Pharmaceut. Ltd. Prev: Chief Exec. Dir. Cortecs Ltd. Isleworth.

FLYNN, Michael Joseph Royal Bolton Hospital, Minerva Rd, Farnworth, Bolton BL4 0JR Tel: 01204 390762 Fax: 01204 390640 — MB ChB 1980 Manch.; FFA RCS Eng. 1984. Cons. Anaesth.Roy. Bolton Hosp. Prev: Sen. Regist. (Anaesth.) N.W. RHA.

FLYNN, Morgan William North Berwick Health Centre, 54 St. Baldreds Road, North Berwick EH39 4PU Tel: 01620 892169 Fax: 01620 897005; Hatley Lodge, Dirleton, North Berwick EH39 5DH Tel: 01620 893771 — MB BCh BAO 1985 NUI; LRCPI 1985; DCH RCPSI 1988; DObst RCPI 1989.

FLYNN, Mr Niall Alastair Kenneth Queen Alexandra Hospital, Portsmouth PO6 3LY Tel: 023 92 286864; Old Mill Cottage, Paradise lane, Bishop's Waltham, Southampton SO32 1AH Email: nakflynn@yahoo.co.uk — MB ChB 1987 Bristol; FRCS 1998 (Tr. And Orth.); FRCS Lond. 1992. (Bristol) Cons. in Orthop. & Trauma Qu. Alexandra Hosp. Portsmouth. Socs: BOTA; Fell. BOA; ESSKA. Prev: Lect. Soton. Univ. Hosp. NHS Trust; Sen Regist. (Orthop.) QAH Portsmouth; Sen Regist. (Orthop.) Lord Mayor Treloar & N. Hants. Hosp.s.

FLYNN, Patricia Josephine Anaesthetics Unit, Bart's and The London Queen Mary School of Medicine and Dentistry, Whitechapel, London E1 2AD Tel: 020 7377 7119 Fax: 020 7377 7126 Email: p.j.flynne@mds.qmw.ac.uk — MB BCh BAO 1970 NUI; FFA RCSI 1977; FFA RCS Eng. (ad eundem) 1987; DCH 1973, DObst 1975, DA 1975. (University College Dublin) Sen. Lect. (Anaesth.) Bart's and The Lond. Qu. Mary Sch. of Med. and Dent.; Hon. Cons. Bart's and The Lond. NHS Trust; Sec. Gen. Brit. Acad. Forens. Sci.

FLYNN, Patrick Mary 14 Montpelier Park, Edinburgh EH10 4NJ Tel: 0131 229 8403 Fax: 0131 221 1550 — MB BCh BAO 1978 NUI; LMCC 1984; DObst RCPI 1987; DCH NUI 1982. (Univ. Coll. Dub.) Prev: SHO (Surg.) Ibl Al Bmar Baghdad, Iraq; GP Canada & Edin.

FLYNN, Paul Desmond University of Cambridge Clinical School, Department of Medicine, Addenbrooke's Hospital, Hills Road, Cambridge CB2 2QQ Tel: 01223 331504 Email: pdf@mole.bio.cam.ac.uk; 23 Iver Close, Cherry Hinton, Cambridge CB1 3JG Tel: 01223 416597 — MB BChir 1990 Camb.; BA Camb. 1987, MA 1991; MRCP (UK) 1993; MRCPI 1993. (Cambridge) Clin. Lect. (Med.) Univ. of Camb. Clin. Sch. Prev: BHF Clin. PhD Stud. (Med.) Univ. Camb. Clin. Sch.; Research Fell. (Clin. Biochem. & Metab.) St. Geo. Hosp. Med. Sch. Lond.; SHO (Med.) Soton. Gen. Hosp.

FLYNN, Paul Edward 22 Cranleigh Road, London SW19 3LU — MB BS 1994 Lond.

FLYNN, Paul Gerard Site 66, 14 Meadowview, Jordanstown, Newtownabbey BT37 0UP — MB BCh BAO 1981 Belf.

FLYNN, Mr Paul Michael Women's Services Directorate, Royal Victoria Infirmary, Queen Victoria Road, Newcastle upon Tyne NE1 4LP Tel: 0191 282 5865 Fax: 0191 227 5173; Fax: 07092 173892 Email: obsngobs@ntlworld.com — MB BCh BAO 1990 NUI; MRCOG 1998. (University College Dublin) Specialist Regist., O & G, S. Cleveland Hosp./Cons. O & G, Roy. Vict. Inf. Socs: N. of Engl. Obs. & Gyn. Soc.; Brit. Soc. for Colposcopy and Cervical Path.; Brit. Gyn. Cancer Soc.

FLYNN, Peter Anthony Department of Neuroradiology, Level 3, A Block, Royal Victoria Hospital, Grosvenor Road, Belfast BT12 6BA Email: paflynn@doctors.org.uk — MB BCh BAO 1989 Belf.; MRCP (UK) 1992; FRCR 1997. Cons. Neuroradiologist, Roy. Vict. Hosp., Belf. Prev: Specialist Regist. (Diag. Radiol.) N.. RHA.

FLYNN, Robert Joseph Flat 14, Lowlands, 2-8 Eton Avenue, London NW3 3EJ — MB BCh BAO 1989 Dub.

FLYNN, Thomas Gerard 2 Hardwick Close, Ipswich IP4 5XB — MB BCh BAO 1982 NUI.

FOADI, Minou Dokht Department of Haematology, Imperial College of Science, Technology and Medicine, Charing Cross Hospital Campus, Fulham Palace Road, London W6 8RP Tel: 020 8846 7121; Flat 9, 69 Courtfield Gardens, London SW5 0NJ Tel: 020 7370 2655 Email: m.foadi@virgin.net — MD 1959 Tehran; 1964 Diploma Amer. Bd. of Paediat.; 1960 Diploma Postgrad. Basic

Sci. & Med. USA; 1973 Diploma American State Board to Pract. Med.; 1961 Diploma Postgrad. Paediat. Univ. Pennsylvania, USA; MB BS 1958; ECFMG Cert. 1961. Hon. Lect. & Emerit. Cons. (Haemat.) Char. Cross. Hosp. Campus, Imperial Coll. of Sci., Technol. & Med., Lond. and Hammersmith Hosps. NHS Trust, Du Cano Rd., Lond. Socs: Brit. Inst. Biol.; Brit. Soc. Haematol. & Brit. Soc. Cancer Research Med.; Collegiate Comm. Exam Univ. Lond. (for Basic Med. Sci. & Pham. And Final MB BS Path.). Prev: Acting Head of Dept. Haemat. Imperial Coll. Sch. Med. Div. Invesy. Sci. Char. Cross Hosp. Campus, Lond.; Sen. Lect. & Hon. Cons. Haemat. Char. Cross Hosp. Med. Sch. Lond.; Leukaemia Research Fell. Inst. Child Health Hosp. Sick. Childr. Lond.

FOALE, Rodney Allan 66 Harley Street, London W1N 1AE Tel: 020 7323 4687 Fax: 020 7631 5431 Email: raf@smht-foale.co.uk; Department of Cardiology, St. Mary's Hospital, Praed St., London W2 1NY Tel: 020 7725 1250 Fax: 020 7631 5431 — MB BS 1971 Meldouane, Australia; 1990 (FESC); FACC 1985; MRCP 1976 UK; FRCP 1994 Lond. (University Of Meldouane, Australia) p/t Cons. Cardiol. & Dir. Surg. & Cardiovasc. Sci. St. Mary's Hosp. Lond.; Hon. Sen. Lect. Imp. Coll. Sch. of Med. Socs: Austral. Med. Assn.; Roy. Soc. Med. Prev: Dir. Cardiac Sci. St Mary's Hosp. Lond.; Sen. Regist. (Cardiol.) Hammersmith Hosp. Lond.; Sen. Clin. Fell. Harvard Univ. & Massachussetts Gen. Hosp., USA.

FOAT, Mr Graham Southport & Formby DGH, Southport PR8 6PN; Greystoke, 94 Victoria Road, Formby, Liverpool L37 1LP Tel: 01704 834990 Fax: 01704 834990 — MB ChB 1979 Liverp.; FRCOG 1997; MObstG Liverp. 1987; MRCOG 1984. Cons. O & G S.port & Ormskirk NHS Trust.

FODDEN, Mr David Ian Accident & Emergency Department, Pinderfields General Hospital, Aberford Road, Wakefield WF1 4DG Tel: 01924 201688 Fax: 01924 214840 — MB ChB 1979 Leeds; FRCS Ed. 1984; DA (UK) 1990; FFAEM 1993. (Univ. Leeds) Cons. (A & E Med.) Pinderfields Gen. Hosp. Wakefield.

FODDY, Sarah Elizabeth Fairhill Medical Practice, 81 Kingston Hill, Kingston upon Thames KT2 7PX Tel: 020 8546 1407 Fax: 020 8547 0075; 187 Sidney Road, Walton-on-Thames KT12 3SD — MB BS 1987 Lond.; MRCGP 1994; DRCOG 1993. (Charing Cross and Westminster)

FOEX, Mr Bernard Andre Dept. Emergency Medicine, Manchester Royal Infirmary, Oxford Road, Manchester M13 9WL Tel: 0161 275 8539; 21 Sunnybrow Road, Middleton, Manchester M24 4AD Tel: 0161 653 5861 — BM BCh 1988 Oxf.; BA (Hons.) Oxf. 1985; FRCS Ed. 1993; PhD (Manchester) 1998. (Oxf.) Specialist Regist. (A & E) NW Rotat.; Hon Research Fell. N. W.ern Injury Research Centre. Socs: Eur. Shock Soc.; Intens. Care Soc.; Porit Avol A & E Med. Prev: MRC Scientist NWIRC Univ. Manch.; Locum Samu. Paris SHO ANE Hope Hosp. Salford.

FOEX, Professor Pierre Nuffield Department of Anaesthetics, Radcliffe Infirmary, Woodstock Road, Oxford OX2 6HE Tel: 01865 224770 Fax: 01865 794191 Email: pierre.foex@nda.ox.ac.uk; 26, Jack Straw's Lane, Oxford OX3 0DW Tel: 01865 761771 — 1960 Dip. Federal (Med.) Geneva; MD 1966 Geneva; MA Oxf. 1976, DPhil 1973; FANZCA 1993; FRCA 1985. (Univ. Geneva) Nuffield Prof. Anaesth. & Hon. Cons. Oxf. Radcliffe Trust; Mem. (Counc.) Roy. Coll. Anaesth. Socs: Anaesth. Res. Soc., Intens. Care Soc. & Europ.; Acad. Anaesth.; Founding mem.Acad.med.Sci.s. Prev: Research Fell., Clin. Lect. & Univ. Lect. (Anaesth.) Univ. Oxf.; Clin. Reader (Clin. Physiol.) Univ. Oxf.

FOGARTY, Mr Adrian Bernard Royal Free Hospital, London NW3 2QG Tel: 020 7830 2126 Fax: 020 7830 2985 Email: afogarty@btinternet.com — MB BCh BAO 1984 Belf.; FRCS (A&E) Ed. 1995; FRCS Ed. 1989; FRCSI 1989; DA (UK) 1993; FFAEM 1996. (Qu. Univ. Belf.) Cons. A & E & Hon. Sen. Lect. Roy. Free Hosp. Lond. Socs: BMA; Brit. Assn. Accid. & Emerg. Med.; Amer. Coll. of Emerg. Phys.s. Prev: Sen. Regist. (A & E) St. Mary's Hosp. Lond.; Regist. (A & E) St. Vincent's Hosp. Dub.; SHO Rotat. (Surg.) Belf.

FOGARTY, Aideen Catherine 337 Billing Road E., Northampton NN3 3LL — MB BS 1962 Lond.; MRCS Eng. LRCP Lond. 1962; DCH Eng. 1965; DObst RCOG 1964.

FOGARTY, Andrew William 337 Billing Road E., Northampton NN3 3LL — BM BCh 1992 Oxf.

FOGARTY, Anthony John Holly Mount, 222B Unthank Road, Norwich NR2 2AH — MB BCh BAO 1965 Dub.; BA, MB BCh BAO Dub. 1965; MRCP Lond. 1969; DObst RCOG 1970. (T.C. Dub.) Socs: BMA. Prev: SHO. Roy. Hosp. Sheff.; SHO Sefton Gen. Hosp. Liverp.; Res. Med. Off. Lond. Chest Hosp.

FOGARTY, Mr Brendan Joseph 21 Belvedere Manor, Windsor Park, Belfast BT9 6FT Tel: 01232 683082 — MB BCh BAO 1991 Belf.; BSc (Hons.) Belf. 1989; FRCS Eng. 1995; FRCSI 1995.

FOGARTY, Damian Gerard Nephrology Unit, Belfast City Hospital, Belfast BT9 7AB Tel: 028 9032 9241 Email: damian.fogarty@bch.n-I.nhs.uk — MB BCh BAO 1989 Belf.; MRCP (UK) 1992; MD (Belf.) 1996. Cons. Nephrologist Belf. City Hosp.; Sen. Lect. Qu.'s Univ. Belf. Prev: Sen. Regist. Regional Nephrol. Unit, Belf. City Hosp.; Research Fell. (Med.), Harvard Med. Sch.; Regist. (Nephrol.), Belf. City Hosp.

FOGARTY, John Philip Francis (retired) Sunnybank, St Helier, Jersey JE2 4GF Tel: 01534 34268 — MB BCh BAO 1950 NUI; FRCP Ed. 1971, M 1957; MRCPsych 1971; DCH Eng. 1955; DPM RCPSI 1954. Hon. Cons. Psychiat. Gen. Hosp. St. Helier, Jersey; Med. Ref. Social Security dpartment States of Jersey. Prev: Cons. Psychiat. Lond.derry & Gransha Hosp.

FOGARTY, Kevin William 168 Park Avenue N., Northampton NN3 2HZ Tel: 01604 716500; 337 Billing Road E., Northampton NN3 3LL Tel: 01604 30546 — MB BCh BAO 1962 Dub.; MRCP Lond. 1969; MRCGP 1974; DObst RCOG 1965; DCH Eng. 1964. (Univ. Dub.) Socs: BMA. Prev: SHO Accid. Serv. Radcliffe Infirm. Oxf.; Ho. Surg., Ho. Off. (Paediat.) & Ho. Phys. N.ampton Gen. Hosp.

FOGARTY, Leo Joseph 67 Acomb Road, York YO24 4EP Tel: 01906 330311 Fax: 01904 330312 Email: lfogarty@cix.co.uk — MB BS 1975 Lond.; MRCGP 1985. Socs: RCGP Healthcare Informatics Task Gp.; RCGP Jt. Computing Gp.; RCGP Acad. Coll.s Informat. Gp.

FOGARTY, Lilian Margaret 24 Lillington Road, Leamington Spa CV32 5YY — MB ChB 1936 Birm.; BA, MB ChB Birm. 1936. (Birm.) Prev: Ho. Surg. Ear & Throat Dept. & Cas. Ho. Surg. Gen. Hosp. Birm.; Ho. Surg. Childr. Hosp. Birm.

FOGARTY, Mary Yvonne Department of Biochemical Medicine, Ninewells Hospital, Dundee DD1 9SY — MB BCh BAO 1983 NUI; MSc Leeds 1986. Sen. Regist. (Biochem. Med.) Ninewells Hosp. Dundee; Hon. Lect. Univs. Dundee & St. And.

FOGARTY, Paul Patrick Ulster Hospital, Belfast BT16 1RH Tel: 02890 9056 1401 Fax: 02890 9056 1402 Email: paul.fogarty@nda.n-i.nhs.uk; Glen House, Crawfordsburn, Bangor BT19 1HY Tel: 02891 853343 — MB BCh BAO 1981 Belf.; FRCOG 1998; MD Belf. 1990; MRCOG 1986, D 1984. (Queen's University Belfast) Cons. O & G Ulster Hosp.; Cons. Obst. and Gyn. Ulster InDepend. Clinic Belf.; Clin. Lect. Dept. Of O&L Qu.'s Univ. Belf. Prev: Lect. & Hon. Sen. Regist. (O & G) Roy. Vict. Hosp. Belf.

FOGAZZI, Giovanni Battista 137A Devonshire Road, London SE23 3LZ — State Exam 1979 Milan.

FOGELL, Anita Mary 131 Watford Road, Birmingham B30 1NP — MB ChB 1991 Leeds.

FOGELL, Maurice 37 Harrisons Road, Edgbaston, Birmingham B15 3QR — MB ChB 1942 Glas. (Univ. Glas.) Clin. Asst. Skin Hosp. Birm. Prev: Ho. Phys. S.. Gen. Hosp. Glas.; Res. Med. Off. Skin Hosp. Birm.; Capt. RAMC 1943-6.

FOGELMAN, Frank Victoria Medical Centre, 7 Longmoore Street, London SW1V 1JH Tel: 020 7821 1531 Fax: 020 7233 5995 — MB BChir 1972 Camb.; MA Camb. 1973; MRCP (UK) 1974; AFOM RCP Lond. 1982. (Middlx) Phys. Dept. Nuclear Cardiol. Cromwell Hosp. Lond.; Chairm. Kensington, Chelsea & W.minster LMC; GP. Med. Adviser, Channel 4 and Nat. magazines. Socs: Assur. Med. Soc.; Soc. Occup. Health; BMA. Prev: Clin. Asst. & Research Fell. (Cardiol.) St. Thos. Hosp. Lond.; Regist. (Cardiothoracic) Centr. Middlx. Hosp. Lond.; SHO (Med.) Hammermsith Hosp.

FOGELMAN, Professor Ignac Department of Nuclear Medicine, Guy's Hospital, St Thomas St., London SE1 9RT Tel: 020 7955 4593 Fax: 020 7955 4657; 16 Canons Drive, Edgware HA8 7QS — MB ChB 1973 Glas.; MD (Hons.) Glas. 1983, BSc (Hons.) 1971; FRCPS Glas. 1987; MRCP (UK) 1975. Prof. Nuclear Med. Guy's Kings & St thomas Sch. of Med., KCL & Hon.Cons. Phys. Guy's & St Thomas NHS Trust. Prev: Cons. Phys. (Nuclear Med.) Guy's Hosp. Lond.

FOGG, Mr Anthony John Blakeley The Ridgeway Hospital, Moormead Road, Wroughton, Swindon SN4 9DD Tel: 01672 541080 Fax: 01672 541080 Email: ajbfogg@totalise.co.uk; Thorn

Hanger, The Common, Marlborough SN8 1DL Tel: 01672 513943 — MB BS 1975 Lond.; BSc (Hons.) Biochem. Lond. 1971; FRCS Eng. 1980. (Roy. Lond.) Cons. Orthop. Surg. P.ss Margt. Hosp. Swindon. Socs: Brit. Orthop. Assn. Prev: Sen. Regist. (Orthop.) Roy. Nat. Orthop. Hosp. Lond.

FOGG, Clare Joanne Whalley Medical Group, 42 King Street, Whalley, Clitheroe BB7 9SL Tel: 01254 823273; Tel: 01200 426015 — MB BS 1991 Lond.; DCH RCP Lond.1997; DRCOG 1997; DFFP 1997; MRCGP 1998. (Guy's Hosp. Med. Sch.) p/t Gen. Practitioner, Whalley. Socs: BMA; MDU. Prev: SHO (Psychiat.) Airedale Hosp.; SHO (O & G & Paediat.) Burnley Hosp.; GP Regist. Clitheroe.

FOGG, Katheryn Jane Department of Anaesthetics, Royal Brompton Hospital, London SW3 6NP; 39 Danbury Street, London N1 8LE Tel: 020 7359 0296 Email: k.fogg@rbh.nthames.nhs.uk — MB BS 1989 Lond.; BA (Hons.) Oxf. 1986; FRCA 1994. Cons. (Anaesth.), Roy. Brompton Hosp., Lond. Prev: Sen. Regist. Rotat. (Anaesth.) Roy. Lond. Hosp.; Regist. Rotat. (Anaesth.) St. Bart. & Whipps Cross Hosps. Lond.; SHO (Anaesth.) Roy. Free Hosp. Lond.

FOGG, Martin Robert 81 Thornbarrow Road, Windermere LA23 2DQ — MB BS 1982 Lond.

FOGGENSTEINER, Lukas Addenbrooke's Hospital, Hills Road, Cambridge CB2 2QQ; 233 Mill Road, Cambridge CB1 3BE — BM 1990 Soton.; BSc Soton. 1989, BM 1990; MRCP (UK) 1993.

FOGGETT, Carolyn Widbrook Surgery, 72 Wingfield Road, Trowbridge BA14 9EN — MB ChB 1984 Leic.; MB ChB Leic. l984.

FOGGIN, William Keith 349 Pensby Road, Pensby, Wirral CH61 9NL Tel: 0151 648 1193; Oakhanger, Queensway, Gayton, Wirral CH60 3SL Tel: 0151 342 1548 — MB ChB 1963 Liverp.; FRCGP 1987; MRCGP 1972; DObst RCOG 1967. Course Organiser Wirral.

FOGGITT, Mr Andrew Charles 17 Clarendon Crescent, Titchfield Common, Fareham PO14 4RE Tel: 01489 583236 Email: andrew@foggitt.com — MB ChB 1990 Liverp.; FRCS Ed. (Tr. & Orth.) 2001; FRCS Ed. 1995. Regist. (Orthop.) Wessex Rotat.

FOGGITT, Cecil Henry 134 Ringinglow Road, Sheffield S11 7PR Tel: 0114 2266 0124 — MB ChB 1941 Sheff. (Sheff.)

FOGGITT, Kenneth Dean (retired) 53 West End Road, Cottingham HU16 5PW Tel: 01482 849513 — MB ChB Sheff. 1939; DO Oxf. 1941; DOMS Eng. 1942. Prev: Cons. Ophth. Surg. Hull Roy. Infirm. Kingston Gen. Hosp. Hull, Castle.

FOGGITT, Mr Paul (retired) Beech House, College Road, Ripon HG4 2AE Tel: 01765 605913 — MB ChB Leeds 1957; FRCS Eng. 1965; FRCS Ed. 1964. Prev: Cons. Surg. (Orthop.) SE Staffs. Health Dist.

FOGIEL, Peter Cooper Woodside Medical Group A, 80 Western Road, Woodside, Aberdeen AB24 4SU Tel: 01224 492631 Fax: 01224 276173; 10 Overton Avenue, Dyce, Aberdeen AB21 7FU Tel: 01224 725391 — MB ChB 1972 Aberd.

FOGUET SUBIRANA, Pedro Ramon Plot 48, 19 Kel Way, Binley, Coventry CV3 2XP — LMS 1983 Barcelona.

FOINETTE, Kathryn Margaret Ruby 7 Woodside, Crowborough TN6 1EG — BM BS 1997 Nottm.

FOIST, Jana Marie Eva Pear Tree Surgery, 28 Meadow Close, Kingsbury, Tamworth B78 2NR Tel: 01827 872755 Fax: 01827 874700; Treleigh, 35 Middle Lane, Nether Whitacre, Coleshill, Birmingham B46 2HX — MB BS 1972 Lond.; DObst RCOG 1975. (St. Thos.)

FOIST, Michael Jan (retired) Treleigh, Middle Lane, Nether Whitacre, Coleshill, Birmingham B46 2HX — MRCS Eng. LRCP Lond. 1973; DA Eng. 1975. Prev: Partner Peautree Surg., 28 Meadow Cl., Kingsbury, B78 2NR.

FOISTER, John Anthony (retired) Dr Foister, Sycamore Close, Fordwater Road, Chichester PO19 4PS Tel: 01243 527847 — MB ChB Birm. 1962; MRCS Eng. LRCP Lond. 1962; DObst RCOG 1964. Prev: Ho. Surg. Qu. Eliz. Hosp. Birm.

FOK, Donald Hin Suen 36 Elliott Square, Elsworthy Rise, London NW3 3SU — MB BS 1987 Lond.

FOK, Mary Elizabeth Gwent Helathcare Trust, Oakfield House, Llanfrechfa Grange, Cwmbran NP44 8YN; Foxhill, Wilcrick, Magor, Caldicot NP26 3DA — MB ChB 1978 Birm. Staff Grade (Comm. Paediat.), Gwent Healthcare Trust. Prev: Staff Grade Glan Hafren Trust; Staff Grade Gwent Community Health Trust; Clin. Med. Off. Berks. HA.

FOK, Mr Peter John Department of Surgery, Perth Royal Infirmary, Taymount Terrace, Perth PH1 1NX Tel: 01738 473677 Email: jfok@pri.tuht.scot.nhs.uk; Bellfield, Dalguise, Dunkeld PH8 0JU Tel: 01350 727380 Fax: 01350 727453 Email: johnfok@aol.com — MB BChir 1975 Camb.; MB BChir Camb. 1974; MA Camb. 1975; FRCS Eng. 1978. (King's College Hospital Medical and Dental School) Cons. Surg. (Gen. Surg.) Perth Roy. Infirm. Prev: Cons. Surg. (Gen. Surg.) Stracathro Hosp. Brechin; Lect. (Surg.) Qu. Mary's Hosp. Univ. Hong Kong.

FOK, Wilson Wai Fung Northumberland Heath Medical Centre, Hind Crescent, Northumberland Heath, Erith DA8 3DB Tel: 01322 336556 Fax: 01322 351475; 4 The Dell, Bexley DA5 2AG — MB 1983 Camb.; BSc (Hons.) St. And. 1979; BChir 1982; DRCOG 1987. Princip. GP Erith Health Centre. Prev: Trainee GP Isle of Thanet VTS; Ho. Phys. New Hinchingbrooke Hosp. Huntingdon; Ho. Surg. Addenbrooke's Hosp. Camb.

***FOLB, Jonathan Eben** 32 Malcolmson Close, Birmingham B15 3LS — BM BCh 1996 Oxf.

FOLCA, Mr Paul Joseph (retired) (cons. rooms), Mount Stuart Hospital, St Vincents Road, Torquay TQ1 4UP — MB 1959 Camb.; BA Camb. 1955, BChir 1958; FRCS Eng. (Ophth.) 1968; FRCS Glas. 1964; FCOphth 1988. Cons. Ophth. Surg. Torbay Hosp. Prev: Regional Adviser SW (Ophth.) RCS Eng.

***FOLEY, Anne Louise** 30 Dale Avenue, Longton, Preston PR4 5YJ — MB ChB 1997 Dundee.

FOLEY, Catherine Ann Copnor Road Surgery, 111 Copnor Road, Portsmouth PO3 5AF Tel: 023 9266 3368 Fax: 023 9278 3203; 85A Finchdean Road, Rowlands Castle PO9 6EN — MB ChB 1980 Leic.; DRCOG 1982.

FOLEY, Catherine Mary Southlands Hospital, Shoreham-by-Sea BN43 6TQ Tel: 01273 455622; 3 St. John's Mews Cottages, John St, Shoreham-by-Sea BN43 5EU Tel: 01273 461994 — MB BCh BAO 1954 NUI; DA RCPSI 1959. (Cork) Assoc. Specialist Anaesth. Worthing AHA. Prev: Regist. (Anaesth.) Lincoln Co. Hosp.; SHO (Anaesth.) Roy. Cornw. Infirm, Truro & Frenchay Hosp. Bristol; Ho. Surg. N.. Infirm. Cork.

FOLEY, Charlotte Louise 56 Wentworth Av, London N3 1YL — BM BCh 1997 Oxf.; MA 1998. SHO Rotat. (Basic Surgic.), Roy. Surrey Co. Hosp., Guildford.

FOLEY, Claire Angela 15 Beech Road, Lenzie, Glasgow G66 4HN — MB ChB 1994 Glas.

FOLEY, Eleanor Isabel (retired) 47 The Grove, Bedford MK40 3JN Tel: 01234 342711 — MB BS 1965 Lond.; MRCS Eng. LRCP Lond. 1965; FFA RCS 1971; DA Eng. 1969. Prev: Cons. Anaesth. Bedford Hosp.

FOLEY, Ellen Patricia (Surgery), 143 Ingrebourne Gardens, Upminster RM14 1BJ Tel: 01708 228888; 10 Engayne Gardens, Upminster RM14 1UZ Tel: 01708 226083 — MB BCh BAO 1951 NUI; DA Eng. 1954. (Cork)

FOLEY, Gerard Peter 7 Muker Grove, Stockton-on-Tees TS19 7RL — MRCS Eng. LRCP Lond. 1988; FRACGP 1996; MRCGP 1995; DRCOG 1994. GP Australia. Prev: Trainee GP Porch Surg. Corsham, Wilts.; SHO (O & G) N. Middlx. Hosp. Lond.; SHO (Paediat.) Qu. Mary's Hosp. Sidcup.

FOLEY, Heather Maxine Woodlands Surgery, Tilgate Way, Tilgate, Crawley RH10 5BS Tel: 01293 525204 Fax: 01293 514778 — BM BS 1987 Nottm.; FRCS Eng. 1992. GP. Socs: Fell.Roy. Coll. of Surg.s; BMA.

FOLEY, J Helen Child Development Centre, Royal Surrey County Hospital, Guildford GU2 7XX Tel: 01483 464135 Fax: 01483 450742 Email: h.foley@virgin.net; 55 Cranley Road, Guildford GU1 2JW Tel: 01483 504830 Fax: 01483 306253 — BM BCh Oxf. 1962; MA Oxf. 1962; FRCP Lond. 1994; MRCP (UK) 1967; FRCPCH 1996; DCH Eng. 1970. (Oxford) Cons. Neuropaediat. Roy. Surrey NHS Trust Guildford. Socs: Brit. Paediat. Neurol. Assn.; Eur. Acad. Childh. Disabil. Prev: Sen. Regist. (Paediat.) Newcomen Centre Guy's Hosp. Lond. & St. Thos. Hosp. Lond.; Regist. (Neurol.) St. Jas. Hosp. Leeds.

FOLEY, Jane Anne Dept. Of Psycological Medicine, Gartnavel Royal Hospital, 1055 Gt Heston Rd, Glasgow G12 0XH Email: r.c.kelly@clinmed.gla.ac.uk; Coull, 57 Brodrick Road, London SW17 7DX — MB BS 1976 Lond.; FRCP; MRCP (UK) 1979. (St. Thos.) p/t Cons. Rheum. Qu. Mary's Hosp. Lond. Socs: Brit. Soc. Rheum.; Brit. Soc. Rehabil. Med. Prev: Civil. Cons. Rheum. &

Rehabil. Qu. Eliz. Milit. Hosp. Lond.; Sen. Regist. (Rheum.) St. Thos. Hosp. Lond.

FOLEY, John The Old House, 54 Ashacre Lane, Worthing BN13 2DE Tel: 01903 265218 — MA 1941, MD Camb. 1953, MB BChir 1941; MD Camb. 1953, MA 1941; FRCP Lond. 1969, M 1947. (Camb. & Lond. Hosp.) Prev: Emerit. Cons. Neurol. SW Thames RHA.; Neurol. Worthing, S.lands & Chichester Hosps.; Hon. Cons. Neurol. St. Geo. Hosp. Lond.

FOLEY, Kieran Noel University Hospital of South Manchester, Nell Lane, Withington, Manchester M20 — MB BCh BAO 1985 NUI; FCAnaesth. 1981. Regist. (Anaesth.) Univ. Hosp. S. Manch. Prev: Regist. (Anaesth.) Blackburn Roy. Infirm.; Regist. (Anaesth.) Bradford Roy. Infirm.

FOLEY, Margaret Ellen Mary 38 Bath Road, Emsworth PO10 7ER Tel: 01234 372065 — MRCS Eng. LRCP Lond. 1943; FRCOG 1970, M 1948. (King's Coll. Hosp.) Dir. Family Plann. Serv. Portsmouth & SE Hants. Health Dist.; Mem. Jt. Comm. Contracep. RCOG. Socs: SW Obst. & Gyn. Soc. Prev: Cons. Gyn. Sevenoaks Hosp.; Regist. (Gyn.) King's Coll. Hosp.; PMO Portsmouth & Dist. Family Plann. Centres.

FOLEY, Martin Francis Upper Ground Floor, 15 Methuen Park, Muswell Hill, London N10 2JR Tel: 020 8365 2030 — MB BS 1993 Lond. (The Royal Free Hospital School of Medicine)

FOLEY, Mary Bridget Noeline Department of Respiratory Medicine, Royal United Hospital, Combe Park, Bath BA1 3NG Tel: 01225 824531 Fax: 01225 824175 — MB BCh BAO 1983 NUI; MD NUI 1991; MRCPI 1985; FRCP Lond. 1998. Cons. Phys. (Respirat. & Gen. Med.) Roy. United Hosp. Bath; Assoc. Edr. Thorax. Socs: Brit. Thorac. Soc. Prev: Cons. Thoracic Med. Roy. Free Hosp.; Lect. (Med.) & Hon. Sen. Regist. Univ. Coll. & Middlx. Med. Sch. Lond.

FOLEY, Michael Augustine 49 Roseberry Avenue, Stokesley, Middlesbrough TS9 5HF — MB BS 1984 Lond.; BSc Lond. 1981; MRCP (UK) 1988; FRCA 1991. (Guy's Hosp.) Cons. Anaesth. S. Cleveland Hosp. Prev: Sen. Regist. (Anaesth.) N.. RHA.

FOLEY, Patrick Edward 56 Wentworth Avenue, London N3 1YL Tel: 020 8346 6962 — MB BS 1962 Lond.; FRCPath 1987, M 1975; Dip. Clin. Biochem. (RCP Lond., RIChem, RCPath &; Assn. Clin. Biochem.) 1975; Dip. Biochem. Lond 1967. Cons. Chem. Path. Whipps Cross Hosp. Lond. Prev: Chief (Clin. Chem.) Univ. Mass. Med. Center, U.S.A.

FOLEY, Paul William Xavier 55 Cranley Road, Guildford GU1 2JW Tel: 07970 167118 Fax: 07970 240043 — MB ChB 1997 Bristol.

FOLEY, Peter Thomas Flat 2, 1 Chester Way, London SE11 4UT; 55 Cranley Road, Guildford GU1 2JW Tel: 01483 504830 — MB BS 1993 Lond.; BSc Lond. 1992. (St Thos.) SHO Rotat. (Surg.) Roy. Sussex Co. Hosp. Brighton. Prev: Ho. Off. (Gen. Med.) St. Peter's Hosp. Chertsey; Ho. Off. (Gen. Surg.) Treliske Hosp. Truro.

FOLEY, Mr Robert John Eugene Bedford Hospital, Kempston Road, Bedford MK42 9DJ Tel: 01234 355122; 20 Park Avenue, Bedford MK40 2LB Tel: 01234 341604 Fax: 01234 269190 — MB BS 1966 Lond.; FRCS Eng. 1971; MRCS Eng. LRCP Lond. 1966. (Lond. Hosp.) Cons. Surg. Bedford Gen. Hosp. Socs: Fell. Roy. Soc. Med.; Assn. of Surg.s of Gt. Britain & Irel.; AUGIS. Prev: Sen. Regist. (Surg.) Roy. Free Hosp. Lond. & Roy. N.. Hosp. Lond.; Regist. (Surg.) Whipps Cross Hosp. Lond.

FOLEY, Sharon Elizabeth The Orchard, Borough Green, Sevenoaks TN15 8BD — MB BS 1991 Lond.

FOLEY, Stephen 9-11 Alexander Road, Harrogate HG1 5JS Tel: 01423 503218 Email: stephen@novasco.demon.co.uk — MB ChB 1979 Leeds; MRCGP 1983. (Leeds)

FOLEY, Mr Stephen John Coopers Department of Urology, Royal Berkshire Hospital, Reading — MB BS 1990 Lond.; FRCS (Urol.) 2000; FRCS Eng. 1994. Cons. Urol., Roy. Berks. Hosp., Reading. Prev: Regist. (Urol.) Roy. Hants. Co. Hosp. Winchester; Regist. (Urol.) St. Mary's Hosp. Portsmouth; Regist. (Urol.) Inst. Urol. Middlx. Hosp. Lond.

FOLEY, Stephen John Royal Shrewsbury Hospital, Mytton Oak Rd, Shrewsbury SY3 8XQ Tel: 01743 261000; c/o 55 Cranley Road, Guildford GU1 2JW Tel: 01483 504830 Fax: 01483 306253 — MB ChB 1996 Ed.; BSc (Hons.) 1994. (Ed.) SHO (Med.) Roy. Shrewsbury Hosp. Socs: Fell. Roy. Med. Soc. Ed. Prev: SHO (A & E) Roy. Lond. Hosp.; RMD (A&E), Cairns Base Hosp., Qu.sland, Australia; HS Roy. Infirm. Edin.

FOLEY, Thomas Henry (retired) 55 Cranley Road, Guildford GU1 2JW Tel: 01483 504830 Fax: 01483 306253 Email: thfoley@uk-consultants.co.uk — MB BS (Hons. Med.) Lond. 1959; BSc (1st cl. Hons.) Lond. 1956, MD 1971; FRCP Lond. 1979, M 1962. Cons. Cardiol. Roy. Surrey Hosp. NHS Trust; Staff Grade Cons. Cardiac Dept. Roy. Surrey Hosp. Prev: Lect. (Med.) St. Thos. Hosp. Med. Sch. Lond.

FOLEY-COMER, Mr Adam Jonathan 15 Brookland Close, Hampstead Garden Suburb, London NW11 6DJ Tel: 020 8455 7064 Email: foley@aol.com — MB ChB 1992 Manch.; FRCS Eng. 1997. SHO (Plastic Surg.) Lister Hosp. Stevenage.

FOLEY-NOLAN, Niall Diare Ross 40 Kingswood Crescent, Leeds LS8 2BG — MB BCh BAO 1983 NUI; MRCPI 1986.

FOLKES, Anne, SSStJ (retired) — MB BS Lond. 1963; MRCS Eng. LRCP Lond. 1963; FRCR 1975; FFR 1970; DMRT Eng. 1967. Prev: Cons. St. Luke's Cancer Centre Roy. Surrey Co. Hosp. Guildford.

FOLKES, Sarah Elizabeth Fiona, Maj. RAMC c/o 5 Regiment Army Air Corps BFPO 808 — MB BS 1983 Lond.; MSc (Occupat. Med.) Lond. 1988; AFOM RCP Lond. 1988. Research Job Occupat. Med. HM Forces.

FOLLETT, Gerald Frederick (retired) 5 White Dales, Edinburgh EH10 7JQ — MB ChB 1957 Sheff.; MRCPath 1970; DObst RCOG 1959.

FOLLETT, Orla Josephine Ingestre, Agar Road, Truro TR1 1JU — MB BCh BAO 1972 Belf.; DObst RCOG 1974. (Belf.) Prev: Jun. Ho. Off. Roy. Vict. Hosp. Belf.; SHO (Obst.) Glas. Roy. Matern. Hosp.; Rotating SHO (Gen. Pract.) Plymouth Gen. Hosp.

FOLLOWS, Dorothy Mary High Trees, Clara Drive, Claverley, Pudsey LS28 5QP — MB ChB 1960 Leeds; DA Eng. 1963; DObst RCOG 1962.

FOLLOWS, George Alexander High Trees, Clara Drive, Calverley, Pudsey LS28 5QP — BM BCh 1994 Oxf.; MA Oxf. 1994; MRCP (UK) 1997. (Oxf.) Specialist Regist. (Haematol.) Yorks. Deanery.

FOLLOWS, Mark Christopher 19 Park Road, Bestwood Village, Nottingham NG6 8TQ Tel: 0115 979 7657 — BM BS 1994 Nottm. SHO (Med.) Kings Mill Centre Sutton-in-Ashfield. Prev: Ho. Off. (Surg.) Kings Mill Centre Sutton-in-Ashfield; Ho. Off. (Med.) Nottm. City Hosp.

FOLLOWS, Oliver John (retired) High Trees, Clara Drive, Calverley, Pudsey LS28 5QP Tel: 01274 612939 Fax: 01274 618481 Email: ojfollows@hotmail.com — MB BChir 1962 Camb.; MA, MB Camb. 1962, BChir 1961; FRCP 1967 London; FRCR 1975; FFR 1973; DMRD Eng. 1971. Prev: Cons. Diag. Radiol. Bradford Gp. Hosps.

FOLLOWS, Patricia Michele 3 Randall Road, Bristol BS8 4TP — MB ChB 1994 Bristol.

FOLLOWS, Roger Lindsey Goodacre and Partners, Swadlincote Surgery, Darklands Road, Swadlincote DE11 0PP Tel: 01283 551717 Fax: 01283 211905; 3 The Limes, Woodville Road, Hartshorne, Swadlincote DE11 7HR Tel: 01283 552210 — MB ChB 1987 Birm.; MB ChB (Hons.) Birm. 1987; MRCGP 1991; DRCOG 1990; Cert. Family Plann. JCC 1989. (Birmingham)

FOLWELL, Gregory Anthony Joseph The Surgery, 6 College Road, Eastbourne BN21 4HY Tel: 01323 735044 Fax: 01323 417705 — MB BS 1988 Lond.; T(GP) 1992; MRCGP 1992; DRCOG 1992. Prev: SHO St. Catherines Hospice Crawley; Trainee GP Leicester Roy. Infirm. VTS.

FON, Mr Lon Jee 101 Green Park Avenue, Belfast BT8 7YF Email: docs@ljf13.demon.co.uk — MB BCh BAO 1991 Belf.; FRCS Ed. 1996. (Queen's Belfast) Specialist Regist. (Surg.).

FON, Peter Josip 21 Cranworth Road, Winchester SO22 6SE Tel: 01962 852869; 6 Nepean Court, Carina, Brisbane, Queensland 4152, Australia — MB BS 1983 Queensland; FFR RCSI 1994. Prev: Regist. St. Lukes Hosp. Guildford; Radiat. Oncol. Trainee Qu.sland Radium Inst. Brisbane, Austral.

FONE, David Lawrence 64 Chapel Road, Abergavenny NP7 7DS — MB BS 1982 Lond.; MFPHM RCP (UK) 1996; MRCGP 1986; DCH RCP Lond. 1986; DRCOG 1985. Cons. Pub. Health Med. Gwent HA.

FONG, Grace Lai Yu Block 3 Orsett Hospital, Rowley Road, Grays RM16 3EU; 42 Gerrard Road, London N1 8AX — MB BS 1992 Lond.

FONG, Jim Chi Wai 80 Brocco Bank, Hunters Bar, Sheffield S11 8RS — MB ChB 1998 Sheff.; MB ChB Sheff 1998.

FONG, Jong Jeng 35 Gateley Road, London SW9 9TA — MB ChB 1994 Ed.

FONG, Kevin Jeremy 4 Tewkesbury Avenue, Pinner HA5 5LH — MB BS 1998 Lond.; MB BS Lond 1998.

FONG, Richard (retired) 163 Newland Park, Cottingham Road, Hull HU5 2DX — MB BS 1963 Sydney; MRCP (UK) 1973; Dip. Ven. Soc. Apoth. Lond. 1976; DPM Leeds 1975. Prev: Cons. Genitourin. Med. N. Humberside HA.

FONSECA, Esther Elise Princess Street Group Practice, 2 Princess Street, London SE1 6JP Tel: 020 7928 0253 Fax: 020 7261 9804; 3 Winterbrook Road, London SE24 9HZ — MB BChir 1969 Camb.; MB BChir Camb. 1968; DCH Eng. 1970. (Camb. & Westm.)

FONT OLIVE, Maria Del Mar Grove Road Surgery, 3 Grove Road, Solihull B91 2AG Tel: 0121 705 1105 Fax: 0121 711 4098; 37 Austcliff Drive, Solihull B91 3XT — LMS 1991 Barcelona; MRCGP 1996.

FONTAINE, Eustace James 81 Forest Road, London E8 3BT — BM 1994 Soton.

FONTAINE, Mark Peter Forum Medical Centre, Mandurah 6210, Australia Tel: 00 61 9 5358155; c/o 49 Brackendale Road, Camberley GU15 2JS Tel: 01276 24790 — MB BChir 1986 Camb.; MA Camb. 1988; DGM RCP Lond. 1990. Prev: GP Clarkson Surg. Wisbech; SHO (ENT) W. Suff. Hosp.

FONTANA, Andrea BUPA Cambridge, Lea Hospital, 30 New Road, Impington, Cambridge CB4 9EL — State Exam 1986 Palermo.

FONTANA, John William Fontana and Partners, Silsden Health Centre, Elliott Street, Silsden, Keighley BD20 0DG Tel: 01535 652447 Fax: 01535 657296; Darkwood House, The St, Addingham, Ilkley LS29 0JY — MB ChB 1969 Birm.; MRCGP 1977; DA Eng. 1972. Clin. Asst. (Anaesth.) Keighley.

FONTEBASSO, Manuela Tel: 01904 794141 Fax: 01904 788304 — MB ChB 1980 Leeds. GP Princip.; Clin. Asst. Headache Clinic York Dist. Hosp.

FOO, Ai Wyne Royal Belfast Hospital for Sick Children, Falls Road, Belfast BT12 Tel: 01232 240503; 16 Meadowbank, Jordanstown, Belfast BT17 0UP — MB BCh BAO 1993 Belf. Socs: BMA.

FOO, Angeline Ming Li 96 Rosemount Place, Aberdeen AB25 2XN — MB ChB 1998 Aberd.; MB ChB Aberd 1998.

FOO, Cheong Keong Grove Medical Group, 1 The Grove, Gosforth, Newcastle upon Tyne NE3 1NU Tel: 0191 210 6680 Fax: 0191 210 6682; 2A Akenside Terrace, Jesmond, Newcastle upon Tyne NE2 1TN — MB ChB 1986 Glas.; MRCP (UK) 1991; MRCGP 1992; DRCOG 1992. (Univ. Glas.) Tutor (Gen. Pract.) & Lect. (Primary Health Care) Univ. Newc. u. Tyne.

FOO, Howard Shing Liang 233 High Street, Edinburgh EH1 1PE — MB ChB 1993 Ed.

FOO, Ina Soke Mun 18 Corringham Court, Corringham Road, London NW11 7BY — MB BS 1985 Lond.

FOO, Irwin Tiang Hoe Department of Anaesthetics, Western General Hospital NHS Trust, Crewe Road, Edinburgh EH4 2XU Tel: 0131 537 1000; 6 Brunstane Road N., Edinburgh EH15 2DJ Tel: 0131 669 6301 — MB BChir 1987 Camb.; MRCP (UK) 1990; FRCA 1992. (University Cambridge School Clinical Medicine) Cons. (Anaesth.) W.ern Gen. Hosp. Edin. Prev: Sen. Regist. (Anaesth.) Roy. Infirm. Edin.

FOO, Ivan Tiang Hei Department Plastic Surgery, Bradford Royal Infirmary, Duckworth Lane, Bradford BD9 6RJ Tel: 01274 542200 — MB BS 1982 Lond.; FRCS Eng 1986; FRCS Ed. 1986; FRCSC Plast. 1993. (Middlesex) Cons. Plastic Surg. Bradford Roy. Infirm. Socs: Brit. Assn. Plast. Surgs.; Brit. Assn. Aesthetic Plastic Surgs.

FOO, Kong Yew Flat 326 Bow Quarter, Manhattan Building, Fairfield Road, London E3 2UQ Tel: 0973 195287 — MB BS 1994 Lond.; MRCP UK 1998. (St. Bartholomews Hosp. Lond.)

FOO, Li Foong Flat 2/1, 12 Millwood St., Glasgow G41 3JX — MB BCh 1994 Wales.

FOO, Loke Kong Flat 36, Marshall House, Upper Newtownards Road, Dundonald, Belfast BT16 1RB — MB BCh BAO 1986 Belf.

FOO, Marjorie Wai-Yin Department of Medicine, G Block, Archway Wing, Whittington Hospital, Archway Road, London N19 3UA Tel: 020 7288 5301 Fax: 020 7288 5302 — MB BCh BAO 1989 Belf.; MRCP (UK) 1992. (Qu. Univ. Belf.) Clin. Research Fell (Med.) Whittington Hosp. Lond. Socs: RCPS Glas.; Roy. Soc. Med. Prev: Regist. S.end Gen. Hosp. & Middlx. Hosp. Lond.

FOO, Patrick Sze Liang Poverest Medical Centre, 42 Poverest Road, St Mary Cray, Orpington BR5 2DQ Tel: 01689 833643 Fax: 01689 891976 — MB BS 1988 Lond.; BSc Lond. 1984. GP. Prev: SHO (Cas.) N. Middlx. Hosp. Lond.; Ho. Surg. Orpington Hosp.; Ho. Phys. Pembury Hosp.

FOO, Rudolph Percival Whitton Croft, 21 South Drive, Sandal, Wakefield WF2 7ND Tel: 01924 50733 — MRCS Eng. LRCP Lond. 1964; FFA RCS Eng. 1972; DA Eng. 1969. (Leeds) Cons. Anaesth. Wakefield Gp. Hosps. Prev: SHO (Anaesth.) Pinderfields Gen. Hosp. Wakefield; Regist. (Anaesth.) Wakefield Gp. Hosps. & N. Staffs. Roy. Infirm.; Stoke-on-Trent.

FOOK, Lisa Joan Royal Liverpool Hospital, Prescot Road, Liverpool Tel: 0161 706 2000; 50 Tothale Turn, Netherley, Liverpool L27 4YB — MB ChB 1990 Sheff.; MRCP (UK) 1994. Regist. (Geriat. Med.) Roy. Liverp. Hosp. Liverp. Prev: SHO (Haemat.) Withington Hosp. Manch.; SHO Rotat. (Med.) King's Mill Hosp. Mansfield; Ho. Off. Roy. Hallamsh. Hosp. & N.. Gen. Hosp. Sheff.

FOOKES, Bernard Harry (retired) 4 Cliveden Coppice, Sutton Coldfield B74 2RG Email: bernard@fookes.which.net — MB BS 1955 London; FRCP 1994 Edinburgh; MRCS Eng. LRCP 1955 London; MRCPsych 1971; DPM Eng. 1960. Prev: Cons. Psychiat. to N. Birm. Hosps.

FOOKES, Jenny Ross (retired) 4 Cliveden Coppice, Sutton Coldfield B74 2RG — MB ChB 1958 Ed.; MRCPsych 1979. Prev: Cons. Child & Adolesc. Psychiat. W. Midl. RHA.

FOOKS, Timothy John Charles Lower Street Surgery, 95 Lower Street, Pulborough RH20 2BP Tel: 01798 872305; Kings & Princes, The Hollows, West Chiltington, Pulborough RH20 2JN — BSc (Hons.) Lond. 1984, MB BS 1987; MRCGP 1992; DCH RCP Lond. 1991; DRCOG 1990. Chairm. Chichester & Rural PCG. Socs: BMA. Prev: Trainee GP Camb. HA.

FOON, Brian Peter Flat 11, Block 3, Prince Charles Hospital, Merthyr Tydfil CF47 9DT — MB BS 1992 West Indies.

FOONG, Jacqueline Flat 101, Holmfield Court, Belsize Grove, London NW3 4TU — MB BS 1985 New South Wales.

FOONG, Lian Cheun 18 Hillcrest, 51/57 Ladbroke Grove, London W11 3AX; #06-04 Kent Vale, Block A, 103 Clementi Rd, Singapore 129788, Singapore Email: obgflc@nus.edu.sg — MB BS 1987 Lond.; MD 1994; BSc Lond. 1984; MRCOG 1992. (Charing Cross & Westminister) Cons. (O & G); Sen. Lect. Prev: Specialist Regist., Qu. Charlotte's Hosp., Lond.

FOORD, Alice Louise Northgate Medical Practice, 1 Northgate, Canterbury CT1 1WL Tel: 01227 463570 Fax: 01227 786147 — MB ChB 1985 Bristol; DRCOG 1989; DCH RCP Lond. 1987.

FOORD, Christopher David Tower House Surgery, 169 West Wycombe Road, High Wycombe HP12 3AF Tel: 01494 526840 — BM 1989 Soton.; MRCGP 1995; DRCOG 1993. GP High Wycombe. Prev: Trainee GP Lymington; SHO (Paediat.) S.lands Hosp. Shoreham-by-Sea; SHO (Med.) Lymington Hosp. Hants.

FOORD, Keith David Department of Radiology, Conquest Hospital, St Leonards-on-Sea TN37 7RD Tel: 01424 758118 Fax: 01424 758013 Email: foord.keith@esht.nhs.uk; Hill Top, Hastings Road, Battle TN33 0TE Tel: 01424 774634 — MB ChB 1977 Sheff.; BMet. Sheff. 1967; FRCR 1983; DMRD 1981. (Sheff.) Cons. Radiol. E. Sussex Hosp.s NHS Trust; Director of Clin. Informatics, Conquest Hosp. Socs: Founder Mem. Brit. Soc. Interven. Radiol.; Cardiovasc. & Interven. Radiol. Soc. Europe; Eur. Congr. Radiol.

FOORD, Magdalen Laura 58a Canning Road, London N5 2JS — MB BS 1998 Lond.; MB BS Lond 1998.

FOORD, Richard David The Surgery, 36 Waverley Road, Southsea PO5 2PW Tel: 02392 828281 Fax: 02392 822275; 36 Dunnock Close, Rowlands Castle PO9 6HQ Tel: 02392 413927 — BM 1989 Soton.; MRCGP 1994; DFFP 1994; DRCOG 1993. (Southampton University) GP Princip.

FOORD, Roy Douglas (retired) The Coach House, Elmswell Road, Great Ashfield, Bury St Edmunds IP31 3HH Tel: 01359 242135 — MB BS Lond. 1954; DTM & H Eng. 1958; DPH Lond. 1961. Prev: Med. Dir. Greenford Div. Glaxo Gp. Research Ltd.

FOORD, Tina Frances Churchill Hospital, New Road, Oxford OX3 7LJ Tel: 01865 741841 — BM 1990 Soton.; MRCP (UK) 1993; FRCR 1997. p/t Cons.(Clin. Oncol.) Ch.ill Hosp., Oxf. Prev:

Regist. (Med.) St. Richards Hosp. Chichester; Regist. (Clin. Oncol.) Ch.ill Hosp. Oxf.

FOOT, Andrew Saville Leybourne Surgery, 1 Leybourne Avenue, Ensbury Park, Bournemouth BH10 6ES Tel: 01202 527003 Fax: 01202 549339 — MB BS 1981 Lond.; DRCOG 1984. p/t Indep. Tribunal Serv. Disabil. Appeal Tribunals.

FOOT, Annabel Brigid Mary Royal Hospital for Children, Upper Mandalin Street, Bristol BS2 8BJ Tel: 0117 927 6988 Fax: 0117 342 8628 Email: annabel.foot@ubht.swest.nhs.uk — MB ChB 1979 Bristol; MRCP (UK) 1982; FRCP 1997. Cons. Paediat. Oncol. Roy. Hosp. Sick Childr. Bristol. Prev: Regist. Rotat. (Paediat.) Reading & Oxf.

FOOT, Herbert Thomas (retired) 79 Boscombe Overcliffe Drive, Bournemouth BH5 2EL Tel: 01202 385336 Fax: 01202 385336 Email: tom@foothome.fsnet.co.uk — MRCS Eng. LRCP Lond. 1943; MA Camb. 1952; FRCGP 1975, M 1958. Prev: Resid. Anaesth. Lond. Hosp.

FOOT, Jean Margaret (retired) Laurel Farm, Little Barningham, Norwich NR11 7AG Tel: 01263 577405 Email: margeo@btinternet.com — MB BS 1965 Lond.; MRCS Eng. LRCP Lond. 1965; MRCGP 1979. Prev: Clin. Asst. Purley Hosp.

FOOT, Jill Lesley Wickham Surgery, Station Road, Wickham, Fareham PO17 5JL Tel: 01329 833121; Little Meads, Station Road, Soberton, Droxford, Southampton SO32 3QU Tel: 01489 877259 — MB BS 1982 Lond.; DFFP 1998; MRCGP 1986; DCH RCP Lond. 1986; DRCOG 1985. (Lond. Hosp.) GP, Wickham Surg., Wickham, Fareham. Socs: BMA; Nat. Assn. Family Plann. Doctors.

FOOT, Vanessa Mary 195 Mansfield Road, Papplewick, Nottingham NG15 8FL Tel: 0115 963 4128 — MB BS 1988 Lond.; MRCGP 1995; DRCOG 1994. Prev: SHO (Med.) S. Cleveland Hosp. Middlesbrough.

FOOT, Victoria Helen HQ HM Prison Service, Room 301A, Cleland House, Page St., London SW1P 4LN Tel: 020 7217 6538 Fax: 020 7217 6345 — MB BS 1979 Lond.; MRCGP 1985; DRCOG 1986. Health Care Adviser HM Prison Serv. Prev: Med. Off. HM Prison Durh.; Maj. RAMC.

FOOTE, Agnethe Ann Rectory Meadow Surgery, School Lane, Amersham HP7 0HG Tel: 01494 727711 Fax: 01494 431790; Thornhay, Hare Lane, Little Kingshill, Great Missenden HP16 0EF Tel: 01494 862204 — MB BS Lond. 1965; MRCS Eng. LRCP Lond. 1965; MRCGP 1989; DObst RCOG 1967. (St. Mary's) Prev: Assoc. Specialist Dept. Geriat. Med. Amersham.

FOOTE, Mr Andrew Veitch (retired) Edgehill Cottage, 45 Culter House Road, Milltimber, Aberdeen AB13 0EN Tel: 01224 732368 — MB ChB 1951 Ed.; ChM Ed. 1966; FRCS Ed. 1956. Prev: Cons. Cardio-Thoracic Surg. Aberd. Roy. Infirm.

FOOTE, Christopher Kenneth Arthur Thornhay, Hare Lane, Little Kingshill, Great Missenden HP16 0EF — MB BS Lond. 1964; FRCP (UK) 1981, M 1971; MRCS Eng. LRCP Lond. 1964. (St. Mary's) Cons. Phys. S. Bucks. NHS Trust. Prev: Cons. Phys. Dept. Geriats. Swindon & Cirencester Area; Squadron Ldr. RAF Med. Br., Med. Specialist; Sen. Regist. Dept. Geriats. & Nuffield Dept. Med. United Oxf. Hosps.

FOOTE, Guinevere Ann The Fryern Surgery, Oakmount Road, Chandlers Ford, Eastleigh SO53 2LH — MB ChB 1976 Bristol; MRCGP 1983; DCH Eng. 1978. Prev: Clin. Asst. (Paediat.) St. Jas. Univ. Hosp. Leeds; Regist. (Paediat.) St. Peter's Hosp. Chertsey; Clin. Asst. (Paediat.) St. Jas. Univ. Hosp. Leeds; SHO (Gen. Med.) Plymouth Gen. Hosps. SHO (Paediat.) Roy. Devon & Exeter Hosps.

FOOTE, John William Department of Diabetes & Endocrinology, Royal Cornwall Hospital, Treliske, Truro TR1 3LJ Tel: 01872 252733 Email: john.foote@rcht.swest.nhs.uk — MB ChB 1975 Liverp.; FRCP (Ed.) 1998; FRCP 1998; FRCPath 1997, M 1987; MD Liverp. 1985; MRCP (UK) 1979; BSc (Hons.) Liverp. 1971. (Liverp.) Cons. Phys. (Diabetes & Endocrinol.) Roy. Cornw. Hosp. Truro. Socs: Brit. Diabetic Assn. Prev: Cons. Phys. Hinchingbrooke Hosp. Huntingdon; Cons. Chem. Path. Papworth Hosp. Camb.; Sen. Regist. (Clin. Chem.) Univ. Hosp. Nottm.

FOOTE, Julian Alasdair James Green Gates, Sandy Way, Woking GU22 8BB — MB BCh 1997 Wales.

FOOTE, Keith Douglas Department Paediatrics, Royal Hampshire County Hospital, Romsey Road, Winchester SO22 5DG Tel: 01962 863535 — MB BS 1977 Lond.; MRCP (UK) (Paediat.) 1983; MRCS Eng. LRCP Lond. 1977; DCH RCP Lond. 1983. Cons. Paediat. Roy. Hants. Co. Hosp. Winchester. Socs: Paediat. Research Soc.; Brit. Assn. Perinatal Med. Prev: Sen. Regist. (Paediat.) King's Coll. Hosp. Lond.; Post Doctoral Fell. (Neonat.) Univ. Brit. Columbia Canada.

FOOTE, Susan Jane Westwind, Milton, Dumbarton G82 2SG — MB ChB 1982 Glas. Clin. Asst. In BrE. Screening.

FOOTERMAN, David Simon 21 Fairfax Place, London NW6 4EJ — MB BS 1976 Lond.; MRCS Eng. LRCP Lond. 1976; FFA RCS Eng. 1983; FFA (SA) 1981. (St. Geo.)

FORAN, Bernadette Hannah Wickham Green, Coldwell Lane, Sheffield S10 5TJ — MB ChB 1994 Sheff.

FORAN, John Dermot 138 Harley Street, London W1; 98 Eversholt Road, London NW1 1BP — MB BS 1963 Lond.

FORAN, John Paul Michael Cardiothoracic Unit, St George's Hospital, Blackshaw Road, London SW17 0QT Tel: 020 8672 1255 Fax: 07070 607836 Email: jpmf@bizonline.co.uk; 39 Sussex Road, Carshalton Beeches, Carshalton SM5 3LT Tel: 0385 221989 Fax: 07070 607836 — MB BS 1988 Lond.; MRCP (UK) 1991. (St. Geo. Hosp. Lond.) Socs: Fell. Roy. Soc. Med. Lond.; Brit. Cardiac Soc.

FORBAT, Lance Nicholas West Cumberland Hospital, NHS Trust, Hensingham, Whitehaven CA28 8JG Tel: 01946 523015 Fax: 01946 523504 — MD 1994 Lond.; BSc (Hons.) Lond. 1977, MD 1994, MB BS 1980; MRCP (UK) 1984. Cons. Cardiol. & Phys. W. Cumbld. Hosp. Whitehaven; Hon. Cons. Cardiol. S. Tees NHS Trust, Middlesbrough. Prev: Regist. (Cardiothoracic) Groby Rd. Hosp. Leicester; Brit. Heart Foundat. Jun. Research Fell. Dept. Physiol. United Med. & Dent. Sch. St. Thos. Hosp. Lond.; Hon. Regist. (Cardiol.) St. Thos. Hosp. Lond.

FORBAT, Sandra Mary Flat B, 173 Brondesbury Park, Brondesbury, London NW2 5JN — MB BS 1985 Lond.

FORBER, Kenneth William Homefield Place, Heavitree, Exeter Tel: 01392 73948 — MB ChB 1943 Birm.; MRCS Eng. LRCP Lond. 1943.

FORBER, Mr Robert Kenneth Jonathan, Col. late RAMC Army Headquarters North Ireland BFPO 825; Homefield Place, 35 Fore St, Heavitree, Exeter EX1 2QN Tel: 01392 50910 — MB BChir 1974 Camb.; MA Camb. 1975; MMed Sc. Birm. 1991; FRCS Lond. 1980; MFOM RCP Lond. 1997, AFOM 1991. (Guy's) Sen. Specialist (Occupat. Med.) Cdr. Med. Scotl. Socs: Soc. Occupat. Med. Prev: SO1 (Prevent. Med.) HQ UKSC(G) Rheindahlen; SO1 Health HQ Land Command Salisbury; DPMO HM Naval Base Portsmouth.

FORBES, Alan Milne Webster Hunts Cross Group Practice, Hunts Cross Health Centre, 70 Hillfoot Road, Hillfoot, Liverpool L25 0ND Tel: 0151 486 1428 Fax: 0151 448 0233; 16 Sinclair Drive, Childwall, Liverpool L18 0HN — MB ChB 1972 Aberd.; MRCP (UK) 1975. Course Organiser (Gen. Pract.) Liverp. Prev: Regist. Renal Med. Sefton Gen. Hosp. Liverp.; Research Fell. Dept. Child Health Aberd. Univ.

FORBES, Alasdair Anderson Scotstown Medical Centre, Cairnfold Road, Bridge of Don, Aberdeen AB22 8LD Tel: 01224 702149 Fax: 01224 706688 — MB ChB 1989 Aberd.

FORBES, Alastair St Marks Hospital, Watford Road, Harrow HA1 3UJ Tel: 020 8235 4016 Fax: 020 8235 4039 Email: alastair.forbes@ic.ac.uk — MB BS 1979 Lond.; ILTM 2000; BSc (Hons.) Lond. 1976, MD 1987; FRCP Lond. 1996; MRCP (UK) 1982. (King's Coll.) Cons. Phys. (Gastroenterol.) St. Marks Hosp. Lond.; Reader Imperial Coll. Sch. Med. Socs: Amer. Gastroenterological Assn.; Brit. Soc. Gastroenterol.; Eur. Assn. Gastroenterol. Prev: Sen. Regist. (Gen. Med. & Gastroenterol.) Char. Cross & W.m. Hosps. Lond.; Research Fell. Liver Unit King's Coll. Hosp. Lond.; Regist. (Gen. Med. & Gastroenterol.) Middlx. Hosp. Lond.

FORBES, Alexander Scott Riverside Medical Centre, Victoria Road, Walton-le-Dale, Preston PR5 4AY Tel: 01772 556703; Goosnargh Mill, Mill Lane, Goosnargh, Preston PR3 2JX Tel: 01772 865172 — MB ChB 1981 Ed.; MRCGP 1985; DCH RCP Lond. 1984; DRCOG 1983.

FORBES, Alison Maria 13 Dorrells Road, Longwick, Princes Risborough HP27 9SL Tel: 01844 342721 — MB ChB 1982 Aberd.; FRCA 1995; DA (UK) 1987. Cons. Anaesth. with on interest in Acute Pain; Stoke Mondeville Hosp. NHS Trust. Prev: Regist. (Anaesth.) Mersey RHA & S. Birm. HA; Med. Off. RAMC.

FORBES, Angela Marilyn Grosvenor Team, West Cheshire Hospital, Liverpool Rd, Chester CH1 2UL Tel: 01244 364038 Fax: 01244 364492 Email: angel.forbes@mta2.wwirralcc-tr.nwestnhs.uk; 16 Sinclair Drive, Liverpool L18 0HN Tel: 0151 722 9539 — MB

ChB 1971 Aberd.; MRCP (UK) 1979. (Aberdeen) Staff Grade Phys. in Psychiat., Acute Adult Psychiat., Qwirral and W. Chesh. NHS Trust Chester. Prev: Med. Off. (Psychiaatry) N. Mersey Community; NHS Trust. Liverp.; Gen. Practitioner P.s Pk. Health Centre, Liverp..

FORBES, Angus Edwin Cokesputt, Payhembury, Honiton EX14 3HD — MB Camb. 1961, BChir 1960; DObst RCOG 1964. (Lond. Hosp.) Socs: BMA. Prev: Ho. Surg. & Res. Accouch. Lond. Hosp.; Colombo Plan Med. Off. Laos.

FORBES, Anne Lesley Kingthorne Group Practice, 83A Thorne Road, Doncaster DN1 2EU Tel: 01302 342832 Fax: 01302 366995 — MB ChB 1983 Bristol. SHO & GP VTS Barnsley HA.

FORBES, Avril Ann Auchengrane, Castle Douglas DG7 2LH — MB ChB 1984 Glas.; MB ChB Glas. l984; DCCH RCP Ed. 1993; DFFP 1993; DCH RCPS Glas. 1991; DRCOG 1986; Joint Committee on Postgraduate Training for General Practice- Certificate of experience 1989. Prev: Clin. Med. Off. (Child Health) Gateshead Healthcare; Clin. Med. Off. (Child Health) Dumfries.

FORBES, Professor Charles Douglas University Department of Medicine, Ninewells Hospital and Medical School, Dundee DD1 9SY Tel: 01382 660111 Fax: 01382 660675; East Chattan, 108 Hepburn Gardens, St Andrews KY16 9LT Tel: 01334 472428 — MB ChB Glas. 1961; DSc Glas. 1986, MD 1973; FRCP Lond. 1979, M 1965; FRCP Ed. 1978, M 1965; FRCP Glas. 1974, M 1964. Prof. Med. & Hon. Cons. Phys. Ninewells Hosp. Dundee; Vis. Prof. Univ. Strathclyde. Socs: Fell. (Counc. on Thrombosis) Amer. Heart Assn.; Assn. Phys. & Europ. Soc. Clin. Investig.; (Pres.) Brit. Soc. Haemostasis & Thrombosis. Prev: Reader (Med.) Univ. Glas.; Research Fell. Case W.. Reserve Univ. Ohio, USA; Lect. Makerere Univ., Uganda.

FORBES, David Ian Gloucester Avenue Surgery, 158 Gloucester Avenue, Chelmsford CM2 9LQ Tel: 01245 353182 Fax: 01245 344479; Forty Hill, Moulsham Thrift, Chelmsford CM2 8BP — MB BS 1987 Lond.; DLO RCS Eng. 1991.

FORBES, Duncan William Department of Anaesthesia, Perth Royal Infirmary, Taymount Terrace, Perth PH1 1NX; 83 Glasgow Road, Perth PH2 0PQ — MB ChB 1984 Glas.; MB ChB Glas. l984; FRCA 1990. Cons. Anaesth. Perth Roy. Infirm. Socs: Assn. Anaesth. GB & Irel.; Glas. & W. Scot. Soc. Anaesth. Prev: Sen. Regist. (Anaesth.) Ninewells Hosp. Dundee; Regist. (Anaesth.) Glas. Roy. Infirm.; SHO & Regist. (Anaesth.) Monklands Dist. Gen. Hosp. Airdrie.

FORBES, Elizabeth Ann 93 Finnart Street, Greenock PA16 8HN — MB ChB 1993 Glas.

FORBES, Elizabeth Karen Firs Clinic, Firs Lane, Smethwick, Warley B67 6A Tel: 0121 558 0105; 48 Bantock Way, Harborne, Birmingham B17 0LX — MB ChB 1985 Birm.; MB ChB (Hons.) Birm. 1985; MRCGP 1989; DCH RCP Lond. 1988; DRCOG 1987.

FORBES, Freda Pathology Department, Vale of Leven District General Hospital, Alexandria G83 0UA Tel: 01389 754121 Fax: 01389 603870; Canna, 17 Victoria Road, Helensburgh G84 7RT Tel: 01436 676961 — MB ChB 1977 Glas.; MRCPath 1983. Cons. Path. Vale of Leven Argyll & Clyde HB. Prev: Cons. Cytopath. Roy. Infirm. Glas.

FORBES, George Barnet (retired) 42 St Lawrence Forstal, Canterbury CT1 3PA Tel: 01227 458936 — MB ChB Aberd. 1937; MD Aberd. 1951; FCPath. 1963. Prev: Cons. Path. Kent & Canterbury Hosp.

FORBES, George Wilson Farrins, Datchworth Green, Knebworth SG3 6TN Tel: 01438 812428 — M.B., Ch.B. Aberd. 1942. (Aberd.) Prev: Ho. Phys. Haymeads E.M.S. Hosp. Bishop's Stortford.

FORBES, Gerald Innes 33 Hope Terrace, Edinburgh EH9 2AP — LRCP LRCS 1951 Ed.; LRCP LRCS Ed. LRFPS Glas. 1951.

FORBES, Hamish (retired) Ballaggan Steading, Gollanfield, Inverness IV2 7QT — MB BS 1954 Lond.; MRCS Eng. LRCP Lond. 1954; FFCM 1987, M 1974; DIH Eng. 1966; DTM & H Eng. 1965; DPH Lond. 1961. Prev: Med. Adviser Div. Bldg. Common Servs. Agency.

FORBES, Henry Finlayson Smiddy Cottage, Shanzie Farm, Alyth, Blairgowrie PH11 8JS — MB ChB 1985 Ed. Ho. Surg. Law Hosp. Carluke; Ho. Phys. City Hosp. Edin.

FORBES, Isabella Mary Barclay (retired) Mansefield, Almswall Road, Kilwinning KA13 6 Tel: 01294 52826 — MB ChB 1943 Glas.

FORBES, Miss Jennifer Ellen The Royal Free Hospital, Pond Street, Hampstead, London NW3 Tel: 020 7794 0500 — MB BS 1984 Lond.; BSc (Hons.) Lond. 1981; FRCS Glas. 1989; FRCOphth 1990. (St. Mary's Hosp. Med. Sch. Lond.) Cons. Ophth., Roy. Free Hosp.; Barnet Gen. Hosp.; Edgeware Community Hosp. Socs: Roy. Soc. Med. Prev: Sen. Regist. Flex. (Ophth.) Moorfields Eye Hosp., Lond.; Sen. Regist. Flex. (Ophth.) Roy. Free Hosp. Lond.; Research Regist. (Ophth.) Clin. Cataract Unit. Oxf. Eye Hosp.

FORBES, Jennifer Helen Durell Top Flat Left, 47 Magdalen Yard Road, Dundee DD1 4NF — MB ChB 1995 Dundee.

FORBES, Jennifer Margaret Dunluce Health Centre, 1 Dunluce Avenue, Belfast BT9 7HR — MB BCh BAO 1984 Belf.

FORBES, John Alexander 8 Colville Drive, Bishop's Waltham, Southampton SO32 1LT Tel: 01489 896482 — MB ChB 1951 Aberd.; MA Aberd. 1947, MD 1963; FRCGP 1971, M 1962. (Aberd.) Prev: Prof. Primary Med. Care Univ. Soton. Med. Sch.; Sen. Lect. (Community Med.) Univ. Soton. Med. Sch.

FORBES, John Ronald (retired) Pen-y-Wern, Pontblyddyn, Mold CH7 4HN Tel: 01978 760531 — MB BS (Hons.) Lond. 1935; MD Lond. 1938; FRCP Lond. 1953, M 1937; MRCS Eng. LRCP Lond. 1935. Prev: Cons. Phys. Clwyd S. Health Dist.

FORBES, John William East Calder Medical Practice, 147 Main St., East Calder, Livingston EH53 0EW Tel: 01506 882882 Fax: 01506 883630; Morven Cottage, Livingston Village, Livingston EH54 7AF Tel: 01506 411950 — MB ChB Ed. 1966.

FORBES, Karen c/o Palliative Care Team, Department of Palliative Medicine, Bristol Oncology Centre, Horfield Road, Bristol BS2 8ED Tel: 0117 928 3507 Fax: 0117 928 3865 Email: k.forbes@bristol.ac.uk; New Hall, Pwllmeyric, Chepstow NP16 6LF Tel: 01291 626554 Fax: 01291 622429 — MB ChB 1984 Birm.; MRCP (UK) 1988; Dip. Palliat. Med. Wales 1992. Cons. & Sen. Lect. (Palliat. Med.) Bristol. Socs: Assn. Palliat. Med. Prev: Sen. Regist. (Palliat. Med.) Leed Yorks. Region; Regist. & SHO (Palliat. Med.) Cardiff; Regist. (Radiother.) Nottm. Gen. Hosp.

FORBES, Kirsten 5 Royal Circus, Edinburgh EH3 6TL — BChir 1992 Camb.

FORBES, Laetitia Janet Williams Mound House, 3 Albert St., Arbroath DD11 1RA — M.B., Ch.B. St. And. 1941. (Dundee) Prev: Capt. R.A.M.C.; Ho. Phys. Stobhill Hosp. Glas.; Ho. Surg. Gleneagles E.M.S. Hosp.

FORBES, Lindsay Jean Lesley 46 Allendale Close, London SE5 8SG Tel: 020 7701 3446 — MB BS 1988 Lond.; MSc 1997; BSc (Med. Sociol.) Lond. 1985; MRCP (UK) 1991. Lect. (Pub. Health Med.) UMDS Lond. Prev: Regist. (Med.) St. Geo. Hosp. Lond.; Regist. (Med.) St. Richard's Hosp. Chichester & Worthing Hosp.; SHO (Med.) Roy. Sussex Co. Hosp. Brighton.

FORBES, Mary Charlotte (retired) 339 Albert Drive, Pollokshields, Glasgow G41 5HJ — MB ChB 1943 Glas. Prev: Ho. Surg. Roy. Matern. & Wom. Hosp. & Roy. Samarit. Hosp. Glas.

FORBES, Maureen Drummond (retired) 8 Christchurch Road, Norwich NR2 2AD Email: cdforbes@paston.cd.uk — MB ChB Liverp. 1958; DPM Eng. 1973.

FORBES, Michael James Shell International, Shell Centre, South Bank, London SE1 7NA Tel: 020 7934 3770 Fax: 020 7934 7046 — MB BChir 1971 Camb.; MFOM RCP Lond. 1997; DIH RCP Lond. 1990; DA Eng. 1976; DCH Eng. 1973. (Camb. & Guy's Hosp. Lond.) Sen. Med. Adviser Shell Internat. Lond. Prev: Sen. Med. Adviser Shell Expo Aberd.; Chief Med. Off. Brunei Shell Petroleum, Brunei.

FORBES, Nadia Jane c/o Mr G. Newman, 3 Bretaneby High St., Seal, Sevenoaks TN15 0AJ — MB ChB 1994 Auckland.

FORBES, Naida Frances c/o Dr & Mrs C Mercer, 22 Kinnear Road, Edinburgh EH3 5PE — MB ChB 1997 Aberd.

FORBES, Mr Patrick Bruce Hinchingbrooke Hospital, Huntingdon PE29 6NT Tel: 01480 416416 Fax: 01480 416248 Email: paddy.forbes@hbhc-tr.anglox.nhs.uk; 168 Hartford Road, Huntingdon PE29 1XQ Tel: 01480 454280 Fax: 01480 436423 Email: pforbes@talk21.com — MB ChB 1974 Aberd.; FRCOG 1996, M 1983; DRCOG 1978. Cons. O & G Hinchingbrooke Health Care NHS Trust Huntingdon. Prev: Cons. O & G RAF; Lect. St. Mary's Hosp. Med. Sch. Lond.

FORBES, Patrick Joseph Wessex Road Surgery, Wessex Road, Parkstone, Poole BH14 8BQ Tel: 01202 734924 Fax: 01202 738957 — MB BCh BAO 1973 NUI.

FORBES, Raeburn Bruce 19 Lochinver Crescent, Dundee DD2 4UA Tel: 01382 660046 — MB ChB 1992 Dundee; MRCP (UK) 1995. SHO (Neurosci.) Dundee Roy. Infirm. Socs: BMA. Prev:

SHO Rotat. (Med. for Elderly) Roy. Vict. Hosp. Dundee VTS; Ho. Off. Profess. Med. Unit. Ninewells Hosp.

FORBES, Robert Duncan (retired) Chattis Hill, Moulsham Thrift, Chelmsford CM2 8BP Tel: 01245 353182 — MB BS 1957 Lond.; DObst RCOG 1959. MPS NZ 1950; Clin. Asst. (ENT) Chelmsford & Essex Hosp. Prev: Ho. Surg. (O & G) OldCh. Hosp. Romford.

FORBES, Robin David Whinfield Cottage, Pennington, Ulverston LA12 0LE; 33 Darnell Road, Trinity, Edinburgh EH5 3PH Tel: 0131 552 9742 Email: goodforbes@hotmail.com — MB ChB 1993 Dundee; FRCA Royal Coll. Anaesthetists 1998; DA Royal Coll. Anaesthetists 1996. (Dundee Univ.) Specialist Regist., Anaesthetics, Roy. Infirm. Edin.

FORBES, Stuart John Gastroenterology Department, Hammersmith Hospital, Du-cane Road, London W12 0NN Tel: 020 8383 3957 Fax: 020 8749 3436; 157 Kyverdale Road, London N16 6PS Tel: 020 8806 3786 — MB ChB 1992 Ed.; BSc Ed. 1990; MRCP (UK) 1995. Wellcome Trust Med. Research Train. Fell. Hammersmith Hosp. Lond.; Lect. St Mary's Hosp. Prev: Hon. Regist. Gastroenterol. Hammersmith Hosp.; Sp. Regist. St Mary's Hosp.; Sp. Regist. Hillingdon Hosp.

FORBES, Walter 13 Buchan Place, Fraserburgh AB43 9TX — MB ChB 1989 Aberd.

FORBES, Wellesley St Clair Department of Clinical Radiology, Hope Hospital, Stott Lane, Salford M6 8HD Tel: 0161 787 4928 Fax: 0161 787 4920 Email: dr forbes@hope.srht.nwest.nhs.uk; Bankfield, 13 Moss Lane, Sale M33 6QD Tel: 0161 969 1638 — MB BCh BAO 1969 Dub.; MA Dub. 1970; FRCR 1975; DMRD Eng. 1974; DObst RCOG 1971. (TC Dub.) Cons. Radiol., Neuroradiol. & Gen. Radiol. Hope Hosp. Salford Roy. Hosps. NHS Trust & Roy. Manch. Childr. Hosp.; Lect. (Diag. Radiol.) Univ. Manch. Socs: Brit. Soc. Neuroradiol.; Brit. Inst. Radiol.; Coun. Mem. Manch. Med. Soc. Prev: Sen. Research Fell. (Diag. Radiol.) Univ. Manch.; Sen. Regist. (Radiodiag.) Radcliffe Infirm. Oxf.

FORBES, William 144 Mayfield Road, Newington, Edinburgh EH9 3AL Tel: 0131 667 4203 Fax: 0131 668 4833 — PhD Glas. 1966, MD 1972, MB ChB 1959; FRCS Ed. 1965; MFCM 1981. (Glas.) The Cunningham Trust St. Andrews. Prev: Sen. Med. Off. Chief Scientist Off. Scott. Home & Health Dept.; Sen. Lect. (Path.) Univ. Edin.; Scientif. Adviser Scott. Hosp. Endowment Research Trust (Edin.) The Linbury Trust Lond.

FORBES, William Raymond (retired) 63 Gabalfa Road, Swansea SA2 8NA Tel: 01792 206377 — MB BCh BAO 1956 Belf.; FRCP Lond. 1978, M 1965; FRCP Ed. 1977, M 1963; DCH Eng. 1959; DObst RCOG 1958. Prev: Cons. Paediat. W. Glam. AHA.

FORBES SMITH, Peter Arthur 4 Home Park, Aberdour, Burntisland KY3 0XA — MRCS Eng. LRCP Lond. 1973; BSc (Hons.) Lond. 1970, MB BS 1973; FRCOG 1992, M 1980; Dip. Ven. Soc. Apoth. Lond. 1977. (St. Bart.) Cons. O & G P.ss Margt. Hosp. Swindon. Prev: Sen. Regist. & Lect. (O & G) Middlx. Hosp. Lond.; Resida. Surg. Off. Wom. Hosp. Soho Sq. Lond.; Resid. Med. Off. Qu. Charlottes Matern. Hosp. Lond.

FORD, Alan Ross The Surgery, 318 Westdale Lane, Mapperley, Nottingham NG3 6EU Tel: 0115 987 7604 Fax: 0115 956 8592; 13A Steedman Avenue, Mapperley, Nottingham NG3 6DL Tel: 0115 993 9554 — MB BS 1972 Lond.; MD Lond. 1980; BSc (Hons.) Lond 1969; MRCP (UK) 1975; MRCGP 1985. (Westm.) GP. Prev: GP Witney, Oxon.; MRC Train. Fell. (Clin. Pharm. Unit) Radcliffe Infirm. Oxf.; Regist. (Gen. & Renal Med.) Addenbrooke's Hosp. Camb.

FORD, Alexander Charles 94 Yorkdale Road, Oldham OL4 3AR Tel: 0161 665 1098 — MB ChB 1997 Leeds. SHO A&E Leeds Gen. Infirm. Prev: SHO Gen. Med. Seacroft Hosp. Leeds; PRHO Surg. Bradford Roy. Infirm.; PRHO Med. Seacroft Hosp. Leeds.

FORD, Angela Dorothy Busby Road Surgery, 75 Busby Road, Clarkston, Glasgow G76 7BW Tel: 0141 644 2669 Fax: 0141 644 5171 — MB ChB 1981 Aberd.; MRCGP 1985; DRCOG 1983.

FORD, Barbara Doris The Nook, Stonebreaks Road, Springhead, Oldham OL4 4BY — MRCS Eng. LRCP Lond. 1961.

FORD, Brian Nevin Neillsbrook Road Surgery, 5 Neillsbrook Road, Randalstown, Antrim BT41 3AE Tel: 028 9447 2575 Fax: 028 9447 3653; Greystone House, 23 Greystone Road, Antrim BT41 1HQ Tel: 018494 62378 — MB BCh BAO 1972 Belf.; MRCGP 1985; DObst RCOG 1974.

FORD, Christine Helen Lonsdale Medical Centre, 24 Lonsdale Road, London NW6 6RR Tel: 020 7328 8331 Fax: 020 7328 8630; 7 Leighton Crescent, London NW5 2QY Tel: 020 7485 2640 — MB ChB 1975 Dundee; MRCP (UK) 1980; MRCGP 1984; DRCOG 1985. GP Facilitator in Subst. Misuse & HIV Presention in Gen. Pract.; Clin. Dir. Brent Specialist Drug & Alcohol Serv.

FORD, Colin David Wingate Medical Centre, 79 Bigdale Drive, Northwood, Liverpool L33 6YJ Tel: 0151 546 2958 Fax: 0151 546 2914; 1 Thornhill, Granville Park, Aughton, Ormskirk L39 5HD Tel: 01695 423768 — MB ChB 1962 Liverp.; MRCGP 1986; DObst RCOG 1964. (Liverp.) Organiser Whiston Hosp.; Trainer (Gen. Pract.) VTS; Chairm. St. Helens & Knowsley LMC. Socs: Roy. Coll. Gen. Pract. Prev: Ho. Phys. Walton Hosp. Liverp.; Ho. Surg. St. Helens Hosp.; Ho. Surg. (Obst.) Whiston Hosp.

FORD, Mr Colin Gagen 79 De Beauvoir Road, Kingsland, Hackney, London N1 4EL Tel: 020 7254 1491 — MB BS 1962 Lond.; FRCS Eng. 1973; DObst RCOG 1964. (St. Mary's)

FORD, Daniel Robert 80 War Lane, Harborne, Birmingham B17 9RR Tel: 0121 427 8057 — MB ChB 1997 Birm.; BSc (Hons.) Birm. 1994. (Birmingham)

FORD, David Edward (retired) Timberly, St Peters Road, Hayling Island PO11 0RT Tel: 023 9246 5817 Email: defordmd@waitrose.com — MB BS Lond. 1955; DPhysMed Eng. 1963; DObst RCOG 1957. Prev: Dep. Med. Dir. Med. Rehabil. Centre Camden Rd. Lond.

FORD, Mr David James Robert Jones and Agnes Hunt, Orthopaedic Hospital, Oswestry SY10 7AG Tel: 01691 404000 — MB BS 1976 Newc.; FRCS (Orth.) Ed. 1984; FRCS Glas. 1980; FRCS Eng. 1980; FRCS Ed. 1980. Cons. Orthop. Trauma Surg. & Hand & Upper Limb Surg. Robt. Jones & Agnes Hunt Orthop. Hosp. OsW.ry. Socs: Fell. BOA; Brit. Soc. Surg. Hand. Prev: Sen. Regist. (Orthop.) Robt. Jones & Agnes Hunt Orthop. Hosp. OsW.ry & N. Staffs. Infirm. Stoke-on-Trent; Research Fell. Microsurg. MRC Clin. Research Centre N.wick Pk.; Regist. (Hand Surg.) Derbysh. Roy. Infirm.

FORD, David John Department of Medicine, Scarborough Hospital, Scarborough YO12 6QL Tel: 01723 342037 Fax: 01723 346424 — MB BChir 1980 Camb.; MA Camb. 1979; MRCP (UK) 1982; FRACP 1987; DCH Otago 1983. Cons. Gen. & Respirat. Med. ScarBoro. Hosp. Prev: Cons. Gen. & Respirat. Med. N. Shore Hosp. Auckland; Clin. Lect. Auckland Med. Sch.

FORD, Deborah Louise Oaklands, Middlewich Medical Centre, St. Anns Walk, Middlewich CW10 9BE Tel: 01606 836481; Sweetbridge Cottage, 32a Church St, Davenham, Northwich CW9 8NF — MB ChB 1989 Manch.; MRCGP 1993; DRCOG 1992; DCH RCP Lond. 1991. (Manch.)

FORD, Diana Elizabeth Hallsteads, Chilworth, Guildford GU4 8RQ Tel: 01483 560044 — MB BS Lond. 1954; MRCS Eng. LRCP Lond. 1954; DCH Eng. 1956. (King's Coll. Hosp.) Assoc. Specialist (Paediat. Neurol.) Frimley Childr. Centre Frimley Pk. Hosp. Prev: Ho. Phys. & Ho. Surg. Qu. Eliz. Hosp. Childr. Lond.

FORD, Edward Hugh Rawlinson (retired) Balsham Place, Balsham, Cambridge CB1 6EP — MB BChir 1949 Camb.; MD Camb. 1955. Prev: Dir. Med. Studies Selwyn Coll. Camb.

FORD, Mrs Elizabeth Magdalene (retired) 26 Harrow Gardens, Orpington BR6 9WD — MD 1939 Basle; MD St. And. 1949. MB ChB 1948. Prev: Sen. Resid. Med. Off. Bangour EMS Hosp. Edin.

FORD, Elizabeth Margaret Sian Hilltop, Sunnybank, Brecon LD3 7RW — MB BCh 1988 Wales; MRCGP 1994; DCH RCP Lond. 1996.

FORD, Fiona Mary 44 Churchgate, Southport PR9 7JH — MB ChB 1978 Liverp.; DRCOG 1980; DTM & H Liverp. 1981. Prev: Med. Off. St. John's Hosp. Mzuzu, Malawi.

FORD, Gareth Victoria Surgery, 5 Victoria Road, Holyhead LL65 1UD; Derva, Maes Meiler, Bethel, Bodorgan LL62 5PH — MB BCh 1990 Wales. Prev: Trainee GP/SHO (O & G) Neath Gen. Hosp.

FORD, Professor Gary Ashley Wolfson Unit of Clinical Pharmacology, The University, Newcastle upon Tyne NE2 4HH Tel: 0191 222 7744 Fax: 0191 222 5826 Email: g.a.ford@ncl.ac.uk — MB BChir 1982 Camb.; MA Camb. 1983; FRCP Lond. 1996; MRCP (UK) 1985. (Camb./King's Coll. Hosp.) Prof. of Pharmacol. of Old Age Univ. of Newc. upon Tyne; Cons. Phys. Stroke and Gen. Med. Newc. upon Tyne Hopsitals NHS Trust Newc. upon Tyne. Socs: Brit. Geriat. Soc.; Brit. Pharmacol. Soc.; Train. Comm. Mem. Brit. Assn. Stroke Phys. Prev: Sen. Lect. (Clin. Pharmacol. & Geriat. Med.) Univ. Newc. upon Tyne; Sen. Regist. (Geriat. & Gen. Med.) Freeman

Hosp. Newc.; Post Doctoral Fell. (Clin. Pharmacol.) Dept. Med. Stanford Univ. Calif., USA.

FORD, George Charles Fronks Road Surgery, 77 Fronks Road, Dovercourt, Harwich CO12 3RS Tel: 01255 556868 Fax: 01255 556969 — MB ChB 1980 Manch.; MRCGP 1984.

FORD, Gillian Dawn Accident and Emergency Group, 54 Cockton Hill Road, Bishop Auckland DL4 6DB Tel: 01388 602728; Tel: 01388 814526 — MB ChB 1988 Leeds; Dip Occ Med 2000; MRCGP 1993; DRCOG 1992.

FORD, Gillian Rachel, CB (retired) 9 Ryecotes Mead, Dulwich Common, London SE21 7EP Tel: 020 8693 6576 Email: gillian.fordmackenzie@care4free.net — BM BCh 1959 Oxf.; FFCM 1974; DO Eng. 1962; MRCP 1978 London; FRCP 1985 London; FRCP 1996 Edinburgh. Prev: Dep. Chief Med. Off. DHSS.

FORD, Mr Glenn Robert Easton Ward, Williams Avenue, Dorchester DT1 2JY Tel: 01305 251150; 9 Linden Avenue, Dorchester DT1 1EJ — MB BS Lond. 1980; BSc Lond. 1977; FRCS Eng. 1986. (Guy's) Cons. ENT Surg. W. Dorset Gen. Hosps. NHS Trust & E. Som. NHS Trust. Prev: Cons. ENT Surg. Camb. Milit. Hosp. Aldershot.

FORD, Gordon Paterson 21 Daleside, Thornhill Edge, Dewsbury WF12 0PJ — MB ChB 1973 Ed.; MRCP (UK) 1978.

FORD, Helen Louise Department of Neurology, St James' University Hospital, Leeds LS9 7TF Tel: 0113 206 6162 — MB ChB 1987 Leeds; BSc (Hons.) Leeds 1984; MRCP (UK) 1990; MD Leeds 1997. (Leeds) Cons. (Neurol.) St. James' Univ. Hosp. Prev: Med. Off. Good Shepherd Hosp., Swaziland; Regist. (Neurol.) St. Jas. Univ. Hosp. Leeds; SHO (Chest Med.) Killingbeck Hosp.

FORD, Henry Robin Clinton Charlton Hill Surgery, Charlton Road, Andover SP10 3JY Tel: 01264 337979 Fax: 01264 334251; Walnut Tree Cottage, Drove Road, Chilbolton, Stockbridge SO20 6AB — MB BS 1981 Lond.; MRCGP 1987; DRCOG 1986. Trainer (Gen. Pract.) Hants. Prev: Trainee GP Wistaria Lymington; SHO (Chest Med.) St. Richard's Hosp. Chichester; SHO (Orthop. & A & E) Swindon.

FORD, Hubert Talbot 26 Arundel Road, Cheam, Sutton SM2 6EU Tel: 020 8642 9611 — MB BS 1952 Lond.; FRCR 1975; FFR 1961; DMRT Eng. 1959. (Westm.) p/t Med. Dir. St. Raphael's Hospice N. Cheam, Surrey. Socs: Brit. Inst. Radiol. Prev: Cons. Radiotherap. St. Geo. Hosp. Lond. & Roy. Marsden Hosp. Lond.; Cons. Radiotherap. N.ampton Gen. Hosp.; Sen. Regist. IrRadiat. Unit, W.m. Hosp. Lond.

FORD, Hugh Kelson, CVO (retired) Brookdale, Church End, Sedgeford, Hunstanton PE36 5NA Tel: 01485 72399 — MB BS 1951 Lond.; FRCGP 1976, M 1965; DObst RCOG 1957. Hon. Med. Dir. W. Norf. Home Hospice Gp. Prev: Surg.-Apoth. to H.M. Ho.hold Sandringham.

FORD, Hugo Edward Rawlinson Royal Marsden Hopsital, Downs Road, Sutton SM2 5NG Email: hugo@icr.ac.uk; 48 Hugh Street, London SW1V 4ER — BChir 1992 Camb.; MB BChir Camb. 1992; MA Camb. 1992, BA 1988; MRCP 1995. (Cambridge University St. Thomas' Hospital) Specialist Regist., Med. Oncol., Roy. Marsden Hosp. Socs: Assn. of Cancer Phys.s, (Mem.); Amer. Soc. of Clin. Oncol., (Jun. Mem.); Europ. Soc. of Med. Oncol., (Jun. Mem.). Prev: Regist. (Med. Oncol.) Roy. Marsden Hosp. Lond.; Regist. (Gen. Med.) St. Richard's Hosp., Chichester; SHO (Med. Oncol.) Roy. Marsden Hosp. Lond.

FORD, James Angus, Capt. RAMC Royal Hospital For Sick Children, Yorkhill G15 6PX Tel: 01268 593422, 0141 201 0827 Email: iyoukham@ntlworld.com; 20 Ralston Road, Bearsden, Glasgow G61 3BA Tel: 0141 942 4273 — MB ChB 1967 Glas.; FRCP Lond. 1993; FRCP Glas. 1983; FRCP Ed. 1983; MRCP (UK) 1971; MRCPCH 1996, FRCPCH 1997; DCH RCPS Glas. 1969. (Glas.) Cons. Paediat. Roy. Hosp. for Sick Childr. Glas. Socs: Scott. Paediat. Soc.; Brit. Med. Assn. Prev: Chairm. Scott. Comm. Hosp. Med. Serv.; Hon Sen. Clin. Lect.; Chairm. Scott. Counc. BMA.

FORD, James Anthony Room 7E09, Department of Health, Quarry House, Quarry Hill, Leeds LS2 7UE Tel: 0113 254 5820 Fax: 0113 254 6347 Email: jford@doh.gov.uk; Nimrod, 42 Hesketh Road, Southport PR9 9PB Tel: 01704 546457 Fax: 01704 545395 Email: drfordetc@aol.com — MB ChB 1977 Liverp.; MSc Manch. 1996; AFOM RCP Lond. 1995; DRCOG 1979. Sen. Med. Off. (Gen. Med. Servs.) Primary Care Div. NHS Exec. HQ Leeds; Hon. Lect. (Health Care Educat.) Univ. Liverp. Socs: Brit. Assn. Med. Managers; Soc. Occupat. Med.; S.port Med. Soc. Prev: Med. Adviser DSS Benefits Agency NW Regional Off.; GP S.port.

FORD, Jane Louise 16 Grantley Place, Bradley, Huddersfield HD2 1LZ Tel: 01484 538011 — MB ChB 1988 Leeds. Prev: Trainee GP Bradford VTS; SHO (Geriat. Med.) Bradford Roy. Infirm.

FORD, Jane Mary Collegiate Medical Centre, Brideoak Street, Manchester M8 0AT Tel: 0161 205 4364 Fax: 0161 203 5511 — MB ChB 1979 Sheff. Princip. GP Manch.

FORD, Jennifer Evelyn Mulberry Lodge, 25 High Shore Road, Peckham, London SE15 5AA — MB BChir 1992 Camb.; MA Camb. 1993, MB Chir 1992. SHO (Psychiat.) Goodmayes Hosp. Socs: MDU & BMA.

FORD, Jennifer Margaret 78 Kingswood Firs, Grayshott, Hindhead GU26 6EX — MB BS 1983 Lond.; Cert. Family Plann. JCC 1987; DCH RCP Lond. 1985. Examg. Med. Practitioner Benefits Agency Med. Servs. Prev: Clin. Med. Off. (Child Health) Hindhead; Staff Grade (Paediat.) Liphook.

FORD, Joan Mary (retired) Green Hallow, 60 Carrwood Road, Wilmslow SK9 5DN Tel: 01625 523928 — MB ChB 1959 Liverp.; MFHom 1983. Prev: Phys. Manch. Homoeop. Clinic.

FORD, John Barrie Crown Street Surgery, 17 Crown Street, Swinton, Rotherham S64 8LY Tel: 01709 583862; The Coppins, 1 Warren Vale Road, Swinton, Mexborough S64 8UR Tel: 01709 583862 — MB ChB 1960 St. And.

FORD, John Cedric (retired) Plum Cottage, Hook Lane, Aldingbourne, Chichester PO20 6TF Tel: 01243 543787 — MB BS 1941 Lond.; MRCS Eng. LRCP Lond. 1939; FRCPath 1964. Prev: Cons. Path. Sandwell Area Hosps.

FORD, John Harold George Lower Nash Farm, Nutbourne, Pulborough RH20 2HS Tel: 01798 812292 — MRCS Eng. LRCP Lond. 1950. (St. Geo.) Prev: Resid. Obst. Asst. & Ho. Surg. St. Geo. Hosp. Lond.

FORD, John Jeffrey Sunnyside Surgery, 4 Sunnyside Road, Clevedon BS21 7TA Tel: 01275 873588 Fax: 01275 875218; The Coach House, 21A Cambridge Road, Clevedon BS21 7DN — MB ChB 1978 Dundee; MRCGP 1983; DRCOG 1980.

FORD, John Michael Tipping Warders, East St., Tonbridge TN9 1LA Tel: 01732 770088 Fax: 01732 771674 — MB BS 1961 Lond.; DHMSA Lond. 1976; DObst RCOG 1965. (St. Thos.) Med. Off. Tonbridge Sch. Socs: Fell. Roy. Soc. Med. Prev: Med. Historian St. Thos. Hosp. Lond.; Cas. Off. & Ho. Phys. (Obst.) St. Thos. Hosp. Lond.; Ho. Surg. Peace Memor. Hosp. Watford.

FORD, Lillian Rose (retired) 19 River Park, Marlborough SN8 1NH Tel: 01672 515321 — MD Philadelphia 1955; BSc Washington 1944; LRCP LRCS Ed. LRCPS Glas. 1970; MFCM 1974; DPH Glas. 1973; Dip. Amer. Bd. Paediat. 1961; MPH 1965 University of California, Berkeley; MPH 1965 University of California, Berkeley. Prev: Clin. Med. Off. Glas., Newham, Hounslow.

FORD, Lisa Isabella Greenbanks, Savage Hill, Newland, Coleford GL16 8NH — MB BS 1989 Lond.; MSc (Trop.) Lond. 1993; BSc Lond. 1986; MSc (Remote Health Care) Aberd. 1997. (London) Prev: Med. Off. Brit. Antartic Survey Base Signy Is., Antartica; SHO (A & E) Basildon Hosp.; Ho. Surg. Waikato Hosp. Hamilton, NZ.

FORD, Lois Brown 5 Kilmardinny Gate, Bearsden, Glasgow G61 3ND Tel: 0141 943 1530 — MB ChB 1951 Glas.; MRCGP 1970. p/t Med. Ref. Benefits Agency Glas.

FORD, Madeleine Sarah The Surgery, Whitecliff Mill St, Blandford Forum DT11 7 Tel: 01258 452501 — MB ChB 1989 Birm.; MRCGP 1995; DRCOG 1994; DCH RCP Lond. 1993. GP Princip. (half-time). Prev: Trainee GP Wessex.; SHO (ENT & Ophth.) Odstock Hosp. Salisbury; SHO (A & E, Paediat. & O & G) Poole Gen. Hosp.

FORD, Mark Rohan Wilfred 107A Cotham Brow, Bristol BS6 6AS — MB BS 1985 Lond.

FORD, Martin Allan 2 Hawkes Place, Sevenoaks TN13 2PF Tel: 01732 743606 Fax: 01732 741968 Email: martin_ford@csi.com — MB BS 1979 Lond.; MBA Lond. 1990; DRCOG 1982; Dip. Pharm. Med. RCP (UK) 1987; DCH RCP Lond. 1983; FFPM 1998. (Roy. Lond. Hosp.) Med. Dir. Rhone Poulenc Rorer. Prev: Head Internat. Clin. Operats. Ciba Pharmaceut.

FORD, Michael Frederick Alderney Hospital, Ringwood Road, Poole BH12 4NB Tel: 01202 305088 Fax: 01202 718619; 19 Wellington Road, Poole BH14 9LF Tel: 01202 734241 — MB BS 1977 Lond.; BA 1971 Lond.; MRCP Lond. 1981; MRCPsych 1984; DCH Eng. 1979; FRCPsych. 1998. (Middlesex Hospital) Cons.

Psychiat. St. Anns Hosp. Poole. Prev: Sen. Regist. (Psychiat.) St. Geo. Hosp. Lond.; Regist. (Psychiat.) Glenside Hosp. Bristol; Regist. (Med.) Ysbyty Glan Clwyd.

FORD, Michael Joseph Tel: 0131 441 0800; 11 West Carnethy Avenue, Edinburgh EH13 0ED — MD 1987 Ed.; MB ChB (Hons.) 1972; FRCP Ed. 1985; MRCP (UK) 1974. Cons. Phys. W.ern Gen. Hosp. Edin. Socs: BSG.

FORD, Nicholas Talbot South Way Medical Practice, 2 South Way, Shirley, Croydon CR0 8RP Tel: 020 8777 1876 Fax: 020 8776 2677 — MB BS 1977 Lond.; MRCOG 1983. Regist. (O & G) Qu. Mary's Hosp. Roehampton.

FORD, Pamela Mary SEMA Medical Services, Sutherland House, 29-37 Brighton Road, Sutton SM2 5AN Tel: 020 8652 6032 Fax: 020 8652 6010; 49 Queens Road, Beckenham BR3 4JJ — MB BChir 1977 Camb.; MB BChir Camb. 1975; Dip Occ Med, 1999; MA Camb. 1973; MRCP (UK) 1979; DMRD Eng. 1982. (St. Bart.) Med. Adviser SEMA Med. Servs. Socs: Soc. Occupat. Med. Prev: Occupat. Med. Phys., BMI Health Servs.; GP Lond.; Sen. Regist. (Radiol.) Lond. Hosp.

FORD, Patricia Mary The Old Vicarage, 260 Manchester Road, Blackrod, Bolton BL6 5AZ — MB BCh 1960 Wales; FFA RCS Eng. 1965; DA Eng. 1962. (Cardiff)

FORD, Paul Andrew 12 Chapel Lane, Barwick-in-Elmet, Leeds LS15 4EG — MB BS 1990 Lond.; MRCP (UK) 1993. Specialist Regist. St. Geo. Hosp. Lond.

FORD, Peter George Tipping (retired) Braeside Cottage, Cannongate Road, Hythe CT21 5PT Tel: 01303 267896 — MB BS 1956 Lond.; MRCGP 1968; DObst RCOG 1960. Prev: Sec. Med. Protec. Soc.

FORD, Peter Neville 4 Harding Road, Epsom KT18 6HN Tel: 01372 276794 — MB BS 1993 Lond.; BSc (Hons.) Anat. & Developm. Biol. Lond. 1990; MRCP (UK) 1996. (St. Bart.) SHO (Anaesth.), W.on Super Mare. Socs: BMA; Roy. Coll. Physchiat. Prev: SHO (Med.) Rotat., Portsmouth; Regist. (IC & Gen. Med.), Fremantle Hosp., W. Australia; Sen. Regist. (IC), Fremantle Hosp., W. Australia.

FORD, Ralph Alan Glendower Road Surgery, 54 Glendower Road, Peverell, Plymouth PL3 4LD Tel: 01752 673336 Fax: 01752 267130 — MB ChB 1980 Liverp. Hosp. Pract. (Ophth.) Plymouth.

FORD, Rebecca Louise 170 Beacon Park Road, Beacon Park, Plymouth PL2 2QS — BM BCh 1997 Oxf.; MA Cantab. 1998. (Oxford) SHO (Gen. Med.), Derriford Hosp., Plymouth. Prev: Temporary Lect. (Anat.), Manch. Univ.; SHO (A & E) Cardiff Roy. Infirm.

FORD, Richard Graham Bideford Medical Centre, Abbotsham Road, Bideford EX39 3AF Tel: 01237 476363 Fax: 01237 423351; Upcott Farm, Bideford EX39 5JQ Tel: 01237 475532 — MB BS 1970 Lond.; MRCS Eng. LRCP Lond. 1970. (St. Mary's)

FORD, Roger Norman St Bede's Medical Centre, Lower Dundas Street, Sunderland SR6 0QQ Tel: 0191 567 5335; Washing Wells Farm, Washing Wells Lane, Whickham, Newcastle upon Tyne NE16 4RT Tel: 0191 488 0640 Fax: 0191 510 2495 — MB ChB 1979 Manch.; DRCOG 1982; MRCGP 1983.

FORD, Ronald Norman Elgar House Surgery, Church Road, Redditch B97 4AB Tel: 01527 69261 Fax: 01527 596856; 373 Birmingham Road, Redditch B97 6RH Tel: 01527 64392 — MB ChB 1969 Bristol.

FORD, Ronald Stanley (retired) Green Hallow, 60 Carrwood Road, Wilmslow SK9 5DN Tel: 01625 523928 — MB ChB 1958 Liverp.; MRCPsych 1971; DPM Eng. 1965. Prev: Cons. Psychiat. Cheadle Roy. Hosp.

FORD, Sally Gillian Upcott, Bideford EX39 5JQ — MRCS Eng. LRCP Lond. 1970.

FORD, Sandra Jane 23 Howford Road, Glasgow G52 3JU — MB ChB 1992 Glas.; DRCOG 1994. Trainee GP Glas.

FORD, Shelagh Ann The Surgery, 318 Westdale Lane, Mapperley, Nottingham NG3 6EU Tel: 0115 987 7604 Fax: 0115 956 8592; 13A Steedman Avenue, Mapperley, Nottingham NG3 6DL — MB 1974 Camb.; BChir 1973; DRCOG 1987; Cert. Family Plann. JCC 1977.

FORD, Sheridan Petrea 33 Cavendish Square, London W1M 0PS Tel: 020 7399 1300 Fax: 020 7399 1301; 2 Hawkes Place, Sevenoaks TN13 2PF Tel: 01732 743606 — MB BS 1980 Lond.; MFPHM RCP (UK) 1988; DCH RCP Lond. 1983; Barrister Middle Temple. (Middlx. Hosp.) Head UK Med. Servs., Lond. Prev: Sen. Medico-Legal Adviser Med. Protec. Soc. Lond.; Regist. (Community Med.) Wessex RHA.

FORD, Simon Michael 19 Alexandra Park, Redland, Bristol BS6 6QB — MB ChB 1997 Bristol.

FORD, Steven Duncan Haydon Bridge Health Centre, North Bank, Haydon Bridge, Hexham NE47 6HG Tel: 01434 684216 Fax: 01434 684144 — MB ChB 1976 Birm.; MRCGP 1981.

FORD, Susan Elizabeth Greengate Medical Centre, 1 Greengate Lane, Birstall, Leicester LE4 3JF Tel: 0116 267 7901; 30 Groby Lane, Newtown, Linford, Leicester LE6 0HH — BM 1984 Soton.; BM (Hons.) Soton. l984; MRCGP 1989; DRCOG 1987; DCH RCP Lond. 1986.

FORD, Tamsin Jane Department of Psychiatry, Royal London Hospital Trust, Whitechapel, London E1; 25B Rosebery Road, London SW2 4DQ — MB BS 1990 Lond. SHO Rotat. (Psychiat.) Roy. Lond. Hosp. Trust.

FORD, Mr Trevor Francis Kent & Sussex Hospital, Mount Ephraim, Tunbridge Wells TN4 8AT Tel: 01892 526111 Fax: 01892 549103; The Mill, Mill Lane, Horsmonden, Tonbridge TN12 8DB Tel: 01892 723627 — BM BCh 1971 Oxf.; BA Oxf. 1968, MA 1972; DM Oxf. 1982, MCh 1985, BM BCh 1971; FRCS Eng. 1977; FRCS Ed. 1976. Cons. (Urol.) Kent & Sussex Weald NHS Trust. Prev: Sen. Regist. (Urol.) St. Peter's Hosp. & Inst. Urol.; Lect. (Surg.) St. Geo. Hosp. Med. Sch.

FORD, Wendy Laura Thornton Practice, Church Road, Thornton-Cleveleys FY5 2TZ Tel: 01253 827231 Fax: 01253 863478; The Spinney, Roseacre Road, Elswick, Preston PR4 3UD — MB ChB 1989 Manch.

FORD-ADAMS, Martha Evelyn Paediatric Department, Farnborough Hospital, Farborough Common, Orpington BR6 8ND Tel: 01689 814072 Fax: 01689 814038 Email: marina.ford-adams@bromleyhospitals.nhs.uk; 10 Vere House, 15 Cheyne Row, Chelsea, London SW3 5HR Tel: 020 7352 6427 Fax: 020 7352 6427 — MB BS 1989 Western Australia; MRCP (UK) 1994; DCH RCP Lond. 1992. (University of W Australia) Cons. Paediat. FarnBoro. Hosp. Socs: BMA; Diabetes UK; Med. Wom.'s Federat. Prev: Regist. (Paediat.) John Radcliffe Hosp. Oxf.; SHO (Respirat. Paediat.) Gt. Ormond St. Hosp. Lond.; Clin. Fell. (Liver Transpl.) Addenbrooke's Hosp. Camb.

FORD-YOUNG, William Paul Douglas Broken Cross Surgery, Fallibroome Road, Macclesfield SK10 3LA Tel: 01625 617300 Fax: 01625 617300 — MB ChB 1984 Liverp.; MB ChB Liverp. l984; MRCGP 1988; DRCOG 1988; Dip. GUM 1998. Clin. Asst. (Genitourin. Med.) Macclesfield Dist. Gen. Hosp. & Withington Hosp. Manch.; Hon. Sec. Macclesfield Dist. LMC. Socs: Med. Soc. Study VD; Assn. Genitourin. Med.

FORDE, Anthony 1 Glebe Road, Hillsborough BT26 6NE — MB BCh BAO 1985 Belf.; MRCGP 1989; DRCOG 1990; Cert. Family Plann. JCC 1990.

FORDE, Hanora Hilda 32 High Road E., Felixstowe IP11 9JW — MB BCh BAO 1947 NUI; DObst RCOG 1951; DPH NUI 1953. (Cork)

FORDE, Ian 88 King Edwards Road, South Woodham Ferrers, Chelmsford CM3 5PH — BM BCh 1998 Oxf.; BM BCh Oxf 1998.

FORDE, Jennifer Wilma 11 Westland Gardens, Magherafelt BT45 5AZ — MB BCh BAO 1995 Belf.

FORDE, Michael Edwin 14 Centre Court, Barlow St., Derby DE1 2TQ — MB ChB 1996 Sheff.

FORDE, Steven Charles Olumide, Squadron Ldr. RAF Med. Br. Anaesthetics Department, Leicester Royal Infirmary, Leicester LE1 5WW Tel: 0116 254 1414 Email: mail@gasco.demon.co.uk — MB ChB 1991 Leeds; FRCA 1996; DA (UK) 1994. (Leeds) Specialist Regist. (Anaesth.) Leicester Roy. Infirm.; Lect. (Anaesth.) Leicester Univ. Socs: Train. Mem. Assn. AnE.h.; Hist. Anaesth. Soc.; Soc. Computing & Technol. in Anaesth. Prev: Specialist Regist. (Anaesth.) PeterBoro.; Regist. (Anaesth.) Soton. Gen.

FORDHAM, Emma Jane 1 Fern Royd, Hathersage, Hope Valley S32 1AU — MB ChB 1991 Dundee.

FORDHAM, Guy Tristan 23 Mount Road, New Malden KT3 3JU — BM 1998 Soton.; BM Soton 1998.

FORDHAM, John Noel Long Stop, 5 The Oval, Wynyard Village, Billingham TS22 5QQ Tel: 01740 644849 — MB BS 1972 Lond.; Hon. Sen. Lect. Newcastle University; MD Lond. 1984; BSc (Hons. Animal Physiol.) Lond. 1970; FRCP 1991; MRCP (UK) 1976; MRCS

Eng. LRCP Lond. 1972. Cons. Rheum. James Cook Un. Hosp. Socs: Brit. Soc. Rheum.; Nat. Osteoporosis Soc. Prev: Sen. Regist. (Rheum.) Lond. Hosp.; Regist. (Med.) Lond. Hosp.; SHO (Neurol. & Med.) Whipps Cross Hosp. Lond.

FORDHAM, Mr Mark Vincent Peter 12 Leigh Road, West Kirby, Wirral CH48 5DY — MB BS 1977 Lond.; MA Camb. 1976; FRCS Eng. 1982. Cons. Urol. Roy. Liverp. Hosp.

FORDHAM, Richard Mayo Myddelton (retired) Brambles, Spring Copse, Hinasey Hill, Oxford OX1 5BJ Tel: 01865 735103 — MB 1959 Camb.; BChir 1958 Camb.; FFA RCS Eng. 1963. Cons. Anaesth. Oxf.

FORDHAM, Simon Ellis Silkhouse Court, Tithebarn Street, Liverpool L2 2LE Tel: 0151 515 3002 Fax: 0151 285 6051 Email: simon-mganga@doctors.org.uk — BM BS 1980 Nottm.; BMedSci Nottm. 1978; MMedSci Birm. 1995; MRCGP 1984; Dip. Pract. Dermat. Wales 1990; FRCGP 1997. Gen. Practitioner, Liverp.; Hon. Research Fell. Dept. Primary Care Liverp. Univ.; Forens. Med. Examr., Merseyside Police Auth. Socs: Fell. Roy. Soc. Med.

FORDY, Keith 8 Bede Kirk, Barnard Castle DL12 8DJ — MB ChB 1994 Manch.

FORDYCE, Mr Andrew Murray Department of Oral & Maxillofacial Surgery, Torbay Hospital, Newton Road, Torquay TQ2 7AA Tel: 01803 654838 Email: andrew.fordyce@sdevonhc-tr.swest.nhs.uk — MB BS 1988 Lond.; BDS Lond. 1979; FRCS Ed. 1992; FDS RCS Eng. 1988. (UCH London, St. Georges Hospital London) Cons. (Oral & Maxillofacial Surg.) Torbay Hosp. Socs: Fell. Brit. Assn. Oral & Maxillofacial Surg.; BMA; BAHNO. Prev: Regist. (Oral. Surg.) Sunderland Gen. Hosp, New Gen. Hosp., MiddlesBoro. Gen.; Regist. (Oral Surg.) Burnley Gen. Hosp.; SHO (Orthop. & A & E) St. Richard's Hosp. Chichester.

FORDYCE, David Timothy 31 House O'Hill Avenue, Blackhall, Edinburgh EH4 5DN — MB ChB 1993 Ed.

FORDYCE, Mr Gordon Esslemont (retired) 23 Meadowfields, Sandsend, Whitby YO21 3SX — MB ChB 1932 Aberd.; FRCS Ed. 1948. Prev: Cons. Surg. Newc. RHA.

FORDYCE, Mr Michael John Forbes Kent & Sussex Hospital, Mount Ephraim, Tunbridge Wells TN4 8AT Tel: 01892 526111 Fax: 01892 528381 — MB BS 1980 Lond.; FRCS Ed. 1985. (Middlesex) Cons. Orthop. Surg. Kent & Sussex Hosp.; Cons. Orthopaedic Surg., The Horder Centre for Arthritis, CrowBoro., E. Sussex. Socs: Brit. Orthop. Assn.; BMA; Brit. Orthopaedic Foot Soc. Prev: Sen. Regist. Rotat. (Orthop. & Trauma.) Exeter & Truro Hosps. SW RHA.; Regist. Rotat. (Orthop. & Trauma) Bristol Hosps.; Regist. (Orthop. & Trauma) Stoke Mandeville Hosp.

FORECAST, David James 97 Harley Street, London W1N 1DF — MB BS 1977 Lond.; MRCP (UK) 1979; MRCS Eng. LRCP Lond. 1977. (King's Coll. Hosp.) Gen. Phys. & Gastroenterol.

FOREMAN, Mr Allan Gillies (retired) 92 The Wynd, Beach Wynd, Preston Road, North Shields NE30 2TE Tel: 0191 272 8205 — LRCP LRCS Ed. LRFPS Glas. 1946; FRCS Ed. 1954. Prev: Cons. Surg. N. Tyneside AHA.

FOREMAN, Anna Jean Eryl Surgery, Eryl, Station Road, Llantwit Major CF61 1ST Tel: 01446 793444 Fax: 01446 793115; Craig Y Don, Colhugh St, Llantwit Major CF61 1RF Tel: 01446 793610 — MB BS 1975 Lond.; FFA RCSI 1982.

FOREMAN, David William The Surgery, Lambsale Meadow, North Entrance, Saxmundham IP17 1AS Tel: 01728 602022 — MB BS 1970 Lond.; DObst RCOG 1972. (St. Thos.) Prev: SHO (O & G) & SHO (Paediat.) St. Mary's Hosp. Portsmouth.

FOREMAN, Edward Anthony (retired) Pennywaste House, Foston, Derby Tel: 01283 812154 — MRCS Eng. LRCP Lond. 1949.

FOREMAN, Mr Jacob Theun Colchester General Hospital, Turner Road, Colchester CO4 5JL — Artsexamen 1986 Groningen; FRCS Glas. 1993.

FOREMAN, Professor John Charles Department of Pharmacology, University College London, Gower Street, London WC1E 6BT Tel: 020 7679 7314 Fax: 020 7679 7314 Email: john.foreman@ucl.ac.uk; 7 Old Bakery Court, Heacham, King's Lynn PE31 7LL Tel: 01485 572669 — MB BS 1976 Lond.; FRCP 2001; PhD Lond. 1974, BSc 1970, DSc 1993. (Univ. Coll. Hosp.) Prof. Immunopharmacol. Univ. Lond.; Vice Dean (Sch. of Med.) UCL & Dean of Stud.s UCL. Socs: Fell. Univ. Coll. Lond.; Brit. Pharm. Soc. & Physiol. Soc. Prev: Prof. Pharmacol. Odense Univ. Sch. Med. Denmark & Univ. Tasmania, Austral.; Instruc. (Med.) Johns Hopkins Univ. Sch. Med. Baltimore, USA.

FOREMAN, Lorraine Patricia Mayfield Medical Centre, 37 Totnes Road, Paignton TQ4 5LA Tel: 01803 558257 Fax: 01803 663353; Highways, 2 Hookhills Grove, Paignton TQ4 7LN Tel: 01803 843145 Fax: 01803 663353 — MB ChB 1973 Birm.; MRCGP 1977.

FOREMAN, Nicholas Edward Colne House Surgery, 99A Uxbridge Road, Rickmansworth WD3 2DJ Tel: 01923 776295 Fax: 01923 777744; Lodore, 15 Chalfont Lane, Rickmansworth WD3 5PR — MB BS 1981 Lond.; BSc Lond. 1978, MB BS 1981; MRCGP 1985; DRCOG 1985.

FOREMAN, Peter Stephen Headley House, 55 Rayens Cross Road, Long Ashton, Bristol BS41 9DY Tel: 01275 392134 Fax: 01275 394576; St. Martins, Long Ashton, Bristol BS41 9HP — BM BS 1979 Nottm.; BSc Manch. 1974; BMedSci Nottm. 1977; MRCP (UK) 1984; MRCGP 1987; DRCOG 1985.

FOREMAN, William Morton (retired) 19 Henley Close, Saxmundham IP17 1EY Tel: 01728 604941 Email: billforeman@compuserve.com — MB BChir 1944 Camb.; MA, MB BChir Camb. 1944; MRCGP 1954. Prev: Ho. Surg. St. Thos. Hosp.

FORESTER, Mr Andrew John Department of Surgery, Charing Cross Hospital, Fulham Palace Road, London W6 8RF Tel: 020 8846 1479 Fax: 020 8846 1439; 10 Brough Close, Off Richmond Road, Kingston upon Thames KT2 5DB Tel: 020 8549 3158 Fax: 020 8549 3158 — MB ChB 1984 Leic.; MB ChB Leic. l984; BSc (Hons.) Open 1993; FRCS Ed (Orth) 1993; FRCS Ed. 1989. (Leicester) Sen. Lect. (Orthop. Surg.) Imperial Coll. Sch. Med. Prev: Vis. Lect. (Orthop. Surg.) Univ. Teach. Hosp. Lusaka, Zambia; Sen. Regist. Rotat. (Orthop.) Hammersmith Hosp. Lond.

FORESTER, Nerys Dawn 1 Bowbank Close, Sunderland SR3 1PW Tel: 0191 528 2964; Flat 3, 30 Street Lane, Roundhay, Leeds LS8 2ET Tel: 0113 295 6709 — BM BCh 1997 Oxf. SHO, St. James', Leeds. Prev: Ho. Off. Newc. & Oxf.

FORFAR, Isobel Mary Langlands 9 Ravelston Heights, Edinburgh EH4 3LX Tel: 0131 315 2184 — MB ChB 1942 St. And.; AFOM RCP Lond. 1979; DPH Ed. 1954. (St. And. & Ed.) Socs: Med. Wom. Federat.; Fac. Occupat. Med. Prev: Med. Off. Marks & Spencer Edin.

FORFAR, John Colin Department Cardiology, John Radcliffe Hospital, Headington, Oxford OX3 9DU Tel: 01865 220326 Fax: 01865 220252 Email: colin.forfar@orh.nhs.uk; The Cullions, Elvendon Road, Goring-on-Thams, Reading RG8 0DT Tel: 01491 875023 — MB ChB 1975 Ed.; MA Oxf. 1985; PhD Ed. 1984, MD 1985, BSc (Hons.) 1972; FRCP Lond. 1991; MRCP (UK) 1977; FRCPE 1987. (Edinburgh) Cons. Phys. & Cardiol. John Radcliffe Hosp. Oxf.; Chairm. Cardiac Clin. Centre Oxf. Radcliffe NHS Trust; Mem. Comm. on Safety of Med.s Med.s Commiss. Socs: Brit. Cardiac Soc. Prev: Clin. Reader (Cardiovasc. Med.) & Fell. Lady Margt. Hall Univ. Oxf.; Sen. Regist. & Lect. John Radcliffe Hosp. Oxf.; Lect. (Cardiol.) Univ. Edin. Roy. Infirm. Edin.

FORFAR, Professor John Oldroyd, MC 9 Ravelston Heights, Edinburgh EH4 3LX Tel: 0131 315 2184 — MB ChB 1941 St. And.; FRSE 1975; BSc St. And. 1938, MD (Commend.) 1958; FRCP Glas. 1978, M 1978; FRCP Lond. 1964, M 1947; FRCP Ed. 1953, M 1948; DCH Eng. 1948; Hon. FRCPCH 1997. (St. And.) Emerit. Prof. Child Life & Health Univ. Edin. Socs: Hon. Fell. RCPCH; Fell. Amer. Coll. Nutrit.; (Ex.Chairm.) Jt. Paediat. Comm. RCP & Brit. Paediat. Assn. Prev: Sen. Phys. (Paediat.) W.ern Gen. Hosp. Edin.; Phys. Roy. Hosp. Sick Childr. Edin. & Cons. Paediat. Simpson Memor. Matern. Pavil.; Capt. RAMC, Med. Off. 47 (RM) Commando (Mentioned in Despatches).

FORGACS, Ian Christopher Department of Gastroenterology, King's College Hospital, Denmark Hill, London SE5 9RS Tel: 020 7737 4000 Fax: 020 7346 6474 Email: ian.forgacs@kcl.ac.uk — MB BS 1975 Lond.; BSc (Hons.) Lond. 1972, MD 1986; FRCP Lond. 1993; MRCP (UK) 1977; MRCS Eng. LRCP Lond. 1975. (Guy's) Cons. Phys. & Gastroenterol. King's Coll. Hosp. Lond.; Assoc. Edr. Brit. Med. Jl. & Gut; Regional Specialty Adviser in Gastrenterlogy (S. Thames), Roy. Coll. of Phys.s of Lond. Socs: Brit. Soc Gastroenterol.; Amer. Gastoenterol. Assn.; Eur. Soc. Clin. Investig. Prev: Lect. Med. (Gastroenterol.) Univ. Camb. & Sen. Regist. (Med.) Addenbrooke's Hosp. Camb.; Regist. (Med.) St. Thos. Hosp. Lond.; SHO (Neurol.) Nat. Hosp. Nerv. Dis. Qu. Sq. Lond.

FORGAN, Barbara Joan Kyleakin, Clwydian Park Crescent, St Asaph LL17 0BJ Tel: 01745 730754 — MB ChB Glas. 1970; DObst RCOG 1974. Prev: Clin. Med. Off. (Child Health) Clwyd AHA; GP Garstang, Lancs.; SHO (Paediat. Surg.) Roy. Hosp. Sick Childr. Edin.

FORGAN, Rachel Claire 134 Witherford Way, Selly Oak, Birmingham B29 4AW — BM BS 1993 Nottm.; BMedSci 1991.

FORGE, Jennifer Anne Clairmont Family Centre, Bishop Auckland DL14 7BB — MB ChB 1986 Leic.; MRCPsych. 1991; DCH RCP Lond. 1988. Cons. Child & Adolesc. Psychiat. Clairmont Family Centre Bishop Auckland.

FORMAN, Adam 203-205 School Road, Sheffield S10 1GN — MB ChB 1984 Sheff.; MB ChB Sheff. l984; MRCGP 1988; DObst RCPI 1988.

FORMAN, Catherine Helen Meadowcroft Surgery, Jackson Road, Aylesbury HP19 9EX Tel: 01296 425775 Fax: 01296 330324 — MB BS 1988 Lond.; FRCGP 2000; MRCGP 1994; DCH RCP Lond. 1993; DRCOG 1992; Dip. Obst. NZ 1992. (University College London)

FORMAN, Clive Wilson The Finsbury Circus Medical Centre, 5 London Wall Buildings, Finsbury Circus, London EC2M 5NS Tel: 020 7638 0909 Fax: 020 7638 9211 Email: cforman@fcmc.co.uk; 120 Lexden Road, West Bergholt, Colchester CO6 3BP — MB BS 1984 Lond.; D Occ Med 2000; DRCOG 1988. (Westm.) Socs: Assur. Med. Soc. Prev: GP Colchester VTS; SHO (ENT Surg.) Essex Co. Hosp. Colchester; Ho. Off. (Surg.) W.m. Hosp. Lond.

FORMAN, Geoffrey Harold 22 Harley Street, London W1N 1AP Tel: 020 7637 0491; 18 Ashgrove House, Lindsay Square, London SW1V 2HW Fax: 0207 976 6065 — MB BS Lond. 1961; MRCS Eng. LRCP Lond. 1961; BDS Univ. Lond. 1958; FDS RCS Eng. 1964, LDS 1957. (Guy's) Recogn. Teach. Univ. Lond.; Cons. Oral & Maxillofacial Surg. KCH Lond. Socs: Fell. Roy. Soc. Med.; Fell. Brit. Assn. Oral & Maxillofacial Surg.; Fell. Internat. Assn. Oral & Maxillofacial Surgs. Prev: Cons. Oral & Maxillofacial Surg. King's Coll. Hosp. Lond.; Sen. Regist. (Oral Surg.) E.man Dent. Hosp.; Sen. Regist. (Oral Surg.) Qu. Vict. Hosp. E. Grinstead.

FORMAN, Judith Diane Annandale, Mutton Lane, Potters Bar EN6 2AT — MB BS 1975 Lond.; BA Physiol. Sci. Oxf. 1972; MRCGP 1980; DRCOG 1977.

FORMAN, Kathleen Department Haematology, University Hospital, Queen's Medical Centre, Nottingham NG7 2UH Tel: 0115 924 9924 Fax: 0115 978 5836; West Cottage, Sunbeam St, Whatton, Nottingham NG13 9ER Tel: 01949 850422 — MB ChB 1974 Aberd.; MRCP (UK) 1978; FRCPath 1997. (Aberd.) Cons. Haemat. Univ. Hosp. Qu. Med. Centre Nottm.

FORMAN, Margaret Louise Springhill Hospice, Broad Lane, Rochdale OL16 4PZ Fax: 01706 644943 Email: julie@springhill.u-net.com; Greycourt, 34 Norford Way, Bamford, Rochdale OL11 5QS Email: forman@supanet.com — MB ChB 1980 Manch.; BSc Med. Sc. St. And. 1977; MRCGP 1994; MFFP 1994; MRCOG 1988; Dip. Palliat. Med. Wales 1996. (St Andrews and Manchester) Cons. Palliat. Med. Springhill Hospice Rochdale. Prev: GP Middleton; Trainee GP Rochdale; Regist. (O & G) St. Mary's Hosp. Manch.

FORMAN, Peter Crawford Banks The Surgery, 2 Mark Street, Rochdale OL12 9BE Tel: 01706 43183 Fax: 01706 526640; 3 Camberley Drive, Bamford, Rochdale OL11 4AZ Tel: 01706 68763 — MB ChB 1976 Manch.; BSc. (Med. Sci.) St. And 1973.

FORMAN, Robert Graham Centre for Reproductive Medicine, 94 Harley St., London W1N 1AF Tel: 020 7487 3456 Fax: 020 7487 5226 Email: forman.crm@virgin.net; 14 De Vere Gardens, Kensington, London W8 5AE Fax: 020 7937 8604 — MB BS 1978 Lond.; MD Lond. 1989; MRCOG 1984; FRCOG 1997. (Middlx.) Med. Dir. Centre for Reproduct. Med. Lond.; Hon. Sen. Lect. Dept. of Obst. & Gyn. UMDS, St Thos. Hosp. Lond. Prev: Sen. Lect. & Hon. Cons. O & G St. Thos. Hosp. Lond.; Lect. & Sen. Regist. Univ. Oxf.; MRC Trav. Fell., Paris.

FORMAN, Sara Margaret St. David's Hospital, Carmarthen SA31 3HB Tel: 01267 237481 Fax: 01267 235840 — BM BCh 1988 Oxf.; MRCPsych 1992. Cons. Psychiat. Pembrokesh. & Derwen NHS Trust.

FORMAN, Winston Michael Chorley Road Surgery, 65 Chorley Road, Swinton, Manchester M27 4AF Tel: 0161 794 6287 Fax: 0161 728 3415; 3 Knights Close, Prestwich, Manchester M25 1PP — MB BS 1968 Lond. Postgrad. Tutor (Gen. Pract.) Salford; Med. Off. Manch. Jewish Home for Aged. Socs: BMA. Prev: Ho. Phys. & Ho. Surg. Crumpsall Hosp.

FORMELA, Ms Laura Janina Department of Surgery, Salford Royal Hospitals NHS Trust, Stott Lane, Salford M6 8WH Tel: 0161 789 7373 — MB ChB 1980 Birm.; BSc Hons 1976; FRCS Ed 1989; FRCS Gen 1998. Cons. Gen. Surg. Socs: Assn. Upper G.I. Surg. Prev: Sen. Regist., Mersey Region.

FORNEAR, Jane Elizabeth The Priory Surgery, 326 Wells Road, Bristol BS4 2QJ Tel: 0117 949 3988 Fax: 0117 778250; Eastfield Lodge, 207 Henleaze Road, Henleaze, Bristol BS9 4NQ Tel: 01179 623569 — MB ChB Bristol 1971; DObst RCOG 1973.

FORNI, Luigi Geraldo 8 Acacia Grove, New Malden KT3 3BJ — MB BS 1989 Lond.; PhD Lond. 1984, BSc 1981, MB BS 1989. SHO (Med. & Oncol.) Roy. Marsden Hosp. Lond.

FOROUGHI, Mansoor 4 Coniston Road, Dronfield Woodhouse, Dronfield S18 8PZ — MB ChB 1992 Sheff.

FOROUHI, Nita Gandhi Department of Epidemiology & Population Sciences, London School of Hygiene & Tropical Medicine, Keppel St., London WC1E 7HT Tel: 020 7927 2465; 199 Bruntsfield Place, Edinburgh EH10 4DQ Tel: 0131 447 3851 — MB BS 1989 Newc.; BMedSc 1986; MRCP (UK) 1993. Hon. Regist. & Research Train. Fell.sh. (Clin. Epidemiol.) Lond. Sch. Hyg. & Trop. Med. Socs: Scott. Thoracic Soc. Prev: SHO (Gen. Med.) Roy. Infirm. Edin.; SHO Rotat. (Gen. & Respirat. Med.) City Hosp. & Roy. Infirm. Edin.

FOROUHI, Parto 28 Moor Close, North Shields NE29 8DB — MB ChB 1984 Ed.

FORRAI, Gabriel Louis (retired) Moray House, 16 Walton Road, Kirby-le-Soken, Frinton-on-Sea CO13 0DU Tel: 01255 852308 — MB ChB 1955 Aberd.

FORRER, Mr John Andrew Department of Genitourinary Medicine, Ormskirk & District General Hospital, Ormskirk L39 2AZ Tel: 01695 571043 — MB BS 1977 Lond.; MRCS Eng. LRCP Lond. 1977; FRCS Ed. 1982; Dip. Ven. Soc. Apoth. Lond. 1985. (St. Mary's) Cons. Genitourin. S.port and Ormskirk Hosp. NHS Trust and Wigan and Leigh NHS Trust. Socs: Med. Soc. Studies VD. Prev: Sen. Regist. (Genitourin. Med.) Gtr. Glas. HB.

FORREST, Adam Keith East Gooseham Farmhouse, Gooseham, Bude EX23 9PG — MB ChB 1996 Liverp.; BA Oxon 1993. RAMC.

FORREST, Alastair John Locality One, Chilton Wing, Sutton hospital, Cotswold Road, Sutton SM2 5NF Tel: 020 8296 4239 Fax: 020 8296 4239 — FRCPsych 1986; MB ChB 1965 Otago; MRCPsych 1972. (Otago) Cons. Psychiat. Sutton Hosp. Prev: Cons. Psychiat. Netherne Hosp. Coulsdon.; Sen. Regist. Dept. Psychiat. St. Geo. Hosp. Tooting Resid. Manhattan; State Hosp. New York, U.S.A.

FORREST, Alexander Lister (retired) — MB ChB 1958 St. And.; FFA RCS Eng. 1963. Prev: Cons. Anaesth. Ninewells Hosp. & Med. Sch. Dundee.

FORREST, Alexander Muir (retired) 2 Ashlawn Drive, Boston PE21 9PT Tel: 01209 436 4299 — MB ChB 1937 Glas.; DPH 1947. Prev: Cons. Chest Phys. Pilgrim Hosp. Boston Lincs.

FORREST, Professor Alexander Robert Walker Department of Forensic Pathology, Medico-legal Centre, Watery St., Sheffield S3 7ES Tel: 0114 273 8721 Fax: 0114 279 8942 Email: r.forrest@sheffield.ac.uk; 3 Betjeman Gardens, Sheffield S10 3FW Tel: 0114 266 9769 Fax: 0114 268 3151 Email: forrearw@doctors.net.uk — MB ChB 1973 Ed.; FRSC, CChem 1983; BSc (Hons.) Ed. 1970; LLM 1993; FRCP Lond. 1992; FRCP Ed. 1989; MRCP (UK) 1977; FRCPath 1992, M 1980; MCB 1981; DObst RCOG 1975. (Ed.) Prof. (Forens. Toxicology) Univ. of Sheff.; Asst. Dep. Coroner S. Yorks. (W. Dist.); Edr. Sci. & Justice; Hon. Cons. (Clin. Chem. & Toxicol.) Sheff. Teachg.. Hosps. NHS Trust. Socs: Amer. Soc. Clin. Chem.; Internat. Assn. Forens. Toxicols.; Forens. Sc. Soc. (Counc.). Prev: Cons. Clin. Chem. & Toxicol. Sheff. Univ. Hosps. NHS Trust; Sen. Regist. (Path. Biochem.) Roy. Infirm. Glas.; Clin. Dir. (Lab Med) CSUH NHS Trust.

FORREST, Sir Andrew Patrick McEwen (retired) 19 St Thomas Road, Edinburgh EH9 2LR Tel: 0131 667 3203 Fax: 0131 662 1193 Email: patrick.forrest@ed.ac.uk — MB ChB 1945 St. And.; FRCS Ed. 1950; Hon. FACS 1978; Hon. FRACS 1987; Hon. FRCR 1988; Hon. FRCSC 1989; FRSE; BSc St. And. 1942, MD (Gold Medal) 1958; LLD Dundee 1986; Hon. DSc Univ. Wales 1981; Hon. DSc Chinese Univ. Hong Kong 1986; ChM (Gold Medal) St. And. 1954;

FRCS Glas. 1962; FRCS Eng. 1952; FIBiol. Prev: Regius Prof. of Clin. Surg. Univ. Edin.

FORREST, Anita 50 Ranfurly Road, Bridge of Weir PA11 3EP Email: anitafla66@aol.com — MB ChB 1991 Manch.

FORREST, Anne Elizabeth Margaret Rutherglen Health Centre, 130 Stonelaw Road, Rutherglen, Glasgow G73 2PQ Tel: 0141 531 6030 Fax: 0141 531 6031; 12 Douglas Avenue, Burnside, Rutherglen, Glasgow G73 4RA — MB ChB 1975 Glas.; MRCGP 1981; DCH RCPS Glas. 1977; DRCOG 1977. (Univ. Glas.)

FORREST, Archibald 5 Atholl Court, 14 Dirleton Drive, Glasgow G41 3BQ — MB ChB 1942 Glas.

FORREST, Colin Archibald 36 Earlspark Avenue, Glasgow G43 2HW — MB ChB 1971 Glas.; MRCOG 1979.

FORREST, Diana Rosemary St Helens and Knowsley Health Authority, Cowley Hill Lane, St Helens WA10 2AP Tel: 01744 457232 Fax: 01744 457339 Email: diana.forrest@sthk-ha.nwest.nhs.uk; 51 Temple Road, Sale M33 2FQ Tel: 0161 973 4536 — MB ChB 1973 Bristol; MSc (Comm. Med.) Lond. Sch. Hyg. & Trop. Med. 1982; MFPHM RCP (UK) 1990; DObst RCOG 1975. (Bristol) Director of Pub. Health St Helens and Knowsley Health Auth. St Helens. Prev: Cons. Pub. Health Med. Liverp. HA; Cons. Pub. Health Med. NW Region, NW & W. Surrey & NE Hants. HAs.

FORREST, Mr Duncan Mouat (retired) 45 Hartfield Crescent, West Wickham BR4 9DW Tel: 020 8462 3951 Fax: 020 8462 3951 Email: duncan@forrest3y.freeseve.co.uk — MB ChB 1947 New Zealand; FRCS Eng. 1951. Volunteer Cons. Med. Foundat. c/o Victims of Torture Lond. Prev: Cons. Surg. W.m. Childr. Hosp., Childr. Hosp. Sydenham & Qu. Mary's Hosp. Childr. Carshalton.

FORREST, Elaine Ford 91 Glassford Tower, Motherwell ML1 2AX — MB ChB 1987 Glas.

FORREST, Ewan Hay 37A Aytoun Road, Glasgow G41 5HW Tel: 0141 424 0173 — MB ChB 1990 Aberd.; BMedBiol Aberd. 1987; MRCP 1993; MD Aberd. 1999. Specialist Regist. Gastroenterol. & Gen. Med.

FORREST, Ewen Thomas Scott Dept. Of Anaesthesia, Countess of Chester Hospital, Liverpool Rd, Chester CH2 1UL Tel: 01244 365461; Holmlea, Moor Lane, Rowton, Chester CH3 7QW Tel: 01244 332231 — MB BS 1983 Lond.; FRCA 1989; DA Eng. 1985. Cons. Anaesth. Countess of Chester Hosp. Prev: Regist. (Anaesth.) Hosp. for Sick Childr. & Char. Cross Hosp. Lond.; Regist. & SHO (Anaesth.) St. Mary's Hosp. Lond.

FORREST, George Williamson (retired) 21 Ambassador Court, Kenilworth Road, Leamington Spa CV32 6JF Tel: 01926 426443 — BSc 1937, MB ChB Glas. 1940. Prev: GP Coventry.

FORREST, Gillian Craig The Park Hospital for Children, Old Road Headington, Oxford OX3 7LQ Tel: 01865 741717 Fax: 01865 226355 — MB BS 1969 Lond.; FRCPSych 1989, M 1977; MRCGP 1974; FRCPCH 1997; DObst RCOG 1973; DCH Eng. 1971. (St. Thos.) Cons. Pk. Hosp. Childr. Oxf.; Hon. Sen. Lect. Univ. Oxf.

FORREST, Gordon Andrew Penn Manor Medical Centre, Manor Road, Penn, Wolverhampton WV4 5PY Fax: 01902 575078; 127 Finchfield Lane, Wolverhampton WV3 8EY Tel: 01902 762675 — MB ChB 1961 Glas. Socs: BMA.

FORREST, Gordon James Johnstone Health Centre, 60 Quarry Street, Johnstone PA5 8EY Tel: 01505 324348 Fax: 01505 323710; 26 Marchbank Gardens, Ralstern, Paisley PA1 3JD Tel: 0141 882 9035 — MB ChB 1982 Glas.; MRCGP 1988. GP Renfrewsh.; Clin. Asst. Accord Hospice Paisley. Prev: Regist. (Med. Oncol.) Glas. Roy. Infirm.; SHO (Gen. Med.) & Research SHO (Med. Oncol.) Glas. Roy. Infirm.

FORREST, Ian Alexander 8 Balmoral Avenue, Gosforth, Newcastle upon Tyne NE3 1YE — MB ChB 1994 Ed.; MB ChB (Hons.) Ed. 1994; BSc (Hons.) Ed. 1992; MRCP (UK) 1997. Research Regist. (Respirat. Med.) Freeman Hosp. Newc. u Tyne.

FORREST, Mr James Frederick The White House, Ashley, Market Drayton TF9 4JY Tel: 01630 672993, 01630 673110 — MB ChB 1967 Birm.; FRCS Eng. 1974. Cons. Surg. N. Staffs. Hosp. Dist. Prev: Sen. Surg. Regist. W. Midl. RHA; Research Assoc. Univ. Calif. Los Angeles USA.

FORREST, James Michael The Westmoreland GP Centre, Fazakerley Hospital, Aintree, Liverpool L9 7AL Tel: 0151 525 6286; 25 Rose Place, Aughton, Ormskirk L39 4UJ — MB ChB 1970 Liverp.; FRCGP 1990, M 1974; DObst RCOG 1973; DCH Eng. 1972. Assoc. Regional Adviser Gen. Pract. Mersey RHA. Socs: Merseyside & N.W. Fac. RCGP.

FORREST, John Arthur Hunter Glasserton, 4A Mosspark Road, Milngavie, Glasgow G62 8NJ Tel: 0141 956 4376 Fax: 0141 956 4376 Email: jforrest@cotignac.freeserve.co.uk — MB ChB 1969 Ed.; MD Ed. 1980, BSc (Hons. Pharmacol.) 1966; FRCP Glas. 1985; FRCP Ed. 1984; MRCP (UK) 1971. (Ed.) Cons. Phys. Stobhill Gen. Hosp. Glas. Socs: Brit. Soc. Gastroenterol. Prev: Sen. Regist. (Gastroenterol.) Roy. Infirm. & W.. Gen. Hosp. Edin.; Regist. (Med. & Gastroentrol.) Roy. Infirm Edin.; SHO (Med.) N.. Gen. Hosp. Edin.

FORREST, John Grant 102/7 Whitehouse Loan, Greenhill, Edinburgh EH9 1AX Tel: 0131 447 9045 Email: g.forest@ukonline.co.uk — MB ChB 1989 Aberd.; FRCA 1996; Msc (IT) Heroit-Watt Univ. 1999. Clin. Research Fell. (Anaesth.) Roy. Infirm. Edin. Socs: Ed. & E. Scot. Soc. Anaesth.; Soc. Computing & Technol. in Anaesth.

FORREST, Karen Mary 33 Richmond Road, Kirby-in-Ashfield, Nottingham NG17 7PR — BM BCh 1996 Oxf.

FORREST, Katharine Margaret East Grange Farmhouse, Grange Road, St Andrews KY16 8LF Email: katfor@hotmail.com — MB ChB Ed. 1991; MRCP (UK) 1995; MRCPCH 1997. (Ed.) Specialist Regist. RHSL Edin. Socs: BMA; Med. & Dent. Defence Union of Scotl.; MDDUS. Prev: Regist. & SHO Roy. Hosp. Sick Childr. Edin.; SHO (Anaesth.) Roy. Infirm. Edin.; SHO Yorkshill Glas.

FORREST, Kirsty Ann Thornton 2 Wellfield Court, Marsh, Huddersfield HD3 4AG — MB ChB 1994 Ed.

FORREST, Mr Leslie 143 St Annes Road E., Lytham St Annes FY8 3HW — MB ChB 1965 Manch.; MD Manch. 1972, MB ChB 1965; FRCS Ed. 1977. Cons. Surg. Blackpool, Wyre & Fylde HA.

FORREST, Lisa Victoria 9 Cedarwood Close, Fairoak, Eastleigh SO50 7LN — MB BCh 1998 Wales.

FORREST, Mark Robert 5 Nelson Road, Harrow HA1 3ET — MB ChB 1990 Manch.

FORREST, Melanie Jane Kas, Gloucester Road, Alveston, Bristol BS35 3RG — MB ChB 1997 Liverp.

FORREST, Neil 38 Wallfield Crescent, Aberdeen AB25 2LA — MB ChB 1998 Aberd.; MB ChB Aberd 1998.

FORREST, Vida Alice (retired) East Grange Farm House, Grange Road, St Andrews KY16 8LL Tel: 01334 472099 — MB ChB St. And. 1960; DCCH 1986; Cert. FPA JCC 1969; DObst RCOG 1964. Prev: SCMO (Child Health) Cheltenham & Dist. HA.

FORREST-HAY, Iain Longfield Road Surgery, 1 Longfield Road, Harpfields, Stoke-on-Trent ST4 6QN; 21 Brough Lane, Trentham, Stoke-on-Trent ST4 8BX — MB ChB 1966 Birm.; MRCPath 1975.

FORRESTER, Agnes Corbett (retired) 7 Ravenscraig Gardens, Dundee Road, West Ferry, Dundee DD5 1LT Tel: 01382 79181 — MB ChB 1928 St. And. Prev: Vis. Anaesth. Bradford Roy. Infirm. & St. Luke's Hosp. Bradford.

FORRESTER, Alan Michael 280 Crookesmoor Road, Sheffield S10 1BE — MB ChB 1993 Sheff.

FORRESTER, Mr Alastair William Department of Radiology, Glasgow Royal Infirmary, Glasgow Tel: 0141 211 4619 Fax: 0141 211 4781; Balblair, 26 Redburn Avenue, Giffnock, Glasgow G46 6RH Tel: 0141 638 6935 — MB ChB 1975 Glas.; FRCS Glas. 1980; FRCR 1987. Cons. Diag. Radiol. Glas. Roy. Infirm.

FORRESTER, Alexander James Maxwell Hillside Cottage, Crowcombe, Taunton TA4 4AW Email: maxforrester@yahoo.co.uk — MB ChB 1982 Bristol; MRCGP 1988; DRCOG 1987. Socs: Brit. Med. Acupunc. Soc.

FORRESTER, Alison McColl 95 Bishopthorpe Road, York YO23 1NX — BM BCh 1981 Oxf.; BA (Hons.) 1978; MRCP (UK) 1985; MPH Leeds 1988; MFPHM RCP (UK) 1991. Clin. Asst. Gastroenerology York Dist. Hosp. York. Prev: Cons. Pub. Health Med. Grimsby & Scunthorpe HA.; Sen. Regist. (Pub. Health Med.) Yorks. RHA.

FORRESTER, Alistair Gilroy Princes Street Surgery, 155 Princes Street, Dundee DD4 6DG Tel: 01382 461090 Fax: 01382 461091; 9 Glasclune Way, Broughty Ferry, Dundee DD5 3TJ Tel: 01382 739914 — MB ChB 1966 St. And.; FRCGP 1999; MRCGP 1975. (St. And.) Sen. Partner, P.s St. Surg., Dundee; Clin. Tutor (Gen. Pract.) Univ. Dundee; GP Trainer Tayside HB; Clin. Asst. Drug Develop. Scotl. Socs: BMA (Ex-Chairm. Dundee Div.); Forfarshire Med. Assn. (Ex-Pres.); Dundee Med. Club (Ex-Pres.). Prev: Dent.

Anaesth. '69-'92; Trainee GP, Dundee '68-'69; Demonstator (Anat) Univ. Dundee '67-'68.

FORRESTER, Andrew John Howard Centre, 2 Crozier Terrace, London E9 6AT Email: andrew.forrester@dial.pipex.com — MB ChB 1991 Ed.; BSc (Hons.) Ed. 1993; MRCPsych 1997. (Edinburgh) Lect. (Forens. Psychiat.) St Bartholomews Med. Sch. Lond. Prev: Regist. (Psychiat.) Maudsley Hosp. Lond.; Research Fell. (Psychiat.) Roy. Edin. Hosp.

FORRESTER, Catriona 17 Fulshaw Av., Wilmslow SK9 5JA — MB ChB 1973 Glas.; MRCP (UK) 1977.

FORRESTER, Mr Donald Wylie Shaftesbury Medical Centre, 480 Harehills Lane, Leeds LS9 6DE Tel: 0113 248 5631 Fax: 0113 235 0658; 15 Broomhill Drive, Moortown, Leeds LS17 6JW Tel: 0113 237 0221 Email: don.forrester@hotmail.com — MB ChB 1971 St. And.; MD Dundee 1981; FRCS Glas. 1977; FRCS Ed. 1977. (St. And.) Socs: BMA. Prev: Wellcome Research Fell. & Hon. Sen. Regist. (Surg.) Ninewells Hosp. Dundee; Demonst. (Anat. & Path.) Univ. of St. And.

FORRESTER, Geoffrey (retired) 2 Llewellyn Court, Elmsleigh Avenue, Leicester LE2 2DH — MRCS Eng. LRCP Lond. 1945; FRCGP 1975, M 1967; DOMS Eng. 1949. Clin. Asst. Roy. Infirm. Leicester. Prev: Ho. Phys. W. Bromwich Gen. Hosp.

FORRESTER, Ian Robert Berry Lane Medical Centre, Berry Lane, Longridge, Preston PR3 3JJ Tel: 01772 783021 Fax: 01772 785809 — MB ChB 1973 Ed.; FRCGP 1994; MRCGP 1977; DRCOG 1977.

FORRESTER, Mr James Cunningham Eastlea, 2 Ellieslea Road, West Ferry, Dundee DD5 1JG Tel: 01382 75452 — MB ChB 1960 St. And.; ChM (High Commend.) Dund 1970; FRCS Glas. 1965; FRCS Ed. 1965; FRCS Eng. 1965. Cons. Surg. Ninewells Hosp. Dundee; Sen. Lect. in Surg. Univ. Dundee; Fell. Assn. Surgs. Gt. Brit. & Irel. Socs: Surg. Research Soc. Prev: Postgrad. Research Surg. (Fulbright Schol.) Univ. Calif. Med. Center; San Francisco, U.S.A.; Anat. Research Asst. St. Salvator's Coll. Univ. St. And.

FORRESTER, James Wylie Ewing (retired) 3 Balone Steading, St. Andrews KY16 8NS Tel: 01334 478273 — MB ChB 1962 Glas.; DObst RCOG 1964. Med. Prescribing Adviser Gtr. Glas. HB. Prev: Chairm. Gtr. Glas. SE Dist. Med. Comm.

FORRESTER, John McColl (retired) 120 Morningside Drive, Edinburgh EH10 5NS Tel: 0131 447 2540 — BM BCh Oxf. 1952; DObst RCOG 1955; FRCP Ed. 1998. Prev: Sen. Med. Off. Scott. Home & Health Dept.

FORRESTER, Marianne 10 Wallfield Place, Aberdeen AB25 2JN — MB ChB 1997 Aberd.

FORRESTER, Marion Brown Turner Nook End Cottage, Nook Lane, Ambleside LA22 9BH Tel: 015394 32027 — MB ChB 1944 Manch. (Manch.)

FORRESTER, Paul Broatch Belltrees, 43 Aytoun Road, Glasgow G41 5HW — MB ChB 1983 Glas.

FORRESTER, Peter (retired) 17 Mckay Road, Wimbledon, London SW20 0HT — MB ChB 1952 Glas. Prev: GP Wimbledon.

FORRESTER, Peter Charles 31 Pelhams Walk, Esher KT10 8QA — MB BS 1977 Lond.; FRCA 1981. Indep. Pract. Lond. Prev: Cons. Anaesth. St. Peter's Hosp. Chertsey; Cons. Anaesth. Char. Cross Hosp. & Chelsea & W.m. Hosp.

FORRESTER, Robert Michael Nook End Cottage, Nook Lane, Ambleside LA22 9BH Tel: 015394 32027 — MB BChir 1943 Camb.; MD Camb. 1955, MA, MB BChir 1943; FRCP Lond. 1970; DCH Eng. 1951. (Camb. & Manch.)

FORRESTER, Robert Smith, Surg. Cdr. RN Retd. (retired) 5 The Mews, Norton Hall Farm, Norton Road, Letchworth SG6 1AL Tel: 01462 679582 — MB ChB 1947 Aberd.; DCP Lond, 1956; FRCPath 1975, M 1963; DMJ (Path.) Soc. Apoth. Lond. 1967. Prev: Cons. Path. RN Hosp. Plymouth.

FORRESTER-WOOD, Mr Christopher Patrick Department of Thoracic Surgery, Bristol Royal Infirmary, Bristol BS2 8HW Tel: 0117 928 4210 Fax: 0117 928 3522; The Olds Stores, Westerleigh, Bristol BS37 8QP — MA, MB Camb. 1970, BChir 1969; FRCS Eng. 1975. (St. Bart.) Cons. Thoracic Surg. Bristol Roy. Infirm. Bristol. Socs: Soc. of Cardiothoracic Surg. Of GB & Irel.; Europ. Soc. for Thoracic Surg. Prev: Sen. Regist. (Cardio-Thoracic Surg.) Glas. Roy. Infirm.

FORSDICK, Dennis Henry (retired) Dean Cottage, 12 Downside Road, Winchester SO22 5LU Tel: 01962 867480 — MB BS Lond. 1947. Prev: Hosp. Pract. (Dermat.) Roy. Hants. Co. Hosp. Winchester.

FORSDICK, Paul Brian 60 Nursery Close, Hurstpierpoint, Hassocks BN6 9WA Tel: 01273 834212 — MB BS 1990 Lond.; MRCGP 1996; DRCOG 1994; Dip. Sports Med. Lond 1993. (St. Geo. Hosp. Med. Sch.) GP Hove; Med. Off. to Sussex Co. Cricket Club.

FORSDICK, Stephen John Park Medical Centre, 19 Bridge Road, St Austell PL25 5HE Tel: 01726 73042 Fax: 01726 74349; Nansladron Farm, Pentewan, St Austell PL26 6DJ — MB BS 1978 Lond.; MA Oxf. 1979; MRCS Eng. LRCP Lond. 1978; MRCGP 1982; DRCOG 1982; Dip. Occ. Med. 1996. (Oxf. & Guy's) Adjudicating Med. Pract. Benefits Agency. Socs: Brit. Soc. Med. & Dent. Hypn.; Cornw. Clin. Soc.; Brit. Med. Acupunc. Soc. Prev: Clin. Asst. (Obst.) Plymouth Gen. Hosp.; Trainee GP Plymouth VTS; Ho. Phys. & Ho. Surg. Guy's Hosp. Lond.

FORSEY, James Peter Hexham General Hospital, Hexham NE46 1QJ Tel: 01434 606161 — MD 1990 Bristol; BSc Wales 1975, MSc 1982; MB BS Newc. 1981; MRCOG 1986. Cons. O & G Hexham Gen. Hosp. Prev: Sen. Regist. (O & G) Univ. Hosp. Wales Cardiff.

FORSEY, Julie Helen Easdale Medical Practice, Seil Island, Oban PA34 4QT — MB BCh 1982 Wales; DRCOG 1984; MRCGP 1986; MRCGP 1986; DRCOG 1984. GP Locum work.

FORSEY, Peter Ronald 41 Wentworth Park Avenue, Harborne, Birmingham B17 9QU — MB ChB 1988 Birm.; MRCP (UK) 1992. Cons. Phys. (Cardiol.) Dudley Gp. Hosps. NHS Trust. Prev: Regist. (Cardiol.) Qu. Eliz. Hosp. Birm.

FORSHALL, Samuel William Stubbs Farm, Midhurst GU29 0PG — MB ChB 1991 Bristol.

FORSHAW, David Michael Broadmoor Hospital, Crowthorne RG45 7EG; Department of Forensic Psychiatry, Institute of Psychiatry, De Crespigny Park, London SE5 8AF — MB ChB 1980 Liverp.; MRCPsych 1985; DPhilMed Soc. Apoth. Lond. 1987; DHMSA 1984. Cons. Forens. Psychiat. (Forens. & Addic. Psychiat.) BRd.moor Hosp. Berks.; Sen. Lect. (Forens. Psychiat.) Inst. Psychiat. Lond. Prev: Research Psychiat. Inst. Psychiat. Lond.; Sen. Regist. & Regist. (Psychiat.) Maudsley Hosp. Lond.

FORSHAW, Henry Brian Bayley The Albion Surgery, 6 Pincott Road, Bexleyheath DA6 7LP Tel: 020 8304 8334 — MRCS Eng. LRCP Lond. 1956; DObst. RCOG 1960. (Lond. Hosp.) Socs: BMA; Roy. Coll. Gen. Pract. Prev: Ho. Phys. Roy. Surrey Co. Hosp. Guildford; Ho. Surg. Poplar Hosp.; Ho. Off. Mothers' Hosp. Lond.

FORSHAW, John Wellington Barlow (retired) Barons Lodge, 12 Baroncroft Road, Woolton, Liverpool L25 6EH Tel: 0151 428 9479 — MB BChir 1945 Camb.; MD Camb. 1953, MA 1946; FRCP Lond. 1970, M 1949. Prev: Cons. Phys. Roy. Liverp. Hosp.

FORSHAW, Mark Lewis Manor Practice, James Preston Health Centre, 61 Holland Road, Sutton Coldfield B72 1RL Tel: 0121 354 2032 Fax: 0121 321 1779 — MB ChB 1990 Birm.; ChB Birm. 1990.

***FORSHAW, Matthew James** 5 The Harlings, Hertford Heath, Hertford SG13 7PQ Tel: 01992 442368 — MB BChir 1994 Camb.; BA (Hons.) Camb. 1992.

FORSHAW, Michael Anthony 13 Kings Hey Dr, Southport PR9 7JB — MB ChB 1997 Manch. SHO Rotat. (Surgic.), Addenbrooke's Hosp., Camb. Prev: Ho. Off. (Gen. Med. & Cardiol.), Manch. Roy. Infirm.; Ho. Off. (Gen. Surg.), Hope Hosp., Salford, Manch.

FORSHAW, Shirley Elizabeth Anne Clanrye Surgery, Monayhan St., Newry BT35 6BW — MB BCh BAO 1992 Belf.; MRCGP 1996; DRCOG 1995; DCH 1994; DGM 1993; DFFP 1997. (Qu. Univ. Belf.) Socs: BMA. Prev: Gen. Practitioner with interest in family Plann..

FORSTER, Alan Walton Centre, Lower Lane, Fazakerly, Liverpool L9 7LJ Tel: 01382 660111 Ext: 32274 Fax: 01382 425739 Email: forstera@wcnn-tr.nhs.nwest.nhs.uk; 103 Derby Drive, Rainford, St Helens WA11 8EH Tel: 01744 606640 — MB ChB 1978 Aberd.; BMedBiol Aberd. 1975; FRCP Glas. 1993. Cons. Clin. Neurophysiol. Walton Centre, Liverp. Socs: (ex Hon. Sec.) Brit. Soc. Clin. NeuroPhysiol. Prev: Cons. Clin. Neurophysiol. Ninewells Hosp. Dundee; Hon. Sen. Lect. Univ. Dundee & Univ. St. And.

FORSTER, Mr Alan Lambert 99 Ayr Road, Prestwick KA9 1TF — MB ChB 1970 Glas.; BSc (Hons.) Physiol. Glas. 1968, MB ChB 1970; FRCS Glas. 1975. Cons. Gen. Surg. Ayrsh. & Arran Health Bd.

FORSTER, David Brian Clarkson Surgery, De-Havilland Road, Wisbech PE13 3AN Tel: 01945 583133 Fax: 01945 464465 — MB BS 1986 Lond.

FORSTER, Mr David Martin Campbell Royal Hallamshire Hospital, Glossop Road, Sheffield S10 2JF Tel: 0114 271 3572 Fax: 0114 275 4930 Email: lgp@rsurgi.sheffield.ac.uk; Half Acre, 49 Church Lane, Dore, Sheffield S17 3GT — MB BChir Camb. 1959; MA Camb. 1960; FRCS Eng. 1964; DObst RCOG 1961. (Camb. & St. Thos.) Cons. Neurol. Surg. Sheff. HA; Dir. Nat. Centre for Stereotactic Radiosurg. Sheff. Socs: Fell. Roy. Soc. Med.; Soc. Brit. Neurol. Surgs. Prev: Cons. Neurosurg. Karolinska Hosp. Stockholm, Sweden.

FORSTER, David Michael Barrywood, Linden Close, Thornton-Cleveleys, Blackpool Tel: 01253 868090 — MB ChB 1964 Liverp.; FFA RCS Eng. 1970. (Liverp.) Cons. (Anaesth.) Blackpool Health Dist. Prev: Sen. Regist. Norf. & Norwich Hosp.; Regist. BRd.green Hosp. Liverp.

FORSTER, David Myrton Cunynghame (retired) 133 Shepherds Hill, Harold Wood, Romford RM3 0NR Tel: 01708 342646 — MB BChir Camb. 1959; MA Camb. 1959; MRCS Eng. LRCP Lond. 1956; FRCOG 1979, M 1966. Prev: Cons. O & G Harold Wood Hosp.

FORSTER, Donald Peter Northumberland Mental Health Trust, Foundry House, The Oval, Stead Lake, Bedlington NE22 5HS; 11 Ashdale, Darras Hall, Ponteland, Newcastle upon Tyne NE20 9DR — MSc (Soc. Med.) (Distinc.) Lond. 1974, MB BS 1967; MRCS Eng. LRCP Lond. 1967; FFPHM 1984, M 1976; FRCPsych 1998, M 1974; DPM Eng. 1972. (St. Mary's) Staff Grade Old Age Psychiat. Dept N.umberland Ment. Health Trust Bedlington. Socs: Soc. Social Med.; BMA. Prev: Sen. Lect. (Epidemiol.) Univ. Newc.; Sen. Regist. Med. Care Research Unit (Community Health) Sheff. Univ.; Regist. (Psychiat.) Knowle Hosp. Fareham.

FORSTER, Edward Mitchell Henry Lisbellaw, Enniskillen BT94 5BE — MB BCh BAO 1946 Dub. Clin. Asst. (Geriat. Med.) Co. Hosp. Enniskillen. Prev: SHO (Surg.) Fermanagh Co. Hosp. Enniskillen; Forens. Off. Police Dept. Co. Fermanagh.

FORSTER, Elizabeth Margaret Church Cottage, Barcombe, Lewes BN8 5TW — MB BS 1951 Lond. (Westm.) JP. Socs: BMA & Roy. Soc. Med. Prev: Assoc. Specialist (Ment. Handicap) Fouchlands & Foredown Hosps.

FORSTER, Elliot David, MC (retired) 16 South Row, Blackheath, London SE3 0RY — MB BChir 1945 Camb.; MRCS Eng. LRCP Lond. 1930.

FORSTER, Eveline Nora 6 Greyfriars Close, Olton, Solihull B92 7DR Tel: 0121 707 5322 Fax: 0121 707 5322 — MB ChB 1975 Liverp.; DRCOG 1978.

FORSTER, Gay Nethergreen Road Surgery, 34-36 Nethergreen Road, Sheffield S11 7EJ Tel: 0114 230 2952 — MB ChB 1965 Sheff.; DA Eng. 1968; DObst RCOG 1967. p/t GP.

FORSTER, Greta Elizabeth The Ambrose King Centre, The Royal London Hospital, Whitechapel, London E1 1BB Tel: 020 7377 7315 Fax: 020 7377 7648 Email: ambrose.kijng@dial.piper.com — MB ChB 1976 Liverp.; MRCOG 1982; Dip. Ven. Soc. Apoth. Lond. 1979; FRCOG 1997; 1994 MFFP. (Liverpool) Cons. Genitourin. Med. Roy. Lond. Hosp. Barts & the Lond. NHS Trust. Socs: Med. Soc. Study VD; Founder Mem. Spec. Interest Gp. in Adolesc. Sexual Health 2000; Coun. Mem., MSSVD 1997-2000 1989-1992. Prev: Sen. Regist. (Venereol.) St. Mary's Hosp. Lond.

FORSTER, Helen Rydon House, Cheddon Rd, Taunton TA2 7AZ Tel: 01823 333438 Fax: 01823 333287 — MB BS 1989 Lond.; MRCGP 1994; DRCOG 1992. (St. Thos. Hosp. Lond.) Flexible Train. SHO (Psychiat.). Prev: Clin. Med. Off. (Family Plann.) Taunton; Trainee GP Taunton VTS; Staff Grade Psychiat.

FORSTER, Mr Ian Douglas The Surgery, Bishops Waltham, Winchester SO23 1GR Tel: 01489 892288 Fax: 01489 894402; Ashwell, Lower Chase Road, Swanmore, Southampton SO32 2PB Tel: 01489 896730 — MB BS 1974 Lond.; FRCS Lond. 1980. (St. Geo.) Clin. Asst. (BrE. Surg.) Roy. Hants. Co. Hosp. Winchester. Prev: Demonst. (Anat.) Univ. St. And.; Regist. (Surg.) Roy. Hants. Co. Hosp. Winchester.; SHO (Surg.) St. Geo. Lond.

FORSTER, Mr Ian William Queen Medical Centre, Nottingham Tel: 01159 249924 Ext: 42042; The Wildernesse, 398 Duffield Road, Allestree, Derby DE22 1ES Tel: 01332 558797 Email: iwforster@compuserve.com — MB BS Lond. 1968; FRCS Eng. 1975; FRCS Ed. 1975. (Univ. Coll. Hosp.) Cons. Orthop. Nottm. Univ. Qu. Med. Centre Nottm. Socs: Fell. BOA; Brit. Orthop. Research Soc.; ESSKA. Prev: Sen. Regist. (Orthop.) Derbysh. Roy. Infirm. & Harlow Wood Hosp.; Sen. Lect. & Lect. (Orthop.) Nottm. Univ.; Clin. Research Asst. Dept. Orthop. Welsh Nat. Sch. Med. Cardiff.

FORSTER, Isobel Dorothy Margaret (retired) Lyndale, Dipe Lane, East Boldon NE36 0PH — MB ChB 1951 Ed.; DCH Eng. 1955. Prev: GP Jarrow.

FORSTER, Janet Elizabeth Brockhurst Medical Centre, 139-141 Brockhurst Road, Gosport PO12 3AX Tel: 023 9258 3564 Fax: 023 9251 0782 — MB ChB 1978 Sheff.; DRCOG 1981.

FORSTER, Joanne Claire 227 Aylestone Road, Leicester LE2 7QJ — MB ChB 1998 Leic.; MB ChB Leic 1998.

FORSTER, John Lewis Macmillan (retired) 111 Finnart Street, Greenock PA16 8HT — MB ChB 1963 Glas. Prev: SHO (Dermat.) Stobhill Hosp. Glas.

FORSTER, Kenneth Brian (retired) 15 Little Bornes, Alleyn Park, Dulwich, London SE21 8SD — MB BS 1955 Durh. Prev: Ho. Surg. Huddersfield Roy. Infirm.

FORSTER, Lorne Fiona Thorntree Villa, Muckart Road, Dunning, Perth PH2 0RW — MB ChB 1991 Ed.; PhD 1997. (Univ. Edin. Glas.) Prev: Clin. Research Asst. (Path. Biochem.) Glas. Roy. Infirm.; SHO & Ho. Off. (Med.) Borders Gen. Hosp. Melrose; Ho. Off. (Surg.) St. John's Hosp. Livingston.

FORSTER, Mark Campbell 398 Duffield Road, Derby DE22 1ES — MB ChB 1993 Sheff.

FORSTER, Martin David Rotheram General Hospital, Rotherham Tel: 01709 820000; Half Acre, 49 Church Lane, Dore, Sheffield S17 3GT Tel: 0114 236 5059 — MB BS 1994 Newc. Med. SHO Rotat., Rotheram Gen. Hosp.

FORSTER, Matthew Osborn (retired) Church Cottage, Church Road, Barcombe, Lewes BN8 5TW Tel: 01273 400484 — MB BS 1949 Lond. Prev: Psychother. Stud. Health Serv.

FORSTER, Michael Richard Dept. of Anaesthesia, Perth Royal Infirmary, Perth PH1 1NX — MB ChB 1989 Bristol; FRCA 1994; BSc (Hons.) Bristol 1986. Cons. Dept. Anaesth., Perth Roy. Infirm. Socs: BMA & Assn. Anaesth. Prev: Career Regist. (Anaesth.) Gtr. Glas. HB.

FORSTER, Neil Duncan 398 Duffield Road, Allestree, Derby DE22 1ES — MB ChB 1998 Manch.; MB ChB Manch 1998.

FORSTER, Nicola Jane Flat 5, 127 New Kings Road, London SW6 4LS — MB ChB 1993 Sheff.

FORSTER, Norma Dorothy 4 Manor Walk, Benton, Newcastle upon Tyne NE7 7XX Tel: 0191 266 5246; 11 Brandling Mews, Gosforth, Newcastle upon Tyne NE3 5PN Tel: 0191 236 4076 — MB BS 1949 Durh. (Durh.) Socs: Med. Wom. Federat.

FORSTER, Paul Melville 10 Hepple Close, Isleworth TW7 6AY Tel: 020 8568 7339 — MB BS 1952 Lond.; MRCS Eng. LRCP Lond. 1952. (St. Mary's) Med. Asst. Path. W. Middlx. Hosp. Isleworth. Socs: Fell. Roy. Soc. Med.; Assn. Clin. Paths. Prev: Asst. Pathol. City Hosp. Nottm.; Ho. Surg. N. Devon Infirm. Barnstaple.

FORSTER, Pauline Marie Department of Child and Family Psychiatry, The Blakesley Centre, 102 Blakesley Rd, Yardley, Birmingham B25 8RN Tel: 0121 683 6151; 4 Pool Meadow Close, Moseley, Birmingham B13 9YP — MB ChB 1977 Manch.; BSc (Hons.) Anat. Manch. 1974; MRCGP 1982; FRCPsych 2001; DRCOG 1980; DA (UK) 1981. Cons. Child & Adolesc. Psychiat. N. Birm. Childr.'s Hosp. NHS Trust; Hon. Clin. Sen. Lect. Univ. Birm. Prev: Sen. Regist. Rotat. (Child & Adolesc. Psychiat.) NW RHA.

FORSTER, Peter John Gibson James Paget Hospital, Lowestoft Road, Great Yarmouth NR31 6LA Tel: 01493 452216 Fax: 01493 452590 Email: forster.proops@btinternet.com — MD 1983 Birm.; MB ChB 1973; FRCP Lond. 1994; MRCP (UK) 1976. (Birmingham) Cons. Phys. & Rheum. Jas. Paget Hosp. Gt. Yarmouth.

FORSTER, Robert Alan Winifred Lee Health Centre, Wartling Road, Eastbourne BN23 7PG Tel: 01323 20555 Fax: 01323 36094 — MB BS 1960 Lond.; MRCS Eng. LRCP Lond. 1960; DObst RCOG 1962. (Guy's) Course Organiser E.bourne GP VTS. Prev: Ho. Phys. & Ho. Surg. Pembury Hosp.; Ho. Off. (Obst.) & Cas. Off. Lewisham Hosp.

FORSTER, Robert Gordon (retired) Featherstone Hall, Featherstone, Pontefract WF7 6AR Tel: 01977 792272 — MRCS Eng. LRCP Lond. 1949. Prev: GP.

FORSTER, Robyn Elizabeth 2 Wester Tarsappie, Rhynd Road, Perth PH2 8PT — MB ChB 1977 Dundee; DCH RCPS Glas. 1980; DRCOG 1979. Clin. Med. Off. Tayside HB.; Staff Grade Paediat. Perth.

FORSTER, Simon St James's University Hospital, Beckett St., Leeds LS9 7TF Tel: 0113 243 3144; 3 Bramstan Avenue, Bramley, Leeds LS13 3JG Tel: 0113 257 1310 — MB BS 1985 Newc.; MRCPsych 1993; MRCGP 1990. Sen. Regist. (Child & Adolesc. Psychiat.) Yorks. Region. Prev: Regist. (Psychiat.) N.. Region.; SHO (Psychiat.) Gateshead Dist.

FORSTER, Simon William Henry Erne Health Centre, Cornagrade Road, Enniskillen BT74 6AY Tel: 028 6632 2707; 11 Hollyhill View, Tonystick, Enniskillen BT74 6FT — MB ChB 1988 Aberd.; MRCGP 1992; DRCOG 1993; Cert. Family Plann. JCC 1991; DCH RCPS Glas. 1991. Prev: Trainee GP Aberd. VTS.

FORSTER, Stephen Douglas 6 Nicola Close, Harrow Weald, Harrow HA3 5HP — MB ChB 1992 Liverp.

FORSTER, Stephen James North Devon District Hospital, Barnstaple EX31 4JB Tel: 01271 22577 — MB ChB 1969 Liverp.; FFA RCS Eng. 1976. Cons. (Anaesth.) N. Devon Hosp. Barnstaple.

FORSTER, Susan Morag Clinic 6, Department Genito-Urinary Medicine, Hinchingbrooke Hospital, Huntingdon PE29 6NT Tel: 01480 416461 — MB BS 1981 Lond.; FRCP Lond. 1997; MRCP (UK) 1984. (Roy. Free Hosp., Lond.) Cons. Genitourin. Med. & Clin. Tutor, Hinchingbrooke Hosp., Huntingdon. Socs: MSSVD; AGUM; BHIVA. Prev: Sen. Lect. (Genitourin. Med.) St. Mary's Hosp., Lond.

FORSTER, Terence Anthony (retired) 11 Brandling Mews, Gosforth, Newcastle upon Tyne NE3 5PN Tel: 0191 236 4076 — MB BS 1948 Durh.; DObst RCOG 1953.

FORSTER, Thomas Woolbert Hill (retired) South Hill, Shirwell, Barnstaple EX31 4LG Tel: 01271 850849 — MB BS Lond. 1947. Prev: Ho. Phys. Paediat. Unit, St. Mary's Hosp.

FORSYTH, Alexander Smith The Strawberry Gardens Medical, 377 Heysham Road, Morecambe LA3 2BP Tel: 01524 850999 Fax: 01524 855688 — MB ChB 1977 Glasgow; MB ChB Glas 1977. (Glasgow) GP Morecambe, Lancs.

FORSYTH, Allan (retired) Drumnakyle, Foss, Pitlochry PH16 5NJ Tel: 01882 634281 — MB ChB Ed. 1959; MRCGP 1973; DObst RCOG 1967. Prev: GP Perth.

FORSYTH, Mr Andrew Thomas Sussex Cardiac Centre, Eastern Road, Brighton BN2 5BE Tel: 01273 696955 Email: andytforsyth@cs.com; Keepers Cottage, Slugwash Lane, Wivelsfield Green, Brighton RH17 7SS Tel: 01444 416220 — MB BS 1970 Melbourne; FRACS 1978. (Melbourne) Cardiothoracic Surg. Roy. Sussex Co. Hosp. Brighton. Prev: Cardiothoracic Surg. Kings Coll. Hosp. Lond. & Lond. Bridge Hosp.

FORSYTH, Angela March End, South Road, Busby, Glasgow G76 8JB Tel: 0141 644 1497 Fax: 0141 644 5731 — MB ChB Glas. 1969; FRCPS Glas. 1985. Cons. Dermat. Contact Dermat. Unit Roy. Infirm. Glas.; Hon. Sen. Clin. Lect. (Dermat.) Univ. Glas. Socs: Brit. Assn. Dermat. & Brit. Contact Dermat. Gp. (Comm. Mem.).

FORSYTH, Anne 1 Sandfield Avenue, Milngavie, Glasgow G62 8NR Tel: 0141 956 2004 — MB ChB Glas. 1962; DObst RCOG 1964; DA Eng. 1967. (Glas.) Clin. Asst. Glas. Drug Probl. Serv. Socs: BMA; FPA. Prev: Partner in Gen. Pract. - Glas. W.; Anaesth. Glas. W.. Gp. Hosps. & Glas. Roy. Matern. Hosp.; SHO (Anaesth.) & Resid. (Med. & Surg.) W.. Infirm. Glas.

FORSYTH, Anne Catherine 2 Baird Drive, Bearsden, Glasgow G61 4BL — MB ChB 1987 Aberd.; MRCGP 1993; DCH RCP Lond. 1991. Staff Grade Community Paediat. Inverness. Prev: SHO (A & E) Raigmore Hosp.; Regist. (Geriat. Med.) Law Hosp. Carluke; SHO (Paediat.) Leeds.

FORSYTH, Charles James North Cottage, Dovers Green Road, Reigate RH2 8BU Tel: 01737 226338 Email: charles@dr-forsyth.demon.co.uk — MB BS 1977 Lond.; MFHom 1982. (Guy's) Pract. Homoeop. Med. Surrey. Socs: Fac. Homoeop.; Brit. Soc. Allergy, Environm. & Nutrit. Med.

FORSYTH, Constance Catherine (retired) Redmyre, 5A Glamis Drive, Dundee DD2 1QG Tel: 01382 566412 — MB ChB 1945 Ed.; MB ChB (Hons.) Ed. 1945; MD (Commend.) Ed. 1949; FRCP Lond. 1972, M 1948; FRCP Ed. 1962, M 1947. Prev: Reader (Child Health) Univ. Dundee.

FORSYTH, David Stevenson Flat 1, 7 Edge Hill, Wimbledon, London SW19 4LR Tel: 01752 813277 Fax: 01752 815733 — MB ChB 1969 Sheff.; BDS, LDS 1963; MRCGP 1980; DRCOG 1979. Socs: Roy. Soc. of Med. Prev: Clin. Asst., Dermat. Dept., Derriford Hosp., Plymouth.

FORSYTH, Dianne Elizabeth 5 Elgin Drive, Broomridge, Stirling FK7 7TZ Tel: 01786 813573 — MB ChB 1995 Glas. SHO (Psychiat.) Stratheden Hosp. Socs: BMA. Prev: JHO/SHO Quensland Health, Australia; SHO (Psychiat. of Old Age & Health c/o Elderly); Jun. Ho. Off. (Surg.).

FORSYTH, Duncan Ronald Department of Medicine For The Elderly, Addenbrooke's Hospital, Hills Road, Cambridge CB2 2QQ Tel: 01223 217785 Fax: 01223 217783 Email: duncan.forsyth@addenbrookes.nhs.uk; 10 Rock Road, Cambridge CB1 7UF Tel: 01223 244602 Fax: 01223 244602 — MB ChB 1978 Manch.; MA Camb. 1995; MRCP (UK) 1984; FRCP 1997. (Manchester) Cons. Geriat. Addenbrooke's Hosp. Camb. Socs: Brit. Med. Assn.; Brit. Geriat.s Soc. Prev: Sen. Regist. (Gen. & Geriat. Med.) Roy. Devon & Exeter Hosp.; Lect. (c/o Elderly) Manor Pk. Hosp. Bristol; Research Fell. Bristol Roy. Infirm.

FORSYTH, Gilbert McIlwrick (retired) 223 Bank Street, Stanecastle, Irvine KA12 0YB Tel: 01294 211118 Email: gforsyth@lineone.net — MB ChB Ed. 1939; FRCOG 1963, M 1948. Prev: Obst. Regist. S.. Gen. Hosp. Glas.

FORSYTH, Hilary Mary Charlton Lane Centre, Charlton Lane, Cheltenham GL53 9DZ Tel: 01242 272017; 12 Windrush, Burford OX18 4TS Tel: 0451 844679 — MB BS 1967 Lond.; MRCS Eng. LRCP Lond. 1966; MRCPsych 1974; DPM Eng. 1971; DObst RCOG 1969. (St. Thos. Hosp. Lond.) Cons. Psychiat. (Gen. Adult & Rehabil.) E. Glos. NHS Trust. Prev: Cons. Psychiat. Kingston Gen. Hosp.

FORSYTH, Hope Glen Milne Community Paediatrics, Royal Liverpool Children's Hospital NHS Trust, Alder Hey Hospital, Eaton Road, Liverpool L12 2AP Tel: 0151 228 4811; 23 Knowsley Park Lane, Prescot L34 3NA Tel: 0151 426 3163 — MB ChB 1967 Aberd.; MSc (Audiol.) Manch. 1993; MRCPCH 1997; DCH RCP Lond. 1969. Cons. Community Paediat. (Audiol.) Roy. Liverp. Childr. Hosp. Socs: BMA; BACDA Research Sub-Gp. and Educat. Sub-Gp. Prev: Sen. Community Med. Off. (Audiol.) Roy. Liverp. Childr. NHS Trust; Regist. (Paediat.) Roy. Berks. Hosp. Reading; Regist. (Audiol.) Nuffield Centre.

FORSYTH, Ian Coulter 47 Quarry Bank, Keele, Newcastle under Lyme, Newcastle ST5 5AG — MB ChB 1994 Cape Town.

FORSYTH, James Ian McLeish (retired) Bankfield, Consett DH8 5NW Tel: 01207 502380 — MB ChB 1950 Ed.; DObst RCOG 1955. Prev: Regist. (O & G) Auckland Hosp. NZ.

FORSYTH, James Stewart Beechlea, 1 Ellieslea Road, West Ferry, Dundee DD5 1JG — MB ChB 1973 Glas.; MD Glas. 1992; FRCP Ed. 1988; MRCP (UK) 1978; DObst RCOG 1975; DCH RCPS Glas. 1975. Clin. Dir. & Cons. Paediat. Ninewells Hosp. & Med. Sch. Dundee; Hon. Sen. Lect. Child Health. Prev: Lect. Child Health Ninewells Hosp. & Med. Sch. Dundee; Regist. (Med. Paediat.) Roy. Hosp. Sick Childr. Edin.

FORSYTH, Joan Downie Johnston Beechlea, 1 Ellieslea Road, West Ferry, Dundee DD5 1JG; Beechlea, 11 Ellieslea Road, Westferry, Dundee DD5 1JH Tel: 01382 778465 — MB ChB 1973 Glas.; MBA (Distinc.) Dundee 1996. Med. Adviser to Local Auth., Dundee City Counc., Perith & Kinross Angus Counc. Socs: Sec. Housing Med. Adv., Scotl. Prev: Head Quality Assur. Unit Dundee City Counc.

FORSYTH, John (retired) 6 Ardrossan Road, Saltcoats KA21 5BW — MB ChB 1949 Glas.

FORSYTH, Katarina Cecilia Inchpark Surgery, 10 Marmion Crescent, Edinburgh EH16 5QU Tel: 0131 666 2121 — MB ChB 1988 Ed.; DCH RCPS Glas. 1991.

FORSYTH, Kenneth David Beaumont Street Surgery, 27 Beaumont Street, Oxford City, Oxford OX1 2NR Tel: 01865 311500 Fax: 01865 311720; 3 Cumnor Hill, Oxford OX2 9EU Tel: 01865 240720 — BM BCh 1968 Oxf.; DRCOG 1975.

FORSYTH, Leigh James 41 Mollington Avenue, Liverpool L11 3BG — MB ChB 1994 Sheff.

FORSYTH, Linda 8 Pinecrest Circle, Bieldside, Aberdeen AB15 9FN Tel: 01224 869657 — MB ChB 1986 Aberd.

FORSYTH, Marie Therese Dr Marie Forsyth, The Surgery, 3 Alloway Place, Ayr KA7 2AA Tel: 01292 610682 Fax: 01292

263322; 3 Alloway Place, Ayr KA7 2AA Tel: 01292 610682 Fax: 01292 263322 — MB ChB 1976 Glas.

FORSYTH, Mary Grant (retired) 8 Narborough Court, 58 Warwick Place, Leamington Spa CV32 5DF Tel: 01926 313319 — MB ChB 1946 Ed.

FORSYTH, Melissa Claire 2 Chaucer Way, Lexden, Colchester CO3 4HA — MB ChB 1995 Birm.; BSc (Hons) Birm. 1994.

FORSYTH, Michael Charles 3 Laurel Grove, Chester CH2 3HU — MB ChB 1995 Manch.

FORSYTH, Philip Athelstan (retired) The Poplars, Wickhambrook, Newmarket CB8 8UR — MRCS Eng. LRCP Lond. 1933.

FORSYTH, Rachel Susannah — MB ChB 1995 Bristol.

FORSYTH, Robert James Children's Outpatients, Newcastle General Hospital, Westgate Road, Newcastle upon Tyne NE4 6BE Tel: 0191 273 8811 Fax: 0191 272 3297 Email: rob.forsyth@trvi.nuth.northy.nhs.uk — BM BCh 1987 Oxf.; PhD Newc. 1995; MRCP (UK) 1990; DCH RCP Lond. 1989. Cons. & Sen. Lect. (Paediat. Neurol.) Univ. Newc. u. Tyne. Socs: Brit. Paediat. Neurol. Assn.; Brit. Neurosci. Assn. Prev: Fell. (Paediat. Neurol.) Univ. Brit. Columbia; 1st Asst. (Child Health) Univ. Newc. u. Tyne; Wellcome Fell. (Child Health) Univ. Newc. u. Tyne.

FORSYTH, Robert Sinclair The Surgery, Croyard Road, Beauly IV4 7DJ Tel: 01463 782794 — MB ChB 1986 Ed.; MRCGP 1993; DObst RCPI 1993. Gen. Pract. Beauly, The Surg., Croyard Rd. Prev: Assoc. Pract. Arisaig & Small Isles Practs.; Trainee, Kinesmill Surg., Inverness.

FORSYTH, Sheila Margaret (retired) 19 Louvain Road, Derby DE23 6DA Tel: 01332 345397 — LRCP LRCS Ed. LRFPS Glas. 1947; DCH Eng. 1950. Prev: GP Derby.

FORSYTH, Sophie 21 Austenway, Gerrards Cross SL9 8NN — MB ChB 1994 Manch.

FORSYTH, Stuart Gordon Adam (retired) 42 Pembury Road, Tonbridge TN9 2HX Tel: 01732 353001 — MB BChir 1945 Camb.; BA Camb. 1945; MRCS Eng. LRCP Lond. 1945; DCH Eng. 1960. Prev: Ho. Phys. Univ. Coll. Hosp.

FORSYTH, William James Danebridge Medical Centre, 29 London Road, Northwich CW9 5HR Tel: 01606 45786 Fax: 01606 331977; 579 London Road, Davenham, Northwich CW9 8LN — MB ChB 1977 Aberd.; AFOM RCP Lond. 1993; MRCGP 1981.

FORSYTHE, Beverley Jill Zeneca Pharmaceuticals, Alderley Park, Macclesfield SK10 4T Tel: 01625 517062 Email: beverley.forsythe@alderley.zeneca.com; 2 Gorsey Road, Wilmslow SK9 5DP Tel: 01625 521410 — MB BChir 1985 Camb.; MA Camb. 1984, MB BChir 1985; DRCOG 1986. Pharmaceut. Phys. Zeneca Pharmaceut. Macclesfield. Prev: GP Princip. Sch. Hill Ho. Lewes.

FORSYTHE, Daphne Elizabeth Sycamore Cottage, The Street, Wenhaston, Halesworth IP19 9EF Tel: 01502 478405 Email: eforsy27@globalnet.co.uk — MRCS Eng. LRCP Lond. 1950; DPH (Tanner Memor. Prize) Eng. 1966. (King's Coll. Hosp.) Socs: BMA; Med. Jl.ists Assn. Prev: SCMO (Family Plann.) Norwich HA; Dep. MOH Saffron Walden; Ho. Phys. King's Coll. Hosp.

FORSYTHE, David Tristram The Surgery, George Holding Centre, Chaucer Way, Larkfield, Aylesford ME20 7SS Tel: 01732 841213 Fax: 01732 841213; 14 Pelican Court, Wateringbury, Maidstone ME18 5DD Tel: 01622 814466 Fax: 01622 814466 — MB BS 1977 Lond.; MRCGP 1983. (Roy. Free) Med. Off. Kenward Trust. Socs: BMA. Prev: Invicta Radio Doctor; Mentor RCGP (Educat.); Postgrad. GP Tutor.

FORSYTHE, Fiona Mary Haslemere Health Centre, Church Lane, Haslemere GU27 2BQ Tel: 01428 653881; April Cottage, Pk Road, Haslemere GU27 2NJ — MB BS 1979 Lond.; MRCS Eng. LRCP Lond. 1978. (Westm.)

FORSYTHE, John Leslie Robert 115 Dene Road, Wylam NE41 8EZ — MB BS 1981 Newc.

FORSYTHE, Professor John Malcolm Centre for Health Services Studies, George Allen Wing, University of Kent, Canterbury CT2 7NF Tel: 01227 823681 Fax: 01227 827868 Email: j.m.forsythe-2@ukc.ac.uk; Buckingham House, 1 Royal Chase, Tunbridge Wells TN4 8AX Tel: 01892 522359 Fax: 01892 522359 — MB BS Lond. 1962; MSc (Social Med.) Lond. 1971, BSc (Hons. Anat.) 1959; FRCP Lond. 1985; MRCS Eng. LRCP Lond. 1961; FFPHM RCP (UK) 1976, M 1974; DObst RCOG 1963. (Guy's) Profess. Fell. Pub. Health Univ. Kent; Sen. Lect. (Pub. Health Med.) King's Coll. Med. Sch.; Profess. Fell. Centre for Health Serv. Studies Univ. Kent; Chairm. Comm. Managem. The Horder Centre for Arthritis; Pres. Epidemiol. & Pub. Health Sect. Roy. Soc. of Med.; Adjunct Prof. St Geo. Univ. Grenada WI; Chairm. Tunbridge Wells PCG Bd; Edit. Bd. Jl. Roy. Coll. Phys; Bd. Hyde Housing Assn. Socs: Fell. Roy. Soc. Med.; Hon. Mem. Internat. Med. Informatics Assn. Prev: Regional Med. Off. & Regional Dir. Pub. Health & Serv. Developm. SE Thames RHA; Vis. Prof. Univ. N. Carolina, USA; Area Med. Off. Kent. AHA.

FORSYTHE, Sarah Louise 12 Kelman Close, London SW4 6JE — MB BS 1992 Lond.; Dip. Obst. & Gyn. Auckland 1996; Cert. Family Plann. NZ 1996. (Guy's Hosp.) Occupat. Health Trainee Unilever Lond. Socs: Soc. Occupat. Health Med. Prev: SHO (O & G) Nat. Wom. Hosp.; SHO (Paediat.) Starship Hosp., NZ.

FORSYTHE, Thomas 3 Moss Vale Road, Dromore BT25 1DG — LRCPI & LM, LRSCI & LM 1940; LRCPI & LM, LRCSI & LM 1940.

FORSYTHE, William Ian (retired) Kenway House, Parton, Castle Douglas DG7 3NE Tel: 0164 47 205 — MB BCh BAO 1945 Belf.; MD Belf. 1949; FRCP Ed. 1969, M 1952. Cons. Paediat. Leeds Gen. Infirm. & St. Jas. Hosp. Leeds. Prev: Trav. Schol. Barnkliniken Qu. Caroline Hosp. Stockholm, Sweden.

FORSYTHE-YORKE, Wulfram Edler Irmler, OBE, KStJ, Brigadier late RAMC Grove House, Horning Upper St., Norwich NR12 8NE — MB BChir 1959 Camb.; MB Camb. 1959, BChir 1958; MA Camb. 1959; MRCS Eng. LRCP Lond. 1958; FFCM 1989, M 1974; FFPHM 1990; DTM & H Eng. 1968. (Camb. & Middlx.) Indep. Med. Advisor Benefits Agency; Cdr. St. John Ambul. Norf.; Pres. RAMC Assn. Norf. Br.; Liveryman Soc. Apoth. Lond. Socs: Fell. Brit. Inst. Managem. Prev: Cons. Pub. Health E. Norf. Health Commiss.; DPH Gt. Yarmouth & Waveney DHA; Commanding Off. Qu. Eliz. Milit. Hosp.

FORTE, Vincent John Charles Balmoral, 1 Victoria Road, Deal CT14 7AU — MB BS 1987 Lond.; BA Hons. Camb. 1983; MRCGP 1992; DA (UK) 1989. Socs: Eur. Undersea Biomed. Soc. Prev: Trainee GP Acle; SHO (Obst. & Gyn, Gen. Med. & A & E) Jas. Paget Hosp. Gt. Yarmouth.

FORTES MAYER, Mr Karl David BUPA Hospital, Little Aston Park Road, Sutton Coldfield B74 3BZ Tel: 0121 353 2444; Dorian, 9 The Limes, Walsall WS1 2RX Tel: 01922 633092 Fax: 01922 633092 Email: karlfm@medix-uk.com — MB BChir 1969 Camb.; MB Camb. 1969, BChir 1968; FRCS Eng. 1973. (St. Geo.) Cons. Surg., Walsall Hosp. NHS trust. Socs: BMA (Med. Ethics Comm.); Assoc. Mem. BAUS; Brit. Assn. of Paediatric Surg. Prev: Director of Sandwell and Walsall BrE. Screening Serv.

FORTH, Agnes Jeanette 271 Killin Street, Sandyhills, Glasgow G32 9TH — MB ChB 1979 Dundee.

FORTH, Michael James (retired) 149 High Street, Street BA16 0EX Tel: 01458 442603 — MB BS Lond. 1947; MRCS Eng. LRCP Lond. 1947; MRCGP 1959. Prev: Med. Ref. (Benefits Agency).

FORTI, Alexander Donald Stoney Green, London Road E., Amersham HP7 9DH Tel: 0124 03 21294 — LRCPI & LM, LRSCI & LM 1973; LRCPI & LM, LRCSI & LM 1973.

FORTIN, Catherine Helene Germaine Stamford Wing, Royal Masonic Hospital, Ravenscourt Park, London W6 0TN Tel: 020 8741 9000; 11 Avenue Gambetta, 94160 Saint Mandé, France Tel: 00 33 3603064073 — MD 1976 Paris; T(GP) 1991; Dip. Confed. Nat. Med. Acupunct. France 1978. (Fac. Med. St. Antoine) Resid. Med. Off. Psychiat. Roy. Masonic Hosp.; Off. Migrations Internat.es Paris; Accredit. Phys. to French. Consulate Lond. Socs: Fell. Roy. Soc. Med.; BMA. Prev: Accredit. Phys. to French Consulate in Lond.; Sch. Med. Off. Lycée Français, Lond.; GP Cromwell Hosp. Lond.

FORTON, Daniel Michael Henrik 98 Galloway Road, London W12 0PJ — MB BS 1993 Lond.

FORTON, Julian Thomas Marcus 25 St Johns Road, Petts Wood, Orpington BR5 1HS — BChir 1995 Camb.

FORTT, Richard Windsor Highlands, 8 Park Road, Radyr, Cardiff CF15 8DG Tel: 029 2084 2206 — MB BCh 1961 Wales; FRCPath 1981, M 1969. Cons. Histopath. Roy. Gwent Hosp. Newport. Prev: Sen. Lect. in Path. Welsh Nat. Sch. Med. Cardiff; Regist. (Morbid Anat.) Hammersmith Hosp. Lond.; Sen. Regist. (Morbid Anat.) Lond. Hosp.

FORTUN, Paul James 24 Jardin de Crocquet, St Aubins High St., St Brelade, Jersey JE3 8BR — BM 1993 Soton.

FORTUNE, Diana Caroline 2 Crockham Way, London SE9 3HE — MB BS 1978 Lond.; BSc (Behavioural Sci.) Lond. 1975; MRCS Eng. LRCP Lond. 1978. (St. Bart.) Med. Examr. Benefits Agency. Prev:

Med. Off. S. Thames Blood Transfus. Serv.; Trainee GP Luton & Dunstable VTS; SHO (Gen. Med.) Luton & Dunstable Hosp.

FORTUNE, Farieda 30 Acacia Road, London NW8 6AS — MB BS 1980 Lond.

FORTUNE, Louise Dorothy 23 The Grove, Hartlepool TS26 9LZ — MB ChB 1973 Leeds; DA (UK) 1980. Prev: SHO (Orthop./Cas.) Raigmore Hosp. Inverness; Regist. (Anaesth.) Roy. Infirm. Hull; GP Fleetwood Lancs.

FORTUNE, Mary Hall Brora Health Centre, Station Square, Brora KW9 6QJ Tel: 01408 621320 Fax: 01408 621535; Glen Ayeron, Golf Road, Brora KW9 6QS — MB ChB 1985 Dundee; MRCGP 1989; DRCOG 1988. Socs: MRCSP 1977.

FORTUNE, Peter-Marc PICU, Great Ormond Street Hospital, London WC1N Tel: 0207 813 8213 Fax: 0207 813 8206 Email: fortune@doctor.com; 41a Cranwich Road, London N16 5HZ Tel: 020 7502 1604 Fax: 020 7502 1605 — BM 1992 Soton.; BM Soton. 1929; PhD Soton. 1988, BSc 1984; MRCP (UK) 1995. Specialist Regist., PICU, Gt. Ormond St. Hosp. Socs: MRCPCH; Paed. Intens. Care Soc. Prev: Specialist Regist. (Paediat.) N.wick Pk. Hosp. Harrow; SHO Soton. Gen. Hosp.

FORTUNE, William Alan Infirmary Drive Medical Group, Consulting Rooms, Infirmary Drive, Alnwick NE66 2NR Tel: 01665 602388 Fax: 01665 604712; Allermuir, Prudhoe St, Alnwick NE66 1PZ — MB BS Durh. 1966; FRCGP 1994, M 1979; FRCOG 1987, M 1971; DObst RCOG 1968.

FORTUNE-JONES, Helen Fax: 0131 661 7028; Fax: 0131 661 7028 — MB ChB 1994 Ed.; DRCOG 1997; DFFP, 1998; MRCGP, 1999. (Edinburgh) GP Non-Princip., Edin. Prev: GP Regist. Pk.Gr. Med. Pract. Edin.; SHO (Paediat.) Vict. Hosp. Kirkcaldy.

FORTY, Mr Frank (retired) Ballyculter, Green Lane, Stanmore HA7 3AH — MB BS 1928 Lond.; FRCS Eng. 1929; MRCS Eng. LRCP Lond. 1927. Prev: Surg. Edgware Gen. Hosp.

FORTY, Mr Jonathan Department of Cardiothoracic Surgery, Freeman Hospital, Newcastle upon Tyne NE7 7DN Tel: 0191 287 3111 — MB BChir 1980 Camb.; MA Camb. 1982, BA 1978, MB BChir 1980; FRCS Eng. 1986; FRCS Ed. 1986; MD 1999 Cambridge. Cons. Cardiothoracic Surg. Freeman Hosp. Newc. Socs: (Pres.) Europ. Soc. Heart & Lung Transpl.ation; Internat. Soc. Heart & Lung Transpl.; Soc. Cardiothoracic Surgs. of GB & Irel. Prev: Sen. Regist. (Cardiothoracic Surg.) Freeman Hosp. Newc.; Regist. (Cardiothoracic Surg.) Papworth Hosp. Camb.

***FORWARD, Daren Paul** 5 Royal Standard House, Standard Hall, Nottingham NG1 6FX — BM BCh 1997 Oxf.

FORWARD, Francis Robert The Glebe, 53 Trumlands Road, St Marychurch, Torquay TQ1 4RA — MB BS 1975 Lond.

FORWARD, Peter John Parkhill Medical Practice, 3 Park Hill Road, Torquay TQ1 2AL; 15 Sherwell Valley Road, Chelston, Torquay TQ2 6EJ — MB ChB 1977 Manch.

FORWARD, Robin Francis Miller Honey Brooke, Sandford Orcas, Sherborne DT9 4RP Tel: 01935 75122 Email: jafoward@ic24.net; Honey Brooke, Sandford Orcas, Sherborne DT9 4RP Tel: 01963 220778 Email: jafoward@ic24.net — MB BS 1959 Lond.; FFA RCS 1971 Eng.; DObst RCOG 1961; DA 1966 Eng.; FFA RCS Eng. 1971; DA Eng. 1966; DObst RCOG 1961. (St. Thos.) Socs: Assn. Anaesths. & S. W. Soc. Anaesths. Prev: Cons. Anaesth. E. Som. NHS Trust; Sen. Regist. (Anaesth.) S. W.. RHB; Regist. (Anaesth.) United Bristol Hosps.

FORWELL, Professor George Dick, OBE (retired) 20 Irvine Crescent, St Andrews KY16 8LG Tel: 01334 472943 — MB ChB Ed. 1950; PhD Ed. 1955; FRCP Lond. 1985; FRCP Glas. 1974; FRCP Ed. 1967, M 1957; FFCM 1972; DPH Eng. 1959; DIH Soc. Apoth. Lond. 1957. Hon. Prof. Univ. St. And. Prev: Chief Admin. Med. Off. & Dir. Pub. Health Gtr. Glas. HB.

FORWOOD, Caroline Margaret Highams Park Fundholding Practice, Health Centre, Handsworth Avenue, Highams Park, London E4 9PD Tel: 020 8527 0913 Fax: 020 8527 6597; 69 Wellesley Road, Walthamstow, London E17 8QX Email: caroline@wxhdoctors.demon.co.uk — MB BS 1994 Lond.; BSc (Biochem. & Molec. Biol.) Lond. 1991; DFFP 1997; DRCOG 1996. (Univ. Coll. Lond. Med. Sch.) GP Regist. Highams Pk. Prev: Trainee GP/SHO Whipps Cross Hosp. Lond. VTS; Ho. Off. (Med.) OldCh. Hosp.; Ho. Off. (Surg.) Basildon Hosp.

FOSBURY, Simon John Fraser Headley House, 55 Rayens Cross Road, Long Ashton, Bristol BS41 9DY Tel: 01275 392134 Fax: 01275 394576 — MB BS 1970 Lond.; MRCS Eng. LRCP Lond. 1970.

FOSDYKE, Neil Antony 19 Craven Lea, Croxteth Park, Liverpool L12 0NF — MB ChB 1985 Liverp.

FOSKETT, Derrick (retired) Pond Farm Cottage, Sonning Common, Reading RG4 9NU Tel: 01189722269 — MB BChir 1938 Camb.; MA Camb. 1944; FRCP Lond. 1969, M 1948; MRCS Eng. LRCP Lond. 1938. Prev: Cons. Phys. Reading Hosps. Sen. Med. Regist. Radcliffe Infirm. Oxf.

FOSKETT, Lesley Anne 46 Gisborne Crescent, Allestree, Derby DE22 2FL Tel: 01332 557138 — BM BS 1981 Nottm.; MRCGP 1985; DRCOG 1984.

FOSKETT, Richard Alan Calcot Medical Centre, Hampden Road, Chalfont St. Peter, Gerrards Cross SL9 9SA Tel: 01753 887311 Fax: 01753 890639 — MB BS 1976 Lond.; MA Oxf. 1977; MRCGP 1981; DCH Eng. 1980. (St. Bart.)

FOSS, Alexander James Easterbrook Queens Medical Centre, Nottingham NG7 2 Fax: 020 7253 4696; 10 Parkside, Nottingham, London NG8 2NW Tel: 0115 925 5540 Email: alexander.foss@btinternet.com — BM BCh 1986 Oxf.; MA Oxf. 1990, BA 1983; MRCP (UK) 1990; FCOphth 1991, M 1990. Cons. Qu.'s Med. Centre Nottm. Socs: Brit. Eye Study Gp.; FRCOPphth; MRCP. Prev: SHO (Ophth.) Roy. Berks. Hosp. Reading; Regist. & SHO (Ophth.) Eye Hosp. Oxf.; SHO (Gen. Med.) Guy's Hosp. Lond.

FOSS, Mr Martin Vincent Lush (retired) Summerhill, Cheverell's Green, Markyate, St Albans AL3 8RN Tel: 01582 840561 — MB BChir 1963 Camb.; MA, MB Camb. 1963, BChir 1962; FRCS Ed. 1967; FRCS Eng. 1968; LMSSA Lond. 1962. Prev: Cons. Traum. & Orthop. Surg. Luton & Dunstable Hosp.

FOSSARD, Christopher Willow House, 84 Lammack Road, Lammack, Blackburn BB1 8LA Tel: 01254 60545 — MB BS 1966 Lond.; MSc Newc. 1969; FRCP Lond. 1986. (Univ. Coll. Hosp.) Paediat. Blackburn Dist. Prev: SHO Paediat. Whitehaven Hosp.; Sen. Regist. (Paediat.) E. Birm. Childr. Hosp.; Regist. (Paediat.) Univ. Newc. on Tyne.

FOSSEY, Susan Mary 4 Chapel Bar, Wymeswold, Loughborough LE12 6UF — MB ChB 1985 Leeds; MRCOG 1992.

FOSTER, Alan Roland (retired) The Old Rectory, Welsdale Road, Donington on Bain, Louth LN11 9QZ Tel: 01507 343215 — MB ChB 1949 Leeds; MB ChB Leeds 1952; BSc (2nd cl. Hons. Physiol.) Leeds 1949; FRCP Ed. 1982, M 1960; FRCPsych 1982, M 1971; DPM Eng. 1958. Prev: Cons. Psychiat. Exeter HAs.

FOSTER, Mr Allen, OBE — MB ChB 1973 Birm.; FRCS Eng. 1981; FRCOphth 1988; DO RCS Eng. 1975. (Birmingham) Med. Dir. to CBM Internat.; Sen. Lect. in Internat. Eye Health. Prev: Hon. Lect. Wilmer Inst. John Hopkins Hosp. Baltimore, USA; Med. Supt. Mvumi Hosp. Tanzania; Sen. Lect. Ist. Opth. Lond.

FOSTER, Brian Joseph Landor House, 59 St Cross Road, Winchester SO23 9RE Tel: 01962 867613 — MB BS 1949 Lond.; MRCS Eng. LRCP Lond. 1949; MRCGP 1965; DPM Eng. 1970. (Lond. Hosp.) p/t Cons. Pall Europe; Cons. Bitterne & Woolston Rotary Club Housing Soc. & Soton. Flower Fund Homes. Socs: BMA; Medico-Legal Soc. Lond.; Fell. of Roy. Soc. of Med. Prev: Hosp. Pract. (Psychogeriat.) Moorgreen Hosp.; Hon. Clin. Teach. (Gen. Pract.) Univ. Soton. Med. Sch.; Med. Off. Shell UK & BP Ltd. Hamble & Texaco Ltd.

FOSTER, Bruce (retired) 22 Clarence Road, Hale, Altrincham WA15 8SF Tel: 0161 928 3985 — MB BS 1957 Lond.; FFA RCS Eng. 1961; DA Eng. 1959. Prev: Cons. Anaesth. Manch. Roy. Infirm.

FOSTER, Carl Andrew Priory View Medical Centre, 2a Green Lane, Leeds LS12 1HU Tel: 0113 295 4260 Fax: 0113 295 4278 — MB ChB 1985 Manch.; MRCGP 1991; DObst Auckland 1988. (Manch.) Socs: Roy. Coll. of Gen. Practitioners. Prev: SHO (Med.) Qu. Pk. Hosp. Blackburn; Ho. Surg. Salford Roy. Hosp.; Ho. Phys. Blackburn Roy. Infirm.

FOSTER, Carol Jane (retired) Lyes Cottage, Shortgate Lane, Laughton, Lewes BN8 6DF Tel: 01825 840643 — MB Camb. 1967, BChir 1966; BA Camb. 1967; FRCP Lond. 1987, M 1969. Prev: Cons. Phys. (Geriat. Med.) Qu. Mary's Hosp. Sidcup.

FOSTER, Caroline Jane Badger Farm House, Badger, Wolverhampton WV6 7JS — MB BS 1992 Lond.; MRCP Paed. 1995.

FOSTER, Catherine Elisabeth The Health Centre, Dunning Street, Stoke-on-Trent ST6 5BE Tel: 01782 425834 Fax: 01782 577599 — MB ChB 1994 Liverp.; DRCOG 1997. GP Regist. N. Staffs. Hosp. Centre Stoke on Trent.

FOSTER, Charles Arthur, ERD (retired) Glebe Farm, Sternfield, Saxmundham IP17 1ND Tel: 01728 602579 — MB BS Lond. 1948; MRCS Eng. LRCP Lond. 1948; FFA RCS Eng. 1954; DA Eng. 1951. Cons. Anaesth. St. Thos. Hosp.; Cons. Anaesth. Roy. Masonic Hosp. Lond. Prev: Sen. Regist., Cas. Off. & Ho. Phys. St. Thos. Hosp.

FOSTER, Charlotte Sarah Stamford Hill Group Practice, 2 Egerton Road, Stamford Hill, London N16 6UA Tel: 020 8800 1000 Fax: 020 8880 2402; 63 Benthal Road, Stoke Newington, London N16 7AR Tel: 020 8806 1675 Fax: 020 8806 4713 Email: cabradbury@compuserve.com — MB ChB 1987 Bristol; MRCGP 1993. (Bristol) Princip. GP. Prev: GP Tutor City & E. Lond. HA.

FOSTER, Christabel Anne Eyre Medical Practice, 31 Eyre Crescent, Edinburgh EH3 5EU Tel: 0131 556 8842 Fax: 0131 557 2177; 46 Inverleith Row, Edinburgh EH3 5PY Tel: 0131 552 5432 Fax: 0131 552 5432 — MB ChB 1978 Ed.; MRCGP 1982; DRCOG 1981. GP Adviser Health Promotion Lothian HB. Prev: GP MuirHo.

FOSTER, Christine Anne New Land Surgery, Grove Medical Centre, Wooton Grove, Sherborne DT9 4DL Tel: 01935 813438 Fax: 01935 817470 — MB ChB 1983 Bristol; BSc Bristol 1980; MRCGP 1988. Principle in Gen. Pract. Prev: Trainee GP Bradford VTS.

FOSTER, Christopher James King Edward VII Hospital, Midhurst GU29 0BL — MB ChB 1973; MD 1987 Bristol; MRCP (UK) 1977. (Bristol University) Cons. Cardiol. (Interven.al Cardiol.) King Edwd. VII Hosp. Midhurst. Socs: Fell. of the Amer. Coll. of Cardiol. Mem. Canad. Cardiovasc. Soc. Prev: Assoc. Prof./Interven.al Cardiol.s Dalharsie Univ./QE HSC Halifax, N.S. Canada.

FOSTER, Professor Christopher Stuart Department of Pathology, Duncan Building, Royal Liverpool University Hospital, Liverpool L69 3BX Tel: 0151 706 4480 Fax: 0151 706 5883 Email: csfoster@liv.ac.uk; 24 Harthill Road, Calderstones, Liverpool L18 6HU — MB BS 1973 Lond.; PhD Lond. 1983, BSc (Hons.) 1969; MRCS Eng LRCP Lond. 1973; MRCPath 1984. (Westminster) Geo. Holt Prof. & Dir. of Path. Univ. Liverp.; Comm. Mem. Communication & Continuing Med. Educat. Amer. Soc. Clin. Pathol.; Europ. Edr. Human Pathol. Socs: Roy. Soc. Med.; Amer. Soc. Clin. Pathologists; Internat. Acad. Path. Prev: Sen. Lect. & Hon. Cons. Histopath. Roy. Postgrad. Med. Sch. & Hammersmith Hosp. Lond.; Sen. Scientist Div. Biochem. & Molecular Dis. Childr. Hosp. Philadelphia, USA.

FOSTER, Crawford Richard Muir, Surg. Lt. RN 4 Cerdic Mews, Hamble, Southampton SO31 4LW — MB ChB 1987 Ed.

FOSTER, David Hugh Christian Lisle 16 St Georges Court, 83-89 St Georges Drive, London SW1V 4DB — MB BS 1992 Lond.

FOSTER, David Norton Birch Hill Hospital, Rochdale OL12 9QB Tel: 01706 377777 Fax: 01706 755884; Pilkington Farm House, Mankinholes, Todmorden OL14 6HR Tel: 01706 814623 Fax: 01706 814623 Email: fosterhq@aol.com — MB BS 1965 Lond.; FRCP Lond. 1987, M 1969; MRCS Eng. LRCP Lond. 1965. (St. Mary's) Cons. Phys. Birch Hill Hosp. Rochdale; Hon. Med Off. Springhill Hosp Rochdale. Socs: Fell. Manch. Med. Soc.; Brit. Soc. Gastroenterol.; Lancs. Amateur Gastroenterol. Soc. Prev: Sen. Regist. (Med.) St. Jas. Hosp. Leeds & Univ. Teachg. Hosp. Lusaka, Zambia; Regist. (Med.) St. Mary's Hosp. Lond. (Harrow Rd. Br.).

FOSTER, David Richard Princess of Wales Hospital, Bridgend CF31 1RQ Tel: 01656 752422; Ty Perllan, Laleston, Bridgend CF32 0HN — MB BCh 1972 Wales; FRCR 1979; DMRD 1977. Cons. Radiol. P.ss of Wales Hosp. Bridgend. Socs: BMA & Brit. Soc. Gastroenterol. Prev: Cons. Radiol. Roy. Perth Hosp., W.. Austral.; Sen. Regist. (Radiol.) Univ. Wales Cardiff; Regist. (Radiol.) Roy. Hosp. Sheff.

FOSTER, David Spencer (retired) 6 Park Road, Tiverton EX16 6AU Tel: 01884 255482 — MB BS 1938 Lond.; MB BS Lond 1938; MRCS Eng. LRCP Lond. 1938; MRCOG 1942. Prev: Regist., & Ho. Surg. (O & G) St. Mary's Hosp.

FOSTER, David Vernon, TD, Flight Lt. RAFVR/ Major (T & AVR) Retd. (retired) 56 Elmbridge Avenue, Surbiton KT5 9HA Tel: 020 8399 1289 — MRCS Eng. LRCP Lond. 1943; DMJ (Clin.) Soc. Apoth. Lond. 1968. Research Assoc. RCS Eng. Prev: Police Surg. Metrop. Police.

FOSTER, Diana Mary Overnhill Family Practice, 14 Overnhill Road, Staple Hill, Bristol BS16 5DN Tel: 0117 970 1656 Fax: 0117 987 2479; 23 Emerson Way, Emersons Green, Bristol BS16 7AP Tel: 0117 956 9643 — MB ChB 1985 Leic.; BSc Leic. 1983; DRCOG 1990.

FOSTER, Dilys Lloyd White Gables, 84 Victoria Road, Penarth CF64 3HZ Tel: 01222 708638 — MB BS 1939 Lond.; MRCS Eng. LRCP Lond. 1939; DPH Wales 1942. (Cardiff) Clin. Med. Off. S. Glam. AHA (T). Prev: Res. Med. Off. Llandough Hosp. Penarth; Asst. MOH Carmarthen Boro. Counc.; Asst. MOH Cardiff City Counc.

FOSTER, Dinah Mary Constance Child Health Department, Mansfield Community Hosptial, Stockwell Gate, Mansfield NG18 5QJ Tel: 01623 785050 Fax: 01623 424062; 13 Woodland View, Southwell NG25 0AG Tel: 01636 813763 Email: tondinw@btinternet.com — MB ChB Liverp. 1968; DPH Liverp. 1972. Cons. Paediat. Community Child Health Centr. Nottm. Healthcare NHS Trust; Med. Adviser Social Servs. Adopt. Agency Notts. Socs: Fell. Roy. Coll. Paediat. Child Health; Fac. Comm. Health. Prev: Princip. Med. Off. (Community Child Health) N. Notts. HA; SCMO (Child Health Serv.) Centr. Notts. HA.

FOSTER, Donald William (retired) 26 Station Road, Radyr, Cardiff CF15 8AA Tel: 01222 842795 — MB BCh 1952 Wales; FFCM 1984, M 1975; DPH 1956. Prev: SCM Mid-Glam. HA.

FOSTER, Dorothy Anne Acorn Cottage, Ingestre, Stafford ST18 0RE Tel: 01889 270126; Hazeldene House, Great Haywood, Stafford ST18 0SU — MB BCh BAO 1953 Dub.

FOSTER, Douglas Alexander Foster, The Surgery, Burns Road, Greenock PA16 0NJ Tel: 01475 631755 Fax: 01475 631755 — MB ChB 1986 Aberd.

FOSTER, Douglas Ferguson, Group Capt. RAF Med. Br. Retd. Heathfield, Collinswood Road, Farnham Common, Slough SL2 3LH Tel: 01753 645316 — MB ChB 1956 Ed.; MFOM RCP Lond. 1980; DAvMed Eng. 1970; DObst RCOG 1960. (Ed.) Socs: Soc. Occupat. Med.; BMA. Prev: Chief Med. Off. Guinness plc; Off. Commanding P.ss Mary's RAF Hosp. Halton; Off. Commanding Aviat. Med. Train. Centre RAF N. Luffenham.

FOSTER, Duncan Stuart Glover Street Medical Centre, 133 Glover Street, Perth PH2 0JB Tel: 01738 639748 Fax: 01738 635133; Sunnybank, 187 Glasgow Road, Perth PH2 0LZ Tel: 01738 635821 — MB ChB 1989 Ed.; MRCGP 1993; Cert. Prescribed Equiv. Exp. JCPTGP 1993; DRCOG 1992; DCH RCPS Glas. 1991. GP Perth. Prev: SHO (A & E) Falkirk & Dist. Roy. Infirm.; Trainee GP Lothian HB.

FOSTER, Elizabeth Ann The Topsham Surgery, The White House, Holman Way, Topsham, Exeter EX3 0EN Tel: 01392 874646 Fax: 01392 875261 — MB ChB 1985 Bristol; MRCGP 1989; DRCOG 1989. Prev: Trainee GP Plymouth VTS.

FOSTER, Elizabeth Mary, TD Tel: 020 8943 3424 Fax: 020 8977 1855; 5 Clifton Drive, Marple, Stockport SK6 6PP Email: elizabeth.foster@btinternet.com — MB BS 1982 Lond.; BSc Lond. 1979; MRCGP 1989; DCH RCP Lond. 1988. (Char. Cross) p/t Locum Gen. Practitioner; Assoc. Cons. in Clin. Risk Managem. (Med. Protec. Soc.). Socs: Fell. Roy. Soc. Med. Prev: GP Princip. Drs. Childs & Foster, Teddington, Middlx.

FOSTER, Eric Jeffrey Heywood Shorpshire Area Health Authority, The Limes, Belle Vue Road, Shrewsbury SY3 — MB ChB 1953 Manch.; DPH 1960; DObst RCOG 1957. Specialist Community Med. Salop AHA. Prev: Dep. Co. MOH Salop.

FOSTER, Gareth Colin 26A Old Cultra Road, Holywood BT18 0AE — MB ChB 1994 Dundee.

FOSTER, Geoffrey David 131 Killylea Road, Armagh BT60 4LL — MB ChB 1979 Sheff.

FOSTER, Mr George Edward Grosvenor Nuffield Hospital, Wrexham Road, Chester CH4 7QP Tel: 01244 680444 Fax: 01244 680812 Email: georgefos@aol.com; Manor House, Manley, Warrington WA6 9HL Tel: 01928 740246 Fax: 01928 740775 — MD 1973 Liverp.; MB ChB 1968; FRCS Eng. 1974. Cons. Surg. Chester HA & Grosvenor Nuffield Hosp. Chester; Clin. Lect. (Surg.) Univ. Liverp. Socs: Fell. Roy. Soc. Med.; Surgic. Research Soc. & Assn. Surgs.; Assn. Coloproctol. Prev: Lect. (Surg.) Univ. Nottm.; Regist. (Surg.) Liverp. Roy. Infirm.; Demonst. & Lect. (Anat.) Univ. Liverp.

FOSTER, Graham Peter Glentworth Surgery, Dalton Terrace, York YO24 4DB Tel: 01904 658542 Fax: 01904 671979 — MB BChir 1975 Camb.; MA Camb. 1975. (Westm.)

FOSTER, Graham Richard Forth Valley Health Board, 33 Spittal Street, Stirling FK8 1DX Email: gfoster@forth-hb.scot.nhs.uk — MB ChB 1988 Dundee; MPH Dundee 1994; MRCGP 1992; T(GP) 1992; MFPHM 1996. Cons. in Pub. Health Med. Forth Valley Health Bd. Socs: BMA. Prev: Sen. MO Pub. Health Policy Unit Scot. Off. Edin.; Sen. Regist. Pub. Health Med. Tayside HB; Trainee GP Tayside HA VTS.

FOSTER, Graham Russell 16 Sherfield Avenue, Rickmansworth WD3 1NH — MB BS 1983 Lond.; PhD Lond. 1993; BA Oxf. 1980; MRCP (UK) 1986. Sen. Lect. & Hon. Cons. St. Mary's Hosp. Lond. Prev: Lect. & Regist. (Med.) St. Mary's Hosp. Lond.; Clin. Research Fell. ICRF Lond.

FOSTER, Helen Elisabeth Rheumatology, Catherine Cookson Burrding, Medical School, University, Newcastle upon Tyne NE7 7DN Tel: 0191 284 3111 Fax: 0191 223 1159 Email: h.e.foster@ncl.ac.uk; 45 Western Way, Darras Hall, Ponteland, Newcastle upon Tyne NE20 9AS Tel: 01661 823408 — MB BS 1985 Newc.; MD Newc. 1992; MRCP (UK) 1988; DCH RCP Lond. 1994; FRCPCH 1997. (Newcastle) Clin. Sen. Lect. Paediatric Rheum., Univ. Newc. upon Tyne; Fell. (Paediat. Rheum.) Univ. Brit. Colombia, Canad. 1993; Exec. Mem. Brit. Paediat. Rheum. Gp. Socs: BMA; Brit. Soc. Rheum.; Exec. Mem. Brit. Paediat. Rheum. Assn. Prev: Research Fell. Arthritis & Rheum. Counc. 1988-1990; Cons. Rheumatologist (Paediat. and Adult), Newc. NHS Hosps. Trust, Newc. upon Tyne.

FOSTER, Helen Elizabeth 3 Oakwood, Kendal LA9 5EG — MB ChB 1987 Ed.; MRCP (UK) 1991. Clin. Asst. (Med. for the elderley), W.morland Gen. Hosp. Prev: Clin. Asst. (Cardiac. Rehabil.) Chesterfield & N. Derbysh. Roy. Hosp.

FOSTER, Helen Love (retired) 52 Old Vicarage Green, Keynsham, Bristol BS31 2DH Tel: 01179 867629 — MB ChB Ed. 1948; BSc Ed. 1948; DObst RCOG 1950. Prev: Clin. Asst. (A & E) Roy. United Hosp. Bath.

FOSTER, Helen Margaret 2 Tythebard Drive, Kingswinford DY6 0DS — BM BS 1988 Nottm.

FOSTER, Henry, Col. late RAMC c/o Williams & Glyns Bank (Holt's), Lawrie House, Victoria Road, Farnborough GU14 7NR; Heybridge Mills, Maldon CM9 4LS Tel: 0621 853100 — MB BS Lond. 1938; FRCP Ed. 1965, M 1953; MRCP Lond. 1953; MRCS Eng. LRCP Lond. 1938; DTM & H Lond 1952. (Guy's) Prev: Cons. (Med.) RAMC; Res. Med. Off. Putney Hosp. & Bromley Hosp.; ENT Ho. Surg. Selly Oak Hosp.

FOSTER, Hilary Daryl 3 Graham Road, Mitcham CR4 2HB Tel: 020 8640 2606 — MB BS 1986 Lond.; BSc Lond. 1983, MB BS 1986; MRCPsych 1990. Sen. Regist. Rotat. (Psychiat.) UMDS Guy's & St. Thos. Hosps. Lond.

FOSTER, Ian Louis Chantry Cottage, 33 Seabrook Road, Hythe CT21 5LX Tel: 01303 268529 — MB BS 1962 Lond.; MRCS Eng. LRCP Lond. 1962; DObst RCOG 1965. (Westm.) Prev: SHO (O & G) & Ho. Phys. Buckland Hosp. Dover; Ho. Surg. (Gyn.) All St.'s Hosp. (W.m. Hosp.).

FOSTER, Irene Olga (retired) 223 Durham Road, Gateshead NE9 5AB Tel: 0191 477 1155 — MB BS 1946 Durh. Prev: GP Gateshead.

FOSTER, James Michael Gerard Private Consulting Rooms, The Princess Grace Hospital, 42-52 Nottingham Place, London W1U 5NY Tel: 020 7486 1234 Ext: 2171 Fax: 020 7908 2168; Heathend Lodge, Windsor Road, Ascot SL5 7LQ Tel: 01344 621549 — MB BS 1974 Lond.; MSc UWCM 2001; FRCA 1992; FFA RCS Eng. 1980; DA Eng. 1979; MRCS Eng. LRCP Lond. 1977. (St. Bart. Hosp. Med. Coll.) Cons. in Pain Manage. Frimley Pk. Hosp. Surrey; Hon. Sen. Lect. St. Bart Hosp. Med. Coll. Socs: Internat. Assn. Study of Pain; The Pain Soc.; Fell.RSM. Prev: Cons. in Anaesth. & Pain Managem. St. Bart. Hosp. Lond.; Sen. Regist. (Pain Managem.) Sir Chas. Gairdner Hosp. W.ern Australia; Sen. Regist. (Anaesth.) Guy's Hosp. Lond.

FOSTER, Jane Elizabeth Jubilee Medical Centre, 52 Croxteth Hall Lane, Croxteth, Liverpool L11 4UG Tel: 0151 546 3956 Fax: 0151 546 3221; 72 Avondale Road, Wavertree, Liverpool L15 3HF Tel: 0151 733 6781 — BM BS 1988 Nottm.; BMedSci Nottm. 1986; MRCGP 1995; T(GP) 1995; DRCOG 1994; DCH RCP Lond. 1991. (Nottm.) Clin. Asst. (Haemat.) Roy. Liverp. Univ. Hosp. Prev: SHO (Psychiat.) BRd.oak Unit BRd.green Hosp. Liverp.; Trainee GP/SHO York; Med. Off. Kagando Hosp. Kasese, Uganda.

FOSTER, Jane Marilyn (retired) 12 St George's Gardens, Pontesbury, Shrewsbury SY5 0TB — MB BS 1959 Lond.; DA Eng. 1961; DObst RCOG 1960. Prev: SCMO S. Downs Health NHS Trust.

FOSTER, Janet Elizabeth Airedale Child & Family Service, Hillbrook, Mayfield Road, Keighley BD20 6LD Tel: 01535 661531 Fax: 01535 691194 — MB ChB 1969 Bristol; MRCPsych. 1981. Cons. Psychiat. Child & Adolesc. Airedale NHS Trust.

FOSTER, Jeffrey William 5 Manor Mansions, Belsize Gr, London NW3 4NB — MB BS 1997 Lond.

FOSTER, Jennifer Elizabeth Gartmore Road Surgery, 2 Old Gartmore Road, Drymen, Glasgow G63 0DP Tel: 01360 660203; 67 Dunmore Street, Balfron, Glasgow G63 0PZ — MB ChB 1982 Ed.

FOSTER, Jillian Ann 172 Hotspur Street, Newcastle upon Tyne NE6 5BH — MB BS 1994 Newc.

FOSTER, John 430 Doncaster Road, Barnsley S70 3RJ; 4 Seckar Lane, Wooley, Wakefield WF4 2LE — MB BS 1954 Durh.

FOSTER, John Princes Street Surgery, 155 Princes Street, Dundee DD4 6DG Tel: 01382 461090 Fax: 01382 461091 Email: j.foster"princesfinix.org.uk; Bennetsfield, 18 Benvie Road, Fowlts, Dundee DD2 5SA — MB BS 1973 Lond.; BSc (Hons.) Lond. 1970; MRCGP 1978; DObst RCOG 1975; FRCGP 1998. (Middlx.) Vice-Chairm. Scott. Counc. RCGP; Hon. Clin. Tutor Gen. Pract. Univ. Dundee; Mem. Counc. RCGP. Socs: Dundee Med. Club; Forfarshire Med. Assn.; BMA. Prev: Trainee GP Edin. VTS; SHO (O & G) Stirling Roy. Infirm.; Ho. Phys. Centr. Middlx. Hosp. Lond.

FOSTER, John Barnes (retired) Briardene, 19 Lindisfarne Road, Newcastle upon Tyne NE2 2HE Tel: 0191 281 1717 Fax: 0191 281 1717 Email: briardent@aol.com — MB BS 1953 Durh.; MB BS (Hons.) Durh. 1953; MD (Commend.) Newc. 1973; FRCP Lond. 1970, M 1955; ACInst.Arb. 1994; FAO 1998. Hon. Reader (Neurol.) Univ. Newc. Prev: Neurol. Regional Neurol. Centre Newc. & Newc. HA.

FOSTER, Mr John Charles Caldew Hospital, 64 Dalston Road, Carlisle CA2 5NW Tel: 01228 531713 Fax: 01228 590158; Green Trees, Burgh-by-Sands, Carlisle CA5 6BD Tel: 01228 576233 — MB ChB Ed. 1945; FRCS Ed. 1953. (Ed.) Hon. Cons. Orthop. Surg. E. Cumbld. Hosp. Gp. Socs: Fell. BOA; (Ex-Pres.) NE Orthop. Assn. Prev: Sen. Regist. (Orthop.) Bradford A & B Hosp. Gps.; Resid. Surg. Off. N. Lonsdale Hosp. Barrow-in-Furness; Ho. Surg. Edin. Roy. Infirm.

FOSTER, John Cordner The Surgery, Nettlebed, Henley-on-Thames RG9 5AJ Tel: 01491 641204 — MB ChB 1945 Birm. (Birm.) Clin. Asst. Roy. Berks. Hosp. & BoroCt. Hosp. Reading. Socs: Oxf. Med. Soc. & Reading Path. Soc. Prev: Ho. Phys. Brompton Hosp. Lond. & Miller Gen. Hosp. Lond.

FOSTER, John Herbert Bridge House Farm, Risley Lane, Breaston, Derby DE72 3BP Tel: 01332 872430 Fax: 01332 875022 — MB ChB Sheff. 1960. (Sheff.) Specialist Med. Adviser Sketchley Hall W.minster Health Care (Specialist Health Care Div.); Med. Adviser PCD Maltron Ltd. Socs: Balint Soc. & Soc. Occupat. Med. Prev: Med. Advisers E. Midl. Elec. plc.

FOSTER, John Huey 54 Ballymaderphy Road, Kilkeel, Newry BT34 4SW — MB BCh BAO 1977 Belf.; FRCR 1983. Cons. Radiol. Belvoir Pk. & Belf. City Hosps.

FOSTER, John Maurice (retired) 3 Kimberley Close, Sutton Coldfield B74 3DU Tel: 0121 353 9782 — MRCS Eng. LRCP Lond. 1952; DObst RCOG 1959. Prev: Ho. Surg. Birm. Matern. Hosp.

FOSTER, John Stuart Manor Surgery, Forth Noweth, Redruth TR15 1AU Tel: 01209 313313; 5 Falmouth Road, Truro TR1 2BL Tel: 01872 261106 — MB ChB 1985 Leic.; BSc Lond. 1979; MRCGP 1993.

FOSTER, Jonathan Charles 4 Lindisfarne Road, Jesmond, Newcastle upon Tyne NE2 2HE — MB ChB 1987 Leeds.

FOSTER, Judith 14 Airthrey Avenue, Glasgow G14 9JR Tel: 0141 959 5207 — MB BChir 1976 Camb.; MA Camb. 1977, MB BChir 1976; FRCS Glas. 1982. Clin. Asst. (A & E) Roy. Infirm. Glas.; Clin. Asst. (A & E) S.ern Gen. Hosp. Glas.

FOSTER, Judith Anne The Orchard, Egloshayle, Wadebridge PL27 6HW — MB ChB 1994 Leeds.

FOSTER, Julie Elizabeth Orchard Surgery, New Road, Melbourn, Royston SG8 6BX Tel: 01763 260220 Fax: 01763 262968;

Ambleside Cottage, 5 Moat Lane, Melbourn, Royston SG8 6EH Tel: 01763 263070 — MB BS 1984 Lond.; MRCGP 1988; DRCOG 1986. Prev: GP Gt. Yarmouth; Trainee GP Gt. Yarmouth VTS; Clin. Med. Off. (Child Health) Gt. Yarmouth.

FOSTER, Justine Elizabeth Longlevens Surgery, 19b Church Road, Longlevens, Gloucester GL2 0AJ Tel: 01452 522695 Fax: 01452 525547; Redbrook House, Lower Farm, Tibberton, Gloucester GL19 3AQ Tel: 01452 790691 — MB BS 1977 Lond.; BSc Lond. 1974; MRCGP 1989. (Middlx. Hosp.) Prev: Med. Off. C.J.M. Hosp. Zululand; SHO (Paediat.) Glos. HA.

FOSTER, Katherine Ann Ashton 3 Bannistre Cl, St Annes, Lytham St Annes FY8 3HS — MB ChB 1997 Leic.

FOSTER, Katherine Emma 25 St Hubert's Close, Gerrards Cross SL9 7EN — BM BS 1995 Nottm.

FOSTER, Kathryn 47 The Chandlers, Leeds LS2 7EJ — MB ChB 1995 Glas.

FOSTER, Kenneth John The East Surrey Hospital, Three Arch Road, Redhill RH1 5RH Tel: 01737 768511; High Brooms, 50 Raglan Road, Reigate RH2 0DY Tel: 01737 245426 — MB BS 1971 Lond.; BSc (Hons.) Lond. 1968; DM Soton. 1979; FRCP Lond. 1993; MRCP (UK) 1973. Cons. Phys. & Endocrinol. E. Surrey HA.

FOSTER, Kirsty Jane 2 Hall Park, Heslington, York YO10 5DT — MB BS 1992 Lond.; MRCP (UK) 1996.

FOSTER, Laura Anne Northumberland Community Health, The Health Centre, Civic Precinct, Forum Way, Cramlington NE23 6QN Tel: 01670 713021 Fax: 01670 735880 — MB BS 1974 Newc.; MRCGP 1978. GP Cramlington, N.d.

FOSTER, Lindsay Margaret 8 Park Hill, Kenilworth CV8 2JG — BM BS 1978 Nottm.; MRCGP 1983.

FOSTER, Lyn Mary 76 Albert Road, Keynsham, Bristol BS31 1AD — MB ChB 1986 Liverp. Clin. Asst. (Gen. Adult Psychiat.) S.mead Hosp. Bristol. Socs: BMA.

FOSTER, Margaret Elizabeth 7 Higher Lydgate Park, Grasscroft, Saddleworth, Oldham OL4 4EF — MB BCh 1973 Wales; DCH Eng. 1975; DObst RCOG 1975. (Welsh National School of Medicine) Clin. Med. Off. (Community Child Health) Stockport Healthcare Trust. Socs: BMA; BACCH. Prev: Regist. (Paediat.) Hillingdon Hosp. Lond.; SHO (Med.) Roy. Free Hosp. Lond.; SHO (Paediat.) Qu. Mary's Hosp. Childr. Carshalton.

FOSTER, Mark Gregory Park Surgery, Windsor Street, Trecynon, Aberdare CF44 8LL Tel: 01685 872040 Fax: 01685 883696; Pengelli Fach Farm, Vaynor, Merthyr Tydfil CF48 2TU — MB BS 1983 Lond. Prev: SHO (O & G) N. Middlx. Hosp. Lond.; SHO (Paediat.) Sydenham Childr. Hosp. Lond.

FOSTER, Mr Michael Charles Good Hope Hospital, Sutton Coldfield B75 7RR Tel: 0121 378 2211 Fax: 0121 378 6082 Email: michael.foster@goodhot.wmids.nhs.uk; 113 Wentworth Road, Harborne, Birmingham B17 9SU Email: mikejofoster@cs.com — MB ChB 1980 Birm.; DM Nottm. 1989; FRCS (Urol.) 1992; FRCS Ed. 1984. Cons. Urol. Good Hope Hosp. W. Midl. Prev: Cons. Urol. Qu. Eliz. Hosp. Birm.; Regist. (Urol.) Stepping Hill Hosp. Stockport; SHO & Regist. (Surg.) & Clin. Research Fell. (Transpl.) Nottm.

FOSTER, Mr Michael Edward Penygroes House, Groes Wen, Taffs Well, Cardiff CF15 7UU — MB BCh 1977 Wales; MChir Camb. 1985, MA 1978, BChir 1977; FRCS Eng. 1981. p/t Cons. Gen. Surg.Roy. Glam. Hosp. Socs: Assn. Surg. & Soc. Minimally Invasive Surg. Prev: Sen. Regist. Univ. Hosp. Wales.

FOSTER, Mr Murray Egerton Department Oral & Maxillofacial Surgery, North Manchester General Hospital, Crumpsall, Manchester M8 5RB Tel: 0161 795 4567 — MB BCh 1973 Wales; MScD 1979, BDS 1968; FRCS Ed. 1985; FFD RCSI 1979; FDS RCS Eng. 1975. Cons. Oral & Maxillofacial Surg. Postgrad. Hosp. Tutor N. W.. RHA. Socs: Fell. Brit. Assn. Oral & Maxillofacial Surg.; BMA. Prev: Sen. Regist. St. Geo. Hosp. Gp. Lond.; Regist. E.man Dent. Hosp. Lond.; Ho. Off. (Oral Surg.) Cardiff Roy. Infirm.

FOSTER, Nicholas James 166 Low Road, Halton, Lancaster LA2 6NU — MB ChB 1998 Leeds.

FOSTER, Nicholas John The Surgery, 34 Teme Street, Tenbury Wells WR15 8AA Tel: 01584 810343 Fax: 01584 819734; Little Oaks Cottage, Hope Bagot, Ludlow SY8 3AE Tel: 01584 891092 — BMedSci Nottm. 1980, MB BS 1982; MRCGP 1987; DCH RCP Lond. 1986. (Nottingham) Prev: Trainee GP Bishops Castle.

FOSTER, Nicholas John Orchard Surgery, The Dragwell, Kegworth, Derby DE74 2EL Tel: 01509 672419 Fax: 01509 674196; The Lodge, Lockington, Derby DE74 2RH Tel: 01509 673359 — MB ChB Sheff. l984, BDS 1978; MRCGP 1987; DCH RCP Lond. 1987; DRCOG 1987. Prev: Trainee GP Nottm. VTS.

FOSTER, Norah May Esson (retired) Cranmore, 15 Cathay Terrace, Cullen, Buckie AB56 4RX — MB ChB 1929 Aberd. Prev: Serv. (Leeds Region).

FOSTER, Oliver James Francis St George's Hospital, St George's Healthcare, Blackshaw Road, London SW17 0QT Tel: 020 8672 1255 — MB BS 1983 Lond.; PhD Lond. 1992; FRCP (UK) 1999; BA Oxf. 1980. (Oxford & Middlesex) Cons. Neurol. & Hon. Sen. Lect. St Geo.'s Hosp. Lond.; Hon. Sen. Lect. Neurol. Nat. Hosp. Lond.; Hon. Cons. Neurol. Roy. Marsden Hosp. Lond. Socs: Fell.Roy. Soc. Med.; Chairm. (Sec.) Clin. Autonomic Research Soc.; Soc. for Neurosci. Prev: Lect. & Sen. Regist. Nat. Hosp. (Neurol. & Neurosurg.) Univ. Coll. Hosps. Lond.; Regist. Nat. Hosp. Neurol. & Neurosurg. Qu. Sq. Lond.; Research Fell. & Hon. Regist. Char. Cross & W.m. Med. Sch. Lond.

FOSTER, Paul Bentham Fore Street Surgery, Fore Street, St Dennis, St Austell PL26 8AG Tel: 01726 822254 — MB ChB 1974 Birm.

FOSTER, Mr Paul James Singapore National Eye Centre, 11 Third Hospital Avenue, Singapore 168751, Singapore Tel: 00 65 2277255 Fax: 00 65 2277290 Email: snecpf@pacific.net.sg; 6 Christmas Lane, High Halstow, Rochester ME3 8SN Tel: 01634 250597 — BM BS 1989 Nottm.; BMedSci Nottm. 1987; FRCS Ed. 1994. (Nottm.) Clin. Research Fell. (Preven. Ophth.) Inst. Ophth. Lond.; Regist. (Ophth.) Singapore Nat. Eye Centre. Socs: Assn. Research in Vision & Ophth.; Internat. Soc. Geogr. & Epidemiological Ophth. Prev: SHO (Ophth.) Oxf. Eye Hosp.; SHO (Ophth.) Roy. Berks. Hosp. Reading; SHO (Ophth.) N.ampton Gen. Hosp.

FOSTER, Paul Michael Myrie Ground Floor, 179 Hemingford Road, London N1 1DA — MB BS 1978 Lond.; BSc (Pharmacol.) Lond. 1975, MB BS 1978; MRCGP 1984; MFHom 1980; DRCOG 1981. Socs: Brit. Holistic Med. Assn.

FOSTER, Paul Nicholas INF, PO Box 1230, Kathmandu, Nepal Email: pfoster@info.org.np; c/o 61 Highfield Road, Lymm WA13 0DT — MB ChB 1987 Manch.; BSc (Med. Sci.) St. And. 1984; FRCA 1994. Baptist Miss. Soc. W.. Reg. Hosp. Pokhara, Nepal. Prev: Sen. Regist. (Anaesth.) NW RHA.

FOSTER, Penelope Jane Madeley Lodge, Hemingford Grey, Huntingdon PE28 9DF — MB ChB 1972 Birm.; DRCOG 1974. Clin. Med. Off. Huntingdon HA.

FOSTER, Peter Alexander Henry McConnell (retired) 33 Osborne Drive, Belfast BT9 6LH Tel: 028 9038 1862 — MB BCh BAO 1942 Belf.; MD Belf. 1947. Prev: Sen. Med. Off. DHSS N. Irel.

FOSTER, Peter Nigel Macclesfield District General Hospital, Macclesfield SK10 3BL Tel: 01625 421000; 47 Barracks Lane, Macclesfield SK10 1QJ — BM BCh 1977 Oxf.; PhD Leeds 1991; MA Oxf. 1978, BM BCh 1977; MRCP (UK) 1980; FRCP 1997. (Oxf. & St. Ths.) Cons. Phys. Macclesfield Dist. Gen. Hosp. Socs: Brit. Soc. Gastroenterol. Prev: Sen. Regist. (Med. & Gastroenterol.) Yorks. RHA; Regist. (Med.) Univ. Hosp. Nottm. & N. Staffs. Hosp. Centre Stoke-on-Trent.

FOSTER, Philip Andrew 198 Roden Street, Belfast BT12 5QE — MB BCh 1998 Belf.; MB BCh Belf 1998.

FOSTER, Phillip Crown House Surgery, Chapelgate, Retford DN22 6NX Tel: 01777 703672 Fax: 01777 710534 — MB BS 1972 Lond.; MRCS Eng. LRCP Lond. 1972; MRCGP 1978. (St. Bart.) Med. Off. Bassetlaw Hospice. Prev: Med. Off. RAF Hereford; Ho. Surg. St. Bart. Hosp. Lond.

FOSTER, Raymond Nigel 37 Shiphay Lane, Torquay TQ2 7DU — MB ChB 1978 Manch.; BSc. Hons. (Med. Sci.) St. And. 1975; MRCGP 1983; DRCOG 1982; DA Lond. 1980.

FOSTER, Richard John The Surgery, 94 High St., Wootton Bridge, Ryde PO33 4PR — BM 1986 Soton.; MRCGP 1991.

FOSTER, Mr Richard Philip (retired) The Manor House, Church Close, Lydeard St Lawrence, Taunton TA4 3SF Tel: 01984 667207 Fax: 01984 667598 — MB BS 1962 Lond.; FRCS Eng. 1968; MRCS Eng. LRCP Lond. 1963. Cons. Orthop. Surg. Taunton & Som. Hosp. Prev: Sen. Orthop. Regist. St. Thos. Hosp. Lond. & Hants. AHA (T).

FOSTER, Robert Marius, RD, Surg. Lt.-Cdr. (retired) Bellfield House, The Street, North Lopham, Diss IP22 2LR — MB ChB 1946 Ed.; FRCP Ed. 1969, M 1954. Clin. Teach. (Med.) Univ. Soton. Prev: Cons. Phys. St. Mary's Hosp. Newport I. of Wight.

FOSTER, Robert Walter (retired) — MB BS Lond. 1963; PhD Lond. 1963, BSc 1958. Prev: Reader (Pharmacol.) Univ. Manch.

FOSTER, Robin — BM BCh 1964 Oxf.; BSc Oxf. 1964, MA 1964. (Oxf.) GP Tutor Univ. Oxf.; Police Surg. Thames Valley Police; Med. Adviser, Thames Valley Police. Socs: Provin. Fell. Roy. Soc. Med; Soc. Med. & Dent. Hypn. Prev: Regist. (Med.) Roy. Hosp. Sheff.; SHO (Med.) Roy. Marsden Hosp. Lond.; Ho. Surg. (ENT) & Ho. Phys. Radcliffe Infirm. Oxf.

FOSTER, Robin Nigel 40 Banastre Drive, Newton-le-Willows WA12 8BE — MB ChB 1987 Dundee; FRCA 1994. Cons. Anaesth. Wigan & Leigh NHS Trust. Prev: Sen. Regist. (Anaesth.) NW Region; Research Fell. (Anaesth.) Hope Hosp. Salford; Regist. (Anaesth.) Stoke on Trent.

FOSTER, Sabeena 94 Highfield Road, Ipswich IP1 6DJ — MB BS 1993 Lond.; DRCOG 1997; DFFP 1998. (King's College School of Medicine and Dentistry) SHO (Gen. Med.) Norf. & Norwich Hosp.; GP VTS Ipswich Hosp. Prev: GP VTS Norwich Hosp.; SHO (A & E) & Ho. Off.(Gen. Surg.) Mayday Hosp.; Ho. Off. (Gen. Med.) King's Coll. Hosp.

FOSTER, Sally 35 Crosby Road, Northallerton DL6 1AA Tel: 01609 779772 — MB ChB 1994 Leeds; BSc (Hons.) Leeds 1992. (Leeds) SHO (Psych. In Learning Disabilities), Bootham Pk. Hosp., York. Prev: SHO (Psych. In older People), Cl. La. Hosp., ScarBoro.; SHO (Gen. Psych.) St. Mary's Hosp., ScarBoro.; Regist. (Psych.) Cambell Town Hosp., New S. Wales.

FOSTER, Samantha 29A Belsize Park Gardens, London NW3 4JH — MB BS 1992 Lond.

FOSTER, Sarah Elizabeth 12 Hayfield Park, New Buildings, Londonderry BT47 2PY Email: sarahfoster@hotmail.com — MB BS 1998 Newc.; MB BS Newc 1998. (Newcastle upon Tyne) SHO (Med.), N. Tees Gen. Hosp., Stockton-on-Tees. Socs: BMA; MSS; MPS. Prev: Ho. Off. (Med.), N. Tees Gen. Hosp., Stockton-on-Tees; Ho. Off. (Surgic.), N. Tees Gen. Hosp., Stockton-on-Tees.

FOSTER, Sarah Frances 32 Prospect Drive, Hest Bank, Lancaster LA2 6HZ — MB BS 1989 Lond.

FOSTER, Sarah Jane 55 North Way, Seaford BN25 3HP — MB ChB 1998 Bristol.

FOSTER, Simon Charles Orchard Barn, Plex Lane, Halsall, Ormskirk L39 7JZ Tel: 01704 840965 — MB ChB 1991 Manch.; MRCFP 1995; DFFP 1994; DCH RCP Lond. 1994; DRCOG 1994; DPD 1999. (Manchester) GP Princip. Clin. Asst. in Dermat.

FOSTER, Stephen John — MB BS 1984 Lond.; BSc Lond. 1981; FFARCS Eng. 1988; DA (UK) 1986. (St. Bart.) Cons. Anaesth. N. Staffs. Hosp. NHS Trust. Socs: Assn. Anaesth. Gt. Brit. & Irel.; Assn. Cardiothoracic Anaesth.; Midl. Soc. Anaesth. Prev: Sen. Regist. (Anaesth.) Midl. Anaesth. Train. Scheme; Regist. (Anaesth.) BRd.green & Roy. Liverp. Hosps.; Regist. (Anaesth.) Manch. Roy. Infirm. & N. Manch. Gen. Hosp.

FOSTER, Stuart Richard Chealltainn, Dervaig, Tobermory, Isle of Mull PA75 6QJ Tel: 01688 400338 — MB BChir 1963 Camb.; MB Camb. 1963, BChir 1962; MA Camb. 1963; DIH Soc. Apoth. Lond. 1978; DObst RCOG 1966. (St. Mary's) Phys. (Occupat. Health). Socs: Soc. Occupat. Health.

FOSTER, Susan Little Oaks Cottage, Hope Bagot, Ludlow SY8 3AE Tel: 01584 891092 — MB BS 1982 Nottm.; BMedSci Nottm. 1980, MB BS 1982. GP Asst. Retainer Scheme Tenbury Wells. Prev: Trainee GP Mansfield VTS.

FOSTER, Susan Joan Public Health Services, Le Bas Centre, St Saviours Road, St Helier, Jersey JE1 4HR Tel: 01534 789933; La Conchiere, Le Clos de la Tour, La Rocque, Grouville JE3 9BX — MB BS 1969 Lond.; Cert. Family Plann. JCC 1970. (St. Geo.) SCMO Jersey Pub. Health Servs. Socs: BMA; Fac. Fam. Plann. Prev: Clin. Med. Off. Berks. & Surrey HAs; Ho. Phys. & Ho. Surg. Cheltenham Gen. Hosp.

FOSTER, Teresa Agnes The Health Centre, PO Box 101(a), The Health Centre, 20 Cleveland Square, Middlesbrough TS1 2NX Tel: 01642 242192 Fax: 01642 231809; 25 Worsley Crescent, Marton, Middlesbrough TS7 8LU Tel: 01642 310723 — MB ChB 1975 Dundee; DCH Eng. 1977; MRCGP 1980.

FOSTER, Thomas John Tel: 028 82 255149 Fax: 028 82 240138 — MB BCh BAO 1983 Belf.; BSc (Hons.) Physiol. Belf. 1980; MRCPsych 1990; MD Belf. 1997. (Queen's University Belfast) Cons. Gen. Adult Psychiat. Tyrone & Fermanagh Hosp. Omagh. Prev: Sen. Regist. Maudsley Hosp. Lond.

FOSTER, Timothy Robert The Surgery, St Andrews Hall, Guildersfield Road, London SW16 5LS Tel: 020 8765 4901 — MB BS 1981 Lond.; MRCGP 1986; DRCOG 1983.

FOSTER, Victoria Joyce 18 Rocky Lane, Heswall, Wirral CH60 0BZ — MB ChB 1995 Sheff.

FOSTER, William Bygrove House, 18 Collingwood Road, Witham CM8 2DZ Tel: 01376 513187 — MB BS 1940 Durh. (Newc. upon Tyne) Obst. & Gyn. Socs: Chelmsford & Colchester Med. Soc. & Internat. Soc. Psychosomatic. Prev: Ho. Surg. & Res. Anaesth. Roy. Vict. Infirm. Newc.; Res. Surg. Off. N. Ormesby Hosp. Middlesbrough; Capt. RAMC.

FOSTER, William Francis 4 Laurelbank, Comber, Newtownards BT23 5EJ — MB BCh BAO 1968 Belf.; FFR 1974; DMRD Eng. 1973; DRCOG 1970. Cons. Radiol. Ulster Hosp. & Dundonald & Ards Hosp. Newtownards.

FOSTER, William Hugh Saintbridge Surgery, Askwith Road, Saintbridge, Gloucester GL4 4SH Tel: 01452 500252 — MB BS 1977 Lond.; MRCGP 1985; DA Eng. 1983. (Middlx. Hosp.) Course Organiser Glos. VTS. Prev: Med. Superintend. C.J.M. Hosp. Zululand.

FOSTER, William Peter (retired) 421 Topsham Road, Countess Weir, Exeter EX2 7AB — MB ChB 1944 Bristol; MRCS Eng. LRCP Lond. 1945; DCH Eng. 1950. Prev: Ho. Phys. Roy. Infirm. Bristol.

FOSTER-SMITH, Valerie Upton (retired) 3 Hall Close, Maids Moreton, Buckingham MK18 1RH Tel: 01280 815110 — MB ChB 1965 Liverp.

FOSTER-THOMPSON, Foster (retired) 1 Clarendon Crescent, Leamington Spa CV32 5NR Tel: 01926 335487 Email: drfoster@cwcom.net — MB BS 1954 Durham; MRCP 1964 Edinburgh; FRCP 2000 Edinburgh. Aviat. Med. Examr. Dept. Transport, Canada; Sen. Aviat. Med. Examr. Fed. Aviat., USA; Authorised Med. Off. Civil Aviat. Auth. Prev: Cons. Gen. Phys. (Cardiol.) Coventry HA.

FOTHERBY, Kenneth John New Cross Hospital, Wolverhampton WV10 0QP Tel: 01902 307999 — MB BChir 1980 Camb.; MB Camb. 1980, BChir 1979; FRCP 1998. Cons. Phys. New Cross Hosp. Wolverhampton.

FOTHERBY, Martin David Glenfield General Hospital, Leicester LE3 9QP Tel: 0116 287 1471 Fax: 0116 232 2976 — MB ChB 1982 Leic.; MD Leic. 1995; BSc Lancaster 1977; MRCP (UK) 1988; FRCP 1999. (Univ. of Leicester) Sen. Lect. (Med. for the Elderly) Univ. Leicester; Hon. Cons. Phys. Glenfield Hosp. Leicester. Socs: Brit. Hypertens. Soc. & Med. Research Soc.; Brit. Geriat. Soc. Prev: Sen. Regist. (Med. & Geriat. Med.) Leicester Teach. Hosps.; Regist. Research Fell. Leicester Gen. Hosp.

FOTHERGILL, Diana Jane The Jessop Wing, Three Rootwark, Sheffield S10 2SF Tel: 0114 226 8166 — MB ChB 1979 Ed.; FRCOG 2000; 1976 (Hons.) BSc Med Sci 1976; MRCOG 1984. Prev: Cons. O & G Chesterfield & N. Derbysh. Roy. Hosp.; Sen. Regist. (O & G) N.. Gen. Hosp.; Research Regist. IVF Unit St. Mary's Hosp. Manch.

FOTHERGILL, Gavin 9 Helmdon Rise, Torquay TQ2 7SA — MB ChB 1981 Bristol; DRCOG 1988; DA (UK) 1986.

FOTHERGILL, Nicola Jane Accident and Emergency Dept, St. John's Hospital, Howden Rd West, Livingston EH54 6PP Tel: 01500 419666 Email: jane.fothergill@wlt.scot.nhs.uk — MB ChB 1980 Bristol; MRCP (UK) 1984; FRCS Ed. 1990; FFAEM 1993; FRCP 1995. (Bristol) Cons. A & E Med. St. John's Hosp. Lond. Socs: Hn. Sec. of Jt. Comm. on higher Train. in Accid. and Emerg. Med., Fac. of A & E Med. Prev: Sen. Regist. Rotat. (A & E) SW Thames RHA.; Cons. Accid. and Emerg. Med., St Mary's Hosp, Lond.

FOTHERGILL, Susan Margaret Leighton Road Surgery, 1 Leighton Road, Linslade, Leighton Buzzard LU7 1LB Tel: 01525 372571 Fax: 01525 850414; 12 Mount Pleasant, Stoke Hammond, Milton Keynes MK17 9EX — MB ChB 1986 Manch.; MRCGP 1991. (Manch.)

FOTHERINGHAM, Mr Timothy Middlesex Hospital, Mortimer St., London W1T 3AA Tel: 020 7636 8333; 35 Mervan Road, Brixton, London SW2 1DR Tel: 020 7274 5027 — MB BS 1989 Lond.; FRCS Eng. 1993. Regist. (Radiol.) Middlx. Hosp. Lond. Prev: SHO (Gen. Surg.) E. Surrey Hosp. Redhill.

FOTIADIS, Richard John 20 Melrose Gardens, London W6 7RW — MB BS 1996 Lond.

FOTIADOU, Maria St Thomas' Hospital, London SE1 7EH Tel: 020 7928 9292 — Ptychio Iatrikes 1986 Thessalonika; MRCPsych 1992. Sen. Regist. (Psychiat.) St. Thos. Hosp. Lond.

FOTTRELL, Edward Michael Elizabeth Ward, St Thomas Hospital, London SE1; 2 Steep Hill, Streatham, London SW16 1UL Tel: 020 8769 7275 — MB BCh BAO NUI 1964; MD 1980; FRCPsych 1988, M 1972; DPM Eng. 1968. (Cork) Cons. Psychiat. Lambeth Community Care NHS Trust; Cons. Psychogeriat. St. Thos. Hosp. Lond.; Clin. Dir. Elderly Ment. Health Servs. Lambeth Community Care NHS Trust; Recognised Univ. Teach. (Psychiat.) Univ. Lond. & United Med. & Dent. Sch. Guy's & St. Thos. Hosps. Prev: Psychiat. Tutor Tooting Bec Hosp. Lond.; Med. Admin. Tooting Bec Hosp.; Sen. Regist. (Psychol. Med.) St. Thos. Hosp. Lond.

FOUAD, Abdalla Abdel Mageed Mohamed 27 Old Bothwell Road, Bothwell, Glasgow G71 8AP — MB BCh 1980 Cairo.

FOUBISTER, Glenn (retired) 3 Farley Court, Church Road, Farley Hill, Reading RG7 1TT — MB ChB 1959 Aberd.; FRCP Lond. 1994; FRCP Ed. 1986, M 1967. Cons. Phys. Geriat. Med. Roy. Berks. & Battle Hosps. NHS Trust. Prev: Sen. Regist. (Geriat. Med.) United Camb. Hosps. & E. Anglian RHB.

FOUBISTER, Mr Graeme Craigie Department of Orthopaedic Surgery, Ninewells Hospital and Medical School, Dundee DD1 9SY Tel: 01382 660111; Newton Bank, Abernyte, Perth PH14 9SY Tel: 01828 686584 — MB ChB 1980 Ed.; FRCS (Orth.) Ed 1993; FRCS Ed. 1985. Cons. Trauma & Orthop. Surg. Dundee Roy. Infirm. Prev: Sen. Regist. (Orthop. Surg.) St. Jas. Univ. Hosp. Leeds; Regist. (Orthop. Surg.) Roy. Infirm. Edin. & P.ss Margt. Rose Orthop. Hosp.; Regist. Rotat. (Surg.) Roy. Infirm. Edin.

FOUBISTER, William John Thornbury Health Centre, Eastland Road, Thornbury, Bristol BS35 1DP Tel: 01454 412599 Fax: 01454 41911; Howard House, Lowerstone, Berkeley GL13 9DJ — MB ChB 1985 Aberd.; MRCGP 1991; DRCOG 1990; T(GP) 1991. (Aberdeen) Socs: BMA. Prev: SHO (Paediat.) S.end Gen. Hosp.; SHO (O & G) Harold Wood Hosp. Essex; Trainee GP Dartmouth, Devon.

FOUIN, Francois Louis Pierre (retired) 147 North Deeside Road, Milltimber AB13 0JS Tel: 01224 868912 — MB ChB 1954 Aberd.; FRCGP 1978, M 1965; DObst RCOG 1958.

FOULDS, Angela Mary Josephine Trent Bridge Family Medical Practice, 28A Henry Road, West Bridgford, Nottingham NG2 7NA Tel: 0115 914 6600 — MB BS 1975 Lond.; MRCS Eng. LRCP Lond. 1975.

FOULDS, Geoffrey Eric Ashby Health Centre, North St., Ashby-de-la-Zouch, Leicester; Strawberry Hill, Kilwardby St, Ashby-De-La-Zouch, Leicester LE65 2FQ — MB ChB 1975 Birm.; MRCGP 1980; DCH Eng. 1978; DRCOG 1977. GP Ashby-de-la-Zouch. Prev: Trainee GP Leicester VTS; Ho. Phys. & Ho. Surg. Kidderminster Gen. Hosp.

FOULDS, Iain Stewart The Birmingham Skin Centre, City Hospital NHS Trust, Dudley Road, Birmingham B18 7QH Tel: 0121 507 6625 Fax: 0121 507 6644; The Shrubbery, Hartlebury, Worcester DY11 7YA Tel: 01299 250930 — MB ChB 1974 Glas.; MB ChB (Commend.) Glas. 1974; FRCP Lond. 1994; MRCP (UK) 1977; MFOM RCP Lond. 1987. Cons. Dermat. The Birm. Skin Centre & Good Hope Hosp. Sutton Coldfield; Sen. Lect. (Occupat. Dermat.) Inst. Occupat. Health Univ. Birm. Prev: Sen. Regist. (Dermat.) Hallamsh. Hosp. Sheff.

FOULDS, John Witham (retired) 7 Wellgarth Court, North Bitchburn, Crook DL15 8EL Tel: 01388 768799 — MA, MB BChir Camb. 1963; FRCOG 1981, M 1968. Prev: Consult. (O & G) Bishop Auckland Gen. Hosp.

FOULDS, Malcolm Sydenham House Surgery, Boulevard, Hull HU3 2TA Tel: 01482 326818 Fax: 01482 218267 — MB ChB 1981 Sheff.

FOULDS, Nicola Clare Department Clinical Genetics, St Georges Healthcare NHS Trust, Blackshaw Road, Tooting, London SW17 0QT; Breezes, Marley Common, Haslemere GU27 3PT Tel: 01428 661552 — MB ChB 1993 Bristol; PhD Camb. 1986; BSc (Biochem. with Pharmacol.) Soton. 1983; MRCP (Paediat.) 1997. Clin. Regist. (Genetics). Prev: SHO (Paediat. Surg.) Soton. Gen. Hosp.; SHO (Paediat. Cardiol.) Soton. Gen. Hosp.; SHO (Paediat.) St. Mary's Hosp. Portsmouth.

FOULDS, Richard Arthur Healthlink Consulting Ltd, 100 Main St, Willoughby on the Wolds, Loughborough LE12 6SZ Tel: 01509 881121 — MB BS 1975 Lond.; FRCP Lond. 1994; MRCP (UK) 1977; FFPM RCP (UK) 1997. (St. George's Hospital) Managing Dir. & Princip. Cons., Healthlink Consg. Ltd. Prev: Med. Dir., Smithkline Beecham Pharmaceut.

FOULDS, Professor Wallace Stewart, CBE Kinnoul Place, 68 Dowanside Road, Glasgow G12 9DL Tel: 0141 334 2463 Fax: 0141 357 4297 Email: wallace@wsfoulds.demon.co.uk; Kinnoul Place, 68 Dowanside Road, Glasgow G12 9DL Tel: 0141 334 2463 Fax: 0141 357 4297 Email: wallace@wsfoulds.demon.co.uk — MB ChB Glas. 1946; DO Eng. 1952; ChM (Hons.) Glas. 1964, MD (Commend.) 1958; Hon DSc Strathclyde 1991; FRCS Glas. 1976; FRCS Eng. 1953; Hon. FRCOphth. 1992; Hon. FCSSA 1992; Hon. FRACO 1988; FCOphth 1988. (Glas.) Cons. Ophth. Glas. Edin. Lond.; Emerit. Prof. Ophth. Univ. Glas.; Vis. Prof. Nat. Univ., Singapore; Co-director Singapore Eye Research Inst.; Hon. Fell. Med. & Dent. Defence Union of Scotl. Socs: Hon. Fell. Roy. Soc. Med.; Mem. Amer. Acad. Ophth.; Mem. Macula Soc. Prev: Tennent Prof. Ophth. Univ. Glas. 1964; Cons. Ophth. United Camb. Hosps. & E. Anglian RHB; Research Fell. Inst. of Ophth. Univ. Lond.

FOULGER, Veronique Anne Louise Moatfield Surgery, St. Michaels Road, East Grinstead RH19 3GW Tel: 01342 327555 Fax: 01342 316240; 12 Maypole Road, Ashurst Wood, East Grinstead RH19 3QN — MB BS 1981 Lond.

FOULIS, Alan Keith Department of Pathology, Royal Infirmary, Glasgow G4 0SF Tel: 0141 211 4224 Fax: 0141 211 4884 Email: a.k.foulis@clinmed.gla.ac.uk; 32 Tannoch Drive, Milngavie, Glasgow G62 8AS Tel: 0141 956 3092 — MB ChB 1974 Glas.; MB ChB (Commend.) Glas. 1974; MD (Hons.) & Bellahouston Medal Glas. 1987, BSc (1st cl. Hons. Path.) 1972; FRCP Ed. 1995; MRCPath 1982. Cons. Path. Roy. Infirm. Glas. Prev: Lect. (Path.) W.. Infirm. Glas.

FOULIS, Keith (retired) 9 Orchard Avenue, Bothwell, Glasgow G71 8NF — MB ChB 1940 Glas.

FOULKES, Alun Lloyd Llwyn Brwydrau Surgery, 3 Frederick Place, Llansamlet, Swansea SA7 9RY Tel: 01792 771465 — MB BCh 1972 Wales.

FOULKES, Mr Andrew Yew Tree Surgery, Yew Tree House, North End Road, Yapton, Arundel BN18 0DU Tel: 01243 551321 Fax: 01243 555101 — MB ChB 1980 Bristol; MB ChB (Hons.) Bristol 1980; BSc Bristol 1977; FRCS Ed. 1985; MRCOG 1987, D 1986; MRCGP 1987. Socs: BMA. Prev: SHO (O & G) Bristol Matern. Hosp.; SHO (O & G) John Radcliffe Hosp. Oxf.; SHO (Surg.) Leicester Roy. Infirm.

FOULKES, Mr John Edward Broster Mount Stuart Hospital, St Vincents Road, Torquay TQ1 4UP Tel: 01803 313881 Fax: 01803 311498 — MB BS 1967 Lond.; FRCS Ed. 1972; MRCS Eng. LRCP Lond. 1967; FRCOG 1991, M 1974; DObst RCOG 1969. (St. Bart.) Cons. O & G S. Devon Health Care Trust. Prev: Sen. Regist. SW Region Bristol; Regist. W.m. Hosp. Lond.; RMO Qu. Charlottes & Chelsea Hosps.

FOULKES, Jonathan Hugh Giles Tel: 01202 523059 Fax: 01202 533239 — BM 1979 Soton.; MRCGP 1986; DRCOG 1983.

FOULKES, Krystyna Karla 18 Amesbury Avenue, Scartho, Grimsby DN33 3HT — State Exam Med 1994 Mainz.

FOULKES, Sally Jane 13 Foxhills Road, Penn, Wolverhampton WV4 4SS — BM 1979 Soton.

FOUND, Sarah Margaret Parkside Group Practice, 27 Wyche Grove, South Croydon CR2 6EX Tel: 020 8680 2588 Fax: 020 8680 1415; 23 Verulam Avenue, Purley CR8 3NR Tel: 020 8660 8877 — MB BS 1975 Lond.; MRCS Eng. LRCP Lond. 1975; MRCGP 1979. (Roy. Free) Prev: GP Newbury Pk. Health Centre Ilford; Ho. Phys. St. And. Hosp. Lond.; Ho. Surg. Roy. Free Hosp. Lond.

FOUNTAIN, Andrew Neil 12 Cromwell Road, Bramhall, Stockport SK7 1DA Tel: 0161 439 8528 — MB BS 1994 Lond.; BSc Experim Path. Lond. 1991. SHO Rotat. (Med.) Roy. United Hosp. Bath.

FOUNTAIN, Arthur Bernard (retired) 1 Stocks Mead, Washington, Pulborough RH20 4AU — MRCS Eng. LRCP Lond. 1938. Prev: Lt.-Col. RAMC, Comm. Med. Off. Libya.

FOUNTAIN, Diana Mary (retired) 36 Oaklands, Somerford Road, Cirencester GL7 1FA — MB BChir 1962 Camb.; FRCPsych 1993, M 1979. Prev: Cons. Psychiat. Swindon Health Dist.

FOUNTAIN, Frances Mary (retired) 24 Victoria Avenue, Harrogate HG1 5PR Tel: 01423 560721 — MB BChir Camb. 1946; MRCS Eng. LRCP Lond. 1946; FRCOG 1976, M 1957. Prev: Cons. O & G Harrogate & Ripon Gp. Hosps.

FOUNTAIN, Margaret Averil Marie Curie Centre, Speke Road, Liverpool L25 8QA; 4 Hamilton Street, Hoole, Chester CH2 3JG — MB BS 1985 Lond.; MRCGP 1993; DRCOG 1991. (St. Bart. Hosp. Med. Coll.) Sen. Regist. Palliat. Med. Marie Curie Centre Liverp. Prev: Sen. Regist (Palliat. Med.), St.John's Hospice-in-Wirral, Bebington, Wirral; Sen. Regist. (Palliat. Med.) Nightingale Macmillan Continuing Care Unit Derbysh. Roy. Infirm.

FOUNTAIN, Mr Saunders William Great Poplars, Rasehill Close, Chorleywood Road, Rickmansworth WD3 4EW — MB ChB 1970 Glas.; FRCS Eng. 1975; T(S) 1991. Cons. Thoracic Surg. Harefield Hosp. Lond. Socs: Soc. Thoracic & Cardiovasc. Surgs.; Brit. Thoracic Soc. Prev: Sen. Regist. Cardiothoracic Surg. Roy. Infirm. Edin.; Cardiothoracic Surg. Regist. Harefield Hosp.; Resid., Glas. Roy. Infirm.

FOUNTAIN, Mr Shaun Arthur Salisbury District Hospital, Salisbury SP2 8BJ Tel: 01722 336262 Fax: 01722 325373; Dovecote House, 155 Lower Road, Salisbury SP2 9NJ Tel: 01722 412776 — MB ChB 1984 Leic.; FRCOG 2001; BSc (Hons.) Leic. 1981; MRCOG 1989. Cons. O & G Salisbury Dist. Hosp. Socs: ESHRE; Amer. Soc. Reproduc. Med.; Brit. Fertil. Soc. Prev: Sen. Regist. (O & G) Norf. & Norwich Hosp.; Research Fell. (Reproduc. Med.) Rosie Matern. Hosp. Camb. & Bourn Hall Clinic Camb.; Regist. (Obst. Gyn.) Hammersmith Hosp. Lond.

FOUQUE, Claire Anne 89 Woodmansterne Road, Carshalton SM5 4JW — MB BS 1992 Lond. SHO (Anaesth.) Torbay Hosp. Torquay.

FOURACRE, Anthony John (retired) Anchorage, Victoria Avenue, Withernsea HU19 2LH Tel: 01964 613929 — MRCS Eng. LRCP Lond. 1946; FRCGP 1980. Prev: Med. Off. Withernsea Hosp.

FOURACRE, Robert Daniel St Nicholas Surgery, Queen Street, Withernsea HU19 2PZ Tel: 01964 613221 Fax: 01964 613960; 377 Queen Street, Withernsea HU19 2NZ Tel: 0196 422209 — MB BS 1976 Lond.; MRCS Eng. LRCP Lond. 1976; MRCGP 1980. (Char. Cross) Prev: Ho. Phys. Char. Cross. Hosp.; Ho. Surg. Hemel Hempstead Gen. Hosp. Trainee Gen. Pract. Boston; Vocational Train. Scheme.

FOURACRES, Mr Michael 25 Bolleynwood Court, Lacey Green, Wilmslow SK9 4DA Tel: 01625 535963 — MB ChB 1971 Bristol; FRCS Ed. 1976; FRCOG 1992,M 1978. Cons. O & G Wythenshawe Hosp. Manch. Prev: Lect. Univ. Manch. St. Mary's Hosp.

FOURIE, Hannelie 19 Hayles Street, London SE11 4SU — MB ChB 1985 Pretoria.

FOURIE, Paul Gerard Leak, Gunn, Fourie, Brennan and Roberts, Witton Medical Centre, 29-31 Preston Old Road, Blackburn BB2 2SU Tel: 01254 262123 Fax: 01254 695759 — MB BS 1993 Newc.; DRCOG 1997; MRCGP 1998. (Newcastle) GP Princip.; GP Regist. Hull. Prev: SHO (A & E) Hull Roy. Infirm.; GP Regist. Willerby Rd. Hull; SHO (O & G) Hull Roy. Infirm.

FOUYAS, Mr Ioannis Department of Clinical Neurosciences, Western General Hospital, Edinburgh EH4 2XU Tel: 0131 537 1000 Fax: 0131 537 2561 Email: if@skull.dcn.ed.ac.uk; Flat 27, 2 Hill Place, Edinburgh EH8 9DS — Ptychio Iatrikes 1988 Athens; FRCS Ed. 1992. (Athens Med. Sch., Greece) Acad. Research Fell. (Clin. Neurosci.) W.. Gen. Hosp. Edin.; Regist. (Neurosurg.) W.. Gen. Hosp. Edin. Prev: Regist. (Neurosurg.) Nat. Hosp. Neurol. & Neurosurg. Lond.; SHO (Gen. Surg.) King's Mill Hosp. Sutton-in-Ashfield; SHO (Plastic Surg. & Orthop.) Withington Hosp. Manch.

FOWDEN, Albert Orchard View, Cove Road, Silverdale, Carnforth LA5 0SQ — MB ChB Liverp. 1955.

FOWELL, Andrew Rhos Newydd, Llangoed, Beaumaris LL58 8PH — MB ChB 1978 Leeds.

FOWELL, Andrew James Palliative Medicine, Radcliffe-On-Trent, Bangor LL57 2PW — BM 1998 Soton.; BM Soton 1998. Cons.

FOWERAKER, Juliet Evelyn Department of Microbiology, Papworth Hospital NHS Trust, Papworth Everard, Cambridge CB3 8RE — MB BChir 1979 Camb.; MB BChir Camb, 1979; PhD Camb. 1987, MA 1980; MRCPath 1992. Cons. Microbiol. (PHLS) Papworth Hosp. NHS Trust Camb. Prev: Sen. Regist. Leicester Pub. Health Laborat.; Regist. (Microbiol.) Univ. Hosp. Wales; Research Regist. (Microbiol.) Leeds W.. HA.

FOWERAKER, Karen Louise Queen's Medical Centre, University Hospital, Nottingham NG7 2UH — BM BS 1996 Nottm.; BMedSci 1994. SHO (Med.) Qu.'s Med. Centre Nottm. Prev: Med. Off. W.. Hosp. Footscray Melbourne Australia; Jun. Ho. Off. (Med.) Qu. Med. Centre Nottm.; Jun. Ho. Off. (Gen. Surg.) York Dist. Hosp.

FOWERS, David Edward Blackburn Road Medical Centre, Blackburn Road, Birstall, Batley WF17 9PL Tel: 01924 478265 — MB ChB 1983 Leeds.

FOWKE, Ruth (retired) 49 Poplar Road, Shalford, Guildford GU4 8DH — MB BCh 1957 Wales; MRCPsych 1973; DPA Exeter 1948; DPM Eng. 1964. Prev: Cons. Psychiat. InterHealth.

FOWKES, Professor Francis Gerald Reid Public Health Sciences, University of Edinburgh Medical School, Teviot Place, Edinburgh EH8 9AG Tel: 0131 650 3220 Fax: 0131 650 6904 Email: gerry.fowkes@ed.ac.uk; 2 McLaren Road, Edinburgh EH9 2BH — PhD Wales 1985; MSc (Soc. Med.) Lond. 1979; MB ChB Ed. 1970; FRCP Ed. 1988; MRCP (UK) 1974; FFPHM 1987; 1980 M; DTM & H Liverp. 1972. Prof. Epidemiol. Univ. Edin.; Dir. Wolfson Unit for Preven. of Peripheral Vasc. Dis. Univ. Edin. Prev: Sen. Lect. (Epidemiol. & Community Med.) Univ. Wales Coll. Med.; Sen. Regist. (Community Med.) Lothian HB; Lect. (Gen. Pract.) Univ. Edin.

FOWLE, Adrian J West Surrey Clinical Neurophysiology, St Peters Hospital, Guildford road, Chertsey KT16 0PZ Tel: 01932 722543 — MB BS 1985 Lond.; BSc (Hons. Physiol.) Lond. 1981; MRCP (UK). (St. Thomas) Cons. Clin. Neurophysiologist, W. Surrey Clin. NeuroPhysiol.(Ashford and St Peters Hosp.s Trust and Frimley Pk. Hosp. NHS Trust). Socs: BMA; Brit. Soc. for Clin. NeuroPhysiol. Prev: Regist. (Neurol.) Glaxo Research Fell. Brook Gen. Hosp. Lond.; Regist. (Med. & Geriat.) Bromley Hosps. NHS Trust; Research Fell. (Neurophysiol.) St. Thos. Campus UMDS Guy's & St. Thos. Hosps. Lond.

FOWLE, Arthur Sydney Edward 29 Manor Way, Beckenham BR3 3LH Tel: 020 8402 1867 Fax: 020 8402 1867 Email: arthur@towk.co.uk — MB BS 1954 Lond.; MD Lond. 1962; FRCP Lond. 1980, M 1957; MRCS Eng. LRCP Lond. 1954. (King's Coll. Hosp.) Indep. Cons. Beckenham; Practitioner, Brit. Performing Arts Med. Trust. Socs: Brit. Pharm. Soc.; Brit. Thorac. Soc. Prev: Princip. Med. Research Phys. Wellcome Foundat. Ltd.; Phys. Chest Unit Lewisham Hosp. Lond; Vis. Prof. Clin. Pharmacol. Guy's Hosp. Lond.

FOWLE, Carolyn Susan 4 Blakeney Road, Wiveton, Holt NR25 7TL Tel: 01263 740880 — MB BS 1964 Lond.; BA (Hons.) Psychol. 1987; MRCS Eng. LRCP Lond. 1964; DCH RCP Lond. 1983; Cert JCC 1981. (Middlx.)

FOWLE, Lise Lotte 29 Manor Way, Beckenham BR3 3LH Tel: 020 8402 1867 Fax: 020 8402 1867 — MB BS Lond. 1954; MRCS Eng. LRCP Lond. 1954; DCH Eng. 1958. (King's Coll. Hosp.) SCMO Lambeth Health Care NHS Trust. Socs: Fac. Community Health; Brit. Soc. Audiol.; Brit. Assn. Community Drs in Audiol. Prev: Regist. (Med.) S. Lond. Hosp. Wom. & Childr.; Ho. Phys. (Paediat.) King's Coll. Hosp.; Fell. (Paediat.) Johns Hopkins Hosp. Baltimore, USA.

FOWLER, Aidan Lewis 26 Clyde Road, Redland, Bristol BS6 6RW — MB BS 1990 Lond.

FOWLER, Mr Alan William (retired) High View, Litchard Rise, Bridgend CF31 1QJ Tel: 01656 652671 — MB BS Lond. 1943; FRCS Eng. 1947. Prev: Hon. Cons. Orthop. Surg. Mid Glam. Area.

FOWLER, Allan 143 Whitchurch Road, Chester CH3 5QE — MB ChB 1966 Liverp. (Liverp.) Prev: SHO (O & G) BRd.green Hosp.; SHO (Neurosurg.) Walton Hosp. Liverp.

FOWLER, Andrew John 2 Stetchworth Road, Woodditton, Newmarket CB8 9SP — MB ChB 1997 Leeds.

FOWLER, Andrew Vaughan 11 Gordon Avenue, Portswood, Southampton SO14 6WJ — BM 1998 Soton.; BM Soton 1998; BSc Soton 1997. SHO (Surg.), Portsmouth QA Hosp.

FOWLER, Christine Elizabeth Lillian 78 Forsyth Road, Newcastle upon Tyne NE2 3EU — MB BS 1998 Newc.; MB BS Newc 1998.

FOWLER, Christine Sharon Blue Dykes Surgery, Eldon Street, Clay Cross, Chesterfield S45 9NR Tel: 01246 862468 — BM 1988 Soton.; MRCGP 1994; DRCOG 1993; DFFP 1992. Prev: SHO (O & G & Paediat.) Chesterfield; SHO (Ophth.) Wolverhampton.

FOWLER, Mr Christopher Gordon Department Urology, The Royal London Hospital, London E1 1BB Tel: 020 7377 7327 Fax: 020 7377 8760; (cons. rooms) The London Independent Hospital, Beaumont Square, Stepney Green, London E1 4NL Tel: 020 7790 0990 Fax: 020 8749 8913 — MB BS 1974 Lond.; 1999 MA (Education); BSc Lond. 1971, MS 1997; FRCS (Urol.) Eng. 1987; FRCS Eng. 1979; FRCP Lond 1997; MRCP (UK) 1977. (Middlx.)

Reader in Surgic. Educat., Hon. Cons. Urol.; Asst. Warden for Educat. Socs: Brit. Assn. Urol. Surg. Prev: Regist. (Surg.) Roy. Free Hosp. Lond.; Regist. (Surg.) Hillingdon Hosp.; Lect. (Urol.) Lond. Hosp.

FOWLER, Mrs Clare Amanda Mow Barton, Frenchay, Bristol BS16 1LU — MB BS 1990 Lond.; FRCS Eng. 1994. (Middlx. Hosp.) Specialist Regist. (Gen. Surg.) Bristol Roy. Infirm. Prev: SHO Rotat. (Surg.) Frenchay Hosp. Bristol.

FOWLER, Professor Clare Juliet Department Uro-Neurology, National Hospital For Neurology & Neurosurgery, Queen Square, London WC1N 3BG Tel: 020 7837 3611 Fax: 020 7813 4587 Email: c.fowler@ion.ucl.ac.uk — MB BS 1973 Lond.; MB BS (Hons.) Lond. 1973; MSc Lond. 1977; FRCP Lond. 1992; MRCP (UK) 1975. (Middlesex Hospital) Cons. Uroneurol. Nat. Hosp. Neurol. & Neurosurg. Lond.; Caldicott Guardian UCLH NHS Trust Lond. Socs: (Hon. Sec.) EEG Soc.; (Chairm.) Clin. Autonomic Research Soc.; (Scientif. Comm.) Internat. Continence Soc. Prev: Cons. Clin. Neurophysiol. St. Barts Hosp. & Univ. Coll. Lond. Hosp.; Dep. Med. Dir. UCL Hosp.; Sen. Regist. (Clin. Neurophysiol.) Middlx. Hosp. & Nat. Hosp. Nerv. Dis. Lond.

FOWLER, Darren Joseth 4 Woodpecker Way, Worthing BN13 2TY — MB BS 1992 Lond. Fell. Harvard Med. Sch., Boston USA. Socs: Brit. Soc. of Human Genetics; Amer. Col. Of Med. Genetics. Prev: Research Fell., Harris Birthright Centre (O & G), Kings Coll. Hosp., Lond.; Research Fell., Mass. Gen. Hosp., Boston, USA; SHO, Paediat., N.wick Pk. Hosp./ Clin. Research Centre, Harrow, Middx.

FOWLER, David Kinorth Medical Centre, 26 Abbotswell Crescent, Aberdeen AB12 5JW Tel: 01224 876000 Fax: 01224 899182; Dykeneuk, Blairs, Aberdeen AB12 5YS — MB ChB 1981 Aberd.; MRCGP 1988. (Aberd.) Socs: Soc. Orthop. Med.

***FOWLER, David Michael** Napp Pharmaceuticals, Cambridge Science Park, Milton Road, Cambridge CB4 0GW Tel: 01223 424444 Fax: 01223 424441 Email: david.fowler@napp.co.uk; 30 Parsonage Street, Cambridge CB5 8DN Tel: 01223 562012 Email: david.m/f@ntlworld.com — MB ChB 1980 Birm.

FOWLER, Denis Byron (retired) Springfield, Station Road, Sway, Lymington SO41 6BA Tel: 01590 682265 — MB ChB 1954 Bristol; DObst RCOG 1956. Prev: Med. Off. St. Peter's Hospice Bristol.

FOWLER, Elijah 34A Leegate Road, Heaton Moor, Stockport SK4 4AX Tel: 0161 432 3521 — MB ChB 1939 Aberd.

FOWLER, Elizabeth Veronica Haxby Wiggington Health Centre, Wiggington, York YO3 3PL Tel: 01904 760125; 54 Towthorpe Road, Haxby, York YO32 3NA Tel: 01904 768715 — MB ChB 1981 Aberd.; BSc Lond. 1975; MRCGP 1986; DRCOG 1986. Socs: Roy. Coll. Gen. Pract.

FOWLER, Emily Fiona Department of Pathology, Southend Hospital NHS Trust, Prittlewell Chase, Westcliff on Sea SS0 0RY Tel: 01702 221214 Fax: 01702 22143 Email: ffowler@southend.nhs.uk; 148 Bishopsteignton, Shoeburyness, Southend-on-Sea SS3 8BQ Tel: 01702 588254 Email: efdonald@btinternet.com — MB ChB 1974 Aberd.; PhD Aberd. 1981, MB ChB 1974; FRCPath 1993, M 1981. (Aberdeen University) Cons. Histopath. & Cytol. S.end NHS Trust. Socs: Brit. Soc. Clin. Cytol. Prev: Clin. Asst. (Cytol.) S.end & Basildon DHAs; Lect. (Histopath.) St. Bart. Hosp. Med. Coll. Lond.; Lect. (Path.) Univ. Aberd.

FOWLER, Gillian Elizabeth 2 Bourtree Road, Hamilton ML3 8QD — MB ChB 1998 Glas.; MB ChB Glas 1998.

FOWLER, Professor Godfrey Heath, OBE University Division of Public Health & Primary Care, Institute of Health Science, Oxford OX3 7LF Fax: 01865 227137; Orchard House, 13 Squitchey Lane, Oxford OX2 7LD Tel: 01865 558331 Email: godfrey.fowler@balliol.ox.ac.uk — BM BCh Oxf. 1956; MA Oxf. 1957; FRCP 1997; FRCGP 1978, M 1965; FFPHM 1998; DCH Eng. 1959; DObst RCOG 1958. (Oxf. & Univ. Coll. Hosp.) Prof. Emerit. Gen. Pract. & Emerit. Fell. Balliol Coll., Univ. Oxf.; GP Cons. ICRF Gen. Pract. Research Gp. Socs: BMA & Oxf. Med. Soc. Prev: WHO Fell.; Ho. Phys. (Paediat.), Ho. Surg. (O & G) & Med. Off. (Cas.) Univ. Coll. Hosp. Lond.

FOWLER, Gordon Stanley (retired) Milbra Garth, 5 Main St, Wetwang, Driffield YO25 9XL Tel: 01377 236403 — MB ChB Leeds 1944; DA Eng. 1953.

FOWLER, Graham John The Surgery, Staunton, Gloucester GL19 3RB Tel: 01452 840228 — MB ChB 1977 Manch.; BA (Hons.) Wales 1971; MRCGP 1982. GP Staunton; GP Trainer Glos.; Med. Co-Ordinator Romanian Challenge. Prev: SHO (A & E & Orthop.) Cheltenham Gen. Hosp.; SHO (Psychiat.) Hill Hosp. Gloucester; Ho. Off. P.ss Margt. Hosp. Swindon.

FOWLER, Gregory The Health Centre, Holmes Road, Broxburn EH52 5JZ Tel: 01506 852008 Fax: 01506 856859 — MB ChB 1974 Ed.; MRCGP 1978.

FOWLER, Guy Richard John Shirley Holms, South Park Drive, Gerrards Cross SL9 8JH Tel: 01753 882394 — MB BS 1985 Lond. Prev: Ho. Phys. St. Bart. & Medway Dist. Hosps. Lond.; Ho. Surg. Colchester Gen. Hosp.

FOWLER, Helen Margaret 123 Strichen Road, Fraserburgh AB43 9QJ — MB ChB 1970 Aberd.

FOWLER, Helen Marie The Surgery, The Gardens, London SE22 9QU Tel: 020 8693 4715 Fax: 020 8299 4418 — MB ChB 1990 Birm.; DRCOG 1995; DGM RCP Lond. 1994.

FOWLER, Iolanthe Avis 12 Aldene Glade, Sheffield S6 4DB — MB ChB 1995 Leic.

FOWLER, James X-Ray Department, Ormskirk District General Hospital, Wigan Road, Ormskirk L39 2AZ Tel: 01695 586573 — MB ChB 1982 Manch.; FRCR 1990; T(R) (CR) 1991. Cons. Radiol. Ormskirk Dist. Gen. Hosp. Prev: Sen. Regist. (Radiol.) W. Midl. Train. Scheme.

FOWLER, Mr James William 7 Nile Grove, Morningside, Edinburgh EH10 4RE — MB ChB 1964 Ed.; FRCS Ed. 1967.

FOWLER, Mr John Leonard Royal Hampshire County Hospital, Winchester SO22 5DG Tel: 01962 824974 — MB BS 1979 Lond.; FRCS (Orthop.) Eng. 1990; FRCS Eng. 1983; FRCS Ed. 1983. Cons. Orthop. Surg. Roy. Hants. Co. Hosp. Winchester. Socs: Brit. Assoc. of Spine Surg.s; Brit. Cervical Spine Soc.; Brit. Orthapeadic Assoc.

FOWLER, John Morris Old Meadows, Silchester, Reading RG7 2LL Tel: 01256 881450 Fax: 01256327670 Email: janegoode@compuserve.com — MB BS 1958 Lond.; FRCP Lond. 1976, M 1963. (Univ. Coll. Hosp.) Cons. Phys. N. Hants. Hosp.; Examr. MRCP.

FOWLER, Joseph Moelwyn Stafford Road Surgery, 470 Stafford Road, Oxley, Wolverhampton WV10 6AR Tel: 01902 783103 Fax: 01902 575114 — MB BCh 1981 Wales.

FOWLER, Julia Charlotte Mary 51 Conway Road, Cardiff CF11 9NU — MB BCh 1993 Wales. Specialist Regist. (Radiol.) Univ. Hosp. Wales Cardiff.

FOWLER, Kathryn Margaret Anne Oakwood House, Hursley, Winchester SO21 2LD — MB ChB 1981 Manch.; MRCP (UK) 1984; MRCGP 1987. Prev: SHO (Med.) Derriford Hosp. Plymouth & N. Manch. Gen. Hosp.; SHO (Paediat.) Booth Hall Childr. Hosp. Manch.

FOWLER, Kenneth George Depratment of Radiology, Perth Royal Infirmary, Perth PH1 1NX Tel: 01738 623311 — MB ChB 1982 Ed.; MRCP (UK) 1986; FFR RCSI 1991; FRCR 1991. (Ed.) Cons. Radiol. Perth Roy. Infirm.; Hon. Sen. Lect. Univ. Dundee. Socs: Roy. Coll. Radiologists BrE. Gp.; Scott. BrE. Gp. Forum; Scott. Radiolog. Soc.

FOWLER, Leslie Keith (retired) 7 Marlborough Close, Mardley Hill, Welwyn AL6 0UG Tel: 01438 715236 — MB BCh 1955 Wales; BSc Wales 1952; FFPM RCP Lond. 1989. Cons. Pharmaceut. Med. Welwyn. Prev: Head Internat. Drug Safety Processing Centre Roche Products Ltd. Welwyn Gdn. City Herts.

FOWLER, Lindsey 53 Bridge Street, King's Cliffe, Peterborough PE8 6XH Tel: 01780 470043 — MB ChB 1992 Leic. SHO (Psychiat.) N. W. Anglia Healthcare Trust PeterBoro. Prev: VTs PeterBoro.

FOWLER, Lindsey Ruth 25 Whitehall Road, Aberdeen AB25 2PP — MB BS 1986 Lond.; MRCGP 1991; T(GP) 1991; DCH RCP Lond. 1989.

FOWLER, Mary Hilltop Cottage, The Collies Common, Gnosall, Stafford ST20 0JD — MB ChB 1981 Liverp.

FOWLER, Nevil Howard The Surgery, Malthouse Meadows, Portesham, Weymouth DT3 4NS Tel: 01305 871468 Fax: 01305 871977; Email: di@dianefowler-lfe.supanet.com — BM 1986 Soton.; MRCGP 1994. Prev: Trainee GP W. Dorset VTS; SHO (O & G) W. Dorset Hosp. Dorchester.

FOWLER, Mr Oliver James William 5 Sunden Heath, Harrogate HG3 2NA Tel: 01423 526501 — MB ChB 1985 Birm.; FRCS Eng. 1990. Regist. Rotat. (Radiol.) Leeds & Bradford.

FOWLER, Percy Bruce Southmayd 152 Harley Street, London W1N 1HH Tel: 020 7935 8868 & 071 935 1858; Shirley Holms,

South Park Drive, Gerrards Cross SL9 8JH Tel: 01753 882394 — BM BCh Oxf. 1944; DM Oxf. 1953, BA 1944; FRCP Lond. 1963, M 1946. (St. Thos.) p/t Hon. Sen. Research Fell. & Hon. Cons. Char. Cross Hosp. Lond. Socs: Assn. Phys & Internat. Soc. Internal Med. Prev: Phys. Char. Cross Hosp. Lond.; Cons. Phys. Wembley Hosp. & Chalfont & Gerrard's Cross Hosp.; Sen. Regist. Char. Cross Hosp. & Bromley Hosp. Gp.

FOWLER, Peter David (retired) 204 Prestbury Road, Macclesfield SK10 3BS Tel: 01625 422708 — MB ChB 1947 Manch.; MB ChB (Hons.) Manch. 1947; FRCP Ed. 1989, M 1985; FFPM RCP (UK) 1989. Prev: Assoc. Specialist & Hon. Clin. Tutor Staffs. Rheum. Centre.

FOWLER, Peter Duncan Tel: 0115 922 5826 — MB BS 1992 Lond.; BSc (Hons.) Biomed. Sc. Lond. 1989; MRCP (UK) 1995. Regist. Rotat. (Med. & Diabetes) Mid Trent.

FOWLER, Rekha Carlton Health Clinic, 61 Burton Road, Carlton, Nottingham NG4 3D Tel: 0115 961 7616 — BM BS 1987 Nottm.; BMedSci Nottm. 1987; MRCP (Paediat.) Lond. 1997; DCH RCP Lond. 1989. (Nottm.) Staff Grade (Community Paediat.) Nottm. Prev: SHO (Neonat. Med.) Roy. Sussex Co. Hosp. Brighton; Resid. (Paediat. ICU) Guy's Hosp. Lond.

FOWLER, Richard Charles Leeds General Infirmary, Great George St., Leeds LS1 3EX — MB BS 1974 Lond.; MRCP (UK) 1978; MRCS Eng. LRCP Lond. 1973; FRCR 1982; DMRD Eng. 1980. Cons. Radiol. Gen. Infirm. Leeds.

FOWLER, Robert William Oldchurch Hospital, Waterloo Road, Romford RM7 0BE Tel: 01708 708183 Fax: 01708 708183; Apartment 103, 190 St. John St, London EC1V 4JY — MB BS 1975 Lond.; BSc (Psychol.) (Hons.) Lond. 1972, MD 1988; FRCP Lond. 1994; MRCP (UK) 1978. (University College London) Cons. Phys. (Geriat. Med. & Respirat. Med.) Havering Hosps. NHS Trust & BHB Community Health Care NHS Trust. Socs: Brit. Geriat. Soc.; Brit. Soc. Rehabil. Med.; Brit. Thorac. Soc. Prev: Sen. Regist. (Geriat. Med.) Bloomsbury & Islington HAs.

***FOWLER, Sarah Elizabeth** 7 Church Street, Gamlingay, Sandy SG19 3JH; 51 Fallow Rise, Hertford SG13 7NL Email: sarahefowler@doctors.org.uk — MB ChB 1997 Birm.

FOWLER, Mrs Sheila Cameron (retired) 3 Whitaker Gardens, Burton Road, Derby DE23 6AW Tel: 01332 366572 — MB ChB 1954 Sheff.; MRCS Eng. LRCP Lond. 1955.

FOWLER, Simon Paul Forest Gate Surgery, Hazel Farm Road, Totton, Southampton SO40 8WU Tel: 023 8066 3839 Fax: 023 8066 7090; 5 Sharvells Road, Milford on Sea, Lymington SO41 0PE — MB ChB 1986 Birm.

FOWLER, Stephen James Church House Barn, South Road, Bretherton, Preston PR26 9AJ — MB ChB 1995 Manch.; MRCP (UK) 1999. (Manchester) SHO (Med. Rotat.), N. Manch. Gen. Hosp.

FOWLER, Thomas Mair, Col. late RAMC Retd. 14 Craigs Road, Ellon AB41 9DP — MB ChB 1936 Aberd. (Aberd.)

FOWLER, Timothy John 2 Kinnaird Avenue, Bromley BR1 4HG — BM BCh 1961 Oxf.; DM Oxf. 1975; FRCP Lond. 1979, M 1965. (St. Bart.) p/t Cons.Neurol Maidstone & Tunbridge Wells NHS Trust. Socs: Fell. Roy. Soc. Med.; Brit. Assn. Neurol. Prev: Sen. Regist. Nat. Hosp. Nerv. Dis. Qu. Sq. & St. Mary's Hosp. Lond.; Regist. (Neurol.) Qu. Eliz. Hosp. Birm.; Formerly Cons Neurol Kings Coll. Hosp., Lond.

FOWLER, William (retired) 37 Codsall Road, Wolverhampton WV6 9QD Tel: 01902 751869 — MD 1948 Glas.; MB ChB 1936. Prev: Consult. in Admin. Charge VD Dept. Gen. Hosp. Birm.

FOWLER-DIXON, Ruth Haslewood Horbury Health Centre, 2A Westfield Road, Horbury, Wakefield WF4 6LL Tel: 01924 270919 — MB ChB 1977 Birm.; MRCPsych 1985; DCH RCPS Glas. 1981. Staff Grade Psychiat. Stanley Royd Hosp. Wakefield.

FOWLER NÉE JUKES), Rosemary 8 Ash Grove, Allington, Maidstone ME16 0AA Tel: 01622 750257 — MB BChir 1975 Camb.; MRCGP 1982; DCH Eng. 1979; DRCOG 1978. Non-Princip. Gen. Pract. Maidstone.

FOWLES, Bryan William (retired) 9A Windmill Lane, Rothwell, Leeds LS26 0DN Email: bryan.fowles@hamphog.fsnet.co.uk — MB ChB Leeds 1957. p/t Adviser Leeds HA. Prev: Surg. Lt.-Cdr. RN.

FOWLES, Maurice Wilson (retired) 29 Langworth Gate, Lincoln LN2 4AD Tel: 01522 529632 — MB ChB Liverp. 1954; MRCPsych 1971; DPM Eng. 1962. Cons. Psychiat. (Forens.) & Med. Dir. Novic Clinic E. Anglia Regional Secure Unit Norwich. Prev: Cons. Psychiat. Harmston Hall Hosp. & Rampton Hosp. Retford.

FOWLES, Richard Gregory Chirnside Medical Practice, South Crofts, Chirnside, Duns TD11 3UH Tel: 01890 818253 Fax: 01890 818595; Coachmans, Maines South Drive, Chirnside, Duns TD11 3LD — MB ChB 1980 Dundee; MRCGP 1989; DCH RCP Lond. 1985; DRCOG 1984.

FOWLES, Stephanie Joy 17 Old Sneed Road, Bristol BS9 1ES Tel: 0117 968 1508 — MB BS 1952 Lond.; MRCP Lond. 1955; FFR 1961; DMRD Eng. 1959. Cons. Radiol. Frenchay Hosp. Bristol.

FOWLIE, Alison Derby City General Hospital, Uttoxeter Road, Derby DE22 3NE Tel: 01332 340131; Southdown, Hollington, Ashbourne DE6 3GB — MB BS 1972 Lond.; MRCS Eng. LRCP Lond. 1972; FRCOG 1991, M 1979. (Roy. Free) Cons. O & G (FetoMatern. Med.) Derby City Gen. Hosp. Socs: Fell. Birm. & Midl. Obst. & Gyn. Soc.; Blair Bell Res. Soc. Prev: Cons. Obst. (Antenatel Diag.) Birm. Matern. Hosp.; Research Regist. (Obst. Ultrasound) & SHO (Gyn.) King's Coll. Hosp. Lond.; SHO (Obst.) Qu. Charlottes Hosp. Wom. Lond.

FOWLIE, Douglas Gibb Royal Cornhill Hospital, Aberdeen AB25 2ZH — MB ChB 1970 Aberd.; FRCPsych 1988, M 1976. Cons. Psychiat. & Sen. Clin. Lect. Roy. Cornhill Hosp. & Univ. Aberd.

FOWLIE, Hector Chalmers, OBE (retired) 21 Clepington Road, Dundee DD4 7EL — MB ChB 1955 St. And.; FRCP Ed. 1969, M 1961; FRCPsych 1973, M 1972; DPM Eng. 1958. Prev: Vice-Chairm. Ment. Welf. Commiss. for Scotl.

FOWLIE, Jill Elizabeth Nithsdale Road Surgery, 162 Nithsdale Road, Glasgow G41 5RU Tel: 0141 424 1831 Fax: 0141 423 7422 — MB ChB 1987 Aberd.

FOWLIE, Marjory Anne Russell Roxburghe House, Tornadee Hospital, Milltimber AB13 0HR Tel: 01224 681818; Esdaile, Sandyhill Road, Banff AB45 1BE — MB ChB 1970 Aberd. Med. Off. (Palliat. Med.) Roxburghe Hse. Aberd.

FOWLIE, Peter Walker Tel: 01382 660111 Fax: 01382 645783; Dundas, Main St, Longforgan, Dundee DD2 5EW — MB ChB 1985 Ed.; MSc Canada 1995; MRCP (UK) 1991; MRCGP 1989; DRCOG 1988; MRCPCh 1997. Cons. Paediat.Tayside Univeristy Hosp.s NHS Trust. Prev: MRC Train. Fell. (Health Servs. Research), Dundee Univ.; Sen. Regist. (Paediat.), Tayside HB; Regist. (Paediat.) Tayside HB.

FOWLIE, Stephen McIntosh Nottingham City Hospital, Hucknall Road, Nottingham NG5 1PB — MD 1992 Ed.; MB ChB 1980; MBA Nottm. 1997. Cons. Phys. (Health c/o the Elderly) Nottm. City Hosp. Prev: Sen. Regist. (Gen. & Geriat. Med.) Oxf.

FOWLIS, Mr George Akindele Urology Department, The North Middlesex Hospital, Sterling Way, London N18 1QX Tel: 020 8887 2431 Fax: 020 8887 4661 Email: ga.fowlis@ferriman.demon.co.uk; naiMing, 23 Lingfield Way, Nascot Wood Road, Watford WD17 4UW Tel: 01923 213435 Fax: 01923 213255 Email: gafowlis@doctors.org.uk — MB BCh BAO 1984 Dub.; BSc Yale 1979; MD Dub. 1993; FRCS Eng. 1989; FRCS (Urol.) 1996. (Dublin) Cons. Urol. Surg. (Oncol.) N. Middlx. Hosp. Lond. Socs: BMA; Fell.Europ. Bd. Urol.; Brit. Assn. Urol. Surgs. Prev: Sen. Regist. Rotat. (Urol.) Whipps Cross & Roy. Free Hosp.; Regist. (Urol.) Hammersmith Hosp. RPMS, Univ. Coll. & Middlx. Hosp.

FOWNES, Helen Elaine 81 St Giles Road, Tile Cross, Birmingham B33 0PB Tel: 0121 783 4468; Flat 2, 180 Westgate Road, Newcastle upon Tyne NE4 6AL Tel: 0191 232 0228 0 — MB ChB 1990 Manch. Clin. Asst. (Gen. Pract. & ENT) Birm.

FOX, Adam Tobias 16 The Crossways, Wembley HA9 9NG — MB BS 1996 Lond.

FOX, Alan Stuart Grahame Park Health Centre, The Concourse, Grahame Park Estate, London NW9 5XT Tel: 0208 905 9195 Fax: 020 8200 9173 — MB BS 1969 Lond.; MRCGP 1975; DObst RCOG 1972.

FOX, Alison Mary Jaunty Springs Health Centre, 53 Jaunty Way, Sheffield S12 3DZ Tel: 0114 239 9453; Tel: 0114 230 8696 — MB ChB 1980 Bristol; DRCOG 1983. p/t Gen. Practitioner. Prev: Trainee GP Cheltenham VTS.

FOX, Allan Robert Wye Surgery, 67 Oxenturn Road, Wye, Ashford TN25 5AY Tel: 01233 812414/812419 Fax: 01233 813236; Court Lodge, Godmersham, Canterbury CT4 7DT Tel: 01227 730568 — MB BS 1989 Lond.; BSc (Hons.) Lond. 1980, MB BS 1989; MRCP (UK) 1992. (St Thomas) Prev: SHO (O & G) All St.s Hosp. Chatham; SHO Rotat. (Med.) Kent & Canterbury Hosp.; SHO & Ho. Off. (Gen. Med.) Kent & Canterbury Hosp.

FOX, Amanda Beatrice Edwina Barrow Hospital, Barrow Gurney, Bristol BS48 3SG — MB BS 1979 Lond.

FOX, Andrew Jonathan Leicester General Hospital, Gwendolen Road, Leicester LE5 4PW Tel: 0116 249 0490 — MB ChB 1988 Glas.; DA (UK) 1993; DRCOG 1992; FRCA 1997. Cons. (Anaes & IC), Leicester Gen. Hosp.; Mem. Roy. Coll. Anaesth. Socs: Assn. Anaesth. GB & Irel.; Intens. Care Soc.; Vasc. Anaesth. Soc. Prev: Specialist Regist. (Anaesth.) Leicester Roy. Infirm.; Trainee GP Dumfries VTS; SHO (Anaesth.) P'boro. Dist. Hosp.

FOX, Andrew Martin Springfield House Medical Centre, 275 Huddersfield Road, Oldham OL4 2RJ Tel: 0161 633 2333 Fax: 0161 628 66832; 24 Oaklands Park, Grasscroft, Oldham OL4 4JY — MB ChB 1981 Manch.; DA Eng. 1984; FFA RCS (Lond.) 1986. GP Oldham.

FOX, Anthony Dunstan (cons. rooms), The Wessex Nuffield Hospital, Winchester Road, Chandlers Ford, Eastleigh SO53 2DW Tel: 01703 266377; 54 Barton Court Avenue, Barton on Sea, New Milton BH25 7HG Tel: 01425 618801 — MB BS Lond. 1968; BSc Lond. 1968; MRCGP 1975; MFHom RCP Lond. 1980; DCH Eng. 1972; DObst RCOG 1971. (Lond. Hosp.) Indep. GP E.leigh. Socs: Fell. Roy. Soc. Med.; BMA; Brit. Soc. Allergy & Environm. Nutrit. Med. Prev: GP Keynsham; SHO (Med.) Roy. Hosp. Chesterfield; SHO (Paediat. & Obst.) City Hosp. Nottm.

FOX, Mr Antony David Royal Shrewsbury Hospital NHS Trust, Mytton Oak Rd, Shrewsbury SY3 8XQ Tel: 01743 261633 Fax: 01743 261122 Email: mradfox@compuserve.com; 61 The Mount, Shrewsbury SY3 8PL Tel: 01743 362115 — MB BS 1987 Lond.; BSc (Hons.) Lond. 1984; FRCS Lond. 1991; FRCS Ed. 1989; FRCS (Gen.) 1998; MS 1998. (Charing Cross/Westminster) Cons. Surg. Socs: Vasc. Surg. Soc.; Assn. Surg. Prev: Sen. Regist. (Surg.) John Radcliffe Hosp. Oxf.; Lect. (Surg.) Bath; Regist. (Surg.) N.ampton & Oxf.

FOX, Benjamin Daniel 3 Alwyne Square, London N1 2JX — BM BCh 1998 Oxf.; BM BCh Oxf 1998.

FOX, Bernard (retired) Flat 2, Adelaide Court, 15 Adelaide Crescent, Hove BN3 2JF — MD 1973 Lond.; MB BS 1953; FRCPath 1977, M 1965. Prev: AGM Path. Servs. Riverside HA.

FOX, Bruce Michael Tregay X-ray Dept., Derriford Hospital, Plymouth PL6 8DH Email: bruce.fox@phnt.swest.nhs.uk — MB BS 1991 Lond.; MRCP (UK) 1995; FRCR (UK) 1997. (Royal Free Hospital School of Medicine) Specialist Regist. (Radiol.); Cons. GT Radiologist, Derrifield Hosp., Plymouth. Socs: Mem. Europ. Soc. GT Radiol.

FOX, Candida 26 Warwick Road, Chorlton, Manchester M21 0AX Email: cand@mcmail.com — MB ChB 1988 Sheff.; MRCPsych 1996; MRCGP 1993.

FOX, Caroline Louise Saltash Health Centre, Callington Rd, Saltash, Saltash PL12 6DL — MB BS 1991 Lond.; MRCGP; DCH RCP Lond. 1996, DRCOG 1998. Gen. Practitioner, Saltash Health Centre, Saltash.

FOX, Charles John Victor Fiveways, Gayton, Northampton NN7 3EX Tel: 01604 859444 Email: charles@foxfam.demon.co.uk — BM BCh 1966 Oxf.; BA Oxf. 1963, BM BCh 1966; FRCP Lond. 1986; MRCP (U.K.) 1970. (St. Thos.) Cons. Phys. N.ampton Gen. Hosp. Prev: Sen. Med. Regist. Roy. Devon & Exeter Hosp. & Bristol Roy. Infirm.; Regist. (Cardiol.) St. Thos. Hosp. Lond.

***FOX, Charles Nicholas Ilya** 292 Globe Road, London E2 0NS — MB BS 1989 Lond.

FOX, Christopher Alan St Johns Lane Health Centre, St. Johns Lane, Bristol BS3 5AS Tel: 0117 966 7681 Fax: 0117 977 9676 — MB BS 1976 Lond.; MRCS Eng. LRCP Lond. 1976; Dip. Palliat. Med. Wales 1992. (Guy's Hosp. Lond.)

FOX, Christopher John Peggy Garth, Thoralby, Leyburn DL8 3SU Tel: 01969 663706 — MB BChir 1985 Camb.; MRCP (UK) 1989; FRACP 1994. (Westminster Medical School) Regist, St. Thomas's Hosp. Prev: Regist., Roy. Liver Unit; Regist., Roy. Sussex Co. Hosp., Brighton; Regist., Roy. Perth Hosp., Perth, Australia.

FOX, Claire Maxine Hollyholm, Sylvan Way, Bognor Regis PO21 2RS — BM BCh 1997 Oxf.

FOX, Cyril Albert (retired) 7 Crepieny Road, Hendon, London NW4 3DT Tel: 0208 202 2181 Email: cyril@foxalma.freeserve.co.uk — MA Camb. 1957, BA 1953, MD 1970, MB BChir 1956; MRCS Eng. LRCP Lond. 1956; MRCGP 1968.

FOX, David Benjamin 47 Newmans Way, Hadley Wood, Barnet EN4 0LR Tel: 020 8441 6787 — MA, MB BChir Camb. 1952; MRCS Eng. LRCP Lond. 1952. (Univ. Coll. Hosp.) Prev: Hosp. Pract. (Dermat. & Rheum.) & Clin. Asst. (Psychol. Med.) N. Middlx. Hosp. Edmonton; Hosp. Pract. Varicose Ulcer Clinic & Dept. Dermat. & Rheum. St Ann's Hosp. Lond.; Ho. Phys. & Clin. Asst. Skin Dept. St. And. Hosp. Bow.

FOX, David George Ross (retired) Hillrise, Leiston Road, Aldeburgh IP15 5QD Tel: 01728 453294 — MB BChir Camb. 1942; MA Camb. 1943, MD 1949; MRCGP 1953; DIH Soc. Apoth. Lond. 1951. Prev: Ho. Phys. Connaught Hosp. Walthamstow.

FOX, David James Hilltop, 2 Durham Drive, Blackburn BB1 9NX — MB ChB 1998 Dund.; MB ChB Dund 1998.

FOX, David Jonathan 20 Beechcroft Road, Gosport PO12 2ER — BM BS 1990 Nottm.; BMedSci Nottm. 1988. Regist. Rotat. (Psychiat.) Mid Trent Nottm. Prev: SHO (Geriat.) Sandwell Dist. Gen. Hosp.

FOX, David Michael West Point Medical Centre, 167-169 Slade Lane, Levenshulme, Manchester M19 2AF Tel: 0161 248 5100 Fax: 0161 225 6258; 6 Clothorn Road, Didsbury, Manchester M20 6BQ Tel: 0161 445 1632 Email: foxs@dial.pipex.com — MB ChB 1969 Manch.; MRCGP 1992. (Manch.) Div. Police Surg. Gtr. Manch. Police; Clin. Lect. (Gen. Pract.) Manch. Univ. Socs: Assn. Police Surg.

FOX, David Philip 27E Elmgrove Road, Cotham, Bristol BS16 2AU — MB BS 1989 Lond.

FOX, Declan Pius Newtownstewart Medical Centre, 5 Millbrook Street, Newtownstewart, Omagh BT78 4BW Tel: 028 8166 1333 Fax: 028 8166 1883; Cill Nua, 6 Ballymullarty Road, Newtownstewart, Omagh BT78 4NP Tel: 016626 61467 Fax: 016626 62353 Email: declanfox@compuserve.com — MB BCh BAO 1979 Dub.; MRCGP 1988; DObst RCPI 1986. (Trinity Coll. Dub.) Represen. N. Irel. Small Practs Assn.; Mem. Primary Health Care Specialist Gp. Socs: GP Writers Assn. (Comm. Mem.); Ulster Med. Soc.; BMA.

FOX, Dennis Henry, MBE (retired) West Hythe, Upper Tockington Road, Tockington, Bristol BS32 4LQ Tel: 01454 612754 — MB ChB Bristol 1951; MRCS Eng. LRCP Lond. 1951. Prev: Med. Off. RAMC.

FOX, Edgar Alexander (retired) 3 Walmer Avenue, Bishop Auckland DL14 6NW Tel: 01388 602755 — MB ChB Aberd. 1949.

FOX, Edward Gerard 17 Roman Road, Kirkintilloch, Glasgow G66 1EF — MB BCh BAO 1937 Dub.; MD Dub. 1941; MRCPI 1952; DCH Eng. 1942. (T.C. Dub.) Paediatr. Stobhill Hosp. Glas. Socs: Roy. M-C Soc. Glas. & Scott. Paediat. Soc. Prev: Sen. Res. Med. Off. Alder Hey Childr. Hosp. Liverp.; Clin. Asst. Roy. Liverp. Childr. Infirm.; Squadron Ldr. RAFVR.

FOX, Elizabeth Ellen 163 Beach Road, Hartford, Northwich CW8 3AD Tel: 01606 75017 — MB BS 1990 Lond.

FOX, Elsie Elizabeth (retired) 19 St Catherines, Lincoln LN5 8LW — MB ChB Liverp. 1963. Locum GP. Prev: Med. Off. St. Barnabas Hospice Lincoln.

FOX, Emma Frances Queen Mary's Hospital, Roehampton Lane, Roehampton, London SW15 Tel: 020 8355 2470; 65 Grand Avenue, Worthing BN11 5BA Tel: 01903 501088 — MB BS 1991 Lond.; MRCP (UK) 1994; DFFP 1996; DGM RCP Lond. 1995. Cons. (Genito-Urin. Med.), Qu. Mary's Hosp. & St Geo.'s Hosp., Lond.; Forens. Med. Examr. Metrop. Police. Socs: Soc. Study VD; Assn. Genitourin. Med. Prev: Regist. (G.U. Med.) St. Thos. Hosp. Lond.; SHO (Med.) E.bourne Dist. Gen. Hosp.

FOX, Ernest Malcolm Fox and Partners, South Park Surgery, 250 Park Lane, Macclesfield SK11 8AA; Willowfield, Bullocks Lane, Sutton, Macclesfield SK11 0HE Tel: 01260 252677 Email: malcom_fox@msn.com — MB ChB 1964 Leeds; FRCGP 1990, M 1976; DObst RCOG 1966. (Leeds) p/t Non- Princip. GP.

FOX, Gabriel Max Nexstar Pharmaceuticals Ltd., The Quorum, Barnwell Road, Cambridge CB5 8RE Tel: 01223 571400 Fax: 01223 571400 Email: gfox@nexstar.com — MB BChir 1989 Camb.; BA Camb. 1987. Med. Dir., Nexstar Pharmaceut.

FOX, Mr Geoffrey Charles (retired) 5 Greenhills Road, Charlton Kings, Cheltenham GL53 9ED Tel: 01242 520574 — MB BS Lond. 1959; FRCS Eng. 1970; FRCS Ed. 1966; MRCS Eng. LRCP Lond. 1959; DLO Eng. 1968. Prev: Cons. ENT Surg. E. Glos. NHS Trust & Glos. Roy. NHS Trust.

FOX, Geoffrey Stewart The Health Centre, Greenside, Cleckheaton BD19 5AN Tel: 01274 872200; Pennygate, Micklefield Lane, Rawdon, Leeds LS19 6BA Tel: 0113 250 6133 — MB BS 1974 Lond.; DRCOG 1978.

FOX, George Christopher 32 Trenchard Gardens, South Cerney, Cirencester GL7 6JA — MB BS 1991 Lond.; BSc Lond. 1988, MB BS 1991; Cert. Av. Med. 1992.

FOX, Harold Department of Pathology, University of Manchester, Stopford Bldg, Oxford Road, Manchester M13 9PT Tel: 0161 275 5301 Fax: 0161 275 5289; 24 Manor Drive, Chorlton, Manchester M21 7GQ Tel: 0161 445 5872 Fax: 0161 445 5872 — MD 1966 Manch.; MD (Gold Medal) Manch. 1966, MB ChB (Hons.) 1955; FRCOG 1984; FRCPath 1977, M 1965. Emerit. Prof. Reproduc. Path. Univ. Manch.; Hon. Cons. Path. St. Mary's Hosp. Manch. Socs: (Pres.) Internat. Soc. Gyn. Path. & (Ex-Pres.) Internat. Acad. Prev: Vis. Prof. Path. Trivandrum Med. Coll., India; Research Fell. Univ. Calif. Med. Center San Francisco; SHO (Haemat.) Manch. Roy. Infirm.

FOX, Helena Junior Common Room, Maudsley Hospital, London SE5; 102 Cumnor Hill, Oxford OX2 9HY — MB BS 1982 Lond.; MRCPsych 1989.

FOX, Hilary Jane Uppingham Surgery, 2 London Road, Oakham LE15 9TY Tel: 01572 823531 Fax: 01572 821145 Email: foxhj@gp-c82077.nhs.uk; The Coach House, Weston Road, Edith Weston, Oakham LE15 8HQ Tel: 01780 720113 Email: hils@moore-fox.denon.co.uk — MB ChB 1985 Leic.; MRCGP 1989; DRCOG 1989; DCH RCP Lond. 1990. Prev: Trainee GP Leicester VTS.

FOX, Howard George 34 Sackville Gardens, Hove BN3 4GH — MB BS 1987 Lond.

FOX, Mr Hugh Jonathan Royal Hampshire County Hospital, Winchester SO22 5DG Tel: 01962 863535 — MB ChB 1986 Bristol; FRCS Ed. 1991; FRCS Ed. (Orth.) 1997. Cons. Orthop. and Trauma Roy. Hants. Co. Hosp. Winchester. Socs: BASK; BOTA; BOA Fell. Prev: Knee Fell. Brisbane Orthop. & Sports Med. Centre, Australia; Sen. Regist. Rotat. (Orthop.) S. Birm.; Regist. Rotat. (Orthop.) S. Birm.

FOX, Jacqueline 35 Hazel Tree Grove, Dorridge, Solihull B93 8HL — MB ChB 1991 Birm.

FOX, Jeffrey John Ivy Farm, Foxhole, Saxlingham Nethergate, Norwich NR15 1UG Tel: 0150 842462 — MB ChB 1968 Liverp.; DObst RCOG 1971.

FOX, Jennifer Ann Roe Lane Surgery, 172 Roe Lane, Southport PR9 7PN Tel: 01704 228439 Fax: 01704 506878; 37 Lulworth Road, Southport PR8 2BG Tel: 01704 69181 — MB ChB 1982 Birm.; DRCOG 1986. Dip. Fac. Sexual Med. & Reproduc. Health. Prev: GP Birm.

FOX, Mr John Adrian (retired) 44 Little Common, Stanmore HA7 3BZ Tel: 020 8954 6733 — MB BS Lond. 1957; FRCS Eng. 1962; MRCS Eng. LRCP Lond. 1957. Prev: Cons. Surg. Edgware Gen. Hosp.

FOX, John Edward Clinical Neurophysiology Department, Queen Elizabeth Hospital, Edgbaston, Birmingham B15 2TH Tel: 0121 472 1311 Fax: 0121 627 2108 — MB ChB Birm. 1970; PhD Birm. 1976, BSc 1967, MD 1987. Cons. Clin. Neurophysiol. Qu. Eliz. Hosp. Birm.; Sen. Clin. Lect. Birm. Univ. Socs: Physiol. Soc.; Brit. Soc. for Clin. NeuroPhysiol.; Brit.Neurosc. Assn. Prev: Cons. Clin. & Experim. Neurophysiol. Midl. Centre for Neurosurg. & Neurol. Smethwick; Hon. Sen. Regist. (Clin. Neurophysiol.) Qu. Eliz. Hosp. Birm. & Midl. Centre Neurosurg. & Neurol. Smethwick; Lect. (Med.) Sch. Birm.

FOX, John Henry 5 North Street, Topsham, Exeter EX3 0AP Tel: 01392 874136 — MB BS 1993 Lond.; BA (Hons.) 1989. (St. Bartholomew's Hospital) GP Regist. Ide La. Surg. Alphington Exeter. Socs: Assoc. Mem. RCGP. Prev: SHO (A & E); SHO (Gen. Med.); SHO (Psychiat.).

FOX, Mr John Norman Castle Hill Hospital, Castle Road, Cottingham HU16 5JQ Tel: 01482 622654 Fax: 01482 622650 Email: jnfox@doctors.org.uk; 32 Molescroft Road, Beverley HU17 7ED — MB ChB 1972 Ed.; BSc (Med. Sci.) Ed. 1969; FRCS Ed. 1977. (Ed.) Cons. Surg. Castle Hill Hosp. & Hull Roy. Infirm.; Hon. Sen. Lect. Univ. Hull. Prev: Cons. Surg. W.wood Hosp. Beverley; Sen. Regist. (Surg.) Edin. Hosps.; Research Fell. (Surg.) Univ. Missouri, USA.

FOX, John Patrick The Gables, 11 Dove Park, Chorleywood, Rickmansworth WD3 5NY — MB BS 1938 Lond.; MD Lond. 1947; MRCS Eng. LRCP Lond. 1936; DPH Lond. 1947. (Westm.)

FOX, Mr John Sherwood West Middlesex University Hospital, Twickenham Road, Isleworth TW7 6AF Tel: 020 8565 5113 Fax: 020 8565 5973; 13 Walpole Road, Twickenham TW2 5SN Tel: 020 8894 4418 — MB BS Lond. 1967; MRCS Eng. LRCP Lond. 1967; FRCOG 1989, M 1975. (St. Mary's) Cons. W. Middlx. Univ. Hosp. Isleworth; Hon. Sen. Lect. (Obst. & Gyn.) Char. Cross & W.m. Med. Sch. Lond.

FOX, Jonathan Gabriel Renal Unit, Stobhill NHS Trust, Glasgow G21 3UW Tel: 0141 201 3645 — MB BS 1981 Lond.; FRCP Glas. 1998; MD Lond. 1994; MRCP (UK) 1984; BSc Lond. 1978. Cons. Phys. Stobhill Hosp. Glas. Prev: Sen. Regist. (Nephrol. & Gen. Med.) Glas. Roy. Infirm.

FOX, Jonathan Peter Southport & Formby District General Hospital, Town Lane, Kew, Southport PR8 6PN Tel: 01704 547471 Fax: 01704 868623; 37 Lulworth Road, Birkdale, Southport PR8 2BG Tel: 01704 569181 Fax: 01704 550616 — MB ChB 1980 Birmingham; FRCP Lond. 1997; MRCP (UK) 1985; T(M) 1992; MD 1991 Birm. (Univ. Birm.) Cons. Phys. & Cardiol. S.port & Formby Dist. Gen. Hosp.; Vis. Cardiol. Cardiothoracic Centre Liverp. Socs: Brit. Cardiac Soc. Prev: Sen. Regist. (Cardiol.) Cardiovasc. Centre Liverp.; Research Fell. (Cardiovasc. Med.) E. Birm. Hosp.; Regist. (Cardiovasc. Med.) P. Chas. Hosp. Brisbane, Austral.

FOX, Judith Eveline 22 Talbot Avenue, Edgerton, Huddersfield HD3 3BG — MB ChB 1978 Dundee.

FOX, Julian Vincent 23 Spencer Street, Eldon Lane, Bishop Auckland DL14 8TL Tel: 01388 776729 Fax: 01388 776553 Email: dr.fox@bigfoot.com; Woodhamm Surgery, Village Close, Woodham Village, Newton Aycliffe DL5 4DU Tel: 01325 311300 — MB ChB 1987 Leic.; DRCOG 1993.

FOX, Julie Meriel 10 Ison Close, Biddenham, Bedford MK40 4BH — MB ChB 1997 Manch.

FOX, June Rose 14 Milton Road, Repton, Derby DE65 6FZ — MB ChB 1959 Birm. SCMO S.. Derbysh. HA.

FOX, Professor Keith Alexander Arthur Department of Cardiology, Royal Infirmary, Lauriston Place, Edinburgh EH3 9YW Tel: 0131 536 2743 Fax: 0131 536 2744 Email: k.a.a.fox@ed.ac.uk — MB ChB 1974 Ed.; BSc Hons. Ed. 1972, MB ChB 1974; FRCP Ed. 1987, M 1977; FESC 1988. Duke of Edin. Prof. Cardiol. & Hon. Cons. Cardiol. Cardiovasc. Research Unit Univ. Edin. & Roy. Infirm. Edin. Socs: Founding Fell. & Mem. Scientif. Comm. Europ. Soc. Cardiol.; Brit. Cardiac Soc. (Counc. Mem.); Edit. Bd. Coronary Artery Dis. (Curr. Sci.). Prev: Sen. Lect. (Cardiol.) & Hon. Cons. Cardiol. Welsh Nat. Sch. of Med.; Asst. Prof. Med. Dept. Cardiol. Univ. Washington, Missouri, USA.

FOX, Kevin Francis Flat 14, Blandford Court, 4-6 Christchurch Avenue, London NW6 7BP Tel: 020 8451 0913 — MB BChir 1991 Camb.; MA Camb. 1991; MRCP (UK) 1993. Research Fell., Nat. Health & Lung Inst. Imperial Coll. Sch. of Med.

FOX, Kim Michael Royal Brompton of Harefield NHS Trust, Sydney St., London SW3 6NP Tel: 020 7352 8121 Fax: 020 7351 8629; 88 Harley Street, London W1N 1AE Tel: 020 7486 4617 Fax: 020 7935 0896 — MD Dundee 1980; MB ChB St. And. 1971; FRCP Lond. 1988; MRCP (UK) 1974; FESC 1988. (St Andrews) Cons. Cardiol. Roy. Brompton Hosp. Lond.; Hon. Cons. Cardiol. Wexham & Heatherwood NHS Trust; Prof. of Clin. Cardiol. Imperial Coll. Lond. Socs: Bd. Mem. Europ. Soc. Cardiol.; Brit. Cardiac Soc. Prev: Cons. Cardiol. Nat. Heart Hosp.; Sen. Regist. Hammersmith Hosp. Lond.; Regist. Rotat. Hammersmith Hosp. & Hosp. Sick Childr. Gt. Ormond St. Lond.

FOX, Liam House of Commons, Westminster, London SW1A 1AA — MB ChB Glas. 1983; MRCGP 1989.

FOX, Linda Caroline Peralta, Ridge Road, Maidencombe, Torquay TQ1 4TD — BM BS 1995 Nottm.; BMedSci Nottm. 1995.

FOX, Marcia Fleur Rosanne 1 Linden Lea, London N2 0RF — MB BS 1983 Lond.

FOX, Margaret Beatrice (retired) Greenhill, 5 Oaklands Road, Bromley BR1 3SJ — MRCS Eng. LRCP Lond. 1937.

FOX, Mark Andrew Department of Cardiothoracic Anaesthesia, Cardiothoracic Centre, Thomas Drive, Liverpool L14 3PE Tel: 0151 228 1616; 14A North Drive, Victoria Park, Liverpool L15 8JG — MB BS 1978 Lond.; FFA RCS Eng. 1983. (Roy. Free) Cons. Anaesth.

Cardiothoracic Centre NHS Trust Hosp. Liverp.; Clin. Lect. (Anaesth.) Univ. Liverp. Prev: Sen. Regist. (Anaesth.) Mersey Regional HA; Lect. (Anaesth.) Univ. Liverp.

***FOX, Mark Robert** West Ridge, Harepath Hill, Seaton EX12 2TA — BM BCh 1994 Oxf.; BA (Hons.) Oxf. 1991, BM BCh 1994.

FOX, Martyn Howard QE2 Hospitals, East and North Hertfordshire NHS Trust, Howlands, Welwyn Garden City Tel: 01707 328111 — MB BS 1985 Lond.; FRCA 1996. (Roy. Free Hosp. Lond.) Cons. Anaesthistic Dept. QE2 Hosp. Aest and N. Herts. NHS Trust. Prev: Yorks. Regist. Rotat. in Anaesthetics; Specialist Regist. (Anaesth.) St. James' Univ. Hosp. Leeds; SHO (Anaesth.) Horton Gen. Hosp. Oxon.

FOX, Matthew Peralta, Ridge Road, Maidencombe, Torquay TQ1 4TD — BM BS 1994 Nottm.; BMedSci Nottm. 1994.

FOX, Maurice Bickerstaffe (retired) 40 Algitha Road, Skegness PE25 2AJ — MB BS 1942 Lond.; MRCS Eng. LRCP Lond. 1942; MRCOG 1950, DObst 1948. Prev: Jun. O & G Regist. Nottm. City Hosp.

FOX, Maxwell Hilton Bognor Medical Practice, West Street, Bognor Regis PO21 1UT Tel: 01243 823864 Fax: 01243 623800 — MB BS 1972 Lond.; BSc (Hons.) Salford 1967. Socs: Brit. Med. Acupunc. Soc.

FOX, Michael James Fax: (+966) 3 890 0316; The Homestead, 154 High Street, Selsey, Chichester PO20 0QE Tel: 01705 524844 Fax: 01705 580873 Email: michaelj.fox@virgin.net — MB BS 1976 Lond.; DAvMed. 1994; DRCOG 1987. (St. Thos.) Aviat. Med. Specialist BAE Systems Dhahran.

FOX, Michael Philip Ground Floor Flat, 22 Lady Somerset Road, London NW5 1UP — MB BS 1996 Lond.

FOX, Mr Miles 54 Stumperlowe Crescent Road, Sheffield S10 3PR Tel: 0114 230 3613 Fax: 0114 230 3613 Email: miles.fox@sheffield.ac.uk — MB ChB 1950 Manch.; ChM 1960 Manc; FRCS 1955 Eng; MD 1965 Manch. (Manch.) Hunt. Prof. RCS Eng. 1976. Socs: Brit. Assn. Urol. Surgs.; Brit. Transpl. Soc.; Internat. Soc. Urol. Prev: Cons. Urol. Roy. Hallamsh. Hosp. Sheff.; Research Fell. Harvard Med. Sch. Boston, USA; Dir. Renal Transpl. Unit Roy. Hallamsh. Hosp. Sheff.

FOX, Mr Nigel John 3 Parkways, Selby YO8 9BB — MB BS 1981 Newc.; FRCS Ed. 1985.

FOX, Patrick Joseph Ballymena Health Centre, Cushendall Road, Ballymena BT43 6HQ Tel: 028 2564 2181 Fax: 028 2565 8919 — MB BCh BAO 1971 Belf. Socs: BMA. Prev: SHO & Ho. Off. Waveney Hosp. Ballymena.

FOX, Paul Alexander 5 Andrews Grove, Ackworth, Pontefract WF7 7NU — MB ChB 1984 Leeds; Diploma Palliative Medicine (UWCM) 2001. GP Castleford, W. Yorks.; MacMillan GP facilitator; Primary Care Trust Cancer Lead. Prev: Trainee GP Castleford Pontefract; SHO (Orthop. & Cas.) Huddersfield Roy. Infirm.; SHO (Gastroenterol. & Gen. Med.) Hull Roy. Infirm.

FOX, Paul Andrew Kobler Clinic, Chelsea and Westminster Hospital, 369 Fulham Road, London SW10 9TH; Email: pfox@kings4.demon.co.uk — MB BChir 1988 Camb.; MA Camb. 1989, BA 1985; MRCP (UK) 1996; Cert. JCPTGP 1995. Specialist Regist. HIV/GUM Chelsea & W.m. Hosp. Socs: MSSVD (Med. Soc. For Study of Venereal Dis.s); Steering Comm. for HPV s/i Gp. Prev: SHO (Gen. Med.) Solihull Hosp.; Indep. Pract. Stress Managem. & Hypnother. & Med. Adviser to PSI Servs. plc; Trainee GP Heanor Derbysh.

FOX, Peter Stobswell Medical Centre, 163 Albert Street, Dundee DD4 6PX Tel: 01382 461363 Fax: 01382 453423 — MB ChB 1984 Dundee.

FOX, Mr Peter David Chichester Nuffield Hospital, 78 Broyle Road, Chichester PO19 4BE Tel: 01243 532244 — MB ChB 1980 Manch.; FRCS Eng. 1987; FCROphth 1989. Cons. Ophth. Surg. Worthing & Chichester.

FOX, Peter Gerald, TD The Mill House, Puncknowle, Dorchester DT2 9BU Tel: 01308 897432 — MRCS Eng. LRCP Lond. 1949. (St. Mary's) Med. Off. Min. of Social Security Med. Bds.; Cons. Wessex Cancer Help Centre Chichester. Prev: Med. Off. Chesh. Home (Phys. & Ment. Handicap. Childr.) Dorchester; Regtl. Med. Off. Qu.s Own Dorset Yeomanry (TA); Port Med. Off. Weymouth.

FOX, Peter Stewart Stirling House, Balliul Business Park Tel: 0191 2705000 Fax: 0191 2705060 — MB ChB 1983 Birm.; MRCGP 1987; DRCOG 1987. (Birm.) Med. Director, Jt. develop. Team, NHS Clin. Assessm. systems. Prev: Trainee GP Newc. VTS; Ho. Off. City Gen. Hosp. Stoke-on-Trent; Ho. Off. Selly Oak Hosp. Birm.

FOX, Peter Stuart (retired) 25 Gillylees, Scarborough YO12 5DR Tel: 01723 360597 — MB ChB 1954 Sheff.

FOX, Peter Thomas Wye Valley Surgery, 2 Desborough Avenue, High Wycombe HP11 2RN Tel: 01494 521044 Fax: 01494 472770; 7 Gosling Grove, Downley, High Wycombe HP13 5UF — MB ChB 1962 Leeds; DCMT . Lond. 1967; DObst RCOG 1964. (Leeds) Fell. Roy. Soc. Trop. Med.

FOX, Raymond Brownlee Centre, Gartnavel General Hospital, Great Western Road, Glasgow G12 0YN — MB ChB 1981 Aberd.; MRCP (UK) 1986; DTM & H Liverp. 1990.

FOX, Richard (retired) Yew Tree House, 16 Coast Road, West Mersea, Colchester CO5 8LH — MB BS 1951 Lond.; MRCP (UK) 1956; MRCS Eng. LRCP Lond. 1951; FRCPsych 1976, M 1971; T(Psychiat.) 1992; Dip. Psychiat. Amer. Bds. Psychiat. & Neurol. 1981; DPM Eng. 1959. Vice-Pres. Phoenix Gp. Homes & Brit. Epilepsy Assn. Prev: Mem. Parole Bd. Lond.

FOX, Richard Michael St Ives Cottage, Bridge St., Bradwell, Hope Valley S33 9HE — MB BS 1987 Lond.

FOX, Richard Simon Ross The Royal National Orthopaedic Hospital Trust, Brockley Hill, Stanmore HA7 4LP Tel: 020 8954 2300 Fax: 020 8954 8914 Email: rfox@hazelwood.force9.net — MB BS 1981 Lond.; FCAnaesth. 1991. Cons. Anaesth. Roy. Nat. Orthop. Hosp. Middlx.

FOX, Robert Department of Obstetrics, Taunton & Somerset Hospital, Taunton TA1 5DA Tel: 01823 333444 — MB ChB 1980 Leeds; MD Bristol 1993; MRCOG 1986. Cons. O & G Taunton & Som. Hosp. Prev: Lect. (O & G) Univ. Bristol.

FOX, Robert McDougall The Green House, Rotherfield, Crowborough TN6 3QU Tel: 01892 853520 Fax: 01892 853520 Email: robinfox1@compuserve.com — MB ChB Ed. 1965; FRCP Lond. 1996; FRCP Ed. 1991. Med. Edr., Jl. Roy. Soc. Med., IPPF Bull., Assoc. Edr. Circulat. Prev: Edr. Lancet; Ho. Phys. W.. Gen. Hosp. Edin.; Ho. Surg. Roy. Infirm. Edin.

FOX, Robin Andrew The Health Centre, Coker Close, Bicester Tel: 01869 249333 — MB BS 1991 Lond.; MRCP UK 1994.

FOX, Ronald Howard 26 St Peter's Way, Chorleywood, Rickmansworth WD3 5QE Tel: 01923 283107 — MRCS Eng. LRCP Lond. 1946; DSc Lond. 1966, PhD 1953, MB BS 1946; MRCP Lond. 1972. (St. Bart.) Socs: Physiol. Soc. & Med. Research Soc. Prev: on Scientif. Staff Div. Human Physiol. Nat. Inst. Med. Research Lond.; Ho. Phys. Med. Profess. Unit. St. Bart. Hosp.; Hosp. Pract. Geriat. Day Hosp. (Shrodells Wing) Watford Gen. Hosp.

FOX, Rosemary 46 Heol Don, Whitchurch, Cardiff CF14 2AS — MB BCh 1984 Wales.

FOX, Sally Elizabeth (Rawlinson) 9 Shire Close, Bagshot GU19 5RA Email: sallyfox@barclays.net; 9 Shire Close, Bagshot GU19 5RA Email: sallyfox@barclays.net — MB BS 1992 Lond.; MRCP Lond. 1996. (Royal Free Hosp. Sch. Of Med.)

FOX, Sally Elizabeth Stonewold, 51 Ben Rhydding Road, Ilkley LS29 8RN — MB ChB 1980 Sheff.; MRCGP 1987; DCH RCP Lond. 1984. Staff Grade (Community Paediat.) W. Yorks.

FOX, Selina 22 St Davids Drive, South Anston, Sheffield S25 5DQ — MB BS 1991 Lond.

FOX, Sharon Ann Elm Barn, The Fields, Hingham, Norwich NR9 4JG — BM BS 1988 Nottm.; DRCOG 1992; DCH RCP Lond. 1990.

FOX, Simon James St Phillips Chambers, Fountain Court, Steelhouse Lane, Birmingham B4 6DR Tel: 0121 246 7000 — MB BS 1990 Lond.; Dip. Law Lond. 1993. Barrister, N. Circuit. Prev: SHO (Cas. & Neurosurg.) Wellington Hosp. NZ; Ho. Surg. Char. Cross Hosp. Lond.; Ho. Phys. St. Richard's Hosp. Chichester.

FOX, Sonia Doreen 51 Crespigny Road, London NW4 3DU Tel: 020 8202 9244 — MB BCh 1937 Wales; BSc 1934, MB BCh Wales 1937, DPH 1941. (Cardiff) Prev: Asst. MOH City Cardiff; Res. Med. Off. Llandough Hosp. Penarth.

FOX, Stephen Foxleigh Family Surgery, Henry Street, Leigh WN7 2PE Tel: 01942 602020 Fax: 01942 609039 — MB ChB 1975 Liverp.; APLS 1996 (Adv Life Support Grp); DA (UK) 1989 Roy Coll Anaesth.; ATLS Roy. Coll. Surg. Lond. 1998. GP Leigh Lancs.; Med. Off. (A & E) Roy. Liver. Childr. Hosp.; Lect. to Acumedic Foundat. Socs: Active Acupunc. Gen. Pract. & Hosp.; Chinese Med. Regist.; Small Pract.s Assn. Vice Chairm. (Nat.).

FOX, Stephen Bernard 18B Frognal Gardens, Hampstead, London NW3 6XA — MB ChB 1986 Bristol; BSc (Hons.) Bristol 1983, MB ChB 1986. Research Fell. Univ. Oxf. Nuffield Dept. Path. Prev: Lect. & Hon. Sen. Regist. (Path.) Univ. Sheff. Med. Sch.; SHO (Path.) John Radcliffe Hosp. Oxf.

FOX, Susan Helen Flat 71, Lancaster House, 71 Whitworth St., Manchester M1 6LQ — MB ChB 1990 Manch.

FOX, Thomas Peter Grange Medical Centre, Seacroft Crescent, Leeds LS14 6NX Tel: 0113 295 1801 Fax: 0113 295 1799 — MB ChB 1982 Leeds; MRCGP 1988; DCH RCP Lond. 1984. GP Leeds.

FOX, Timothy David Castley Gamages Lodge, Audley End, Saffron Walden CB11 4JJ Tel: 01799 540860 Fax: 01799 542030 Email: timfox.gamages@dial.pipex.com; Camages Lodge, Audlem End., Safforn Walden CB11 4JJ Tel: 01799 540860 Fax: 01799 542030 Email: timfox.gamages@dial.pipe-x.com — MB BS 1973 Lond.; Member of the British Association of Psychothesapists 1997; MRCP (UK) 1977. (St Georges Hospital London) p/t Psychoanalytic Psychotherapist; Assoc. Edr. Drug & Therap Bull. Prev: Princip., the Surg. Buckden, Huntingdom, Cambs.

FOX, Valerie Mary (retired) Longs Camps, St Sampsons, Guernsey GY2 4UQ Tel: 01481 720940 — MB BS 1949 Lond.; MRCS Eng. LRCP Lond. 1949; DCH Eng. 1953. Prev: Ho. Surg. Fulham Hosp.

FOX, Victoria Judith Clare 129 Croydon Road, London SE20 7TT — MB BS 1991 Lond.

FOX, Vivian Edward Noel North Hill Surgery, 18 North Hill, Colchester CO1 1DZ Tel: 01206 578070 Fax: 01206 769880; 22 Queens Road, Colchester CO3 3PB Tel: 01206 540919 Fax: 01206 769194 Email: foxes@queens.frech.co.uk — BM 1979 Soton.; MRCGP 1983; DRCOG 1982; Dip. Occ. Med. 1998. (Soton.) Med. Off. Betts (UK) Colchester Inst. & Essex Co. Newspapers. Socs: Soc. Occup. Med.; GP Asthma Gp. Prev: Trainee GP Colchester VTS; SHO (Cas.) Soton. Gen. Hosp.; Ho. Phys. W.. Hosp. Soton.

FOX, Wallace, CMG 28 Mount Ararat Road, Richmond TW10 6PG Tel: 020 8940 9662 — MB BS 1943 Lond.; MD (Distinc.) Lond. 1951; FRCP Lond. 1962, M 1950; MRCS Eng. LRCP Lond. 1943; FFCM 1976, M 1973. (Guy's) Emerit. Prof. Community Therap. Cardiothoracic Inst. Lond. Univ. Lond. Socs: Corr. Mem. Mexican Nat. Acad. Med.; Hon. Foreign Corr. Mem. Argentine Nat. Acad. Med. Prev: Cons. Phys. & Dir. MRC Tuberc. & Chest Dis. Unit Brompton Hosp.Lond.; WHO Sen. Med. Off. Tuberc. Chemother. Centre, Madras; Asst. Chest Phys. Chest Clinic, Hammersmith.

FOX, William Thomas Adam 22 Ravenswood Avenue, Crowthorne RG45 6AY — MB BS 1996 Lond.

FOX, Zoe Denise Flat 4, Kingsley House, N.D.D.H., Raleigh Park, Barnstaple EX31 4JB Tel: 01271 322577 Ext: 2854 Fax: 01271 322577 — BM BS 1997 Nottm. GP VTS, Barnstable.

FOX-HILEY, Paul Jonathan St Lukes Hospital, Blackmoorfoot Road, Huddersfield HD4 5RQ Tel: 01484 846128 Email: paul.fox-hiley@virgin.net — MB BS 1984 Lond.; MRCPsych 1991. (Lond. Hosp. Med. Coll.) Cons. Psychiat. St. Lukes Hosp. Huddersfield. Prev: Sen. Regist. (Psychiat.) Roy. Lond. Hosp.; Regist. (Psychiat.) Claybury Hosp. Woodford Bridge.

FOX-MALE, Patricia Overdown, 23 Richmond Road, Barnet EN5 1SA Tel: 020 8441 1732 Fax: 020 8441 1732 — MB BS 1971 Lond.; MRCS Eng. LRCP Lond. 1971; DObst RCOG 1973. (Roy. Free) Prev: Med. Off. Lifestyle AMI Portland Hosp. Lond.; SCMO Brent & Harrow AHA; SHO Obst. Edgware Gen. Hosp.

FOX-RUSSELL, Pamela Mary (retired) Birchcroft, The Sands, Farnham GU10 1ND Tel: 01252 782627 — LRCPI & LM, LRSCI & LM 1955; LRCPI & LM, LRCSI & LM 1955; LAH Dub. 1954; MFCM Eng. 1974; DPH Eng. 1963.

FOX-RUSSELL, William (retired) 1 Park Gate, Park Road, London N2 8DJ Tel: 020 8444 8714 — MB BS 1956 Lond.; MRCP (UK) 1972; DCH Eng. 1962; DObst RCOG 1960. Cons. Geriat. City & E. Lond. AHA (T). Prev: Sen. Regist. (Geriat. Med.) Chelsea & Kensington AHA (T).

FOXELL, Richard Maurice Dorset County Hospital, Williams Avenue, Dorchester DT1 2JY Tel: 01305 251150 Fax: 01305 254688; The Old Rectory, West Stafford, Dorchester DT2 8AB — MB BS 1973 Lond.; FFA RCS Eng. 1980; DObst RCOG 1975. Cons. Anaesth. W. Dorset Hosps. Prev: Sen. Regist. (Anaesth.) Soton. & Winchester HAs.

FOXEN, Mr Eric Harry Miles (retired) Chestnuts, Allington, Devizes SN10 3NN Tel: 01380 860371 Email: milesfoxen@aol.com — FRCS Eng. 1948; MRCS Eng. LRCP Lond. 1942; DLO Eng. 1944. Cons. Surg. ENT Dept. W.m. Hosp. Lond. Prev: Surg. i/c ENT Dept. W.m. Hosp. & W.m. Childr. Hosp. Lond.

FOXEN, Patricia Portugal Place Health Centre, Portugal Place, Wallsend NE28 6RZ Tel: 0191 262 5252 Fax: 0191 262 5252; 34 Queens Way, Tynemouth, North Shields NE30 4NS Tel: 0191 257 4924 — MB BChir 1989 Camb.

FOXLEY, Michael Ewen MacDonald Craig Nevis Surgery, Belford Road, Fort William PH33 6BU; 2 Achaphubuil, Fort William PH33 7AL Tel: 01397 772775 Fax: 01397 700655 — MRCS Eng. LRCP Lond. 1973; DA Eng. 1977. (Middlx.) Prev: Clin. Asst. (Anaesth.) Belford Hosp. Fort William; SHO (Paediat.) St. Albans City Hosp.; SHO (Anaesth.) Middlx. Hosp. Lond.

FOXTON, Richard Hartas, MBE (retired) 45 Gainsborough Lane, Scawby, Brigg DN20 9BY Tel: 01652 658332 Email: richardfoxton@virgin.net — MB ChB Leeds 1943; DMJ (Clin.) Soc. Apoth. Lond. 1972. Prev: Capt. RAMC.

FOXTON, Theresa Mary Weston General Hospital, Grange Road, Uphill, Weston Super Mare BS23 4TQ Tel: 01934 636363 Email: tfoxton@doctors.org.uk — MB ChB 1985 Glas.; DFFP 1994; DRCOG 1993; DA RCP (UK) 1991. (University of Glasgow) Clin. Asst. (Gen. Med. & Cardiol.) W.on Gen. Hosp. Socs: Brit. Soc. of Echocardiography. Prev: Trainee GP E. Quay Med. Centre Bridgwater; Regist. Rotat. (Med.) Liverp.

FOXWORTHY, Mr James Vincent King Acre, Corby Hill, Carlisle CA4 8QA — MB ChB 1974 Glas.; FRCS Glas. 1979. (Glas.) Regist. (Surg.) I. of Man Health Servs. Bd.

FOXWORTHY, Mary (retired) 16 Mornington Walk, Ham, Richmond TW10 7LY — MB BCh BAO 1954 NUI; BA Kingston Univ. 1996. Prev: Princip. Phys. (Child Health) Richmond Twickenham & Roehampton DHA.

FOXWORTHY, Mr Michael Patrick Department of Orthopaedics, Crosshouse Hospital, Kilmarnock KA2 0BE Tel: 01563 521133 — MB ChB Glas. 1986; FRCS (Orth.) 1997; FRCS Glas. 1990; Dip. Bioeng. Strathclyde 1996. Cons. Orthop. Surg. CrossHo. Hosp. Kilmarnock.

FOY, Charles John 6 St Johns Avenue, Belfast BT7 3JE — MB BCh BAO 1989 Belf.; MRCP (UK) 1993.

FOY, Dina Maria Walderslade Village Surgery, 62A Robin Hood Lane, Chatham ME5 9LQ; 7 Greenhurst Road, West Norwood, London SE27 0LH — MB BS 1983 Lond.; MRCGP 1988; DCH RCP Lond. 1987. Trainee GP Chatham. Prev: Family Health Progr. Adviser, Vanuatu, S. Pacific.

FOY, Gillian Elm Tree Farm, 90 Elm Tree Road, Locking, Weston Super Mare BS24 8EH Tel: 01934 823334 — MB ChB 1969 Liverp.; DObst RCOG 1972. (Lond.) Clin. Med. Off. W.on Area Health Trust.

FOY, John Gerard Donnelly Foy and Partners, 106 Splott Road, Splott, Cardiff CF24 2XY Tel: 029 2046 2848 Fax: 029 2045 2123; 96 Penylan Road, Penylan, Cardiff CF23 5HX Tel: 029 2049 8501 Email: gerry_foy@msn.com — MB ChB 1977 Glas.

FOY, Judith Margaret Department of Anaesthetics, University Hospital of Wales, Heath Park, Cardiff CF14 4XW Tel: 029 2074 7747; 96 Penylan Road, Penylan, Cardiff CF23 5HX — MB BCh 1963 Wales; FFA RCS Eng. 1968. (Cardiff) Cons. (Anaesth.) Univ. Hosp. Wales Cardiff. Prev: Sen. Regist. (Anaesth.) Univ. Hosp. Wales Cardiff; Lect. (Anaesth.) Welsh Nat. Sch. Med. Cardiff; Teachg. Fell. in Anaesth. Boston Univ. Hosp., U.S.A.

FOY, Julia Mary 140 Ballynoe Road, Downpatrick BT30 8AT — MB BCh BAO 1992 Belf.

FOY, Mr Michael Anthony Ridgeway Hospital, Moormead Road, Wroughton, Swindon SN4 9DD Tel: 01793 814848 Fax: 01672 512810; Leigh Hill, Savernake, Marlborough SN8 3BH Tel: 01672 810230 — BM Soton. 1977; FRCS Ed. 1982. Cons. Orthop. Surg. P.ss Margt. Hosp. Swindon. Socs: Fell. Roy. Soc. Med.; Medico-Legal Soc.; Brit. Orthop. Assn. Prev: Cons. Orthop. Surg. RAF Hosp. Wroughton; Sen. Regist. (Fract. & Orthop. Surg.) Univ. Hosp. Qu. Med. Centre Nottm.; Sen. Regist. (Orthop.) RAF Hosp. Ely.

FOY, Mr Patrick Michael The Walton Centre for Neurology and Neurosurgery, Lower Lane, Fazakerley, Liverpool L9 7LJ Tel: 0151 525 3611 Fax: 0151 529 5500 — MB ChB Leeds 1970; FRCS Eng. 1975.

FOY, Robert Colin Department of Obs & Gyn, University of Edinburgh, 37 Chalmers St., Edinburgh EH3 9ER Email:

r.foy@ed.ac.uk — MB ChB 1988 Ed.; DCH Lond. 1991; MRCGP 1992; MSc 1995; MEPHM 1997.

FOY, William Thomas 140 Ballynoe Road, Downpatrick BT30 8AT — MB BCh BAO 1988 Belf. SHO (Psychiat.) Gransha Hosp. Prev: SHO (Med.) Altnagelvin Area Hosp.

FOYLE, Marjory Florence (retired) Flat 14, 3 Lansdowne Walk, London W11 3LN Tel: 020 7229 9295 Email: mfoyle@compuserve.com — MB BS Lond. 1945; FRCPsych 1980, M 1973; MD Lond. 1999. Cons. Psychiat. to Missions. Prev: Cons. Psychiat. Interhealth 157 Waterloo Rd. Lond.

FOZARD, John Roger Heatherdale House, Compton Way, Farnham GU10 1QY — MB BS Lond. 1970; MRCS Eng. LRCP Lond. 1970; DObst RCOG 1972; FFA RCS Eng. 1974. (Roy. Free) Cons. Anaesth. Roy. Surrey Co. Hosp. Guildford. Socs: Assn. Anaesths.; Pain Soc.; World Soc. of Pain Clinicians. Prev: Sen. Regist. (Anasth.) Middlx. Hosp. Lond.; Regist. & SHO (Anaesth.) Lond. Hosp.

FOZARD, Mr Jonathan Basil James Royal Bournemouth Hospital, Castle Lane E., Bournemouth BH7 7DW Tel: 01202 704614; Bedborough, Uddens Drive, Wimborne BH21 7BQ — MB BS 1979 Lond.; MS Lond. 1987; FRCS Eng. 1983. Cons. Surg. Roy. Bournemouth Hosp. Prev: Lect. & Hon. Sen. Regist. (Surg.) Univ. Wales Coll. of Med. Cardiff.; Clin. Fell. (Colon & Rectal Surg.) Mayo Clinc, USA; Regist. (Surg.) St. Jas. Univ. Hosp. Leeds.

FOZARD, Lindy Anne Weybridge Health Centre, 22 Church Street, Weybridge KT13 8DW Tel: 01932 853366 Fax: 01932 844902; 15 Vaillant Road, Weybridge KT13 9EP Tel: 01932 855753 — MB BS 1984 Lond.; MRCGP 1989; DRCOG 1988. Prev: Trainee GP Chertsey VTS; SHO (O & G) St. Peter's Hosp. Chertsey; SHO (Paediat.) Heatherwood Hosp. Ascot.

FOZZARD, Miss Constance Ethel (retired) 64 Lemon Street, Truro TR1 2PN Tel: 01872 276160 Fax: 01872 276160 Email: constance@cfozzard.freeserve.co.uk — MB BS 1958 Lond.; FRCS Eng. 1967; FRCOG 1979, M 1964. Hon. Sen. Lect. (Obst. & Gyn.) Univ. Bristol. Prev: Cons. O & G Roy. Cornw. Hosps. Trust.

FRACKOWIAK, Professor Richard Stanislaus Joseph Wellcome Department of Cognitive Neurology, Institute of Neurology, 12 Queen Square, London WC1N 3BG Tel: 020 7833 7456 Fax: 020 7813 1445 Email: r.frackowiak@fil.ion.ucl.ac.uk — MB BChir 1975 Camb.; DSc Lond 1996; MD Camb. 1982, MA 1975; FRCP Lond. 1987, M 1976; Docteur Honoris causa, Liege 1999. (Camb. & Middlx.) Director, Inst. of Neurol., Univ. Coll., Lond.; Prof. & Head Wellcome Dept. Cognitive Neurol. Inst. Neurol. Lond.; Dir. Leopold Muller Func.al Imaging Laborat.; Cons. Nat. Hosp. Nerv. Dis.; Adjunct Prof. Neurol. Cornell Univ. Med. Sch., NY. Socs: Assn. Brit. Neurol.; French Soc. Neurol. & Academia Europ.; Belgian Roy. Acad. Med. Prev: Prof. Clin. Neurol. Roy. Postgrad. Med. Sch. & Inst. Neurol.; Cons. Neurol. Hammersmith Hosp. Lond.; MRC Clin. Sci. Cyclotron Unit.

FRADD, Mr Simon Oakley Greenwood and Sneinton Family Medical Centre, 249 Sneinton Dale, Sneinton, Nottingham NG3 7DQ Tel: 0115 950 1854 Fax: 0115 958 0044 — MB BS 1976 Lond.; BSc (Hons.) Lond. 1973, MB BS 1976; FRCS Eng. 1983. (Westm.) Mem. GMSC Negotiators; Mem. GMC. Socs: BMA & JCPTGP; Nottm. Non-Fundholders Exec. Prev: Mem. Med. Pract. Comm.; Regist. (Gen. Surg.) Burton Gen. Hosp.; Regist. (Urol.) Univ. Hosp. Wales Cardiff.

FRADD, Victoria Jane Neonatal Unit, Birmingham Heartlands Hospital, Solihull B91 2NL; Lode Heath Cottage, 74 School Lane, Solihull B91 2NL — MB BS 1988 Lond.; MRCP 1995 (UK); MRCP (UK) 1995. (Guy's Hosp.) Specialist Regist. (Paediat.) Heartlands NHS Trust Birm. Socs: Brit. Assn. of Perinatal Med. Prev: Sen. Regist. (Paediat.) St Richard's Chichester; Sen. Regist. (Paediat.) St Geo.'s Hosp. Lond.; SPR Birm. Wom.s Hosp.

FRAENKEL, Mildred (retired) 78 Shaftesbury Avenue, Kenton, Harrow HA3 0RE Tel: 020 8909 3914 — MB BCh BAO 1950 Dub.; BA Dub. 1948; LAH Dub. 1952; MPSI 1952. Prev: GP Lond.

FRAIN, Anastasia Elizabeth Pickering 6, North Tees General Hospital, Stockton-on-Tees TS19 8PE; 17 Arncliffe Avenue, Stockton-on-Tees TS18 3QB — MB ChB 1988 Bristol. SHO (Med.) N. Tees Gen. Hosp.

FRAIN, Isobel Katherine Margaret 151 Knighton Lane E., Leicester LE2 6FT — MB ChB 1989 Leic.

FRAIN, John Desmond James, RD 51 Tynemouth Street, London SW6 2QS — MB BCh BAO 1947 NUI.

FRAIN, John Patrick James Pickering 6, North Tees General Hospital, Hardwick, Stockton-on-Tees TS19 8PE; 4 Ferndene Drive, Long Eaton, Nottingham NG10 3RR — MB ChB 1989 Bristol. Demonst. (Anat.) Univ. Newc.

FRAIN, Simon Paul Thomas 349 Holyhead Road, Wellington, Telford TF1 2EZ — MB ChB 1982 Manch.

FRAIN-BELL, Catherine Elaine Easson (retired) Woodlands, Forfar Road, Coupar Angus, Blairgowrie PH13 9AN Tel: 01828 628465 — MB ChB St. And. 1948; FFCM 1982, M 1972; FRCPCH 1997; DCH Eng. 1950. Prev: Cons. Paediat. (Educat. Med.) Tayside HB.

FRAIN-BELL, Lockhart Dumfries & Galloway Royal Infirmary, Nithbank, Dumfries DG1 4AP — MB ChB 1944 St. And.; MB ChB (Commend.) St. And. 1944; FFR 1958; DMRD Ed. 1955. (St. And.) Radiol. Dumfries & Galloway Roy. Infirm. Socs: Fell. Roy. Soc. Med.; Brit. Inst. Radiol. Prev: Asst. Radiol. St. Thos. Hosp. Lond.; Sen. Regist. in Radiodiag. Dundee Roy. Infirm. & Tutor in Clin.; Radiol. Univ. St. And.

FRAIS, Montague Mark 241 Mather Avenue, Liverpool L18 9UD Tel: 0151 427 7172 — MB ChB Leeds 1939. (Leeds) Prev: Res. Med. Off. Leeds Pub. Disp. & Middleton Sanat.

FRAISE, Adam Paul Microbiology Department, City Hospital, Dudley Road, Birmingham B18 7QH; 11 Crosbie Road, Birmingham B17 9BG — MB BS 1983 Newc.; MRCPath 1990; FRCPath 1998. Cons. Microbiol. City Hosp. Birm.; Hon. Sen. Lect. Dept. Infec. Univ. Birm. Socs: Treas. Of the Hosp. Infec. Soc. Prev: Clin. Lect. (Bacteriol.) Oxf. Univ.

FRAISE, Mary Claire Cofton Medical Centre, 2 Robinsfield Drive, Off Longbridge Lane, West Heath, Birmingham B31 4TU Tel: 0121 693 4414 — BM 1986 Soton. Prev: Trainee GP Oxf.

FRAME, Alan Gibson Shanklin Medical Centre, 1 Carter Road, Shanklin PO37 7HR Tel: 01983 862245 Fax: 01983 862310; Greystones, High St, Newchurch, Sandown PO36 0NN Tel: 01983 864646 — MB BS 1975 Lond.

FRAME, Alexander (retired) West Lintmailing, Manse St, Galashiels TD1 1NA Tel: 01896 753739 — MB ChB 1962 Ed.; MRCGP 1975; DObst RCOG 1973; DPH Lond. 1967; DCH RCPS Glas. 1964.

FRAME, Archibald Hamilton (retired) 59 Russell Drive, Bearsden, Glasgow G61 3BB Tel: 0141 942 6040 — MB ChB 1957 Glas.; FRCP Ed. 1979, M 1966; FRCP Glas. 1977, M 1966; FRCPsych 1987, M 1972; DPM Ed. & Glas. 1963; DObst RCOG 1958. Prev: Cons. Psychiat. Stobhill Gen. Hosp. Glas.

FRAME, David Wilson Fenwick Road Surgery, 261 Fenwick Road, Giffnock, Glasgow G46 6JX Tel: 0141 531 6993 Fax: 0141 531 6997 — MB ChB 1987 Glas.; MRCGP 1992; DFFP 1993.

FRAME, James (retired) 40 West Coats Road, Cambuslang, Glasgow G72 8AD Tel: 0141 641 8922 — MB ChB 1951 Glas.; DObst RCOG 1957. Prev: Phys. i/c BUPA Med. Centre Glas.

FRAME, Mr James Donaldson St Andrews Centre for Plastic Surgery and Burns, Broomfield Hospital, Chelmsford CM1 7ET Tel: 01277 516199 Email: framejames@aol.com — MB BS 1977 Lond.; FRCS Eng. 1982; FRCS Ed. 1982; FRCS (Plast Surg.) 1989; MRCS Eng. LRCP Lond. 1977. (St. Bart.) Cons. Plastic Surg. St And.Centre for Plastic & Burns Chelmsford; Sen. Lect. (Plastic Surg.) St Barts Hosp. Lond. Socs: Brit. Assn. Plast. Surgs.; Brit. Assn. Aesthetic Plastic Surgs.; (Comm.) Internat. Soc. Burn Injuries. Prev: Cons. Plastic Surg. NE Thames Regional Plastic Surg. & Burns Unit St. Andrews Hosp. Billericay; Sen. Regist. (Plastic Surg.) St. And. Hosp. Billericay; Regist. (Plastic Surg.) Mt. Vernon Hosp. N.wood.

FRAME, John 2 Gilchrist Row, St Andrews KY16 8XU Tel: 01334 74580 — MB ChB 1949 Glas. (Glas.) Sen. Lect. (Biol. & Pre Clin. Med.) St. And. Socs: Anat. Soc. Gt. Brit. & Path. Soc. Prev: Sen. Lect. (Anat.) St. Salvator's Coll. Univ. St. And.; SHO (Orthop.) Killearn Hosp.; Capt. RAMC.

FRAME, Mary Alice 59 Russell Drive, Bearsden, Glasgow G61 3BB Tel: 0141 942 6040 — MB BS 1959 Lond.; DPM Ed. & Glas. 1965; DObst RCOG 1961; DCH Eng. 1962. (Char. Cross.)

FRAME, Mary Henderson Elmgrove, 9 Lenzie Road, Stepps, Glasgow G33 6DU — LRCP LRCS 1953 Ed.; LRCP LRCS Ed. LRFPS Glas. 1953.

FRAME, Mary Young Woodside Health Centre, Barr Street, Glasgow G20 7LR Tel: 0141 531 9560 Fax: 0141 531 9572; 46

Pinewood Avenue, Lenzie, Glasgow G66 4EQ — MB ChB 1980 Glas.; MRCGP 1984; DRCOG 1982.

FRAME, Robert James Corner Cottage, Beoley Court, Icknield St., Beoley, Redditch B98 9AL Tel: 01527 61771 — LRCP LRCS 1944 Ed.; LRCP LRCS Ed. LRFPS Glas. 1944. (Anderson Coll. Glas.)

FRAME, William Douglas Glasgow & West of Scotland Blood Transfusion Service, Law Hospital, Carluke ML8 5ES Tel: 01698 373315 Fax: 01698 376291 — MB ChB 1978 Glas. Assoc. Specialist Transfus. Med.

FRAME, William Thomas 46 Pinewood Avenue, Lenzie, Glasgow G66 4EQ Tel: 0141 776 4893 — MB ChB 1977 Glas.; FFA RCS Eng. 1982. (Glasgow) Cons. Anaesth. Glas. Roy. Infirm.; Clin. Dir. (Anaesth. Theatres & Intens. Care).

FRAME, William Tinto (retired) The Surgery, Frew Terrace, Irvine KA12 9DY Tel: 01294 72326 — MB ChB 1952 Glas.; MRCGP 1972; DObst RCOG 1956. Prev: GP Irvine.

FRAMPTON, Catherine The Tump, Gwehelog, Usk NP15 1RD Tel: 01291 673705 — MB BCh 1995 Wales. (University of Wales, College of Medicine) SHO Psychiat. P.ss of Wales Hosp. Bridgend S. Wales. Prev: SHO (Paediat.) P.ss of Wales Hosp. Bridgend S. Wales; SHO (A & E) P.ss of Wales Hosp. Bridgend S. Wales; GP Regist. Portway Surg. Portway Porthcawl.

FRAMPTON, David Rodmell (retired) The Old Bake House, 315 Main Road, Broomfield, Chelmsford CM1 7AX Tel: 01245 441976 Fax: 01245 441976 — MB BS 1963 Lond.; MRCGP 1975; DCH Eng. 1966; DObst RCOG 1965. Prev: Med. Director Farleigh Hospice Chelmsford.

FRAMPTON, John (retired) 11 Cloister Way, Leamington Spa CV32 6QE Tel: 01926 428383 — MB BS 1955 Lond.; MD Lond. 1966; FRCOG 1975, M 1962. Examr. CMB, PLAB & RCOG. Prev: Cons. O & G Warwick Hosp.

FRAMPTON, Maria Ann 124 Mill Road, Colchester CO4 5LL — MB BCh BAO 1990 NUI.

FRAMPTON, Mr Michael Charles, Surg. Cdr. RN Retd. ENT Department, Bedford Hospital (South Wing), Kempston Road, Bedford MK42 9DJ Tel: 01234 792113 Fax: 01234 795860 Email: michael.frampton@bedhos.anylox.nhs.uk; The Little House, The Drive, Church Lane, Oakley, Bedford MK43 7ST Tel: 01234 822181 Fax: 01234 826908 — MB BS 1975 Lond.; FRCS (Orl.) Eng. 1982. (St. Thos.) Cons. ENT Surg. Bedford Hosp. Socs: Fell. Roy. Soc. Med.; Harveian Soc. Prev: Cons. ENT Surg. RN Hosp. Haslar; Sen. Regist. (Head & Neck Unit) Roy. Marsden Hosp. Lond.; Ho. Surg. St. Thos. Hosp. Lond.

FRAMPTON, Simon Peter Leyland House Surgery, 18 Derby Street, Ormskirk L39 2BY Tel: 01695 579501 Fax: 01695 571724; 32 Redcliffe Gardens, Aughton, Ormskirk L39 4UR — MB ChB 1985 Liverp.; DRCOG 1989; Cert. Family Plann. JCC 1988. Socs: Brit. Assn. Sport & Med. Prev: Clin. Asst. (Genitourin. Med.) Ormskirk Dist. Gen. Hosp.; SHO (Anaesth.) S.port & Formby Dist. Gen. Hosp.; Trainee GP/SHO Warrington Dist. Gen. Hosp. VTS.

FRANC, Nicola Louise Hillcote, Doctors Commons Road, Berkhamsted HP4 3DR — MB BS 1998 Newc.; MB BS Newc 1998.

FRANCE, Anthony James Minewells Hospital, East Block Level 4, Dundee DD1 9SY Tel: 01382 496456 Fax: 01382 425650 Email: tony.france@tuht.scot.nhs.uk — MB BChir 1978 Camb.; MB Camb.1979, BChir 1978; MA Camb. 1978, BA 1975; FRCP Ed. 1995; MRCP (UK) 1981. (Magdalene Coll. Camb. & St. Thos. Hosp. Lond.) Cons. Phys. (Infec., ImmunoDefic. & Respirat. Dis.) NHS Tayside Dundee; Hon. Sen. Lect. (Med.) Univ. Dundee. Socs: Brit. Infec. Soc.; Brit. Thorac. Soc.; Scott. HIV and AIDS Gp. Prev: Sen. Regist. Gen. Med. & Communicable Dis.s Edin.; Regist. (Respirat. Med.) Edin.; Nat. Panel Specialists (Infec. Dis.) The Scott. Office.

FRANCE, Dorothy McCulloch Deanlands, Stockcroft Road, Balcombe, Haywards Heath RH17 6LN Tel: 01444 811586 Fax: 01444 811586 Email: d.france@btopenword.com — MB ChB Glas. 1964; FRCP Lond. 1986; MRCP (UK) 1970. Cons. Dermat. Surrey & Sussex Health Care Trust Crawley Hosp. & P.ss Roy. Hosp. Haywards Heath (Retd.). Socs: St. John's Hosp. Dermat. Soc.; Roy. Soc. Med. Prev: Sen. Regist. (Dermat.) Univ. Coll. Hosp. Lond.; Regist. (Dermat.) Aberd. Roy. Infirm.

FRANCE, James Edward 18 Broadshoard, Cowbridge CF71 7DB Tel: 01446 773351 — MB BS 1993 Lond.; BSc (Hons.) Lond. 1990. SHO (Med.) Co. Hosp. Hereford. Prev: SHO (Anaesth.) P.ss of Wales Hosp. Bridgend; SHO (A & E) St. Mary's Hosp. Lond.

FRANCE, Jonathan Keith 3 Mowbray Court, Kirkby Malzeard, Ripon HG4 3RU — MB BS 1994 Lond.

FRANCE, Margaret Mary Withnell Health Centre, Railway Road, Withnell, Chorley PR6 8UA Tel: 01254 830311 Fax: 01254 832337 — MB ChB 1978 Manch.

FRANCE, Martin John Norfolk Park Health Centre, Tower Drive, Sheffield S2 3RE Tel: 0114 276 9661 Fax: 0114 276 9471 — MB BS 1985 Lond.; BSc Lond. 1982, MB BS 1985.

FRANCE, Michael William Department of Chemical Pathology, Manchester Royal Infirmary, Oxford Road, Manchester M13 9WL Tel: 0161 276 1234 — MB BS 1986 Lond.; MSc Surrey 1975; BSc Wales 1971; FRCPath 1991, M 1979. Cons. Chem. Path. Manch. Roy. Infirm.; Dir. (Laborat. Med.) Centr. Manch. Hosp. & Community NHS Trust. Prev: Regist. (Chem. Path.) Epsom Gen. Hosp.

FRANCE, Richard The Medical Centre, Oaklands, Yateley GU46 7LS Tel: 01252 872333 Fax: 01252 860236 — MB BS 1961 Lond.; DObst RCOG 1964. (St. Bart.) Med. Off. Frimley Pk. Hosp. Socs: Fell. Roy. Soc. Med.; Stress Managem. Working Party RCGP; (Chairm.) Brit. Assn. Behavioural & Cognitive Psychothers. Prev: Clin. Asst. (ENT) Aldershot Gen. Hosp.; Ho. Phys., Ho. Surg. (Obst.) & SHO (ENT) St. Helier Hosp. Carshalton.

FRANCE, Robert Dennis (retired) Sandford, Streamcross, Claverham, Bristol BS49 4LL Tel: 01934 835849 Fax: 01934 834509 — MB BChir Camb. 1954; LMSSA Lond. 1952. Prev: Dep. Sec. Med. Protect. Soc.

FRANCES, Vino Medway Hospital, Windmill Road, Gillingham ME7 5NY — MB BS 1975 Sri Lanka; MRCPsych 1984.

FRANCIOSI, Paola Ginevra Abraham Cowley Unit, St Peter's Hospital, Chertsey KT16 0QA Tel: 01932 872010 — State DMS Catholic Univ. Rome 1970; Specialist Psychiatry Univ. of Milan 1973; MRCPsych 1983. (Catholic University, Rome) Cons. Psychother. St. Peter's Hosp. Chertsey. Prev: Sen. Regist. (Psychother.) Addenbrooke's Hosp. Camb.; Regist. (Psychiat.) St. Mary's Hosp. Lond.

FRANCIS, Adele Bushwood Oak, Irelands Lane, Lapworth, Solihull B94 5PH — MB ChB 1990 Birm.; ChB Birm. 1990.

FRANCIS, Alan Christopher Manor House Surgery, Providence Place, Bridlington YO15 2QW Tel: 01262 602661 Fax: 01262 400891 — MB ChB 1988 Liverp.; MRCGP 1994.

FRANCIS, Anne 7 St Brannocks Well Close, Braunton EX33 1BE — MB ChB 1985 Bristol.

FRANCIS, Mrs Anne Elizabeth Wythall Health Centre, May Lane, Hollywood, Birmingham B47 5PD — MB BS 1969 Lond. (Univ. Coll. Hosp.)

FRANCIS, Anthony John West Road Surgery, 170 West Road, Fenham, Newcastle upon Tyne NE4 9QB Tel: 0191 273 6364; 20 Osbaldeston Gardens, Gosforth, Newcastle upon Tyne NE3 4JE Tel: 0191 213 0747 — MB ChB 1974 Birm.; BSc (Hons.) Birm. 1971; MRCP (UK) 1979; MRCGP 1989; DFFP 1993. Prev: Sen. Regist. Dryburn Hosp. Durh.; Sen. Regist. Newc. Gen. Hosp.; Regist. (Med.) Singleton Hosp. Swansea.

FRANCIS, Antony Frank Dept of Psychiatry, Hergest Unit, Ysbyty Gwynedd, Bangor LL57 2PW Tel: 01248 384075 Fax: 01248 371397; Tal y Bont Mawr, Dwyran, Llanfairpwllgwyngyll LL61 6UU — MB BCh 1969 Wales; FRCPsych 1996; MRCPsych 1975; DPM Eng. 1974. (Welsh Nat. Sch. Med.) Cons. Psychiat. Gwynedd Hosp. Bangor. Prev: Sen. Regist. (Psychiat.) Univ. Hosp. S. Manch.; Regist. MRC Biochem. Psychiat. Unit WhitCh. Hosp. Cardiff.

FRANCIS, Carol Yvette 10 Long Acres, Wirral CH49 2SP — MB BCh 1987 Wales.

FRANCIS, Charles Mark 21 Dudley Avenue, Edinburgh EH6 4PL — BM BCh 1986 Oxf.; DPhil Oxf. 1982, MA, BM BCh 1986; MRCP (UK) 1991.

FRANCIS, Christopher Richard Thomas Bacon Road Medical Centre, 16 Bacon Road, Norwich NR2 3QX Tel: 01603 503917 Fax: 01603 458793; 5 Carrow Hill, Norwich NR1 2AA Tel: 01603 666121 — MB ChB Bristol 1980; MRCGP 1986; DGM RCP Lond. 1986; DRCOG 1985; Cert. FPA JCC 1985; DCH RCP Lond. 1984. (Univ. Bristol) Mem. Norf. Health (GP Commiss. Gp.). Socs: MPU; BMA & SHA. Prev: Trainee GP Norwich VTS; Regist. (Ment. Handicap) Little Plumstead Hosp. Norwich; SHO (Orthop.) & (A & E) Kent & Canterbury Hosp.

***FRANCIS, Claire Louise** 26 Copthall Way, New Haw, Addlestone KT15 3TX — MB ChB 1998 Birm.

FRANCIS, Claire Patricia Pittenweem and Elie Surgeries, 2 Routing Row, Pittenweem, Anstruther KY10 2RG Tel: 01333 311307; Hill House, 1 Main St, Kilconquhar, Leven KY9 1LF Tel: 01333 340302 — BM BCh 1983 Oxf.; MRCGP 1988; DRCOG 1987. (Oxf.)

FRANCIS, Darrel Parthipan 63 Queen Ediths Way, Cambridge CB1 8PL — MB BChir 1994 Camb.

FRANCIS, David Alan 1 Claverdon Drive, Sutton Coldfield B74 3AH Fax: 0121 353 7426 Email: d.a.francis@bham.ac.uk — MB ChB 1977 Manch.; MB ChB (Hons.) Manch. 1977; PhD Lond. 1987; BSc (Hons.) Manch. 1974; FRCP Lond. 1996; MRCP (UK) 1980. Sen. Lect. (Neurol.) Qu. Eliz. Hosp. Birm. & Manor Hosp. Walsall. Socs: Assoc. Mem. Assn. Brit. Neurol. Prev: Sen. Regist. (Neurol.) Nat. Hosp. Nerv. Dis. & Guy's Hosp. Lond.; Regist. Nat. Hosp. Nerv. Dis. Lond.; Clin. Asst. Moorfields Eye Hosp. Lond.

FRANCIS, Deborah Mary 35 Elsie Road, Dulwich, London SE22 8DX Tel: 020 8693 3803 — MB 1973 Camb.; MA Camb. 1974, MB 1973, BChir 1972; FFA RCS Eng. 1976. (St. Thos.) Cons. Anaesth. Lithotripter Centre St. Thos. Lond. Socs: BMA; Assn. Anaesth. GB & Irel. Prev: Clin. Lect. (Anaesth.) St. Thos. Hosp. Med. Sch. Lond.; Research Assoc. Anaesth. Brigham & Wom. Hosp. & Harvard Med. Sch. Boston, USA; Sen. Regist. (Anaesth.) St. Thos. Hosp. Lond.

FRANCIS, Eileen Mary 49 Glen Avenue, Worsley, Manchester M28 2RP Tel: 0161 790 9766 — MB BCh BAO 1986 NUI; MRCGP 1990.

FRANCIS, Ernest Patrick The Surgery, 28 Holes Lane, Woolston, Warrington WA1 4NE Tel: 01925 653218 Fax: 01925 244767; 42 Glebe Avenue, Grappenhall, Warrington WA4 2SQ Tel: 01925 860537 — MB BCh BAO 1983 Belf.

FRANCIS, Gareth Huw The Surgery, 107 Weoley Castle Road, Weoley Castle, Birmingham B29 5QD Tel: 0121 427 1530; 72 Meadow Hill Road, Kings Norton, Birmingham B38 8DA — MB BS 1969 Lond.; DObst RCOG 1971. Prev: Hon. Sen. Lect. Dept. Med. Birm. Univ.

FRANCIS, Geoffrey Charles Linden Medical Centre, 9A Linden Avenue, Maidenhead SL6 6HD Tel: 01628 20846 Fax: 01628 789318 — MB BS 1985 Lond.; MRCGP Lond. 1989; DRCOG 1988; DGM RCP Lond. 1988.

FRANCIS, Gilbert Geoffrey 189A St James Road, Croydon CR0 2BZ Tel: 020 8684 5353 Fax: 020 8665 1229; 1A Castle Hill Avenue, Croydon CR0 0TH Tel: 01689 43636 — MB BS 1959 Lond.; MRCS Eng. LRCP Lond. 1957. (St. Geo.)

FRANCIS, Gillian Elizabeth Polymasc Pharmaceuticals plc, Fleet Road, London NW3 2EZ Tel: 020 7830 2800 Fax: 020 7830 2800 Email: admin@polymasc.com; Summer Cottage, Cave End, Reading RG4 9EH Tel: 01734 723030 — MB BS 1971 Lond.; MSc Lond. 1978, MB BS 1971; MRCPath 1983; BSc (Med) Lond 1995. (Royal Free Hospital School of Medicine) Head & Sen. Lect. (Molecular Cell Path.) Roy. Free Hosp. Sch. Med. Lond.; Chief Exec. Off. Polymasc Pharmaceut. plc. Prev: Wellcome Sen. Clin. Research Fell. Roy. Free Hosp. Sch. Med. Lond.

FRANCIS, Gillian Gwyneth Lancelyn Precinct Practice, 1 Lancelyn Precinct, Spital Road, Wirral CH63 9JP Tel: 0151 334 4019 Fax: 0151 346 1063; Windward, Fleck Lane, West Kirby, Wirral CH48 1LA Tel: 0151 625 1747 Email: 113303.3373@compuserve.com — BM BCh 1977 Oxf.; MA Oxf. 1978, BM BCh 1977; DRCOG 1980. (Oxford) GP; GP Tutor Wirral 1997.

FRANCIS, Graham John Queens Avenue Surgery, 14 Queens Avenue, Dorchester DT1 2EW Tel: 01305 262886 Fax: 01305 250607; 14 Queens Avenue, Dorchester DT1 2EW — MB BS 1979 Lond.; MRCGP 1983; DRCOG 1982. (Guy's)

FRANCIS, Gwenda Muriel (retired) 14 Bedford Road, Horsham RH13 5BJ Tel: 01403 266182 — MB BS 1939 Lond.; MRCS Eng. LRCP Lond. 1937. Prev: Sen. Ho. Surg. Roy. I. of Wight Co. Hosp. Ryde.

FRANCIS, Mr Harold Hugh (retired) Esmeralda, Carnatic Road, Mossley Hill, Liverpool L18 8BY Tel: 0151 724 4505 Fax: 0151 724 4505 — MB ChB New Zealand 1944; BSc New Zealand 1938; FRCS Ed. 1953; FRCS Eng. 1953; FRCOG 1959, M 1950. NZ Trav. Schol. Obst. & Gyn. Univ. Otago. Prev: Cons. O & G United Liverp. Hosps.

FRANCIS, Helen Claire 118 Glanmor Road, Sketty, Swansea SA2 0RS — MB ChB 1992 Leeds; BSc (Hons.) Human Biol. Lond. 1987. SHO (Gen. Surg.) Swansea. Socs: MDU.

FRANCIS, Hugh (retired) 3 Mawddach Crescent, Arthog LL39 1BJ Tel: 01341 427 — MB ChB 1943 Liverp.; DPH 1962.

FRANCIS, Hugh Bowen (retired) Dunstable Road Surgery, 163 Dunstable Road, Luton LU1 1BW Tel: 01582 23553 — MB BChir 1960 Camb.; MB Camb. 1960, BChir 1959; DObst RCOG 1961. Prev: SHO (Cas.) W. Middlx. Hosp.

FRANCIS, Huw Wesley Stephen (retired) 22 Clovelly Road, Ealing, London W5 5HE Tel: 020 8579 9589 — MB BChir 1952 Camb.; MA Camb. 1952; FFPHM RCP (UK) 1989; FFCM RCP (UK) 1972; DPH Lond. 1956. Prev: Area Med. Off. Camden & Islington AHA (T).

FRANCIS, Ian Stuart 2 Ralph Cottages, Ford Manor Road, Dormansland, Lingfield RH7 6NZ — MB BS 1992 Lond.; BDS Lond. 1985.

FRANCIS, Ithel Lloyd (retired) Powys, 5 Old Quay Close, Parkgate, South Wirral CH64 6UA Tel: 0151 336 5733 — MB ChB 1947 Liverp.; FFA RCS Eng. 1954; DA Eng. 1952. Prev: Cons. Anaesth. Mersey RHA.

FRANCIS, Jason Kevin Jacksons Farmhouse, Maltings Lane, Witham CM8 1DZ — MB BS 1996 Lond.

FRANCIS, John George 83 Bowes Hill, Rowlands Castle PO9 6BS — MB ChB 1962 Manch.; MRCS Eng. LRCP Lond. 1963; FRCOG 1980, M 1967, DObst 1964. Cons. O & G St. Mary's Hosp. Portsmouth. Socs: Blair Bell Research Soc. Prev: Sen. Regist. (O & G) Cardiff & Newport Hosps.; Research Fell. Welsh Nat. Sch. Med. Cardiff; Regist. (O & G) Wythenshawe Hosp. Manch.

FRANCIS, John Gwilym, TD (retired) The Oaks, Lower Lane, Ebford, Exeter EX3 0QT Tel: 01392 875428 — MB BS Lond. 1955; FFA RCS Eng. 1961; DA Eng. 1958; DObst RCOG 1959. Prev: Sen. Anaesth. Regist. St. Thos. Hosp. Lond.

FRANCIS, John Nicholas Thornbrook Surgery, Chapel-en-le-Frith, High Peak SK23 0RH Tel: 01298 812725; Oak House, Chapel Milton, Chapel-en-le-Frith, High Peak SK23 0QQ — MB ChB 1974 Sheff.; DRCOG 1980.

FRANCIS, Jonathan Damon 14 Beaulands Close, De Freville Avenue, Cambridge CB4 1JA Tel: 01223 31665 Email: postmaster@jonfrancis.demon.co.uk — BM 1990 Soton.; FRCA 1997. Regist. (Anaesth.) Addenbrooke's Hosp. Camb. Prev: SHO (Anaesth.) Univ. Hosp. Wales, Cardiff.

FRANCIS, Juliet Rachel 147 Lonnen Road, Wimborne BH21 7AU — MB ChB 1997 Birm.

FRANCIS, Karl Martin Jonothon Flat 4, 9 Hartfield Road, Eastbourne BN21 2AP — MB BS 1989 Lond.

FRANCIS, Kay Lesley 1 Brighton Terrace Road, Sheffield S10 1NT — MB ChB 1989 Sheff.

FRANCIS, Kollannur Sebastian Tanyfron, 199 The Barley Lea, Coventry CV3 1DZ Tel: 024 7645 8151 Fax: 024 7645 8881 — MB BS Kerala 1973. (Calicut Med. Coll. Kerala, India)

FRANCIS, Mary (retired) 4 New Court, Strides Lane, Ringwood BH24 1EE — MB BS 1943 Durh.; MD Durh. 1945; MRCS Eng. LRCP Lond. 1943; DObst RCOG 1946. Prev: Regist. (Med.) King Geo. V Hosp. Godalming.

FRANCIS, Nicholas David Charing Cross & Westminster Medical School, Department of Histopathology, Charing Cross Hospital, Fulham Palace Road, London W6 8RF Tel: 020 8746 8232 Fax: 020 8846 1364; Gable End, 46 North Park, Gerrards Cross SL9 8JP Tel: 01753 889728 — MB BS 1979 Lond.; MRCPath 1986. (St. Mary's Hosp.) Cons. (Histopath.) Hammersmith Hosp.s Trust; Mem. (Counc.) Internat. Acad. Path. Socs: Fell. Roy. Soc. Trop. Med. & Hyg.; Assn. Clin. Path.; Path. Soc. Prev: Sen. Lect. (Histopath.) Char. Cross & W.m. Med. Sch. Lond.; Lect. (Histopath.) St. Marys Hosp. Lond.

FRANCIS, Patricia Elizabeth Quane (retired) Quy Hall, Quy, Cambridge CB5 8AJ — MB BS 1944 Lond.

FRANCIS, Peter William Fairfield Surgery, 1 Park Crescent, Llanelli SA15 3AE Tel: 01554 773133 — MB BCh 1973 Wales; DPM Eng. 1981. Prev: Specialist in Psychiat. RAMC.

FRANCIS, Raymond 9 Maxwell Drive, Glasgow G41 5DR — MB ChB 1994 Dundee.

FRANCIS, Richard Randolph Maxwell 1/25 North Werber Park, Edinburgh EH4 1SY — MB BS 1988 West Indies.

FRANCIS, Rodrigues Stanley (retired) 14 Densworth Grove, Lower Edmonton, London N9 0LJ — MB BS 1954 Andhra; DIH Eng. 1966; DPH Eng. 1962. Prev: Med. Off. HM Overseas Civil Serv. 1954-1980.

FRANCIS, Roger Michael Bone Clinic, Freeman Hospital, Newcastle upon Tyne NE7 7DN Tel: 0191 223 1160 Fax: 0191 223 1161 Email: rmfrancis@compuserve.com; 4 Dene Road, Wylam NE41 8EY Tel: 01661 852642 — MB ChB 1975 Leeds; FRCP Lond. 1991; MRCP (UK) 1979. Reader (Geriat. Med.) Univ. Newc.; Cons. Phys. Freeman Hosp. Newc. Socs: Coun. Mem. Nat. Assn. for the Relief of Paget's Dis.; Internat. Bone & Mineral Soc.; Amer. Soc. for Bone & Mineral Research. Prev: Sen. Regist. (Geriat. Med.) Univ. Coll. Hosp. Lond.; Sen. Regist. (MRC Mineral Metabol. Unit) Gen. Infirm. Leeds; Research Fell. (Path.) Jewish Hosp. St. Louis, USA.

FRANCIS, Ronald Charters, TD, Lt.-Col. RAMC Retd. (retired) 301 Durham Road, Low Fell, Gateshead NE9 5AE Tel: 0191 477 8793 — MB BS 1953 Lond.; MRCS Eng. LRCP Lond. 1953; DTM & H Eng. 1963; FRCOG 1980, M 1966; DObst RCOG 1955. Prev: Cons. O & G RAMC.

FRANCIS, Rowan Nigel Kingsmuir, Forncett St Mary, Norwich NR16 1JJ — MB BS 1970 Lond.; FFA RCS Eng. 1975. (Middlx.) Cons. Anaesth. Qu. Eliz. Hosp. King's Lynn.

FRANCIS, Sadie Bentz Craighyfryd, Cambria St., Holyhead LL65 1NH Tel: 01407 764231 Fax: 01407 762159 — MB ChB 1973 Manch.; MRCPsych 1985; FRCPsych 1999. Cons. Psychiat. N. W. Wales NHS Trust. Prev: Sen. Regist. (Psychiat.) Clwyd HA; Regist. (Psychiat.) Univ. Hosp. S. Manch.; SHO (Gen. Med.) Profess. Med. Unit Manch. Roy. Infirm.

***FRANCIS, Tania** 9 Lyme Street, London NW1 0EH — BM 1997 Soton.

FRANCIS, Thottungal Antony Deepcar Medical Centre, 241-245 Manchester Road, Deepcar, Sheffield S36 2QZ Tel: 0114 288 2146 — MB BS 1968 Mysore. (Kasturba Med. Coll. Mangalore) Socs: BMA. Prev: Regist. Hartwood Hosp. Shotts.

FRANCIS, William Harvey 15 Middleton Road, Ilkley LS29 9EX — MB BS Lond. 1994; BSc Lond. 1991. (UMDS) Specialist Regist. Clin.Oncol.Cookridge Hosp. Leeds.

FRANCIS-LANG, Andrew Michael Hewletts, Love Lane, Petersfield GU31 4BU — MB BS 1992 Lond.

FRANCOMBE, James 23 Beachfield Road, Liverpool L18 3EG — MB ChB 1991 Liverp.; FRCS Eng. 1995. Specialist Regist. (Surg.) Mersey.

FRANGOULIS, Miss Medea Angelica Sutton Hospital, Consworld Road, Sutton SM2 5NF Tel: 020 8269 4359 — MB BS 1972 Lond.; FRCOphth; FRCS Eng. 1977; MRCS Eng. LRCP Lond. 1972; DO Eng. 1976. (Char. Cross) p/t Cons. Ophth. Epsom and St Helier Trust Health Auth. Merton Sutton and Wandsworth Health Auth. Prev: Sen. Regist. & Regist. Moorfields Eye Hosp. Lond.; Regist. Sutton Hosp. Surrey.

FRANK, Alexander John Martin Steyning Health Centre, Tanyard Lane, Steyning BN44 3RJ Tel: 01903 814100 Fax: 01903 812981; Penfold House, 17 High St, Steyning BN44 3GG Tel: 01903 879622 — MB BS 1963 Lond.; MRCGP 1979; Cert. Family Plann. JCC 1967; DObst RCOG 1965. (St. Bart.) Indust. Med. Adviser Shamrock Farms, Smalldole; Trainer (Gen. Pract.) SE Thames RHA. Socs: BMA. Prev: Organiser Day Release Course, Worthing; Clin. Asst. (Sclerother.) Worthing Hosp. & S.lands Hosp. Shoreham; SHO (Anaesth.) S.lands Hosp. Shoreham-by-Sea.

FRANK, Andrew Oliver Departments of Rehabilitation Medicine & Rheumatology, Northwick Park Hospital, Harrow HA1 3UJ Tel: 020 8869 2102 Fax: 020 8426 4358 — MB BS Lond. 1968; FRCP Lond. 1990; MRCP (UK) 1971. (Middlx.) Cons. Rehabil. Med. & Rheum. N.wick Pk. Hosp.; Prof. (Assoc.) Dept. Health Studies, Brunel Univ.; Cons. Rehabil. Med. Disablem. Serv. Centre, RNOH Stanmore. Socs: Brit. Soc. Rheum.; (Counc.) Soc. Research, Redhill; Brit. Soc. Rehabil. (Pres.). Prev: Clin. Dir. & Mem. Operat.al Bd. 1990-1995; Sen. Regist. (Rheum. Rehabil. & Gen. Med.) Salisbury Gen. Hosp.; Lect. (Med.) Univ. Malaya Kuala Lumpur, Malaysia.

FRANK, David Charles Cleveland Clinic, 12 Cleveland Road, St Helier, Jersey JE1 4HD Tel: 01534 722381/734121; La Fontenelle, Rue Des Fontaines, St. Martin, Jersey JE3 6EF — MB ChB 1982 Glas.; MRCGP 1987; DRCOG 1987.

FRANK, Miss Helena Janet Eye Unit, Royal Bournemouth Hospital, Castle Lane, Bournemouth Tel: 01202 303626 — MB BS 1969 Lond.; BMedSc Adelaide 1972; FRCS Eng. 1975; MRCS Eng. LRCP Lond. 1969; FCOphth 1989; DO Eng. 1974. (Roy. Free) Cons. Ophth. Eye Unit Roy. Bournemouth Hosp. Bournemouth; Ophth. Plastic Surg. & Strabismus ONLY. Socs: Europ. Soc. Ophth. & Plastic Reconstruc. Surg. Prev: Sen. Regist. Ophth. Soton. Eye Hosp. & Qu. Alexandra Hosp.; Portsmouth; Regist. (Ophth.) & SHO (Ophth.) Bristol Eye Hosp.

FRANK, Hugh Grahame (retired) 17 Hayfield Avenue, Boston Spa, Wetherby LS23 6EG Tel: 01937 842159 — MB ChB 1942 Liverp.; MD Liverp. 1952, MRad 1948; FRCR 1975; FFR 1955; DMRT Eng. 1948. Prev: Cons. (Radiother. & Oncol.) Leeds W.. HA.

FRANK, Joanna Ruth 31 Armitage Road, London NW11 8QT — BM 1995 Soton.

FRANK, Mr John David Bristol Royal Hospital for Children, Paul O'Gurvian Building, Upper Maudlin Street, Bristol BS2 8BJ Tel: 01179 285454 Fax: 01179 285701; Phippens Farm, Butcombe, Bristol BS40 7UR — MB BS Lond. 1969; FRCS Eng. 1973; MRCS Eng. LRCP Lond. 1969. (St. Mary's) Cons. Paediat. Urol. Bristol Roy. Hosp. Childr. Socs: Brit. Assn. Paediat. Surgs.; Brit. Assn. Urological Surg.s; Brit. Assn. Paediat. Urol.s. Prev: Cons. Paediat. Urol. Hosp. Childr. Gt. Ormond St.; Sen. Lect. (Paediat. Urol.) Inst. Urol. Lond.; Sen. Regist. (Surg.) St. Peters Hosp. Lond.

FRANK, John William Cosultant in Nuclear Medicine and Radiology, Hammersmith Hospitals NHS Trust, Charing Cross Hospital, London W6 8RF Tel: 020 8846 1428 Fax: 020 8846 1426 Email: jfrank@hhnt — MRCS Eng. LRCP Lond. 1971; MSc Lond. 1978, MB BS 1971; FRCR 1978; DMRD Eng. 1975; DObst RCOG 1974. (St. Bart.) Cons. (Radiol. & Nuclear Med.) Whipps Cross Hosp. Socs: Brit. Inst. Radiol. & Brit. Nuclear Med. Soc. Prev: Cons. Radiol. Soton. Univ. Hosps.

FRANK, Michael Jeffrey The Parkwood Health Centre, Long Catlis Road, Parkwood, Rainham, Gillingham ME8 9PR Tel: 01634 233491; Maryfield, 7 Hoath Lane, Wigmore, Gillingham ME8 0SL — MB ChB 1965 Manch.; MRCS Eng. LRCP Lond. 1967; DObst RCOG 1967. (Manch.) Med. Adviser Sava Centre Gillingham; Kent Final M.O. Exam. for Roy. Navy, Roy. Marines, RAF Recruitment; Med. Ref. Brit. Sub Aqua Club Kent. Prev: Med. Off. Chemelil Sugar Co. Kenya; Sen. Med. Off. (Govt.) Grand Turk; Med. Off. S. Caicos, Turks & Caicos Is.s.

FRANK, Miriam 27 Duncan Terrace, London N1 8BS Tel: 020 7278 3688 Email: miriamfk@aol.com — MB ChB 1960 N.Z.; FFA RCS Eng. 1975; DA Eng. 1971. (Otago) Sen. Lect & Hon. Cons. Anaesth. Unit Roy. Lond. Hosp. & Newham Health Dist. Socs: Anaesth. Research Soc. & Obst. Anaesth. Assn. Prev: Sen. Regist. (Anaesth.) Lond. Hosp. & Hosp. Sick Childr. Gt. Ormond St.; N.E.Thames Reg. Assessor Anaesth. Confidential Enquires into Marend Deaths.

FRANK, Nicholas Jeremy 5/10 Northwood Hall, Hornsey Lane, London N6 5PL — MB BS 1990 Lond.; MRCGP 1995; DRCOG 1994; DFFP 1993. (Lond. Hosp. Med. Coll.) Prev: GP VTS City & Hackney Lond.

FRANK, Otto Stephen, TD 14 Devonshire Place, London W1N 1PB Tel: 020 7935 0640 Fax: 020 7224 6256; 12 Montana Road, Wimbledon, London SW20 8TW Tel: 020 8946 2784 — MB BS 1963 Lond.; MRCP (UK) 1970; FRCPsych. 1982, M 1972; DPM Eng. 1968. (Char. Cross) Cons. Psychiat.Bken.Mlt.Trust.Gordon Hosps.W1; Cons. Psychiat. Riverside Ment. Health Trust. Gordon Hosp. SW1; Hon. Cons. Psychiat.Qu.Mary's Hosp.Roehampton, Roy,Hosp.Chelsea & Hosps.t John & St Eliz.Lond. Prev: Maj. RAMC, Specialist (Psychiat.) Qu. Alexandra's Milit. Hosp. Millbank; Sen. Regist. Foren. Unit Maudsley Hosp.

FRANK, Peter Ivan (retired) Bowland Road, 52 Bowland Road, Baguley, Manchester M23 1JX Tel: 0161 998 2014 Fax: 0161 945 6354 — MD Liverp. 1970, MB ChB 1957; MRCS Eng. LRCP Lond. 1957; FRCGP 1976, M 1967; DObst RCOG 1960; DCH Eng. 1959. Dir. GP Research Unit N. W. Lung Research Centre Wythershawe Hosp. Prev: GP.

FRANK, Mr Peter Leo 21 St John Street, Manchester M3 4DT Tel: 0161 834 8362 Fax: 0161 834 5722; 504 Castle Quay, Castlefield, Manchester M15 4NT — MRCS Eng. LRCP Lond. 1957; FRCS Ed. 1967. Hons. Cons. Salford HA. Socs: Fell. Roy. Soc. Med.; Eur. Spine Soc.; Soc. for Sport & Law. Prev: Cons. Orthop. & Traum. Surg. Hope Hosp., Salford Roy. Hosp., Roy. Manch. Childr. Hosp. & Worsley Rehabil. Centre Regional Pain Clinic.

FRANK, Ruth (retired) La Rocque à Chancre, Rue Du Dos D'ane, Castel GY5 7LB Tel: 01481 58470 — MB BS 1958 Lond.; MRCS Eng. LRCP Lond. 1958; DA Eng. 1961.

FRANK, Thomas George Parkside Family Practice, Eastleigh Health Centre, Newtown Road, Eastleigh SO50 9AG Tel: 023 8061 2032 Fax: 023 8062 9623; 18 Holly Hill, Bassett, Southampton SO16 7ER — MB ChB 1985 Birm.; MRCGP 1989; DRCOG 1988.

FRANK, Thomas Lesley (retired) Riseborough Hall, Marton Lane, Pickering YO18 8LU — MB BS 1943 Lond.; MRCS Eng. LRCP Lond. 1940. Prev: Ho. Surg. & Cas. Off. St. Mary Abbots Hosp. Kens.

FRANK, Timothy Laszlo Ash House, Ash Lane, Altrincham WA15 8PH — MB ChB 1989 Leeds.

FRANKAU, Timothy George May Lane Surgery, Dursley GL11 4JN Tel: 01453 540540 Fax: 01453 540570; 68 Kingshill Road, Dursley GL11 4EG Tel: 01453 543524 — MB BS 1973 Lond.; DA Eng. 1978; DObst RCOG 1976. Prev: Trainee GP Wessex VTS; Ho. Phys. St. Geo. Hosp. Lond.; Ho. Surg. Ashford Hosp. Middlx.

FRANKE, Bernd Middlesborough General Hospital, Room 2, Admin Block, Ayresome Green Lane, Middlesbrough TS5 5AZ — State Exam Med 1992 Dusseldorf.

FRANKEL, Andrew Howard 12 Sunningdale Close, Stanmore HA7 3QL — MB BS 1982 Lond.; BSc Lond. 1979, MD 1991; MRCP (UK) 1985. Cons. Phys & Nephrol. Hammersmith Hosps. Trust. Prev: Sen. Regist. (Nephrol.) Char. Cross Hosp. Lond.

FRANKEL, Eric 20 Hermon Hill, London E11 2AP Tel: 020 8989 5482 Email: efrankel@doctors.org.uk — MB BS Lond. 1939; MD Lond. 1942; FRCP Lond. 1969, M 1942; MRCS Eng. LRCP Lond. 1939. (St. Geo.) Cons. Phys. Wanstead Hosp.; Cons. Med. Claybury Ment. Hosp. Woodford Bridge. Socs: (Counc.) Hunt. Soc. Lond.; BMA. Prev: Clin. Asst. St. Geo. Hosp. & Neurol. Clinic Lond. Hosp.; Maj. RAMC, Med. Specialist.

FRANKEL, Hans Ludwig, OBE National Spinal Injuries Centre, Stoke Mandeville Hospital NHS Trust, Aylesbury HP21 8AL Tel: 01296 315852 Fax: 01296 315868; Seytons Manor, Terrick, Aylesbury HP17 0UA Tel: 01296 612215 — MB BS 1956 Lond.; FRCP Lond. 1977, M 1964; MRCS Eng. LRCP Lond. 1956. (Univ. Coll. Hosp.) Cons. & Clin. Dir. Nat. Spinal Injuries Centre Stoke Mandeville Hosp.; Cons. Star & Garter Home for Disabled Soldiers, Sailors & Airmen; Chairm. Trustees Internat. Spinal Research Trust. Socs: (Pres.) Internat. Med. Soc. Paraplegia. Prev: Sen. Regist. Stoke Mandeville Hosp.; Cas. Off. Hampstead Gen. Hosp.

FRANKEL, Jonathan Paul Wessex Neurological Centre, Southampton General Hospital, Trenoma Road, Southampton SO16 6YD Tel: 02380 796567 Fax: 02380 798793 Email: jonny@frankel.demon.co.uk — MB BS 1983 Lond.; MRCP (UK) 1988. (Univ. Coll. Hosp.) Cons. Neurol. Wessex Neurol. Centre Soton. Univ. Hosps. Trust. Prev: Sen. Regist. (Neurol.) Roy. Lond. Hosp.; Regist. (Neurol.) Nat. Hosp. Neurol. & Neurosurg. Lond. & St. Thos. Hosp. Lond.

FRANKEL, Richard John The Priory, Holybourne, Alton GU34 4HH Tel: 01420 883326 Fax: 01420 542927 Email: r.frankel@btinternet.com — MB BCh 1962 Witwatersrand; FRCP Lond. 1967. (Witwatersrand) Cons. Phys. Frimley Pk. Hosp. Frimley. Socs: Fell. RCP; Soc. Endocrinol. Prev: Sen. Med. Regist. St. Geo. Hosp. Lond.

FRANKEL, Professor Stephen John 11 Worcester Terrace, Clifton, Bristol BS8 3JW Tel: 0117 973 7054 — BM BCh Oxf. 1970; PhD Camb. 1981; DM Oxf. 1984, MA 1970; FFPHM RCP (UK) 1991; MFCM 1985. Prof. Epidemiol. & Pub. Health Med. Univ. Bristol. Prev: Dir. Health Care Eval. Unit. (Epidemiol. & Community Med.) Bristol Univ.; Sen. Lect. (Epidemiol. & Community Med.) Univ. Wales Coll. Med.; Research Fell. Clare Hall Camb.

FRANKEL, Tanya Leonora 25A Frognal, London NW3 6AR — BM BS 1997 Nottm.

FRANKENTHAL, Jacob (retired) 4 The Elms, Parker Avenue, Gosforth, Newcastle upon Tyne NE3 4BD Tel: 0191 285 7401 — LRCP LRCS Ed. LRFPS Glas. 1940; DOMS Eng. 1948. Prev: Cons. Ophth. Sunderland & Hartlepools Hosp. Gps.

FRANKISH, John Barry Burvill Street Health Centre, Burvill Street, Lynton EX35 6HA Tel: 01598 753226; Rock Lodge, Lynton EX35 6LA — MB BS 1978 Lond.; DRCOG 1980; DCH 1981; MSc (Exon) 1998. (St. Thos.) Prev: SHO (Cas.) St. Thos. Hosp. Lond.; SHO (O & G) St. Thos. Hosp. Lond.; SHO (Paediat.) Frimley Pk. Hosp. Surrey.

FRANKL, Andrew Robert 439 Archway Road, London N6 4HT — MB BS 1988 Lond.; DCH RCP Lond. 1992. (Univ. Coll. & Middlx. Sch. of Med.) Locum GP; Mem. N. Lond. & NW Thames Palliat. Care Gp. Prev: SHO (O & G) UCL Hosps.; SHO Barnet VTS; SHO (Radiother. & Oncol.) Mt. Vernon Hosp.

FRANKLAND, Alfred William London Allergy Clinic, 66 New Cavendish St., London W1G 8TD Tel: 020 7637 9711 Fax: 020 7580 9749; 46 Devonshire Close, London W1G 7BG Tel: 020 7637 1994 — BM BCh 1938 Oxf; MA Oxf. 1940, DM 1956; FRCP Lond. 1995. (St marys Lond) Cons. Lond. Allergy Clinic. Socs: (Ex-Pres.) Brit. Soc. Allergy & Clin. Immunol.; (Vice-Pres.) Internat. Assn. Aerobiol.; (Ex-Pres.) Europ. Acad. Allergol. Prev: Phys. i/c Clinic for Allergic Disorders St. Mary's Hosp. Lond.; Capt. RAMC; Ho. Phys. St. Mary's Hosp.

FRANKLAND, Andrew William Fore Street Surgery, 26 Fore Street, Totnes TQ9 5DX Tel: 01803 862671; 26 Fore Street, Totnes TQ9 5DX Tel: 01803 862671 — MRCS Eng. LRCP Lond. 1980; DCCH MRCGP 1986; DRCOG 1983. GP Totnes.

FRANKLAND, Henry William John Flat 3/1 Fords La, Dundee DD2 1DW — MB ChB 1997 Dundee.

FRANKLAND, John Charles (retired) Green Beck House, Halton Green, Lancaster LA2 6PA Tel: 01524 811382 — MB ChB 1964 Manch.; BSc (Physiol., Hons.) Manch. 1961; FRCGP 1978, M (Distinc.) 1970; DObst RCOG 1967. Prev: Assoc. Regional Advisor (Gen. Pract.) NW Region.

FRANKLAND, Susan Margaret St Damiens Surgery, 1 Place Road, Melksham SN12 6JN Tel: 01225 791212 Fax: 01225 700767 — MB ChB 1984 Leeds; MRCGP 1995.

FRANKLEN-EVANS, Mary Ursula (retired) 64 The Crossway, Portchester, Fareham PO16 8NT Tel: 01705 379922 — MRCS Eng. LRCP Lond. 1950; DCH Eng. 1953; DObst RCOG 1954. Prev: Med. Regist. W. Herts. & St. Paul's Hosps. Hemel Hempstead.

FRANKLIN, Alan James (retired) 11 Braemar Avenue, Chelmsford CM2 9PN Tel: 01245 352185 Fax: 01245 252421 — MRCS Eng. LRCP Lond. 1960; FRCP Ed. 1983, M 1968; FRCP Lond. 1982; FRCPCH 1997; DCH Eng. 1962; DObst RCOG 1962. Med. Adviser ME Assoc.; Med. Adviser W.care. Prev: Cons. Paediat. Mid Essex Hosps. Trust Chelmsford.

FRANKLIN, Mr Alfred 66 Cumberland Road, Bromley BR2 0PW Tel: 020 8464 0120 — MB ChB 1970 Liverp.; ChM Liverp. 1987, MB ChB 1970; FRCS Eng. 1976; FRCS Ed. 1976. Cons. (Orthop. Surg.) Bromley & Orpington Hosps.; Hon. Sen. Lect. (Dept. Surg.) Guys Hosp.Lond. Socs: Fell. Brit. Orthop. Assn. Prev: Sen. Regist. Rotat. (Orthop.) Guys & St. Tho. Hosp. Lond.; Hon. Sen. Regist. Fast Neutron Clinic Hammersmith Hosp. Lond.; Regist. (Orthop.) Univ. Coll. Hosp. Lond.

FRANKLIN, Clifford Bruton (retired) 95 Oldfield Road, Altrincham WA14 4BL Tel: 0161 928 3418 Fax: 0161 928 5857 Email: clifford_franklin@msn.com — MB ChB MB ChB Birm. 1955; MRCS Eng. LRCP Lond. 1955; FFA RCS Eng. 1959. Prev: Cons. Anaesth. Univ. Hosps. S. Manch. NHS Trust.

FRANKLIN, David Hamilton Chest Unit, Raigmore Hospital NHS Trust, Inverness IV2 3UJ Tel: 01463 704362 Fax: 01463 705358; Fidra, Cantray, Croy, Inverness IV2 5PS Tel: 01667 493331 — MB ChB 1964 Ed.; BSc Ed. 1964; FRCP Glas. 1994; FRCP Ed. 1980, M 1968; MRCP Lond. 1968. (Ed.) Cons. Chest Phys. Raigmore Hosp. Inverness NHS Trust; Hon. Sen. Lect. Univ. Aberd. Socs: Scott. Thoracic Soc.; Brit. Thorac. Soc. Prev: Lect. (Med.) Roy. Infirm. Edin.

FRANKLIN, Doris (retired) 95 Oldfield Road, Altrincham WA14 4BL Tel: 0161 928 3418 Fax: 0161 928 5857 Email: clifford_franklin@btinterneet.com — MB ChB MB ChB Liverp. 1956. Prev: Clin. Med. Off. Trafford HA.

FRANKLIN, George Herbert Massey (retired) The Coach House, Weston, Shrewsbury SY4 5XA Tel: 0193 924267 — MB ChB 1931 Manch. Prev: Vis. Phys. Shrops. CC Sanat. Prees Heath.

FRANKLIN, Mr Ian John Department of Vascular Surgery, Charing Cross Hospital, Fulham Palace Road, London W6 8RF Tel: 020 8846 7335 Fax: 020 8846 7330; 20A Nevern Mansions, 42 Warwick Road, London SW5 9TJ Email: ijfranklin@msn.com — MB BS 1990 Lond.; FRCS Eng. 1995. (St. Mary's Hospital) Specialist Regist. Rotat. (Gen Surg.), Char. Cross; Specialist Regist. Rotat. (Gen. Surg.) Char. Cross. Socs: Surg. Research Soc.; Vasc. Surg. Soc. GB & Irel.; Eur. Soc. Vasc. Surg. Prev: Specialist Regist. (Surg.), Lister Hosp., Imperial Coll. of Med. at Char. Cross; Lect. (Surg.) Imperial Coll.

Sch. of Med. at Char. Cross; SHO Rotat. Roy. Berks. & Battle NHS Trusts.

FRANKLIN, Professor Ian Maxwell Department of Medicine, Royal Infirmary, 10 Alexandra Parade, Glasgow G31 2ER Tel: 0141 211 1202 Fax: 0141 552 2953 Email: imf1c@clinmed.gla.ac.uk; 82 Langside Drive, Glasgow G43 2SX — MB ChB 1974 Leeds; PhD Lond. 1982; BSc (Biochem.) Leeds 1971; FRCP Ed. 1996; FRCP Glas. 1993; FRCP Lond. 1990; MRCP (UK) 1976; MRCPath. 1981. (Univ. Leeds) Prof. Transfus. Med. Univ. Glas. & Nat. Med. & Scientif. Dir., Scott. Nat. Blood Transfus. Serv. Socs: Brit. Soc. Haematol.; Amer. Soc. Hemat.; Assn. Phys. Prev: Dir., Glasg. & W. Scotl. Blood Transfers Serv.; Cons. Haemat. Roy. Infirm. Glas. & Qu. Eliz. Hosp. Birm.; Sen. Regist. (Haemat.) Univ. Coll. Hosp. Lond.

FRANKLIN, Jeremy John Southdene Surgery, The Shrubberies, George Lane, South Woodford, London E18 1BD Tel: 020 8530 3731; 43 The Drive, South Woodford, London E18 2BL Tel: 020 8989 6006 — MB BS 1959 Lond.; Dobst RCOG 1966; MRCGP 1971; DObst RCOG 1966; MRCGP 1971. (St. Mary's)

FRANKLIN, Joanne St Quintin 10 Hall Close, Worsbrough, Barnsley S70 5LN — MB ChB 1992 Sheff.

FRANKLIN, John Wirral & West Cheshire Community NHS Trust, Ashton House Hospital, Columbia Road, Oxton, Birkenhead L43 6TH Tel: 0151 653 9660; 5 Abbey View, Childwall, Liverpool L16 5EZ — MB ChB 1986 Leeds; MRCPsych 1993. Cons. Psychiat. in Learning Disabilities.

FRANKLIN, John Rafe Stoke Surgery, Belmont Villas, Stoke, Plymouth PL3 4DP Tel: 01752 562569 Fax: 01752 607299 — MB BS 1979 Lond.

FRANKLIN, Julian Seymour West Road Surgery, 12 West Road, Westcliff on Sea SS0 9DA Tel: 01702 344492 Fax: 01702 437051; 55 Quorn Gardens, Leigh-on-Sea SS9 2TA Tel: 01702 557104 — MB BS 1987 Lond.; DA 1992; DRCOG Lond. 1993. (Lond. Hosp. Med. Coll.) Prev: SHO (Obstet. & Gyn.) Newham Hosp.; SHO (Paediat.) Newham Hosp.; SHO (Anaesth.) Roy. Lond. Hosp.

FRANKLIN, Julie Alison Clare Catherine House Surgery, The Plains, Totnes TQ9 5HA Tel: 01803 862073 Fax: 01803 862056; 40 Mile End Road, Newton Abbot TQ12 1RW — MB BCh 1989 Wales; DRCOG 1993. p/t GP (Retainer). Socs: MDU. Prev: Assoc. GP Dawlish; Trainee GP Newton Abbot; SHO (ENT) Torbay Hosp.

FRANKLIN, Leona Louise 54 The Ridings, Portsmouth PO2 0UF — MB BS 1998 Lond.; MB BS Lond 1998.

FRANKLIN, Mary The Surgery, 127 Trinity Road, Tooting, London SW17 7HJ Tel: 020 8672 3331 — MB BCh BAO 1969 Dub.; DObst RCOG 1971. (TC Dub.) Prev: SHO (Paediat.) Kingston Hosp.; Ho. Surg. Connaught Hosp. Lond; Ho. Phys. & Ho. Off. (O & G) Bethnal Green Hosp.

FRANKLIN, Mary Elizabeth 7 Lexcroft, Droitwich WR9 7RD — MB BCh BAO 1964 NUI; FFA RCS Eng. 1969; DA Eng. 1966. (Univ. Coll. Dub.)

FRANKLIN, Paula Catherine Heather 31 Burtons Road, Hampton Hill, Hampton TW12 1DB — MB BS 1983 Lond.; MPH John Hopkins Univ. USA 1991. (St. Bart.)

FRANKLIN, Peter John The Surgery, 132 Liverpool Road, Cross Heath, Newcastle ST5 9EQ Tel: 01782 616573; 11 The Villas, Stoke-on-Trent ST4 5AH — MB BS 1976 Lond.; MRCS Eng. LRCP Lond. 1976; DMJ Clin. Soc. Apoth. Lond. 1987. Police Surg. Stoke on Tent (N).

FRANKLIN, Peter Keith Holt Medical Practice, High Street, Holt NR25 6BH Tel: 01263 712461 Fax: 01263 713211 — BM BS 1980 Nottm.; BMedSci. (Hon.) Nottm. 1978; MRCGP 1989.

FRANKLIN, Reginald Bernard The Beacon, Goathland, Whitby YO22 5AN Tel: 01947 896469 Fax: 01947 896431 — MB BS 1963 Durh.; FRCSC 1975; FRCOG 1986, M 1972. (King's Coll. Newc., Univ. Durh.) Socs: Fell. Soc. Gyn. & Obst. Canada; Canad. Soc. Colprocopists. Prev: Specialist (O & G) Sudbury Ontario, Canada.

FRANKLIN, Robert Adrian (retired) Verno House S., Lyndhurst Road, Christchurch BH23 4SG Tel: 01425 273062 — MB BChir 1964 Camb.; BA Camb. 1959; MA Camb. 1963; MRCS Eng. LRCP Lond. 1963; FRCPsych 1984, M 1972; T(Psych) 1991; DPM Eng. 1970. Prev: Cons. Psychiat. Dorset Health Care NHS Trust.

FRANKLIN, Robert Michael (retired) 51 Chapeldown Road, Torpoint PL11 2HU Tel: 01752 814317 — MB BS 1954 Lond. Prev: GP Torpoint.

FRANKLIN, Rodney Cyril George Royal Brompton and Harefield NHS Trust, Harefield Site, Harefield, Uxbridge UB9 6JH Tel: 01895 828659 Fax: 01895 828659 Email: r.franklin@rbh.nthames.nhs.uk — MB BS 1979 Lond.; FRCP Lond. 1994; MRCP (UK) 1982; MD 1997; FRCPCH 1997. (UCH) Cons. Paediat. Cardiol. Harefield Hosp. Middlx.; Hon. Sen. Lect. Nat. Heart & Lung Inst. Imperial Coll.; Hon. Cons. Paediactric Cardiol Gt. Ormond St Hosp for Childr. Lond. Prev: Sen. Regist. (Paediat. Cardiol.) Univ. Hosp. for Childr. Utrecht, Netherlands; Research Fell. Brit. Heart Foundat. Inst. Child Health Lond.

FRANKLIN, Simon Budleigh Salterton Medical Centre, 1 The Lawn, Budleigh Salterton EX9 6LS Tel: 01395 441212 Fax: 01395 441244; 26 Swains Road, Budleigh Salterton EX9 6HU — MB BS 1983 Lond. (Charing Cross Hospital Medical School) Prev: SHO (O & G) W. Lond. Hosp.; SHO & Clin. Med. Off. (Paediat.) Char. Cross Hosp. & Riverside HA; SHO (Gen. Med. & Geriat.) Watford Gen. Hosp.

FRANKLIN, Stephen Mark Hillview Medical Centre, 60 Bromsgrove Road, Redditch B97 4RN Tel: 01527 66511; 60 Station Road, Studley B80 7JS Tel: 01527 854613 — MB ChB 1983 Bristol; BSc (Cell. Path.) Bristol 1980.

FRANKLIN, Suzette Louie Diabetes Centre, Radcliffe Infirmary, Oxford OX2 6HE; The Manor, Culham, Abingdon OX14 4LZ Tel: 01235 520020 — MB BS 1977 Lond.; MRCOphth 1990. Med. Ophth. for Screening Diabetes Centre & Eye Hosp. Oxf. Prev: Regist. (Ophth.) Oxf. Eye Hosp. Radcliffe Infirm.

FRANKLIN, Terry Charles Chesterfield Hospital, Clifton Hill, Clifton, Bristol BS8 1BP Tel: 0117 730391; Smallway Farm, Congresbury, Bristol BS49 5AA Tel: 01934 876150 — MB ChB 1969 Bristol; BSc (Hons.) Zool. Leic 1963; MRCS Eng. LRCP Lond. 1969; DObst RCOG 1973. Orthop. Phys. Chesterfield Hosp., Bristol. Socs: Brit. Assn. Manip. Med. & Brit. Assn. Sport & Med. Prev: Orthop. Phys. Sports Injuries Clin. Brist. Roy. Infirm.

FRANKLIN, Tessa Susan Margaret Rose Cottage, Foredraught Lane, Crowle, Worcester WR7 4AS — MB ChB 1989 Dundee.

FRANKLIN, Victoria 71 Moat Lane, Slade Green, Erith DA8 2ND — MB BS 1996 Lond.

FRANKLIN, Victoria Louise Peadiatric Dept, Ward Tich, Ninewells Hospital, Dundee DD1 9SY — MB ChB 1995 Dundee; MPCPCH 1999; Dip. Paediatrics (Sydney) 1997; BMSc 1992 Dundee Univ. Specialist Regist. Paediat., Ninewells Hosp. Dundee; Paediatric diabetes Research Fell.ship Diabetes UK.

FRANKLIN, William Hugh White Lodge Practices, 21 Grosvenor Street, St Helier, Jersey JE1 4HA Tel: 01534 23892 Fax: 01534 601955; Abbotsfield, Highview Lane, St Helier, Jersey JE2 3GE Tel: 01534 58850 — MB BS 1969 Lond.; MRCS Eng. LRCP Lond. 1969; DRCOG 1976. (Guy's) Socs: Fell. Roy. Soc. Med.; BMA. Prev: Hon. Clin. Asst. Dept. Med., Ho. Phys. & Ho. Surg. Guy's Hosp. Lond.; Ho. Surg. (Obst & Gyn.) St. Thos. Hosp. Lond.

FRANKLIN-ADAMS, Joan Inman, MBE Redwood, Lewes Road, East Grinstead RH19 3ND Tel: 01342 321799 — MB BS 1934 Lond.; DCH Eng. 1940. (Lond. Sch. Med. Wom.) Socs: BMA & Med. Assn. for Preven. of War. Prev: Med. Off. Save the Childr.

FRANKLYN, Professor Jayne Agneta Department of Medicine, University of Birmingham, Queen Elizabeth Hospital, Edgbaston, Birmingham B15 2TH Tel: 0121 6272381 Fax: 0121 627 2384 Email: j.a.franklyn@bham.ac.uk — MB ChB 1979 (Hons) Birm.; 2000 Fmedsci; MB ChB (Hons.) Birm. 1979; PhD Birm. 1988,; FRCP Lond. 1993; MRCP (UK) 1982. Prof. Med. Univ. Birm.; Hon. Cons. Phys. Qu. Eliz. Hosp. Birm. Socs: Soc. Endocrinol.; Assn. Phys.; Amer. Endocrine Soc. Prev: Wellcome Trust Sen. Research Fell. Clin. Sci. Univ. Birm.; Lect. & Hon. Sen. Regist. (Med.) Univ. Birm.; MRC Train. Fell. (Med.) Univ. Birm.

FRANKLYN, Patricia Pearl (retired) 16 Emm Lane, Bradford BD9 4JJ Tel: 01274 541997 — MB ChB 1942 St. And.; FRCR 1975; DMR Lond. 1944. Hon. Cons. Radiologist Bradford Area Health Auth. Prev: Resid. (Radiol.) New Eng. Center Hosp. Boston, USA.

FRANKS, Alison Lynda Department of Radiotherapy, Walsgrave Hospital, Clifford Bridge Road, Coventry CV2 2DX Tel: 024 7653 8779 Fax: 024 7653 8905 Email: dralfranks@ic24.net; Fernie Cottage, The Old Stables, East Langton, Market Harborough LE16 7SB Tel: 01858 545140 Email: dral.franks@ic24.net — MB ChB 1985 Dundee; MRCGP 1990; DMRT 1994; DObst RCPI 1990;

FRCR 1998. (Ninewells Hosp. & Med. Sch. Dundee Univ.) Cons. in Palliat. Med. and Oncol. Walsgrave Hosp. Coventry. Socs: Brit. Oncol. Assn.; Assn. Palliat. Med.; BMA. Prev: Sen. Regist. (Clin. Oncol.) St. Thomas' Hosp. Lond.; Sen. Regist. (Palliat. Med.) Leics. Hospice; Regist. (Clin. Oncol.) Cookridge Hosp Leeds.

FRANKS, Andrea Rosalind Department of Dermatology, Countess of Chester NHS Trust, Liverpool Road, Chester CH2 1UL Tel: 01244 365000 Fax: 01244 365112; 9A Fulwood Park, Liverpool L17 5AA Tel: 0151 728 7303 — BM BCh 1972 Oxf.; FRCP (UK) 2000; MA Camb. 1972; MRCP (UK) 1974; MRNZGP 1988; DCH RCP Lond. 1975. Cons. Dermat. Countess of Chester NHS Trust. Prev: Regist. (Dermat.) Roy. Liverp. Hosp.

FRANKS, Antony Campbell (retired) 4 Links View Way, Southampton SO16 7GR Tel: 01703 769299 — MA, MB BChir. Camb. 1946; MRCS Eng. LRCP Lond. 1940; DTM & H Eng. 1949. Prev: Sen. Med. Off. (Community Health) Soton.

FRANKS, Antony John Institute of Epidemiology & Health Services Research, University of Leeds, 34 Hyde Terrace, Leeds LS2 9LN Tel: 0113 292 6151 Fax: 0113 292 6452 — MB ChB Ed. 1972; BSc (Hons.) Ed. 1969, MD 1989; MPH Leeds 1989; FRCPath 1990, M 1978; MFPHM RCP (UK) 1990. (Ed.) Sen. Lect. (Pub. Health Med.) Univ. Leeds; Hon. Cons. Neuropath. Leeds Gen. Infirm.; Med. Care Epidemiol. N.. & Yorks. Regional Off. Prev: Dist. Med. Off. Centr. Kiribati; Vis. Lect. (Path.) Univ. Accra, Ghana.

FRANKS, Christopher Ralph Quintiles (UK) Ltd, Ringside, 79 High St., Bracknell RG12 1DZ Tel: 01344 749200 Fax: 01344 749246; Church House, Wantage Road, Eddington, Hungerford RG17 0HA Tel: 01488 684261 Fax: 01488 686996 — MB BS 1973 Lond.; MD Lond. 1983; MRCS Eng. LRCP Lond. 1972; FACP 1985; FFPM 1993, M 1990; T(M) 1991; FIBiol 1987, MIBiol 1976, CBiol 1984; FRSH 1979. (Guy's) Managing Dir. Quintiles (UK) Ltd. Berks. Socs: Fell. Roy. Soc. Med.; Brit. Oncol. Assn. & Amer. Soc. Clin. Oncol. Prev: Vice-Pres. (Med.) Euro Cetus BV, Amsterdam; Hon. Cons. Phys. (Med. Oncol.) W.m. Hosp. Lond.; Dir. Anti Cancer Clin. Research Europe, Middle E., Afr., Bristol Myers Co.

FRANKS, Daniel Martin 66 St Albans Road, Edinburgh EH9 2PG — MB ChB 1998 Dund.; MB ChB Dund 1998.

FRANKS, Deirdre Michelle The Maltings Family Practice, 10 Victoria Street, St Albans AL1 3JB Tel: 01727 853296 Fax: 01727 862498; Ailsa Craig, 28 Jennings Road, St Albans AL1 4PD — MB BS 1984 Lond.; MRCGP 1989; DRCOG 1988. (Univ. Coll. Hosp.) Socs: Soc. Occupat. Med. Prev: SHO St. Peter's Hosp. Chertsey VTS.

FRANKS, Harold Leslie (retired) 5 Oakfield Road, Gosforth, Newcastle upon Tyne NE3 4HS — MB BS 1943 Durh. Hon. Capt. RAMC:. Prev: Mem. Managem. Team Newc. HA.

FRANKS, Karen Lisa 37 Little Road, Liberton, Edinburgh EH16 6SH — MB BS 1997 Newc.

FRANKS, Kevin Nicholas The Alleys, Pimlico Rd, Clitheroe BB7 2AG — MB ChB 1997 Leic.

FRANKS, Leonard Maurice 13 Allingham Street, London N1 8NX Tel: 020 7359 9202 — MB BS Durh. 1942; MD Durh. 1957; FCAP 1959; FRCPath 1969, M 1963. (Univ. Durh.) Sen. Cons. Scientist Imperial Cancer Research Fund FCS; Cons. Edr. Cancer Surveys; Terry Fox Vis. Prof. Univ. Brit. Columbia; Erasmus Wilson Lect. RCS 1954; Vis. Fell. Johns Hopkins Hosp. 1960-1. Prev: Sec. Gen. Internat. Federat. for Cell Biol. 1972-1984; Head Dept. Cell. Path. ICRF Lond.; Edr. Cell Biol. Internat. Reports 1977-86.

FRANKS, Oliver Hugh Basil The Oaks Surgery, Applegarth Avenue, Park Barn, Guildford GU2 8LZ Tel: 01483 563424 Fax: 01483 563789; The Old House, Pk Road, Albury Heath, Guildford GU5 9DF Tel: 01483 202056 — MB ChB 1980 Bristol; DCH RCP Lond. 1983. Prev: Trainee GP Torbay Hosp. Torquay VTS; Ho. Phys. Som. HA; Ho. Surg. Worthing HA.

FRANKS, Paul 19 Rosewood Gardens, Kenton, Newcastle upon Tyne NE3 3DH — MB ChB 1979 Ed.

FRANKS, Peter Spencer (retired) Tailors Green, Bacton, Stowmarket IP14 4LL — MB BS Lond. 1959; DObst RCOG 1962.

FRANKS, Philip Irvin, OBE c/o Grindlays Bank Plc, 13 St James's Square, London SW1 — MRCS Eng. LRCP Lond. 1930; DOMS Eng. 1948. (St. Bart.) Brunei Ct. Hons. Socs: Fell. Roy. Soc. Med. Prev: Dir. Med. Servs. Brunei & Ophth. Specialist Brunei & Malaya; Sen. Regist. (Ophth.) Aberd. Roy. Infirm.; Regist. (Ophth.) Vict. Hosp. Blackpool.

FRANKS, Quentin Benjamin 2 Littlemead, Esher KT10 9PE — MB BChir 1990 Camb.

FRANKS, Mr Roger Ernest Cardiac Unit, Royal Liverpool Childrens Hospital, Alder Hey, Liverpool L12 2AP Tel: 0151 252 5635 Fax: 0151 252 5643 Email: rogerfranks@rlch-tr.nwest.nhs.uk; 9A Fulwood Park, Liverpool L17 5AA Tel: 0151 728 7303 — MB BS Lond. 1969; FRCS Eng. 1974. Cons. Cardiothoracic Surg. Roy. Liverp. Childr. Hosp. Prev: Cons. Cardiothoracic Surg. Wellington, NZ; Sen. Regist. Nat. Heart & Chest Hosps.

FRANKS, Sally Elizabeth 199A Crookes, Sheffield S10 1TE — MB ChB 1998 Sheff.; MB ChB Sheff 1998.

***FRANKS, Sarah Caroline** 105 Jacoby Place, Priory Road, Edgbaston, Birmingham B5 7UW — MB ChB 1998 Birm.

FRANKS, Professor Stephen Department Reproductive Science & Medicine, Imperial College School of Medicine, St Mary's Hospital, London W2 1PG Tel: 020 7886 1461 Fax: 020 7886 6054 Email: s.franks@ic.ac.uk; 15 Huddleston Road, London N7 0AD — MD 1978 Lond.; MB BS 1970; FRCP Lond. 1988; MRCP (UK) 1972; Hon MD Uppsata 1995. Prof. Reproduc. Endocrinol. St. Mary's Hosp. Med. Sch. Lond.; Hon. Cons. Phys. St. Mary's Hosp. Lond. W2. Socs: Soc. Endrocrinol.; Assn. Phys. Prev: Lect. (Med.) Qu. Eliz. Hosp. Univ. Birm.; Research Fell. & Med. Regist. Middlx. Hosp. Lond.; MRC Trav. Research Fell. McGill Univ. Montreal, Canada.

FRANKS, Stephen Hugh The Surgery, 134 Baffins Road, Portsmouth PO3 6BH — MB ChB 1984 Ed.; MRCGP 1988. Gen. Pract. Princip. Portsmouth. Prev: Trainee GP Lothian HB VTS.

FRANKS, Ursula (retired) The Meadow, Main St., Longforgan, Dundee DD2 5ET Tel: 01382 360582 — MB BCh 1954 Wales; M.Litt St. And. 1993; BSc Wales 1951; DO Eng. 1958. Prev: Assoc. Specialist (Ophth.) Ninewells Hosp. Dundee.

FRANKS, Virginia Elizabeth The Old House, Park Road, Shalford Rd., Albury, Guildford GU4 9DF — MB ChB 1983 Bristol; BSc (Hons.) (Psychol.) Bristol 1981. Prev: Ho. Surg. & Ho. Phys. Torquay Hosp.

FRANKS, Miss Wendy Alison Moorfields Eye Hospital, London EC1V 2PD Tel: 020 7253 3411 Fax: 020 7253 4696 Email: wendy.franks@moorhelds.nthames.nhs.co.uk; Email: wafranks@aol.com — MB BChir 1980 Camb.; BSc Lond. 1977; FRCS Eng. 1986; FRCOphth 1988. Cons. Ophth. Moorfields Eye Hosp. Lond. Prev: Cons. Ophth. York Dist. Hosp.; Retinal Fell. Roy. Vict. Eye & Ear Hosp. Melbourne, Austral.; Sen. Regist. St. Thos. Hosp. & Moorfields Eye Hosp. Lond.

FRANKTON, Sarah The Molecular Endocrinology Group, MRC Clinical Sciences Centre, Hammersmith Hospital, London W12 0HS Tel: 020 8743 2030; 83 Mayfield Road, London W12 9LT Tel: 020 8740 5979 — MB BS 1993 Lond.; MRCP 1996; BSc Lond. 1990. (St Bartholomews) Specialist Regist. (Gen. Med., Diabetes & Endocrinol.) Hammersmith Hosp. Reseach Regist. Socs: BMA; Roy. Coll. Phys.; Med. Protec. Soc. Prev: Specialist Regist. (Endocrinol., Diabetes, Gen. Med.) Univ. Coll. Hosp., Middlx. Hosp., Hammersmith Hosp. & Char. Cross Hosp.

FRANKUM, Stuart Charles Kennington Health Centre, 200 Kennington Road, Kennington, Oxford OX1 5PY Tel: 01865 730911 Fax: 01865 327759; 126 Oxford Road, Abingdon OX14 2AG — MB BS 1976 Lond.; BSc Lond. 1973, MB BS 1976; MRCGP (Distinc.) 1981; DRCOG 1982; Cert. Family Plann. JCC 1982. (St. Thos.)

FRANZ, Eva Christiane North Tyneside General Hospital, Rake Lane, North Shields NE29 8NH — State Exam Med 1991 Saarland.

FRANZI, Stephen John Bungalow 27, Valentia Close, Reading RG30 1DQ — MB BS 1983 Melbourne.

FRAPPELL, Mr Jonathan Martin Nuffield Hospital, Plymouth PL6 8BG Tel: 01752 775861 Fax: 01752 778421; Sowton, Buckland Monachorum, Yelverton PL20 6DB Tel: 01752 855541 Email: j.f.@phnt.swest.nhs.uk — MB BS 1977 Lond.; FRCS Eng. 1983; FRCS Ed. 1983; MRCOG 1986; FRCOG 1998. (St. Bart.) Cons. O & G Derriford Hosp. Plymouth. Socs: Bd. Mem. Brit. Soc. Gyn. Endoscopy; (Counc.) Brit. Soc. Study Vulval Dis.; Brit. Gyn. Cancer Soc.

***FRASER, Adam Alexander** 14 Admiral Place, Moseley, Birmingham B13 8BQ Tel: 0121 449 4792 Email: adam@fraser99.freeserve.co.net — MB ChB 1998 Birm.; MBChB (Hons).

FRASER, Alan Alexander Department of Psychiatry, Southern General Hospital, Glasgow G51 4TF Tel: 0141 201 1960 Fax: 0141 201 1961; 65 Dowanside Road, Glasgow G12 9DL Tel: 0141 357 2283 — MB ChB 1979 Glas.; BSc (Hons.) Pharmacol. Glas. 1976; MRCPsych 1984. (Univ. Glas.) Cons. Psychiat. S.. Gen. Hosp. Glas.; Vis. Cons. Priory Hosp. Glas. Prev: Sen. Regist. Duke St. Hosp. Glas.; Regist. S.. Gen. Hosp. Glas.

FRASER, Alan Gordon Department of Cardiology, University of Wales College of Medicine, Heath Park, Cardiff CF14 4XN — MB ChB 1975 Ed.; BSc Ed. 1972, MB ChB 1975; MRCP (UK) 1980. (Edin.) Sen. Regist. (Gen. Med. & Cardiol.) Univ. Hosp. Wales. Prev: Research Fell. Dept. Cardiol. Univ. Wales Coll. Med.; Regist. (Med.) Raigmore Hosp. Inverness; Lect. (Med.) Univ. Edin.

FRASER, Alan Keill Spa Well Medical Group, Denburn Health Centre, Rosemount Viaduct, Aberdeen AB25 1QB Tel: 01224 640952 Fax: 01224 404422 — MB ChB 1983 Aberd.; FRCGP 2000; MRCGP 1987; DRCOG 1986. Socs: BMA. Prev: Trainee GP/SHO Grampian VTS; Ho. Off. Stirling Roy. Infirm.

FRASER, Alan Robert Coquet Medical Group, Amble Health Centre, Percy Drive, Amble, Morpeth NE65 0HD Tel: 01665 710481 Fax: 01665 713031 — MB ChB 1975 Bristol; MRCP (UK) 1977; MRCGP 1983.

FRASER, Alasdair Campbell (retired) 9 The Common, London W5 3TR Tel: 020 8567 1285 — MB BS 1955 Lond.; MRCS Eng. LRCP Lond. 1953; FRCOG 1972, M 1960. Examr. Univ. Lond., RCOG & Conj. Bd. etc.; Regional Adviser Matern. Mortality Report DoH; Mem. Pension Appeal Tribunal. Prev: Cons. O & G St. Mary's Hosp. & Samarit. Hosp. Wom. Lond.

FRASER, Alexander John 50 Fall Birch Road, Lostock, Bolton BL6 4LG — MB ChB 1971 Sheff.

FRASER, Alison Margaret Annabel Child & Adolescent Unit, Birch Hill Hospital, Rochdale OL12 9QB — MB ChB 1975 Aberd.; MRCPsych 1979. Cons. Child & Adolesc. Psychiat. Rochdale HA.

FRASER, Alistair Edward MCO/3, Petroleum Developments Oman Ltd.,, PO Box 81, Muscat, Oman Fax: 00 968 677 441; 76 Desswood Place, Aberdeen AB15 4DQ Tel: 01224 635989 — MB ChB 1982 Aberd.; AFOM RCP Lond. 1991. Occupat. Health Adviser Shell Internat. Oman. Prev: Med. Advisor Shell Expro.;; Brit. Antartic Survey Med. Off.;; SHO Rotat. (Surg.) Grampian HB.

FRASER, Allison Margaret West Park, Pitfodels, Cults, Aberdeen Tel: 01224 47781 — MB ChB 1960 Aberd. (Aberd.) Prev: Ho. Phys. Roy. Aberd. Hosp. Sick Childr.; Ho. Surg. Woodend Gen. Hosp. Aberd.

FRASER, Andrea Jean Trent View Medical Practice, 45 Trent View, Keadby, Scunthorpe DN17 3DR Tel: 01724 782209 Fax: 01724 784472; The Laurels, 85 Godnow Road, Crowle, Scunthorpe DN17 4EE — MB ChB 1980 Manch.; MRCGP 1984; DRCOG 1983.

FRASER, Rev. Andrew (retired) Duncree, 29 Parklands Way, Hartlepool TS26 0AP Tel: 01429 275129 — MB ChB Glas. 1942; BSc Glas. 1939; MRCGP 1953; FFA RCS Eng. 1954; DA Eng. 1947. Hon. Cons. Anaesth. Hartlepool Health Dist.; Min. of United Reformed Ch. 1980. Prev: Sen. Cons. Anaesth. Hartlepool Health Dist.

FRASER, Andrew Aberdeen Royal Infirmary, Foresterhill, Aberdeen AB25 2ZN Tel: 01224 681818 Email: a.fraser@abdn.ac.uk; Top Floor Flat, 557 Great Western Road, Mannofield, Aberdeen AB10 6PA Tel: 01224 326677 Email: 101553.1326@compuserve.com — MB ChB 1989 Glas.; MRCP (UK) 1993. Regist. (Gastroenterol.) Aberd. Roy. Infirm.

FRASER, Andrew Gordon (retired) — MB ChB 1962 Ed.; BSc (1st cl. Hons. Bact.) Ed. 1960, MD 1984, MB ChB 1962. Prev: Sen. Lect. (Med. Microbiol.) Univ. Edin.

FRASER, Andrew Hunter (retired) Canmore, 90 Chapeltown Road, Bromley Cross, Bolton BL7 9ND — MB ChB 1945 Ed.

FRASER, Andrew Kerr St Andrew's House, Department of Health, Scottish Executive, Edinburgh EH1 3DG Tel: 0131 244 2270 Fax: 0131 244 3477 Email: andrew.fraser@scotland.gsi.gov.uk — MB ChB 1981 Aberd.; FFPHM 1999; FRCP 2001 Glasgow; MRCP (UK) 1987; MFPHM RCP (UK) 1993; MPH Glas. 1990; FRCP Ed. 1997. Dep. Chief Med. Off. Scott. Exec. Prev: Med. Dir. Nat. Servs. Div. Common Servs. Agency Scotl.; Dir. Pub. Health Highland Health Bd.

FRASER, Angus Charles Lovat 80 Wickham Hill, Hurstpierpoint, Hassocks BN6 9NR — BM BCh 1969 Oxf.; MA; MRCP (U.K.) 1973; FFA RCS Eng. 1977. Cons. (Anaesth.) Roy. Sussex Co. Hosp. Brighton. Prev: Sen. Regist. (Anaesth.) Nuffield Dept. Anaesth. Oxf. United Hosps.; Regist. (Anaesth.) Bristol Roy. Infirm.; Med. Regist. Edendale Hosp. Pietermaritzberg, S. Afr.

FRASER, Anne Sheila, Squadron Ldr. RAF Med. Br. Medical Centre, RAF Kinloss, Forres IV36 0UH Tel: 01309 72161 — MB ChB 1982 Aberd.; MRCGP 1986; DRCOG 1986.

FRASER, Barbara Elizabeth Alexandra Hospital, Woodrow Drive, Redditch B98 7UB Tel: 01527 503030 — MB ChB 1983 Sheff.; FRCPCH; MRCP (UK) 1990.

FRASER, Brian Joseph Gorsey Lane Surgery, 93 Gorsey Lane, Ford, Liverpool L21 0DF Tel: 0151 928 7757 Fax: 0151 928 9125 — MB ChB 1990 Liverp.; MRCGP 1995; DRCOG 1993. Clin. Asst. (Cas.) Alder Hey Childr. Hosp. Liverp. Socs: BMA.

FRASER, Campbell Victor (retired) 6 Lansdowne Road, Bedford MK40 2BU — MB ChB 1953 Aberd. Prev: Ho. Phys. City Hosp. Aberd.

FRASER, Caroline Bishopdams, Kingswells, Aberdeen AB15 8SQ — MB ChB 1978 Aberd.

FRASER, Caroline Margaret The Shrubbery, 65A Perry Street, Northfleet, Gravesend DA11 8RD Tel: 01474 356661 Fax: 01474 534542; 8 Shawfield Park, Bromley BR1 2NG — MB BS 1980 Lond.; MRCGP 1985; DRCOG 1983; Dip. Occ. Med. 1997. (Guys)

FRASER, Carolyn Jane University Medical Centre, Claremont Road, Newcastle upon Tyne NE2 4AN Tel: 0191 232 2973 Fax: 0191 230 3631; Stable Cottage, Whorlton Hall Farm, Newcastle upon Tyne NE5 1NP — MB ChB 1981 Leeds; BSc Leeds 1978; MRCGP 1985; DRCOG 1985.

FRASER, Charles Stewart Magdalen Medical Practice, Lawson Road, Norwich NR3 4LF Tel: 01603 475555 Fax: 01603 787210; Riverside, Markshall, Caistor St Edmunds, Norwich NR14 8QT Tel: 01508 494553 — MB ChB 1973 Aberd.; DRCOG 1976. (Aberdeen) Indust. Med. Off. Prev: Mem. Norwich VTS; Ho. Phys. Qu. Eliz. Hosp. Birm.; Ho. Surg. St. Bernard's Hosp. Gibraltar.

FRASER, Christopher Paul Govanhill Health Centre, 233 Calder Street, Glasgow G42 7DR Tel: 0141 531 8361 Fax: 0141 531 8375; 28 Essex Drive, Jordanhill, Glasgow G14 9NA — MB ChB 1988 Glas.; MRCGP 1994; DRCOG 1994; DCH RCPS Glas. 1993.

FRASER, Claire Margaret Barber Directorate Diagnostic Imaging, Farnborough Hospital, Farnborough Common, Orpington BR6 8ND Tel: 01689 814264 Fax: 01689 814157; St George's House, The Square, Wrotham, Sevenoaks TN15 7AA — MB BS 1970 Lond.; MRCS Eng. LRCP Lond. 1970; FRCR 1983; DObst RCOG 1972. Cons. Radiol. Bromley Hosps. NHS Trust. Prev: Cons. Radiol. Orpington & FarnBoro. Hosps.

FRASER, Colin Donald Andrew 29 Kildrummy Road, Aberdeen AB15 8HJ — MB ChB 1990 Dundee.

FRASER, David Edward 11 Glen Road, Dyce, Aberdeen AB21 7FB Tel: 01224 722595 — MB ChB 1949 Aberd.; FRCGP 1973. (Aberd.) Socs: Aberd. M-C Soc. Prev: Med. Adviser Grampian Region; SHO Woodend Hosp. Aberd.; RAMC.

FRASER, David Ian Norfolk & Norwich Hospital, Brunswick Road, Norwich NR1 3SR Tel: 01603 286541 Fax: 01603 287532 Email: david.fraser@norfolk-norwich.thenhs.com; Tel: 01603 758133 Email: david.fraser2@tesco.net — MB BS 1982 Lond.; BSc Lond. 1979; MRCOG 1990; MD Lond. 1993. (King's College Hospital) Cons. O & G Norf. & Norwich Hosp. Socs: Brit. Menopause Soc.; Brit. Matern. Fetal Med. Soc. Prev: Sen. Regist. (O & G) Soton./Winchester.

FRASER, David McKee Hayfield House, Hayfield Road, Kirkcaldy KY2 5AH Tel: 01592 648137 Fax: 01592 648060; Gowanbrae House, 120 Garvock Hill, Dunfermline KY11 4JY Tel: 01383 729957 Fax: 01383 735255 — MB ChB 1971 Ed.; FRCP Ed. 1983; MRCP (UK) 1974. Med. Director, FifeAcute Hosps. NHS Trust; Med. Dir. Qu. Margt. Hosp. NHS Trust. Prev: Cons. Phys. Milesmark Hosp. Dunfermline.

FRASER, Donald Alexander Stewart (retired) 21A Island Bank Road, Inverness IV2 4QS Tel: 01463 230669 Fax: 01463 230669 Email: sandsal@mingulay.fsnet.co.uk — MB ChB 1952 Glas.; MRCGP 1966; DObst RCOG 1963. Prev: Med. Off. Brit. Petroleum Co. Ltd.

FRASER, Donald Finlayson 53 Lime Avenue, Badgers Way, Buckingham MK18 7JJ — MB ChB 1983 Dundee.

FRASER, Donald James 5 Lothersdale Close, Burnley BB10 2BU — MB ChB 1993 Bristol.

FRASER, Donald Rankin Kerr Inchpark Surgery, 10 Marmion Crescent, Edinburgh EH16 5QU Tel: 0131 666 2121; 18 Midmar Gardens, Edinburgh EH10 6DZ Tel: 0131 447 1346 — MB ChB 1972 Ed.; BSc (Med. Sci.) Ed. 1969; MRCGP 1977; DObst RCOG 1976. (Ed.) Hosp. Pract. (Geriat. & Orthop.) Astley Ainslie Hosp. Edin. Socs: BMA. Prev: Trainee GP Edin. VTS; Ho. Surg. Roy. Infirm. Edin.; Ho. Off. (Med.) City Hosp. Edin.

FRASER, Donald Ross McLennan Gergask Surgery, Laggan, Church Terrace, Newtonmore PH20 1AH Tel: 01528 544225 Fax: 01528 544388; Creag-a-Bhile, Laggan, Newtonmore PH20 1BS Tel: 01528 544288 Email: calgacus@zetnet.co.uk — MB ChB 1969 Glas.; DObst RCOG 1971.

FRASER, Douglas George William 15 Lower Oxford Road, Newcastle ST5 0PB — MB BChir 1992 Camb. SHO Rotat. (Med.) N. Staffs. Hosp. Stoke-on-Trent.

FRASER, Douglas John Uplands, Basingstoke Road, Swallowfield, Reading RG7 1PY Tel: 01734 883446 — MB BS 1988 Lond. SHO (Psychiat.) Old Manor Hosp. Salisbury. Prev: Ho. Off. Kingston Hosp. Surrey; Ho. Off. (Med.) St. Peters Hosp. Chertsey.

FRASER, Douglas McLaren (retired) Uplands, Basingstoke Road, Swallowfield, Reading RG7 1PY Tel: 01159 883446 — MB ChB 1949 Aberd.; DObst RCOG 1955; DCH Eng. 1954. Prev: Regist. (Med.) & SHO (Paediat. & Infec. Dis.) York Hosps. Gp.

FRASER, Edith Victoria 37 Gunters Mead, Queens Drive, Oxshott, Leatherhead KT22 0PD Tel: 0137 284 3488; 37 Gunters Mead, Queens Drive, Oxshott, Leatherhead KT22 0PD Tel: 0137 284 3488 — MB BS 1943 Lond.; MRCS Eng. LRCP Lond. 1943; MFCM 1972. (Lond. Sch. Med. Wom.) A. M. Bird Postgrad. Schol. in Path. 1944 Roy. Free Hosp.; Asst. Med. Adviser Elmbridge Boro. Counc. Prev: SCMO Esher; Ho. Phys. P. of Wales' Hosp. Plymouth; Res. Anaesth., Med. & Paediat. Regist. Roy. Free Hosp.

FRASER, Elaine Margaret Busby Road Surgery, 75 Busby Road, Clarkston, Glasgow G76 7BW Tel: 0141 644 2666 Fax: 0141 644 5171; 10 Seyton Avenue, Giffnock, Glasgow G46 6QA — MB ChB 1978 Glas.; MRCGP 1982; DRCOG 1981.

FRASER, Ellis Mary (retired) 10 Nicholas Avenue, Whitburn, Sunderland SR6 7DB Tel: 0191 529 2127 — MB ChB 1941 Ed.

FRASER, Ewen Duncan c/o 146 Wenallt Road, Rhiwbina, Cardiff CF14 6TQ — MB ChB 1989 Ed. Resid. Med. Off. Wanganui Hosp., NZ. Prev: Ho. Off. Roodlands Hosp. Haddlington.

FRASER, Fiona Heath Poole, Heath Lane, Willaston, South Wirral CH64 1TR Tel: 0151 327 5107 Fax: 0151 327 5107 — MB BS 1978 Lond.; BSc (1st cl. Hons.) Lond. 1975, MB BS 1978; MRCP (UK) 1985; FRCR 1986; DRCOG 1980. (Lond. Hosp.) Cons. Radiol. Halton Gen. Hosp. Runcorn.; Cons. Radiol.. Roy. Liverp. Univ. Hosp., Liverp. Prev: Sen. Regist. (Radiol.) Mersey RHA; Sen. Regist. & Regist. (Radiol.) Lond. Hosp.; SHO (Med.) Harefield & Mt. Vernon Hosps.

FRASER, Frederick Earle (retired) 3 Countisbury, St Mark's Hill, Surbiton KT6 4LR — MB BS 1946 Lond.; MRCS Eng. LRCP Lond. 1941; MRCGP 1968. Prev: Ho. Phys. & Cas. Ho. Surg. Luton & Dunstable Hosp.

FRASER, Gary Smith The Bondgate Practice, Bondgate Surgery, Infirmary Close, Alnwick NE66 2NL Tel: 01665 510888 Fax: 01665 510581 — MB ChB 1983 Aberd.

FRASER, George 1398 Dumbarton Road, Glasgow G14 9XS Tel: 0141 959 1520; 5 Wardlaw Road, Bearsden, Glasgow G61 1AL — MB ChB 1951 Glas. (Glas.) Prev: Ho. Surg. Glas. Roy. Infirm.; Ho. Phys. Gartloch Hosp.; Ho. Surg. (O & G) Stirling Roy. Infirm.

FRASER, George Alfred (retired) Seven Acres, Pyecombe, Brighton BN45 7EE — MB ChB 1931 Ed.; DLO Eng. 1937. Prev: Cons. Otolarying E Sussex Health Auth.

FRASER, George Robert ICRF Cancer Genetic Clinic, Department of Clinical Genetics, Churchull Hospital, Oxford OX3 7LJ Tel: 01865 226048 Fax: 01865 226011; 1 Woodstock Close, Oxford OX2 8DB Tel: 01865 515745 — MB BChir 1956 Camb.; DSc Lond. 1978, PhD 1960; MA Camb. 1960, BA 1953, MD 1966; FRCP Lond. 1995; MRCP (UK) 1990; FRCPC 1975. Sen. Clin. Research Fell. ICRF Oxf.; Hon. Cons. Med. Genetics Oxon. HA; Hon. Vis. Geneticist St. Barts. Hosp. Lond.; Dip. Amer. Bd. Med. Genetics. Socs: Fell. Canad. Coll. Med. Geneticists; Fell. Amer. Coll. Med. Geneticists. Prev: Prof. Human Genetics Univ. Leiden, Netherlands; Prof. Med. Genetics Memor. Univ. Newfld., Canada; Assoc. Prof. Med. & Genetics Univ. Washington, Seattle, USA.

FRASER, Ghislaine Margaret 3 Albion Gate, Albion St., Glasgow G1 1HE — MB ChB 1986 Glas.; MRCP (UK) 1993; MRCGP 1990; DRCOG 1989; MSc 1996; FRCR 1998. (Glasgow)

FRASER, Gillian Barbara Northumbria Healthcare NHS Trust, Ashington Hospital, West View, Ashington NE63 0SA Tel: 01670 521212; 5 Kings Avenue, Morpeth NE61 1HX — MB BS 1973 Newc.; MRCGP 1977; DObst RCOG 1976. Community GP N.umbria Healthcare NHS Trust; Med. Director (Community), N.umbria Healthcare NHS Trust. Prev: Med. Director, N.umberland Community Trust; GP Princip., Morpeth, Nothumberland.

FRASER, Gordon Martin (retired) 17 Park Road, Edinburgh EH6 4LE Tel: 0131 552 4872 — MB ChB 1951 Ed.; FRCP Ed. 1988, M 1984; FRCR 1975; FFR 1964; DMRD Ed. 1959. Cons. Radiol. W.. Gen. Hosp. & N. Gen. Hosp. Edin. Prev: Sen. Regist. (Radiodiag.) United Cardiff Hosps.

FRASER, Hamish Scott Findlay 7 Strathfillan Road, Edinburgh EH9 2AG — MB ChB 1986 Ed.; BSc Med. Sci. (Hons.) Physiol. Ed. 1984; MSc Knowledge Based Systems Ed. 1991; MRCP (UK) 1990. Career Regist. (Cardiol.) E. Scotl. Scheme; Regist. (Cardiol.) Edin. Roy. Infirm. Prev: SHO (Gen. Med./Cardiol.) N.. Gen. Hosp. Sheff.; SHO (Med.) Stirling Roy. Infirm.; SHO (Med. Falkirk Roy. Infirm.

FRASER, Harriet Mary 10 Melford Court, Fendall Street, London SE1 3DX Tel: 0207 237 7851; 10 Melford Court, Fendall Street, London SE1 3DX Tel: 0207 237 7851 — MB BS 1994 Lond.; BSc (Hons.) Lond. 1991; DRCOG 1997; DFFP 1998; MRCGP 1998. (University College, London) Socs: Nat. Assn. Non- Princip.s.

FRASER, Mr Iain Donald Windmill Farm, Beckwithshaw, Harrogate HG3 1QL — MB ChB 1965 St. And.; FRCS Ed. 1970. Cons. Surg. (ENT) St. Jas. Hosp. Leeds.

FRASER, Iain Sullivan Department of Infectious Diseases, North Manchester General Hospital, Delauneys Road, Crumpsall, Manchester M8 6RL — MB 1987 Camb.; BChir 1986; MRCP (UK) 1990; DTM & H Liverp. 1990. Prev: Regist. (Infec. Dis. & Chest Med.) Monsall Hosp.

FRASER, Mr Ian Arthur 66 Kenilworth Road, Coventry CV4 7AH Tel: 024 7641 0004 — MD 1983 Leics.; BSc Birm. 1969, MB ChB 1972; FRCS Eng. 1979. Cons. Gen. Surg. Walsgrave Hosp. Coventry.

FRASER, Ian Donaldson (retired) 14 Station Approach, Pensford, Bristol BS39 4AE Tel: 01761 490894 — MB ChB Bristol 1957; MD Bristol 1961; FRCP Ed. 1987; FRCPath 1976, M 1964. Prev: Med. Dir. Regional Transfus. Centre Bristol.

FRASER, Mr Ian Douglas Livingstone Warwick Hospital, Lakin Road, Warwick CV34 5BW Tel: 01926 495321 Fax: 01926 408 2602; Warwickshire Nuffield Hospital, The Chase, Old Milverton Lane, Leamington Spa CV32 6RW Tel: 01926 427971 Fax: 01926 428791 — MB BS 1969 Lond.; MS Lond. 1981; FRCS Eng. 1974; MRCS Eng. LRCP Lond. 1969; T(S) 1991; DObst RCOG 1971. (St. Bart.) Cons. Surg. Warwick Hosp. & Warks. Nuffield Hosp.; Mem. of Ct. of Examr.s Roy. Coll. of Surg.s of Eng. Socs: Fell. Roy. Soc. Med.; BMA; Assn. Colo-proctol. GB & Irel. Prev: Resid. Surg. Off. St. Mark's Hosp. Lond.; Vince Lombardi Cancer Research Fell. Med. Coll. Wisconsin, USA; Demonst. (Anat.) Univ. Oxf.

FRASER, Ian Macleod Eastfield Medical Centre, Eastfield Drive, Penicuik EH26 8EY Tel: 01968 675576 Fax: 01968 674395; Kirklands, Milton Bridge, Penicuik EH26 0NY Tel: 01968 674845 Fax: 01968 674395 Email: kirklandsmb@compuserve.com — MB ChB 1972 Ed.; MRCGP 1981; DRCOG 1976. Hosp. Pract. (Geriat.) Orthop. Rehabil. Astley Ainslie Hosp. Edin.

FRASER, Mr Ian Marcus Moore Church House, Church Lane, Tonbridge TN9 1DA Tel: 01732 353225; The Hermitage, Tonbridge Road, Hadlow, Tonbridge TN11 0AS — MB 1965 Camb.; MA; BChir 1964; FRCSI 1971; DRCOG 1983; DA Eng. 1978. (Middlx.) GP Tonbridge. Prev: SHO (Anaesth.) Roy. Vict. Hosp. Belf.

FRASER, Mr Ian Rae, TD, Lt.-Col. RAMC Retd. (retired) 126 Harley Street, London W1G 7JS Tel: 020 7935 2030 Fax: 020 7224 2520 — MB BS 1966 Lond.; BSc Lond. 1960; FRCS Eng. 1975; MRCS Eng. LRCP Lond. 1966. Hon. Cons. Surg. Hammersmith Hosp. Trust/ Char. Cross Hosp.; Cons. Surg. Cromwell Hosp. & New Vict. Hosp./ Portland Hosp. Wom. & Child. Prev: Cons. Surg. Otolaryngol. Kingston Hosp. & Qu. Mary's Univ. Hosp.

FRASER, Mr Ian Urquhart Anatomy Department, St Bartholomew's Hospital Medical School, Charterhouse Square, London EC1 Tel: 020 7253 0661; 18 Breton House, Barbican,

London EC2Y 8DQ Tel: 020 7638 3841 — MRCS Eng. LRCP Lond. 1954; FRCS Eng. 1966. (Guy's) Lect. Dept. Anat. St. Bart. Hosp. Med. Sch.

FRASER, Isobel Marjorie Copperkins, Yarrowside, Little Chalfont, Amersham HP7 9QL — MB ChB 1996 Birm.; ChB Birm. 1996. SHO Birm. Childr.s Hosp.

FRASER, Jacqueline Helen 6 Adams Drive, Fleet GU51 3DZ — MB BS 1979 Lond.; BSc Psychol. Manch. 1973.

FRASER, James 2 Glenburn Road, Bearsden, Glasgow G61 4PT — MB ChB 1943 Glas. (Glas.) RAMC. Prev: Med. Resid., Glas. Corp. Pub. Health Dept.

FRASER, James Hamish Elrick Station House, Monymusk, Inverurie AB51 7HR — MB ChB 1997 Aberd.

FRASER, James Ian Clement Flat 18, Walterton Lodge, Walterton Road, London W9 3DG — MB BS 1989 Lond.

FRASER, Mr James Penny (retired) The Cottage, 245 Brandlesholme Road, Bury BL8 1DH Tel: 0161 764 4947 — MB ChB 1947 St. And.; FRCS Glas. 1962; FRFPS Glas. 1953.

FRASER, Jane Clare The Bondgate Practice, Bondgate Surgery, Infirmary Close, Alnwick NE66 2NL Tel: 01665 510888 Fax: 01665 510581 — MB ChB 1984 Leeds; MB ChB Leeds l984; MRCGP 1989.

FRASER, Jean Mary Kennedy Medical Research Unit, Wrightington Hospital, Hall Lane, Appley Bridge, Wigan WN6 9EW Tel: 01257 251616 Fax: 01257 251617; 28 Springwood Close, Walton Park, Preston PR5 4AF Tel: 01772 312678 Fax: 01772 312678 — MB BS 1968 Lond.; MRCS Eng. LRCP Lond. 1968. (Roy. Free) Clin. Research Phys. Med. Research Unit Wrightington Hosp. Wigan. Prev: GP King's Langley; Ho. Phys. (Paediat.) Hampstead Gen. Hosp.; Ho. Off. (Surg.) Hosp. SS John & Eliz. Lond.

FRASER, Jocelyn Sophie Gastroenterology, The Rayne Institute, St Thomas Hospital, London SE1 7EH — MB BS 1992 Lond.; MRCP (UK) 1996. (St. Geo. Hosp. Med. Sch.) Specialist Regist., Gastroenterol., St Thomas Hosp., Lond. Prev: Regist. (c/o Elderly & Gastroenterolgy) Canterbury; SHO (Gen. Med.) Kent & Canterbury Hosp.; Regist. (Gen. Med. & Gastroenterol.) Canterbury.

FRASER, John 11/2 Cobden Road, Edinburgh EH9 2BJ — MB ChB 1972 Glas.

FRASER, John Andrew Braeside Surgery, Gorse Hill, Farningham, Dartford DA4 0JU Tel: 01322 862110 Fax: 01322 862991; The White House, The St, Horton, Kirby, Dartford DA4 9BY Tel: 01322 864374 — MB BS 1976 Lond.; MRCS Eng. LRCP Lond. 1976; DObst 1983. (Westm.) Socs: Pinocchios Med. Soc.; (Chairm.) Kent Medico Legal Soc. Prev: SHO (Obst.) Kings Coll. Hosp. Lond.; SHO (Orthop.) Roy. Nat. Orthop. Hosp. Lond.; Ho. Surg. W.m. Hosp. Lond.

FRASER, John Murray 161 Hillcrest, Weybridge KT13 8AS — MB BS 1986 Lond.; MRCGP 1994.

FRASER, John Stuart (retired) Byrnera, 2 Hackers Close, East Bridgford, Nottingham NG13 8PU Tel: 01949 20678 — MB ChB 1953 Aberd.

FRASER, Judith Ann Whelley Hospital, Community Health Services HQ, Bradshaw St., Whelley, Wigan WN1 3XD Tel: 01942 822623 Fax: 01942 822692 Email: judith.fraser@wiganlhs-tr.nwest.nhs.uk; 11 Hillside, Heaton, Bolton BL1 5DT Tel: 01204 847182 Fax: 01204 496909 Email: jfraser@flowerj.freeserve.co.uk — MB BS 1967 London; MRCS Eng. LRCP 1967 London; FRCPCH 1997; DCH Eng. 1970. (King's Coll. Hosp.) Cons. Paediat. (Community Child Health) Whelley Hosp. Wigan. Socs: Fell. Manch. Med. Soc.

FRASER, Karen Elizabeth Chrisp Street Health Centre, 100 Chrisp St., London E14 6PG Tel: 020 7515 4860; 125 Mildenhall Road, London E5 0RY Tel: 020 8533 7804 — MB ChB 1989 Glas.; MRCGP 1993; DRCOG 1993. GP Princip.; Clin. Tutor Dept. of Gen. Pract. Qu. Mary & W.field Coll. Lond.

FRASER, Karen Elizabeth Grovemead Health Partnership, 67 Elliot Road, Hendon, London NW4 3EB Tel: 020 8203 4466 Fax: 020 8203 1682 — MB ChB Glas. 1978; MRCGP 1983; DRCOG 1980.

FRASER, Katherine Mary Sunderland Eye Infirmary, Sunderland SR2 9HP; Tornaveen House, Torphins, Aberdeen AB31 4PD — MB BS 1998 Newc.; MB BS Newc 1998; BSc (Hons.) Edin. 1993. (Newcaslte) SHO (Opthalmology), Sunderland Eye Infirm.

FRASER, Keith Gordon Cuminestown Health Centre, Auchry Road, Cuminestown, Turriff AB53 5WJ Tel: 01888 544232 Fax: 01888 544701 — MB ChB 1973 Aberd.

FRASER, Keith Philip Lamorna, Half Mile, Leeds LS13 — MB BS 1981 Lond.

FRASER, Kenneth Boyd, MC (retired) Lagan Lian, Altnaha, Tomintoul, Ballindalloch AB37 9HP — MD 1950 Aberd.; DSc Aberd. 1961, MD 1950, MB BCh 1940. Prev: Prof. Microbiol. Qu.'s Univ. Belf.

FRASER, Kenneth Munro (retired) 34 Waldron Road, Broadstairs CT10 1TB Tel: 01843 862429 Email: kenfraser@breathemail.net — MB ChB 1951 Liverp.; FRCPsych 1978, M 1971; DPM Eng. 1958; DCH Eng. 1955. Prev: Cons. Child Psychiat. Canterbury.

FRASER, Kerr Houston (retired) Longridge, Kilmacolm PA13 4NU — MB ChB 1946 Glas.; FFCM 1982, M 1972; DMSA Ed. 1961. Prev: Chief Admin. Med. Off. Argyll & Clyde Health Bd.

FRASER, Kim Armand St Nicholas Hospital, Jubilee Road, Gosforth, Newcastle upon Tyne NE3 3XT Tel: 0191 223 2503 Fax: 0191 223 2241 Email: k.a.fraser@ncl.ac.uk — MB ChB 1981 Aberd.; MMedSci. (Clin. Psychiat.) Leeds 1986; MRCPsych 1985; FRCPsych 2000. Cons. Forens. Psychiat. Newc. City Health NHS Trust. Prev: Lect. (Forens. Psychiat.) Inst. Psychiat. & Hon. Cons. Psychiat. Bethlem Roy. Hosp. & Maudsley Hosp.; Sen. Regist. (Forens. Psychiat.) Maudsley & BRd.moor Train. Scheme; Sen. Regist. (Psychiat.) N.. RHA.

FRASER, Kirsteen Catherine Bell 34 Birkenburn Road, Cumbernauld, Glasgow G67 3QS Tel: 0141731446; Wycombe General Hospital, Queen Alexandra Road, High Wycombe HP11 2TT Tel: 01494 526161 — MB BS 1996 Lond.; BSc Lond. 1993; DRCOG 1998; DFFP 1998. (University College London) SHO (GP VTS) Wycombe Gen. Hosp.

FRASER, Lesley Doreen 436 Mosspark Boulevard, Glasgow G52 1HX Tel: 0141 882 5494 Fax: 0141 883 1015; Tel: 0141 639 2018 — MB ChB 1985 Aberd.; LFHon (Med) 1994 Glasgow; MRCGP 1989. GP Retainer Glas.; Clin. Asst. Diabetes Centre S. Gen. Hosp. NHS Trust Glas. Prev: GP Retainer Edin.; SHO (Psychiat.) & Clin. Med. Off. (Community Paediat.) Edin.

FRASER, Malcolm Hugh Tams Brig Surgery, 107 New Road, Ayr KA8 8DD Tel: 01292 262697 Fax: 01292 265926; 35 The Loaning, Alloway, Ayr KA7 4QL — MB ChB 1972 Glas.; MRCGP 1976; DObst RCOG 1975.

FRASER, Maria Public Health Laboratory, Level 5, Sandringham Building, Leicester Royal Infirmary NHS Trust, Aylestone St., Leicester LE1 5WW Tel: 01162 586516 Fax: 01162 551949; 1 Woodstock Close, Oxford OX2 8DB Tel: 01865 515745 — Ptychio Iatrikes 1974 Thessalonika; MSc Med. Microbiol. Lond. 1986, MSc Virol. 1990; MRCPath 1994. Cons. (Med.Virol) PHL Leicester Roy. Infirm. Socs: Soc. Gen. Microbiol.; New York Acad. of Sci.s; Amer. Assoc. for the Advancem. of Sci.

FRASER, Marion Anne Nicolson (retired) Delness, 11B Island Bank Road, Inverness IV2 4QN Tel: 01463 232897 — MB ChB Ed. 1963.

FRASER, Mark Donald 3 Whitegate Close, Prescot L34 0JD — MB ChB 1990 Liverp.

FRASER, Mark Stewart (retired) 7 West Fergus Place, Kirkcaldy KY1 1UR Tel: 01592 261441 — MB ChB Ed. 1942; FRCP Ed. 1965, M 1948. Prev: Cons. Paediat. Fife HB.

FRASER, Marrion Armstrong McKeand (retired) 5A Lennox Court, 14 Sutherland Avenue, Bearsden, Glasgow G61 3JW Tel: 0141 931 5056 — MB ChB 1939 Glas.; MA Glas. 1934. Prev: Ho. Surg. Vict. Infirm. & Roy. Matern. Hosp. Glas.

FRASER, Mary (retired) Flat 1, Ponsonby House, Wherton Road, Oxford OX3 8AH — MD 1933 Lond.; MB BS Lond. 1928; DObst RCOG 1935.

FRASER, Mr Matthew Hamilton 2 Catrine Court, Glasgow G53 7FH — BM 1979 Soton.; FRCS Ed. 1986.

FRASER, Mr Michael 31 Dolphin Gardens W., Currie, Edinburgh EH14 5RJ — MB ChB 1985 Aberd.; FRCS Glas. 1990. Regist. (Gen. Surg.) S.. Gen. Hosp. Glas.

FRASER, Mr Michael Ronald Fawkham Manor Hospital, Manor Lane, Fawkham, Longfield DA3 8ND Tel: 01474 879900 Fax: 01474 879827; St. Georges House, The Square, Wrotham, Sevenoaks TN15 7AA Tel: 01732 883685 Fax: 01474 883685 — MB BS 1970 Lond.; FRCS Eng. 1976; MRCS Eng. LRCP Lond. 1970.

(Westm.) p/t InDepend. Cons. Orthopaedic Surg. Socs: Fell. BOA; BMA; Roy. Soc. of Med. Prev: Cons. (Orthop. Surg.) Dartford & Gravesham NHS Trust; Sen. Regist. (Orthop.) Roy. Nat. Orthop. Hosp. Lond.; Regist. Rotat. (Surg.) Soton Univ. Hosp.

FRASER, Moray Ewen Canisbay Surgery, Canisbay, Wick KW1 4YH Tel: 01955 611205 Fax: 01955 611327; St. Leonards, Canisbay, Wick KW1 4YH — MB ChB 1979 Glas. Socs: BMA.

FRASER, Natasha Colette 2 Park Lodge Close, Cheadle SK8 1HU — MB ChB 1991 Manch.; MRCGP 1997.

FRASER, Neil Chalmers Childrens Unit, Hereford Hospitals NHS Trust, County Hospital, Hereford HR1 2ER Tel: 01432 355444 Fax: 01432 364036 Email: neil.fraser@hh-tr.wmids.nhs.uk; 14 Coningsby Court, Coningsby St, Hereford HR1 2DF Tel: 01432 276765 — FRCPCH 1997; MB ChB Ed. 1970; BSc (Hons.) Ed. 1967; FRCP Lond. 1997; FRCP Ed. 1987, M 1974; DCH RCPS Glas. 1972. Cons. Paediat. Co. Hosp. Hereford; Sen. Clin. Lect. Univ. Birm.; Hon. Cons. Birm. Childr. Hosp. Prev: Sen. Regist. Roy. Hosp. Sick Childr. Edin.

FRASER, Neil Stuart — MB ChB 1982 Glas.; DA (UK) 1987. GP Sherborne; Clin. Asst. (Anaesth.) Dorset. Prev: SHO (Anaesth.) Winchester HA.

FRASER, Nicola Louise Tel: 0117 962 0652 Fax: 0117 962 0839; Ridgewood, Drybridge, Buckie AB56 5LB — BM BS 1981 Nottm.; BMedSci Nottm. 1979; MRCGP 1990; DRCOG 1990; DFFP. (Nottingham) p/t Locum Gen. Practitioner Bristol. Prev: GP Princip.

FRASER, Nigel Bryce 92a Roman Road, Basingstoke RG23 8HD — MB BS 1992 Lond.

FRASER, Nigel Charles Belgrave Surgery, 16-18 Falsgrave Road, Scarborough YO12 5AT — MB ChB 1988 Manch.; DCH 1998; BSc (Hons.) Manch. 1986; Dip. IMC RCS Ed. 1998; MRCGP 1998. GP Princip., ScarBoro. Socs: BASICS; Fac. Immediate Care Ed.

FRASER, Norman Douglas (retired) 186 Newton Road, Newcastle upon Tyne NE7 7HQ — MB BS 1948 Durh. Prev: Med. Off. Uganda Med. Serv.

FRASER, Norman Gordon (retired) 28A Muirfield Road, Inverness IV2 4AY Tel: 01463 224829 — MD 1973 Glas.; MB ChB 1961; FRCP Ed. 1977, M 1966; DObst RCOG 1963. Prev: Cons. Dermat. Raigmore Hosp. Inverness.

FRASER, Norman Grant (retired) Glenbarry, 58 Victoria Road, Lenzie, Glasgow G66 5AP Tel: 0141 776 1281 — MB ChB 1950 Aberd.; FRCPsych 1979, M 1971; DPM Eng. 1956. Prev: Phys. Supt. Woodilee Hosp. Lenzie & Stoneyetts Hosp. Chryston.

FRASER, Pamela Ann 8 Cairnie View, Westhill, Aberdeen AB32 6NB — MB ChB 1983 Aberd.; DA (UK) 1986. p/t Clin. Med. Off., Family Plann. and Reproductive Health, Aberd. Prev: Gen. Practitioner, Aberd.

FRASER, Pamela Anne Flat 3R, 64 Lauderdale Gardens, Hyndland, Glasgow G12 8QW — MB ChB 1991 Glas. SHO (Gen. Med.) Monklands Dist. Gen. Hosp. Airdrie.

FRASER, Pauline Anne Department of Genitourinary Medicine, Chesterfield & North Derbyshire Royal Hosptial, Calow, Chesterfield S44 5BL Tel: 01246 209582 — MB BS 1983 Newc.; FRCP 2000. Cons. Genitourin. Med. Chesterfield & N. Derbysh. Roy. Hosp. & Roy. Hallamsh. Hosp. Sheff. Prev: Sen. Regist. (Genitourin. Med.) Yorks RHA.; Regist. (Med.) Vict. Hosp. Kirkcaldy; SHO (Med.) N. Tees Gen. Hosp. Stockton on Tees.

***FRASER, Rachel Ann** Royal Alexandra Hospital, Corsebar Road, Paisley PA2 9PN Tel: 0141 887 6701 Email: fraufraser@hotmail.com — MB ChB 1998 Glas.

FRASER, Rhona Barbara Isobel Health Centre, Balmellie Road, Turriff AB53 4DQ Tel: 01888 562323 Fax: 01888 568682; Corserine, 22 Delgaty Terrace, Turriff AB53 4GA — MB ChB 1977 Glas.; DRCOG 1981.

FRASER, Richard James 60 Hatchard Road, London N19 4NQ — MB BS 1989 Lond.

FRASER, Robert Ashley Department of Pathology, Royal Shrewsbury Hospital (North), Mytton Oak Road, Shrewsbury SY3 8XQ Tel: 01743 261168 Fax: 01743 355963 Email: raf@rshhis.demon.co.uk; Kinder, 10 Port Hill Road, Shrewsbury SY3 8SE Tel: 01743 343130 Fax: 01743 272285 Email: tenphr@globalnet.co.uk — MB ChB 1972 Aberd.; PhD Aberd. 1984; FRCPath 1995; MRCPath 1984. Cons. Histopath. & Med. Dir. Roy. Shrewsbury Hosp. NHS Trust. Socs: Assn. Clin. Pathol. & Path. Soc. GB. & N. Irel.; (Sec.) Nat. Assn. Clin. Tutors; Brit. Assn. Med. Managers. Prev: Lect. (Pathol.) Univ. Aberd.; Hon. Sen. Regist. Grampian HB.

FRASER, Robert Bruce Univ. Dept. Obsegynae, Level 4, The Jessop Wing, Tree Root Walk, Sheffield S10 2SF Tel: 0114 226 8537 Fax: 0114 226 8538 Email: r.b.fraser@sheffield.ac.uk — MB ChB 1971 Sheff.; MD Sheff. 1984; FRCOG 1989, M 1976; DCH Eng. 1973. Hon. Cons. Sheff. Teachg. Hosp. NHS Trust; Sen. Reader (Obst. & Gyn.) Univ. Sheff.

FRASER, Professor Robin Charles The East Leicester Medical Practice, 131 Uppingham Road, Leicester LE5 4BP Tel: 0116 276 7145 Fax: 0116 246 1637; 167 Spencefield Lane, Leicester LE5 6GG Tel: 01162 584871 Fax: 01162 584982 — MB ChB Aberd. 1963; MD Aberd. 1974; FRCGP 1974, M 1969. (Aberd.) Prof. Gen. Pract. Univ. Leicester; RCGP Internat. Developm. Adviser (Kuwait). Prev: Ho. Phys. (Profess. Unit) & Ho. Surg. Cas. Dept. Aberd. Roy. Infirm.; Ho. Phys. (Profess. Unit) Roy. Aberd. Hosp. Sick Childr.; James Mckenzie Lect & medallist 1994.

FRASER, Sarah Ann 49 Park Hill, Clapham, London SW4 9NS — MB BS 1991 Lond.; BSc Lond. 1988; DA (UK) 1994; MRCP (UK) 1996. (St. Geos.) Specialist Regist. (Palliat. Med.), Trinity Hospice, Clapham, Lond. Prev: Specialist Regist., The P.ss Alice Hospice, Esher; Specialist Regist. (Palliat. Med.) Roy. Marsden Hosp. Surrey; SHO Roy. Marsden Hosp. Lond.

FRASER, Sarah Elizabeth 95 Harlow Crescent, Harrogate HG2 0AL — MB ChB 1990 Bristol; MRCGP 1995; DCH RCP Lond. 1993. GP Harrogate. Prev: Trainee GP Bristol; SHO (O & G & Paediat.) Taunton & Som. Hosp.; SHO (Psychiat.) Coney Hill Hosp. Glos.

FRASER, Mr Scott George Sunderland Eye Infirmary, Sunderland SR4 9HP — MB ChB 1988 Leic.; MD 2000; FRCS Ed. 1992; FRCOphth 1994, M 1993. (Leic.) Cons. Ophthalmorogist Sunogrand Exe. Infirm. Prev: Friends of Moorfields Research Fell. Moorfields Eye Hosp.; Specialist Regist. Moorfields Eye Hosp.; Clin. Research Fell. Ophth. Epidemiol. Unit Moorlands.

FRASER, Sheila Edith, OBE (retired) Cornerways, Dragon's Well Road, Brentry, Bristol BS10 7BU Tel: 0117 950 6989 — MB ChB 1947 Bristol; FRCGP 1972. Prev: GP Bristol.

FRASER, Shona 35 The Loaning, Alloway, Ayr KA7 4QL — MB ChB 1998 Aberd.; MB ChB Aberd 1998.

FRASER, Mr Simon Charles Alexander Department Vascular Surgery, King's College Hospital, Denmark Hill, London SE5 9RS Tel: 020 7346 3339; Flat 1, 20 Streatham Common Northside, London SW16 3HJ Tel: 020 8769 2514 — MB ChB 1981 Ed.; MD Ed. 1993; FRCS Eng. 1987; FRCS Ed. 1986. Cons. Vasc. Surg. King's Coll. Hosp. Lond. Socs: Vasc. Surg. Soc. GB & Irel.; Eur. Soc. Vasc. & Endovasc. Surg.; Assn. Surg. Prev: Fell. (Clin. Vasc.) St. Mary's Hosp. Lond.; Sen. Regist. King's Coll. Hosp. Lond.

FRASER, Simon Douglas Stafford Grove Medical Practice, Shirley Health Centre, Grove Road, Shirley, Southampton SO15 3UA Tel: 023 8078 3611 Fax: 023 8078 3156; 14 Highcrown Street, Highfield, Southampton SO17 1QF Tel: 02380 558239 — BM 1992 Soton.; MRCGP 1998; DCH RCP Lond. 1995; DFFP 1995; DRCOG 1994. (Southampton) Hospice doctor, Naomi Ho. Childr.'s Hospice, near Winchester. Prev: SHO Roy. Hants. Co. Hosp. Winchester.

FRASER, Stuart Muir Findlay Melbourne Street Medical Centre, 56 Melbourne Street, Leicester LE2 0AS Tel: 0116 262 2721; Church Cottage, 2 Church Lane, Stroughton, Leicester LE2 2FJ Tel: 0116 271 7180 Email: sfraser46@hotmail.com — MB BS Lond. 1969; FRCGP 1991, M 1977; DCH Eng. 1972; DObst RCOG 1971. (St. Mary's) Treas. Leics. LMC; Trainer Trent RHA. Socs: BMA; Leic. Med. Soc. Prev: Ho. Off. (O & G) City Hosp. Nottm; Ho. Off. (Gyn.) Samarit. Hosp. Lond.; Ho. Phys. St. Mary's Hosp. (Harrow Rd. Br.) Lond.

FRASER, Susan Anne 27 Upper Glenburn Road, Bearsden, Glasgow G61 4BN Tel: 0141 942 0235 — MD 1971 Glasgow; MB ChB 1966 Glasgow; FRCP 1983 Glasgow; MRCP 1972 UK; MB ChB 1966 Glasgow. Cons. Phys. Geriat. Med. S.. Gen. Hosp. Glas. & Hon. Clin. Sen. Lect. (Geriat. Med.) Univ. Glas.; Clin. Dir. (Geriat. Med.) S. Gen. Hosp. NHS Trust. Socs: Roy. M-C Soc. Glas. & Brit. Geriat. Soc. Prev: Cons. Phys. Geriat. Med. Glas. Roy. Infirm. & Lightburn Hosp.; MRC Research Asst. (Med.) W.. Infirm. Glas.; Sen. Regist. (Endocrinol.) Univ. Dept. Med. Glas. Roy. Infirm.

FRASER, Susan Marjorie 66 Coatbridge Road, Glenboig, Coatbridge ML5 2PU — MB ChB 1979 Glas.; FRCP Glas. 1993; MRCP (UK) 1982. Cons. Phys. Rheum. Vict. Infirm. Glas.

***FRASER, Susannah Jane** 31 Hazledene Road, Aberdeen AB15 8LB Tel: 01224 315954 — MB ChB 1998 Ed.; MB ChB Ed 1998.

FRASER, Thomas Law (retired) 11 Ridgepark Drive, Lanark ML11 7PG Tel: 01555 663707 — MB ChB 1957 Glas.; FFA RCS Eng. 1965; DA Eng. 1960. Prev: Cons. Anaesth. Law Hosp. Carluke.

FRASER, Thomas Walter Gerrard (retired) 23 Carlton Road, Derby DE23 6HB Tel: 01332 292084 — MB ChB 1949 Ed. Prev: Ho. Phys. Roy. Infirm. Edin.

FRASER, Uilleam Somerled The Surgery, Station Road, Fortrose IV10 8SY Tel: 01381 620909 Fax: 01381 620505; Comerscroft, Fortrose IV10 8RX Tel: 01381 620285 Email: willfa@globalnet.co.uk — MB ChB 1968 Ed. (edinburgh) Socs: Highland Med. Soc.

FRASER, Victoria Grace Windycleve, Southdown Road, Millbrook, Torpoint PL10 1EQ — MB BCh 1995 Wales. (Univ. Wales Coll. Med.) GP Regist. & SHO N. Herts NHS Trust Stevenage VTS.

FRASER, Violet Eleanor Nutt (retired) Sotwell Hill House, Brightwell-Cum-Sotwell, Wallingford OX10 0PS Tel: 01491 34654 — MB BS 1939 Lond.; MRCS Eng. LRCP Lond. 1938.

FRASER, Wallace Robert Urmston Group Practice, 154 Church Road, Urmston, Manchester M41 9DL Tel: 0161 755 9870 Fax: 0161 755 9896 — MB ChB 1975 Manch.; MRCGP 1980; DRCOG 1980. (Manch.) Tutor (Gen. Pract.) Trafford; Clin. Governance Lead Trafford N. PCG.

FRASER, William Charles Village Medical Centre, 400-404 Linthorpe Road, Middlesbrough TS5 6HF Tel: 01642 851234 Fax: 01642 820821 — MB ChB 1981 Aberd.; MRCGP 1991. SHO (Geriat.) Roy. Alexandra Hosp. Paisley. Prev: Trainee GP Oldmeldrum Med. Gp.

FRASER, Professor William Duncan University Department of Clinical Chemistry, Royal Liverpool University Hospital, Prescott Road, PO Box 147, Liverpool L69 3GA Tel: 0151 706 4247 Fax: 0151 706 5813 Email: w.d.fraser@liv.ac.uk; 3 Harebell Close, Formby, Liverpool L37 4JP — MB ChB 1982 Glas.; BSc (Hons.) Glas. 1977, MB ChB 1982; MRCPath 1990; MD (Hons.) 1995; FRCPath 1998; MRCP (London) 1999. (Glasgow University) Prof. & Hon. Cons. Clin. Chem., Roy. Liverp. Univ. Hosp. & Univ. of Liverp. Socs: Assn. of Clin. Biochem.s (ACB); Chairm. of Scientif. Comm. Prev: Sen. Lect. & Hon. Cons. Clin. Chem. Roy. Liverp. Univ. Hosp. & Univ. Liverp.; Sen. Regist. (Clin. Biochem.) Glas. Roy. Infirm.; Reader & Hon. Cons. Clin. Chem. Roy. Liver. Univ. Hosp. & Univ.

FRASER, Professor William Irvine, CBE 146 Wenallt Road, Rhiwbina, Cardiff CF14 6TQ Tel: 029 2056 2323 Email: wpcw.f@shor.ef.ae.uk — MD (Commend.) Glas. 1969, MB ChB 1963; FRCPsych 1979, M 1971; DPM Ed. & Glas. 1967. Prof. Ment. Handicap Univ. of Wales Coll. Med.; Dir. Welsh Centre for Learn. Disabil.; Edr. Jl. Internat. Disabil. Research. Socs: Chairm. Welsh Div. Roy. Coll. Psychiat. Prev: Cons. Psychiat. Roy. Edin. & Gogarburn Hosps. Edin.; Supt. Phys. Lynebank Hosp. Dunfermline; Sen. Lect. (Rehabil. Studies) Univ. Edin.

FRASER, William Ross (Surgery), 22 Albyn Place, Aberdeen AB10 1YJ Tel: 01224 587946 Fax: 01224 580325; 31 Hazledene Road, Aberdeen AB15 8LB Tel: 01224 315954 — MB ChB 1972 Aberd.; BSc Aberd. 1966, MB ChB 1972; MRCGP 1976. Prev: Trainee GP Aberd. VTS; Ho. Phys Profess. Med. Unit & Ho. Surg. Accid. Orthop. Aberd. Roy. Infirm.

FRASER, Zilla Margaret (retired) Uplands, Swallowfield, Reading RG7 1PY Tel: 01734 883446 — MB BS 1951 Lond.; MB BS (Hons.) Lond. 1951; MRCS Eng. LRCP Lond. 1951; DCH Eng. 1953. JP. Prev: Regist. (Med.) York. Gp. Hosps.

FRASER-ANDREWS, Elisabeth Ann St John's Institute of Dermatology, St Thomas's Hospital, London SE1 7EH Tel: 020 7928 9292 Fax: 020 7922 8738 Email: e.fraser-andrews@umds.ac.uk; 123 Wakehurst Road, London SW11 6BZ Tel: 020 7922 0689 — MB BChir 1993 Camb.; MRCP (Lond.) 1995. (Camb./UMDS) Research Specialist Regist. St. John's Inst. Dermat. Lond. Socs: Train. Mem. Brit. Assn. Dermat.

FRASER-DARLING, Alasdair, MBE The Surgery, 52 High St., Caythorpe, Grantham NG32 3DN Tel: 01400 72215; St Vincent House, Caythorpe, Grantham NG32 3EJ Tel: 01400 72656 — MB ChB 1951 Ed.; BA Oxf. 1949; FRCGP 1974; DObst RCOG 1955. DL. Socs: Roy. Med. Soc. Edin. & Lincoln Med. Soc. Prev: Trainee Asst. Edin. Univ. Gen. Pract. Teachg. Unit; Ho. Surg. Roy. Infirm. Edin.; Col. late RAMC T & AVR (retd.), late CO 222 Field Ambul.

FRASER JONES, John (retired) 47 Manor Road, Solihull B91 2BL Tel: 0121 705 2100 — MB BS 1949 Lond.; FRCA 1992; FFA RCS Eng. 1959. Prev: Cons. Anaesth. E. Birm. HA & Solihull HA.

FRASER-MOODIE, Fanny Christina 2 Sheen Common Drive, Richmond TW10 5BN Tel: 020 8876 6663 — MRCS Eng. LRCP Lond. 1932. (Lond. Sch. Med. Wom.) Prev: Ho. Surg. Bootle Gen. Hosp.; Ho. Phys. Roy. Liverp. Childr. Hosp.

FRASER-MOODIE, Mr William Alistair 73 Hazelwood Road, Duffield, Derby DE56 4AA — MB BS 1966 Lond.; FRCS Ed. 1971; FRCS Eng. 1972; MRCS Eng. LRCP Lond. 1965; DCH Eng. 1969; DObst RCOG 1968. (St. Thos.) Cons. (A & E) Derbysh. Roy. Infirm. Derby. Prev: Regist. (Gen. Surg.) Ashford Hosp. Middlx.; Regist. (Gen. Surg.) Hammersmith Hosp. Lond.; SHO (Plastic Surg.) Qu. Mary's Hosp. Roehampton.

FRASSEK, Barbara 19 Parliament Street, Bury BL9 0TE — MB ChB 1978 Pretoria.

FRATER, Alexander John 14 Carisbrooke House, Courtlands, Richmond TW10 5AZ — MB BS 1993 Lond.

FRATER, John Kenneth Scott Department of Pathology, Hartlepool General Hospital, Holdforth Road, Hartlepool TS24 9AH Tel: 01429 522413 — MB ChB 1983 Ed.; BSc (Anat.) Ed. 1980; MRCPath 1994. Cons. Chem. Path. N. Tees and Hartlepool NHS Trust. Socs: Fell. Roy. Med. Soc.; Assn. Clin. Pathol.; Assn. Clin. Biochem. Prev: Sen. Regist. (Clin. Biochem.) W.. Infirm. & Gartnavel Gen. Hosp. Glas.; Trainee (Path.) RAF Inst. Path. & Trop. Med.; Ho. Surg. Dunfermline & W. Fife Hosp.

FRATER, Nelda Elizabeth Fircroft, 9 Hollingbourne Road, London SE24 9NB — MB BChir 1990 Camb.

FRATER, Robert Andrew Scott Harrogate District Hospital, Lancaster Park Road, Harrogate HG2 7SX Tel: 01423 885959 — MB ChB 1978 Ed.; MRCP (UK) 1981; FRCA 1984. Cons. Anaesth. Harrogate Health Care N. Yorks. Socs: Assn. Anaesth. GB & Irel.; (Treas.) Harrogate Med. Soc.; Obst. Anaesth. Assn. Prev: Sen. Regist. (Anaesth.) N.. RHA; Lect. Univ. Leicester; Regist. (Anaesth.) Oxf.

FRAY, David Lawton House Surgery, Bromley Road, Congleton CW12 1QG Tel: 01260 275454 Fax: 01260 298412; Brackenrigg, Crouch Lane, Timbersbrook, Congleton CW12 3PT Tel: 01260 276898 — MB ChB 1986 Dundee; MRCGP 1990; DRCOG 1989. Prev: Trainee GP Bury HA VTS; Ho. Off. (Med.) Bury Gen. Hosp.; Ho. Off. (Surg.) Oldham Roy. Infirm.

FRAY, Neil Francis Lime Grove Medical Centre, Lime Grove Walk, Matlock DE4 3FD Tel: 01629 582107 Fax: 01629 57006 — BM BS 1991 Nottm.; BMedSc (Hons.) Nottm. 1989; MRCGP 1995; DFFP 1995. Vis. Phys. Whitworth Hosp. Matlock. Prev: Regist. Derby VTS.

FRAYLING, Ian Martin Dept. Medical Genetics, Molecular Genetics Laboratory, Box 158, Addenbrooke's Hospital, Cambridge CB2 2QQ Tel: 01223 217971 Fax: 01223 217972 Email: ian.frayling@addenbrookes.nhs.uk — MB BChir 1982 Camb.; PhD Manch. 1995; MA Camb. 1984, BA (Hons.) 1980. (Cambridge) Specialist Regist. (Genetic Path.), Addenbrooke's Hosp., Camb. Socs: Clin. Molec. Genetics Soc.; Cancer Genetics Gp. Prev: Clin. Research Fell. ICRF Colorectal Unit. St. Mark's Hosp. Harrow; CRC Research Fell.sh. Paterson Inst. Cancer Research Christie Hosp. Manch.; Regist. (Rotat.) (Chem. Path.) Roy. Manch. Childr. Hosp.

FRAYN, Elizabeth Helen 24 Ramsay Road, Headington, Oxford OX3 8AX — MB ChB 1998 Glas.; MB ChB Glas 1998.

FRAYNE, James Matthew Wrightington NHS Trust, Hall Lane, Appley Bridge, Wigan WN6 9EP Tel: 01257 256244 — MB ChB 1971 Leeds; FFA RCS Eng. 1977; MBA Brad. Cons. Anaesth. Wrightington Hosp.

FRAZER, Alan Campbell Brondeg, Llanelly Church Road, Gilwern, Abergavenny NP7 0EL Tel: 01873 831531 Email: frazal@hotmail.com — MRCS Eng. LRCP Lond. 1944; MRCGP 1957. (Liverp.) Prev: Regional Med. Off. DHSS Leeds.

FRAZER, Alan Neil Lee Grove Medical Practice, 49 Richford Gate, Richford Street, London W6 7HY Tel: 020 8846 7555 Fax: 020 8846 7538 — BM BCh 1975 Oxf.; MRCGP 1980.

FRAZER, Alison Forrest All Saints Vicarage, 20 Limavady Road, Waterside, Londonderry BT47 1JD — MB BCh BAO 1969 Belf.

FRAZER, Christopher Keith 20B Morrison Road, London SW11 5PA; 23 Albert Terrace, Beverley HU17 8JU — MB ChB 1984 Liverp. Regist. (Radiol.) Hull Roy. Infirm.

FRAZER, David Craig Northville, Milton St., Fairford GL7 4BW — MB ChB 1994 Liverp.

FRAZER, Mr David George Department of Ophthalmology, Royal Victoria Hospital, Grosvenor Road, Belfast BT12 6BA Tel: 028 9089 4786; 2 Seapark Grove, Holywood BT18 0NS — MB BCh BAO 1982 Belf.; BSc (Hons.) Belf. 1979; FRCS Glas. 1988; FCOphth 1990. Cons. Ophth. Surg. Roy. Vict. Hosp. Belf.

FRAZER, John Bernard Firlands, 6 Rockwood Road, Calverley, Leeds LS16 5PG Tel: 0113 236 1447 Fax: 0113 229 8199 Email: jbfraz@email.msn.com — MB BS 1981 Newc.; BMedSc (Hons.) Newc. 1978, MB BS 1981; DRCOG 1985. (Newc.) Clin. Asst. (Forens. Psychiat.) Waddiloves Hosp. Bradford.; SHO (Psychiat.) Leeds Psychiat. Train. Scheme. Socs: BMA.

FRAZER, John Francis Deryk (retired) Warren Farm, Boxley, Maidstone ME14 3EA Tel: 01622 752524 — BM BCh 1942 Oxf.; PhD Lond. 1953; DM Oxf. 1955, BM BCh 1942. Prev: Sen. Lect. in Physiol. Char. Cross Hosp. Med. Sch.

FRAZER, Margaret Whittington (retired) Knitsley Station, Hownsgill Drive, Consett Tel: 01207 505166 — MB ChB 1945 Manch. Prev: Anaesth. Regist., Res. Anaesth. & Sen. Ho. Surg. Profess. Unit.

FRAZER, Muriel Josephine Louise, MBE (retired) 48 Wellington Park, Belfast BT9 6DP Tel: 01232 666412 — MB BCh BAO 1938 Belf.; MB BCh BAO (1st cl. Hons. & 1st Pl.) Belf. 1936; BA Belf. MD (High Commend.) 1938; FRCP Lond. 1953, M 1938; FRCSI 1939. Prev: Cons. Paediat. Roy. Belf. Hosp. for Sick Childr., Belf. City Hosp. & Mater Infirm. Hosp. Belf.

FRAZER, Richard Scott Gillbrow Farm House, Mosser, Cockermouth CA13 0SR — MB ChB 1982 Liverp.

FRAZER, Ruth Sara Golwg y Maes, Pen y fai, Bridgend CF31 4LS — MB ChB 1973 Dundee; MFFP 1993; Dip. Forens. Med. Glas 1995. (Dundee) Community Paediat. Rhondda. Socs: BACCH; Assn. Inst. Psychosexual Med. Prev: Community Med. Off. Plymouth Health Dist.; sen.clin.med.off(psychosexual Med) Glas.; Sen.Clin.Med.Off.(Community Child health)Glas.

FRAZER, Sheila Josephine Learning Disability Service, Burton Place, Taunton TA1 4HE Tel: 01823 423126 — MB BCh BAO 1986 NUI; MRCPsych. Cons. Psychiat. in Learning Disabil., Som. Partnership NHS and Social Care Trust.

FRAZER COX, Malcolm Great Sutton Medical Centre, Old Chester Road, Great Sutton, Ellesmere Port CH66 3PB Tel: 0151 339 3079 Fax: 0151 339 9225; 26 Cherry Garden Avenue, Folkestone CT19 5LD Tel: 01303 275465 — MB ChB 1982 Liverp.; MRCS Eng. LRCP Lond. 1982; DRCOG 1986. (Liverp.) Hosp. Practitioner Mersey Regional Drug & Alcohol Rehabil. Unit Countess of Chester Hosp. Socs: BMA; Chester & N. Wales Med. Soc. Prev: Demonst. (Anat.) Liverp. Univ. Med. Sch.; Ho. Off. Roy. Liverp. Hosp. (T).

FREAKE, Deborah Adelaide Medical Centre, Adelaide Terrace, Benwell, Newcastle upon Tyne NE4 8BE Tel: 0191 219 5599 Fax: 0191 219 5596 — MB BS 1987 Newc.

FREAKER, Wendy Ann 1 Woodside Cottages, Fortis Green, London N2 9HE — MB ChB 1967 Liverp.; MRCPsych 1973.

FREAKLEY, Geoffrey Charles Hugh Hawthorn Medical Centre, May Close, Swindon SN2 1UU Tel: 01793 536541 Fax: 01793 421049 — MB ChB 1968 Bristol; MRCGP 1979; DMRD Eng. 1972.

FREARS, Janna Felicity The Staithe, 41 Northgate, Beccles NR34 9AU Tel: 01502 713661 Fax: 01502 713661 — MB BS 1965 Lond.; BSc Lond. 1962; DCH Eng. 1970. (St. Bart. Hosp. Lond.) Socs: SW Paediat. Club; Brit. Thorac. & Tuberc. Assn.; Plymouth Med. Soc. Prev: Assoc. Specialist Childr. Asthma Clin. Plymouth Gen. Hosp.; Regist. (Paediat.) Whittington Hosp. Lond.; Ho. Phys. (Paediat.) St. Bart. Hosp. Lond.

FREARSON, Richard James Robin 49 Tranby Lane, Anlaby, Hull HU10 7DT — MB BS 1996 Newc.

FREDERICKS, Briony Jane X-Ray Department, Royal Hospital for Sick Children, Glasgow G3 8SJ Tel: 0141 339 8888 — MB BS 1979 Lond.; MRCP (UK) 1995; FRCPC 1989; FRCR 1984; FRCPG 1997.

FREDRIKSSON, Sten Thomas 36 St Davids Hill, Exeter EX4 4DT — Lakarexamen Lund 1985.

FREE, Amanda Jane Old Cottage Hospital Surgery, Alexandra Road, Epsom KT17 4BL Tel: 01372 724434 Fax: 01372 748171 — MB BS 1981 Lond.; DRCOG 1985; DCH RCP Lond. 1984. (St. Geo.) GP Epsom. Prev: Trainee GP Epsom Dist. Hosp. VTS.

FREE, Anthony John 48 Mulgrave Road, Belmont, Sutton SM2 6LX — MB BS 1979 Lond.; MRCGP 1983; DRCOG 1982; DCH RCP Lond. 1981.

FREE, Caroline Jane Guy's King's & St Thomas' School of Medicine, Waterloo Bridge House, 57 Waterloo Road, London SE1 8WA — MB ChB 1988 Leeds. Research Fell. Prev: SHO (O & G) Hull HA.

FREE, Daniel George Charles The Health Centre, Oakleigh Road North, Whetstone, London N20 0DH Tel: 020 8368 6550 — MB BS 1985 Lond. (Royal Free Hospital) Prev: Lect./Primary Care, RFHSM/UCL Med. Schs.

FREE, Gary 141 Ferrers Avenue, Tutbury, Burton-on-Trent DE13 9JJ — BM BS 1993 Nottm.

FREE, Lucy Caroline The Health Centre, Windmill Avenue, Hassocks BN6 8LY Tel: 01273 844242 Fax: 01273 842709; 2 Sandfield Cottages, New Way Lane, Hurstpierpoint, Hassocks BN6 9BA Tel: 01273 834393 — MB BS 1980 Lond.; DRCOG 1983. Med. Off. Plumpton & Brighton Racecourse. Socs: (Comm.) Med. Equestrian Assn.; Racecourse Med. Offs. Assn.

FREE, Mark Christopher Stonecot Surgery, 115 Epsom Road, Sutton SM3 9EY Tel: 020 8644 5187; 40 West Hill, Epsom KT19 8LF Tel: 01372 743284 Email: mark.free@btinternet.com — MB BS 1981 Lond.; BSc Lond. 1978; MRCGP 1987; DRCOG 1984. (St. Geo.) Course Organiser St. Geo.'s VTS Release Course S. Thames; Chief Med. Off. Cornhill PMI Guildford & Connolly Leather Wimbledon; Mem. Merton, Sutton & Wandsworth LMC. Socs: Epsom Med. Soc.

FREEBAIRN, Alice Judith Elizabeth Berkshire Cancer Centre, Royal Berkshire Hospital, London Road, Reading RG1 5AN Tel: 01189 878030 Fax: 01189 877877 — MB BS 1992 Lond.; FRCR 1998; BSc Lond. 1989; MRCP (UK) 1995. (King's Coll. Lond.) Prev: Regist. (Clin. Oncol.) Poole Gen. Hosp.; SHO (Gen. Med.) Reading; Regist. (Clin. Oncol.) Roy. S. Hants. Hosp. Soton.

FREEBORN, Catherine Marion Cudworth Health Centre, Rose Tree Avenue, Cudworth, Barnsley S72 8UA Tel: 01226 712018; 49 Clayfields Lane, Wentworth, Rotherham S62 7TD Tel: 01226 745486, 01980 597702 Email: cathy@collinson.freeserve.co.uk, russellowers@doctors.org.uk — BM BS 1980 Nottm.; DRCOG 1996; DCCH RCP Ed. 1993. Gen. Practitioner Barnsley HA. Prev: Clin. Med. Off. Rotherham HA.; Ho. Off. Univ. Hosp. Nottm.; Ho. Off. Derby City Hosp.

FREEBURN, Elizabeth Margaret Highfields, Shoreditch, Taunton TA3 7BL — MB BCh BAO 1958 Belf. Prev: Ho. Off. & SHO (Anaesth.) Belf. City Hosp.

FREED, David Leon Joshua 14 Marston Road, Salford M7 4ER Tel: 0161 795 6225 Fax: 0161 795 6225 Email: dljfreed@doctors.org.uk — MB ChB 1977 Manch.; MB ChB Manch. 1968; MD Manch. 197. (Manch.) Allergist. Socs: Brit. Soc. Allergy; Internat. Lectin Soc.; Brit. Toxicol. Soc. Prev: Lect. (Immunol.) Manch. Univ.

FREED, Laura Elms Medical Centre, Green Lane, Whitefield, Manchester M45 7FD Tel: 0161 766 2311 Fax: 0161 767 9544 — MB ChB 1983 Manch.; BSc (Med Sci) St. And. 1980; MRCGP 1988. Prev: Clin. Med. Off. N. Manch. HA.

FREEDLANDER, Mr Eric Department of Plastic Surgery, Northern General Hospital, Herries Road, Sheffield S5 7AU — MB ChB 1972 Glas.; BSc (Hons.) Glas. 1970, MD 1991; FRCS (Plast) Ed. 1986; FRCS Ed. 1979; FRCS Glas. 1979. Cons. Plastic Surg. N. Gen. Hosp. & Sheff. Childr. Hosp.

FREEDLANDER, Stanley Cecil (retired) 9 Priory Gardens, St Andrews KY16 8XX Tel: 01334 478532 — LRCP LRCS Ed., LRFPS Glas. 1944; FRCGP 1975, M 1960.

FREEDMAN, Abraham 21B Chesterford Gardens, London NW3 7DD Tel: 020 7435 4587 — MB BS 1941 Lond.; MD Lond. 1948; FRCP Lond. 1972, M 1947; MRCS Eng. LRCP Lond. 1939. (Lond. Hosp.) Clin. Dir. Laborat. Applied Biol. Ltd. Lond. Socs: Brit. Soc. Rheum.& BMA. Prev: Cons. Phys. Hackney Hosp.; Asst. Med. Off. Lewisham Hosp.; Squadron Ldr. RAFVR.

FREEDMAN, Andrew Robert Department of Medicine, University of Wales College of Medicine, Heath Park, Cardiff CF14 4XN Tel:

029 2074 7747 Fax: 029 2074 3819 Email: freedman@cardiff.ac.uk — MB BChir 1981 Camb.; MA Camb. 1981, MD 1991; MRCP (UK) 1983; FRCP 1998. Sen. Lect. & Hon. Cons. Phys. Infec. Dis. Univ. Wales Coll. Med. Cardiff. Prev: Sen. Regist. (Communicable Dis.) St. Geo. Hosp. Lond.

FREEDMAN, Mr Arnold (retired) 5 Chadlington Road, Oxford OX2 6SY Tel: 01865 515224 — BM BCh 1955 Oxf.; MA Oxf. 1955; FRCS Eng. 1964; FCOphth RCS Eng. 1990; DO Eng. 1959. Prev: Cons. Ophth. United Oxf. Hosps.

FREEDMAN, Barbara Alexandra Mary RPR House, 52 St Leonard's Road, Eastbourne BN21 3UU Tel: 01323 534415 Fax: 01323 534081; 24 Constantine Road, London NW3 2NG Tel: 020 7482 6251 — MB BChir 1980 Camb.; BA (Biochem.) Camb. 1977, MB BChir (Hons.) 1980; MRCP (UK) 1983. (Univ. Camb.) Med. Dir. Rhône-Poulenc Rorer UK. Prev: Med. Research Counc. Train. Fell.sh.; SHO Rotat. (Med.) Univ. Coll. Hosp. Lond.; Ho. Off. (Med. & Surg.) St. Mary's Hosp. Lond.

FREEDMAN, Beth 51 Lynton Drive, Southport PR8 4QG; 19 Sewers Hall Close, Finchley, London N3 1JL — MB ChB 1995 Manch.; MRCP (Paeds). SHO (Paediat.) Gt. Ormond St.Oncol.Hosp. Socs: BMA. Prev: SHO (Paediat. Cardiol.), Harefield Hosp.; SHO Paediat. Chelsea & W.m. Hosp.; SHO (A & E) N. Manch. Gen. Hosp.

FREEDMAN, Danielle Beverley 54 The Green, Little Gaddesden, Berkhamsted HP4 1PL — MB BS 1976 Lond.; FRCPath. 1995, M 1983. (Roy. Free) Cons. Chem. Path. & Clin. Dir. Path. Luton & Dunstable Hosp.; Clin. Dir. (Path.) & Assoc. Phys. (Clin. Endocrinol.) Luton & Dunstable Hosp. NHS Trust. Socs: Med. Res. Soc.; Brit. Diabetic Assn. Prev: Lect. (Clin.) Chem. Path. Middlx. Hosp. Med. Sch. Lond. Univ.; Regist. (Chem. Path.) & SHO (Clin. Path.) Roy. Free Hosp. Lond.

FREEDMAN, Deborah Judith 35 Church Street, Thriplow, Royston SG8 7RE; 67 Berkely Road, Bishopston, Bristol BS7 8HQ — MB BS 1994 Lond.; MRCP 1998. (Lond. Hosp. Med. Coll.) Staff Grade Community Paediat., S.mead Hosp., Bristol. Prev: SHO (Paediat.) Soton. Gen. Hosp.; SHO (Paediat.) Portsmouth; SHO (Paediat.) Whipps Cross Hosp. Lond.

FREEDMAN, Freda 489 Palatine Road, Manchester M22 Tel: 0161 998 3206 — MB BS 1951 Durh. (Durh.)

FREEDMAN, George Roland (retired) 41 Elmfield Road, Gosforth, Newcastle upon Tyne NE3 4BA — MB BChir 1947 Camb.; FRCGP 1970. Lect. Family Med. Univ. Newc. Prev: Provost N. Eng. Fac. RCGP.

FREEDMAN, Harold Joshua Handa, 77 Campsie Drive, Mosshead, Bearsden, Glasgow G61 3HX Tel: 0141 942 6625 — MB ChB 1955 Glas.; DA Eng. 1957. Cons. Anaesth. N. Glas. Health Dist.

FREEDMAN, Isidore (retired) Flat 46, Green Park, 91 Manor Road, Bournemouth BH1 3HR — MRCS Eng. LRCP Lond. 1958; BSc Lond. 1980; BA Open 1988; MRCPsych 1973; T(Psych) 1991; DPM Eng. 1967. Prev: Cons. Psychiat. (Ment. Handicap) & Clin. Tutor (Psychiat.) Monyhull Hosp. Birm.

FREEDMAN, Jonathan Elliot Parkbury House Surgery, St. Peters Street, St Albans AL1 3HD Tel: 01727 851589 Fax: 01727 854372 Email: jonathan.freedman@gp-E82060.nhs.uk; 77 Gurney Court Road, St Albans AL1 4QX — MB BS 1989 Lond.; Dip. Med. Acupunct. (Brit. Med.); MRCGP 1994; DRCOG 1992; DCH RCP Lond. 1991. (St. Georges Med. Sch. Lond.) GP Trainer St. Albans; Local Med. Comm.; Vice Chaim. Herdfordshire LMC; Clin. Avd. on Employm.s.; Health Serv. Ombudsman. Socs: Acred. Mem. Brit. Med. Acupunc. Soc. Prev: Trainee GP St. Albans VTS.

FREEDMAN, Judith The Portman Clinic, 8 Fitzjohns Avenue, London NW3 5NA Tel: 020 7794 8262 Fax: 020 7447 3748 Email: jfreedman@tavi-port.org — MD 1975 Stanford Univ. USA; BA Harvard 1971. p/t Cons. Psychother. Portman Clinic Lond.; Dip. Amer. Bd. Psychiat. & Neurol. Socs: Fell. Roy. Coll. Psychiat.; Boston Psychoanalytic Soc. Prev: Asst. Psychiat. McLean Hosp. Boston, MA, USA.

FREEDMAN, Mr Lawrence Samuel Clementine Churchill Hospital, Sudbury Hill, Harrow HA1 3RX Tel: 01923 286337; 49 Thames Street, St Albans, Christchurch, New Zealand Email: chricthurnell@hotmail.com — MB BS 1978 Lond.; FRCS Eng. 1982. Cons. Orthop. Surg. N.wick Pk. Hosp. Harrow.

FREEDMAN, Louis Wellington Hospital Consultant Surgery, Wellington Place, London NW8 9LE; 11 St. James' Close, Prince Albert Road, London NW8 7LG Tel: 020 7722 7011 — MB ChB Manch. 1945; BA (Hons.) (Philosophy) Lond. 1971; MD Manch. 1963. (Manch.) Med. Off. Confederat. Brit. Industs. & Gen. Electric Company. Socs: Fell. Roy. Soc. Med.; BMA. Prev: Clin. Asst. (Gyn.) P. of Wales Hosp. Tottenham & Bearsted Memor. Hosp.; Resid. Surg. Off. Lond. Jewish Hosp.; Ho. Surg. (Orthop.) & Cas. Off. Beckett Hosp. Barnsley.

FREEDMAN, Peter Sydney Dept. of Metabolism, St Bartholomews Hospital, Dominion House 3rd Floor, 59 Bartholomew Close, London EC1A 7BE Tel: 020 7601 7450 Fax: 020 7601 7449 Email: p.s.freedman@mds.qmw.ac.uk; Beech House, Church St, Thriplow, Royston SG8 7RE Tel: 01763 208204 — MB BS Lond. 1969; MA Camb. 1977; BSc (Special) Lond. 1965; MRCP (UK) 1972; MRCS Eng. LRCP Lond. 1968. (Lond. Hosp.) Cons. Phys. & Endocrinol. Homerton Hosp., Lond. E9; Cons. Phys. (Diabetes) The Roy. Hosps. Lond.; Hon. Sen. Lect. St Barts & Roy. Lond. Sch. Med. & Dent. Socs: Soc. Endocrinol. BDA. Prev: Lect. (Med.) Univ. Camb.; Hon. Regist. (Cardiac) Lond. Hosp.

FREEDMAN, Roger Charles Manchester Health Authority, Gateway House, Piccadilly South, Manchester M60 7LP; 31 Coppice Road, Poynton, Stockport SK12 1SL Email: rfreedman@doctors.org.uk — MB BS 1968 Lond.; 1996 Dip Presc Sci, Liverp.; MRCS Eng. LRCP Lond. 1967; MRCGP 1974; DObst RCOG 1970. (Univ. Coll. Hosp.) Primary Care Med. Adviser, Manch. Health Auth. and Salford & Trafford Health Auth.; Dep. Port Med. Off., Manch. Airport; Hon. Med. Adviser, Granada TV. Prev: Gen. Practitioner, Margate, Kent (1970-91); Ho. Surg. (Obst.) I. of Thanet Dist. Hosp.; Med. Adviser, Tameside FHSA (1991-93).

FREEDMAN, Sarah Anne Imperial College Health Centre, Southside, Watt;s Way, London SW7 1LU Tel: 020 7584 6301 Fax: 020 7594 9390 — MB BS 1986 Lond.; DRCOG 1991. (UMDS (Guy's)) Prev: Trainee GP Hastings VTS; SHO (A & E) William Harvey Hosp. Ashford.

FREEDMAN, Stanley 55 Twyford Avenue, London N2 9NR Tel: 020 8883 8038 — MB BS 1960 Lond.; PhD Lond. 1969, BSc 1957; FRCP Lond. 1980, M 1964. (Middlx.) Sen. Med. Off. Med. Control Agency; Hon. Cons. Phys. Char. Cross Hosp. Socs: Physiol. Soc. Prev: Cons. Phys. Chase Farm Hosp. Enfield; Sen. Regist. Hammersmith Hosp. Lond.

FREEDMAN, Wendy 24 Aldenham Avenue, Radlett WD7 8HX — MB BS 1989 Lond.; MRCGP 1996; DCH RCP Lond. 1992.

FREEGARD, Simon Peter Stennack Surgery, The Old Stennack School, St Ives TR26 1RU Tel: 01736 793333 Fax: 01736 793746; The Ship House, Church Road, Lelant, St Ives TR26 3LB Tel: 01736 756337 — MB BS 1978 Lond.; MRCGP 1985; MRCP 1982 (UK); MSc (Exon) 1997 Univ. Exeter; MB BS (Hons.) Lond. 1978; MRCP (UK) 1982; MRCGP 1985; MSc (Exon) 1997 Univ. Exeter. (St. Bart.) Hosp. Practitioner (Cardiol.).

FREEGARD, Mr Timothy James Royal Eye Infirmary, Apsley Road, Mutley, Plymouth PL4 6PL Tel: 01752 203142 — MB BS Lond. 1983, MD 1997; FRCS Glas. 1989; FCOphth 1990. (St. Bart.) Cons. (Ophth.) Roy. Eye Infirm. Plymouth. Prev: Sen. Regist. Roy. Free & UCL; Sen. Regist. Lond. Hosp. & St. Bart. Hosp.

FREELAND, Mr Andrew Peter Felstead House, 23 Banbury Road, Oxford OX2 6NX Tel: 01865 404142 — MB BS 1967 Lond.; FRCS Eng. 1972; MRCS Eng. LRCP Lond. 1967. (Guy's) Cons. Surg. (ENT) Radcliffe Infirm. Oxf. Socs: Fell. Roy. Soc. Med.; Roy. Soc. Med. (Ex-Pres. Sect. Laryngol. & Rhinol.). Prev: Sen. Regist. Radcliffe Infirm. Oxf.; Clin. Research Fell. Banting Inst. Univ. Toronto, Canada.

FREELAND, Malcolm Scott Gillingham Road Surgery, Gillingham Road, Silton, Gillingham SP8 5DF Tel: 01747 840226 Fax: 01747 840950 — MB 1975 Camb.; BChir 1974. Doctor,G.P,Silton.

FREELAND, Mr Peter Accident & Emergency Department, St Johns Hospital, Livingston EH54 6PP Tel: 01506 419666 — MB BCh BAO 1980 Belf.; FRCP Ed. 1993; FRCS Ed. 1985; FFAEM 1994. Cons. A & E St. Johns Hosp. Livingston.

FREELAND, Robin (retired) 9 Riverside Park, Linnpark Avenue, Netherlee, Glasgow G44 3PG Tel: 0141 637 2407 — MB ChB 1940 Glas.; BSc Glas. 1937, MB ChB 1940, DPH 1942; DMRD Eng. 1963. Prev: Cons. Radiol. (in Admin. Charge) Monkland Dists. Hosps.

FREELAND, William Alexander, Lt.-Col. RAMC Retd. RGIT Ltd., 338 King St., Aberdeen AB24 5BQ Tel: 01224 619619 Fax: 01224 619519 Email: waf@rgit.co.uk; Franorst, Kincardine O'Neil, Aboyne

AB34 5AB Tel: 0133 988 4350 — MB ChB 1976 Aberd.; MSc Occupat. Med. Lond. 1985; MFOM RCP Lond. 1988, AFOM 1987. Exec. Med. Dir. RGIT Ltd. Aberd.; Mem. Internat. Commiss. on Occupat. Health. Socs: Soc. Occupat. Med. Prev: Cons. Occupat. Med. & Head Army Occupat. Health Research Unit APRE FarnBoro.

FREELING, Professor Paul, OBE The Brocklebank Health Centre, 249 Garratt Lane, London SW18 4UE Tel: 020 8870 1341; 59 Spencer Park, Wandsworth, London SW18 2SX Tel: 020 8870 4444 — MB BS 1952 Lond.; FRCGP 1972. (St. Mary's) Prof. Gen. Pract. & Head Dept. Gen. Pract. & Primary Care St. Geo. Hosp. Med. Sch. Lond.; Vice Dean St. Geo. Hosp. Med. Sch. Lond.; Sub-Dean MSc in Health Sci. Prev: Mayne Guest Prof. Univ. Qu.sld.; Nuffield Tutor RCGP; Vis. Expert Family Med. to Health Manpower Developm. Progr. MoH Singapore.

FREEMAN, Adam Roger Mark Tel: 020 8997 1999 Fax: 0870 094 0166 Email: armfreeman@doctors.org.uk — MA, BM BCh Oxf. 1959; FRCPsych 1988, M 1973; DPM Eng. 1965; DObst RCOG 1962; AMQ 1960. (Oxf.) Socs: Chair Parliamentray Liaison Comm. Roy. Coll. of Psychiat.s. Prev: Cons. Psychiat. Hillingdon Hosp. Uxbridge.; Cons. Psychiat. St. Bernard Hosp. S.all; Sen. Regist. (Psychiat.) Middlx. Hosp. Lond. & Shenley Hosp. St. Albans.

FREEMAN, Adrian Clifford Waterside Primary Care, Combe Martin Health Centre, Castle Street, Combe Martin, Ilfracombe EX34 0JA Tel: 01271 882406 Fax: 01271 883821 — MB ChB 1979 Birm.; MRCGP 1984; DRCOG 1986.

FREEMAN, Alan Hugh Victoria Cottage, 16 Main St., Hardwick, Cambridge CB3 7QS Tel: 01954 210633 — MB BS 1968 Lond.; MRCS Eng. LRCP Lond. 1968; FFR 1974; DMRD Eng. 1972. (Westm.) Cons. Radiol. Addenbrooke's Hosp. Camb.

FREEMAN, Miss Alexandra Simone Jacqueline 69 Abercrombie Gardens, Southampton SO16 8FR — BM 1988 Soton.

FREEMAN, Alfred Michael (retired) Fingringhoe Hall, Church Road, Fingringhoe, Colchester CO5 7BN Tel: 01206 729312 Email: xrw68@dial.pipex.com — MB BChir Camb. 1955; MA Camb. 1965; MRCS Eng. LRCP Lond. 1954; LMSSA Lond. 1954; DPhysMed Eng. 1970. Locum Cons. P.ss Alexandra Hosp. Trust Mid-Essex Hosps. Trust Chelmsford. Prev: Clin. Asst. N. Middlx. Hosp., P.ss Alexandra Hosp. Harlow & S.end Gen. Hosp.

FREEMAN, Amanda Emma Louise Department of Paediatrics, St Mary's Hospital, Milton Road, Portsmouth PO3 6AD Tel: 023 92 286000 — MB BS 1986 Lond.; MRCP (UK) 1989. (St Thomas's Hospital Medical School) p/t Cons. in Paediat. St Mary's Hosp. Portsmouth. Prev: Sen. Regist. (Paediatric Neurol.) Soton. Gen. Hosp.; Regist. (Paediat.) St. Geo. Hosp. Lond.; SHO (Paediat. Cardiol.) Hosp. for Sick Childr. Gt. Ormond St. Lond.

FREEMAN, Anthony Leon Greenford Avenue Medical Centre, 322 Greenford Avenue, London W7 3AH Tel: 020 8578 1880; 18A Lion Gate Gardens, Kew, Richmond TW9 2DW Tel: 020 8940 0420 Email: anthony.freeman@virgin.net — MB BS 1968 Lond.; MRCP (UK) 1973; MRCS Eng. LRCP Lond. 1968; DCH Eng. 1970; Dip Occ Med 1998. (Kings Coll. Hosp.) Med. Adviser HM Customs & Excise (p/t); Local Med. Offcer Civil Serv. Prev: Phys. & Lect. (Med.) Univ. Natal & King Edwd. VIII Hosp.; SHO (Med.) Wexham Pk. Hosp. Slough; Regist. (Med.) Epsom Dist. Hosp.

FREEMAN, Anthony Simon Mitford St Clinic, Mitford St., Stretford, Manchester M32 8AG Tel: 0161 866 8556 Fax: 0161 865 4937; 18 Henley Avenue, Firswood, Manchester M16 0EW — MB ChB 1963 Manch.; MRCS Eng. LRCP Lond. 1963; DObst RCOG 1967. (Manch.) GP Princip.; Crowd Doctor at Manch. United Football Club. Prev: Trainee GP Edin.

FREEMAN, Brendan Melbourne Health Care Centre, Penn Lane, Melbourne, Derby DE73 1EF Tel: 01332 862124 Fax: 01332 865154; The Hollies, High St, Tickmae, Derby DE73 1JH Tel: 01332 862799 — MB ChB Liverp. 1951; DObst RCOG 1973; DTM & H Liverp. 1962. Clin. Asst. Sue Ryder Hospice. Prev: Med. Off. Pahang Consolidated Co. Sungai Lembing Hosp., Malaysia; SHO Off. Liverp. Roy. Infirm. & Walton Hosp. Liverp.

FREEMAN, Mr Brian James Christopher Frenchay Hospital, Beckspool Road, Bristol BS16 1LE Tel: 0117 970 1212; 11 The Hornbeams, Marlborough Drive, Frenchay, Bristol BS16 1PW Tel: 0117 956 5703 — MB BCh BAO 1988 NUI; MB BCh NUI BAO 1988; FRCS Eng. 1992; LRCPSI 1988. Regist. (Trauma & Orthop. Surg.) Frenchay Hosp. Bristol. Socs: Assoc. Mem. BOA; Brit. Orthop. Train. Assn.; BMA. Prev: Regist. (Orthop.) A.O.C. S.mead; Regist. (Trauma & Orthop. Surg.) Bristol Roy. Infirm.; Regist. & SHO (Orthop.) Cheltenham Gen. Hosp.

FREEMAN, Brian Sidney All Hallows Farm House, Wimborne BH21 5NJ Tel: 01725 517 678. Fax: 01725 517678 Email: hallows@dircon.co.uk — BM BCh 1950 Oxf.; MA Oxf. 1950. (Oxf. & St. Thos.) Prev: Ho. Off. St. Thos. Hosp. Lond.

FREEMAN, Carol Ann 5 Davan Pl, Broughty Ferry, Dundee DD5 3HG — MB ChB 1997 Glas.

FREEMAN, Caroline Judith Shawbirch Medical Centre, 5 Acorn Way, Shawbirch, Telford TF5 0LW Tel: 01952 641555 Fax: 01952 260913; Wharf House, Wappenshall, Telford TF6 6DE Tel: 01952 603271 — MB ChB 1985 Liverp.; MRCGP 1990; DRCOG 1988. (Liverpool) Prev: Trainee GP St. Helen's & Knowsley HA VTS; SHO (Psychiat.) Greaves Hall S.port; SHO (Psychiat.) Fazakerley Hosp. Liverp.

FREEMAN, Charles Bryan Chapeloak Practice, 347 Oakwood Lane, Leeds LS8 3HA; 460 Harrogate Road, Leeds LS17 6DN Tel: 0113 295 3764 Email: freeman@ukonline.co.uk — BM BCh 1966 Oxf.; MA Oxf. 1966, BA 1963, DM 1977; MRCP (UK) 1970; FRCP (UK) 1999. (Oxf. & St. Geo.) Socs: BMA; MDU. Prev: Vis. Assoc. (Pediat. Oncol.) Nat. Insts. Health Bethesda, USA; MRC Research Fell., Clin. Lect. & Hon. Sen. Regist. (Med. Genetics) St. Mary's Hosp. Manch.

FREEMAN, Christopher Paul Lindsay Royal Edinburgh Hospital, Morningside Terrace, Edinburgh EH10 5HF Tel: 0131 537 6708 Fax: 0131 537 6104; (cons. rooms), 14 Moray Place, Edinburgh EH3 6DT Tel: 0131 225 4843 Fax: 0131 225 6749 — MB ChB 1971 Ed.; MPhil Ed. 1978; FRCPsych 1990, M 1975; FRCP 1999. (Ed.) Cons. Psychother. Roy. Edin. Hosp.; Hon. Sen. Lect. Edin. Univ.; Regional Adviser SE Region Scotl.; Chairm. Roy. Coll. Psychiat. Special Comm. on ECT. Prev: Lect. (Psychiat.) Edin. Univ.; Sen. Lect. & Hon. Cons. Psychiat. Edin. Univ. & Roy. Edin. Hosp.; Chairm. Roy. Coll. Psychiat. Research Comm.

FREEMAN, Clare 60 Park Grange Croft, Sheffield S2 3QL — MB ChB 1990 Sheff.

FREEMAN, Clive Anthony Martin Stockton Heath Medical Centre, The Forge, London Road, Stockton Heath, Warrington WA4 6HJ Tel: 01925 604427 Fax: 01925 210501 — MB ChB 1976 Dundee; Dip Occ Med 2000; MRCGP 1985; DRCOG 1978.

FREEMAN, Cyril (retired) 19 Woodmere Way, Beckenham BR3 6SJ Tel: 020 8650 1291 — LRCPI & LM, LRCSI & LM 1947. Prev: Ho. Phys. & Ho. Surg. Drumcondra Hosp. Dub.

FREEMAN, Daryl Glenfield Surgery, 111 Station Road, Glenfield, Leicester LE3 8GS; 63 Maplewell Road, Woodhouse Eaves, Loughborough LE12 8RG Tel: 01509 891403 Email: freeman@gpiag-asthma.org — MB ChB 1986 Leic.; MRCGP 1991; DRCOG 1990. GP Glenfield Surg., Leicester. Socs: Roy. Soc. Med.; BTS. Prev: Trainee GP Market HarBoro. & Leicester VTS; SHO (Paediat.) Nuneaton; SHO (Gen. Med.) Gibraltar.

FREEMAN, Eleanor Anne Department of Geriatric Medicine, St Woolos Hospital, Newport Tel: 01633 238321 Email: anne.freeman@gwent.wales.nhs.uk; 248 Cyncoed Road, Cyncoed, Cardiff CF23 6RT Email: anne.freeman@anne51.fsnet.co.uk — MB ChB 1973 Manch.; FRCP Lond. 1994; MRCP (UK) 1980. Cons.Physi. c/o the Elderly Med. Roy. Gwent & St. Woolos Hosp. Newport, Gwent; Health Professional Adviser, Nat. Assembly for Wales, Cardiff, 1 session per week. Socs: Brit. Geri. Soc; Nat. Assoc of Clin Tutors; Assoc. for study of Med Edu. Prev: Sen. Regist. (Geriat.) Cardiff Roy. Infirm.; Regist. (Med.) Univ. Hosp. Wales; SHO (Med.) N.. Gen. Hosp. Sheff. & N. Manch. Gen. Hosp.

FREEMAN, Emma Jean Karin 105 Runnymede, Merton Abbey, London SW19 2RQ — MB BS 1985 Lond. Regist. (Med.) William Harvey Hosp. Ashford Kent. Prev: SHO (Med.) Roy. Sussex Co. Hosp. Brighton; SHO (Oncol.) RMH; SHO (Med.) Kingston Hosp.

FREEMAN, Eric Burton House, Withington Hospital, Manchester M20 2LR Tel: 0161 291 4524 — MRCS Eng. LRCP Lond. 1961; FRCP Lond. 1983, M 1966; FRCP Ed. 1981, M 1965. (Manch.) Cons. Geriat. Univ. Hosp. S. Manch. Socs: Brit. Geriat. Soc.; BMA.

FREEMAN, Frances Elizabeth (retired) Warriors, Millfield Lane, Hitchin SG4 7NH — MB BS Lond. 1958; MRCS Eng. LRCP Lond. 1958; DObst RCOG 1961. Prev: Clin. Asst. (Med.) Lister Hosp. Stevenage.

FREEMAN, Professor George Kenneth Fulham Clinic, 82 Lillie Road, London SW6 1TN Tel: 020 7386 9299 Fax: 020 7610 0635

— MB BChir 1969 Camb.; MD Camb. 1993; MRCP (UK) 1971; FRCGP 1985, M 1975. (St. Thos.) Prof. Gen. Pract. Imperial Coll. Sch. of Med.; GP Fulham. Socs: (Ex-Sec.) Assn. Univ. Dept. Gen. Pract. Prev: Sen. Lect. & Lect. (Primary Med. Care) Soton. Univ.; GP Soton.

FREEMAN, Heather Gillian Minchin Woodpecker's End, Longridge Grove, Pyrford, Woking GU22 8PG — MB BCh BAO 1958; MD Dub. 1973; MRCPath 1974; DObst RCOG 1961. Emerit. Cons. St. Peter's Hosp. Chertsey. Prev: Cons. Chem. Pathologist St Peter's Hosp. Chertsey; Sen. Lect. (Chem. Path.) Roy. Postgrad. Med. Sch. Lond.; Sen. Regist. (Chem. Path.) Centr. Middl. Hosp. Lond.

FREEMAN, Helen Catherine Nelson Health Centre, Cecil St., North Shields NE29 0DZ Tel: 0191 257 4001; 58 The Grove, Gosforth, Newcastle upon Tyne NE3 1NJ Tel: 0191 285 7067 — MB BS 1983 Newc.; MRCGP 1987; DRCOG 1987. Prev: Trainee GP N.umbria VTS.

FREEMAN, Howard Michael The Tod Practice, 12 Durham Road, Raynes Park, London SW20 0TW Tel: 020 8946 0069 Fax: 020 8944 2927; Little Burgh, The Drive, Banstead CR5 3LT Tel: 01737 355248 — MB BS 1979 Lond.; MA Camb. 1980; MRCS Eng. LRCP Lond. 1979; MRCGP 1987. (Camb. & Univ. Coll. Hosp.) Chairm. Exec. Nelson & W. Merton PCT.

FREEMAN, Hugh John Hackwood Partnership, Essex House, Worting Road, Basingstoke RG21 8SU Tel: 01256 470464 Fax: 01256 357289 — MB BS 1973 Lond.

FREEMAN, Professor Hugh Lionel 21 Montagu Square, London W1H 2LF Tel: 020 7224 4867 Fax: 020 7224 6153 — BM BCh Oxf. 1954; MSc Salford 1980; MA Oxf. 1954, DM 1988; FRCPsych 1971; FFPHM 1989; DPM Eng. 1958; Hon. FRCPsych 1998. (Oxf. & Manch.) Hon. Prof. Univ. Salford; Hon. Cons. Psychiat. Salford Ment. Health Trust; Hon. Vis. Fell. Green Coll. Oxf.; Hon. Research Fell. UCL; Capt. RAMC (RARO); Edr. Brit. Jl. Psychiat. & Curr. Opinion in Psychiat. (1983-93). Socs: Fell. Roy. Soc. Med.; Fell. (Pres.) Manch. Med. Soc.; Harv. Soc. Prev: Sen. Regist. Littlemore Hosp. Oxf.; Regist. Bethlem Roy. & Maudsley Hosps. Lond.; Ho. Surg. (Neurosurg.) Manch. Roy. Infirm.

FREEMAN, Mr James Church Stile, 11 Yealm Road, Newton Ferrers, Plymouth PL8 1AH Tel: 01752 872250 — MB BS 1940 Lond.; FRCS Eng. 1948; MRCS Eng. LRCP Lond. 1940; DLO Eng. 1950. (Middlx.) Prev: Cons. ENT Surg. United Bristol Hosps.

FREEMAN, James Old Stones, Great Addington, Kettering NN14 4BL — MB BS 1971 Lond.; FFA RCSI 1977. (Middlx.) Cons. Anaesth. Kettering Gen. Hosp. Prev: Sen. Regist. (Anaesth.) W. Midl. RHA.; Sen. Regist. (Anaesth.) City Gen. Hosp. Stoke-on-Trent; Regist. (Anaesth. & Pulmon. Func.) Middlx. Hosp. Lond.

FREEMAN, Jan George 32 Huntingdon Close, Kingston Park, Newcastle upon Tyne NE3 2XY — MB BS 1973 Newc.; MRCP (UK) 1976. Sen. Regist. (Gen. med. & Gastroentero.) Roy. Vict. Infirm. Socs: Brit. Soc. Gastroenterol.; Caledonian Soc. Gastroenterol. Prev: Research Fell. Univ. Newc.; Regist. Birkenhead Gen. Hosp.; SHO Gloucester Roy. Hosp.

FREEMAN, Jeffrey Stuart Tameside General Hospital, Fountain St., Ashton-under-Lyne OL6 9RW Tel: 0161 331 5040 Fax: 0161 331 5255 Email: jefffreeman.exchange.tgcps.tr-nwest.nhs.uk; 6 Pine Road, Didsbury, Manchester M20 6UY Tel: 0161 445 3559 Fax: 0161 445 3559 Email: debfreeman@compuserve.com — MB ChB Leeds 1968; FRCP Lond. 1991; MRCP (UK) 1980. (Leeds) Cons. Paediat. Tameside & Glossop Community & Priority Servs. NHS Trust. Socs: Manch. Paediat. Club; Brit. Paediat. Assn. Prev: Sen. Regist. (Paediat.) Booth Hall Childr. Hosp. Manch.; Resid. (Paediat.) Ashkelon, Israel; Regist. (Paediat.) St. Mary's Hosp. Manch.

FREEMAN, Joanna Streatham Common Group Practice, Guildersfield Road, London SW16 5LS Tel: 020 8765 4901 — MB BS 1987 Lond.; MRCGP 1991; DRCOG 1991. (St. Thos. Hosp.) Clin. Asst. BrE. Clinic St. Thos. Hosp. Lond. Socs: MDU.

FREEMAN, John Russell 8 Snelston Crescent, Littleover, Derby DE23 6BL — MB ChB 1954 Manch.; MRCGP 1963; DObst RCOG 1955. Princip. Police Surg. Derbysh. Constab. Socs: Derby Med. Soc. & Assn. Police Surg. Prev: Ho. Surg. Salford Roy. Hosp.; Ho. Off. St. Mary's Hosp. Manch.

FREEMAN, Jonathan William Tel: 0121 472 1311 Fax: 0121 440 0262 Email: jonathan.freeman@university-b.wmids.nhs.uk; Tel: 0121 440 0262 Email: jonathan.freeman@blueyonder.com — MB ChB 1978 Birm.; FFA RCS Eng. 1983. (Birmingham) Cons. Transpl. Anaesth. & Intens. Care Specialist Qu. Eliz. Hosp. Birm.; Hon. Sen. Clin. Lect. Univ. Birm.; Div.al Director UHBT. Socs: Liver IC Gp. Europe.; Internat. Liver Transpl. Soc.

FREEMAN, Julie Anne Royal Hospital for Sick Chidlren, Edinburgh Tel: 0131 536 0000; 18 Warrender Park Road, Edinburgh EH9 1JG — MB ChB 1983 Ed.; FFA RCS Eng. 1988. Cons. Anaesth. Roy. Hop. Sick Childr. Edin. Prev: Sen. Regist. (Anaesth.) Roy. Infirm Edin.

FREEMAN, Kathryn Ann West Street Surgery, 89 West Street, Dunstable LU6 1SF Tel: 01582 664401 Fax: 01582 475766; The Old Wrestlers, Leighton Road, Northall, Dunstable LU6 2HA Tel: 01525 222428 — MB ChB 1978 Manch. GP Princip.

FREEMAN, Keith tds (Telemedicine) Ltd, Kingfisher, Lissington Road, Wickenby, Lincoln LN3 5AB Tel: 01673 885533 Fax: 01673 885815 Email: keith.freeman@btinternet.com; Kingfisher, Lissington Road, Wickenby, Lincoln LN3 5AB Tel: 01673 885533 Fax: 01673 885815 Email: keith.freeman@btinternet.com — MB BS 1975 Lond.; FRCP Lond. 1996; MRCP (UK) 1979; MRCS Eng. LRCP Lond. 1975; LMSSA Lond. 1975. (Guy's) Dir. tds (TeleMed.) Ltd; Hon. Prof. TeleMed. Univ. Wales Swansea. Socs: Brit. Assn. Dermat.; Uk TeleMed. Assoc. - Vice Chair; Amer. TeleMed. Assoc. Prev: Cons. Dermat. Lincoln & Louth NHS Trust; Cons. Dermat. W. Wales Gen. Hosp. Carmarthen; Cons. Adviser (Dermat.) MOD (Army) & Camb. Milit. Hosp. Aldershot.

FREEMAN, Kenneth Berkeley Norman 6 Dunsdon Close, Liverpool L25 6JG — MB ChB 1944 Liverp.; MRCS Eng. LRCP Lond. 1944; MRCGP 1954. (Liverp.) Prev: Flight Lt. RAFVR; Sen. Ho. Surg. S.port Gen. Infirm.; Ho. Phys. Roy. S.. Hosp. Liverp.

FREEMAN, Mr Laurence Brian c/o Leighton Hospital, Leighton, Crewe CW1 4QJ Tel: 01270 255141 Fax: 01270 612085; 10 Rivington Road, Hale, Altrincham WA15 9PH Tel: 0161 928 7317 — MB Camb. 1967, BChir 1966; FRCS Eng. 1976; DO Eng. 1972; FRCOphth. (Univ. Coll. Hosp.) Cons. Ophth. Mid Chesh. Hosps. Trust. Socs: Fell. Roy. Soc. Med. Prev: Ho. Phys. Univ. Coll. Hosp.; Ho. Surg. Hillingdon Hosp.

FREEMAN, Leisa Joan Norfolk & Norwich Hospital, Brunswick Road, Norwich NR3 1SR Tel: 01603 289666 Fax: 01603 287494 Email: leisa.freeman@norfolk-norwich.thenhs.com; The Dairy House, High St, Dunwich, Saxmundham IP17 3DN Tel: 01728 648388 Fax: 01628 648833 — MB ChB 1979 Birm.; MRCP (UK) 1982. (University of Birmingham) Assoc. Specialist, Cardiol.; Hon. Lect. (Cardiol.), Univ. of E. Anglia. Socs: Brit. Cardiac Soc. Prev: Regist., Nat. Heart Hosp., Lond.

FREEMAN, Lesley Marsh Street Surgery, 25A Marsh Street, Rothwell, Leeds LS26 0AG Tel: 0113 282 1571 Fax: 0113 282 4720; Ingledew Cottage, Cross Ingledew Crescent, Leeds LS8 1BR — MB ChB 1987 Leics.; MRCGP 1991; DRCOG 1990.

FREEMAN, Louise Jennet Goldthorn, Eden Mount Road, Grange-over-Sands LA11 6BN — MB ChB 1991 Birm.; FFAEM 2001; FRCS Ed. 1996; DA 1996. (Birm.) Specialist Regist. (A & E) SW Thames. Socs: Brit. Assn. Accid. & Emerg. Med.; BMA. Prev: SHO (Elderly Care) St. Helier; SHO (ITU) Lewisham; SHO (Orthop.) Roy. Orthop. Hosp. Birm.

FREEMAN, Marie Joyce (retired) Wingfield House, Darlington Place, Bath BA2 6BY Tel: 01225 466670 Fax: 01225 466670 — MB BS 1959 Lond.; LMSSA Lond. 1958; FFCM 1984, M 1972; DPH Eng. 1969. Prev: Indep. Health Care Managem. Cons. Avon.

FREEMAN, Mark James 9 Showell Green, Droitwich WR9 8UE — BM BS 1991 Nottm.

FREEMAN, Mark Peter The Surgery, 174 Lower Glen Road, St Leonards-on-Sea TN37 7AR Tel: 01424 721616/852270 Fax: 01424 854812; Pheasants, Butchers Lane, Three Oaks, Hastings TN35 4NE Tel: 01424 813932 — BM BCh 1986 Oxf.; MA Camb. 1987, BA 1983; MRCGP 1990; DCH RCP Lond. 1990; DFFP 1994. Socs: Brit. med. Acupunct. Soc.

FREEMAN, Mark Steven 74 High Ash Avenue, Alwoodley, Leeds LS17 8RT — MB BS 1992 Lond.; BSc Lond. Univ. 1989; MRCP (UK) 1996. (Univ. Coll. Hosp.) Specialist Regist. (Gen. Med., Diabetes & Endocrinol.) Pinderfields Hosp. Wakefield. Prev: SHO (Neurol., Renal Med. & Med.) St. Jas. Univ. Hosp. Leeds.

FREEMAN, Martin John The Orchard Medical Centre, Fairmead, Cam, Dursley GL11 5NE Tel: 01453 548666 Fax: 01453 548124; Sills Leaze, Sandpits, Dursley GL11 6PB Tel: 01453 547430 — MB

ChB 1975 Bristol; MA Ethics of Health Care Wales 1996; MRCGP 1996. Socs: BMA.

FREEMAN, Matthew Pallett Farm, Bury Road, Turton, Bolton BL7 0BX — MB ChB 1994 Dundee.

FREEMAN, Matthew Neil 25 Astral Avenue, Hipperholme, Halifax HX3 8NN — MB BS 1996 Lond.

FREEMAN, Mr Michael Alexander Reykers (retired) 79 Albert Street, London NW1 7LX Tel: 020 7388 5731 Fax: 020 7388 5731 — MB BChir 1964 Camb.; MD Camb. 1964; FRCS Eng. 1959. Hon. Cons. Surg. Lond. Hosp.; Europ. Edr.-in-Chief Arthroplasty. Prev: Cons. Orthop. Surg. Roy. Lond. Hosp.

FREEMAN, Michael Keith Trennal, Germoe, Penzance TR20 9BA — MB BS 1966 Lond.; FFA RCS Eng. 1977; DA Eng. 1971; DObst RCOG 1970. Cons. Anaesth. Cornw. & I. of Scilly AHA.

FREEMAN, Michael Russell Mill Street, Crewe CW2 7AQ — MB ChB 1987 Sheff.; BMedSci Sheff. 1986; MRCGP 1991. (Sheffield University)

FREEMAN, Murray John Victoria Park Health Centre, Bedford Avenue, Birkenhead CH42 4QJ Tel: 0151 645 8384 Fax: 0151 644 9561; 1 Waterpark Road, Prenton, Birkenhead CH42 9NZ Email: murray.freeman@virgin.net — MB ChB 1977 Dundee; MRCGP Lond. 1983; DRCOG 1979.

FREEMAN, Myra Joan 14 Ridings Avenue, London N21 2EL Tel: 020 8363 7283 — MB ChB Leeds 1960. (Leeds) JP. Socs: Fac. Community Health. Prev: SCMO Camden & Islington Health Auth.; Clin. Med. Off. Enfield & Haringey AHA; Asst. Med. Off. Lond. Boro. Enfield.

FREEMAN, Nicole Josephine Westoak Surgery, 319 Westdale Lane, Carlton, Nottingham NG7 6BG — MB BS 1989 Lond.; MRCGP 1993; DRCOG 1993. GP Retainee. Prev: GP Attachment to Kensington, Chelsea & W.m. Commiss. Agency.

FREEMAN, Pearl Edna (retired) 37 Harrisons Road, Edgbaston, Birmingham B15 3QR — M.B., Ch.B. Glas. 1945. Prev: Asst. Med. Off. Matern. & Child Welf. Oldbury.

FREEMAN, Peter (retired) 7 Lillington Road, Leamington Spa CV32 5YS Tel: 01926 428153 — MB ChB 1962 St. And.; FRCGP 1978, M 1972; DObst RCOG 1964. Prev: GP Leamington Spa.

FREEMAN, Peter 2 Meadow Avenue, Preesall, Poulton-le-Fylde FY6 0HA Tel: 01253 811032 Email: pfreem@bigfoot.com — MRCS Eng. LRCP Lond. 1973; LLB 1991; MA, BM BCh Oxf. 1973; MRCOG 1981. Med. Off, War Pens. Agency, Blackpool. Prev: Ho. Phys. Epsom Dist. Hosp.; SHO (Gyn.) Hosp. Wom. Leeds; Regist. (O & G) St. Luke's Hosp. Bradford.

FREEMAN, Richard Antony The Castle Medical Group, Clitheroe Health Centre, Clitheroe BB7 2JG Tel: 01254 823273 Fax: 01254 824891 — MB ChB 1984 Manch.; 1999 Dip. Sports Medicine; 2001 Dip. Muscoloskelctal Medicine; MLCOM 2000; MRCGP 1989. Gen. Practitioner; Ostheopath; Sports Phys. Socs: Brit. Assn. Sport & Med.; BMA; AMO OSCA.

FREEMAN, Ricky Frederick 147 Rowanberry Avenue, Braunstone, Leicester LE3 6PQ — BM 1988 Soton.

FREEMAN, Mr Robert Maxwell Directorate Obstetrics and Gynaecology, Derriford Hospital, Plymouth PL6 8DH Fax: 01752 763721 Email: robtfreeman@aol.com; Email: robtfreem@aol.com — MB ChB 1977 Dundee; MD Dundee 1984; MRCOG 1984; FRCOG 1997. Cons. Obst. and Gynaecologist Plymouth Hosp.s NHS Trust Plymouth. Socs: Internat. Continence Soc.; BMA; Internat. Urogyn. Assn. (Europ. Represen. to the Internat. Bd. of IUGA. Prev: Regist. Dept of Ob/Gyn St Geo.s Hosp. Lond.; Regist. Deot og Ob/Gyn Qu. Charlottes Chelsea Hosp. for Wom., Lond.; Sen. Regist. Dept Ob/Gyn Plymouth Gen. Hosp. & S.end Hosp.

FREEMAN, Robert Thomas 12 Pitt Street, London W8 4NY — BM BCh 1996 Oxf.

FREEMAN, Robin 120 Whirlowdale Road, Sheffield S7 2NJ — MB ChB 1980 Birm; FFARCS 1988. Cons. Anaesth. Centr. Sheff. Univ. Hosps.

FREEMAN, Robin Craig Bridge Street Practice, 21 Bridge Street, Driffield YO25 6DB Tel: 01377 253441 Fax: 01377 241962; Monks Walk, 8 The Green, Cranswick, Driffield YO25 9QU — MB ChB 1982 Leeds; MRCGP 1986.

FREEMAN, Mr Roger Harvey, CBE, Brigadier late RAMC Retd. (retired) 9 Keepers Wood, Chichester PO19 4XU Tel: 01243 528665 Email: rogerf@chich2.demon.co.uk — MB ChB 1945 Birmingham; FRCS 1950 Edinburgh; MRCS Eng. LRCP 1945 London. Prev: Sen.Orthop. Regist. King's Coll. Hosp. Lond. 1955-1959.

FREEMAN, Rosemary Anne Veronica Firs House Surgery, Station Road, Impington, Cambridge CB4 9NP Tel: 01223 234286 Fax: 01223 235931 — BM BCh 1985 Oxf.; BA Oxf. 1982, BM BCh 1985; MRCP (UK) 1988; MRCGP 1990; DRCOG 1987. Prev: Research Fell. (Neurol.) Univ. Calif. San Francisco, USA.

FREEMAN, Mr Samuel Vaani 9 Goodman Crescent, London SW2 4NR Tel: 020 8671 2768 Fax: 020 8671 2768 — Laurea Bologna 1966; FRCSI 1976. Socs: Fell. W. Afr. Coll. Surgs.

FREEMAN, Simon John Derriford Hospital, Plymouth PL6 8DH Tel: 01752 777111 — MB BS 1985 Lond.; MRCP (UK) 1989; FRCR 1994. (Middlesex Hospitlal, University of London) Cons. Radiol., Derriford Hosp., Plymouth. Prev: Sen. Regist. (Diagn. Radiol.) S & W RHA; Regist. (Diag. Radiol.) Bristol Roy. Infirm.; SHO (Med.) S.mead Hosp. Bristol.

FREEMAN, Simon Philip Lavender Hill Group Practice, 19 Pountney Road, Battersea, London SW11 5TU Tel: 020 7228 4042 Fax: 020 7738 9346 — MB BS 1979 Lond.; BA Camb. 1976; MRCGP 1987; DRCOG 1982. (Westm.) Dip. Addic. Behaviour for GP. Univ. Lond. Prev: Clin. Lect. Div. of Primary Care St Geo.'s Med. Sch. Lond.; GP St. Thos. Hosp. Lond. VTS; SHO Chest Dept. St. Thos. Hosp. Lond.

FREEMAN, Simon Richard Mackenzie 14 Lombard Grove, Manchester M14 6AN — MB ChB 1995 Manch.

FREEMAN, Susan Laura 34 Sturmer Close, Yate, Bristol BS37 5UR — BM 1998 Soton.; BM Soton 1998.

FREEMAN, Sylvie Denyse Institute of Molecular Medicine, John Radcliffe Hospital, Headington, Oxford OX3 9DS Tel: 01865 222433 Email: freemans@scip.icnet.uk — MB ChB 1987 Birm.; MRCP (UK) 1990; DPhil Merton Oxford 1996; Dip. MRCPath 1997. Clin. Scientist Inst. Molecular Med. Oxf.; Clin. Lect. Oxf.; Hon. Clin. Fell. UCH Lond. Prev: Res. Regist. MRC Train. Fell.sh. Inst. Molecular Med. Oxf.; Regist. (Haemat.) John Radcliffe Hosp. Oxf.; SHO (Med.) Dudley Rd. Hosp. Birm.

FREEMAN, Thomas 75 Ballybentragh Road, Muckamore, Antrim BT41 2HJ Tel: 01849 432882 — MB BCh BAO 1942 Belf.; MD (High Commend.) Belf. 1947; FRCP Ed. 1969, M 1964; FRCPsych 1971; DPM Lond. 1947. (Qu. Univ. Belf.) Cons. Psychiat. Anna Freud Centre Lond.; Vis. Prof. Postgrad. Med. Sch. Univ Otago, NZ 1966. Socs: Fell. Roy. Soc. Med.; Hon. Mem. Brit. Psychoanalyt. Soc.; (Pres.) N.. Irel. Assn. Study Psychoanal. Prev: Cons. Psychiat. Roy. Dundee Liff Hosp.; Med. Dir. Lansdowne Clinic Glas.; Maj. RAMC.

FREEMAN, Victor (retired) Birchwood, Cokes Lane, Chalfont St Giles HP8 4TZ Tel: 01494 762238 — MRCS Eng. LRCP Lond. 1927; DPH Eng. 1930. Prev: Assoc. MOH Lond. Boro. Islington.

FREEMAN, Walter Harvey 1 Bowland Drive, Walton, Chesterfield S42 7LZ — MB ChB 1991 Leeds.

FREEMAN, Zoe Rose Lolohea Trennel Farm, Germoe, Penzance TR20 9SA — BM 1994 Soton.

FREEMAN-ARCHER, Margaret Isabel (retired) 15 Exmoor Way, Minehead TA24 8AZ — MB BS 1943 Lond.; MD Lond. 1951, DPH 1951; MRCS Eng. LRCP Lond. 1943; DObst RCOG 1950; DCH Eng. 1950. Prev: Sen. Med. Off. Matern. & Child Welf. Worcs. CC & Kingston Upon Hull.

FREEMAN-WANG, Theresa Bernadette Regin 46 Langdale Avenue, Mitcham CR4 4AF; Ist Floor Flat, Woodhurst, 61 Fortis Green, East Finchley, London N2 9JJ Email: theresa.freeman-wang@which.net — MB ChB 1989 Bristol; MRCOG 1997. Clin. Research Fell. in Colposcopy Servs.

FREEMAN WELHAM, Susan 10 Purbeck Terrace Road, Swanage BH19 2DE Tel: 01929 424272 — MB ChB 1992 Manch.; BSc (Hons.) Psychol. Wales 1972. (Manch.)

FREEMANTLE, Ruth (retired) 8 Wetherby Close, Blandford Forum DT11 0JN Tel: 01258 488737 — MB BS 1959 London; MRCS Eng. LRCP 1959 London; MRCPsych 1990; MRCOG 1980. Prev: Cons. Psychiat. St. Lawrence Hosp. Bodmin.

FREEMONT, Professor Anthony John Pathological Sciences, University of Manchester, Oxford Road, Manchester M13 9PL Tel: 0161 275 5269; 10 Harewood Avenue, Sale M33 5BY — MB BS 1976 Lond.; BSc Lond. 1973, MD 1984; FRCP Lond. 1995; FRCP Ed. 1990; MRCP (UK) 1979; MRCS Eng. LRCP Lond. 1976;

MRCPath 1986. Prof. (Path.) Univ. Manch. Med. Sch. Socs: Internat. Skeletal Soc. & Amer. Coll. Rheum.

FREER, Charles Bernard Health-Sure, 208 West George St., Glasgow G2 2P2 Tel: 0141 204 1585 Fax: 0141 204 1590; 1 Grange Road, Glasgow G61 3PL Tel: 0141 942 0632 — MB ChB 1968 Glas.; MRCGP 1974. Company Med. Adviser Healthcare Consultancy Glas.; Med. Adviser Ashbourne Homes; Chairm. Brit. Assn. for Serv. to Elderly. Socs: Soc. Occup. Med.; Roy. Soc. Med. Prev: Sen. Lect. (Gen. Pract.) Univ. Soton.; Asst. Prof. Family Med. Univ. Michigan.

FREER, Maryanne Christine Brockwell View, Long Ridge Road, Blaydon-on-Tyne NE21 6JN — MB BS 1987 Newc. Ho. Phys. Ashington Gen. Hosp. N.umberland. Prev: Ho. Phys. Ashington Gen. Hosp.; Ho. Surg. Newc. Gen. Hosp.

FREER, Tegwedd Helen Wonford House Hospital, Dryden Road, Exeter EX2 5AF Tel: 01392 403624 — MB ChB 1986 Aberd.; MRCPsych 1991. (Aberd.) Cons. (Gen. Adult & Old Age Psychiat.) Exeter Community Health Servs. NHS Trust. Prev: Sen. Regist. Exeter Community Health Servs. NHS Trust; Sen. Regist. Plymouth Community Trust; Cons. Psychiat. Albert Pk. Clinic, Austral.

FREESE, Mr Arthur James The Glebes, New Road, Long Melford, Sudbury CO10 9JY — MRCS Eng. LRCP Lond. 1939; FRCS Ed. 1946; LDS RCS Eng. 1936. (Lond. Hosp.) Cons. Emerit. Dent. Surg. Chelmsford & Essex Hosp.; Hon. Maj. RAMC. Socs: BMA; BAOMS (Brit. Assn. of Oral and Maxillo-Facial Surg.s). Prev: Sen. Regist. (Dent.) Lond. Hosp.; Maj. RAMC Surg. Specialist; Resid. Surg. Off. Roy. Hosp. Chesterfield.

FREESTON, Una de Havilland Lenworth Clinic, 329 Hyth Road, Ashford TN24 0QE Tel: 01233 204180; 6 The Mill, Wickhambreaux, Canterbury CT3 1RQ Tel: 01227 728270 — MB BS Lond. 1951; FRCPsych 1994, M 1972; DPM 1971; DCH RCP Lond. 1954. Cons. Child Psychiat. EKHA Ashford Kent. Socs: BMA; RCPsych. Prev: Psychiat. (Child & Adolesc.) Canterbury and Thames Health Auth. BRd.stone; Sen. Lect. Chinese Univ. Hong Kong; Sen. Specialist (Child Psychiat.) Canberra, Austral.

FREESTON, William Essex House Medical Centre, 59 Fore Street, Chard TA20 1QB Tel: 01460 63071 Fax: 01460 66560; Old Mill House, Wadeford, Chard TA20 3AU Tel: 01460 62283 Fax: 01460 66560 — MB ChB 1968 Liverp.; DObst RCOG 1971. (Liverp.) Prev: SHO (O & G) BRd.green Hosp. Liverp.; SHO Med. (Neurol.) Walton Hosp. Liverp.; Ho. Off. (Cardio-Thoracic Unit) BRd.green Hosp. Liverp.

***FREESTONE, Bethan Esme Louise** 12 Maes-y-Brenin, Rhayader LD6 5EP — MB ChB 1998 Birmingham; ChB Birm 1998.

FREESTONE, Michael David Barrack Lane Medical Practice, 1 Barrack Lane, Ipswich IP1 3NQ Tel: 01473 252827 Fax: 01473 250463; 158 Valley Road, Ipswich IP4 3AJ Tel: 01473 258726 — MB ChB 1969 Liverp.; DObst RCOG 1971; DObst RCOG 1971.

FREESTONE, Stephen Inveresk Research, Edinburgh EH14 4AP Tel: 01875 618187 Fax: 01875 614555 Email: steve_freestone@sgsgroup.com; 18 White Dales, Edinburgh EH10 7JQ Tel: 0131 445 4772 — MB ChB 1975 Sheff.; MD Sheff. 1991; MRCP (UK) 1978; FRCPE 1998. Med. Dir. Inveresk Research. Socs: Brit. Pharm. Soc. & Brit. Hypertens. Soc.; Med. Res. Soc. Prev: Hon. Cons. Phys. W. Gen. Hosp. Edin.; Lect. (Clin. Pharmacol.) Roy. Infirm. Edin.; Research Fell. (Therap.) Roy. Hallamsh. Hosp. Sheff.

FREETH, Audrey Irene (retired) Alma House, Dalbeattie DG5 4HE Tel: 01556611900 — MB BS Lond. 1937; FRCOG 1962. Prev: Regist. Birm. Matern. Hosp.

FREETH, Harold Derek (retired) Balcary Tower, Auchencairn, Castle Douglas DG7 1QZ Tel: 01556 640325 — MD Lond. 1950, MB BS 1942; MRCS Eng. LRCP Lond. 1941; FRCOG 1961, M 1948. Prev: Cons. O & G Leighton Hosp. Crewe.

FREETH, Malcolm Owen Marine Surgery, 29 Belle Vue Road, Southbourne, Bournemouth BH6 3DB Tel: 01202 423377 Fax: 01202 424277; del Cantano, 5 Keswick Road, Boscombe Manor, Bournemouth BH5 1LP Tel: 01202 303973 — MB BS Lond. 1969; MRCS Eng. LRCP Lond. 1967; FRCGP 1996, M 1980. (St. Bart.) Med. Adviser Dorset LMC. Socs: BMA (Ex-Chairm. E. Dorset Div.). Prev: Chairm. Dorset LMC; Ho. Surg. (O & G) Roy. Vict. Hosp. Bournemouth.

FREETH, Mark Graham Department of Histopathology, New Cross Hospital, Wolverhampton WV10 0QP Tel: 01902 307999 — MB ChB 1978 Sheff.; MRCPath 1984. Cons. Path. Wolverhampton HA.

FREETH, Rachel Katherine The Vicarage, Mount Skippet, Ramsden, Chipping Norton OX7 3AP — BM 1994 Soton.

FREIJ, Ramzi Mounir Kent and Canterbury Hospital, Accident and Emergency Department, Ethelbert Road, Canterbury CT1 3NG Tel: 01227 766877 Fax: 01227 864138 Email: ramzi.freij@ekh_tr.sthames.nhs.uk — MB BS 1986 Lond.; FRCS Glas. 1993; FFAEM 1997. (King's Coll. Sch. Med.) Cons. A & E Kent and Canterbury Hosp. Canterbury.

FREMANTLE, Janet Elizabeth Meres Cliff, Laflouder Lane, Mullion, Helston TR12 7HU Tel: 01326 240119 — MB BS Lond. 1960; MRCS Eng. LRCP Lond. 1960; DPH Eng. 1966. (Roy Free)

FREMPONG, Joseph Rotton Park Medical Centre, 264 Rotton Park Road, Edgbaston, Birmingham B16 0LU Tel: 0121 429 1543 Fax: 0121 434 — BChir 1965 Camb.; MB 1966; MRCP (UK) 1972. (Cambridge University/ The London Hospital) Socs: BMA; Birm. Med. Inst.; Diabetes UK.

FREMPONG, Mr Robert Yeboah 214 Central Road, Morden SM4 5PP — MB ChB 1965 Bristol; FRCS Ed. 1973; FRCS Eng. 1974.

FRENCH, Adrian John The Banks Surgery, 9 The Banks, Sileby, Loughborough LE12 7RD Tel: 01509 812343 — BM BCh 1975 Oxf.; BA Oxf. 1972, BM BCh 1975; MRCP (UK) 1978; MRCGP 1981.

FRENCH, Alistair John 35 Hanover House, St John's Wood High St., London NW8 7DY Tel: 020 7722 1072 — MB BS 1957 Lond.; MRCS Eng. LRCP Lond. 1958; DA Eng. 1963. (Lond. Hosp.) Prev: SHO (Anaesth.) Lond. Hosp.; Capt. RAMC Anaesth. Brit. Milit Hosp. Taiping, Malaya; Regist. (Anaesth.) N. Middlx. Hosp. Lond.

***FRENCH, Allison May** St Leonards Avenue, Blandford Forum DT11 7NY — MB ChB 1994 Birm.

FRENCH, Anne Jane 16 Cliff Avenue, Gorleston, Great Yarmouth NR31 6EQ — MB ChB 1991 Leic. SHO (Orthop.) Leicester Roy. Infirm. Prev: Demonst. (Anat.) Leicester Univ.

FRENCH, Antony Eric 7 Standarhay Close, Elburton, Plymouth PL9 8PL — BM 1998 Soton.; BM Soton 1998.

FRENCH, Arthur Harper (retired) Wickford Health Centre, Market Road, Wickford SS12 0AG Tel: 01268 766222 — MB ChB Ed. 1952. Prev: GP Wickford.

FRENCH, Brian Thomas James Department of Pathology, King Edward VII Hospital, Midhurst GU29 0BL Tel: 01730 812341 Fax: 01730 815996; Holmlea, 8 Barncroft Close, Tangmere, Chichester PO20 6FE Tel: 01243 527795 — MB BS 1968 Sydney; DCP Lond 1972; MRCPath 1978; FRCPA 1980; FRCPath 1990. (Sydney) Cons. Path. King Edwd. VII Hosp. Midhurst; Cons. Pathologist St. Richard's Hosp. Chichester W. Sussex. Prev: Cons. Path. Noble's Hosp. Douglas Isle of Man.

FRENCH, Charles Marcus 15 Louise Road, Northampton NN1 3RP — MB BChir 1963 Camb.; MD Camb. 1967, MA 1963; MRCGP 1972; DTM & H Eng. 1971. (Lond. Hosp.) Socs: FRSM.

FRENCH, David Douglas Kidsgrove Medical Centre, Mount Road, Kidsgrove, Stoke-on-Trent ST7 4AY Tel: 01782 784221 Fax: 01782 781703; Ivybank Farm, Cloudside, Timbersbrook, Congleton CW12 3QB Tel: 0126 02 275010 — MRCS Eng. LRCP Lond. 1962; DObst RCOG 1964. (Guy's) Clin. Asst. (Sclerother.) Haywood Hosp. Stoke-on-Trent; Apptd. Fact. Doctor. Socs: BMA. Prev: Ho. Phys. (Paediat.) St. Albans City Hosp.; Ho. Surg. (Obst.) Sussex Matern. Hosp. Brighton; Dept. Family Pract. Pasqua Hosp. Regina, Canada.

FRENCH, Elizabeth Marine Surgery, 29 Belle Vue Road, Bournemouth BH6 3DB — MB BS 1981 Lond.

FRENCH, Ernest Alexander (retired) 2 Hatfield Road, Mapperley Park, Nottingham NG3 5EQ Tel: 0115 960 5439 — MB BChir 1958 Camb.; MRCS Eng. LRCP Lond. 1957; FRCPath 1981, M 1969. Cons. Haematol. Univ. Hosp. Qu.'s Med. Centre Nottm. Prev: Sen. Regist. (Haemat.) St. Geo. Hosp. Lond.

FRENCH, Professor Gary Lawrence Department Microbiology, Guy's, King's and St Thomas' School of Medicine, St Thomas' Hospital, London SE1 7EH Tel: 020 7928 9292 Ext: 3244 Fax: 020 7928 0730 Email: gary.french@kcl.ac.uk — MB BS 1970 Lond.; BSc Lond. 1967; MD Lond. 1987; FRCPath 1989, M 1977; FRCPA 1985. (St. Thos.) Counc. of the Hosp. Infec. Med. Socs: Hosp. Infec. Soc.; Brit. Soc. Antimicrob. Chemother.; Path. Soc. Prev: Prof. & Hon. Cons. Microbiol. Chinese Univ. & P. of Wales Hosp., Hong Kong; Sen. Lect. & Hon. Cons. (Microbiol.) St. Thos. Hosp. Lond.; Lect. (Microbiol.) Univ. W. Indies, Jamaica.

FRENCH, Gillian Samantha Mortimer Surgery, Victoria Road, Mortimer Common, Reading RG7 1HG Tel: 0118 933 2436 Fax: 0118 933 3801 — BM BS 1990 Nottm.; MRCGP 1994.
FRENCH, Gordon William Galloway 163 Uttoxeter Road, Derby DE22 3NP — MB ChB 1980 Glas.
FRENCH, Graham Christopher 47 Chelmsley Lane, Birmingham B37 7BJ Tel: 0121 779 3446; 37 Helena Road, Norwich NR2 3BY Tel: 01603 666795 — MB ChB 1991 Manch. Trainee GP Norwich VTS. Socs: BMA; MDU.
FRENCH, James Lawrence Hepburn Copperfield, Station Road, Much Hadham SG10 6AX — BM BS 1998 Nottm.; BM BS Nottm 1998.
FRENCH, Janet 24 Weysprings, Haslemere GU27 1DE — MB BS 1960 Lond.; MRCS Eng. LRCP Lond. 1960. (Roy. Free) Prev: Ho. Surg. Roy. Free Hosp.
FRENCH, Jennifer Caroline 3 Turnstone Wharf, Castle Marina, Nottingham NG7 1GT — BM BS 1998 Nottm.; BM BS Nottm 1998.
FRENCH, Jeremy Jules Melford Hall, The Green, Dungworth, Sheffield S6 6HE — MB BS 1996 Newc.
FRENCH, Joan Mary (retired) 66 Three Elms Road, Hereford HR4 0RH Tel: 01432 270365 — MB ChB 1965 St. And.; DFFP 1994. Prev: GP Hereford & N.d.
FRENCH, John Anthony 2 Longburgh Fauld, Longburgh, Burgh-by-Sands, Carlisle CA5 6AE — MB ChB 1991 Sheff.
FRENCH, John Charles Paxton Green Health Centre, 1 Alleyn Park, London SE21 8AU Tel: 020 8670 6878 Fax: 020 8766 7057 — MB BS 1974 Lond.; DCH Eng. 1977. (St. Mary's)
FRENCH, Judith Anne The Congregational Hall, Town Street, Marple Bridge, Stockport SK6 5AA Tel: 0161 427 2049/1074 Fax: 0161 427 8389; Quarrybank House, 8 Quarry Rise, Romiley, Stockport SK6 4DD Tel: 0161 494 1478 — BM BCh 1976 Oxf.; MA Oxf. 1976; MRCGP 1991. (Oxford) Socs: Roy. Coll. Gen. Pract.
FRENCH, Mark Jeremy Richard Ilkley Health Centre, Springs Lane, Ilkley LS29 8TQ Tel: 01943 609255 Fax: 01943 430005; 68 Main Street, Addingham, Ilkley LS29 0PL — MB BS 1984 Newc.; MB BS Newc. l984; DRCOG 1989. (Newcastle upon Tyne) Clin. Asst. (Palliat. Care) Ardenlea Marie Curie Hospice Ilkley. Prev: Clin. Asc. Oncol. Airedale Gen. Hosp.
FRENCH, Mr Michael Edward Barn House, Clayton Road, Clayton, Newcastle ST5 4AB — MB BChir 1966 Camb.; MD Camb. 1973, MB BChir 1966; FRCS Ed. 1977. Cons. Surg. (Urol. & Transpl.) N. Staffs. Hosp. Stoke.
FRENCH, Neil 183 Leechmere Road, Sunderland SR2 9DL — MB ChB 1987 Ed.; MRCP (UK) 1990.
FRENCH, Nicholas Mark 16 Lindale Close, Anston, Sheffield S25 4FD — MB ChB 1994 Leeds.
FRENCH, Pamela Ann Church Road Surgery, 261 Church Road, Stannes on Sea, Lytham St Annes FY8 1EH Tel: 01253 728911 Fax: 01253 732114; 23 Albany Road, Ansdell, Lytham St Annes FY8 4AT — MB ChB 1984 Manch.; MB ChB Manch. l984; MRCGP 1989; DCCH RCP Ed. 1987. Prev: SHO (ENT) Blackburn Roy. Infirm.; Ho. Off. (Surg.) W. Cornw. Hosp. Penzance; Ho. Off. (Med.) Blackburn Roy. Infirm.
FRENCH, Patrick Dag The Mortimer Market Centre, University College Hospital, Mortimer Market, London WC1E 6AU Tel: 020 7530 5077 Fax: 020 7530 5044 Email: pfrench@gum.ucl.ac.uk — MB ChB 1985 Liverp.; FRCP (UK) 1999; MRCP (UK) 1988. Cons. Genitourin. Med. Univ. Coll. Lond. Hosps.; Hon. Sen. Lect. (Genitourin. Med.) Roy. Free Hosp. & UCL Med. Sch. Prev: Sen. Regist. (Genitourin. Med.) Middlx. Hosp. Lond.; Regist. (Genitourin. Med.) St Marys Hosp. Lond.; SHO Rotat. (Med.) Walton & Fazakerley Hosp. Liverp.
FRENCH, Paul Frederic Marine Surgery, 29 Belle Vue Road, Southbourne, Bournemouth BH6 3DB Tel: 01202 423377 Fax: 01202 424277 — MB BS 1980 Lond.; DRCOG 1982.
FRENCH, Rebecca Joy Upper Lodge, Brooms Green, Dymock GL18 2DP — BM 1998 Soton.; BM Soton 1998.
FRENCH, Richard Anthony 23 Green Walk, Timperley, Altrincham WA15 6JN — MB BS 1989 Lond.
FRENCH, Robert Stephen St Nicholas Surgery, Queen Street, Withernsea HU19 2PZ Tel: 01964 613221 Fax: 01964 613960; Town Farm, Southsiide, Patrington, Hull HU12 0RN Tel: 01964 631207 Email: stephen.french@btinternet.com — MB ChB 1978 Liverp.; MRCGP 1985; DRCOG 1984. Med. Off. Withernsea Hosp.; Trainer Humberside VTS. Socs: Hull Med. Soc. Prev: Trainee GP Liverp. VTS; SHO (ENT) Roy. Liverp. Hosp.
FRENCH, Rowena Bourne Pels House, Junction Rd, Alderbury, Salisbury SP5 3A2 — MB ChB 1978 Birm.; MRCGP 1982; DRCOG 1981.
FRENCH, Roy 5 Broad Street, Kingswinford DY6 9LP Tel: 01384 336466 — M.R.C.S. Eng., L.R.C.P. Lond. 1947. (Guy's)
FRENCH, Ruth Caroline Old Harlow Health Centre, Jenner House, Garden Terrace Road, Harlow CM17 0AX Tel: 01279 418136 Fax: 01279 429650; Copperfield, Much Hadham SG10 6AX Tel: 01279 842404 — MB BS Lond. 1969; DObst. RCOG 1971.
FRENCH, Sarah Loveday 64 Wood Vale, London N10 3DN — MB BS 1967 Lond.; DObst RCOG 1972; DA Eng. 1969. (St. Geo.) Prev: SHO (Obst.) Radcliffe Infirm. Oxf.; SHO (Anaesth.) St. Geo. Hosp. Lond.; Ho. Phys. P'boro. & Dist. Memor. Hosp.
FRENCH, Stephanie Roberta Sandford, Streamcross, Claverham, Bristol BS49 1LL Tel: 01934 835849 Fax: 01934 834509 — MB BS 1971 Lond.; MRCS Eng. LRCP Lond. 1971; MRCGP 1975; DObst RCOG 1973. (Char. Cross) Medico-Legal Adviser Osborne Clarke Solicitors; Medico-Legal Adviser, United Bristol Healthcare NHS Trust. Prev: GP Princip., Bristol; Asst. Sec. Med. Protec. Soc.; Med. Off., Univ. of Bristol Stud. Health Servs.
FRENCH, Terence Austin Central Pathology Laboratory, Hartshill, Stoke-on-Trent ST4 7PA Tel: 01782 554241 — MB ChB Birm. 1967; MRCS Eng. LRCP Lond. 1967; FRCPath 1986, M 1974. (Birm.) Cons. Path. Centr. Path. Laborat. Hartshill; Home Office Path. Socs: Assn. Clin. Paths. Prev: Asst. Path. Addenbrooke's Hosp. Camb.; Sen. Regist. Birm. AHA.
FRENCH, Timothy Joseph Paediatric Department, Taunton & Somerset Hospital, Musgrove Park, Taunton TA1 5DA Tel: 01823 342214 Fax: 01823 343777 Email: claire.bell@tauntonsom.tr.swest.nhs.uk; Annadale, Curland, Taunton TA3 5SG Tel: 01460 234410 Fax: 01460 234410 — MB BS 1973 Queensland; MSc Queensland 1975; FRCP Lond. 1994; MRCP (UK) 1978; MRCPCH 1996; FRCPCH 1997. (University of Queensland Brisbane, Australia) Cons. Paediat. Taunton & Som. Hosp. MusGr. Pk. Taunton. Prev: Cons. Paediat. MusGr. Pk. Hosp. Taunton & Yeovil Dist. Hosp.; Sen. Regist. Bristol Roy. Hosp. Sick Childr.; Regist. Guy's Hosp. Lond.
FRENCH, Valentine Isabelle (retired) Mulberry House, Harnham Lane, Withington, Cheltenham GL54 4DD — MB BS Lond. 1957; DCH Eng. 1960. Prev: Clin. Asst. (Allergy) Cheltenham Gen. Hosp.
FRENCH, William George (retired) 7 Murray Place, Stonehaven AB39 2GG Tel: 01569 762878 — MB ChB 1942 Aberd.; FRCGP 1975.
FRENKEL, Joost 8 Penn Court, 12/28 North End Road, London W14 0SH — Artsexamen 1986 Amsterdam.
FRENKIEL, Anna Leonora Cedry, 6 Clement Road, London SW19 7RJ Tel: 020 8946 9030 — MRCS Eng. LRCP Lond. 1952; BA (Med.) Amer. Univ. Beirut 1946; MFCM 1972; DObst RCOG 1954; DCH Eng. 1961, DPH 1965. (Sheff.) Sen. Med. Off. Richmond, Twickenham & Roehampton DHA. Socs: Fell. Soc. MOH; FRIPHH. Prev: Ho. Surg. Childr. Hosp. Sheff.; Ho. Phys. Montague Hosp. MexBoro.; SHO Scarsdale Hosp. Chesterfield.
FRERK, Christopher Martin Northampton General Hospital, Billing Road, Northampton NN1 5BD Tel: 01604 634700 Fax: 01604 545672 — MB ChB 1984 Liverp.; FRCA 1990. (Liverp.) Cons. Anaesth. N.ampton Gen. Hosp.
FRESCHINI, Angela Joy Louise Harvest Lodge, Bowers Court, Standon, Stafford ST21 6RW — MB ChB 1990 Birm.
FRESCHINI, David Leandro 15 Watling Street, Bury BL8 2JD — MB ChB 1988 Manch.
FRESHWATER, Dennis Andrew, Surg. Lt. RN Medical Department, MDHU Frimley Park, Frimley Park Hospital, Frimley, Camberley Tel: 01276 604604 Email: dennis_freshwater@msn.com; Cheyne Cottage, Birch Drive, Hawley, Camberley GU17 9BY Tel: 01276 34508 — MB BS 1992 Lond. (Middlesex) SHO MDHU Frimley Pk. Socs: BMA.
FRESHWATER, Gerald Thomas Shetland Medical Services, Hill House, Lower Hill Head, Lerwick ZE1 0EL Tel: 01595 695448 Fax: 01595 695858 Email: freshwater@zetnet.co.uk — MB ChB 1972 Birm.; AFOM RCP UK 1993; CIH Dund 1987; DA Eng. 1978; DRCOG 1977; Cert. Family Plann. JCC 1977. Dir. Occupat. Health Shetland HB; Ltd. Specialist (Anaesth.) Gilbert Bain Hosp. Socs: Soc.

Occupat. Med.; BMA; Fac. Pre Hosp. Care. Prev: GP Lerwick Doctors Gp.; Ho. Phys. Lewis Hosp. Stornoway.

FRESHWATER, Jane Valerie Anaesthetic Dept, Western General Hospital, Crewe Road South, Edinburgh EH4 2XU Tel: 0131 537 1652 Email: 537 1025; 43 Corstorphine Road, Edinburgh EH12 5QQ Tel: 0131 337 7049 Email: hillfoot.demon.co.uk — MB ChB 1968 Birm.; FFA RCS Eng. 1972; DA Eng. 1971. (Univ. Birm.) Cons. Anaesth.s E.ern Gen. hopsital Edin. Socs: Scott. Soc. Anaesth.; Assn. Anaesth. GB & Irel.; Obst. Anaesth. Assn. Prev: Cons. Anaesth. Monklands & Bellshill Hosps. Lanarksh.; Sen. Regist. W.. Gen. Hosp. Edin.; Sen. Regist. W. Midl. RHA.

FRESHWATER, Kenneth Haughan Maryfield Medical Centre, 9 Morgan Street, Dundee DD4 6QE Tel: 01382 462292 Fax: 01382 461052; Ardfern, Murroes, Broughty Ferry, Dundee DD5 3PB Tel: 01382 350292 — MB ChB 1969 St. And.; MRCGP 1979; DObst RCOG 1971. (St. And.)

FREUDENBERG, Sebastian 24 Boscastle Road, London NW5 1EG Tel: 020 7485 0172 — MB BS 1960 Lond.; MRCS Eng. LRCP Lond. 1960; MRCGP 1973; DCH Eng. 1967. (St. Thos.) Prev: GP Kentish Town; Regist. (Paediat.) Whittington Hosp. Lond.; Ho. Phys. Evelina Childr. Hosp. of Guy's Hosp. Lond.

FREUDMANN, Matthew Steven Bryn Coed, Asney Lane, Erbistock, Wrexham LL13 0DS — MB BCh 1995 Wales.

FREW, Anthony James Medical Specialties Clinical Group, Southampton General Hospital, Southampton SO16 6YD Tel: 02380 794069 Fax: 02380 798492 Email: ajf1@soton.ac.uk — MB BChir 1980 Camb.; FAAAI 1997; MA Camb. 1983, BA 1977, MD 1989; FRCP Lond. 1997; MRCP (UK) 1983. Reader (Med.) & Hon. Cons. Phys. Univ. Soton.; Hon. Cons. Phys. Roy. Bournemouth & ChristCh. Hosp. NHS Trust. Socs: Sen. Gen. Europ. Acad. Allergy & Clin. Immunol.; (Counc.) Brit. Soc. Allergy & Clin. Immunol.; Fell. Amer. Acad. of Allergy, Asthma & Immunol. Prev: Vis. Sc. Univ. Brit. Columbia Respirat. Div. Vancouver Gen. Hosp.; Clin. Lect. (Allergy & Clin. Immunol.) Nat. Heart & Lung Inst. Brompton Hosp. Lond.; Sen. Regist. City Gen. Hosp. Stoke-on-Trent.

FREW, David 87 Whitehouse Road, Barnton, Edinburgh EH4 6PB — MB ChB 1962 Ed.

FREW, Iain David Owen (retired) 17 Catherine Drive, Sutton Coldfield B73 6AX Tel: 0121 354 8332 — MB ChB 1959 Glas.; MD Glas. 196. Prev: Cons. Haemat. Good Hope Gen. Hosp. Sutton Coldfield.

FREW, Mr Ivor James Cunningham (retired) 6 Wentworth Grange, The Grove, Gosforth, Newcastle upon Tyne NE3 1NL Tel: 0191 285 1511 — MB ChB 1944 Liverp.; FRCS Eng. 1949. Prev: Cons. Surg. (ENT) Newc. AHA (T).

FREW, James Mair (retired) Brackens, Castledon Road, Downham, Billericay CM11 1LD Tel: 01268 711345 — MB BChir 1948 Camb.; BA Camb. 1944; DObst RCOG 1951. Prev: Ho. Surg. & Cas. Off. St. Thos. Hosp.

FREW, James Shearer (retired) East Ardblair, 494 A Perth Road, Dundee DD2 1LR Tel: 01382 667862 — MB ChB (Hons.) Glas. 1941; BSc Glas. 1938; FRCP Ed. 1974, M 1970; FRCP Lond. 1970, M 1947. Prev: Cons. Phys. Ninewells Hosp. Dundee.

FREW, Janine Marie West Wing, Esk Medical Centre, Ladywell Way, Musselburgh EH21 6AB Tel: 0131 665 2594 Fax: 0131 665 2428 — MB ChB 1986 Ed.; DCCH RCP Ed. 1991.

FREW, Nicola Caroline 18 Broomhill Manor, Belfast BT9 5HG Tel: 01232 682925 — MB ChB 1993 Dundee; MB ChB Dund. 1993. SHO (O & G) Vale of Leven Hosp. Alexandria Dunbaronsh. Prev: Surg. Lt. RN; SHO (A & E).

FREW, Patrick William Bullock Fair Close Surgery, Bullock Fair Close, Harleston IP20 9AT Tel: 01379 853217 Fax: 01379 854082; 11A The St, Brooke, Norwich NR15 1JW Tel: 01508 550264 — MB BChir 1982 Camb.; MA Camb. 1982; MRCGP 1989; DRCOG 1989; DCH RCP Lond. 1985.

FREW, Ronald Linkstone (retired) Seaforth, The Esplanade, Oban PA34 5AQ Tel: 01631 563755 — MB ChB Ed. 1955. Prev: Regist. N.. Hosp. Dunfermline.

FREW, William Alan Anaesthetic Department, Royal Alexandra Hospital, Corsebar Road, Paisley PA2 9P Tel: 0141 887 9111; 8 Drummond Way, Newton Mearns, Glasgow G77 6XW Tel: 0141 616 2700 — MB ChB 1993 Glas. (Univ. Glas.) SHO (Anaesth.) R.A.H. Paisley; SHO Anaesth. Roy. Alexandra Hosp. Paisley. Prev: SHO (Neurosurg.) S.. Gen. Hosp. Glas.; SHO Neurosurg. S. Gen. Hosp. Glas.; SHO (Thoracic Surg.) Hairmyres Hosp. E. Kilbride.

FREWER, John David 29 Amberlands Close, Bristol BS48 3LW — MB BS 1992 Lond.; BDS Lond. 1984; LDS RCS Eng. 1985.

FREWIN, Rebecca Jane 4 The Otters, Bolham, Tiverton EX16 7SD — MB ChB 1991 Ed.; MRCP (UK) 1994; Dip. RCPath 1999.

FREWIN, Tom The Surgery, 52 Clifton Down Road, Bristol BS8 4AH Tel: 0117 973 2178 Fax: 0117 925 6178; 13 Mortimer Road, Clifton, Bristol BS8 4EY Tel: 0117 973 6407 — MB ChB Bristol 1970; MRCS Eng. LRCP Lond. 1970; DRCOG 1983. (Univ. Bristol) Med. Edr. Small Pract.s Assn.; Pub. Affairs Spokesperson for Bristol Div. & Brit. Med. Assn. Socs: (Hon. Pub. Affairs Sec.) BMA; Brit. Medico-Legal Soc. Prev: Regist. (Gen. & Respirat. Med.) Derby Roy. Infirm.; SHO (Paediat.) Hammersmith Hosp. Lond.; SHO (Neurosurg.) Roy. Free Hosp. Lond.

FREYTAG, Christine Ursula Cowes Health Centre, 8 Consort Road, Cowes PO31 7SH Tel: 01983 295251 Fax: 01983 280461; Curtle Mead, Baring Road, Cowes PO31 8DS Tel: 01983 294312 — MB BS 1982 Lond.; LMSSA Lond. 1982; MRCGP 1987; DRCOG 1988; Cert. Family Plann. JCC 1987. (St. Thos.) Prev: SHO Rotat. (Med.) Oxf.; Ho. Phys. (Med. Unit) St. Thos. Hosp. Lond.; SHO (Oncol.) Roy. Marsden Hosp. Lond.

FRIED, Michal John 67A Leamington Terrace, Edinburgh EH10 4JT — MB BS 1982 Lond.; BSc Ed. 1976; MRCGP 1991; FFA RCSI 1989. Sen. Regist. (Anaesth.) Roy. Infirm. Edin. Prev: Research Fell. Edin.; Staff & GP (Anaesth.) Canada.

FRIEDLAND, Jonathan Samuel Department of Infectious Diseases, Imperial College, Hammersmith Hospital, Du Cane Road, London W12 0NN Tel: 020 8383 1000 Fax: 020 8383 3394 Email: j.friedland@ic.ac.uk; Tel: 020 7607 6063 — MB BS 1984 Lond.; PhD Lond. 1993; MRCP (UK) 1987; MA Camb. 1985, BA 1981; FRCP 1999 London; FRCP 1999 Edinburgh. (Cambridge and King's College Hospital London) Reader (Infect. Dis. & Med.) Imperial Coll. Lond.; Hon. Cons. Infect. Dis. & Med. Hammersmith Hosp. Lond. Socs: Fell. Roy. Soc. Trop. Med. & Hyg. (Chair Educat. and Train. Comm.); Brit. Soc. Antimicrob. Chemother.; Specialist Advisery Comm. Infec. & Trop. Dis. Roy. Coll. of Phys.s. Prev: Lect. (Communicable Dis.) St. Geo. Hosp. Med. Sch. Lond.; MRC Train. Fell. St. Geo. Hosp. Med. Sch. Lond.; Regist. Nuffield Dept. Med. John Radcliffe Hosp. Oxf.

FRIEDMAN, Dennis Emanuel Israel 99 Harley Street, London W1N 1DF Tel: 020 7487 3930 Fax: 020 7935 7207; 2 St Katherine's Precinct, Regent's Park, London NW1 4HH Tel: 020 7935 6252 Fax: 020 7486 2398 Email: dennisfriedman@compuserve.com — MRCS Eng. LRCP Lond. 1948; FRCPsych 1978, M 1972. (St. Bart.) Med. Dir. Charter Clinic Lond.; Vis. Cons. Priory Hosp. Roehampton. Socs: Fell. Roy. Soc. Med. Prev: Hon. Lect. Psychiat. St. Barts. Hosp. Lond.; Lect. Postgrad. Med. Federat.; Mem. Univ. Teach. Assn.

FRIEDMAN, Ellis Harold Ian West Pennine Health Authority, Westhulme Avenue, Oldham OL1 2PL Tel: 0161 455 5700 Fax: 0161 455 5760 Email: ellis.friedman@wpennine-ha.nwest.nhs.uk; 16 Hastings Close, Whitefield, Manchester M45 6UQ — MB ChB 1977 Manch.; MSc Manch. 1985, MB ChB 1977; FFPHM 1996; MFCM 1988. (Manch.) Dir. Pub. Health Med. W. Pennine HA.; Regional Dir. for BrE. Screening Quality Assur., NW Region. Prev: Dir. Pub. Health Med. Oldham HA; Manager Gtr. Manch. BrE. Screening Serv.; Head Community Med. S. Manch. HA.

FRIEDMAN, Emma Pandora Royal London Hospital, Radiology Department, London E1 1BB Tel: 020 7377 7657 Fax: 020 7377 7094; 5 Kingstown Street, London NW1 8JP Tel: 020 7722 5531 — MB BS 1985 Lond.; MRCP (UK) 1989; FRCR 1993. Cons. Radiol. Roy. Lond. Hosps. Trust. Prev: Sen. Regist. (Radiol.) Middlx. Hosp. Lond.

FRIEDMAN, Trevor 227 Plains Road, Mapperley, Nottingham NG3 5RF Tel: 0115 926 8971 — MB BS 1982 Lond.; BSc (Hons.) (Cell Path.) Lond. 1979, MB BS 1982; MRCPsych 1987. (Middlx.) Cons. Liaison Psychiat. Leicester Gen. Hosp. Prev: Lect. (Psychiat.) Univ. Nottm. Qu. Med. Centre; Regist. (Psychiat.) Warneford Hosp. Oxf.; SHO (A & E) St. Mary's Hosp. Lond.

FRIEDMANN, Adam Charles 141 Beresford Road, Birkenhead CH43 2JD; Flat 14, 55 Barrington Road, Brixton, London SW9 7JG Tel: 020 7738 6165 — MB BS 1997 Lond. Ho. Surg. King's Coll. Hosp.

FRIEDMANN, Mr Allan Isadore Keythorpe Lodge, 25 Manor Road, Bournemouth BH1 3ET — MB BCh 1940 Witwatersrand; FRCS Eng. 1961; DOMS Eng. 1946. Socs: Internat. Perimetric Soc. Prev: Reader (Ophth.) RCS Eng.; Cons. Roy. Eye. (St. Thos.) Hosp. Lond.

FRIEDMANN, Batia Queens Avenue Surgery, 46 Queens Avenue, Muswell Hill, London N10 3BJ Tel: 020 8883 1846 Fax: 020 8365 2265 — MB BS 1984 Lond.

FRIEDMANN, Bridget Ann The Firs, Newtown Road, Sherfield English, Romsey SO51 0GJ Tel: 01794 342160 — MB BS Lond. 1969; MFFP 1993; Cert. JCC Lond. 1978. (Univ. Coll. Hosp.) Mem. Inst. Psychosexual Med.

FRIEDMANN, Professor Imrich 11 Hathaway Close, Stanmore HA7 3NR Tel: 020 8954 0124 — MD Prague 1931; DSc Lond. 1967; FRCS Eng. 1979; MRCS Eng. LRCP Lond. 1942; FRCPath 1964; DCP Lond 1944. (Prague & Univ. Coll. Hosp.) Vis. Prof. Path. Univ. Calif. San Francisco, Los Angeles, Colorado & Denver, USA; Emerit. Prof. Path. Univ. Lond.; Hon. Cons. Path. Roy. Nat. Throat, Nose & Ear Hosp. & N.wick Pk. Hosp. & Clin Research Centre; Cons. Electron Microscopy Ear Research Inst. Los Angeles, USA; Research Fell. Imperial Cancer Research Fund; Emerit. Cons. Pathol. N.wick Pk. & St. Mark's Hosps. Trust. Socs: Hon. Fell. Czech. Assn. Otolaryng.; Hon. Fell. Dutch Assn. Otolaryng.; Hon. Fell. Laryngeal Cancer Soc. (Italy). Prev: Prof. Path. Univ. Lond.; Dir. Dept. Path. Inst. Laryngol. & Otol. Lond.; Pathol. Bata Hosp. Zlin, Czechoslovakia & Univ. Hosp., Kosice.

FRIEDMANN, Peter Simon The Firs, Newtown Road, Awbridge, Romsey SO51 0GJ — MD 1978 Camb.; MB 1970, BChir 1969; FRCP Lond. 1984; MRCP (UK) 1971. (Univ. Coll. Hosp.) Prof. Dermat. Univ. Liverp.; Hon. Cons. (Dermat.) Roy. Liverp. Univ. Hosp. Trust. Socs: Pres. Europ. Soc. Dermatol. Res.; (Ex-Chairm.) Brit. Soc. Investigative Dermat. Prev: Sen. Lect. (Dermat.) Univ. Newc.

FRIEL, Andrea Maria 120 Ballycastle Road, Coleraine BT52 2DZ — MB ChB 1991 Dundee.

FRIEL, Catherine Mary Lord Lister Health Centre, 121 Woodgrange Road, Forest Gate, London E7 0EP Tel: 020 8250 7510 Fax: 020 8250 7515 — MB BCh BAO 1976 Belf.; DCH RCP Lond. 1983. Socs: Assoc. Mem. BPA.

FRIEL, Francis Columba Riverside Practice, Upper Main Street, Strabane BT82 8AS Tel: 028 7138 4100 Fax: 028 7138 4115 — LAH Dub. 1966.

FRIEL, James Charles (retired) Rose Cottage, The Gardens, Sandbach CW11 1BB Tel: 01270 763470 — MB BCh BAO NUI 1946; AFOM RCP 1979. Med. Off. MoD.

FRIEND, Andrew Richard Windmill Health Centre, Mill Green View, Leeds LS14 5JS Tel: 0113 273 3733 Fax: 0113 232 3202; 48 Aviary Road, Armley, Leeds LS12 2NS — MB ChB 1989 Leeds; MRCGP 1995; DFFP 1994; DRCOG 1994. (Leeds) GP Princip. Leeds. Prev: Trainee GP Bradford; SHO (A & E) Leeds Gen. Infirm.; SHO (Geriat.) St. Luke's Hosp. Bradford.

FRIEND, Howard Michael The Surgery, Morchard Bishop, Crediton EX17 6NZ — MB BS 1976 Lond.; MRCGP 1983; DCH RCP Lond. 1992; DRCOG 1980. Prev: Lect. (Med.) Specialist Malawi, Afr.

FRIEND, Professor James Anthony Ritson Aberdeen Royal Infirmary, Foresterhill, Aberdeen AB25 2ZN Tel: 01224 681818 Fax: 01224 840766 Email: jamesfriend@arh.grampian.scot.nhs.uk — MB ChB 1962 Ed.; BA Camb. 1959; FRCP Ed. 1977, M 1965. (Camb. & Ed.) Cons. Thoracic Med. & Clin. Prof. (Med.) Aberd. Teachg. Hosps.; Clin. Prof. (Med.) Aberd. Univ.; Chairm. Scientif. Comm. on Tobacco and Health Dept. of Health. Socs: Fell. (Ex-Pres.) Roy. Med. Soc. Edin.; (Ex-Pres.) Brit. Thoracic Soc.; (Pres.) Scott. Thoracic Soc. Prev: Sen. Regist. United Oxf. Hosps.; Regist. City Hosp. Edin.; Dorothy Temple Cross Fell. Univ. Hosp. Seattle, USA.

FRIEND, John Henry (retired) 52 Whittlesford Road, Little Shelford, Cambridge CB2 5EW Tel: 01223 842860 — MD 1947 Lond.; MB BS 1943; FRCP Lond. 1969, M 1944. Prev: Cons. Phys. N. Staffs. Roy. Infirm. City Gen. Hosp. Stoke-on-Trent.

FRIEND, Mr John Richard (retired) Nuffield Hospital, Derriford Road, Plymouth PL6 8BG Tel: 01752 707345 Fax: 01752 778421 — MA, BM BCh 1962; FRCOG 1987, M 1968; BM BCh 1962; DM 1979 Oxford; MRCP 2000. Hon. Cons. RN Hosp. StoneHo. Plymouth. Prev: Cons. Plymouth Gen. Hosp.

FRIEND, Jonathan Peter Daniel Newtyning, Stone Allerton, Axbridge BS26 2NJ Tel: 01934 712971 Email: drjfriend@hotmail.com — MB BS Lond. 1972; MRCS Eng. LRCP Lond. 1972; FFA RCS Eng. 1978. (King's Coll. Hosp.) Cons. Anaesth. W.on Area Health Trust.

FRIEND, Katherine Joyce Furneaux The Square House, Peppard, Henley-on-Thames RG9 5EJ — MB BS 1966 Lond.; MRCPsych 1972; DPM Eng. 1970; DObst RCOG 1969. (Univ. Coll. Hosp.) Cons. Child Adolesc. Psychiat. Berks. Health Care NHS Trust.

FRIEND, Nichola Helen 9 Burlington Road, Portishead, Bristol BS20 7BG — MB ChB 1997 Bristol.

FRIEND, Peter Anthony Public Health Laboratory, Royal Cornwall Hospital (City), Infirmary Hill, Truro TR1 2HZ Tel: 01872 79361 — MB ChB 1977 Ed.; MRCPath 1986. Cons. Microbiol. Pub. Health Laborat. Truro.

FRIEND, Professor Peter John Nuffield Department of Surg, John Radcliffe Hosp, Oxford OX3 9DU — MB BChir 1979 Camb.; MA, MD Camb. 1993; FRCS Eng. 1983. Prof. of Transpl.ation & Cons. Surg Nuffield Dept. Surg John Radcliffe Hosp & Oxf. Transpl. Centre. Prev: Univ. Lect. In Surg Univ. of Camb.; Vis. Asst. Prof. Indiana Univ Med Centre USA.

FRIER, Professor Brian Murray Department of Diabetes, Royal Infirmary of Edinburgh, Edinburgh EH3 9YW Tel: 0131 536 2074 Fax: 0131 536 2075 Email: brian.frier@luht.scot.nhs.uk; 100 Morningside Drive, Edinburgh EH10 5NT Tel: 0131 447 1653 — MB ChB 1972 Ed.; BSc (1st cl. Hons. Physiol.) Ed. 1969; MD Ed. 1981; FRCP Glas. 1986; FRCP Ed. 1984; MRCP (UK) 1974. (Ed.) Cons. Phys. (Diabetes) Roy. Infirm. Edin.; Hon. Prof. (Diabetes) Univ. Edin.; Chairm. Hon. Advisery Panel on Driving & Diabetes. Socs: Diabetes UK; Assn. Phys. GB & Irel.; Eur. Assn. Study Diabetes. Prev: Cons. Phys. Gartnavel Gen. Hosp. & W.. Infirm. Glas.; Sen. Regist. (Med.) Roy. Infirm. Edin.; Research Fell. Cornell Univ. Med. Centre New York, USA.

FRIER, Julie Ann Cofton, Whiteball, Wellington TA21 0LS — BM BCh 1992 Oxf.; MRCP (Paed.) 1996. Specialist Regist. (Paediat.) S.W. Region.

FRIER, Sally Rachel Conway Road Health Centre, Conway Road, Sale M33 2TB Tel: 0161 962 7321 Fax: 0161 973 1151; 32 Albert Road, Hale, Altrincham WA15 9AJ Tel: 0161 928 0294 — MB BS 1988 Lond.; MRCGP 1992; DRCOG 1991.

FRIEZE, Marshall 16 Church Farm Garth, Shadwell, Leeds LS17 8HD — LRCP LRCS 1950 Ed.; LRCP LRCS Ed. LRCPS Glas. 1950; MRCPsych 1972.

FRIMPONG, Gifty Akosua Addai Akuoko 177 Croydon Road, Beckenham BR3 3QH — MB ChB 1996 Bristol.

FRIMPONG-ANSAH, Kwabena Nana Hillhurst, Kewferry Drive, Northwood HA6 2PA — MB BS 1990 Lond.; BSc (Hons.) Lond. 1987, MB BS 1990. Demonst. (Anat. & Cell Biol.) UMDS Guy's Hosp. Lond. Prev: Cas. Off. (A & E) St. Thos. Hosp. Lond.; Ho. Off. (Surg.) Guy's Hosp. Lond.; Ho. Off. (Med.) Lewisham Hosp. Lond.

***FRISBY, Jacqueline Jane** 85 Rockhill Drive, Mountsorrel, Loughborough LE12 7DS — MB ChB 1996 Birm.

FRISBY, Jean Spence (retired) Fox Barn, Cholesbury, Tring HP23 6ND — MB ChB 1956 Glas. Prev: SCMO (Family Plann.) Bucks.

FRISBY, Paul Alexander The Surgery, 1 Arlington Road, Eastbourne BN21 1DH Tel: 01323 727531 Fax: 01323 417085 — MB BS 1991 Lond.

FRISCHMAN, William John 47 Balfour Road, Walmer, Deal CT14 7HY — MB BS 1976 Lond.; MRCP (UK) 1980. Regist. (Paediat.) Leicester Roy. Infirm. Prev: SHO Qu. Eliz. Hosp. Childr. Lond.

FRISKEN, Isobel Katherine Parc Lea, North Corner, Coverack, Helston TR12 6TJ — MB BS 1997 Lond.

FRISTON, Karl John 23 Batchworth Hill, London Road, Rickmansworth WD3 1JL — MB BS 1984 Lond.; MA Camb. 1985; MRCPsych 1988. Wellcome Sen. Fell. (Clin. Sci.) & Hon. Cons. Inst. Neurol.; Reader (Imaging Neurosci.). Prev: MRC Clin. Sci. Hammersmith Hosp. Lond.; Psychiat. Rotat. Scheme Oxf.

FRISTON, Mark Harpham The Chambers of Kieran Coonan QC, 6 Pump Court, Temple, London EC4Y 7AR Tel: 020 7583 6013 Fax: 020 7353 0464 Email: mhfriston1@aol.com; 31 Chessington Mansions, Colworth Road, Leytonstone, London E11 1HZ — MB BChir Camb. 1990; MA Camb. 1990; MRCP (UK) 1993; Barrister at Law 1997. (Camb.) Barrister The Chambers of Kieran Coonan Q.C. Prev: Med. Regist. Guy's Rheum. Rotat.

FRITH, Anthony George Bradshaw Castlefields Health Centre, Chester Close, Castlefields, Runcorn WA7 2HY Tel: 01928 566671 Fax: 01928 581631 — MB ChB 1973 Liverp. (Liverp.)

FRITH, Christopher William Greyfriars Surgery, 25 St. Nicholas Street, Hereford HR4 0BH Tel: 01432 265717 Fax: 01432 340150; Meadowside Cottage, Hemhill, Lugwardine, Hereford HR1 4AL Tel: 01432 850330 — MB ChB 1982 Birm.; DObst. RCOG 1986. Mem. Community Serv. Unit Managem. Bd. Socs: Heref. Med. Soc. Prev: SHO (Geriat. & A & E) Heref. Gen. Hosp.; SHO (O & G & Paediat.) Heref. Co. Hosp.; Ho. Off. Birm. Accid. Hosp.

FRITH, Kathleen May (retired) 152 Harley Street, London W1N 1HH Tel: 020 7935 3834 — MB BS 1949 Lond.; MRCS Eng. LRCP Lond. 1948; FRCOG 1968, M 1953; DMJ (Clin.) Soc. Apoth. Lond. 1962. Prev: Cons. O & G Romford Hosp. Gp.

FRITH, Maria-Dolores Sylvia The Old Post Office, Knayton, Thirsk YO7 4AU — MB BS 1987 Newc.

FRITH, Peggy Alison The Eye Hospital, Radcliffe Infirmary, Oxford OX2 6HE Tel: 01865 228578 Fax: 01865 224515 — MB 1975 Camb.; BChir 1974; FRCP Lond. 1997; FRCOphth 2000; MD 1999 Cambridge. (Camb./Oxf.) Cons. Med. Ophth. Oxf. Radcliffe Infirm. Trust & Univ. Coll. Hosp. Lond.; Dep. Director of Clinincal Studies, Oxf. Univ. Med. Sch.; Hon. Sen. Clin. Lect. (Ophth.) Oxf. Univ. Socs: (Ex-Counc.) Roy. Soc. Med.; Med. Wom. Federat. (Counc.).

FRITH, Peter John Bradshaw Oakwood Surgery, Church Street, Mansfield Woodhouse, Mansfield NG19 8BL Tel: 01623 633111 Fax: 01623 423480; 22 Salisbury Road, Mansfield NG19 6EY — MB BChir 1978 Camb.; BChir 1977; DRCOG 1980. Princip. in Gen. Pract., Mansfield WoodHo.; Tutor (Gen. Pract.) Preclin. Studies Qu. Med. Centre Nottm.

FRIZELLE, Pamela Christina (retired) Main Street, Lisnaskea, Enniskillen BT92 0JG Tel: 013657 21424 — MB BCh BAO 1945 NUI.

FRIZZELL, Robert Alan 76 Warwick Road, Carlisle CA1 1DU Tel: 01228 24477 — MB BS 1965 Durh.; MRCGP 1974. (Newc.) Prev: SHO (Paediat.) Cumbld. Infirm. Carlisle; SHO (Obst.) City Matern. Hosp. Carlisle; Ho. Surg. Gen. Hosp. Bishop Auckland.

FRODSHAM, Peter Francis 16 Uppingham Drive, Woodley, Reading RG5 4TH — MRCS Eng. LRCP Lond. 1964.

FRODSHAM, William Arthur (retired) 65 Kimberley Drive, Lydney GL15 5AG Tel: 01594 842934 — LMSSA 1963 Lond.; DA Eng. 1969.

FROGGATT, Mr David Lewis (retired) 2 Gilstead Hall, Bingley BD16 3NP Tel: 01374 565716 Email: david.froggatt@lineone.net — MB BChir 1961 Camb.; MA, MB Camb. 1961, BChir 1960; FRCS Eng. 1966; DObst RCOG 1961. Prev: Surg. Bradford Roy. Infirm.

FROGGATT, Paul Andrew 21 Blackthorn Avenue, Manchester M19 1FT — MB BS 1998 Lond.; MB BS Lond 1998.

FROGGATT, Sir Peter 3 Strangford Avenue, Belfast BT9 6PG Tel: 01232 667954 Fax: 01232 687806 — LLD (Hon. Causa) Belf. 1991, PhD 1967; LLD (hon. causa) Dub. 1981; FRCSI (hon.) 1988; MD Dub. 1958, MB BCh BAO 1952; FRCPI 1973; FRCP Lond. 1980, M 1974; FFCM 1974; FFCM RCPI 1976; FFOM RCPI 1975; DPH Belf. 1956; DSc (hon. causa) NUI 1982. Socs: Hon. Mem. Soc. Social Med.; Hon. Mem. Soc. Occupat. Med.; Hon. Fell. Roy. Acad. Med. Irel. Prev: Vice-Chancellor & Pres. Qu. Univ. Belf.; Prof. Epidemiol. Qu. Univ. Belf.; Cons. E. Area Health Bd. (N.Irel.).

FROGGATT, Robert Clive 129 St George's Road, Cheltenham GL50 3ER Tel: 01242 580468 Fax: 01242 253591; 59 Hatherley Road, Cheltenham GL51 6EG Tel: 01242 580911 Fax: 01242 228975 — MB BS 1970 Lond.; MRCS Eng. LRCP Lond. 1970; FRCGP 1986, M 1975; DObst RCOG 1973. (St. Bart.) Hosp. Pract. Cheltenham & Gloucester Child Guid. Clinics; Hon. Sec. Conservat. Med. Soc. Socs: BMA & Cheltenham Gen. Pract. Assn.; RCGP (Hon. Treas. Severn Fac.). Prev: Ho. Surg. & Ho. Phys. St. Bart. Hosp. Lond.

FROGGETT, Sonja Mary 33 Sedley Taylor Road, Cambridge CB2 2PN — MB ChB 1958 Leeds. (Leeds) Prev: Med. Regist. Newmarket Gen. Hosp.; Surg. Regist. Bradford Roy. Infirm.

FROHN, Mr Maurice John Nicholas (retired) Oakwood House, 22 Rectory Close, Woodchurch, Ashford TN26 3QD Tel: 01233 861359 Fax: 01223 861359 Email: frohn@clara.co.uk — MB BS Lond. 1956; FRCS Eng. 1965; MRCS Eng. LRCP Lond. 1956; DObst RCOG 1958. Hon. Cons. Surg. Benenden Hosp. Trust & Post Office & Civil Serv. Sanat. Prev: Sen. Regist. (Surg.) St. Mark's Hosp. Lond.

FROHNSDORFF, Kenneth George Edward Little Folly, 105 The Street, Lacton Green, Willesborough, Ashford TN24 0NB — MB BS 1961 Lond.; MRCP (UK) 1973; MRCS Eng. LRCP Lond. 1960; DCH Eng. 1963. (King's Coll. Hosp.) Cons. (Geriat. Med.) S.E. Kent Health Dist.

FROLEY, Alan Francis Beeches Surgery, 9 Hill Road, Carshalton SM5 3RB Tel: 020 8647 6608/6609; 20 South Rise, Carshalton Beeches, Carshalton SM5 4PD Tel: 020 8642 5255 — MB ChB 1970 Liverp.; MRCP (UK) 1978; Cert. Family Plann. JCC 1975; DObst RCOG 1973; DCH Eng. 1973. Prev: Clin. Lect. (Paediat. Research) & Hon. Sen. Regist. Middlx. Hosp. Med. Sch.; Sen. Resid. (Paediat.) Hosp. Sick Childr. Toronto, Canada; Regist. Rotat. (Paediat.) Qu. Mary's Hosp. Childr. Carshalton.

FROMET DE ROSNAY, Edgar Louis Philippe 11 Cleves Court, Firs Avenue, Windsor SL4 4EF — MB BCh 1995 Witwatersrand.

FROMMER, Eva Ann (retired) Raphael Medical Centre, Coldharbour Lane, Hildenborough, Tonbridge TN11 9LF — MB BS 1952 Lond.; MRCS Eng. LRCP Lond. 1952; FRCPsych 1981, M 1971; DCH Eng. 1954, DPM 1962. Cons. Child Psychiat. St. Thos. Hosp.

FROOD, John David Lamb St Lukes Hospital, Marton Road, Middlesbrough TS4 3AF Tel: 01642 854953 Fax: 01642 821810; 45 Marske Mill Lane, Saltburn-by-the-Sea TS12 1HT — MB BS 1963 Durh. Med. Dir. S. Tees Community & Ment. Health NHS Trust.

FROOD, Richard Andrew William Weaver Vale Practice, Hallwood Health Centre, Hospital Way, Runcorn WA7 2UT Tel: 01928 711911 Fax: 01928 717368; West Wind, Meadow View Drive, Frodsham, Warrington WA6 6UP Tel: 01928 732238 Email: richardfrood@hotmail.com — MB ChB 1972 Liverp.; FRCGP 1995, M (Distinc.) 1976. Course Organiser Mersey VTS; GP UnderGrad. Tutor - Liverp. Univ. Prev: Trainee GP Macclesfield VTS; Chairm. N. Chesh. LMC.

***FROOME, Victoria Anne** Arlberg House, Kiln Lane, Bourne End SL8 5JE Tel: 01628 523320 Fax: 01628 526718; Arlberg House, Kiln Lane, Bourne End SL8 5JE Tel: 01628 523320 Fax: 01628 526718 — MB BS 1998 Lond.; MB BS (Hons.) Lond 1998.

FROOTKO, Mr Nicholas John Goldings, Clays Lane, Loughton IG10 2RZ Tel: 020 8508 0895 — MB BCh 1969 Witwatersrand; MSc Oxf. 1984; FRCS Eng. 1978. Cons. Otolaryngol. Whipps Cross Hosp. Lond. & King Geo. Hosp. Ilford. Socs: Fell. Roy. Soc. Med. Prev: Clin. Lect. (Otolaryngol.) Nuffield Dept. Surg. & Dept. Otolaryngol. Radcliffe Infirm. Univ. Oxf.

FROSH, Mr Adam Carl 4 Grosvenor Avenue, East Sheen, London SW14 8BX Email: a.fresh@btinternet.com — MB BCh 1988 Wales; FRCS (Otol.) Ed. 1994; FRCS Ed. 1992; FRCS (ORL) 1998. (University of Wales College of Medicine) Specialist Regist., Head & Neck Surg., Roy. Marsden Hosp., Lond.; Hon. Research Fell. MRC 1999. Prev: Regist. (ENT) Char. Cross Hosp. Lond.

FROSH, Barbara Jayne Pennine Drive Surgery, 6-8 Pennine Drive, London NW2 1PA Tel: 020 8455 9977; 318 Whitchurch Lane, Canons Park, Edgware HA8 6QX — MB BS 1980 Lond.; MRCGP 1984; DRCOG 1983. (Royal Free) GP Lond.

FROSSARD, Rosalind Jeanne Middlesex Hospital, Mortimer St., London W1T 3AA Tel: 020 7636 8333; 168A Sutherland Avenue, Maida Vale, London W9 1HR Tel: 020 7221 3477 — MB ChB 1977 Bristol; FFA RCS Eng. 1985. Cons. Anaesth. Middlx. Hosp. Lond.

FROST, Andrew Reginald 46 Rosemary Hill Road, Four Oaks, Sutton Coldfield B74 4HJ — MB ChB 1976 Manch.; FFA RCS Eng. 1984. Cons. Anaesth. Walsgrave Hosp. Coventry. Prev: Sen. Regist. (Anaesth.) W. Midl. RHA.

FROST, Ann 37 Skibereem Close, Pontprennau, Cardiff CF23 8PT — MB ChB 1990 Leeds.

FROST, Christopher Stephen 30 Rochester Way, Rhos-on-Sea, Colwyn Bay LL28 4NJ — MB ChB 1975 Liverp.

FROST, Claire Elizabeth Ann Sand Farm, Sand Farm Lane, Sand Bay, Weston Super Mare BS22 9UF — BM BS 1997 Nottm.

FROST, David Lochmaben Medical Group, The Surgery, 42-44 High Street, Lochmaben, Lockerbie DG11 1NH Tel: 01387 810252 Fax: 01387 811595; Harefield, Nurse's Loaning, Watchhill Road,

Lochmaben, Lockerbie DG11 1RX — MB ChB 1978 Aberd.; MRCGP 1987.

FROST, Deborah Karen Millway Medical Practice, Hartley Avenue, Mill Hill, London NW7 2HX Tel: 020 8959 0888 Fax: 020 8959 7050 — MB BS 1987 Lond.; MA Camb. 1988; MRCGP 1991; T(GP) 1991; DRCOG 1990. Prev: Trainee GP Edgware Gen. Hosp. VTS.

FROST, Dorothy Marjorie (retired) Staploe Medical Centre, Brewhouse Lane, Soham, Ely CB7 5JD Tel: 01353 624121 Fax: 01353 624203 — MB BS 1972 Lond.; MRCS Eng. LRCP Lond. 1972.

FROST, Emma Victoria 220 Bassett Avenue, Southampton SO16 7FU — BM 1995 Soton.

FROST, Geoffrey John Childrens Department, Kidderminster General Hospital, Bewdley Road, Kidderminster DY11 6RJ Tel: 01562 823424; 501 Chester Road S., Kidderminster DY10 1XD Tel: 01562 823880 — MB BS 1971 Lond.; MD Lond. 1992; MRCP (UK) 1975; MRCS Eng. LRCP Lond. 1971; DCH Eng. 1973. (King's Coll. Hosp.) Cons. Paediat. Kidderminster Gen. Hosp. & Worcester Roy. Infirm.

FROST, Gerard 3 Parklands Court, Castle Eden, Hartlepool TS27 4TQ — MB BCh BAO 1977 Dub.; AFOM 2000; MRCGP 1981; DRCOG 1981; DCH Dub. 1981.

FROST, Ian Sam's Cottage, 131 Kirby Rd, Walton on the Naze CO14 8RJ — MB BS 1998 Lond.; MB BS Lond 1998; BSc Lond. 1996. (SGHMS)

FROST, James Bradshaw (retired) 34 Ben Rhydding Road, Ilkley LS29 8RL — MB BChir 1946 Camb.; MA Camb. 1948, MB BChir 1946; DCH Eng. 1951.

FROST, James Shabelle East Harling Surgery, Market St., East Harling, Norwich NR16 2AD Tel: 01953 717204; The Limes, Market Place, Kenninghall, Norwich NR16 2AH Tel: 01953 887666 — MB BChir 1991 Camb.; BSc (Hons.) St. And. 1988; MRCGP 1995; DFFP 1995; Dip. Travel Med. Glas. 1999.

FROST, Jeremy Clive Grosvenor House Surgery, Grosvenor House, Warwick Square, Carlisle CA1 1LB — MB ChB 1981 Aberd.; BMedBiol 1978; MRCGP 1986; DCH RCP Lond. 1984. Prev: SHO (Paediat., O & G & Dermat.) Cumbld. Infirm Carlisle.

FROST, Julie Ann Westrop Surgery, Newburgh Place, Highworth, Swindon SN6 7DN Tel: 01793 762218 Fax: 01793 766073; 2 Artis Avenue, Wroughton, Swindon SN4 9BP Tel: 01793 813369 Email: jafrost@bigfoot.com — MB BCh 1994 Wales; MRCGP 1999. (UWCM) p/t GP, W.rop Surg., Highworth.

FROST, Lloyd Andrew (retired) Oakdene, 151A Wigton Lane, Leeds LS17 8SH Tel: 0113 268 4768 — MB ChB 1963 Leeds. Prev: Ho. Phys. & Ho. Surg. St. Jas. Hosp. Leeds.

FROST, Michael Fisher Quorn Medical Centre, 1 Station Road, Quorn, Loughborough LE12 8PB Tel: 01509 412232 Fax: 01509 620652; 24 Cradock Drive, Quorn, Leicester LE12 8ER — MB ChB 1985 Leic.; DCH RCP Lond. 1988; DRCOG 1987.

FROST, Michael William 26 Parkland Crescent, Horning, Norwich NR12 8PJ Tel: 01692 630559 Email: michealwfrost@hotmail.com; 3 Culverdon Park, Tunbridge Wells TN4 9QT — MB ChB 1994 Dundee; BSc (Hons.) Dund 1989. (Dundee) Specialist Regist. (Anaesth.), Kent & Sussex NHS trust (King's Coll. Specialist Regist. Rotat.). Socs: BMA; MDDUS. Prev: SHO (A & E) St. Johns NHS Trust Livingston; SHO (Anaesth.) Dundee Teachg. Hosps. NHS Trust.

FROST, Mr Neil Tel: 01224 553571 Fax: 01224 552584; West-Town, By Newmachar, Aberdeen AB21 0UP Tel: 01651 862809 — MB ChB 1978 Dundee; FRCS Ed. 1986. Staff Grade Surg. (ENT) Aberd. Hosps. Socs: Mem.: Scott. Otolaryngol. Soc.; BMA. Prev: Reg. (ENT) Aberd. Hosp.; Reg. (ENT) Glas. (Gantnavel & Yorkhill); SHO (ENT) Dundee & Edin.

FROST, Mr Neil Andrew Bristol Eye Hospital, Lower Maudlin St, Bristol BS1 2LX — MB ChB 1985 Sheff.; BA Camb. 1983; FRCS Eng. 1989; MRCP (UK) 1991; FRCOphth 1993.

FROST, Nia 14 Llys Pen y ffordd, Pentre Lane, Rhuddlan, Rhyl LL18 6HJ — MB ChB 1992 Manch.

FROST, Paul John 5 Rowan Close, Penarth CF64 5BU — MB ChB 1988 Sheff.

FROST, Peter Graham Department of Clinical Biochemistry, North West London Hospitals Trust, Acton Lane, London NW10 7NS Tel: 020 8453 2299 Fax: 020 8965 1117 Email: peter.frost@cmh-tr.nthames.nhs.uk; 32 Pitshanger Lane, London W5 1QY Tel: 020 8930 7002 Fax: 020 8930 7002 Email: pgfrost@hotmail.com — MB Camb. 1971, BChir 1970; MRCPath 1977. (Lond. Hosp.) Cons. (Chem. Path.) N. W. Lond. Hosp. Trust. Socs: Assn. Clin. Pathol.; Brit. Hyperlipidaemia Assn.; Roy. Soc. Med. Prev: Sen. Regist. (Clin. Chem.) N.wick Pk. Hosp. Harrow & St. Mary's; Hosp. Lond.; Regist. Chem. Path. W.m. Hosp. Lond.

FROST, Roger Adrian Department of Clinical Radiology, Salisbury District Hospital, Salisbury SP2 8BJ Tel: 01722 429197 Fax: 01722 414008 Email: dr.r.frost@shc-tr.swest.nhs.uk; Mayfly Cottage, Netton Island, Bishopstone, Salisbury SP5 4DD Tel: 01722 780823 — MB BS 1976 Lond.; MRCP (UK) 1978; FRCR 1985; FRCP 1997. (Lond. Hosp.) Cons. Radiol. Salisbury Health Care NHS Trust. Socs: Brit. Soc. Gastroenterol.; Pres. Eur. Soc. Gastrointestinal & Abdom. Radiol.; s/i Gp. Gastrointest.& Abdom. Radiol. Prev: Sen. Regist. (Radiol.) Middlx. Hosp. Lond.; Regist. (Med.) Soton. Gen. Hosp.; Regist. (Radiol.) Plymouth Gen. Hosp.

***FROST, Rosemarie** 5 Rowan Close, Penarth CF64 5BU — MB BCh 1997 Wales.

FROST, Sara Michaela The Long House, 23 West St., Axbridge BS26 2AA — MB ChB 1998 Bristol.

FROST, Sarah Fiona Moresdale Lane Surgery, 95 Moresdale Lane, Leeds LS14 6GG Tel: 0113 295 1200 Fax: 0113 295 1210; 6 Ash Gardens, Leeds LS6 3LD — MB ChB 1987 Leeds; MRCGP 1993; DRCOG 1991.

FROST, Sheila Margaret Pond Tail Surgery, The Green, Godstone RH9 8DY Tel: 01883 742279 Fax: 01883 742913 — MB ChB 1975 Bristol. (Bristol)

FROST, Simon Anthony Hyde Brechin Health Centre, Infirmary Street, Brechin DD9 7AY Tel: 01356 624411 Fax: 01356 623259 — MB ChB 1978 Dundee.

FROST, Stephen James Department Psychiatry, Leicester General Hospital, Gwendolen Road, Leicester LE5 4PW — MB BS 1974 Newc.; MRCPsych 1979. Cons. Psychiat. Carlton Hayes Hosp. NarBoro..

FROST, Susan Kay Woodside, Centre Vale, Todmorden Road, Littleborough OL15 9JY — MB ChB 1991 Leic. SHO (A & E) N. Manch. Gen. Hosp. Prev: Ho. Off. (Surg.) Leicester Gen. Hosp.; Ho. Off. (Med.) Geo. Eliot Hosp. Nuneaton.

FROST-SMITH, Brian Meredith The Long House, Little Strickland, Penrith CA10 3EG Tel: 01931 716214 Fax: 01931 716926 Email: bfrostsmit@aol.com — BSc, MB BCh Wales 1950. (Cardiff)

FROST-SMITH, Marjorie Jean The Long House, Little Strickland, Penrith CA10 3EG Tel: 01931 716214 Fax: 01931 716926 Email: bfrostmit@aol.com — MRCS Eng. LRCP Lond. 1948. (Cardiff) Prev: Ho. Phys. & Ho. Surg. Morriston Hosp. Swansea; Ho. Phys. Walton Hosp. Liverp.

FROSTICK, Professor Simon Peter Department of Musculoskeletal Science, Royal Liverpool University Hospital, Liverpool L69 3GA Tel: 0151 706 4120 Fax: 0151 706 5815 Email: s.p.frostick@liverpool.ac.uk; Rose Cottage, Old Quay Lane, Neston, South Wirral CH64 6QR Tel: 0151 336 2197 Email: simon.frostick@btinternet.com — BM BCh 1978 Oxf.; MA Oxf. 1983, DM 1988; FRCS Eng. 1983. (Oxford) Prof. Orthop. Univ. Liverp. Roy. Liverp. Univ. Hosp.; Hon. Cons. Roy. Liverp. Univ. Hosp. Socs: Fell. BOA; Brit. Soc. Surg. Hand; Eur. Federat. Soc. Microsurg. Prev: Sen. Lect. Univ. Notts.; Clin. Lect. (Orthop.) Univ. Nottm.; Stanley Johnson Fell. (Microsurg.) N.wick Pk. Hosp. Harrow.

FROUD, Eleanor Baird Arborfield Garrison Group Practice, Arborfield Garrison, Reading RG2 3NJ — MB ChB 1982 Manch.; MRCGP 1987; Cert. Family Plann. JCC 1989.

FROW, Jennifer Ann Bewdley Medical Centre, Dog Lane, Bewdley DY12 2EG Tel: 01299 402157 Fax: 01299 404364; 63 Park Lane, Bewdley DY12 2HA Tel: 01299 403810 — MB BS 1966 Lond.; MB BS (Hons.) Lond. 1966; MRCS Eng. LRCP Lond. 1966; FRCGP 1987, M 1975; DObst RCOG 1969; DCH Eng. 1968. (St. Geo.) Socs: Nat. Assn. Family Plann. Doctors. Prev: Ho. Off. (Obst.) St. Helier Hosp. Carshalton; Ho. Off. (Paediat.) Hillingdon Hosp. Uxbridge; Ho. Phys. St. Geo. Hosp. Lond.

FROW, Michael William Oliver 53a Stephendale Road, Fulham, London SW6 2LT — MB BS 1993 Lond.; BSc (Hons.) Lond. 1990. (UCLMS) Research Fell., Qu.s Mary's Hosp., Sidcup. Prev: SHO (Anaesth.) Guy's Hosp.; SHO (Anaesth.) Lewisham Hosp.; SHO (A & E) Colchester Gen. Hosp. & Qu. Eliz. II Hosp. Welwyn Garden City.

FROW, Richard William 288 Dogsthorpe Road, Peterborough PE1 3PL — MB BS 1998 Lond.; MB BS Lond 1998.
FRUITHOF, Michael Herman 8 Baldock Road, Letchworth SG6 3LB — MB BCh BAO 1948 Dub. (T.C. Dub.)
FRY, Abigail Department of Accident and Emergency, Royal Sussex County Hospital, Eastern Road, Brighton BN2 5BE — MB BS 1997 Lond.
FRY, Alan John (retired) 46 Banbury Road, Brackley NN13 6AT — MB BS Lond. 1953; DCH Eng. 1956; DObst RCOG 1957.
FRY, Anthony Harold Emblem House, London Bridge Hospital, 27 Tooley St., London SE1 2PR Tel: 020 7607 3937 Fax: 020 7607 3815 Email: anthony@frydoc.demon.co.uk; 14 Devonshire Place, London W1G 6HX Tel: 020 7607 3937 — MB BS Lond. 1966; MPhil (Psychiat.) Lond. 1972; MRCS Eng. LRCP Lond. 1966; MRCPsych 1972; DPM Eng. 1972. (King's Coll. Hosp) p/t Cons. Psychiat. Lond. Bridge Hosp.; Cons. Psychiat. & Med. Dir. Stress Managem. Unit Lond. Bridge Hosp.; Cons. Psychiat. Charter Nightingale Hosp.; Cons. Psychiat, Devonshire. Socs: R.S.M.; City Med. Book Club; Trustee Indep. Doctors Forum Educ. Trust. Prev: Cons. Phys. (Psychol.) Med. Guy's Hosp. Lond.; Recognised Teach. (Psychiat.) Univ. Lond. & United Med. Schs. Guy's & St. Thos. Hosps. Lond.; Examr. Roy. Coll. Psychiat.
FRY, Caroline Elizabeth Pondsmead House, Halstock, Yeovil BA22 9RY — MB BS 1978 Lond.; DA (UK) 1984. Med. Off. Mondial Assistance Croydon.
FRY, Derek John Home Office, Mansion House, Monkmoor Road, Shrewsbury SY2 5AN Tel: 01743 241612; Department of Anatomy & Physiology, The University, Dundee DD1 4HN Tel: 01382 23181 — BM BCh 1969 Oxf.; MA, DPhil, BM BCh Oxf. 1969. (Oxf. & St. Bart.) Med. Civil Servant Home Off. Shrewsbury. Socs: Anat. Soc. & BMA. Prev: Sen. Lect. (Anat.) Univ. Dundee; Ho. Phys. Med. Profess. Unit St. Bart. Hosp. Lond.
FRY, Donald Ian Taliesin, 31 Knoll Road, Abergavenny NP7 7AN Tel: 01873 854218 — MA, BM BCh Oxf. 1960; LMSSA Lond. 1959; FFA RCS Eng. 1968; DA Eng. 1962. (Westm.) Cons. Anaesth. N. Gwent Health Dist. Socs: Assn. Anaesths.; Assn. Anaesths. Prev: Sen. Regist. (Anaesth.) United Bristol Hosps.; SHO (Anaesth.) United Oxf. Hosps.; Regist. (Anaesth.) Roy. Cornw. Hosp. Truro.
FRY, Edwin Norman Sargood 8 Countisbury Road, Norton, Stockton-on-Tees TS20 1PZ Tel: 01642 554397 — MB ChB 1946 Ed.; FFA RCS Eng. 1954; DA Eng. 1949. (Ed.) Cons. Anaesth. N. & S. Tees Health Dists. Socs: (Ex-Pres.) N.. Soc. Anaesths. Prev: Res. Anaesth. Doncaster Roy. Infirm. Regist. (Anaesth.) Wolvertampton; Hosp. Gp.; Sen. Regist. (Anaesth.) Roy. Bucks. & Assoc. Hosps. Gp.
FRY, Ian Kelsey (retired) The Pines, Woodlands Road, Bickley, Bromley BR1 2AE Tel: 020 8467 4150 — BM BCh 1948 Oxf.; DM Oxf. 1962; FRCP Lond. 1972, M 1956; FRCR 1975. Prev: Cons. Radiol. St. Bart. Hosp. Lond.
FRY, John Mervyn Rushey Mead Health Centre, 8 Lockerbie Walk, Leicester LE4 7ZX Tel: 0116 266 9616; 12 Tynedale Close, Oadby Grange, Leicester LE2 4TS — MB ChB 1978 Aberd.
FRY, Professor Lionel 96 Harley Street, London W1G 7HY Tel: 020 7935 2421 Fax: 020 7224 0656; 16 Caroline Place, London W2 4AN Tel: 020 7229 7790 — MB BS (Hons.) Lond. 1957; BSc (Hons.) Lond. 1954, MD 1964; FRCP Lond. 1976, M 1960; MRCS Eng. LRCP Lond. 1957. (King's Coll. Hosp.) Emerit. Prof. of Dermat. Imperial Coll. Sch. of Med. Lond.; Vis. Cons. Dermatiologist Skin and Cancer Hosp. Dub. Socs: Fell. Roy. Soc. Med. Prev: Cons. Dermat. St. Mary's Hosp. Lond.; Sen. Regist. Skin Dept. Lond. Hosp.; Regist. (Med.) & Ho. Phys. (Med.) King's Coll. Hosp. Lond.
FRY, Lore Marguerite (retired) 25 Serpentine Road, Sevenoaks TN13 3XR — LRCP LRCS 1943 Ed.; LRCP LRCS Ed. LRFPS Glas. 1943; MFCM 1972; DObst RCOG 1946; DPH Lond. 1950. Prev: Dep. Div. Med. Off. LCC.
FRY, Margaret Fisher 25 Marchmont Road, Richmond TW10 6HQ — MB BCh BAO 1942 Belf.; DCH Eng. 1950; DPM Eng. 1973. (Belf.) Asst. MOH Middlx. CC. Prev: Ho. Surg. Ulster Hosp. Childr. & Wom. Belf.; RAF Med. Br.; Res. Med. Off. P.ss Louise Kens. Hosp. Childr.
FRY, Nicholas Martin North Wales Hospital, Denbigh LL16 4ST — MB ChB 1984 Glas.; MB ChB Glas. l984.
FRY, Richard Paul William Child, Family and Adolescent Consultation Service, 26 Bennett's Yard, Lancaster Road, Uxbridge UB8 1BN Tel: 01895 256521 Fax: 01895 232219 — MB BS 1980 Lond.; MSc Lond. 1994; MD Lond. 1993; MRCPsych 1987; MRCGP 1984; DCH RCP Lond. 1984; DRCOG 1982. (St. George's) Cons. Child & Family Psychiat. Hillingdon Child & Family Serv. & Hillingdon Hosp. Middlx. Prev: Sen. Regist. (Child Psychiat.) Gt. Ormond St. & Univ. Coll. & Middlx. Hosps. Lond.; Clin. Research Fell. (Psychiat.) St. Geo. Hosp. Med. Sch. Lond.; Regist. (Psychiat.) St. Geo. Hosp. Lond.
FRY, Roland Werner 25 Serpentine Road, Sevenoaks TN13 3XR — MB BS 1979 Lond.; MRCS Eng. LRCP Lond. 1977; DRCOG 1984. (Char. Cross)
FRY, Mrs Thea 97 Colindeep Lane, London NW9 6DJ Tel: 020 8205 7690 — MD Czechoslovakia 1945; MFHom. 1967. Prev: Med. Off. Brook Advis. Centres.; Med. Off. Bowes Rd. Clin. Lond.; Med. Off. Fortis Green Clin. e.
FRY, Thomas Michael Prospect Medical Practice, 95 Aylsham Road, Norwich NR3 2HW — MB BS 1993 Lond.
FRY, Violet (retired) The Grange, Townsend Hill, Ipplepen, Newton Abbot TQ12 5RU Tel: 01803 812189 — MB ChB 1934 Bristol; MRCS Eng. LRCP Lond. 1934; DA Eng. 1948. Prev: Anaesth. Torbay Hosp. Gp.
FRYAR, Christopher Paul Heath Lane Medical Centre, Heath Lane, Chester CH3 5UJ Tel: 01244 348844 Fax: 01244 351057; 3 Haydan Mews, Godscroft Lane, Frodsham, Warrington WA6 6XU Tel: 01928 732462 — MB ChB 1988 Liverp.; MRCGP 1993; DRCOG 1991. (Liverp.) GP Heath La. Med. Centre Chester. Prev: Trainee GP Chester VTS.
FRYATT, Robert John c/o Foreign & Commonwealth Office (New Dehli), King Charles St., London SW1A 2AH; 39 St Cuthberts Lane, Locks Heath, Southampton SO31 6TE — MB BS 1982 Lond.; MSc Lond. 1993; MRCP (UK) 1985; MFPHM RCP (UK) 1994; DTM & H RCP Lond. 1988. Cons. Health Systems Developm. Advisor Overseas Developm. Admin., India.
FRYER, Alan Edward Royal Liverpool Childrens Hospital, Alder Hey, Liverpool L12 2AP Tel: 0151 252 5238 Fax: 0151 252 5951 Email: alan.fryer@rlch-tr.nwest.nhs.uk — MB BS 1978 Lond.; FRCPCH 1997; FRCP Lond. 1994; MD Lond. 1989; MRCP (UK) 1983; BSc (Hons.) Lond. 1975. (St. Thos. Hosp. Med. Sch. Lond.) Cons. Clin. Geneticist Roy. Liverp. Hosp. & Roy. Liverp. Childr. Hosp. And Liverp. Wom.s Hosp.; Hon. Lect. (Med. & Child Health) Univ. Liverp.
FRYER, Hilary Ann Mintaro, Stewarts Drive, Farnham Common, Slough SL2 3LB Tel: 01753 644400 — MB BS 1977 Lond.; DRCOG 1980. (Univ. Coll. Hosp.) Prev: Clin. Med. Off. (Family Plann.) Ealing HA; Trainee GP Watford VTS; Ho. Phys. Hillingdon Hosp. Uxbridge.
FRYER, James Maxwell Department Anaesthesia, Royal Preston Hospital, Preston PR2 9HT Tel: 01772 716565 Fax: 01772 710992 — MB ChB 1972 Manch.; FFA RCS Eng. 1977; DObst RCOG 1974. (Manchester) p/t Cons. Anaesth. Preston Acute Hosps. NHS Trust. Socs: Obst. Anaesth. Soc.; Intractable Pain Soc.; ESRA. Prev: Sen. Regist. (Anaesth.) Wythenshawe Hosp.; Staff Mem. (Anaesth.) Wilhelmina Gasthuis Amsterdam; Sen. Regist. (Anaesth.) Manch. Roy. Infirm.
FRYER, Jane Anne The Grange Road Practice, 108 Grange Road, London SE1 3BW Tel: 020 7237 1078 Fax: 020 7771 3550; 90 Adys Road, Peckham, London SE15 4DZ Tel: 020 7358 9929 — MB BS 1980 Lond.
FRYER, Jeffrey Harwood (retired) Caythia, The Warren, Kingswood, Tadworth KT20 6PQ Tel: 01737 832415 — MB BS 1951 Lond. Prev: Managing Dir. CIBA-GEIGY Pharmaceut. Div.
FRYER, Lynne Carmen 33 Victoria Road, Malden CM9 JHE — MB BCh 1994 Wales; BSc Birm. 1982, BDS 1986; FDS RCS Ed. 1990; BDS Birm. 1986; FRCSI 1998. Specialist Regist. (Oral & Maxillofacial Surg.) Addenbrooke's/Ipswich/Guys. Socs: BAOMS; BMA; MDU.
FRYER, Malcolm Edward Mill House, Cruckmeole, Hanwood, Shrewsbury SY5 8JN — MB BS 1966 Lond.; FFA RCS Eng. 1974; DA Eng. 1970. Cons. (Anaesth.) Roy. Shrewsbury Hosp. Socs: Roy. Soc. Med. & Obst. Anaesth. Assn. Prev: Sen. Regist. (Anaesth.) Oxon. RHA.
FRYER, Peter John The Grove House, Lower St., Stutton, Ipswich IP9 2SE Tel: 01473 328230 — MB BS 1957 Lond.; MRCS Eng. LRCP Lond. 1957; Dip. Med. Acupunc. 1997; DObst RCOG 1959. (Char. Cross) Phys. & Acupunct. Shrubland Hall Health Clinic, Coddenham, Suff. Socs: Med. Offs. Sch. Assn.; Brit. Med. Acupunct.

Soc. Prev: Ho. Surg. Harrow Hosp.; Ho. Phys. Hackney Gen. Hosp.; Ho. Surg. (O & G) Chase Farm Hosp. Enfield.

FRYERS, Gordon Robert Cedar House, 31 Mill Road, Loddon, Norwich NR14 6DR Tel: 01508 520534 Fax: 01508 520534 — MD 1947 Leeds; MB ChB (Hons.) 1945; MRCP Lond. 1946. (Leeds) Socs: Fell. Roy. Soc. Med. Prev: Ho. Phys. Gen. Infirm. Leeds.

FRYERS, Sylvia Grace 47 Greer Park Avenue, Newtownbreda Road, Belfast BT8 4QE — MB BCh BAO 1986 Belf.

FRYERS, Thomas Department Public Health, South Cumbria HA., Priors Lea, Abbey Road, Barrow-in-Furness LA13 9JU Tel: 01229 870870 Fax: 01229 830242; Lambrigg Foot, Grayrigg, Kendal LA8 9BL Tel: 01539 824202 — MB ChB 1961 Manch.; PhD Manch 1978, MD 1974; DObst RCOG 1962; FFCM 1979, M 1974; DPH Manch. 1964. (Manch.) Dir. (Pub. Health) S. Cumbria Dist. HA; Adjunct Prof. New York Med. Coll. Prev: Reader (Pub. Health & Epidemiol.) Manch. Univ.; Cons. UNICEF & WHO, Zambia, Kampuchea, Belize, Mauritius & China; Sen. Lect. (Epidemiol.) Univ. Ilorin Nigeria.

FRYETT, Diana Clare (retired) 3-4 Widcombe Parade, Widcombe, Bath BA2 4JT Tel: 01225 310883 — MB ChB 1965 Bristol.

FRYMANN, Robert James 19 Coombe Road, Sheffield S10 1FF — MB ChB 1993 Sheff.

FRYMANN, Sarah Jane 2 Doulton Gardens Road, Lower Parkstone, Poole BH14 8RG — MB ChB 1991 Sheff.

FRYSSIRA, Eleni 19 Russell Court, 3 Woburn Place, London WC1H 0LL — Ptychio Iatrikes 1975 Athens.

FRYSZMAN-FENTON, Aleksandra Joanna White Lodge, 68 Silver St., Enfield EN1 3EW Tel: 020 8363 4156; 9 Woodleigh, 7 Churchfields, South Woodford, London E18 2RF Tel: 020 8504 8948 — Lekarz 1970 Warsaw; MD Warsaw 1979; Cert. Prescribed Equiv. Exp JCPTGP 1992. GP Enfield; Clin. Asst. (Urol.) S.end Healthcare NHS Trust. Socs: Eur. Assn. Urol. & BMA. Prev: Trainee GP Enfield; Regist. (Urol.) Kent & Canterbury Hosp.; SHO (A & E) S.end Hosp.

FSADNI, Mr John Kingsbury Court Surgery, Church Street, Dunstable LU5 4RS Tel: 01582 663218 Fax: 01582 476488; 36 Waveney Road, Harpenden AL5 4QY Tel: 01582 761421 — MRCS Eng. LRCP Lond. 1977; FRCS Eng. 1988; MD Malta 1989; DFFP 1993. (Univ. Malta Med. Sch.) Socs: Brit. Med. Acupunct. Soc. Prev: SHO (c/o Elderly) Lister Hosp. Stevenage; SHO (O & G) Qu. Eliz. II Hosp. Welwyn Gdn. City; SHO (Orthop.) Lister Hosp. Stevenage.

FTYARAS, George Elias 27 Longdene Road, Haslemere GU27 2PG Tel: 01428 644868 — MD 1931 Athens.

FU, Yuen Lung 424 St Vincent Street, Glasgow G3 8EU — MB BCh BAO 1983 Belf.

FUAD, Filzah 43 Ombersley Road, Bedford MK42 9JX — MB BS 1997 Newc.

FUAT, Ahmet Carmel Surgery, Nunnery Lane, Darlington DL3 8SQ Tel: 01325 463149; 35 Abbey Road, Darlington DL3 7RD — MB ChB 1982 Aberd.; MRCGP 1986; DRCOG 1984. (Aberdeen) GP Tutor S. Durh.; Co-Edr. Darlington Postgrad. Jl.; Hon. Research Fell. Centre for Health Studies Durh. Univ. Socs: Rheum. Soc.

FUCHS-GOLDFARB, Susan 138A Hempstead Road, Watford WD17 4LG Tel: 01923 36707 — MD 1939 Basle; FRCPath 1976, M 1964. Cons. Pathol. (Histopath. & Cytol.) Barnet Hosp. Gp. Socs: Assn. Clin. Pathols. & Brit. Soc. Clin. Cytol. Prev: Regist. Gp. Laborat. Watford; Brit. Emp. Cancer Campaign Schol. At Harefield Hosp.

FUDGE, Bernard John Lyndhurst, Heol-y-Parc, Pentyrch, Cardiff CF15 9NB Tel: 029 2089 1411 — BSc Wales, MB BCh 1950. (Cardiff) Prev: Med. Regist. Bridgend Gen. Hosp.; Ho. Phys. Llandough Hosp. Cardiff; Capt. RAMC.

FUEST, Margaret (retired) Little Matford, 35 Wonford Road, Exeter EX2 4PG Tel: 01392 273116 — MB BS Lond. 1956; MRCS Eng. LRCP Lond. 1956. Prev: Ho. Phys. & Ho. Surg. (Gyn. & Obst.) St. Nicholas' Hosp. Lond.

FUGE, Bernadette Welsh Office, Cathays Park, Cardiff CF10 3NQ Tel: 029 2082 3924; Cwm Telyn, Church Road, Pentyrch, Cardiff CF15 9QF Tel: 029 2089 0758 — MB BCh Wales 1969; LLM Wales 1993; MPH Wales 1997. (Welsh Nat. Sch. Med.) Med.Dir. NHS Direct.Nat.Assembly.Wales. Prev: Princip. GP; Princip.Med.Off.Welsh.Off.

FUGE, Charles Alistair Mayfield House, Claverton Down Road, Combe Down, Bath BA2 7AD Tel: 01225 832500 — BM BCh 1959 Oxf.; BA Oxf. 1956; FFA RCS Eng. 1967; DA Eng. 1965. (Oxf. & St. Bart.) Socs: (Counc.) Assn. Anaesths. & Hist. Anaesth. Soc. Prev: Cons. Anaesth. Bath HA; Sen. Regist. (Anaesth.) St. Geo. Hosp. Lond. & Soton. Hosp. Gp.; Specialist in Anaesth. RAF.

FUGE, Emma Rhian 2 Marchlands, Stoke Park Road S., Bristol BS9 1LS Tel: 0117 968 7139 Email: rhianfugr@chase12.freeserve.co.uk — MB BS 1993 Lond.; MRCP UK 1997. (St. Bartholomews) Specialist Regist. in Haemetology, Oxf. Radcliffe NHS Trust, Oxf.

FUGGLE, Alison Rosemary Community Unit, Avenue House, The Avenue, Eastbourne BN21 3XY Tel: 01323 440022 — MB ChB 1973 Glas.; Cert. Family Plann. JCC 1985. Community Med. Off. (Child Health) Community Unit E.bourne.

FUGGLE, William James Histopathology Department, New Cross Hospital, Wolverhampton WV10 0QP Tel: 01902 644810 Email: dr.fuggle@rwh-tr.wmids.nhs.uk — MB ChB 1977 Bristol; MRCPath 1986. Cons. Path. W. Midl. RHA., Cons. Histopath, Roy. Wolverhampton Hosps. NHS Trust. Socs: Assn. of Clin. Pathologists Counc. Mem. Roy. Coll. of Pathologists regional Counc. Mem.

FUJITA, Yoshihiro c/o 7 Temple Avenue, Whetstone, London N20 9EJ — BChir 1990 Camb. (Univ. Camb.) Clin. Lect. (Med. Oncol.) Univ. Manch.; Hon. Regist. Christie Hosp. Manch.; CRC Clin. Research Fell. Socs: RCP. Prev: SHO S. Birm. HA, S. Manch. HA & John Radcliffe Hosp. Oxf.

FUKS, Kazimierz North Street Medical Centre, 274 North Street, Romford RM1 4QJ Tel: 01708 764477 Fax: 01708 757656; 11 Wakerfield Close, Emerson Park, Hornchurch RM11 2TH Tel: 01708 471216 Email: docf@aol — MB ChB 1976 Birm.; BSc (Hons.) Birm. 1971; MRCGP 1984; DCH Eng. 1980; DRCOG 1980; DFFP 1991. (Birmingham) Provide Vasectomy Serv. Boro.s of Barking, Havering & S. Essex. Socs: BMA. Prev: SHO (O & G) Hallam Hosp. W. Bromwich; SHO (Paediat. & Gen. Med.) Sandwell Dist. Gen. Hosp. W. Bromwich.

FULBROOK, Richard David Morthen Road Surgery, 2 Morthen Road, Wickersley, Rotherham S66 1EU Tel: 01709 549711; 56 Broom Crescent, Rotherham S60 2SS Tel: 01709 518862 Fax: 01709 518862 Email: drrdfulbrook.s602ss.uk@networkmed.com — MB ChB 1987 Sheff.; MRCGP 1992.

FULCHER, Robert Anthony Norfolk and Norwich University Hospital, Norwich — MB BCh BAO 1974 NUI; MRCPI 1980. Cons. Phys. (Geriat.) Norf. & Norwich Univ. Hosp. Socs: Brit. Geriat. Soc. Prev: Sen. Regist. (Geriat.) Camb. HA.

FULD, Heinz (retired) Fern Cottage, Llanarmon-Yn-Ial, Mold CH7 4QX Tel: 01824 780240 — LRCP LRCS Ed. LRFPS Glas. 1934; MD Heidelberg 1931; FRCP Ed. 1964, M 1936. Prev: Hon. Phys. Sefton Gen. Hosp. Liverp.

FULFORD, Charlotte Jane 3 Craven Road, Reading RG1 5LF Tel: 0118 986 2277; 26 Hamilton Road, Reading RG1 5RD — MB BS 1973 Lond.; BSc Lond. 1970; DCH RCP Lond. 1988; DObst RCOG 1975; MsC (Community Paediat.) Lond. 1997. (London Hospital Medical College) Assoc. Specialist (Community Paediat.) Roy. Berks. & Battle Hosps. NHS Trust. Prev: Staff Grade (Community Paediat.) Roy. Berks. & Battle Hosps. NHS Trust Reading; Clin. Med. Off. W. Berks. HA; Clin. Asst. Roy. Berks. Hosp. Reading.

FULFORD, Professor Kenneth William Musgrave Department of Philosophy, University of Warwick, Coventry CV4 7AL Tel: 024 76 524961 Fax: 024 76 523019 Email: pysak@warwick.ac.uk — MB BChir Camb. 1968; DPhil. Oxf. 1982; PhD Lond. 1976; MA Camb. 1968; MRCP (UK) 1970; FRCPsych 1994; MRCPsych 1976; FRC Psych 1999. (Middlx.) Prof. of Philosophy & Ment. Health Univ. Warwick; Hon. Cons. Psychiat. Univ. Dept. Psychiat. Oxf. Socs: Founder Chair, Philosophy Special Interest Gp., Roy. Coll. of Psychaitrists. Prev: Clin. Lect. (Psychiat.) Oxf.

FULFORD, Laura Geraldine 6 Arran Way, Christchurch BH23 5LP — MB BS 1994 Lond.

FULFORD, Mary Ruth (retired) Shockerwick House Nursing Home, Shockerwick, Bath BA1 7LL Tel: 01225 74363 Ext: 234 — MB ChB 1942 Birm.; MRCS Eng. LRCP Lond. 1942.

FULFORD, Mr Paul Edwin 50 Murrayfield Gardens, Edinburgh EH12 6DF — MB BS 1991 Lond.; FRCS Ed. 1995. Specialist Regist. (Gen. Surg.) NW RHA.

***FULFORD, Richard Kenneth** 14 Hargate Hill, Stapen Hill, Burton-on-Trent DE13 9GH; Broad Sawyers, 57 Loom Lane, Radlett WD7 8NX — MB ChB 1996 Birm.

FULFORD, Mr Simon Charles Venton Department of Urology, Leicester General Hospital, Leicester LE5 4WQ Tel: 0116 249 0490 Fax: 0116 273 0639; 9 Orchid Place, Broughton Astley, Leicester LE9 6NN — MB BS 1987 Lond.; FRCS Eng. 1992. (King's Coll. Lond.) Specialist Regist. (Urol.) Leicester Gen. Hosp. Socs: BMA; Roy. Soc. Med.; Brit. Assn. Urol. Surgs. Prev: Research Fell. (Urol.) Cardiff Roy. Infirm.

FULFORD, William George Newtons, The Health Centre, Heath Road, Haywards Heath RH16 3BB Tel: 01444 412280 Fax: 01444 416943 — MB BChir 1977 Camb.; MRCGP 1980; MRCGP 1987; MA 1997.

FULFORD-KIRBY, John (retired) Room 31, Verulam House, Nursing Home, Verulam Road, St Albans AL3 4DH Tel: 01727 866937 — MB BS 1952 Sydney. Prev: Hon. Clin. Asst. (Med.) Roy. N. Shore Hosp. Sydney & Sydney Hosp., Austral.

FULFORD-SMITH, Antony William — MB BS 1984 Lond.; BSc Pharmacol. (Hons.) 1981; MRCGP 1989; DCH RCP Lond. 1988; DRCOG 1987. (Westm.) Regional Med. Adviser, Glaxosmithkline, Uxbridge; Clin. Assis. St Marys Hosp. Lond. Prev: GP, Judges Cl. Surg., E. Grinstead.

FULLAGAR, Ivo Reginald Arthur (retired) Linbeck, Birkby, Ravenglass CA18 1RT — MB BS 1958 Lond. Prev: Resid. Med. Off. Roy. Free Hosp. Lond.

FULLALOVE, Simon Quay Lane Surgery, Old Quay Lane, St Germans, Saltash PL12 5LH Tel: 01503 230088 Fax: 01503 230713; South Bake Cottage, Trerulefoot, Saltash PL12 5BP — MB ChB 1987 Manch.; MRCP (UK) 1991; MRCGP 1995; DRCOG 1995; DFFP 1994. Clin. Asst. (Endoscopy) Saltash.

FULLARD, Mark Jonathan 6 Tennyson Street, Leicester LE2 1HS — MB ChB 1995 Leic.

FULLBROOK, John Edward Clarendon Lodge Medical Practice, 16 Clarendon Street, Leamington Spa CV32 5SS Tel: 01926 422094 Fax: 01926 331400 — BM BS 1989 Nottm.; MRCGP 1996; DFFP 1995; DCH RCP Lond. 1994. (Nottingham)

FULLER, Mr Alan Pearce (retired) C.R.S. Royal Masonic Hospital, Ravenscourt Park, London W6 0TN Tel: 020 8748 4611 Fax: 020 8748 3817 — MB BS 1951 Lond.; FRCS Eng. 1958; FRCS Ed. 1957; DLO Eng. 1954. Cons. ENT Surg. Roy. Masonic Hosp. Lond.; Mem. Ct. Exam. RCS Eng. Prev: Cons. ENT Surg. St. Bart. Hosp. Lond.

FULLER, Andrew Thomas Radburne (retired) Cedar Trees, 3 Bassett Wood Drive, Southampton SO16 3PT Tel: 023 8076 9095 Email: elizabeth3@onetel.net.uk — MB BS 1954 Lond.; FFA RCS Eng. 1960; DObst RCOG 1957; DA Eng. 1957. Prev: Med. Off. Stud. Health Serv. Soton. Univ.

FULLER, Anne Rosemary Cheadle Hulme Health Centre, Smithy Green, Cheadle Hulme, Cheadle SK8 6LU Tel: 0161 485 7233; 15 Torkington Road, Wilmslow SK9 2AE Tel: 01625 531084 — MB ChB Manch. 1967. (Manchester)

FULLER, Claire Royal Lancaster Infirmary, Ashton Road, Lancaster LA1 4RP Tel: 01524 65944 Fax: 01524 846346; Plas-Yr-Afon, Glanrafon, Llangoed, Beaumaris LL58 8PE — MB ChB 1989 Aberd. MacMillan Fell.sh. (Hons.) Regist. (Med. Oncol. & Palliat. Care) Roy. Lancaster Infirm. Prev: SHO (Gen. Med.) Gwynedd HA; Ho. Off. (Gen. Med. & Surg.) Grampian HA.

FULLER, Clare Elizabeth Department of Pathology, Salisbury District Hospital, Odstock, Salisbury SP2 8BJ Tel: 01722 336262 Fax: 01722 425251; Tel: 01722 718280 — BM BCh 1985 Oxf.; MRCPath 1992. Cons. Histopath. Salisbury Dist. Hosp. Prev: Lect. (Histopath.) Univ. Sheff. Med. Sch.; Regist. (Histopath.) Univ. Hosp. of Wales Cardiff.

FULLER, David John Link End Surgery, 39 Pickersleigh Road, Malvern WR14 2RP Tel: 01684 568466 Fax: 01684 891064; 125 West Malvern Road, Malvern WR14 4NG Tel: 01684 561596 — MRCS Eng. LRCP Lond. 1978; BSc (Hons.) Lond. 1975, MB BS 1979; MRCGP 1984; DRCOG 1983. (St. Mary's) Vaccination & Immunisation Adviser Worcester Gen. Pract. Assn. Socs: BMA & Assn. Clin. Biochem.

FULLER, Frances Margaret Lavender Cottage, 2 Hayle Road, Fraddam, Hayle TR27 6EH Email: frances.fuller@virgin.net — MB BS 1994 Lond.; MRCGP 1999; DFFP 1998. (Univ. Coll. Lond. Med. Sch.)

FULLER, Geraint Nicholas Department of Neurology, Gloucester Royal Hospital, Great Western Road, Gloucester GL1 3NL Tel: 01452 394497 Fax: 01452 394499; Ashmead House, Leckhampton Hill, Cheltenham GL53 9QH Tel: 01242 576649 Fax: 01242 576649 — MB BS 1983 Lond.; FRCP 1998; MA Camb. 1983, BA 1980; MD Lond. 1990; MRCP (UK) 1986. (St. Mary's) Cons. Neurol. Glos. Roy. Hosp. & Cheltenham Gen. Hosp. Prev: Sen. Regist. (Neurol.) Char. Cross Hosp. Lond.; MRC Research Traing. Fell. Dept. Med. (Neurol.) Char. Cross & W.m. Med. Sch. Lond.; Regist. (Med. & Neurol.) St. Stephens Hosp. Lond.

FULLER, Geraldine 83 Clifford Road, New Barnet, Barnet EN5 5NZ — MB BS 1979 Lond.; MRCS Eng. LRCP Lond. 1979; MRCGP 1984; DCCH RCGP & FCM 1988; DRCOG 1980. Clin. Med. Off. E. Herts. HA.

FULLER, Mr Harold William Charles (retired) Villa Kedros, 11 Dover Close, Alresford SO24 9PG Tel: 01962 733424 — MB BS 1937 Lond.; MB BS (Hnrs. Gold Medal) Lond. 1937; FRCS Eng. 1940; MRCS Eng. LRCP Lond. 1937. Prev: Ho. Surg. & Ho. Phys. King's Coll. Hosp.

FULLER, Ian Charles (retired) Connor Lodge, Sedgfield, Stockton-on-Tees TS21 3DW Tel: 01740 622677 Email: ianfuller@dial.pipex.com — MB BS Lond. 1953; FRCGP 1972; DObst RCOG 1955.

FULLER, Jean Elizabeth Anderson Bodey Medical Centre, 363 Wilmslow Road, Fallowfield, Manchester M14 6XU Tel: 0161 248 6644 Fax: 0161 224 4228 — MB ChB 1974 Dundee.

FULLER, John Duncan (retired) Park House, Thorney, Peterborough PE6 0SA Tel: 01733 270325 — MRCS Eng. LRCP Lond. 1946. Prev: Res. Surg. Off. Luton & Dunstable Hosp.

FULLER, John Harry 53 Kent Avenue, Ealing, London W13 8BE — MB BS 1969 Lond.; MA Oxf. 1970; FRCP Lond. 1995; MRCS Eng. LRCP Lond. 1969; MRCP (UK) 1973; FFPHM 1990; MFCM RCP (UK) 1984. (Char. Cross) Prof. Clin. Epidemiol. Univ. Coll. Lond. Prev: Reader (Epidemiol.) Univ. Coll. Lond. Med. Sch.

FULLER, John Robert 19 St Mary's Cottages, Church St., Eastbourne BN20 8BD — BM 1988 Soton.; MRCP (UK) 1991; FRCOphth 1993.

FULLER, Jonathan Henry Shaw The Lawson Practice, 85 Nuttall Street, London N1 5HZ Tel: 020 7739 9701; 94 Lenthall Road, London E8 3JN Tel: 020 7683 0046 Email: j.fuller@ic.ac.uk — MB BS 1974 Lond.; FRCGP 1995, M 1979; DRCOG 1977. Sen. Lect. (Primary Health Care & Gen. Pract.) Imperial Coll. Sch. of Med. Prev: Lect. (Gen. Pract. & Primary Care) Roy. Lond. & St. Bart. Hosp. Med. Coll.; Trainee GP Hackney VTS.

FULLER, Lucinda Claire King's College Hospital, London SE5 Tel: 020 7346 3824 Fax: 020 7346 3616; 88 Claylands Road, London SW8 1NJ Tel: 020 7735 3217 — MB BChir 1988 Camb.; MRCP (UK) 1992. Cons. Dermat. King's Coll. Hosp. Lond. Socs: BMA; Brit. Assn. Dermat.; St. John's Dermat. Soc. Prev: Sen. Regist. (Dermat.) King's Coll. Hosp. Lond.; Regist. (Dermat.) Guy's Hosp. Lond.

FULLER, Martin David 4 Rochester House, Rushford Road, London SW2 1JR — MB ChB 1991 Leeds.

FULLER, Richard 27 Cliff Street, Wakefield WF2 0DW — MB ChB 1995 Leeds. SHO Rotat. (Gen. Med.) Pinderfields Hosp. Wakefield. Prev: Ho. Off. (Gen. Med.) Bradford & (Gen. Surg.) Leeds.

FULLER, Richard William Glaxo Wellcome Research & Development, Uxbridge UB11 1BT Tel: 020 8990 8451 Fax: 020 8990 8309 — MB BS 1977 Lond.; BSc (Hons.) Lond. 1974, MD 1989; FRCP Lond. 1995; MRCP (UK) 1980.

FULLER, Mr Robert Charles (retired) Well Cottage, Goodrich, Ross-on-Wye HR9 6JA Tel: 01600 890226 — MB BS 1940 Lond.; FRCS Eng. 1947; MRCS Eng. LRCP Lond. 1939. Prev: Cons. Surg. Hammersmith Hosp. Lond., Acton Hosp. Lond. & Wembley Hosp.

FULLER, Sidney 'Cuilfail', Firle Road, Seaford BN25 2JD Tel: 01323 898622 — M.B., Ch.B. St. And. 1942. (St. And.) Prev: Ho. Phys. Roy. Infirm. Falkirk.

FULLERTON, Alexander Getty Turton Villa, Turton St., Weymouth DT4 7DU Tel: 01305 772309 — MB BCh BAO 1950 Belf.; FRCPsych 1979, M 1971; DPM RCPSI 1957. (Qu. Univ. Belf.) Prev: Lord Chancellor's Med. Vis. Lord Chancellor's Dept. Lond.; Cons. Psychiat. & Med. Dir. Barnsley Hall Hosp.; Asst. Psychiat. Herrison Hosp. Dorchester.

FULLERTON, Archibald Thomas Duncastle Road Surgery, 275 Duncastle Road, Donermara, Strabane BT82 0LR Tel: 028 7139 8226 — MB BCh BAO 1978 Belf.

FULLERTON, Donald Stuart (retired) La Maison Ville És Philippes, Grouville JE3 9UZ Tel: 01534 852920 Fax: 01534 852920 — MB BCh BAO 1952 Belf.; FRCOG 1989. Prev: Cons. Obst. Jersey Matern. Hosp.

FULLERTON, Duncan Gordon 18 Sandhurst Dr, Ruddington, Nottingham NG11 6HY — MB ChB 1997 Liverp.

FULLERTON, George Denis (retired) 13 Highbury Avenue, Springwell, Gateshead NE9 7PX Tel: 0191 416174 — MB BS Durh. 1945. Prev: Capt. RAMC.

FULLERTON, Iain Samuel Herbert Avenue Surgery, 268 Herbert Avenue, Poole BH12 4HY Tel: 01202 743333 Fax: 01202 738998; 1 Glen Road, Parkstone, Poole BH14 0HF Tel: 01202 739144 — MB BS 1989 Lond.; MRCGP 1993. (St. Mary's Hosp. Med. Sch. Lond.) Prev: Trainee GP Bournemouth & Wimborne; SHO (Anaesth.) Weymouth Dist. Hosp. Dorset.

FULLERTON, John Richard Red Gables, Kite Hill, Wootton, Ryde PO33 4LG — MB BCh 1957 Dub.; BA, MB BCh BAO Dub. 1957; FRCR 1975; DRMD Lond. 1969. Cons. (Radiol.) I. of Wight Health Auth. Prev: Cons. (Radiol.) Roy. Naval Hosp. Plymouth; Cons. (Radiol.) King Abdul Aziz Milit. Hosp. Tabuk, Saudi Arabia.

FULLERTON, Joyce Muir 42 Chaine Memorial Road, Larne BT40 1AD — MB BCh BAO 1953 Dub. (T.C. Dub.) Prev: Ho. Off. Massereene Hosp. Antrim.

FULLERTON, Kenneth James Belfast City Hospital, Lisburn Road, Belfast BT9 7AB Tel: 01232 329241 Fax: 01232 263946 — MB BCh BAO 1978 Belf.; MD Belf. 1984; FRCP Lond. 1993; FRCP Ed. 1992; MRCP (UK) 1981; FRCP (Glas.) 1998. (The Queens University of Belfast) Med. Dir. Belf. City Hosp. HSS Trust; Hon. Lect. Qu.'s Univ. Belf.; Cons. Phys. (Geriat. Med.) Belf. City Hosp. Trust. Prev: Cons. Phys. Craigavon Area Hosps. Trust; Sen. Lect. (Geriat. Med.) Univ. Manch.

FULLERTON, Lesley Ann Priory Court Surgery, 1 High Street, Beauly IV4 7BY Tel: 01463 782214 Fax: 01463 782129; 7 Broallan, Kilmorack, Beauly IV4 7AH Tel: 01463 782731 — MB ChB 1985 Aberd. GP.

FULLERTON, Mark Edwin Nelson David Place Medical Practice, 56 David Place, St Helier, Jersey JE1 4HY; Ville Ès Philippes, Grouville JE3 9UZ Tel: 01534 856115 — MB ChB 1981 Birm; DRCOG 1984.

FULLERTON, Sally Ann 29 Findon Road, London W12 9PP — MB BS 1980 Lond. (St. Mary's) SHO (Obst.) W.m. Hosp. Lond. Prev: SHO (Anaesth.) Ealing & St. Bart. Hosp. Lond.; SHO (Paediat.) W.m. Hosp. Lond.

FULLILOVE, Susan Margaret 8 Aveling Park Road, Walthamstow, London E17 4NU Tel: 020 8523 3467 — MB BS 1990 Lond.; FRCS; MA 1991 Oxf. SHO (Surg.) St. Bart. Hosp. Lond. Socs: MDU & BMA.

FULLMAN, Mr Peter Michael (retired) 47 London Road, Canterbury CT2 8LF Tel: 01227 456352 — MB BS 1958 Lond.; LLB (Hons.) Lond. 1996; FRCS Ed. 1967; MRCS Eng. LRCP Lond. 1958; T(OG) 1991; FRCOG 1980, M 1967, DObst 1959; LLM 1998; Barristter- at- Law (Middle Temple) 1997. Specialist Obst. & Gyn. Under Europ. Specialist Med. Quals. Order 1995. Prev: Cons. O & G Surg. Kent & Canterbury Hosps NHS Trust & Thanet NHS Healthcare Trust.

FULLWOOD, Helen Frances (retired) Aston House, 65 Sunderland St., Tickhill, Doncaster DN11 9PT — MB ChB 1919 Glas. Prev: Asst. Co. Med. Off. W. Riding CC.

FULTON, Ailsa Jane 7 Abbey Park, Bangor BT20 4BY — MB BCh BAO 1997 Belf. SHO (Med.), Belf. City Hosp., Belf. Prev: Pre-Regist. Ho. Off., Belf. City Hosp., Belf.

FULTON, Barbara Department of Anaesthesia, Newcastle General Hospital, Westgate Road, Newcastle upon Tyne NE4 6BE Tel: 0191 273 8811; The Hollies, 2 The Ridgeway, Kenton, Newcastle upon Tyne NE3 4LN — MB BS 1981 Newc.; BMedSci Newc.; FFARCS. Cons. Anaesth. & Intens. Care Newc. Gen. Hosp. Prev: Sen. Regist. Addenbrooke's & Ipswich Hosps.; Regist. Rotat. Newc. & Camb.

FULTON, Charles Stewart 27 Avon Mill View, Linlithgow Bridge, Linlithgow EH49 7SH — MB ChB 1980 Ed.

FULTON, Christina Anne (retired) 5 Braidmount Crest, Edinburgh EH10 6JN — MB ChB 1956 Ed.; FRCS Ed. (Ophth.) 1962. Assoc. Specialist Ophth. Vict. Kirkcaldy. Prev: Sen. Regist. (Ophth.) Leeds Gen. Infirm.

FULTON, Denise Ingham (retired) 44 Malone Heights, Upper Malone, Belfast BT9 5PG Tel: 028 90 615402 — MB BCh BAO 1943 Belf. Prev: Family Plann. Off. E. Health & Social Servs. Bd.

FULTON, George William Ogilvie 8A Rydal Avenue, Grimsby DN33 3EL — MB BS 1994 Lond.

FULTON, Heather Scott (retired) Glebe house, Tweedsmuir, Biggar ML12 6QP — MB ChB 1958 Ed.; MA Ed. 1953. Prev: Sen. Med. Off. DSS Newc.

FULTON, James Douglas Health Care of Elderly, Directorate of Medicine, Derriford Hospital, Plymouth PL6 8DH Tel: 01752 792892 Fax: 01752 792894 Email: jamie.fulton@phnt.swest.nhs.uk — MB ChB 1982 Glas.; FRCP Glas. 1994; MRCP (UK) 1985. Cons. Phys. Derriford Hosp. Plymouth. Prev: Cons. Phys. Stracathro Hosp. Brechin.

FULTON, James Finlay The Surgery, Newton Port, Haddington EH41 3NF Tel: 01620 825497 Fax: 01620 824622 — MB ChB 1985 Ed.; MRCGP 1989; DCH RCP Glas. 1988; DRCOG 1987.

FULTON, James Kerr Heathlind, Knocksilla Park, Hospital Road, Omagh BT79 0AR — MB BCh BAO 1947 Belf. (Belf.)

FULTON, James McLellan 2 Wellbrae, Chapleton, Strathaven ML10 6RT — MB ChB 1980 Glas.

FULTON, John Alexander Health Centre, Newgate Street, Worksop S80 1HP Tel: 01909 500266 Fax: 01909 478014; 15 Glebe Close, Worksop S80 3QX Tel: 01909 479748 Email: sandy24125@aol.com — MB ChB 1976 Manch.; BSc St. And. 1973; MRCGP 1980.

FULTON, Karen Anne 7 Collinbridge Dr, Newtownabbey BT36 7SX — MB BCh BAO 1997 Belf. SHO (Psychiat.).

FULTON, Patrick 110 Chapel Street, Leigh WN7 2DB Tel: 01942 672169; 6 Waltham Avenue, Glazebury, Warrington WA3 5NL Tel: 01925 763660 — MB ChB 1951 Manch. (Manch.) Socs: Fell. Manch. Med. Soc.; Wigan & Leigh Postgrad. Med. Soc. Prev: Ho. Phys. & Ho. Off. (Paediat.) Lake Hosp. Ashton-under-Lyne; RAMC (Nat. Serv.).

FULTON, Phyllis Mary (retired) 8 Claverhouse Drive, Edinburgh EH16 6BS — MB ChB 1957 Ed.; FRCP Ed. 1972, M 1961; FFPHM 1975, M 1972; DPH Ed. 1964; DObst RCOG 1963. Prev: Sen. Lect. (Epidemiol.) Dept. Pub. Health Sci. Univ. Edin.

FULTON, Raymond Alexander Limavady Health Centre, Scroggy Road, Limavady BT49 0NA Tel: 028 7776 6641 — MB BCh BAO 1974 Dub.; BA Dub. 1971; FRCP Lond. 1992; MRCP (UK) 1978. Cons. Dermat. Altnagelvin Hosp. Lond.derry. Prev: Trainee GP York VTS; Sen. Regist. (Dermat.) Glas. Roy. Infirm.; MRC Exchange Fell. Hosp. Edouard Herriot Lyon, France.

FULTON, Robert Fieldfares, Church Lane, Barnham, Bognor Regis PO22 0BP Tel: 01243 552151 — MB BCh BAO 1945 Belf.; MRCGP 1964. Prev: Ho. Phys. & Ho. Surg. Belf. City Hosp.

FULTON, Rosemary Jill Holywood Arches Health Centre, Belfast BT4 1; 5 Knockburn Park, Belfast BT5 7AY — MB ChB 1978 Bristol; MRCGP 1983; DRCOG 1980; DCH Dub. 1982.

FULTON, Thomas Terence, OBE (retired) 44 Malone Heights, Upper Malone, Belfast BT9 5PG Tel: 02890 615402 — MB BCh BAO 1944 Belf.; MB BCh BAO (Hons.) Belf. 1944; MD Cincinnati 1943; MD (Commend.) Belf. 1951; FRCP Lond. 1967, M 1948; FRCPI 1977. Hon. Cons. Phys. Roy. Vict. Hosp. Belf. Prev: Cons. Phys. Roy. Vict. Hosp. Belf.

FULTON, William Francis Monteith (retired) Woodhill, Braemar, Ballater AB35 5XX Tel: 01339 741239 — MB ChB 1945 Glas.; BSc Glas. 1941; MD (Hnrs.) 1961. MB ChB (Commend.) 1945; FRCP Lond. 1972, M 1949; FRCP Ed. 1968, M 1962; FRCP Glas. 1969, M 1966. Prev: Prof. Med. Univ. Nairobi.

FUMI, Lucio Monmouth Pharmaceuticals Ltd., 3-4 Huxley Rd, The Surrey Research Park, Guildford GU2 7RE Tel: 01483 565299 Fax: 01483 563658 Email: lfumi@monmouth.pharma.uk.com; 2 Wyfold Cottages, Wyfold, Reading RG4 9HX Tel: 01491 680072 Fax: 01491 680072 Email: lucio.fumi@talk21.com — State Exam 1983 Trieste. (Trieste, Italy) Med. Dir., Monmouth Pharmaceut. Ltd. Socs: Brit. Assn. Pharmaceut. Phys.; Eur. Soc. Parenteral & Enteral Nutrit.; Amer. Soc. Parenteral & Enteral Nutrit. Prev: Med. Dir. Convatec Europe Ickenham; Med. Dir. Clintec Nutrit. Ltd.; Med. Dir. Carex Europ. Gp.

FUNAKI, Ayano 44 Fortismere Avenue, London N10 3BL — MB BS 1998 Lond.; MB BS Lond 1998.

FUNG, Caroll Chee-Chiu 27 Parkfield Road, Coleshill, Birmingham B46 3LD — BM 1981 Soton.

FUNG, Debra Ann Acers, Doggetts Wood Lane, Chalfont St Giles HP8 4TH — MB BS 1982 Lond.; DObst. 1985; DCH RCP Lond. 1986.

FUNG, Peter Jeremy Lordshill Health Centre, Lordshill District Centre, Lordshill, Southampton SO16 8HY Tel: 023 8073 8144 Fax: 023 8073 0722 — BM 1977 Soton.; MRCGP 1982.

FUNG, Yuk Yu 6 Manor House Court, 11 Warrington Gardens, London W9 2PZ — MB BS 1975 Lond.

FUNG-A-FAT, Arnold George Elmswood (Surgery), 22 Fryent Way, London NW9 9SA Tel: 020 8204 8228; 33 Glanleam Road, Stanmore HA7 4NW Tel: 020 8954 1528 — MB BS 1952 Lond.; MRCS Eng. LRCP Lond. 1952. (Guy's)

FUNKEL, Helga Dudley Group of Hospitals, Russells Hall Hospital, Dudley DY1 2HQ; 3 Edge Hill, Stourbridge DY7 6DP — State Exam Med 1987 Berlin; FCA 1997. Specialist Regist. (Anaesth.) & Cons. Anaesth./ Pain Managem.

FUNNEKOTTER, Robert Pieter 1 Millhall Farmhouse, Stirling FK7 7LP — MB ChB 1992 Cape Town.

FUNNELL, Anthony Ronald Heene and Goring Practice, 145 Heene Road, Worthing BN12 4PY Tel: 01903 235344 Fax: 01903 247099; 18 St. Valerie Road, Worthing BN11 3LL — MB BS 1982 Lond.; MRCGP 1995; DRCOG 1995; DFFP 1994. (Roy. Free Hosp. Med. Sch.) Prev: Trainee GP E.bourne VTS.

FUNNELL, Mark Stewart 124 Bunning Way, London N7 9UW — MB BS 1989 Lond.

FUNNELL, Nicola Jane 52 Kelsey Lane, Beckenham BR3 3NE — MB ChB 1992 Leeds.

FURBANK, Ian David James Little Bushey Surgery, 128 Little Bushey Lane, Bushey, Watford WD23 4SA Tel: 020 8386 8888 Fax: 020 8386 8898 — MB BS Lond. 1982; MRCGP 1986. Prev: Trainee GP Barnet Gen. Hosp. VTS.

FURBER, Peter John Alpine House Surgery, 86 Rothley Road, Mountsorrel, Loughborough LE12 7JU Tel: 0116 230 3062 Fax: 0116 237 4218 — MB ChB 1983 Leicester; MB ChB 1983 Leicester.

FUREY, Alison Hilary Merton, Sutton & Wandsworth Health Auth., The Wilson, Cranwer Road, Mitcham CR4 4TP Tel: 020 8687 4649 — MB BS 1985 Lond.; MRCOG 1992. p/t Cons. in Pub. Health Med. Lond. - Marton, Sutton & Wandsworth Health Auth. Prev: Health Cons. Brit. Counc.; Regist. (Obst. Gyn.) Univ. Hosp. Wales; Regist. PH Med.

FURLEPA, Krzysztof Antoni Bersted Green Surgery, 32 Durlston Drive, Bognor Regis PO22 9TD; April Cottage, Aldwick St, Bognor Regis PO21 3AW — MB BS 1975 Lond.

FURLEY SMITH, Elizabeth Anne The Surgery, Carisbrooke House, Stockleigh Road, St Leonards-on-Sea TN38 0JP Tel: 01424 423190/432925 Fax: 01424 460473; Linton Lodge, 26 Linton Road, Hastings TN34 1TW Tel: 01424 460582 Fax: 01424 435226 — MB BS 1983 Lond.; DRCOG 1987. GP St. Leonards-on-Sea. Prev: Trainee GP Hastings VTS; Ho. Phys. Inverness & Fort William; Ho. Surg. Hastings.

FURLONG, Annemarie Christine Town Farm, Southside, Hull HU12 0RN — MB ChB 1978 Liverp.; Cert. Family Plann. JCC 1983; DRCOG 1983; DCH RCP Lond. 1981. Med. Panel Mem. Independant Appeals Serv. Prev: GP Sessions on retainer scheme, E.Yorks.; Clin. Asst., Psychogenatrics & BrE. Clinic, Hull; Clin. Med. Off. Wirral.

FURLONG, Carol Mary 201B Swithland Lane, Rothley, Leicester LE7 7SJ — MB BCh BAO 1984 Dub.

***FURLONG, Elizabeth** 33 Windmill Lane, Henbury, Bristol BS10 7XE — MB ChB 1998 Birm.

FURLONG, Leon Roger Oakdale, Kingmoor, Carlisle CA3 9QZ — MB BS 1979 Lond.

FURLONG, Mary Barbara (retired) 1 The Meadows, Stiles Way, Antrim BT41 2RJ Tel: 02894466525 — MB BCh BAO 1947 NUI. Cons. Psychiat. Holywell Hosp. Antrim. Prev: Regist. St. Luke's Hosp. Armagh.

FURLONG, Olive Cynthia (retired) Cliff Hill House, Low Burnham, Epworth, Doncaster DN9 1DE Tel: 01427 752300 — MB ChB 1949 Manch.; MFCM 1975; DCH Eng. 1952. Prev: Cons. Pub. Health Med. Doncaster HA.

FURLONG, Mr Ronald John 11-12 Wimpole Street, London W1M 7AB Tel: 020 7436 1919 Fax: 020 7636 4351; Flat 3, 8 Wimpole St., London W1M 7AB Tel: 020 7580 5213 — MB BS 1931 Lond.; FRCS Eng. 1934; MRCS Eng. LRCP Lond. 1931. (St. Thos.) Socs: Fell. Roy. Soc. Med. & BOA. Prev: Cons. Orthop. Surg. King Edwd. VII Hosp. For Off.s; Orthop. Surg. St. Thos. Hosp. & Qu. Vict. Hosp. E. Grinstead; Cons. Orthop. Surg. to Army.

FURLONG, Rosalind Claire Spenser St Ann's Hospital, St Ann's Road, London N15 3TH Tel: 020 8442 6000 Fax: 020 8442 6354 — MB BS 1971 Lond.; MRCS Eng. LRCP Lond. 1971; MRCPsych 1977; FRCPsych 1998. (Univ. Lond. & Guy's Hosp. Med. Sch.) Cons. Psychiat. St. Ann's Hosp. Haringey Healthcare NHS Trust; Clin. Dir. Haringey Healthcare NHS Trust; Hon. Sen. Lect. Roy. Free Hosp. Sch. Med. Lond. Prev: Cons. Psychait. Friern Hosp.

FURLONGER, Andrew James 2 High Meadow, Hathern, Loughborough LE12 5HW — MB ChB 1994 Leic.

FURMAN, Gita 6 Apsley Grove, Bowdon, Altrincham WA14 3AH — MB ChB 1982 Manch.; DRCOG 1987.

FURNACE, Graham Fraser RGIT Ltd, 338 King St., Aberdeen AB24 5BQ Tel: 01224 619606 Fax: 01224 619540 Email: gff@rgit.co.uk — MB ChB 1985 Glas.; MRCGP 1990; AFOM 1997; DRCOG 1989. Occupat. Phys. Aberd.

FURNACE, Jacqueline Clinical Pharmacology Unit, Ward 6, Aberdeen Royal Infirmary, Foresterhill, Aberdeen AB25 2ZN — MB ChB 1983 Ed.; BSc (Med. Sci.) Ed. 1980; Dip. Forens. Med. Glas. 1991; MEd. Aberd. 1998.

FURNEAUX, James 14 Hillfoot Avenue, Bearsden, Glasgow G61 3QB; 14 Hillfoot, Bearsden, Glasgow G61 2QJ — MB ChB 1982 Aberd.

FURNEAUX, Peter John Sidney The Surgery, Church Street, Hartfield TN7 4AQ Tel: 01892 770402 Fax: 01892 770189; Southenay House, Church St, Hartfield TN7 4AQ — MB BS 1978 Lond.; PhD McGill 1966; MA Camb. 1964; MRCS Eng. LRCP Lond. 1978. (Lond. Hosp.) Prev: SHO (Paediat.) William Harvey Hosp. WillesBoro.

FURNELL, Phyllis Marie 11 Michael Road, South Norwood, London SE25 6RW Tel: 020 8653 5705 — MB BS 1963 Poona. (B.J. Med. Coll.) Regist. (Microbiol.) Roy. Free Hosp. Hampstead. Prev: Regist. (Path.) Mayday Hosp. Thornton Heath; SHO (Path.) St. Olave's Hosp. Lond.; Ho. Phys. & Ho. Surg. Mile End Hosp.

FURNESS, Anthony Gaskell Elizabeth Ave Group Practice, 2 Elizabeth Avenue, London N1 3BS Tel: 020 7226 6363; 16 Birchington Road, London N8 8HP Tel: 020 8340 5156 Fax: 020 7226 5048 — MB Camb. 1971, BChir 1970; MRCGP 1997; MRCPsych 1978; DObst RCOG 1973. (Middlx.) Prev: Regist. (Child Psychiat.) Child Guid. Train. Centre; SHO (Psychiat.) Hillingdon Hosp.; SHO (Paediat.) St. Chas. Hosp. Lond.

FURNESS, Frank Cockill and Partners, Group Surgery, Church St, Ossett WF5 9DE Tel: 01924 273118 Fax: 01924 261321; Grange Cottage, 170 Old Road, Overton, Wakefield WF4 4RL — MB ChB Birm. 1969. Prev: Ho. Phys. Stepping Hill Hosp. Stockport; Ho. Surg. (O & G) Selly Oak Hosp. Birm.

FURNESS, Gregory 2 Grangewood Park, Kilfennan, Londonderry BT47 5SH — MB BCh BAO 1979 Belf.

FURNESS, John Charles Dept of Paediatrics, Sunderland Royal Hospital, Sunderland SR4 7TP — MB BS 1992 Newc.

FURNESS, Michael John 31 Wilton Place, Knightsbridge, London SW1X 8SH Tel: 020 7235 0417 Fax: 020 7259 5386 — MB BS 1969 Lond.; BDS Lond. 1964. (St. Georg. Lond; Roy. Dental Hosp.)

FURNESS, Professor Peter Norman Department of Pathology, General Hospital Leicester, Gwendolen Road, Leicester LE5 4PW Tel: 0116 258 4582 Fax: 0116 258 4573 Email: pnf1@le.ac.uk — BM BCh 1981 Oxf.; PhD Nottm. 1989; MA Camb. 1981, BA 1978; FRCPath 1997, M 1989. Prof. (Renal Path.) Univ. Leicester; Hon. Cons. Path. Leicester Gen. Hosp. Prev: Lect. (Path.) Univ. Nottm.; Hon. Sen. Regist. (Histopath.) Nottm. HA; Sen. Lect. (Path.) Univ. of Leic.

FURNESS, Robert Harvey Scott Magnolia House Practice, Magnolia House, Station Road, Ascot SL5 0QJ Tel: 01344 637800 Fax: 01344 637823 — MB BS Lond. 1971; MRCS Eng. LRCP Lond. 1970. (St. Bart.) Socs: Fell. Hunt. Soc. Prev: Trainee GP Lond. (St. Bart.) VTS; SHO (Cas.) St. Bart. Hosp. Lond.; Demonst. (Anat.) Char. Cross Hosp. Med. Sch.

FURNESS, Sandra Jean Wickenden Farm, The Street, Plaxtol, Sevenoaks TN15 0QG Tel: 01732 810334 — MB ChB 1974 Sheff.; DRCOG 1975.

FURNISS, Andrew Edward Ansdale, Kiln Lane, Hambleton, Poulton-le-Fylde, Blackpool — MB ChB 1980 Leeds.

FURNISS, David Anthony 14 Leadhall Grove, Harrogate HG2 9ND Tel: 01423 871353 — MRCS Eng. LRCP Lond. 1956. Adjudicating Med. Pract. DSS.

FURNISS, Debra Louise Skinner 40 Newfield Green Road, Sheffield S2 2BR — MB ChB 1995 Sheff.

FURNISS, Michael John Preston (retired) 51 Manor Road, Ashford TW15 2SL Tel: 01784 255300 — MB BChir 1957 Camb.; MA, MB Camb. 1957, BChir 1956. Prev: Sen. Med. Off. HM Remand Centre & Y.O.I. Feltham.

FURNISS, Patrick 10 Mile End Road, Norwich NR4 7QY — MB BChir 1967 Camb.; MA, MB Camb. 1967, BChir 1966; FFA RCS Eng. 1970. (St. Thos.) Cons. Anaesth. United Norwich Hosps. Socs: Ass. Anaesth.; IC Soc. Prev: Jt. Sen. Regist. (Anaesth.) Hosp. Sick Childr. Gt. Ormond St. & St. Thos. Hosp. Lond.; Regist. (Anaesth.) St. Thos. Hosp. Lond.

FURNISS, Stephen Spencer Meads Lodge, Elmfield Road, Gosforth, Newcastle upon Tyne NE3 4AY Tel: 0191 284 7598 — MB BS 1979 Lond.; MA Camb. 1979; FRCP Lond. 1995; MRCP (UK) 1982. Cons. Cardiol. Freeman Hosp. Newc. u. Tyne; Brit. Heart Foundat. Sen. Lect. (Acad. Cardiol.) Univ. Newc. u. Tyne. Prev: Research Assoc. Freeman Hosp. Newc.; Regist. (Cardiol.) Freeman Hosp. Newc.; Lect. Med. Unit Lond. Hosp.

FURROWS, David Charles 43 Wellington Road, Timperley, Altrincham WA15 7RQ — MB BS 1993 Lond.

FURROWS, Sarah Jillian 43 Wellington Road, Temperley, Altrincham WA15 7RQ — MB BS 1994 Lond.

FURSDON, Diana Muriel (retired) Silverton Surgery, Silverton, Exeter EX5 4HX Tel: 01392 860176 — MRCS Eng. LRCP Lond. 1956. Prev: Mem. Huddersfield Med. Soc. Ho. Phys. Gloucester Roy. Hosp.

FURSDON, Paul (retired) Pleasure House, Thorverton, Exeter EX5 5PJ Tel: 01392 860251 — MRCS Eng. LRCP Lond. 1958; MRCGP 1969; DHMSA 1987. Prev: Ho. Off. City Matern. Hosp. Gloucester.

***FURSE, Rosanne Marie** 15 Great Western Road, Dorchester DT1 1UF Tel: 01305 269482 — MB BS 1997 Lond.

FURST, Herbert Charles (retired) Great Fish Hall, Hadlow, Tonbridge TN11 0AA — LRCP LRCS 1928 Ed.; BSc (Hons.) Sydney 1924; LRCP LRCS Ed. LRFPS Glas. 1928. Prev: Gen. Surg. St. And. Hosp. Lond.

FURTADO, Alexandra 80 Lodore Gardens, Kingsbury, London NW9 0DN — MB BS 1965 Karachi. (Dow Med. Coll.) Clin. Asst. Hosp. Sick Childr. Gt. Ormond St. Lond. Socs: Assoc. Mem. Fac. Homoeop. UK. Prev: SHO (Paediat.) Centr. Middlx. Hosp. Lond., W. Middlx. Hosp. Isleworth; & Evelina Childr. Hosp. of Guy's Hosp. Lond.

FURZE, Richard John High Street Surgery, 25 High Street, Tollesbury, Maldon CM9 8RG Tel: 01621 869204 Fax: 01621 869023; 25 High Street, Tollesbury, Maldon CM9 8RG Tel: 01621 869204 — MB BChir 1974 Camb.; MA, MB Camb. 1974, BChir 1973; MRCP (UK) 1978; DRCOG 1983; DCH Eng. 1976.

FUSI, Luca Department of Obstetrics & Gynaecology, Hammersmith Hospital, Du Cane Road, London W12 0NN Tel: 020 8743 2030 Fax: 020 8383 8065; Department of Obstetrics & Gynaecology, Ealing Hospital, Uxbridge Road, Southall UB1 3HW Tel: 020 8574 2444 Fax: 020 8767 5727 — MD 1976 Rome; MRCOG 1985. Cons. O & G Hammersmith & Ealing Hosp.; Sen. Lect. (Obst. & Gyn.) Imperial Coll. Med. Hammersmith Campus. Socs: Brit. Fertil. Soc.; Brit. Fetal Matern. Med. Soc.; Internat. Fetal Med. & Surg. Soc.

FUSSELL, Ian James Pengarth Road Surgery, Pengarth Road, St Agnes TR5 0TN Tel: 01872 553881 Fax: 01872 553885; Carn Cottage, Town Hill, St Agnes TR5 0QT Tel: 01872 553081 Email: surfdocfus@england.com — BM BS 1989 Nottm.; BMedSci (Hons.) Nottm. 1986; MRCGP 1994. (Nottingham) GP St Agnes Cornw.; Assoc. Specialist Genitourin. Med. Socs: BMA; MDU. Prev: Regist. (A & E) Newc. Australia; GP/Regist. Constantine Cornw.

FUSSELL, Miss Katharine Mary (retired) 17 Mendip Avenue, Winstanley, Wigan WN3 6EB Tel: 01942 222545 Fax: 01942 228323 Email: kmfussell@aol.com — MB ChB Birm. 1951; FRCS Eng. 1957; MRCS Eng. LRCP Lond. 1951. Prev: Cons. Surg. Roy. Albert Edwd. Infirm. Wigan.

FUSSEY, Catherine Elizabeth Cliff Villages Medical Practice, Mere Road, Waddington, Lincoln LN5 9NX Tel: 01522 720277 Fax: 01522 729174; March House, 7 Greetwell Road, Lincoln LN2 4AQ Tel: 01522 529181 — MB ChB 1980 Sheff.; BSc Surrey 1972; MSc Birm. 1975.

FUTERS, George Ilkeston Health Centre, White Lion Square, Ilkeston DE7 5PZ Tel: 0115 932 2968 — MB BCh BAO 1956 Dub.; DA Eng. 1959. (T.C. Dub.) Med. Staff Ilkeston Community Hosp. Prev: Ho. Phys. & Cas. Off. Sir P. Dun's Hosp. Dub.; Med. Off. Irish Nat. Blood Transfus. Assn.; Resid. Anaesth. City Hosp. Nottm.

FUZZEY, George Jeremy John St Peter's Hospital, Chertsey KT16 — MA; MB Camb. 1962, BChir 1961; FFA RCS Eng. 1966. (Camb. & St. Thos.) Cons. Anaesth. N.W. Surrey Hosp. Gp. Prev: Sen. Regist. (Anaesth.) St. Thos. Hosp. Lond.; Regist. (Anaesth.) St. Thos. Hosp. Lond. & United Sheff Hosps.

FYALL, Andrew Aitken Wilson Street Surgery, 11 Wilson Street, Derby DE1 1PG Tel: 01332 344366 Fax: 01332 348813 — MB ChB 1980 Sheff.; MRCGP 1985; DRCOG 1984.

FYANS, Philip Geoffrey Upper Chorlton Road Surgery, 171 Upper Chorlton Road, Manchester M16 9RT Tel: 0161 881 4293 Fax: 0161 860 5265 — MB ChB 1978 Manch.; MSc Manch. 1975, BSc 1972, MB ChB 1978. GP Manch. Prev: SHO (Cardiothoracic Med.) Wythenshawe Hosp. Manch.; Ho. Phys. Manch. Roy. Infirm.; Ho. Surg. Chester Roy. Infirm.

FYDLER, Terence John (retired) Langland House, 1 Rockingham Road, Cottingham, Market Harborough LE16 8XS — MB ChB 1960 Birm.; DA Eng. 1962; DObst RCOG 1969.

FYFE, Mr Alasdair Hunter Beattie 59 Old Mearns Road, Clarkston, Glasgow G76 7ES — MB ChB 1971 Glas.; FRCS Glas. 1976. Cons. Paediat. Surg. Roy. Hosp. Sick Childr. Glas.

FYFE, Alexander Ewing The Blackheath Hospital, 40-42 Lee Terrace, Blackheath, London SE3 9UD Tel: 020 8318 4900; 40 Heath Lane, London SE3 0UT Tel: 020 8852 8347 — MB BS 1950 Lond.; MRCS Eng. LRCP Lond. 1945; FRCOG 1968, M 1953. (St. Bart.) Cons. O & G Greenwich Health Dist.; Examr. RCOG & Centr. Midw. Bd. Socs: Fell. Roy. Soc. Med.; (Counc.) Roy. Coll. Gyn. & English Nat. Bd. for Nursing Midw. & Health Visit. Prev: Sen. Regist. (O & G) Roy. Free Hosp. Lond.; Obst. Ho. Surg. Qu. Charlotte's Hosp. Lond.; Orthop. Ho. Surg. St. Bart. Hosp.

FYFE, Alison Laura Ann 46 Vale Road, Claygate, Esher KT10 0NJ — MB BS 1994 Lond.

FYFE, David Richard New Southgate Surgery, Buxton Place, off Leeds Road, Wakefield WF1 3JQ Tel: 01924 334400 Fax: 01924 334439; 3 Castle Terrace, Sandal, Wakefield WF2 6AZ Tel: 01924 253369 — MB BS 1981 Lond.; DRCOG 1984.

FYFE, David Walter 405 Barlow Moor Road, Chorlton-cum-Hardy, Manchester M21 7FZ — MB ChB 1989 Manch.

FYFE, Elizabeth Lydia (retired) 77 Drymen Road, Bearsden, Glasgow G61 3RL — MB ChB Glas. 1949; DCH Eng. 1953.

FYFE, George (retired) Breich, Gowanlea Place, Comrie, Crieff PH6 2EJ Tel: 01764 670523 — MB ChB St. And. 1946, DPH 1952; MFCM 1972. Prev: Dist. Med. Off. Falkirk Health Dist.

FYFE, Mr Ian Stuart Department of Orthopaedics, Northwick Park Hospital, Watford Road, Harrow HA1 3UW — MB ChB 1969 Liverp.; FRCS Eng. 1975; FRCS Ed. 1975; FRCS Ed. (Orth.) 1982; MRCS Eng. LRCP Lond. 1969. (Liverp.) Cons. (Orthop.) N.wick Pk. Hosp. Lond.; Hon. Sen. Lect., Imperial Coll. Socs: Brit. Assn. for Surg. of the Knee (BASK); Brit. Cervical Spine Soc.; Brit. Spine Soc. Prev: Sen. Regist. (Orthop.) Centr. Notts. Health Dist.; Regist. (Orthop.) Harlow Wood Orthop. Hosp. Mansfield; Squadron Ldr. RAF Med. Br.

FYFE, Isobel Mary (retired) Breich, Gowanlea Place, Comrie, Crieff PH6 2EJ Tel: 01764 670523 — MB ChB (Commend.) St. And. 1949; DPH St. And. 1952. Prev: Clin. Asst. Path. Dept. St. And. Univ. Med. Sch.

FYFE, John The Medical Centre, Caledonian Road, Perth PH2 8HH Tel: 01738 28234 Fax: 01738 24945; Redlands, 40 Viewlands Terrace, Perth PH1 1DA Tel: 01738 25986 — MB ChB 1958 Glas.; DObst RCOG 1961.

FYFE, Mr Neil Cameron Matthew Disablement Services Centre, Freeman Hospital, Newcastle upon Tyne NE7 7AF Tel: 0191 223

1183 Fax: 0191 284 0379 Email: neil.fyfe@nuth.northy.nhs.uk — MB BChir 1971 Camb.; MA, MChir Camb. 1985, BA 1968; FRCS Eng. 1976; FRCP Lond. 1998. (Univ. Camb. & St. Thos. Hosp.) Cons. Rehabil. Med. Newc. Hosps. NHS Trust; Hon. Cons. Rehabil. Med. Tees Health NHS Trust; Hon. Lect. (Surg.) Univ. Newc.; Hon. Med. Adviser Nat. Rifle Assn.; Mem. Med. Appeals Tribunal. Socs: (Hon. Treas.) Brit. Soc. Rehabil. Med.; N. Eng. Medico-Legal Soc. Prev: Sen. Med. Off. Disablem. Servs. Auth. Newc.; Med. Off. DHSS Artific. Limb & Appliance Serv. Lond.; Lect. (Surg.) & Hon. Sen. Regist. St. Thos. Hosp. Lond.

FYFE, Thomas Drummochy, Port Glasgow Road, Kilmacolm PA13 4QQ Tel: 0150 587 2367 — MD 1970 Glas.; MB ChB 1962; FRCP Glas. 1977, M 1967. (Glas.) Cons. Phys. S.. Gen. Hosp. Glas. Prev: Cons. Phys. Vale of Leven Dist. Gen. Hosp. Alexandria; Med. Regist. Vict. Infirm. Glas.; Regist. Atheroma Research Unit W.. Infirm. Glas.

FYFE, William Morton (retired) 77 Drymen Road, Bearsden, Glasgow G61 3RL Tel: 0141 942 2166 — MB ChB Glas. 1945; MD (Commend.) Glas. 1957; FRCP Lond. 1974, M 1952; FRCP Ed. 1971, M 1951; FRCP Glas. 1965, M 1962; DCH Eng. 1949. Prev: Cons. Paediat. & Sen. Regist. (Paediat.) Roy. Hosp. For Sick Childr. Glas.

FYFIELD, Jill (retired) Bourn House, South Knighton, Newton Abbot TQ12 6NP Tel: 01626 821743 — MB BS 1960 Lond.; MRCS Eng. LRCP Lond. 1960; Cert. Contracep. & Family Plann. RCOG & RCGP 1975. Prev: Princip. Clin. Med. Off. (Community Health) S. Devon Healthcare Trust.

FYNES, Michelle Maria Department of Obstetrics & Gynaecology, Cambridge University, Addenbrookes Hospital, Robinson Way, Cambridge CB2 2SW — MB BCh BAO 1991 NUI.

FYNN, Julia Abigail 6 Broadhill Close, Bramhall, Stockport SK7 3BY — MB ChB 1989 Dundee. SHO P. Wales Hosp. Sydney, Austral.

FYNN, Simon Patrick 13 Arundel Street, Ashton-under-Lyne OL6 6RD — BChir 1991 Camb.

FYVIE, Andrew Duncan 24 Chatsworth Road, Croydon CR0 1HA Tel: 020 8688 3430 Fax: 020 8688 4150 — MB ChB 1978 Ed.; DRCOG 1986.

FYVIE, Kathleen Roberta Joan 17 Laurel Hill Road, Coleraine BT51 3AY — MB BCh BAO 1988 Belf.

GAAL, Eugene 58 Coldharbour Road, Redland, Bristol BS6 7LZ — MB ChB 1995 Bristol; BA (Pol & Econ) Konstane 1988. Socs: Med. Defence Union; BMA.

GABA, Martin David 10 Canning Cresent, Oxford OX1 4XB — MB ChB 1980 Dundee.

GABALLA, Mohammad Anwar Ahmad Orthopaedic Department, Royal Hospital for Sick Children, Yorkhill, Glasgow G3 8SJ — MB BCh 1979 Assiut.

GABALLA, Naguib Edward The Surgery, 315 Sheldon Heath Road, Sheldon, Birmingham B26 2TY Tel: 0121 743 2626 Fax: 0121 244 8383 — MB BCh 1969 Cairo.

GABATHULER, Helen Barlich House, Binton, Stratford-upon-Avon CV37 9TW — BM 1987 Soton.; MRCP (UK) 1991; MRCGP 1993; DRCOG 1992. Asst. (Gen. Pract.); Clin. Asst. (Rheum.) Warwick Hosp.

GABAY, Anita Maureen 474 Street Lane W., Moortown, Leeds LS17 6HA Tel: 0113 267 4411 — MB ChB 1963 Aberd.; Dip. Community. Med. Tel-Aviv 1974. Regional Med. Off. DHSS.

GABB, John Harry, Surg. Capt. RN Fleet Medical Division, South Terrace, HM Naval Base, Portsmouth PO1 3LS — MB BS 1976 Lond. Dep. Director Med. Operat.s.

GABB, Patricia (retired) 31 Langholm Crescent, Darlington DL3 7ST — MB ChB 1945 Leeds; BA Open 1988. Prev: SCM (Child Health) Durh. AHA.

GABB, Richard John Escott 5 Lovell Close, South Wonston, Winchester SO21 3EN Tel: 01962 880404 Email: aay95@dial.pipex.com — MRCS Eng. LRCP Lond. 1973; MB BS Lond. 1973, MSc (Occupat. Med.) 1991. (St. Bart.) SCMO (Communicable Dis. Control) Winchester HA. Socs: BMA. Prev: Trainee GP Wessex VTS; SHO (O & G) St. Mary's Hosp. Portsmouth; SHO (Microbiol.) Soton. Gen. Hosp.

GABBAY, Felicity Jane PPD Gabbay, Ambassador House, 8 Carlton Crescent, Southampton SO15 2EY Tel: 02380 230511 Fax: 02380 230513; 10 Park Lane, Milford on Sea, Lymington SO41 0PT — MB ChB 1976 Manch.; BSc Manch. 1976; FRCP Lond. 1995; FFPM RCP (UK) 1989; Dip. Pharm. Med. RCP (UK) 1982. Managing Dir. PPD Gabbay; Fell. Acad. Regist. Fac. Pharmaceut. Med. RCP (UK). Socs: Soc. Pharmaceut. Med. Prev: Regional Dir. Clin. Research N.. Europe Warner Lambert Soton.

GABBAY, Professor John Wessex Institute for Health Research and Development, University of Southampton, Mailpoint 728, Biomedical Sciences Building, Southampton SO16 7PX Tel: 02380 595649 Fax: 02380 596539 Email: jg3@soton.ac.uk; 10 Park Lane, Milford on Sea, Lymington SO41 0PT Tel: 01590 645542 Fax: 01590 642742 — MB ChB 1974 Manch.; MSc (Community Med.) Lond. 1984; BSc Manch. 1971; FFPHM RCP (UK) 1994, M 1991; MFCM 1989. Prof. Pub. Health Univ. Soton.; Exec. Dir. Nat. Coordinating Centre for Health Technol. Assessm.; Dir. Wessex Inst.Health R & D Univ. of Soton. Prev: Sen. Lect. (Pub. Health.) St. Mary's Hosp. Med. Sch. Lond.; Research Assoc. Templeton Coll. (NHS Train. Auth. Research) Oxf.; Assoc. Lect. Wellcome Unit Hist. of Med. Univ. Camb.

GABBE, David Michael Brooklyn, Barrack Lane, Ravensmoor, Nantwich CW5 — MB BCh BAO 1960 Dub.; FFA RCS Eng. 1969. (T.C. Dub.) Sen. Anaesth. Regist. Liverp. RHB. Socs: Liverp. Soc. Anaesths. & BMA. Prev: SHO BRd.green Hosp. Liverp.; Regist. Clatterbridge Hosp.; Regist. Whiston Hosp. Prescot.

GABBITAS, David Graham Gabbitas, Cronehills Health Centre, Cronehills Linkway, West Bromwich B70 8TJ Tel: 0121 500 6455 Fax: 0121 580 1813; 39 Albert Road, Harborne, Birmingham B17 0AP — MB ChB 1971 Birm.

GABBITAS, Stuart Michael 15 Ferrands Park Way, Harden, Bingley BD16 1HZ Tel: 01535 273928 — MRCS Eng. LRCP Lond. 1973; MRCGP 1977; DObst RCOG 1976. Trainer GP W. Yorks.

GABBOTT, David Anthony Dept of Anaesthetics, Gloucestershire Royal NHS Trust, Great Western Road, Gloucester GL1 3NN Tel: 01452 394194/4810 — BM BCh 1987 Oxf.; MA Oxf. 1991, BA (Physiol. Sci.) 1984; FRCA 1992. Cons. Anaesth. Gloucester Roy. Infirm. Socs: Resusc. Counc. Prev: Sen. Regist. Rotat. S. & W. Region; Regist. Rotat. (Anaesth.) S. & W. Region; Attend. Anaesthesiol. & Vis. Asst. Prof. Shock Trauma Centre Maryland, USA.

GABBOTT, Mary Catherine BUPA Hospital, Fordcombe, Tunbridge Wells TN3 0RD Tel: 01892 740042 Fax: 01892 740046; Tithe Barn, Clay Hill Road, Hook Green, Lamberhurst, Tunbridge Wells TN3 8LS Tel: 01892 890154 Fax: 01892 890155 Email: 104716.3245@compuserve.com — MB ChB 1973 Manch.; MRCGP 1977; Joint Comm. Postgrad. Train. (Gen. Pract.) 1982; Cert. JCC Lond. 1978; DObst RCOG 1975. Assoc. Specialist (Psychosexual Med.) Kent & Sussex Weald NHS Trust. Socs: Inst. Psychosexual Med. Prev: Regist. (Psychiat.) Middlewood Hosp. Sheff.

GABE, Clare Irena 37 Sandringham Avenue, Wimbledon Chase, London SW20 8JY Tel: 020 8540 4211 — MB BS 1988 Lond.; BSc (Hons.) Anat. Lond. 1985; MRCGP 1997; DRCOG 1992. (Char. Cross & Westm.) Asst. GP Lond. Prev: Trainee GP/SHO Rotat. Ealing Gen. Hosp. VTS.; SHO (Cas.) Watford Gen. Hosp.; Ho. Surg. (Orthop.) W.m. Hosp.

GABE, Ivor Thomas Lancewood, Carron Lane, Midhurst GU29 9LE Tel: 01730 813933 Fax: 01730 813933 Email: ivor.gabe@dial.pipex.com — BS Lond. 1950; MD Lond. 1953; FRCP Lond. 1972, M 1952; MRCS Eng. LRCP Lond. 1950. (King's Coll. Lond. & St. Geo.) Emerit. Cons. Phys. & Late Med. Dir. King Edwd. VII Hosp., Midhurst; Hon. Cons. (Cardiol.) Roy. Brompton Hosp.; Hon. Sen. Lect. (Med.) Char. Cross & W.m. Hosp. Med. Sch. Socs: Med. Research Soc. & Brit. Cardiac. Soc. Prev: Mem. Scientif. Staff MRC & Lect. (Med.) Roy. Postgrad. Med. Sch. Lond.; Research Fell. (Cardiol. Br.) Nat. Inst. Health Bethesda, Maryland USA.

GABE, Simon Mark St Marks Hospital, Northwick Park,, Watford Road,, Harrow HA1 3UJ Tel: 0208235 4177 Fax: 0208235 4001 Email: s.gabe@ic.ac.uk — MB BS 1988 Lond.; MSc (Clin. Nutrit.) Distinc. Univ. Surrey 1997; BSc (Hons.) Physiol. Lond. 1985; MRCP (UK) 1991; MD 2000. (Char. Cross & Westm. Hosp. Med. Sch. Lond.) Sen. Lect. In Intestinal Failure & Nutrit., Hon. Cons. Gastroenterologist. Imperial Coll. Sch. of Med., St Marks Hosp., Lond.. Socs: Nutrit. Soc.; Brit. Soc. of Gastroenterol.; Internat. mem. Amer. Gastroenterol. Assn. Prev: Specialist Regist. (Gastroenterol.) Hammersmith Hosp. Lond.; Research Regist. Centr. Middlx. Hosp.

Lond. & Hon. Regist. Liver Unit King's Coll. Hosp. Lond.; Regist. Liver Unit King's Coll. Hosp. Lond.

GABIE, Israel 334 Watling Street Road, Ribbleton, Preston PR2 6UA — MB BCh 1952 Witwatersrand. Prev: Ho. Off. Baragwanath Non-Europ. Hosp. Johannesburg, Lambeth Hosp.; Lond. & Roy. Albert Edwd. Infirm. Wigan.

GABLE, David Raymond 3 St Martins Close, Canterbury CT1 1QG — MB BS 1996 Lond.

GABR, Saad Mohamed North Glamorgan NHS Trust, Prince Charles Hospital, Merthyr Tydfil CF47 9DT — MB ChB 1978 Med-Delta U, Tanta; LRCP Ed. LRCPS Glas. 1994.

GABRA, Gamal Saber Regional Blood Transfusion Centre - National Blood Service, Vincent Drive, Edgbaston, Birmingham B15 2SG — MB BCh 1961 Cairo; FRCPath 1990, M 1978. Cons. Haemat. Regional Blood Transfus. Centre Birm.; Hon. Sen. Clin. Lect. Birm. Univ.; Head of WHO Collaborating Centre for Train. and Developm. in Transfus. Med. Socs: Internat. Soc. Blood Transfus.; Founder Mem. Brit. Blood Transfus. Soc. Prev: Cons. Haemat. & Sen. Regist. Glas. & W. Scotl. Blood Transfus. Centre Carluke.

GABRA, Hani ICRF Medical Oncology Unit, MRC Building, Western General Hospital, Crewe Road, Edinburgh EH4 2XU Tel: 0131 332 2471 Fax: 0131 332 4889 — MB ChB 1987 Glas.; MSc (Clin. Oncol.) Edinburgh 1993; BSc (Hons.) Glas 1984; MRCP (UK) 1990; PhD Ed. 1996. (Glasgow) ICRF Clin. Scientist & Hon. Cons. (Med. Oncol.) W.ern Gen. Hosp. Edin.; Hon. Sen. Lect. (Med. Oncol.) Univ. of Edin. Socs: Assn. Cancer Phys.; Eur. Soc. Med. Oncol. Prev: Sen. Regist. (Med. Oncol.) ICRF Med. Oncol. Unit W. Gen. Hosp.; Clin. Research Fell. ICRF Med. Oncol. Unit. W.. Gen. Hosp. Edin.; Regist. (Med. Oncol.) W.. Gen. Hosp. Edin.

GABRI, Refaat Abdel Moneem Ibrahem Royal Hospital for Sick Children, Yorkhill, Glasgow G3 — MB BCh 1984 Cairo; MRCP (UK) 1994.

GABRIEL, Carolyn Marie Department of Neurology, Guy's Hospital, London Bridge, London SE1 9RT; 52 Carlton Mansions, Randolph Avenue, London W9 1NR — MB BS 1990 Lond.; MB BS (Hons.) Med. 1990; BSc Biochem Lond. 1987; MRCP (UK) 1993. (St. Bart. Hosp. Med. Coll.) Research Assoc. (Neurol.) Guy's Hosp. Lond.

GABRIEL, David Wilson (retired) The Manor, Ludham, Great Yarmouth NR29 5AB — MB BS Lond. 1955. Prev: GP Gt. Yarmouth.

GABRIEL, Diana (retired) The Manor, Ludham, Great Yarmouth NR29 5AB Tel: 01692 678378 — MB BChir Camb. 1954; DA Eng. 1957. Prev: Ho. Surg. & Ho. Phys. S.end Gen. Hosp.

GABRIEL, Gabriel Marlborough Department, The Royal Free Hospital, Pond Street, London NW3 2QP Tel: 020 7830 2404 (Secretary) Email: gabriel.gabriel@rhf.nthames.nhs.org.uk; 32 Lauriston Road, London SW19 4TQ Tel: 020 8946 9074 Email: gabriel.gabrield@blueyonder.co.uk — MB BS 1974 Lond.; FRCP 1997, M 1979. (St. Thos.) Cons. (Genitourin. Med.) Roy. Free Hosp. Lond. & HM Prison Holloway. Socs: Med. Soc. Study of VD; Assn. Genitourin. Med. Prev: Sen. Regist. (Genital Med.) St. Bart. Hosp. Lond.; Regist. (Gen. & Genitourin. Med.) St. Thos. Hosp. Lond.

GABRIEL, John Roger Thomas Gulf Veterans' Medical Assessment Programme, Gassiot House, St Thomas' Hospital, London SE1 7EH Tel: 020 7202 8320 Fax: 020 7202 8327; Tel: 01483 505658 — MB BS Lond. 1962; BA (Hist. & Politics) Open 1978; MSc (Biochem.) Soton. 1970; FRCP Lond. 1979, M 1966; MRCS Eng. LRCP Lond. 1962; DTM & H Lond. 1993; DCH Eng. 1967. (Char. Cross) Cons. Phys., MOD, Gulf Veteran's Med. Assessm. Progr.St Thomas' Hosp. Lond. SE1 7E. Socs: Renal Assn.; BMA. Prev: Renal Phys. St. Mary's Hosp. Lond. & N.wick Pk. Hosp. Middlx.; Sen. Regist. (Nephrol.) Med. Unit W.m. Hosp. Lond.; Regist. (Med.) Hammersmith Hosp.

GABRIEL, Mrs Phyllis (retired) Somerville House, Somerville Road, Willand, Cullompton EX15 2PP Tel: 01884 820241 — MB BS Lond. 1940. Prev: Ho. Phys. Manch. Roy. Infirm. & W. Suff. Gen. Hosp. Bury St. Edmunds.

GABRIEL, Richard William (retired) 11 Park Hill, Toddington, Dunstable LU5 6AW Tel: 01525 872146 — MRCS Eng. LRCP Lond. 1959; MB BChir Camb. 1960; MA Camb. 1962; FFA RCS Eng. 1964; DA Eng. 1961. Prev: Sen. Regist. & Regist. St. Bart. Hosp. Lond.

GABRIEL, Rupert James Spa Medical Centre, Snowberry Lane, Melksham SN12 6UN Tel: 01225 703236 — MB BS 1983 Lond.; FPCert; DGM RCP Lond. 1990; DCH RCP Lond. 1987; DRCOG 1987.

GABRIEL, Mr Sabry Selim 10 Harley Street, London W1N 1AA Tel: 020 7467 8300 Fax: 020 8989 6658; 17B Woodford Road, Snaresbrook, London E18 2EL Tel: 020 8989 5055 — MB BCh Cairo 1960; FRCS Ed. 1965; FRCS Glas. 1965; MRCS Eng. LRCP Lond. 1977. Indep. Gen. Surg. Lond. Prev: Assoc. Specialist (Accid. Surg.) Whipps Cross Hosp. Lond.; Sen. Cons. Surg. NE State, Nigeria.

GABRIEL, Sara Louise 371 Banbury Road, Oxford OX2 7RE Tel: 01865 59501 — MB BS 1992 Lond. SHO (Intens. Care) N.ampton Gen. Hosp. Prev: SHO (Anaesth.) Manch. Roy. Infirm.

GABRIEL, Stephen Grant Julian Dudley Park Medical Centre, 28 Dudley Park Road, Acocks Green, Birmingham B27 6QR Tel: 0121 706 0072 Fax: 0121 707 0418 — MB ChB 1981 Dundee; BSc St. And. 1978; MRCGP 1986; DCCH RCP Ed. 1988; DRCOG 1985. GP Acocks Green.

GABRIELCZYK, Marek Ryszard Department of Anaesthesia, Southend District Hospital, Prittlewell Chase, Westcliff on Sea SS0 0RY — MB BS 1978 Lond.; FFA RCS Eng. 1983. (St. Bart.) Cons. Anaesth. S.end DHA. Socs: BMA & Assn. Anaesth. Gt. Brit. & Irel. Prev: Sen. Regist. (Anaesth.) St. Geo. Hosp. Lond.; Sen. Regist. (Anaesth.) Nat. Heart Hosp. Lond.; Regist. (Anaesth.) Edgware Gen. & Colindale Thoracic Hosps. Lond.

GADALLAH, Mr Ekram Friege 29 Cumberland Avenue, Blackpool FY1 5QL Tel: 01253 791449 — MB ChB 1981 Assuit; LRCP LRCS Ed. LRCPS Glas. 1993; FRCS Eng. 1994; DRCOG 1996; DCH RCP Lond. 1996; DFFP 1997; MRCGP 1998; FRCS AIE (Ed) 1999. GP & Med. Off. of Special Scale (MOSS) AIE, New Zealand. Prev: GP Regist.,Blackpool Vict. Hosp. VTS; Surgic. Regist., NZ.

GADD, Christine Mary Mitchell Road Surgery, 9 Mitchell Road, Canferd Heath, Poole BH17 8UE Tel: 01202 672474 Fax: 01202 660926 — MB BS 1977 Lond. GP Poole.

GADD, Elaine Margaret Skipton House, 80 London Road, London SE1 6LH Tel: 020 7972 1517 Fax: 020 7972 5147 Email: elaine.gadd@doh.gsi.gov.uk — MB ChB 1983 Birm.; MA 1999 (King's Coll. Lond.); MRCPsych 1987. (University of Birmingham) Prin. Med. Off. DoH. Prev: Sen. Research Fell. & Hon. Cons. Psychiat. Univ. Birm.

GADD, John Robert Schlumberger SEMA Medical Services, Albert Bridge House, Bridge Street, Manchester M60 9DA Tel: 0161 831 2089 Fax: 0161 831 2108 — MB BS 1979 Lond.; 2001 DDAM, Fac. Of Occupational. Med. RCP.; DRCOG 1982. (Lond. Hosp.) Med. Adviser, Schlumberger Sema Med. Serv.s.; Clin. Asst. (Ophth.) Manch. Roy. Eye Hosp. Socs: Mem. Of Soc. Of Occupat.al Med.; Mem. Of Assur. Med. Soc. Prev: Princip. GP Romiley, Stockport; SHO (Ophth.) P.ss Margt. Hosp. Swindon; Ho. Phys. Lond. Hosp.

GADD, Martin Christopher Longmead, Summerhill, Polegate BN26 6QY — MB BS 1983 Lond.

GADD, Mr Robert Lisle (retired) The Heys, 63 Roundcroft, Romiley, Stockport SK6 4HZ Tel: 0161 427 2031 — MB ChB 1945 Manch.; MD Manch. 1964; FRCS Ed. 1958; FRCOG 1965, M 1952. Prev: Cons. O & G St. Mary's Hosp. Manch.

GADD, Rosemary Lisle The Oaks Surgery, Applegarth Avenue, Park Barn, Guildford GU2 8LZ Tel: 01483 563424 Fax: 01483 563789 — BA Oxf. 1979, BM BCh 1982; DCH RCP Lond. 1986; DRCOG 1984; Cert. Family Plann. JCC 1984. Prev: Trainee GP Sandhurst VTS; SHO (O & G & Paediat.) Roy. Berks. Hosp. Reading; SHO (Psychiat.) St. Johns Hosp. Stone.

GADD, Veronica Mary (retired) The Heys, 63 Roundcroft, Romiley, Stockport SK6 4HZ Tel: 0161 427 2031 — MB ChB 1950 St. And. Prev: Clin. Med. Off. Tameside & Glossop HA.

GADDIE, John Tel: 01896 826000 Fax: 01896 823476; Bothendene, Bowden, Melrose TD6 0SS Tel: 01835 823590 Fax: 01896 823476 — MB ChB 1968 Aberd.; MD (Hons.) Aberd. 1975; FRCP Ed. 1985; MRCP (UK) 1977. (Aberd.) Med. Dir. Borders Gen. Hosp. NHS Trust. Socs: Med. Mem. Unit Managem. Team; Brit. Thorac. Soc. & Scott. Soc. Phys. Prev: Sen. Regist. (Respirat. Med.) Grampian HB; Ho. Phys. Profess. Med. Unit & Ho. Surg. Profess. Surgic. Unit Roy. Infirm. Aberd.

GADDIS, Stephen 25 Galloway Avenue, Hamilton ML3 7UR — MB ChB 1985 Glas.

GADELRAB, Raafat Rifaat St Mary's Hospital, Praed Street, London W2 1NY Tel: 0207 886 6709 Fax: 0207 886 1847; 7 Warwick Drive, Putney, London SW15 6LB Tel: 020 8789 5320 Email: raafatgadelrab@hotmail.com — MB BCh Cairo 1969; DLO Lond 1979. ENT Surg.

GADEL RAB, Mr Ragai Refaat Newham General Hospital, Glen Road, Plaistow, London E13 8SL Tel: 020 7363 8109 Fax: 020 7363 8064 — MB BCh 1974 Ain Shams; FRCS Glas. 1989. Cons. Orthop. Surg. Newham Gen. Hosp. Lond. Socs: Fell.Brit. Orthopaedic Assoc.; Fell.BASK; Fell.LRS. Prev: Cons. Orthop. Surg. Qu. Eliz. Milit. Hosp. Lond.; Regist. (Orthop.) S.end Gen. Hosp. Essex.

GADELRAB, Rita Refaat Royal National Orthopaedic Hospital, Brockley Hill, Stanmore HA7 4LP Tel: 020 8954 2300; 7a Leinster Mansions, 1 Langland Gardens, Hampstead, London NW3 6QB — MB BCh 1982 Cairo; FFARCSI 1990. Cons. Anaesth.

GADHIA, Dhirajlal Jagjivandas 42 Brambling Way, Oadby, Leicester LE2 5PA — MB BS 1963 Karnatak; DTM & H Liverp. 1964. (Kasturba Med. Coll. India)

GADHIA, Nina 37 Eddington Lane, Herne Bay CT6 5TT — MB ChB 1998 Manch.; MB ChB Manch 1998.

GADHVI, Bharatkumar 37 East Quay, Wapping Dock, Liverpool L3 4BU — MB BS 1994 Lond.

GADHVI, Deepa Flat 37, East Quay, Wapping Quay, Liverpool L3 4BU — MB BS 1995 Lond.

GADHVI, Harish Mulraj Whipps Cross Hospital, Whipps Cross Road, Leytonstone, London E11 1NR Tel: 020 8531 1851; Naseberry Court, 2 Merriam Close, London E4 9JQ Tel: 020 8535 6877 Fax: 020 8925 5761 — MB BS Gujarat 1969; MRCPsych 1979; DPM Eng. 1977; FRCPsych 1996. (Gujarat Univ.) Cons. Psychiat. Forest Health Care Trust Whipps Cross Hosp. & Thorpe Coombe Hosp. Lond.; Med. Mem. Ment. Health Review Tribunals. Socs: Fell. Roy. Soc. Med. Prev: Sen. Regist. Oxf. RHA; Regist. Mapperley Hosp. Nottm.

GADHVI, Mulu Raja Fountayne Road Health Centre, 1A Fountayne Road, London N16 7EA Tel: 020 8806 3311 Fax: 020 8806 9197 — MB BS 1970 Poona. (B.J. Med. Coll.) Prev: Res. Med. Off. Nairobi Hosp., Kenya.

GADHVI, Neela Mulubhai Fountayne Road Health Centre, 1A Fountayne Road, London N16 7EA Tel: 020 8806 3311 Fax: 020 8806 9197 — MB BS 1971 Poona. (B.J. Med. Coll.) Prev: Med. Off. Nairobi Hosp., Kenya.

GADIYAR, Vinod Department of Anaesthetics, Fairfield General Hospital, Bury BL9 7TD Tel: 0161 705 3645; 4 Greenwich Close, Bamford, Rochdale OL11 5JN Tel: 01706 646126 Email: vinodgadiyan@hotmail.com — MB BS 1987 Gulbarga; FFA RCSI 1995. (Govt. Med. Coll. Bellary, India) Cons. Anaesth. Bury NHS Health Care Trust Bury. Socs: Assn. Anaesths.; BMA; Scott. Soc. Anaesth. Prev: Cons. Anaesth. Caithness Gen. Hosp. Wick; Staff Grade (Anaesth.) P. Philip Hosp. LLa.lli; Regist. (Anaesth.) Neath Gen. Hosp., P. Philip Hosp. LLa.lli & Roy. Vict. Hosp. Belf.

GADSBY, Ian Christopher Cinderford Health Centre, Dockham Road, Cinderford GL14 2AN Tel: 01594 598020; Blakemore Hale, Popes Hill, Newnham GL14 8LE Tel: 01452 760509 — BM BCh 1972 Oxf.; BM BCh Oxf.. 1972; MRCGP 1980.

GADSBY, James Burnet (Surgery), 36 Colne Road, Burnley BB10 1LQ Tel: 01282 26029; 7 Queens Park Road, Burnley BB10 3LB — MB ChB 1944 Aberd. (Aberd.) Prev: Mem. Med. Bds. Min. of Pens. & Nat. Insur.; Cas. & Orthop. Regist. Nottm. Gen. Hosp.; Dep. Res. Surg. Off. & Orthop. Ho. Surg. Hosp. of St. Cross, Rugby.

GADSBY, Roger Red Roofs, 31 Coton Road, Nuneaton CV11 5TW Tel: 02476 357100 Fax: 02476 642036; Rivendell, School Lane, Exhall, Coventry CV7 9GF Tel: 01203 362126 — MB ChB 1971 Birm.; BSc (Hons.) (Med. Biochem.) Birm. 1971; FRCGP 1992, M 1979; DRCOG 1978; DCH Eng. 1978. (Birm.) Hon. Sen. Lect. (Primary Care) Univ. Warwick. Socs: Previous Chairm. Midl. Fac. RCGP; Chairm.ship GNOGO May 99. Prev: SHO (Med., Paediat. & O & G) City Gen. Hosp. Stoke-on-Trent.

GADSDEN, Paul Michael 27 Woburn Av, Tuffley, Gloucester GL4 0SN — MB ChB 1997 Sheff.

GAER, Mr Jullien Anthony Roger 95 Brook Green, London W6 7BD — MB BS 1983 Lond.; FRCS Ed. 1988. Regist. (Cardiothoracic Surg.) Hammersmith Hosp. Lond. Prev: Regist. (Gen. Surg.) W.. Gen. Hosp. Edin.; Regist. (Cardiothoracic Surg.) Harefield Hosp. Middlx.; SHO (Cardiothoracic Surg.) Brompton Hosp. Lond.

GAETE, Helen Patricia The Princess Royal Hospital, Colwell Road, Villa Unit, Haywards Heath RH16 4EX Tel: 01444 441881; Helianthus Farm, Spathan Lane, Ditchling, Hassocks BN6 8XH — MRCS Eng. LRCP Lond. 1977. Assoc. Specialist (Psychiat.) P.ss Roy. Hosp. Haywards Heath. Socs: BMA & ISPNE. Prev: Staff Grade (Psychiat.) P.ss Roy. Hosp. Haywards Heath; Regist. (Psychiat.) St. Francis Hosp. Haywards Heath; Clin. Asst. (Psychiat.) P.ss Roy. Hosp. Haywards Heath.

GAFAR, Amin Hamza The Lister Hospital, IVF Unit, Chelsea Bridge Road, London SW1W 8RH Tel: 020 7730 3417 Ext: 261; 45 Arundel Avenue, Morden SM4 4DR Tel: 020 8542 3914 Email: amin.gafar@talk21.com — Medic 1982 Bucharest; MRCOG 1991. (Bucharest) Fertil. Specialist IVF Unit Lister Hosp. Socs: Europ. Soc. of Obs./Gyn.; ESHRE.

GAFFAN, Judith 19 Richmond Road, Oxford OX1 2JL — BM BS 1997 Nottm.

GAFFEY, Mr Andrew 165 Lothair Road, Leicester LE2 7QE Tel: 0116 291 9433 Email: a.gaffey@virgin.net — MB ChB 1993 Leic.; FRCSI 1997.

GAFFIKIN, Peter George Montgomery (retired) 16 Bentley Close, Kings Worthy, Winchester SO23 7LG Tel: 01962 885301 — BM BCh Oxf. 1951; MA Oxf. 1957. Prev: Indust. Med. Adviser Conder Gp. Companies, Bendicks (Mayfair) Ltd., Millflex Gp. Culverlands Press.

GAFFIKIN, Philippa Elizabeth (retired) 14 Tyne Road, Oakham LE15 6SJ — MB ChB 1941 St. And.

GAFFNEY, Brian Patrick 42 English Street, Downpatrick BT30 6AB Tel: 028 4461 2861 Email: brianpgaffney@hotmail.com — MB BCh BAO 1984 NUI; BSc Belf. 1978; MSc Ed. 1990; MRCGP 1988; MFPHM RCP (UK) 1993; MD 2000 Queen's Univ. Belfast. (University College, Dublin) Chief Exec. Health Promotion Agency for N. Irel. Belf.

GAFFNEY, Christopher Charles Velindre Hospital, Whitchurch, Cardiff CF14 2TL Tel: 029 2061 5888 Fax: 029 2031 6267 Email: chris.gaffney@velindre-tr.wales.nhs.uk — MB ChB 1976 Bristol; FRCR 1984. (University of Bristol) Cons. Clin. Oncol. Velindre Hosp. Cardiff. Prev: Sen. Regist. (Radiother. & Oncol.) Newc. Gen. Hosp.

GAFFNEY, David Apsley Street Surgery, 14 Apsley Street, Glasgow G11 7SY Tel: 0141 339 2960; 33 Riverside Road, Newlands, Glasgow G43 2EG — MB ChB 1976 Glas.; BSc (1st cl. Hons.) (Biochem.) Glas. 1972, MB ChB 1976; FRCP Glas. 1992; MRCP (UK) 1980; MRCGP 1983; Dip. Forens. Med. Glas 1992. (Glasgow) GP Glas.; Asst. Police Surg. Glas. (B Div.); Sen. Tutor (Gen. Pract.) Univ. Glas.

GAFFNEY, John Edward 7/107 Ramsgate Avenue, Bondi NSW 2026, Australia; 4 Wellington Road, Bury BL9 9BG — MB ChB 1983 Manch.; BSc (Med. Sci.) St. And. 1981; DRCOG 1986; DCH RCP Lond. 1985. Trainee GP W. Timperley Health Centre. Prev: SHO (Paediat.) Duchess of York Hosp. for Babies Manch.; SHO (Obst. & Gyn.) Univ. Hosp. S. Manch.; Ho. Off. (Surg. & Med.) Withington Hosp. Manch.

GAFFNEY, John Karl Department of Rheumatology, Norfolk & Norwich Hospital, Brunswick Road, Norwich NR1 3SR; 122 Newmarket Road, Norwich NR4 6SA Tel: 01603 503487 Fax: 01603 287004 Email: karl@norrheum.demon.co.uk — MB BCh BAO 1988 NUI; MRCPI 1990. (Univ. Coll. Dubl.) Cons. Rheumat. Norf. & Norwich Hosp. Brunswick Rd. Norwich; Hon. Sen. Lect. Univ. E. Anglia; BUPA Hosp. Norwich Old Watton Rd. Colney Norwich. Socs: BMA; Brit. Soc. Rheum.; Amer. Coll. Rheum.

GAFFNEY, Mark St John Green Street Clinic, 118-122 Green Street, Eastbourne BN21 1RT Tel: 01323 722908 Fax: 01323 723136 — MB BS 1983 Lond.; DCM 1999 Beijing Univ. Of Chinese Med. & Acupunc. (Guys.) Gen. Practitioner, Green St. Clinic, E.bourne; Med. Off., The Chaseley Trust, E.bourne (52 bed spinal injuries unit); Med. Off., Kestrel Ho., E.bourne (50 bed terminal care unit); Director E.bourne Med. Acupunc. Centre; E. Sussex LMC Mem. Socs: Fell. Chinese Med. Inst. and Register, Lond.; Brit. Med. Acpuncture Soc. Prev: Med. Advisor for E. Sussex FHSA for Health Promotion & Minor Surg.

GAFFNEY, Michael John Patrick 7 Novara Park, Antrim BT41 1PA — MB BCh BAO 1962 NUI; DPM Eng. 1978; MA QUB 1996. (Univ. Coll. Cork) Assoc. Specialist Holywell Hosp. Antrim.

Socs: BMA. Prev: Rotat. Psychiat. Regist. Notts. AHA (T); Disp. Med. Off. Labasheeda Disp. Dist.; Med. Regist. St. Jas. Hosp. Dub.

GAFFNEY, Michael Patrick Mill Street Medical Centre, Mill Street, St Helens WA10 2BD Tel: 01744 23641 Fax: 01744 28398; 79 Heyes Avenue, Rainford, St Helens WA11 8AP Tel: 01744 882958 Fax: 01744 28398 — MB ChB 1974 Liverp.; MRCGP 1979; DFFP 1996; DRCOG 1977. Socs: St. Helens Med. Soc. Prev: Trainee GP Whiston Hosp. Liverp. VTS.

GAFFNEY, Paul Gerard Portland Road Surgery, 34 Portland Road, Kilmarnock KA1 2DL Tel: 01563 522411 Fax: 01563 573556; 34 Portland Road, Kilmarnock KA1 2DL Tel: 22411 — MB ChB 1981 Ed.; BSc (Med. Sci.) Ed. 1978, MB ChB 1981; MRCGP 1985; DRCOG 1983. (Edinburgh) Clin. Asst. (Diabetes). Prev: Regist. (Med.) CrossHo. Hosp. Kilmarnock & Ballochmyle Hosp.; Mauchline; SHO (Obst.) Ayrsh. Centr. Hosp. Irvine.

GAFFNEY, Siobhan Sarah Mary 23 Ashley Avenue, Armagh BT60 1HE — MB BCh BAO 1993 NUI.

GAGE, Andrew John 140 Parkville Road, Manchester M20 4TY — MB BS 1998 Lond.; MB BS Lond 1998.

GAGE, Paul Richard The Green Surgery, The Green, Church Lane, Brailsford, Ashbourne DE6 3BX Tel: 01335 360328 Fax: 01335 361095 — MB ChB 1969 Manch.; DA Eng. 1972. Clin. Asst. (Anaesth.) S.. Derbysh. HA. Prev: Regist. (Anaesth.) Salford Hosps. Gp.; Ho. Surg. & Ho. Phys. Hope Hosp. Salford.

GAGE, Rebecca Juliette Brodie Middle Court, Church St., Beckington, Bath BA3 6HD — MB BS 1996 Lond.

GAGE, Susan 11 The Oaks, Wangfield Lane, Curdridge, Southampton SO32 2DA Tel: 01489 783563 — MB ChB 1967 Bristol; DCH Eng. 1970. (Bristol) SCMO Soton. & S.W. Hants. HA. Socs: BMA. Prev: Asst. Res. Med. Off. Roy. Hosp. Sick Childr. Bristol; Ho. Surg. W.on-super-Mare Gen. Hosp.

GAGUINE, David Shemtob Horton Park Surgery, 99 Horton Park Avenue, Bradford BD7 3SG Tel: 01274 504956 Ext: 7 Fax: 01274 504951 Email: dgaguine2@bradford-ha.nhs.uk; 4 Bantree Court, Thackley, Bradford BD10 0SG Tel: 01274 610045 Email: david@gaguine.freeserve.co.uk — MB ChB 1978 Leeds.

GAHAN, Anthony Dermot 157 Crescent Road, Crumpsall, Manchester M8 5UE — MB BS 1994 Lond.; BSc (Med. Sci.) Hons. St. And. 1991. (St. And. & St. Bart. Lond.) SHO (Psychiat.) Homerton Hosp. Lond.

GAHIR, Manjit Singh Nottingham Forensic Service, The Wells Road Centre, The Wells Road, Nottingham NG3 3AA Tel: 0115 969 1300 Fax: 0115 952 9420 Email: mgahir@nadt.org.uk — MB ChB 1988 Birm.; MSc (Criminology) 1998 Loughborough University; MRCPsych 1994. (Birm.) Cons. (Forens. Psychiat.) Nottm. Forens. Serv.; Clin. Teach. Univ. of Nottm. 1998. Socs: Brit. Soc. of Criminology; Nat. Assn. Treatm. of Sex Offenders. Prev: Sen. Regist. (Forens. Psychiat.) Reaside Clinic; Regist. (Psychiat.) Birm.

GAIER, Sylvia 16 Beauclair Drive, Liverpool L15 6XG Tel: 0151 722 3949 & profess. 051 220 9191 — MB BCh BAO 1950 Dub.; BA, MB BCh BAO Dub. 1950; MRCGP 1968; DCH Eng. 1954. (T.C. Dub.) Socs: (Ex-Chairm.) Liverp. Jewish Med. Soc. Prev: Paediat. Regist. Alder Hey Childr. Hosp. Liverp.; Neo-Natal Regist. St. Mary's Hosp. Manch.; Sen. Ho. Off. (Paediat.) Maelor Gen. Hosp. Wrexham.

GAIK CHENG OOI, Dr Dudley Road Hospital, Birmingham Tel: 0121 554 3801; 70 Blount Road, Off Colby Drive, Thurmaston, Leicester LE4 8LJ Tel: 0116 269 2257 — MB BCh BAO 1985 Belf.; MRCP (UK) 1987; FRCR 1994. Sen. Regist. Rotat. (Radiol.) W. Midl. Socs: Roy. Coll. Radiol. Prev: Regist. (Med.) Leicester Roy. Infirm.

GAIKWAD, Girrao Annarao The Cherries, 19 Doonholm Road, Alloway, Ayr KA7 4QQ — MB BS 1971 Marathwada.

GAILEY, David Andrew Hamilton Adelaide Medical Centre, Andover SP10 1HA Tel: 01264 351144 — MB BCh BAO 1963 Dub.; BA Dub. 1963; DObst RCOG 1968. (TC Dub.) Chairm. Med. Staff Andover War Memor. Hosp. Socs: BMA. Prev: Ho. Phys. & Ho. Surg. Adelaide Hosp. Dub.; Capt. RAMC.

GAILEY, Michael David Hewson Jenisa, Livery Road, Winterslow, Salisbury SP5 1RF — MB BS 1996 Lond.

GAILI, Hassan El-Mubarak El Neonatal Unit, Leicester General Hospital, Gwendolen Road, Leicester LE5 4PW Tel: 0116 249 0490; 6 Fox Hollow, Oadby, Leicester LE2 4QY Tel: 0116 271 3132 Email: hassan.gaili@virgin.net — MB BS 1980 Khartoum, Sudan; MB BS Khartoum, Sudan; MRCP (UK) 1992; MRCPCH 1997. Staff Grade (Neonates) Leicester Gen. Hosp. Socs: ARICD; Soc. Sudanese Doctors; Arab Doctors. Prev: Career Regist. Leicester Roy. Infirm.

GAILLARD, Brigitte 23 Cowdrey Road, London SW19 8TU — State Exam Med 1989 Aachen.

GAILLEMIN, Oliver Simon Georges Raymond Butlers Gate, Kidbrooke Park, Forest Row RH18 5JA — MB ChB 1997 Manch.

GAIN, Richard Thomas Garner 26 Woolley Avenue, Poynton, Stockport SK12 1XU Tel: 01625 267352 Email: richard.gain@mcmail.com; Semantic Technologies Limited, Enterprise House, Manchester Science Park, Manchester M15 6SE Tel: 0161 226 3859 — MB BS 1982 Lond.; DRCOG 1986. (Guy's) Clin. Developm. Manager. Prev: GP Beckenham; Trainee GP Basingstoke Hosp. VTS.

GAIN, Robin Graham Garner (retired) Minstead, Red Lion Lane, Sarratt, Rickmansworth WD3 6BW Tel: 01923 268762 Fax: 01923 268762 Email: robin@gain.screaming.net — MB BS Lond. 1957; MRCS Eng. LRCP Lond. 1957; FRCGP 1983, M 1975; DObst RCOG 1963. Prev: GP.

GAIND, Raghunandan Keats House, Guy's Hospital, London SE1 9RT Tel: 020 7955 4290 Fax: 01622 851375 Email: raghugaind@lindia.com; The Old School House, Otterden ME13 0BX Tel: 01622 859889 — MB BS 1954 Punjab; FRCP Ed. 1974, M 1959; FRCP Glas. 1973; FRFPS Glas. 1957; FRCPsych 1977, M 1971; DPM Lond. 1965. (Amritsar Med. Coll.) Cons. Neuropsychiat. Suttons Manor Clinic Stapleford Tawny Essex/The Priory Clinic, Keats Ho., Lond. SE1 9RT; Chairm. Inst. Social Psychiat. Lond.; Edr. Curr. Themes Psychiat. Socs: Fell. Roy. Soc. Med.; Brit. Med. Assoc. Prev: Sen. Phys. (Psychol. Med.) Guy's Hosp. Lond.; Chairm. SE Thames Regional Psychiat. Speciality Sub Comm.; Sen. Regist. Bethlem Roy. & Maudsley Hosps. Lond.

GAINER, Alan Joseph Rossmore, Homer, Much Wenlock TF13 6NQ — MB ChB 1968 St. And.; MRCGP 1977.

GAINER, Nigel St Clair (retired) 1 Midland Road, Thrapston, Kettering NN14 4JS Tel: 01832 734726 Email: nigel08@aol.com — MB BS 1955 Lond. Prev: RAMC.

GAINS, Jennifer Elizabeth Longridge, Farm Lane, East Markham, Newark NG22 0QH — MB BS 1998 Lond.; MB BS Lond 1998.

GAINSBOROUGH, Nicola Department of Medicine for Elderly, Brighton General Hospital, Elm Grove, Brighton BN2 3EW Tel: 01273 696955 Fax: 01273 665013 — MB ChB 1984 Bristol; MB ChB Bristol I984; FRCP 1998. Cons. Geriat. & Gen. Phys. Brighton Gen. Hosp. & Roy. Sussex Co. Hosp. Prev: Sen. Regist. Guy's Hosp. Lond.; Research Fell. King's Coll. Hosp. Lond.

GAINZA, Carlos Federico Acre Edgware Community Hospital, Edgware HA8 0AD Tel: 020 8732 6400 Fax: 0208 732 6401; 126 Hillfield Avenue, London N8 7DJ Tel: 020 8341 3485 — MB ChB 1971 Buenos Aires; MRCPsych Lond. 1983. Cons. Child & Adolesc. Psychiat. & Med. Dir. N.gate Clinic Barnet Healthcare NHSTrust. Prev: Cons. Child & Family Psychiat. Ealing & Chatham.

GAIR, Esther Janice Moorfields Eye Hospital, City Road, London EC1V 2PD Email: pposner@netcomuk.co.uk; 7 Spencer Rise, London NW5 1AR — MB BS 1990 Lond.; BSc (Hons.) Lond. 1987; FRCOphth 1995. (Univ. Coll. & Middlx. Sch. Med. Lond.) Specialist Regist. (Ophth.).

GAIR, James Donald Cherry Tree Cottage, The Green, Thorpe Market, Norwich NR11 8TL — MB BS 1986 Lond.

GAIR, Margaret Rennie Hurll 28 Riverside Road, Wormit, Newport-on-Tay DD6 8LQ Tel: 01382 541537 — MB ChB 1950 Glas.

GAIR, Richard William COSC (Eastern), Institute of Public Health, Forvie Site, Robinson Way, Cambridge CB2 2SR; 38 Cotesbach Road, London E5 9QJ — MB BS 1982 Lond.; FFPHM 2001 RCP (UK); MSc (Community Med.) Lond. 1991; BSc (Hons. 2.1 Social Appl. Med.) Lond. 1979; MFPHM RCP (UK) 1995. Regional Epidemiologist CDSC (E.ern) - NHS E.ern Region. Prev: Sen. Regist. Communicable Dis. Surveillance Centre; Cons. Communicable Dis. Control for Hillingdon & Princip. Med. Off. (Health Control) Heathrow Airport.

GAIR, Terence Middlestown Health Centre, Ramsey Crescent, Middlestown, Wakefield WF4 4QQ Tel: 01924 272121 — MB ChB 1985 Leeds; MRCGP 1989.

GAIRE, Catherine Paula 4 Coastguard Cottages, Kings Saltern Road, Lymington SO41 3QJ — MB BCh BAO 1987 NUI.

GAIRIN DEULOFEU, Isaura Newton Lodge, Ouchthorpe Lane, Wakefield WF1 3SP Tel: 01924 327375 Fax: 01924 327383 — LMS 1989 Barcelona; LMS Autonoma Barcelona 1989. Specialist Regist. in Forens. Psychiat. Leeds CMHT.

GAIT, Andrea Jane Owl Hill, Dunhampton, Stourport-on-Severn DY13 9SS — MB ChB 1998 Leic.; MB ChB Leic 1998.

GAITONDE, Alison Myra Redhill Child & Family Consultation Service, Shaw's Corner, Redhill RH1 6BD Tel: 01737 764704; 7 Ashurst Road, Tadworth KT20 5ET Tel: 01737 812646 — MB ChB 1955 NZ; MRCPsych 1973; DPM Eng. 1960. Cons. Psychiat. Redhill & Oxted Child Guid. Clinics; Cons. Psychiat. Guildford Child Guid. Clinic. Socs: BMA. Prev: Clin. Asst. Roy. N.. Hosp. Holloway; Psychiat. Leatherhead Child Guid. Clinic; Vis. Psychiat. Beechcroft Sch., Pine End Sch., Red Ho. Sch. & Wey Ho. Sch.

GAITONDE, Emma Jane Louise Department of Child and Adolescent Psychiatry, Brookside Family Consultation Clinic, 18d Trumpington Road, Cambridge CB2 2AH Tel: 01223 746001 Fax: 01223 746002 Email: ejg1003@cus.cam.ac.uk — MB BChir 1989 Camb.; MA Camb. 1993, BA 1986; MRCPsych 1997. (Cambridge and the London Hospital) Clin. Lect. in Developm. Psychiat. & Honarary specialist Regist. in Child & Adolesc. Psychiat., Camb. Socs: Brit. Neuropsychiat. Assn.; Tuberous Sclerosis Assn.; Br. Secret. Assoc of child Psychiat.s and Psychologists. Prev: Specialist Regist. (Developm. Psychiat.) Camb.; SHO (Pschiatry) Addenbrooke's Hosp., Camb.; Research Regist. (Psychiat.) Addenbrooke's Hosp. Camb.

GAITONDE, Michael David Shire Pharmaceutical Development Ltd, East Anton, Andover SP10 5RG Tel: 01264 348552 Fax: 01264 348539 Email: mgaitonde@shiregroup.com — MB BChir 1990 Camb.; MA Camb. 1993, BA 1986; MRCP (UK) 1993; Dip. Pharmaceut. Med. 1996; AFPM 1997. (Cambridge and St Georges Hospital) Med. Dir. New Projects, Shire Pharmaceut. Developm. Andover. Socs: Medico-Legal Soc. Prev: Med. Dir. Shire Pharmaceut. Contracts Andover; Sen. Med. Adviser Roche Products Ltd; Clin. (Pharmacol.) Hoechst, Marion Roussel.

GAJAWIRA, Nilani Pushpakanthi 127 Clifton Drive S., Fairhaven, Lytham St Annes FY8 1DX Tel: 01253 734478; Blackpool Wyre & Fylde Community Health Services NHS Trust, Department of Child Psychiatry, Blackpool FY3 8NR — MB BS Ceylon 1967; MRCPsych 1980. Cons. Child & Adolesc. Psychiat.

GAJDA, Andrew 15 Blackpark Terrace, Inverness IV3 8NE — MB ChB 1997 Aberd.

GAJDATSY, Adam Dominic 4 Castle Grove Drive, Leeds LS6 4BR — MB ChB 1991 Leeds. SHO (A & E) Leeds Gen. Infirm. Trust.

GAJEBASIA, Surjeet Singh Rookery Lane Health Centre, 26 Rookery Lane, Groby, Leicester LE6 0GL Tel: 0116 231 3331 — MB BS 1975 Punjabi U.; MB BS 1975 Punjabi U.

GAJEK, Anna Llwyn Brwydrau Surgery, 3 Frederick Place, Llansamlet, Swansea SA7 9RY Tel: 01792 771465 — MB BCh 1979 Bristol. Regist. (Anaesth.) Singleton Hosp. Swansea. Prev: SHO (Anaesth.) Singleton Hosp. Swansea; SHO (Med.) Morriston Hosp. Swansea.

GAJEK, Wieslaw Roman 63 Higher Lane, Langland, Swansea SA3 4PD Tel: 01792 205666, 01792 285292 Fax: 01792 285292 — Lekarz 1967 Lodz; MSc (Physics) Torun 1960; FRCR 1978; DMRT Eng. 1974. (Med. Sch. Lodz) Cons. Radiother. & Oncol. Singleton Hosp. Swansea. Socs: FRCR (Lond). Prev: Tutor (Radiother.) Med. Sch. Bristol; Sen. Regist. Bristol Radiother. & Oncol. Centre; Regist. (Radiother.) Velindre Hosp. Cardiff.

GAJEWSKA, Anna Maryon Sexy's Farm House, Spring St, Wool, Wareham BH20 6DB Tel: 01929 463657 — MB BCh 1982 Wales; BSc Sheff. 1976; MSc Wales 1978, MB BCh 1982. Staff Phys. (Palliat. Med.), Poole Hosp. NHS Trust. Prev: Clin. Asst. (c/o Elderly) Wareham Hosp.; Regist. (Psychol. Med.) Wales Coll. Med. Cardiff; Regist. (Med. Microbiol.) Univ. Hosp. Wales Cardiff.

GAJJAR, Ameeta 15 Guildersfield Road, London SW16 5LS Tel: 020 8764 9489 Email: ameeta_gajjar@hotmail.com — MB BS 1998 Lond.; MB BS Lond 1998; BSc (Hons) 1995. Surgic. Ho. Off. Qu. Eliz. The Qu. Mother Hosp., Margate Kent. Prev: Med. Ho. Off. Char. Cross Hosp.

GAJJAR, Arvind Purshottam Anaesthetic Department, Kidderminster General Hospital, Bewdley Road, Kidderminster DY11 6RJ Tel: 01562 823424 Fax: 01562 67412; 49 Cairndhu Drive, Kidderminster DY10 2TB Tel: 01562 864259 — MB BS 1972 Gujarat; MB BS Gurarat 1972; FFA RCS Eng. 1981. Clin. Asst. (Anaesth.) Kidderminster Health Care NHS Trust. Socs: Assn. Anaesth. GB & Irel.; Hosp. Cons. & Spec. Assn. Prev: Cons. Anaesth. Armed Forces Hosps. S.. Region Khamis Mushyt, Saudi Arabia.

GAJJAR, Bharatrai 60 Wolsey Road, Moor Park, Northwood HA6 2EH Tel: 01923 823993 — MB ChB 1972 Cape Town; FRCR 1982. Cons. Radiol. Watford Gen. Hosp. & N.wick Pk. Hosp. Harrow.

GAJJAR, Mr Girish Sankalchand c/o Barclays Bank, PO Box 85, Ramsgate CT11 9UP — MB BS 1967 Gujarat; FRCS Eng. 1994.

GAJJAR, Jeannette Gillian Karibu, 4 The Fields, Ouzlewell Green, Lofthouse, Wakefield WF3 3RZ — MB ChB 1968 Leeds; DA Eng. 1971. (Leeds) SCMO (Sch. Health) Wakefield & Pontefract Community Health Trust.

GAJJAR, Paresh Damji Sheffield Teaching Hospitals NHS Trust, Northern General Hospital, Herries Road, Sheffield S5 7AU Tel: 0114 243 4343 Fax: 0114 271 4289 Email: P.Gajjar@Sheffield.ac.uk; Karibu, 4 The Fields, Ouzlewell Green, Lofthouse, Wakefield WF3 3RZ Tel: 0113 282 1920 Fax: 0113 393 4325 Email: pdg@doctors.org.uk — MB ChB 1969 Leeds; FRCGP 1996, M 1975; DObst RCOG 1973. (Leeds) Cons. Palliat. Med. Hon Sen. Lect.N.ern.Gen.Hosp.Sheff. Socs: Pain Soc.; Assn. Palliat. Med. Mem. Exec. Comm. 2001; Nat. Counc. for Hospices and Spec. Palliat. Care Serv. Regional and Co. Repr. Comm. 2001. Prev: Med. Director, Wakefield Hospice. 1990-2000; Cons. Phys. Palliat. Med. Pinderfileds Hosp. NHS Trust, Wakefield, 1990-2000.; GP & CME Tutor Wakefield.

GAJJAR, Shilpa 48 The Ruffetts, South Croydon CR2 7LR — MB BS 1995 Lond.

GAJRAJ, Mr Haroun Department of Surgery, Yeovil District Hospital, Higher Kingston, Yeovil BA21 4AT Tel: 01935 707599 — MB BS 1980 Lond.; MB BS (Hons.) Lond. 1980; BSc (1st cl. Hons.) Lond. 1977, MS 1989; FRCS Eng. 1984. (Kings Coll. Hosp.) Cons. Gen. & Vasc. Surg. Yeovil Dist. Hosp. Som.; Hon. Cons. MusGr. Hosp. Taunton, Som. Socs: Vasc. Soc. GB & Irel.; BA Surgic. Oncols. Prev: Sen. Regist. St. Geo. & St. Thos. Hosps. Lond.

GAJRAJ, Malcolm University Hospital of Wales, Department of Paediatrics, Cardiff CF1 7JJ Tel: 029 2074 7747; 5 Claymore Place, Windsor Quay, Cardiff CF11 7JJ Tel: 029 2039 0661 — BM 1990 Soton.; MRCP (UK) 1994. Sen. Regist. (Paediat. Neurol. & ICU) Univ. Hosp. Wales Cardiff. Prev: Sen. Regist. Roy. Gwent Hosp. Newport.

GAJRAJ, Mohamed Kemel 18 Beauchamp Road, East Molesey KT8 0PA — MRCS Eng. LRCP Lond. 1970.

GAJRAJ, Noor Mahamood 45 Beauchamp Road, East Molesey KT8 2PG Tel: 020 8979 6993 — MB BS 1983 Lond.; FRCA 1991. Asst. Prof. Anaesth. Pk.land Hosp. Dallas, Texas, USA. Prev: Sen. Regist. (Anaesth.) Univ. Hosp. Nottm.; SHO (Anaesth.) St. Thos. Hosp. Lond.; Ho. Off. (Med.) King's Coll. Hosp. Lond.

GAJREE, Anoop Kumar Ardoch Medical Centre, 6 Ardoch Grove, Cambuslang, Glasgow G72 8HA Tel: 0141 641 1255 Fax: 0141 646 1988 — MB ChB 1976 Glas.; MRCGP 1983; DRCOG 1983.

GAKHAL, Rapinder Kaur Victoria House, Victoria Road, Stocksbridge, Sheffield S36 2FX — MB ChB 1993 Ed.

GAL, Isabel (retired) 11 The Fairways, Broom Road, Teddington TW11 Tel: 020 8977 7791 — MD 1951 Budapest; PhD Lond. 1979; LRCP LRCS Ed. LRFPS Glas. 1959. Joseph Sen. White Fell. RCP Inst. O & G Univ. Lond.; Hon. Cons. Chelsea Wom. Hosp. Prev: Research Fell. Qu. Mary's Hosp. Carshalton.

GALAAL, Khadhra Ahmed 57 Bullsmoor Way, Waltham Cross EN8 8HW — MB ChB 1992 Dundee.

GALAN, Yvonne Sara 10 Little Potters, Bushey Heath, Watford WD23 4QT — MB ChB 1993 Manch.; DRCOG 1996; DTM & H 1998; DFFP 1998. (Manchester) Health Worker, Leprosy Control Project, Alfredo Da Matta Inst., Amazonas, Brazil. Prev: Locum GP, Manch.

GALASKO, Professor Charles Samuel Bernard Hope Hospital, Eccles Old Road, Salford M6 8HD Tel: 0161 787 4291 Fax: 0161 787 4706 — MB BCh Witwatersrand 1962; MSc (Hon.) Manch. 1980; ChM Witwatersrand 1969; FRCS Eng. 1966; FRCS Ed. 1966. (Witwatersrand) Prof. Orthop Surg. Univ. Manch.; Hon. Cons. Orthop. Surg. Salford Roy. Hosps. NHS Trust Manch. & Childr. Hosps. NHS Trust; Mem. Counc. RCS. Socs: (Ex-Pres.) Internat.

Orthop. Research Soc.; (Ex-Counc.) BOA, Pres.-Elect 2001; Chairm. Jt Comm. on Surg. Train. of GB & Irel. 1997-. Prev: Hunt. Prof. RCS Eng.; Dir. Orthop. Unit Roy. Postgrad. Med. Sch. Hammersmith Hosp.; Sen. Regist. Nuffield Orthop. Centre Oxf. & Accid. Serv. Radcliffe Infirm.

GALAUD, John Bryant 25 Hamilton Street, Chester CH2 3JG — MRCS Eng. LRCP Lond. 1966. (Middlx.)

GALAZKA, Leszek Stanislaw 9 Alderside Walk, Egham TW20 0LX — LRCPI & LM, LRSCI & LM 1951; LRCPI & LM, LRCSI & LM 1951. Prev: Ho. Surg. Black Notley Hosp.; Ho. Phys. Highlands Hosp. Lond.; Sen. Cas. Off. Hillingdon Hosp. Uxbridge.

GALAZKA, Nuala Mary Irene Ithaca, 9 Alderside Walk, Egham TW20 0LX — MB BS 1983 Lond.

GALBALLY, Bryan Peter 1 Marlborough, 61 Walton St., London SW3 2JU — MB BS 1949 Melbourne; FRACP 1978.

GALBRAITH, Alan William (retired) 107 Randolph Avenue, London W9 1DL Tel: 020 7449 1261 — MB BChir 1958 Camb.; MB BChir Camb. 1957; MA Camb. 1958; DCH Eng. 1960; DObst RCOG 1959. Phys. Amer. Sch. Lond. Prev: Regist. (Paediat.) & Ho. Surg. St. Bart. Hosp. Lond.

GALBRAITH, Deborah Child Health Department, Pendragon House, Gloweth, Truro TR1 3LS Tel: 01872 254552 Fax: 01872 225506; Warleigh, Rock Road, St. Minver, Wadebridge PL27 6PW — MB ChB 1972 Ed. SCMO (Child Health) Roy. Cornw. Hosps. Trust. Prev: Sessional Pract. (Child Health & Family Plann.) Leics. HA; Research Asst. (Gyn.) P'boro. Dist. Hosp.

GALBRAITH, Dorothy Joyce 20 The Horseshoe, York YO24 1LX Tel: 01904 706666 — MB ChB 1951 St. And.; MRCPsych 1971; DPM Leeds 1956. (St. And.) Socs: BMA. Prev: Cons. Child Psychiat. (Adolesc.) York Health Dist.; Fulbright Grantee For Study in USA At McCook Hosp. Hartford; SHO (Med.) The Retreat York.

GALBRAITH, Elizabeth Adelaide 25 Mill House Close, Leamington Spa CV32 6AN Tel: 01926 27759 — MB BCh BAO 1943 Dub.; MA Dub. 1971, MB BCh BAO 1943. (T.C. Dub.) Prev: Ho. Phys. Gloucester Roy. Infirm. & Derby Childr. Hosp.; Cas. Off. Bristol Gen. Hosp.

GALBRAITH, James Pollokshaws Doctors Centre, 26 Wellgreen, Glasgow G43 1RR Tel: 0141 649 2836 Fax: 0141 649 5238; 22 Ballantrae Drive, Newton Mearns, Glasgow G77 5TB Tel: 0141 639 7577 — MB ChB 1981 Glas.; MRCGP 1986; DRCOG 1983.

GALBRAITH, Jennifer 1 Rockfield Avenue, Monmouth NP25 5BB — MB BCh 1971 Wales; DObst RCOG 1973. Clin. Med. Off. (Community Gyn & Sexual Health) Gwent Healthcare NHS Trust.

GALBRAITH, Nicol Spence, CBE (retired) 22 Fen Road, Chesterton, Cambridge CB4 1TX — MB BS 1950 Lond.; FRCP Lond. 1983, M 1978; MRCS Eng. LRCP Lond. 1950; FFCM 1974; DPH Lond. 1954. Prev: Dir. Communicable Dis. Surveillance Centre Lond.

GALBRAITH, Olive Achnameadhonach, Taynuilt PA35 1JS — MB ChB Glas. 1934. (Univ. Glas.) Prev: Ho. Phys. & Ho. Surg. Roy. Infirm. Glas.; Dist. Med. Off. Qu. Charlotte's Hosp. Lond.; Sen. Med. Off. (Child Health) Argyll & Bute Health Dist.

GALBRAITH, Patricia Sarah Red House Surgery, 96 Chesterton Road, Cambridge CB4 1ER Tel: 01223 365555 Fax: 01223 356848 — BM Soton. 1982; MRCGP 1989; Dip. Palliat. Med. Wales 1993; DRCOG 1988; DCH RCP Lond. 1987. (Southampton)

GALBRAITH, Mr Samuel Laird 48 Woodend Drive, Jordanhill, Glasgow G13 1TQ Tel: 0141 959 5127 Fax: 0141 950 2055 Email: galbraith@udcf.gla.ac.uk — MB ChB Glas. 1971; BSc Glas. 1968, MD 1977; FRCS Glas. 1975. (Glas.) Cons. Neurosurg. Gtr. Glas. HB.

GALBRAITH, Sarah Nichol Asrmy Medical Directorate (Medical-Legal), Former Army Staff College, Slim Road, Camberley GU15 4NP Tel: 01276 412727; The Old Stables, College Lane, Ellisfield, Basingstoke RG25 2QE Tel: 01256 381247 Fax: 01256 381974 Email: sngkag@msn.com — MB BChir 1986 Camb.; MA (Hons.) Camb. 1987, BA (Hons.) 1983; MRCGP 1991; MFFP 1993; T(GP) 1992; LLM Cardiff 1999. Cons. & Head of Dept. Army Medico-Legal Dept. Prev: Med. Adviser Dept. of Social Security; GP Minden Garrison Med. Centre; Maj. RAMC.

GALBRAITH, Stephen Brown 23 Royal Crescent, Glasgow G3 7SL — MB ChB 1991 Dundee.

GALBRAITH, Susan Mary 5 Bernard Grove, Beaulieu Drive, Waltham Abbey EN9 1JR Email: galbraith@graylab.ac.uk — MB BChir 1990 Camb.; BSc (Hons.) Manch. 1987; FRCR 1997; MRCP (UK) 1992. Regist. (Clin. Oncol.) Middlx. Hosp. Lond. & Mt. Vernon Hosp. N.d. Middlx.; Research Fell. Mt. Vernon Hosp. Middlx. Prev: Regist. (Clin. Oncol.) Middlx. Hosp. Lond. & Mt. Vernon Hosp. Middlx.; SHO Leukaemia Unit Roy. Marsden Hosp. Sutton; SHO Rotat. (Med.) Addenbrooke's Hosp. Camb.

GALDOS TOBALINA, Maria Paloma 47 Ruskin Walk, London SE24 9NA — LMS 1984 Basque Provinces.

GALE, Alison Clare Hope Hospital, Eccles Old Road, Salford, Manchester; 71 Bicknell Close, Great Sankey, Warrington WA5 8EX Tel: 01925 710803 — MB ChB 1990 Leic. Regist. (O & G) Hope Hosp. Manch. Prev: SHO (O & G) Countess of Chester Hosp. & Fazakerley Hosp. Liverp.; SHO (Oncol.) Clatterbridge Centre Radiother. & Oncol. Wirral.

GALE, Andrew Neil 50 Cassiobury Drive, Watford WD17 3AE — MD 1982 Liverp.; MB ChB Liverp. 1971; FRCP Lond. 1990; MRCP (UK) 1974. Cons. Neurol. Roy. Free Hosp. Lond. & Luton & Dunstable Hosp. Prev: Sen. Regist. (Neurol.) Univ. Coll. Hosp. & Nat. Hosp. Nerv. Dis. Lond.; Regist. (Neurol.) Nat. Hosp. Qu. Sq. Lond.; Fell. (Med.) Johns Hopkins Hosp. Baltimore, USA.

GALE, Christopher Peter 16 Northfield Avenue, Radcliffe on Trent, Nottingham NG12 2HX — MB BS 1994 Lond.

GALE, Colin William Little Orchard, Prinsted, Emsworth PO10 8HT — LRCPI & LM, LRSCI & LM 1953; LRCPI & LM, LRCSI & LM 1953; FRCOG 1974, M 1961. (RCSI) Cons. O & G Portsmouth Hosp. Gp.; Hon. Clin. Teach. (Obst. & Gyn.) Univ. Soton.

GALE, Diana Gwendolen Leigh The Old School, Coates, Cirencester GL7 6NN — DPhil Oxf. 1977; MB BCh Witwatersrand 1966; FCP(SA) 1970. (Witwatersrand) Clin. Asst. & Med. Off. (Genitourin. Med.) Glos.; Clin. Asst. Diabetes Swindon; Clin. Asst. Gastro-Enterology Swindon.

GALE, Professor Edwin Albert Merwood Diabetes and Metabolism, Medical School Unit, Southmead Hospital, Bristol BS10 5NB Tel: 0117 959 5337 Fax: 0117 959 5336 Email: edin.gale@bristol.ac.uk; 9 Carnarvon Road, Bristol BS6 7DR Tel: 0117 924 3123 — MB 1973 Camb.; BChir 1972; FRCP Lond. 1987; MRCP (UK) 1975. Prof. (Diabetic Med.) Univ. of Bristol; Phys. S.mead Hosp. & Bristol Roy. Infirm. Prev: Prof. Diabetes. St. Bart. Hosp. Lond.; Phys. St. Bart. & Homerton Hosp. Lond.; Sen. Research Fell. Oxf. Diabetes Unit.

GALE, Janet Hutton Beck House, Stokesley Road, Guisborough TS14 8DL Tel: 01287 632500 — MB BS Durh. 1962; MFFP 1993. Sen. Med. Off. N. Tees Family Plann. Serv. Socs: Fell. Roy. Soc. Med.; Fac. Comm. Health; BMA (Vice-Chair. S. Tees Div.).

GALE, Joanna Wessex Medical Oncology Unit, Royal South Wales Hospital, Off Brintons Terrace, St Mary's — BM 1990 Soton.; MRCP (UK) 1994. (Univ. Soton.) Clin. Research Fell. & Hon. Sen. Regist. (Med. Oncol.) Wessex Med. Oncol. Unit Roy. S. Hants. Hosp. Soton.

GALE, Jonathan Ennion Sadler St Barnabas Surgery, St. Barnabas Terrace, Stoke, Plymouth PL1 5NN Tel: 01752 607006 Fax: 01752 560166 — BM 1982 Soton.; BSc (Hons.) Wales 1976; MRCGP 1987; DCH RCPS Glas. 1986; DRCOG 1985. (Soton.)

GALE, Matthew St John Collison Avenue Health Centre, Collison Avenue, Chorley PR7 2TH Tel: 01257 262104 Fax: 01257 232285; 3 Sandringham Drive, Brinscall, Chorley PR6 8SU Tel: 01254 830519 — MB BS 1982 Lond. Prev: Trainee GP Earby VTS; SHO (O & G) Airedale Gen. Hosp.; SHO (Psychiat.) Scalebor Pk. Hosp.

GALE, Richard Francis 9 Malmains Way, Beckenham BR3 6SA — MB BS 1985 Lond.

GALE, Richard Gareth 56 Manston Close, Launton, Bicester OX26 4FB — BM BCh 1988 Oxf.; MA Oxf. 1990, BM BCh 1988. Trainee GP Oxf.; Regtl. Med. Off. 1st Bn. Roy. Green Jackets. Prev: SHO (A & E) John Radcliffe Hosp. Oxf.

GALE, Richard Newlyn Glendevon Medical Centre, 3 Carlton Place, Teignmouth TQ14 8AB — MB BS 1983 Lond.

GALE, Richard Peter 16 Northfield Av, Radcliffe-on-Trent, Nottingham NG12 2HX — MB ChB 1997 Leeds.

GALE, Robert Stephen Foxe's Barn, Clyffe Pypard, Swindon SN4 7PD Tel: 01793 731910 Fax: 01793 731319; 13 Padgate, Thorpe End, Norwich NR13 5DG Tel: 01603 701360, 01793 731910 Fax: 01793 731319 — MB BS 1967 Lond.; MRCS Eng. LRCP Lond. 1967; DObst RCOG 1970. p/t Locum GP; Examg. Med. Practitioner for Benefits Agency.

GALE, Sally Ann Wallis and Partners, The Health Centre, 5 Stanmore Road, Stevenage SG1 3QA Tel: 01438 313223 Fax:

01438 749734; 99 Pondcroft Road, Knebworth SG3 6DE Tel: 01438 813425 — MB BS 1979 Lond.; BSc (Hons.) Lond. 1972; MRCGP 1983; DRCOG 1982; DCH Eng. 1981. (Univ. Coll. Lond.) Prev: SHO (Obst.) N. Herts. Hosp. Hitchin; SHO (Paediat.) Lister Hosp. Stevenage; Ho. Phys. Univ. Coll. Hosp. Lond.

GALEA, Carmel Vange Health Centre, Southview Road, Vange, Basildon SS16 4HD Tel: 01268 533151 Fax: 01268 282059 — MD 1967 Malta; MRCS Eng. LRCP Lond. 1974. (Malta)

GALEA, Frank Ingledene, 106 Junction Road, Deane, Bolton BL3 4NE — MD 1949 Malta; BSc Malta 1946, MD 1949. (Malta) Prev: Jun. Hosp. Med. Off. Vict. Hosp. Blackpool; Med. Off. Min. of Health, N. Nigeria.

GALEA, George Tissue Services Department, Protein Fractionation Centre, Ellens Glen Road, Edinburgh EH17 7QT Tel: 0131 536 5700; 58A Garscube Terrace, Ravelston, Edinburgh EH12 6BN Tel: 0131 346 2836 — MD Aberd. 1990; FRCP Ed. 1993; MRCP (UK) 1981; MRCS Eng. LRCP Lond. 1977. Nat. Tissues Servs. Dir. Socs: Assn. Clin. Path.; Brit. Blood Transfus. Soc.; Brit. Assn. Tissue Banks- Chair- Med. SIG. Prev: Regional Transfus. Dir. E. Scotl. BTS; Regional Transfus. Dir. Inverness & N. Scotl. BTS; Cons. Blood Transfus. Serv. Aberd. & Roy. Infirm.

GALEA, Ivan Alexander Askew Avenue Surgery, 143A Askew Avenue, Hull HU4 6NH Tel: 01482 354251 — MB ChB 1988 Ed.; MRCGP 1992. (Edinburgh)

GALEA, Mr Joseph Section of Cardiac Surgery, Clinical Sciences Centre, Northern General Hospital, Herries Road, Sheffield S5 7AU Tel: 0114 271 4922; 284 Herries Road, Sheffield S5 7AH Tel: 0114 271 5761 — MD 1985 Malta; LRCP LRCS Ed. LRCPS Glas. 1989; FRCS Ed. 1992. Research Assoc. (Cardiac Surg.) Univ. Sheff. Socs: Brit. Soc. Cardiovasc. Research.; Internat. Soc. Heart Research; (Scientif. Sect. Carditharacic & Vasc. Surg.) Amer. Heart Assn.

GALEA, Mr Marcus Hugh Department of Surgery, Princess Margaret Hospital, Okus Road, Swindon SN1 4JU — MB BS 1983 Lond.; DM Nottm. 1993; BSc 1980 Lond.; FRCS Lond. 1988. Cons. Gen. Surg. Maj. Interest in BrE. Endocrine Surg. P.ss Margt. Hosp. Swindon. Prev: Lect. (Surg.) Nottm.; Regist. Nottm. & Cardiff.

GALEA, Paul Francis Yorkhill NHS Trust, Royal Hospital for Sick Children, Yorkhill, Glasgow G3 8SJ — MD 1973 Malta; FRCP Glas. 1990; MRCP (UK) 1978; DCH RCPS Glas. 1976; FRCPCH 1997. (Malta) Cons. Paediat. Roy. Hosp. For Sick Childr., Glas.; Hon. Clin. Sen. Lect. Univ. of Glas. Socs: Brit. Paediat. Assn.; Brit. Assn. Perinatal Med.; Brit. Paediat. Rheum. Gp. Prev: Cons. Paediat. Rutherglen Matern. Hosp. Glas.; Cons. Paediat. Glas. Roy. Matern. & Roy. Hosp. for Sick Childr. Glas.

GALEY, Stuart Martin St Christophers Cottage, Postlip Hall, Winchcombe, Cheltenham GL54 2AG — MB ChB 1982 Leic.; MRCGP 1986. Socs: Assn. Brit. Med. Acupunc. Soc.

GALI, Mohamed Hassan Ali Russell Hall Hospital, Dudley DY1 2LH Tel: 01384 456111; 85 John House, Busheyfield Road, Dudley DY1 2LU — MRCS Eng. LRCP Lond. 1986; MB BS Khartoum 1981; MRCP (UK) 1989.

GALIATSOU, Eftihia Lister House, 22 Winton Drive, Kelvindale, Glasgow G12 0QA — Ptychio Iatrikes 1986 Ioannina.

GALIMBERTI, Andrea 95A High Street, Weston, Bath BA1 4DQ — State Exam 1992 Milan. Prev: Specialist Regist. (O & G) S.mead Hosp. Bristol; Regist. (O & G) Roy. United Hosp. Bath; Sen. SHO (O & G) Roy. United Hosp. Bath.

GALIOT GARCIA, Francisco Flat 54 Barony Court, Barony Road, Nantwich CW5 5RD — LMS 1992 Cordoba; PhD Cordoba 1992, MD 1990. SHO (O & G) Leeds Gen. Infirm. Prev: SHO (O & G) Sharoe Green Hosp. Preston, Roy. Lancaster Infirm. & Burton Hosp.

GALIZIA, Edward John (retired) Carlingcott Mill, Carlingcott, Bath BA2 8AP — MB BS 1961 Lond.; MRCS Eng. LRCP Lond. 1961; FFA RCS Eng. 1971. Cons. Anaesth. Bath Health Dist. Prev: Sen. Regist. (Anaesth.) United Bristol Hosps.

GALL, Alan Ronald Unthank Road Surgery, 38 Unthank Road, Norwich NR2 2RD Tel: 01603 624715 — MB ChB 1979 Aberd.

GALL, Amy Jane 18 St Pegas Road, Peakirk, Peterborough PE6 7NF — MB BS 1992 Newc.

GALL, Angela 110 Braehead Way, Bridge of Don, Aberdeen AB22 8SD — MB ChB 1991 Aberd. SHO (Elderly Care & Med.) Perth Roy. Infirm. Prev: SHO (Med.) W. Cornw. & Treliske; SHO (A & E) Warrington.

GALL, Jane Fraser Stranraer Health Centre, Edinburgh Road, Stranraer DG9 7HG Tel: 01776 706566 — MB ChB 1980 Glas.; MRCGP 1984; DRCOG 1983.

GALL, Joanna North Hampshire Hospital, Aldermaston Road, Basingstoke RG24 9NA Tel: 01256 473202; Little Orchard, 5 New Road, Twyford, Reading RG10 9PS Tel: 0118 934 5269 — BM 1979 Soton.; MRCOphth 1988; DO RCS Eng. 1984. Assoc. Specialist N. Hants. Hosps. Trust. Prev: Clin. Asst. (Ophth.) Basingstoke Dist. Hosp. & Roy. Berks. Hosp. Reading; SHO (Ophth.) Roy. Berks. Hosp. Reading.

GALL, Nicholas Peter Dept. Of Cardiology, King's College Hospital, Denmark Hill, London SE5 9RS — MB BS 1993 Lond.; MSc 1998 Univ. Sussex; BSc (Hons.) Lond. 1990; MRCP (UK) 1996. (UMDS, Guy's Campus Univ. Lond.) Regist. (Cardiol.) King's Coll. Hosp., Lond. Socs: Mem. of Brit. Cardiac Soc. Prev: Reg. (Cardiol.) Roy. Sussex Co., Brighton; Reg. (Cardiol.) Conquest Hosp., Hastings; Research Fell. Cardiol., GKT Sch. of Med., Univ. Lond.

GALL, Robert Graham Heatherwood Hospital, Ascot, Ascot SL5 8AA Tel: 01344 877462; 15 Leigh Park, Datchet, Slough SL3 9JP Tel: 01753 541063 Email: graham.gall@btinternet.com — MB BS 1977 Newc.; BA Oxf. 1974; FRCPsych 1997. Cons. (Psychiat.) Berks. Healthcare Trust. Prev: Ho. Off. (Gen. Med.) Newc. Gen. Hosp.; Ho. Off. (Gen. Surg.) Qu. Eliz. Hosp. Gateshead.

GALL, Scott Alexander 11 Lonsdale Terrace, Newcastle upon Tyne NE2 3HQ — MB BS 1998 Newc.; MB BS Newc 1998.

GALL, Mr William James (retired) Cornerstones, 40A Culver Road, Saltash PL12 4DS Tel: 01752 842067 Email: bilgwen@msn.com — MB ChB 1947 Bristol; FRCS Eng. 1954; MRCS Eng. LRCP Lond. 1947. Prev: Cons. Gen. Urol. Derriford Hosp. Plymouth.

GALLACHER, Christine 1 Rose Park E., Belfast BT5 7RL — MB ChB 1994 Glas.

GALLACHER, James Brown (retired) Viewfield, Saline, Dunfermline KY12 9TL Tel: 01383 852297 — MB ChB Ed. 1958. Chairm. Fife Primary Care (NHS) Trust.

GALLACHER, Jane Helen Park Terrace Surgery, 7A Park Terrace, Stirling FK8 2JT Tel: 01786 445888 Fax: 01786 449154; Hillfoot Cottage, 47 Ochil Road, Menstrie FK11 7BP Tel: 01259 762916 — MB ChB 1989 Dundee; MRCGP 1993; DRCOG 1991. Clin. Asst. Family Plann.

GALLACHER, Karen Geraldine The Swan Medical Centre, 4 Willard Road, Yardley, Birmingham B25 8AA Tel: 0121 706 0216 Fax: 0121 707 3105 — MB ChB 1987 Glas.

GALLACHER, Rodney Hall West Croft House, 66 Main Street, Egremont CA22 2DB Tel: 01946 820348 Fax: 01946 821611 — MB BS 1972 Newc. (Newc.)

GALLACHER, Stephen John Medical Unit B, Southern General Hospital NHS Trust, 1345 Govan Road, Glasgow G51 4TF Tel: 0141 201 1100 Fax: 0141 201 1783 — MB ChB 1983 Glas.; MD Glas. 1993; MRCP (UK) 1986. Cons. Phys. S.. Gen. Hosp. Glas. Prev: Lect. & Sen. Regist. (Med.) Glas. Roy. Infirm.; Regist. (Med.) Glas. Roy. Infirm.

GALLACHER, Thomas 52 Pereira Road, Birmingham B17 9JN — MB ChB 1987 Glas.; FRCA 1994. Career Regist. Rotat. (Anaesth.) W. Midl.

GALLACHER, William (retired) — MB ChB 1953 Glas. Prev: Asst. Psychiat. Ailsa Hosp. Ayr.

GALLACHER, William Angus Benreary Surgery, Seaview Place, Buckie AB56 1JT Tel: 01542 831555 Fax: 01542 835799 — MB ChB 1983 Glas.; MB ChB (Commend.) Glas. 1983; MRCP (UK) 1987; MRCGP 1991; DRCOG 1988. Socs: Roy. Coll. Phys. Edin.

GALLAGHER, Andrew Charles 28 Flowery Field, Woodsmoor, Stockport SK2 7ED Tel: 0161 483 2887 Email: galla@globalnet.co.uk — MB ChB 1988 Sheff.; MRCP (UK) 1994; DObst. Otago 1991; DCH RCP Lond. 1990. Specialist Regist. John Radcliffe Hosp, Oxf. Prev: Regist. (Paediat.) Brighton; Community Med. Off. (Paediat.) Camberwell; SHO (Paediat.) St. Geo. Hosp. Lond.

GALLAGHER, Andrew Peter Flat 2/2, 9 Novar Drive, Glasgow G12 9PX — MB ChB 1988 Glas.

GALLAGHER, Andrew Robert Rosebank Surgery, Ashton Road, Road, Lancaster LA1 4JS Tel: 01524 842284 Fax: 01524 844839 — MB ChB 1985 Manch.; MRCGP 1989; DFFP 1997; DRCOG 1988; DCH RCP Lond. 1987. Partner, Rosebank Med. Pract.,

Lancaster; Crowd doctor Bolton Wonderars F.C; Clin. Asst.. Accid. & Emerg., Roy. Lanc. Infirm. Prev: Trainee GP Longridge Preston; SHO (Gen. Med. & Paediat.) Roy. Preston Hosp.

GALLAGHER, Ann Carmel 19 Belvedere Manor, Windsor Park, Belfast BT9 6FT — MB BCh BAO 1988 NUI; MRCPI 1994; FFARCSI 1997.

GALLAGHER, Annamaria The Old Rectory, 697 Antrim Road, Belfast BT15 4EH — LRCPI & LM, LRCSI & LM 1976; MRCGP 1980; MICGP 1986; DCH RCPSI 1980; DRCOG 1979. Locum GP. Prev: Doctor's Retainer Scheme Belf.; Intern (Med. & Surg.) E.. HB Irel.; Trainee GP Qu. Mary's Hosp. Lond. VTS.

GALLAGHER, Anthony Brian Employment Health Advisors, Core House, Puladuff Road Tel: 003532 1497 5888 Fax: 003532 1497 5890; 50 West Avenue, Parkgate, Frankfield — MB BCh BAO 1982 NUI; MRCGP 1988; DCH RCPSI 1986; DObst RCPI 1987. (University College Cork) Occupat.al Phys. Occupat.al Med. Employm. Health Advisers Cork. Prev: Gen. Practitioner Timplerley Health Centre Altrincham.

GALLAGHER, Anthony James 9 Hunter Avenue, Manby, Louth LN11 8TY — MB BS 1996 Lond.

GALLAGHER, Aoibhin Bernadette Kilgartnaleague, Ballinamallard, Enniskillen BT94 2GZ — MB BCh BAO 1997 Belf.

GALLAGHER, Bernadette Agnes Newton Cottage, 19 Quarry Road, Fauldhouse, Bathgate EH47 9ES — MB ChB 1959 Ed.; FRCP Ed. 1994; MRCP Ed. 1963; DPH Glas. 1968; DCH Eng. 1961. (Ed.) Cons. Community Paediat. Lanarksh. Healthcare NHS Trust; Sen. Clin. Med. Off. (Community Child Health) Lanarksh. HB; Asst. Med. Off. Lanark CC. Socs: Soc. Pub. Health; Scott. Assn. Community Child Health; Fac. Community Health. Prev: Sen. Regist. (Paediat.) Univ. Coll. Hosp. W. Indies, Mona, Jamaica; Regist. (Med.) Leith Hosp. Edin.; Regist. (Paediat.) Roy. Vict. Infirm. Newc. u. Tyne.

GALLAGHER, Betty Clifton Road Surgery, 22 Clifton Road, Rugby CV21 3QF Tel: 01788 544744/544718 Fax: 01788 553902; 9 Oswald Way, Rugby CV22 7PL Tel: 01788 546141 — MB BS Lond. 1975. (Roy. Free) Prev: Clin. Asst. (Paediat.) Hosp. of St. Cross Rugby; Trainee GP Hosp. St. Cross Rugby VTS.

GALLAGHER, Bryonie Susan 5 High Laws, South Gosforth, Newcastle upon Tyne NE3 1RQ — MB BS 1984 Newc.; MRCGP 1988; DRCOG 1988.

GALLAGHER, Charles John Tudor House Surgery, 43 Broad Street, Wokingham RG40 1BE Tel: 0118 978 3044 Fax: 0118 977 0420 — MB BS 1979 Lond.; MRCGP 1987; DRCOG 1986. Prev: Princip GP Harrow; Sen. Med. Off. Sch. of Infantry Warminster.

GALLAGHER, Christopher Joseph St Bartholomew's Hospital, Department of Medical Oncology, West Smithfield, London EC1A 7BE Tel: 020 7601 8521 Fax: 020 7601 7577 Email: chris.gallagher@bartsandthelondon.nhs.uk — MB ChB 1974 Auckland; PhD Lond. 1986; BSc Auckland 1971; FRCP Lond. 1995; T(M) 1991. (Auckland) p/t Cons. Med. Oncol. St. Bart. Hosp. Lond. Socs: Assoc. Cancer Phys.s; Brit. Gyn. Soc.; Amer. Soc. Clin. Oncol. Prev: Sen. Regist. (Med. Oncol.) Roy. Marsden Hosp. Sutton; Sen. Regist. & ICRF Clin. Research Fell. (Med. Oncol.) St. Bart. Hosp.; Sen. Lect. St. Bart. & Roy. Lond. Hosps.

GALLAGHER, Claire 44 Troutbeck Crescent, Beeston, Nottingham NG9 3BP — MB BS 1993 Lond.

GALLAGHER, Claire Michelle 36A Cavendish Road, London NW6 7XP — MB BS 1989 Lond.

GALLAGHER, Conal 47 Salisbury Road, Cressington Park, Liverpool L19 0PH — MB ChB 1956 Liverp.

GALLAGHER, David (Surgery), 19 High Street, Penistone, Sheffield S36 6BR — MB BS 1977 Newc.; MRCGP 1981; DRCOG 1980; DA Eng. 1983.

GALLAGHER, Dermot Francis Health & Safety Executive, Sovereign House, 110 Queen St., Sheffield S1 2ES Tel: 0114 291 2300 Fax: 0114 291 2345 Email: frank.gallagher@hse.gsi.gov.uk — MB ChB 1980 Newc.; LLB 2002 (Hons.); MRCGP 1984; MFOM RCP Lond. 1996; DRCOG 1983. Med. Insp. of Health & Safety, Health and Safety Exec., Sheff. Socs: Soc. Occupat. Med. Prev: Occupat. Phys. IBH/AMARC Washington Hosp. Tyne & Wear; GP Bishop Auckland.

GALLAGHER, Dominic Martin 151 (Basement Left) Broomhill Drive, Glasgow G11 7ND — MB ChB 1990 Glas.

GALLAGHER, Eleanor Jean Burn Brae Surgery, Hencotes, Hexham NE46 2ED Tel: 01434 603627 Fax: 01434 606373; 7 Leazes Crescent, Hexham NE46 3JX Tel: 01434 604567 — MB ChB 1989 Dundee; BMSc Dund 1986; MRCGP 1993; DRCOG 1992. Prev: Trainee GP Newc. VTS.

GALLAGHER, Elizabeth Gibb 2D Intwood Road, Cringleford, Norwich NR4 6XD — MB ChB 1965 Glas.; BSc Glas. 1957; MRCPsych 1972; DPM Eng. 1970. (Glas.) Med. Mem. - Ment. Health Review Tribunal. Prev: Cons. Psychiat. Towers Hosp. Leicester; Sen. Regist. (Psychiat.) Hellesdon Hosp. Norwich; SHO (Path.) Stobhill Hosp. Glas.

GALLAGHER, Elizabeth Joanne 54 Circular Road, Belfast BT4 2GB — MB BCh BAO 1990 Belf.; MRCGP 1995; DRCOG 1994; DCH Dub. 1993.

GALLAGHER, Francis Joseph 27 Marguerite Park, Newcastle BT33 0PE — MB BCh BAO 1953 Belf. (Qu. Univ. Belf.)

GALLAGHER, Gabrielle Agnes Alison Lea Medical Centre, Calderwood, East Kilbride, Glasgow G74 3BE Tel: 01355 236444; 6 Attow Road, Glasgow G43 1BZ Tel: 0141 632 2527 — MB ChB 1974 Glas.

GALLAGHER, Geraldine Marian 84 Marlborough Park N., Belfast BT9 6HL — MB BCh BAO 1979 Belf.; FRCS Ed. 1984.

GALLAGHER, Gerard Michael 19 Kynaston Close, Harrow Weald, Harrow HA3 6TQ — MB BS 1978 Lond.; MRCS Eng. LRCP Lond. 1978; MRCGP 1983.; DGM RCP Lond. 1985.

GALLAGHER, Mr Herbert William (retired) 80 Belfast Road, Comber, Newtownards BT23 5QP Tel: 02891 878551 — MB BCh BAO Belf. 1939; FRCSI 1976; FRCS Ed. 1946. Prev: Cons. Surg. N. Down. Hosp. Gp. & Banbridge Hosp.

GALLAGHER, Hugh 247 Chipstead Way, Banstead SM7 3JW — MB BS 1994 Lond.

GALLAGHER, Hugh Joseph Glenavy Family Practice, 47 Main Street, Glenavy, Crumlin BT29 4LN Tel: 028 9442 2287 Fax: 028 9442 2100; Tel: 0184 94 22202 — MB BCh BAO 1984 NUI; BSc Belf. 1978; LRCPI & LM, LRCSI & LM 1984; MRCGP 1989; DGM RCP Lond. 1987.

GALLAGHER, Mr Hugh Joseph Royal Victoria Infirmary, Newcastle upon Tyne NE1 4LP Tel: 0141 282 4662 — MB ChB 1988 Glas.; FRCS Glas. 1992; FRCS Gen 2000. (Glas.) Cons. GI Surg., Roy. Vict. Infirm., Newc., Specialist Colorectal & Laparoscope Surg. Socs: Roy. Coll. Surgs.; Assn. of ColoProctol.; Assn. of Surg.s. Prev: SPR (Gen Surg) St Jas. Leeds.

GALLAGHER, James The Health Centre, Victoria Road, Hartlepool TS26 8DB Tel: 01429 272945 Fax: 01429 867797 — MB ChB 1982 Glas.

GALLAGHER, James 6 Attow Road, Glasgow G43 1BZ Tel: 0141 632 2527 — MB ChB 1974 Glas.; MRCPsych 1979. Cons. Psychotherapist. Dykebar Hosp. Paisley. Socs: Roy. Coll. Psychiat.; Scott. Assn. Psychoan. Psychother.

GALLAGHER, James Owen The Health Centre, 20 Duncan Street, Greenock PA15 4LY Tel: 01475 724477; 79 Union Street, Greenock PA16 8BG — MB ChB 1988 Glas.; MRCGP 1992; DGM RCP Lond. 1993; DRCOG 1991. (Glasgow) Prev: SHO (Geriat. Med.) Ravenscraig Hosp. Greenock; SHO (Psychiat.) Dykebar Hosp. Paisley; Ho. Off. (Gen. Med. & Surg.) Roy. Alexandra Hosp. Paisley.

GALLAGHER, James Ronan 13 Denmark Road, Poole BH15 2DB — MB BS 1996 Lond.

GALLAGHER, Janet Elizabeth Family Planning Service, Stanhope Parade Health Centre, Gordon St., South Shields NE34 4JP Tel: 0191 451 6105 Fax: 0191 451 6106 — MB BS 1978 Newc.; MFFP 1994. Contracept. & Sexual Health Serv. Manager; Sen. Clin. Med. Off. (Family Plann.) S. Tyneside Health Care Trust.

GALLAGHER, Mrs Johanna Patricia 45 Main Street, Glenavy, Crumlin BT29 4LN Tel: 0184 94 53738 — MB BCh BAO 1947 NUI. (Univ. Coll. Dub.) Socs: MICGP. Prev: Ho. Surg. & Ho. Phys. St. Vincent's Hosp. Dub.; Ho. Surg. Roy. Albert Edwd. Infirm. Wigan.

GALLAGHER, John Mourneside Medical Centre, 1A Ballycolman Avenue, Strabane BT82 9AF Tel: 028 7138 3737 Fax: 028 7138 3979 — MB BCh BAO 1964 NUI.

GALLAGHER, John (retired) Station Road Surgery, Sowerby Bridge HX6 3AB — MB BCh BAO 1948 Belf.

GALLAGHER, John Charles (retired) Grove House, 35 Church Lane, Normanton WF6 1AD — LRCP LRCS Ed. LRFPS Glas. 1949; DObst RCOG 1962. Prev: Ho. Phys. Law Hosp. Carluke.

GALLAGHER, John Charles Medical Centre, Imphal Barracks BFPO 36 — BM 1979 Soton.; FRCGP 2001; MRCGP I988; DRCOG l983. Civil. Med. Practitioner (GP) Brit. Forces Germany Health Serv. Prev: Trainee GP Newport I. of Wight VTS; Chief Med. Off. (GP) Company Clinic Kitwe, Zambia.

GALLAGHER, John Mark 3 Lowland Road, Stockport SK2 7EG — MB ChB 1991 Dundee.

GALLAGHER, John Martin The Surgery, High Street, Epworth, Doncaster DN9 1EP Tel: 01427 872232 Fax: 01427 874944 — MB BCh BAO 1990 NUI; MRCOP 1998; DRCOG 1995; MMedSc NUI 1992. (University College Dublin) Prev: Trainee GP Doncaster; SHO (Paediat. & O & G) Doncaster Roy. Infirm.; SHO (Med.) Montagu Hosp. MexBoro..

GALLAGHER, John Michael Linfield Surgery, 7 Belmont Road, Portswood, Southampton SO17 2GD Tel: 023 8058 5858 Fax: 023 8039 9858 — MB BS 1971 Newc.; MRCGP 1975; DObst RCOG 1974. Prev: Trainee Gen. Pract. Newc. Vocational Train. Scheme.

GALLAGHER, John Patrick (retired) 45 Main Street, Glenavy, Crumlin BT29 4LN Tel: 0184 94 53738 — LRCPI & LM, LRSCI & LM 1947; LRCPI & LM, LRCSI & LM 1947. JP. Prev: GP Crumlin.

GALLAGHER, Joseph Brendan (retired) Inisfree, Clifton Square, Peterlee SR8 5HQ Tel: 0191 586 2583 — LRCPI & LM, LRCSI & LM 1949. Prev: MRCGP.

GALLAGHER, Julie Margaret Claire 64 Newlands Road, Glasgow G43 2JH Tel: 0141 632 5325; 6/7 Maxwell Street, Morningside, Edinburgh EH10 5HU Tel: 0131 447 4259 — MB ChB 1992 Manch.; DRCOG Glas. 1998. SHO (O & G) St. John's Hosp. Livingstone; GP Regist. Leith Mt. Pract. Edin. Socs: BMA. Prev: SHO (I.D.) Ruchill Hosp. Glas.; SHO (Paediat.) Roy. Hosp. Sick Childr. Glas.; SHO (Paediat. ICU & Infec. Dis.) St. Mary's Hosp. Lond.

GALLAGHER, Kevin Thomas Department of Child Psychiatry, Eaglestone H. C, Standing Way, Milton Keynes MK6 5AZ Tel: 01908 607501 — BM 1987 Soton. SHO (Anaesth.) Nottm. City Hosp.

GALLAGHER, Lorna Miriam Gretta 199 London Road, Twickenham TW1 1EJ — MB BS 1997 Lond.

GALLAGHER, Louis Brian Stephens, TD 19 Staveley Road, Shipley BD18 4HD Tel: 01274 582180 — MB BCh BAO 1966 Belf.; FFA RCS Eng. 1976. Cons. Anaesth. Bradford Hosps. NHS Trust. Socs: Roy. Coll. Anaesth.; BMA; Assn. Anaesth.

GALLAGHER, Louise Martina 43 Woolmead Avenue, London NW9 7AX — MB ChB 1997 Liverp.

GALLAGHER, Mark Michael Department of Cardiological Sciences, The Medical School, St George's Hospital, Cranmer Terrace, London SW17 0RE Tel: 020 8725 5733 Fax: 020 8767 7141 Email: gallagh@sghms.ac.uk — MB BCh BAO 1990 NUI; BSc NUI 1987; MD NUI 1996; MRCPI 1992. (Univ. Coll. Cork) Research Fell. Clin. Cardiol. St. Geo.'s Hosp. Med. Sch. Prev: Regist. Clin. Cardiol. Cork Univ. Hosp.

GALLAGHER, Mary (retired) Dunedin, 67 Clydesdale Road, Bellshill ML4 2QE Tel: 01698 843120 — MB ChB Glas. 1960, DPH 1968. SCMO Gtr. Glas. Area Health Bd. Prev: Ho. Phys. Glas. Roy. Infirm.

GALLAGHER, Michael Christopher John Department of Anesthesia, Central Newfoundland Regional Health Centre, Union St., Grand Falls Windsor NFLD A2A 2EI, Canada Tel: 00 1 709 2922231; 38 Sutherland Avenue, Maida Vale, London W9 2HQ — MB ChB 1983 Liverp.; FRCPC 1994; DA (UK) 1988. Chief Anesthesia Centr. Newfld. Regional Health Center., Canada.

GALLAGHER, Michael Henry 6 Highfield Road, Purley CR8 2JG Tel: 020 8660 6345 — MB BS 1980 Lond.; MRCGP 1986; DFFP 1993.

GALLAGHER, Monica Elizabeth 93 Augharainey Road, Mullaghconnor, Dungannon BT70 3NF — MB BCh BAO 1977 Belf.

GALLAGHER, Morris Stanhope Parade Health Centre, Gordon Street, South Shields NE33 4HX Tel: 0191 455 4621 Fax: 0191 427 3180 — MB BS 1979 Newc.; FRCGP 1991, M 1983; DCCH RCP Ed. RCGP & FCM 1983; DRCOG 1982. Prev: Research Fell. RCGP.

GALLAGHER, Neil James 26 Thompson Road, London SE22 9JR; 1 Chapel Terrace, Brighton BN2 1HB Tel: 01273 696955 — MB BCh BAO 1989 Dub.

GALLAGHER, Owen Thomas Glenavy Family Practice, 47 Main Street, Glenavy, Crumlin BT29 4LN Tel: 028 9442 2287 Fax: 028 9442 2100; 10 Glen Road, Glenavy, Crumlin BT29 4LU — MA Dub. 1992, MB BCh BAO Dub. 1976; MICGP 1986; MRCGP 1985; DObst RCPI 1981; DCH NUI 1981. GP Glenavy. Prev: Med. Off. St. Lukes Hosp. Anna, SE Nigeria; Med. Supt. St. Josephs Hosp. Masaka, Uganda; Trainee GP HornCh..

GALLAGHER, Patricia Mary 66 Bay Road, Wormit, Newport-on-Tay DD6 8LZ — MB ChB 1988 Dundee. Clin. Med. Off. (Community Paediat.) Tayside HB. Prev: SHO (O & G) Stirling Roy. Infirm.

GALLAGHER, Mr Patrick Ael-y-Don, 13 Mayfield Road, Bramhall, Stockport SK7 1JU Tel: 0161 439 7240 — MB ChB 1973 Manch.; BSc (Physiol.) Manch. 1970, MB ChB 1973; FRCS Eng. 1977. Cons. Surg. Stepping Hill Hosp. Stockport.

GALLAGHER, Patrick Gerrard 2 Blenkinsopp Court, Peterlee SR8 1JH — MB BCh BAO 1978 NUI; LRCPI & LM, LRCSI & LM 1978; DRCOG 1983. Socs: BMA; Irish GMC; Assn. Police Surg.

GALLAGHER, Patrick Joseph Department Pathology, Southampton University Hospitals, Tremona Road, Southampton SO16 6YD Tel: 02380 796664 Fax: 02380 705580 Email: pjg4@soton.ac.uk — MB BS Lond. 1967; PhD Soton. 1979; MD Lond. 1980; FRCPath 1986, M 1975. (St. Thos.) Reader (Path.) Soton. Univ. Hosp. Prev: Cons. Path. Bath; Fulbright Vis. Fell. (Path.) Stanford Univ., USA; Jun. Asst. Path. Univ. Camb.

GALLAGHER, Mr Paul 31 Sheepwalk Lane, Townville, Castleford WF10 3HU — MB ChB 1965 Leeds; FRCS Eng. 1972. Prev: Ho. Phys. Profess. Med. Unit St. Jas. Hosp. Leeds; Ho. Surg. & Cas. Off. Leeds Gen. Infirm.

GALLAGHER, Mr Paul Vincent Wilson Lodge, Great Whittington, Newcastle upon Tyne NE19 2HP — MB BS 1990 Newc.; FRCS Ed. 1994.

GALLAGHER, Paula Mary Omagh Health Centre, Mountjoy Road, Omagh BT79 7BA Tel: 028 8224 3521; 73 Dublin Road, Omagh BT78 1HQ Tel: 01662 244158 — MB BCh BAO 1983 Dub.; MRCGP 1987; DRCOG 1986; DCH NUI Dub. 1986; DGM RCP Lond. 1985. GP Omagh.

GALLAGHER, Peter Finian 65 Wellesley Avenue, Belfast BT9 6DG — MB BCh BAO 1976 NUI. (Galway)

GALLAGHER, Sarah Katherine 14 Sandelswood End, Beaconsfield HP9 2NW — MB BS 1997 Lond.

GALLAGHER, Theresa Marion Royal Surrey County Hospital, Egerton Road, Guildford GU2 7XX Tel: 01483 464116 Email: tessgallagher@usa.net — MD 1985 NUI; MPhil Belf. 1993; MB BCh BAO 1977; FRCPI 1993, M 1982; MRCP (UK) 1990; FFA RCSI 1981. Cons. Anaesth. Roy. Surrey Co. Hosp. Prev: Cons. Paediat. Anaesth. Roy. Belf. Hosp. Sick Childr.

GALLAGHER, Thomas Bernard The Rogerstone Practice, Chapel Wood, Western Valley Road, Rogerstone, Newport NP10 9DU Tel: 01633 893272 Fax: 01633 895079 — MB BCh BAO 1987 NUI; DGM RCP Lond. 1990. SHO (O & G) Llandough Hosp. Cardiff.

GALLAGHER, Valerie Anne Selsdon Park Medical Practice, 95 Addington Road, South Croydon CR2 8LG Tel: 020 8657 0067 Fax: 020 8657 0037 — MB BS 1989 Lond.; MRCGP 1993. (Charing Cross and Westm.) Prev: Trainee GP Croydon VTS.

GALLAGHER, Wendy Jayne Department of Anaesthesia, St Bartholomew's Hospital, West Smithfield, London EC1 Tel: 020 7601 7518 Fax: 020 7601 7520 — MB BS 1980 Lond.; FFARCS 1984. Cons. Anaesth. & Pain Relief St. Bart. Hosp. Lond.

GALLAGLEY, Andrew Chorley South Ribble & District General Hospital, Preston Road, Chorley PR7 1PP Tel: 01257 245152; 2 Windsor Drive, Brinscall, Near Chorley, Chorley PR6 8PX Tel: 01254 830531 Email: andygee@doctors.org.uk — MB ChB 1990 Leeds; MRCPsych 2001. Specialist Regist. Old Age Psychiat., Manch. Train. Scheme. Prev: SHO Basic Train. Scheme (Psychiat.) Lancs. & S. Cumbria.

GALLAHER, Janet Michelle, Capt. RAMC 4 Cruise Road, Sheffield S11 7EF — MB ChB 1995 Sheff. Trainee GP Regist. RAMC.

GALLAND, Mr Robert Brian Little Orchard, Gardeners Lane, Upper Basildon, Reading RG8 8NL — MB ChB 1971 Manch.; MB ChB (Hons. Surg.) Manch. 1971; MD Manch. 1983; FRCS Eng. 1976. Cons. Surg. Roy. Berks. Hosp. Reading; Sen. Regist. (Surg.) Hammersmith Hosp. Lond. & Reading Hosps.; Surg. Research & RCS Trav. Fell.sh. 1980-81; Mem. Ct. Examr. RCS. Socs: Vasc. Surg. Soc.; Assn. Surg. Prev: Price Research Fell. Univ. Louisville Kentucky USA; Regist. (Surg.) W. Middlx. & Hammersmith Hosps.; Ho. Surg. & SHO (Surg.) Manch. Roy. Infirm.

GALLANNAUGH, Mr Stuart Charles The Horder Centre for Arthritis, St Johns Road, Crowborough TN6 1XP Tel: 01892 665577

Fax: 01892 662142; Trumpetts Farm, Bodle Street Green, Hailsham BN27 4RD Tel: 01323 833734 Fax: 01323 833318 Email: trumpetts@compuserve.com — MB BS 1961 Lond.; MS Lond. 1973; FRCS Eng. 1969; FRCS Ed. 1969. (St. Thos.) p/t Surg. Dir. Horder Centre for Arthritis CrowBoro. Socs: Fell. Roy. Soc. Med. (Ex-Pres. Orthop. Sect.); Brit. Assn. Surg. Knee; Brit. Hip. Soc. Prev: Cons. Surg. Orthop. Conquest Hosp. Hastings; Regional Advisor Orthop. Surg. RCS Eng.; Cons. Surg. Orthop. St. Geo. Hosp. Lond. & Redhill Hosp.

GALLANT, Michael John (retired) The Old Rectory, Ashley, Market Harborough LE16 8DH Tel: 01858 565518 Fax: 01858 565518 — MRCS Eng. LRCP Lond. 1959; FRCR 1975; FFR 1971; DMRD Eng. 1968. Cons. Radiol. N.ampton Gen. Hosp. Prev: Sen. Regist. (Diag. X-Ray) W.m. Hosp.

GALLARD, Stephanie Clair Alyson 15 Wellington Road, Wallasey CH45 2JR — MB ChB 1996 Liverp.; BSc (Hons.) (Pharmacy) 1990.

GALLEGOS, Mr Christopher Robert Rollings Royal United Hospital, Combe Park, Bath BA1 3NG Tel: 01225 824574 Fax: 01225 824192; Waverley House, 53 Bloomfield Avenue, Bath BA2 3AE — MB BS 1983 Lond.; MS Lond. 1993; FRCS (Urol) 1994; FRCS Eng. 1987. Cons. Urol. Roy. United Hosp. Bath. Prev: Sen. Regist. (Urol.) Roy. United Hosp. Bath.

GALLEGOS, Mr Nicholas Charles Weston General Hospital, Grange Road, Uphill, Weston Super Mare BS23 4TQ — MB BS 1981 Lond.; MS Lond. 1993; FRCS Eng. 1986; FRCS Ed. 1985. Cons. Surg. W.. Gen. Hosp. Prev: Sen. Regist. Univ. Coll. & Middlx. Sch. Med.; Regist. (Surg.) Wexham Pk. Hosp. Slough.

GALLEN, Bedelia Connolly (retired) 2 The Grove, Collearn, Auchterarder PH3 1PT Tel: 01964 663158 — MB ChB 1936 Glas.; DPH Glas. 1941. Prev: GP, Kensington Lond. & Ealing Lond..

GALLEN, Derek Desmond Oxford PGMDE, The Triangle, Roosevelt Drive, Headington OX3 7XP Tel: 01865 740644 Fax: 01865 740641 Email: dgallen@oxford-pgmde.co.uk; 139 Doddington Road, Earls Barton, Northampton NN6 0NW — FRCGP 1996; MRCGP 1988; DRCOG 1986; 1985 Lond.; M.Med. Ed. 2001 (Dundee); DCH RCP 1985 Lond.; BSc Lond. 1980, MB BS 1983; MRCGP 1988; DRCOG 1986; DCH RCP Lond. 1985. (Univ. Coll. Hosp.) Director of Post Grad. Gen. Pract. Educat., Oxf. Deanary.

GALLEN, Ian William Diabetes Centre, Wycombe General Hospital, High Wycombe HP11 2TT Tel: 01494 526161 Fax: 01494 425865 — MB BS 1983 London; MD 1990 Nottingham; MRCP 1986 UK; FRCP 2000 UK. (Westminster Medical Schooll) Cons. Phys. (Diabetes) Wycombe Gen. Hosp. Socs: Soc. Endocrinol.; Roy. Coll. Phys.s Lond.; Brit. Diabetic Assn. Prev: Sen. Regist. (Gen. Med. & Endocrinol.) Roy. Devon, Exeter Hosp. & Bristol Roy. Infirm.; Fell. (Endocrine) NW Univ. Med. Sch. Chicago, USA; Regist. Univ. Hosp. Nottm.

GALLETLY, Neil Philip Flat 4, 12 Kew Gdns. Road, Richmond TW9 3HG — MB BS 1993 Lond.; BA Camb. 1989, MA 1993; MRCP (UK) 1997. (UMDS) Specialist Regist. (Gastroenterol.) Chelsea & W.minster Hosp. Lond. Prev: SHO (Neurol.) Roy. Free Hosp.; SHO (Communicable Dis.) St. Geo. Hosp. Lond.; SHO (Respirat. & ITU) Roy. Brompton Hosp. Lond.

GALLETLY, Susan Catrina Chorley & District Hospital, Preston Road, Chorley PR7 1PP; 12 Eton Park, Midgery Lane, Fulwood, Preston PR2 9NL — MB ChB 1977 Dundee; MRCP (UK) 1981; FRCR 1986. Cons. Radiol. Chorley & Dist. Hosp. Prev: Sen. Regist. (Radiol.) Manch. Univ. Med. Sch.; Regist. (Radiol.) Manch. Univ. Med. Sch.; Regist. (Med.) Vict. Hosp. Blackpool.

GALLI, Emilia Maria (retired) Wild Oak Cottage, Wild Oak Lane, Trull, Taunton TA3 7JS Tel: 01823 278057 Email: emg@casamia.free-online.co.uk — MB ChB 1965 Glas.; FFA RCS Eng. 1968. Prev: Sen. Regist. (Anaesth.) Vict. & W.. Infirm. Glas.

GALLI, Peter Richard School Road Health Centre, School Road, Kingskerwell, Newton Abbot TQ12 3HN Tel: 01803 873551 Fax: 01803 875774; 21 Broadlands, Shaldfon, Teignmouth TQ14 0EH — MB BS 1967 Lond. (Middlesex) Socs: Torbay Med. Soc.; Brit. Italian Med. Soc.

GALLIFORD, David (retired) 226 Hillmorton Road, Rugby CV22 5BG Tel: 01788 565101 — MB ChB Birm. 1959; DObst RCOG 1961; DCH Eng. 1962. Prev: GP Rugby.

GALLIFORD, Jack William Primrose House, 13 Albany Hill, Tunbridge Wells TN2 3RX; Meadow Cottage, 122 Waggon Road, Hadley Wood, Barnet EN4 0PN — MB BS 1998 Lond.; MB BS Lond 1998; BSc Lond 1997. (Royal Free Hospital School of Medicine) SHO N. Middlx. Hosp. Edmonton. Prev: Ho. Surg. Hemel Hempstead Hosp.; Ho. Phys. Roy. Free Hosp.

GALLIFORD, Thomas Michael 13 Albany Hill, Tunbridge Wells TN2 3RX — MB BS 1998 Lond.; MB BS Lond 1998; BSc (Hons) 1995. (Imperial College School of Medicine, St. Mary's)

GALLIMORE, Charles Hill Oakham Medical Practice, Cold Overton Road, Oakham LE15 6NT Tel: 01572 722621/2; The Stone House, Wing, Oakham LE15 8SD Tel: 01572 737343 — MB BChir 1967 Camb.; MA Camb. 1967; MRCS Eng. LRCP Lond. 1966; DA Eng. 1971; DObst RCOG 1968. (Lond. Hosp.) Socs: BMA. Prev: SHO (Anaesth.) St. And. Hosp. Billericay; Ho. Surg. Roy. United Hosp. Bath; Receiv. Room Off. Lond. Hosp.

GALLIMORE, David John The Sheilings, Lodge Lane, Kingswinford DY6 9XE; The Limes, 172 High St, Lye, Stourbridge DY9 8LL — MB BCh 1974 Wales; MRCGP 1978; DRCOG 1976. Clin Asst. (Neonat.. Ultrasonography) New Cross Hosp. Wolverhampton.

GALLIMORE, Graham Reginald Three Hedges, Cerne Abbas, Dorchester DT2 7JT — MB BS 1971 Lond.; MRCPsych 1976. (St. Geo.) Cons. Psychiat. Forston Clinic Herrison Dorchester.

GALLIMORE, Jacqueline Casalini, 17 Main Road, Milford, Stafford ST17 0UL — MB BS 1988 Lond. Clin. Asst. (Psychiat.) St. Geo. Hosp. Stafford. Prev: SHO (Psychiat.) Highcroft Hosp. Staffs.; Ho. Off. (Surg.) Roy. Hosp. Wolverhampton; Ho. Off. (Med.) Worcester Roy. Infirm.

GALLIMORE, John Robert Moss Street Surgery, Chadsmnoor, Cannock WS11 2DE Tel: 01543 504477 Fax: 01543 504636; Casalini, 17 Main Road, Milford, Stafford ST17 0UL — MB BS 1988 Lond.; DRCOG 1991.

GALLIVAN, Michael Patrick (retired) Newlands, 13 Waungron Road, Llandaff, Cardiff CF5 2JJ — MB BCh 1969 Wales; MRCS Eng. LRCP Lond. 1971.

GALLIVAN, Philippa Rachel 12 Forthview Road, Blackhall, Edinburgh EH4 2DE — MB BChir 1990 Camb.

GALLIVAN, Richard James Goldington Avenue Surgery, 85 Goldington Avenue, Bedford MK40 3DB Tel: 01234 349531 Email: richard.gallivan@gp-e81047.nhs.uk; 32 Kimbolton Avenue, Bedford MK40 3AA — MB BS 1982 Lond. (St Mary's) Prev: Trainee GP Bedford Gen. Hosp. VTS; Ho. Surg. St. Chas. Hosp. Lond.

GALLIVAN, Terence James (retired) Chiverton, 6 Gwent Close, Garston, Watford WD25 9LG — LMSSA 1953 Lond.; MRCGP 1974. Prev: Health & Temperance Dir. Brit. Union Confer. of Seventh-Day Adventists.

GALLON, Maureen Elizabeth Westholm, 15 Carlogie Road, Carnoustie DD7 6DA Tel: 01241 55101 — MB ChB 1977 Aberd. Prev: Lect. (Path.) Univ. Aberd.

GALLOP, Amanda Joy Long Clawson Medical Practice, The Surgery, The Sands, Long Clawson, Melton Mowbray LE14 4PA Tel: 01664 822214/5 — MB BS 1979 Nottm.

GALLOP, Andrew Michael (retired) Rycart House, Belvoir Road, Denton, Grantham NG32 1LJ Tel: 01476 870345 — MB BS Lond. 1961; DA (UK) 1965. Prev: Regist. (Anaesth.) Norf. & Norwich Hosp.

GALLOP, Deidre Mary (Gould) Swingbridge Surgery, Swingbridge Road, Grantham NG31 7XT Tel: 01476 571166 Fax: 01476 570397; Ryecourt House, Belvoir Road, Denton, Grantham NG32 1LJ Tel: 01476 870345 — MB ChB 1976 Birm.; DCH Eng. 1978. GP Grantham, Lincs. Prev: GP Mildenhall Suff.; Clin. Asst. (Paediat.) W. Suff. Hosp. Bury St. Edmunds.

GALLOP-EVANS, Eve Mei Ling Velindre Hospital, Cardiff CF14 2TL Tel: 029 2061 5888; 20 Palace Road, Cardiff CF5 2AF Email: eve@meurig.com — MB BS (Hons.) Lond. 1988; BSc (Hons.) Lond. 1985; MRCP (UK) 1991; Ph D (Cardiff) 1997. Specialist Regist. Clin. Oncol. Prev: MRC Train. Fell. (Med.) Univ. Wales Coll. Med. Cardiff; Regist. (Gen. Med. & Chest Med.) Caerphilly & Llandough Hosps. Cardiff; SHO (Med.) Hammersmith Hosp. Lond.

GALLOW, Richard Jonathan The Surgery, Parkwood Drive, Warners End, Hemel Hempstead HP1 2LD Tel: 01442 250117 Fax: 01442 256185; Tel: 01923 856291 Email: richardgallow@hotmail.com — MRCS Eng. LRCP Lond. 1971; MRCGP 1977. GP Tutor Hemel Hempstead Dist.

GALLOWAY, Alexander McLaren Cosham Health Centre, Vectis Way, Portsmouth PO6 3AW Tel: 023 9238 1117 Fax: 0223 9221

4266 — MB BS 1981 Lond.; MRCGP 1985; DRCOG 1983. (Middlx.)

GALLOWAY, Alexandra Jane 35C Cleghorn Street, Dundee DD2 2NL — MB ChB 1998 Dund.; MB ChB Dund 1998.

GALLOWAY, Alison Wrythe Green Surgery, Wrythe Lane, Carshalton SM5 2RE Tel: 020 8669 3232/1717 Fax: 020 8773 2524; 4 Brier Lea, Tadworth KT20 6TR Tel: 01737 833112 — MB BS 1983 Lond.; MRCGP 1987; DRCOG 1987; DCH RCP Lond. 1986.

GALLOWAY, Angela Royal Victoria Infirmary, Queen Victora Road, Newcastle upon Tyne NE1 4LP Tel: 0191 282 4884 Fax: 0191 201 0156 Email: angela.galloway@nuth.northy.nhs.uk — MB BS 1978 Lond.; BSc (Hons.) Lond. 1975; MD Liverp. 1993; MRCS Eng. LRCP Lond. 1978; FRCPath 1996, M 1985. (Roy. Free) Cons. Microbiol. Newc. Roy. Vict. Infirm. Newcaslte upon Tyne. Prev: Cons. Microbiol. N. Durh. Acute Hosps. NHS Trust; Cons. Microbiol. St. Helens & Knowsley HA; Sen. Regist. (Med. Microbiol.) Roy. Liverp. Hosp.

GALLOWAY, Colin Alexander Stewart (retired) Heathcote, 10 Muirfield Road, Inverness IV2 4AY Tel: 01463 231445 — MB ChB 1960 Ed.; FRCP Ed. 1972, M 1963; FRCPCH 1997; DCH RCPS Glas. 1962. Prev: Cons. Paediat. Raigmore Hosp. Inverness.

GALLOWAY, Colin Francis 7 Torbothie Road, Shotts ML7 5JJ — MB BS 1994 Lond.

GALLOWAY, David Brian Medicines Assessment Research Unit (MARU), Ward 9, Aberdeen Royal Infirmary, Foresterhill, Aberdeen AB25 2XG Tel: 01224 553096 Fax: 01223 840559 Email: d.b.galloway@abdn.ac.uk; 212 Springfield Road, Aberdeen AB15 8JL — MB ChB 1964 Aberd.; FFPM RCP UK 1991; FRCP Lond. 1995; FRCP Ed. 1993; MRCP (UK) 1971; DObst RCOG 1966. (Aberd.) Dir. Meds. Assessm. Research Unit Aberd. Socs: Fell. Roy. Soc. Med.; BMA; Aberd. M-C Soc. Prev: Cons. Clin. Pharmacol. Pharma Industry; Dir. Cardiovasc./Critical Care Gps. Upjohn Ltd. Crawley; Dir. Clin. Research Napp Research Centre Camb.

GALLOWAY, Mr David James Gartnavel General Hospital, 1053 Great Western Road, Glasgow G12 0YN Tel: 0141 211 3192 Fax: 0141 211 3211; Email: djgalloway@lineone.net — MD 1985 Glas.; MB ChB 1977; FRCS Glas. 1981. Cons. Gen. & Colorectal Surg. W. Gartnavel Gen. Glas. Socs: Surg. Research Soc.; Brit. Assn. Surg. Oncol. Prev: Clin. Fell. Surg. Oncol. Memor. Sloan Kettering Cancer Center New York USA; Lect. & Hon. Sen. Regist. (Surg.) W.. Infirm. Glas.; Surg. Regist. W. Scot. Rotat. Train. Scheme in Gen. Surg.

GALLOWAY, Dennis Charles (retired) 6 Lugg View, Hereford HR1 1JF Tel: 01432 50800 — MB ChB 1939 Birm.; FRCOG 1963, M 1948. Hon. Consg. O & G Bishop Auckland Gen. Hosp.

GALLOWAY, Donald Walter 22 Broad Street, Carlisle CA1 2AQ Tel: 01228 42438 — MB ChB 1979 Ed.; FFA RCSI 1985. Cons. Anaesth. Cumbld. Infirm. Carlisle.

GALLOWAY, Fiona Dorothy Beech House Surgery, St. Bridget's Lane, Egremont CA22 2BD Tel: 01946 820203 Fax: 01946 820372; Orchard Brow, Haile, Egremont CA22 2PD Tel: 01946 841313 Fax: 01946 820372 Email: galloway1@btinternet.com — MB ChB 1979 Liverp.; FRCGP 2000; MRCGP 1983; DCH RCP Glas. 1985; DRCOG 1984. (Liverpool) Socs: Cumbria Fac. Roy. Coll. of GPs (Hon. Sec.).

GALLOWAY, Heather Jane 20 Selborne Avenue, Low Fell, Gateshead NE9 6ET — MB BS 1982 Newc.; DCCH RCP Ed. 1986.

GALLOWAY, Ian William Young Kellyfield, 8 Lawhill Road, Dollar FK14 7BG — MB ChB 1969 Ed.; BSc (Med. Sci.) Ed. 1966, MB ChB 1969.

GALLOWAY, Mr James Brown Wallace (retired) 25A Park Circus, Ayr KA7 2DJ Tel: 01292 265293 — MB ChB 1956 Glas.; MA Glas. 1950, MB ChB 1956; FRCS Glas. 1962; FRCS Ed. 1962; FRCS Eng. 1965. Prev: Cons. Gen. Surg. Garrick Hosp. Stranraer.

GALLOWAY, Jean Christina Ruth Ingerlsey Unit, Macclesfield District General Hospital, Victoria Road, Macclesfield SK10 3BL Tel: 01625 421000 Fax: 01625 663107 — MB ChB 1977 Birm.; MRCP (UK) 1982; MRCPsych 1985; FRCPsych 1999. Cons. Phychiat. Macclesfield Dist. Gen. Hosp.; Chair of Basic Train. Subcommitee of N.W. PostGrad. Deanery (E.) Spenalty Train. Comm.. Psychiat.. Socs: Manch. Med. Soc. Prev: Cons. Psychiat (Community Psychiat. & Old Age Psychiat.) Stepping Hill Hosp. Stockport; Sen. Regist. (Psychiat.) Univ. Hosp. S. Manch.

GALLOWAY, John Kerr Lorn & Islands Distric General Hospital, Glen Gallan Road, Oban PA34 4HH Tel: 01631 567500; Ach-Na-Clach, Clachan Seil, Isle ofSeil, Oban PA34 4TL Tel: 01852 300264 — MB ChB 1965 Glas.; DMRD Eng. 1970. (Glas.) p/t Cons. Radiol. Lorn & Is.s Dist. Gen. Hosp. Oban. Prev: Cons. Radiol. Vale of Leven Dist. Gen. Hosp.; Cons. Radiol. Inverclyde Dist., Argyll & Clyde HB; Asst. Lect. Anat. Dept. Glas. Univ.

GALLOWAY, Mr John Millie Dow (retired) Cherry Trees, Kemp Road, Swanland, North Ferriby HU14 3LZ — MB ChB 1960 Ed.; ChM Ed. 1969, MB ChB 1960; FRCS Ed. 1964. Cons. Surg. Hull Hosp. Gps.

GALLOWAY, John Murray St James House Surgery, County Court Road, King's Lynn PE30 5SY Tel: 01553 774221 Fax: 01553 692181; Darkwood, St. Augustines Way, South Wootton, King's Lynn PE30 3TE Tel: 01553 675010 — MB BS 1977 Lond.; FRCP (UK) 1997, MR 1980; MRCGP 1984. (Middlx.) Hosp. Pract. (Gen. Med.) Qu. Eliz. Hosp. King's Lynn; Steering Gp. Mem. Primary Care Soc. Gastroenterol. Prev: Regist. (Med.) Lister Hosp. Stevenage.

GALLOWAY, John Perryman Glamis Medical Practice, Glamis Centre, Glenrothes KY7 4RH Tel: 01592 771177 Fax: 01592 631208 — MB ChB 1976 Ed.

GALLOWAY, Lynne 2 Blackfaulds Street, Coalsnaughton, Tillicoultry FK13 6JR — MB ChB 1998 Aberd.; MB ChB Aberd 1998.

GALLOWAY, Malcolm James 13 Ashbourne Avenue, London E18 1PQ — MB BS 1997 Lond.; BSc (Hons) 1994. (Royal London and St. Bartholomews) Specialist Regist. (Histopath.), Roy. Lond. & St. Bartholomews Hosps. Prev: SHO (Histopath.), UCL.

GALLOWAY, Michael John City Hospitals Sunderland NHS Trust, Sunderland Royal Hospital, Kayll Rd, Sunderland SR4 7TP Tel: 0191 565 6256 — MB BS 1977 Lond.; MBA Keele 1994; BSc Lond. 1974, MD 1987; FRCP Lond. 1994; FRCP Ed. 1992; MRCP (UK) 1980; MRCS Eng. LRCP Lond. 1977; MRCPath 1986; FRCPath 1996. (Royal Free) Cons. Haemat. Sunderland Roy. Hosp. Prev: Sen. Regist. (Haemat.) Roy. Liverp. Hosp.; Wellcome Research Fell. Roy. Liverp. Hosp.; Regist. (Haemat.) Roy. Liverp. Hosp.

GALLOWAY, Mr Nicholas Robert 14 Park Terrace, The Park, Nottingham NG1 5DN Tel: 0115 941 1366 — MB ChB Camb. 1959; BA Camb. 1956; MD Ed. 1970; FRCS Eng. 1966; DO Eng. 1963; FRCOphth 1988. (Camb. & Ed.) Emerit. Cons., Qu. Med. Centre Nottm. Socs: Fell. Roy. Soc. Med.; Bd. Mem Europ. Assoc for vision and Eye Research. Prev: Sen. Regist. Moorfields Eye Hosp. Lond.; SHO (Ophth.) Edin. Roy. Infirm.; Ho. Surg. Edin. W.. Gen. Hosp.

GALLOWAY, Paul David Marston Medical Centre, 24 Cherwell Drive, Headington, Oxford OX3 0LY Tel: 01865 761234 Fax: 01865 74406; 44 Eaton Road, Appleton, Abingdon OX13 5JH — MB ChB 1987 Sheff.

GALLOWAY, Mr Peter Hamilton Plymouth Royal Eye Infirmary, Plymouth PL4 6PL; 12 Station Road, South Brent TQ10 9BE Email: p_galloway@hotmail.com — MB BS 1994 Newc.; FRCOphth; BMedSc Newc. 1991. (Newcastle upon Tyne) Specialist Regist. (Ophth.) S. W. Rotat. Plymouth Exeter Bristol; SHO (Ophth) W. Norwich Hosp. Socs: Fell.. Roy. Coll. Opthalmol. Prev: Ho. Off. (Med.) Roy. Vict. Infirm. Newc.; SHO (Opthalmology) W. Norwich Hosp.; SHO (Ophth.) Manch. Roy. Eye Hosp.

GALLOWAY, Peter John Department of Clinical Biochemistry, Royal Hospital for Sick Children, Glasgow G3 8SF Tel: 0141 201 0345 Email: peter.galloway@yoskhill.scot.nhs.uk — MB ChB 1987 Ed.; BSc (Med. Sci.) Ed. 1984; MRCP (UK) 1991; DCH Glas. 1993; MRCPath 1997. (Edinburgh) Cons. Clin. Biochem., Roy. Hosp. for Sick Childr./N. Galsgow NHS Trust, Glas. Prev: Regist. (Med.) Lothian HB.; Specialist Regist. (Clin. Chem.) Glas.

GALLOWAY, Raymond William (retired) 52 Knowsley Road, Liverpool L19 0PG Tel: 0151 427 5113 Fax: 0151 427 5113 — MD Liverp. 1961, MB ChB 1953, DMRD 1957; DObst RCOG 1955; FRCR 1959; DMRD Eng. 1957. Prev: Cons. Radiol. Liverp. DHA.

GALLOWAY, Robert Kemp (retired) 28 Douglas Gardens, Uddingston, Glasgow G71 7HB Tel: 01698 815000 Email: rkglloway@netscapeonline.co.uk — MB ChB Ed. 1958; FRCS Ed. 1966; FRCOG 1979, M 1966. Prev: Cons. Obst. Bellshill Matern. Hosp. & Cons. Gyn. Monklands Dist. Gen. Hosp. Airdrie.

GALLOWAY, Robert Neil (retired) 7Abbey Farm, St Bees CA27 0DY Tel: 01946 822424 — MB BChir 1954 Camb.; BA Camb. 1951, MB BChir 1954; FRCGP 1988; DObst RCOG 1956.

GALLOWAY, Ronald Matthew 1A Ardenlee Avenue, Belfast BT6 0AA — MB BCh BAO 1961 Dub.

GALLOWAY, Rosmairi Johnstone Mooredge, Chapel St., Carluke ML8 4BD — MB ChB 1988 Glas.; BSc Glas. 1985; DFFP 1995; DCCH 1998. Staff Grade Doctor, Community Child Health, Lanarksh. Primary Care NHS Trust.

GALLOWAY, Sarah Caroline 14 Park Terrace, The Park, Nottingham NG1 5DN — MB BS 1992 Lond.; MRCGP 2000; DRCOG 1994; DFFP 1997. (St. George Hospital Medical School) GP Retainer S. Brent Health Centre Devon. Socs: MPS; MRCGP. Prev: Med. Off. Kunde Hosp. Nepal.

GALLOWAY, Sheila Joan Psychiatric Day Unit, Whyteman's Brae, Victoria Hospital, Kirkcaldy KY1 2ND; Eden Villa, The Barony, Cupar KY15 5ER — MB ChB 1977 Aberd.; MRCPsych 1985. Assoc. Specialist (Psychiat.) Vict. Hosp. Kirkcaldy.

GALLOWAY, Simon Jonathan 14 South Parade, Pudsey LS28 8NZ — MB ChB 1995 Leeds.

GALLOWAY, Mr Simon William Department of Surgery, Royal Liverpool University Hospital, Prescot St., Liverpool L7 8XP Tel: 0151 706 4170; 1 Merecroft, Great Boughton, Chester CH3 5US Tel: 01244 345916 — MB ChB 1988 Liverp.; FRCS Eng. 1992.

GALLOWAY, Susan McLaren Tel: 0131 228 6081 Fax: 0131 229 4330 — MB ChB 1976 Ed.; FRCGP 2000; DCH Glas. 1979; DRCOG 1979.

GALLOWAY, William Hugh (retired) 312 Queen's Road, Aberdeen AB15 8DT Tel: 01224 314651 — MB ChB 1939 Ed.; MD Ed. 1964; DCH Eng. 1946; FRCP Ed. 1952, M 1948. Prev: Cons. Paediatr. Aberd. Special Hosp. Gp.

GALLWEY, Barbara Ann Annfield Plain Surgery, Durham Road, Annfield Plain, Stanley DH9 7TD Tel: 01207 215005 — MB BCh BAO 1979 Dub.

GALLWEY, Patrick Lionel Grattan St Alban, 8 Lyndhurst Road, Exeter EX2 4PA Tel: 01392 425525 Fax: 01392 421889 Email: plg@saint-alban.com; Tel: 01364 621462 Fax: 01364 621462 — MB BS 1956 Lond.; FRCPsych 1980, M 1971; DPM Eng. 1960. (St. Thos.) Indep. Medico-Legal Consultancy; Vis. Consg. Psychiat. HM Prison Exeter; Tutor Psychother. Butler Clinic Devon. Socs: Exeter Medico-Legal Soc.; Expert Witness Inst.; Fell.Roy.Soc.Med. Prev: Cons. Forens. Psychiat. Butler Clinic Devon; Cons. Forens. Psychiat. St. Geo.s Hosp. Lond.; Sen. Tutor (Psychother.) Inst. Psychother. Lond.

GALPIN, Grant William 4 Crown Court, Sun Hill, Cowes PO31 7HZ — MB ChB 1991 Cape Town.

GALPIN, Oliver Patrick (retired) Craigfryn, 22 Roumania Crescent, Llandudno LL30 1UP Tel: 01492 876250 — MB BS Lond. 1950; FRCP Lond. 1976, M 1959. Chairm. St David's Hosp. Llandudno. Prev: Cons. Phys. Gwynedd HA.

GALT, Owen Vaughan 29 Rivelin Valley Road, Sheffield S6 5FE — MB BS 1996 Lond.

GALTON, Clare Judith 27 Hillway, Highgate, London N6 6QB — MB BChir 1993 Camb. Socs: MRCP (UK).

GALTON, Professor David Jeremy Department of Medicine, St Bartholomew's Hospital, West Smithfield, London EC1A 7BE Tel: 020 7882 6064, 020 8348 3309 Email: djgalton@mds.qmw.ac.uk; 27 Hillway, London N6 6QB — BSc (1st Class Hons); MB BS (Hons.) Lond. 1960; MSc (Biochem.) Lond. 1962; FRCP Lond. 1976, M 1964; FRCOphth 1989. (Univ. Coll. Hosp.) Prof. Human Metab. Univ. Lond.; Cons. Phys. i/c Dept. Diabetes & Lipids St. Bart. Hosp. Lond. & Moorfields Eye Hosp Lond. Socs: Chairm. Brit. Hyperlipidaemia Assoc.; Sec. Europ. Atherosclerosis Soc.; Brit. Diabetic Assn. Prev: Lect. (Clin. Biochem.) Roy. Postgrad. Med. Sch. Lond.; Research Fell. Nat. Inst. Health Bethesda, USA; Ho. Phys. Univ. Coll. Hosp.

GALTON, Ernest Manuel Goitein (retired) 5 West Heath Lodge, Branch Hill, London NW3 7LU Tel: 020 7435 5558 — MB BS 1930 Lond.; MRCS Eng. LRCP Lond. 1928; DOMS Eng. 1936. Prev: Liston Gold Medal, Univ. Coll. Hosp. Liston Gold Medal, Univ. Coll. Hosp.

GALTON, James Seth 27 Hillway, London N6 6QB — MB 1994 Birm.

GALTON-FENZI, Fiona Caroline Evelyn Kings Corner Surgery, Kings Road, Ascot SL5 0AE Tel: 01344 623181 Fax: 01344 875129 — MB BS 1981 Lond.; BA (Hons.) Jurisprudence Oxf. 1991; MRCGP 1985; DRCOG 1983. (Westm.) Med. Adviser Ealing, Hammersmith & Hounslow FHSA.

GALTREY, Anne Cecilia Edge Hill Health Centre, Crosfield Road, Liverpool L7 5QL Tel: 0151 260 2777 — MB ChB 1973 Liverp.; MRCGP 1977; DObst RCOG 1975.

GALUSZKA, John Andrew Victoria House Surgery, Victoria Road, Bicester OX26 6PB Tel: 01869 248585 — MB ChB 1980 Birm.; MRCGP 1985; DCH RCP Lond. 1983; DRCOG 1982. Prev: SHO (Obst.) Derby City Hosp.; SHO (Paediat.) Derby Childr. Hosp.

GALVAN DE LA HOZ, Alfonso 63 Wolsey Road, East Molesey KT8 9EW — LMS 1986 Complutense de Madrid.

GALVANI, David William 14 Reservoir Road N., Birkenhead CH42 8LU — MB ChB 1979 Liverp.; FRCP 1998; Cert Med Educat 2001; MD Liverp. 1990. Cons. Haemat. Arrowe Pk. Hosp. Wirral; Clin. Tutor Arrowe Pk. Hosp., Wirral. Prev: Clin. Lect. (Haemat.) Univ. Liverp.

GALVIN, Elizabeth Anne Susan Woodlands Surgery, 55 Southend Road, Hockley SS5 4PZ Tel: 01702 202514 Fax: 01702 204110 — MB BS 1971 Lond.; MRCS Eng. LRCP Lond. 1971; DObst RCOG 1973. (Roy. Free)

GALVIN, Fionuala Delia Maria 5 Braemar Road, Brentford TW8 0NR — MB BCh BAO 1990 NUI.

GALVIN, Gerard Paul 2 Skip Lane, Walsall WF5 3LL — MB BCh BAO 1974 NUI; MRCP (UK) 1979. (Cork) Regist. (Haemat.) Kingston Gen. Hosp. Hull. Prev: Regist. (Gen. Med.) Hull Roy. Infirm.; Regist. (Gen. Med.) Geo. Eliot Hosp. Nuneaton; Ho. Phys. St. Finbarr's Hosp. Cork.

GALVIN, Hazel Patricia Elm House, 89 Pontefract Road, High Ackworth, Pontefract WF7 7EF — MB ChB 1967 Leeds. Staff Grade (Paediat. Oncol.) St. Jas. Univ. Hosp. Leeds. Socs: Brit. Paediat. Assn.

GALVIN, Helen Louise Department of Dermatology, Halifax General Hospital, Salterhebble, Halifax HX3 0PW Tel: 01422 357171 — MB ChB 1980 Leeds; MB ChB (Hons.) Leeds 1980. Assoc. Specialist (Dermat.) Halifax Gen. Hosp.

GALVIN, John (retired) 45 Fitzwilliam Street, Wath upon Dearne, Rotherham S63 7HG Tel: 01709 877580 — MB ChB Leeds 1952. Prev: Ho. Surg. & Orthop. Off. Gen. Infirm. Leeds.

GALVIN, Michael Christopher Elm House, 89 Pontefract Road, High Ackworth, Pontefract WF7 7EF — MB ChB 1967 Leeds; FRCP Lond. 1991; FRCPath. 1990, M 1977; MRCP (UK) 1973. Cons. (Clin. Haemat.) Pinderfields Hosp. Wakefield.

GALVIN, Timothy John Heath House Surgery, Free School Lane, Halifax HX1 2PS Tel: 01422 365533 Fax: 01422 345851 — MB ChB 1979 Leeds; BSc Hons. (Med. Microbiol.) Leeds 1976, MB ChB 1979. (Leeds) Socs: Brit. Assoc. Sport and Med.

GALWAY, John Edgar (retired) Tara, Brompton Park, Derryhale, Portadown, Craigavon BT62 3SP Tel: 01762 871757 — MD Belf. 1972, MB BCh BAO 1965; FFA RCSI 1968. Dir. Regional Hyperbaric Med. Unit. Prev: Cons. Anaesth. S.. Health & Social Servs. Bd.

GALWAY, John Patrick Muckamore Abbey Hospital, Antrim BT41 4SH Tel: 018494 63333; 89 Brentwood Way, Newtownards BT23 8RY — MB BCh BAO 1975 Belf. Assoc. Specialist N & W Belf. Health & Social Serv. Trust.

GAMA, Joubert Gratia (Surgery), 1 Childwall Park Avenue, Liverpool L16 0JG Tel: 0151 722 1077 Fax: 0151 488 6601; 22 Opal Way, Wokingham RG41 3UL — MB ChB 1981 Liverp. Socs: Brit. Assn. Sport & Med.; Assoc. Mem. Brit. Med. Acupunc. Soc.; Assoc. Mem. Brit. Soc. Orthop. Med.

GAMA, Rousseau Mariano Dept. of Clinical Chemistry, New Cross Hospital, Wolverhampton WV10 0PU; Tel: 01902 750062 — MB ChB 1980 Liverp.; 2000 Cchem MRSC; BSc (Hons.) Biochem. Liverp. 1977, MD Chem. Path. 1993; MSc Clin. Biochem. Surrey 1988; MRCP (UK) 1985; MRCPath 1998. Cons. (Chem Path) New Cross Hosp. Wolverhampton; Hon.Sen. Lect. (Med.) Birm. Uni.; Hon.Sen Llect. (Chem.Path) Wolverhampton Uni. Socs: Assoc. of Clin. Pathologist; Roy. Soc. Chem.; Assoc.of Clin. Biochem.s. Prev: Sen. Regist. (ChemPath) Roy.Surrey Co Hosp.; Resarch Fell.. Wolfson Res. Lab. QEMC Birm.; Ergist. Rotat. (Med) Liverp.

GAMAGE, Donald Henry (retired) 22 Grange Road, West Cross, Swansea SA3 5ES Tel: 01792 405879 — MB BS 1951 Lond.; MRCS Eng. LRCP Lond. 1951. Prev: GP Swansea.

GAMBA, Eleanor 378 The Meadway, Tilehurst, Reading RG30 4NX — MB BS 1998 Lond.; MB BS Lond 1998.

GAMBHIR, Anil Kumar 20 Stetchworth Drive, Worsley, Manchester M28 1EX — MB ChB 1991 Manch.; FRCS (Eng.) 1995. (Manch.) Specialist Regist. (Orthop.) N. W. Region.

GAMBIER, Donald Morley (retired) 2 Marlborough Place, Lymington SO41 9LX — MB ChB (Hons.) Bristol 1949; FRCGP 1984, M 1966. Prev: Sen. Med. Off. The Welsh Off. Cardiff.

GAMBLE, Adrian Roger 1 Acrefield, Beardwood, Blackburn BB2 7BJ — BM BS 1993 Nottm.

GAMBLE, Donald (retired) Haxells, 49 East Road, West Mersea, Colchester CO5 8EP Tel: 01206 382739 — BM BCh Oxf. 1961; FRCR 1975; FFR 1967; DMRT Eng. 1965. Prev: Cons. Radiother. Colchester Health Dist.

GAMBLE, Douglas Samuel Clarke, Col. L/RAMC Department Psychiatry, HQNI BFPO 825 Tel: 028 9226 6079 Email: dcp.ni@ukf.net — MB BCh BAO 1976 Belf.; MRCPsych 1982. Cons. Psychiat. HQ, N Irel.; Cons. Adviser (Psych) to Director Gen. Army Med. Serv.s. Prev: Cons. Psychiat. Brit. Milit. Hosp., Hong Kong.; Cons. Psychiat. Brit. Milit. Hosp., Rinteln, Germany.

GAMBLE, Elizabeth Anne 7 Franklin House, Watts St., London E1W 2PY Email: liggamble@cwcom.net — BM 1992 Soton.; MRCP (UK) 1995. Research Regist. Lond. Chest Hosp. Prev: Regist. (Gen. Med.) S.end Hosp.; SHO (Med.) Brighton Gen. Hosp. & Leicester Gen. Hosp.; SHO (A & E) Roy. Sussex Co. Hosp. Brighton.

GAMBLE, Giles Edward 49 East Road, West Mersea, Colchester CO5 8EP — MB ChB 1991 Manch.

GAMBLE, Harvey Paul 99 Kenneth Road, Romford RM6 6LR — MB ChB 1994 Dundee; BA Hull 1987. (Dundee) SHO (Ophth.) Middlesbrough. Prev: SHO (O & G) Romford.; Ho. Off. (Surg.) OldCh. Hosp. Romford; Ho. Off. (Med.) Ninewells Hosp. Dundee.

GAMBLE, James Alexander Samuel 66 Circular Road, Jordanstown, Newtownabbey BT37 0RQ Tel: 01232 866566 — MD 1975 Belf.; MB BCh BAO 1969; FFA RCSI 1973. (Belf.) Cons. (Anaesth.) Belf. City Hosp. & Musgrave Pk. Hosp. Prev: Sen. Lect. (Anaesth.) Qu. Univ. Belf.; Sen. Regist. (Anaesth.) & Research Fell. Roy. Vict. Hosp. Belf.

GAMBLE, Kate Rebecca Meadow View, Coronation Avenue, Bradford-on-Avon BA15 1AX — MB BS 1998 Newc.; MB BS Newc 1998.

GAMBLE, Peter 21 St Mary's Drive, Perth PH2 7BY Tel: 01738 35626 — MB ChB 1974 Ed.; BSc Ed. 1971, MB ChB 1974; FRCR 1980; DMRD Ed. 1978. Cons. Radiol. Perth Roy. Infirm. Prev: Sen. Regist. (Radiol.) Roy. Infirm. Edin.; Ho. Phys. W.. Gen. Hosp. Edin.; Fell. (Radiol.) Toronto Gen. Hosp. Canada.

GAMBLE, Raymond White House, 22 Rectory Lane, Preston, Hull HU12 8UE — MB ChB 1959 Manch. (Manch.) Med. Off. BAMS. Socs: Hull Med. Soc.; Assoc. Mem. Brit. Assn. Manip. Med. Prev: GP Hull; SHO (O & G) W.mld. Co. Hosp. Kendal; Resid. Med. Off. Stockport Roy. Infirm.

GAMBLE, William Drumnagee, Greenisland, Antrim BT41 — MB BCh BAO 1965 Belf. (Belf.) Socs: BMA. Prev: Ho. Surg. & Ho. Phys. Roy. Vict. Hosp. Belf.; SHO (O & G) Route Hosp. Ballymoney; SHO (Cardiol. & Med.) Waveney Hosp. Ballymena.

GAMBLE, William Graham Hickey Sleaford Medical Group, Riverside Surgery, 47 Boston Road, Sleaford NG34 7HD Tel: 01529 303301 Fax: 01529 415401; 39 St. John's Close, Leasingham, Sleaford NG34 8LU Tel: 0529 305257 Email: gamble39@aol.com — MB BCh BAO 1972 Belf.; MRCGP 1977; DObst RCOG 1974. (Queen's University Belfast) Police Surg. Sleaford Sub Div. Socs: BMA; RCGP; Assn. of Police Surgs.

GAMBLE, William James Farlough Lodge, Newmills, Dungannon — MB BCh BAO 1960 Belf.; DObst RCOG 1962. Assoc. Specialist (Geriat.) S. Tyrone Hosp. Dungannon. Socs: Brit. Geriat. Soc.

GAMBLE, William Rodney Integrated Health Services, Dupont (UK) Ltd., Maydown Works, Londonderry BT47 1TU — MB BCh BAO 1984 Belf.; MFOM RCP 2000; AFOM RCP Lond. 1997; Dip. Occ. Med. RCP Lond. 1995. Med. Advisor IHS Manager Dupont. Socs: Soc. Occupat. Med. Prev: GP Isle of Harris & Isle of Lewis.

GAMBLES, Caroline Sian Flat 2, 4 Ashwood Terrace, Leeds LS6 2EH — MB ChB 1996 Leeds.

GAMBLIN, Alfred Joseph Kingsmills Medical Practice, 18 Southside Road, Inverness IV2 3BG Tel: 01463 235245 Fax: 01463 01443 714400 — MB ChB 1969 Aberd.; DObst RCOG 1971.

GAMBLING, Maurice Douglas 4 Church Way, Tarring, Worthing BN13 1HD Tel: 01903 234957 Fax: 01903 234957 Email: mdgambling@classic.msn.com — MB BS 1971 Lond.; BA Durham. 1962. (Middlx.) Freelance Med. Writer & Edr.; Clin.Asst. Oncol. Worthing Hosp. Socs: Fell. Roy. Soc. Med. Prev: Head, Ciba-Geigy Sci. Pub.ations, Lond.; GP Worthing; Asst.Sec.Med.Defence.Union.

***GAME, David Stanley** Flat 1, 21 Church St., Kingsbridge TQ7 1BT — BM BCh 1996 Oxf.

GAME, Diana Mary (retired) 19 The Shimmings, Boxgrove Road, Guildford GU1 2NG — MB ChB 1950 Glas.; DCH Eng. 1953. Prev: SCMO Essex HA.

GAME, Frances Louise 190 Curborough Road, Lichfield WS13 7RB — MB BCh 1985 Wales; BSc Wales 1982, MB BCh 1985; MRCP (UK) 1988. Sen. Regist. (Chem. Path.) Centr. Path. Laborat. Stoke-on-Trent.

GAME, Lily Maclennan West Hallam Medical Centre, The Dales, West Hallam, Derby DE4 4EJ Tel: 0115 932 5462 Fax: 0115 944 4859; Craggie, 128 Longfield Lane, Ilkeston DE7 4DB — MB ChB 1974 Sheff.; Cert. Family Plann. JCC 1980. (Sheffield University) Prev: Trainee GP Chesterfield VTS; SHO Childr. Hosp. Sheff.

GAMELL, Annet Petrina Kingswood Surgery, Hollis Road, Totteridge, High Wycombe HP13 7UN Tel: 01494 474783 Fax: 01494 438424 — MB BS 1980 Lond.; MRCS Eng., LRCP Lond. 1980; MRCGP 1984; DRCOG 1983. (Char. Cross Hosp.)

GAMIE, Esame Mohamed Khalil St Luke's Hospital, Little Horton Lane, Bradford BD5 0NA Tel: 01274 542200; 21 Birchtree Close, Wakefield WF1 4TF — MB BCh 1970 Cairo; FRCS Glas. 1991. Staff Surg. St. Luke's Hosp. Bradford.

GAMINARA, Elizabeth Jane 33 Countess Road, London NW5 2XH — MB 1974 Camb.; BChir 1973; MRCP (UK) 1976; MRCPath. 1982.

GAMINARA, Monica (retired) 1 Waldock Barton, Stratton, South Petherton TA13 5NZ — MRCS Eng. LRCP Lond. 1949. Prev: Med. Off. (Family Plann. & Child Welf.) Som. AHA.

GAMLEN, Gordon William (retired) 8 Southfield Drive, Kenilworth CV8 2FR Tel: 01926 852155 — MB BChir Camb. 1962; MRCS Eng. LRCP Lond. 1961; FFA RCS Eng. 1967; DObst RCOG 1963. Cons. Anaesth. S. Warks. Hosp. Gp. Prev: Sen. Regist. (Anaesth.) United Bristol Hosps.

GAMLEN, Timothy Richard Milton Keynes District General Hospital, Standing Way, Eaglestone, Milton Keynes MK6 5LD — MB BS 1969 Lond.; MRCP (U.K.) 1972. (St. Thos.) Cons. Chem. Path. Milton Keynes Gen. Hosp.

GAMLIN, Caroline Grace Worthy House, Lympsham Road, Lympsham, Weston Super Mare BS24 0DN — MB ChB 1983 Leic.; MFPHM 1997; MRCGP 1987; DRCOG 1986. Cons. Pub. Health Med. Som. Health Auth.

GAMM, Frederick Geoffrey Shelton (retired) Rock Cottage, Bishopswood, Chard TA20 3RS Tel: 01460 234274 — MB BS 1957 Lond.; MRCS Eng. LRCP Lond. 1957; DObst RCOG 1959. Prev: Regist. (Geriat.) SE RHB.

GAMMACK, Andrew John 110 Kings Road, Harrogate HG1 5HW Tel: 01423 503035 — MB BCh 1993 Wales.

GAMMACK, Evaline Anne Joan c/o Mrs. Mulholland, 13 Broomhill Avenue, Partick, Glasgow G11 7AE — MB ChB 1960 Aberd.; MRCOG 1964.

GAMMAGE, Michael Dennis Department of Cardiovascular Medicine, Queen Elizabeth Hospital, Edgbaston, Birmingham B15 2TH Tel: 0121 697 8338 Fax: 0121 627 2582 Email: m.d.gammage@bham.ac.uk; Dyott End, 30 Dyott Road, Moseley, Birmingham B13 9QY Tel: 0121 449 5515 Fax: 0121 449 5515 — MB ChB 1979 Birm.; MD Birm. 1987; FRCP Lond. 1994; MRCP (UK) 1982. (Univ. Birm.) Reader (Cardiovasc. Med.) Univ. Birm. & Qu. Eliz. Hosp. Birm.; Hon. Cons. Cardiol. Qu. Eliz. Hosp. Birm. Socs: Brit. Cardiac Soc.; N. Amer. Soc. for Pacing & Cardiac Electrophysiol.; Fell., Europ. Soc. of Cardiol. Prev: Brit. Heart Foundat. Sen. Lect. (Cardiovasc. Med.) Univ. Birm. & Qu. Eliz. Hosp. Birm.; Sen. Regist. (Cardiol.) Qu. Eliz. Hosp. Birm.; Regist. (Med.) Leic. Roy. Infirm.

GAMMAN, Francis Richard (retired) Oatridge House, Coaley, Dursley GL11 5DT — MRCS Eng. LRCP Lond. 1959; MB Camb. 1960, BChir 1959; MRCGP 1974.

GAMMANPILA, Seetha Mangalika De Parys, 62 Boughton Lane, Loose, Maidstone ME15 9QS Tel: 01622 44611 — LMSSA 1978 Lond.; Vrach, Peoples' Friendship Univ. 1968; Dip. Community Paediat. Warwick 1989; DFFP 1994. (Peoples' Friendship Univ.

Moscow) Clin. Med. Off. Maidstone Health Dist. Socs: Fac. Community Health.; Fell. of Roy. Inst. of Pub. Health & Hyg. May 1998. Prev: Ho. Phys. Moscow City Teachg. Hosp., USSR; Ho. Off. (Gyn. & Obst.) Greenwich Dist. Hosp.; SHO (Gyn. & Obst.) Leighton Hosp. Crewe.

GAMMANPILA, Sumathipala Wijesena De Parys, 62 Boughton Lane, Loose, Maidstone ME15 9QS — MD 1968 Moscow; MD Peoples Friendship Univ. Moscow 1968; LMSSA Lond. 1976; FFA RCSI 1973. (Peoples Friendship Univ. Moscow) Cons. Anaesth. Maidstone Health Dist. Prev: Ho. Surg. Moscow City Teach. Hosp. No. 64; Regist. (Anaesth.) Leighton Hosp. Crewe; Sen. Regist. (Anaesth.) St. Mary's Gp. Hosps. Lond.

GAMMELL, Hilary Jane Bethea Clifton Road Surgery, 26 Clifton Road, Rugby CV21 3QF Tel: 01788 543088 Fax: 01788 551496; School House, Rugby CV22 5EH — MB BS 1977 Lond. (St. Thos.)

***GAMMELL, Samantha Joy** 6 Southampton Road, Belsize Park, London NW5 4HX; 68 Bell Lane, Brookmans Park, Hatfield AL9 7AY Tel: 01707 663434 — MB BS 1997 Lond.

GAMMIE, Helen Davidson (retired) 7 Friars Park, Institution Road, Elgin IV30 1QU Tel: 01343 543256 — MB ChB Aberd. 1941.

GAMMIE, John Wilson 7 Friars Park, Institution Road, Elgin IV30 1QU Tel: 01343 543256 — MB ChB Aberd. 1941; DA Eng. 1958.

GAMMIE, Kenneth Miller 147 Bath Road, Hounslow TW3 3BU Tel: 01491 575966 — MB BS 1951 Lond.; AFOM RCP Lond. 1978; MRCGP 1968. (St. Thos.) Med. Off. United Biscuits (Osterley); Med. Off. Fiat. Auto (UK) Ltd. Socs: BMA. Prev: Clin. Asst. (Med.) Hounslow Hosp.; Ho. Surg. & Ho. Phys. Roy. Hosp. Richmond.

GAMMIE, Sheila Christine Sunnyside Royal Hospital, Hillside, Montrose DD10 9JP Tel: 01674 830361; Mill of Conveth, Laurencekirk AB30 1ND Tel: 01561 378188 — MB ChB 1980 Ed.; DRCOG 1982. Staff Grade (Psychiat.) Sunnyside Roy. Hosp. Montrose.

GAMMON, Alison Patricia Joan Accident & Emergency Department, Stoke Mandeville Hospital, Aylesbury HP21 8AL Tel: 01296 316514; 83 Wendover Road, Stoke Mandeville, Aylesbury HP22 5TD Tel: 01296 613165 — BSc Lond. 1977, MB BS 1980; FRCS Ed. 1991; DCH RCP Lond. 1989. Cons. A & E Stoke Mandeville Hosp.

GAMMON, Kenneth Tan Lan, Dwyran, Llanfairpwllgwyngyll LL61 6YD Tel: 01248 430742 — MB BCh 1949 Wales; BSc, MB BCh Wales 1949. Prev: GP Mold; SHO (Obst.) Morriston ENS Hosp.; Med. Off. RAF 1950-52.

GAMMON, Max (Alfred William Maxwell) 92 Southwark Park Road, London SE16 3RS Tel: 020 7237 1429 — MB BS 1967 Lond.; MRCS Eng. LRCP Lond. 1967. (Univ. Coll. Hosp.) Dir. Roy. Hosp. St. Bart. Charitable Foundat. Socs: Roy. Soc. Med. Prev: Regist. (Cardiac Surg.) Nat. Heart Hosp. Lond.; SHO (Gen. Surg.) Redhill Gen. Hosp.; SHO (Urol. & Gen. Surg.) St. Jas. Hosp. Balham.

GAMMON, Rosalind Sarah Griffith Millbrook, Clarbeston Road, Haverfordwest SA62 5RG — MB BCh 1980 Wales; DRCOG 1984; DCH RCP Lond. 1983.

GAMMON, Veronica May (retired) 7 Heol Iscoed, Efail Isaf, Pontypridd CF38 1BP — MB BS 1948 Lond.; FRCS Eng. 1961; DLO Eng. 1971. Prev: Cons. ENT Surg. Mid Glam. AHA.

GAMPER, Mary Aileen Wings, Burley Road, Winkton, Christchurch BH23 7AN Tel: 01425 73449 — MB BS 1973 Lond.; Dip. Palliat. Med. Wales 1993. (St. Bart.) Staff Grade (Palliat. Med.) MacMillan Unit ChristCh. Hosp. Prev: SHO (A & E) Freedom Fields Hosp. Plymouth; Ho. Phys. Roy. S. Hants. Hosp.

GAMPER, Nicholas Hunter Burton Medical Centre, Burton Green, 123 Salisbury Road, Burton, Christchurch BH23 7JN Tel: 01202 474311 Fax: 01202 484412; Wings, Burley Road, Winkton, Christchurch BH23 7AN Tel: 01425 673449 — MB BS 1970 Lond.; MRCS Eng. LRCP Lond. 1970; DCH Eng. 1974; DRCOG 1972. (Char. Cross) Gen. Practitioner. Prev: SHO (Obst.) Truro Hosp.; SHO (Paediat.) Roy. Devon & Exeter Hosp.; Ho. Off. Char. Cross Hosp. Lond.

GAMSU, Harold Richard 26 Calton Avenue, London SE21 7DG Tel: 020 8693 9920 Fax: 020 8693 9920 Email: harold.gamsu@kcl.ac.uk — MB BCh Witwatersrand 1954; FRCP Lond. 1984; FRCP Ed. 1973, M 1962; DCH Eng. 1959; FRCPCH 1997. (Witwatersrand) Emerit. Prof. Neonat. King's Coll. Hosp. Lond. Prev: Hon. Cons. Paediat. King's Coll. Hosp.; Regist. Childr. Hosp. Sheff.; Chief Resid. Cleveland Metrop. Hosp.

GAMSU, M J Mill Road Surgery, 98A Mill Road, Ecclesfield, Sheffield S35 9XQ Tel: 0114 246 9419.

GAN, Juliet Holmes Flat 1/2, 87 Glencairn Drive, Pollockshields, Glasgow G41 4QW — MB ChB 1995 Glas.

GAN, Mr Kong Bok The Elms, 4 West End, Beeston, Nottingham NG9 1GL Tel: 0115 925 7238 Fax: 0115 925 7238 — MB BS 1971 Malaya; FRCS Eng. 1977. (Malaya) Plastic Surg. Pk.field Hosp. Rotherham. Socs: Assoc. Mem. Brit. Assn. Plastic Surgs.; Brit. Assn. Cosmetic Surg. Prev: Regist. (Plastic Surg.) Qu. Mary's Hosp. Roehampton.

GAN, Yee Chiung Flat 1/R, 37 Glencairn Drive, Pollockshields, Glasgow G41 4QW Tel: 0141 424 3355 — MB ChB 1995 Glas. (Univ. Glas.) SHO (Cardiothoracic Surg.) W. Infirm. Glas. Basic Surgic. Train. Scheme W. Scotl. Socs: BMA. Prev: SHO (Orthop. & Gen. Surg.); SHO (Med.) Stobhill Hosp. Glas.

GAN, Yoke Cheng 37 Ranelagh Road, Pendlebury, Swinton, Manchester M27 4HG — MB BS 1988 Malaya; MRCP (UK) 1994.

GANA, Mr Baba Mallam West Wales General Hospital, Carmarthen SA31 2AF Tel: 01267 227514 Fax: 01267 227514 Email: ganabm@epnise.net — MB BS 1983 Zaria Nigeria; FRCS Glas. 1990; Dip. Urol. Lond 1991. (Bello University Zaria, Nigeria) Socs: Brit. Assoc. Urological Surg.s; Fell.Internat. Coll. of Surg.s; Fell.Roy. Soc. of Med. Prev: Regist. in Urol. Dundee Roy. Infirm.; Demonstartor in Anat.,Newc. Med. Sch.

GANA, Mr Hosea Baba-Yisa Urology Department, Whiston Hospital, Warrington Road, Prescot L35 5DS Tel: 0151 426 1600 Fax: 0151 430 1405; 12 Irton Road, Southport PR9 9DY Tel: 01704 549379 Fax: 01704 541175 — MB BS 1977 Ahmadu Bello Univ. Nigeria; MB BS Ahmadu Bello U Nigeria 1977; FRCS Ed. 1984; Dip. Urol. Lond 1989. Cons. Urol.Fairfield InDepend. Hosp.Crank St Helens NHS Trust. Socs: Brit. Assn. Urol. Surgs.; Founding Mem. Brit. Erectile DysFunc. Soc.; BMA. Prev: Cons. Surg. & Urol. Gen. Hosp. Minna, Nigeria; Regist. (Urol.) Walton & Fazakerley Hosp. Liverp.; SHO (Surg.) Whiston & St. Helens Hosps.

GANAI, Nripendra Kumar The Health Centre, 20 Duncan Street, Greenock PA15 4LY Tel: 01475 724477 — MB BS 1965 Calcutta. (Nilratan Sircar Med. Coll.)

GANAPATHI, Erode Nallathambi Camphill Road Surgery, 10 Camp Hill Road, Nuneaton CV10 0JH — MB BS 1973 Madras. (Stanley Med. Coll., Madras, India)

GANAPATHY, Davangere Hiremutt Donnybank, 41 Priory Road, Newcastle ST5 2EN Tel: 01782 616599 — MB BS 1961 Mysore. (Mysore Med. Coll.) Socs: Med. Protec. Soc. Prev: Clin. Asst. Orthop. Trauma.

GANAPATHY, Murughian 61 Ayreville Road, Beacon Park, Plymouth PL2 2RB Tel: 01752 563359 — MB BS 1968 Madras; DO RCPSI 1981; DOMS Agra 1969.

GANAPATHY, Trichur Sundaram Harold Street Surgery, 2 Harold Street, Sheffield S6 3QW Tel: 0114 233 5930; 10 Studfield Hill, Wadsley, Sheffield S6 4SJ Tel: 0114 234 3446 — MD 1966 New Delhi; MB BS Osmania 1958; FFA RCSI 1976; DA Osmania 1963. (Osmania) Prev: GP Walkley Sheff.; Regist. (Anaesth.) Univ. Hosp. Wales, Cardiff; Regist. (Anaesth.) Roy. Gwent Hosp. Newport.

GANCKE, Anne Elizabeth The Surgery, 8 Oakleigh Gardens, Orpington BR6 9PL — MB BS 1987 Lond. Trainee GP Medway Hosp. Gillingham, Kent VTS. Prev: Community Med. Off. Medway Hosp.

GANCZ, Gordon King Edward Street Surgery, 9 King Edward Street, Oxford OX1 4JA Tel: 01865 242657 — BM BCh 1972 Oxf.; MA.

GANCZAKOWSKI, Mary Elizabeth Department of Haematology, Queen Alexandra Hospital, Cosham, Portsmouth PO6 3LY Tel: 023 92 286688 Fax: 023 92 374204; 22 Sheep Street, Petersfield GU32 3JX — MB BS 1980 Lond.; BSc (Hons.) Lond. 1977; MRCP (UK) 1983; MRCPath (Haemat.) 1988. (Guy's) Cons. Haemat. Qu. Alexandra Hosp. Portsmouth. Prev: MRC Train. Fell. & Wellcome Research Fell. Inst. of Molecular Med. John Radcliffe Hosp., Oxf.; Sen. Regist. & Regist. (Haemat.) Roy. Free Hosp. Lond.

GANCZAKOWSKI, Stanislaw Kazimierz (retired) 188 Kimbolton Road, Bedford MK41 8DP Tel: 01234 217714 — MB ChB 1944 Polish Sch. of Med.; DA Eng. 1955. Prev: Cons. Anaesth. Bedford Gp. Hosps.

GANDAMIHARDJA, Tasha Anggara-Kasih 69 Page Street, London NW7 2EE — MB BS 1996 Lond.

GANDE, Anthony Richard Dacre House, Wicken Bonhunt, Saffron Walden CB11 3UG — BM BCh 1993 Oxf. SHO (Anaesth.) Soton. Gen Hosp. Socs: Ostetic Anaesth. Assn.; Assoc of Anaethetists. Prev: SHO (Elderly Care) Poole Gen. Hosp.; SHO (Neonat. Med.) P.ss Anne Hosp. Soton.; SHO (A & E) Poole Hosp. Dorset.

GANDECHA, Dinesh Jamnadas Tel: 0116 273 7569 Fax: 0116 273 7443 — MB BS 1975 Poona; MB BS 1975 Poona.

GANDER, Derek Reginald 7 Wimpole Street, London W1M 7AB Tel: 020 7580 1584 Email: derekgander@lineone.net; 8 St. Peter's Close, St Albans AL1 3ES Tel: 01727 850584 Fax: 01727 850584 — MB BS 1953 Lond.; MRCP Lond. 1959; FRCPsych 1977, M 1971; DPM Lond. 1962. (Middlx.) Indep. Psychiat. Lond. Socs: Fell. Roy. Soc. Of Med.; Brit. NeuroPsychiat. Assn. Prev: Cons. Psychiat. Qu. Eliz. II Hosp. Welwyn Gdn. City; Regist. Bethlem Roy. & Maudsley Hosps.; Chief Asst. (Psychol. Med.) St. Thos. Hosp. Lond.

GANDERTON, Marianne Antonie (retired) The Dell, 33 Gringer Hill, Maidenhead SL6 7LY Tel: 01628 626455 — MB BS Adelaide 1953; DCH Eng. 1957. Prev: Cons. (Allergy) Med. Dept. Dome Hollister Stier.

GANDERTON, Philip 303 Winslow Road, Bromyard HR7 4TX — MB BCh 1994 Wales.

GANDHAM, Sayi Ramesh Staffordshire Police HQ, Emplyee Healthcare Services, Cannock Road, Stafford ST17 0QG — MB BS 1974 Andhra; MCGPI 1984; MFFP 1993; LFOM RCPI 1990; MRCGP 1980; DIH (Eng.) 1987 & Diploma in Venerology DV (1978) Eng. (Andhra Med. Coll.) Head.Employee Health Care Serv. Socs: Soc. Occupat. Med.; Fell. Amer. Bd. Forens. Examr. (Bd. Certified in Forens. Med.); Fell. Inst. Occupat. Safety & Health.

GANDHE, Advait Jayant 142 John Silkin Lane, London SE8 5BE — MB BS 1996 Lond.

GANDHI, Anil Goverhandas 35 Norwich Road, Northwood Hills, Northwood HA6 1ND — MB BS 1972 Madras; MB BS 1972 Madras.

GANDHI, Mr Ashu 45 Francis Road, Withington, Manchester M20 4XP — MB ChB 1989 Manch.; FRCS Eng. 1994; FRCS Ed. 1994. Higher Surgic. Trainee NW Region.

GANDHI, Bhavesh Rameshchandra 30 Yew Tree Close, Lapworth, Solihull B94 6NB — MB BS 1990 Lond.

GANDHI, Mr Bhogilal Prabhudas (retired) 50 Frome Valley Road, Stapleton, Bristol BS16 1HE Tel: 0117 965 4304 — MB BS Bombay 1949; FRCS Eng. 1961; LCPS Bombay 1944.

GANDHI, Mr Harjeet Singh 78 Craig Road, Stockport SK4 2BG — MB BS 1978 Ed.; MSc (Biomed. Eng.) Dundee 1991; BSc Guru Nanak Dev India 1973, MB BS 1978; FRCS Glas. 1987; LRCP LRCS Ed., LRCPS Glas. 1985. Regist. (Orthop.) Manor Hse. Hosp. Lond. Prev: Regist. (Orthop.) Kidderminster Gen. Hosp.

GANDHI, Mr Hemendra Babulal South Tyneside District Hospital, Hasten Lane, South Shields NE34 0PL; 7 Brandling Court, South Shields NE34 8PA — MB BS 1978 Gujarat; FRCS Ed. 1984.

GANDHI, Imtiyaz Kaderali Jiggins Lane Medical Centre, 17 Jiggins Lane, Bartley Green, Birmingham B32 3LE Tel: 0121 477 7272 Fax: 0121 478 4319 — MB ChB 1985 Ed.; MRCGP 1991. Trainee GP S. Birm. HA.

GANDHI, Jagdish Dwarkadas 41 Moss Road, Billinge, Wigan WN5 7BU — MB BS 1977 Gujarat; MB BS Gujaret 1977; MD Gujarat 1980; LMSSA Lond. 1983; MFFP 1995; MRCOG 1988; DGO 1979; FRCOG 2000. Staff Grade (O & G) S.port Dist. Gen. Hosp. Socs: Brit. Soc. of Colposcopy and Cervical Path.; Brit. Menopause Soc. Prev: Regist. (O & G) Warneford Hosp. Leamington Spa; SHO (Gyn.) St. Chad's Hosp. Birm.; SHO (Obst.) City Hosp. Derby.

GANDHI, Kamala Bhogilal (retired) 50 Frome Valley Road, Stapleton, Bristol BS16 1HE Tel: 0117 965 4304 — MB BS Bombay 1950; LCPS Bombay 1946; DGO CPS Bombay 1947.

GANDHI, Maher Kadirali Box 234, Dept.Haematology, Cambridge CB2 2QQ — MB ChB 1989 Aberd.; MRCP (UK) 1994. Hon. Sen. Regist. (Haemat.) Addenbrooke's Hosp. Camb.

GANDHI, Manish Mahendra Cardiac Centre, Royal Devon & Exeter Hospital, Barrack road, Exeter EX2 5DW — MB ChB 1986 Glas.; MD (Hons.) Glas. 1994; MRCP (UK) 1989. Cons. Cardiol., The Roy. devon & Exeter Hosp. Socs: Brit. Cardiovasc. Interven. Soc.; Brit. Cardiac Soc.; Amer. Heart Asson. Counc. on Clin. Cardiol. Prev: Sen. Regist. (Cardiol.) Soton. Gen. Hosp.; Sen. Regist. (Cardiol.) Wessex Cardiac Centre; Regist. (Cardiol.) Middlx. Hosp. Lond.

GANDHI, Meena Navnitlal 55 Hamilton Road, London NW11 9EH — MB BS 1994 Lond.; BSc Lond. 1991, MB BS 1994; MRCOG Part 1; DFFP; MFFP. (UCL) SHO (O & G) Hemel Hempstead Gen. Hosp. Prev: Ho. Off. (Gen. Med.) Brighton Health Care; SHO (A & E) Ealing Hosp.; SHO (Genitourin. Med.) Char. Cross Hosp. Lond.

GANDHI, Minal Mahendra 37 Worcester Crescent, Woodford Green IG8 0LX — MB ChB 1992 Glas.; MRCP(UK) 1998. (Glasgow) Specialist Regist. Paediat. N. Thames Deanery. Socs: RCP; MRCPCH. Prev: SHO Rotat. (Paediat.) Hillingdon Hosp. & St. Mary's Hosp. Paddington; SHO Rotat. (Med.) Bristol Roy. Infirm.; SHO (Paediat.) Mayday Univ. Hosp.

GANDHI, Naimishchandra Sharadchandra 27 Priestfields, Rochester ME1 3AB — MB BCh 1992 Wales.

GANDHI, Naresh Dahyalal Academic Department of Psychiatry, St Mary's Hospital, Praed St., London W2 1NY Tel: 020 7725 6032 — MD 1989 Bombay; MB BS 1986; MRCPsych. 1993.

GANDHI, Nimita 35 Swallow Close, Totton, Southampton SO40 7JA — MB BS 1990 Lond.

GANDHI, Professor Noshir Jamshedji South Durham Health Care NHS Trust, Orthopaedic Directorate, Bishop Auckland General Hospital, Bishop Auckland DL14 6AD Tel: 01388 454000 Fax: 01388 454136; 11 Ashbourne Drive, Featherstones, Coxhoe, Durham DH6 4SE Tel: 0191 377 9773 Fax: 0191 377 9773 — MB BS 1957 Bombay; FICS 1990 US; MS Bombay 1965; MChOrth Liverp. 1965; FRCS Ed. 1962. (GS Med. Coll. & KEM Hosp. Bombay) Cons. Orthop. Surg. (Orthop. Surg. & Trauma Directorate) Darlington Memor. Hosp., Bishop Auckland Gen. Hosp.; Prof. Orthop. Open Internat. Univ. For Complementary Med.; Hon. Sen. Cons. Orthop. Surg. Parsi Gen. Hosp. Socs: Brit. Med. Assn.; Soc. Internat. Coll. Orthop. Surgs. & Traumatol. Belguim; Assn. Study & Application of Methodol. of Ilizarov (Life Mem.). Prev: Cons. Orthop. Surg. Univ. Hosp. Of N. Durh.; Hon. Prof. Orthop. Surg. & Sen. Med. Teach. J.J. Gp. of Hosps. & G.M. Coll. Bombay Univ.; Cons. Orthop. Masina Hosp. (Head of Orthop. Dept.).

GANDHI, Pankaj 40 Deanscroft Avenue, Kingsbury, London NW9 8EN — MB ChB 1982 Leic.

GANDHI, Mr Pankaj Navnitlal — MB BS 1988 Lond.; FRCS Ed. 1994. (UCL) Specialist Regist. (Surg.) SE Thames.

GANDHI, Paul Singh 128 Pencisely Road, Cardiff CF5 1DR — MB BCh 1997 Wales.

GANDHI, Rajiv Anant 189 Harvie Avenue, Newton Mearns, Glasgow G77 6LJ — MB ChB 1992 Glas.

GANDHI, Mr Rameshchandra Govindlal (retired) Blackpool Victoria Hospital NHS Trust, Fundraising, 4 Furness Drive, Poulton-le-Fylde, Blackpool FY6 8JT Tel: 01253 303142 Fax: 01253 303106 Email: rggandi@april-cott.freeserve.co.uk — MB BS Gujarat 1961; FRCS Eng. 1974; FRCS Ed. 1973. Cons. Cardiothoracic Surg. Vict. Hosp. Blackpool; JP.; DL. of Lancs.; Dir. Fundraising Vict. Hosp. Blackpool. Prev: Sen. Regist. (Cardiothoracic Surg.) Univ. Hosp. Wales Cardiff & Llandough Hosp. Penarth.

GANDHI, Sandeep Sharadchandra 27 Priestfields, Rochester ME1 3AB — MB BS 1993 Lond.; MRCP (UK) 1996. Specialist Regist. (Cardiol. & Gen. Internal Med.) Basildon & Thurrock Gen. Hosp. Prev: SHO (Cardiol.) W.. Gen. Hosp. Edin.; SHO (Med.) Qu.'s Md. Centre Nottm.

GANDHI, Vandna 12 Priory Avenue, Wembley HA0 2SB — MB ChB 1993 Manch.

GANDY, Alexis Sharon Wallsend Road Surgery, 34 Wallsend Road, North Shields NE29 7BJ Tel: 0191 296 1456; 4 Elmfield Grove, Gosforth, Newcastle upon Tyne NE3 4XA Tel: 0191 285 4156 Email: sharon.gandy@btinternet.com — MB BS 1981 Newc.; MRCGP 1986; DRCOG 1985.

GANDY, Christopher Patrick 78 Llangorse Road, Aberdare CF44 0LD — MB ChB 1992 Bristol.

GANDY, Gillian Margaret (retired) The Old Post Office, 65 High St., Barrington, Cambridge CB2 5QX — MB BS Lond. 1953; MD Lond. 1971; MRCS Eng. LRCP Lond. 1953; MRCP (UK) 1986; DCH Eng. 1958. Prev: Cons. Paediat. Cambs. AHA (T).

GANDY, Peter John Wooda, Throwleigh, Okehampton EX20 2HX — MB BS 1995 Lond.

GANERI, Puran 42 Eastgate Street, Stafford ST16 2LY — MB BS 1953 Calcutta; MRCP Ed. 1958; MRCGP 1968; DCH Eng. 1957. (Med. Coll. Calcutta) Socs: BMA.

GANESAN, Kunnathur Lakshmivenkataraman The Galleries Health Centre, Washington Centre, Washington NE38 7NQ — MB BS 1967 Madras; DCH RCPSI 1975. (Stanley Med. Coll. Madras)

GANESAN, Trivadi Sundaram Cancer Research UK Department of Medical Oncology, Churchill Hospital, Old Road, Headington, Oxford OX3 7LJ Tel: 01865 226185 Fax: 01865 226179 Email: ganesan@cancer.org.uk; Tel: 01865 222458 Fax: 01865 222431 — M.N.A.M.S 1981; MB BS Madras 1977; PhD Lond. 1989; MD Madras 1980; FRCP Lond. 1995; MRCP (UK) 1983. (Jipmer Pondicherry, India) Cons. Med. Oncol. Cancer Research UK Ch.ill Hosp. Oxf.; Cons. Clin. Sci. Inst. Molecular Med. John Radcliffe Hosp. Oxf.; Sen. Lect. Univ. oxf. Socs: Brit. Assn. Cancer Research; Assn. Cancer Phys. (UK); Amer. Assn. Cancer Research.

GANESAN, Vijeyarani 22 St Paul Street, London N1 7AB — MB ChB 1990 Bristol.

GANESH, Iyer Sudha Flat 5, Endsleigh Road Flats, Bedford Hospital (South Wing), Kempston Road, Bedford MK42 9DJ — MB BS 1988 Kerala; MB BS University of Kerala 1988; MRCP (UK) 1992.

GANESH, Subrahmanyam Dowlais Medical Practice, The Surgery, Ivor St., Dowlais, Merthyr Tydfil CF48 3LU Tel: 01685 721400 Fax: 01685 375287; 17 West Grove, Merthyr Tydfil CF47 8HJ Tel: 01685 722078 Fax: 01685 722078 — MB BS 1955 Mysore; BSc Mysore 1948; LMSSA Lond. 1961; DCH Eng. 1963. (Mysore) Prev: Regist. (Paediat.) Merthyr & Aberdare Hosp. Gp.; SHO Port Talbot Gen. Hosp.; Ho. Phys. & Ho. Surg. KR Hosp. Mysore.

GANESH, Thambimuttu Cressingham Road Surgery, 36 Cressingham Road, Edgware HA8 0RW Tel: 020 8959 1496 Fax: 020 8906 8713 — MB BS 1971 Ceylon; MB BS 1971 Ceylon.

GANESHALINGAM, Kandeepan 84 Rugby Avenue, Greenford UB6 0EZ — MB ChB 1997 Aberd.

GANESHALINGHAM, Ramesh 54a Upper Tooting Road, London SW17 7PD — MB BS 1996 Lond.

GANESHANANTHAM, Saravanamuthu Llwyneryr Hospital, 151 Clasemont Road, Morriston, Swansea SA6 6AH; 4 The Croft, Castle St, Loughor, Swansea SA4 6TB — MB BS 1976 Ceylon; MRCS Eng. LRCP Lond. 1981; MRCPsych 1985; DPM Eng. 1983. (Univ. Ceylon) Cons. Psychiat. Llwyneryr Hosp. Swansea. Socs: BMA; Roy. Coll. Psychiat. Prev: Regist. (Psychiat.) St. David's Hosp. Carmarthen.

***GANESHANANTHAN, Mallikadevi** 72 Standard Road, Hounslow TW4 7AS — MRCS Eng. LRCP Lond. 1987.

GANESHANANTHAN, Vimaladevi c/o Drive K. Makeswaran, 4 Buckingham Close, Petts Wood, Orpington BR5 1SA — MB BS 1963 Ceylon.

GANG, Judith Maria Magdolna (retired) 3 Gunnersbury Crescent, Acton, London W3 9AA Tel: 020 8992 9877 — MB BS 1963 Durh. Prev: Chief of Sect. Pharmacol. S.A. Labaz Brussels.

GANGAHAR, Mr Rajat 45 Birch Road, Rochdale OL12 9QJ — MB BS 1989 Calcutta; FRCS Ed. 1994.

GANGAR, Mr Kevin Francis Department of Obstetrics & Gynaecology, St Mary's Hospital, London W2 1PG — MB BChir 1980 Camb.; MA, MB BChir Camb. 1980; FRCS Ed. 1986; MRCOG 1987. Lect. & Sen. Regist. St. Mary's Hosp. Med. Sch. Lond. Socs: Fell. Roy. Soc. Med. Prev: Research Fell. Acad. Dept. O & G Kings Coll. Hosp. Sch. of Med. Lond.; Regist. (O & G) Kings Coll. Hosp. Lond.

GANGE, Philip David (retired) 14 South Hook Road, Gellyswick, Milford Haven SA73 3RU Tel: 01646 692080 — MRCS Eng. LRCP Lond. 1941; DObst RCOG 1948. Prev: Admiralty Surg. & Agent.

GANGI, Moshin Tauqir 13/7 Medical City, King Khalid National Guard Hospital, PO Box 9516, Jeddah 21423, Saudi Arabia Tel: 9662 665 3400 Fax: 9662 665 3031; 34 Maplewood Gardens, Bolton BL1 3NR — MB ChB 1984 Aberd.; MB ChB Aberd. l984; MRCP UK 1988. Cons. Internal Med. King Khalid Nat. Guard Hosp. Jeddah, Saudi Arabia. Prev: Specialist Regis. in Gastroenterol. GI Unit Woodend Gen. Hosp. Aberd.; Regist. N. Gen. Hosp. Sheff.; Regist. Roy. Gwent Hosp.

GANGOLA, Rajendra Lal The Surgery, 6 Barretts Grove, Stoke Newinton, London N16 8AR Tel: 0207 254 1661 Fax: 0207 275 8777; 115 Selborne Road, London N14 7DE Tel: 020 8886 9368 — MB BS 1962 Lucknow; BSc Agra 1957; DTM & H Liverp. 1971.

GANGOLI, Sameer Vivek 116 Plover Way, London SE16 7TZ — MB BS 1997 Lond.

***GANGOTRA, Gursharon** 32 Worlds End Road, Handsworth Wood, Birmingham B20 2NP — MB ChB 1998 Birm.; ChB Birm. 1998.

GANGULI, Ashim Canklow Road Surgery, 245/247 Canklow Road, Canklow, Rotherham S60 2JH Tel: 01709 363398; Streema-Heasley, Sledgate Lane, Wickersley, Rotherham S66 1AN — MB BS 1967 Gauhati; MRCP (UK) 1985.

GANGULI, Prafulla Kumar (retired) Annapurna, 15 Pen-y-Groes, Groes-Faen, Pontyclun CF72 8PA Tel: 01222 891177 — MB BS 1946 Calcutta; FRCR 1989; DMRD Liverp. 1953, DMRT 1954. Hon. Clin. Tutor (Radiodiag.) Welsh Nat. Sch. Med.; Tutor (Radiodiag.) Univ. Bristol. Prev: Cons. Radiol. i/c Taff Ely & Rhondda Units Mid. Glasm. HA.

GANGULY, Dilip Kumar Linwood Health Centre, Ardlamont Square, Linwood, Paisley PA3 3DE Tel: 01505 321051 Fax: 01505 383302 — MB BS 1963 Calcutta. (Calcutta) GP Paisley, Renfrewsh.

GANIWALLA, Mr Turaabali Mohamedali Jivanjee The Surgery, 157-159 Reservoir Road, Erdington, Birmingham B23 6DN Tel: 0121 373 6902 Fax: 0121 373 3263; 2 Hanwell Close, Walmley, Sutton Coldfield B76 1UD — MB ChB 1978 Nairobi, Keyna; MB ChB Nairobi, Kenya 1978; FRCS Ed. 1988; LMSSA Lond. 1984; DLO RCS Eng. 1990. (University of Nairobi, Kenya) GP Princip. & Clin. Asst. Wolverhampton; Trainee GP Dudley VTS. Prev: Staff Otolaryngol. Wolverhampton & Dudley Gp. of Hosps. W. Midl.

GANJU, Durga (Surgery) 3 Medina Road, Luton LU4 8BD; 117 Montrose Avenue, Luton LU3 1HP Tel: 22475 — MB BS 1954 Punjab; MB BS Punjab (India) 1954; DGO CPS Bombay 1959. (Amritsar Med. Coll.)

GANKANDE, Mr Ananda Upali Heenilama Poole Hospital NHS Trust, Long Fleet Road, Poole BH15 2JB Tel: 01202 665511; 25 Twyford Way, Poole BH17 8BL — MB BS 1979 Peradeniya, Sri Lanka; FRCS Ed. 1992. Staff Grade Surg. (A & E) Poole Hosp. Trust. Socs: BMA.

GANKERSEER, Simon Alexander The Meadows Surgery, Temple Grove, Gatehouse Lane, Sussex Way, Burgess Hill RH15 9XH Tel: 01444 242860 Fax: 01444 870496; Windlesham, North Common, North Chailey, Lewes BN8 4DP — MB BS 1990 Lond.

GANLEY, Patrick Dennis 60 Bole Hill Road, Sheffield S6 5DD — MB ChB 1993 Sheff.

GANLEY, Yvonne Susan PO Box 658, Hlabisa, Kwazulu/Natal 3937, South Africa Email: y.ganley@iafrica.com; 48 Hawkenbury, Harlow CM19 4JA — MB ChB 1987 Sheff.; MRCGP 1992; DTM & H Liverp. 1992. Community Med. Off. Hlabisa, S. Afr. Prev: Clin. Lect. (Travel Med.) Liverp. Sch. Trop. Med.

GANLY, Mr Ian 57 Gallagher Avenue, Lousdale, Paisley PA2 9HE Tel: 01505 816226 — MB ChB 1989 Glas.; BSc (Hons.) Glas. 1984, MB ChB 1989; FRCS Glas. 1993; FRCS Ed. 1993. Prev: SHO (Gen. Surg.) Vale of Leven Gen. Hosp., Glas. Roy. Infirm. & Law Hosp. Carluke.

GANLY, Nigel Anthony The Bell Surgery, York Road, Henley-on-Thames RG9 2DR Tel: 01491 572261 Fax: 01491 411295 — MB BChir 1977 Camb.; MA Camb. 1976; MRCS Eng. LRCP Lond. 1976; MRCGP 1980; DRCOG 1980.

GANLY, Sarah Ann Dr's Gooden and Partners, 111 Pembrooke Road, Clifton, Bristol BS9 Tel: 0117 973 3790 — BM BCh 1983 Oxf.; BA Camb. 1980; MRCGP 1992. GP Retainer, Bristol.

GANN, Michael John Edling Oak Tree House, New Pale Road, Manley Common, Frodsham WA6 9EP Tel: 01928 740569 Fax: 01928 740569 Email: mikegann@doctors.org.uk — MB BS Lond. 1968; FRCS Eng. 1974; FFOM 2002; T(OM) 1991. (Univ. Coll. Hosp.) p/t Indep. Pract. Occupat. Health; Cons. Occupat. Phys. Bolton Hosps. NHS Trust. Socs: Soc. Occupat. Med. Prev: Sen. Med. Adviser Civil Servs. OHS; Sen. Med. Adviser Shell Gp. Companies; Surg. Brunei Shell Petroleum Company Ltd.

GANNER, Anthony Neville Rother House Medical Centre, Alcester Road, Stratford-upon-Avon CV37 6PP Tel: 01789 269386 Fax: 01789 298742 — MB BChir 1964 Camb.; MA, MB Camb. 1964, BChir 1963; MRCS Eng. LRCP Lond. 1963; DObst RCOG 1966. (Camb.) Course Organiser Coventry VTS. Assoc. MRCGP. Socs: BMA. Prev: Ho. Off. (Surg.) Qu. Eliz. Hosp. Birm.; Ho. Off. (Paediat.) Childr. Hosp. Birm.; Ho. Off. (Obst.) Birm. Matern. Hosp.

GANNON, Caroline Dawn 8 Birch Grove, Golcar, Huddersfield HD7 4BQ — MB BCh BAO 1991 Belf.

GANNON, Isobel Diana Adeline Road Surgery, 4 Adeline Road, Boscombe, Bournemouth BH5 1EF Tel: 01202 309421 Fax: 01202 304893; Glebe House, Green Lane, Fordingbridge SP6 1JT — MB BS 1980 Lond. (Lond. Hosp.)

GANNON, John Patrick Dept of Anaesthesia, Wirral Hospital, Arrowe Park Road, Upton, Wirral CH49 5PE Email: jpgannon@msn.com; Email: jpgannon@msn.com — MB BCh BAO 1980 NUI; FCAnaesth 1991; FFA RCSI 1991; DA (UK) 1987. (Univ. Coll. Cork, Irel.) Cons. Anaes. Wirral Anaes.Gp. BUPA Murrayfield Hosp. Wirral; Cons. Anaesth. The Wirral Hosp. Merseyside. Socs: Intens. Care Soc.; Liverp. Soc. Anaesth.; Assoc. Anaesth. of G. Britain & Irel.

GANNON, Mr Mark Xavier Dell Cottage, 21 Bears Hill Road, King's Norton, Birmingham B38 8BJ — MB ChB 1979 Birm.; MD Birm. 1988; FRCS Eng. 1984; FRCS Ed. 1984. Cons. Surg. Birm. Heartlands Hosp. Socs: Vasc. Soc.; Assn. Surg.

GANNON, Martin Craig Princess Alice Hospice, West End Lane, Esher KT10 8NA Tel: 01372 461803; 9 Southerland Close, Weybridge KT13 9EN Tel: 01932 702535 Email: cgsg@cwcom.net — MB ChB 1988 Birm.; MRCGP 1993; Dip. Palliat. Med. Wales 1996. (Birm.) Cons. (Palliat. Med.); Cons. (Palliat. Med.) Houslow & Spelthorne Community & Ment. Health NHS Trust; Cons. (Palliat. Med.) P.ss Alice Hospice Esher; Hon. Cons. (Palliat. Med.) Ashford Hosp. Socs: Assn. Palliat. Med. Prev: Sen. Regist. (Palliat. Med.) P.ss Aice Hospice Esher; Regist. (Palliat. Med.) Myton Hamlet Hospice Warwick & Compton Hospice Wolverhampton; SHO (Palliat. Med.) St. Giles Hospice Lichfield.

GANNON, Martin John Fordingbridge Surgery, Bartons Road, Fordingbridge SP6 1RS Tel: 01425 652123 Fax: 01425 654393; Glebe House, Green Lane, Fordingbridge SP6 1JT — MB BS 1980 Lond.; MRCGP 1984; DRCOG 1984. (Lond. Hosp.) Prev: Trainee GP Salisbury VTS.

GANNON, Mr Michael Joseph 14 Glen Road, Leeds LS16 5NJ — MB BCh BAO 1977 NUI; FRCSI 1983; MRCOG 1990.

GANNON, Paul Francis Gerard DuPont (UK), P.O. Box 401, Wilton Site, Middlesbrough TS6 8JJ Tel: 01642 445766 Fax: 01642 445555 Email: paul.gammon@gbr.duponts.com — MB ChB 1985 Birm.; MRCP (UK) 1988; MFOM RCP Lond. 1996; MD 1999. UK Integrated Health Servs. Manager. Prev: Employm. Med. Advisor Health & Safety Exec. Leeds; Research Regist. (Respirat. Med.) E. Birm. Hosp.

GANNUSHKIN, Eugene Alexander — Vrach 1969 1st Moscow Med. Inst.; Vrach 1st Moscow Med. Inst. USSR 1969; FRCR 1988. Cons. Radiol. Colchester Gen. Hosp. Socs: Fell. Roy. Soc. Med. Prev: Sen. Regist. (Radiol.) Edin. Roy. Infirm.; Regist. (Radiol.) N.wick Pk. Hosp.

GANNY, Atoshi Sule 79 Coles Green Road, London NW2 7JH — MB BS 1981 Ahmadu Bello, Nigeria.

GANORKAR, Vijay Dhundiraj Department of Radiology, General Infirmary, Pontefract WF8 1PL Tel: 01977 606612 Fax: 01977 606135 — MB BS 1970 Nagpur; DMRD Eng. 1976. (Nagpur) Cons. Radiol. Pontefract Gen. Infirm. Friarwood. Prev: Sen. Regist. (Radiol.) Manch. & Salford AHAs (T); Regist. (Radiol.) Manch. Roy. Infirm.

GANT, Catherine Elizabeth c/o Mrs J Austin, 24 Linwood Road, Bournemouth BH9 1DW — MB BS 1986 Lond.; MRCP (UK) 1990; DCH RCP Lond. 1988. Paediat. GP Hong Kong.

GANT, Laurence James 118 Old Ford Road, London E2 9PW — MB BS 1991 Lond.

GANT, Richard Michael Arbury Road Surgery, 114 Arbury Road, Cambridge CB4 2JG Tel: 01223 364433 Fax: 01223 315728 — MB ChB 1973 Bristol; DA Eng. 1977.

GANTLEY, Jacqueline Mary North Road Medical Practice, 182 North Road, Cardiff CF14 3XQ Tel: 029 2061 9188 Fax: 029 2061 3484; 182 North Road, Cardiff CF14 3XQ Tel: 619188 — MB BCh 1981 Wales; MRCGP 1985.

GANVIR, Mr Pralhad Laxmanrao Church Street Surgery, 169 Church Street, Eccles, Manchester M30 0LU Tel: 0161 787 8880 Fax: 0161 787 8864 — MB BS 1959 Nagpur; FRCS Ed. 1964. Prev: Capt. AMC (India), Surg. Specialist; Regist. (Surg.) Hope Hosp. Salford; SHO (Neurosurg.) W.. Gen. Hosp. Edin.

GANVIR, Shishir Pralhad Church Street Surgery, 169 Church Street, Eccles, Manchester M30 0LU Tel: 0161 787 8880 Fax: 0161 787 8864; 15 Hardy Grove, Swinton, Manchester M27 0DA — MB ChB 1984 Birm.; MRCGP 1994. Prev: SHO (Geriat.) Ladywell Hosp. Salford; SHO (O & G & A & E) Hope. Hosp. Salford; SHO (Paediat.) Bolton Gen. Hosp.

GANVIR, Usha Pralhad (retired) Dr's Ganvir Practice, 169 Church Street, Eccles, Manchester M30 0LU Tel: 0161 787 8880 — MB BS 1964 Nagpur. Prev: Ho. Off. (O & G) & (Surg.) Hope Hosp. Salford.

GAON, David (retired) The Beeches Consulting Centre, The Alexandra Hospital, Mill Lane, Cheadle SK8 2PY Tel: 0161 428 4185 Fax: 0161 428 1692 — MB BCh 1955 Cairo; MRCS Eng. LRCP Lond. 1959; FRCP Ed. 1986; FRCP Lond. 1982. Cons. Phys. (Neurol.) Stepping Hill Hosp. Stockport. Prev: Regist. (Med.) Nottm. City Hosp. & United Sheff. Hosps.

GAON, Paul David 2 Waiting Court, Jesmond Way, Stanmore HA7 4QP — MB BS 1993 Lond.

GARABET, Ghazi George (retired) Collieston, Letterwalton, Ledaig, Oban PA37 1SA Tel: 0163 172 0368 — MB ChB 1964 Baghdad; FRCP Glas. 1993; MRCP (UK) 1975; MRCS Eng. LRCP Lond. 1979. Cons. Phys. (Geriat.) Lorn & Is.s Dist. Gen. Hosp. Oban. Prev: Sen. Regist. (Geriat. Med.) St. Francis' Hosp. Lond.

GARAI, Gaurchandra C/O Dr G Haldar, 5 Haithwaite, Two Mile Ash, Milton Keynes MK8 8LJ — MB BS 1972 Calcutta.

GARAI, Mrs Joan Glover (retired) Abney, Bagshot Road, Worplesdon, Guildford GU3 3PZ — MRCS Eng. LRCP Lond. 1944; MRCPsych 1971; DPM Eng. 1952. Prev: Asst. Psychiat. Roy. Free Hosp. Gp.

GARAI, Oliver Frank Parksuite, Frimley Park Hospital, Frimley, Camberley GU16 5UJ Tel: 01276 604606 Fax: 01276 604773; Abney, Bagshot Road, Worplesdon, Guildford GU3 3PZ Tel: 01483 232049 — MRCS Eng. LRCP Lond. 1941; FRCP Lond. 1972; MRCP (UK) 1943. (King's Coll. Lond.) Indep. Cons. Woking. Socs: Fell. Roy. Soc. Med.; Soc. Apoth. Liveryman.; BMA. Prev: Cons. Phys. Frimley Pk. Hosp. Camberley; Cons. Phys. (Cardiol.) Brompton Hosp. Lond.

GARALA, Kirit Health Centre, High Street, Bedworth, Nuneaton CV12 8NQ Tel: 024 7631 5432 Fax: 024 7631 0038 — MB ChB 1979 Birmingham; MB ChB 1979 Birmingham.

GARALA, Madhu Govind Health Centre, 77c Moor Street, Coventry CV5 6EU Tel: 024 7667 5016 Fax: 024 7671 7405 — MB ChB 1981 Manch.; DRCOG 1984. GP Coventry.

GARAS, Salah Fahmy Golf Green Road Surgery, 96-98 Golf Green Road, Jaywick, Clacton-on-Sea CO15 2RN Tel: 01255 423151 Fax: 01255 429208 — MB BCh 1969 Cairo.

GARBER, Ian Henry Flat C, 13 St Georges Drive, Pimlico, London SW1V 4DJ Tel: 020 7821 7180 Fax: 020 7821 7180; Flat C, 13 St. Georges Drive, Pimlico, London SW1V 4DJ Tel: 020 7821 7180 Fax: 020 7821 7180 — LRCPI & LM, LRSCI & LM 1964. (Royal College of Surgeons Ireland)

GARBER, Sebastian Adrenele Frimley Park Hospital, Portsmouth Road, Frimley, Camberley GU15 2RF Tel: 01276 604604; 7 Jonson Close, Mitcham CR4 1DP — MB BCh 1976 Nigeria; MRCOG 1990. Locum Staff Grade (Obstet. & Gyn.) Frimley Pk. Hosp. Camberley. Prev: Regist. (O & G) N. Devon Dist. Hosp.

GARBER, Steven Jeremy Department of Diagnostic Imaging, Ipswich Hospital NHS Trust, Ipswich IP4 5PD; Salisbury House, 92 Church St, Sudbury CO10 9QT Tel: 01787 248164 — MB BS 1984 Lond.; BSc Lond. 1981; MRCP (UK) 1987; FRCR 1990. (Roy. Free) Cons. Radiol. Ipswich Hosp. Socs: Roy. Coll. Radiol.; BMA. Prev: Sen. Regist. (Radiol.) Middlx. Hosp. & Univ. Coll. Hosp.; Regist. (Radiol.) Univ. Coll. Hosp. Middlx.; SHO (Med.) Luton & Dunstable Hosp. Luton & Qu. Eliz. Hosp. Welwyn.

GARBETT, Neil Denis International Clinical Research, Glaxo Wellcome Research & Development, Greenford Road, Greenford UB6 0HE Tel: 020 8077 3147 Fax: 020 8966 2030 Email: ndg44796@ggr.co.uk; The Beeches, Beech Waye, Gerrards Cross SL9 8BL Tel: 01753 893526 Fax: 01753 893525 — MB ChB 1977 Otago; MFPM RCP (UK) 1993; FRACP 1988. (Otago University Dunedin, New Zealand) Dir. Internat. Clin. Research Glaxo Wellcome Research & Developm. Greenford. Prev: Cons. Respirat. Phys. Wellington Hosp., NZ; Sen. Regist. Brompton Hosp. Lond.

GARBUTT, Dale 127 North Wingfield Road, Grassmoor, Chesterfield S42 5EB — MB ChB 1986 Ed.; BSc (Hons. Psychol.)

Ed. 1984; MRCPsych 1991. (Edinburgh) Cons. in Old Age Psychol. Midlothian.

GARBUTT, Freya Elizabeth 2 Church Lane, Creeton, Grantham NG33 4QB Tel: 01780 410563 — BChir 1996 Camb.; MB BChir Camb. 1996; BA (Hons.) Cantab. 1994. (Camb.)

GARBUTT, Ian Trevor 12 Fernbank, Bristol BS6 6PZ — BM BS 1985 Nottm.; DRCOG 1988.

GARBUTT, Nigel Isaac Barry, Surg. Lt.-Cdr. RN Retd. Southwest Occupational Health, Tudor Cottage, Minsterworth, Gloucester GL2 8JP Tel: 01452 750128 Fax: 01452 750138 — MB BS 1974 Lond.; DRCOG 1976; LLM 1999. (Lond. Hosp.) Indep. Specialist (Occupat. Med.) & Forens. Med. Pract. SW Eng.; Police Surg. Avon & Som. Constab. & Glos. Constab.; HM Dep. Coroner Worcs. Socs: Brit. Assn. Immed. Care Schemes; Soc. Occupat. Med.; Assn. Police Surg. Prev: Employm. Med. Adviser Health & Safety Exec. Bristol; Princip. GP W.bury-on-Severn.

GARCHA, Parvinder Singh 77 Lampton Road, Hounslow TW3 4DH Tel: 020 8572 1497 Fax: 020 8577 7322; 14 Lampton Avenue, Hounslow TW3 4EN — MB BS 1982 Lond.; MRCP (UK) 1988; MRCGP 1987; DCH 1986. Clin. Asst. (Dermat.) W. Middlx. Univ. Hosp. Socs: Soc. Occupat. Med.

GARCIA, Jose Anthony 120 Peveril Road, Sheffield S11 7AR — MB ChB 1991 Sheff.

GARCIA, Stephane Henry C/O Alan Orchover, 42 Pangbourne Dr, Stanmore HA7 4QT — MB BS 1984 Lond.

GARCIA, Steven Paul 52 Sussex Street, London SW1V 4RG — MB BS 1992 Lond.

GARCIA ABREU, Tania 19 Harrow Way, Weavering, Maidstone ME14 5TU — LMS 1993 Cordoba.

GARCIA ALEN GARCIA, Luciano 119 Moston Lane E., New Moston, Manchester M40 0GJ — LMS 1991 Santiago de Compostela.

GARCIA ASENSIO, Maria del Pilar 24 Hoyle Road, London SW17 0RS — LMS 1988 Barcelona.

GARCIA-BAQUERO MERINO, Maria Teresa 11 Greystone Crescent, Dumfries DG1 1PG Tel: 01387 55165 — LMC Extremadura 1989.

GARCIA CEBALLOS, Jose Ignacio Flat 3, Charnwood Court, 2 Farncombe Road, Worthing BN11 2BE — LMS 1993 Basque Provinces.

GARCIA CIFUENTES, Bernardo 28A Laurel Gardens, London W7 3JG — LMS 1983 Oviedo.

GARCIA DE VINUESA, Carola MRC Centre for Immune Regulation University of Birmingham, Medical school, Vincent Drive, Birmingham B15 2TT Tel: 0121 414 6970 Fax: 0121 414 3599 Email: c.g.vinuesa@bham.ac.uk; Flat 4, 31 Oxford Road, Mosely, Birmingham B13 9EH Tel: 0121 442 2085 Email: cgvinuesa@yahoo.com — LMS 1993 Madrid; LMS Autonoma Madrid 1993; DRCOG 1995; DFFP 1996; MSc 1997. Clin. Research Fell. Immunol., Univ. of Birm. Socs: Brit. Soc. for Immunol.

GARCIA GARCIA, Miguel Angel Royal Lancaster Infirmary, 25 Pointer Court, Ashton Road, Lancaster LA1 4JT — LMS 1993 Granada.

GARCIA HINAREJOS, Juan Alberto Drumlang Lodge, Gruline, Isle of Mull PA71 6HR — LMS 1987 Valencia.

GARCIA-LOZANO GOMES, Francisco Javier Top Flat, 22 Eccleston Square, London SW1V 1NS — LMS 1982 Oviedo.

GARCIA-MIRALLES, Jose Ramon The Surgery, Front St., Pelton, Chester-le-Street DH2 1DE Tel: 0191 370 0263 Fax: 0191 370 0243 — LMS 1989 Saragossa. (Saragossa) GP Chester le St., Co. Durh.

GARCIA-OCHOA FERNANDEZ, Juan Yeovil District Hospital, Higher Kingston, Yeovil BA21 4AT Tel: 01935 75122; 9 Oliver Close, The Prinnels, Swindon SN5 6NP — LMS 1992 Complutense Madrid.

GARCIA-ORAD CARLES, Cristina 1 Burns Street, Nottingham NG7 4DS Tel: 0115 978 5792 — LMS 1989 Basque Provinces. (University of Basque Country Bilbao) Socs: MDU; BMA; I H Exchange.

GARCIA-ORMAETXEA, Milagros 41 Manchester Road, Ashton-under-Lyne OL7 0DA — LMS 1990 Basque Provinces.

GARCIA-PRADERAS, Ignacio 90 Antrobus Road, London W4 5NQ — LMS 1993 Saragossa.

GARCIA-RODRIGUEZ, Charles Robert 28 Lime Tree Avenue, Retford DN22 7BA — MB BS 1989 Lond.; FRCA (UK) 1993. Vis. Assoc. Anaesthesiol. Duke Univ. Med. centre, Durh., N. Carolina USA. Prev: Sen. Regist. Anaesth. St Mary's Hosp., Paddington.

GARCIA RODRIGUEZ, Ruth c/o Postgraduate Department, Department of Psychiatry, St George's Hospital Medical School, Tooting, London SW17 0RE — LMS 1994 Seville.

GARCIA-VARGAS, Jose Eliseo Zeneca Pharmaceuticals, Mereside Alderley Park, Macclesfield SK10 4TG Tel: 01625 582828 Fax: 01625 669 3288; 7 Greenhythe Road, Heald Green, Cheadle SK8 3NS — Medico Cirujano Peru 1982; BMSc Peru 1982; DMRT Lond. 1992. (Univ. Nacional Federico Villarreal) Med. Advisor (Oncol.) Zeneca Pharmaceut. Macclesfield. Socs: Roy. Coll. Radiol.; Eur. Soc. Therap. Radiat. & Oncol.; Brit. Oncol. Assn. Prev: Med. Advisor (Oncol.) Pharmacia & Upjohn; Staff Med. Oncol. St. Jas. Univ. Hosp. Leeds; Regist. (Clin. Oncol.) Velindre Hosp. Cardiff.

GARCIA ZARCO, Maria del Mar 47 Russell Drive, Nottingham NG8 2BA — LMS 1987 Valencia.

GARD, Philip David The Health Centre, High Street, Arnold, Nottingham NG5 7BG Tel: 0115 926 7257; 34 Doverbeck Drive, Woodborough, Nottingham NG14 6ER Tel: 0115 965 4502 — MB ChB 1977 Bristol; BSc Bristol 1974; MRCGP 1983; DRCOG 1982; DA Eng. 1980.

GARD, Richard John Llynyfran Surgery, Llynyfran Road, Llandysul SA44 4JX Tel: 01559 363306 Fax: 01559 362896 — MB ChB 1987 Birm.; MRCGP 1993.

GARD, Walter John (retired) The Dow Surgery, William St., Redditch B97 4AJ Tel: 01527 62285 Fax: 01527 64764 — MB ChB 1961 Birm.; MRCS Eng. LRCP Lond. 1961; DA Eng. 1966. Hosp. Pract. (Anaesth.) Alexandra Hosp. Redditch. Prev: SHO (Anaesth.) Gen. Hosp. Birm.

GARDECKI, Mr Teodor Ignacy Marek New Cross Hospital, Wolverhampton WV10 0QP Tel: 01902 307999; 8 Summerfield Road, West Park, Wolverhampton WV1 4PR Tel: 01902 429044 — MB BS 1973 Lond.; MS Lond. 1989; FRCS Ed. 1978; FRCS Eng. 1978. (St. Thos.) Cons. Gen. & Vasc. Surg. New Cross Hosp. Wolverhampton. Socs: Vasc. Surg. Soc. GB & Irel.; W Midl. Surg. Soc. Prev: Sen. Regist. (Surg.) W. Midl.; Regist. (Surg.) N. Staffs. Roy. Infirm. Stoke on Trent; Research Fell. Qu. Eliz. & Roy. Orthop. Hosp. Birm.

GARDEE, Mohammed Rafique 21 Cleveden Drive, Kelvinside, Glasgow G12 0SD — MB ChB 1997 Glas.

GARDEN, Anne Strachan Liverpool Women's Hospital, Crown St., Liverpool L8 7SS Tel: 0151 702 4101 Fax: 0151 702 4024; 6 Queen's Park, Pipers Lane, Heswall, Wirral CH60 9HP — MB ChB 1973 Aberd.; FRCOG 1992, M 1979. Sen. Lect. & Hon. Cons. O & G Univ. Liverp.; Lect. (Child Health & Gyn.) Liverp. Wom. Hosp.; Asst. Dir. (Med. Educat.) Liverp. Socs: BMA. Prev: Sen. Regist. (O & G) Roy. Infirm. & Simpson Matern. Mem. Pavil. Edin.; Regist. (O & G) Groote Schuur Hosp. Cape Town S. Afr. & Matern. Hosp. Aberd.

GARDEN, Gillian Margaret Flett Department of Psychiatry, Pilgrim Hospital, Sibsey Road, Boston PE21 9QU Tel: 01205 364801 Ext: 3634 Fax: 01205 351251 — MB ChB 1983 Birm.; BSc (Pharmacol.) Birm. 1980; MRCP (UK) 1986; MRCPsych 1989. Cons. Psychiat. Pilgrim Hosp. Boston; Hon. Cons. Psychiat. St. Luke's Hosp. for Clergy Lond.

GARDEN, Ian Allardyce (retired) 10 Kynance Close, South Normanton, Alfreton DE55 2FD — MB ChB Aberd. 1958.

GARDEN, Professor Olivier James Department of Clinical and Surgical Sciences (Surgery), Royal Infirmary, Lauriston Place, Edinburgh EH3 9YW Tel: 0131 536 3812 Fax: 0131 228 2661 Email: ojgarden@ed.ac.uk; 22 Moston Terrace, Newington, Edinburgh EH9 2DE Tel: 0131 667 3715 Email: ojgarden@aol.com — MB ChB 1977 Ed.; BSc Ed. 1974, MD 1987; FRCS Ed. 1993; FRCS Glas. 1981. (Univ. Ed.) Regius Prof. of Clin. Surg., Dept. of Clin. and Surgic. Sci. (Surg.), Univ. of Edin., Roy. Infirm., Edin.; Cons. Surg. Scott. Liver Transpl. Unit. Roy. Infirm. Edin.; Hon. Cons. Surg. Roy. Infirm. Edin. Socs: Mem. Assn. Surg.; Mem. Eur. Surgic. Assn.; Mem. Internat. Surgic. Soc. Prev: Sen. Lect. & Hon. Cons. Surg. Univ. Dept. Surg. Roy. Infirm. Edin.; Lect. Univ. Dept. Surg. Glas. Roy. Infirm.; Chef de Clinique Hosp. Paul Brousse, Villejuif, France.

GARDEN, Thomas Buchan Horsefair Practice, Horse Fair, Rugeley WS15 2EL Tel: 01889 582244 Fax: 01899 582244 — MB ChB

1966 Aberd.; Cert. Family Plann. JCC 1975. (Aberd.) Med. Off. (Family Plann.) S. Staffs HA. Socs: BMA & Nat. Assn. Family Plann. Doctors. Prev: Cas. Off. Aberd. Roy. Infirm.; Ho. Off. Roy. Aberd. Hosp. Sick Childr. & Aberd. Matern. Hosp.

GARDHAM, Mr John Richard Carr The Kings Oak Hospital, Chase Farm, The Ridgeway, Enfield EN2 8SD Tel: 020 8370 9500; The Old School House, Great Amwell, Ware SG12 9SJ Tel: 01920 871179 — MB BChir Camb. 1962; MD Camb. 1977, MChir 1966; FRCS Eng. 1964. (Middlx.) Socs: Fell. Roy. Soc. Med.; Vasc. Surgic. Soc. GB & Irel. Prev: Sen. Regist. (Surg.) Norf. & Norwich Hosp.; Sen. Regist. (Surg.) Middlx. Hosp.; Regist. (Surg.) St. Thos. Hosp. Lond.

GARDI, Pravinchandra Dayalal c/o Mr G Z Chhatrisha, 77 Ethel Road, Leicester LE5 5ND Tel: 0116 273 8148; PO Box 89, Malindi, Kenya — MB BS 1966 Bombay. (Topiwala Nat. Med. Coll.)

GARDINER, Alan Seath (retired) 9 Earls Avenue, Folkestone CT20 2HW Tel: 01303 256818 Fax: 01303 256818 Email: drasgar@btinternet.com — BM BCh Oxf. 1951; MA Oxf. 1951; FFA RCS Eng 1961; DA Eng. 1955. Cons. Anaesth. SE Kent HA. Prev: Cons. Anaesth. Univ. Hosp. W. Indies.

GARDINER, Alexander Quentin (retired) Baylissburn House, Dalmuinzie Road, Bieldside, Aberdeen AB15 9EB — MB ChB 1962 Aberd.; PhD Aberd. 1967, MB ChB 1962; FRCPsych 1981, M 1971; DPM Ed. & Glas. 1966. Prev: Cons. Psychiat. Roy. Cornhill Hosp. Aberd.

GARDINER, Alison Oriel Patricia The Private GP Service, Bournemouth Nuffield Hospital, 63 Lansdowne Road, Bournemouth BH1 1RN Tel: 01202 702808 Fax: 01202 294247 — MB BS 1981 Lond.; DFFP 1998; MRCGP (Distinc.) 1986; DA (UK) 1987; DRCOG 1986. (Guy's Hosp. Lond.) Dir. Health Screening Unit Bounemouth Nuffield Hosp. Socs: BMA.

GARDINER, Alistair John Park Gate Surgery, 28 St. Helens Road, Ormskirk L39 4QR Tel: 01695 72561 Fax: 01695 571709; Highlands, 99 Ruff Lane, Ormskirk L40 6HA Tel: 01695 572486 — MB ChB 1974 Liverp.

GARDINER, Anne Elizabeth Hilary Cottage Surgery, Keble Lawns, Fairford GL7 4BQ Tel: 01285 712377 Fax: 01285 713084; Cleeve Lodge, Baunton Lane GL7 2NQ Fax: 01285 659186 Email: wgardiner@ill.org — MB ChB 1983 Sheff.; MRCGP 1987; DRCOG 1988; DCH RCP Lond. 1986. (Sheffield University) p/t GP Princip. Prev: Trainee GP/SHO Cirencester Memor. Hosp. VTS; SHO (O & G) P.ss Margt. Hosp. Swindon.

GARDINER, Austen James Sutherland 'Farringford', St Margaret's Drive, Dunblane FK15 0DP Tel: 01786 823183 — MD 1974 Aberd.; MB ChB 1960; FRCP Glas. 1979; FRCP Ed. 1979, M 1978; MRCP Lond. 1966. (Aberd.) Cons. Phys. Med. Unit Monklands Hosp. Airdrie; Surg. Research Fell. & Garden Research Fell. Dept. Med. Aberd. Univ.; Research Fell. Cardio-Respirat. Serv., McGill Univ. Clinic Roy. Vict. Hosp. Montreal. Socs: Scott. Soc. Experim. Med. & Scott. Thoracic Soc. Prev: Research Fell. Cardio-Respirat. Serv., McGill Univ. Clinic Roy. Vict.; Hosp. Montreal; Sen. Regist. Aberd. Roy. Infirm.

GARDINER, Carol Anne Bonerick Farmhouse, Iron Gray, Dumfries DG2 9SE Tel: 0138 773464 — MB ChB 1985 Dundee.

GARDINER, Charlotte McElheran 21 Tweskard Park, Stormont, Belfast BT4 2JY Tel: 01232 763522 — MB BCh BAO 1949 Belf.; FFA RCS Eng. 1954; DA Eng. 1953. (Belf.) Socs: Assn. Anaesth. Gt. Brit. & Irel. Prev: Cons. Anaesth. Belf. City Hosp. Gp.; Head, Dept. Anaesth. Christian Med. Coll. Ludhiana, India; Med. Off. Jiwan Jyoti Christian Hosp. Robt.sganj, India.

GARDINER, Christine Ann Glebe Street Surgery, 1 Glebe Street, Chiswick, London W4 2BD Tel: 020 8747 4800 Fax: 020 8995 4388; 55 Airedale Avenue, Chiswick, London W4 2NW Tel: 020 8747 4742 — MB ChB 1981 Leic.

GARDINER, David Alan Hartland Way Surgery, 1 Hartland Road, Shirley, Croydon CR0 8RG Tel: 020 8777 7215 Fax: 020 8777 7648; 22 Forest Ridge, Beckenham BR3 3NH — MB BCh 1981 Wales; DRCOG 1984; BSc 1998; Dip. Computing 1998.

GARDINER, David Stuart Department of Pathology, Monklands District General Hospital, Airdrie ML6 0JS Tel: 01236 746105 Fax: 01236 770117 — MB ChB 1986 Glas.; BSc (Hons. Path.) Glas. 1984, MD Glas. 1991; MRCPath 1993. (Glasgow) Cons. Histopath. Monklands Dist. Gen. Hosp. Airdrie. Prev: Sen. Regist., Regist. & SHO (Histopath.) W.. Infirm. Glas.; Lect. (Histopath.) Roy. Infirm. Glas.

GARDINER, Eileen Wendy 17 Kings Court, Templepatrick, Ballyclare BT39 0EB — MB ChB 1986 Dundee.

GARDINER, Mr Gavin Thomas Mt Vernon Hospital, Northwood Tel: 020 8423 9474 — MB BS 1973 Lond.; BDS Otago 1964; FRCS Ed 1986; MRCS Eng. LRCP Lond. 1973; FDS RCS Eng. 1968; FRACDS 1969. Cons. Oral & Maxillofacial Surg. Hillingdon Hosp. Uxbridge, Mt. Vernon Hosp. N.wood & N.wick Pk. Hosp. Harrow. Prev: Sen. Regist. (Oral & Maxillofacial Surg.) St. Geo. Hosp. Lond. & Roy. Dent. Hosp. Lond.

GARDINER, George David 2 Shankbridge Road, Cromkill, Ballymena BT42 3DJ Tel: 01266 653684 Email: george gardiner@compuserve.com — MB ChB 1988 Ed.

GARDINER, Heather Marion Adolescent Unit, Gartnavel Royal Hospital, 1055 Great Western Road, Glasgow G12 0XH Tel: 0141 211 3589; 32 Biggar Road, Symington, Biggar ML12 6FT Tel: 01899 308331 Email: heather@tinto.demon.co.uk — MB ChB 1981 Manch.; MPhil Ed. 1994; MRCPsych 1992; DRCOG 1983. Cons. (Adolesc. Psychiat.) Gartnavel Roy. Hosp. Glas.; Hon. Clin. Lect. Univ. of Glas. Prev: Sen. Regist. (Child & Adolesc. Psychiat.) Yorkhill NHS Trust Glas.

GARDINER, Helena Maria Cardiothoracic Unit, Freeman Hospital, Newcastle upon Tyne NE7 7DN Tel: 0191 284 3111; 76 Valiant House, Vicarage Crescent, London SW11 3LX Tel: 020 7738 0991 — MB BCh 1981 Wales; MD Bristol 1993; MRCP (UK) 1988. Sen. Regist. (Paediat. Cardiol.) Freeman Hosp. Newc. u. Tyne. Prev: Regist. (Paediat. Cardiol.) Gt. Ormond St. Hosp. Lond.; Research Fell. Inst. Child Health Univ. Bristol; Bliss Neonat. Fell. S.mead Hosp. Bristol.

GARDINER, Hilary Jean (retired) 10 Nelson Close, Stockbridge SO20 6ES Tel: 01264 810365 Fax: 01264 810365 — MB BS 1948 Lond.; MRCPsych 1973; DPM Eng. 1971. Prev: Asst. Psychiat. Roy. Hants. Co. Hosp. Winchester.

GARDINER, Jacqueline 26 Whitecraigs, Kinnesswood, Kinross KY13 9JN — MB ChB 1997 Aberd.

GARDINER, James Stewart 5 Haddon Close, Alderley Edge SK9 7RD Tel: 01625 582639 — MD 1972 Aberd.; MB ChB 1946; FFOM 2000 RCP Lond.; MFOM RCP Lond. 1978; MRCGP 1959; DIH Soc. Apoth. Lond. 1973. (Aberd.) Cons. Occupat. Health Phys. Chesh. Prev: Div. Med. Off. ICI Ltd. (Organics Div.) Manch.; Div. Med. Off. ICI Ltd. (Pharmaceut. Div.) Alderley Edge.

GARDINER, Jill ICRF Department of Medical Oncology, Western General Hospital, Crewe Road, Edinburgh Tel: 0131 332 2471 Email: gardinj@callisto.lif.icnet.uk; 37 Kettil'stoun Grove, Linlithgow EH49 6PP Tel: 01506 671083 — MB ChB 1988 Glas.; BSc (Hons.) Glas. 1985; MRCP (UK) 1992. (Glas.) Specialist Grade Regist. (Med. Oncol.) W.ern Gen. Hosp. Edin. Prev: Clin. Research Fell. (Med. Oncol.) W.ern Gen. Edin.; Regist. (Med. Oncol.) W.. Gen. Hosp. Edin.; SHO (Gen. Med. & Med. Oncol.) Glas. Roy. Infirm.

GARDINER, Joanne Sheena 14 Duddington Park, Edinburgh EH15 1JN — MB ChB 1994 Ed.; DRCOG 1997; MRCP (Ed.) 1998. (Edinburgh) GP Regist. Rose Garden Med. Centre Edin. Prev: SHO (Oncol.) W.ern Gen. Hosp. Edin.; SHO (Paediat.) St. John's Hosp. Livingston; SHO (O & G) St. John's Hosp. Livingston.

GARDINER, Mr Jonathan Croxon Andover Lodge, Redenham Park, Andover SP11 9AQ — MB BS 1985 Lond.; FRCS Eng. 1990.

GARDINER, Katharine Helen 4 Castle Grove Drive, Far Headingley, Leeds LS6 4BR — MB ChB 1990 Leeds. SHO (Paediat.) Harrogate Dist. Hosp. Prev: SHO (Paediat.) Leeds Gen. Infirm.; SHO (Infec. Dis.) Seacroft Hosp. Leeds.

GARDINER, Mr Keith Reginald Colorectal Surgical Unit, Royal Victoria Hospital, Grosvenor Road, Belfast BT12 6BA — MB BCh BAO 1983 Belf.; MD Belf. 1993; FRSCI 1987; FRCS Ed. 1987; MCh Belf. 1994; FRCS (Gen.) 1995. Cons. Surg. Roy. Vict. Hosp. Belf.; Hon. Sen. Lect. (Surg.) The Qu. Univ. of Belf.; Chairm., NI Basic Surgic. Train. Comm., NI Counc. for PostGrad. Med. and Dent. Educat.; Progr. Director, Gen. Surg., NI Counc. for PostGrad. Med. and Dent. Educat., Belf. Socs: Surg. Research Soc.; Brit. Soc. Gastroenterol.; Assn. Coloproctol. Prev: Research Fell. (Surg.) Johns Hopkins Med. Inst. Baltimore, Maryland, USA; Sen. Lect. (Surg.) The Qu. Univ. of Belf.

GARDINER, Kerry Jeanetta Flat 4, 105 Buccleuch St., Edinburgh EH8 9NG — MB ChB 1998 Ed.; MB ChB Ed 1998.

GARDINER, Louise Jayne 2 Peacock Way, Bretton, Peterborough PE3 9AA Tel: 01733 266194 Fax: 01733 266194 Email: lgardner@doctors.org.uk — MB ChB 1998 Bristol.

GARDINER, Martin Richard 51 Cornwall Street, Chester CH1 3JE — MB ChB 1996 Liverp.

GARDINER, Matthew Forrest (retired) Long Garretts, Hawkedon, Bury St Edmunds IP29 4NP Tel: 01284 789481 — MB BS Lond. 1950. Prev: Indep. GP Surrey.

GARDINER, Michael Craig Portrush Medical Centre, Dunlace Avenue, Portrush BT56 8DW Tel: 028 7082 3767 Fax: 028 7082 3413 — MB BCh BAO 1973 Dub.

GARDINER, Patricia Susan Abbey House Surgery, Golding Close, Daventry NN11 5RA Tel: 01327 877770 Fax: 01327 310267 Email: patti.gardiner@abbeyhousesurgery.co.uk; 5 London Road, Daventry NN11 4DA Tel: 01327 878741 Email: pattigardiner@cs.com — MB ChB 1977 Aberd.; MRCGP (Distinc.) 1994; DCH RCPS Glas. 1979. (Aberd.) p/t GP; Examr. Panel of RCGP.

GARDINER, Penny Victoria 12 Thorpe Lodge, Cotham Side, Bristol BS6 5TJ — MB ChB 1990 Aberd.

GARDINER, Peter Ambrose 18 Crown Place, Woodbridge IP12 1BU — LMSSA 1937 Lond.; DOMS Eng. 1941; MD Lond. 1960; FCOphth 1989. (Guys Hosp) Emerit. Consult. Ophth. Guy's Hosp. Socs: Fell. Roy Soc. Med.; Fell Roy. Soc. Med. Prev: Emerit. Cons. (Ophth.) Guy's Hosp. Lond.; Cons. (Ophth.) Surg. Miller Hosp. Lond.; Surg. (Ophth.) Surg. Barnet Gen. Hosp.

GARDINER, Philip Victor Ward 2, Altnagelvin Hospital, Londonderry BT47 6SB Tel: 028 7134 5171; 76 Stoneypath, Victoria Road, Londonderry BT47 2AF Email: pvgardiner@yahoo.co.uk — MB BCh BAO 1985 Belf.; MD Belf. 1993; MRCP (UK) 1988. (Queen's University Belfast) Cons. Phys. (Rheum.) Altnagelvin Hosp. Belf. Socs: FRCP (Lond.) 1999; FRCP (Glas) 1998. Prev: Sen. Regist. (Med.) Altnagelvin Hosp. Belf.; Sen. Regist. (Rheum.) Musgrave Pk. Hosp.; Research Fell. (Respirat. Med.) Newc. u. Tyne.

GARDINER, Mr Quentin Dept of Otolaryngology, Ninewells Hospital & Medical school, Dundee DD1 9SY Tel: 01382 660111 Fax: 01382 632816 Email: g.gardiner@dundee.ac.uk; 31 Dundee Road W., Broughty Ferry, Dundee DD5 1NB Tel: 01382 477707 — MB ChB 1986 Ed.; FRCS Eng. 1991. (University of Edinburgh) Cons. (Otolaryngol.) Ninewells Hosp. & Med. Sch. Dundee.; Hon. Cons. Fife Acute Health Care Trust Kirkcaldy; Hon. Sen. Clin. Teach. Univ. of Dundee Dundee. Socs: Societe Francaise D'Orl Mem.; Scott. Otolaryngol. Soc.; Brit. Assoc. of ORL HNS Mem. Prev: Fell. (Rhinology) Hopital St Chas. Montpellier, France; Regist. (Otolaryngol.) Roy. Lond. Hosp.; SHO (Otolaryngol.) Roy. Nat. ENT Hosp. Lond. & Roy. Infirm. Edin.

GARDINER, Professor Richard Mark Department of Paediatrics, UCL Medical School, Rayne Institute, University St., London WC1E 6JJ Tel: 020 7209 6100 Fax: 020 7209 6103 — MB BChir 1973 Camb.; MB Camb. 1973, BChir, 1972; BA Camb. 1969, MD 1981; FRCP Lond. 1989; MRCP (UK) 1974; DCH Eng. 1974. (St. Thos.) Prof. Paediat. Univ. Coll. Lond. Socs: Neonat. Soc.; Phys. Soc.; Paediat. Research Soc. Prev: Clin. Reader (Paediat.) Univ. Oxf.; Wellcome Sen. Research Fell. (Clin. Sc.) Univ. Coll. Lond.; Regist. (Paediat.) Addenbrooke's Hosp. Camb.

GARDINER, Robert (retired) 74 Bowhouse Drive, Kirkcaldy KY1 1SB Tel: 01592 643399 — MB ChB 1951 Aberd.; FRCP Ed. 1988, M 1984; FFCM 1980, M 1974; DIH Eng. 1959; DPH St. And. 1957. Prev: Chief Admin. Med. Off. Fife HB.

GARDINER, Roger Alec Belle Vue Medical Practice, 271 Rayleigh Road, Thundersley, Benfleet SS7 3FX Tel: 01702 553140 Fax: 01702 556539 — MB BS 1978 Lond. (London Hospital)

GARDINER, Sarah Evelyn 2 Peacock Way, Wood Acres, South Bretton, Peterborough PE3 9AA — MB ChB 1995 Leeds.

GARDINER, Stephen Tay Court Surgery, 50 South Tay Street, Dundee DD1 1PF Tel: 01382 228228 Fax: 01382 202606; 369 Blackness Road, Dundee DD2 1ST — MB ChB 1990 Dundee. GP Princip. Prev: Trainee GP Tayside HB.

GARDINER, Stephen East Quay Medical Centre, East Quay, Bridgwater TA6 5YB Tel: 01278 444666 Fax: 01278 445448; Upland, 37 Wembdon Rise, Wembdon, Bridgwater TA6 7PN Tel: 01278 446162 — MB BS 1986 Lond.; MA Camb. 1987; MRCGP 1992; DRCOG 1990.

GARDINER, Stephen Clive (retired) Branscombe, Agaton Road, St Budeaux, Plymouth PL5 2EW Tel: 01752 361955 — MB ChB St. And. 1956. Prev: Ho. Surg. Craigtown Matern. Hosp. St. And.

GARDINER, Susan 215 Woodfield Road, Harrogate HG1 4JE — MB ChB 1998 Aberd.; MB ChB Aberd 1998.

GARDINER, Susan Carole 51 Sandbeds Road, Pellon, Halifax HX2 0QL; Woodview, 59 Hollins Lane, Sowerby Bridge HX6 2RS Tel: 01422 834052 — MB ChB 1984 Manch.; DRCOG 1987; Cert. Family Plann. JCC 1987. Prev: Trainee GP Luton VTS.

GARDINER, Mr Thomas Baxter (retired) 77 Norwood Park, Bearsden, Glasgow G61 2RZ Tel: 0141 942 0305 — MB ChB 1942 Glas.; FRFPS Glas. 1949; FRCS Glas. 1962. Prev: Cons. Orthop. Surg. W.. Infirm. Glas., Killearn Hosp. & Gartnavel.

GARDINER, Victor Reid (retired) 21 Tweskard Park, Belfast BT4 2JY Tel: 01232 763522 — MB BCh BAO Belf. 1949. Prev: Assoc. Specialist (Geriat. Med.) Ulster Hosp. Dundonald.

GARDINER, William McGregor (retired) 31 Oxford Street, Dundee DD2 1TH Tel: 01382 668203 — MB ChB St. And. 1960. Prev: GP Dundee.

GARDNER, Adrian Christopher 22B O'Connell Road, Eastleigh SO50 9GL — BM 1998 Soton.; BM Soton 1998.

GARDNER, Alan Waters Edge, Derwent Drive, Baslow, Bakewell DE45 1RS — MRCS Eng. LRCP Lond. 1950.

GARDNER, Alan (retired) 2A Penrhyn Avenue, Walthamstow, London E17 5DB Tel: 020 8527 2563 — MRCS Eng. LRCP Lond. 1966. Prev: Ho. Phys. Buckland Hosp. Dover.

GARDNER, Mr Alan David Hyde (retired) 1 Hyde Lane, Danbury, Chelmsford CM3 4QX Tel: 01245 223456 Fax: 01245 222130 Email: alan@adhg.demon.co.uk — MB BS 1962 Lond.; FRCS Eng. 1971; T(S) 1991. Vis. Prof. Spinal Surg. Denver Colorado, USA; Guest Lect. Dutch Spine Soc. & Austral. Spine Soc. Prev: Cons. Orthop. Surg. Basildon Hosp. & Orsett Hosp. Gray's & Black Notley Hosp. Braintree.

GARDNER, Angela Ruth (retired) 19 Hunter Road, Wimbledon, London SW20 8NZ Tel: 020 8946 7785 — MRCS Eng. LRCP Lond. 1958; MRCPsych 1973; DPM Eng. 1971. Prev: Cons. Psychiat. St. Mary Abbots & St. Stephens Hosps. Lond.

GARDNER, Antony Kenneth 11 Towton Road, West Norwood, London SE27 9EE Email: tgardner@cix.co.uk — MB BS 1987 Lond. (Guy's Hospital) Prev: Trainee GP Taunton & Som. Hosp. VTS; Ho. Phys. Frenchay Hosp. Bristol; Ho. Surg. Orpington Hosp. Kent.

GARDNER, Mr Arthur Michael Newsam (retired) The Priory, Ipplepen, Newton Abbot TQ12 5RT Tel: 01803 812213 — BM BCh 1943 Oxf.; DM, MCh Oxf. 1967; FRCS Eng. 1951. Hon. Cons. Gen. Surg. Torbay Health Dist. Prev: Sen. Regist. (Surg.) Radcliffe Infirm. Oxf.

GARDNER, Mr Brian Patrick National Spinal Injuries Centre, Stoke Mandeville Hospital, Aylesbury HP21 8AL Tel: 01296 315000 Fax: 01296 315867; 2 Northumberland Avenue, Aylesbury HP21 7HG Tel: 01296 423420 Fax: 01296 424627 Email: bgardner@indognet.co.uk — BM BCh 1973 Oxf.; MA Oxf. 1976, BA 1971; FRCP Ed. 1996; FRCP Lond. 1995; FRCS Eng. 1980; MRCP (UK) 1978. (Oxf. & Lond. Hosp.) p/t Cons. Surg. Spinal Injuries Nat. Spinal Injuries Centre Stoke Mandeville. Socs: BMA; Internat. Med. Soc. Paraplegia. Prev: Sen. Regist. (Spinal Injuries) Merseyside Regional Centre S.port; Regist. (Neurol. Surg.) Roy. Vict. Hosp. Belf.; Regist. Rotat. (Surg.) Addenbrooke's Hosp. Camb.

GARDNER, Catherine Agnes 65 Stratherrick Road, Inverness IV2 4LL Tel: 01463 235044 — MB ChB Glas. 1958; DO Eng. 1963. Asst. Ophth. Raigmore Hosp. Inverness. Prev: Asst. Surg. Greenock Eye Infirm.; Regist. Glas. Ophth. Inst.

GARDNER, Catherine Mary Thorkhill Road Surgery, 115A Thorkhill Road, Thames Ditton KT7 0UW Tel: 020 8398 3141 Fax: 020 8398 7836; 99 Manor Road N., Hinchley Wood, Esher KT10 0AB Tel: 020 8398 6517 — MB BS 1974 Lond.; MRCGP 1978; DRCOG 1977. (Univ. Coll. Hosp.) Socs: Brit. Med. Acupunct. Soc. Prev: Regist. (Psychiat.) Qu. Eliz. II Hosp. Welwyn Garden City; Trainee GP VTS Watford; Ho. Phys. Med. Unit Univ. Coll. Hosp. Lond.

GARDNER, Christopher Shand (retired) Wayside Cottage, Route des Houguettes, Zion, St John, Jersey JE3 4FR Tel: 01534 862377 Fax: 01534 862377 — MA, BM BCh Oxon. 1943. Prev: Ho. Phys. & Out-pat. Off. Guy's Hosp.

GARDNER, Christopher Stanley Holywood Road Surgery, 54 Holywood Road, Belfast BT4 1NT Tel: 028 9065 4668 — MB BCh BAO 1980 Belf.; MRCGP 1986; DRCOG 1985.

GARDNER, Clive Alan 24 Ravenscourt Place, Gateshead NE8 1PP — MB BS 1981 Newc.

GARDNER, David Alan Dept. of Chemical Pathology, Windeyer Building, 46 Cleveland Street, London W1T 4JF Tel: 020 7679 9235 Fax: 020 7679 9496 Email: david.gardner@uclh.org; 200 Sandridge Road, St Albans AL1 4AL Tel: 01727 862019 Email: dagardner@ntlworld.com — MRCS Eng. LRCP Lond. 1963; MRCS Eng. LRCP Lond. 1963; FRCPath 1983, M 1971. (Leeds) Cons. Chem. Path. Univ. Coll. Lond. Hosps.; Hon. Sen. Lect. UCL. Prev: Cons. Chem. Pathol. Chelsea & Kensington Gp. Hosps.; Regist. (Chem. Path.) Roy. Free Hosp. Lond.; Regist. (Path.) Guy's Hosp. Lond.

GARDNER, David William Hill House Surgery, West St., Aspatria, Carlisle CA7 3HG Tel: 01228 20209; 11 Station Road, Aspatria, Carlisle CA7 2AJ — MB ChB 1981 Ed.; MRCGP 1994; DCCH RCP Ed. 1985; DRCOG 1984.

GARDNER, Denis, MBE, TD 50 Wallasey Village, Wallasey CH45 3NL Tel: 0151 638 8221 Fax: 0151 639 6512 — MB ChB 1954 Liverp.; MRCS Eng. LRCP Lond. 1955; DGM RCP Lond. 1989.

GARDNER, Mr Donald Cecil (retired) 4 Bracken Hill, Cat St., Upper Hartfield, Hartfield TN7 4DU Tel: 01342 823135 — MB BS 1953 Lond.; FRCS Eng. 1960; MRCS Eng. LRCP Lond. 1953. Cons. Orthop. Surg. Tunbridge Wells Dist. Hosp. Gp. Prev: Sen. Regist. (Orthop.) & Ho. Surg. King's Coll. Hosp. Lond.

GARDNER, Professor Dugald Lindsay Department of Pathology, University Medical School, Teviot Place, Edinburgh EH8 9AG; 5/4 Fountainhall Court, Fountainhall Road, Edinburgh EH9 2NL Tel: 0131 662 4776 Email: dugaldgardner@mcmail.com — MB ChB Ed. 1948; PhD Ed. 1957, MD 1958; MSc Manch. 1981; ScD Camb. 1986, MA 1950, BA 1945; FRCS Ed. 1990; FRCP Lond. 1975, M 1969; FRCP Ed. 1963, M 1950; FRCPath 1975, M 1963. (Camb. & Ed.) Hon. Fell. (Path.) Univ. Edin. & Emerit. Conservator Roy. Coll. Surg. Edin. Socs: Path. Soc.; Amer. Assn. Anatomists; Scot. Soc. Hist. Med. Prev: Emerit. Prof. Histopath. Univ. Manch.; Musgrave Prof. (Path.) Qu. Univ. Belf.; Dir. Kennedy Inst. of Rheum. Lond.

GARDNER, Edmund Paul (retired) Christmas Maltings Surgery, Camps Road, Haverhill CB9 8HF Tel: 01440 702203 — MRCS Eng. LRCP Lond. 1963; MB Camb. 1964, BChir 1963; DObst RCOG 1965. Clin. Asst. (Med.) Risbridge Hosp. Kedington; Clin. Asst. (Ment. Handicap) W. Suff. Gen. Hosp. Bury St Edmunds. Prev: Ho. Off. (Gen. & Rectal Surg.) & Ho. Off. (O & G) Middlx. Hosp. Lond.

GARDNER, Elizabeth Scoon 20 Thornhill Terrace, Sunderland SR2 7JL Tel: 0191 565 9007 — LRCP LRCS Ed. LRFPS Glas. 1951; MCOphth 1988; DO Dub. 1979. (Roy. Colls. & Univ. Ed.) Assoc. Specialist Sunderland Eye Infirm. Socs: N. Eng. Ophth. Soc.; Internat. Soc. Ophth. Ultrasound. Prev: Regist. (Ophth.) Univ. Coll. Hosp., Ibadan; Med. Off. (Ophth.) Mulago Hosp., Kampala; SHO (Ophth.) NW Metrop. RHB.

GARDNER, Eric Kay (retired) 80 Hurn Road, Christchurch BH23 2RW Tel: 01202 471424 — MB BChir Camb. 1938; FRCS Eng. 1948; LMSSA Lond. 1938; FFA RCS Eng. 1953; DA Eng. 1944. Prev: Med. Adviser Lond. Ambul. Serv.

GARDNER, Mr Eric Richardson 45 Aytoun Road, Pollockshields, Glasgow G41 5HW — MB ChB 1981 Dundee; FRCS Glas. 1985. Sen. Regist. (Orthop.) W.. Infirm. Glas.

GARDNER, Faith Mary 73A London Road, Kilmarnock KA3 7BP Tel: 01563 537306 Fax: 01563 537306 — MB BS 1985 Lond.; Dip. Sports Med. RCS. Scotl. 1992; Dip. Sports Med. Lond 1990; DRCOG 1989. Staff Grade (A & E) Ayr Hosp.; Specialist (Orthop. & Sports Med.) Ayr & Irvine. Socs: (Vice-Chairm. & Sec.) Brit. Assn. Sports Med. Scotl.; (Chairm.) Brit. Assn. Sports Med. Scol.

GARDNER, Fiona Lanarkshire Hospitals NHS, Eaglesham Rd, East Kilbride, Glasgow G75 8RG Tel: 01355 220292 Fax: 01355 234064; West Deyne, 2 Bishops Park, Thorntonhall, Glasgow G74 5AF — MB ChB 1973 Glas.; MRCP (UK) 1978; FRCR 1983; DMRD Ed. 1981. Cons. Radiol. Haimyres Hosp. S Lanarksh.; Cons. Radiol. StoneHo. Hosp, Lanarksh.

GARDNER, Francis John Edward Department of Obst. & Gyn., Univ.of Leicester Medical School, Robert Kilpatrick Clinical Sciences Building, Leicester Royal Infirmary, PO Box 65, Leicester LE2 7LX; 15 Rosslyn Avenue, Mountsorrel, Loughborough LE12 7UQ — MB ChB 1992 Leic.; BSc Leic. 1990. (Univ. Leicester Med. Sch.) Specialist Regist. (O & G) Leicester Roy. Infirm.; Hon. Research Fell. (O & G), Univ. of Leicester & Warwick. Prev: Clin. Research Fell. (O & G) Leicester Roy. Infirm.; Specialist Regist. (O & G) Pilgrim Hosp., Boston; SHO (O & G) Leicester Roy. Infirm.

GARDNER, Geoffrey Ian Miller Street Surgery, Miller Street, Off Kings Street, Newcastle ST5 1JD Tel: 01782 711618 Fax: 01782 713940 — MB ChB 1973 Sheff.; Dip. Sports Med. Ed. 1991. Mem. GP Comiss. Forum N. Staffs. HA.

GARDNER, George Clifford Edward Torbay Hospital, Lawes Bridge Road, Torbay, Torquay TQ2 7AA; The Red House, Fordens Lane, Holcombe, Dawlish EX7 0LD — MB BS 1996 Lond.; BMedSci 1995. (St Mary's London) GP Regist. Torbay Hosp., Torquay, Devon.

GARDNER, George Scott Ivy Farmhouse, 31 Station Road, Great Coates, Grimsby DN37 9NP Tel: 01472 882899 — MB ChB 1962 Glas. (Glas.) Prev: Sen. Aviat. Med. Examr. Federal Aviat. Auth. USA; Authorised Med. Examr. Civil Aviat. Auth. UK; Chief Med. Off. Lockheed Aircraft, Saudi Arabia.

GARDNER, Mr Graham John Accident & Emergency Department, Torbay Hospital, Lawes Bridge, Newton Road, Torquay TQ2 7AA Tel: 01803 864515 Fax: 01803 616331 Email: gjgardner1@aol.com; Email: gjgardnerl@aol.com — MB BS 1978 Lond.; FFA 1983 RCS, Eng; FRCS 1989 Ed; FFAEM 1994; LLM 1998. (St. Thos.) Cons. A & E Torbay Hosp. Socs: Brit. Assn. Accid. & Emerg. Med.; BMA; BASICS. Prev: Sen. Regist. (A & E) Manch. Roy. Infirm., Stockport & S. Manch. Hosps.; Regist. (Accid & Emerg.) Countess of Chester Hosp.; Cons. A&E Epsom Gen.Hosp.

GARDNER, Grazyna Anna The Quintin Medical Centre, Hawkswood Road, Hailsham BN27 1UG; The Old Farmhouse, Vines Cross Road, Horam, Heathfield TN21 9EE — MB BS 1989 Lond.; DRCOG 1994; DFFP 1998. (Guy's) p/t GP Asst. The Quintin Med. Centre, Hailsham.

GARDNER, Gregory Thomas Gerard 45 Elizabeth Road, Birmingham B13 8QH Tel: 0121 449 8580 Email: g.gardner@clara.co.uk — MB ChB 1980 Liverp.; MRCGP 1991. (Liverp.) GP Non-Princip. Socs: BMA; Doctors Who Respect Human Life Soc.; Christ. Med. Fell.sh.

GARDNER, Harry (retired) 5A Golf Court, Strathview Park, Glasgow G44 3LD Tel: 0141 637 7260 — LRCP LRCS 1945 Ed.; LRCP LRCS Ed. LRFPS Glas. 1945; DPH St. And. 1948; FFR 1962; DMRD Ed. 1953. Prev: Cons. Radiol. Vict. Infirm. Glas.

GARDNER, Harry Ward, MBE Central Scotland Occupational Health Unit, Fire Brigade Headquarters, Maddiston, Falkirk FK2 0LG Tel: 01324 710227; Mollan, Thornhill, Stirling FK8 3QJ Tel: 01786 850320 — LRCP LRCS Ed. LRFPS Glas. 1951; AFOM RCP Lond. 1980; MRCGP 1965. (Glas.) p/t Princip. Centr. Scotl. Occupat. Health Serv.; Occupat. Health Adviser Clackmannan Coll.; Med. Off. Centr. Region Fire Brig. Socs: Soc. Occupat. Med.; BAHSWE; Assn. Local Auth. Med. Advisers. Prev: Occupat.al Health Adviser Scott. Soc. for autistic Childr.; Med. Adviser Centr. Regional Counc.; Occupat. Health Adviser Stirling Univ.

GARDNER, Mr Iain Dugald The Eye Department, Derbyshire Royal Infirmary, London Road, Derby DE1 2QY Tel: 01332 254884 Fax: 01332 254884; 158 Main Street, Kings Newton, Melbourne, Derby DE73 1BS — MB ChB 1976 Birm.; FRCS Eng. (Ophth.) 1984; FCOphth 1988; DO RCS Eng. 1982. Cons. Ophth. Surg. Derbysh. Roy. Infirm. Prev: Wellcome Research Fell. Nuffield Laborat. Ophth. Oxf.

GARDNER, Isabel Mary (retired) Three Ways, 24 Mentone Avenue, Aspley Guise, Milton Keynes MK17 8EQ Tel: 01908 582246 — MB BCh BAO Dub. 1940; BA Dub. 1940. Prev: Med. Off. (Family Plann.) Beds. AHA.

GARDNER, Isobel Craig Bristol Royal Informery, Bristol BS2 8HW Tel: 0117 923 0000 — MB ChB 1987 Ed.; FRCA 1998; DRCOG 1995. p/t Specialist Regist. (Anaesth.) Bristol/S. W. Deanary. Socs: Obstetric Anaes. Assn.; BMA.

GARDNER, James Edward The Surgery, East Grinstead Road, Lingfield RH7 6ER Tel: 01342 833456 Fax: 01342 836347 — MB BS 1989 Lond.; DRCOG 1993. Prev: Trainee GP Brighton VTS.

GARDNER, Mr John Mark Department of Ophthalmology, Leicester Royal Infirmary, Leicester LE1 5WW Tel: 0116 258 5929 Fax: 0116 258 5927; 72 Stoneygate Road, Leicester LE2 2BN Email: john.m.gardner@dial.pipex.com — MB BS 1981 Lond.; FRCS Ed. 1992; MRCGP 1989; FRCOphth. 1992, M 1989. (St Thomas'

Hospital) Socs: Christ. Med. Fell.sh. Prev: Clin. Research Fell. (Gen. Pract.) Univ. Leicester; Hon. Regist. (Ophth.) Leicester Roy. Infirm.; SHO (Ophth.) W. of Eng. Eye Infirm. Exeter.

GARDNER, Joy Marjorie 5 Roseberry Green, North Stainley, Ripon HG4 3HZ — MB BS 1945 Lond.

GARDNER, Judith Anne Barlborough Medical Practice, The Old Malthouse, 7 Worksop Road, Barlborough, Chesterfield S43 4TY Tel: 01246 819994 Fax: 01246 812293 — MB ChB 1987 Manch.; MRCGP 1992. Prev: Trainee GP Preston; SHO Rotat. (A & E & Med.) Roy. Preston Hosp. Lancs.

GARDNER, Juliet Catanach Fordton House, Crediton EX17 3PS Tel: 01363 772608 — MB BS Lond. 1963; MRCS Eng. LRCP Lond 1963. (Guy's) Occupat. Med. Crediton area. Prev: Co-ordinator Jt. Agency Child Abuse Team, Exeter HA.

GARDNER, Justin Mark 93 Bradley Street, Crookes, Sheffield S10 1PA — MB ChB 1995 Sheff.

GARDNER, Katharine Anne Princes Park Health Centre, Bentley Road, Liverpool L8 0SY Tel: 0151 728 8313 Fax: 0151 728 8417 — MB BChir 1975 Camb.; FRCGP 1994, M 1979.

GARDNER, Katherine Alice 85 North Road, St Andrews, Bristol BS6 5AQ — MB BS 1990 Lond.; DA (UK) 1993. SHO (Anaesth.) St. Thos. Hosp. Lond. Prev: SHO (Anaesth.) Roy. United Hosp. Bath; SHO (A & E) Frenchay Hosp. Bristol; Ho. Off. (Gen. Surg.) Roy. United Hosp. Bath.

GARDNER, Kathleen Melrose 14 Burnfield, Livingston Vill., Livingston EH54 7AS — MB ChB 1964 Ed.; MRCOG 1977, DObst 1966.

GARDNER, Lawrence Guy — MB ChB 1962 Ed.; FFA RCS Eng. 1969; DObst RCOG 1964. (Ed.) Cons. Anaesth. (Paediat.) Gen. Infirm. Leeds. Socs: Assoc. Paediat. Anaeath. GB & Irel.; Assoc. Dent. Anaesth. & Yorks. Soc. Anaesth.; Yorks. Soc. of Anaesth.s.

GARDNER, Lionel Dalrymple (retired) Tillyloss, West Baldwin, Douglas IM4 5HE Tel: 01624 851281 — MB ChB 1934 Glas.; BSc Glas. 1929, MB ChB 1934; FRFPS Glas. 1948; MRCP Glas. 1962; MRCPsych 1971; DPM Eng. 1949. Prev: Psychiat. Specialist St. Brendan's Hosp. Bermuda.

GARDNER, Louise Blackbird Leys Health Centre, Blackbird Leys, Oxford OX4 6HL Tel: 01865 778244 Fax: 01865 774686; St luke's, 3 The Terrace, Edgcumbe Road, Lostwithiel PC22 0DT Tel: 01208 871325, 01865 718828 — MB BS 1985 Lond.; MRCGP 1990; DRCOG 1989; DCH RCP Lond. 1988. (Univ. Coll. Hosp.) p/t GP Princip., Blackbird Leys Health Centre Oxf. Prev: Trainee GP Ealing Gen. Hosp. Lond. VTS; SHO (A & E) N.ampton Gen. Hosp.

GARDNER, Martin William 71 St James Road, Sutton SM1 2TG — MB BS 1987 Lond.; FRCA 1994; DRCOG 1991. Specialist Regist. (Anaesth.) St. Geo. Hosp. Lond.

GARDNER, Mary Lynn York Medical Practice, St John's Health Centre, Oak Lane, Twickenham TW1 3PA Tel: 020 8744 0220 Fax: 020 8892 6855 — MB ChB 1984 Bristol; MRCGP 1990; DFFP 1995; T(GP) 1991; Cert. Family Plann. JCC 1988; DRCOG 1988. (Univ. Bristol)

GARDNER, Matthew Charles Department of Anaesthetics, William Harvey Hospital, Kennington Road, Willesborough, Ashford TN24 0LZ Tel: 01303 616041; 3 Orpins Close, Lees Road, Brabourne Lees, Ashford TN25 6PT — MB BS 1988 Lond.; BSc Lond. 1985; FRCA 1994. Cons. Anaesth. William Harvey Hosp. Ashford Kent. Socs: Sec. Ashford Med. Soc.; Assn. Anaesth.; Difficult Airway Soc. Prev: Sen. Regist. (Anaesth.) Guy's Hosp. Lond.; Regist. Rotat. (Anaesth.) SE Thames RHA; SHO (Paediat., A & E & Anaesth.) Plymouth HA.

GARDNER, Mr Nigel Hedley Noall (cons. rooms), 1 The Quadrant, Wonford Road, Exeter EX2 4LE Tel: 01392 56774 Fax: 01392 421662; Fordton House, Crediton EX17 3PS Tel: 01363 772608 — MB ChB 1956 Birm.; FRCS Eng. 1963; FRCOG 1979, M 1966. Cons. Gyn. & Obst. Exeter & Mid Devon Health Dist. Prev: Sen. Regist. St. Thos. Hosp. Lond.; SHO Qu. Charlotte's Hosp. Lond.; Resid. Surg. Off. Chelsea Hosp. Wom.

GARDNER, Peter Anthony (retired) 31 Battye Avenue, Huddersfield HD4 5PW — LAH 1955 Dub.; FFCM 1980, M 1974; DPH Liverp. 1965. Prev: Dist. Med. Off. Huddersfield HA.

GARDNER, Peter Tom, Col. late RAMC Retd. (retired) Nantcellan, Clarach, Aberystwyth SY23 3DR — MB ChB Bristol 1958; FRCOG 1980, M 1967. Prev: Cons. & Med. Dir. O & G Bronglais Gen. Hosp. Aberystwyth.

GARDNER, Phyllis Annette (retired) 4 St Winifred's Drive, Bath BA2 7HR — MB BS 1953 Lond.; DObst RCOG 1955. Prev: SCMO Bath HA.

GARDNER, Ramon 34 Wilberforce Road, Cambridge CB3 0EQ Tel: 01223 363531 — MB BS Lond. 1958; MA Camb. 1976; MRCP Lond. 1964; MRCS Eng. LRCP Lond. 1958; FRCPsych 1981, M 1972; DPM Lond. 1967; DObst RCOG 1960. (Lond. Hosp.) Emerit. Cons. Addenbrooke's Hosp. Camb. Prev: Cons. Psychiat. Camb. HA (T); Assoc. Lect. Camb. Clin. Med. Sch.

GARDNER, Mr Raymond David (retired) Bow Bridge House, Bowbrook, Shrewsbury SY5 8PG Tel: 01743 362901 — MB ChB 1957 Liverp.; BSc Lond. 1952; MD Liverp. 1964; FRCS Eng. 1967; FRCS Ed. 1966; MRCS Eng. LRCP Lond. 1957. Prev: Cons. Surg. Roy. Shrewsbury Hosp.

GARDNER, Richard (retired) Green View, Bainbridge, Leyburn DL8 3EF Tel: 01969 650484 Fax: 0870 734 9105 Email: ribag@gardner96.freeserve.co.uk — MB BChir 1953 Camb.; FRCGP 1982, M 1965; DObst RCOG 1957. Prev: Ho. Surg. W.m. Hosp.

GARDNER, Richard Ronan Orchard House, The Green, Great Brington, Northampton NN7 4JD — MB BS 1982 Lond.; BSc (Hons.) Lond. 1978, MB BS 1982; DRCOG 1985. (St. Bart.) Prev: SHO (Gen. Med., Neurol. & O & G) Harold Wood Hosp. Essex.

GARDNER, Richard William 3 Milton Crescent, Cheadle SK8 1NT — MB ChB 1978 Manch.; BSc Manch. 1972, MB ChB 1978; MRCGP 1981; DRCOG 1980.

GARDNER, Robert (retired) 6 Woodlands Avenue, Swinton, Manchester M27 0DJ — MRCS Eng. LRCP Lond. 1948. Prev: GP Little Hulton, Salford Gtr. Manch.

GARDNER, Robert John Trendlechell, Comeytrowe Road, Trull, Taunton TA3 7NE — MB BChir 1982 Camb.; MB BChir Camb. l983.

GARDNER, Robin Francis Anson Brewer Street, 4 Brewer Street, Maidstone ME14 1RU Tel: 01622 755401/755402 Fax: 01622 695378 — MB 1979 Camb.; BChir 1978; MRCGP 1983; DRCOG 1983; Cert Family Plann. JCC 1983.

GARDNER, Rosemary Lesley Farnborough Hospital, Farnborough Common, Orpington BR6 8ND — MB BS 1977 Lond.; MRCOG 1985; FRCOG 1998. (Westm.) Cons. O & G FarnBoro. Hosp. Orpington. Prev: Lect. & Hon. Sen. Regist. (O & G) Roy. Free Hosp. Lond.; Research Fell. (O & G) Roy. Free Hosp. Lond.; Regist. (O & G) W.m. Hosp. Lond.

GARDNER, Samantha Jane Torbay Hospital, Lawes Bridge Road, Torbay, Torquay TQ2 7AA; Owl Corner, 4 Parkhill Road, Torquay TQ1 2AL — MB BS 1996 Lond.; BSc 1991. GP Regist. Torbay Hosp., Torquay, Devon. Prev: SHO (Geriat. Med.) N. Shore Hosp., New Zealand.

GARDNER, Sharryn Elizabeth 17 Harbury Avenue, Southport PR8 2TA — MB ChB 1994 Glas.

GARDNER, Simon 42 Fairfield Road, Stockton-on-Tees TS19 7AW Tel: 01642 884356 — MB BS 1994 Newc. Trainee Mem. Roy. Coll. Anaesth.

GARDNER, Simon James Nicholas Kerigan and Partners, The Surgery, 4 Captain French Lane, Kendal LA9 4HR Tel: 01539 720241 Fax: 01539 725048; 3 Bankfield, Kendal LA9 5DR Tel: 01539 729750 Fax: 01539 735154 Email: 100413.3472@compuserve.com — MB BChir 1988 Camb.; MA Lancaster 1998; BA Camb. 1985; MRCGP 1993; DRCOG 1992. Prescribing Lead S. Lakeland PCG; Dir. W.morland Primary Care Co-op.

GARDNER, Stephen Geoffrey Springfield House, High St., Stanford-in-the-Vale, Faringdon SN7 8LH — MB BCh 1991 Wales; MRCP (UK) 1996. (Univ. Wales Coll. Med.) Clin. Research Fell. (Diabetes) Diabetes & Metab. Univ. Bristol. Socs: BMA; Brit. Diabetic Assn. Prev: Clin. Research Fell. (Diabetes) Dept. Diabetes & Metab. St. Bart. Hosp. Lond .; SHO (Cardiol. & ITU) Middlx. Hosp. Lond.; SHO (Med.) William Harvey Hosp. Ashford, Kent.

GARDNER, Tarek Dhia Imutran Ltd., Douglas House, 18 Trumpington Road, Cambridge CB1 2AH Tel: 01223 300151 Fax: 01223 300153; Bell Marsh, Golf Club Road, Weybridge KT13 0NN Tel: 01932 855479 Fax: 01932 828154 Email: tarek-gardner@msn.com — LMSSA 1984 Lond. Dir. Clin. Developm. Imutran Ltd. Camb. Socs: Fell. Roy. Soc. Med. Prev: Sen. Project Manager Sandoz Pharma Ltd. Basle, Switz.; Gp. Med. Off. Sandoz

Pharma Ltd. Basle, Switz.; Med. Adviser Sandoz Pharmaceut. Frimley Surrey.

GARDNER, Thomas Main (retired) 35 Austen Road, Glasgow G13 1SJ Tel: 0141 959 4069 — MB ChB 1944 Glas.; BSc Glas. 1940, MB ChB 1944. Prev: Ho. Surg. Vict. Infirm. Glas.

GARDNER, Thomas Martin 2 Tadcaster Road, Dringhouses, York YO24 1LH — MB ChB 1980 Manch.

GARDNER, William Norman Department of Respiratory Medicine & Allergy, Guy's, Kings & St Thomas's School of Medicine, Denmark Hill Campus, London SE5 9PJ Tel: 020 7346 3165 Fax: 020 7346 3589 Email: william.gardner@kcl.ac.uk; 92 Holmdene Avenue, London SE24 9LE Tel: 020 7274 3572 — MB BS Sydney 1965; DPhil Oxf. 1975; FRCP Lond. 1991; MRCP (UK) 1971. Reader in Respirtory Med. & Hon. Cons. Phys. Kings Coll. Sch. Med. & Dent. & Dept. of Physiol. Socs: Fell. Coll. Phys. & Brit. Thoracic Soc.; Eur. Respirat. Soc. (Chairm. Control of Breathing Gp. & Head Clin. Physiol. Assembly); Ex-Head Clin. Physiol. Assembly Europ. Respir. Soc. (1995-1997). Prev: Sen. Lect. (Med. & Thoracic) Kings Coll. Sch. Med. & Dent. Kings Coll. Lond.; Researcher (Phys.) Univ. Oxf. & Nuffield Inst.; SHO W.m. Hosp. Lond.

GARDNER, Zoe Nora Conquest c/o Mrs Barnam, 41 Pendre, Brecon LD3 9EA Tel: 01874 622672 — MB BS Lond. 1963; BA (Hons.) Open 1983; FRCS Eng. 1971; MRCS, 1963, LRCP Lond. 1963. (St. Bart. Hosp. Lond.) Working in develping countries on short term contracts.

GARDNER-MEDWIN, David (retired) Flocktons, Station Road, Heddon-on-the-Wall, Newcastle upon Tyne NE15 0EG Tel: 01661 852318 — MB BChir 1962 Camb.; FRCPCH 1997; MD Camb. 1972; FRCP Lond. 1977, M 1965. Hon. Lect. Hist. of Med. Univ. Newc. Prev: Cons. Paediat. Neurol. Newc. Gen. Hosp.

GARDNER-MEDWIN, Janet Mary McCrae Department of Rheumatology, University of Birmingham, Edgbaston, Birmingham B15 2TT Tel: 0121 414 6792 Fax: 0121 414 6793 Email: j.m.gardner-medwin@bham.ac.uk; 9 Harrison's Road, Edgbaston, Birmingham B15 3QR Tel: 0121 454 0277 — MB ChB 1988 Bristol; BSc (Biochem.) Bristol 1985; PhD Nottm. 1997; MRCP (UK) 1991. (Bristol) Lect. (Paediat. Rheum.) Univ. Birm. Prev: Clin. Research Fell. (Immunol.) Univ. Hosp. Nottm.

GARDNER-THORPE, Catherine Clare 15 St Leonards Road, Exeter EX2 4LA — MB BS 1992 Lond.; DA (UK) 1996; DGM RCP Lond. 1994; DTM & H, Liverp 1999. SHO Poole Gen. Hosp. Prev: SHO (Anaesth.) W. Dorset Gen. Hosp. NHS Trust; Ho. Surg. Roy. Devon & Exeter Hosp.; Ho. Phys. Hereford Co. Hosp.

GARDNER-THORPE, Christopher (cons. rooms), The Coach House, 1A College Road, Exeter EX1 1TE Tel: 01392 433941 Email: csardnerthorpe@doctors.org.uk — MB BS 1964 Lond.; MD Lond. 1973; FRCP Lond. 1985; FACP 2001. (St. Thos.) Cons. Neurol. S. W.. RHA. Socs: Exeter Medico-Legal Soc. (Chairm.); Curator Devon & Exeter Med. Soc.; Assoc. Brit. Neurol.

GARDNER-THORPE, Sheelah Mary Robertson 15 St Leonards Road, Exeter EX2 4LA Tel: 01392 31927 — MB BS 1965 Lond.; MRCS Eng. LRCP Lond. 1965. (Roy. Free) Clin. Asst. Psychogeriat. Exeter HA. Prev: Ho. Phys. Roy. Free Hosp. Lond.; Ho. Surg. Soton. Gen. Hosp.; SHO Wessex Neurol. Centre.

GAREEBOO, Mohammad Shafick Queen Elizabeth II Hospital, Howlands, Welwyn Garden City AL7 4HQ — MB ChB 1997 Aberd. SHO (Gen. Med.), Qu. Eliz. II Hosp., Welwyn Garden City.

GAREH, Michael David Llangollen Health Centre, Regent Street, Llangollen LL20 8HL; Maes y Rhuddallt, Llanderfel LL23 7RE Tel: 01678 530787 Email: mike@gareh.co.uk — MRCS 1969 Eng.; LRCP 1969 Lond. (Liverp.) Prev: Ho. Surg. Maelor Gen. Hosp. Wrexham; Ho. Phys. & Cas. Off. War Memor. Hosp. Wrexham.

GARELICK, Antony Ian Psychotherapy Clinic, Forest House, Thorpe Coombe Hospital, 714 Forest Road, London E17 3HP; 133 Huddleston Road, London N7 0EH — MB BS Lond. 1970; MRCP (UK) 1973; FRCPsych 1992, M 1977. (Univ. Coll. Hosp. Lond.) Cons. Psychotherap. Thorpe Coombe Hosp. Lond.; Cons. Psychotherap. Tavistock Clinic Lond.; Hon. Sen. Lect. UCL. Socs: (Past Chairm.) Assn. Psychoanal. Psychother.; Brit. Assn. of Psychother.; Hon.Sec. Psychother. Fac. Exec. Roy. Coll. in Psychiat.s. Prev: Sen. Regist. & Regist. Maudsley Hosp. Lond.; Hon. Sen. Regist. Kings Coll. Hosp. Med. Sch. Lond.

GAREWAL, Clare 118-120 Stanford Avenue, Brighton BN1 6FE Tel: 01273 506361; 24 Pembroke Crescent, Hove BN3 5DD Tel: 01273 220220 — MB ChB 1989 Birm.; MRCGP 1994; DCH RCP Lond. 1993; DRCOG 1993. (Birmingham) Socs: MDDU Scotl.

GAREWAL, Davinder Singh 5 Kings Ride House, 289 Sheen Road, Richmond TW10 5AW — MB BCh BAO 1981 NUI; MRCP (UK) 1987; FCAnaesth 1990; DA (UK) 1987. Asst. Prof. Univ. Texas, Houston USA. Prev: Regist. (Anaesth.) The Lond. Hosp. & Walsgrave Hosp. Coventry; SHO (Anaesth.) Hartlepool Gen. Hosp. & Roy. Berks. Hosp. Reading.

GAREWAL, Sheila 39 Lostock Junction Lane, Lostock, Bolton BL6 4JW — MB ChB 1979 Manch.; FRCR 1987. Cons. Radiol. Bury Health Care NHS Trust. Prev: Sen. Regist. Rotat. (Radiol.) N. W. RHA.

GAREWAL, Surrinderbir Singh (retired) Arrowe Park Hospital, Arrowe Park Road, Upton, Birkenhead L43 5PE Tel: 0151 678 5111 — MB BS 1959 Madras; BSc Punjab 1953; MRCP Ed. 1968. Prev: Cons. Phys. (Geriat. Med.) Arrowe Pk. Hosp. Birkenhead.

GARFIELD, Anna Maria The Surgery, 321 Shirland Road, London W9 3JJ Tel: 020 8969 2626 Fax: 020 8964 0353 — MRCS Eng. LRCP Lond. 1977. GP Lond.

GARFIELD, Mr John Samuel Keyhaven, Hadrian Way, Chilworth, Southampton SO16 7HY Tel: 02380 767674 — MChir Camb. 1963, MB 1955, BChir 1954; FRCP Lond. 1977, M 1957; FRCS Eng. 1961; MRCS Eng. LRCP Lond. 1954. (St. Mary's) Hon. Emerit. Cons. Neurosurg. Soton. Univ. Trust Hosps. Socs: Fell. Roy. Soc. Med.; (Counc.) Med. Defence Union. Prev: Sen. Regist. Nat. Hosp. Qu. Sq.

GARFIELD, Mark Jon 54 George Road, Oldbury, Oldbury B68 9LJ — MB ChB 1993 Birm.; ChB Birm. 1993.

GARFIELD, Paul Child, Adolescent and Family Consultation Service, Ivry House, 23 Henley Road, Ipswich IP1 3TF Tel: 01473 214811 Fax: 01473 280809 — MB BS 1986 Lond.; MRCPsych 1991; BA, Cambridge, 1980; 2000 Mphil, Leicester. Cons. Child & Adolesc. Pschiatry, Ipswich.

GARFINKEL, Henry Abraham (cons. rooms), Hospital of St John & St Elizabeth, 60 Grove End Road, London NW8 9NH Tel: 020 7286 5126 Fax: 020 7266 2316; 7 Kinloss Gardens, London N3 3DU Tel: 020 8349 1319 — MB BS 1958 Lond.; 1982 LRCP MRCS (UK) 1982; 1958 MRCS Eng. LRCP Lond. 1958; 1968 MRCGP 1968; 1982 MRCP (UK) 1982; 1999 FRCP (Lond.) 1999; 1997 FACP 1997; 1999 FRCP (Edin.) 1999. (St. Geo.) Consg. Phys. St. John & St. Eliz. Lond. Hosp; Clin. Asst. Cardiol. St Mary's Hosp Lond.; Adviser to Media Resources Serv.s (CIBA Foundat.) In Hypnother. and Acupunc.; Med. Registra St Geo.'s Hosp Lond. Socs: Fell. Roy. Soc. Med.; Brit. Med. Acupunct. Soc.; Worshipful Soc. Apoth. Lond. Prev: Regist. (Med.) Epsom Dist. Hosp.; Med. 2nd Asst. & Ho. Phys. Profess. Med. & Metab. Units St. Geo. Hosp. Lond.

GARG, Anil Kumar Worthing Hospital, Park Avenue, Worthing BN11 2DH Tel: 01903 205111 Fax: 01903 285175 Email: anil.garg@wash-tr.sthames.nhs.uk; 62 Ladydell Road, Worthing BN11 2JU Tel: 01903 823467 Email: anilgarg@doctors.org.uk — MB BS 1976 Delhi; MRCPI 1982; DCH RCPS Glas. 1978. Cons. Paediat. Worthing Hosp. Socs: FRCPI-1993 FRCPH - 1997. Prev: Sen. Cons. Neonat. N W Armed Forces Hosp. Tabuk, Saudi Arabia.

GARG, Anupam Division of Cardiology, Hammersmith Hospital, Dulcane Road, London W12 0NN Tel: 020 8383 1000 Email: a.garg@ic.ac.uk — MB BS 1991 Lond.; BSc Lond. 1988; MRCP (UK) 1994. Regist. Rotat. (Cardiol.) Poole Hosp., Roy. Bournemouth Hosp. & Soton. Gen. Hosp.; Clin. Research Fell. Hammersmith Hosp. Prev: SHO Rotat. (Gen. Med.) Derriford Hosp. Plymouth.

GARG, Archana Croston Medical Centre, 30 Brookfield, Croston, Preston PR26 9HY Tel: 01772 600081 Fax: 01772 601612; Higher Hey, Highfield Road, Croston, Preston PR26 9HH Tel: 01772 600820 — MRCS Eng. LRCP Lond. 1977. (Goa Med. Coll. India) GP Princip. f/t. Prev: Clin. Asst. Aidiology; Clin. Asst. Family Plann.

GARG, Kamlesh Kumar Croston Medical Centre, 30 Brookfield, Croston, Leyland PR26 9HY Tel: 01772 600081 Fax: 01772 601612; Higher Hey, Highfield Road, Croston, Leyland PR26 9HH Tel: 01772 600820 — MB BS 1968 Gout. Medical College, Patiala, Punjabi Univ. India; MD 1972 Univ. of Delhi, India. Gen. Pract., S. Lancs. Health Auth. Socs: BMA; Overseas Doctor's Assoc.; Small Pract.'s Assoc.

GARG, Nirmal 31 Somersby Way, Boston PE21 9PQ Tel: 01205 353444 Fax: 01205 353444 — MB BS 1971 Rajasthan. (RNT Med. Coll. Udaipur, India) Staff Grade (Community Paediat.) Lincs.
GARG, Nita 14 Ribble Drive, Bury BL9 6RT — MB ChB 1998 Liverp.; MB ChB Liverp 1998.
GARG, Rekha 59 Seaford Close, Ruislip HA4 7HN — MB BS 1992 Lond.
GARG, Mr Shivraj Skegness & District Hospital, Dorothy Avenue, Skegness PE25 2BS Tel: 01754 762401; 31 Somersby Way, Boston PE21 9PQ Tel: 01205 353444 Fax: 01205 353444 — MB BS 1972 Indore; FRCS Eng. 1983. (MGM Medical College Indore, India) Assoc. Specialist.
GARG, Tarsem Lal Manchester Road Surgery, 7 Manchester Road, Worsley, Manchester M28 3NS Tel: 0161 790 3132 Fax: 0161 703 7463; 16 Thornway, Worsley, Manchester M28 1YS Tel: 0161 702 9731 — MB BS 1971 Punjab; DCH Punjab 1994; FLEX USA 1980. (Rohtak Med. Coll.) GP Manch. Socs: Amer. Coll. Advancem. in Med.; MPS. Prev: Clin. Asst. Fazakerley Hosp. Liverp.; Regist. (Gen. Med.) Jersey, CI & Roy. Inverclyde Hosp. Greenock.
GARGAN, Mr Martin Francis RUTHERGLEN, 3 Stione Park road South, Sneyd Park, Bristol BS9 1L5 Email: email@gargan.fsnet.co.uk — BM BCh 1984 Oxf.; FRCS (Orth.) 1994; FRCS Eng. 1988. Cons. Sen. Lect. (Trauma & Orthop. Surg.) Bristol. Socs: Brit. Orthop. Assn.; BMA.
GARGAN, Rosemary Elizabeth Crouch Oak Family Practice, 45 Station Road, Addlestone, Weybridge Tel: 01932 840123 Fax: 01932 821589 — MB ChB 1969 Glas. Socs: Fac. Homoeop. & Brit. Soc. Nutrit. Med. & Brit. Holistic Med. Assn.
GARGASH, Husnia Abdulla 16 Serlby Court, Addison Road, London W14 — MB ChB 1982 Baghdad; MRCOG 1991.
GARGAV, Archana (Surgery), 66 Westwood Road, Tilehusrt, Reading RG3 5PP Tel: 01734 427421 — MB BS 1964 Vikram.
GARGAV, Mr Ashok Kumar Whitley Wood Lane Surgery, 96 Whitley Wood Lane, Reading RG2 8PP Tel: 0118 987 6522 Fax: 0118 975 7067; 34 Hazel Road, Purley Beeches, Reading RG8 8BB Tel: 01734 26536 — MB BS 1964 Vikram; MS Bhopal 1973. (Gandhi Med. Coll.)
GARGYA, Satish Chandra 3 Timbers Way, Erdington, Birmingham B24 0QJ — MB BS 1962 Lucknow.
GARGYE, Usha 95 Warrenside Close, Wilpshire, Blackburn BB1 9PE — MB BS 1968 Allahabad.
GARIOCH, Jennifer Jessie Dermatology Centre, West Norwich Hospital, Norfolk and Norwich NHS Trust, Norwich NR2 3TU Tel: 01603 288210 Fax: 01603 288601 Email: jennifer.garioch@norfolk.norwich.thenhs.com — MB ChB 1983 Glas.; FRCP 1997; MD. (Univ. Glas.) Cons. Dermat. W. Norwich Hosp. Socs: BMA; Roy. Soc. Med. Prev: Sen. Regist. (Dermat.) St. Mary's Hosp. Lond.; Regist. (Dermat.) Glas. Roy. Infirm.; Regist. (Med.) Roy. Alexandra Hosp. Paisley.
GARKAL, Anila The Surgery, 61 Farmhill Road, Waltham Abbey EN9 1NG Tel: 01992 713891 Fax: 01992 714278 — MB BS 1960 Vikram. (Gwalior) Socs: BMA.
GARLAND, Anthony Philip (retired) Hawthorn Cottage, Balaclava Lane, Wadhurst TN5 6EG Tel: 01892 782645 — MB BS Lond. 1953; DA Eng. 1966; DTM & H Liverp. 1958. Prev: Clin. Asst. (Cas.) Kent & Sussex Hosp. Tunbridge Wells.
GARLAND, Benjamin White Lodge Medical Practice, 68 Silver Street, Enfield EN1 3EW Tel: 020 8363 4156 Fax: 020 8364 6295 — BM 1985 Soton.; MRCGP 1995.
GARLAND, Mrs Jean Shirley (retired) Bridge House, The Green, Dunsfold, Godalming GU8 4LA Tel: 01483 200368 — MB BS 1959 Lond.; MRCS Eng. LRCP Lond. 1959; DObst RCOG 1962.
GARLAND, Joan Eleanor Margaret (retired) 57 Sark Close, Lowry Hill, Carlisle CA3 0DY Tel: 01228 32840 — MB ChB 1941 Liverp.; DPH 1948; MFCM 1974. Prev: Sen. Med. Off. E. Cumbria Health Dist.
GARLAND, Mr John Bowden Ambleside, 10 Pinfold Lane, Whitefield, Manchester M45 7JS — MD 1967 Manch.; MB ChB 1959; FRCS Ed. 1964; FRCS Eng. 1965. (Manch.) Cons. Urol. N. Manch., Salford Roy. & Roy. Manch. Childr. Hosps.
GARLAND, John Kennedy 2 Surrey Gardens, Birchington CT7 9SA Tel: 01843 41384; 92 Minnis Road, Birchington CT7 9NZ Tel: 01843 445969 Fax: 01843 848609 — MA Fuller 1988; MB BS Lond. 1968; FRCP Thailand 1984; MRCP (UK) 1977; MRCGP 1987; DRCOG 1970; MTh. Oxf. 1997. (Lond. Hosp.) Prev: Superinten. Christian Hosp. Saiburi, Thailand.
GARLAND, John Martin 27 Grove Park, Bangor BT20 5QG — MB BCh BAO 1986 Belf.; MRCGP 1992; DRCOG 1991; DMH Belf. 1990; DCH RCPS Glas. 1990; DGM RCP Lond. 1986.
GARLAND, John Michael 3 Vine Cottages, The Square, Whimple, Exeter EX5 2SR — MB ChB 1966 Ed.
GARLAND, Martin Harry Barnet General Hospital, Wellhouse Lane, Barnet EN5 3DJ — MB BS 1971 Lond.; FRCP Lond. 1994; MRCP (UK) 1973; MRCS Eng. LRCP Lond. 1971; MRCGP 1977. (Univ. Coll. Hosp.) Cons. Phys. i/c Elderly Barnet Gen. Hosp. (Well Ho. Trust) & Colindale Hosp. Socs: Brit. Geriat. Soc. Prev: Sen. Regist. Univ. Coll. Hosp. Lond.; Sen. Regist. (Geriat.) Whittington Hosp. Lond.; Research Fell. (Clin. Pharmacol. & Therap.) Univ. Coll. Hosp. Lond.
GARLAND, Natasha Helen 88B Hackford Road, London SW9 0RG — MB ChB 1986 Manch.; MA (Med. Anthropol.) Lond. 1995; MRCPsych 1993.
GARLAND, Suzanne Johanna 32 Nansen Avenue, Oakdale, Poole BH15 3DB — MB BS 1993 Lond.
GARLAND-COLLINS, John Richard The Grange, Highfield Road, Hemsworth, Pontefract WF9 4DP Tel: 01977 610009 Fax: 01977 617182 — MB BS 1970 Lond.; MB BS Lond. 1970.; MRCS Eng. LRCP Lond. 1970. (Lond. Hosp.) Prev: SHO (Geriat.) Doncaster Roy. Infirm.; SHO (O & G) W. Suff. Gen. Hosp. Bury St. Edmunds; Ho. Surg. Cas. Dept. Lond. Hosp.
GARLANT, Arthur James Alfred (retired) Dunsden, Tunstall Road, Sittingbourne ME10 1YG Tel: 01795 472207 — MB BS 1957 Lond.; DObst RCOG 1960.
GARLICK, Alan 44 Loughborough Road, Coleorton, Leicester LE67 8HG Tel: 01530 224116 — MB ChB 1977 Manch.; Dip. Clin. Hypn. Sheff. 1991.
GARLICK, Mr David John Esperance House, Hartington Place, Eastbourne BN21 3BG Tel: 01323 726828 Fax: 01328 730313; Greenleas, 10 Old Camp Road, Eastbourne BN20 8DH Tel: 01323 737679 Fax: 01323 416769 — MRCS Eng. LRCP Lond. 1970; BSc Lond. 1967, MB BS 1970; FRCS Eng. 1978; FRCOphth 1989; DObst RCOG 1973; DO Eng. 1975. (Univ. Coll. Hosp.) Cons. Ophth. Surg. E.bourne Dist. Gen. Hosp. Prev: SHO (Ophth.) Soton. Eye Hosp.; Research Fell. Ophth. St. Thos. Hosp. Lond.; Resid. Surg. Off. Moorfields Eye Hosp. Lond.
GARLICK, George Granby 47 Fulbrooke Road, Cambridge CB3 9EE Tel: 01223 352354 — MB BS 1948 Lond.; MRCS Eng. LRCP Lond. 1945. (St. Mary's) Prev: Ho. Phys. Addenbrooke's Hosp. Camb.; Jun. Asst. Pathol. Dept. of Path. Univ. Camb.; Res. Obst. Off. Camb. Matern. Hosp.
GARLICK, Martin John Jay Lane Health Centre, Jay Lane, Leintwardine, Craven Arms SY7 0LG Tel: 01547 540355 Fax: 01547 540355; Mill Cottage, Mill Lane, Leintwardine, Craven Arms SY7 0LA Tel: 01547 540288 — MB ChB 1974 Birm.
GARLICK, Mr Nicholas Ian 9 Dovecot Close, Pinner HA5 2RE — MB BS 1984 Lond.; FRCS (Orth.) 1995; FRCS Eng. 1989; FRCS Ed. 1989. (St. Bart.) Cons. & Hon. Sen. Lect. (Orthop. & Trauma Surg.) Roy. Free Hosp. Lond. Prev: Lect. Roy. Nat. Orthop. Hosp. Lond.; Sen. Regist. Rotat. Roy. Free & Roy. Nat. Orthop. Hosp. Lond.; Regist. Rotat. St. Geo. Hosp. Lond.
GARLICK, Peter Richard The Surgery, Much Birch, Hereford HR2 8HT Tel: 01981 540310 Fax: 01981 540748 — MB BS 1971 Lond.; DObst RCOG 1974. (The London Hospital)
GARLICK, Mr Richard Eric — MB BS 1978 Lond.; FRCS Eng. 1985; FRCS Ed. 1983; MRCGP 1999; MFPHM 1994. (St. Thos.)
GARMAN, John Godfrey (retired) Buckton Mill, Nr. Leintwardine, Craven Arms SY7 0JU Tel: 01547 3615 — MRCS Eng. LRCP Lond. 1935.
GARMAN, John Paul 23 Swan Quay, Vespasian Road, Bitterne Manor, Southampton SO18 1DU — MB BS 1998 Lond.; MB BS Lond 1998.
GARMAN, Wendy Margaret Thornhill Park Road Surgery, 90 Thornhill Park Road, Thornhill, Southampton SO18 5TR Tel: 023 8047 4207 Fax: 023 8047 0004; 61 Thornhill Park Road, Thornhill, Southampton SO19 5JX — MB ChB 1969 Sheff.
GARMANY, David Humphrey 21 Forthill Road, Broughty Ferry, Dundee DD5 3DL — MB ChB 1992 Glas.

GARMANY, Humphrey Camperdown Street Surgery, 15 Camperdown Street, Broughty Ferry, Dundee DD5 3AA Tel: 01382 778881 Fax: 01382 731884 — MB BChir 1968 Camb.; MA, MB Camb. 1968, BChir 1967; MRCGP 1976. (Guy's) Clin. Asst. Dept. Ophth. Ninewells Hosp. Dundee.

GARNER, Adrienne Jean Julie 10 Meadway, Berkhamsted HP4 2PN Fax: 01442 876848 — MB BS 1970 Lond.; MRCS Eng. LRCP Lond. 1970; Dip. Sports Med. Lond 1991; DCH RCP Lond. 1974. Asst. GP Herts. Socs: Med. Protec. Soc. Prev: Dep. Med. Off. Health Nassau, Bahamas.

GARNER, Professor Alec (retired) 33 Rosslyn Road, Billericay CM12 9JN Tel: 01277 623389 Fax: 01277 633838 — MB ChB 1960 Manch.; PhD Lond. 1972; MD Manch. 1966; FRCP Lond. 1988; MRCP (UK) 1983; FRCOphth 1989; FRCPath 1979, M 1973. Prev: Prof. Path. Inst. Ophth. Univ. Lond.

GARNER, Anne Ashford Hospital, London Road, Ashford TW15 3AA Tel: 01784 884488; Harold Lodge, Elwyn Road, March PE15 9DB Tel: 0780 1051 707 — MB BS 1998 Lond.; MB BS Lond 1998. (St Georges Hospital Medical School, London) SHO A&E Ashford Hosp. Middlx.; PRHO Med. St Heliers Hosp., Surrey. Prev: PRHO Surg. Ashford Hosp. Middlx.

GARNER, Anne Helen c/o Dubai Petroleum Co.mpany, PO 2222, Dubai, United Arab Emirates Tel: 00 97143432222 Fax: 00 9713012144; 56 Clifton Gardens, London W9 1AU Tel: 020 7286 4707 — MB BChir 1970 Camb.; MB BChir Camb. 1971; MA Camb. 1970; Cert. FPA 1972. (Camb. & St. Mary's) Med. Off. Dubai Petroleum Company, UAE; Assoc. Phys. Amer. Hosp. Dubai. Socs: BMA; Emirate Med. Assn. Prev: GP Surrey FPC; Ho. Phys. N.wick Pk. Hosp.; Ho. Surg. St. Mary's Hosp. Lond.

GARNER, Anthony David c/o Dubai Petroleum Co., PO 2222, Dubai, United Arab Emirates Tel: 00 971 43432222 Fax: 00 971 43062144 Email: tony.garner@conoco.com; 19 Mallow Crescent, Burpham, Guildford GU4 7BU Tel: 01483 302814, 020 7286 4707 Email: garner@emirates.net.ae — MB BS 1971 Lond.; AFOM 1979. (St. Mary's Hospital (Imperial College of Medicine)) Reg.Med.Dir.Africa & Mid E. Conoco.Inc; Staff Phys. Amer. Hosp. Dubai; Sch. Med Advis. Amer. Sch Dubai. Socs: BMA; Roy. Soc. Med.; Soc. Occupat. Med. Prev: GP Staines; SHO (Psychiat.) Wexham Pk. Hosp. Slough.

GARNER, B Jane Department of Old Age Psychiatry, Chase Farm Hospital, The Ridgeway, Enfield EN2 8JL Tel: 020 8366 9147 — MB BS 1977 Lond.; BSc (Hons.) Lond. 1974; FRCPsych 1997, M 1981. (Univ. Coll. Hosp.) Cons. Psychiat. (Old Age Psychiat.) Chase Farm Hosp. Enfield. Prev: Sen. Regist. (Psychiat.) Middlx. Hosp. Lond.; Regist. & SHO (Psychiat.) Univ. Coll. Hosp. Lond.

GARNER, David Philip 16 Cherry Tree Cl, Worthing BN13 3QJ — BM 1997 Soton.

GARNER, Edward Brian (retired) Cubstocks, Haydon Bridge, Hexham NE47 6NF Tel: 01434 688936 — MB BS 1954 Lond.; FFR 1974; DMRD Eng. 1971; DObst RCOG 1958. Prev: Cons. Radiol. Hexham Gen. Hosp.

GARNER, Gillian Mary 60 Sydner Road, London N16 7UG Tel: 020 7241 1618 — MB BS 1984 Lond.; BSc Lond. 1981; MRCP (UK) 1989. (Univ. Coll. Lond.)

GARNER, James Stuart 56 Clifton Gardens, London W9 1AU — MB BS 1997 Lond.

GARNER, Jane Elizabeth Gloucester Road Medical Centre, Tramway House, 1A Church Road, Horfield, Bristol BS7 8SA Tel: 0117 949 7774 Fax: 0117 949 7730; 19 Julian Road, Sneyd Park, Bristol BS9 1JZ Tel: 0117 968 1737 — MB ChB 1985 Bristol. Prev: GP Oxf.; Trainee GP Oxf.; SHO (O & G, ENT & A & E) Bristol.

GARNER, Jean Fenwick Health Centre, St Philip's Building, The London School of Economics & Political Science, Houghton St., London WC2A 2AE — MB ChB 1965 Ed.; BSc (Physiol.) Ed. 1962; MRCPsych 1981; DPM Eng. 1969. (Ed.) Cons. Psychother. Stud. Health Serv. Lond. Sch. Economics & Political Sci. Socs: Inst. Gp. Anal.; Brit. Psychoanal. Soc.

GARNER, Jeffrey Philip 8 Chiltern Drive, Winstanley, Wigan WN3 6DY — MB ChB 1993 Sheff.

GARNER, John Angus McVicar St Triduanas Medical Practice, 54 Moira Park, Edinburgh EH7 6RU Tel: 0131 657 3341 Fax: 0131 669 6055; 25 Murrayfield Avenue, Edinburgh EH12 6AU Tel: 0131 337 6120 Fax: 0131 313 0503 Email: johncathygarner@compuserve.com — MB ChB 1974 Ed.; FRCGP 1995, M 1980; DCH Eng. 1977; DObst RCOG 1976. (Edinburgh) Mem. Scott. Gen. Med. Servs. Comm.; Vice-Chairm. Med. & Dent. Defence Union of Scotl.; Treas. Gen. Med. Serv. Defence Fund Ltd. Socs: (Counc.) BMA (Vice-Chairm. Scott. Counc.). Prev: Regist. (Med.) Roy. Alexandra Hosp. Rhyl; SHO (Paediat.) Ninewells Hosp. Dundee; Ho. Surg. Leith Hosp. Edin.

GARNER, Margaret Isabel 49 Croft Road, Carlisle CA3 9AG — MB ChB 1974 Leeds.

GARNER, Margaret Ruth Cheadle Heath Clinic, Stockport Road, Cheadle Heath, Stockport SK3 0NW Tel: 0161 480 0584; 71 Fog Lane, Didsbury, Manchester M20 6AR Tel: 0161 434 4984 — MB ChB 1981 Manch.; BSc (Hons.) Manch. 1978; MRCGP 1985; DRCOG 1984. (Manch.) Staff Grade (Community Paediat.) Stockport Healthcare NHS Trust; Clin. Med. Off. (Family Plann.) Trafford NHS Trust. Socs: Assoc. Mem. RCPCH; BACCH; RCGP.

GARNER, Paul The Howdale Surgery, 48 Howdale Road, Downham Market PE38 9AF Tel: 01366 383405 Fax: 01366 383433 — MB ChB 1974 Leeds; MRCGP 1978.

GARNER, Professor Paul Adrian International Health Research Group, Liverpool School of Tropical Medicine, Pembroke Place, Liverpool L3 5QA Tel: 0151 705 3201, 0151 707 1702 Fax: 0151 707 1702 Email: pgarner@liv.ac.uk; Glebelands, 1 St Michaels Church Road, Liverpool L17 7BD — MB BS 1979 Lond.; MD Lond. 1990; MFPHM 2000. (UCTL) Prof. (Internat. Health) Liverp. Univ. & Hon. Cons. Pub. Health Merseyside; Hon research fell St Geo.s Med. Sch. Grenada.

GARNER, Penelope Jane Cruddas Park Surgery, 178 Westmorland Road, Newcastle upon Tyne NE4 7JT Tel: 0191 226 1414; Cubstocks, Haydon Bridge, Hexham NE47 6NF Tel: 01434 688936 — MB BS 1961 Lond.; MRCS Eng. LRCP Lond. 1961; FRCGP 1993, M 1977. (St. Mary's)

GARNER, Peter 21 Marston Ferry Court, Summertown, Oxford OX2 7XH — MB ChB 1955 Manch.

GARNER, Miss Rachel Ellen Flat A, Cairney House, 10A Osborne Vilals, Osborne Avenue, Jesmond, Newcastle upon Tyne NE2 1JU — BM BS 1988 Nottm.

GARNER, Stefan Dominic Tel: 01708 852318 Fax: 01708 853216; La Semilla, Peartree Lane, Doddinghurst, Brentwood CM15 0RJ Tel: 01277 823957 — MB BS 1967 Lond.; MRCP (UK) 1980; MRCS Eng. LRCP Lond. 1967. (Westm.) Socs: Brit. Diabetic Assn. (Med. & Scientif. Sect.).

GARNERY, Didier 12 Marie Close, London SW4 8LL — MD 1978 Tours.

GARNETT, Adam Giles Gadsden Plas Isaf, Abergele LL22 7AR — MB BS 1988 Lond.; BSc Lond. 1985, MB BS 1988.

GARNETT, Andrew Richard Anaesthetics Department, South Cleveland Hospital, Marton Road, Middlesbrough TS4 3BW — MB ChB 1970 Leeds; FFA RCS Eng. 1981. Cons. Anaesth. S. Cleveland Hosp. Middlesbrough.

GARNETT, Catherine Ann 34 Acresgate Court, Liverpool L25 4UF — MB ChB 1989 Liverp.

GARNETT, James Francis Philip Filey Surgery, Station Avenue, Filey YO14 9AE Tel: 01723 515881 Fax: 01723 515197; 15 Northgate, Hunmanby, Filey YO14 0NT Tel: 01723 891232 — MB ChB 1973 Leeds; MRCP (UK) 1976; MRCGP 1987; DCH Eng. 1977. Med. Dir. E. Yorks. Community Healthcare NHS Trust.

GARNETT, Jane Elizabeth 21 Hobberton Green, Sowerby Bridge, Halifax HX6 1NR — MB ChB 1981 Leeds.

GARNETT, Matthew Romney 29 Church Road, Wheatley, Oxford OX33 1LZ — BM BCh 1993 Oxf.

GARNETT, Robin, OBE, QHP, Brigadier late RAMC Defence Medical Rehabilitation Unit, Headley Court, Leatherhead Tel: 01732 378271 Fax: 020 8781 2366; 23 Holbrook Lane, Chislehurst BR7 6PE Tel: 020 8467 7823 — MB ChB 1967 Bristol; PhD Lond. 1979; DPhysMed. Eng. 1971; BSc (Anat.) Bristol 1963; FRCP Ed. 1985. (Bristol) Dir. Defence Rehabil. (Rheum. & Rehabil.) Leatherhead; Hon. Cons. Phys. (EMG) St. Thos. Hosp. Lond.; Chairm. SAC Rehabil. Med. (JCMMT) 1992. Socs: Fell. Roy. Soc. Med. (Counc. Mem. & Edit. Represen. United Serv. & MoD Sect.); (Ex-Pres.) Brit. Soc. Rehabil. Med.; Brit. Soc. Rheum. Prev: Smith & Nephew Trav. Schol. Spinal Injury Rehabil. Aust. & USA; Medelec Research Fell. (Clin. Neurophysiol.) Rayne Inst. St. Thos. Hosp. Lond.

GARNETT, Shelagh Mary South Lancashire Health Authority, The Green, Eccleston, Chorley PR7 5PD Tel: 01257 452222 — MB ChB

1976 Sheff.; MSc Manch. 1991; MRCP (UK) 1983; MFPHM RCP (UK) 1992. (Sheffield) Director of Health Improvement, Chorley & S. Ribble Primary Care Trust.

GARNETT, Timothy John Eli Lilly & Co, Lilly Research Centre, Erl Wood Manor, Sunninghill Road, Windlesham GU20 6BH; 3 Dorset Road, Windsor SL4 3BA Tel: 01753 714606 Fax: 01753 714606 — MB BS 1984 Lond.; MFPM RCP (UK) 1995; MFFP 1993; MRCOG 1992; Cert. Family Plann. JCC 1985. Europ. Clin. Developm. Phys. Socs: BMA; (Counc.) Roy. Soc. Med.; Internat. Menopause Soc. Prev: Dir. of Med. Affairs Organon Laborat. Camb. Sci. Pk.; Research Regist. (O & G) Kings Coll. Hosp. Lond.; SHO (Med. Oncol.) Roy. Marsden Hosp. Lond.

GARNHAM, Mr Andrew William 56 School Road, Moseley, Birmingham B13 9SW Tel: 0121 684 8814 Email: andy@wgarnham.freeserve.co.uk — MB BCh 1988 Wales; FRCS Ed. 1992.

GARNHAM, Francesca Emma Kynance, Manor Road, Penn, High Wycombe HP10 8JB; Homerton Hospital, Homerton Row, Hackney, London E9 6SR — MB BS 1994 Lond. SHO (ITU) Homerton Hosp. Socs: Fell. Lond. Med. Soc.

GARNHAM, Ian Roy Cuckow 29 Amigo House, Westminster Bridge Road, London SE1 7QE Tel: 020 7928 8191 — MB BS 1989 Lond.

GARNHAM, John Claude Kynance, Manor Road, Penn, High Wycombe HP10 8JB Tel: 01494 812177 Fax: 01494 816281 — MB BS 1957 Lond.; MRCS Eng. LRCP Lond. 1957; FFPM RCP (UK) 1989. (St. Bart.) Chairm. Chiltern Internat. Ltd. Socs: Fell. Roy. Soc. Trop. Med. & Hyg.; Emerit. Amer. Soc. Clin. Pharmacol. & Ther.; Brit. Soc. Pharmacol. Prev: Vice-Pres. Med. Affairs, Pharmaceut. Products Div. Abbott Laborats., USA; Dir. Clin. Research Dow Pharmaceuts., USA.

GARNHAM, Mr John Richard (retired) Belton, Poplar Lane, Bransgore, Christchurch BH23 8JE — MA, MB Camb. 1961, BChir 1960; FRCS Eng. 1964. Prev: Cons. Gen. Surg. Harefield Hosp., Mt. Vernon Hosp. N.wood & N.wood & Pinner Hosp.

GARNHAM, Patricia Anne Rosemary Community Child Health, Bedford House, Havelock Place, Shelton, Stoke-on-Trent ST1 4PR; 66 Beech Avenue, Rode Heath, Stoke-on-Trent ST7 3JD — MB ChB 1981 Manch. (Manch.) Staff Grade (Community Child Health) N. Staffs. NHS Hosp. Trust.

GARNISH, Rosalind Petra 51 Dartmouth Avenue, Westlands, Newcastle ST5 3NT — MB ChB 1970 Ed.; BSc Ed. 1967; DFFP 1993; Dip. Community Paediat. Sheff. 1991; Cert. Family Plann. JCC 1975. Socs: Fac. Comm. Health; Diplomate Fac. Family Plann. & Reproduc. Healthcare. Prev: Assoc. Specialist (Child Health) Wakefield & Pontefract Community Trust.

GAROFALIDES, Basil 32 Mount Avenue, Westcliff on Sea SS0 8PT — MB BCh BAO 1957 Dub. Counc.lor Cyriax Foundat.; Clin. Asst. (Orthop.) S.end Gen. Hosp. Socs: Brit. Med. Acupunct. Soc.; Brit. Inst. Musculoskel. Med. Prev: Assoc. Specialist (Orthop. Surg.) S.end Gen. Hosp.; Regist. (Orthop.) S.end Gen. Hosp.

GAROUSHA, Soliman Ali 56 Oak Lane, Upchurch, Gillingham Tel: 01634 231423; 32 Heathfield Close, Penenden Heath, Maidstone ME14 2AB — MB BCh 1957 Cairo; LMSSA Lond. 1963; FRCOG 1979, M 1966, DObst 1963. (Cairo) Prev: Cons. Gyn. Surg. Al-Galaea Hosp. Tripoli.

GARRALDA HUALDE, Professor Maria Elena Academic Unit of Child & Adolescent Psychiatry, Imperial College Faculty of Medicine, St Mary's Campus, Norfolk Place, London W2 1PG Tel: 0207 886 1145 Fax: 0207 886 6299 — LMS 1971 Navarra Spain; MPhil Lond. 1979; MD Navarra 1981; MRCPsych 1975; T(Psych) 1991; DPM Eng. 1975. (Navarra Spain) Prof. Child & Adolesc. Psychiat. Fac. of Med. Imperial Coll. St. Mary's Campus; Hon. Cons. (Child & Adolesc. Psychiat.). Socs: Fell. Roy. Coll. Psychiat.; Roy. Soc. Med.; Fell.Roy.Coll.Paediat. & Child health. Prev: Sen. Lect. & Reader (Child & Adolesc. Psychiat.) Univ. Manch.; Regist. (Psychiat.) & Sen. Regist. (Child Psychiat.) The Maudsley & Bethlem Roy. Hosp. Lond.

GARRARD, Alison Clare 19 Montacute Way, Wimborne BH21 1UB Tel: 01202 887460 — MB ChB 1995 Bristol. SHO (Anaesth.) Ysbyty Glan Clwyd, Rhyl. Prev: SHO (Med.) Ysbyty Glan Clwyd, Rhyl; SHO (A & E) Ysbyty Gwynedd Bangor.

GARRARD, Olga Neve Immacolata Larby Young People's Unit, Victoria Park Road, Exeter EX2 4NU — MB BS 1990 Lond.; BSc (Hons.) Nutrit. with Basic Med. Sci. Lond. 1987; MRC Psych 1996. Specialist Regist. in Child & Adolesc. Psychiat. Prev: SHO (Psychiat.) Tottenham Mews Day Hosp. Lond.; SHO (Psychiat.) St. Lukes Woodside Hosp. Lond.

GARRARD, Peter Institute of Cognitive Neuroscience, Alexandra House, 17 Queen Square, London W4N 3AR Email: p.garrard@ulc.ac.uk; 22 St Paul Street, London N1 7AB Tel: 0207 226 2064 Email: p.garrard@ulc.ac.uk — MB ChB 1990 Bristol; PhD 2000 Cambridge; MA Oxf. 1985; MRCP (UK) 1994. (Bristol) MRC Clinician Scientist, Inst. of Neurol., Qu. Sq. Lond. Socs: Assoc. Mem. Assn. Brit. Neurol. Prev: Regist. Neurol. Camb.; Regist. Neurol. Nt. Hosp. Qu. Sq. Lond.; Regist. Rotat. (Neurol.) Bristol.

GARRATT, Ann (retired) Garratt, 27 Little Gaddesden, Berkhamsted HP4 1NU Tel: 01442 842275 — MB BS 1950 Lond.; MRCS Eng. LRCP Lond. 1949; DO Eng. 1953. Prev: Med. Asst. (Ophth.) Watford Gen. Hosp.

GARRATT, Cecil Douglas (retired) 27 Little Gaddesden, Berkhamsted HP4 1NU Tel: 01442 842275 — MB BS 1947 Lond.; MRCP Lond. 1948; MRCS Eng. LRCP Lond. 1942. Prev: Regist. (Med.) Roy. Masonic Hosp.

GARRATT, Christopher John 41 School Lane, Chilwell, Nottingham NG9 5EH — MB ChB 1988 Dundee; AFPM RCP Lond. 1995; Dip. Pharm. Med. RCP (UK) 1994; DA (UK) 1990. Research Phys. Knoll Pharmaceut. Nottm. Prev: SHO (Anaesth.) Qu. Med. Centre Nottm.

GARRATT, Donald Michael The Chantries, 1 Blundells Croft, Welford on Avon, Stratford-upon-Avon CV37 8EP Tel: 01789 750907 — MB ChB 1946 Birm. Prev: Chairm. Wilts LMC; Vice-Chairm. Wilts. FPC.

GARRATT, Frank Neville (retired) 21 Stafford Road, Bloxwich, Walsall WS3 3NJ Tel: 01922 475807 — PhD Birm. 1958, MB ChB 1951; FFCM 1977, M 1972; DPH Lond. 1956. Hon. Cons. Pub. Health Med. Walsall H.A. Prev: Asst. Gen. Manager (Med.) Wolverhampton HA.

GARRATT, Patrick Martin 23 Foxearth Road, Selsdon, South Croydon CR2 8EL — BM BS 1996 Nottm.

GARRATT, Peter Philip The Surgery, 66-68 Stoke Road, Gosport PO12 1PA Tel: 023 9258 1529 Fax: 023 9250 1417 — MB ChB 1986 Birm.; MRCGP 1995; DRCOG 1990. (Birm.)

GARRAWAY, William Michael Druim Mhor Alvie, Aviemore PH22 1QB Tel: 01479 810215 Fax: 01479 810215 — MD 1980 Ed.; MB ChB 1966; MSc (Social Med.) Lond. 1972; FRCP Ed. 1988, M 1985; FRCGP 1983, M 1970; DCH RCP Glas. 1970; DObst RCOG 1968. (Ed.) . Prev: Prof. Dept. Pub. Health Sci. Univ. Edin; Cons. Epidemiol. Mayo Clinic Rochester Minnesota; Assoc. Prof. (Epidemiol.) Mayo Grad. Sch. of Med. Rochester Minnesota.

GARRETT, Anne Mary Gabrielle Lissadell, Rocklands Lane, Thornton Hough, Wirral CH63 4JX — MB BS 1980 Lond.; FRCR 1987; DMRD Liverp. 1985. Cons. Radiol. Arrowe Pk. Hosp. Wirral. Prev: Sen. Regist. (Radiol.) Mersey RHA.

GARRETT, Arthur Stephen, MBE (retired) Greenfields, Kerdiston Road, Reepham, Norwich NR10 4LQ Tel: 01603 870739 — MB BS 1938 Lond.; MRCS Eng. LRCP Lond. 1938. Prev: GP Reepham, Norf.

GARRETT, Canice James Marsh Street Surgery, 25A Marsh Street, Rothwell, Leeds LS26 0AG Tel: 0113 282 1571 Fax: 0113 282 4720; Lane End House, Church Lane, Adel, Leeds LS16 8DE Tel: 0113 267 6488 — MB ChB 1972 Leeds; MRCGP 1978; Cert. Family Plann. JCC 1978; Dip. Ven Soc. Apoth. Lond. 1977; DObst RCOG 1974.

GARRETT, Carol Ann Robert Street Surgery, 140 Robert Street, Milford Haven SA73 2HS Tel: 01646 690690 Fax: 01646 690402; Bulford Cottage, Bulford Road, Johnston, Haverfordwest SA62 3ET Tel: 01437 890341 — MB ChB Manch. 1976; MRCGP 1980.

GARRETT, Christine Kennedy-Galton Centre, Level 8V, Northwick Park and St Mark's Hospitals, North West London Hospitals NHS Trust, Watford Road, Harrow HA1 3UJ Tel: 020 8869 2795 Fax: 020 8869 3106 — MB BS Lond. 1967; FRCP Lond. 1994; FRCPC 1979; MRCP (UK) 1973; MRCS Eng. LRCP Lond. 1967; DCH Eng. 1969. (Guy's) p/t Cons. Clin. Geneticist N. Thames RHA. Prev: Sen. Regist. (Clin. Genetics) Guy's Hosp. Lond.; Cons. Clin. Geneticist S. W.. RHA.

GARRETT, Christopher John, OStJ, Brigadier late RAMC Retd. (retired) Pilgrims Hospice, 56 London Rd, Canterbury CT2 8JA Tel: 01227 459700 Fax: 01227 784156 — MB ChB Birm. 1956; FRCP

Lond. 1980; MRCP Lond. 1963; T(M) 1991; DTM & H Eng. 1961. p/t Cons. Phys. Pilgrims Hospices Canterbury. Prev: Command Cons. Phys. HQ BAOR.

GARRETT, Geoffrey (retired) Ash Fell, 306 Leigh Road, Worsley, Manchester M28 1LH Tel: 0161 790 3505 — MD 1960 Manch.; MB ChB 1950; FRCPath 1972, M 1963; DPath Eng. 1957. Cons. Pathol. Oldham & Dist. Hosp. Gp.; Home Office Pathol. Fell. Manch. Med. Soc. Prev: Sen. Regist. Path. & Ho. Surg. Manch. Roy. Infirm.

GARRETT, Helen Mary Carol Kendrick Unit, Duchess of York Hospital, Nell Lane, West Didsbury, Manchester M20 2LR Tel: 0161 291 3131 Fax: 0161 291 3952 — MB ChB 1982 Liverp.; MRCPsych 1986. Cons. Child & Adolesc. Psychiat. S. Manch. Univ. Hosps. NHS Trust. Socs: Manch. Med. Soc. Prev: Cons. Child & Adolesc. Psychiat. Oldham NHS Trust; Sen. Regist. (Child Psychiat.) N.. W.. RHA.

GARRETT, Jennifer 38 Baker Street, Potters Bar EN6 2EB — MB BS 1990 Lond.

GARRETT, John Graham 19 St Agnes Road, Heath, Cardiff CF14 4AN Tel: 029 2062 3496 Fax: 029 2062 3496 — MB BS 1984 New South Wales.

GARRETT, John Norton (retired) Les Blanches, St Martin's, Guernsey GY4 6AE Tel: 01481 37630 — MB BS 1957 Lond.; MRCS Eng. LRCP Lond. 1956; DObst RCOG 1958. Prev: Med. Regist. Worthing Hosp.

GARRETT, John Patrick Robinhurst House, Blackhurst Lane, Tunbridge Wells TN2 4QA — MB ChB 1978 Liverp.; MRCP 1981; FRCR 1987. Cons. Radiol. Tunbridge Wells Hosps. Prev: Sen. Regist. (Radiol.) John Radcliffe Hosp. Oxf.; Regist. (Cardiol.) Mater Miser. Hosp. Dub.

GARRETT, Professor John Raymond Department of Oral Pathology, The Rayne Institute, King's College Medical & Dental School, 123 Coldharbour Lane, London SE5 9NU Tel: 020 7346 3019 Fax: 020 7346 3019; 15 Deepdene Road, Denmark Hill, London SE5 8EG Tel: 020 7274 6488 — MB BS 1959 Lond.; MB BS (Hons. Obst. & Gyn.) Lond. 1959; PhD Lond. 1965, BSc (Physiol. 1st cl. Hons.) 1956; MD (Hon. Causa) Lund, Sweden 1985; MRCS Eng. LRCP Lond. 1959; FRCPath 1977, M 1965; LDS RCS Eng. 1949. (King's Coll. Hosp.) Emerit. Prof. & Former Head of Oral Path. King's Coll. Sch. Med. & Dent.; Liveryman Worshipful Soc. Apoth. Socs: Fell. Roy. Soc. Med.; Path. Soc.; Liveryman Worshipful Soc. Apoth. Prev: Nuffield Dent. Research Fell.; Ho. Phys. (Paediat.) & Ho. Surg. (ENT) King's Coll. Hosp. Lond.

GARRETT, Katharine Raye 62 Southway, London NW11 6SA Tel: 020 8458 1518 — MB BS 1953 Lond. (St. Geo.) Prev: Clin. Med. Off. Barnet AHA; Ho. Phys. Gt. Ormond St. Childr. Hosp. Lond.; Regist. (Paediat.) Centr. Middlx. Hosp. Lond.

GARRETT, Marshall McIntyre 30 Buckingham Terrace, Glasgow G12 8ED — MB ChB 1984 Glas.; MB ChB Glas. l984.

GARRETT, Martina Broadhaven, Well Lane, Gayton, Wirral CH60 8NQ Tel: 0151 342 3866 — MB BCh BAO 1950 NUI. (Galway) Prev: Ho. Surg. Bootle Gen. Hosp.; Jun. Hosp. Med. Off. Clatterbridge Hosp. Bebington.

GARRETT, Michael John Broadhaven, Well Lane, Gayton, Wirral CH60 8NQ Tel: 0151 342 3866 — MB BCh BAO 1947 NUI; MD NUI 1966; FRCR 1973; FFR 1958; FFR RCSI 1962; DMRT Eng. 1952. Vis. Prof. Gadenski Regional Radiother. Centre Alberta Univ. & Dir. Educat. Univ. Liverp.; Lect. (Clin. Radiother.) Univ. Liverp. Socs: BMA & Liverp. Med. Inst. Prev: Cons. Radiother. & Oncol. Liverp. Regional Radiother. Servs.; Res. Med. Off. Christie Hosp. & Holt Radium Inst. Manch.; Regist. Roy. Vict. Infirm. Newc.

GARRETT, Peter John Renal Unit, Tyrone County Hospital, Hospital Road, Omagh BT79 0AP Tel: 02882 245211 Fax: 02882 240115 Email: pgarrett@slt.n-i.nhs.uk; 101 Cavan Road, Fintona, Omagh BT78 2LU Tel: 02882 897077 Email: cavan@enterprise.net — MB ChB 1975 Liverp.; MD Liverp. 1985; FRCP Ed. 1995; FRCP Lond. 1997; MRCP (UK) 1979. (Liverp.) Cons. Phys. & Nephrol. Tyrone Co. Hosp. Omagh. Socs: Renal Assn.; Eur. Renal Assn.; Irish Mephrological Soc. Prev: Sen. Regist. (Nephrol. & Gen. Med.) Wessex RHA; Lect. (Med.) Mater Hosp. & Univ. Coll. Dub.; SHO (Nephrol.) St. Peter's Hosp. Lond.

***GARRETT, Simon James** 23 Horsecastles Lane, Sherborne DT9 6BU Tel: 01935 814400 — BM 1998 Soton.; BM Soton 1998.

GARRETT, Stewart MacFarlane (retired) The Holt, Craighouse PA60 7XR Tel: 01496 820350 — MB ChB Glas. 1957. JP. Prev: JP.

GARRETT, Thomas St Augustines Medical Practice, 4 Station Road, Keynsham, Bristol BS31 2BN Tel: 0117 986 2343 Fax: 0117 986 1176; 12 St. Ladoc Road, Keynsham, Bristol BS31 2DR Tel: 0117 986 2254 Fax: 0117 986 2254 Email: tgarret@cix.co.uk — MB BChir 1969 Camb.; MA Camb. 1969; MRCGP 1980; DObst RCOG 1971; DTM & H Liverp. 1970; M Ed UWE 1997; FRCGP 1997. (Camb. & Lond. Hosp.) Assoc. Adviser Postgrad. Med. Dept. Univ. Bristol. Socs: Clin. Soc. Bath; Fell. Roy. Coll. Gen. Pract. (Severn Fac.); World Organisation Nat. Coll. & Acads. of Family Practs. Prev: Med. Off. i/c Wusasa Hosp. Zaria, Nigeria.

GARRETT, William (retired) 198 Hamilton Road, Mount Vernon S., Glasgow G32 9QU Tel: 0141 778 6529 — MB ChB 1946 Glas. Prev: RAMC.

GARRETT, William Robert 11 Parkstone Avenue, Poole BH14 9LW Tel: 01202 735523 — MB BS 1992 Lond.; BSc (1st. cl. Hons.) Pharmacol. Lond. 1989; FRCA 1998. (Lond. Hosp. Med. Coll.) Specialist Regist. (Anaesth.) Soton. Gen. Hosp. Prev: SHO (Anaesth.) Soton. Gen. Hosp.; SHO (Med.) Broomfield Hosp. Chelmsford; Ho. Off. (Surg.) Roy. Lond. Hosp.

GARRETT, Mr William Vere 1 Portland Mews, St Georges Road, Brighton BN2 1EQ — MB BS 1994 Lond.; BSc (Hons.) Lond. 1993; FRCS (Eng.) 1998. (Char. Cross & Westm.) SHO (Gen. Surg.) Roy. Sussex Co. Hosp. Brighton. Socs: Surg. Research Soc.; BMA. Prev: SHO (Gen. Surg.) RSCH; SHO (Neuro Surg.) HPNC Hurstwood Pk. Neurosci.s Centre Haywards Heath; SHO (Orthop. Surg.) RSCH.

GARRETT-ANDERSON, Dominic 174 Camberwell Grove, London SE5 8RH — MB BS 1988 Lond.

GARRETT-COX, Robin Guy Shrubhill, Dunblane FK15 9PA — BChir 1994 Camb.

GARRETT RYAN, Fiona Jane The Old Schoolhouse, Ferndale Road, Horsell, Woking GU21 4AJ — MB BS 1994 Lond.; MA Oxf. 1994, BA (Hons.) 1990. Trainee GP Frimley, Surrey; GP Retainer, Camberley, Surrey. Prev: GP Regist. Lightwater, Surrey.

GARRETTS, Maurice (retired) 23 Eversleigh Road, Finchley, London N3 1HY Tel: 020 8349 1459 — MB BS (Hons. Distinc. Pharmacol. & Applied; Therap.) Lond. 1950; FRCP Lond. 1970, M 1952. Lect. (Dermat.) Univ. Manch. Prev: Cons. Dermat. United Manch. Hosps., Manch. & Salford Hosp. Dis. Skin., Roy. Manch . Childr. Hosp., Withington Hosp. & Wythenshawe Hosp.

GARREY, Mr Matthew Macmaster 21 Lauderdale Drive, Newton Mearns, Glasgow G77 5AR Tel: 0141 639 4775 — MB ChB 1936 Glas.; MB ChB (Commend.) Glas. 1936; FRCS Glas. 1973; FRCOG 1963, M 1944; DPH Glas. 1940. (Glas.) Socs: Fell. (Ex-Pres.) Roy. M-C Soc. Glas.; Fell. Obst. Soc. Glas.; S.. Med. Soc. Glas. Prev: Emerit. Cons. Glas. Roy. Matern. Hosp.; Cons. Obst. Glas. Roy. Matern. Hosp.; Cons. Gyn. Roy. Samarit. Hosp. For Wom. Glas.

GARRICK, Mr Herbert David Oluwole Grantham & District Hospital, Manthorpe Road, Grantham NG31 8DG Tel: 01476 565232 Fax: 01476 590441 Email: drgarrick@aol.com; Cameron House, High Road, Mauthorpe, Grantham NG31 8NG Tel: 01476 560199 Fax: 01636 685971 Email: dgarrick45@hotmail.com — MD 1972 Moscow; FRCS Eng. 1979; FFAEM 1994; MSc (Sports Med.) 1997; Dip. IMC (RCS Ed.) 1996. Cons. A & E Grantham & Dist. Hosp. & Newark Gen. Hosp.; Mem. Lincs. Integrated Volun. Emerg. Servs. Socs: Brit. Assn. Accid. & Emerg. Med.; Brit. Assn. Immed. Care Med.; Brit. Assn. Sports Med. Prev: Cons. Surg. Geo. Town Hosp. Cayman; Cons. Surg. P.ss Margt. Hosp. Nassau.

GARRIDO, Maria Consuelo Central Pathology Laborotory Stoke on Trent, Department of Histopathology & Cytology, North Staffs Hospital Trust, Hartshill Road, Stoke-on-Trent ST4 7PA Tel: 01782 716662 ext. 5207; Leatop House, Weston Bank, Stafford ST18 0BA — Medico y Cirujano 1984 Univ. de Valle Colombia; DRCPath 1994. Cons. Path. N. Staffs. Hosp. Trust Stoke on Trent. Socs: Assn. Clin. Paths. Prev: Lect. (Path.) Univ. Oxf.; Lect. (Path.) Univ. Birm.

GARRIDO FERRER, Anselmo Flat 44 Room 2, Glenfrith Close, Leicester LE2 9QQ; Flat 4, 49 Cliff Road, Leeds LS6 2EZ — LMS 1992 U. Autonoma Barcelona.

GARRIGAN, Christopher Thomas (retired) The Health Centre, 203 Main Street, Barrhead G78 1HG Tel: 0141 880 6161 Fax: 0141 881 7063 — MB ChB 1968 Glas.; DObst RCOG 1970; MRCGP 1974.

GARRIOCH, David Brown Pembury Hospital, Pembury, Tunbridge Wells TN2 4QJ Tel: 01892 823535; Windwood, Nevill Court, Tunbridge Wells TN4 8NL Tel: 01892 545463 Fax: 01892 515305

— MB ChB 1971 Aberd.; MD Aberd. 1978, MB ChB 1971, BMedBiol (Immunol.) 1968; FRCOG 1990, M 1977. Cons. O & G Kent & Sussex Weald NHS Trust; Tutor St. Thos. & Guy's Med. Sch. Lond. Prev: Cons. O & G Pembury & Sevenoaks Hosps.; Ho. Phys. & Ho. Surg. Aberd. Roy. Infirm.; Hon. Sen. Regist. St. Thos. Hosp. Lond. Lect. Univ. Lond.

GARRIOCH, Magnus Allan 44 Hamilton Avenue, Pollokshields, Glasgow G41 4JD; Southern General Hospital, Department of Anaesthetics, 1345 Govan Road, Glasgow G51 4TF Tel: 0141 201 1658 Fax: 0141 201 1321 — MB ChB 1984 Birm.; FRCA 1989; DA (UK) 1986. (Birm.) Cons. Anaesth. & Intens. Care S.. Gen. Hosp. Glas.; Sen. Lect. Anaesth. Univ. Glas. Socs: FRCAnaesth.; Assn. Anaesth. GB & Irel.; Europ. Soc. of Intens. Care. Prev: Sen. Regist. (Anaesth.) Lothian Region; Fell. (Shock Trauma) Washington Hosp. Centre Washington DC, USA; Regist. & SHO (Anaesth.) Glas. Roy. Infirm.

GARROD, Andrew Charles Church Field Medical Centre, Church Field, Camelford PL32 9YT Tel: 01840 213894 — MB BCh 1986 Wales.

GARROD, David Cubitt Hamilton (retired) 'Penlan', Gipsy Lane, Wokingham RG40 2HP Tel: 0118 978 3799 — MB BChir 1950 Camb.; DObst RCOG 1951. Prev: Ho. Surg. & Obst. Intern St. Bart.

GARROD, Graham David Bottreaux Surgery, Boscastle PL35 0BG Tel: 01840 250209 Fax: 01840 250666; Trevillett Barton, Trevillett, Tintagel PL34 0HL Tel: 01840 770563 — MB BCh 1976 Wales; MRCGP 1982; DObst N. Zealand 1981; DA Eng. 1979; Cert. Family Plann. JCC 1982. Prev: SHO (Med.) Harrogate Gen. Hosp. Yorks.; Regist. (Med.) Green La. Hosp. Auckland, New Zealand; SHO (Paediat.) N. Devon Dist. Hosp. Barnstaple.

GARROD, James Anthony (retired) 16 Hale Road, Wendover, Aylesbury HP22 6NF Tel: 01296 622978 — MB BS 1960 Lond.; DObst RCOG 1962. Prev: SHO Luton Matern. Hosp.

GARROD, Patrick John 122 Longstomps Avenue, Chelmsford CM2 9LB — BM Soton 1988; MRCGP 1996. (Univ. Soton.)

GARROD, Timothy John Bradley Stoke Surgery, Brook Way, Bradley Stoke North, Bristol BS32 9DS Tel: 01454 616262 Fax: 01454 619161; 3 Kings Avenue, Bishopstow, Bristol BS7 8JL Tel: 0117 924 4291 — MB ChB 1991 Bristol; BSc ARCS (Biochem.) Lond. 1985; MRCGP 1996; DFFP 1996; DGM RCP Lond. 1994. (Bristol) Princip. GP. Prev: Trainee GP Glos.; SHO (O & G) W.on Gen. Hosp.; SHO (O & G) St. Michael's Hosp. Bristol.

GARROOD, Penelope Victoria Ann 46 Coniston Avenue, Newcastle upon Tyne NE2 3HA — MB BS 1998 Newc.; MB BS Newc 1998.

GARROW, Alan Davidson Eborall and Partners, Fountain Medical Centre, Sherwood Avenue, Newark NG24 1QH Tel: 01636 704378/9 Fax: 01636 610875; Willowmere, Wyke Lane, Farndon, Newark NG24 3SP Tel: 01636 74977 Fax: 01636 610875 — MB ChB 1972 Aberd.; DA Eng. 1976; DObst RCOG 1974. Staff Anaesth. Newark Hosp. Socs: Nottm. M-C Soc.; Mansfield Med. Soc.; Trent Anaesth. Soc. Prev: SHO (Anaesth.) Nottm. Hosps. Gp.; SHO (Obst.) Aberd. Matern. Hosp.; Ho. Phys. (Phys. Surg.) Woodend Hosp. Aberd.

GARROW, Professor John Stuart (retired) The Dial House, 93 Uxbridge Road, Rickmansworth WD3 7DQ Tel: 01923 775747 Fax: 01923 710665 — MB ChB 1952 St. And.; PhD St. And. 1961, MD 1957; FRCP Lond. 1988; FRCP Ed. 1976, M 1961. Hon. Cons. Phys. St. Bart., St. Marks & Roy. Lond. Hosp.; Edr. Europ. Jl. Clin. Nutrit. Prev: Rank Prof. Human Nutrit. St. Bart. Hosp. Med. Coll.

GARROW, Katharine Joyce (retired) The Dial House, 93 Uxbridge Road, Rickmansworth WD3 7DQ Tel: 01923 775747 — MB ChB Aberd. 1950; DCH Eng. 1953. Prev: GP Rickmansworth.

GARRY, Anne Catherine St Leonards Hospice, 185 Tadcaster Road, York YO24 1GL Tel: 01904 708553; Millview, 77 Acomb Road, York YO24 4EP Tel: 01904 794763 — MB ChB 1984 Leeds; MRCGP 1991; DTM & H Liverp. 1992; T(GP) 1991; DRCOG 1986. (Leeds) Cons. Palliat. Med. St.Leonards Hospice & York Dist. Hosp. Prev: Sen. Regist. (Palliat. Med.) Liverp. Marie Curie Centre Mersey Regional Train. Progr.; Regist. (Palliat. Med.) Yorks. Regional Train. Progr.

GARRY, Gerard Martin 42 Dawlish Drive, Coventry CV3 5NB — MB BS 1991 Lond.

GARRY, John William (retired) 4 Curle Avenue, Lincoln LN2 4AN — LM 1952 Dub.; MB BCh BAO NUI 1951, DPM 1954; MRCPsych 1971; LAH Dub. 1950; FRCPsych 1989. Prev: Cons. Psychiat. Trent RHA.

GARRY, Martin Joseph 69 Linkside Drive, Southgate, Gower, Swansea SA3 2BS Tel: 01792 234046 — MB BCh 1989 Wales; DA 1995; FRCA 1998. Specialist Regist. (Anaesth.) Univ. Hosp. Wales. Prev: Specialist Regist. (Anaesth.) Morriston Hosp. Swansea.

GARRY, Raymond Westgarth, Westgate, Guisborough TS14 6AP Tel: 01287 634545 — MB BS 1967 Newc.; MD Newc. 1983; FRCOG 1989, M 1976; DObst RCOG 1969. (Newc.) Cons. Gyn. & Dir. Minimal Access Gyn. Surg. St. Jas. Univ. Hosp.; Cons. Obst. & Gyn. Cleveland AHA & S. Tees HA i/c Minimal Access Surg. Med. Dir. Wom. Endoscopic Laser Foundat; Edr. Gyn. Endoscopy. Socs: (Pres.) Brit. Soc. Gyn. Endoscopy. Prev: Lect. (O & G) Univ. Leicester & Hon. Sen. Regist. Leicester AHA; Wellcome Research Fell. Endocrinol. Roy. Vict. Infirm. Newc.

GARSED, Martin Paul Pilgrims Hospice, 56 London Road, Canterbury CT2 8JA Tel: 01277 459700 Fax: 01277 812606 Email: martin_garsed@pilgrimshospice.org — MRCS Eng. LRCP Lond. 1973; Dr. Med. Cordoba Catholic Univ. Argentina 1970; MSc (Clin. Psychother.) Lond. 1992; MRCGP 1976; Dip. Palliat. Med. Wales 1998; DObst RCOG 1974. Hospice Phys. Prev: Hosp. Pract. Psychother. Canterbury Ment. Health Servs.; Trainee GP W. Sussex. VTS; Resid. Med. Off. Buenos Aires Brit. Hosp.

GARSED-BENNET, David John Carver Fleet Medical Centre, Church Road, Fleet GU51 4PE — MB BS 1972 Lond.

GARSIDE, John Harold The Health Centre, Chapel Street, Thirsk YO7 1LG Tel: 01845 523154 Fax: 01845 526213 — BM BCh 1971 Oxf.; MRCGP 1979.

GARSIDE, Jonathan Paul 17 Westrope Way, Bedford MK41 7YX — MB BS 1994 Lond.

GARSIDE, Julian Michael Holmfirth, 224 Thorpe Road, Great Clacton, Clacton-on-Sea CO15 4QA — MB BS 1994 Lond.

GARSIDE, Lydia Jane 8 Branpole Road, Bournemouth BH8 9NZ; 9 Sidney Gardens, Muscliffe, Bournemouth BH9 3SG Tel: 01202 516473 — BM Soton. 1994; MRCP (UK) 1998. (Southampton) SHO Paediat. Prev: SHO Paediat. Guy's Hosp. Lond.; SHO Paediat. Canterbury.

GARSIDE, Peter James Circuit Lane Surgery, 53 Circuit Lane, Reading RG30 3AN Tel: 0118 958 2537 Fax: 0118 957 6115 Email: pgarside@doctors.org.uk — MB BS 1983 Lond.; BSc (Hons.) Lond. 1980; MRCP (UK) 1987; MRCGP 1993; DTM & H RCP Lond. 1989. GP Princip., Reading. Socs: Roy. Soc. of Med. Fell. Prev: Regist. (Gen. Med.) Roy. Berks. Hosp. Reading; SHO (Rheum., Rehabil. & Metab. Med.) Nuffield Orthop. Centre Oxf.; SHO (Dermat.) Inst. Dermat. Lond.

GARSIDE, Sarah Helen Saddleworth Medical Practice, The Clinic, Smithy Lane, Uppermill, Oldham OL3 6AH Tel: 01457 872228 Fax: 01457 876520; The Grange, Millcroft Lane, Delph, Oldham OL3 5UX Tel: 01457 876293 — MB ChB 1982 Manch.; BSc St. And. 1979.

GARSIN, Mitcholl Douglas 31 Boleyn Way, New Barnet, Barnet EN5 5LH — MB BS 1983 Lond.; LMSSA Lond. 1983. (St. Bart.) Trainee GP Lond. Prev: SHO (Psychiat.) Claybury Hosp. Lond.; SHO (Accid & Emerg.) OldCh. Hosp. Romford; SHO (Geriat. Med.) Whipps Cross Hosp. Lond.

GARSON, Jeremy Alexander Division of Virology, UCL Medical School, Windeyer Building, 46 Cleveland St., London W1T 4JF Tel: 020 7380 9490 Fax: 020 7580 5896 — MB ChB 1977 Birm.; PhD Lond. 1988; MSc (Immunol.) Birm. 1979, BSc (Hons.) 1974, MD 1983; MRCP (UK) 1980; MRCPath 1995; FRCPath 1997. (Univ. Birm. Med. Sch.) Sen. Lect. (Med. Microbiol. & Virol) Univ. Coll. Lond.; Hon. Cons. Virol. UCL Hosps. NHS Trust. Socs: Soc. Gen. Microbiol. Prev: ICRF Clin. research fell.sh. Inst. Child Health Lond.; MRC Special Train. Fell.sh. (Neuropath.) Frenchay Hosp. Bristol; Research Fell. (Neurosurg. & Oncol.) Mass. Gen. Hosp. & NIH Bethesda, USA.

GARSON, Meir 74 Singleton Road, Salford M7 4LU Fax: 0161 740 0662 Email: emrservices@btinternet.com — MB ChB 1974 Manch.; MRCP (UK) 1977. (Manchester) Socs: BMA. Prev: Ho. Phys. Manch. Roy. Infirm.; SHO (Paediat.) Booth Hall Childr. Hosp. Manch.; SHO (Med.) Univ. Hosp. S. Manch.

GARSON, Paul Anthony Richard Peel Health Centre, Market St., Bury BL9 0BT Tel: 0161 763 7790 Fax: 0161 761 3077 — MRCS

Eng. LRCP Lond. 1974; DObst RCOG 1976. Chairm. NW Region Med. Audit Advis. Gps.

GARSON, Robert Arnold 17 Paddock, Shibden, Halifax HX3 7TA — MRCS Eng. LRCP Lond. 1949; FRCPath 1963. Socs: Leeds M-C Soc. & Brit. Soc. Cytol. Prev: Cons. Pathol. Roy. Halifax Infirm.; Capt. IMS; Army Path. Serv. India Command.

GARSON, Sonia Moat House, Hinstock, Market Drayton TF9 2TL — MB BS 1994 Lond.

GARSON, William Philip (retired) Greenways, Glaziers Lane, Normandy, Guildford GU3 2DQ — MB BS 1965 Lond.; MRCS Eng. LRCP Lond. 1967; DCH Eng. 1969; DObst RCOG 1967. Prev: Med. Regist. Hackney Hosp. Lond.

GARSTANG, Andrew Richard Lytham Road, Blackpool FY5 5AX Tel: 01253 345086; White Lodge, Linden Close, Thornton, Thornton-Cleveleys FY5 2RA Tel: 01253 859631 — MB BS 1993 Lond.; BSc (Hons.) Lond. 1989; MRCGP 1998. (King's Coll. Med. & Dent. Lond.) GP Princip., St Mary's Surg., 467 Lytham Rd, Blackpool. Prev: SHO Rotat. (Geriat. & Med.) Vict. Hosp. Blackpool NHS Trust; Trainee GP/SHO Vict. Hosp. Blackpool NHS Trust VTS.

GARSTANG, Charles Neville (retired) The Surgery, 5A Brookfield Road, Hucclecote, Gloucester GL3 3HB Tel: 01452 617295 Fax: 01452 372236 — MB BChir 1964 Camb.; MA, MB Camb. 1964, BChir 1963; MRCGP 1974; DCH Eng. 1965; DObst RCOG 1966.

GARSTANG, James Simon Hangersley Hill, Hangersley, Ringwood BH24 3JP Email: simon_garstang@msn.com — MB ChB Bristol 1995. (Bristol) SHO (Anaesth.), Soton. Gen. Hosp. Prev: SHO Paediat. Basingstoke; Ho. Off. Surg. Salisbury; Ho. Off. Med. Salisbury.

GARSTANG, Joanna Jane, Capt. RAMC Dept of Paediatrics, St Mary's Hospital, Portsmouth — MB ChB 1995 Bristol; DCH. (Bristol) SHO Paediat., St Mary's Hosp. Portsmouth. Prev: Med. Off. Med. Reception Station Colchester; Ho. Off. Med. Defence Med. Unit Bristol Roy. Infirm.; SHO (Paediat.) Qu. Mary's Hosp. Sidcup.

GARSTANG, Jonathan Edward Bond End Farm, Bond End Lane, Upton St Leonards, Gloucester GL4 8ED Tel: 01452 371916 — MB BS 1993 Lond.

GARSTIN, Mr William Ian Hamilton Antrim Area Hospital, 45 Bosh Road, Antrim BT41 2RL Tel: 01849 424123 Fax: 01849 424293; 105 Glenarm Road, Larne BT40 1DY Tel: 01574 260495 Fax: 01574 260495 — MB BCh BAO 1979 Belf.; MD Belf. 1987, MB BCh BAO 1979; FRCS Ed. 1983.

GARSTON, Brian (retired) 38 Delamere Road, Ainsdale, Southport PR8 2RG Email: bgarstonmb@btinternet.com — MB ChB 1961 Liverp. Prev: GP S.port.

GARSTON, Helen Noreen 38 Delamere Road, Southport PR8 2RG; 11 Third Avenue, Selly Park, Birmingham B29 7EX — MB ChB 1989 Liverp.; FRCA Lond 1998.

GARSTON, Mr Joseph Bernard 16 St John Street, Deansgate, Manchester M3 4DF Tel: 0161 832 9954; Lancaster House, 174 Chamber Road, Oldham OL8 4BU Tel: 0161 652 1227 — MB BS 1960 Durh.; FRCS Eng. 1968; DO Eng. 1964. Cons. Ophth. Surg. Roy. Oldham Hosp. Socs: Fell. Roy. Soc. Ophth. Surgs.; BMA (Ophth. Gp. Comm.). Prev: Sen. Regist. United Sheff. Hosps.; Regist. Soton. Eye Hosp.; Ho. Surg. Roy. Vict. Infirm. Newc.

GARTELL, Mr Paul Chantrey Royal Hampshire County Hospital, Romsey Road, Winchester SO22 5DG Tel: 01962 824830 Fax: 01962 824640; Highcroft, Fairfield Road, Shawford, Winchester SO21 2DA Tel: 01962 713176 Fax: 01962 715448 — MB BS 1972 Lond.; MS Soton. 1988; FRCS Eng. 1979; MRCS Eng. LRCP Lond. 1972; DA Eng. 1975. Cons. Surg. Roy. Hants. Co. Hosp. Winchester. Socs: Mem. of Assn. of Surg.s GB & I; Mem. of Assn. of Upper GI Surg.s; Mem. of RSM.

GARTH, Mr Richard John Nicholas Consulting Rooms:, 8 Lyndhurst Road, Exeter EX2 4PA Tel: 01392 411611; Whelmstone Barton, Coleford, Crediton EX17 5DG — MB ChB 1980 Manch.; FRCS (Otol) 1991; FRCS 1987 Glas. (Manch.) Cons. ENT Surg. Roy. Devon & Exeter Hosp. (Wonford). Prev: Cons. Adviser (Otolayngol.) to MDG (N); Sen. Regist. Head & Neck Unit Roy. Marsden Hosp. Lond.; Med. Off. HM Submarines.

GARTHWAITE, Elizabeth Thorn Tree Garth, Gilling East, York YO62 4HS — MB BS 1977 Lond.; MRCS Eng. LRCP Lond. 1977. (Westm.)

GARTHWAITE, Elizabeth Anne Broad Cut Farm, Denby Dale Road, Calder Grove, Wakefield WF4 3AB — MB ChB 1997 Leeds.

GARTHWAITE, Mark Edward Kaye Flat 2/12, 21 Queensborough Gardnes, Glasgow G12 9PP — MB ChB 1986 Glas.

GARTHWAITE, Sarah Elizabeth St. James Medical Centre, 11 Carlton Road, Tunbridge Wells TN1 2JS Tel: 01892 541634; Matfield Oast, Chestnut Lane, Matfield, Tonbridge TN12 7JJ Tel: 01892 722264 Fax: 01892 724022 Email: jands.garthwaite@virgin.net — MB BS 1985 Lond. (Middlx. Hosp.)

GARTNER, Clive Paul Kingsway Medical Centre, Kingsway, Billingham TS23 2LS Tel: 01642 553738 Fax: 01642 533011; 58 Junction Road, Norton, Stockton-on-Tees TS20 1PW — MRCS Eng. LRCP Lond. 1971; Dip. Pract. Dermat. Wales 1991. Prev: Regist. (Med.) ScarBoro. Hosp.; Regist. (Paediat.) Wolverhampton Gp. Hosps.

GARTON, Fiona Mary Queens Road Medical Group, 6 Queens Road, Aberdeen AB15 4NU Tel: 01224 641560 Fax: 01224 642773 — MB ChB 1979 Aberd.; MF Hom 1998; MRCGP 1983; DRCOG 1982. (Aberdeen) p/t Sen. Clin. Tutor (Gen. Pract.) Aberd. Univ.; NHS Homeopathic Practitioner; Mem.s Represen. for N. Scotl. for Fac. of Homaopathy.

GARTON, Frederick Paul Anthony (retired) Bleach Green Farm, Wingfield, Diss IP21 5RG Tel: 01379 586609 — MB BS 1950 Lond.; MRCS Eng. LRCP Lond. 1947; MFOM RCP Lond. 1979; DIH Eng. 1956. Prev: Resid. Fell. Inst. Occupat. Health Lond. Sch. Hyg.

GARTON, Mark James Perth Royal Infirmary, Perth PH1 1NX Tel: 01382 660111; Terrace House, Perth Road, Stanley, Perth PH1 4NF Email: charlie.garton@btinternet.com — MB BS 1985 Lond.; FRCP (Edin) 2001; MSc Aberd. 1993, MD 1996; MRCP (UK) 1988. (St. Geo. Hosp. Med. Sch.) Cons. Gen. Med. & Rheum. Perth Roy. Infirm. Prev: Sen. Regist. (Gen. Med. & Rheum.) City Hosp. Aberd.; Regist. (Gen. Med.) Aberd. Roy. Infirm.; SHO (Gen. Med.) Hope Hosp. Salford.

GARTRY, Mr David Stanley Moorfields Eye Hospital, City Road, London EC1V 2PD Tel: 020 7253 3411 Fax: 020 7253 4696; 149 Harley Street, London W1G 6DE Tel: 020 7486 3112 Fax: 020 7935 5429 Email: david@gartry.demon.co.uk — MB BS 1984 Lond.; BSc (Hons.) Glas. 1978; MD Lond. 1995; FRCS Eng. 1988; FRCOphth. 1988; DO RCS Eng. 1988; MD (London) 1995. (Univ. Coll. Lond.) Cons. Ophth. Surg. (Corneal, Cataract & Refractive Surg.) Moorfields Eye Hosp. Lond.; Past Pres., The Brit. Soc. for refractive Surg.; Examr., The Roy. Coll. of Ophth.s; Examr., The Brit. Coll. of Optometrists. Socs: Fell. Roy. Coll. Ophth.; Roy. Inst. GB; Fell. Amer. Acad. Ophth. Prev: Sen. Regist. (Ophth.), Sen. Resid. & Corneal Fell. Moorfields Eye Hosp. Lond.; Research Fell. (Ophth.) St. Thos. Hosp. & Inst. Ophth. Lond.; Iris Fund Research Fell.

GARTSIDE, John Michael Bowns Green Cottage, Dark Lane, Milford, Derby DE56 0TH — MB BS 1967 Lond.; MA Camb. 1960; FRCP Lond. 1987; MRCP (U.K.) 1971. (Middlx) Cons. Dermat. Derby Roy. Infirm. Prev: Sen. Regist. (Dermat.) Gen. Hosp. Nottm.; Ho. Phys. Middlx. Hosp.; Ho. Surg. Centr. Middlx. Hosp.

GARTSIDE, Malcolm Wall 3 Lower House Drive, Lostock, Bolton BL6 4JX Tel: 01204 42799 — MB ChB 1965 Liverp.; FRCOG 1984, M 1972. Cons. (O & G) Bolton Gp. Hosps.

GARTSIDE, Timothy Westgate Medical Centre, Braddon Close, Morecambe LA4 4UZ Tel: 01524 832888 Fax: 01524 832722; Middlebarn, 6 Manor Lane, Slyne, Lancaster LA2 6RD Tel: 01524 822784 — MB ChB Manch. 1983; BSc Med. Sc. (Hons.) St. And. 1980.

GARUD, Suresh Padmanabh X-Ray Department, Horton General Hospital, 81a Oxford Road, Banbury OX16 9AL — MB BS 1974 Poona.

GARVAN, Mr Cornelius John Dept. Of Neurosurgery, Oldchurch Hospital, Romford RM7 0BE Tel: 01708 708277 Fax: 01708 732184 — MB BCh BAO 1968 NUI; FRCSI 1973; T(S) 1979. (University Coll Dublin) Cons. Neurosurg. Regional Centre Neurosurg. & Neurol. OldCh. Hosp. Romford. Socs: Roy. Soc. Med. Prev: Sen. Regist. (Neurosurg.) Midl. Centre for Neurosurg. & Smethwick & Qu. Eliz. Hosp. Birm.

GARVEY, Angela Josepha Professional Address, Altnagelvin, Glenshane Road, Londonderry BT47 6SB Tel: 02871 345171 — MB BCh BAO 1977 Belf.; FRCP Ed. 1995; MRCP (UK) 1981; FRCP 2000 London. Cons. In Palliat. Med. Altnagelvin NHS Trust, Lond.derry. Prev: Cons. In Palliat. Med. NI Hosace.

GARVEY, Colin Neil Palatine Group Practice, Murray's Road, Douglas IM2 3TD Tel: 01624 623931 Fax: 01624 611712 — MB

BS 1991 Lond.; DFFP 1997; DCH 1996. (St. Geo. Hosp. Med. Sch.) GP Palatine Gp. Pract., Douglas, I. of Man. Socs: Isle of Man Med. Soc. Prev: GP Regist. Sandy La. Surg. Leyland, Lancs.; GP Regist. Tarleton Health Centre, Tarleton, Lancs.; SHO (O & G) Ormskirk Hosp. Lancs.

GARVEY, Conall John (Surgery), 35 Rodney St., Liverpool L1 9EN Tel: 0151 708 7410 Fax: 0151 708 6950; Tel: 0151 608 5412 — MB BCh BAO 1978 NUI; 2000 DBE; FRCR 1983. Cons. Radiol. Roy. Liverp. Univ. Hosp.; Hon. Clin. Lect. (Radiodiag.) Univ. of Liverp.; Clin. Dir. (Radiol.) Roy. Liverp. Univ. Hosp.; Chirm. Dist. Med. Advis. Com. Of Liverp. HA; Nat. Clin. Lead for Radiol., Cancer Servs. Collaborative. Socs: RSNA; BMA; MPS. Prev: Sen. Regist. N.wick Pk. Hosp. Harrow.; Clin. Director 1995-2001; Chairm. Dist. 1999-2001.

GARVEY, Gerard Nicholas Graham Road Surgery, 22 Graham Road, Weston Super Mare BS23 1YA Tel: 01934 62811 Fax: 01934 645842 — MB ChB 1986 Bristol; MRCGP 1993; DRCOG 1991. (Bristol)

GARVEY, James Castlederg Surgery, 13A Lower Strabane Road, Castlederg BT81 7AZ Tel: 028 8167 1211 Fax: 028 8167 9700; Brackenbridge, Castlederg — MB BCh BAO 1979 Belf.; MRCGP 1983.

GARVEY, Jonathan Charles Beauchamp House Surgery, 37 Baddow Road, Chelmsford CM2 0DB Tel: 01245 262255 Fax: 01245 262256 — MB BChir 1977 Camb.; MA Camb. 1977; MRCS Eng. LRCP Lond. 1976.

GARVEY, Mary Teresa The Haven, Main St., Edingley, Newark NG22 8BG — MB ChB 1981 Leeds. SHO (Microbiol.) Nottm. Hosps. Prev: Regist. (Psychiat.) Sheff. HA.

GARVEY, Niall 12 The Braes, Lochgelly KY5 9QH — MB ChB 1995 Ed.

GARVEY, Ronan James Patric 3 Shirley Drive, Grappenhall, Warrington WA4 2PA — MB BCh BAO 1972 NUI; BSc NUI 1974, MB BCh BAO 1972; MRCPath 1980. (Galway) Cons. (Microbiol.) Warrington Dist. Gen. Hosp. Prev: Sen. Regist. (Microbiol.) Leicester Roy. Infirm.; Intern & SHO (Microbiol.) Regional Hosp. Galway.

GARVEY, Timothy Patrick Noel Drugs Northwest, Kenyon House, Prestwich Hospital, Bury New Road, Manchester M25 3BL Tel: 0161 772 3538 Fax: 0161 772 3595 — MB ChB 1978 Manch.; MRCPsych 1982; LLB (Hons) 1993. (Manchester) Cons. Drug Depends. Drugs N.W. Manch. Prev: Cons. Drug Depends. S. Sefton HA; Sen. Regist. Camb. HA; Regist. Centr. Birm. HA.

GARVIE, Alison Catherine Ethel Allison and Partners, Maryhill Health Centre, 41 Shawpark Street, Glasgow G20 9DR Tel: 0141 531 8840 Fax: 0141 531 8848 — MB ChB 1978 Glas.; FRCGP 2001; MRCGP 1982; DRCOG 1980. Gen. Practitioner; Assoc. Adviser GP Retainer Scheme (W. Scotl.) DPGME 1 Horselethiu Rd. Glas. G12. Socs: Bearsden & Milngavie Med. Soc.; BMA; Full Mem. Brit. Med. Acupunc. Soc.

GARVIE, Dorothy Claire Childrens Hospital Lewisham, Lewisham High St., London SE13 6LH Tel: 020 8690 4311; 86 Lee Road, Blackheath, London SE3 9DE Tel: 020 8318 5899 — MB ChB 1980 Sheff.; MRCP (UK) 1984. Sen. Lect. (Neonat. & Paediat.) UMDS Guy's & St. Thos. Hosp. Lond.; Hon. Cons. Paediat. Lewisham Hosp. Prev: Regist. (Paediat.), Lect (Neonat. Paediat.) & Research Regist. (Paediat.) St. Thos. Hosp. Lond.

GARVIE, Douglas Gow, OBE (retired) 5 Repton Drive, Newcastle ST5 3JF Tel: 01782 619795 Fax: 01782 629929 — MB ChB 1956 Glas.; MB ChB (Commend.) Glas. 1956; FRCGP 1974, M 1964. Prev: Occupat. Phys. N. Staffs. HA.

GARVIE, James MacKenzie (retired) 31 Skip Lane, Walsall WS5 3LL Tel: 0121 357 2160 — BM BCh 1943 Oxf.; MA Oxf. 1945, BM BCh 1943; FRCP Lond. 1975, M 1949; DCH Eng. 1949. Prev: Cons. Paediatr. St. Margts. Hosp. Birm. & Walsall & W. Bromwich Hosp.

GARVIE, Stephen James Valleyfield Health Centre, Chapel Street, High Valleyfield, Dunfermline KY12 8SJ Tel: 01383 880511 Fax: 01383 881848 — MB ChB 1984 Ed.

GARVIN, Catherine Claire Armagh Health Centre, Dobbin Lane, Armagh BT61 7QG Tel: 028 3752 3165 Fax: 028 3752 2319 — MB BCh BAO 1988 Belf.; MRCGP 1992; DRCOG 1991. Prev: SHO (Paediat., Med. & O & G) Craigavon Area Hosp. N. Irel.

GARVIN, James Stephen Marshall The Garvin Surgery, Barrack St, Coalisland BT71 4LS Tel: 028 8775 3575 Fax: 028 8772 7544 — MB BCh BAO 1976 Dub.; DRCOG 1978.

GARVIN, John Stephen (retired) Ring Hill, 24 Mullaghbane Road, Armagh BT61 9HW Tel: 028 3752 3004 — MB BCh BAO 1959 Belf.; FRCGP 1983, M 1968; DCH RCPS Glas. 1967; DObst RCOG 1962.

GARWAY-HEATH, David Fitzgerald Garway 7 Islington Park Mews, Islington Park St., Islington, London N1 1QL — MB BS 1987 Lond.; BSc (Hons.) Lond. 1984; FRCOphth 1992. (UMDS (St. Thomas' Hospital London)) Specialist Regist. (Ophth.) N. Thames Region; Glaucoma Fell. Moorfields Eye Hosp. Prev: Research Fell. Glaucoma Unit Moorfields Eye Hosp. Lond.

GARWOOD, Alfred The Old Hall Surgery, 237 Hall Lane, Chingford, London E4 8HX Tel: 020 8524 3410 Fax: 020 8524 6424; 74 Monkhams Avenue, Woodford Green IG8 0ET Tel: 020 8504 0216 — MB ChB 1977 Sheff.; MRCS Eng. LRCP Lond. 1977. GP Trainer Chingford; Clin. Tutor Roy. Free Hosp. Med. Sch. Lond.; Clin. Asst. (Psychother.) Claybury Hosp. Essex. Socs: Soc. Clin. Psychiat.

GARWOOD, David John 7 High Street, Withernwick, Hull HU11 4RP — MB BS 1987 Lond.; MRCGP 1991; DRCOG 1991; DCH RCP Lond. 1989.

GARWOOD, Elizabeth Jane Croftfoot Road Surgery, 30 Croftfoot Road, Glasgow G44 5JT Tel: 0141 634 0431 Fax: 0131 633 5284; 26 Essex Drive, Glasgow G14 9NA Tel: 0141 959 1046 — MB ChB 1971 Leeds; MRCOG 1977. (Leeds) Socs: BMA & Med. Soc. Study VD. Prev: Regist. (O & G) Stobhill Hosp. Glas.; Sen. Regist. (Sexually Transm. Dis.) Roy. Infirm. Glas.

GARWOOD, Norman (retired) Drayton, 17 Raddenstile Lane, Exmouth EX8 2JL Tel: 01395 265396 — MRCS Eng. LRCP Lond. 1947; DA Eng. 1954. Prev: Regist. (Anaesth.) Co. Hosp. York & S.end Gen. Hosp.

GARWOOD, Peter Jacques (retired) Church Barn, Bale Road, Sharrington, Melton Constable NR24 2PF Tel: 01263 860700 — MB ChB 1958 Ed. Prev: Ho. Phys. Roy. Infirm. Edin.

GARWOOD, Philip John Department Radiology, Blackburn Royal Infirmary, Blackburn; Rookwood, Colne Road, Trawden, Colne BB8 8NU — MB ChB 1977 Bristol; FRCR 1985. Cons. Radiol. Blackburn Roy. Infirm. Prev: Sen. Regist. (Radiol.) Manch.

GARWOOD, Richard Edmund 25 St James Close, Warden, Sheerness ME12 4NW — MB BS 1965 Lond. Socs: Fell. Roy. Soc. Med.; BMA; Bristol Medico-Legal Soc. Prev: Med. Off. HM Prison Bristol.; Managing Med. Off. HM Prison Swaleside; Clin. Asst. (Venereol.) Roy. Sussex Co. Hosp. Brighton.

GASCOIGNE, Alistair Donald 1 Stoneycroft E., Newcastle upon Tyne NE12 6YU Tel: 0191 268 8878; Royal Victoria Infirmary, Victoria Road, Newcastle upon Tyne NE1 4LP — MB BS 1984 Newc.; FRCP 2000 Lond.; BSc (Hons.) Physiol. Newc. 1979; MRCP (UK) 1990. Cons. Phys. (Intens. Care & Respirat. Med.) Roy. Vict. Infirm. Newc. Socs: Brit. Thorac. Soc.; Intens. Care Soc. Prev: Sen. Regist. (Intens. Ther. & Gen. Med.) Newc.; Research Regist. (Cardiopulm. Transpl.) Freeman Hosp. Newc. u. Tyne.

GASCOIGNE, Donald (retired) 9 Balroy Court, Forest Hall, Newcastle upon Tyne NE12 9AW Tel: 0191 266 5813 Email: donaldgascoigne@tinyworld.co.uk — MB BS Durh. 1951. Chairm. N. Newc. upon Tyne Mem. Med. Adviser Comm. Health Call (Newc. upon Tyne). Prev: Clin. Tutor in Family Med. Univ. Newc-upon-Tyne.

GASH, Amanda Jane 60 Guisborough Road, Great Ayton, Middlesbrough TS9 6AD — MB BCh 1979 Wales.

***GASH, Andrew John** Rhos Farm, Pen Mon, Beaumaris LL58 8RN — MB BCh 1986 Wales.

GASH, Stephen Raymond Salgar House, Hamsterley, Bishop Auckland DL13 3PX Tel: 01388 488251 — MB BCh 1978 Wales; MRCGP 1984; DCH Eng. 1981; DRCOG 1980. Med. Advisor Benefits Agency.

GASIM, Ahmed Crownhill Surgery, 103 Crownhill Road, Plymouth PL5 3BN Tel: 01752 771713 — MB BS 1977 Khartoum; MB BS 1977 Khartoum.

GASIOROWSKI, Edward Robert 25 Cumberland Road, Brooklands, Sale M33 3EW — MB ChB 1993 Manch.

GASK, John 5 Old School House, Garrett St., Cawsand, Torpoint PL10 1PD Tel: 01752 822136 — BM BCh 1947 Oxf.; LMSSA Lond. 1940. (St. Bart.)

GASK, Linda Guild Academic Centre, Royal Preston Hospital, Sharoe Green Lane, Preston PR2 9HT Tel: 01772 710072 Fax: 01772 710772; 4 Cliffe Cottages, Roper lane, Thurgoland, Sheffield

S35 8AA Email: linda.gask@man.ac.uk — MB ChB 1979 Ed.; PhD Manch. 1992, MSc 1984; FRCPsych 1996, M 1984. (Ed.) (Community Psychiat.)/ reader Univ. Manch. & Hons. Cons. Psychiat. Guild Community Healthcare Trust; Jt. appointment with Nat. Primary cave research and Developm. centre, univ Manch. Prev: Sen. Research Fell. Univ. Sheff. & Hon. Cons. Psychiat. Barnsley Dist.HA.

GASKARTH, Matthew Thomas Gerrard 2 Redwing Lane, Stockton-on-Tees TS20 1LL Email: mattgaskarth@hotmail.com — MB BChir 1994 Camb.; BA 1991; FRCS (Eng) 1998. (Cambridge) Specialist Regist. in Diagnostic Radiol., Addenbrooke's Hosp, Camb. Prev: SHO (Transpl. Surg.) Addenbrooke's Hosp.; SHO (Paediat. Urol.) Gt. Ormond St. Hosp.

GASKELL, Mr Alan 10 Cairn Crescent, Alloway, Ayr KA7 4DX Tel: 01292 445260 — MB ChB 1982 Ed.; FRCS Ed. 1987; FRCOphth 1989.

GASKELL, David Edward Holmwood Drummond Terrace, Crieff PH7 4AN — MB ChB 1988 Ed.; MRCGP 1993.

GASKELL, David Frederick, MBE Lomond and Argyll PC NHS Trust, Trust Headquarters, Aros, Lochgilphead PA31 8LB Tel: 01546 606600 Email: david.gaskell@aandb.scot.nhs.uk; Brookfield, Inverneill, Ardrishaig, Lochgilphead PA30 8ES Tel: 01546 603885 — MB ChB 1976 Ed.; MPhil Ed. 1988, BSc (Med. Sci.) 1973; MRCPsych 1985; MRCGP 1983. Lead Clinician in R&D Lomond and Argyll P.C. NHS Trust HQ. Prev: Cons. Psychaitrist Lomond and Argyll PC NHS Trust Lochgilphead.

GASKELL, Mary Valerie Marie Stopes, Whitfield St., London W1 Tel: 020 7388 0662; 75 St. Leonards Road, Chesham Bois, Amersham HP6 6DR Tel: 01494 727577 — MB ChB 1964 Liverp.; DPM Eng. 1968. (Liverp.) Sessional Med. Off. Pregn. Advice Serv. Lond. Socs: Affil. RCPsych. Prev: SHO (Neurol.) & Ho. Surg. Walton Hosp. Liverp.; Ho. Phys. Sefton Gen. Hosp. Liverp.

GASKELL, Peter Gordon (retired) 17 The Green, Pencaitland, Tranent EH34 5HE Tel: 01875 340916 — MB ChB 1949 Glas.; MD Glas. 1967,; FRCGP 1976.

GASKELL, Philip Aldroyd Eyre Medical Practice, 31 Eyre Crescent, Edinburgh EH3 5EU Tel: 0131 556 8842 Fax: 0131 557 2177; 4 West Savile Road, Edinburgh EH16 5NG Tel: 0131 667 4725 — MB ChB 1976 Ed.; BSc (Med. Sci.) Ed. 1973; MRCGP 1981. (Ed.) Prev: Hosp. Pract. Young Disabled Unit Liberton Hosp. Edin.; Regist. (A & E) Roy. Infirm. Edin.; Med. Dir. E. & Mid Lothian NHS Trust Edenhall Hosp. Musselburgh.

GASKELL, Ronald Keith Ridge Lea Hospital, Quernmore Road, Lancaster LA1 3JT Tel: 01524 586213 — MB ChB 1978 Ed.; MRCPsych 1985. Cons. Psychiat. Ridge Lea Hosp. Lancaster.

GASKELL, Wendy Gillian 109 Crocus Way, Springfield, Chelmsford CM1 6XH — MB BS 1984 Lond.

GASKIN, Gillian Renal Section, Department of Medicine, Imperial College School of Medicine, The Hammersmith Hospital, London W12 0NN Tel: 020 8383 3152 Fax: 020 8746 2410 — MB BChir 1983 Camb.; PhD Lond. 1996; MA Camb. 1986, BA 1981; MRCP (UK) 1986. (Univ. Camb.) Sen. Lect. & Hon. Cons. Renal Med. Imperial Coll. Sch. Med. & Hammersmith Hosp. Lond. Prev: Sen. Regist. Hammersmith Hosp. Lond. MRC Train. Fell. RPMS Lond.; Regist. (Renal) Hammersmith Hosp. Lond.

GASKIN, Mark Andrew The Blofield Surgery, Plantation Road, Blofield, Norwich NR13 4PL Tel: 01603 712337 Fax: 01603 712899 — MB BCh 1985 Wales; DRCOG 1990; DCH RCP Lond. 1989.

GASKIN, Pauline Mary Daisy Hill Hospital, 6 Hospital Road, Newry BT35 8DR Tel: 01693 65511 Fax: 01693 65226; The Close, 60 Derrymore Road, Bessbrook, Newry BT35 7DN Tel: 01693 838443 — LRCPI & LM, LRSCI & LM 1978; LRCPI & LM, LRCSI & LM 1978; MRCOG 1991. Assoc. Specialist (O & G) Daisy Hill Hosp. Newry. Socs: Ulster Obst. Gyn. Soc.; (Comm.) Ulster Gyn. Urol. Soc.

GASPAR, Arul Savio 96 Olton Boulevard E., Acocks Green, Birmingham B27 7ND — MB ChB 1992 Dundee; MRCGP 1997.

GASPAR, Duraiswami 71 Cotton Lane, Moseley, Birmingham B13 9SE — MB BS 1958 Madras; MD (Gen. Med.) Madras 1963; FRCP Eng. 1995; MRCP (UK) 1970; FRCPsych 1985, M 1972; DPM Eng. 1970. (Stanley Med. Coll. Madras) Postgrad. Clin. Tutor Psychogeriat. Univ. Birm.; Cons. Psychiat. N. Birm. Ment. Health Trust. Prev: Sen. Regist. (Psychiat.) United Birm. Hosps.; Regist. (Psychiat.) Moorhaven Hosp. Ivybridge.

GASPAR, Hubert Babu Raj 6A Milverton Street, London SE11 4AP — MB BS 1989 Lond.

GASPAR, Katerina 96 Olton Boulevard E., Acocks Green, Birmingham B27 7ND — BM 1992 Soton.; MRCGP 1996.

GASPAR, Lourdes Selvan 71 Cotton Lane, Birmingham B13 9SE — MB ChB 1989 Dundee.

GASPAR, Margaret V (retired) — MBBS. Full Time Gen. Practitioner in Uk for 28 years. Prev: 1972-1981 worked Clin. Asst., Accid. & Emerg. Dept., Sellyoak Hosp., Birm.

GASPER, Terence Malcolm Tel: 01789 269386 Fax: 01789 298742; Wasen Hill, Evesham Road, Binton, Stratford-upon-Avon CV37 9UD — MB BS 1975 Lond.; Dip Sports Med 2000; MRCP (UK) 1978; DRCOG 1979. (King's Coll. Hosp.) Princip. Gen. Pract.; Clin. Asst. Rheum. Warwick Hosp. Socs: Brit. Assn. Sports Med. Prev: Clin. Asst. (Gastroenterol. & Chest Med.) Warwick Hosp.

GASSER, Alison Judith Harrogate District Hospital, Lancaster Park Road, Harrogate HG2 7SX Tel: 01423 885959; 86 Glebe Field Drive, Wetherby LS22 6WG — MB ChB 1983 Leeds; FRCA 1988; DA (UK) 1986. (Leeds University) Cons. Anaesth. Harrogate Health Care NHS Trust Harrogate. Socs: BMA; Assn. Anaesth.; Roy. Coll. Anaesth. Prev: Sen. Regist. (Anaesth.) W. Midl.; Research Fell. (Anaesth.) Manch. Roy. Infirm.; SHO Post Fell. (Anaesth.) Killingbeck Hosp. Leeds.

GASSON, George Bernard 67 Vernon Road, Edgbaston, Birmingham B16 9SQ — MA Camb. 1956, BA 1952, MB BChir 1956; MRCS Eng. LRCP Lond. 1956; AFOM RCP Lond. 1979; DCH Eng. 1961; DPH Lond. 1961; DObst RCOG 1959. (Camb. & Lond. Hosp.) Socs: Midl. Dermat. Soc.; Midl. Rheumat. Soc.; Fell. Roy. Soc. Med. Prev: Regist. (Cardiac & Med. Outpats.) & Ho. Phys. & Receiv. Room Off. Lond. Hosp.; Ho. Phys. Addenbrooke's Hosp. Camb.

GASSON, Jeremy Nicholas 1 Chestnut Street, Rhydyfelin, Pontypridd CF37 5NG — MB ChB 1989 Leic. Regist. (O & G) Hartlepool Gen. Hosp. Prev: Regist. (O & G) S. Cleveland Hosp. Middlesbrough.; SHO (O & G) City Hosp. Nottm.

GASSON, Patricia Marjorie 3 The Avenue, Crossgates, Leeds LS15 8JN — MB ChB 1983 Glas.

GASTER, Basil Sidney Carrington (retired) 33 Farmadine House, Saffron Walden CB11 3HS — MB BChir 1937 Camb.; MRCGP 1953. Prev: Ho. Surg. Vict. Hosp. Childr.

GASTER, Rebecca Anne 9 High Park Road, Kew, Richmond TW9 4BL Tel: 020 8878 1331 — BM 1995 Soton.

GASTON, Andrew Cecil Robert Ekwendi Hospital, P.O. Box 19, Ekwendeni, Malawi, Malawi Email: ccaphealth@malawi.net; 26 Frys Road, Ballymena BT43 7EW — MB ChB 1990 Bristol; MRCGP 1995; DTM & H. RCP Lond. 1997. (Univ. Bristol) Med. Off. Mission Hosp. Malawi Employed by Ch. of Scotl. Prev: Trainee GP Plymouth VTS.

GASTON, Christine Mary Cornford House Surgery, 364 Cherry Hinton Road, Cambridge CB1 8BA Tel: 01223 247505 Fax: 01223 568187; 6 Parsonage Court, Whittlesford, Cambridge CB2 4PH Tel: 01223 837554 — BM BCh 1976 Oxf.; MRCGP 1980; DRCOG 1979. (Oxford)

GASTON, Colin Hill 15 Woodville Road, Harborne, Birmingham B17 9AS — MB ChB 1980 Birm.; FRCP 1988; LMCC 1983; DRCOG 1982; DCH RCP Lond. 1982. Paediat. Dr. Everett Chalmers Hosp., Frederilton, Canada; Paediat. Resid. Isaac Walton Childr. Hosp. Halifax Canada. Prev: Sen. Paediat. Resid., Lannipeg Childr. Hosp., Canada; SHO (Paediat.) Birm. Childr. Hosp.; Ho. Surg. Birm. Accid. Hosp.

GASTON, Hannah 68 Newlands Avenue, Southampton SO15 5ES Tel: 02380 777924 — MB BS 1972 Lond.; DM Soton 1986; FRCS Eng. 1977; MRCS Eng. LRCP Lond. 1972; FCOphth 1988; DO Eng. 1975. (Roy. Free) Assoc. Specialist Soton. Eye Hosp. Socs: BMA; Med. Wom. Federat.; Research Into Spina Bifida & Hydrocephalus. Prev: Sen. Regist. Soton. Eye Hosp.; Lect. (Ophth.) Univ. Soton.; SHO (Ophth.) Soton. Eye Hosp. & Birm. & Midl. Eye Hosp.

GASTON, Jacqueline Carol 97 Holland Road, Maidstone ME14 1UN Tel: 01622 754874 — MB BS 1989 Lond.; BSc 1986 Lond.; MRCP (UK) 1992; MRCGP 1996. (St. Georges) p/t GP St Lukes Sugery, Maidstone, Kent. Prev: Regist. (ITU) St. Geo. Hosp. Lond.; Regist. (Gen. Med.) P.ss Roy. Hosp. Haywards Heath; SHO (Cardiol.) St. Geo. Hosp. Lond.

GASTON, Professor John Stanley Hill University of Cambridge, School of Clinical Medicine, Box 157, Level 5 Addenbrooke's

Hospital, Hills Road, Cambridge CB2 2QQ Tel: 01223 330161 Fax: 01223 330160 Email: jshg2@medschl.cam.ac.uk; 6 Parsonage Court, Whittlesford, Cambridge CB2 4PH Tel: 01223 837554 — BM BCh 1976 Oxf.; PhD Bristol 1983; MA 1973; BM BCh 1975; FRCP Lond. 1995; MRCP (UK) 1979. (Oxf.) Prof. Rheum. Univ. Camb. Socs: Brit. Soc. Rheum.; Brit. Soc. Immunol.; Amer. Coll. of Rheum. Prev: Prof. Experim. Rheum. Univ. Birm.; Wellcome Sen. Research Fell. & Hon. Cons. Rheum. Univ. Birm.; Research Fell. Stanford Univ. Sch. Med. Calif., USA.

GASTON, Joseph Tate 122 Ballinlea Road, Armoy, Ballymoney BT53 8TY Tel: 012657 51266 — MB BCh BAO 1955 Dub.

GASTON, Mr Paul 2 Quarry High Street, Headington, Oxford OX3 8JT — MB ChB 1993 Ed.; FRCS Ed 1997. Specialist Regist. Orthop. & Trauma Oxf. Deanery. Socs: BOA Assoc. Mem.; BOTA Mem.; BMA Mem.

GASTON, William Donald McIntyre Maine Medical Practice, Old Mill Park, Main Street, Cullybackey, Ballymena BT42 1GP Tel: 028 2588 2222 Fax: 028 2588 3900; Morven, 45 Dunnygarron Road, Cullybackey, Ballymena BT43 5PS Tel: 01266 880340 — MB BCh BAO 1956 Belf.; FRCGP 1982, M 1974. Socs: BMA; Ulster Med. Soc. Prev: Ho. Off. Massereene Hosp. Antrim & Roy. Belf. Hosp. Sick Childr.

GATA DIAZ, Amparo Isabel 247 Southcroft Road, London SW16 6QT — LMS 1994 Granada.

GATAURE, Preminder Singh The Department of Anaesthetics, Princess of Wales Hospital, Coity Road, Bridgend CF31 1RQ Tel: 01656 752361; 17 Homeway Road, Leicester LE5 5RH — MB BCh 1984 Wales; FRCA 1991; FFA RCS Long. 1988. Cons. Anaesth. & Intens. Care P.ss of Wales Hosp. Bridgend. Prev: Sen. Regist. (Anaesth.) Welsh Nat. Sch. Med. Univ. Hosp. of Wales; SHO (Anaesth.) Roy. Gwent Hosp. Newport.

GATE, Barbara Ashwell House, Bloxham, Banbury OX15 4PT Tel: 01295 720356; Ashwell Cottage, Stonehill, Bloxham, Banbury OX15 4PT — MB ChB 1949 Sheff.; MRCS Eng. LRCP Lond. 1949; DCH Eng. 1952. (Sheff.)

GATE, Howard Barton Strathpeffer Medical Practice, The Surgery, Strathpeffer IV14 9BA Tel: 01997 421455 Fax: 01997 421172; Strathview, Strathpeffer IV14 9DX Tel: 01997 421455 — MB ChB 1976 Ed.; BSc (Med. Sci.) Ed. 1973, MB ChB 1976. Med. Asst. Highland Rheum. Unit Ross Memor. Hosp. Dingwall.

GATE, Mr James Malcolm Ashwell Cottage, Stonehill, Bloxham, Banbury OX15 4PT Tel: 01295 720356 — MRCS Eng. LRCP Lond. 1947; FRCS Ed. 1959; FRCOG 1969, M 1953; LLB 1993. (Leeds) Cons. O & G Surg. Banbury & Dist. Gp. Hosps. Prev: Cons. O & G Surg. Banbury & Dist. Gp. Hosps.; Sen. Regist. Jessop Hosp. Wom. Sheff.; Regist. St. Mary's Hosp. Manch.

GATECLIFF, John Richard Rydings Hall Surgery, Church Lane, Brighouse HD6 1AT Tel: 01484 715324 Fax: 01484 400847; 89 Wilson Road, Wyke, Bradford BD12 9HA Tel: 01274 691271 Email: rgatecliff@csi.com — MB BS 1980 Newc. Prev: SHO (Anaesth.) Bradford Roy. Infirm.; Ho. Off. W. Cumbld. Hosp. Whitehaven; Ho. Off. Newc. Gen. Hosp.

GATECLIFF, John Stratton (retired) 68D Pontefract Road, Featherstone, Pontefract WF7 5HG Tel: 01977 792212 — MB ChB 1953 Leeds.

GATECLIFF, Margaret (retired) 68D Pontefract Road, Featherstone, Pontefract WF7 5HG Tel: 01977 791974 — MB ChB 1955 Leeds. Prev: Assoc. Specialist (Dermat.) Pontefract Gen. Infirm.

GATEHOUSE, David Hexham General Hospital, Hexham NE46 1QJ Tel: 01434 606161 Fax: 01434 607920; Viewfield, Cutlers Hall Road, Shotley Bridge, Consett DH8 8RD Tel: 01207 500681 — MB ChB 1968 Birm.; MSc Birm. 1972, MB ChB 1968; FRCS Eng. 1974. Cons. Surg. (Gen. & BrE. Surg.) Hexham Gen. Hosp.; Hon. Lect. Surg. Roy. Vict. Infirm. Newc. Socs: N. Eng. Surg. Soc., W. Midl. Surg. Soc. & Midl. Gastro-Enterol. Soc. Prev: Cons. Surg. Shotley Bridge Hosp.; Sen. Regist. Rotat. (Surg.) Birm.; Regist. (Surg.) Selly Oak Hosp. Birm.

GATELEY, Mr Christopher Alan Royal Gwent Hospital, Newport NP20 2UB Tel: 01633 234234; 6 Craig Yr Haul Drive, Castleton, Cardiff CF3 2SA Tel: 01633 681547 — MB BCh 1983 Wales; FRCS (Gen.) 1995; FRCS Eng. 1988; MCh Wales 1998. Cons. BrE. & Gen. Surg. Roy. Gwent Hosp. Newport. Prev: Lect. & Hon. Sen. Regist. (Surg.) Roy. Preston Hosp. & Univ. Hosp. S. Manch.; Career Regist. (Surg.) E. Glam. Gen. Hosp.

GATELEY, Mr David Robert St George's Healthcare NHS Trust, Blacks Law Road, Tooting, London SW17 0QT Tel: 020 8672 1255 Fax: 020 8672 5304 — MB BS 1984 Lond.; MA Cantab.; FRCS (Plast.). (Cambridge and King's College Hospital) Cons. Plastic & Reconstruc. Surg. St. Geo.'s Hosp. Lond.

GATENBY, Jacquelyn Dunstan Medical Centre, 284 Bury Road, Bolton BL2 6AY Tel: 01204 531557 Fax: 01204 364407 — MB BS 1992 Lond. SHO (Med.) Bolton Roy. Infirm. Prev: Ho. Off. (Med.) Manch. Roy. Infirm.; Ho. Off. (Surg.) Leigh Infirm.

GATENBY, Robin Alix Bronte Gatenby and Lyons, The Surgery, Parkview, Aberchirder, Huntly AB54 7SW Tel: 01466 700213 Fax: 01466 780580 — MB BCh BAO 1977 Dub.; MB BCh Dub. 1977; MRCGP 1984; DObst. RCPI 1980; DCH NUI 1979. GP Aberchirder. Prev: Med. Off. St. Eliz. Hosp. Transkei.

GATER, Richard Andrew Psychiatry Directorate, Rawnsley Building, Manchester Royal Infirmary, Oxford Road, Manchester M13 9WL Tel: 0161 276 5348 Fax: 0161 273 2135 — MB ChB 1980 Manch.; MSc Manch. 1987, MD 1995; MRCPsych 1985. Sen. Lect. (Psychiat.) Univ. of Manch.; Hon. Cons. Psychiat. Centr. Manch. Healthcare NHS Trust.

GATES, Catherine 12 Argyle Crescent, Edinburgh EH15 2QG — MB ChB 1997 Aberd.

GATES, Clare Denise 10 St Elmo Road, London W12 9EA — MB BS 1988 Lond.

GATES, David Tel: 01332 674173 Fax: 01332 280387; 25 Darley Park Road, Darley Abbey, Derby DE22 1DA — BM BS 1975 Nottm.; BMedSci (Hons.) 1973; MRCGP 1981. Tutor (Gen. Pract.) Univ. Nottm.

GATES, John Charles The Health Centre, East Looe, Looe PL13 1HA Tel: 01503 263195 Fax: 01503 265680; Portlooe House, West Looe, Looe PL13 2HZ Tel: 01503 262438 — MB BCh BAO 1957 Belf.

GATES, Laura Jane Aberdeen Royal Infirmary, Foresterhill, Aberdeen AB25 2ZN — MB BS 1990 Lond.

***GATES, Simon** 56 Leigh Road, Prestbury, Macclesfield SK10 4HX — MB ChB 1994 Birm.

GATH, Ann-Mary Gethin (retired) Jasmine Cottage, The Green, Tostock, Bury St Edmunds IP30 9NY — BM BCh 1960 Oxf.; DM Oxf. 1975; FRCPsych 1984, M 1972; DPM Eng. 1968; DCH Eng. 1964. Prev: Prof. Developm. Psychiat. & Hon. Cons. W. Essex HA.

GATH, Anthony Morton Stroud Road Surgery, 102 Stroud Road, Gloucester GL1 5JN Tel: 01452 524506; Flat 8 Oakbank House, Oakbank, Gloucester GL4 0AZ — MB ChB 1978 Birm.; BSc (Physiol.) Birm. 1975, MB ChB 1978; DLO RCS Eng. 1985. (Birm.)

GATH, Charlotte Emily The Old Plume of Feathers, Stubbs Road,, Everdon, Daventry NN11 3BN Tel: 01327 361315 — MB BS 1987 Lond.; MSc (Pub. Health Med.) Lond. 1994; MFPHM RCP (UK) 1996; DRCOG 2000. (University College London) GP Regist., N.ampton Gen. Hosp. Train. Scheme. Socs: Roy. Soc. Med. Prev: SHO (Psychiat.) Roy. Free Hosp. Lond.; Ho. Phys. Univ. Coll. Hosp. Lond.; Ho. Surg. Cheltenham Gen. Hosp.

GATHA, Dhiraj Nanalal Department of Anaesthetics, Heatherwood Hospital, Ascot SL5 8AA; 47 Gainsborough Drive, Blythewood, Ascot SL5 8TA — MB BS 1967 Gujarat; MD (Anaesth.) Gujarat 1970; DA 1970. (B.J. Med. Coll. Ahmedobad & M.P. Shah Med. Coll. Jamnagar) Assoc. Specialist (Anaesth.) Heatherwood Hosp. Ascot.

GATHERCOLE, Mr Nicholas John Macclesfield District General Hospital, Victoria Road, Macclesfield SK10 3BL Tel: 01625 661455 Fax: 01625 511314; Norwood, 253 Blakelow Road, Macclesfield SK11 7EH Tel: 01625 420571 Email: john@gathercole.net — MB BS 1976 Lond.; FRCS Eng. 1982; MRCS Eng. LRCP Lond. 1976; FFAEM 1994. (Charing Cross Hospital) Cons. A & E Macclesfield Gen. Hosp. Chesh.; Cons. A & E Alexandra Hosp., Cheadle,Chesh.; Cons. A & E Regancy Hosp., Macclesfield, Chesh.; Chief Med. Off., Roy. Lond. Assur., Wilmslow, Chesh. Socs: Manch. Medico-legal Soc.

GATHERCOLE, Raymond, Col. late RAMC (retired) Sherwood, Chiltern Hill, Chalfont St Peter, Gerrards Cross SL9 9TH Tel: 01753 880472 Email: ray@zimmer.demon.co.uk — MRCS Eng. LRCP Lond. 1949; DLO Eng. 1961.

GATHERER, Alexander (retired) Bagley Frith, 42 Bagley Wood Road, Kennington, Oxford OX1 5LY Tel: 01865 735939 — MD

1960 (Commend.) Aberd.; MB ChB 1951 Aberd.; FFCM 1973; DPH Manch. 1958; DIH Eng. 1959.

GATISS, Sarah-Jane 17/10 St Leonard's Lane, Edinburgh EH8 9SD — MB ChB 1996 Ed.

GATLAND, Mr David John Department of ENT, Southend Hospital, Westcliff on Sea SS0 0RY Tel: 01702 435555 Fax: 01702 479986; 90 Chalkwell Avenue, Westcliff on Sea SS0 8NN Tel: 01702 479986 Fax: 01702 479986 — MB BS 1972 Lond.; FRCS Ed. 1985; FRCS Eng. 1985. (Guys) Cons. ENT Surg. S.end Hosp. Socs: Mem. Brit. Assn. OtoLaryngol. Prev: Cons. Surg., Sen. Regist. & Regist. (ENT) St. Bart. Hosp. Lond.; SHO (ENT) Roy. Nat. Throat, Nose & Ear Hosp. Lond.

GATLAND, Jonathan Christopher Mersea Road Surgery, 272a Mersea Road, Colchester CO2 8QY Fax: 01206 517100 — MB BS 1978 Lond.; MRCS Eng. LRCP Lond. 1978; DRCOG 1981. (Char. Cross) Prev: Trainee GP Colchester VTS; Ho. Phys. Chesterton Hosp. Camb.; Ho. Surg. Char. Cross Hosp. Lond.

GATLEY, Malcolm Stanley 16 St John Street, Manchester M3 4EA Tel: 0161 835 1144 Fax: 0161 835 1465 Email: gatleyl@quista.net; 1 Eaton Drive, Alderley Edge SK9 7RA Tel: 01625 576134 Fax: 01625 576134 Email: mgatleyl@quista.net — MB ChB Liverp. 1957; MRCS Eng. LRCP Lond. 1957; FFOM RCP Lond. 1985, MFOM 1980, AFOM 1978; DIH Soc. Apoth. Lond. 1975; DMJ (Clin.) Soc. Apoth. Lond. 1967; DLO Eng. 1962. p/t Cons. Phys. Occupat. Med.; Hon. Lect. (Occupat. Med.) Univ. Manch. Socs: Soc. Occupat. Med. & BMA; Manch. Dist. Tediogist Soc. Prev: Dir. Occupat. Health Serv. N. Manch. NHS Trust; Occupat. Phys. Salford AHA (T) & Salford City Counc.; Med. Off. Centr. Electricity Generating Bd.

GATLING, Wendy Department of Diabetes, Poole Hospital NHS Trust, Longfleet Road, Poole BH15 2JB Tel: 01202 442514 Fax: 01202 442069 Email: wgatling@poole-tr.swest.hns.uk; Oak Apple, Holtwood, Holt, Wimborne BH21 7DS — MB ChB 1977 Liverp.; DM Soton. 1986; FRCP Lond. 1994; MRCP (UK) 1981; T(M) 1991. Cons. Phys. Poole Hosp. NHS Trust. Prev: Cons. Phys. E. Herts. NHS Trust; Sen. Regist. Poole & Soton. Gen. Hosps.; Research Fell. Poole Gen. Hosp.

GATOFF, H Dam Head Medical Centre, 1020 Rochdale Road, Blackley, Manchester M9 7HD Tel: 0161 720 9744 Fax: 0161 720 9755 — MB ChB 1976 Manchester; MB ChB 1976 Mnachester.

GATRAD, A H M Ross Road, Coalpool, Walsall WS2 1RE — MB ChB 1973 Sheffield; MB ChB 1973 Sheffield.

GATRAD, Abdul Rashid 3 Chesterwood, Aldridge, Walsall WS9 0PT Tel: 0121 352 0068 — MB ChB 1971 Leeds; MRCS Eng. LRCP Lond. 1971; PhD 1994; Dip Hlth Managem Keele 1998; FRCP Lond. 1991; MRCP (UK) 1977; DCH Eng. 1974; DObst RCOG 1973. Cons. Paediat. Manor Hosp. Walsall; Hon. Sen. Lect. Univ. Birm.; Asst. Prof. Paediat. Univ. Kentucky.USA. Socs: Brit. Paediat. Assn. & BMA. Prev: Sen. Regist. St. Mary's Hosp. Manch. & Booth Hall Hosp. Manch.; Regist. (Paediat.) Roy. Manch. Childr. Hosp.; Med. Dir. Mlambe Miss. Hosp. Malawi, Africa.

GATRILL, Rachel Bridget Wells Health Centre, Glastonbury Road, Wells BA5 1XJ Tel: 01749 672137; Vespasian Farm, Green Ore, Wells BA5 3ET Tel: 01761 241282 Email: rachel@gatrill.globalnet.co.uk — MB BCh 1977 Wales; DRCOG 1981. GP Princip.

GATTAMANENI, Hanumantha Rao Clinical Oncology, The Christie Hospital & Holt Radium Institute, Withington, Manchester M20 4BX Tel: 0161 446 3000 Fax: 0161 446 3092 — MB BS 1973 Kurnool; MD Chandigarh 1976; FRCR 1980. (Kurnool Med. Sch.) Cons. Clin. & Oncol. The Christie Hosp. & Holt Radium Inst. Manch.

GATTAS, Amin Alexan, Capt. RAMC 98 Bristol Road, Edgbaston, Birmingham B5 7XH Tel: 0121 440 1038 — MB ChB Birm. 1939. (Birm. & Paris) Private Pract.; Insur. Med. Examr. Socs: BMA; MDU.

GATTENS, Michael 19 Culbin Drive, Knightswood, Glasgow G13 4PR Tel: 0141 954 3613 — MB ChB 1986 Glasg.; MRCPI 1995. (Glas.) Specialist Regist. (LAS) Haemat. St. Thos. Hosp. Lond. Socs: Fell. Roy. Soc. Med.; MRCPCH. Prev: Clin. Asst. (Haemat. & Oncol.) Gt. Ormond St. Hosp. for Sick Childr. Lond.

GATTER, Kevin Charles University Department of Cellular Science, John Radcliffe Hospital, Oxford OX3 9DU Tel: 01865 220559 — BM BCh 1979 Oxf.

GATTIE, Charles Hubert (retired) The Cottage, lenlyn, Lostwithiel PL22 0 Tel: 01208 873905 — MB ChB Manch. 1932; BSc Manch. 1929. Prev: MOH Bucklow RD.

GATTONI, Frank Emilio Godfrey Pasley Road Health Centre, Pasley Road, Eyres Monsell, Leicester LE2 9BU Tel: 0116 278 5182; Fosse House, Coventry Road, Croft, Leicester LE9 3GP — MSc (Statis.) Lond. 1966, BSc (Econ.) 1965, MBBS 1977.

GATTUSO, Jennifer May Breast Unit, St. Bartholomew's Hospital, London — MB BS 1985 Lond.; MPhil Lond. 1988, MD1997; MA Camb. 1986; FRCS Eng. 1991; MD Lond 1997. (Camb. Univ. & Middlx. Hosp.) p/t SP. Reg. BrE. Unit. Barts.

GATWARD, Colin Christopher Crown Dale Medical Centre, 61 Crown Dale, London SE19 3NY Tel: 020 8670 2414 Fax: 020 8670 0277; 5 Southolme Close, London SE19 2QU — MB ChB 1986 Leeds; DRCOG 1992. Chairm. S. Lond. Area Multifund.

***GATWARD, Jonathan James** The Old Manse, Cutsdean, Cheltenham GL54 5RX — MB ChB 1997 Liverp.

GATZEN, Mr Christopher Wycombe Hospital, Queen Alexandra Road, High Wycombe HP11 2TT Tel: 01494 526161 — State Exam Med 1985 Aachen; FRCS 1990 Edinburgh; FRCS 1998 General. (Aachen) Cons. Colorectal Surg. Socs: Assn.Coloproctologists Gt. Britain & Irel.; Surgic. Research Soc.; Fell. Assoc. of Surg.s of Gt. Britain and Irel. Prev: Resid. Surgic. Off., St. Mark's Hosp.; Sen. Surgic. Regist., St. Mary's & Assoc. Hosps.; Surgic. research fell., Harvard Med. Sch., Boston, USA.

GAU, Donald William (retired) Upper Burgess, 11 Stratton Road, Beaconsfield HP9 1HR Tel: 01494 676018 Fax: 01494 676018 Email: dgau335533@aolcom — MB 1962 Camb.; BChir 1961; MRCP Lond. 1968; FRCGP 1979, M 1973. Prev: GP Beaconsfield.

GAU, Gillian Sarah (retired) Upper Burgess, Stratton Road, Beaconsfield HP9 1HR Tel: 01494 676018 Fax: 01494 676018 Email: dgau335533@aol.com — MB BS Lond. 1962; MD Lond. 1978; MRCS Eng. LRCP Lond. 1962. Hon. Research Fell. Postgrad. Med. Sch. Prev: Cons. Histopath. Qu. Charlotte's & Chelsea Hosp. Lond.

GAUBERT, Diana Rhys Ashleigh, Quarry Lane, N> Anston, Sheffield S25 4DB — MB ChB 1969 Leeds. (Leeds)

GAUBERT, Roger Alan Peter Dinnington Group, New Street, Dinnington, Sheffield S25 2EZ — MB ChB 1969 Leeds; MRCGP 1976; DObst RCOG 1972. GP Trainer Rotherham VTS.

GAUCI, Charles Anton, Lt.-Col. RAMC Retd. Whipps Cross Hospital, Whipps Cross Road, Leytonstone, London E11 1NR Tel: 020 8535 6885 Fax: 020 8535 6467; King George Hospital, Barley Lane, Goodmayes, Ilford IG3 8YB Tel: 020 8970 8158 Fax: 020 8950 8474 — MD 1971 Malta; FRCA 1975. (Malta) Cons. Pain Relief Ther. Whipps Cross Hosp. Lond. & King Geo. Hosp. Essex. Socs: Assn. Anaesth. GB & Irel. & Pain Soc. GB & Irel.; (Region. Sec.) Pain Intervent. Interest Gp. (PIIG). Prev: Cons. Anaesth. Resuscitat. & Cons. i/c Pain Relief Clinic Qu. Eliz. Milit. Hosp. Lond.; Hons. Cons. Pain Clinic Guy's Hosp. Lond.

GAUDOIN, Mark Roland 28 Urrdale Road, Glasgow G41 5DD Tel: 0141 427 3384 — MB ChB 1987 Ed.; MD 2001; MRCOG 1995. (Univ. Ed.) Cons. (O. & G.), Roy. Alexandra Hosp., Paisley. Socs: Glas. Obst. Soc.; Brit. Fertil. Soc. Prev: Spr (O. & G.), W. of Scotl.; Clin. Scientist MRC Human Genetics Unit W.. Gen. Hosp. Edin.; Trainee GP Earlston Berwicksh. VTS.

GAUGAIN, John Victor Prince Charles Hospital, Merthyr Tydfil CF47 9DT Tel: 01685 721721 — MB ChB 1990 Manch. SHO (Anaesth.) P. Chas. Hosp. Mid. Glam. HA. Prev: Ho. Off. (Surg.) Withington Hosp. S. Manch. HA; Ho. Off. (Med.) Furness Gen. Hosp. S. Cumbria HA.

GAUGHAN, Anthony Fabian 45 Dawlish Drive, Southport PR9 9RB — MB ChB 1980 Liverp.

GAUGHT, Fiona Jane Hanway Road Surgery, 2 Hanway Road, Buckland, Portsmouth PO1 4ND Tel: 023 9281 5317 Fax: 023 9289 9926 — MB ChB 1989 Leic.; DRCOG 1993.

GAUKROGER, Mr Michael Christopher Department Oral & Maxillofacial Surgery, Chase Farm Hospital NHS Trust, The Ridgeway, Enfield EN2 8JL Tel: 020 8342 1201 Fax: 020 8967 5925 Email: mcgaukroger@hotmail.com — MB BS 1985 Lond.; BDS 1977; FRCS Ed. 1990; FDS RCS Eng. 1989, LDS 1977. (Charing Cross) Cons. (Maxillofacial Surg.) Chase Farm Hosp. NHS Trust. Socs: Fell. Brit. Assn. Oral & Maxillofacial Surg.; Brit. Assn. of

Head & Neck Oncol. Prev: Lect. & Hon. Sen. Regist. King's Coll. Hosp.

GAULD, Alexander Riddell Mintlaw Group Practice, Newlands Road, Mintlaw, Peterhead AB42 5GP Tel: 01771 623522 Fax: 01771 624349; Little Knock, Mintlaw, Peterhead AB42 5BU Tel: 01771 22925 — MB ChB 1977 Aberd.; MRCGP 1981; DA Eng. 1980; DRCOG 1982. Princip. GP Grampian HB.

GAULD, David Andrew Burnham Medical Centre, Love Lane, Burnham-on-Sea TA8 1EU Tel: 01278 795445 Fax: 01278 793024; Penmill, Townsend, Curry Rivel TH10 0MP Email: dgauld@penmill.fsnet.co.uk — MB BS 1987 Lond.; DRCOG; MRCGP. (St. Georges Hospital Medical School)

GAULD, Graham Douglas West Denburn Medical Practice, West Wing, Denburn Health Centre, Rosemount Viaduct, Aberdeen AB25 1QB Tel: 01224 642955 Fax: 01224 637736 — MB ChB 1984 Aberd.; MRCGP 1988; DCH RCPS Glas. 1987; DRCOG 1986. Prev: Trainee GP Raigmore Hosp. Inverness.

GAULD, Helen Mary Graham Little Knock, Mintlaw, Peterhead AB42 5BU Tel: 01779 622925 — MB ChB 1977 Aberd. Disabil. Exams. DHSS. Prev: GP Aberd.sh. Retainer Scheme.

GAULE, Edward William Forsythe and Gaule, 14 Pelican Court, Wateringbury, Maidstone ME18 5SS Tel: 01622 814466 Fax: 01622 817647 — MB BS 1977 Lond.; DRCOG 1984; MRCS Eng. LRCP Lond. 1977. (Kings College Hospital, London)

GAULT, Betty (retired) The Old Orchard, Raby Road, Thornton Hough, Wirral CH63 4JS Tel: 0151 336 1512 — MB ChB 1951 Cape Town; DA Eng. 1956. Prev: Clin. Asst. Med. Wirral AHA.

GAULT, Mr David Thomas Department of Plastic Surgery, Mount Vernon Hospital, Rickmansworth Road, Northwood HA6 2RN Tel: 01923 826111; Bishopswood Hospital, Rickmansworth Road, Northwood HA6 2JW Tel: 01628 891333 Fax: 01628 891334 Email: dg@davidgault.com — MB ChB 1977 Ed.; FRCS Eng. 1982. (Ed.) Cons. Plastic Surg. Gt. Ormond St. Hosp. Socs: Life Mem. Roy. Med. Soc. Edin.; Assoc. Mem. Brit. Assn. Plastic Surgs.; Assoc. Mem. BSSH. Prev: Sen. Regist. (Plastic Surg.) St. Thos. Hosp. & Hosp. for Sick Childr. Gt. Ormond St. Lond.

GAULT, Lisa Dawn 19 Robinson Crescent, Bangor BT19 6NP — MB BCh 1998 Belf.; MB BCh Belf 1998.

GAULT, William (retired) The Old Orchard, Raby Road, Thornton Hough, Wirral CH63 4JS Tel: 0151 336 1512 — MB BCh BAO Dub. 1951; FRCOG 1971, M 1957. Prev: Cons. Gyn Centr. Wirral Gp. Hosps.

GAUNT, David Ramon 20 The Readings, Red Road, Borehamwood WD6 4SS Tel: 020 8953 5272 — MB BS 1988 Lond. SHO (A & E) Wexham Pk. Hosp. Slough.

GAUNT, Joan Kirkgate Surgery, 215 Kirkgate, Wakefield WF1 1JJ Tel: 01924 371331 Fax: 01924 378121; 8 Stocksmoor Road, Midgley, Wakefield WF4 4JQ Tel: 01924 830270 — MB ChB 1972 Leeds. Primary Care Advis.Pinderfields Trust.

GAUNT, Katie Jane School House, Wigmore, Leominster HR6 9UD — MB BS 1992 Lond.

GAUNT, Martha Louise 3 Beech Tree Court, Baildon, Shipley BD17 5TB — MB ChB 1980 Leics.; FRCR 1987. Cons. (Diagn. Radiol.) Bradford Dist. HA.

GAUNT, Mr Michael Ellis Department of Surgery, Robert Kilpatrick Building, Leicester Royal Infirmary, Leicester LE2 7LX Tel: 0116 252 3142; 2 Worsh Close, Whetstone, Leicester LE8 6QS — MB ChB 1988 Leic.; BSc (Hons.) Leic. 1985, MD (Distinc.) 1996; FRCS Eng. 1992; FRCS Ed. 1992. (Leic.) Regist. (Gen. Surg.) Leicester Roy. Infirm.; Lect. Surg. Leicester Univ. Socs: Assn. Surg.; Eur. Soc. Vasc. Surg. Prev: Surgic. Research Fell. Univ. Leicester.

GAUNT, Peter Nicholas Public Health Laboratory, Derriford Hospital, Derriford Road, Plymouth PL6 8DH Tel: 01752 792370 Fax: 01752 771561 Email: nick.gaunt@phnt.swest.nhs.uk; 67 Cardinal Avenue, Plymouth PL5 1UR — MRCS Eng. LRCP Lond. 1978; BSc (Hons.) Lond. 1974, MB BS 1978; FRCPath 1996; MRCPath 1984. (Guy's) Cons. Microbiol. Derriford Hosp. Plymouth; Hon. Princip. Lect. Univ. Plymouth.

GAUNT, Rebecca Mary Hollow Meadow House, Priors Hardwick, Rugby CV47 7SP — MB ChB 1998 Bristol.

GAUNT, Richard Martin Charles Rowden Surgery, Rowden Hill, Chippenham SN15 2SB Tel: 01249 444343 Fax: 01249 446797 — MB ChB 1986 Leic.; MRCGP 1991.

GAUNT, Robert Musgrave (retired) 2 Rectory Close, Bolton Percy, York YO23 7AX Tel: 01904 744581 — MB ChB Leeds 1947; DObst RCOG 1950. Prev: Ho. Surg. Hosp. Wom. & Matern. Hosp. Leeds.

GAUNT, Simon Peter 29 Vitre Gardens, Lymington SO41 3NA — MB ChB 1991 Leic. Trainee GP ChristCh..

GAUNT, Valerie Patricia 315 Cotton End Road, Wilsread, Bedford MK45 3DT — BM 1981 Soton.

GAUNTLETT, Ian Sidney Department Anaesthetics, Musgrove Park Hospital, Milverton, Taunton TA1 5DA; 4 Bickley Cottages, Milverton, Taunton TA4 1PZ — MB BS 1976 Lond.; FFA RCS Eng. 1982; DA Eng. 1979. Cons. Anaesth. MusGr. Pk. Hosp. Taunton.

GAUNTLETT, Sidney Leonard, MBE 5 Goodhart Way, West Wickham BR4 0ER Tel: 020 8777 7250 — MB BS 1946 Lond.; DTM & H Eng. 1948. (Lond. Hosp.) Prev: Salvation Army Internat. Alcohol/Drug Coordinator; Med. Off. Salvat. Army Hosp. Dhariwal, India; Chief Med. Off. Salvat. Army Hosp. Chikankata, Zambia.

GAUNTLEY, Karen Ann 42 Sheepfold Lane, Ruddington, Nottingham NG11 6NS — MB BCh 1987 Wales.

GAUR, Arjun Singh 39 Montagu Avenue, Newcastle upon Tyne NE3 4JH — MB BS 1973 Kanpur.

GAUTAM, Leela Mani Grampian Health Care NHS Trust, Community Health Division, Bucksburn Clinic, Kepplehills Road, Bucksburn, Aberdeen AB21 9DG Tel: 01224 715541; 13 Westholme Avenue, Aberdeen AB15 6AA Tel: 01224 321063 — MB BS 1971 Bangalor; MB BS Bangalore 1971; DRCOG 1981; MFFP 1996; FRIPHH 1998. (Bangalore Medical College, India) SCMO (Community Health) Grampian Health Care NHS Trust. Socs: MFCH. Prev: SCMO (Community Health) Liverp. HA; Clin. Med. Off. Liverp. HA; SHO Roy. Liverp. Hosp.

GAUTAM, Prasanna Chandra Grampian Health Care NHS Trust, Department of Medicine for the Elderly, Woodend General Hospital, Queens Road, Aberdeen AB15 6XS Tel: 01224 663131; 13 Westholme Avenue, Aberdeen AB15 6AA Tel: 01224 321063 Email: pgautam@aol.com — MB BS 1970 Bangalore; MRCP (UK) 1981; FRIPHH 1993; FRCP Ed. 1994; FRCP Glas. 1996. (Bangalore Medical College, India) Cons. Phys. Woodend Hospial Aberd.; Hon. Sen. Clin. Lect. Aberd. Univ. Med. Sch. Socs: Brit. Geriat. Soc.; Fell. Fac. Community Health; Internat. Continence Soc. Prev: Sen. Regist. (Gen. & Geriat. Med.) Sunderland; Regist. (Geriat. Med.) Liverp.; Regist. (Cardiol.) Liverp.

GAUTAM, Mr Shri Kumar K S Medical Centre, 33 Dormers Wells Lane, Southall UB1 3HY Tel: 020 8574 3986/8571 7632 Fax: 020 8893 6188 — MB BS 1968 Lucknow; MS (ENT) Allahabad 1972. (G.S.V.M. Med. Coll.) Regist. (ENT) Wexham Pk. Hosp. Slough. Prev: Regist. (ENT) Roy. N.. Infirm. Inverness.

GAUTAM, Srijania 16 Alpine Way, Sunderland SR3 1TN — MB BS 1997 Lond.

GAUTAM, Mr Vijayshil Queen Elizabeth II Hospital, East Herts. NHS Trust, Howlands, Welwyn Garden City AL7 4HQ Tel: 01707 328111/0850 996 376 Fax: 01707 391228 Email: 100271.511@compuserve.com — MB BS 1982 Patna; FRCS Ed. 1990; FRCSI 1990; Dip. IMC RCS Ed. 1989. Cons. A & E Directorate QEII Hosp. Welwyn Gdn. City Herts.; Adj. Asst. Prof. Allegheny Univ. of Health Scis. Philadelphia, USA; Dir. Centre for Train. in Clin. Skills, Univ. Herts. Socs: Fell. Fac. A & E Med.; Amer. Coll. Emerg. Phys.; Founder Mem. Fac. Pre-Hosp. Care. Prev: Fell. (Emerg. Med.) Penn State Univ. MSH Med. Center, Penn., USA; Sen. Regist. (A & E) SW RHA.

GAUTAMA, Pragati 45 Woodford Avenue, Gants Hill, Ilford IG2 6UH — MB BS 1990 Lond.

GAUTAMA, Sanjay Anaesthetic Dept, St Mary's Hosp, Praed St, London W2 1NY Tel: 020 7725 6666; Flat A8 Lloyds Wharf, Mill Street, London SE1 2BD Tel: 0207 252 1078 Fax: 0207 252 1078 Email: sanjay@gautama.co.uk — MB BS 1990 Lond.; BSc (Hons.) Lond. 1987; FRCA 1996. (Guy's Hosp. Med. Sch.) Locum Cons (Anaesthetics) St Mary's Hosp Lond.

GAUTHIER, Jean-Baptiste Michel Knowsley Child and Adolescent Mental Health Services, The Wellcroft Centre, Wellcroft Road, Huyton, Liverpool L36 7TA Tel: 0151 489 6137 Fax: 0151 480 2460; 10 Wicks Lane, Liverpool L37 3JG Tel: 01704 876329 — MB ChB 1971 Liverp.; MA Oxf. 1978, BA (Phil. & Psychol.) 1974; MRCS Eng. LRCP Lond. 1971; MRCPsych 1979; DCH Eng. 1980; DPM Eng. 1979. Cons. Child & Adolesc. Psychiat. St. Helens

& Knowsley Community Health (NHS) Trust. Socs: Liverp. Med. Inst.; Brit. Med. Assn. Prev: Sen. Regist. (Child & Adolesc. Psychiat.) Alder Hey Childr. Hosp. Liverp.; Regist. (Psychiat.) Walton Hosp. Liverp.; SHO (Psychiat.) Sefton Gen. Hosp. Liverp.

GAVAGHAN, Siobhan Wendy Maria 30 Douglas Road, Chingford, London E4 6DA — MB ChB 1984 Leeds; AFOM RCP Lond. 1994; MRCGP 1990. Sen. Regist. (Occupat. Health) Worcester Roy. Infirm.

GAVALAS, Mr Manolis Costa 9 Gordon Road, Wanstead, London E11 2RA Tel: 020 7387 9300 — MB ChB 1984 Sheff.; MB ChB Sheff. l984; FRCS Ed. 1989. Cons. A & E Lond.

GAVAN, Duncan Ross Blackburn Royal Infirm, Bolton Road, Blackburn BB2 3LR; 5 Browgate, Sawley, Clitheroe BB7 4NB — MB ChB 1984 Manch.; BSc St. And. 1981; MRCP (UK) 1988; FRCR 1992. Cons. Radiol. Blackburn & Ribble Valley. Prev: Sen. Regist. (Radiol.) Newc.; Regist. (Radiol.) Edin.

GAVAN, Jacqueline Riverside, Sawley Manor, Sawley, Clitheroe BB7 4NG Tel: 01200 440189 — MB BCh 1986 Wales; BSc (Hons.) St. And. 1982. Prev: GP Newc. & Edin. Doctors Retainer Scheme.

GAVEL, Felix Fabius Gil von Gwynedd Hospital NHS Trust, Rsbyty Gwynedd, Penrhosgarnedd, Bangor LL57 2PW — MB ChB 1991 Birm.; ChB Birm. 1991.

GAVILAN, John 142 Bushey Mill Lane, Watford WD24 7PB — MB BS 1984 Lond.

GAVIN, Alice Jane Muirhead, St Cyrus, Montrose DD10 0DR — MB ChB 1992 Aberd.

GAVIN, Andrew Robertson Top Right Flat, 63 Airlie St., Glasgow G12 9SR — MB ChB 1994 Glas.

GAVIN, Anna Teresa Northern Ireland Cancer Registry, Mulhouse Building, Grosvenor Road, Belfast BT12 6BJ Tel: 01232 263136 Fax: 01232 248017 Email: nicr@qub.ac.uk; The Lodge, Mount Irwin, 59 Derryhaw Road,Tynan, Armagh BT60 4ST Tel: 01861 568192 — MB BCh BAO 1981 Belf.; MSc (Community Med.) Lond. 1985; RCP (UK) 1988; FFPHM RCP (UK) 1997; FFPHM RCPI 1977; MFPHM 1988. (Qu. Univ. Belf.) Dir. N. Irel. Cancer Registry Qu. Univ. Belf. Prev: Cons. Pub. Health Med. EHSSB N. Irel.; Cons. Pub. Health Med SHSSB N1.

GAVIN, Frances Mary Low Moor House, 167 Netherlands Avenue, Low Moor, Bradford BD12 0TB Tel: 01274 606818 Fax: 01274 691684; 50 Brecon Avenue, Low Hills Lane, Huddersfield HD3 3QF — MB ChB 1988 Leeds; BSc Leeds 1985, MB ChB 1988; MRCGP 1993; DRCOG 1992.

GAVIN, Ian (retired) 51 Balmoral Road, Accrington BB5 6DB Tel: 01254 392082 — MB ChB 1951 Glas. Hon. Sen. Clin. Asst. Blackburn & E. Lancs. Hospice. Prev: SHO (Orthop.) Vict. Infirm. Glas.

GAVIN, John St Andrews Surgery, 166 Market Street, Eastleigh SO50 5PT Tel: 023 8061 2472 Fax: 023 8061 1717; Bramley, Roman Road, Twyford, Winchester SO21 1QW Tel: 01962 713521 — MB BChir 1988 Camb.; MRCGP 1992; DCH RCP Lond. 1992.

GAVIN, Judith Mary 57 Marlborough Road, Chingford, London E4 9AJ — MB BCh BAO 1979 NUI; LRCPI 1979; MRCGP 1989.

GAVIN, Lewis Den Munro, OStJ (retired) Priory Gate, The Green, Datchet, Slough SL3 9JL Tel: 01753 543585 — MB ChB 1939 Aberd.; MD Aberd. 1947; MRCGP 1968. Hon. Lt. Col. Prev: GP Slough.

GAVIN, Mary Elizabeth (retired) — MB BCh BAO 1968 NUI.

GAVIN, Michael John White Lodge, Wepre Drive, Connah's Quay, Deeside CH5 4HE Tel: 01244 831686 — MB BCh BAO 1938 NUI. (Galway) Socs: BMA. Prev: Hon. Surg. to HM the King; Ho. Phys. & Ho. Surg. Galway Centr. Fev. & Matern. Hosp.

GAVIN, Michael Joseph (retired) 2 Fron Road, Connah's Quay, Deeside CH5 4NF — MB BCh BAO 1968 NUI.

GAVIN, Mr Michael Paul Department of Ophthalmology, Stibhill Hospital, Balornock Road, Glasgow G21 3UW Tel: 0141 201 3479 Fax: 0141 201 4153 — MB ChB 1986 Aberd.; BMedBiol (Hons.) Aberd. 1984; FRCS Ed. 1993; MRCP (UK) 1989; FRCOphth 1994. (Univ. Aberd.) Cons. Ophth., N. Glas. NHS Trust. Prev: Sen. Regist. (Ophth.) G.G.H.B.

GAVIN, Neil Gow Sinclair Kensington Group Practice, Kensington Road, Road, Douglas IM1 3PF Tel: 01624 676774 Fax: 01624 614668; Raeburn, Quarterbridge Road, Douglas IM2 3RF Tel: 01624 621895 — MB ChB Aberd. 1970; MRCGP 1978; DObst RCOG 1975.

GAVIN, Noel Alexander 3 Cairnside, Eastherrington, Sunderland SR3 3LT — MB BS 1993 Newc.

GAVIN, Noel James 58 Mill Lane, Heatley, Lymm WA13 9SQ — MB BCh BAO 1980 NUI; LRCPI & LM, LRCSI & LM 1980; FCAnaesth. 1989; FFA RCSI 1988. Sen. Regist. (Anaesth.) N. W.. RHA Manch.

GAVIN, Vera Jean (retired) Priory Gate, The Green, Datchet, Slough SL3 9JL Tel: 01753 543585 — MRCS Eng. LRCP Lond. 1943. JP. Berks. Prev: Sen. Med. Off. Slough Family Plann. Clinic.

GAVIN, William Bernard John Deeside Medical Centre, 17-21 Chester Road E., Shotton, Deeside CH5 3NA Tel: 01244 831698; Old Banks, Killins Lane, Shotton, Deeside CH5 1RF — MB BCh BAO 1966 NUI. Hosp. Pract.(Ment. Handicap) Broughton Hosp.; Police Surg. Clwyd HA; Med. Adviser Brit. Aerospace plc. Chester. & Continental Can Co. Deeside. Prev: Ho. Surg. & Ho. Phys. Roy. S.. Hosp. Liverp.; Ho. Surg. (Obst.) Nat. Matern. Hosp. Dub.

GAVINS, Edward Neil 44 Lyndon Road, Manton, Oakham LE15 8SR — MB BS 1991 Lond.

GAVINS, Philip William Littleton Surgery, Buckland House, Esher Park Avenue, Esher KT10 9NY Tel: 01372 462235 Fax: 01372 470622; 20 Tottington Road, Claygate, Esher KT10 0SA Tel: 01372 65135 — MB BS 1985 Lond.; DRCOG 1984.

GAVOURIN, Mr Brian Alan (retired) Crispin Cottage, Travellers End, Stockbridge Road, Winchester SO22 5JZ — MB BS 1948 Lond.; FRCS Glas. 1964; MRCS Eng. LRCP Lond. 1947; FRCOG 1969, M 1955, DObst 1950. Prev: Col. Late RAMC, CO Brit. Milit. Hosp. Iserlohn.

GAVRIELIDES, Iliada 9 Fircroft Road, London SW17 7PR — MB BS 1992 Lond.

GAVRILOVIC, Anica Valley Surgery, 81 Bramcote Lane, Chilwell, Nottingham NG9 4ET; 5 Linden Grove, Beeston, Nottingham NG9 2AD — MB BS 1978 Newc.; MRCGP 1984. Trainer Nottm. VTS.

GAW, Allan Department of Pathological Biochemistry, Royal Infirmary, University NHS Trust, Glasgow G31 2ER Tel: 0141 211 4599 Fax: 0141 553 2558 — MB ChB 1984 Glas.; MB ChB Glas. l984; PhD Glas. 1992; MD Glas. 1996. Dep. Study Dir., Prosper Study (Path. Biochem.ry) Roy. Infirm. Univ. NHS Trust. Socs: (Comm.) Brit. Hyperlipidaemia Assn. Prev: Brit. Heart Foundat. Research Fell. (Path. Biochem.ry); Research Fell. (Molecular Genetics) S.W.. Med. Centre Dallas, Texas, USA; Lect. (Path. Biochem.ry) Roy. Infirm. Glas..

GAW, David Hugh Warrenpoint Health Centre, Summerhill, Warrenpoint, Newry BT34 3JD — MB BCh BAO 1977 Belf.; MRCGP 1981.

GAW, Norman James Woodside Health Centre, Barr Street, Glasgow G20 7LR Tel: 0141 531 9507 Fax: 0141 531 9509; 1 Horseshoe Road, Bearsden, Glasgow G61 2ST Tel: 0141 942 0728 — MB ChB 1979 Glas.; MRCGP (Distinc.) 1983; DRCOG 1981.

GAWARIKAR, Sudhir Bhaskar Lurgan Hospital, Sloan St., Lurgan, Craigavon BT66 8NX — MB BS 1974 Indore.

GAWITH, Donald Hugo (retired) 1 Church Fields Avenue, Ulverston LA12 7HJ — MRCS Eng. LRCP Lond. 1945; DPH Glas. 1952.

GAWKRODGER, David John Brook Cottage, Back Lane, Sheffield S17 4HP — MB ChB (Hons.) (Distinc. Surg.) Birm. 1976; MD (Hons.) Birm. 1988; FRCP Lond. 1994; FRCP Ed. 1992; MRCP (UK) 1979. Cons. Dermat. Roy. Hallamsh. Hosp. Sheff.; Hon. Sen. Clin. Lect. (Dermat.) Univ. Sheff. Prev: Lect. (Dermat.) Univ. Edin. & Hon. Sen. Regist. Roy. Infirm. Edin.; Regist. (Med.) N. Staffs. Hosp. Centre Stoke-on-Trent; Ho. Phys. Med. Profess. Unit Qu. Eliz. Hosp. Birm.

GAWLER, Jeffrey 149 Harley Street, London W1G 6DE Tel: 020 7224 0640 Fax: 020 7935 7245; Tel: 020 8850 0025 — MB BS 1968 Lond.; FRCP Lond. 1982, M 1970. (St. Bart.) Phys. Roy. Hosps. Trust; Cons. Neurol. N. Middlx. Hosp. Socs: Assn. Brit. Neurol. Prev: Sen. Regist. Nat. Hosp. Nerv. Dis. Qu. Sq. Lond.

GAWLER, Tracy Jane 5 Burma Crescent, Canterbury CT1 1AQ Tel: 01227 785832 — MB ChB 1989 Auckland.

GAWLEY, Sarah Pamela Geriatric Medical Unit, Musgrave Park Hospital, Balmoral, Belfast BT9 7JB Tel: 02890 669501; 29A Carnreagh, Hillsborough BT26 6LJ — MB BCh BAO 1972 Belf.; MD Belf. 1989; FRCP Lond. 1993; MRCP (UK) 1979; DCH RCPS Glas. 1974. Cons. Phys. Geriat. Med. Musgrave Pk. Hosp. Belf. & Lagan

Valley Hosp. Lisburn; Hon. Clin. Lect., Qu. Univ. Belf. Socs: Fell. Ulster Med. Soc.; Fell. Ulster Soc. Internal Med.; Irish Gerontol. Soc. Prev: Sen. Regist. (Geriat. Med.) Roy. Vict. Hosp. Belf.; Research Fell. DHSS; Counc. of Europe Med. Fell.

GAWLINSKA, Maria Helena Seymour House Surgery, 154 Sheen Road, Richmond TW9 1UU Tel: 020 8940 2802 Fax: 020 8332 7877; 23 Park Road, Richmond TW10 6NS Tel: 020 8940 5860 Fax: 020 8332 6101 — MB BS 1979 Lond.; MRCGP 1985; DRCOG 1984. (St. Bartholomew's)

GAWN, Allyson de Voy Bo'ness Road Medical Practice, 31-33 Bo'ness Road, Grangemouth FK3 8AN Tel: 01324 482653; 4 Cullin Place, Grangemouth FK3 0DA Tel: 01324 665563 Email: gawn@btinternet.com — MB ChB 1985 Ed.; MRCGP 1989; DCH RCPS Glas. 1988; DRCOG 1987; Dip. Occ. Med. RCP Lond. 1997.

GAWNE CAIN, Mary Louise Wessex Neurological Centre, Southampton General Hospital, Tremona Road, Southampton SO16 6YD Tel: 02380 796641 — MB BChir 1987 Camb.; FRCR 1993; MRCP (UK) 1989. Cons. NeuroRadiol. Prev: Sen. Regist. (Neuroradiol.) Radcliffe Infirm. Oxf.; Research Fell. Inst. Neurol. Qu. Sq. Lond.; Sen. (Radiol.) St. Geo. Hosp. Lond.

GAWRONSKI, Jan Gerard Stefan Flat A, Kerry House, 67B Kelvin Road, London N5 2PQ — MB ChB 1996 Liverp.

GAY, Alan Leon 4 Belvedere Court, Alwoodley, Leeds LS17 8NF — MB ChB 1962 Leeds; MRCPsych 1972; T(Psych) 1991; DPM Leeds 1965. (Leeds) Socs: BMA.

GAY, David Allin Thomas 8 Badger Hill, Rastrick, Brighouse HD6 3QX — MB BS 1997 Lond.

GAY, Frederick William Green Storthe, 68 Coast Road, West Mersea, Colchester CO5 8LS — MB BCh BAO 1972 Belf.; PhD Belf. 1967, MD 1992, BSc 1965. Reader (Biomed. Sci.) Anglia Polytechnic Univ. Camb. Socs: Roy. Soc. Med. & Rowhook Med. Soc. Prev: GP W. Mersea; Tutor Regist. (Path.) Qu. Univ. Belf.; Clin. Lect. (Microbiol.) Middlx. Hosp. Lond.

GAY, John Christopher Colwell 19 Westlands Court, West Road, Bransgore, Christchurch BH23 8BQ — MB BS 1978 Lond. (Guy's)

GAY, Kenneth Harry Rosevean, Constantine Bay, Padstow PL28 8JG Tel: 01841 520789 — MB ChB 1961 Bristol. Socs: FRCGP.

GAY, Martin Alan 923 Warwick Road, Solihull B91 3EP — MB BS 1975 Lond.; MRCS Eng. LRCP Lond. 1975. (Char. Cross) Med. Quality Manager Benefits Agency Med. Servs. Prev: Trainee GP New Mills; SHO (Radiother.) Christie Hosp. Manch.; SHO Rotat. (Surg.) Norf. & Norwich Hosp.

GAY, Martyn John (retired) PO Box 22, Sidmouth EX10 0YS Tel: 01395 568943 Fax: 01395 568831 — MB ChB Bristol 1960; MD Bristol 1969; FRCPsych. 1981, M 1971; DCH Eng. 1962, DPM 1965. Clin. Lect. (Ment. Health) Univ. Bristol. Prev: Cons. Child & Adolesc. Psychiat. Bristol & W.on DHA.

GAY, Michael Preston Manor Farm Cottage, Browston Lane, Browston, Great Yarmouth NR31 9DP — MB ChB 1975 Cape Town.

GAY, Simon Phillip Merlin Dyeing & Finishing Ltd., Manor Lane, Holmes Chapel, Crewe CW4 8AB Tel: 01477 537336 Fax: 01477 535304 — MB BS 1988 Lond.; MRCGP 1993; DRCOG 1992; DCH RCP Lond. 1992. (St. George's H.M.S.) Prev: GP Market HarBoro.; Represen. Leics. Locality Purchasing Forum.

***GAYA, Daniel Richard** 21 Windsor Avenue, Newton Mearns, Glasgow G77 5NX Tel: 0141 639 4456 — MB ChB 1998 Glas.; MB ChB Glas 1998.

GAYA, Doorendranath Sanjeev 95 Warren Drive S., Surbiton KT5 9QD — MB BS 1994 Lond.

GAYA, Harold Microbiology Department, 20 Devonshire Place, London W1N 2DH Tel: 020 7935 4444 Ext: 3156 Fax: 020 7935 5314; 16 Berry Hill, Stanmore HA7 4XS Tel: 07733 260399 Email: h.gaya@bigfoot.com — MB ChB 1963 Glas.; FRCPath 1981, M 1970. (Glas.) Cons. Microbiol. Lond. Clinic; Hon. Sen. Lect. Nat. Heart & Lung. Inst. Imperial Coll. Lond. Univ. Socs: Fell. Roy. Soc. Med.; Fell. Infec. Dis. Soc. Amer. Prev: Reader (Bact.) St. Mary's Hosp. Med. Sch. Lond.; Cons. & Hon. Lect. (Bact.) Roy. Postgrad. Med. Sch. & Hammersmith Hosp. Lond.; Cons. Microbiologist Roy. Brompton & Harefield NHS Trust Lond.

GAYED, Emil Shawky 98 Wadham Gardens, Greenford UB6 0BS — LRCP 1982 Ed.; MB BCh Egypt 1976; LRCS Ed. 1982; LRCPS Glas. 1982; MRCOG 1985.

GAYED, Halim Wadie 186 Malden Road, New Malden KT3 6DS Tel: 020 8949 3624 — MB BCh 1972 Cairo. (Ksr El-Ani - Cairo University) Med. Advisor & Disabil. Analyst, Med. Servs., Sutton, Surrey; Disabil. Analyst & EMP to Benefits Agency Med. Serv. Sutton Surrey. Socs: Fell. Roy. Soc. Med. Lond. Prev: Med. Off. HMP Bullingdon Bicester Oxon; Med. Off. HMP Brixton & Wandsworth; Med. Off. Spinal & Neurol. Rehabil. Unsted Pk.-Godalmig, Private Back Clinic, Lond.

GAYED, Shoukry Latif Mickleover Surgery, 10 Cavendish Way, Mickleover, Derby DE3 5BJ Tel: 01332 519160 Fax: 01332 523054 — MB BCh 1977 Ain Shams; MRCS Eng. LRCP Lond. 1984.

GAYEN, Ajit Kumar 198 Brooklands Road, Sale M33 Tel: 0161 962 1010 — MB 1951 Calcutta. Socs: BMA.

GAYER, Arthur Hugh Sheiling School, Ashley, Ringwood BH24 2EB Tel: 01425 477488 Fax: 01425 479536 Email: sheilingco@aol.com — MB BS 1970 Lond.; MFHom. 1974; DObst RCOG 1972. (The London Hospital) Med. Off. Sheiling Sch. Ringwood, Hants. Socs: Anthroposop. Med. Assn. Counc. Mem.

GAYER, Mark Alan North House Surgery, North House, Hope Street, Crook DL15 9HU Tel: 01388 762945 Fax: 01388 765333 — MB ChB 1988 Manch.; MRCGP 1993. Prev: Trainee GP Bolton; SHO Blackburn GP VTS; Ho. Off. Surg. Furness Gen. Hosp.

GAYER, Sally Jane 14 Millbrook Park, Lisvane, Cardiff CF14 0UH — MB ChB 1990 Leic.

GAYFORD, Jasper John Purley Resource Centre, 50 Pampisford Road, Purley CR8 2NE Tel: 020 8700 8900 Fax: 020 8700 8944 — MB BS 1965 Lond.; MD Lond. 1978; MRCS Eng. LRCP Lond. 1965; FDS RCS Eng. 1964; BDS Lond. 1961; FRCPsych 1985, M 1973; DPM Eng. 1972; AKC. (Roy. Dent. & St. Geo.) Cons. Psychiat. (Psychosexual Disorders) Croydon Ment. Health Serv. - Bethlem & Maudsley NHS Trust; Hon. Cons. St. Luke's Hosp. Clergy; Hon. Sen. Lect. St. Geo. Hosp. Lond. Socs: Fell. Roy. Soc. Med.; Brit. Acad. Foren. Sc. Prev: Sen. Regist. (Psychiat.) W.m. Hosp. Lond.; Regist. (Med.) Roy. W. Sussex Hosp. Chichester; Lect. & Hon. Sen. Regist. Inst. Dent. Surg. Lond.

GAYLE, Carol Marcia King's College Hospital, Denmark Hill, Camberwell Green, London SE5 9RS Tel: 020 7737 4000 Fax: 020 7346 3313 — MB BS 1987 Lond.; BSc (1st cl. Hons.) Lond. 1984; MRCP (UK) 1991. Research Regist. (Endocrinol.) Dept. Med. King's Coll. Hosp. Lond. Prev: Regist. (Diabetes & Endocrinol.) King's Coll. Hosp. Lond.; SHO Rotat. (Gen. Med.) Dulwich & King's Coll. Hosp. & Centr. Middlx. Hosp. Lond.

GAYMER, Adrian Raymond The Cross Surgery, The Cross, Milborne Port, Sherborne DT9 Tel: 01963 250334 Fax: 01963 251180; Pond Farm, Henstridge, Templecombe BA8 0QH Tel: 01963 363222 — MB BS 1972 Lond.; DObst RCOG 1975. (Middlx.) Med. Off. (Staff Occupat. Health) Yeovil Dist. Hosp.

GAYNER, Mr Allan Davidson North Tyneside General Hospital, Rake Lane, North Shields NE29 8NH — MB BS 1968 Lond.; FRCS Eng. 1976; MRCS Eng. LRCP Lond. 1968. (Roy. Free)

GAYNER, John Reynolds (Surgery), 6 Sloane Square, London SW1W 8EE Tel: 020 7730 3700 Fax: 020 7730 6500; 4 Upper Cheyne Row, London SW3 5JN Tel: 020 7351 6801 — MB BS 1970 Lond. (St. Thos.) GP Lond.; Company Med. Adviser. Socs: Soc. Occupat. Med.; Soc. Apoth.; Assur. Med. Prev: Ho. Surg. (Orthop.) St. Thos. Hosp. Lond.

***GAYNOR, Edward Sebastian** Student Services Centre, 150 Mount Pleasant, Liverpool L69 3BX Tel: 0151 794 4720; Carfax, St Michaels Church Road, Liverpool L17 7BD — MB ChB 1986 Liverp.; MRCGP 1993; DRCOG 1990; DCH RCP Lond. 1989; DTM & H Liverp. 1989.

GAYNOR, Patricia Alice Anaesthetic Division, East Surrey Hospital, Three Arch Road, Redhill RH1 5AE Tel: 01737 768511; Thornthrift, Clay Lane, South Nutfield, Redhill RH1 4EG Tel: 01737 761028 — MB BS 1967 Lond.; MRCS Eng. LRCP Lond. 1967; FFA RCS Eng. 1972; DA Eng. 1969. (Char. Cross) Cons. Anaesth. E. Surrey Hosp. Redhill. Socs: Assn. Anaesth. & Pain Soc. Prev: Sen. Regist. (Anaesth.) Redhill Hosp.; Regist. (Anaesth.) P. Henry's Hosp. Melb. Austral.; SHO (Anaesth.) Char. Cross Hosp.

GAYTON, Paul 161 New Church Road, Hove BN3 4DB — MB ChB 1975 Bristol.

GAZE, B I Rutherford Medical Centre, 1 Rutherford Road, Mossley Hill, Liverpool L18 0HL Tel: 0151 722 1803 Fax: 0151 738 0083.

GAZE, Mark Nicholas Meyerstein Institute of Oncology, The Middlesex Hospital, Mortimer St., London W1T 3AA Tel: 020 7636 8333 Fax: 020 7436 0160; 8 Clarkson Row, Mornington Terrace, London NW1 7RA Tel: 020 7387 4565 — MB BS 1981 Lond.; MD Lond. 1993; FRCP Ed. 1995; MRCP (UK) 1984; T(R) (CO) 1993; FRCR 1988; DMRT Ed. 1987. (St. Bart.) Cons. Oncol. Univ. Coll. Lond. Hosps. & Gt. Ormond St. Hosp. Childr. Lond. Socs: Bd. Fac. Clin. Oncol.; RCR. Prev: Sen. Regist. (Clin. Oncol.) Beatson Oncol. Centre Glas.; Lect. (Radiat. Oncol.) Univ. Edin. & Glas.

GAZE, Mr Nigel Raymond Fulwood Hall Hospital, Midgery Lane, Preston PR2 9SZ Tel: 01772 704111; Priory House, 35 Priory Lane, Penwortham, Preston PR1 0AR Tel: 01772 743821 — MB ChB 1966 Liverp.; FRCS Eng. 1973; FRCS Ed. 1972. (Liverp.) Cons. Plastic Surg. Roy. Preston Hosp. & Vict. Hosp. Blackpool. Socs: Brit. Acad. Experts; Fell. Roy. Soc. Med.; BMA (Chairm. Preston & S. Ribble Br.). Prev: Sen. Regist. (Plastic Surg.) Yorks RHA; Regist. (Plastic Surg.) Wordsley Hosp. Stourbridge; Regist. (Surg.) Chester Roy. Infirm.

GAZELEY, Simon David 1 Palmcroft Close, Ipswich IP1 6RB — MB BS 1997 Newc.

GAZET, Anne Caroline 3 The Green, Northleach, Cheltenham GL54 3EX Tel: 01451 860200 — MB BS 1987 Lond.; DRCOG 1992. (St. Geo. Hosp. Med. Sch.)

GAZET, Mr Jean-Claude Vine Cottage, 48 Wayneflete Tower Avenue, Esher KT10 8QG Tel: 01372 463235 Fax: 01372 463235 — MRCS Eng. LRCP Lond. 1951; MS Lond. 1965, MB BS 1951; MS Univ. Illinois 1963; FRCS Eng. 1956. (Guy's) Cons. Surg. St. Geo. Hosp. & Roy. Marsden Hosp. Lond. Socs: Fell. Assn. Surgs.; Fell. Med. Soc. Lond.; ESSO. Prev: Sen. Regist. (Surg.), Ho. Phys. & Ho. Surg. Guy's Hosp. Lond.; Lect. (Anat.) King's Coll. Univ. Lond.

GAZI, Thrity Framroze Law Hospital, Carluke ML8 5ER Tel: 01698 72621 — MB BS 1965 Bombay; DA Eng. 1970; DGO CPS Bombay 1967. (Grant Med. Coll.)

GAZIS, Anastasios George 37 Leander Gardens, Birmingham B14 6EZ — BM BS 1991 Nottm.

GAZZARD, Andrew Mark c/o Craven Tor, Harewood Road, Skipton BD23 1QR — MB BChir 1994 Camb.

GAZZARD, Professor Brian George Chelsea & Westminster Hospital, 369 Fulham Road, London SW10 9NH Tel: 020 8746 8239 Fax: 020 8746 5611 Email: eileen.witney@chelwest.nhs.uk; Old Blew House, Dulwich Common, London SE21 7EW Tel: 020 8693 1151 — MB BChir 1971 Camb.; MB BChir (Hons.) Camb. 1971; MD Camb. 1976; FRCP Lond. 1983; MRCP (UK) 1972. Cons. Phys. Chelsea & W.minster Hosp.; Research Dir. (HIV & GUM Unit) Chelsea & W.minster Hosp. Socs: Chairm. Brit. HIV. Assn. Prev: Sen. Regist. St. Bart. Hosp. Lond.; Lect. Liver Unit King's Coll. Hosp. Lond.

GAZZARD, Joanna Alice Wonstanley Group Practice, Huitt Square Surgery, Winstanley Estate, Battersea, London SW11 2HS Tel: 020 7228 8988 Fax: 020 7978 4550; Old Blew House, Dulwich Common, London SE21 7EW Tel: 020 8693 1151 — MRCS Eng. LRCP Lond. 1972; BSc Lond. 1969, MB BS 1972. (Guy's Hosp. & King's Coll. Hosp.)

GBECKOR-KOVE, David Mahu HM Prison, Wormwood Scrubs, PO Box 757, Du Cane Road, London W12 0AE Tel: 020 8743 0311 — MB ChB Ghana 1970; MRCP (UK) 1975; MRCGP 1983. Head of Healthcare & Sen. Med. Off. HM Prison Wormwood Scrubs Lond. Prev: Research Regist. St. Geo. Hosp. Lond.; Regist. (Med.) Blackburn Roy. Infirm.

GBEGBAJE, Mary Eyewunmi c/o Mr A. Oshunniyi, 15 Honister Gardens, Stanmore HA7 2EH — MB BS 1983 Ibadan.

GBELEE, Henry Olusegun Doctor's Mess, Harold Wood Hospital, Romford RM3 0BE — LMSSA 1993 Lond.

GBINIGIE, Andrew Osahon Wordsley Hospital, Stourbridge DY8 5QX Tel: 01384 456111 Fax: 01384 244308; The Iroko, Tanglewood, Barnt Green, Birmingham B45 8QR — MB BS (Distinc.) Benin 1978; MFFP 1994; MRCOG 1989. Cons. O & G Dudley Hosps. NHS Trust.

GBOLADE, Babatunde Abiodun The Leeds Teaching Hospitals NHS Trust, Fertility Control Unit, Department of Obstetrics and Gynaecology, St James's University Hospital, Beckett St., Leeds LS9 7TF Tel: 01132 065381 Fax: 01132 065381 — MB BS 1978 Ibadan, Nigeria; 1983 LM Dub. 1983; 1994 MRCPI 1994; 1993 MFFP 1993; 1992 MRCOG 1992; 1983 DGO TC Dub. 1983. (Univ. Ibadan, Nigeria) Cons. Gyn. & Dir. of Fertil. Control Unit Dept. O & G St. Jas. Univ. Hosp. Leeds; Hon. Sen. Clin. Lect. Univ. Leeds. Socs: Fell. Roy. Soc. Health Lond.; NY Acad. Sci.; Fell. N. of Eng. Obst. and Gyn. Soc. Prev: Clin. Lect. (Family Plann. & Reproduc. Health Care) & Sen. Regist. (Community Gyn.) Univ. Manch.; Regist. (Genitourin. Med.) Manch. Roy. Infirm.; Regist. (O & G) N. Manch. Gen. Hosp. & St. Mary's Hosp. Manch.

GEACH, Anthony Richard Gillies Health Centre, Sullivan Road, Brighton Hill, Basingstoke RG22 4EH Tel: 01256 479747 Fax: 01256 20627; 135 Worting Road, Basingstoke RG22 6HJ Tel: 01256 465624 — MB BS 1960 Lond.; DObst RCOG 1965. (St. Bart.) Prev: Resid. Med. Off. Childr. Hosp. Sydenham; Resid. Intern. (Midw. & Gyn.) & SHO (Surg.) St. Bart. Hosp. Lond.

GEADAH, Monir Wakim 23 Mote Avenue, Maidstone ME15 7SU Tel: 01622 751984 — MB BCh 1965 Ain Shams; FFA RCS Eng. 1974; FFA RCSI 1973. (Ain Shams) Cons. Anaesth. Maidstone Health Dist. Prev: Sen. Regist. (Anaesth.) Guy's Hosp. Lond.; Regist. (Anaesth.) Brook Hosp. Lond. & King's Coll. Hosp. Lond.

GEAKE, Michael Richard (retired) The Old Cottages, Pentireglaze, St Minver, Wadebridge PL27 6QY — MB BChir 1943 Camb.; FRCP Lond. 1971, M 1964; MRCS Eng. LRCP Lond. 1943. Prev: Hon. Sen. Lect. Char. Cross Hosp. Lond.

GEALS, Michael Forbes Department of Obstetrics & Gynaecology, Dumfries & Galloway Royal Infirmary, Bankend Road, Dumfries DG1 4AP Tel: 01387 246246; Heathermbank, Ryedale Road, Dumfries DG2 7EP Tel: 01387 251075 — MB ChB 1968 Aberd.; FRCOG 1988, M 1975; DObst 1972. (Aberd.) Cons. O & G Dumfries & Galloway Acute & Matern. Servs. NHS Trust. Prev: Lect. (O & G) Roy. Infirm. Aberd.; Regist. (Obst & Gyn.) Roy. Infirm. Glas. & Duke St. Hosp. Glas.; Regist. (O & G) Inverness Hosp. Gp.

GEALY, Sian Elizabeth Maesafallen, Tregaron SY25 6HY — MB BCh 1992 Wales.

GEANEY, David Patrick Charter House, Wellington St., Thame OX9 3BN Tel: 01844 217446 Fax: 01844 217451 — MB ChB Sheff. 1973; MD Sheff. 1985; MRCP (UK) 1976; MRCPsych 1986. Cons. Psychiat. S. Oxon.

GEAR, Mr Michael William Leishman (retired) Gloucestershire Royal Hospital, Great Western Road, Gloucester GL1 3NN Tel: 01452 394675 — BM BCh 1958 Oxf.; MA Oxf. 1958, DM 1970; MCH 1970 Oxf.; FRCS Eng. 1963. Cons. Surg. Gloucester Roy. Hosp. Prev: Examr. Surg. Oxf. Univ.

GEAR, Philippa Castle Gardens Medical Centre, 78 East Hill, Colchester CO1 2QS Tel: 01206 866626 Fax: 01206 869575; Hill Farm, Frating Hill, Frating, Colchester CO7 7DG — BM 1976 Soton.; BM (Hons.) Soton. 1976; MRCP (UK) 1980; MRCGP 1983; DRCOG 1978.

GEAR, Sarah Louise 3A Tivy Dale, Cawthorne, Barnsley S75 4EY — MB ChB 1995 Manch.

GEARING, Kathleen Elizabeth Albia House, Gillan, Manaccan, Helston TR12 6HJ — MB BCh BAO 1979 Dub. Socs: Fac. Homoeop.

GEARTY, Joan Catherine Department Histopathology, City Hospital NHS Trust, Dudley Road, Birmingham B18 7QH — MB BCh BAO 1966 NUI; FRCPath 1993, M 1981. Cons. Histopath. City Hosp. NHS Trust Birm.

GEARY, Colin Garton (retired) Dunedin, South Park Drive, Poynton, Stockport SK12 1BN Tel: 01625 873584 — MB 1956 Camb.; BChir 1955; FRCP Lond. 1981, M 1966; FRCP Ed. 1972, M 1964; FRCPath 1978, M 1965. Hon. Haemat. United Manch. Hosps.; Hon. Lect. (Clin. Haemat.) Univ. Manch. Prev: Dir. (Haemat.) Manch. Roy. Infirm.

GEARY, John Adrian Bramhall Health Centre, 66 Bramhall Lane South, Bramhall, Stockport SK7 2DY Tel: 0161 439 8213 Fax: 0161 439 6398 — MB ChB 1971 Manch.; Cert Av. Med. (Manchester) Brit. Airways Apptd. Dr. for Manch.; Clin. Asst. (Occupat. Med.) Stepping Hill Hosp. Stockport; Company Doctor, JMC Airlines; Contract Phys., Lufthansa Airlines. Socs: Assn. Aviat. Med. Examrs.; BMA.

GEARY, Kathryn Gabrielle 11 Cochrane Road, Benson, Wallingford OX10 6ED — MB ChB 1992 Manch.

GEARY, Mr Nicholas Paul Jonathan BUPA Murrayfield Hospital, Holmwood Drive, Thingwall, Wirral CH61 1AU Tel: 0151 678 5111 Fax: 0151 604 7087 Email: nick.geary@dial.pipex.com; Email: nick.geary@dial.pipex.com — MB ChB 1976 Liverp.; FRCS Eng.

1981. Cons. Orthop. Surg. Arrowe Pk. & Clatterbridge Hosps. Wirral. Socs: Fell. Roy. Soc. Med. (Mem. Orthop. Sect.); Fell. BOA; Pres. Orthop. Foot Surgic. Soc. Prev: Sen. Regist. Rotat. (Orthop.) Char. Cross Hosp. Lond.; Research Fell. (Orthop.) N.wick Pk. Hosp. Harrow; Regist. (Orthop.) St. Albans City Hosp.

GEARY, Mr Philip Michael 155 High Street, Northwood HA6 1ED — MB ChB 1987 Manch.; FRCS Eng. 1993.

GEARY, Richard John 14 Wyaston Gardens, Willow Meadow Road, Ashbourne DE6 1HH — BM BS 1992 Nottm.

GEARY, Susan Christine 28 Harbut Road, London SW11 2RB — BM BS 1995 Nottm.

GEATER, John Gwilliam (retired) 45 Wellington Square, Hastings TN34 1PN — MB ChB 1967 Birm.; MRCGP 1979; DObst RCOG 1969; DTM & H Liverp. 1969. Prev: Med. Supt. Gidakom Hosp., Bhutan & Mongar Hosp. Bhutan.

GEBBIE, Ailsa Elizabeth 18 Dean Terrace, Edinburgh EH4 1NL Tel: 0131 332 7941; 32 Garscube Terrace, Edinburgh EH12 6BN Tel: 0131 337 6775 Fax: 0131 467 0007 — MB ChB 1981 Ed.; MRCOG 1986; DCH RCP Lond. 1984; DRCOG 1983. Cons. (Community Gyn.) Lothian Primary Care NHS Trust. Prev: SCMO Lothian HB; Regist. (O & G) Simpson Memor. Matern. Pavil. Edin.; SHO (Paediat.) Leicester Roy. Infirm.

GEBBIE, Henry Hugh (retired) 8/4 Back Dean, Edinburgh EH4 3UA Tel: 0131 343 1518 — MB ChB Glas. 1953; FRCP Ed. 1993; FRCGP. Prev: Hon. Apoth. to HM The Qu.

GEBRIAL, Wafik Nosshi 8 Ryefield Road, London SE19 3QU — MB BCh 1976 Cairo; MCOphth 1988; DO RCS Eng. 1983.

GEDDES, Professor Alexander (Alasdair) McIntosh, CBE 34 The Crescent, Solihull B91 1JR Tel: 0121 705 8844 Fax: 0121 705 2314 Email: a.m.geddes@bham.ac.uk — MB ChB Ed. 1957; FRCP Lond. 1981, M 1977; FRCP Ed. 1971, M 1963; FRCPath 1995; FFPHM 1998. Assoc. Dean. sch. Med. Univ. Birm; Cons. Phys. E. & S. Birm. Hosps.; Civil. Cons. Infec. Dis. & Trop. Med. RN; Examr. MRCP (UK); Dep. Dean Fac. Med. Univ. Birm. Socs: Assn. Phys.; Jt. Comm. on Vaccination & Immunization DoH; Health Educat. Auth. DoH. Prev: Cons. Adviser (Infec. Dis.) to Chief Med. Off. DoH; Examr. Final MB Univs. Sheff., Glas. & Newc.; Mem. Expert Advis. Comm. on AIDS DoH.

GEDDES, Christine Margaret South Barnbeth Farm, Bridge of Weir PA11 3RS Tel: 01505 612493 — MB ChB 1976 Aberd. Clin. Asst. (Anaesth.) Hairmyres Hosp. E. Kilbride.

GEDDES, Colin Charles Flat 3F1, 7 Havelock St., Glasgow G11 5JB — MB ChB 1989 Ed.; MRCP (UK) 1992. Career Regist. (Nephrol.) Glas. Prev: SHO III (Neprol.) Glas. Roy. Infirm.; Sho (Med.) Morriston, Swansea.

GEDDES, David Robert The Clifton Health Centre, Water Lane, Clifton, York YO30 6PS Tel: 01904 623259; 98 Heworth Green, York YO31 7TQ Tel: 01904 423609 Email: drgeddes@aol.com — MB BS 1987 Lond.; MRCGP 1992; Dip. Pract. Dermat. Wales 1993; DRCOG 1991; DCH RCP Lond. 1991. (Royal London Hospital Medical College) Socs: York Med. Soc.

GEDDES, Doris M (retired) 21 Highview Avenue, Clacton-on-Sea CO15 4DY Tel: 01255 423023 Email: dmgeddes@clara.co.uk — MB ChB 1955 Aberd.; Cert. Family Plann JCC 1961. Prev: GP & SCMO Essex.

GEDDES, Professor Duncan Mackay Royal Brompton Hospital, Sydney St., London SW3 6NP Tel: 020 7351 8182 Fax: 020 7351 8999 — MRCS Eng. LRCP Lond. 1971; MB BS (Hons.) Lond. 1971; MA Camb. 1967; MD Lond. 1979; FRCP (UK) 1982, M 1973. Cons. Phys. Brompton Hosp.; Civil. Cons. Dis. Chest. to Army & Navy. Socs: Pres. Brit. Thoracic Soc.; Brit. Thorac. Soc.; Chairm. Nat. Asthma Campaign.

GEDDES, Gabrielle Bernardine Kensington Road Surgery, 148 Kensington Road, Coventry CV5 6HY Tel: 024 7667 2466 Fax: 024 7671 7311; The Cedars, Red Lane, Burton Green, Kenilworth CV8 1PB — MB ChB Birm. 1964. (Birm.) GP. Prev: Clin. Asst. Anaesth. Birm. Hosp. Wom.; SHO Anaesth. Dudley Rd. Hosp. Birm.; Ho. Phys. E. Birm. Hosp.

GEDDES, Ian Campbell 123 Kilmarnock Road, Glasgow G41 3YT Tel: 0141 649 6231; 42 caird Gardens, Hamilton ML3 0AT Tel: 01698 420639 — MB ChB 1992 Glas.; MRCGP 1996; DFFP 1997. (University of Glasgow)

GEDDES, Jennian Ford Department of Morbid Anatomy, Royal London Hospital, Whitechapel, London E1 1BB Tel: 020 7377 7000 Ext: 2239 Fax: 020 7377 0949 Email: j.f.geddes@qmul.ac.uk — MB BS 1978 Lond.; BA (Hons.) Reading 1969; FRCPath 1997. (Roy. Free Hosp. School of Med.) Reader (Neuropath.) St. Bart. & The Lond. Sch. of Med. & Dent. Qu. Mary Univ. Lond. Socs: Amer. Assn. Neuropath.; Coun.lor of Intern Soc of Neuropath. Prev: Sen. Regist. (Neuropath.) Nat. Hosps. for Neurol. & Neurosurg. Maida Vale & Roy. Free Hosp. Lond.; Hon. Lect. (Histopath.) Roy. Free Hosp. Sch. Med.

GEDDES, John Dalziel The Surgery, Sixpenny Handley, Salisbury SP5 5PA Tel: 01725 552500 Fax: 01725 552029; Old North Farm House, Gussage St. Michael, Wimborne BH21 5JE Tel: 01725 552395 — MB BChir 1961 Camb.; MA, MB Camb. 1961, BChir 1960; DObst RCOG 1962. (Camb. & Lond. Hosp.) Prev: Clin. Asst. Diabetic Dept. Salisbury Gen. Infirm.

GEDDES, John Richard University Department of Psychiatry, Warneford Hospital, Headington, Oxford OX3 7JX Tel: 01865 226480 Fax: 01865 793101 Email: john.geddes@psychiatry.ox.ac.uk — MB ChB 1985 Leeds; MD Leeds 1994; MRCPsych 1989. Sen. Clin. Research Fell. Univ. Dept. Psychiat. Oxf.; Hon. Cons. Psychiat. Oxf. Prev: Sen. Regist. (Psychiat.) Roy. Edin. Hosp.

GEDDES, Justine Helena The Cedars, Red Lane, Burton Green, Kenilworth CV8 1PB — MB ChB 1990 Birm.; ChB Birm. 1990.

GEDDES, Karen Moore Alison Lea Medical Centre, Calderwood, East Kilbride, Glasgow G74 3BE Tel: 01355 236444; 69 Holehouse Road, Eaglesham, Glasgow G76 0JF — MB ChB 1984 Glas.; MRCGP 1988; DRCOG 1986. Prev: Trainee GP Vict. Infirm. Glas. VTS.

GEDDES, Murray Clinton 12/3b Hart Street, Edinburgh EH1 3RN — MB ChB 1993 Stellenbosch.

GEDDES, Mr Neil Kelman South Barnbeth Farm, Bridge of Weir PA11 3RS Tel: 01505 612493 — MB ChB 1977 Aberd.; FRCS Glas. 1983; Cert Gen. Av. Med. 1983. Cons. ENT Surg. Roy. Hosp. for Sick Childr. Yorkhill Glas. & GartnavelGen. Hosp. Glas.; Hon. Sen. Clin. Lect. (Otolaryngol.) Univ. Glas. Prev: Sen. Regist. (ENT) Glas. Health Bd.

GEDDES, Nicola Anne 26 Inverleith Row, Edinburgh EH3 5QH Tel: 0131 551 5091 — MB ChB 1978 Ed.; MSc (Nutrit.) Lond. 1988; MFHom RCP Lond. 1990. (Ed.) Homoeop. Phys. Edin.; Clin. Asst. (Homoeop.) Glas. Homoeopath. Hosp.

GEDDES, Pamela Mary Milton Medical Centre, 109 Egilsay Street, Glasgow G22 7JL Tel: 0141 772 1183 Fax: 0141 772 2331; 16 Durness Avenue, Glasgow G61 2AL — MB ChB 1978 Glas.; MRCGP 1984; DRCOG 1979. GP Glas.; Clin. Med. Off. (Family Plann.) Townhead Clinic Kirkintilloch.

GEDDES, Susan Margaret Division of Anaesthesia, Glasgow Royal Infirmary, Glasgow G4 08F Tel: 0141 552 3535; 28 Westbourne Gardens, Glasgow G12 9PF Tel: 0141 334 7142 — MB ChB 1984 Aberd.; FRCA 1989. Sen. Regist. (Anaesth.) Glas. Infirm. Prev: Regist. (Anaesth.) W.. Infirm. Glas.; SHO (Anaesth.) Aberd. Hosps.

GEDDIS, Arlene Elizabeth Lurgan HSSC, 100 Sloan St., Lurgan, Craigavon BT66 8NT Tel: 01762 327824 Fax: 01762 329353; Karwar, 42 Banbridge Road, Waringstown, Craigavon BT66 7QD Tel: 01762 881339 — MB BCh BAO 1972 Belf.; MRCPCH 1997; DObst RCOG 1974. SCMO Craigavon & Banbridge Health & Social Servs. Trust. Socs: Fac. Community Health.

GEDDIS, Carolyn Jane 2 Dukestown La, Lurgan, Craigavon BT66 8TB — MB BCh BAO 1997 Belf.

GEDDIS, Thomas Henry 1 Kingsway Grove, Lurgan, Craigavon BT66 7TE — MB BCh BAO 1958 Belf.; DTM & H Liverp. 1964; DRCOG 1960.

GEDDY, Paul Martyn Department of Pathology, Alexandra Hospital, Woodrow Drive, Redditch B98 7UB Tel: 01527 503030 Fax: 01527 517434 Email: pmspathology@bigfoot.com — BM 1984 Soton.; 2002 CHE in ICT, Durham Univ.; MRCPath 1993. Cons. Histopath.Alexandra Hosp. Redditon. Socs: Assn. of Clin. Pathologists; Brit. Soc. of Clin. Cytol. Prev: Sen. Regist. (Histopath.) Yorks. Regional Train. Sch.; Regist. (Histopath.) Freeman Hosp. Newc.; Cons histopath Ntees Gen. Hosp.

GEDGE, Ann Sarah Newbold Surgery, 3 Windermere Road, Chesterfield S41 8DU Tel: 01246 277381 Fax: 01246 239828 — MB ChB 1990 Bristol; MRCGP 1995; DRCOG 1994. (Univ. Bristol) G.P. Prev: Trainee GP Chesterfield; SHO (O & G) St. Mary's Hosp. Portsmouth; SHO (A & E & Psychiat.) Salisbury Gen. Infirm.

GEDGE, Jennifer South Cleveland Hospital, Marton Road, Middlesbrough TS4 3BW Tel: 01642 850850; 3 Fanacurt Road, Guisborough TS14 8BJ — MB BS 1988 Newc.; MRCP (UK) 1993. Cons. Phys. with an Interest in Elderly Care. Socs: Brit. Geriat. Soc. Prev: Sen. Regist. (Gen. & Geriat. Med.) Roy. Hallamshire Hosp. Sheff.; Regist. (Gen & Geriat. Med.) S.Cleveland Hosp. Middlesbrough.

GEDMAN, John Keith 29 Thornfield Road, Thornton, Liverpool L23 9XY — MB BCh 1977 Wales.

GEDNEY, Jacqueline Anne James Cook University Hospital, Marton Road, Middlesbrough TS4 3BW — MB BS 1985 Lond.; BSc Physics Nottm. 1980; MRCP (UK) 1992; FRCA 1993. (St. Thos.) Cons. (Anaes & IC),James Cook Univ. Hosp., Middlesbrough.

GEDNEY, John 34 West Pastures, Ashington NE63 8LB; 91 Highfield Road, South Shields NE34 6HY — BM BS 1979 Nottm.; MRCP (UK) 1984; MRCGP 1983; DRCOG 1983. GP Ashington. Prev: Regist. Univ. Edin. Rheum. Dis. Unit N.. Gen. Hosp. Edin.

GEDROYC, Wladyslaw Michal Witold — MB BS 1978 Lond.; MRCP (UK) 1982; FRCR 1985. Cons. (Radiol.) St. Mary's Hosp. Lond. Prev: Sen. Regist. (Radiol.) Guy's Hosp. Lond.; Asst. Prof. Pennsylvania State Univ.

GEE, Andrew Stephen 25 Great Norwood Street, Cheltenham GL50 2AW — MB BChir 1989 Camb.

GEE, Rev. Doctor Anne Alison, OBE 37 Floral Farm, Canford Magna, Wimborne BH21 3AT Tel: 01202 887078 Email: a.gee@ukgateway.net; 37 Floral Farm, Canford Magna, Wimborne BH21 3AT — BA 2001 Surrey; MB ChB Manch. 1966. (Manch.) p/t Clin. Asst. (Diabetes) Bournemouth. Prev: GP Bournemouth; Tutor (Gen. Pract.) Bournemouth; Chairm. Wessex GP Educat.al Trust.

GEE, Bruce Colin 24 Cameo Way, Stafford ST16 1SR — MB ChB 1996 Birm.; ChB Birm. 1996.

GEE, Charles Edward Robinson (retired) Lodge Barn, Hatton, Cotes Heath, Stafford ST21 6SH Tel: 01782 796550 — MB ChB 1947 Birm.; MRCS Eng. LRCP Lond. 1947; MRCGP 1960. Prev: Capt. RAMC.

GEE, Christopher Peter 6 The Hollies, Queen Elizabeth Hospital, Gayton Road, King's Lynn PE30 4ET — BChir 1994 Camb.

GEE, Douglas George New Bridges Acute Unit, Birkdale Way, Newbridge Road, Hull HU9 2BH Tel: 01482 321703 Fax: 01482 336926 Email: douglas.gee@herch.tr.nhs.uk — MB ChB 1990 Ed.; MMedSc Leeds 1997; MRCPsych 1995. Cons. Psychiat. Hull & E. Riding Community Health NHS Trust. Prev: Sen. Regist. (Gen. Adult Psychiat.) Yorks.; Regist. (Psychiat.) Yorks.

GEE, Duncan Roderick (retired) 28 Hungerford Road, Bournemouth BH8 0EH — MB ChB 1966 Manch. Benefits Agency Med. Serv. Prev: GP Bournemouth.

GEE, Harold Director of Postgraduate Education, Birmingham Women's Hospital, Edgbaston, Birmingham B15 2TG Tel: 0121 627 2657 Fax: 0121 678 5922 Email: harry.gee@bham-womens.thenhs.com — MB ChB 1974 Liverp.; MD Liverp. 1982; FRCOG 1993, M 1980. Cons. Obst., Director of Postgrad. Educat., Med. Director. Socs: Roy. Coll. Obst. & Gyns.; Mem. Brit. Assn. Perinatal Med.

GEE, Ian Bradshaw Cobo Surgery, Route De Carteret, Castel Tel: 01481 56404 Email: healthcaregroup@compuserve.com; Eventai, Oakmore Drive, St Martins, Guernsey GY4 6DZ Tel: 01481 34116 — MB BS 1987 Lond.; MRCGP 1995.

GEE, Ian Roderick — MB ChB 1993 Leic.; MRCP (UK) 1996. Research Regist. (Hepat. & Transpl.), Addenbrookes Hosp., Camb.

GEE, Martin Alexander — MB ChB 1984 Birm.; MRCPsych 1989; T(Psych) 1994. Cons. Psychiat. Combined Health Care Trust N. Staffs. Prev: Sen. Regist. (Psychiat.) W. Midl. RHA; Regist. (Psychiat.) Birm.

GEE, Mary Elizabeth Solihull HA, 6th Floor, Mell House 46 Diwy Lane, Solihull B91 3BU Tel: 0121 712 8300 Fax: 0121 712 8301; Wood Farm, 31 Main Street, Bagworth, Leicester LE67 1DN Email: mary.gee@solihull-ha.wmids.nhs.uk — MB BS 1977 Lond.; BA Open 1987; MRCS Eng. LRCP Lond. 1977; MFPHM RCP (UK) 1993. Cons. in Pub. Health Med. Prev: Sen. Regist. (Pub. Health Med.) Leics. HA.; Cons Pub. Health Med. Tees HA; Med. Adviser Ofsted & DFES.

GEE, Monica Naomi 1 Wansbeck Road N., Newcastle upon Tyne NE3 2LR Tel: 0191 213 5475 — MB BS 1995 Newc.

***GEE, Peter** Penn Surgery, 2A Coalway Road, Penn, Wolverhampton WV3 7LR Tel: 01902 332040 Fax: 01902 621540; Castlecroft Farm House, Radford Lane, Lower Penn, Wolverhampton WV3 8JT — MB ChB 1986 Birm.; MRCGP 1992; DFFP 1993; DRCOG 1991.

GEE, Richard Peter Lakeside Lodge, Madley, Hereford HR2 9PT — MB BS 1981 Lond.

GEE, Richard William Lower Gornal Health Centre, Bull Street, Gornal Wood, Dudley DY3 2NQ Tel: 01384 459621 Fax: 01384 359495 — MB ChB 1970 Birm.

GEE, Roger Alan Caythorpe Surgery, 52-56 High Street, Caythorpe, Grantham NG32 3DN Tel: 01400 272215 Fax: 01400 273608; Fernleigh, Frieston, Caythorpe, Grantham NG32 3BD Tel: 01400 272345 Email: roger.g@doctorupdate.net — MB ChB 1973 Manch.; BSc Nottm. 1966; MFFP 1993. GP Caythorpe Sen. Partner since 1994; Trainer GP Caythorpe; Trainer (Family Plann.) S. Lincs. HA; Clin. Med. Off. S. Lincs. HA. Prev: Trainee GP Lincoln VTS; Ho. Phys. Stepping Hill Hosp. Stockport; Ho. Surg. Wythenshawe Hosp. Manch.

GEE, Sidney 19 Victoria Street, Rochester ME1 4JE Tel: 01634 843338 Fax: 020 7486 4660; 42 Chester Close N., Regents Park, London NW1 4JE Tel: 020 7486 4660 Fax: 020 7486 4660 — MB BS 1943 Lond.; MRCS Eng. LRCP Lond. 1943. (Lond. Hosp.) Socs: Fell. Roy. Soc. Med. Prev: Ho. Phys. St. And. Hosp. Bow; Resid. Surg. Off. Tilbury Hosp.

GEE, Steven Davenport Department of Public Health, Wesham Park Hospital, Derby Road, Wesham, Nr. Kirkham, Preston PR4 3PL Tel: 01253 306344 Fax: 01253 306374; Wagtails Barn, Fleetwood Road, Esprick, Preston PR4 3HE Tel: 01253 836053 Fax: 01253 836053 Email: wagtails@blackpool.net — MB ChB 1975 Sheff.; BA Canterbury 1986; FAFPHM 1994; MCCM (NZ) 1985; DPH Otago 1980; Dip. Obst Otago 1979. Cons. Communicable Dis. Control NW Lancs. HA; Hon. Lect. Manch. Med. Sch. Prev: Dep. Med. Off. Health ChristCh., NZ; Med. Off. Health Timaru, NZ.

GEELAN, Stephen David East Midlands Centre for Forensic Mental Health, Arnold Lodge, Cordelia Close, Leicester LE5 0LE Tel: 0116 225 6066 Fax: 0116 225 6127 — MB BS 1990 Lond.; MRCPsych 1995; DHCL 1995; MA (Oxford) 1998. Cons. Forens. Psychiat., Leicester. Prev: Sen. Regist. (Forens. Psychiat.) Reaside Clinic Birm.

GEEN, Isobel Glenbourne Unit, Derriford Hospital, Plymouth Tel: 01752 777111 — MB ChB 1988 Bristol.

GEER, Penny Louise 22 Beacon Way, Banstead SM7 1DY — MB BS 1996 Newc.

GEEVES, Nolan Paul 41 Fullwell Road, Bozeat, Wellingborough NN29 7LX — BM 1995 Soton.

GEEWATER, Mr David Michael Julian The Butchery Surgery, 7 The Butchery, Sandwich CT13 9DL Tel: 01304 612138 — MB BS 1969 Lond.; FRCS Eng. 1976; MRCS Eng. LRCP Lond. 1969; Cert. Occupat. Med. Manch. 1994; Dip. Biochem. (Distinc.) Lond 1969. (Lond. Hosp.) Socs: Fell. Roy. Soc. Med. Prev: SHO (Obst.) P'boro. Dist. Hosp.; Ho. Phys. Childr. Dept. Lond. Hosp.

GEFFEN, Terence John Boris 2 Stonehill Close, London SW14 8RP Tel: 020 8878 0516 — MD Lond. 1948, MB BS 1943; FRCP Lond. 1970, M 1948. (Univ. Coll. Hosp.) Med. Advisor Capsticks Solicitors. Socs: Roy. Soc. Med. Prev: Cons. Pub. Health Med. NW Thames RHA; Sen. PMO DHSS; Ho. Phys. & Sen. Regist. (Med.) Univ. Coll. Hosp. Lond.

GEFFIN, Basil Brian Southgate Surgery, 270 Chase Side, Southgate, London N14 4PR Tel: 020 8440 9301 Fax: 020 8449 9349; 3 Elmscott Gardens, London N21 2BP Tel: 020 8364 0335 Fax: 020 8351 0568 Email: brian.geffin@btinternet.com — MB BCh Witwatersrand 1969. (Witwatersrand) Clin. Asst. (Endocrinol.) N. Middlx. Hosp. Lond. Prev: SHO (Gen. Med.) N. Middlx. Hosp. Lond.

GEGG, Jennifer Mary 161 Old Ferry Road, Saltash PL12 6BN — MB BS 1962 Lond.; MRCS Eng. LRCP Lond. 1962.

GEGGIE, David Alan Richard 4 Greystoke Avenue, Sale M33 3NT; 54 Bucklow Gardens, Lymm WA13 9RQ — MB ChB 1992 Manch.; FRCS (Eng.) 1997. Specialist Regist. (A & E) Rotat.

GEH, Esther 19 Ingham Grove, Nottingham NG7 2LQ — BM BS 1993 Nottm.

GEH, Ju Ian Charing Cross Hospital, Fulham Palace Road, London W6 8RF Tel: 020 8846 1234; 26 St Crispins Close, Hampstead, London NW3 2QF — MB BS 1988 Lond.; MRCP (UK) 1992; FRCR

1997. (University College Hospital) Sen. Regist. (Clin. Oncol.) Char. Cross Hosp. Prev: Regist. Rotat. (Clin. Oncol.) Middlx. & Mt. Vernon Hosps.; SHO Rotat. (Med.) St. Bart. Hosp. Lond.; Ho. Off. (Med.) Univ. Coll. Hosp. Lond.

GEH, Lung Chu Jenny 11 Glade Croft, Sheffield S12 2UZ — BM BS 1992 Nottm.

GEH, Shing Yang Vernon 24 Horsford Road, London SW2 5BN — BM BS 1990 Nottm.; FRCOphth 1995. Specialist Regist. - S. Thames Rotat.

GEHLHAAR, Eric William St Luke's Hospital, Crosland Moor, Huddersfield HD4 5RQ Tel: 01484 343000; Tel: 01484 604442 Email: ericgehlhaar@doctors.org.uk — MB BS 1979 Lond.; MRCPsych 1984; DGM RCP Lond. 1986. (St. Mary's) Cons. Psychiat. St. Luke's Hosp. Huddersfield. Prev: Lect. Psychiat. St. Mary's Hosp. Lond.; Regist. Bethlem Roy. Maudsley Hosp. Lond.

GEIDER, Stefan Camphill Medical Practice, St John's, Murtle House, Bieldside, Aberdeen AB15 9EP Tel: 01224 868935 Fax: 01224 868971 — State Exam Med 1993 Herdecke.

GEISER, P The Health Centre, 20 Cleveland Square, Middlesbrough TS1 2NX Tel: 01642 245069 Fax: 01642 230388 — MB BS 1973 London; MB BS 1973 London.

GELDARD, Jonathan Andrew Frederick The Surgery, Vicarage Lane, Walton on the Naze CO14 8PA Tel: 01255 674373 Fax: 01255 851005; Mayfield, Kirby Road, Walton on the Naze CO14 8RB — MRCS Eng. LRCP Lond. 1973.

GELDART, John Richard Borough Road Surgery, 167a Borough Road, Middlesbrough TS4 2EL Tel: 01642 243668 Fax: 01642 222252; 48 Church Lane, Eston, Middlesbrough TS6 9DB — MB BS 1986 Newc.

GELDART, Richard Ean Morton (retired) Arrowfield, Main St, Kirkby Malzeard, Ripon HG4 3SE Tel: 01765 658240 — MB BS 1953 Lond.; MRCS Eng. LRCP Lond. 1953; DObst RCOG 1955. Prev: Ho. Surg. (Obst.) S.lands Hosp. Shoreham.

GELDART, Thomas Richard Southampton Hospital, Tremour Rd, Southampton Tel: 02380 777222; Low Lickbarrow Farm, Lickbarrow Close, Heathwaite, Windermere LA23 2NF Email: tan.geldart@talk21.com — MB BS 1993 Lond.; BSc (Hons.) Lond. 1990; MRCP (UK) 1996. (Univ. Coll. & Middlx. Hosp.) Specialist Regist. (Med. Oncol.) Soton. Hosp. Prev: Regist. (Med. Oncol.) Roy. Bournemouth Hosp.; Regist. (Oncol.) ChristCh., New Zealand; SHO (Gen. Med.) Roy. Bournemouth Hosp.

GELDER, Alison Daphne 40A North Street, Winterborne Kingston, Blandford Forum DT11 9AZ — BM BS 1992 Nottm.

GELDER, Colin Malcolm Department of Medicine, University of Wales College of Medicine, Heath Park, Cardiff CF14 4XN; 10 Windsor Terrace, Penarth CF64 1AA — MB BS 1984 Lond.; MB BS (Hons.) Lond. 1984; PhD Lond. 1996, BSc (Hons) Immunol 1981; MRCP (UK) 1987. (Univ. Coll. Hosp.) Wellcome Trust Sen. Clin. Research Fell. & Hon. Cons. Phys. Univ. of Wales Coll. of Mecicine Cardiff; Sen. Lect. (Med.) Univ. of Wales Coll. of Med. Cardiff. Socs: Brit. Thorac. Soc.; Brit. Soc. Allergy & Clin. Immunol. Prev: Lect. (Med.) Univ. of Wales Coll. of Med. Cardiff; Wellcome Trust Advanced Train. Fell. Dept. Immunol. St. Mary's Hosp. Lond.; MRC Train. Fell. Dept. Thoracic Med. Nat. Heart & Lung Inst. Lond.

GELDER, Fiona Jane Lambeth Road Group Practice, 80 Kennington Road, London SE11 Tel: 020 7735 7918 Fax: 020 7587 5296; 60 Cleaver Square, Kennington, London SE11 4EA — MB BS 1986 Lond.; MRCGP 1990; DRCOG 1990; MSc Lond. 1993. GP Retainer Scheme. Prev: Lect. (Gen. Pract.) St. Thos. Hosp. Lond.

GELDER, Michael Graham University Department of Psychiatry, Warneford Hospital, Oxford OX3 7JX — BM BCh 1953 Oxf.; MA Oxf. 1957, BA (1st cl. Hons.) 1950, DM 1965; FRCP Lond. 1970, M 1958; FRCPsych 1972; DPM (Distinc.) Lond. 1961; DObst RCOG 1955. (Oxf. & Univ. Coll. Hosp.) Emerit. Prof. Psychiat. Univ. Oxf. Socs: Fell. RCPhys.; Fell. Roy. Coll. Psychiat.; Fell. Acad. Of Med. Sci.s. Prev: Phys. Bethlem Roy. & Maudsley Hosps.; MRC Fell. Clin. Research.; Hons. Cons. Psychiat., Oxf. Ment. Health Trust.

GELDING, Susan Valerie Newham General Hospital, Glen Road, London E13 8SL Tel: 020 7363 8001 Fax: 020 7363 8577 Email: susangelding@newhamhealth.nhs.org — MB BS 1983 Lond.; FRCP 1999; MD Lond. 1995; MRCP (UK) 1987. (Middlx. Hosp. Med. Sch. Lond.) Cons. Phys. & Sen. Lect. (Gen. Med. & s/i Diabetes & Endocrinol.) Newham Gen. Hosp. Lond., St. Bart. & Roy. Lond. Sch. Med.; Sen. Lect. and Hon. Cons., Dept of Diabetes and Metab. Med., St. Bart. and Roy. Lond. Sch. of Med., Lond.. Prev: Lect. (Med.) & Hon. Sen. Regist. The Lond. Hosp. Med. Coll.; R. D. Lawrence Research Fell. St. Mary's Hosp. Med. Sch. Lond.

GELFER, Richard Asher (retired) 27 Fortis Green, London N2 9JL — LRCP LRCS 1950 Ed.; LRCP LRCS Ed. LRFPS Glas. 1950; DPM Eng. 1954. Prev: Sen. Regist. Napsbury Hosp. & (Psychol. Med.) Char. Cross Hosp.

GELIPTER, David Mosborough Health Centre, 34 Queen Street, Mosborough, Sheffield S20 5BQ Tel: 0114 248 7488 — MRCS Eng. LRCP Lond. 1978; MRCGP 1983; DRCOG 1981. Lect. (Gen. Pract.) Univ. Sheff. Socs: Assn. Univ. Depts. Gen. Pract. Prev: GP & Primary Care Med. Adviser Trent RHA.

GELISTER, Mr James Samuel Kerr BUPA Hospital, Bushey, Watford WD2 1RD Tel: 020 8950 8550 Fax: 01923 421 8537; Garden Hospital, Hendon, London NW4 1RX Tel: 020 8203 6832 Fax: 020 7421 8537 — MB BS 1978 Lond.; MS Lond. 1988; FRCS Eng. 1982. (Univ. Coll. Hosp.) Cons. Urol. WellHo. NHS Trust Barnet, Herts. Prev: Sen. Regist. (Urol.) Roy. Marsden, St Mary's & St Helier Hosps. Lond.; Regist. (Urol.) Middlx. Hosp. Lond.; Regist. (Surg.) & Research Fell. Univ. Coll. Hosp. Lond.

GELL, Anne Elizabeth 79A Woodbury Avenue, Petersfield GU32 2EB — MB BS 1990 Lond. Trainee GP Roy. Surrey Co. Hosp. Guildford.

GELL, Ian Raymond Chesterfield & North Derbyshire Royal Hospital, Calow, Chesterfield S44 5BL Tel: 01246 277271 Fax: 01246 552607; 15 The Grange, Ashgate, Chesterfield S42 7PS Tel: 01246 567361 Email: igell@aol.com — MB ChB 1977 Leeds; FRCA Eng. 1981. Cons. Anaesth. Chesterfield & N. Derbysh. Roy. Hosp.; Clin. Dir. Critical Care. Prev: Sen. Regist. (Anaesth.) Sheff. HA.

GELLATLY, Lilian Audrey (retired) 10 Ailsa Road, Twickenham TW1 1QW Tel: 020 8892 3249 Email: audrey-gallatly@tesco.net — MB BChir 1945 Camb.; MA Camb. 1947. Prev: Deptm. Med. Off. Lond. Boro. Hounslow.

GELLER, Rosemary Janet Shropshire Health Authority, William Farr House, Royal Shrewsbury Hospital, Copthorne, Shrewsbury SY3 8XL Tel: 01743 261356 Fax: 01743 261357; Park House, Sandford, Oswestry SY11 4EX Tel: 01691 610692 Fax: 01691 610692 — MB ChB 1984 Birm.; MFPHM 1990. Dir. (Pub. Health) Shrops. HA; Hon. Sen. Clin. Lect. (Pub. Health & Epidemiol.) Univ. Birm. Prev: Cons. Pub. Health Med. Solihull HA; Regist. & Sen. Regist. (Pub. Health Med.) W. Midl. RHA.

GELLERT, Andrew Ronald Brentfield Medical Centre, 10 Kingfisher Way, London NW10 8TF Tel: 020 8459 8833 Fax: 020 8459 1374 — MB BS 1977 Lond.; MD Lond. 1987; MRCP (UK) 1979; MRCS Eng. LRCP Lond. 1977; MRCGP 1992; DRCOG 1986. (Roy. Free) Course Organiser N.wick Pk. Hosp. Prev: Trainee GP Lond.; Regist. Rotat. (Med.) Univ. Coll. Hosp. & Whittington Hosp. Lond.; SHO (Obst.) Roy. Free Hosp. Lond.

GELLERT, Selina Louise Brentfield Medical Centre, 10 Kingfisher Way, London NW10 8TF Tel: 020 8459 8833 Fax: 020 8459 1374 — MB BS 1977 Lond.; MRCS Eng. LRCP Lond. 1977; MRCGP 1982; DRCOG 1979. (Roy. Free) GP Lond. Prev: Ho. Phys. & Ho. Surg. Roy. Free Hosp. Lond.

GELLETT, Laura Rosalind 16 Woodland Grove, Bristol BS9 2BB — MB BS 1992 Lond.

GELLY, Keith James Ninewells Hospital and Medical School, Ninewells Drive, Dundee DD1 9SY Tel: 01382 660111; 20E Taylor's Lane, Dundee DD2 1AQ Tel: 01382 641070 — MB ChB 1991 Ed.; BSc (Hons) Ed. 1989; MRCP (UK) 1994; DRCPath 1988. (Edinburgh) Specialist Regist. (Haemat.) Dept. of Haemat. Ninewells Hosp. & Med. Sch. Dundee.

GELMAN, Wolf Abbey Wing, St. Peter's Hospital, Guildford Road, Chertsey KT16 0PZ; Email: wgelman@doctors.org.uk — MB BS 1991 Lond.; BSc (Hons.) Lond. 1985; MRCOG 1997; DFFP 1995. (Univ. Coll. Hosp. Lond.) Socs: Internat. Continence Soc. and Roy. Soc. Med. Prev: Sen. Regist. (O & G) P.ss Anne Hosp. S.ampton; Dist. Med. Off. SE Labrado GRHS, Canada; SHO (O & G) W.m. Hosp. & W. Lond. Hosp.

GELSON, Alan David Norman Sawston Health Centre, Link Road, Sawston, Cambridge CB2 4LB Tel: 01223 832711 Fax: 01223 836096 — MB 1968 Camb.; BA Camb. 1964, MB 1968, BChir 1967; MRCP (UK) 1970; MRCGP 1981. (Camb. & Middlx.) Prev: Ho. Phys. Middlx. Hosp. Lond.; SHO Hammersmith Hosp. Lond.; Sen. Regist. (Med.) St. Geo. Hosp. Lond.

GELSON, John 52 Mitchell Avenue, Jesmond, Newcastle upon Tyne NE2 3LA; Vine Cottage, Main St, Corbridge NE45 5LE Tel: 01434 632427 — MB ChB 1956 Birm.; MRCS Eng. LRCP Lond. 1956; MLCO 1975; LMCC 1971. (Birm.) Prev: Mem. Med. Staff Nanaimo Gen. Hosp., Canada & Riverside Memor. Hosp. Turtleford, Canada.

GELSTHORPE, Elfrida (retired) Oversley Nursing Home, 24 Epsom Road, Leatherhead KT22 8TE — MRCS Eng. LRCP Lond. 1927; BA Camb. 1924, MB 1929, BChir 1928. Prev: Med. Off. CMS N.. Sudan.

GEMBALI, Murali Friargate Surgery, Agard Street, Derby DE1 1DZ Tel: 01332 294040; 17 Priory Gardens, Oakwood, Derby DE21 4TG Tel: 01322 833663 — MB ChB 1987 Leeds; DRCOG 1992. GP Princip. Socs: Derby Med. Soc. Prev: SHO (O & G) Derby City Hosp.; SHO (Psychiat.) Kingsway Hosp. Derby.

GEMMEKE, Marie Catherine Martine Hillstones, Kemming Road, Whitwell, Ventnor PO38 2RA — Artsexamen 1992 Utrecht.

GEMMELL, Agnes Cunningham Lindsay (retired) Blairside, 1 Foundry Wind, Kilwinning KA13 Tel: 01294 552589 — MB ChB Glas. 1946.

GEMMELL, Alexander Jamieson (retired) 22 Turnberry Wynd, Castlepark, Bothwell, Glasgow G71 8EE Tel: 01698 854144 Fax: 01698 854144 — MB ChB 1973 Glas.

GEMMELL, Donald Fraser Wallacetown Health Centre, Lyon Street, Dundee DD4 6RB Tel: 01382 457629 Fax: 01382 450365 — MB ChB 1979 Aberd.; MRCGP 1983; DRCOG 1983.

GEMMELL, Elizabeth Carlops, Morehall Lane, Bolsterstone, Sheffield S36 3ST Tel: 0114 288 2530 — MB ChB Ed. 1939; MRCPsych 1971; DPM Eng. 1962; DTM & H Liverp. 1940. (Univ. Ed.) Emerit. Cons. Psychiat. Middlewood Hosp. Sheff. Socs: BMA. Prev: Sen. Asst. Psychiat. Middlewood Hosp. Sheff.; Med. Supt. Ganesh Das Hosp. Shillong.

GEMMELL, Helen Margaret 75 Swanston Avenue, Edinburgh EH10 7DA — MB ChB 1993 Sheff.

GEMMELL, Hugh Douglas (retired) Drumadoon, Westbury, Shrewsbury SY5 9BZ Tel: 01743 884282 — MB ChB 1945 Glas.; MRCGP 1968. Prev: Ho. Phys, Vict. Infirm. Glas.

GEMMELL, Ian Michael McKinley, Lt.-Col. RAMC SO1 Occ Med, Army Personnel Centre, Kentigern House, Brown Street, Glasgow Tel: 0141 224 2360 Fax: 0141 224 3284; Email: ian.gemmell@virgin.net — MB ChB 1986 Leic.; MSc (Remote Healthcare) 1996; Cert. In Occupat. Health 1997; MFOM 2000 RCP. Cons. Occ Med, APC, Glas.. Socs: Roy. Soc. Med.; Soc. Occupat. Med. Prev: Sr Occ Med, HQ ATRA Upavon; Med. Off. Rothera Base, Antarctica; GP Brit. Gp. Pract., Berlin.

GEMMELL, Jean Armour 'Beechwood', 33 Wellshot Drive, Cambuslang, Glasgow G72 8BT Tel: 0141 641 9530 — MB ChB 1951 Glas. (Univ. Glas.) Assoc. Specialist (Dermat.) S.. Gen. Hosp., Glas.

GEMMELL, John Hamilton Old Fletton Surgery, Rectory Gardens, Old Fletton, Peterborough PE2 8AY Tel: 01733 343137 Fax: 01733 894739 Email: fletton.surgery@virgin.net — MB ChB 1982 Aberd.; MRCGP 1986; DRCOG 1985. Prev: Trainee GP Aberd. VTS.

GEMMELL, Judith Anne 52 Kilbarchan Road, Bridge of Weir PA11 3EZ; 52 Kilbarchan Road, Bridge of Weir PA11 3EZ — MB ChB 1979 Ed.; MRCOG 1988. (Ed.) Cons. O & G Roy. Alexandra Hosp. Paisley. Socs: Brit. Fertil. Soc.; Brit. Menopause Soc.; Glas. Obst. & Gyn. Soc. Prev: Sen. Regist. (O & G) Glas. Roy. Infirm.

GEMMELL, Leslie William Bryn Hyfryd, Sunbank, Llangollen LL20 8EG — MRCS Eng. LRCP Lond. 1976; BSc Lond. 1973, MB BS 1976; FFA RCS Eng. 1981. (St. Mary's) Cons. Anaesth. Maelor Gen. Hosp. Wrexham.

GEMMELL, Phoebe Catherine Burns (retired) Drumadoon, Westbury, Shrewsbury SY5 9BZ Tel: 01743 884282 — M.B., Ch.B. Glas. 1945. Prev: Asst. Anat. Dep of Anaesth. Univ of Glas.

GEMMELL, Robert John Cornerways Medical Centre, Parkers Close, Gorley Road, Poulner, Ringwood BH24 1SD Tel: 01425 476688 Fax: 01425 470030; 31 St. Ives Wood, Ashley Heath, Ringwood BH24 2EA Tel: 01425 472186 — MB ChB 1976 Dundee; DRCOG 1981.

GEMMELL, Wilma Elizabeth Barrhead Health Centre, 201 Main St., Barrhead G18 1SA — MB ChB 1989 Glas.; MRCGP 1993; DRCOG 1992. Prev: Trainee GP Glas. S. VTS.

GEMMILL, John Douglas The Ayr Hospital, Dalmellington Road, Ayr KA6 6DX Tel: 01292 610555 Fax: 01292 265265 — MD 1992 Ed.; BSc (Hons.) Ed. 1980, MD 1992, MB ChB 1983; MRCP (UK) 1986. (Edinburgh) Cons. Phys. The Ayr Hosp. Socs: Brit. Cardiac Soc.; Coun. Mem. Scott. Cardiac Soc.; Scott. Soc. Phys. Prev: Regist. (Cardiol.) Roy. Infirm. Glas.; Regist. (Cardiol.) Univ. Dept. Mat. Med. Stobhill Gen. Hosp.; Regist. Roy. Infirm. Edin.

GEMMILL, Susan Health Centre, 14 Market Place, Carluke ML8 4AZ Tel: 01555 752150 Fax: 01555 751703 — MB ChB 1987 Ed.

GENDALL, Lois Frideswide (retired) 48 Wall Road, Gwinear, Hayle TR27 5HA Tel: 01209 831448 — MB ChB Leeds 1957. Prev: GP Praze Cornw.

GENDI, Nagui Safwat Tawfik Rheumatology Department, Basildon Hospital, Nether Mayne, Basildon SS16 5NL Tel: 01268 593397 Fax: 01268 593799; Whiteacre, 24 Hall Green Lane, Hutton, Brentwood CM13 2QX Tel: 01277 233447 Fax: 01277 233447 Email: ngendi@yahoo.com — MB ChB 1977 Alexandria; FRCP 1999; MRCP (UK) 1986; MSc Alexandria 1984. Cons. Rheum. & Rehabil. Basildon Hosp. Socs: Brit. Soc. Rehabil. Med.; Brit. Soc. Rheum. Prev: Sen. Regist. (Rheum. & Rehabil.) Nuffield Orthop. Centre Oxf.; Regist. (Rheum.) Roy. Free Hosp. Lond.

GENDY, Raafat Khalaf Dorset County Hospital, Dorchester DT1 2JY — MB BCh 1975 Cairo; FRCS Glas. 1987; FRCS Ed. 1986; MMedSci Birm. 1997; Intercollegiate Exam Gen.Surg.1999. Socs: Brit. Assn. Surgic. Oncol.; Brit. Trauma Soc.; Brit. Assn. Day Surg.

GENEVER, Edward Ernest 89 Chatsworth Drive, Mansfield NG18 4QU Tel: 01623 653398 Fax: 01623 460128 Email: eegenever@hotmail.com — MB ChB Birm. 1958; MRCGP 1977; FFA RCS Eng. 1973; DA Eng. 1964; DObst RCOG 1960. (Birm.) Med. Examr. Nottm. BAMS. Socs: Mansfield Med. Soc. Prev: GP Mansfield; GP (Anaesth.) Morwell Med. Clinic, Austral.

GENEVER, Richard William 89 Chatsworth Drive, Mansfield NG18 4QU — MB ChB 1997 Sheff.

GENEVIEVE, Michele Yvette Grange Lodge, Bols Cheri, Felcourt Road, Felcourt, East Grinstead RH19 2LA — MB BS 1998 Lond.; MB BS Lond 1998. SHO Surg., Sir Chas. Gairdner Hosp., W.Australia.

GENNERY, Andrew Richard Newcastle General Hospital, Westgate Road, Newcastle upon Tyne NE4 6BE Email: argennery@aol.com; Honeysuckle House, Oakwood, Hexham NE46 4LE — MB ChB 1988 Sheff.; MRCP (UK) 1993; DCH RCP Lond. 1992; Dip. Med.Sci. Newc. 1997; MRCPCH (founder member) 1996. (Sheffield) Regist. (Paediat.) N. RHA. Socs: Roy. Coll. Paediat. & Child Health; Brit. Soc. Immunol.

GENNERY, Brian Albert 6 Qualitas, Roman Hill, Bracknell RG12 7QG Tel: 01344 427927 Fax: 01344 300114 Email: bagqnal@aol.com — MB ChB 1964 Bristol; FFPM RCP (UK) 1989; Dip. Pharm. Med. RCP (UK) 1977; FRCP 1998. Cons. Pharm.med. Socs: Fell. Roy. Soc. Med.; BMA. Prev: Ho. Phys. Ham Green Hosp. Bristol; Ho. Surg. Roy. Infirm. Bristol; Capt. RAMC.

GENT, Adrian Laurence Tel: 01953 602118 Fax: 01953 605313; Badgers Well, Wreningham Road, Wymondham NR18 9NS Tel: 01953 602527 — MB BS Lond. 1970; MRCS Eng. LRCP Lond. 1970; DObst RCOG 1972. (Roy. Free) Socs: BMAS. Prev: SHO (Paediat.) St. Peter's Hosp. Chertsey; Resid. Med. Off. Qu. Charlotte's Matern. Hosp. Lond.; SHO (Gyn.) Dept. O & G Hammersmith Hosp.

GENT, Anthony Michael 57 Longford Road, Sheffield S17 4LP — MB ChB 1990 Leeds; DRCOG 1994; DFFP 1995. Med. Coordinator Humanitarian Aid Organisation HMD Internat. Lond.

GENT, Christine Barbara 67 Marks Court, Southchurch Avenue, Southend-on-Sea SS1 2RJ — MB BS 1981 Lond.; BSc (Hons.) Lond. 1978; MRCP (UK) 1986. Cons. Phys. For Elderly S.end Hosp.

GENT, Edward David 8 Wellands Close, Bromley BR1 2AQ — MB BS 1989 Lond.

GENT, Graham Michael Shanklin Medical Centre, 1 Carter Road, Shanklin PO37 7HR Tel: 01983 862245 Fax: 01983 862310; 4 Youngwoods Copse, Alverstone Garden Village, Sandown PO36 0HJ — MB BChir 1965 Camb.; MA, MB BChir Camb. 1965. (Lond. Hosp.)

GENT, Keith Steven 22 Ratcliffe Avenue, Branston, Burton-on-Trent DE14 3DA Tel: 01283 562134 — MB ChB 1977 Birm. Dip. Philosophy of Med. Soc. Apoth. 1996.

GENT, Neal Robert Edward 4 Youngwoods Copse, Alverstone Garden Village, Sandown PO36 0HJ — MB BS 1997 Lond.

GENT, Nicholas Sefton Chamberlain (retired) 35 New Road, Kirkby Lonsdale, Carnforth LA6 2AB Tel: 015242 72049 — BM BCh 1948 Oxf.; DObst RCOG 1954.

GENT, Peter Michael 69 High Street, Watchfield, Swindon SN6 8TL — MB BS 1998 Lond.; MB BS Lond 1998.

GENT, Peter Nigel Conway The Meads Surgery, Grange Road, Uckfield TN22 1QU Tel: 01825 765777 Fax: 01825 766220 — MB BS 1968 Lond.; MRCP (UK) 1976; LMCC 1971; DCH Eng. 1973.

GENT, Robert Nicolas 1 High Meadows, Bromley Cross, Bolton BL7 9AR; Hazel Grove, South View, Lindale-in-Cartmel, Grange-over-Sands LA11 6LF — MB ChB 1984 Liverp.; MSc Newc. 1989; MB ChB Liverp. l984. Dir. (Pub. Health) Morecambe Bay HA; Hon. Lect. (Pub. Health & Epidemiol.) Univ. Newc. Socs: Fac. Pub. Health Med. Prev: Dir. (Pub. Health) Lancaster HA; Cons. Pub. Health Med. S. Cumbria HA.

GENT, Roger John Four Oaks Medical Centre, Carlton House, Mere Green Road, Sutton Coldfield B75 5BS Tel: 0121 308 2080 Fax: 0121 323 4694; 158 Blake Street, Little Aston, Sutton Coldfield B74 4EU — MB ChB 1989 Leic.; MRCGP 1993; DRCOG 1992.

GENT, Timothy Matthew The Bridge Street Surgery, 30-32 Bridge Street, Downham Market PE38 9DH Tel: 01366 388888 Fax: 01366 383716; 15 Broadlands, Downham Market PE38 9JB Tel: 01366 385181 — MB BS 1979 Lond.; MRCGP 1984; DRCOG 1986. (Charing Cross) Prev: RAF Med. Br.

GENTILI, Nicoletta 75A Top Floor Flat, Woodside, London SW19 7QL — State Exam Rome 1991.

GENTLE, Peter Henderson — MB BChir 1967 Camb.; MSc (Social Med.) Lond. 1972; MA (Engineering); FRCP Lond. 1996; FFPHM 1979, M 1974; T(PHM) 1991. (Camb. & King's Coll. Hosp.) Cons. Pub. Health N. & E. Devon HA.

GENTLE, Stephen Charles Basement Flat, 7 St Andrews Square, Surbiton KT6 4EA — MB BS 1996 Lond.

GENTLE, Susan Mary Moston Lodge Children's Centre, The Countess of Chester Health Park, Liverpool Road, Chester CH2 1UL Tel: 01244 364803 Fax: 01244 365838; 5 The Stables, Station Lane, Guilden Sutton, Chester CH3 7SY — MB ChB 1982 Sheff.; MRCP (UK) 1990. (Sheffield) Cons. Community Paediat. Prev: SCMO (Child Health) Community Health Sheff.

GENTLE, William Ainslie (retired) 6 Meadow Close, Hampsthwaite, Harrogate HG3 2EX Tel: 01423 770742 — MB ChB 1948 Ed.; DObst RCOG 1953. Prev: GP Harrogate.

GENTLEMAN, Mr Douglas de Regnéville Centre for Brain Injury Rehabilitation, Royal Victoria Hospital, Jedburgh Road, Dundee DD2 1SP Tel: 01382 423196 Fax: 01382 423177 Email: douglas.gentleman@tpct.scot.nhs.uk; 49 Clepington Road, Dundee DD4 7EL Tel: 01382 462496 — MB ChB 1978 Glas.; BSc (Hons.) Glas. 1976; FRCS Eng. 1982; FRCS Glas. 1982. (University of Glasgow) Cons. Neuro-Rehabil. Tayside Primary Care Trust; Hon. Cons. Neurosurg. Tayside Univ. Hosps. Trust; Hon. Sen. Lect. (Med.) Univ. Dundee. Socs: GMC (Former Chairm. Br. Counc. Scotl.); Soc. Brit. Neurol. Surg.; Scott. Head Injury Forum. Prev: Cons. (Neurosurg.) Dundee Roy. Infirm.; Sen. Regist. (Neurosurg.) Inst. Neurol. Sci. S. Gen. Hosp. Glas.

GENTLES, Mr Andrew William (retired) 11 Hollins Crescent, Harrogate HG1 2JG Tel: 01423 565011 — MB 1958 Camb.; BChir 1957; FRCS 1968 Eng; FRCOphth 1989; DO 1962 Eng. Cons. Ophth. Surg. Harrogate Dist. Gen. Hosp. & Ripon & Dist. Hosp. Prev: Resid. Surg. Off. & Chief Clin. Asst. Moorfields Eye Hosp. Lond.

GENTLES, Helen 40 Frankland Close, Weston, Bath BA1 4EJ — MB BS 1994 Lond.; BSc Lond. 1991; MRCP (UK) 1998. (King's) SHO (Gen. Med.) Roy. Sussex Co. Hosp. Brighton.

GENTON, Alfred Michael (retired) Romansleigh, Sunny Hill, Bruton BA10 0DD Tel: 01749 813304 — MB ChB 1964 Birm.; MRCS Eng. LRCP Lond. 1964; DObst RCOG 1967. Locum GP. Prev: Jt. Med. Off., King's Sch. Bruton.

GENTON, Helen Elizabeth Romansleigh, Sunny Hill, Bruton BA10 0DD — MB ChB 1991 Birm.; ChB Birm. 1991.

GEOGHEGAN, Anthony John Maternity Department, John Radcliffe Hospital, Oxford OX3 9DZ — MB BCh BAO 1991 NUI; LRCPSI 1991.

GEOGHEGAN, Antoinette Teresa c/o Prospect House Medical Group, Prospect Place, Newcastle upon Tyne NE4 6QD Tel: 0191 284 8651; 8 Broadway W., Gosforth, Newcastle upon Tyne NE3 2JD — MB BCh BAO 1980 NUI; MRCPsych 1986. (Galway) Cons. Child & Adolesc. Psychiat./Psychotherapist (Childr.). Prev: Sen. Regist. (Child & Adolesc. Psychiat.) Fleming Nuffield Unit Newc.; Sen. Regist. (Adolesc. Psychiat.) Young Peoples Unit Newc. u. Tyne.

GEOGHEGAN, Colin John Occupational Health Service, Royal Mail Mount Pleasant, Farringdon Road, London EC1 1BB Tel: 020 7239 2286 Fax: 020 7239 2339 — MB BCh BAO 1981 NUI; MSc (Occupat. Med.) Lond. 1986; MRCPI 1985; LRCPI & LM, LRCSI & LM 1981; AFOM RCP Lond. 1988. Area Med. Adviser Lond. Socs: Fell. Roy. Soc. Med.; Soc. Occupat. Med. Prev: Sen. Med. Off. BBC; Employm. Med. Adviser EMAS; SHO Renal Unit Jervis St. Hosp. Dub.

GEOGHEGAN, Hugh Francis The Health Centre, Queensway, Billingham TS23 2LA Tel: 01642 552700/552151 Fax: 01642 532908; Arncliff, 188 Station Road, Billingham TS23 2RT Tel: 01642 553740 — MB BCh BAO 1977 Dub.; MA Dub. 1980, BA 1977; MRCGP 1981; DRCOG 1981; DCH RCPSI 1980. (Univ. Dub.) Prev: Trainee GP Cleveland VTS; Ho. Off. St. Jas. Hosp. Dub.

GEOGHEGAN, James 1 Tulip Gardens, Havant PO9 3BQ — MB ChB 1997 Birm.

GEOGHEGAN, John Martin 23 Holt Coppice, Aughton, Ormskirk L39 6SD Tel: 01695 421243 — BM BS 1997 Nottm.; BMedSci. Nottm. 1995. (Nottingham) Surg. SHO Rotat. Nottm.

GEOGHEGAN, Stephen Landsborough The Westmoreland Centre, 22 Railway Road, Leigh WN7 4AU Tel: 01942 679703; Fairways, Broseley Avenue, Culcheth, Warrington WA3 4HH Tel: 01925 762660 Fax: 01925 762660 — LMSSA 1959; MB Camb. 1960; BChir Camb. 1961; MA Camb. 1964, BA 1956; BA Oxf. 1956; LMSSA Lond. 1959. (Univ. Oxf.) Socs: BMA; Anglo German Med. Soc. (Former Pres.). Prev: Chairm. NW RHA Speciality Train. Comm. for Gen. Pract.; Chairm. NW RHA Med. Comm.; Capt. RAMC (Nat. Serv.) & War Office Civil. Med. Pract. Mönchen Gladbach, Germany.

GEORGALLOU, Marina 45 Broad Walk, London N21 3BL — MB BS 1998 Lond.; MB BS Lond 1998.

GEORGE, Abraham 18 Oakfields Road, Cringleford, Norwich NR4 6XE — MB BS 1982 Madras.

GEORGE, Ajay 19 Karslake Road, Mossley Hill, Liverpool L18 1EY — MB ChB 1996 Liverp.

GEORGE, Alan Michael 11 Queen Wood Close, Cyncoed, Cardiff CF23 9JH Tel: 029 2049 9234 — MB ChB 1964 Wales; FFCM 1983, M 1973; DPH Bristol 1969. (Cardiff) Dep. Chief Med. Off. Welsh Off. Prev: Specialist Community Phys. (Acute Sickness Servs.) S. Glam. AHA (T).

GEORGE, Alison Mary 38 Larkspur Terrace, Newcastle upon Tyne NE2 2DU; 22 Mitchell Avenue, Jesmond, Newcastle upon Tyne NE2 3LA Tel: 0191 281 0307 — MB BS 1990 Newc.; MRCGP 1996; DFFP. (Newcastle upon Tyne)

GEORGE, Alun Michael Staploe Medical Centre, Brewhouse Lane, Soham, Ely CB7 5JD Tel: 01353 624121 Fax: 01353 624203 — MB BS 1987 Lond.; MA Camb. 1887, BA 1984; MRCGP 1991; DCH RCP Lond. 1990; DRCOG 1990. (The Roy. Lond.)

GEORGE, Mr Amin Fouad Princess Margaret Hospital, Okus Road, Swindon SN1 4JU Tel: 01793 536231 Fax: 01793 426595; 109 Bath Road, Swindon SN1 4AX Tel: 01793 534330 — MB ChB 1975 Cairo; FRCS Ed. 1984; FRCS Glas. 1984. (Cairo Univ. Eygpt) Assoc. Specialist (Trauma & Orthop.) P.ss Margt. Hosp. Swindon. Socs: Brit. Orthop. Assn. Prev: Staff Grade Surg. (Trauma & Orthop.) P.ss Margt. Hosp. Swindon; Cons. Orthop. Surg. Abha, Saudi Arabia; Regist. (Orthop.) P.ss Alexandra Hosp. Harlow.

GEORGE, Andrew Tel: 01606 883410 — MB ChB 1987 Manch.; 2001 MRCA; BSc (Med. Sci.) St. And. 1984; FFA RCSI 1992; DA (UK) 1989. Cons. Anaesth. Leighton Hosp. Crewe. Prev: Regist. Rotat. (Anaesth.) Countess of Chester Hosp.

GEORGE, Arnold (retired) Holmwood, 20 New Wokingham Road, Crowthorne RG45 6JJ Tel: 01344 774790 — MB BS 1949 Lond.; MRCGP 1976. Prev: Ho. Phys. W.m. Childr. Hosp.

GEORGE, Batheswa 10A Woodside Avenue, North Finchley, London N12 8BG — MB BS 1968 Poona; FRCPath 1993.

GEORGE, Boniface 90 Heston Grange, Heston, Hounslow TW5 0HD — LRCPI & LM, LRSCI & LM 1963; LRCPI & LM, LRCSI & LM 1963; FRCPI 1968; MRCPI 1969.

GEORGE, Brychan (retired) Low Ridge, 6 Aldersgate Road, Cheadle Hulme, Cheadle SK8 7PJ — MRCS Eng. LRCP Lond. 1945; MFOM RCP Lond. 1979. Prev: Regional Med. Adviser N. W. Gallaher Gp. Cos.

GEORGE, Catharine Mary The Long House, 73-75 East Trinity Road, Edinburgh EH5 3EL Tel: 0131 552 4919; 125 Trinity Road, Edinburgh EH5 3LB — MB ChB 1989 Manch.; MRCGP 1994; DIP IMC 1992. Partner in Gen. Pract.; Course Organiser N. Lothian Train. (VTS).

GEORGE, Professor Sir Charles Frederick British Heart Foundation, 14 Fitzhardinge St., London W1H 6DH Tel: 020 7487 7122 Fax: 020 7486 1273; 15 Westgate Street, Southampton SO14 2AY — MB ChB 1965 Birm.; BSc (Hons.) Birm. 1962, MD 1974; FRCP Lond. 1978, M 1968; MRCS Eng. LRCP Lond. 1965; FFPM RCP Lond. 1989. (Birm.) Med Dir. BHF; Dean of Med. Univ. Soton.; Mem. Gen. Med. Counc. (Chairm. Educat. Comm.); Chairm. Jt. Formulary Comm. Brit. Nat. Formulary; Prof. Clin. Pharmacol. Univ. Soton. Socs: BMA; Brit. Pharm. Soc.; Roy. Soc. Med. Prev: Sen. Lect. (Med.) Univ. Soton.; Sen. Regist. Hammersmith Hosp. Lond.; Regist. (Med.) Gen. Hosp. Birm.

GEORGE, Mr Christopher David Department of Diagnostic Radiology, Epsom General Hospital, Dorking Road, Epsom KT18 7EG Tel: 01372 735173 — MB BS 1980 Lond.; FRCS Eng. 1985; FRCR 1991; T(R) (CR) 1993. (Westm.) Cons. Diag. Radiol. Epsom Gen. Hosp.; Price Fell. Surgic. Research Univ. Louisville, Kentucky, USA 1985-6. Socs: Fell. Roy. Soc. Med.; Radiol. Soc. N. Amer.; Amer. Roentgen Ray Soc.. Prev: Sen. Regist. & Regist. (Radiol.) St. Geo. Hosp. Lond.; Regist. (Surg.) Ealing & Hammersmith Hosps. Lond.; Regist. (Surg.) W.m. Hosp. Lond.

GEORGE, Colette Mary 16 Hanover Road, Norwich NR2 2HD — MB ChB 1987 Manch.; MA Camb. 1988. Trainee GP Norwich.

GEORGE, David Michael 3 Darlow Drive, Biddenham, Bedford MK40 4AX — MB BS 1955 Lond.; DObst RCOG 1960. (Univ. Coll. Hosp.) Prev: Ho. Surg. W. Middlx. Hosp. Isleworth; Ho. Phys. N. Middlx. Hosp. Lond.; Ho. Surg. (Obst.) Mayday Hosp. Thornton Heath.

GEORGE, David William Rowland The Health Centre, Canterbury Way, Stevenage SG1 4LH Tel: 01438 357411 Fax: 01438 720523 — MB BS 1958 Lond.; MRCS Eng. LRCP Lond. 1958. (Univ. Coll. Hosp.)

GEORGE, Diane (retired) 15 Park An Gwarry, Carnon Downs, Truro TR3 6XB Tel: 01872 864953 — MB ChB Aberd. 1962; DPH Dundee 1968. Prev: SCMO Cornw. & I. of Scilly HA.

GEORGE, Doreen Emily The Old Rectory, Himley, Dudley DY3 4LB — MB ChB 1945 Birm. Prev: Ho. Surg. Gen. Hosp. Walsall.

GEORGE, Eku Melissa 8 Stumpcross Way, Stumpcross Fields, Pontefract WF8 2DF — MB ChB 1981 Manch.

GEORGE, Emmanuel Arrowe Park Hos[ital, Arrowe Park Road, Upton CH49 5PE Tel: 0151 604 7244 Fax: 0151 604 7214; The White House, 34 Meols Drive, Hoylake, Wirral CH47 4AN Tel: 0151 632 4545 Fax: 0151 632 4575 Email: manegeorge@aol.com — MB ChB 1984 Liverp.; PhD (Pharmacol.) CNAA 1979; BSc (Hons.) Liverp. 1977; MRCP (UK) 1987. Cons. Phys. specialising in Rheum. Wirral health Auth. Wirral. Socs: FRCP. Prev: Regist. Rotat. (Gen. Med.) Countess of Chester Hosp. Chester; Regist. Rotat. Walton Hosp. Liverp.; SHO (Gen. Med. Rotat.) Walton & Fazakerley Hosps. Liverp.

GEORGE, Frederick Owens Baronscourt Surgery, 89 Northfield Broadway, Edinburgh EH8 7RX Tel: 0131 657 5444 Fax: 0131 669 8116 — MB ChB 1977 Ed.; MRCGP 1981; DRCOG 1980. (Ed.) Lect. (Gen. Pract.) Univ. Edin. Socs: BMA. Prev: SHO (A & E) W.. Gen. Hosp. Edin.; SHO (Paediat.) W.. Gen. Hosp. Edin.; SHO (O & G) Bangour Gen. Hosp.

GEORGE, Gerald Harold Matthias 99 Howards Road, London E13 8AZ — BM 1990 Soton.; BSc (Hons.) Portsmouth 1986; MRCP (UK) 1994. Regist. (Rheum.) Guy's Hosp. Lond. Prev: Regist. (Rheum. & Med.) Maidstone Hosp.

GEORGE, Gillian (retired) Genitourinary Medicine Office, Exmoor Unit, North Devon District Hospital, Raleigh Park, Barnstaple EX31 4JB Tel: 01271 22483 Email: gill.george@virgin.net — MB ChB Ed. 1961. Prev: Cons. Genitourin. Med. N. Devon Dist. Hosp. Barnstaple.

GEORGE, Grizelda Jane Celia Accident & Emergency Department, The Horton Hospital, Oxford Radcliffe Hospitals NHS Trust, Banbury OX16 9AL Tel: 01295 229661 Fax: 01295 229389; 3 Field House Drive, Oxford OX2 7NT Tel: 01865 559124 Fax: 01865 556181 Email: grizelda_graham@talk21.com — BM BCh 1977 Oxf.; MA, DPhil Oxf. 1977; FRCS Eng. 1987; FFAEM 1996. (Guy's Hosp. Med. Sch.) Cons. A & E Med. Horton Gen. Oxf. Radcliffe Hosp.s NHS Trust. Socs: Fell. Roy. Soc. Med.; Brit. Assn. Accid. & Emerg. Med.; St Hildas Med. Soc. Prev: SHO (Surg.) Battle Hosp. Reading; Ho. Phys. Guy's Hosp. Lond.; Ho. Surg. Guy's Hosp. Lond.

GEORGE, Helen Brenda-Lee 9 Leslie Road, London E11 4HF — MB BS 1989 Lond.

GEORGE, Helen Mary Shingler Priory Avenue Surgery, 2 Priory Avenue, Caversham, Reading RG4 7SE Tel: 0118 947 2431 Fax: 0118 946 3340 — MB ChB 1985 Birm.; DRCOG 1990. Prev: Trainee GP Sandwell Dist. Gen. Hosp. VTS.

GEORGE, Henry Robin (retired) 75 Cunliffe Close, Oxford OX2 7BJ Tel: 01865 511969 — MD 1972 Lond.; MB BS 1952; DPM Eng. 1960. Prev: Cons. Psychiat. Brighton, & Cuckfield & Crawley Health Dists.

GEORGE, Hilary Margaret 22 Whitehall Pl, Aberdeen AB25 2PA — MB ChB 1997 Aberd.

GEORGE, Iain Roger 2 Claypool Farm Close, Hutton Henry, Hartlepool TS27 4QZ — MB ChB 1969 Glas.

GEORGE, James c/o Department of Medicine for the Elderly, Cumberland Infirmary, Carlisle CA2 7HY — MB ChB 1977 Liverp.; FRCP 1993; MRCP (UK) 1980. Cons. Phys. Cumbld. Infirmiary Carlisle; Hon. Sen. Lect. Univ. Newc. Socs: BMA & Brit. Geriat. Soc. Prev: Sen. Regist. (Geriat. & Gen. Med.) Leeds & Bradford HAs; Regist. (Neurol.) Leeds Gen. Infirm.; Lect. (Med.) Univ. Aberd.

GEORGE, Mr James Douglas Eaton Chase, Unthank Road, Norwich NR4 7QW Tel: 01603 54137 — MB BCh BAO 1961 Belf.; FRCSI 1965; FRCS Ed. 1966. (Belf.) Cons. Surg. Norf. & Norwich Hosp.

GEORGE, Jennie Ceridwen (retired) 32 Coventry Road, Ilford IG1 4QU Tel: 020 8554 3442 Email: ceridwen.george@talk121.com — MB BS 1950 Lond.; MRCS Eng. LRCP Lond. 1950. Prev: Asst. Med. Off. Lond. Boro. Newham.

GEORGE, John Roderick Graham Hilton Lodge, Hilton, Derby DE65 5FP — MRCS Eng. LRCP Lond. 1952. (Birm.) Maj. RAMC, TA, Med. Off. Qu.'s Own Roy. Regt., Staffs. Yeomanry. Prev: Med. Off. Roy. Milit. Acad. Sandhurst & Staff Coll. Camberley.

GEORGE, Julie Yvette 3 Surrendon Crescent, Brighton BN1 6WE — BM 1992 Soton.

GEORGE, Kadayath Abraham Department of Clinical Anaesthesia, Belfast City Hospital, Lisburn Road, Belfast BT9 7AB Tel: 02890 263842, 02890 329241 Email: kadayath@aol.com; 4 Piney Park, Belfast BT9 5QU Tel: 02890 667898 Email: kadayath@aol.com — MB BS 1967 Panjab, India; MS (Anaesth.) Panjab, India 1971, MB BS 1967; FFA RCSI 1975; DA Panjab, India 1969. (Christian Med. Coll. Ludhiana) Cons. Anaesth. Belf. City Hosp. Socs: Assn. Anaesth. UK & Irel.; BHA; Intens. Care Soc. UK & I. Prev: Vis. Asst. Prof. Anaesthsiol. Oregon Health Scis. Univ. Portland, Oregon, USA.

GEORGE, Kurien 23 Ravenswood Crescent, Harrow HA2 9JL — MB BS 1953 Ceylon; DTM & H Ceylon 1963. (Ceylon) Socs: BMA. Prev: Med. Off. Govt. Health Servs. Ceylon.

GEORGE, Mrs Leelamma 159 Burton Road, Eastbourne BN21 2RU Tel: 01323 27934 — MB BS 1976 Kerala; MCOphth Lond. 1989; DO RCPSI 1989.

GEORGE, Lesley Meadowside, Hemhill, Lugwardine, Hereford HR1 4AL Tel: 01432 850330 Fax: 01432 850330; Hereford Community NHS Trust, Belmont Abbey, Hereford HR1 4AL Tel: 01432 850330 — MB ChB 1982 Birm.; MFCM 1988; MFPHM 1989. Community Paediat. Hereford Community NHS Trust. Prev: SR (Pub. Health Med.) W. Midl. RHA; Trainee GP Much Birch; SHO (Geriat.) Roy. Shrewsbury Hosp.

GEORGE, Lindsay David 4 St Agatha Road, Heath, Cardiff CF14 4EB — MB BCh 1991 Wales; MRCP (UK) 1994.

GEORGE, Marc Dominic 10 Birch Street, Nayland, Colchester CO6 4JA — MB BS 1994 Lond.

GEORGE, Marguerite (retired) 2 Frobisher Way, Goring-by-Sea, Worthing BN12 6EU Tel: 01903 246251 — MB BS 1939 Lond.; MRCS Eng. LRCP Lond. 1940.

GEORGE, Marina Sanu 107 Upper Selsdon Road, South Croydon CR2 0DP — MB BS 1997 Lond.

GEORGE, Mr Mark Lawrence 33 The Avenue, Radlett WD7 7DQ Email: m.l.george@btinternet.com — MB BS 1991 Lond.; BSc (1st. cl. Hons.) Lond. 1988; FRCS Eng. 1995. (St Mary's Hospital London) Higher Surg. Trainee (Gen. Surg.) S. Thames HA Kings Coll. Hosp.; Research Regist. at Inst. of Cancer Research & Roy. Marsden Hosp., Sutton. Prev: SHO Rotat. (Surg.) St. Mary's Hosp. Lond.

GEORGE, Marta Joy Anna The Health Centre, 103 Brown Street, Broughty Ferry, Dundee DD5 1EP Tel: 01382 731331 Fax: 01382 737966 — MB ChB 1968 St. And. (St. And.)

GEORGE, Mary O & G Department, Royal Victoria Infirmary, Newcastle upon Tyne; Flat 7, 40 Burdon Terrace, Newcastle upon Tyne NE2 3AE Tel: 0191 281 6795 Fax: 0191 281 6795 Email: thefamilygeorge@aol.com — MB BS 1982 Kerala; DFFP; MRCOG 1991. (T D Medical College, Alleppey, Kerala) Cons. Gynaecologist (locum), Roy. Vict. Infirm., Newc.-upon-Tyne; Cons.(locum) in O & G, Univ. Hosp. Of N. Durh., Durh.; Cons. (locum) in O & G, PeterBoro. Dist. Hosp. PeterBoro. Socs: Eur. Soc. Obst. & Gyn.; Menopause Soc.; Roy. Soc. Med. Prev: Regist. (O & G) Ealing Hosp. Lond.; Regist. (Urogyn.) Roy. Vict. Infirm. Newc. u. Tyne; SHO (O & G) N. Tyneside Gen. Hosp. Tyne & Wear.

GEORGE, Mecheril Itty 2 Glebe Avenue, Bothwell, Glasgow G71 8AA — MB BS 1972 Mysore.

GEORGE, Melanie June 12 Milner Green, Warmsley, Bristol BS30 7BF — MB BS 1991 Adelaide.

GEORGE, Melapurethu Georgie Lisnaskea Health Centre, Drumhaw, Lisnaskea, Enniskillen BT92 0JB Tel: 028 6772 1443 Fax: 028 6772 2526 — MB BS 1974 Mysore.

GEORGE, Michael (retired) Northfield Cottage, Northfield Lane, Barnstaple EX31 1QD Tel: 01271 42967 — MB ChB 1958 Ed.; MB ChB (Hons.) Ed. 1962; BSc (Physiol., Hons.) Ed. 1958; FRCP Lond. 1980, M 1967; FRCP Ed. 1977, M 1966. Prev: Cons. Phys. N. Devon Dist. Hosp.

GEORGE, Michael (retired) Paglesham, 17 The Causeway, Boxford, Sudbury CO10 5JR Tel: 01787 211789 Fax: 01787 211808 — MB BS Lond. 1961; MB BS Lond. 1961; DObst RCOG 1963.

GEORGE, Michael John 46 Chase Way, Southgate, London N14 5DE — MB BS 1984 Lond.; BSc (Hons.) Lond. 1981, MB BS 1984; MRCP (UK) 1988. (Westm. & King's Coll. Hosp.)

GEORGE, Michelle Margaret Haydon Bridge Health Centre, North Bank, Haydon Bridge, Hexham NE47 6HG — MB ChB 1990 Aberd.; MRCGP 1995. (Aberdeen University)

GEORGE, Mohan Medical Centre, Manor Court Avenue, Nuneaton CV11 5HX — MB BS 1984 Magadh.

GEORGE, Mohan Edward The Surgery, Marlborough, Seaham SR7 7TS Tel: 0191 581 2866 Fax: 0191 513 0393 — MB BS 1974 Kerala. (Med. Coll. Trivandrum)

GEORGE, Mr Nicholas James Robert The Old Rectory, Wolverhampton Road, Himley, Dudley DY3 4LB — MB BS 1970 Lond.; MD Bristol 1987; FRCS Eng. 1975. Fell. Europ. Bd. Urol.

GEORGE, Mr Nicolas David Langley 19 Wynford Avenue, Leeds LS16 6JN Tel: 0113 275 7820 — BM BS 1985 Nottm.; BMedSci Nottm. 1983; FRCOphth 1990. Cons. Ophth. Leeds Gen. Infirm. & Dewsbury Dist. Hosp. Socs: BMA. Prev: Sen. Regist. Leeds Gen. Infirm. Regist. Addenbrooke's Hosp. Camb.

GEORGE, P K Hirwaun Health Centre, Hirwaun, Aberdare CF44 9NS Tel: 01685 811999 Fax: 01685 814145.

GEORGE, Philip 1 Hall Park, Swanland, North Ferriby HU14 3NL Email: medical.philip@pkgeorge.karoo.co.uk — MB ChB 1997 Ed.

GEORGE, Philip Jeremy Maplesden Department of Thoracic Medicine, The Middlesex Hospital, Mortimer St., London W1T 3AA Tel: 0207 380 9005 Fax: 0207 637 5809 Email: jeremy.george@uclh.org — MB BS 1979 Lond.; MA (Zool.) 1976, MSc (Neuroendocrinol.) Oxf. 1981; MD Lond. 1993; FRCP 1997. (St. Thos.) Cons. Phys. (Respirat. & Gen. Med.) Univ. Coll. Hosps. Lond. Socs: Roy. Soc. of Med.; Brit. Thoracic Soc.; Europ. Respirat. Soc. Prev: Cons. Phys. (Respirat. & Gen. Med.) N. Middlx. & St. Bart. Hosps. Lond.; Sen. Regist. (Thoracic Med.) Lond. Chest Hosp. & Lond. Hosp.; Research Fell. & Regist. (Med.) Univ. Coll. Hosp. Lond.

GEORGE, Miss Phyllis Ann (retired) 9B Rosslyn Hill, Hampstead, London NW3 5UL Tel: 020 7794 3476 — MB BS Lond. 1948; FRCS Eng. 1953; MRCS Eng. LRCP Lond. 1948. Prev: Vice-Pres. RCS Eng. 1988-90.

GEORGE, Puthukudiyil Mathai 10A Woodside Avenue, London N12 8BG — MB BS 1968 Poona.

GEORGE, Mr Pynadath Pathross Chorley & South Ribble NHS Trust General Hospital, Chorley PR7 1PP; 11 The Croft, Euxton, Chorley PR7 6LH — MB BS 1974 Kerala; FRCS Glas. 1988. Cons. Gen. Surg. Chorley & S. Ribble NHS Trust. Socs: BMA; Brit. Assn. Surgic. Oncol.; Assn. Surg.

GEORGE, Rani Louisa The Medical Centre, Grove Green, Maidstone ME14 5TQ Tel: 01622 736777; 350A Loose Road, Maidstone ME15 9TT — MB BS 1970 Kerala. (Trivandrum Med. Coll.) Socs: Brit. Med. Acupunct. Soc. & Brit. Med. & Dent. Hypn. Soc. Prev: GP Maidstone; Regist. (Med.) S. Lond. Hosp. Wom.

GEORGE, Rhodri Iwan Davies and Partners, Meddygfa Teilo, Crescent Road, Llandeilo SA19 6HL Tel: 01558 823435 Fax: 01558 824045; Llys Nini, Church Road, Llanedi, Pontardulais, Swansea SA4 1YS Tel: 01792 884878 — MB BCh 1989 Wales; MRCGP 1994.

GEORGE, Richard David, OStJ, Col. late RAMC Ashley Stud Farm, Ashley Lane, Box, Corsham SN13 8AW Tel: 01225 742901 Fax: 01225 744902 — MB BS 1968 Lond.; FRCGP 1987, M 1975; MFFP 1993; DObst RCOG 1974. (Lond. Hosp.) p/t Sessional Med. Off.- MOD. Prev: Command Adviser (Gen. Pract.) UK.; Cdr. Med. 5th Div.; Staff Med. Off., DNBCC.

GEORGE, Richard Hugh Birmingham Childrens Hospital, Steelhouse Lane, Birmingham B4 6NH Tel: 0121 333 9816 Fax: 0121 333 9811; Belle Walk, 21 Mucklow Hill, Halesowen B62 8NT Tel: 0121 421 3200 — MB ChB Birm. 1967; FRCPath 1986, M 1974. Cons. Microbiol. Birm. Childr. Hosp. & Birm. Wom. Hosp.; Sen. Clin. Lect. Birm. Med. Sch. Socs: Brit. Soc. Antimicrob. Chemother.; Hosp. Infec. Soc.; Assn. Med. Microbiol. Prev: Lect. (Clin. Bacteriol.) Birm. Univ. Med. Sch.

GEORGE, Rina Rachel 4 Piney Park, Belfast BT9 5QU — BM BS 1998 Nottm.; BM BS Nottm 1998.

GEORGE, Robert Charles Respiratory & Systemic Infection Laboratory, Central Public Health Laboratory, 61 Colindale Avenue, London NW9 5HT Tel: 020 8200 4400 Fax: 020 8205 6528 Email: rgeorge@phls.org.uk — MB BS 1976 Lond.; MSc (Med. Microbiol.) Lond. 1980, BSc 1973; FRCPath 1995, M 1983. (Lond. Hosp.) Dir. & Cons. Med. Microbiol. Respirat. & Systemic Infec. Laborat. Centr. Pub. Health Laborat. Lond.; Hon. Sen. Lect. (Clin. Scs.) Lond. Sch. Hyg. & Trop. Med. Lond. Socs: (Ex-Counc.) Brit. Soc. Antimicrobial Chemother.; Assn. Med. Microbiol.; Assn. Clin. Path. Prev: Cons. Med. Microbiol. Antibiotic Ref. Laborat. Div. Hosp. Infec, Centr. Pub. Health Laborat. Lond.; Asst. Med. Microbiol. (Pub. Health Lab. Serv. Bd.); Hon. Sen. Regist. Centr. Middlx. Hosp. Lond.

GEORGE, Robert Ernest James East Wing, Esk Medical Centre, Ladywell Way, Musselburgh EH21 6AA Tel: 0131 665 2267 Fax: 0131 653 2348 — MB ChB 1969 Glas. (Glas.) Prev: Ho. Surg. Glas. Roy. Infirm.; SHO (Obst.) Vale of Leven Hosp. Alexandria.

GEORGE, Robert John Dunnett Camden & Islington Community Health Services, NHS Trust & UCL Medical School 1st Floor Wolfson Building, Palliative Care Centre, 48 Riding House St., London W1N 8AA Tel: 020 7530 6200 Fax: 020 7530 6220 Email: rob.george@ucl.ac.uk; 250 Devonshire Road, London SE23 3TQ Tel: 020 8699 5141 Fax: 020 8699 5141 Email: rob@ari-el.org.uk — MB BChir 1977 Camb.; MA, MD Camb. 1986 MB, BChir 1977; MRCP (UK) 1979; FRCP (UK) 1997. (King's Coll. Hosp.) Sen. Lect. & Hon. Cons. Palliat. Med. Univ. Coll. Lond. Hosps. Trust & Camden & Islington Community NHS Trust; Dir. Palliat. Care Centre Camden & Islington Community Health Servs. NHS Trust & UCL Med. Sch.; Hon. Cons. Hospice of St. Johns Lond.; Hon Cons. (Oncol.) UCL Hosps. Trust. Socs: Assn. Palliat. Med.; Fell.RSM. Prev: Sen. Regist. Lond. Chest Hosp. & Univ. Coll. Hosp. Lond.; MRC Research Fell. Lond. Chest & Brompton Hosp. Lond.; Regist. Centr. Middlx. Hosp. Lond.

GEORGE, Rosemary Hillside, Bircham Road, Snettisham, King's Lynn PE31 7NG — MB ChB 1967 Birm.; FFA RCS Eng. 1972.

GEORGE, Sabina Elizabeth 107 Upper Selsdon Road, Selsdon, Croydon CR2 0DF — MB BS 1996 Lond.

GEORGE, Shane John 7 Poplars, Breakspear Road N., Harefield, Uxbridge UB9 6NR — MB BS 1986 Lond.; MRCP (UK) 1991; DA (UK) 1991.

***GEORGE, Sheena Mariam** 262 Alwyn Road, Rugby CV22 7RR — MB BS 1988 Lond.; DO RCPSI 1991.

GEORGE, Sheila Elizabeth (retired) Rams Corner, Little Cowarne Bromyard, Hereford Tel: 01885 400274 — MB BCh BAO 1951 Dub. Exam. Med. Pract. for DSS. Prev: Clin. Asst. Diabetic Clinic Worcester Roy. Infirm.

GEORGE, Sheru Abraham Dermatology Department, Amersham Hospital, Amersham HP7 0JD Tel: 01494 734612 Fax: 01494 734620; 5 Oakdene, Beaconsfield HP9 2BZ Tel: 01494 673478 — MB ChB 1985 Dundee; MRCP (UK) l988. Cons. Dermat. Amersham Hosp.; Hon. Cons. Dermat. Oxf. Socs: Fell. Roy. Soc. Med. Prev: Sen. Regist. (Dermat.) Amersham & Oxf.

GEORGE, Simon Pynummootil Greenwich District General Hosptial, Vanburgh Hill, London SE10 Tel: 020 8858 8141 — MB BS 1975 Kerala; BSc Kerala 1965; MRCPsych 1987. Cons. Psychiat. Greenwich Dist. Gen. Hosp. Lond.

GEORGE, Sonia William 35 Devonshire Place, London W1N 1PE Tel: 020 7935 5252; 39 Temple Sheen Road, London SW14 7QF — MB BCh 1976 Cairo; FFA RCSI 1989. Cons. Anaesth. Obst. Unit Portland Hosp. for Wom. & Childr. Lond.; Indep. Dent. Anaesth. Pract. Lond. Prev: Cons. Anaesth. (IVF & Fertil. Unit.) Humana Wellington Hosp. Lond.

***GEORGE, Stella** 1 Fountain Road, Edgbaston, Birmingham B17 8NJ — MB ChB 1996 Birm.

GEORGE, Stephen Llanyon University of Southampton, Health Care Research Unit, Mailpoint 805, Southampton General Hospital, Tremona Road, Southampton SO16 6YD Tel: 023 809 6530 Fax: 023 8079 6529 Email: pluto@soton.ac.uk; Email: pluto@sotn.ac.uk — MB BS 1980 Lond.; MB BS Lond.1980; MSc Lond. 1984; MD Sheff. 1994; MFPHM RCP (UK) 1991. (St. Bart.) Sen. Lect. ReaderHealth Med.) Univ. Soton.; Director, Univ. of S.ampton Health Care Research Unit; Hon. Cons. epidemiologist, S.ampton Uni. Hosps. Trust. Socs: Fell. Roy. Statistical Soc.; Soc. Social Med. Prev: Lect. (Epidemiol.) Univ. Sheff. 1988-1992; Sen. Lect. In Pub. Health Med., Uni. Of S.ampton 1992-2000.

GEORGE, Mr Thomas Kunniparampil Blackburn Royal Infirmary, Blackburn BB2 3LR Tel: 01254 294033 Fax: 01254 294566 — MB BS 1975 Poona; 1999 Dip HSM Univ. of S. Lancs., Preston; FRCS Ed. 1980; FFAEM 1993. (Armed Forces Med. Coll.) Cons. A & E Blackburn Roy. Infirm. Blackburn. Prev: Sen. Regist. (A & E) Manch. & Blackp. Rotat.; Regist. (A & E) Leic. Roy. Infirm.

GEORGE, Trevor Hugh Gronow Lister Medical Centre, Lister House, Staple Tye, Harlow CM18 7LU Tel: 01279 414882 Fax: 01279 439600 — MB BS 1964 Lond.; MRCS Eng. LRCP Lond. 1966; DObst RCOG 1966. (Univ. Coll. Hosp.)

GEORGE, Varghese Kanisseril Central Surgery, 23 Boston Avenue, Southend-on-Sea SS2 6JH Tel: 01702 342589 Fax: 01702 437015 — MB BS 1977 Kerala.

GEORGE, William Andrew Strathearn (retired) 11 Lymister Avenue, Moorgate, Rotherham S60 3DR — MB ChB 1950 Ed.

GEORGE, Mr William David 21 Kingsborough Gardens, Glasgow G12 9NH — MB BS 1966 Lond.; MS Lond. 1977, MB BS 1966; FRCS Eng. 1971.

GEORGE, William Thomas 22 Hamilton Terrace, Milford Haven SA73 3JL Tel: 01646 690674 Fax: 01646 690553; Rathbank, 17 The Rath, Milford Haven SA73 2QA Tel: 01646 693307 — MB BS Lond. 1964; MRCS Eng. LRCP Lond. 1967; AFOM RCP Lond. 1979; DObst RCOG 1968. (St. Bart.) Socs: BMA. Prev: Ho. Surg. (Neurosurg.) St. Bart. Hosp. & Roy. Berks. Hosp. Reading; Ho. Phys. Norf. & Norwich Hosp.

GEORGE SAMRAJ, Ponnumperumal Narayan 296 Burges Road, East Ham, London E6 2ES — MB BS 1982 Madras, India; MB BS Madras 1982; MRCOG 1994.

GEORGEKUTTY, Mr Kurudamannil Kulangara Abraham 107 Upper Selsdon Road, Selsdon, South Croydon CR2 0DP Tel: 020 8657 3360 — MB BS 1968 Allahabad; MS Allahabad 1972; FRCS Eng. 1980. Assoc. Specialist (Surg.) Bromley Hosps. NHS Trust. Prev: Cons. Surg. Centr. Hosp. Riyadh; Regist. (Surg.) Plymouth Gen. Hosp. & Bridend Gen. Hosp.

GEORGELIN, Dene John St Suliac, Oxford Road, St Helier, Jersey JE2 4LJ Tel: 01534 20797 — BM 1993 Soton. SHO (A & E) Salisbury Dist. Gen. Hosp. Prev: SHO (Med.) Health Waikato, New Zealand; SHO (Orthop. & Trauma) Treliske Hosp. Truro; Ho. Off. (Med.) Treliske Hosp. Truro.

GEORGELIN, Donald Henry (retired) White Lodge, Arnworth Avenue, Fauvic, Grouville JE3 9BP Tel: 01534 853550 Fax: 01534 853880 — MB BS Lond. 1960; MRCS Eng. LRCP Lond. 1960; DObst RCOG 1962. Prev: SHO (Paediat.) & Ho. Surg. (Obst.) St. Mary's Hosp. Portsmouth.

GEORGEOU, Theodore 54 Melbourne Road, Crookes, Sheffield S10 1NS — MB ChB 1988 Sheff.

GEORGESON, Eileen Janet Tor-Na-Coille, 5 Walnut Grove, Kinfauns, Perth PH2 7JX Tel: 01738 24629 — MB ChB 1961 St. And.

GEORGIANNOS, Stavros Flat 7, 2 St John's Avenue, London SW15 2AG — Ptychio Iatrikes 1985 Athens.

GEORGIOU, Alison Mary Haresfield House Surgery, 6-10 Bath Road, Worcester WR5 3EJ Tel: 01905 763161 Fax: 01905 67016; 3 Gargen Cottages, Marlsbrook Lane, Sale Green, Droitwich WR9 7LW — MB ChB 1984 Birm.; M.Med. Sci. Birm. 1998; MRCGP 1988; DRCOG 1988; DCH RCP Lond. 1987.

GEORGIOU, Christos Chelsea & Westminster Hospital, 369 Fulham Road, London SW10 9NH Tel: 020 8746 8000 — MB BS 1996 Lond.; BSc (Hons.) Sheff. 1987; PhD 1991. (Charing Cross and Westminster London) SHO (O & G) Chelsea & W.minster Hosp. Lond.; Lect. (Anat.) Lond. Sch. of Osteop. Socs: Med. Protec. Soc.; Med. Sickness Soc.

GEORGIOU, George 851 Forest Road, London E17 4AT — MB BS 1989 Lond.; MRCGP 1993; T(GP) 1993.

GEORGIOU, George Andrew 212 London Road, Worcester WR5 2JT; October House, Blacksmith's Lane, Lower Moor, Pershore WR10 2PA — MB ChB 1985 Birm.; BSc (Anat.) Birm. 1981, MB ChB 1985.

GEORGIOU, Melina Flat B, 1st Floor, 13B Thornton Avenue, Stretham, London SW2 4HL — MB ChB 1996 Manch.

GEORGIOU, Tassos Flat 36, Stanley Court, Stanley Road, Cambridge CB5 8LW — MB ChB 1994 Leeds. SHO (Ophth.) York Dist. Hosp. Socs: BMA; MDU.

GEORGUI, Mounir Megalli Child & Family Unit, Rose Cottage, 27/28 Hallchurch Road, Holly Hall, Dudley DY2 0TH Tel: 01384 482909 — MB ChB 1968 Cairo; MRCPsych 1983. Cons. Child Psychiat. Dudley HA. Prev: Cons. Child Psychiat. N. Staffs. HA; Sen. Regist. (Child Psychiat.) W. Berks. HA.

GEORGY, Michel Salib 36 Rollswood Drive, Solihull B91 1NL Tel: 0121 709 0407 — MB BCh Ain Shams 1970; FRCOG 1995, M 1982. Socs: Med. Protec. Soc.; Birm. & Midl. Obst. & Gyn. Soc.; Internat. Continence Soc. UK. Prev: Cons. O & G Nat. Guard K. Khalid Hosp. Jeddah, Saudi Arabia.

GEPI-ATTEE, Mr Samuel 64 Sandringham Road, Stoke Gifford, Bristol BS34 8PY Tel: 0117 940 6814; 64 Sandringham Road, Stoke Gifford, Bristol BS34 8PY Tel: 0117 940 6814 — MB ChB 1976 Ghana; FRCSI 1985; MD Bristol 1998. Research Fell. (Urol.) S.mead Hosp. Bristol.

GERADA, Anthony 104 Eastfield Road, Peterborough PE1 4AX Tel: 01733 54885 — MD 1949 Malta; DTM & H Eng. 1951; DCH Eng. 1956.

GERADA, Clare The Hurley Clinic, Ebenezer House, Kennington Lane, London SE11 4HJ Tel: 020 7735 7918 Fax: 020 7587 5296 — MB BS 1983 Lond.; MRCGP 1996; MRCPscyh 1988. Princip. GP Hurley Clinic; GP Cons. Consultancy Liason Addic. Serv.; Sen. Med. Off., DOH, Health promotion Div..; Vice Chairm. LMC. Prev: Regist. Maudsley Hosp. Lond.

GERAGHTY, Elspeth Margaret Blackbrook Surgery, Lisieux Way, Taunton TA1 2LB Tel: 01823 259444 Fax: 01823 322715 — MB BS 1990 Newc.

GERAGHTY, Ian Franklin, MBE Intensive Care Directorate, Hope Hospital, Stott Lane, Salford M6 8HD Tel: 0161 787 5107; 21 The Firs, Bowdon, Altrincham WA14 2TG Tel: 0161 929 9277 — MB BCh BAO 1976 Dub.; FFA RCS Eng. 1983. Cons. Anaesth. (Adult Intens. Care Med.) Hope Hosp. Salford. Prev: Cons. Anaesth. RN Hosp. Hasler Gosport.

GERAGHTY, John Michael Department of Histopathology, Taunton & Somerset Hospital, Musgrove Park, Taunton TA1 5DA — MB BS 1985 Newc.; BMedSc Newc. 1984, MB BS 1985; MRCPath 1993. Cons. Histopath. Taunton & Som. Hosp. Prev: Sen. Regist. (Histopath.) Addenbrooke's Hosp. Camb.; Regist. (Histopath.) St. Bart. & St. Mary's Hosps. Lond.

GERAGHTY, Julia Rachel 34 Royal Terrace, Edinburgh EH7 5AH Tel: 0131 478 1394 Fax: 0131 478 1395 Email: drgeraghty@connectfree.co.uk — MB ChB 1984 Cape Town; MFHom 1994; DCH RCP Lond. 1988. (Univ. of Cape Town, S. Afr.) Indep. Homoeop. Phys. Glas. & Indep. Homeop. Phys. Edin.; Clin. Asst. (Homoeop.) Glas. Socs: Med. Protec. Soc. Prev: GP/Regist. Glas.; SHO (Homoeop. Med.) Glas.; SHO (Paediat.) Lond.

GERAGHTY, Patrick Gerard Mary Vesper Road Surgery, 43 Vesper Road, Leeds LS5 3QT Tel: 0113 275 1248 Fax: 0113 274 9090; The Laurels, 7 The Lane, Alwoodley, Leeds LS17 7BR Tel: 0113 267 8459 — MB BCh BAO 1982 NUI; DRCOG 1987; Cert. Family Plann. JCC 1987. (Univ. Coll. Dub.) Clin. Asst. Meanwood Pk. Hosp.; Med. Off. Yorks. Blood Transfus. Serv.; Stadium Doctor Leeds United FC; Police Surg. Leeds. Socs: Leeds M-C Soc.; Leeds Med. Golf Soc.; (Ex-Pres.) W. Riding Irish Med. Soc.

GERAGHTY, Richard James c/o Elderly Medical Unit, Queen Mary's Sidcup NHS Trust, Frognal Avenue, Sidcup DA14 6LT; 253 Southlands Road, Bromley BR1 2EG — MB BS 1985 Lond.; MRCP (UK) 1988. Cons. Phys. Geriat. Med. Qu. Mary's Sidcup NHS Trust. Prev: Sen. Regist. Rotat. (Geriat. Med.) SE Thames RHA.

GERAGHTY, William Joseph Aidan Apple Grove, Radnar Road, Luton LU4 0QQ — LRCP 1949 Irel.; 1949 LRCPI & LM, LM RCSI 1949.

GERAINT, Michael Norgine Pharmaceuticals Ltd, Chaplin House, Moorhall Road, Harefield, Uxbridge UB9 6NS Tel: 01895 826600 Email: mgeraint@norgine.com; 29 Carlingford Road, London NW3 1RY Tel: 020 7681 0586 Fax: 020 7681 0586 Email: mike.geraint@which.net — MB ChB 1975 Liverp.; BSc (Hons.) Pharmacol. Liverp. 1970; MFPM 1989. (Liverp.) Med. Dir. Norgine Pharmaceut. Ltd. Prev: Med. Dir., Smith & Nephew Healthcare Ltd.; Div. Med. Adviser, Smith & Nephew Pharmaceut. Ltd.; Technical Developm. Dir. Schering Hosp. Supply Div.

GERANMAYEH, Ardeshir RMO Building, Leicester General Hospital NHS Trust, Gwendolen Road, Leicester LE5 4PW; 85 Regent Road, Leicester LE1 6YG — MB ChB 1995 Leic.

GERARD, Ewan Moray Port Health, South Terminal, Gatwick Airport, Crawley RH11 0TG Tel: 01293 533229 Fax: 01293 502665; Church House, 71 Elmer Road, Middleton-On-Sea, Bognor Regis PO22 6EH Email: ewan_gerard@compuserve.com — MB ChB 1982 Birm.; MSc Oxf. 1987; FRCS Ed. 1988; MRCGP 1989. Med. Dir. Port Health; Dep. Police Surg. Sussex Police. Prev: Princip. GP Littlehampton; Trainee GP Bishops Waltham & Harvant Hants.; Regist. Rotat. (Gen. Surg.) E. Dorset & Soton. HA's.

GERARD, Sian Wynne Fitzalan Medical Centre, Fitzalan Road, Littlehampton BN17 5JR Tel: 01903 733288 Fax: 01903 733773 — BM 1986 Soton.; BSc (Biochem.) Cardiff 1982. Health Screening Sessional Doctor Goring Hall Hosp. (Amicus Healthcare) Goring by Sea. Prev: Trainee GP W. Sussex; SHO (A & E & Ophth.) Qu. Alexandra Hosp. Portsmouth; SHO (Gen. Med. & O & G) St. Mary's Hosp. Portsmouth.

GERAUD, Christian Medicare Francais, 3 Harrington Gardens, London SW7 4JJ — MD 1981 Paris.

GERBER, Aubrey (retired) 9 Bishopsgate, Thorntonhall, Glasgow G74 5AX Tel: 0141 644 4330 — LRCP LRCS Ed. LRFPS Glas. 1945; DPM Eng. 1969. Hosp. Pract. (Psychiat.) S.. Gen. Hosp. Glas. Prev: Ho. Surg. Roy. Vict. & W. Hants. Hosp. Bournem.

GERBER, David Glynn Gransha Hospital, Clooney Road, Londonderry BT47 6TF — MB ChB 1995 Cape Town.

GERBER, Harry (retired) Roseholm, 1 Lanrig Road, Newton Mearns, Glasgow G77 5AA Tel: 0141 639 7183 — LRCP LRCS Ed. LRFPS Glas. 1948.

GERBER, Stephen 28 Hillfoot Crescent, Stockton Heath, Warrington WA4 6SB — MB ChB 1985 Cape Town.

GERG, Rajesh Kumar Queens Drive Surgery, 339 Queens Drive, Liverpool L4 8SJ Tel: 0151 226 6024; 2 Fox Wood, Parklands Estate, West Derby, Liverpool L12 0HZ — MB BS 1973 Panjab; MB BS Panjab (India) 1973. (Med. Coll. Rohtak)

GERGEL, Ivan Philip 34 Gresham Gardens, London NW11 8PD; The Basement Flat, 2 Sandwell Crescent, London NW6 1PB — MB BS 1983 Lond. (Roy. Free) SHO (Psychiat.) N.wick Pk. Hosp. Harrow. Prev: SHO (Cas.) Roy. Free Hosp. Lond.

GERGIS, Eibhlin Maria Frances 4 Mount Frost Place, Markinch, Glenrothes KY7 6JH — LRCPI & LM, LRSCI & LM 1976; LRCPI & LM, LRCSI & LM 1976; T(GP) 1991.

GERGIS, Maher Ibrahim Anaesthetic Department, Victoria Hospital, Hayfield Road, Kirkcaldy KY1 5AH Tel: 01592 643355 Fax: 01592 647090; 4 Mount Frost Place, Markinch, Glenrothes KY7 6JH Tel: 01592 612777 — MB BCh 1968 Cairo; FFA RCS Eng. 1979; FFA RCSI 1978; T(Anaesth) 1991. Cons. Anaesth. Vict. Hosp. Kirkcaldy. Socs: Fell. Roy. Coll. Anaesth.; BMA; Anaesth. Assn. Prev: Cons. Anaesth. Nat. Guard Hosp., Saudi Arabia & Bishop Auckland; Sen. Regist. (Anaesth.) Leicester Hosps.

GERHARD, Sheila Decima (retired) Little Dowding, Dorking Road, Walton on the Hill, Tadworth KT20 7TJ Tel: 01737 813045 — MB BS 1950 Lond.; MRCS Eng. LRCP Lond. 1950. Prev: Clin. Med. Off. Merton & Sutton HA.

GERHARDS, Martin Blackthorn Medical Centre, St. Andrews Road, Barming, Maidstone ME16 9AL Tel: 01622 726277 Fax: 01622 725774 — Artsexamen 1985 Rotterdam.

GERKEN, Anne James Paget Hospital NHS Trust, Lowestoft Road, Great Yarmouth NR31 6LA Tel: 01493 452478; East Wood, 132 Corton Long Lane, Lowestoft NR32 5HD — MB BS 1965 Lond.; MRCS Eng. LRCP Lond. 1965; FRCPath 1984, M 1972; DObst RCOG 1967. (Char. Cross) Cons. Microbiol. Jas. Paget Hosp. NHS Trust. Prev: Cons., Regist. & Lect. (Microbiol.) Char. Cross Hosp.

GERLIS, Kim Linda Osler House Surgery, Potter Street, Harlow CM17 9BG Tel: 01279 422664/629707 Fax: 01279 422576; 200A Old Road, Harlow CM17 0HQ Tel: 01279 639143 — MB BS 1982 Lond.; MRCGP 1985; DRCOG 1984. (Lond. Hosp.)

GERLIS, Laurence Stanley 21 Devonshire Place, London W1G 6HZ Tel: 020 7935 0113 Fax: 020 7486 0505 Email: laurence@gerlis.com — MB BChir 1974 Camb.; MA (1st Cl. Hons.) Camb. 1975, MB BChir 1974; MRCP (UK) 1976; Dip. Pharm. Med. 1979; FFPM. (Lond. Hosp.) Specialist (Diabetes & Endocrinol.) Lond. Vocational Train. Exemption; TV Doctor BBC. Prev: Dir. Clin. Research Biogen Med. Research Geneva; Med. Dir. Novo Laborat. (UK).

GERLIS, Professor Leon Monty, CStJ (retired) National Heart & Lung Institute, Dovehouse St., London SW3 6LY — MB BS 1944 London; MRCS Eng. LRCP Lond. 1943; FRCPath 1971, M 1963. Vis. Prof. of Cardiac Path. Imperial Coll. Sch. of Med. at the Nat. Heart & Lung Inst. Lond.; Hon. Cons. Cardiac Path. Brompton Hosp. Lond. Prev: Cons. Path. Grimsby Dist. Hosp.

GERLIS, Robin David The Ross Practice, Keats House, Bush Fair, Harlow CM18 6LY Tel: 01279 692747 Fax: 01279 692737 Email: rob.gerlis@gp-f81106.nhs.uk; 200A Old Road, Old Harlow, Harlow CM17 0HQ — MB BS 1982 Lond.; MRCGP 1985; DRCOG 1984. (London Hospital Medical College) Harlow PCT Exec. Mem./IT lead. Socs: Harlow Med. Soc. Prev: Clin. Asst. (Dermat.) Herts & Esssex Hosp. Bishop's Stortford.

GERMAIN, Sarah Janet 11 Coventry Road, Nuneaton CV11 4NL Tel: 01203 736658 — MB BS 1997 Lond.; MA 1998. (Cambridge University; St. Bart's and the Royal London School of Medicine) SHO (O & G), The John Radcliffe Hosp., Oxf. Prev: SHO (Gyn), N.wich Pk. Hosp., Harrow; Ho. Off. (Med.), The Qu. Eliz. Hosp., Birm.; Ho. Off. (Surg.), The Horton Gen. Hosp., Banbury, Oxon.

GERMAINE, Daniel Derek Arthur (retired) Oatlands, The Street, Bulmer, Sudbury CO10 7EP — MB ChB 1961 St. And. Prev: Regist. (Anaesth.) Ipswich & E. Suff. Hosp. & Glas. Roy. Infirm.

GERMAN, Mr Karl Andrew Basement Flat, 17 Alfred Road, Acton, London W3 6LH Tel: 020 8993 3449; c/o Karinya, Misrah Kola, Attard, Malta — MB BS 1983 Lond.; MS Lond. 1993; FRCS Urol. 1994; FRCS Ed. 1987; FRCS Lond. 1987. Sen. Regist. (Urol.) Inst. Urol. Middlx. Hosp. Lond. Prev: Sen. Regist. Rotat. (Urol.) Edith Cavell Hosp., Middlx. Hosp., Battle Hosp. & Roy. P. Alfred Hosp., Sydney; Research Regist. Cardiff Roy. Infirm.; Regist. Rotat. (Urol.) Cleveland Hosp. & Freeman Hosp.

GERMER, Michael David Liquorpond Street Surgery, 10 Liquorpond Street, Boston PE21 8UE Tel: 01205 362763 Fax: 01205 358918 — MB BS 1976 Lond.; FRCS Glas. 1983; MRCGP 1984; DRCOG 1985; Cert. FPA 1984; MSc (Sports Med.) Nottm. 1997. GP; Clin. Asst. Endoscopy Pilgrim Hosp. Boston.

GERMER, Stephanie Boston Health Clinic, Lincoln Lane, Boston PE21 8RU — MB BS 1975 Lond.; MFPHM 1989; FRCPCH 1997; DCH Eng. 1980. (St. Bart.) Cons. Community Paediat., United Lincs. Hosps. NHS Trust, Boston, Lincs. Prev: Clin. Med. Off. S. Lincs. HA & Fife; Clin. Asst. Paediats. Goroka Base Hosp., Papua New Guinea; Cons. Community Paediat. Pilgrim Health NHS Trust Boston Lincs.

GERMON, Mr Timothy John Department of Neurosurgery, Frenchay Hospital, Bristol BS16 1LE Tel: 0117 970 1212 — MB ChB 1987 Bristol; BSc Bristol 1984, MB ChB 1987; FRCS Eng. 1992.

GEROW, Evelyn Ruth (retired) Lothian Health, Primary Care Services, Stevenson House, Edinburgh EH11 3LG Tel: 0131 537 8443 Fax: 0131 537 8456 — MB ChB 1961 Ed. Med. Admin. Cervical Screening Lothian Health Edin. Prev: Research Asst. (Path.) Univ. Edin.

GERRAND, Mr Craig Hamilton Department of Orthopaedics, Freeman Hospital, Newcastle upon Tyne NE7 7DN Tel: 0191 2843111 Fax: 0191 2231238 Email: craig.gerrand@northy.nvth.nhs.uk; First Floor Right, 11 Dowanside Road, Glasgow G12 9YB — MB ChB 1989 Ed.; FRCS Ed. 1993; FRCS ed (TR and ORTH) 1999. Cons. or Thopaedic Surg.

GERRARD, Catherine Alexandra Mount Farm, Cruckton, Shrewsbury SY5 8PR — MB ChB 1983 Manch.; BSc St. And. 1980; DRCOG 1986.

GERRARD, Mr David James 94A Abdevill Road, Clapham, London SW4 9NA Tel: 020 7498 1557 — MB BS 1989 Lond.; FRCS Eng. 1992. SHO (Gen. Surg.) St. Bart. Hosp. Lond. Prev: Demonst. & SHO (Orthop.) St. Geo. Hosp. Lond.; SHO (Gen. Surg.) Kingston-upon-Thames.

GERRARD, Frances Elizabeth Ystwyth Medical Group, Ystwyth Primary Care Centre, Parc Y Llyn, Llanbadarn Fawr, Aberystwyth SY23 3TL Tel: 01970 613500 Fax: 01970 613505 — MB BS 1985 Lond.; MA Oxf. 1984; MRCGP 1992; DRCOG 1991.

GERRARD, George (retired) 14 Langside Drive, Comrie, Crieff PH6 2HR Tel: 01764 670771 — MB ChB Glas. 1939. Prev: Cons. Chest Phys. Rushden Hosp.

GERRARD, Georgina Elizabeth Cookridge Hospital, Leeds LS16 6QB Tel: 0113 267 3411 Fax: 0113 392 4052; 40 St. Georges Square, Chadderton, Oldham OL9 9NY Tel: 0161 681 3718 — MB BChir 1986 Camb.; BA 1982, BSc (Hons.) 1984; MRCP (UK) 1991; FRCR 1993. Cons. (Clin. Oncol.) Cookridge Hosp. Leeds. Prev: Sen. Regist. (Clin. Oncol.) Cookridge Hosp. Leeds.; Regist. (Clin. Oncol.) Cookridge Leeds & Bristol Oncol. Centre; SHO (Med.) Nottm.

GERRARD, James William Windmill Health Centre, Mill Green, Leeds LS14 5JS Tel: 0113 273 3733 Fax: 0113 232 3202 — MB ChB 1985 Manch.; BSc St. And. 1982; MRCGP 1993; DGM RCP Lond. 1991; DCH RCP Lond. 1989.

GERRARD, John Lembrook Cottage, Lem Hill, Far Forest, Kidderminster DY14 9DU Tel: 01299 266509 — BM BCh 1954 Oxf. (Oxf.) Chairm. Cuxson Gerrard & Co. Ltd.

GERRARD, John Miller 57 Market Street, Stoneywood, Bucksburn, Aberdeen AB21 9JE — MB ChB 1991 Aberd.

GERRARD, Julia The Stanmore Medical Centre, 85 Crowshott Avenue, Stanmore HA7 1HS Tel: 020 8951 3888 Fax: 020 8952 5093; 17 Harley Road, Harrow HA1 4XF Tel: 020 8863 8094 — MB BS 1991 Lond.; MRCGP 1995; DFFP 1995; DCH RCP Lond. 1994. (Char. Cross & Westm.)

GERRARD, Mary Pauline Childrens Hospital, Western Bank, Sheffield S10 2TH Tel: 0114 271 7366 Fax: 0114 275 2289 Email: mary.gerra@sheffch_tr.trent.nhs.uk; 26 Rutland Park, Sheffield S10 2PB Tel: 0114 268 2089 — MB ChB 1977 Manch.; BSc (Hons.) (Med. Sci. & Biochem.) St. And. 1974; FRCP Lond. 1994; DCH Eng. 1979; FRCPCH. (St Andrews Manchester) Cons. Paediat. Oncol. Sheff. Childr. Hosp. Prev: Research Fell. (Paediat. Oncol.) St. Bart. Hosp. Lond.

GERRARD, Timothy John Dukes Avenue Surgery, 1 Dukes Avenue, London N10 2PS Tel: 020 8883 9149 — MB BS 1982 Lond.; MA Oxf. 1979; MRCGP 1989; DRCOG 1987; DCH RCP Lond. 1984. Prev: Trainee GP Highgate.; SHO (O & G & Paediat.) Whipps Cross Hosp.; SHO (A & E) Lond. Hosp.

GERRIE, Linda Margaret 9 Westholme Crescent S., Aberdeen AB15 6AF — MB ChB 1989 Aberd.; PhD Aberd. 1982, BSc 1978, MB ChB 1989; MRCP (UK) 1994. Specialist Regist. (Neurol.) Aberd. Roy. Infirm. (Train. Post).

GERRIE, Sara Elaine 2 Elms Drive, Quorn, Loughborough LE12 8AF — MB BS 1993 Lond.

GERRISH, Stephen Paul 38 Hallam Grange Crescent, Fulwood, Sheffield S10 4BD Tel: 0114 230 8453 — MB BCh 1978 Wales; FFA RCS Eng. 1983. Cons. Anaesth. Sheff..

GERRITSEN, Elisabeth Rengelina Pembury Hospital, Pembury, Tunbridge Wells TN2 4QJ — Artsexamen 1991 Maastricht.

GERRY, Bruce Alexander William 2A Conyngham Road, Manchester M14 5SA — MB ChB 1996 Manch.

GERSHUNY, Anthony Robert Department of Clinical Oncology, Oldchurch Hospital, Romford RM7 0BE Tel: 01708 746090 Fax: 01708 737690; 19 Colchester Drive, Pinner HA5 1DE Tel: 020 8866 7276 Fax: 020 8933 0177 Email: arg270953@aol.com — MB BChir 1979 Camb.; MB Camb 1979, BChir 1978; MA Camb. 1979; MRCP (UK) 1983; FRCR 1987. (Westm.) Cons. Clin. Oncol. OldCh. Hosp. Romford E. Lond. Regional Cancer Centre; Hon. Cons. The Roy. Hosps. Socs: BMA; Brit. Oncol. Assn.; Fell. Roy. Coll. Radiologists. Prev: Sen. Regist. (Clin. Oncol.) Char. Cross Hosp. & Chelsea & W.m. Hosp. Lond.; Sen. Regist. (Radiother. & Oncol.) W.. Hosp. Lond. & St. Luke's Hosp. Guildford; Regist. (Radiother.) Roy. Marsden Hosp. Lond.

GERSON, David Arthur Harold 3 Dawlish Close, De Mowbray Court, Newton, Swansea SA3 4UT — MB BCh 1983 Wales. Trainee GP Swansea VTS.

GERSTEN, Abbey Elizabeth 6 Somerton Road, London SE15 3UG — MB BS 1992 Lond.; MRCGP 1998. (King's College London) Gen. Pract. Retainer Scheme S.E.Lond.

GERTNER, David Jotham Basildon Hospital, Nether Mayne, Basildon SS16 5NL Tel: 01268 593314 Fax: 01268 593151; 180 Holders Hill Road, London NW7 1LU Tel: 020 8349 4627 — MB BS 1982 Lond.; BSc Lond. 1979; MRCP (UK) 1985. (University College Hospital) Cons. Phys. & Gastroenterol. Basildon Hosp. Essex. Prev: Sen. Regist. (Gastroenterol., Human Nutrit. & Gen. Med.) Roy. Lond. Hosp.; Research Fell. St. Mark's Hosp. Lond.; Regist. Rotat. (Med.) UCH Lond.

GERTNER, Gillian Rosslyn Hill Surgery, 20 Rosslyn Hill, London NW3 1PD Tel: 020 7435 1132; 169 Holders Hill Road, London NW7 1ND — MB BS 1982 Lond. (Univ. Coll. Hosp.)

GERVAIS, Gordon Fraser Tel: 028 8283 1275 Fax: 028 8283 1620 — MB BCh BAO 1967 Dub.; MA Dub. 1967; DObst RCOG 1971; DCH RCPSI 1969.

GERVAIS, Trevor Gordon 12 Omagh Road, Drumquin, Omagh BT78 4QY — MB BCh 1998 Belf.; MB BCh Belf 1998.

GERVAL, Marie-Odile Beech lawn, 3 Church Road, Skelmersdale WN8 8ND — MB BS 1996 Lond.

GERVIS, John Harvey (retired) Nazeingbury, Nazeing, Waltham Abbey EN9 2JN — MB BChir 1957 Camb.; MRCS Eng. LRCP Lond. 1956; DObst RCOG 1958.

GERWAT, Mr John ENT Department, Level 7, Derriford Hospital, Plymouth PL6 8DH Tel: 01752 777111; Purps Farm, Shaugh Prior, Plymouth PL7 5EN Tel: 01752 839576 — MB BS 1961 Lond.; MB BS (Hons.) Lond. 1961; FRCS Eng 1972; MRCS Eng LRCP Lond. 1961. Civil Cons. ENT RN DHU Plymouth & Hon. Cons. Plymouth Hosp. Socs: Brit. Assn. Otol. Prev: Cons. ENT Surg. Wellington Hosp. Univ. Otago, NZ; Cons. ENT Surg. Jersey Hosp., C.I.

GESINDE, Mojisola Olufunmilayo National Blood Service Yorkshire, Leeds Blood Centre, Bridle Path, Leeds LS15 7TW Tel: 0113 214 8689 Fax: 0113 214 8696 Email: moji.gesinde@nbs.nhs.uk — MB BS Univ. Ibadan Nigeria 1980; FRCPath Lond. 1999; MRCPath Roy. Coll. Pathol. Lond. 1990. (University College Ibadan Nigeria) Cons. Haematologist Leeds Blood Centre. Socs: Brit. Soc. Haematol.; Brit. Blood Transfus. Soc.; Internat. Soc. Blood Transfus. (ISBT). Prev: Sen. Regist. Haemat. & Blood Transfusioon Manch.; Regist. Haemat. Derby.

GETACHEW, Hennock 43B Averill Street, London W6 8EP — State Exam Med 1988 Leipzig; MD Berlin 1995.

GETACHEW, Uta c/o Ulrike Krause, 371A Holloway Road, London N7 0RN — State Exam Med 1990 Berlin.

GETHEN, Ronald Charles Ricketts (retired) 5 Priory Close, Boxgrove, Chichester PO18 0EA Tel: 01243 776487 — MRCS Eng. LRCP Lond. 1938. Prev: Surg. Lt.-Cdr. RNV(S)R (King's Commend.).

GETHEN SMITH, Edward Brian (retired) Sherwood, 137 Kingston Rd, Taunton TA2 7SR Tel: 01823 73091 — MRCS Eng. LRCP Lond. 1946; MA, MB, BChir, Camb. 1945; MRCS Eng., LRCP Lond. 1946. Prev: Ho. Surg. Guy's Hosp. Med. Sector.

GETHIN, Ian Paris Gethin, Davies and Knowles, Harris Memorial Surgery, Robartes Terrace, Illogan, Redruth TR16 4RX Tel: 01209 842515 Fax: 01209 842380; Meadowside Cottage, Wheal Clifford, St. Day, Redruth TR16 5HZ Tel: 01209 821447 Fax: 01209 822299

Email: ian_gethin@iangethin.eurobell.co.uk — MB BCh 1978 Wales; MFFP 1994; MRCOG 1987; DCH RCP Lond. 1985. (Welsh Nat. Sch. Med. Cardiff) Prev: Regist. (O & G) Roy. Devon & Exeter Hosp., S.mead Hosp. Bristol & Basingstoke Dist. Hosp.

GETHING, Elizabeth Jasmine Cottage, 63 West Hill, Portishead, Bristol BS20 6LG — MB ChB 1993 Liverp. GP Regist Clevedon, Bristol. Prev: SHO (Cardiol.) Cardiothoracic Centre Liverp.; SHO (Gen. Med.) Whiston Hosp. Liverp.

GETHING, Joshua Foxwood, Waste Lane, Kelsall, Tarporley CW6 0PE Tel: 01829 51397 — MB ChB 1955 Sheff.; FFOM RCP Lond. 1989, MFOM 1978; DIH Soc. Apoth. Lond. 1968. Chief Med. Off. Assoc. Octel Co. Ellesmere Port. Prev: SHO (O & G) Qu. Vict. Hosp. Morecambe; Ho. Phys. & Cas. Off. Sheff. Roy. Hosp.

GETHING, Nora Jessie (retired) Cressage, 122 Streetly Lane, Four Oaks, Sutton Coldfield B74 4TE — MB BS 1933 Lond. Prev: Dermat. Off. Childr. Hosp. Birm.

GETTY, Mr Charles John Moore Northern General Hospital, Sheffield S5 7AU Tel: 0114 243 4343 Ext: 4958; Great Gilling, 11 Chorley Road, Sheffield S10 3RJ Tel: 0114 230 2892 Fax: 0114 230 9444 Email: info@johngelty.co.uk — MB 1972 Camb.; MB BChir Camb. 1972; MA Camb. 1972; FRCS Eng. 1976; FRCS 1999 Edinburgh. (Cambrige) Cons. Orthop. Surg. Sheff. AHA(T); Hon. Clin. Lect. (Orthop.) Univ. Sheff. Socs: Fell. BOA; Internat. Soc. Study Lumbar Spine; Eur. Rheum. Arthrit. Surg. Soc. Prev: Sen. Regist. (Orthop. Train. Scheme) St. Bart. Hosp. Lond.; Regist. (Surg.) Ipswich Hosp.; Ho. Surg. Middlx. Hosp. Lond.

GEUTJENS, Mr Guido 114 Britannia Avenue, Nottingham NG6 0EB — MD 1987 Louvain; FRCS Eng. 1991; FRCS Ed. 1991.

GHADIALI, Hemlata Himanshu The Mount, North Avenue, Ashbourne DE6 1EZ — MB BS 1971 Gujarat; MRCPsych 1977; DPM Gujarat 1973. (Ahmedabad) Cons. Psychiat. Kingsway Hosp. Derby. Prev: Sen. Regist. (Psychiat.) Lond. Hosp.; Sen. Regist. (Psychiat.) Claybury Hosp. Woodford Bridge; Regist. Bexley Hosp.

GHADIALI, Himanshu Nautambhai The Mount, North Avenue, Ashbourne DE6 1EZ Tel: 01335 45552 — MD 1973 Bombay; MD (Psychol. Med.) Bombay 1973, MB BS 1972; MRCPsych 1976; DPM CPS Bombay 1973. (Seth G.S. Med. Coll.) Cons. Psychiat. Kingsway Hosp. Derby; Assoc. Prof. Mem. Soc. Analyt. Psychol. Ltd. Prev: Cons. Psychiat. St. Geo. Hosp. Stafford; Sen. Regist. (Psychiat.) St. Clements Hosp. Lond. & Runwell Hosp. Wickford; Clin. Asst. Ingrebourne Centre St. Geo. Hosp. HornCh..

GHADIALI, Mr Pesi Erach (retired) 35 Cole Park Road, Twickenham TW1 1HP Tel: 020 8892 7373 — MB BS 1946 Bombay; FRCS Eng. 1953. Prev: Cons. Clin. Physiol. Brompton Hosp.

GHADIMI, Hooshand The Surgery, 45 Rosary Gardens, London SW7 4NQ Tel: 020 7373 6557 Fax: 020 7373 6426 — MRCS Eng. LRCP Lond. 1964; DCH RCPS Glas. 1967.

GHAEM-MAGHAMI HEZAVEH, Sadaf Infectious Diseases Unit, St George's Hospital Medical School, Cranmer Terrace, London SW17 0RE Tel: 020 8725 3474 Fax: 020 8725 3487 Email: sghaem@sghms.ac.uk; The Surgey, 121 Wrythe Lane, Carshalton SM5 2RT — MB BS 1990 Lond.; DFFP 1993; MRCOG 1999. (London hospital medical school) Specialist Regist. (O & G) N. W. Thames Region. Socs: BMA; Med. Protec. Soc.; BSI. Prev: Clin. Research Fell. & Hon. Regist. (O & G & Infec. Dis.) St. Geo. Hosp. Lond.; SHO (Genitourin. Med.) St. Geo. Hosp. Lond.; SHO (Neonat.) St. Mary's Hosp. Lond.

GHAFAR, Mr Fazal Flat 4, The Maples, Queen Elizabeth Hospital, Gayton Road, King's Lynn PE30 4ET — MB BS 1974 Peshawar, Pakistan; FRCSI 1993.

GHAFFAR, Abdul The Surgery, Abbey Square, Walsall WS3 2RH Tel: 01922 408416 Fax: 01922 400372; 418 Sutton Road, Walsall WS5 3BA Tel: 01922 614269 — MB BS Patna 1966. (Prince of Wales Med. Coll.)

GHAFFAR, Abdul Rahemtulla Khadiyawala Willowmere, Mere Road, Newton le Willow, St Helens — MB BS 1965 Karachi; DCH Eng. 1979. (Dow Med. Coll.)

GHAFFAR, AJM Abdul 6 Rosemoor Gardens, Longwood Road, Appleton, Warrington WA4 5RG — MB BS 1957 Dacca; MRCP (U.K.) 1971; LMSSA Lond. 1967; DCH RCPS Glas. 1963. Cons. (Geriat.) Warrington Gen. Hosp. Socs: BMA & Acad. W.. Acupunc. Prev: SHO (Paediat.) Good Hope Gen. Hosp. Sutton Coldfield; SHO Chest Dis. Gateforth Hosp. nr. Selby; Regist. Chest Dis. Scotton Banks Hosp. KnaresBoro..

GHAFFARI, Kamran 121 Harley Street, London W1N 1DH Tel: 020 7935 0525 — MD 1975 Milan; MD (Hons.) Milan 1975; MRCPsych 1980. (University of Milan Medical School) p/t Cons. Psychother. W. Middlx. Univ. Hosp. & Ashford Hosp.; Hon. Cons. Lond. Clinic of Psychoanal. Socs: Assn. Psychoanal. Psychotherap. NHS; Brit. Psychoanal. Soc.; Internat. Psychoan. Soc. Prev: Lect. & Sen. Regist. (Psychiat.) St. Thos. Hosp. Lond.; Sen. Regist. (Psychiat.) St. Bernard's Hosp. Lond.; Regist. (Psychiat.) Char. Cross. Hosp. Lond.

GHAFOOR, Abdul Bents Lane Medical Practice, 100 Lower Bents Lane, Bredbury, Stockport SK6 2NL Tel: 0161 430 8708 Fax: 0161 406 6528; 27 Withypool Drive, Mile End, Stockport SK2 6DT — MB ChB 1977 Manch. GP Stockport; Clin. Asst. (Ophth.) Stepping Hill Hosp. Stockport.

GHAFOOR, M B Baillie Street Health Centre, Baillie Street, Rochdale OL16 1XS Tel: 01706 525384 Fax: 01706 861625 — MB BS 1986 Bahauddin Zakariya; MB BS 1986 Bahauddin Zakariya.

GHAFOOR, Nadeem Haider 30 Valley Road, Liversedge WF15 6DF — MB ChB 1997 Leeds.

GHAHARIAN, Khashayar Lincoln and Louth NHS Trust, Lincoln County Hospital, Greetwell Road, Lincoln LN2 5QY Tel: 01522 512512 Fax: 01522 548820; 28 Southgate Spinneys, South Rauceby, Sleaford NG34 8QF Tel: 01529 488622 — MB BS 1997 Lond.; BSc (Hons) Lond 1994. (King's College School of Medicine & Dentistry) GPVTS Course August 1998 - July 2001.

GHAIE, Saveena Suzane 1 Tullybeg Av, Coleraine BT51 3NG — MB ChB 1997 Manch.

GHALAYINI, Marwan Standish Medical Practice, Rodenhurst, Church Street, Standish, Wigan WN6 0JP Tel: 01257 421909 Fax: 01257 424259; Lakewood, Brandreth Delph, Lancaster Lane, Parbold, Wigan WN8 7AQ — MD 1973 Damascus.

GHALI, Anis Aziz 50 Lynwood Avenue, Wall Heath, Kingswinford DY6 9AL Tel: 01384 95261 — MB BCh 1965 Cairo. (Kasr El Aini) Assoc. Specialist Anaesth. Dudley AHA. Prev: Clin. Asst. Dudley AHA; Regist. (Anaesth.) Newc. Gen. Hosp.; Regist. (Anaesth.) Dudley AHA.

GHALI, Fouad Abdel Messiah Hayes Grave Priory Hospital, Prestons Road, Hayes, Bromley BR2 7AS Tel: 020 8462 7722 Fax: 020 8462 5028; Snappers Hill, High St, Chipstead, Sevenoaks TN13 2RW Tel: 01732 455944 — MB BCh 1955 Cairo; MRCP (UK) 1970; MRCS Eng. LRCP Lond. 1972; FRCPsych 1987, M 1973; DPM Cairo 1960. (Ein-Shams) Med Dir Cons Psychiat. The Priory Hosp Hayes Gr. Bromley Kent. Socs: BMA; RSM; Egyptian Med Soc. Prev: Sen. Regist. Neuropsychiat. Unit Cairo; Sen. Regist. Hellingly Hosp.; Hon. Sen. Regist. Maudsley Hosp.

GHALI, Mr Nabeel Nassif Coxley Grange, Coxley Lane, Middlestown, Wakefield WF4 4PU Tel: 01924 274176 Fax: 01924 270732 — MB BCh 1962 Cairo; DS Cairo 1965, MB BCh 1962, DOS 1967; FRCS Ed. 1976; MRCS Eng. 1974. (Cairo) Cons. Orthop. Surg. Pinderfields Hosp. Wakefield. Socs: Fell. Roy. Soc. Med. Prev: Sen. Regist. (Orthop. & Traum.) Leeds & Bradford Health Dist.

***GHALI, Shadi** 12 Claire Court, 144 Sussex Gardens, London W2 1UE Email: shadi@btinternet.com — MB BS 1998 Lond.; MB BS Lond 1998; BSc Pharm 1995.

GHALY, Ahmos Farid Fahmy 51 Balgreen Road, Murrayfield, Edinburgh EH12 5TY Tel: 0131 337 0807 — MB BCh 1982 Ain Shams; MRCOG 1986. Regist. (O & G) W.. Gen. Hosp. Edin.

GHALY, Melvinderpal Singh Woodbrook Medical Centre, 28 Bridge Street, Loughborough LE11 1NH Tel: 01509 239166 Fax: 01509 238747; Parklands, 27 Pantain Road, Loughborough LE11 3LZ Tel: 01509 214515 — MB ChB 1984 Leeds; DFFP 1987; MRCGP 1988; DObst 1987. Clin. Tutor (Gen. Pract.) & Clin. Asst. (Rheum.) LoughBoro. Gen. Hosp.; GP Tutor. Socs: BMA; Med. Protec. Soc.

GHALY, Raouf George Anaesthetic Department, Royal Albert Edward Infirmary, Wigan Lane, Wigan WN1 2NN Tel: 01942 822088 Fax: 01942 822089 Email: rgghaly@gofornet.co.uk; 12 Brandreth Delph, Parbold, Wigan WN8 7AQ Tel: 01257 462245 Fax: 01257462245 Email: rgghaly@gofornet.co.uk — MB BCh 1970 Cairo; 2001 DP Med. Dublin; PhD Belf. 1989; FFA RCSI 1982; DA Cairo 1973. (Cairo Univeristy) Cons. Anaesth. & Chronic Pain Managem. Roy. Albert Edwd. Infirm. Wigan. Socs: BMA, Chairm. Wigan Div.; Assn. Anaesth. GB & Irel.; Anaesth. Res. Soc. Prev:

Lect. (Anaesth.) Qu. Univ. Belf.; Sen. Regist. (Anaesth.) Roy. Vict. Hosp. Belf.

GHANCHI, Mr Faruque Daudbhai 79 Track Road, Batley WF17 7AB Tel: 01924 478330 — MB BS 1992 Gujarat; MS (Ophth.) Gujarat 1989, MB BS 1992; FRCOphth 1992.

GHANDI, Seema 25 Beech Hill, Haywards Heath RH16 3RY — BM 1994 Soton.

GHANEH, Paula 2 Tanyard Drive, Hale Barns, Altrincham WA15 0BS — MB ChB 1989 Liverp.; FRCS Ed. 1994.

GHANEM, Hani Ibrahim Mostafa Carlton Hayes Hospital, Leicester LE9 5ES Tel: 0116 286 3481 Fax: 0116 275 1839; 98 Long Lane, Carlton-in-Lindrick, Worksop S81 9AU Tel: 01909 731604 — MB BCh 1972 Cairo; LRCP LRCS Ed. LRCPS Glas. 1978; DRCOG 1980; DObst. RCPI 1980. (Cairo) Staff Psychiat. Carlton Hayes Hosp. Leicester. Prev: GP Eccles Health Centre Manch.; SHO (Gen. Med.) Kilton Hosp. Worksop Notts.; SHO (Psychiat.) Derriford & Moorhaven Hosp. Plymouth.

***GHANI, Khurshid Ridwan** 19 Kingsmere Park, London NW9 8PJ — MB ChB 1998 Leeds.

GHANI, Mr Mahboob 9 Belle Vue Court, Belle Vue Gardens, Brighton BN2 2AN Tel: 01273 696955 — MB BS 1982 Punjab; FRCSI 1991.

GHANI, Patric Nasimul 68 Silverdale Avenue, Westcliff on Sea SS0 9BD — MB BS 1996 Lond.

GHANI, Rauf 4 Holwood Drive, Chorlton-cum-Hardy, Manchester M16 8WS Email: rauf@rghani.freeserve.co.uk — MB ChB 1994 Leic.; DFP 1998. (Leicester) Specialist Regist. (O & G), NW Deanery/Rotat. Prev: Specialist Regist. (O & G) RVI Newc.; SHO (Gyn.) Birm. Wom.'s Hosp.; SHO (Oncol.) Qu. Eliz. Hosp.

GHANI, Usman William Way Doctors Surgery, William Way, Wainfleet, Skegness PE24 4DE Tel: 01754 880212 Fax: 01754 880788 — MB BS 1967 Karachi.

GHANIM, Saeed Nashoor 16 Hannerton Road, Shaw, Oldham OL2 8HS; Royal Oldham Hospital, Rochdale Road, Oldham OL1 2JH Tel: 0161 624 0420 — MB ChB 1973 Mosul, Iraq; MRCP (UK) 1986; DCH RCP Lond. 1983. Staff Grade Paediat. Lancs. Socs: BMA; BPA; ODA. Prev: Cons. Paediat. Sanaa Yemen; Specialist Paediat. Baghdad.

GHANNAM, Issam Mohammed Taysir 110 Starbold Crescent, Knowle, Solihull B93 9LA Tel: 01564 778345 Fax: 01564 778345 — MD 1976 Damascus; MD Damascus, Syria 1976; DTCD Wales 1984.

GHARIB-OMAR, Adnan Bahlul Glenfield General Hospital, Leicester LE3 9DZ Tel: 0116 250 2550 Fax: 0116 250 2770; 12 Gavenny Way, Abergavenny NP7 5LX Tel: 01873 850806 — MB ChB 1970 Baghdad; DM Baghdad 1975. Socs: Fell. Roy. Soc. Med.; Fell. Roy. Soc. Health. Prev: Staff. Psychiat. Pen-y-Fal Hosp. Abergavenny; Med. Off. Alexandra Clinic Plymouth; Regist. (Psychiat.) Moorhaven & E. Glam. Gen. Hosps.

GHATAK, Mr Sunit Kumar Portland Hospital, 209 Great Portland St., London W1W 5AH Tel: 020 7935 4577 Fax: 020 7390 8266 Email: dulal@doctors.org.uk; 1 Bourne Avenue, Southgate, London N14 6PB Tel: 020 8882 0209 Fax: 020 8882 0209 Email: indira@ghatak.freeserve.co.uk — MB BS 1965 Calcutta; FRCOG 1990, M 1973; DObst 1968; DGO Calcutta 1966. (R.G. Kar Med. Coll.) Indep. Cons. O & G Lond. Socs: Indian Med. Soc.; Overseas Doctors Assn. Prev: Hon. Assoc. Specialist Colposcopy & Laser Clinic Rush Green Hosp. Romford; Clin. Asst. & Regist. (Gyn. & Obst.) St Mary's Hosp. Lond.; Regist. (Gyn. & Obst.) St. Mary's Hosp. Plaistow.

GHATAORE, Kulwinder Singh 16 Beaufort Avenue, New Cubbington, Leamington Spa CV32 7TA — MB ChB 1996 Leic.

GHATAURA, Sukhvinder Singh 11 Ellesmere Road, Greenford UB6 9ES Email: sukghataura@hotmail.com — MB ChB 1994 Leeds; FRCS Ed 1999. SHO Surg. (Curr.ly Plastic Surg.).

GHATGE, Ramesh The Surgery, 22 Maple Drive, Yew Tree Estate, Walsall WS5 4JJ Tel: 01922 620961 Fax: 01922 637387; 46 Jesson Road, Walsall WS1 3AX — MB BS 1973 Jiwaji.

GHATTAORA, Avtar Singh High Street, Arnold, Nottingham NG5 7BG.

GHATTAORA, Rashbal Singh 1 Gedling Grove, Arboretum, Nottingham NG7 4DU — MB BS 1993 Lond.

GHATTAS, Khaled Top Flat, 57 Harley St., London W1 — MB BS 1982 Lond.; MSc. Lond. 1988, MB BS 1982.

GHAURI, Abdus Saboor Khan 41 Quintin Avenue, London SW20 8LD — BM BCh 1990 Oxf.; BA Camb. 1987. SHO (Trauma & Orthop.) Glos. Roy. Hosp. Prev: Demonst. (Anat.) St. Geo. Hosp. Med. Sch. Lond.

GHAURI, Javed Bashir Hawkesbury Road Surgery, 1A Hawkesbury Road, Canvey Island SS8 0EX Tel: 01268 682303 — MB BS 1970 Sind. (Liaquat Med. Coll. Hyderabad) Local Civil Serv. Med. Off; Clin. Asst. S.end Gen. Hosp.

GHAUS, Pervez 35 Manse Crescent, Houston, Johnstone PA6 7JN — MB ChB 1984 Glas.; MRCGP 1991; DRCOG 1991. Clin. Asst. Artific. Limb & Appliance Centre Belvidere Hosp. Glas.

GHAWSS, Mr Mohammad Idriss Mahomathoo 80 Uxendon Hill, Wembley HA9 9SL — MB ChB 1973 Ed.; FRCS Ed. 1990.

GHAZAL, Mohamad Anwar 97 Weymouth Bay Avenue, Weymouth DT3 5AD Tel: 01305 778158 — MD 1969 Damascus. Assoc. Specialist (Orthop.) W. Dorset Hosps.

GHAZAL ASWAD, Saad North Tyneside General Hospital, Rake Lane, North Shields NE29 8NH Tel: 0191 293 2504 Fax: 0191 293 2594; 8 Salters Court, Gosforth, Newcastle upon Tyne NE3 5BH Tel: 0191 284 3018 Fax: 0191 284 3018 Email: soad.ghazol_aswad@newcastle.ac.uk — MD 1980 Aleppo; PhD Newc. 1995; MRCOG 1988; CCST (GMC) 1995; DFFP 1998; Mangt. Cert. (OU) 1996. Cons. O & G N. Tyneside Gen. Hosp.; Lect. (Cancer Research) Univ. Newc. u. Tyne. Prev: Research Regist. (Gyn. Oncol. & Cancer Research) Newc.; Regist. (Gyn. Oncol.) Qu. Eliz. Hosp. Gateshead; Regist. (O & G) Huddersfield Roy. Infirm.

GHAZANFAR, Reza Flat 5, Monckton Court, Strangways Terrace, London W14 8NF — MB BS 1998 Lond.; MB BS Lond 1998.

GHAZAWY, Ghazawy Shenouda (retired) 10 Edenbridge Gardens, Pewter Spear, Warrington WA4 5FH Tel: 01925 213367 Fax: 01924 213368 — MB ChB Alexandria 1973; DLO RCS Eng. 1978. Prev: GP Rochdale.

GHAZAWY, Samer 10 Edenbridge Gardens, Pewterspear, Warrington WA4 5FH — MB ChB 1998 Manch.; MB ChB Manch 1998.

GHAZI, Amer 17 Waldon Point, 56 Lukes Road, Torquay TQ2 5YE — MD 1986 Damascus; MD Damascus, Syria 1986; DA UK. GP Regist. Walnut Lodge Surg.

GHAZI, Arif Hussain 150 St Mary's Road, London N9 8NN Email: arifghazi@virgin.net — MB BS 1996 Lond.; BSc 1995. SHO Anaesth. P.ss Roy., Haywoods Heath Sussex. Socs: RCA; Assoc. of Anaesth.s. Prev: SHO Anaesth. Kent & Sussex; Ho. Off. Med. Romford; Ho. Off. Surg. Whipps Cross Leytonston.

GHAZNAVI, Mr Abdul Hameed St Helier Hospital, Wrythe Lane, Carshalton SM5 1AA Tel: 020 8644 4343; 92 Boundary Road, Carshalton SM5 4AB Tel: 020 8669 1813 — MB BS 1964 Sind; FRCS Eng. 1972; FRCS Ed. 1972. (Liaquat Med. Coll.) Assoc. Specialist (Urol.) St. Helier Hosp. Carshalton & Epsom Dist. Hosp. Socs: Sutton Med. Soc.; Epsom Med. Soc.; Assoc. Mem. BAUS. Prev: Clin. Asst. (Urol.) St. Helier Hosp. Carshalton; Regist. (Surg.) Warrington Gen. Hosp.; Regist. (Surg.) S.E. Kent Hosps.

GHEBREHEWET, Samuel Communicable Disease Surveillance Centre NW, Chester CH1 4EF Email: sg1samg1@hotmail.com — MD 1988 Addis Ababa.

GHEY, Eileen Mary Ruth (retired) 14 Elm Court Gardens, Truro TR1 1DS Tel: 01872 74797 — MRCS Eng. LRCP Lond. 1938; MA, BM BCh Oxf. 1958; DA Eng. 1944.

GHILCHIK, Margaret 10 Harley Street, London W1G 9PF Tel: 020 7467 8300 Fax: 020 7467 8312 Email: margaret@ghilchik.demon.co.uk; 6 Morland Close, Hampstead Way, London NW11 7JG Tel: 020 8458 3039 — MB BS 1961 Lond.; BSc (Hons.) Lond. 1957, MS 1972; FRCS Eng. 1967. (St. Bart.) Cons. Surg. St. Mary's Hosp., Dir. of BrE. Unit, St. Chas. Hosp., Centr. Middlx. & Eliz. Garrett Anderson Hosp. Lond.; Hon. Sen. Lect. (Surg.) St. Mary's Hosp. Med. Sch.; Surgic. Tutor RCS; Postgrad. Clin. Tutor St. Chas. Hosp. Lond.; Examr. MB BS Univ. Lond.; Penrose May Tutor RCS Eng.; Mem. Bd. Managem. & Med. & Sci. Comm. Wom. Nationwide Cancer Control Campaign. Socs: Surgic. Research Soc.; Brit. Assn. Surgic. Oncol.; Assn. Surg. Prev: Research Fell. Johns Hopkins Univ., USA; Regist. (Surg.) W.m. Hosp. & Harold Wood Hosp.; Ho. Surg. St. Bart. Hosp.

GHOBRIAL, Emeel Isaac Kidderminster NHS Trust, Bewdley Road, Kidderminster DY11 6RJ Tel: 01562 823424; 5 Isaacs Way, Droitwich WR9 8UZ Tel: 01905 774438 — MB BCh 1977 Cairo;

FFA RCSI 1992; DA (UK) 1989. (Univ. Cairo Coll. Med.) Cons. Anaesth. Kidderminster NHS Trust. Socs: Roy. Coll. Anaesth.; Assn. Anaesth. GB & Irel.; BMA. Prev: Specialist Regist. (Anaesth.) Stoke Sch. of Anaesth.; Sen. Regist. (Anaesth.) Leeds Gen. Infirm.; Locum Sen. Regist. Rotat. (Anaesth.) W. Midl.

GHOBRIAL, Laila Adly Iskander 189 Billing Road, Northampton NN1 5RS Tel: 01604 38947 — MB BCh 1966 Cairo.

GHOBRIAL, Onsi Samuel Health Centre, Park Drive, Stenhousemuir, Larbert FK5 3BB Tel: 01324 554411 Fax: 01324 553629; Stenhousemuir Health Centre, Larbert FK5 — MB BCh 1964 Cairo; LRCP LRCS Ed. LRCPS Glas. 1975; MRCGP 1977; DRCOG 1976; Dip. Dermat. Lond 1972. (Cairo) Prev: SHO (Dermat.) Fulford & City Hosps. York; SHO (Gen. Med.) Heathfield Gen. Hosp. Ayr.; Regist. (Gen. Med.) Falkirk Roy. Infirm.

GHOBRIAL, Mr Sherif Aziz Faragalla 47A Philpot Street, London E1 2JH — MB BCh 1975 Cairo; LRCS LRCP Ed. LRCPS Glas. 1983; FRCS Ed. 1985; MRCOG 1982.

GHODSE, Professor Abdol Hamid Department of Addictive Behaviour and Psychological Medicine, St George's Medical School, Cranmer Terrace, London SW17 0RE Tel: 020 8672 9516 Fax: 020 8725 2914 — FRCP Ed 1997; FFPHM (UK) 1997; DPM Eng. 1974; MD Tabriz 1965; PhD Lond. 1976, FRCP 1992; MRCP (UK) 1988; MFPHM RCP (UK) 1996; FRCPsych 1985, M 1980. Prof. Psychiat. St. Geo. Hosp. Med. Sch. Lond. & Dir. Addic. Resource Agency for Commiss.airs S. Thames (W.) Region; Hon. Cons. St. Geo. Healthcare & S.W. Lond & St Geo. Ment NHS Trusts & Merton, Sutton & Wandsworth HA; Adviser Jt. Formulary Comm. (Brit. Nat. Formulary); Pres. Internat. Narcotics Control Bd.; Mem. WHO Expert Advis. Panel (Alcohol & Drug Depend.). Prev: Cons. St. Geo. & St. Thos. Hosp. Lond.; Regist. Maudsley Hosp. Lond.; Lect. Inst. Psychiat. Lond.

GHODSE, Barbara Wilson Hospital, Cranmer Road, Mitcham CR4 4TP Tel: 020 8648 4021; 42 Alwyne Road, London SW19 7AE Tel: 020 8947 1400 — MB BChir 1971 Camb.; MA, MB Camb. 1971, BChir 1970; MRCP (UK) 1972; MRCS Eng. LRCP Lond. 1970. (St. Bart.) Commiss. Manager Acute Servs. Merton, Sutton & Wandsworth HA. Prev: Research Fell. & Hon. Regist. (Neurol.) Char. Cross Hosp. Lond.; SHO (Neurol.) Brook Hosp. Lond.; Ho. Phys. (Neurol.) & Ho. Surg. Surgic. Unit St. Bart. Hosp. Lond.

GHOLKAR, Anil Rajaram Neuroradiology Department, Newcastle General Hospital, Westgate Road, Newcastle upon Tyne NE4 6BE Tel: 0191 273 8811 Fax: 0191 256 3270 Email: anil@gholkar.demon.co.uk; 1 Fernwood Grove, Hamsterley Mill, Rowlands Gill NE39 1HJ — MB BS 1978 Bombay; FRCR 1985. Cons. Neuroradiol. Regional Neurosci. Centre Newc. Gen. Hosp. Prev: Sen. Regist. (Neuroradiol.) Manch. Roy. Infirm.

GHOLKAR, Joanne Hexham General Hospital, Hexham NE46 1QJ — MB ChB 1978 Manch.; MRCP (UK) 1981; FRCR 1984. Cons. Radiol. Hexham Gen. Hosp. Prev: Cons. Radiol. Shotley Bridge Gen. Hosp.

GHOLKAR, Santosh Anant 18 Wood Lane Close, Sheffield S6 5LY — MB ChB 1994 Sheff.

GHONEIM, Adeeb Taha Mohamed 35 West End Drive, Horsforth, Leeds LS18 5JR — MB BCh 1964 Cairo; PhD (Microbiol.) 1st Med. Inst. Moscow 1971; LMSSA Lond. 1976; MRCPath 1974. (Cairo) Cons. Microbiol. St. Jas. Univ. Hosp. Leeds; Sen. Clin. Lect. Univ. Leeds. Socs: Assn. Clin. Pathols. Mem. Brit. Soc. Antimicrobial Chemother. Prev: Sen. Lect. Microbiol. Univ. Leeds & Hon. Cons. Microbiol. Leeds AHA; Sen. Regist. (Microbiol.) Area Dept. Path. Exeter.

GHOORAH, Sanyukta Kaushalya Bharathi 24 Mavis Avenue, Leeds LS16 7LJ — MB ChB 1990 Leeds.

GHOORAHOO, Haroun Israel 9 Furzefield Road, Blackheath, London SE3 8TU Tel: 020 8293 3808 — MB BS 1993 Lond.; BSc Lond. 1990; MRCP (UK) 1996. (UMDS of Guy's & St. Thos. Hosps. Lond.) Prev: SHO (Thoracic Med.) Lond. Chest Hosp.; SHO (Cardiol. & Thoracic Med.) Harefield Hosp.; SHO (Gen. Med.) Hillingdon Hosp.

GHOORBIN, Vidya Bhushan 4 Heathdene Road, Wallington SM6 0TD — MB BS 1977 Rajasthan.

GHORASHIAN, Sala 54 Albert Road, Caversham, Reading RG4 7PF — BM BCh 1998 Oxf.; BM BCh Oxf 1998.

GHORBAL, Mr Murad Muhammed Shafik (retired) Lourdes Hospital, 57 Greenbank Road, Liverpool L18 1HQ Tel: 0151 733 7123 — LMSSA 1965 Lond.; MChOrth Liverp. 1971; FRCS Ed. 1968; FRCS Eng. 1968. Cons. Orthop. Surg. Walton Hosp. Liverp. Prev: SHO (Orthop.) Norf. & Norwich Hosp.

GHORI, Mr Moin Uddin Burton Hospital NHS Trust, Belvedere Road, Burton-on-Trent DE13 0RB — MB BS 1985 Karachi; FRCS Ed. 1992.

GHORI, Shabbir Salim Woodplumpton Road Surgery, 104 Woodplumpton Road, Fulwood, Preston PR2 2LR Tel: 01772 729756 — MB BS 1974 Indore; MB BS 1974 Indore.

GHOSAL, Shomik 63 Duncan Road, Sheffield S10 1SN — MB BS 1983 Calcutta; MRCP (UK) 1990.

GHOSE, Mr Amit 28 Ashdown Drive, Stourbridge DY8 5QY — MB BS 1983 Calcutta; FRCS Ed. 1991.

GHOSE, Arup Ratan South Warwickshire General Hospitals NHS Trust, Department Microbiology, Warwick Hospital, Lakin Road, Warwick CV34 5BW Tel: 01926 495321/482618 Fax: 01926 482600 Email: arup.ghose@swarkhosp-tr.wmids.nhs.uk; 28 Myton Crescent, Warwick CV34 6QA Tel: 01926 407700 Email: arup.ghose@virgin.net — MB BS 1979 Calcutta; LRCP LRCS Ed. LRCPS Glas. 1984; FFPath RCPI 1991; MRCPath 1989; FRCPath 1997. Cons. Clin. Microbiol. & Communicable Dis. Control S. Warks. Gen. Hosps. NHS Trust. Socs: Brit. Soc. Antimicrob. Chemother.; Brit. Soc. Study of Infec.; Hosp. Infec. Soc. Prev: Sen. Regist. (Clin. Microbiol.) Qu. Eliz. Childr. Hosp. & Gen. Hosp. Birm.

GHOSE, Bharati St Michael's Hospital, St Michael's Road, Warwick CV34 5UW Tel: 01926 406789; 28 Myton Crescent, Warwick CV34 6QA Tel: 01926 407700 — MB BS 1979 Calcutta. (NRS Med. Coll. Calcutta) Clin. Asst. (Gen. Psychiat.) St. Michael's Hosp. Warwick. Socs: Med. Protec. Soc. Prev: Regist. (Psychiat.) New Cross Hosp. Wolverhampton & St. Margts. Hosp. Birm.; SHO (Psychiat.) Barnsley Hall Hosp.

GHOSE, Roy Ranjeet 7 Manor Grove, Danygraig, Porthcawl CF36 5HD — MB BCh 1957 Wales; FRCP Ed. 1971, M 1961; FRCP Lond. 1982, M 1966. (Cardiff) Socs: BMA. Prev: Cons. Phys. Gen. Med. Singleton Hosp. Swansea & LLa.lli Hosp.; Sen. Regist. (Med.) Cardiff Roy. Infirm.; Regist. (Med.) St. Peter's, St. Paul's & St. Philip's Hosps. Lond.

GHOSE, Somendra Lal Poulter Road Medical Centre, 34 Poulter Road, Liverpool L9 0HJ Tel: 0151 525 5792 — MB BS 1970 Dibrugarh.

GHOSH, Adhir Kumar 23 Turnberry Drive, Wilmslow SK9 2QW — MB BS 1969 Calcutta.

GHOSH, Ajit Kumar Pontefract General Infirmary, Friarwood Lane, Pontefract WF8 1PL — MD 1963 Bihar; MB BS 1961; FRCP Lond. 1986; FRCP Ed. 1984; MRCP (UK) 1972. (Darbhanga Med. Coll.) Cons. Phys. (Geriat. Med.) Pontefract HA. Prev: Regist. (Chest Med.) Castle Hill Hosp. Cottingham; Regist. (Gen. Med.) Halifax Roy. Infirm.; Sen. Regist. (Geriat. Med.) St. Jas. Hosp. Leeds.

GHOSH, Mr Ajoy Kumar The Surgery, 8 Elmfield Avenue, Atherton, Manchester M46 0HW Tel: 01942 882001 Fax: 01942 886707; 10 Dalton Fold, Westhoughton, Bolton BL5 2QN Tel: 01942 813665 — MRCS Eng. LRCP Lond. 1973; MS Patna 1961, MB BS 1958; FRCS Ed. 1972. (P. of Wales Med. Coll. Patna) JP; Clin. Asst. (Gen. Surg.) Leigh Infirm.; Div. Surg. St. John's Ambul. Tyldsley. Socs: Wigan Med. Inst. & Overseas Doctors Assn. Prev: Regist. (Surg.) Vict. Hosp. Burnley; Regist. (Thoracic Surg.) City Hosp. Nottm.; Regist. (Orthop. Surg.) Promenade Hosp. S.port.

GHOSH, Amal Kumar 266 Tiverton Road, Tottenham, London N15 6RT Tel: 020 8800 5326; 80 Ashurst Road, Cockfosters, Barnet EN4 9LG Tel: 020 8449 6848 — MB BS 1965 Calcutta. (R.G. Kar Med. Coll.) Princip. GP Enfield & Haringey. Prev: SHO (Gen. Surg.) Bootle Hosp. Liverp.; SHO (Orthop.) Torbay Hosp. Torquay; SHO Rowley Bristow Orthop. Hosp. Pyrford.

GHOSH, Amitav (retired) 3 Mere Farm Road, Oxton, Prenton CH43 9TS Tel: 0151 653 4246 — MB BS 1959 Nagpur; FRCP Glas. 1981, M 1966; FFHom 1982, M 1979; DCH RCPS Glas. 1968; DTM & H Liverp. 1967. Prev: Clin. Dir. & Cons. Homoeop. Med. Mossley Hill Hosp. Liverp.

GHOSH, Anindya Raja Heath House Priory Hospital, (Priory Group of Hospitals), Heath House Lane, Bristol BS16 1EQ Tel: 0117 952 5255 Fax: 0117 952 5552 Email: rajaghosh@compuserve.com; Overdale, Church Town, Backwell, Bristol BS48 3JQ Tel: 01437 766546 — MBBS 1969; MD (Psych) 1976; MAMS 1974; MRC Psych 1981. Staff Cons. Psychiat. (p/t) Heath Ho. Priory Hosp.

Bristol; Hon. Lect. Univ. Hosp. of Wales, Cardiff. Socs: Roy. Coll. Psychiat.; Brit. Assn. of Behavioural & Cognitive Psychother.; Fell.Indian Psychiatric Soc. Prev: Cons. Psychiat. UBHT, Bristol; Cons. Psychiat. Derwen HNS Trust, Carmarthen; Lect. Inst. of Psychiat. Lond.

GHOSH, Aniruddha c/o Scunthorpe General Hospital, Cliff Gardens, Scunthorpe DN15 7BH; 42 Liskeard Road, Walsall WS5 3ES — MB BS 1974 Calcutta. (Med. Coll. Calcutta) Regist. Summerlands & Yeovil Dist. Hosp. Prev: SHO Roy. Shrewsbury & CrossHo.s Hosps.; SHO Sandwell Dist. Gen. Hosp. W. Bromwich; SHO S.lands Hosp. Shoreham-by-Sea.

GHOSH, Anuradha 53 Avenue Clamart, Scunthorpe DN15 8EQ — MB BS 1974 Calcutta.

GHOSH, Aparna Pentire, 18 Woodcote Road, Tettenhall, Wolverhampton WV6 8LP Tel: 01902 756081 — MB BS 1967 Calcutta; MFCM RCP (UK) 1989; DCP Warwick 1984; DA Eng. 1977; DObst RCOG 1970; DGO Calcutta 1967. (R.G. Kar Med. Coll.) Sen. Clin. Med. Off (Community Med.) Wolverhampton HA.

GHOSH, Apurba Lumar c/o Dr A Palit, Hillside, Coxhill, Narberth SA67 8EH — MB BS 1979 Gauhati; MRCPI 1995.

GHOSH, Asim Kumar 109 High Street, Feltham TW13 4HG Tel: 020 8751 3394 Fax: 020 8890 0547. GP Feltham, Middlx.

GHOSH, Asit Kumar c/o Drive C. Chattopadya, Department of Rheumatology, Wrightington Hospital of Joint Diseases, Hall Lane, Appley Bridge, Wigan WN6 9EP — MB BS 1963 Calcutta.

GHOSH, Avijit New City Medical Centre, Tatham St., Sunderland SR1 2QB Tel: 0191 567 5571 Fax: 0191 510 2746; 21 Cottonwood, Burdon Vale, Sunderland SR3 2NU — MB BS 1991 Newc.; DFFP 1995. ((Newc.)) GP Sunderland. Socs: BMA.

***GHOSH, Baisakhi Reenee** 10 Dalton Fold, Westhoughton, Bolton BL5 2QN — MB ChB 1997 Manch.; BSc MB ChB (Hons.) Manch. 1997.

GHOSH, Bani 194 Chesterfield Road S., Mansfield NG19 7EE — MB BS 1948 Calcutta; DA Eng. 1963; Cert FPA (Inc. IUD) 1969. (Calcutta Med. Coll.) Clin. Asst. (Anaesth.) Centr. Notts. Health Dist.; Clin. Med. Off. Family Plann. Clinics Notts. AHA (T) & Derbysh. AHA.

GHOSH, Biman Behari (retired) Medical Unit, 1 Croston Road, Lostock Hall, Preston PR5 5RS Tel: 01772 30724 Fax: 01772 620160 — MB BS 1960 Calcutta.

GHOSH, Biswa Nath Alvanley Surgery, 1 Auburn Avenue, Bredbury, Stockport SK6 2AH Tel: 0161 430 2727 Fax: 0161 406 7999.

GHOSH, Caroline 103 Little Sutton Road, Sutton Coldfield B75 6PT — MB ChB 1992 Sheff.

GHOSH, Chhanda 343 Wokingham Road, Earley, Reading RG6 7EB — MB BS 1971 Calcutta.

GHOSH, Deb Baran 119 Northcote Road, London SW11 6PW — MB BS 1963 Calcutta; MRCOG 1971.

GHOSH, Debabrata Whytemans Brae Hospital, Kirkcaldy KY1 2ND Tel: 01592 643355 Fax: 01592 640159; 15 Long Craigs Terrace, Kinghorn, Burntisland KY3 9TA Tel: 01529 890879 — MB BS 1962 Calcutta; FRCP Glas. 1986; FRCP Ed. 1984; MRCP (UK) 1973; DCH NUI 1969. (R.G. Kar Med. Coll.) Cons. Phys. Geriat. Med. Fife HB. Socs: Brit. Med. Assoc.; Brit. Geriat.s Soc.; Roy. Coll. Phys.s Edin.

GHOSH, Debi Sankar (retired) 42 Carmarthen Avenue, Cosham, Portsmouth PO6 2AQ Tel: 01705 379152 — MB BS Calcutta 1958; DO Eng. 1968.

GHOSH, Dipali Flat 2B Oak House, St Annes Hospital, St Annes Road, London N15 3TH — MB BS 1965 Calcutta.

GHOSH, Dulal Chandra Weston Street Surgery, 28-30 Weston Street, Adderly Green, Longton, Stoke-on-Trent ST3 5DQ Tel: 01782 311266; 32 Constance Avenue, Trentham, Stoke-on-Trent ST4 8XJ — MB BS 1965 Calcutta.

GHOSH, Gautam Kumar 12 Oakley Avenue, Ealing, London W5 3SD — MB BS 1967 Calcutta; MS (PGI) 1972; DO Lond. 1977. Assoc. Specialist Ophth., Char. Cross Hosp. & Diabetic Retinopathy Unit, Hammersmith Hosp. Lond.; Specialist Diabetic Eye Clinic, St. Peter's Hosp., Chertsey.

GHOSH, Gunnen Joachim York Clinic, Guy's Hospital, 47 Weston St., London SE1 9RT — MB BS 1990 Lond.; BSc Lond. 1987, MB BS 1990; MSc Lond. 1996; MRCPsych 1995. Specialist Regist. Guy's Hosp. Lond. Prev: Specialist Regist. (Gen. Adult Psychiat.) Guy's Hosp.; Clin. Research Fell. (Psychol. Treatm.s) Guy's Hosp. & UMDS; Regist. Rotat. (Psychiat.) Guy's Hosp.

GHOSH, Indrajit Robert Red Cottage, Brick Kiln Lane, Great Horkesley, Colchester CO6 4EU Tel: 01206 271735 Fax: 01206 271735 Email: irghosh@aol.com — MB ChB 1988 Ed.; MRCP (UK) 1995. Sen. Regist. in Gen. Med., Clin. Neurophysiol. & IC Med. Socs: Collegiate Mem. Roy. Coll. Phys.s, Lond.; Brit. Soc. Clin. Neurophysiol.; Assn. Brit. Neurol. Prev: Sen. Regist. Clin. Neurophysiol. St. Bart. Hosp. Lond.

GHOSH, Mr Jayantabrata 6 Forest Grove, Prescot L34 2RZ — MB BS 1956 Calcutta; FRCS Ed. 1966; DO Eng. 1969. (Med. Coll. Calcutta) Cons. Ophth. Surg. Providence Hosp. St. Helen's. Prev: Regist. Plastic Surg. Whiston. Hosp. Prescot.

GHOSH, Jayanti Kumar Blyth Health Centre, Thoroton Street, Blyth NE24 1DX Tel: 01670 396500 Fax: 01670 396516; Malda-Villa, 14 Herring Gull Close, Blyth NE24 3RH Tel: 01670 353635 — MB BS Calcutta 1962; FRSH 1996. (NRS Med. Coll. Calcutta) Princip. Gen. Med. Pract.; Clin. Adviser NHS Ombudsman Panel; Med. Off. Blyth Community Hosp. N.d.; Chairm. Med. Exec. Comm. Blyth Community Hosp. (1988-1989 1990-91); Mem. N.d. LMC; Mem. Health Serv. Appeal Auth. Med. Panel; Clin. Adviser NHS Ombudsman Panel. Socs: BMA (Ex-Chairm. Mid. N.d. Div.); Chairm. Blyth Community Health Care Assn. Prev: Regist. (Orthop.) Ashington Gen. Hosp. N.d.; SHO (Orthop. Cas. & Gen. Surg.) Middlesbrough Gen. Hosp.; Clin. Asst. (A & E) Isle of Thanet Dist. Hosp. Margate & Ashington Hosp.

GHOSH, Jonathan 32 Constance Av, Stoke-on-Trent ST4 8XJ — MB ChB 1997 Manch.

GHOSH, Justin Mathew 226c Haverstock Hill, London NW3 2AE — MB BS 1998 Lond.; MB BS Lond 1998.

GHOSH, Jyotish Chandra 121 Harley Street, London W1N 1DH Tel: 020 7935 0244; 957 Finchley Road, London NW11 7PE Tel: 020 8458 8725 — MB 1951 Calcutta; MRCP (UK) 1958; FRCP Ed. 1972. Hon. Clin. Asst. Nat. Heart Hosp. Lond. Prev: Chief Cons. Phys. Gen. Hosp. Lagos, Nigeria; Assoc. Lect. & Cons. Univ. Teach. Hosp. Lagos, Nigeria.

GHOSH, Karen 103 Little Sutton Road, Sutton Coldfield B75 6PT — MB ChB 1993 Dundee.

GHOSH, Kiron 27 Broom Road, Newton Mearns, Glasgow G77 5DP — MB BS 1976 Calcutta; MRCPath 1990; DGO 1978. Sen. Regist. (Virol.) Ruchill Hosp. Gtr. Glas. Hosp. Prev: Regist. (Microbiol.) S.. Gen. Hosp. Glas.

GHOSH, Madhumita Lambeth Walk Group Practice, 5 Lambeth Walk, London SE11 6SP Tel: 020 7735 4412 Fax: 020 7820 1888 — MB BCh 1992 Wales.

GHOSH, Manju The Well House, 64 Blakes Avenue, New Malden KT3 6RF — MB BS 1963 Calcutta; FRCOG 1985, M 1972; DObst 1969; DGO Calcutta 1964. (Calcutta Med. Coll.)

GHOSH, Mr Manoj Kumar 28 Alford Court, Bonchurch Close, Sutton SM2 6AY — MB BS 1974 Calcutta; FRCS Ed. 1985.

GHOSH, Mohan Hjertholm Northumberland Heath Medical Centre, Hind Crescent, Northumberland Heath, Erith DA8 3DB Tel: 01322 336556 Fax: 01322 351475; Maytrees, 24 Baldwyns Park, Bexley DA5 2BA Tel: 01322 522767 — MB ChB 1986 Dundee. Socs: Protec. Soc.

GHOSH, Monimoy 29 Richmond Road, Ilford IG1 1JY — MB BS 1988 Calcutta; MRCP (UK) 1991; MD Warwick 1998.

GHOSH, Mrinal Kanti Rotherham District General Hospital, Moorgate Road, Rotherham S60 2UD Tel: 01709 820000; 79 Woodfoot Road, Moorgate, Rotherham S60 3EH Tel: 01709 363770 — MB BS 1961 Calcutta; FRCP Lond. 1988; FRCP Glas. 1987; MRCP (UK) 1974; DTCD Delhi 1963. (Med. Coll. Calcutta) Cons. Phys. Med. for Elderly Rotherham HA; Hon. Clin. Lect. (Med. for Elderly) Univ. Sheff.

GHOSH, Nila 2 Hiram Drive, East Boldon NE36 0TA Tel: 0191 536 7963 — MB BS 1963 Calcutta; FFA RCS Eng. 1978; DA Eng. 1968. (Calcutta Med. Coll.) Cons. Anaesth. Sunderland AHA. Socs: Assn. Anaesth. Prev: Sen. Regist. (Anaesth.) Sunderland AHA; Regist. (Anaesth.) W. Middlx. Hosp. Isleworth; Sen. Regist. (Anaesth.) Newc. AHA (T).

GHOSH, Niranjan East Street Surgery, 1 East Street, Rochdale OL16 2EG Tel: 01706 639002 — MB BS 1969 Calcutta; DLO 1979 Lond.

GHOSH, Pabitra Kumar 371 Broad Lane, Coventry CV5 7BW Tel: 024 76 465313 — MB BS 1953 Calcutta. (R.G. Kar Med. Coll.)
GHOSH, Pinaki Bridgeton Health Centre, 201 Abercromby Street, Glasgow G40 2DA Tel: 0141 531 6500 Fax: 0141 531 6505 — MB BS 1974 Calcutta; MB BS 1974 Calcutta.
GHOSH, Mr Pradeep Chandra Bransholme South Health Centre, Goodhart Road, Bransholme, Hull HU7 4DW Tel: 01482 825496 — MB BS 1965 Patna; BSc (Hons.) Patna 1959, MS 1968, MB BS 1965. (P. of Wales Med. Coll.)
GHOSH, Pratima The Surgery, 19 Lichfield St., Walsall WS1 7UG Tel: 01922 623780; 12 Buchanan Road, Walsall WS4 2EN — MB ChB 1985 Leic.; DRCOG 1989. (Univ. Leic.) GP; Clin. Asst. (Dermat.) Skin Hosp. Birm. Prev: Trainee GP Shepshed Health Centre Leics. VTS; SHO (Psychiat.) Carlton Hayes Hosp. Leicester; SHO (O & G) W. Birm.
GHOSH, Priti Kana 24 Woodlands Avenue, New Malden KT3 3UN — MB BS 1976 Calcutta.
GHOSH, Purab Ratan Higher Broughton Health Centre, Bevendon Square, Salford M7 4TP Tel: 0161 792 6888 Fax: 0161 708 8510.
GHOSH, Purnima (retired) Ryhope Health Centre, Ryhope, Sunderland SR2 0RY Tel: 0191 521 0220/0617 — MB BS 1963 Calcutta; DA Eng. 1967. Asst. Anaesth. Dryburn Hosp. Durh.
GHOSH, Ratan Kanti 3 Buttermere Drive, Priorslee, Telford TF2 9RE — MD 1979 Calcutta; MB BS 1976.
GHOSH, Roma Mary 12 Old Larne Road, Ballynure, Ballyclare BT39 9QB — MB BS 1970 Panjab; FFA RCSI 1976.
GHOSH, Sagar Chandra (retired) — MB BS 1965 Calcutta. Prev: Med. Off. Brit. Pregn. Advis. Serv. P'boro.
GHOSH, Sajal Kumar (retired) Breeze Hill, Halifax Road, Briercliffe, Burnley BB10 3QS Tel: 01282 431172 — MB BS 1955 Calcutta; DMRD Liverp. 1966. Prev: Cons. Radiol. Burnley & Dist. Gp. Hosps.
GHOSH, Salil Kumar (retired) Medical Department, Middlesbrough General Hospital, Middlesbrough TS5 5AZ Tel: 01642 854462 Fax: 01642 854462 — MB BS 1959 Calcutta; FRCP Ed. 1981, M 1966; FRCP Glas. 1980, M 1965. Cons. Phys. (Gen. Med. & Infec. Dis.) S. Tees Acute Hosp. NHS Trust. Prev: Sen. Phys. MAMC Hosp. Durgapur, India.
GHOSH, Samantha Renee Mary Flat 1/2, 31 Barterholm Road, Paisley PA2 6PA — MB ChB 1992 Glas.
GHOSH, Samit Kumar 12 Ash Close, Abbots Langley WD5 0DN — MB ChB 1998 Liverp.; MB ChB Liverp 1998.
GHOSH, Sandip Kumar 27 Broom Road, Newton Mearns, Glasgow G77 5DP — MD 1980 Calcutta; MB BS 1976; MRCP (UK) 1987; MRCPI 1987. Regist. (Respirat. Med.) W.. Infirm. Glas. Prev: Regist. (Med.) Ballochmyle Hosp.; SHO (Med.) Ashington Gen. Hosp.
GHOSH, Mr Sankardas Singleton Hospital, Swansea SA2 8QA Tel: 01792 205666 Fax: 01792 208647; 4 Dysgwylfa, Sketty, Swansea SA2 9BG Tel: 01792 296485 Fax: 01792 285292 — MB BS Calcutta 1963; BSc Calcutta 1957, MS (Gen. Surg.) 1973. (Nilratan Sircar Med. Coll.) Staff Oncol. (Clin. Oncol.) Singleton Hosp. Swansea. Prev: Sen. Off. (Radiother. & Oncol.) Unit Singleton Hosp. Swansea; Med. Off. (Outpats.) Dept. Surg. R.G. Kar Med. Coll. & Hosp. Calcutta; Regist. (Surg.) Med. Coll. Hosps., Calcutta.
GHOSH, Mr Santanu Kumar c/o Mrs Sue Reed Accommodation Manager, Nurses Home, Maidstone General Hospital, Hermitage Lane, Maidstone ME16 9QQ — MB BS 1980 Calcutta; FRCS Glas. 1987; MRCS Eng. LRCP Lond. 1988.
GHOSH, Sisir Kumar The Surgery, 110 Sandy Hill Road, Plumstead, London SE18 7BA Tel: 020 8854 3736 Fax: 020 8854 4381; 1 Farrington Place, Chislehurst BR7 6BE — MB BS Calcutta 1970; BSc Calcutta 1960. (R.G. Kar Med. Coll.) Family Plann. Off. Bexley Health. Socs: BMA (Sec. Bexley & Greenwich Div.). Prev: Course Organiser PGEA.
GHOSH, Subrata Gastrointestinal Unit, Western General Hospital, Edinburgh EH4 2XU Tel: 0131 537 1754 Fax: 0131 537 1007 Email: sg@srv0.med.ed.ac.uk; 107 Craigleith Hill Avenue, Edinburgh EH4 2NB Tel: 0131 332 5131 Email: subrata@sghosh.freeserve.co.uk — MB BS 1982 Calcutta; MD Ed. 1996; MD Calcutta 1986; FRCP (Ed.) 1997. Cons. Gastroenterol. GI Unit W.. Gen. Hosp. Edin.; Sen. Lect. Univ. Edin. Socs: Brit. Soc. Gastroenterol.; Scott. Assn. Phys.; Caledonian Soc. Gastroenterol. Prev: Research Fell. Edin. Univ. GI Unit W.. Gen. Hosp.; Regist. (Gastroenterol.) W.. Gen. Hosp. Edin.; Hon. Regist. & Clin. Research Fell. (Med. & Gastroenterol.) Bristol Roy. Infirm.
GHOSH, Sukhamay 2 Hiram Drive, East Boldon NE36 0TA Tel: 0191 536 7963 — MB BS 1963 Calcutta; MB BS (Hons.) Calcutta 1963; FRCP Ed. 1991; FRCP Lond. 1990; MRCP (UK) 1972. (Calcutta Med. Coll.) Cons. Phys. (Geriat. Med.) Sunderland HA; Hon. Clin. Lect. (Geriat. Med.) Univ. Newc. Socs: Brit. Geriat. Soc. & BMA. Prev: Sen. Regist. (Geriat.) St. Mary's Hosp. Lond. & W. Middlx. Hosp. Isleworth; Regist. (Gen. Med.) King Edwd. VII Hosps. Windsor & Maidenhead.
GHOSH, Sukumar (retired) 58 Bowdon Avenue, Barlborough, Chesterfield S43 4JE Tel: 01246 810944 — MB BS 1956 Calcutta.
GHOSH, Mr Tarak Nath 15 St Johns Street, Huntingdon PE29 3DD — MB BS 1962 Calcutta; FRCS Ed. 1976; FRCS Glas. 1976; DO Eng. 1969; DO RCPSI 1969; DOMS Calcutta 1965.
GHOSH, Tushar Kanti The Surgery, The Gables, 284 Porters Avenue, Dagenham RM8 2EQ Tel: 020 8592 7679 Fax: 020 8593 8110; 29 Roy Gardens, Newbury Park, Ilford IG2 7QG Tel: 020 8597 5992 — MB BS 1967 Bangalore; DGM RCP Lond. 1986; MRCGP. (Bangalore) Hosp. Pract. (Geriat. Med.) Chadwell Heath Hosp. Romford; Clin. Asst. (Cardiol.) King Geo. Hosp. Essex.; GP Trainer; GP Tutor; GMC Assessor; Med. Stud. Pl.ments with Local Hosps. in Witten Germany. Socs: (Pres. 98/99) Ilford Med. Soc.
GHOSH, Utpal Kumar 5 Farington Terrace, Dundee DD2 1LP Tel: 01382 69204 — MB BS 1959 Gauhati. (Assam Med. Coll.) Assoc. Specialist (Geriat. Med.) Roy. Vict. Hosp. Dundee; Hon. Lect. Geriat. Med. Univ. Dundee.
GHOSH-CHOWDHURY, Neeta 7 Crescent Lane, London SW4 9PT — MB BS 1998 Lond.; MB BS Lond 1998.
GHOSH RAY, Goures Chandra Castle Hill Hospital, Castle Road, Cottingham, Hull HU16 5JQ Tel: 01482 875875; 71 Valley Drive, Kirk Ella, Hull HU10 7PW — MB BS Calcutta 1966; FRCOG 1986, M 1972; DGO Calcutta 1968. (Calcutta Med. Coll.) Staff Grade (O & G) Castle Hill Hosp. Hull. Prev: Regist. (O & G) N. Cambs. Hosp. Wisbech.
GHOTRA, Malkit Singh Lazy End, 25B Newark Road, Windlesham GU20 6NE — MB BS 1993 Lond.; BSc (Hons.) Lond. 1989. (King's Coll. Hosp. Med. Sch.) Pharmaceut. Phys. Socs: BMA; MDU. Prev: SHO (Ent) FarnBoro. Hosp., Orpington Kent; SHO (Anaesth.) Greenwich Dist. Hosp. Lond.; Ho. Phys. Qu. Mary's Hosp. Sidcup.
GHOURI, Nayeem Ahmed Peel Street Surgery, 11 Peel Street, Glasgow G11 5LL Tel: 0141 334 9331 Fax: 0141 334 9332; 20 Second Avenue, Bearsden, Glasgow G61 2LR — MB BS 1972 Bangalore. (Bangalore Med. Coll.)
GHOUZE, Aysha 45 Dukes Wood Av, Gerrards Cross SL9 7JY — MB BS 1997 Lond.
GHUFOOR, Mr Khalid ENT Department, Royal Glamorgan General Hospital, Ynys Maerdy, Llantrisant CF72 8XR — MB BS 1990 Lond.; BSc Lond. 1987; FRCS (ENT) 1995; FRCS Eng. 1995. Prev: Regist. (ENT) St. Mary's Hosp. Lond.
GHUFOOR, Wasima Naheed 8 Scutari Road, East Dulwich, London SE22 0NN — MB BCh 1990 Wales; MRCGP 1995; DRCOG 1993. Prev: Trainee GP Raynes Pk.
GHUFOOR, Zahid 7 Graces Road, London SE5 8PF — MB BS 1994 Lond.
GHULAM, Sahera Jassim The Knoll, Lees Road, E. Bradbourne, Ashford TN25 5LE Tel: 01303 850202 — MB ChB 1976 Baghdad; MRCP (UK) 1983; DCH RCP Lond. 1983.
GHUMAN, Baljit Singh Mayhill Surgery, 108 Pen-y-Graig Road, Mayhill, Swansea SA1 6JZ — MB ChB 1990 Leeds; DFFP Lond. 1998; T(GP) Lond. 1997. (Leeds University) GP Princip. Prev: SHO (Gen. Med.) E. Glam. Gen. Hosp. Ch. Village; SHO O & G E. Glam. Gen. Hosp.; Regist. (Gen. Md.) Llandough & Caerphilly Hosp. Cardiff.
GHURA, Harvinder Singh 9 Highcroft Avenue, Oadby, Leicester LE2 5UH — MB BS 1993 Newc.; MRCP (UK) 1996. Specialist Regist. (Dermat.) Leicester Roy. Infirm. Socs: BMA; Newc. & Durh. Med. Grad. Assn.; Brit. Assn. Dermatol. Prev: SHO (Gen. Med.) Freeman Hosp. Newc.; Ho. Off. (Surg.) Dryburn Hosp. Durh.; Ho. Off. (Med.) Newc. Gen. Hosp.
GHURA, Parminder Singh 30 Queensway, Gosforth, Newcastle upon Tyne NE3 5NS — MB BS 1997 Newc.
GHURAN, Azad Valentine 10 Pitfold Road, Lee, London SE12 9HX Tel: 020 8857 3499 Email: azad@globalnet.co.uk — MB ChB 1993 Ed.; MRCP (UK) 1996. (Edinburgh) Research Fell. St.Geo.s Hosp. Med. Sch. Socs: BMA; Med. Protec. Soc. Prev:

Regist. (Cardiol.) N. Staffs. City Gen. Hosp. Stoke on Trent; SHO (Cardiol./Gen. Med.) St. James' Univ. Hosp. Leeds; SHO (Gen. Med.) Harrogate Dist. Hosp.

GHURYE, Rajiv Shantaram Shanklin Medical Centre, 1 Carter Road, Shanklin PO37 7HR Tel: 01983 862245 Fax: 01983 862310; Parkwall, Redhill Lane, Wroxhall, Ventnor PO38 3ER — MD 1980 Nagpur; MB BS 1977; MRCP (UK) 1986. GP Shanklin Med. Centre; Phys. i/c Open Access Endoscopy Serv. Orchard Hosp. Newport I. of Wight. Prev: Hon. Sen. Regist. (Gen. Med./Gastroenterol.) St. Mary's Hosp. I. of Wight th; Hon. Regist. (Gastroenterol.) Qu. Alexandra Hosp. Cosham Portsmouth; Resid. Phys. I. of Wight Private Hosp.

GIALLOMBARDO, Elio Princess Margaret Hosp, Okus Road, Swindon SN1 4JU; Trabbs House, Goose Green, Lambourn, Hungerford RG17 8YB — State DMS 1984 Ancona; MRCP (UK) Ed. 1988; FRCP 1999. Cons. Phys. Dept.of med for the elderly P.ss Margt. Hosp Swindon. Socs: BGS.

GIAM, Nigel Kim Lin 23A Park Hill, London W5 2JS — MB BS 1998 Lond.; MB BS Lond 1998.

GIANCOLA, Giorgio Luigi X-Ray Department, Queen Elizabeth The Queen Mother Hospital, St Peters Road, Margate CT9 4AN Tel: 01843 225544 Fax: 01843 220049 — MB ChB 1983 Birm.; FRCR 1989. Cons. Radiol. QEQM Hosp. Margate/WHH Hosp. Ashford, E. Kent NHS Trust. Socs: BSIR (Brit. Soc. of Interneutional Radiol.); CIRSE (CadioVasc. & Interven.al Soc. of Europe). Prev: Sen. Regist. W. Midl. RHA; SHO (Med.) Dudley HA.

GIANGRANDE, Paul Leo Francis Oxford Haemophilia Centre, Churchill Hospital, Oxford OX3 7LJ Tel: 01865 225300 Fax: 01865 225608 Email: paul.giangrande@ndm.ox.ac.uk; Home Close, Southend, Garsington, Oxford OX44 9DH Tel: 01865 361394 Fax: 01865 368112 Email: raw36@dial.pipex.com — MB ChB 1979 Manch.; MB ChB (Hons.) Manch. 1979; T(Path) 1991; T(M) 1991; DHMSA 1988; Cert. Av. Med. 1993; FRCPI (Ireland) 1999; BSc (Hons.) Pharmacol. Manch. 1976, MD 1991; FRCP Lond. 1996; FRCP Ed. 1997; MRCP (UK) 1982; LMSSA Lond. 1979; MRCS Eng. LRCP Lond. 1979; FRCPCH 1997; FRCPath 1996, M 1986; FRCPI 1999 (Ireland). (Univ. Manch.) Cons. Haemat. Oxf. Radcliffe Hosps. NHS Trust; Hon. Sen. Lect. (Haemat.) Univ. Oxf.; Vice-pres. (med.) World Fed. Of Haemophilia, Canada. Prev: Clin. Research Fell. Haemophilia & Thrombosis Centre Milan, Italy; Clin. Research Fell. (Haemat.) Roy. Free Hosp. Lond.; Lect. & Hon. Sen. Regist. (Haemat.) W.m. & Char. Cross Hosps. Lond.

GIANNAKIS, Ioannis Birmingham and Midland Eye Hospital, Church St., Birmingham B3 2NS — Ptychio Iatrikes 1987 Thessalonika.

GIANNAS, John 8 Essan House, 1A Victoria Road, London W5 1TB — Ptychio Iatrikes 1990 Athens.

GIANNELLI, Professor Francesco Bruno Paediatric Research Unit, Div. Medical & Molecular Genetics, King's College GKT Medical College, Guy's Campus, Guy's Tower, Guy's Hospital, London SE1 9RT Tel: 020 7955 4450 Fax: 020 7955 4444 — State DMS Rome 1960; DSc Lond. 1989, PhD 1967; DSc Rome 1970. (Rome) Prof. Molecular Genetics & Hon. Cons. Cytogenetics & Cell. Biol. UMDS Lond. Socs: Fell. RCP. Prev: Reader (Cell Biol. & Cytogenetics) Guy's Hosp. Med. Sch. Lond.; Sen. Lect. & Lect. (Cytogenetics) Guy's Hosp. Med. Sch. Lond.

GIANNELLI, Paolo Biagio Luigi Churchtown Medical Centre, 137 Cambridge Road, Southport PR9 7LT Tel: 01704 224416 Fax: 01704 507168; 11 Hesketh Road, Southport PR9 9PD — MB ChB 1988 Manch.; MRCGP 1992.

GIANNOUDIS, Panagiotis 16 Oakdene Court, Leeds LS17 8XS — Ptychio Iatrikes 1991 Ioannina.

GIANNOULATOS, Spyridon c/o Mrs D. Tringala, 13 Edgehill Avenue, London N3 3AY — Ptychio Iatrikes 1984 Athens.

GIANNOULIS, Kleanthis 33 St James Street, Weston Super Mare BS23 1ST — Ptychio Iatrikes 1993 Thessalonika.

GIATROMANOLAKI, Alexandra 7 Skene Close, Headington, Oxford OX3 7XQ — Ptychio Iatrikes 1990 Patras.

GIBB, Mr Alan George (retired) 19 Westpark Gardens, Dundee DD2 1NY Tel: 01382 640867 Fax: 01382 640867 Email: aande.gibb@tesco.net — MB ChB Aberd. 1941; FRCS Ed. 1948; FCS Hong Kong 1994; DLO Eng. 1944. Prev: Vis. Prof. Otolaryngol. Nat. Univ., Singapore.

GIBB, Alan Patrick Royal Infirmay of Edinburgh, University Medical School, Teviot Place, Edinburgh EH8 9AG — MB ChB 1980 Ed.; PhD Ed. 1993, BSc (Hons.) 1977, MB ChB 1980; MRCP (UK) 1983; MRCPath 1988. (Edinburgh) Cons. Microbiologist Lothian Univ. Hospiatls NHS Trust Edin.; Hon. Clin. Sen. Lect. Univ. of Edin. Prev: Regist. (Med. Microbiol.) N. Manch. Gen. Hosp.; SHO (Infect. Dis.) City Hosp. Edin.; Lect. (Bacteriol.) Edin. Univ.

GIBB, Alison Mary 33 Griffiths Drive, Southport PR9 7DP — MB BS 1992 Newc.

GIBB, Allan David 37 Upper Gordon Road, Camberley GU15 2HJ Tel: 01276 26424; Stony Ridge, Pine Avenue, Camberley GU15 2LY — MB BS 1959 Lond.; DObst RCOG 1963. (St. Thos.) Prev: Squadron Ldr. RAF Med. Br.; Obst. Ho. Surg. W. Suff. Gen. Hosp. Bury St. Edmunds.

GIBB, Christopher Alan South Molton Health Centre, 10 East Street, South Molton EX36 3BZ Tel: 01769 573101 Fax: 01769 574371 Email: gibb@gp-683137.nhs.uk — BM 1986 Soton.; MRCGP 1991; Dip. Pract. Dermat. Wales 1996; DRCOG 1993; Cert. Family Plann. JCC 1992; T(GP) 1991; DA (UK) 1988. (Southampton) GP Princip. Socs: BMA; RCGP (MRCGP). Prev: Trainee GP Barnstaple; SHO (O & G) Barnstaple.

GIBB, Diana Mary Institute of Child Health, 30 Guildford St., London WC1N 1EH Tel: 020 7242 9789 Fax: 020 7380 9972 Email: d.gibb@ctu.mrc.ac.uk; 70 Beversbrook Road, London N19 4QH — MB ChB Bristol 1977; MSc (Epidemiol.) Lond. 1990; MD Bristol 1989; MRCP (UK) 1985; Dip. Obst. Auckland 1979. Sen. Lect. (Paediat. Epidemiol.) & Hon. Cons. Infec. Dis. Inst. Child Health Lond. Hosp. for Childr. Gt. Ormond St. Trust; Sen. Lect. Epidemiol.; MRC Clin. Trials Unit Lond. Socs: Roy. Coll. Paediat. & Child Health. Prev: Hon. Sen. Regist. (Renal) Hosp. for Sick Childr. Gt. Ormond St. & Inst. Child Health Lond.; Med. Off. Delek Tibetan Hosp. Dharamsala, India; Lect. (Infec. Dis.) Inst. Child Health Lond.

GIBB, Donald McKenzie Fotheringham Women's Services Care Group, King's College Hospital, Denmark Hill, London SE5 8RX Tel: 020 7346 3629 Fax: 020 7346 3617; 38 Hertford Avenue, East Sheen, London SW14 8EQ — MB ChB 1974 Ed.; MD Ed. 1990; MRCP (UK) 1981; FRCOG 1993, M 1980. Cons. O & G King's Coll. Hosp. Lond.; Head of Teach. (Obst. & Gyn.) King's Coll. Sch. of Med. & Dent. Prev: Lect. (O & G) Nat. Univ., Singapore.

GIBB, Duncan Beveridge 278 Bonkle Road, Newmains, Wishaw ML2 9QQ Tel: 01698 2185 — MB ChB 1950 St. And.; DObst RCOG 1966.

GIBB, Eileen Fyffe (retired) 12 Hillside Drive, Grantham NG31 7EZ Tel: 01476 561596 — MB ChB Glas. 1940. Prev: Gen. Med. Practioner, Grantham.

GIBB, Elizabeth Lynn Adult Department, Tavistock Clinic, 120 Belsize Lane, London NW3 5BA Tel: 020 7435 7111 — MB ChB 1982 Sheff.; 2001 BPAS; MRCPsych 1988; TQAP 1998. p/t Locum Cons. Tavistock Clinic Lond. (Psychother). Prev: (Locum) Cons. (Psychother.) Maudsley Hosp.; Sen. Regist. (Psychother.) Tavistock Clinic Lond.

GIBB, Fraser Duncan McKay 15 Etive Drive, Airdrie ML6 9QQ — MB ChB 1990 Glas.

GIBB, Iain Edward 19 Prebend Mansions, Chiswick High Road, London W4 2LU — MB ChB 1991 Dundee.

GIBB, Ian Alastair Macfarlane (retired) Greyfriars, 2 Alwood Avenue, Blackpool FY3 8NG Tel: 01253 391295 — MB ChB 1950 Glas.

GIBB, Jackie Karen 76 Cheshire Gardens, Chessington KT9 2PS — MB BS 1989 Lond.

GIBB, Jacqueline Sarah Stile Close, 4 Newland Gardens, Sherborne DT9 3AF Tel: 01963 812819 — MB BS Lond. 1951; MRCS Eng. LRCP Lond. 1951. (Roy. Free) Socs: Inst. Psychosexual Med. Prev: Sen. Med. Clin. Off. Family Plann. Som. HA & W. Dorset HA.

GIBB, John Watson (retired) 31 Kings Road, Elderslie, Johnstone PA5 9LY Tel: 01505 320480 — MB ChB 1944 Ed.; MB ChB (Hons.) Ed. 1944; FRCP Ed. 1981, M 1949. Prev: Sen. Med. Off. Regional Med. Serv. Scott. Home & Health Dept.

GIBB, Margaret Winifred 149 North Deeside Road, Bieldside, Aberdeen AB15 9EA — MB ChB 1945 Aberd.; BSc, MB ChB Aberd. 1945. (Aberd.)

GIBB, Muriel Elizabeth (retired) Craigweil Lodge, 3 Craigweil Road, Ayr KA7 2XJ Tel: 01292 263038 — MB ChB 1942 St. And.; MA Aberd. 1932; DLO Eng. 1959. Prev: Cons. ENT Surg. Ayrsh. Hosps.

GIBB, Mr Paul Alistair Kent & Sussex Hospital, Mount Ephraim, Tunbridge Wells TN4 8AT Tel: 01892 526111; Pinehurst, Mayfield Lane, Wadhurst TN5 6JE — MB BS Lond. 1983; FRCS (Orth.) 1992; FRCS Eng. 1988; FRCS Ed. 1988. Cons. Trauma & Orthop. Kent & Sussex Hosp. Tunbridge Wells. Prev: Sen. Regist. (Orthop.) King's Coll. Hosp. Lond.

GIBB, Peter Walker (retired) 20 Corbiehill Avenue, Edinburgh EH4 5DR Tel: 0131 336 1951 — MB ChB 1962 Ed.; DTM & H 1964.

GIBB, Robert (retired) Church Hill, Church Brough, Kirkby Stephen CA17 4EJ Tel: 017683 41428 — MB ChB 1942 Aberd.; FRCR 1975; FFR 1953; DMRT Eng. 1948. Prev: Dir. (Radiother.) Christie Hosp. & Holt Radium Inst. Manch.

GIBB, Robert Cameron Department of Forensic Psychiatry, St Nicholas Hospital, Newcastle upon Tyne NE3 3XT; 15 Etive Drive, Airdrie ML6 9QQ — MB ChB 1985 Glas.; MRCPysch 1991. Lect. (Forens. Psychiat.) Univ. Newc. u. Tyne. Prev: Clin. Research (Forens. Psychiat.) Inst. Psychiat. Maudsley Hosp. Lond.; SHO & Regist. Gartnavel Roy. Hosp. Glas.

GIBB, William Richard Glenny Wessex Neurological Centre, Southampton General Hospital, Tremona Road, Shirley, Southampton SO16 6YD Tel: 02380 794793 Fax: 02380 798793; Queen Alexandra Hospital, Cosham, Portsmouth PO6 3LY Tel: 02392 286807 Fax: 02392 286054 — MB BS 1979 Lond.; MD Lond. 1987; FRCP Lond. 1995; MRCP (UK) 1982. (Royal Free) Cons. Neurol. Soton. Gen. Hosp.; Cons. Neurol. Portsmouth NHS Hosp.s. Prev: Sen. Lect. (Neurol.) King's Coll. Sch. Med. & Dent. Lond.; Sen. Regist. (Neurol.) Nat. Hosps. Nerv. Disorders & Guy's Hosp. Lond.; Regist. (Neurol.) Middlx. Hosp. & Nat. Hosps. Nerv. Disorders Lond.

GIBBENS, Carol Lesley Glebe House, Moreton, Dorchester DT2 8RQ Tel: 01929 462468 — MB BS 1965 Lond.; MFFP 1993. (St. Thos.) Clin. Asst. (O & G) W. Dorset HA.; Sessional Clin. Med. Off. Dorchester. Prev: SHO (Paediat.) St. Mary's Hosp. Portsmouth; Ho. Phys. & Ho. Surg. St. Thos. Hosp.

GIBBENS, George Lawrence Declan Glebe House, Moreton, Dorchester DT2 8RQ Tel: 01929 462468 — MB BS 1964 Lond.; MD Lond. 1976; FRCOG 1989, M 1970. (St. Thos.) Prev: Cons.O&GW.DorsetHealth Dist.; Regist. St. Bart. Hosp. Lond.; Lect. (O & G) Soton. Univ.

GIBBENS, Mary Virginia Queen Mary's Hospital, Sidcup DA14 6LT Tel: 020 8302 2678 — MB BS 1980 Lond.; BSc (1st. cl. Hons.) Lond. 1977; FRCS Eng. 1987; MD 1990; FRCOphth. (St. Thos.) Cons. (Ophth) Qu. Mary's Hosp. Sidcup. Socs: Fell. Roy. Soc. Med.; Fell. Med. Soc. Lond. Prev: Regist. (Ophth.) St. Thos. Hosp. Lond.; SR (Ophth) St Bart's The Roy. Lond. Univ Coll. Hosp. Roy. Free & Moorfields Eye Hosp.

GIBBERD, Frederick Brian Chelsea & Westminster Hospital, 369 Fulham Road, London SW10 9NH Tel: 020 8746 8599 Fax: 020 8746 8594; 2 Ferrings, Dulwich, London SE21 7LU Tel: 020 8693 8106 Fax: 020 8693 8106 — MB BChir 1957; MD Camb. 1974; FRCP Ed. 1993; FRCP Lond. 1972, M 1960; MRCS Eng. LRCP Lond. 1957; Hon. FFOM RCP Lond. 1995. (Camb. & Westm.) Hon. Phys. (Neurol.) Chelsea & W.m.Hosp.; Nero.Lister.Hosp.Lond. Socs: Assn. Brit. Neurols.; Harveian Soc. Lond. (Pres. 1995); Past Master Soc. Apoth. Prev: Sen. Regist. (Neurol.) Lond. Hosp. & Maida Vale Hosp. Lond.; Asst. Ho. Phys. Nat. Hosp. Qu. Sq. Lond.; Ho. Phys. Brompton Hosp.

GIBBIN, Mr Kevin Patrick 11 Regent Street, Nottingham NG1 5BS — MB 1969 Camb.; BChir 1968; FRCS Eng. 1974. (Camb. & St. Mary's) Cons. Otolaryngol. Univ. Hosp. Nottm. Socs: Roy. Med. Soc. (Sects. Otol. & Laryngol.); BMA; Nottm. M-C Soc. Prev: Sen. Regist. (Otolaryngol.) Univ. Hosp. Wales. Cardiff; Ho. Surg. & Ho. Phys. St. Mary's Hosp. Lond.; Demonst. (Anat.) Camb. Univ.

GIBBIN, Phillip Picton Mapsland, Laugharne, Carmarthen SA33 4QP — MB BChir 1974 Camb.; BA Camb. 1970, MA, MB 1974, BChir 1973; MRCS Eng. LRCP Lond. 1973; DObst RCOG 1975. (Camb. & Westm.) Prev: Ho. Phys. Poole Gen. Hosp.; SHO (O & G) W. Wales Gen. Hosp.; SHO (Paediat.) Morriston Hosp.

GIBBINGS, Charlotte Rosemary Winkfield Plain Farm, Winkfield Lane, Windsor SL4 4RU — MB BS 1977 Lond.; MRCOG 1983.

GIBBINS, Frederick Johnson (retired) Hamilton Lodge, West Park Lane, Sedgefield, Stockton-on-Tees TS21 2BA — MB ChB 1960 St. And.; FRCP Ed. 1979, M 1964. Prev: Cons. Phys. Geriat. N & S Tees Hosp. Gps.

GIBBINS, Nicholas Edmund 3 Quarry Gardens, Tonbridge TN9 2SG — MB BS 1998 Lond.; MB BS Lond 1998.

GIBBINS, Pamela Mary (retired) Hill Top, Bower Bank, Areley Kings, Stourport-on-Severn DY13 0AF — MB ChB 1948 Birm.; MRCS Eng. LRCP Lond. 1948. Prev: Clin. Asst. Droitwich Centre For Rheum. Dis.

GIBBINS, Peter Anthony Milestone, 29 West St., Chickerell, Weymouth DT3 4DY — MB BS 1973 Newc.; AFOM RCP Lond. 1995; DA Eng. 1975. Med. Adviser (Occupat. Health) GKN - W.land Helicopters, Yeovil.; Med. Adviser (Occupat. Health) W. Dorset Gen. Hosps. NHS Trust Dorset Community NHS Trust. Socs: Soc. Occupat. Med. Prev: Med. Adviser (Occupat. Health) Merck UK; GP Wyke Regis, Weymouth.

GIBBINS, Robert Llewellyn Maes-y-Coed Doctors Surgery, Maes-y-Coed, Glandwr Park, Builth Wells LD2 3DZ Tel: 01982 552207 Fax: 01982 553826 — MB BChir 1975 Camb.; MA, MB BChir Camb. 1975; DRCOG 1982.

GIBBINS, Stephen Roland Moss Street Surgery, Chadsmnoor, Cannock WS11 2DE Tel: 01543 504477 Fax: 01543 504636 — MB ChB 1979 Birm.; MRCGP 1995; DA (UK) 1987; DRCOG 1981.

GIBBINS, Steven John 155 Penns Lane, Sutton Coldfield B72 1BN — MB ChB 1998 Leic.; MB ChB Leic 1998.

GIBBON, Mr Anthony Joseph Tel: 01904 725946 Fax: 01904 453578; Marston House, 27 Lockwood House, Earswick, York YO32 9FT Tel: 01904 767600 Email: tony.gibbon@nkgateway.net — MB BS 1987 Lond.; BSc (Hons.) Lond. 1984; FRCS (Orth.) 1996; FRCS Eng. 1991. Cons. Orthop. Surg. York Dist. Hosp. Prev: Research Fell. (Orthop.) Harvard Med. Sch. Boston, USA; Sen. Regist. (Orthop.) St. Bart. Train. Progr. Lond.

***GIBBON, Caspar Edward Acton** 51 Highworth Avenue, Cambridge CB4 2BQ — BM 1994 Soton.

GIBBON, Edward Anthony Acton Lower Street Surgery, 95 Lower Street, Pulborough RH20 2BP Tel: 01798 872305 — MB BS 1974 London. GP PulBoro., W. Sussex.

GIBBON, Frances Mary Department of Child Health, University Hospital of Wales, Heath Park, Cardiff CF14 4XW Tel: 029 2074 3542 Fax: 029 2074 6322 Email: frances.gibbon@uhw-tr.wales.nhs.uk — MB ChB 1987 Manch.; BSc (Med. Sci) St. And. 1984; MRCP (UK) 1993. Cons. Paediat. Neurol. Univ. Hosp. Wales.

GIBBON, Gareth James 103 Chapel Road, Abergavenny NP7 7DR — BM BS 1997 Nottm.

GIBBON, Gemma Victoria Far Willow, Welsh St., Chepstow NP16 5LS — MB ChB 1996 Ed.

GIBBON, Karen Lesley Whipps Cross Univ. Hospital NHS Trust, Whipps Cross Hospital, Department of Dermatology, Whipps Cross Road, London E11 1NR Fax: 020 8505 0174 Email: kgibbon@doctors.org.uk; Fax: 0208 505 0174 Email: kgibbonal@doctors.org.uk — MB ChB 1983 Leeds; BSc (Hons.) Leeds 1983; MRCP (UK) 1987; DFFP 1996; Dip. Pract. Dermat. Wales 1996; DRCOG 1987; DCH RCP Lond. 1985.

GIBBON, Mr Norman Otway Knight (retired) 43 Jubilee Road, Formby, Liverpool L37 2HT Tel: 017048 73799 — MB ChB 1941 Liverp.; ChM Liverp. 1951; FRCS Eng. 1947; FRCS Ed. 1945. Prev: Cons. in Admin. Charge Dept. Urol. Roy. Liverp. Hosp.

GIBBON, Raymond Holt (retired) 78 Aylestone Hill, Hereford HR1 1HX Tel: 01432 273342 — MB 1954 Camb.; BChir 1953; FFR 1963; DMRD Eng. 1961. Prev: Cons. Radiol. Hereford AHA.

GIBBON, Simon Paul 105 Watling Street Road, Fulwood, Preston PR2 8BQ — MB ChB 1982 Manch.

GIBBONS, Adam Matthew Saddleworth Medical Practice, The Clinic, Smithy Lane, Uppermill, Oldham OL3 6AH Tel: 01457 872228; 66 Church Road, Uppermill, Oldham OL3 6EH — MB ChB 1986 Leic.; MRCGP 1990; DRCOG 1989. (Leicester)

GIBBONS, Andrew Jonathan 10 Boughton Lane, Loose, Maidstone ME15 9QN — MB BChir 1995 Camb.; BA Camb. 1993; BDS Lond. 1983; FDS RCS Ed. 1988; LDS RCS Eng. 1984; MA Camb 1997; FRCS Ed 1998. (Camb.) Sen. Specialist RAF. Socs: Brit. Assn. Oral & Maxillofacial Surg.; BMA.

GIBBONS, Andrew Neil Milestone Surgery, 208 Farnborough Road, Farnborough GU14 7JN Tel: 01252 545078 Fax: 01252 370751; Aintree House, 63 Salisbury Road, Farnborough GU14 7AG — BM BCh 1980 Oxf.; MA Oxf. 1980, BA 1977, BM BCh 1980;

MRCGP 1984. GP Milestone Surg. FarnBoro. Prev: SHO (O & G) Llandough & St. Davids Hosp. Cardiff; SHO (CardioPulm. Med.) Univ. Hosp. Wales Llandough; Ho. Phys. John Radcliffe Hosp. Oxf.

GIBBONS, Andrew Robert Feldon Lane Surgery, Feldon Lane, Halesowen B62 9DR Tel: 0121 422 4703; Riverside, 21 High St, Kinver, Stourbridge DY7 6HG Tel: 01384 873373 — MB ChB 1971 Birm.; MRCP (UK) 1976.

GIBBONS, Anita Helen 3 Water Lane CB4 9XW; 3 Water Lane, Cambridge CB4 9XW — MB BS 1988 Lond.; BSc Lond. 1985; MRCP (UK) 1991; DTM & H Lond. 1992; MD Lond. 1997. p/t Specialist Regist. (Gastroenterol.) E.ern. Prev: Wellcome Research Fell. (Gastroenterol.) Roy. Postgrad. Med. Sch. Lond.; Regist. (Med. & Gastroenterol.) Whittington Hosp. Lond.; SpR (Gastroenterol.), N. W. Thames.

GIBBONS, Ann Eleri 29 Cressy House, Hannibal Road, London E1 3JE — MB BS 1989 Lond.

GIBBONS, Brian Joseph Gwynfi Health Centre, Blaengwynfi, Port Talbot SA13 3YE Tel: 01639 850345 — MB BCh BAO 1974 NUI; FRCGP 1995, M 1980; DRCOG 1979; Cert. FPA 1979. (University College Galway, Ireland) Mem. (Sec.) Morgannwg LMC.

GIBBONS, Carmel Philomena 6 Woodbury Rise, Great Glen, Leicester LE8 9ER — MB BCh BAO 1984 NUI.

GIBBONS, Mr Charles Edward Richard 42 Shortlands Road, Kingston upon Thames KT2 6HE Tel: 020 8541 0965 — MB BS 1989 Lond.; FRCS Eng. 1993; FRCSI 1993. (Lond. Hosp. Med. Coll.) Regist. Rotat. (Orthop.) Chelsea & W.m. Hosps. Lond. Prev: Regist. Chelsea & W.minster Hosp.; SHO (Gen. Surg.) Bath Roy. United Hosp.; Ho. Surg. & Cas. Off. Roy. Lond. Hosp.

GIBBONS, Mr Christopher Leonard Maxime H Nuffield Orthopaedic Centre, Windmill Road, Headington, Oxford OX3 7LD Tel: 01865 741155; Easter Barn, Rousham Road, Tackley, Oxford OX5 3BB Tel: 01869 331025 — MB BS 1985 Lond.; MA Oxf. 1983; FRCS (Orth.) 1995; FRCS Eng. 1990. (Lond. Hosp.) Cons. Nuffield Orthop. Centre Oxf. Prev: Sen. Regist. Nuffield Orthop. Centre Oxf.; Regist. (Accid. Serv.) John Radcliffe Hosp. Oxf.; Regist. (Gen. Surg.) Profess. Unit. Qu. Eliz. Hosp. Birm.

GIBBONS, Mr Christopher Peter Department of Surgery, Morriston Hospital, Swansea SA6 6NL Tel: 01792 703581 Fax: 01792 703583; Tel: 01792 204202 Email: c.p.gibbons@email.msn.com — BM BCh 1976 Oxf.; MA, DPhil Oxf. 1978, MCh 1985; FRCS Eng. 1980. (Oxford) Cons. Surg. Morriston Hosp. Swansea. Socs: BMA; Assn. of Surg.s of GB & Irel.; Vasc. Surgic. Soc. of GB & Irel. Prev: Sen. Regist. (Gen. Surg.) Univ. Hosp. of Wales Cardiff; Sen. Regist. (Gen. Surg.) Singleton Hosp. Swansea; Clin. Research Fell. (Transpl.) Roy. Hallamsh. Hosp. Sheff..

GIBBONS, Mr Christopher Thomas 7 Oaklands, Newcastle upon Tyne NE3 4YQ Email: chrisgibbons@compuserve.com — MB BCh 1992 Wales; FRCS 1997. Specialist Regist. Trauma & Orthop. Socs: Assoc. Mem. of Brit. Orthopaedic Assoc.; Brit. Orthop. Train. Assn.

GIBBONS, Clare Rachel Brocklebank Group Practice, Brocklebank Health Centre, 249 Garratt Lane, London SW18 4UE Tel: 020 8870 1341 — MB ChB 1992 Manch.; DRCOG; MRCGP. GP. Prev: Acad. Asst. in Gen. Pract., St. Geo.s Hosp. Med. Sch.

GIBBONS, David Oliver (retired) Gwel Towans, Treloyhan Pk Road, St Ives TR26 2AH Tel: 01736 796059 — MB BS Lond. 1965; FRCP Lond. 1983, M 1969; T(M) 1991. Prev: Cons. Phys. W. Cornw. Hosp. Penzance & Cornw. Clin. Area.

GIBBONS, David Robert Stanley Burnacre, Stocks Lane, Over Peover, Knutsford WA16 8TW — MB ChB 1976 Manch.; MRCOG 1989. Staff O & G E. Chesh. NHS Trust Macclesfield.

GIBBONS, Eileen Mary Squires Lane Medical Practice, 2 Squires Lane, Finchley, London N3 2AU Tel: 020 8346 1516 Fax: 020 8343 2537 — MB BCh BAO 1970 Dub.

GIBBONS, Gordon Robert 24 Great Arler Road, Leicester LE2 6FF — MB ChB 1994 Leic.

GIBBONS, Professor James Leo 45 South Entrance, Saxmundham IP17 1DG Tel: 01728 603777 — MD 1967 Newc.; MB BS Durh. 1948; FRCP Lond. 1968, M 1954; FRCPsych 1972; DPM Lond. 1952. (King's Coll Univ of Durham) Emerit. Prof. Psychiat. Univ. Soton. Prev: Clin. Sub-Dean & Reader in Psychiat. Univ. Newc.; Sen. Lect. Inst. Psychiat. & Hon. Phys. Maudsley Hosp.; Research Asst. in Neurol. Roy. Vict. Infirm. Newc.

GIBBONS, Jennifer Whiteman The Surgery, The Street, Wonersh, Guildford GU5 0PE Tel: 01483 898123 — MB 1980 Camb.; BChir 1979; MRCGP 1983; DRCOG 1983.

GIBBONS, John Joseph Patrick 22 Bridgecroft Road, Wallasey CH45 7NX — MB BCh BAO 1975 NUI; FFA RCS Eng. 1982. Sen. Regist. (Anaesth.) Mersey RHA.

GIBBONS, Kevin Joseph The Surgery, 8 Leicester Terrace, Northampton NN2 6AL Tel: 01604 33682; South View, Glebe Lane, Harlestone, Northampton NN7 4ET Tel: 01604 843148 — MB BCh BAO 1959 Dub. (T.C. Dub.) Mem. (Ex-Chairm.) N.ants. LMC. Socs: N.ampton Med. Soc. Prev: Represen. N.ants. Dist. Managem. Team.

GIBBONS, Leslie Alfred (retired) Jessamine Cottage, 57 The Street, Rustington, Littlehampton BN16 3NU Tel: 01903 775348 — MRCS Eng. LRCP Lond. 1941; FRCGP 1972, M 1956; FRCA 1972. Prev: Cons. Aanesth. Redhill Gp. Hosp. & Crawley Hosp.

GIBBONS, Mary Beeches Medical Centre, 20 Ditchfield Road, Widnes WA8 8QS Tel: 0151 424 3101/423 6632 Fax: 0151 495 2925 — LRCPI & LM, LRSCI & LM 1975; LRCPI & LM, LRCSI & LM 1975; MRCGP 1980; DRCOG 1978. Princip. GP Widnes.

***GIBBONS, Michael Anthony** 113 Duncruin Street, Maryhill, Glasgow G20 0EU Tel: 0141 579 5230 — MB ChB 1998 Glas.; MB ChB Glas 1998; BSc Glas. 1996.

GIBBONS, Michael Joseph 218 Malone Road, Belfast BT9 5LQ Tel: 01232 201703 — MB BCh BAO 1991 Belf.; MRCP (UK) 1994. (Qu. Univ. Belf.) Specialist Regist. (Gastroenterol.) Roy. Vict. Hosp. Belf.

GIBBONS, Nigel Christopher Woodbridge Road Surgery, 165-167 Woodbridge Road, Ipswich IP4 2PE Tel: 01473 256251; 150 Woodbridge Road, Ipswich IP4 2NS Tel: 01473 257877 — MB BS 1982 Lond.; DRCOG 1986.

GIBBONS, Patricia May The Flat, 223 London Road, Waterlooville PO8 8DA Tel: 01705 648765 — MB ChB 1959 Birm.; DObst RCOG 1966.

GIBBONS, Mr Paul Jeremy Birmingham Children's Hospital, Department of Orthopaedics, Steelhouse Lane, Birmingham B4 6NH Tel: 0121 333 8099 — MB BS 1983 Lond.; FRCS Ed. 1991; FRCS (Orth.), 1996. Cons. Orthop. Surg., Birm. Childr.s Hosp.; Cons. Orthop. Surg. Roy. Orthop. Hosp., Birm. Prev: Sen. Regist. Roy. Orthop. Hosp. Birm.; Regist. Roy. Orthop. Hosp. Birm.; Regist. Rotat. (Surg.) Roy. & New Cross Hosps. Wolverhampton.

GIBBONS, Peter Frank Osteopathic Medicine Unit, Faculty of Human Development, City Campus, Victoria University, P.O. Box 14428, Melbourne Vic. 8001, Australia Tel: 00 61 03 92481190 Fax: 00 61 03 92481110 Email: petergibbons@vut.edu.au; 32 Rochford Road, Chelmsford CM2 0EF Tel: 01245 283626 — MB BS 1983 Lond.; DMS Med. Soc. Apoth. Lond. 1997. (Roy. Free) Sen. Lect. Vict. Univ. Melbourne, Austral.

GIBBONS, Rachel Kathe 16 Southwood Avenue, London N6 5RZ — MB BS 1998 Lond.; MB BS Lond 1998.

GIBBONS, Richard James Nuffield Department of Clinical Biochemistry, University of Oxford, John Radcliffe Hospital, Headdington, Oxford OX3 9DU Tel: 01865 222367 Email: rgibbons@immsvr.jr2.ox.ac.uk; 33 Portland Road, Summertown, Oxford OX2 7EZ — BM BCh 1986 Oxf.; MA, DPhil Oxf. 1984; MRCP (UK) 1989. (Oxf.) Univ. Lect. Clin. Biochem. (Med.) Nuffield Dept. Clin. Biochem. Oxf. Univ.

GIBBS, Alan Edward Russell Rectory Meadow Surgery, School Lane, Amersham HP7 0HG Tel: 01494 725705 Fax: 01494 431790; Clumber Cottage, Oakway, Amersham HP6 5PQ Tel: 01494 726386 Fax: 01494 431790 — MRCS Eng. LRCP Lond. 1954. (St. Bart.) Socs: Internat. Soc. Clin. & Experim. Hypn.; Brit. Med. Acupunct. Soc. Prev: JHMO Roy. Nat. Hosp. Rheum. Dis. Bath; Res. Med. Off. Stoke Mandeville Hosp. Aylesbury; Med. Regist. Amersham Gen. Hosp.

GIBBS, Allen Robert Dept. of Histopathology, Llandough hospital, Cardiff & Vale NHS Trust, Penarth LF64 2XX Tel: 01222 715283 Fax: 01222 712979; 36 Fields Park Road, Newport NP20 5BB — MB ChB 1970 Newc.; MRCPath 1978. Cons. Histopath. Llandough Hosp. Penarth.

GIBBS, Mr Andrew Nicholas Orthopaedic Department, The Ipswich Hospital, Heath Road, Ipswich IP4 5PD Tel: 01473 712233 — MRCS Eng. LRCP Lond. 1968; BSc (Physiol.) Lond. 1965, MB BS 1969; FRCS Eng. 1973. (Lond. Hosp.) Orthop. Surg. Ipswich Hosp. Prev: Rotating Orthop. Regist. St. Bart. & Assoc. Hosps.; Rotating

Regist. Soton. Univ. Gp. Hosps.; Regist. Orthop. Hammersmith Hosp. Lond.

GIBBS, Anthony Entwistle Whisper Wood, Newton Green, Sudbury CO10 0QS Tel: 01787 373033 — MB BChir 1953 Camb.; MA Camb. 1944; MRCS Eng. LRCP Lond. 1944; MFHom 1968. (Guy's Hosp. Lond.) Prev: Asst. Phys. Walnuttree Hosp. Sudbury; Regist. (Med.) Geriat. Unit Rochford; Sen. Ho. Phys. Lond. Seamen's Hosp. Tilbury.

GIBBS, Antony James (retired) Mercer's Cottage, The Common, Cranleigh GU6 8NS — BM BCh 1930 Oxf.; MA, DM Oxf. 1932, BM BCh 1930; MRCS Eng. LRCP Lond. 1930.

GIBBS, Avis Patricia (retired) 1 Nursery Road, Bitterne Park, Southampton SO18 1NS Tel: 01703 554452 — MB ChB Manch. 1956.

GIBBS, Betty Price Foel Fodig, Corwen LL21 9BY — MB ChB 1967 Sheff. (Sheff.)

GIBBS, Caryl Rosalie The Taff Riverside Health Practice, Meddygfa Min Afon Taf, Riverside Health Centre, Wellington St., Cardiff CF11 9SH Tel: 029 2034 3615 Fax: 029 2064 0419 — MB BCh 1963 Wales; MA Cardiff 1995; DObst RCOG 1965; DPH Bristol 1968. (Cardiff) Prev: SHO (O & G) Griffithstown Co. Hosp.; Ho. Phys. & Ho. Surg. Llandough Hosp.; Asst. MOH Mon. CC.

GIBBS, Catherine Elizabeth 36 Wellington Hill, Horfield, Bristol BS7 8SR — MB ChB 1990 Bristol; MRCGP 1995.

GIBBS, Charles James Queen Elizabeth Hospital, Stadium Road, Woolwich, London SE18 4QH Tel: 020 836 6004 — MB ChB 1976 Cape Town; MRCP (UK) 1980; FRCP 2000. Cons. Phys. (Diabetes & Endocrinol.) Qu. Eliz. Hosp. NHS Trust (formely known as Greewich Healthacre Trust). Prev: Sen. Regist. St. Mary's Hosp. Portsmouth; Regist. MRC Mineral Metab. Unit Gen Infirm. Leeds; Regist. (Med.) Frenchay Hosp. Bristol.

GIBBS, Christopher Richard 2 Friday Lane, Barston, Solihull B92 0HY — MB ChB 1990 Leic.; MRCP (UK) 1994. Regist. (Med. & Cardiol.) City Hosp. Birm. Prev: SHO Rotat. (Med.) Derby City Gen. Hosp.

GIBBS, Denis Dunbar (retired) Kingsweston, Appleford, Abingdon OX14 4PD Tel: 01235 848309 — BM BCh Oxf. 1952; BA Oxf. 1950, DM 1962; FRCP Lond. 1973, M 1955; DHM Soc. Apoth. 1989; DCH Eng. 1957. Hon. Cons. Phys. Roy. Lond. Hosp. Prev: Examr. Univs. Oxf., Lond., Basrah & ConJt. Bd.

GIBBS, Duncan Stuart Stannary Surgery, Abbey Rise, Whitchurch Road, Tavistock PL19 9BB Tel: 01822 613517 Fax: 01822 618294; Lanherne, Chollacott Lane, Whitchurch, Tavistock PL19 9DD Tel: 01822 614159 — MB ChB 1965 Otago; MRCGP 1984; DObst RCOG 1973; DA Eng. 1971. (Otago) Socs: BMA; MDU; RCGP.

GIBBS, Eileen (retired) Barley Croft, commonside, crowle, Scunthorpe DN17 4EX Tel: 01724 712078 — MB ChB 1954 Leeds.

GIBBS, Elaine Ruth The Cripps Health Centre, University Park, Nottingham NG7 2QW Tel: 0115 950 1654; 18 Brookhill Drive, Woolaton, Nottingham NG8 2PS — BM BS 1986 Nottm.; MRCGP 1991; DRCOG 1991.

GIBBS, Elizabeth Patricia (retired) 83 Church Street, Great Burstead, Billericay CM11 2TS Tel: 01277 652724 — MB BS 1955 Lond.; MRCS Eng. LRCP Lond. 1955; FFA RCS Eng. 1967; DA Eng. 1960. Prev: Cons. Anaesth. & Intens. Care Basildon & Thurrock HA.

GIBBS, Gerard Harry Raleigh Hartcliffe Health Centre, Hareclive Road, Hartcliffe, Bristol BS13 0JP Tel: 0117 9645588/9647925 Fax: 0117 964 9055; Woodbine Cottage, North Wick, Dundry, Bristol BS41 8NN — MB ChB 1978 Bristol; BSc Bristol 1975; MRCGP 1983; DRCOG 1981. (Bristol) GP Princip.

GIBBS, Gilbert William (retired) 1 Danecourt Road, Poole BH14 0PG Tel: 01202 676660 — MB ChB Liverp. 1942. Prev: Cas. Off. City Hosp. Plymouth.

***GIBBS, Hannah Georgina** 3 Bampton Drive, Downend, Bristol BS16 6BJ Tel: 0117 957 4425 — BM BS 1998 Nottm.; BM BS Nottm 1998.

GIBBS, Irene Elizabeth (retired) 29 Park Grove, Henleaze, Bristol BS9 4LF Tel: 0117 942 1062 — MB ChB 1956 Bristol; BSc St. And. 1951; DCH Eng. 1968. Prev: Dist. SCMO (Child Health) Bristol & W.on HA.

GIBBS, James George Flat 6, Lucerne Close, Aldermans Hill, London N13 4QJ — MB BS 1998 Lond.; MB BS Lond 1998.

GIBBS, Jeremy Michael Department of Neuroscience, Royal Free Hospital, Pond St., London NW3 2QG Tel: 020 7794 0500 — MD 1987 Camb.; MB 1976, BChir 1975; MRCP (UK) 1977. Cons. Neurol. Roy. Free Hosp. & Lister Hosp. Stevenage.; Hon. Sen. Lect. Roy. Free Hosp. Sch. Med. Lond. Prev: Sen. Regist. Nat. Hosp. & King's Coll. Hosps. Lond.; Research Fell. MRC Cyclotron Unit Hammersmith Hosp. Lond.

GIBBS, John Lister Department of Paediatric Cardiology, Yorkshire Heart Centre, Leeds Tel: 0113 392 5750 Email: jgibbs@cwcom.net — MB BS Lond. 1978; FRCP Lond. 1994; MRCP (UK) 1980; MRCS Eng. LRCP Lond. 1977. (Roy. Free) Cons. Paediat. Cardiol. Killingbeck Hosp. Leeds; Sen. Lect. (Paediat. & Child Health) Univ. Leeds. Prev: Sen. Regist. (Paediat. Cardiol.) Killingbeck Hosp. Leeds; Regist. (Cardiol.) Harefield Hosp.; SHO Roy. Sussex Co. Hosp. Brighton.

GIBBS, John Michael Department of Paediatrics, Countess of Chester Hospital, Liverpool Road, Chester CH2 1UL Tel: 01244 365058 — MB BS 1983 Lond.; FRCPCH 1997 Lond.; BSc Lond. 1980, MD 1996; MRCP (UK) 1987; DCH RCP Lond. 1987. Cons. Paediat. Countess of Chester Hosp. Prev: Sen. Regist. (Paediat.) Sheff.; Research Fell. Univ. Coll. Lond.; Regist. Rotat. (Paediat.) Liverp.

GIBBS, Mr John Reynell (retired) 9 Lee Orchards, Boston Spa, Wetherby LS23 6BJ — MB ChB 1932 Bristol; FRCS Ed. 1938. Prev: Cons. Neurosurg. Brook Gen. Hosp. Woolwich.

GIBBS, John Roger Long Frie Surgery, St Peter Port, Guernsey GY7 9RZ Tel: 01481 254883 Fax: 01481 264185; Maison Des Varendes, Les Varendes, Castel, Guernsey GY5 7RF Tel: 01481 254883 Fax: 01481 255409 — MB BS 1967 Lond.; MRCS Eng. LRCP Lond. 1966; DA Eng. 1971; DObst RCOG 1969. (Guy's) Socs: MCOH 1996. Prev: SHO Anaesth. Medway Gp. Hosps.; SHO Psychiat. Univ. Coll. Hosp.; Ho. Phys. (Paediat.) Evelina Hosp.

GIBBS, John Simon Russell Department of Cardiology, 5 South, Charing Cross Hospital, Fulham Palace Road, London W6 8RF Tel: 020 8846 1032 Fax: 020 8746 8182 Email: s.gibbs@ic.ac.uk; Department of Cardiology, Hammersmith Hospital, London W12 0HS Tel: 020 8383 3037 Fax: 020 8740 8373 — MB BChir 1980 Camb.; MA Camb. 1980, MD 1993; MRCP (UK) 1983. (Camb. & St. Thos.) Sen. Lect. (Cardiol.) Imperial Coll. Sch. Med. Nat. Heart & Lung Inst.; Hon. Cons. Cardiol. Hammersmith Hosps. NHS Trust. Socs: Fell. Roy. Soc. Med.; Brit. Cardiac. Soc. Prev: Sen. Regist. Roy. Brompton & St. Geo. Hosp. Lond.; Brit. Heart Foundat. Jun. Research Fell.; Regist. (Med.) Hammersmith Hosp. & Nat. Heart Hosp. Lond.

GIBBS, Jonathan Crispin The Minster Practice, Cabourne Court, Cabourne Avenue, Lincoln LN2 2JP Tel: 01522 568838 Fax: 01522 546740; 14 Heath Road, Nettleham, Lincoln LN2 2XZ Tel: 01522 753598 — MB BS 1988 Lond.; MRCGP 1994; DRCOG 1991; Cert. Family Plann. JCC 1991.

GIBBS, Kate Josephine Market Street Health Group, 52 Market St., East Ham, London E6 2RA; 10 Pemberton Court, Portelet Road, Stepney, London E1 4EN — MB BS 1992 Lond. (Lond. Hosp. Med. Coll.)

GIBBS, Kenyatta Hawthorn Surgery, Wilfrid Terrace, Branch Road, Lower Wortley, Leeds LS12 5NR Tel: 0113 295 4770 Fax: 0113 295 4771 — BM 1985 Soton.; BSc Essex 1979. Prev: Regist. (Geriat. Med.) Leeds Gen. Infirm.

GIBBS, Louise Mary Elizabeth St Christopher's Hospice, 51-59 Lawrie Park Road, Sydenham, London SE26 6DZ Tel: 0208 778 9252 Fax: 0208 659 8680; Tel: 0207 350 2280 Fax: 0207 978 6390 — MB BChir 1988 Camb.; MA Camb. 1988; MRCP (UK) 1991. Cons. Phys. Palliat. Med. St. Christopher's Hospice. Prev: Locum Cons.(Pall Med) Roy. Marsden Hosp., Sutton; Sen. Regist. (Palliat. Med.) UMDS. Lond.; Lect. & Sen. Regist. (Palliat. Med.) Trinity Hospice Lond.

GIBBS, Marilyn Dorothy Cefn Coed Hospital, Cockett, Swansea SA2 0GH Tel: 01792 561155 Fax: 01792 580740; 65 Pastoral Way, Tycoch, Swansea SA2 9LY Tel: 01792 201808 Fax: 01792 418697 — MB ChB 1968 Bristol; MB ChB Bristol. 1968; FRCPsych 1995, M 1973; T (Psych) 1991; DPM Eng. 1972. Cons. Psychiat. Glan-Y-Mor NHS Trust. Prev: Sen. Regist. (Psychiat.) S. Glam. AHA (T).

GIBBS, Martin Gibbs and Oakley, Doctors Surgery, Millend, Blakeney GL15 4ED Tel: 01594 510225 Fax: 01594 516074; Chelsea House, New Road, Blakeney GL15 4DD — MB BCh 1984 Wales; BSc (Hons.) Wales 1981, MB BCh 1984; MRCGP 1990;

DRCOG 1990. Socs: Primary Care Soc. Gastroenterol. Prev: Trainee GP Glos. HA VTS; Regist. Rotat. (Med.) Sheff. HA; SHO Rotat. (Med.) Leicester HA.

GIBBS, Mr Martin Laurence Poynings, Upper St., Stratford St Mary, Colchester CO7 6LW Tel: 01206 322516 — MB BS 1985 Lond.; FRCS Glas. 1990; FRCOphth 1991; DO RCS Eng. 1990. Community Based Ophth. & Company Dir. Suff.

GIBBS, Mary Georgina City Road Surgery, 204 City Road, Hulme, Manchester M15 4EA Tel: 0161 872 8129 Fax: 0161 877 0321; 7 Norman Road, Rusholme, Manchester M14 5LF — MB ChB 1976 Manch.; MRCGP 1984; DRCOG 1978; Cert. Family Plann. JCC 1980.

GIBBS, Maxwell Leonard Health Centre, Green Lane, Corwen LL21 0DN Tel: 01490 412362; Foel Fodig, Corwen LL21 9BY — MB ChB 1967 Sheff.; FRCP (U.K.) 2000; DCH Eng. 1969. (Sheff.)

GIBBS, Nesta Jeanne (retired) 28 Beulah Road, Rhiwbina, Cardiff CF14 6LX Tel: 029 2061 8334 — MB ChB Birm. 1948; MRCS Eng. LRCP Lond. 1948. Prev: Med. Off. S. Glam. AHA (T).

GIBBS, Professor Norman Martin Dellwood, Beechway, Merrow, Guildford GU1 2TA Tel: 01483 68057 — MB ChB 1948 Bristol; MRCP Lond. 1951; MRCS Eng. LRCP Lond. 1947; FRCPath 1969. (Bristol) Cons. Path. Histopath. Audit Roy. Sussex Hosp. Brighton; Cons. Histopath. SE Thames RHA; Hon. Prof. Path. Univ. Surrey. Socs: Assn. Clin. Path. Prev: Regional Co-ordinator BrE. Screening Path. SW Thames RHA; Demonst. Path. Univ. Bristol; Sen. Regist. (Clin. Path.) Sheff. United Hosps. & RHB.

GIBBS, Norman Peter Henry (retired) Hollydene, Fulmer Common Road, Fulmer, Iver SL0 0NP Tel: 01753 663672 — MB BS 1952 Lond.; MRCS Eng. LRCP Lond. 1952. Prev: Mem. BMA & Harefield & N.wood Med. Soc.

GIBBS, Mr Paul University of cambridge, University Department of Surgery, Addenbrooke's Hospital, Cambridge CB2 2QQ Tel: 01223 336978 Email: pg224@cam.ac.uk — MB BCh 1981 Wales; FRCS Ed. 1986. Lect./Hon Cons. Surg., Dept. of Surg., Addlerbrooke's Hosp. Socs: Brit. Transpl. Soc.; BMA; BSI. Prev: Sen. Lect./Hon Cons., Inst. of Liver Studies, Kings Coll. Hosp.

GIBBS, Paul John 3 Coronation Cottages, Routs Way, Rownhams, Southampton SO16 8JG — MB BS 1992 Lond.

GIBBS, Rebecca Ann (Geary) The Cottage, 2 Friday Lane, Barston, Solihull B92 0HY — MB ChB 1994 Birm. (Birm.) p/t GP Sandwell. Prev: Trainee GP/SHO Worcester Roy. Infirm VTS; SHO (A & E) City Hosp. NHS Trust Birm.; Ho. Off. (Med.) City Hosp. NHS Trust.

GIBBS, Richard Geoffrey James Victoria House, 47A Kings St., Arundel BN18 9BN — MB ChB 1990 Manch.

GIBBS, Richard Henry Worfield House, Worfield, Bridgnorth WV15 5LH — MB BS 1997 Lond.

GIBBS, Roger John Yew Tree Cottage Surgery, 15 Leyton Road, Harpenden AL5 2HX Tel: 01582 712126 Fax: 01582 462414; Wisteria, 28 The Broadway, Gustard Wood, Wheathampstead, St Albans AL4 8LP Tel: 01438 833466 — MB BS 1974 Lond.; BSc Lond. 1971; MRCS Eng. LRCP Lond. 1974; DRCOG 1978; DCH Eng. 1977. Trainer (Gen. Pract.) Harpenden.

GIBBS, Roland Geoffrey (retired) North Cove House, Beccles NR34 7PP Tel: 0150 276203 — MB BChir 1948 Camb.; FRCP Lond. 1974, M 1954; MRCS Eng. LRCP Lond. 1948. Cons. Phys. Gt. Yarmouth & LoW.oft Hosp. Gp. Prev: Ho. Phys. & Sen. Med. Cas. Off. St. Thos. Hosp.

GIBBS, Sally Louise 111 Station Road, Beaconsfield HP9 1UT — BM BS 1994 Nottm.

GIBBS, Sam Simon Sebastian Dermatology Department, Ipswich Hospital NHS Trust, Heath Road, Ipswich IP4 5PD Tel: 01473 704043 Fax: 01473 704712 — MB BChir 1983 Camb.; MA Camb. 1983; MRCP (UK) 1989; DTM & H (Liverp.) 1990. (Middlesex Hospital) Cons. (Dermatol.) Dermat. Dept. Ipswich Hosp. NHS Trust Heath Rd. Ipswich IP4 5PD. Socs: Brit. Assn. Dermatol. Prev: Med. Off. Murgwanza Hosp. Ngara, Kagera, Tanzania; SPR Dermat, Norwich & Camb.

GIBBS, Mr Simon Ashley Lawson 6 The Bowmans, Victoria Road, Macclesfield SK10 3JA — MB BS 1987 Lond.; MA Camb. 1988; FRCS Lond. 1991; FRCS Glas. 1991. (St. Mary's) Lect. & Hon. Sen. Regist. (Gen. Surg.) Univ. Manch. Hosps. Socs: BMA; Assn. Accid. & Emerg. Surg. Prev: Regist. Rotat. S. Manch. Hosps.; Research Fell. Brigham & Wom. Hosp. Boston Mass, USA; SHO Rotat. (Surg.) Liverp. & Chester.

GIBBS, Siobhan Ellen Marie Abraham and Partners, 21-23 Morden Hill, Lewisham, London SE13 7NN Tel: 020 8469 2880 Fax: 020 8692 9399 — MB BCh BAO 1991 Dub.

GIBBS, Stephanie Juliet Oldchurch Hospital, Romford RM7 0BE Tel: 01708 708317; 9a Lansdowne Walk, London W11 3LN — MB BS 1986 Lond.; MRCP (UK) 1990; FRCR 1996. Cons. Radiother., OldCh. & St. Bartholomews Hosp.s Lond. Prev: Sen. Regist. St Bart's & Roy. Lond. Hosps.; Regist. (Radiother.) Middlx. Hosp. Lond.

GIBBS, Susannah Margaret Royal Edinburgh Hospital, Morningside Terrace, Edinburgh EH10 5HF — MB ChB 1993 Leeds; BSc Leeds 1990. (Leeds) SHO (Psychiat.) Edin.

GIBBS, Timothy John St Giles Road Surgery, St. Giles Road, Watton, Thetford IP25 6XG Tel: 01953 889134/881247 Fax: 01953 885167 — MB BS 1982 Lond.; BA Camb. 1974; DRCOG 1986.

GIBBS, Trevor John 27 Upton Road, Moreton, Wirral CH46 0PE Tel: 0151 677 2327 Fax: 0151 604 0419; 11 Queens Avenue, Meols, Wirral CH47 0LR Tel: 0151 632 0906 — MB ChB 1973 Liverp.; MMedSci Leeds 1988; FFHom 1992, M 1985; FRCGP 1990, M 1981; MICGP 1986; DGM RCP Lond. 1986; DCH Eng. 1980; DRCOG 1978. Assoc. Adviser (Continuing Med. Educat.) Univ. Liverp. Socs: Inst. Health Serv. Managers. Prev: Examr. RCGP; Sen. Research Asst. (Haemat.) Univ. Liverp.; Regist. (Med.) Liverp. Roy. Infirm.

GIBBS, Zaida Katharine 1 Stoke Mead, Midford Lane, Limpley Stoke, Bath BA2 7GX — MB ChB 1976 Bristol; MRCGP 1981; DRCOG 1979. Prev: SHO (Paediat.) S.mead Hosp. Bristol; SHO (Cas.) Roy. United Hosp. Bath; GP Beckington.

GIBBY, Martin John Ashcroft Surgery, Stewkley Road, Wing, Leighton Buzzard LU7 0NE Tel: 01296 688201 Fax: 01296 681421; The Walnuts, 20 Ridings Way, Cublinton, Leighton Buzzard LU7 0LW — MB ChB 1978 Liverp.; MRCGP 1984; DRCOG 1980. Prev: SHO Roy. Liverp. Childr. Hosp.; Ho. Off. Ormskirk & Dist. Gen. Hosp.

GIBBY, Owain Morris Royal Gwent Hospital, Newport NP20 2UB Tel: 01633 252244; Plas Newydd, Portycarne St, Usk NP5 1RZ Tel: 01291 673637 — MB BS 1972 Lond.; FRCP Lond. 1993; MRCP (UK) 1975. (Roy. Free) Cons. Phys. Roy. Gwent Hosp. Socs: Eur. Assn. for Study Diabetes; Brit. Diabetic Assn. (Med. & Scientif. Sect.). Prev: Lect. (Med.) Univ. Birm.; MRC Train. Fell. (Clin. Biochem.) Univ. Camb.; Regist. (Med.) Univ. Hosp. of Wales.

GIBBY, Sion Aled Bwlch-Newydd, Peniel, Carmarthen SA32 7DJ Tel: 01267 232782 Email: siongibby@hotmail.com — BM BCh 1998 Oxf.; BM BCh Oxf 1998; MA OXON 1995.

GIBEON, Simon Heathfield Medical Centre, Lyttelton Road, Hampstead Garden Suburb, London N2 0EE Tel: 020 8458 9262 Fax: 020 8458 0300; 21 Thornton Way, London NW11 6SL Tel: 020 8455 6981 Fax: 020 8455 6981 Email: drsgibeon@mcmail.com — MB BS 1973 Lond.; MRCS Eng. LRCP Lond. 1973. (Royal Free) Primary Care Phys. Roy. Free Hosp. Socs: Lond. Jewish Med. Soc.; Assur. Med. Soc.

GIBLIN, Mary Emma 19 St James Street, Castle Hedingham, Halstead CO9 3EW — MB BS 1993 Lond.; DRCOG; DFFP. (Charing Cross and Westminster)

GIBLIN, Michael Wayside, Lower Contour Road, Kingswear, Dartmouth TQ6 0AL; 1 Greenswood Road, Brixham TQ5 9HN — MB ChB 1978 Birm.

GIBLIN, Myfanwy Mary Wayside, Lower Contour Road, Kingswear, Dartmouth TQ6 0AL — MB ChB 1981 Birm.

GIBSON, Alan Calvert (retired) 73 Canford Cliffs Road, Poole BH13 7AH Tel: 01202701593 — MB BChir 1950 Camb.; MA Camb. 1950; FRCP Ed. 1971, M 1957; FRCPsych 1977, M 1971; DPM Durham. 1956. Prev: Cons. Psychiat. Bournemouth & E. Dorset Hosps.

GIBSON, Mr Alan Graeme Faulds 38 Stoke Lane, Bristol BS9 3DN Tel: 0117 962 2827 Email: 106014.3210@compuserve.com — MB ChB 1970 Bristol; FRCS Eng. 1977. Assoc. Specialist Orthop. Surg. N. Bristol NHS Trust; Med. Adviser Brit. Hang-gliding & Paragliding Assn. Prev: Sen. Specialist (Orthop.) Qaboos Hosp. Salalah, Sultanate of Oman; Staff Orthop. Surg. S.mead Hosp. Bristol.

GIBSON, Alan James (retired) Meadow Farm, Rudbaxton, Haverfordwest SA62 4DB — MB ChB 1954 Glas.; DObst RCOG 1957. Prev: GP HaverfordW.

GIBSON, Alan Tregarthen 162 Tranmere Road, Earlsfield, London SW18 3QU — MB BS 1982 Lond.; PhD Lond. 1976, BSc 1973, MB BS 1982. SHO (Med. Rotat.) N.wick Pk. Hosp. Harrow.

GIBSON, Alexander Brian Forsyth 31 St John Street, Oxford OX1 2LH Tel: 01865 515770 — MRCS Eng. LRCP Lond. 1934; BA Camb. (St. Thos.)

GIBSON, Alexander George Penn, Out Elmstead Lane, Barham, Canterbury CT4 6PH — MB BS 1962 Lond.; FRCPath 1984, M 1972; DObst RCOG 1964. (Char. Cross) Cons. Path. Canterbury & Thanet Health Dist.; Hon. Sen. Lect. Foren. Path. Lond. Hosp. Socs: Brit. Assn. Foren. Med. Prev: Sen. Lect. Foren. Path. Lond. Hosp. Med. Coll.; Regist. Path. Char. Cross & Roy. Marsden Hosps. Lond.

GIBSON, Alexander James 4 Crammond Close, London W6 8QS — MB BS 1996 Lond.; BSc Lond. 1993. (Char. Cross & Westm. Med. Sch.) SHO (Trauma & Orthop.) Centr. Middlx. Hosp.; SHO (Vasc. Surg.) St Mary's Hosp. Paddington; SHO (Paediat. Surg.) Gt. Ormond St. Hosp. Prev: SHO (A & E) Hillingdon Hosp. Middlx.; Ho. Off. (Med.) Ashford Hosp. Middlx.; Ho. Off. (Surg.) Watford & Mt. Vernon Hosp.

GIBSON, Andrea Julie 1/L, 191 Clarkston Road, Glasgow G44 3BS — MB ChB 1995 Glas. SHO (A & E) Bradford Roy. Infirm.

GIBSON, Andrew 78 Dalewood Road, Sheffield S8 0EF — MB BS 1990 Lond.; MRCP (UK) 1993.

GIBSON, Andrew Forbes Butler North Bicester Surgery, Holm Square, Southwold, Bicester OX26 3YQ Tel: 01869 323600 Fax: 01869 323300; Cowley Lodge, Preston Bisset, Buckingham MK18 4DX Tel: 01296 738154 — LMSSA 1981 Lond.; MA Camb. 1981, MB BChir 1982; DRCOG 1985. (St. Thos.) Socs: BMA & Christian Med. Fell.sh.

GIBSON, Andrew Gilmore The Surgery, Norwich Road, Saxlingham Nethergate, Norwich NR15 1TP Fax: 01508 498207; The Surgery, St. Mary's Close, Newton Flotman, Norwich NR15 1AH Tel: 01508 470300 Fax: 01508 471346 — MB BS 1973 Lond.; BSc Lond. 1970; MRCGP 1977; DObst RCOG 1976. (Lond. Hosp.) Socs: Christ. Med. Fell.sh. Prev: Princip. GP Chelmsford.

GIBSON, Andrew Neale 65 Castle Wemyss Drive, Wemyss Bay PA18 6BU — MB ChB 1994 Glas.

GIBSON, Andrew Richard 82 Sugden Road, London SW11 5EE — MB BS 1993 Lond.

GIBSON, Angus Alexander Mackintosh (retired) 8 Rosslyn Terrace, Glasgow G12 9NB — MB ChB 1956 Ed.; FRCP Ed. 1971, M 1961; FRCPath 1978, M 1966. Prev: Cons. Pathol. Roy. Hosp. Sick Childr. & Qu. Mother's Hosp. Glas.

GIBSON, Anthony David Flints, Lower Station Road, Henfield BN5 9UR — MB BCh 1997 Wales.

GIBSON, Anthony Leo 3 Woodlands Park Drive, The Parklands, Blaydon-on-Tyne NE21 5PQ Tel: 0191 414 5441 — MB BChir 1966 Camb.; MA, MB Camb. 1966, BChir 1965; FRCP Lond. 1980, M 1967. (St. Geo.) Prev: Phys. Qu. Eliz. Hosp. Gateshead; Sen. Regist. (Med.) Roy. Vict. Infirm. Newc.; Ho. Phys. Brompton Hosp. Lond.

GIBSON, Audrey 40 Tyrone Drive, Rochdale OL11 4BE — MB ChB 1982 Manch.

GIBSON, Brenda Elizabeth Simpson 7 Redlands Road, Glasgow G12 0SJ — MB ChB 1973 Aberd.; MRCP (UK) 1977; MRCPath 1982; DFM 1987 Glas. 1987. Cons. Haemat. Roy. Hosp. for Sick Childr. Glas.

GIBSON, Bruce Malcolm Department of Anaesthetics, Newcastle General Hospital, Westgate Road, Newcastle upon Tyne NE4 6BE — MB BCh 1990 Wales; FRCA 1997. Specialist Regist. (Anaes), Newcatle upon Tyne.

GIBSON, Carol Vivien Blandford House Surgery, 7 London Road, Braintree CM7 2LD Tel: 01376 347100 Fax: 01376 349934; Little Priory, Shalford Road, Panfield, Braintree CM7 5AS — MB ChB 1969 Manch.; DObst RCOG 1971.

GIBSON, Carolyn 6 Bexley Drive, Bangor BT19 7ZQ Tel: 01247 468478 — MB BCh BAO 1989 Belf.; DFFP 1998; MRCGP 1994; DRCOG 1993; DCH RCSI 1992; DGM RCP Lond. 1991. Trainee GP Bangor.

***GIBSON, Christine Elaine** 28 Wilsham Road, Abingdon OX14 5LD Tel: 01225 313352; 28 Wilsham Road, Abingdon OX14 5LD Tel: 01225 313352 — MB ChB 1994 Birm.

GIBSON, Daren Joseph 79 Morshead Mansions, Morshead Road, London W9 1LG — MB BS 1994 Lond.

GIBSON, David Alexander 52/6 Laichpark Road, Edinburgh EH14 1XB — MB ChB 1993 Ed.

GIBSON, David Arnold (retired) Woodside Surgery, Woodside Road, Woodlands, Doncaster DN6 7JR Tel: 01302 330212 Fax: 01302 330591 — MB ChB 1984 Leeds; DA (UK) 1986. Prev: Trainee GP Scunthorpe VTS.

GIBSON, David Howard 7 Benston Crescent, Hollybush, Ayr KA6 7EA — MB BCh BAO 1978 Belf.; MRCOG 1983. Cons. O & G Ayrsh. & Arran HB. Prev: Sen. Regist. & Sen. Tutor Belf. City Hosp. & Jubilee Matern. Hosp. Belf.

GIBSON, David John Ker Victor Street Surgery, Victor Street, Shirley, Southampton SO15 5SY Tel: 023 8077 4781 Fax: 023 8039 0680; 96 Wilton Row, Shirley, Southampton — BM 1987 Soton.; MRCGP 1991; DRCOG 1990.

GIBSON, David Richard Comber Health Centre, 5 Newtownards Road, Newtownards BT23 5BA — MB BCh BAO 1972 Belf.; M.M.Ed 1999 University of Dundee; FRCGP 1993, M 1978; DCH RCPSI 1976. (Queens University Belfast) Gen. Med. Practitioner; Assoc. Dir. Postgrad. Gen. Pract. Educat. N.I.C.P.G.M.D.E. Belf.

GIBSON, David William Ramsay Richards and Partners, The Surgery, North Street, Langport TA10 9RH Tel: 01458 250464 Fax: 01458 253246; Southview, Currywoods Way, Curry Rivel, Langport TA10 0NR Tel: 01458 251697 — MB ChB Bristol 1967; Dip. Obst. NZ 1976. (Bristol)

GIBSON, Derek Gair Royal Brompton Hospital, London SW3 6NP Tel: 020 7351 8636 Fax: 020 7351 8776 — MB BChir Camb. 1962; FRCP Lond. 1975, M 1963. (Westm.) Cons. Cardiol. Roy. Brompton Hosp. Lond. Socs: Fell. Roy. Soc. Med.; Brit. Cardiac Soc.; Fell Europ. Soc. Cardiol. Prev: Sen. Regist. St. Bart. Hosp. Lond.; Regist. Nat. Heart Hosp. & Med. Unit W.m. Hosp.

GIBSON, Eileen McCreary (retired) 1 Silvermere, Byfleet Road, Cobham KT11 1DZ Tel: 01932 863486 — MB BCh BAO 1928 Belf.; MB BCh BAO (Hons.) Belf. 1928; FFA RCS Eng. 1954; DA Eng. 1947. Prev: Cons. Anaesth. NW Surrey Gp. Hosps.

GIBSON, Elisabeth Eunice University College Hospital, Gower St., London WC1E 6AU Tel: 020 7387 9300; 13 Longfellow Way, London SE1 5TB Tel: 020 7252 3867 — MB BS 1994 Lond.; BSc Lond. 1990. (UMDS Lond.) SHO (Obst.) Univ. Coll. Hosp. Lond. Prev: SHO (Neonates & Gyn.) Univ. Coll. Hosp.; SHO (O & G) Lewisham Hosp. Lond.

GIBSON, Eric Osborne Health Centre, Rodney Road, Walton-on-Thames KT12 3LB Tel: 0193 22 28999; The Acre, Goose Rye Road, Worplesdon, Guildford GU3 3RJ Tel: 01483 233629 — MB ChB 1951 Glas.; DObst RCOG 1953; FRCGP 1982, M 1962. (Glas.) Walton Hosp; Vice-Chairm. Surrey Family Pract. Comm. Socs: BMA & NW Surrey DHA; Surrey Local Med. Comm. Prev: Ho. Surg. Roy. Alexandra Infirm. Paisley & Roy. Matern. & Wom. Hosp. Glas.; Ho. Phys. W.. Infirm. Glas.; Ho. Surg. Roy. Matern. Hosp. Glas.

GIBSON, Fiona Alison Murray 15 Croft Road, Charlton Kings, Cheltenham GL53 8LD — MB ChB 1984 Bristol.

GIBSON, Fiona Jane House 2, The Grange Farm, St Andrews KY16 8LL Tel: 01334 78486 — MB ChB 1988 Manch.; BSc (Med. Sci.) St. And. 1985; DRCOG 1992.

GIBSON, Fiona Malcolm The Ayr Hospital, Dalmellington Road, Ayr KA6 6DX Tel: 01292 610555 — MB ChB 1984 Glas.; FFAEM 1998; FRCS (A&E) Ed 1996; MRCGP 1992; DA (UK) 1994; Dip. IMC RCS Ed. 1988; DRCOG 1986. Cons. (A & E) The Ayr Hosp. Prev: Regist. (A & E) Alder Hey Childr.s Hosp. Liverp. & PeterBoro. Dist.; Specialist Regist. (A & E) Roy. Vict. Hosp. Belf.

GIBSON, Fiona Mary 35 Knockdene Park, Belfast BT5 7AD — MB BCh BAO 1978 Belf.

GIBSON, George Anderson 1 Holly Avenue, Stenhousemuir, Larbert FK5 4DN — MB ChB 1984 Glas.; MB ChB Glas. l984.

GIBSON, Professor Gerald John Freeman Hospital, Newcastle upon Tyne NE7 7DN Tel: 0191 284 3111 Fax: 0191 213 1575 Email: g.j.gibson@ncb.ac.uk — FRCP 2000 Edin.; MB BS (Hons.) Lond. 1968; BSc (1st cl. Hons.) Lond. 1965; MD Lond. 1976; FRCP Lond. 1982; MRCP (UK) 1970. (Guy's) Cons. Phys. Regional Cardiothoracic Centre Freeman Hosp. Newc.; Prof. Respirat. Med. Univ. Newc. u. Tyne. Socs: Chairm. of Exec. 1997-99 (Pres.-Elect 2001-2); Brit. Thorac. Soc.; Eur. Respirat. Soc. Prev: Sen. Regist. (Med.) Hammersmith Hosp. Lond.; Resid. Phys. St. Joseph's Hosp. McMaster Univ. Hamilton, Canada; Ho. Phys. Guy's Hosp. Lond.

GIBSON, Grace Ellen Tigh Na Coille, Budhmor, Portree IV51 9DJ — MB ChB 1977 Glas.

GIBSON, Graham Cornelius Strensall Medical Practice, Medical Centre, Southfields Road, Strensall, York YO32 5UA Tel: 01904 490532 — MB ChB 1981 Ed.; BSc (Med. Sci.) Ed. 1978; MRCGP 1986. (Edin.) Prev: Trainee GP York; Med. Off. Ruttonjee Sanat., Hong Kong.

GIBSON, Helen Yorkhill NHS Trust, Royal Hospital for Sick Children, Glasgow G3 8SJ Tel: 0141 201 0000; 9 Torr Crescent, Rhu, Helensburgh G84 8LZ — MB ChB 1983 Manch.; MSc Physiol. Lond. 1986; MRCP (UK) 1990; DCH RCP Lond. 1989. SHO (Paediat.) Roy. Hosp. for Sick Childr. Glas. Prev: Regist. (Pub. Health Med.) Argyll & Clyde Health Bd.; Regist. (Pub. Health Med.) Cheltenham HA.

GIBSON, Helen Grace Avences Medical Centre, 149-155 Chancerlands Ave, Hull HU5 3TJ Tel: 01482 343614 — MB ChB 1981 Sheff.; DFFP 1996; MRCGP 1985; DRCOG 1984. GP Princip.

GIBSON, Helen Margaret The Old Barn, Rue Des Caches, St Saviours, Guernsey GY7 9TJ Tel: 01481 65295 — MB BS 1966 Durh.; MRCOG 1971. (Newc.) Partner Qu.s Rd. Med. Pract. Guernsey; Guernsey Health Bd.; Guernsey Family Plann. Socs: Roy. Coll. Obst & Gyn.; Fac. Fam. Plan. Doctors.

GIBSON, Henry 233 Minster Ct, Liverpool L7 3QH — MB ChB 1997 Liverp.

GIBSON, Howard Norman The General Hospital, Gloucester St., St Helier, Jersey JE2 3 Tel: 01534 59000; Mont de la Mare, Chemin du Mont de la Mare, St Peter, Jersey JE3 7FT Tel: 01534 483582 — MB ChB 1982 Manch.; FRCP Ed. 1996; MRCP (UK) 1986. (Manch.) Cons. Phys. (Neurol.) Jersey Gen. Hosp. Socs: N. Eng. Neurol. Assn.; Assoc. Brit. NeUrol.s. Prev: Sen. Regist. (Med.) Manch. Roy. Infirm.; Regist. (Med.) N. Manch. Gen. Hosp.; Research Regist. (Neurol.) Roy. Preston Hosp.

GIBSON, Hugh Farquhar Rubislaw Place Medical Group, 7 Rubislaw Place, Aberdeen AB10 1QB Tel: 01224 641968 Fax: 01224 645738 — MB ChB 1973 Aberd.; FRCGP 1998; MRCGP 1977.

GIBSON, Ian Brodie (retired) 2 Townend Terrace, Symington, Kilmarnock KA1 5QH Tel: 01563 830295 Fax: 01563 830295 — MB ChB 1956 Glas.; MRCGP 1966. Prev: GP Dundonald, Ayrsh.

GIBSON, Ian Duncan Fairways, 1 The Mount, Esher KT10 8LQ — MB ChB 1998 Dund.; MB ChB Dund 1998.

GIBSON, Ian George Longrigg Blandford House Surgery, 7 London Road, Braintree CM7 2LD — MB ChB 1966 Manch.; MRCGP 1981; Dip. IMC RCS Ed. 1991; DObst RCOG 1968. (Manch)

GIBSON, Ian Stewart Brundall Medical Partnership, The Dales, Brundall, Norwich NR13 5RP Tel: 01603 712255 Fax: 01603 712156 — MB ChB 1988 Aberd.; MRCGP 1992; DRCOG 1991.

GIBSON, Ian William Department of Pathology, Western Infirmary, Glasgow G11 6NT Email: gcl059@clinmed.gla.ac.uk — MB ChB 1988 Glas.; BSc (Hons.) Glas. 1985, MD (Hons.) 1995; MRCPath 1995; DRCPath 1993. Cons. Pathol. W. infirm. Glas. Socs: Internat. Acad. Path. (Brit. Div.); Assn. Clin. Path. Prev: Sen. Regist. (Path.) W.. Infirm. Glas.; SHO (Path.) W.. Infirm. Glas.; Ho. Off. (Gen. & Vasc. Surg.) Gartnavel Gen. Hosp. Glas.

GIBSON, Isabel Young (retired) — MB ChB Glas. 1945. Prev: SCMO (Family Plann.) Basingstoke & N. Hants. HA.

GIBSON, Isobel Margaret The Surgery, 171 Main Street, Callander FK17 8BJ Tel: 01877 331000; Robertson House, Bridgend, Callander FK17 8AS Tel: 01877 330341 — MB ChB 1985 Glas.; MRCGP 1992; DCH RCP Lond. 1990; Cert. Family Plann. JCC 1988. p/t GP Princip. Callander. Prev: Regist. (Psychiat.) Gtr. Glas. HB; Trainee GP Shetland; SHO (Paediat.) Gtr. Glas. HB.

GIBSON, Ivan Hamilton Dumfries & Galloway Royal Infirmary, Department of Histopathology & Cytology, Bankend Road, Dumfries DG1 4AP — MB BCh BAO 1970 Belf.; FRCPath 1976. Cons. Path. Dumfries & Galloway HB.

GIBSON, James Charles 45 Bryansford Road, Newcastle BT33 0DW Tel: 013967 24627 — LM 1945 Rotunda; LRCPI & LM LRCSI & LM 1943.

GIBSON, James Maurice Radiology Department, Cheltenham General Hospital, Sandford Road, Cheltenham GL53 7AN Tel: 01242 273000 Fax: 01242 273589; Bluegates, Clapton, Berkeley GL13 9QU — MB BS 1979 Lond.; MA Camb. 1979; MRCP (UK) 1984; FRCR 1987. (King's Coll. Hosp.) Cons. Radiol. Cheltenham Gen. Hosp.

GIBSON, Jane Harvey Rheumatic Diseases Unit, George Sharp Unit, Cameron Hospital, Windygates, Leven KY8 5RR Tel: 01592 712472 Fax: 01592 750851; Aila, 1 Bishop Terrace, Kinnesswood, Kinross KY13 9JW Tel: 01592 840355 Email: jg2gg@aol.com — MB ChB 1988 Ed.; BSc (Hons.) Ed. 1980; MRCP (UK) 1991; MD Ed 1998. Cons. (Rheum.) Fife Primary Care NHS Trust. Prev: Sen. Regist. (Rheum.) Manch.; Clin. Lect. Univ. Manch.; Regist. (Rheum.) N.wick Pk. Hosp.

GIBSON, Jane Isabella (retired) Glen O'Dee Hospital, Banchory AB31 5SA — MB ChB 1940 Aberd.; FRCPath. 1964. Prev: Lect. (Path.) Univ. Aberd.

GIBSON, Janet Isobel (retired) Stokewood Surgery, Fair Oak, Eastleigh SO50 7LU Tel: 01703 692000 — MB BS 1958 Lond.; DObst RCOG 1962. Prev: SHO Qu. Charlotte's Matern. Hosp. Lond.

GIBSON, Janice Lesley 25 Hillview Avenue, Dumfries DG1 4DX — MB ChB 1992 Ed.

GIBSON, Jeanne Tower House Practice, St. Pauls Health Centre, High Street, Runcorn WA7 1AB Tel: 01928 567404; Mill Lane House Farm, Mill Lane, Kingsley, Warrington WA6 8HZ — MB BS Lond. 1981; MRCGP 1985; DRCOG 1983.

GIBSON, Jeannette Robertson Bennett Bennetdale, Paganel Drive, Dudley DY1 4AY — LRCS 1944 Ed.; L.R.C.P., L.R.C.S. Ed., L.R.F.P.S. Glas. 1944. (Anderson Coll. Glas.) Asst. M.O.H. Dudley.

GIBSON, Jennifer Anne 14 Carnhill Avenue, Newtownabbey BT36 6LE — MB BCh BAO 1994 Belf.

GIBSON, Jennifer Mary Doidge, MBE (retired) 38 Galsworthy Road, Goring, Worthing BN12 6LW Tel: 01903 504968 — MB BChir 1956 Camb.; MRCP (UK) 1971; FRCP Lond. 1987; DTM & H Liverp. 1967; DA (UK) 1963; DObst RCOG 1958. Volun. Med. report writer Med. Foundat. c/o Survivors of Torture. Prev: Acting Med. Supt. Nixon Memor. Hosp. Segbwema, Sierra Leone.

GIBSON, Jeremy Clarence 96 Edinburgh Road, Dumfries DG1 1JU — MB ChB 1994 Glas.

GIBSON, Jeremy John Stuart The Surgery, Marlpits Road, Honiton EX14 2NY Tel: 01404 41141 Fax: 01404 46621; St Michaels Mount, 55 Church Hill Road, Honiton EX14 2DB Tel: 01404 42870 Fax: 01404 42870 Email: gibsonjjs@globalnet.uk.uk — MB BChir Camb. 1967; MA Camb. 1968; MRCGP 1973; DObst RCOG 1969. (Camb. & Middlx.) Clin. Asst. (Endoscopy) Honiton Hosp. Socs: (Comm.) Primary Care Soc. Gastroenterol.; Exec. Comm. Digest. Dis.s Found. Prev: Ho. Off. Surgic. Unit Middlx. Hosp. Lond.; Ho. Phys. Ipswich & E. Suff. Hosp.

GIBSON, John (retired) Primrose Bolt, Primrose Lane, Woodfalls, Salisbury SP5 2NA — MB ChB Glas. 1966.

GIBSON, John Department of Oral Medicine, Glasgow Dental Hospital & School, 378 Sauchiehall St., Glasgow G2 3JZ — MB ChB 1992 Glas.; BDS Glas. 1986; FDS (OM) RCPS Glas. 1996; FDS RCPS Glas. 1990; FFD RCSI 1990; PhD 1998. (Glasgow) Sen. Lect. and Cons. in Oral Med. Univ. of Glas. Socs: BMA; Brit. Soc. Oral Med.; Brit. Soc. Med. Mycol. Prev: Lect. (Oral Med.) Univ. Glas.; Clin. Asst. (Oral Med.) Glas. Dent. Hosp. & Sch.

GIBSON, John Alan Ewing Street Surgery, 26 Ewing Street, Kilbarchan, Johnstone PA10 2JA Tel: 01505 702410; Foremount House, Kilbarchan, Johnstone PA10 2EZ Tel: 01505 702410 — MB ChB 1951 Glas.; MD Dalhousie 1954; FRCGP 1992, M 1959; — DObst RCOG 1955; CBiol, FIBiol 1985. (Univ. Glas.) Vis. Phys. Merchiston Hosp. & Elderslie Hosp. for Handicap. Childr.; Chairm. Scott. Natural Hist. Library; Edr. Scott. Naturalist. Socs: Fell. Roy. Soc. Med.; Fell. BMA (Sen. Hon. Sec. UK); Life Fell RCGP. Prev: Sen. Demonst. (Anat.) Univ. Glas.; Regist. (Surg.) S.. Gen. Hosp. Glas.; SHO Roy. Matern. & Wom. Hosp. Glas.

GIBSON, John Alexander Mid Staffordshire NHS Trust, Staffordshire General Hospital, Weston Road, Stafford ST16 3SA Tel: 01785 257731 Fax: 01785 230771 Email: john.gibson@msgh-tr.wmids.nhs.uk; Brocton Gate, Brocton, Brocton, Stafford ST17 0SS Tel: 01785 662858 Fax: 01785 662858 Email: jagibson@doctors.org.uk — MB BChir Camb. 1965; MD Camb. 1978, MA 1965; FRCP Lond. 1984; MRCP (UK) 1971; DObst RCOG 1968. (Camb. & St. Bart.) Cons. Phys. Staffs. Gen. Hosp. Socs: Roy. Soc. Med.; Brit. Soc. Gastroenterol. Prev: Sen. Regist. (Med.) W. Middlx. Hosp. & St. Mary's Hosp. Paddington.

GIBSON, John Anthony Longford Street Surgery, Longford Street, Heywood OL10 4NH Tel: 01706 621417 Fax: 01706 622915 — MB BS 1978 Lond.; MRCS Eng. LRCP Lond. 1978; MRCGP 1984; DRCOG 1981. (Guy's) GP Heywood. Prev: Trainee GP N.ampton Gen. Hosp.; Ho. Surg. Guy's Hosp. Lond.; Ho. Phys. Lewisham Hosp. Lond.

GIBSON, John Dudley Department Neurology, Derriford Hospital, Plymouth PL6 8DH Tel: 01752 792618 Email: john.gibson@phnt.swest.nhs.uk; Thorn House, Wembury, Plymouth PL9 0EQ Tel: 01752 862494 — MB BS 1970 Lond.; BSc (1st cl. Hons.) Lond. 1967, MD 1976; FRCP Lond. 1995; MRCP (UK) 1973. (Univ. Coll. Hosp.) Cons. Neurol. Derriford Hosp. Plymouth. Prev: Sen. Regist. Leeds Gen. Infirm.; Regist. Nat. Hosp. Lond.

GIBSON, John Edward West Suffolk Hospital, Hardwick Lane, Bury St Edmunds IP33 2QZ; 41 Hopkins Close, Cambridge CB4 1FB Tel: 01223 513461 — MB BChir 1992 Camb.; MA Camb. 1993; FRCS (Eng.) 1997.

GIBSON, John Fintan Joseph April Cottage, 11 Carbery Avenue, Southbourne, Bournemouth BH6 3LL Tel: 01202 428406 — MB BCh BAO 1971 NUI; MRCGP 1975; MICGP 1984; DObst RCPI 1974; DCH RCPSI 1973. Staff Grade Community Paediat. E. Dorset Health Auth. Prev: GP Co-Carlow, Eire.

GIBSON, Mr John Mackintosh Cowan (retired) Hillside, 277 North Deeside Road, Milltimber AB13 0HA Tel: 01224 732237 Fax: 01224 732237 — MB ChB 1950 Ed.; FRCS Ed. 1956. Prev: Clin. Sen. Lect. (Orthop. Surg.) Univ. Aberd.

GIBSON, John Mark Ward 21, Royal Victoria Hospital, Belfast BT12 6BA — MD 1985 Dub.; MB BCh BAO Dub. 1976; FRCP Lond. 1994; MRCP (UK) 1979. Cons. Neurol. Roy. Vict. Hosp. Belf. Prev: Sen. Regist. (Neurol.) Roy. Vict. Hosp. Belf.; Research Fell. The Lond. Hosp.; Regist. Wessex Neurol. Centre Soton.

GIBSON, John Martin Glenbrooke House, 30 Knutsford Road, Alderley Edge SK9 7SD — MB ChB 1987 Liverp.

GIBSON, Mr John Nicolas Alastair Princess Margaret Rose Orthopaedic Hospital, Fairmilehead, Edinburgh EH10 7ED Tel: 0131 536 4600 Fax: 0131 536 4754 Email: j.n.a.gibson@ed.ac.uk; 14 White Dales, Fairmilehead, Edinburgh EH10 7JQ Email: j.n.a.gibson@cableinet.co.uk — MB BS 1978 Lond.; MD Lond. 1987; FRCS Ed. (Orth.) 1990; FRCS Ed. 1983. Cons. Orthop. Surg. & Sen. Lect. Lothian Univ. Hosps. NHS Trust; Cons. Orthop. Surg. St John's Hosp., Livingston; Cons. Orthop. Surg. The BUPA Murrayfield Hosp., Edin. Socs: Med. Res. Soc. & Brit. Orthop. Research Soc.; NY Acad. Sci. Cervical Spine Soc.; Internat. Soc. Study Lumbar Spine. Prev: Spinal Fell. Roy. N. Shore Hosp. Sydney; Regist. (Orthop.) Roy. Infirm. Dundee; Ho. Surg. Lond. Hosp.

GIBSON, Mr John Robin Munro (retired) 54 Victoria Drive, Bognor Regis PO21 2TF Tel: 01243 865003 Fax: 01243 865166 Email: jenjohn@viconline.co.uk — MB BS Lond. 1957; MRCS Eng. LRCP Lond. 1956; FRCOG 1978, M 1964; T(OG) 1991; DObst RCOG 1961. Prev: Cons. O & G Chichester & Graylingwell Hosp. Gp.

GIBSON, John Stanley Department of Anaesthesia, The General Infirmary, Leeds LS1 3EX — MB BChir 1974 Camb.; MB Camb. 1974, BChir 1973; MA Camb. 1974; FFA RCS Eng. 1977. (St. Mary's) Cons. Anaesth. Gen. Infirm. Leeds; Sen. Clin. Lect. Univ. Leeds. Socs: Assn. Anaesth. Prev: Lect. (Anaesth.) Univ. Leeds; Regist. (Anaesth.) Sheff. HA; SHO (Anaesth.) Roy. United Hosp. Bath.

GIBSON, Mr Jonathan Mark Birmingham and Solihull NHS TruStreet, Bordesley Green E., Birmingham B9 5SS Tel: 0121 766 6611 Email: gibsonj@heartsol.wmids.nhs.uk; 203 Station Road, Knowle, Solihull B93 0PU Tel: 0156 4 778964 Email: gibsonj@heartsol.wmids.nhs.uk — MB BS 1976 Lond.; MD Leic. 1987; FRCS Ed. 1981; FCOphth 1988. (St. Bart.) Cons. Ophth. Birm. Heartlands and Solihull NHS Trust & Birm. & Midl. Eye Centre, City Hosp. NHS Trust; Hon. Clin. Sen. Lect. Univ. Birm.; Vis. Lect. Aston Univ.; Director Research & Developm., Heartlands and Solihull NHS Trust. Socs: BMA; Counc. Mem. Roy. Coll. Ophth.s; Midl. Ophth. Soc. - Pres. Prev: Lect. & Sen. Regist. (Ophth.) Univ. Leicester; SHO & Regist. P.ss Alexandra Eye Pavil. Edin.; Ho. Surg. Roy. Infirm. Edin.

GIBSON, Julia Mary (retired) 3 Woodlands Park Drive, The Parklands, Blaydon-on-Tyne NE21 5PQ Tel: 0191 414 5441 Email: gibson@julton.demon.co.uk — MB BS Lond. 1964; MRCS Eng. LRCP Lond. 1964. Prev: GP Gateshead & S. Tyneside HA.

GIBSON, Kathryn 104 Fordwich Rise, Hertford SG14 2DE — MB BCh 1991 Wales.

GIBSON, Kirstie Ann Alison 18 Blackstone Hill, Redhill RH1 6BE Tel: 01737 767101 — MB BS 1988 Lond.; MSc Soton. 1994. (Guy's Hosp.) Clin. Serv. Manager BUPA Lond. Socs: Fell. Roy. Soc. Med. Prev: Clinc. Developm. Manager Norwich Union Healthcare; Trainee GP Bournemouth; SHO (A & E) St. Helier Hosp.

GIBSON, Lorna Margaret 1 Holly Avenue, Stenhousemuir, Larbert FK5 4DN — MB ChB 1998 Glas.; MB ChB Glas 1998.

GIBSON, Margaret Gault 9 Green Lane, Liverpool L18 6HA Tel: 0151 724 1303 — MB BCh BAO 1942 Belf. (Belf.)

GIBSON, Margaret Hunter Hayes Barton, Totteridge Lane, London N20 — MB ChB 1963 Ed.; DCH RCPS Glas. 1965. Prev: Ho. Phys. St. Stephen's Hosp. Chelsea; SHO Qu. Eliz. Hosp. Childr. Lond.; SHO (Paediat.) Roy. N.. Infirm. Inverness.

GIBSON, Mr Mark Frankland Accident & Emergency Department, York District Hospital, Wiggington Road, York YO31 8HE Tel: 01904 725616 Fax: 01904 454415 — MB ChB 1980 Manch.; FRCS Ed. 1984. Cons. A & E York Health Servs. Trust. Socs: Fell. Fac. Accid. & Emerg. Med. Prev: Sen. Regist. (A & E) Yorks. RHA; Clin. Tutor (A & E & Plastic Surg.) Leeds Univ.; Regist. Rotat. (Surg.) Roy. Hallamsh. Hosp. Sheff.

GIBSON, Mary The Gables, Rue de Causie, St Clement, Jersey JE2 6SQ Tel: 01534 52941 — MB ChB 1947 St. And. (St. And.) Prev: Med. Off. Freetown, Sierra Leone; Anaesth. Regist. Roy. Hants. Co. Hosp. Winchester; Cas. Off. Roy. Infirm. Dundee.

GIBSON, Mary Isobel (retired) 6 Maris Drive, Burton Joyce, Nottingham NG14 5AJ — MRCS Eng. LRCP Lond. 1933. Prev: Ho. Phys. Roy. Free Hosp.

GIBSON, Mary Teresa Royal Victoria Infirmary, Newcastle upon Tyne NE1 4LP Tel: 0191 285 5131; 36 High Street, Gosforth, Newcastle upon Tyne NE3 1LX Tel: 0191 285 2162 — MB BS 1966 Lond.; MRCP (UK) 1971; MRCS Eng. LRCP Lond. 1966; DCH Eng. 1969. (Guy's) Cons. Paediat. Child Developm. Roy. Vict. Infirm. Newc. Socs: Brit. Paediat. Assn. & Brit. Paediat. Neurol. Assn. Prev: Ho. Off. Hosp. Sick. Childr. Gt. Ormond St. Lond.; Regist. (Paediat.) Hammersmith Hosp. Lond.; Lect. Dept. Paediat. Guy's Hosp. Lond.

GIBSON, Matthew Robert Main X-ray Department, Royal Berkshire Hospital, London Road, Reading RG1 5AN Tel: 0118 987 8035 — BM BS 1986 Nottm.; BMedSci Nottm. 1984; MRCP (UK) 1989; FRCR 1994. Cons. Radiol. Roy. Berks. Hosp. NHS Trust. Prev: Sen. Regist. (Diag. Radiol.) St. Mary's Hosp. Lond.

GIBSON, Mr Michael John 4 Westfield Grove, Gosforth, Newcastle upon Tyne NE3 4YA — MB BS 1977 Lond.; FRCS Eng. 1982.

GIBSON, Nancy Elizabeth Penny Lane Surgery, 7 Smithdown Place, Liverpool L15 9EH Tel: 0151 733 2800 — MB BCh BAO 1974 Belf.

GIBSON, Neil Alexander Department of Respiratory Medicine, Royal Hospital for Sick Children, Glasgow G3 8SJ Tel: 0141 201 0035 Fax: 0141 201 0671 Email: neil.gibson@yorkhill.scot.nhs.uk; 24 Thorn Drive, Bearsden, Glasgow G61 4LT — MB ChB 1983 Ed.; MD Ed. 1995; MRCP (UK) 1986; FRCPCH 1997. (Ed.) Cons. Paediat. Respirat. Med. Roy. Hosp. Sick Childr. Glas.; Hon. Sen. Lect. Glas. Univ. Socs: Amer. Thoracic Soc.; Brit. Thorac. Soc.; Brit. Sleep Soc. Prev: Respirat. Fell. Perth, Austral.; Regist. (Paediat.) Roy. Vict. Infirm. Newc.; Research Regist. (Child Health) Leicester Roy. Infirm.

GIBSON, Nicholas Henry Bodriggy Health Centre, 60 Queens Way, Bodriggy, Hayle TR27 4PB Tel: 01736 753136 Fax: 01736 753467 — MB BS 1983 Lond.; MRCGP 1991. (Char. Cross Hosp. Med. Sch.)

GIBSON, Nicola Margaret Carmondean Medical Group, Carmondean Health Centre, Livingston EH54 8PY Tel: 01506 430031 Fax: 01506 432775 — MB ChB 1983 Dundee; Cert. Family Plann. JCC 1989; DRCOG 1989. Prev: SHO Tayside HB.

GIBSON, Patrick Howard Department of Renal Medicine, Royal Infirmary of Edinburgh, Lauriston Place, Edinburgh EH3 9YW Tel: 0131 229 2477; 50 The Causeway, Duddingston, Edinburgh EH15 3PZ Tel: 0131 661 5348 — MB ChB 1987 Leeds; MRCP Ed. 1991. Cons. Nephrologist, Renal Unit, Roy. Infirm., Edin.

GIBSON, Patrick Wilfred Flood and Partners, Essex House Surgery, Station Road, Barnes, London SW13 0LW Tel: 020 8876 1033 Fax: 020 8878 5894 — MB BS 1985 Lond.; MA Camb. 1985; MRCGP 1990; DRCOG 1990. Trainee GP Qu. Mary's Univ. Hosp., Lond. VTS.; Princip. Essex Hse. Barnes. Prev: Princ. Fairhill Med. Pract. Kingston upon Thames.

GIBSON, Paul Alexander Gerald Royal Lancaster Infirmary, Lancaster LA1 4RP Fax: 01524 583911 Email: paul gibson@l.bay-tr.nwest.nhs.uk — MB ChB 1981 Manch.; MRCP (UK) 1984; FRCPch. Cons. Paediat. Roy. Lancaster Infirm.

GIBSON, Paul Edward 79 Morshead Mansions, Morshead Road, Maida Vale, London W9 1LG Tel: 020 7266 2602; 34 Queens Walk, Kingsbury, London NW9 8ER Tel: 020 8200 4340 — MB BS 1990 Lond.; MRCP (UK) 1994; FRCR 1997. (Royal Free Hospital) Regist. (Radiol.) N.wick Pk. Hosp. Harrow. Prev: SHO & Regist. (Gen. Med.) Barnet Gen. Hosp.; SHO (Cas.) Watford Gen. Hosp.; SHO (Med.) W. Essex Health Auth.

GIBSON, Paul James 35A Calderstones Road, Liverpool L18 6HR Email: paulgibson@doctors.org.uk; 105 West Street, Harrow HA1 3ES — MB ChB 1993 Leeds; DCH 1997. GP Regist. Chalkhill Health Centre, Wembley. Socs: Med. Protec. Soc. Prev: SHO Paediat. Centr. Middl. Hosp.; SHO (c/o Elderly) Whipps Cross Hosp. Lond.; SHO (Genitourin. Med. & HIV) St. Bart. Hosp. Lond.

GIBSON, Paul John Department of Radiology, Grantham & Kesteven General Hospital, 101 Manthorne Road, Grantham NG31 8DG; Bayswater House, Main Road,, Long Bennington, Newark NG23 5DJ Tel: 01400 281693 — MB ChB 1984 Leic.; FRCR 1992. Cons. Diag. Radiol. Grantham & Kesteven Gen. Hosp. Prev: Sen. Regist. & Regist. (Diag. Radiol.) Leicester.

GIBSON, Penelope Jane Surrey Hampshire Borders NHS Trust, Jarvis Centre, 60 Stoughton Road, Guildford GU1 1LH Tel: 01483 783113 Fax: 01483 783199 — MB BS 1978 Lond.; MRCP (UK) 1980; FRCP Lond. 1997; FRCPCH. (St. Geo.) Cons. Community Paediat. Surrey Hants. Borders NHS Trust. Prev: Lect. (Community Child Health) St. Geo. Hosp. Med. Sch. Lond.; Sen. Regist. (Paediat.) Char. Cross Hosp. Lond. & Kingston Hosp. Surrey; Lect. (Child Health) St. Geo. Hosp. Med. Sch. Lond.

GIBSON, Peter David Department of Medicine for the Elderly, North Manchester General Hospital, Crumpsall, Manchester M8 5RB Tel: 0161 795 4567 — MB ChB 1985 Manch.; MRCP (UK) 1990. Cons. Phys. Med. N. Manch. Gen. Hosp. Socs: Brit. Geriat. Soc.

GIBSON, Mr Peter Hugh 316 Queen's Road, Aberdeen AB15 8DT — MB ChB 1971 Liverp.; FRCS Eng. 1978; FRCS Ed. 1977. Cons. Orthop. Surg. Aberd. Roy. Infirm. Prev: Surg. Cdr. RN; Sen. Regist. Nuffield Orthop. Centre & Accid. Serv. John Radcliffe; Hosp. Oxf.

GIBSON, Peter Lindsay The Smethwick Medical Centre, Regent Street, Smethwick, Warley B66 3BQ Tel: 0121 558 0105 Fax: 0121 555 7206; 435 Hagley Road W., Quinton, Birmingham B32 2AD Tel: 0121 423 1205 Fax: 0121 423 2757 — MB ChB 1978 Birm.; DRCOG 1980.

GIBSON, Philip Ronald Hopkin 30 Garfield Avenue, Litchard, Bridgend CF31 1QA — MB BCh 1974 Wales; DObst RCOG 1976.

GIBSON, Ridley Morven, Blackhall, Hartlepool TS27 4LQ Tel: 0191 586 4331 — MB BS 1956 Durh. Socs: BMA. Prev: Ho. Surg. Sunderland Matern. Hosp.; Ho. Phys. Sunderland Roy. Infirm.

GIBSON, Mr Robert 12 Harberton Drive, Belfast BT9 6PF Tel: 01232 665418 — MB BCh BAO 1957 Belf.; FRCS Eng. 1964; FRCS Ed. 1962. (Belf.) Cons. Otolaryngol. Roy. Vict. Hosp. Belf. Socs: Assn. Head & Neck Oncol.; Roy. Soc. Med. Prev: Ho. Surg. & Regist. (ENT Surg.) Roy. Vict. Hosp. Belf.; Fell. (Otolaryngol.) Washington Univ. St. Louis, USA.; Chair. Med. Staff, Roy. Vic. Hosp.

GIBSON, Mr Robert Andrew Hele Cottage, 3 Old Torrington Road, Sticklepath, Barnstaple EX31 2DD Tel: 01271 371006; Hele Cottage, 3 Old Torrington Road, Sticklepath, Barnstaple EX31 2DD Tel: 01271 371006 — BM BCh 1972 Oxf.; MA Oxf. 1972; FRCS Ed. 1978; FRCOphth 1989; DO RCS Eng. 1977. (Oxford) Cons. Ophth. N. Devon Dist. Hosp. Barnstaple. Prev: Sen. Regist. Bristol Eye Infirm.

GIBSON, Robert Ernest Craig (retired) The Croft, 18 High Seaton, Workington CA14 1PD Tel: 01900 603275 — MB ChB 1950 Glas.; FFA RCS Eng. 1961. Prev: Cons. Anaesth. W. Cumbld. Hosp. Gp.

GIBSON, Mr Robert Myles, OBE, ERD, TD, CStJ 27 Clarendon Road, Leeds LS2 9NZ Tel: 0113 243 0822 Fax: 0113 243 1186; 152 Harley Street, London W1N 1HH — MB ChB 1949 Glas.; 2000 F.I.M.C. Ed.; Dip. Sports Med. 1996; Dip. IMC RCS Ed. 1994; FFAEM 1993; FRCS Eng. 1968; FRCS Ed. 1956; MD (Commend.) Glas. 1952; MSc McGill 1951. (Glas.) Cons. Neurosurg. Gen. Infirm. Leeds, Leeds (St. Jas.) Univ. Hosp. & King Edwd VII Hosp; Sen. Lect. (Neurosurg.) Univ. Leeds; Hon. Cons. Neurosurg. to Army; Hon. Cons. Football League FA; Surg. Specialist RAMC TAVR OC Mobile Neurosurg. Units; Mem. Armed Forces Med. Advis. Bd.; Dep. Chairm. Centr. Comm. for Hosp. Med. Servs.; Chairm. Fac. Pre Hosp. Care RCS Ed. & Vice-Pres. RCS Ed. Socs: Pres. Milit. Surg. Soc.; Chairm. Fac. Pre-Hosp. Care R.C.S. Edin.; Coun. Mem. Soc. Brit. NeUrol. Surg.s. Prev: Glas. Univ. Schol. to McGill Univ.. Montreal 1950-1; Ho. Phys. Roy. Infirm. Glas.; Ho. Surg. W.. Infirm. Glas.

GIBSON, Robin Gordon Dun Aluinn, 354 Albert Drive, Glasgow G41 5PJ Tel: 0141 427 1505 — MB ChB Glas. 1960; BDS Ed. 1955; FRCP Glas. 1982, M 1965; LMSSA Lond. 1960; FFHom 1969; DCH RCPS Glas. 1962. (Glas.) p/t Indep. Cons. Phys. (Homoeop. Med.) Glas. Socs: Brit. Soc. Sport & Med.; Brit. Soc. Med. & Dent. Hypn.; Fell.Fac of Homeopathy. Prev: Cons. Med. Homoeop. Hosp. Glas.; Regist. (Immunol.) W.. Infirm. Glas.; Regist. (Infec. Dis.) Belvidere Hosp. Glas.

GIBSON, Roderick John 4 Fair-A-Far Shot, Whitehouse Road, Cramond, Edinburgh EH4 6LD — MB ChB 1982 Ed.; MRCP (UK) 1985; FRCR 1989; T(R)(CR) 1992. Cons. (Neuroradiol.) W.. Gen. Hosp. Socs: Fell. Roy. Coll. Radiol.

GIBSON, Roger James 9 Queens Gate Villas, Victoria Park Road, London E9 7BU — MB BS 1994 Lond.

GIBSON, Ruth Brodie (retired) 43 Ridgewood Drive, Harpenden AL5 3LJ Tel: 01582 761005 Fax: 01582 761005 — MB ChB Glas. 1949; DO Eng. 1955. SCMO Beds. AHA. Prev: SCMO Luton & Dunstable Hosp.

GIBSON, Samuel Strachan (retired) The Close, 385 Barnsley Road, Sandal, Wakefield WF2 6BA Tel: 01924 256279 — MB ChB 1956 Ed. Civil. Med. Pract. Territorial Army.

GIBSON, Sean Fearon Albert Street Health Centre, Ross Road, Belfast BT12 4AT Tel: 028 225185 — MD 1962 Belf.; MB BCh BAO 1948. (Belf.)

GIBSON, Sheila Lilian Marjory Glasgow Homoeopathic Hospital, 1000 Great Western Road, Glasgow G12 0NR Tel: 0141 211 1609 Fax: 0141 211 1610; Dun Aluinn, 354 Albert Drive, Glasgow G41 5PJ Tel: 0141 427 1505 Fax: 0141 427 1505 — MB ChB (Hons.) Glas. 1965; BSc (Hons.) Glas. 1959, MD 1969. (University of Glasgow) Research Co-Ordinator (Clin. Pharmacognosy) Glas. Homoeop. Hosp. Prev: Lect. (Med. Genetics) Univ. Glas.; Mem. Genetical Soc. & Roy. M-C Soc. Glas.

GIBSON, Sheila Mary Red Lion Cottage, 228 High Road, Chilwell, Nottingham NG9 5DB — BM BS 1977 Nottm.; MRCPsych 1981.

GIBSON, Shirley Jean 2 Pinewood Road, Aberdeen AB15 8NA — MB ChB 1982 Aberd.; MRCGP 1986.

GIBSON, Simon Peter 124 St Michael's Road, Great Cosby, Liverpool L23 7UW — MB ChB 1981 Sheff.

GIBSON, Stella Elizabeth Grace 35 Stanely Avenue, Paisley PA2 9LE — MB ChB 1954 Glas.; MA Glas. 1949; MFCM 1972; DPH Glas. 1959. (Glas.) Prev: Cons. Pub. Health Med. Argyll & Clyde HB; Dep. MOH Paisley & Clydebank.

GIBSON, Stephen Harvey Church Street Surgery, St Mary's Courtyard, Church Street, Ware SG12 9EG Tel: 01920 468941 Fax: 01920 465531 — MB BS 1977 Lond.; MA Camb.; MRCGP 1983; Cert. Av. Med. 1990; DRCOG 1981. (Univ. Coll. Hosp.) Med. Computing & Occupat. Med. Adviser. Socs: Brit. Computer Soc.; BMA (E. Herts. Div.); Soc. Occupat. Med. Prev: GP Trainer Qu. Eliz. II Hosp. Herts.; Herts. MAAG Audit Facililator; Herts. Police Staff Surg.

GIBSON, Suzy Montgomerie 2 Townend Terrace, Symington, Kilmarnock KA1 5QH Tel: 01563 830295 — MB ChB 1994 Aberd.; MRCS (Glasgow) 1999. (Aberdeen University)

GIBSON, Terence James 60B Copers Cope Road, Beckenham BR3 1RJ Tel: 020 8650 9884 — MD 1966 Lond.; MD Lond. 1980 MB BS 1966; FRCP 1982, M 1969; MRCS Eng. LRCP Lond. 1966. (Guy's) Cons. Rheum. Guy's Hosp. Lond. Prev: Sen. Regist. Rheum. Guy's Hosp. Lond.

GIBSON, (Terence) Michael, OStJ, Group Capt. RAF Med. Br. 22 Queen Anne's Gate, Caversham, Reading RG4 5DU Tel: 01734

483250 — MB ChB 1970 Aberd.; PhD Surrey 1977; MFOM RCP Lond. 1980; DAvMed. 1982. Sen. Med. Off. RAF Med. Br.; Cons. Occupat. Med. RAF. Socs: BMA & Soc. Occupat. Med. Prev: Cons. Aviat. Med. RAF Med. Br.; Ho. Phys. & Ho. Surg. Stratford-upon-Avon Hosp.

GIBSON, Thomas (retired) 163 High Street, Harston, Cambridge CB2 5QD — MRCS Eng. LRCP Lond. 1953; DPH Lond. 1960. Prev: Dep. Dir. (Cons.) Regional Transfus. & Immuno-Haemat. Centre Camb.

GIBSON, Thomas Campsie c/o Knox, 5 Tower Avenue, Upton, Pontefract WF9 1ED — MB ChB 1977 Ed.

GIBSON, Thomas Stanley (retired) Penrhiw Farm, Llanfynydd, Wrexham LL11 5HL — MB BCh BAO 1948 Belf. Prev: Res. Med. Off. & Res. Surg. Off. Belf. City Hosp.

GIBSON, Thomas Walter (retired) High Barn, Bog Lane, Stirton, Skipton BD23 3LQ Tel: 01756 795578 — MB CAmb. 1959, BChir 1958; MA Camb. 1966; DObst RCOG 1962. Assoc. Dir Airdale NHS Trust. Prev: GP Skipton.

GIBSON, William John Alexander (retired) 19 Rosamunde Pilcher Drive, Longforgan, Dundee DD2 5EF — MB ChB 1960 Glas.; FRCR 1993; DMRD Eng. 1964. Cons. Radiol. with Admin. Responsibil. Angus Unit Stracathro Hosp. Brechin Tayside HB; Hon. Sen. Lect. Univ. Dundee.

GIBSON, William Martin (retired) Birdlip Cottage, Mutton Hall Hill, Heathfield TN21 8NB Tel: 01435 864088 — BM BCh 1938 Oxf.; MA, BM BCh Oxf. 1938. Prev: Ho. Surg. & Cas. Off. St. Geo. Hosp.

GIBSON, Yvonne Agnes Beryl (retired) Pen Rhiw Farm, Llanfynydd, Wrexham LL11 5HL — MB BCh BAO 1949 Belf. Prev: Res. Med. Off. & Res. Surg. Off. Roy. Vict. Hosp. Belf.

GIBSON-GLUBB, Sharon Margaret 25 Upper Maze Hill, St Leonards-on-Sea TN38 0LB; St. Wilfrids Hospice, Millgap Road, Eastbourne BN21 2HS Tel: 01323 644500 Fax: 01323 450487 — MRCS Eng. LRCP Lond. 1966; MPH Amer. Univ. Beirut 1972; Dip. Palliat. Med. Wales 1992. (Guy's) Med. Dir.St Wilfrids Hospice E.bourne. Socs: BMA & Assn. Palliat. Med. Prev: GP Lond.; Sen. Regist. (Med.) Al Qassimi Hosp. Sharjah, UAE; Gen. Phys. MoD Hosp. Jeddah, Saudi Arabia.

GIBSON-SMITH, Barry Kirk 5 Lorraine Gardens, Glasgow G12 9NY — MB ChB 1994 Glas.; BSc (Immunol.) Glas. 1992. SHO (Infec. Dis.) Ruchill Hosp. Glas. Prev: SHO (Med.) Roy. Alexandra Hosp. Paisley; SHO & Ho. Off. (Med.) Gartnavel Gen. Hosp. Glas.; Ho. Off. (Surg.) S.. Gen. Hosp. Glas.

GIBSON-SMITH, Sarah Lansdowne, Whitelane, Guildford GU4 8PR — MB BS 1998 Lond.; MB BS Lond 1998.

GIBSON-SMITH, Susan Maryhill Health Centre, 41 Shawpark Street, Glasgow G20 9DR Tel: 0141 531 8800 Fax: 0141 531 8851; 5 Lorraine Gardens, Glasgow G12 9NY — MB ChB 1992 Glas.; MRCGP 1996; DRCOG 1995. Prev: Trainee GP Glas.; SHO (Paediat.) Yorkhill Hosp. Glas.; SHO (O & G) S.. Gen. Hosp. Glas.

GIDDEN, Mr David John Department of Orthopaedics and Trauma, Northampton General Hospital, Weston Favell, Northampton NN1 5BD Tel: 01604 544639 — MB ChB 1987 Dundee; 1999 FRCS (Tr. & Orth.); MSc Biomed. Engin. Sci. Dundee 1993; FRCS Ed. 1993. Cons. Orthopaedic and Trauma Surg. Socs: BOA; BSSM.

GIDDEN, Fiona Alice The Grange Cottage, 105 High Street, Weston Favell NN 3JX Tel: 01604 403714 Email: fgidden@aol.com — MB ChB 1989 Dundee; MRCPath 2001; PhD Lond. 1982, BSc 1976; Dip RCPath 1998. Prev: Regist (chem.path) Roy. Liverp. Hosp..Liverp.; Regist. (Chem. Path.) Ninewells Hosp. & Med. Sch. Dundee.

GIDDENS, Joanne Elizabeth 15 Captains Row, Portsmouth PO1 2TT Tel: 023 92 431570; The Surgery, Salisbury Road, Southsea PO4 9QX Tel: 023 92 731458 — BM 1992 Soton.; MRCGP 1996; DRCOG 1995. (Soton.)

GIDDINGS, Mr Anthony Edward Buckland 6 Fairway, Guildford GU1 2XG Tel: 01483 561826 Email: aebgiddings@compuserve.com — MD Bristol 1978, MB ChB 1966; MRCS Eng. LRCP Lond. 1966; FRCS Eng. 1971; FRCS 1999. (Bristol) Cons. Gen. & Vasc. Surg. King's Coll., Guy's & St. Thomas' Hosps., Lond.; Chairm. SAC in Gen Surg 1998; Chairm. Federat. of Surg Spec. Assoc 1998. Socs: Roy. Soc. Med. (Ex-Pres. Surgic. Sect.); Assoc. of Surg. GB & Irel. Pres. 1996; James IV Assoc. of Surg. Inc. Director 1998. Prev: Cons. Gen. & Vasc. Surg. Roy. Surrey Co. Hosp. Guildford; Sen. Regist. Gen. Surg. Roy. Infirm. Bristol; Lect. Surg. Univ. Sheff.

GIDDINGS, Mr Peter 1 Goodrest Croft, Yardley Wood, Birmingham B14 4JU Tel: 0121 474 2059 — MB BS 1980 Bristol; MB BS (Hons. Clin. Pharm. & Therap.) Bristol 1984; BSc (Hons.) Lond. 1980; FRCS Ed. 1989; MRCGP 1990. (Westm.) p/t Hon. Clin. Lect. Dept. Gen. Pract. Univ. Birm. Prev: Regist. (Orthop. Surg.) E. Birm. Hosp.; Regist. (Urol.) E. Birm. Hosp.; SHO (A & E Med.) Qu. Med. Centre Nottm.

GIDDINS, Alan Grey (retired) Blacknest Hall, 18 Grand Avenue, Worthing BN11 5AG Tel: 01903 202965 — MB BS 1955 Lond.; MRCP Lond. 1959; MRCS Eng. LRCP Lond. 1955; DMRD Eng. 1959, DCH 1957. Prev: Cons. Radiol. Worthing Hosp.

GIDDINS, Esther Ann Blacknest Hall, 18 Grand Avenue, Worthing BN11 5 Tel: 01903 202965 — MB BS 1955 Lond.; LLM Wales 1995; MRCS Eng. LRCP Lond. 1955; DObst RCOG 1957. (Roy. Free Hosp.) Edith Pechey Phipson Postgrad. Schol. 1958; Doctor Benefits Agency; DAT Tribunal Mem. Socs: Med. Wom. Federat.; BMA; Roy. Soc. Med. Prev: Regist. (Plastic Surg.) Lond. Hosp.; Jun. Cas. Off. Roy. Free Hosp.; Ho. Surg. Plastic Unit Qu. Vict. Hosp. E. Grinstead.

GIDDINS, Mr Grey Edward Bence Royal United Hospital, Combe Park, Bath BA1 3NG Tel: 01225 824456; The Hayes, Newton St. Loe, Bath BA2 9BU Tel: 01225 873592 — MB BChir 1986 Camb.; BA Camb. 1982; FRCS (Orth.) 1992; FRCS Eng. 1989; FRCS Ed. 1989; Europ. Dip. Hand Surg. (Cambridge and St. Thomas's) Cons. Orthop. & Hand Surg. Roy. United Hosp. Bath; Cons. Orthopaedist & Hand Surg. Roy. Nat. Hosp. Rheumatoid Dis. in Bath; Hon. Sen. Lect. Univ. of Bath. Prev: Hand. Fell. Oxf. & Wexham Pk. Hosps.; Sen. Regist. (Orthop.) Roy. Nat. Orthop. Hosp. Stanmore; Regist. (Orthop.) John Radcliffe Hosp. & Nuffield Orthop. Centre Oxf.

GIDDINS, Jane Clare 112 Cator Lane, Chilwell, Nottingham NG9 4BB; Dr Bridgewater and Partners, The Valley Surgery, 81 Bramcote Lane, Chilwell, Nottingham NG9 4ET — BM BS 1991 Nottm.; DRCOG 1995. p/t GP Retainee Chilwell Nottm. Prev: Asst. GP Derby.

GIDLOW, David Arthur 253 Pensby Road, Heswall, Wirral CH61 5UA Tel: 0151 342 6876 Fax: 0151 342 3392 — MB ChB 1973 Liverp.; FFOM RCP Lond. 1992, MFOM 1983; DIH Eng. 1979. Managing Dir Health in Business LTD Ellesmere Port. Socs: Soc. Occupat. Med.

GIDWANI, Fatehchand Nanikram 14 Queen Edith's Way, Cambridge CB1 7PN Tel: 01223 212476 — MB BS 1953 Bombay; FRCR 1975; FFR 1970; DMRD Eng. 1967; DMRT Eng. 1966. (Grant Med. Coll.) Cons. Radiol. Lister Hosp. Stevenage.

GIENCKE, Kai 10 Carloway Avenue, Fulwood, Preston PR2 9PN — State Exam Med 1992 Kiel.

GIETZEN, Timothy William Seaside Medical Centre, 18 Sheen Road, Eastbourne BN22 8DR Tel: 01323 725667 Fax: 01323 417169; 42 Baldwin Avenue, Eastbourne BN21 1UP Tel: 01323 20549 — MB ChB 1984 Sheff.; MB ChB Sheff. l984; MRCGP 1988. GP E.bourne.

GIFFIN, Nicola Jane 19 Burntwood Road, Sevenoaks TN13 1PS — MB BS 1991 Lond.

GIFFORD, Clive Stanley Edward (retired) 40 Castlemaine Avenue, South Croydon CR2 7HR Tel: 020 8688 9637 — MRCS Eng. LRCP Lond. 1942. Prev: SHO (Surg.) P. of Wales Gen. Hosp. Tottenham.

GIFFORD, Joanne 51 Radernie Place, St Andrews KY16 8QR — MB ChB 1998 Aberd.; MB ChB Aberd 1998.

GIFFORD, Leonard Aitchison (retired) 4 Forth Vean, Godolphin Cross, Helston TR13 9RH — MB ChB 1940 Manch.; FFA RCS Eng. 1954; DA Eng. 1947. Prev: Sen. Cons. Anaesth. Ashton, Hyde & Glossop Hosp. Gp.

GIFFORD, Peter Walter Willison (retired) The Paddocks, Hengoed, Oswestry SY10 7ET Tel: 01691 659737 — MB ChB Birm. 1939; MRCS Eng. LRCP Lond. 1939. Prev: Dir. Stud. & Nurses Health Serv. Univ. Sheff. & United Sheff.Hosps.

GIGLI, Cristina c/o 97 Fairfield Road, Burgess Hill RH15 8NP — State DMS 1993 Ancona.

GIHOOLY, Thomas C Parkhead Health Centre, 101 Salamanca Street, Glasgow G31 5BA Tel: 0141 531 9060 Fax: 0141 531 9042 — MB ChB 1983 Glasgow; MB ChB 1983 Glasgow.

GIL CANDON, Rosario 5 Silverstone Close, Bicton Heath, Shrewsbury SY3 5JE — LMS 1993 Seville.

GIL OROZCO, Susana Maria Department of Sports Medicine, Mann Ward, The Royal London Hospital, Bancroft Road, London E1 4DG — LMS 1990 Basque Provinces.

GIL RIVAS, Sara 49 Ullswater Crescent, London SW15 3RG — MB BS 1993 Lond.

GIL-RODRIGUEZ, Juan Antonio 13 De Walden Street, London W1G 8RW Tel: 020 7486 2284 Fax: 020 7935 1649 — LMS Madrid 1957; LAH Dub. 1965; FFA RCS Eng. 1971; DA Eng. 1963. (Madrid) Hon. Cons. Anaesth. St. Mary's Hosp. Lond. Socs: Fell. Roy. Soc. Med. Prev: Sen. Regist. (Anaesth.) Lond. Hosp.; Wellcome Research Fell. in Anaesth. Dept. Anaesth. RCS Eng.; Regist. Anaesth. Regional Thoracic & Cardiac Surg.

GILANI, Muhammad Shah 55 Tamar Square, Woodford Green IG8 0EA — MB BS 1974 Punjab; MRCS Eng. LRCP Lond. 1984.

GILANI, Natasha Harewood, Wood Lane, Iver Heath, Iver SL0 0LG — MB BS 1997 Lond. SHO Paediat.

GILANI, Shamim Sadrudin Manji Knightswood House, Dragon Lane, Weybridge KT13 0NG Tel: 01932 858020 Fax: 01932 858071 Email: gilani.jamal@lineone.net — MB ChB 1975 Bristol; MSc (Nuclear Med.) Lond. 1996; MRCP (UK) 1978; MRCS Eng. LRCP Lond. 1974; FRCR 1982. Cons. Radiol. St Peters Hosp. Chertsey; BrE. Screening. W. of Lond. BrE. Screening Serv.s, Char. Cross Hosp.. Socs: FRCR; RCP; BrE. Gp. Prev: Cons. Radiol. Hillingdon Hosp.; Sen. Regist. (Radiol.) Hammersmith Hosp. Lond.; Regist. (Radiol.) Bristol Roy. Infirm.

GILANI, Mr Syed Ahmed Ali Hulton District Health Centre, Haysbrook Avenue, Worsley, Manchester M28 0AY Tel: 0161 790 3276 Fax: 0161 703 7948; 7 Victoria Road, Ellesmere Park, Eccles, Manchester M30 9HU Tel: 0161 789 2505 — MB BS 1956 Punjab; MB BS Punjab (Pakistan) 1956; FRCS Eng. 1967; MRCS Eng. LRCP Lond. 1968. (Nishter) Socs: Fell. Manch. Med. Soc.; BMA. Prev: Cons. Surg. Saudi Arabian Airlines Jeddah; Cons. Surg. Giad Hosp. Mecca, Saudi Arabia; Surg. Regist. Macclesfield Hosp. (Infirm. Br.).

GILANI, Syed Mujtaba Nawaz The Iver Health Centre, Trewarden Avenue, Iver Heath, Iver SL0 05B — MB BS 1963 Karachi.

GILBART, William Stephen Westway Surgery, 1 Wilson Road, Ely, Cardiff CF5 4LJ Tel: 029 2059 1729 Fax: 029 2059 9956; 1 Fairwater Avenue, Fairwater, Cardiff CF5 3AR Tel: 029 2056 7246 — MB BCh 1970 Wales. Socs: BMA & MDU.

GILBERT, Aaron 20 Highview Gardens, Finchley, London N3 3EX — MRCS Eng. LRCP Lond. 1940.

GILBERT, Angela Margaret The Wellcome Research Laboratories, Langley Court, Beckenham BR3 3BS Tel: 020 8658 2211 — MD 1986 Bristol; MB ChB 1978. Socs: Fac. Pharmaceut. Med.

GILBERT, Anne Elizabeth Brooklyn Medical Practice, 65 Mansfield Rd, Hewor DE75 7AL — MB BChir 1985 Camb.; DRCOG 1991; MRCGP 1996. (Camb.) p/t GP Princip. Nott. Prev: Trainee GP Long Eaton; Trainee GP Nottm.; SHO (Psychiat.) Mapperley Hosp. Nottm.

GILBERT, Basil, OBE, SBStJ (retired) 9 Hollywood, Stamford Road, Bowdon, Altrincham WA14 2LL Tel: 0161 928 2768 — MRCS Eng. LRCP Lond. 1952; FFPHM 1978, M 1974; DPH Manch. 1960. Prev: Dist. Med. Off. & Area Med. Off. Oldham HA.

GILBERT, Christopher Julian The Health Centre, Wroughton, Swindon SN4 9LW Tel: 01793 814570 — MB BS 1972 Newc.; MRCGP 1985.

GILBERT, Christopher Peter Swiftsden Farm Oast, Ticehurst Rd, Hurst Green, Etchingham TN19 7QT — MB BS 1997 Lond.

GILBERT, Christopher Roy Mill Road Surgery, 61 Mill Road, Mile End, Colchester CO4 5LE Tel: 01206 845900 Fax: 01206 844090 — MB BS 1973 Lond.; MRCS Eng. LRCP Lond. 1973; DRCOG 1977. (Guy's) Prescribing Lead Colchester PCG. Prev: Med. Off. BT Colchester; Occupat. Health Phys. New Possibilites Trust.

GILBERT, Clare Elizabeth Department of Preventive Ophthalmology, Institute of Ophthalmology, Bath St., London EC1V 9EL Tel: 020 7608 6900 Fax: 020 7250 3207 Email: clare.gilbert@ucl.ac.uk — MB ChB 1976 Bristol; MSc Epidemiol. Lond. 1995; MD Bristol 1995; FRCS (Ophth.) Eng. 1980; FRCOphth 1990. Sen. Research Fell. (Ophth); Med. Adviser Sight Savers InterNat. Prev: Research Fell. (Ophth.) Inst. Ophth. Lond.

GILBERT, David John Adshall Road Surgery, Adshall Road, Cheadle SK8 2JN; 10 Depleach Road, Cheadle SK8 1DZ — MB ChB 1979 Leeds; LLM 2001 Cardiff; MRCGP 1985; AFOM RCP Lond. 1992; Cert. Family Plann. 1986. Clin. Asst. (Cas. & Occupat. Health) Stockport Infirm.; Guandian Media Gp.; Corporate Med. Managem.; Anniva N. W. Bus Company. Socs: Manch. Medico-Legal Soc.; Soc. Occupat. Med.; Manch. Med. Soc.

GILBERT, Debra Jane Church Street Surgery, St Mary's Courtyard, Church Street, Ware SG12 9EG Tel: 01920 468941 Fax: 01920 465531 — MB BS 1983 Lond.; DFFP 1999; BSc (Hons.) Lond. 1980, MB BS 1983. (Middlx.) p/t Gen. Practitioner, Ch. St. Surg., Ware, Herts. Prev: Gen. Practitioner, Stanhope Surg., Waltham Cross.

GILBERT, Edgar Laurence, Wing Cdr. RAF Med. Br. Retd. Lodge Farm, Hopton, Hodnet, Market Drayton TF9 3LF — LMSSA 1948 Lond. (St. Mary's) Prev: Ho. Surg. ENT & Orthop. Dept. & Res. Anaesth. St. Mary's Hosp.

GILBERT, Professor Fiona Jane Lilian Sutton Building, University of Aberdeen, Foresterhill, Aberdeen AB25 2ZN Tel: 01224 559253 Fax: 01224 559718 Email: f.j.gilbert@abdn.ac.uk; 17 Rubislaw Den N., Aberdeen AB15 4AL Tel: 01224 314152 Fax: 01224 209691 — MB ChB 1978 Glas.; FRCP Ed. 1994; FRCP Glas. 1991; MRCP (UK) 1981; FRCR 1986; DMRD Aberd. 1984. (University of Glasgow) Prof. of Radiol., Univ. of Aberd.; Hon. Cons. Radiol., Aberd. Roy. Infirm. Socs: Fell. Roy. Coll. of Radiologists; Fell. Roy. Coll. of Phys.s & Surg.s of Glas.; Fell. Roy. Coll. of Phys.s of Edin.

GILBERT, Harold 5 Wentworth Grange, The Grove, Newcastle upon Tyne NE3 1NL Tel: 01632 852939 — MB BS 1943 Durh.; MRCS Eng. LRCP Lond. 1943. (Durh.) Prev: Clin. Asst. Matern. Dept. Newc. Gen. Hosp.; Ho. Surg. Roy. Vict. Infirm. Newc-on-Tyne; Capt. RAMC.

GILBERT, Mr Hugh William Department of Urology, Cheltenham General Hospital, Cheltenham GL52 7AN Tel: 01242 274271; 17 Christ Church Road, Cheltenham GL50 2NY Email: hugh.gilbert@egnhst.org.uk — MB BChir 1985 Camb.; FRCS Ed. 1989; FRCS Eng. 1989; FRCS (Urol.) 1995; MD 1995. Cons. Urol. Surg. Cheltenham Gen. & Glos. Roy. Hosp.

GILBERT, Irving 42 Links Avenue, Gidea Park, Romford RM2 6ND Tel: 01708 762535 — MRCS Eng. LRCP Lond. 1940; MD Lond. 1949, MB BS 1940; FRCP Lond. 1972, M 1948. (Lond. Hosp.) Prev: Cons. Phys. Basildon & Dist. Hosp., St. Andrews Hosp. Billericay & Orsett Hosp.

GILBERT, Ivan John Tall Trees Surgery, Rectory Road, Retford DN22 7AY Tel: 01777 701637 Fax: 01777 710619 — MB BChir 1975 Camb.; BA Camb. 1971, MA, MB 1975, BChir 1974; MRCS Eng. LRCP Lond. 1974; DRCOG 1977.

GILBERT, Jame Exeter & District Hospice, Dryden Road, Exeter EX2 5JJ Tel: 01392 402555 Fax: 01392 495981 Email: j.f.gilbert@exeter.co.uk — MB ChB 1983 Birm.; MRCP (UK) 1987; FRCP 1997. Cons. Palliat. Med. Roy. Devon & Exeter Hosp.; Med. Dir., Exeter & Dist. Hospice; Lect. (Palliat. Med.) Univ. Exeter 1992. Prev: Sen. Regist. Leics. Hospice; Regist. St. Gemma's Hospice Leeds; Epidemiol. MRC Epidemiol. Unit Cardiff.

GILBERT, James Strathloanhead, Avonbridge, Falkirk FK1 2JZ — MB ChB 1989 Aberd.

GILBERT, Jeffrey Hamilton 20B Mountstewart Road, Newtownards BT22 2AL; 22 Lutton Place (3F1), Edinburgh EH8 9PE Tel: 0131 668 2899 — MB BCh BAO 1986 Belf.

GILBERT, Jeremy Heathcote Fairfield Park Health Centre, Tyning Lane, Camden Road, Bath BA1 6EA Tel: 01225 331616 Fax: 01225 482932 — MB BS 1984 Lond.; DRCOG 1990; DCH RCP Lond. 1989; MRCGP 1991. GP Princip. Fairfield Pk. Health Centre Bath. Prev: SHO (O & G) Bedford Gen. Hosp.; SHO (Paediat.) Hillingdon Hosp. Lond.; SHO (Gen. Med.) Basingstoke Dist. Hosp.

GILBERT, Jill Katherine Mental Health Unit, Ards Hospital, Church St., Newtownards BT23 4AS Tel: 028 9151 0106 — MB BCh BAO 1977 Belf.; MRCPsych. 1982. Cons. Psychiat. Ards Hosp. Newtownards.

GILBERT, John Macclesfield District General Hospital, Victoria Road, Macclesfield SK10 3BL — MB BS 1978 Lond.; FRCP Lond. 1995; MRCP (UK) 1983; MRCS Eng. LRCP Lond. 1978. Cons. Paediat. Macclesfield Dist. Gen. Hosp. Chesh. Prev: Sen. Regist. (Paediat.) To Sheff. Hosps.

GILBERT, John Gardens Lane Health Centre, Gardens Lane, Conisborough, Doncaster DN12 3JW Tel: 01709 862150 Fax: 01709 868322; Pear Tree Lodge, The Wapping, Hooton Roberts, Rotherham S65 4PG Tel: 01709 850475 Fax: 01709 850475 Email: j.gilbert@doctors.org.uk — MB BS 1971 Kerala. (Trivandrum Med. Coll.) Socs: Fell. Roy. Soc. Med.

GILBERT, John Edward Gilbert and Partners, Cronehills Health Centre, Cronhills Walkway, West Bromwich B70 6TJ Tel: 0121 553 0287 Fax: 0121 580 1821; 63 Pear Tree Drive, Great Barr, Birmingham B43 6HT Tel: 0121 357 4327 Email: 113136.2462@compuserve.com — MB ChB 1974 Birm.; MRCGP 1989; D.Occ.Med. RCP Lond. 1995. Socs: Soc. Occupat. Med. Prev: SHO (Med.) E. Birm. Hosp.; SHO (Neurol.) Midl. Centre for Neurosurg. & Neurol. Smethwick; Ho. Surg. Dudley Rd. Hosp. Birm.

GILBERT, Mr Jonathan Michael Wexham Park Hospital, Slough SL2 4HL Tel: 01753 633000 Fax: 01753 633632; South Lodge Consulting, Wexham St, Wexham, Slough SL2 4HS Tel: 01753 516852 Fax: 01753 516275 — MB BS 1971 Lond.; MS Lond. 1984; FRCS Eng. 1977; MRCS Eng. LRCP Lond. 1971; DObst RCOG 1973. (Lond. Hosp.) Cons. Surg. Wexham Pk. Hosp. Slough. Socs: Coun. Mem. Roy. Soc. Med. (Sect. of ColoProctol.); BMA; Assn. Coloproctol. Prev: Sen. Regist. Rotat. (Gen. Surg.) W.m. Hosp. Lond.; Resid. Surgic. Off. St. Mark's Hosp. Lond.; Clin. Scientif. Off. MRC Clin. Research Centre Harrow.

GILBERT, Lynne Kathryn 41 St Michaels, Longtanton, Cambridge CB4 5BZ — MB BChir 1986 Camb.; PhD Bristol 1981; MA Camb. 1977; BA (Hons.) 1975; MFFP 1995; DRCOG 1991. Clin. Med. Off. (Family Plann. & Clin. Asst. (Genitourin. Med.) Camb.; Dir. Med. & Veterin. Studies Newnham Coll. Camb. Prev: SHO (O & G) Rosie Matern. Hosp. Camb.; Ho. Phys. Addenbrooke's Hosp. Camb.; Ho. Surg. Hinchingbrooke Hosp. Huntingdon.

GILBERT, Margaret Ruth 66 Leicester Road, Salford M7 4AR — MB ChB 1975 Leeds. (Leeds) Socs: BMA. Prev: GP Child Health Clinics Manch.

GILBERT, Marie Patricia (retired) 4 Churchfields, Welford on Avon, Stratford-upon-Avon CV37 8ES Tel: 01789 750426 — MB BS 1955 Lond.; MRCS Eng. LRCP Lond. 1955; FRCPCH 1997; DObst RCOG 1958. Prev: Hon. Vis. Sen. Lect. (Child Health) Warwick Univ.

GILBERT, Michael Alan (retired) Hadley, 9 Bassett Wood Drive, Southampton SO16 3PT Tel: 01703 769095 — MB ChB 1954 St. And.; DA Eng. 1958; MRCGP 1969. Prev: GP Soton.

GILBERT, Mr Michael Chaplain (retired) Quayside, 49 Northgate, Beccles NR34 9AU Tel: 01502 713036 — MB BS (Hons.) Lond. 1949; FRCS Eng. 1954; LMSSA Lond. 1949. Prev: Asst. Surg. LoW.oft & N. Suff. Hosp. & War Memor. Hosp. Beccles.

GILBERT, Michael Edward Johnson and Partners, Langley House, 27 West Street, Chichester PO19 1RW Tel: 01243 782266/782955 Fax: 01243 779188 — MB BS 1975 Lond.; BSc Lond. 1969; MRCP (UK) 1983; DRCOG 1984. Prev: Trainee GP W. Suff. VTS; Regist. (Med.) Newmarket Gen. Hosp.; Temp. Lect. Bland-Sutton Inst. Lond.

GILBERT, Michael John BG International Ltd, 100 Thames Valley Park Drive, Reading RG6 1PT Tel: 0118 929 3146 Fax: 0118 929 3140; 5 Hawkewood Road, Lower Sunbury, Sunbury-on-Thames TW16 6HL Tel: 01932 886491 — MB ChB 1959 Birm.; AFOM RCP Lond. 1982; DObst RCOG 1961. Chief Med. Adviser BG Internat. Ltd. Socs: Fell. Roy. Soc. of Med.; Soc. Occupat. Med. Prev: Chief Med. Off. Petroleum Dev., Oman; Med. Off. Brunei Shell Petroleum; Sen. Med. Adviser Shell Internat. Petroleum Co.

GILBERT, Nicholas James Heathville Road Surgery, 5 Heathville Road, Gloucester GL1 3DP Tel: 01452 528299 Fax: 01452 522959 — MB ChB 1985 Birm.; MRCGP 1990; DRCOG 1988. (Birm.) GP Glos.; Police Surg. Glos. Socs: BMA.

GILBERT, Penelope Stella Nailsea Family Practice, Tower House Medical Centre, Stockway South, Nailsea BS48 2XX Tel: 01275 866700 Fax: 01275 866711 — MB BS 1991 Lond.; BSc Lond. 1988; MRCGP 1996; DRCOG 1995; DFFP 1993. (Roy. Free Hosp. Lond.) GP Princip. Prev: GP Princip. Brislington, Bristol; GP Regist. Portishead, Bristol.

GILBERT, Peter Huw The Thorndike Centre, Longley Road, Rochester ME1 2TH Tel: 01634 817217; 8 Priestfields, Rochester ME1 3AG Tel: 01634 409353 — MB BCh 1982 Wales; DCH RCP Lond. 1989; DRCOG 1988. Socs: Roy. Coll. Gen. Pract.

GILBERT, Peter Norval (retired) The Fairway, Millbeck Green, Collingham, Wetherby LS22 5AJ — LDS Leeds 1960; BChD Leeds 1961.

GILBERT, Peter Sam Oxford Terrace Medical Group, 1 Oxford Terrace, Gateshead NE8 1RQ; 22 Denewell Avenue, Low Fell, Gateshead NE9 5HD — MB BChir 1974 Camb.; MA Camb. 1976; MRCGP 1979; DRCOG 1975.

GILBERT, Mr Philip Martin The Queen Victoria Hospital, Holtye Road, East Grinstead RH19 3DZ Tel: 01342 410210 Fax: 01342 317907; 2 Blubell Close, East Grinstead RH19 1RS Tel: 01342 315532 — MB BS 1977 Lond.; BDS Lond. 1968; FRCS (Plast) 1994; FRCS Ed. 1982; FDS RCS Eng. 1972. (St. Geo. Hosp. Lond.) Cons. Plastic Surg. Qu. Vict. Hosp. E. Grinstead. Socs: Brit. Assn. Plastic Surg.; Brit. Burns Assn.; BMA. Prev: Cons. Plastic Surg. St. John's Hosp. Livingston; Cons. Plastic Surg. Academisch Ziekenhuis Rotterdam, Netherlands; Sen. Regist. (Plastic Surg.) Qu. Vict. Hosp. E. Grinstead.

GILBERT, Rachel Frances 17 Woodbury Rise, Malvern WR14 1QZ — MB ChB 1995 Manch.

GILBERT, Ralph Kerr (retired) Garden Cottage, Belford Close, Sunderland SR2 7TY Tel: 0191 567 9008 — LRCPI & LM, LRSCI & LM 1956; LRCPI & LM, LRCSI & LM 1956; FDS RCS Eng. 1951; LDS RCS Ed. 1942. Postgrad. Dent. Tutor Univ. Newc. u. Tyne. Prev: Postgrad. Dent. Tutor Univ. Newc. u. Tyne.

GILBERT, Rebekah Joy 56 Sutton Street, Walkergate, Newcastle upon Tyne NE6 4RE — MB BS 1997 Newc.

GILBERT, Richard Frederick Tracey Gurney Surgery, 101-103 Magdalen Street, Norwich NR3 1LN Tel: 01603 448800; 53 The Avenues, Norwich NR2 3QR — MB BChir 1984 Camb.; PhD Camb. 1981, MA 1980; MRCGP 1989; DCH RCP Lond. 1987; DRCOG 1987. Hosp. Pract. (Respirat. Med.) Norf. & Norwich NHS Trust. Prev: Trainee GP Norwich VTS.

GILBERT, Robert Angus Fletcher (retired) 10 Arbuthnot Street, Camelon, Falkirk FK1 4BW Tel: 01324 20777 — MB ChB 1946 Ed.; Cert. Av Med. MoD (Air) & Civil; Aviat. Auth. 1975.

GILBERT, Mr Roger Gordon (retired) 1 Fisherman's Walk, Barrack Lane, Craigweil, Bognor Regis PO21 4BU Tel: 01243 262967 — MB BS 1932 Lond.; FRCS Eng. 1937; MRCS Eng. LRCP Lond. 1932; FRCGP 1978, M 1952. Prev: SHMO (Surg.) Leatherhead Hosp. Surrey.

GILBERT, Russell James Cross Hills Farm, Cross Hill Lane, Warmfield, Wakefield WF1 5TJ — MB ChB 1987 Leeds.

GILBERT, Ruth Elizabeth Centre for Paediatric Epidemiology & Prosthetics, Institute of Child Health, Guilford St., London WC1N 1EH Tel: 0207 242 9789 Email: r.gilbert@ich.vcl.ae.uk; 85 Mackenzie Road, London N7 8QY — MD 1993 Sheff.; FRCPCH 1998; MSc Epidemiol. Lond. 1992; MB ChB 1982; MRCP (UK) 1985. Sen. Lect. Clin. Epidemiol. Inst. Child Health Lond.; Hon. Cons. Gt. Ormond St. Hosp. Socs: BMA; Roy. Coll. of Paediat. & Child Health. Prev: Lect. (Paediat.) Bristol.

GILBERT, Stephen Samuel Queen Margaret Hospital, Whitefield Road, Dunfermline KY12 0SU — MB ChB 1985 Glas.; FRCA 1990. Cons. Anaesth. Qu. Margt. Hosp. Dunfermline.

GILBERT, Timothy James, Wing Cdr. RAF Med. Br. Monklands Hospital, Monkscourt Avenue, Airdrie ML6 0J Tel: 012236 748748 — MB BS 1985 Lond.; MRCP (UK) 1992. (St. Geo. Hosp. Lond.) Cons. (Cardiol. & Gen. Med.). Socs: Brit. Cardiac Soc.; Brit. Cardiac Interven. Prev: Cons. (cardiol&gen.med) Derriford Hosp. Plymouth; Sen. Regist (Gen. Med.) PeterBoro. Dist. Hosp.; Sen. Regist. (Cardiol.) John Radcliffe Hosp. Oxf.

GILBERTHORPE, Christopher Centre Surgery, Hinckley Health Centre, 27 Hill Street, Hinckley LE10 1DS Tel: 01455 632277 Fax: 01455 890635; 105 Main Street, Thornton, Coalville LE67 1AH Tel: 01530 230653 — MB ChB 1976 Bristol; DRCOG 1981; DCH Eng. 1980. (Bristol)

GILBERTHORPE, John Medical Defence Union, 192 Altrincham Road, Manchester M22 4RZ; 2 Laneside Farm House, Peaslows, Chapel en le Firth, High Peak SK23 0QX Tel: 01298 815263 — MB BChir 1972 Camb.; MA Camb. 1972; MRCGP 1975; DObst RCOG 1975; DCH Eng. 1974. (Camb. & St. Mary's) Medico-Legal Adviser MDU. Prev: GP Burton-on-Trent; Trainee GP Kings Lynn VTS; Ho. Surg. St. Mary's Hosp. Lond.

GILBERTSON, Alfred Anthony Francis 2 Longworth Way, Woolton Park, Liverpool L25 6JJ Tel: 0151 428 5745 — MB ChB Liverp. 1956; FFA RCS Eng. 1962. (Liverp.) Emerit. Cons. Roy. Liverp. Univ. Hosp.; Staff Anaesth. Montreal Gen. Hosp.; Vis. Prof. McGill Univ. Montreal. Socs: Fell. Roy. Soc. Med. (Regional Dean); Liverp. Med. Inst. (Vice Pres.). Prev: Cons. Anaesth. Roy. Liverp. Hosp.; Sen. Regist. (Anaesth.) United Liverp. Hosps.; Squadron Ldr. RAF Med. Br., Anaesth. Specialist.

GILBERTSON, Clive (retired) Chain Orchard, Chapel Lane, Abergavenny NP7 7BT Tel: 01873 853643 — MB BCh Wales 1955; FRCP Lond. 1979, M 1963. Prev: Regist. W.m. Hosp.

GILBERTSON, Michael Henry Marshall (retired) Rockbank, Broadford, Isle of Skye IV49 9AQ — BM BCh 1942 Oxf.; MA, BM BCh Oxf. 1942. Prev: Dep. Coroner Hitchin Dist.

GILBERTSON, Nicola Jane Royal Cornwall Hospital (Treliske), Truro TR1 3LJ Tel: 01872 74242 Fax: 01872 252017; Treskewis, Trewithen Moor, Stithians, Truro TR3 7DU — MB ChB 1981 Liverp.; FFGMS 1988; MRCP (UK) 1985. Cons. Paediat. Roy. Cornw. Hosps. Trust.; Clin. Dir. (Child Health). Prev: Sen. Regist. (Paediat.) Char. Cross Hosp. Lond.

GILBERTSON, Richard James Cancer Research Unit Medical School, University of Newcastle upon Tyne, Framlington Place, Newcastle upon Tyne NE2 4HH Tel: 0191 222 8221 Fax: 0191 222 7556 Email: r.j.gilbertson@newcastle.ac.uk — MB BS 1992 Newc.; BMedSc Newc. 1991, MB BS (Hons.) 1992; MRCP (UK) 1995; PhD (Newcastle) 1999. Med. Research Counc. (MRC) Clin. Scientist. Prev: UK MRC Clin. Train. Fell.; Specialist Regist. Paediat.

GILBERTSON, Robert Colin Verno House West, Lyndhurst Road, Highcliffe, Christchurch BH23 4SG Tel: 01425 275686 Email: bobgilb@globalmer.co.uk — MB BS 1966 Lond.; MRCS Eng. LRCP Lond. 1966; DA Eng. 1969; DObst RCOG 1968. (St. Bart.)

GILBEY, Andrew Graham Gilbey, 4 Gwilym Road, Cwmllynfell, Swansea SA9 2CH Tel: 01639 844738; 52 Gurnos Road, Ystalyfera, Swansea SA9 2HY Tel: 01639 844738 — MB BS 1982 Lond.; DLO RCS Eng. 1984. (Middlx.)

GILBEY, Jane Elizabeth Manston Surgery, 72-76 Austhorpe Road, Leeds LS15 8DZ Tel: 0113 264 5455 Fax: 0113 232 6181; Birch Rose Allod Surgeryilla, 2E Lidgett Park Road, Leeds LS81 1EQ — MB ChB 1978 Birm.; MRCGP 1982; DRCOG 1980.

GILBEY, Stephen George Birch Villa, 2E Lidgett Park Road, Leeds LS8 1EQ Tel: 0113 206 5064 Fax: 0113 216 6244 Email: stephen.gilbey@gw.sjsuh-northy.nhs.uk — MB ChB 1981 Birm.; BA Oxf. 1975; MD Birm. 1989; FRCP 1997; MRCP (UK) 1984. Cons. Phys. St. Jas. Univ. Hosp. Leeds. Prev: Sen. Regist. (Med.) Hammersmith Hosp. Lond.; Research Fell. Diabetic Dept. King's Coll. Hosp. Lond.; SHO (Med.) Selly Oak Hosp. Birm.

GILBODY, John Stephen P.O.Box 7210, Hook RG27 9GE Tel: 01256 764944 Fax: 01256 760100 Email: john@johngilbody.com — MB BS 1992 Lond.; BSc Pharmacol. & Toxiocol. (1st Cl. Hons.) Lond. 1989. (UMDS London) Sen. Med. Advisor Wyeth Laboratories, Taplow. Socs: BMA; MDU; Brit. Assn. Pharmaceut. Phys. Prev: Med. Advisor Procter & Gamble Ltd. Staines; Sen. Med. Adviser Solvey Healthcare, S.ampton.

GILBODY, Julian Northampton General Hospital, Northampton NN1 5BD Tel: 01604 634100; 99 Twickenham Road, Newton Abbot TQ12 4JG Tel: 01626 367273 — MB BS 1997 Lond.; BSc Lond. 1994, MB BS 1997. (Roy. Free Hosp.) SHO Basic Surgic. Train. Rotat. N.ampton Gen. Hosp. N.ampton. Prev: Princip. Ho. Off. (Surg.) Lister Hosp. Stevenage.

GILBODY, Mary Spencer (retired) 53 Kenilworth Road, Sale M33 5DU Tel: 0161 973 5875 — MB BCh BAO Belf. 1952; FFCM RCP (UK) 1983, M 1972; DPH Manch. 1956. DMO Trafford Health Auth. Prev: SCM (Child Health) Trafford AHA.

GILBODY, Simon Martin Academic Unit of Psychiatry, 15 Hyde Terrace, University of Leeds, Leeds LS2 GLT Email: s.m.gilbody@leeds.ac.uk — MB ChB 1991 Leeds; MMedSci. (Clin. Psychiat.) Leeds 1996, BSc (Hons.) Psychol. 1989; MRCPsych 1995. Lect. in Psychaitry; Hon. Sen. Regist. (Psychiat.) Yorks. Deanery. Prev: Regist. Rotat. (Psychiat.) Leeds; Tutor (Psychiat.) Univ. Leeds; MRC Special Train. Fell. NHS Centre for Reviews & Dissemination Univ. York.

GILBY, Edward Daniel (cons. rooms) Longwood House, The Bath Clinic, Claverton Down Road, Bath BA2 7BR Tel: 01225 835555; Stillmeadow, 18 Bradford Road, Winsley, Bradford-on-Avon BA15 2HW Tel: 01225 722119 — MRCS Eng. LRCP Lond. 1965; MSc (Biochem.) Lond. 1975, MB BS 1965; FRCP Lond. 1984, M 1969. (Univ. Coll. Hosp.) Cons. Phys. Oncol. Roy. United Hosp. Bath. Prev: Research Fell. (Hon. Sen. Regist.) Roy. Marsden Hosp. Sutton; Research Fell. (Hon. Sen. Regist.) St. Thos. Hosp. Lond.

GILBY, Elizabeth Maria Lister Hospital, Coreys Mill Lane, Stevenage SG1 4AB Tel: 01438 314333; 66 Whitley House, Churchill Gardens, London SW1V 3BJ — MB BS 1992 Newc.; FRCS Eng. 1996. (Newc.) SHO Anaesth. Lister Hosp. Herts. Socs: BMA; Wom. Surgic. Train.

GILBY, John Arthur Brook Medical Centre, 98 Chell Heath Road, Bradeley, Stoke-on-Trent ST6 6PD Tel: 01782 838355 Fax: 01782 836245; 77 Woodhall Road, Rookery, Stoke-on-Trent ST7 4QY Tel: 01538 775918 — MB ChB 1984 Manch.; MB ChB Manch. l984. GP Stoke-on-Trent; Clin. Asst. (Cas.) Leighton Hosp. Crewe.

GILCHRIST, Alison Mary Gospatric Cottage, Dalmeny, South Queensferry EH30 9TT — MB BCh BAO 1980 Belf.; FRCR 1985.

GILCHRIST, Andrew Martin 23 Spinney Hill, Melbourne, Derby DE73 1GT — MB ChB 1994 Sheff.

GILCHRIST, Anne Carol Young Peoples Department, Royal Cornhill Hospital, Aberdeen AB25 2ZH Tel: 01224 557317 Fax: 01224 840691 Email: anne.gilchrist@gpct.grampian.scot.nhs.uk — MB ChB 1981 Aberd.; MSc Manch. 1991; MRCPsych 1987. p/t Cons. Adolesc. Psychiat. Grampian Primary Healthcare Trust Aberd.; Hon. Sen. Lect. (Psych.) Aberd. Univ. Prev: Cons. (Child & Adolesc. Psychiat.) Ment. Health Servs. of Salford; Tutor (Child & Adolesc. Psychiat.) Univ. Manch.

GILCHRIST, Audrey Portglenone Road Surgery, 23 Portglenone Road, Ahoghill, Ballymena BT42 1LE Tel: 028 2587 1200 Fax: 028 2587 8628 — MB BCh BAO 1983; DRCOG 1987; DMH Belf. 1989; DCH Dub. 1989. Trainee GP Ahoghill Ballymena VTS. Prev: SHO (O & G) Waveney Hosp. Ballymena; SHO (Paediat.) Waveney Hosp. Ballymena; SHO (Psychiat.) Holywell Hosp. Antrim.

GILCHRIST, Caroline-Anne Marion 47 Polnoon Street, Eaglesham, Glasgow G76 0BB — MB ChB 1994 Glas.

GILCHRIST, Caroline Margaret Priory View Medical Centre, 2A Green Lane, Leeds LS12 1HU Fax: 01422 345851 — MB ChB 1978 Dundee.

GILCHRIST, Ceilidh Rhona 63 Millbrae Road, Glasgow G42 9UT — MB ChB 1996 Glas.

GILCHRIST, David Thomas (retired) 1 Cedar Court, The Gables, Fairoak Lane, Oxshott, Leatherhead KT22 0SD Tel: 01372 844055 — MB BCh BAO; MD Belf. 1952, MB BCh BAO 1945; FFA RCS Eng. 1955; DA Eng. 1946; MD 1952 Belf. Prev: Cons. Anaesth. Qu. Mary's Hosp. Roehampton.

GILCHRIST, Edith (retired) 95 Hillway, Highgate, London N6 6AB Tel: 020 8348 2606 — MB BS 1938 Lond.; FRCA RCS Eng. 1953; DA Eng. 1942. Hon. Archiv. Roy. Free Hosp. Lond. Prev: Cons. Anaesth. Roy. Free Hosp. Lond. & Hampstead Gen. Hosp.

GILCHRIST, Frances Catherine 11 Kilkie Street, Fulham, London SW6 2SH — MB BS 1992 Lond.; MRCP (UK) 1995. (UCH) Hon. Regist. (Respirat. Med.) Roy. Brompton Hosp. Lond.

GILCHRIST, Helen The Spinney, Gwaelodygarth Close, Merthyr Tydfil CF47 8DX — MB BS 1997 Lond.

GILCHRIST, Iain Cameron The Surgery, Broomfields, Hatfield Heath, Bishop's Stortford CM22 7EH Tel: 01279 730616 Fax: 01279 730408 — MB ChB 1968 Glas.; MRCGP 1972; DObst RCOG 1970. (Glas.) Socs: (Hon. Treas.) Primary Care Rheum. Soc. Prev: Lect. (Gen. Pract.) Univ. Manch.; SHO S.. Gen. Hosp. Glas.; Ho. Off. (O & G) Redlands Hosp. Wom. Glas.

GILCHRIST, Ian Neilson Townhead Health Centre, 16 Alexandra Parade, Glasgow G31 2ES Tel: 0141 531 8945 Fax: 0141 531 8935; 20 Sutherland Avenue, Glasgow G41 4JH Tel: 0141 427 4775 — MB ChB 1960 Glas.

GILCHRIST, Ian Robert Jubilee Medical Centre, 52 Croxteth Hall Lane, Croxteth, Liverpool L11 4UG Tel: 0151 546 3956 Fax: 0151 546 3221 — MB ChB 1981 Bristol; DRCOG 1983.

GILCHRIST, James 5 Woodlands Avenue, Rochdale OL11 5HJ Tel: 01706 44978 — MB ChB 1933 Glas. (Glas.)

GILCHRIST, James Norman Gray Tel: 01908 611767 Fax: 01908 615099; 80 Wolverton Road, Newport Pagnell MK16 8JG Tel: 01908 610866 — MB BS 1969 Lond.; MRCS Eng. LRCP Lond. 1969. (St. Bart.)

GILCHRIST, James Thomas 10 Stockmore Street, Oxford OX4 1JT — MB BS 1993 Lond.; MRCP (Lond) 1996. (London Hospital Medical College)

GILCHRIST, Jennifer Jane 14 North Park Terrace, Edinburgh EH4 1DP — MB ChB 1984 Manch.; MB ChB Manch. l984; MRCGP 1989. Doctors Retainer Scheme Ladywell HC Edin. Prev: Trainee GP Edin. VTS; Ho. Off. Withington Hosp. Manch. & Blackburn Roy. Infirm.

GILCHRIST, John (retired) 10 Knowehead Drive, Uddingston, Glasgow G71 7PX — MB ChB 1941 Glas.

GILCHRIST, Judith Anne 13 Chorley Avenue, Sheffield S10 3RP — BM BS 1989 Nottm.; MRCP (UK) 1996.

GILCHRIST, Mary Lindsay (retired) 6/6 Succoth Court, Succoth Park, Edinburgh EH12 6BY Tel: 0131 337 2150 — MB ChB 1920 Ed.

GILCHRIST, Natasha Ashburnham Cottage, Ashburnham Drive, Walters Ash, High Wycombe HP14 4UD Tel: 01494 565627 Fax: 01494 564360 Email: natashagilchrist@hotmail.com — MB BS 1998 Lond.; MB BS Lond 1998. PRHO Surg. & Med.; PRHO Med. Wycombe Hosp., High Wycombe Bucks. Socs: BMA. Prev: PRHO Surg. Barnet Gen. Hosp.

GILCHRIST, Norah Elizabeth (retired) 371 Hendon Way, London NW4 3LY Tel: 020 8202 7179 — MB BS 1946 Lond.; MD Lond. 1975. Prev: Asst. Dir. Regional Neurol. Rehabil. Unit Homerton Hosp. Lond.

GILCHRIST, Robert Adam Sampson (retired) The Old Vicarage, Shotteswell, Banbury OX17 1JB Tel: 01295 730213 — MB BChir 1958 Camb.; FRCGP 1979, M 1971; DObst RCOG 1959. Prev: GP Banbury.

GILCHRIST, Sian South Street Doctors Surgery, South Street, Cockermouth CA13 9QP Tel: 01900 324123 Fax: 01900 324122 — MB ChB 1987 Liverp.; MRCGP 1991; DRCOG 1989.

GILDEA, Eileen (retired) 8 Rathmore Avenue, Bangor BT19 1DH — MB BCh BAO 1940 NUI. Prev: Med. Asst. (Psychiat.) Mater Infirm. Hosp. Belf.

GILDEH, Peter B Guelder Rose Medical Centre, Headcorn Road, Staplehurst, Tonbridge TN12 0BU Tel: 01580 893045 Fax: 01580 890252 — MD 1972; MD 1972, DTCD 1975. GP. Socs: MPS. Prev: Cons. Phys., Roy. Albert Hosp., Wigan, Lancs.

GILDER, Fay Josephine Anaesthetic Department, Addenbrooke's Hospital, Cambridge CB2 2QQ Tel: 01223 245151 Fax: 01223 217223; 31 Cyprus Road, Cambridge CB1 3QA Tel: 01223 412295 — MB BS 1991 Lond.; BSc (Hons.) Lond. 1990; FRCA 1995. (St. Geo. Hosp. Med. Sch. Univ. Lond.) Specialist Regist. Rotat. (Anaesth.) Addenbrooke's Hosp. Camb. Socs: Fell. Roy. Soc. Med.; Assn. Anaesth. Prev: SHO (Anaesth. & Neonat. Intens. Care) Addenbrooke's Hosp. Camb.; SHO (Anaesth.) Qu. Eliz. Hosp. King's Lynn; SHO (Anaesth.) St. Richards Hosp. Chichester.

GILDER, Jane Elizabeth The Medical Centre, Badgers Crescent, Shipston-on-Stour CV36 4BQ Tel: 01608 661845 Fax: 01608 663614 — MB BS 1986 Lond.; MRCGP 1992; DRCOG 1991; DCH RCP Lond. 1990. Prev: Trainee GP Cookham Med. Centre Berks; SHO (Paediat.) Qu. Eliz. Hosp. Sick. Childr.; SHO (O & G) Roy. Free Hosp. Lond.

GILDERSLEVE, Albert Alan (retired) 30 Kenwood Park Road, Sheffield S7 1NF Tel: 0114 255 2114 — MB ChB 1955 Sheff.; DObst RCOG 1960. Prev: Med. Ref. DoH.

GILDERSLEVE, Christopher David Department of Anaesthetics, University Hospital of Wales, Heath Park, Cardiff CF14 4XW Tel: 029 2074 3107 Fax: 029 2074 5489 Email: chris@steambunny.demon.co.uk — MB BCh 1982 Wales; FRCA 1989; FFA RCSI 1988. (University Wales) Cons. (Paediat. Anaesthtics) Univ. Hosp. Wales Cardiff. Socs: BMA; Assn. Paediat. Anaesth.; Assn. Anaesth. Prev: Sen. Regist. (Anaesth.) Univ. Hosp. Wales; Clin. Research Fell. (Anaesth.) Univ. Wales.

GILDERSLEVE, James Quentin Berkshire Cancer Centre, Royal Berkshire & Battle Hospitals NHS Trust, London Road, Reading RG1 5AN Tel: 0118 987 7861 Fax: 0118 987 7877 — MB BS 1982 Lond.; MA Oxf. 1982; MRCP (UK) 1985; T(R) (CO) 1991; FRCR 1989; FRCP 1998. Cons. Clin. Oncol. Roy. Berks. & Battle Hosps. NHS Trust. Prev: Tutor & Sen. Regist. (Clin. Oncol.) Cookridge Hosp. Leeds; Regist. (Radiother. & Oncol.) Roy. Marsden Hosp. Lond.; Regist. (Med.) Edgware Gen. Hosp.

GILES, Alison Anne 18 Moss Gate Road, Liverpool L14 0JP — MB ChB 1989 Ed.

GILES, Andrew Peter 31 Durnford Way, Cambridge CB4 2DP — BM BS 1989 Nottm.

***GILES, Angela** 54 Copsewood Avenue, Nuneaton CV11 4TQ Tel: 01203 381162 — MB ChB 1997 Sheff.

GILES, Antony James Hassall 77 Lily Close, St Paul's Court, London W14 9YB Tel: 020 8741 2988 — MB BChir 1973 Camb.; MA, MB Camb. 1973, BChir 1972; Dip. Ven. Soc. Apoth. Lond. 1975. (Camb. & St. Thos.) Assoc. Specialist (Genitourin. Med.) Chelsea & W.m. Hosp. Lond.; Venereol. HM Prison Holloway. Socs: BMA & Med. Soc. Study VD. Prev: Cons. Phys. Venereol. & Genitourin. Med. Trent RHA; Sen. Regist. (Venereol.) Char. Cross Hosp. & St. Stephens Hosp. Lond.

GILES, Christopher (retired) 42 Richmond Village, St Josephs Way, Nantwich CW5 6TD Tel: 01270 629341 Email: chris@dsgiles.freesaveco.uk — MD 1948 Manch.; BSc Manch. 1937, MD 1948, MB ChB 1940; FRCPath 1964. Prev: Cons. Haemat. Centr. Path. Laborat. Stoke-on-Trent.

GILES, Claire Elizabeth Mount Farm Surgery, Lawson Place, Bury St Edmunds IP32 7EW Tel: 01284 769643 Fax: 01284 700833; West Mill, Horringer Road, Bury St Edmunds IP33 2EE Tel: 01284 702040 — MB ChB 1984 Liverp.; MB ChB Liverp. l984; MRCGP 1988; DRCOG 1987. (Liverpool)

GILES, Claire Margaret 31 Malone Park, Belfast BT9 6NJ — MB BCh BAO 1996 Belf.

GILES, Cyril Joseph Springfield Road Surgery, 44-46 Springfield Road, Belfast BT12 7AH Tel: 028 9032 1454 Fax: 028 9020 1106 — MB BCh BAO 1962 Belf.

GILES, David Peter Vaughan Lindsay (retired) 5 Ocean View Road, Bude EX23 8NW Tel: 01288 352061 Fax: 01288352061 — MB BS Lond. 1959; FRCGP 1996, M 1976; DA Eng. 1965; DObst RCOG 1965. Chairm. & Bd. Mem. Surveyor Hosp. Accredit. Progr. Prev: GP Bude.

GILES, Elspeth Anne Hill House, May Lane, Claughton-on-Brock, Preston PR3 0PD Tel: 01995 640087 — MB BS 1997 Newc. Prev: PRHO (Med.) N. Tyneside Dist. Gen.; PRHO (Surg.) Roy. Lancaster Infirm.

GILES, Emma Louise 38 Horseshoe Crescent, Beaconsfield HP9 1LL — MB BCh 1990 Wales; DGM RCP Lond. 1994. Trainee GP High Wycombe VTS.

GILES, Graeme Macpherson Strathcarron Hospice, Randolph Hill, Denny FK6 5HJ; Kiscadale, 28 Chalton Road, Bridge of Allan, Stirling FK9 4DX — MB ChB 1973 Glas.; FRCR 1983. Med. Cons. Strathcarron Hospice, Denny; Hon. Cons. Palliat. Med. Forth Valley HB.

GILES, Ian Philip 35 Hillary House, Teviot St., London E14 6PU — MB BS 1992 Lond.

GILES, Jan 329 Springvale Road, Sheffield S10 1LL — MB ChB 1998 Sheff.; MB ChB Sheff 1998.

GILES, John Adolphus Mileham Lodge, Hinton St George TA17 8SN Tel: 01460 74942 — MB BS 1978 Lond.; FRCS Eng. 1983; FRCOG 1997, M 1984; LM 1981. (Middlx.) Cons. Gyn. E. Som. Hosp. Trust.

GILES, John Alan Conquest Hospital, The Ridge, Hastings TN34 2 Tel: 01424 757000 Fax: 01424 757006/758118; North Ridings, 39 Baldslow Down, St Leonards-on-Sea TN37 7NJ — MB BS 1980 Lond.; MRCP (UK) 1984; FRCR 1987. Cons. Radiol. Hastings & Rother NHS Trust. Prev: Sen. Regist. (Radiol. King's Coll. Hosp. Lond.; Asst. Prof. Radiol. Hershey Med. Center Penn. State Univ., USA.

GILES, John Peter (retired) Winter Court, Twemlows Avenue, Higher Heath, Whitchurch SY13 2HD Tel: 01948 840040 — MRCS Eng. LRCP Lond. 1956; DObst RCOG 1962; DA Eng. 1964. Prev: SHO (Anaesth.) Leeds Gen. Infirm.

GILES, Julian Henry The Surgery, 30 Old Road West, Gravesend DA11 0LL Tel: 01474 352075/567799 Fax: 01474 333952; Corner Cottage, Round St, Cobham DA13 9BA — MB BS Lond. 1979; MRCS Eng. LRCP Lond. 1979. (St. Bart.) Prev: GP Harbury; SHO (Gyn.) St. Bart. Hosp. Lond.; SHO (Anaesth.) W.m. Hosp. Lond.

GILES, Julian William Greenhurst Farm, Fowley Lane, High Hurstwood, Uckfield TN22 4BG — MB BS 1992 Lond.

GILES, Mr Keith Wilson (retired) 35 Woodland Way, Stevenage SG2 8BU Tel: 01438 368741 — MB BS 1953 Lond.; FRCS Eng. 1965; FRCS Ed. 1963; MRCS Eng. LRCP Lond. 1953. Liveryman Soc. Apoth. Lond. Prev: Cons. Surg. Lister Hosp. Stevenage & Qu. Vict. Memor. Hosp. Welwyn.

GILES, Margaret Doris Melfort, 7 Ossian Road, Newlands, Glasgow G43 2JJ Tel: 0141 632 3870 — MD Glas. 1946, MB ChB 1940; DCH Lond. 1944. (Glas.) Cons. Paediatr. Roy. Hosp. Sick Childr. Glas. Socs: Brit. Paediat. Assn. & Scott. Paediat. Soc. Prev: Ho. Phys. & Hall Tutor Glas. Roy. Infirm.; Ho. Surg. Roy. Matern. Hosp. Glas.

GILES, Mark Julian The Medical Centre, 7E Woodfield Road, London W9 3XZ Tel: 020 7266 1449 Fax: 020 7451 8155 — MB BS 1988 Lond.; MRCGP 1993; DRCOG 1992.

GILES, Martin Andrew Bryr Aweton, The Castle, Denbigh LL16 3NB — MB ChB 1982 Leic.

GILES, Michael Brian The Windsor Road Surgery, Windsor Road, Garstang, Preston PR3 1ED Tel: 01995 603350 Fax: 01995 601301; Hill House, Claughton-on-Brock, Preston PR3 0PD — MB ChB 1971 Liverp.; BSc (Hons. 1st cl. Physiol.) Liverp. 1968, MB ChB 1971. Hosp. Pract. (Psychiat.) Ribbleton Hosp. Preston. Prev: Clin. Asst. (Paediat.) Preston Roy. Infirm.; Hosp. Pract. (Psychiat.) Whittingham Hosp. Preston.

GILES, Mr Nigel Christopher Lindsay 94 Durnford Street, Stonehouse, Plymouth PL1 3QW — MB BS 1986 Lond.; BSc (Hons.), MB BS Lond. 1986; FRCS Ed. 1992.

GILES, Paul David Department of Biochemistry, Manor Hospital, Moat Road, Walsall WS2 9PS Tel: 01992 721172 Fax: 01992 656787 Email: gilesp@wht.walsallh-tr.wmids.nhs.uk — BM 1981 Oxf.; FRCP (Lond.) 1997, (Edin.) 1997, M 1984; FRCPath 1997, M 1989. (Oxf.) Cons. Chem. Path. Walsall NHS Hosp. Trust; Hon. Sen. Lect., Dept. of Med. Univ. Birm. Socs: BMA & Assoc. Clin. Biochem. Prev: Med. Dir. Walsall Hosp. NHS Trust; Sen. Regist., Dept. of Clin. Chem., Edin. Roy. Infirm.; Regist. in Chem. Path., Leeds Gen. Infirm. & St. James Univ. Hosp. Leeds.

GILES, Paul Richard 83 Badshot Park, Badshot Lea, Farnham GU9 9NE — MB ChB 1993 Bristol.

GILES, Rachel Mary 118 Forest Glade, Basildon SS16 6SX — MB BS 1984 Lond.; DRCOG 1995 London; MRCGP 1988; DCH RCP Lond. 1987. (Guy's) Prev: GP Princip. 1988-1996 Stiffard Clays Grays Essex (f/t).

GILES, Roger Walton Howard West Suffolk Hospital, Hardwick Lane, Bury St Edmunds IP33 2QZ; West Mill, Horringer Road, Bury St Edmunds IP33 2EE — MB ChB 1973 Liverp.; FRCOG 1995; T(OG) 1991; MObstG Liverp. 1983. Cons. O & G W. Suff. Hosp. Bury St. Edmunds. Prev: Sen. Regist. Guy's Hosp. Lond.

GILES, Simon Higdon Bermina, Lower Ashton, Exeter EX6 7QW — MB BS 1973 Lond. (Roy. Free) Prev: Pres. Torquay & Dist. Med. Soc.

GILES, Simon Louis 23 Bosmere Gardens, Emsworth PO10 7NP — MB BS 1995 Lond.

GILES, Stephen Nicholas 166 Wrexham Road, Whitchurch SY13 1HU — MB BS 1992 Lond.; FRCS Ed. 1997. (Char. Cross & Westm. Med. Sch.) Specialist Regist. Stoke-on-Trent/OsW.ry. Prev: SHO (Orthop.) N.. Gen. Hosp. Sheff.; SHO (Plastics) Withington Hosp. Manch.; SHO (Gen. Surg.) Withington Hosp. Manch.

GILES, Thomas Ernest Department of Histopathology, Hull Royal Infirmary, Anlaby Road, Hull HU3 2KZ Tel: 01482 328541 — MB ChB 1987 Birm.; ChB Birm. 1987. Cons., Histopath., Hull Roy. Infirm.

GILES, Vera Archer 4 Blundells Lane, Rainhill, Prescot L35 6NA Tel: 0151 426 4198; 529 Warrington Road, Rainhill, Prescot L35 6NA Tel: 0151 426 2141 — LRCPI & LM, LRCSI & LM 1938. (RCSI) Asst. Widnes. Socs: BMA & St. Helens Med. Soc.

GILFEATHER, Leonard Bernard Christopher Farnham Road Surgery, 301 Farnham Road, Slough SL2 1HD Tel: 01753 520917 Fax: 01753 550680; 53 Botham Drive, Chalvey Road East, Slough SL1 2L2 Tel: 01753 691216 — MB ChB 1969 Glas.; DObst RCOG 1971. (Glas.) Assoc. Specialist (Sports Med.) The Winidsor sports.

GILFILLAN, Lindsay John Lintonville Medical Group, Old Lane, Ashington NE63 9UT Tel: 01670 812772 Fax: 01670 521573; 9 Leland Place, Morpeth NE61 2AN — MB ChB 1983 Manch.; BSc St. And. 1980; MRCGP 1991; DRCOG 1991; Cert. Family Plann. JCC 1990; DCH RCP Lond. 1989; DCCH RCP Ed. 1989; DGM RCP Lond. 1988. Prev: Trainee GP St. And.

GILFILLAN, Richard Cameron Urbal Road Surgery, 67 Urbal Road, Coagh, Cookstown BT80 0DP Tel: 028 7973 7243 Fax: 028 7973 7602; 5 Ruskey Road, Coagh, Cookstown BT80 0AA Tel: 01648 737243 — MB BCh BAO Belf. 1978; MRCGP 1982; DRCOG 1980.

GILFILLAN, Thomas Graham (retired) 40 Deepdale Avenue, Scarborough YO11 2UF Tel: 01723 366117 Email: graham.gilgillian@tesco.net — MB BS 1959 Lond.; MRCS Eng. LRCP Lond. 1959.

***GILFORD, Beth Gourlay** 25 Marchlyn Crescent, Millbrook, Ingleby Barwick, Stockton-on-Tees TS17 5DP — MB ChB 1998 Dund.; MB ChB Dund 1998.

GILFORD, Hilary Jane St Helier Hospital, Wrythe Lane, Carshalton SM5 1AA; 35 Waterer Gardens, Burgh Heath, Tadworth KT20 5PD — MB BS 1974 Lond.; FRCR 1983; DMRD Eng. 1980. Cons. Radiol. St. Helier Hosp. Carshalton.

GILHAM, Deborah The Village Surgery, Marford Road, Wheathampstead, St Albans AL4 8BT Fax: 01582 834693; 20 Lyndhurst Drive, Harpenden AL5 5RJ Tel: 01582 713001 — MB BS 1981 Lond.; MRCGP 1985; DRCOG 1984. GP Wheathampstead.

GILHAM, Penelope Anne Clapham Park Surgery, 72 Clarence Avenue, London SW4 8JP Tel: 020 8674 4436; 39A Red Post Hill, London SE24 9JJ Tel: 020 7326 4368 — MB BS 1985 Lond.; MRCGP 1991; DRCOG 1989.

GILHOOLY, Charlotte Jane Anaesthetics Directorate, Glasgow Royal Infirmary, 84 Castle St., Glasgow G12 9NA Tel: 0141 211 4620; 9A Rosslyn Terrace, Glasgow G12 9NA — MB ChB 1987 Glas.; FRCA 1993. (Glas.) Specialist Regist. (Intens. Care) 1997 Glas. Roy. Infirm.; Sen. Regist. (Anaesth.) 1995 Vict. Infirm. Glas. Prev: Res. Fell. Univ. Glas.; Career Regist. (Anaesth.) Glas. Roy. Infirm.

GILHOOLY, Gary The Surgery, 4 Old Steine, Brighton BN1 1EJ Tel: 01273 685588 Fax: 01273 624328; 4 The Old Steine, Brighton BN1 1EJ Tel: 01273 685588 — MB BS 1979 Lond.; BSc (Hons.) Lond. 1976, MB BS 1979; MRCGP 1986; DRCOG 1984. GP Brighton; Med. Off. John Howard Ho. Long Term Disabled.

GILHOOLY, Marie Veronica 2 Claremont Terrace, Glasgow G3 7XR; 36 Hawthorn Avenue, Bearsden, Glasgow G61 3NH — MB ChB 1980 Glas.; DFFP 1993; Cert. Family Plann. JCC 1987; DCH RCP Lond. 1984. Socs: BMA.

GILI, Nicholas Lluis 42 Neill Road, Sheffield S11 8QG — MB ChB 1998 Sheff.; MB ChB Sheff 1998.

GILKAR, Ghulam Mohammad Manchester Road Medical Centre, 774 Manchester Road, Bradford BD5 7QP Tel: 01274 392108 — MB BS 1967 Jammu & Kashmir. (Govt. Med. Coll. Jammu & Kashmir) GP.

GILKES, Jeremy John Heming 115A Harley Street, London W1N 1DG Tel: 020 7935 6465 Fax: 020 7935 5014 — MB BS 1964 London; MRCP 1970 UK; MD 1976 London; FRCP 1983 London. (St. Bart.) Hon. Cons. Dermat. St. Lukes Hosp. for Anglican Clergy & King Edwd. VII Hosp. for Offs. Lond. Socs: Fell. Roy. Soc. Med. (Mem. Sect. Dermat.); Brit. Assn. Dermat. Prev: Cons. Dermat. Univ. Coll. Hosps. Lond.; Sen. Regist. (Dermat.) St. Bart. Hosp. Lond.

GILKES, Mr Michael John (retired) — LRCP 1946 MRCG Eng. LRCP Lon. 1946; MB BS Lond. 1950; FRCS Eng. 1954; MRCS Eng. LRCP Lond. 1946; FRCOphth 1988. Hon. Cons. Ophth. Brighton Health Dist. Sussex Eye Hosp. Prev: Ophth. Trachoma Research Gp. Med. Research Counc.

GILKISON, John Noble, Lt.-Col. RAMC Retd. The Granary, Baadsmill, West Calder EH55 8LG — MB ChB 1966 Ed.; MRCGP 1976; DDerm Lond 1977; DObst RCOG 1973.

GILKS, Andrew Weston (retired) 50 Temple Fortune Lane, London NW11 7UE Tel: 020 8458 3017 — MB BS Lond. 1954, DPH (Distinc.) 1949; MRCS Eng. LRCP Lond. 1945; MFOM RCP Lond. 1978; DIH Eng. 1952. Prev: Sen. Med. Off. Lond. Transp. Exec.

GILKS, John Michael Langton (retired) 29 Sadler Street, Wells BA5 2RR Tel: 01749 676564 — BM BCh 1950 Oxf.; MA Oxf. 1949, BM BCh 1950; FFOM RCP Lond. 1984, MFOM 1978; DIH Soc. Apoth. Lond. 1972. Prev: Chief Med. Adviser Kuwait Petroleum Internat.

GILL, Adarsh Deepak Singh Guy's Hospital, Newcomen Centre, St Thomas St, London SE1 9RT Tel: 020 7955 5000 Fax: 020 7955 4950; 9 Belsize Avenue, Ealing, London W13 9TF Tel: 020 8840 5543 — MB BS 1991 Lond.; BSc Hons. Lond. 1988; MRCP (UK) 1994; MRCPCH 1997. (Guy's Hospital) Specialist Regist. (Paediat. Neurol.) Guy's Hosp. Lond. Prev: Regist. (Paediat.) Roy. Alexandra Hosp. for Silk Childr. Brighton.

GILL, Aftab Ahmed 30 Richmond Street, Totterdown, Bristol BS3 4TQ — LRCP LRCS LRCPS 1998 Ed., Glas.

GILL, Aidan Patrick 87 Hackworth Point, Rainhill Way, London E3 3EX — MB BS 1991 Lond.

GILL, Alan Bryan Peter Congdon Neonatal Unit, Clarendon Wing, Leeds General Infirmary, Leeds LS1 3EX Tel: 0113 392 2936 Fax: 0113 392 6068 — MB ChB 1985 Manch.; MRCP (UK) 1989; FRCPCN 1996. (Manchester) Cons. (Neonatologist) Leeds Gen. Infirm.; Clin. Director for Neonat. Serv.s at Leeds Teachg. Hosps. NHS Trusts. Socs: Roy. Coll. Of Paediats. & Child Health (Fell.); Neonat. Soc. (Mem.); Brit. Assoc. of Perinatal Med. (Mem.). Prev: Sen. Regist. (Neonat. Med.) Leeds Gen. Infirm.

GILL, Amarjit Kaur Fairview Medical Centre, 131-133 Flixton Road, Urmston, Manchester M41 5ZZ Tel: 0161 748 2021 Fax: 0161 748 7974.

GILL, Amrik Singh 40 Pencombe Drive, Wolverhampton WV4 5EW — MB ChB 1979 Birm.; BPharm (Hons.) Lond. 1973. GP Wolverhampton.

GILL, Andrew Leonard Arthur Beckmill House, Shap Road, Kendal LA9 6NY Tel: 01539 720429 — MB BS 1951 Lond.; MRCS Eng. LRCP Lond. 1950. (Middlx.) Indep Hypnotherap. Kendal. Prev: Ho. Phys. Whittington Hosp. Lond.; Ho. Surg. Mt. Vernon Hosp. N.wood.

GILL, Anil 247B Abbey Lane, Beauchief, Sheffield S8 0BT — MB ChB 1995 Sheff.

GILL, Bhavita Kaur 12 Skelwith Rise, Nuneaton CV11 6JP — MB ChB 1998 Leic.; MB ChB Leic 1998. SHO (Anaesth.), Leicester Sch. of Anaes. Rotat. Prev: HO, Staffs. Gen. Hosp.

GILL, Brian (retired) 3 Leefields Close, Uppermill, Oldham OL3 6LA — MB ChB 1948 Manch.

GILL, Brian Vincent (retired) Follifoot, The Green, Frant, Tunbridge Wells TN3 9DN Tel: 01892 750266 — MB BS 1961 Lond.; FRCGP 1993, M 1968. Prev: Nuffield Pract.

***GILL, Caroline Ruth** 4 Mews Cottages, The Sands, Appleby-in-Westmorland CA16 6XN — MB BS 1994 Newc.

GILL, Charan Preeti Hillingdon Hospital, Pield Heath Road, Uxbridge UB8 3NN Tel: 01895 238282 — BSc (Hons.) Lond. 1986, MB BS 1989; FRCA 1994; DA (UK) 1991. (University College and Middlesex Hospital Medical School) Cons. (Anaesth.), Hillingdon Hosp. Socs: RCA; Assoc. fo Anaesth.s; Obst. Anaesth. Assn. Prev: Sen. Regist. (Anaesth.),UCH & Middlx. Hosps.; Post Fell.ship Regist. (Anaesth.) Gt. Ormond St. Hosp. Lond.; Regist. (Anaes), Hammersmith Hosp., Lond.

GILL, Charles Raymond Wells Blooms Inn Medical Centre, 21 Garlick Hill, London EC4V 2AU Tel: 020 7606 6159 Fax: 020 7489 1134 Email: info@bimc.co.uk; Firs, 6 Broadwater Road, Burwood Park, Walton-on-Thames KT12 5DB Tel: 01932 227357 Fax: 01932 227357 Email: rgilliclam@aol.com — MB BS 1966 Lond.; MRCP (UK) 1970; MRCS Eng. LRCP Lond. 1966; MRCGP 1974; AFOM RCP Lond. 1978; FRCP Lond 1999. (Char. Cross) Chief Med. Off. Bank of Eng., Swiss Life Pension Fund & Assecurazioui Gen.; Staff Med. Adviser Bank of Eng.; Pres. Elect Internat. Comm. Life, Health & Disabilities Insur. (ICLAM); Swiss Life Pension Fund & Assecurazioui Gen; Chief Med Off.; Med. Adviser Nat. & Internat. Pension organisations. Socs: Fell. Roy. Soc. Med. & Med. Soc. Lond.; Hon.Mem Mexican Assn. Life Med. Insur.; Fell. (Ex-Pres.) Assur. Med. Soc. Prev: Regist. (Gen. Med. & Infec. Dis.) Neasden & Centr. Middlx. Hosps.; Bank Med. Off., Bank of Eng.; Hon. Sen. Clin. Fell. in Med. Char. Cross Hosp. Lond.

GILL, Daljeet Singh 50 Freshwell Avenue, Romford RM6 5DT — MB BS 1989 Lond.; MSc Lond. 1992, MB BS 1989; MRCP (UK) 1994. Regist. (Med.) P.ss Alexandra Hosp. Harlow.

GILL, David Bertram Edwin Cecil 5 Oaklands, Ruyton Eleven Towns, Shrewsbury SY4 1HT — BM BCh 1983 Oxf.

GILL, David Christopher 1 Malvern Court, 29 Mapperley Road, Mapperley Park, Nottingham NG3 5SS Tel: 0115 962 2351; Knoydart, 2 Calligary, Ardvasar, Isle of Skye IV45 8RU — MB ChB St. And. 1963; FRCPsych 1987, M 1976; DPM Eng. 1975; DTM & H Liverp. 1967; DObst RCOG 1965. (St. And.) Med. Dir. Nottm. Clinic; Indep. Cons. Psychiat. Nottm. Socs: Nottm. M-C Soc.; BMA. Prev: Cons. Psychiat. Mapperley Hosp. Nottm.; Clin. Teach. Univ. Nottm. Med. Sch.; Sen. Regist. (Psychiat.) Knowle Hosp. Fareham.

GILL, David Kirtland Belford Medical Practice, The Belford Health Centre, Croftfield, Belford NE70 7ER Tel: 01668 213738 Fax: 01668 213072 — MB BS 1978 Newc.; MRCGP 1982; Dip. Med. Educat. Dund 1995; DRCOG 1982. GP Trainer Belford; PCG Bd. Mem. Socs: Brit. Soc. Med. & Dent. Hypn.

GILL, Deborah Patricia 153A Victoria Road, London N9 9BA — MB BS 1990 Lond.

GILL, Donald (retired) Church Croft, Baker St., Appleton Wiske, Northallerton DL6 2AQ — MRCS Eng. LRCP Lond. 1942; FRCP Ed. 1977, M 1959. Prev: Cons. Dermatol. Teesside Gp. Hosps.

GILL, Geoffrey Munro, MBE (retired) Beechcroft, Old Chapel Rd, Inverurie AB51 4QN Tel: 01467 620574 — MB ChB 1953 Aberd.; FRCGP 1979, M 1960. Prev: GP Inverurie.

GILL, Geoffrey Victor Department of Diabetes & Endocrinology, University Hospital Aintree, Liverpool L9 1AE Tel: 0151 529 4749 Fax: 0151 529 4688 — MB BS 1972 Newc.; MD Newc. 1980, MSc Newc. 1974; MA Liverpool 1999; BA (Hons) Open University 1995; FRCP Lond. 1990; MRCP (UK) 1975; DTM & H Liverp. 1975; MSc Newc 1975. (Newcastle upon Tyne) Reader in Med. & Trop. Med. Univ. of Liverp.; Hon. Cons. Phys. Univ. Hosp. Aintree Liverp.; Hon. Lect. Liverp. Sch. Trop. Med. Socs: Fell.Roy. Coll. Phys.s; Diabetes UK; Soc. Endocrinol. Prev: Post Cons. Phys. & Endoc., Walton Hosp, Liverp 1990-1996.

GILL, Gurdave Singh 282 Greenford Avenue, London W7 3AB — MB ChB 1993 Sheff.

GILL, Hannah Fazakerley Hospital, Longmoor Lane, Liverpool L9 7AL — MB ChB 1998 Liverp.; MB ChB Liverp 1998.

GILL, Har Mohander Singh Fairview Medical Centre, 131-133 Flixton Road, Urmston, Manchester M41 5ZZ Tel: 0161 748 2021 Fax: 0161 748 7974.

GILL, Harbans Kaur The Surgery, 398 High Street North, Manor Park, London E12 6PH Tel: 020 8548 4898 Fax: 020 8548 4898; 45 Ranelagh Gardens, Ilford IG1 3JP Tel: 020 8554 9911 — MB BS 1964 Panjab; MB BS Panjab (India) 1964; DCD Delhi 1974; DGO Delhi 1972. (Med. Coll. Amritsar) SHO Qu.'s Pk. Hosp. Blackburn.

GILL, Harinder Kaur Loughborough University Medical Centre, Loughborough University of Technology, Loughborough LE11 3TU Tel: 01509 222061 — BM 1985 Soton.; DRCOG 1991.

GILL, Harinder Kaur 89 Central Ave, Stapleford, Nottingham NG9 8PR — MB BS 1990 Newc.

GILL, Herpal Kaur Chineworth, 81 Kenilworth Road, Coventry CV4 7AF — MB BS 1996 Lond.

GILL, James Murray (retired) The Gables, 34 Bodenham Rd, Hereford HR1 2TS Tel: 01432 358723 — MB ChB 1946 Ed. Prev: Ho. Surg. Roy. Hosp. Sick Childr. Edin. & W. Gen. Hosp. Edin.

GILL, Jane Cecilia University of Bradford Health Centre, Laisteridge Lane, Bradford BD5 0NH Tel: 01274 234979 Fax: 01274 235940 Email: jgill2@bradford-ha.nhs.uk — MB ChB 1976 Manch.; BSc Manch. 1974; DRCOG 1980. (Manchester) Med. Off. Stud. Health Serv. Univ. Bradford; Med. Off., Family Plann., Bradford City PCT. Prev: Trainee GP Taunton VTS.

GILL, Janet 26 St Michael's Avenue, Highworth, Swindon SN6 7JZ — MB BS 1993 Lond.

GILL, Jasjit Kaur 3 High Trees, Birmingham B20 1HS — MB BS 1992 Newc.; MRCP (UK) 1996; DTM & H Liverp. 1996.

GILL, Jasper Anthony 214 Lambeth Road, London SE1 7JY — MB BS 1998 Lond.; MB BS Lond 1998.

GILL, Jaswinder Singh 19 Park Hill, London W5 2JS — MB 1980 Camb.; MA Camb. 1979, MB 1980, BChir 1979; MRCP (UK) 1982; LDS RCS Eng. 1992. Res. Fell. Univ. Birm. Dept. Med.

GILL, Jaswinder Singh 1 Everest Avenue, Llanishen, Cardiff CF14 5AP — MB ChB 1996 Liverp.

GILL, Jean The Surgery, Harriet St., Walkden, Manchester M4 6HB — MB ChB 1948 Ed.; MRCPsych 1980; DPM Manch. 1977. (Ed.)

GILL, Jean Carolyn Spear Ling House Surgeries, 130 Skipton Road, Keighley BD21 3AN Tel: 01535 605747 Fax: 01535 602901 — MB BS 1977 Lond.; DRCOG 1980. (Middlesex Hospital Medical School)

GILL, Jennifer Margaret Memorial Medical Centre, Bell Rd, Sittingbourne ME10 4XX; Hucking Court Barn, Hucking, Maidstone ME17 1QT Tel: 01622 884120, 0208 473 6668 Fax: 01622 884120 — MB BS 1968 Lond.; FRCGP 2000; MBA Newc. 1993; MRCS Eng. LRCP Lond. 1968; MRCGP 1980; Dip. Community. Med. Ed. 1975. (St. Geo.) p/t GP Princip. Prev: GP Coldstream.

GILL, John Barry, LVO, Surg. Cdr. RN (retired) Wychbold, Church Road, Tattingstone, Ipswich IP9 2NA — MB BCh BAO 1953 Dub. Prev: Ho. Surg. & Cas. Off. Sir P. Dun's Hosp. Dub.

GILL, John Rupert The Health Centre, Chapel Road, Mendlesham, Stowmarket IP14 5SQ Tel: 01449 767722 — MB BS 1967 Lond.; MRCS Eng. LRCP Lond. 1966; DCH Eng. 1970; DObst RCOG 1970. (Guy's) Prev: Ho. Phys. Roy. Hants. Co. Hosp. Winchester; SHO (Paediat.) & SHO (O & G) Ipswich & E. Suff. Hosp.

GILL, Kanwalprit Singh 18 Briarwood, Wilmslow Park, Wilmslow SK9 2DH — MB ChB 1989 Liverp.

GILL, Kanwarpal Singh — MB ChB 1990 Liverp.; FRCR 1997; MRCP (UK) 1993; DTM & H RCP Lond. 1994. Cons. Radiologist Pinderfields and Pontefract NHS Trust, W. Yorks. Prev: SHO (Infec. Dis.) Birm. Heartlands Hosp.; SHO (Gen. Med.) New Cross Hosp. Wolverhampton; Ho. Off. Arrowe Pk. Hosp. Wirral.

GILL, Kathryn Elizabeth Woodpeckers, Chapel La, Blackboys, Uckfield TN22 5LB — MB BS 1997 Lond.

GILL, Kelvin Charles Yusuf and Partners, Alexander House Health Centre, 600-602 Liverpool Road, Platt Bridge, Wigan WN2 5BB Tel: 01942 866137 Fax: 01942 866891 — MB ChB 1985 Liverp.; MRCGP 1991.

GILL, Kenneth James Anaesthetic Dept, Dorset County Hospital, Williams Avenue, Dorchester DT1 2JY Tel: 01305 254500 Fax: 01305 254413 Email: gill@wali.co.uk; The Acers, Alington Ave, Dorchester DT1 2AB Tel: 01305 267813 Fax: 01305 267844 Email: gill@wdi.co.uk — MB ChB 1971 Ed.; BSc (Hons.) Med. Sci., Physiol. Ed. 1968; FFA RCS Eng. 1975. (Edinburgh) Cons. (Anaesth.) & Clin. Dir. (Anaesth. & Theatres) W. Dorset Gen. Hosps. NHS Trust Dorchester. Socs: Assn. Anaesth. GB & Irel.; Pain Soc.; Brit. Assn. Day Surg. Prev: Lect. (Anaesth.) Univ. Bristol.

GILL, Mr Kevin Patrick Mary 39 Arundel Crescent, Boston PE21 7QH — MB BCh BAO 1982 NUI; FRCR 1993; FRCSI 1986.

GILL, Kiranjit 48 Shelley Crescent, Heston, Hounslow TW5 9BJ — MB BS 1998 Lond.; MB BS Lond 1998.

GILL, Kuljit (Surgery) 6 Valley Road, Galley Common, Nuneaton CV10 9NH Tel: 01203 394427; 13 Northumberland Avenue, Stockingford, Nuneaton CV10 8E Tel: 01203 386344 — MB BS 1959 Rajasthan; DA Eng. 1967. (S.M.S. Med. Sch. Jaipur) Asst. Sch. Med. Off. Nuneaton (N. Warks.) Health Dist.

GILL, Kultar Singh 72 Chadwell Health Lane, Chadwell Heath, Romford RM6 4AF Tel: 020 8590 2800 — MB BS 1958 Bombay. (Grant Med. Coll.) Prev: SHO (Orthop.) St. Helier Hosp. Carshalton; SHO (Cas.) St. Chas. Hosp. Lond.; SHO (O & G) Risedale Matern. Hosp. Barrow-in-Furness.

GILL, Lovereet Singh Flat 35, Chepstow House, 16 Chepstow St., Manchester M1 5JF — MB ChB 1992 Liverp.

GILL, Mandeep Singh 15 Alden Close, Helmshore, Rossendale BB4 4AX — MB ChB 1991 Manch.

GILL, Margaret Elizabeth Cunningham 8 Redcrest Gardens, Camberley GU15 2DU Tel: 01276 22774 Email: moygill@aol.com — MB BS Lond. 1968; MRCS Eng. LRCP Lond. 1968. (St. Bart.) SCMO (Psychosexual Clin.) Bournewood Community Health Trust & Harrow & Hillingdon Healthcare NHS Trust. Socs: Fac. Fam. Plann. & Reproduc. Health Care; Inst. Psychosexual Med. Prev: Clin. Med. Off. (Family Plann. Instruc.) E. Herts. HA; Ho. Surg. & Ho. Phys. Mildmay Miss. Hosp. Lond.

GILL, Margaret Mary Patricia (retired) Dykeheads, Wauchope, Hawick TD9 9TG Tel: 01450 860718 Fax: 01450 860718 — MB ChB 1953 Leeds; MRCPsych 1984.

GILL, Martin John Department of Immunity & Infection, The Medical School, The University of Birmingham, Edgbaston, Birmingham B15 2TT Tel: 0121 414 3634 Fax: 0121 414 3454 Email: m.j.gill@bham.ac.uk — MB ChB 1984 Leeds; 2001 FRCPath; PhD Lond. 1994; BSc Leeds 1981, MB ChB 1984; MRCPath 1992. Sen. Clin. Lect. (Med. Microbiol.) Univ. Birm. & Hon. Cons. Birm. City Hosp. NHS Trust. Prev: Wellcome Trust Fell. & Hon. Sen. Regist. (Med. Microbiol.) St. Mary's Hosp. Med. Sch. Lond.

GILL, Martyn David — MB ChB 1987 Bristol; MRCP (UK) 1991; MRCGP 1994; DRCOG 1992.

GILL, Michael William 21 Priory Terrace, London NW6 4DG — MB BS 1979 Lond.; MSc Lond. (Community Med.) 1983; FRCP Lond. 1996; MRCP (UK) 1981; FFPHM RCP (UK) 1993; MFCM 1985. Dir. (Pub. Health) Brent & Harrow HA. Prev: Cons. Pub. Health Med. Bloomsbury & Islington; Dir. (Pub. Health) Riverside HA.

GILL, Michael William St Andrew's Hospital, Devas St., Bow, London E3 3NT Tel: 020 7363 8222 Fax: 020 7363 8256 Email: mgill@nht.thenhs.org — MB BS 1981 Lond.; MRCP (UK) 1985; FRCP (UK) 1995. (Middlx.) Cons. Phys. Geriat. Med. Newham Healthcare NHS Trust. Socs: Mem. Brit. Geriat. Soc.; Brit. Stroke Research Gp. Prev: Sen. Regist. & Lect. (Geriat. & Internal Med.) St. Bart. Hosp. Med. Coll. Lond. & Waltham Forest HA; Regist. (Gen. Med.) Homerton Hosp. Lond.

GILL, Naseem Tariq 3 Crossfield Close, Wardle, Rochdale OL12 9JP — MB ChB 1987 Manch.

GILL, Nicola Jane 18 Kerver Lane, Dunnington, York YO19 5SH — MB ChB 1990 Sheff. GP York Retainer Scheme; Mem. Roy. Coll. Gen. Pract.

GILL, Nigel Patrick Ratten Row, Stainborough Lane, Hood Green, Barnsley S75 3HA — MB ChB 1977 Bristol; BSc Bristol 1974, MB ChB 1977; FCAnaesth 1989; DA Eng. 1980. Cons. Anaesth. Barnsley. Socs: Assn. Anaesth. & Obst. Anaesth. Assn.

GILL, Owen Patrick Noel PHLS Commuicable Disease Surveillance Centre, 61 Colindale Avenue, London NW9 5EQ Tel: 020 8200 6868 Fax: 020 8200 7868 Email: ngill@phls.nhs.uk; 94 Durham Road, East Finchley, London N2 9DS Tel: 020 8444 6220 Email: noel.gill@btinternet.com — MB BCh BAO 1974 NUI. Cons. Epidemiologist.

GILL, Paramjeet Kaur 5 Ventnor Way, Fareham PO16 8RU — LRCPI & LM, LRSCI & LM 1977; LRCPI & LM, LRCSI & LM 1977; DCH NUI 1979. Regist. (Paediat.) Childr. Hosp. Dub.; Regist. (Neonat. Paediat.) Rotunda Hosp. Dub. Prev: SHO (Paediat.) Childr. Hosp. Dub.; SHO (Geriat. Med.) St. Laurence's Hosp. Dub.; Ho. Off. (Neonat. Paediat.) Rotunda Hosp. Dub.

GILL, Paramjit Singh 2 Froxmere Close, Solihull B91 3XG — BM 1982 Soton. Research Tutor Centre Research Prim. Care Acad. Unit Gen. Pract. Univ. Leeds.

GILL, Pardeep Singh 48 Shelley Crescent, Hounslow TW5 9BJ — MB ChB 1990 Leic.

GILL, Parwinder Singh 32 Harlington Road E., Feltham TW14 0AB Tel: 020 8893 1160 — LMSSA 1983 Lond.; MB BS Bhopal 1978; DRCOG 1996. GP Feltham. Prev: Trainee GP Liverp.; SHO (Paediat.) Arrowe Pk. Hosp. Wirral; Ho. Off. Birkenhead.

GILL, Paul Anthony Regents Park Surgery, Park St., Shirley, Southampton SO16 4RJ Tel: 02380 783618; 2 Howells Crescent, Cardiff CF5 2AJ — MB BCh 1986 Wales; MRCGP 1996; DFFP 1995; DRCOG 1994; FRCA 1992. (Welsh Med. Sch.) Prev: GP/Regist. Soton.

GILL, Paul Vivian Liaison Psychiatry, The Longley Centre, Norwood Grange Drive, Sheffield S5 7JT Tel: 0114 226 1621 Fax: 0114 226 1620 Email: jennyb@chsheff-tr.trent.nhs.uk; 53 Woodstock Road, Loxley, Sheffield S6 6TG — MB BS 1978 Newc.; MRCPsych 1985. Cons. Liaison Psychiat. Community Health Sheff.; Cons. The Porterbrook Clinic. Prev: Sen. Regist. (Psychiat.) Sheff. HA; Regist. (Psychiat.) Sheff. HA; SHO (Gen. Med.) Sunderland HA.

GILL, Pelvender Singh 84 Northam Road, Southampton SO14 0PB — BM 1998 Soton.

GILL, Peter Bodey Medical Centre, 363 Wilmslow Road, Fallowfield, Manchester M14 6XU Tel: 0161 248 6644 Fax: 0161 224 4228 — MB ChB 1987 Manch.; MRCGP 1993.

GILL, Peter Howard Richard, Group Capt. RAF Med. Br. (retired) Beatrice House, 19/21 Lansdowne Road, Aldershot GU11 3ER Tel: 01252 314254 — MRCS Eng. LRCP Lond. 1968; MSc Birm. 1979; MFOM RCP Lond. 1980; DAvMed Eng. 1976. Prev: Cons. RAF Inst. Aviat. Med. FarnBoro.

GILL, Mr Peter John Sunderland Royal Hospital, Kayll Road, Sunderland SR4 7TP Tel: 0191 565 6256 — MD 1988 Belf.; MB BCh BAO Belf. 1980; FRCS Ed. 1984. Cons. Orthop. Surg. Sunderland Roy. Hosp.

GILL, Peter Treloar North Tees General Hospital, Stockton-on-Tees TS19 8PE Tel: 01642 617617 — MB BS 1975 Newc.; MRCP (UK) 1978; FRCR 1980. Cons. Radiol. N. Tees Health Dist. Prev: Sen. Regist. & Regist. (Radiodiag.) Bristol Roy. Infirm.; SHO (Gen. Med.) N. Tees Gen. Hosp.

GILL, Prudence Mary 40 Prince of Wales Apartments, Esplanade, Scarborough YO11 2BB — MB ChB Bristol 1955. (Bristol.)

GILL, Rajindra Singh Stockingford Medical Centre, 13 Northumberland Avenue, Stockingford, Nuneaton CV10 8EJ Tel: 024 7638 6344 Fax: 024 7638 4512; 135 Lutterworth Road, Nuneaton CV11 6PY — MB BS 1958 Lucknow; DObst RCOG 1965. (King Geo. Med. Coll.) Socs: BMA (Ex-Chairm. Nuneaton Div.). Prev:

Regist. & SHO (O & G) Gen. Hosp. Bishop Auckland; SHO (Med.) Roy. Bath Hosp. Harrogate.

GILL, Ranjit Singh Edgeley Medical Practice, 1 Avondale Road, Edgeley, Stockport SK3 9NX Tel: 0161 477 8230 Fax: 0161 476 1915 — MB ChB 1985 Manch.; MRCGP 1991; T(GP) 1990; DRCOG 1989; Dip. Palliat. Med. 1998. (Manch.)

GILL, Ravijit Singh 12 Salts Drive, Broadstairs CT10 2SY — BM 1986 Soton.; FCAnaesth 1991.

GILL, Richard George Harefield Health Centre, Rickmansworth Road, Harefield, Uxbridge UB9 6JY Tel: 01895 822944 Fax: 01895 823755; Kingsbury House, 23 Berks Hill, Chorleywood, Rickmansworth WD3 5AG Tel: 01923 283031 — MB BS 1970 Lond.; BSc Lond. 1967; MRCP (UK) 1973; MRCGP 1986; DTM & H Liverp. 1978; DObst. RCOG 1972. (Lond. Hosp.) Prev: Phys. Vom Christian Hosp. Nigeria.

GILL, Richard John The Surgery, 280 Havant Road, Drayton, Portsmouth PO6 1PA Tel: 023 9237 0422 Fax: 023 9261 8383 — BM 1984 Soton.; Dip Occ Med 2001; MRCGP 1989; DCH RCP Lond. 1989; DGM RCP Lond. 1988; DRCOG 1986; Cert. Family Plann. JCC 1986. (Southampton) GP Princip., Occupat.al Health Adviser Portsmouth City Counc. & Others; Hosp. Pract. (Orthop.) & GP Trainer Portsmouth; Occupat.al Health. Prev: Trainee GP St. Mary's Hosp. VTS Portsmouth; SHO (Anaesth.) Qu. Alexandra Hosp. Portsmouth; SHO (Orthop.) Soton. Gen. Hosp.

***GILL, Robbie** 74 Dorchester Way, Clifford Park, Coventry CV2 2LX Tel: 024 76 622945 — BM BS 1996 Nottm.

GILL, Robert Ward Harvyn, 80 Main Road, Slyne, Lancaster LA2 6AU Tel: 01524 824089 — MRCS Eng. LRCP Lond. 1972; BSc Lond. 1969, MB BS 1972.

GILL, Roop 16 Victoria Drive E., Salisbury District Hospital, Odstock Road, Salisbury SP2 8BJ — BM 1995 Soton.

GILL, Sarah 20A Kathleen Road, London SW11 2JS — MB BS 1984 Lond.; MRCP (UK) 1987. Lect. Genito-Urin. Med. Middlx. Hosp. Lond.

GILL, Satwant Singh Department of Anaesthesia, Pinderfields Hospital NHS Trust, Aberford Road, Wakefield WF1 4DG Tel: 01924 201688; 10, Lidgett Park Road, Roundhay, Leeds LS8 1EQ Tel: 0113 268 7208 Fax: 0113 266 9316 — MB BCh 1980 Wales; FRCA 1985. Cons. Anaesth. Pinderfields Hosp. Wakefield HA. Socs: Assn. Anaesth.; Anaesth. Res. Soc.; Intens. Care Soc. Prev: Lect. (Anaesth.) Med. Sch. Sheff.; Regist. (Anaesth.) Univ. Hosp. Wales Cardiff & Roy. Gwent Hosp.

GILL, Satwant Singh Benfleet Surgery, 12 Constitution Hill, Benfleet SS7 1ED — MB BS 1976 Utkal.

GILL, Shahid Khurshid The Surgery, 26 Oakwood Road, Sparkhill, Birmingham B11 4HA Tel: 0121 777 3082 — MB BS 1981 Karachi; MRCS Eng. LRCP Lond. 1984; DRCOG 1990; Cert. Family Plann. JCC 1988; DCH RCPS Glas. 1986. Socs: MDU; BMA. Prev: SCMO (Pub. Health & Communicable Dis.) Birm.

GILL, Mr Steven Streatfield Department of Neurosurgery, Frenchay Hospital, Frenchay, Bristol BS16 1LE Tel: 0117 970 1212 — MB BS 1982 Lond.; MS Lond. 1993; FRCS Eng. 1986. Cons. Neurosurg. Frenchay Hosp. Bristol. Prev: Sen. Regist. (Neurosurg.) Soton. Gen. Hosp.; Regist. (Neurosurg.) Nat. Hosp. Nerv. Dis. Maida Vale Lond.

GILL, Sukhwinder Kaur 81 Sudbury Court Drive, Harrow HA1 3SS — MB BS 1998 Lond.; MB BS Lond 1998.

GILL, Surinder Singh 34 Packman Lane, Kirk Ella, Hull HU10 7TL — MB BS 1971 Panjab.

GILL, Surryia Longsite Health Centre, 526-528 Stockport Road, Manchester M13 0RR Tel: 0161 256 4488 — MB ChB 1983 Manch.; ECFMG 1982; MRCGP 1993; DFFP 1993.

GILL, Sydney James (retired) Shiellow Crag, Shiellow Wood, Belford NE70 7PH — MB BS Durh. 1951. Employm. Med. Adviser EMAS. Prev: GP.

GILL, Thomas John Harlestone Road Surgery, 117 Harlestone Road, Northampton NN5 7AQ Tel: 01604 751832 Fax: 01604 586065; Church Hill House, 32 Cross St, Moulton, Northampton NN3 7RZ Tel: 01604 644404 — MB BCh 1971 Wales; FRCGP 2000; MRCGP 1976; DObst RCOG 1974; Cert. Family Plann. JCC 1974. Prev: Unit Gen. Manager Elderly & Community Unit N.ampton HA.; SHO (Child Health) Llandough Hosp.; SHO (O & G) & Ho. Off. (Gen. Med. & Surg.) Univ. Hosp. Wales.

GILL, Timothy Robert Rohais Medical Centre, Rohais Road, St. Peter Port, Guernsey GY1 1FF Tel: 01481 723322 Fax: 01481 725200; Les Hougues, Rue Des Hougues, St. Andrew, Guernsey GY6 8XH — MB BS 1980 Lond.; MRCP (UK) 1983; MRCGP 1988; DCH RCP Lond. 1987. Prev: Regist. (Med.) Cardiff Hosps.

GILL, Valerie Harvyn, 80 Main Road, Slyne, Lancaster LA2 6AU — MRCS Eng. LRCP Lond. 1972; BSc Lond. 1969, MB BS 1972.

GILL, Virinderjit Singh (retired) 109A Horsham Avenue, Peacehaven BN10 8DU Tel: 01273 581079 — MB BS 1953 Punjab; BA (Open Univ.) Lond. 1991; MB BS Punjab (India) 1953. Prev: GP E. Sussex.

GILL-CAREY, Michael Chapple Summer Tides, Trevaunance Cove, St Agnes TR5 0RY Tel: 01872 553225 Fax: 01872 553225 — BM BCh Oxf. 1951; MA Oxf. 1953; DObst RCOG 1953. (Oxf. & Guy's) Examg. Med. Pract. Benefits Agency; Examr. Insur. Companies; Med. Off. TA Truro. Socs: (Ex-Pres.) Cornw. Clin. Soc. Prev: Ho. Phys. (Paediat. & Infec. Dis.) Joyce Green Hosp. Dartford; Ho. Surg. (O & G) Canad. Red Cross Memor. Hosp.; RAF Med. Br.

GILLAM, David Maxwell Abington Park Surgery, Christchurch Medical Centre, Ardington Road, Northampton NN1 5LT Tel: 01604 630291 Fax: 01604 603524; Woad Cottage, Preston Deanery, Northampton NN7 2DY — BM BCh 1971 Oxf.; MA, DPhil Oxf. 1968; MRCP (UK) 1974; MRCGP 1978.

GILLAM, Mary Louise Breast Screening Service, Northampton General Hospital Trust, Cliftonville Road, Northampton NN1 5BD; Woad Cottage, Preston Deanery, Northampton NN7 2DY — BM BCh Oxf. 1970; MA Oxf. 1970. Clin. Co-ordinator BrE. Screening Serv. N.ampton. Prev: GP N.ampton.

GILLAM, Patrick Geoffrey (retired) The Surgery, Cysgod-Yr-Eglwys, Solva, Haverfordwest SA62 6TE Tel: 01437 721306 — MB BS 1957 Lond.; DObst RCOG 1960. Prev: Regist. (Med.) Pembs. Co Hosp.

GILLAM, Peter Michael Stephen (retired) Ash Hill House, Sherfield English, Romsey SO51 6FU Tel: 01794 884200 — MB BChir 1955 Camb.; MD Camb. 1967; FRCP Lond. 1974, M 1960; DObst RCOG 1957. Prev: Cons. Phys. Salisbury Gen. Hosp.

GILLAM, Stephen John Church Farm House, Luffenhall, Walkern, Stevenage SG2 7PX; King's Fund, 11-13 Cavendish Square, London WIG 0AN Tel: 020 7307 2692 Fax: 0207 7307 2817 Email: sgilliam@kingsfund.org.uk — MB BS 1980 Lond.; MSc Lond. 1990; MA Camb. 1981; FRCP 1997, MRCP (UK) 1984; MFPHM RCP (UK) 1992; MRCGP 1985; DCH RCP Lond. 1983; MD 1998; FPHM 1999. (UCH) Dir. Primary Care Progr. King's Fund; Hon. Sen. Lect. Dept. Primary Care & Populative Scis. Roy. Free & UCH; Vis. Reader Inst. Health Serv. Research Univ. Luton. Prev: Cons. Pub. Health Med. Beds. Health; Trainee GP N.wick Pk. Hosp. VTS; Sen. Regist. (Pub. Health Med.) NW Thames RHA.

GILLAM, Steven Charles West Barn, Somersall Hall Drive, Chesterfield S40 3LH Tel: 01246 568513 — MB BS 1975 Lond.; DRCOG 1979. (St. Geo.) Socs: Brit. Soc. of Med. & Dent. Hypn. Prev: GP Chesterfield; Clin. Asst. (A & E) Hallamshire Hosp. Sheff.; SHO (Obst.) N.. Gen. Hosp. Sheff.

GILLAMS, Alison Rosemary 41 Lady Margaret Road, London NW5 2NH — MB ChB 1981 Bristol; MRCP (UK) 1986; FRCR 1989.

GILLAMS, Charlotte Louise West Drove Lodge, Swanborough, Lewes BN7 3PE Tel: 01273 474987 Email: boyd.family@dios.pipe@aol.com — MB ChB 1987 Leic.; MRCGP 1994. GP Partner St. Andrews Surg. Lewes.

GILLAN, Richard Urquhart Merchlyn Farm House, Henryd, Conwy LL32 8YE — MB ChB 1954 Birm.; MRCP Lond. 1959; MRCPsych 1971; DPM Lond. 1962. (Birm.) Prev: Cons. Psychiat. Runwell Hosp. Wickford; Sen. Regist. Bethlem Roy. & Maudsley Hosps.

GILLAN, Shaun Anthony East Cowes Health Centre, Down House, York Avenue, East Cowes PO32 6RR Tel: 01983 295611 Fax: 01983 280815 — MB BCh BAO 1973 NUI; MRCGP 1980; DRCOG 1978.

GILLANDERS, Edwina M. EMAS Health & Safety Executive, Arden House, Regent Centre, Gosforth, Newcastle upon Tyne NE3 3JN Tel: 0191 202 6200 Fax: 0191 202 6300 Email: edwina.gillanders@hse.gsi.gov.uk — MB BCh BAO Belf. 1968; FFOM RCP Lond. 1990, M 1984; FFOM RCPI 1993, M 1978; DIH Soc. Apoth. Lond. 1977; CIH Dund 1976. (Belf.) Sen. Med. Insp., EMAS Yorks. & N. E. Div., Newc. Socs: Brit. Occupat. Hyg. Soc. & Soc. Occupat. Med. Prev: Employm. Med. Adv. EMAS Dundee.

GILLANDERS, Ian Alexander "A Block", Stracathro Hospital, Brechin DD9 7QA Tel: 01356 647291; 2 Whiterashes, Kingswells, Aberdeen AB15 8QE — MB ChB 1985 Aberd.; FRCP Ed. 1998. Cons. Geriat.,Angus Region (NHS Tayside). Socs: Brit. Geriat. Soc.; Scott. Soc. of Phys.s. Prev: Lect. (Geriat. Med.) City Hosp. Edin.; Cons. Phys. (AMAU) Aberd. Roy. Infirm.; Cons. Phys. Stracathro Hosp. Brechin.

GILLANDERS, Professor Lewis Alexander 17 Denhead, Kirk Brae, Cults, Aberdeen AB15 9QT Tel: 01224 862408 — MB ChB Glas. 1947; FRCP Ed. 1974, M 1971; FRCR 1975; Hon. FFR RCSI 1979; FFR 1958; DMRD Eng. 1955. Emerit. Clin. Prof. Radiol. Univ. Aberd. Socs: Brit. Inst. Radiol. Prev: Cons. i/c Regional Radiol. Servs. Grampian HB; Sen. Regist. (Radiodiag.) Selly Oak Hosp. Birm. & Glas. Roy. Infirm.; Ho. Surg. Roy. N. Infirm. Inverness.

GILLANDERS, Nora Ellen (retired) 17 Denhead, Kirk Brae, Cults, Aberdeen AB15 9QT Tel: 01224 862408 — MB ChB Birm. 1958; DObst RCOG 1960. Prev: GP Aberd.

GILLANDERS, Vivienne Theresa Ormskirk Street Surgery, 51A Ormskirk Stret, St Helens WA10 2TB Tel: 01744 29209; 16 Wearhead Close, Golborne, Warrington WA3 3YE — MB ChB 1983 Manch.; MFFP 1993; MRCGP 1987; DCH RCP Lond. 1991; DRCOG 1986. (Manch.) Prev: Clin. Lect. (Genitourin. Med.) Univ. Manch.; Staff Grade (Genitourin. Med.) Bolton Gen. Hosp.; Clin. Med. Off. (Genetics) St. Mary's Hosp. Manch.

GILLANI, Nasim Abronhill Health Centre, Pine Road, Cumbernauld, Glasgow G67 3BE Tel: 01236 727654; 29 Glen View, Kildrum, Cumbernauld, Glasgow G67 2DA Tel: 0123 67 727800 — MB BS 1967 Punjab.

GILLARD, Emma Susan Elizabeth 1 The Arch, 71 High St., Bottisham, Cambridge CB5 9BA Tel: 01223 811769 — MB ChB 1990 Leic.; MRCGP 1996; Dip Pub Health, Camb. 1997. (Leic.) Specialist Regist. (Pub. Health) N.W. Anglia P'boro. Prev: GP/Regist. RedHo. Surg. Camb.

***GILLARD, Jonathan David** 1 Wissons Cottages, Bishops Tawton, Barnstaple EX32 0BB — MB ChB 1995 Birm.

GILLARD, Jonathan Harvey University Department of Radiology, Addenbrooke's Hospital, Cambridge CB2 2QQ Tel: 01223 336890 Fax: 01223 330915 Email: jhg21@cam.ac.uk; 1 The Arch, 71 High St, Bottisham, Cambridge CB5 9BA Tel: 01223 811769 — MB BS 1988 Lond.; BSc (Hons.) Lond. 1985, MD 1997; FFR RCSI 1998; FRCR 1999. (UMDS - Guy's) Clin. Lect. (Radiol.) Addenbrooke's Hosp. Camb. Socs: Soc. Magnetic Resonance. Prev: Clin. & Research Fell. (Neurol. Radiol.) Johns Hopkins Hosp. Baltmore, USA; SHO (Neurol.) Nat. Hosp. Neurol. Lond.

GILLARD, Mr Malcolm George First Floor Suite, 1 Devonshire Place, London W1G 6HH Tel: 020 7486 2856 Fax: 020 7486 2858; 11 Harley Place, London W1G 8QE — MB BS 1972 Lond.; FRCS Eng. 1978; MRCS Eng. LRCP Lond. 1972; FRCOG 1994, M 1980; T(OG) 1991. (St. Bart.) Cons. O & G. Socs: Fell. Roy. Soc. Med.; BMA; Yeoman Soc. of Apoth. Prev: Cons. Obst. St. Bart. & Homerton Hosps. Lond.; Regist. (O & G) City Hosp. Nottm.; SHO Qu. Charlottes Hosp. Lond.

GILLATT, Darren Clive 290 Nottingham Road, Ripley DE5 3JT — MB ChB 1997 Birm.

GILLATT, Mr David Antony Woodleigh Cottage, Vicarage Road, Leigh Woods, Bristol BS8 3PH — MB ChB 1980 Manch.; FRCS Eng. 1985; FRCS Ed. 1984. Regist. Frenchay Hosp. Bristol; SHO Stockport Infirm., Wythenshawe Hosp., Stepping Hill Hosp. Stockport & S.mead Hosp. Bristol; Ho. Posts Stepping Hill Hosp. Stockport & Manch. Roy. Infirm.

GILLATT, Mairidh Anna Macdonald Nicolson (retired) 31 Weeping Cross, Stafford ST17 0DG Tel: 01785 662109 — MB ChB 1936 Glas.; MFCM 1972; DObst RCOG 1942; DPH Glas. 1940. Prev: PMO Matern. & Child. Welf. Staffs. CC.

GILLBARD, George Dennis (retired) 84 Wrottesley Road, London NW10 5YE Tel: 020 8965 9519 — M.R.C.S. Eng., L.R.C.P. Lond. 1925.

GILLBARD, Jean 12 Morden Road, London SE3 0AA Tel: 020 8852 3680 — MB BS Lond. 1950. (King's Coll. & W. Lond.) Med. Off. to the Brit. Pregn. Advisery Serv. Lond.; Sen. Clin. Med. Off. (Housing) Lewisham & N. S.wark HA. Prev: SCMO (Housing) Lewisham & N. S.wark HA.; Staff Med. Off. Univ. Coll. Hosp. Lond.; Asst. MOH & Sch. Med. Off. Co. Boro. Ipswich.

GILLBE, Charles Edward Royal Brompton Hospital, Sydney St., London SW3 6NP Tel: 020 7351 8291 Fax: 020 7351 8524 Email: cegillbe@hotmail.com; 32 Luttrell Avenue, London SW15 6PF Tel: 020 8785 9613 Fax: 020 8789 0221 Email: cegille@hotmail.com — MB ChB 1972 Aberd.; FRCA 1979. (Aberdeen) p/t Cons. Anaesth. Brompton Hosp. Lond.; Hon. Sen. Lect. Heart & Lung Inst. Univ. Lond.; Regional Adviser Roy. Coll. of Anaesths., N. W. Thames; Lead Regional. Adviser Roy. Coll. Anaesth. N. Thames; Chairm. spec train comit. For Anaesth. N. Thames; Mem. Intercollegiate Bd. for train.in Intens. Care med. Socs: Anaesth. Res. Soc. & Intens. Care Soc.; Assn. Cardiothoracic Anaesth.; Assn for study of med edu. Prev: Sen. Regist. (Anaesth.) Roy. Free Hosp. & Nat. Hosp. Nerv. Dis. Lond.

GILLBERRY, Margaret Anne Langham House, Little London, Oakhill, Bath BA3 5AU — MB BS 1991 Lond. GP Regist. Prev: SHO (Paediat.) St. Geo. Hosp. Lond.; SHO (O & G) St. Geo. Hosp. Lond.; SHO (Psychiat.) Epsom Hosp. & Kingston Hosp.

GILLEECE, Maria Helena Department Hematology, Ysbyty Gwynedd, Bangor LL57 2PW Tel: 01248 384384 Email: maria.gilleece@nww-tr.wales.nhs.uk — MB ChB 1984 Liverp.; BSc (Hons.) Liverp. 1981; MD Manch. 1995; MRCP (UK) 1988; MRCPath 1996. (Liverpool) p/t Cons. Haematologist. Prev: Sen. Regist. (Haemat.) NW RHA Manch; Kay Kendall Leukaemia Fund Research Fell. Dana-Farber Cancer Inst. Boston, USA; BonemarrowTranspl. Coord. Hammersmith Hosp. Lond.

GILLEECE, Yvonne Catherine Chelsea & Westminster Hospital, 369 Fulham Road, London SW10 9NH Tel: 020 8746 8000 Fax: 020 8846 6198 — MB BCh BAO 1993 NUI; DFFP 2000; MRCP (UK). Specialist Regist. (HIV & Genitourin. Med.), Chelsea & W.minster Hosp., Lond. Socs: MSSVD; BHIVA; HIV Trainees Club.

GILLEGHAN, James Donald (retired) — MB ChB 1959 Ed.; LRCP LRCS Ed. LRFPS Glas. 1958; FRCP Ed. 1995; FRCGP 1980, M 1969; DObst RCOG 1964. Prev: Dir. of Studies (Gen. Pract.) Univ. Edin. (Lister Postgrad. Inst.).

GILLEGHAN, Shona Bridget Fulford Surgery, 2 Fulford Park, Fulford, York YO10 4QE Tel: 01904 625566 Fax: 01904 671539 — MB BChir 1988 Camb.; MA Camb. 1989; MRCP (UK) 1991; MRCGP 1993; DRCOG 1992.

GILLEN, Christopher David Taunton & Somerset NHS Trust, Musgrove Park, Taunton TA1 5DA Tel: 01823 342126 — MB ChB 1981 Dundee; MRCP 1988; DTM & H 1993. (Dundee) Cons. Phys. Gastroenterol. Taunton & Som. NHS Trust MusGr. Pk. Hosp. Taunton. Socs: Brit. Soc. Gastroenterol.; Brit. Assn. for Enterol. & Parenteral Feeding; W Country Phys. Prev: Cons. Phys. & Gastroenterol. Roy. Hosp. Haslar Gosport Hants.

GILLEN, David Palmer Carrowreagh, Hannah's Lane, Westbury sub Mendip, Wells BA5 1EX — MB BS 1992 Lond.

GILLEN, Derek 45 Melville Gardens, Bishopbriggs, Glasgow G64 3DE — MB ChB 1991 Glas.

GILLEN, Jennifer 45 Melville Gardens, Bishopsbriggs, Glasgow G64 3DE — MB ChB 1992 Glas.

GILLES, Herbert Michael Joseph William P. Hartley Building, Brownlow St., PO Box 147, Liverpool L69 3BX Tel: 0151 708 9393 Fax: 0151 794 5540; 3 Conyers Avenue, Birkdale, Southport PR8 4SZ Tel: 01704 566664 — MD 1946 Malta; MSc Oxf. 1951; DSc (Hon. Causa) Malta 1984, BSc 1943; MD (Hon. Causa) Karolinska, Stockholm 1979; FRCP Lond. 1969, M 1963; FFPHM RCP (UK) 1972. (Roy. Univ. Malta) Sen. Research Fell. (Pharmacol. & Ther.) Univ. Liverp.; Vis. Prof. Pub. Health Univ. Malta; Emerit. Prof. Trop. Med. Univ. Liverpol; Vis. Prof. Internat. Health RCS Dub.; Vis. Prof. Trop. Med. Fac. Trop. Med. Bangkok; Vice Pres. Liverp. Sch. Trop. Med. Socs: Roy. Soc. Med.; Internat. Epidemiol. Assn.; (Ex-Pres.) Roy. Soc. Trop. Med. & Hyg. Prev: Dean & Prof. Trop. Med. Univ. Liverp.; Prof. Preven. Med. Univ. Ibadan; Mem. Scientif. Staff Med. Research Counc.

GILLESPIE, Mr Alan (retired) 26 Victoria Road, Fleet GU51 4DN Tel: 01252 819253 — MB BS 1951 (Hons) Lond.; FRCS Eng. 1958; MRCS Eng. LRCP Lond. 1951; FRCOG 1974, M 1961, DObst 1952. Cons. (O & G) W. Surrey NE Hants. Dist. & Frimley Pk. Hosp.; Hon. Cons. (O&G) Cape Town Univ. S. Africa. Prev: Res. Med. Off. Samarit. Hosp. Wom. Lond.

GILLESPIE, Alan Macleod 3 Ash Court, Fairfield Manor, Sprotbrough, Doncaster DN5 7JZ — MB BS 1992 Lond.

GILLESPIE, Andrew Valentine (retired) Chantry, 24 Woodend Drive, Sunninghill, Ascot SL5 9BG Tel: 01344 621843 — MB BChir 1962 Camb.; MRCS Eng. LRCP Lond. 1958; MFPHM 1989; DPH Eng. 1973; FRIPHH 1997. Prev: Sen. Community Med. Off., S.W. Herts Health Auth., Watford.

GILLESPIE, Anne Jacqueline Fleming Bon Secours Hospital, 36 Mansion House Road, Langside, Glasgow G41 Tel: 0141 632 9231; The Spittal, Balfron, Glasgow G63 0QR — MB ChB Glas. 1968. (Glas.) Med. Off. Stakis plc., Alexander StenHo., Brit. Airways & Amer. Airlines, Hilton Internat., Pilkington Alexander Clay & Nat. Austral. Bank; Vice Chairm. Health Reform Gp.; Dir. Occumedic Med. (Harley St.) Ltd.; Dir. Fastrack Health Ltd. Socs: Exec. Mem. Conserv. Med. Soc. Prev: Ho. Surg. Glas. Roy. Infirm.; Ho. Off. Redlands Hosp. Wom. Glas.

GILLESPIE, Aran 50 Stockport Road, Marple, Stockport SK6 6AB Tel: 0161 426 0299; Email: aran@gillespie.uk.net — DFFP (RCOG Lond.) 2001; MB BS Lond. 1994; MA Cantab. 1995; DRCOG (R.C.O.G. Lond.) 1998. (The London Hospital Medical College) GP Princip., Marple, Stockport (Stockport Rd. Med. Pract.). Prev: SHO Psychiat. Canterbury; SHO O & G Canterbury; GP Regist. - Whitstable Health Centre.

GILLESPIE, Barbara Ann (retired) 3 Dartan Ree, Tynan, Armagh BT60 4QT Tel: 02837 568583 Fax: 02837 568583 — MB BCh BAO 1959 Dub.; MA Dub. 1992.

GILLESPIE, Christopher Martin Torbay General Hospital, Torquay; Auld Reekie, Torquay Road, Shaldon, Teignmouth TQ14 0BQ — MB BS 1977 Lond.; MRCS Eng. LRCP Lond. 1976; MRCPsych 1983. Cons. Psychiat. Torbay Gen. Hosp. Torquay.

GILLESPIE, Colin Vanbrugh Hill Health Centre, Vanbrugh Hill, London SE10 Tel: 020 8312 6095 Fax: 020 8293 1226; 73 Mycenae Road, Blackheath, London SE3 7SE Fax: 020 8293 8918 — Dobst RCOG 1965; MBBS 1962 Lond.; MB BS Lond. 1962; DObst RCOG 1965. (Char. Cross) Sen. Consg. Phys. Health Linx Dept. Blackheath Hosp.; Sen. Med. Off. The Marine Advis. Med. & Repatriation Serv. Cornhill Lond. Socs: (Ex-Pres.) W. Kent. M-C Soc. (Hon. Archiv.). Prev: Clin. Asst. (Gyn.) Greenwich Dist. Hosp.; Ho. Surg. & Cas. Off. Memor. Hosp. Woolwich; Ho. Phys. Brook Gen. Hosp. Woolwich.

GILLESPIE, Craig 6 Menlove Avenue, Liverpool L18 2EE — MB ChB 1992 Liverp.

GILLESPIE, David Henry Eastfield Medical Centre, Eastfield Drive, Penicuik EH26 8EY Tel: 01968 675576 Fax: 01968 674395; 6 Kirkhill Way, Penicuik EH26 8HH Tel: 01968 678397 — MB ChB 1978 Ed.; MRCGP 1982; DRCOG 1980; Dip. Occ. Med. 1995.

GILLESPIE, Eileen Marjorie (retired) 26 Breck Hill Road, Woodthorpe, Nottingham NG5 4GP Tel: 0115 967 6939 — MB ChB 1957 Leeds. Prev: Gen. Practioner, Nottm.

GILLESPIE, Elaine Barrhead Health Centre, 101 Main St., Barrhead, Glasgow G78 1SD Tel: 0141 880 6161 — MB ChB 1976 Glas.; DCCH RCP Ed. 1993; DFFP 1993; DRCOG 1978. Clin. Med. Off. (Child Health) Argyll & Clyde HB. Prev: Clin. Med. Off. Lanarksh. HB.

GILLESPIE, Emily Marjorie (retired) 2 Church Avenue, Stoke Bishop, Bristol BS9 1LD Tel: 0117 968 2297 — MB BCh BAO Dub. 1933; MA Dub. 1939, MD 1936; DPH Dub. 1937. Prev: Serol. Blood Transfus. Centre Bristol.

GILLESPIE, Mr Eric James Dow (retired) 9 Court Road, Tunbridge Wells TN4 8EB Tel: 01892 531607 — MB ChB Ed. 1931; FRCS Ed. 1934. Hon. Maj. RAMC. Prev: SHO (Surg.) Hull Roy. Infirm. & S.port Gen. Infirm.

GILLESPIE, Ernest Harper (retired) 1 Baronsmead, Henley-on-Thames RG9 2DL Tel: 01491 575683 — MB ChB 1933 Ed.; FRCPath 1963. Prev: Dir. Pub. Health Laborat. Serv. Sheff.

GILLESPIE, Gail Flat 3/L, 108 Novar Drive, Hyndland, Glasgow G12 9SU — MB ChB 1993 Glas. SHO (Anaesth.) Glas.

GILLESPIE, Gerard Desmond Hospital Hill Surgery, 7 Izatt Avenue, Dunfermline KY11 3BA Tel: 01383 731721 Fax: 01383 623352; 4 Dalmeny View, Dalgety Bay, Dunfermline KY11 9LU Tel: 01383 823550 — MB ChB 1980 Manch.; BSc St. And 1978; MRCGP 1985. (Manch.) Med. Off. Exxon Chem Mossmorran, Fife; Club Doctor, Dunfermline Athletic F.C.

GILLESPIE, Mr Gordon 23 Monreith Road, Newlands, Glasgow G43 2NY Tel: 0141 632 4312 — MD 1971 Glas.; MD (Commend.) Glas. 1971, MB ChB 1959; FRCS Ed. 1966; FRCS Glas. 1966; DObst RCOG 1961. Cons. Gen. Surg. Vict. Infirm. Glas. Socs: Brit. Soc. Gastroenterol. & Surg. Research Soc.

GILLESPIE, Gordon Neil 23 Monreith Road, Glasgow G43 2NY — MB BS 1998 Lond.; MB BS Lond 1998.

GILLESPIE, Hugh Michael The Meanwhile Garden Medical Centre, Unit 5, 1-31 Elkstone Road, London W10 5NT Tel: 020 8960 5620 Fax: 020 8964 1964; 14 Milverton Road, Brondesbury Park, London NW6 7AS — MB BS 1961 Lond.; LMSSA Lond. 1960; DObst RCOG 1964. (St. Bart.) Prev: Sen. Regist. (Geriat. Med.) Guy's Hosp. Lond.; Regist. (Geriat.) Paddington Hosp. Gp.; SHO (Med. & Geriat.) Whittington Hosp. Lond.

GILLESPIE, Hugh Richard Edmund 16 Golborne Road, London W10 5PE — MRCS Eng. LRCP Lond. 1949.

GILLESPIE, Professor Iain Erskine (retired) 27 Athol Road, Bramhall, Stockport SK7 1BR Tel: 0161 439 2811 Email: profandmrs_gillespie@yahoo.com — MB ChB 1953 Glas.; MSc Manch. 1974; MD (Hons.) Glas. 1963; FRCS Glas. 1970; FRCS Eng. 1963; FRCS Ed. 1959. Prev: Prof. Surg. & Dean Med. Sch. Univ. Manch.

GILLESPIE, Ian Alexander Belfast City Hospital, Lisburn Road, Belfast BT9 7AB Tel: 028 9032 9241 Email: ian.gillespie@bch.n-i.nhs.uk; 5 Glendarragh, Belfast BT4 2WB Email: iangillespie@ntlworld.com — MB BCh BAO 1981 Belf.; Dip. Pain Med. (CARCSI) 2001; FFA RCSI 1985. (Queens Univ. of Belfast) Cons. Anaesth. & Chronic Pain Relief Belf. City Hosp.

GILLESPIE, Mr Ian Hugh Ashtead Hospital, Ashtead KT21 2SB Tel: 01372 276161 Fax: 01372 278704; 11 Netherton Road, St. Margaret's, Twickenham TW1 1LZ Tel: 020 8892 6334 — MB BS 1969 Lond.; FRCS Eng. 1977; FRCOphth 1988; DO Eng. 1973. (Middlx.) Cons. Ophth. Surg. Roy Eye Unit Kingston. Socs: Fell. Roy. Soc. Med.; Amer. Acad. Ophth. Prev: Sen. Regist. (Ophth.) W.m. Hosp. Lond.; Regist. (Ophth.) St. Thos. Hosp. Lond.; Resid. Surg. Off. Moorfields Eye Hosp. Lond.

GILLESPIE, Mr Ian Norman Dept. of Radiology, Edinburgh Royal Infirmary, Lauriston Place, Edinburgh EH3 9YW Tel: 0131 536 2900/2901 Fax: 0131 536 2921 Email: ian.gillespie@luht.scot.nhs.uk; 18 Lyne Park, West Linton EH46 7HP Tel: 01968 660097 Email: in.gillespie@virgin.net — MB ChB 1977 Dundee; FRCS Ed. 1982; FRCR 1985; DMRD Ed. 1983. Cons. Radiol. Edin. Roy. Infirm.

GILLESPIE, Jacqueline Ashington Hospital, West View, Ashington NE63 0SA — MB ChB 1989 Glas.

GILLESPIE, Mr James Alexander Hartsridge, South Godstone, Godstone RH9 8LZ — MB ChB 1951 St. And.; MB ChB (Commend.) St. And. 1951; ChM (Hons.) St. And. 1959, MD (Commend.) 1953; FRCS Ed. 1956. Hon. Cons. Surg. St. Geo. Hosp. Lond.; Regius Reader Emerit. in Surg. Univ. Lond. Socs: (Ex-Sec.) Vasc. Surg. Soc. GB & Irel. Prev: Examr. Surg. Univ. Lond.

GILLESPIE, James Allan 25 Mardale, Stewartfield, East Kilbride, Glasgow G74 4ND — MB ChB 1985 Glas.

GILLESPIE, James Edward Neuroradiology Department, Manchester Royal Infirmary, Oxford Road, Manchester M13 9WL Tel: 0161 276 4233; Holmleigh, 212 Bramhall Lane S., Bramhall, Stockport SK7 3AA Tel: 0161 439 2697 — MB BCh BAO 1978 NUI; FRCR 1983; DMRD Eng. 1983. Cons. Neuroradiol. Manch. Roy. Infirm.

GILLESPIE, James Finlayson (retired) 19 Erskine Hill, Polmont, Falkirk FK2 0UH Tel: 01324 715020 — MB ChB 1970 Glas. Prev: GP Falkirk.

GILLESPIE, James Gerard Mourneside Medical Centre, 1A Ballycolman Avenue, Strabane BT82 9AF Tel: 028 7138 3737 Fax: 028 7138 3979; 38 Melmount Road, Strabane BT82 9EF Tel: 01504 883196 — MB BCh BAO 1977 NUI; MRCGP 1988.

GILLESPIE, James Ross, MBE (retired) 2 Westwood View, Beverley HU17 8EL Tel: 01482 869371 — MB ChB 1954 Aberd.; DObst RCOG 1956.

GILLESPIE, James Ross Field House Surgery, 18 Victoria Road, Bridlington YO15 2AT Tel: 01262 673362 Fax: 01262 400218 — MB BChir 1977 Camb.; MB Camb. 1977, MA, BChir 1976; MRCGP 1980; DRCOG 1979. (Westm.) Prev: Trainee GP Kettering VTS; Ho. Phys. Kent & Canterbury Hosp.; Ho. Surg. Ipswich & Dist. Hosp.

GILLESPIE, Janet Patricia 2 Church Gate, Church Lane, Therfield, Royston SG8 9QD — MB BCh BAO 1981 Belf.; MRCGP 1987.

GILLESPIE, Jean Margaret East Yorkshire Community Trust, Temperton House, Westwood Hospital, Beverley HU17 8EL Tel: 01482 886600 — MB ChB 1973 Ed.; DObst RCOG 1976. (Ed.) SCMO E. Yorks. Community Trust. Socs: MRCPCH.

GILLESPIE, Jeremy Scott James 4 Osborne Place, Belfast BT9 6YP — MB BCh BAO 1993 Belf.; MRCP (UK) (Ed.) 1996.

GILLESPIE, John Fitzroy Tynan Surgery, 15 Dartan Ree, Tynan, Armagh BT60 4QT; 3 Dartan Ree, Tynan, Armagh BT60 4QT Tel: 01861 568583 Fax: 01861 568583 — MB BCh BAO 1956 Dub.; MA Dub. 1992; LM Rotunda 1957. (Trinity Coll. Dub.) JP; DL. Socs: BMA. Prev: High Sheriff Co. Armagh.

GILLESPIE, Professor John Spence (retired) Camptower, 5 Boclair Road, Bearsden, Glasgow G61 2AE — MB ChB (Commend.) Glas. 1949; PhD Glas. 1955; FRCP Glas. 1972; D. Univ. (Hons.) 1998. Prof. Pharmacol. Univ. Glas.

GILLESPIE, John Stewart Brigade Court, 104E Titchfield St., Kilmarnock KA1 1PH — MB ChB 1995 Glas.; BSc (Hons.) Glas. 1992. (Glas.) SHO (Dermat.) CrossHo. Hosp. Kilmarnock. Prev: SHO (Paediat.) CrossHo. Hosp.; SHO (O & G) Ayrsh. Centr. Hosp.; SHO (A & E Med.) Ayr Hosp.

GILLESPIE, Keith, Surg. Cdr. RN Retd. Knowle House Surgery, 4 Meavy Way, Crownhill, Plymouth PL5 3JB Tel: 01752 771895; Kingston House, Yelverton PL20 6HY Tel: 01822 852909 — MB ChB 1979 Bristol; MRCGP 1986. Princip. in Gen. Pract. Knowle Ho. Surg.; Med. Adviser, BRd.reach Ho., Addition Treatm. Centre, Plymouth. Prev: MoD Lond.; Princip. Med. Off. HMS Raleigh; Sen. Med. Off. Brit. Servs. Families Clinic, Naples.

GILLESPIE, Lorna Melanie 15 Hillside Road, Dundee DD2 1QZ — MB ChB 1993 Aberd.

GILLESPIE, Marjorie Marie 33 Hever Road, Edenbridge TN8 5DH — BM BCh 1996 Oxf.; BA Harvard 1991. Socs: Fell.- Roy. Soc. Of Med.

GILLESPIE, Morven Douglas 19 Erskine Hill, Polmont, Falkirk FK2 0UH — MB ChB 1970 Glas.

GILLESPIE, Neil David Department of Medicine (Ageing and Health), Ninewells Hospital and Medical School, Dundee DD1 9SY Tel: 01382 660111 Ext: 32450 Email: n.d.gillespie@dundee.ac.uk — MB ChB 1990 Glas.; BSc (Hons.) Glas. 1987; MRCP (UK) 1993; MD Dndee 1999. (Glas.) Sen. Lect. in Ageing & Health, Dept. Med., Ninewells Hosp., Dundee; Cons. Phys. (Med. for the Elderly), Dundee Primary Care NHS Trust. Prev: Lect. Dept. Med. (Ageing and Health), Ninewells Hosp. & Med. Sch., Dundee.

GILLESPIE, Pamela Erica 225 Saintfield Road, Belfast BT8 6PS — MB ChB BAO 1987 Belf. (Belfast) Indep. Med. Dir. Obesity Clinic Belf. Prev: SHO (Psychiat.) Belf. City Hosp.; SHO (Psychiat.) Downshire Hosp. Downpatrick; Ho. Off. (Med./Surg.) Craigavon Area Hosp.

GILLESPIE, Mr Patrick Hamilton 4 Demesne Gate, Saintfield, Ballynahinch BT24 7BE — BM BCh 1993 Oxf.; FRCS Eng. 1997; MA 1995 (Cambridge). (Oxford) Research Fell., Burns abd Plastic Surg., Stoke Madeville Hosp.

GILLESPIE, Peter Neal, OStJ, Lt.-Col. RAMC Medical Centre, Stirling Lines, Hereford HR2 6JA Tel: 01432 357311 — MB BCh BAO 1982 Belf.; MRCGP 1990; Dip. Pract. Dermat. Wales 1996; DTM & H Liverp. 1992; Dip IMC RCS Ed. 1992; DRCOG 1987. (Qu. Univ. Belf.) Sen. Med. Off. Hereford. Prev: Regtl. Med. Off. to 1/7 DEO Gurka Rifles; Regtl. Med. Off. to 1/2 KEO Gurka Rifles; Ho. Off. Mater Infirmorum Hosp. Belf.

GILLESPIE, Ruth Jean Simpson 2nd Floor Flat, 332 Morningside Road, Edinburgh EH10 4QJ — MB ChB 1990 Glas. SHO (Gen. Med.) Stobhill Gen. Hosp. Glas.

GILLESPIE, Shaun Francis 225 Saintfield Road, Belfast BT8 6PS Tel: 01232 703437 — MB BCh BAO 1988 Belf.; MRCPsych 1996; DMH Belf. 1993; DRCOG 1991. (Qu. Univ. Belf.) Specialist Regist. Rotat. (Psychiat.) N. Irel. Prev: Specialist Regist. (Psychiat.) Whiteabbey; SHO (Psychiat.) Belf. City Hosp.

GILLESPIE, Siobhan Mary 64 Gaskarth Road, London SW12 9NL — MB BS 1998 Lond.; MB BS Lond 1998.

GILLESPIE, Professor Stephen Henry Department of Medical Microbiology, Royal Free Hospital School of Medicine, Rowland Hill St., London NW3 2PF Tel: 020 7794 0500 Fax: 020 7794 0433 Email: stepheng@rfhsm.ac.uk; 2 Church Gate, Church Lane, Therfield, Buntingford SG9 9QD — MB BCh BAO 1980 Belf.; MD Belf. 1994; FRCP Ed. 1995; MRCP (UK) 1983; MRCPath 1986; T(Path) 1991; FRCPath 1996. Reader & Hon. Cons. Med. Microbiol. Roy. Free Hosp. Sch. Med. Lond. Socs: Path. Soc. of GB & Irel. (Counc. Mem.); Internat. Union Against Tuberc. & Lung Dis. (Clin. Trials Comm.); Soc. Gen. Microbiol. Prev: Mercers Lect. Clin. Trop. Med. Lond. Sch. Hyg. & Trop. Med.

GILLESPIE, Thomas Andrew 2nd Floor Right, 47 Viewforth, Edinburgh EH10 4LA — MB ChB 1989 Glas.

GILLESPIE, Professor William Alexander (retired) 2 Church Avenue, Bristol BS9 1LD Tel: 0117 968 2297 — MB BCh BAO Dub. 1936; MD Dub. 1942; FRCP Lond. 1971, M 1964; FRCPI 1957, M 1938; FRCPath 1963; DPH Dub. 1938. Prev: Prof. Clin. Bact. Univ. Bristol.

GILLETT, Adam Paul 55 Furlong Lane, Bishops Cleeve, Cheltenham GL52 8NJ — MB BCh 1995 Wales; DCH 1997; DRCOG 1997.

GILLETT, Adrian Paul Dept of Microbiology, Stoke mandeville Hospital, Mandeville Road, Aylesbury HP21 8AL Tel: 01296 31522 Fax: 01296 315389 Email: giletta@doctors.org.uk — MB ChB Birm. 1969; MRCP (UK) 1974; FRCPath 1991, M 1979. Cons. Med. Microbiol. Stoke Mandeville Hosp. Aylesbury.

GILLETT, Miss Anthea Sarah Blunden Hall, Bishops Castle SY9 5AX — MB ChB 1988 Manch.

GILLETT, Donald Satterthwaite Department of Haematology, Pembury Hospital, Tunbridge Wells TN2 4QJ Tel: 01892 823535 Fax: 01892 824370 — MB BS 1976 Lond.; BSc (Hons.) Lond. 1973; FRCP Lond. 1995; FRCP (UK) 1995, M 1980; FRCPath 1995, M 1985. (St. Bart. Hosp.) Cons. Haemat. Pembury Hosp. Kent. Socs: ACP; BSH; BBTS. Prev: Dir. Med. Educat. Kent & Sussex Weald NHS Trust; Lect. (Haemat.) Kings Coll. Hosp. Lond.; SHO (Gen. Med.) Kent & Canterbury Hosp.

GILLETT, George Bryan (retired) 5 Campton Road, Gravenhurst, Bedford MK45 4JB Tel: 01462 711268 — MB BS 1956 Lond.; FFA RCS Eng. 1961; DA Eng. 1958. Prev: Cons. Anaesth. St. Bart. Hosp. Lond.

GILLETT, Godfrey T Department of Clinical Biochemistry, Great Ormond Street Hospital for Children NHS Trust, Great Ormond St., London WC1N 3JH Tel: 020 7813 8321 Fax: 020 7829 8624 Email: ggillett@hgmp.mrc.ac.uk — MB ChB 1981 Sheff.; MA Camb. 1982, BA 1978; MRCP (UK) 1988; MRCPath 1995. Sen. Regist. & Clin. Lect. (Clin. Biochem.) Gt. Ormond St. Hosp. NHS Trust Lond.; Clin. Research Assoc. (Metab. Med.) UCL. Socs: Assn. Clin. Biochems.; Genet. Soc.; SSIEM. Prev: Lect. (Genetics) Inst. Child Health Lond.; MRC Train. Fell. (Human Biochem.) Genetics Unit Univ. Coll. Lond.; Regist. (Clin. Biochem.) Univ. Hosp. & City Hosp. Nottm.

GILLETT, James Cooper (retired) New Briton, Cresswell Quay, Kilgetty SA68 0TH Tel: 01646 651311 — MA Oxf., BM BCh 1946; MRCS Eng. LRCP Lond. 1939.

GILLETT, Marion 13 Burnt Stones Close, Sheffield S10 5TS Tel: 0114 230 5749 — MB ChB 1960 Birm. (Birm.) Dist. Med. Off. N. Derbysh. Health Auth. Socs: BMA. Prev: SCM (Health Care Plann., Epidemiol. & Dist.; Support) Derbysh. AHA; Regist. & Sen. Regist. (Community Med.) Trent RHA.

GILLETT, Mark James 12 Burnbrae Road, West Parley, Ferndown, Wimborne — MB BS 1992 Lond.

GILLETT, Martin Bancroft Department of Histopathology, Arrowe Park Hospital, Upton, Wirral CH49 5PE Tel: 0151 678 5111 Fax: 0151 604 1733; The Cottage, 7 Grange Cross Lane, West Kirby, Wirral CH48 8BJ Tel: 0151 625 5686 — MB BS 1972 Lond.; BSc Lond. 1969, MB BS 1972; MRCPath 1986; DObst RCOG 1974; FRCPath 1996. (St. Bart.) Cons. Histopath. Arrowe Pk. & Clatterbridge Hosps. Wirral. Socs: Assn. Clin. Path. & Internat. Acad. Path. Prev: Sen. Regist. (Path.) John Radcliffe & Ch.ill Hosps. Oxf.; Regist. (Path.) Kingston upon Thames Hosp.; Med. Off. Ngora Hosp. Uganda.

GILLETT, Roger (retired) Fernroyd, St Margaret's Road, Altrincham WA14 2AW Tel: 0161 928 5112 — BM BCh 1945 Oxf.; BM BCh Oxon. 1945; DPath Eng 1960; FRCPath 1971, M 1964. Prev: Cons. Path. Hope Hosp. Salford.

GILLETT, Roger Howitt (retired) 11 Lakeside Road, Poole BH13 6LS Tel: 01202 765855 — MB BChir 1965 Camb.; MA Camb. 1965; DObst RCOG 1966. Clin. Asst. (H.I.V.) Roy. Bournemouth Hosp. Bournemouth (p/t). Prev: Gen. Pract. Bournemouth.

GILLETT, Timothy Paul Sir Martin Roth Young Peoples' Unit, Newcastle General Hospital, Westgate Road, Newcastle upon Tyne NE4 6BE Tel: 0191 219 5023 Fax: 0191 219 5022 Email: tgillett@ncht.northy.nhs.uk; 23 Southwood Gardens, Kenton, Newcastle upon Tyne NE3 3BU Tel: 0191 284 4797 Fax: 0191 284 4797 Email: tim@timtom.demon.co.uk — MB BS 1984 Lond.; MRCPsych 1991. Cons. Adolesc. Psychiat. Young People's Unit New. Gen. Hosp. Newc. u. Tyne; Hon. Sen. Lect. (Child Health) Univ. Newc.

GILLEY, Judith Ann 42 Avondale Avenue, London N12 8EN Tel: 020 8445 1654 Fax: 020 8446 9997 — MB BS 1969 Lond.; FRCGP 2000; MRCGP 1992; DFFP 1994. (Lond. Hosp. Med. Sch.) Chief Executions The Secretariat. Beds. & Herts LMCS, Stevenage. Socs: Inst. Psychosexual Med.; BMA Counc. Prev: Partner, GP Pract., Cornw. Ho., Cornw. St. Lond.; Sen. Lec. Pub. Health & Primary care Roy. Free. Hosp.

GILLGRASS, James William The Birdhurst Medical Practice, 1 Birdhurst Avenue, South Croydon CR2 7DX Tel: 020 8686 2070 Fax: 020 8686 0824 — MB BS 1976 Lond.; MRCP (UK) 1978; MRCS Eng. LRCP Lond. 1976. (Char. Cross) GP Croydon; Chairm. Croydon LMC 1995-. Prev: Clin. Asst. (Cardiol.) Croydon; Regist. (Rheum.) Guy's Hosp. Lond.

GILLHAM, Adrian Bayley The Priory Hospital Woking, Chobham Road, Knaphill, Woking GU21 2QF Tel: 01483 485141 Fax: 01483 797053 Email: dragillham@whc.co.uk; Seven Steps, Crondall Road, Crookham Village, Fleet GU51 5SS Tel: 01252 810285 Fax: 01252 810285 Email: gillham.7steps@tinyonline.co.uk — MB BChir 1972 Camb.; MA Camb. 1973; MRCP (UK) 1976; MRCPsych 1989; MRCGP 1981. (Jesus Coll. Camb. & St. Mary's) Cons. Psychiat. (Independant); Med. Dir. Priory Hosp. Woking; Regional Cons. Psychiat. The Ex Serv. Ment. Welf. Soc.; cons Psychiat., surrey Hants. borders -NHS Trust. Socs: Assn. Cognitive Anal. Ther.; Europ. Soc. for Traum. stress studies. Prev: Cons. Psychiat. Camb. Milit. Hosp. Aldershot; Hon. Sen. Regist. Maudsley Hosp. & Guy's Hosp. Lond.

GILLHAM, Charles Martin — MB BS 1994 Lond.; BSc Lond. 1991; MRCP 1998. (UCLMSM) Sen. Specialist Regist.(Clin. onc.) Middlx. Hosp. Marthes St. Lond. Prev: SHO Med. Rotat. Barnet Gen. Hosp. Herts.; Specialist Regist. (Clin. Oncol.) St Bartholomews Hosp. Lond.

GILLHAM, Margaret Imogen 5 Fox's Close, Milton, Cambridge CB4 4BT Tel: 01223 863305 — MB BS 1981 Newc.

GILLHAM, Michael James Auckland Hospital, Park Road, Auckland 1, New Zealand Tel: 019 379 7440 Fax: 019 307 4933; 21 Leicester Road, Croydon CR0 6EB Tel: 020 8 654 0476 — MB BS 1990 Lond.; BSc (Hons.) Lond. 1989. Regist. (Gen. Med.) Auckland Hosp., NZ. Prev: SHO (Gen. Med.) Hull Roy. Infirm.

GILLHAM, Mr Nicholas Richard Horton Hospital, Oxford Road, Banbury OX16 9AL Tel: 01295 229401 Fax: 01295 229055; 4 Victoria Terrace, Deddington, Banbury OX15 0TU Tel: 01869 338169 — BM BCh 1981 Oxf.; MA Camb. 1986, BA 1978; FRCS Ed. (Orth.) 1993; FRCS Ed. 1986. Cons. Trauma & Orthop. Surg. Horton Gen. Hosp. NHS Trust.

GILLIAM, Andrew Douglas 21 Ancaster Road, Wesk Park, Leeds LS16 5HH — MB ChB 1995 Dundee; MRCS 1998. SHO Surg. ScarBoro. Hosp.

GILLIAM, Gillian Spindrift, Pyrford Road, West Byfleet KT14 6RE — MB BS 1961 Lond. (Lond. Hosp.) Prev: Ho. Phys. Orsett Hosp. Grays.; Ho. Surg. Nottm. Gen. Hosp.; Clin. Research Asst. Woking Vict. Hosp.

GILLIAT, Joanna Mary Frances The Garth Surgery, Westgate, Guisborough TS14 6AT Tel: 01287 632206 Fax: 01287 635112; Throstle Nest Farm, Moorsholm, Saltburn-by-the-Sea TS12 3JJ Tel: 01287 643605 Fax: 01287 660696 — MB BS 1984 Newc.; MB BS Newc. l984; MRCGP 1991. Princip. GP GuisBoro.. Prev: SHO (O & G) Lincoln Co. Hosp.; SHO (Psychiat. & Paediat.) Darlington Memor. Hosp.; SHO (Geriat.) Poole Hosp.

GILLIBRAND, Angela Hamilton, Chilworth Road, Southampton SO16 7JT Tel: 02380 768618 Fax: 02380 760757 — MB BS 1993 Lond.

GILLIBRAND, Mr Pharic Nelson Hamilton, Chilworth Road, Southampton SO16 7JT Tel: 02380 768618 Fax: 02380 760757 — MD Lond. 1969, MB BS 1958; FRCOG 1977, M 1965. (St. Mary's) Emerit. Cons. (O & G) S.ampton Univ. Hosp.; Hon. Clin. Teach. Soton. Univ. Med. Sch. Socs: BMA & RSM. Prev: Sen. Regist. St. Geo. Hosp. Lond.; Regist. St. Mary's Hosp. & Samarit. Hosp. Wom. Lond.

GILLIBRAND, Rebecca Anvil Cottage, Letcombe Regis, Wantage OX12 9LA — MB BS 1996 Lond.

GILLIBRAND, Susanna Ingleford, Leigh Road, Southampton SO17 1EF Tel: 02380 554775 Email: shoghton@aol.com — MB BS 1989 Lond.; MRCGP 1993; DRCOG 1992; Dip. Occ. Med. 1997. (St. Mary's Hosp. Med. Sch.) Clin. Asst. (Dermat.) Haslar Hosp. Soton.; Med. Adviser Vosper Thornycroft UK; Adviser (Occupat. Health) Soton. City Counc. Prev: Trainee GP Portsmouth VTS.

GILLIE, Anne Katherine (retired) 9 Algarth Rise, Heworth, York YO31 1HD — MB ChB Glas. 1949; MRCPsych 1973; DPM Lond. 1952. Prev: Cons. Psychiat. Clifton Hosp. York.

GILLIE, Christopher Philipson Alveley Medical Centre, Village Road, Alveley, Bridgnorth WV15 6NG Tel: 01746 780553; The Rowans, Oldbury, Bridgnorth WV16 5LW Tel: 01746 767912 — MB BS 1958 Durh.; MRCGP 1968. (Newc.) Socs: Brit. Geriat. Soc. Prev: JHMO (Psychiat.) W. Cumbld. Hosp. Whitehaven; SHO (Med.) Preston Hosp. N. Shields; Ho. Phys. Paediat. Gen. Hosp. Newc. u Tyne.

GILLIE, Ian (retired) 12 Sydalls Way, Catterick Vill., Richmond DL10 7ND — MB ChB 1964 Manch. Prev: Resid. Clin. Pathol., Ho. Surg. (ENT) & Ho. Phys. (Haemat.) Manch. Roy. Infirm.

GILLIE, Isla Margaret Sinclair (retired) — MB ChB 1943 Ed.; DPH Ed. 1963; MFCM 1972. Prev: SCM Newc. HA.

GILLIE, Mr Roger Fairgreave Department of Ophthalmology, Royal Victoria Infirmary, Newcastle upon Tyne NE1 4LP Tel: 0191 232 5131 — MB BS 1967 Newc.; FRCS Ed. 1973; FRCOphth 1991; DO Eng. 1972. (Newc.) Cons. Ophth. Roy. Vict. Infirm. Prev: Sen. Regist. Eye Dept. Roy. Hosp. Sheff.; Regist. Eye Dept. Roy. Vict. Infirm. Newc.; SHO Eye Dept. Edin. Roy. Infirm.

GILLIES, Alexander Kenneth (retired) 5 Drumdevan Road, Inverness IV2 4BZ — MB ChB 1952 Glas. Prev: Princip. GP Tongue & Brora Sutherland.

GILLIES, Anne Juliet 38 Selly Wick Road, Selly Park, Birmingham B29 7JA — MB BCh 1988 Wales. SHO (O & G) E. Birm. Hosp.

GILLIES, Carolyn Govan Health Centre, 5 Drumoyne Road, Glasgow G51 4BJ Tel: 0141 531 8490 Fax: 0141 531 8487; 14 Larchfield Avenue, Newton Mearns, Glasgow G77 5PW Tel: 0141 639 6027 — MB ChB 1981 Dundee; DRCOG 1984.

GILLIES, Douglas Ritchie Neri District Hospital, Lancaster Park Road, Harrogate HG2 7SX Tel: 01423 885959; 6 Greengate Drive, Scriven, Knaresborough HG5 9EN Tel: 01423 868758 — MB ChB 1975 Ed.; BSc Ed. 1972; MRCP (UK) 1981. (Ed.) Cons. Paediat. Harrogate Health Care Trust. Prev: Sen. Regist. (Paediat.) Yorks. RHA.

GILLIES, Elisabeth Ann Drummond 17 Pembridge Road, London W11 3HG Tel: 020 7221 0174 Fax: 020 7229 0774 — MB ChB 1986 Ed.; MRCGP 1996; DCH RCP Lond. 1995; DA (UK) 1988. p/t GP Asst. Lond.; Palliat. Care Hosp. Practitioner.

GILLIES, Elizabeth Mary Viewfield Lane Health Centre, Viewfield Lane, Selkirk TD7 4LJ Tel: 01750 21674 Fax: 01750 23176; The Maples, 19 Heatherlie Park, Selkirk TD7 5AL — MB ChB 1976 Ed.; MRCP (UK) 1979; MFHom 1995. (Ed.)

GILLIES, Frances Claire Louise 31 Minster Way, Bath BA2 6RH — MB ChB 1991 Birm.; ChB Birm. 1991.

GILLIES, Graham William Armstrong 14 Larchfield Avenue, Newton Mearns, Glasgow G77 5PW — MB ChB 1980 Dundee; FFA RCS Eng. 1984. Cons. Anaesth. Vict. Infirm. Glas.

GILLIES, Helen Catherine Farndon Health Centre, Church Lane CH3 6QD Tel: 01829 270206 — MB BS 1980 Lond.; BSc (Hons.) Lond. 1977; MRCP (UK) 1983; DRCOG 1988. (Guy's Hospital) GP employed non-Princip., Farndon, Chesh.; Clin. Asst., Cardiol., Countess of Chester Hosp. Prev: Lect. (Clin. Pharmacol.) & Hon. Regist. (Gen. Med.) Guy's Hosp. Med. Sch. Lond.

GILLIES, Hugh Graham Tel: 01295 259484 — MB ChB 1976 Manch.; BSc St. And. 1973; DRCOG 1979. (St Andrews and Manchester) Prev: Regist. (A & E) Hope Hosp. Salford; Ho. Surg. Dumfries & Galloway Roy. Infirm.; Ho. Phys. Univ. Hosp. S. Manch.

GILLIES, Hunter (retired) Roseway, 9 Watling Lane, Dorchester on Thames, Wallingford OX10 7JG — MB ChB 1934 Glas.; MB ChB (Commend.) Glas. 1934; MD (High Commend.) Glas. 1938; FRCP Ed. 1952, M 1947; MRCP Glas. 1968; FRCPsych 1971; DPM Eng.

1936. Hon. Cons. Psychiat. Stobhill Gen. Hosp. Glas. Prev: Cons. i/c Psychiat. Unit Stobhill Gen. Hosp.

GILLIES, John Calum MacDonald Viewfield Lane Health Centre, Viewfield Lane, Selkirk TD7 4LJ Tel: 01750 21674 Fax: 01750 23176 Email: john.gillies@selkirhc.borders.scot.nhs.uk; The Maples, Heatherlie Park, Selkirk TD7 5AL — MB ChB 1976 Ed.; FRCGP 2000; FRCP Ed. 1992; MRCP (UK) 1978; MRCGP 1985; DTM & H Liverp. 1980; DCH NUI 1979. (Ed.) p/t GP Princip.; Guidelines Adviser NHS borders. Prev: Undergrad. Tutor (Gen. Pract.) Univ. Glas.; Dist. Med. Off. Ntcheu, Malawi.

GILLIES, Katherine Mary Tel: 020 7835 0979 — MB ChB 1989 Manch.; BSc (Med. Sci.) St. And. 1986; MRCGP 1995; DCH RCP Lond. 1994; DRCOG 1993. (Manchester/St Andrews) GP. Socs: BMA. Prev: Asst. GP Lond.; SHO (Paediat.) 1993.

GILLIES, Liesel 45A Lonsdale Square, London N1 1EW — MB ChB 1990 Stellenbosch.

GILLIES, Michael Alexander Munoz 19 Glen Grove, E. Kilbride, Glasgow G75 0BG — MB ChB 1994 Glas.

GILLIES, Neil Radasi The Moorings, 6 Newton St., Stornoway, Isle of Lewis HS1 2RE — MB ChB 1954 Aberd.

GILLIES, Neil William Kingsmills Medical Practice, 18 Southside Road, Inverness IV2 3BG Tel: 01463 235245 Fax: 01463 01443 714400; 5 Bellfield Terrace, Inverness IV2 4ST Tel: 01463 716515 Fax: 01463 716515 Email: administrator@gp55817.highland.hb.scot.nhs.uk — MB ChB Ed. 1970; BSc Ed. 1967; DCH Eng. 1973; DObst RCOG 1972. (Ed.) Socs: Highland Med.Soc.

GILLIES, Pauline Mary 1 Hilldowntree Mill, Leggart Terrace, Aberdeen AB12 5TX — MB ChB 1992 Aberd.

GILLIES, Mr Robert Malcolm Department of Orthopaedics, Leighton Hospital, Middlewich Road, Crewe CW1 4QJ Tel: 01270 612382 Fax: 01270 612382 — MB ChB 1982 Liverp.; FRCS Ed. 1987. Cons. Orthop. Surg. Leighton Hosp. Crewe. Socs: Fell. BOA; Brit. Orthop. Sports Trauma Assn.; Brit. Assn. for Surg. of Knee.

GILLIES, Roderick Church Place Surgery, 6 Church Place, Moffat DG10 9ES Tel: 01683 220197 Fax: 01683 221320; Park Cottage, Old Well Road, Moffat DG10 9AP — MB ChB 1981 Dundee.

GILLIES, Ruth Margaret Fairfield Park Health Centre, Tyning Lane, Camden Rd, Bath BA1 6EA Tel: 01225 331616 Fax: 01225 482932; 31 Minster Way, Warminster Road, Bath BA2 6RH Tel: 01225 463649 — MB BS 1961 Lond.; MRCS Eng. LRCP Lond. 1961; MFFP 1993. (Univ. Coll. Hosp.)

GILLIES, Sheila Elizabeth (retired) 23 Matheson Road, Stornoway HS1 2LR Tel: 01851 703138 — MB ChB 1947 St. And.

GILLIES, Shona Ross Church Place Surgery, 6 Church Place, Moffat DG10 9ES Tel: 01683 220197 Fax: 01683 221320; Park Cottage, Old Well Road, Moffat DG10 9AP — MB ChB 1986 Aberd.; DRCOG 1988.

GILLIES, Tracey Elizabeth 26 Craighouse Avenue, Edinburgh EH10 5LN — MB ChB 1989 Bristol.

GILLIES, Walter John Larchhill, Moffat DG10 9AJ Tel: 01683 221022 — MB ChB Ed. 1945; BA Camb. 1942. (Camb. & Ed.) GP Dumfriessh. Prev: Ho. Surg. Roy. Infirm. Edin.; Ho. Phys. Roy. Hosp. Sick Childr. Edin.; Capt. RAMC.

GILLIESON, Elizabeth Celia (retired) 8 Welby Gardens, Grantham NG31 8BN Tel: 01476 63539 — MB BS 1938 Lond.; MRCS Eng. LRCP Lond. 1938. Prev: Ho. Phys. Univ. Coll. Hosp.

GILLIGAN, Mr Conor John 3 Shrewsbury Drive, Belfast BT9 6PL Tel: 01232 665152 — MB BCh BAO 1945 Belf.; FRCSI 1949. Cons. Surg. Mater Infirm. Hosp. Belf. Socs: Fell. Assn. Surgs.; Ulster Surg. Club.

GILLIGAN, David Oncology Centre, Box 193, Addenbrooke's NHS Trust, Hills Road, Cambridge CB2 2QQ Tel: 01223 216555 Fax: 01223 274409 Email: david.gilligan@msexc.addenbrookes.anglox.nhs.uk; 55 Hinton Avenue, Cambridge CB1 7AR — MB BChir 1985 Camb.; BSc Ed. 1983; MRCP (UK) 1989; FRCR 1993; FRCP 1999 (Edin). Cons. Clin. Oncol. Addenbrooke's & Papworth Hosps. Camb. Prev: Sen. Regist. (Clin. Oncol.) Middlx. Hosp. Lond.; Clin. Research Fell. (Radiother.) Inst. Cancer Research Sutton, Surrey; Regist. (Radiother. & Oncol.) Roy. Marsden Hosp. Lond. & Surrey.

GILLIGAN, Marie Theresa Albert Street Health Centre, Albert Street, Belfast BT12 4JR Tel: 028 9032 0777 — MB BCh BAO 1980 Belf.; MRCGP 1984; DRCOG 1982.

GILLIGAN, Rebecca Elizabeth 55 Central Avenue, Prescot L34 1NA — MB ChB 1998 Manch.; MB ChB Manch 1998.

GILLIGAN, Stephen John Blackburn Hyndburn and Ribble Valley NHS Trust, Blackburn Royal Infirmary, Bolton Road, Blackburn BB2; 74 Rogersfield, Langho, Blackburn BB6 8HD — MB ChB 1986 Manch.; FRCA 1994. Cons. (Anaesth. & IC) Blackburn, Hyndburn & Ribble Valley NHS Trust.

GILLIGHAN, John Christopher Verdon The Medical Centre, Market St., Whitworth, Rochdale OL12 8QS Tel: 01706 852238 Fax: 01706 853877; 6 Lowerford Drive, Rochdale OL12 7JA — LRCPI & LM, LRSCI & LM 1974; LRCPI & LM, LRCSI & LM 1974.

GILLILAND, Andrew Edward William Dunluce Health Centre, 1 Dunluce Avenue, Belfast BT9 7HR — MD Belf. 1992, MB BCh BAO 1980; MRCGP 1984; MICGP 1987; DCH Dub. 1983; DRCOG 1982. Sen. Lect. & Princip. (Gen. Pract.) Qu. Univ. Belf. Prev: Lect. (Family Pract.) Univ. Manitoba, Canada.

GILLILAND, Mr Eric Leslie North Tees General Hospital, Stockton-on-Tees TS19 8PE Tel: 01642 617617 Fax: 01642 624976; Ashleigh, 4 Ashville Avenue, Eaglescliffe, Stockton-on-Tees TS16 9AX Email: gilliland@hotmail.com — MB BS 1972 Lond.; BSc (Hons.) Lond. 1969; MS Lond. 1988; FRCS Eng. 1977. (St. Mary's) Cons. Surg. N. Tees Gen. Hosp. Stockton-on-Tees. Prev: Sen. Regist. (Surg.) St. Mary's Hosp. Lond.; Regist. (Surg.) Qu. Eliz. II Hosp. Welwyn Garden City; Harvard Research Fell., USA.

GILLILAND, Helen Elizabeth Margaret — MB ChB 1987 Ed.; FRCA 1992. Cons. Anaethsthetist, Roy. Gp. of Hosp.s, Belf. Socs: Train. Mem. Assn. AnE.h.; Fell. of Roy. Coll. of Anaesth.s.

GILLILAND, Mr Robert Altnagelvin Area Hospital, Glenshane Road, Londonderry BT47 6SB — MD Belf. 1997; MB BCh BAO Belf. 1983; FRCS (Gen) Ed. 1997, FRCS 1987. (Queen's Univ. Belf.) Cons. Surg. (Specialist Interest in ColoProctol.) Altnagelvin Area Hosp. Lond.derry; Clin. Lect., Qu.'s Univ. of Belf. Socs: Assn. of ColoProctol. GB & Irel.; Irish Assn. of Coloproctol. (Ex-Sec.).

GILLILAND, Stephen James 11 Monkwood Place, Ayr KA7 4UL — MB ChB 1989 Aberd.; MRCGP 1995.

GILLING-SMITH, Carole Marie-Therese Laura Department Obstetrics & Gynaecology, St Mary's Hospital Medical School, London W2 1PG Tel: 020 7886 1061 Fax: 020 7886 6054; 18 Lysia Street, London SW6 6NG Tel: 020 7381 5803 — MB BChir 1984 Camb.; PhD 1997; MA Camb. 1982; MRCOG 1990. Lect. & Hon. Sen. Regist. (O & G) St. Mary's Hosp. Lond. Prev: MRC Train. Fell. & Hon. Regist. (O & G) St. Mary's Hosp. Lond.; SHO (Obst.) Qu. Charlotte's Hosp. Lond.; SHO (Gyn.) Chelsea Hosp. for Wom. Lond.

GILLING-SMITH, Mr Geoffrey Lawrence Department of Vascular Surgery, Link 8C, Royal Liverpool University Hospital, Prescot St., Liverpool L7 8XP Tel: 0151 706 3481 Fax: 0151 706 5827; Old Hall, Puddington, South Wirral L64 5SS — MB BS 1980 Lond.; MS Lond. 1994; FRCS Eng. 1987; FRCS Ed. 1987; MRCS Eng. LRCP Lond. 1980. (Char. Cross) Cons. Vasc. Surg. Roy. Liverp. Univ. Hosp.; Surgic. Tutor RCS Eng. Socs: BMA; Vasc. Surg. Soc. GB & Irel.; Eur. Soc. Vasc. Surg. Prev: Sen. Regist. (Vasc. Surg.) St. Mary's Hosp. Lond.; Research Fell. Roy. Postgrad. Med. Sch. Hammersmith Hosp. Lond.

GILLINGHAM, Professor Francis John, CBE, MBE(Mil) Easter Park House, Barnton Avenue, Edinburgh EH4 6SN Tel: 0131 336 3528 Fax: 0131 228 8118; El Rodat, Javea, 03730, Alicante, Spain Tel: 00 34 965 771955 Fax: 00 34 965 771955 Email: jgillinghm@aol.com — MB BS 1939 Lond.; Hon. Fell. Coll. Surgs. Sri Lanka 1975; MRCS Eng. LRCP Lond. 1939; FRS Ed.; Hon. MD Thessaloniki 1973; FRCP Ed. 1967; FRCS Ed. 1955; FRCS Eng. 1947; Hon. FRCSI 1982 Hon FRACS; Hon. FRCS Glas. 1982; Hon. FRACS 1980. (St. Bart.) Emerit. Prof. Neurol. Surg. Univ. Edin. Socs: (Ex-Pres.) Edin. M-C Soc.; Hon. Mem. Roy. Acad. Med. Valencia; Fell. RSA. Prev: Prof. Surg. Neurol. & Adviser Neurosurg. King Saud Univ. Kingdom of Saudi Arabia; Maj. RAMC Neurosurg. Specialist, Milit. Hosp. (Head Injuries) Oxf.; Hon. Cons. Neurosurg. St. Bart. Hosp. Lond.

GILLINGHAM, Naomi Susan Lisson Grove Health Centre, Gateforth St, London NW8 8EG Tel: 020 7262 1366 Fax: 020 7258 1943; 5 Fortnam Road, London N19 3NS Tel: 020 7272 3438 — MB BS 1981 Lond.; BSc (Hons.) Surrey 1975; Cert. Family Plann. JCC 1985; DRCOG 1983. (Roy. Free) GP Tutor Co-ordinator Roy. Free Hosp. Lond. Prev: Trainee GP Edgware Gen. Hosp. VTS.

GILLINGS, Martin Jonathon Oak Street Medical Practice, Oak Street, Norwich NR3 3DL Tel: 01603 613431 Fax: 01603 767209; Victoria House, 96 Newmarket Road, Norwich NR2 2LB Tel: 01603 504486 — MB BChir 1975 Camb.; FRCP 2001; DRCOG 1980. (Queens Coll.Camb & St Barts Lond) Socs: Brit. Thorac. Soc.& BMA. Prev: SHO (Med.) Roy. Portsmouth Hosp.; Regist. (Med.) W. Norwich & Norf. & Norwich Hosps.; Ho. Phys. Hackney Hosp. Lond.

GILLIS, Professor Charles Raphael 20 Craignethan Road, Whitecraigs, Giffnock, Glasgow G46 6SQ Tel: 0141 639 1718; West of Scotland Cancer Surveillance Unit, University Department of Public Health, Glasgow G12 8RZ Tel: 0141 330 3281 Fax: 0141 330 3283 — MD (Commend.) Glas. 1971, MB ChB 1961; FFCM 1979, M 1974; MRCP (Glas.) 1987; FRCP (Glas.) 1989. (Glasgow) Cons. (Epidemiol. of Cancer) & Dir. W. Scotl. Cancer Surviellance Unit.; Hon. Prof. Univ. of Glas. 1997. Prev: Sen. Lect. (Community Med.) Univ. Glas.; Hon. Cons. Epidemiol. Ruchill Hosp. Glas.

GILLIS, Clive Victor Stonebow Cottage, Eastertown, Lympsham, Weston Super Mare BS24 0HT — MB ChB 1968 Leeds; DObst RCOG 1971.

GILLIS, Sarah 47a Rotherfield Street, London N1 3BU — MB BS 1991 Lond.

GILLIS, Victor Emmanuel (retired) 23 Ettrick Lodge, 36 The Grove, Gosforth, Newcastle upon Tyne NE3 1NH Tel: 0191 284 9195 — MB BS 1935 Durh.

GILLISON, Mr Ewen Walford (retired) Fairfield, Brushford, Dulverton TA22 9AT Tel: 01398 323351 Email: gillison@frgeuk.com — MB BS Lond. 1959; FRCS Eng. 1967; FRCS Ed. 1966; DObst RCOG 1961. Hon. Cons. Surg., City Hosp., Dudley Rd, Birm. Prev: Cons. (Surg.) Kidderminster Gen. Hosp.

GILLIVER, Ann (retired) 13 Earl Close, Dorchester DT1 1DY — MB BS 1959 Lond.; MRCS Eng. LRCP Lond. 1959. Regist. (Rheum. & Rehabil.) W. Dorset Health Dist.

GILLMER, Michael David George Women's Centre, John Radcliffe Hospital, Headley Way, Oxford OX3 9DU Tel: 01865 221624 Fax: 01865 221188; Royston, Church Lane, Islip, Oxford OX5 2TA Tel: 07774 235627 Email: mike.gillmer@obs-gyn.ox.ac.uk — MB BS 1968 Lond.; MD Lond. 1979; MRCS ENg. LRCP Lond. 1968; FRCOG 1983, M 1972. (King's Coll. Hosp.) Cons. O & G John Radcliffe Hosp. Oxf.; Hon. Lect. Nuffield Dept. Obst. & Gyn. Oxf. Socs: Gyn. Vis. Soc.; Green Coll.; Blair Bell Res. Soc. Prev: Clin. Reader (O & G) Oxf.; Lect. (Obst.) Univ. Natal Durban S. Afr. & (O & G) St. Mary's Hosp. Lond.

GILLMORE, John Holton (retired) 31 White Oak Way, Nailsea, Bristol BS48 4YS Tel: 01275 852103 Email: jgillm6356@aol.com — MB ChB (Hons.) Bristol 1970; MRCGP 1975. Prev: Sen. Part. The Health Centre Som. Sq. Nailsea Bristol.

GILLMORE, Julian David Queen Mary's Hospital, Frognal Avenue, Sidcup DA14 6LT — MB BS 1991 Lond.

GILLMORE, Roopinder Jit 236 Twyford Avenue, Portsmouth PO2 8NP — MB BS 1994 Lond.

GILLON, John SE Scotland Blood Transfusion Service, Royal Infirmary, Edinburgh EH3 9HB Tel: 0131 536 5320 Fax: 0131 536 5301 Email: jack.gillon@snbts.csa.scot.nhs.uk; 20 Suffolk Road, Edinburgh EH16 5NJ Tel: 0131 667 1565 — MB ChB 1973 Ed.; MRCP (UK) 1975; MD Ed. 1984; FRCP Ed. 1991. Cons. Phys. Edin. & SE Scotl. Blood Transfus. Serv. Roy. Infirm. Edin.; Hon. Sen. Lect. Univ. Edin. Socs: Brit. Blood Transfus. Soc. Prev: Lect. (Med. & Gastrointestinal) W.. Gen. Hosp. Edin.

GILLON, Professor Raanan Evelyn Zvi ICHS, Southside Prince's Gardens, London SW7 1LU Tel: 020 7584 6301 Fax: 020 7594 9390; 42 Brynmaer Road, London SW11 4EW Tel: 020 7622 1450 — MB BS Lond. 1964; BA (Phil) (1st cl. Hons.) Lond. 1979; FRCP Lond. 1988, M. 1974. (Univ. Coll. Hosp. & Oxf.) Sen. NHS Partner, Imperial Coll. Health Serv. Med. Partnership. Socs: Fell. Roy. Soc. Med.; BMA; Internat. Assn. Bioethics. Prev: Edr. Jl. Med. Ethics; Dir., Imperial Coll. Health Serv.; Vis. Prof., MA Course Dir. & Examr. Centre Med. Law & Ethics, King's Coll. Lond. Univ.

GILLOTT, John Henry 110 Westbourne Road, Sheffield S10 2QT Tel: 0114 60341 — MB ChB 1961 Sheff. Prev: Regist. Path. United Sheff. Hosps.; SHO Med. Lincoln Hosp. Gp.

GILLOTT, Timothy John 110 Westbourne Road, Sheffield S10 2QT — MB ChB 1990 Sheff.

GILLOW, Janice Louise 4 St Mary's Lane, Ecclesfield, Sheffield S35 9YE — MB ChB 1983 Leeds. SHO Rotat. (Psychiat.) Pontefract Gen. Infirm. Train. Scheme. Prev: SHO (Psychiat.) Stanley Royd Hosp. Wakefield; SHO (Path.) Leeds Gen. Infirm.; Research Asst. Dept. Surg. Leeds Gen. Infirm.

GILLOW, John Timothy Joseph — MB BS 1987 Lond.; BA (Cantab.) 1982; MRCP (UK) 1991; FRCOphth 1994.

***GILLSON, John Andrew** 1 Grosvenor Crescent, Droitwich WR9 7SX — BM BS 1998 Nottm.; BM BS Nottm 1998.

GILLSON, Simon Toby La Fe, Quarry Lane, Birstall, Batley WF17 0DF — BM BS 1995 Nottm.

GILLULEY, Paul Francis Academic Department of Psychiatry, Charing Cross & Westminster Medical School, 24 St Dunstan Road, Hammersmith, London W6 — MB ChB 1991 Glas.; MRCPsych 1996.

GILLVRAY, Karen Elizabeth 16 Knockmarloch Park, Belfast BT4 2LD — MB BCh BAO 1990 Belf.

GILMAN, Alan Richard Brinnington Health Centre, Brinnington Road, Stockport SK5 8BS Tel: 0161 430 4002 Fax: 0161 430 2918 — MB ChB 1976 Manch.

GILMAN, David Howard The Rex Binning Department of Anaesthetics, Royal Sussex County Hospital, Eastern Road, Brighton BN2 5BE Tel: 01273 609060 Fax: 01273 664791; The Cottage, Station Road, Isfield, Uckfield TN22 5XG Tel: 01825 750492 Fax: 01825 750492 — MB BS 1980 Lond.; BSc Lond. 1977; FFA RCS Eng. 1985. (King's College Hospital) Cons. Anaesth. Roy. Sussex Co. Hosp. Brighton. Prev: Sen. Regist. King's Coll. Hosp. Lond.

GILMAN, Margaret Millicent (retired) 3 Ashley Mill Lane N., Hale, Altrincham WA14 3NQ — MB ChB 1956 Manch.; DA Eng. 1958.

GILMARTIN, Gail Mackintosh House, 120 Blythswood St., Glasgow G2 4EH Tel: 0141 221 5858; 35 Gates Road, Lochwinnoch PA12 4HF — MB ChB 1984 Liverp.; MPhil Glas. 1994. Med. Adviser Med. & Dent. Defence Union Scotl.

GILMARTIN, Laurence Mary Declan Accident & Emergency Department, Princess of Wales Hospital, Coity Road, Bridgend CF31 1RQ Tel: 01656 752752 — MB BCh BAO 1978 NUI; FRCSI 1982; FRCS Ed. 1988; BSc (Anat.) NUI 1980. Cons. (A & E) P.ss of Wales Hosp. Bridgend.

GILMER, Samuel Owens Holywood Arches Health Centre, Westminster Avenue, Belfast BT4 1NS Tel: 028 9056 3354 Fax: 028 9065 3846 — MB BCh BAO 1979 Belf.

GILMORE, Andrew Leicester Terrace Health Care Centre, 8 Leicester Terrace, Northampton NN2 6AL Tel: 01604 33682 Fax: 01604 233408 — MB ChB 1989 Leic.; BSc (Hons.) Sheff. 1983; MRCGP 1996; DRCOG 1994. (Univ. Leic.) Socs: BMA; MDU. Prev: Trainee GP/SHO Kettering Gen. Hosp. VTS.

GILMORE, Anna Benedicta Claire Ecohost, London School of Hygiene & Tropical Medicine, Geppel St, London — MB BS 1991 Lond.; DTM & H Liverp. 1993; MPH 1997; MFPHM 1999. Sen. Regist. in Pub. Health Med.

GILMORE, Antonia Mary Clare 17 Nursery Walk, Cambridge CB4 3PR — MB BS 1983 Lond. Clin. Asst. (Ophth.) Addenbrookes Hosp. Camb. Prev: SHO (Ophth. & Geriat.) Cheltenham Gen. Hosp.; Ho. Off. (Phys.) Lister Hosp. Stevenage.

GILMORE, Mrs Cathryn Patricia Bangor Health Centre, Newtownards Road, Bangor BT20 4LD Tel: 028 9146 9111; 2 Maxwell Park, Bangor BT20 3SH Tel: 02891 271063 — MB BCh BAO 1976 Belf.; MRCGP 1981; DCH RCPSI 1982.

GILMORE, Christine EMH Team, Wirral and West Cheshire Community NHS Trust, Liverpool Road, Chester CH2 1UL Tel: 01244 364268 Fax: 01244 364268 — MB ChB 1983 Liverp.; MRCPsych 1990. Cons. (Old Age Psychiat.) Wirral & W. Chesh. Community NHS Trust. Socs: Liverp. Psychiat. Soc. Prev: Sen. Regist. (Old Age Psychiat.) S.port & Formby Comm. NHS Trust; Sen. Regist. (Gen. & Rehabil. Psychiat.) W. Chesh. Comm. NHS Trust; Sen. Regist. (Old AGe Psychiat.) N. Mersey Com. Trust.

GILMORE, David Anthony Kings Road Surgery, 67 Kings Road, Harrogate HG1 5HJ Tel: 01423 875875 Fax: 01423 875885; 6 Station Lane, Burton leonard, Harrogate HG3 3RU — MB ChB 1991 Sheff.; DRCOG 1996. (Sheffield) p/t GP Princip. The Surg., 67 Kings Rd, Harrogate; Health Screening Duchy Nuffield Hosp. Prev: Clin. Med. Off. Community Paediat. Harrogate; Sen. Clin. Med. Off., Goulburn Valley Base Hosp. Australia; GP /Occ Health Phys., RAF Menwith Hill Harrogate.

GILMORE, David Hugh Geriatric Medical Unit, Royal Victoria Hospital, Belfast BT12 6BA Tel: 01232 240503; 2 Maxwell Park, Bangor BT20 3SH Tel: 01247 271063 — MB BCh BAO 1972 Belf.; MRCP (UK) 1977; FRCP Lond. 1993. Cons. Phys. (Geriat. Med.) Roy. Vict. Hosp. Belf.

GILMORE, David Richard New Park Medical Practice, 163 Robertson Road, Dunfermline KY12 0BL Tel: 01383 629200 Fax: 01383 629203; 31 Morrison Drive, Dunfermline KY11 8DJ Tel: 01383 720192 — MB ChB 1993 Ed.; MRCGP 1997. (Univ. of Edin.) Prev: GP/Regist. Galashiels; SHO (Gen. Pract.) Borders Gen. Hosp. Melrose VTS.

GILMORE, Eric Joseph (retired) Linton Lodge, Stoney Furlong Road, Baslow, Bakewell DE45 1ST Tel: 01246 582480 — MB BS Madras 1947.

GILMORE, Ian Ross 5 Cloverhill Gardens, Belfast BT4 2LH — MB BCh BAO 1948 Belf.; DObst RCOG 1953. (Qu. Univ. Belf.) Prev: Ho. Surg. Roy. Vict. Hosp. Belf.

GILMORE, Professor Ian Thomas (cons. rooms), 88 Rodney St., Liverpool L1 9AR Tel: 0151 709 0669; Birchways, Oldfield Drive, Heswall, Wirral CH60 6SS Tel: 0151 342 3264 — MD 1979 Camb.; MA Camb. 1972, MD 1979, MB BChir 1971; FRCP Lond. 1985; MRCP (UK) 1973. (Cambrige and St Thomas') Cons. Phys. Roy. Liverp. Univ. Hosp.; Prof. (Med.) Univ. of Liverp.; Regist. RCP Lond. Socs: Brit. Soc. Gastroenterol.; Assn. Phys. Prev: Vis. Schol. Univ. Calif., San Diego; Sen. Regist. (Med.) Char. Cross Hosp. Lond.; Regist. (Med.) St. Thomas' Hosp. Lond.

GILMORE, James Edward Whiteabbey Hospital, Station Road, Newtownabbey BT37 9RH; 35 Malone Park, Malone, Belfast BT9 6NL Tel: 01232 682171 — MD 1989 Belf.; MB BCh BAO Belf. 1979; MRCP (Ed.) 1983.

GILMORE, James McCaughey (retired) 10 Averill Court, Hill Road, Clevedon, Clevedon BS21 7NE Tel: 01275 341817 — MB ChB 1937 St. And.; MD St. And. 1950; DPH 1940. Prev: Cons. Chest Phys. N.. RHA.

GILMORE, John Strahan (retired) 77 North Road, Saltash PL12 6BD — MB BCh BAO Belf. 1949; FRCGP 1979, M 1972. Prev: Med. Sec. Devon LMC.

GILMORE, Karen Janette Top Floor Flat, 25 Fernbank Road, Bristol BS6 6PZ — MB ChB 1988 Leic.; DTM & H Liverp. 1994; DRCOG 1991. Regist. (Anaesth.) Bristol. Prev: SHO (Anaesth.) Oxf. & Torbay.

GILMORE, Margaret McIntosh (retired) 3 Newbattle Terrace, Edinburgh EH10 4RU Tel: 0131 447 2614 Email: margaret_m_gilucre@hotmail.com — MB ChB St. And. 1940; MFCM 1974; DPH Ed. 1960. Prev: Sen. Lect. Dept. Nursing Studies Univ. Edin.

GILMORE, Martin Manor Park Surgery, Belmount Close, Bramley, Leeds LS13 2UP Tel: 0113 257 9702; 2 Sandmoor Lodge, Sandmoor Lane, Leeds LS17 7EA Tel: 0113 269 1514 — MB ChB 1956 Leeds. Prev: Clin. Asst. (Dermat.) Leeds Gen. Infirm.

GILMORE, Morag Campbell Meadowpark Street Surgery, 214 Meadowpark Street, Glasgow G31 2TE Tel: 0141 554 0464 — MB ChB 1977 Glas.

GILMORE, Nicholas Mark Stanhope Oakenhall Medical Practice, Bolsover Street, Hucknall, Nottingham NG15 7UA Tel: 0115 963 3511 Fax: 0115 968 0947; 14 Byron Gardens, Southwell NG25 0DW — MB BS 1985 Lond.; DCH RCP Lond. 1991; DRCOG 1990.

GILMORE, Mr Owen Jeremy Adrian 108 Harley Street, London W1G 7ET Tel: 020 7637 8820 Fax: 020 7935 3901 Email: gilmore@harley_street108.demon.co.uk; Whitewater Mill, Hook RG27 9EH Tel: 01256 766868 Fax: 01256 768747 Email: gilmore@wwmill.demon.co.uk — MB BS Lond. 1966; MS Lond. 1976; FRCS Ed. 1971; FRCS Eng. 1971; MRCS Eng. LRCP Lond. (Begley Prize RCS) 1966; Fell. Inst. Sports Med. 1995. (St. Bart) Cons. i/c Lond. BrE. Clinic 108 Harley St. Lond.; Surg. Dir. Groin & Hernia Clinic Lond. Socs: Fell. Roy. Soc. Med.; BMA; BASO. Prev: Cons. Gen. Surg. & Cons. i/c BrE. Unit St. Bart. Hosp. Lond.; Designated Surg. Assessor NE Thames Region Nat. BrE. Screening Progr.; Sen. Lect. (Surg.) Univ. Lond.

GILMORE, Paul 22 Burnside Road, Portstewart BT55 7LB — MB BCh BAO 1973 Belf.; MRCP (UK) 1978. Cons. Phys. Coleraine Hosp.

GILMORE, Robert John 20 The Grove, Bearsted, Maidstone ME14 4JB — MB BCh 1994 Wales.

GILMORE, Rodney The Deganwy Medical Centre, York Road, Deganwy, Conwy LL31 9PX Tel: 01492 583304 Fax: 01492 572967; The Medical Centre, Plas Penrhyn, Penrhyn Bay, Llandudno LL30 3EU Tel: 01492 549368 Fax: 01492 548103 Email: rodgilmore@enterprise.net — MB BCh 1976 Wales; MRCGP 1980; DMJ(Clin) Soc. Apoth. Lond. 1995; DRCOG 1979; DCH Eng. 1978. (Welsh Nat. Sch. Med.) Div.al Police Surg. Conwy. Socs: (Counc.) Assn. Police Surgs.

GILMORE, Russell David Manor Park Surgery, Bell Mount Close, Leeds LS13 2UP Tel: 0113 257 9702 Fax: 0113 236 1537 — MB ChB 1983 Leeds. Princip. GP Leeds.

GILMORE, Samuel James Boyd 12 Ermine Street, Ancaster, Grantham Ng32 3PP Tel: 01400 230226 Fax: 01400 273608; 3 Granary Court, Wilsford, Grantham NG32 3NP — MB BCh BAO 1983 Belf.; MRCGP 1989; Dip. IMC RCS Ed. 1989; DCH RCSI 1989; DRCOG 1987; DGM RCP Lond. 1987. (Queen's University Belfast)

GILMORE, William Arthur (retired) 11 The Birches, Burn Road, Doagh, Ballyclare BT39 0QG Tel: 01960 341274 — MB BCh BAO 1945 Belf. Prev: Med. Off. DHSS Med. Ref. Serv.

GILMORE, William Robert (retired) 9 Coastguard Lane, Groomsport, Bangor BT19 6LR Tel: 01247 882410 — MB BCh BAO 1945 Belf.; FFA RCSI 1961; FFA RCS Eng. 1953; DA Eng. 1949. Hon. Cons. Anaesth. Roy. Vict. & Ulster Hosp. Belf. Prev: Cons. Anaesth. Belf. Gp. Hosps. Ulster Hosp. & N. Antrim Gp. Hosps.

GILMOUR, Alexander McHaig 51 Prideaux Road, Eastbourne BN21 2NE — MB ChB 1969 St. And.; MRCPath 1979. Cons. Histopath. Dist. Gen. Hosp. E.bourne.

GILMOUR, Beverley Dawn Centre for Nutritional Medicine, 43 Devonshire St., London W1G 7AL — MB BS 1987 Lond.; BSc 1984; DRCOG 1990.

GILMOUR, Carol Anne Myrtlebank, Achachork, Portree IV51 9HT Tel: 01478 2597 Fax: 01478 2597 — MB ChB 1990 Aberd.; MRCPsych. Specialist Regist. Rotot. (Child Psychiat.) E. Anglian.

GILMOUR, Christopher Alan 5 Delamont Park, Upper Knockbreda Road, Belfast BT6 9RJ Tel: 01232 583353 — MB BCh BAO 1991 Belf. (Queens University of Belfast) Med. Off. N.ern Irel. Hospice.

GILMOUR, Mr Douglas Graham Peripheral Vascular Unit, Royal Infirmary, 16 Alexandra Parade, Glasgow G31 2ER Tel: 0141 211 4772 Fax: 0141 552 5337; 27 Kessington Road, Bearsden, Glasgow G61 2HL Tel: 0141 942 0425 Fax: 0141 942 0425 Email: dougmour@globalnet.co.uk — MB ChB 1971 Glas.; BSc (Hons.) Glas. 1969, MD 1979; FRCS Glas. 1975. (Glasgow) Cons. Surg. Roy. Infirm. Glas.; Hon. Clin. Sen. Lect. Univ. Glas. Socs: Vasc. Soc. GB & N. Irel. Prev: Sen. Lect. (Surg.) Roy. Infirm. Glas.

GILMOUR, Elizabeth The Birmingham Childrens Hospital, Dermatology Department, Steelhouse Lane, Birmingham B4 6NL — MB ChB 1989 Sheff.; MA Oxf. 1987; MRCP (UK) 1993.

GILMOUR, Fergus Buchanan Alyth Health Centre, New Alyth Road, Alyth, Blairgowrie PH11 8EQ Tel: 01828 632317 Fax: 01828 633272 — MB ChB 1982 Dundee. Clin. Asst. (A & E) Dundee Roy. Infirm. Socs: BMA.

GILMOUR, Helen Nicola Williamwood Medical Centre, 85 Seres Road, Clarkston, Glasgow G76 7NW Tel: 0141 638 7984 Fax: 0141 638 8827 — MB ChB 1990 Glas.; MRCGP 1995; DRCOG 1994. Clin. Asst., Accord Hospice, Paisley. Prev: SHO (Oncol.) Beatson Oncol. Centre W.ern Infirm. Glas.; SHO (Palliat. Care) Hunters Hill Marie Curie Centre Glas.; Trainee GP, Bathgate W. Lothian.

GILMOUR, Hugh Montgomery Department of Pathology, University Medical School, Teviot Place, Edinburgh EH8 9AG Tel: 0131 650 3001 Fax: 0131 650 6528; 58 Polwarth Terrace, Edinburgh EH11 1NJ Tel: 0131 337 4203 — MB ChB 1967 Ed.; FRCS 2001; FRCPath 1986, M 1974. (Ed.) Sen. Lect. (Path.) Univ. Edin.; Hon. Cons. Lothian Univ. Hosp. NHS Trust. Socs: Assn. Clin. Path. & Brit. Soc. Gastroenterol.

GILMOUR, Iain Merry Tel: 0191 567 0961 — MB ChB 1981 Glas.

GILMOUR, Janice Elizabeth 19 Linnet Close, Winsford CW7 3FA — MB ChB 1990 Manch.; BSc (Hons.) Med Sci. St. And. 1987. Trainee GP Chester VTS; Trainee GP Hoole Chester. Prev: Ho. Off.

(Gen. Med. & Geriat.) Macclesfield Dist. Gen. Hosp.; Ho. Off. (Surg.) Stockport Infirm. & Stepping Hill Hosp. Stockport.

GILMOUR, Jeffrey Paul 17 Clos Nant Mwlan, Cardiff CF23 8NA — MB BCh 1995 Wales.

GILMOUR, Joan (retired) 47 Edenhurst Drive, Formby, Liverpool L37 2LH Tel: 0170 48 76758 — MB ChB 1960 Sheff. Princip. Clin. Med. Off. S.port & Formby Community Health Serv. Trust. Prev: Clin. Med. Off. Sefton AHA.

GILMOUR, John McCulloch (retired) Rowan Cottage, 1 Hele Cottage, Bickleigh, Plymouth PL6 7AF — MB ChB 1946 Glas.; MFOM RCP Lond. 1981; DIH Eng. 1977.

GILMOUR, John Roderick Kirriemuir Health Centre, Tannage Brae, Kirriemuir DD8 4DL Tel: 01575 573333 Fax: 01575 574230 — MB ChB 1966 Ed.; DCH RCPS Glas. 1970. (Ed.)

GILMOUR, Mark Frank Winstan Forth View Practice, Dean Road, Bo'ness EH51 0DQ Tel: 01506 822466 Fax: 01506 826216; 36 Strathalmond Park, Edinburgh EH4 8AH — MB ChB 1975 Ed.; BSc (Med. Sci.) (Hons.) Ed. 1971, MB ChB 1975; MRCGP 1979; DRCOG 1978. (Edin. Univ. Med. Sch.)

GILMOUR, Nigel Christopher The Old Manor, Stanton St John, Oxford OX33 1HF — MB BS 1978 Lond.

GILMOUR, Robert Fraser Room 5, The Villa, Whipps Cross Hospital, Whipps Cross Road, London E11 1NR — MB BS 1997 Lond.

GILMOUR, Ruth Janet Culduthel Road Health Centre, Ardlarich, 15 Culduthel Road, Inverness IV2 4AG Tel: 01463 712233 Fax: 01463 715479 — MB ChB 1989 Glas.; MB ChB (Hons.) Glas. 1989; BSc (Hons.) Glas. 1986; MRCGP 1995; DRCOG 1991. GP. Prev: SHO (Psychiat.) Craig Dunain Hosp. Inverness; Trainee GP Grantown-on-Spey.

GILMOUR, Sally Ann Dumville 8 Kinross Avenue, Woodsmoor, Stockport SK2 7EL — MB ChB 1994 Manch.

GILMOUR, Samuel Kyle 8 Kinross Avenue, Woodsmoor, Stockport SK2 7EL — MB ChB 1994 Manch.

GILMOUR, Sharron Helena 11 Belford Mews, Edinburgh EH4 3BT Tel: 0131 225 2249 — MB BS 1960 Lond.; MB BS (Hnrs.) Lond. 1960; MRCS Eng. LRCP Lond. 1960.

GILMOUR, William Maxwell 32 Oxgangs Road, Edinburgh EH10 7AX — MB ChB 1950 Glas.; FRCGP 1981, M 1969. (Glas.) Socs: BMA.

GILMOUR-WHITE, Shona Ellen Greenfield, Adsborough, Taunton TA2 8RP — MB ChB 1981 Bristol; MRCGP 1986; DRCOG 1985; DA (UK) 1984. Clin. Asst. Gen. Pract.

GILPIN, Mr David Alastair (retired) Daisy Hill Hospital, 5 Hospital Road, Newry BT35 8DR — MB BCh BAO 1986 Belf.; FRCS (Gen. Surg.) 2000; BSc (Hons.) Belf. 1983, MD 1995; FRCSI 1990. Regist. (Surg.) N. Irel. Train. Scheme. Prev: Research Fell. Shriners Inst. for Burned & Crippled Childr. & Univ. Texas Med. Br. Galveston Texas, USA.

GILPIN, George Noel 16 Clonevin Park, Lisburn BT28 3BL — MB BCh BAO 1985 Belf.

***GILPIN, James Lloyd** 2 Royal Oaks, Kesh Road, Maze, Lisburn BT27 5RR — MB BCh BAO 1997 Belf.

***GILPIN, Teresa Jayne** 355 Crewe Road, Willaston, Nantwich CW5 6NW — MB ChB 1993 Liverp.

GILPIN, Thomas Shanks Coursebeer Farm, Whiddon Down, Okehampton EX20 2QZ — LRCPI & LM, LRSCI & LM 1953; LRCPI & LM, LRCSI & LM 1953; LAH Dub. 1953.

GILRAY, George (retired) 10 Barntongate Avenue, Edinburgh EH4 8BB Tel: 0131 339 1431 Email: george@caledoncapital.freeserve.co.uk — MB ChB Ed. 1953; FFCM 1984, M 1974; DPH Glas. 1968. Prev: Princip. Med. Off. Scott. Home & Health Dept.

GILROY, Mr Douglas Gerard 91 Upper Malone Road, Belfast BT9 6UF — MB BCh BAO 1978 Belf.; FRCSI 1985; MRCP (UK) 1980; FFA RCSI 1983. Regist. (Surg.) Daisy Hill Hosp. Newry.

GILROY, Fiona Mary Jubilee Field Surgery, Yatton Keynell, Nr. Chippenham SN14 7EJ Tel: 01249 782204 — MB ChB 1982 Aberd.; Cert. Family Plann. JCC 1985; DRCOG 1984; PHEC Cert 1995; ATLS Provider 1996; Cert. Travel Med Glasg. 1997. GP Non-Princip. Chippenham. Socs: GP Writer's Assn.; Brit. Assn. Immed. Care Schemes; Media Medics. Prev: GP Princip. Cheltenham; Clin. Med. Off. (Child Heath) Leamington Spa.

GILROY, John Bernard Derrylea, Derrylin, Enniskillen BT92 9QR Tel: 013657 48441 — MB BCh BAO 1980 Dub.; DRCOG 1987; DCH Dub. 1983; DDerm Dublin 1997. Socs: Irish Coll. Gen. Pract.; Roy. Coll. Gen. Pract.

GILROY, Kenneth James 82 Cadwell Drive, Maidenhead SL6 3YR — MB ChB 1998 Leic.; MB ChB Leic 1998.

GILROY, Patricia Louise 21 Brynteg Est, Llandegfan, Menai Bridge LL59 5TY — MB ChB 1998 Sheff.; MB ChB Sheff 1998.

GILRUTH, Agnes Jean Menzies (retired) 110 Perth Road, Blairgowrie PH10 6ED Tel: 01250 872024 — MB ChB 1939 Ed.; BSc (Pure Sci.) Ed. 1939; DObst RCOG 1943; DCH Eng. 1944. Prev: Asst. MOH Matern. & Child Welf. Dept. City Birm.

GILSENAN, Kevin Luis The Charter Medical Centre, 88 Davigdor Road, Hove BN3 1RF Tel: 01273 738070/770555 Fax: 01273 220 0883; 18 Hartington Villas, Hove BN3 6HF Tel: 01273 278663 — MB BS 1965 Lond.; MRCP (UK) 1971; MRCS Eng. LRCP Lond. 1965; MRCGP 1977. (St. Bart.) Prev: Regist. (Paediat.) Guy's Hosp. Lond.; Ho. Phys. Hosp. Sick Childr. Gt. Ormond St. Lond.; Ho. Phys. S.end Gen. Hosp.

GILSON, Dianne Cookridge Hospital, Leeds LS16 6QB — MB ChB 1979 Manch.; MD Manch. 1990; FRCR 1990; MRCP (UK) 1983. (Manch) Cons. Clin. Oncol. Cookridge Hosp. United Leeds Teach. Hosps. NHS Trust. Prev: Lect. (Radiother.) Univ. Leeds; Tutor & Research Fell. (Radiother.) Univ. Leeds; Regist. (Radiother. & Oncol.) Notts Gen. Hosp.

GILSON, Joanne Mary Heathgate Surgery, The Street, Poringland, Norwich NR14 7JT Tel: 01508 494343; Woodton Grange, Bungay NR35 2LP — BM 1978 Soton.

GILSON, Richard John Cary Department of Sexually Transmitted Diseases, Roy Free & Univ College Med Sch, The Mortimer Market Centre, off Capper St., London WC1E 6AU Tel: 020 7380 9778 Fax: 020 7380 9669 Email: rgilson@gum.ucl.ac.uk — MB 1982 Camb.; BChir 1981; FRCP 1997; MRCP (UK) 1985; MD (cambridge Univ) 1999. Sen. Lect. & Hon. Cons. Dept. of Sexually Transm. Dis.s Roy Free & Univ. Coll. Lond. Med. Sch., Camden & Islington Community Health Servs. NHS Trust.; Hon. Cons. UCL Hosps. NHS Trust.

GILSON, Roger Alfred James Rosser and Partners, Crewkerne Health Centre, Middle Path, Crewkerne TA18 8BX Tel: 01460 72435 Fax: 01460 77957 Email: roger.gilson@gp-l85004.nhs.uk; Old Barn House, Merriottsford, Merriott TA16 5NH Tel: 01460 77075 Email: gilson@btinternet.com — MB ChB 1976 Birm.; MRCGP 1983; DFFP 1995. (Birmingham) Socs: BMA; Med. Protec. Soc.

GILSTON, Alan (retired) 20 Hocroft Avenue, London NW2 2EH Tel: 020 7435 1483 Fax: 020 7431 9878 — MB ChB 1953 Leeds; FFA RCS Eng. 1959. Vis. Prof. Dalhousie Univ. Fac. Med. Halifax Nova Scotia 1984. Prev: Cons. Anaesth. Nat. Heart Hosp. Lond.

GILTHORPE, Helen Margaret 5 Richmond Mews, Elmfield Road, Newcastle upon Tyne NE3 4BQ — BM BCh 1945 Oxf.; BM BCh Oxon. 1945; DCH Eng. 1946.

GILTINAN, William Michael St Thomas Surgery, Ysyol Street, St. Thomas, Swansea SA1 8LH Tel: 01792 653992; Headland Lodge, Headland Road, Bishopston, Swansea SA3 3HD Tel: 01792 233548 — MB BCh 1973 Wales.

GILVARRY, Anne Marie 176 Sutton Court Road, Chiswick, London W4 3HR — MB BCh BAO 1978 NUI; MRCPI 1980; FRCSI 1984.

GILVARRY, Eilish Plummer Court, Carliol Place, Newcastle upon Tyne NE1 6UR Tel: 0191 219 5600 Fax: 0191 219 5601 — MB BCh BAO 1978 NUI; MRCGP 1982; MRCPsych 1984. Cons. Psychiat. Ment. Health Trust Newc. u. Tyne.

GILVARRY, Margaret Claire Orford Lodge Surgery, 100 Bancroft, Hitchin SG5 1ND Tel: 01462 432042 Fax: 01462 436505; 25 Pasture Road, Letchworth SG6 3LP Tel: 01462 678955 — MB BCh BAO 1976 NUI. GP. Prev: Trainee GP Letchworth VTS; Regist. (Psychiat.) Luton & Dunstable Hosp.; SHO (Obst.) Lister Hosp. Stevenage.

GIMBLETT, Marc Louis 8 Clarendon Road, London E18 2AW; 5 Grassways Avenue, Pakuranga, Auckland, New Zealand — MB ChB 1984 Otago; FRACO 1994; FRACS 1994.

GIMBRETT, Roy Christopher Mill View Hospital, Nevill Avenue, Hove BN3 7HZ Tel: 01273 696011 — BM 1986 Soton.; MRCPsych 1990. Cons. Psychiat. S. Downs Health NHS Trust. Prev: Cons. (Psychiat.) Edith Cavell Hosp. PeteBoro.

GIMENEZ BURGOS, Myriam 7 Almond Grove, Worksop S80 1AU — LMS 1990 Saragossa.

GIMENO SENTAMANS, Clare Maria Cookridge Hospital, Hospital Lane, Leeds LS16 6QB; 19 Eddison Walk, Leeds LS16 8DA Tel: 0113 281 7377 — LMS 1989 Basque Provinces. Regist. (Oncol. & Radiother.) Cookridge Hosp. Leeds; Dip. Clin. Oncol. Course Roy. Marsden Hosp. Inst. Cancer Research Univ. Lond. Socs: Assoc. Mem. Roy. Coll. Radiotherap. Prev: Regist. (Radiother. & Oncol.) Clatterbridge Oncol. Centre Wirral.

GIMLETTE, Thomas Michael Desmond (retired) 50 Hurlingham Court, London SW6 3UP — MB BChir 1950 Camb.; BA (1st cl. Hons. Nat. Sc. Trip) Camb. 1946, MD; 1957, MB BChir 1950; FRCP Lond. 1973, M 1951; FRCR 1986. Phys. (Nuclear Med.) Liverp. HA & Liverp. RHB. Prev: Sen. Regist. (Med.), Regist. (Cardiac.) & Ho. Phys. St. Thos. Hosp. Lond.

GIMMACK, George 12 Hillcrest Gardens, Finchley, London N3 3EY Tel: 020 8346 8866; 12 Hillcrest Gardens, Finchley, London N3 3EY Tel: 020 8346 8866 — MRCS Eng. LRCP Lond. 1942; MRCGP 1968. (Middlx.) Med. Ref. Norwich Union Insur. Soc., Legal & Gen. Assur. Soc. & Scott. Amicable Life Assur. Soc. Socs: BMA. Prev: Ho. Phys. Gen. & Eye Hosps. Cheltenham; Capt. RAMC 1942-46.

GIMSON, Alexander Edward Stanford Hepato Biliary & Liver Transplant Unit, Addenbrookes NHS Trust, Cambridge CB2 2QQ Tel: 01223 216110; The Grove, High St, Brinkley, Newmarket CB8 0SF — MB BS 1975 Lond.; FRCP Lond. 1994; MRCP (UK) 1978. Cons. Phys. Hepatol. Addenbrooke's NHS Trust. Prev: Cons. Hepatol. Inst. Liver Studies Kings Coll. Hosp. Lond.

GIMSON, Leslie Victor, VRD (retired) Ducklings, Church Lane, Bury, Pulborough RH20 1PB Tel: 01798 831357 — MB BS Lond. 1939.

GINBEY, Derald William Department of Paediatrics, St Luke's Hospital, Little Horton Lane, Bradford BD5 0NA — MB ChB 1986 Leeds; MRCP (UK) 1992.

GINEVER, Doreen Mary (retired) Flat 11, Dunham Lawn, Bradgate Road, Altrincham WA14 4QJ Tel: 0161 928 4229 — MB ChB 1948 Manch. Prev: Community Med. Off. Trafford HA.

GING, John Edward Villiers House, Tolworth Hospital, Red Lion Road, Surbiton KT6 7QU Tel: 020 8390 0102 — MB BS 1990 Lond.; BSc Lond. 1987; MRCPsych 1995. (St. Mary's Hosp. Med. Sch.) Sen. Regist. S. Thames (W..) Gen. Psychiat. Rotat. Train. Scheme St. Geo. Hosp. Lond.

GINGELL, Mr John Clive Litfield House, 1 Litfield Place, Clifton Down, Bristol BS8 3LS Tel: 0117 973 1323 Fax: 0117 973 3303 — MB BCh 1960 Wales; FRCS Eng. 1966; FRCS Ed. 1966; MRCS Eng. LRCP Lond. 1960. Cons. Surg. Urol. S.mead Health Trust Hosp. Bristol; Sen. Clin. Lect. (Urol.) Bristol Univ. Socs: Fell. Roy. Soc. Med. (Mem. Sect. Urol.); Brit. Assn. Urol. Surg. Prev: Sen. Regist. & Tutor (Urol.) United Bristol Hosps.; Regist. (Surg.) Postgrad. Med. Sch. Lond.; Research Asst. Surgic. Unit Cardiff Roy. Infirm.

GINGELL, Katherine Helen The Elms Health Centre, Slade Road, Cradley, Halesowen B63 2UR; 42 Summervale Road, West Hagley, Stourbridge DY9 0LX Tel: 01562 883429 — MB ChB 1979 Liverp.; MRCPsych 1991. Cons. Child & Adolesc. Psychiat. Elms Health Centre Halesowen. Prev: Sen. Regist. (Child & Adolesc. Psychiat.) Healthlands Hosp. Birm.

GINIMAV, Prabhuraj Shankarappa — MB BS 1970 Karnatak; DA Eng. 1981; Dip. Orthop. Karnatak 1972. (Karnatak Med. Coll. Hubli)

GINIMAV, Shreegowri Prabhuraj 121 Eastbourne Road, Willingdon, Eastbourne BN20 9NE — MB BS 1969 Karnatak; DGO Karnatak 1974. (Karnatak Med. Coll. Hubli)

GINKS, Susan Elizabeth La Chasse, St John, Jersey JE3 4 — MB ChB 1968 Manch.

GINKS, William Richard General Hospital, St Helier, Jersey Tel: 01534 59000 — MB ChB Manch. 1965; FRCP Lond. 1987, M 1968. (Manch.) Cons. Phys. St. Helier, Jersey. Socs: Brit. Cardiac. Soc.; Brit. Thorac. Soc. Prev: Sen. Regist. (Cardiol.) St. Geo. Hosp. Lond.; Regist. (Cardiol.) Roy. Postgrad. Med. Sch. Lond.

GINN, Arthur Edward, OStJ (retired) Strood Cottage, Tenterden Road, Rolvenden, Cranbrook TN17 4JJ Tel: 01580 3516 — MRCS Eng. LRCP Lond. 1942; LMSSA Lond. 1934. Prev: Div. Med. Off. Brit. Rlys. (S. Region).

GINN, Elizabeth Alexandra Room 1, 14 Park Avenue, Worthing BN11 2DH — MB BS 1998 Lond.; MB BS Lond 1998.

GINN, Hilary Elizabeth Montbrison, 14 Grange Park, Henleaze, Bristol BS9 4BP — MB BCh BAO 1972 Belf.; DObst RCOG 1974. GP Bristol. Prev: Med. Dir. JJ Ventilation (Internat. Ltd.) Bristol; GP Chepstow; SHO (Paediat.) Roy. Belf. Hosp. Sick Childr.

GINNS, Anthony David The Quakers Lane Surgery, Quakers Lane, Richmond DL10 4BB Tel: 01748 850440 Fax: 01748 850802; Whitecliffe Cottage, Westfields, Richmond DL10 4SB — BM BCh 1972 Oxf.; MA Oxf. 1972; MRCGP 1976; DRCOG 1975. Prev: Clin. Asst. (Psychiat.) Friarage Hosp. N.allerton.

GINSBERG, Lionel Department of Clinical Neurosciences, Royal Free Hospital School of Medicine, Pond St., London NW3 2QG Tel: 020 7794 0500 Fax: 020 7431 1577 — MB BS 1982 Lond.; MB BS (Hons. Betuel Prize) Lond. 1982; BSc (Hons. 1st. cl.) Lond. 1976, PhD 1980; MRCP (UK) 1985; FRCP 1996. (Middlx.) Cons. NeUrol., Roy. Free Hosp. Lond. and Chase Farm Hosp, Enfield; Hons. Cons. Phys., Nat. Hosp. For Neurol. and Neurosurg., Qu. Sq, Lond.; Hon. Sen. Levct. Inb Clin. Neurosurg., Uni. Of Lond..; Cons. NeUrol., P.ss Grace Hosp. Garden & Kings Oak Hosp. Enfield. Socs: Assn. Brit. Neurol. Prev: Clin. Lect. (Neurol.) Univ. Camb.; Vis. Sci. Nat. Inst. Health Bethesda Md., USA; Regist. (Neurol.) Nat. Hosp. Lond.

GINSBURG, Jean Royal Free Hospital, Pond St, London NW3 2QG Tel: 020 7794 0500 Ext: 3751 Fax: 020 7431 5816; 7 Ardwick Road, London NW2 2BX Tel: 0207435 5388 Fax: 020 7431 2592 — BM BCh Oxon.; BA (Hons.) Oxf. 1948, MA 1952, DM 1959; FRCP Lond. 1978, M 1971. (Oxf. & St. Mary's) p/t Hon. Cons. Endocrinol. Roy. Free Hosp. NHS Trust. Prev: Sen. Lect. (Endocrinol.) Roy. Free Hosp. Med. Sch. Lond.; Sen. Lect. Char. Cross Hosp. Med. Sch.; Research Fell. St. Thos. Hosp. Med. Sch.

GINSBURG, Robert Department of Anaesthetics, King's College Hospital, Denmark Hill, London SE5 9RS Tel: 020 7346 3154 Fax: 020 7346 3632 Email: 100101.2633@compuserve.com — MB BS 1975 Lond.; BSc (Hons.) Lond. 1972; MRCS Eng. LRCP Lond. 1975; FFA RCS Eng. 1983. Cons. Anaesth. King's Coll. Hosp. Lond.; Regional Adviser Roy. Coll. Anaesth. S. Thames (E.). Prev: Sen. Regist. (Anaesth.) Lond. Hosp.; Clin. Research Fell. (Anaesth.) UCLA Sch. Med. Los Angeles, USA; Sen. Regist. (Anaesth.) Hosp. Sick Childr. Lond.

GINZ, Beryl (retired) 29 Chestnut Way, Repton, Derby DE65 6FQ — MB ChB Aberd. 1964; MSc Leeds 1974; FRCOG 1984, M 1971. Cons. O & G Burton Dist. Hosp. Prev: Cons O & G Burton Dist Hosp.

GIORA, Asher Reuven 25 Cervantes Ct, Northwood HA6 1AL — BM 1997 Soton.

GIORGI, Luigi 5 Brook Lane, Plaxtol, Sevenoaks TN15 0RF — State Exam 1987 Rome.

GIOTAKIS, Ioannis 41 Glasslyn Road, London N8 8RJ — Ptychio Iatrikes 1975 Athens.

GIOVANNELLI, Marco Andrea 3 The Mews, Outwoods, Eaton Bank, Duffield, Belper DE56 4BP Tel: 01332 840314 — MB BS 1994 Lond.; MRCP (UK) 1998. (The Royal Free Hospital School of Medicine) SHO (Anaesth.) Qu.s Med. Centre Univ. Hosp. Nottm. Prev: SHO (Med.) Derby Roy. Infirm. NHS Trust.

GIOVANNONI, Gavin Department of Neurology, Institute of Neurology, Queen Square, London WC1N 3BG Tel: 020 7837 3611 Fax: 020 7837 3558 Email: ggiovannoni@ion.ucl.ac.uk; 42 Taybridge Road, Battersea, London SW11 5PT Tel: 020 7228 1117 — MB BCh 1987 Witwatersrand; PhD London University 1998; FCP (Neurol) 1993. (Univ. Witwatersrand) Research Fell. (Clin. Neuroimmunol, Multiple Sclerosis) Inst. Neurol. Lond. Socs: SA Coll. of Med.

GIPSON, Mr Michael 144 Rupert Road, Huyton, Liverpool L36 9TH Tel: 0151 489 4246 — MRCS Eng. LRCP Lond. 1963; MA Camb. 1969, MB 1964, BChir 1963; FRCS Eng. 1970. (Westm.) Cons. Plastic Surg. St. Helens & Knowsley AHA & Liverp. AHA (T). Socs: Brit. Assn. Plastic Surg. & Brit. Soc. Surg. Hand. Prev: Resid. Surg. Off. Roy. Marsden Hosp. Lond.; Regist. (Surg.) W.m. Hosp. Lond.; Sen. Regist. (Plastic Surg.) United Sheff. Hosps.

GIRACH, Aniz — MB ChB 1990 Leeds; MRCGP 1996; MRCOphth 1994. (Leeds)

GIRALDI, Douglas Joseph Sixways Clinic, London Road, Charlton Kings, Cheltenham GL52 6HS Tel: 01242 583520 — MB BS 1971 Lond.; MRCS Eng. LRCP Lond. 1971; MRCGP 1980; DCH RCPS

Glas. 1973; Cert JCC Lond. 1978. (St. Thos.) Med. Off. Family Plann. Assn. Cheltenham; Clin. Asst. (Venereol.) Cheltenham Gen. Hosp. Socs: BMA. Prev: SHO (Paediat.) Soton. Gen. Hosp.; Regist. (Paediat.) Redhill Gen. Hosp. & Qu. Mary's Hosp. Sick Childr.; Carshalton.

***GIRDHER, Andrew Rajesh** 56 Beeston Fields Drive, Beeston, Nottingham NG9 3DD — MB ChB 1996 Birm.

GIRDWOOD, Robert Walter Anthony Department of Microbiology, Stobhill NHS Trust, Glasgow G21 3UW; 5 Corsebar Drive, Paisley PA2 9QB — MB ChB 1965 Glas.; FRCPath 1986, M 1972; DTM & H Liverp. 1973. Cons. Bacteriol. Stobhill NHS Trust Glas.; Cons. Admin. Charge of Scott. Meoningococcal/Pneumococcal Refer. Laborat.; Cons. Admin. Charge of Scott. Legionella Refer. Laborat.; Dir. Scott. Salmonella Refer. Laborat. & Scott. Inborn Errors Screening Laborat.; Dir. Scott. Parasite Diag. Laborat.; Hon. Sen. Lect. (Microbiol.) Univ. Glas.

GIRDWOOD, Professor Ronald Haxton, CBE 2 Hermitage Drive, Edinburgh EH10 6DD Tel: 0131 447 5137 — MB ChB 1939 Ed.; MB ChB (Hons. & Leslie Gold Medal) Ed. 1939; FRSE 1978; PhD Ed. 1952, MD (Gold Medal) 1954; FRCPI 1984; FRCP Lond. 1956, M 1944; FRCP Ed. 1945, M 1941; FRCPath 1964; Hon. FACP 1983; Hon. FRACP 1985. (Univ. Ed. & Michigan) Emerit. Prof. Therap. & Clin. Pharm. Univ. Edin. Socs: (Ex-Counc.) Scott. Soc. Hist. Med.; Assn. Phys.; Internat. Soc. Haematol. Prev: Pres. Roy. Coll. Phys. Edin.; Dean Fac. Med. Univ. Edin.; Lt.-Col. RAMC.

GIRDWOOD, Thomas Grossart (retired) Aultbea House, Matty Lonning, Carlisle CA5 6PQ Tel: 01228 710166 — MB ChB 1959 Ed.; DMRD 1964; FRCR 1975; FFR 1967; DObst RCOG 1961. Cons. Radiol. Cumbld. Infirm. Carlisle.

GIRGIS, Amira Julie 39 Swaby Road, London SW18 3PX Tel: 020 8946 1078 Email: amirajg@aol.com — MB BS 1994 Lond.; BSc (Hons.) Lond. 1991. (St. George's Hospital Medical School) Specialist Regist. N. Hants. Hosp. Basingstoke. Socs: BMA; AAGBI; OAA. Prev: SHO (IC) Lewisham Univ. Hosp.; SHO (Anaesth.) N. Hants. Hosp. Basingstoke; SHO (A & E & Anaesth.) Mayday Univ. Hosp. Croydon.

GIRGIS, Fayez Loucas North Middlesex Hospital, London N18 1QX; 28 Nightingale Court, Maltings Place, Bagleys Lane, London SW6 2BU Tel: 0208 887 2845 — MB BCh 1966 Ain Shams; DM Ain Shams 1968; MRCP (UK) 1975; MRCS Eng. LRCP Lond. 1976. Cons. Rheum. Gdn. Hosp. Lond., N. Lond. Nuffield Hosp. Enfield, BUPA Hosp. Bushey, Herts.; Cons. Rheum. N. Middlx. Hosp. Lond. Socs: BMA; BSR. Prev: Sen. Regist. (Med.) Dept. Rheum. St. Mary's Hosps. Lond. & Roy. Nat. Orthop. Hosp. Lond.; Cons. Rheum. Barnet & Finchley Memor. Hosp.

GIRGIS, Magdy Sobhy Rozel, Wilson Road, Hartlebury, Kidderminster DY11 7XU Tel: 01299 250224 Fax: 01299 250224 — MB BCh 1968 Cairo; FFA RCS Eng. 1978. (Cairo) Cons. Anaesth. Kidderminster Gen. Hosp.

GIRGIS, Maged Mourad Ramsis Chessel Surgery - Bitterne Branch, 4 Chessel Avenue, Bitterne, Southampton SO19 4AA Tel: 023 8044 7777 Fax: 023 8042 5429 — MB BS 1993 Lond.

GIRGIS, Maurice Hanna Wrightington Hospital, Hall Lane, Wrightington, Wigan WN6 9EP Tel: 01257 256244 Fax: 01257 253809; 2 Broomholme, Shevington, Wigan WN6 8DT Tel: 01257 255367 — MB ChB 1966 Egypt; DA Eng. 1972. (Alexandria Univ.) Assoc. Specialist (Anaesth.) Wrightington Hosp. NHS Trust. Prev: Regist. (Anaesth.) Roy. N.. & St. And. Hosps. Lond.; SHO (Anaesth.) Darlington Memor. Hosp.

GIRGIS, Samia Ibrahim Department of Metabolic Medicine, Imperial College School of Medicine, Hammersmith Campus, Du Cane Road, London W12 0NN Tel: 020 8383 3232 Fax: 020 8383 3232 Email: sgirgis@ic.ac.uk; 139 Horsenden Lane S., Greenford UB6 7NS Tel: 020 8991 0493 — MB BCh 1967 Assiut; FRCPath 1998; MRCPath 1990; PhD Lond. 1981. Sen. Lect. (Metab. Med.) Imperial Coll. Sch. Med. Hammersmith Campus; Hon. Cons. (Chem. Path.) Univ. Lond. Hammersmith Hosps NHS Trust. Socs: Brit. Endocrine Soc. & Brit. Diabetic Assn.; Nat. Osteoporosis Soc. Prev: Sen. Lect. & Hon. Cons. (Chem. Path.) Univ. Lond. Roy. Post. Med. Sch.; Lect., Hon. Sen. Regist. & Regist. (Chem. Path.) Univ. Lond. Roy. Post. Med. Sch. & Hammersmith Hosp. Lond.; Research Fell. Endocrine Unit RPMS Lond.

GIRIJA, Nagarajan 56 Lockesley Drive, Orpington BR5 2AF — MB BS 1971 Madras; DA Madras 1979.

GIRLING, Anne Carol 220 Unthank Road, Norwich NR2 2AH — MB BS 1981 Lond.; MD Lond. 1990; MRCPath 1994. Cons. Histopath. Cytopath Norf. & Norwich Health Care NHS Trust.

GIRLING, David John MRCClinical Trials Unit, 222 Euston Road, London NW1 2DA Tel: 020 7670 4734 Fax: 020 7670 4818 Email: djg@ctu.mrc.ac.uk; 11 Bateman Mews, Cambridge CB2 1NN Tel: 01223 354333 Email: djg@ctu.mrc.ac.uk — BM BCh Oxf. 1964; MA Oxf. 1965; FRCP Lond. 1980, M 1969. (Oxf. & Lond. Hosp.) Sen. Scientif. Staff MRC Clin. trials unit; Sec. MRC Lung Cancer Working Party & Sec. MRC Upper Gastrointestinal Tract Cancer Working Party. Socs: Brit. Thorac. Soc.; Internat. Assn. Study Lung Cancer; Brit. Oncol. Assn. Prev: Research Fell. & Regist. (Child Health & Neonat. Unit) Hammersmith Hosp. Lond.

GIRLING, David Keith 19 Oakhurst Drive, Newcastle upon Tyne NE3 4JS — MB BS 1963 Lond.; MRCS Eng. LRCP Lond. 1962; FFA RCS Eng. 1969. (Univ. Coll. Hosp.) Cons. Anaesth. Regional Cardiothoracic Surg. Serv. Newc. u. Tyne; Hon. Clin. Lect. Univ. Newc. Socs: BMA & Assn. Cardiothoracic Anaesths. Prev: Ho. Phys. Univ. Coll. Hosp.; Regist. Bournemouth & E. Dorset Hosp. Gp.

GIRLING, Deborah Michelle Fulbourn Hospital, Cambridge CB1 5EF Tel: 01223 218995 Fax: 01223 218892 Email: deborah.girling@addenbrookes.nhs.uk — MB BChir 1985 Camb.; MA Camb. 1986; MRCPsych 1989. (Cambridge) p/t Cons. Old Age Psychiat. Fulbourn Hosp. Camb. Prev: Sen. Regist. (Old Age Psychiat.) Fulbourn Hosp. Camb.

GIRLING, Joanna Caroline West Middlesex University Hospital, Twickenham Road, Isleworth TW7 6AF — MB BS 1986 Lond.; MA Camb. 1986; MRCP (UK) 1991; MRCOG 1992. Cons. O & G W. Middlx. Hosp.; Hon. Cons. Qu. Charlottes Hosp. Socs: MacDonald Club. Prev: Sen. Regist. (O & G) Hammersmith & N.wich Pk. Hosps. Lond.; Regist. (Med.) Baragwanath Hosp. Univ. Witwatersrand, S. Afr.; SHO (O & G) Qu. Charlottes & Chelsea Hosp.

GIRLING, Keith Julian 48 Tavistock Drive, Nottingham NG3 5DW — MB BS 1987 Lond. SHO (Gen. Med.) MiddlesBoro. Gen. Hosp.

GIRLING, Patricia Ann (retired) 15 Normanby Road, Wollaton, Nottingham NG8 2TA Tel: 01159 284443 — MB ChB 1957 Sheff.; DCH Eng. 1960. Prev: GP Bramcote Nottm.

GIRLING, Philippa Jane Elizabeth St Edwards Vicarage, Tadcaster Road, Dringhouses, York YO24 1QG — MB ChB 1994 Leic.

GIRLING, Simon Danford Department of Radiology, Norfolk & Norwich Hospital, Brunswick Road, Norwich NR1 3SR Tel: 01603 286286; Hill Grove, 220 Unthank Road, Norwich NR2 2AH — MB BS 1981 Lond.; BSc Lond. 1978, MB BS 1981; MRCP (UK) 1984; FRCR 1987. Cons. Diag. Radiol. Norwich HA. Prev: Regist. & Sen. Regist. (Radiol.) Guy's Hosp. Lond.

GIRN, Sukhdev Singh 82 Littleover Lane, Derby DE23 6JG — MB ChB 1990 Leeds.

GIROLAMI, Miss Anna North-Western Injury Research Centre, Stopford Buildings, University of Manchester, Oxford Road, Manchester Tel: 0161 275 5183 Fax: 0161 275 5190; 3 Blackbrook Glade, Buxton Road, Chapel-en-le-Firth, High Peak SK23 0PJ Tel: 01298 816124 — MB ChB 1991 Sheff.; FRCS Eng. 1996. Research Fell. N. W.. Injury Research Centre Univ. Manch.'. Socs: Wom. Surgic. Train.; BMA.

GIRVAN, Ruth Barbara Bennetts Road North Surgery, 2 Bennetts Road North, Keresley End, Coventry CV7 8LA Tel: 024 7633 2636 Fax: 024 7633 7353 — MB BS 1981 Lond. Socs: Diplomate Fac. Family Plann.; Roy. Coll. of Gen. Practitioners.

GIRVENT MONTLLOR, Meritxell Department of Surgery, Hope Hospital, Eccles Old Road, Salford M6 8HD — LMS 1990 U Autonoma Barcelona.

GIRVIN, Francis Gerard 12 Mullagmmarget Road, Dungannon BT71 6QX — MB ChB 1995 Glas.

GISBERT PUJALS, Froilan 42 Crowell Road, Oxford OX4 3LN — LMS 1992 Barcelona.

GISHEN, Faye Sara 10 Denman Drive, London NW11 6RG — MB BS 1997 Lond.; BSc. SHO (Gen. Med.) Barnet Hosp. Lond. Socs: BMA; MDU.

GISHEN, Phillip 126 Harley Street, London W1; 38 Southway, London NW11 6SA — MB BCh 1968 Witwatersrand; FRCR 1976; DMRD Eng. 1974. (Witwatersand) Dir. Of Radiol. Hammersmith & Char. Cross Hosp.s Lond.; Diagnostic Radiologists Harley St Lond.

Prev: Sen. Cons. Radiol. Johannesburg Gen. Hosp.; Cons. Radiol. & Dir of Radiol King's coll Hosp Lond.

GISSEN, Paul 38 Walker Avenue, Barassie, Troon KA10 6SA — MB ChB 1995 Glas.

GITTENS, Malcolm James Kingsway Medical Centre, Kingsway, Billingham TS23 2LS Tel: 01642 553738 Fax: 01642 533011 — MB BS 1987 Lond.; MRCGP 1992; DRCOG 1992; DCH RCP Lond. 1991. Prev: Trainee GP Cleveland VTS.

GITTINS, Catherine Stewart 57 Ridge Road, London N8 9LJ — BM Soton. 1987; DCH RCP Lond. 1992.

GITTINS, Jeremy Charles The Surgery, 6 Queens Walk, Ealing, London W5 1TP Tel: 020 8997 3041 Fax: 020 8566 9100; 24 Milton Road, Acton, London W3 6QA — MB BS 1986 Lond.; MA Oxf. 1986, BA 1980; MRCGP 1990; DRCOG 1989; DCH RCP Lond. 1988. Course Organiser Ealing Hosp. VTS; GP Trainer.

***GITTINS, Nicola Susan** 5 Rooks Meadow, Hagley, Stourbridge DY9 0PT — MB ChB 1994 Birm.

GITTINS, Peter Robert 39 Carpenter Road, Edgbaston, Birmingham B15 2JJ Tel: 0121 440 1715 Fax: 0121 440 1715 — MB BChir Camb. 1950; DObst RCOG 1956. (Camb. & Birm.) Indep. Psychother. Birm. Socs: Fell. Brit. Soc. Med. & Dent. Hypn.; Internat. Soc. Hypn. Prev: Med. Dir. Robt. Nursing Home Birm.; Med. Off. Monyhull Hall Birm.; Clin. Asst. Midl. Nerve Hosp. Birm.

GITTINS, Samantha Blyth Health Centre, Thoroton Street, Blyth NE24 1DX Tel: 01670 396560 Fax: 01670 396579 — MB BS 1991 Newc.

GITTLESON, Neville Leon (retired) 1 Button Hill, Sheffield S11 9HF Tel: 0114 236 6565 — BM BCh Oxf. 1953; MA Oxf. 1954, BA 1950, DM 1965; FRCPsych 1974, M 1971; DPM Manch. 1960. Med. Mem. Ment. Health Review Tribunal. Prev: Cons. Psychiat. Sheff. HA.

GITTOES, Neil John Lloyd Department of Medicine, Queen Elizabeth Hospital, Edgbaston B15 2TH Tel: 0121 4721311 Fax: 0121 6272384 Email: n.j.gittoes@bham.ac.uk — MB ChB 1990 Birm.; BSc Birm. 1987; MRCP (UK) 1993; PhD 1997. (Birmingham) Sen. Clin. Lect. & Hon. Cons. in Endocrinol., Univ. Birm. & Univ. Hosp. Birm. Socs: RCP; Endocrine Soc.; Thyroid Club. Prev: Clin. Research Fell. Regist. (Med.); Clin. Lect. Univ. of Birm.

GITTOS, Mark John Brander St Andrew's Centre, East Wing, Broomfield Hospital, Court Road, Chelmsford CM13 0AB — MB ChB 1984 Auckland. Cons. (Plastic Surg.) Broomfield Hosp.

GITTOS, Rosemary Ann Brander Anaesthetic Department, Colchester General Hospital, Colchester CO4 5JL Tel: 01206 853535; 1 Hollymead Close, Turner Road, Colchester CO4 5JU — MB ChB 1991 Otago. SHO (Anaesth.) Colchester Gen. Hosp. Socs: Protec. Soc.

GIUNTI, Paola 158 Regents Park Road, London NW1 8XN — State Exam 1985 Rome.

GIVANS, Robert John 30 Kings Road, Harrogate HG1 5JP Tel: 01423 60261 — MB BS 1957 Lond.; MRCS Eng. LRCP Lond. 1957; DTM & H Eng. 1960. (Middlx.) Force Med. Off. N. Yorks. Police; Sec. N. Yorks. L.M.C. Socs: Fell. Roy. Soc. Med.; BMA. Prev: Ho. Surg. Mt. Vernon Hosp.; Ho. Phys. Ipswich & E. Suff. Hosp.; Cas. Off. Padd. Gen. Hosp.

GIVEN-WILSON, Rosalind Margaret 20 Vardens Road, London SW11 1RH Tel: 020 7207 0333 — MB BS 1980 Lond.; BA Camb. 1977; MRCP (UK) 1983; FRCR 1986. Cons. Radiol. St. Geo. Hosp. Lond.

GIWA, Suleiman Olayiwola 7 Winbourne Court, Winbourne St., London N1 7HB — MB BS 1981 Lagos.

GIWA-OSAGIE, Osatohamwen Onasere 22 Trinity Rise, London SW2 2QR — MB 1973 Camb.; MSc Leeds 1976; BChir 1972; MRCOG 1977; DObst RCOG 1974. (King's Coll. Hosp.) Lect. King's Coll. Hosp. Lond. Prev: Adrian Stokes Research Fell. (Endocrinol.) Univ. Leeds; SHO (Gyn.), & Ho. Surg. & Ho. Phys. King's Coll. Hosp. Lond.

GJERTSEN, Thomas Alan Stanley House Farm, Great Ayton, Middlesbrough TS9 6QD — MB BS 1970 Lond.

GLACKIN, Patrick Tyrone County Hospital, Hospital Road, Omagh BT79 0AP — MB BCh BAO 1988 NUI.

GLACKIN, Sarah 5 Chichester Gardens, Antrim Road, Belfast BT15 5FS — MB BCh BAO 1994 Belf.

GLADDEN, Margaret Hay 91 Woodend Drive, Glasgow G13 1QF Tel: 0141 959 3849 — MB BS 1965 Lond.; PhD Liverp. 1971; MRCS Eng. LRCP Lond. 1965; DCH Eng. 1968. (Roy. Free) Sen. Lect. Physiol. Inst. Glas. Univ. Prev: Jun. Research Fell. Med. Research Counc.; Holt Research Fell. Univ. Liverp.

GLADDISH, Sarah Jane 22 Cromwell Grove, London W6 7RG Tel: 020 7603 9357 — MB BS 1994 Lond.; BSc (Hons) 1991; MRCP 1997. (St. Georges Hospital Medical School London) Specialist Regist. N. W. Thames Geriats. Char. Cross Hosp. Lond.

GLADMAN, Esther Yanne Davenport House, 91 Main St., Woodborough, Nottingham NG14 6DA Tel: 0115 965 2609 — MB ChB 1985 Birm.; MRCGP 1990; DRCOG 1989; DA (UK) 1988. Prev: GP Retainer Scheme Nottm.; SHO (O & G) Kingsmill Hosp. Sutton in Ashfield; SHO (Anaesth.) Nottm. City, Univ. & Mansfield Dist. Hosps.

GLADMAN, Gordon Manchester Childrens Hospital, Hospital Road, Pendlebury, Manchester M27 4HA Tel: 0161 727 2662 Fax: 0161 727 2662; Springfield, 13 Ogden Road, Bramhall, Stockport SK7 1HJ Tel: 0161 439 4031 — MB ChB 1982 Manch.; MRCP (UK) 1986. Cons. Paediat. Cardiol. Manch. Childr. Hosp. NHS Trust. Prev: Cardiol. Fell. Hosp. Sick Childr. Toronto, Canada.

GLADMAN, John Raymond Fletcher Ageing and Disability Research Unit, B Floor Medical School, University Hospital, Nottingham NG7 2UH Tel: 0115 942 1421 Fax: 0115 942 3618 Email: john.gladman@nottingham.ac.uk — MB ChB 1983 Birm.; BSc (Hons.) Birm. 1980; DM Nottm. 1991; MRCP (UK) 1986; FRCP Lond. 1998. Sen. Lect. (Med.) Univ. Hosp. Nottm. Socs: Brit. Stroke Research Gp.; Soc. for Research in Rehabil. (Sen. Sec. & Pres. Elect).

GLADMAN, Lisa Marie Squirrels Lodge, Crossway, Walton-on-Thames KT12 3JA — MB BS 1997 Lond.; BSc (Hons) Lond1994. (UCL Medical School) SHO Geriat. Med. UCL.

GLADMAN, Marc Anthony 4 Fairway Drive, Dartford DA2 6AR — MB BS 1996 Lond.

GLADSTONE, David Ian 28 Scotts Way, Tunbridge Wells TN2 5RG — MB ChB 1970 Ed.; MRC Path. 1980.

GLADSTONE, Gerald Sewell (retired) Tylers, Little Bushey Lane, Bushey, Watford WD23 3RU Tel: 020 8950 2546 — MA, MB BChir Camb. 1940; MRCPsych 1971; DPM Eng. 1948. Prev: Cons. Psychiat. Napsbury Hosp. St. Albans.

GLADWELL, Stephen Robert Fox Devon House, Uffculme Psychotherapy Service, Mindelsohn Way, Edgbaston, Birmingham B15 2QR Tel: 0121 678 2471 Fax: 0121 678 2499 Email: stephen.gladwell@sbmht.wmids.nhs.uk — MB BS 1973 Lond.; MA (Psychoanalyt. Studies) Lond. 1996; MRCS Eng. LRCP Lond. 1973; MRCPsych 1977; FRCPsych 1997. (Roy. Free) Cons. Psychiat. in Psychother. Devon Ho. Birm. Prev: Cons. Psychother. Uffculme Clinic Birm.; Sen. Lect. & Hon. Cons. Child Psychiat. Birm. Univ.; Sen. Regist. (Child Psychiat.) The Pk. Hosp. Childr. Oxf.

GLADWIN, Barbara Cecilia (retired) 3 Victoria Mead, Thame OX9 3HY Tel: 01844 4958 — MRCS Eng. LRCP Lond. 1942. Prev: Asst. Med. Off. Oxf. Blood Transfus. Serv.

GLAHOLM, John 56 Witherford Way, Bourneville Village, Birmingham B29 4AS Tel: 0121 628 9154 Email: john.glaholm@virgin.net — MB BS 1980 Lond.; BSc Biochem. Lond. 1977; MRCP 1983; FRCR (Clin. Oncol.) 1987. (Charing Cross Hospital Medical School) Cons. Clinc. Oncol. Qu. Eliz. Hosp. Edgebaston Birm. Prev: Sen. Regist. & Regist. Roy. Marsden Hosp.

GLAHOLM, John Bilton (retired) 55 Claremont Road, Whitley Bay NE26 3TP Tel: 0191 252 5719 — MB BS 1949 Durh. Prev: SHO (O & G) Ashton-under-Lyne Gen. Hosp.

GLAISHER, Brian Douglas (retired) Mill House, Mill Lane, Hildenborough, Tonbridge TN11 9LX Tel: 01732 832782 — MRCS Eng. LRCP Lond. 1954. Prev: Ho. Phys. Roy. E. Sussex Hosp. Hastings.

GLAISTER, Alison Margaret Wickham Market Medical Centre, Chapel Lane, Wickham Market, Woodbridge IP13 0SB Tel: 01728 747101 Fax: 01728 747580 — MB ChB 1984 Bristol; MRCGP 1989; DRCOG 1988.

GLAISYER, Hilary Ruth Great Ormond St. Hospital, Great Ormond St., London WC1 Tel: 0207 405 9200 — MB BS 1989 Lond.; MRCP (UK) 1992; FRCA 1995. Prev: Regist. Rotat. (Anaesth.) Middlx. Hosp. Lond.; SHO (Anaesth.) St. Thos. Hosp. Lond.; SHO Rotat. (Postgrad.) Whittington Hosp. Lond.

GLAISYER, John Michael The Surgery, Cerne Abbas, Dorchester DT2 7JG Tel: 01300 341666 Fax: 01300 341090; Picketts Farm, Newlands Lane, Glanvilles Wootton, Sherborne DT9 5QG Tel: 01300

345215 — MB BS 1959 Lond.; MRCS Eng. LRCP Lond. 1959; DObst RCOG 1964. (Middlx.) Socs: BMA. Prev: Ho. Surg. Middlx. Hosp.; Ho. Phys. Centr. Middlx. Hosp.; Ho. Off. (O & G) St. Alfege's Hosp. Greenwich.

GLANCEY, Gerald Robert Renal Unit, Ipswich Hospital, Heath Road, Ipswich IP4 5PD Tel: 01473 704168 — MB BS 1983 Lond.; BA Camb. 1980; MD Lond. 1991; MRCP (UK) 1986. (Guy's) Cons. Phys. and Nephrologist & Director of Ipswich Hosp. Drug Research Unit.

GLANCY, Bernard Patrick Garden Street Surgery, 29 Garden Street, Magherafelt BT45 5DD Tel: 028 7938 6237 Fax: 028 7930 1302 — MB BCh BAO 1978 Belf.

GLANCY, Claire Isabella Harper 2A Speirs Grove, Thornliebank, Glasgow G46 7RL — MB ChB 1993 Glas. SHO (Anaesth.) Vict. Infirm. Glas. Prev: SHO (Paediat.) CrossHo. Hosp. Kilmarnock; Ho. Off. (Surg.) Monklands Dist. Gen. Hosp. Airdrie; Ho. Off. (Med.) Roy. Alexandra Hosp. Paisley.

***GLANCY, Damian Gerard** 14A All Saints Road, Clifton, Bristol BS8 2JJ Tel: 0117 923 9701 Email: damianglancy@hotmail.com — MB ChB 1998 Bristol; BSc (Hons) 1995.

GLANCY, James Michael Department of Cardiology, County Hospital, Union Walk, Hereford HR1 2ER; St. John's House, Burghill, Hereford HR4 7RX — MB ChB 1983 Manch.; MRCP (UK) 1989; MD Leic. 1996. Cons. Cardiol. Phys. Co. Hosp. Hereford. Socs: Med. Res. Soc.; Brit. Cardiac Soc. Prev: Research Regist. (Cardiol.) Leicester; RN Short Career Commiss.

GLANCY, Stephen John 2A Spiers Grove, 9 Main St., Thornliebank, Glasgow G46 7RL — MB ChB 1992 Glas. SHO (Med.) Roy. Alexandra Hosp. Paisley.

GLANCY, Thomas Terence (retired) Brandsby House, Ambleside Road, Windermere LA23 1AX — MB ChB 1951 Manch.

GLANFIELD, Michael Dennis 71 Aylesford Avenue, Beckenham BR3 3RZ — MB BS 1978 Lond.; BA Open 1990; MRCS Eng. LRCP Lond. 1978; DAvMed FOM RCP Lond. 1996; Cert. Gen. Av. Med. 1983. (Westm.) SMO DERA; Authorized Med. Examr. Civil Aviat. Auth. Socs: Roy. Aeronaut. Soc.; Roy. Inst. Prev: Med. Dir. AA Alert Assistance; Company Med. Off. Dan Air Gatwick.

GLANFIELD, Patricia Ann 2 The Gables, Oddfellows Road, Hathersage, Hope Valley S32 1DU — MB ChB 1980 Sheff. Community Med. Off. (Family Plann.) Centr. Health Clinic Sheff. HA.

GLANVILL, Andrew Peter Glanvill and Partners, Springmead Surgery, Summerfields Road, Chard TA20 2HB Tel: 01460 63380 Fax: 01460 66483; Gables, Touchstone Close, Chard TA20 1QZ Tel: 01460 64262 Email: pglanv@aol.co.uk — MB BS 1974 Lond.; DRCOG 1979. (St. Bart.) Approved Doctor Dept. of Energy (Certified Med. Fitness to Dive); Med. Ref. for UK Sport; Diving Med. Comm. Socs: Eur. Undersea Biomed. Soc. Prev: SHO (Psychiat.) Tone Vale Hosp. Taunton; SHO (A & E & Paediat.) Glos. Roy. Hosp.

GLANVILL, Michael Edward, OStJ (retired) Wetherlaw, 5 Brutten Way, Mitchell Gardens, Chard TA20 2HB Tel: 01460 63348 — MRCS Eng. LRCP Lond. 1948; BA Open 1986; MRCGP 1953; DMJ (Clin.) Soc. Apoth. Lond. 1967. Barrister-at-Law, Middle Temple; Master Diver Brit. Underwater Centre; Authorised Med. Examr. Civil Aviat. Auth.; Div. Surg St. John Ambul. Brig. Prev: Med. Adviser Underwater Med. Inst. Oceanographic Scs.

GLANVILLE, Hugh Josolyne Allington House, Allington, Salisbury SP4 0DA Tel: 01980 610254 — FRCP Lond. 1975, M 1968; MRCS Eng. LRCP Lond. 1942; DPhysMed Eng. 1948. (St. Mary's) Research & Rehabil. Prev: Emerit. Europe Prof. Rehabil. Soton. Univ.; Phys. Rheum. & Rehabil. Salisbury Health Dist.; Consult. i/c Nuffield Rehabil. Centre, Odstock Hosp.

GLANVILLE, Mr John Dixon Woodside, The Crescent, Romsey SO51 7NG Tel: 01794 516982 — MB BS Lond. 1945; FRCS Eng. 1953; DLO Eng. 1952. (St. Mary's) Emerit. Cons. ENT Surg. Soton. & SW Hants. HA. Socs: Fell. Roy. Soc. Med. Prev: Ho. Surg. (ENT) St. Mary's Hosp. Padd.; Regist. (ENT) Bristol United Hosps.; Sen. Regist. (ENT) Roy. Free Hosp. Lond.

GLANVILLE, John Norman (retired) Cartref, London Road, Barkston Ash, Tadcaster LS24 9PW Tel: 01937 557379 Fax: 01937 557379 Email: jglanville@freenet.co.uk — MB BCh 1952 Wales; FRCR 1984; DMRD Eng. 1961. Prev: Cons. Radiol. Pinderfields Gen. Hosp. Wakefield & St. Jas. Hosp. Leeds.

GLANVILLE, Samuel Basil Christopher 26 Ember Farm Way, East Molesey KT8 0BL — BM 1998 Soton.; BM Soton 1998.

GLANVILLE, Thomas Anthony Clapham Park Surgery, 72 Clarence Avenue, London SW4 8JP Tel: 020 8674 4436; 39 Spring Grove, London W4 3NH Tel: 020 8995 8929 — MB BChir 1962 Camb.; MA Camb. 1962; MRCOG 1967. (St. Thos.) Prev: Sen. Regist. (O & G) Lusaka Teachg. Hosp., Zambia; Regist. (O & G) St. Bart. Hosp. Lond.

GLANVILLE, Tracey Jane 2/1, 61 Airlie Street, Glasgow G12 9SR — MB ChB 1991 Glas.; BSc (Hons.) Biochem. Ed. 1986.

GLASBY, Martin Stephen Woodside Surgery, High Street, Loftus, Saltburn-by-the-Sea TS13 4HW Tel: 01287 640385 Fax: 01287 644071 — MB ChB 1981 Leeds; MRCGP 1985; DRCOG 1983.

GLASBY, Mr Michael Arthur Department of Clinical Neurosciences, Edinburgh University, Western General Hospital NHS Trust, Crewe Road, Edinburgh EH4 2XU Tel: 0131 537 2905 Fax: 07713513193 Email: michael.glasby@ed.ac.uk — BM BCh 1977 Oxf.; MA Camb. 1986; MSc, MA Oxf. 1975, BA (1st cl. Hons.) (Animal Physiol.) 1971; FRCS Ed. 1993; FRCS Eng. 1981; FICS 1995; CBiol, MIBiol 1993. (Oxford) Reader & Hon. Cons Experim. Neurol.) Univ. of Edin.; Examr. (Cardiothoracic Surg. & Orthop. Surg.) Intercollegiate Bd. RCS GB & Irel.; Examr. RCS Edin. & Glas. Socs: Brit. Orthop. Research Soc.; Assoc. Mem. Brit. Soc. Surg. Hand. Prev: Reader (Anat.) Univ. of Edin.; Fell. & Lect. (Anat.) New Hall Camb.; Surg. Harefield Heart Transpl. Trust.

***GLASBY, Michael James** Owlsden, The Green, Fornham All Saints, Bury St Edmunds IP28 6JX — MB BS 1997 Lond.; BSc (Psychol.) Lond. 1994.

GLASCOE, Stephen Paul Kings Road Surgery, 180 Kings Road, Canton, Cardiff CF11 9DQ Tel: 029 2034 1547 Fax: 029 2064 0499 — MB ChB 1974 Liverp.; MRCGP 1979; DRCOG 1977. (Liverp.)

GLASER, Adam Woolf Yorkshire Regional Centre for Paediatric Oncology & Haematology, St. James's University Hospital, Beckett Street, Leeds LS9 7TF Tel: 0113 206 4985 Fax: 0113 247 0248; 2 Belgravia Gardens, North Lane, Leeds LS8 2SW — MB BS 1989 Lond.; BSc (Hons.) Lond. 1986; MRCP (UK) 1993; FRCPCH; DM 1999. (Charing Cross and Westminster) Cons. Paediatric & Adolesc. Oncologist. Prev: Locum Cons., Gt. Ormond St. Hosp. Lond.; Fell. Paediat. Oncol. Hosp. Sick. Childr. Toronto, Canada; Lect. & Hon. Sen. Regist. (Paediat.) Qu. Med. Centre Univ. Nottm.

GLASER, Danya Ruth Dept. of Psychological Medicine, Great Ormond Street Hospital, London WC1N 3JH Tel: 020 7829 8679 Fax: 020 7829 8657 — MB BS Lond. 1966; MRCS Eng. LRCP Lond. 1966; FRCPsych. 1992, M 1977; DCH Eng. 1968. (Univ. Coll. Hosp.) Cons. Child Psychiat. Gt. Ormond St. Hosp. Childr. Lond. Prev: Cons. Child Psychiat. Guy's Hosp. Lond.; Sen. Regist. (Child Psychiat.) Hosp. for Sick Childr. Gt. Ormond St. Lond.

GLASER, Leonard Henry Shelley, Firfields, Cobbetts Hill, Weybridge KT13 0UD Tel: 01932 841808 Fax: 01932 841808 Email: drlhglaser@aol.com — MB BS Lond. 1954; DObst RCOG 1959. (Char. Cross) JP; Med. Adv. & Adjudicating Med. Auth. Benefits Agency Med. Servs. DSS. Socs: Worshipful Soc. Apoth. Prev: Clin. Asst. (Paediat.) Fulham Hosp. (Char. Cross Hosp.); Ho. Phys. & Ho. Surg. (O & G) Selly Oak Hosp. Birm.

GLASER, Mark Gordon Charing Cross Hospital, Department Radiotherapy & Oncology, Fulham Palace Road, London W6 8RF Tel: 020 8846 1733/1740 — MB BS 1971 Lond.; MRCS Eng. LRCP Lond. 1971; DMRT Eng. 1978; FFR RCSI 1978; FRCR 1979. (Char. Cross) Cons. Radiother. & Oncol. Char. Cross Hosp. Lond.; Hon. Cons. W. Middlx. Hosp.; Hon. Cons. Radiother. & Oncol. Hammersmith Hosp. Lond. Prev: Regist. (Radiother.) Lond. Hosp.; Ho. Phys. St. Stephen's Hosp. Chelsea; SHO (Radiother.) Christie Hosp. Manch.

GLASER, Sholem 54 Church Street, Bathford, Bath BA1 7RS Tel: 01225 859353 — MB BS (Hons.) Lond. 1936; MSc (Hons.) Cape Town 1932; FRCS Eng. 1937; MRCS Eng. LRCP Lond. 1936. (Lond. Hosp. & Cape Town) Prev: Surg. Bath Hosp. Gp.; Lt.-Col. RAMC.

GLASGOW, Alastair Charles Arthur Dunluce Avenue Surgery, 1-3 Dunluce Avenue, Belfast BT9 7AW Tel: 028 9024 0884; 52 Richmond Court, Lisburn BT27 4QX Tel: 01846 678533 — MB BCh BAO 1974 Belf.; MFOM 1999; MFHom 1982; DObst RCOG 1976. (Qu. Univ. Belf.) Occupat. Health Phys. Visteon UK; Mem. Fac. Homoeop. Lond.; Regional Med. Off. BBC, N. Irel. Socs: Fell.ship Ulster Med. Soc.; Soc. Occup. Med. N Irel. Gp. Prev: SHO Roy.

Matern. Hosp. Belf. & Samarit. Hosp. Belf.; SHO Roy. Belf. Hosp. Sick Childr.

GLASGOW, Isobel Little (retired) Danny, Hurstpierpoint, Hassocks BN6 9BB Tel: 01273 832299 — MB BCh BAO 1923 Belf. Prev: Capt. RAMC.

GLASGOW, John Frederick Turnbull Royal Belfast Hospital Sick Children, Falls Road, Belfast BT12 6BE Tel: 01232 240503 Fax: 01232 235340; 12 Old Coach Road, Upper Malone Road, Belfast BT9 5PR Tel: 01232 290298 Fax: 01232 290286 Email: j.glasgow@qub.ac.uk — MB BCh BAO Belf. 1963; BSc Belf. 1960, MD 1982; FRCP 1979, M 1966; FRCPI 1979, M 1966; FFAEM 1993; DCH RCPS Glas. 1967; FRCPCH 1997. (Belf.) Cons. Paediat. (A & E) & Reader (Child Health) Qu. Univ. Belf. Socs: Brit. Assn. Accid. & Emerg. Med.; (Ex-Pres.) Irish Paediat. Assn. Prev: Sen. Regist. Roy. Belf. Hosp. Sick Childr.; Fell. (Gastroenterol.) Hosp. Sick Childr. Toronto, Canada; Ho. Phys. Hosp. Sick Childr. Gt. Ormond St. Lond.

GLASGOW, Louise Victoria Mary Copper Hall, Watts Rd, Thames Ditton KT7 0BX — BM BCh 1997 Oxf.

GLASGOW, Mr Malcolm Mervyn Stanley 77 Newmarket Road, Norwich NR2 2HW Tel: 01603 667195 Fax: 01603 761554 Email: glasknee@yahoo.com; Holverston Hall, Holverston, Norwich NR14 7PH Tel: 01508 480739 — MB BS Lond. 1970; FRCS Eng. 1975. Cons. Orthop. Norf. & Norwich Hosp. Socs: Fell. BOA; Pres. Brit. Assn. Surg. of Knee (BASK); Europ. Soc Surg. of the Knee Sports and Arthroscopy (ESSKA). Prev: Sen. Regist. (Orthop.) W.m. Hosp. Lond.; Regist. (Orthop.) Roy. Nat. Orthop. Hosp. Lond.

GLASGOW, Mark Charles Copnor Road Surgery, 111 Copnor Road, Portsmouth PO3 5AF Tel: 023 9266 3368 Fax: 023 9278 3203; 154c Havant Road, Hayling Island PO11 0LJ Tel: 023 92 466023 — MB ChB 1976 Ed.; MRCGP 1981; DRCOG 1980. (Manch.)

GLASGOW, Thomas Clemens (retired) Sunnyhurst, 22 Greenham Drive, Seaview PO34 5LL — LRCP LRCS 1949 Ed.; LRCP LRCS Ed. LRFPS Glas. 1949. Prev: GP Chorley.

GLASGOW, William Victor 12 Rosevale Avenue, Newtownards BT23 7BZ Tel: 01247 812239 — MB BCh BAO Belf. 1941. (Belf.)

GLASIER, Annabelle Frances 22 India Street, Edinburgh EH3 6HB Tel: 0131 225 3962 — MB ChB 1976 Bristol; BSc (Psychol.) Bristol 1973, MD 1983, MB ChB 1976; FRCOG 1995, M 1983. Cons. Gyn. & Dir. Family Plann. Well Wom. Servs. Lothian HB; Sen. Lect. Univ. Edin. Prev: Clin. Research Scientist MRC Unit Reproduct. Biol. Edin.; Hon. Cons. Lothian HB; Lect. (Reproduc. Med.) Univ. Edin.

GLASON, Matthew Sean Lawrence Squire and Partners, Market Place, Hadleigh, Ipswich IP7 5DN Tel: 01473 822961 Fax: 01473 824895 — MB BS 1986 Lond.; Dip Occ Med 1999; DFFP 1996. (Roy. Free Hosp. Lond.) Prev: Phys. Occupat. Health Dept. HM Naval Base Portsmouth; Princip GP. Gibraltar Servs. Med. & Dent. Centre.

GLASPER, Anthony James 40 Liverpool Grove, Walworth, London SE17 2HJ — MB BS 1996 Lond.

GLASS, Alan 123 Russell Road, Moseley, Birmingham B13 8RS Tel: 0121 449 3294 — MB ChB 1954 Birm.; BSc (Anat. & Physiol.) Birm. 1951, MD 1964, MB ChB 1954. (Birm.) Sen. Lect. Dept. Anat. Univ. Birm. Socs: EEG Soc. & Anat. Soc. Gt. Brit. & Irel. Prev: Surg. Lt. RNVR, Att. RN Physiol. Laborat.; Lect. Dept. Anat. Univ. Birm.

GLASS, Andrew Lewis Clayton Health Centre, 89 North Road, Clayton, Manchester M11 4EJ Tel: 0161 223 9229 Fax: 0161 223 1116 — MB ChB 1975 Manch.; BSc (Med. Sci.) St. And. 1973.

GLASS, Camilla Elizabeth Black Causeway House, 2 Black Causeway Road, Strangford, Downpatrick BT30 7LX — MB ChB 1995 Dundee.

GLASS, David Thompson (retired) 'Highwayes', Templepatrick, Ballyclare BT39 0AA Tel: 0184 94 32751 — MD 1952 Belf.; MB BCh BAO 1946; FFR RCSI 1964; DMRD Eng. 1950. Prev: Cons. Radiol. Massereene Hosp. Antrim & Waveney Hosp. Ballymena.

GLASS, Douglas James Allan Tel: 013397 55686 Fax: 013397 53510; Deecastle, Dinnet, Aboyne AB34 5NU Tel: 013398 85217 — MB ChB 1977 Aberd. Apoth. to the Roy. Ho.hold Balmoral. Prev: GP Peterhead.

GLASS, Elizabeth Jean Douglas Pinderfields General Hospital, Aberford Road, Wakefield WF1 4DG Tel: 01924 213755 Fax: 01924 212132 — MD 1984 Ed.; BSc Ed. 1970, MB ChB 1973; FRCP Ed. 1993; FRCPCH 1997. (Edinburgh) Cons. Paediat. Pinderfield Gen. Hosp. Wakefield.

GLASS, Gerard Malmuire (retired) Casetta, Castle St., Strangford, Downpatrick BT30 7NF Tel: 01396 881656 — MD 1957 Belf.; MB BCh BAO 1943. Hon. Cons. Vasc. Surg. Mater Infirm. Hosp. Belf. Prev: Clin. Teach. (Gen. Surg.) Qu.'s Univ. Belf.

GLASS, Janice Margaret 73 Telford Avenue, Leamington Spa CV32 7HQ — MB ChB 1973 Aberd. Clin. Med. Off. S. Warks. HA.

GLASS, John Aboyne Health Centre, Bellwood Road, Aboyne AB34 5HQ Tel: 01339 886345; 8 Queens Hill Drive, Aboyne AB34 5GD Tel: 013398 86079 — MB ChB 1981 Aberd.; MRCGP 1986; DRCOG 1985.

GLASS, John Bellairs 322 Singlewell Road, Gravesend DA11 7RZ — MB BS Lond. 1951; DObst RCOG 1961. (St. Thos.) Prev: Ho. Surg. & Ho. Phys. Roy. Vict. Hosp. Folkestone; Ho. Surg. (Obst.) Soton. Gen. Hosp.

GLASS, Mr Jonathan Mark 46 Hart Grove, Ealing, London W5 3NB Fax: 020 8354 0324 Email: jo46hg@aol.com — MB BS 1989 Lond.; BSc Lond. 1986; FRCS Eng. 1993; FRCS (Urol) 1998. (St. Mary's Hosp. Med. Sch. Lond.) Cons. Urol., Guy's & St.Thomas' Hosps., Lond. Socs: Fell. Roy. Soc. Med.; Brit. Assn. Urol. Surgs.; Brit. Soc. Endocrinol. Prev: Specialist Regist. (Urol.) N.wick Pk. Hosp. Lond.; Regist. (Urol.) Hammersmith Hosp. Lond.; Research Regist. (Urol.) St. Mary's Hosp. Lond.

GLASS, Karen Sandra Queens Medical Centre, University Hospital, Nottingham NG7 2UH — BM BS 1988 Nottm.

GLASS, Leslie George Alderman Jack Cohen Health Centre, Springwell Road, Sunderland SR3 4HG Tel: 0191 522 9908 Fax: 0191 528 8294 — MB ChB 1975 Manch.

GLASS, Martin Robert Clarendon Wing, Leeds General Infirmary, Leeds LS2 9NS; 25 Sandmoor Drive, Alwoodley, Leeds LS17 7DF — MD Birm. 1977, MB ChB 1967; MRCS Eng. LRCP Lond. 1968; FRCOG 1984, M 1972. (Birm.) Cons. O & G Clarendon Wing Leeds Gen. Infirm. Prev: Sen. Lect. (O & G) Univ. Leeds; Sen. Regist. W. Midl. RHA; Research Regist. Birm. & Midl. Hosp. Wom. Birm.

GLASS, Mr Richard Edmund Princess Margaret Hospital, Okus Road, Swindon SN2 4JU Tel: 01793 536231; Lower Easton Piercy, Kingston St. Michael, Chippenham SN14 6JS — MB BS 1971 Lond.; MS Lond. 1983; FRCS Eng. 1976. (Lond. Hosp.) Cons. Surg. Gastroenterol. P.ss Margt. Hosp. Swindon. Socs: Fell. Roy. Soc. Med.; St. Mark's Assn.; Assn. Surg. Prev: Regist. (Surg.) Gordon Hosp. Lond.; Research Fell. Cleveland Clinic Ohio, USA; Resid. Surg. Off. St. Mark's Hosp. Dis. Colon & Rectum Lond.

GLASS, Robert Kewrin, Garvagh, Coleraine — MB BCh BAO 1941 Belf.

GLASS, Robert Gavin 123 Russell Road, Moseley, Birmingham B13 8RS — MB ChB 1988 Bristol; BSc (Hons.) Bristol 1985, MB ChB 1988; MRCP (UK) 1993. Regist. (Med.) Dorset Co. Hosp.

GLASS, Sharon Anne Department of Child Health, Elm Street Clinic, Elm St., Ipswich IP1 1HB Tel: 01473 275301 Fax: 01473 275375 Email: sharon.glass@lhp.nhs.uk; 82 Belstead Road, Ipswich IP2 9AW Tel: 01473 601009 — MB ChB 1978 Ed.; FRCP(E) 1999; MRCP (UK) 1982. Cons. Community Paediat. Local health Partnership NHSTrust Ipswich. Socs: FRCPCH; FRCPCH; BACCH Brit. Assoc. Comm. Child Health. Prev: Sen. Regist. Roy. Hosp. Sick Childr. Edin.

GLASS, Susan 38 Timberbottom, Bolton BL2 3DL — MB ChB 1990 Manch.

GLASS, Sylvia Ethel Priorslegh Medical Centre, Civic Centre, Park Lane, Poynton, Stockport SK12 1GP Tel: 01625 872299; 138 Gill Bent Road, Cheadle Hulme, Cheadle SK8 6NJ Tel: 0161 486 0151 — MB BChir 1979 Camb.; PhD Camb. 1976; BSc Birm. 1972. (Camb.) GP Manch. Prev: SHO (Obst.) Camb. Matern. Hosp.; Ho. Phys. Ipswich Hosp.; Ho. Surg. Addenbrooke's Hosp. Camb.

GLASS, William John (retired) 29 Gorsedene Road, Whitley Bay NE26 4AH Tel: 0191 252 5887 Email: bill@wglass.fsnet.co.uk — MB ChB 1957 Ed.

GLASSBOROW, Ruth Tel: 020 8655 1223; 145 Addiscombe Court Road, Croydon CR0 6TX Tel: 020 8654 0331 — BM BS 1994 Nottm.; BMedSci Nottm. 1992; DRCOG 1996; DCH 1997; MRCGP 1998. (Nottm.) GP Princip. Woodside Health Centre S. Norwood SE25 5NT. Socs: RCGP; Diplomate RCOG. Prev: SHO (Geriat.s, Paediat.) Mayday Hosp.; SHO (A & E & O & G) Mayday Hosp.; Ho. Off. (Gen. Surg., Gen. Med. & ENT) Mayday Hosp. Croydon.

GLASSER, Abraham I 1 Lonsdale Avenue, Giffnock, Glasgow G46 6HG — MB ChB 1935 Glas.

GLASSER, Jonathan Michael 65 Langside Drive, Newlands, Glasgow G43 2QX — MB ChB 1973 Glas.; FFA RCS Eng. 1978. Cons. Anaesth. Hairmyres Hosp. E. Kilbride. Prev: Sen. Regist. (Anaesth.) Manch. AHA; Regist. (Anaesth.) Vict. Infirm. Glas.

GLASSON, Carole The Clapham Park Surgery, 72 Clarence Avenue, London SW4 8JP Tel: 020 8674 0101 Fax: 020 8674 2941; 72 Clarence Avenue, London SW4 Tel: 020 8674 0101 — MB BS 1978 Lond.; MRCS Eng. LRCP Lond. 1978; MRCGP 1982; DRCOG 1981.

GLASSPOOL, John Alan Victor Street Surgery, Victor Street, Shirley, Southampton SO15 5SY Tel: 023 8077 4781 Fax: 023 8039 0680 — BM 1980 Soton.; FRCP 2000; MRCP (UK) 1984. Hon. Clin. Tutor (Primary Med Care) Univ. Soton.; Mem. Standing Comm. of GPs, Roy. Coll. of Phys.s, Lond. Prev: Regist. (Med.) Salisbury Gen. Infirm.

GLASSPOOL, Mr Michael Gillo (retired) Rookery Cottage, Chevening Lane, Knockholt, Sevenoaks TN14 7LB Tel: 01959 533265 — MB BChir Camb. 1962; FRCS Eng. 1972; FRCOphth 1989; DO Eng. 1967. Cons. Ophth. Orpington Hosp. & Qu. Mary's Hosp. Sidcup. Prev: Sen. Regist. Moorfields Eye Hosp. (Holborn Br.) Lond.

GLASSPOOL, Rosalind Margaret Beatson Oncology Centre, Western Infirmary, Glasgow Tel: 0141 211 2000; 27 Banavia Road, Glasgow G11 5AW Tel: 0141 357 5916 — MB BS 1994 Oxf.; MSc (Univ. Glas.) 1999; MBBS Lond. 1994; BA (Hons.) Oxf. 1989; MRCP (UK) 1997. (St. Geo. Med. Sch.) Specialist Regist. (Med. Oncol.) W.. Infirm. Glas.; Clin. research Fell., Univ. of Glas., Glas. Socs: Roy. Coll. of Phys.s, Lond.; Assn. of Cancer Phys.s; Brit. Assn. of Cancer Research. Prev: SHO Rotat. (Med.) Guy's Hosp. Lond.; Ho. Off. (Med.) St. Geo. Hosp. Lond.; Ho. Off. (Gen. Surg. & Urol.) Ipswich Hosp.

GLASTONBURY, Rachel Ruth Top Flat, 61 Alma Road, Clifton, Bristol BS8 2DW; 33 Bulwer Road, Clarendon Park, Leicester LE2 3BW Tel: 0116 270 7520 — MB ChB 1991 Leic.; DRCOG 1995; MRCGP 1997. (Leicester)

GLATT, David The Southwick Health Centre, The Green, Sunderland SR5 2LT Tel: 0191 548 6634 Fax: 0191 548 1281; 12 Ashbrooke Mount, Tunstall Road, Sunderland SR2 7SD Tel: 0191 522 6813 — MRCS Eng. LRCP Lond. 1960. (Leeds)

GLATT, Hyman Sam 33 Greetlands Road, Tunstall, Sunderland SR2 9EB Tel: 0191 528 4606 — MB ChB 1958 Sheff.; MRCS Eng. LRCP Lond. 1949.

GLATT, Max Meier 16 Southbourne Crescent, London NW4 2JY Tel: 020 8346 4810 Fax: 020 8343 1989; 16 Southbourne Crescent, London NW4 2JY Tel: 020 8346 4810 Fax: 020 8343 1989 — MD 1937 Leipzig; DSc Open 1978; FRCP Lond. 1975, M 1970; FRCPsych 1971; Hon. FRCPsych 1985; DPM Eng. 1950. (Berlin & Leipzig) Serv. Dir. Addic. Dis. Unit Cons. Psychiat. Charter Nightingale Hosp. Lond.; Vis. Psychother. HM Prison Wormwood Scrubs; Recognised Teach. (Med.) Univ. Lond.; Emerit. Edr. Brit. Jl. Addic.; Vice-Pres. Med. Counc. on Alcoholism; Ex-Pres. Nat. Counc. on Alcoholism. 1984. Socs: Vice-Pres. Med. Counc. Alcoholism; Honourary Fell. Soc. Study Addic.; Honourary Mem. German Soc. Addic. Research & Ther. Prev: Cons. i/c Regional Alcoholic Addic. Unit NW Thames RHA & St. Bernard's Hosp.; Hon. Cons. & Hon. Sen. Lect. UCH; WHO Cons. & Mem. WHO Expert Advis. Panel on Drug Dependence.

GLATZEL, Therese Gabriele Robert Jones & Agnes Hunt Orthopaedic & District Hospital, Oswestry SY10 7AG — State Exam Med 1987 Berlin.

GLAVES, Ian Scarborough Hospital, Woodlands Drive, Scarborough YO12 6QL Tel: 01723 368111 — MB ChB 1972 Sheff.; FRCR 1979; DMRD Eng. 1977. (Sheff.) Cons. Radiol. ScarBoro. Hosp. Prev: Sen. Regist. (Radiol.) Sheff. AHA (T).

GLAVES, Jeffrey Department of Medical Imaging, Chesterfield Royal Hospital NHS Trust, Calow, Chesterfield S44 5BL Tel: 01246 277271 — MB BS 1971 Newc.; FRCR 1978; DMRD Eng. 1977. Cons. Radiol. Chesterfield & N. Derbysh. Roy. Hosp. Socs: RCR BrE. Gp. Prev: Cons. Radiol. City Hosp. Nottm.; Sen. Regist. (Radiol.) Leeds AHA (T); Regist. (Radiol.) Notts. AHA (T).

GLAVES, Philip The Health Centre, Bridge Street, Thorne, Doncaster DN8 5QH Tel: 01405 812121 Fax: 01405 741059; 57 Lancaster Avenue, Kirk Sandall, Doncaster DN3 1NR — MB BS 1977 Newc.

GLAVIN, Ronnie Jack 229 Queen Victoria Drive, Jordanhill, Glasgow G13 1UU — MB ChB 1978 Glas.; MPhil Glas. 1993, MB ChB 1978; FFA RCS Eng. 1984. Cons. Anaesth. Vict. Infirm. Glas.

GLAVINA, Anne Hazelwood (retired) High Ground, Manesty, Keswick CA12 5UG Tel: 01768 777277 — MB BS 1950 Durh.; MRCPsych 1981. Prev: Cons. (Psychogeriat.) Walsgrave Hosp. Coventry.

GLAVINA, Helen Margaret 74 Cherry Orton Road, Orton Waterville, Peterborough PE2 5EH — MB BS 1978 Newc.; DRCOG 1982. Prev: Trainee GP Newc. VTS.

GLAVINA, Michael John 74 Cherry Orton Road, Orton Waterville, Peterborough PE2 5EH Tel: 01733 236107 — MB BS 1978 Newc.; FFARCS Eng. 1984; DA Eng. 1982. Cons. Anaesth. P'boro. HA. Prev: Sen. Regist. (Anaesth.) E. Anglian RHA; Lect. (Anaesth.) Chinese Univ., Hong Kong; Cons. Anaesth. Dunedin, NZ.

GLAYSHER, Christopher Michael Robert St Ann Street Surgery, 82 St. Ann Street, Salisbury SP1 2PT Tel: 01722 322624 Fax: 01722 410624; The Old Farm House, Quidhampton, Salisbury SP2 9AS — MB BS 1970 Lond.; FRCGP 2001; MRCS Eng. LRCP Lond. 1970; MRCGP 1979; DObst RCOG 1973; DCH Eng. 1972.

GLAZE, Margaret Elizabeth Taylor and Partners, The Surgery, Hexton Road, Barton-le-Clay, Bedford MK45 4TA Tel: 01582 882050 — MB ChB 1973 Liverp.

GLAZE, Robin Christopher John Young People's Unit, Tipperlin Rd, Edinburgh EH10 5HF Tel: 0131 537 6523 Fax: 0131 537 6102 — MB ChB 1984 Birm.; MRCPsych. 1989. Cons. Adoloescent Psychiat., Lothian Primary Care NHS Trust Edin. Prev: Cons. Child & Adolesc. Psychiat. N. Staffs Combined Healthcae NHS Trust.

GLAZEBROOK, Clive William 15 Bentley Road, Cambridge CB2 2AW — MB BS 1973 Lond.; MA Camb. 1987; BSc (Hons.) Lond. 1971, MB BS 1973; FFA RCS Eng. 1978; DObst RCOG 1975. (King's Coll. Hosp.) Cons. Anaesth. New Addenbrooke's Hosp. Camb.; Assoc. Lect. Univ. Camb. Socs: BMA; Obst. Anaesth. Assn. Prev: Sen. Regist. (Anaesth.) Radcliffe Infirm. Oxf.; Regist. (Anaesth.) Univ. Otago Dunedin, New Zealand; Resid. (Obst. & Med.) Internat. Grenfell Assn. Newfld. Canada.

GLAZEBROOK, William Rimington Flat 1, 51 Earls Court Sq, London SW5 9DG — MB BS 1997 Lond.

GLAZENER, Cathryn Margaret Anne Health Services Research Unit, University of Aberdeen, Drew Kay Wing, Polwarth Building, Foresterhill, Aberdeen AB25 2ZD Tel: 01224 681818 Fax: 01224 663087 Email: c.glazener@abdn.ac.uk; 1 Gladstone Place, Queen's Cross, Aberdeen AB10 6UX Tel: 01224 322959 Email: c.glazener@adbn.ac.uk — MB ChB 1979 Dundee; BMSc Dund 1976; MD Bristol 1984; MRCOG 1986. Clin. Research Fell. Univ. Aberd. Prev: Wellcome Train. Research Fell. Health Serv. Research Univ. Aberd.

GLAZER, Mr Geoffrey 84A St John's Wood, High St., London NW8 7SH Tel: 020 7483 3020 Fax: 020 7483 3087 Email: g.glazer@surg.freeserve.co.uk; 28 Twyford Ave, London N2 9NJ Tel: 020 8883 3737 Fax: 020 8442 1408 Email: g.glazer@ic.ac.uk — MB BS 1964 Lond.; MS Lond. 1983; FRCS Eng. 1969; MRCS Eng. LRCP Lond. 1964; FACS 1982. (St. Mary's) Cons. Surg. St. Mary's Hosp. Lond. Prev: Asst. Dir. Surg. Unit, Hon. Cons. & Sen. Lect. St. Mary's Hosp. Lond.; Sen. Regist. (Surg.) St. Mary's Hosp. Lond.

GLAZER, Philip (retired) Westbury House, Grove Road, Bladon, Woodstock OX20 1RD Tel: 01993 811287 — MB BS 1936 Lond.; MRCS Eng. LRCP Lond. 1935; FFA RCS Eng. 1953; DA Eng. 1939. Prev: Cons. Anaesth. United Oxf. Hosps.

GLEADHILL, Mr David Norman Sholto The Consulting Rooms, 29 Upper Lisburn Road, Belfast BT10 0GX Tel: 02890 301461 Fax: 02890 612448 Email: gleadhill@fsbusiness.co.uk — FRCP Lond. 1996; MB ChB 1977 Bristol; FRCS Ed. 1981; MRCP (UK) 1983; FRCS Glas. 1984; FFAEM 1993; FRCP (Ed.) 1995. Cons. Accid. & Emerg. Med. (Belf. & Antrim). Socs: Mem. of the Ulster Med. Soc.; Brit. Med. Assn.; Fell. of the Roy. Coll. of Phys.s (Edin & Lond). Prev: Sen. Regist. (A & E) Walton Hosp. Liverp.; Regist. (Surg.) N.. Health & Social Servs. Bd.; Regist. (Med.) E.. Health & Social Servs. Bd.

GLEADHILL, Iain Colin Lewis Medical Unit, Lagan Valley Hospital, Lisburn BT28 1JP Tel: 02892 665141; 33 Rugby Road, Belfast BT7 1PT Tel: 02890 248512 — MB BCh BAO 1975 Belf.;

FRCP Ed. 1995; MRCP (UK) 1982. (Qu. Univ. Belf.) Cons. Phys. (Gen. & Respirat. Med.) Lagan Hosp. & Belf. City Hosp. Socs: Amer. Coll. Phys. & Brit. Thoracic Soc.

GLEADHILL, Valerie Frances Deirdre Ulster Community & Hospitals Trust, Ulster Hospital, Dundonald, Belfast BT16 1RH Tel: 02890 484511; Penultimate, Sketrick Island, Killinchy, Newtownards BT23 6QH Tel: 02897 541525 — MB BCh BAO Belf. 1966; FRCP Lond. 1988; MRCP (UK) 1974; DCH RCPS Glas. 1968; FRCPCH 1998. (Glas.) Cons. Paediat. Ulster Hosp. Belf. Socs: Brit. Paediat Assn.; Brit. Diabetic Assn.; Ex-Pres. Ulster Paediat. Soc.

GLEADLE, Jonathan Mark 27B Upper High Street, Thame OX9 3EX — BM BCh 1988 Oxf.; BA (Hons.) Physiol. Sci. Oxf. 1985; MRCP (UK) 1991. MRC Research Fell. Inst. Molecular Med. John Radcliffe Hosp. Oxf. Prev: Regist. (Renal & Gen. Med.) St. Helier Hosp. Carshalton; Regist. (Neurol. & Gen. Med.) Atkinson Morley & St. Geo. Hosp. Lond.; SHO (Intens. Care & Med.) Addenbrooke's Hosp. Camb.

GLEADLE, Ronald Ian c/o Barclays Bank, St Mary's TR21 0PN — MB BS 1963 Lond.; MRCP Lond. 1968; MRCS Eng. LRCP Lond. 1963. Prev: Clin Scientist MRC Blood Pressure Research Unit W.. Infirm. Glas.; Med. Regist. Renal Unit St. Mary's Hosp. Portsmouth; Med. Regist. Ashford Hosp. Middlx.

GLEASURE, Aideen Joanna A & E Department, Queen Elizabeth II Hospital, Welwyn Garden City Tel: 01707 328111 — MB ChB 1992 Glas.; MRCGP 1996; DGM RCP Lond. 1994; DRCOG 1994. p/t staff Grade in Acute Med./ Elderly \Med. Socs: BMA. Prev: Trainee GP Glas.; SHO (Psychiat. & Geriat. Med.) Gartnavel Roy. Hosp. Glas.

GLEAVE, Catherine Ruth 72 Buchanan Road, Sheffield S5 8AL Tel: 0114 245 6679 Fax: 0114 257 7369; 175 Wortley Road, High Green, Sheffield S35 4LT Tel: 0114 284 5697 — MB ChB 1994 Liverp.; MB ChB Hons 1994 Liverpool; DFFP 1999; DRCOG 1999. (Liverpool) GP Sheff.; GP Regist. VTS Pontefract. Prev: GP Regist. VTS Pontefract; SHO Rotat. (Gen. Psychiat.) Mersey Train. Scheme; Ho. Off. Roy. Liverp. Univ. Hosp.

GLEAVE, Charles Michael Tudor (retired) 62 Sandford Road, Bromley BR2 9AN Tel: 020 8460 5057 — MB BChir 1962 Camb.; MA Camb. 1962; MRCS Eng. LRCP Lond. 1961; FFA RCS Eng. 1965; DA Eng. 1963. Cons. Anaesth. St. Thos. Hosp. Lond. Prev: Cons. Anaesth. Brook Hosp. Lond.

GLEAVE, David Alan 1 Ferndale Close, Woolston, Warrington WA1 4NT — MB ChB 1982 Leeds; MRCGP 1988; DCH Lond. 1988. Sen. Med. Off. Aboriginal Med. Serv. Carnarvon, W.. Austral. Socs: BMA & Austral. Med. Assn. Prev: Regist. (O & G) Swan Dist. Hosp. Viveash, W.. Australia; Trainee GP Thornton Cleveleys Lancs.

GLEAVE, Mr John Reginald Wallace Riversdale, 13 Woodlands Road, Great Shelford, Cambridge CB2 5LW Tel: 01223 843309 Fax: 01223 847807 — MA Camb. 1975; MA, BM BCh Oxf. 1950; FRCS Eng. 1957. (Oxf.) Emerit. Cons. Neurosurg. Addenbrooke's Hosp. Camb.; Assoc. Lect. Camb. Univ. Med. Sch; Coll. Lect. Magdalene Coll. Camb. Socs: Fell. Roy. Soc. Med.; Sen. Mem. Soc. Brit. Neurol. Surgs.; World and Europ. Soc. Func.al & Stereotactic Neosurg. Prev: Sen. Cons. Neurosurg. United Camb. Hosps. & E. Anglian RHB; Off. i/c Army Neurosurg. Unit; Sen. Regist. (Neurosurg.) Radcliffe Infirm. Oxf.

GLEDHILL, Ann Department of Histopathology, Harrogate District Hospital, Lancaster Park Rd, Harrogate HG2 7SX Tel: 01423 553107 Fax: 01423 553 2330 Email: ann.gledhill@hhc-tr.northy.uk — MB BS 1980 Lond.; MBA Leeds 1993; BSc Lond. 1977, MB BS 1980; MRCPath 1989. (St Bartholomews) Cons. (Histopath.), Harrogate Healthcare Trust.

GLEDHILL, James Martin The Cross, Milborne Port, Sherborne DT9 5DH Tel: 01963 250334; Old Angel Inn, Milborne Port, Sherborne DT9 5EQ — MB ChB 1979 Bristol; MA Oxf. 1972; MRCGP 1984; DRCOG 1983. Clin. Asst. (Orthop.) Yeatman Hosp. Sherborne.

GLEDHILL, Jeremy Robin (retired) Broadstairs Health Centre, The Broadway, Broadstairs CT10 2AJ Tel: 01843 862304 Fax: 01843 869177 — MB BS Lond. 1963; MRCS Eng. LRCP Lond. 1963; DObst RCOG 1965. Prev: Ho. Surg. (Obst.) Canad. Red Cross Memor. Hosp. Taplow.

GLEDHILL, John Eric 7 Bamburgh Close, Pendas Fields, Leeds LS15 8UQ — MB BS 1988 Newc.

GLEDHILL, Julia Anne 528 Finchley Road, London NW11 8DD — MB BS 1988 Lond.; BSc Lond. 1985; MRCP (UK) 1992; MRCPsych 1996. Clin. Research Fell. (Child & Adolesc. Psychiat.) Imperial Coll. Sch. Med. St Mary's. Prev: Research Regist. (Psychiat.) Roy. Free Hosp. Sch. Med.; SHO Regist. Rotat. (Psychiat.) Roy. Free & Assoc. Hosps. Lond.; Tutor (Med. Oncol.) Univ. Manch.

GLEDHILL, Maureen Thelma 528 Finchley Road, London NW11 8DD Tel: 020 8731 8642; 528 Finchley Road, London NW11 8DD Tel: 020 8455 7211 — MB ChB 1957 Sheff.; MRCPsych 1970; DCH Eng 1960. p/t Indep. Cons. Psychother. Lond. Socs: Fell. Roy. Soc. Med.; Europ. Soc, Communicative Psychother.; Brit. ConFederat. Psychother. Prev: Cons. Psychother. 'Open Door' Hornsey Lond.; Sen. Regist. Child Guid. Train. Centre Lond.

GLEDHILL, Peter Donald Kings Road Surgery, 27b Kings Road, Sandy SG19 1EJ Tel: 01767 682277 Fax: 01767 691436; 3 Filland Court, Sandy SG19 1HW Tel: 01767 691842 — MB BS 1981 Newc.; MRCGP 1986; DRCOG 1986.

GLEDHILL, Raymond Clive 1 Edward Mews, Flat 1, Redhill St., London NW1 4AT Tel: 020 7383 2611 — MD 1949 Leeds; MB ChB 1943; FRCP Lond. 1978, M 1949; FRCPsych 1971; DPM Lond. 1952. (Leeds) Cons. Psychiat. Ct. Div. Scheme Tottenham Magistrates Ct. Socs: Assoc. Mem. Brit. Psychoanal. Soc.; Ment. Health Rev. Tribunal NW Thames Region. Prev: Vis. Psychother. HM Prison Holloway Lond.; Cons. Psychiat. Goodmayes & King Geo. Hosps. Ilford & Barking Hosp.

GLEDHILL, Richard Forsyth 10 The Pines, South Terrace, Dorking RH4 2BE — MD 1974 Lond.; MB BS 1965; MRCP (UK) 1968.

GLEED, Daphne Isabella Leonore 32 Carmel Court, Beach Avenue, Birchington CT7 9JT Tel: 01843 41595 — MRCS Eng. LRCP Lond. 1942. Prev: Gyn. Ho. Surg. S. Lond. Hosp.

GLEEK, Robin Nigel Harrison Park Road Health Centre, Park Road, Tarporley CW6 0BE Tel: 01829 732401 Fax: 01829 732404 — MB ChB 1978 Manch.; MRCGP 1982; DRCOG 1982. PCG Bd. Mem.; IT Lead; CME Lead.

GLEES, John Paul 10 Ravenscourt Place, Hammersmith, London W6 0UN Tel: 020 8741 8739 Fax: 020 8741 8739 — MD Gottingen 1967; State Exam Med. 1966; FRCR 1976; DMRT Eng. 1975. (Bonn, Oxf. & Goettingen) Cons. Radiother. & Oncol. St. Geo., Roy. Marsden, Cromwell Hosps., Kingston Hosp. & Ashstead Hosp.; Hon. Sen. Lect. Univ. Lond. & Inst. Cancer Research. Socs: Fell. Roy. Soc. Med.; Brit. Inst. Radiol.; Assoc. Mem. Amer. Soc. Therap. Radiol. Prev: Cons. Radiother. & Clin. Oncol. Epsom Gen. Hosp.

GLEESON, Carmel Marie Anne 123 Booth Lane S., Weston Favell, Northampton NN3 3EY — MB BS 1991 Lond.

GLEESON, Catherine Mary Aileen St Catherine's Hospice, Malthouse Road, Crawley RH10 6BH Tel: 01293 447333 Fax: 01293 611977; Cambridge House, Cherry Lane, Bolney, Haywards Heath RH17 5PR — MB BS 1985 Lond.; MRCGP Lond. 1990; DRCOG 1990; DCH RCP Lond. 1988. (Guy's) Med. Dir. St. Catherine's Hospice, Crawley.

GLEESON, Claire Marie Tenterleas, Mill Lane, Alwalton, Peterborough PE7 3UZ; 29 Manor Park, Redland, Bristol BS6 7HJ — MB BS 1993 Lond.; BSc 1990. (University College & Middlesex) Specialist Regist. (Anaesth.) Bath. Prev: SHO (Anaesth.) St. Thomas Hosp.

GLEESON, Dermot Christopher Royal Hallamshire Hospital, Glossop Road, Sheffield S10 2JF Tel: 0114 276 6222 — MD 1988 NUI; BSc (Physiol.) NUI 1978, MB BCh BAO 1976; MRCP (UK) 1980; MRCPI 1980. Cons. Phys. Roy. Hallamsh. Hosp. Prev: Sen. Regist. Univ. Dept. Gastroenterol. Manch. Roy. Infirm.; MRC Trav. Fell. Yale Univ. Sch. Med., USA; Clin. Research Fell. Guy's Hosp. Lond.

GLEESON, Fergus Vincent 26 Staverton Road, Oxford OX2 6XJ — MB BS 1983 Lond.; MRCP (UK) 1986; FRCR 1989; FRCP 1998. Cons. Radiol. Ch.ill John Radcliffe NHS Trust Oxf. Prev: Regist. (Radiol.) Addenbrooke's Hosp. Camb.

GLEESON, Helena Kate 16 Rutland Terrace, Stamford PE9 2QD — MB BS 1993 Newc.; MRCP UK 1996.

GLEESON, Jane Mary 37 Deronda Road, London SE24 9BQ — BChir 1990 Camb.

GLEESON, Joseph Albert (retired) 7 Bishop Kirk Place, Summertown, Oxford OX2 7HJ Tel: 01865 516294 — MB BCh

BAO 1955 NUI; FRCP Ed. 1995; FRCP Lond. 1978, M 1962; MRCP Ed. 1962; FFR 1962; DMRD Eng. 1960; Hon. FRCRI 1996. Prev: Cons. Radiol. Chelsea & W.m. Hosp. Lond.

GLEESON, Mr Malachy Joseph Collingwood, South Hill Avenue, Harrow HA1 3PB — MB BCh BAO 1981 NUI; MCh NUI 1989; FRCS (Urol.) 1992; FRCSI 1985; LRCPI & LM, LRCSI & LM 1981. Cons. Urol. Centr. Middlx. Hosp. Lond.

GLEESON, Mary Deirdre 7 Bishop Kirk Place, Summertown, Oxford OX2 7HJ Tel: 01865 516294 — MB BCh BAO 1955 NUI; DPM Eng. 1974. (NUI) Assoc. Specialist in Psychother. NE RHA. Prev: Med. Off. of Health.

GLEESON, Michael Howard The General Hospital, St Helier, Jersey Tel: 01534 59000; Beauvoir House, Rue de la Croiserie, Trinity, Jersey JE3 7EA Tel: 01534 866446 — MB ChB Manch. 1965; FRCP Lond. 1982, M 1968. Cons. Phys. (Gen. Med. & Gastroenterol.) Gen. Hosp. St. Helier. Socs: Brit. Soc. Gastroenterol. Prev: Sen. Regist. (Gastroenterol.) & SHO (Med.) Manch. Roy. Infirm.; Regist. (Med.) Hammersmith Hosp. Lond.

GLEESON, Professor Michael John Department of Otolaryngology, Guy's Hospital, London SE1 9RT Tel: 020 7955 5000 Fax: 020 7955 8878 Email: michael.gleeson@kcl.ac.uk; 93 Southborough Road, Bickley, Bromley BR1 2EP Fax: 020 8402 6664 — MB BS 1976 Lond.; MD Lond. 1993, BDS (Hons.) 1971; FRCS Eng. 1981; MRCS Eng. LRCP Lond. 1976; LDS RCS Eng. 1971. (Guy's Hosp. Med. Sch.) Prof. Otolaryngol.Guy's & St. Thos. Hosp. Lond. & King's Coll. Hosp. Socs: Brit. Assn. Otol.; Otolaryng. Research Soc.; Med. Soc. Lond. Prev: Reader & Cons. Surg. Guy's Hosp. Lond.; Janet Nash Fell. Dept. Otolaryng. Univ. Zurich, Switz.; Chief Resid. (Otolaryng.) Head & Neck Surg. Univ. Washington, USA.

GLEESON, Mr Robert Edward 29 Manor Park, Bristol BS6 7HJ — MB BS 1994 Lond.; BSc 1991; MRCS 1998. Clin. Fell. Orthop. Surg. Socs: Roy. Coll. Surg.

GLEKIN, Barnet Melvyn Tel: 0141 531 9550 Fax: 0141 531 9555 Email: barryglekin@doctors.org.uk; 34 Beech Avenue, Newton Mearns, Glasgow G77 5PP — MB ChB 1973 Glas.; MRCGP 1983.

GLEN, Ailish Ann 27 Knowehead Gardens, Uddingston, Glasgow G71 7PY — MB ChB 1987 Glas.

GLEN, Alastair Campbell Agnew Biochemistry Department, Victoria Infirmary, Glasgow G42 9TY Tel: 0141 201 5620 Email: alastair_glen@gvic.scot.nhs.uk; 27ba Nithsdale Road, Glasgow Tel: 0141 427 2131 Email: alastair_glen@msn.com — MB ChB 1960 Glas.; BSc Glas. 1963, MD (Commend.) 1972; FRCP Glas. 1988. Cons. Biochem. Vict. Infirm. Glas. Prev: Sen. Regist. Vict. Infirm. Glas.; Research Assoc. Mass Inst. Technol., USA; Regist. W.. Infirm. Glas.

GLEN, Alexander Iain Munro Highland Psychiatric, Research Foundation, The Green House,Beechwood Business Pk, Inverness IV2 3ED Tel: 01463 667318 Fax: 01463 667338 Email: iain.glen@hprf.sol.co.uk; Dalnavert Farm House, Kincraig, Kingussie PH21 1NQ Tel: 01540 651347 Fax: 01540 651213 — MB ChB 1954 Glas.; FRCP Glas. 1980, M 1962; FRCPsych. 1980, M 1971; DPM Eng. 1959. (Glas.) p/t Director, Highland Psych. Res. Foundat. The GreenHo. Inverness; Director, Psychiatric Disgnostics Ltd Inverness. Socs: Roy. Coll. Psychiat. (Fell.). Prev: Cons. Clin. Director, Psychiatric Serv. Highland; Mem. Scientif. Staff MRC Brain Metab. Unit, Pharmacol. Dept. Univ. Edin.

GLEN, Dugald Alexander Department of Radiology, Stirling Royal Infirmary, Stirling FK8 2AU Tel: 01786 434000 Email: dugaldq@sri.scot.nhs.uk; 9 Abercromby Place, Stirling FK8 2QP Tel: 01786 471892 Email: dugald.glen@btinternet.com — MB ChB 1981 Ed.; BSc Ed. 1978; FRCR 1988; MRCP (UK) 1984; DMRD Aberd. 1986. Cons. Diagn. Radiol. Stirling Roy. Infirm. Socs: Brit. Med. Ultrasound Soc.; Brit. Soc. Of Internat. Radiol.; Scot. Med. Soc. Prev: Regist. & Sen. Regist. (Diagn. Radiol.) Aberd. Roy. Infirm.

GLEN, Mr Eric Stanger (retired) 9 StJohn's Road, Pollokshields, Glasgow G41 5RJ Tel: 0141 423 1648 Email: eric@pollocjkshields.fsnet.co.uk — MB ChB Glas. 1960; FRCS Glas. 1967; FRCS Ed. 1967. Prev: Hon.Clin.Sen.Lect.URDL. Univ.Glas.

GLEN, Euan Meldrum 15 Campbell Park Drive, Colinton, Edinburgh EH13 0HS — MB ChB 1991 Aberd.

GLEN, Jennifer Lesley Newington Surgery, 14 East Preston Street, Edinburgh EH8 9QA Tel: 0131 662 4400 Fax: 0131 662 4400 — MB ChB 1989 Dundee; BSc (Hons.) Med. Sc. St. And. 1986; MRCGP 1994; T(GP) 1994. Trainee GP Edin. Prev: Resid. Med. Off. Wanganui Base Hosp. Wanganui, NZ; Ho. Surg. Perth Roy. Infirm.; Ho. Phys. City Hosp. Edin.

GLEN, Kirsten Anne Camelon Medical Practice, 3 Baird Street, Camelon, Falkirk FK1 4PP Tel: 01324 622854 Fax: 01324 633858; 24 Abbots Moss Drive, Falkirk FK1 5UA — MB ChB 1988 Glas.; DRCOG 1992.

GLEN, Patricia Alexa Scott (retired) 9 St John's Road, Pollokshields, Glasgow G41 5RJ Tel: 0141 423 0759 — MB ChB 1959 Glas.; DA Eng. 1962. Prev: GP Rutherglen.

GLEN, Paul 50 Threestanes Road, Strathaven ML10 6EB — MB ChB 1998 Glas.; MB ChB Glas 1998.

GLEN, Robert Thom 142 Old Bath Road, Cheltenham GL53 7DP Tel: 01242 514360; 142 Old Bath Road, Cheltenham GL53 7DP Tel: 01242 514360 — MB ChB 1958 Glas.; FFA RCS Eng. 1967; DA Eng. 1960; DObst RCOG 1960. GP Cheltenham. Socs: BMA; Assn. Anaesths. Prev: Sen. Regist. (Anaesth.) Roy. Infirm. Stobhill Hosp. Glas.; Regist. (Anaesth.) W.. Infirm. Glas.; Med. Off. RAMC/Irish Guards (Nat. Serv.).

GLEN, Sarah Elizabeth Child & Adolescent Mental Health Services, Andrew Lang Unit, Viewfield Lane, Selkirk TD7 4LJ Tel: 01750 23392; Southbank, Bowden, Melrose TD6 0ST — MB ChB 1982 Dundee; MRCPsych 1987; DCH RCP Glas. 1984. Cons. Child & Adolesc. Psychiat. Child & Adolesc. Ment. Health Servs. Prev: Cons. (Child & Adolesc. Psychiat.) Larkfield Child & Family Centre Inverclyde Roy. Hosp. Greenock; Sen. Regist. (Child. & Adolesc. Psychiat.) Dept. Child & Family Psychiat. Roy. Hosp. Sick Childr. Glas.

GLEN, Stephen Blaney, Squadron Ldr. RAF Med. Br. Retd. Kirkhall Surgery, 4 Alexandra Avenue, Prestwick KA9 1AW Tel: 01292 476626 Fax: 01292 678022; 27 Lomond View, Symington, Kilmarnock KA1 5QS Tel: 01563 830870 — MB ChB 1978 Manch.; BSc (Med. Sci.) St. And. 1975; AFOM RCP Lond. 1987; MRCGP 1986; DGM RCP Lond. 1989; DCH RCP Lond. 1986; DRCOG 1985. Med. Adviser Brit. Aerospace Prestwick. Prev: Sen. Med. Off. RAF AlderGr. N. Irel.

GLEN, Stephen Kenneth Department Edinbugh Royal Infirmary, Department of Cardiology, Edinburgh Royal Infirmary, Lauriston Place, Edinburgh EH3 9YW Tel: 0131 536 1000 — MB ChB 1990 Glas.; MD 1998 Glas.; MRCP (UK) 1993. (Glas.) Career Regist. Rotat. (Med. & Cardiol.) SE Scotl.; Med. Adviser Scott. Sub Aqua Club; Sec., UK Sport Diving Med. Committe. Prev: Research Fell. W.. Infirm. Glas.; SHO (Med.) Gtr. Glas. HB.

GLEN, Thomas Glencurr, Mid Curr, Dulnain Bridge, Grantown-on-Spey PH26 3LU — MB ChB 1989 Dundee.

GLEN-BOTT, Agnes Mary (retired) 31 Green Street, Hereford HR1 2QH — MB BS 1951 Lond.; DObst RCOG 1953. Prev: Med. Off. DHSS: Secretariat. to Comm. on Safety of Med.

GLENCROSS, Avril Harriet Mayfield, Dalkeith E22 4AD Tel: 0131 663 1051 — MB ChB 1980 Glas.; MRCGP 1988; DCH RCPS Glas. 1986; DRCOG 1984.

GLENCROSS, Iain Hamilton Frank Swire Health Centre, Nursery Lane, Halifax HX3 5TE Tel: 01422 345798; 25 Savile Crescent, Halifax HX1 2EN — MB ChB 1978 Dundee; MRCGP 1982; DRCOG 1984. Trainer GP Halifax.

GLENCROSS, Janet Doreen Lincolnshire HA, Cross o'Cliff, Bracebridge Heath, Lincoln TN7 LN4 Tel: 01522 513355 Email: janet.glencross@lines-ha.nhs.uk — MB BCh 1979 Witwatersrand; MFPHM 2000; MPH 1998 Nottm.; MMedSci Nottm. 1992. (Univ. Witwatersrand) Cons. Pub. Health, Lincs. HA. Prev: Assoc. Med. Advisor Leicester Health; GP Leicester.

GLENCROSS, Joseph Fergusson 4 Belmont Avenue, Ayr KA7 2JN Tel: 01292 281439 — MB ChB 1956 Glas.

GLENCROSS, Simon James Belvoir Vale, 17A Walford Close, Bottesford, Nottingham NG13 0AN; 65 Harrowby Lane, Grantham NG31 9HZ — MB BS 1980 Lond. (St. Geo.) Prev: GP P'boro VTS; SHO (Orthop. & Cas.) Roy. Berks. Hosp. Reading; Ho. Surg. St. Geo. Hosp. Lond.

GLENDENING, John David 4 Castle Gate, Nottingham NG1 7BJ — MB ChB 1987 Sheff.

GLENDINNING, David (retired) The Hollows, South Rauceby, Sleaford NG34 8QL — MB ChB 1939 Glas.; DPH Glas. 1942; DPM Eng. 1953. Prev: Cons. Psychiat. Rauceby Hosp.

GLENDINNING, Gillian Mary (retired) The Old Court House, South Petherton, Taunton TA13 5BN Tel: 01460 240237 — MB BS Lond. 1955; MRCS Eng. LRCP Lond. 1955. Prev: Ho. Phys. Paediat. Dept. Guy's Hosp.

GLENDINNING, Neil Whittingham (retired) The Old Court House, South Petherton TA13 Tel: 01460 240237 — MD Lond. 1976, MB BS 1955; MRCS Eng. LRCP Lond. 1955; DObst RCOG 1959. Hon. Cons. Huntington's Dis.s. Prev: Obst. Ho. Surg. MusGr. Pk. Hosp. Taunton.

GLENDINNING, Sheila Mary Rose The Surgery, Newton Port Surgery, Haddington EH41 3NF — MB ChB 1970 Ed.; BSc (Med. Sci) Ed. 1967; DFFP. (Edinburgh) GP Partner Haddington. Socs: BMA; Med. Wom. Federat. Prev: Gen. Med. Off. Shanta Bhawan Hosp. Kathmandu, Nepal.

GLENESK, Alison Doreen Holburn Medical Group, 7 Albyn Place, Aberdeen AB10 1YE; 1 Rubislaw Den Gardens, Aberdeen AB15 6FE Tel: 01224 315367 — MB ChB 1978 Aberd.; MRCGP 1982. GP Princip. & GP Trainer.

GLENFIELD, Jacqueline Emma 52 Castlemore Avenue, Belfast BT6 9RG — MB BCh BAO 1993 Belf.

GLENFIELD, John Rodger Currie Road Health Centre, Currie Road, Galashiels TD1 2UA Tel: 01896 752419 Fax: 01896 753876; 1 Lochend, Abbotsferry Park, Tweedbank, Galashiels TD1 3RY — MB BCh BAO 1982 Belf.; FRCGP 1998; MRCGP 1987; DFFP 1993; Cert. Family Plann. JCC 1984; T (GP) 1990; DCH Dub. 1986; DRCOG 1984. (Queen's University Belfast) Socs: Christ. Med. Fell.sh. Prev: GP S. Shields; Undergrad. Tutor (Gen. Pract.) Univ. Newc. u. Tyne; Clin. Asst. (A & E) Addenbrooke's Hosp. Camb.

GLENISTER, Peter Wilfrid 20 Kings Hall Road, Beckenham BR3 1LU — MB 1978 Camb.; BA Camb. 1973, MB 1978, BChir 1977.

GLENN, Mr Andrew Martin Seething House, Brooke Road, Seething, Norwich NR15 1DP — MB BS 1983 Newc.; FRCS (Ophth.) Eng. 1987; DO RCS Eng. 1987. Cons. W. Norwich Hosp. Prev: Regist. (Ophth.) Roy. Vict. Infirm. Newc.

GLENN, David Richard John 12 Springhill Road, Bangor BT20 3NR — MB BCh BAO 1993 Belf.

GLENN, Michael Paul Diamond Hall Farm, Moorside Fold, Longton, Preston PR4 5RE — MB BS 1963 Lond.; MRCS Eng. LRCP Lond. 1963. (St. Geo.) Occupat. Health Phys. Preston.

GLENN, Michael Stephen College Health Service, Queen Mary and Westfield College, Charterhouse Square, London EC1M 6BQ Tel: 020 7982 6057 — MB BCh BAO 1976 Belf.; AFOM RCP Lond. 1993; MRCGP 1982; DRCOG 1981; DCH RCP Lond. 1981. Med. Adviser Qu. Mary & W.field Coll.

GLENN, Roger Wesley (retired) Little Sutton, 29 Dukes Road, Lindfied, Haywards Heath RH16 2JQ Tel: 01444 484250 Email: rogerglenn@hotmail.com — MB BS 1949 Lond. Prev: Ho. Phys. & Ho. Surg. (Throat & Ear) Guy's Hosp. Lond.

GLENNIE, Allen Charles Loughview Surgery, 2 Main Street, Kircubbin, Newtownards BT22 2SP Tel: 028 9173 8532; The Stables, 189c Main Road, Newtownards BT22 1EP — MB BCh BAO 1968 Belf.; MRCP (UK) 1973; DCH RCPS Glas. 1970; DObst RCOG 1970.

GLENNIE, Elsie Margaret (retired) Moor House, Cambus, O'May, Ballater AB35 5SD Tel: 01339 755325 — MB ChB 1950 Ed.; DObst. RCOG 1953. Prev: Obst. Ho. Off. City Hosp. Derby.

GLENNIE, Hugh Rinder Newtown Hospital, Newton Road, Worcester WR5 1JG Tel: 01905 763333 Fax: 01905 33315; 1 Denison Close, Malvern WR14 2EU Tel: 01684 563934 — MB BChir 1973 Camb.; BA Camb. 1968, BA 1971; FRCP Lond. 1994; MRCP (UK) 1975; MRCS Eng. LRCP Lond. 1971. (St. Bart. & Camb.) Cons. Geriat. Med. Worcester Dist. HA. Prev: Sen. Regist. (Geriat. Med.) E. Birm. Hosp.; Lect. & Clin. Research Fell. (Geriat. Med.) Qu. Eliz. Hosp. Birm.

GLENNIE, John Alexander Oakeswell Health Centre, Brunswick Park Road, Wednesbury WS10 9HP Tel: 0121 556 2114 Fax: 0121 505 1843; 55 Broadway, Walsall WS1 3EZ Tel: 01922 21037 — MB ChB 1962 Aberd. (Aberd.) Prev: Ho. Phys. Ballochmyle Hosp.; Ho. Surg. Kilmarnock Infirm. & Glas. Roy. Matern. Hosp.

GLENNIE, John Robert (retired) Thatched Cottage, Widdington, Saffron Walden CB11 3SJ Tel: 01799 41375 — MB 1964 Camb.; BChir 1963. Prev: Ho. Surg. & Ho. Phys. St. Mary's Hosp. Portsmouth.

GLENNIE, Richard 38 Haig Avenue, Whitley Bay NE25 8JG — MB ChB 1998 Dund.; MB ChB Dund 1998.

GLENNIE-SMITH, Keith, TD (retired) 13 Boulnois Avenue, Parkstone, Poole BH14 9NX Tel: 01202 742250 — MB BS 1951 Lond.; FFA RCS Eng. 1960; DA Eng. 1957; FICAE 1980. Cons. i/c Med. Acupunc. Clin. Poole Hosp.; Corr. Edr. (UK) Acupunc. & Electro-therap. Research; Lt.-Col. RAMC/RARO, Sen. Specialist Anaesth.; Mem. (Counc.) Europe Fell.sh. Audio-Visual Technol. Continuing Educat. Prev: Cons. Anaesth. & Cons. i/c Med. Illustr. Servs. E. Dorset.

GLENNON, Catherine Mary Grappenhall Residential School, Church Lane, Grappenhall, Warrington WA4 3EU — MB ChB 1993 Liverp.

GLENNON, John Edward Anthony (retired) 1A St Andrew's Road, Blundellsands, Liverpool L23 7UP — MB BCh BAO 1956 NUI; LMCC 1958. Prev: Ho. Off. St. Michael's Hosp. Dunloaghaire.

GLENNON, Peter The Surgery, 10 Browning St., Stafford ST16 3AT Tel: 01785 258249 Fax: 01785 253119 — MB BS 1982 Lond.; MA Oxf. 1983, BA (1st cl. Hons.) Physiol. Sci. 1979; MMedSc Birm. 1994; MRCGP 1986; Dip IMC RCS Ed. 1988; DRCOG 1986; DCH RCP Lond. 1985. GP.

GLENNON, Peter Edward Priscilla Bacan Lodge, Colman Hospital, Unthark RD, Norwich NR2 2PJ — MB ChB 1987 Leeds; MB ChB (Hons.) Leeds 1987; MD (Distinc.) Leeds 1996; MRCP (UK) 1990; Cert. Specialist Training (Cardiol) 1998. (Univ. Leeds) Socs: RCP Lond.; Brit. Cardiac Soc. Prev: Clin. Research Fell. (Cardiol.) Nat. Heart & Lung Inst. Lond.

GLENNON, Vivienne 27 Pulleyn Drive, York YO24 1DY — MB ChB 1973 Leeds; DCH RCP Lond. 1979; DRCOG 1977. Community Med. Off. Family Plann. York HA.

GLENVILLE, Brian Eric 66 Harley Street, London W1N 1AE Tel: 020 7636 3059 Fax: 020 7631 5341 Email: brian.glenville@virgin.net; 33 Carlton Hill, London NW8 0JX Tel: 020 7624 6500 — MB BS 1978 Lond.; BSc (Hons.) (Immunol.) Lond. 1975; MS Lond. 1992; FRCS Ed. 1983. Cons. Cardiothoracic Surg. St. Mary's Hosp. Lond.; Hon. Cons. Cardiothoracic Surg. N.wich Pk. Hosp. Harrow; Hon. Sen. Lect. in Cardiothoracic Surg. Imperial Coll. Lond. Socs: Fell. Roy. Soc. of Med.; Soc. Cardiothoracic Surg. (UK). Prev: Sen. Regist. (Cardiothor. Surg.) Freeman Hosp. Newc.; Research Fell. Cardiothoracic Inst. Lond.

GLEW, Christine 19 Wadham Dr, Bristol BS16 1PF — BM 1997 Soton.

GLEW, David Department of Radiology, Royal United Hospital, Combe Park, Bath BA1 3NG Tel: 01225 824369; Marshstone Cottage, 89 High St, Marshfield, Chippenham SN14 8LT — BM BCh 1983 Oxf.; BA Camb. 1980; MRCP (UK) 1986; FRCR 1990. Cons. Radiol. Roy. United Hosp. Bath. Prev: Cons. Radiol. S.mead Hosp. Bristol; Regist. & Sen. Regist. (Radiol.) Bristol Roy. Infirmiary.

GLEW, Margaret Silverbirches, High Banks, Coast Rd, Rampside, Barrow-in-Furness LA13 0QW — MB ChB 1997 Glas.

GLEW, Miss Susan Sylvia Department of Obstetrics & Gynaecology, St Michael's Hospital, Bristol BS2 8EG — MB ChB 1981 Manch.; BSc (Hons.) Manch. 1978, MD 1993; MRCOG 1986; DRCOG 1984; MD Manch. 1992. (Manchester) Cons. & Sen. Lect. (O & G) Univ. Bristol & St. Michael's Hosp. Prev: Sen. Regist. (O & G) Roy. Devon & Exeter Hosp.; Joseph Starke Clin. Reseach Fell. Paterson Inst. Christie Hosp. Manch.; Vis. Lect. (O & G) Univ. Hosp. Kuala Lumpar, Malaysia.

GLICHER, Susan Rosamund Cheadle Medical Practice, 1-5 Ashfield Crescent, Cheadle SK8 1BH Tel: 0161 428 7575 Fax: 0161 283 8884 — MB ChB 1984 Manch.; MRCGP 1989; DRCOG 1989.

GLICK, Mr Selwyn (retired) — MB ChB Birm. 1958; FRCS Eng. 1963; DObst RCOG 1960. Hons. Cons. Surg. Burton Hosps. NHS Trust. Prev: Surg. Winnipeg Gen. Hosp.

GLICKMAN, Mr Scott Academic Medical Rehabilitation Unit, Charing Cross Hospital, Fulham Palace Road, London W6 8RF Tel: 020 8846 7135; Flat 22, Alexa Court, 73 Lexham Gardens, London W8 6JL — MB BS 1981 Lond.; FRCS Eng. 1988. Imperial Coll. Sch. of Med.; Hon. Cons. Char. Cross Hosp.; Europ. Bd. Physical Med. & Rehabil. Socs: Fell. Roy. Soc. Med.; Brit. Soc. Rehabil. Med.; Assn. for Med. Educat. in Europe. Prev: Sen. Regist. (Rehabil.) Roy. Nat. Orthop. Hosp. NHS Trust; Regist. (Surg.) St. Helier Hosp. Carshalton.

GLIDDEN, John McRorie Newbattle Group Practice, Mayfield, Dalkeith EH22 4AD Tel: 0131 663 1051 — MB ChB 1973

Edinburgh; MB ChB Edin 1973. (Edinburgh) GP Dalkeith, Midlothian.

GLIDDON, Roland Peter Noel Park Surgery, Albion Way, Horsham RH12 1BG Tel: 01403 217100 Fax: 01403 214639; Shalom, 14 Crawford Gardens, Horsham RH13 5AZ Tel: 01403 241601 — MB BS 1981 Lond.; MRCS Eng LRCP Lond. 1980; MRCGP 1985. (St Thomas's London) Socs: BMA. Prev: GP Stafford.

GLITHERO, Mr Philip Robert The Royal Orthopaedic Hospital NHS Trust, The Woodlands, Bristol Road South, Northfield, Birmingham B31 2AP Tel: 0121 685 4156 Fax: 0121 685 4213 Email: prglitheno@mcsed.ac.uk; 61 Stonerwood Avenue, Hall Green, Birmingham B28 0AX — BM BS 1981 Nottm.; FRCS 1995 (Orth.); FRCS 1988 Ed.; Dip Biomechanics 1993 Strathclyde; FRCS (Orth.) 1995; FRCS Ed. 1988; Dip. Biomechanics Strathclyde 1993. (Nottm.) Cons. Paediat. Orthop. Surg. Roy. Orthop. Hosp. & Childr. Hosp. Birm. Socs: Fell. BOA; Eur. Soc. Motion Anal. in Childr.; Brit. Soc. Childr. Orthop. Surg. Prev: Clin. Fell. (Paediat. Orthop.) Gt. Ormond St. Hosp.; Sen. Regist. (Orthop.) Roy. Orthop. Hosp. Birm.

GLOSSOP, Mr Lawrence Paul Tel: 01902 429044 Fax: 01902 710290; Willow Lawn, 5 Danescourt Road, Tettenhall, Wolverhampton WV6 9BE Tel: 01902 758729 — MB BS 1973 Lond.; FRCS (ENT) Eng. 1982; FRCS Eng. 1977; MRCS Eng. LRCP Lond. 1973. (St. Mary's) Cons. ENT Surg. Wolverhampton, Dudley & Kidderminster HAs. Socs: Mem.: Europ. Acad. of Facial Plastic Surg. Prev: Sen. Regist. Hosp. Sick Childr Gt. Ormond St. & Roy. Nat. Throat, Nose& Ear Hosp. Lond. & Brighton Gp. Hosps.

GLOSTER, John 14 Church Place, Ickenham, Uxbridge UB10 8XB — MB BChir Camb. 1946; PhD Lond. 1959; MD Camb. 1953; MRCS Eng. LRCP Lond. 1946; DOMS Eng. 1950. (St. Bart.) Emerit. Prof. of Experim. Ophth. Inst. Ophth. Lond.; Hon. Cons. Ophth. Moorfields Eye Hosp. Prev: Mem. Staff Ophth. Research Unit Med. Research Counc.; Regist. Research Dept. Birm. & Midl. Eye Hosp.; Dean Inst. Ophth. Lond.

GLOVER, Benedict Daniel Antrim Coast Medical Practice, The Cloney, Glenarm, Ballymena BT44 0AB Tel: 028 2884 1214 Fax: 028 2884 1202; Antrim Villa, Glenarm, Ballymena BT44 0AB Tel: 01574 841202 — MB BCh BAO 1964 Belf.; DObst RCOG 1966. (Qu. Univ. Belf.) Socs: Ulster Med. Soc. & BMA. Prev: Ho. Off. (Med. & Surg.) & Clin. Asst. (ENT) Moyle Hosp. Larne; SHO (O & G) Route Hosp. Ballymoney.

GLOVER, David Andrew 36 Meadow Mead, Frampton Cotterell, Bristol BS36 2BE — MB BCh 1998 Wales.

GLOVER, David Henry 45 Links Drive, Radlett WD7 8BD — MB ChB 1976 Bristol.

GLOVER, David Neill (retired) The Cobham Health Centre, 168 Portsmouth Road, Cobham KT11 1HT Tel: 01932 867231 Fax: 01932 866874 — MB BS 1963 Lond. Prev: Ho. Surg. (O & G) St. Bart. Hosp. Lond.

GLOVER, David Roy Cambridge Antibody Technology Ltd., Granta Park, Great Abington, Cambridge CB1 6GD Tel: 01763 269219 Fax: 01763 269468 Email: david.glover@camb-antibody.co.uk — MB BChir 1977 Camb.; MB Camb. 1976, BChir 1976; MA Camb. 1977; MRCP (UK) 1979; MFPM 1990; FFPM 1997. Med. Dir., Camb. Antibody Technol. Gp. plc. Socs: BMA; Brit. Pharm. Soc. (BPS); Eur. Tissue Repair Soc. (ETRS). Prev: Clin. Research Fell. Dept. of Cardiovasc. Med. Univ. of Birm.; Med. Dir. Schering-Plough Welwyn Gdn City; Dir. of Med. Affairs Merck Sharp & Dohme Ltd. Hoddesdon.

GLOVER, Frederick Richard, MC (retired) Gwrdy Cottage, Llanybydder SA40 9TY Tel: 01570 480566 — MB BS 1934 Lond.; MRCS Eng. LRCP Lond. 1931; DPH Eng. 1938. Prev: Cons. Geriatr. Bury & Rossendale Hosp. Gp.

GLOVER, Mr Garry Winston 6 Birch Court, Rickmansworth Road, Northwood HA6 2QZ Tel: 01923 829922 Fax: 01923 824144; 33 Northbrook Drive, Northwood HA6 2YU Tel: 01923 827354 — MB BS 1964 Sydney; FRCS Eng. 1969. (Sydney) Cons. ENT Surg. N.wick Pk., Mt. Vernon & Hillingdon Hosp.; Regional Adviser N. Thames (W.) RCS Eng. Socs: Fell. Roy. Soc. Med. (Ex-Sec. & Vice-Pres. Otol. Sect.); Scott. Otolaryngol. Soc. Prev: Sen. Regist. ENT Dept. Dundee Teachg. Hosps.; Fell. (Otolaryng.) Univ. Melb., Austral.; Sen. Regist. & Hon. Lect. ENT Dept. Middlx. Hosp. Lond.

GLOVER, Geraldine 35 Pendragon Close, Cardiff CF14 9BD — MB BCh BAO 1984 NUI.

GLOVER, Gyles Roderick 21 Morgan Street, Mile End, London E3 5AA Tel: 020 8981 5741 — MB BS 1978 Lond.; MSc Lond. 1985, BSc 1975, MB BS 1978; MRCPsych 1983; MFPHM 1988. Sen. Lect. Dept. Community Med. Char. Cross Hosp. & W.m. Med. Sch. Lond. Prev: Regist. (Community Med.) Newham HA.; Regist. (Psychiat.) The Lond Hosp.

GLOVER, Huw Francis Bernard Penn Manor Medical Centre, Manor Road, Penn, Wolverhampton WV4 5PY Tel: 01902 331166 Fax: 01902 575078 — MB BS 1988 Lond.; MRCGP 1992; DFFP 1994; T(GP) 1992; DRCOG 1990. Bd. Mem. S.W. Wolverhampton PCG. Socs: B.M.A.S.

GLOVER, Jason Daniel 2 Long Wood Drive, Jordans, Beaconsfield HP9 2SS — BM 1991 Soton.

GLOVER, Jenifer Imogen Manor View Practice, Bushey Health Centre, London Road, Bushey, Watford WD23 2NN Tel: 01923 225224 Fax: 01923 213270; Crooklets, 39 Oxhey Road, Oxhey, Watford WD19 4QG — MB BS 1971 Lond.; MRCS Eng. LRCP Lond. 1971; DObst RCOG 1974; DCH Eng. 1973. (Char. Cross)

GLOVER, John Richard Department Occupational Health, Swindon Health Authority, 9 The Mall, Swindon SN1 4HZ Tel: 01793 36231; Woodlands, New Road, Chisledon, Swindon SN4 0PE Tel: 01793 740357 — MB BChir 1951 Camb.; MA, MB BChir Camb. 1951; FFOM RCP Lond. 1982, M 1978; MFCM 1974; DIH Soc. Apoth. Lond. 1956; Specialist Accredit. (Occupat. Med.) RCP Lond. 1978. (Middlx.) Dist. Occupat. Health Phys. Swindon HA. Socs: Hon. Mem. Brit. Assn. Manip. Med.; Soc. Occupat. Med. Prev: Gp. Chief Med. Adviser Burmah Gp. Cos.; Cons. W.ingHo. Brake & Signal Co.; Sen. Lect. (Occupat. Med.) Univ. Wales Coll. Med. Cardiff.

GLOVER, John Robin (retired) 49 High Street, Stilton, Peterborough PE7 3RA Tel: 01733 240772 — MB BS 1963 Lond.; MRCS Eng. LRCP Lond. 1962; FFAEM 1993. Cons. A & E P'boro. Dist. Hosp. Prev: Regist. (Cas.) Sheff. Childr. Hosp. & Derby Roy. Infirm.

GLOVER, Jonathan Michael Royal Flying Doctor Service, PO Box 744, Mount Isa Qld 4825, Australia; Woodlands, New Road, Chiseldon, Swindon SN4 0PE Tel: 01793 740357 Email: jonathan.glover@compuserve.com — MB ChB 1990 Aberd.; MRCGP 1995. Med. Off. Roy. Flying Doctor Serv. Mt. Isa Qu.sland, Austral.

GLOVER, Jonathan Robert Department of Radiology, Ashford & St Peter's NHS Trust, Guildford Road, Chertsey KT16 0PZ Tel: 01932 872000; Cranbrook, Ruxbury Road, Chertsey KT16 9NH Tel: 01932 562600 — MB BS 1980 Lond.; MA Oxf. 1978; FRCS Eng. 1984; FRCR 1990. Cons. Radiol. St. Peter's Hosp. Chertsey. Prev: Sen. Regist. Middlx. & Univ. Coll. Hosps. Lond.

GLOVER, Josephine Mary 6 Fairlawn Park, Kettlewell Hill, Woking GU21 4HT Tel: 01483 771104 Fax: 01483 764956 — MB BS 1983 Lond.; MA Oxf. 1982; MFPM 1992. (St. Bart.) Europ. Med. Dir. ISIS Pharmaceut. Inc. Calif., USA. Socs: Fell. Roy. Soc. Med. Prev: Cons. Pharm. Med.; Head UK Cardiovasc. Gp. SmithKline & French Research Ltd. Welwyn.

GLOVER, Katherine Jane 8 Hill Crest Drive, Molescroft, Beverley HU17 7JG — MB ChB 1998 Leeds.

GLOVER, Lynne Alison 109 Hales Road, Cheltenham GL52 6ST Tel: 01242 524715 — MB BS 1975 Lond.; MRCS Eng. LRCP Lond. 1975; MFFP 1995; DRCOG 1978. (Guy's) SCMO (Family Plann.) E. Glos. NHS Trust & Severn NHS Trust; Sen. Clin. Med. Off. (Psychosexual Med.) E. Glos. NHS Trust. Prev: Trainee GP Chislehurst Kent; SHO (O & G) Lewisham Hosp. Lond.; SHO (Paediat.) FarnBoro. Hosp.

GLOVER, Margaret Elizabeth Relly Farm, Broom Park, Durham DH7 7RJ Tel: 0191 384 8725 — MB ChB 1969 St. And. Sen. Med. Off. & SCMO N. Durh. HA.

GLOVER, Mark Alec 75 Woodville Drive, Pembroke Park, Portsmouth PO1 2TQ — BM BCh 1987 Oxf.; BA Oxf. 1984; MRCGP 1996; AFOM RCP Lond. 1996.

GLOVER, Martin William Mews Close Health Centre, Mews Close, Ramsey, Huntingdon PE26 1BP Tel: 01487 812611 Fax: 01487 711801; The Thatched Cottage, High St, Bury, Huntingdon PE26 2NQ Tel: 01487 814377 — MB BS 1976 Lond.; BSc Lond. 1973; MRCGP 1980. (Middlesex Hospital Medical School)

GLOVER, Mary (retired) 5 Dunedin Drive, Twatling Road, Barnt Green, Birmingham B45 8HZ Tel: 0121 445 1012 — MB ChB 1950 Birm. Prev: Research Fell. (Cytol.) Qu. Eliz. Matern. Hosp. Birm.

GLOVER, Mary Teresa Dermatology, St Andrew's Hospital, Devas St., London E3 3NT — MB BS 1980 Lond.; MA Camb. 1981; MRCP (UK) 1983; DCH RCP Lond. 1984; FRCP 1998. (London) Cons. Dermat. Newham Healthcare Lond.; Sen. Lect. (Dermat.) Roy. Lond. Hosp.; Hon. Cons. (Dermat.) The Hosp. for Sick Childr. Gt. Ormond St.

GLOVER, Michael Pond Tail Surgery, The Green, Godstone RH9 8DY Tel: 01883 742279 Fax: 01883 742913; Greenfields, Rabies Heath Road, Bletchingley, Redhill RH1 4l7 Tel; 01883 743266 — MB BS 1980 Lond.; MRCS Eng. LRCP Lond. 1979; MRCGP 1985; DRCOG 1985; DCH RCP Lond. 1984.

GLOVER, Michelle 3 Lampeter Sq, London W6 8PS — MB BS 1997 Lond.

GLOVER, Nicholas Alexander Joseph Northfield Road Surgery, Northfield Road, Blaby, Leicester LE8 4GU Tel: 0116 277 1705 — MB ChB 1992 Leic.; MRCGP 1996; DFFP 1996; DRCOG 1996; T (GP) 1996. (Leicester) Clin. Asst. (Dermat.).

***GLOVER, Nicholas Mark** 8 New College Road, Shrewsbury SY2 6PU Tel: 0370 902023 — MB BS 1994 Lond.; BSc Medl Microbiol 1991.

GLOVER, Paul David Undercliffe Surgery, 273 Healey Lane, Batley WF17 8DQ Tel: 01924 403406 Fax: 01924 412890 — MB BS 1984 Lond.; DRCOG 1988.

GLOVER, Paul Joseph 42 Sandymount Street, Belfast BT9 5DP — MB BCh BAO 1989 Belf.; BSc Belf. 1986; MRCP (UK) 1992; FRCA 1995.

GLOVER, Peter Church View Surgery, Burley House, 15 High Street, Rayleigh SS6 7DY Tel: 01268 774477 Fax: 01268 771293 — MB BS 1978 Lond.; BSc Reading 1970; MSc Newc. 1972; MRCGP 1982; DRCOG 1982; DPD 1992; Dip. Ther. 1997. GP Rayleigh.

GLOVER, Richard Berry Scermer, Manor Way, Oxshott, Leatherhead KT22 0HU Tel: 01372 843088 — MB BS Lond. 1953; MRCS Eng. LRCP Lond. 1952. (Middlx.) Sen. Med. Off. Epsom, Sandown Pk., Kempton Pk. & Lingfield Pk. Racecourses. Socs: BMA & Med. Equest. Assoc.; Racecourse Med. Offs. Assn. Prev: GP Oxshott; Flight Lt. RAF Med. Br.; Ho. Surg. & Ho. Surg. (ENT) Middlx. Hosp.

GLOVER, Roy Austen (retired) 5 Dunedin Drive, Twatling Road, Barnt Green, Birmingham B45 8HZ Tel: 0121 445 1012 — MB ChB 1950 Birm. GP Birm. Prev: Surgic. Hosp. Pract. S. Birm. HA.

GLOVER, Ruth Elsbeth Nova, 1 Glebelands Meadow, Loxwood Road, Alfold, Cranleigh GU6 8EA; 49 Calcott Park, Yateley GU46 6JJ Tel: 01252 879672 — MB ChB 1995 Leeds.

GLOVER, Samuel Rowan, 48-50 Muswell Road, London N10 Tel: 020 8883 5600 — MB BCh BAO 1944 Belf.

GLOVER, Simon James 76 Gipsy Lane, Kettering NN16 8UA — MB BS 1991 Lond.

GLOVER, Stephanie Caroline 31 Applehaigh View, Royston, Barnsley S71 4JG — MB ChB 1994 Leic. SHO (Anaesth.) Leicester.

GLOVER, Stuart Cunningham Southmead District General Hospital, Southmead Road, Westbury-on-Trym, Bristol BS10 5NB Tel: 0117 959 5549 Fax: 0117 959 6156; 14 Ormerod Road, Stoke Bishop, Bristol BS9 1BB Tel: 0117 968 4245 Fax: 0117 968 8168 — MB ChB 1972 Aberd.; MB ChB (Hons.) Aberd. 1972; FRCP Lond. 1988; FRCP Ed. 1986; MRCP (UK) 1974. Cons. Phys. with s/i in Communicable & Trop. Dis. S.mead Hosand. Bristol. And HIV Med.; Hon. Lect. (Med.) Univ. Bristol.

GLOVER, Tyrone Frederick 7 St Helens Road, Rainford, St Helens WA11 7QX — MB 1988 Camb.; BChir 1987.

GLOVER, William John (retired) The Hospital for Sick Children, Great Ormond St., London WC1N 3JH Tel: 020 7405 9200 — MB BCh BAO 1950 Belf.; FFA RCS Eng. 1957; DObst RCOG 1953. Prev: Mayo Foundat. Fell. (Anaesth.).

GLOZIER, Nicholas Simon Maudsley Hospital, Denmark Hill, London SE5 — MB BS 1992 Lond.; MA Oxon 1995; MSc Lond 1998; MRC Psych 1997.

GLUCK, Timothy Adam 12 Parolles Road, London N19 3RD — MB BS 1988 Lond.; MRCP (UK) 1991.

GLUCK-BARDI, Susan 61 Lyndhurst Gardens, Finchley, London N3 1TA — MB ChB 1924 Liverp.

GLUCKMAN, Mr Paul Geoffrey Calvin ENT Department, Medway Hospital, Windmill Road, Gillingham ME7 5NY Tel: 01634 830000 Fax: 01732 822541 — MB BS 1979 Lond.; FRCS Ed. 1988; FRCS Eng. 1984; DLO RCS Eng. 1987. (St. Bart.) Cons. ENT Surg. Medway Hosp. NHS Trust. Socs: Fell. Roy. Soc. Med.; Brit. Assn. Otol. Prev: Cons. ENT Surg. BMH Iserlohn Germany; Vis. Lect. & Hon. Sen. Regist. (Surg.) Chinese Univ. of Hong Kong; Sen. Regist. Rotat. (ENT) Roy. Devon & Exeter Hosp. & Roy. Marsden Hosp.

GLUCKSMAN, Edward Accident & Emergency Department, King's College Hospital, Denmark Hill, London SE5 9RS Tel: 020 7346 3235 Fax: 020 7346 3531 — MD 1972 Virginia, USA; MD Virginia 1972, FRCP 1988; FFAEM 1993. Cons. A & E King's Coll. Hosp. Lond. Socs: Fell. Fac. Accid. & Emerg. Med.; Fell. Roy. Soc. Med.; Fell.Roy. Coll. of Phys.s.

GLYN, John Harry Howard 35 Sussex Square, London W2 2SP Tel: 020 7262 9187 — MRCS Eng. LRCP Lond. 1946; MA Camb. 1947, MD 1955, MB BChir 1947; FRCP Lond. 1971, M 1952. (Camb. & Middlx.) Emerit. Cons. (Rheum.) St Mary's Hosp., St. Chas. Hosp. & Camden Rd. Med. Rehabil. Centre; Emerti. Cons. (Rheum.) St. Dunstan's & Osborne Ho.; Assoc. Teach. St. Mary's Hosp. Med. Sch. Lond. Socs: Heberden Soc. & Brit. Assn. Rheum. & Rehabil. Prev: Sen. Regist. Dept. Rheum. Lond. Hosp.; Research Fell. Dept. Rheum. Dis. N.Y. Univ. Bellevue Med. Centre; Consult. Dept. Rheum. Dis. P. of Wales Gen. Hosp. Lond.

GLYN-JONES, Sion Yr Hen Reithordy, Dwyran, Llanfairpwllgwyngyll LL61 6BJ — MB BS 1996 Lond.

GLYNN, Ada (retired) 35 Old Park Avenue, Enfield EN2 6PJ Tel: 020 8366 7239 — MRCS Eng. LRCP Lond. 1940; PhD Lond. 1930, BSc 1928; DPM Eng. 1942. Prev: Cons. Psychiat. Winterton Hosp. Sedgefield & S.W. Durh. Hosp. Gp.

GLYNN, Alan Anthony (retired) 1 Pembridge Crescent, London W11 3DT Tel: 020 7229 8878 Fax: 020 7229 8878 — MD 1960 Lond.; MB BS 1946; FRCP Lond. 1974, M 1954; FRCPath 1972, M 1964. Prev: Dir. Centr. Pub. Health Laborat. Colindale.

GLYNN, Angela Frances Mary 329 Nottingham Road, Nottingham NG7 7DB Tel: 0115 975788 — MB BCh BAO 1942 NUI; LM Dub. 1942. (Galw.) Prev: Med. Off. Gen. Hosp. Galway, Roy. Infirm. Stoke-on-Trent & Kendal; Gen. Hosp.

GLYNN, Barbara Gail St Marys Medical Centre, Wharf Road, Stamford PE9 2DH — MRCGP, DRCOG, MBBS. (King's College Hospital London) GP.

GLYNN, Christopher James Oxford Regional Pain Relief Unit, Churchill Hospital, Oxford OX3 7LJ Tel: 01865 226193 Fax: 01865 226160 — MB BS 1968 Sydney; MSc Oxf. 1977; FFA RCS Eng. 1973; DCH RCP Lond. 1971. Cons. Anaesth. Oxf. Regional Pain Relief Unit Oxon HA; Lect. Univ. Oxf. Socs: Internat. Assn. for Study of Pain; (Treas.) Intractable Pain Soc. GB & Irel. Prev: Fell. Oxf. Regional Pain Relief Unit Abingdon Hosp.; Sen. Staff Specialist (Anaesth. & Inten. Care) Flinders Med. Centre Adelaide, Austral.

GLYNN, Gerard Martin Anthony Microbiolgy Laboratory, Level 2, Altnagelvin Area Hospital, Londonderry BT47 6SB Tel: 01504 45171 — MB BCh BAO 1983 NUI; MMedSc (Med. Microbiol.) NUI 1987; BSc (Anat.) 1980; MRCPath 1992. Cons. Med. Microbiol. Altnagelvin Area Hosp. Lond.derry. Socs: Hosp. Infec. Soc. & Path. Soc. Gt. Brit. & Irel.; Amer. Soc. Microbiol. Prev: Sen. Regist. (Med. Microbiol.) Pub. Health Laborat. John Radcliffe Hosp. Oxf.; Regist. & SHO (Med. Microbiol.) Univ. Coll. Hosp. Galway Irel.; SHO (Path.) St. Vincents Hosp. Dub.

GLYNN, Professor Ian Michael (retired) Trinity College, Cambridge CB2 1TQ Fax: 01223 333840 Email: img10@cam.ac.uk — MB BChir 1952 Camb.; FRS; PhD Camb. 1956, MD 1970, MA 1953; MD (Hon) Aarhus 1988; FRCP Lond. 1987. Fell. Trinity Coll. Camb. Prev: Univ. Prof. Physiol. Univ. Camb.

GLYNN, Joanne Catherine 17 Bickley Street, London SW17 9NF — MB BS 1997 Lond.

GLYNN, John Patrick (retired) 30 The Coppice, Shirebrook, Mansfield NG20 8EF Tel: 01623 742730 — MB BCh BAO NUI 1952; LM Rotunda.

GLYNN, Judith Rebecca London School of Hygiene & Tropical Medicine, London WC1E 7HT — BM BCh 1986 Oxf.; PhD Lond. 1993; MSc Lond. 1991; MA Camb. 1987, BA 1983; MRCP (UK) 1989. Sen. Lect. (Epidemiol.) Lond. Sch. Hyg. & Trop. Med. Prev: Lect. (Epidemiol.) Lond. Sch. Hyg & Trop Med.; Wellcome Research Train. Fell. (Clin. Epidemiol.) Lond. Sch. Hyg. & Trop. Med.; Regist. (Med.) City Hosp. Nottm.

GLYNN, Leonard Eleazar (retired) Four Winds, Hammersley Lane, Penn, High Wycombe HP10 8HG Tel: 01494 812285 — MB BS 1934 Lond.; MB BS (Hons.) Midw., Gyn. & Path. Lond. 1934; BSc (1st cl. Hons. Physiol.) Lond. 1931, MD 1945; FRCP Lond. 1963, M 1936; MRCS Eng., LRCP Lond. 1934; FRCPath 1965. Prev: Dir. Kennedy Inst. Rheum.

GLYNN, Liam Joseph Francis (retired) 2 Croft Lane, Roade, Northampton NN7 2QZ Tel: 01604 862352 — MB BCh BAO 1956 NUI; DPH 1959, DCH 1959; MRCPI 1965. Prev: SCMO N.ants. AHA.

GLYNN, Michael Jonathan The Royal London Hospital, Barts and the London NHS Trust, Whitechapel, London E1 1BB Tel: 020 7377 7000 or 020 377 7486 Fax: 020 7377 7337 Email: drmichael.glynn@bartsandthelondon.nhs uk — MB BChir 1978 Camb.; MILT 2001; MA Camb. 1978; MD Camb. 1995; FRCP Lond. 1993; MRCP (UK) 1980; T(M) 1991. (St. Mary's) Cons. Physiol. (Gastroenterol.) Barts & the Lond. Hosps.; Dep. Med. Director Barts & the Lond. Hosps. Socs: Brit. Soc. Gastroenterol.; Eur. Soc. Parenteral & Enteral Nutrit.; Eur. Assn. Study Liver. Prev: Cons. Gastroenterol. Newham Gen. Hosp.; Sen. Regist. (Med. & Gastroenterol.) Lond. Hosp.; Research Fell. (Clin. Nutrit.) & Hon. Sen. Regist. Char. Cross Hosp. Lond.

GLYNN, Oona Elizabeth Gertrude 11 Cleaver Square, Kennington, London SE11 4DW — MB BCh BAO 1962 NUI; DPH NUI 1967; DCH NUI 1965.

GLYNN, Paul Michael Lingwell Croft Surgery, Ring Road, Middleton, Leeds LS10 3LT Tel: 0113 270 4848 Fax: 0113 272 0030; Highbrook, 33 Blackmoorfoot, Linthwaite, Huddersfield HD7 5TR Tel: 01484 846134 — MB ChB 1983 Leeds; MRCGP 1987; Cert. Family Plann. JCC 1987; DRCOG 1987. Prev: Regional Med. Off. BT plc Leeds.

GLYNN, Peter Jeremy Haden Crahamel Medical Practice, Crahamel House, 2 Duhamel Place, St Helier, Jersey JE2 4TP Tel: 01534 735742 Fax: 01534 735011 — MB BS 1972 Lond.

GLYNN, Rory Paul Bellevue Surgery, Bellevue Terrace, Newport NP20 2WQ Tel: 01633 256337 Fax: 01633 222856 — MB BCh BAO 1987 NUI; DObst. RCPI 1991; DGM RCP Lond. 1990.

GLYNN, Ruth Hannah 48 East End Road, Finchley, London N3 3QU Tel: 020 8346 0359 Email: drruth@psynet.net — MRCS Eng. LRCP Lond. 1965; BA Camb. 1961. (Camb. & King's Coll. Hosp.) Staff Grade (Community Paediat.) Lond.

GLYNNE, Alan 97 Harley Street, London W1G 6AG Tel: 020 7935 5896 Fax: 020 7935 6617 — MB ChB 1965 Ed.; BSc (Hons.) Ed. 1963; MRCP Lond. 1968; FFPM 1990; T(M) 1991; Dip Pharm Med RCP (UK) 1977; FRCP 2000 London. (Univ. Ed.) Cons. Phys. (Gen. Medicinie) Cromwell Hosp. Clinic, Wellington Hosp., Pk.side Hosp., Lond.; Assoc. Lect. Univ. Surrey 1997-; Med. Adviser, HarCt. Publishers. Socs: Brit. Diabetic Assoc. (Mem. Med. & Scientif. Assoc.); Brit. Thyroid Assn.; Soc. Endocrinol. Prev: Hon. Lect. & Cons. Med. Guy's Hosp. Lond.; Sen. Regist. (Med.) Manch. Roy. Infirm. & Univ. Hosp. S. Manch.; Regist. (Gen. Med. & Endocrinol.) Glas. Roy. Infirm.

GLYNNE, Gaynor Llwyd (retired) — MB ChB 1949 Manch. Prev: Clin. Asst. (Anaesth.) Univ. Hosp. S. Manch.

GLYNNE, Paul Alexander Renal Section & Department of Infectious Diseases, Division of Medicine & Investigative Sciences, Imperial Coll. Sch. of Med., Hammersmith Hosp., Du Cane Road, London W12 0NN Tel: 020 8383 2065 Fax: 020 8383 3394 Email: p.glynne@rpms.ac.uk; Flat 7, 81 Sinclair Road, London W14 0NR — MB BS 1992 Lond.; MRCP (UK) 1995. (University College & Middlesex School of Medicine) Wellcome Research Train. Fell. & Hon. Specialist Regist. (Nephrol.) Imperial Coll. Sch. Med. Hammersmith. Socs: Renal Assn.; Eur. Dialysis & Transpl. Assn.; Internat. Soc. Nephrol. Prev: Specialist Regist. (Renal Med.) Hammersmith Hosp. Lond.; Regist. (Med.) Ealing Hosp.; SHO (Renal Med.) St. Geo. Hosp. Lond.

GLYNNE-JONES, Robert George Thorburn Mount Vernon Centre for Cancer Treatment, Northwood HA6 2RN Tel: 01923 844012 Fax: 01923 844138 — MB BS 1978 Lond.; BA Oxf. 1972; MRCP (UK) 1981; FRCR 1986; FRCP 1998. Cons. Clin. Oncol. Mt. Vernon Hosp. Middlx.; Macmillan lead clinician in gastrointestinal cancer. Socs: Amer. Soc. Of Clin. Oncol.; Brit. Inst. Of Radiol.; Roy. Soc. Of Med. Prev: Lect. & Hon. Sen. Regist. (Radiother.) Middlx. Hosp. Lond.; Sen. Regist. (Radiother.) St. Bart. Hosp. Lond.

GNANACHELVAN, K The Surgery, 10 Highland Road, Bromley BR2 4AD Tel: 020 8460 2368 Fax: 020 8313 9908.

GNANACHELVAN, Sivagnanapragasam Saishyam, 3 Courtenay Drive, Beckenham BR3 6YE Tel: 020 8663 0892; 10 Highland Road, Bromley BR1 4AD Tel: 020 8460 2368 Fax: 020 8658 7378 — MB BS 1973 Sri Lanka; MRCS Eng. LRCP Lond. 1985; MRCOG 1988; DRCOG 1987. Socs: BMA; Overseas Doctors Assn.; Med. Inst. of Tamil.

GNANADURAI, Thevathanjan Victor c/o Anaesthic Secretary, Russells Hall Hospital, Dudley DY1 2HQ Tel: 01384 456111; 56 Redlake Drive, Pedmore, Stourbridge DY9 0RX Tel: 01562 885398 — MB BS 1965 Ceylon; FFA RCS Eng. 1975. (Ceylon) Cons. Anaesth. Dudley HA. Socs: Intractable Pain Soc. Gt. Brit. & Irel.; Internat. Soc. Hypn.; Internat. Assn. for the Study of Pain. Prev: Cons. Anaesth. W. Midl. Regional Centre for Plastic, Jaw & Maxillofacial Surg.; Sen. Regist. & Research Asst. Brompton Hosp. Lond.

GNANAKUMARAN, Gnanasegaram 57B Day's Lane, Biddenham, Bedford MK40 4AE — BM 1993 Soton. (Univ. Soton.) Socs: Mem. MDU; BMA.

GNANALINGHAM, Giritharalingham Muhuntha Academic Division of Child Health, School of Human Development, Floor E, East Block, Queen's Medical Centre, Nottingham NG7 2UH Tel: 0115 924 9924 Ext: 43504 Fax: 0115 970 9382 Email: mg.gnanalingham@nottingham.ac.uk — MB ChB 1995 Manch.; MRCPH 1999. (Manch.) Clin. Lect. In Child Health, Acad. Div. of Child Health, Qu.'s Med. Centre, Nottm. NG7 2UH. Socs: MDU; Roy. Coll. of Paediat. & Child Health; Intercollegiate Comm. for Train. in Paediatric Intens. care Med. Prev: Paediat.Specialist Regist. Liverp. Wom.'s Hosp. Liverp.; Paediat.Specialist Regist. Alder Hey Childr.'s Hosp, Liverp.; Paediat.Specialist Regist. Warington Gen. Hosp. Warringtonl.

GNANANANDAN, Jayanthy Keats Surgery, 290A Church Street, Edmonton, London N9 9HJ; 39 Bush Hill, Winchmore Hill, London N21 2BT Tel: 020 8360 9733 — MB BS 1976 Ceylon; LMSSA Soc Apoth. Lond. 1992; DFFP 1993; DA (UK) 1988. (University of Ceylon, Peradeniya, Sri Lanka) GP; Clin. Asst. A & E. Prev: CMO Child Health.

GNANANANDHA, Mr Chellathurai 69 Hillside Avenue, Worthing BN14 9QT; 4 Alston Close, Silkstone, Barnsley S75 4NW — MB BS Ceylon 1970; FRCS Ed. 1980. (Ceylon) Regist. (ENT) Birm. AHA.; Assoc. Specialist ENT Barnsley Dist. Gen. Hosp. Prev: SHO (A & E) Suff. AHA; Locum Cons. ENT Barnsley Dist. Hosp.; Locum Cons. Pilgram Hosp. Boston.

GNANAPRAGASAM, Jagathambikai 141 Mostyn Road, London SW19 3LS — MB BS 1955 Ceylon.

GNANAPRAGASAM, James Peter Mail Point 46, Southampton General Hospital, Southampton SO16 6YD Tel: 023 8079 6243 — MB BS 1983 Colombo; MRCS Eng LRCP Lond. 1987; MRCP (UK) 1988; FRCP 2000. Cons. Paediat. Cardiol. Soton. Gen. Hosp.

GNANAPRAGASAM, Jewel Jebaseeli 2 Wallington Drive, Chandlers Ford, Eastleigh SO53 1TR — MB BS 1985 Colombo; LMSSA Lond. 1992.

GNANAPRAGASAM, John Baptist 141 Mostyn Road, Merton Park, London SW19 3LS Tel: 020 8542 1616 — MB BS 1951 Ceylon; MRCOG 1961; FRCOG 1974.

GNANAPRAGASAM, Vasanthakumar Cuthbert 141 Mostyn Road, Mevtan Park, London SW19 3LS — MRCS Eng. LRCP 1991 Lond.; MRCS Eng LRCP Lond. 1991; MRCGP 1996; DRCOG 1995. GP Asst. Sutton.

***GNANAPRAGASAM, Vincent Jeyaseelan** 93 Glenthorn Road, Newcastle upon Tyne NE2 3HJ; 174 Jalan 5/45, Petaling Jaya, Selangor 46000, Malaysia — MB BS 1994 Newc.; BMedSci 1993.

GNANARATNAM, Jeevarathi 56 Farnham Gardens, London SW20 0UE — MB BS 1980 Colombo; MRCS Eng. LRCP Lond. 1985; MRCP (UK) 1994.

GNANASEGARAM, Dhurga 118 Finchfield Lane, Finchfield, Wolverhampton WV3 8EU Tel: 01902 766337 — MB ChB 1995 Manch.; BSc (Hons.) Biomed. Sci. Manch. 1993. (Manchester) SHO (Gen. Med.) Wythenshawe Hosp. Manch. Socs: Brit Med Assoc.

GNANENTHIRAN, Subramaniam 5 The Parklands, Wolverhampton WV3 9DG; Child Health Clinic, Red Hill St, Wolverhampton WV1 1NR — MB BS 1970 Ceylon; MSc Univ.

Warwick 1993; DCH RCP Lond. 1981. SCMO (Child Health) Wolverhampton. Socs: ODA; BMA; Brit. Paediat. Assn.

GNANI, Shamini 86 Elmfield Road, South Croydon CR2 0EF — MB ChB 1991 Birm.

***GOAD, Claire Elizabeth** Buckland Edge, Cliftons Lane, Reigate RH2 9RA — MB ChB 1998 Birm.

GOADBY, Jack Weldon, Wing Cdr. RAF Med. Br. Retd. High House Farm, 54 High House Drive, Rednal, Birmingham B45 8ET Tel: 0121 445 5169 Fax: 0121 447 8206; High House Farm, 54 High House Drive, Rednal, Birmingham B45 8ET Tel: 0121 445 5169 Fax: 0121 447 8206 — MRCS Eng. LRCP Lond. 1966; FFOM RCP Lond. 1994, MFOM 1980; DAvMed FOM RCP Lond. 1975; DObst RCOG 1971. (St. Thos. Hosp. Lond.) Indep. Cons. Birm.; Occupat. Phys. W. Bromwich. Socs: Soc. Occupat. Med.; Fell. Fac. Occupat. Med. Prev: Regional Med. Adviser (N.) Lucas Industries plc; Sen. Med. Off. Powergen plc; Occupat. Health Phys. Austin Rover Longbridge.

GOADSBY, Peter James Institute of Neurology, The National Hospital for Neurology & Neurosurgery, Queen Square, London WC1N 3BG Tel: 020 7837 3611 Fax: 020 7813 0349 — MB BS 1985 New South Wales; MB BS (Hons.) New South Wales 1985; PhD Newc South Wales 1985, BMedSc 1982, MD 1989; FRACP 1990. Wellcome Sen. Lect. & Reader (Clin. Neurol.) Nat. Hosp. for Neurol. & Neurosurg. Lond.; Hon. Cons. Neurol. Nat. Hosp. for Neurol & Neurosurg. Lond. Prev: Assoc. Prof. Neurol. Univ. NSW, Austral.; Cons. Neurol. P. Henry Hosp. Sydney, Austral.

GOATER, Nicola Lesley 40A Gloucester Gardens, Bishops Bridge Road, London W2 6BN Tel: 0121 262 8628 Email: anar@glgdns.freeserve.co.uk — MB BS 1991 Lond.; BSc (1st cl. Hons.) Clin. Sci. Lond. 1991; MRCPsych 1996. (St. Mary's Hosp. Lond.) Specialist Regist. Psychiat. (Gen. Adult) Roy. Free Hosp. Rotat. Lond.,. Socs: Fell. Roy. Soc. Med. Prev: Research Fell. (Psychiat.) Roy. Free Hosp. Med. Sch. Lond.; Regist. (Old Age Psychiat.) & Regist. Acad. (Psychiat.) Roy. Free Hosp. Lond.

GOBBETT, Anne Mary Orchard House, Emlyns St., Stamford PE9 1QP Tel: 01780 762963 — MB BS 1989 Newc.; FRCOphth 1994. Clin. Asst. (Ophth.) Sunderland Eye Infirm. Prev: SHO (Ophth.) Sunderland Eye Infirm.; SHO (Neurosurg.) Middlesbrough Gen. Hosp.

GOBERDHAN, Pratibha Daulat 2A Sylvan Hill, London SE19 2QF Tel: 020 8771 9415 — LRCPI & LM, LRSCI & LM 1965; LRCPI & LM, LRCSI & LM 1965; MSc Audiol. Med. Manch. 1989. (RCSI) Paediat. Audiol. Med. Croydon Community Health Trust. Socs: Hon. Fell. Soc. Pub. Health 1989; BMA; Brit. Soc. Audiol. Prev: Ho. Phys. St. Mary's Hosp. Lond.; Cas. Off. Paddington Green Childr. Hosp. Lond.; Cas. Off. St. Geo. Hosp. Lond.

GOBLE, Catherine Mary — MB BS 1986 Lond.; MRCGP 1991; T(GP) 1992. (St. Thos. Hosp. Med. Sch.) Prev: GP FarnBoro.; GP Hants./Wilts.

GOBLE, Mr Nigel Mark 6 Tynewydd Drive, Castleton, Cardiff CF3 2SB — MB BS 1977 Lond.; FRCS Eng. 1981.

GOBLE, Orla Ann 7 Little St. John Street, Woodbridge IP12 1EE Tel: 01394 382046 — MB BS 1989 Lond.; DRCOG 1995; DFFP 1995. (St. Thos. Hosp. Med. Sch.) p/t GP Retainer, 7 Little St. John's, Woodbridge. Prev: GP Regist. Woodbridge; SHO (Psychiat. & Paediat.) Alexandra Hosp. Redditch; SHO (O & G) Pembury Hosp.

GOCMAN, Michael Charles Abernethy House, 70 Silver Street, Enfield EN1 3EP Tel: 020 8366 1314 Fax: 020 8364 4176 — MB ChB 1981 Leic.; DRCOG 1983; Cert. Family Plann. JCC 1983. (Leicester) Chairm. New River Total Care Project; Ex-Chairm. New River Fund Holders Gp.; Chairm. GP Unit Staff Comm. Socs: LJMS; Assoc. Mem. RCGP; BMA.

GODBEHERE, Peter Raymond 32 Highertown, Truro TR1 3QA Tel: 01872 262104 — MB ChB 1992 Leic. Prev: SHO (Gen. Med.) Solihull Hosp.

GODBER, Colin Moorgreen Hospital, Botley Road, West End, Southampton SO30 3JB Tel: 02380 475241 Fax: 02380 465014; Tel: 02380 558065 — BM BCh 1964 Oxf.; MPhil Lond. 1971; FRCP Lond. 1982, M 1967; FRCPsych 1981, M 1973. (Middlx.) Cons. Old Age Psychiat. W. Hants. NHS Trust. Prev: Med.dir.Soton.Community health; Lect. (Psychiat.) Soton Univ.

GODBER, Sir George Edward, GCB (retired) 21 Almoner's Avenue, Cambridge CB1 8NZ Tel: 01223 247491 — BM BCh Oxf. 1933; Hon. FRCPsych 1973; Hon. FRCOG 1966; DPH Lond. 1936; FRCGP, FRCP (Hon) 1972; DM Oxf. 1939; Hon. LLD Manch. 1964, Hull 1970, Nottm. 1973; Hon. DCL Newc. 1972, Oxf. 1973; Hon. DSc Bath 1979; FRCP Lond. 1947, M 1935; Hon. FRCS Eng. 1973; FFCM 1974; Hon. FRCGP 1973. Prev: Chief Med. Off. DHSS.

GODBER, Greville Noel Lambert 27 Eaton Court, Eaton Gardens, Hove BN3 3PL — MB BS 1940 Lond.; MRCS Eng. LRCP Lond. 1938. (Guy's)

GODBERT, Kenneth 27a St Owens Street, Hereford HR1 2JB Tel: 01432 262403 — MB BS 1980 Lond.; MSc Manch. 1989; MRCPsych. 1984. Cons. Psychiat. Hereford Co. Hosp.

GODBOLE, Maheshwar Krishnarao 11 Lowerfold Way, Healey, Rochdale OL12 7HX Tel: 01706 53747 — MB BS 1960 Nagpur; DO Eng. 1964. (Med. Coll. Nagpur) Assoc. Specialist (Ophth.) Oldham HA.

GODBOLE, Shibani 11 Lowerford Way, Healey, Rochdale OL12 7HX Tel: 01706 53747 — MB BS 1959 Nagpur; BSc Nagpur 1953; DObst RCOG 1964. (Med. Coll. Nagpur) Prev: Clin. Med. Off. Rochdale AHA.

GODBOLE, Vaidehi 14 Turnberry Walk, Bedford MK41 8AZ — MB ChB 1994 Leeds.

GODBOLT, Alison Kate 22 Merton Road, Bedford MK40 3AF — MB ChB 1997 Ed.

GODBOLT, Hayley Louise 14 Selwyn Avenue, Richmond TW9 2HA — MB BS 1997 Newc.

GODBY, Clifford, TD Wigan & Leigh Hospice, Kildare St., Hindley, Wigan WN2 3HZ Tel: 01942 525566 Fax: 01942 525577; Broughton House, 10 Windsor Road, Chorley PR7 1LN — MB ChB 1981 Manch.; DRCOG 1985; DPM Wales 1998. Hospice Phys. Wigan & Leigh Hospice.

GODDARD, Andrew Francis 10 Brompton Way, West Bridword, Nottingham NG2 7SU — MB BChir 1991 Camb.; BA Camb. 1988, MB BChir 1991; MRCP (UK) 1993; MA Camb. 1997; MD Camb. 1997. Specialist Regist. (Gastroenterol.) City Hosp. Nottm. Prev: Research Fell. & Hon. Regist. (Gastroenterol.) Univ. Hosp. Nottm.; SHO & Ho. Off. (Med.) Addenbrooke's Hosp. Camb.

GODDARD, Ann Victoria 28 Deacons Hill Road, Elstree, Borehamwood WD6 3LH Tel: 020 8953 1436 — MB BS Lond. 1958; MRCS Eng. LRCP Lond. 1958; DA Eng. 1961. (St. Mary's) Clin. Asst. (Anaesth.) Shenley & Napsbury Hosps. & Centr. Middlx. Hosp. Acton.

GODDARD, Anthony James Patrick St James University Hospital, Beckett St., Leeds LS9 7TF Tel: 0113 243 3144; 11 Hawks Nest Rise, Alwoodley, Leeds LS17 7JH Tel: 0113 268 9432 Email: tony.goddard@bt.internet.com — MB ChB Leeds 1991; MRCP (UK) 1995; FRCR (UK) 1998. Regist. Rotat. (Radiol.) Leeds-Bradford Train. Scheme. Socs: Roy. Coll. Radiol. Prev: SHO Rotat. (Clin. Med.) Seacroft & Killingbeck Hosps.

GODDARD, Caroline Louisa Heron House, Bridge, Chard TA20 4HR — MB ChB 1992 Manch. SHO Gosford Hosp. NSW Australia. Socs: BMA; Roy. Coll. Gen. Pract.; DFFP. Prev: Trainee GP Bristol VTS; Trainee GP/SHO Leighton Hosp. VTS.

GODDARD, Catherine Ann Oxleas NHS Trust, Upton Road Day Hospital, 14 Upton Road, Bexleyheath DA6 8LQ Tel: 020 8301 7904 Fax: 020 8301 7927 — MB BS 1979 Newc.; MRCPsych 1984. Cons. Psychiat. Old Age Oxleas NHS Trust.

GODDARD, Clive John Russell 23 Chevington Drive, Heaton Mersey, Stockport SK4 3RF — MB ChB 1984 Manch.; MRCP (UK) 1988. Sen. Regist. Glas. Roy. Infirm. Prev: Lect. (Gastroenterol.) Univ. Hosp. S. Manch.

GODDARD, Dennis Max 28 Deacons Hill Road, Elstree, Borehamwood WD6 3LH Tel: 020 8953 1436 — MB BCh Witwatersrand 1951. (Witwatersrand) Med. Off. Haberdashers' Aske's Sch. Elstree; Med. Off. Elstree Manor Home For Retd. Teach.; Med. Off. Med. Centre Metrop. Police Train. Coll. Hendon; Med. Adviser Teach. Benevolent Fund; Princip. Metrop. Police Recruit Assessm. Aybrook St. Centre. Socs: Med. Off. Sch. Assn. Prev: Clin. Asst. (Med.) Barnet Gen. Hosp.; Sen. Regist. (Med.) Johannesburg Gen. Hosp.; Regist. (Med.) Hackney Hosp.

GODDARD, Deryck Lake Hepworth (retired) Rose Dene, Goosnargh Lane, Goosnargh, Preston PR3 2BP Tel: 01772 865232 — MB BS 1936 Lond.; MB BS (Hons. Forens. Med. & Pub. Hyg.) Lond. 1936; MD Lond. 1939; FRCP Lond. 1971, M 1940; MRCS Eng. LRCP Lond. 1936. Prev: Cons. Phys. Preston & Chorley Gp. Hosps. & Brompton Hosp. Frimley.

GODDARD, Dorothy Ann Royal United Hospital, Combe Park, Bath BA1 3NG Tel: 01225 824384 Fax: 01225 825515 Email: dorothy.goddard@ruh_bath.swest.nhs.uk; 12 Ash Grove, Wells BA5 2LX Email: hdgoddard@tesco.net — MB ChB 1977 Bristol; MRCP (UK) 1980; DMRD Lond. 1984. (University of Bristol Medical School) Cons. Diagnostic BrE. Imaging & Radiol.Roy. United Hosp. Socs: Roy. Coll. Radiol.; RCR BrE. Gp; Community Mem. SW Radiologists Assoc. Prev: Assn. Specialist (Radiol.) Roy. United Hosp. Bath; Regist. (Diagnostic Radiols.) Bristol Roy. Infirmiary.

GODDARD, Francis John (retired) 17 Third Avenue, Hove BN3 2PB Tel: 01273 731322 — MRCS Eng. LRCP Lond. 1943; MRCGP 1953. Prev: Med. Off. Brighton Racecourse.

GODDARD, Gerald Frank Anaesthetic Department, Frimley Park Hospital, Portsmouth Road, Frimley, Camberley GU16 7UJ Tel: 01276 604161 Fax: 01276 604606; 1 High Street, Odiham, Hook RG29 1LE Tel: 01256 702164 — MB BS 1972 Lond.; FFA RCS Eng. 1979. (Univ. Coll. Hosp.) p/t Cons. Anaesth. Frimley Pk. Hosp. Surrey. Prev: Sen. Regist. (Anaesth.) Manch. Train. Rotat.; Regist. (Anaesth.) Hobart & Adelaide Australia; Regist. & SHO Rotat. (Anaesth.) Bristol Train.

GODDARD, Helen Clare 18 Bedmond Road, Hemel Hempstead HP3 8LJ — MB ChB 1997 Liverp.

GODDARD, Ian Michael The Hawthorns, St Andrews Gardens, Shepherdswell, Dover CT15 7LP — MB ChB 1998 Bristol.

GODDARD, Jane 34 Amerland Road, Wandsworth, London SW18 1PZ — MB ChB 1989 Ed.; BSc (Med. Sci.) Ed. 1987, MB ChB 1989.

GODDARD, Jane Margaret Shackleton Department of Anaesthetics, Southampton General Hospital, Tremona Road, Southampton SO16 6YD Tel: 02380 777222; Braemar, 10 Botley Road, Romsey SO51 5AH — MB BS 1983 Lond.; BDS (Hons.) 1979; FRCA 1989; DA (UK) 1985. Cons. Anaesth. Soton. Univ. Hosp. NHS Trust. Prev: Sen. Regist. (Anaesth.) Soton. Gen. Hosp.; Regist. (Anaesth.) St. Geo. Hosp. Lond.; SHO (Anaesth.) Basingstoke Dist. Hosp. & Soton Gen. Hosp.

GODDARD, John David (retired) 58 Queen Mary Avenue, Morden SM4 4JR Tel: 020 8540 5082 — MB BS 1964 Lond.; MRCP (UK) 1974; MRCS Eng. LRCP Lond. 1964. Prev: GP Morden, Surrey.

GODDARD, John Martin, TD Sheffield Childrens Hospital, Western Bank, Sheffield S10 2TH — MB BS 1977 Lond.; MRCP (UK) 1981; FFA RCS Eng. 1983. (St. Bart.) Cons. Paediat. Anaesth. Sheff. Childr.'s Hosp. NHS Trust. Prev: Sen. Regist. (Anaesth.) Sheff. HA; Regist. (Paediat. Anaesth.) Liverp. HA; Regist. (Anaesth.) Soton. Hosps.

GODDARD, Julie Ann 12 Wheatfield Road, Bilton, Rugby CV22 7LN — MB BS 1998 Newc.; MB BS Newc 1998.

GODDARD, Kim Alexander 44a New Dover Road, Canterbury CT1 3DT — MB BS 1988 Lond.

GODDARD, Lisa 92 Emlyn Avenue, Ebbw Vale NP23 5TZ — MB BS 1996 Lond.

GODDARD, Margaret Linda The Westmoreland GP Centre, Fazakerley Hospital, Aintree, Liverpool L9 7AL Tel: 0151 525 6286; 23 Grange Park, Maghull, Liverpool L31 3DP — MB ChB 1976 Liverp.; MRCGP 1981; DRCOG 1979. (Liverpool)

GODDARD, Maria Johanne 22 Bellshaugh Lane, Kelvinside, Glasgow G12 0PE — MB ChB 1988 Manch. (St Andrews and Manchester)

GODDARD, Martin Summerleigh, Pinfold Hill, Curbar, Calver, Hope Valley S32 3YL — MB BS 1998 Lond.; MB BS Lond 1998. SHO (Surgic.) Rotat., Lincoln & Louth NHS Trust, Co. Hosp., Lincoln. Prev: Ho. Surg., St. Thomas' Hosp., Lond.; Ho. Phys. Kent & Sussex Hosp., Tunbridge Wells.

GODDARD, Martin James 36 The Vale, Coulsdon CR5 2AW — BM BCh 1984 Oxf. SHO Nuffield Orthop. Centre Oxf.

GODDARD, Mr Nicholas Julian Department of Orthopaedics, Royal Free Hospital, Pond St., London NW3 2QG Tel: 020 7794 0500 Fax: 020 7830 2947; 43 Rowhampton Lane, Putney, London SW15 5LT Tel: 020 8788 3921 Fax: 020 8785 4759 — MB BS 1978 Lond.; FRCS Eng. 1983; DU Chir Main Paris VII 1989; DU Tech Microchir Paris VII 1989. (St. Bartholomews) Cons. Orthop. Surg. & Hon. Sen. Lect. Roy. Free Hosp. & Sch. Med. Lond.; Arnott Lect. RCS; Examr. FRCS; Examr. Europ. Dept. Hand Surg.; Hon. Orthops. Surg. Surrey C.C.C. & L.T.A.; Mem. Etranger De Gp.e D'Etude De La Main. Socs: Fell. BOA; Brit. Soc. Surg. Hand. Prev: Sen. Regist. (Orthop.) St. Bartholomews Train. Scheme; Regist. (Orthop.) Roy. Free Hosp. Train. Scheme; Surgic. Fell. Inst. Francais De La Main, Paris.

GODDARD, Nicholas Paul Lewisham Child and Family Therapy Centre, 78 Lewisham Park, London SE13 6QJ Tel: 020 8690 1086 — MB BS 1989 Lond.; BSc Lond. 1986; MRCPsych 1994. (King's College) Cons.; Sen. Lect. Guy's Hosp. Prev: Sen. Regist. Maudsley.

GODDARD, Professor Paul Richard X-Ray Department, Bristol Royal Infirmary, Marlborough Street, Bristol BS2 8HW Tel: 0117 928 2728 Fax: 0117 928 3267 Email: kay.angell@ubht.swest.nhs.uk; Redland Green Farm, Redland Green, Redland, Bristol BS6 7HF Tel: 0117 942 0256 Fax: 0117 942 0256 — MB BS 1974 Lond.; BSc 1971 ((Pharmacol., Hons.)) Lond.; DMRD 1979; FRCR 1982; MD 1983 Bristol. (Univ. Coll. Hosp.) Cons. Diag. Radiol. Bristol Roy. Infirm.; Vis. Prof., Uni. Of the W. of Eng.; Edr. in Chief Clin. MRI; Civil Cons. RAF; Head of Train. Bristol Radiol. Train. Scheme; Clin. Sen. Lect. (Radiol.) Univ. of Bristol. Socs: Coun. Mem. Brit. Inst. Of Radiol.; Past Pres. Magnetic Resource Radiol. Assn.; Past Chair. Chest Radiol. Assn. Prev: Lect. (Diag. Radiol.) Bristol Univ.; Sen. Regist. (Diag. Radiol.) Bristol Roy. Infirm.; SHO (Chest Med.) Univ. Coll. Hosp. Lond.

GODDARD, Penelope Gay Merrow Park Surgery, Kingfisher Drive, Guildford GU4 7EP Tel: 01483 503331 Fax: 01483 303457; 74 Charlock Way, Burpham, Guildford GU1 1XZ Tel: 01483 826321 — MB BS 1972 Lond.; MRCS Eng. LRCP Lond. 1972. (Char. Cross)

GODDARD, Peter Frank Honorary Librarian, The Royal College Of Pathologists, 2 Carlton House Terrace, London SW1Y 5AF Tel: 020 7451 6708 Fax: 020 7451 6702 — MB BS 1957 Lond.; FRCPath 1978, M 1966. (Char. Cross) Socs: Assn. Clin. Biochem. Prev: Cons. Chem. Pathol. Epsom Healthcare NHS Trust; Regist. Dept. Chem. Path. Postgrad. Med. Sch. Lond.; Ho. Surg. Char. Cross Hosp. Lond.

GODDARD, Raymond St Clements Hospital, Ipswich IP3 8LS Tel: 01473 715111 Fax: 01473 270653; Sycamore Cottage, Church Common, Snape, Saxmundham IP17 1QL — MB BS 1968 Lond.; MRCS Eng. LRCP Lond. 1968; MRCPsych 1984. Cons. Psychiat. Rehabil. E. Suff. Health Dist.

GODDARD, Richard Keith 4 Longdown Road, Epsom KT17 3PT — MB ChB 1997 Leeds.

GODDARD, Robert Hugh Wells City Practice, 22 Chamberlain Street, Wells BA5 2PF Tel: 01749 673356 Fax: 01749 670031; 12 Ash Grove, Wells BA5 2LX — MB ChB 1976 Bristol; MRCGP 1986; FRCA Eng. 1984; DRCOG 1985. Prev: Regist. (Anaesth.) Bristol Roy. Infirm.; SHO (Med. & Paediat.) Yeovil Dist. Hosp.

GODDARD, Rosemary Jane Email: ros_goddard@hotmail.com — MB ChB 1991 Bristol; CCST 2001; PhD Camb. 1986; BSc York 1980; MRCOG 1996. (Bristol) Specialist Regist. Cheltenham Gen. Hosp. Socs: Soc. Study of Fertil.; BMA; RCOG. Prev: Regist. (O & G), St Michael's Hosp., Bristol; Regist. (O & G) S.mead Hosp. Bristol; Regist. (O & G) Cheltenham Gen.

GODDARD, Sarah The Farm, Eardiston, Tenbury Wells WR15 8JS — BM 1994 Soton.; MRCP 1997. Research Fell. Qu. Eliz. Liver Unit Lab's, Birm. Prev: N. Staffs (SHO Med.); Addenbrooke's SHO(Hepat.).

GODDARD, Suzanne Louise Flat 8 Gt Sanders House, Hurst Lane, Seddlescombe, Tunbridge Wells TN33 0PE Tel: 01424 870167 — MB BS 1997 Lond. (Charing Cross and Westminster) SHO Med. Rotat. (Cardiol. Gen.Med) Conquest Hosp. Hastings. Socs: BMA; MDU; MPS.

GODDARD, Mrs Una Kathleen (retired) 18 New Walk, Beverley HU17 7DJ Email: kgoddard@vinden.karoo.co.uk — MB ChB 1955 Sheff.; LLB Hull 1985; FRCS Eng. 1959; FCOphth. 1988; DO Eng. 1959. Prev: Sen. Ophth. Regist. United Sheff. Hosps.

GODDARD, William Peter City Hospital, Hucknall Road, Nottingham NG5 1PJ; Cheney Cottage, Rearsby Lane, Gaddesby, Leicester LE7 4XE — MB BChir 1988 Camb.; BA (Hons.) Camb. 1986; MRCP (UK) 1992; DM 1998. (Camb. Clin. Sch.) Cons. (Gastero & Gen. Med.) Nottm. City Hosp. Prev: Sen. Regist. (Gastroenterol.) Nottm. City Hosp.; Research Regist. (Gastroenterol.) Nottm. City Hosp.; Regist. (Gen. Med., Gastroenterol. & Diabetes) Leicester Roy. Infirm.

GODDEN, Charles William Department of Paediatrics, Royal Surrey County Hospital, Egerton Road, Guildford GU2 7XX Tel: 01483 464115 — MB BS 1983 Lond.; MRCP Paediat. (UK) 1991; FRCPCH 1997; DCH RCP Lond. 1986; DRCOG 1986. (Char. Cross)

Cons. Paediat. Roy. Surrey Co. Hosp. Guildford. Socs: BMA; RCPCH; BPRS. Prev: Sen. Regist. (Paediat.) Poole & Soton.; Regist. (Paediat.) Ealing Hosp. & W.m. Childr. Hosp. Lond.; Regist. (Paediat.) P.ss Margt. Hosp. Child. Perth, W.. Austral.

GODDEN, Dagmar Patricia 3 Oak Coppice, off Overdale Drive, Bolton BL1 5JD — MB ChB 1988 Aberd.; DFFP 1997. (Aberd.) Clin. Asst. (Genito-Urin. Med.), p/t,Hope Hosp., Salford. Socs: AGUM. Prev: Family Plann. Sessions; SHO (Psychiat.) Rotherham Dist. Gen Hosp.

GODDEN, Mr Daryl Richard Philip Gloucestershire Royal Hospital, Great Western Road, Gloucester, Bolton GL1 3NN Tel: 01452 528555 — MB ChB 1991 Sheff.; BDS 1981; FRCS 1996 Eng.; FDS RCS 1993 Eng.; FRCS(OMFS) 1999. (Sheff.) Cons. (Oral, Maxillofacial Surg.) Cheltenham and Gloucester. Socs: Jun. Fell. Brit. Assn. Oral & Maxillofacial Surg.; BMA; BAHNO. Prev: Specialist Regist. (Oral) Blackburn Roy. Infirm.; Specialist Regist. (Oral) N. Manch. Hosp.; Specialist Regist. (Oral) Manch. Roy. Infirm.

GODDEN, Professor David John Highland islands Health Institute, The Geeen House, Inverness IV2 3ED Tel: 01463 667320, 01463 667310; Western Clone House, Lethen, Nairn IV12 5LD Tel: 01667 451087 — MB ChB 1977 Ed.; MD Ed. 1991; FRCP Ed. 1996; MRCP (UK) 1982; FRCP 1998 Glasgow. Clin. Prof. Uni .of Aberd. Prev: Cons. Thoracic & Hyperbarie Aberd. Roy,. Infirm.; Lect. (med) Uni. Aber.; Res. Fell. Uni.Brit. Colombia, Canada.

GODDEN, Michael John Flatt Walks Health Centre, 3 Castle Meadows, Catherine Street, Whitehaven CA28 7QE Tel: 01946 692173 Fax: 01946 590406 — MB ChB 1968 Aberd. GP Whitehaven.

GODFRAY, Deirdre Margaret North Swindon Practice, Home Ground Surgery, Thames Avenue, Haydon Wick, Swindon SN25 1QQ Tel: 01793 705777 Fax: 01793 705737; 5 Grosvenor Road, Kingshill, Swindon SN1 4LT Tel: 01793 541063 Email: deirdregodfray@supanet.com — BM 1988 Soton.; Southampton. GP Swindon.

GODFREE, Valerie Ann Saxonbury, 4 North Parade, Horsham RH12 2BE Tel: 01403 251398 — MB ChB 1981 Manch.; BSc St. And. 1978; MFFP 1995; MRCOG 1987. Dep. Dir. Amarant Centre Lond. & Hon. Lect. Acad. O & G Kings Coll. Hosp. Lond.; Clin. Asst. (Obst. & Gyn.) Brighton Healthcare NHS Trust.

GODFREY, Mr Alan Michael Felstead House, 23 Banbury Road, Oxford OX2 6NX Tel: 01865 244421 Fax: 01865 244421 Email: ag2u@iname.com; Tel: 01865 244421 — MB BCh 1968 Wales; MA Oxf. 1985; FRCS Ed. 1974. (Cardiff) Indep. Cons. Plastic Surg. Oxf. & N. Wessex and GloucesterRegions; Tutor in Anat. (p/t) Lincoln Coll. Oxf. (Curr.). Socs: Brit. Assn. Plastic Surg.; (Counc.) Brit. Assn. Aesthetic Plastic Surgs.; Sec.-Gen. Europ. Soc. Laser Aesthetic Surg. Prev: Cons. Plastic Surg. Oxf. HA; Sen. Regist. (Plastic Surg.) Oxf. AHA (T); Regist. (Plastic Surg.) Stoke Mandeville Hosp. Aylesbury.

GODFREY, Andrew John Health Centre, High Street, Bedworth, Nuneaton CV12 8NQ Tel: 024 7631 5432 Fax: 024 7631 0038; 9 Moorcroft Close, Whitestone, Nuneaton CV11 6TB Tel: 01203 343492 — MB ChB 1984 Leic.; MB ChB Leic. l984.

GODFREY, Andrew William Helm Church Plain Surgery, Church Plain, Loddon, Norwich NR14 6EX Tel: 01508 520222 Fax: 01508 528579 — MB BS 1983 Lond. Princip. in Gen. Pract.; Hosp. Practitioner, Cardiol., Norfolf & Norwich Hosp.; Co. Med. Off., Norf. St Johns Ambul. Prev: Regist. (Med.) Edgware Gen. Hosp.

GODFREY, David John Meanwood Group Practice, 548 Meanwood Road, Leeds LS6 4JN Tel: 0113 295 1737 Fax: 0113 295 1736; 19 North Park Avenue, Roundhay, Leeds LS8 1EJ Tel: 0113 266 4250 — MB ChB 1955 Leeds. (Leeds) Clin. Asst. in Paediat. St. Jas. Hosp. Leeds. Socs: Leeds Regional Paediat. Club. Prev: Paediat. Regist. Leeds Gen. Infirm.; Med. Regist. Chapel Allerton Hosp.

***GODFREY, Derek** 125 Drum Brae Drive, Edinburgh EH4 7SL Tel: 01313399467 Email: derekgodfrey@hotmail.com; 125 Drum Brae Drive, Edinburgh EH4 7SL Tel: 01313399467 Email: derekgodfrey@hotmail.com — MB ChB 1998 Dund.; MB ChB Dund 1998.

GODFREY, Gerald 8a The Avenue, King Lane, Leeds LS17 7BE Tel: 0113 267 5210 — MRCS Eng. LRCP Lond. 1941. (Leeds)

GODFREY, Gerald Flat 2, 33-36 Chester Square, London SW1W 9HT Tel: 020 7730 6050 Email: gg.jethro@virgin.net — MRCS Eng. LRCP Lond. 1951; MRCGP 1960. (Glas.) Socs: BMA; Wellington Soc.; Roy. Soc. Med.

GODFREY, Hugh William 1 Seafield Avenue, Wirral CH60 4SJ — MB ChB 1991 Liverp.

GODFREY, Hyman Eric West Point Medical Centre, 167/9 Slade Lane, Levenshulme, Manchester M19 2AF Tel: 0161 248 5100 5101 Fax: 0161 225 6258; 2 Depleach Road, Cheadle SK8 1DZ Tel: 0161 428 5868 Fax: 0161 428 1627 — MB ChB 1954 Manch.; FRCGP 1987, M 1965; DObst RCOG 1958. Police Surg. Manch.; Mem. Criminal Injuries Compensation Appeal Panel. Socs: Fell. Manch. Med. Soc.; Assn. Police Surg. Prev: Med. Off. HM Prison Styal.

GODFREY, Ian Blake 2 Montrose Avenue, Bristol BS6 6EQ — MB ChB 1994 Bristol.

GODFREY, Isabel Magdalen The Bear Garden, 3 Railway Terrace, Avenue Road, Brockenhurst SO42 7RU — MB ChB 1982 Aberd.

GODFREY, Ivan Chandra (retired) Floreal, Vicarage Lane, Barlaston, Stoke-on-Trent ST12 9AG — MB ChB 1941 Ed.

GODFREY, Jacqueline Lesley Ruth Priory Medical Group, Cornlands Road, Acomb, York YO24 3WX Tel: 01904 781423 Fax: 01904 784886 — MB BS 1983 Lond.

GODFREY, James Brendan Ayrshire Central Hospital, Irvine KA12 8SS — MB BCh BAO 1975 Dub.; MRCPI 1977. Cons. Geriat. Med. CrossHo. Hosp. Kilmarnock.

GODFREY, Joan Frances Woodlands Gairlochy, Spean Bridge PH34 4EQ Tel: 0139 782232 — LRCP LRCS 1949 Ed.; LRCP LRCS Ed. LRFPS Glas. 1949; MRCGP 1958. (Roy. Colls. Ed.) Sen. Med. Off (Child Health) Highland Health Bd. (Lochaber).

GODFREY, Jonathan Mark Green Lane Hospital, Devizes SN10 5DS Tel: 01380 731200 — BM 1987 Soton.; MMedSci Birm. 1994; MRCPsych 1992. Cons. Psychiat. Prev: Sen. Regist. Rotat. (Gen. & Old Age Psychiat.) N. Wales; Sen. Regist. (Child & Adolesc. Psychiat.) Devon; Regist. & SHO (Psychiat.) Birm. Train. Scheme.

GODFREY, Joseph John Breckfield Road North Surgery, 141 Breckfield Road North, Liverpool L5 4QU Tel: 0151 263 6534; 106 Druids Cross Road, Wooltan Hill, Liverpool L18 3HN Tel: 0151 737 1631 — MB BS 1971 Ceylon. (Colombo) Prev: Regist. (Paediat. Surg.) Alder Hey Childr. (Teach.) Hosp. Liverp.; Regist. (Gen. Surg.) Roy. Liverp. (Teach.) Hosp.

GODFREY, Keith Malcolm Department of Dermatology, Royal South Hants Hospital, Graham Road, Southampton SO14 0YG; Briar Cottage, Hazel Grove, Ashurst, Southampton SO40 7AJ — BM 1983 Soton.; BM (Hons.) Soton. 1983; MRCP (UK) 1985; FRCP (UK) 1999; PhD (soton) 1999. MRC Clin. Scientist Med. Research Counc. Environm. Epidemiol. Unit. Univ. of Soton.; Hon. Cons. Dermat. Roy. S. Hants. Hosp. Soton. Prev: Sen. Lect. (Dermat.) Soton. Univ.; MRC Train. Fell. MRC Env. Epidemiol. Unit Soton; Regist. (Dermat.) Roy. Berks. Hosp. Reading & St. Thos. Hosp. Lond.

GODFREY, Malcolm Paul Weston, CBE (retired) 17 Clifton Hill, St John's Wood, London NW8 0QE Tel: 020 7624 6335 Fax: 020 7328 9474 — MB BS (Univ. Medal) Lond. 1950; FRCP Lond. 1972, M 1955; MRCS Eng. LRCP Lond. 1950. Prev: Chairm. Pub. Health Laborat. Serv. Bd.

GODFREY, Martin 5-11 Theobolds Road, London WC1X 8SH Tel: 020 7413 3120; 90 Kensington Church Street, London W8 4BU Tel: 020 7792 4952 — MB ChB 1979 Birm.; MRCGP 1983. Managing Dir. EuroSci.s Communication. Socs: Roy. Soc. Med. (Pres. Sect. Gen. Pract.); Med. Jl.ists Assn.

GODFREY, Paul Stuart Andrew 2 Melita Road, Bristol BS6 5AZ — MB BS 1978 Newc.

GODFREY, Peter Frederick 72 York Road, Montpelier, Bristol BS6 5QF — MB ChB 1974 Bristol; MRCGP 1978; T(GP) 1991.

GODFREY, Philip d'Arcy Leighton 63 Shelford Road, Radcliffe on Trent, Nottingham NG12 1AJ Tel: 0115 910 3947 — BM BS 1977 Nottm. Managing Dir. Protos Ltd. Nottm. Prev: Research & Developm. Dir. Protos Ltd. Bristol; Software Designer Abies Informatics Lond.; GP Ilkeston.

GODFREY, Philip Walter (retired) 23 West Park Crescent, Roundhay, Leeds LS8 2HE Tel: 0113 266 1447 — MRCS Eng. LRCP Lond. 1931; DTM & H Eng. 1934.

GODFREY, Philippa Kaye Fryern and Millers Dale Partnership, Millers Dale Surgery, 9 Ormesby Drive, Chandlers Ford, Eastleigh SO53 1SH Tel: 023 8026 2488 Fax: 023 8025 5524 — BM 1980

Soton.; MRCGP 1985; DRCOG 1984; Cert. Family Plann. JCC 1983. GP.

GODFREY, Richard Charles Southampton General Hospital, Southampton SO16 6YD Tel: 02380 794626 Fax: 02380 701771; The Wardenry, Church Road, Farley, Salisbury SP5 1AH Tel: 01722 712231 Fax: 01722 712553 Email: rgodfrey78@hotmail.com — MB BChir Camb. 1966; MD Camb. 1974; FRCP Lond. 1981. (Univ. Coll. Hosp.) Cons. Phys. Soton. Gen. Hosp.; Internat. Consultancy (Med. Educat.). Prev: Prof. Med. Moi Univ., Kenya.

GODFREY, Ronald Grimmett Darentlea, High St., Eynsford, Dartford DA4 0AA Tel: 01322 863092 — MRCS Eng. LRCP Lond. 1949. (Lond. Hosp.)

GODFREY, Sonia Jane The Health Centre, Testwood Lane, Totton, Southampton SO40 3ZN Tel: 023 8086 5051 Fax: 023 8086 5050; 17 Jeffries Close, Rownhams, Southampton SO16 8DS — BM 1984 Soton.; BM Soton 1984; MRCGP 1988; DRCOG 1987; DCH RCP Lond. 1987; Cert. Family Plann. JCC 1987. Prev: Clin. Med. Off. (Community Child Health) Reading & Soton.; Trainee GP Lymington; SHO (Paediat., Geriat. & O & G) Soton. Gen. Hosp.

GODFREY-GLYNN, Patricia Michele Noelle Llanilar Health Centre, Llanilar, Aberystwyth SY23 4PA Tel: 01974 241556 Fax: 01974 241579 — MB BCh BAO 1983 NUI.

GODHANIA, Virambhai Rajabhai (retired) 9 Lime Tree Walk, Chorley Wood, Rickmansworth WD3 4BX Tel: 01923 770899 — MB BS 1968 Baroda.

GODKIN, Andrew James 18 Myrdle Court, Myrdle St., Whitechapel, London E1 1HP Tel: 020 7247 3659 — MB BChir 1989 Camb.; MA Camb. 1990, MB BChir 1989; MRCP (UK) 1991. Regist. (Gastroenterol. & Gen. Med.) Chelsea & W.m. Hosp. Lond.

GODLEE, Carolyn Jane Summertown Group Practice, 160 Banbury Road, Oxford OX2 7BS Tel: 01865 515552 Fax: 01865 311237; 40 Lonsdale Road, Oxford OX2 7EW Tel: 01865 510367 — MB BChir 1981 Camb.; BSc Lond. 1979; DRCOG 1984.

GODLEE, Fiona Nicolette BMJ, Tavistock Square, London WC1H 9JR Tel: 020 7383 6597 Fax: 020 7383 6418 Email: fionagodlee@compuserve.com; Sheephouse Farm, East Knoyle, Salisbury SP3 6BB Tel: 01747 830157 Fax: 01747 830023 — MB BChir 1985 Camb.; BSc Lond. 1983; MRCP (UK) 1988. (Cambridge) Asst. Edr. BMJ; Exec. Edr. Clin. Evidence '99. Prev: Harkness Fell.; Lect. Harvard Med. Sch.; Regist. (Gen. Med.) Whittington Hosp. Lond.

GODLEE, John Nicholas (retired) White Lodge, Rectory Lane, Angmering, Littlehampton BN16 4JU Tel: 01903 774212 — MA, MB Camb. 1955, BChir 1954; MRCS Eng. LRCP Lond. 1955; FRCR 1975; FFR 1960; DMRT Eng. 1958. Prev: Dir. Radiother. & Oncol. Dept. Univ. Coll. Hosp. Lond.

GODLEE, Julian Raymond Lister Maltings Surgery, 8 Victoria Street, St Albans AL1 3JB Tel: 01727 855500 Fax: 01727 845537; Ayres Barn, Ayres End Lane, Harpenden AL5 1AL Tel: 01582 764629 — MB BChir 1984 Camb.; BSc (Hons.) Lond. 1981; MRCGP 1989; DRCOG 1988. (Addenbrooke's Camb.) Socs: (Sec.) St. Albans Med. Soc.; Sec. St. Albans GP Forum; Exec. Comm. Mem. St. Albans Total Purchasing Project. Prev: SHO (O & G & Paediat.) Roy. Free. Hosp. Lond.; SHO (Psychiat.) Friern Hosp. Lond.

GODLEE, Rickman James Philip Wantage Health Centre, Church Street Practice, Wantage Health Centre, Wantage OX12 7AY Tel: 01235 770245 Fax: 01235 770727 Email: rickman.godlee@gp-k84033.nhs.uk; The Willows, Manor Road, Wantage OX12 8DW Tel: 01235 764619 — MB BS 1978 Lond.; MA Camb. 1975; MRCGP 1985; DRCOG 1983. Tutor (Primary Care) Oxf. Univ.

GODLEY, Clifford Craig Avondale Medical Practice, Strathaven Health Centre, The Ward, Strathaven ML10 6AS Tel: 01357 529595 Fax: 01357 529494; 7 Kibblestane Place, Strathaven ML10 6EL Tel: 01357 22325 Email: administrator@gp63739.law.lanark-hb.scot.nhs.uk — MB ChB 1977 Glas.; FRCP Glas. 1991; MRCP (UK) 1981; MRCGP 1983. Hosp. Pract. (Respirat. Med.) Strathclyde Hosp. Motherwell. Prev: Regist. (Gen. & Respirat. Med.) Glas. Roy. Infirm.

GODLEY, Heather Daphne Saint Vincent Medical Centre, 77 Thorne Road, Doncaster DN1 2ET — MB ChB 1978 Sheff.; MRCGP 1982.

GODRICH, John Edward Orchard House, 5 Little Orchard, Woodham, Addlestone KT15 3ED Tel: 01932 354713 Fax: 01932 354713 Email: godrich.email@virgin.net — MB BChir 1959 Camb.; MA Camb. 1959; MRCS Eng. LRCP Lond. 1958; DObst RCOG 1960. (Camb. & St. Bart.) Indep. Pract.; EMP for Benefits Agency. Socs: BMA; Woking Med. Soc. Prev: Ho. Surg. Profess. Surgic. Unit Qu. Eliz. Hosp. Birm.; Ho. Surg. (O & G) Brighton Gen. Hosp.; Ho. Phys. Radcliffe Infirm. Oxf.

GODRIDGE, Anne Carol Tieve Tara, Rear of Park Dale, Airedale, Castleford WF10 2QT Tel: 01977 552360 Fax: 01977 603470; 6 Ridgedale Mount, Pontefract WF8 1SB Tel: 01977 793056 — MB ChB 1987 Manch. Prev: Trainee GP Pontefract.

GODRIDGE, Helen 53 Borough Street, Castle Donington, Derby DE74 2LB Tel: 01332 811480; 229 Derby Road, Long Eaton, Nottingham NG10 4BS Tel: 0115 973 3518 — BM BS 1988 Nottm.; BMedSci Nottm. 1986; MRCGP 1993. (Nottm.) GP; Clin. Asst. (Diabetes); Clin. Asst. (Geriat. Rehabil.). Socs: BMA. Prev: SHO (A & E) Stafford Dist. Gen. Hosp.; SHO (Paediat.) Derbysh. Childr. Hosp.; SHO (O & G) Derby City Hosp.

GODSIFF, Leisha Sarah Jeremiah's Cottage, High St., Little Abington, Cambridge CB1 6BG — MB BS 1989 Lond.

GODSIFF, Mr Steven Paul Orthopaedic Department, Leicester General Hospital, Gwendolen Road, Leicester LE5 4PW Tel: 0116 249 0490 Fax: 01162 588111 — MB BS 1984 Lond.; FRCS (Orth.) 1995; FRCS Eng. 1988. (King's Coll. Hosp. Lond.) Cons. Orthop. Surg. Leicester Gen. Hosp. & Roy. Infirm. Leicester. Socs: BMA; BOA. Prev: Sen. Regist. Roy. Nat. Orthop. Hosp. Stanmore, Norf. & Norwich Hosp. & Gt. Ormond St. Hosp. Childr. Lond.

GODSLAND, Judith 12 Blewitt Court, Oxford Road, Littlemore, Oxford OX4 4PB — MRCS Eng. LRCP Lond. 1980; BSc Lond. 1975, MB BS 1981; MRCPsych 1988. (Guy's) Analytic Psychotherapist.

GODSMARK, Christopher James Bearsted Medical Practice, Yeoman Lane, Bearsted, Maidstone ME14 4DS Tel: 01622 737326 Fax: 01622 730745 Email: yeomanla@btinternet.com — BM 1994 Soton. (Soton.) GP Princip. Bearsted Med. Pract. Socs: BMA; MDU. Prev: GP Locum (MFDDOC); GP Regist., Woodlands Med. Centre, Paddock Wood; SHO (c/o the elderley), Pembury Hosp.

GODWARD, Sally 81B Ashburnham Road, Kensal Rise, London NW10 5SE — MB BS 1991 Lond.

GODWIN, Dawn Sheena Bath Lodge Practice, Bitterne Health Centre, Commercial Street, Bitterne, Southampton SO18 6BT Tel: 023 8044 2111 Fax: 023 8042 1316; 25 Bilberry Close, Locks Heath, Southampton SO31 6XX — BM Soton. 1982; DRCOG 1988; DCH RCP Lond. 1987.

GODWIN, Eric George (retired) Upperton, Petworth GU28 9BE Tel: 01798 343073 — MRCS Eng. LRCP Lond. 1937; FFA RCS Eng. 1954; DA Eng. 1945. Prev: Cons. (Anaesth.) Croydon AHA.

GODWIN, John Christopher Queens Park Surgery, 146 Drove Road, Swindon SN1 3AG — MB BS 1980 Lond.; MRCGP 1985; DRCOG 1983. (Roy. Free) Prev: Trainee GP Abergavenny.

GODWIN, Lucy Charlotte Conquest, Hillworth Road, Devizes SN10 5ET — MB BS 1993 Lond.

GODWIN, Raymond John West Suffolk Hospital, Hardwick Lane, Bury St Edmunds IP33 2QZ Tel: 01284 713000; Fornham End, Sheepwash Bridge, Fornham All Saints, Bury St Edmunds IP28 6JJ Tel: 01284 769772 — MB BChir 1972 Camb.; BChir 1971; MA Camb. 1972; FRCP Lond. 1995; MRCP (UK) 1973; FRCR 1977; DMRD Eng. 1975. (Camb. & King's Coll. Hosp.) Cons. Radiol. W. Sussex Hosp. Bury St. Edmunds; Recognised Clin. Teach. Fac. Clin. Med. Camb. Univ. Sch. Clin. Med.; Grad. Med. Course supervisor Univ. Camb.; Fell. Hughes Hall Camb. Prev: Sen. Regist. (Radiol.) Addenbrooke's Hosp. Camb.; Assoc. Post Grad. Dean Univ. Camb.

GODWIN, Stanley Thomas (retired) 30 Lillington Road, Leamington Spa CV32 5YY Tel: 01926 424658 — MB BS 1958 Lond.; MRCGP 1972; DObst RCOG 1961. Prev: Hosp. Pract. (Anaesth.) Warwick Hosp.

GODWIN, Yvette Nottingham City Hospital, Department of Plastic Surgery, Hucknall Road, Nottingham NG5 1PB — MB BChir 1987 Camb.; FRCS Eng. 1991. RMO N.land Base Hosp. Whangarei, NZ.; Specialist Regist. Plastic Surg.

GODWIN-AUSTEN, Richard Bertram Papplewick Hall, Nottingham NG15 8FE Tel: 0115 963 3491 Fax: 0115 964 2767 — MD 1968 Lond.; MB BS 1959; FRCP Lond. 1976, M 1963. (St. Thos.) Cons. neUrol. (Emerit.) Nottm. & Derby Hosp.s; Sec.Treas.Gen.World.Fed.Nerology. Socs: Fell. Roy. Soc. Med.; Assn. Brit. Neurol.; mem.Amer..Acad.Neurol. Prev:

Univ.Hosp.Nottm.CityHosp. & Pilgrim Hosp. Boston.; Pres. Assn. Brit. Neurol.; Regist. Middlx. Hosp. Lond.

GOEBELLS, Ponnusamy 63 Burniston Road, Hull HU5 4JX — MB BS 1975 Madras.

GOEDKOOP, Lina Cornelia Harcourt Farm, Zeals Row, Zeals, Warminster BA12 6PE — Artsexamen 1985 Free U Amsterdam; Artsexamen Free Univ Amsterdam 1985. Clin. Asst. Adult Psychiat. Frome Comalomity Ment. Health Team (p/t).

GOEL, Ajay 56 Tryfan Close, Ilford IG4 5JY — MB BS 1991 Lond.

GOEL, Ambar 3 Roydscliffe Road, Bradford BD9 5PT — MB BS 1994 Newc.

GOEL, G S Roselawn Surgery, Roselawn, 149 Malden Road, New Malden KT3 6AA Tel: 020 8949 0555 Fax: 020 8395 5666.

GOEL, Mr Ishwar Prasad c/o Drive P.D. Gupta, 4 Hazel Road, Dudley DY1 3EW — MB BS 1974 Delhi; MS (Surg.) Delhi 1978, MB BS 1974; FRCS Ed. 1982.

GOEL, Krishna Murari Royal Hospital for Sick Children, Yorkhill, Glasgow G3 8SJ Tel: 0141 201 0000; Eredine House, Eredine, Dalmally PA33 1BP Tel: 01866 844207 — MB BS 1960 Lucknow; BSc Lucknow 1955, MD 1964; FRCP Lond. 1983; FRCP Glas. 1978; FRCP Ed. 1980, M 1970; DCH Lucknow 1962. (G.S.V.M. Med. Coll. Kanpur) Cons. Paediat. Roy. Hosp. Sick Childr. Glas.; Hon. Clin. Sen. Lect. Univ. Glas. Socs: Scott. Paediat. Soc. & Brit. Paediat. Assn.; Scott. Soc. Phys. Prev: Sen. Regist. & Regist. (Med. Paediat.) Roy. Hosp. Sick Childr. Glas.; SHO W.. Infirm. Glas.

GOEL, Kusum Lata 11 Crichton Road, Carshalton Beeches, Carshalton SM5 3LS Tel: 020 8643 3030 Fax: 020 8643 1013; 3 Peaks Hill, Purley CR8 3JG Tel: 020 8668 2664 Fax: 020 8643 1013 — MB BS 1974 Panjab; MB BS Panjab (India) 1974; DRCOG 1981. (Med. Coll. Rohtak) Prev: Ho. Off. Vict. Zannana Hosp. Delhi & Med. Coll. Rohtak.

GOEL, M Roselawn Surgery, Roselawn, 149 Malden Road, New Malden KT3 6AA Tel: 020 8949 0555 Fax: 020 8395 5666.

GOEL, Pramod Kumar The Surgery, Sough Hall Avenue, Thorpe Hesley, Rotherham S61 2QP Tel: 0114 257 8787 Fax: 0114 245 0412; Laithe Cottage, Hoober, Rotherham S62 7SA Tel: 0114 252 2665 — MB BS 1966 Lucknow. (King Geo. Med. Coll.)

GOEL, Raj Kumar Goel, 11 Crichton Road, Carshalton SM5 3LS Tel: 020 8643 3030/9551 Fax: 020 8643 1013; 3 Peaks Hill, Purley CR8 3JG Tel: 020 8668 2664 — MB BS 1968 Rajasthan; DPM Eng. 1977; DTCD Delhi 1972. (SMS Med. Coll. Jaipur) Prev: Regist. (Psychiat.) FarnBoro. Hosp.; Regist. (Psychiat.) Kingston Hosp.; SHO Willingdon Hosp. Delhi.

GOEL, Rajendra Kumar Bassetlaw District General Hospital, Worksop S81 0BD Tel: 01909 500990; 7 Alpine Court, Worksop S80 3DY Tel: 01909 472613 Fax: 01909 472613 — MB BS 1971 Lucknow; FRCR 1980; DMRD Eng. 1978; DMRD Delhi 1975. (King Geo. Med. Coll. Lucknow) Cons Radiol. Doncaster & Bassetlaw NHS Trust Worksop Notts. Socs: Roy. Austral. Coll. Radiol.; Radiol. Soc. N. Amer.; Eur. Assn. Radiol. Prev: Cons. Radiol. Dubai Hosp. UAE.; Cons. Radiol. Solihull Gen. Hosp., Holymoor Hosp. N.field Birm. & Solihull Pk.way Hosp.; Rotat. Sen. Regist. (Radiol.) Wexham Pk. Hosp. Slough, King Edwd. VII Hosp. Windsor & N.wick Pk. Hosp. & Clin. Research Centre Harrow.

GOEL, Mr Rajinder Parkash 22 Lyndhurst Road, Stretford, Manchester M32 8DY — MB ChB 1987 Dundee; FRCS Ed. 1991. Career Regist. (Orthop.) NW Region. Prev: SHO Rotat. (Surg.) Salford HA; SHO (Orthop.) Roy. Preston Hosp.; Demonst. (Anat.) & Cas. Off. Univ. Dundee.

GOEL, Rajiv 202 Redbridge Lane E., Ilford IG4 5BH — MB BS 1993 Lond.; BSc (Hons.) Lond. 1990; DRCOG 1996; DFFP 1996; MRCGP 1998. (St. Bart.) GP.

GOEL, Mr Ram Niwas Kingston Hospital, Galsworthy Road, Kingston upon Thames KT2 7QB Tel: 020 8546 7711 Ext: 2991 Fax: 020 8934 3274 — MB BS Delhi 1966; FRCS Glas. 1977; FRCS Ed. 1977; FFAEM 1996. (Maulana Azad Med. Coll.) Cons. A & E Med. Kingston Hosp. Socs: Fac. Accid. & Emerg. Med; Brit. Assn. Accid. & Emerg. Med.; BMA.

GOEL, Rashmi Plumstead Health Centre, Tewson Road, Plumstead, London SE18 Tel: 020 8854 8027 Fax: 020 8317 3030; Oakwood, Priory Close, Chislehurst BR7 5LB Tel: 020 8468 7421 — MB BS 1976 Kanpur; LRCP LRCS Ed. LRCPS Glas. 1983; MRCOG 1993.

GOEL, Mr Vijai Kumar 2 Netherstone Grove, Four Oaks, Sutton Coldfield B74 4DT — MB BS 1964 Agra; FRCSI 1978.

GOEL, Wishav Parkash 9 Coneymead, Stalybridge SK15 1HF — MB BS 1982 Lond. (Westm.) SHO (A & E) Roy. Liverp. Hosp.; SHO (Gen. Med.) Tameside Gen. Hosp. Rotat. Ashton-u-Lyne. Prev: Ho. Off. (Gen. Surg.) W. Suff. Hosp. Bury St. Edmunds; Ho. Off. (Gen. Med.) Manor Hosp. Walsall.

GOEL, Y K Riverside Centre for Health, Park Street, Liverpool L8 6QP Tel: 0151 706 8317.

GOENKA, Gopal Edge Hill Health Centre, Crosfield Road, Liverpool L7 5QL Tel: 0151 260 2777 — MB BS 1972 Bihar. (Darbhanga Med. Coll. Laheriasarai) Prev: Civil Asst. (Surg.) Chak Sikander Health Sub-Center Samastipur, India.

GOENKA, Nirupam Hemangan, New Mill Stile, Liverpool L25 6JY — MB ChB 1994 Liverp. SHO Rotat. (Med.) Wirral Hosps. Trust Merseyside. Prev: Ho. Off. (Gen. Med. & Surg.) Roy. Liverp. Univ. Hosp.

GOEPEL, John Robert Department of Histopathology, Royal Hallamshire Hospital, Glossop Road, Sheffield S10 2SF Tel: 0114 271 2728 Fax: 0114 271 2200 — MB ChB 1972 Sheff.; FRCPath 1991, M 1979. Cons. Histopath. Centr. Sheff. Univ. Hosp. Sheff. Socs: Path. Soc.; Internat. Acad. Path.; Assn. Clin. Path. Prev: Hon. Cons. Path. W.on Pk. Hosp. Roy. Hallamsh. Hosp. Sheff.; Lect. (Path.) Sheff. Univ.; Sen. Lect. (Path.) Sheff. Univ.

GOETZ, Sarah Carroll 62 New Road, Harmer Green, Welwyn AL6 0AN Tel: 0143 871 4737 — MB BS 1988 Lond. Ho. Off. (Cas.) Gold Coast Hosp. Qu.sland, Australia. Prev: Ho. Phys. Heather Wood Hosp.; Ho. Surg. Homerton Hosp. Lond.

GOETZEE, Arthur Edouard (retired) 10 Honeyhole, Blackburn BB2 3BQ Tel: 01254 667121 Email: arthurgoetzee@aol.com — MB ChB 1952 Liverpool; MD Liverp. 1960, MChOrth 1963, MB ChB 1952; FRCS Ed. 1962. Prev: Med. Off. Benefits Agency War Pens. Norcross Blackpool.

GOFF, David George X-Ray Department, Raigmore Hospital, Inverness — MB ChB 1977 Dundee; FRCR 1983. Cons. Radiol. Raigmore Hosp. Inverness. Prev: Cons. Radiol. Ninewells Hosp. Dundee.

GOFF, David Kenston Hazard Grange, North Road, Hetton-Le-Hole, Houghton-le-Spring DH5 9JY Tel: 0191 262671 — MB BS 1969 Newc.; FRCPath 1988, M 1977. (Newc.) Cons. (Haemat.) Sunderland AHA. Socs: Assn. Clin. Paths. & Brit. Soc. Haemat. Prev: Sen. Specialist (Haemat.) RAF Med. Br.

GOFFE, Timothy Rhys Powell 46 Heath Crescent, Free School Lane, Halifax HX1 2PW Tel: 01422 368103 Fax: 01422 250011 Email: hm.goffe@which.net; Ferodo, Chapel-en-le-Frith, High Peak SK23 0JP Tel: 01298 812520 — MB BS 1970 Lond.; DObst RCOG 1972. (Lond. Hosp.) Occupat.Phys.; Co. Med. Adviser Ferodo Federal -Mogul; Transco Med. Advis.Yorks & E. Midl.s. Prev: GP Telford.; comp.Med.Advis. T&N Plc.

GOFFIN, Paul Stuart 81 Curzon Avenue, Birstall, Leicester LE4 4AG — MB ChB 1980 Leic.; MRCGP 1987; DRCOG 1986; DA (UK) 1985; Cert Av. Med. 1985.

GOFFIN, Richard Bligh (retired) 144 Falcondale Road, Westbury-on-Trym, Bristol BS9 3JF Tel: 0117 950 0033 Email: dick-goffin@btinternet.com — MB ChB 1959 Bristol; DObst RCOG 1962. Prev: Assoc. Specialist Nat. Blood Serv. Bristol.

GOFFMAN, Harold Louis 19 Druids Park, Liverpool L18 3LJ Tel: 0151 722 8544 — MB ChB 1948 Liverp. (Liverp.) Prev: Res. Surg. Off. Clatterbridge Gen. Hosp. Bebington; Capt. RAMC 1949-51; on Med. Staff Sir Alfred Jones Memor. Hosp. Liverp.

GOGAN, Michael Patrick 80A Sewell Road, Lincoln LN2 5LY — LMSSA 1966 Lond.

GOGBASHIAN, Charles Andrew Chells Way Surgery, 265 Chells Way, Stevenage SG2 0HN Tel: 01438 313001 Fax: 01438 362322; 30 Chatsworth Road, London W5 3DB Tel: 020 8998 1816 — MB BS 1972 Lond.; BSc Lond. 1969, MB BS 1972. (Middlx.)

GOGGIN, Michael James 32 Dover Street, Canterbury CT1 3HQ Tel: 01227 454335 Fax: 01227 454335 Email: mikegoggin@tinyworld.co.uk — MB BS 1958 Lond.; FRCP Lond. 1983; MRCP (UK) 1968; MRCS Eng. LRCP Lond. 1958. (St. Mary's) Indep. Cons. Phys. (Nephrol.) / Health Screening, Chaucer Hosp. Canterbury; Hon. Sen. Research Fell. Kent Inst. Med. & Health Scis. Univ. Kent, Canterbury; Mem. Independ Trib.Serv.; Mem. Multicentre Research Ethics Centre (S. Thames Region). Socs: Renal Assn. Prev: Cons. Nephrol. Kent & Canterbury Hosp.; Lect.

(Nephrol.) Inst. Urol. Lond.; Regist. (Cardiol. & Gen. Med.) Harefield Hosp.

GOGNA, Charan Jeev Bridge St Surgery, 3 Bridge St., Otley LS21 1BQ Tel: 01943 464001 Fax: 01943 461465; 23 Hillside, Follifoot, Harrogate HG3 1EF Tel: 01423 879932 — MB ChB 1989 Leeds; MRCGP 1995. (Leeds)

GOGNA, Jill Denise 199 Bannerdale Road, Sheffield S11 9FB — MB BS 1990 Newc.; MRCGP 1994.

GOGNA, Sabodh Chander 2 Wrekin Drive, Tettenhall, Wolverhampton WV6 8UJ — MB BS 1990 Newc.

GOGOI, Mr Nirjan Kumar 21 Tabard Road, Eggborough, Goole DN14 0UP — FRCSI 1989.

GOH, Beng Tin Ambrose King Centre, The Royal London Hospital, Whitechapel, London E1 1BB Tel: 020 7377 7308 Fax: 020 7377 7648 Email: ambrose.king@dial.pipex.com; 44 Upwood Road, London SE12 8AN — MB BS 1977 Singapore; FRCPI 1994; FRCP Lond. 1993; MRCP (UK) 1980; MRCPI 1980; Dip. Ven. Soc. Apoth. Lond. 1981; Dip. Dermat. Lond 1980. (University of Singapore) Cons. Venerol. Lond. Hosp. & Moorfields Eye Hosp. Lond.; Cons. Genitourin. Phys., Barts & the Lond. NHS Trust & Moorfields Eye Hosp. NHS Trust Lond. Socs: N. Thames Rep. Assn. for Genitourin. Med.; Med. Soc. Study VD. Prev: Sen. Regist. (Venereol.) Roy. Lond. Hosp. & Moorfields Eye Hosp. Lond.; Regist. (Venereol.) Kings Coll. Hosp. Lond.

GOH, David Kok Yew 47 Silverburn Drive, Oakwood, Derby DE21 2JH — BM BS 1994 Nottm.

GOH, Day Eel Edenhall Hospital, Pinkieburn, Musselburgh EH21 7TZ — MB ChB 1983 Ed.; MRCP (UK) (Paediat.) 1986; MD Ed. 1996. (University of Edinburgh) Cons. Community Paediat. Edenholt Hosp. Musselburgh.

GOH, Gaik Cheng Department of Anaesthetics, Barnsley District General Hospital, Gawber Road, Barnsley S75 2EP; 4 Hallam Grange Road, Fulwood, Sheffield S10 4BJ — MB ChB 1984 Glas.; MB ChB Glas. l984; DA (UK) 1986. Clin. Asst. Anaesth. Barnsley Dist. Gen. Hosp.

GOH, Geraldine Tsui Yen 267 Clarendon Park Road, Leicester LE2 3AQ — MB ChB 1998 Leic.; MB ChB Leic 1998.

GOH, Grace Joo Min Department of Radiology, Kettering General Hospital, Rothwell Road, Kettering NN16 8UZ Tel: 01536 492000; 5 Cross Lane, Aldwincle, Kettering NN14 3EG — MB ChB 1985 Liverp.; MRCP (UK) 1989; FRCR 1994; DMRD Liverp. 1991. (Univ. Liverp.)

GOH, Kah Lay Department of Vascular Medicine, Postgraduate Medical School, Barrade Road, Exeter EX2 5AX Tel: 01392 403087 Fax: 01392 403027 Email: k.l.goh@exeter.ac.uk; 7 Hales Close, Exwick, Exeter EX4 2NX Email: kl.goh@virgin.net — MB ChB 1992 Leic.; MRCP (UK) 1996. (University of Leicester) Research Fell. (Diabetes & Endocrinol.) Exeter.

GOH, Kai Kee 255 Loxley Road, Sheffield S6 4TG — MB ChB 1997 Sheff.

GOH, Suan-Gaik Julia Lifespan Healthcare NHS Trust, Management Office, Ida Darwin, Fulbourn, Cambridge CB1 5EE Tel: 01223 884268 Fax: 01223 884004 Email: suan.goh@l:fespan-tr.anglox.nhs.uk; The Conifers, Hayter Close, West Wratting, Cambridge CB1 5LY — MB BS 1970 Newc.; MFPHM RCP (UK) 1990; FFPHM 2000. Cons. Pub. Health Med. Lifespan Health Care NHS Trust, Camb.& Cabridgeshire Health Auth.

GOH, Vicky Joo-Lin 54 Williamson Way, Rickmansworth WD3 8GL — MB BChir 1994 Camb.

GOH, Mr Yew-Heng Hugh Department of Surgery, North Devon District Hospital, Raleigh Park, Barnstaple EX31 4JB Tel: 01271 322577 — MB BS 1994 Monash; MB BS (Honours) 1994; AFRCS Ed Roy College Surgs Ed 1998; FRCS 1999. SHO (Gen. Surg.), NDDH, Barnstable. Prev: SHO (Gen. Surg.), E. Glam. Hosp., Pontypridd; SHO (Neurosurg.), Qu. Eliz. Hosp., Birm.; SHO (Orthop.) S.end Hosp. 1996.

GOH HUAT SENG, Mr Martin 436 Edinburgh Road, Glasgow G33 2PW — MB BS 1988 Singapore; FRCS Ed. 1993; FRCS Glas. 1993.

GOHEIR, Mr Ali Atif 25 Shore Court, Shore Lane, Sheffield S10 3BW — MB BS 1984 Punjab; FRCSI 1991.

GOHIL, Jayeschandra 243A Prince Regent Lane, London E13 8SD — MB BS 1992 Lond.

GOHIL, Kishor Bhimji New Ford Health Centre, 2 Baden Road, Smallthorne, Stoke-on-Trent ST6 1SA Tel: 01782 834288 — MB BChir 1983 Camb.; MA Camb. 1983; LMSSA Lond.1983; MRCGP 1987; DRCOG 1981. SHO (ENT) Ipswich Hosp. Prev: SHO (O & G) Ipswich Hosp.; SHO (Geriat. & Rhuem.) Mid. Glam. HA; Ho. Surg. Ipswich Hosp.

GOHIL, Nathalal Mepa (Surgery) 113 Church La, Stechford, Birmingham B33 9EJ Tel: 0121 783 2861; 105 Brockhurst Road, Hodge Hill, Birmingham B36 8JE Tel: 0121 783 4699 — MB BS 1974 Saurashtra. (M.P. Shah Med. Coll. Jamnagar) Prev: SHO (Anaesth.) Bolton Roy. Infirm.

GOHIL, Satyen Rajendrasinh 50 Green Lane, Harrogate HG2 9LP — MB BS 1998 Lond.; MB BS Lond 1998.

GOHIL, Suresh 68 Balsall Heath Road ., Edgbaston, Birmingham B5 7NG Tel: 0121 440 1878 — MB ChB 1992 Dundee.

GOHIL, Vinod Natha Lila 1 Owen Close, Leicester LE4 7TT — MB ChB 1967 Liverp.

GÖHMANN, Heinz-Dieter Queen Elizabeth II Hospital, Welwyn Garden City AL7 4HQ; Sonnenweg 3, 83346 Bergen, Germany, Germany — State Exam Med 1982 Heidelberg.

GOING, James Jensen Department of Pathology, Glasgow Royal Infirmary, 84 Castle St., Glasgow G4 0SF Email: going@udcf.gla.ac.uk — MB ChB 1980 Ed.; FRCPath 1998; MRCPath 1990; PhD Ed. 1989; MRCP (UK) 1983; BSc (Hons. Path) 1977. Sen. Lect. (Path.) Glas. Univ.; Hon. Cons. Path. N. Glas., Univ. Hosp. Prev: Sen. Regist. (Path.) Glas. Roy. Infirm.; MRC Train. Fell. Path. Dept. Univ. Edin.

GOING, Sheila Margaret 15 Broomley Drive, Giffnock, Glasgow G46 6PD — MB ChB 1977 Ed.; BSc Ed. 1974, MB ChB 1977; MRCP (UK) 1980. (Ed.) Clin. Asst. (Dermat.) Glas. Roy. Infirm. Prev: Clin. Asst. (Dermat.) Roy. Infirm. Edin.; Regist. (Dermat.) Roy. Infirm. Edin.; Regist. (Gen. Med.) Vict. Hosp. Kirkcaldy.

GOK, Muhammed Asim Rowan House, Doctors Residence, Royal Liverpool University Hospital, Prescot St., Liverpool L7 8XP — MB ChB 1991 Manch.

GOKA, Agbe Koku John 41 Ethelbert Road, Canterbury CT1 3NF — MB ChB 1976 Ghana; MRCP (UK) 1982.

GOKAL, Ramanlal Department Renal Medicine, Manchester Royal Infirmary, Manchester M13 9WL Tel: 0161 276 1234 Fax: 0161 276 8022 Email: rgokal@renal.cmht.nwest.nhs.uk — MD Birm. 1980, MB ChB 1970; FRCP Lond. 1987. Cons. Nephrol. Phys. Manch. Roy. Infirm. Socs: Pres. Internat. Soc. Peritoneal Dialysis 1998-2001. Prev: Lect. (Med.) Univ. Newc.; MRC Clin. Research Fell. & Hon. Sen. Regist. Nuffield Dept. Clin. Med.Radcliffe Infirm. Oxf.

GOKHALE, Jay Andrew 6 Markham Croft, Rawdon, Leeds LS19 6NR Tel: 0113 250 0893 — MB ChB 1992 Leeds; BSc (Hons.) Sheff. 1983; FRCS (Eng.) 1997. Specialist Regist. (Gen Surg), Yorks. Deanery, Hull Roy. Infirm. Socs: Surg. Research Soc.; BMA. Prev: Research Fell., Ho. Off. (Surg.) & Clin. Asst. (A & E) St. Jas. Univ. Hosp. Leeds; SHO Postgrad Rotat. (Surg.) St. Jas. Univ. Hosp. Leeds; Specialist Regist. (Gen. Surg.) ScarBoro. Hosp.

GOKHALE, Nandini Suhas 41 Wharfdale Road, Long Eaton, Nottingham NG10 3HG — MB BS 1974 Bombay; LRCP LRCS Ed. LRCPS Glas. 1988.

GOKHALE, Ravindra Occupational Health, Arrowe Park Hospital, Arrowe Park Road, Wirral CH49 5PE Tel: 0151 604 7175 Fax: 0151 604 7338 Email: ravindragokhale@yahoo.com; 2nd Floor GUM, Arrowe Park Hospital, Wirral CH49 5PE Tel: 0151 604 7175 Fax: 0151 604 7338 — MBBS 1983; Dip Ven 2001 (Distinction) University of Liverpool; Dip Occ Med 1991 University of Sydney. Staff Phys. in GU/HIV Med., Arrowe Pk. Hosp. Socs: Med. Soc. for Study of Venereal Dis.s; Soc. of Occupat.al Med.; Indian Assn. of Dermatol.s, Venereologists & Leprologists. Prev: Specialist Regist. in Occupat.al Med., Manch.; Specialist Regist. in Genito - Urin. Med. Stoke-on-Trent; Sen. Ho. Off., Med. Rotat. Castle Hill Hosp. Hull.

GOKHALE, Shakuntala Nagesh 2 Coleridge Road, London N12 8DE — MB BS 1963 Nagpur; MS (Ophth.) Bombay 1966, DOMS 1964. (Med. Coll. Nagpur) Socs: BMA. Prev: Regist. & Tutor Ophth. Nair Hosp. Bombay; Regist. (Ophth.) Gen. Hosp. S.end-on-Sea & Chelmsford & Essex; Hosp.

GOKHALE, Suhas Laxman The Surgery, 41 Wharfedale Road, Long Eaton, Nottingham NG10 3HG Tel: 0115 946 2690 Fax: 0115 946 2690 Email: suhas.gokhale@gp-c81642.nhs.uk; 1 Heyes Grove,

Rainford, St Helens, St Helens WA11 8BW Tel: 0115 925502, 01744 889021 — MB BS 1974 Bombay.
GOKHALE, Vasudeo Laxmanrao Helsby House, 120 Biddulph Road, Congleton CW12 3LY Tel: 01260 273469 — MRCS Eng. LRCP Lond. 1960; DO Eng. 1957. (Nagpur Med. Coll.) Ophth. (Community Health) N. Staffs. HA. Prev: Asst. Ophth. Crewe Memor Hosp.; Ho. Surg. Roy. Infirm. Leicester; Regist. Roy. Eye & Ear Hosp. Bradford.
GOKUL, Mr Krishnan House No. 2, Southport District Hospital, Townlane Kew, Southport PR8 6PN Tel: 01704 547471; c/o Drive S. G. Subbuswamy, 11 Scrub Rise, Billericay CM12 9PG Tel: 0127 76 52094 — MB BS 1985 Madras; FRCS Ed. 1989. (Stanley Medical School Madras) Staff Specialist (Surg.) S.port Dist. Hosp. Socs: BMA; Med. Protec. Soc.; NW Surg. Soc. Prev: Regist. (Surg.) Roy. Liverp., Macclesfield & Birm. Childr. Hosps. & Clatterbridge Hosp.
GOL, Berta (retired) 35 Middle Lane, Nether Whitacre, Coleshill, Birmingham B46 2HX — MD Prague 1938. Prev: GP Kingsbury Health Centre.
GOLARA, Moneli 51 Eversley Park Road, London N21 1NR Email: m.gorara@virgin.net — MB BS 1991 Lond.; MRCOG 1997.
GOLCHIN, Kambiz 24 Willowbank, Craigavon Area Hospital, Lurgan Road, Portadown, Craigavon BT63 5QQ; 65 Lockview Road, Stranmillis, Belfast BT9 5FJ — MB BCh BAO 1994 NUI; LRCPSI 1994.
GOLD, Aaron Parkside Family Practice, Green Road Surgery, 224 Wokingham Road, Reading RG6 1JT Tel: 0118 966 3366 Fax: 0118 926 3269 — MB BS 1976 Sydney; MB BS 1976 Sydney.
GOLD, Ann Elizabeth Aberdeen Royal Infirmary, Ward 27/28, Forrester Hill, Aberdeen AB25 2ZN Email: ann.gold@arh.grampian.scot.nhs.uk — MB ChB 1988 Ed.; FRCP (UK) 2001; MB ChB (Hons.) Ed. 1988; BSc (Hons.) Ed. 1985, MD (Distinc.) 1994; MRCP (UK) 1991. (Univ. Ed.) p/t Cons. in Diabetes & Gen. Med. Socs: Collegiate Mem. RCP Edin.; Eur. Assn. Study Diabetes.; Diabetes UK. Prev: Sen. Regist. (Diabetes & Endocrinol.) Roy. Vict. Infirm,. Newc.; Research & Career Regist. (Diabetes) Roy. Infirm. Edin.; SHO Rotat. (Med.) Edin.
GOLD, Charles (retired) 5 Belleisle Place, Kilmarnock KA1 4UD Tel: 01563 543874 — MB ChB 1950 Glas.; MRCGP 1952; DObst RCOG 1952. Prev: Ho. Phys. Profess. Unit Roy. Infirm. Glas.
GOLD, Colin James Bartongate Surgery, 115 Barton Street, Gloucester GL1 4HR Tel: 01452 422944 Fax: 01452 387871; 27 Alexandra Road, Gloucester GL1 3DR Tel: 01452 415205 — MB BS 1977 Lond.; MRCP (UK) 1981. (Middlx. Hosp. Univ. Lond.)
GOLD, Mr Darren Marc 58 Argent Street, Grays RM17 6PG — MB BS 1989 Lond.; FRCS Eng. 1993. Regist. (Surg.) Guy's Hosp. Lond. Socs: Assn. Surg. Train. (SE Thames Rep.).
GOLD, David Victor Rowley Regis Hospital, Moor Lane, Rowley Regis B65 8DA Tel: 0121 607 3513; 97 Gravelly Hill N., Erdington, Birmingham B23 6BJ Tel: 0121 350 4006 — MB ChB 1989 Birm. (Univ. Birm.) Staff Psychiat. (Psychiat. of Old Age) Rowley Regis Hosp. W. Midl. Prev: Regist. Rotat. (Psychiat.) Solihull HA Train. Scheme; SHO (Psychiat.) All St.s Hosp. Birm.; SHO (A & E) Selly Oak Hosp. Birm.
GOLD, Deborah Blanche 80 Wildwood Road, Hampstead Garden Suburb, London NW11 6UJ — MB BS 1971 Lond.; MRCP (U.K.) 1973.
GOLD, Ellis Neville (retired) 80 Childwall Park Avenue, Liverpool L16 0JQ Tel: 0151 722 6577 Email: elson@waitrose.com — MB BCh; BSc (Hons.) Manch. 1948; MRCGP 1968. Prev: GP Liverp.
GOLD, Herbert John Bruntsfield Health Centre, 11 Forbes Road, Edinburgh EH10 4EY — MB ChB 1961 Ed.; DObst RCOG 1964.
GOLD, Iain Lockhart Academy Street Surgery, 2 Academy Street, Hurlford, Kilmarnock KA1 5BU Tel: 01563 525314 Fax: 01563 573561; 15 Mount Avenue, Kilmarnock KA1 1UF — MB ChB 1973 Glas.; MRCGP 1978; DObst RCOG 1975. Prev: Sen. Med. Off. RAF Med. Br.; SHO (O & G) Paisley Matern. Hosp.; Ho. Off. (Paediat. Med.) Roy. Hosp. Sick Childr. Glas.
GOLD, Ian David Red House Surgery, 124 Watling Street, Radlett WD7 7JQ Tel: 01923 855606 Fax: 01923 853577; Pathways, Loom Lane, Radlett WD7 8NZ Tel: 01923 857702 Fax: 01923 859363 Email: info@confplus.demon.co.uk — MB BChir 1980 Camb.; MA Camb. 1980; MRCP (UK) 1982; MRCGP (Distinc.) 1984; DCH RCP Lond. 1983; DRCOG 1983. (Cambridge and Guy's Hospital) GP Tutor Roy. Free Hosp. Lond. Prev: SHO (Paediat.) Edgware Gen. Hosp.; SHO (Med.) Centr. Middlx. Hosp. Lond.; SHO (Cardiol. & Respirat. Med.) Guy's Hosp. Lond.
GOLD, Mr James Munro (retired) Great Seaside Farm, Branscombe, Seaton EX12 3DP — MB ChB 1941 Ed.; MChOrth Liverp. 1953; FRCS Ed. 1948. Cons. Rehabil. Tayside HB.
GOLD, Janet Suzanne Middleton and Partners, Sele Gate Surgery, Hencotes, Hexham NE46 2EG Tel: 01434 602237 Fax: 01434 609496 — MB BS 1987 Newc.; MRCGP 1991; DRCOG 1991; DCCH RCP Ed. 1990. GP.
GOLD, June-Anne 16 Theydon Grove, Epping CM16 4PU — MB BS 1996 Lond.
GOLD, Lorna Margaret The Surgery, 190 Aston Lane, Handsworth, Birmingham B20 3HE Tel: 0121 356 4669 Fax: 0121 356 7020; 97 Gravelly Hill N., Erdington, Birmingham B23 6BJ Tel: 0121 350 4006 Email: lornagold@hotmail.com — MB ChB 1986 Dundee; MRCGP 1993.
GOLD, Maurice, Flight Lt. (retired) 49 Townshend Road, St John's Wood, London NW8 6LJ Tel: 020 7586 4030 — MRCS Eng. LRCP Lond. 1940; DObst RCOG 1948. Prev: Regist. (O & G) Centr. Middlx. Hosp. Lond.
GOLD, Maurice Roderick Moseley Avenue Surgery, 109 Moseley Avenue, Coventry CV6 1HS Tel: 024 7659 2201 Fax: 024 7660 1226; Yew Tree Cottage, 41 Fieldgate Lane, Kenilworth CV8 1BT Tel: 01926 53647 — MB ChB 1969 Birm.; LMCC 1974; Cert. Contracep. & Family Plann. JCC 1976; DA Eng. 1973; DObst RCOG 1971. Liaison Off. Dep. Serv. Coventry FPC. Socs: BMA; Sands Cox Soc. Birm. Prev: Regist. & SHO (Anaesth.) Walsgrave Hops. Coventry; SHO (O & G) Warneford Gen. Hosp. Leamington Spa.
GOLD, Nicholas Guy Old Byland Hall, Helmsley, York YO62 5LG Tel: 0143 96 254 — MB BS 1973 Lond.
GOLD, Ronald Geoffrey Department of Cardiology, Freeman Hospital, Freeman Road, Newcastle upon Tyne NE7 7DN Tel: 0191 284 3111 Fax: 0191 213 1968; 8 High Mill Road, Hamsterley Mill, Rowlands Gill NE39 1HE Tel: 01207 542517 — MB BS 1952 Adelaide; FRCP Lond. 1973, M 1961; FRACP 1972, M 1956. (Adelaide) Cons. Cardiol. Freeman Hosp. Newc.; Clin. Lect. (Cardiol.) Univ. Newc. u. Tyne. Socs: Brit. Cardiac Soc. & Brit. Pacing & Electrophysiol. Gp. Prev: Sen. Regist. (Cardiac) Brompton Hosp. Lond.; Sen. Regist. Cardiac Unit Papworth Hosp.; Regist. (Med.) Roy. Adelaide Hosp.
GOLD, Stephen Charles (retired) 10 Devonshire Mews W., London W1G 6QE — MB BChir 1941 Camb.; MRCS Eng. LRCP Lond. 1940; MA Camb. 1941, BA (2nd cl. Nat. Sc. Trip.) 1937; MD Camb. 1952; FRCP Lond. 1958, M 1947. Hon. Cons. Phys. St. Johns Hosp. Dis. of Skin Lond.; Hon. Cons. Phys. Skin Dept. St. Geo. Hosp. Prev: Phys. Skin Dept. St. Geo. Hosp.
GOLD, Tara 6 Duchy Grove, Harrogate HG2 0ND — BM BS 1992 Nottm.; DRCOG 1994.
GOLDACRE, Michael John Institute of Health Sciences, University of Oxford, Old Road, Oxford OX3 7LF Tel: 01865 226994 Fax: 01865 226993; 83 Rose Hill, Oxford OX4 4HT — BM BCh Oxf. 1969; MSc (Distinc.) (Social Med.) Lond. 1974; MA Oxf. 1969, BA (1st cl. Hons.) 1966; FFPHM 1983, M 1976. (Univ. Coll. Hosp.) Cons. Pub. Health S. E. Regional Office NHS Exec.; Reader (Pub. Health) Oxf. Univ.; Hon. Dir. Healthcare Epidemiol. Unit Oxf. Record Linkage Study; UK Med. Careers Res. Gp, Univ. Oxf.; Fell. Magdalen Coll. Oxf. Prev: Ho. Phys. Univ. Coll. Hosp. Lond.; Ho. Surg. Brighton Gen. Hosp.
GOLDBECK, Rainer Dept of Psychological Medicine, Aberdeen Royal Infirmary, Phase II 3rd Floor Forresthill, Aberdeen AB25 2ZN Tel: 01224 554806 Email: rainer.goldbeck@gpct.grampian.scot.nhs.uk — State Exam Med 1987 Hannover; MRCPsych 1992. Cons. Liaison Psychiat.
GOLDBECK-WOOD, Sandra Jane 92 Gilbert Road, Cambridge CB4 3PD Tel: 01223 365653 — MB ChB 1993 Bristol. Asst. Edr. Brit. Med. Jl.
GOLDBERG, Sir Abraham (retired) 16 Birnam Crescent, Bearsden, Glasgow G61 2AU — MB ChB Ed. 1946; FRS Ed. 1971; DSc Glas. 1966; MD (Gold Medal) Ed. 1956; FRCP Lond. 1967, M 1951; FRCP Ed. 1965, M 1963; FRCP Glas. 1964, M 1962; FRFPS Glas. 1951; FFPM 1989; MB ChB 1946. Hon. Cons. Med. W. Infirm. Glas.; Mem. Edit. Bd. Pharmaceut. Med.; Hon. Prof.ial Research Fell. Dept. Modern Hist. Univ Glas.. Prev: Regius Prof. Pract. Med. Univ. Glas.

GOLDBERG, Mr Andrew Julian — MB BS 1994 Lond.; FRCS (Irel) 1997; FRCS (Eng) 1998. Specialist Regist. in Trauma & Orthop., Stanmore Roy. Nat. Orthop. Hosp. Prev: SHO (Trauma & Orthop.) Whittington Hosp. NHS Trust, Lond.; IRC Clin. Research Fell. (Researching MD); Specialist Regist. Orthop., N. Thames.

GOLDBERG, Anthony Aaron Joseph 37 Lyttelton Road, London N2 0DQ Tel: 020 8455 9117 — MB BS 1966 Lond.; MPharm Lond. 1962, BPharm (Hons.) 1960; MRCS Eng. LRCP Lond. 1966; FFPM RCP (UK) 1989; MPS 1961. (Univ. Coll. Hosp.) Chairm. & Chief Exec. Off. Clin. & Technical Research Assocs. Lond. Socs: Brit. Pharm. Soc. & Brit. Inst. Regulatory Affairs.

GOLDBERG, Charles David Simon Adolescent Service, 32 York Rd, Battersea, London SW11 3QJ — MB ChB 1975 Manch.; MSc Social Anthropol. Lond. 1988; MRCP (UK) 1981; MRCPsych 1986. Cons. & Hon. Sen. Lect. Child & Adolesc. Psychiat. St. Geo. Hosp. Lond.; Advanced Clin. Train. Inst. Family Ther. Lond. Prev: Sen. Regist. (Child Psychiat.) St. Geo. Hosp. Lond.; Regist. (Psychiat.) The Bethlem Roy. & Maudsley Hosps. Lond.

GOLDBERG, Professor David Julian Scottish Centre for Infection & Environmental Health, Clifton House, Clifton Place, Glasgow G3 7LN Tel: 0141 300 1103 Fax: 0141 300 1170; 34 Beaconsfield Road, Glasgow G12 0NY Tel: 0141 339 1516 — MB ChB 1982 Glas.; DSc. (St. And.) 2000; FFPHM (UK) 2000; BSc St. And. 1979; MRCP (UK) 1986; MFPHM RCPI 1993; FRCP Glas. 1997; FRCP Ed. 1998. Dep. Dir., Cons. Epidemiol. & Head of HIV, Hepatitis & STD Sect. Scott. Centre for Infec. & Env. Health; Henry Mechan Prof. of Pub. Health, Dept. of Pub. Health, Univ. of Glas. Prev: MRC Funded Sen. Research Fell. (Cons. Grade) Communicable Dis. Unit Scotl.; Research Assoc. (MRC Funded) AIDS Surveillance Prog. Scotl. Communicable Dis. Unit; Jun. Fell. (Community Med. & Clin. Epidemiol.) Communicable Dis. Unit Scotl.

GOLDBERG, David Owen 83 Stanley Road, Bootle L20 7DA Tel: 0151 476 7962 Fax: 0151 476 7985 Email: drdaurdgoldberg@pccb.sefton-ha.nhs.uk — MB ChB 1986 Liverp.; DRCOG 1991. (Liverpool) Forens. Med. Examr. Merseyside Police. Socs: Assn. Police Surg.; BMA. Prev: GP Princip. Bridge Rd. Med. Centre Litherland; SHO (Geriat.) Kingston Gen. Hosp. Hull; SHO (Paediat.) Hull Roy. Infirmiary.

GOLDBERG, Professor Sir David Paul Brandes Institute of Psychiatry, De Crespigny Park, London SE5 8AF Tel: 020 7919 3100 Fax: 020 7277 1586 Email: d.goldberg@iop.kcl.ac.uk — MSc Manch. 1976; DM Oxf. 1970, MA, BM BCh (Hons.) 1959; FRCP Lond. 1976, M 1967; FRCP Ed. 1974, M 1967; FRCPsych 1974, M 1971; DPM Lond. 1967. (St. Thos.) Prof. Psychiat. Inst. of Psychiat. Socs: Neurosc. Bd. MRC.; Fell. Roy. Soc. Med. Prev: Lect. (Psychiat.) Inst. Psychiat. Lond.; Regist. (Med.) St. Thos. Hosp.; Asst. Ho. Phys. Nat. Hosp. Nerv. Dis. Qu. Sq.

GOLDBERG, Gerald James (retired) 57 Compayne Gardens, London NW6 3DB Tel: 020 7328 3967 — MB BCh 1945 Witwatersrand; FRCP Lond. 1972, M 1952; FRCPsych 1975, M 1971; DPM Lond. 1951. Prev: Cons. Psychiat. Goodmayes Hosp. Ilford.

GOLDBERG, Mr H Martin (retired) Park Cottage, Albemarle Avenue, Manchester M20 1HX Tel: 0161 445 1984 — MB BS 1938 Lond.; BSc CNAA 1983; FRCS Eng. 1941; MRCS Eng. LRCP Lond. 1939. Prev: Hon. Cons. Surg. N. Manch. Gen. Hosp., Vict. Memor. Jewish Hosp. & Booth Hall Hosp. Manch.

GOLDBERG, Ian Jack Leonard Willow Bank, Blundellsands Road W., Blundellsands, Liverpool L23 6TE Tel: 0151 924 8499 Email: ian-goldberg@doctors.org.uk — MRCS Eng. LRCP Lond. 1951; PhD, BA (Hons.), BSc (Hons.) Rhodes & Natal; FRCPath 1972. (Witwatersrand & W. Lond.) Med. Ref., Thornton Crematorium, Mersyside. Socs: FRCPath.; Assoc. of Clin. Biochem. Prev: Cons. Chem. Pathol. St. Mary's Hosp. Lond.; Sen. Lect. Chem. Path. Univ. W. Indies; Dan Mason Research Fell. W. Lond. Hosp. Med. Sch.

GOLDBERG, Ilfra Joy (retired) Thames Postgraduate Medical & Dental Education, 33 Millman St., London WC1N 3EJ Tel: 020 7692 3137 Fax: 020 7692 3101 — MB BS 1961 Lond.; MRCS Eng. LRCP Lond. 1961. Assoc. Dean. Flexible Train. N. & S. Thames Depts. Postgrad. Med. Prev: Assoc. Dean for Flexible Train. N&S Thames Depts. Post Grad. Med.

GOLDBERG, Miss Jacqueline Ann Department of Surgery, Hairmyres Hospital, East Kilbride, Glasgow G75 8RG Tel: 013552 20292 Fax: 013552 41527 — MB ChB 1981 Birm.; MD Birm 1990; FRCS Glas. 1985. (Birm.) Cons. Surg. Hairmyres Hosp. E. Kilbride; Hon. Sen. Lect. Univ. Glas. Socs: Assn. Surg. Prev: Cons. Surg. Law Hosp. Carluke; Sen. Regist. (Gen. Surg.) W. Scotl.; Resid. Med. Off. St. Mark's Hosp. for Dis. Rectum & Colon Lond.

GOLDBERG, Katherine Ann 77 Tasker Road, Sheffield S10 1UY — MB ChB 1992 Sheff.

GOLDBERG, Lawrence Charles Royal Sussex County Hospital, Eastern Road, Brighton BN2 5BE Tel: 01273 696955 Fax: 01273 679788 Email: lawrence.goldberg@brighton-healthcare.nhs.uk — MB ChB 1984 Bristol; MRCP (UK) 1987; MD Bristol 1995. (Bristol) Cons. nephrologist, Roy. Sussex Co. Hosp., Brighton, E.Sussex. Socs: EDTA; Brit. Transpl. soc..; Renal Assn. Prev: Research Fell. (Transpl. Med.) & Regist. (Nephrol.) St. Mary's Hosp. Lond.; Regist. (Liver Unit) King's Coll. Hosp. Lond.; Sen. Regist. in Nephrol. & Gen. Med. Hammersmith Hosp. NHS Trust Lond.

GOLDBERG, Miram 12 Southway, London NW11 6RU — MRCS Eng. LRCP Lond. 1961; AFOM RCP Lond. 1981. (Witwatersrand & W. Lond.) Adviser BRd.gate Med. Centre; Mem. Dis. Appeal Tribunal. Socs: BMA & Roy. Soc. Med. Prev: Med. Adviser Sedgewick Noble Lowndes Occupat. Health Dept.; Sen. Med. Adviser Med. Centre for Cardiac Research; Med. Off. Marks & Spencer Occupat. Health Dept.

GOLDBERG, Montague Joshua (retired) 4 St Davids Crescent, Leicester LE2 2RL Tel: 0116 274 5767 — MB BCh 1948 Witwatersrand; Hon. DSc Leicester 1989; FRCP Lond. 1973, M 1964; Dip. Med. Witwatersrand 1956. Prev: Cons. Cardiol. Regional Cardiothoracic Unit Groby Rd. Hosp.

GOLDBERG, Peter Leslie Department of Anaesthesia, Queen Elizabeth II Hospital, Howlands, Welwyn Garden City AL7 4HQ — MB BChir 1979 Camb.; BA Camb. 1976, MA 1981; FFA RCS Eng. 1984. (Camb. & St. Bart.) Cons. Anaesth. E. Herts. HA. Socs: BMA. Prev: Sen. Regist. (Anaesth.) St. Mary's Hosp. Lond.; Regist. (Anaesth.) Liverp. HA; Ho. Phys. St. Bart. Hosp. Lond.

GOLDBERG, Raymond Stanley 16 Kneeton Park, Middleton Tyas, Richmond DL10 6SB Tel: 01325 377487 — MB ChB 1958 Manch.; FRCP Lond. 1988; DCH Eng. 1965. Cons. Paediat. Darlington Memor. Hosp. Prev: Cons. Paediat. Duchess of Kent's Milit. Hosp. Catterick.

GOLDBERG, Roger Gary The Group Practice, 34 Ritchie St., London N1 0DG Tel: 020 7837 1663 Fax: 020 7837 3656 — MB BS 1983 Lond.; MRCGP 1989; DRCOG 1986. Trainee GP Kentish Town Lond. VTS. Prev: SHO (Obst. & Paediat.) Univ. Coll. Hosp. Lond.; SHO (Geriat.) N. Middlx. Hosp. Lond.

GOLDBERG, Stephen Howard Doctors Surgery, 79-81 Bowman Street, Glasgow G42 8LF Tel: 0141 423 1398 Fax: 0141 423 1845; Torridon, 53 Milverton Road, Whitecraigs, Glasgow G46 7JN — MB ChB 1981 Manch.; BSc St. And. 1978; MRCGP 1985.

GOLDBERG, Susan Marie St Peter's Surgery, 6 Oaklands Avenue, Broadstairs CT10 2SQ Tel: 01843 860777 Fax: 01843 866647 — MB BS 1982 Lond.; MRCGP 1986; DCH RCP Lond. 1986; DRCOG 1986; Cert. Family Plann. JCC 1986. Sch. Med. Off. Prev: Trainee GP Hackney Hosp. VTS; Ho. Surg. Hackney Hosp.; Ho. Phys. (Endocrinol. & Cardiol.) St. Bart. Hosp. Lond.

GOLDBLATT, Beryl 17 Ferncroft Avenue, London NW3 7PG Tel: 020 7435 8633 — MB BCh 1948 Witwatersrand; MRCPsych 1974.

GOLDBLATT, Teddy William (retired) 3 Keats Close, London NW3 2RP Tel: 020 7435 8825 — MB BCh Witwatersrand 1944; DPM 1951. Prev: Cons. Psychiat. Tavistock Clinic, Lond.

GOLDBY, Frank Stephen (retired) 11 Sicklesmere Road, Bury St Edmunds IP33 2BN Tel: 01284 755172 Fax: 01284 755172 — MB BChir 1963 Camb.; MD Camb. 1975; FRCP Lond. 1980; MRCP (UK) 1967. Prev: Med. Dir. St. Nicholas Hospice & Cons. Phys. W. Suff. Hosps. NHS Trust.

GOLDEN, Brian Jonathan Ravenscroft Medical Centre, 166-168 Golders Green Road, London NW11 8BB Tel: 020 8455 2477 Fax: 020 8201 8298; 61 Southway, London NW11 6SB Tel: 020 8455 8777, 020 8946 4516 — MB ChB 1971 Leeds; MB ChB 1971 (Hons.) Leeds; MRCP (UK) 1977; MRCGP (Distinc. & Fraser Rose Gold Medal) 1978; DCH Eng. 1974; DObst RCOG 1973. (University of Leeds) GP Princip. Barnet HA; Med. Off. Middlx. Univ. Lond.; Clin. Tutor (Gen. Pract.) Roy. Free Hosp. Lond. Prev: Regist. (Gen. Med.) Liverp. AHA; SHO (Paediats.) Alder Hey Childr. Hosp. Liverp.; SHO (Obst.) Leeds Matern. Hosp.

GOLDEN, Eric Charles Elliott (retired) Wingate Cottage, South Newington, Banbury OX15 4JG Tel: 01295 720334 — MRCS Eng. LRCP Lond. 1941; MA Camb. 1943, MB BChir 1942.

GOLDEN, Francis St Clair, OBE, OStJ 15 Beech Grove, Alverstoke, Gosport PO12 2EJ Tel: 023 9258 2833 Email: golden_biomed@msn.com — MB BCh BAO 1960; PhD (Physiol.) Leeds 1979; DAvMed Eng. 1969. (Cork (NUI)) Hon. Cons. Human & Applied Phys.and Hon. Lecture Univ. of Portsmouth; Chairm. RNLI Med. & Survival Comm. Socs: Fell. Roy. Soc. Med. Prev: Surg. Rear-Admiral RN.

GOLDEN, Geraldine Anne The Surgery, 369 Kenton Road, Harrow HA3 0XF Tel: 020 8907 0991; 32 Littleton Crescent, Harrow HA1 3SX Tel: 020 8422 3600 Fax: 020 8909 1164 — MB BCh BAO 1981 NUI; LRCPI & LM, LRCSI & LM BAO 1981; MRCGP 1986; DCH RCP Dub. 1983. (Royal College of Surgeons) Socs: Assoc. Mem. Brit. Med. Acupunc. Soc.

GOLDEN, Lorraine Alexandra Mackay 2 Bullock Steads Farm Cottages, Ponteland Road, Kenton Bank Foot, Newcastle upon Tyne NE13 8AH — MB BS 1986 Newc.; MRCPsych 1991. Sen. Regist. (Psychiat.) The Grange, Benton. Prev: Sen. Regist., Regist. & SHO (Psychiat.) Cherry Knowle Hosp. Sunderland.

GOLDEN, Maureen Patricia 371 Chepstow Road, Newport NP19 8HL Tel: 01633 277771 — MB BCh 1973 Wales; DRCOG 1976.

GOLDEN, Patrick Nial Henry TFL 252 Blackness Road, Dundee DD2 1RS; Broomvale, Inchferry, Maryculter, Aberdeen AB12 5FX Tel: 01224 734786 — MB ChB 1996 Dundee. SHO (A & E) Fremantel Hosp. W. Australia. Socs: MPS; BMA. Prev: SHO (Med.) Ninewells Hosp. Dundee; SHO (Surg.) Stracathro Hosp. W. Australia.

GOLDENBERG, Solomon Maurice The Garratt Lane Surgery, 657-659 Garratt Lane, London SW17 0PB Tel: 020 8944 6827 Fax: 020 8947 7357; 657 Garratt Lane, London SW17 0PB Tel: 020 8946 7274 — MSc 1996; MB BS Khartoum 1963; MRCS Eng. LRCP Lond. 1964; FRCGP 1981, M 1971; DObst RCOG 1967. (Khartoum) Clin. Asst. Wandsworth Community Drug Team; Prison Med. Off. HMP Wandsworth. Socs: BMA; RCGP. Prev: Regist. Blood Coagulat. Research Unit Ch.ill Hosp. Oxf.; SHO (O & G) King Geo. Hosp. Ilford; Ho. Off. Tuberc. & Meningitis Unit United Oxf. Hosps.

GOLDER, Neil David Boyd c/o Countess of Chester Hospital, Department of Paediatrics, Chester CH2 1UL — MB ChB 1991 Manch.; LLB (Hons.) Manch. 1980. SHO (Paediat.) Countess of Chester Hosp.

GOLDFOOT, Mandy Tanya 34 Manor Way, Harrow HA2 6BY — BM 1993 Soton.

GOLDHILL, David Raymond The Anaesthetics Unit, The Royal London Hospital, London E1 1BB Tel: 020 7377 7725 Fax: 020 7377 7126 Email: dgoldhill@mds.qmw.ac.uk; White Lodge, Monken Hadley, Barnet EN5 5PY — MB BS 1979 Lond.; BA Oxf. 1974, MA 1983; FFA RCS Eng. 1983. Sen. Lect. & Hon. Cons. Roy. Lond. Hosp.

GOLDIE, Alison Mary East Quay Medical Centre, East Quay, Bridgwater TA6 5YB Tel: 01278 444666 Fax: 01278 445448; Mulberry, Brook St, North Newton, Bridgwater TA7 0BL — MB ChB 1979 Bristol; MRCP (UK) 1984; DRCOG 1984; DA (UK) 1983.

GOLDIE, Alison Mary 172 Penn Road, Wolverhampton WV3 0EJ — MB ChB 1989 Leic.

GOLDIE, Mr Andrew Martin David Biggar Health Centre, South Croft Road, Biggar ML12 6BE Tel: 01899 220383 Fax: 01899 221583; 12 Lochknowe Street, Braidwood, Carluke ML8 5PW — MB ChB 1987 Aberd.; FRCS Glas. 1993; DCH RCPS Glas. 1994. Prev: SHO (Geriat.) Law Hosp. Carluke; SHO (Paediat.) Ayr Hosp.; SHO (ENT) CrossHo. Hosp. Kilmarnock.

GOLDIE, Anne Scott Anaesthetic Department, Royal Hospital for Sick Children, Yorkhill, Glasgow G£ 8SJ Tel: 020 7586 2992; 24 Bentinck Close, Prince Albert Road, St. Johns Wood, London NW8 7RY Tel: 020 7586 2992 — MB ChB 1987 Glas.; FRCA 1993. Cons. (Anaes & IC), Roy. Hosp. for Sick Childr., Glas.

GOLDIE, Mr Boyd Stephen Department of Orthopaedics, Whipps Cross Hospital, Leytonstone, London E11 1NR Tel: 020 8535 6667 Email: boyd.goldie@whippsx.nhs.uk; Tudor House, 12A The Green, London N14 7EH Tel: 020 8245 7157 Fax: 020 8245 7157 — MB BS 1982 Lond.; BSc (Hons.) Lond. 1979; FRCS Eng. 1987; DHMSA 1981. (Westm.) Cons. Orthop. Surg. Whipps Cross Hosp. Lond. Socs: Fell. BOA; Brit. Soc. Surg. Hand; Brit. Soc. Elbow & Shoulder Surg. Prev: Sen. Regist. Rotat. (Orthop.) Roy. Lond. Hosp. & Assoc. Hosps.; Regist. Rotat. (Orthop.) St. Mary's Hosp. Lond.; Resid. (Orthop.) Mass. Gen. Hosp. Boston, USA.

GOLDIE, Christopher John Phoenix Surgery, 9 Chesterton Lane, Cirencester GL7 1XG Tel: 01285 652056 Fax: 01285 641562 Email: chris.goldie@1-84012.nhs.uk; Garden House, Berkeley Road, Cirencester GL7 1TY Tel: 01255 657592 Email: chris.goldie@lineone.net — MB ChB 1979 Glas.; MRCGP 1984; DCH RCP Lond. 1985; DRCOG 1984; DA Eng. 1983. (Glas.) Hosp. Pract. (Anaesth.) Cirencester. Socs: BMA; RCGP. Prev: Trainee GP Carlisle; Trainee SHO/GP Dudley Rd. Hosp. Birm. VTS; SHO (Anaesth.) Good Hope Gen. Hosp. Sutton Coldfield.

GOLDIE, David John Chapel House, Nupdown Lane, Oldbury-on-Severn, Bristol BS35 1RR Tel: 01454 260526 — MB BS Lond. 1965; BSc (Physiol.) Lond. 1962; MD Bristol 1973; FRCPath 1985, M 1973. (St. Bart.) Cons. Path. (Clin. Chem.) S.mead Hosp. Bristol.; Sen. Lect. Clin. Pathol. Univ. of Bristol. Prev: Lect. (Chem. Path.) St. Bart. Hosp. Lond.

GOLDIE, John Gerard Scott Easterhouse Health Centre, 9 Auchinlea Road, Glasgow G34 9HQ Tel: 0141 531 8170 Fax: 0141 531 8110; 50 White Street, Glasgow G11 5EA — MB ChB 1982 Glas.; MRCGP 1987; DRCOG 1985. Prev: Trainee GP Glas. Roy. Infirm. VTS.

GOLDIE, June Baillieston Health Centre, 20 Muirside Road, Baillieston, Glasgow G69 7AD Tel: 0141 531 8050 Fax: 0141 531 8067 — MB ChB 1976 Glas.

GOLDIE, Lawrence 111 Harley Street, London Tel: 020 7935 0977 Fax: 020 7935 0728; 40 Parkhill Road, London NW3 2YP Tel: 020 7485 6558 Fax: 020 7916 8203 — MB ChB 1953 Manch.; MD Manch. 1961; MRCS Eng. LRCP Lond. 1953; FRCPsych 1975, M 1971; DPM Lond. 1958. (Manch.) Cons. Med. Psychoanal. Psychother., Cons. Psychiat. & Hon. Cons. Tavistock Clinic Lond. Socs: Fell. Roy. Soc. Med.; Hon. Mem. Internat. Psychosocial Oncol. Soc.; (Counc.) Psychologie et Cancer Assn. France. Prev: Cons. Psychiat. & Cons. Med. Psychother. Roy. Marsden Hosp. Lond.; Sen. Lect. (Psychiat.) Inst. O & G Hammersmith Hosp. Lond.; Cons. Psychiat. & Med. Psychother. Roy. Nat. Throat Nose & Ear Hosp. Lond.

GOLDIE, Matthew Winsor Chapel House, Nupdown Lane, Bristol BS35 1RR — MB BS 1992 Lond.; DCH 1997; DCROG 1998; DFFP 1999; MRCGP 1999. (Charing Cross and Westminster)

GOLDIN, David — MB BS 1969 Lond.; FRCP Lond. 1990; MRCP (UK) 1973. (St. Thos.) Cons. Dermat. Qu. Eliz. The Qu. Mother Hosp. Margate & Kent & Canterbury Hosp. Prev: Sen. Regist. (Dermat.) Addenbrooke's Hosp. Camb.; Regist. (Med. & Dermat.) Wycombe Gen. Hosp.; Med. Off. Zambia Flying Doctor Serv.

GOLDIN, Eric Joseph 18 Carrick Crescent, Giffnock, Glasgow G46 6PP — MB ChB 1985 Glas.

GOLDIN, Mr Jacob Henry Birmingham Nuffield Hospital, 22 Somerset Road, Birmingham B15 2QQ Tel: 0121 643 9167 Fax: 0121 633 4206; Rose Cottage Farm, Ullenhall, Solihull B95 5PJ Tel: 01564 793496 Fax: 01564 794975 — MB ChB 1962 Cape Town; FRCS Ed. 1967; FRCS 1998 Eng. (Cape Town) Cons. Plastic Surg.Birm. Nuffield Hosp., Wye Valley Nuffield & The Garden Hosp. Lond.. Socs: Fell. Roy. Soc. Med.; Brit. Assn. Plastic Surg.; Brit. Assn. Aesthetic Plastic Surgs. Prev: Sen. Regist. (Plastic Maxillofacial & Oral Surg.) St. Thos. Hosp. & Hosp. Sick Childr. Lond.; Ho. Off. Profess. Med. & Surg. Units Groote Schuur Hosp., Cape Town; Cons. Plastic Surg. Wordesley Hosp.

GOLDIN, Jonathan Gerald 39 St George's Road, London NW11 0LU — MB ChB 1983 Cape Town.

GOLDIN, Jonathan Mark The Tavistock Clinic, 120 Belsize Lane, London NW3 5BA Tel: 020 7435 7111 Email: jongoldin@doctors.org.uk — MB ChB 1992 Manch.; BSc (Hons.) Psychol. Manch. 1989; DCH RCP Lond. 1994; MRCPsych 1998. (Manch.) Tavistock and Portman NHS Trust, Lond. Socs: Assn. Child Psychol. & Psychiat.; Assn. Psychoanalyt. Psychother. NHS; Assn. Infant Ment. Health (UK). Prev: Specialist Regist. (Child & Adolesc. Psychiat.).

GOLDIN, Joshua Alec Tel: 020 8458 9262 Fax: 020 8458 0300 — MB ChB 1973 Cape Town; MB ChB 1973 Cape Town.

GOLDIN, Robert David Dept of Histopathology, St Mary's Hospital Medical School, Norfolk Place, London W2 1PG Tel: 020 7723 1252 Fax: 020 7724 7349 — MB ChB 1980 Zimbabwe; MD

Zimbabwe 1987, MB ChB 1980; LRCP LRCS Ed. LRCPS Glas. 1980; MRCPath 1986. Sen. Lect. (Histopath.) St. Mary's Hosp. Med. Sch. Lond. Socs: Eur. Soc. Study of Liver; Internat. Assn. Study of Liver; Internat. Acad. Path.

GOLDING, Anthony Mark Barrington (retired) 12 Clifton Hill, London NW8 0QG Tel: 020 7264 0504 Fax: 020 7264 0504 — MB BChir 1952 Camb.; MA Camb. 1954; MRCOphth. 1989; FFPHM RCP (UK) 1979; FRIPHH 1983; FFCM 1979, M 1972; DO RCS Eng. 1956. Prev: Edr. Health & Hyg.

GOLDING, Catherine Elizabeth Marian 12 Clifton Hill, London NW8 0QG — BM BS 1991 Nottm.; BMedSci. Nottm. 1989; MRCP 1996. Specialist Regist. (Paediat.) N. Thames Calman Rotat. Socs: RCP; RCPCH.

GOLDING, Catherine Louise Field House, Treegarn Road, Langstone, Newport NP18 2JS — MB BS 1992 Lond.

GOLDING, Daniel John 22 Starcross Ct, Mickleover, Derby DE3 5PW — MB ChB 1997 Birm.

GOLDING, Douglas Noel (retired) 152 Harley Street, London W1 Tel: 020 8203 3395 — MB BCh BAO 1954 Dub.; MA, MD Dub. 1956; FRCPI 1968, M 1959; DPhysMed Eng. 1963. Cons. Rheum. BUPA Roding, Holly Hse. & The Rivers Private Hosps. Essex; Examr. RCPI; Examr. Dip. Musculoskeletal Med.; Vis. Lect. (Rheum.) Univ. Dub. (TCD). Prev: Cons. Phys. (Rheum.) P.ss Alexandra Hosp. Harlow.

GOLDING, John Hemingford The Surgery, Regal Chambers, 50 Bancroft, Hitchin SG5 1LL Tel: 01462 453232; 35 Priory Way, Hitchin SG4 9BL — MB BS 1972 Lond.; MRCS Eng. LRCP Lond. 1972; DObst RCOG 1975. (Roy. Free) Prev: SHO (A & E) & Ho. Surg. Roy. Free Hosp. Lond.; Ho. Off. (Obst.) Edgware Gen. Hosp. Lond.

GOLDING, Jonathan Laurence 58 Park Road, Prestwich, Manchester M25 0FA; Blackford House Medical Centre, 137 Croft Lane, Bury BL9 8QA Tel: 0161 766 6622 — MB ChB 1981 Leeds; MRCGP (Distinc.) 1985; DRCOG 1983. (Leeds)

GOLDING, Michael John 11 Ravendale Drive, Lincoln LN2 2JN — MB ChB 1980 Liverp. Asst. Laege, Nordland Psykiatriske Sykehus, Norway. Prev: Medarbeider Vidaräsen Landsby, Norway; Specialist Paediat. Brit. Milit. Hosp., Rintelln, W. Germany.

GOLDING, Patricia Frances (retired) Langstone Manor, 42 Lanstone Road, Havant PO9 1RF Tel: 023 9248 4979 — MB BS Lond. 1962; FRCR 1977; DMRT Eng. 1975. Prev: Cons. (Radiother. & Oncol.) Portsmouth Hosps. Trust.

GOLDING, Patrick Joseph 'Kingscote', Malpas Road, Truro TR1 1QJ — MB BCh BAO 1943 NUI. (Galw.) Prev: Ho. Surg. & Ho. Phys. Richmond Hosp. Dub. & Centr. Hosp. Galway; Res. Med. Off. Camborne-Redruth Hosp.; Clin. Asst. Barncoose Geriat. Hosp. Redruth.

GOLDING, Peter Lee Royal Hospital Haslar, Gosport PO12 2AA Tel: 02392 584255; Langstone Manor, 42 Langstone Rd, Havant PO9 1RF Tel: 02392 484979 — MB BS 1962 Lond.; FRCP Lond. 1979, M 1967; MRCS Eng. LRCP Lond. 1962. (Lond. Hosp.) Cons. Phys. Portsmouth & SE Hants. Health Dist. Socs: Brit. Soc. Gastroenterol. & Liver Club. Prev: Sen. Regist. (Gen. Med.) Lond. Hosp.; Regist. (Gen. Med.) Soton. Gen Hosp.; Surg. Lt. RN.

GOLDING, Peter Roger Yewcroft, 41 Church St., Littleover, Derby DE23 6GF — MB ChB 1959 Bristol; BSc (Hons.) Bristol 1956, MD 1974, MB ChB (Hons.) 1959; FRCP Lond. 1980, M 1963. Cons. Phys. Derby City Hosp. & Derby Roy. Infirm. Socs: Europ. Organisat. Research & Treatm. Cancer; Fell. Roy. Soc. Med. Prev: Regist. (Med.) Centr. Middlx. Hosp. Lond.; MRC Fell. Char. Cross Hosp. Lond. 1971-2; Sen. Med. Regist. Char. Cross Hosp. Lond.

GOLDING, Mr Robert Howard Field House, Tregarn Road, Langstone, Newport NP18 2JS Tel: 01633 412876 — MB BS 1965 Lond.; FRCS Ed. 1972; FRCOG 1983, M 1970, DObst 1967. (Lond. Hosp.) Cons. (O & G) Roy. Gwent Hosp.; Hon. Clin. Lect. Univ. Wales Coll. Med. Cardiff. Prev: Sen. Regist. (O & G) Univ. Hosp. of Wales Cardiff.

GOLDING, Samantha Kim Barrowford Surgery, Ridgeway, Barrowford, Nelson BB9 8QP Tel: 01282 612621 Fax: 01282 611958; 3 Whiteacre Lane, Barrow, Clitheroe BB7 9BJ Tel: 01254 824691 — MB ChB 1990 Leeds; T(GP) 1995. GP Lancs. Retainer Scheme; GP Lancs. Asst. Prev: Trainee GP Huddersfield HA VTS; Ho. Phys. St. Jas. Univ. Hosp. Leeds; Ho. Surg. Seacroft Hosp. Leeds.

GOLDING, Sarah Jane Lawrence Hill Health Centre, Hassell Drive, Bristol B52 0AN Tel: 0117 555241 — MB BS 1985 Lond.; DFFP 1993; MRCGP 1991; DRCOG 1992; T (GP) 1991; DCH RCP Lond. 1989; AKC. (Westm.) p/t GP Retainer Lawrence Hill Health Centre, Bristol; SCMO Family Plann., Keynsham. Socs: Avon Doctors Gp. Contracep. & Sexual Health. Prev: GP Princip. St Martins Surg. Bristol; Trainee GP Bristol; SHO (O & G) St. Geo. Hosp. Lond.

GOLDING, Stephen John Oxford Magnetic Resonance Imaging Centre, John Radcliffe Hospital, Oxford OX3 9DU Tel: 01865 221904 Fax: 01865222019 Email: stephen.golding@radiology.ox.ac.uk; 89 Shelley Close, Abingdon OX14 1PR Tel: 01235 831305 — MB BS 1972 Lond.; MA Oxf. 1988; MRCS Eng. LRCP Lond. 1972; FRCR 1980; DMRD Eng. 1977. (Guy's) Univ. Lect. (Radiol.) Univ. Oxf.; Hon. Cons. Radiol. Oxf. Radcliffe Hosp.; Oxf. Instruments Fell. Radiol. Univ. Coll. Oxf. Socs: Eur. Soc. Head & Neck Radiol.; Brit. Inst. Radiol. (Pres. 1996/7); Internat. Soc. Strategic Studies in Radiol. Prev: Sen.lect.Caneer.Research; Clin. Dir. Oxf. MRI Centre; Dir. Regional CT Unit Oxf.

***GOLDING, Steven John Joseph** 39 West Avenue, Wallington SM6 8PH — MB ChB 1998 Birm.

GOLDING, Timothy Michael Sabden & Whalley Medical Group, Whalley Medical Centre, The Surgery, 42 King St., Whalley, Clitheroe BB7 9SL Tel: 01254 823273 Fax: 01254 824891; 3 Whiteacre Lane, Barrow, Clitheroe BB7 9BJ Tel: 01254 824691 — MB ChB 1990 Leeds; MRCGP 1994; DFFP 1995. (Leeds) Prev: Trainee GP Huddersfield VTS; Ho. Surg. St. Jas. Univ. Hosp. Leeds; Ho. Phys. Chapel Allerton Hosp. Leeds.

GOLDING, Warren Reuben Shadwell Medical Centre, 137 Shadwell Lane, Leeds LS17 8AE Tel: 0113 293 9999 Fax: 0113 248 5888; 16 Grange Court, Primley Copse, Alwoodley, Leeds LS17 7TX — MB ChB 1984 Leeds; MB ChB Leeds l984; MRCGP 1988; DRCOG 1987. (Leeds)

GOLDING-COOK, Anthony Nigel The Ridgeway Practice, Plympton Health Centre, Mudge Way, Plympton, Plympton PL7 1AD Tel: 01752 346634 Fax: 01752 341444 Email: dr.golding-cook@ridgeway.org.uk; Oakwood House, 9 Oakwood Close, Woolwell, Plymouth PL6 7RP Email: anthony@golding-cook.com — BM (Hons.) Soton. 1988; BM 1988 Soton.; BSc (Hons.) Dund 1984; DRCOG 1993; DFFP 1993. (Soton.) GP Ridgeway Pract., Plympton; Area Surg. St John Ambul. (W. Devon); Med. Advisor, Christian Aid Trust. Socs: Brit. Assn. for Immediate Care; Plymouth Immediate Med. Supp. (Dir. of Educat.). Prev: Woolwell Med. Centre, Plymouth; Trainee GP Plymouth VTS; SHO (A & E) Derriford Hosp. Plymouth.

GOLDING-WOOD, Mr David Gordon Department ENT & Head & Neck Surgery, Farnborough Hospital, Orpington Common, Orpington BR6 8ND Tel: 01689 814000 Fax: 01689 814127; Tel: 01959 522220 Fax: 01959 525097 — MB BS 1980 Lond.; BSc Lond. 1977; FRCS (Otol.) Eng. 1987; FRCS Ed. 1985. (St. Thos.) p/t Cons. Otolaryngol. Bromley Hosps NHS Trust; Hon. Cons. Otolaryngol. Qu. Marys, Sidcup NHS Trust. Socs: Fell. Roy. Soc. Med.; Brit. Assn. Otorhinol. Head & Neck Surg. Prev: Sen. Regist. (ENT) Roy. Free Hosp. Lond.; Fell. (Neuro-otol.) Univ. Michigan; Regist. (ENT) Roy. Nat. Throat, Nose & Ear Hosp. Lond.

GOLDMAN, Aaron Joseph 46 Ballantrae Road, Liverpool L18 6JQ — MB ChB 1941 Liverp.

GOLDMAN, Allan Paul 1 Gladsmuir Road, London N19 3JY — MB BCh 1986 Witwatersrand; MSc (Med) Cape Town; MRCP Lond. Cons. (Paediat. IC) Gt. Ormond St. Hosp. for Childr. Lond.

GOLDMAN, Ann Jane Hospital for Children NHS Trust, Great Ormond St., London WC1N 3JH Tel: 020 7829 8678 Fax: 020 7813 8588; 92 Hampstead Way, London NW11 7XY Tel: 020 8458 2989 Fax: 020 8381 4740 Email: a.goldman@ich.ucl.ac.uk — MB 1974 Camb.; BChir 1973; FRCP Lond. 1994; MRCP (UK) 1977. Cons. Palliat. Care Hosp. Childr. NHS Trust Gt. Ormond St. Lond. Prev: Dir. Symptom Care Team Dept. Haemat. & Oncol. Hosp. Sick Childr. Gt. Ormond St. Lond.

GOLDMAN, Arlene (retired) 10 Berkeley Court, 39 Ravenscroft Avenue, London NW11 8BG Tel: 020 8458 9989 Fax: 020 8455 3411 Email: arl@dircon.co.uk — MB BCh 1957 Witwatersrand; MRCP (UK) 1974; MACP 1976; Cert. Av. Med. 1984; ECFMG Cert. 1976; FLEX Lic. (USA) 1977; FRCP 1999. Contrib. Jl. on Internet &

Med. Online. Prev: Hon. Sen. Lect. & Hon. Cons. Univ. Coll. Hosp. Lond.

GOLDMAN, Deborah Lynne Hollow Way Medical Centre, 58 Hollow Way, Cowley, Oxford OX4 2NJ Tel: 01865 777495 Fax: 01865 771472 — MB ChB 1985 Cape Town; MB ChB 1985 Cape Town.

GOLDMAN, Eleanor (retired) 31 Hill Top, London NW11 6ED Tel: 020 8455 5950 Email: elizzy@dircom.co.uk — MB BCh Witwatersrand 1952. Prev: Assoc. Specialist Roy. Free Hosp. Haemophilia Centre Lond.

GOLDMAN, Ian Gerald Thatcher's Cottage, Chadwich Lane, Bromsgrove — MB ChB 1958 Birm. Socs: BMA. Prev: Ho. Phys. Bridgend Gen. Hosp.; Ho. Surg. Guest Hosp. Dudley; Clin. Off. in Psychiat. Brit. Milit. Hosp. Singapore.

GOLDMAN, Jeremy Eric 15 Lawsone Rise, Conningsby Road, High Wycombe HP13 5NS Tel: 01494 463757 — MB BS 1983 Lond.; BSc Lond. 1979, MB BS 1983. Business Developm. Project Manager Connect Pharma Oxf. Prev: Sen. Market Research Exec. G.D. Searle High Wycombel; Ho. Phys. Ealing Hosp. S.all; Ho. Surg. Gravesend & N. Kent Hosps.

GOLDMAN, Professor John Michael 33 Northumberland Place, London W2 5AS — BM BCh 1963 Oxf.; DM Oxf. 1981; FRCP Lond. 1979, M 1967; FRCPath 1986, M 1985. (St. Bart.) Prof. Leukaemia Biol. & Chairm. Dept. Haemat. Roy. Postgrad. Med. Sch.; Dir. LRF Centre Adult Leukaemia, Lond.; Phys. Hammersmith Hosp. Lond. Prev: Ho. Off. Hammersmith Hosp.; Fell. (Med.) Univ. Miami, USA; Fell. (Med.) Mass. Gen. Hosp. Boston, USA.

GOLDMAN, Jonathan Howard 55 Southbourne Crescent, London NW4 2JX; Department Cardiology, St. George's Hospital, Blackshaw Road, London SW17 0QT Tel: 020 8672 1255 Email: jonathangoldman@compuserve.com — MB BS 1989 Lond.; MB BS Lond. 1989 + distinction; BSc (Hons.) Lond. 1986; MRCP (UK) 1992; MD U.LOND. 1996. (St. Bartholomew's Hospital) Specialist Regist. (Cardiol.) St. Geo. Hosp. Lond. Socs: Fell. Roy. Coll. Phys.; Med. Res. Soc.; Brit. Soc. Immunol. Prev: Regist. Rotat. (Med.) St. Geo. Hosp. Lond.; Specialist Regist. (Cardiol. & Gen. Med.) Guildford Hosp. Surrey; Regist. (Cardiol.) St. Geo. Hosp. Lond.

GOLDMAN, Jonathan Mervyn Torbay Hospital, Lawes Bridge, Torquay TQ2 7AA Tel: 01803 655116 Fax: 01803 655580 Email: jon.goldman@sdevonhc_tr.swest.nhs.uk — MB BS 1978 Lond.; MD Lond. 1986; MRCP (UK) 1981; FRCP Lond. 1997. (Middlx.) Cons. Gen. & Respirat. Phys. Torbay Hosp. Torquay. Socs: Brit. Thorac. Soc.; Eur. Respirat. Soc. Prev: Sen. Regist. (Thoracic & Gen. Med.) Leeds & Hull Hosps.; Regist. (Thoracic Med.) Brompton Hosp. Lond.; Research Fell. Lung Func. Unit Brompton Hosp. Lond.

GOLDMAN, Kenneth Peter (retired) 8 Southwark Place, Bromley BR1 2LT — MB BChir 1955 Camb.; MB BCh Camb. 1955; MD Camb. 1964; FRCP Lond. 1977, M 1961. Prev: Cons. Phys. Dartford & Gravesham Health Dist.

GOLDMAN, Leopold 26 Crosby Road, Westcliff on Sea SS0 8LG Tel: 01702 349861 — MB ChB 1935 Birm.; DIH Soc. Apoth. Lond. 1946. Prev: Sen. Med. Off. Min. of Supply, Roy. Ordnance Fact.

GOLDMAN, Leslie Harry Eisner, Goldman and Ship, Shipley Health Centre, Alexandra Road, Shipley BD18 3EG Tel: 01274 589153 Fax: 01274 770882; 2 The Coach House, Derry Hill, Menston, Ilkley LS29 6NG — MB ChB 1979 Birm.; BA (Hons.) Oxf. 1973; MRCGP 1983; DRCOG 1982.

GOLDMAN, Mr Mark David 15A Ampton Road, Edgbaston, Birmingham B15 2UJ — MD 1985 Birm.; MB ChB 1974; FRCS Eng. 1980; FRCSI 1979. Sen. Lect. (Surg.) Univ. Birm. Socs: Surg. Research Soc. Gt. Brit. & Assn. Surgs. Prev: Sen. Lect. E. Birm. Hosp.; Lect. (Surg.) Qu. Eliz. Hosp. Birm.; Regist. (Surg.) Selly Oak Hosp. Birm.

GOLDMAN, Martin Harris 19 Myddelton Park, Whetstone, London N20 0HT Tel: 020 8445 7128 Fax: 020 8445 7128 Email: martingoldman@easynet.co.uk — MB BS 1975 Lond.; BSc (Hons.) Lond. 1971; MRCP (UK) 1979; FFPM 1989; Dip. Pharm. Med. (RCP UK) 1982. (Middlx.) Med. Adviser Pharmax Ltd. Bexley.; Med. Cons. Nomad; Edr. Gastroenterol. Today. Prev: Clin. Project Manager Sterling-Winthrop Research Gp. (Europe) Guildford; Regist. N. Middlx. Hosp. Lond.; SHO St. Geo. Hosp. Med. Unit Bolingbroke Hosp. Lond.

GOLDMEIER, David 7 Golders Close, Edgware HA8 9QD — MD 1977 Lond.; MB BS 1971; MRCP (U.K.) 1973. Cons. Venereol. St. Mary's Hosp. Lond. W2. Socs: Assn. of Sexual & Marital Therap.; Soc. Psychosomatic Research; Med. Soc. Study VD. Prev: MRC Research Regist. Lond. Hosp.; Sen. Regist. Univ. Coll. Hosp. Lond.

GOLDREIN, Sonia Hannah Jane Torreno, St Andrews Road, Blundellsands, Liverpool L23 7UR Tel: 0151 924 2065 Fax: 0151 924 2065 Email: goldrein@aol.com — MB BS Durh. 1947. (Newc-on-Tyne)

GOLDRING, Hymon Jack 2 Frognal, London NW3 — MB BCh BAO 1930 Belf. (Belf.) Med. Off. Sch. Clinics Camden & W.m.; Med. Adviser ABC Television; Med. Examr. Scott. Widows Insur. Co.; Exam. Gen. Nurs. Counc. Socs: Fell. Roy. Soc. Med.; Dermat. Soc. Prev: Sen. Ho. Phys. W. Lond. Hosp.; Sen. Res. Phys. Lambeth Hosp.; Squadron Ldr. RAF Med. Br., Specialist Venereol. & Dermat. RAF.

***GOLDRING, James Joshua Peter** 53 Wykeham Road, London NW4 2SS Tel: 020 8202 0333 Fax: 020 8203 0764 Email: jjpgoldring@hotmail.com — BMedSc 1995 Birm.; MBChB 1998.

GOLDRING, Mr Julian Richard 24 Lochbroom Drive, Newton Mearns, Glasgow G77 5PF Tel: 0141 639 3346 — MB ChB Glas. 1967; FRCS Glas. 1982; FRCS Ed. 1971; DObst RCOG 1969. (Glas.) Cons. Surg. Hairmyres Hosp. E. Kilbride. Socs: Vasc. Surg. Soc. GB & Irel. Prev: Sen. Regist. (Surg.) Roy. Infirm. Glas.; Regist. (Surg.) Vict. Infirm. Glas.; SHO Stobhill Hosp. Glas.

GOLDRING, Simon David Arthur 28 Whiteways, Newtownards BT23 4UW — MB BCh BAO 1994 Belf.

GOLDRING, Stephen Timothy 11 The Verne, Church Crookham, Fleet GU52 6LT — MB ChB 1997 Manch.

GOLDSACK, Anne Michele Littleton Surgery, Buckland House, Esher Park Avenue, Esher KT10 9NY Tel: 01372 462235 Fax: 01372 470622; 2 Rydens Grove, Hersham, Walton-on-Thames KT12 5RX Tel: 01932 246599 — MB BS 1981 Lond.; MA Oxf. 1980.

GOLDSACK, Craig Flat 4, 36 Petherton Road, London N5 2RE — MB ChB 1988 Ed.; BSc (Hons.) Ed. 1985; MRCP (UK) 1992. SHO (Anaesth.) St. Thos. Hosp. Lond.; SHO (IC) Nat. Hosp. Neurol. & Neurosurg. Lond. Prev: SHO (Med.) Leeds Gen. Infirm.; Ho. Phys. Edin. Roy. Infirm.

GOLDSBOROUGH, David (retired) Cobblers Cottage, Glasshouses, Harrogate HG3 5QH — MB ChB 1953 Manch. Prev: Princip. GP Yorks.

GOLDSBROUGH, Joyce 7 Kirk Lane, Ruddington, Nottingham NG11 6NN Tel: 0115 921 3500 — MB BS Durh. 1954; MFCM 1972; DPH Eng. 1969. (Durham University Medical School) Indep. Cons. Nottm.; Med. Ref. Nottm. City. Socs: Soc. Community Med. Prev: Med. Off. Health Arnold & Carlton UDCs; Regist. (Chest Dis.) Castle Hill Sanat. Cottingham.

GOLDSER, David Stephen West Pottergate Health Centre, 137 West Pottergate, Norwich NR2 4BX Tel: 01603 628705 Fax: 01603 766789 — MB BS 1977 Lond.; MRCS Eng. LRCP Lond. 1977; MRCGP 1985; DCH RCP Lond. 1984.

GOLDSMITH, Amal R 364 Birmingham Road, Walsall WS5 3NX — MB BS 1959 Gauhati; MRCPath 1975. (Assam Med. Coll. Dibrugarh) Cons. (Histopath.) Manor Hosp. Walsall. Prev: Sen. Regist. (Histopath.) W. Midl. RHA; Regist. (Morbid Anat.) United Birm. Hosps. & Birm. RHB; SHO (Path.) Glos. Roy. Infirm. Gloucester.

GOLDSMITH, Arthur Landrey Royal Hampshire County Hospital, Romsey Road, Winchester SO22 5DG Tel: 01926 825042 Fax: 01962 825044 — MB ChB 1986 Cape Town; MRCP (UK) 1992; FRCA 1993. Cons. Anaesth., Roy. Hants. Co. Hosp., Winchester. Socs: Intens. Care Soc.; Difficult Airway Soc.; Assn. of Anaesth.s. Prev: Sen. Regist. (Anaesth.) Wessex Rota.

GOLDSMITH, Carol Haresfield House Surgery, 6-10 Bath Road, Worcester WR5 3EJ Tel: 01905 763161 Fax: 01905 767016 — MB ChB 1988 Birm.; MRCGP 1993; DCH RCP Lond. 1991; DRCOG 1991. Prev: Trainee GP Worcester; SHO Worcester Roy. Infirm. GP VTS.

GOLDSMITH, Christy Saron The Mount, Bostal Road, Steyning BN44 3PD — MB BS 1998 Lond.; MB BS Lond 1998.

GOLDSMITH, David Julian Alexander Guy's Hospital Renal Unit, 4th Floor, Thomas Guy House, Guy's Hospital, St Thomas' St., London SE1 9RT Tel: 020 7955 8791 Fax: 020 7955 4909 Email: davidogoldsmith@gstt.sthomas.nhs.uk — MB BChir 1983 Camb.; MA Camb. 1984, MB BChir 1983; FRCP 1999; MRCP (UK) 1986.

(St. Thos.) Cons. (Nephrol.) Guy's Hosp. Lond. Socs: Eur. Dialysis & Transpl. Assn.; Renal Assn.; Fell. Roy. Soc. Med. Prev: Cons. (Nephrol.) Roy. Sussex Co. Hosp. Brighton; Sen. Regist. (Nephrol.) Manch. Roy. Infirmiary; Sen. Regist. (Nephrol.) Withington Hosp. Manch.

GOLDSMITH, Derek Harold Edge Hill Health Centre, Crosfield Road, Liverpool L7 5QL Tel: 0151 260 2777; 7 Rockbourne Avenue, Woolton, Liverpool L25 4TG Tel: 0151 428 9202 — MB ChB 1954 Liverp. Examg. Med. Off. DHSS; Med. Off. Family Plann. Liverp. HA (T); Med. Off. Automotive Products Ltd. Liverp. & R.S. Clare Ltd. Liverp. Socs: Assoc. Mem. Coll. GP; Liverp. Med. Inst. Prev: Orthop. Ho. Surg. Liverp. Roy. Infirm.; Ho. Phys. Warrington Gen. Hosp.; Cas. Off. BRd.green Hosp.

GOLDSMITH, Edmond Colin 17 Wynchurch Road, Belfast BT6 0JH — MB BCh BAO 1989 Belf.

GOLDSMITH, Eric Eversley, 12 Holmdene Avenue, Mill Hill, London NW7 2NA Tel: 020 8959 3971 — LRCP LRCS 1940 Ed.; MD Koenigsberg 1936; LRCP LRCS Ed. LRFPS Glas. 1940; FFA RCS Eng. 1954; DA Eng. 1949. (Koenigsberg & St. Mungo's Coll.) Socs: Assn. Anaesths. Prev: Cons. Anaesth. Roy. Eye Hosp., Dreadnought Seaman's Hosp. & Woolwich Hosp. Gp. Lond.; Sen. Regist. (Anaesth.) W. Herts. Hosp. Hemel Hempstead; Capt. RAMC.

GOLDSMITH, Henry John (retired) Deep Dene, 7 Rose Lane, Liverpool L18 8AD Tel: 0151 724 5555 — MB BS 1947 Lond.; MD Lond. 1952; MD NY State Univ. 1960; FRCP Lond. 1970, M 1949. Prev: Cons. Nephrologist. Roy. Liverp.. Univ. Hosp.

GOLDSMITH, Michael John Medigold health Consultancy Ltd., Preston Lodge Court, Preston Deanery, Northampton NN7 2DS Tel: 01604 870888 Fax: 01604 870780 Email: mike.goldsmith@medigold.health.com; Cromwell House, Wollaston, Wellingborough NN29 7QW Tel: 01933 665533 Fax: 01933 665175 Email: mike.goldsmith@virgin.net — MB BS 1973 Lond.; MRCS Eng. LRCP Lond. 1972; MRCGP 1977. (St. Bart.) Managing Dir. Medigold Health Consultancy Ltd; Chief Med.Off.Medisure; Hon. Med. Off. E Midl. Co. Rugby Club. Socs: Dep. Chairm. Conserv. Med. Soc.; Assur. Med. Soc.; Fell.Roy. Soc. Med. Prev: Research Fell. Centre For Policy Studies; Founder & Exec. Med. Dir. Harrow Health Care Centre; SHO (Orthop.) & Cas. Off. Barnet Gen. Hosp.

GOLDSMITH, Paul St John's College, Cambridge CB2 1TP — BM BCh 1994 Oxf.; MA Camb. 1991; MRCP (UK) 1994.

GOLDSMITH, Pauline Veronica Whitburn Surgery, 3 Bryers Street, Whitburn, Sunderland SR6 7EE Tel: 0191 529 3039 Fax: 0191 529 5436 — MB ChB 1973 Liverp.; MRCGP 1978; AFOM RCP Lond. 1989; DRCOG 1976.

GOLDSMITH, Professor Rainer (retired) Ivy House Farm, 69 Duck St., Egginton, Derby DE65 6HG Tel: 01283 730358 Fax: 01283 730970 Email: ragoldy@aol.com — MB BChir 1952 Camb. Emerit. Prof. Physiol. Univ. Lond. Prev: Prof. Human Biol. LoughBoro. Univ.

GOLDSPINK, Daniel Rufus — MB BS 1994 Newc.; MRCGP 2001; DTM & H Liverp. 1997. p/t Gen. Practitioner Princip.

GOLDSPINK, Madeline Hermione Fortescue 9 Avenue Road, Bishop's Stortford CM23 5NS Tel: 01279 656634 Fax: 01279 755447 — MB BS Lond. 1965. (St. Mary's)

GOLDSTEIN, Amanda Ruth Birmingham Children's Hospital, Steelhouse Lane, Birmingham B4 6NH Tel: 0121 333 6184; 130 Westfield Road, Birmingham B15 3JQ — MB ChB 1980 Manch.; MRCP (UK) 1984; FRCPCH 1997. Cons. Paediat. Childr. Hosp. Birm. Prev: Sen. Regist. Rotat. (Paediat.) W. Midl. Train. Sch.; Clin. Fell. Hosp. for Sick Childr. Toronto, Canada; Scientif. Off. MRC Laborat. Jamaica.

GOLDSTEIN, Andrew Leslie Mirfield Surgery, Scholars Gate, Lea Village, Birmingham B33 0DL Tel: 0121 785 0795 — MB ChB 1985 Birm.; MRCGP 1989; DGM RCP Lond. 1987. Clin. Med. Off. Sandwell HA.

GOLDSTEIN, Daniel John Department of Biomedical Science, University Sheffield, Sheffield S10 2TN Tel: 0114 276 8555 — MB BCh 1955 Witwatersrand; BSc (Hons.) Witwatersrand 1952, DSc 1976, MB BCh 1955. Reader Dept. Biomed. Sci. Univ. Sheff.

GOLDSTEIN, Hugh School Lane Surgery, School Lane, Washingborough, Lincoln LN4 1BN Tel: 01522 792360 Fax: 01522 794144; 7 School Lane, Washingborough, Lincoln LN4 1BL Tel: 01522 790323 — MB BS 1972 Newc.

GOLDSTEIN, Janet Elizabeth 41A Chantry Road, Moseley, Birmingham B13 8DN — MB ChB 1975 Birm.; MFFP 1994; MRCGP 1984.

GOLDSTEIN, Sheila Yvette 4 Wellacre Road, Kenton, Harrow HA3 0BN — MB ChB 1974 Manch.; MFFP 1993; DRCOG 1977.

GOLDSTONE, Professor Anthony Howard Private Patients Wing, University College Hospital, Grafton Way, London WC1 6DB Tel: 020 7380 9678 Fax: 020 7387 3025 Email: anthony.goldstone@uclh.org; 67 Loom Lane, Radlett WD7 8NX Tel: 01923 856954 Fax: 01923 859231 — BM BCh 1968 Oxf.; MA, BM BCh Oxf. 1968; FRCP Lond. 1984; FRCP Ed. 1979; MRCP (UK) 1971; FRCPath 1988, M 1975. (Univ. Coll. Hosp. Oxford Univ.) Cons. Haematologist Dir. N. Lond. Cancer Network. Socs: Brit. Soc. Haematol. & Brit. Soc. Immunol.; Pres. Brit Soc. Haem. 2000/1; Pres. Brit Soc for Blood & Marrow Transpl. 1998- 2000. Prev: Sen. Regist. (Haemat. & Haematol.) Addenbrookes Hosp. Camb.; Cancer Research Campaign Research Fell. (Therap.) Roy. Infirm.; Med. Dir. Univ. Coll. Hosp. & Middlx. Hosp. Lond.

GOLDSTONE, Anthony Peter ICSM Endocrine Unit, Hammersmith Hospital, Du Cane Road, London W12 0NN Tel: 020 8383 3242 Fax: 020 8383 3142 Email: agoldsto@rpms.ac.uk; Flat 2, 10 West Bourne Gardens, Bayswater, London W2 5PU Tel: 020 7221 6732 — BM BCh 1990 Oxf.; BA Camb. 1987; MRCP (UK) 1993. Samuel Leonard Simpson Fell. in Endocrinol. Hammersmith Hosp. Lond. Prev: MRC Clin. Train. Fell. Hammersmith Hosp. Lond.; Regist. (Endocrinol.) Hammersmith Hosp. Lond.

GOLDSTONE, Jeffrey Wingate Medical Centre, 79 Bigdale Drive, Northwood, Liverpool L33 6YJ Tel: 0151 546 2958 Fax: 0151 546 2914 — MB ChB 1979 Liverp.; MRCGP 1986.

GOLDSTONE, Jessie 24 Craigwell Road, Prestwich, Manchester M25 0EF Tel: 0161 740 2093 — MB ChB 1931 Manch. (Manch.)

GOLDSTONE, John Charles Department of Anaesthesia, University College London Hospitals, Room 103, Middlesex Hospital, London W1A 8AA Tel: 020 7636 8333 Fax: 0207 580 6423 Email: j.goldstone@ucl.ac.uk — MB BS 1981 Lond.; MD Lond. 1992; MRCS Eng. LRCP Lond. 1981; FFA RCS Eng. 1987. (Char. Cross) Cons. in Anaesth. and Intens. Care, Univ. Coll. Lond. Hosps..; Hon Sen. Lect.. Roy. Free & Univ. Coll. Med. Sch. Socs: Fell. Roy. Soc. Med.; Intens. Care Soc. & Brit. Thoracic Soc. Prev: Sen. Regist. (Anaesth.) Univ. Coll. Hosp. Lond.; Research Fell. Chest Unit Brompton & King's Coll. Hosp. Lond.; Regist. (Anaesth.) King's Coll. Hosp. Lond.

GOLDSTONE, Julian Patrick 81 Knowland, Highworth, Swindon SN6 7ND — MB ChB 1988 Stellenbosch.

GOLDSTRAW, Emma Jayne 33 Southleigh Road, Clifton, Bristol BS8 2BQ — MB ChB 1998 Bristol.

GOLDSTRAW, Paul William 5 Menai Drive, Knypersley, Stoke-on-Trent ST8 7BN — MB ChB 1972 Dundee; MRCP (UK) 1975; FRACP 1986; FAFRM 1996; FRCP 1998. Private Pract. Socs: BGS; NZGS; ASGM. Prev: Specialist Phys. to Old People Tauranga, New Zealand; Lect. (GM) Soton. Univ.

GOLDSTRAW, Mr Peter The Royal Brompton Hospital, Sydney St., London SW3 6NP Tel: 020 7351 8558 Fax: 020 7351 8560 Email: p.goldstraw@rbh.nthames.nhs.uk — MB ChB Birm. 1968; FRCS Eng. 1973; FRCS Ed. 1972. Cons. Thoracic Surg. Roy. Brompton Hosp. Lond.; Civil. Cons. RAF; Civil. Adviser RN; Hon. Cons. Benenden Hosp.; Hon. Sen. Lect. Cardiothoracic Inst. Univ. Lond.; Guest Reviewer Annals Thoracic Surg.; Mem. Edit. Bd. Thorax & Respirat. Socs: (Ex-Exec.) Soc. Cardiothoracic Surgs.; Roy. Soc. Med. (Counc. Respirat. Sect.); (Ex-Counc.) Brit. Thoracic Soc. Prev: Cons. Thoracic Surg. Middlx. & Univ. Coll. Hosps. Lond.; Sen. Regist. (Cardio-Thoracic Surg.) Gtr. Glas. HB; Regist. (Cardio-Thoracic Surg.) Roy. Infirm. & City Hosp. Edin.

GOLDSWORTHY, Basil Martin, Surg. Capt. RN Retd. 19 Western Way, Alverstoke, Gosport PO12 2NE Tel: 01705 580523 — MB BS 1935 Lond.; MRCS Eng. LRCP Lond. 1935; DMRD Eng. 1957.

GOLDSWORTHY, Lisabeth Lesley British Royal Hospital for Sick Children, St Michael's Hill, Bristol BS2 8BJ Tel: 0117 921 5411 Fax: 0117 928 5667 Email: margaret.howls@ubht.swest.nhs.uk; 81 Concorde Drive, Westbury-on-Trym, Bristol BS10 6PX — MB BS 1984 Lond.; BSc Lond. 1981; MRCP (UK) 1988; MRCPCH; DCH RCP Lond. 1988. (St. Bart.) Cons. Paediat. (Ambulatory & A & E) Bristol Roy. Childr. Hosp. Socs: Roy. Coll. Paediat. & Child Health; Brit. Paediat. Accid. & Emerg. Gp; Roy. Coll. Phys.s. Prev: Sen. Regist.

(Paediat.) S. W. Region; Regist. (Paediat.) Roy. Cornw. Hosp. Truro; Regist. (Paediat.) Roy. Childr. Hosp. Brisbane, Austral.

GOLDTHORP, Steven Lawrence Kenland House Surgery, 37 Station Road, Milngavie, Glasgow G62 8BT Tel: 0141 956 1005 Fax: 0141 955 0342; Croftcroyne, 8 Briarwell Road, Milngavie, Glasgow G62 6AW Tel: 0141 956 4145 Fax: 0141 956 4145 Email: tillthorp@briarwell.dfman.co.uk — MB ChB 1981 Leeds; BSc (Hons.) Leeds 1978; MRCGP 1988. (Leeds) GP Glas. Prev: Regist. (Dermat.) Stobhill Gen. Hosp. Glas.; Regist. (Anaesth.) W.. Infirm. Gtr. Glas. HB; SHO (O & G) Vale of Leven Dist. Gen. Hosp

GOLDTHORP, William Oates (retired) Pennine House, Pennine Drive, Ashton-under-Lyne OL6 9SE Tel: 0161 368 2541 — MB ChB Manch. 1956; FRCOG 1977, M 1963, DObst 1958. Prev: Sen. Regist. Profess. Unit St. Mary's Hosp. Manch.

GOLDTHORPE, Selwyn Brendon 45 Trent View, Keadby, Scunthorpe DN17 3DR — MB BS 1977 Newc.; MRCGP 1981; DRCOG 1980; DCH Eng. 1980.

GOLDWATER, Daniel Edward 18 Castle Hill Road, Prestwich, Manchester M25 0FR — MB ChB 1995 Manch.

GOLDWATER, Harry Leon (retired) 18 Castlehill Road, Prestwich, Manchester M25 0FR Tel: 0161 740 1016 — MB BS Durh. 1958; FFA RCS Eng. 1964; DObst RCOG 1960. Prev: Cons. Anaesth. Manch. Childr. Trust & N. Manch. Healthcare Trust.

GOLDWATER, Mr Stanley (retired) 33 Coleridge Walk, London NW11 6AT Tel: 020 8458 8192 — MB BS 1947 Lond.; FRCS Eng. 1952; MRCS Eng. LRCP Lond. 1946. Prev: Surg. Regist. OldCh. Hosp. Romford.

GOLDWYN, Charmian Rosemary Lilla The Surgery, 17 Rosslyn Road, Twickenham TW1 2AR Tel: 020 8892 1991 Fax: 020 8744 0533; 77 Elm Bank Gardens, London SW13 0NX Tel: 020 8876 3700 Fax: 020 8878 5031 — MB BS Lond. 1960; MRCS Eng. LRCP Lond. 1960. (Roy. Free) GP Trainer Twickenham. Socs: GP Writer's Assn.; Primary Care Rheum. Soc.; Primary Care Gastroenterol. Soc. Prev: Clin. Asst. (Diabetes) W. Middlx. Hosp.

GOLEBIOWSKI, Mr Adam (retired) Pelham House, 246 London Road, West Malling ME19 5AU Tel: 01732 842149 — Med. Dipl. 1938 Lwow; FRCS Eng. 1969. Prev: Resid. Surg. Off. Lond. Chest. Hosp.

GOLEN, Zbigniew 2 Rounall Avenue, Dalbeattie DG5 4TA Tel: 01556 611776 — MB ChB 1947 Polish Sch. of Med. (Polish Sch. Med.) Prev: Asst. Psychiat. Whittingham Hosp. Preston; Sen. Hosp. Med. Off. Winterton Hosp. Sedgefield; Ho. Surg. & Cas. Off. Newark Gen. Hosp.

GOLIGHER, Jane Elizabeth Queen Mary's Hospital, Sidcup DA14 6LT Tel: 020 8302 2678; 18 Lordship Park, Stoke Newington, London N16 5UD Tel: 020 8802 7188 — MB BS 1978 Lond.; DCH RCP Lond. 1982. Regist. (Radiol.) Univ. Coll. Hosp. Lond. Socs: BMA. Prev: SHO (Radiother.) St. Bart. Hosp. Lond.; SHO (Paediat.) High Wycombe Hosp.

GOLIGHTLY, Donald Lawrence, TD (retired) Moresby, Main Road, Stocksfield NE43 7NJ Tel: 01661 843291 — MB BS 1947 Durh.; BA (Hons. Fine Art) Univ. Sunderland 1997; BA (Hons.) Open 1992; BA Open Univ. 1975; MRCGP 1978; DObst RCOG 1952.

GOLIGHTLY, Kay Louise 227 Addycombe Terrace, Newcastle upon Tyne NE6 5TY Tel: 0191 276 5978 — MB BS 1990 Newc.; MRCPsych 1996. (Newc.) Specialist Regist. Hadrian Clinic Newc. Gen. Hosp.

GOLIK, Paul Orchard Surgery, Knypersley Road, Norton-in-the-Moors, Stoke-on-Trent ST6 8HY Tel: 01782 534241 Fax: 01782 541068 — MB ChB 1975 Birm.

GOLIN, Malcolm Robert Colne House Surgery, 99A Uxbridge Road, Rickmansworth WD3 2DJ Tel: 01923 776295 Fax: 01923 777744 — MB BS 1980 Lond.; MB BS (Dist. Med. & Path.) Lond. 1980; Dip. GU Med. Soc. Apoth. Lond. 1990; DCH RCP Lond. 1984; DRCOG Lond. 1983. (Westm.) Med. Adviser to Three Rivers Dist. Counc. Rickmansworth; Med. Off. Kvaener Construction InterNat. Ltd. Socs: W Herts & Watford Med. Soc. Prev: Clihnical Asst. (Genitourin. Med.) Watford Gen. Med.; Trainee GP Medway VTS; Ho. Phys. & Gen. Surg. Qu. Mary's Hosp. Roehampton.

GOLIN, Monty (retired) 21 Uplands Park Road, Enfield EN2 7PU Tel: 020 8363 1717 — MB ChB Cape Town 1951; DA Eng. 1957. Prev: GP Waltham Cross.

GOLLAN, James 7 Heatherlaw, Blackfell, Washington NE37 1JX — MB ChB 1958 Ed.; DPM Ed. & Glas. 1964. (Ed.) Socs: BMA. Prev: Ho. Off. W.. Gen. Hosp. Edin.; Regist. Centr. Hosp. Warwick & Bellsdyke Hosp. Larbert.

GOLLAND, Ian Morris Rose Lodge, 16 Hereford Road, Southsea PO5 2DH Tel: 01705 738046 Fax: 01705 738046 — MB ChB 1981 Ed.; BSc (Hons.) Ed. 1978, MD 1991; MRCOG 1986. Cons. O & G Portsmouth & SE Hants. HA. Prev: Sen. Regist. Rotat. (O & G) St. Mary's Hosp. Portsmouth & Hammersmith; Regist. & Research Fell. (O & G) Univ. Hosp. S. Manch.

GOLLAPUDI, Mr Sriramamurti 4 The Stables, Walton, Wakefield WF2 6TA Tel: 01924 249528 Email: gsmurti@globalnet.co.uk — MB BS Andhra 1969; MCh Liverp. 1987; MS (Orth.) Andhra 1973; FRCS Glas. 1983. Cons. Trauma & Othopaedic Surg. Ponderfields & Pontefract Hosp.s NHS Trust. Socs: Fell. BOA. Prev: Regist. Centre for Hip Surg. & Hand Surgic. Unit Wrightington; Regist. BRd.green Hosp. Liverp.; Asst. Prof. Orthop. Andhra Univ., India.

GOLLEDGE, Jonathan 7 Warwick Place, Thornbury, Bristol BS35 1EZ — MB BChir 1990 Camb.

GOLLEDGE, Norman Hedley Hedworth (retired) St Mary's, Bridge Road, Kingswear, Dartmouth TQ6 0DZ Tel: 01803 752506 Fax: 01803 752506 — MRCS Eng. LRCP Lond. 1939; MRCGP 1952.

GOLLEDGE, Peter 1 Hawthorn Terrace, Sunderland SR6 8BE Email: gollburns@supanet.com — MB ChB 1989 Manch.; MRCP (UK) 1993. Specialist Regist. (Cardiol. & Med.) N. E. Thames Deanery Lond.

GOLLIN, Teresa Jean Harptree Surgery, Bristol Road, West Harptree, Bristol BS40 6HF Tel: 01761 221406 Fax: 01761 221882 Email: teresa.gollin@gp-l81030.nhs.uk — MB ChB 1980 Birm.; MRCGP 1984; LFHom 1996; DRCOG 1983. (Birmingham)

GOLLINGS, Anthony John Group Practice Surgery, Middle Chare, Chester-le-Street DH3 3QD Tel: 0191 388 4857 Fax: 0191 388 7448; 2 Park Road N., Chester-le-Street DH3 3SD — MB BS 1971 Newc.

GOLLINS, Simon William North Wales Cancer Treatment Centre, Glan Clwyd NHS Trust, Rhyl LL18 5UJ Tel: 01745 445161 Fax: 01745 445212 — BM BCh 1988 Oxf.; MA Oxf. 1986, DPhil 1985, BA 1982; MRCP (UK) 1991; FRCR 1994. (Oxford University) Cons. in Clin. Oncol., N. Wales Cancer Treatm. Centre, Rhyl. Prev: Cons. in Clin. ColOncol. Velindre NHS Trust Cardiff; Sen. Regist. (Clin. Oncol.) Velindre NHS Trust Cardiff; Regist. (Radiother. & Oncol.) Christie Hosp. Manch.

GOLLINS, William James Frederick Dikoya, Croft Drive W., Caldy, Wirral CH48 2JQ Tel: 0151 625 9584 — MB ChB 1960 Liverp.; MFOM RCP Lond. 1988; DPH Leeds 1965; DObst RCOG 1963. (Liverp.) Med. Adviser Dista Products & Ford Motor Co. Prev: Med. Off. DHSS; Med. Off. Unilever (Merseyside) Ltd.; Departm. Med. Off. Boros. Kingston-upon-Hull & Birkenhead.

GOLLOCK, Mr John Maurice Windyknowe House, Windyknowe Road, Galashiels TD1 1RQ Tel: 01896 757025 — MB ChB 1969 Ed.; FRCS Ed. 1974. Cons. Surg. Borders Gen. Hosp. Melrose, Roxburghsh. Scotl. Socs: Moynihan Chirurgical Club; St. Marks Assn.; Ed. Harveian Soc. Prev: Resid. Surgic. Off. St. Mark's Hosp. Lond.

GOLSHETTI, Virupaxi Golappa Rapid Access Chest Pain Clinic, Clinic D, Glenfield Hospital, Leicester LE3 9QS Tel: 0116 250 2481 Fax: 0116 250 2653; 23 Lindhurst Lane, Mansfield NG18 4JE Tel: 01623 653528 — MB BS 1965 Karnatak; DFFP 1994. Hosp. Specialist in Cardiol. i/c of rapid access chest pain clinic, Dept. of Cardiol., Glenfield Hosp., Leicester. Prev: Med. Off. (Cardiac Pacemaker Implant.) Glenfield Unit; Regional Cardiac Centre Leics.; Regist. in Cardiol., Leicester.

GOLTON, Andrea Gayl 15 Ravenscroft Avenue, Wembley HA9 9TJ Tel: 020 8904 3097 Fax: 020 8904 3097 — MB BS 1971 Lond.; DMRD Eng. 1974. (Roy. Free Lond.) Socs: Fell.Roy. Soc. Med. Prev: Sen. Regist. (Radiol.) N.wick Pk. Hosp. Harrow & Roy. Free Hosp.; Lond.

GOLTON, Michael John Rotherfield Surgery, Rotherfield, Crowborough TN6 3QW Tel: 01892 852415/853288 Fax: 01892 853499 — MB BS 1986 Lond.; DCH; DRCOG.

GOMAA, Mr Hany El Sayed Mousa 9 Dyke Nook Close, Whickham, Newcastle upon Tyne NE16 5TD — MB BCh 1976 Cairo; FRCS Ed. 1989.

GOMARA, Carita Julia Boyd 4 St Peters Road, Cirencester GL7 1RG — MB BS 1989 Lond.; MRCGP 1994; DCH RCP Lond. 1993; DRCOG 1992. (Char. Cross & Westm. Med. Sch. Lond.)

GOMATHINAYAGAM, Alagappan Browns Buildings, 1/2 Front Street, Dipton, Stanley DH9 9AB Tel: 01207 571222 Fax: 01207 570070; Kripa, 15 Lee Hill Court, Lanchester, Durham DH7 0QE Tel: 01207 529081 — MB BS 1972 Madras. (Madurai Med. Coll.) Prev: SHO (Med.) Shotley Bridge Hosp. & Leigh Infirm.

GOMERSALL, Charles David 40 De Vere Gardens, London W8 5AH — MB BS 1985 Lond.

GOMERSALL, Charles Roger (retired) The Lodge, Hamsterley, Bishop Auckland DL13 3QF Tel: 01388 488476 Fax: 01388 488476 — MS BS 1966 Durh.; FRCOG 1984, M 1971. Cons. O & G S. Durh. Hosps. NHS Trust. Prev: 1st Asst. (O & G) Univ. Newc.

GOMERSALL, Patricia Mary Doctors Surgery, Newton Way, Baildon, Shipley BD17 5NH Tel: 01274 582506 Fax: 01274 532426; Kingsleigh, 22 Kings Road, Ilkley LS29 9AN Tel: 01943 607445 — MB ChB 1974 Bristol; DRCOG 1979.

GOMES, A N V Dean House Surgery, 193 High Street, Ponders End, Enfield EN3 4DZ Tel: 020 8804 1060 Fax: 020 8367 8787 — MB BS 1966 Mysore; MB BS 1966 Mysore.

GOMES, Aloysius Joseph Eric Moore Health Centre, Tanners Lane, Warrington WA2 7LY Tel: 01925 417252 — LRCPI & LM, LRSCI & LM 1960; LRCPI & LM, LRCSI & LM 1960. (RCSI)

GOMES, Judith Adelina 45 Cranhurst Road, Willesden Green, London NW2 4LL Tel: 020 8450 6861 — MB BS 1987 Lond.; MRCGP 1993; Cert. Family Plann. JCC 1991; DRCOG 1991. Prev: Trainee GP Lond.; SHO (O & G) Barking Hosp. Essex; SHO (Paediat.) Hillingdon Hosp. Uxbridge Middlx.

GOMES, Maria De Fatima Almeida Sefton Avenue Surgery, 3 Sefton Avenue, London NW7 3QB Tel: 020 8959 1868 Fax: 020 8906 0595 — MRCS Eng. LRCP Lond. 1974; MRCP (UK) 1979.

GOMES, Peter John The Medical Specialist Group, PO Box 113, Alexandra House, Les Frieteaux, St Martin's, Guernsey GY1 3EX Tel: 01481 238565 — BM 1984 Soton.; 2000 FRCP Ed.; MRCP (UK) 1988; Dip. IMC RCS Ed. 1993. (Soton.) Cons. Phys. & Med. Oncologist, P.ss Eliz. Hosp. Le Vanquiedor, St. Martin's, Guernsey, CI. Prev: Sen. Regist. (Med. Oncol.) Char. Cross Hosp. Lond.; Sen. Regist. (Gen. Internal Med.) RAF Hosp. Wegberg; Cons. Phys. & Med. Oncol. Roy. Hosp. Haslar, Gosport.

GOMES DERANIYAGALA, Gorakanage Basil Abercromby Health Centre, Grove Street, Edge Hill, Liverpool L7 7HG Tel: 0151 708 9370; 15 Loyola Hey, Rainhill, Prescot L35 6PZ Tel: 0151 430 6759 — MB BS Ceylon 1964; MCGP (Sri Lanka) 1976; MACF. GP Liverp. Prev: SCMO (Occupat. Health) & Clin. Med. Off. Community Health St. Helens & Knowsley HA; SHO (A & E) Frimley Pk. Hosp.; GP Colombo, Sri Lanka.

GOMES DERANIYAGALA, Gorakanage Reshmaal Deepthi Royal Free Hospital, Hampstead, London NW3 Tel: 020 7794 0500; 15 Loyola Hey, Rainhill, Prescot L35 6PZ Tel: 0151 430 6759 Fax: 020 7430 6759 — MB ChB 1994 Liverp.; MRCP (Lond.) 1998. (Liverp.) SHO (Geriat. Med.) Roy. Free Hosp. Lond. Socs: BMA & Med. Defence Union. Prev: SHO (Critical Care) Rotat. Whiston Hosp.; Med. SHO (Endocrin/Diabetes/Gen. Med.); Med. Heinsman Mayday Univ Hosp.

GOMESZ, Felix Anthony Remegius Gatwick Park Hospital, Povey Cross Road, Horley RH6 0BB Tel: 01293 785511; Colley House, Reigate Heath, Reigate RH2 9JP Tel: 01737 241018 — MB BS 1962 Ceylon; FFA RCS Eng. 1971. (Univ. Ceylon) Cons. Anaesth. Pain Relief Clinic E. Surrey Hosp. Redhill. Socs: Assoc. Mem. Intractable Pain Soc. GB & Irel.; Internat. Assn. Study of Pain; Internat. Neuromodulation Soc.

GOMEZ, Bandula Kamala 17 Ferndale Road, Chichester PO19 4QJ — MB BS 1970 Ceylon. (Univ. Colombo, Sri Lanka) Staff Grade (psychiat.) Worthing Priority Cave. Prev: SHO Portsmouth Healthcare NHS Trust; Clin. Asst. Winehuter & E.leigh Healthcare NHS Trust.

GOMEZ, Charles Keith Rizleigh 55 Pirbright Road, Southfields, London SW18 5ND Tel: 020 8870 0424 Email: kgomez@globalnet.co.uk — MB BS 1992 Lond.; BSc Lond. 1989; MRCP (UK) 1995; Dip RCPath (UK) 1999. (St. Thos. Hosp. Lond.) Regist. (Haemat) W. Middlx. Hosp, Twickenham. Prev: Regist. (Haemat.) Hammersmith Hosp. Lond.; Regist. (Haemat.) Ealing Hosp. Lond.; SHO (Haemat.) Roy. Free Hosp. Lond.

GOMEZ, George 103 Dora Road, Wimbledon Park, London SW19 7JT — MB BS 1945 Lond.; FRCGP 1975, M 1953. (Lond. Hosp.) Hosp. Pract. Allergy ENT Dept. St. Geo. Hosp. Tooting; Hon. Sen. Lect. Dept. Gen. Pract. & RCGP Tutor St. Geo. Hosp. Med. Sch. Lond.; Clin. Asst. ENT Dept. Qu. Mary's Hosp. Roehampton; Occupat. Health Med. Off. Lond. Boro. Wandsworth; Attached To MRC Social Med. Research Unit Lond. Sch. Hyg. & Trop. Socs: Med. Mem. Brit. Allergy Soc. & Hunt. Soc. Prev: Clin. Asst. ENT Dept. St. Mary Abbot's Hosp. Lond.; Flight Lt. RAF Med. Br.

GOMEZ, Joan Rae (retired) Natterjack, Thursley Road, Churt, Farnham GU10 2LG Tel: 01428 606354 Fax: 01428 606354 Email: jrgomez966@aol.com — MB BS Lond. 1945; FRCPsych 1985, M 1974; DPM Eng. 1973; DHMSA 1996; DPMSA 1997. Hon. Cons. Psychiat. Chelsea & W.m. Hosp. Lond.; Friend of the Wellcome Inst. Prev: Cons. Psychiat. W.m. Hosp. Lond. & Gordon Hosp. Lond.

GOMEZ, Kumudini Renuka 55 Pirbright Road, Southfields, London SW18 5ND Tel: 020 8870 0424 Email: kgomez@globalnet.co.uk — MB BS 1994 Lond.; BSc Lond. 1991; MRCP (UK) 1997. (UMDS (Guy's & St. Thos. Hosps.)) Specialist Regist. (Paediat.) W. Middliesex Hosp. Twickenham. Prev: SHO (Paediat.) Roy. Brompton Hosp. Lond.; SHO (Paediat.) Guy's & St. Thos. Hosps. Lond.; SHO (Paediat.) All St.s Hosp. Chatham Kent.

GOMEZ, Michael Peter Gaspar Anthony The Royal West Sussex Hospital Trust, St Richards, Spitalfield Lane, Chichester PO19 4SE Tel: 01243 831608 Fax: 01243 831606 Email: mikegomez@rws-tr.sthames.nhs.uk — MB BS Colombo 1969; FRCOG 1995, M 1977; FSLCOG 1999. (Univ. Colombo, Sri Lanka) Cons. Genitourin. Med. Roy. W. Sussex Hosp. Trust, St. Richards Chichester & War Memor. Hosp. Bognor Regis. Socs: Soc. Study VD; Fell. Roy. Coll. Obst. & Gyn.; BMA. Prev: Regist. (Genitourin. Med.) Fletcher Clinic Chichester; Cons. O & G Matern. Hosp. & K. Faisal Hosp. Taif, Saudi Arabia; Sen. Lect. & Hon. Cons. Ragama Gen. Hosp. & N. Colombo Med. Sch. Colombo.

GOMEZ BORDAS, Luis Alfonso 308A Heathwood Road, Cardiff CF14 4HT — LMS 1990 Cantabria.

GOMEZ MARTIN, Julien 425 Stanningley Road, Leeds LS13 4BL — LMS 1990 Navarre.

GOMEZ-REINO SANCHIS, Jose Maria Greenwich District Hospital, Geriatric Department, London SE10 9HE — LMS 1990 Alicante.

GOMM, Stephanie Audrey St Ann's Hospice, Little Hutton, Manchester M38 0EL Tel: 0161 702 8181 Fax: 0161 790 0181; 18 Briksdal Way, Lostock, Bolton BL6 4PQ — MB ChB 1973 Manch.; MD Manch. 1986; MRCP (UK) 1977. (Manchester) Med. Dir. St. Ann's Hosp. Manch.; Hon. Cons. Salford Roy. Hosp. NHS Trust. Socs: Fell. Manch. Med. Soc.; Assn. Palliat. Med.; Brit. Thorac. Soc. Prev: Sen. Regist. (Palliat. Med.) Leeds; Sen. Regist. (Gen. & Respirat. Med.) Manch.; Univ. Tutor (Med.) Manch. Roy. Infirm.

GOMMERSALL, Lyndon Mark Spider Cottage, Kings End, Powick, Worcester WR2 4RE — BM BS 1997 Nottm.

GOMPELS, Brian Malcolm 7 Heathfield, Cobham KT11 2QY Tel: 0137 284 3668 — MB BS 1963 Lond.; MRCS Eng. LRCP Lond. 1963; FFR 1971; DMRD Eng. 1968. (King's Coll. Hosp.) Cons. Radiol. Epsom Dist. Hosp. Socs: Hosp. Cons. & Specialist Assn. Prev: Sen. Regist. St. Thos. Hosp. Lond.

GOMPELS, Mark Martin Albert Dept Immunology, Southmead Hospital, Westbury on Tym, Bristol BS10 5NB — MB BS 1986 Lond.; BSc Lond. 1983; MRCP (UK) 1989; MRC Path 1998; MD 1998. Cons. Immunol. S.mead Hosp., Bristol Roy. Infirm.; Cons Immunol. & Allegy, Taunton. Prev: Research Regist. (Immunol.) St. Bart. Hosp. Lond.; Sen. Regist. (Immunol.) Newc. Gen. Hosp.

GOMPELS, Mary Anne Barbara Market Lavington Surgery, 15 Church Street, Market Lavington, Devizes SN10 4DT Tel: 01380 812500 — MB BS 1986 Lond.; MRCGP 1990; DRCOG 1989. (St. Mary's Hosp. & Med. Sch. Lond.) Prev: Trainee GP/SHO Whipps Cross Hosp. Lond. VTS; Ho. Off. (Surg. & Med.) St. Chas. Hosp. Lond.

GOMPERTZ, David 17 Oakmere Lane, Potters Bar EN6 5LS Email: dgomp@compuserve.com — PhD Lond. 1965; BSc (Hons.) Anat. Birm. 1957, MD 1976, MB ChB 1960; FFOM RCP Lond. 1988, M 1981; FRCPath 1984, M 1975. (Birm.) Prev: Cons. Occupat. & Environm. Health MRC Inst. of Environm. & Health; Dep. Dir. Med. Servs. (Res. & Path.) Health & Safety Exec. Lond.; Sen. Lect. & Cons. Biochem. Genetics Roy. Postgrad. Med. Sch. Hosp. Lond.

GOMPERTZ, Deborah Alexandria 45 Eastbury Grove, Chiswick, London W4 2JT Email: debdoc@doctors.org.uk — MB ChB 1994 Birm.; ChB Birm. 1994; MRCP 1997. Ho. Surg. Qu. Eliz. Hosp. Birm.

GOMPERTZ, Hugh Richard, OBE (retired) 41 Ocean Drive, Ferring, Worthing BN12 5QP Tel: 01903 244879 — MB BS 1953 Lond.; MRCS Eng. LRCP Lond. 1953; DObst RCOG 1955. Prev: Med. Off. W. View Hosp. Tenterden.

GOMPERTZ, Patrick Hugh Department of Health Care of the Elderly, The Royal London Hospital (Mile End), Bancroft Road, London E1 4DG Tel: 020 7377 7843 Fax: 020 7377 7844 Email: patrick.gompertz@thht.org — MB ChB 1985 Bristol; FRCP (UK) 1999. Cons. Phys. Geriat. Med. Roy. Lond. Hosp. Socs: Amer. Geriat. Soc. & Brit. Geriat. Soc. Prev: Sen. Regist. (Geriat. & Gen. Med.) Newham Healthcare; Research Regist. Roy. Free Hosp. & Lond. Hosp.; Regist. (Med.) Whipps Cross Hosp. Lond.

GOMPERTZ, Mr Richard Henry Kent Queens Hospital, Belvedere Road, Burton-on-Trent DE13 0RB Tel: 01283 566333; Consulting Rooms, Worthington House, 146 High St, Burton-on-Trent DE14 1JE Email: henry.gompertz@btinternet.com — MB BS 1980 Lond.; MS Lond. 1990; MRCS Eng. LRCP Lond. 1980; FRCS Eng. 1984. (Westm.) Cons. Gastroenterol. Surg. Qu.s Hosp. Burton. Socs: Brit. Soc. Gastroenterol.; Surg. Research Soc. GB & Irel. Prev: Lect. & Sen. Regist. (Surg.) Freeman Hosp. & Univ. Dept. Surg. Roy. Vict. Infirm. Newc.; MRC Research Fell. Roy. Postgrad. Med. Sch. Hammersmith Hosp. Lond.; Regist. (Surg.) Hammersmith Hosp. Lond.

GOMPERTZ, Richard Michael Henry (retired) 14 Ashfield House, Bayshill Lane, Cheltenham G50 3AX Tel: 01242 513600 — MB BS Lond. 1952; MRCS Eng. LRCP Lond. 1953; DObst RCOG 1954; DCH Eng. 1955; LMCC 1964. Prev: Assoc. Specialist (Paediat.) Cheltenham Gen. & Matern. Hosps.

GOMPERTZ, Simon Martin 76 Limes Road, Tettenhall, Wolverhampton WV6 8RB Tel: 01902 744747 Email: randsgomp@compuserve.com — MB ChB 1990 Birm.; ChB Birm. 1990; BSc (Hons.) Birm. 1987; MRCP (UK) 1994. (Univ. Birm.) Clin. Research Fell. Qu. Eliz. Hosp. Birm. Socs: BMA; Brit. Thorac. Soc.

GONCALVES-ARCHER, Edward Bernard Hook and Hartley Wintney Medical Partnership, 1 Chapter Terrace, Hartley Wintney, Hook RG27 8QJ Tel: 01252 842087 Fax: 01252 843145; Greensleeves, Deptford Lane, Greywell, Basingstoke RG29 1BS — MB BS 1978 Lond.; MRCS Eng. LRCP Lond. 1978.

GONÇALVES-ARCHER, Helena Cristina North Lane Practice, 38 North Lane, Aldershot GU12 4QQ Tel: 01252 344434; Greensleeves, Greywell, Basingstoke — MB BS 1978 Lond. (Roy. Free) Clin. Asst. (Diabetes) Basingstoke Dist. Hosp. Socs: BMA. Prev: Ho. Surg. (Gen. Surg. & Orthop.) & Ho. Phys. (Gen. Med. & Nephrol.) Roy. Free Hosp. Lond.

GONDE, Jennifer Elizabeth 33 Linwood Close, London SE5 8UT — MB BS 1993 Lond.

GONDHIA, Anjalee 22 Wychwood Avenue, Edgware HA8 6TH — MB BS 1993 Lond.

GONEM, Mr Mohammed Nabil Hassaan 25 Cams Hill, Fareham PO16 8RB Tel: 01329 280975 — MB BCh 1964 Alexandria; FRCS Eng. 1971; MRCS Eng. LRCP Lond. 1975; FRCR 1978; DMRD Eng. 1977. (Alexandria) Cons. Radiol. Qu. Alexandra Hosp. Portsmouth. Prev: Sen. Regist. (Radiol.) St. Thos. Hosp. Lond.; Regist. (Radiol.) King's Coll. Hosp. Lond.

GONET, Mr Leon Casimir Louis 'Heatherwood', 70 Coombe Lane W., Kingston upon Thames KT2 7DA — MB BS 1940 Lond.; FRCS Eng. 1950; MRCS Eng. LRCP Lond. 1939. (St. Geo. & King's Coll.) Hon. (Emerit.) Cons. Orthop. Surg. Chelsea, Kensington & W.m. Vict. Health Auth. (T); Cons. Orthop. Surg. New Vict. Hosp. Kingston upon Thames, St. Anthony's Hosp. Cheam, & Cromwell Hosp. Lond.; Chairm. DHSS Med. Bds. Indust. Injuries. Socs: Sen. Fell. Brit. Orthop. Assn.; Founder Mem. Int. Arthroscopy Assn. Prev: 1st Asst. Orthop. & Traum. Dept. W. Middlx. Hosp.; Sen. Regist. Heatherwood Orthop. Hosp.; Maj. RAMC 1940-46 (Mentioned in Despatches).

GONI, Ahsan-Ul-Haq Shakespeare Road Surgery, 50 Shakespeare Road, Eastwood, Rotherham S65 1QY Tel: 01709 836969 Fax: 01709 837000 — MB BS 1971 Jammu & Kashmir; DCH Jammu Univ. 1981; Cert. Community. Paediat. Sheff. 1989; FPA (UK) 1987; DFFP (UK) 1999. GP; Hon. Clin. Teach. Sheff. Inst. of Gen. Pract. & Primary Care Sheff. Univ.; GP Tutor Quality in Pract. Rotherham S. Yorks. Socs: MDU.

GONI, Riyaz Ahmad Health Clinic, Gardens Lane, Conisborough, Doncaster DN12 3JW Tel: 01709 862150 — MB BS 1966 Jammu & Kashmir.

GONI SARRIGUREN, Alberto 5 Ffordd Beck, Copper Meadow, Gowerton, Swansea SA4 3GE — LMS 1987 Navarre; DRCOG 1995.

GONSAI, Ramnikgiri Bachugiri The Surgery, 179 Cumberland Road, London E13 8LS Tel: 020 7476 1029 Fax: 020 7476 6616 — MB BS 1967 Gujarat.

GONSALKORALE, Mahendra Hope Hospital, Stott Lane, Salford M6 8HD Tel: 0161 787 4044 Fax: 0161 787 4031 Email: mgonsalkorale@hope.srht.nwest.nhs.uk — MSc Manch. 1990; MD Ceylon 1973, MB BS 1967; FRCP Lond. 1992; MRCP (UK) 1975. (Faculty of Medicine, Sir Lanke) Cons. Phys. Elderly Care Hope Hosp. Salford; Hon. Assoc. Lect. (Geriat. Med.) Univ. Manch.; Project Dir., Salford Roy. Hosp. NHS Trust. Socs: Brit. Geriat. Soc. & Internat. Continence Soc. Prev: Cons. Neurol. Gen. Hosp. Kandy, Sri Lanka; Sen. Regist. (Geriat. Med.) S. Manch. HA; Regist. (Neurol.) Addenbrooke's Hosp. Camb.

GONSALVES, Mr Hannibal Joseph Billy General Hospital, Bishop Auckland DL14 6AD Tel: 01388 454000 Fax: 01388 454136; Tower Lodge, Morley, Bishop Auckland DL14 0PH Tel: 01388 718374 Email: hjbgonsalves@aol.com — MB BS Dacca 1967; LRCP LRCS Ed. LRCPS Glas. 1977; FRCS Eng. 1976; FRCS Ed. 1976. (Chittagong Med. Coll.) Cons. Surg. (A & E Med.) S. Durh. Healthcare NHS Trust. Socs: Fell. Roy. Soc. Med.; N. Eng. Surgic. Soc.; Brit. Assn. Accid. & Emerg. Med. Prev: Cons. Surg. Vict. Hosp. Castries St. Lucia, W. Indies; Regist. (Surg.) Louth Co. Hosp. & Hartlepool Gen. Hosp.

GONSALVES, J V Fulwood Green Medical Centre, Fulwood Green Medical Centre, Jericho Lane, Liverpool L17 4AR Tel: 0151 727 2440 Fax: 0151 726 1936.

GONSALVES, Olive Joan 337 Cannon Hill Lane, Raynes Park, London SW20 9HQ — MB BS 1950 Bombay; DTM & H Eng. 1965; DCH Eng. 1957. (Grant Med. Coll.) Sessional Med. Off. Health Dept. Lond. Boro. Wandsworth.

GONSALVES, Patrick The Surgery, 432 Kingstanding Road, Kingstanding, Birmingham B44 9SA Tel: 0121 377 8244 Fax: 0121 350 0150; 2 Honiley Drive, New Oscott, Sutton Coldfield B73 6RN Tel: 0121 355 5999 — MB BS 1970 Madras. (Christian Med. Coll. Vellore)

GONTEB, Gerson Pinderfields General Hospital, Aberford Road, Wakefield WF1 4DG — MB ChB 1980 Natal.

GONZAGA, Rabindran Thuraisingham 23 Whetstone Close, Farquhar Road, Edgbaston, Birmingham B15 2QL — MB BCh BAO 1990 NUI.

***GONZALEZ, Dominic Michael** 114 Banner Cross Road, Ecclesall, Sheffield S11 9HR Tel: 0114 235 0221 — MB ChB 1988 Sheff.

GONZALEZ, Elizabeth 110 Common Road, Wombourne, Wolverhampton WV5 0LN — MB ChB 1997 Leeds.

GONZALEZ, Maria Luisa Rosa 121 Penarth Haven, Penarth Marina, Penarth CF64 1TT — MB BS 1988 W. Indies.

GONZALEZ, Michael Angelo Flat 2, 17 St Phillips Road, Surbiton KT6 4DU — BM BS 1998 Nottm.; BM BS Nottm 1998.

GONZALEZ, Orlando Manthorpe Centre for Elderly Services, 101 Manthorpe Road, Grantham NG31 8DG Tel: 01476 578901 Fax: 01476 578897; Frith House, Normanton-on-Cliffe, Grantham NG32 3BH Tel: 01400 250302 Fax: 01400 250302 Email: orlandogonzalez@tinyworld.co.uk — D Med y Cir Pontificia Univ. Javeriana, Colombia 1970; DPH RCP Lond. 1975; MRCPsych 1983. Cons. Psychiat. S. Lincs.Healthcare NHS Trust. Prev: SHO Regist. Rotat. W.minster Hosp.; Sen. Regist. (Psychiat.) Roy. S. Hants. Hosp. Soton; Sen. Regist. (Psychiat.) Char. Cross Hosp. Lond.

GONZALEZ, Mr Vicente Gaston 39 Shaftesbury Avenue, Penwortham, Preston PR1 0EL Tel: 01772 744019 — LRCP LRCS 1985 Ed.; MD Chile 1972; FRCS Glas. 1984; LRCP LRCS Ed. LRCPS Glas. 1985.

GONZALEZ CARVAJAL, John Ramon 37 Cambridge Road, Twickenham TW1 2TJ — MB ChB 1988 Manch.

GONZALEZ CASTRO, Aurora Leeds General Infirmary, Leeds LS1 3EX; 37 Ridgeway, Randhay, Leeds LS8 4DD Tel: 0113 217

9212 — LMS 1990 Oviedo; FRCS Glas. 1997; MSc Teesside 1996. Specialist Regist. (Orthop.) Leeds Gen. Infimary Leeds.

GONZALEZ CONTRERAS, Raquel Begona Central Surgery, Bell Street, Sawbridgeworth CM21 9AQ Tel: 01279 723172 — LMS 1988 Basque Provinces.

GONZALEZ ELOSEGUI, Ana Maria Doctor's Quarters Block 1, Room 4, Worcester Royal Infirmary, Newtown Road, Worcester WR5 1HN; Apartment 4, Grove House, Harrow Croft, off Farmbrook Close, Worcester WR2 5UG Tel: 01905 422938 — LMS 1991 Navarre. SHO (A & E) Alexandra Redditch Hosp. NHS Trust. Prev: Ho. Off. Worcester Roy. Infirm. & Countess of Chester Hosp.

GONZALEZ GARCIA, Laura Virginia 66 Hazel Drive, Woodley, Reading RG5 3SA — LMS 1989 Valladolid.

GONZALEZ GRACIA, Isabel Maria Barts & London NHS Trust Tel: 01642 854600; 2 The Gardens, (Rear of 35 High Street), Normanby, Middlesbrough TS6 0LD — LMS 1988 Saragossa; FRCA 2001; MRCP (UK) 1994. Specialist Regist. (Anaesth.) Newc. Hosps. Socs: RCP (Glas.); RCA (Lond.); Assn. Anaesth.

GONZALEZ-MARTIN, Jose Argelio Flat 202c, Waterloo Warehouse, Waterloo Road, Liverpool L3 0BH — LMS 1991 La Laguna.

GONZALEZ NARANJO, Domingo Salvador 192 Highbridge Road, Sutton Coldfield B73 5QT — LMS 1994 Valencia.

GONZALEZ POLLEDO, Javier Eastbourne Hospitals NHS Trust, Kings Drive, Eastbourne BN21 2UD Tel: 01323 417400 Email: javiergonz-poll@freeserve.co.uk; Flat 2, 19 St. John's Road, Meads, Eastbourne BN20 7NQ Tel: 01323 639320 — LMS 1984 Santiago de Compostela; DRCOG 1997. (Santiago de Compostela) GP Regist. Socs: BMA; MDU. Prev: GP/ Regist. E.bourne; SHO Paediat.; SHO (Psychiat.) E.bourne Dist. Gen. Hosp.

GONZALEZ PRIETO, Maria de la Concepcion 1 The Cedars, Colinton Road, Edinburgh EH13 0PT Tel: 0131 441 6485 — LMS 1985 Cantabria.

GONZALEZ SANTOS, Rafael 49 Brambleside, Kettering NN16 9BH — LMS 1987 Malaga.

GONZALEZ SANZ, Nuria Plot 48, 19 Kelway, Binley, Coventry CV3 2XP — LMS 1984 Barcelona.

GONZALEZ SORDO, Maria Dolores Doctors' Mess, Huddersfield Royal Infirmary, Acre St., Huddersfield HD3 3EA; Riding Edge, Scotland Lane, Horsforth, Leeds LS18 5SF — LMS 1993 Cantabria.

GOOCH, Christopher Leeds 106 Hillview Drive, Clarkston, Glasgow G76 7JD — MB ChB 1993 Glas.

GOOCH, Ingrid Joanne Flat 3, Over Dinsdale Hall, Over Dinsdale, Darlington DL2 1PW — MB BCh 1996 Witwatersrand.

GOOCH, Jocelyn Amanda Hebden Bridge Health Centre, Hangingroyd Lane, Hebden Bridge HX7 6AG Tel: 01422 842333 Fax: 01422 842404; 8 Freshwater East Road, Lamphey, Pembroke SA71 5JX — MB BS 1990 Lond. GP Hebden Bridge Gp Pract.

GOOD, Mr Anthony Malcolm Thomas Accident & Emergency, Royal Liverpool University Hospital, Liverpool Tel: 0151 706 2026 — MB BS 1983 Lond.; FRCS Ed. 1990; FRCS Ed. 1992 (A&E); FFAEM 1996; M MED SCI 1999. Cons. A & E Med. Roy. Liverp. Univ. Hosp.; Hon. Lect., Univ. Dept. of Med.

GOOD, Brian John The Health Centre, Tavanagh Avenue, Portadown, Craigavon BT62 3BU Tel: 01762 351497; Park House, Tandragee, Craigavon BT62 2AY — MB ChB 1975 Bristol.

GOOD, Catriona Diana c/o Miss Fiona Good, Flat 8, 7 Wetherby Place, London SW7 4NG — MB ChB 1985 Cape Town; FRCR 1993.

GOOD, Christopher Douglas Drybrook Surgery, Drybrook Road, Drybrook GL17 9JE Tel: 01594 542239 Fax: 01594 544501; Windmill Cottage, Vention Lane, Lydbrook GL17 9RL Tel: 01594 860542 — MB ChB 1978 Bristol; MRCGP 1984. Prev: Med. Med. Glos. FHSA & HA.

GOOD, Mr Christopher John (retired) The Blackheath Hospital, 40 Lee Terrace, London SE3 9UD Tel: 020 8318 4900 — MB BS 1969 Lond.; MRCS Eng. LRCP Lond. 1969; FRCS Eng. 1974. Cons. Orthop. Surg. Qu. Mary's Hosp. Sidcup. Prev: Sen. Regist. (Orthop.) St. Geo. Hosp. Lond.

GOOD, Christopher Saxty Spinney Cottage, Thicket Grove, Maidenhead SL6 4LW Tel: 01628 628157 Fax: 01628 627007 Email: chris.good@three-stacks.demon.co.uk — BM BCh 1963 Oxf.; MA Oxf. 1963; FRCS Eng. 1970; MRCS Eng. LRCP Lond. 1964. (Oxf. & Guy's) Socs: Fell. Roy. Soc. Med.

GOOD, Harry William Whateley, TD (retired) 27 Lenham Road E., Saltdean, Brighton BN2 8AF Tel: 01273 304707 — MB BCh BAO 1936 Dub.; MA, MB BCh BAO Dub. 1936. Prev: Lt.-Col. RAMC (V).

GOOD, Mr Peter Dudley Tandragee Health Clinic, 3 Montague Street, Tandragee, Craigavon BT62 2AN Tel: 028 3884 0223; 8 Old Scarva Road, Tandragee, Craigavon BT62 2ED — MB ChB 1972 Ed.; FRCS Ed. 1978.

GOOD, Mr Stewart Ian Accident and Emergency Department, Royal Shrewsbury Hospital, Mytton Oak Road, Shrewsbury SY3 8XQ Tel: 01743 261313 Fax: 01743 261166 Email: sgood@injury-reports.co.uk; Thje Old Vicarage, Ford, Shrewsbury SY5 9LL Tel: 01743 851027 — MB ChB 1982 Birm.; FRCS Glas. 1987; FFAEM 1994; DA (UK) 1992; Dip IMC Res (Ed) 2000. Cons. A & E Roy. Shrewsbury Hosp.; Med. Off. to amateur swimming Assoc./Amateur Swimming Federat. of Gt. Britain, covering Dist., Nat. and Interntl and aquatic experts. Socs: Fell. Fac. Accid. & Emerg. Med.; BMA; Brit. Assn. Accid. & Emerg. Med. Prev: Sen. Regist. (A & E) Univ. Coll. Hosp. Lond.; SHO (Anaesth.) N. Staffs. Hosp. Centre; Regist. (A&E) Lincoln Co. Hosp.

***GOOD, Vanessa Jane** The Vicarage, Ditton Priors, Bridgnorth WV16 6SQ Tel: 01746 712636 — MB BS 1997 Lond.; BA (Hons - Class I Physiol. Sci.) Oxon 1994.

GOOD, William Ross Algitha Lodge Surgery, 4 Algitha Road, Skegness PE25 2AQ Tel: 01754 766766 Fax: 01754 760632 — MB ChB 1975 Dundee. GP Skegness; Clin. Asst. Geriat. Day Unit Skegness. Prev: SHO (Neurol.) Dundee Roy. Infirm.; Regist. (Med.) Perth Roy. Infirm.; Regist. (Med.) Ninewells Hosp. & Med. Sch. Dundee.

GOODA, Susan Elizabeth (retired) The Limey, Sutherland Farm, Hartland, Bideford EX39 6EY Tel: 01237 441819 — MB BS 1961 Lond.; MRCS Eng. LRCP Lond. 1961.

GOODACRE, John Alan 49 Holly Avenue, Jesmond, Newcastle upon Tyne NE2 2PX — MD 1990 Newc.; PhD Newc. 1989, MD 1990; BM BS Nottm. 1976, BMedSci 1974; MRCP (UK) 1980. Lect. (Rheum.) Univ. Newc. u Tyne.

GOODACRE, Selwyn Hugh Tel: 01283 551717 Fax: 01283 211905; 69 Ashby Road, Woodville, Swadlincote DE11 7BZ Tel: 01283 221652 Fax: 01283 221652 — MB ChB Birm. 1963; DObst RCOG 1965. (Birm.) Socs: BMA; GP Writers Assn.; S. Derbysh. Gen. Med. Pract. Gp. Prev: Ho. Surg. Roy. Hosp. Wolverhampton & Sorrento Matern. Hosp. Birm.; Ho. Phys. Qu. Eliz. Hosp. Birm.

GOODACRE, Stephen Walter Medical Care Research Unit, Sheffield University, Regent Court, 30 Regent Street, Sheffield S1 4DA; Flat 3, 4 Shad Thames, London SE1 2YT Tel: 0114 267 0508, 020 7403 3606 Fax: 020 7357 6172 — MB ChB 1989 Leic.; MSc 2000; MRCP (UK) 1992; FFAEM 1997; Dip. IMC RCS Ed. 1996. Health Servs. Research Fell., Sheff. Univ.; Research Fell. in Accid. & Emerg., N.. Gen. Hosp., Sheff. Prev: Yorks. Region Higher Specialist Train. Rotat. in Accid. & Emerg.; Specialist Regist. (A & E) Yorks. Region.

GOODACRE, Mr Timothy Edward Elliott Department of Plastic surgery, Radcliffe Infirmary, Woodstock Road, Oxford OX2 6HE Tel: 01865 224792 Fax: 01865 311673; Felstead House, 23 Banbury Road, Oxford OX2 6NX Tel: 01865 350821 Secretery, 01865 404142 — MRCS Eng. LRCP Lond. 1978; BSc Lond. 1975, MB BS 1978; FRCS Ed. 1982; FRCS Eng. 1982. (St. Thos.) Cons. Plastic Surg. Radcliffe Infirm. Oxf. & Roy. Berks. Hosp. Reading; Hon. Sen. Lect. (Surg.) Univ. Oxf.; Reg. Speciality Avd. Plast. Surg. Oxf. Socs: Brit. Assn. Plastic Surg.; Brit. Assoc. Head & Neck Oncol.; Coll. Of Surg. of E. S.ern Africa, Foundat. Fell. Prev: Sen. Regist. (Plastic Surg.) Qu. Mary's Hosp. Roehampton; Regist. (Plastic Surg.) MT. Vernon Hosp. N.wood; Surg. Mvumi Hosp. Dodoma, Tanzania.

GOODALE, Alissa Jocelyn 94 Boston Avenue, Southend-on-Sea SS2 6JD — BM 1993 Soton.

GOODALL, Brian Clayton Health Centre, 89 North Road, Clayton, Manchester M11 4EJ Tel: 0161 223 9229 Fax: 0161 223 1116; 8 Apsley Close, Altrincham WA14 3AJ — MB ChB 1971 Manch.

GOODALL, Christopher Michael Andrew Milton Heyes, Sandfield Lane, Acton Bridge, Northwich CW8 2RH — MB ChB 1987 Leeds. SHO (O & G) Wakefield HA.

GOODALL, David Queens Park Hospital, Haslingden Road, Blackburn BB2 3HH; 44 Park Lane, Great Harwood, Blackburn BB6 7RF Tel: 01254 889163 — MRCS Eng. LRCP Lond. 1963;

MRCOG 1974. (Liverp.) Cons. O & G Blackburn, Hyndburn & Ribble HA; Hon. Sen. Lect. Dept. Trop. Paediat. Liverp. Sch. Trop. Med. Socs: BMA Fell. Roy. Soc. Trop. Med. & Hyg.; N. Eng. Obst. Soc. Prev: Med. Superintendent Khristiya Seva Niketan (Ch. of N. India) W.; Bengal, India.

GOODALL, David Michael Tel: 01242 580668 Fax: 01242 707699 — MB ChB Bristol 1969; DObst RCOG 1971. (Bristol) GP Princip.; Clin. Asst. (Oncol.) Cheltenham. Prev: SHO (O & G) Gen. Hosp. Bishop Auckland; Ho. Surg. Cossham Memor. Hosp. Bristol; Ho. Phys. Frenchay Hosp. Bristol.

GOODALL, Helen Jane Killamarsh Medical Practice, 209 Sheffield Road, Killamarsh, Sheffield S31 8DZ Tel: 0114 251 0000 Fax: 0114 248 9380; 4 Park Farm Mews, The Lane, Spinkhill, Sheffield S21 3YQ Tel: 01246 430120 — MB ChB 1988 Liverp.; MRCGP 1992; DCH RCP Lond. 1992; DGM RCP Lond. 1990.

GOODALL, Henry Bushman (retired) 16 Hazel Avenue, Dundee DD2 1QD Tel: 01382 665247 — MB ChB 1944 St. And.; MB ChB (Commend.) St. And. 1944; MD (Hons. & Rutherford Gold Medal) St. And. 1959; FRCPath 1970. Prev: Reader (Haemat.) Dept. Path. Ninewells Hosp. Dundee.

GOODALL, Henry Nathan Ford Motor Company, 43/311, Occupational Health Department, Wide Lane, Swaythling, Southampton SO18 2NQ Tel: 02380 587241 Fax: 02380 587395; Trewendoc, Bramshaw, Lyndhurst SO43 7JL — MB BS Lond. 1969; AFOM RCP Lond. 1990; MFOM RCP Lond. 1998. (King's Coll. Hosp.) Med. Off. Ford Motor Co. Soton., Leamington & Daventry Plants. Socs: BMA (Ex-Chairm., Ex-Hon. Sec. & Ex-Hon. Treas. Soton. & SW Hants. Div.); SOM. Prev: Med. Off. IBM Hursley Laborat. Winchester; Hosp. Pract. (A & E) Soton. Gen. Hosp.; Demonst. (Anat.) Univ. Camb.

GOODALL, Ian David 55 Millers Rise, St Albans AL1 1QW — MB BS 1987 Lond.

GOODALL, Janet (retired) Melton, Burrington Drive, Trentham, Stoke-on-Trent ST4 8SP Tel: 01782 659304 — MB ChB 1954 Sheff.; MA Keele 1991; FRCP Ed. 1974, M 1964; MRCS Eng. LRCP Lond. 1955; Hon. FCPCH 1996; DCH Eng. 1957; DObst RCOG 1956. Prev: Cons. Paediat. N. Staffs. Hosp. Centre Stoke-on-Trent.

GOODALL, Jeremy Rees Fisher Medical Centre, Millfields, Coach Street, Skipton BD23 1EU — MB ChB 1974 Leeds.

GOODALL, John Alexander Durell Belford Hospital, Fort William PH33 6BS Tel: 01397 702481 Fax: 01397 702772; Achanellan, Glen Loy, Banavie, Fort William PH33 7PD Tel: 01397 712798 — MB ChB 1965 Ed.; FRCP Ed. 1979; MRCP (UK) 1970.

GOODALL, John Donald 23 Churchill Gardens, London W3 0JN — MB BS 1984 Lond.

GOODALL, John Francis (retired) 8 Rockwood Drive, Skipton BD23 1NF — MRCS Eng. LRCP Lond. 1935; MD Camb. 1940, MB BChir. 1937. Prev: Pathol. 14th B.G.H. India 1943-45.

GOODALL, Jonathan Richard 18 Whitbarrow Road, Lymm WA13 9AF — MB BS 1986 Lond.; FRCA. 1991. (Guy's Hosp. (UMDS)) Cons. Anaesth. (IC Med.). Socs: Assn. Anaesth.s; Intens. Care Soc.; BMA. Prev: Sen. Regist. (Anaesth.) NWRHA; Regist. (Anaesth.) NW RHA.

GOODALL, Mrs Karen Lesley 1 Warwick Road, Worsley, Manchester M28 7BW — MB ChB 1990 Sheff. Specialist Regist. Manch. Roy. Eye Hosp. Manch. Prev: SHO Manch. Roy. Eye; SHO Wolverhampton Eye Infirm.; SHO Roy. Liverp. Hosp.

GOODALL, Merica Doreen Maud (retired) Easterley Grange, Foxton, Sedgefield, Stockton-on-Tees TS21 2HX — MB BS 1960 Durh.; DPM Eng. 1964. Prev: Cons. Psychiat. Winterton Hosp. Sedgefield.

GOODALL, Michael Stewart Bridgnorth Medical Practices, Northgate House, 7 High St., Bridgnorth WV16 4BU Tel: 01746 767121 — MB ChB 1979 Bristol; DRCOG 1983; DA (UK) 1981.

GOODALL, Mr Peter (retired) Green Trees, Chapel St., Duffield, Derby DE56 4EQ Tel: 01332 840008 — MRCS Eng. LRCP Lond. 1951; MA, MChir Camb. 1962; MB BChir 1951; FRCS Eng. 1957. Prev: Cons. Surg. Derbysh. Roy. Infirm. & City Hosp. Derby.

GOODALL, Peter Charles Anthony Tel: 023 8033 3326 Fax: 023 8033 3008 — MB BS 1981 West. Austral.; BSc West. Austral. 1976. Prev: Med. Off. Brit. Aerospace Dhahran, Saudi Arabia; Trainee GP Whiteparish VTS; Regist. (Geriat.) Soton. Gen. Hosp.

GOODALL, Robert Colin Kingsway Lodge, King St., Much Wenlock TF13 6BL Tel: 01952 727352 Fax: 01952 728479; Clifton Lodge, Cressage, Shrewsbury SY5 6DH Tel: 01952 510318 Fax: 01952 510570 — MB ChB 1979 Birm.; DA Eng. 1984; DRCOG 1981. Prev: SHO (O & G) N. Staffs Roy. Infirm.; SHO (Paediat. & Anaesth.) Roy. Shrewsbury Hosp.

GOODALL, Mr Robert John Rhodes Calderdale Royal Hospital, Salterhebble, Halifax HX Tel: 01422 357222; Wheatstone, Skircoat Green Road, Halifax HX3 0LJ — MB ChB 1970 Leeds; ChM Leeds 1982; FRCS Eng. 1975; FRCS Ed. 1975. Cons. Surg. Halifax. Socs: Assn. Surg.; Assn. Endoscopic Surgs.; Hosp. Cons.s and Specialists Assn. (Co. Chairm.). Prev: Sen. Regist. Rotat. Leeds & Bradford; Tutor (Surg.) Hope Hosp. Salford.

GOODALL, Susan Charlotte — MB ChB 1989 Sheff.; MRCGP 1993; DRCOG 1992. Prev: Trainee GP S. Clwyd VTS.

GOODALL-COPESTAKE, John The Primary Care Centre, Harpers Lane, Presteigne LD8 2AN Tel: 01544 267985 — MB ChB 1967 St. And.; DObst RCOG 1971. (St. And.) Prev: Ho. Phys. & Ho. Surg. (Paediat.) Warwick Hosp.; Ho. Off. (O & G) Warneford Hosp. Leamington Spa.

GOODAY, Helen Margaret Kirby Astley Ainslie Hospital, Canaan Lane, Edinburgh EH9 2HL Tel: 0131 537 9000 Fax: 0131 537 9080 — MB ChB 1984 Birm.; MRCPsych 1990. (Birmingham) Specialist Regist. (Rehabil. Med.) Astley Ainslie Hosp. Cunaan La. Edin. Socs: MRCPsych.; Scott. Soc. Rehabilit.; Brit. Soc. Rehabilit.Med. Prev: Staff Grade Psychiat. (Adolesc. Psychiat.) Roy. Edin. Hosp.; Staff Grade Psychiat. & Asst. Clin. Dir. Robt.. Fergasson Unit Roy. Edin. Hosp.; Regist. (Forens. Psychiat.) State Hosp. Carstairs.

GOODBODY, Richard Anthony, VRD Little Dene, Kingsway, Chandlers Ford, Eastleigh SO50 1FH Tel: 0142 152495 — MRCS Eng. LRCP Lond. 1943; MD (Path.) Lond. 1951, MB BS 1947; FRCPath 1963. (St. Bart.) Cons. Pathol. Soton. Univ. Hosps.; Surg. Lt.-Cdr. RNVR. Socs: Path. Soc. & Assn. Clin. Pathols. Prev: Sen. Regist. & Pathol. to Neurosurg. & Neurol. Units Centr. Middlx. Hosp.; Research Fell. in Neuropath. Inst. Neurol. Univ. Lond.; Regist. (Path.) Guys Hosp. Lond.

GOODBOURN, Colin Gregory Mark Department of Microbiology, Whipps Cross Hospital, Whipps Cross Road, Leytonstone, London E11 1NR Tel: 020 8539 5522; Brook Cottage, Greensward Lane, Hockley SS5 5HR Tel: 01702 200193 — MB BS 1989 Lond.; MSc 1994; MRCPath 1999; BSc (Hons.) Lond. 1981. (Univ. Coll. and Middlx. Hosp. Med. Sch.) Cons. Microbiologist at Whipps Cross Hosp. Prev: Regist. (Microbiol.) Pub. Health Laborat. Serv. Chelmsford; Sen. Regist. (MicroBiol.) St. Barths. Hosp., Lond.

GOODBRAND, Theodore Allan (retired) Inchgarth, Longside Road, Mintlaw, Peterhead AB42 5EJ Tel: 01771 623588 Fax: 01771 624349 — MB ChB 1960 Aberd. Prev: Ho. Phys. City Hosp. Aberd.

GOODCHILD, Christopher Alan Vivian Southchurch Boulevard Surgery, 27 Southchurch Boulevard, Southend-on-Sea SS2 4UA Tel: 01702 468443 Fax: 01702 603281 — MB BS 1969 Lond.; MRCS Eng. LRCP Lond. 1969. (St. Geo.) Police Surg.; Exam. Med. Off. DHSS. Prev: Clin. Asst. Dept. Rheum. & Physical Med. S.end Gen. Hosp.

GOODCHILD, Helena 6 Westholm, London NW11 6LH Fax: 020 8455 2483 — BM 1993 Soton.; DFFP 1997; DCH RCP Lond. 1996. GP Regist. Lond. Prev: SHO (O & G) N.wick Pk. Hosp.; SHO (Paediat. & Accid. Emerg.) Watford Gen. Hosp.; SHO (Geriat.) Barnet Gen. Hosp.

GOODCHILD, Jeremy Uppingham Road Medical Centre, 46-48 Uppingham Road, Leicester LE5 0QD Tel: 0116 276 7133 Fax: 0116 276 4464; Hanjague, Rocky Hill, St Mary's TR23 0PR Tel: 01720 422531 — MB BS 1957 Lond.; MRCS Eng. LRCP Lond. 1957; DObst RCOG 1961. (Westm.) Prev: Ho. Phys. St. Chas. Hosp. Lond.; Ho. Surg. Beckenham Hosp.; Ho. Off. (Obst.) St. Mary's Matern. Hosp. Croydon.

GOODCHILD, Kathleen Anne 172 Emlyn Road, London W12 9TB — MB BS 1988 Lond.; MRCP (UK) 1992; FRCR 1996. Year 5 Specialist Regist. (Clin.Oncol) Meyersten Inst. of Oncol., Middlx. Hosp. Prev: Hon. Sen. Regist. (Clin. Oncol.) Marie Curie Research Wing Mt. Vernon Hosp. N.wood.

GOODCHILD, Leonard Philip 1 Uxendon Crescent, Wembley HA9 9TW Tel: 020 8904 3883 — MB BS 1952 Lond.; MRCGP 1965. (Char. Cross) Prev: Vis. Med. Pract. Hillcrest Residen. Welf. Home Harrow; Clin. Asst. (Med.) Wembley Hosp.; Capt. RAMC.

GOODCHILD, Mary Catherine (retired) 4 Jerningham House, 18 Mount Sion, Tunbridge Wells TN1 1UE Tel: 01892 513592 — MB

BS Lond. 1960; MD Birm. 1980; DCH Eng. 1963. Prev: Assoc. Specialist in Cystic Fibrosis Dept. Child Health Univ. Hosp.

GOODCHILD, Patricia Ann Plas-Newydd, Portcarne St., Usk NP5 1RZ — MRCS Eng. LRCP Lond. 1969.

GOODDEN, Griselda Frances Clare The Surgery, 111 Pembroke Road, Clifton, Bristol BS8 3EU Tel: 0117 973 3790; 12 Westbury Park, Bristol BS6 7JA Tel: 0117 973 0999 Fax: 0117 973 0912 Email: hulls@epulse.net — MB BS 1974 Lond.; MRCS Eng. LRCP Lond. 1974; DObst RCOG 1976. (St. Marys Hospital London) Socs: Bristol Medico-ChiroSurgic. Soc. Prev: Ho. Surg. & Ho. Off. (Obst.) St. Mary's Hosp. Lond.; Ho. Phys. Edgware Gen. Hosp.

GOODDY, Ethel Lomax Old Birtley, Brook, Godalming GU8 5LB — MB BS 1942 Lond.; MRCS Eng. LRCP Lond. 1942. (Univ. Coll. & W. Lond. Hosp.) Prev: Ho. Phys. W. Lond. Hosp.; Capt. RAMC.

GOODDY, William Walton Old Birtley, Brook, Godalming GU8 5LB Tel: 01428 682377 — MB BS 1942 Lond.; MD Lond. 1946; FRCP Lond. 1953, M 1945; MRCS Eng. LRCP Lond. 1941. (Univ. Coll. Hosp.) Socs: Fell. Univ. Coll. Lond. 1966; (Ex-Pres.) Assn. Brit. Neurol.; Hon. Foreign Mem. of the Neurol. Societies of France, Australia & Canada. Prev: Cons. Phys. Nat. Hosp. Nerv. Dis. Qu. Sq. & Univ. Coll. Hosp. Lond. St. Richard's Hosp. Chichester; Emerit. Cons. Neurol. K. Edwd. VII Hosp. Midhurst; Cons. Neurol. to RN.

GOODE, Andrew Gareth Woodcote Health Centre, Wayside Green, Woodcote, Reading RG8 0PR Tel: 01491 680686; 41 Holinlea Road, Goring on Thames, Reading RG8 9EX — MB BS 1989 Lond.; BSc (Pharm.) Lond. 1986; MRCGP 1994; DRCOG 1993; DCH RCP Lond. 1992. GP; Dip. Family Plann. Socs: BMA; Med. Defence Union. Prev: Trainee GP Reading.

GOODE, Anthea Felicity Westbar Surgery, 1 Westbar, Banbury OX16 9SF; Horn Hill Cottage, Adderbury, Banbury OX17 3EU — MB ChB 1987 Bristol; MRCGP 1992.

GOODE, Professor Anthony William The Surgical Unit, The London Hospital, London E1 Tel: 020 7601 8888; The Surgical Unit, The West Wing, St. Bartholomews Hospital, London EC1 Tel: 020 7601 7032 — MB BS Newc. 1968; MD Newc. 1978; FRCS Eng. 1974. Prof. Endocrinol. & Metabol. Surg. Surgic. Unit Roy. Lond. Hosp. & St. Bart. Hosp. Lond.; Hon. Prof. Bagrit Centre Imperial Coll. of Sci., Technol. & Med. Lond.; Trustee Smith & Nephew Foundat.; Edr. in Chief Med. Sci. & The Law; Clin. Dir. Helicopter Emerg. Med. Servs. Socs: Fell. Roy. Soc. Med.; (Hon. Sec. & Treas.) Brit. Assn. Endocrine Surgs. 1983-1996; Brit. Assn. Surg. Oncol. Prev: Cons. Surg. & Sen. Lect. Char. Cross Hosp. Med. Sch. Lond.; Sen. Regist. & Tutor (Surg.) Hammersmith Hosp. & Roy. Postgrad. Med. Sch.

GOODE, Beryl (retired) Rustlings, High Kilburn, York YO61 4AJ — MB ChB 1957 Leeds; DCH Eng. 1964; DObst RCOG 1960. Prev: Clin. Med. Off. E. Yorks. HA.

GOODE, Helen Montrose/ Brechin CMHT Offices, Sunnyside Royal Hospital, Hillside, Montrose DD10 9JP — MB ChB 1988 Manch.; 1997 Dip Cog. + Behav. Psych. (Dund.); BSc 1985 (Hons) Psycology; MRCPsych 1993. Prev: Sen. Regist. (Gen. Psychiat.) Roy. Dundee Liff Hosp.; Regist. (Psychiat.) Craig Dunain Hosp. Inverness & Roy. Cornhill Hosp. Aberd.

GOODE, Inez Mary Patricia Health Building, North Holmwood, Dorking RH5 4HX Tel: 01306 885802; The Oaks, Ridgeway Road, Dorking RH4 3EY Tel: 01306 889873 — MB BChir 1953 Camb.; MA Camb. 1955, MB BChir 1953; MRCGP 1974. (Camb. & St. Bart.) Hosp. Pract. Dept. Dermat. E. Surrey Hosp. Redhill & Long Gr. Hosp. Epsom; Div. Surg. St. John Ambul. Brig.; Mem. E. Surrey Dist. Health Auth. Socs: BMA & St. John's Hosp. Dermat. Soc. Prev: Ho. Phys. & Jun. Regist. Skin Dept. St. Bart. Hosp.; Asst., Dept. Dermat. King. Edwd. VII Hosp. Windsor.

GOODE, John David (retired) Rustlings, High Kilburn, York YO61 4AJ Tel: 01347 868127 — MB ChB 1955 Birm.; FRCP Lond. 1978, M 1966; BA Hull 1999. Prev: Cons. Phys. Rheum. & Gen. Med. Hull & E. Yorks. HAs.

GOODE, Nicola Judith The Surgery, 2314 Coventry Road, Sheldon, Birmingham B26 3JS; 21 Whitefields Crescent, Solihull B91 3NU — BM BS 1986 Nottm.; BMedSci Nottm. 1984; MRCGP 1990; DCH RCP Lond. 1994; DRCOG 1990. (Nottingham) GP Sheldon, Birm. Prev: Clin. Med. Off. (Community Child Health) Nottm. Community Health NHS Trust; Trainee GP/SHO Pilgrim Hosp. Boston VTS.

GOODE, Mr Peter Nicholas The Accident Department, Newcastle General Hospital, West Road, Newcastle upon Tyne NE4 6BE Tel: 0191 273 8811 — MB BS 1981 Newc.; FRCS Glas. 1987; FFAEM 1993; DFM Glas. 1989. Cons. (A & E) Newc. Gen. Hosp. Socs: Fell. Roy. Soc. Med.; Brit. Accid. & Emerg. Med. Soc. Prev: Cons. (A & E) S. Tyneside Dist. Hosp.; Sen. Regist. (A & E, Med. & Surg.) Glas. Roy. Infirm.; Regist. (Gen. Surg.) Newc. & Gateshead HA.

GOODE, Sarah Jane 74 Adelaide Road, St Denys, Southampton SO17 2HW — BM 1994 Soton.

GOODE, Thomas Darcy c/o Department Radiotherapy & Oncology, Poole General Hospital, Poole BH15 2JB Tel: 01202 675100 — MB BS 1972 Lond.; FRCS 1997; MRCP (UK) 1976; MRCS Eng. LRCP Lond. 1972; FRCR 1981. (Roy. Free) Cons. Radiother. & Oncol. Wessex RHA; Mem. of Counc., Joseph Weld, Hospice, Dorchester, Dorset. Socs: BMA & Assn. Palliat. Care & Hospice Doctors.; Fell. Roy. Soc. of Med. Prev: Sen. Regist. (Radiother. & Oncol.) Roy. Marsden Hosp. Sutton; Regist. (Radiother. & Oncol.) Ch.ill Hosp. Oxf.; Regist. (Gen. Med.) P.ss Margt. Hosp. Swindon.

GOODE, Timothy Bruce Donnington Medical Practice, Wrekin Drive, Donnington, Telford TF2 8EA Tel: 01952 605252 Fax: 01952 677010; Moorhead Cottage, 32A Moorhead, Preston-on-the-Weald Moors, Telford TF6 6DN Tel: 01952 670242 — BM BCh 1979 Oxf.; BA Camb. 1976; DRCOG 1982. Princip. GP; Clin. Asst. (Diabetes) P.ss Roy. Hosp. Telford; Chairm. Shrops. Primary Care Audit Gp. Socs: Chairm. Shrops. Med. Audit Advisory Gp.

GOODER, Mr Peter David Consulting Rooms, Beardwood Hospital, Preston New Road, Blackburn BB2 7AE Tel: 01254 693711 Fax: 01254 691874; Old Newshams, Old Buckley Lane, Ribchester, Preston PR3 3YN Tel: 01254 878798 — MB BS 1967 Lond.; FRCS Ed. 1977; FRCS Eng. 1972; MRCS Eng. LRCP Lond. 1967. (Char. Cross) Cons. Otolaryngol. Blackburn, Hyndburn & Ribble Valley HA. Socs: Fell. Roy. Soc. Med. & Manch. Med. Soc. Prev: Sen. Regist. (Otolaryng.) Manch. AHA; Demonst. (Anat.) Char. Cross Hosp. Med. Sch.; Ho. Phys. & Ho. Surg. Char. Cross Hosp.

GOODESS, John Edward 14 Burlington Road, Ipswich IP1 2EU Tel: 01473 211661; Church Cottage, The Green, Flowton, Ipswich IP8 4LG Tel: 01473 658446 — MB BChir 1953 Camb.; DObst RCOG 1961. (St. Mary's) Socs: BMA. Prev: Ho. Phys. Hillingdon Hosp.; Cas. Off. Padd. Green Childr. Hosp.; Obst. Ho. Off. St. Asaph Hosp.

GOODEY, Frank John Rose Cottage, 84 Strand-on-the-Green, London W4 3PU — MRCS Eng. LRCP Lond. 1945.

GOODFELLOW, Amy Elizabeth 13 Cameron Close, Warley, Brentwood CM14 5BX — MB ChB 1995 Manch.

GOODFELLOW, Mr Christopher Francis White Oaks, Hyde Lane, Danbury, Chelmsford CM3 4QT Tel: 01245 222362 Fax: 01245 224224 Email: chrisgoodfellow@skynow.net — MB BS 1972 Lond.; MRCS Eng. LRCP Lond. 1971; FRCOG 1992, M 1976. (Lond. Hosp.) Cons. O & G Chelmsford & Essex Hosp. & St. Johns Hosp. Chelmsford. Socs: Brit. Soc. Colpos. & Cerv. Path. Prev: Cons. (O & G) Leeds Univ.; Sen. Regist. (O & G) Leeds AHA (T); Regist. (O & G) Lond. Hosp. & Bristol Matern. Hosp.

GOODFELLOW, David Peter Cantilupe Surgery, 51 St Owen Street, Hereford HR1 2JB — MB ChB 1992 Leic.; MRCGP 1996; DFFP 1996; DRCOG 1994. (Leicester) Clin. Asst. BrE. Surg., Hereford Co. Hosp.

GOODFELLOW, Jill Caroline Cantilupe Surgery, 51 St. Owen Street, Hereford HR1 2JB Tel: 01432 268031 Fax: 01432 352584 — MB ChB 1992 Leic.; MRCGP 1996; DGM RCP Lond. 1995; DRCOG 1994. (Leic.)

GOODFELLOW, Mr John William St Lukes, Latimer Road, Oxford OX3 7PF Tel: 01865 744935 Fax: 01865 744455; 4 Upland Park Road, Summertown, Oxford OX2 7RU Tel: 01865 53006 Fax: 01865 310735 — MB BS 1951 Lond.; MS Lond. 1982; FRCS Eng. 1957; MRCS Eng. LRCP Lond. 1951. (Guy's) Consg. Edr. Jl. Bone & Jt. Surg. (Brit. Vol.); Cons. Emerit. Nuffield Orthop. Centre Oxf. Socs: Hon. Fell. S. Afr. Orthop. Assn.; Hon. Fell. Italian Orthop. Assn.; Fell. Amer. Orthop. Assn. Prev: Cons. (Orthop. Surg.) Nuffield Orthop. Centre Oxf.; Orthop. Surg. Rancho Los Amigos Hosp. Los Angeles, USA; Consg. Edr. Jl. Bone & Jt. Surg. (Brit. Volume).

GOODFELLOW, Jonathan Wales Heart research Institute, University of Wales College of Medicine, Cardiff CP4 4XN Tel: 01222 746243 Fax: 01222 743500 Email: goodfellowj@cardiff.ac.uk; Pen-Y-Garreg, Piccadilly, Llanblethian,

Cowbridge CF71 7JL — MB BS 1985 Lond.; BSc (Hons.) Lond. 1982; MRCP (UK) 1989. (St Bartholomews) Cons. Cardiol. P.ss of Wales Hosp. Coity Rd; Sen. Lect. Cardiol. Wales Heart Research Inst. Socs: Brit. Cardiac Soc.; RCP; Brit. Cardiac Interven. Soc. Prev: Sen. Regist. (Cardiol.) Univ. Hosp. Wales Cardiff; Regist. (Cardiol.) S.mead Hosp. Bristol & Bristol Roy. Infirm.; SHO (Med.) Roy. United Hosp. Bath.

GOODFELLOW, Mair Elunis (retired) 148 Westbourne Road, Penarth CF64 5BQ Tel: 02920 707827 Fax: 01222 707827 — MB BCh Wales 1960; DCH Eng. 1962. Prev: Princip. in Gen. Pract.

GOODFELLOW, Peter Bryan c/o Ty Gwyn, Wyfordby Avenue, Blackburn BB2 7AR — MB ChB 1993 Sheff. Regist. (Surg.) Caboolture Hosp. Qu.sland, Austral.

GOODFELLOW, Rhian Mair 1 Amesbury Road, Penylan, Cardiff CF23 5DW — MB BCh 1989 Wales; MRCP (UK) 1992.

GOODFELLOW, Rodney Christopher British Nuclear Fuels plc, Springfields Works, Salwick, Preston PR4 0XJ — MB ChB 1962 Birm.; AFOM RCP Lond. 1982. Sen. Med. Off. Brit. Nuclear Fuels plc. Springfields.

GOODFELLOW, Susan Jane Deepfield Close Medical Centre, 10 Deepfield Close, Cardiff CF5 4SH — MB BS 1985 Lond.; MRCP (UK) 1990; MRCGP 1993; DRCOG 1991. Asst. GP Cardiff. Prev: SHO (Paediat.) Roy. United Hosp. Bath.

GOODFELLOW, Thomas Radiology Department, Walsgrave Hospital NHS Trust, Clifford Bridge Road, Coventry CV2 2DX Tel: 024 76 602020 Fax: 024 76 622197; 68 Lutterworth Road, Pailton, Rugby CV23 0QF Tel: 01788 832039 Email: goodfellow.family@tesco.net — MB BS 1973 Lond.; BSc (Hons.) Lond. 1970; FRCS Eng. 1979; FRCR 1987. Cons. Radiol. The Walsgrave Hosp. Coventry.; Clin. Dir. Support Servs. Prev: Sen. Regist. (Radiol.) Wessex RHA.

GOODFIELD, Nicholas Ewen Ross ECG Dept, Stobhill Hospital, Balornock Rd, Glasgow G21 3UW Tel: 0141 201 3000 Fax: 0141 558 5693 Email: nicholas.goodfield@northglasgow.scot.nhs.uk; 20 Forrest Dr, Bearsden, Glasgow G61 4SJ Tel: 0141 931 5968 Fax: 0141 931 5968 Email: n.e.r.g@tesco.net — MB ChB 1986 Ed.; BSc (Hons. Med. Sci.) Ed. 1983; MRCP (UK) 1989. Cons. Cardiol. Stobhill NHS Trust Glas. Prev: Lect. Cardiovasc. Research Unit Univ. Edin.; Regist. (Cardiol.) Roy. Infirm. Edin.; Regist. Rotat. (Gen. Med.) Borders Gen. Hosp. & W.. Gen. Hosp. Edin.

GOODGAME, Kathleen Winifred Mary (retired) 35A New Road, Bournemouth BH10 7DW — MB BS Lond. 1966; MRCS Eng. LRCP Lond. 1966. Prev: Ho. Phys. Roy. N.. Infirm. Inverness.

GOODGE, Andrew Mobil Medical Department, Mobil Court, 3 Clements Inn, London WC2A 2EB Tel: 020 7412 2865 Fax: 020 7412 2935 Email: andrew_goodge@email.mobil.com; Mustow House, 4 High Road, Layer De La Haye, Colchester CO2 0DS Tel: 01206 734438 — MB ChB 1978 Sheff.; MRCGP 1982; DRCOG 1981; MFOM RCP (UK) 1997. (Sheffield) Sen. Med. Adviser Mobil N. Sea & Mobil Shipping Companies.

GOODGE, Brian Malcolm The Surgery, Stradbroke, Eye IP21 5HX Tel: 01379 384220; Crown House, Worlingworth, Woodbridge IP13 7PD Tel: 01728 628464 — MB BS 1964 Lond.; MRCP (UK) 1970; MRCS Eng. LRCP Lond. 1964. (King's Coll. Hosp.)

GOODGER, Abigail Roberta 114 Dean Drive, Wilmslow SK9 2EY — MB ChB 1994 Liverp.

GOODGER, John Lloyd (retired) Applegarth, 16 Orchard Road, Burpham, Guildford GU4 7JH Tel: 01483 575916 — MB BS 1948 Lond.; MFOM RCP Lond. 1979; DObst RCOG 1952; DIH Soc. Apoth. Lond. 1965. Prev: Dep. Head John Lewis Partnership Med. Serv.

GOODGER, Nicholas Mark 10 Hudsons, Tadworth KT20 5TZ — MB ChB 1994 Lond.; MBBS Lond. 1994; BSc Lond. 1993; BDS Lond. 1985; LDSRCS (Eng.) 1986; FDSRCS (Eng.) 1989. (St. Georges' Hosp. Med. Sch.) Lect./Hon. Sen. Regist. (Oral & Maxillofacial Surg.) Guy's Hosp. Lond.

GOODGER, Rachel Caroline Clarence Cottage, Felindre, Brecon LD3 0TE — MB ChB 1993 Bristol.

GOODGER, Valmai Rhian Clarence Cottage, Felindre, Brecon LD3 0TE Tel: 01497 847474 — MB ChB 1995 Bristol. SHO Med. Rotat. Swindon & MarlBoro. NHS Trust Swindon. Prev: SHO (Oncol.) Qu. Eliz. Hosp. Birm.; SHO (A & E) Newport Gwent; PRHO (Med.) Hereford.

GOODHARDT, Lionel Sidney 152 Harley Street, London W1N 1HH Tel: 020 7935 0444 — MB BS Lond. 1946. (Middlx.) Med. Ref. Commercial Union & Other Assur. Assns. Prev: Clin. Asst. Roy. Nat. Throat, Nose & Ear Hosp. Lond.; Capt. RAMC; Ho. Surg. Middlx. Hosp.

GOODHART, Louisa Clare Statham Grove Surgery, Statham Grove, London N16 9DP Tel: 020 7254 4327 Fax: 020 7241 4098 — MB ChB 1980 Birm.; MRCP (UK) 1983; MRCGP 1987; DCH RCP Lond. 1985. Facilitator Child Health Surveillance Hackney.

GOODHART, Sir Robert Anthony Gordon Barton House Surgery, Barton House, Beaminster DT8 3EQ Tel: 01308 862233 Fax: 01308 863785; Orchard Hill, Netherbury, Bridport DT6 5NB — MB BS 1972 Lond.; MRCS Eng. LRCP Lond. 1972; MRCGP 1976; DObst RCOG 1975. (Guy's) Prev: GP Bromley.

GOODHEAD, David George Doncaster Royal Infirmary, Armthorpe Road, Doncaster DN2 5LT Tel: 01302 366666 Fax: 01302 761317 — MB BS 1972 Lond.; MRCS Eng. LRCP Lond. 1972; MRCPsych 1977; FRCPsych 1995. (King's Coll. Hosp.) Cons. Psychiat. Doncaster Roy. Infirm.; Med. Dir. Doncaster Healthcare NHS Trust; Med. Dir. Trent & Yorks. Sect. 12(2) Approvals Serv. Prev: Sen. Regist. (Psychiat.) Univ. Nottm.; Regist. (Psychiat.) Doncaster Roy. Infirm.; Regist. (Psychiat.) Univ. Sheff. & Middlewood Hosp. Sheff.

GOODIER, John Christopher Limeleigh Medical Centre, 169 Narborough Road, Leicester LE3 0PE Tel: 0116 255 2688; Whirlow House, Forest Drive, Kirby Muxloe, Leicester LE9 2EA Tel: 0116 239 2659 — MB ChB 1964 Sheff. Socs: Leic. Med. Soc.

GOODIER, Valerie Anne St Anne's Hospital, 69 Haven Road, Poole BH13 7LN Tel: 01202 708881 Fax: 01202 399649; 109 Penn Hill Avenue, Lower Parkstone, Poole BH14 9LY Tel: 01202 740940 Email: dode hooker@virgin.net — BM 1986 Soton. Staff Grade (Psychiat.) St. Ann's Hosp. Poole.

GOODIER, Mr William David Consultant Orthopaedic Surgeon, The Royal London Hospital, Whitechapel, London E1 Tel: 020 7377 7000 — MB BS 1985 Lond.; FRCS Eng. 1990; FRCS (Orth) 1996. (London Hospital Medical Centre) Cons. Orthop. Surg. Roy. Hosps. NHS Trust.

GOODIN, Stephanie Judith (retired) Lauriston, Riverside Road, Dittisham, Dartmouth TQ6 0HS Tel: 01803 722319 — MB BS 1952 Lond. Prev: Regist. (Anaesth) King Edwd. VII Hosp. Windsor.

GOODING, Alan Holly Tree Surgery, 42 Boundstone Road, Wrecclesham, Farnham GU10 4TG Tel: 0125 225 3183 — MB BS 1958 Lond.; MRCS Eng. LRCP Lond. 1959; DObst RCOG 1960. (Guy's) Socs: BMA. Prev: Regist. (Med.) St. Luke's Hosp. Guildford; Ho. Surg. (Orthop.) Guy's Hosp. Lond.; Ho. Surg. (O & G) Wanstead Hosp.

GOODING, Christopher Rees Bay Tree Cottage, School Lane, Kirk Ella, Hull HU10 7NT — MB BS 1998 Lond.; MB BS Lond 1998.

GOODING, Claire Juliet Dalmage Email: clairegooding@doctors.org.uk — MB BS 1992 Lond.; BSc Lond. 1989. (St. Bart.) Gen. Practitioner; Clin. Asst., Neurol. Dept., Wythenshawe Hosp., Manch.

GOODING, Donald John, OStJ (retired) The Old Granary, Offham, Lewes BN7 3QA Tel: 01273 473583 — MB BS Lond. 1955; MRCS Eng. LRCP Lond. 1955. JP. Prev: HM Coroner E. Sussex.

GOODING, Dulcie Grace (retired) 43 Burford Lodge, Pegasus Grange, Whitehouse Road, Oxford OX1 4QG Tel: 01865 790705 — MB BS 1959 Lond.; MRCS Eng. LRCP Lond. 1959; FFCM 1975, M 1972; DPH Eng. 1962. Prev: SCM Bloomsbury DHA.

GOODING, Hubert Keith 8 Hook Road, Surbiton KT6 5BH Tel: 020 8390 3396 — MB ChB 1957 Glas.; DObst RCOG 1961. (Glas.) Med. Staff Surbiton Gen. Hosp. Socs: Brit. Soc. Med. Hypn. Prev: Regist. (Obst.) Lennox Castle Hosp.; Ho. Phys. & Ho. Surg. Stobhill Hosp. Glas.

GOODING, Ian Robert Lister Hospital, Corey's Mill Lane, Stevenage SG1 4 Tel: 01438 314333; 55 Hazelwood Close, Cambridge CB4 3SW Tel: 01223 721085 — BChir 1994 Camb.; MB BChir Camb. 1996; MA Camb. 1996; MRCP Lond. 1998. (Cambridge) SHO (Gen. Med.) Lister Hosp. Stevenage. Prev: SHO (A & E) Hinchingbrooke Hosp. Huntingdon.

GOODING, Jane Helen 8 Chiltern Drive, Upper Hopton, Mirfield WF14 8PZ — MB ChB 1972 Leeds; MRCPsych 1978; DPM Leeds 1976.

GOODING, Mr Michael Rees (retired) Department of Neurosurgery, Hull Royal Infirmary, Hull HU3 2JZ — MSc Lond. 1964, BSc 1956, MD 1975, MB BS 1959; FRCS Eng. 1967 MRCS

Eng. LRCP Lond. 1959. Cons. Neurosurg. Hull Roy. Infirm. Prev: Research Neurosurg. Atkinson Morley's Hosp. Lond. & Univ. Calif.

GOODING, Michelle The Surgery, Cross Road, Sacriston, Durham DH7 6LJ Tel: 0191 371 0232; 28 Lee Hill Court, Lanchester, Durham DH7 0QE Tel: 01207 529195 — MB BS 1994 Newc.; MRCGP 1998.

GOODING, Paul Simon 23 Alexandra Road, Brecon LD3 7PB — MB BCh 1997 Wales.

GOODING, Roger Graham Pemberley Avenue Surgery, 32 Pemberley Avenue, Bedford MK40 2LA Tel: 01234 351051 Fax: 01234 349246 — MB 1972 Camb.; BChir 1971; DObst RCOG 1975.

GOODING, Sylvia Margot Dorothy 14 Winchester Drive, Exmouth EX8 5QA — MB ChB 1979 Glas. GP Fivemiletown Co. Tyrone.

GOODING, Trevor Nigel The Atherstone Surgery, 1 Ratcliffe Road, Atherstone CV9 1EU Tel: 01827 713664 Fax: 01827 713666 — MB ChB 1985 Birm; MRCGP 1990; Cert. Family Plann. JCC 1989; DRCOG 1988. Socs: Brit. Med. Acupunc. Soc. Prev: Trainee GP Bishops Castle VTS; SHO (Med., O & G & Paediat.) Solihull Hosp. W. Midl. VTS; Ho. Off. Rotat. (A & E) Bundaberg Base Hosp. Qu.sland, Austral.

GOODISON, Simon James Findlay Blackthorn Surgery, 73 Station Road, Netley Abbey, Southampton SO31 5AE Tel: 023 8045 3110 Fax: 023 8045 2747 — MB BS 1980 Lond.; MRCP (UK) 1984; MRCGP 1990; DRCOG 1989. (Middlesex Hospital) GP Princip.

GOODLAD, John Robert Ceol Na Mara, Brecknish, Allanfearn, Inverness IV2 7HY Tel: 01463 234299 Email: john.goodlad@virgin.net — MB ChB 1986 Aberd.; MRCPath 1993. Cons. (Path.) Raigmore Hosp. Inverness.

GOODLAND, Duncan Stuart Kennedy Way Surgery, Kennedy Way, Yate, Bristol BS37 4AA Tel: 01454 313849 Fax: 01454 329039 — MB ChB 1973 Bristol; MRCGP 1977; DObst RCOG 1976.

GOODLASS, Jayne Bridwood, Scarborough Rd, Driffield YO25 7EH Tel: 01377 252832 — BM BS 1997 Nottm.

GOODLIFFE, Arnold David Robert (retired) 144 Church Hill Road, Sutton SM3 8NA Tel: 020 8644 8787 — MRCS Eng. LRCP Lond. 1956; MB Camb. 1957, BChir 1956. Prev: Ho. Surg. (Obst.) & Cas. Off. Redhill Co. Hosp.

GOODLIFFE, Charles David Penistan and Partners, Cordell Road, Long Melford, Sudbury CO10 9EP Tel: 01787 378226 Fax: 01787 311287; Bishop's Rock, New Road, Long Melford, Sudbury CO10 9JY — LRCPI & LM, LRSCI & LM 1971; LRCPI & LM, LRCSI & LM 1971; DObst RCOG 1974; DCH RCPSI 1973. Prev: Rotat. Intern St. Eliz. Hosp. Youngstown Ohio U.S.A.; Paediat. Ho. Phys. Our Lady's Hosp. for Sick Childr. Dub.; SHO (O & G) New Cross Hosp. Wolverhampton.

GOODMAN, Mr Aaron Isaac (retired) 15 St John Street, Manchester M3 4DG Tel: 0161 834 7373 — MB ChB 1942 Manch.; BSc (Hons. Physiol.) Manch. 1939, MD 1947; FRCS Ed. 1947. Prev: Cons. ENT Surg. Tameside & N. Manch. HAs.

GOODMAN, Andrew Gordon Royal Devon & Exeter NHS Trust, Barrack Road, Exeter EX2 5DW Tel: 01392 402102; Lower Upcroft House, Torquay TQ13 0DH — MB ChB 1983 Birm.; MA Oxf. 1976, BA 1973; MRCP (UK) 1986; FRCR 1990; T(R) (CO) 1991. Cons clin oncologist Roy. Devon & Exeter Hosp & Torbay Hosp. Prev: Sen. Regist. (Radiother. & Oncol.) Qu. Eliz. Hosp. Birm.; Regist. (Radiother. & Oncol.) W.m. Hosp. Lond.; Cons radiotherapist , Qu. Eliz. Hosp Birm.

GOODMAN, Mr Anthony John Cheltenham General Hospital, Sandford Road, Cheltenham GL53 7AN Tel: 01242 222222 Fax: 01242 571466 — MD 1989 Sheff.; MB BS Lond. 1978; FRCS Eng. 1982. (King's Coll. Hosp.) Cons. Gen. Surg. Cheltenham Gen. Hosp. Glos. Socs: Assn. Surg.; Pancreatic Soc. Gt. Brit. & Irel.; Brit. Stomach Cancer Gp. Prev: Sen. Regist. (Surg.) Leicester; Lect. (Surg.) Roy. Hallamsh. Hosp. Sheff.; Regist. (Surg.) Leicester Roy. Infirm.

GOODMAN, Aveen Maria 40 Clontara Park, Lisburn BT27 4LB — MB BCh BAO 1990 Belf.

GOODMAN, Benjamin Elkan Apartment 324, The Colonnades, Albert Dock, Liverpool L3 4AB — MB ChB Liverp. 1966.

GOODMAN, Bernard 1 Highfield Gardens, Bassaleg, Newport NP10 8LR — MB ChB 1947 Manch. (Manch.)

GOODMAN, Carol Margaret 28 Kings Road, Harrogate HG1 5JP Tel: 01423 560261 — BM BS 1978 Nottm.; BMedSci Nottm. 1976, BM BS 1978; MRCGP 1984. (Nottingham) GP Princip. Prev: Regist. (Gen. Surg.) Roy. Infirm. Bradford; SHO (Gen. Surg.) Balfour Hosp. Kirkwall Orkney; SHO (O & G) Nottm. City Hosp.

GOODMAN, Mr Christopher Michael Department of Urology, Ninewells Hospital, Dundee DD1 9SY — MB ChB 1979 Manch.; MD Manch. 1989; FRCS Ed. 1984. Cons. Urol. Surg. Dundee Teach. Hosps.; Hon. Sen. Lect. Fac. Med. Univ. Dundee. Socs: Btir.Assn.Urol.Surgs. Prev: Sen. Regist. (Urol.) Morriston Hosp. Swansea & Univ. Hosp. Wales Cardiff.

GOODMAN, Frances Rebecca Molecular Medicine Unit, Institute of Child Health, 30 Guilford St., London WC1N 1EH Tel: 020 7242 9789 Ext: 2432 Fax: 020 7404 6191 Email: fgoodman@hgmp.mrc.ac.uk; 30B Northampton Square, London EC1V 0ES — MB BS 1990 Lond.; 2000 PhD London; MSc Lond. 1995; MA Camb. 1984; MRCP (UK) 1993. (St. Bart.) MRC Clinician Scientist & Hon. Clin. Lect., Inst. of Child health, Lond.; Hon. Specialist Regist. in Clin. Genetics, Gt. Ormond St. Hosp., Lond. Socs: Brit. Soc. Human Genetics; Skeletal Dysplasis Gp. Prev: SHO (Paediat.) St. Geo. Hosp. Lond.; SHO Rotat. (Gen. Med.) King's Coll. Dulwich Hosp. Lond.

GOODMAN, Mr Gavin Cecil Hillhead Farm, Maltfield, Wedmore BS28 4TP Tel: 01934 713006 Fax: 01934 713006 — MB ChB 1967 Leeds; FRCS Ed. 1973; MFOM RCP Lond. 1991, A 1988; FRACGP 1977; FFOM 1997. Prev: Sen. Employm. Med. Advisor Health & Safety Exec.

***GOODMAN, Hannah Elizabeth** Maryborough Base Hospital, 185 Walker St., Maryborough Qld 4650, Australia Tel: 07 4123 8222 Email: h900@health.gld.gov.au; 25 Sunnybank Cl, Scholes, Cleckheaton BD19 6PP Tel: 01274 877187 Fax: 01274 877187 — MB ChB 1997 Ed.; BSc Hons. Med. Sci. 1995.

GOODMAN, Helene Valerie (retired) 51 Maresfield Gardens, London NW3 5TE Tel: 020 7794 6365 — BM BCh Oxf. 1951; MA Oxf. 1952, DM 1961; FRCS Eng. 1962; DPhysMed Eng. 1958. Recognised Teach. (Rheum.) Univ. Lond. Prev: Cons. Rheum. W.m. Hosp. Lond.

GOODMAN, Ian Lawrence The Surgery, Northwood Health Centre, Mount Vernon Hospital, Rickmansworth Road, Northwood HA6 1TQ Tel: 01923 820626; 5 Dalkeith Grove, Stanmore HA7 4SQ Tel: 020 8958 9073 Email: ian@iangood.demon.co.uk — MB BChir 1982 Camb.; MA Camb. 1983; MRCS Eng. LRCP Lond. 1982; FRCGP 1997; MRCGP 1986; DRCOG 1985; DGM RCP Lond. 1985; DCH RCP Lond. 1984. (St. Geo.) Mem. Hillingdon FPC Computer Facilitator. Socs: (Treas.) NW Thames Fac. RCGP. Prev: Trainee GP N.wick Pk. VTS.

GOODMAN, James Stuart York House Medical Centre, 20-21 York Street, Stourport-on-Severn DY13 9EH; Hazeland Farm, Netherton Lane, Abberley WR6 6BS Tel: 01299 896597 — MB ChB 1986 Birm.; MRCGP 1990; DRCOG 1990. Prev: Trainee GP Worcs. VTS.

GOODMAN, Janet Christine The Red House Surgery, 241 Queensway, Bletchley, Milton Keynes MK2 2EH Tel: 01908 375111 — MB 1979 Camb.; MB 1979; BChir 1978; MRCP (UK) 1980; MRCGP 1983; DRCOG 1982.

GOODMAN, Jennifer 83 Clifford Road, Barnet EN5 5NZ — MB ChB 1982 Leeds. Master of Arts in Psychol. of Ther. & Counselling Antioch Univ. USA 1994. Prev: Ho. Off. (Surg. & Neurosurg.) Hull Roy. Infirm.; Ho. Off. (Med.) Roy. Halifax Infirm.

GOODMAN, Jennifer Lesley 38 Wells Road, Folkestone CT19 4PW — BM 1979 Soton. Prev: SHO (Psychiat.) Guy's Hosp. Lond.; Ho. Off. (Gen. Surg., Gen. Med. & Urol.) Kent.

GOODMAN, Joanna Frances Mary 1 Rosedale, Abberley, Worcester WR6 6BA Tel: 01299 896597 — MB ChB 1984 Birm.; MRCGP 1989; DRCOG 1988. Asst. GP Droitwich Health Centre; Sen. Clin. Med. Off. (Family Plann.) Kidderminster; Clin. Asst. (Ophth.) Kidderminster Gen. Hosp.

GOODMAN, Mr Jonathan Delman Samuel Somerfield Hospital, London Road, Maidstone ME16 0DU; 7 Hanover Steps, St. Georges Fields, London W2 2YG Tel: 020 7402 5838 — MD Lond. 1982, MB BS 1970; FRCS Ed. 1983; MRCS Eng. LRCP Lond. 1970; FRCOG 1978, DObst 1972. (St. Geo.) Cons. O & G, Maidstone Gen. Hosp., Maidstone. Socs: Blair-Bell Soc.; Fell. Roy. Soc. Med. Prev: Sen.

Regist. (O & G) St. Thos. Hosp. Lond.; Regist. (O & G) Pembury Hosp.; Research Off. Nuffield Inst. Med. Research Oxf.

GOODMAN, Karen Louise 250 Langworthy Road, Salford M6 5WW Tel: 0161 736 7422 Fax: 0161 736 4816; 5 Sunningdale Avenue, Whitefield, Manchester M45 7GW — MB ChB 1980 Manch.; MFHom RCP Lond. 1992; DRCOG 1984.

GOODMAN, Karen Michele 1 Winthorpe Street, Grove Lane, Headingley, Leeds LS6 4AN — MB ChB 1991 Leeds.

GOODMAN, Kathryn 7 Moyle Grove, Ponthir, Newport NP18 1GP — MB BS 1987 Lond.; T(GP) 1991.

GOODMAN, Kirsty Anna St Budeaux, Newbury Lane, Cousleywood, Wadhurst TN5 6HA — MB BS 1996 Lond.

GOODMAN, Marion Ann 489 Palatine Road, Northenden, Manchester M22 4DH; 16 Turnberry Road, Heald Green, Cheadle SK8 3EP Tel: 0161 282 8591 — MB ChB 1969 Birm.; LF Hom (MED) 2000; BSc Bristol 1966. GP Manch. Socs: Brit. Menopause Soc.; The Fac. of Homeopathy.

GOODMAN, Martin Henderson 3rd Floor S Block, Selly Oak Hospital, Raddleburn Rd, Selly Oak, Birmingham B29 6JD Tel: 0121 627 8482 Fax: 0121 627 8282; 211, Beaumont Road, Bournville, Birmingham B30 1NU Email: martin\goodman2@compuserve.com — MB BS 1983 Lond.; FRCP 1999; BSc London 1980; MRCP 1986 U.K. Cons. Geriat. Med. Birm.. Specialist Community Health NHSTrust. Prev: Lect. (Geriat. Med.) Univ. Birm.

GOODMAN, Mervyn (retired) 1 Hornby Lane, Liverpool L18 3HH Tel: 0151 722 7125 Fax: 0151 722 7125 — MRCS Eng. LRCP Lond. 1951; FRCGP 1978, M 1959; DObst RCOG 1953. Trustee BMA Charities. Prev: Med. Ref. Benefits Agency Med. Serv.

GOODMAN, Michael John (cons. rooms & resid.), 3 Ringley Drive, Whitefield, Manchester M45 7DR Tel: 0161 796 9414 Fax: 0161 766 4994 Email: michaelgoodman@gofree.co.uk — BM BCh Oxf. 1968; DPhil Oxf. 1975, BA (Hons. Physiol.) 1965, MA 1968; FRCP Lond. 1987; MRCP (UK) 1971. (Oxf. & Westm.) Cons. Phys. (Gen. Med. & Gastroenterol.) Bury Gen. Hosp.; Chas. Murchison Schol. RCP Lond. 1970. Socs: Brit. Soc. Gastroenterol.; BMA (Dep. Chairm. of Centr. Cons.s and Specialists Comm.). Prev: Asst. Prof. (Med.) Univ. Chicago, USA; Wellcome Research Schol. Nuffield Dept. Clin. Med. Radcliffe Infirm. Oxf.

GOODMAN, Neville Walter Department of Anaesthetics, Southmead Hospital, Bristol BS10 5NB Tel: 0117 950 5050 Email: nev.w.goodman@bris.ac.uk; 5 Northover Road, Westbury on Trym, Bristol BS9 3LW — BM BCh 1975 Oxf.; DPhil Oxf. 1974, MA 1975; FRCA 1979. Cons. Anaesth. S.mead Hosp. Bristol; Examr. FRCA Exam. (Primary). Prev: Cons. Sen. Lect. (Anaesth.) Univ. Bristol.

GOODMAN, Raymond Emmanuel BUPA Hospital Manchester, Russell Road, Whalley Range, Manchester M16 8AJ Tel: 0161 226 0112 Fax: 0161 227 9405; 13 Drayton Manor, 507 Parrswood Road, Didsbury, Manchester M20 5GJ — LMSSA Lond. 1963; MSc Salford 1976; MRCS Eng. LRCP Lond. 1964; MRCGP 1983; DObst RCOG 1965; MIBiol. 1985. (Manch.) p/t Cons. Psycho Sexual Med. Salford AHA; Hon. Teach. Clin. Med. Univ. Manch. Socs: BMA; Inst. Psychosexual Med.; Soc. Scientif. Study of Sex NY. Prev: Med. Off. Brit. Pregn. Advis. Serv.; Clin. Asst. (Psychiat.) Sale & Brooklands War Memor. Hosp.; Ho. Surg. & Ho. Phys. Ashton-under-Lyne Gen. Hosp.

GOODMAN, Professor Robert Nicholas Department of Child and Adolescent Psychiatry, Institute of Psychiatry, De Crespigny Park, London SE5 8AF Tel: 020 7703 5411 — BM BCh 1978 Oxf.; PhD Camb. 1997; BA (1st cl. Hons.) Camb. 1975, MA 1979; MRCP (UK) 1983; FRCPsych 1997, M 1986; T(Psychiat.) 1991. Prof. (Brain & Behavioural Med.) Inst. Psychiat. Lond.; Sen. Lect. Inst. Child Health; Hon. Cons. Childr. Maudsley Hosp. Lond. & Gt. Ormond St. Hosp. Lond. Prev: Research Fell. (Child Psychiat.) Gt. Ormond St. Hosp. Lond.; Regist. (Psychiat.) Maudsley Hosp. Lond.; SHO (Paediat.) Gt. Ormond St. Hosp. Lond.

GOODMAN, Sally Eileen Bristol Oncology Centre, Horfield Road, Bristol BS2 8ED Tel: 0117 928 2418; 5 Northover Road, Westbury-on-Trym, Bristol BS9 3LW — BM BCh 1976 Oxf.; MA Oxf. 1976; MRCP (UK) 1980; FRCR 1984; FRCP 2000. Cons. Clin. Oncol. Bristol Oncol. Centre.

GOODMAN, Sarah 15 Bincleaves Road, Weymouth DT4 8RS Tel: 01305 785891 — MB BS 1976 Lond.; MRCS Eng. LRCP Lond. 1974; DRCOG 1978. (St. Mary's) GP Portland. Prev: Cas. Off. S.mead Hosp. Bristol; SHO (Paediat.) Addington Hosp. Durban, S. Afr.; Ho. Off. (O & G) St. Mary's Hosp. Lond.

GOODMAN, Sarah Elizabeth Beechwood, St Bridget's Lane, Egremont CA22 — MB BS 1986 Newc.; MRCGP 1994; DRCOG 1992.

GOODMAN, Thomas Robin Department of Radiology, John Radcliffe Hospital, Oxford OX3 9DU — MB BChir 1989 Camb.; BMSc (Hons.) Dund 1986; MRCPI 1992; FRCR 1995. Cons. Paediatric Radiologist, John Radcliffe Hosp., Oxf.. Prev: Fell. in Paediatric Radiol., The Hosp. for Sick Childr.; Regist. Rotat. (Radiol.) Oxf.; SHO (Gen. Med.) John Radcliffe Hosp. Oxf.

GOODRICH, Bryan Henry Lilliput Surgery, Elms Avenue, Lindisfarne, Poole BH14 8EE Tel: 01202 741310 Fax: 01202 739122; Evening Cottalge, 23 Bingham Avenue, Poole BH14 8ND — MB ChB 1968 Birm.; FRCA 1973. (Birm.) Hosp. Pract. (Anaesth.) Roy. Bournemouth Gen. Hosp. Socs: BMA; Birm. Sands Cox Soc. Prev: Sen. Regist. (Anaesth.) Soton. Univ. & Bournemouth & E. Dorset Hosps; Ho. Phys. Gen. Hosp. Birm.; Ho. Surg. Qu. Eliz. Hosp. Birm.

GOODRICK, Margaret Jean Department of Haematology, Frenchay Hospital, Frenchay, Bristol BS16 1LE Tel: 0117 970 1212 — MB ChB 1982 Manch.; FRCPath 1998; MD Manch. 1994; MRCP (UK) 1985; MRCPath 1988. Cons. Haemat. Nat. Blood Auth. & N. Bristol NHS Trust. Prev: Sen. Regist. (Blood Transfus. & Immunohaemat.) Bristol.

GOODRIDGE, David Martin Gostwyck Warders Medical Centre, 47 East Street, Tonbridge TN9 1LA Tel: 01732 770088 Fax: 01732 770033; 43 The Drive, Tonbridge TN9 2LR Tel: 01732 770055 Email: d.goodridge@virgin.net — MB BChir 1973 Camb.; FRCGP 1989, M 1980; DRCOG 1977. (Guy's) Chairm. Sevenoaks & Tonbridge PCG. Prev: Chairm. Kent Trainers Selection Comm.; Coll. Tutor RCGP, Tunbridge Wells.

GOODRUM, David Thomas Cheltenham General Hospital, Sandford Road, Cheltenham GL53 7AN — MB ChB 1978 Bristol; FRCA. 1987. Cons. Anaesth. E. Glos. NHS Trust.

GOODRUM, Elissa Jacqueline 8 The Pavilions, Sandford Road, Cheltenham GL53 7AJ — MB BS 1987 Lond.

GOODSHIP, Judith Anne 13 North Avenue, Gosforth, Newcastle upon Tyne NE3 4DT — MB ChB 1981 Ed.; BSc (Hons.) Ed. 1978; MD Ed. 1990; MRCP (UK) 1984; DRCPath. 1988; FRCP 1997. Cons. & Sen. Lect. N. Region Genetics Serv. Newc. u. Tyne.

GOODSON, Mary Elizabeth (retired) Hopewell House, 15 Calverley Road, Oulton, Leeds LS26 8JD Tel: 0113 282 3292 — MB ChB Leeds 1939, DCH 1947; MRCGP 1965; DObst RCOG 1946; DCH Lond. 1944. Prev: GP Oulton & Woodlesford.

GOODSON, Paul Law Street Surgery, 49-51 Laws Street, Pembroke Dock SA72 6DJ Tel: 01646 683113 / 682002 Fax: 01646 622273; 45 St. Leonards Avenue, Crundale, Haverfordwest SA62 4DW — MB BS 1986 Lond.; MRCGP 1991.

GOODSON, Trevor Colin Peppers, La Mielle Clement, St Brelade, Jersey JE3 8FW — MB ChB 1995 Bristol.

GOODSON-WICKES, Charles (retired) Flat 23, 37 St James's Place, London SW1A 1NS Tel: 020 7629 0981 — MB BS Lond. 1970. Dir. Gyrus Gp. plc & Nstor Healthcare Gp. Plc; Chairm.MRDARC Ltd. Prev: Clin. Asst. St. Bart. Hosp. Lond.

GOODSPEED, Alan Herbert (retired) 147 Browning Road, Enfield EN2 0HJ Tel: 020 8363 1604 — MB BS Lond. 1952; MRCS Eng. LRCP Lond. 1952; Dip Pharm Med. RCP (UK) 1978.

GOODSTONE, Andrew Stephen The Surgery, 17 Marylebone Road, London NW1 5LT Tel: 020 7935 6328 — MB ChB 1992 Sheff.

GOODWILL, Christopher John Department Rheumatology & Rehabilitation, Kings College Hospital, Denmark Hill, London SE5 9RS; 9 Kemerton Road, Beckenham BR3 6NJ Tel: 020 8650 0894 — MB BS 1957 Lond.; FRCP Lond. 1977, M 1961; MRCS Eng. LRCP Lond. 1957; DPhysMed Eng. 1964. (King's Coll. Hosp.) Cons. Phys. Rheum. & Rehabil. King's Coll. Hosp. Lond. Socs: Brit. Soc. Rheum. & Brit. Soc. Rehabil. Med. Prev: Sen. Regist. (Physical Med. & Rheum.) King's Coll. Hosp.; Ho. Phys. Brompton Hosp.

GOODWIN, Alexander Paul Lamy, Surg. Lt.-Cdr. RN Retd. Department of Anaesthetics, Royal United Hospital, Coombe Park, Bath BA1 3NG Tel: 01225 825061 Fax: 01225 825056 Email: alexandergoodwin@patrol.i.way.co.uk — MB BS 1981 Lond.; FCAnaesth 1990; DA (UK) 1986. Cons. Anaesth. Roy. United Hosp.

Bath; Lead Clinician - Day Surg. Bath; RCA Coll. Tutor; Educat. Dir. - Bristol Sch. Anaesth. Prev: Sen. Regist. (Anaesth.) Oxf. Regional Train Scheme; Trainee & Research Fell. (Anaesth.) Addenbrooke's Hosp. Camb.

GOODWIN, Alison Mary The Bunches, Aldham, Colchester CO6 3PH — MB BS 1987 Lond.; FRCA 1992. Cons. Kings Coll. Hosp. Lond. Socs: Fell. Roy. Soc. Med.; BMA. Prev: Regist. (Anaesth.) Univ. Coll. Lond. Hosps.

GOODWIN, Andrew John 20 West Road, Bromsgrove B60 2NQ — BM 1980 Soton.

GOODWIN, Mr Andrew Timothy Woodfield House, Chalfont Lane, Chorleywood, Rickmansworth WD3 5PP Tel: 01923 282282; 1 Madge Hill, Church Road, Hanwell, London W7 3BW Tel: 020 8567 2728 Email: goodwinat@msn.co.uk — MB BS 1990 Lond.; FRCS Eng. 1995. (St. Mary's Lond.) Specialist Regist. (Cardiothoracic) Papworth Hosp. Cambs. Prev: Research Regist. (Cardiothoracic Surg.) Harefield Hosp. Middlx.; SHO Rotat. (Surg.) N.wick Pk. Hosp. Harrow HA; Ho. Off. (Cardiothoracic Surg.) St. Mary's Hosp. Lond. & (Med.) St. Chas. Hosp. Lond.

GOODWIN, Angela Mary Warden Lodge Surgery, Albury Ride, Cheshunt, Waltham Cross EN8 8XE Tel: 01992 622324 Fax: 01992 636900 — MB BS 1979 Lond.

GOODWIN, Anthony Princess of Wales Hospital, Coity Road, Bridgend CF31 1RQ Tel: 01656 752661 Fax: 01656 752280 — MB BCh 1972 Wales; DCH Eng. 1977. (Welsh Nat. Sch. Med.) Cons. Paediat. P.ss of Wales Hosp. Bridgend. Socs: Welsh Paediat. Soc. Prev: Assoc. Specialist (Paediat.) P.ss of Wales Hosp. Bridgend; Regist. (Paediat.) E. Glam. Hosp. Pontypridd; Ho. Phys. Roy. Gwent Hosp. Newport.

***GOODWIN, Anthony Myles** 18 Ascot Park, Great Crosby, Liverpool L23 2XH — MB ChB 1988 Sheff.; MRCGP 1992; DRCOG 1992.

GOODWIN, Asmara Mirelle 20 Julian Road, Folkestone CT19 5HW — BM 1997 Soton.

GOODWIN, Cathryn Philippa Joondalup Community Mental health, Regents Park Rd, Joondalup WA 6027, Australia Tel: 08 9400 9499; 12 The Chase, Chervil Way, Reading RG7 3YX Tel: 08 9400 9499 — MB BCh 1994 Wales; DRCOG; DCH; FFP. (UWCM) GP Princip.; Staff Grade Family Plann.; Occupat.al Health Phys.

GOODWIN, Professor Charles Stewart Division of Gastroenterology, St George's Hospital Medical School, Cranmer Terrace, London SW17 0RE; 12 Pine Grove, Wimbledon, London SW19 7HE Tel: 020 8879 3317 Fax: 020 8879 1611 Email: stewart@pylori.demon.co.uk — MB BChir Camb. 1958; MD Camb. 1965; FRCPA 1977; FRCPath 1982, M 1970; Dip. Bact. Lond 1966. (St. Bart.) Hon. Vis. Prof. in MicroBiol. Dept. of Gastroenterol. St Geo.s Hosp. Med. Sch.; Hon. Cons. Div. of Med. St. Geo. Health Care. Prev: Prof. Bacteriol. United Arab Emirates Univ.; Assoc. Prof. (Clin. Microbiol.) Univ. W.. Austral.; Cons. Microbiol. N.wick Pk. Hosp. Harrow.

GOODWIN, Daphne Mary (retired) 150 Buckswood Drive, Gossops Green, Crawley RH11 8JF Tel: 01293 612906 — MB BS (Hnrs. Path.) Lond. 1960; MRCS Eng. LRCP Lond. 1960. Prev: Paediat. Ho. Phys. Hampstead Gen. Hosp.

GOODWIN, Daryl Patrick Sandgate Road Surgery, 180 Sandgate Road, Folkestone CT20 2HN Tel: 01303 221133 Fax: 01303 261068 — BM BCh 1979 Oxf.; MA, BM BCh Oxf. 1979; MRCGP 1984; DRCOG 1984. Prev: SHO (Paediat.) Birm. Childr. Hosp.; SHO (Med.) Good Hope Gen. Hosp. Sutton Coldfield; Ho. Surg. (Paediat. & Gen. Surg.) John Radcliffe Hosp. Oxf.

GOODWIN, David (retired) 17 Glenbroome Park, Jordanstown, Newtownabbey BT37 0RL Tel: 851642 — MB BCh BAO 1944 Belf.

GOODWIN, Mr David Pryce Royal Berkshire Hospital, Reading RG1 5AN; 72 Berkeley Avenue, Reading RG1 6HY Tel: 01734 584711 — MB BS 1961 Lond.; BSc (Special, Hons.) Lond. 1958, MS 1973, MB BS (Hons. Surg.) 1961; FRCS Eng. 1966; FACS 1989. (St. Mary's) Cons. Surg. Roy. Berks. Hosp. Reading; Assoc. Teach. St. Mary's Hosp. Med. Sch. Lond. Socs: Fell. Roy. Soc. Med.; Vasc. Soc. GB; Brit. Assn. Surgic. Oncol. Prev: Sen. Regist. (Surg.) St. Mary's Hosp. Lond.; Ho. Surg. Hammersmith Hosp.; Fell. (Surg.) TuLa. Univ. New Orleans, USA.

GOODWIN, Donald Philip 43 Holymoor Road, Holymoorside, Chesterfield S42 7EB Tel: 01246 566710 — MB ChB 1985 Sheff.; DRCOG 1989. GP Trainee Chesterfield VTS. Prev: SHO (Psychiat.) Chesterfield Roy. Hosp.; SHO (O & G) Scardale Hosp. Chesterfield; SHO (Paediat.) Chesterfield & N. Derbysh. Roy. Hosp. Chesterfield.

GOODWIN, Fiona Clare Bayliss Farm, Corse, Staunton, Gloucester GL19 3RJ — MB ChB 1987 Birm.

GOODWIN, Mr Frank Raymond Church House, Bury, Dulverton TA22 9NE — MB ChB Birm. 1946; FRCS Ed. 1967; MRCS Eng. LRCP Lond. 1946; DObst RCOG 1951. (Birm.) Socs: BMA; Sen. Fell. Brit. Orthop. Assn. Prev: Cons. i/c A & E Dept. Good Hope Hosp. Sutton Coldfield; Cons. (Orthop. Surg.) Riyadh Milit. Hosp. Saudi Arabia; Capt. RAMC.

GOODWIN, Gareth Wyn The Surgery, Scotland St., Llanrwst LL26 0AL Tel: 01492 640411; Garreg Wen, Llanddoged, Llanrwst LL26 0BJ — MB ChB 1979 Liverp.

GOODWIN, Gerald Leopold (retired) 9 Greenclose Road, Whitchurch, Cardiff CF14 1QP Tel: 01222 625404 — MRCS Eng. LRCP Lond. 1956; MA Camb. 1953; LMSSA Lond. 1954; BDS St. And. 1962. Prev: Surg. (Dent.) Porth M. Glam. & Cwmbran Gwent.

GOODWIN, Professor Guy Manning University Department of Psychiatry, Warneford Hospital, Warneford Lane, Headington, Oxford OX3 7JX Tel: 01865 226451 Fax: 01865 204198 Email: guy.goodwin@psych.ox.ac.uk — BM BCh 1978 Oxf.; BA Oxf. 1968, DPhil 1972; FRCP Ed. 2000; MRCP (UK) 1980; FRCPsych 1995, M 1982. (Oxf. Univ.) W.A. Handley Prof. & Hon. Cons. Oxon. Ment. Health Trust. Socs: (Counc.) Brit. Assn. Psychopharmacol. & Pres. (2002-2004). Prev: Prof. Psychiat. Univ. Edin.

GOODWIN, Mr Harold Penthouse W., Albany, Manor Road, East Cliff, Bournemouth BH1 3EL Tel: 01202 553479 — MB BS 1933 Lond.; FRCS Eng. 1938; MRCS Eng. LRCP Lond. 1933; MRCGP 1953; FRCGP 18/11/94. (Univ. Coll. Hosp. & St. Bart.) Cons. Obstetr. & Gynaecol. SW, NW & Metrop. & Wessex RHBs; Cons. (Gyn.) P. of Wales Hosp. Lond.; Cons. (Obst.) Bearsted Memor. Hosp. Lond.; Examr. Gen. Nurs. Counc. Eng. & Wales; Hon. Capt. RAMC. Socs: Fell. Roy. Soc. Med. Prev: Sen. Gyn. & Obst. Regist. Char. Cross Hosp.; Gyn. Regist. Postgrad. Med. Sch. Hammersmith Hosp.; Res. Med. Off. Qu. Charlotte's Matern. Hosp. & Hosp. Wom. Soho Sq.

GOODWIN, Herbert Alan (retired) Tanglewood Cottage, Gurrey Bank, Llandeilo SA19 6AX Tel: 01558 822240 — MB BCh 1959 Wales; DCH Eng. 1966, DA 1966. Prev: Cons. Paediat. W. Wales Gen. Hosp. Carmarthen.

GOODWIN, Hilary Anne Woodfield House, Chalfont Lane, Chorleywood, Rickmansworth WD3 5PP Tel: 01923 282282 — MB BS 1965 Lond.; AFOM RCP Lond. 1988; MFFP 1993; DIH Lond. 1988; DObst RCOG 1967. (St. Mary's) Occupat. Health Phys. Woodfield Hse. Chorleywood. Prev: Sen. Med. Adviser Shell UK; Dist. Med. Off. Centr. Elec. Generating Bd. & Nat. Power Co.; GP Pinner.

GOODWIN, Ian David 24 Essex Road, Sutton Coldfield B75 6NS — MB ChB 1987 Liverp.

GOODWIN, Jane Featherstone 1 Dovergrove, Egginton, Derby — MB ChB 1969 Liverp.; DObst RCOG 1972 DO Eng. 1975. (Liverp.)

GOODWIN, Janet Elizabeth (retired) Upcott Cottage, Eardisley, Hereford HR3 6PR — MB ChB Manch. 1963; DA Eng. 1976. Assoc. Specialist (Anaesth.) Hereford Health Dist.

GOODWIN, Professor John Forrest 12 Fillenton Court, 27 Valuey Pk Road, Teddington TW11 9BF — MB BS 1942 Lond.; MD Lond. 1946; MD Hon Causa Lisbon 1984; FRCP Lond. 1957, M 1944; MRCS Eng. LRCP Lond. 1942; FESC 1989; Hon. FACP 1984; FACC 1967. (St. Mary's) Emerit. Prof. Clin. Cardiol. Roy. Postgrad. Med. Sch. Lond. Socs: Fell. Roy. Soc. Med.; (Pres.) Cardiomyopathy Assn.; Assn. Phys. Prev: Hon. Cons. Phys. Hammersmith Hosp.; Hon. Cons. Cardiol. St. Geo. Hosp. Lond.; Mem. Expert Comm. (Cardiovasc. Dis.) WHO.

GOODWIN, John Spencer 2B St Pauls Road, Manchester M20 4PG — MB ChB 1997 Manch.

GOODWIN, Leonard George, CMG Shepperlands Farm, Park Lane, Finchampstead, Wokingham RG40 4QF Tel: 0118 973 2153 — MB BS 1950 Lond.; FRS 1976; Hon. DSc Brunel 1986; BPharm Lond. 1935, BSc 1937; FRCP Lond. 1972, M 1966; Hon. FRPS 1977. (Univ. Coll. Hosp.) Fell. UCL. Socs: Fell. Roy. Soc. Med.; Hon. Mem. (Ex-Pres.) Roy. Soc. Trop. Med. & Hyg. Prev: Dir. Laborats. Comparative Med. Inst. Zool. & Dir. Sc. Zool. Soc. Lond.; Head Wellcome Laborats. Trop. Med. Lond.

GOODWIN, Mark David 47 St Mary's Road, Sindlesham, Wokingham RG41 5DA — BM BCh 1996 Oxf.; BA Oxf. 1992. (Oxford) SHO (Gen. Med.) MusGr. Pk. Hosp. Taunton.
GOODWIN, Mr Mark Ivor The Royal Bournemouth Hospital, Castle Lane E., Bournemouth BH7 7DW Tel: 01202 704458 Fax: 01202 704506 — BM 1980 Soton.; FRCS 1986 Ed. (Southampton) Cons. Orthop. & Trauma Roy. Bournemouth Hosp. & Poole Hosp. NHS Trust. Socs: Fell. BOA. Prev: Sen. Regist. (Orthop. & Trauma) United Hosp. Bath; Clin. Fell. (Orthop. & Trauma) Vancouver Gen. Hosp. Vancouver, BC, Canada; Regist. (Orthop. Paediat.) Lord Mayor Treloar Hosp. Alton, Hants..
GOODWIN, Mark Jonathan Glyncorrwg Health Centre, Waun Avenue, Glyncorrwg, Port Talbot SA13 1DP Tel: 01639 850407 Fax: 01639 850895 — MB BCh 1985 Wales; MRCGP 1990. GP.
GOODWIN, Michael William Peter 20 Church Street, Weedon, Northampton NN7 4PL Tel: 01327 340521 — MB BS 1991 Lond. Specialist Regist. (Anaesth.) John Radcliffe Hosp. Oxf.
GOODWIN, Naomi 26 The Rise, Llanishen, Cardiff CF14 0RD — MB ChB 1994 Leic.; BSc 1991. Specialist Regist. (Anaesth.) Welsh Train. Scheme; Flexible Trainee. Prev: SHO (Anaesth.) Leicester Train. Scheme.
GOODWIN, Paul Raymond Murray Road Surgery, 1 Murray Road, Northwood HA6 2YP Tel: 01923 824588 Fax: 01923 840534 — MB BS 1971 Lond.
GOODWIN, Paul Richard Mayfield Surgery, Mayfield, Buckden St. Neots, Huntingdon PE19 5SZ Tel: 01480 810216 Fax: 01480 810745; 17 Brampton Road, Grafham, Huntingdon PE28 0UR Tel: 01480 810297 — MB BS 1987 Lond.; MRCGP 1991; DRCOG 1990. Prev: Trainee GP W. Essex. VTS.
GOODWIN, Peter Geoffrey Summerhill, Forest Lane, Ringwood BH24 3HF Tel: 01425 472010 — MD 1978 Lond.; MB BS Lond. 1966; FRCP Lond. 1980; MRCP (U.K.) 1970. (St. Mary's) Cons. Dermat. Roy. Bournemouth & ChristCh. NHS Trust & Soton. Hosp. NHS Trust (T). Socs: Fell. Roy. Soc. Med.; Fell. Brit. Assn. Dermat.; Solent Skin Soc. Prev: Sen. Regist. (Dermat.) Middlx. Hosp. Lond.; Regist. Edgware Gen. Hosp.; Hon. Sen. Regist. Dermat. St. Mary's Hosp. Lond.
GOODWIN, Philip 58A Wimpole Street, London W1M Tel: 020 7935 3351 Fax: 020 7487 2504; Pinehurst, Shootersway Lane, Berkhamsted HP4 3NW Tel: 01442 871849 — MB ChB 1957 Leeds. Prev: SHO (Gen. Med. & Haemat.) & SHO (Chemother.) Bradford Roy. Infirm.; Clin. Asst. (Haemat.) Hull Roy. Infirm.
GOODWIN, Philip Edward Speeds Cottage, Church Road, HavenSt., Ryde PO33 4DN — MB BS 1972 Lond.; FFA RCSI 1976. Cons. Anaesth. St. Mary's Hosp. Trust Newport I. of Wight. Prev: Sen. Regist. St. Mary's Hosp. & Edgware Gen. Hosp.; Regist. St. Mary's Hosp. Lond. & Nat. Heart Hosp.
GOODWIN, Philip John 30 West End Cottages, Congleton CW12 4DZ — MB ChB 1989 Manch.
GOODWIN, Richard Bupa Hospital, Washington NE38 9JZ Tel: 0191 415 1272 Fax: 0191 415 5541; 32 South Street, Durham DH1 4QP Tel: 0191 384 4255 Email: dick.goodwin@clara.net — MRCS Eng. LRCP Lond. 1968; FFA RCS Eng. 1975; DA Eng. 1971; DObst RCOG 1970.
GOODWIN, Richard Geoffrey 26 The Rise, Llanshen, Cardiff CF14 0RD — MB BS 1994 Lond.; MRCP Lond. 1998. (St Mary's) Specialist Regist. (Dermat.) Cardiff. Prev: Med. SHO N.ampton.
GOODWIN, Richard Michael Beechwood Surgery, 57 John Street, Workington CA14 3BT Tel: 01900 64866 Fax: 01900 871561 — BM BCh 1983 Oxf.; LMSSA Lond. 1982; MRCGP 1988; DCH RCPS Glas. 1986.
GOODWIN, Richard William Barnet & Chase Farm Hospitals NHS Trust, Barnet General Hospital, Well House Lane, Barnet EN5 3DJ Tel: 020 8216 4000; 84 Lofting Road, London N1 1JB Tel: 0385 916463 Email: richgoodwin@hotmail.com — MB BS 1998 Lond.; MB BS Lond 1998; BSc Hons Lond. 1995. (UCL Medical School) SHO Basic Surgic. Train. Rotat. Barnet Gen. Hosp.
GOODWIN, Mr Robert John 150 Buckswood Drive, Crawley RH11 8JF Tel: 01293 612906; 39 Kentish Lane, Hatfield AL9 6NG Tel: 01707 664534 Fax: 020 7453 2439 Email: roburol@aol.com — MB BChir 1991 Camb.; MA Camb. 1987; FRCS Eng. 1994; MSc Lond. 1997. (Royal Free) Regist. (Uroneurol.) Nat. Hosp. Neurol. & Neurosurg. Lond.; Specialist Regist. (Urol.) St Geo. Hosp. Lond.; Lect. (Urol.) St. Peter's Hosp. Lond. Prev: Regist. (Uroneurol.) Nat. Hosp. Lond.; Lect. (Urol.) St Peters Lond.; Specialist Regist. (Urol.) Centr. Middlx. Hosp. Lond.
GOODWIN, Stephanie Helen Jeanette 4 Birch Road, Gatley, Cheadle SK8 4NE — MB ChB 1987 Manch.
GOODWIN, Stephen Anthony Airport Medical Services, Forte Posthouse Hotel, Povey Cross Road, South Area, London Gatwick Airport, Horley RH6 0BA Tel: 01293 775336 Fax: 01293 775344 Email: amsgatwick@compuserve.com; 132 Worlds End Lane, Chelsfield, Orpington BR6 6AS Tel: 01689 857121 — MRCS Eng. LRCP Lond. 1962. (Guy's) Authorised Med. Examr. Civil Aviat. Auth. & others Airport Med. Servs. Gatwick Airport Lond.; Med. Adviser Brit. Airline Pilots Assn.; Med. Adviser Virgin Atlantic Airways. Socs: Aerospace Med. Assn. Prev: GP W. Wickham; Med. Off. RAF Changi, Singapore.
GOODWIN, Susan Mary Pheasants Clough Farm, Upper Hulme, Leek ST13 8UB — BM BS 1994 Nottm. Regist. Rotat. (Psychiat.) S. Manch. Univ. Hosp.
GOODWIN, Tania Gisele Yew Tree Cottage Surgery, 15 Leyton Road, Harpenden AL5 2HX Tel: 01582 712126 Fax: 01582 462414; 6 Beesowend Cottages, Beesowend Lane, Harpenden AL5 2AA — MB ChB 1993 Birm.; MRCGP 1998; DFFP. (Birmingham) GP Partner, Yew Tree Cottage Surg. Harpenden. Prev: SHO Qu. Eliz. II Hosp. Welwyn Garden City VTS; Ho. Phys. Alexandra Hosp. Redditch; Ho. Surg. Qu. Eliz. II Hosp Welwyn Garden City.
GOODWIN, Timothy John (retired) Northwood Consulting Rooms, 25B Green Lane, Northwood HA6 2UZ Tel: 01923 826948 — MB BS Lond. 1964; FRCP Lond. 1983, M 1967. Clin. Tutor Mt. Vernon Postgrad. Med. Centre; Dir. (Med. Educat.) & Cons. Phys. Mt. Vernon & Watford Hosps. NHS Trust; Vis. Phys. Harefield Hosp. N.wood & Pinner Hosp. Prev: Sen. Regist. Med. Unit St. Mary's Hosp. Lond.
GOODWIN, Trevor Stockton Heath Medical Centre, The Forge, London Road, Stockton Heath, Warrington WA4 6HJ Tel: 01925 604427 Fax: 01925 210501; Midway, 11 Woodlands Drive, Thelwall, Warrington WA4 2EU — MB ChB 1971 Manch.; MRCGP 1978; DCH RCP Lond. 1986; DObst RCOG 1975. Prev: Trainee GP Salford; SHO (Obst. & Gyn, Paediat. & A & E) Hope Hosp. Salford.
GOODWIN, Victoria Helen 101 Windemere Avenue, Cardiff CF2 5PS — MB BCh 1994 Wales.
GOODWIN HUDSON, Ellen Elisa (retired) 14 Newton Park, Newton Solney, Burton-on-Trent DE15 0SX — MRCS Eng. LRCP Lond. 1924.
GOODWIN-JONES, Roger Banwell Grange Park Surgery, Grange Road, Burley in Wharfedale, Ilkley LS29 7HG Tel: 01943 862108 Fax: 01943 864997; 4 Chantry Court, Chantry Drive, Ilkley LS29 9HU — MB ChB 1979 Leeds; MRCGP 1984; Cert. Family Plann. JCC 1983; DRCOG 1982.
GOODWORTH, David Jeremy Birchwood Practice, Birchwood Medical Centre, Northmead Drive, Poole BH17 7XW Tel: 01202 697639 Fax: 01202 659323 — MB ChB 1984 Manch.; DRCOG 1988. (Manchester) GP Princip. Prev: Trainee GP Truro VTS; SHO (A & E) & Ho. Off. (Surg.) Bury Gen. Hosp.
GOODWYN, Jasper Richard Derby Road Practice, 52 Derby Road, Ipswich IP3 8DN Tel: 01473 728121 Fax: 01473 718810 — MB BChir 1989 Camb.; MA Camb. 1989; MRCGP 1995; DRCOG 1993. (Clare College Cambridge & St Bartholomews)
GOODYEAR, Geoffrey Martin Penn Fields Health Centre, Upper Zoar St., Wolverhampton WV3 0JH Tel: 01902 22313; Rosslaw, Penstone Lane, Lower Penn, Wolverhampton WV4 4XE Tel: 01902 340782 — MB BChir 1966 Camb.; MB Camb. 1966, BChir 1965; DObst RCOG 1969. (St. Thos.) Socs: Inst. Psionic Med. Prev: Med. Off. Lesotho Flying Doctor Serv.; SHO Rotat. Wolverhampton Hosp. Gp.; SHO (O & G) Hallam Hosp. W. Bromwich.
GOODYEAR, Helen Margaret The North Middlesex Hospital, Sterling Way, London N18 1QX Tel: 020 8887 2000; 55 Muswell Road, London N10 2BS Tel: 020 8444 4185 — MB ChB 1982 Bristol; MRCP (UK) 1986. Sen. Regist. N. Middlx. Hosp. & Hosp. Sick Childr. Gt. Ormond St. Lond. Socs: BMA & Brit. Paediat. Assn. Prev: Lect. & Hon. Sen. Regist. Qu. Eliz. Hosp. for Childr. Lond.; Regist. & SHO (Paediat.) Hosp. for Sick Childr. Gt. Ormond St. Lond.
GOODYEAR, John Edwin Casterbridge, The Green, Finningley, Doncaster DN9 3BT Tel: 01302 770217 — MB ChB 1948 N.Z.; FRCPA 1987; FRCPath 1977, M 1965; DMJ Soc. Apoth. Lond. 1977. Socs: Brit. Assn. Forens. Med. & Brit. Acad. Forens. Sci.;

Assn. of Clin. Pathologists; Brit. Soc. of Haemat. Prev: Cons. Path. MOD (Army) Brit. Milit. Hosp. Rintein.

GOODYEAR, Kathryn 31 Monkswood Close, Newbury RG14 6NR — BM 1998 Soton.; BM Soton 1998.

GOODYEAR, Mary Louisa (retired) 17 Penns Court, Horsham Road, Steyning BN44 3BF Tel: 01903 815705 — MB ChB 1949 Leeds.

GOODYEAR, Patricia Ann Judy 139 Knightlow Road, Birmingham B17 8PY Tel: 0121 429 2364 Fax: 0121 429 2364 Email: patricia.goodyear@talk21.com; 139 Knightlow Road, Birmingham B17 8PY Tel: 0121 429 2364 Fax: 0121 429 2364 Email: patricia.goodyear@talk21.com — MB ChB Birm. 1962; MRCPsych. 1973; DPM 1969; MSc. 1998 UCL. (Birm.) p/t Indep. Cons. Birm.; Hon. Sen. Lect. (Psychiat.) Univ. Birm.; Mem. W. Midl. Inst. Psychother.; Mem. Birm. Med. Inst. Socs: Assn. Psychoanalyt. Psychother.; W Midl. Inst. Psychother.; Birm. Med. Inst. Prev: Cons. Psychiat. Yewcroft Ment. Health Resource Centre Birm.; Clin. Tutor (Psychiat.) John Conolly Hosp. Birm.; Hon. Sen. Lect. (Psychiat.) Univ. Birm.

GOODYEAR, Paul William Alexander 12 D'Ayncourt Walk, Farnsfield, Newark NG22 8DP — MB ChB 1998 Manch.; MB ChB Manch 1998.

GOODYER, Professor Ian Michael Section of Developmental Psychiatry, Douglas House, 18 Trumpington Road, Cambridge CB2 2AH Tel: 01223 336098 Fax: 01223 746122 Email: ig104@cus.cam.ac.uk; 13 High Street, Oakington, Cambridge CB4 5AG — MB BS 1974 Lond.; MD Lond. 1985; FRCPsych 1989, M 1978; DCH Eng. 1976; F. Med Sci 1999; FRCPCH 1995; F Med Sci 1999. (Sr Georges Hosp) Prof. Child & Adolesc. Psychiat. Univ. Camb.; Hon. Cons. Lifespan Healthcare Trust Camb. Socs: Fell. Acad. of Med. Sci. Prev: Lect. (Child & Adolesc. Psychiat.) Univ. Camb.; Sen. Lect. (Child & Adolesc. Psychiat.) Univ. Manch.; Hon. Cons. Salford HA.

GOOI, Hock Chye Department of Immunology, Chancellor Wing, St James' University Hospital, Beckett St., Leeds LS9 7TF — MB BS 1971 Malaya; MRCP (UK) 1976; MRCPath 1983. Cons. Immunol. St. Jas. Univ. Hosp. Leeds.

GOOLAMALI, Saleem Karim (cons. rooms), 25 Highfield Road, Northwood HA6 1EU Tel: 01923 824342 Fax: 01923 829229 Email: mediderm@talk21.com; Parkside, 28 Bedford Road, Moor Park, Northwood HA6 2AZ Fax: 020 8869 2939 Email: mediderm@btinternet.com — MB BS Lond. 1967, MRCP (UK) 1970; MD Lond. 1976; FRCP Lond. 1982. (Univ. Coll. Lond. & Univ. Coll. Hosp.) Cons. Dermat. N.wick Pk. & St Mark's NHS Trust Harrow; Recognised Clin. Teach. Univ. Lond.; Examr. MRCP (UK) RCP Lond.; Hon Sen. Lect. Imperial Coll. Sch. of Med., Lond. Socs: Fell. Roy. Soc. Med. (Mem. Sect. Dermat.); Brit. Assn. Dermat.; Fell. Amer. Acad. Dermat. Prev: Sen. Regist. (Dermat.) Roy. Vict. Infirm. Newc.; SHO Lond. Hosp. Whitechapel Lond.; Ho. Phys. (Med. & Neurol.) & Ho. Surg. Univ. Coll. Hosp. Lond.

GOOLD, Isobel Joyce Odiham Health Centre, Deer Park View, Odiham, Hook RG29 1JY Tel: 01256 702371 Fax: 01256 701180; Coudray House, Herriard, Basingstoke RG25 2PN Tel: 01256 381787 Fax: 01256 381787 — MB BS 1968 Lond.; MRCS Eng. LRCP Lond. 1968; DObst RCOG 1971; DCH Eng. 1971. (Roy. Free)

GOOLD, Janet Eileen (retired) 42 Digswell Rise, Welwyn Garden City AL8 7PW Tel: 01707 322398 — MB BS 1962 Lond.; MRCS Eng. LRCP Lond. 1962; FFA RCS Eng. 1974; DA Eng. 1968. Cons. Anaesth. Qu. Eliz. II Hosp. Welwyn Garden City & Hertford Co. Hosp. Prev: Sen. Regist. (Anaesth.) Roy. Berks. Hosp. Reading.

GOOLD, Marian Anne 35 Vincam Close, Whitton, Twickenham TW2 7AB — MB BS 1976 Lond.; MRCS Eng. LRCP Lond. 1976. AKC 1976.

GOOLD, Mary Josephine 15 Downs Road, Newcastle BT33 0AG Tel: 013967 22398 — MB BCh BAO 1933 Belf.; LM Nat. Matern. Hosp. Dub. 1935. (Belf.) Socs: BMA. Prev: Asst. MOH LLa.lly Municip. Boro. & St. Helens Co. Boro.

GOOLD, Michael Francis Britton and Partners, 10 Spencer Street, Carlisle CA1 1BP Tel: 01228 29171; Appleby House, Kirkbride, Carlisle CA7 5JH Tel: 0169 73 51810 — MB BCh BAO 1981 NUI; MRCGP 1987; DObst RCPSI 1987; DCH RCPI 1987.

GOOLDEN, Alan Wilfrid Gough (retired) Orchard House, Summerhouse Lane, Aldenham, Watford WD25 8DL Tel: 01923 855395 — MB BS 1953 Lond.; FRCP Lond. 1985, M 1979; MRCS Eng. LRCP Lond. 1943; FRCR 1975; DMRT Eng. 1949. Prev: Cons. Radiotherap. Hammersmith Hosp.

GOON, Peter Kin Cho Department of Virology, St Mary's Hospital, South Wharf Road, London W2 1BL Tel: 020 7886 1746 Fax: 020 7886 6505 Email: pgoon@compuserve.com — MB BCh BAO 1994 Belf.; BSc (Med. Genetics) Belf. 1991; MRCP (Lond) 1998. (Queen's University, Belfast) Specialist Regist. (Virol.) St. Mary's Hosp. Lond.

GOONATILLEKE, Mestiyage Don Arnold Pemasiri Department of Psychiatry, Mersey Care NHS Trust, University Hospital Aintree, Longmoor Lane, Liverpool L9 7AL — MB BS 1967 Ceylon; FRCPsych 1993, M 1979; DPM Eng. 1978. (Colombo) Cons. Psychiat. Mersey Care NHS Trust Univ. Hosp. Aintree. Prev: Sen. Regist. Exevale Hosp. Exminster Devon.

GOONAWARDANA, Priyanthie Renuka 8 Manor Park Gardens, Edgware HA8 7NA — MB ChB 1991 Ed.

GOONERATNE, H Galpins Road Surgery, 6 Galpins Road, Thornton Heath CR7 6EA Tel: 020 8684 3450 Fax: 202 8683 0439 — MB BS 1966 Ceylon; MB BS 1966 Ceylon.

GOONESINGHE, N S Allport Surgery, 87 Allport Lane, Bromborough, Wirral CH62 7HL Tel: 0151 334 3621 Fax: 0151 334 3080.

GOONETILLEKE, Chitralal Ranjan Department of Haematology, Dorset County Hospital, Williams Avenue, Dorchester DT1 2JY — MB BS 1968 Ceylon; MRCP (UK) 1979; MRCPath 1981.

GOONETILLEKE, Udugama Koralalage Don Ajith Neurology Department, Regional Neuroscience Centre, Newcastle General Hospital, Westgate Road, Newcastle upon Tyne NE4 6BE Tel: 0191 273 8811 — MB BS Lond. 1985; MRCP (UK) 1989. (St Thomas's Hospital) Cons. & Hon. Sen. Lect. Neurol. Socs: Assn. Brit. Neurols.; Roy. Coll. Phys.; Peripheral Nerve Soc. Prev: Sen. Regist. (Neurol.) Roy. Vict. Infirm. (Newc.) & Middlesbrough Gen. Hosp. (Middlesbrough); Reg. (Neurol.) Manch. Roy. Infirm. N. Manch. Gen. Hosp.; Research & Hon. Regist. (Neurol.) W.m. & Char. Cross Hosp. Lond.

GOONETILLEKE, Udugama Koralalage Don Albert Dept. of Histopathology, Harold Wood Hospital, Romford RM3 0BE Tel: 01708 708413; 4 Ascott Avenue, Ealing, London W5 5QB — MD BS 1962 Colombo; MD Univ. Colombo 1984; MB BS Ceylon 1962; FRCPA 1976; FRCPath 1992, M 1980; DMJ Soc. Apoth. Lond. 1970. (Colombo) Cons. Histopath., Romford. Socs: Counc. Mem. Brit. Assn. Forens. Med.; (Ex-Chairm.) Forens. Med. Soc. Prev: Lect. (Forens. Path.) Char. Cross Hosp. Med. Sch. Lond.; Lect. (Forens. Med.) Leeds Univ.; Regist. (Path.) King Edwd. Memor. Hosp. Lond.

GOONEWARDENE, Swendrini De Fonseka Block 3, Orsett Hospital, Rowley Road, Orsett, Grays RM16 3EU Tel: 01375 891100; 119 Shenfield Place, Shenfield, Brentwood CM15 9AG — MB BS 1978 Sri Lanka; LRCP LRCS Ed. LRCPS Glas. 1986; FFA RCSI 1987; DA Eng. 1984. Staff Grade (Anaesth.) Orsett Hosp. & Basildon & Thurrock HA. Prev: Regist. (Anaesth.) Qu. Eliz. II Hosp. Welwyn Gdn. City; Regist. (Anaesth.) Hemel Hempstead Gen. Hosp.

GOONEWARDENE, Tyrone Ignatius 50 Queens Walk, Harrow HA1 1XS — MB BS 1994 Lond.

GOOPTU, Chandralekha Dermatology Department, The Oxford Radcliffe Hospital, Oxford OX3 7LJ Tel: 01865 228266 Fax: 01865 228260 — MB BChir 1991 Camb.; BA (Hons.) Oxf. 1988; MRCP (UK) 1994. Specialist Regist. (Dermat.) The Oxf. Radcliffe Hosp. Oxf. Prev: Regist. (Dermat.) Ch.ill Hosp. Oxf., Roy. Berks. & Battle Hosp. Reading & St. Johns Inst. Dermat. Lond.; SHO (Dermat.) Chelsea & W.m. Hosp. Lond.; SHO (Med.) E. Birm. Hosp.

GOOPTU, Debabrata South Tyneside District Hospital, Harton Lane, South Shields NE34 0PL Tel: 0191 454 8888 Fax: 0191 202 4180; 2 Meadowfield Drive, Cleadon Village, Sunderland SR6 7QW Tel: 0191 536 2073 — MB BS Calcutta 1954; DPhil Oxf. 1965; FRCP Lond. 1977, M 1960; FRCP Ed. 1977, M 1959. (Med. Coll. Hosps. Calcutta) Cons. Phys. Gen. Med. & Gastroenterol. S. Tyneside HA. Socs: Brit. Soc. Gastroenterol.; BMA; Caledonian Gut Club. Prev: Wellcome Foundat. Fell. Nuffield Dept. Med. Radcliffe Infirm. Oxf.; Sen. Regist. (Med.) Birm. RHB; Regist. (Respirat. Dis.) Hammersmith Hosp. & Roy. Postgrad. Med. Sch. Lond.

GOORAH, Sulackshana Devi Flat H474, Castle Leazes Halls, Newcastle upon Tyne NE2 4NY — MB BCh BAO 1992 Belf. SHO (Obst. & Gyn.) Belf. City Hosp.

GOORBARRY, Madan Deo Marsh House Medical Centre, 254 Marsh House Avenue, Billingham TS23 3EN Tel: 01642

561282/565068 Fax: 01642 565982 — MB ChB 1970 Glas. (Glas.) Prev: SHO (Paediat.) Hawkhead Hosp. Paisley; SHO (Obst. & Gyn) Paisley Matern. Hosp.; Ho. Phys. Roy. Alexandra Infirm. Paisley.

GOORNEY, Anthony Bryan (retired) Hook Green Farmhouse, Hook Green, Lamberhurst, Tunbridge Wells TN3 8LL — MB ChB 1950 Ed.; BSc Ed. 1949; FRCPsych 1982, M 1972; DPM Eng. 1965; DIH Soc. Apoth. Lond. 1961. Prev: Med. Dir. Ticehurst Hse. Hosp.

GOORNEY, Benjamin Philip Department of Genito Urinary Medicine, Hope Hospital, Salford M6 8HD Email: bgoorney@hope.srht.nwest.nhs.uk — MB ChB Manch. 1979; FRCP Lond. 1994; MRCP (UK) 1983. Cons. Genitourin. Phys. Salford & Manch. Hosps. Socs: Med. Soc. Study VD; Regional Represen. for (AGUN) Assn. Genito. Urin. Med., N.W. Region; Assn. Genitourin. Med. Prev: Sen. Regist. (Genitourin. Med.) Gen. Infirm. Leeds; Regist. (Venereol.) Char. Cross. Hosp. Lond.; SHO (Med.) S.mead Hosp. Bristol.

GOOSE, David Hugh (retired) 4 Old Hall Drive, Dersingham, King's Lynn PE31 6JT — MB ChB Ed. 1969; BDS Ed. 1964; FRCS Ed. 1974; FDS RCS Ed. 1971. p/t Locum Gen. Practitioner. Prev: Partner in full time Gen. Pract.

GOOSE, Gillian Lesley Tollgate Health Centre, 220 Tollgate Road, London E6 5JS Tel: 020 7445 7700 Fax: 020 7445 7715 — MB BS 1984 Lond.; MRCGP 1995; DCH RCP Lond. 1989; DRCOG 1988; DFFP 1997. (St. Geo. Hosp. Lond.) GP Princip. Prev: Trainee GP Newham VTS.

GOOZEE, Paul Royston The Hildenborough Medical Group Westwood, Tonbridge Road, Hildenborough, Tonbridge TN11 9HL Tel: 01732 838777 Fax: 01732 838297 — MB BS 1983 Lond.; BPharm 1977; MRCP (UK) 1987; MRCGP 1988. (Middlx.) Hosp. Practitioner Lardiology Kent & Sussex Hosp. Tunbridg, Wells, Kent.

***GOPAKUMAR, Bhaskaran Nair** 8 Adel Park Court, Leeds LS16 8HS Tel: 0113 267 1254 — MB ChB 1997 Leeds.

GOPAKUMAR, Chempakserry Gopalapanicker 12 Hathaway Crescent, Manor Park, London E12 6LR — MB BS 1970 Kerala; MRCPI 1977; MRCP (UK) 1977.

GOPAKUMAR, Choonattu Kuttanpillai 40 Main Road, Danbury, Chelmsford CM3 4NQ — MB BS 1977 Kerala.

GOPAL, Bipin 18 Hollingbourne Gardens, Ealing, London W13 8EN — MB ChB 1973 Leeds; MSc Surrey 1978; MRCP (UK) 1980.

GOPAL, David Terence Kilmeny Surgery, 50 Ashbourne Road, Keighley BD21 1LA Tel: 01535 606415 Fax: 01535 669895; Woodlands Cottage, Calton Road, Thwaites Brow, Keighley BD21 4UT Tel: 01535 211096 — MB BS 1985 Newc.

GOPAL, Mayur Naresh 64 Wakerley Road, Leicester LE5 6AQ — MB ChB 1992 Leeds.

GOPAL, Rookmeen 1 Harebell Close, Exeter EX4 2PE — MB ChB 1986 Leeds; MRCPI 1992; T(GP) 1993.

GOPALA KRISHNA, Peddiraju Horeb Street Surgery, Horeb Street, Treorchy, Cardiff CF42 6RU Tel: 01443 772185 Fax: 01443 773083.

GOPALAKRISHNAN, Geetha 42 Kynaston Road, Enfield EN2 0DB — MB BS 1983 Madras.

GOPALAN, Janaki Department of Obstetrics & Gynaecology, Royal Alexandra Hospital, Corsebar Road, Paisley PA2 9PN — MB BS 1986 Madras; MRCOG 1991.

GOPALAN, Mr Vallipuram House 19, Doctors Residence, North Staffordshire Hospital, Hilton Road, Stoke-on-Trent ST4 6SE — MB BS 1985 Colombo; FRCSI 1994.

GOPALASWAMY, Adoni Kuppuswamy Bootham Park Hospital, Bootham Park, York YO30 7BY Tel: 01904 454079 Fax: 01904 453794 — MB BS 1966 Mysore; FRCPsych 1995, M 1976; DPM Bangalore 1971. (Mysore Med. Coll.) Cons. Psychiat. Rehabil. York Health Serv.s NHS Trust Bootham Pk. York. Socs: BMA; Fell the Roy. Soc of Med. Prev: Cons. Psychiat. St. Wulstans Hosp. Malvern; Sen. Regist. (Psychiat.) SE Thames RHA; Regist. (Psychiat.) NW Surrey Health Dist.

GOPALJI, Mr Bipinchandra Thakordas Consultant Orthopaedic Surgeon, BUPA Alexandra Hospital, Walderslade, Chatham ME5 9PG Tel: 01634 687166 — MRCS Eng. LRCP Lond. 1978; FRCS Ed. 1984. (St. Mary's) Cons. Orthop. Surg. Medway Hosp. Prev: Regist. (Orthop.) St. Thos., Lewisham & Guy's Hosps. Lond.

GOPASHETTI, Shidharamappa Chanabasappa Glan Clwyd Hospital, Bodelwyddan, Rhyl LL18 5UJ Tel: 01745 583910; Basav Belagu,2 Rhodfa Sant Elian, Colwyn Bay LL29 8PY Tel: 01492 512456 — MB BS 1965 Karnatak. Assoc. Specialist (A & E) Glan Clwyd Hosp. Rhyl. Prev: Resid. Surg. Off. Colwyn Bay & W. Denbighsh. Hosp. Clwyd.

GOPEE, Mr Keshkar Debendranath Reetoo 12 Saundersfoot Way, Oakwood, Derby DE21 2RH — MD 1983 Brussels; FRCS Ed. (Ophth) 1997. (Faculty of Medicine University of Brussels)

GÖPFERT, Michael Johannes Webb House Democratic, Therapeutic Community, Victoria Avenue, Crewe CW2 7QS Tel: 01270 614400 Fax: 01270 614401 Email: mgopfert@webbhouse.mhss-tr.nwest.nhs.uk — State Exam Med 1975 Univ. Munich; MD Technical Univ. Munich 1978; MSc Advanced Family Ther. Brunel Univ. 1990; MRCPsych 1981; FRCPsych 1997. Cons. Psychiat. in Psychother. Ment. Health Serv.s of Salford Prestwich. Socs: Fell. Amer. Orthopsychiat. Assn.; Mem. Inst. of Gp. Anal. (Lond.); Fell. Roy. Soc. Of Med. Prev: Oberarzt Psychother. Konstanz, Germany 1986; Sen. Resid. Clarke Inst. Psychiat. Toronto, Canada 1983-85; Sen. Regist. (Child & Adolesc. Psychiat.) Lond. Hosp. 1981-83.

GOPINATH, Mulayil Krishnan The Surgery, 142 Furlong Road, Bolton on Dearne, Rotherham S63 8HA Tel: 01709 890771 Fax: 01709 889704 — MB BS 1979 Madras.

GOPINATH, Shashikala Charing Cross Hospital, Fulham Palace Road, London W6 8RF; 86 Mendip Crescent, Putnoe, Bedford MK41 9EP Tel: 01234 270463 — MB BS 1977 Calicut, India; FRCA 1987; DA (UK) 1985. Sen. Regist. (Anaesth.) Char. Cross Hosp. Lond. Prev: Regist. (Anaesth.) Bedford Gen. Hosp.

GOPINATHAN, Kesavan Kodappilly Nova Scotia Medical Centre, Leeds Road, Allerton Bywater, Castleford WF10 2DP Tel: 01977 552193 Fax: 01977 518891 — MB BS 1967 All-India Institute of Med Sci. GP Castleford, W. Yorks.

GOPINATHAN, Kizhakke Palakkath Warwick Hospital, Lakin Road, Warwick CV34 5BW Tel: 01926 495321; 1 Goodwood Close, Aintree Road, Stratford-upon-Avon CV37 9FP Tel: 01789 261489 — MB BS Kerala 1970; MRCPI 1988; LRCP LRCS Ed. LRCPS Glas. 1985. Staff Grade Phys. (Gen. Med.) Warwick Hosp. Socs: BMA. Prev: Staff Grade Phys. (Geriat.) Stratford-on-Avon Hosp.; Regist. (Geriat.) Pontefract Gen. Infirm. & Vict. Hosp. Kirkcaldy.

GOPINATHAN, Mahendra 11 Bullivant Close, Greenhithe DA9 9PB — MB ChB 1987 Dundee; BSc (Hons.) Dund 1982, MB ChB 1987; T(GP) 1991.

GOPINATHAN, Vazhapilly 4 Stanley Park, North Biggar Road, Airdrie ML6 6EJ — MB BS 1971 Madras; BSc Kerala 1963; DPM Eng. 1977.

GOR, Amrish Sukhadevbhai 4 Chaplin Road, Wembley HA0 4TX — MB BS 1990 Mangalore, India; LRCP LRCS Ed. LRCPS Glas. 1994.

GOR, Mayur Sukhadevbhai 4 Chaplin Road, Wembley HA0 4TX — MB BCh 1984 Dundee.

GOR, Meenal 3 Bean Leach Avenue, Stockport SK2 5JA — MB ChB 1997 Manch.

GORAM, Jane Beryl Kathleen 10 Upland Crescent, Truro TR1 1LU Tel: 01872 279927; Flat 1, 261 The Vale, Acton, London W3 7QA Tel: 020 8354 4249 — MB ChB 1994 Bristol. (Bristol) SHO Hillingdon Hosp. Hillingdon Middlx. Prev: Chelsea & W.minster Hosp. Lond.; MaryBoro. Base Hosp. MaryBoro., Qu.sland, Australia; Worthing Hosp. W. Sussex.

GORARD, David Angelo Wycombe Hospital, High Wycombe HP11 2TT Tel: 01494 425267; 38 Woodville Road, London W5 2SF — MB BS 1984 Lond.; MD Lond. 1994; MRCP (UK) 1987; FRCP 2000. Cons. Phys. (Gen. Med. & Gastroenterol.) Wycombe Hosp. Socs: Roy. Coll. Phys.; Brit. Soc. Gastroenterol. Prev: Sen. Regist. (Gastroenterol. & Med.) Roy. Lond. & OldCh. Hosps.; Research Fell. (Gastroenterol.) St. Bart. Hosp. Lond.; Regist. (Med.) Qu. Mary's & W.m. Hosp. Lond.

GORAYA, Anita New Road Surgery, Bounds Green Group Practice, Gordon Road, New Southgate, London N11 2PF Tel: 020 8888 9044 — MB BS 1992 Lond.; DRCOG 1994; BSc (Hons) Lond. 1988; MRCGP 1997; DFFP 1995. p/t Gen. Practitioner, Lond. Socs: Counc. Mem., Brit. Med. Assn.; Mem. of Ethics Comm. of the Brit. Med. Assn.; Freelance Med. Jl.ist.

GORAYA, Bhupinder Singh 21 Downing Drive, Greenford UB6 8BD — BM 1993 Soton.

GORAYA, Jasmine 22 Partridge Way, Oakham LE15 6BX — BM BS 1998 Nottm.; BM BS Nottm 1998.

GORAYA, Paramjit Singh Fosse Health Trust, Child Health Services, 8/12 University Road, Leicester LE1 7RG Tel: 0116 255 9600 Fax: 0116 254 4051; 22 Partridge Way, Oakham LE15 6BX — MB BS Panjab, India 1968; BSc Alld Univ., India 1962; DCH RCP Lond. 1980. SCMO (Child Health) Fosse Health Trust Leicester. Prev: Regist. (Paediat.) S. Shields Gen. Hosp.; Capt. Army Med. Corp., India.

GORAYA, Surjit Singh Allendale Road Surgery, 35 Allendale Road, Greenford UB6 0RA Tel: 020 8902 8146 — BM Soton 1985; DCH RCP Lond. 1990.

GORBUTT, Norman Sherwood Health Centre, Elmswood Gardens, Sherwood, Nottingham NG5 4AD Tel: 0115 960 7127; 2 Norfolk Park, Plains Road, Nottingham NG5 6PN Tel: 0115 926 1260 — MB ChB 1957 Sheff.; DA Eng. 1977; DObst RCOG 1959. (Sheff.) Clin. Asst. (Anaesth.) City Hosp. Nottm. Socs: Fell. Roy. Soc. Med.; BMA.

GORCHEIN, Abel Department of Clinical Pharmacology, St Mary's Hospital Medical School, London W2 1NY Tel: 020 7725 1140 Fax: 020 7725 6145 Email: a.gorchein@ic.ac.uk — PhD Lond. 1966; MB ChB (Hnrs.) Glas. 1959; FRCP Ed. 1982, M 1962; FRCP Lond. 1997, M 1968. (Glasgow University) Sen. Lect. (Clin. Pharmacol. & Therap.) St. Mary's Hosp. Med. Sch. Lond.; Hon. Cons. Phys. St. Mary's Hosp. Lond. Socs: Biochem. Soc.; Brit. Pharm. Soc. Prev: Ho. Phys. W.. Infirm. Glas.; Lect. (Med. & Chem. Path.) & Clin. Research Fell. (MRC) St. Mary's Hosp. Med. Sch. Lond.

GORDGE, Kalpita The Moat House Surgery, Worsted Green, Merstham, Redhill RH1 3PN Tel: 01737 642207 Fax: 01737 642209; 52 Grovehill Road, Redhill RH1 6DB — MB BS 1978 Lond.; MRCS Eng. LRCP Lond. 1978; MRCGP 1983; DRCOG 1982. (St. Bart.) Prev: SHO Crawley Hosp. VTS; Ho. Surg. Crawley Hosp.; Ho. Phys. Roy. Sussex Co. Hosp. Brighton.

GORDHANDAS, Arun Mangaldas The Clinic, Collum Lane, Ashby, Scunthorpe DN16 2SZ — MB BS 1956 Bombay.

GORDINSKY, Tanja Janine c/o Dewsbury District Hospital, Healds Road, Dewsbury WF13 4HS — State Exam Med 1988 Berlin.

GORDON, Adam Forbes Department of Obstetrice & Gynaecology, Caithness General Hospital, Wick KW1 5UG Tel: 01955 605050 — MB ChB 1988 Manch.; MRCOG 1995. Cons. (O & G), Caithness Gen. Hosp. Prev: Specialist Regist. (O & G) Ninewells Hosp. Dundee.

GORDON, Adriana Katharina Roydon, 6 Golfview Road, Bieldside, Aberdeen AB15 9DQ — MB BCh 1941 Witwatersrand.

GORDON, Agnes Morison (retired) 12 Central Avenue, Cambuslang, Glasgow G72 8AY Tel: 0141 641 1064 — MB ChB 1946 Glas; 1974 MFCM; 1960 DPH Glasgow. Prev: GP Denny, Stirlingsh.

GORDON, Mr Alan George (retired) — MB BCh BAO Belf. 1953; FRCS Ed. 1962; FRCOG 1974, M 1961, DObst 1955. Hon. Cons. Gyn. P.ss Roy. Hosp. Hull. Prev: Cons. O & G P.ss Roy. Hosp. Hull.

GORDON, Alan Ian Dunbar Medical Centre, Abbey Road, Dunbar EH42 1JP Tel: 01368 862327 Fax: 01368 865646 — MB ChB 1976 Aberd.; MRCGP 1984; DCH Otago 1981; DO Auckland 1980; LFHom.; DFFP. (Aberdeen) Prev: GP Arbroath; Regist. (Paediat.) Palmerston N. Hosp., NZ.

GORDON, Alan John Ivy House, Swan Lane, Kelvedon Hatch, Brentwood CM15 0AW — MB ChB Birm. 1963; FRCP Ed. 1994; MRCP Lond. 1969; MRCP Ed. 1967; Dip. Gen. Psychiat. Keele 1994; MSc (Gen. Psychiat.) Keele Univ. 1998. (Birm.) Cons. Clin. Neurophysiol. S.end Healthcare NHS Trust. Prev: Sen. Regist. (Neuroscs.) St. Bart. Hosp. Lond.; Wellcome Research Fell. Middlx. Hosp. Med. Sch. Lond.; Regist. (Neurol.) Gen. Infirm. Leeds.

GORDON, Mr Alasdair Duncan 107 Chiltern Avenue, Bushey, Watford WD23 4QE — MB BS 1987 Lond.; FRCS Ed. 1991; MFFP 1995; MRCOG 1994. Hon. Clin. Lect. Nat. Med. Laser Centre Univ. Coll. Lond. Med. Sch. Prev: Regist. Rotat. Univ. Coll. Hosp. & Whittington Hosp.

GORDON, Alastair Charles Henry Department of Medicine, Northampton General Hospital, Northampton NN1 5BD; 15 St Matthews Parade, Northampton NN2 7HF — MB ChB 1980 Ed.; BSc Ed. 1977; MRCPI 1991. Cons. Phys. (Med. for Elderly) N.ampton. Prev: Sen. Regist. (Health c/o the Elderly) City Hosp. Nottm.

GORDON, Alastair David George Waterside Health Centre, Southampton SO45 5WX Tel: 02380 845955; Blackfield Medical Centre, Southampton SO4 1XA Tel: 02380 899119 — MB BS 1961 Lond.; MRCS Eng. LRCP Lond. 1961. (Middlx.) Hon. Tutor (Primary Med. Care) Soton Univ. Med. Sch.; Hon. Med. Adviser RNLI Calshot Life Boat; Sch. Med. Off. Soton. & SW Hants. Educat. Auths.; Clin. Asst. Ment. Handicap Soton HA. Socs: BMA & New Forest Med. Soc. Prev: SHO (Cas.) Roy. Vict. Hosp. Bournemouth; Ho. Off. (Obst.) Edgware Gen. Hosp.; Ho. Surg. (Genitourin.) Middlx. Hosp. Lond.

GORDON, Alexander (retired) 29 Braid Road, Edinburgh EH10 6AN Tel: 0131 447 7774 — MD 1966 Ed.; MB ChB 1948. Prev: Hon. Sen. Lect. (Neuropath.) Dept. Path. Univ. Edin.

GORDON, Alison Catherine Viewfield, 28 Inverleith Terrace, Edinburgh EH3 5NU Tel: 0131 332 4725 — MB ChB 1973 Ed. Assoc. Specialist St. Columba's Hospice Edin.

GORDON, Alistair John 14 Walton Place, London SW3 1RJ Tel: 020 7584 7980 Fax: 020 584 8676 Email: doctoraj@gordongp.freeserve.co.uk — MB Camb. 1962, BChir 1961; MA Camb. 1962. (Camb. & St. Bart.) Gen. Practitioner, Lond.; Gp. Med. Adviser, P & O. Socs: Assoc. Mem. RCGP; Indep. Doctors Forum; BMA. Prev: Clin. Asst. & Regist. (Gen. Pract.) St. Bart. Hosp. Lond.; Med. Off. Roy. Hosp. & Home Putney; Med. Off., News Internat. Newspapers.

GORDON, Allan Jan Borders General Hospital, Melrose TD6 9BS Tel: 01896 826728 Fax: 01896 826728 — MB ChB 1971 Glas.; BSc Glas. 1967; MA Camb. 1979; FRCOG 1995, M 1976; Dip FPA 1973. (Glas.) Cons. O & G & Hon. Sen. Lect. Univ. Ed.; Dist. Tutor RCOG; Chairm. Med. Equipm. Comm. Socs: Ed. Obst. Soc.; Brit. Soc. Colpos. & Cerv. Cytol.; Glas. Obst.Soc. Prev: Cons. O & G Elsie Inglis Matern. Hosp., Bruntsfield Hosp. & E. Gen. Hosp. Edin.; Lect. (O & G) Univ. Camb.; Regist. (O & G) Roy. Matern. Hosp. Glas.

GORDON, Mr Andrew Charles Home Farm, Hill Road, Lewknor, Watlington OX49 5TS — MB BS 1979 Lond.; MS Lond. 1993; FRCS Eng. 1984. Cons. Surg. Wexham Pk. & Heatherwood Hosps. Prev: Clin. Tutor (Surg.) Univ. Oxf.

GORDON, Andrew Christian 24 Burnham Wood, Fareham PO16 7UD — MB BS 1986 Lond.

GORDON, Mr Angus Buchan 67 Harley Street, London W1G 8QZ Tel: 020 7935 2734; Department of Surgery, Royal Marsden Hospital, Fulham Road, London SW3 6JJ Tel: 020 7352 8171 — MB BS 1970 Lond.; FRCS Eng. 1973; MRCS Eng. LRCP Lond. 1968. (St. Bart.) Hon. Cons. Surg. Hosp. St. John & St. Eliz. Lond. Socs: Fell. Roy. Soc. Med.; Brit. Assn. Surg. Oncol. Prev: Sen. Regist. (Surg.) Centr. Middlx. Hosp. Lond.; Research Fell. Univ. Colorado, Denver USA; Regist. (Surg.) Luton & Dunstable Hosp.

GORDON, Ann Franklin c/o Neonatal Secretary, The Royal Berkshire Hospital, London Road, Reading RG1 5AN Tel: 0118 987439 Fax: 0118 987 8113; 4 Ammanford, Caversham, Reading RG4 7XN Email: a.f.gordon@btinternet.com — MB ChB 1988 Glas.; BSc (Hons.) Glas. 1985; MRCP (UK) 1991; DCH RCP Lond. 1991; SR - MRCPCH. Cons. Paediat. Roy. Berks. Hosp. Reading. Socs: MRCPCH; BMA. Prev: Sen. Regist. (Paediat.) Addenbrooke's Hosp. Camb.; Regist. (Paediat.) Mayday Hosp. Croydon & St. Geo. Hosp. Lond.; SHO (Neonatol.) St. Geo. Hosp. Lond.

GORDON, Anthony Christopher 11 St Helens Road, London W13 9AG — MB BS 1993 Lond.; BSc Lond. 1990. (St. Bart. Hosp.) Specialist Regist. Rotat. Imperial Sch. of Anaesth. N. W. Thames. Socs: Train. Mem. Anaesth. Assn.; Train. Mem. Intens. Care Soc. Prev: Regist. (ICU) Roy. N. Shore Hosp. Sydney Australia; SHO Rotat. (Anaesth.) Char. Cross. Hosp. Lond.; SHO (Cardiothoracic Surg.) St. Bart. Hosp. Lond.

GORDON, Ashley Robert New Road Surgery, New Road, Brighstone, Newport PO30 4BB Tel: 01983 740219 Fax: 01983 741399 — MB BCh 1980 Witwatersrand; MB BCh 1980 Witwatersrand.

GORDON, Barbara Shepherd Gosfield Hall, Halstead CO9 1SF Tel: 01787 473844 — MB ChB 1938 Glas. (Glas.) Ho. Surg. Roy. Infirm. & Roy. Matern. & Wom. Hosp. Glas. Prev: Ho. Phys. Roy. Hosp. Sick Childr. Glas.

GORDON, Caroline (Pamela) Department Rheumatology, The Medical School, University of Birmingham, Birmingham B15 2TT Tel: 0121 414 6778 Fax: 0121 414 6794 Email: p.c.gordon@bham.ac.uk; Department Rheumatology, City Hospital,

Dudley Road, Birmingham B18 7QH Tel: 0121 5075793 Fax: 0121 5075451 — MB BS 1981 Lond.; FRCP 2000; BA (Camb.) 1978; MD Lond. 1994; MRCP (UK) 1984; MA (Camb.) 1982. (Lond. Hosp.) Sen. Lect. & Hon. Cons. Rheum. Univ. Birm., City Hosp. & Univ. Hosp. Birm. NHS Trusts. Socs: Brit. Soc. for Rheum., (Mem.); Amer. Coll. of Rheum., (Mem.); Roy. Coll. of Phys.s, (Fell.). Prev: Clin. Lect. & Hon. Sen. Regist. (Rheum.) Univ. Birm. & Qu. Eliz. Hosp. Birm.; Harkness Fell.sh. (Rheum. & Immunol.) Univ. Calif., San Francisco; Regist. (Med.) Frenchay Hosp. Bristol.

GORDON, Catherine Ann 38 Orchard Way, Cogenhoe, Northampton NN7 1LZ Email: kateg@ndirect.co.uk; Email: kate@ndirect.co.uk — MB ChB 1991 Birm.; ChB Birm. 1991; MRCPsych. (Birm.) Cons. Psychiat. Older People, Nottm. Health care NHS Trust. Socs: Roy. Coll. Psychiat.

GORDON, Charles Swallowfield, Conniford Lane, Ipplepen, Newton Abbot TQ12 5UD — MB BS 1996 Lond.

GORDON, Charles Eddie Talbot (retired) Bridgend House, Inverkeithny, Huntly AB54 7XJ Tel: 01466 730203 — MB ChB 1946 Aberd. Prev: Ho. Phys. Aberd. Roy. Infirm.

GORDON, Claire Jean Saddlers, High St., Bramley, Guildford GU5 0HP — MB ChB 1987 Ed.; MRCGP 1992; DCH RCP Lond. 1989.

GORDON, Clare 2 Hindle Street, Stacksteads, Bacup OL13 8LL — MB ChB 1983 Leeds.

GORDON, Mr David 12 Brookfield Road, Littleborough OL15 8RH — MB ChB 1975 Glas.; BSc (Hons.) Glas. 1973, MB ChB 1975; FRCS Glas. 1979. Cons. ENT Surg. Birch Hill Hosp. Rochdale.

GORDON, David 81 Rouken Glen Road, Giffnock, Glasgow G46 7JD Tel: 0141 638 2522 — MB ChB 1937 Glas. (Glas.)

GORDON, Professor David Faculty of Medicine, Dentistry, Nursing and Pharmacy, Stopford Building Univ.Manchester, Oxford Road, Manchester M13 9PT Tel: 0161 275 5027 Fax: 0161 275 5784 Email: dean.mdn.gordon@man.ac.uk — MB BChir 1971 Camb.; MB BChir Camb. 1970; FRCP Lond. 1989; MRCP (UK) 1972; F Med Sci 1999. (Camb.) Dean Fac. of Med. Dent. & Nursing and Pharmacy Univ. of Manch.; Prof. of Med.; Hon. Cons. Phys., Centr. Manch. Healthcare NHST, Salford Roy. Hosp., NHST, S. Manch. Univ. Hosp.s NHST. Prev: Progr. Dir. Wellcome Trust; Asst. Dir. Med. Unit St. Mary's Hosp. Med. Sch. Lond.; Hons. Cons. Phys. St. Mary's Hosp. Lond.

GORDON, David Hirsch (Surgery), 464 Garratt Lane, London SW18 4HP — MB ChB 1973 Cape Town.

GORDON, David John 10 Ings Way, Arksey, Doncaster DN5 0TE — MB ChB 1990 Ed.

GORDON, David Jonathan 16 Corkran Road, Surbiton KT6 6PN — MB ChB 1998 Liverp.; MB ChB Liverp 1998.

GORDON, David Neil 145b High Street, Cherry Hinton, Cambridge CB1 9LN Tel: 01223 244563 — MB ChB 1992 Aberd.; BMedBiol (Hons.) Aberd. 1989; DA (UK) 1994. Med. Adviser Napp Laborat. Camb. Prev: Regist. (Emerg. Med.) Brisbane, Austral.; PHO (Med.) Toowoomba, Austral.; SHO (Anaesth.) Aberd.

GORDON, David Neville Health Centre, Pond St., Shoreham-by-Sea BN43 5WJ Tel: 01273 461101; 36 Atlantic Court, Shoreham Beach, Shoreham-by-Sea BN43 5UJ Tel: 01273 463883 — MB BS 1961 Lond.; DObst RCOG 1964. (King's Coll. Hosp.) Hon. Med. Off. Sussex Co. FA. Prev: Ho. Surg., Ho. Phys. & Cas. Off. Freedom Fields Hosp. Plymouth.

GORDON, David Sydney 3 Beaconsfield Park, Ludlow SY8 4LY Tel: 01584 3076 — MB ChB 1967 Ed.; DObst RCOG 1970. Socs: BMA. Prev: SHO (Cas. & Orthop.) Poole Gen. Hosp.; Ho. Phys. Brighton Gen. Hosp.; Ho. Surg. Roy. Sussex Co. Hosp. Brighton.

GORDON, Derek Medical Unit, Stobhill NHS Trust, Balornock Road, Glasgow G21 3UW Tel: 0141 201 3000 Fax: 0141 201 3888 Email: derek.gordon@northglasgow.scot.nhs.uk; 44 Milverton Road, Giffnock, Glasgow G46 7LP Email: drdee23@aol.com — MB ChB 1979 Glas.; MB ChB 1979 Glasgow; BSc 1974; FRCP 1993 Glasgow; MRCP 1983 UK; FRCP 2000 Edinburgh; MD 1988 Glasgow. (Glasgow) Cons. Phys. Diabetes & Endocrinol. Stobhill NHS Trust Glas.; Hon. Sen. Lect. Glas. Univs. Socs: Sec. Caledonian Soc. Endocrinol.; Brit. Diabetic Assn. Prev: Cons. Phys. (Gen. Med., Diabetes & Endocrinol.) Law Hosp. Carluke; Sen. Regist. (Gen. Med, Diabetes & Endocrinol.) S.. Gen. Hosp. Glas.; Regist. (Gen. Med. & Endocrinol.) Glas. Roy. Infirm.

GORDON, Mr Derek John Department of Plastic Surgery, Ulster Hospital, Dundonald, Belfast BT16 1RH — MB BCh BAO 1983 Dub.; BA Dub. 1981, MB BCh BAO 1983; FRCS Ed. 1988; FRCSI (Plast) 1994; FRCSI 1988. Cons. Plastic Surg. Ulster Hosp. Belf. Prev: Sen. Regist. (Plastic Surg.) Frenchay Hosp. Bristol.; Intern Adelaide Hosp. Dub.

GORDON, Mr Derek Stanley, CBE 149 Ballycoan Road, Purdysburn, Belfast BT8 8LN Tel: 028 9082 6640 — MB BCh BAO 1948 Belf.; MCh Belf. 1957, MB BCh BAO (Hons.) 1948; FRCS Ed. 1954. (Ed.) Socs: Ulster Neuropsychiat. Soc. Mem. (Pres 1982); Brit. Soc. Neurol. Surgs. Full Mem. Pres 1986- 88. Prev: Cons. Neurol. Surg. Roy. Vict. Hosp. Belf.; Research Fell. (Surg.) Harvard Med. Sch. Boston & Clin. Fell. Mass. Gen. Hosp. USA; Asst. Lect. Path. & Physiol. Qu. Univ. Belf.

GORDON, Dorothy Ray The Surgery, 100 Lower Clapton Road, London E5 0QR — MRCS Eng. LRCP Lond. 1958; DMRT Eng. 1967. (Leeds) Prev: Regist. Radiother. St. Thos. Hosp. Lond.; SHO Gyn. Marie Curie Hosp. Lond.

GORDON, Douglas Thomson (retired) 33 Burnett Road, Plymouth PL6 5BH Tel: 01752 777886 — MB ChB 1950 Aberd.; MD Aberd. 1962; DPH Aberd. 1954. Prev: Asst. Phys. Scott Hosp. Plymouth.

GORDON, Douglas Victor 6 Calwell Park, Ballycarry, Carrickfergus BT38 9HJ Tel: 01960 72767 — MRCS Eng. LRCP Lond. 1957. Med. Off. N. Irel. Blood Transfus. Serv.; Anaesth. Ards Dist. Health & Social Serv. Bd.; Doctor-in-Charge Action Cancer Early Warning Serv. Belf. Socs: BMA.

GORDON, Edward Benjamin 55 Rodney Road, West Bridgford, Nottingham NG2 6JH Tel: 0115 923 5124 Fax: 0115 923 5124 — MB ChB 1958 Ed.; FRCPsych 1980, M 1971; DPM Eng. 1962. (Ed.) Emerit. Cons. Psychiat. Univ. Hosp. Qu. Med. Centre Nottm.; Second Opinion Apptd. Doctor Ment. Health Act Commiss.; Mem. Ment. Health Rev. Tribunal; Lord Chancellor's Med. Visitor. Socs: Fouding Mem. Inst. of Expert Witnesses. Prev: Cons. Psychiat. Qu. Med. Centre Nottm.; Sen. Regist. (Psychiat.) Long Gr. Hosp. Epsom & United Birm. Hosps.; Ho. Surg. Edin. Roy. Infirm.

GORDON, Edward Guy (retired) 46 Lax Lane, Bewdley DY12 2DZ Tel: 01299 403247 — LRCP LRCS 1941 Ed.; LRCP LRCS Ed. LRFPS Glas. 1941; FRCPath 1968, M 1964; DPath Eng. 1955. Prev: Cons. Path. Dudley HA.

GORDON, Elizabeth Anne Clover Kempston House, Green End, Kempston, Bedford MK43 8RL — MB ChB 1989 Bristol.

GORDON, Miss Elizabeth Mary 90 Taybridge Road, Clapham, London SW11 5PZ Tel: 020 7228 7418 — MS Lond. 1977, MB BS (Hons. Surg., Pharmacol. &; Therap.) Lond. 1962; FRCS Eng. 1967. (Char. Cross) Sen. Lect. Surg. Char. Cross Hosp. Lond. Prev: Cons. Surg. S. Lond. Hosp.; Edwd. Wilson Research Fell. Monash Univ.; at Alfred Hosp. Melbourne Australia; Cons. Urol. St. Geo. Hosp. Lond.

GORDON, Elsie Robertson (retired) 116 Southbrae Drive, Glasgow G13 1UE Tel: 0141 959 4567 — MB ChB 1946 Glas.; MRCGP 1953.

GORDON, Ernest, Lt.-Col. RAMC 4 Brackendale Close, Camberley GU15 1HP Tel: 01276 64053 — LMSSA 1966 Lond.; MRCGP 1987; DRCOG 1985; Cert. Family Plann. JCC 1984; DPhysMed Eng. 1968. Sen. Med. Off. HM Forces; Sen. Med. Off. Kowloon Gp. Pract. BMH, Hong Kong. Prev: Regist. (Rheum. & Rehabil.) Guy's Hosp. Lond.; Regist. Norf. & Norwich Hosp.; Sen. Regist. Roy. Free & N. Middlx. Hosps. Lond.

GORDON, Fiona Hutchison Netherwood Bank, Glencaple Road, Dumfries DG1 4TY — MB BChir 1991 Camb.; MA Camb. 1991; MRCP (UK) 1994. Clin. Fell. Liver Unit Kings' Coll. Hosp. Prev: Regist. Liver Unit King's Coll. Hosp. Lond.; Regist. (Gen. Med.) Medway Hosp. Gillingham; SHO (Med.) Addenbrooke's Hosp. Camb.

GORDON, Florence Catherine (retired) 9 Coolsara Park, Lisburn BT28 3BG Tel: 01846 662558 — MB BCh BAO 1952 Belf.; DO Eng. 1960. Clin. Med. Off. EHSSB, N. Irel. Prev: Ophth. Med. Pract. Sch. Clinics N. Irel.

GORDON, Gabriella 8 Wellgarth Road, London NW11 7HS — MB ChB 1993 Manch.

GORDON, Gavin 14 Sydney Road, Ealing, London W13 9EY — MB ChB 1972 Glas.

GORDON, Mr Gavin The Beanstalk, Dordon, Tamworth B78 1SX Tel: 01827 893381 Fax: 01827 893360 — MB BS 1969 Lond.; FRCS Eng. 1977; MRCS Eng. LRCP Lond. 1969. Cons. Surg. (A & E)

Geo. Eliot Hosp. NHS Trust. Prev: Cons. Surg. (A & E) Manor Hosp. Nuneaton.

GORDON, Mr Gavin Chapman (retired) 22 London Road, Saffron Walden CB11 4ED — MB ChB 1934 Glas.; FRCS Ed. 1946. Prev: Cons. Orthop. Surg. Cumbria HA.

GORDON, Mr George (retired) Netherwood Bank, Glencaple Road, Dumfries DG1 4TY Tel: 01387 254653 — MB ChB Ed. 1959; FRCS Ed. 1967; FRCOG 1977, M 1964. Cons. O & G Dumfries & Galloway Health Bd. Prev: Ho. Phys. Roy. Hosp. Sick Childr. Edin.

GORDON, George 20 The Moors, Kidlington OX5 2AJ — BM BCh 1943 Oxf.; BSc Oxf. 1942, DM 1949. (Oxf.) Emerit. Fell. Brasenose Coll. Oxf.; Emerit. Reader (Sensory Physiol.) Oxf. Socs: Sen. Mem. Assn. Brit. Neurol.; Physiol. Soc. Prev: Dean of Med. Sch. Oxf.; Ho. Surg. Wingfield-Morris Orthop. Hosp. Oxf. & Radcliffe Infirm. Oxf.

GORDON, George Douglas (retired) Rosehill, Clint Bank, Burnt Yates, Harrogate HG3 3DW Tel: 01423 770357 — MD 1935 Leeds; MB ChB 1924. Prev: Maj. RAMC.

GORDON, George Hector Miller (retired) Braeriach, Manse Road, Killin FK21 8UY Tel: 01567 820470 — MB ChB 1951 Aberd. Prev: Ho. Surg. Roy. Infirm. Aberd. & Aberd. Matern. Hosp.

GORDON, George Mark The Lomond Practice, Napier Road, Glenrothes KY6 1HL Tel: 01592 611000 Fax: 01592 611639 — MB BCh BAO 1990 Belf.; MRCGP 1995; DFFP 1994; DRCOG 1994. (Qu. Univ. Belf.)

GORDON, Graham Stewart 4 Cairahill Road, Fraserburgh Tel: 01346 28058; 17 Saltown Place, Fraserburgh Tel: 01346 28088 — MB ChB 1980 Aberd.

GORDON, Gwenda Jane Craignorth House, Balthayock, Perth PH2 7LQ — MB ChB 1994 Glas.

GORDON, Harold Leslie Whiston Hospital, Dragon Lane, Prescot L35 5DR Tel: 0151 426 1600 — MB ChB 1976 Liverp.; FFA RCS Eng. 1981. Cons. Anaesth. Whiston Hosp. Prescot.

GORDON, Harriet Mary Royal Hampshire County Hospital, Romsey Road, Winchester SO24 0NL; Little Gastons, Kilmeston, Nr. Alresford, Alresford SW24 0NL — MB BS 1988 Lond.; MD 2000 Lond.; MRCP (UK) 1992; DA (UK) 1990. (St. Bart. Hosp. Lond.) Cons. Phys. and Gastroenterologist at the Roy. Hants. Co. Hosp., Winchester. Prev: Research Fell. Roy. Free Hosp. Lond.; Regist. Rotat. (Med. & Gastroenterol.) Middlx. Hosp. & Roy. Free Hosp. Lond .; SHO Rotat. & Ho. Off. (Med.) St. Bart. Hosp. Lond.

GORDON, Mr Harry 26 Kent Gardens, Ealing, London W13 8BU Tel: 020 8997 4572 — MB BS 1954 Lond.; FRCS Ed. 1961; FRCOG 1975, M 1963. (St. Thos.) Cons. (O & G) N.wick Pk. Hosp. & Clin. Research Centre; Harrow. Socs: Neonat. Soc. Prev: Sen. Lect. Inst. O & G Lond. & Hon. Cons. (O & G); Hammersmith Hosp. Lond.; Sen. Regist. & Tutor (O & G) Hammersmith Hosp.

GORDON, Harvey 3 Saxonbury Gardens, Long Ditton, Surbiton KT6 5HF — MB ChB 1956 Liverp.; MRCGP 1972; FFPHM (T) RCP (UK) 1990; FFCM RCP (UK) 1988, M 1974; DPH Liverp. 1960. Med. Ref. Randalls Pk. Crematorium Leatherhead. Socs: BMA. Prev: Cons. Communicable Dis. Control Epsom Health Care Trust; Dir. (Pub. Health) Mid-Surrey Health Dist.; Dep. MOH Dep. Princip. Sch. MO & Dep. Med. Ref. Crematorium Wandsworth.

GORDON, Harvey Leon Bethlem Royal Hospital, Denis Hill Unit, Monks Orchard Road, Beckenham BR3 3BX Tel: 0208 776 4241 — MB ChB 1974 Ed.; FRCPsych 1997; BSc (Med. Sci.) Ed. 1971; MRCPsych 1979. Cons. Forens. Psychiat. S. Lond. and Maudsley NHS Trust, Lond.; Hon. Lect. in Forens. Psychiat., Inst. of Psychiat., Lond. Prev: Sen. Regist. (Psychiat.) The Bethlem Roy. & Mandsley Hosp. Lond.; SHO Regist. (Psychiat.) The Lond. Hosp. & St. Clements Hosp. Lond.; SHO (Psychiat.) Middlx. Hosp. Lond.

GORDON, Helen Jacqueline Lochgelly Health Centre, David Street, Lochgelly KY5 9QZ Tel: 01592 783400 Fax: 01592 784200; 2 Heriot Gardens, Burntisland KY3 9HY Tel: 01592 872308 — MB ChB 1969 St. And.; DObst RCOG 1971.

GORDON, Helen Katherine Bellshill Maternity Hospital, Bellshill ML4 3JN Tel: 01698 747292; Craigownie, 6 Briarwell Road, Milngavie, Glasgow G62 6AW — MB ChB 1980 Glas.; MRCOG 1986. Cons. O & G Bellshill Matern. & Hairmyres Hosps. Prev: Regist. (O & G) St. Mary's Hosp. Lond.; Regist. (O & G) Greenwich Dist. Hosp.; SHO (O & G) Kings Coll. Hosp. & St. Thos. Hosp. Lond.

GORDON, Helen Ruth — MB ChB 1980 Manch.; MRCGP 1984. (Manch.) p/t Locum GP. Prev: Asst. GP Lond.

GORDON, Hilary 17 Hartland Drive, Edgware HA8 8RJ — MB BS 1968 Lond.; MRCS Eng. LRCP Lond. 1968; LMSSA Lond. 1968.

GORDON, Iain Drummond Tel: 01776 706566; Taigh Ban, Ryanview Crescent, The Larg, Stranraer DG9 0JL Tel: 01776 703792 — MB ChB 1968 Glas.; FRCP Glas. 1988; MRCP (UK) 1971. (Glas.)

GORDON, Ian Dean Branksome House, St Aldhelms Road, Branksome Park, Poole BH13 6BS — MB BS 1978 Lond.; BSc (Hons.) Lond. 1975, MB BS 1978. (King's Coll. Hosp.) GP Bournemouth. Prev: SHO/Regist. (Med.) Soton. Univ. Hosps.; Ho. Phys. Roy. Sussex Co. Hosp. Brighton; Ho. Surg. King's Coll. Hosp. Lond.

GORDON, Ian Jonathan Flat 1, Archbishop's House, Church Road, Liverpool L25 5JF — MB ChB 1979 Liverp.; MRCS Eng. LRCP Lond. 1979; MRCP (UK) 1983.

GORDON, Ian Mitchell Hendry Kenmure Medical Practice, 7 Springfield Road, Bishopbriggs, Glasgow G64 1PJ Tel: 0141 772 6309 Fax: 0141 762 2018; 26 Pinewood Avenue, Lenzie, Glasgow G66 4EQ — MB ChB 1976 Glas. Med. Off. Gen. Counc. Brit. Shipping Glas.

GORDON, Ian Robert Oscar Claudy Health Centre, Irwin Crescent, Claudy, Londonderry BT47 4AB Tel: 028 7133 8371 — MB BS 1968 Lond.; MRCS Eng. LRCP Lond. 1968; MRCGP 1975. (Guy's) Prev: High Sheriff of Co. Lond.derry 1981.

GORDON, Professor Isky Great Ormond St Hospital for Children, London NW1N 3JH Tel: 0207 829 8615 Fax: 020 829 8665 Email: i.gordon@ich.wcc.ac.uk — MB BCh 1966 Witwatersrand; FRCR 1975; FFR 1973; DMRD Eng. 1971; T (R) (CR) 1991; FRCP 1998; FRCPCH 1997. (Witwatersrand) Cons. Radiol. Hosp. Sick Childr. Gt. Ormond St. Lond.

GORDON, Jacqueline Coraletta 16 Homewell Walk, Clifton Est., Nottingham NG11 8HA — MB ChB 1993 Ed.

GORDON, Jacqueline Therese 311 Upper ShorehamRoad, Shoreham-by-sea BN43 5QB — MB BChir 1989 Camb.; MRC Psych 1997.

GORDON, Jane Alison 140 Thurston Road, Glasgow G52 2AZ Tel: 0141 883 8838 Fax: 0141 810 1511 — MB ChB 1978 Glas.; MRCGP 1982; DRCOG 1982.

GORDON, Jane Elizabeth The Dovercourt Surgery, 309 City Road, Sheffield S2 5HJ Tel: 0114 270 0997 Fax: 0114 276 6786; 11 Dalewood Road, Sheffield S8 0EB Tel: 0114 270 0997 — BM BS 1984 Nottm.; BM BS Nottm. l984; DRCOG 1987.

GORDON, Janet Rosemary Kingswood Health Centre, Alma Road, Kingswood, Bristol BS15 4EJ Tel: 0117 961 1774 Fax: 0117 947 8969 — MB ChB 1982 Manch.; MRCGP 1986; DRCOG 1985; DCH RCP Lond. 1984.

GORDON, Jessie (retired) 30 Weston Way, Weston Favell, Northampton NN3 3BL Tel: 01604 406394 — MB ChB Ed. 1959; MRCPsych 1978. Level II EMDR Train. Prev: Cons. Child & Family Psychiat. Springfield Child & Family Cons. Serv. N.ampton Retd. Feb. 97.

GORDON, John 183 Nithsdale, Glasgow G41 5QR — MB ChB 1956 Ed.; BA Camb. 1953. (Ed.) Lect. in Bact. Univ. Glas. Socs: Path. Soc. Gt. Brit. & Irel. Prev: Surg. Ho. Off. & Med. Ho. Off. Edin. Roy. Infirm.; Regist. Laborat. Med. (Path. & Bact.) W.. Infirm. Glas.

GORDON, John Edward Warwick Road Surgery, 65 Warwick Road, Carlisle CA1 1EB Tel: 01228 36303 — MB ChB 1974 Liverp. Clin. Asst. (A & E) Cumbld. Infirm. Carlisle.

GORDON, John Fraser Park Medical Centre, 164 Park Road, Peterborough PE1 2UF Tel: 01733 562060 Fax: 01733 425015; 32 Westwood Park Road, Peterborough PE36 6JL Tel: 01733 568516 Email: otsib@hotmail.com — MB ChB 1967 Aberd.; DObst RCOG 1969. (Aberd.)

GORDON, John Frederick HM Prison Grendon, Grendon Underwood, Aylesbury HP18 0TL — MB BChir 1968 Camb.; MA, MB Camb. 1968, BChir 1967; DPM Eng. 1973; Registered Psychotherapist (UKCP) 1997. (Camb. & St. Bart.) Med. Off. HM Prison Grendon Aylesbury. Prev: Psychother. Philadelphia Assn.; Surg. Lt. RN.

GORDON, John Gregory Gordon Rubislaw Terrace Surgery, 23 Rubislaw Terrace, Aberdeen AB10 1XE Tel: 01224 643665 Email: john.davidson@rudislawterrace.grampian.scot.nhs.uk — MB ChB 1968 Aberd. (Aberd.)

GORDON, John Nicholas 183 Withsdale Road, Glasgow G41 5QR — MB BS 1993 Lond.

GORDON, John Simpson (Tim) 9 Hammersmith Terrace, London W6 9TS Tel: 020 8748 9673 — MB BCh 1953 Witwatersrand; DCP Lond 1955; Lic. Acupunc. 1981. (Witwatersrand) Traditional Chinese Acupunc. Lond.
GORDON, Johnathan James Taigh Ban, Ryanview Crescent, Stranraer DG9 0JL — MB ChB 1995 Glas.
GORDON, Jonathan Samuel Gorbals Health Centre, 45 Pine Place, Glasgow G5 0BQ Tel: 0141 531 8290 Fax: 0141 531 8208; 15 Park Drive, Thorntonhall, Glasgow G74 5AS — MB ChB 1973 Glas.; DObst RCOG 1975.
GORDON, Joseph Edward (retired) The Villa, Seaton Burn, Newcastle upon Tyne NE13 6ES — LRCPI & LM, LRSCI & LM 1959; LRCPI & LM, LRCSI & LM 1959. Prev: Mem. Regional Med. Comm.
GORDON, Judy West Cliff Medical Centre, 14 West Cliff Road, Bournemouth BH2 5HD Tel: 01202 314888 Fax: 01202 780303 Email: postmaster@gp-j81622.nhs.uk; Branksome House, St. Aldhelm's Road, Branksome Park, Poole BH13 6BS — MB BS (Hons. Med.) 1978 Lond.; MRCP (UK) 1980. (King's Coll Lond.) Prescribing G.P.; Lead Poole Bay PCT - GP Prescribing Lead, Poole Bay PCT.
GORDON, Katharine Jean Meddygfa Teifi Surgery, New Road, Llandysul SA44 4QJ Tel: 01559 362221 Fax: 01559 362080 — MB ChB 1980 Bristol; MRCGP 1985; DRCOG 1983.
GORDON, Kathryn Louise The Old Barn, Heads Lane, Bolsterstone, Sheffield S36 3ZF — MB ChB 1988 Sheff.; BMedSci Sheff. 1988; MRCGP 1995; DFFP 1995; DRCOG 1991. Prev: GP Barnsley; Trainee GP Matlock.
GORDON, Leslie Robert Forest Hall Medical Centre, Station Road, Forest Hall, Newcastle upon Tyne NE12 9BQ Tel: 0191 266 5823 — MB BS 1979 Newc.; MRCGP 1984; DRCOG 1983. (Newc. u. Tyne)
GORDON, Malcolm Keith 39 Christchurch Road, Norwich NR2 2BX Tel: 01603 288971 — MB ChB 1984 Otago; FRACS 1993.
GORDON, Mr Malcolm William George Accident & Emergency Department, Southern General NHS Trust, 1345 Govan Road, Glasgow G51 4TF Tel: 0141 201 1455 Fax: 0141 201 1232 Email: malcolm.gordon@sgh.scot.nhs.uk; Email: mwg.gordon@ntlworld.com — MB ChB 1981 Glas.; FRCS Glas. 1986; FFAEM 1993; FRCS Ed. 1998. Cons. A & E Med. S.. Gen. Hosp. NHS Trust Glas.; Hon. Clin. Sen. Lect. Glas. Socs: BMA; Brit. Assn. Accid. & Emerg. Med.; BASICS. Scot. Prev: Sen. Regist. (A & E Med.) Roy. Infirm. Edin.
GORDON, Margaret Mary 19 Farm Court, Bothwell, Glasgow G71 8BU — MB ChB 1991 Glas.
GORDON, Martin Winston 38 Carlisle Close, Mobberley, Knutsford WA16 7HD — MB ChB 1965 Leeds.
GORDON, Mary Balmford (retired) 41 Sandy Lane, Romiley, Stockport SK6 4NQ Tel: 0161 430 2500 — MB, ChB Manch. 1938; MRCS Eng., LRCP Lond. 1939. Prev: Sen. Resid. Med. Off. Alder Hey Childr. Hosp. Liverp.
GORDON, Mary Lilian (retired) 34 Westella Way, Kirkella, Hull HU10 7LW — MB BCh BAO Belf. 1960; DObst RCOG 1962. Prev: GP Hull.
GORDON, Melita Alison Royal Hallamshire Hospital, Glossop Road, Sheffield S10 Tel: 0114 271 1900; P. O. Box 30096, Blantyre 3, Malawi, Central African Republic Tel: +265 630129 — BM BCh 1990 Oxf.; MA Camb. 1993; MRCP (UK) 1993; DTM & H RCP Lond. Liverp. 1993. (Oxf.) Regist. (Gastroenterol.) Roy. Hallamsh. Hosp. Sheff. Prev: SHO (Med.) Roy. Vict. Hosp. Belf.; SHO (Gen. Med. & Geratol.) John Radcliffe Hosp. Oxf.; Med. Off. Chikankata Hosp., Zambia.
GORDON, Mildred Forsyth (retired) Vishabreck, Evie, Orkney KW17 2PF Tel: 01856 751349 — MB ChB 1948 St. And.
GORDON, Nanette Lilian Margaret, OBE The Briars, 3 Golfview Road, Bieldside, Aberdeen AB15 9AA Tel: 01224 867816 Fax: 01224 867816 — MB ChB Aberd. 1965; FFA RCS Eng. 1969. (Aberd.) Prev: Med. Off. Grampian Oncol. Research Project; Med. Off. (Anaesth.) Aberd. Gp. Hosps.
GORDON, Neil Simson (retired) Huntlywood, 3 Styal Road, Wilmslow SK9 4AE Tel: 01625 525437 Email: neil_gordon@doctors.org.uk — MD 1943 Ed.; MB ChB 1940; FRCP Lond. 1971, M 1947; FRCP Ed. 1962, M 1946. Prev: Cons. Neurol. Roy. Manch. Childr. Hosp. & Booth Hall Childr. Hosp. Manch.
GORDON, Norman Langley Health Centre, Common Road, Slough SL3 8LE Tel: 01753 544288 Fax: 01753 592415; Longdown Farm House, Cadsden, Princes Risborough, Aylesbury — MB ChB Ed. 1958; DObst RCOG 1961; MRCGP 1969. (Ed.)
GORDON, Patricia Mary Department Dermatology, Raigmore Hospital, Inverness IV2 3UJ Tel: 01463 704000; 4 Lovat Road, Inverness IV2 3NT Email: trishpmg@aol.com — MB ChB 1988 Aberd.; MRCP (UK) 1991. Cons. Dermatol. Raigmore Hosp. Inverness. Prev: Sen. Regist. Dermat. Roy. Vic. Infirm. Newc.; Career Regist. (Dermat.) Roy. Infirm. Edin.; SHO Rotat. (Gen. Med.) Aberd. Teach. Hosp.
GORDON, Patrick Anthony 257 Lower Road, Bookham, Leatherhead KT23 4DX — MB BS 1991 Lond.
GORDON, Patrick Naylor 6 Pearsonville, Great Ayton, Middlesbrough TS9 6BY Email: patrickg@globalnet.co.uk — MB BS 1992 Newc.; MRCP (UK) 1996; DCH Lond 1998; DFFP 1999. GP Non-Princip.
GORDON, Patrick William Neil Department of Clinical Chemistry, Basildon Hospital, Nether Mayne, Basildon SS16 5NL Tel: 01268 593016; 4 Silver Street, Maldon CM9 4QE Tel: 01621 858454 — BM BCh 1966 Oxf.; MA Camb. 1971; MA Oxf. 1966; FRCPath 1985, M 1973. (Middlx.) Cons. Chem. Path. Basildon & Thurrock Gen. Hosps. Trust. Prev: Sen. Regist. Addenbrooke's Hosp. Camb.; Asst. Lect. Middlx. Hosp. Med. Sch.; Ho. Phys. Middlx. Hosp.
GORDON, Penelope Anne Leith Queen Alexandra Hospital, Southwick Hill Road, Cosham, Portsmouth PO6 3LY Tel: 023 9282 2444 Fax: 023 9229 3437; Midlington Farmhouse, Southampton SO32 3PU — BM 1977 Soton.; FRCR 1985; DMRD Eng. 1982. Cons. (Radiol.) Portsmouth Hosp.s. Prev: Con. (Radiol.) Brighton HA.; Sen. Regist. (Radiol.) St. Thos. Hosp. Lond.; Regist. (Radiol.) St. Thos. Hosp. Lond.
GORDON, Peter (retired) 105 Lanark Road W., Currie, Edinburgh EH14 5LB Tel: 0131 449 3355 — MB ChB Ed. 1959; FRCGP 1982, M 1968; DObst RCOG 1962. Prev: Hosp. Pract. Roy. Infirm. Edin.
GORDON, Peter David The Health Centre, Gotham Lane, East Leake, Loughborough LE12 6JG Tel: 01509 852181 Fax: 01509 852099; Lynwood, 6 Station Road, East Leake, Loughborough LE12 6LQ Tel: 01509 853866 Email: fam.gordon@btinternet.co — MB BS 1969 Lond.; MRCP (U.K.) 1973; MRCGP 1977; DRCOG 1973. (Roy. Free) Hosp. Pract. (Rheum.) Univ. Hosp. Nottm. Prev: Med. Regist. N. Middlx. Hosp. Lond.; Ho. Phys. Roy. Free Hosp. & Brompton Hosp. Lond.
GORDON, Peter John 2 Westerton Drive, Bridge of Allan, Stirling FK9 4AX Email: pgsg@ukgateway.net — MB ChB 1990 Aberd.; MRCPsych 1997. Locum Cons., Old Age Psychiat., Kildean Hosp., Stirling. Prev: Specialist Regist. Psychiat., Grampian Primary Care NHS Trust, Cornhill Hosp., Aberd.
GORDON, Peter John Gordon and Partners, The Redwell Medical Centre, 1 Turner Road, Wellingborough NN8 4UT Tel: 01933 400777 Fax: 01933 671959 — MB ChB 1971 Aberd.; T(GP) 1991; DObst RCOG 1974. Med. Adviser & Div. Police Surg. N.ants.; Med. Adviser N.ants Co. Counc. Socs: Fell. Roy. Soc. Med. (Clin. Forens. Med. Sect.); Assn. Police Surg.; Alama. Prev: SHO, Resid. Med. Off. & Resid. Surg. Off. Aberd. Roy. Infirm.
GORDON, Philip George St Thomas Road Surgery, St. Thomas Road, Featherstone, Pontefract WF7 5HF Tel: 01977 792212 Fax: 01977 600278; Allweathers, 132 Carleton Road, Carleton, Pontefract WF8 3NP Tel: 01977 602072 — MRCS Eng. LRCP Lond. 1972; DCH Eng. 1975. Clin. Asst. (Ophth.) Pinderfields Hosp. Wakefield. Prev: SHO (Paediat. & O & G) Pontefract Gen. Infirm.
***GORDON, Rachel Irma** Whitley Road Medical Centre, 1 Whitley Road, Collyhurst, Manchester M40 7QH Tel: 0161 205 4407 Fax: 0161 203 5269; 19 Ravensway, Prestwich, Manchester M25 0EU — MB ChB 1986 Manch.; DRCOG 1990; DCH RCP Lond. 1988.
GORDON, Richard Bruce 24D Fraser Road, Aberdeen AB25 3UH Tel: 01224 643110 Email: r.b.gordon@abdn.ac.uk — MB ChB 1994 Aberd.; BSc (Hons.) 1985. SHO (Surg.) Aberd.
GORDON, Robert Michael Gleadless Medical Centre, 636 Gleadless Road, Sheffield S14 1PQ Tel: 0114 239 6475 Fax: 0114 264 2277; 11 Dalewood Road, Beauchief, Sheffield S8 0EB Tel: 0114 262 1811 — BM BS 1984 Nottm.; BMedSci. Nottm. 1982; DRCOG 1988. Hon. Clin. Teach. Sheff. Univ. Med. Sch.
GORDON, Ronald Andrew Croftfoot Road Surgery, 30 Croftfoot Road, Glasgow G44 5JT Tel: 0141 634 0431 Fax: 0131 633 5284;

108 Herries Road, Glasgow G41 4AN Tel: 0141 423 1544 — MB ChB 1967 Glas.; BSc Glas. 1964, MB ChB 1967. (Glas.) Prev: Ho. Phys. Larkfield Hosp. Greenock; Ho. Surg. Vict. Infirm. Glas.

GORDON, Ronald David Lodge Family Centre, Child & Adolescent. Ment. Health Service, Sedgefield, Stockton-on-Tees TS21 3EJ Tel: 01740 622486 Fax: 01740 623207 — MRCS Eng. LRCP Lond. 1972. (Char. Cross Hosp. Lond.) Med. Off. & Psychother, Child & Adolesc. Ment. Healrh Serv., Co. Durh. & Darlington Priority Servs. NHS Trust), Sedgefield, Co. Durh.; Med. Psychother. (Specialist Psychother. Serv.) Woodlands Rd. Clinic Middlesbrough. Socs: Assn. for Psychother. in NHS; Affil. Roy. Coll. Psychiat. Prev: SHO (Psychiat.) St. Luke's Hosp. Middlesbrough; GP Glen Aplin, Qu.sland, Austral.; Asst. Med. Off. Camphill-Rudolf Steiner Schs. Aberd.

GORDON, Ronald Rodger, MC (retired) Gosfield Hall, Halstead CO9 1SF Tel: 01787 473844 — MB ChB 1937 Glas.; MD Glas. 1948; FRCP Lond. 1966, M 1948; DCH Eng. 1947; DObst RCOG 1941. Prev: Paediat. Sheff. Childr. Hosp. & N.. Gen. Hosp. Sheff.

GORDON, Rosemary G Netherwood Bank, Glencaple Road, Dumfries DG1 4TY Tel: 01387 54653 — MB ChB Ed. 1962. (Ed.) SCMO (Family Plann.) Dumfries & Galloway HB. Prev: Resid. Ho. Surg. (Obst.) Forth Pk. Matern. Hosp. Kirkcaldy; Resid. Ho. Surg. (O & G) W.. Gen. Hosp. Edin.; SHO (O & G) E.. Gen. Hosp. Edin.

GORDON, Ross Barclay (retired) Gordon and Partners, 1 North Street, Peterborough PE1 2RA Tel: 01733 312731 Fax: 01733 311447 — MB ChB Aberd. 1967. Prev: Ho. Surg. & Ho. Phys. Memor. Hosp. P'boro.

GORDON, Sandy Richard Tain and Fearn Area Medical Practice, Health Centre, Scotsburn Road, Tain IV19 1PR Tel: 01862 892759 Fax: 01862 892579; Viewfield, Tain IV19 1RJ Tel: 01862 893969 — MB ChB 1985 Aberd.; BMedBiol Aberd. 1985; MRCGP 1995; DCH Otago 1991; Dip. Obst. Otago 1989. (Aberdeen)

GORDON, Sarah Elizabeth Hook Green Farm House, Melliker La, Meopham, Gravesend DA13 0JB — MB BS 1997 Lond.

GORDON, Shane Anton 24 Emmanuel Road, Wylde Green, Sutton Coldfield B73 5LZ — BM BS 1996 Nottm.

GORDON, Sheila Muriel Janet 3A Tarff Avenue, Eaglesham, Glasgow G76 0LN — MB ChB 1983 Glas.

GORDON, Sian Fiona 2 Westerton Drive, Bridge of Allan, Stirling FK9 4AX Email: pgsg@ukgateway.net — MB ChB 1988 Aberd.; MRCGP 1992; DCCH RCP Ed. 1993. Princip. in Gen. Pract., Viaduct Med. Pract., Denburn Health Centre, Aberd. Prev: Trainee GP (Paediat.) Lothian Health Bd.; Trainee GP Grampian Health Bd.

GORDON, Stephen John Heathcroft, Sandy Lane, Kingswood, Tadworth KT20 6NE — MB BS 1996 Lond.

GORDON, Susan 7 Bracken Ridge, Lancaster Park, Morpeth NE61 3SY — MB ChB 1981 Manch.; MFPHM RCP (UK) 1993; MRCGP 1988; DRCOG 1986. Cons. Pub. Health Med. N.d. DHA.

GORDON, Tania Esther Department of Rheumatology, Southend Hospital, Prittlewell Chase, Westcliff on Sea SS0 0RY Tel: 01702 221322 Fax: 01702 221049 — MB BS 1977 Lond.; MRCP (UK) 1980; Middlx. Hosp; FRCP. Cons. Rheumatologist S.end Hosp. Prev: Sen. Regist. (Rheum.) Roy. Free & N. Middlx. Hosps. Lond; Regist. (Gen. Med. Regist. Rotat.) Bloomsbury HA; SHO Nat. Hosp. Nerv. Dis. Lond.

GORDON, Tina Louise 37 Porthamal Road, Rhiwbina, Cardiff CF14 6AQ — MB BCh 1995 Wales. (University of Wales College of Medicine) SHO (Paediat.), VTS Scheme EGGH.

GORDON, Treasa Mary Redwood, Sheethanger Lane, Felden, Hemel Hempstead HP3 0BG — MB ChB 1975 Sheff.; DRCOG 1978.

GORDON, Uma deve Division of Obstetrics & Gynaecology, St Michaels Hospital, Southwell St., Bristol BS2 8EG Tel: 0117 9285704 Fax: 0177 9285290 Email: u.d.gordon@bris.ac.uk; 12 Queens Drive, Bishopston, Bristol BS7 8JR Tel: 0117 942 2189 Email: acgordo@aol.com — MB BS 1981 Sri Venkateswara; MB BS Sri Venkateswara, India 1981; MRCOG 1986; MD 1999. Cons. Sen. Lect. Univ. Bristol. Socs: Irish Perinatal Soc. & Brit. Fertil. Soc.; ESHRE; BMA. Prev: Asst. Master Rotunda Hosp. Dub. Eire; Subspec Train.Human Assisted Reproduc. Unit. RCS Irel. (O & G) Rotunda Hosp. Dub.

GORDON, Vincent William Crombie The Well, Dollar FK14 7LN Tel: 01259 742169 — LRCP LRCS 1935 Ed.; LRCP LRCS Ed. LRFPS Glas. 1935. (Roy. Colls. Ed.)

GORDON, William Ian King Edward VII Hospital, Midhurst GU29 0BL Tel: 0173 081 2341 — MB BS 1944 Melb.; FRCPath 1972. (Melb.) Cons. Path. King Edwd. VII Hosp. Midhurst. Socs: Path. Soc. Prev: Dep. Med. Supt. Roy. Perth Hosp. W. Australia.

GORDON, William John (retired) 108 Fernlea, The Spinney, Bearsden, Glasgow G61 1NB Tel: 0141 943 2544 Fax: 0141 943 0614 — MB ChB Glas. 1947; MD (Commend.) Glas. 1958; FRCS Glas. 1972; FRCOG 1966, M 1952. Prev: Cons. Gyn. Glas. Nuffield Hosp.

GORDON, William Lindsay 182 Wake Green Road, Moseley, Birmingham B13 9QE — BM BCh 1947 Oxf.; BM BCh Oxon. 1947.

GORDON, Willie 1 Stanhope Gardens, Mill Hill, London NW7 2JD Tel: 020 8906 0398 — LMSSA 1941 Lond.; MRCS Eng. LRCP Lond. 1944. (St. Bart.) Prev: On Rehabil. Bd. Boscombe Hosp.; On Rehabil. Bd. for the Disabled Cape Town, S. Afr.; Dist. Surg. Health Dept. Cape Town, S. Afr.

GORDON, Yehudi Boris Sunny House, 1 Sunny Gdns. Road, London NW4 Tel: 020 8202 1114 — MD 1978 Witwatersrand; MB BCh 1964; FRCOG 1990, M 1971; FRCOG S. Afr. 1970. (Witwatersrand) Cons. O & G Hosp. St. John & St. Eliz. Lond. Prev: Cons. O & G The Garden Hosp. Lond.

GORDON-BROWN, Alistair David 45 Erlanger Road, New Cross, London SE14 5TF — MB BS 1983 Lond.

GORDON-BROWN, John (retired) 31 George Street, Cambridge CB4 1AL — MRCS Eng. LRCP Lond. 1943. Prev: Med. Off. Uganda.

GORDON-NESBITT, David Charles Staffordshire General Hospital, Weston Rd ST16 3SA; Strathdoon, Cameron Road, Fort William PH33 6LG Email: ericwirving@hotmail.com — MD 1962 Tehran; FRCPI; MRCP (U.K.) 1975; MRCS Eng. LRCP Lond. 1968. Cons. (Paediat.) Stafford Dist. Gen. Hosp. Socs: Brit. Paediat. Assn. Prev: Sen. Regist. (Paediat.) St. Mary's Hosp. Manch.; Regist. (Paediat.) St. Stephen's Hosp. Lond.; Regist. (Paediat. & Gen. Med.) Roy. Infirm. & Lodge Moor Hosps. Sheff.

GORDON-SMITH, Professor Edward Colin Department of Haematology, Cellular & Molecular Sciences, St George's Hospital Medical School, Tooting, London SW17 0RE Tel: 020 8725 5448 Fax: 020 8725 0245 Email: e.gordon-smith@sghms.ac.uk; 35 Park Road, Chiswick, London W4 3EY — BM BCh Oxf. 1963; MSc Lond. 1971; BSc Oxf. 1961, MA 1963; FRCP Lond. 1978, M 1968; FRCPath 1987. (Westm.) Prof. Haemat. St. Geo. Hosp. Med. Sch. Lond. Socs: (Ex-Pres.) Internat. Soc. Experim. Haematol.; (Pres.) Brit. Soc. Haematol. Prev: Sen. Lect. & Reader Roy. Postgrad. Med. Sch. Lond.

GORDON-WATSON, Margaret Ann (retired) Eaton House, Sidlesham, Chichester PO20 7QD Tel: 01243 641262 — MB BS 1956 Lond. Prev: Med. Regist. Roy. W. Sussex Hosp. Chichester.

GORDON-WRIGHT, Anthony Peter 5 Blackstone Hill, Redhill RH1 6BE Tel: 01737 762552 Fax: 01737 277997 — MB BS (Hons.) Lond. 1969; MD Lond. 1982; FRCOG 1989, M 1977. (Univ. Coll. Hosp.) Cons. O & G E. Surrey Hosp. Socs: Brit. Soc. Gyn. Endoscopy; Brit. Menopause Soc.; Brit. Soc. Colpos. & Cerv. Path. Prev: Sen. Regist. (O & G) Hammersmith Hosp. Lond.; Sen. Regist. Portsmouth Hosp.; Regist. Char. Cross Hosp. Lond.

GORDON-WRIGHT, Hilary Margaret 5 Blackstone Hill, Redhill RH1 6BE Tel: 01737 762552 Fax: 01737 277997 — MB BS 1974 Lond.; MRCS Eng. LRCP Lond. 1974; MRCOG 1981; DCH Eng. 1977. Socs: Brit. Med. Ultrasound Soc. Prev: Assoc. Specialist (Obst. Ultrasound) Roy. Surrey Co. Hosp. Guildford; Regist. (O & G) St. Mary's Hosp. Portsmouth; SHO Qu. Eliz. Hosp. Childr. Lond.

GORE, Charles Patrick (retired) 10 Castle Gate, New Brook St., Ilkley LS29 8DF Tel: 01943 607370 — MB BCh BAO 1940 Dub.; BA, MD Dub. 1943; FRCPI 1968, M 1953; FRCPsych 1973, M 1971; DPM Eng. 1953. Prev: Sen. Regist. Maudsley Hosp. Lond.

GORE, Mr David Marcus Department of Surgery, Royal Liverpool University Hospital, Liverpool L69 3GA Tel: 0151 706 4170 Fax: 0157 706 5826 Email: dmg@dnet.co.uk — MB BChir 1992 Camb.; FRCS Ed. 1996; FRCS Eng. 1996; MA 1996. (Camb.) Clin. Research Fell., Univ. of Liverp. Dept. of Surg. Prev: Regist. Rotat. (Surg.) N. Irel.

GORE, Dilip Gore and Pawar, 81-85 Cleggs Lane, Little Hulton, Manchester M38 9WU Tel: 0161 799 4988 Fax: 0161 799 5271.

GORE, Hema Cleggs Lane Surgery, 131 Cleggs Lane, Little Hulton, Manchester M38 9RS Tel: 0161 799 4001 Fax: 0161 703 8276.

GORE, Mr James (retired) Field House, 110 Harborne Park Road, Birmingham B17 0BS — MB ChB 1925 Birm.; ChM Birm. 1931; FRCS Eng. 1928; MRCS Eng. LRCP Lond. 1925; FICS 1959. Prev: Cons. Surg. Selly Oak Hosp. Birm.

GORE, Jonathan Charles Patrick The Lawson Practice, 85 Nuttall Street, London N1 5HZ Tel: 020 7739 9701 — MB BS 1974 Newc.; MSc 1995 Univ. of Lond.; MRCGP 1978.

GORE, Martin Eric 4 Pembroke Villas, The Green, Richmond TW9 1QF — MB BS 1974 Lond.; PhD Lond. 1985; FRCP Lond. 1994; MRCP (UK) 1979. (St. Bart.) Cons. Cancer Phys. Roy. Marsden Hosp. Lond. & Sutton; Hon. Sen. Lect. Inst. Cancer Research Lond. & Sutton. Prev: Regist. (Gen. Med.) Univ. Coll. Hosp. Lond.; Sen. Lect. Inst. Cancer Research Sutton.

GORE, Mr Peter James Alexandra Hospital, Cheadle SK8 2PX Tel: 0161 428 3656; 16 Gorse Bank Road, Halebarns, Altrincham WA15 0AL Tel: 0161 903 9474 — MB ChB 1967 Liverp.; FRCS Eng. 1978. Princip. Med. Off. Alexandra Hosp. Cheadle Chesh. Socs: Manch. Med. Soc.; Manch. Med. Soc.; Sale Med. Soc.

GORE, Mr Ratnakumar Viswanath Lewisham Hospital, High St., London SE13 6LH Tel: 020 8333 3170 Fax: 020 8333 3159; 55 Osprey Heights, The Falcons, Grant Road, London SW11 2NG Tel: 020 7924 1366 — MB BS 1962 Nagpur; FRCS Ed. 1971. Cons. & Sen. Lect. (Orthop. & Trauma) Lewisham & Guy's Hosps. Lond. Socs: Fell. BOA & Roy. Soc. Med. Prev: Assoc. Prof. Orthop. Imam Reza Med. Centre Univ. Meshad, Iran; Cons. Orthop. Surg. Emdadi Hosp. Meshad, Iran; Regist. (Orthop. & Trauma) Canterbury I. of Thanet Gp. of Hosps.

GORE, Robin Brian Department of Medicine, Furness Hospitals NHS Trust, Dalton Lane, Barrow-in-Furness LA14 4LF; Flat 4, Fell House, Abbery Way, Barrow-in-Furness LA14 1BP — MB ChB 1992 Ed.; BSc (Med. Sci.) Ed. 1990, MB ChB 1992. Prev: SHO Rotat. (Med.) Aberd. Roy. Infirm.; Ho. Off. Roy. Hosp. Sick Childr.; Ho. Off. W.. Gen. Hosp. Edin.

GORE, Stephen Department of Medicine, Yeovil District Hospital, Yeovil BA21 4AT Tel: 01935 475122 Fax: 01935 426850; Headland Cottage, Babcary, Somerton TA11 7EQ Tel: 01458 223335 — MB ChB 1983 Liverp.; FRCP 1999; MD Liverp. 1993; MRCP (UK) 1987. Cons. Phys. with interest in Gastroenterol. Yeovil Dist. Hosp. Socs: Brit. Soc. Gastroenterol. S.W. Gastro Gp. Prev: Sen. Regist. (Med. & Gastroenterol.) Frenchay Hosp. Bristol; Regist. (Med.) Gloucester Roy. Infirm. & Bristol Roy. Infirm.; Research Regist. (Med.) Roy. Liverp. Hosp.

GORE-REES, Peter John Tel: 0151 228 4811 Email: peter.gorerees@tesco.net; 226 Pensby Road, Heswall, Wirral CH61 6UF — MB ChB 1983 Liverp.; MRCPsych 1989; DRCOG 1986. Cons. Child & Adolesc. Psychiat. Alder Hey NHS Trust.

GORHAM, Christopher John 51 Locks Road, Locks Heath, Southampton SO31 7ZL Tel: 01489 583777 Fax: 01489 583777 — MB BS 1967 Lond.; MRCS Eng. LRCP Lond. 1967; DObst RCOG 1969. (St. Thos.) Socs: Sec. Fareham Med. Soc.; Soton Med. Soc. Prev: SHO Addenbrooke's Hosp. Camb.

GORHAM, Desmond Joseph 42 Carlton House, Western Parade, Southsea PO5 3ED Tel: 01705 826031 — MB BS Lond. 1954; DObst RCOG 1962. (Univ. Coll. Hosp.)

GORHAM, Paul Francis Dewsbury & District Hospital, Healds Road, Dewsbury WF13 4HS Tel: 01924 816158/512000 Mob- 0705 013 0500 Fax: 01924 816175 Email: gorham@doctor.com — MB BS 1977 Lond.; MRCP (UK) 1986; T(M) (Paediat.) 1991; DCH RCP Lond. 1983; DRCOG 1979; FRCPCH (1997); FRCP (1999). (Lond. Hosp. Med. Coll.) Cons. Paediat. Dewsbury; Sen. Lect. (Child Health) Univ. Leeds. Socs: Brit. Paediat. Neurol. Assoc.; Eur. Paediat. Neurol. Soc.; Eur. Acad. Childh. Disabil. Prev: Cons. Paediat. St James Univ. Hosp. Leeds; Cons. Paediat. (Community Child Health.) S. Warks. HA.

GORHAM, Tanya Jane 88C Walterton Road, London W9 3PQ — MB BS 1998 Lond.; MB BS Lond 1998.

GORIAH, Harrydewa, SBStJ (retired) Bon Air, Carmarthen Road, Newcastle Emlyn SA38 9DA Tel: 01239 710644 — MB ChB 1955 Birm.; MRCGP 1971.

GORIAH, Sonya Annette Haematology Dept, West Wales General Hospital, Dolgwili Road, Carmarthen SA31 2AF — MB BCh 1994 Wales; BSc (Hons.) Birm. 1989.

GORING, Mr Charles Clairmonte North Tyneside Gen. Hospital, Rake Lane, North Shields NE29 8NH Tel: 0191 293 2514; 84 Marine Avenue, Whitley Bay NE26 3LR — MB ChB 1973 Sheff.; FRCS Ed. 1979; FFAEM 1997. Cons. A & E N. RHA; Consulltant Hand Surg., N. Tyneside Gen Hosp. Socs: Cas. Surg. Assn. & Hand Soc. Prev: Hon. Lect. (Surg.) Univ. Aberd.; Regist. Rotat. (Gen. Surg.) Newc.-on-Tyne Hosp.s; Sen. Regist. (A & E & Plastic Surg.) Aberd.

GORING, Julie Alice Dr D J McNie and Partners, 4 St. Barnabas Road, Caversham, Reading RG4 8RA Tel: 0118 478123 — MB BS 1988 Lond.; MRCGP 1992. GP Princip. Emmer Green Reading. Prev: Trainee GP Oxon. VTS.

GORING-MORRIS, Joanne Anaesthetic Department, Royal Hull Hospitals Trust, Hull Royal Infirmary, Anlaby Road, Hull HU3 2JZ — MB BS 1987 Lond.; DA (UK) 1993. (Lond. Hosp. Med. Coll.) Specialist Regist. (Anaesth.). Socs: Assn. Anaesth.; BMA. Prev: SHO (Anaesth.) Roy. Hull Hosps. Trust; Clin. Asst. (Anaesth.) Roy. Hull Hosps. Trust; SHO (Anaesth.) Hull Roy. Infirm., Newham Gen. Hosp. & Lond. Hosp.

GORINGE, Andrew Paul 69 Sandfield Road, Oxford OX3 7RW — MB BCh 1990 Wales.

GORMALLY, Joanne 11 Avon Drive, Bury BL9 6SN — MB ChB 1998 Leic.; MB ChB Leic 1998.

GORMAN, Andrew Paul 15 Moor Lane, Wilmslow SK9 6AG — MB ChB 1990 Manch.; FRCA 1996. Regist. Rotat. (Anaesth.) NW Manch. Socs: Manch. Med. Soc.; Assn. Anaesth.; Obst. Anaesth. Assn.

GORMAN, Angela Mary National Blood Service, Crescent Drive, Brentwood CM15 8DP Tel: 01277 306000 Fax: 01277 306071; 25 Ollards Grove, Loughton IG10 4DW — MB BCh BAO 1970 NUI; FRCPI 1985, M 1972; MRCP (UK) 1973; MRCPath 1977; Dip. Stat. Dub. 1974. Cons. Haemat. Nat. Blood Serv., Brentwood. Socs: Brit. Soc. Haematol.; Brit. Blood Transfus. Soc. Prev: Cons. Haemat. Whipps Cross Hosp. Lond.; Sen. Regist. Univ. Coll. Hosp. Lond.; Lect. (Haemat.) Roy. Free Hosp. Lond.

GORMAN, Christopher 15 Keswick Avenue, Chadderton, Oldham OL9 9JG — MB ChB 1988 Leeds.

GORMAN, Claire Christine 4 Cambourne Park, Belfast BT9 6RL — MB ChB 1997 Dundee.

GORMAN, Conor Charles 45 Newington Avenue, Belfast BT15 2HP — MB BCh BAO 1993 Belf.

GORMAN, Mr David Francis 3 Millhouse Avenue, Stockton Heath, Warrington WA4 2XF — MD 1985 Ed.; BSc Ed. 1968, MD 1985, MB ChB 1971; FRCS Ed. 1986. Sen. Regist. (A & E) Warrington Gen. Hosp. Prev: SHO. (Paediat.) Alder Hey Childr. Hosp. Liverp.; SHO (A & E) Birkenhead Gen. Hosp.; Regist. (A & E) Chester Roy. Infirm.

GORMAN, James Hamilton (retired) 1 Rathmore Road, Bangor BT19 1DF — MB BCh BAO 1926 Belf.; DPH 1936. Prev: Gen. Med. Pract. Belf. Lt.-Col. IMS.

GORMAN, John James 2 Sispara Gardens, London SW18 1LF — MB BCh BAO 1960 Dub.; BA, MB BCh BAO Dub. 1960. (T.C. Dub.)

GORMAN, Lesley Jane Medical Microbiology Department, Ninewells Hospital, Dundee DD1 9SY — MB ChB 1985 Ed. Cons. Microbiologist. Socs: BMA & Assn. Clin. Path.

GORMAN, Michael S 15 Waterfield Close, Bishops Hull, Taunton TA1 5HB — MB BCh BAO 1994 Belf.

GORMAN, Peter Jeffrey Rastrick Health Centre, Chapel Croft, Rastrick, Brighouse HD6 3NA Tel: 01484 710853/4 Email: PETER.GORMAN@GP_B84014.NHS.UK; 14 Ashleigh Dale, Birkby, Huddersfield HD2 2DL Email: peterjgorman@lineone.net — MB ChB 1971 Manch.; DObst RCOG 1974; Cert FPA 1974. Prev: Ho. Surg. Manch. Roy. Infirm.; Ho. Phys. & SHO (O & G) Hope Hosp. Salford.

GORMAN, Sarah Louise 13 Alvechurch Highway, Lydiate Ash, Bromsgrove B60 1NZ Tel: 0121 453 3958; 13 Alvechurch Highway, Lydiate Ash, Bromsgrove B60 1NZ Tel: 0121 453 3958 — MB ChB 1997 Ed. (Edinburgh University) Ho. Off. (Med.) St Johns Hosp.. Livingston. Socs: BMA. Prev: Ho. Off. (Surg.) E.ern Gen. Hosp. Edin.

GORMAN, Shaun Rodney St James's University Hospital, Beckett St., Leeds LS9 7TF Tel: 0113 243 3144 — MB BChir 1991 Camb.; MRCP (UK) 1996. Specialist Regist. (Paeds), St. James' Univ. Hosp. & Leeds Gen. Infirm.

GORMAN, William Peter Derbyshire Royal Infirmary, London Road, Derby DE1 2QY — MB BChir 1980 Camb.; MD Sheff. 1990; MA, MB Camb. 1980, BChir 1979; FRCP Lond. 1994; MRCP (UK) 1982. Cons. Phys. (Gen. & Geriat. Med.) S. Derbysh. HA. Prev: Sen.

Regist. (Med. & Geriat.) Roy. Hallamsh. & Nether Edge Hosps. Sheff.; Regist. (Neurol.) Frenchay Hosp. Bristol.

GORMLEY, Desmond Gerard Omagh Health Centre, Mountjoy Road, Omagh BT79 7BA Tel: 028 8224 3521 — MB BCh BAO 1987 Belf.; MRCGP 1991. (Queen's University Belfast) GP Mt.joy Rd. Health Centre Omagh.

GORMLEY, Francis Conrad Finsbury Health Centre, Pine St., London EC1R 0JH Tel: 020 7837 9750 — MB BCh BAO 1958 NUI. (Univ. Coll. Dub.)

GORMLEY, George Donald The Laich Medical Centre, Clifton Road, Lossiemouth IV31 6DJ; Garmony, Dunbar St, Lossiemouth IV31 6AL — MB ChB 1960 Aberd. JP. Prev: Res. Surg. Off. Eye Dept. & Res. Med. Off. Glenburn Wing Woodend; Hosp. Aberd.

GORMLEY, Gerrard Joseph 18 Mount Michael Park, Belfast BT8 6JX — MB BCh BAO 1995 Belf.

GORMLEY, Hilda Kathryn Josephine French Weir Health Centre, French Weir Avenue, Taunton TA1 1NW Tel: 01823 331381 Fax: 01823 323689; Swan Cottage, Mount St, Bishops Lydeard, Taunton TA4 3AN Tel: 01823 432723 — MB BCh BAO 1987 Belf.; MRCGP 1991. Socs: BMA. Prev: Trainee GP Taunton & Bishops Lydeard VTS.

GORMLEY, Mr James Desmond The Old School House M/C, 1 Antrim Road, Lurgan, Craigavon BT67 9bW Tel: 028 3831 1900; 49 Kilmore Road, Lurgan, Craigavon BT67 9HT — MB BCh BAO 1981 Belf.; FRCS Ed. 1986; MRCGP 1989; DRCOG 1989. Med. Manager Moylinn Co Op.

GORMLEY, Kevin Michael 18 Gloucester Road, Tewkesbury GL20 5SY — BM BCh 1992 Oxf.

GORMLEY, Mark John James 25 Deramore Park, Belfast BT9 5JX Tel: 01232 660322 — MB BCh BAO 1977 Belf.; BSc (Hons. Physiol.) Belf. 1974, MD 1985; FRCP Lond. 1996; FRCPI 1996; FRCP Glas. 1993; MRCPI 1981; MRCP (UK) 1980; DCH RCPSI 1979. Cons. Phys. Mater Infirmorum Hosp. Belf. Prev: Intern. Resid. Etranger (Diabetes & Endocrinol.) Bichat Hosp. Paris.

GORMLEY, Michael Aidan 3 Basil Street, London SW3 1AU Tel: 020 7235 6642 Fax: 020 7235 6052; 2 Victoria Rise, London SW4 0NZ Tel: 020 7720 2292 — MB BChir 1970 Camb.; MA Camb. 1970; MRCP (UK) 1972; MRCGP 1976; DObst RCOG 1975; DCH Eng. 1971; FRCP 1999. (Middlx.) Prev: Clin. Asst. Brompton Hosp.; SHO (Neurosurg.) Whittington Hosp. Lond.; SHO Qu. Eliz. Hosp. Childr. Lond.

GORMLEY, Miss Paula Dorinda Department of Ophthalmology, B Floor, South Block, Queens Medical Centre, Nottingham NG7 2UH Tel: 0115 924 9924; Cules, Killadeas, Enniskillen, County Fermanagh, Republic of Ireland — MB BCh BAO 1985 Belf.; FRCS (Ophth.) Glas. 1991; DO RCPSI 1991. (Qu. Univ. Belf.) Lect. & Sen. Regist. (Ophth.) Qu. Med. Centre Nottm.

GORMLEY, Mr Peter John Anthony (retired) 23 Windsor Park, Belfast BT9 Tel: 01232 668300 — MB BCh BAO Belf. 1944; FRCSI 1964; DOMS Eng. 1948; FRCOphth 1989. Cons. Ophth. Surg. Mater Infirm. Hosp. Belf.

GORMLEY, Sheena Mary Catherine 22 Laganvale Court, Stranmillis, Belfast BT9 5BH — MB BCh BAO 1992 Belf.; FFA RCSI 1997; DA (UK) 1994.

GORMLEY, Stephen John 12 Anderson Close, London N21 1TH — MB BS 1996 Lond.

GORMLY, Lynn Margaret Graham 11 The Paddocks, Falksworth, Peterborough PE7 3TZ — MB BS 1987 Newc.

GORNALL, Christopher Brian 24 Five Acres, Dursley GL11 4JP — BM BS 1992 Nottm.

GORNALL, James Brian, LVO (retired) Parc Wollas, Laflouder Lane, Mullion, Helston TR12 7HT — MRCS Eng. LRCP Lond. 1957.

GORNALL, Michael Tel: 01282 426840 Fax: 01282 433252; East Dene House, Whalley Road, Simonstone, Burnley BB12 6LH Tel: 01282 773188 — MB ChB Liverp. 1960; DCH Eng. 1967; DObst RCOG 1963. Prev: Ho. Surg. & Ho. Surg. (O & G) Chester City Hosp.; Ho. Phys. Roy. S.. Hosp. Liverp.

GORNALL, Mr Peter Birmingham Children's Hospital, Steelhouse Lane, Birmingham B4 6NH Tel: 0121 333 8078 Fax: 0121 333 8081 Email: petergornall@bhamchildrens.wmids.nhs.uk; 7 Anstruther Road, Edgbaston, Birmingham B15 3NN Tel: 0121 455 8201 Email: petergornall@bhamchildrens.wmids.nhs.uk — BChir 1965; MB 1966 Camb.; FRCS Eng. 1970. (St. Thomas) Cons. Paediat. Surg. Birm. Childr.'s Hosp. Socs: UK Childr. Cancer Study Gp.; Brit. Assn. Paediat. Surg. & Craniofacial Soc. Prev: Sen. Regist. (Surg.) Roy. Hosp. Sick Childr. Edin.; Regist. (Surg.) Roy. Manch. Childr.'s Hosp.; Resid. Asst. Surg. Hosp. Sick Childr. Gt. Ormond St. Lond.

GOROG, Diana Adrienne 106 Queen's Quay, 58 Upper Thames St., London EC4V 3EJ — MB BS 1993 Lond.; MRCP (UK) 1996. (St. Bart.) Specialist Regist. (Cardiol.) Hammersmith Hosp. Prev: Research Fell. (Cardiol.) Roy. Postgrad. Med. Sch. Lond.; SHO (Intens. Care & Cardiol.) St. Thos. Hosp. Lond.; SHO (Neurol.) Nat. Hosp. Neurol & Neurosurg. Lond.

GORONWY, Sally Ruth 1 Field Fare, Dewchurch Green, Little Dewchurch, Hereford HR2 6PU Tel: 01432 840755 — MB BCh 1989 Wales; DCH RCP Lond. 1993; GP (T). Staff Grade (Community Paediat.) Newport Gwent. Prev: Staff Grade (Community Paediat.) Premier Health (SE Staffs.).

GORRIE, George Henry 14 Bristol Gardens, Chichester PO19 4EA; Flat 21 E, Hughendon Lane, Glasgow G12 9XU Email: g.gorrie@btinternet.com — MB ChB 1992 Ed.; MA Camb. 1993; PhD London 1998; MRCP (UK) July 1999. (Ed.) SHO (Med.) Gartnavel Hosp. Glas. Socs: BMA. Prev: Ho. Off. Falkirk; Ho. Off. Roy. Infirm. Edin.; Med. Rotat. W.ern Infirm. Glas.

GORRIE, Morag Joan Western Infirmary Renal Unit, Dumbarton Road, Glasgow G11 6NT Tel: 0141 211 2000 — MB ChB 1986 Ed.; MRCP (UK) 1990.

GORRIE, Sheila Mary 94 Breval Crescent, Hardgate, Clydebank G81 6LS — MB ChB Sheff. 1967; MFFP 1994; DObst RCOG 1969. Med. Counsellor HIV Counselling Clinic Gartnavel Gen. Hosp. Glas.; Instruc. Doctor Gtr. Glas. HB; Clin. Med. Off. (Community Health) Gtr. Glas. HB. Prev: SHO (Gyn.) Jessop Hosp. Wom. Sheff.; Ho. Phys. & Ho. Surg. Roy. Hosp. Chesterfield.

GORRIGAN, John Hippolyte Stoneleigh Surgery, Police Square, Milnthorpe LA7 7PW Tel: 015395 63307 — BM 1983 Soton.

GORRINGE, Heather Rosemary Red Roofs, 31 Coton Road, Nuneaton CV11 5TW Tel: 024 7635 7100 Fax: 024 7664 2036; 254 Nuneaton Road, Bulkington, Nuneaton CV12 9RZ Tel: 01203 310449 — MB BS 1982 Lond.; DCH RCP Lond. 1985; DRCOG 1985. (St. Mary's Hosp. Med. Sch. Lond.) Mem. Roy. Coll. Gen. Pract.

GORRINGE, Sheila Mary (retired) Horslees House, Great Coxwell, Faringdon SN7 7NG Tel: 01367 240395 — MRCS Eng. LRCP Lond. 1959; DObst RCOG 1962. Clin. Asst. (O & G) P.ss Margt. Hosp. Swindon. Prev: SHO (O & G) Nottm. Hosp. Wom.

GORROD, Eileen Ross St Andrews Surgery, 166 Market Street, Eastleigh SO50 5PT Tel: 023 8061 2472 Fax: 023 8061 1717; Lambs Hill, Southdown Road, Shawford, Winchester SO21 2BY Email: eileen@gorrod99.freeserve.co.uk — BM 1977 Soton.; MRCGP 1981; DCH RCP Lond. 1980; DRCOG 1979. (Southampton)

GORROD, Richard George The Old Buck, Houghton St Giles, Walsingham NR22 6AQ — MB BS 1988 Lond.; DCH RCP Lond. 1991; DGM RCP Lond. 1991.

GORROD, Sarah-Jane Rosalind The Old Buck, Houghton St Giles, Walsingham NR22 6AQ — MB BS 1987 Lond.

GORROD, William David Old Fire Station Surgery, 68A Portsmouth Road, Woolston, Southampton SO19 9AN Tel: 023 8044 8558/8901 Fax: 023 8043 5569; Little Ridge, High St, Old Bursledon, Southampton SO31 8DJ Tel: 02380 403135 Email: dacid.gorrod@btinternet.com — MB BS 1970 Lond.; MRCS Eng. LRCP Lond. 1970; DCH Eng. 1972. (St. Mary's) Local Med. Off. Civil Serv. Occupat. Health Serv. Soton. & Local Med. Dir. Health Call plc; Med. Adviser Roy. Yachting Assoc. Socs: Assur. Med. Soc.; Soton. Med. Soc. Prev: SHO (Med. & O & G) Freedom Fields Hosp. Plymouth; SHO (Paediat.) Roy. Cornw. Hosp. Truro.

GORST, David Wilson Royal Lancaster Infirmiary, Ashton Road, Lancaster LA1 4RP Tel: 01524 583752 Fax: 01524 583568 Email: david.gorst@hotmail.com; Langwarren, High Knott Road, Arnside, Carnforth LA5 0AW Tel: 01524 761440 Fax: 000 — BM BCh 1971 Oxf.; MA, BM BCh Oxf. 1971; FRCP Lond. 1990; MRCP (UK) 1973; FRCPath 1989, M 1977. (Guy's) Cons. Haemat. Roy. Lancaster Infirm. Socs: Fell. Manch. Med. Soc.

GORSUCH, Andrew Nicholas Conquest Hospital, The Ridge, St Leonards-on-Sea TN37 7RD Tel: 01424 755255 Fax: 01424 757012 Email: gersuch.andrew@mail.har-tr.sthames.nhs.uk; West Lodge, 1 Hastings Road, Bexhill-on-Sea TN40 2HJ Tel: 01424 733007 Email: andrew_gorsuch@compuserve.com — BM BCh 1973 Oxf.; MA Oxf.

1973, DM 1989; FRCP Lond. 1994; MRCP (UK) 1976. (Westm.) Cons. Phys. (Gen. Med., Diabetes & Endocrinol.) Hastings & Rother NHS Trust. Socs: Soc. Endocrinol.; Diabetes UK (Professional Mem.ship); Assn. of Brit. Clin. Diabetologists. Prev: Sen. Regist. (Gen. Med. Diabetes & Endocrinol.) Whittington Hosp. & Univ. Coll. Hosp. Lond.; Hon. Clin. Lect. St. Bart. Hosp. Med. Coll. Lond.; Regist. (Gen. Med.) King Edwd. VII Hosp. Windsor.

GORTON, Heather Jane 85B Victoria Road, Leeds LS6 1DR — MB ChB 1992 Leeds.

GORTON, James Duncan 13/15 Russell Avenue, St Albans AL3 5HB Tel: 01727 831888 Fax: 01727 845520; 37 Clarence Road, St Albans AL1 4NP Tel: 01727 863571 — MB Camb. 1963, BChir 1962; MA Camb. 1963; DObst RCOG 1964. (Middlx.) Socs: BMA. Prev: Regist. (Med.) Chase Farm Hosp. Enfield; Ho. Phys. Brompton Hosp. Lond.; Ho. Phys. Middlx. Hosp. Lond.

GORTON, Russell Keith 35 Telford Close, High Shincliffe, Durham DH1 2YJ — MB ChB 1980 Manch.

GORU, Mr Siva Sundareswara Rao 32 Ipswich Gardens, Barrowby Gate, Grantham NG31 8SE — MB BS 1973 Andhra; FRCS Glas. 1983; Dip. Urol. Lond 1988. Assoc. Specialist (Gen. Surg.) Lincs. Prev: Specialist (Urol.) Saudi Arabia.

GORZENSKI, Marian Bronislaw (retired) 4 Halecroft Avenue, Wednesfield, Wolverhampton WV11 1TS — MD 1931 Cracow.

GOSAI, Pratapgar Madhavgar 35 Maplestead Road, Dagenham RM9 4XH — MB BS 1975 Saurashtra.

GOSAIN, Roop Kawal 22 Faber Gardens, London NW4 4NR — MB BS 1974 Rajasthan. (Sardar Patel Med. Coll. Bikaner)

GOSAL, Mr Harminder Singh 10 Gatley Drive, Burpham, Guildford GU4 7JJ — MB BS 1988 Lond.; FRCS Eng 1993; FRCS Ed. 1993. (Lond. Hosp.)

GOSAL, Manjit Singh 41 Lonsdale Road, Southall UB2 5LS — MB ChB 1992 Manch.

GOSALIA, Mr Nalin Hiralal c/o J K B Patel, Glendora, Wolviston Road, Wolviston, Billingham TS22 5JT — MB BS 1970 Poona; FRCS Ed. 1980; FRCS Eng. 1980. (B. J. Med. Coll. Poona) Rotat. SHO Surg. Shotley Bridge Hosp. Consett. Prev: SHO Gen. Surg. & Cas. Perth Roy. Infirm. & Radiother. Ninewells Hosp.; Dundee.

GOSALL, Gurpal Singh 16 Meadowbrook Close, Bury BL9 7LE Email: GSG@gosall.com — MB BChir 1995 Camb.; 2001 MRC Psych; MA Camb. 1996, BA 1992. (Camb. & Guy's & St. Thos.) Specialist Regist., Psychiat., Manch. Prev: SHO Med. Huddersfield Roy. Infirm.; Ho. Phys. Leeds Gen. Infirm.; Ho. Surg. Guy's Hosp. Lond.

GOSDEN, Clifford William The Medical Centre, Kingston Avenue, East Horsley, Leatherhead KT24 6QT — MB BS 1979 Lond.; MA Camb. 1979; MRCGP 1984.

GOSDEN, Pauline Elizabeth Dpet. Of Medical Microbiology, Western Area NHS Trust, Weston General Hospital, Grange Road, Uphill, Weston Super Mare BS23 4TQ 2BQ Tel: 01934 647053 Fax: 01934 647051 Email: pauline.gosden@waht.swest.nhs.uk — MB BS 1983 Newc.; PhD Univ. Bristol 1977; BSc Microbiol. Univ. Bristol 1973; MRCPath 1989; Dip. Bact. Univ. Manch. 1986. (Newcastle-upon-Tyne) Cons. Med.Microbiologist, (Med. MicroBiol.) MicroBiol. Dept, W.ern Gen. Hosp., W.ern-Super-mare. Socs: Fell. Roy. Coll. Path; AMM.

GOSHAI, Hemprakash Medical Centre, Oxford Barracks BFPO 17 — MB ChB 1985 Birm.

GOSLING, Oliver Edward Woodbine House, Borrough End, Great Dalby, Melton Mowbray LE14 2EW — BM 1998 Soton.; BM Soton 1998.

GOSLING, Richard Herbert (retired) 7 Bradgate Road, Altrincham WA14 4QU — MB ChB 1946 Ed.; FRCP Ed. 1971, M 1953. Prev: Med. Dir. Labaz Sanofi UK Ltd.

GOSLING, Roland Daniel Top Flat, 10 Kemplay Road, London NW3 1SY — BM BS 1994 Nottm.

GOSNEY, John Roy University Department Pathology, Duncan Building, Royal Liverpool Hospital, Liverpool L69 3GA Tel: 011 706 4490 Fax: 0151 706 5859 Email: jrgosney@liv.ac.uk; 79 Waterloo Ware House, Waterloo Road, Liverpool L3 0BQ Tel: 0151 236 6910 — MB ChB 1980 Liverp.; BSc (Hons.) (Physiol.) Liverp. 1977, MD 1985, MB ChB 1980; MRCPath 1987; FRCPath 1997. (Liverpool University) Reader in Thoracic Path. & Cons. Path. Liverp. Univ. Med. Sch.; Vis. Prof. (Path.) Chas. Univ. Prague, Czech RePub. Socs: Path. Soc. Prev: Sen. Lect. (Path.) Liverp. Univ. Med. Sch.; Lect. Path. Liverp. Univ. Med. Sch.

GOSNEY, Judith Mary Sutton Medical Group, Allenby's Chase, Spalding PE12 9SY Tel: 01406 362081; 136 Chapelgate, Sutton St. James, Spalding PE12 0EE Tel: 01945 440692 — MB ChB 1970 Leeds.

GOSNEY, Margot Ann Geriatric Medicine, University Clinical Department, The Duncan Building, Daulby St., Liverpool L69 3GA Tel: 0151 706 4062 Fax: 0151 706 4064 Email: m.gosney@liverpool.ac.uk; Tudor House, Gorsedd, Holywell CH8 8QY Tel: 01352 711157 — MD 1993 Liverp., MB ChB Liverp. 1983; MRCP Glas. Roy. Coll. 1986; FRCP Lond 1999. Sen. Lect. Geriat. Med. Univ. Liverp. Socs: Brit. Geriat. Soc.; Med. Res. Soc. Prev: Sen. Regist. Univ. Liverp.; Res. Fell. Univ. Liverp.; Regist. Univ. Liverp.

GOSNOLD, John Kenelm Hull Royal Infirmary, Anlaby Road, Hull HU3 2JZ Tel: 01482 674730 Email: jgosnold@aol.com; Kenelm House, Main St, Lelley, Hull HU12 8SN Tel: 01482 897492 Fax: 01482 896280 Email: jgosnold@netcom.uk.co.uk — MB BS Lond. 1966; BSc (Anat.) Lond. 1963, MB BS 1966; MRCGP 1975; FFAEM 1994; DObst RCOG 1969. (St. Thos.) Cons. A & E Servs. Hull Roy. Infirm.; Forens. Med. Exam. Hull; Dir. Postgrad. Med. Edin. Socs: Hull Med. Soc. Prev: Regist. (A & E) Vict. Hosp. Blackpool; SHO (Obst.) W.wood Hosp. Beverley; Ho. Surg. St. Thos. Hosp. Lond.

GOSPEL, Rachel Louise 56 Underwood Road, Birmingham B20 1JS; 4 Cobble Court Mews, Shaws Terrace, York YO24 1BB — MB ChB 1994 Leeds. York Gen. Pract. VTS.

GOSS, Brian Michael The Beeches, 67 Lower Olland Street, Bungay NR35 1BZ Tel: 01986 892055 Fax: 01986 895519 — MB BS Lond. 1972; BSc (Hons.) Lond. 1969; MRCGP 1976; DA 1980. (Lond. Hosp.) GP Bungay. Prev: SHO VTS Ipswich Hosp.; Ho. Phys. Ipswich Hosp.; Ho. Surg. Lond. Hosp.

GOSS, David Biddulph (retired) 24 Barleycroft Road, Welwyn Garden City AL8 6JU Tel: 01707 887677 — MB BS 1948 Lond.; MRCS Eng. LRCP Lond. 1947; MRCGP 1959. Prev: Employm. Med. Off. DHSS.

GOSS, Douglas Royston Littlecovet, Brentfield, Polperro, Looe PL13 2JJ — MB BS 1984 Lond.; MRCGP 1988.

GOSS, Kevin Colin William 14 Windsor Hill, Newry BT34 1ER — MB ChB 1998 Dund.; MB ChB Dund 1998.

GOSSAGE, Adrian Anthony Robert Crawley Hospital, West Green Drive, Crawley RH11 7DH Tel: 01293 600300; Meadow Brook House, Brook St, Cuckfield, Haywards Heath RH17 5JJ Tel: 01444 453721 — MB BS 1971 Lond.; MRCS Eng. LRCP Lond. 1971; MD Lond. 1982; FRCP 1993; MRCP (UK) 1975. (Westm.) Cons. Phys. Crawley & Horsham Hosps. Socs: Endocrine Soc. Prev: Lect. Sheff. Univ.; Sen. Regist. N.. Gen. Hosp. Sheff.; Hon. Scientif. Staff Clin.

GOSSAIN, Jagdeep Balram Gowan Avenue Surgery, 21 Gowan Avenue, Fulham, London SW6 6RH Tel: 020 7736 2379 Fax: 020 7731 6384 — MB BS 1981 Lond.; DRCOG 1985.

GOSSAIN, Ravi Nandan The Surgery, Chancery Lane, Chapel End, Nuneaton CV10 0PD Tel: 024 7639 4766 Fax: 024 7639 6870; 51 Bulkington Lane, Nuneaton CV11 4SP — LRCPI & LM, LRSCI & LM 1963; LRCPI & LM, LRCSI & LM 1963.

GOSSAIN, Savita Good Hope Hospital, Rectory Road, Sutton Coldfield, Sutton Coldfield B75 7RR Tel: 0121 378 2211 — MB BS 1987 Lond.; BSc 1984 Lond.; MRC Path 1998. (Charing Corss & Westminister, London) Cons. Microbiologist, Goodhope Hosp., Sutton Coldfield. Prev: Regist. (Microbiol.) W. Midl. Region.; Regist. (Microbiol.) Qu. Mary's Univ. Hosp. Lond.

GOSSAIN, Sunita Rani 106A Burdon Lane, Sutton SM2 7DA — MB BS 1997 Lond.; MRCP 2000. (Guy's and St. Thomas') SHO (Gen. Med.) Lond.

GOSSE, Charles Noel (retired) Coney's Cottage, Bighton, Alresford SO24 9RE Tel: 01962 733555 — BA (Hons.) Camb. 1932, MB BChir 1936; MRCS Eng. LRCP Lond. 1935; DObst RCOG 1941. Prev: Clin. Asst. P.ss Beatrice Matern. Hosp. & St. Stephens Hosp. Gyn. Dept. Lond.

GOSSIEL, Rashaad 73A St Albans Road, Sheffield S10 4DN — MB ChB 1995 Manch.

GOSSIP, Joyce Margaret c/o 43 Magdalene Yard Road, Roseangle, Dundee DD1 4NE Tel: 01382 346500; 9 Minto Place, Dundee DD2 1BR Tel: 01382 668135 Fax: 01382 668135 — MB

ChB 1971 Glas.; DObst RCOG 1974. Med. Assessor BAMS Dundee. Prev: GP Dundee Retainer Scheme; GP Aberd.

GOSSMAN, Mr Henry H (retired) Westwood, 118 Looseleigh Lane, Derriford, Plymouth PL6 5HJ Tel: 01752 793031 — MB BS Durh. 1949; FRCS Ed. 1957. Cons. Surg. (Neurol.) Plymouth Gen. Hosp., Devon & Cornw. & I. of Scilly DHAs. Prev: Cons. Surg. (Neurol.) Plymouth Gen. Hosp., Devon & Cornw. & I. of Scilly DHAs.

GOSTELOW, Brian Edgar 4 The Sorrels, Isham, Kettering NN14 1HU — MB BS 1974 Lond.; MRCS Eng. LRCP Lond. 1974; MRCPath 1982. Cons. Histopath. Kettering Gen. Hosp.

GOSTICK, Nigel Karl (retired) The Rickyard, 2 Paddox Court, Kilsby, Rugby CV23 8XX — MB ChB 1961 Birm. Prev: GP Rugby.

GOSTLING, Anthony Charles Abraham and Partners, 21-23 Morden Hill, Lewisham, London SE13 7NN Tel: 020 8469 2880 Fax: 020 8692 9399 — MB BS 1982 Lond.; MRCGP 1989; DRCOG 1987. (Char. Cross Hosp.) GP Princip.; 1998 GP Clin. Tutor Lewisham (Postgrad.). Prev: SHO (Gen. Med.) Newham Health Dist.; Ho. Phys. (Med.) & Ho. Surg. Char. Cross Hosp. Lond.

GOSTLING, Dorothy Pamela (retired) Greenbank, Howell's Road, Tewkesbury GL20 5PW Tel: 01684 292279 — MB BS Lond. 1947; BA (Hons.) Open 1982. Prev: Ho. Phys. Roy. Free Hosp.

GOSWAMI, Debdas Clydebank Health Centre, Kilbowie Road, Glasgow; 30 Kilmardinny Grove, Bearsden, Glasgow G61 3NY Tel: 0141 942 5271 — MB BS 1968 Calcutta. (N.R.S. Med. Coll.)

GOSWAMI, Tapas Kumar Addison Road Surgery, Wimblington Village Hall, Addison Road, Wimblington, March PE15 0QT — MB BS 1969 Calcutta. (Nilratan Sircar Med. Coll.) GP Doddington, Benwick & Wimblington; Mem. Brit. Inst. Radiol. Prev: Trainee GP PeterBoro. VTS; Regist. (Radiodiag.) Roy. Berks. Hosp. Reading; Regist. (Radiodiag.) Roy. Infirm. Glas.

GOSWAMI, Mr Ved Parkash Birmingham Heartlands & Solihull NHS Trust, Bordesley Green East, Birmingham B9 S55 Tel: 0121 424 1315 Fax: 0121 424 1318; 40 Hamilton Avenue, Harborne, Birmingham B17 8AJ Tel: 0121 429 3188 Fax: 0121 429 4202 — MB BS 1981 Maharshi Dayanand, India; MChOrth Liverp. 1991; FRCS Eng; MS Ortho 1985. Cons. Orthop. Birm. Heartland & Solihull Hosp NHS Trust. Socs: BOA Fell; BMA Mem.

GOTHAM, Christopher Ronald Whiteparish Surgery, Common Road, Whiteparish, Salisbury SP5 2SU Tel: 01794 884269 Fax: 01794 884109 — MB BS 1979 Lond.; BSc (Hons.) Lond. 1976, MB BS 1979; MRCP (UK) 1984. (The Royal London) Prev: Med. Regist. Rotat. Salisbury Gen. Infirm. & S. Gen. Hosp.; SHO (Neurol.) Kings Coll. Hosp. & Maudsley Hosp. Lond.; SHO (Cardiol.) The Lond. Chest Hosp.

GOTHARD, Catherine Jane 143 Coppice Drive, Northampton NN3 6NQ — MB BS 1998 Lond.; MB BS Lond 1998.

GOTHARD, John Winston Walton Three Leaves, 4A Crescent Wood Road, London SE26 6RU Email: johnww@gothard.com — MB BS 1971 Lond.; FFA RCS Eng. 1975; DObst RCOG 1973. (St. Mary's) Cons. Anaesth. Roy. Brompton Hosp. Lond.; Hon. Cons. Anaesth. King Edwd. VII Hosp. Midhurst. Socs: Assn. Anaesth.; Roy. Soc. Med. Prev: Sen. Regist. (Anaesth.) W.m. Hosp. Lond.; Regist. (Anaesth.) Hosp. Sick Childr. Lond.

GOTHARD, Philip Kevin Department od Infectious Diseases, Hammersmith Hospital, du Cane Road, London W12 9RS Tel: 020 8383 1000 Email: pkgothard@hotmail.com; Email: pkgothard@hotmail.com — MB ChB 1992 Ed.; BSc St. And. 1988; MRCP Ed. 1997. (Edinburgh) Spec. Reg. Infec. Dis.s Hammersmith Hosp. Lond. Socs: MRCP (Edin.). Prev: SHO Rotat. (Med.) Oxf. Train. Scheme; Wellcome Research Regist. (Psychiat.) Oxf. Univ.; Clin. Research Fell. Immunol. of Infec. Dis.s Inst. of Molcular Med. Oxf.

GOTHARD, Samantha Carrie Flat 1, 18 Berkeley Road, Crouch End, London N8 8RU Tel: 020 8442 9088 — MB ChB 1996 Birm.; ChB Birm. 1996. SHO (Psychiat.) Chase Farm Hosp. Enfield Lond. Prev: SHO (Psychiat.) St Ann's Hosp. Tottenham Lond.; PRHO (Surg.) N. Staffs. Hosps. Stoke-on-Trent; PRHO (Med.) Manor Hosp. Walsall.

GOTLA, Dudley William 77 Gartree Road, Leicester LE2 2FD Tel: 0116 270 4747 — MRCS Eng. LRCP Lond. 1935; FFA RCS Eng. 1954; DA Eng. 1946. (Lond. Hosp.) Emerit. Cons. Anaesth. Leicester Gp. Hosps. Socs: BMA; (Ex-Pres.) Leic. Med. Soc. Prev: Regist. (Anaesth.) Univ. Coll. Hosp. Lond. & Brompton Hosp. Lond.; Hon. Clin. Asst. Brompton Hosp. & Hon. Phys. CMS; Capt. RAMC.

GOTT, Elizabeth Jayne 59 Stumperlower Crescent Road, Sheffield S10 3PR — MB BS 1984 Lond.; MRCGP 1992.

GOTTARDO, Nicola Giuseppe 192 Deighton Road, Huddersfield HD2 1JJ Tel: 01484 431591 — MB ChB 1993 Leeds. SHO (Paediat. A & E) Sheff. Childr. Hosp. Prev: SHO (Gen. Paediat., Paediat. Neurol. & Neonat.) Leeds Gen. Infirm.

GOTTLIEB, Isaac 3 Eden Lodge, Willesden Lane, London NW6 7YU Tel: 020 8459 4719 — LRCP LRCS 1939 Ed.; LRCP LRCS Ed. LRFPS Glas. 1939. (Durh.) Prev: Sen. Surg. Beer-Sheba Hosp. Israel; Sen. Resid. Surg. Off. Oldham Roy. Infirm.; Clin. Asst. (Anaesth.) N.wick Pk. Harrow.

GOTTO, James Flat A, 106 Keslake Road, Queens Park, London NW6 6DG — MB BS 1993 Lond.; BSc (Hons.) 1992; MRCP 1996. (St. Mary's) Specialist Regist. (Gastroenterol.) The Middlx. Hosp. Lond. Prev: SHO (Med.) Wexham Pk. Hosp.

GOTTSCHALK, Bodo Park Attwood Clinic, Trimpley, Bewdley DY12 1RE — State Exam Med 1985 Marburg.

GOTTUMUKKALA, Venkatarama Raju The Dowlais Medical Practice, Ivor Street, Dowlais, Merthyr Tydfil CF48 3LU Tel: 01685 721400 Fax: 01685 375287 — MB BS 1976 Madras; MRCPI 1987.

GOTZARIDIS, Efstratios Southampton General Hospital, Eye Unit, Tremona Road, Southampton SO16 6YD — Ptychio Iatrikes 1988 Thessalonika.

GOUBRAN, Mr Goubran Farag Charing Cross Hospital, Fulham Palace Road, London W6 8RF Tel: 020 8846 1471 Fax: 020 8423 5220 — MB BS 1973 Lond.; BDS Lond. 1962; FRCS (Ed.) 1988, M 1973; MRCS Lond. 1973; FDS RCS Eng. 1968. Cons. Oral & Maxillofacial Surg. Char. Cross Hosp. Lond.; Cons. Oral & Maxillofacial Surg. Ealing Hosp. Uxbridge Rd. Prev: Cons. Oral & Maxillofacial Surg. Centr. Middlx. Hosp. Lond.

GOUD, Atmakur Bharathi 27 Triandra Way, Yeading, Hayes UB4 9PB — MB BS 1975 Andhra.

GOUDA, Mr Mahmoud Abdul-Hamid Mohamed Hillside Health Centre, Tan-House Road, Skelmersdale WN8 6DS Tel: 01695 22424; 15 Hazel Lane, Woodley Park, Skelmersdale WN8 6UN — MRCS Eng. LRCP Lond. 1968; MB BCh Cairo 1958, DGO 1961; FRCS Ed. 1967; MRCOG 1968. (Ain Shams Univ. Cairo) Clin. Asst. (Gyn.) Wigan HA. Socs: Assoc. Police Surgs. GB.

GOUDGE, Mary Louise 14 The Pastures, Redhill Grange, Wellingborough NN9 5YR Tel: 01933 402012 Email: mary@credo.demon.co.uk — MB ChB 1996 Manch. (Manchester)

GOUDIE, Alexander William Motherwell Health Centre, 138-144 Windmill Street, Motherwell ML1 1TB Tel: 01698 266688 Fax: 01698 253230; 6 Gailes Park, Bothwell, Glasgow G71 8TS — MB ChB 1972 Glas. Prev: Regist. (Anaesth.) W.. Infirm. Glas.

GOUDIE, Barclay Munro West Gate Health Centre, Charleston Drive, Dundee DD2 4AD Tel: 01382 632771 Fax: 01382 633839; 28 Farington Street, Dundee DD2 1PJ — MD 1987 Dundee; MB ChB 1977; MRCP (UK) 1980; FRCPS Glas. 1991; MRCGP 1986.

GOUDIE, David Edward 45 Earlbank Avenue, Glasgow G14 9HE — MB ChB 1989 Ed.; MRCP (UK) 1993; DCH RCP Ed. 1992.

GOUDIE, David Robert Ninewells Hospital & Medical School, Dundee DD1 9SY Tel: 01382 60111 — MB ChB 1981 Glas.; FRCP Glas. 1994; MRCP (UK) 1984. Cons. Clin. Geneticist & Hon. Sen. Lect. Ninewells Hosp. & Med. Sch. Dundee.

GOUDIE, Helen Michie 9 Carruth Road, Bridge of Weir PA11 3HQ Tel: 01505 690050 — MB ChB 1980 Dundee. Clin. Asst. Psychiat. Gartnavel Roy. Hosp. Glas. Prev: SHO (Psychiat.) Roy. Dundee Liff Hosp.

GOUDIE, John Gordon (retired) 59 Octavia Terrace, Greenock PA16 7SR Tel: 01475 722316 — MB ChB Glas. 1944; FRCPath 1968. Prev: Cons. Bacteriol. Inverclyde Roy. Hosp. Greenock.

GOUDIE, Richard Angus Houghton Health Centre, Church Street, Houghton-le-Spring DH4 4DN Tel: 0191 584 2106 Fax: 0191 584 9493; Gaudeamus, 4 Pimlico, Durham DH1 4QW Tel: 0191 384 0013 Email: drgoudie@gp-a8902l.northy.nhs.uk — MB BChir 1977 Camb.; MB Camb. 1977, BChir 1976; MRCGP 1981. (Camb. & King's Coll. Hosp.) Mem. Sunderland MAAG. Socs: 1st HC Specialist Gp. BCS; Christian Med. Fell.sh.; Primary Care Spec. Gp. of Brit. Computer Soc. Prev: GP Newc.; Trainee GP Newc. VTS.

GOUDIE, Professor Robert Barclay (retired) 19 Dumgoyne Drive, Bearsden, Glasgow G61 3AP Tel: 0141 942 2495 Email: robert.goudie@virgin.net — MB ChB 1951 Glas.; MB ChB (Hons.) Glas. 1951; FRSE; MD (Hons.) Glas. 1967; FRCP Glas. 1971, M 1970; MRCP Lond. 1953; FRCPath 1975, M 1963. Prev: Prof. Path. Univ. Glas.

GOUDIE, Scott Graham 86 Dowanhill Street, Glasgow G12 9EG — MB ChB 1993 Glas.

GOUDIE, Stella Elizabeth Gordon 37 Hamilton Avenue, Pollokshields, Glasgow G41 4JE — MB ChB 1977 Glas.; FRCR 1983; DMRD Eng. 1981.

GOUDIE, Thomas Alexander 12 Roman Drive, Bearsden, Glasgow G61 2QL — MB ChB 1979 Dundee; FFA RCSI 1983. Sen. Regist. (Anaesth.) Glas. Roy. Infirm. Prev: Regist./SHO (Anaesth.) Ninwells Hosp. Dundee; Ho. Off. (Med.) Kings Cross Hosp. Dundee; Ho. Surg. Stracathro Hosp. Brechin.

GOUGH, Alan Denis (retired) 62 Deramore Park S., Belfast BT9 5JY Tel: 028 9080 9919 — MB BCh BAO Belf. 1956; FRCR 1975; FFR RCSI 1975; FFR 1965; DMRD Eng. 1961. Prev: Cons. Radiol. Roy. Vict. Hosp. Belf. & Ulster Hosp. Dundonald.

GOUGH, Alexander Merrilees (retired) Ravenscourt, Church St., Buckhaven, Leven KY8 1JL — MB ChB 1959 St. And.

GOUGH, Amanda Claire The Surgery, 713 Yardley Wood Road, Kings Heath, Birmingham B13 0PT Tel: 0121 444 3597; 34 Buryfield Road, Solihull B91 2DG — MB ChB 1989 Birm.; MRCGP 1995; DRCOG 1993. GP Partner.

GOUGH, Andrew 31 Moorhill Road, Whitnash, Leamington Spa CV31 2LG — MB ChB 1988 Bristol.

GOUGH, Andrew Kenneth Simon The Garvan Institute, St. Vincents Hospital, Sydney NSW ZO10, Australia; The Barn House, Burnett, Keynsham, Bristol BS31 2TF Tel: 01179 869437 — MD 1994 Lond.; MB BS 1985; MRCP Lond. 1988. Research Sabbatical St. Vincents Hosp. Sydney, Austral. Prev: Sen. Regist. (Rheum.) Birm.

GOUGH, Mr Andrew Leslie Swallows, Brent St., Brent Knoll, Highbridge TA9 4EQ — MD 1978 Manch.; MB ChB 1968; FRCS Ed. 1972. Cons. Surg. W.on-super-Mare Gen. Hosp.

GOUGH, Ann 18 West End, Osmotherley, Northallerton DL6 3AA — MB BS 1962 Lond.; MRCS Eng. LRCP Lond. 1962.

GOUGH, Beryl Elizabeth (retired) 1 The Paddock, 44 Bramhall Park Road, Bramhall, Stockport SK7 3NN Tel: 0161 486 9594 — MB ChB 1977 Manch.; DRCOG 1980. Screening Phys. Alexandra Hosp. Cheadle.

GOUGH, Brian Robert Fern House Surgery, 125-129 Newland Street, Witham CM8 1BH Tel: 01376 502108 Fax: 01376 502281 — MB ChB 1974 Manch.; MRCGP 1980; DRCOG 1979; DCH Eng. 1977.

GOUGH, Mr David Christopher Simmonds Aysgarth, 41 Stafford Road, Ellesmere Park, Eccles, Manchester M30 9HN Tel: 0161 288 1149 Email: dcsgough@aol.com — MB ChB Liverp. 1969; FRCS Ed. 1974; FRCS Eng. 1975 DCH Eng. 1971; FRACS 1977. (Liverp.) Cons. Paediat. Surg. Roy. Manch. Childr. Hosps. Socs: Manch. Med. Soc. & Manch. Paediat. Club.; Treas. Europ. Soc. Paediatric Urol. Prev: Sen. Regist. (Surg.) Roy. Manch. Childr. Hosp.; Chief Regist. (Surg.) Roy. Childr. Hosp. Melbourne Australia; Regist. (Surg.) United Cardiff Hosps.

GOUGH, David Graeme Alderman Jack Cohen Health Centre, Springwell Road, Sunderland SR3 4HG Tel: 0191 528 2727 Fax: 0191 528 3262 — MB BS 1985 Newc.

GOUGH, Donald The White House, Little Missenden, Amersham HP7 0QX — MB BChir 1949 Camb.; MA Camb. 1950, BA 1946, MB BChir 1949; MRCPsych 1971; DPM Eng. 1956. (Univ. Coll. Hosp. & Camb.) Socs: Assoc. Mem. Brit. Psycho-Analyt. Soc.; Fell. Roy. Soc. Med. Prev: Sen. Regist. (Psychiat.) Dept. Childr. & Parents Tavistock Clinic; Med. Off. Tone Vale Hosp.

GOUGH, Francis Christopher 32 Hillhead Crescent, Belfast BT11 9FS — MB BCh BAO 1992 Belf.; MRCGP 1996; DRCOG 1994.

GOUGH, George William Department of Obstetrics & Gynaecology, Lincoln County Hospital, Greetwell Road, Lincoln LN2 5QY — BA Oxf. 1980; MBBS Lond. 1983.

GOUGH, Janet Susan 7 Woodbury Drive, Sutton SM2 5RA Tel: 020 8642 4788 — MB ChB 1976 Ed.; BSc Ed. 1973, MB ChB 1976; MRCGP 1984.

GOUGH, John Department of Pathology, Llandough Hospital, Penarth CF64 2XX Tel: 01222 711711 — MB BChir 1960 Camb.; MD Camb. 1965; MRCS Eng. LRCP Lond. 1959; FRCPath 1980, M 1968. (Middlx.) Cons. Path. Llandough Hosp. Socs: Path. Soc. & Assn. Clin. Path. (Educat. Sec.). Prev: Sen. Lect. (Path.) Univ. Wales Coll. Med.; Lect. (Path.) Univ. Bristol; Lect. (Path.) Univ. Manch.

GOUGH, John Hugh Campbell (retired) The Wiillows, Howfield Lane, Chartham Hatch, Canterbury CT4 7HG Email: johngough@doctors.org.uk & thegoughs@hotmail.com — MRCS Eng. LRCP Lond. 1957.

GOUGH, Keith Maitland (retired) Little Ease, Rodmell, Lewes BN7 3HE — MB BS 1943 Lond. Prev: Dir. Univ. Sussex Health Serv.

GOUGH, Kenneth Raymond (retired) The Barn House, Burnett, Keynsham, Bristol BS31 2TF Tel: 0117 986 9437 — MD 1958 Bristol; MB ChB (Hnrs.) 1954; FRCP Lond. 1972, M 1961. Vis. Prof. Univ. Bath; Cons. Phys. Roy. United Hosp. Bath. Prev: Hon. Cons. Phys. United Bristol Hosps.

GOUGH, Mr Malcolm Howard (retired) Church End House, Church End, Bletchington, Kidlington OX5 3DL — MB BS 1951 Lond.; MS Lond. 1964; FRCS Eng. 1957. Hon. Cons. Gen. Surg. Oxon. HA. Prev: Assoc. Dir. Postgrad. Med. Educat. Univ. Oxf.

GOUGH, Martin David Quidi Vidi, Church Lane, North Thonesby, Grimsby DN36 5QG — MB ChB 1995 Dundee.

GOUGH, Michael Anthony 30 Alexandra Court, The Esplanade, Penarth, Cardiff CF64 3LA — MB BCh 1991 Wales; DA 1995; FRCA 1998. (Cardiff) Specialist Regist., Swansea. Socs: Assn. of Anaesth.s; Vasc. Anaesthetic Soc.; Fell. Roy. Coll. of Anaesth.

GOUGH, Michael Brian Quidi Vidi, Church Lane, North Thoresby, Grimsby DN36 5QG Tel: 01472 840828 Email: michael.gough@doctors.net.uk — MB ChB 1971 Birm.; FFA RCS Eng. 1976. Cons. Anaesth. Diana P.ss of Wales Hosp., Grimsby. Prev: Sen. Regist. Leeds Hosp.; Staff Anaesth. Janeway Child Health Centre Canada.

GOUGH, Mr Michael John The General Infirmary Leeds, Great George St., Leeds LS1 3EX Tel: 0113 243 2799; Laurel Cottage, Gilstead Lane, Bingley BD16 3LN Tel: 01274 564328 — MB ChB 1975 Leeds; ChM Leeds 1984; FRCS Eng. 1980. Cons. Vasc. Surg. Gen. Infirm. Leeds & Sen. Clin. Lect. Univ. Leeds; Dir. Vasc. Research Unit Univ. Bradford. Socs: Vasc. Soc. GB. & Irel.; Assn. Surg. Prev: Cons. Surg. Bradford Roy. Infirm.; Sen. Regist. (Gen. Surg.) Yorks. RHA; Regist. (Surg.) Roy. Free Hosp. Lond.

GOUGH, Michael Wentworth Robinson Old School House, 200 Main Road, Meriden, Coventry CV7 7NG Tel: 01676 22252 Fax: 01676 23865; 12 Old Station Road, Hampton-in-Arden, Solihull B92 0EY — MB ChB 1966 Birm. (Birm.) Prev: Ho. Surg. (Gen. Surg. & ENT) & Ho. Phys. Gen. Hosp. Birm.; SHO O & G Good Hope Hosp. Sutton Coldfield.

GOUGH, Nigel Anthony Station Approach Health Centre, Station Approach, Bradford-on-Avon BA15 1DQ Tel: 01225 866611; Hunterscombe, Turleigh, Bradford-on-Avon BA15 2HF Tel: 01225 862027 — MB BS 1977 Lond.; MB BS (Hons.) Lond. 1977; MRCP (UK) 1980; MRCS Eng. LRCP Lond. 1977; MRCGP 1982; Dip. Occ. Med. RCP Lond. 1997; DRCOG 1981. (St. Thos. Hosp.) GP Trainer Bradford-on-Avon.; Regional Med. Off. Marks & Spencer.

GOUGH, Norman Lyon (retired) Little Orchard, 17A haybridge Avenue, Hagley, Stourbridge DY8 2XG Tel: 01562 882944 — LRCPI & LM, LRSCI & LM 1951; LRCPI & LM, LRCSI & LM 1951. Prev: Med. Off. Nat. Blood Transf. Serv. Birm.

GOUGH, Pamela Joan 32 Hillhead Crescent, Stewartstown Road, Belfast BT11 9FS Tel: 01232 625471 — MB BCh BAO 1992 Belf. Trainee GP/SHO Rotat. Daisy Hill Hosp. Newry.

GOUGH, Peter The Surgery, High Street, Barley, Royston SG8 8HY Tel: 01763 848244 Fax: 01763 848677; 40 High Street, Chrishall, Royston SG8 8RP Tel: 01763 838410 — MB BS 1978 Lond.; MRCS Eng. LRCP Lond. 1978; MRCGP 1984; Cert. Family Plann. JCC 1984; DRCOG 1983. (St. Bart.) Div. Surg. St. John's Ambul. Prev: Trainee GP Banbury VTS; Ho. Surg. St. Bart. Hosp. Lond.; Ho. Phys. Whipps Cross Hosp. Lond.

GOUGH, Peter Michael 7 Woodbury Drive, Sutton SM2 5RA Tel: 020 8642 4788 — MD 1985 Bristol; BSc Ed. 1970, MB ChB Ed. 1973; FRCOG 1993, M 1979; Dip. Ven. Soc. Apoth. Lond. 1983. Cons. O & G St. Helier Hosp. Carshalton; Hon. Sen. Lect. St. Geo. Hosp. Med. Sch. Lond.

GOUGH, Rachel 34 Nutgrove Avenue, Bristol BS3 4QF — MB BS 1988 Lond.; MRCP (UK) 1993.

GOUGH, Sarah Louise 25 Shelburne Road, Calne SN11 8ER — MB BS 1998 Lond.; MB BS Lond 1998.

GOUGH, Mr Sidney George William (retired) 11 St John Street, Manchester M3 4DW Tel: 0161 832 9398 — MB ChB 1960

Manch.; FRCS Eng. 1969. Prev: Cons. Orthop. Surg. Salford Roy. Hosps. Trust & Roy. Manch. Childr. Hosp.

GOUGH, Sophie Louise 6 Southampton Road, London NW5 4HX — MB BS 1997 Lond.

GOUGH, Susan Patricia Medical Defence Union, 192 Altringham Road, Manchester M22 4RZ Tel: 0161 428 1234 — MB ChB 1979 Manch.; MSc Liverp. 1991; MRCPsych 1987; DFFP 1993; DRCOG 1983. Medico-Legal Advisor Med. Defence Union Manch. Prev: GP Crosby, Liverp.; Med. Off. (Psychiat.) Sefton Gen. Hosp., Liverp.

GOUGH, Vivienne Mary Flat 1, 4 York Road, Chorlton, Manchester M21 9HP — MB ChB 1998 Manch.; MB ChB Manch 1998.

GOUGH-THOMAS, Hugh Prospect House, Bromeswell, Woodbridge IP12 2PW Tel: 01394 460942 — MB BChir Camb. 1951; MA (Nat. Sc.) Camb. 1948; MRCS Eng. LRCP Lond. 1949; MFCM 1974; AFOM RCP Lond. 1980; DPH Lond. 1956; DObst RCOG 1951. (Camb. & St. Mary's) Indep. Pract. Occupat. Health; Div. Surg. St. John Ambul. Brig. Socs: Gen. Comm. Guardianship Soc. Prev: Nuffield Anaesth. Univ. Oxf.; Dep. MOH Boro. Watford; Univ. Lond. Bygott Schol.

GOULANDRIS, Mariana Little Crawley Surgery, Little Crawley, Yarcombe, Honiton EX14 9AY Tel: 01460 63359 — MB BCh BAO 1960 Dub.; L.F. Hom 1998. Prev: Med. Staff Peel Mem. Hosp. Brampton, Ontario, Canada; Regist. (Med.) Richmond Hosp. Dub.

GOULD, Adrian James (retired) Mint House, St John's Hill, Wareham BH20 4LZ — MB BS Lond. 1959; MRCS Eng. LRCP Lond. 1959; FRCR 1975; FFR 1971; DMRD Eng. 1968. Prev: Cons. Dorset Hosp. Gp. Wessex RHA.

***GOULD, Alastair Brian** 69 The Street, Boughton-under-Blean, Faversham ME13 9BE — MB BS 1986 Lond.

GOULD, Alison Jane — MB ChB 1991 Leeds; MRCP (UK) 1994. SpR (Endocrinol.) Norf. & Norwich NHS Trust Norwich. Prev: Regist. (Gen. Med.) Addenbrooke's Hosp. Camb.

GOULD, Allen Malcolm The Stanmore Medical Centre, 85 Crowshott Avenue, Stanmore HA7 1HS Tel: 020 8951 3888; Kerry House, Kerry Avenue, Stanmore HA7 4NL Tel: 020 8954 2949 — MB BS 1959 Lond.; MRCS Eng. LRCP Lond. 1959; MCOphth. 1988; DO Eng. 1966. (St. Bart.) Prev: Ho. Surg. Eye Dept. St. Bart. Hosp. Lond.; Regist. Eye Dept. Guy's Hosp. Lond.

GOULD, Andrew Armstrong Mill Street Health Centre, Mill Street, Crewe CW2 7AQ Tel: 01270 212725 Fax: 01270 216323; Dairy House Farm, Colleys Lane, Willaston, Nantwich CW5 6NS Tel: 01270 669470 Email: gould@netcentral.co.uk — MB BS 1980 Lond.; BSc Lond. 1977; MRCGP 1986; DRCOG 1985. (St. Bart.) GP Trainer. Prev: SHO (O & G) Qu. Pk. Hosp. Blackburn; SHO (Orthop.) Qu. Eliz. II Hosp. Welwyn Gdn. City.

GOULD, Anthony Douglas William The Cresta Private Hotal, 83 Manchester Road, Southport PR9 9BN — MB ChB 1978 Manch.

GOULD, Brian Alastair Queen Mary's Hospital, Sidcup DA14 6LT Tel: 020 8308 3000 Fax: 020 8308 3077; 5 Marlowe Close, Chislehurst BR7 6ND Tel: 020 8295 1765 — MB BS Lond. 1973; MD Lond. 1984; FRCP Lond. 1993; MRCP (UK) 1977. (St. Mary's) Cons. Cardiol. & Phys. Qu. Mary's Hosp. Sidcup; Hon. Cons. St. Thos. & Guy's Hosp. Lond. Socs: Brit. Cardiac Soc.; Brit. Hypertens. Soc. Prev: Sen. Regist. Rotat. (Cardiol. & Gen. Med.) Bristol Roy. Infirm. & Plymouth Gen. Hosp.; Regist. (Cardiol. & Gen. Med.) N.wick Pk. Hosp. Harrow; Research Fell. & Hon. Regist. (Cardiol.) N.wick Pk. Hosp. Harrow.

GOULD, Charles Herbert Gerard Whiteabbey Health Centre, 95 Doagh Road, Newtownabbey BT37 9QN Tel: 028 9086 4341 Fax: 028 9086 0443 — MB BCh BAO 1957 Belf.; DObst RCOG 1959. Prev: Ho. Phys. & Ho. Surg. Roy. Belf. Hosp. Sick Childr.

GOULD, David Charles Keith Medical Group, Health Centre, Turner St, Keith AB55 5DJ Tel: 01542 882244 Fax: 01542 882317; Ardmohr, Broomhill Road, Keith AB55 5EX — MB ChB 1985 Ed.; MRCGP 1991; T(GP) 1991; DRCOG 1991. Prev: SHO (Orthop. & A & E) Borders Gen. Hosp.; Trainee GP Hawick.

GOULD, David John The Granary, Park Meadows, St Clement, Truro TR1 1SX Tel: 01872 272804 Fax: 01872 320005 Email: davidgould@101324.276 — MB ChB 1972 Leeds; FRCP Lond. 1991; MRCP (UK) 1975. (Leeds) Cons. Dermat. Roy. Cornw. Hosp. Truro. Prev: Lect. (Dermat.) Univ. Sheff.

GOULD, Deborah Ann The Poplars, Minsterley, Shrewsbury SY4 4BP — MB BS 1988 Lond.

GOULD, Derek Alan X-Ray Department, Broadgreen Hospital, Thomas Drive, Liverpool L14 3LB Tel: 0151 706 2744 Fax: 0151 228 0625 Email: dgould@rcbuh-tr.nwest.nhs.uk; 52 Dunbabin Road, Liverpool L16 7QH Tel: 0151 722 6612 Email: derekgould@hotmail.com — MB ChB 1972 Liverp.; MRCP (UK) 1975; FRCR 1981; DMRD Liverp. 1979. Cons. Radiol. Roy. Liverp. & BRd.green Hosps. Socs: Brit. Soc. Interven. Radiol.; Cardiovasc. & Interven. Radiol. Soc. Europe. Fell. Prev: Cons. Radiol. N. Manch. Gen. Hosp.; Regist. (Med.) BRd.green Hosp. Liverp.; SHO (Orthop. & Cas.) Roy. S.. Hosp. Liverp.

GOULD, Duncan Christopher 37 Weymouth Street, London W1N 3FA Tel: 020 7352 6351 — MB BS 1982 Lond.; MBA Lond. 1992; Dip. Pharm. Med. RCP (UK) 1993; Dip. Obst. Otago 1987. Managem. Cons. Pharmaceut. & Healthcare Industries; GP. Socs: Assn. Fac. Pharmaceut. Med.

GOULD, Frances Kate Dept of Microbiology, Freeman Hospital, High Heaton, Newcastle upon Tyne NE7 &DN Tel: 0191 223 1248 Fax: 0191 223 1224 Email: kate-goucd@ffh.nuth.northy nhs .uk; 22 Kensington Gardens, Whitley Bay NE25 8AR — MB BS 1980 Newc.; MRCPath 1987; FRCP 1997. Cons. (Med. Microbiol.) Freeman Hosp. Newc. upon Tyne. Socs: BSAC Edr. JAC (Meetings /Educat. Sec.).

GOULD, Gerald Montague (retired) 8 Lower Byfield, Monks Eleigh, Ipswich IP7 7JJ — MRCS Eng. LRCP Lond. 1948. Prev: GP Lond.

GOULD, Gordon Clifford (retired) 33 Grinstead Lane, Lancing BN15 9DU Tel: 01903 754900 Email: cliffordgould@compuserve.com — MB BS Lond. 1955. Prev: Hosp. Pract. (Cardiothoracic Med.) S.lands Hosp. Shoreham-by-Sea.

GOULD, Gordon Thomas 68 Lifstan Way, Thorpe Bay, Southend-on-Sea SS1 2XE Tel: 01702 582687 — MB BS 1951 Lond.; BA Toronto 1942; LMSSA Lond. 1950. (St. Bart.) Med. Off. DHSS (Social Security), Lond. Co-op. Soc. & Infant Welf.; Clinic, Essex AHA. Socs: BMA. Prev: Ho. Surg. & Cas. Off. E. Suff. & Ipswich Hosp.

GOULD, Grahame Albert Department of Medicine, Weston General Hospital, Grange Road, Weston Super Mare BS23 4TQ Tel: 01934 636363 Fax: 01934 647029; 23 Parsonage Road, Berrow, Burnham-on-Sea TA8 2NJ — MD 1990 Lond.; MB BS 1977; MRCP (UK) 1979; FRCP 1998. (Lond. Hosp.) Cons. Phys. W.on Gen. Hosp. Prev: Sen. Regist. (Med.) Bristol Roy. Infirm.; Research Fell. Rayne Laborat. City Hosp. Edin.; SHO Whittington Hosp. Lond.

GOULD, Ian Malcolm Department of Clinical Microbiology, Royal Infirmary, Aberdeen AB25 2ZD Tel: 01224 681818 Fax: 01224 662979 — MB ChB 1976 Ed.; FRCP Ed. 1990; MRCP (UK) 1980; MRCPath 1987; FRCOphth 1997. (Ed.) Cons. Clin. Microbiol.; Hon. Sen. Lect. (Med. Microbiol.) Univ. Aberd.; Hon Prof. (Med Micro Epidimiology Pub. Health) Univ of Trnava Slovak RePub.

GOULD, Jack (retired) — MB ChB 1943 Liverp. Medicolegal Phys. Prev: Div. Police Surg. Liverp. City Police.

GOULD, James Cameron 16 Church Hill, Edinburgh EH10 4BQ Tel: 0131 447 4327 — MB ChB 1945 Ed.; FRS Ed. 1964; BSc, MD Ed. 1959; FRCP Ed. 1966, M 1963; FRCPath 1972; FFPHM 1975, M 1972; FIBiol, C.Biol 1967. Socs: Fell. Roy. Phys. Soc.; Fell. Roy. Soc. Med. Prev: Dir. Centr. Microbiol. Laborats. Edin.; Path. RAMC; Sen. Asst. Bacteriol. Roy. Infirm. Edin.

GOULD, James Duncan McEwan Ipswich Hospital, Ipswich IP4 5PD Tel: 01473 702174 Fax: 01473 702180; Ivy Lodge Farm, Chimers Lane, Hoo, Woodbridge IP13 7QF Tel: 01473 737245 Fax: 01473 737897 Email: jgould@anglia.co.net — MB ChB Glas. 1970; BSc Ed. 1967; FRCP Ed. 1988; FRCP Glas. 1987; MRCP (UK) 1975; DObst RCOG 1972; DCH RCPS Glas. 1974; FRCPCH 1998. (Ed.) Cons. Paediat. Heath Rd. Wing Ipswich Hosp. Socs: M-C Soc. Edin. & Roy. Soc. Med. Prev: Cons. Paediat. Al Nahdha Hosp. Sultanate of Oman; Sen. Regist. (Med. Paediat.) Hosp. Sick Childr. Gt. Ormond St.; Regist. (Med. Paediat.) Roy. Hosp. Sick Childr. Glas.

GOULD, Jane Cherry Hill, The Square, Braishfield, Romsey SO51 0PR; 31 Wilford Road, Ruddington, Nottingham NG11 6BN — MB ChB 1989 Sheff.; MRCP (UK) 1992; MRCPath 1998.

GOULD, Jeanette Newtown Surgery, 147 Lawn Avenue, Great Yarmouth NR30 1QP Tel: 01493 853191 Fax: 01493 331861; The Laurels, High Road, Burgh Castle, Great Yarmouth NR31 9QL Tel: 01493 781423 — MB ChB 1981 Glas.; DRCOG 1984.

GOULD, John Christopher Gilbert Knight The Health Centre, Glastonbury Road, Wells BA5 1XJ — MB BCh BAO 1971 Dub.

GOULD, John Edward Shapland (retired) 47 The Crescent, Rutherway, Oxford OX2 6QY Tel: 01865 311361 — MB BS Lond. 1949; DA Eng. 1954; MRCGP 1956.

GOULD, Judith Mary Pelhams Clinic, Milham Lane, Kinson, Bournemouth BH10 7LH Tel: 01202 570821; 77 Canford Cliffs Road, Canford Cliffs, Poole BH13 7AH Tel: 01202 701577 — BM BS 1980 Nottm.; BMedSci Nottm. 1978; MRCGP 1985; DRCOG 1984; DCH RCP Lond. 1983. Staff Grade Community Paedit. Bournemouth.

GOULD, Juliet Mary High Street Surgery, 188 High Street, Cottenham, Cambridge CB4 8RX Tel: 01954 250079 Fax: 01954 206078 — MB BS 1973 Lond.; MRCP (UK) 1977; MRCS Eng. LRCP Lond. 1973.

GOULD, Lawrence Nigel The Stanmore Medical Centre, 85 Crowshott Avenue, Stanmore HA7 1HS Tel: 020 8951 3888 Fax: 020 8952 5093; 28 Frithwood Ave, Northwood HA6 3LU — MB BS 1987 Lond.; MRCS Eng. LRCP Lond. 1987; DRCOG 1991. Clin. Asst. (Special Needs) Harrow & Hillingdon CHCT; Clin. Asst. (Neurol.) Hemel Hempstead Gen. Hosp. Herts.; Bd. Mem. Harrow E. Kingsbury PCG; Prescribing LEAD Harrow E.Kingsbury PCG.

GOULD, Lincoln Neville 82 Mill Road, Swanland, North Ferriby HU14 3PL Tel: 01482 634832 — MRCS Eng. LRCP Lond. 1943; MFCM 1972; DPH Liverp. 1950. (Manch.) Staff Med. Off. Castle Hill & De La Pole Hosps. Cottingham; Med. Off. Negas E.. Region. Prev: Clin. Asst. (Psychiat.) BRd.gate Hosp. Beverley; Asst. Co. Med. Off. Heref.; Div. & Dep. Co. Med. Off. E. Riding CC.

GOULD, Martin Colchester District General Hospital, Turner Road, Colchester CO4 5JL; Breewood House, School Lane, Great Horkesley, Colchester CO6 4BW Tel: 01206 272176 — MB ChB 1976 Sheff.; FRCR 1983; DMRD Eng. 1982. Cons. Radiol. NE Essex HA.; Clin. Director Radiol. Prev: Sen. Regist. (Radiol.) Manch. Roy. Infirm.

GOULD, Martin Geoffrey (retired) 22 Narrow Street, London E14 8DQ Tel: 020 7791 0436 Email: 100142.1360@compuserve.com — MRCS Eng. LRCP Lond. 1943; FACS 1956.

GOULD, Michael Ian 2 Upland Road, Leeds LS8 2SQ Tel: 0113 240 1234 Fax: 0113 217 9988 Email: independent@doctors.uk.menet.net; Bedside Manor, 25 Sandhill Oval, Leeds LS17 8EB Tel: 0113 268 6858 Fax: 0113 228 3753 Email: genla@bedsidemanor.demon.co.uk — MB BChir 1975 Camb.; MA, MB Camb. 1975, BChir 1974; MRCP (UK) 1977.

GOULD, Michael John Brooklands, Coleshill Road, Marston Green, Birmingham B37 7HL Tel: 0121 779 6981; 22 Wyken Close, Dorridge, Solihull B93 8RP Tel: 01564 230093 — MB BS 1979 Lond. (St. Thos.) Clin. Med. Off. (Psychiat. of Learning Disabilities) Brooklands. Prev: GP Birm.; GP Trainee Reading; SHO (Rheum.) Battle Hosp. Reading.

GOULD, Michael John Student Health Centre, De Montfort University, The Gateway, Leicester LE1 9BH Tel: 0116 257 7594 Fax: 0116 257 7614 — MB ChB 1986 Leic.; BSc Leic. 1983; MRCGP 1995; Dip. Sports Med. (RCS Ed. & Glas.) 1997; Dip. IMC RCS Ed. 1990. (Leicester) GP Stud. Health Serv.; Sports Phys. Leicester Sports Med. Clinic. Socs: Fell. Roy. Geogr. Soc.; Brit. Assn. Sports Med.; Soc. Orthop. Med.

GOULD, Nicholas Victor Health Centre, Midland St., Long Eaton, Nottingham NG10 1NY Tel: 0115 973 2285 Fax: 0115 946 3894 — MB ChB 1973 Sheff.; MRCGP 1977; DObst RCOG 1976; DCH Eng. 1975. (Sheff.) GP Bd. Mem. Prescribing Lead. Erewash P.C.T. Prev: Trainee GP Doncaster VTS; Ho. Off. (Gen. Med. & Dermat.) Roy. Hosp. Chesterfield; Ho. Off. (Surg.) Roy. Infirm. Doncaster.

GOULD, Nigel Stuart King Street Surgery, 55 King Street, Great Yarmouth NR30 2PW Tel: 01493 855589 Fax: 01493 332824; The Laurels, High Road, Burgh Castle, Great Yarmouth NR31 9QL Tel: 01493 781423 — BM BS 1980 Nottm.; BMedSci (Hons.) Nottm. 1978; MRCGP 1984; DRCOG 1982. Clin. Asst. (Geriat.) N.gate Hosp. Gt. Yarmouth.

GOULD, Peter Charles Ernest Castle Circus Health Centre, Abbey Road, Torquay TQ2 5YH Tel: 01803 298441 — BM BCh 1955 Oxf.; MA, BM BCh Oxf. 1955. (Oxf. & Lond. Hosp.) GP Torquay. Socs: Torquay & Dist. Med. Soc. Prev: Cons. Primary Care Phys. RKH Progr. Saudia Arabia; Ho. Phys. Lond. Hosp.; SHO Torbay Hosp. Torquay.

GOULD, Robert Allan The Surgery, 133 London Road, Cowplain, Waterlooville PO8 8XL Tel: 023 9226 2387; Knightswood Closewood Road, Denmead, Waterlooville PO7 6JD Tel: 02392 263788 — MB BS 1956 Lond.; DCH Eng. 1958; DObst RCOG 1960. (St. Bart.) Prev: Ho. Off. Sydenham Childr. Hosp.; Res. Med. Off. Hosp. Sick Childr. Country Br. Tadworth; Obst. Ho. Off. St. Mary's Hosp. Portsmouth.

***GOULD, Sarah Helen Louise** 7 The Spinney, Cheltenham GL52 3JX Tel: 01242 250224 — MB ChB 1997 Birm.

GOULD, Sheila Elizabeth (retired) Knightswood, Closewood Road, Denmead, Waterlooville PO7 6JD Tel: 023 9226 3788 — MB BS Lond. 1960. Prev: Ho. Surg. St. Mary's Hosp. Portsmouth.

GOULD, Sheila Mary Croft Hall Medical Practice, 19 Croft Road, Torquay TQ2 5UA Tel: 01803 298441 Fax: 01803 296104; Alderley, 3 Bishops Close, Torquay TQ1 2PL Tel: 01803 294141 — MB ChB 1958 Birm.; Cert. Av. Med. 1983; Cert. Family Plann. JCC 1982. (Birm.) p/t GP Torquay & Pricipal in Gen. Pract. Socs: BMA; Torquay & Dist. Med. Soc.; Brit. Assn. for Accid. & Emerg. Med. Prev: Ho. Off. (Obst.) St. Mary's Hosp. Manch.; SHO (Paediat.) Roy. Manch. Childr. Hosp.; Ho. Off. (Med. & Surg.) N. Staffs. Roy. Infirm. Stoke-on-Trent.

GOULD, Stephen John Paediatric Pathology, Maternity Department, John Radcliffe Hospital, Headington, Oxford OX3 3DU; 10 Inkerman Close, Abingdon OX14 1NH — MB BS 1977 Lond.; MRCPath 1983. Cons. (Paediat. Path.) John Radcliffe Hosp. Oxf. Prev: Sen. Lect. Perinatal & Neonat. Path. Univ. Coll. Lond.

GOULD, Stuart Raeburn Epsom General Hospital, Dorking Road, Epsom KT18 7EG Tel: 01372 735129; The Coppice, 22 Downs Road, Epsom KT18 5JD Tel: 01372 722624 — MB BS 1969 Lond.; BSc Lond. 1966, MD 1979; FRCP Lond. 1989; MRCP (UK) 1972. (Lond. Hosp.) Cons. Phys. & Gastroenterol. Epsom & St Helier NHS Trust. Socs: Roy. Soc. Med.; Brit. Soc. Gastroenterol. Prev: Sen. Regist. (Med.) Lond. Hosp.; Research Fell. St. Mark's Hosp. Lond.; Regist. (Gen. Med.) W.m. Hosp. Teach. Gp.

GOULD, Stuart William Thomas 21 Columbine Road, Kempshott, Basingstoke RG22 5RW — MB BS 1986 Lond.; BSc (Hons.) Infec. & Immunity Lond. 1986, MB BS 1989.

GOULD, Terence Ronald (retired) 14 Chalgrove Road, Sutton SM2 5JT Tel: 020 8642 0466 Fax: 020 8404 6415 Email: tgould@cableinet.co.uk — MB BS 1959 Lond.; MRCS Eng. LRCP Lond. 1959; FRCA Eng. 1966; DA Eng. 1964; DObst RCOG 1960; LIHSM 1986. Prev: Cons. Anaesth. St. Geo. Hosp. & Atkinson Morley's Hosp. Lond.

GOULD, Timothy Howard Department of Anaesthetics, Bristol Royal Infirmary, Upper Maudlin St., Bristol BS8 2HW — MB ChB 1984 Bristol; MRCP (UK) 1988; FCAnaesth 1991. Cons. Anaesth. & Intens. Care Bristol Roy. Infirm. Prev: Sen. Regist. Rotat. Derriford Hosp. Plymouth SW Regional Train. Scheme Bristol Roy. Infirm.; Research Fell. (Anaesth.) Univ. Hosp. Wales Cardiff; Regist. (Anaesth.) Univ. Hosp. Wales Cardiff.

GOULD, Timothy John The Surgery, South Hermitage, Belle Vue, Shrewsbury SY3 7JS Tel: 01743 343148 Fax: 01743 357772 — MB ChB 1980 Bristol; BSc (Hons. Physiol.) Bristol 1975, MB ChB 1980; DRCOG 1987.

GOULD, William Michael, OBE (retired) Trenhayle, 73 Rea Barn Road, Brixham TQ5 9EE Tel: 01803 859598 Email: goulds@73reabarn.freeserve.co.uk — MB ChB 1958 Manchester University; FRCS 1964 Edinburgh; DTM and H Liverp. 1970; MB ChB 1958 Manchester University. Prev: Heath Serv. Dir. United Mission to Nepal.

GOULDEN, Annette Diana Department Child & Adolescent Psychiatry, 88 Newtown Road, Newbury RG14 5LF — MB BS 1975 Lond.; BSc (Zool.) Lond. 1969; MRCPsych 1986. Cons. Child Adolesc. Psychiat. Berks. Health Care Trust. Socs: BMA; Assoc. Mem. Gp. Anal. Soc.; ACPP.

GOULDEN, Geoffrey William (retired) 2 Adare Drive, Coventry CV3 6AD — MRCS Eng. LRCP Lond. 1951; DPM Eng. 1967. Prev: Cons. Psychiat. Abbeyfields Hosp. Studley.

GOULDEN, Michael Robert Department of Anaesthesia, 12th Floor, Royal Liverpool University Hospital, Prescot Street, Liverpool L7 8XP — MB BS 1990 Newc.

GOULDEN, Nicholas John 9 Wood Berry Grove, London N12 0DN — MB ChB 1986 Ed.; MRCP (UK) 1990. Research Fell. Sick Childr. Hosp. Bristol. Prev: Regist. (Haemat.) Edin.; Regist. & SHO (Med.) Gateshead.

GOULDEN, Paul 29 Birkdale Road, Dewsbury WF13 4HG Tel: 01924 500177 Fax: 01924 500177 — MB ChB 1974 Leeds; FFA RCS Eng. 1978; DObst RCOG 1976. Cons. Anaesth. Dewsbury Dist. Hosp. Socs: BMA (Honourable Sec. Drewsbury Div.). Prev: Sen. Regist. (Anaesth.) Yorks. RHA.; Regist. (Anaesth.) St. Jas. Univ. Hosp. Leeds; SHO (Anaesth.) Wharfedale Gen. Hosp. Otley.

GOULDEN, Philippa Kathleen 9 Wood Bury Grove, London N12 0ND; 1 Claremont Avenue, Bishopston, Bristol BS7 8JD — MB BS 1984 Lond.; MRCGP 1989; DCH RCP Lond. 1988; DRCOG 1987. Med. Off. Anthony Nolan Bone Marrow Trust. Socs: BMA. Prev: Clin. Asst. Roy. Free; Clin. Asst. Bristol Childr.s; Clin. Asst. Edin. (W.ern).

GOULDEN, Susan Elizabeth The Winterbourne Hospital, Herrington Rd, Dorchester DT1 2DR Tel: 01305 263252 Fax: 01305 257167; Tel: 01935 816831 Fax: 01935 816831 Email: celtique@clara.co.uk — MB BS 1982 Lond.; MRCGP 1991; DA (UK) 1985. p/t Health Promotion, The Winterbourne Hosp., Dorchester.

GOULDEN, Victoria Dermatology Department, Leeds General Infirmary, Great George St., Leeds LS1 3EX — MB ChB 1987 Manch. Ho. Off. (Med.) Qu.'s Pk. Hosp. Blackburn.

GOULDER, Philip Jeremy Renshaw 24 Beaumont Road, Headington, Oxford OX3 8JN — MB 1986 Camb.; BA Oxf. 1982; MB Camb. 1987 BChir 1986; MRCP (UK) 1989. Regist. (Paediat.) Roy. Childr. Hosp. Melbourne, Austral. Prev: SHO (Paediat.) John Radcliffe Hosp. Oxf. & Roy. Hosp. Sick Childr. Edin.

GOULDER, Raymond Victor Honywood (retired) Mount Haviland Cottage, 97 Lansdown Lane, Weston, Bath BA1 4NB — MB BS Lond. 1946; MRCS Eng. LRCP Lond. 1946.

GOULDER, Timothy John Denmead Health Centre, Hambledon Road, Denmead, Waterlooville PO7 6NR Tel: 02392 257112 Fax: 02392 257113 — MB BS 1975 Lond.; MRCP (UK) 1978; MRCS Eng. LRCP Lond. 1975; MRCGP 1979. (Guy's) Hosp. Practitioner Diabetes; Regional Audit Assesor; GP Trainer; HSE Registered Professional Divers Doctor. Socs: Chairm. Vinus Medicus; Soc. Apothec. (Hist. of Med. Sec.). Prev: SHO (Med.) Soton. Gen. Hosp.

GOULDESBROUGH, David Robert Bradford Royal Infirmary, Duckworth Lane, Bradford BD9 6RJ Tel: 01274 364209 Fax: 01274 364190 — MB ChB 1982 Ed.; BSc (Med. Sci.) Ed. 1979; FRCPath 1997, M 1989. Cons. Histopath. Bradford Hosps. NHS Trust. Prev: Lect. (Path.) Univ. Edin. Med. Sch.

GOULDIE, Michell Rita 138 Roseberry Gardens, Upminster RM14 1NE — MB BS 1996 Lond.

GOULDING, Helen Department of Histopathology, Jersey General Hospital Gloucester St., St Helier, Jersey JE2 3QS — MB BS 1986 Newc.; BA Camb. 1983; MRCPath 1993.

GOULDING, John Alexander 75 Leadhall Lane, Harrogate HG2 9NX Tel: 01423 871117; 5 Devon Road, Bedford MK40 3DJ — MB BCh 1986 Wales; MRCGP 1992; T (GP) 1992; DObst. Otago 1989. Prev: Trainee GP Bristol & Ross-on-Wye.

GOULDING, Niall Joseph 242 Nottingham Road, Mansfield NG18 4SH — MB BCh BAO 1957 NUI; LAH Dub. 1956; DA Eng. 1962.

GOULDING, Paul Gerard Ruthven Corney Place Medical Group, The Health Centre, Bridge Lane, Penrith CA11 8HW Tel: 01768 245226 Fax: 01768 245229 — BM BCh 1973 Oxf.; MA Oxf. 1973, BA 1970, BM BCh 1973; MRCGP 1978; DRCOG 1976. Prev: Ho. Phys. Radcliffe Infirm. Oxf.; Ho. Surg. Roy. United Hosp. Bath; Med. Off. C.J.M. Hosp. Nqutu, Zululand.

GOULDING, Peter Jonathan Department of Neurology, St James' Hospital, Leeds LS9 7TF Tel: 0113 283 6927 Fax: 0113 246 5231; 13 Leadhall Crescent, Harrogate HG2 9NG — MB ChB 1982 Ed.; MD Ed. 1990; FRCP (UK) 1985. Cons. Neurol. St. Jas. Hosp. Leeds; Hon. Sen. Lect. (Neurol.) Univ. Leeds. Socs: Assn. Brit. Neurols.; Brit. Neuropath. Soc. Prev: Lect. (Neurol.) Univ. Manch.; Regist. (Neurol.) Manch. Roy. Infirm. & N. Manch. Gen. Hosp.; Clin. Research Fell. (Neurol.) Manch. Roy. Infirm.

GOULDING, Stephen Ronald Queensview Medical Centre, Thornton Road, Northampton NN2 6LS Tel: 01604 713315 Fax: 01604 714378; The Cedars, 63 Church Way, Weston Favell, Northampton NN3 3BY Tel: 01604 409299 Email: skgoulding@hotmail.com — MB BS 1973 Lond.; DA Eng. 1977; DObst RCOG 1975. (Lond. Hosp.) Prev: SHO (Anaesth.) N.ampton Gen. Hosp.; Ho. Surg. & Ho. Phys., & SHO (O & G) Orsett Hosp. Grays.

GOULDING, Steven Tarquin 75 Leadhall Lane, Harrogate HG2 9NX — MB BS 1986 Lond.

GOULDING, Timothy John 43 Shirehampton Road, Bristol BS9 2DN — MB ChB 1989 Birm.

GOULDS, Roger Kenneth Sheet Street Surgery, 21 Sheet Street, Windsor SL4 1BZ Tel: 01753 860334 Fax: 01753 833696 — MB ChB 1978 Sheff.; MRCGP 1984; DRCOG 1981. Socs: Windsor & Dist. Med. Soc.; BMA.

GOULDSON, Rodney Department of Anaesthetics, University Hospital of Wales, Cardiff CF4 4XN Tel: 029 2074 3107; c/o 53 Thingwall Road E., Thingwall, Wirral CH61 3UZ — MB BCh 1986 Wales; FRCA 1992. Cons. Anaesth. Univ. Hosp. Wales Cardiff. Prev: Sen. Regist. (Anaesth.) Cardiff Hosps.; Vis. Asst. Prof. Anaesth. UTSWMC Dallas, Texas, USA; Regist. Rotat. (Anaesth.) Gwynedd & Cardiff Hosps.

GOULSTINE, Mr David Bernard Ophthalmology Department, The Leicester Royal Infirmary, Leicester LE1 5WW — MB BS 1965 Newc.; FRCS Eng. 1970; FCOphth. 1988; DO Eng. 1969. (Newc. upon Tyne) Cons. Ophth. Roy. Infirm. Leic. Prev: Sen. Regist. (Ophth.) Roy. Hosp. Sheff.; Demonst. (Anat.) Newc. Univ.; Ho. Phys. & Ho. Surg. Roy. Vict. Infirm. Newc.

GOULSTINE, Marilyn Bryna 10 The Fairway, Oadby, Leicester LE2 2HH — MB ChB 1971 Leeds; MRCGP 1976; DFFP 1993. Prev: Ho. Phys. St. Jas. Hosp. Leeds; SHO (O & G) King Edwd. VIII Hosp. Durban, S. Afr.; SHO (Paediat.) Transvaal Memor. Hosp. Childr. Johannesburg, S. Afr.

GOULSTON, Roy Frank (retired) 43 Gilkes Crescent, Dulwich Village, London SE21 7BP Tel: 020 8693 2035 — MB BS 1952 Sydney; FRCGP (1996).

GOULSTONE, William (retired) 37 Parkhill Road, Bexley DA5 1HX Tel: 01322 521034 — MB BChir 1938 Camb.; BA Camb. 1934; MRCS Eng. LRCP Lond. 1938. Prev: Squadron Ldr. RAFMS.

GOULT, Ian (retired) Corner Cottage, Brampton, Lincoln LN1 2EG — MB ChB 1975 Sheff.; MB BChir Camb. 1975; MA Camb. 1975; DCH Eng. 1978.

GOULTON, John (retired) Tarifa, Best Beech, Wadhurst TN5 6JL — MB BS Lond. 1955; MRCS Eng. LRCP Lond. 1955; FFPM RCP (UK) 1989; LMCC 1959. Prev: Princip. Med. Adviser Ciba-Geigy Pharmaceut. Horsham W. Sussex.

GOULTY, Leonora Helen (retired) 57 Kirkley Park Road, Lowestoft NR33 0LQ Tel: 01502 565211 — BM BCh 1951 Oxf.; MA (Hons. Physiol.) Oxf. 1947; MRCGP 1964; DObst RCOG 1952; FRCGP 1997. Prev: Ho. Surg. Univ. Dept. Neurosurg. Manch. Roy. Infirm.

GOUNDRY, Gregory Guy Randall Ellerslie, Hexham Old Road, Ryton NE40 3JH — MB BS 1985 Newc. SHO (Orthop.) Newc. Gen. Hosp. Prev: Ho. Off. (Med. & Surg.) Qu. Eliz. Hosp. Gateshead.

GOUNDRY, Lucy Annabel Finchdale, 1 Lubbock Road, Chislehurst BR7 5JG Tel: 020 8295 1086 Email: drgoundry@aol.com — MB BS 1992 Newc.; DCH 1997; DFFP 1998; DRCOG 1998. (Newcastle) GP Princip. Prev: GP Regist. Barnard Med. Pract. Sidcup; Med. Regist. Hammersmith Hosp.; GP Regist. Hammersmith Hosp.

GOURDIE, Ronald William 6 Paterson Street, Kirkcaldy KY2 5AS Tel: 01592 264412 — MB ChB 1971 Dundee; FRCS Eng. 1977. (Dundee) Sen. Cons. & Chief Surg. King Khalid Hosp. Nahjran, Saudi Arabia; Chief Surg. NAAF Hosp. Hafra Al Batan, Saudi Arabia. Prev: SHO Bradford Roy. Infirm.; SHO (Cas.) Vict. Hosp. Kirkcaldy; Ho. Phys. & Ho. Off. (Orthop.) Bridge of Earn Hosp.

GOUREVITCH, Mr Arnold, MC, TD (retired) 40 Greening Drive, Ampton Road, Edgbaston, Birmingham B15 2XA Tel: 0121 454 2002 — MB ChB 1948 Birm.; FRCS Eng. 1939; MRCS Eng. LRCP Lond. 1936. Mem. Ct. Examrs. RCS Eng. Prev: Cons Surg. United Birm. Hosps.

GOUREVITCH, Mr David 20 Chantry Road, Moseley, Birmingham B13 8DH — MD 1989 Birm.; MB ChB 1977; FRCS Ed. 1983. Cons. Gastrointestinal Surg. Sandwell Dist. Gen. Hosp. W. Bromwich. Socs: Brit. Assn. Surg. Oncol.; Brit. Assn. Surgs. Prev: Sen. Regist. (Surg.) Qu. Eliz. Hosp. Birm.

GOURLAY, Catriona Maclaine (retired) The Views, Hill Green, Clavering, Saffron Walden CB11 4QS — MB ChB 1946 Glas.;

MFCM 1973; DPH Lond. 1954. Prev: Sen. Med. Off. (Occupat. Health) Camb. HA.

GOURLAY, Duncan Patterson (retired) Gean Cottage, Clachan of Myrton, Whauphill, Newton Stewart DG8 9PU Tel: 01988 700382 — MB ChB 1950 Glas.

GOURLAY, Evelyn Joyce Dr Forbes and Partners, East Calder Medical Practice, 147 Main Street, East Calder, Livingston EH53 0EW Tel: 01506 882882 Fax: 01506 883630 — MB ChB 1978 Aberd.

GOURLAY, John Crawford 12 Rannoch Drive, Bearsden, Glasgow G61 2JJ Tel: 0141 943 1114 — MB ChB 1963 Glas. (Glas.)

GOURLAY, Kathryn Anne McIntosh, Gourlay and Partners, 1 India Place, Edinburgh EH3 6EH Tel: 0131 225 9191 Fax: 0131 226 6549; 2 Blinkbonny Terrace, Edinburgh EH4 3NA — MB ChB 1971 Ed.; MRCGP 1979; DObst RCOG 1973. GP Edin.

GOURLAY, Michael Victor Oxford Street Surgery, 20 Oxford Street, Workington CA14 2AL Tel: 01900 603302; 4B Rubbybanks Road, Cockermouth CA13 9RG — MB BS 1975 Newc.

GOURLAY, Nigel Gordon (retired) Woodhurst, Balcombe Road, Horley RH6 9SW — MB BS 1947 Lond.; MRCS Eng. LRCP Lond. 1947; FRCOG 1967, M 1953. Prev: Cons. Obstetr. & Gynaecol. Redhill Gen. Hosp. & Crawley Hosp.

GOURLAY, Norman James Muasdale Surgery, Muasdale, Tarbert PA29 6XD Tel: 01583 421206 Fax: 01583 421220; Siavonga House, Muasdale, Tarbert PA29 6XD — MB ChB 1979 Glas.; MA (Distinc.) Swansea 1994; MRCGP 1983. Socs: BMA & Christian Med. Fell.sh. Prev: Med. Pract. Minbank Clinic Lusaka, Zambia; GP Exeter.

GOURLAY, Ralph Peter 24 Rhiwlas, Thornhill, Cardiff CF14 9AD — BMed 1986 Newc; BMed. Newc. 1986.

GOURLAY, Richard Grieve 8 Mid Road, Biggar ML12 6AW — MB ChB 1998 Glas.; MB ChB Glas 1998.

GOURLEY, Aileen Anne Medical Centre, Caledonian Road, Perth PH2 8HH Tel: 01738 628234 Fax: 01738 624945 — MB BS 1974 London; MB BS 1974 Lond; MRCS Eng LRCP Lond 1974. (London) GP Perth.

GOURLEY, Charles Mclaren Flat 5, 24 Westhall Gardens, Edinburgh EH10 4JQ — MB ChB 1994 Glas.

GOURLEY, David Galbraith (retired) Farm Office, Barton Meadows, Cerne Abbas, Dorchester DT2 7JS Tel: 01300 341336 Email: gourley@bartonmeadows.com — MB BS 1965 Lond.; MRCS Eng. LRCP Lond. 1965; DObst RCOG 1969. Prev: GP Cerne Abbas, Dorset.

GOURLEY, Patricia Elizabeth Mary 34 St Michaels Drive, Cupar KY15 5BS — MB ChB 1997 Glas.

GOUTA, Ezzedin Abdoulhadi Yosif 19 Shore Court, Shore Lane, Sheffield S10 3BW Tel: 0114 267 8084 — MB BS 1983 Garyounis; MB BS Garyounis, Libya 1983; MRCPI 1988.

GOUTAM, Pravin Kumar Houghton Regis Medical Centre, Peel Street, Houghton Regis, Dunstable LU5 5EZ Tel: 01582 866161 Fax: 01582 865483; 30 Bampton Road, Luton LU4 0DD — MB BS 1977 Lond.; BA Oxf. 1974. (Guy's Hospital)

GOUTCHER, Colin Mark Flat 1/R, 99 Oban Drive, Glasgow G20 6AA — MB ChB 1995 Glas.

GOVAN, Angela Jane 191 Booker Avenue, Liverpool L18 9TA — MB ChB 1969 Liverp.; MRCGP 1974; DObst RCOG 1971. Prev: Ho. Off. Roy. S.. Hosp. & Sefton Gen. Hosp. Liverp.

GOVAN, Graeme Castlehill Health Centre, Castlehill, Forres IV36 1QF Tel: 01309 672233; Cathkin, Nelson Road, Forres IV36 1DR Tel: 01309 672952 — MB ChB 1980 Dundee; MRCGP 1984; DRCOG 1982. (Dundee Univ. Med. Sch.) GP Trainer; Co-ordinator SHO Teachg. for Moray Vocational Train. Scheme. Socs: Highland Med. Soc. Inverness. Prev: Trainee GP Inverness VTS; Ho. Off. King's Cross Hosp. Dundee & Stracathro Hosp. Brechin.

GOVAN, James 96 Terregles Avenue, Glasgow G41 4PQ — LRCP LRCS 1949 Ed.; LRCP LRCS Ed. LRFPS Glas. 1949. Prev: Ho. Phys. Glas. Roy. Infirm.

GOVAN, Mr James Anthony Alistair Bishop's Square, Castle Hill, Farnham GU9 0AD Tel: 01252 712772 Fax: 01252 712625 Email: jgovan@doctors.org.uk — MB BS 1970 Lond.; FRCS Eng. 1978; MRCP (UK) 1972; MRCS Eng. LRCP Lond. 1970; FRCOphth 1990; DO Eng. 1977. (Guy's) Cons. Ophth. Surg. Frimley Pk. Hosp. & Farnham Hosp. Socs: FRCOphth; Roy. Soc. Med.; UK & Irel. Soc. Cataract & Refractive Surgs. Prev: Sen. Regist. Guy's Hosp. Lond.; Sen. Resid. Moorfields Eye Hosp. Lond.

GOVAN, Jonathan Robert Hillingdon Hospital, Pield Heath Road, Uxbridge UB8 3NN Tel: 01895 279266 Fax: 01895 279890 Email: jon.govan@120.hillingh_tr.nthames.nhs.uk; Belvedere, Baker's Wood, Denham, Uxbridge UB9 4LF Tel: 01895 832962 Fax: 01895 831301 Email: jon.@docgovan.demon.co.uk — MB BS Lond. 1966; FRCP Lond. 1988; MRCP (UK) 1970; MRCS Eng. LRCP Lond. 1966. (Guy's) Cons. Phys. Hillingdon & Harefield Hosps.; Hon. Clin. Tutor Char. Cross & W.m. Med. Sch. Socs: Brit. Thorac. Soc. Prev: Sen. Regist. St. Geo. Hosp. Sydney, Austral., Regist. (Med.) Wycombe Gen. Hosp.; SHO Roy. Sussex Co. Hosp. Brighton.

GOVARDHAN DAS, Kuthupady Flat 4-C Bellaway Homes, St Mary's Gardens, Upper Parliment St., Liverpool L8 1TE — MB BS 1986 Karnatak, India.

GOVE, Alasdair Roy West Street Surgery, 16 West Street, Newport PO30 1PR Tel: 01983 522198 Fax: 01983 524258 — MB BS 1981 Lond.; MRCP (UK) 1988; MRCGP 1988; DRCOG 1986.

GOVE, Mr John Robert William The Swan Surgery, Northgate St., Bury St Edmunds IP33 1HY Tel: 01284 750011 Fax: 01284 723565 Email: theswansurgery@dial.pipex.com; The Chestnuts, Brockley Road, Whepstead, Bury St Edmunds IP29 4TW Tel: 01284 735646 Email: thosegoves@aol.com — MB BS 1981 Lond.; MA Oxf. 1984; FRCS Glas. 1985. (Oxford University & St. Bartholomew's Hospital London) Prev: Regist. (Surg.) Lond. Hosp.; SHO (Paediat. & O & G) Chase Farm Hosp. Enfield.

GOVE, Roderick Ian Southampton University Hospitals Trust, Tremona Road, Shirley, Southampton SO16 4XY Tel: 01489 798964 Email: iangove@suht.swet.nhs.uk; 15 The Vale, Locks Heath, Southampton SO31 6NL Tel: 01489 577842 Email: ianrgove@rgove.freeserve.co.uk — MB BS 1977 Lond.; MD Lond. 1987; FRCP Lond. 1994; MRCP (UK) 1981. (Lond. Hosp. Med. Coll.) Cons. Elderly Care Med. Soton. Univ. Hosp. Trust & Soton. Community Servs. Trust. Socs: Brit. Geriat. Soc.

GOVENDEN, Vanunathan Furness General Hospital, Dalton Lane, Barrow-in-Furness LA14 4LF Tel: 01229 870870; Bank House, Sandside, Kirkby-in-Furness LA17 7UA — MB BCh BAO 1978 Dub.; BA, MB BCh BAO Dub. 1978; FRCA. 1987; FFA RCSI 1986. Cons. Anaesth. Furness Gen. Hosp. Cumbria.

GOVENDER, Suren 28 Beeches Road, Sutton SM3 9NA — MB BS 1998 Lond.; MB BS Lond 1998.

GOVER, David Edward Williton and Watchet Surgeries, Robert Street, Williton, Taunton TA4 4QE Tel: 01984 632701 Fax: 01984 633933; Ford Farm, Bicknoller, Taunton TA4 4EH Tel: 01984 656252 Email: d.gover@btinternet.com — BM BCh 1976 Oxf.; MA, BM BCh Oxf. 1976; FRCGP 1996, M 1981. (Oxf. & St. Thos.)

GOVER, Geoffrey (retired) Clare Cottage, 5 Orchard Close, Wedmore, Wedmore BS28 4DQ Tel: 01934 713932 Email: geoff.gover@lineone.net — MB BS 1954 Lond.; MRCS Eng. LRCP Lond. 1954. Prev: Regist. (Med.) Miller Gen. Hosp. Greenwich.

GOVER, Pamela Ann c/o District General Hospital, Kings Drive, Eastbourne BN21 2UD — MB ChB 1969 Manch.; FRCP Lond. 1991; MRCP (UK) 1973; FRCPath 1988, M 1976. Cons. Phys. Haemat. E.bourne Dist. Gen. Hosp. Prev: Lect. (Haemat.) St. Thos. Hosp. Lond.; Regist. (Haemat.) St. Geo. Hosp. Lond.; SHO (Rheum.) Middlx. Hosp. Lond.

GOVER, Shirley Margaret Williton and Watchet Surgeries, Robert Street, Williton, Taunton TA4 4QE Tel: 01984 632701 Fax: 01984 633933; Ford, Bicknoller, Taunton TA4 4EH Tel: 01984 656252 — MB BS 1977 Lond.; DCH RCP Lond. 1982. Prev: Clin. Med. Off. (Community Paediat.) Som. HA.

GOVERNOR, Ian Stewart, Col. late RAMC (retired) Liddington Cottage, Badbury, Swindon SN4 0EU Tel: 01793 740480 Fax: 01793 740480 Email: lidcot@tinyworld.co.uk — MB BS 1958 Lond.; FRCOG 1982; DTM & H RCP Lond. 1964. Cons. O & G HM Armed forces. Prev: Cons. O & G P.ss Alexandra Hosp. Wroughton.

GOVES, John Raymond The Charlbury Medical Centre, Enstone Road, Charlbury, Chipping Norton OX7 3PQ Tel: 01608 810210 Fax: 01608 811636 — MB BS 1977 Lond.; MRCGP 1981; DCOG 1980; DFFP 1998. (St. Bart.) Socs: Oxf. Med. Soc.

GOVEWALLA, Pauras 87 Northiam, London N12 7HL — MB BS 1994 Lond.

GOVIER, Christine Beatrice Ellen (retired) 159 Old Winton Road, Andover SP10 2DR — MB BS 1980 Lond.; DRCOG 1982. Prev: GP Andover.

GOVIER, Elizabeth Ann 20 Castle Road, Sandgate, Folkestone CT20 3AG Tel: 01303 40570 — MB BS 1956 Lond.; MRCS Eng. LRCP Lond. 1956. (Roy. Free)

GOVIER, Jayne Laura 10 Russell Court, Woodstock Road, Oxford OX2 6JH Tel: 01865 311736 — MB BS 1987 Lond.; DA (UK) 1992; DRCOG 1991. Regist. Rotat. (Anaesth.) Dudley Rd. & Qu. Eliz. Hosps. Birm. Prev: SHO (Anaesth.) Qu. Eliz. Hosp. W. Midl.; SHO (Anaesth.) MusGr. Pk. Hosp. Som.

GOVIER, Katie Louise 12 Burcot Park, Burcot, Abingdon OX14 3DH — BM 1997 Soton. SHO (Paediat.) PeterBoro. Dist. Hosp. Prev: Ho. Off. (Surg.) Roy. United Hosp. Bath; Ho. Off. (Med.) Roy. Bournemouth Hosp.

GOVIND, Abha 12 Aisne Road, Deepcut, Camberley GU16 6SS Tel: 01252 836634 — MB BS 1982 Delhi; MRCOG 1990; DGO 1984. Cons. O & G N. Middlx. Hosp. Socs: BMA; Brit. Midl.s Obst. & Gyn. Soc.; Brit. Soc. Colpos. & Cerv. Path. Prev: Sen. Regist. (O & G) Birm. Wom.'s Hosp. Edgbaston Birm.; Sen. Regist. Stoke-on-Trent; Research Regist. Stoke-on-Trent.

GOW, Alistair Cameron 17 Monument Road, Ayr KA7 2RL Tel: 01292 262668 — MB ChB 1950 Glas.; DObst RCOG 1954. (Glas.) GP Clin. Asst. Ophth. Heathfield Hosp. Ayr. Prev: Sen. Ho. Off. O & G Bellshill Matern. Hosp.; Ho. Surg. & Ho. Phys. W. Infirm. Glas.; Ho. Surg. Roy. Hosp. Sick Childr. Glas.

GOW, Arthur Henry Ferguson (retired) 6 Downs Court, Meads St., Eastbourne BN20 7RJ — MRCS Eng. LRCP Lond. 1941. Hon. Cons. Chest Phys. E.bourne Gp. Hosps. Prev: Med. Off. Ch. of Scotl. Mission Hosp. Kwazulu.

GOW, David Peter Flat 2, 37 Clyde Road, Manchester M20 2JJ — MB ChB 1994 Liverp.

GOW, George Argyle House, Lady Lawson St., Edinburgh EH3 9 Tel: 0131 222 5584 Fax: 0131 222 5720; 15 Avon Place, Edinburgh EH4 6RE Tel: 0131 317 8994 — MB ChB 1980 Ed.; BSc (Med. Sci.) Ed. 1977. (Ed.) Med. Advisor Benefits Agency Med. Servs. Edin. Prev: GP Grangemouth; Trainee GP Falkirk Roy. Infirm. VTS.

GOW, Isobel Alexandra St Michaels Hospital, Aylsham, Norwich NR11 6NA; 394 Unthank Road, Norwich NR4 7QE — MB ChB 1982 Birm.; MRCGP 1986; DRCOG 1986. Clin. Med. Off. (Geriat. & Rehabil.) St. Michaels Hosp. Norwich. Prev: GP Birm.

GOW, James Gordon (retired) (cons. rooms), Lourdes Private Hospital, Greenbank Road, Liverpool L18 1HQ Tel: 0151 733 7123 — MB ChB Liverp. 1940; MD Liverp. 1962, ChM 1963; FRCS Eng. 1948. JP. Prev: Cons. Urol. BRd.green Hosp. Liverp.

GOW, Mairi (retired) 29 Ballifeary Road, Inverness IV3 5PJ — MB ChB 1951 Aberd.

GOW, Phyllis Clare (retired) Denovo, 27 Addington Road, Sanderstead, Croydon CR2 8RF Tel: 020 8651 6195 — MB Calcutta 1946.

GOW, Rona Lucea 2/1, 60 Ashley St., Glasgow G3 6HW — MB ChB 1997 Glas.

GOW, Winifred Mary Horse Shoe, Bar Road, Curbar, Sheffield S30 1YB — MB ChB 1943 Sheff. (Sheff.)

GOWA, S H N Trinity Street Surgery, 124 Trinity Street, Huddersfield HD1 4DT Tel: 01484 535152 Fax: 01484 532311 — MB BS 1975 Nagpur; MB BS 1975 Nagpur.

GOWA, Shoshanna Beckside Road Surgery, 47 Beckside Road, Bradford BD7 2JN Tel: 01274 576035 — MB BS 1970 Nagpur. (Nagpur) GP Bradford, W. Yorks.

GOWAN, Antonia Sonja Olivia 21 Sudbrook Gardens, Richmond TW10 7DD Tel: 020 8940 7917 Email: antoniagowen@hotmail.com — MB BS 1998 Lond.; MB BS Lond 1998. (St Georges Hospital Medical School) Roy. Perth Hosp. SHO. Prev: St Geo.s PRHO Med.; Kingston Hosp. PRHO Surg.

GOWANS, Gordon Tait 9 Queen's Gardens, Edinburgh EH4 2DA — MB ChB 1992 Manch.

GOWANS, Ian Duncan 9 Queens Gardens, Blackhall, Edinburgh EH4 2DA — MB ChB 1993 Ed.

GOWANS, Sir James (Learmonth), CBE (retired) 75 Cumnor Hill, Oxford OX2 9HX Tel: 01865 862304 Fax: 01865 865548 — MB BS (Hons.) Lond. 1947; DPhil, MA Oxf. 1953, BA (1st cl. Hons. Physiol.) 1948; Hon. LLD Glas. 1988; Hon. DSc Chicago 1971, Birm. 1978, Rochester NY 1987; Hon. MD Soton. 1987; Hon. MD Ed. 1979; FRCP Lond. 1975; Hon. ScD Yale 1966; Hon MD Sheff. 1999. Hon. Fell. Exeter Coll. Oxf. 1983, Lincoln Coll. Oxf. 1984 & St. Catherine's Coll Oxf 1987; Mem. Counc. Managem. St. Christopher's Hospice; Fell. King's Coll. Lond. Prev: Sec. Gen. Human Frontier Sci. Program Strasbourg, France.

GOWANS, Jennifer The Surgery, Chestnut Walk, Stratford-upon-Avon CV37 6HU — MB BS 1985 Lond.; DFFP 2000; BA (Hons.) Camb. 1982; MRCGP 1989; DRCOG 1988. GP Princip. Stratford on Avon; GP Stratford on Avon Retainer Scheme. Socs: BMA; Roy. Coll. of Gen. Practitioners. Prev: GP Salisbury Retainer Scheme; Trainee GP Overton.

GOWANS, Maureen New Park Medical Practice, 163 Robertson Road, Dunfermline KY12 0BL Tel: 01383 629200 Fax: 01383 629203; 19 Old Kirk Road, Dunfermline KY12 7SX — MB ChB 1971 Ed.; BSc (Med. Sci.) Ed. 1968. MB ChB 1971; DObst RCOG 1975; DCH RCPS Glas. 1975. (Edinburgh) Prev: SHO (Paediat.) Vict. Hosp. Kirkcaldy; SHO (Obst.) Forth Pk. Matern. Hosp. Kirkcaldy; Trainee Gen. Pract. W. Fife Vocational Train. Scheme.

GOWANS, William John Mytton Oak Medical Practice, Racecourse Lane, Shrewsbury SY3 5LZ Tel: 01743 362223 Fax: 01743 244 5811; Cadogen House, 53 The Mount, Shrewsbury SY3 8PP Tel: 01743 362223 — MB 1984 Camb.; BChir 1983; MRCP (UK) 1986; MRCGP 1989; DRCOG 1988; Cert. Family Plann. JCC 1989. GP Shrewsbury. Prev: SHO (O & G) Roy. Shrewsbury Hosp. Lond.; SHO (Paediat.) Roy. Hosp. Shrewsbury; Regist. (Gen. Med.) Watford Gen. Hosp.

GOWAR, Mr John Penrose The Priory Hospital, Priory Road, Edgbaston, Birmingham B5 7UG Tel: 0121 440 2323 Fax: 0121 440 0804; 48 Worcester Road, Hagley, Stourbridge DY9 0LD — MB BS Lond. 1963; FRCS Eng. 1971; FRCS Ed. 1971; MRCS Eng. LRCP Lond. 1963; DObst RCOG 1967. (St. Thos.) Socs: Brit. Assn. Plastic Surg.; Brit. Burns Assn.; Birm. Medico-Legal Soc. Prev: Sen. Regist. (Plastic Surg.) Hosp. Sick Childr. Gt. Ormond St. & St. Thos. Hosp. Lond.; Regist. (Gen. Surg.) Roy. Hosp. Wolverhampton; Formerly Cons Plastic Surg Burns Unit Selly Oak Hosp Univ Hosp Birm. NHS Trust.

GOWDA, Chandra Keerthi Chestnut Cottage, Garlands, Carlisle CA1 3SU — MB BS 1997 Lond.

GOWDA, Rajesh 128 Boothroyd Lane, Dewsbury WF13 2LW — MB ChB 1995 Birm.; ChB Birm. 1995. SHO (Psychiat. with Rehabil.) All St.s Hosp. Birm. Prev: SHO (Old Age Psychiat.) Solihull; SHO (Psychiat.) All St.s Birm.

GOWDA, Ravish 21A Osborne Road, Jesmond, Newcastle upon Tyne NE2 2AH Tel: 0191 212 1330 Fax: 0017079888738 Email: vari.gowda@virgin.net; 128 Boothroyd Lane, Dewsbury WF13 2LW Tel: 01924 510994 — MB BS 1991 Newc.; MRCP (UK) 1994; DRCOG 1996; DCH 1997; MRCGP 1998. (Newcastle) GP Regist. Greystoke Surg. Morpeth. Prev: GP Regist. Boldon Sunderland; SHO (Paediat.) Sunderland Dist. Gen. Hosp.; SHO (O & G) Jersey Gen. Hosp.

GOWDA, Simon Tal-y-Bont Surgery, Station Road, Pontardulais, Swansea SA4 1TL Tel: 01792 882368 — MB BCh 1998 Wales.

GOWENLOCK, Alan John 130 Ravensbourne Avenue, Shortlands, Bromley BR2 0AX — MB BChir 1983 Camb.

GOWER, Andrew 3 Hesleyside Road, South Wellefield, Whitley Bay NE25 9HB — MB BS 1990 Newc.

GOWER, Ann Jacquelyn (retired) 53 Fursby Avenue, Finchley, London N3 1PJ Tel: 020 8346 1627 — MB ChB 1963 Glas.; DCH RCPS Glas. 1966. Prev: Clin. Med. Off. Pk.side NHS Trust.

GOWER, Gareth Emlyn 28 Bryn-y-Mor, Burry Port SA16 0LA — MRCS Eng. LRCP Lond. 1968; DObst RCOG 1971. Socs: BMA.

GOWER, Mr John (retired) 3 Holm Oak Close, Bexhill-on-Sea TN39 3SF — MB BS 1950 Lond.; FRCS Ed. 1976; MRCS Eng. LRCP Lond. 1950; MRCGP 1971; DObst RCOG 1952. Prev: Clin. Asst. (Gastroenterol. Endoscopy) Conquest Hosp. Hastings.

GOWER, John David Goronwy Hendford Lodge Medical Centre, 74 Hendford, Yeovil BA20 1UJ Tel: 01935 470200 Fax: 01935 470202 — MB BS 1969 Lond.; MRCS Eng. LRCP Lond. 1969; DObst RCOG 1971.

GOWER, Norman David (retired) 141 Hyperion Road, Stourton, Stourbridge DY7 6SJ Tel: 01384 377658 — MB BS 1949 Lond.; MD Lond. 1962; MRCS Eng. LRCP Lond. 1949; FRCPath 1975, M 1964.

GOWER, Peter Edward Charing Cross Hospital, Fulham Palace Road, London W6 8RF Tel: 020 8846 1753 Fax: 020 8846 7569; 2 West Drive, Cheam, Sutton SM2 7NA Tel: 020 8661 9578 — BSc Lond. 1959, MD 1972, MB BS 1963; FRCP Lond. 1977, M 1966; MRCS Eng. LRCP Lond. 1962. (Lond. Hosp.) Cons. Phys. Char. Cross Hosp. Fulham; Examr. Med. Univ. Lond. Socs: Med. Research Soc.; Eur. Renal Assn.; Renal Assn.

GOWER, Mr Richard Lewis Longfield Consulting Rooms, 196 Stow Hill, Newport NP20 4HB — MB BS 1970 Lond.; FRCS Eng. 1976; MRCS Eng. LRCP Lond. 1970.

GOWER, Sean Graham Station Road Surgery, 24 Station Road, Long Buckby, Northampton NN6 7QB Tel: 01327 842360 Fax: 01327 842302 — MB BS 1989 Lond.; MRCGP 1993; DRCOG 1991. (Roy. Free Hosp.) Prev: Trainee GP N.ampton Gen. Hosp. VTS; Ho. Surg. P.ss Margt. Hosp. RAF Halton; Ho. Phys. N.ampton Gen. Hosp.

GOWER, Simon Nicholas Anaesthetic Dept Castle Mill Hospital, Castle Road, Cottingham HU16 5JQ Tel: 01482 875875; 2 Eppleworth Road, Cottingham HU16 5YE — MB BS 1986 Lond.; DA (UK) 1988; FRCA 1993; BSc Lond 1983. (Guys Hospital) Cons. in Cardiothoracic Anaesth. & IC, Castle Hill Hosp. Prev: Sen. Regist. Leeds Gen. Infirm.; Regist. (Anaesth.) Kent & Canterbury Hosp.

GOWER-THOMAS, Kathleen Lorna Radiology Dept, Royal Glamorgan Hospital, Llantrisant, Pontyclun CF72 8XR; Tel: 029 2075 0282 — MB BCh 1985 Wales; BSc 1980 Wales; FRCR 1991. Cons. Radiol. Roy. Glam. Gen. HospMid Glam. & BrE. Test Wales Cardiff. Prev: Sen. Regist. (Radiol.) Univ. Hosp. Wales Cardiff.

***GOWERS, Christopher James Dafydd** 21 Donnington Square, Newbury RG14 1PJ — BM BS 1997 Nottm.; BMedSci Nottm. 1995.

GOWERS, Lesley Elizabeth Parklands Hospital, Aldermaston Road, Basingstoke RG24 9RH; 94 Hartsbourne Road, Reading RG6 5SJ Tel: 0118 987 4510 — BM BS 1985 Nottm.; MRC Psych. Staff Grade (Psychiat.) Pk.lands Hosp. Basingstoke.

GOWERS, Philip Shirley Downing (retired) Long Ridge, Derwent Lane, Hathersage, Hope Valley, Sheffield S32 1AS Tel: 01433 650265 — MB ChB 1941 Sheff.; MRCGP 1952.

GOWERS, Professor Simon Geoffrey Pine Lodge YPC, 79 Liverpool Road, Chester CH2 1AW Tel: 01244 364776 Fax: 01244 364778 — MB BS 1980 Lond.; MPhil Lond. 1987, BSc 1977; FRCPsych 1996, M 1984. (St. Geo.) Prof. Adolesc. Psychiat. Univ. Liverp.; Hon. Cons. (Adolesc. Psychiat.) W. Chesh. NHS Trust. Prev: Sen. Lect. (Child & Adolesc. Psychiat.) Univ. Manch.; Sen. Regist. (Child Adolesc. Psychiat.) Roy. Manch. Childr. Hosp.; Lect. (Hon. Sen. Regist.) Psychiat. St. Geo. Hosp. Med. Sch. Lond.

GOWING, Katherine Louise — MB BS 1988 Lond.; MRCGP 1992.

GOWING, Noel Frank Collett 258 Coombe Lane, West Wimbledon, London SW20 0RW — MRCS Eng. LRCP Lond. 1941; MD Lond. 1948, MB BS 1946; FRCPath 1964. (St. Geo.) Emerit. Prof. Tumour Path. Inst. Cancer Research Roy Cancer Hosp. Socs: Path. Soc. Gt. Brit.; (Ex-Pres.) Assn. Clin. Paths. Prev: Examr. in Morbid Anat. RCPath.; Cons. in Morbid Anat. & Histopath. Roy. Marsden Hosp. Lond.; Hon. Cons. Pathol. St. Geo. Hosp.

GOWLAND, Deryck Newton 1/19 Cranley Gardens, London SW7 3DB Tel: 020 7835 1231; 1/19 Cranley Gardens, London SW7 3BD Tel: 020 7835 1231 — MB BS 1970 Lond.; MRCS Eng. LRCP Lond. 1970; DRCOG 1976; DA (UK) 1972.

GOWLAND, Eric (retired) 88 Borrowdale Avenue, Gatley, Cheadle SK8 4QQ Tel: 0161 282 5465 — MB BS 1959 Lond.; PhD A.N.U. 1967; MRCS Eng. LRCP Lond. 1959; FRCPath 1981, M 1969. Prev: Cons. Chem. Path. S. Manch. Univ. Hosps. NHS Trust & Christie Hosp. NHS Trust.

GOWLAND, Maureen Rita 34 Albert Road, Heaton, Bolton BL1 5HF — MB ChB 1968 Birm.; FRCR 1976; FRCP Ed. 1991; MRCP (UK) 1986; DMRD Eng. 1972. Cons. Radiol. Bolton HA; Postgrad. Med. Tutor Bolton. Socs: Hon. Sec. Brit. Inst. Radiol.; Counc. Manch. Med. Soc.

GOWLAND, Stephen Norman 15 Braeworth Close, Yarm TS15 9SB — MB BS 1991 Lond. (St. Geo. Hosp. Med. Sch.) GP (Princip.) Coulby Med. Practical Middlesbrough. Prev: SHO Rotat. (Surg.) Walsgrave Hosp. Coventry; SHO (ENT Surg.) Fairfield Gen. Hosp. Bury; SPO GP Train. Scheme Bury.

GOWLETT, Sarah Jane Main X-Ray, Northern General Hospital, Herries Road, Sheffield S5 7AU; 46 White Ox Way, Penrith CA11 8QP Tel: 0114 268 5289, 01768 891272 Email: sarah.gowlett@talk21.com — FRCR 2000 Nov.; MB BChir. Camb. 1993. (Addenbrookes) Cons., Radiol., Sheff. Teachg. Hosps. NHS Trust, Sheff. Prev: Specialist Regist. (Radiol.) Roy. Vict. Infirm. Newc.

GOWLING, George Eric Ardenlea, 124 Greenock Road, Bishopton PA7 5AS — MB ChB 1970 Glas.; MRCP (U.K.) 1974; DCH RCPS Glas. 1973; DObst RCOG 1972.

GOWRIBALAN, Ratnam Department of Obstetrics & Gynaecology, Grimsby District General Hospital, Scartho Road, Grimsby DN33 2BA — MB BS 1978 Sri Lanka.

GOWRIE MOHAN, Shanmugasundaram 38 Shaftesbury Avenue, Norwood Green, Southall UB2 4HJ Tel: 020 8571 1344 — MB BS 1983 Sri Lanka; FCAnaesth 1991; DA (UK) 1988. Sen. Regist. (Anaesth.) Hammersmith Hosp. Lond. Socs: Fell. Roy. Coll. Anaesth.; Assn. Anaesth. Prev: Regist (Anaesth.) Luton & Dunstable Hosp.; Regist. (Anaesth.) Basingstoke Dist. Gen. Hosp. & W. Middlx. Univ. Hosp.; SHO (Anaesth.) Old Ch. Hosp. Romford.

GOY, Jennifer Anne Anaesthetic Department, Stoke Mandeville Hospital, Mandeville Road, Aylesbury HP21 8AL Tel: 01296 315000 — MB BS London 1970; FRCA 1975. (Middlx.) Cons. Anaesth. Stoke Mandeville Hosp. Aylesbury. Socs: Assn. Paediat. Anaesth; BMA; Assn. Anaesth. Prev: Sen. Regist. Hosp. Sick Childr. Gt. Ormond St., Univ. Coll. Hosp. & Nat. Heart Hosp. Lond.

GOYAL, Aaliya Doctors Mess, Dewsbury & District Hospital, Healds Rd, Dewsbury WF13 4HS — MB ChB 1997 Leeds.

GOYAL, Amrit Lal The Manors, Elgin Drive, Wallasey CH45 7PR — MB BS 1972 Punjab; MB BS Punjabi 1972.

GOYAL, Arun Kumar The Health Centre, Wallsgreen Road, Cardenden, Lochgelly KY5 0JE Tel: 01592 722445 — MB BS 1970 Punjabi. (Punjabi) GP Lochgelly, Fife.

GOYAL, Mina The Doctors House, 40 Cameron Road, Seven Kings, Ilford IG3 8ZF Tel: 020 8590 0282 Fax: 020 8599 0282; Tel: 020 8590 0282 Fax: 020 8599 0282 — MB BS 1987 Lond.; MRCGP 1992; DRCOG 1991; DFFP 2001. (The Royal London hospital, UL)

GOYAL, Poonam Iona, Green Lane, Rochdale Road, Halifax HX2 7JJ Tel: 01422 51831 — MB BS 1973 Delhi. (Lady Hardinge Med. Coll.) Clin. Med. Off. (Community Med.) Calderdale AHA.

GOYAL, Ratan Lal Agrawal The Surgery, 53 Eastbrooks Place, Chalvedon, Basildon SS13 3QS Tel: 01268 553455 Fax: 01268 556809; 15 Furrow Felde, Basildon SS16 5HB Tel: 01268 521035 — MB BS 1961 Bihar. (Darbhanga Med. Coll. Laheriasarai) Prev: Regist. (Orthop. & Accid.) Roy. Alexandra Infirm. Paisley & S.end Gen. Hosp. Essex; SHO (Orthop.) Mt.gould Hosp. Plymouth; SHO (Gen. Surg.) Medway & Gravesend Gp. Hosps.

GOYAL, Sudeshna Tel: 0151 228 4811; Pragati, 22 Winchester Close, off School Lane, Woolton, Liverpool L25 7YD Tel: 0151 486 0392 Email: sue.goyal@rlch_tr.nwest.nhs.uk — MB BS 1969 All India Inst. Med. Scs. New Delhi; MCOphth 1991; DRCOG 1978; DO Eng. 1971. (All India Inst. Med. Scs. New Delhi) Assoc. Specialist (Ophth.) Alder Hey Childr. Hosp. Liverp. Prev: Clin. Med. Off. (Ophth. Sch. Health) Liverp. HA; Regist. (Ophth.) Alder Hey Childr. Hosp. Liverp.

GOYAL, Surinder Kumar Queens Road Surgery, 252 Queens Road, Halifax HX1 4NJ Tel: 01422 330636; Iona, Green Lane, Rochdale Road, Halifax HX2 7JJ Tel: 01422 51831 — MB BS 1968 Punjab; MB BS Punjabi 1968. (Govt. Med. Coll. Patiala)

GOYDER, Elizabeth Claire Manor House, Old London Road, Capel St Mary, Ipswich IP9 2JU — MB BChir 1990 Camb.; MRCGP 1994.

GOYDER, John Francis (retired) Apperley Mount, Apperley Lane, Rawdon, Leeds LS19 6BJ Tel: 0113 250 3054 — MB BS 1951 Lond.; MRCS Eng. LRCP Lond. 1951. Prev: GP Leeds.

GOYDER, Nicholas Peter Air Balloon Surgery, Kenn Road, St George, Bristol BS5 7PD Tel: 0117 909 9914 Fax: 0117 908 6660; Rosemary, 20 Northumbria Drive, Henleaze, Bristol BS9 4HP Tel: 0117 962 4126 — MB ChB 1986 Bristol; MRCGP 1991; T (GP) 1991; Cert. Family Plann. JCC 1990; DRCOG 1990. (Bristol)

GOYDER, Patricia Angela (retired) Apperley Mount, Apperley Lane, Rawdon, Leeds LS19 6BJ Tel: 0113 250 3054 — MB BCh BAO 1953 Dub.; MA Dub. 1965. Prev: Dent. Anaesth. Bradford Community Health.

GOYNE, Raymond Leslie Portslade Health Centre, Church Road, Portslade, Brighton BN41 1LX Tel: 01273 422525 — MB ChB 1957 Liverp.

GOZALI, Sukardi 6 Walton Court, 51 Fairfax Road, London NW6 4EN Email: sgozali@doctors.org.uk — MB BS 1988 Lond. (UCH, London)

GOZZARD, Alicia Priory Lane Surgery, Priory Lane, Prestatyn LL19 9DH Tel: 01745 854496; Craig Dulas, Rhyd-Y-Foel Road, Llanddulas, Abergele LL22 8EG Tel: 01492 516418 — MB ChB 1977 Birm.; MSc 2000 Birm.; DCH NUI 1980; DRCOG 1979. Rotat. SHO E. Birm. Hosp. Prev: Ho. Surg. E. Birm. Hosp.; Ho. Phys. N. Staffs. Roy. Infirm. Stoke-on-Trent.

GOZZARD, Charles 3 Riverdene Place, Dell Wharf, Bitterne Park, Southampton SO18 1UG — MB BS 1994 Lond.; BSc (Hons.) Physiol. Lond. 1991. Demonst. (Anat.) Qu. Mary & W.field Coll. Lond.; Resid. Med. Off. Pk.side Hosp. Wimbledon. Prev: Ho. Phys. S.end Gen. Hosp.; Ho. Surg. Roy. Lond. Hosp.

GOZZARD, David Ian Department of Haematology, Ysbyty Glan Clwyd, Bodelwyddan, Rhyl LL18 5UJ Tel: 01745 583910; Craig Dulas, Rhyd-Y-Foel Road, Llanddulas, Abergele LL22 8EG Tel: 01492 516418 — MB ChB 1977 Birm.; MRCP (UK) 1980; MRCPath 1986. Cons. Haemat. Glan Clwyd Hosp.

GOZZARD, John Gilbert Manston Surgery, 72-76 Austhorpe Road, Leeds LS15 8DZ Tel: 0113 264 5455 Fax: 0113 232 6181 — MB ChB 1966 Leeds. (Leeds) Prev: Ho. Phys. & Ho. Surg. St. Jas. Hosp. Leeds.

GRABARSKA-KREISS, Beata Kamilla Hanscombe House Surgery, 52A St. Andrew Street, Hertford SG14 1JA Tel: 01992 582025 — MRCS Eng. LRCP Lond. 1990. SHO (ENT) Whipps Cross Hosp. Lond.; SHO (Paediat.) Wexha Ph Hosp. Slough. Prev: SHO (A & E) Qu. Eliz. Hosp. Welwyn Gdn. City; Ho. Off. (Surg.) Orsett Hosp. Essex; Ho. Off. (Med.) Wexham Pk. Hosp. Slough.

GRABAU, Wolfgang Joachim James Paget Hospital, Lowestoft Road, Gorleston, Great Yarmouth NR31 6LA Tel: 01493 452452 Fax: 01493 452052; Storrs, Marsh Road, Halvergate, Norwich NR13 3QB Tel: 01493 700272 Fax: As above — MB ChB Liverp. 1966; FRCP Lond. 1988; MRCP (U.K.) 1970. Cons. Phys. & Cardiol. James Paget Hosp. Gt. Yarmouth Norf. Prev: Cons. Phys. Gt. Yarmouth & Waveney Health Dist.; Sen. Med. Regist. Guy's Hosp. Lond.; Med. Regist. Nat. Heart Hosp. Lond.

GRABCZYNSKA, Sophie Anne Watford General Hospital, Vicarage Road, Watford WD18 0HB — MB BS 1990 Lond. SHO (Gen. Med.) Watford Gen. Hosp. Prev: SHO (Gen. Med.) Chelsea & W.m. Hosp. Lond.

GRABHAM, Sir Anthony Herbert (retired) Rothesay House, 56 Headlands, Kettering NN15 6DG Tel: 01536 513299 — MB BS Durh. 1953; FRCS Eng. 1960. Chairm. BMA Servs.; Governor PPP Healthcare Med. Trust; Chairm. BMJ Comm. Prev: Chairm. Counc. (Chairm. CCHMS) BMA.

GRABHAM, Mr John Anthony 22 Southcliffe Road, Southampton SO14 6GE Tel: 02380 634695 — MB ChB 1988 Leic.; FRCS Glas. 1993.

GRABHAM, Ruth Elisabeth Newbridge Surgery, 129 Newbridge Hill, Bath BA1 3PT Tel: 01225 425807 Fax: 01225 447776; 29 Richmond Place, Lansdown, Bath BA1 5PZ — MB BS 1987 Lond.; MRCGP 1992; DRCOG 1990. (Char. Cross. & Westm.) Partner Newbridge Surg.; Clin. Asst. Cardiol. Roy. United Hosp.; Roy. United Hosp., Bath. Socs: BMA. Prev: SHO (Paediat. & Psychiat.) W. Middlx. Univ. Hosp. Twickenham; SHO (O & G) Char. Cross Hosp. Lond.; SHO (A & E) Char. Cross Hosp. Lond.

GRABINAR, John The Surgery, 80 Torridon Road, London SE6 1RB Tel: 020 8698 5281 Fax: 020 8695 1841 — BM BCh 1968 Oxf.; MA Oxf. 1968; MRCGP 1980; DCH Eng. 1972; DObst RCOG 1971. (Univ. Coll. Hosp.) Local Civil Serv. Med. Examr. Crematorium Ref., Lewisham. Socs: BMA. Prev: SHO (Cas.) Lewisham Hosp.; Ho. Phys. Univ. Coll. Hosp. (St. Pancras); Ho. Phys. (Paediat.) Brook Gen. Hosp. Woolwich.

GRABS, Anthony John c/o McKay, 3 Tigh-Na-Mara Court, Wemyss Bay Road, Wemyss Bay PA18 6AE — MB BS 1985 Queensland; FRACS 1993. Clin. Lect. (Surg.) Glas. Roy. Infirm.

GRACE, Andrew Ashley Papworth Hospital, Papworth Everard, Cambridge CB3 8RE Tel: 01480 364350 Fax: 01480 364799 Email: ag@mole.bio.cam.ac.uk; Department Biochemistry, University of Cambridge, Tennis Court Road, Cambridge CB2 1QW Tel: 01223 333631/333630 Fax: 01233 333345 — MB BS 1983 Lond.; FRCP Lond.1999; FACC 1998; PhD (Hons.) Camb. 1993; MRCP (UK) 1986. (St. Thos.) Brit. Heart Foundat. Sen. Research Fell. Univ. Camb.; Hon. Cons. (Cardiol.) Papworth & Addenbrooke's Hosp. Camb. Socs: Fell. Amer. Coll. Cardiol.; Amer. Heart Assn. Counc.s; Brit. Cardiac Soc. Prev: Fulbright Sen. Research Schol. Univ. Calif. San Diego USA; BHF Clin. Scientist Research Fell. Univ. of Camb.; Regist. (Cardiol.) Papworth Hosp. Camb.

GRACE, Mr Andrew Ronald Holmes Department of Otolaryngology, York District Hospital, Wigginton Road, York YO31 8HE Tel: 01904 631313; The Granary, Overton, York YO30 1YL — MB BS 1978 Lond.; FRCS Eng. 1984. Cons. Ent. Surg. York Dist. Hosp. Prev: Sen. Regist. Addenbrooke's Hosp. Camb. & Roy. Nat. Throat Nose & Ear Hosp.; SHO (ENT) Addenbrooke's Hosp. Camb.; Regist. (ENT) Roy. Nat. Throat Nose & Ear Hosp. Lond.

GRACE, Archibald Hew 8 Minsted Square, Cooden, Bexhill-on-Sea TN39 3BQ — MRCS Eng. LRCP Lond. 1930; FFA RCS Eng. 1954; DA Eng. 1947. (St. Bart.) Hon. Cons. (Anaesth.) Hastings Gp. Hosps. Socs: Assn. Anaesths. Gt. Brit. Prev: Maj. RAMC, Specialist Anaesth.; Specialist Anaesth. EMS; Cons. Anaesth. Hastings Gp. Hosps.

GRACE, Mr David Leslie Chase Farm Hospitals NHS Trust, The Ridgeway, Enfield EN2 8JL Tel: 020 8366 6600; 22 Dryden Road, Bush Hill Park, Enfield EN1 2PP Tel: 020 8360 2700 Fax: 020 8360 2700 — MB ChB 1975 Leeds; FRCS Eng. 1979. p/t Cons. Orthop. Surg. Chase Farm Hosp. Enfield. Middlx. Prev: Sen. Regist. (Orthop.) St. Bart. Hosp. Lond.

GRACE, Declan Altnagelvin Hospital Health & Social Services Trust, Glenshane Road, Londonderry BT47 6SB Tel: 028 7134 5171 Fax: 028 7161 1222 — MB BCh BAO 1986 Belf.; FFA RCSI 1990; MD Belf. 1995; Dip. ICM RCSI 1998. (Queens University of Belfast) Cons. Anaesth. Altnagelvin Hosp. Health & Social Servs. Trust Derry. Socs: Intens. Care Soc. Irel.; Assn. Anaesth. GB & Irel.; N. Irel. Soc. Anaesth. Prev: Overseas Fell. Anaesth. Roy. Perth Hosp.; Sen. Tutor (Anaesth.) Qu. Univ. Belf.

GRACE, Donna Maria 19 Harecastle Close, Hayes UB4 9RE — MB ChB 1987 Sheff.

GRACE, Janet Barbara Department of Old Age Psychiatry, Institute for the Health of the Elderly, Newcastle General Hospital, West Road, Newcastle upon Tyne NE4 6BE Tel: 0191 273 6666 Fax: 0191 273 1156 Email: j.b.grace@ncl.ac.uk — BM BS 1991 Nottm.; MRCPsych 1997. Lect. Old Age Psychiat.; Hon. Specialist Regist.

GRACE, John Francis The Surgery, Miller Way, Wainscott, Rochester ME2 4LP Tel: 01634 717450; Alexander House, School Lane, Higham, Rochester ME1 1YW — MB BS 1973 Lond.; MRCS Eng. LRCP Lond. 1973; MRCGP 1978. Prev: Ho. Off. Guy's Hosp. Lond.; SHO Med. Medway Dist. Hosp. Gillingham.

GRACE, Miss Katie Louise Russell Woodhall, Woodhall Lane, Ascot SL5 9QW Tel: 01344 621312 Fax: 01344 620399 — MB BS 1994 Lond.; BSc Lond. 1991; FRCS (Eng.) 1998. (St Thomas' Hospital) Research Regist. Bristol Roy. Infirm. Socs: MDU; GMA; BMA. Prev: Sen. SHO (Gen. Surg.) Frenchay Hosp.; SHO (Gen. Surg.) Rotat. Bristol Roy. Infirm.; (A & E) St Thomas'.

GRACE, Kevin Roger Cullums Cottage, Whepstead Road, Horringer, Bury St Edmunds IP29 5PU — MB BS 1968 Lond.; DCH Eng. 1971.

GRACE, Lilla Marguerite Vandyk, Amberley, Stroud GL5 5AT — MB BCh BAO 1929 Dub. Prev: Ho. Surg. Adelaide Hosp. Dub.

GRACE, Pauline May 63 Kenmore Road, Sale M33 4LG — MB ChB 1980 Manch.; MRCP (UK) 1983; MRCGP 1986; DRCOG 1986.

GRACE, Philip Henry (retired) Cae Maes Mawr, Llanddona, Beaumaris LL58 8UN Tel: 01248 810752 — MB ChB 1950 Liverp. Prev: Ho. Phys. David Lewis N.. Hosp. Liverp.

GRACE, Richard John Department of Haematology, Eastbourne District General Hospital, Kings Drive, Eastbourne BN21 2UD — MB ChB 1984 Manch.; BSc (Hons) Physiol. 1981; FRCPath 2001; FRCP 1997; MRCPath 1992. Prev: Sen. Regist. (Haemat.) St. Thos. Hosp. Lond.; Regist. Rotat. (Haemat.) Yorks.

GRACE, Professor Roger Hew (retired) Springfield Lodge, Oaken, Wolverhampton WV8 2BA Tel: 01902 842278 Fax: 01902 845154 Email: rhg@nuffieldhospital.freeserve.co.uk — MB BS Lond. 1960; FRCS Eng. 1964. Prev: Prof. Colorectal Surg. Roy. Wolverhampton Hosps. NHS Trust.

GRACE, Sarah Helen Elizabeth — MB BS 1984 Nottm.; MRCGP 1988; DRCOG 1987. Prev: GP Newark.

GRACE, Tania Cullums Cottage, Whepstead Road, Horringer, Bury St Edmunds IP29 5PU — MB BS 1993 Lond.

GRACEY, David George Robert 11 Earlsfort, Moira, Craigavon BT67 0LY — MB ChB 1997 Glas.

GRACEY, Mr Lionel Rodney Hubert (retired) Queenswood, Cross Road, Sunningdale, Ascot SL5 9RX Tel: 01344 625989 — MB BChir Camb. 1951; MA Camb. 1952, BA 1948, MChir 1961; FRCS Ed. 1957; FRCS Eng. 1957. Hon. Cons. Surg. Roy. Free Hosp. Lond.; Hon. Cons. Surg. Hosp. St. John & Eliz. Lond. & King Edwd. VII Hosp. For Offs Lond; Hon. Surg. Italian Hosp. Lond. Prev: Sen. Regist. (Surg.) St. Bart. Hosp. & Roy. Free Hosp.

GRACEY, Nigel Gerard Adrian 5 Sydney Court, St Peter, Jersey JE3 7YS Tel: 01534 33400 — MRCS Eng. LRCP Lond. 1956; BA Camb. 1953, MB BChir 1957. (Guy's) Socs: Jersey Med. Soc. Prev: Ho. Surg. Orpington Hosp.; Ho. Phys. Warwick Gen. Hosp.; Clin. Asst. (Geriat.) Heathcote Hosp. nr. Warwick.

GRACEY, Sharon Elizabeth Wing D, Belfast City Hospital, Lisburn Road, Belfast BT9 7AB Tel: 01232 329241; 6 Malone Park, Belfast BT9 6NH Tel: 01232 660394 — MB BCh BAO 1988 Belf.; MRCGP 1993; DFFP 1994; DRCOG 1992; DCH RCS Dub. 1992; DGM RCP Lond. 1990. Clin. Asst. (Dermat.) Belf. City Hosp. Prev: GP Locum.

GRACEY-WHITMAN, Lionel Joseph Akenside Court, Belsize Crescent, London NW3 5QT Email: zagreb@globalnet.co.uk — MB BS 1994 Lond.; MRCP (UK) 1998.

GRACIAS, Cornelio Joao Lourenco 11 Sinnott Road, Walthamstow, London E17 5PL — MB BS 1982 Bombay.

GRACIAS, Shirley Ann Child & Family Therapy Service, Family Health Centre, The Halve, Trowbridge BA14 8SA Tel: 01225 352280 Fax: 01225 775769 — MB ChB 1983 Bristol; MRCPsych. 1988; DCH RCP Lond. 1987. p/t Cons. Child & Adolesc. Psychiat. Avon & Wilts. Ment. Health Care NHS Trust. Prev: Cons. Child & Adolesc. Psychiat. S. Glam.; Sen. Regist. Rotat. (Child & Adolesc. Psychiat.) S. Wales; Regist. (Psychiat.) Barrow Hosp. Bristol.

GRACIE, Stephen William Personnel Department, Royal Infirmary, 84 Castle St., Glasgow G4 0SF; 52C Cleveden Drive, Kelvinside, Glasgow G12 0NU Tel: 0141 334 1724 — MB ChB 1996 Dundee. Prev: SHO (Neonatology) Qu. Mother's Hosp. Glas.; SHO (Gen. Med. Paediat.) Roy. Hosp. of Sick Childr. Glas.; PRHO (Gen. Med.) Hairmyres Hosp. Glas.

GRADDEN, Craig William Department of Medicine & Nephrology, University Hopital Aintree, Longmoor Lane, Liverpool Tel: 0151 525 5980 Email: farndon@freeuk.com — MB ChB 1990 Ed.; MRCP (UK) 1994. Regist. (Renal Med.) Roy. Liverp. Hosp., Cons. (Med. & Nephrol., Univ. Hosp. Aintree, Liverp.). Socs: BMA; Roy. Soc. of Med; Europ. Dialysis & Transport Assn. Prev: SHO (Renal & Gen. Med., Intens. Care & Neurol.) Derby City Hosp.; SPR Nephrol. & Gen. Med., Roy. Liverp. Univ. Hosp.

GRADILLAS, Vicente 169 Plough Way, Rotherhithe, London SE16 7FN — MB BS 1996 Lond.; BSc (Hons). (United Medical and Dental Schools of Guy's and St. Thomas') SHO (Psychiat.) Bethlem & Maudsley Hosp. Trust Lond.

GRADWELL, David Peter, Wing Cdr. RAF Med. Br. RAF Centre Of Aviation Medicine, Henlow, Hitchin SG14 6DN Tel: 01462 851515 Fax: 01462 850928 Email: caqumed@rafeane.oug.atc — MB ChB 1981 Dundee; BSc (Hons.) Dund 1976, MB ChB 1981; PhD Lond. 1993; DAvMed 1988; FRACS 1999. (Dundee) Cons. Adviser Aviat. Med. (RAF); O.C. Operat.al Support RAFCAM; Head Altitude Med. RAFCAM; Hon. Sen. Lect. KCL. & Univ. of Surrey; Reader (Aviat. Physiol.) RCP. Socs: Fell.Roy. Soc. Med.; Fell.Roy. Aeronautical Soc.; Assoc. Fell. Aerospace Med. Assoc. Prev: Regist. (Med.) Perth Roy. Infirm.; Regist. (Med.) Ninewells Hosp. Dundee; Ho. Phys. & Surg. Ninewells Hosp. Dundee.

GRADWELL, Ernest Appley Moor House, Robin Hood Lane, Wrightington, Wigan WN6 9QG — MB ChB 1974 Liverp.; MRCPath 1981; FRCPath 1992. (Liverpool) Cons. Histopath. Whiston Hosp. Prescot Merseyside.

GRADWELL, Mark Whitmore Priorslegh Medical Centre, Civic Centre, Park Lane, Poynton, Stockport SK12 1GP Tel: 01625 872299 — MB ChB 1983 Leeds; MRCGP (Distinc.) 1989; DRCOG 1988; DCH RCP Lond. 1988; DO RCS Eng. 1986. Clin. Asst. (Ophth.) Macclesfield Dist. Hosp. Prev: Trainee GP W. Cumbria VTS; SHO (Ophth.) St. Paul's Eye Hosp. Liverp.; Ho. Off. Leeds Gen. Infirm.

GRADWELL, Rosemary Zara 201 Belper Road, Stanley Common, Ilkeston DE7 6FT — MB ChB 1983 Dundee. Clin. Med. Off. (Community Child Health) Nottm. HA.

GRADY, Alison Kerry 9 Bridge Croft, Lynwood Park, Clayton Le Moors, Accrington BB5 5XP — MB ChB 1985 Manch.

GRADY, Kathryn Barbara Hartley Corner Surgery, 51 Frogmore Road, Blackwater, Camberley GU17 0DB Tel: 01252 872791 Fax: 01252 878910; 24 Pinecroft Road, Wokingham RG41 4AL Tel: 01189 894212 Email: kgrady@doctors.org.uk — MB BChir 1980 Camb.; MRCGP 1987; MRCOG 1985. (Univ. Camb. Sch. Clin. Med.) GP. Socs: Brit. Menopause Soc. Prev: Trainee GP Sheff VTS; Regist. (O & G) N.. Gen. Hosp. Sheff.

GRADY, Kathryn Maria 52 Medway Crescent, John Leigh Gardens, Altrincham WA14 4UB Tel: 0161 941 7720 — MB BS 1984 Lond.; BSc Lond. 1981; FRCA 1992. (Univ. Coll. Hosp. Med. Sch.) Cons. Anaesth. & Chronic Pain Relief S. Manch. Univ. Hosps. NHS Trust. Socs: Pain Soc.; Obst. Anaesth. Assn.

GRAEME, Patricia Doreen (retired) Little Baltilly, Ceres, Cupar KY15 5QG Tel: 01334 828238 — MB BS 1946 Lond.; MRCP Lond. 1949; MRCS Eng. LRCP Lond. 1944. Prev: Med. Asst. St. Mary's Hosp. Lond.

GRAEME-BARBER, Melanie 1 Ashen Green, Great Shelford, Cambridge CB2 5EY — BM 1994 Soton.

GRAETZ, Keith Philip Cumberstone Chase Lane, Tittensor, Stoke-on-Trent ST12 9HH — BChir 1995 Camb.

GRAETZ, Paul Alexander Penton House, Queen Anne Street, Shelton, Stoke-on-Trent ST4 2EQ Tel: 01782 848642 Fax: 01782 747617; Cumberstone, Chase Lane, Tittensor, Stoke-on-Trent ST12 9HH Tel: 01782 372356 — MB ChB 1971 Birm.

GRAF, Kurt Anthony (retired) 17 Park View Gardens, London NW4 2PR Tel: 020 8202 6120 — MD 1935 Vienna; LRCP LRCS Ed. LRFPS Glas. 1938; MRCPsych. 1971; DPM Eng. 1940. Prev: Med. Dir. Kilburn & Muswell Hill Child Guid. Servs.

GRAF, Roland Eric Briarwood, 14 Springfield Road, Leicester LE2 3BA Tel: 0116 270 4324 — MB BChir 1969 Camb.; BA (1st cl. Hons.) Open 1981; MA Camb. 1970. (Camb. & Lond. Hosp.) Prev: SHO (Paediat.) Nottm. Childr. Hosp.; SHO (Psychiat.) Carlton Hayes Hosp. NarBoro.; Ho. Off. (Paediat.) Gulson Hosp. Coventry & Kettering Gen. Hosp.

GRAFEN, Lucy Child and Family Therapy Services, Havart Health Centre, Civic Centre Road, Havant PO9 2AZ Tel: 02392 344205 — MB ChB 1983 Glas.; MRCPsych 1989. Cons. (Child & Adolesc. Psych.), Havant Health Centre, Havant. Prev: Sen. Regist. (Child & Adolesc. Psychiat.) Pk. Hosp. Oxf. HA.

GRAFF, Christine Tresa Lister Hospital, Chelsea Bridge Road, Chelsea, London SW1W 8RH Tel: 020 7730 3417 Fax: 020 7824 8564; 5 Redcliffe Place, London SW10 9DB Tel: 020 7351 2825 — BM 1979 Soton.; BSc (Hons) St. And. (Zool.) 1970.

GRAFF, Mr Derek John Charles Summerfield Road Consulting Rooms, 8 Summerfield road, Wolverhampton WV1 4PR Tel: 07950 340057 Fax: 01952 291192; 17 Brookvale Road, Priorslee, Telford TF2 9RL Tel: 01952 299085 — MRCS Eng. LRCP Lond. 1951; FRCS Eng. 1957; LRCP Lond. 1951. (King's Coll. Hosp.) Hon. Cons. Orthop. Surg. Wolverhampton HA. Socs: Fell. BOA; (Ex-Pres.) Pres. Naughton Dunn Club.; Birm. Medico-Legal Soc. Prev: Cons. Orthop. Surg. Wolverhampton, Robt. Jones & Agnes Hunt Orthop. Hosp. OsW.ry; Sen. Regist. (Orthop.) Hartshill Orthop. Hosp. Stoke on Trent & N. Staffs. Roy. Infirm.

GRAFFY, Jonathan Peter Statham Grove Surgery, Statham Grove, London N16 9DP Tel: 020 7254 4327 Fax: 020 7241 4098 — MB ChB 1980 Birm.; FRCGP 1994, M 1984; DRCOG 1983. (Birmingham) Sen. Lect. (Gen. Pract. & Primary Care) St. Bart. & The Lond. Med. Coll.; Dir. E. Lond. & Essex Network Researches.

GRAFTON, Andrew John Parkfield Medical Centre, The Walk, Potters Bar EN6 1QH Tel: 01707 651234 Fax: 01707 660452; 8 Mandeville Road, Potters Bar EN6 5LQ Tel: 01707 645693 — BM BS 1988 Nottm.; MRCGP 1992.

GRAHAM, Alasdair 15 Golf View, Strathaven ML10 6AZ — MB ChB 1981 Glas.; MRCGP 1991; DRCOG 1990. Prev: Trainee GP Leeds; Regist. (Med.) Wharfedale Gen. Hosp. Otley; Regist. (Med.) Inverclyde Roy. Hosp. Greenock.

GRAHAM, Alastair Baker Brooklyn Surgery, 65 Mansfield Road, Heanor DE75 7AL Tel: 01773 712552; Hawthorne House, Agnes Meadow, Offcote, Ashbourne DE6 1JQ Tel: 01335 344072 — MB

ChB 1987 Manch. (Manchester Medical School, Oxford Road Manachester)

GRAHAM, Alastair Campbell 14 Shandon Park, Belfast BT5 6NW — MB BCh BAO 1990 Belf.

GRAHAM, Mr Alastair John 46 Cholmeley Park, London N6 5ER — BM BCh 1991 Oxf.; MA Oxf. 1993; FRCS Eng. 1996. (Oxf.) Specialist Regist. Rotat. (Orthop. Surg.) Oxf. Socs: Med. Defence Union; Roy. Soc. Med.; Brit. Orthop. Train. Assn. Prev: SHO (Gen. Surg. & Orthop. Surg.) Roy. Free Hosp.; SHO (Orthop. & Plastic Surg.) Qu. Mary's Univ. Hosp. Roehampton; SHO (Neurosurg.) Qu. Sq. Lond.

GRAHAM, Mr Alastair Noel John 49 Belverdere Park, Belfast BT9 5GT — MB BCh BAO 1986 Belf.; FRCS Ed. 1990; FRCSI 1990.

GRAHAM, Alexander John Tenby Lodge, Sion Hill, Bath BA1 2UW — MRCS Eng. LRCP Lond. 1949. (Middlx.) Prev: Ho. Surg. (ENT) & Cas. Off. (Surg.) Middlx. Hosp.; Asst. Med. Off. Bahamas Gen. Hosp.

GRAHAM, Alexander John (retired) 1 Blue Knowes Road, Law, Carluke ML8 5JE — MB ChB 1951 Aberd.; FRCP Glas. 1974; MRCP Ed. 1961; DPM Eng. 1955. Prev: Cons. Psychiat. & Phys. Supt. Hartwood Hosp. Shotts.

GRAHAM, Alexandria Mary Robertson Central Health Centre, North Carbrain Road, Cumbernauld, Glasgow G67 1BJ Tel: 01236 731738 — MB ChB 1980 Ed. GP. Prev: Med. Examr. Benefits Agency Med. Servs.

GRAHAM, Alison Wobett House, Manchester Royal Infirmary, Oxford Road, Manchester M13 9WL — MB BChir 1992 Camb.

GRAHAM, Alison Jane Hillside, Upper Myrtlefield, Navriside, Inverness IV2 5BX — MB ChB 1987 Dundee; DCCN Edin 1991; MFPHM 1995.

GRAHAM, Alison Jayne Tel: 01733 240478 Fax: 01733 244645 — MB BS 1989 Newc.; MRCGP (Distinc.) 1993. (Newc.) Occupat. Health Adviser Camb. Constab.; Med. Director Scancare Serv.s Ltd. (Health Assessm. Company) based in Grantham. Prev: Trainee GP P'boro.

GRAHAM, Alison Shirley Fairview Surgery, 69 Fairview Road, London SW16 5PX Tel: 020 8764 6666 Fax: 020 8764 4659; 4 Broadlands Avenue, London SW16 1NA — LMSSA 1968 Lond. GP; Tutor to the Sub-Dept. of GP, St. Geo. Hosp. Med. Sch. Prev: Ho. Phys. St. Anthony's Hosp. Cheam; Ho. Surg. (Gyn.) St. Jas. Hosp. Lond.

GRAHAM, Alistair David 1F1, 3 Gladstone Terrace, Edinburgh EH9 1LX — MB ChB 1994 Ed.

GRAHAM, Allison Nationa Spinal Injury Centre, Stoke Mandeville Hospital, Aylesbury — MB ChB 1985 Glas.; FRCP Glas 2001; MSc Glas. 1994; MRCP (UK) 1991. Cons.. (Spinal Injuries) Nat. Spinal Injury Centre Stoke Mandeville. Prev: Sen. Regist. (Spinal Injuries) Qu. Eliz. Nat. Spinal Injuries Unit Glas.; Regist. (Spinal Injuries) SMH Aylesbury; SHO (Spinal Injuries) Stoke Mandeville Hosp. Aylesbury.

GRAHAM, Andrea Nicole Holly Leigh, 41 St Anns Road, Middlewich CW10 9BN Tel: 01270 582233 — MB ChB 1992 Manch.; BSc (Hons.) Med. Biochem. Manch. 1989.

GRAHAM, Andrew Alastair (retired) 6 Richmond Hill, Bath BA1 5QT Tel: 01225 422525 — MB BS Lond. 1949; MRCS Eng. LRCP Lond. 1948. Prev: Med. Off. Kingswood Sch. Bath.

GRAHAM, Andrew John MRC Cognition &Brain Sciences Unit, 15 Chaucer Road, Cambridge CB2 2EF — MB BChir 1992 Camb.; MA Camb. 1992; MRCP (UK) 1995. Wellcome Research Fell.

GRAHAM, Andrew Robert Blantyre Health Centre, Victoria St., Blantyre, Glasgow; 40 Millhouse Dr, Glasgow G20 0UE Tel: 0141 337 1937 — MB ChB 1990 Aberd. Trainee GP Blantyre. Prev: SHO (Obst.) Bellshill Matern. Hosp. Lanarksh.; SHO (A & E & Med.) Hairmyres Hosp. E. Kilbride; SHO (Psych.) Hartwood Hosp. Shotts.

GRAHAM, Angela Elizabeth Glen Isla, Copleigh Drive, Kingswood, Tadworth KT20 6BJ — MB ChB 1981 Glasgow; MB ChB Glasgow1981. (Glasgow)

GRAHAM, Anna Louise University of Bristol, Division of Primary Healthcare, Canynge Hall, Whiteladies Road, Bristol BS8 2PR Tel: 0117 928 7205 Fax: 0117 928 7346 Email: a.graham@bristol.ac.uk; 59 Shaftesbury Avenue, Bristol BS6 5LU — MB BS 1989 Lond.; MSc (Epidemiol.) Lond. 1997; MRCP (UK) 1993; MRCGP 1995; DFFP 1995; DCH RCP Lond. 1992. NHS R&D Stud.ship Dept. of Gen. Pract. Univ. of Bristol.

GRAHAM, Annabel Martyn The Manse, Austenwood Lane, Chalfont St Peter, Gerrards Cross SL9 9DA — MB ChB 1956 Ed.

GRAHAM, Anne Louis Margaret (retired) 9 Bemersyde Drive, Newcastle upon Tyne NE2 2HL Tel: 0191 281 4400 — MB ChB 1950 St. And.; FRCGP 1987; MRCOG 1956. Prev: Regist. O & G Dryburn Hosp. Durh., & P.ss Mary Hosp. &.

GRAHAM, Annika Huddersfield Royal Infirmary, Lindley, Huddersfield HD3 3EA Tel: 01484 342130 — MB ChB 1985 Manch.; BSc (Hons.) Manch. 1982, MD 1993; MRCP (UK) 1988; FRCP 2000. Cons. Phys. (Respirat. Med.) Huddersfield Roy. Infirm. Prev: Sen. Regist. (Gen. & Respirat. Med.) Leeds Gen. Infirm.; Sen. Regist. Bradford Roy. Infirm. & St. Luke's Hosp. Bradford; Regist. (Cardiothoracic Med.) Wythenshawe Hosp. Manch.

GRAHAM, Anthony Cherry Valley Health Centre, King's Square, King's Road, Belfast BT5 7BP Tel: 01232 401844 Fax: 01232 402069; 72 Wandsworth Road, Belfast BT4 3LW Tel: 01232 471925 — MB BCh BAO Belf. 1966; DObst RCOG 1968; DCH RCPSI 1971. (Belf.)

GRAHAM, Anthony Richard Pieter Beech Hill Medical Practice, 278 Gidlow Lane, Wigan WN6 7PD Tel: 01942 821899 Fax: 01942 821752; 14 Chorley Road, Hilldale, Parbold, Wigan WN8 7AL — MB BS 1975 Lond.

GRAHAM, Arthur Stevenson Central Health Centre, North Carbrain Road, Cumbernauld, Glasgow G67 1BJ Tel: 01236 731738; Roodlands, 3 Queen's Drive, Cumbernauld, Glasgow G68 0HN Tel: 01236 732280 — MB ChB 1980 Ed.; DRCOG 1982.

GRAHAM, Barry Hope Family Medical Centre, Hawarden Road, Hope, Wrexham LL12 9NL Tel: 01978 760468 Fax: 01978 760774; Cross Farm, Hope Mountain, Caergwrle, Wrexham LL12 9HE — MB ChB 1971 Liverp.; MRCGP 1980; DCH Eng. 1973.

GRAHAM, Candida Rae South London & Maudsley NHS Trust, Bethlem Royal Hospital, Monkd Orchard Road, Beckenham BR3 3BX Email: crg09@aol.com; 6 Peckarmans Wood, Dulwich Estate, London SE26 6RY — MB ChB 1989 Leics.; MRCPsych 1994; MMedSci Birm.1997. Cons (Psychiat.) S. Lond. & Maudsley Hosp. NHS Trust Lond.

GRAHAM, Caroline Tracy Department of Cellular Pathology, State Mandeville Hospital NHS Trust, Mandeville Rd, Aylesbury HP21 8AL Tel: 01296 315341; Kop Farm, Kop Hill, Princes Risborough HP27 0LB — BM 1988 Soton.; MRCPath 1999. p/t Cons. Cellular Path. State Mandeville Hosp. NHS Trust Aylesbury.

GRAHAM, Carys Mair Catherine Gladstone House, Manlot, Deeside CH5 2EP Tel: 01244 538883 — MB ChB 1971 Liverp.; FRCPCH 1997; DCH Eng. 1974; DObst RCOG 1973. Cons. Community Paediat. N. E. Wales NHS Trust; Designated Doctor (Child Protection) N. Wales HA. Socs: Roy. Coll. Paediat. & Child Health. Prev: SCMO Clwyd AHA.

GRAHAM, Catherine Sarah A&E Department, Whiston Hospital, Prescot L35 5DR Tel: 0151 430 1606 Fax: 0151 430 1973 Email: sarah.graham@gwise.sthkh-tr.nwest.nhs.uk — MB ChB 1979 Liverp.; FRCP 1996. Cons. A & E Med. Whiston Hosp. Prescot, Merseyside. Prev: Sen. Regist. (A & E Med.) Walton Hosp. Liverp.

GRAHAM, Mr Christopher Mark Torbay Hospital, Lawes Bridge, Torquay TQ2 7AA Tel: 01803 64567; 9 Greenway Road, Galmpton, Brixham TQ5 0LR — MB BChir 1979 Camb.; MA Camb. 1979, BA (Hons.) Pharmacol. 1976, MB 1979, BChir 1978; FCOphth 1988; FRCS Eng. 1985; DO RCS Eng. 1982. Cons. Ophth. Torbay Hosp. Torquay. Prev: SHO (Ophth.) W. Norwich Hosp.; Regist. (Ophth.) Addenbrooke's Hosp. Camb.; Sen. Regist. (Ophth.) Moorfields Eye Hosp. Lond.

GRAHAM, Christopher Michael Kop Farm, Kop Hill, Princes Risborough HP27 0LB Tel: 01844 275386 — MB ChB 1983 Otago; FCAnaesth 1991. Cons. Anaesth. Wycombe Hosp. High Wycombe. Prev: Sen. Regist. W. Midl.

GRAHAM, Christopher Nicholas The Grange Medical Centre, 39 Leicester Road, Nuneaton CV11 6AB Tel: 024 7632 2810 Fax: 024 7632 2820; The Lilacs, 17 Church Street, Atherstone CV9 3PJ — BM BS 1989 Nottm.; BMedSci (Hons.) Nottm. 1987; MRCGP 1995. (Nottingham) GP Nuneaton. Socs: BMA. Prev: SHO (Gen. Med.) Geo. Eliot Hosp. Nuneaton; SHO (A & E) N. Staffs. Roy. Infirm.

GRAHAM, Colin The Medical Centre, Forest Gate Road, Corby NN17 1TR Tel: 01536 202507 Fax: 01536 206099 — MB ChB 1981 Sheff.; MRCGP 1985; DRCOG 1985. Prev: Trainee GP Lincoln VTS.

GRAHAM, Colin John Cherryvalley Health Centre, Kings Square, Belfast BT5 7AR; 61 Rose Park, Belfast BT57 — MB BCh BAO 1983 Belf.; MRCGP 1989; DRCOG 1987.

GRAHAM, Colin Macleod (retired) Ash Tree House, Everdon, Daventry NN11 4EJ — MB ChB 1961 Ed. Med. Adviser Cummins Ltd. Daventry. Prev: Clin. Asst. Danetre Hosp. Daventry.

GRAHAM, Colina (retired) Greenloaning, Herington Grove, Hutton Mount, Shenfield, Brentwood CM13 2NN — LRCP LRCS Ed. LRFPS Glas. 1952.

GRAHAM, Cyril William Erne Health Centre, Enniskillen BT74 6AY; 1 Killyvilly Heights, Enniskillen BT74 4DT — MB BCh BAO 1991 Belf.; MRCGP 1995; DObst. RCPI 1994; DME RCPI 1993. Forens. Med. Off., Enniskillen. Prev: Assoc. GP Ederney Co Fermanagh.

GRAHAM, Mr David Andrew 72 Wandsworth Road, Belfast BT4 3LW — MB ChB 1993 Dundee; FRCS Edinbugh 1998. (University of Dundee) Specialist Regist. Trauma & Orthop. Percival Pott Rotat., NE. Thames Deanery.

GRAHAM, David Anthony Adam Practice, 306 Blandford Road, Poole BH15 4JQ Tel: 01202 679234 Fax: 01202 667127; The Birches, Merley Pk Road, Ashington, Wimborne BH21 3DB Tel: 01202 882655 Fax: 01202 888666 Email: dagram@cwmail.co.uk — MB ChB 1970 Birm.; BSc (Anat.) Birm. 1967; MRCGP 1978; DObst RCOG 1972. (Birm.)

GRAHAM, Mr David Francis 10 Harley Street, London W1N 1AA Tel: 020 7636 6504 Fax: 020 7637 5227; 26 Cranbrook Drive, Pinkneys Green, Maidenhead SL6 6SB Tel: 01628 33722 Fax: 01628 33722 — MB BS 1970 Newc.; FRCS Eng. 1976; FRCS Ed. 1975. (Newc.) Cons./Hon. Sen. Lect. Roy. Postgrad. Med. Sch. Hammersmith Hosp. Lond. Socs: Fell. Roy. Soc. Med.; Belg. Chir. Soc. Prev: Cons. Surg. Fife Health Bd. & Clin. Tutor (Surg.) Edin. Univ.; Lect. (Surg.) Glas. Roy. Infirm.; Regist. Gen. Surg. Luton & Dunstable Hosp. & United Oxf. Hosps.

GRAHAM, Professor David Ian University Department of Neuropathology, Southern General Hospital ., South Glasgow University Hospitals NHS Trust, Glasgow G51 4TF Tel: 0141 201 2113 Fax: 0141 201 2998 Email: d.graham@clinmed.gla.ac.uk — MB BCh 1963 Wales; PhD Glas. 1972; FRSE 1986; FRCP ANDS Glas. 1986; FRCPath 1983, M 1971; F Acad. Med. Sci 2000. (Cardiff) Prof. Dept. Neuropath. Inst. Neurol. Sci. S.. Gen. Hosp. Glas. NHS Trust. Socs: Brit. Neuropath. Soc. & Path. Soc.; Internat. Soc. Neuropath.; Internat. Neurotrauma Soc. Prev: Fogarty Internat. Research Fell. Laborat. of Neuropath. Univ. Penna. Philadelphia, USA; Lect. & Reader (Neuropath.) Univ. Glas.

GRAHAM, David Robert Whiston Hospital, Prescot L35 5DR Tel: 0151 426 1600 Fax: 0151 430 1913 — MB ChB 1977 Liverp.; MD Liverp. 1990; FRCP Lond. 1996; MRCP (UK) 1981. (Liverp.) Cons. Phys. (Gen. Med. & Respirat. Med.) Whiston Hosp. Merseyside; Clin. Lect. & Dep. PostGrad. & Dean 1998; Dept. Regional Adviser RCP 1997; Med. Off. GB Rugby League 1997; Med. Off. St. Helens RLFC. Prev: Sen. Regist. (Gen. Med.) Walton Hosp. Liverp.; Clin. Fell. Univ. Hosp. Lond. Ontario, Canada; Postgrad. Clin. Tutor.

GRAHAM, David Thomas 14 Shandon Park, Belfast BT5 6NW — MB BCh BAO 1959 Belf.; FRCR 1980; DMRD Eng. 1979.

GRAHAM, Deborah 71 Palmerston Road, Denton, Manchester M34 2NZ Tel: 0161 336 6677 Email: docdebgraham@yahoo.com — MB ChB 1989 Sheff.; MRCGP 1994; ALS 1995; Cert. Prescribed Equiv. Exp. JCPTGP 1994; DFFP 1994 - recert 1999; Cert. Family Plann. JCC 1993. (Sheffield) Clin. Asst. (Genito-Urin. Med.) N. Manch. Gen. Hosp. & Bolton Centre for Sexual Health; Non-Princip. GP Manch. Prev: Clin. Asst. (Genitourin. Med.) Manch. Roy. Infirm. & hope Hosp.; Asst. Ship's Doctor P & O Cruises (UK) Ltd. Soton.; Clin. Asst. (Dermat. & Genitourin. Med.) Oldham Hosp. Manch.

***GRAHAM, Denise Mary** 77 Bryansford Av, Newcastle BT33 0LG; Flat 3/5, 15 Clarendon St, Glasgow G20 7QP Tel: 0141 353 2467 — MB ChB 1997 Glas.

GRAHAM, Donald Department of Anaesthetics, York District General Hospital, Wiggington Road, York YO3 7HE; Lavender Cottage, 68 Westgate, Tickhill, Doncaster DN11 9NQ — MB ChB 1982 Dundee; DA (UK) 1986. SHO (Anaesth.) Vict. Infirm. Glas.; Regist. (Anaesth.) Vict. Infirm. Glas.; Regist. (Psych.) Timaru Hosp. Timaru, NZ; Regist. (Anaesth.) Middlemore Hosp. Auckland, NA. Prev: SHO (Cas.) Hairmyres Hosp. E. Kilbride; Jun. Ho. Off. (Surg.) Roy. Hosp. Sick Childr. Glas.; Jun. Ho. Off. (Med.) Raigmore Hosp. Inverness.

GRAHAM, Dudley James Morton 49 South Union Street, Cupar KY15 5BB — MB ChB 1989 Aberd.

GRAHAM, Duncan George Priory Avenue Surgery, 24-26 Priory Avenue, High Wycombe HP13 6SH Tel: 01494 448132 Fax: 01494 686407 — MB BS 1986 Newc.; MRCGP 1992; DCH RCP Lond. 1991.

GRAHAM, Effie (retired) The Cottage (Old Laundry), Rheda Park, Frizington CA26 3TE — MB ChB 1962 Manch. Non-Exec. Dir. W. Cumbria Health Care NHS Trust. Prev: Ho. Surg. City Gen. Hosp. Carlisle.

GRAHAM, Elaine Mary 22 Church Road, Almondsbury, Bristol BS32 4DT — MB BCh 1987 Wales. SHO (A & E) Gwent HA; SHO (Paediat., Geriat. & Gen. Med.) Gwent HA. Prev: Trainee GP Gwent VTS.

GRAHAM, Elizabeth Ann Northern Ireland Radiotherapy Centre, Belvoir Park Hospital, Hospital Road, Belfast; Apartment 12, 6 Broomhill Manor, Belfast BT9 5HG — MB BCh BAO 1980 Belf.; DMRT RCR 1987; DRCOG 1982.

GRAHAM, Elizabeth Mary Medical Eye Unit, St Thomas' Hospital, London SE1 7EH Tel: 020 7928 9292 Fax: 020 7922 8165 — MB BS 1972 Lond.; FRCP Lond. 1992; MRCP (UK) 1975; FRCOphth 1989; DO Eng. 1978. Cons. (Med. Ophth.) St. Thos. Hosp. Lond.; Cons. (Ophth.) Nat. Hosp. Neurol. & Neurosurg. Prev: Iris Research Fell. (Med. Ophth.) St. Thos. Hosp. Lond.

GRAHAM, Eric William Long View, Maple Avenue, Bexhill-on-Sea TN39 4ST Tel: 01424 843182 — MB BS 1948 Lond. (Guy's) Socs: Brit. Med. Acupunct. Soc.

GRAHAM, Erica Louise Department of Therapeutics, Queen's University, Belfast; 5 Park Avenue, Donaghadee BT21 0EB — MB ChB 1974 Birm. Research Clin. Asst. (Therap.) Qu. Univ. Belf.

GRAHAM, Fiona 13 Aubigny Drive, Fulwood, Preston PR2 3QL — MB ChB 1989 Manch. SHO (Anaesth.) Manch. Roy. Infirm. Prev: SHO (Paediat.) Qu. Pk. Hosp. Blackburn; SHO (A & E) Warrington Dist. Gen Hosp.; SHO (Anaesth.) Stepping Hill Hosp. Stockport.

GRAHAM, Fiona Margaret St Barnabas Hospice, Nettleham Road, Lincoln LN2 1RE; Rose Farm House, Main St, Marston, Grantham NG32 2HH — MB ChB 1986 Dundee; MRCGP 1993; DCH RCP Lond. 1990. Dep. Med. Dir. St Barnabas Hospice Lincoln. Prev: Clin. Asst. (Palliat. Care) Fife Healthcare Trust; Med. Off. Myton Hamlet Hospice Warwick.

GRAHAM, Fiona Mary Greenfield, Big Brae, Tarbert PA29 6UQ — MB ChB 1993 Ed.

GRAHAM, Frances Caroline The Manor, Winterbourne Monkton, Swindon SN4 9NW — MB BChir 1968 Camb.; FFA RCS Eng. 1971.

GRAHAM, Freda Mary Olwyn (retired) White Gate Lodge, Bridge Road, Llandaff, Cardiff CF5 2PT — MRCS Eng. LRCP Lond. 1939.

GRAHAM, Mr Geoffrey Paul University Hospital of Wales, Heath Park, Cardiff CF14 4XW; Palla House, St Brides Super Ely, Cardiff CF5 6ND — MB BS 1982 Lond.; FRCS Lond. 1986. (Univ. Coll. Hosp.) Cons. (Trauma & Orthop.) Univ. Hosp. of Wales; Hon. Sen. Lect. in Sport & Exercise Med., Univ. of Wales Coll. of Med., Health Pk., Cardiff.

GRAHAM, George Smith (retired) 7 Farnley Ridge, Neville's Cross, Durham DH1 4HB Tel: 0191 384 3339 — MB BS 1945 Durh.; MRCPath. 1965. Prev: Cons. Path. Dryburn Hosp. Durh.

GRAHAM, George Stewart (retired) 73 Hepburn Gardens, St Andrews KY16 9LS Tel: 01334 73659 — MB ChB 1956 Ed.; DCH Eng. 1959; DObst RCOG 1960; MRCGP 1969. Prev: GP Bathgate.

GRAHAM, Gerald Ralph (retired) The Kennels, Whaddon, Milton Keynes MK17 0LT Tel: 01908 501000 Fax: 01908 501000 Email: gerald.graham@talk21.com — MD 1949 West. Reserve Univ. Ohio; BA Minn. 1943; LMSSA Lond. 1959. Hon. Cons. Clin. Physiol. Hosp. Sick Childr. Lond.; Founding Edr. Paediat. Cardiol.; Med. Adviser Springer Verlag Lond. Ltd; Dir. MPT Cons.s Ltd. Prev: Cons. i/c Dept. Clin. Physiol. Hosp. Sick Childr. Gt. Ormond St. Lond.

GRAHAM, Godfrey Earlam Lester (retired) 297 Wigan Lane, Wigan WN1 2QY Tel: 01942 242748 Email: earlamgraham@talk21.com — MA, BM BCh Oxf. 1944; MRCS Eng. LRCP Lond. 1944; DObst RCOG 1949. JP. Co. Lancaster. Prev: Capt. RAMC.

GRAHAM, Gregory Ian Trosnant Lodge Surgery, Trosnant Lodge, Trosnant Street, Pontypool NP4 8AT — MB BS 1972 Lond.; 1993 Dip Phil (Health Care) Swansea. (St. George's London)

GRAHAM, Guy Wayland Seymour Simpson House Medical Centre, 255 Eastcote Lane, South Harrow, Harrow HA2 8RS Tel: 020 8864 3466 Fax: 020 8864 1002 — MB BS 1970 Lond. Prev: Research Fell. Cardiol. St. Mary's Hosp. Paddington; Ho. Surg. & Psychiat. Ho. Phys. St. Thos. Hosp. Lond.; Regist. Gen. Med. High Wycombe Gen. Hosp.

GRAHAM, Heather Margaret Oliver and Partners, The Guildhall Surgery, Lower Baxter Street, Bury St Edmunds IP33 1ET Tel: 01284 701601 Fax: 01284 702943; 8 Orchard Way, Horringer, Bury St Edmunds IP29 5SF Tel: 01284 735355 Fax: 01284 735120 — MB BS 1968 Lond.; MRCS Eng. LRCP Lond. 1968; MRCGP 1978; DPH Glas. 1974; DCH RCP Lond. 1971; DObst RCOG 1969. Prev: Med. Off. Social Paediat. Research Unit Glas.; Clin. Med. Off. DoH, Bermuda.

GRAHAM, Helen Christine 16 Bowfield Road, West Kilbride KA23 9JY — MB ChB 1977 Manch.

GRAHAM, Helen Elizabeth 48 Woodruff Avenue, Hove BN3 6PH — MB BS 1989 Lond.

GRAHAM, Helen Judith The Surgery, 1 Forest Hill Road, London SE22 0SQ Tel: 020 8693 2264 Fax: 020 8299 0200 — MB ChB Manch. 1969; MRCGP 1985; DCH Eng. 1973; FRCGP 1999. (Univ. Manch.) Sen. Lect. (Gen. Pract.) King's Coll. Sch. Med. & Dent. Lond.; Trainer, Lond. Deanery; Dept. of Med. Educat., Guys, Kings and St Thomas Sch. of Med. Kings Coll. Lond.. SEIART. Socs: BMA; Brit. Geriat. Soc.; AUDGP. Prev: Resid. Ho. Off. Roy. Canberra Hosp., Austral.; Resid. SHO Childr. Hosp. Sydenham; Regist. (Radiother. & Oncol.) King's Coll. Hosp. Lond.

GRAHAM, Henry 31 Green Lane, Hendon, London NW4 2AG — MRCS Eng. LRCP Lond. 1952; BA (Hons.) Camb. 1948, MA 1952; DPH Eng. 1957. (Camb. & Westm.) Socs: BMA. Prev: O & G Ho. Surg. Chase Farm Hosp. Enfield; Paediat. Ho. Phys. Hillingdon Hosp. Uxbridge; Ho. Phys. Whipps Cross Hosp. Lond.

GRAHAM, Henry Cresswell (retired) Brookside, Gorstage Lane, Weaverham, Northwich CW8 2ST — MB 1945 Liverp.; MB, ChB Liverp. 1945.

GRAHAM, Hilary Hamill (retired) 29 Benhall Green, Benhall, Saxmundham IP17 1HT Tel: 01728 602563 — BSc (Anat.) (1st cl. Hons.) Lond. 1964, MB BS (Hons.) 1968; MRCS Eng. LRCP Lond. 1968. Family Therapist Highgate Gp. Pract. Family Clinic Highgate Lond.; Family Therapist Norf. Ment. Health Care Trust Child & Adolesc. Ment. Health Serv.s LoW.oft. Prev: Ho. Phys. Univ. Coll. Hosp.

GRAHAM, Iain Crosshouse Hospital, Kilmarnock KA2 0BE; 9 Broomfield Road, Ayr KA7 2SP — MB ChB 1977 Aberd.; MPhil Glas. 1996; LLM Cardiff 1992; FRCPath 1996, M 1984; Dip. Hlth. Servs. Managem. 1992; DFM Glas. 1988; DMJ(Path) Soc. Apoth. Lond. 1986. Cons. Path. Ayrsh. & Arran HB.

GRAHAM, Iain Frank Miller 18 College Road N., Blundellsands, Liverpool L23 8UT — MB BS 1973 Lond.; FFA RCS Eng. 1977. (St. Mary's)

GRAHAM, Iain Kirkpatrick 52 Munro Road, Jordanhill, Glasgow G13 1SF — MB ChB 1998 Glas.; MB ChB Glas 1998.

GRAHAM, Ian Charles Anthony David Paul, TD (retired) Horsdon Close, 25 Blundell's Avenue, Tiverton EX16 4DL Tel: 01884 252981 — MRCS Eng. LRCP Lond. 1936; MA Camb. 1937, MB BChir 1937; DA Eng. 1951. Prev: Sen. Surg. Cas. Off. & Ho. Surg. St. Thos. Hosp.

GRAHAM, Isabel Mary Health Centre, Cowbridge CF7; Palla House, St Brides-super-Ely, Cardiff CF5 6ND — MB BCh 1984 Wales; DRCOG 1988.

GRAHAM, Isobel Anne Southern General Hospital, 1345 Govan Road, Glasgow G51 4TF; 155 Paisley Road, Barrhead, Glasgow G78 1HT — MB ChB 1982 Glas.; MRCPsych. 1988. Cons. Gen. Psychiat. & Learning Disabil. Gtr. Glas. HB. Prev: Sen. Regist. (Gen. Psychiat. & Ment. Handicap) Gtr. Glas. HB; Regist. (Psychiat.) Dykebar Hosp. Paisley.

GRAHAM, Jacqueline Anne Birchgrove Surgery, 104 Caerphilly Road, Cardiff CF14 4AG Tel: 029 2052 2344 Fax: 029 2052 2487; 22 Bristow Park, Upper Malone Road, Belfast BT9 6TH Tel: 01232 667245 — MB ChB 1987 Bristol; MRCP (UK) 1992; MRCGP 1996. Clin. Asst. (Genitourin. Med.) Roy. Gwent Hosp. Newport. Prev: SHO (A & E) Nevill Hall Hosp. Abergavenny; Regist. (Gen. Med.) Roy. Gwent Hosp. Newport; Trainee GP E. Glam. VTS Scheme.

GRAHAM, Mr James (retired) 56 Falloch Road, Milngavie, Glasgow G62 7RR Tel: 0141 563 7443 Email: jimmy.g@ntlworld.com — MB ChB 1959 Glas.; FRCS Ed. 1964; FRCS Glas. 1964. Prev: Cons. Orthop. Surg. W.. Infirm. & Gartnavel Gen. Hosp. Glas.

GRAHAM, James Cara, 29 Broomfield Avenue, Newton Mearns, Glasgow G77 5JW Tel: 0141 639 6768 — MB ChB 1972 Glas. Prev: GP Argyll & Clyde HB; GP Cambuslang; Ho. Surg. Roy. Hosp. Sick Childr. Glas.

GRAHAM, James Anthony Gordon 7 Longlands, Worthing BN14 9NS Tel: 01903 522535 — MB ChB 1949 Ed.; FFCM 1980, M 1974; DPH Leeds 1957. Med. Ref. Worthing Boro. Counc. Socs: Fell. Soc. Pub. Health & Fac. Pub. Health Med. Prev: Dir. (Pub. Health) Worthing HA; MOH Worthing Boro.; Dep. MOH Croydon Co. Boro.

GRAHAM, James Christopher Green Lane Medical Centre, 15 Green Lane, Stoneycroft, Liverpool L13 7DY Tel: 0151 228 9101 Fax: 0151 228 2472; Blue Ridge, Woolton Hill Road, Liverpool L25 4RF Tel: 0151 228 9101 — MB ChB 1985 Liverp.; MRCGP 1990; DFFP 1993; DRCOG 1988.

GRAHAM, James Lloyd Turner (retired) Nyassa, Granville Road, St Margaret's Bay, Dover CT15 6DS Tel: 01304 853155 — LRCPI & LM, LRSCI & LM 1939; LRCPI & LM, LRCSI & LM 1939; LM Rotunda 1947. Prev: Med. Off. GCBS Dover.

GRAHAM, James McClellan Crichton Royal Hospital, Dumfries DG1 4TG — MB ChB 1977 Ed.; MMedSci Leeds 1987; MRCPsych 1985. (Edinburgh) Cons. Psychiat. Dumfries & Galloway Health Bd. Prev: Sen. Regist. (Psychiat.) S. Glam. HA.

GRAHAM, James Peter (retired) Lindishaven, Manor Brow, Keswick CA12 4BA — MB BS 1953 Durh.

GRAHAM, James Reid 48 Woodruff Avenue, Hove BN3 6PH — MB BS 1986 Lond.; MRCGP 1992; DCH RCP Lond. 1993; DRCOG 1988; Cert. Family Plann. JCC 1988.

GRAHAM, James Young 28 Lesbury Road, Heaton, Newcastle upon Tyne NE6 5LB — MB ChB 1992 Dundee; FRCR 2001; BMSc 1989; MRCP (UK) 1996. Clin. Fell., Clin. Radiol., Leeds Gen. Infirm., Leeds. Prev: Specialist Regist. (Clin. Radiol.) N.ern Deanery Newc. Gen. Hosp. Newc.

GRAHAM, Janet Fraser (retired) Flat 12, Westpark, 65 Partickhill Road, Glasgow G11 5AD Tel: 0141 339 8660 — MB ChB Glas. 1944; DPH 1950; DCH Eng. 1948; MFCM 1972. Prev: Sen. Med. Off. (Matern. & Child Welf.) Gtr. Glas. Health Bd.

GRAHAM, Jeffrey Martin 31 Alma Square, St John's Wood, London NW8 9PY Tel: 020 7286 6685 — BM BCh 1975 Oxf.; PhD Lond. 1974; MA Oxf. 1973, BA (Physiol.) 1969, BM BCh 1975; MFCM 1981. Princip. Med. Off. DHSS. Prev: Ho. Surg. Lond. Hosp. (Whitechapel); Ho. Phys. Lond. Hosp. (Mile End); Lect. in Physiol. Lond. Hosp. Med. Coll.

GRAHAM, Jill Victor Street Surgery, Victor Street, Shirley, Southampton SO15 5SY Tel: 023 8077 4781 Fax: 023 8039 0680 — BM 1980 Soton.; MRCGP 1985; DRCOG 1984. Socs: MRCGP.

GRAHAM, Jill Eileen 51 Tannery Road, Sawston, Cambridge CB2 4UW — MB BCh BAO 1990 Belf.; MRCGP 1994; DFFP 1996; DRCOG 1993; DGM RCPS Glas. 1992. (Qu. Univ. Belf.)

GRAHAM, Joan Logan 61 Banbridge Road, Gilford, Craigavon BT63 6DL — MB BCh BAO 1966 Belf.; FFA RCSI 1972. Cons. (Anaesth.) Craigavon Area Hosp.

GRAHAM, Mr John Alistair Oakrigg Farm, Moffat DG10 9QW — MD 1971 Glas.; MB ChB 1963; FRCS Eng. 1969; FRCS Glas. 1969.

GRAHAM, John Douglas Bristol Oncology Centre, Horfield Road, Bristol BS2 8ED Tel: 0117 928 2409 Fax: 0117 928 3572; Howgrove Cottage, The Batch, Butcombe, Bristol BS40 7UY — MB ChB 1981 Glas.; BSc (Hons.) Glas. 1979, MB ChB 1981; FRCR 1989; MRCP (UK) 1984. Cons. Clin. Oncol. Bristol Oncol. Centre. Prev: Sen. Regist. (Radiother.) Middlx. Hosp. Lond.; Regist. (Radiother.) Roy. Marsden Hosp. Lond.; Regist. (Oncol.) Gartnavel Gen. Hosp. Glas.

GRAHAM, John Galbraith (retired) 4 St Edeyrns Close, Cyncoed, Cardiff CF23 6TH Tel: 01222 751175 — MB ChB Glas. 1956; FRCP Ed. 1973, M 1963; FRCP Lond. 1975, M 1963. Hon. Clin. Tutor Welsh Nat. Sch. Med. Prev: Cons. Neurol. S. Glam. AHA (T).

GRAHAM, John Gordon Ismay Paediatric dept, Ninewells Hospital, Dundee DD1 9SY Tel: 01382 660777; the Rock House, Woodhaven Pier, Newport-on-Tay DD6 8LB Tel: 01382 540026 Email: johnnygigraham@hotmail.com — MB ChB 1997 Dundee; BSc (Hons) 1992. SHO (Paediat.) Ninewells Hosp. Dundee.

***GRAHAM, John Joseph** 16 Lauder Drive, Linwood, Paisley PA3 3EY Tel: 01505 323195 — MB ChB 1995 Glas.; BSc (Hons.) Glas. 1992.

GRAHAM, John Leonard (retired) Oakbank, Laggan Road, Crieff PH7 4LQ Tel: 01764 2300 — MB ChB 1952 St And.; FFCM 1979, M 1972; DObst RCOG 1955.

GRAHAM, Mr John Malcolm 150 Harley Street, London W1G 7LQ Tel: 020 7486 9583 Fax: 020 7935 3635 Email: johngraham@150harleystreet.com — MA, BM BCh Oxf. 1966; FRCS Ed. 1975; FRCS Eng. 1971; DM Lambeth 1998. (Oxf. & Middlx.) Cons. ENT Surg. Roy Nat. Throat, Nose & Ear Hosp. Lond.; Corr. Mem. Soc. de Otorrinolaring. del Uruguay; Hon. Cons. UCLH, Lond. Chairm. Med. Comm., St Lukes Hosp. Fro the clergy, Lond..; Hon.Cons. ENT Surg., Med. Foundat. fro the c/o victims of torture. Socs: Europ. Soc. Paediatric Otorhinolaryng. (Pres.- Elect); Brit. Assn. Paediat. Otorhinol. (Counc. Founding Pres.); Brit. Assn. Otol. (Counc.. Mem.). Prev: Cons. ENT Surg. Univ. Coll. Hosps.

GRAHAM, John Montague (retired) The Firs, Forest Road, Chandler's Ford, Eastleigh SO53 1NA — MB BS 1949 Lond.; FRCPath 1973, M 1963; Dip. Bact. Lond 1956. Cons. Bacteriol. Roy. Hants. Co. Hosp. Winchester. Prev: Regist. (Clin. Path.) Manch. Roy. Infirm.

GRAHAM, Jonathan Clive 18 High Dene, Jesmond Park W., Newcastle upon Tyne NE7 7TL Tel: 0191 281 5909 Email: j.c.graham@ncl.ac.uk — MB BS 1991 Lond.; MRCP (UK) 1994; DTM & H Liverp. 1995; Dip RC Path 1998. (St Thomas)

GRAHAM, Jonathan David 11 Tudor Close, Woodford Green IG8 0LF — MB ChB 1990 Manch.

GRAHAM, Jonathan Paul The Health Centre, Victoria Road, Ulverston LA12 0EW Tel: 01229 582223 — MB BS 1979 Newc.

GRAHAM, Jonathan William 16 Kelly Court, Borehamwood WD6 5QU — MB BS 1994 Lond. (Charing Cross and Westminster Medical School) Specialist Regist. Radiol., Guy's & St. Thomas' Radiol. Rotat.

GRAHAM, Juliet Helen 73 Athenlay Road, London SE15 3EN Tel: 020 7732 6522 — MB BChir 1988 Camb.; MSc Lond. 1993; BA Camb. 1985; MRCP (UK) 1991; DCH 1997; DRCOG 1998; DGM 1997.

GRAHAM, Karen Cuminestown Health Centre, Auchry Road, Cuminestown, Turriff AB53 5WJ Tel: 01888 544232; 25 Walker Avenue, Banff AB45 1AQ Tel: 01261 812956 — MB ChB 1985 Glas.; MRCGP 1989; DRCOG 1987. Assoc. GP Cuminestown Health Centre; Asst. Banff Health Centre. Socs: Banff Med. Soc. Prev: SHO (Gen. Paediat. Med.) Roy. Hosp. Sick Childr. Edin.; Ho. Off. (Gen. Surg.) Stobhill Gen. Hosp.; Ho. Off. (Gen. Med.) Glas. Roy. Infirm.

GRAHAM, Karen Elizabeth 19 Quarry Road, Banbridge BT32 3TW — MB BCh BAO 1986 Belf.; DRCOG 1990. Trainee GP Crewe.

GRAHAM, Karl Alexander 28 Lovedean Lane, Lovedean, Waterlooville PO8 8HJ — BM 1998 Soton.; BM Soton 1998.

GRAHAM, Kathryn 95 Paterson Avenue, Irvine KA12 9LW — MB ChB 1998 Ed.; MB ChB Ed 1998.

GRAHAM, Kenneth Anthony 19 Enterpen Close, Yarm TS15 9RT — MB BS 1985 Lond.

GRAHAM, Mr Kenneth Ekundayo 463 Watford Way, London NW4 4TR — MB BS 1977 Lagos, Nigeria; FRCS Ed. 1986; FRCS Glas. 1986.

GRAHAM, Kenneth Thompson (retired) Beaulieu, 11 Green Acres, Birdham, Chichester PO20 7HL Tel: 01243 512989 — MRCS Eng. LRCP Lond. 1943. Prev: GP Teddington.

GRAHAM, Laura Ann 28 Lesbury Road, Heaton, Newcastle upon Tyne NE6 5LB — MB ChB 1991 Dundee; MRCP (UK) 1995. p/t Specialist Regist., Rehabil. Med., Hunters Moor Regional Rehabil. Centre, Newc. upon Tyne.

GRAHAM, Lesley Jane Crammond 148 The Pleasance, Edinburgh EH8 9RS Tel: 0131 536 9000; 6 St. Ronans Terrace, Edinburgh EH10 5NG Tel: 0131 447 5072 — MB ChB 1981 Aberd.; MSc Community Health Ed. 1990; MRCGP 1985; DRCOG 1984. Sen. Regist. (Pub. Health Med.) Lothian HB. Socs: BMA; Fac. Pub. Health Med. Prev: GP Sighthill Edin.; Med. Off. Murchison S. Is., New Zealand.

GRAHAM, Lorraine Elizabeth 31 Whitla Road, Lisburn BT28 3PS — MB BCh BAO 1994 Belf.

GRAHAM, Lynne Sylvia Weavers Medical Centre, 50 School Lane, Kettering NN16 0DH Tel: 01536 513494 Fax: 01536 416521; Highfields, 18 Stanion Road, Brigstock, Kettering NN14 3HW — MB ChB 1981 Sheff.; MRCGP 1985; DRCOG 1985. Prev: Trainee GP Lincoln VTS.

GRAHAM, Malcolm Arthur Holmes (retired) 1 Osborne Road, Potters Bar EN6 1RZ Tel: 01707 662515 — MB BS Lond. 1954; DObst RCOG 1956. Clin. Asst. (Diabetes) Barnet Gen. Hosp. Prev: Ho. Surg. (Obst.) W. Middlx. Hosp.

GRAHAM, Margaret Elizabeth Springfield Medical Practice, 463 Springfield Road, Belfast BT12 7DN Tel: 028 9032 7126 Fax: 028 9032 5976; 26 Ballyhenry Drive, Newtownabbey BT36 5BD Tel: 028 9080 1738 Email: margaret.graham@ntlworld.com — MB BCh BAO 1972 Belf.; MRCGP 1981; DCH RCPSI 1974. (Queen's University Belfast) Socs: BMA; Hon. Treas. Ulster Med. Soc. Prev: Regist. (Med.) Roy. Vict. Hosp. Belf.; Regist. (Paediat.) Roy. Belf. Hosp. Sick Childr.

GRAHAM, Margaret Marie Rose Anne Killiecrankie, 3 Brickwood Place, Burton on the Wolds, Loughborough LE12 5AW Tel: 01509 880558 — MB BS 1972 Lond.; MRCP (UK) 1977; MRCS Eng. LRCP Lond. 1972; DObst RCOG 1974; DCH Eng. 1974. (Roy. Free) Research Assoc. Nat. ECMO Project. Prev: SHO (Paediat.) Kingston Hosp. Kingston-on-Thames & Guy's Hosp. Lond.; SHO (Med. & Chest Dis.) Mayday Hosp. Thornton Heath.

GRAHAM, Marilyn Helen Fairview Surgery, 69 Fairview Road, London SW16 5PX Tel: 020 8679 1700 Fax: 020 8764 4659; 155 Rosendale Road, London SE21 8HE Tel: 020 8761 5897 — MB ChB 1984 Leic.; MB ChB Leic. I984; DIP Homeopathy 1998; DRCOG 1986. (Leicester)

GRAHAM, Mary Patricia Havard 19 Bellhouse Lane, Grappenhall, Warrington WA4 2SG — MB ChB 1949 Aberd.; MFCM 1972; DPH Manch. 1962.

GRAHAM, Meyrick (retired) 8 Sherringham Road, Southport PR8 2HQ — MB BS 1950 Durh. Med. Off. Hesketh Pk. Hosp. S.port. Prev: Ho. Surg. (O & G) Dryburn Hosp. Durh.

GRAHAM, Mr Michael David Dorset County Hospital, Williams Avenue, Dorchester DT1 2JY Tel: 01305 255476 — MB BChir 1986 Camb.; MChir Camb. 1994; BSc (Hons.) St. And. 1982; FRCS Eng. 1989. Cons. Surg. (Gen. Surg.) Dorset Co. Hosp. Dorchester. Socs: BASO; ASGBI. Prev: Specialist Regist. Kingston Hosp.; Sen. Regist. St. Helier Hosp. Carshalton; Regist. (Surg.) Flinders Med. Centre Adelaide, Austral.

GRAHAM, Moira Jean The Rowans, Broallan, Beauly IV4 7AH — MB ChB 1992 Glas.

GRAHAM, Nicholas William Staunton Group Practice, 3-5 Bounds Green Road, Wood Green, London N22 8HE Tel: 020 8889 4311 Fax: 020 8826 9100 — MB BChir 1973 Camb.; BA Camb. 1970, MB BChir 1973. Prev: Trainee GP Whittington Hosp. VTS.

GRAHAM, Nora 27 St Albans Road, London NW5 1RG Tel: 020 7485 7937 Fax: 020 7267 4628 — BM BCh Oxf. 1961; MRCPsych 1976; FRCPsych 1988, M 1976. Cons. Psychogeriat. Roy. Free Hosp. Lond.; Chairm. Alzheimer's Dis. InterNat.

GRAHAM, Patricia Cran 85 Durham Road, Bromley BR2 0SP — MB ChB 1982 Glas.; MRCPath 1989.

GRAHAM, Paula Jane Kathleen 27 Cleland Park N., Bangor BT20 3EN — MB ChB 1998 Dund.; MB ChB Dund 1998.

GRAHAM, Paula Maria Anne Blackhall & Peterlee Group Practice, Morven, Hesleden Road, Blackhall, Stanley Tel: 0191 586 4331; 56 Grinstead Way, Carrville, Durham DH1 1LZ Tel: 0191 384 8883 — MB BS 1989 Newc.; BSc (Hons.) Newc. 1984; MRCGP 1995; DFFP 1993; DRCOG 1992. (Newcastle upon Tyne) Prev: Trainee GP N.umbria VTS.

GRAHAM, Peter Wordsworth Health Centre, 19 Wordsworth Avenue, Manor Park, London E12 6SU Tel: 020 8548 5960 Fax: 020 8548 5983; 11 Tudor Close, Woodford Green IG8 0LF Tel: 020 8505 1520 Fax: 020 8552 7397 Email: petergra@globalnet.co.uk — MB ChB Ed. 1962; BSc (Hons.) Ed. 1959; FRCGP 1994, M 1974. (Ed.) Socs: (Ex-Pres.) Balint Soc.; (Chairm.) Newham Med. Soc. Prev: Ex-Course Organiser Newham VTS.

GRAHAM, Mr Peter Anderson (retired) 1 Llandennis Avenue, Cyncoed, Cardiff CF23 6JD Tel: 01222 751507 — MB ChB 1950 Glas.; FRCS Eng. 1957; FRCOphth 1988. Prev: Cons. Ophth. Surg. Univ. Hosp. of Wales.

GRAHAM, Peter David Tain and Fearn Area Medical Practice, Health Centre, Scotsburn Road, Tain IV19 1PR Tel: 01862 892759 Fax: 01862 892579; Erracht, Rhynie, Tain IV20 1TS Tel: 01862 832494 — MB ChB 1981 Aberd.; MRCGP 1997; DRCOG 1997. Trainer (Gen. Pract.) Tain Ross-Sh.

GRAHAM, Peter Jeffrey 36 Fern Road, Ellesmere Port, South Wirral CH65 6PB — MB ChB 1989 Liverp.

GRAHAM, Philip Jeremy 27 St Albans Road, London NW5 1RG Tel: 020 7485 7937 Fax: 020 7267 4628 — MB BChir 1960 Camb.; FRCP Lond. 1973, M 1961; FRCPsych 1972, M 1971; DPM Lond. 1964. (Univ. Coll. Hosp.) Prof. Child Psychiat. Univ. Oslo, Norway. Socs: Fell. Roy. Soc. Med.; Brit. Paediat. Assn. Prev: Prof. Child Psychiat. Inst. Child Health & Hon. Cons. Phys. Childr. Hosp. Ormond St. Lond.; Dean Inst. Child Health; Cons. Phys. Bethlem Roy. & Maudsley Hosps.

GRAHAM, Mr Philip Yates London Independent Hospital, 1 Beaumont Square, Stepney Green, London E1 4NL Tel: 020 7790 0990; 10 Harley Street, London W1N 1AA Tel: 020 7636 6540 — MB BS 1979 Newc.; FRCS Eng. 1984; T(Plastic Surg.) 1992. Aesthetic Plastic Surg. Lond. Indep. Hosp. Socs: Eur. Acad. of Facial Surg.; Assoc. Mem. Brit. Assn. Plastic Surgs.

GRAHAM, Ralph Scorer The Surgery, Parkwood Drive, Warners End, Hemel Hempstead HP1 2LD Tel: 01442 250117 Fax: 01442 256185; Melbury, Meadway, Berkhamsted HP4 2PL — MB BS 1971 Lond.; MRCP (U.K.) 1974; MRCGP 1979. Assoc. Specialist Dept. Gastroenterol. Watford Gen. Hosp. & W. Herts. Gen. Hosp. Socs: Brit. Soc. Gastroenterol. Prev: Course Organiser Hemel Hempstead VTS.

GRAHAM, Raymond Wheldon (retired) Branch End Surgery, Stocksfield NE43 7LL Tel: 01661 842626 Fax: 01661 844392 — MB BS 1964 Durh.; MD Newc. 1969; DMRD Eng. 1972. Prev: Ho. Phys. & Ho. Surg. & Regist. (Radiol.) Roy. Vict. Infirm. Newc.

GRAHAM, Reginald Edgar (retired) 11 Lambton Crescent, Sedgefield, Stockton-on-Tees TS21 2DE Tel: 01740 620455 Email: g20248@exdir — MRCS Eng. LRCP Lond. 1950; BA Lond. 1933; FFA RCS Eng. 1961; DA Eng. 1954. Hon.Cons. Anaesth. N.. RHA. Prev: Regist. (Anaesth.) Birm. Accid. Hosp. & Gulson Hosp. Coventry.

GRAHAM, Rena Louise 14 Denewood Road, Highgate, London N6 4AJ — MB BS 1972 Lond.; DA Eng. 1974.

GRAHAM, Richard Darcy 183 Main Road, Duston, Northampton NN5 6RD — MB BS 1987 Lond.

GRAHAM, Richard Gordon (retired) Game Keepers Cottage, Corkscrew Lane, Coleorton, Leicester LE67 8FF Tel: 01530 412571 — BM BCh 1941 Oxf.

GRAHAM, Richard James Doctors Residence, Heartlands Hospital, Bordesley Green, Birmingham B14 7ET — MB ChB 1991 Birm.; MB ChB (Hons.) Birm. 1991. SHO (Med.) Birm. Heartlands Hosp.

GRAHAM, Robert 35 Osborne Drive, Belfast BT9 6LH Tel: 028 665444 — MB BCh BAO 1945 Dub. (TC Dub.)

GRAHAM, Robert Donald 2B Wyndham Way, Oxford OX2 8DF — BM BCh 1970 Oxf.; MA Oxf. 1967, BM BCh 1970; FFA RCS Eng. 1981. Cons. Anaesth. Whittington Hosp. Lond. Prev: Staff Anaesth. Harvard Univ. Boston Mass., USA.

GRAHAM, Robert James Ogle Birchwood Surgery, 232-240 Nevells Road, Letchworth SG6 4UB Tel: 01462 683456; 84 Lytton Avenue, Letchworth SG6 3HY — MB BS 1988 Lond.; MRCGP 1992. Prev: Trainee GP Lister Hosp. Stevenage; Ho. Surg. Roy. Free Hosp. Lond.; Ho. Phys. Qu. Eliz. Hosp. King's Lynn Norf.

GRAHAM, Robert Marshall (retired) The Rufflets, 115 Gartree Road, Oadby, Leicester LE2 2FF Tel: 0116 270 5368 — MB ChB 1960 Glas.; FRCOG 1977, M 1964. Prev: Cons. (O & G) Leicester Gen. Hosp.

GRAHAM, Robert Martin James Paget Hospital, Gorleston, Great Yarmouth NR31 6LA Tel: 01493 452613 Fax: 01493 452801 — MB BS 1977 Lond.; FRCP Lond. 1994; MRCP (UK) 1980. Cons. Dermat. Jas. Paget NHS Trust. Socs: Fell. Internat. Soc. Dermat. Surg.; Brit. Assn. Dermat.; Amer. Acad. Dermat. Prev: Sen. Regist. (Dermat.) Roy. Liverp. Hosp.; Hon. Tutor (Dermat.) Univ. Liverp.; Regist. (Dermat.) St. Thos. Hosp. Lond. & Roy. Berks. Hosp.

GRAHAM, Robin Charles Pieter Beech Hill Medical Practice, 278 Gidlow Lane, Wigan WN6 7PD Tel: 01942 821899 Fax: 01942 821752 — MB BS 1973 Lond. (St. Mary's) Prev: Resid. Emerg. King Edwd. VII Hosp. Bermuda; SHO Anaesth. Freedom Fields Hosp. Plymouth; Ho. Phys. St. Mary's Hosp. Lond.

GRAHAM, Ronald Cairns, CBE (retired) 34 Dalgleish Road, Dundee DD4 7JT Tel: 01382 455426 — MB ChB Glas. 1956; FRCP Ed. 1983, M 1981; FFCM 1973; Dip. Soc. Med. Ed. 1968. Prev: Chief Admin Med. Off. Tayside Health Bd.

GRAHAM, Ronald David Carolside Medical Centre, 1 Carolside Gardens, Clarkston, Glasgow G76 7BS Tel: 0141 644 3511 Fax: 0141 644 5525; 6 The Grove, Giffnock, Glasgow G46 6RW — MB ChB 1973 Glas.; MRCGP 1977; DRCOG 1975. Police Surg. F & G Div. Glas.

GRAHAM, Rosemary Dickson (retired) Leemost House, Radnor Cliff Crescent, Sandgate, Folkestone CT20 2JQ Tel: 01303 240100 Fax: 01303 240100 — MB BS Lond. 1946; FRCPCH 1997; FFPHM 1989; FFCM 1977. Prev: Cons. Pub. Health Med. St. Geo.'s Hosp., Lond. SW17.

GRAHAM, Russell Frederick The Regency Hospital, West Street, Macclesfield SK11 8DW Tel: 01625 501150; Brae-Side, Buxton Old Rd, Macclesfield SK11 0AG Tel: 01625 426913 — MB ChB Liverp. 1957; FFA RCS Eng. 1967. (Liverp.) Cons. Anaesth. E. Chesh. NHS Trust. Socs: Fell. Manch. Med. Soc.; Soc. for Intravenous Anaesthesa (UK); Brit. Soc. of Urthopaedic Anaesth.s. Prev: Capt. RAMC; Regist. (Anaesth.) United Liverp. Hosps. & Chester Roy. Infirm.

GRAHAM, Sara Marguerite 38 My Ladys Mile, Holywood BT18 9EN — MB BCh BAO 1989 Belf.; MRCGP 1993; DRCOG 1992. Trainee GP Co. Antrim VTS.

GRAHAM, Simon Matthew 142 Lightwood Road, Buxton SK17 6RW — MB ChB 1994 Leeds.

GRAHAM, Stephen Geoffrey Department of Anaethesia, Cheriton House, South Cleveland Hospital, Marton Road, Middlesbrough TS4 3BW — MB ChB 1982 Leeds; FRCA 1989. Cons. Anaesth.

GRAHAM, Stephen Henry Parliament Hill Surgery, 113-117 Highgate Road, London NW5 1TR Tel: 020 7485 1095 Fax: 020 7284 4677; 5 Sumerlee Avenue, London N2 9QP Tel: 020 8444 8220 — MB BS 1983 Lond.; BSc (Hons.) Lond. 1980; MRCGP 1998. (Middlx.) Bd. Mem. N. Camden PCG; GP Tutor, Thames Postgrad. Med. & Dent. Educat. Univ. Lond. Prev: Trainee GP Lond.; Clin. Med. Off. (Paediat.) St. Giles Hosp. Lond.; SHO (Paediat.) Whittington Hosp. Lond.

GRAHAM, Stuart James 10 Borrowdale Gardens, Camberley GU15 1QZ Email: prism_ian@compuserve.com — MB BS 1994 Lond.; BSc Lond. 1991. (UMDS) Prev: Surg. Rotat. (Obst.) Frimley Pk. Hosp.

GRAHAM, Susan c/o Evans, 14 Meads Grove, Astley, Tyldesley, Manchester M29 7HE — MB ChB 1998 Ed.; MB ChB Ed 1998.

GRAHAM, Susan Mary 84 Lytton Avenue, Letchworth SG6 3HY — MB BS 1988 Lond.; DRCOG 1991. Asst. GP Letchworth. Prev: Trainee GP/SHO (Obst. & Paediat.) & Ho. Off. (Phys.) Lister Hosp. Stevenage; Ho. Off. (Surg.) Qu. Eliz. II Hosp. King's Lynn.

GRAHAM, Tanya Carole 9 Helen Terrace, Port Dinorwic LL56 4SZ — MB ChB 1991 Dundee; DRCOG 1995; DCH RCP Lond. 1995.

GRAHAM, Thomas British Military Hospital, Rinteln BFPO 29 — MB BCh BAO 1965 Belf.; FRCPI 1986, M 1976; DCH Eng. 1971. Paediat. Brit. Milit. Hosp. Rinteln. Prev: Paediat. Brit. Milit. Hosp. Iserlohn & Camb. Milit. Hosp.; Aldershot.

GRAHAM, Mr Timothy Robin Department Cardiothoracic Surgery, Queen Elizabeth Hospital, Edgbaston, Birmingham B15 2TH Tel: 0121 627 2541 Ext: 2533 Fax: 0121 627 2542; Tel: 0791 660845 Email: tim.graham@university_b.wnyds.nhs.uk — MB ChB 1979 Dundee; FECTS 1999; FRCS (Hons.) Glas. 1997; FRCS Ed. 1984; FRCS Eng 1998. (Dundee) Cons. Cardiothoracic Surg. Qu. Eliz. Hosp. Birm.; Hon. Sen. Lect. Birm. Univ. Socs: Soc. Cardiothoracic Surg.; Brit. Cardiac Soc.; Eur. Assn. Cardiothoracic Surg. UK. Prev: Cons. & Sen. Lect. (Cardiothoracic Surg.) Roy. Lond. Hosp.; Sen. Regist. (Cardiothoracic Surg.) Leicester, Nottm. & Papworth Hosp. Camb.; Research Fell. Hon. Lect. (Cardiothoracic Surg.) Lond. Hosp. Med.

GRAHAM, Vanessa Auriol Lindsay Willesden Chest Clinic, Willesden Hospital, Robson Avenue, London NW10 — BM BCh 1973 Oxf.; MRCP (UK) 1976.

GRAHAM, Victoria Helen Jane 180 Rhymney Street, Cardiff CF24 4DJ — MB BCh 1998 Wales.

GRAHAM, Walter (retired) 9 Preston Road, Lytham St Annes FY8 5BL Tel: 01253 737523 Fax: 01253 737523 — MB BS 1953 Lond.; LMSSA Lond. 1948.

GRAHAM, William (retired) Aston House, Whitburn Road, Cleadon, Sunderland SR6 7QL Tel: 0191 536 7003 — MB BS 1953 Durh. Prev: GP S. Shields.

GRAHAM, Mr William Bryce Bramhall Health Centre, 66 Bramhall Lane South, Bramhall, Stockport SK7 2DY Tel: 0161 439 8213 Fax: 0161 439 6398; 21 The Mere, Cheadle Hulme, Cheadle SK8 5LA Tel: 0161 485 5118 — MB BChir 1968 Camb.; MA Camb. 1970; FRCS Ed. 1975. (St. Bart.) Clin. Asst. (Gen. Med.) Stepping Hill Hosp. Stockport. Prev: Regist. (Surg.) Manch. Roy. Infirm.; Demonst. (Anat.) Univ. Bristol; Resid. Ho. Surg. St. Bart. Hosp. Lond.

GRAHAM, Mr William Henry Bowers Wood Retirement Home, Nateby, Preston; Forton Lodge, Fornton, Preston PR3 0AJ Tel: 01524 203 — MB ChB 1927 Glas.; FRCS Eng. 1934. (Glas. & King's Coll. Lond.) Urol. Surg. Roy. Infirm. Preston, Chorley & Dist. Hosp., W.morland Co. Hosp. Kendal & Lytham Cottage Hosp.; Cons. Urol. Surg. Roy. Infirm. Lancaster; Hon. Lt.-Col. RAMC. Socs: Counc. Brit. Assn. Urol. Surgs.; Internat. Soc. Urol. Prev: Asst. Surgic. Unit, Brit. Postgrad. Med. Sch. Lond.; Surg. St. Mary's Hosp. Islington.

GRAHAM, William Henry (retired) Knowehead, Slaggyford, Carlisle CA8 7PH Tel: 01434 320272 — MB ChB Ed. 1945; DIH 1949.

GRAHAM, Mr William John Hill (retired) Whitestones, 8 The Green, Carrickblacker, Portadown, Craigavon BT63 5LH Tel: 0283 833 2130 — MB BCh BAO Belf. 1953; FRCSI 1980; FRCS Eng. 1962; FRCS Ed. 1961; DObst RCOG 1955. Prev: Cons. Surg. Craigavon Area Hosp., N. Armagh Hosp. & Banbridge &.

GRAHAM, William McKenzie Crookston Medical Centre, Glasgow G53 7FY Tel: 0141 883 8887; 3 Shuna Place, Newton Mearns, Glasgow G77 6TN Tel: 0141 639 1693 — MB ChB 1983 Glas.; MRCGP 1987; DRCOG 1987. GP Glas..

GRAHAM-BROWN, Katherine Elizabeth 26 Letheren Place, Eastbourne BN21 1HL Tel: 01323 439024 — MB BS 1985 Lond.; FRCS Lond. 1990; FCOphth 1990; DO RCS Eng. 1989. Clin. Asst. Roy. Free Hosp. Lond. Prev: Regist. (Ophth.) Roy. Berks. Hosp. Reading.; SHO (Ophth.) Kings Coll. Hosp. Lond.; SHO (Ophth.) Kent Co. Ophth. & Aural Hosp. Maidstone.

GRAHAM-BROWN, Robin Alan Charles The Leicester Royal Infirmary, Leicester LE1 5WW Tel: 0116 258 5162 Fax: 0116 258 6792; Killiecrankie, 46 Barrow Road, Burton on the Wolds, Loughborough LE12 5TB Tel: 01509 880558 Email: rgrahamb@aol.com — MB BS 1973 Lond.; BSc Lond. 1970; FRCP Lond. 1990; MRCP (UK) 1976; MRCS Eng. LRCP Lond. 1973. (Royal Free Hospital) Cons. Dermat. Leicester Roy. Infirm.; Hon. Sen. Lect. (Dermat.) Univ. Leicester; Clin. Dir. (Med.) Leicester Roy. Infirm. Socs: Brit. Assn. Dermatol.; Dowling Club; Fell. Roy. Soc. Med. Prev: Sen. Regist. (Dermat.) Roy. Free Hosp. Lond.; Regist. (Med.) Qu. Mary's Hosp. Roehampton; Ho. Phys. Roy. Free Hosp. Lond.

GRAHAM-CUMMING, Andrew Nesbitt, Group Capt. RAF Med. Br. DDAvMed (RAF), Headquarters Personnel & Training Command, RAF Innsworth, Gloucester GL3 1EZ Tel: 01452 712612 ext 5816 Fax: 01452 510841 Email: avmed@ddavmed.demon.co.uk — MB BS 1974 Lond.; MRCS Eng. LRCP Lond. 1974; MRCGP 1980; DAvMed 1982; MFOM RCP Lond. 1996. (St. Mary's) RAF Med. Off. Gloucester; Dep. Dir. Aviat. Med. Socs: Roy. Aeronaut. Soc.

GRAHAM-EVANS, John Nigel (retired) Felpham & Middleton Health Centre, 109 Flansham Park, Felpham, Bognor Regis PO22 6DH Tel: 01243 582384 Fax: 01243 584933 — MB BS 1957 Lond.; MRCS Eng. LRCP Lond. 1957; FRCGP 1982, M 1972; DObst RCOG 1959. Prev: Ho. Off. (O & G) Brighton Gen. Hosp.

GRAHAM-JONES, Susanna Department of Primary Care, Institute of Health Sciences, Headington, Oxford OX3 7LF Tel: 01865 226621 Fax: 01865 513017 Email: susanna.grahamjones@dphpc.ox.ac.uk; 11 St. Margaret's Road, Oxford OX2 6RU Tel: 01865 557245 Fax: 01865 513017 Email: susanna.graham-jones@dphpc.ox.ac.uk — MB BS 1975 Lond.; BA Oxf 1971, DPhil 1981; MRCGP 1986. (St. Mary's) Lect. (Gen. Pract.) Oxf. Univ. Socs: Wom. in Med. Assn.; Assn. Univ. Depts. Gen. Pract. Prev: GP & Lect. (Gen. Pract.) Liverp.; Trainee GP Wantage Health Centre; Med. Off. Save the Childr. Fund Nepal.

GRAHAM MUNRO, Fiona Jane 151 Bisley Road, Stroud GL5 1HS — MB ChB 1988 Leeds.

GRAHAM-SERVICE, David Martin (retired) Cleveden, 6A Gartconnell Drive, Bearsden, Glasgow G61 3BL Tel: 0141 942 3334 Email: david@graham-service.ponet.co.uk — MB ChB St. And. 1942. Doctor Osteop. Kirksville, Mo. 1948. Prev: Resid. Surg. Off. Thoracic Unit, Harefield Hosp.

GRAHAM-STEWART, John Cameron Mulberry Grange, St Boniface Road, Ventnor PO38 1PP — MRCS Eng. LRCP Lond. 1949; Apptd. Fact. Doctor.

GRAHAME, Professor Rodney, CBE 46 Clifton Hill, London NW8 0QG Tel: 020 7624 4364 Fax: 020 7625 4364 Email: rodneygrahme@cs.com; Hospital of St John and St Elizabeth, 60 Grove End Road, London NW8 9NH Tel: 020 7286 5126 Fax: 020 7266 2316 — MB BS Lond. 1955; MD Lond. 1969; FRCP Lond. 1975, M 1959; MRCS Eng. LRCP Lond. 1956; FACP 1988. (Lond. Hosp.) Emerit. Prof. Clin. Rheum. Univ. Lond.; Cons. Rheum. Emerit. Guy's Hosp. Lond.; Chairm. Disabil. Living Allowance Adviser Bd. (DSS).; Cons. Rheum UCL Hosps.; Emerit. Prof. Clin. Rheum Guy's King's Coll. & St Thomas Hosps. Med. & Dent. Sch.; Hon. Cons., Gt. Ormond St. Childr.'s Hosp., Lond.. Socs: (Ex-Pres.) Brit. Soc. for Rheum.; (Ex-Chairm.) Educat. Comm. Internat. League of Assns. of Rheumat.; Ex-Pres. Brit. League Against Rheum. Prev: Cons. Rheum Guy's & St Thos Hosps. Trust; Maynard Jenour Clin. Research Fell. Kennedy Inst. Rheum. Lond.; Sen. Regist. (Med., Rheum. & Physical Med.) W. Lond. Hosp.

GRAHAME-CLARKE, Cairistine Naomi Ellinor The Old Hall, E. Tuddenham, Dereham NR20 3ND — BM BCh 1990 Oxf.; BA, BM BCh Oxf. 1990; MRCP (UK) 1994. Regist. Rotat. (Med.) Addenbrooke's Hosp. Camb. Prev: SHO Lond. Chest Hosp.; SHO Rotat. (Med.) Whittington Hosp. Lond.

GRAHAME-SMITH, Professor David Grahame, CBE (retired) — MB BS Lond. 1956; PhD Lond. 1966; FRCP Lond. 1972, M 1958; MRCS Eng. LRCP Lond. 1956. Fell. Corpus Christi Coll. Oxf. Prev: Rhodes Prof. Clin. Pharmacol. Univ. Oxf.

GRAHAME-SMITH, Harvey Neil 34 Spring Meadow, Ballinderry Upper, Lisburn BT28 2RN Tel: 01846 613109 — MB BS 1981 Lond.; MRCP (UK) 1985; MRCGP 1988; DRCOG 1986. (St. Mary's) Prev: SHO (Paediat.) Norf. & Norwich Hosp.; SHO (Obst.) St. Marys Hosp. Lond.; SHO (Med.) City Hosp. Nottm.

GRAIN, Lucy Alice Thurlow Department of Paediatrics, Princess Margaret Hospital, Swindon Tel: 01793 536231; 24 Edwards Meadow, Marlborough SN8 1UD Tel: 01672 516755 Email: lucy.grain@smnhst.swest.nhs.uk — MB ChB 1985 Liverp.; MRCP (UK) 1990. Cons. Paediat. P.ss Margt. Hosp. Swindon Wilts. Socs: Roy. Coll. Paediat. and Child Health. Prev: Regist. (Paediat.) St. Geo. Hosp. Lond.; Sen. Regist.(Paediat) Oxf. RHA; Flexible trainee Paediatric Intens. care.

***GRAINGE, Christopher Leonard,** Surg. Lt. 20 Van Gogh Place, Bognor Regis PO22 9BQ Tel: 01243 829424 — MB BS 1998 Lond.; MB BS Lond 1998.

GRAINGE, Simon Michael Wyatt High Street Surgery, 116-118 High Street, Hythe CT21 5LE Tel: 01303 266652 Fax: 01303 261711; Seaton House, 12 Hillcrest Road, Hythe CT21 5EU Tel: 01303 265640 — MB ChB 1973 Bristol; DObst RCOG 1976.

GRAINGER, Andrew James 202 Derwent Court, Freeman Hospital, High Heaton, Newcastle upon Tyne NE7 7DN; 76 Stoke Valley Road, Exeter EX4 5ER — BM BS 1990 Nottm.

GRAINGER, Caron Roberta NHS Executive West Midlands, 142 Hagley Road, Birmingham B16 9PA Tel: 0121 224 4679 Fax: 0121 224 4680 Email: cgrainge@doh.gov.uk — MB ChB 1988 Leeds; MFPHM RCP (UK) 1994; MD Leeds 1998. Cons. Pub. Health Med. NHS Exec. W. Midl.; Hon. Sen. Clin. Lect. Univ. Birm. Prev: Sen. Regist. (Pub. Health Med.) Solihull Health.

GRAINGER, Cecil Richard Public Health Services, St Helier, Jersey JE1 4HR Tel: 01534 623700 Fax: 01534 730353 Email: hss03@itl.net; St Clair Cottage, La Ruelle de Ste Clair, St Lawrence, Jersey JE3 1HD Tel: 01534 871932 — MB ChB Leeds 1963, DPH 1970; DObst RCOG 1966; FFPHM RCP Lond. 1993; MFCM 1983; T(PHM) 1991. (Leeds) Med. Off. Health Jersey. Socs: Fell. Roy. Soc. Trop. Med. & Hyg.; BMA. Prev: SCM Cornw. & Isles of Scilly HA; MOH Seychelles.

GRAINGER, David John 3 Old Grange Avenue, Ballymena BT42 2EA; Antrim Hospital, 45 Bush Road, Antrim BT41 2RL Tel: 01849 424000 — MB BCh BAO Belf. 1968; FFA RCSI 1973; DObst RCOG 1971. Cons. (Anaesth.) Antrim Hosp. Antrim. Prev: Sen. Regist. (Anaesth.) Roy. Vict. Hosp. Belf.; Ho. Off. Roy. Vict. Hosp.

GRAINGER, David Nicholas Throckley Surgery, Back Victoria Terrace, Throckley, Newcastle upon Tyne NE15 9AA Tel: 0191 267 4005 Fax: 0191 229 0646; Old School House, Towne Gate, Heddon-on-the-Wall, Newcastle upon Tyne NE15 0DT Tel: 01661 853182 — MB BS 1988 Newc.; BMedSci 1987; MRCGP (Distinc.) 1993; DFFP 1993; T(GP) 1993; DRCOG 1991. Clin. Asst. (A & E) Newc. Gen. Hosp. Socs: BMA. Prev: Trainee GP Heston Med. Centre Newc.; SHO (Psychiat. & O & G) N. Tyneside Gen. Hosp. N. Shields.

GRAINGER, Freda (retired) 9 Fairway, Upper Hopton, Mirfield WF14 8PY Tel: 01924 497291 — MB ChB 1955 Manch.; DA Eng. 1957. Prev: SCMO Huddersfield DHA.

GRAINGER, Iain Michael Eden Medical Group, Port Road, Carlisle CA2 7AJ Tel: 01228 24477 — MB ChB 1989 Manch.; BSc St. And. 1986; MRCGP 1993; DRCOG 1992. Chairm. Carlisle & Dist. Commiss.ing Gp.

GRAINGER, Jacqueline 15 Braeworth Close, Yarm TS15 9SB — MB ChB 1994 Leic.

GRAINGER, Jessie Ellen Joyce (retired) 6 Succoth Place, Edinburgh EH12 6BL Tel: 0131 337 5861 — MB ChB 1946 Ed.; FRCP Ed. 1970. Prev: Phys. & Sen. Med. Regist. Bangour Gen. Hosp.Broxburn.

GRAINGER, John David 38 Grasmere Road, Huddersfield HD1 4LJ — MB ChB 1994 Sheff.

GRAINGER, John Michael 28 Snailbeach, Minsterley, Shrewsbury SY5 0NS — MB ChB St. And. 1961; MRCPath 1973. Cons. Cytologist P.ss Roy. Hosp. Telford.

GRAINGER, Leslie Nuffield Health Centre, Witney OX28 6JQ Tel: 01993 703641 — MB ChB 1965 Leeds.

GRAINGER, Mark Adrian — MB BS 1991 Lond.; BPharm Lond. 1985; DFFP 1995. (St. Thos. Hosp.) GP Princip.; Clin. Asst. (Dermat.) ChristCh. Hosp.; Clin. Asst. (Occupat.al Health) Roy. Bournemouth Hosp. Socs: Roy. Pharmaceut. Soc. GB.

GRAINGER, Melvin Frank 38 Broughton Road, Stourbridge DY9 0XP — MB ChB 1992 Manch.

GRAINGER, Paul George South Tyneside District General Hospital, Harton Lane, South Shields NE34 0PL; 11 Kingsway, South Shields NE33 3NN — MB BS 1990 Lond.; BSc (Psychol.) Lond. 1987; MRCP (UK) 1994. Regist. (Med.) S. Tyneside Dist. Gen. Hosp. Prev: SHO (Neurol.) Middlesbrough Gen. Hosp.; SHO (Cardiol.) S. Cleveland Hosp.; SHO (Gen. Med. & Geriat.) N. Tees Hosp.

GRAINGER, Robert Housman (retired) 19 Low Green, Woodham Village, Newton Aycliffe DL5 4TR Tel: 01325 315577 — MB ChB Leeds 1954.

GRAINGER, Professor Ronald Graham Little Orchard, 8 Clumber Road, Sheffield S10 3LE Tel: 0114 230 5476 Fax: 0114 230 5476 Email: profgrai@aol.com — MB ChB (Hons.) Leeds 1945; MD Leeds 1948; FRCP Lond. 1971, M 1951; FRCR 1975; FFR 1954; Hon. FRACR 1979; Hon. FACR 1974; DMRD Eng. 1952. (Leeds) Emerit. Kodak Prof. Radiol. Univ. Sheff.; Hon. Edr. Clin. Radiol.; Examr. RCR & Edin. DMRD. Socs: Fell. of Roy. Coll. of Radiologists; Brit. Inst. Radiol.; BMA. Prev: Cons. Radiol. Lond. Chest Hosp. Sheff. Uni. Hosps.; Sen. Hosp. Med. Off. & Sen. Regist. St Thos. Hosp.

GRAINGER, Ruth Louise The Barn, Green End, Hebden Bridge HX7 8SQ — MB ChB 1992 Manch.

GRAINGER, Stephen Leigh King George Hospital, Barley Lane, Goodmayes, Ilford IG3 8YB Tel: 020 8983 8000 Fax: 020 8970 8124; Rockhills Farm, Willingale, Ongar CM5 0QG Email: dr.rockhills@lineone.net — MB BS 1973 Lond.; MD Lond. 1986; FRCP Lond. 1995; MRCP (UK) 1977. (St. Bart.) Cons. Phys. King Geo. Hosp. Redbridge. Socs: Brit. Soc. of Gastroenterol.; Brit. Asst. for Study of the Liver. Prev: Lect. St. Thos. Hosp. Med. Sch. Lond.; Sen. Regist. St. Thos. Hosp. Lond.

GRAIS, Morad The Cottage Ashfield, Falmouth TR11 2RZ Tel: 01326 311355 — MB BCh 1965 Alexandria.

GRALTON, Ernest James Frederick St Andrews Hospital, Cliftonville, Northampton NN1 5BE Tel: 01604 615500 Fax: 01604 615501 Email: eec.ernest@virgin.net — MB BS 1986 New South Wales; MRCPsych 1994. Socs: N.ampton Med. Soc.; BMA. Prev: Specialist Regist. (Forens. Psychiat.) Langdon Hosp. Devon; Regist. Rotat. (Psychiat.) Cornw. & W. Devon.; Sen. Regist. (Psychiat.) Cornw. & Isles of Scilly Learning Disabil. NHS Trust.

GRAMMENA, Paschalia Room 267 West Wing N/H, Guy's Hospital, St Thomas St., London SE1 9RT — Ptychio Iatrikes 1989 Thessalonika.

GRAMSMA, A The Surgery, Stock Hill, Biggin Hill, Westerham TN16 3TJ Tel: 01959 573352 Fax: 01959 570785.

GRANDE, Michael John 13 Kingsdown Road, London N19 4LD — MB BS 1981 Lond.; MA Camb. 1978; MSc Lond. 1976, MB BS 1981. (Guy's)

GRANDE, Ricardo Alfonso 185 Cromwell Road, London SW5 0SE — MB BS 1954 Lond.; MRCP Lond. 1961; MRCS Eng. LRCP Lond. 1954. (Westm.) Cons. Phys. N. Middlx. Hosp. Lond.; Cons. Phys. St. Ann's Hosp. Tottenham. Socs: BMA. Prev: Sen. Regist. Brompton & Lond. Chest Hosp.

GRANDEY, Frederick Michael 38 Carlbury Avenue, Acklam, Middlesbrough TS5 8SQ Tel: 01642 821690 — BM BCh 1984 Oxf.; MRCGP 1990; DGM RCP Lond. 1990. (Oxford)

GRANDHI, Valli Northwood Park Road Surgery, 85 Northwood Park Road, Bushbury, Wolverhampton WV10 8EX Tel: 01902 831500 / 931700 Fax: 01902 831996 / 834700 — MB BS 1972 Osmania; DCH RCP Lond. 1980; DRCOG 1976; DObst RCPI 1980. GP.

GRANDISON, Alistair Laidlaw 34B Barnsbury Street, London N1 1ER — MB ChB 1986 Aberd. SHO (Histopath.) Lond. Hosp.

GRANDISON, Ian Menmuir Rowden Surgery, Rowden Hill, Chippenham SN15 2SB Tel: 01249 444343 Fax: 01249 446797; Broome Corner, Tytherton Lucas, Chippenham SN15 3RL Tel: 01249 740215 — MB BS 1967 Lond.; MRCS Eng. LRCP Lond. 1967; DObst RCOG 1970; DA Eng. 1970. (St. Geo.) Prev: Ho. Surg., Ho. Phys. & Cas. Off. St. Geo. Hosp. Lond.

GRANEEK, Bernard John Occupational Health Department, Royal Marsden Hospital, Fulham Road, London SW3 6JJ Tel: 020 7808 2139 Fax: 020 7808 2670 Email: bernard.graneek@rmh.nthames.nhs.uk — MB BS 1977 Lond.; BSc Lond. 1974; MRCP (UK) 1982; AFOM RCP Lond. 1990; FRCP 1999. (Royal Free Hospital) Cons. Phys. (Occupat. Health) Roy. Brompton & Harefield NHS Trust & Roy. Marsden Hosp.; Hon. Sen. Lect. (Occupat. & Environent. Med.) Nat. Heart & Lung Inst. Lond. Socs: Brit. Thorac. Soc.; Assn. Nat. Health Serv. Occupat. Phys.; Soc. of Occupat.al Med. - Chairm., Lond. Gp. Prev: Employm. Med. Adviser Health & Safety Exec. Barking; Clin. Lect. (Occupat. Med.) Brompton Hosp. Lond.; Regist. (Med.) St. Mary's Hosp. Lond.

GRANET, David (retired) 21 Broomcroft Road, Newton Mearns, Glasgow G77 5ER Tel: 0141 639 1100 — LRCP LRCS Ed. LRFPS Glas. 1941.

GRANGE, Anthony Robert St James Surgery, 89 Wash Lane, Clacton-on-Sea CO15 1DA Tel: 01255 222121; 14 Connaught Gardens E., Clacton-on-Sea CO15 6HY Email: grange@compuserve.com — MB BS 1976 Lond.; MRCGP 1984; DRCOG 1983. Prev: Med. Regist. Torbay Hosp.; SHO (Gen. Med.) Hull Roy. Infirm.; Ho. Off. The Lond. Hosp.

GRANGE, Caroline Sara Nuffield Department of Anaesthetics, The John Radcliffe Hospital, Headly Way, Headington, Oxford OX3 9DY; 18 Rewley Road, Oxford OX1 2RD — MB BS 1983 Lond.; FRCA 1990; DCH RCP Lond. 1987; DA (UK) 1985. Cons. Anaesth. Radcliffe Hosp. Oxf. Prev: Sen. Regist. (Anaesth.) St. Bart., Gt. Ormond St. Hosp. Childr. & Whipps Cross Hosp. Lond.; Clin. Fell. Brit. Columbia Wom.s Hosp., Vancouver, Canada.

GRANGE, John Michael Imperial College School of Medicine, National Heart and Lung Institute, Dovehouse St., London SW3 6LY Tel: 020 7351 8456 Fax: 020 7376 3442 Email: j.grange@ic.ac.uk; 29 Stanley Road, Northwood HA6 1RQ — MD 1974 Lond.; MSc Lond. 1981, MD 1974, MB BS 1967. (Middlx.) Reader MicroBiol. Imperial Coll. Sch. Med. Nat. Heart & Lung Inst. Lond.; Hon. Cons. Microbiol. Roy. Brompton Hosp. Lond.; Assoc. Edr. InterNat. Jl. of Tuberc. & Lung Dis.; Vis. Prof. UCL Med. Sch. Socs: Roy. Soc. Med.; Internat. Union Against Tuberc. & Lung Dis. Prev: Lect. (Microbiol.) Middlx. Hosp. Med. Sch.; Ho. Phys. Mt. Vernon Hosp. N.wood.; Ho. Surg. St. And. Hosp. Dollis Hill.

GRANGE, Richard Vernon (retired) 85 Long Road, Cambridge CB2 2HE Tel: 01223 841360 — MB BChir Camb. 1949; MA Camb. 1949; MRCP Lond. 1956. Prev: Regist. (Dermat.) Lond. Hosp.

GRANGE, Simon Andre Welham Apartment 30, Fort Picklecombe, Maker, Torpoint PL10 1JB — MB ChB 1991 Bristol.

GRANGE, Mr William John The Royal London Hospital, Whitechapel, London E1 1BB Tel: 020 7377 7000 Ext: 2322; The London Independent Hospital, 1 Beaumont Square, Stepney Green, London E1 4NL Tel: 020 7791 3422 — MB BChir 1971 Camb.; MA Camb. 1970, FRCS Eng. 1975. (Camb. & Lond. Hosp.) Cons. Orthop. Surg. Lond. Hosp. Prev: Sen. Regist. (Orthop.) Lond. Hosp.; Lect. (Surg.) Lond. Hosp. Med. Coll.; Surg. Specialist RAF.

GRANGER, Allan Frederic (retired) 28 Castle Gardens, Kimbolton, Huntingdon PE28 0JE Tel: 01480 860806 — MB ChB 1938 Glas.; MRCGP 1963.

GRANGER, Annabel Catherine Phoebe Maudsley Hospital, Denmark Hill, London SE5 8AZ Tel: 020 7703 6333; 16 Colomb Street, Greenwich, London SE10 9EW — MB BS 1994 Lond.; BSc Lond. 1991; DRCOG 1997; DFFP 1997. (UCL) SHO Rotat. Maudsley. Prev: GP Regist. Leytonstone; SHO (O & G) Whipps Cross; SHO (Paediat.) Whipps Cross.

GRANGER, Charles Edmund Pringle Head, Pringle Bank, Warton, Carnforth LA5 9PW — MB BS 1983 Lond.; BSc Lond. 1980; FRCA. 1992. Cons. Anaesth. & IC Roy. Lancaster Infirm.

GRANGER, David Edmund (retired) 45 Clifton Road, Poole BH14 9PW Tel: 01202 745674 Email: davidgranger@denecote.freeserve.co.uk — MB BS Lond. 1952. Red Cross Examr. (W. Dorset); Volun. Gp Volunteer at E. Dorset Drugs & Alcohol Serv. Prev: Dist. Med. Off. Remploy.

GRANGER, John Douglas (retired) St Just, Sandbourne Road, Bournemouth BH4 8JH Tel: 01202 763518 — BM BCh 1951 Oxf.; MRCGP 1968; DObst RCOG 1958. Prev: GP Bournemouth.

GRANGER, John McLean Grantley Street Surgery, 1 Grantley Street, Glasgow G41 3PT Tel: 0141 632 4698 Fax: 0141 649 6671; 1 Grantley Street, Glasgow G41 3PT — MB ChB 1965 Glas.; DObst RCOG 1967. (Glas.) Prev: Jun. Ho. Off. (Med.) S.. Gen. Hosp. Glas.; Jun. Ho. Off. (Surg.) Ayr Co. Hosp.; Jun. Ho. Off. (Obst.) Stobhill Gen. Hosp. Glas.

GRANGER, Katherine Alexandra Barnsley District general Hospital, Gamber Road, Barnsley S75 2EP; 1 Brighton Terrace, Crookes, Sheffield S10 1NT — MB BS 1986 Lond.; MRCOG 1992. Cons. (O & G). Prev: Sen. Regist. (O & G) N.. Gen. Hsop. Sheff.

GRANGER, Mary Elizabeth Flat 1, Cathedral Court, Cathedral Green, Llandaff, Cardiff CF5 2EB — MB BCh 1957 Wales.

GRANGER-TAYLOR, Claudia Pollock 54 Albert Street, London NW1 7NR — MB BS 1974 Newc.; MRCGP 1979; DRCOG 1980.

GRANIER, Stephen Kneal Whiteladies Health Centre, Whatley Road, Clifton, Bristol BS8 2PU Tel: 0117 973 1201 Fax: 0117 946 6850; Tel: 0117 973 1113 — MB ChB 1991 Cape Town; D OCC Med 2000; MRCGP 1996. GP Princip.; Med. Adviser, BCWA Healthcare, Bristol. Socs: BMA; RCGP. Prev: Research Fell. (Gen. Pract.) King's Coll. of Med. & Dent. Lond.; Clin. Research Fell. (Gen. Pract.) Univ. Wales Coll. Med. Cardiff.

GRANNE, Ingrid Elizabeth Crossways, Hempton, Banbury OX15 0QY; C/O Dept of Obs Gyna, St Mary's Hospital, Oxford Road, Manchester M13 9WL Email: ingrid.granne@lineone.net — MB BS 1998 Lond.; MB BS Lond 1998. (Royal Free Hospital School of medicine) SHO (O & G) St Mary's Hosp., Manch.

GRANNELL, Jonathan The Surgery, 3 Austin Road, Battersea, London SW11 5JP Tel: 020 7498 0232 Fax: 020 7498 0271 — MB BS 1984 Lond.; BSc Lond. 1977, MB BS 1984; DRCOG 1986. SHO (Psychiat.) Hill End. Hosp. St. Albans. Prev: SHO (O & G) W. Herts. Hosp. Hemel Hempstead; SHO (Geriat. Med./Gen. Med.) St. Pauls Hosp. Hemel Hempstead.

GRANNUM, Patrick Neville (retired) Friary House Surgery, 2A Beaumont Road, Plymouth PL4 9BH — MB ChB 1961 Ed. Mem. Plymouth Postgrad. Centre.

GRANOWSKA, Maria St Bartholomews Hospital, Nuclear Medicine Department, West Smithfield, London EC1A 7BE Tel: 020 7601 7144 Fax: 020 7796 3753; 709 Willoughby House, Barbican Est., London EC2Y 8BN Tel: 020 7628 8518 — Lekarz 1964 Warsaw; MSc (Nuclear Med.) Univ. Lond. 1977; FRCR 1997. (Acad. Med. Warsaw) Reader (Nuclear Med.) Univ. Lond. & Hon. Cons. Nuclear Med. St. Bart. Hosp. Med. Coll. & St. Marks Hosp. Lond. Socs: Eur. Assn. Nucl. Med.; Brit. Nuclear Med. Soc.; Soc. Nucl. Med., USA. Prev: Sen. Clin. Lect. & Hon. Cons. St. Bart. Hosp. Med. Coll.; Sen. Clin. Lect. & Hon. Cons. (Nucl. Med.) Middlx. Hosp. & Med. Sch. Lond.; Wellcome Trust Research Fell. Dept. Nucl. Med. St. Bart. Hosp. Lond.

GRANSDEN, William Robert Department of Microbiology, Guy's Hospital, London SE1 9RT — MB BChir 1979 Camb.; MA, MB Camb. 1979, BChir 1978; MRCPath 1986.

GRANT, Professor Adrian Maxwell Health Services Research Unit, Drew Kay Wing, Polwarth Building, Foresterhill, Aberdeen AB25 2ZD Tel: 01224 553908 Fax: 01224 663087 Email: a.grant@abdn.ac.uk; 66 Tillydrone Avenue, Aberdeen AB24 2TN Tel: 01224 484752 Fax: 01224 484752 — BM BCh 1973 Oxf.; MA Oxf. 1974, DM 1986; MSc (Epidemiol.) Lond. 1980; MFPHM RCP (UK) 1995; FRCOG 1991, M 1979; FRCP 1999. (St. Thos.) Dir. Health Servs. Research Unit. Aberd.; Prof. Health Servs. Research Univ. Aberd. Prev: Dir. (Perinatal Trials Serv.) & Epidemiol. Nat. Perinatal Epidemiol. Unit Radcliffe Infirm. Oxf.

GRANT, Alan Jack The Hendon Medical Practice, 5 Sunningfields Road, Hendon, London NW4 4QR Tel: 020 8203 5246 — MB ChB 1971 Manch.; DObst RCOG 1973. Specialist (Med. Acupunc.) Chase Farm Hosps. NHS Trust Enfield; Clin. Asst. Diabetic Clin. N. Middlx. Hosp. Lond.; Ed. Brit. Med. Acupunc. Soc. Jl. Socs: Brit. Med. Acupunct. Soc. Prev: Chairm. Brit. Med. Acupunc. Soc.

GRANT, Alan John 10 Jones Green, Knightsbridge W., Livingston EH54 8QB — MB ChB 1981 Ed.; BSc (Hons.) Ed. 1978, MB ChB 1981; DRCOG 1985.

GRANT, Alexander Chrystal 55 Tiel Path, Glenrothes KY7 5AX — MB ChB 1981 Ed.

GRANT, Allister James 188 Widney Manor Road, Solihull B91 3JW Email: allisterjg@aol.com; 5 Torkington Road, Gatley, Cheadle SK8 4PR — MB ChB 1990 Birm.; MRCP (UK) 1993. MRC Clin. Train. Fell.; Line Research Labs.; Clin. Research Block; Qu. Eliz. Hosp. Birm. Prev: Specialist Regist. QEH Liver & Hepatobiliary Unit Birm.; Specialist Regist. (Gastroenterol. & Gen. Med.) Selly Oak Hosp.; Regist. (Gen. Med. & Gastroenterol.) Worcester Roy. Infirm.

GRANT, Mr Andrew John 60 Plymouth Road, Penarth CF64 3DJ Tel: 01222 703603 — MB BCh 1985 Wales; FRCS (Orth.) 1994; FRCS Ed. 1989. Cons. Orthop. Surg. Roy. Gwent Hosp.

GRANT, Andrew John Addison Court Medical Centre, 4 Brondesbury Road, Kilburn, London NW6 6AS Tel: 020 7624 9853 Fax: 020 7372 3660; 12 Leopold Mews, London E9 7NL Tel: 020 8985 5728 Email: andygrant@dial.pipex.com — MB BS 1983 Lond.; MRCGP 1987; DRCOG 1987. (Char. Cross Hosp. Med. Sch.) Sen. Teachg. Fell.; Non Princip. in Gen. Pract. E. Lond. Socs: Exec. Comm. Mem., Brit. HIV Assoc.; Assn. Univ. Depts. Gen. Pract. Prev: Trainee GP Twickenham VTS; GP Princip., Kilburn, Lond.

GRANT, Angela Claire Campion House, Standen St., Iden Green, Cranbrook TN17 4LB — MB BS 1961 Lond.; MRCS Eng. LRCP Lond. 1961; MRCP Ed. 1969; MRCOG 1967.

GRANT, Angus Robert 5 Concorde Way, Inverkeithing KY11 1PS — MB ChB 1988 Ed.

GRANT, Anne Mackie 10 Harley Street, London W1N 1AA Tel: 0131 447 5263, 0207 467 8471 Fax: 0207 467 8312 Email: mikebowen@quista.net — MB ChB Ed. 1968; DCCH RCP Ed. 1984. Cons. Community Paediat. Lothian Universities NHS Trust. Prev: SCMO (Community Child Health) Lothian HB.

GRANT, Anne Mary 13 Braedale Road, Lanark ML11 7AW — MB ChB 1979 Aberd. Prev: Regist. & SHO (Anaesth.) S.. Gen. Hosp. Glas.

GRANT, Anthony William (retired) The Park Medical Group, Fawdon Park Road, Fawdon, Newcastle upon Tyne NE3 2PE Tel: 0191 285 1763 Fax: 0191 284 2374 — MB BS 1961 Durh.; MRCGP 1978; DObst RCOG 1963.

GRANT, Brian 114 Laurelgrove Dale, Belfast BT8 6ZF — MB BCh BAO 1995 Belf.

GRANT, Bridget Mary 10 Bentley Lane, Grasby, Barnetby DN38 6AW — MB ChB 1980 Leic.; MRCGP 1984; DCH RCP Lond. 1984; DRCOG 1983.

GRANT, Carl Anthony 14D Bibury Court, Hestia Drive, Raddlebarn Road, Birmingham B29 6JD — MB BS 1987 West Indies.

GRANT, Caroline Elizabeth 177 Chastilian Road, Dartford DA1 3LW — MB BS 1994 West Indies.

GRANT, Carolyn Elizabeth Tomintoul House, Flichity, Inverness IV2 6XD Tel: 01808 521213 Fax: 01808 521213; Crown Medical Practice, 12 Crown Avenue, Inverness IV2 3NF — MB ChB 1974 Glas.; MRCGP 1981; DRCOG 1979. (Glasgow)

GRANT, Catherine Elizabeth Links Medical Practice, 144A King Street, Aberdeen AB24 5B Tel: 01224 644463 — MB ChB 1996 Dundee; DFFP 1999 Aberdeen; DRCOG 1999 Aberdeen; MRCGP 2000 (Merit) Aberdeen. (Dundee) GP Princip. Links Med. Pract., 144A King St., Aberd.; Clin. Med. Off., Dept. Of Genito-Urin. Med., Woolmanhill Hosp., Aberd. Socs: Roy. Coll. of Gen. Practitioners; Diplomate of Roy. Coll. of Obst.s & Gynaecologists; Diplomate of Fac. of Family Plann. & Reproductive Healthcare. Prev: Jun. Ho. Off. (Gen. Surg./ENT) Aberd. Roy. Infirm., 1996-97; GP VTS Aberd. Roy. Infirm.; GPVTS Aberd. Roy. Infirm., 1997-1999.

GRANT, Charles Baring Travers (retired) Chowles, Rusper, Horsham RH12 4RH Tel: 01293 871425 — MB BS 1956 Lond.; MA Oxf. 1955; DObst RCOG 1960; DCH Eng. 1961. Prev: Ho. Phys. Qu. Eliz. Hosp. Childr. Lond.

GRANT, Mr Charles Evan Proctor The Manor, Little Cawthorpe, Louth LN11 8NB Tel: 01507 603148 — MB BS 1972 Lond.; FRCS Eng. 1980. (UCH London) Cons. Orthop. Surg. N. Lincs. HA.

GRANT, Charles Pearson Dingwall (retired) The Inclosure, 14 Windsor Place, Stirling FK8 2HY Tel: 01786 465158 Fax: 01786 465158 — MB ChB 1948 Glas.; AFOM RCP Lond. 1982; MRCGP 1957. Prev: GP.

GRANT, Christine Isabel Greyfriars Medical Centre, 33-37 Castle Street, Dumfries DG1 1DL Tel: 01387 257752; Mayfield, 2 Hill St., Dumfries DG2 7AQ Tel: 01387 263309 — MB ChB Aberd. I984; DRCOG 1987. p/t Asst. GP Dumfries. Prev: Trainee GP Dumfries & Galloway HB VTS.

GRANT, Christine Joan 10 Grange Road, Cambridge CB3 9DU — MB BS 1969 Lond.; MB BS (Hons.) Lond. 1969; MRCS Eng. LRCP Lond. 1969. (Westm.) Prev: SHO (O & G) Roy. Hants. Co. Hosp. Winchester; Ho. Phys. Med. Unit Qu. Mary's Hosp. Roehampton; Ho. Surg. W.m. Hosp. Lond.

GRANT, Christopher Alexander 2 The Hawthorns, Newburgh, Wigan WN8 7LL — MB BS 1996 Lond.

GRANT, Christopher Mark Yaxley Group Practice, Yaxley Health Centre, Landsdowne Road, Yaxley, Peterborough PE7 3JX Tel: 01733 240478 Fax: 01733 244645; 47 Sunningdale, Orton Waterville, Peterborough PE2 5UB Email: cms.grant@gp-d8to31.anglox.nhs.uk — MB ChB 1983 Wales; BSc (Hons.) Wales 1980; MRCGP 1987. GP; Chairm. S. PeterBoro. PCG; GP Trainer. Prev: Clin. Asst. (Rheum.) PeterBoro. Dist. Hosp.; GP Couse Organiser PeterBoro. Dist.

GRANT, Christopher William (retired) Corrour, Larchwood Road, Pitlochry PH16 5AS Tel: 01796 472930 — MB ChB St. And. 1949; FRCGP 1988; DObst RCOG 1953. Prev: GP Pitlochry.

GRANT, Clare Mace 18 Southwood Lawn Road, London N6 5SF — MB ChB 1990 Bristol; BSc (Psychol.) Bristol 1987; MRCGP 1995; DRCOG 1994.

GRANT, David Ivan School Lane Surgery, School Lane, Washingborough, Lincoln LN4 1BN Tel: 01522 792360 Fax: 01522 794144; Bramley Cottage, Main St, Hayton, Retford DN22 9LH — MB BS 1986 Lond.; DPD 1999; BSc Lond. 1983; MRCGP 1992; DRCOG 1992; T(GP) 1992; Cert. Family Plann. (Adv & Gen.) JCC 1991; DGM RCP Lond. 1990. (St Barth. Med. Sch.) Prev: SHO (ENT) Doncaster Roy. Infirm.; SHO (A & E & Paediat.) Bassetlaw Dist. Gen. Hosp.

GRANT, David Jonathan Liberton Hospital, Lasswade Road, Edinburgh EH16 6UB; 37 Bonaly Wester, Edinburgh EH13 0RQ Email: d.j.grant@btinternet.com — MB BS 1984 Lond.; MA Camb. 1985; FRCPE 1997. Cons. Phys. (Geriat. Med.) Lothian Univ. Hosp.s NHS Trust Edin. Prev: Sen. Regist. & Hon. Lect. (Geriat. Med.) Ninewells Hosp. Dundee.

GRANT, David Paul Carregwen Surgery, Church Road, Blaenavon NP4 9AF Tel: 01495 790264 Fax: 01495 790334; Beilu Ddu, Llanover Lane, Cwmavon, Pontypool NP4 8UW Tel: 01495 774449 — MB BS 1986 Lond.; BSc Lond. 1983; MRCGP 1990; DRCOG 1989. (St. Mary's Hosp. Lond.) Prev: Trainee GP E. Surrey VTS.

GRANT, David Seafield, Group Capt. Retd. Green Gables, Pershore Road, Hampton, Evesham WR11 6PL — MRCS Eng. LRCP Lond. 1940. (St. Bart.) Prev: RAF Med. Br.

GRANT, David Stephen Department of Imaging, Whittington Hospital NHS Trust, St Mary's Wing, Highgate, London N19 5NF Tel: 020 7288 5019 Fax: 020 7288 5233; 4 Linden Lea, London N2 0RG — MB ChB 1978 Sheff.; BSc (Hons.) Sheff. 1975; MRCP (UK) 1982; FRCR 1986. (Univ. Sheff.) Cons. Radiol. Whittington Hosp. NHS Trust; Hon. Clin. Lect. Inst. Nuclear Med. Lond.; Dir. Imaging Whittington Hosp. NHS Trust. Prev: Sen. Regist. (Radiol.) Univ. Coll. Hosp. Lond.; Regist. Rotat. (Med.) Profess. Scheme. Sheff.

GRANT, Dermot Joseph 46 Ballyarton Road, Killaloo, Londonderry BT47 3TA — MB BCh BAO 1985 Belf.; DRCOG 1988.

GRANT, Donald Andrew The Surgery, 11 Chiphouse Road, Kingswood, Bristol BS15 4TR Tel: 0117 967 1363 — MB ChB 1985 Bristol; MRCGP 1991; DRCOG 1991.

GRANT, Donald Austin (retired) Cornhill, 11 Latch Gardens, Brechin DD9 6LN — MB ChB 1940 Aberd. Prev: Med. Off. Co. Hosp. Brechin.

GRANT, Donald Frederick Community Child Health, Lorn & Islands District General Hospital, Glengallan Road, Oban PA34 4HH Tel: 01631 567613 Fax: 01631 567134; An Eala Bhan, 5 Rathad Achanaiseig, A'Choingheal (Connel Ferry), Oban PA37 1SR — MB ChB Ed. 1965. SCMO & Clin. Co-ordinator (Community Child Health) Argyll & Bute Sectors, Argyll & Bute NHS Trust. Socs: Roy. Coll. Paediat. & Child Health; Scott. Soc. Hist. of Med.; BMA. Prev: Clin. Med. Off. Tayside HB; GP Cardenden Fife; GPAdvis. Inverness-sh.

GRANT, Donald Morris Caversham Group Practice, Kentish Town Health Centre, 2 Bartholomew Road, London NW5 2AJ — MB BChir 1951 Camb.; BA, MB BChir Camb. 1951; FRCGP 1981, M 1969. (Univ. Coll. Hosp.) Sen. Lect. Univ. Coll. Hosp. Med. Sch. Lond. Prev: Nuffield Trav. Fell.; SHO Dept. O & G Ilford Matern. Hosp.; Ho. Phys. Univ. Coll. Hosp.

GRANT, Donna Louise 32 Acacia Drive, Southend-on-Sea SS1 3JX — MB BS 1998 Lond.; MB BS Lond 1998.

GRANT, Elizabeth Dorothy Mary Jones Alyth, 63 Monument Road, Ayr KA7 2UE Tel: 01292 266199 — MB ChB 1949 Glas.; DPH 1954. Prev: Asst. MOH Flints.

GRANT, Elizabeth Mary 50 Radnormere Drive, Cheadle Hulme, Cheadle SK8 5JS; 37 The Circuit, Wilmslow SK9 6DA Tel: 01625 532381 — MB ChB 1990 Sheff.; MRCGP 1995; DFFP 1993; DRCOG 1993. Prev: Regist. (Palliat. Care) Wellington, New Zealand; Trainee GP N.umbria & Gateshead; SHO (Paediat.) Newc. Gen. Hosp.

GRANT, Ellen Catherine Gardner Coombe Heights, 20 Coombe Ridings, Kingston Hill, Kingston upon Thames KT2 7JU Tel: 020 8546 9482 Fax: 020 8546 9482 Email: elleneggrant@onetel.net.uk — MB ChB 1958 St. And.; MB ChB (Commend.) St. And. 1958; DObst RCOG 1960. (St. Andrews University) p/t Priv. Phys. & Med. Gynaecologist; Mem. Edit. Bd. Mem. Jl. Nutrit. & Environm. Med.; Med. Adviser Foresight & Dyslexia Inst. Socs: HACSG; Brit. Soc. Allergy, Environm. & Nutrit. Med.; Dyslexia Inst. - life Mem. Prev: Hon. Clin. Asst. (Neurol.) Char. Cross Hosp. Lond.; Med. Off. Counc. Investig. Fertil. Control Lond.

GRANT, Fiona May 131 Lodge Road, Writtle, Chelmsford CM1 3JB — MB BS 1996 Lond.

GRANT, George Scotsburn Road Health Centre, Scotsburn Road, Tain IV19 1PR Tel: 01862 892203 Fax: 01862 892165; (home), 3 Mayfield Wynd, Tain IV19 1LL — MB ChB 1972 Glas.; BSc (Physiol., Hons.) Glas. 1970, MB ChB 1972. Prev: SHO (Anaesth.) Roy. Infirm. Glas.; Jun. Ho. Off. (Surg.) & Jun. Ho. Off. (Med.) Roy. Infirm. Dumfries.

GRANT, George Bryce (retired) 1 Dene Park, Darras Hall, Ponteland, Newcastle upon Tyne NE20 9AH — MB BS Durh. 1943; FRCGP 1975, M 1952. Hon. Lect. (Primary Health Care) Newc. Univ. Prev: Princip. GP Jarrow.

GRANT, Geraldine Ann 262 Culmore Road, Londonderry BT48 8JL — MB BCh BAO 1979 NUI.

GRANT, Hamish Sutherland Monearn, 4 Dalgleish Gardens, Bishopgate, Cupar KY15 4DL Tel: 01334 656649 — MB ChB 1971 Aberd.; MFOM RCP Lond. 1984; DObst RCOG 1975; DAvMed 1978. RAF Civil. Med. Pract. RAF Leuchars Fife. Socs: FOM; SOM.

GRANT, Helen Christina (retired) 10 Antrim Grove, London NW3 4XR Tel: 020 7483 4065 Email: drhelengrant@hotmail.com — MB BS 1946 Lond.; MD Lond. 1951; FRCP Lond. 1975, M 1948. Prev: Sen. Lect. & Cons. Neuropath. Char. Cross Hosp. Lond.

GRANT, Mr Henry Richard 31 Wimpole Street, London W1G 8GS Tel: 020 7935 3593 Fax: 020 7224 1957 Email: hrgrant@lineone.net; 1A Allison Grove, London SE21 7ER Tel: 020 8693 5105 — MB BS 1964 Lond.; FRCS Eng. 1971; MRCS Eng.

LRCP Lond. 1964; Specialist Accredit. (Orl.) RCS Eng. 1976. (King's Coll. Hosp.) Cons. Surg. (ENT) Roy. Free Hosp. Trust Roy. Nat. Throat Nose & Ear Hosp.; Cons. Surg. (ENT) Whitttington Hosp. Trust. Socs: Roy. Soc. Med. (Ex-Pres. Sect. Laryngol. and Rhinol.); Assn. Head & Neck Oncol. Prev: Cons. Surg. (ENT) Univ. Coll. Hosps. Lond.; Sen. Regist. (ENT) King's Coll. Hosp. Lond.; Regist. (Gen. Surg.) Brook Gen. Hosp. Lond.

GRANT, Hilary Mary Bernadette 138 Goodyers End Lane, Bedworth, Nuneaton CV12 0HU — MB BCh BAO 1991 NUI.

GRANT, Mr Iain Chalmers Derriford Hospital, Derriford Road, Plymouth PL6 8DH Tel: 01752 777111/52516 Fax: 01752 792995 Email: iain.grant@phnt.swest.nhs.uk; The Lodge, Crapstone, Yelverton PL20 7PS — MB ChB 1975 Ed.; BSc (Med. Sci) Ed. 1972; FRCS Ed. 1980; FFAEM 1993. (Edinburgh) Cons. A & E Derriford Hosp.; Cons. A & E Plymouth Hosps. NHS Trust; Sen. Med. Off. Brit. Antarctic Survey Med. Unit; Hon. Sen. Lect. Plymouth Postgrad. Med. Sch. Socs: Brit. Assn. Accid. & Emerg. Med.; Brit. Assn. Immed. Care Schemes; Med. Equestrian Assn. Prev: Cons. Adviser A & E Med. to Med. Dir. Gen. RN; Cons. A & E Med. RN Hosp. Plymouth; Surg. Cdr. RN.

GRANT, Mr Ian Department of Plastic Surgery, Addenbrookes Hospital, Cambridge CB2 2QQ — BM BCh 1991 Oxf.; FRCS 1995 Edin.; MA 1991 Oxford; FRCS Eng. 1995. (Oxford) Specialist Regist. (Plastic Surg.) Addenbrookes Hosp. Camb. Prev: Research Fell. (Plastic Surg.) The Blond McIndoe Centre Qu. Vict. Hosp. E. Grinstead.

GRANT, Ian Cameron 420 Wood Lane, Stannington, Sheffield S6 6AQ Tel: 0114 233 9503 — BM BCh 1974 Oxf.; MA Oxf. 1986, BA 1969, BM BCh 1974; FFA RCS Eng. 1983; DRCOG 1981. (Oxford University) Cons. (Anaesth.) Rotherham Dist. Gen. Hosp.; Dir. Intens. Care. Prev: Sen. Regist. (Anaesth.) Sheff. HA.

GRANT, Mr Ian James Mackay 713 Yardley Wood Road, Birmingham B13 0PT Tel: 0121 444 3597; 348 Sarehole Road, Birmingham B28 0AQ Tel: 0121 778 2672 — MB BS 1957 Lond.; FRCS Ed. 1966. (Middlx.) Prev: Regist. Roy. Orthop. Hosp. Birm.; SHO Birm. Accid. Hosp.; Ho. Phys. & Ho. Surg. Middlx. Hosp. Lond.

GRANT, Ian Rene King George Hospital, Barley Lane, Goodmayes, Ilford IG3 8YB Tel: 020 8983 8000 Fax: 020 8970 8065; 41 Lynwood Drive, Collier Row, Romford RM5 2QX Tel: 01708 769921 Email: ianrg@msn.com — BM 1977 Soton.; MRCP (UK) 1981; FRCPath 1996, M 1985. Cons. Haemat. King Geo. Hosp. Ilford. Prev: Sen. Regist. (Haemat.) Leicester Roy. Infirm.; Regist. (Haemat.) Roy. Liverp. Hosp.; SHO (Haemat.) Gen. Hosp. Soton.

GRANT, Mr Ian Robert (retired) 1 Calderwood Road, Newlands, Glasgow G43 2RP Tel: 0141 637 5755 Email: igrantuk@aol.com — MB ChB Ed. 1961; FRCS Ed. 1970; DObst RCOG 1964; DTM & H Liverp. 1963. Prev: Cons. (Orthop. Surg.) Law Hosp. Carluke.

GRANT, Ian Scott Intensive Care Unit, Western General Hospital, Crewe Road, Edinburgh EH4 2XU Tel: 0131 537 1666 Fax: 0131 537 1021 Email: i.s.grant@ed.ac.uk; 2 Ashburnham Gardens, South Queensferry EH30 9LB Tel: 0131 331 3296 — MB ChB 1972 Ed.; FRCP Glas 1987; FRCP Ed. 1985; MRCP (UK) 1974; FFA RCSI 1978. (University of Edinburgh) Cons. Anaesth. & Dir. IC Unit W.ern Gen. Hosp. Edin. Socs: Coun. Mem. Intens. Care Soc.; Past-Pres. Scott. Intens. Care Soc. Prev: Cons. Anaesth. Ninewells Hosp. Dundee.

GRANT, Ian William Ballantyne (retired) Nether Balchandy, Pitlochry PH16 5JT Tel: 01796 482360 — MB ChB 1941 Ed.; FRCP Ed. 1954; MRCP (UK) 1944. Prev: Cons. Phys. Respirat. Unit, N.. Gen. Hosp. Edin.

GRANT, Isobel Hilary (retired) Braecroft, Tame Bridge, Stokesley, Middlesbrough TS9 5LQ Tel: 01642 710242 — MB BChir 1951 Camb.; FRCPCH 1997; FRCP Ed. 1981, M 1961; DCH Eng. 1954. Prev: Cons. Paediat. N & S Tees Hosp. Gps.

GRANT, James Alexander St Margarets Health Centre, St. Margaret's Drive, Auchterarder PH3 1JH Tel: 01764 662614/662275 Fax: 01764 664178 — MB ChB 1975 Glas.; BSc (Hons.) Glas. 1971, MB ChB 1975; FRCP Ed. 1992; FRCP Glas. 1992; MRCP (UK) 1978; FRCGP 1990.

GRANT, James Alexander Tel: 01674 673400 Fax: 01674 672175; Rosebank, 2 Wellington Gardens, Montrose DD10 8QF Tel: 01674 672123 — MB ChB 1971 Aberd.; CIH Aberd. 1991; DObst RCOG 1974.

GRANT, James Russell (Surgery) Gatesden, Cromer St., London WC1 Tel: 020 7837 8559; 255 Creighton Avenue, London N2 9BP Tel: 020 8883 2382 — MB ChB 1951 Glas. (Glas.) Princip. Gen. Pract. Lond.; Med. Off. Thomas Coram Foundat. & Camden Reception Centre King's Cross Lond. Prev: Psychiat. Provin. Govt. Red Deer, Alta.; Regist. Maudsley Hosp. Lond.; Ho. Phys. Bethnal Green Hosp. Lond.

GRANT, Jamie Thomas 32 Acacia Drive, Thorpe Bay, Southend-on-Sea SS1 3JX — MB BS 1998 Lond.; MB BS Lond 1998.

GRANT, Jane Alyson 3 Pen y Cae, Ystrad Mynach, Hengoed CF82 7FA; Benefit Agency Medical Services, Government Buildings, Gabalfa, Cardiff CF14 4YJ Tel: 01222 586962 — MB BCh 1981 Wales; DRCOG 1985. Med. Adviser Benefits Agency Cardiff. Prev: Clin. Med. Off. (Spinal Injuries & Rehabil.) Rookwood Hosp. Llandaff.

GRANT, Jean Malcolm (retired) Le Clos de Vin, Sark, Guernsey Tel: 01481 832123 — MB ChB 1939 Ed.; FRCP Ed. 1953; FRCPath 1964. Prev: Dir. Regional Transfus. Centre, Oxf.

GRANT, Jennifer Anne 6 Sunniside Terrace, Cleadon, Sunderland SR6 7XE — BM 1982 Soton.; MRCGP 1986; DRCOG 1985. (Soton.) Community Med. Doctor (Family Plann.) S. Shields. Prev: GP Whitburn & Yeovil; Trainee GP Langport.

GRANT, Jeremy John Herring Department of Histopathology, Worthing Hospital, Park Avenue, Worthing BN11 2DH Tel: 01903 285090 Fax: 01903 285077 Email: jenny.grant@wash-tr.sthames.nhs.uk; Dyke House, Lavant, Chichester PO18 0BG Fax: 01243 775109 Email: jgrant@doctros.org.uk — MB BS 1982 Lond.; MRCPath 1995; DRCOG 1987. Cons. Histopath. Worthing & S.lands NHS Trust. Prev: Sen. Specialist AHR RAMC Millbank, Lond.

GRANT, Jill Penelope Longroyde Surgery, 38 Castle Avenue, Rastrick HO6 3HT Tel: 01484 721102 — MB ChB 1986 Sheff.; MRCGP 1991; DRCOG 1991; Cert. Family Plann. JCC 1988. (Sheff.) p/t GP Princip. Longroyde Surg., Rastrick. Socs: BMA; Brit. Menopause Soc.; Diplomate Fac. Family Plann. Prev: GP Princip. Broomhill Surg., Sheff.

GRANT, Joanne Susan Greenend, Coach Road, Overton, Ashover, Chesterfield S45 0JN — MB BChir 1994 Camb.

GRANT, John (retired) 10 Moray Drive, Balloch, Inverness IV2 7HS — MB ChB 1950 Ed.

GRANT, John Silver Willows, Chapel Lane, West Bergholt, Colchester CO6 3EF Tel: 01206 240863 — MB BS 1958 Lond.; FICS 1968; MRCS Eng. LRCP Lond. 1958; DPath Eng. 1964. (Lond. Hosp.) Sen. Lect. Med. Microbiol. Lond. Sch. Hyg. & Trop. Med. (Univ. Lond.). Socs: Fell. Roy. Soc. Trop. Med. & Hyg. Prev: Maj. RAMC, Pathol. Brit. Milit. Hosps. Hannover & Berlin; Lect. & Clin. Pathol. Qu. Mary Hosp. Univ. Hong Kong Fac. Med.

GRANT, John James (retired) 3 Hamilton Road, Glasgow G32 9QD Tel: 0141 778 3241 — MB BCh BAO 1952 NUI.

GRANT, John Leslie The Health Centre, Holding Street, Rainham, Gillingham ME8 7JP Tel: 01634 262333; 10 Berengrave Lane, Rainham, Gillingham ME8 7LS Tel: 01634 231717 — MB ChB 1978 Manch.; DRCOG 1981; DPD 1997.

GRANT, John McGregor 31 Meikle Crescent, Hamilton ML3 7QA — MB ChB 1968 Ed.; FRCS Glas. 1994; MRCP (UK) 1972; MRCOG 1974; DObst 1970; FRCS (Glas) 1994. Cons. O & G Bellshill Matern. Hosp.

GRANT, John William Histopathology Department, Box 235, Addenbrooke's Hospital, Hills Road, Cambridge CB2 2QQ Tel: 01223 216744 Fax: 01223 216980 Email: jwg21@cam.ac.uk; 243 Hinton Way, Great Shelford, Cambridge CB2 5AN Tel: 01223 842733 — MB ChB 1977 Aberd.; MA Camb. 1995; MD Aberd. 1989; FRCPath 1996, M 1984. Cons. Histopath. Addenbrooke's Hosp. Camb.; Assoc. Lect. Univ. Camb; Fell. Emmanuel Coll. Camb. Socs: Path. Soc.; Brit. & Swiss Neuropath. Socs.; Assn. of Clin. Pathologists (ACP). Prev: Sen. Regist. (Neuropath & Histopath.) Soton Gen. Hosp., Oberarzt, Inst. Path. Univ. Hosp. Zurich, Switz.; Regist. (Morbid Anat. & Histopath.) Ninewells Hosp. Dundee.

GRANT, Judith Department Neonatal Medicine and Surgery, University Hospital, Queens Medical Centre, Nottingham NG7 2UH Tel: 01159 249924 Ext: 43429; 66 Hallfields, Edwalton, Nottingham NG12 4AA Tel: 0115 923 1614 — MB BCh 1980 Wales; MRCP (UK) 1984; DCH RCP Lond. 1983. Cons. Neonatologist Qu. Mary Centre Nottm. Prev: Sen. Regist. & Lect. (Child Health) Leic. Univ.

GRANT, Judith 25 Melrose Grove, Spinneyfield, Rotherham S60 3NA Email: j(amelrosegrove.freeserve.co.uk — MB ChB Liverp. 1970; FFOM RCP Lond. 1993, MFOM 1983, AFOM 1980; DIH Eng. 1980; DObst RCOG 1975; DA Eng. 1974. p/t Cons. Occupat.l Phys. - Self Employed; Occupat. Phys.Chesterfield & N Derbys Hosp.NHS Trust. Socs: Fell. Fac. Occupat. Med.; Soc. Occupat. Med. Prev: Cons. in Occupat. Med. Stoke Mandeville Hosp. NHS Trust; Sen. Employm. Med. Adviser Health & Safety Exec. Sheff.

GRANT, Karen Tracey Trosnant Lodge Surgery, Trosnant Lodge, Trosnant Street, Pontypool NP4 8AT Tel: 01495 762709 Fax: 01495 758177; Beilu Ddu, Llanover Lane, Cwmavon, Pontypool NP4 8UW Tel: 01495 774449 — MB BS 1984 Lond.; MRCGP 1990; DRCOG 1989. (St. Mary's Hosp. Lond.) Prev: Trainee GP Reigate VTS; SHO (Geriat. & Paediat.) Redhill Gen. Hosp.

GRANT, Katherine 42 Langhorn Close, Newcastle upon Tyne NE6 1XL — MB BS 1997 Newc.

GRANT, Kathryn Elizabeth Tobias and Grant, 19 Culver Road, Lancing BN15 9AX Tel: 01903 753279 Fax: 01903 851339; 11 Browning Road, Lancing BN15 0PY Tel: 01903 751766 — BM BS 1980 Nottm.; BMedSci Nottm. 1978, BM BS 1980; MRCGP 1984; DRCOG 1982. (Nottm. Med. Sch.)

GRANT, Keith Alexander Diagnostic Imaging, Clatterbridge Centre for Oncology, Clatterbridge Road, Bebington, Wirral CH63 4JY Tel: 0151 334 4000 Fax: 0151 334 0882; Glen Shira, Queens Drive, Heswall, Wirral CH60 6SH — MB BS 1974 Lond.; BSc Lond. 1971, MB BS 1974; MRCP (UK) 1981; FRCR 1984. (Univ. Coll. Hosp.) Cons. Radiol. Clatterbridge Centre for Oncol. Wirral. Prev: Sen. Regist. & Regist. (Radiol.) John Radcliffe Hosp. Oxf.

GRANT, Keith Peter Mark Wallacetown Health Centre, Lyon St., Dundee DD4 6RB Tel: 01382 458333; 34 Strathern Road, Dundee DD5 1PN — MB ChB 1980 Dundee. Socs: MRCGP. Prev: Trainee GP Ninewells Hosp. Dundee VTS; Asst. Med. Off. St. Lukes Hosp. Hiranpur, India.

GRANT, Kenneth Alexander Compthall, Sunnyside Road, Brightons, Falkirk FK2 0RW — MB ChB 1967 Ed.; FRCOG 1986, M 1972. Cons. O & G Forth Valley Health Bd.

GRANT, Lee Alexander 83 Smeeth Road, St Johns Fen End, Wisbech PE14 8JF — MB ChB 1997 Bristol.

GRANT, Liam James 15 Windermere Crescent, Southport PR8 3QS — MB ChB 1998 Liverp.; MB ChB Liverp 1998.

GRANT, Linda 7 Earlspark Way, Bieldside, Aberdeen AB15 9BY — MB ChB 1975 Ed.; MRCP (UK) 1978. GP Asst. Socs: BMA.

GRANT, Linda Joyce Craig 31 Craiglockhart Grove, Edinburgh EH14 1ET — MB ChB 1980 Glas.; MRCGP 1985; DRCOG 1983. Clin. Asst. Inveresk Clin. Research Edin. Prev: GP Glas.

GRANT, Lisa Jane 1 Cedar Walk, 45 Romsey Road, Winchester SO22 5DG — MB BS 1991 Queensland.

GRANT, Lisa Jane 62 Tredelar Square, Bow, London E3 5AE — MB BS 1993 Lond.

GRANT, Lloyd John Peter 44 Cranbrook Road, Redland, Bristol BS6 7BT — MB BS 1988 West Indies.

GRANT, Louise 4 North Gargieston Road, Kilmarnock KA1 1TE — MB ChB 1994 Aberd.; MRCP UK (Paediatrics) Glas 1998. (Aberd.)

GRANT, Lyndsay Jan 4 Dalgleish Gardens, Cupar KY15 4DL — MB ChB 1997 Glas.

GRANT, Margaret Irene 12 Leahill Close, Malvern WR14 2UE Tel: 01684 563216 — MB ChB St. And. 1968; FFA RCS Eng. 1975; DA Eng. 1971. (St. And.) Community Paediat. Worcs.; Sen. Clin. Med. Off. Worcester Community NHS Trust. Socs: Brit. Paediat. Assn.; Dep. Chairm. Roy. Inst. of Publ. Health & Hyg. Soc. Pub. Health.

GRANT, Marion Kirkwood 24 Blackroot Road, Sutton Coldfield B74 2QH Tel: 0121 354 6884 — MB ChB 1956 Birm. (Birm.) Clin. Asst. Accid. Dept. Good Hope Hosp. Sutton Coldfield. Prev: Ho. Phys. Gen. Hosp. Birm.; Ho. Surg. Childr. Hosp. Birm.

GRANT, Marjorie Macaulay (retired) 17 Woodland Close, Chelford, Macclesfield SK11 9BZ Tel: 01625 861170 — MRCS Eng. LRCP Lond. 1956. Prev: SCMO Crewe HA.

GRANT, Mary (retired) 6 Torfield Road, Eastbourne BN21 2HN Tel: 01323 734089 — BM BCh 1955 Oxf.; MA, BM BCh Oxf. 1955. Prev: Assoc. Specialist (Rheum.) E.bourne Dist. Gen. Hosp.

GRANT, Michael Edward Inglewood, 13 Crawley Road, Horsham RH12 4DR Tel: 01403 52875 — MB BCh BAO 1949 NUI; FRCPsych 1983, M 1972; DPM Eng. 1958. Socs: Fell. Roy. Soc. Med. Prev: Cons. Psychiat. Forest Hosp. Horsham; Vis. Cons. Psychiat. St. Thos. More Approved Sch.; Regist. Warlingham Pk. Hosp.

GRANT, Michael Owen (retired) The Woodlands, Hanchurch, Stoke-on-Trent ST4 8RY Tel: 01782 657085 Fax: 01782 657363 — MB BCh BAO 1959 Dub.; FRCOG 1979, M 1966; 2000 BA Dub. Prev: Sen. Regist. Birm. RHB.

GRANT, Neil Colin Robert 26 Eskview Grove, Dalkeith EH22 1JW — MB ChB 1998 Aberd.; MB ChB Aberd 1998.

GRANT, Neil John Crawford (retired) 63 Somerford Road, Cirencester GL7 1TX — MB 1958 Camb.; BChir 1957; DTM & H Eng. 1963; DObst RCOG 1962.

GRANT, Neil Mackie 95 Main Street, Colinsburgh, Leven KY9 1LW — MB ChB 1992 Aberd.

GRANT, Nicola Anne 3 Craighouse Terrace, Edinburgh EH10 5LH — MB ChB 1993 Aberd.

GRANT, Norman Marshall 12 Hathaway Court, The Esplanade, Rochester ME1 1QX Tel: 01634 826092 — MB ChB 1956 Aberd. (Aberd.) Socs: BMA. Prev: Ho. Phys. & Ho. Surg. Woodend Gen. Hosp. Aberd.; Ho. Surg. (Obst.) German Hosp. Lond.

GRANT, Patrick Keith The Ayrshire Hospice, 35-37 Racecourse Rd, Ayr KA7 2TG Tel: 01292 269200 Email: kg@ayrshirehospice.org; 5 Shanter Place, Alloway, Ayr KA7 4RD — MB ChB 1985 Aberd.; MRCGP 1992.

GRANT, Mr Patrick Thomas Accident and Emergency Department, Western Infirmary, Glasgow G11 6NT Tel: 0141 211 2651 Fax: 0141 211 6303 Email: patrick.grant.wg@northglasgow.scot.nhs.uk; 48 Eastwoodmains Road, Giffnock, Glasgow G46 6QD Tel: 0141 571 7365 Email: patrick.grantl@ntlworld.com — MB ChB 1979 Manch.; BSc St. And. 1976; FRCS Ed. 1984; FFAEM 1993; Dip. Forens. Med. Glas 1991. (St. Andrews and Manchester) Cons. (A & E Med.) W. Infirm. Glas.; Hon. Clin. Sen. Lect. Univ. Glas. Socs: Resusc. Counc.; BAEM Soc.; BMA. Prev: Sen. Regist. (A & E) NW RHA.

GRANT, Pauline Ann 65 Phoenix Drive, Wateringbury, Maidstone ME18 5DR — MB ChB 1989 Birm.

GRANT, Peter Craig 65 Sandeman Street, Dundee DD3 7LB — MB ChB 1980 Dundee.

GRANT, Peter Francis Ian Charles Cottage Hospital, The Health Centre, Castle Road East, Grantown-on-Spey PH26 3HR Tel: 01479 872484 Fax: 01479 873503; Rosemount, 3 Woodside Avenue, Grantown-on-Spey PH26 3JN Tel: 01479 872196 Email: 113466.2556@compuserve.com — MB ChB 1978 Ed.; MRCGP 1982; DRCOG 1981. (Edinburgh)

GRANT, Peter Harold The James Preston Health Centre, 61 Holland Road, Sutton Coldfield B72 1RL Tel: 0121 354 2032 Fax: 0121 323 2121 — MB ChB 1956 Birm. (Birm.) Prev: Ho. Surg. & Ho. Phys. Qu. Eliz. Hosp. Birm.

GRANT, Professor Peter John Unit Mol. Vasc. Med., Leeds General Infirmary, Great George St., Leeds LS1 3EX Tel: 0113 3923476 Fax: 0113 2423811 Email: p.j.grant@leeds.ac.uk; 46 Cottage Road, Headingley, Leeds LS6 4DD Tel: 0113 275 2363 — MD 1987 Bristol; MB ChB 1976; FRCP 1995; MRCP (UK) 1981. (University of Bristol) Prof. Med. Hon. Cons. Med. Leeds Gen. Infirm. Socs: Brit. Diabetic Assn.; Assn. Phys. Prev: Sen. Lect & Sen. Regist. (Med.) Leeds Gen Infirm.; Medicin Asst. Boursier C.H.U.V. Lausanne, Switz..

GRANT, Peter Julian Vittoria Health Centre, Vittoria Street, Birkenhead CH41 3RH Tel: 0151 647 7321 — MB ChB 1969 Sheff.; DObst RCOG 1971. (Sheff.) Socs: Birkenhead Med. Soc. Prev: Clin. Asst. & Med. Adviser (Occupat. Health) Wirral HA; SHO (Geriat.) New End Hosp. Lond.

GRANT, Peter Watson (retired) 12 Marina Court Avenue, Bexhill-on-Sea TN40 1BN Tel: 01424 223730 — MB ChB 1949 Ed.; MRCGP 1963; DMJ Soc. Apoth. Lond. 1962.

GRANT, Peter Weir (retired) Park Avenue Medical Centre, Park Avenue, Dundee DD4 6PP — MB ChB St. And. 1949; MRCGP 1963.

GRANT, Richard Hugh Edward 26 The Highlands, Bunbury, Tarporley CW6 9NT Tel: 01829 260165; Little Crosby, 26 The Highlands, Bunbury, Tarporley CW6 9NT Tel: 01829 260165 — MB BS 1956 Lond.; DCH Eng. 1959. (Middlx.) Assoc. Medico-Legal Cons. Old Docks Off. Glos. Prev: Chief Med. Off. Pub. Health Dept. Jamestown I. St. Helena, S. Atlantic Ocean; Dir. David Lewis Centre for Epilepsy Chesh.; Rehabil. Phys. Al Hada Hosp. Taif, Saudi Arabia.

GRANT, Robert Western General Hospital, Edinburgh EH4 2XU Tel: 0131 537 2088 Fax: 0131 537 1132; 6 Netherlaw, Grange Road, North Berwick EH39 4RF — MD 1985 Glas.; MB ChB 1980; FRCP Glas. 1993; MRCP (UK) 1983; FRCP 1996 Edin. Cons. Med. Neurol. W.. Gen. Hosp. Edin.; Sen. Lect. W.. Gen. Hosp. Edin. Socs: Assoc. Brit. Neurol.; Amer. Acad. Neurol. Prev: Sen. Regist. (Neurol.) W.. Gen. Hosp. Edin.; Research Fell. (Neuro-oncol.) Univ. Michigan, USA; Clin. Research Fell. (Neurosurg.) Univ. Glas.

GRANT, Robert Livingstone (retired) 23 Gartcows Cres, Falkirk FK1 5QH Tel: 01324 621725 Email: rigrant@blueyonder.co.uk — MB ChB Ed. 1954; MRCGP 1962; DObst RCOG 1958. Prev: Ho. Surg., Ho. Phys. & Ho. Off. (Obst.) Falkirk & Dist. Roy. Infirm.

GRANT, Robert Morrison Markinch Medical Centre, 19 High Street, Markinch, Glenrothes KY7 6ER Tel: 01592 610640 Fax: 01592 612089; 29 Braid Drive, Glenrothes KY7 4ES Tel: 01592 610396 — MB ChB 1970 Aberd. Hosp. Pract. Young Disabled Unit Rehabil.Unit Glenrothes Hosp. Fife; Macmillian GP Facilitator Lead Cancer Team Fife; Lead GP SE Scotl. Cancer Network (SCAN). Prev: GP Dumfriessh; MRC Fell. Cancer Research Counc. Unit Radiother. & Clin. Oncol. Addenbrooke's Hosp. Camb.

GRANT, Roderick William Department of Radiology, Oldchurch Hospital, Romford RH7 0BE Tel: 01708 345533 Fax: 01708 736646 Email: grant@cobbold65.fsnet.co.uk; 65 Cobbold Road, London W12 9LA Tel: 020 8932 4420 Email: grant@cobbold65.fsnet.co.uk — MB BS 1965 Lond.; MRCS Eng. LRCP Lond. 1965; FRCR 1981; DMRD Eng. 1979. Cons. Radiol. OldCh. Hosp. Romford Essex. Socs: Brit. Inst. of Radiol.; Europ. Soc. of Radiol.; Internat. Bone and Mineral Soc. Prev: Sen. Regist. Radiol. Char. Cross Hosp.; Regist. Radiol. & Regist. Nuclear Med. Soton. Gen. Hosp.; Cons. Radiologist Heatherwood and Wrexham Pk. NHS Trust.

GRANT, Ronald Napier Robertson (retired) Beechgrove, 6 Stainburn Road, Workington CA14 4EA Tel: 01900 602885 Email: r.grant@dial.pipex.com — MB BChir 1943 Camb.; MA Camb. 1943, MD 1950; FRCGP 1975, M 1953.

GRANT, Ronald William, TD 187 King Street, Aberdeen AB24 5AH — MB ChB 1967 Aberd. (Aberd.) Lt.-Col. RAMC (V); Hon. Surg. St. And. Ambul. Assn.; Hon. Surg. Aberd. Lifeboat. Socs: Aberd. M-C Soc.; Scott. Med. & Dent. Hypn. Soc. Prev: Regtl. Med. Off. Barbados Regt.; Traing. Off. 6 Med. Company Canad. Militia; Chairm. Med. Staff Comm. St. Eliz. Hosp. N. Sydney, Nova Scotia.

GRANT, Sandra Helen Victoria Street Medical Group, 7 Victoria Street, Aberdeen AB10 1QW Tel: 01224 641930 Fax: 01224 644081; 3 Springdale Place, Bielside, Aberdeen AB15 9FD — MB ChB 1978 Dundee; MRCGP 1993; Cert. Family Plann. JCC 1988.

GRANT, Sandra Mary, OBE Scottish Health Advisory Service, Elliot House, 8-10 Hillside Crescent, Edinburgh EH7 5EA Tel: 0131 623 4320 Email: sandra.grant@shas.csa.scot.nhs.uk; 57 Dowanside Road, Glasgow G12 9DL Tel: 0141 357 1828 Email: sandra.grant@dial.pipex.com — MB ChB 1971 Ed.; BSc (Med. Sci.) Ed. 1968; FRCPsych 1989, M 1975; MBA 1994. Dir. Scott. Health Advisery Serv. Edin.; Cons. Psychotherapist Gartnavel Roy. Hosp. Glas. Socs: BAMM. Prev: Clin. Dir. Adult Commnity Ment. Health Servs. Glas.; Sen. Regist. (Psychiat.) Roy. Edin. Hosp.; Regist. (Psychiat.) Roy. Edin. Hosp.

GRANT, Sandra Mary Thomson Oliver and Partners, Millhill Surgery, 87 Woodmill Street, Dunfermline KY11 4JW Tel: 01383 621222 Fax: 01383 622862; Byeways, 12 Bruchaven Crescent, Limekilns, Dunfermline KY11 3JJ — MB ChB 1966 Glas.

GRANT, Sheila Anne Melbourne Grove Medical Practice, Melbourne Grove, London SE22 8QN Tel: 020 8299 0499 Fax: 020 8299 1954; 1A Allison Grove, London SE21 7ER Tel: 020 8693 5105 — MB BS 1964 Lond.; MRCS Eng. LRCP Lond. 1964.

GRANT, Sheila Booth Royal Cornhill Hospital, Aberdeen AB25 3HG Tel: 01224 681818 — MB ChB 1971 Aberd.; MRCPsych 1978. Assoc. Specialist (Psychiat.) Roy. Cornhill Hosp. Aberd.

GRANT, Simon Charles Donovan Halifax General Hospital, Salterhebble, Halifax HX3 0PW Tel: 01422 357171 — MB ChB 1983 Leeds; BSc (Hons.) Leeds 1980, MB ChB 1983; MRCP (UK) 1988; MD 1997. Cons. Cardiol. Calderdale Healthcare NHS Trust. Prev: SR Cardiol. Sheff.; SR Cardiol. Manch.; RES Reg Cardiol. Manch.

GRANT, Simon Ewart Adebayour Sarephed Medical Centre, 60 Arden Road, Smethwick, Smethwick B67 6AJ Tel: 0121 558 0263 Fax: 0121 558 9071 — MB BCh BAO 1962 Belf. (Belf.) Prev: Ho. Off. Befl. City Hosp.; Med. Off. Gambia Med. Serv.

GRANT, Stanley William (retired) 8 Endrick Road, Killearn, Glasgow G63 0TY — LRCP LRCS 1942 Ed.; LRCP LRCS Ed. LRFPS Glas. 1942. Prev: Med. Asst. Kt.swood Hosp. Glas.

GRANT, Stefan Charles 64 Ashdown Drive, Borehamwood WD6 4NA — MB BCh 1981 Witwatersrand.

GRANT, Stephen Charles Abbey Medical Practice, The Health Centre, Merstow Green, Evesham WR11 4BS Tel: 01386 761111 — MB BS 1986 Lond.; BSc Lond. 1983; MRCP (UK) 1990. (UCL) GP Princip.; Hosp. Practitioner Gen. Med. Prev: SHO (Haemat.) Univ. Coll. Hosp. Lond.

GRANT, Steven John 1 Cedar Walk, 45 Romsey Road, Winchester SO22 5DG — MB BS 1989 Queensland.

GRANT, Stuart Alan 15 Fern Avenue, Lenzie, Glasgow G66 4LE — MB ChB Glas. 1989; FRCA 1995. Specialist Regist. Anaesth. S. W. of Scotl. Deanery. Socs: BMA; DAGBI.

GRANT, Susan Joy Lincoln Road Practice, 63 Lincoln Road, Peterborough PE1 2SF Tel: 01733 565511 Fax: 01733 569230; 47 Sunningdale, Orton Waterville, Peterborough PE2 5UB — MB BCh 1982 Wales; MRCGP 1986; DRCOG 1986. (Welsh National School of Medicine) Prev: Clin. Med. Off. Child & Sch. Health Serv. P'boro.

GRANT, Susan Marie 118/4 Nicolson Street, Edinburgh EH8 9EJ — MB ChB 1979 Aberd.

GRANT, Thomas Edward (retired) 71/2 Canongate, Edinburgh EH8 8BS Tel: 0131 557 0532 — LRCP LRCS Ed. LRFPS Glas. 1948; BA (Econ. & Soc Stud) Univ. Manch. 1965; MRCPsych 1973; DPM Eng. 1955. Prev: Cons. Psychiat. (Child, Adolesc. & Family) Sunderland Gen. Hosp.

GRANT, Valerie Elizabeth Cargans House, 54 Cargans Road, Tandragee, Craigavon BT62 2EA — MB BCh BAO 1994 Belf.; DRCOG 1997; DGM 1996. (Queen's Univ. Belf.)

GRANT, Warren Carnegie Derwent Practice, Norton Road, Malton YO17 9RF Tel: 01653 600069 Fax: 01653 698014; Lowfield Farm, Settrington, Malton YO17 — MB BS 1973 Lond.; BSc (Hons.) Physiol. Lond. 1970; DRCOG 1977.

GRANT, Mr William Eoin Department of Otolaryngology, Royal Infirmary of Edinburgh, Lauriston Place, Edinburgh EH3 9YW Tel: 0131 536 6340; 2 Bardny Street, Edinburgh EH3 6PE Tel: 0131 556 6440 Fax: 0131 556 6440 Email: willie@grosbil.demon.co.uk — MB BCh BAO 1984 NUI; M.Ch. Dub. 1996; FRCS (Orl.) 1996; LRCPSI 1984; FRCSI 1989; FRCS ED 1999. (R.C.S. Irel.) Cons. Otolaryngol. Roy. Infirm. Edin.; Hon. Sen. Lect. (Otolaryngol.) Univ. Edin. Socs: Brit. Assn. Otol. Head & Neck Surg.; Roy. Soc. Med. (Sect. Otol. Larngol & Rhinol.); Young Cons. Otolaryngol. Head & Neck Surg. Prev: ENT Regist. Train. Scheme, Dub.; Research Fell. (Laser Surg.) Univ. Coll. Hosp. Lond.; Sen. Regist. Roy. Free Hosp. Lond.

GRANT, William Neil McNab St Georges Hospital, Morpeth NE61 2BU Tel: 01670 512121 — MB ChB 1980 Aberd.; MRCPsych 1984. Cons. Psychiat. St. Geo. Hosp. Morpeth. Prev: Sen. Regist. Newc. Gen. Hosp.; Sen. Regist. Rotat. (Psychiat.) N.. Reg. HA; Regist. (Psychiat.) Roy. Edin. Hosp. Edin.

GRANT, Yvonne Anna Maria 333 Glossop Road, Sheffield S10 2HP — MB BS 1987 Lond.

GRANT DE LONGUEUIL, Michael Charles Riverlyn Medical Centre, Station Road, Bulwell, Nottingham NG6 9AA Tel: 0115 927 9214 Fax: 0115 977 0971; 141 Woodthorpe Drive, Mapperley, Nottingham NG3 5JL Tel: 0115 955 3545 — MB BS 1972 Lond. (Char. Cross) Socs: Roy. Soc. Med. Prev: Clin. Asst. Hayward Ho. Continuing Care Unit City Hosp. Nottm.; SHO (Med. Oncol.) New Char. Cross Hosp. Lond.; SHO (Paediat.) New Char. Cross Hosp.

GRANT DUFF, Leslie Grant (retired) Tillers Green Farm, Dymock GL18 2AP Tel: 01531 85437 — MB BCh BAO 1945 Dub.; MA Dub. 1945; MRCGP 1965; Cert. Av Med. MoD (Air) & CAA 1975. Prev: Regist. (Med.) Essex Co. Hosp. Colchester.

GRANTHAM, Catherine Frances Wychwood, Preston, Cirencester GL7 5PR — MB ChB 1987 Leeds. Trainee GP Bristol. Prev: SHO (Otorhinolaryngol. & A & E) Bath Roy. United Hosp.; SHO (Geriat. Med.) Manor Pk. Hosp. Bristol.

GRANTHAM, Charles Edward Dumaresq Trosnant Lodge Surgery, Trosnant Lodge, Trosnant Street, Pontypool NP4 8AT Tel:

01495 762709 Fax: 01495 758177 — MB ChB 1989 Bristol; MRCGP 1993; DRCOG 1991. (Bristol)

GRANTHAM, Elizabeth Brenda (retired) Overwell House, Mill Road, Oundle, Peterborough PE8 4BW — MB BS 1953 Lond. Prev: Assoc. Specialist (Child Developm.) P'boro. Dist. Hosp.

GRANTHAM, Kathleen Mary Haven Home, The Street, Hapton, Norwich NR15 1AD — MB BS 1992 Newc.

GRANTHAM, Vincent Alpe (retired) 15A Mill Road, Oundle, Peterborough PE8 4BW Tel: 01832 73548 — MB BS 1953 Lond. Prev: Med. Off. Oundle Sch.

GRANTHAM, Vincent Alpe Mark Twyford Health Centre, Loddon Hall Road, Twyford, Reading RG10 9JA Tel: 0118 934 0112 Fax: 0118 934 1048 — MB BS 1988 Lond.; MRCP (UK) 1993.

GRANTLEY, Bernard Flat 9, Highlands, Oakleigh Road N., London N20 9HA — MB ChB 1952 Bristol. (Bristol) Local Civil Serv. Med. Off. Prev: Sen. Cas. Ho. Surg. Bristol Roy. Infirm.; Ho. Surg. ENT Bristol Gen. Hosp.

GRANVILLE, Carmel Marie 177 Wolverhampton Road, Oldbury B68 0LR Tel: 01384 422 2189 — LRCPI & LM, LRSCI & LM 1952; LRCPI & LM, LRCSI & LM 1952; CPH Dub. 1955. Assoc. Specialist Rubery Hill Hosp. Birm. Prev: Asst. MOH Pub. Health Dept. Birm. & Dudley Co. Boros.; Jun. Hosp. Med. Off. St. Margt.'s Hosp. Birm.

GRAPE, Angela Mary (retired) King's Arms, Michaelchurch Eskley, Hereford HR2 0JY Tel: 01981 510689 — MB BS Lond. 1962; DA Eng. 1964. Assoc. Specialist Mid Wales Hosp. Talgarth.

GRASBY, Michael Paul 41 Norreys Avenue, Oxford OX1 4ST — BSc Lond. 1977, MB BS 1980; MRCPsych 1986; DCH RCP Lond. 1985. MRC Clin. Pharmacol. Dept. Radcliffe Infirm. Oxf.; MRC Train. Fell.

GRASON, Howard Graeme The Health Centre, Doctor Lane, Mirfield WF14 8DU Tel: 01924 495721 Fax: 01924 480605 — MB ChB 1969 Leeds. Prev: Ho. Phys. & Ho. Surg. Huddersfield Roy. Infirm.

GRASSE, Alan Samuel Muir 16 Hollycroft Avenue, Hampstead, London NW3 7QL — MB BS 1980 Lond.

GRASSE, Michael Ellerston Muir West End Lane Surgery, 125 West End Lane, London NW6 1DS Tel: 020 7624 1769 — LMSSA 1950 Lond.

GRASSET-MOLLOY, Gabrielle Josephine Marie Flat 17, Wentworth Court, Downview Road, Worthing BN11 4RJ — MB BS 1957 Lond.; DPH Eng. 1961. (St. Bart.) Prev: Sen. Med. Off. Brighton Co. Boro.; PMO Lond. Boro. Hackney; Med. Off. Worthing Municip. Boro.

GRASSICK, Brian Douglas Miller Pollards, Oval Way, Gerrards Cross SL9 8PY Tel: 01753 888434 — MB ChB Aberd. 1961; AFOM RCP Lond. 1983; DObst RCOG 1965. Indep. GP Gerrards Cross.; Cons. Occupat. Med. Hillingdon Hosp. Uxbridge. Socs: Soc. Occupat. Med. Lond. Prev: Sen. Med. Off. (Occupat. Med.) Slough Occupat. Health Serv.; Regist. (O & G) P.ss Margt. Hosp. Nassau, Bahamas; Ho. Phys. Aberd. Roy. Infirm.

GRASSIE, Mr Alistair Duncan Shiskine Surgery, Inglewood, Shiskine, Brodick KA27 8EW Tel: 01770 860247 Fax: 01770 860298 — MB ChB 1970 Glas.; FRCS Ed. 1975.

GRASSIE, Mrs Elizabeth Helen Salton Shiskine Surgery, Inglewood, Shiskine, Brodick KA27 8EW — MB ChB 1970 Glasgow.

GRASSO, Paul 131 Old Lodge Lane, Purley CR8 4AU Tel: 020 8660 0315 Fax: 020 8763 1843 Email: paul.grasso@which.net — BSc, MD Malta 1949; DTM & H Liverp. 1954; DCP Lond 1959; FRCPath 1975. Prof. of Experim. Path. Surrey Univ. Socs: Fell. Roy. Soc. Trop. Med. & Hyg.; Path. Soc.; RSM. Prev: Chief Path. & Dep. Dir. BIBRA; Med. Off. i/c Creek Hosp. Lagos, Nigeria; Specialist (Pathol.) Gen. Hosp. Lagos.

GRATION, John Charles David Occupational Health, Praxis 42 Ltd., 26 Red Lion Square, London WC1R 4HQ Tel: 020 7528 1390 Email: john.grationb@cw.com — MB ChB 1988 Bristol; MIS 1996; LLM Wales 1991; AFOM RCP Lond. 1995; MRCGP 1992; DRCOG 1992; DGM RCP Lond. 1991; DCH RCP Lond. 1990; DHMSA 1987; MFOM 1999; MIS 1996 B'HAM. (Bristol) Grp. Med. Advis. Cable & Wireless; Occupat.al Health Director, Praxis 42 Ltd. Socs: Soc. Occupat. Med.; Inst. Occupat. Health & Safety. Prev: Sen. Regist. (Occupat. Med.) Sandwell Gen. Hosp.; Head of Occup. Health Rover Gp. Swindon.

GRATTAGE, Mr Trevor James Ashby Turn Primary Care Centre, Ashby Link, Scunthorpe DN16 2UT Tel: 01724 842051 Fax: 01724 280346 — MB ChB 1972 Sheff.; FRCS Ed. 1976; FRCS Eng. 1977; DRCOG 1981; MRCGP 1991. Socs: Brit. Soc. Of Med. & Dent. Hypn.; Chair Ethical Sub-Comm.

GRATTAN, Clive Edmund Hume Dermatology Centre, West Norwich Hospital, Bowthorpe Road, Norwich NR2 3TU Tel: 01603 288265 Fax: 01603 288601 — MB BChir 1978 Camb.; MA 1981 Cambridge; FRCP Lond. 1994; MRCP (UK) 1980; M.D. (Cambridge) 1997. (St. Thos) Cons. Dermat. Norf. & Norwich Univ. Hosp. NHS Trust. Prev: Hon. Sen. Lect. St. John's Inst. Dermat.; Research Fell. Inst. Dermat. St. Thos. Hosp. Lond.; Regist. (Dermat.) Bristol. Roy. Infirm.

GRATTIDGE, Isobel Riddell 5 Cults Court, Cults, Aberdeen AB15 9SZ Tel: 01224 868110 — MB ChB 1942 Aberd. (Aberd.) Socs: BMA. Prev: Ho. Phys. Hertford CC Hosp.; Ho. Surg. Bradford Childr. Hosp. & Vict. Hosp. Childr. Hull.

GRATTON, Dorothy Marian (retired) (cons. rooms), 275 Cardiff Road, Aberaman, Aberdare CF44 6YA Tel: 01685 876414 — MB ChB Manch. 1951; FRCOG 1972, M 1957, DObst 1954. Prev: Cons. O & G Merthyr & Cynon Valley Health Unit.

GRATWICK, Linda Catherine 6 Fountain Avenue, Hale, Altrincham WA15 8LY — MB ChB 1988 Ed.

GRAVATT, Derek Bernard (retired) 9 Willow Park, Otford, Sevenoaks TN14 5ND Tel: 01959 523034 — MB BChir 1967 Camb.; MA Camb. 1967; DIH Eng. 1973. Prev: Sen. Med. Adviser PO Occupat. Health Servs. Lond Area.

GRAVE, Mr George Frank, Maj. RAMC Retd. (retired) Lychgate Cottage, Salwarpe, Droitwich WR9 0AH Tel: 01905 773696 — MB BS Lond. 1951; FRCS Ed. 1964. Prev: Cons. Surg. Droitwich Private Hosp. & Alexandra Hosp. Redditch.

GRAVELL, Delyth Lois LLwynhendy Health Centre, Llwynhendy, Llanelli SA14 9BN Tel: 01554 772946 Fax: 01554 752570; 58 Hendre Park, Llangennech, Llanelli SA14 8UP — MB BS 1983 Lond.; MRCGP 1988; DRCOG 1985.

GRAVELL, Emyr Wyn LLwynhendy Health Centre, Llwynhendy, Llanelli SA14 9BN Tel: 01554 772946 Fax: 01554 752570; 28 Bryngwyn Road, Dafen, Llanelli SA14 8LW Tel: 01554 778844 — MB BS 1988 Lond.

GRAVELL, Rhiannon Mair 16 Meadow Street, Pontcanna, Cardiff CF11 9PY — MB BCh 1990 Wales; MRCGP 1994; DRCOG 1995.

GRAVELLE, Idris Paul St Peters Surgery, St. Peters Street, Carmarthen SA31 1LN Tel: 01267 236241 Fax: 01267 236241 — MB BCh 1984 Wales; MRCGP 1989; DRCOG 1989. Gen. Practitioner; Clin. Asst., ENT.

GRAVELLE, Iwan Huw (retired) Heathcliffe House, 9 Bronwydd Close, Cardiff CF23 5RA Tel: 029 2048 6588 — MB ChB 1957 Ed.; BSc Wales 1950; FRCP Ed. 1971; MRCP (UK) 1965; FRCR 1975; FFR 1966; DMRD 1963. Cons. Radiol. Univ. Hosp. of Wales. Prev: Regist. & Sen. Regist. Radiodiag. Dept. Roy. Infirm. Edin.

GRAVENEY, Michael James Meadowbank, Mill Lane, Fenny Compton, Leamington Spa CV47 2YF Tel: 0129 577486 — MB BS 1976 Lond.; BSc Reading 1967; PhD Lond. 1974, MB BS 1976. (St. Bart.) Dep. Dir. Unit of Clin. Epidemiol. Univ. Oxf. Socs: Aerospace Med. Assoc.; Soc. Occupat. Med.; Mem.Biol. Engin. Soc. Prev: Sen. Med. Off. Office of Chief Sci. DHSS Lond.; Research Med. Off. RAF Inst. Aviat. Med. FarnBoro.; Ho. Surg. Stratford upon Avon Gen. Hosp.

GRAVER, Hilary Joan (retired) 45 Bishopsthorpe Road, London SE26 4PA Tel: 020 8778 9560 — MB BS 1957 Lond.; DA Eng. 1960. Prev: Resid. Anaesth. St. Giles' Hosp. Lond.

GRAVES, Alastair Clydesdale Saint Vincent Medical Centre, 77 Thorne Road, Doncaster DN1 2ET Tel: 01302 361318; Brompton House, 1 Brompton Road, Sprotbrough, Doncaster DN5 7LB Tel: 01302 853932 Email: alastairgraves@compuserve.com — MB ChB 1984 Liverp.; MB ChB Liverp. l984; MRCGP 1988.

GRAVES, Emma Louise 31 Garrett Court, Gertrude Road, Norwich NR3 4SD Tel: 01603 402549 — BM BS 1994 Nottm. SHO (Anaesth.) Norf. Norwich Hosp.

GRAVES, Mr Frederick Thomas (retired) Mole End, Wormley Lane, Hambledon, Godalming GU8 4HB Tel: 01428 682771 Fax: 01428 682771 — MB BS 1943 Lond.; DSc Lond. 1974, MS 1955; FRCS Eng. 1949; MRCS Eng. LRCP Lond. 1943. Prev: Vis. Prof. Urol. Wake Forest Univ. N. Carolina, USA.

GRAVES, John (retired) March Cottage, Beaulieu Road, Walhampton, Lymington SO41 5RE Tel: 01590 676038 — MRCS Eng. LRCP Lond. 1951. Prev: GP Fawley.

GRAVES, Peter Bernard The Medical Centre, 106 Gold St., Wellingborough NN8 4BT Tel: 01933 224679 Fax: 01933 229236; 27 Neale Close, Wollaston, Wellingborough NN29 7UT — MB BS 1980 Lond.; MRCGP 1990.

GRAVES, Valerie, OBE (retired) 12 Piper Road, Lexden, Colchester CO3 3SF Tel: 01206 578226 — MB BS Lond. 1946; FRCGP 1970, M 1964. Hon. Dir. Graves Med. Audiovisual Library. Prev: Asst. Lect. Anat. Univ. Coll. Lond.

GRAVES-MORRIS, John Wyn (retired) 24 Turnpike, Sampford Peverell, Tiverton EX16 7BN Tel: 01884 820307 — MRCS Eng. LRCP Lond. 1942. Prev: Surg. Lt. RNVR.

GRAVES-STANWICK, Theodore Roman 12 East St Helens Street, Abingdon OX14 5EA — MRCS Eng. LRCP Lond. 1952. (Ed. Birm. & Oxf.) Socs: BMA & Oxf. Med. Soc. Prev: Med. Off. Abingdon Hosp.

GRAVESTOCK, Nicholas Measham Medical Unit, High Street, Measham, Swadlincote DE12 7HR Tel: 01530 270667 Fax: 01530 271433; Blue Tiles, 28 Measham Road, Ashby-de-la-Zouch LE65 2PF Tel: 01530 414743 Email: bluetiles@leicester.anglican.org — MB BS 1979 Lond.; MRCGP 1983; DRCOG 1984. (Univ. Coll. Hosp.) GP Trainer Leicester. Socs: BMA; RCGP; Christ. Med. Fell.sh. Prev: SHO (Obst.) St. Paul's Hosp. Cheltenham; Trainee GP Cirencester VTS.

GRAVESTOCK, Shaun Michael Oxleas NHS Trust, 183 Lodge Hill, Goldie Leigh, Greenwich Abbeywood, London SE2 0AY Tel: 020 8319 7113 Fax: 020 8319 7129 Email: shaun.gravestock@oxleas.nhs.uk; 3 Scoter Close, Woodford Green IG8 7DH Tel: 020 8559 2586 — MB BS 1985 Newc.; MRCPsych 1989; T(Psych) 1994. (Newcastle) Cons. Psychiat. (Learning Disabilities) Oxleas NHS Trust Lond.; Hon. Sen. Lect. GKT Med. Schs. Univ. of Lond. Socs: Sec. Penrose Soc.; Assn. Univ. Teach. Psychiat. Prev: Hon. Lect. Univ. of Newc.; Cons. Psychiat. Learning Disabilities N.gate Hosp. N.umberland; Lect. & Sen. Regist. (Psychiat.) UMDS Guy's Hosp. Lond.

GRAVESTON, Nigel Humphrey, Maj. RAMC (retired) Burnley General Hospital, Casterton Avenue, Burnley BB10 2PQ Tel: 01282 425071 — MB BS 1978 Lond.; MRCS Eng. LRCP Lond. 1978; FFA RCS Eng. 1983. Cons. Anaesth. Burnley Gen. Hosp. Prev: Cons. Anaesth. 33 Field Hosp.

GRAVETT, Peter James Department of Haematology, The London Clinic, 20 Devonshire Place, London W1G 6BW Tel: 020 7935 4444 Fax: 020 7486 3782 Email: p.gravett.@thelondonclinic.co.uk — MB BS Lond. 1969; MRCS Eng. LRCP Lond. 1969; FRCPath 1991, M 1979. (Guy's) Cons. Path. (Haemat.) The Lond. Clinic; Med. Dir. Stemuell Transp. Unit. the Lond. Clinic. Socs: Fell. Roy. Soc. Med.; Brit. Soc. Haematol.; Founder Mem. Brit. Blood Transfus. Soc. Prev: Hon. Cons. Path. (Haemat.) W.m. Hosp. Lond.; Cons. Path. (Haemat.) Qu. Eliz. Milit. Hosp. Lond.; Off. i/c John Boyd Laborat.

GRAVIL, Jane Helen Royal Alexandra Hospital, Paisley PA2 9PN Tel: 0141 887 9111; 83 Ormonde Drive, Glasgow G44 3RF — MB ChB 1987 Glas.; FRCP 2000 Glas.; BSc (Hons.) Glas. 1984; MRCP (UK) 1991. Cons. Respirat. & Gen. Med. Roy. Alexandra Hosp. Paisley. Socs: Brit. Thorac. Soc.; BMA; Scott. Thorac. Soc.

GRAY, Alan Geoffrey 2 Alma Cottages, Church Lane, Great Warley, Brentwood — MB BChir 1968 Camb.; MA, MB Camb. 1968, BChir 1967; DObst RCOG 1973. (St. Bart.) Prev: Med. Regist. & Ho. Surg. & Ho. Phys. Harold Wood Hosp.

GRAY, Alan Henry Health Centre, Edwinstowe, Mansfield NG21 9QS Tel: 01623 822303 — MB BS 1950 Lond.; MRCGP 1968. (Westm.) Med. Off. Civil Serv. Socs: Balint Soc. Prev: Capt. RAMC; Ho. Phys. W.m. Hosp. Lond.

GRAY, Alasdair James Health Centre, Bank Street, Cupar KY15 4JN Tel: 01334 653478 Fax: 01334 657305 — MB ChB 1982 Aberd.; MRCGP 1988. Prev: Regist. (Psychiat.) Fife HB.

GRAY, Alexandra Emma Southend General Hospital, Prittlewell Close, Westcliffe on Sea SS0 0RY; 32 Barnsdale Avenue, Millwall, London E14 9WR Tel: 020 7537 0937 — MB BChir 1989 Camb.; FRCS 2001 (Gen. Surg.); FRCS Eng. 1993. Cons. Gen. Surg., S.end Hosp. NHS Trust. Prev: Specialist Regist. (Gen. Surg.), N.E. Thames; Research Fell. (Gen. Surg.) Roy. Free Hosp.

GRAY, Alison Jane 5 Sandringham Drive, Aldridge, Walsall WS9 8HD — MB BChir 1987 Camb.; MA Camb. 1989; MRCPsych 1995. Sen. Regist. (Psychiat.) Hereford Co. Hosp. Prev: Regist. (Psychiat.) Worcester Roy. Infirm.

GRAY, Mr Alistair John Ashtree Cottage, Roundy Lane, Adlington, Macclesfield SK10 4JZ Tel: 01625 573395 — MB ChB 1975 Ed.; FRCS Eng. 1981; FFAEM 1995; DRCOG 1977. Cons. A & E Stepping Hill Hosp. Stockport. Prev: Sen. Regist. (A & E) Manch. Roy. Infirm.; Regist. (A & E) Countess of Chester Hosp.; Ho. Surg. Edin. Roy. Infirm.

GRAY, Mr Alistair John Russell Department of Orthopaedic Surgery, Western Infirmary, Dumbarton Road, Glasgow G11 6NT Tel: 0141 211 1853; Carrick House, Station Road, Balfron, Glasgow G63 0SX Tel: 01360 441037 Fax: 01360 441037 — MB ChB 1982 Aberd.; FRCS (Orth.) 1995; FRCS Ed. 1988. (Aberd.) Cons. Orthop. Surg. W.. Infirm. Glas.; Hon sen lec in Orthopaedic surg Univ of Glas. Socs: BMA; Fell. BOA. Prev: Sen. Regist. & Career Regist. (Orthop.) Addenbrooke's Hosp. Camb.; Regist. (Orthop.) Dundee.

GRAY, Amanda Louise Donkleywood House, Donkleywood, Hexham NE48 1AQ — MB ChB 1992 Liverp.

GRAY, Andrew George 72 Beechgrove Terrace, Aberdeen AB15 5EY Email: andy_g_gray@msn.com — MB ChB 1991 Ed.; MRCPsych 1997.

GRAY, Andrew Phillip Goldington Road Surgery, 2 Goldington Road, Bedford MK40 3NG Tel: 01234 351341 Email: andrew.gray@gp-e81011.nhs.uk; 117 Putnoe Lane, Bedford MK41 8LB Tel: 01234 407249 Fax: 01234 341464 — MB BS 1975 Lond. (Middlx.) Sen. Med. Off. Bedford Sch.; Med. Off. HM Prison Bedford. Prev: Course Organiser Bedford VTS; Dist. Surg. Venda, S. Afr.; Ship Surg. RMS St Helena.

GRAY, Andrew Richard Caldicot Medical Group, Gray Hill Surgery, Woodstock Way, Caldicot, Newport NP26 4DB Tel: 01291 420282 Fax: 01291 425853; 24 Ostringen Close, Abergavenny NP7 5LY Tel: 01873 852173 — MB BCh 1992 Wales; BDS Wales 1983; MRCGP 1996; FDS RCS Ed. 1987. (Warks.)

GRAY, Ann Betty (retired) 2 Whatman Close, Off Sittingbourne Road, Maidstone ME14 5HX Tel: 01622 765051 — MRCS Eng. LRCP Lond. 1956; MB BS Lond. 1956; MFCM 1974; DPH Lond. 1967; DCH Eng. 1965. Prev: Cons. Psychiat. Tunbridge Wells & Maidstone Health Dists.

GRAY, Anne Margaret 6 Station Road, Helensburgh G84 7BQ Tel: 01436 673283 Fax: 01436 673285 Email: anne.gray@helensburgh.co.uk; 6 Station Road, Helensburgh G84 7BQ Tel: 01436 673283 Fax: 01436 673285 Email: anne.gray@helensburgh.co.uk — MB ChB 1945 Glas.; FRCPsych 1987, M 1971; DPM Ed. & Glas. 1966. (Glasgow University) Cons. Psychiat. Leverndale Hosp. Glas. (Now Retd.).

GRAY, Anthony Edward Beechwood Surgery, 371 Chepstow Road, Newport NP19 8HL Tel: 01633 277771 Fax: 01633 290631; Beckscott, Isca Road, Caerleon, Newport NP18 1QG Tel: 01633 421525 — MB BCh 1966 Wales. (Cardiff) Socs: BMA & Gwent Med. Soc. Prev: Clin. Asst. (Diabetol.) Roy. Gwent Hosp. Newport.

GRAY, Anthony John Gordon Norfolk & Norwich Hospital, Brunswick Road, Norwich NR1 3SR Tel: 01603 287086; Oaklands, 66 Colney Lane, Cringleford, Norwich NR4 7RF Tel: 01603 505118 — MB BChir 1973 Camb.; MB BChir Camb. 1972; MA Camb. 1973; FRCA 1977; DObst RCOG 1974. (Camb. & St. Bart.) Cons. Anaesth. Norf. & Norwich Healthcare NHS Trust. Prev: Sen. Regist. (Anaesth.) S. W.. RHA.

GRAY, Atherton Gerald Princess Margaret Hospital, Okus Road, Swindon SN1 4JU Tel: 01793 426759; White House Cottage, Callow Hill, Brinkworth, Chippenham SN15 5DZ — MD 1992 Ed.; MB ChB 1976; MRCP (UK) 1980; MRCPath. 1989; DTM & H Eng. 1978. Cons. Haemat. P.ss Margt. Hosp. Swindon.

GRAY, Barry James Department of Thoracic Medicine, Kings College School Medicine & Dentistry, Bessemer Road, London SE5 9PJ Tel: 020 7326 3165; 25 Eaglesfield Road, Shooters Hill, London SE18 3BX Tel: 020 8854 5579 — MRCS Eng. LRCP Lond. 1972; MA Dub. 1990, MD 1990, BA, MB BCh BAO 1972; MRCPI 1975; MRCP (UK) 1977. Cons. Phys. (Thoracic Med.) Kings Coll. Hosp. Lond. Socs: Brit. Thoracic Soc. & Amer. Thoracic Soc. Prev: Lect. (Med.) & Hon. Sen. Regist. Chest Unit King's Coll. Hosp. Med. Sch. Lond.; Lect. (Med.) Trinity Coll. Dub.; Ho. Off. Roy. City Dub. Hosp.

GRAY, Mr Basil Kenneth (retired) Birkie Brae, Hawick TD9 0PS Tel: 01450 850235 — MB BCh BAO 1956 Belf.; FRCS Ed. 1961.

Cons. Urol Surg. Bradford Roy. Infirm. & Bradford Childr. Hosp. Prev: Cons. Urol Surg. Bradford Roy. Infirm. & Bradford Childr. Hosp.

GRAY, Beverley Anne Lordshill Health Centre, Lordshill District Centre, Lordshill, Southampton SO16 8HY Tel: 023 8073 8144 Fax: 023 8073 0722 — MB BS 1980 Lond.; MRCP (UK) 1983; MRCGP 1988. (Char. Cross) Prev: Trainee GP Kingston upon Thames VTS; Regist. (Radiother.) Middlx. Hosp. Lond.; SHO (Med. & Cardiol.) Harefield Hosp. Middlx.

GRAY, Beverley Margaret Department of Anaesthesia, Hull Royal Infirmary, Anlaby Road, Hull HU3 2JZ Tel: 01482 674542; Toft House, 46-48 Main St, Swanland, North Ferriby HU14 3QR Tel: 01482 631536 — MB BS 1983 Lond.; FRCA 1988. Cons. Anaesth. Hull Roy. Infirm.

GRAY, Brendan Matthew (retired) Tullyvin, Pwllmeyric Close, Chepstow NP16 6LQ Tel: 01291 623557 — LRCPI & LM, LRCSI & LM 1950. Prev: Assoc. Specialist (Anaesth.) St. Lawrence Hosp. Chepstow.

GRAY, Brian Department of Diabetic Medicine, The County Hospital, Hereford HR1 2ER; The Fountain, Twyning, Tewkesbury GL20 6DB Tel: 01684 292529 — MB BChir 1964 Camb.; MA Camb. 1964; DObst RCOG 1967. (Univ. Coll. Hosp.) p/t Clin. Asst. Diabetes, Hereford Co. Hosp.; Community Retinopathy Screening Serv., Hereford Primary Care Trust. Socs: Brit. Diabetic Assn. (Med. & Scientif. Sect.). Prev: Ho. Surg. Cheltenham Gen. Hosp.; Ho. Phys. (Paediat.) Hillingdon Hosp.; Res. Obst. Off. Cheltenham Matern. Hosp.

GRAY, Carl Department of Histopathology, Harrogate District Hospital, Lancaster Park Road, Harrogate HG2 7SX Tel: 01423 553071 Fax: 01423 553230 Email: carlgray@btinternet.com — MB ChB 1978 Leeds; BSc (Hons.) Leeds 1975; FRCPath 1996, M 1985; DMJ(Path) Soc. Apoth. Lond. 1987. Cons. Histopath. Harrogate HA. Prev: Hon. Cons. Histopath. & Morbid Anat. Leeds W.. HA; Sen. Lect. (Path.) Univ. Leeds; Hon. Sen. Regist. (Path.) Yorks RHA.

GRAY, Carol 75 Heaton Road, Heaton, Newcastle upon Tyne NE6 5HH Tel: 0191 276 3720 — MB BS 1989 Newc. SHO (Dermat.) Roy. Vict. Infirm. Newc. Prev: SHO (ENT) Freeman Hosp. Newc.; SHO (Paediat.) S. Cleveland Hosp. Middlesbrough.

GRAY, Mrs Carol Amanda Maria N. Staffs. Hospital, Emergency Department, Windsor House, Princes Road, Hartshill, Stoke-on-Trent ST4 7LN Tel: 01782 554503 Fax: 01782 747179; 51 Chesterwood Road, Burslem, Stoke-on-Trent ST6 7EL Email: gray@chesterwood.freeserve.co.uk — MB BS 1982 Lond.; FFAEM 1998; FRCS Ed. 1994; BSc Lond. 1979. (St. Bart.) Cons. (A & E) N. Staffs. Hosp. Stoke-on-Trent; Sen. Lect. & Director of Clin. underGrad. studies, Univ. of Keele. Prev: Sen. Regist. (A & E) W. Midl.; Regist. (A & E) Mersey; GP Stoke-on-Trent.

GRAY, Catherine Janet Auckland Surgery, 84A Auckland Road, Upper Norwood, London SE19 2DF Tel: 020 8653 5146 Fax: 020 8653 1195; 55 Franciscan Road, Tooting, London SW17 8EA — MB BS 1985 Lond.; MRCP (UK) 1988; MRCGP 1992; DCH RCP Lond. 1989.

GRAY, Catherine Rosemary Sun House, Capon Tree Road, Brampton CA8 1QL — BM BS 1981 Nottm.; BMedSci Nottm. 1979; MRCGP 1985; Dip. Occ. Med. RCP Lond. 1997; DRCOG 1984. (Nottm.) Occupat. Phys. Nestlé, Dalston & Dumfries & Brake Bros. Lancaster; Clin. Asst. (BrE. Clinic) Cumbld. Infirm. Carlisle.

GRAY, Catherine Tweedie 133 Leamington Road, Coventry CV3 6GT Tel: 024 76 414853 — MB ChB Glas. 1941. (Glas.) Socs: BMA. Prev: Dep. Asst. MOH Coventry Co. Boro.; Indian Med. Serv.; Ho. Phys. & Ho. Surg. Roy. Infirm. Glas.

GRAY, Cavin 194A White Lane, Sheffield S12 3GL Tel: 0114 239 5233 — MB ChB 1985 Ed.; FRCA 1994. Cons. Anaesth., N.ern Gen. Hosp., Sheff. Prev: Regist. (Anaesth.) Roy. Hallamsh. Hosp. Sheff.; SHO (Anaesth.) Roy. Hallamsh. Hosp. Sheff.

GRAY, Charles Philip (retired) 24 St Mary's Avenue, Alverstoke, Gosport PO12 2HX Tel: 023 9258 3481 — MB ChB 1956 Birm.; DA Eng. 1961; DObst RCOG 1958.

GRAY, Charles Richardson White (retired) Hornpipe, Park Road, Forest Row RH18 5BX Tel: 01342 822537 Fax: 01342 822585 Email: hompipe@mistral.co.uk — BA Camb. 1955; MB BS Lond. 1963; FFA RCS Eng. 1973. Prev: Research Asst. (Med.) King's Coll. Hosp. Lond.

GRAY, Professor Christopher Stuart Department of Geriatric Medicine, Sunderland District General Hospital, Kayll Road, Sunderland SR4 7TP Tel: 0191 565 6256 Fax: 0191 569 9767; Broadstone, Front St, Tynemouth, North Shields NE30 4RG Email: c.s.gray@ncl.ac.uk — MB BS 1982 Newc.; MD Newc. 1991; FRCP Lond. 1995; MRCP (UK) 1985. (Newc. u. Tyne) Prof. Clin. Geriat. Univ. Newc. u. Tyne; Hon. Cons. City Hosps. Sunderland. Prev: Cons. Phys. & Geriat.ian Qu. Eliz. Hosp. Gateshead; Sen. Lect. (Geriat. Med.) Edin. Univ.; Sen. Regist. (Med.) with s/i in Geriat. Lothian HB.

GRAY, David Department of Medicine, Division of Cardiovascular Medicine, Queen's Medical Centre, University Hospital, Nottingham NG7 2UH Tel: 0115 970 9344 Fax: 0115 970 9384 Email: d.gray@nottingham.ac.uk; 15 Redwood Avenue, Wollaton, Nottingham NG8 2SG Tel: 0115 928 3750 — BM BS 1983 Nottm.; FRIPHH; DM Nottm. 1992, BMedSci 1981; MRCP (UK) 1986; MPH Nottm. 1995; FRCP 1998. (Nottm.) Reader (Med.) & Hon. Cons. Phys. & Cardiol. Univ. Hosp. Nottm. Socs: Chartered Soc. Physiother. Prev: Sen. Lect. Cardiol. Univ. Hosp. Nottm.; Vis. Fell. Duke Univ. Med. Centre Durh. N. Carolina, USA; Lect. (Cardiovasc Med.) Univ. Hosp. Nottm.

GRAY, David Grant Rowan Villa, 127 Old Greenock Road, Bishopton PA7 5BB Tel: 01505 863727 Email: dooleygray@compuserve.com — MB ChB 1993 Aberd.; MRCP 1998. SHO Palliat. Care, Huntershill Marie Curie Centre. Prev: SHO (Med.) Inverclyde Roy. NHS Trust.

GRAY, David Thomas (retired) 27 Knightsbridge Manor, Belfast BT9 5ET Tel: 02890 682304 — MB BCh BAO 1960 Belf.; DObst. RCOG 1963. Prev: SHO (Clin. Path.) Belf. City Hosp.

GRAY, Deborah Ann 1 Pitcairn Avenue, Bangor BT20 4UJ — MB BCh BAO 1983 Dub.; MRCGP 1987. Socs: Roy. Coll. Gen. Pract.

GRAY, Derek William George Great Western Road Medical Group, 327 Great Western Road, Aberdeen AB10 6LT; 29 Angusfield Avenue, Aberdeen AB15 6AR Tel: 01224 316156 Email: derekgray29@btinternet.com — MB ChB Aberd. 1963. Club Doctor Aberd. Football Club. Prev: Regist. & Ho. Phys. Roy. Aberd. Hosp. Sick Childr.; Ho. Surg. (Cas.) Aberd. Roy. Infirm.

GRAY, Prof. Derek William Russell c/o Nuffield Department of Surgery, Headington, Oxford OX3 0EX — MB ChB 1974 Leeds; FRCP 1998 UK; FRCS 1979 Eng.; DPhil 1984 Oxf.; DPhil Oxf. 1984; FRCS Eng. 1979; MRCP (UK) 1976. Prof. (Surg.) Univ. Oxf.; Prof. & Hon Cons. Univ., Oxf. Socs: Sec. Int. Pancreas & Islet Transpl. Ass. Prev: Clin. Lect. (Surg.) Univ. Oxf.; Regist. (Surg.) Gloucs. Roy. Hosp.; Clin. Reader (Surg.) Univ. Oxf.

GRAY, Douglas Anderson 4 Melville Place, Newburgh, Cupar KY14 6HB Tel: 01337 40658; Langhame, Station Cottages, E. Daviot, Inverness IV1 2EP Tel: 01463 772232 Email: douglas.gray@btinternet.com — MB BS 1987 Newc.; BSc (Hons.) Ed. 1975; DPhil Sussex 1980; MRCPsych 1996; MRCGP 1991. (Newcastle) Specialist Regist. (Forens. Psychiat.) Roy. Cornhill Hosp. Aberd.; Specialist Regist. Craig Dunain Hosp. Inverness. Socs: Brit. Assn. Psychopharmacol. Prev: Specialist Regist. Roy. Cornw. Hosp. Aberd.; Trainee GP Highland VTS; MRC Research Fell. King's Coll. Hosp. Med. Sch. Lond.

GRAY, Douglas James Luska, Langley Road, Claverdon, Warwick CV35 8QA — MB ChB 1998 Leeds.

GRAY, Duncan Allan 2 Redford Terrace, Edinburgh EH13 0BT — MB ChB 1991 Aberd.

GRAY, Mr Duncan Charles St Thomas's Hospital, Lambeth Palace Road, London SE1 7EH — MB ChB 1981 Aberd.; FRCS Ed. 1992; Dip. Sports Med. Lond. 1988. Prev: Trainee GP Aviemore.; Regist. (Anaesth.) Vict. Infirm. Glas.

GRAY, Eileen Norah Fax: 01403 730660 — MB ChB 1978 Glas.; BSc Glas. 1978; DRCOG 1980. (Glasgow) p/t S.water W. Sussex. Socs: Med. Protec. Soc. & Guild of Catholic Doctors. Prev: SHO (Paediat. & O & G) S.. Gen. Hosp. Glas.; SHO (Geriat.) Horsham Hosp.

GRAY, Eleanor Ruth (retired) 1 Hatton Way, Perth PH2 7DP Tel: 01738 624807 — MB ChB Ed. 1960.

GRAY, Elizabeth Sim 22 Binghill Crescent, Milltimber, Aberdeen Tel: 01224 868322 — MB ChB 1967 Aberd.; MRCPath 1976. (Aberd.) Cons. (Paediat,/Perinatal Path.) Aberd. Med. Sch. Prev: Lect. (Path.) Univ. Aberd.

GRAY, Elspeth Catherine Hollycroft, Newton of Pitcairn, Dunning, Perth PH2 0SL — MB ChB 1991 Aberd.

GRAY, Fiona Mairi 8/18 Sheriff Bank, Edinburgh EH6 6ES — MB ChB 1990 Glas.; MRCGP 1994.

GRAY, Francesca Margaret 7 Old Coach Road, East Kilbride, Glasgow G74 4DS — MB ChB 1998 Glas.; MB ChB Glas 1998.

GRAY, George Allan 2 Gourleys Lane, West Kirby, Wirral CH48 8AS Tel: 0151 632 3014 Fax: 0151 625 8265 — MB ChB Ed. 1948; LMCC 1977.

GRAY, George Leslie Archway Medical Practice, 16 Francis Street, Stornoway HS1 2XB Tel: 01851 703588 Fax: 01851 706338; Torwoodlee, 12 Goathill Crescent, Stornoway HS1 2TA Tel: 01851 702899 Email: docglgray@aol.com — MB ChB 1977 Ed.; MRCGP 1981; DRCOG 1981; Dip. Palliat. Med. Wales 1993. Med. Dir. Bethesda Hospice Stornoway.

GRAY, Mr George Russell 6 Calderwood Road, Newlands, Glasgow G43 2RP Tel: 0141 637 9104 Email: llygra@aol.com — MB ChB 1968 Glas.; FRCS Eng. 1974; FRCS Glas. 1974. Cons. Surg. Vict. Infirm. Glas. Prev: Sen. Regist. (Surg.) Vict. Infirm. Glas.; Research Regist. (Gastroenterol.) Univ. Dept. Surg. W.. Infirm. Glas.; Lect. (Path.) Univ. Dundee.

GRAY, Gilbert Henry (retired) Saltcoats Health Centre, 17-19 Raise Street, Saltcoats KA21 5LX — MB ChB 1970 Glas.; MRCP (UK) 1973.

GRAY, Hamish David Royal Sussex County Hospital, Eastern Road, Brighton BN2 5BE — MB ChB 1992 Otago.

GRAY, Harry (retired) Stillington, York YO61 1LR Tel: 01483 200368 — MD 1948 Leeds; MB ChB 1942, DPH 1947. Prev: MOH Easingwold Flaxton, Wath & Thirsk RDS.

GRAY, Harry Richardson, VRD (retired) 17 Davy's Place, Gravesend DA12 4DL Tel: 01474 324613 Email: sue.harry.gray@lineone.net — MB ChB 1941 Liverp.; MRCGP 1953. Surg. Cdr. RNR (Retd.) (mentioned in despatches). Prev: Sen. Regist. & SHO (Surg.) Gen. Hosp. Birkenhead.

GRAY, Heather Clare Bellevue Crescent Surgery, 26 Huntingdon Place, Edinburgh EH7 4AT Tel: 0131 556 8196 Fax: 0131 557 0535 — MB ChB 1985 Aberd.; MRCGP 1989.

GRAY, Helen Clare 45 Stoke Hill, Stoke Bishop, Bristol BS9 1LQ Tel: 0117 968 7505 Email: helengray20@hotmail.com; 39 North Circular Road, Belfast BT15 5HD Tel: 02890 776887 — MB BChir 1987 Camb.; BA Oxf. 1985; MRCP (UK) 1990. Cons. Phys. in Diabeties/Endocrinol., Cheltenham Gen. Hosp., Cheltenham; Hon. Clin. Research Fell. Bristol Roy. Infirm. Prev: Research Fell. & Hon. Sen. Regist. (Med.) Addenbrooke's Hosp. Camb.; Regist. Rotat. (Med.) Qu. Med. Centre Nottm.; SHO Rotat. (Med.) Addenbrooke's Hosp. Camb.

GRAY, Helen Grace McIntyre Monklands & Bellshill Hospitals NHS Trust, Monklands Hospital, Monkscourt Avenue, Airdrie ML6 0JS Tel: 01236 746116; 17 Holm Road, Crossford, Carluke ML8 5RG Tel: 01555 860434 — MB ChB 1964 Glas.; MSc Ed. 1980; MRCOG 1973. Med. Dir. Monklands & Bellshill Hosps. NHS Trust. Prev: Cons. Pub. Health Med. Lanarksh. HB; Trainee (Community Med.) Argyll & Clyde HB; Regist. (O & G) William Smellie Matern. Hosp. Lanark, Law Hosp. Carluke & S.. Gen. Hosp. Glas.

GRAY, Henry St John Swindells Gate Farm, Hedgerow, Rainow, Macclesfield SK10 5DA Tel: 01625 573020 — MB BS 1978 Lond.; MRCP (UK) 1981; FRCA 1987. Cons. Anaesth. Wythenshawe Hosp. Manch. Prev: Sen. Regist. (Anaesth.) N. W.. RHA.

GRAY, Henry Withers Tel: 01355 229525 Fax: 0141 211 4386; 4 Winton Park, East Kilbride, Glasgow G75 8QW Tel: 0141 211 4761 Fax: 0141 211 4386 Email: hwg1q@clinmed.gla.ac.uk — MB ChB Glas. 1965; MD Glas. 1974; FRCP Glas. 1986, M 1984; FRCP Lond. 1984, M 1968. (Jackson Primary, Rutherglen Academy ackton Primary, Rutherglen Academy) Cons. Phys. Roy. Infirm. Glas. Med. and Nuclear Med. Socs: Brit. Nuclear Med. Soc.; Assn. Phys.; Soc. of Nuclear Med.

GRAY, Hermina Mary Meddygfa Pengorof, Gorof Road, Ystradgynlais, Swansea SA9 1DS Tel: 01639 843221 Fax: 01639 843790; The Lamb & Flag House, 12 Heol Rheolau, Abercraf, Swansea SA9 1TE Tel: 01639 730151 — MB ChB 1979 Sheff.

GRAY, Huon Hamilton Wessex Cardiac Unit, Southampton University Hospital, Southampton SO16 6YD Tel: 02380 794703 Fax: 02380 798693 Email: huon@dial.pipex.com — MB BS 1977 Lond.; FACC 1998; FESC 1997; FRCP Lond. 1994; MD Lond. 1986; MRCP (UK) 1980. (St. Thos.) Cons. Cardiol. Wessex Cardiac Unit Soton. Socs: Hon. Sec. Brit. Cardiac Soc.-1998-2000. Prev: Sen. Regist. (Cardiol.) Brompton Hosp. & St. Geo. Hosps. Lond.; Regist. (Cardiol.) Brompton Hosp. Lond.; Brit. Heart Foundat. Jun. Research Fell. St. Thos. Hosp. Lond.

GRAY, Mr Iain Cairns Maxwell 45 Rodney Street, Liverpool L1 9EN Tel: 0151 708 0842; 70 Trafalgar Road, Southport PR8 2NJ — MB ChB 1970 Glas.; MB ChB (Commend.) Glas. 1972; BSc (Hons. Physiol.) Glas. 1970; FRCS (Orthop.) Ed. 1984; FRCS Glas. 1976, FRCS Ed. 1976. (University of Glasgow) Cons. Orthop. Surg. Roy. Liverp. Univ. Hosp. Trust. Socs: Fell. Brit. Orthop. Assn. & Brit. Hand Soc. Prev: Sen. Regist. (Orthop.) W.. Infirm. Glas.

GRAY, Iain Gilfillan 14 Westwater Place, Wormit, Newport-on-Tay DD6 8NS — MD 1972 Dundee; MB ChB St. And. 1964; FFA RCS Eng. 1968; DObst RCOG 1966. (St. And.) Cons. Anaesth. Dundee Teach. Hosps. Prev: Sen. Regist. Dundee Roy. Infirm.; Fell. (Anaesth.) Hosp. Sick Childr. Toronto, Canada.

GRAY, Ian Gilmour (retired) 22 Highfield Close, Thorpe St Andrew, Norwich NR7 0RQ Tel: 01603 436134 — MB BS 1944 Lond.; MRCGP 1966. Prev: Ho. Surg. St. Geo. Hosp.

GRAY, Ian Ramsay (retired) 21 Bridge End, Warwick CV34 6PB Tel: 01926 492270 — MD 1943 Wisconsin; MB BS Lond. 1944; MD Lond. 1949; FRCP Lond. 1964. M 1945. Consult. Cardiol. Coventry & S. Warks. Gp. Hosps. Prev: Sen. Regist. Nat. Heart Hosp.

GRAY, Jacqueline Dorothy Lane End, Ladycutter Lane, Corbridge NE45 5RR — MB BS 1987 Newc.; MSc Newc. 1992; MFPHM RCP (UK) 1994; MRCGP (UK) 1998. (Newcastle upon Tyne) Cons. Pub. Health Med. Prev: GP Princip. Tynedale N.umberland; Sen. Regist. (Pub. Health) Univ. Newc. u. Tyne.

GRAY, James Allan (retired) St Andrews Cottage, 15 Lauder Road, Edinburgh EH9 2EN Tel: 0131 667 4124 — MB ChB 1959 Ed.; FRCP Ed. 1974, M 1965. Prev: Cons. Communicable Dis. City Hosp. Edin.

GRAY, James Geoffrey Rosehall Medical Practice, Glengormley, Newtownabbey BT36 8P Tel: 01232 832188; 39 North Circular Road, Belfast BT15 5HD Tel: 01232 776887 — MB BCh BAO 1949 Belf. (Qu. Univ. Belf.)

***GRAY, James Michael** 30 Toller Road, Quorn, Loughborough LE12 8AH — MB ChB 1995 Birm.

***GRAY, James Thorburn** 53 Forres Road, Sheffield S10 1WD Email: james.gray@cwcom.net — MB ChB 1998 Sheff.; MB ChB Sheff 1998.

GRAY, James William The Holt, Lapworth St., Lowsonford, Solihull B95 5HG — MB ChB 1985 Aberd.

GRAY, Jane Glenlyn Medical Centre, 115 Molesey Park Road, East Molesey KT8 0JX Tel: 020 8979 3253 Fax: 020 8941 7914; 7 Armstrong Close, SudBury Lane, Walton-on-Thames KT12 2JQ Tel: 01932 231774 — MB BS 1971 Lond.; MRCS Eng. LRCP Lond. 1971. Socs: BSMDH.

GRAY, Jane Lesley Moss Lane Surgery, Moss Lane, Madeley, Crewe LW5 9NQ — MB ChB 1989 Manch.; MRCGP 1994; DRCOG 1992. GP Retainee, Moss La. Surg., Madeley. Prev: Asst. GP Malpas Chesh.

GRAY, Janet Frances Spence Group Practice, Westcliffe House, 48-50 Logan Road, Bishopston, Bristol BS7 8DR Tel: 0117 944 0701; Kuchana, St. Martin's Lane, Marshfield, Chippenham SN14 8LZ Tel: 01225 891115 Fax: 01225 892240 — MB BChir 1974 Camb.; MFHom 1988; MRCGP 1978; DRCOG 1977. (Univ. Camb. & St. Mary's Med. Sch. Lond.)

GRAY, Mrs Jean Annette (retired) 21 Bridge End, Warwick CV34 6PB Tel: 01926 492270 — MRCS Eng. LRCP Lond. 1951; MRCPsych 1979. Cons. Psychiat. S. Warks. HA. Prev: Sen. Regist. (Psychiat.) W. Midl. RHA.

GRAY, Jean Margaret 4 Crowthers Hill, Dartmouth TQ6 9QX — MB ChB 1947 Birm. (Birm.) Socs: Inst. Psycho-Sexual Med.; Assoc. Mem. W. Midl. Inst. of Psychother.

GRAY, Jenifer Rose (retired) 42 Colthurst Drive, Hanham, Bristol BS15 3SG — MB ChB 1978 Birm. Clinc. Asst. in Urodynamics S.mead Hosp. Bristol. Prev: GP BRistol.

GRAY, Jennifer (retired) Syed, Dibdin and Asker, 511 Fox Hollies Road, Hall Green, Birmingham B28 8RJ Tel: 0121 777 1180 Fax: 0121 777 6265 — MB ChB 1973 Birm.; BMus (Hons.) Birm. 1964,

MB ChB 1973. Non-Princip. GP. Prev: Clin. Asst. Dalton Pl. Drug AlcoholUnit Solihull.

GRAY, Jennifer Mary Somercotes Medical Centre, 22 Nottingham Road, Somercotes, Derby DE72 3FL Tel: 01773 602141; 76 Chesterfield Road, Tibshelf, Derby DE55 5NL — MB BS 1976 Lond.; MRCS Eng. LRCP Lond. 1976; MRCGP 1983; DCH Eng. 1980. Prev: Jun. Regist. (Paediat.) St. Bart. Hosp. Lond.; SHO (Paediat.) St. Jas. Univ. Hosp. Leeds; Trainee GP E.bourne VTS.

GRAY, Mr Jeremy David 8 Tennyson Road, Bath BA1 3BG — MB BChir 1979 Camb.; MA, MB BChir Camb. 1979; FRCS Eng. 1988. (Guy's)

GRAY, Jeremy David Kingsland, Leominster HR6 9QL Tel: 01568 708214 Fax: 01568 708188; Plainsbrook, Bircher, Leominster HR6 0BW Tel: 01568 780279 — BM BS 1986 Nottm.; MRCGP 1996; DRCOG 1992; MRCP (Ed.) 1991; BmedSci (Nottm.) 1984. (Nottingham) GP Full Partner. Prev: SHO (O & G) Chester HA.; SHO (Dermat.) Leeds Gen. Infirm.

GRAY, Jeremy Pieter Tel: 020 7585 1358 Email: joemy@6rg123.net — MB BS 1985 Lond.; MA Camb. 1982; MRCP (UK) 1990; MRCGP 1994; DGM RCP Lond. 1988. (Roy. Hosp. Lond.) Princip. in Gen. Pract.; Director of Battersea Research Gp.; Director of Primary Care Developm. Gp. Prev: Lect. (Community Med. Educat.) Kings Coll. Sch. Med. & Dent.; Regist. (Gen. Med.) Whipps Cross Hosp. Lond.; SHO Rotat. (Gen. Med.) W.m. Med. Sch. Lond.

GRAY, Jessie Katherine Minnie (retired) 6 Royal Terrace, Linlithgow EH49 6HQ Email: jkmgray@compuserve.com — LRCP LRCS Ed. LRFPS Glas. 1948; MFCM 1972; DPH Ed. 1951. Prev: Med. Off. & Lect. Callendar Pk. Coll. of Educat. Falkirk.

GRAY, Jill Caroline Scott Clun Surgery, Turnpike Meadow, Clun, Craven Arms SY7 8HZ Tel: 01588 640573 Fax: 01588 640084; 36 High Street, Bishops Castle SY9 5BQ Tel: 01588 638436 — MB ChB 1977 Ed.; BSc Ed. 1974; MRCGP 1982; DRCOG 1980. Shrops. Family Practitioner Comm. Socs: Roy. Soc. Gen. Pract.; Diplomate Roy. Coll. Obst. & Gyn.

GRAY, Jillian Sandra 26 Stuart Road, Bishopton PA7 5BX — MB BS 1996 Lond.

GRAY, Joan (retired) 2 Snells Wood Court, Cokes Lane, Little Chalfont, Amersham HP7 9QT — MB ChB 1943 Birm.; FRCPCH 1997; FFPHM RCP (UK) 1977, M 1972; DPH Lond. 1961. Prev: Cons. Pub. Health Med. Aylesbury Vale HA.

GRAY, Joanna Croix Farm, Main St., Tur Langton, Leicester LE8 0PJ — MB BS 1984 Lond.

GRAY, Johannah Geneen Mayday University Hospital, London Rd, Thornton Heath, Croydon CR7 7YE — MB BS 1997 Lond.

GRAY, John (retired) Innisfree, Walwyn Road, Colwall, Malvern WR13 6QG Tel: 01684 540418 — MB ChB 1942 Aberd. Prev: GP Thornley, Durh.

GRAY, John Public Health Laboratory, Central Pathology Laboratory, Hartshill Road, Hartshill, Stoke-on-Trent ST4 7PX Tel: 01782 46956 Fax: 01872 744568; 193 London Road, Newcastle ST5 7HZ — MB BS 1970 Lond.; MRCS Eng. LRCP Lond. 1970; FRCPath 1988, M 1976; Dip. Bact. Lond 1975. (Char. Cross.) Dir. Cons. Microbiol. Pub. Health Laborat. Stoke-on-Trent. Prev: Asst. Microbiol. Pub. Health Laborat. Serv. E. Birm. Hosp.; Trainee Microbiol. Pub. Health Laborat. Serv. N.. Gen. Hosp. Sheff.

GRAY, John Alexander 111 Hatton Gardens, Crookston, Glasgow G52 3PU — LRCP LRCS 1947 Ed.; LRCP LRCS Ed. LRFPS Glas. 1947.

GRAY, Sir John Archibald Browne (retired) Seaways, Kingsway, Kingsand, Torpoint PL10 1NG Tel: 01752 822745 Fax: 01753 822745 Email: jabgray@seaways.u-net.com — MB BChir Camb. 1942; FRS; MA, ScD Camb. 1962; Hon. DSc Exeter 1985; FRCP Lond. 1974; FIBiol. Hon. Fell. Clare Coll. Camb. Prev: Mem. Extern. Scientif. Staff Med. Research Counc. (Marine Biol. Assn.).

GRAY, John Armstrong Muir, CBE Institute of Health Sciences, Old Road, Oxford OX3 7LF Tel: 01865 226833 Fax: 01865 226775 Email: mini.gray@his.ox.ac.uk; 59 Lakeside, Oxford OX2 8JQ Tel: 01865 554066 — MB ChB Glas. 1969; MD Glas. 1981; FRCP Glas. 1988; FRCP (UK) 1984; MRCGP 1983; DSc UEA 1999. Dir. of the Inst. Of Health Sci.; Dir. Nat. Electronic Library for Health; Sec. Cochrane Collaboration. Prev: Jt. Dir. Nat. Screening Comm.

GRAY, John Cuthbertson (retired) Uppingham Road Medical Centre, 190 Uppingham Road, Leicester LE5 0QG Tel: 0116 276 6605 — MB ChB 1957 Glas. Prev: SHO (Anaesth.) Lord Mayor Treloar Orthop. Hosp. Alton.

GRAY, John Dennis 35 Oaks Drive, Lexden, Colchester CO3 3PR — MB BS 1962 Lond.; FRCR 1975; FFR 1974; DMRD Eng. 1971. (Char. Cross) Cons. Radiol. Dist. Gen. Hosp. Colchester. Prev: Sen. Regist. Diag. Radiol. Dept. Lond. Hosp.; Med. Regist. Hackney Hosp.; SHO Sully Hosp.

GRAY, John Edward Gosbury Hill Health Centre, Orchard Gardens, Chessington KT9 1AG Tel: 020 8397 2142 Fax: 020 8974 2717 — MB BS 1971 Lond.; M.I.T. 2001; MRCGP 1977; DObst RCOG 1973. Socs: Eur. Hair Research Soc.; Amer. Hair Research Soc.; Eur. Soc. Contact Dermat.

GRAY, John Emmerson 5 Littel Dene, Lodore Road, Newcastle upon Tyne NE2 3NZ — MB BS 1936 Durh.

GRAY, Mr John Gowan 12 Park Avenue, Wolstanton, Newcastle ST5 8AU Tel: 01782 626679 — MB ChB 1950 Ed.; FRCS Ed. 1956; FRCS Eng. 1958. Cons. Surg. N. Staffs. Roy. Infirm. Stoke-on-Trent. Prev: Lect. (Surg.) Univ. Birm.; Sen. Regist. (Surg.) Glas Roy. Infirm.

GRAY, John Michael 3 The Brake Yard, St Mawes, Truro TR2 5BP — MB BS 1956 Lond.

GRAY, Jonathon Robin Email: jonathongray@ultw-tr.wales.nhs.uk — MB ChB 1988 Dundee; BMSc (Hons.) Dund 1985; MRCP (UK) 1991; MRCPI 1990; PhD 1994. Cons. (Clin. Genetics) Inst. Med. Genetics Univ. Hosp. Wales. Prev: Clin. Research Fell. (Molecular Genetics) Ninewells Hosp. Dundee; Ho. Off. (Med.) Ninewells Hosp. Dundee; Ho. Off. (Surg.) Perth Roy. Infirm. Scotl.

GRAY, Judith Elizabeth 12 Old Coad Road, Upper Malone Road, Belfast BT9 5PR Tel: 01232 613808 — MB BCh BAO 1964 Belf.; MFFP 1994. (Belf.) Med. Off. Belf. E. HB. Socs: Fac. Fam. Plann. & Reproduc. Health Care; Assoc. Mem. Inst. Psycho-Sexual Med. Prev: Ho. Off. & SHO S. Belf. Gp. Hosps.

GRAY, Julia Katharine Mary Macniven House, Gartnavel Royal Hospital, 1055 Great Western Road, Glasgow G12 0XH — MB ChB 1989 Sheff.; MRCPsych 1996; DRCOG 1993. Specialist Regist. (Psychiat.) Glas.

GRAY, Julian Arnold The Leasowes, Ewyas Harold, Hereford HR2 0ES — MB BS 1981 Lond.; DPhil Oxf. 1988, BA (1st Cl. Hons) 1978; MRCP (UK) 1984. Med. Expert CNS Clin. Research Sandoz Ltd. Basle, Switz.. Prev: MRC Train. Fell. & Hon. Med. Regist. (Dept. Clin. Pharmacol.) Radcliffe Infirm. Oxf.; Research Regist. (Neurol.) Roy. Surrey Co. Hosp. Guildford; SHO (Neurol.) Radcliffe Infirm. Oxf.

GRAY, Julian Malcolm 31 Woodfield Drive, Winchester SO22 5PY — MB BCh 1984 Wales.

GRAY, Juliet Clare 80 Brands Hill Avenue, High Wycombe HP13 5PU; 2 Bembridge Crescent, Southsea PO4 0QU Tel: 01705 734208 Email: jcxgray@aol.com — MB BS 1994 Lond.; MA Camb. 1991; MRCP (UK) 1997. (Roy. Free Hosp. Sch. Med.) Specialist Regist. (Paeds), St. Mary's Hospitla, Portsmouth. Prev: SHO (Neonat.) St. Geo. Hosp. Lond.

GRAY, Karen Elizabeth 6 Calderwood Road, Glasgow G43 2RP — MB ChB 1997 Glas. SHO (O & G), Souhthern Geberal Hosp., Glas.

GRAY, Katherine Jane Broomhouse Mains Farm, Duns TD11 3PP — MB ChB 1990 Ed.; MRCP (UK) 1993.

GRAY, Kathleen Elizabeth Craig Fowlers Bench, Higher Burwardsley, Tattenhall, Chester CH3 9PQ — MB ChB 1950 Liverp. Prev: Ho. Surg. Liverp. Roy. Infirm.; Ho. Phys. & Sen. Ho. Off. Clatterbridge Hosp. Bebington.

GRAY, Kenneth Edward Barnet General Hospital, Wellhouse Lane, Barnet EN5 3DJ Tel: 020 8216 4000 Fax: 020 8216 5480 Email: kennethgray@classicfm.net; 19 Loom Lane, Radlett WD7 8AA Tel: 01923 857712 Email: kennethgray@classicfm.net — MB BChir Camb. 1962; MA Camb. 1968; FRCP Lond. 1979, M 1968. (St. Bart.) p/t Cons. Phys. Barnet Gen. Hosp. & Finchley Memor. Hosp, & Potters' Bar Hosp; Hon. Cons. Cardiol. Harefield Hosp.; Hon. Phys. & Cardiol. Dispensaire Francais. Socs: Brit. Cardiac Soc. Prev: Sen. Regist. (Med.) United Bristol Hosps. & SW RHB; Regist. (Cardiol.) Nat. Heart Hosp. Lond.; Ho. Phys. St. Bart. Hosp. Lond.

GRAY, Libby Jane 34 Ladywood Road, Upper Marham, King's Lynn PE33 9NY — MB BS 1990 New South Wales.

GRAY, Mrs Margaret Eleanor Rosamond (retired) 11 Ullswater, 53 Putney Hill, London SW15 6RY Tel: 020 8789 9813 — MB BS

1943 Lond.; MD Lond. 1947; DPH (Distinc.) 1947; MRCS Eng. LRCP Lond. 1942.

GRAY, Margaret Winifred Abbey Health Centre, East Abbey Street, Arbroath DD11 1EN Tel: 01241 870311 Fax: 01241 875411; 27 Viewfield Road, Arbroath DD11 2DN — MB ChB 1972 St. And.; BSc St. And. 1969, MB ChB 1972; MRCGP 1980.

GRAY, Maria-Danuta (retired) 14 St Mary's Road, Harborne, Birmingham B17 0HA Tel: 0121 427 6525 — LRCPI & LM, LRSCI & LM 1962; LRCPI & LM, LRCSI & LM 1962; FRCOG 1989, M 1968; DRCOG 1966. Prev: Cons. Gyn. Birm. Nuffield Hosp.

GRAY, Marion Findlay (retired) 396 Cyncoed Road, Cardiff CF23 6SA Tel: 02920 753918 — MB ChB 1947 Ed. Prev: Ho. Phys. (Paediat.) City Hosp. Nottm.

GRAY, Marion Yvonne 17 Fields Park Road, Cardiff CF11 9JP — MB BCh 1987 Wales; MRCP (UK) 1991.

GRAY, Mark Stephen 50 The Park, Bookham, Leatherhead KT23 3LS — MB ChB 1997 Liverp.

GRAY, Martin Peter 5 Moss Bank, Aughton, Ormskirk L39 5DD — MB ChB 1993 Glas.

GRAY, Mary Elizabeth Stanhope (retired) Crookledy, Worton, Leyburn DL8 3ET — MB BS 1950 Durh.; DObst RCOG 1953. Prev: Gen. Practitioner, York.

GRAY, Maureen Mary 107 Crown Road N., Glasgow G12 9HS — MB ChB 1974 Glas.; MFFP 1993. Staff Grade (Med. Oncol.) Glas. Roy. Infirm. Prev: SCMO (Family Plann.) Gtr. Glas. HB; Research Fell. (Clin. Oncol.) Univ. Glas.

GRAY, Michael Ancrum Medical Centre, 12-14 Ancrum Road, Dundee DD2 2HZ Tel: 01382 833399 Fax: 01382 832484 — MB ChB 1981 Dundee. (Dundee) GP Dundee.

GRAY, Michael Ian Hart Nut Tree Cottage, Lower Chicksgrove, Tisbury, Salisbury SP3 6NB Tel: 01722 714382 — MB ChB St. And. 1965; MFOM RCP Lond. 1981; DAvMed Eng. 1976. Indep. Aviat. Med. Cons. Salisbury. Prev: Chief Med. Off. Gulf Air Bahrain; Sen. Specialist (Aviat. Med.) HQ Dir. Army Air Corps Middle Wallop; Regtl. Med. Off. 4th/7th Roy. Dragoon Guards.

GRAY, Michael James John Caen Health Centre, Braunton EX33 1LR Tel: 01271 812005 Fax: 01271 814768; North Buckland House, North Buckland, Braunton EX33 1HY Tel: 01271 890789 — MB ChB 1972 Bristol; DA Eng. 1975; DObst RCOG 1976.

GRAY, Moyra Noelle 1 Shandon, Pond Park Road, Lisburn BT28 3LQ — MB BCh BAO 1978 Belf.

GRAY, Nigel Ian Douglas Beaumont Clinton Road Surgery, 19 Clinton Road, Redruth TR15 2LL Tel: 01209 216507 Fax: 01209 218262 — MB BS 1967 Lond.; DObst RCOG 1971; DA Eng. 1970.

GRAY, Nigel Richard Homestead Clinic, Homestead Drive, Wakefield WF2 9PE Tel: 01924 384498 Fax: 01924 200373; 28 Woodthorpe Park Drive, Wakefield WF2 6NE Tel: 01924 256378 — MB ChB 1987 Leeds. Sen. Part. GP Pract.

GRAY, Mr Norman, Lt.-Col. RAMC 48 Mereworth Drive, Shooters Hill, London SE18 3EE Tel: 020 8854 1771 — MB BCh BAO 1964 Dub.; MA Dub. 1978, BA 1962, MB BCh BAO 1964; FRCS Ed. 1971. (TC Dub.) Cons. Urol. Qu. Eliz. Milit. Hosp. Woolwich. Socs: Brit. Assn. Urol. Surgs. & Transpl. Soc. S.. Africa. Prev: Sen. Lect. Univ. Natal Durban, S. Africa; Regist. S. Gen. Hosp. Glas.; Ho. Surg. Stirling Roy. Infirm.

GRAY, Olivia Sharon Margaret Roselea Cottage, Dalby, Peel IM5 3BR — MB ChB 1987 Liverp.

GRAY, Orla Mary 13 Slievemoyne Park, Newcastle BT33 0JD; 2 Rockfield Glen, Bangor BT19 7SF Tel: 01247 460422 — MB BCh BAO 1997 Belf. (Queens University of Belfast) SHO (Gen. Med.) Ulster Hosp. Dundonald. Prev: Jun. Ho. Off. Antrim Area Hosp.

GRAY, Pamela Frances Uplands, High Casterton, Carnforth LA6 2SE — MB ChB 1980 Manch.

GRAY, Patricia High Street Surgery, 87 High Street, Abbots Langley WD5 0AJ Tel: 01923 262363 Fax: 01923 267374 Email: pgray@gp-e82046.nhs.uk — MB BS 1986 Lond.; DO Auckland 1989. GP. Prev: Trainee GP Abbots Langley; SHO (O & G) Nat. Wom. Hosp. Auckland, NZ.

GRAY, Patricia Mary (retired) Birklands, Edwinstowe, Mansfield NG21 9NJ — MB BS Lond. 1952; MRCS Eng. LRCP Lond. 1952. JP.; Clin. Asst. (Anaesth.) Mansfield & Newark Health Dist.; Bd.ing Med. Off. DHSS. Prev: Clin. Asst. (Anaesth.) Mansfield & Newark Health Dist.

GRAY, Patrick John Brampton Medical Practice, 4 Market Place, Brampton CA8 1NL Tel: 016977 2551 Fax: 016977 41944; Plum Cottage, Farlam, Brampton CA8 1LA Tel: 016977 46187 Fax: 016977 41944 — BM BS 1981 Nottm.; BMedSci Nottm. 1979; FRCGP 1994, M 1985; Dip. Pract. Dermat. Wales 1991; DCH RCP Lond. 1984; DRCOG 1983.

GRAY, Paul Anthony Boundary House, 462 Northenden Road, Sale M33 2RH Tel: 0161 972 9999 — MB ChB 1984 Manch.; Dip. Med Acupunc 1996; MRCGP 1988; DCH RCP Lond. 1986. Socs: Brit. Med. Acupunc. Soc. Prev: SHO (Med./Paediat./O & G) Tameside Gen. Hosp.

GRAY, Paul Stephen Leslie Grove Surgery, Grove Lane, Thetford IP24 2HY Tel: 01842 752285 Fax: 01842 751316 — MB BS 1983 Lond.; BSc (Hons.) Lond. 1977, MB BS 1983. GP Thetford Norf. Prev: Trainee GP Tunbridge Wells.

GRAY, Penelope Jane Pereira 4 Hammelton Road, Bromley BR1 3PY Tel: 020 8290 1911 — MB ChB 1988 Bristol.

GRAY, Peter The Medical Centre, 32 London Road, Sittingbourne ME10 1ND Tel: 01795 472109/472100 — MB ChB 1983 Manch.; BSc St. And. 1980; MRCGP 1988; T(GP) 1991. GP Sittingbourne. Socs: Kent Medico-Legal So. Prev: Barrister Stour Chambers Canterbury; Med. Off. P & O Cruises; Trainee GP Whitehaven Cumbria VTS.

GRAY, Peter Boswell Department of Pathology, Royal Hospital, Chesterfield S44 5BL — MRCS Eng. LRCP Lond. 1970; FRCPath 1990, M 1978. Cons. Histopath. Chesterfield Roy. Hosp.

GRAY, Mr Peter John 31 Swan Mead, Hemel Hempstead HP3 9DQ — MB BChir 1982 Camb.; MA, MB Camb. 1982, BChir 1981; FRCS Eng. 1991; FRCOphth 1991. Sen. Regist. (Ophth.) Roy. Lond. Hosp. & Moorfields Eye Hosp. Socs: Internat. League Against Epilepsy. Prev: Regist. (Ophth.) Regional Eye Unit. OldCh. Hosp. Romford; SHO (Ophth.) The Roy. Eye Unit Kingston-upon-Thames; SHO (Neurosurg.) Atkinson Morley's Hosp. Lond.

GRAY, Peter Lawrence Portadown Health Centre, Portadown, Armagh BT62 5BU; Chilton, Cadeleigh, Tiverton EX16 8RT — MB BCh BAO 1979 Belf.; BSc (Hons.) (Physiol.) Belf. 1976; MRCGP 1983; Cert. Family Plann. JCC 1983; DRCOG 1981.

GRAY, Peter Louis Thomas The Surgery, 226 Rutland Street, Grimsby DN32 7LT Tel: 01472 342349; 3 Beckhythe Close, Grimsby DN33 2ES — MB ChB 1959 Sheff. (Sheff.) Clin. Asst. (Geriat.) Diana, P.ss of Wales Hosp. Grimsby; Clin. Asst. (Dermat.) Diana, P.ss of Wales Hosp. Grimsby. Socs: Fell. Roy. Soc. Med. Prev: Regist. (Med.) Co. Hosp. Louth; Clin. Asst. (Paediat.) Grimsby Matern. Hosp.; SHO (Med.) City Hosp. Derby.

GRAY, Peter William Spencer (retired) 9 The Avenue, Wivenhoe, Colchester CO7 9AH — MB BS 1945 Lond.; FFA RCS Eng. 1954, DA Eng. 1947. Prev: Sen. Resid. St. Bart. Hosp. Lond.

GRAY, Philip Andrew Department of Anaesthesia, Hull Royal Infirmary, Anlaby Road, Hull HU3 2JZ Tel: 01482 674542; Toft House, 46-48 Main St, Swanland, North Ferriby HU14 3QR Tel: 01482 631536 — MB BS 1982 Lond.; FRCA 1988. (Middlx.) Cons. Anaesth. & IC, Hull Roy. Infirm.

GRAY, Philip John Bath Lodge Practice, Bitterne Health Centre, Commercial Street, Bitterne, Southampton SO18 6BT Tel: 023 8044 2111 Fax: 023 8042 1316; Lower Swanwick Farm House, 240 Swanick Lane, Lower Swanwick, Southampton SO31 7GS — MB BS 1970 Newc.; MRCGP 1984; DObst RCOG 1975. Prev: Trainee GP Portsmouth VTS.

GRAY, Philip John Sutterton Surgery, Spalding Road, Sutterton, Boston PE20 1LD Tel: 01205 460254 Fax: 01205 460779 — MB ChB 1969 Leeds; DPM Leeds 1973; DObst RCOG 1971. (Leeds)

GRAY, Pieter Francis (retired) Old Glebe, Waldron, Heathfield TN21 0RB Tel: 01435 863865 — MB BChir 1956 Camb.; MA Camb. 1956; MRCS Eng. LRCP Lond. 1955. Prev: Ho. Off. Dept. Skin & Eyes Middlx. Hosp. Lond.

GRAY, Richard Park Crescent New Surgery, 1A Lewes Road, Brighton BN2 3JJ — MB BS 1974 Lond.; MRCS Eng. LRCP Lond. 1974; FRCGP 1989; MRCGP 1978; DRCOG 1977; MA Sussex 1998. (St. Mary's) Princip. Lect. In Primary Care, PostGrad. Med. Sch., Uni. Of Brishton. Prev: Assoc. Dean (Gen. Pract.) S. Thames (E.); GP Tutor Brighton Postgrad. Med. Centre; Ho. Phys. St. Mary's Hosp. Lond.

GRAY, Richard Edward Stuart Royal Surrey County Hospital, Egerton Road, Guildford GU2 7XX Tel: 01483 464159 Fax: 01483

406668 — MB ChB 1979 Sheff.; MA Camb. 1979; FRCP Lond. 1997; MRCP (UK) 1983. (Sheff. Univ. Med. Sch.) Cons. Rheum.; Clin. Tutor Roy. Surrey Co. Hosp. Socs: Brit. Soc. Rheum.; BMA; Nat. Ostroporosis Soc. Prev: Sen. Regist. (Rheum.) Wexham Pk. Hosp. Slough & Stoke Mandeville Hosp. Aylesbury; Regist. (Human Metab. & Clin. Biochem.) Roy. Hallamsh. Hosp. Sheff.; SHO (Rheum., Gen. Med. & Geriat.) Nether Edge Hosp. Sheff.

GRAY, Richard John Saville Medical Group, 7 Saville Place, Newcastle upon Tyne NE1 8DQ Tel: 0191 232 4274 Fax: 0191 233 1050; Beaulieu, Linden Avenue, Gosforth, Newcastle upon Tyne NE3 4HD Tel: 0191 284 0997 — MB BS 1975 Lond.; MRCS Eng. LRCP Lond. 1975; DRCOG 1977. (Char. Cross.) Med. Off. Stagecoach Bus Co. & Tyne & Wear PTE. Socs: N. Eng. Medico-Legal Soc. Prev: SHO (Paediat.) Char. Cross Hosp. Lond.; SHO (Obst.) W. Lond. Hosp.; Ho. Phys. Mt. Vernon Hosp. N.wood.

GRAY, Richard Nicholas Manning 530 New Hythe Lane, Aylesford ME20 7TH Tel: 01622 791322; 150 Linden Road, Coxheath, Maidstone ME17 4RA — MB BS 1969 Lond.; FFOM 1994 London; MSc (Occupat. Med.) Lond. 1974, MB BS 1969; MFOM RCP Lond. 1980. Socs: Soc. Occupat. Med. Prev: Area Med. Adviser Post Office SW Region Bristol; Naval Med. Off. Health to Flag Off. Scotl. & N.. Irel.; Sen. Med. Off. HM Naval Base Rosyth.

GRAY, Robert Cecil (retired) 3 Strathallan Park, Upper Malone, Belfast BT10 0AY Tel: 01232 622965 — MB BCh BAO 1949 Dub.; BA Dub. 1949, MD 1961; FFA RCSI 1962; DA RCPSI 1953. Prev: Cons. Anaesth. Roy. Vict. Hosp. Belf.

GRAY, Robert Donald 24 Alloa Road, Clackmannan FK10 4HG — MB ChB 1998 Aberd.; MB ChB Aberd 1998.

GRAY, Robert Fraser 15 Cardwell Road, Gourock PA19 1UG — MB ChB 1982 Glas.

GRAY, Robert McNally 58 Aytoun Road, Glasgow G41 5HE — MB ChB 1987 Glas.; BSc Glas. 1984; MRCPsych 1997. Specialist Regist. (Psychiat.) Glas. Prev: Career Regist. (Psychiat.) Glas.

GRAY, Robert Stuart 24 Murrayfield Drive, Edinburgh EH12 6EB — MB ChB 1971 Ed.; MRCP (UK) 1974.

GRAY, Mr Roger Frank Evelyn Hospital, Cambridge CB2 2AF Tel: 01223 216486; 5 Pemberton Terrace, Cambridge CB2 1JA — MB BS 1973 Lond.; MA Camb. 1987; FRCS Eng. 1977; MRCS Eng. LRCP Lond. 1973. (St. Mary's) Cons. ENT Surg. Addenbrooke's Hosp. Camb.; Cons. ENT Surg. Hinchingbrooke Hosp. Huntingdon; Assoc. Lect. Camb. Univ; Mem. Brit. Cochlear Implant Gp. Socs: Brit. Assn. Otol.; RCS (Regional Adviser); BMA. Prev: Sen. Regist. Rotat. (ENT) Roy. Free Hosp. Lond.; Regist. (ENT) St. Mary's Hosp. Lond.; SHO Roy. Nat. Throat, Nose & Ear Hosp. Lond.

GRAY, Mr Roger Hamilton Woodram Oaks, Pitminster, Taunton TA3 7AS — MB ChB 1980 Liverp.; FRCS Eng. 1987; MRCP (UK) 1984; FCOphth 1988; DO RCS Eng. 1987. (Liverp.) Cons. Ophth. Taunton & Som. NHS Trust. Prev: Sen. Regist. Oxf. Eye Hosp.; Vitreo-Retinal Fell. Moorfields Eye Hosp. Lond.; Sen. Regist. (Ophth.) Vitreo-Retinal Unit Roy. Perth Hosp. W.. Austral.

GRAY, Ronald Fraser Parkhead Hospital, 81 Salamanca St., Glasgow G31 5ES Tel: 0141 211 8300 Fax: 0141 211 8380; 44 Westbourne Crescent, Bearsden, Glasgow G61 4HE — MB ChB 1982 Glas.; MRCPsych 1987; T(Psych) 1991. Cons. Psychiat. Pk.head Hosp. Glas.; Hon. Sen. Clin. Lect. Univ. Glas. Prev: Sen. Regist. (Psychiat.) Gtr. Glas. HB; Regist. (Psychiat.) Gartnavel Roy. Hosp.

***GRAY, Samuel Brennan** 130 Upper Waterloo Road, Larne BT40 1EF; 2 Rockfield Glen, Bangor BT19 7SF Tel: 01247 460422 — MB BCh BAO 1997 Belf.

GRAY, Sarah Jane 18 Lemon Street, Truro TR1 2LZ Tel: 01872 273133 Fax: 01872 260900 Email: sarah.gray@18lemst.cornwall.nhs.uk; Egloserme Farm, St. Erme, Truro TR4 9BW Email: sarahgray@lineone.net — MB BS 1986 Lond.; MRCGP 1990; DRCOG 1988; BSc 1983 Lond.; T (GP) 1991; BSc Lond. 1983; MRCGP 1990; DFFP 1996; T(GP) 1991; DRCOG 1988. (Lond. Hosp.) Carrick Menopause Clinic, 18 Lemon St., Truro; Duchy Hosp. Meuopause Clinic, Penventiunie La., Truro. Socs: (Instruc.) Fac. Family Plann.; Brit. Menopause Soc. (Comm. Mem.); LMC Cabinet (Cornw.). Prev: Trainee GP S.end VTS.

GRAY, Sarah Kirkpatrick Ruth 105 Netherby Road, Edinburgh EH5 3LR Tel: 0131 552 4338 — MB ChB 1943 Ed.; DPM Eng. 1956. (Ed.) Med. Asst. Roy. Edin. Hosp. Nerv. Dis. Socs: Affil. RCPsych; Geriat. Soc. Prev: Med. Off. Warlingham Pk. Hosp.

GRAY, Selena Felicity Research & Development Directorate, Westward House, Lime Kiln Close, Stoke Gifford, Bristol BS34 8SR Tel: 0117 984 1842 Fax: 0117 984 1776 Email: s.gray@doh.gov.uk; Whitewood Lodge, Norton Lane, Whitchurch, Bristol BS14 0BU — MB ChB 1982 Leeds; MRCP (UK) (Paediat.) 1985; MFPHM RCP (UK) 1991; DCH RCP Lond. 1984; FFPHM 1997; FRCP 1998. Clin. Adviser Research & Developm. Directorate NHSE S. & W. Bristol. Prev: Sen. Regist. (Pub. Health Med.) Bristol & Dist. HA; Regist. (Community Med.) SW RHA Frenchay HA.

GRAY, Sheila Mary (retired) 7 Glen Court, Dunblane FK15 0DY — MB ChB 1949 Glas. Prev: Cons. Diag. Sonar Stirling Roy. Infirm.

GRAY, Shirley Anne Dr. S. Gray, 50 Argyle Street, Inverness IV2 3BB Tel: 01463 240166; Dr. S. Gray, 50 Argyle Street, Inverness IV2 3BB Tel: 01463 240166 — MB ChB 1985 Aberd.; MRCGP 1990. GP Retainer. Prev: GP Inverness.

GRAY, Simon Robert Walnut Tree Health Centre, Blackberry Court, Walnut Tree, Milton Keynes MK7 7NR Tel: 01908 691123; 23 Boulters Lock, Giffard Park, Milton Keynes MK14 5QR Tel: 01908 617010 — MB BS 1987 Lond.; MRCGP 1992; DTM & H RCP Lond. 1993; DRCOG 1991. (St. Mary's Hosp. Lond.) Prev: Med. Supt. Mbale Health Centre, Uganda, E. Afr.

GRAY, Stephen John Papworth Hospital NHS Trust, Papworth Everand, Cambridge CB3 8RE; Applebarne, Houghton Hill, Houghton, Huntingdon PE28 2BS — MB BS 1981 New South Wales; BSc 1976; FRCA 1991. (University of New South Wales) Cons. Cardiothoracic Anaesth. Papworth Hosp. Socs: Assoc. Cardiothor. Anaesth. (ACTA).

GRAY, Stephen Paul (retired) Greystoke Surgery, Kings Avenue, Morpeth NE61 1JA Tel: 01670 511393 Fax: 01670 503282 — MB ChB Leeds 1968; MRCGP 1984; DObst RCOG 1971. Hosp. Pratitioner in Geriat. Morpeth Cottage Hosp. Prev: Regist. Psychiat. Clifton Hosp. York.

GRAY, Stuart Reed 89 Belbroughton Road, Blakedown, Kidderminster DY10 3JJ — MB BCh 1985 Wales; MRCGP 1994; DRCOG 1989.

GRAY, Tanusree Mistu Kilmarnock Road Surgery, 123 Kilmarnock Road, Glasgow G41 3YT Tel: 0141 649 6231 Fax: 0141 632 2012 — MB ChB 1989 Glas.

GRAY, Professor Thomas Cecil, CBE, OStJ, KCSG 6 Raven Meols Lane, Formby, Liverpool L37 4DF Tel: 01704 871008 — MB ChB Liverp. 1937; MD Liverp. 1947; FRCP Lond. 1972; FRCS Eng. 1968; FRCA 1990; FRCA 1948; Hon. FFA RCSI 1962; DA Eng. 1941; Hon. FANZCA 1992. (Univ. Liverp.) Socs: Hon. Mem. (Ex-Pres.) Assn. Anaesths. Silver Medal 1982; Hon. Fell. Roy. Soc. Med. 1979 (Ex-Pres. Sect. Anaesth. Hy.; Henry Hill Hickman Medal 1972. Prev: Emerit. Prof. Anaesth. Univ. Liverp.; Emerit. Civil Cons. Anaesth. Army (Guthrie Medal 1977), Mitchener MEML, RAMC, 1983); Asst. Dir.-Gen. St. John Ambul. Assn.

GRAY, Timothy John Pereira 85 Merton Hall Road, London SW19 3PX — BChir 1995 Camb.

GRAY, Trevor Alan Department of Clinical Chemistry, Northern General Hospital, Herries Road, Sheffield S5 7AU — MB ChB 1979 Dundee; MSc Dundee 1977; BSc Birm. 1971; FRCP Lond. 1996; MRCPath 1986; FRCPath 1996, M 1986. Cons. Chem. Path. N. Gen. Hosp. Sheff. Prev: Sen. Regist. (Chem. Path.) Dudley Rd. Hosp. Birm.

GRAY, Trevor Buchanan 2 Cambridge Terrace, Regents Park, London NW1 4JL Tel: 020 7486 0009 Fax: 020 7486 0524 — MB ChB 1986 Cape Town; FRACS 1995; FRACO 1995. Corneal & Extern. Dis. Fell. Moorfields Eye Hosp. Prev: Uveitis Fell. Uveitis Serv. Moorfields Eye Hosp. Lond.; Sen. Regist. Auckland Hosp., NZ.

GRAY, William (retired) 1 Hatton Way, Kinnoull, Perth PH2 7DP Tel: 01738 24807 — MB ChB Ed. 1961; FRCP Ed. 1972, M 1965. Prev: Cons. Phys. Perth Roy. Infirm.

GRAY, William Campbell John Priory Medical Group, Cornlands Road, Acomb, York YO24 3WX Tel: 01904 781423 Fax: 01904 784886 — MB BCh BAO 1974 Dub.

GRAY, William John (retired) Hady House, Hady Hill, Chesterfield S41 0EE Tel: 01246 236078 — MB BCh BAO 1953 Belf.; FRCGP 1986, M 1968. Prev: Course Organiser Chesterfield VTS.

GRAY, Mr William John Department of Neurosurgery, Royal Victoria Hospital, Belfast BT12 6BA Tel: 02890 894974 Fax: 02890 237733; 92 Kings Road, Belfast BT5 7BW Tel: 02890 793594 —

MB BCh BAO 1976 Belf.; FRCSI 1981. Cons. Neurosurg. Roy. Vict. Hosp. Belf.

GRAY, William McWhinnie (retired) 92 Sandy Lane, Hucknall, Nottingham NG15 7GP Tel: 0115 963025 — MB ChB 1952 Glas. Prev: Ho. Phys. S.. Gen. Hosp. Glas.

GRAY, Mr William Peter Wessex Neurological Centre, Southampton General Hospital, Southampton SO16 6YD — MB BCh BAO 1986 NUI; FRCSI 1990.

GRAY, William Roslyn (retired) Southgate Lodge, Westfield Lane, Middle Handley, Eckington, Sheffield S21 5RN Tel: 01246 435450 — MB BS 1960 Lond.

GRAY, Winifred John Radcliffe Hospital, Oxford OX3 9DU Tel: 01865 220501 Fax: 01865 220516; 67 Divinity Road, Oxford OX4 1LH Tel: 01865 248513 Fax: 01865 794867 — MB BS 1960 Adelaide; FRCPath 1984, M 1972. Cons. Cytopath. & Histopath. John Radcliffe Hosp. Oxf.; Examr. MRCPath & Dip. Cytopath.; Hon. Cons. Cytopathologist to the army. Socs: (Ex-Counc.) Brit. Soc. Clin. Cytol. (Cytopath. Subcomm. Mem.). Prev: Cons. Cytopath. & Histopath. Wycombe Gen. Hosp. Bucks.

GRAY-HENRY, Donna-Marie Anthea 94 Jacoby Place, Priory Rd,, Edgbaston, Birmingham B5 7UW — MB BS 1990 West Indies.

GRAYEFF, Sharon Batia 29 Ilmington Road, Kenton, Harrow HA3 0NQ — MB BS 1995 Lond.

GRAYLING, George Grindley (retired) — MB BS 1967 Lond.; MRCS Eng. LRCP Lond. 1965; FFA RCS Eng. 1974; DA Eng. 1969; DObst RCOG 1968. Cons. Anaesth. Glos. AHA.

GRAYLING, Matthew Plum Tree House, School Road, Apperley, Gloucester GL19 4DJ — MB BS 1994 Lond.

GRAYMORE, Roderick Ian Trenoweth, HR Trevilla, Feock, Truro TR3 6QG — MRCS Eng. LRCP Lond. 1951; MRCGP 1967; DObst RCOG 1958. (Manch.) Indep. GP Cornw.; Med. Ref. Cornw. Crematorium Auth., Truro. Socs: BMA. Prev: Resid. Off. (Obst.) Cheltenham Matern. Hosp.; Ho. Off. Duchess of York Hosp. Babies, Manch.; Resid. (Path.) Univ. Coll. Hosp. Lond.

GRAYSON, Caroline 27 Oaklands, Gosforth, Newcastle upon Tyne NE3 4YQ — MB BS 1993 Newc.

GRAYSON, Christina Elizabeth Alice Jezierski and Partners, The Health Centre, Sheen Lane, London SW14 8LP — MB BS 1985 Lond.; MRCGP 1989. Prev: Trainee GP Clapton Lond. VTS.

GRAYSON, Michael Felix 148 Harley Street, London Tel: 020 7935 1900 Fax: 020 7224 1528; 3 Stormont Road, Highgate, London N6 4NS Tel: 020 8340 2045 Fax: 020 8340 2045 — MB ChB Birm. 1959; BSc (Hons.) Birm. 1956; FRCP Lond. 1987, M 1969; MRCS Eng. LRCP Lond. 1959. (Birm.) Cons. Rheumatologist in Private Pract. Socs: Fell. Roy. Soc. Med.; Brit. Soc. Rheum.; Medico Legal Soc. Prev: Sen. Regist. (Rheum.) Roy. Free Hosp. Lond.; Head (Med. Research) Merck, Sharp & Dohme Ltd.; Cons. Rheumatologist, N. Middlx. Hosp. Lndon.

GRAYSON, Michael John Cardio-Analytics, Tamar Science Park, 1 Davy Road, Derriford, Plymouth PL6 8BX Tel: 01752 201144 Fax: 01752 201145; 6 The Esplanade, The Hoe, Plymouth PL1 2PJ Tel: 01752 667163 Fax: 01752 667163 — MB ChB 1952 Ed.; MD (Commend.) Ed. 1965; FRCP Lond. 1974; MRCP (UK) 1957. (Ed.) p/t Cons. Phys. Plymouth. Socs: Brit. Soc. Gastroenterol.; Plymouth Med. Soc. Prev: Cons. Phys. Plymouth Health Dist.; Sen. Regist. (Med.) King's Coll. Hosp. Lond.; Regist. St. Geo. Hosp. Lond.

GRAYSON, Robert Paul 19 Oak Close, Rishton, Blackburn BB1 4JU — MB BS 1997 Lond.

GRAYSTONE, Stephen John 12 Miller Close, Longlevens, Gloucester GL2 0XT — BM 1987 Soton.

GREADY, Elizabeth Margaret Pugshole, Higher Bridmore, Tollard Royal, Salisbury SP5 5QF — MB BCh 1983 Wales; DRCOG 1987. Sen. Community Med. Off. N. Dorset HA. Prev: Community Med. Off. E. Dorset HA.

GREALY, Mark Gerard Westgate Medical Centre, Braddon Close, Morecambe LA4 4UZ Tel: 01524 832888 Fax: 01524 832722; 9 Hunters Gate, Haverbreaks, Lancaster LA1 5BX — MB BCh BAO 1983 NUI; DObst RCPI 1988.

GREALY, Sara Elizabeth 9 Hunters Gate, Haverbreaks, Lancaster LA1 5BX — MB ChB 1985 Manch.

GREANEY, Mr Martin Gerrard Arrowe Park Hospital, Arrowe Park Road, Upton, Wirral CH49 5PE Tel: 0151 604 7054; Lyndale, 7 Telegraph Road, Heswall, Wirral CH60 8NA Tel: 0151 342 6492 Email: mgg@doctors.org.uk — MB ChB 1970 Sheff.; ChM Sheff. 1979; FRCS Eng. 1975. Cons. Surg. Wirral Hosp. Trust. Prev: Sen. Regist. (Surg.) Nottm. HA; Regist. (Surg.) Roy. Infirm. Sheff.

GREANEY, Mr Michael Justin Department of Opthalmology, Southampton General Hospital, Tremona Road, Southampton SO16 6YD — MB BCh BAO 1988 NUI; FRCS Ed. 1994. Prev: SHO Postgrad. Research (Anat.) Univ. Coll. Galway; SHO (Ophth.) W. Norwich Hosp.; Med. Intern Portiuncula Hosp. Ballinasloe, Co. Galway.

GREASLEY, Lorraine Ann 43 Forest Road, Skegby, Sutton-in-Ashfield NG17 3BG — MB BS 1996 Lond.

GREATOREX, Derek George Kingsteignton Surgery, Whiteway Road, Kingsteignton, Newton Abbot TQ12 3HN Tel: 01626 883312 Fax: 01626 336406; Cockhaven House, Cockhaven Road, Bishopsteignton, Teignmouth TQ14 9RF Tel: 01626 779628 — MB ChB 1989 Bristol; BSc (Hons.) Bath 1979; MRCGP 1993; DRCOG 1992; DGM RCP Lond. 1991. Socs: Torbay & Dist. Med. Soc.

GREATOREX, Ian Frederick (retired) — MB ChB 1971 Ed.; HON DSc 1999 Salford; BSc Ed. 1968, MD 1988; MSc Manch. 1986; MRCP (UK) 1975; FRCP Ed. 1998; MFPHM 1987; MRCGP 1979; DCH Eng. 1979; DRCOG 1977. Prev: SHO (Med.) Hammersmith Hosp. Lond.

GREATOREX, Mr Robert Albert Department of Surgery, Queen Elizabeth Hospital, King's Lynn PE30 4ET Tel: 01553 613613 — MB BChir 1977 Camb.; MA Camb. 1977; BDS Lond. 1971; FRCS Eng. 1980; LDS RCS Eng. 1971. (Camb. & Lond. Hosp.) Cons. Gen. Surg. Qu. Eliz. Hosp. King's Lynn. Socs: Assn. Surgs. GB & Irel.; Vasc. Surg. Soc. GB; BMA. Prev: Sen. Regist. (Gen. Surg.) Ipswich & Camb.; Burghard Research Fell. RCS Eng.; Regist. Rotat. (Surg.) Addenbrooke's Hosp. Camb.

GREATREX, Andrew Francis Northcote House Surgery, Northcote House, 8 Broad Leas, Huntingdon PE27 5PT Tel: 01480 461873 Fax: 01480 460612; 8 Daintree, Meedingworth, St Ives, Huntingdon PE27 4SP Tel: 01480 460475 — MB ChB 1992 Leic.; MRCGP 1996. (Leic.) GP Partner N.cote Hse. Surg. St. Ives. Prev: GP Asst. Spinney Surg. Cambs.

GREATREX, Anita Joan (retired) Long Close Cottage, Shappen Hill Lane, Burley, Ringwood BH24 4EP Tel: 01425 403232 — MB BS Lond. 1964; MRCS Eng. LRCP Lond. 1964; DObst RCOG 1970; DCH Eng. 1967. Prev: SHO (O & G) Soton. Gen. Hosp.

GREATREX, Susan Joan 14 Priory Close, Royston SG8 7DU Tel: 01763 49700 — MB ChB 1974 Sheff.

GREAVES, Mr Brian Peter William Harvey Hospital, Kennington Road, Ashford TN25 0DM Tel: 01233 633331; 15 Church Street, Wye, Ashford TN25 5BN Tel: 01233 812442 Fax: 01233 813661 — MB ChB 1969 Cape Town; FRCS Ed. 1974; FRCOphth 1993; FCOphth 1989. (Univ. Cape Town, S. Afr.) Cons. Ophth. William Harvey Hosp. Ashford. Socs: Internat. Strabismol. Assn.; Eur. Strabismological Assn.; S.. Ophth. Soc. Prev: Cons. Ophth. Red Cross Childr. Hosp. Cape Town, S. Afr.

GREAVES, Cyril William Kendall Handley The Hollies Medical Centre, 20 St. Andrews Road, Sheffield S11 9AL Tel: 0114 255 0094 Fax: 0114 258 2863; Galen House, Sharrow Head, Sheffield S11 8FS Tel: 0114 255 0094 — BM BCh 1960 Oxf.; MA Oxf. 1960. (Oxf. & St. Bart.) Socs: Sheff. M-C Soc. & BMA.

GREAVES, David John Tudor Cottage, The Street, Staple, Canterbury CT3 1LL — MRCS Eng. LRCP Lond. 1977. (Guy's)

GREAVES, Desmond Noel Joseph St Stephens Surgery, Adelaide Street, Redditch B97 4AL Tel: 01527 65444 Fax: 01527 69218; 4 Dagtail Lane, Astwood Bank, Redditch B97 5QT Tel: 01527 892740 Fax: 01527 69218 — MB ChB 1978 Birm.; DRCOG 1981; DA Eng. 1982. (Birmingham) Lead GP Redditch GPFH Consortium.

GREAVES, Mr Desmond Peel (retired) Bradfield Lodge, 22 Kivernell Road, Milford on Sea, Lymington SO41 0PQ Tel: 01590 644492 — MB ChB Sheff. 1944; BSc Sheff. 1943; FRCS Eng. 1950; FRCOphth 1988; DOMS Eng. 1947. Hon. Cons. Surg. Moorfields Eye Hosp. Lond.; Hon. Cons. Ophth. Surg. UCH Lond.; Recognised Teach. Univ. Lond.; Mem. Ct. Examrs. RCS Eng. Prev: Pres. 6th Europ. Congr. Ophth. (UK) 1980.

GREAVES, Enid Anne Elizabeth — MB BCh BAO 1972 Dub. (Trinity Coll. Dub.)

GREAVES, Francis Henry The Red Practice, Waterside Health Centre, Beaulieu Road, Hythe SO45 4WX Tel: 023 8084 5955 Fax: 023 8084 1292; 10 Brocks Close, Dibden Purlieu, Southampton SO45 5ST Tel: 02380 845295 Fax: 02380 840787 Email:

francis.greaves@dial.pipex.com — MB BS Lond. 1970; MRCS Eng. LRCP Lond. 1970; DObst RCOG 1973. (Univ. Coll. Hosp.) Socs: New Forest Med. Soc. Prev: SHO (Cas.) & Ho. Phys. Univ. Coll. Hosp. Lond.; SHO (O & G) Soton. Gen. Hosp.

GREAVES, Ian A&E Department, Peterborough District Hospital, Peterborough PE3 6DA Tel: 01733 875806 Fax: 01733 875806 — MB ChB 1986 Birm.; MRCP (UK) 1990; 2001 FIMC. RCSEd; Dip Med Educat 2001; DTM & H RCP Lond. 1992; FFAEM 1999; DMCC 1999. (Birmingham) Cons. in Emerg. Med.; Hon. Sen. Lect. in Conflict Med. UCL. Socs: Hon. Sec. Trauma Care. Prev: Regist. Rotat. (A & E Med.) Yorks.

GREAVES, John David Simonside, 32 Thorpe Avenue, Morpeth NE61 1JR Tel: 01670 512705 Email: david.greaves@ncle.ac.uk — MB ChB 1974 Birm.; MB ChB Birm. 1970; Dip. Med. Educat. Dund 1993; FFA RCS 1974.; FRCA 1997; MMed Dundee 1998. Cons. (Anaesth.) Roy. Vict. Infirm. Newc. u. Tyne. Prev: Cons (Anaesth.) Cheviot & Wansbeck Hosp. Trust; Regist. (Anaesth.) United Birm. Hosps. & Soton. AHA (T); Dir. (Anaesth. & Intens. Care) Rockhampton Base Hosp. Qu.sland, Australia.

GREAVES, John Robert (retired) Exchange House, 18 Upper Strand St., Sandwich CT13 9EE — MB BS 1949 Lond.; MRCS Eng. LRCP Lond. 1949. Prev: Ho. Phys. & Cas. Off. Putney Hosp.

GREAVES, Judith Margaret Lutterworth Health Centre, Gilmorton Road, Lutterworth LE17 4EB Tel: 01455 553531; 13 Tealby Close, Gilmorton, Lutterworth LE17 5PT — MB ChB 1976 Leeds; MRCGP 1981; DA (UK) 1983.

GREAVES, Julian Alexander Handley 309 Cemetery Road, Sheffield S11 8FS — MB ChB 1991 Glas.

GREAVES, Kim Department of Cardiology, St Peter's Hospital, Guildford Road, Chertsey KT16 0PZ Tel: 01932 872000; Dovecote House, Church St, Guilden Morden, Royston SG8 0JD — MB BS 1991 Lond.; BSc (Hons.) Lond. 1988, MB BS Lond. 1991. SHO Rotat. (Med.) St. Geo. Hosp. Lond.; Vis. Research Fell. (Med.) Univ. Wisconsin 1988. Prev: Ho. Off. (Cardiol. & Respirat. Med.) Univ. Coll. Middlx. Sch. Med.; Ho. Off. (Surg.) Ipswich Hosp.

GREAVES, Malcolm Watson St Thomas's Hospital, Lambeth Palace Road, London SE1 7EH Tel: 020 7401 2008 Fax: 020 7401 2008; Dovecote House, Church Street, Guilden Morden, Royston SG8 0JD Tel: 01763 853013 Fax: 01763 853014 — MB BS 1957 Lond.; PhD Lond. 1968, MD 1966; FRCP Lond. 1974; MRCP (UK) 1961. (Char. Cross) Hon. Emerit.. Prof. Dermat. St. John's Inst. Dermat. St. Thos. Hosp. Lond.; Hon. Cons. Dermat. St. John's Hosp. Dis. Skin. Lond.; Hon. Lect. (Pharmacol.) UCL; Adviser Brit. Nat. Formulary; Cons. Adviser Egyptian Armed Forces Hosp. Maadi, Cairo; Cons. Adviser Cutaneous Biol. Research Centre Boston, USA; Mem. Managem. Bd. Exec. United Med. & Dent. Schs. Lond.; Mem. (Counc.) Sch. Pharmacy Univ. Lond.; Mem. Indep. Television Commercial Med. Advis. Panel. Socs: Consultative Gp. Brit. Pharmacocoepia; (Pres.) Europ. Soc. Dermat. Research & Skin Pharmacol. Soc.; Roy. Soc. Med. (Pres. Sect. Dermat.). Prev: Dean St. John's Inst. Dermat. United Med. & Dent. Schs. St. Thos. Hosp. Lond.; Reader (Dermat.) Univ. Newc.; MRC Clin. Research Fell. (Pharmacol.) Univ. Coll. Lond.

GREAVES, Professor Michael Department of Medicine & Therapeutics, University of Aberdeen, Polwarth Building, Foresterhill, Aberdeen AB25 2ZD Tel: 01224 553 016 Fax: 01224 554 761 Email: m.greaves@abdn.ac.uk — MB ChB 1972 Sheff.; 1979 MD Sheff.; FRCP Ed. 1990; FRCP Lond. 1988, M 1975; FRCPath 1990, M 1982; FRCP 1996 Glas. Prof. Haemat. Univ. Aberd., Head Of Dept. Of Med. & Therap.; Head Dept. Med. Univ. Aberd. Prev: Reader, Hon. Cons. Haemat. & Hon. Cons. Phys. Roy. Hallamsh. Hosp. Sheff.; Edr. Brit. Jl. Haemat.

GREAVES, Percy Sidney Sarn Cottage, Rhosygadfa, Oswestry SY10 7AU — MB BChir 1951 Camb.; MA, MB BChir Camb. 1951; MRCS Eng. LRCP Lond. 1951. (Guy's)

GREAVES, Peter (retired) 4 The Orchards, Wyton, Huntingdon PE28 2JG Tel: 01480 469419 Fax: 0705 685270 Email: pewyt@lineone.net — MB ChB St. And. 1954; DObst RCOG 1956. Prev: Ho. Off. (O & G) & Ho. Phys. Memor. Hosp. P'boro.

GREAVES, Peter 64 Shaws Road, Northgate, Crawley RH10 8DH Tel: 01293 28654 — MB ChB 1969 Birm.; MRCPath 1977.

GREAVES, Ralph Robert Sissak Handley Whipps Cruiss University Hospital, Whipps Cruiss Road, London Tel: 020 8535 6708 Fax: 020 8535 6708 — MB BS 1987 Lond.; MD 2000 (Lond.); MRCP (UK) 1989. (Charing Cross and Westminster Medical School) Cons.(Gastroenterol. & Gen. Med.) Whipps Cross Univ. Hosp. Lond. Socs: Roy. Coll. Phys. Prev: Specialist Regist. (Gastroenterol.) Roy. Free Hosp. Lond.; Specialist Regist. (Gastroenterol.) Whipps Cross Univ. Hosp. Lond.; Hon. Regist. (Gastroenterol.) St. Bartholomews Hosp. Lond.

GREAVES, Robert Corder Castle Road, 2 Castle Road, Chirk, Wrexham LL14 5BS Tel: 01691 772434 Fax: 01691 773840; Ashfield, Bronygarth, Oswestry SY10 7LY Tel: 01691 773663 — MB ChB 1975 Birm.; MA Camb. 1975; MRCGP 1980; DRCOG 1977. Prev: Course Organiser Wrexham VTS.

GREAVES, Ruth Jane Church House Surgery, Church House, Shaw Street, Ruddington, Nottingham NG11 6HF Tel: 0115 984 7101 Fax: 0115 984 7404 — BM BS 1988 Nottm.; DRCOG 1994; MRCGP 1994; DFFP 1995.

GREAVES, Sharon Heather Lois Staithes Surgery, Seaton Crescent, Staithes, Saltburn-by-the-Sea TS13 5AY Tel: 01947 840480 Fax: 01947 841034 — MB BS 1985 Lond. (St. Bart.) p/t GP Retainee. Prev: GP Princip. 1995.

GREAVES, Suki 15 Collard Place, London NW1 8DU — MB BS 1994 Lond. Ho. Off. (Surg.) Edgware Gen. Hosp. Middlx.

GREAVES, Susan Jane College Medical Centre, Christ Church College, North Holmes Road, Canterbury CT1 1QU Tel: 01227 767700; 2 Wacher Close, St. Stephens, Canterbury CT2 7JY Tel: 01227 769737 — MB BS 1989 Lond.; MRCGP 1994; DRCOG 1993; DFFP 1993; DCH RCP Lond. 1993. (Guys) GP Princip. Canterbury. Prev: GP Kent & Canterbury Hosp. VTS.

GREAVES, Susan Melanie 19 Bath Terrace, Gosforth, Newcastle upon Tyne NE3 1UH — MB BS 1986 Lond.

GREAVES, Wilfred Edward Tramways Medical Centre, Holme Lane, Sheffield S6 4JQ Tel: 0114 234 3418; Westwood, 37 Stumperlowe Hall Road, Sheffield S10 3QS Tel: 0114 230 2717 — MB ChB 1959 Sheff.; MRCS Eng. LRCP Lond. 1959. (Sheff.) Hon. Clin. Tutor in Gen. Pract. Univ. Sheff. Socs: (Treas.) Sheff. Local Med. Comm.

GREBBELL, Frederick Searle, TD 'Cuan View', 1B Net Walk, Killyleagh, Downpatrick BT30 9QX Tel: 01396 826661 — MB BCh BAO 1947 Belf.; MD Belf. 1957; FFR RCSI 1964; DMRD Eng. 1954. Socs: Brit. Soc. Neuroradiol. Prev: Cons. Neuroradiol. Roy. Vict. Hosp. Belf.; Fell. Ulster Med. Soc.; Mem. Roy. Coll. Radiols.

GREBENIK, Catherine Rachael Nuffield Department of Anaesthesia, John Radcliffe Hospital, Oxford OX3 9DU Tel: 01865 741166; 52 Church Street, Kidlington OX5 2BB Tel: 01865 842026 — MB ChB 1978 Leeds; FFA RCS Eng. (Nuffield Prize) 1982. Cons. Cardiothoracic Anaesth. John Radcliffe Hosp. Oxf. Prev: Sen. Regist. (Anaesth.) St. Bart. Hosp. Lond.

GRECH, Ever 4 Barton House, Halton Road, London N1 — MB BS 1983 Lond.; MRCP (UK) 1989; MRCGP 1987; DRCOG 1986. (St. Bart.) Trainee GP Tunbridge Wells VTS.

GRECH, Henri Department of Haematology, Royal Berkshire Hospital, London Road, Reading RG1 5AN — MB BS 1983 Lond.; MRCP (UK) 1989; MRCPath 1993. Cons. Haemat. Roy. Berks. Hosp. Reading. Socs: Brit. Soc. Haemat.; Assoc. Clin. Pathologists. Prev: Sen. Regist. Rotat. S.ampton Univ. Hosp. Trust & Roy. Bournemouth Hosp.; Lect. & Hon. Regist. St. Thos. Hosp. Lond.; Regist. (Haemat.) St. Lukes Hosp. Guildford.

GRECH, Mark Andrew Tel: 01371 872105 Fax: 01371 873679; Chelmers, Great Easton, Dunmow CM6 2DJ — MRCS Eng. LRCP Lond. 1979; DRCOG 1982; T(GP) 1991. (St. Bart.)

GRECH, Mary Patricia (retired) 8 Stafford Mansions, Stafford Place, London SW1E 6NL Tel: 020 7 828 7594 — MB BS 1951 Lond. Prev: SCMO Sheff. AHA (T).

GRECH, Paul (retired) 8 Stafford Mansions, Stafford Place, London SW1E 6NL Tel: 020 7828 7594 — MD 1949 Malta; FRCR 1976; DTM & H Eng. 1956, DMRD 1963. Prev: Cons. Radiol. N.. Gen. Hosp. & Lodge Moor Hosp. Sheff.

GRECH, Paul Department of Radiology, Hereford County Hospital, Hereford HR1 2TU Tel: 01432 355333; The Beeches, Staunton-on-Wye, Hereford HR4 7NG Tel: 01981 500694 — MB ChB 1981 Sheff.; BSc Sheff. 1978, MB ChB (Hons.) 1981; MRCP (UK) 1984; FRCR 1990. (Sheff.) Cons. Radiol. Hereford NHS Trust. Prev: Asst. Prof. Radiol. Duke Univ. Med. Centre.

GRECH, William 11 Tresta Close, Radbrook Green, Shrewsbury SY3 6AJ — MB ChB 1985 Manch.; MRCGP 1990.

GREELEY, Nevil Charles 19 Watson Cr, Peterhead AB42 2WS — MB ChB 1997 Aberd.

GREEN, Mr Adrian Nicholas Top Maisonette, 22 Cromwell Grove, London W6 7RG Tel: 020 7603 9357 — MRCS Eng. LRCP Lond. 1988; MRCOG 1997. (Charing Cross and Westminster)

GREEN, Alain Jacques Charles Hicks Centre, 75, Ermine Street, Huntingdon PE29 3EZ Tel: 01480 457275 — MB BS 1974 Lond.; JCPTGP Cert. of Equivalent Experience; LLM 1994; MRCS Eng. LRCP Lond. 1974; FRCPath 1995, M 1983; T(Path) 1991. (Roy. Free) GP with Dr. A. Turnill & Partners. Prev: Hon. Cons. Chem. Path. Stoke Mandeville Hosp.; Cons. Chem. Path. RAF Med. Br.; GP Vocational Trainee E. Anglian Deanery.

GREEN, Alan (retired) Cromwell House, Tithe Barn St., Horbury, Wakefield WF4 6LL Tel: 01924 274367 — MB ChB Leeds 1939. Prev: Capt. RAMC.

GREEN, Alan Graham Harley The Surgery, Darvel KA17 0JR Tel: 01560 320205 Fax: 01560 321643 — MB ChB 1973 Glas. (Glasgow University) Hosp. Pract. Kirklanding Hosp. Kilmarnock; Past Chairm. LMC (GP Sub. Comm.). Socs: SGPC (SGMSC); LMC/GP JUB. Prev: Regist. (Respirat. Med.) W.. (Glas.) Health Dist.; Regist. Med. Kilmarnock Infirm.; SHO Seafield Sick Childr. Hosp. Ayr.

GREEN, Alastair Scott Church Lane Surgery, Boroughbridge, York YO51 9BD Tel: 01423 322309 Fax: 01423 324458; The Smithy, Roecliffe, Boroughbridge, York YO5 9LY Tel: 01423 322820 — MB BS 1968 Newc.; MRCGP 1972; DObst RCOG 1972. Civil Med. Pract. Army Air. Corps. N. Yorks. Socs: Harrogate Med. Soc.; York Med. Soc.

***GREEN, Alexander Laurence** 14 Vine Close, Stapleford, Cambridge CB2 5BZ — MB BS 1997 Lond.; BSc (Hons.) Lond. 1994.

GREEN, Alexander Theodore Gastroenterology Unit, Burnley General Hospital, Casterton Avenue, Burnley BB10 2PQ Tel: 01282 474663 Fax: 01282 474884; 7 Brookes Lane, Whalley, Clitheroe BB7 9RG Tel: 01254 823245 — BM BCh 1979 Oxf.; MA Oxf. 1983, DM 1995; MRCP (UK) 1982; FRCP (UK) 1998. (Oxf.) Cons. Phys. (Gastroenterol.) Burnley Gen. & Rossendale Hosps. Socs: BMA; Brit. Soc. Gastroenterol. Prev: Sen. Regist. Rotat. Liverp.; Regist. & Research Fell. St. Thos. Hosp. Lond.

GREEN, Alison Fiona 538 Great Western Road, Aberdeen AB10 6PG — MB BS 1993 Lond.

GREEN, Alison Iola Dunsbury Way Clinic, Dunsbury Way, Leigh Park, Havant PO9 5BG Tel: 01705 482154; 61 Southleigh Road, Havant PO9 2QQ — MB ChB 1981 Glas.; DCH RCP Lond. 1986; MSc (UCL) 1997. SCMO (Community Child Health) Havant.

GREEN, Alison Margaret Garden Flat, 40 Arley Hill, Cotham, Bristol BS6 5PR — MB BS 1986 Lond.; BSc, MB BS Lond. 1986. Trainee GP Whittington Hosp. VTS.

GREEN, Allan John Argyll House, 78 West Street, Ryde PO33 2QJ Tel: 01983 562955 Fax: 01983 883481; 3 Spencer Close, Ryde PO33 3AW Tel: 01983 611589 — MB BS 1976 Lond.; MRCS Eng. LRCP Lond. 1976; DRCOG 1979. (Char. Cross) Surg. & Agent RN; Med. Off. Ryde Sch. Prev: SHO Centr. Middx. Hosp. Lond.; SHO Roy. Lond. Homoeopath. Hosp.; Ho. Surg. Char. Cross Hosp. Lond.

GREEN, Andrew David, Wing Cdr. RAF Med. Br. Surgeon Generals Department, Army Medical Directorate, FSAC Camberley, Slim Road, Camberley GU15 4PQ Tel: 01276 412935 Fax: 01276 412737 Email: zorria@epinet.co.uk — MB BS 1981 Lond.; MFPHM 1999; MRCPath 1990; T(Path) 1991; DTM & H Liverp. 1989; FRCPath 1998. (St. Geo. Hosp. Lond.) Cons. Communicable Dis. Control, Defence Med. Servs. Socs: Fell. Roy. Soc. Trop. Med. & Hyg.; Hosp. Infec. Soc. Prev: Cons. Med. Microbiol. RAF Inst. Path. & Trop. Med. Aylesbury; Lect. (Med. Microbiol.) St. Thos. Hosp. Lond.; Sen. Regist. (Med. Microbiol.) RAF Hosp. Wegberg.

GREEN, Andrew John Malago Surgery, 40 St. Johns Road, Bedminster, Bristol BS3 4JE Tel: 0117 966 3587 Fax: 0117 963 1422; Rydal Mount, 2 Tyne Road, Bristol BS7 8EE — MB ChB 1987 Bristol. Prev: Trainee GP Bristol VTS.

GREEN, Andrew Martin Hedon Group Practice, 4 Market Hill, Hedon, Hull HU12 8JD Tel: 01482 899111 Fax: 01482 890967 — MB ChB 1984 Sheff.; MB ChB Sheff. I984; MRCGP 1988. Prev: Trainee GP Rotherham VTS.

GREEN, Andrew Nicholas Faulkner 5 Orchard Way, Congleton CW12 4PW — MB BS 1990 Lond.

GREEN, Andrew Robert Yorkleigh Surgery, 93 St. Georges Road, Cheltenham GL50 3ED; 2 Deacon Close, Hatherley, Cheltenham GL51 3NY — MB ChB 1990 Birm.; DCH RCP Lond. 1994. (Birm.) Police Surg. Glos. Prev: SHO (Paediat.) Childr. Hosp. Birm.; SHO (O & G) Selly Oak Hosp. Birm.; SHO (A & E) Jersey Gen. Hosp.

GREEN, Ann Children's Centre (Child Development Centre), City Hospital Campus, Hucknall Road, Nottingham NG5 1PB Tel: 0115 962 7658; The Willows, 5 Wood Lane, Gedling, Nottingham NG4 4AD — MB ChB 1964 Manch.; DCH RCPS Glas. 1967. SCMO Notts. HA; Med. Adviser Adoption & Fostering Nottm. Prev: Regist. (Paediat.) Nottm. City Hosp.; Med. Supt. Wenchi Methodist Hosp., Ghana; Asst. Med. Off. City of Soton.

GREEN, Anna Frances Belvoir House, Tattam Close, Woolstone, Milton Keynes MK15 0HB — MB ChB 1991 Leeds.

GREEN, Anne Marie Weybridge Health Centre, 22 Church Street, Weybridge KT13 8DW Tel: 01932 853366 Fax: 01932 844902 — MB BS 1969 Lond.; MRCP (UK) 1973; DCH Eng. 1972; DObst RCOG 1971. (Roy. Free) Prev: Regist. Paediat. Qu. Mary's Hosp. Carshalton; SHO Qu. Eliz. Hosp. Childr. Hackney; SHO Neonat. Paediat. Whittington Hosp. Lond.

GREEN, Mr Anthony David Logan Nobles Hospital, Douglas — MB BCh BAO 1974 Belf.; FRCS Ed. 1978. Cons. Orthop. Surg. Noble's Hosp. Douglas. I. of Man.

GREEN, Anthony Leroy Lodge Medical Centre, 1A Grange Park Avenue, Leeds LS8 3BA Tel: 0113 265 6456 Fax: 0113 295 3710; 47 High Ash Avenue, Leeds LS17 8RS Tel: 0113 295 3709 — BM BCh 1981 Oxf.; MA Camb. 1982; DRCOG 1985. (Camb. & Oxf.)

GREEN, Anthony Richard Department of Haematology, MRC Centre, Hills Road, Cambridge CB2 2QH Tel: 01223 336835 Fax: 01223 336827 — MB BS 1980 Lond.; PhD Lond. 1987; BA Camb. 1977; FRCP Lond. 1995; MRCP (UK) 1983; MRCPath 1988.

GREEN, Mr Antony Edward Royal Free Hospital, Pond St, London NW3 2QG Tel: 01282 613827, 020 794 0500 Fax: 01282 613827 — MB BS 1970 Lond.; BDS Lond. 1965; MRCS Eng. LRCP Lond. 1970; FDS RCS Eng. 1973. (St. Geo.) Cons. Oral & Maxillofacial Surg. Burnley Gen. Hosp., Bury Gen. Hosp., Blackburn Roy. Infirm. & Bolton Dist. Gen. Hosp. Socs: Fell. Brit. Assn. Oral & Maxillofacial Surg.; Brit. Dent. Assn.

GREEN, Antony Markham Timbercombe Annexe, Broomfield, Bridgwater TA5 1AU Tel: 01823 451547 — MRCS Eng. LRCP Lond. 1948.

GREEN, Arnold Richard (retired) Bardsey, Longfield Avenue, Longfield DA3 7LA Tel: 01474 702156 — MB Calcutta 1947.

GREEN, Aud Reidunn Teodora Department of Histopathology, Arrowe Park Hospital, Wirral Tel: 0151 678 5111; Tel: 0151 924 5823 Fax: 0151 932 0953 — LRCPI & LM, LRSCI & LM 1974; MRCPath 1993; FRCPath 2001. p/t Cons. Histopath. Wirral Hosps NHS Trust. Socs: Assn. Clin. Path.; Path. Soc. Prev: Sen. Regist. (Histopath.) Mersey RHA; Regist. (Histopath.) Fazakerley & Walton Hosps. Liverp.; SHO (Histopath.) Mt. Vernon Hosp. N.wood & Univ. Hosp. Wales.

GREEN, Mr Aylmer Roger Mersey Regional Plastic Surgery Centre, Whiston Hospital, Prescot L35 5DR Tel: 0151 430 1664 Fax: 0151 430 1855; Rowan House, 8 Roehampton Drive, Blundellsands, Liverpool L23 7XD Tel: 0151 924 5823 Email: argreen@rowan.u-net.com — LRCPI & LM, LRSCI & LM 1974; FRCS Eng. 1982. Cons. Plastic Surg. Mersey Regional Plastic Surg. & Burns Centre Whiston Hosp. Prescot; Lect. Plastic Surg. to Univ. Liverp. Socs: Fell. Roy. Soc. Med.; (Counc.) Brit. Assn. Plastic Surgs.; Brit. Assn. Aesthetic Plastic. Surgs. Prev: Sen. Regist. (Plastic Surg.) Whiston Hosp.; Regist. (Plastic Surg.) Mt. Vernon Hosp. N.wood & Univ. Coll. Hosp. Lond.; SHO (Plastic Surg.) St. Lawrence Hosp. Chepstow.

GREEN, Barbara Ann 'Woodlea', 22 Havant Road, Horndean, Portsmouth PO2 7HH Tel: 023 92 595779 — MB BCh BAO 1957 NUI; FFA RCS Eng. 1968. (Univ. Coll. Dub.) Cons. Anaesth. Portsmouth Hosp. Gp.

GREEN, Barnaby George James Kis Chur, Chynoweth, Rose Valley, Mabe, Penryn TR10 9JF — MB BS 1972 Lond.; T(Anaesth) 1991; FFA RCS Eng. 1983; DObst RCOG 1974. (St. Mary's) Locum Cons. (Anaesth.).

GREEN, Barry John Green Meadows Surgery, Winkfield Road, Ascot SL5 7LS Tel: 01344 21628 Fax: 01344 875136; Oaklands, 25 Locks Ride, Ascot SL5 8RA Tel: 01344 885275 — MB BS 1976

Lond.; MRCS Eng. LRCP Lond. 1976; MRCGP 1980; DRCOG 1979. (Char. Cross)

GREEN, Basil 21 Rutland Place, Glasgow G51 1TA Tel: 0141 427 3121; 4 Ravenscourt, Thorntonhall, Glasgow G74 5AZ — MB ChB 1949 Glas.; MRCGP 1957. (Glas.)

GREEN, Belinda Kathryn Woodward c/o 10 Brougham Place, Tollcross, Edinburgh EH3 9HW — MB ChB 1981 Ed.; MRCP Ed. 1984.

GREEN, Benjamin (retired) 36 Dean Court Road, Rottingdean, Brighton BN2 7DJ Tel: 01273 305318 — MRCS Eng. LRCP Lond. 1944; FRCR 1986; DMRD Eng. 1951; DMRD Lond 1951. Cons. Radiol. Greenwich Health Dist. Prev: Cons. Radiol. Greenwich Health Dist.

GREEN, Benjamin 16 Broad Oak, Woodford Green IG8 0LH Tel: 020 8504 9888 Fax: 020 8504 9126 — MRCS Eng. LRCP Lond. 1943. (St. Bart.) Socs: BMA. Prev: Asst. Med. Off. Mayday Hosp.; Ho. Surg. Roy. Berks. Hosp. Reading; Ho. Phys. Metrop. Hosp. Lond.

GREEN, Benjamin Hugh Department of Psychiatry, Halton General Hosptial, Runcorn WA7 2DA Tel: 01928 753252 Fax: 0151 606 1812 Email: ben@priory.com — MB ChB 1985 Manch.; ILTM 2001; MRCPsych 1990. Cons. Psych. & Clin. Dir. Ment. Health N. Chesh. Hosp.; Sen. Lect. (Psychiat.) Univ. Liverp. Socs: Manch. Med. Soc. & Liverp. Psychiat. Soc. Prev: Lect. Univ. Liverp.; Sen. Regist. Clatterbridge Hosp. Liverp.

GREEN, Benjamin James Stable Cottage, Hollybush Hill, Stoke Poges, Slough SL2 4QN — MB BS 1998 Lond.; MB BS Lond 1998.

GREEN, Brian George Chalmers and Partners, Cogges Surgery, Cogges Hill Road, Witney OX28 3FP Tel: 01993 700505 Fax: 01993 706610 — MB ChB 1981 Bristol; MRCGP 1994; MRCPsych 1988. (Bristol)

GREEN, Brian Paice (retired) Wistaria House, 7 Tower Grove, Weybridge KT13 9LX Tel: 01932 241105 — MB BS 1950 Lond.; MRCS Eng. LRCP Lond. 1950; DObst RCOG 1952; MRCOP. Prev: Res. Obst. Off. & Ho. Surg. Char. Cross Hosp. Lond.

GREEN, Bryan Department of Pathology, Royal Hampshire County Hospital, Romsey Road, Winchester SO22 5DG Tel: 01962 824379 Fax: 01962 824664 — MB ChB 1980 Birm.; MRCPath 1993. Cons. Histopath. & Cytopath. Winchester & E.leigh Healthcare NHS Trust. Prev: Lect. (Path.) Univ. Liverp.

GREEN, Caroline Emma 153A Wokingham Road, Reading RG6 1LP — MB BS 1992 Lond.

GREEN, Catherine Mary c/o Department Dermatology, Ninewells Hospital, Dundee DD1 9SY — MB ChB 1980 Dundee; FRCP (UK) 1999. Cons. Dermat. Ninewells Hosp. Dundee. Prev: Sen. Regist. & Regist. (Dermat.) Ninewells Hosp. Dundee; Clin. Research Assoc. (Dermat.) St. John's Hosp. Lond.

GREEN, Charles Roger Heyden (retired) 9 Cosbie Close, Bury St Edmunds IP33 3ST Tel: 01284 753685 — MB BChir 1944 Camb.; MA, MB BChir Camb. 1944; DObst RCOG 1948. Clin. Asst. Dept. Obst. W. Suff. Gen. Hosp. Bury St. Edmunds; Assoc. Mem. E. Anglian Obst. & Gyn. Soc. Prev: Cas. Surg. Off. Middlx. Hosp.

GREEN, Charlotte Jessop Drayton Medical Practices, The Health Centre, Cheshire Street, Market Drayton TF9 3BS; Stycheview, Longford, Market Drayton TF9 3PW Tel: 01630 638710 Fax: 01630 638710 — MB BS 1986 Lond.; BSc 1982 (Hons); DRCOG 1989. (University College Hospital London) Prev: Trainee GP Kidderminster Gen. Hosp. VTS.

GREEN, Christina Ann Green Gables, 97 High St., Sandy SG19 1AL; North Hertfordshire NHS Trust, Corey's Mill Lane, Stevenage SG1 4AB Tel: 01438 781129 Fax: 01438 781436 — MB BChir 1980 Camb.; MA Oxf. 1981; MRCP (UK) 1983; FRCP 1998. Cons. Dermat. N. Herts. NHS Trust. Socs: RSM; MWF; Fell. RCP. Prev: Sen. Regist. (Dermat.) Addenbrooke's Hosp. Camb.

GREEN, Christina Anne The Surgery, 61 Wroxham Road, Sprowston, Norwich NR7 8TT Tel: 01603 427153 Fax: 01603 787341 — MB ChB 1982 Glas.; MRCGP 1987; DRCOG 1985. (Glasgow) Prev: GP Congleton, Wigan & Barnsley; Trainee GP Salford HA VTS.

GREEN, Christine Anne Bewdley Medical Centre, Dog Lane, Bewdley DY12 2EG Tel: 01299 402157 Fax: 01299 404364 — MB ChB 1984 Birm.; MRCGP 1988; DRCOG 1987.

GREEN, Christopher John Liverpool House Surgery, 69 Risedale Road, Barrow-in-Furness LA13 9QY Tel: 01229 832232 Fax: 01229 432156 — MB ChB 1985 Manch.; MRCGP 1990.

GREEN, Clare Lesley 48 Earlswells Road, Cults, Aberdeen AB15 9NY — MB ChB 1994 Ed.

GREEN, Clive Robert Studds Farm, Whitstable Road, Herne Bay CT6 8BH — MB BS 1994 Lond.

GREEN, Colin Peter William Harvey Hospital, Kennington Road, Willesborough, Ashford TN24 0LZ Tel: 01233 633331 — MB BS 1982 Lond.; MRCP (UK) 1988. Cons. Paediat. William Harvey Hosp. Ashford.

GREEN, Colin Philip Gloucester Royal Hospital, Great Western Road, Gloucester GL1 3NN Tel: 01452 528555 Fax: 01452 394249; The Court House, Oakley Road, Battledown, Cheltenham GL52 6NZ Tel: 01242 528452 — MB BS 1982 Lond.; MSc Physiol. Lond. 1988, MB BS 1982; FFA RCS Eng. 1987. (St. Bartholomew's (London)) Cons. Anaesth. & IC Gloucestershire Roy. Hosp. Socs: BMA & Mem. Assn. Anaesth.; Intens. Care Soc. Prev: Sen. Regist. & Regist. (Anaesth.) St. Geo. Hosp. Lond.; Regist. (Anaesth.) St. Geo. Hosp. Lond.; SHO (Anaesth.) Roy. Postgrad. Med. Sch. Lond.

GREEN, Dale Thomas Stonecroft Medical Centre, 871 Gleadless Road, Sheffield S12 2LJ Tel: 0114 398575 Fax: 0114 265 0001 — MB ChB 1963 Birm.; DObst RCOG 1965.

GREEN, Daphne Elizabeth Marlborough Road Surgery, 143 Marlborough Road, Swindon SN3 1NJ Tel: 01793 431303 Fax: 01793 495779 — MB BS 1984 Lond.; MRCGP 1988; DRCOG 1986. (Middlx. Hosp. Med. Sch.) GP. Prev: Trainee GP N. Staffs. VTS.

GREEN, David 32 Channel Road, Clevedon BS21 — MB BS 1966 Lond.; MRCP (U.K.) 1971. (King's Coll. Hosp.) Clin. Asst. in Dermat., Brit. Roy. Infirm., Bristol. Socs: BMA. Prev: Regist. (Gen. Med.) Roy. Alexandra Hosp. Rhyl.; SHO (Cardiol.) Sully Hosp. Penarth; Ho. Off. King's Coll. Hosp. Lond.

GREEN, David Ashley 24 Church Road, Wawne, Hull HU7 5XL — MB ChB 1995 Leeds; BSc Lond. 1989. GP Regist. Bradford Hosp. VTS. Socs: BMA. Prev: Ho. Off. (Gen. Med.) Dewsbury Dist. Gen. Hosp.; Ho. Off. (Gen. Surg.) Bradford Roy. Infirm.

GREEN, David Henry Garthacre, Noctorum Road, Noctorum, Birkenhead CH43 9UQ — MB ChB 1982 Liverp.; PhD Liverp. 1977, BSc (Mathemat. Statist.) 1974; FRCR 1987; DMRD 1986. (Liverpool) Cons. Radiol. Wirral Hosp. Trust; Clin. Dir. Wirral BrE. Screening Unit.

GREEN, David Henry c/o 5 Arundel Close, Alresford SO24 9PJ — MB ChB 1990 Birm.; FRCA 1996. Specialist Regist. Rotat. (Anaesth.) S. Midl. Train. Scheme. Socs: BMA; Train. Mem. Assn. AnE.h. Prev: Regist. (Anaesth.) P.ss Alexandra Hosp. Brisbane Qu.sland, Austral.; SHO (Anaesth.) Cheltenham Gen. Hosp.

GREEN, David Ian 6 Thetford Gardens, Wednesfield, Wolverhampton WV11 1TR Email: david.green10@virgin.net — BM BS 1993 Nottm. Staff Grade (A & E) Roy. Shrewsbury Hosp. Socs: Assoc. Soc. Orthopaedic. Med.

GREEN, David James Michael 24 Woodside Lodge, Tivoli Crescent, Brighton BN1 5ND — MB BS 1964 Lond.; MRCS Eng. LRCP Lond. 1964.

GREEN, David John Alresford Surgery, Station Road, Alresford SO24 9JL Tel: 01962 732345 Fax: 01962 736034; High Dell Cottage, Bighton, Alresford SO24 9SE Tel: 01962 733491 — MB ChB 1978 Leeds; MRCGP 1993; DRCOG 1982.

GREEN, David Martin Department of Histopathology, Queen's Hospital, Belvedere Road, Burton-on-Trent DE13 0RB — MB BS 1980 Lond.; MRCPath 1988. Cons. Histopath. Burton Hosps. NHS Trust. Prev: Sen. Regist. (Histopath.) Yorks. RHA.

GREEN, David William Department of Anaesthetics, King's College Hospital, Denmark Hill, London SE5 9RS Tel: 020 7346 3154 Fax: 020 7346 4106; 34 Ponsonby Terrace, London SW1P 4QA Email: info@dr-green.co.uk — MB BS 1973 Lond.; FFA RCS Eng. 1977. (King's Coll. Hosp.) Cons. Anaesth. King's Coll. Hosp. Lond. Socs: Fell. Roy. Soc. Med.; Amer. Soc. Anaesth. & Europ. Acad. Anaesth.; Hon. Sec. Sect. of Anaesth. Roy.Soc. Med. Prev: Asst. Prof. Anaesth. Univ. Texas SW Med. Sch. Dallas, USA; Sen. Regist. (Anaesth.) Qu. Vict. Hosp. E. Grinstead; Ho. Phys. Dulwich Hosp. Lond.

GREEN, Deborah Frances 27 Sibsey Road, Boston PE21 9QY Tel: 01205 362000; 37 Baronsway, Whitkirk, Leeds LS15 7AW Tel: 01132 609070 — MB ChB 1994 Sheff. Paediat. Rotat. Leeds Gen. Infirm. Prev: SHO (A & E) Leeds Gen. Infirm.; SHO (Paediat.) Rotherham; SHO (O & G) Chesterfield.

GREEN, Desmond John 7 Oundle Drive, Wollaton Park, Nottingham NG8 1BN — MB ChB 1975 Birm.; FRCR 1985. Cons. Radiol. City Hosp. Nottm.

GREEN, Diana Muir Cottesmore House, Lower Kingsdown Road, Kingsdown, Corsham SN13 8BG — MB ChB 1971 Liverp. Staff Grade Paediat. (Community Health) Bath & W. Community NHS Trust.

GREEN, Digby Michael 1 Station Terrace, London NW10 5RS — MB ChB 1989 Stellenbosch.

GREEN, Donald James St James Medical Centre, 11 Carlton Road, Tunbridge Wells TN1 2HW Tel: 01892 541634 Fax: 01892 545170 — MB BS 1979 Lond.; MRCS Eng. LRCP Lond. 1980. (Char. Cross) Socs: Christian Med. Fell.sh. Prev: SHO & Ho. Off. I. of Wight Hosps.

GREEN, Dorothy Ferrier 81A Shore Road, Greenisland, Carrickfergus BT38 8TZ Tel: 01232 852542 — MB BCh BAO 1957 Belf.; DA RCPSI 1960. (Qu. Univ. Belf.)

GREEN, Duncan Campbell Hyslop 16 John Campbell Street, The Moorings, Gourock PA19 1RZ — MB ChB 1994 Glas.

GREEN, Duncan Currie 'The Croft', 19 Victoria Road, Gourock PA19 1LD Tel: 01475 24477 — MB ChB 1968 Glas.; DObst RCOG 1970.

GREEN, Edward Lorin 5 Hertford Lockhouse, 201 Parnell Road, London E3 2JZ — MB BS 1971 Melbourne; PhD Lond. 1988, MSc 1983; FRACP 1978; DTM & H RCP Lond. 1980.

GREEN, Edwin Nicholas 20 Orchard Close, Wenvoe, Cardiff CF5 6BW — BM 1990 Soton.; MRCGP 1997.

GREEN, Edwina Elsie 2 Sanderstead Hill, Sanderstead, South Croydon CR2 0HA; 91 Mount Nod Road, London SW16 2LJ — MB ChB 1948 Leeds; MRCS Eng. LRCP Lond. 1948; DObst RCOG 1950; DMJ (Clin.) Soc. Apoth. Lond. 1965. (Leeds) Prev: GP Streatham; Jun. Receiv. Room Off. Leeds Gen. Infirm.; Ho. Surg. Leeds Matern. Hosp.

GREEN, Elizabeth (retired) Hawthorn Cottage, 12 Dunnyfell Road, Muchalls, Stonehaven AB39 3RP Tel: 01569 30508 — MB ChB 1947 St. And.; FFA RCS Eng. 1975; DA Eng. 1954. Prev: Assoc. Specialist (Anaesth.) Tayside Health Bd.

GREEN, Elizabeth Aimee (retired) 32 Foxcroft, St Albans AL1 5SP — MB ChB 1951 Aberd.; DPM Eng. 1959. Prev: Cons. Psych. Cell Barnes Hosp. St. Albans.

***GREEN, Elizabeth Catherine** 41 Orchard Street, Otley LS21 1JU — MB BS 1997 Lond.

GREEN, Elizabeth Mary Chailey Heritage, Clinical Services, Beggars Wood Road, North Chailey, Lewes BN8 4JN Tel: 01825 722112 Fax: 01825 724719 Email: Elizabeth.Green@southdowns.nhs.uk; Farthings, Furners Green, Uckfield TN22 3RP Tel: 01825 740380 — MB ChB St. And. 1970; MD Dundee 1991; BA (Hons.) Psychol. Open 1991; DCH Eng. 1973; Dip Health Mgt Keele 1997. (St Andrews University) Cons. Paediat. Rehabil. & Neurodevelopm. Paediat. Chailey Heritage S. Downs. Health NHS Trust.; Clin. Dir. Rehabil. Prev: Assoc. Specialist (Neurodevelopm. Paediat.) Chailey Heritage Hosp. & Mackeith Centre Brighton; SCMO W. Sussex AHA.

GREEN, Elizabeth Sarah Princess Margaret Hospital, Okus Road, Swindon SN1 4JU Tel: 01793 426759 Fax: 01793 426827 Email: sarah.green@smnhst.swest.nhs.uk — MB BS 1980 Lond.; MB BS (Hons.) Lond. 1980; MA Camb. 1982; FRCP Lond. 1996; MRCP (UK) 1983; FRCPath 1997, M 1989. (Univ. Coll. Hosp. Lond.) Cons. Haemat. P.ss Margt. Hosp. Swindon. Prev: Sen. Regist. (Haemat.) Univ. Coll. Hosp. Lond.

GREEN, Eric William (retired) Springwood, Blawith, Ulverston LA12 8EQ — MB ChB 1948 Leeds; MRCGP 1965; DObst RCOG 1971; DO Eng. 1970.

GREEN, Esther Mary Manford Way Health Centre, 40 Foremark Close, Ilford IG3 9SN — MB ChB 1995 Manch.; DRCOG 2001. GP partner, Hainault IG7. Prev: GP Regist., Wanstead, E11.

GREEN, Everel Catharine (retired) Willow House, 38 Totteridge Common, London N20 8NE Tel: 020 8959 6616 — MB BS Lond. 1951; MRCS Eng. LRCP Lond. 1951; DObst RCOG 1957. Prev: Med. Off. Finchley Memor. Hosp.

GREEN, Fergus Robinson Alloa Health Centre, Marshill, Alloa FK10 1AQ Tel: 01259 216701; 76 Arns Grove, Alloa FK10 2EF — MB ChB 1988 Ed.; MRCGP 1992; DCCH RCP Ed. 1993; DRCOG 1992.

GREEN, Fiona Christine 3 Stevenson Court, Bridge of Allan, Stirling FK9 4TN Email: fgreen1270@aol.com — MB ChB 1993 Aberd.; MB ChB (Commend.) Aberd. 1993; MRCP Ed. 1996. (Aberdeen) Clin. Research Fell. Univ. of Dundee Ninewells Hosp. & Med. Sch.; Hon. Clin. Lect. Ninewells Hosp. & Med. Sch. 1997. Prev: SHO (Med.) Falkirk Roy. Infirm.; SHO Rotat. (Med.) Aberd. Roy. Infirm.

GREEN, Mr Frank Douglas Glenburnie, Maryculter, Aberdeen AB12 5FS — MB ChB 1974 Glas.; FRCS Ed. 1982; MRCP (UK) 1978. Cons. Ophth. Aberd. Roy. Hosp. Trust. Socs: Fell. Coll. Ophth.

GREEN, Mr Gavin Anthony (retired) Queens Hospital, Belvedere Road, Burton-on-Trent DE13 0RB Tel: 01283 566333 — MB BChir 1966 Camb.; MB Camb. 1966, BChir 1965; MA Camb. 1966; FRCS Eng. 1970. Cons. Orthop. Surg. Burton Hosps. NHS Trust. Prev: Sen. Regist. (Orthop.) King's Coll. Hosp. Lond.

GREEN, George Jeffrey Glan Clwyd Hosp, Rhyl LL18 5UJ Tel: 01745 534576; Lon Wilkin, Henllan, Denbigh LL16 5BS Tel: 01745 812065 — MB ChB 1973 Liverp.; MB ChB (Hons.) Liverp. 1973; BSc (Distinc.) Liverp. 1969, MD 1979; FRCP Lond. 1991; MRCP (UK) 1976. (Liverp.) Cons. Phys. (Cardiol.) Glan Clwyd Hosp. Bodelwyddan, Rhyl. Socs: Chairm. Welsh Cardiac Gp.; Hon Sec Jt. speciality for Cardiol. Roy. Coll. Phys. Lond. Prev: Sen. Regist. (Med.) Regional Cardiac Centre Sefton Gen. Hosp. Liverp.; Lect. (Clin. Pharmacol.) Univ. Liverp.; Research Fell. (Pharmacol. & Therap.) Brit. Heart Foundat.

GREEN, George William The Flower House, Lewes Road, Blackboys, Uckfield TN22 5LF Tel: 01825 890454 — MB ChB Leeds (2nd Cl. Hnrs.) 1937; MRCPsych 1972; DPM Eng. 1944. (Leeds) Prev: Cons. Psychiat. Tunbridge Wells Dist. Hosp. Gp. & DHSS; Med. Supt. Ticehurst Ho. Ticehurst; Vis. Psychiat. & Sen. Asst. Med. Off. York Clinic, Guy's Hosp.

GREEN, Gerald Francis (retired) 33 Mallin Court, Turnberry, Girvan KA26 9PB Tel: 01655 331457 — MB BChir 1942 Camb.; MA Camb. 1942; MRCGP 1952; DMRT 1949.

GREEN, Graham Bernard Department of Occupational Health, Aintree Hospital Trust, Fazakerley Hospital, Longmoor Lane, Liverpool L9 7AL Tel: 0151 525 3622 Fax: 0151 525 6086 — MB ChB 1976 Sheff.; AFOM RCP Lond. 1987. Dir. (Occupat. Med.) Aintree Hosps. Trust Liverp. Prev: Chief Occupat. Phys. Atomic Energy Auth. Technol.

GREEN, Harry Lee (retired) 1 Barrhill Road, Kirkcudbright DG6 4BG — MB ChB 1954 Manch.; DIC (Engin. in Med.) 1970. Prev: Cons. Clin. Engin. Char. Cross Hosp.

GREEN, Helen May Lyne of Carron, Aberlour AB38 9NS; Balliemulloch, Aberlour — MB ChB 1980 Aberd. Clin. Med. Off. Grampian HB.

GREEN, Helen Therese (retired) Oakwood House, Eastbury, Hungerford RG17 7JP Tel: 01488 71531 — MD Liverp. 1952, MB ChB 1948; FRCPath 1984. Prev: Cons. Microbiol. Walton Hosp. Liverp.

GREEN, Ian Avon Valley Practice, Fairfield, Uravon, Pensey SN9 6DZ Tel: 01908 630221 — BM 1992 Soton. Trainee GP/SHO Salisbury Dist. Hosp. VTS.

GREEN, Ian Douglas Ladbrook Cottage, Penn Lane, Tanworth-in-Arden, Solihull B94 5HJ — MRCS Eng. LRCP Lond. 1956; PhD Lond. 1968, MB BS 1956; FRCP Lond. 1976, M 1965. (Guy's) Sen. Lect. (Med.) Qu. Eliz. Hosp. Birm.; Hon. Cons. Phys. Selly Oak Hosp. Birm. Prev: Dorothy Temple Cross Trav. Fell. Dept. Physiol., Harvard Sch. Pub.; Health Boston, U.S.A. Specialist Aviat. Med. High Altitude; nst. Aviat. Med. FarnBoro.

GREEN, Ian Linley Garlands, Chineham Lane, Sherborne St John, Basingstoke RG24 9LR Tel: 01256 463963 — MB BS 1981 Lond.; PhD Lond. 1987; FRCR 1992. Cons. Radiol. N. Hants. Hosp. Socs: Brit. Med. Ultrasound Soc. Prev: Sen. Regist. (Radiol.) Soton. Gen. Hosp.

GREEN, Jacques Mortimore 8 Brooklyn Park, Bangor BT20 5PA — MD 1949 Paris; MRCS Eng. LRCP Lond. 1953. Prev: Ho. Off. Fulham Hosp.

GREEN, Mr James Bisdee Malcolm Stone Cross, 90 Lexden Road, Colchester CO3 3TG Tel: 01206 574320 — MA, BM BCh Oxf. 1937; FRCS Ed. 1946; MRCS Eng. LRCP Lond. 1936; DLO Eng. 1943. (Oxf. & St. Thos.) Hon. Cons. ENT Surg. Colchester Health Dist. Socs: Fell. Roy. Soc. Med.; (Ex-Pres.) Colchester Med. Soc.

Prev: Ho. Surg. & Regist. ENT Dept. St. Thos. Hosp.; Med. Off. 1937 'Discovery' Expedition to Antarctic.

GREEN, James Daniel Frank Flat 3, 44 Grosvenor Road, Newcastle upon Tyne NE2 2RP — MB BS 1996 Newc.; PHD Camb. 1991; BSc (Hons.) Bristol 1988. SHO (Basic Surg. Train. Progr.) Newc.-u-Tyne.

GREEN, James Niall Stevenson Salisbury Medical Centre, 474 Antrim Road, Belfast BT15 5GF Tel: 028 9077 7905; 81A Shore Road, Greenisland, Carrickfergus BT38 8TZ Tel: 01232 852542 — MB BCh BAO 1958 Belf.; DObst RCOG 1960. (Qu. Univ. Belf.) Prev: Ho. Off. (Obst.) & Resid. Ho. Off Belf. City Hosp.

GREEN, Mr James Patrick 27 Sibsey Road, Boston PE21 9QY Tel: 01205 362000 — MB ChB 1952 Sheff.; FRCS Eng. 1962. Cons. Orthop. Surg. Pilgrim Hosp. Boston. Prev: Sen. Orthop. Regist. Harlow Wood Orthop. Hosp. Mansfield; Surg. Regist. Roy. Infirm. Sheff.; Demonst. Anat. Univ. Sheff.

GREEN, Mr James Stephen Arthur — MB BS 1989 Lond.; LLM 1998.

GREEN, Jane Louise 7 Dinas Dr, Llangollen LL20 7PL — MB BCh 1997 Wales.

GREEN, Jane Margaret 13 Cumnor Rise Road, Oxford OX2 9HD — BM BCh 1983 Oxf.

GREEN, Janet Maria 10 Laburnum Grove, Irby, Wirral CH61 4UT — MB ChB 1990 Sheff.; MRCGP 1994; DRCOG 1993. (Sheff.) Prev: Trainee GP Cornw. VTS; Ho. Off. (Surg.) Sheff.; Ho. Off. (Med.) Truro.

GREEN, Jennifer Barbara 5 Grosvenor Park, Allerton Hill, Chapel Allerton, Leeds LS7 3QD Tel: 0113 268 0825 Fax: 0113 268 0825 Email: mike_jen_green@dial.pipex.com — MB ChB Leeds 1960; FFPHM RCP (UK) 1995, M 1988; MPH Leeds 1985; MCOphth Eng. 1973; DA (UK) 1967. (Leeds) Indep. Pub. Health Pract.; Clin. Asst. (Eye) Leeds Gen. Infirm. Socs: (Exec. Comm.) BMA; Pres. (Exec. Comm.) Leeds & W. Riding Medico-Legal Soc. Prev: Cons. Pub. Health Med. Wakefield Healthcare; Sen. Regist. (Community Med.) Leeds.

GREEN, Jeremy Simon Coed Duon, Tremeirchion, St Asaph LL17 0UH Tel: 01745 730284 — MB ChB 1988 Birm.; MRCP (UK) 1992; FRCR (UK) 1996. Cons. Radiologist, Dept. of Radiol., Cheltenham Gen. Hosp.

GREEN, Joanne Claire Riverside Cottage, Tittensor Road, Tittensor, Stoke-on-Trent ST12 9HQ — MB ChB 1998 Dund.; MB ChB Dund 1998.

GREEN, Joanne Elizabeth Boringdon House, 1 Church Rd, Dartmouth TQ6 9HQ — MB ChB 1997 Birm.

GREEN, Joel Marcus Jeremy 70 Heol Don, Whitchurch, Cardiff CF14 2AT — MB BCh 1995 Wales. SHO (Paediat.) E. Glam. Gen. Hosp.

GREEN, John Lister Medical Centre, Lister House, Staple Tye, Harlow CM18 7LU Tel: 01279 414882 Fax: 01279 439600 — MB ChB 1980 Cape Town.

GREEN, John Alan Clatterbridge Centre for Oncology, Bebington, Wirral CH63 4JY Tel: 0151 604 7479 Fax: 0151 482 7675 Email: johng@ccotrust.co.uk; CRC Oncology Research Unit, Department of Medicine, University of Liverpool, PO Box 147, Liverpool L69 3BX Tel: 0151 706 4530 Fax: 0151 706 5802 — MB ChB 1973 Glas.; DM Soton. 1983; BSc Glas. 1969; FRCP Lond. 1993; FRCP Ed. 1988; MRCP (UK) 1977. Sen. Lect. (Med. Oncol.) Univ. Liverp. & Roy. Liverp. Univ. Hosp.; Mem. (Counc.) Clatterbridge Cancer Research Trust; Cons. (Hon) Liverp. Woms. Hosp. Socs: Brit. Assoc. for Cancer Research; Amer. Assoc. Cancer Research; Brit. Gyn. Cancer Soc. Prev: Vis. Fell. Nat. Cancer Inst. Washington DC, USA; CRC Research Fell. (Med. Oncol.) Univ. Soton.; Regist. (Med.) Aberd. Roy. Infirm.

GREEN, John David Department of Anaesthesia, Sunderland Royal Hospital, Sunderland SR4 7TP Tel: 0191 565 6256 — MB ChB 1982 Sheff.; FRCA 1994. Cons. Anaesth. & Intens. Care Sunderland Roy. Hosp.

GREEN, John Edward 1 Nudger Green, Dobcross, Oldham OL3 5AW — MB BS 1996 Newc.

GREEN, John Geoffrey 35 Birch Tree Way, Maidstone ME15 7RP Tel: 01622 672723 Email: johngreen@ukonline.co.uk — MB BS 1997 Lond.; BSc (Hons). VTS, Maidstone.

GREEN, John Joseph South Parade Surgery, 7 South Parade, Llandudno LL30 2LN Tel: 01492 876907 Fax: 01492 871480; Rapallo House, Fferm Bach Road, Craig Y Don, Llandudno LL30 1UA Tel: 01492 874683 Email: jjgreen@mistral.co.uk — MB ChB 1980 Birm.; MRCGP 1988; Cert. Family Plann. JCC 1988; DObst RCPI 1983. Princip. (Gen. Pract.); Med. Ref. RNLI (W. Div.); Hon. Med. Adviser Llandudno Lifeboat Station (RNLI); Med. Off. Llandudno Rugby Club. Prev: Trainee GP Llandudno; Regist. (Med.) Letterkenny Gen. Hosp. Co. Donegal, Irel.; SHO (Obst.) Portiuncula Hosp. Ballinasloe, Co. Galway, Irel.

GREEN, John Philip 85 Finchfield Road W., Wolverhampton WV3 8BA — MRCS Eng. LRCP Lond. 1950. (Sheff.) Prev: Ho. Phys. Wharncliffe Hosp. Sheff., Myland Hosp. Colchester & Chelmsford & Essex Hosp.

GREEN, John Toby Herbert Whitcombe Farm, Beaminster DT8 3NE — BM BCh 1949 Oxf.; MA, BM BCh Oxon. 1949. (Middlx.) Prev: Surg. Lt. RN; Ho. Surg. Gyn. Dept., Mt. Vernon Hosp. N.wood; Obst. Ho. Surg. Dorset Co. Hosp.

GREEN, John Trevor Department of Gastroenterology, Llandough Hospital, Penarth CF64 2XX Tel: 01222 711711 Email: greenjt@cdf.ac.uk; Flat 7, 168 Cathedral Road, Pontcanna, Cardiff CF11 9JD Tel: 01222 233642 — MB BCh 1991 Wales; MRCP (UK) 1994. Specialist Regist. (Gastroenterol.) Llandough Hosp. Socs: Brit. Soc. Gastroenterol. (Mem.). Prev: Regist. (Med.) Roy. Gwent Hosp.; SHO Rotat. (Med.) S. Glam.; Research Regist. (Med.) Univ. Hosp. Wales Cardiff.

GREEN, Jonathan Ferrier Mental Health Unit Ards Hospital, Newtownards BT23 4AS Tel: 01247 510106 Fax: 01247 510119 Email: jonathan.green@nda.n-i.nhs.uk — BSc (Hons.) Lond. 1984, MB BS 1987; MRCPsych 1993; DMH Belf. 1991. (Westminster Medical School) Cons. (Adult Gen. Psychiat.), Ards Hosp., Co. Down. Prev: Cons. Psychiat. Ards Hosp. Newtownards, Co Down.

GREEN, Jonathan Michael Department of Child & Family Psychiatry, Booth Hall Childrens Hospital, Charlestown Road, Blackley, Manchester M9 7AA Tel: 0161 795 7000 Fax: 0161 741 5387; 87 South Drive, Manchester M21 8ED — MB BS 1977 Lond.; MA Camb. 1973; MRCPsych 1985; DCH Eng. 1979. (Univ. Coll. Hosp.) Cons. Child & Adolesc. Psychiat. Booth Hall Childr. Hosp. Manch.; Sen. Lect. (Child & Adolesc. Psychiat.) Univ. Manch. Prev: Sen. Regist. Rotat. (Child Psychiat.) Manch.; Regist. Pk. Hosp. Oxf.; SHO Qu. Eliz. Hosp. for Childr. Lond.

GREEN, Jonathan Rupert Bailey N. Staffs Hospital, Gastroenterology Department ST4 6QG Tel: 01782 552390; Southleys, 43 Barlaston Old Road, Trentham, Stoke-on-Trent ST4 8HD Tel: 01782 657972 — BM BCh 1970 Oxf.; DM Oxf. 1978, MA 1970; FRCP Lond. 1987; MRCP (UK) 1973. Cons. Phys. (Gastroenterol.) N. Staffs. Hosp. NHS Trust Stoke-on-Trent. Prev: Sen. Regist. (Gen. Med. & Gastroenterol.) St. Mary's Hosp. Lond.; Hon. Lect. (Gastroenterol.) St. Bart. Hosp. Lond.

GREEN, Joseph James 49 New Court Dr, Egerton, Bolton BL7 9XA — MB ChB 1997 Liverp.

***GREEN, Juliet** 13 Turncliff Crescent, Marple, Stockport SK6 6JP — MB ChB 1994 Birm.; ChB Birm. 1994.

GREEN, June Havergal Weaver Vale Surgery, High St., Winsford CW7 2AS Tel: 01606 551311 Fax: 01606 550689; 81 Chester Road, Winsford CW7 2NG Tel: 01606 556111 — MB BS Melbourne 1951; DObst RCOG 1954; DTM & H Liverp. 1954. (Melb.) Med. Off. Pain Clinic Winsford. Socs: Fell Manch. Med. Soc.; Liverp. Med. Inst. Prev: Regist. (Med.) Barony Hosp. Nantwich & Whiston Hosp.; Med. Off. Sefton Gen. Hosp. Liverp.

GREEN, Karen Lesley Devonshire Road Surgery, 467 Devonshire Road, Blackpool FY2 0JP Tel: 01253 352233 — MB ChB 1982 Manch.; MRCGP 1986; DRCOG 1985. p/t Partner, Gen. Pract.

GREEN, Keith Nicholas The Firs, Broad Lane, Tanworth-in-Arden, Solihull B94 5DP Tel: 015644 2274 — MB ChB 1977 Birm.; MRCP (UK) 1981.

GREEN, Mr Kevin Michael John 34 Potato Wharf, Manchester M3 4NB — MB ChB 1991 Ed.; FRCS Ed. 1995.

GREEN, Klaus Square Medical Practice, High Street, Godalming GU7 1AZ Tel: 01483 415141 Fax: 01483 414881 — MB BChir 1993 Camb.; MA Camb. 1989, MB BChir 1993. Prev: SHO (A & E) N. Middlx. Hosp. Lond.

GREEN, Laura Eileen 46 The Vineries, Liverpool L25 6EX — MB ChB 1995 Sheff.

GREEN, Leslie Melvin (retired) 4 Wellesley Avenue, Northwood HA6 3HY Tel: 019238 28695 Email: ling4@tinyworld.co.uk — MB BS Lond. 1946. Prev: Clin. Asst. Out-pats. St. Mary's Hosp.

GREEN, Louise Catherine Hedon Group Practice, 4 Market Hill, Hedon, Hull HU12 8JB — MB ChB 1983 Sheff.; MRCPsych 1988.

GREEN, Lucinda Caroline Needwoodside, Tatenhill Common, Rangemore, Burton-on-Trent DE13 9RS — MB ChB 1998 Bristol.

GREEN, Lynette Ruby Calder Cottage, Philcote St., Deddington, Oxford Tel: 01869 338527 — MB BS 1964 Sydney; FFA RCS Eng. 1970; DA Eng. 1967. Clin. Asst. Nat. Blood Auth. Prev: Cons. Anaesth. Horton Gen. Hosp. Banbury.

GREEN, Maeve Jocelyn Clarendon Lodge Medical Practice, 16 Clarendon Street, Leamington Spa CV32 5SS Tel: 01926 422094 Fax: 01926 331400; Argyll, 2B Union Road, Leamington Spa CV32 5LT Tel: 01926 313782 — MB ChB 1974 Birm.; MRCGP 1986.

GREEN, Malcolm (retired) Vale House, Lea Road, Dronfield S18 1SB Tel: 01246 413675 — MB ChB Sheff. 1957; MD Sheff. 1964.

GREEN, Professor Malcolm Royal Brompton Hospital, London SW3 6NP Tel: 020 73518708 Email: malcolm.green@ic.ac.uk; 38 Lansdowne Gardens, London SW8 2EF Tel: 020 7622 8286 Fax: 020 7720 4099 Email: malcolm.green@ic.ac.uk — BM BCh Oxf. 1967; MA Oxf. 1967, BSc 1965, BA 1963, DM 1978; FRCP Lond. 1980; MRCP (UK) 1970. (Oxf. & St. Thos. Hosp.) Cons. Phys. Roy. Brompton Hosp. Lond.; Vice-Princip.Fac. of Med.. Imperial Coll. (1997); Head of Nat. Heart & Lung Inst. (2001) Imperial Coll. Socs: Brit. & Amer. Thoracic Socs.; Assn. Phys.; Fell. Fac. Med. Sci. Prev: Dir. Brit. Postgrad. Med. Federat. Lond.; Dean Nat. Heart & Lung Inst. Lond.; Phys. i/c Chest Dept. St. Bart. Hosp. Lond.

GREEN, Malcolm Henry Peter Halton General Hospital, Halton, Runcorn WA7 2DA Tel: 01928 753251 Fax: 01928 753219 — MB ChB Bristol 1970; MRCPsych 1975; DPM Manchester 1975. Cons. Psychiat. Halton Gen. Hosp.; Clin. Dir. Ment. Health Halfon. Prev: Cons. Psychiat. Lancaster Moor Hosp. & N. Manch. Gen. Hosp.; Sen. Regist. (Psychiat.) Univ. Hosp. S. Manch.

GREEN, Mr Marcus Adrian Hillside House, 8 Kendal End Road, Cofton Hackett, Birmingham B45 8PY Tel: 0121 445 4417 — MB ChB 1987 Birm.; BSc Birm. 1986; FRCS Eng. 1991; Dip IMC ECS Ed. 1993; FRCS 1998. (Birmingham) Regist. (Orthop. & Trauma) W. Midl. Train. Scheme; Hon. Lect. Univ. Birm. (Surg.).

GREEN, Margaret Brenda Glen Arleen, Station Road, Coltishall, Norwich NR12 7JG Tel: 01603 738567 — MB ChB 1951 Leeds; DCH Eng. 1955. (Leeds) Prev: Regist. (Paediat.) St. Geo. Hosp. Lond.

GREEN, Mark Alistair East Surrey Hospital, Canada Avenue, Redhill RH1 5RH Tel: 01737 768511; 10 Beverstone Road, Thornton Heath CR7 7LT Fax: 020 8689 2292 — MB BS 1986 Lond.; FRCA 1993; MRCGP 1991; DA (UK) 1991. (St. Geo. Hosp. Med. Sch. Lond.) Cons. Anaesth. E. Surrey Hosp. Redhill Surrey. Prev: GP Croydon; Sen. Regist. (Anaesth.) St. Geo. Hosp. Lond.

GREEN, Mark Stuart 14 Mostyn Avenue, West Kirby, Wirral CH48 3HW — MB ChB 1989 Liverp.

GREEN, Martin Roy The Medical Health Centre, Gray Avenue, Sherburn, Durham DH6 1JE Tel: 0191 372 0441 Fax: 0191 372 1238 — MB ChB 1986 Birm.; MRCGP 1990; DCH RCP Lond. 1990.

GREEN, Martin William Llys Meddyg, Caersws SY17 5EX Tel: 01686 688225 Fax: 01686 688344; Wern Trefeglwys, Caersws SY17 5PN Tel: 01686 430209 — MB BCh Wales 1980; MA Camb. 1981; MRCGP 1986; DCH RCP Lond. 1986; DGM RCP Lond. 1985; DRCOG 1984.

GREEN, Mary Cecilia Dorothy Northwick Park Hospital, Watford Road, Harrow HA1 3UJ — MB BCh BAO 1978 Dub.; MRCPsych 1983. Prev: Sen. Regist. (Psychiat.) N.wick Pk. Hosp. Middlx. & St. Mary's Hosp. Lond.; Research Fell. Calif. Coll. Med. Univ., Calif.; Regist. N.wick Pk. Hosp. Harrow.

GREEN, Mary Elizabeth 65 St Nicholas Road, St Pauls, Bristol BS2 9JJ — MB ChB 1998 Sheff.; MB ChB Sheff 1998.

GREEN, Matthew Bruce Medical Centre, Clive Barracks, Ternhill, Market Drayton TF9 3QE Tel: 01630 698207 Fax: 01630 698200; 7 Dan Y Crug, Brecon LD3 9LD Tel: 0467 782697 — MB BS 1997 Lond. Regt.. Med. Off. 1st Bn. Staffs. Regt.

GREEN, Matthew James 207A Berrow Road, Burnham-on-Sea TA8 2JG — MB ChB 1990 Birm.

GREEN, Maureen Irene (retired) Wells City Practice, 22 Chamberlain Street, Wells BA5 2PF Tel: 01749 673356 Fax: 01749 670031 — MB ChB 1967 Bristol.

GREEN, Mervyn Thomas Old Road Surgery, Old Road, Llanelli SA15 3HR Tel: 01554 775555 Fax: 01554 778868 — MB BCh 1978 Wales; MRCGP 1982; DRCOG 1982.

GREEN, Michael 284 Barnsley Road, Hoylandswaine, Sheffield S36 7JA — MB ChB 1980 Leeds.

GREEN, Michael Alan 9 Tollbridge Road, Woodthorpe, Mastin Moor, Chesterfield S43 3BL — MB ChB 1993 Sheff.

GREEN, Professor Michael Alan The Medico-Legal Centre, Watery St., Sheffield S3 7ES Tel: 0114 273 8721 Fax: 0114 279 8942 Email: forensic.path@sheffield.ac.uk; 5 Grosvenor Park, Allerton Hill, Leeds LS7 3QD Tel: 0113 268 0825 Email: mike_jen_green@dial.pipex.com — MB ChB 1962 Leeds; FRCPath 1993, M 1981; DMJ (Clin. & Path.) Soc. Apoth. Lond. 1970; DObst RCOG 1966; DCH Eng. 1965. (Leeds) Prof. Forens. Path. Univ. Sheff. & Hons. Cons. Path. Cent. Sheff. Univ. Hosp. Trust. Socs: Fell. Brit. Assn. Forens. Med. Prev: Regist. Profess. Paediat. Unit Leeds; Med. Off. Roy. Flying Doctor Serv. Austral.; Med. Off. NSW Govt. Forens. Servs.

GREEN, Mr Michael Frederick Glamorgan House, BUPA Hospital Cardiff, Croescadarn Road, Pentwyn, Cardiff CF23 8XL Tel: 029 2073 6011; Yew Tree Farm, Mountain Road, Upper Cwmbran, Cwmbran NP44 5AA Tel: 01495 756978 Fax: 01495 769684 — MB BS 1964 Lond.; FRCS Eng. 1971; FRCS Ed. 1968; MRCS Eng. LRCP Lond. 1964. (St. Mary's) Aesthetic (Plastic & Reconstruc. Surg.) BUPA Hosp. Cardiff. Socs: Brit. Assn. Plastic Surg.; (Counc.) Brit. Assn. Aesthetic Plastic Surgs. Prev: Cons. Plastic & Reconstruc. Surg. Welsh Regional Centre for Burns & Plastic Surg. St. Lawrence Hosp. Chepstow; Sen. Regist. (Plastic Surg.) St. Jas. Hosp. Leeds; Regist. Rotat. (Surg.) Roy. Hosp. Sheff.

GREEN, Michael Gurnell, MBE Junction Lane Surgery, 14 Junction Lane, Burscough, Ormskirk L40 5SS Tel: 01704 893743 — MB ChB 1942 St. And.; MRCGP 1952. (St. And.) Mem. Liverp. Med. Inst.

GREEN, Michael John 80 Tollgate Road, Salisbury SP1 2JJ Tel: 01722 34951 — MB ChB 1992 Manch.; MRCP (UK) 1995. SHO (Gen. Med.) Trafford Gen. Hosp. Manch. Prev: SHO (Gen. Med.) Trafford Gen. Hosp. & Burnley Gen. Hosp.; Ho. Off. (Gen. Med.) Trafford Gen. Hosp.

GREEN, Michael John 20 Speedwell Road, Birkenhead CH41 0DP — MB ChB 1997 Liverp.

GREEN, Michael Robert The Childrens Hospital, The Leicester Royal Infirmary NHS Trust, Leicester LE1 5WW Tel: 0116 258 6794 Fax: 0116 258 7637 — MB BS 1983 Lond.; MRCP (UK) 1988; FRCPCH. (Roy. Free) Cons. Paediat. Childr. Hosp. Leicester Roy. Infirm. Prev: Univ. Tutor & Hon. Sen. Regist. St. Jas. Univ. Hosp. Leeds; Research Fell. MRC Dunn Nutrit. Unit. Camb.; Regist. (Paediat.) Alder Hey Childr. Hosp. Liverp.

GREEN, Monica 5 Austrey Close, Knowle, Solihull B93 9JE Tel: 01564 775155 — MRCGP 2000; MB ChB Ed. 1994; DGM 1997 Glas. (Edinburgh) p/t GP Regist.

GREEN, Myer Solomon (retired) Ramat-Gan, 40 Castleton Drive, Newton Mearns, Glasgow G77 5LE Tel: 0141 639 4618 Email: msg@cqm.co.uk — MB ChB Glas. 1961; DObst RCOG 1963. Prev: GP Asst. (Gyn.) Hairmyres Hosp. Glas.

GREEN, Nathaniel Mayer 200 Sloane Street, London SW1 Tel: 020 7245 9565 — MD 1936 Lond.; MRCS Eng. LRCP Lond. 1932; DTM & H Lond 1963, DPH 1966. (Univ. Coll. Hosp.) Socs: Fell. Roy. Soc. Med. & Roy. Soc. Trop. Med. & Hyg. Prev: Capt. RAMC.

GREEN, Nicholas Donald Charles, Squadron Ldr. RAF Med. Br. RAF Centre of Aviation Medicine, RAF Harlow SG16 6DN Tel: 01462 851515 Email: ocbiodynamics@rafcam.mod.uk — MB BS 1988 Lond.; BSc (Hons.) Physiol. Lond. 1985; DAvMed. FOM RCP Lond. 1993. (Charing Cross and Westminster) Specialist Regist. (Radiol.), Middlx. Hosp., Lond. Specialist Regist., Aviat. Med., RAF Centre of Aviat. Medcine Harlow. Socs: Brit. Medicial Assn.; Aerospace Med. Assn. Prev: SHO (Med.) Haskar Hosp.; Specialist (Aviat. Med.) RAF S.A.M. FarnBoro..; Specialist Regist. (Radiol.) Middlx. Hosp. Lond.

GREEN, Nicholas Eric Carteknowle and Dore Medical Practice, 1 Carterknowle Road, Sheffield S7 2DW Tel: 0114 255 1218 Fax:

0114 258 4418; 10 Whirlow Park Road, Sheffield S11 9NP — MB ChB 1987 Sheff.; MRCGP 1991; DRCOG 1991.

GREEN, Nicholas James 5 The Russets, Sanal, Wakefield WF2 6JF — MB BS 1992 Lond.

GREEN, Nicholas James Department of Pathology, Royal Shrewsbury Hospital, Mytton Oak Road, Shrewsbury SY3 8XQ Tel: 01743 261168 Fax: 01743 355963 Email: njg@rshhis.demon.co.uk — MB ChB 1984 Leeds; FRCPath 1999; MRCPath 1990; BSc (Hons.) Path. Leeds 1981. (Leeds) Prev: Sen. Regist. (Histopath.) W. Midl. HA.

GREEN, Nicola Jane 60 Mountwood, Greystoke Gardens, Sandyford, Newcastle upon Tyne NE2 1PY — BM BS 1996 Nottm.

GREEN, Nigel Darren 12 Noon Sun Close, Greenfield, Oldham OL3 7JA — MB BS 1997 Newc.

GREEN, Nigel Thomas Wilkes St Ann's Medical Centre, Effingham St., Rotherham S65 1BL Tel: 01709 379283 — MRCS Eng. LRCP Lond. 1962.

GREEN, Mr Norman Alan 60A The Close, Norwich NR1 4EH Tel: 01603 613198 Fax: 01603 633331 — MB BS 1950 Lond.; MS Lond. 1964; FRCS Ed. 1990; FRCS Eng. 1954; MRCS Eng. LRCP Lond. 1950. (St. Bart.) Indep. Medico-Legal Cons. & Clin. Anat.; Med. Mem. Med. Appeals Tribunal; Hon. Med. Off., Dean & Chap. Norwich Cathedral; Examr. RCS Edin. Socs: Hon. Fell. (Ex-Pres.) Brit. Assn. Clin. Anats.; Fell. Roy. Soc. Med. (Ex-Pres. Sect. Urol.); Sen. Mem. Brit. Assn. Urol. Surgs. Prev: Cons. Urol. BUPA Hosp. Norwich; Cons. Urol. Norf. & Norwich Hosp. & Cromer & Dist. Hosp.; Sen. Regist. (Surg.) St. Bart. Hosp. Lond. & Chase Farm Hosp. Enfield.

GREEN, Patricia Anne Tanya Brockwell Centre, Brockwell Centre, Northumbrian Road, Cramlington NE23 1XZ Tel: 01670 733700 Fax: 01670 590606; 2 Highbury, West Jesmond, Newcastle upon Tyne NE2 3BX — MB BS 1984 Newc.; MRCGP 1988; DRCOG 1987.

GREEN, Patrick Gordon 34 Church Street, Oswestry SY11 2SP — LMSSA 1948 Lond. (St. Mary's) Med. Off. OsW.ry & Dist. Hosp.; Clin. Asst. (Geriat.) Robt. Jones & Agnes Hunt Orthop. Hosp. OsW.ry. Socs: Brit. Geriat. Soc. Prev: Maj. RAMC; Ho. Surg. City & Marston Green Matern. Hosps. Birm.

GREEN, Paul Nicholas 21 Kale Close, Ashton Park, West Kirby, Wirral CH48 3LE — MB ChB 1982 Liverp.

GREEN, Paul William (retired) 14 The Common, Evington, Leicester LE5 6EA — MB ChB 1952 Liverp. Prev: Clin. Asst. (Psychiat.) Towers Hosp. Leicester.

GREEN, Peter Andrew The Health Centre, Rosehill, Great Ayton, Middlesbrough TS9 6BL Tel: 01642 723421 Fax: 01642 724575; 100 Newton Road, Great Ayton, Middlesbrough TS9 6DG Tel: 01642 724522 — MB BS 1986 Newc.; MRCGP 1990; DRCOG 1995. (Newc.)

GREEN, Peter Ford (retired) Samburu Cottage, Russells Green, Hooe Road, Ninfield, Battle TN33 9EH Tel: 01424 892033 Email: green@samburu.sambaru.com — MB ChB Ed. 1948. Prev: Cons. A & E Roy. Free Hosp. Lond.

GREEN, Peter Geoffrey 38 Nightingale Square, London SW12 8QN Tel: 020 8673 4494 Fax: 020 8675 9436 — MB BS 1974 Lond.; MRCS Eng. LRCP Lond. 1978; DMJ(Path) Soc. Apoth. Lond. 1990. (Lond. Hosp. Med. Coll.) Indep. Forens. Phys. Lond. Socs: Assn. Police Surg. (Chairm. Metrop. & City Gp.); Fell. Roy. Soc. Med. (Counc. Clin. Forens. Med. Sect.). Prev: Lect. (Forens. Med.) Lond. Hosp. Med. Coll.; Resid. Med. Off. Harley St. Clinic. Lond.; Regist. (Med.) Stepping Hill Hosp.

GREEN, Peter Huw The Surgery, Miller Way, Wainscott, Rochester ME2 4LP Tel: 01634 717450 — MB BS 1984 Lond.; DRCOG 1988; DCH RCP Lond. 1987.

GREEN, Peter James Central Laboratory, St Mary's Hospital, Milton Road, Portsmouth PO3 6AG — BM BCh 1969 Oxf.; MA; FRCPath 1988, M 1976. Cons. Haemat./Dir. Haemophilia Centre St. Mary's Hosp. Portsmouth.

GREEN, Peter Michael 38 Whidborne Avenue, Torquay TQ1 2PQ Tel: 01803 212613 — MB ChB 1956 Birm.; MFPHM RCP (UK) 1986; MFCM 1972; DPH Liverp. 1962. Dist. Med. Off. Torbay.; Hon. Emerit. Cons. Torbay. Prev: Dist. Community Phys. BromsGr. & Redditch Health Dist.; Dist. Community Phys. Cuckfield & Crawley Health Dist.; MOH Henley-on-Thames Municip. Boro. & RD, Thame & Bicester UDs.

GREEN, Philip Anthony Pembroke House Surgery, 1 Fortescue Road, Paignton TQ3 2DA Tel: 01803 553558 Fax: 01803 663180; Hill House, Westerland, Marldon, Paignton TQ3 1RR Tel: 01803 527771 Fax: 01803 663180 Email: pgreen143@aol.com — MB ChB 1973 Bristol; FRCGP 1996, M 1986; DRCOG 1977; DCH Eng. 1976. (Bristol) Chairm. Torbay PCG.

GREEN, Philip Charles (retired) The Grove, South St., Colyton EX24 6ER Tel: 01297 551013 Fax: 01297 551013 Email: greenthegrove@ukonline.co.uk — MB BChir Camb. 1958; MA Camb. 1955; LMSSA Lond. 1955; MRCGP 1979. Prev: GP Trainer.

GREEN, Philippa Mary 18 Whitbarrow Road, Lymm WA13 9AF — MB BS 1986 Lond.; DFFP Lond. 1990; Dip. GU Med. Lond. 1995. Clin. Asst. (Genitourin. Med.) Rochdale; Clin. Med. Off. (Family Plann.) Rochdale.

GREEN, Phillippa Jane 20 Newbridge Hill, Bath BA1 3PU — MB BChir 1986 Camb.; BA, MB BChir Camb. 1986; DGM 1996; DFFP 1997; MRCGP 1997. Community Hosp. GP Paulton Memor. Hosp. Bristol. Prev: GP Regist. Gt. Pulteney St. Bath; SHO Rotat. Bath.

GREEN, Phyllis Ruth Headley House, 55 Rayens Cross Road, Long Ashton, Bristol BS41 9DY Tel: 01275 392134 Fax: 01275 394576; 55 Rayens Cross Road, Long Ashton, Bristol BS41 9DY Tel: 01275 392134 — MB ChB 1976 Bristol; DRCOG 1978.

GREEN, Rachel Clare 246 Forest Road, Loughborough LE11 3HX Tel: 01509 239687 — MB ChB 1997 Birm. (Birmingham) GP VTS Dudley Gp. of Hosps., SHO Med. Wordsley Hosp. Stourbridge. Socs: MDU. Prev: Ho. Off. Surg. Worcester Roy. Infirm.; Ho. Off. Med. Russells Hall Hosp.

GREEN, Rachel Helen Ann 11 Braid Crescent, Morningside, Edinburgh EH10 6AX — MB ChB 1982 Aberd.; BMedBiol Aberd. 1979, MB ChB 1982; MRCP (UK) 1985.

GREEN, Raymond George Hugh Templepatrick Surgery, 80 Castleton, Templepatrick, Ballyclare BT39 0AZ Tel: 028 9443 2202 Fax: 028 9443 3707 — MB BCh BAO 1974 Belf.; MICGP 1988; Dip. Occ. Med. RCP Lond. 1997; Cert. Av. Med. 1990.

GREEN, Rebecca Mary Tel: 023 8079 4015; 28 Raymond Road, Southampton SO15 5AL Tel: 023 8023 1314 — MB ChB 1993 Bristol; BSc 1990; MRCP II Lond. 1996. (Bristol) Specialist Regist. (Radiol.) Soton. Gen. Hosp. Socs: Roy. Coll. of Radiologists; Brit. Med. Assn.

GREEN, Professor Richard Gender Identity Clinic, Department of Psychiatry, Charing Cross Hospital, Fulham Palace Road, London W6 8RF Tel: 020 8846 1394 Fax: 020 8846 1599 Email: richardgreen@ic.ac.uk — MD Johns Hopkins Univ. USA 1961; FRCPsych 1997, M 1995; JD Yale 1987. (Johns Hopkins) Cons. Psychiat. Gender Identity Clinic Imperial Coll. Med.; Vis. Prof. Imperial Coll. Med.; Sen. Research Fell. Inst. Criminol. Univ. Camb.; Mem. Amer. Bd. Psychiat. & Neurol. 1969. Socs: BMA; RSM; Fell. Roy. Med. Soc. Prev: Emerit. Prof. Psychiat. Univ. Calif., Los Angeles.

GREEN, Richard Arthur Donnington Health Centre, 1 Henley Avenue, Oxford OX4 4DH Tel: 01865 771313; 14 Beech Road, Headington, Oxford OX3 7RR Tel: 01865 764776 — MB BS 1986 Lond.; MA Oxf. 1983; MRCGP 1990; DRCOG 1990; Cert. Family Plann. JCC 1990. (St. Bart's London) Vis. Med. Off. Warwick Hse. Social Servs. Home for Childr.; Med. Off. Linden Unit for Continuing Care.

GREEN, Richard Charles Lister 78 Ormond Avenue, Hampton TW12 2RX — MB BCh BAO 1992 NUI; LRCPS & I 1992.

GREEN, Richard James 50 Mount Pleasant, Newcastle ST5 1DP — MB ChB 1997 Birm.

GREEN, Richard John, TD (retired) 1 Mount Pleasant Road, Alverstoke, Gosport PO12 2HP Tel: (023) 9258 7211 Fax: (023) 9258 7211 — MB BS Lond. 1960; MRCS Eng. LRCP Lond. 1960. Prev: GP Waterlooville.

GREEN, Richard Kenneth Penny's Hill Practice, St Mary's Road, Ferndown BH22 9HB Tel: 01202 897200 Fax: 01202 877753; 64 Wesley Road, Highland Park, Colehill, Wimborne BH21 2QD Tel: 01202 883283 — MB BS 1973 Lond. (Guy's)

GREEN, Robert William Health Centre, Minniecroft, Burnham, Slough SL1 7DE Tel: 01628 605333 Fax: 01628 663743; 9 Dawes East Road, Burnham, Slough SL1 8BT Tel: 01628 602210 — MB ChB 1967 St. And.; MRCGP 1976; DObst RCOG 1971. GP Trainer Windsor VTS. Socs: (Ex-Pres.) Windsor & Dist. Med. Soc. Prev:

Trainee GP Stratford-upon-Avon VTS; GP Represen. RCSP Sports Counc. Fitness & Health Advis. Gp.

GREEN, Rodney Irwin (retired) Coed Duon, Tremeirchion, St Asaph LL17 0UH Tel: 01745 730254 — MD 1957 Liverp.; MB ChB 1949; FRCR 1975; DMRD Eng. 1953, Liverp. 1953. Prev: Cons. Radiol. Clwyd HA.

GREEN, Roger 105 Heaton Park Road, Manchester M9 0QQ Tel: 0161 795 9983 — MB ChB 1965 Sheff. (Sheff.) Prof. Physiol. Univ. Manch.; Dean Med. Sch. Socs: BMA; Phys. Soc. Prev: Reader (Physiol.) Univ. Manch.; Research Assoc. (Physiol.) Yale Univ.; Ho. Surg. & Ho. Phys. Roy. Hosp. Sheff.

GREEN, Roger Ernest, MBE, Maj. Retd. 14 Overnhill Road, Bristol BS16 5DN; 20 Newbridge Hill, Bath BA1 3PU Tel: 01225 315765 — MB ChB 1982 Leeds; MRCGP 1987; DRCOG 1989; DCCH 1988. Police Surg.; Clin. Asst., learning difficulties. Prev: Regtl. Med. Off. 2nd Roy. Tank Regt.; Med. Off. MRS Rheindahlen; SHO (O & G) BMH Rinteln.

GREEN, Roger Leonard, TD 8 Lynwood Chase, Bracknell RG12 2JT — MB ChB 1958 Leeds; MFOM RCP Lond. 1979; DAvMed Eng. 1969. (Leeds) Authorised Med. Examr. Civil Aviat. Auth. UK Federal Aviat. Admin.USA & Austral. Civil Aviat. Auth.; Lt. Col. RAMC(V). Socs: Fell. Aerospace Med. Assn. Prev: Princip. Med. Off. Brit. Airways; Cas. Off. Gen. Infirm. Leeds; Med. Off. RAF.

GREEN, Ronald Alan (retired) Fordside, Hovis Mill Lane, Halstead CO9 3AL Tel: 01787 60281 Fax: 01787 469329 — MRCS Eng. LRCP Lond. 1945; MA Camb. 1944, MB BChir 1945; FFA RCS Eng. 1954; DA Eng. 1951. Hon. Cons. Roy. Free Hosp. Lond. Prev: Cons. Anaesth. St. Geo. Hosp., Sydenham Childr. Hosp., Milford Chest Hosp. & Roy. Free Hosp. Lond.

GREEN, Rosalind Margaret No 3 OPD Chest Clinic, Blackburn Royal Infirmary, Infirmary Road, Blackburn BB2 3LR — MB BS 1990 Lond.; BSc (1st cl. Hons.) Experim. Path. Univ. Lond. 1987; MRCP (UK) 1993. Sen. Regist. (Respirat. & Gen. Med.) Wythenshawe Hosp. Manch. Prev: Research Regist. (Respirat. Med.) NW Lung Centre Manch.; Regist. (Gen. & Chest Med.) Birm. Heartlands Hosp.

GREEN, Rosalind Victoria Dock Cottage, Dock Lane, Beaulieu, Brockenhurst SO42 7YH — MB BS 1996 Newc.

GREEN, Rosemary St Peters Medical Centre, Colbeck Road, West Harrow, Harrow HA1 4BS Tel: 020 8864 4868 — MB ChB 1974 Sheff.; DRCOG 1976.

GREEN, Ruth Amanda Rachel The Royal National Orthopaedic Hospital, Brockeley Hill, Stanmore HA7 4LP Tel: 0208 909 5443 Fax: 020 954 0281; 64 Eastbury Road, Northwood HA6 3AR Tel: 01923 826965 Email: ruth.green@ucl.ac.uk — MB BS Lond. 1988; MRCP (UK) 1993; FRCR 1996. (King's Coll. Sch. Med. & Dent.) Cons. Radiol. Roy. Nat. Orthop. Hosp., Stanmore, Middlx. Socs: Eur. Soc. Skeletal Radiol.; Brit. Soc. Skeletal Radiol.; Roy. Coll. of Radiol. Prev: Sen. Regist. (Radiol.) John Radcliffe Hosp. Oxf.; Sen. Regist. (Radiol), Gt. Ormond St. Hosp. Lond.; Regist. (Radiol), St.Geo.Hosp.Lond.

GREEN, Ruth Helen 71 Park Street, Beeston, Nottingham NG9 1DH — MB ChB 1993 Manch.; MRCP (UK) 1996. (Manch.) Specialist Regist. (Gen. & Respirat. Med.) P'boro Dist. Hosp. Prev: SHO (Med.) Countess of Chester Hosp.

GREEN, Ruth Margaret 14 Meadowcroft Road, Wirral CH47 6BG — BChir 1994 Camb.

GREEN, Samatha Nichole Appleby, Pilley Hill, Pilley, Lymington SO41 5QF — MB ChB 1997 Leic.

GREEN, Sarah Rebecca 21 Southedge Close, Hipperholme, Halifax HX3 8DW — MB ChB 1997 Manch. SHO (Paediat.) Roy. Oldham Hosp. Prev: SHO, Emerg. Med., Hope Hosp Salford.

GREEN, Sheila Alice Community Health Clinic, Blackhall Unit, Westmorland General Hospital, Kendal LA9 7RG Tel: 01539 727564; Southwold, 16 Woodland Road, Ulverston LA12 0DX Tel: 01229 581185 — MB BS 1963 Lond.; MB BS (Hons.) Lond. 1963; MRCS Eng. LRCP Lond. 1963; MFFP 1993; DA Eng. 1965. (St. Bart.) Clin. Med. Off. (Family Plann.) S. Cumbria Community & Ment. Health NHS Trust. Socs: BMA. Prev: Clin. Med. Off. (Family Plann.) Gt. Yarmouth & Waveney HA; Clin. Asst. (Anaesth.) Soton. Gen. Hosp.; SCMO (Family Plann.) Winchester HA.

GREEN, Sheila Margaret (retired) Buckhurst Lodge, Best Beech, Wadhurst TN5 6JR Tel: 01892 782094 — MB ChB 1958 Glas.; DObst RCOG 1960. Prev: Asst. GP CrowBoro.

GREEN, Simon Lomas Monkspath Surgery, 27 Farmhouse Way, Monkspath, Shirley, Solihull B90 4EH Tel: 0121 711 1414 Fax: 0121 711 3753; Great Pinley Farm, Claverdon, Warwick CV35 8NB Email: greensimon@aol.com — MB ChB 1982 Birm.; MRCGP 1986; DRCOG 1985. Princip. GP Solihull.; Hon. Clin. Lect. Birm. Med. Sch. Socs: Chairm. Solihull Drugs Action Team. Prev: Trainee GP S. Birm. HA VTS.

GREEN, Siobhan Johanna Stable Cottage, Hollybush Hill, Stoke Poges, Slough SL2 4QN; Medical Department, Wexham Park Hospital, Slough SL2 4HL Tel: 01753 633000 — MB BS 1996 Lond.; BSc; MRCP. (Charing Cross & Westminster) Med. SHO Wexham Pk. Hosp. Slough.

GREEN, Stella Belinda Jane The White Lodge, Kings Road, Thame OX9 3JJ Tel: 01844 212360 Fax: 01844 217145 — MB BS 1987 Lond.; MRCGP 1991; DRCOG 1989. Prev: Asst. GP, Old Cross Keys Surg., P.s RisBoro.; Trainee GP Aylesbury VTS.

GREEN, Stephen Ashley Medical Defence Union Ltd., 192 Altrincham Road, Manchester M22 4RZ Tel: 0161 428 1234 Fax: 0161 491 3301; Underwood, Queen's Road, Kendal LA9 4PH Tel: 01539 722824 — MB BS 1975 Lond.; BSc (Hons.) Lond. 1972; MRCP (UK) 1978; MRCS Eng. LRCP Lond. 1975; MRCGP 1981. (Guy's) Head Risk Managem. MDU. Socs: Anglo-French Med. Soc. Prev: SHO New Cross Hosp. Lond.; Ho. Surg. Greenwich Dist. Hosp.; Ho. Phys. Lewisham Hosp.

GREEN, Stephen David Rigden St Lukes Hospital, Little Horton Lane, Bradford BD5 0NA Tel: 01274 365455 Fax: 01274 365333; 14 Rockwood Road, Calverley, Pudsey LS28 5AA Tel: 0113 257 4195 Email: greens@thecafe.co.uk — MB ChB 1974 Dundee; BSc (Med. Sci.) St. And. 1971; FRCP Ed. 1992; MRCP (UK) 1979; DTM & H Antwerp 1980; FFCRCPCH. (St andrews & Dundee) Cons. Paediat. St. Lukes Hosp. Bradford. Socs: Fell. Roy. Coll. (Paediat. & Child Health); Yorks. Paediat. Soc. Prev: Paediat. Baptist Miss. Soc. IME, Kimpese, D.R.Congo.

GREEN, Stephen Mark 58 Bath Terrace, Gosforth, Newcastle upon Tyne NE3 1UJ — MB BS 1993 Newc.; FRSC (Eng.) 1998.

GREEN, Stephen Thomas St. Johns Medical Centre, High Street, Walsall Wood, Walsall WS9 9LP Tel: 01543 364500 Fax: 01543 364510; 178 Erdington Road, Aldridge, Walsall WS9 0RZ Tel: 01922 455903 — MB ChB 1971 Birm. (Birmingham)

GREEN, Stephen Thomas Department of Infection and Tropical Medicine, Royal Hallamshire Hospital, Sheffield S10 2JF Tel: 0114 271 1900 Fax: 0114 275 3061 — MB ChB 1982 Dundee; BSc Dund 1978, MD (Commend.) 1988; MRCP (UK) 1985; DTM & H RCP Lond. 1996; 1996 (Glasgow) FRCP; (London) FRCP 1999. (Dundee) Cons. Phys. (Infec. Dis. & Trop. Med.) Roy. Hallamsh. Hosp. Sheff.Teachg. Hosp.s NHS Trust; Hon. Sen.. Lect. (Med.) Univ. Sheff. Socs: Brit. Infect. Soc.; Internat. Soc. of Travel Med. Prev: Sen. Regist. (Gen. Med. & Infec. Dis.) Ruchill & Stobhill Hosps. Glas.; Regist. & SHO Rotat. (Gen. Med.) Stobhill Gen. Hosp. Glas.; Ho. Off. (Profess. Med. & Surg. Units) Ninewells Hosp. Dundee.

GREEN, Stuart Gary 126 Osbaldeston Road, London N16 6NJ — MB BS 1989 Lond.; MRCGP 1993; T(GP) 1993.

GREEN, Stuart Harvey Birmingham Children's Hospital, Institute of Child Health, 4th Floor Clinical Research Block, Whittall St., Birmingham B4 6DH; 45 Moorcroft Road, Moseley, Birmingham B13 8LT Tel: 0121 449 2128 — MA, MB Camb. 1964, BChir 1963; FRCP Lond. 1983, M 1967; MRCS Eng. LRCP Lond. 1963. (Middlx.) Sen. Lect. (Paediat.) Inst. Child Health Univ. Birm. Socs: Sec. Brit. Paediat. Neurol. Assn.; Brit. Paediat. Assn. Prev: Ho. Phys. Hosp. Sick Childr. Gt. Ormond St. Lond.; Asst. Ho. Phys. Nat. Hosp. Nerv. Dis. Qu. Sq. Lond.; Fell. (Paediat. Neurol.) Lexington, USA.

GREEN, Susan Park House Surgery, 55 Higher Parr Street, St Helens WA9 1BP Tel: 01744 23705 Fax: 01744 454601 — MB ChB 1983 Liverp.

GREEN, Susan Catherine 21 Regency Court, Park Cl, London E9 7TP — MB BS 1997 Lond. Med. SHO, OldCh. Hosp, Romford.

GREEN, Susan Elizabeth Freeman Road Hospital, Newcastle upon Tyne NE7 7DN Tel: 0191 284 3111; 43A Leazes Terrace, Newcastle upon Tyne NE1 4LZ Tel: 0191 222 0938 — MB BS 1987 Newc.; MB BS (2nd cl. Hons.) Newc. 1987; FRCS Eng. 1992. Sen. Regist. (Surg.) Freeman Hosp. Prev: Sen. Regist. S. Cleveland Hosp.; Regist. Dryburn Hosp.; Research Regist. (Surg.) Univ. Newc. u. Tyne.

GREEN, Susan Margaret The Culverhay Surgery, Culverhay, Wotton-under-Edge GL12 7LS Tel: 01453 843252; Avondale, Dye

House Yard, Kingswood, Wotton-Under-Edge GL12 8RA Tel: 01453 843309 — MB ChB 1978 Leeds; LF HOM Bristol 1998; Dip. Obst. Auckland 1980.

GREEN, Susan Mary Taylor and Partners, Shirehampton Health Centre, Pembroke Road, Shirehampton, Bristol BS11 9SB Tel: 0117 916 2233 Fax: 0117 930 8246; 9 Westbury Park, Bristol BS6 7JB Tel: 0117 974 3405 — MB ChB 1985 Bristol; MRCGP 1993; DRCOG 1992; DFFP 1996; DCH RCP Lond. 1991. (Bristol Univ.)

GREEN, Tana 11 Bramwith Road, Sheffield S11 7EZ — MB ChB 1993 Sheff.

GREEN, Thomas Henry Hayes (retired) 16 Links View, Wallasey CH45 0NQ Tel: 0151 639 5958 — MB ChB 1947 Liverp.; FRCGP 1972, M 1952; MPS 1935.

GREEN, Mr Timothy Piers Leicester Royal Infirmary, Infirmary Square, Leicester LE1 5WW Tel: 0116 258 6241 Fax: 0116 258 7668; 1 Manor Road (Extension), Oadby, Leicester LE2 4FG Tel: 0116 258 8172 — MB ChB 1982 Birm.; FRCS (Orth.) 1994; FRCS Ed. 1987. (Birmingham) Cons. Orthop. Surg. Leicester Gen. Hosp. & Leicester Roy. Infirm. Socs: Brit. Scoliosis Soc.; Brit. Orthopaedic Research Soc. Prev: Sen. Regist. (Orthop.) Leicester Roy. Infirm.; Spinal Research Fell. Stoke-on-Trent; Regist. (Orthop.) United Bristol Hosps. & Gloucester Roy. Hosp.

GREEN, William John (retired) 5 Tullis Close, Castlefields, Stafford ST16 1AX Tel: 01785 228947 — MB ChB Sheff. 1958; FFPHM 1989; FFCM 1981, M 1973; DPH Manch. 1970. Prev: Cons. Pub. Health Med. Yorks. RHA.

GREEN, Mr William Thomas Eye Department, Queen Alexandra Hospital, Cosham, Portsmouth PO6 3LY Tel: 023 92 286933 Fax: 023 92 286440 — MB BS 1982 Lond.; BSc Physiol. Lond. 1979; FRCS Eng. 1988; FRCOphth 1989; DO RCS Eng.1986. Cons. Ophth. Qu. Alexandra Hosp. Portsmouth. Prev: Sen. Regist. (Ophth.) St. Thos. Hosp. & Moorfields Eye Hosp. Lond.

GREEN-ARMYTAGE, Gretel Kathryn Holsworthy Health Centre, Western Road, Holsworthy EX22 6DH Tel: 01409 253692 Fax: 01409 254184 — MB ChB 1991 Leic.; Dip Paediat. Auckland 1995; DRCOG 1997. (Leics.) Dip. Paediat. Auckland 1995.

GREEN HEMMINGS, Claudine Elizabeth 47 Oldstead Grove, Bolton BL3 4XW — MB BS 1990 West Indies.

GREENACRE, Judith Anne Tawelfan, LLanegwad, Nantgaredig, Carmarthen SA32 7NJ Tel: 01267 290578 — MB BCh 1980 Wales; MFPHM RCP (UK) 1992; DCH RCP Lond. 1987. Cons. Pub. Health Med. E. Dyfed & Pembrokesh. HA.

GREENALL, The Hon. Gilbert, CBE Bromesberrow Place, Ledbury HR8 1RZ Tel: 01531 650202 Fax: 01531 650056 — MB ChB 1988 Bristol; MBA Insead 1979. Cons. Adviser Conflict and Humanitarian Dept.., Dept. for Internat. Developm.; UN Disaster Assessm. & Coordination Team (OCHA). Prev: Staff Grade (A & E) Cheltenham Gen. Hosp.

GREENALL, Mr Michael John c/o John Radcliffe Hospital, Department of Surgery, Headington, Oxford OX3 9DU — MB ChB 1972 Leeds; BSc Leeds 1969, ChM 1983, MB ChB 1972; FRCS Ed. 1976; FRCS Eng. 1977. Cons. Gen. Surg. & Surgic. Oncol. Oxf. Radcliffe Hosp. NHS Trust; Edit. Bd. Europ. Jl. Surg. Oncol. Socs: Comm. Mem. Brit. Assn. Surg. Oncol. Prev: Fell. Surgic. Oncol. Memor. Sloan Kettering Cancer Centre, New York, USA; Sen. Regist. (Gen. Surg.) Oxon. AHA (T); Regist. Rotat. United Leeds Hosps.

GREENAN, Joseph 7 The Park, Scalby, Scarborough YO13 0PY Tel: 01723 351073 — MB BCh BAO 1950 NUI; FRCA 1993; FFA RCS Eng. 1959; DA Eng. 1954; FFA RCSI 1962; DA RCPSI 1954. (NUI) Socs: Ex-Pres. Assn. Dent. Anaesths. GB & Irel.; Fell. Assn. Anaesths. GB & Irel. Prev: Cons. Anaesth. ScarBoro. Gp. Hosps.; Sen. Regist. (Anaesth.) United Manch. Hosps.; Regist. Anaesth. Selly Oak Gp. Hosps.

GREENAWAY, Brian James Ilford Medical Centre, 61-63 Cleveland Road, Ilford IG1 1EE Tel: 020 8514 7761/8478 0367 Fax: 020 8478 4448; 9 Stewards Green Road, Epping CM16 7BX Tel: 01992 572576 — MB BS 1978 Lond.; MRCGP 1984; DRCOG 1981. (St. Bart.) Socs: (Treas.) Ilford Med. Soc. Prev: Trainee GP Ilford VTS; Ho. Off. Whipps Cross Hosp.; Ho. Phys. Rochford Hosp.

GREENAWAY, John Richard 19 Cloister Garth, South Gosforth, Newcastle upon Tyne NE7 7LW Tel: 0191 213 5911 Fax: 0191 213 5911 Email: jrg@greenaway.freeserve.co.uk — MB BS 1990 Newc.; MRCP (UK) 1994. Specialist Regist. (Gastroenterol. & Gen. Internal Med.)Freeman Rd. Hosp., Newc. Prev: Research Regist. (Gastroenterol.) S. Tees Acute NHS Trust Middlesbrough; Specialist Regist. (Gastroenterol. & Gen. Internal Med.) Cumbld. Infirm. Carlisle.

GREENAWAY, Michael Edward Wellway Medical Group, The Surgery, Wellway, Morpeth NE61 6TB Tel: 01670 517300 Fax: 01670 511931 — MB BS 1992 Newc.; MRCGP 1996. (Newc.) GP Morpeth, N.d.

GREENAWAY, Timothy James Alexandra Practice, 365 Wilbraham Road, Manchester M16 8NG Tel: 0161 860 4400 Fax: 0161 860 7324 — MB ChB 1981 Manch.; FRCP 2001; MRCP (UK) 1987; MRCGP 1989; DRCOG 1988; DCH RCP Lond. 1984. (Manchester) Gen. Pract. Princip. Prev: SHO (Paediat. & O & G) Wigan HA; SHO (Paediat.) Roy. Manch. Childr. Hosp.; Tutor (Gen. Pract.) Centr. Manch.

GREENAWAY, Wilman Evered 75 Mere Road, Blackpool FY3 9AU — MB BS 1983 W. Indies.

GREENBAUM, Mr Adam Raphael Department of Burns & Plastic Surgery, South Manchester University Hospitals NHS Trust, Withington Hospital, Nell Lane, West Didsbury, Manchester M20 2LR Tel: 0161 291 4075 — MB BS 1987 Lond.; PhD Lond. 1995; MBA Open Univ. 1994; FRCS Eng. 1996. (St. Bart. Hosp.) Specialist Regist. (Plastic Surg.) S. Manch. Univ. Hosp. NHS Trust. Socs: RSM; BAPS. Prev: SHO (Plastic Surg.) Lister Hosp. Stevenage; SHO (Plastic Surg.) St. And. Hosp. Billericay.

GREENBAUM, Agnes Sara Sheepwood, The Ridgeway, Mill Hill, London NW7 1QU — MB ChB 1964 Leeds. (Leeds)

GREENBAUM, Jonathan David The Cottage, Village St., Edwalton, Nottingham NG12 4AB Tel: 0115 974 6066 — MB ChB 1995 Manch.; BSc (Biomedical Scs.) Manch.; MRCP (UK) 1999. (Manch. Univ.) SHO (Anaesth.), Roy. Bolton Hosp. Prev: SHO (Med.), Manch. Roy. Infirm.

GREENBAUM, Louis (retired) 43 Ringmore Rise, London SE23 3DE — MRCS Eng. LRCP Lond. 1936. Prev: Resid. Med. Off. Albert Dock Hosp. Lond.

GREENBAUM, Robert Anthony Cardiology Department, Barnet Hospital, Barnet EN5 6DJ Tel: 020 8216 5490 Fax: 020 8449 2334; Cardiology Department, The Royal Free Hospital, Hampstead, London NW3 2QG Tel: 020 7794 0500 — MB BS 1974 Lond.; BSc (1st cl. Hons. Physiol.) Lond. 1971, MD 1980; FRCP Lond. 1995; FESC 1994. (Univ. Coll. Hosp.) Hon. Sen. Lect. Univ. Coll. Lond. Socs: Fell Roy. Soc. Med.; Brit. Cardiac Soc. Prev: Sen. Regist. (Cardiol.) Harefield Hosp. & Roy. Free Hosp. Lond.; Brit. Heart Foundat. Research Fell., Hon. Regist. & SHO (Cardiol.) Brompton Hosp. Lond.; Regist. (Cardiol.) Lond. Chest Hosp.

GREENBAUM, Ronald (retired) Department of Anaesthesia, The Middlesex Hospital, Mortimer St., London W1T 3AA — MB ChB 1958 Manch.; FFA RCS Eng. 1964; DObst RCOG 1960. Prev: Cons. Anaesth. Univ. Coll. Hosps. Lond.

GREENBERG, Maurice Philip Private Patients Wing, University College London Hospital, 25 Grafton Way, London WC1E 6DB Tel: 020 7383 7911 Fax: 020 7380 9816; Student Counselling Service, University College London, Gower St, London WC1E 6BT Tel: 020 7391 1487 Fax: 020 7419 7023 Email: m.greenberg@ucl.ac.uk — MB BS 1971 Lond.; MPhil Lond. 1983, Acad. Dip. Biochem. Lond. 1967; FRCP Lond. 1995; MRCP (UK) 1974; FRCPsych 1991, M 1979. (Lond. Hosp.) Cons. Psychiat. Univ. Coll. Lond. Hosp.; Cons. Psychiat. Roy. Nat. Throat, Nose & Ear Hosp. Lond.; Head Stud. Counselling Serv. UCL. Prev: Psychiat. Adviser Univ. Coll. Lond.; Sen. Regist. Bethlem Roy. & Maudsley Hosps. Lond.; Lect. & Hon. Sen. Regist. St. Bart. Hosp. Lond.

GREENBERG, Morris 74 North End Road, London NW11 7SY Tel: 020 8458 2376 — MB BS 1953 Lond.; FRCP Lond. 1977, M 1958; FFOM RCP Lond. 1982, M 1979. (Univ. Coll. Hosp.) Sen. Cons. Edr. Amer. Jl. Indust. Med.; Hon. Lect. Brompton Hosp. Lond. Socs: Fell. Roy. Statistical Soc.; Coun.lor & Fell. Collegium Ramazzini.; New York Acad. Sci. Prev: Vis. Prof. Mt.. Sinai New York, USA.; Sen. Research Fell. Nat. Int. Imperial Coll. Sch. Med.; Cons. In Pub. Health, Demography & Health Div. O.N.S.

GREENBERG, Neil 101 Dunvegan Drive, Lordswood, Southampton SO16 8DB — BM 1993 Soton.

GREENBURGH, Anthony Leon 73 Eaton Place [illegible] SW1X 8DR Tel: 020 7235 [illegible] LRCPI & LM, LRSCI & LM 1956; LRCPI & LM [illegible] & LM 1956; MA Oxf. 1956; MRCGP. Prev: Ho.

Phys. Qu. Eliz. Hosp. Childr. Lond.; SHO (O & G) Newmarket Gen. Hosp.

GREENBURY, Enid The Surgery, 153 Park Road, London N8 8JJ Tel: 020 8340 7940 Fax: 020 8348 1530 — MRCS Eng. LRCP Lond. 1975; BSc (Hons.) Lond. 1972, MB BS 1975.

GREENE, Alice Mary Fourth Floor Flat, 86 Harley St., London W1N 1AE Tel: 020 7580 4188 Fax: 020 7580 6466 Email: algreene@globalnet.co.uk — MB BCh BAO 1977 NUI; BA NUI 1977; DIP AP 1997; DIP PSET 1993; MFHom 1982; MRCGP 1981; DObst RCPI 1980; DCH NUI 1980. (TC Dub.) Cons. Homoeop. Phys. Lond.; Lect. (Homoeop.) Roy. Lond. Homoeop. Hosp.; Lect. (Homoeop. Phys.) Teach. Gp Oxf.; Lect. Brit. Autogenic Soc. Ondon. Socs: Fell.of Brit. Autogenic Soc.; Fac. Homoeop. (Ordinary Mem.); Roy. Coll. Gen. Pract. Prev: Regist. (Med.) Roy. Lond. Homoeop. Hosp.

GREENE, Aubrey 19 Woodhouse Road, Davyhulme, Urmston, Manchester M41 7DA — MB ChB 1953 Manch.; MRCS Eng. LRCP Lond. 1956; MRCGP 1973. (Manch.) Socs: Manch. Med.-Leg. Soc. & Stretford Med. Soc. Prev: GP Manch.; Med. Off. RAF; Ho. Surg. & Ho. Phys. Crumpsall Hosp. Manch.

GREENE, Mr Damian Raymond John Department of Surgery, City Hospitals Sunderland NHS Trust, Kayll Road, Sunderland SR4 7TP; 25 West Avenue, Gosforth, Newcastle upon Tyne NE3 4ES Tel: 0191 284 5303 — MB BCh BAO 1983 NUI; ChM NUI 1992; LRCPSI 1983; FRCS (Urol.) 1995; FRCSI 1987. Cons. Urol. City Hosps. NHS Trust Sunderland. Socs: Brit. Assn. Urol. Surgs. & Irish Soc. Urol. Prev: Sen. Regist. Mater Hosp. Dub.; Post Doctoral Fell. (Urol.) Baylor Coll. Houston, Texas.

GREENE, Daphne Margaret Tel: 028 9260 3090 Fax: 028 9250 1310 Email: daphne.greene@lisburncgin-i.nhs.uk; 91 Lisban Road, Saintfield, Ballynahinch BT24 7BT Tel: 01846 638548 Email: daphne.gilmore@lineone.net — MB BCh BAO 1971 Dub.; BA Dub. 1971. (T.C. Dub.) GP Lisburn, N. Irel. Prev: Ho. Off. Ulster Hosp. Dundonald.

GREENE, John Davidson Webster Department of Neurology, Western General Hospital, Crewe Road, Edinburgh EH4 2XU Tel: 0131 537 1000 — MB ChB 1987 Glas.; MD Glas. 1996; MRCP (UK) 1991. (Glas.) Specialist Regist. (Neurol.) W.ern Gen. Hosp. Edin. Socs: Assn. Brit. Neurol.; Brit. Neuropsychiat. Assn. Prev: Clin. Research Fell. (Neurol.) Inst. of Neurol. Lond.; Research Regist. (Neurol.) Addenbrooke's Hosp. Camb.; Regist. (Neurol.) Inst. of Neurol. Sci. Glas.

GREENE, John Richard Timothy MRC Centre For Synaptic Plasticity, Dept. of Anatomy, School of medical Science, University of Bristol, Bristol BS8 1TD — MB BS (Distinc. Clin. Pharmacol.) Lond. 1991; PhD Pharmacol. Lond. 1989; BSc 1986 London. (Char. Cross & Westm. Med. Sch. Lond.) Sen. Lect. MRC Centre for Synaptic Plasticity, Univ. of Bristol. Socs: Physiol. Soc.; Bri. Pharmacol. Soc.; Soc. Neurosc. (USA). Prev: Lect. in BioMed. Sci., Univ. of Sheff.; Med. Res. Counc. Career Developm. Award Holder Dept. Pharmacol. Univ. of Oxf.; Wellcome Trust Clin. Ment. Health Train. Fell. Univ. Oxf.

GREENE, Josephine Frances 95 Poulton Crescent, Woolston, Warrington WA1 4QP — MB ChB 1988 Birm. Trainee GP Liverp. Prev: SHO (Cas.) Dudley Rd. Hosp. Birm.; Ho. Off. Dudley Rd. Hosp. Birm. & New Cross Hosp. Wolverhampton.

GREENE, Karen Julie Fairladies, 102 Main St., St Bees CA27 0AD Tel: 01946 824302 — MB BS 1988 Lond.; DA 1993. (CXWMS) Staff Grade (Anaes); Clin. Asst. (A & E). Prev: SHO Rotat. (Anaesth.) Derby & Nottm.

GREENE, Professor Keith Richard Nuffield hospital, Derriford Road, Plymouth PL6 8BG Tel: 01752 774146 Fax: As Phone Email: k.greene@prg.plym.ac.uk — MB BS 1969 Lond.; DM Soton. 1984; MRCS Eng. LRCP Lond. 1969; FRCOG 1990, M 1976. (King's Coll. Hosp.) Cons. O & G Plymouth Hosps.; Director Perinatal Research Gp.; PostGrad. Med. Sch.; Univ. of Plymouth. Socs: Materno-fetal Med. Soc. Prev: Lect. & Sen. Regist. Soton. & Winchester Health Dists.; Research Fell. Nuffield Inst. Med. Research & Nuffield Dept. Obst. Oxf..; Regist. (O & G) Brighton Gp. Hosps.

GREENE, Linda Anne 82 Popes Lane, London W5 4NT — MB ChB 1990 Bristol.

GREENE, Malcolm John (retired) 21 Crossfield Road, Hale, Altrincham WA15 8DU — MB ChB Bristol 1963; FFA RCS Eng. 1969; DA Eng. 1965. Cons. Anaesth. Withington Hosp. Manch. Prev: Sen. Regist. Manch. Roy. Infirm.

GREENE, Marie Louise 39 Beeleigh Link, Chelmsford CM2 6PH — MB BCh BAO 1978 NUI; MRCPI 1981.

GREENE, Mr Michael Keith Fairladies, 102 Main St., St Bees CA27 0AD Tel: 01946 824302 — MB BS 1981 Lond.; FRCS Ed. 1986. Cons. A & E Med. Cumbria. Socs: Brit. Assn. Accid. & Emerg. Med. Prev: Regist. (A & E) Nottm. Univ. Hosp.; Regist. (Gen. Surg.) Bedford Gen. Hosp.; SHO Rotat. (Surg.) Char. Cross. Hosp. Lond.

GREENE, Stephen Alan Tayside Instituet Child Health, Ninewells Hospital & Medical School, Dundee DD1 9SY Tel: 01382 660111 Fax: 01382 633849 Email: s.a.greene@dundee.ac.uk — MB BS 1973 Lond.; FRCP Ed. 1991; MRCP (UK) 1976. Sen. Lect. Chiild Health and Cons. Paediat. Endocrinol. Ninewells Hosp. & Med. Sch. Dundee. Prev: Wellcome Lect. Dept. Paediat. & Metab. Med. Guy's Hosp. Lond.; Research Fell. John Radcliffe Hosp. Oxf.; Smith & Nephew Trav. Fell.sh. Zurich.

GREENE, William James The Medical Unit, The Manor Drive, Worcester Park KT4 7LG Tel: 020 8337 3309 Fax: 020 8335 0880; 36 Cardinal Close, Worcester Park KT4 7EH Tel: 020 8224 2769 Fax: 020 8224 2769 — MB BS 1976 Lond. (Guy's Hospital) Socs: Anglo-French Med. Soc.; Anglo-German Med. Soc.

GREENE, William Jeremy Wybrants Castle Cottage, Collins Road, Totnes TQ9 5PL Tel: 01803 863282 Email: wjgreene@clara.co.uk — MB BCh BAO Dub. 1961; FRCR 1975; FFR 1972; DMRD Eng. 1970. Cons. Radiol. Torbay Hosp. Torquay.

GREENER, John Simpson Abbey House, Cockfield, Bury St Edmunds IP30 0LB — MB BS 1966 Durh.; MSc Newc. 1968, MD 1973; FRCP Lond. 1995; MRCP (UK) 1975. (Newc.) Cons. Phys. Geriat. Med. W. Suff. Hosp. Bury St Edmonds. Prev: Sen. Regist. (Geriat. Med.) Leicester Gen. Hosp.; Research Assoc. Dept. Clin. Biochem. Univ. Newc.

GREENER, Winifred Ann Abbey House, Cockfield, Bury St Edmunds IP30 0LB — MB BS 1966 Durh.; MFFP 1993. Clin. Med. Off. Mid Anglia Community Health Trust. Socs: Assoc. Mem. Inst. Psycho-Sexual Med.

GREENFIELD, Archibald David Mant, OStJ, CBE 25 Sutton Passeys Crescent, Nottingham NG8 1BX Tel: 0115 978 2424 — MB BS 1940 Lond.; DSc Lond. 1953, MSc 1947, BSc (1st cl. Hons. Physiol.) 1937; LLD (Hon. Causa.) Nottm. 1977; DSc (Hon. Causa.) Belf. 1978; FRCP Lond. 1973, M 1968; MRCS Eng. LRCP Lond. 1940. (St Mary's) Emerit. Prof. Univ. Nottm. Socs: Hon. Mem. Physiol. Soc.; Med. Res. Soc.; Biochem. Soc. Prev: Foundat. Dean Med. Sch. & Prof. Physiol. Univ. Nottm. & Hon. Cons. Physiol. Nottm. AHA (T); Prof. Physiol. Univ. Lond. St. Mary's Hosp. Med. Sch.; Dunville Prof. Physiol. Qu. Univ. & Cons. Physiol. N.. Irel.

GREENFIELD, Janice Eleri Wirral Services for Child Health, St Catherine's Hospital, Derby Road, Birkenhead CH42 0LQ Tel: 0151 604 7364 Fax: 0151 604 7310; 5B Stanley Avenue, Birkdale, Southport PR8 4RU — MB ChB 1985 Liverp. Staff Grade (Community Paediat.) Wirral Hosps. Trust.

GREENFIELD, Maureen Ruth Clark and Partners, 20 Aitken Street, Largs KA30 8AU Tel: 01475 674545 Fax: 01475 689645 — MB ChB 1987 Dundee; MRCGP 1992; DGM RCP Lond. 1991. GP Largs. Prev: Trainee GP Whiteabbey Hosp. Belf. VTS.

GREENFIELD, Patricia Mary The Surgery, 2 Church Lane, Merton Park, London SW19 3NY; 41 Merton Hall Road, London SW19 3PR Tel: 020 8540 4500 — MB BS 1968 Lond.; MRCP (UK) 1973; MRCS Eng. LRCP Lond. 1968; DObst RCOG 1970; DCH Eng. 1971. (Roy. Free) Prev: Regist. Med. P. of Wales Hosp. Tottenham; SHO (Med.) St. Chas. Hosp. Lond.; SHO Paediat. Qu. Mary's Hosp. Carshalton.

GREENFIELD, Peter Rex (retired) Lorne House, Bellhurst Road, Robertsbridge TN32 5DW Tel: 01580 880209 — MB Camb. 1958, BChir 1957; MA Camb. 1985; Hon. FRCPCH 1996; DObst RCOG 1960. Chairm. Chaseley Trust for Severely Disabled People E.bourne; MQPM 1999 The Appeals Serv. Prev: Sen. Princip. Med. Off. DoH.

GREENFIELD, Philippa Jane Obstetrics & Gynaecology Department, Liverpool Women's Hospital, Crown St., Liverpool L8 7SS — MB BS 1996 Lond.

GREENFIELD, Raymond Michael Bere Regis Surgery, Manor Farm Road, Bere Regis, Wareham BH20 7HB Tel: 01929 471268 Fax:

01929 472098; Glebe House, Bloxworth, Wareham BH20 7EE — MB ChB 1971 Bristol; DFFP RCOG 1997.

GREENFIELD, Simon Mark Queen Elizabeth II Hospital, Howlands, Welwyn Garden City AL7 4HQ Tel: 01707 328111 — MB BS 1984 Lond.; MD Lond. 1994; MRCP (UK) 1987; FRCP 2000. (King's Coll. Hosp.) Cons. Phys. & Gastroenterol. Qu. Eliz. II & Lister Hosps. Herts. Prev: Sen. Regist. Rotat. (Gastroenterol.) Whittington Hosp. & Univ. Coll. Lond. Hosps.; Hon. Sen. Regist. (Gastroenterol.) Rayne Inst. St. Thos. Hosp. Lond.; Regist. Rotat. (Med.) St. Thos. Hosp. Lond. & Kent & Sussex Hosp. Tunbridge Wells.

GREENGRASS, Amanda Clerklands Surgery, Vicarage Lane, Horley RH6 8AR Tel: 01293 783802 Fax: 01293 823590; Tanyard Farm Cottage, Langshott, Horley RH6 9LN Tel: 01293 782684 — MB BS 1983 Lond.; DRCOG 1987; Cert. Family Plann. JCC 1987. (Char. Cross) Prev: Community Med. Off. (Paediat.) Merton & Sutton HA; Trainee GP Leatherhead VTS; SHO (O & G) W. Middlx. Univ. Hosp. Isleworth.

GREENGRASS, Sally Ruth C/o Central Sheffield Teaching, Hospital Trust, Sheffield; 24, Hardwick Crescent, Brincliffe, Sheffield S11 8WB Tel: 01708 747267 — BM BS 1987 Nottm.; BMedSci Nottm. 1985; Cert. Prescribed Equiv. Exp. JCPTGP 1994; DFFP 1994; DA (UK) 1993; DCH RCPS Glas. 1992; FRCA 1997. (Nottingham) Specialist Regist. (Anaesth.) Sheff. Prev: SHO Rotat. (Anaest.) Sheff.; GP Trainee Rugby; SHO (Anaesth.) Leicester.

GREENGROSS, Mr Mark Peter 9A Dawson Place, London W2 4TD Tel: 020 7727 5268 Email: peter.greengross@orh.amglox.nhs.uk — MB BS 1987 Lond.; MA Camb. 1988; FRCS Eng. 1992; MFPHM (UK) 1998. (London Hospital) Asst. Med. Dir., Oxf. Radcliffe Hosps. NHS Trust; Hon. Cons. in Pub. Health Med., Oxon. HA; Clin. Asst. (A & E) Oxf. Radcliffe Hosps.

GREENHALF, Mr John Owen 72 Berkeley Avenue, Reading RG1 6HY Tel: 01734 584711; Scythe House, Green Lane, Pangbourne, Reading RG8 7BG Tel: 01734 843013 — MB BS 1964 Lond.; FRCS Ed. 1969; MRCS Eng. LRCP Lond. 1964; FRCOG 1981, M 1968. (Westm.) Examr. Centr. Midw. Bd.; Cons. Obst. & Gyn. Roy. Berks. Hosp. Reading. Prev: Sen. Regist. (O & G) W.m. Hosp.; Regist. W.m. Hosp. Lond.; Regist. (O & G) Kingston Hosp.

GREENHALGH, Anne Marie East Kent Hosps. Trust,, QEQM Hospital, Ramsgate Rd, Margate CT9 4AN; Anne Court, Church Lane, Barham, Canterbury CT4 6PB — MB ChB 1976 Sheff.; FRCR 1982. Cons. (Radiol.) E. Kent Hosps. Trust, Qu. Eliz., The Qu.mother Hosp., Ramsgate Rd, Margate, Kent; Assoc. Med. Director, Cancer Clinician, E.K.H. Trust. Prev: Med. Director, Thanet Healthcare Trust, QEQM Hosp. Margate, Kent.

GREENHALGH, Christopher Barnett Avondale Health Centre, Avondale St., Bolton BL1 4JP Tel: 01204 43803; 141 Armadale Road, Ladybridge, Bolton BL3 4UN — MB ChB 1970 Manch.; MRCGP 1974; DObst RCOG 1973. Socs: Bolton Med. Soc.

GREENHALGH, Edith Alice (retired) Flat 1, Francis Hill Court, Church Lane, Lincoln LN2 1QJ — MB ChB 1938 Manch.

GREENHALGH, George Phethean (retired) Chy Vean, St Mawes, Truro TR2 5AP Tel: 01326 270615 — MB BChir 1952 Camb.; MA 1952; MRCGP 1965. Prev: Temp. Surg. Lt. RNVR.

GREENHALGH, Ian Lower Clapton Health Centre, 36 Lower Clapton Road, London E5 0PQ — LMSSA 1966 Lond.

GREENHALGH, James Howard Eastleigh Health Centre, Newtown Road, Eastleigh SO50 9AG Tel: 023 8061 2197 Fax: 023 8065 0786; 4 Bassett Close, Bassett, Southampton SO16 7PE Tel: 01703 769148 — MB ChB 1978 Manch.

GREENHALGH, Jill Elizabeth Towcester Medical Centre, Link Way, Towcester NN12 6HH Tel: 01327 359953 Fax: 01327 358929; Fawe Park, 17 Wappenham Road, Abthorpe, Towcester NN12 8QU Tel: 01327 858101 — MB BS 1980 Lond.; DRCOG 1982.

GREENHALGH, Karen Lynn 14 Church Road, Easton-in-Gordano, Bristol BS20 0PQ — MB BS 1991 Lond.

GREENHALGH, Lisa Jane Milman Road Health Centre, Milman Road, Reading RG2 0AR Tel: 0118 987 1297 Fax: 0118 975 1172 — BM BS 1993 Nottm.

GREENHALGH, Mark Christopher Stephen The Avenue Surgery, 14 The Avenue, Warminster BA12 9AA Tel: 01985 846224 Fax: 01985 847059 — LMSSA 1993 Lond.; DFFP 1996. (Univ. Coll. Lond. Med. Sch.) Non-Princip. GP Sydney Hse. Surg. Hatfield Peverel. Socs: Fell. Roy. Soc. Med. Prev: GP/Regist. Sidney Ho. Surg. Hatfield Peveral, Essex; SHO Mid Essex Hosps. NHS Trust VTS; Ho. Off. (Surg. & Med.) OldCh. Hosp. Romford.

GREENHALGH, Michael George Towcester Medical Centre, Link Way, Towcester NN12 6HH Tel: 01327 359953 Fax: 01327 358929; Fawe Park, 17 Wappenham Road, Abthorpe, Towcester NN12 8QU Tel: 01327 858102 — MB BS 1981 Lond.; DRCOG 1986.

GREENHALGH, Nancy Mary Department of Old Age Psychiatry, St Lukes Hospital, Blackmoorfoot, Huddersfield HD4 5RQ — MB ChB 1985 Leeds; MRCPsych 1990. Sen. Regist. Rotat. (Psychiat.) Yorks. RHA. Prev: Tutor (Psychiat.) & Hon. Regist. Univ. Leeds; Regist. (Psychiat.) Leeds.

GREENHALGH, Professor Patricia Mary, OBE Holborn Union Building, Highgate Hill, London N19 5LW Tel: 020 7288 3246 Fax: 020 7281 8004 — BM BCh 1983 Oxf.; FRCGP 2000 UK; MA Camb. 1985, BA 1980, MD 1995; MRCP (UK) 1986; MRCGP 1990; FRCP (UK) 1998. (Cambridge) Prof. (Primary Care) Univ. Coll. Lond. Med. Sch.; Med. Writer & Jl.ist; Edit. Adviser Brit. Med. Jl.; Postgrad. Med. Tutor UCLMS.

GREENHALGH, Rebecca 17 Livingstone Mansions, Queens Club Gardens, London W14 9RW — MB BS 1996 Lond.

GREENHALGH, Professor Roger Malcolm Department of Surgery, Charing Cross Hospital, London W6 8RF Tel: 020 8846 7316 Fax: 020 8846 7330; 271 Sheen Lane, East Sheen, London SW14 8RN Tel: 020 8878 1110 — MB BChir Camb. 1967; MA Camb. 1967, MD 1983, MChir 1974; FRCS Eng. 1972. (Camb. & St. Thos.) Prof. Surg. Head Dept. Vasc. Surg. Imperial Coll. Sch. Med.; Chief Div. Vasc. Surg. Hammersmith Hosp. Trust; Regional Dir. Vasc. Sci.; Hon. Cons. Surg. Hammersmith Hosps. Trust, Chelsea & W.m. Trust, Chelsea Roy.Hosp & Qu Mary's Roehampton Hosp; Mem. Health Serv. Research Bd. MRC. Socs: Pres. Vasc. Surg. Soc. 1999-2000; (Sec. Gen.) Assn. Internat. Vasc. Surg.; (Chairm. Trustees) Europ. Soc. Vasc. Surg. Prev: Chairm. Directorate of Surg. Hammersmith Hosps. Trust 1994-1998; Dean Char. Cross & W.m. Med. Sch. 1993-1997; Prof. Surg. & Head Dept. Surg. Char. Cross & W. Med. Sch.

GREENHALGH, Sidney Alfred (retired) 113 Lutterworth Road, Nuneaton CV11 6QA Tel: 01203 347271 — MRCS Eng. LRCP Lond. 1955; DPH Liverp. 1968, DTM & H 1968. Prev: Wing Cdr. RAF Med. Br.

GREENHALGH, Stephen The Pikes Lane Centre, Deane Road, Bolton BL3 5HP Tel: 01204 874300 Fax: 01204 874305 Email: stephen.greenhalgh@gp-p82002.nhs.uk — MB BS 1980 Lond.

GREENHALGH LOWE, Gladys Jennie (retired) 10 Cambridge Gardens, Langland, Swansea SA3 4PP — MRCS Eng. LRCP Lond. 1935.

GREENHALL, Elizabeth Ann 19 Chalfont Road, Oxford OX2 6TL — BM BCh 1968 Oxf.; MFFP 1993; MFCM RCP (UK) 1987; DCH RCP Lond. 1971. (Univ. Oxf. & Westm. Med. Sch.) Cons. Family Plann. Oxon. DHA. Prev: Sen. Regist. (Community Med.) Oxf. RHA; GP Oxf.

GREENHALL, Richard Christopher David Department of Neurology, Radcliffe Infirmary, Oxford OX2 6HE — MB 1969 Camb.; DM Oxf. 1978; BChir 1968; FRCP Lond. 1984; MRCP (UK) 1971. Cons. Neurol. Radcliffe Infirm. Oxf. & Stoke Mandeville Hosp. Aylesbury.

GREENHAM, Ronald (retired) — MB ChB Birm. 1966; FRCP Lond. 1987; MRCP (UK) 1972; DTM & H Liverp. 1977; DCH Eng. 1969; DObst RCOG 1969. Prev: Tutor (Child Health) Roy. Manch. Childr. Hosp.

GREENHAM, Ruth Mary Tansley and Partners, Chalkhill Health Centre, Chalkhill Road, Wembley HA9 9BQ Tel: 020 8904 0911; 19 Bulmer Gardens, Kenton, Harrow HA3 0PA Tel: 020 8904 0321 — MB BS Lond. 1967; MRCS Eng. LRCP Lond. 1967. (Roy. Free) Prev: Ho. Phys. Roy. Free Hosp.; Ho. Surg. Wembley Hosp.

GREENHILL, Michael David (retired) Flat 6/A, Southwood Place, Rosemount Avenue, Newton Mearns, Glasgow G77 5TN — MB ChB 1962 Glas.; DMRD Eng. 1967. p/t Cons. Radiol. S.. Ayrsh. Hosp. Gp.

GREENHILL, Robert, OStJ (retired) 10 Richmond Drive, Cambuslang, Glasgow G72 8BH Tel: 0141 641 3040 — MB ChB Glas. 1949; MRCGP 1955. Prev: Asst. Med. Off. H.M. Prison Barlinnie.

GREENHORN, David James 19 Montrose Gardens, Blantyre, Glasgow G72 9NN — MB ChB 1997 Dundee.

***GREENHORN, Karen Hazel Irene** 1 Barclay Cl, Cullingworth, Bradford BD13 5AX — MB ChB 1997 Dundee.

GREENHOUGH, Christina Mary Mossley Medical Practice, 187 Manchester Road, Mossley, Ashton-under-Lyne OL5 9AB Tel: 01457 833315 Fax: 01457 834496 — MB ChB 1978 Manch.

GREENHOUGH, David McDonald (retired) Kinellan, 15 Victoria Road, Leven KY8 4EU Tel: 01333 425222 Fax: 01333 425222 Email: dung@kinellan.enterprise-plc.com — MB ChB 1969 Ed.; BSc (Med. Sci.) Ed. 1966. Prev: GP Leven Fife.

GREENHOUGH, Sarah Gillian Clerkenwell Medical Practice, Finsbury Health Centre, Pine Street, London EC1R 0HJ — MB ChB 1985 Manch.; BSc (Med. Sci.) St. And. 1982; MRCGP 1994; MPH Leeds 1992. Jt. Sen. Partner, Clerkwell Med. Pract. Prev: Clin. Lect. (Gen. Pract.) Rusholme Health Centre Manch.; Sen. Regist. (Pub. Health Med.) Yorks. RHA.; SHO (O & G) Wythenshaw Hosp. Manch.

GREENHOUGH, Stephen George 20 Cavendish Road, Heaton Mersey, Stockport SK4 3DN — MB ChB 1978 Manch.; FFA RCS Eng. 1982. Cons. Anaesth. Manch. Roy. Infirm. Socs: Fell. Manch. Med. Soc.

GREENHOUSE, Mr Peter Robin David Haig Department of Sexual Health Medicine, Milne Centre for Sexual Health, Bristol Royal Infirmary, Bristol BS2 8HW Tel: 0117 928 4865 Fax: 0117 928 2385; The Courtyard, 23 Royal York Crescent, Clifton, Bristol BS8 4JX Tel: 0117 974 1197 Fax: 0117 973 2180 Email: peter.gh@virgin.net — MFFP 1995; MB BChir (Hons.) Camb. 1980; MA Camb. 1980; MRCS Eng. LRCP Lond. 1979; MRCOG 1988. (Camb.) Cons. In Sexual Health Med., Bristol Roy. Infirm., Bristol; Cons. Sexual Health Med. Bristol Roy. Infirm., Bristol; Vis. Specialist in Sexual Health, H.M. Prison, Bristol; Vis. Specialist in Sexual Health, H.M. Prison, Bristol. Socs: Med. Soc. Study VD; Med. Soc. Study VD; Soc. for the Advancem. of Sexual Health. Prev: Cons. Sexual Health Ipswich Hosp.; Cons. (Sexual Health), Ipswich Hosp.; Sen. Regist. (Genitourin. Med.) St. Bart. Hosp. Lond.

GREENHOW, Denys Shackleton 1 Columbus Gardens, Northwood HA6 1TL Tel: 01923 823946 — MB BS 1988 Lond.; BSc (Intercoll. Intercalated Hon. Biochem.) Lond. 1985; MRCP (UK) 1995; MRCGP 1992; DRCOG 1993; DCH RCP Lond. 1992. Locum GP. Prev: Lond. Acad. GP Regist. Univ. W.m.; Regist. (Diabetes & Endocrinol.) Bristol Roy. Infirm.; Jun Clin. Lead (Diabetes & Endocrinol.) OldCh. Hosp. Romford.

GREENHOW, Timothy John Crosshall Brow Farm, Crosshall Brow, Wigan Road, Ormskirk L39 2BE — MB ChB 1977 Liverp.

GREENING, Alison Pamela St Fillan's Medical Centre, 2 Liverpool Road, Penwortham, Preston PR1 0AD Tel: 01772 745427 Fax: 01772 752562; 2 Lodge View, Farington Moss, Preston PR26 6RG — MB ChB 1988 Liverp.

GREENING, Andrew Peter Western General Hospital, Crewe Road S., Edinburgh EH4 2XU Tel: 0131 537 1780 Fax: 0131 343 3989 Email: a.greening@ed.ac.uk; 80 Murrayfield Gardens, Edinburgh EH12 6DQ — MB ChB 1973 Ed.; BSc (Hons.) Ed. 1970; FRCP Ed. 1986; MRCP (UK) 1975. Cons. Phys. W.. Gen. Hosp. Edin. Socs: Brit. Thorac. Soc.; Assn. Phys.; Brit. Soc. Immunol. Prev: Sen. Research Fell. Edin. Univ.; Sen. Regist. Hammersmith Hosp. Lond.; MRC Train. Fell. Roy. Postgrad. Med. Sch. Lond.

GREENING, James Edwin 147 Beaufort Street, London SW3 6BS — MB BS 1991 Lond.

GREENING, Jayne Sandra St Michaels Hosp, St Michaels Road, Warwick CV34 5QW Tel: 01926 496789 Email: jaynegreening@yahoo.co.uk — MB BS 1990 Lond.; MRC Psych. 1997; MMed Sci. 1999. (St Georges) Specialist Regist. Psychiat. W. Midl. Rotat.

GREENING, Sarah Lindsay Langham Place Surgery, 11 Langham Place, Northampton NN2 6AA Tel: 01604 38162 Fax: 01604 602457; 6 Edgemont Road, Weston Favell, Northampton NN3 3DF — MB ChB 1987 Leic.; MRCGP 1992; DRCOG 1991.

GREENISH, Rev. Brian Vivian Isitt (retired) 69 Chaucer Road, Bedford MK40 2AL Tel: 01234 352498 — MB BS 1944 Lond.; MRCS Eng. LRCP Lond. 1944. Prev: Hosp. Pract. (Dermat.) Bedford Gen. Hosp.

GREENISH, Keith Brian The Surgery, Marshall House, Bancroft Court, Hitchin SG5 1LH Tel: 01462 420740 — MB BS 1972 Lond.; DObst RCOG 1975.

GREENISH, Timothy Snowdon, Squadron Ldr. RAF Med. Br. RAF Centre for Aviation Medicine, RAF Henlow, Henlow SG16 6DN Tel: 01462 851515 Ext: 6179 Fax: 01462 851515 ext 7017 Email: timg@amtw.rafcam.org.uk; 5 Northern Avenue, Henlow SG16 6ET Tel: 01462 850654 — MB BS 1985 Lond.; MRCGP 1992; DRCOG 1992; DFFP 1994; DAvMed 1994. (Middlx.) Med. Off. RAF Centre for Aviat. Med. Socs: MRAes Aviat. Med. Div. Prev: Sen. Med. Off. RAF Valley; Sen. Med. Off. RAF Mt. Pleasant; SMO RAF Decimomannu.

GREENLAND, Andrew David Rosewood, 25 Stag Lane, Chorleywood, Rickmansworth WD3 5HP — MB BS 1997 Lond.

GREENLAND, Jennifer Helen Low Wood, The Street, South Stoke, Reading RG8 0JS — MB BS 1990 Lond.; BSc Lond. 1984; MRCGP 1995; DFFP 1996; DRCOG 1993.

***GREENLAND, Jonathan Edward** Hoops Cottage, 2 Baldon Lane, Marsh Baldon, Oxford OX44 9LT — MB ChB 1987 Birm.

GREENLAW, Griffith John Keith (retired) Bryn Blodau, 79 Hafod Cwnin, Carmarthen SA31 2AS Tel: 01267 222987 — MB BS Lond. 1959; DObst RCOG 1961. Prev: Head of Psychother. Myddfai Psychother. Centre Pembrokesh. Derwen NHS Trust.

GREENLEES, Frank Raymond The Surgery, 83 South St., Bishop's Stortford CM23 3AP Tel: 01279 653225 Fax: 01279 504658; 2 Dane Acres, Bishop's Stortford CM23 2PX Tel: 01279 655715 — MB 1962 Camb.; BChir 1961; DObst RCOG 1964. (Univ. Coll. Hosp.) Prev: Ho. Phys. N. Middlx. Hosp. Lond.; Ho. Surg. Surgic. Unit Univ. Coll. Hosp. Lond.; Ho. Surg. (Obst.) Chester City Hosp.

GREENOUGH, Professor Anne Department of Child Health, King's College Hospital, London SE5 9RS Tel: 020 7346 3037 Fax: 020 7924 9365 — MB BS 1978 Lond.; MD Camb. 1985, MA 1979; FRCP Lond. 1991; MRCP (UK) 1981; DCH Eng. 1980; FRCPCH Lond. 1997; MD 1986. Prof. Clin. Respirat. Physiol. & Hon. Cons. Paediat. King's Coll. Hosp. Lond.; Head Acad. Dept. (Child Health) United Med. Sch. Guys King's & St Thos. Hosps. Socs: Neonat. Soc. (Treas.); Head PICU & MCU of Paediatric Assembly Europ. Respirat. Soc.; ESPR. Prev: Sen. Lect. (Neonat.) & Hon. Cons. Paediat. King's Coll. Hosp. Lond.; Clin. Lect. (Paediat.) Univ. Camb.; Clin.Dir.(Chlid Health) KCH.

GREENOUGH, Mr Charles Geoffrey Middlesbrough General Hospital, Ayresome Green Lane, Middlesbrough TS5 5AZ Tel: 01642 854311 Fax: 01642 854136 — MB BS 1978 Lond.; MD Camb. 1991, MA 1979; MB BS (Hons.) (Surg.) Lond. 1978; FRCS Eng. 1982. Cons. Orthop. Middlesbrough Gen. Hosp. Socs: Internat. Soc. Study Lumbar Spine; Comm. Spine Soc. Europe; Brit. Scoliosis Soc. Prev: Sen. Regist. (Orthop.) Roy. Free & Roy. Nat. Orthop. Hosps. Lond.; Regist. (Surg.) Univ. Coll. Hosp. Lond.

GREENOUGH, Katharine Ruth 33 Stanhope Street, Greenside, Ryton NE40 4AL — MB BS 1990 Newc.

GREENSIDES, Jonathan Lowery Elm Tree Farm, Eastgate, Patrington, Hull HU12 0RG — MB ChB 1992 Manch.

GREENSLADE, Alexander Murray The Clinic, 162 Mayne St., Hanford, Stoke-on-Trent ST4 4QY; 253 New Inn Lane, Trentham, Stoke-on-Trent ST4 8BE Tel: 01782 644355 — MB BS Lond. 1970; MRCS Eng. LRCP Lond. 1972; ECFMG Cert 1970; Cert. Family Plann. JCC 1975; CRS (College of Distribution Trades, London). (Middlx.) GP Overweight Clinic. Prev: Ho. Surg. (O & G) Hillingdon Hosp.; Ho. Phys. (Gen. Med.) Middlx. Hosp. Lond.; Ho. Surg. (Orthop. & Ophth.) St. Albans City Hosp.

GREENSLADE, Gareth Lloyd Anaesthetics Department, Frenchay Hospital, Bristol BS16 1LE Tel: 0117 970 2020 Fax: 0117 957 4414 Email: gareth.greenslade@north-bristol.swest.nhs.uk — MB BS 1985 Lond.; MBA 1999 (Open); FRCA 1992; DA (UK) 1990. (Guy's) Cons. in Pain Managem. & Anaesth. N. Bristol NHS Trust. Socs: Fell. Roy. Soc. Med.; Pain Soc.; IASP. Prev: Clin. Lect. (Anaesth.) Univ. Bristol.

GREENSLADE, Julie Hopkins 49 Oakley Lane, Oakley, Basingstoke RG23 7JT — MB ChB 1982 Leic.; T(GP) 1991. Clin. Med. Off. (Child Health) W. Glam. HA.

GREENSLADE, Phyllis Dora (retired) Homestall, South Moreton, Didcot OX11 — MB BS 1928 Lond. Prev: Med. Off. (Family Plann.) Oxon. AHA (T).

GREENSMITH, Malcolm George Edward Koinnoyia, Holt Road, Llan-y-Pwll, Wrexham LL13 9SD Tel: 01978 660206 Fax: 01978 660206 Email: malcolm@mgreensmith.fsnet.co.uk — MB ChB 1967 Liverp.; FRCR 1974; DMRD Liverp. 1972. (Liverp.) Cons. Radiol.

Wrexham Gp. Hosps. Prev: Sen. Regist. Neuro Radiol. Walton Hosp. Liverp.; Sen. Regist. (Radiol.) Liverp. Roy. Infirm.; Ho. Off. Walton Hosp. Liverp.

GREENSTEIN, Adam Seth 24 Hodford Road, London NW11 8NP — MB ChB 1997 Manch.

GREENSTEIN, Mr David Northwick Park Hospital, Watford Road, Harrow HA1 3UJ Tel: 020 8869 2617 Fax: 020 8869 2577 Email: greensteindavid@hotmail.com — MB ChB 1989 Leeds; BSc Leeds 1986, MB ChB 1989; FRCS Glas. 1994; FRCS Ed. 1994; MD Leeds, 1996. Cons. Gen./Vasc. Surg. Socs: Europ. Soc. of Vasc. Surg.; Surgic. Res. Soc.

GREENSTONE, Michael Adrian c/o Medical Chest Unit, Castle Hill Hospital, Cottingham HU16 5JQ Tel: 01482 623010 Fax: 01482 623255 — MD 1986 Bristol; MB ChB 1974; FRCP Lond. 1993; MRCP (UK) 1977. Cons. Phys. Gen. & Thoracic Med. E. Yorks. & Hull Hosp. Trusts. Prev: Sen. Regist. (Thoracic Med.) Yorks. RHA; Clin. Lect. Cardiothoracic Inst. Lond.; Regist. (Gen. Med.) St. Mary's Hosp. Lond.

GREENSTREET, David Sloan Practice, 251 Chesterfield Road, Sheffield S8 0RT Tel: 0114 255 1164 Fax: 0114 258 9006; 25 Alms Hill Road, Ecclesall, Sheffield S11 9RR Tel: 0114 262 1030 — MB ChB 1992 Sheff.; DRCOG 1996.

GREENSTREET, Yvonne Lydia Akua 16 The Vale, London NW11 8SG — MB ChB 1985 Leeds.

GREENWAY, Mr Brian Arthur Derriford Hospital, Plymouth PL6 8DH — MB BS 1971 Lond.; MS Lond. 1982; FRCS Eng. 1976; MRCP (UK) 1979. (King's Coll. Hosp.) Cons. Surg. Derriford Hosp. Plymouth. Prev: Sen. Regist. (Surg.) Lond. Hosp.; Research Regist. King's Coll. Hosp. Lond.

GREENWAY, Ian Peter Cleveland Anaesthetic Department, Royal Gwent Hospital, Newport NP20 2UB Tel: 01633 252244; 14 Llwyn y Grant Place, Penylan, Cardiff CF23 9ET — MB ChB 1985 Auckland; FANZCA 1993. Cons. Anaesth. Roy. Gwent Hosp. Newport. Socs: Assn. Anaesth. GB & Irel.; Welsh IC Soc. Prev: Sen. Regist. (Anaesth.) Wrexham Maelor Hosp.; Regist. (Anaesth.) Auckland, NZ.

GREENWAY, Janet Hazel The Old Vicarage, Church Lane, Barnham, Bognor Regis PO22 0DA Tel: 01243 552334 — MB ChB 1973 Ed.; FFA RCS Eng. 1978; DA Eng. 1975. (Univ. Ed.) Prev: Regist. (Anaesth.) Soton. Gen. Hosp.

GREENWAY, Julie Leeds Student Medical Practice, 4 Blenheim Court Walk, Leeds LS2 9AE Tel: 0113 295 4488; 5 Lindley Farm, Cinder Lane, Lindley, Otley LS21 2QN — MB ChB 1983 Leeds; Dip. Sports Med. Soc. Apoth. Lond. 1995; DRCOG 1986. GP Leeds Stud. Med. Pract. Socs: Brit. Assn. Sport & Med. (Treas. Yorks. Div.).; Soc. Orthop. Med. Prev: Med. Off. Univ. Health Serv. Leeds; Clin. Asst. (A & E) Bradford Roy. Infirm.; SHO (O & G & ENT) Leeds E.. HA.

GREENWAY, Kathleen Joyce (retired) Hall Close, Tysoe, Warwick CV35 0TW Tel: 01295 680630 — MB ChB Birm. 1944. Prev: Gp Kineton & Tysoe.

GREENWAY, Mary Email: mary@greenway.freeserve.co.uk; Mallards, 25 Goffs Park Road, Southgate, Crawley RH11 8AX Tel: 01293 512978 Email: mary@greenway.freeserve.co.uk — MB BS 1986 Lond.; DA (UK) 1989. (Char. Cross) Regist. Rotat. (Anaesth.) St. Geo. Hosp. Lond. Socs: Jun. Mem. Assn. Anaesth.

GREENWAY, Michael Wyn Glan Clwyd Hospital, Bodelwyddan, Rhyl LL18 5UJ Tel: 01745 583910 — MB BCh 1974 Wales; FRCP Lond. 1993; MRCP (UK) 1980. Cons. Phys. (Health c/o Elderly) Glan Clwyd Hosp. Bodelwyddan, Clwyd. Socs: Brit. Geriat. Soc. (Counc. Mem. Welsh Br.). Prev: Sen. Regist. (Geriat.) Withington Hosp. Manch.; Sen. Regist. (Med.) Crumpsall Hosp. N. Manch.; Regist. (Med.) Liverp. Hosps.

GREENWAY, Neil Dominic Wimbourne Private Clinic, Knobcrook Road, Wimborne BH21 1NL; 52 Parkstone Avenue, Parkstone, Poole BH14 9LS — MB BS 1984 Lond.; BDS Lond. 1988. GP (Dent.) Wimborne; Hosp. Practitioner (Maxillofacial Surg.) Poole NHS Hosp. Trust.

GREENWAY, Peter Bridge Medical Centre, Wassand Close, Three Bridges Road, Crawley RH10 1LL Tel: 01293 526025 — MB BS 1986 Lond.; Dip. Sports Med. Lond 1991; MRCGP (1997). (Westminster) GP.

GREENWAY, Richard Alan Charles 80 Carlyle Road, London W5 4BJ — MB BS 1991 Lond.

GREENWELL, David George Southover Medical Practice, Bronshill Road, Torquay TQ1 3HD Tel: 01803 327100 Fax: 01803 316295 — MB BS 1988 Lond.; MRCGP 1993; DCH RCP Lond. 1992; DRCOG 1991.

GREENWELL, David George 25 Crossgate Peth, Durham DH1 4PZ — MB ChB 1990 Manch.

GREENWELL, Frederick Peter (retired) 14 Westbourne Park Road, London W2 5PH — BM BCh 1956 Oxf.; FRCR 1975; FFR 1964; DMRD Eng. 1962.

GREENWELL, Stephanie Kathleen North Tyneside General Hospital, Rake Lane, North Shields NE29 8WH Tel: 0191 259 6660 Fax: 0191 293 2519; 16 Osborne Avenue, Jesmond, Newcastle upon Tyne NE2 1JQ Tel: 0191 281 2863 Fax: 0191 281 2863 Email: step@lightlinesystems.co.uk — MB BS 1975 Newc.; FFA RCS Eng. 1979. Cons. Anaesth. N. Tyneside Gen. Hosp. Socs: Coun. Mem. Assoc. Anaesth.s GB & Irel. 1998-; N. Engl. Soc. Anaesth. Prev: Sen. Regist. (Anaesth.) Newc. RHA (T).; Regist. (Anaesth.) Roy. Vict. Infirm. Newc.; Ho. Off. Dryburn Hosp. Durh.

GREENWELL, Tamsin Jillian 21 Vivian Road, Sheffield S5 6WJ — MB ChB 1990 Manch.; FRCS Eng. 1995. (Manch. Univ. Med. Sch.) Specialist Regist. Rotat. (Urol.) S. Thames Guy's Hosp. Prev: Regist. (Gen. Surg.) Barnsley Dist. Gen. Hosp.; SHO Rotat. (Surg.) N.. Gen. Hosp. Sheff.; Research Fell. (Gen. Surg.) Univ. Sheff.

GREENWOLD, Natalie Karen Helen 51 Highpoint, North Hill, London N6 4AZ — MB BS 1987 Lond.

GREENWOOD, Alan The Health Centre, Greenside, Cleckheaton BD19 5AP; 26 New Road E., Scholes, Cleckheaton BD19 6EW Tel: 01274 877019 — MB BS Lond. 1967; MRCGP 1977; Cert. Family Plann. JCC 1975; DCH Eng. 1970; DObst RCOG 1969.

GREENWOOD, Alan The Avenue Surgery, 14 The Avenue, Warminster BA12 9AA Tel: 01985 846224 Fax: 01985 847059 — MB ChB 1976 Birm.; DA Eng. 1978. Local Med. Off. Civil Serv. Socs: Fac. Anaesth. RCS Eng.

GREENWOOD, Andrew Paul Hindley Prison, Wigan WN2 5TH Tel: 01942 866255 Fax: 01942 862483 — BM BS 1981 Nottm.; BMedSci 1979; Dip Addictive Behaviour 1998.

GREENWOOD, Andrew Paul 83 Higher Reedley Road, Brierfield, Nelson BB9 5EY — MB ChB 1994 Manch. GP Non-Princip. Prev: GP Regist. Saddleworth Med. Pract.; SHO (O & G) Burnley Gen. Hosp.; SHO (Paediat.) Burnley Gen. Hosp.

GREENWOOD, Anne Marie The Strawberry Gardens Medical, 377 Heysham Road, Morecambe LA3 2BP Tel: 01524 850999 Fax: 01524 855688; 1 Cannon Hill, Lancaster LA1 5LL — MB BS 1980 Newc.; DCH RCP Glas. 1982. (Newcastle upon Tyne) GP Morecambe; Med. Manager (Family Plann.); Clin. Asst. (Dermat.). Socs: FFP.

GREENWOOD, Anthony John 5 Onslow Avenue Mansions, Onslow Avenue, Richmond TW10 6QD — MB BS 1991 Lond. SHO (Ophth.) Lond.

GREENWOOD, Bernard Paul Accident & Emergency Department, Royal Devon & Exeter Hospital, Barrack Road, Exeter EX2 5DW Tel: 01392 402305 Email: bgreenwood@doctors.org.uk; Woodcote, Chagford, Newton Abbot TQ13 8JF Tel: 01647 433562 — MB BS 1964 Lond.; PhD (Social Anthropol.) Camb. 1984; BSc Physiol. Lond. 1961, MB BS 1964; MRCS Eng. LRCP Lond. 1964; Dip. IMC RCS Ed. 1995; Cert. Soc. Anthropol. Camb. 1975. (Oxf.) Assoc. Specialist (A & E) Roy. Devon & Exeter Hosp. Socs: BMA; BAEM. Prev: Research Fell. (Gen. Pract.) Univ. Exeter; Research Stud. (Social Anthropol.) Univ. Camb.; Research Asst. (Surgic Sci.) Univ. Edin.

GREENWOOD, Brian 48 Firs Road, Houghton on the Hill, Leicester LE7 9GU — MB BS 1959 Lond.; MB BS (Hons. Surg.) Lond. 1959; PhD Lond. 1966, BSc (1st cl. Hons. Physiol.) 1956; MRCS Eng. LRCP Lond. 1961. (St. Thos.) Hon. Lect. (Path.) Univ. Leicester. Socs: Pharmacol. Soc.; Path. Soc.; Brit. Soc. Immunol. Prev: Mem. Scientif. Staff Inst. Animal Physiol. Camb.; Lect. Sherrington Sch. of Physiol. St. Thos. Hosp.; Head Path. R & D Laborats. Fisons Pharmaceuts.

GREENWOOD, Brian Kenneth 11 Carlton Road, Hale, Altrincham WA15 8RH Tel: 0161 980 4084 — MB ChB 1968 Manch.; FFA RCS Eng. 1977; DA Eng. 1973. Cons. Anaesth. Trafford HA; Founder Mem. Europ. Soc. Regional Anaesth. Socs: Manch. Med. Soc., Assn. Anaesth. & Obst. Anaesth. Assn. Prev: Sen. Regist.

(Anaesth.) Manch. Roy. Infirm.; Chief Med. Off. Nevis W. Indies; Dist. Med. Off. Chililabombue, Zambia.

GREENWOOD, Carolyn Ann 7 Melrose Road, Galashiels TD1 2AE Tel: 01896 758635 — MB ChB 1979 Dundee; MRCPsych 1984. (Dundee Univ.) Med. Off. Ment. Welf. Commiss. Prev: Sen. Regist. (Child & Adolesc. Psychiat.) Tayside HB; Regist. (Psychiat.) Roy. Dundee Liff Hosp.; Ho. Phys. Monklands Dist. Gen. Hosp. Airdrie.

GREENWOOD, Carolyn de Havilland 32 Paradise Walk, London SW3 4JL — MB BCh 1972 Witwatersrand.

GREENWOOD, Catherine Elizabeth Leslie 80 Hilltop Road, Oxford OX4 1PE — MB BS 1987 Lond.

GREENWOOD, Catherine Mary 15 Best Avenue, Burton-on-Trent DE15 9GU — MB ChB 1997 Sheff.

GREENWOOD, Catriona Elizabeth Flat 2, 197 Kingsway, Hove BN3 4FD — MB ChB 1992 Sheff.

GREENWOOD, Celia Rosemary 13 Windmill Way, Southam, Leamington Spa CV47 0LF — MB ChB 1962 Sheff. (Sheff.)

GREENWOOD, Derek (retired) Rimington, 29 Hesketh Lane, Tingley, Wakefield WF3 1AS Tel: 0113 253 3407 — MB ChB 1952 Leeds. Prev: GP Wakefield.

GREENWOOD, Elizabeth Jane 7 Bovinger Way, Southend-on-Sea SS1 3SZ — MB BS 1989 Lond.

GREENWOOD, Emma Healey Dene, Healey Dell, Rochdale OL12 6BG — MB BCh 1977 Wales.

GREENWOOD, Heather (retired) Medical Services, Government Buildings, Flowers Hill, Brislington, Bristol BS4 5LA — BM BCh 1983 Oxf.; MA Camb. 1984; MRCGP 1988; T(GP) 1991; DCH RCP Lond. 1986; DRCOG 1985. Med. Adviser Benefits Agency Bristol. Prev: GP Malmesbury.

GREENWOOD, Jaime John 26 Earlswood Road, Redhill RH1 6HW — MB BS 1998 Lond.; MB BS Lond 1998.

GREENWOOD, Jeremy Devine Stacksteads Surgery, 20 Farholme Lane, Stacksteads, Bacup OL13 0EX Tel: 01706 873122 Fax: 01706 874152 — MB BS 1979 Lond.; MRCS Eng. LRCP Lond. 1979; MRCPsych 1984; MRCGP 1987. (St. Mary's) GP; Clin. Asst. (Rheum.) Burnley Gen. Hosp.; Med. Off. (Drug Abuse Rehabil.). Socs: Soc. Med. Orthop. Prev: Regist. (Psychiat.) Shelton Hosp. Shrewsbury.

GREENWOOD, John 38 The Street, Rustington, Littlehampton BN16 3NX — MRCS Eng. LRCP Lond. 1936. (Manch.) Socs: BMA & Coll. GP. Prev: Asst. Med. Off. Oldham Gen. Hosp. & St. Geo. Hosp. Stafford; Cas. Off. Qu. Mary's Hosp. Lond.

GREENWOOD, Mr John Edward Department of Plastic Surgery, Wythenshawe Hospital, Southmoor Rd, Wythenshawe, Manchester M23 9LT Tel: 0161 998 7070; 18 Blackchapel Drive, Dean Farm, Rochdale OL16 4QU Tel: 01706 648922 Email: helengr@hotmail.com — MB ChB 1989 Manch.; FRACS 2001 (plast); BSc (Hons.) Anat. Manch. 1986; FRCS Eng. 1994; MD March 1998. (Manchester) Specialist Regist. (Plastic. Surg.) Univ. Hosp. S. Manch. W. Didsbury; Sen. Fell. In Burns and Plastic Surg. Roy. Adelaide Hosp. N. Terr. Adelaide S. Australia. Socs: Brit. Burns Assn.; Brit. Assn. Of Plastic Surg.s. Prev: Research Regist. (Surg.) Univ. Hosp. S. Manch. W. Didsbury; SHO Rotat. Withington & Wythenshawe Hosps.; Ho. Surg. Stepping Hill Hosp. Stockport.

GREENWOOD, John Paul Tain and Fearn Area Medical Practice, Health Centre, Scotsburn Road, Tain IV19 1PR Tel: 01862 892759 Fax: 01862 892579; 6 Springfield Gardens, Tain IV19 1RA — MB ChB 1973 Manch.

GREENWOOD, John Pierre 24 Ashfield Park, Headingley, Leeds LS6 2QT — MB ChB 1991 Leeds; MRCP (UK) 1994. (Leeds) Research Regist. (Cardiol.) St. Jas. Univ. Hosp. Leeds. Prev: SHO (Cardiol.) St. Jas. Univ. Hosp. Leeds; SHO Rotat. (Med.) York Dist. Hosp.

GREENWOOD, Judith, DBE (retired) Royal Edinburgh Hospital, Morningside Place, Edinburgh EH10 5HF Tel: 0131 447 2011 — MB BS 1961 Lond.; MRCS Eng. LRCP Lond. 1961; FRCPsych 1996; MRCPsych 1977. Prev: Cons. Psychiat. Community Drug Problem Serv. Roy. Edin. Hosp.

GREENWOOD, Kathryn Mary St Annes Road East, 24 St. Annes Road East, Lytham St Annes FY8 1UR Tel: 01253 722121 Fax: 01253 781121; 65 Headroom Gate Road, Staines on Sea, Lytham St Annes FY8 3BE — MB ChB 1984 Liverp.

GREENWOOD, Linda Jayne 65 Freedom Road, Walkley, Sheffield S6 2XA Tel: 0114 233 4503; 65 Freedom Road, Walkley, Sheffield S6 2XA Tel: 0114 233 4503 — MB ChB 1984 Liverp.; DRCOG 1986. Prev: GP Sheff.; Trainee GP Ormskirk.

GREENWOOD, Mary Catherine Child Health Bureau, PO Box 115, Chichester PO19 4YT Tel: 01243 815400 Fax: 01243 815225; Thurlow, 9 Finchdean Road, Rowlands Castle PO9 6DA — MB BChir 1972 Camb.; MA Camb. 1972; MRCP (UK) 1976; DCH Eng. 1974. SCMO (Paediat.) Community Health Chichester. Socs: BMA; RCPCH; BACCH. Prev: Clin. Asst. (Paediat.) S.mead Hosp. Brist.; Regist. Hosp. Sick Childr. Lond.; Regist. (Paediat.) Whittington Hosp. Lond.

GREENWOOD, Monica Hazel 152 Harley Street, London W1G 7LH Tel: 020 7935 0444 Fax: 020 7224 2574 Email: monicagreenwood@lineone.net — MB BS 1967 Lond.; MRCS Eng. LRCP Lond. 1967; FRCPsych 1986, M 1972; DA Eng. 1970; DPM Eng. 1972. (St. Mary's) p/t Emerit. Cons. Brent Kensington Chelsea & W.minster NHS (Ment. Health Trust). Prev: Cons. Psychiat. Shenley Hosp. Radlett; Cons. Psychiat. Middlx. Hosp. Lond.; Hon. Sen. Lect. UCL.

GREENWOOD, Neil Pathology Department, St Mary's Hospital, Newport PO30 5TG Tel: 01983 524081 Fax: 01983 822569 — MB BS 1966 Lond.; MRCS Eng. LRCP Lond. 1966; FRCPath 1985, M 1973. (St. Bart.) Cons. Path. I. of Wight AHA. Prev: Lect. (Path.) Univ. Manch.; Ho. Phys. City Gen. Hosp. Stoke-on-Trent; Ho. Surg. Roy. Infirm. Huddersfield.

***GREENWOOD, Nicola Katy** 32 Crimscote Close, Shirley, Solihull B90 4TT — MB ChB 1998 Birm.

GREENWOOD, Mr Peter Andrew Department of Obstetrics & Gynaecology, James Paget Hospital, Gorleston-on-Sea, Great Yarmouth NR31 6LA Tel: 01493 452209; Green Farm House, Green Lane, Somerleyton, N Lowestoft NR31 9HQ — MB BChir 1981 Camb.; DObst Ultrasound (RCR/RCOG) 1998; FRCS Ed. 1987; MRCOG 1987. (Univ. Camb. Med. Sch.) Cons. O & G Jas. Paget Hosp. Gt. Yarmouth; Hon. Cons. Obst. & Gyn. Roy. Lond. Hosps. Trust; Director Waveney Clinic for Reproductive Health. Socs: Fell. Edin. Obst. Soc.; Brit. Fertil. Soc.; Internat. Soc. Ultrasound in Obst. & Gyn. Prev: Sen. Regist. (O & G) Simpsons Memor Matern. Pavil. Edin.; Regist. (O & G) City Hosp. Nottm.; Resid. Med. Off. Qu. Charlotte's Matern. Hosp. Lond.

GREENWOOD, Rachel Derwent House, Flatgate, Howden, Goole DN14 7AG — BM BCh 1977 Oxf.; MRCP (UK) 1979. Cons. Dermat. Scunthorpe Gen. Hosp. Socs: Fell. Roy. Coll. Phys.

GREENWOOD, Richard Edward Hillview House, Kencot, Lechlade GL7 3QX Tel: 01367 860870 Fax: 01367 860870 — MB ChB Birm. 1971; BDS Lond. 1965; FDS RCS Eng. 1973. Civil. Cons. Oral & Maxillofacial Surg. Mayday Hosp.Croydon. Socs: BMA & Brit. Assn. Oral & Maxillofacial Surg.

GREENWOOD, Richard Henry Oak Lodge, 19 Branksome Road, Norwich NR4 6SN Tel: 01603 503135 Fax: 016030 452535 — MB BS (Hons. Med.) Lond. 1968; BSc (Anat.) (1st cl. Hons.) Lond. 1965; FRCP Lond. 1986, MRCP (UK) 1970; MRCS Eng. LRCP Lond. 1968. (Guy's) Cons. Phys. Norf. & Norwich Univ. Hosp. Socs: Europ. Assn. for the Study of Diabetes; Amer. Diabetes Assn.; Hon. Sec. Assoc. Brit. Clin. Diabeteol. (ABCD). Prev: Lect. & Sen. Regist. (Med.) Univ. Hosp. Wales Cardiff; Lect. Med. Unit. Lond. Hosp.; Regist. (Metab. Dis.) St. Thos. Hosp. Lond.

GREENWOOD, Richard James National Hospital for Neurology & Neurosurgery, Queen Square, London WC1N 3BG Tel: 020 7837 3611 Fax: 020 7813 2126; 43 Cunningham Avenue, St Albans AL1 1JJ Tel: 01727 853385 Fax: 01727 834103 — MB BChir 1971 Camb.; MD Camb. 1978; MRCP (UK) 1973; FRCP 1988. Cons. Neurol. Nat. Hosp. Neurol. & Neurosurg., Homerton Hosps. Lond. & Homerton Regional Neurol. Rehabil. Unit. Socs: Fell. Roy. Soc. Med.; Assn. Brit. Neurol. Prev: Cons. Neurol. St. Bart. Hosp. Lond.; Cons. Neurol. Worthing, Chichester & Mid-Downs Dists.; Sen. Regist. The Nat. Hosp. for Nerv. Dis. & St. Bart. Hosp. Lond.

GREENWOOD, Mr Richard Kay (retired) Herongate, 30 The Ridgeway, Rothley, Leicester LE7 7LE Tel: 0116 230 3466 — MB BChir 1961 Camb.; MA Camb. 1953, MD 1964, MChir 1961, MB BChir 1952; FRCS Eng. 1957. Cons. Gen. Surg. Leics. AHA (T); Clin. Tutor Fac. Med. Univ. Leicester; Hon. Clin. Tutor (Surg.) St. Thos. Hosp. Med. Sch. Lond.; Mem. Jt. Consults. Comm. & Centr. Med. Manpower Comm. Prev: Demonst. (Anat.) Univ. Camb.

GREENWOOD, Roger Major (retired) 62 Gayton Road, Harrow HA1 2LS Tel: 020 8427 2755 Email:

rogo6@greenhillha1.demon.co.uk — MB BS 1961 Lond.; PhD Lond. 1967, BSc (Hons. Physiol.) 1958. Prev: Gp. Informat. Manager Roy. Marsden NHS Trust Lond. & Surrey.

GREENWOOD, Roger Newton Renal Unit, North Herts NHS Trust, Lister Hospital, Coreys Mill Lane, Stevenage SG1 4AB Tel: 01438 781157 Fax: 01438 781130 Email: dr.greenwood@nherts_tr.nthames.nhs.uk; 20 Newlands Lane, Hitchin SG4 9AU — MD 1986 Bristol; BSc (Eng.) ACGI Univ. Lond. 1968; MSc Bristol 1969, MD 1986, MB ChB 1976; FRCP Lond. 1994; MRCP (UK) 1980. Lead Clin. Dir. (Renal Med.) N. Herts NHS Trust. Socs: Pres. Brit. Renal Symp.; Audit & Standards Comm. Renal Assn. Prev: Dir. (Renal Med. & Urol.) N Herts. NHS Trust; Sen. Regist. (Nephrol. & Gen. Med.) St. Bartholomews Hosp. Lond.

GREENWOOD, Roger Sterndale 28 Woodfield Road, Coventry CV5 6AL Tel: 024 76 675688 Fax: 024 76 675688 Email: greenwd@clocknet.co.uk — MB BS 1959 Lond.; MRCS Eng. LRCP Lond. 1958. (Guy's) Prev: Ho. Phys. Croydon Gen. Hosp.; Ho. Surg. (Obst.) Mayday Hosp. Thornton Heath; Capt. RAMC.

GREENWOOD, Samuel Fletcher Clifton Drive South, 300 Clifton Drive South, Lytham St Annes FY8 1LJ Tel: 01253 723194; 19 Hall Park Drive, Ansdell, Lytham St Annes FY8 4QR — MB ChB 1954 Manch. (Manch.)

GREENWOOD, Sian Baker, Greenwood and Gammack, 110 King's Road, Harrogate HG1 5HW Tel: 01423 503035 Fax: 01423 562665 — MB ChB 1980 Sheff.; MRCGP 1984; DCH RCP Lond. 1984; DRCOG 1983. Princip. GP Harrogate.

GREENWOOD, Susan Rosemary (retired) Timbertops, Cadbury Camp Lane, Clapton-in-Gordano, Bristol BS20 7SB Tel: 01275 852005 — MRCS Eng. LRCP Lond. 1960; DCH Eng. 1969; DObst RCOG 1963. Prev: Gen. Practitioner, Hartcliffe Health Centre, Hartcliffe Bristol.

GREENWOOD, Susan Tracy 24 Houghton Road, Penwortham, Preston PR1 9HS — MB ChB 1998 Ed.; MB ChB Ed 1998.

GREENWOOD, Thomas Frederick (retired) West Ashby Lodge, Horncastle LN9 5PT Tel: 01507 523314 — MRCS Eng. LRCP Lond. 1934. Prev: Ho. Surg. & O & G Ho. Phys. Middlx. Hosp.

GREENWOOD, Trevor William West Middlesex University Hospital, Isleworth TW7 6AF Tel: 020 8565 5336 Fax: 020 8565 5581; 43 St. James's Avenue, Hampton Hill, Hampton TW12 1HL Tel: 020 8979 9041 — MB BChir 1965 Camb.; MA Camb. 1967; FRCP Lond. 1984, M 1969. (Camb. & St. Mary's) Cons. Phys. W. Middlx. Univ. Hosp. Isleworth & Teddington Memor. Hosp.; Hon. Cons. Cardiol. Hammersmith Hosp. NHS Trust; Hon. Sen. Lect. Imperial Coll. Sch. Med.; Hon. Med. Off. Brit. Athletic Federat. Socs: BMA & Brit. Cardiac Soc. Prev: Dir. Clin. Studies Imperial Coll. Sch. Med.; Sen. Regist. (Med.) Char. Cross Hosp. Lond.; Sen. Research Regist. (Hyperbaric & Coronary Care) W.m. Hosp.

GREENWOOD, William Eric (retired) Little Ranch, Rookwood, West Wittering, Chichester PO20 8QH — MRCS Eng. LRCP Lond. 1939; MD Lond. 1947, MB BS 1939, DPH 1947.

GREER, Alexander McConnell 10 Cormorant Park, Lower Braniel Road, Belfast BT5 7NB — MB BCh BAO 1984 Belf.; MB BCh Belf. l984.

GREER, Alexander William (retired) Newton Hall, Hall Road, Walpole Highway, Wisbech PE14 7QE Tel: 01945 880226 Fax: 01945 880226 — MB BChir Camb. 1963; MA Camb. 1963, BA 1959; DObst RCOG 1965. Med. Assessor TAS. Prev: Ho. Off. Norf. & Norwich Hosp.

GREER, Andrew John Greengate Medical Centre, 1 Greengate Lane, Birstall, Leicester LE4 3JF Tel: 0116 267 7901 — BM BS 1988 Nottm.; BMedSci (Hons) Nottm. 1986; MRCGP 1994; DRCOG 1993.

GREER, Angela Elizabeth (retired) 37 Schonberg Avenue, Belfast BT4 2JR — MB BCh BAO 1957 Belf.; FFPHM RCP (UK) 1981, M 1972; DPH 1961. Prev: Cons. Communicable Dis. Control E. Health & Social Servs. Bd.

GREER, Anne Department of Adolescent Psychiatry, 129 Knightswood Road, Glasgow G13 2XJ — MB ChB 1980 Glas.; MSc (Med. Sci.) Glas. 1986; MRCPsych. 1985. Cons. Adolesc. Psychiat. Kt.swood, Glas. Prev: Sen. Regist. (Child & Adolesc. Psychiat.) Roy. Edin. Hosp. & Roy. Hosp. for Sick Childr. Edin.; Regist. (Child & Family Psychiat.) Roy. Hosp. for Sick Childr. Glas.; MRC Research Stud. Inst. Physiol. Univ. Glas.

GREER, Antony John Flat 3, Doctors Residences, 47 Cleveland St., London W1P 9P2 — MB ChB 1994 Glas. SHO (Gen. Surg.) Univ. Coll. Hosp. Lond. Prev: SHO (Orthop. & A & E) Glas. Roy. Infirm.

GREER, Bridget Louise 11 Roseberry Gardens, Dartford DA1 2NX — MB ChB 1990 Sheff.; MRCGP 1994; DRCOG 1994. (Sheff.)

GREER, Henry Steven St Raphael's Hospice, North Cheam, Sutton SM3 9DX; 15 Parklands Road, Streatham, London SW16 6TB Tel: 020 8677 9106 — MB BS Adelaide 1952; MD Adelaide 1966; FRANZCP 1979; FRCPsych 1973; DPM Eng. 1958. (Adelaide) Cons. Psychiat. St. Raphael's Hospice N. Cheam, Sutton. Socs: Fell.Roy. Coll. of Psychiat.s. Prev: Emerit. Reader (Psychol. Med.) Inst. Cancer Research & Hon. Cons. Psychiat. Roy. Marsden Hosp. Sutton; Regist. Maudsley Hosp. Lond.

GREER, Professor Ian Andrew Department of Obstetrics & Gynaecology, University of Glasgow, Royal Infirmary, 10 Alexandra Parade, Glasgow G31 2ER Tel: 0141 211 4703 Fax: 0141 553 1367 Email: gqta03@udcf.gld.ac.uk — MB ChB 1980 Glas.; MD Glas. 1986; FRCP Glas. 1994; MRCP (UK) 1984; MFFP 1994; MRCOG 1987. Muirhead Prof. & Head. Dept. O & G Univ. Glas. & Roy. Infirm. Glas.; Hon. Cons. Obst. & Gyn. Roy. Infirm. & Roy. Matern. Hosp. Glas. Prev: Clin. Research Scientist MRC Reproduc. Biol. Unit Edin.; Lect. & Hon. Sen. Regist. (O & G) Simpson Memor. Matern. Pavil. & Roy. Infirm. Edin.; Regist. (O & G) Glas. Roy. Matern. Hosp. & Glas. Roy. Infirm.

GREER, John Ruari 626 Lanark Road, Juniper Green, Edinburgh EH14 5EW — MB BCh BAO 1990 Belf.; DGM RCPS Glas. 1993; FRCA 1998. (Queen's Univ. Belf.) Specialist Regist. (Anaesth.) NW Region. Socs: Intens. Care Soc.; BMA. Prev: Clin. Research Fell. (Intens. Care) Manch. Roy. Infirm.

GREET, David Michael Tollgate Health Centre, 220 Tollgate Road, London E6 5JS Tel: 020 7474 7709 Fax: 020 7445 7715; The Old Vicarage, 16 Northumberland Avenue, Wanstead, London E12 5HD Tel: 020 8989 8527 — MB ChB 1979 Bristol; MRCGP 1983; DRCOG 1982.

GREEVES, Colin Malcomson (retired) Antrim Health Centre, Station Road, Antrim BT41 4BS Tel: 028 9446 4938 Fax: 028 9446 4930 — MB BCh BAO 1968 Belf.; MRCOG 1973.

GREEVES, John Anthony 10 Harley Street, London W1N 1AA Tel: 020 7580 1454 — MB BS 1955 Lond.; MRCPsych 1973; DPM Eng. 1959. (Guy's) Examr. (Psychiat.) Coll. of Speech Therapists; Lect. (Psychiat.) Centr. Speech Sch. Socs: Fell. Roy. Soc. Med. & Roy. Anthropol. Inst. Prev: Psychiat. Skin Dept. St. Bart. Hosp. Lond.

GREEVES, Lindsey Gilbert Royal Belfast Hospital for Sick Children, Falls Road, Belfast BT12 6BE; Lislea, 10 Armagh Road, Portadown, Craigavon BT62 3DP — MB BCh BAO 1977 Belf.; MD Belf. 1992; MRCGP 1981; DRCOG 1980; DCH RCPS Glas. 1980.

GREGAN, Andrew Conal Finbarr 12 Kingsley Road, St Helens WA10 6JN — MB BS 1993 Lond.

GREGAN, Anne Catherine Mary Washington Cottage, Finchfield Gardens, Finchfield, Wolverhampton WV3 9LT Tel: 01902 420501 — MB BS 1986 Lond.; BSc (Hons.) Lond. 1983; MRCP (UK) 1990; FRCR 1995. Cons. Radiol. Dudley Gp. Hosp. NHS Trust. Prev: Sen. Regist. (Radiol.) W. Midl.

GREGAN, Mary Jude Lynwood, 12 Kingsley Road, St Helens WA10 6JN — MB BCh BAO 1952 NUI; DCH Eng. 1956. (Univ. Coll. Dub.) Prev: Med. Regist. Our Lady's Hosp. Sick Childr. Crumlin & Alder Hey; Childr. Hosp. Liverp.; Ho. Off. St. Vincent's Hosp. Dub.

GREGAN, Patrick 12 Kinglsey Road, St Helens WA10 6JN — MB BCh BAO 1950 NUI; LM Coombe 1954.

GREGG, Andrew Kieron 1 Church Row, Little Stretton, Leicester LE2 2FT Tel: 0116 259 3774 Email: andy.sue@andygregg.freeserve.co.uk — BM 1993 Soton.; MRCP (UK) 1996; FRCA 1999. Specialist Regist., (Anaesth.) Leicester Roy. Infirm. Prev: Specialist Regist. (Anaes), Lincoln; Specialist Regist. (Anaesth.), PeterBoro.; Specialist Regist. (Renal) Leicester Gen. Hosp.

GREGG, Anne Cecilia 75 Manchester Road, Wilmslow SK9 2JQ — MB BS 1991 Lond.

GREGG, Elizabeth Mary Queen Elizabeth Psychiatric Hospital, Edgbaston, Birmingham B15 2QZ; 16 Croftdown Road, Harborne, Birmingham B17 8RB — MB ChB 1962 Birm.; FRCPsych 1992, M 1978. Cons. Psychiat. S. Birm. Ment. Health Trust. Prev: Cons. Psychiat. Kidderminster Gen. Hosp.

GREGG, Ian (retired) 1 Queens Close, Eynsham, Witney, Oxford OX29 4HN Tel: 01865 464233 Fax: 01865 464234 — BM BCh Oxf. MA OXF1954; DM Oxf. 1983, MA 1954; FRCP Lond. 1986, M 1978; FRCGP 1972; DObst RCOG 1958. Hon. Fell. Univ Exeter. Prev: Sen. Lect. & Dir. (Clin. Epidemiol.) Cardio-Thoracic Inst. Lond.

GREGG, Jacqueline Elizabeth Margretta Community Child Health, Royal Liverpool Childrens NHS Trust, Alder Hey, Liverpool L12 2AP Tel: 0151 228 4811; Aspen House, 28 Pilkington St, Rainford, St Helens WA11 8HG Tel: 01744 886408 — MB ChB 1980 Manch.; MRCP (UK) 1984; DCH RCP Lond. 1982; FRCP 1997; FRCPCH. Cons. Community Paediat. Roy. Liverp. Childr. NHS Trust.

GREGG, Professor Paul James Department of Orthopaedics Surgery, School of Surgical Sciences Medical School, Framlington Place, Newcastle upon Tyne NE2 4 Tel: 0191 222 5659; The Old Vicarage, Grinton, Swaledale, Richmond DL11 6HR — MB BS 1969 Newc.; MD (Commend.) Newc. 1977; FRCS Eng. 1974; T(S) 1991. Prof. Orthop. Surg. Univ. Newc. u. Tyne. Socs: Fell. BOA; (Ex-Pres.) Brit. Orthop. Research Soc.; Brit. Hip Soc. Prev: Prof. Orthop. Surg. Univ. Leicester Sch. Med.; Sen. Lect. (Orthop. Surg.) Univ. Edin. & Hon. Cons. Orthop. Surg. Roy. Infirm. Edin. & P.ss Margt. Rose Orthop. Hosp.; Lect. (Orthop. Surg.) Univ. Newc.

GREGG, Rosaleen Catherine 75 Manchester Road, Wilmslow SK9 2JQ — MB BS 1987 Lond.; BSc Lond. 1984; MRCGP 1993; DCH RCP Lond. 1992; DRCOG 1992.

GREGG, William Victor Harold Holywell Hospital, Antrim BT41 2RJ Tel: 018494 65211 — MB BCh BAO 1980 Belf.; MRCPsych 1989; MRCGP 1984; DCH RCP Lond. 1984; DRCOG 1983. Cons. Psychiat. (Subst. Misuse) Holywell Hosp. Antrim.

GREGG-SMITH, Simon Jeremy John Radcliffe Hospital, Headington, Oxford OX3 9DU; 4 Old Quarry, Bloomfield Drive, Bath BA2 2BP — BM BCh 1984 Oxf.

GREGOR, Anna Department of Clinical Oncology, Western General Hospital, Crewe Road, Edinburgh EH4 2XU Tel: 0131 537 3051 Fax: 0131 537 2184 Email: anna.gregor@luht.nhs.scot.uk; 45 Spylaw Bank Road, Edinburgh EH13 0JF Tel: 0131 441 6360 — MRCS Eng. LRCP Lond. 1973; FRCP Ed. 1993; MRCP (UK) 1975; FRCR 1981. Cons. in Clin. Oncol.; Hon. Sen. Lect. Univ. Edin.

GREGOR, Catherine Binnie (retired) The Old Mill House, Crossmichael, Castle Douglas DG7 3BD — LRCP LRCS Ed. LRFPS Glas. 1953.

GREGOR, Mr Zdenek 94 Harley Street, London W1N 1AF Tel: 020 7935 0777 Fax: 020 7935 6860 Email: zjgregor@aol.com; Moorfields Eye Hospital, City Road, London EC1V 2PD Tel: 020 7253 3411 Fax: 020 7253 4696 — MRCS Eng. LRCP Lond. 1971; FRCS Eng. 1977; FRCOphth 1989; DO Eng. 1975. (Westm.) Cons. Ophth. Surg. Moorfields Eye Hosp. Lond. Socs: Fell. Roy. Soc. Med. (Mem. Counc. Ophth. Sect.); Fell. Roy. Coll. Ophth. (Examr. Final Exams.).; Counc. Europ. Soc. Ophth. (Sec. Gen.). Prev: Resid. Surg. Off. Moorfields Eye Hosp. City Rd. Lond.; Asst. Prof. Univ. S.. Calif., Los Angeles; Sen. Lect. (Ophth.) Univ. Lond.

GREGORI, Mr Alberto Carlo Paul Nethershields, Quarter, Hamilton ML3 7XP Email: gregoribub@aol.com — MB ChB 1982 Glas.; FRCS Eng. 1988; FRCS Ed. 1988; DFM Glas. 1993; FRCS (Orth.) Ed. 1995. (Glasgow) Cons. Surg. (Orthop.) Hairmyres & StoneHo. NHS Trust. Socs: Brit. Orthop. Assn.; World Orthopaedic Concern. Prev: Sen. Regist. (Orthop.) Vict. Infirm. Glas.; Regist. Rotat. (Orthop.) Roy. Infirm. Edin.; Govt. Med. Off. St. Paul's Mission, Zimbabwe.

GREGORI, Michael Doctors Surgery, 2 Padnell Road, Waterlooville PO8 8DZ Tel: 023 9226 3138 Fax: 023 9261 8100; 96 London Road, Cowplain, Waterlooville PO8 8EW Tel: 01705 368609 — MRCS Eng. LRCP Lond. 1974. (Westm.)

GREGOROWSKI, Lennox Fyfe The Riverside Surgery, Waterside, Evesham WR11 6JP Tel: 01386 40121 Fax: 01386 442615; Chandlers, Chandlers End, Ashton under Hill, Evesham WR11 6SS Tel: 01386 881454 — MB ChB 1973 Cape Town; 2000 Dip. Pall. Med. (University of Wales, Cardiff); MMedSc 1996; DRCOG 1978. (Univ. Birm.) Clin. Asst. Macmillan Unit, Evesham Hosp.

GREGORY, Adrian Bede The Health Centre, Cakeham Road, East Wittering, Chichester PO20 8BH Tel: 01243 673434 Fax: 01243 672563 — MB BS 1985 Lond.; BSc (Mech. Engineering) Lond. 1977, MB BS 1985; MSc (Biomech.) Surrey 1978; MRCGP 1989.

GREGORY, Amanda Lindsay Cherry Valley Health Centre, Kings Square, Belfast BT5 7BP Tel: 01232 401844; 5 Kensington Manor, Cherry Valley, Belfast BT5 6PE Tel: 01232 705999 — MB BCh BAO 1991 Belf.; MB BCh BAO (Hons.) Belf. 1991; DRCOG 1993. GP Retainee. Socs: BMA; Assoc. Mem. Roy. Coll. Midw.. Prev: GP Locum Belf.; Trainee GP/SHO Roy. Vict. Hosp. Belf. VTS; Ho. Off. Roy. Vict. Hosp.

GREGORY, Andrew Martin X-Ray Department, Epsom General Hospital, Dorking Road, Epsom KT18 7EG Tel: 01372 735735; 59 The Green, Ewell, Epsom KT17 3JU — MB BS 1972 Lond.; MRCP (UK) 1975; MRCS Eng. LRCP Lond. 1972; FRCR 1979; DMRD Eng. 1977. (Westm.) Cons. Radiol. Epsom & St Helier Trust; Cons. Radiologist, Ashtead Hosp., The Warren, Ashtead, Surrey KT21 2JB. Prev: Sen. Regist. Hammersmith Hosp. Lond.

GREGORY, Anna Lovisa 5 Blisworth Road, Gayton, Northampton NN7 3EY Tel: 01604 858028 — BM 1994 Soton.; MRCP 1998; MRCPCH 1998. (Soton.) Regist. (Paediat.), Roy. Childr.s Hosp., Melbourne, Australia. Prev: SHO Rotat. (Paediat.) QMC Nottm.

GREGORY, Anthony John Middle Barn, Rimpton, Yeovil BA22 8AB Tel: 01935 850708 — MRCS Eng. LRCP Lond. 1958. (Liverp.) Clin. Asst. (Dermat.) Weymouth & Dist. Hosp. & Salisbury Dist. Hosp. & Bridport Comm. Hosp. Prev: Clin. Asst. (Rheum. & Rehabil.) Salisbury Gen. Infirm.; SHO (Phys.) All St.s Hosp. Chatham; Ho. Surg. & Ho. Phys. St. Bart. Hosp. Rochester.

GREGORY, Barbara Anne 18 Leofric Close, Kings Bromley, Burton-on-Trent DE13 7JP — MB ChB 1972 Birm.; DA Eng. 1974. Asst. GP Barton-under-Needwood. Prev: Regist. (Anaesth.) Good Hope Hosp. Sutton Coldfield.

GREGORY, Bernadette Clare Woodeaves, Pleasant Harbour, Bewdley DY12 1AD Tel: 01923 262306 Email: jon.stratton@ntlworld.com — MB BS 1985 Lond.; MRCGP 2001; DMRD Liverp. 1991. (St. George's Hosp. Lond) p/t Salaried GP, Stourbridge. Socs: BMA.

GREGORY, Carol Anne Box 311, Fulbourn Hospital, Addenbrooke's NHS Trust, Fulbourn, Cambridge CB1 5EF Tel: 01223 218995 Fax: 01223 218992 — BM 1981 Soton.; MRCP (UK) 1984; MRCPsych 1990. (Southampton University Medical School) Cons. (Psychiat. of Old Age).

GREGORY, Carole Anne 54 Victoria Walk, Horsforth, Leeds LS18 4PP — MB ChB 1992 Leeds.

GREGORY, Darryl Ross Warneford Hospital, Headington, Oxford OX3 7JX Tel: 01865 741717 — BM BS 1994 Nottm.; BMedSci Nottm. 1992; MRCPsych 1998. (Nottm.) Specialist Regist. (Psychiat.) Oxf. Deanery.

GREGORY, David Andrew Cartington Terrace Medical Group, 1 Cartington Terrace, Heaton, Newcastle upon Tyne NE6 5RS Tel: 0191 265 5755 Fax: 0192 276 2921; 13 Claremont Street, Newcastle upon Tyne NE2 4AH — MB BS 1974 Lond.; MRCGP 1982. Lect. Dept. Family & Community Med. Univ. Newc. upon Tyne.

GREGORY, David Wynne White Gates, Orchard Lane, Crickhowell NP8 1BA Tel: 01873 810671 — MB BCh 1966 Wales; FRCP Lond. 1992, M 1969; FFR 1974; FRCR 1975; DMRD Eng. 1972; FRCP 1992. (Cardiff) Cons. Radiol. Mid Glam. AHA. Prev: Sen. Regist. Univ. Hosp. of Wales Cardiff; SHO (Chest Med.) Sully Hosp. Penarth.

GREGORY, Douglas Gordon Dr J M Beck and Partners, 21 Beaufort Road, Southbourne, Bournemouth BH6 5AJ Tel: 01202 433081 Fax: 01202 430527 — MB BCh 1977 Wales; DRCOG 1980.

GREGORY, Frances Patricia 50 The Keep, Blackheath, London SE3 0AF; Apart 3, Dundrum, Dublin 16, Republic of Ireland — MB BCh BAO 1979 NUI; FRCSI 1989; DTM & H RCP Lond. 1982; DCH NUI 1981. GP Thamesmead; Clin. Asst. (Gen. Surg.) Greenwich Dist. Hosp. Lond.

GREGORY, Gabriella 4 Rivers Cl, Ivybridge PL21 0JN — MB ChB 1997 Manch.

GREGORY, Geraldine Anne 91 Drift Road, Stamford PE9 1XB — MB BS 1984 Lond.; MRCP (UK) 1990; DCH RCP Lond. 1988. Regist. (Paediat.) Leicester Roy. Infirm.

GREGORY, Grace Kathleen (retired) 20 Green Lane, Hendon, London NW4 2NP — LMSSA 1955 Lond.; MB BS Rangoon 1935; DTM Calcutta 1946; DPH Eng. 1959.

GREGORY, Helen Department of Medical Genetics, Medical School, Forester Hill, Aberdeen AB25 2ZD Tel: 01224 552120 — MB BS 1981 Newc.; MRCGP 1988. (Newcastle-Upon-Tyne) Staff

Grade Med. Genetics (p/t) Dept. Med. Genetics Aberd.; GP Asst. Socs: RCGP; Clin. Genetics Soc.; Cancer Genetics Gp. Prev: research fell. Med. Genetics (p/t).

GREGORY, Ian Colin Tel: 020 7233 6464 Fax: 020 7624 7309 Email: ian.maclaren@laht.scot.nhs.uk — MB 1965; MA Camb. 1966, MD 1975; BChir 1964; MRCP Lond. 1967; FFA RCS Eng. 1969. (Univ. Coll. Hosp.) p/t Hon. Cons. Anaesth. Char. Cross Hosp. Lond. Prev: Cons. Anaesth. Char. Cross Hosp. Lond.; Sen. Regist. (Anaesth.) St. Thos. Hosp. Lond.; Ho. Phys., Ho. Surg. Surgic Unit & Research Asst. Med. Unit Univ. Coll. Hosp.

GREGORY, Irene Dorothy Rosalie (retired) 29 Homewood Crescent, Chislehurst BR7 6PS — MB ChB Bristol 1944; FRCS Eng. 1953; DOMS Eng. 1946. Prev: Cons. Ophth. Qu. Mary's Hosp. Sidcup.

GREGORY, Janet Elizabeth Joan CIBA-GEIGY Pharmaceuticals, Wimblehurst Road, Horsham RH12 4AB Tel: 01403 272827 — MB ChB 1977 Manch.; DPM Eng. 1985. Med. Adviser CIBA-GEIGY Pharmaceut. Prev: GP N. Yorks.; Trainee GP Lancs. VTS; SHO (A & E) Preston Roy. Infirm.

GREGORY, Jill 31 Beech Court, Darras Hall, Ponteland, Newcastle upon Tyne NE20 9NE Tel: 01661 872784 Email: jillgregory@compuserve.com — MB BS Newc. 1969; MSc Newc. 1990; DCH RCP Lond. 1972; MRCPCH 1997. SCMO Newc. City Health Trust. Socs: N. Eng. Paediat. Soc.; Brit. Assn. Community Child Health. Prev: Regist. Darlington HA; SHO (Paediat.) Babies Hosp. Newc.

GREGORY, John Stuart (retired) The Knoll, 15 Aughton Road, Swallownest, Sheffield S26 4TF Tel: 0114 287 2446 — MB ChB 1954 Sheff. Prev: SHO Rheum. Research Centre Stoke Mandeville Hosp.

GREGORY, John Welbourn Department of Child Health, University of Wales, College of Medicine, Heath Park, Cardiff CF14 4XN Tel: 029 2074 2274 Fax: 029 2074 4283 Email: wchjwg@cardiff.ac.uk — MB ChB 1981 Dundee; MD Dundee 1992; MRCP (UK) 1986; DCH RCP Lond. 1984; FCPCH 1997; FRCP (UK) 1997. Sen. Lect. (Paediat. Endocrinol.) & Hon. Cons. Univ. Wales Coll. Med. Cardiff. Socs: Brit. Diabetic Assn. (Med. & Scientif. Sect.); Eur. Soc. Paediat. Endocrinol. (Progr. Organising & Summer Sch. Comm. Mem.); Brit. Soc. for Paediatric Endocrinol. & Diabetes (Acad. Waison Off.). Prev: 1st. Asst. (Child Health) Univ. Newc.; Clin. Research Fell. (Paediat., Endocrinol. & Diabetes) Univ. Dundee Ninewells Hosp. & Med. Sch. Dundee; Regist. (Paediat.) Tayside HB.

GREGORY, Karen Linda, Flight Lt. RAF Med. Br. Brownhill Road Surgery, 2 Brownhill RD, Chandlers Ford, Eastleigh SO53 2ZB Tel: 02380 252414 Fax: 02380 366604; Tulluce, Romsey Road, West Wellow, Romsey SO51 6EB — MB ChB 1991 Liverp.; MRCGP 1995; DCH 1997; DFFP 1998. Partner, GP Brownhill RD Surg. Socs: MRCGP; BMA. Prev: Princip. GP RAF Oldham.

GREGORY, Katharine Susan Timbers, Rowney Court, Rowney Green Lane, Birmingham B48 7QU — MB ChB 1988 Birm.

GREGORY, Keith Morley 31 Beech Court, Darras Hall, Ponteland, Newcastle upon Tyne NE20 9NE Tel: 01661 872784 — MB BS Newc. 1969; MFOM RCP Lond. 1990, AFOM 1985; MFFP 1993; MRCOG 1974; FFOM 1998. Occupat. Phys. BUPA Occupat. Healthcare. Socs: Soc. Occupat. Med. Prev: Ho. Off. Shotley Bridge Hosp.; Trainee (O & G) Newc. HA Train. Scheme; Demonst. (Path.) Roy. Vict. Infirm. Newc.

GREGORY, Margaret Badgers Cross, Longwood Lane, Failand, Bristol BS8 3TQ — MB ChB 1980 Bristol; FFARCS Eng. 1984. Cons. Anaesth. Frenchay Hosp. Bristol.

GREGORY, Michael Andrew Royal Oldham Hospital, Rochdale Road, Oldham OL1 2JH Tel: 0161 627 8828; 3 Turnfield Close, Rochdale OL16 2QF — MB BS 1981 Lond.; FFA RCS Eng. 1986. Cons. Anaesth. Roy. Oldham Hosp. Prev: Lect. (Anaesth.) Chinese Univ. of Hong Kong.

GREGORY, Michael William West Timperley Medical Centre, 21 Dawson Road, Altrincham WA14 5PF Tel: 0161 929 1515 Fax: 0161 941 6500 — MB ChB 1989 Liverp.; MRCGP 1994; DCH RCP Lond. 1994; DRCOG 1992. Prev: Civil Med. Pract. Rhine Garrison, Germany.

GREGORY, Monica Mary Lister Hospital, Stevenage SG1 4AB — MRCS Eng. LRCP Lond. 1965; BSc (Hons. Physiol.) Lond. 1962, MB BS 1965; FRCPath 1984, M 1972. (Roy. Free)

GREGORY, Nigel Angus Patrick The Barn Surgery, Hill Road, Watlington OX49 5AF Tel: 01491 612444 Fax: 01491 613988 Email: gregory.angus@gp-k84008.nhs.uk; Tel: 01491 614360 Fax: 01491 614362 — MB ChB 1986 Birm.

GREGORY, Peter Andrew 3 Gainsborough Court, Skipton BD23 1QG — MB ChB 1982 Manch.; MRCGP 1991.

GREGORY, Peter John 78 Manor Rise, Lichfield WS14 9RF — MB 1984 Camb.; BChir 1983.

GREGORY, Peter Leslie Tel: 0115 924 9924 — MB BS 1987 Lond.; MSc (Sports Med.) 1997 Nottingham; BSc Lond. 1984; MRCGP 1991; DCH RCP Lond. 1990. MSc Course Director, Sports Med., Univ. of Nottm., Nottm. Socs: Roy. Coll. Gen. Pract.; Brit. Assn. Sport & Exercise Med.; Brit. Med. Assn. Prev: Princip. Gen. Pract. Lower Quinton; Clin. Asst. Orthop. Warwick Hosp.; Clin. Fell., Centre for Sports Med., Nottm.

GREGORY, Peter Robin 11 Scholars Walk, Gerrards Cross SL9 0EJ — MB BS 1963 Lond.

GREGORY, Mr Peter Thomas Sherwood Conquest Hospital, The Ridge, St Leonards-on-Sea TN37 7RD Tel: 01424 755255; Westcourt House, Caldbec Hill, Battle TN33 0JS Tel: 01424 772553 — MB BChir Camb. 1977; FRCS Eng. 1986; FCOphth 1988; DO RCS Eng. 1983. (Camb. & St. Bart.) Cons. Ophth. Hastings & Rother NHS Trust. Socs: Fell. Roy. Soc. Med. Prev: Sen. Regist. (Ophth.) Char. Cross & Moorfields Hosps. Lond.; Regist. (Ophth.) Qu. Alexander Hosp. Cosham; SHO (Neurosurg. & Ophth.) & Temp. Lect. (Anat.) St. Bart. Hosp. Lond.

GREGORY, Philipp Henry Blackfield Medical Centre, Blackfield, Southampton SO4 1XA Tel: 02380 899119; 47 Roman Way, Dibden Purlieu, Southampton SO45 4RP Tel: 02380 849339 — MB BS 1982 Lond.; MA Oxf. 1985; MRCGP 1986; DRCOG 1986; DCH RCP Lond. 1985. Tutor & GP Trainer Soton.

GREGORY, Ralph Peter Neurology Department, Battle Hospital, Reading RG1 3AG Tel: 0118 963 6475 Fax: 0118 963 6472 Email: ralphgregory@compuserve.com — BM 1982 Soton.; MRCP (UK) 1986; FRCP 1997. Cons. Neurol. Roy. Berks. & Battle Hosp. Trust Reading; Cons. Neurol. Radcliffe Infirm. Oxf.; Sen. Clin. Lect. Oxf. Univ. Prev: Cons. Neurol. RAF Med. Br.

GREGORY, Richard John November Cottage, Stody, Melton Constable NR24 2ED — MB BS 1979 Lond.; MRCS Eng. LRCP Lond. 1978; DRCOG 1983; Cert. Av. Med. 1989.

GREGORY, Richard Mark, Surg. Lt. RN The Wardroom, Royal Naval Hospital, Haslar, Gosport PO12 2AA Tel: 01705 584255; 41 Gaulby Lane, Stoughton, Leicester LE2 2FL Tel: 0116 271 2072 — MB ChB 1993 Sheff.

GREGORY, Robert Department of Medicine, University Hospitals of Leicester NHS Trust, Leicester General Hospital, Gwendolen Road, Leicester LE5 4PW Tel: 0116 258 8017 Fax: 0116 273 3067; 41 St. Catharine's Way, Houghton on the Hill, Leicester LE7 9HE — MB BS 1982 Lond.; BA (Hons.) Oxf. 1979; DM Nottm. 1989; MRCP (UK) 1985; FRCP 1998. (Univ. Oxf. & St. Thos. Hosp.) Cons. Phys. (Gen. Med., Diabetes & Endocrinol.) Leicester Gen. Hosp.; Assoc. Postgrad. Dean Leicester Univ. Prev: Sen. Regist. (Gen. Med., Diabetes & Endocrinol.) Addenbrooke's Hosp. Camb.; Clin. Research Regist. (Diabetes & Immunol.) Univ. Hosp. & Qu. Med. Centre Nottm.

GREGORY, Robert John Heywood Flat 3, Burdon Terrace, Jesmond, Newcastle upon Tyne NE2 3AE — MB BS 1981 Newc.

GREGORY, Rosemary Kate Lower Perwood Farm, Hindon, Salisbury SP3 6TA; 6 Tenham Avenue, Streatham Hill, London SW2 4XR Tel: 01747 820687 Email: rosemarykate@aol.com — MB BS 1991 (Hons.) Newc.; MRCP (UK) 1994; MD 1999. Cons. Med. Oncol. S.ampton Univ. Hosp. Trust. Prev: Sen. Regist. Med. Oncol., Roy. Marsden Hosp. Sutton.

GREGORY, Sarah McColl 79 Christ Church Road, London SW14 7AT Tel: 020 8 878 2447; 4 Darke Street, Torrens ACT 2607, Australia Tel: 00 61 2862074 — MB BS 1994 Sydney. (Univ. Sydney & Concord Hosp.) Regist. (Med.) & Resid. Concord Hosp. Sydney, NSW, Austral.

GREGORY, Simon Andrew 6 Weston Court, Denmark Road, Kingston upon Thames KT1 2RX — MB BS 1985 Lond.

GREGORY, Simon David Dr A Willis and Partners, King Edward Road Surgery, Christchurch Medical Centre, King Edward Road, Northampton NN1 5LY Tel: 01604 633466 Fax: 01604 603227 — MB BS 1990 Lond.; BSc (Hons.) Lond. 1987; MRCGP 1994; DCH

RCP Lond. 1993; DRCOG 1993; DFFP 1993. (St. Bartholomew's Hospital) Prev: Trainee GP N.ampton VTS; Ho. Surg. Profess. Surg. Unit St. Bart. Hosp. Lond.; Ho. Phys. N.ampton Gen. Hosp.

GREGORY, Wendy Louise Wansbeck & Ashington Hospital, Ashington NE63 9JJ Tel: 01670 521212 Fax: 01670 529341 Email: wgregory@doctors.org.uk; 36 Rothwell Road, Gosforth, Newcastle upon Tyne NE3 1UA — MB BS 1987 Newc.; PhD Newc. 1994, BSc (Hons.) 1982, MB BS 1987; MRCP (UK) 1990. Cons. Phys. in Gen. Med. with an interest in Gastroenterol., Wansbeck & Ashington Hosp. Socs: RSM; Brit. Soc. of Gastroenterol. Prev: Regist. Liver Transpl. RPAH Sydney Australia; Specialist Regist. (Gastro) Darlington Memor. Hosp.; Specialist Regist. (Gastro) Sundeland Roy. Hosp.

GREGORY-EVANS, Mr Kevin Imperial College School of Medicine, Western Eye Hospital, Marylebone Road, London NW1 5YE Tel: 020 7886 3202 Fax: 020 7886 3203 Email: k.gregory-evans@ic.ac.uk; 50 Powys Lane, Palmers Green, London N13 4HS Tel: 020 8886 6093 — MB BS 1985 Lond.; BSc (Hons.) Phys. Lond. 1982, MD 1996; FRCS Glas. 1989; FRCOphth 1990; DO RCS Eng. 1988. (St. Bartholomews Medical School London) Sen. Lect. Imperial Coll. Sch. of Med. Lond.; Hon. Cons. (Ophth.) W.ern Eye Hosp. Lond. Prev: Sen. Regist. Moorfields Eye Hosp. Lond.; Research Fell. (Opthalmology) Inst. Opthalmology Lond.; Regist. St. Paul's Eye Hosp. Liverp.

GREGSON, Mr Arthur Edwin Ward (retired) 27 Netherthorpe Way, North Anston, Sheffield S25 4FL Tel: 01909 563544 — MB ChB 1947 Leeds; FRCS Glas. 1962; FRFPS Glas. 1960.

***GREGSON, Catherine Ann** North Cumbria HA, Wavell Drive, Rosehill Industrial Estate, Carlisle CA1 2SE — MB ChB 1986 Ed.

GREGSON, Dorothy Jean 36 The Street, Croxton, Thetford IP24 1LN — MB BChir 1989 Camb.; MA Camb. 1990, MB BChir 1989. Regist. (Pub. Health Med.) Norwich HA. Prev: SHO (O & G) Hinchingbrooke Hosp VTS.

GREGSON, Ernest David Clifton Medical Centre, 571 Farnborough Road, Clifton, Nottingham NG11 9DN Tel: 0115 921 1288; 6 Manor Park, Ruddington, Nottingham NG11 6DS — MB BS 1975 Newc.

GREGSON, Ernest Renaud Lewtas (retired) Craig Dunain, 51 Dundee Road, Perth PH2 7AN Tel: 01738 639120 — MB ChB Ed. 1941. Prev: GP Kirkcaldy 1948-1984.

GREGSON, Jacqueline The Grange, Dishforth Road, Copt Hewick, Ripon HG4 5DF — MB ChB 1998 Manch.; MB ChB Manch 1998.

GREGSON, Janine Mary Fazakerley Hospital, Liverpool L9 7AL Tel: 0151 525 5980 — MB ChB 1992 Liverp.; MRCP (UK) 1997. Specialist Regist. (Research) Fazakerley Hosp. Liverp.

GREGSON, John Francis Psychiatry Training Programme, Wellington School of Medicine, Mein St., Wellington, New Zealand Tel: 00 64 4 385 5541; 29 Meadway Park, Gerrards Cross SL9 7NN Tel: 01753 892005 — MB ChB 1986 Leic.; BSc (Med. Sci.) Leic. 1984; MRCP (UK) 1991. Regist. (Psychiat.) Wellington Train. Program. Prev: Regist. (Psychiat.) ChristCh. Train. Progr., NZ; SHO (Psychiat.) S. Trent; Regist. (Med.) Glenfield Gen. Hosp. Leics.

GREGSON, Mr John Stephen Kennedy Way Surgery, Kennedy Way, Yate, Gloucester BS37 4AA Tel: 01454 313849 Fax: 01454 329039; Woodlands, Dodington Road, Chipping Sodbury, Gloucester BS37 6HS — MB BS Lond. 1965; FRCS Eng. 1972; MRCS Eng. LRCP Lond. 1965. (Guy's) Socs: BMA. Prev: SHO (Plastic Surg.) Frenchay Hosp. Bristol; SHO Rotat. (Surg.) Bristol Roy. Infirm.; Cas. Off. & Ho. Surg. (Orthop.) Guy's Hosp. Lond.

GREGSON, Jonathan 11 Waverley Drive, Tarleton, Preston PR4 6XX — MB ChB 1998 Liverp.; MB ChB Liverp 1998.

GREGSON, Juliet Pamela Grove Surgery, 83 The Grove, Christchurch BH23 2EZ Tel: 01202 481192 Fax: 01202 479732; The Grove Surgery, 83 The Grove, Christchurch BH23 2EZ Tel: 01202 481192 Fax: 01202 479732 — MB BS 1992 Lond.; DRCOG 1995. (King's Coll. Sch. Med. & Dent. Lond.)

GREGSON, Mr Patrick Alan North Staffordshire Royal Infirmary, Princes Drive, Stoke-on-Trent ST4 7LN Tel: 01782 714565; 20 Basford Park Road, Maybank, Newcastle ST5 0PT Tel: 01782 611520 — MB BS 1987 Lond.; FRCS Eng. 1992. (Char. Cross & Westm. Med. Sch.) Specialist Regist. (Orthop.) N. Staffs. Roy. Infirm. Socs: Brit. Orthop. Assn. Prev: Regist. Rotat. (Orthop.) Robt. Jones & Agnes Hunt Orthop. Hosp. OsW.ry.

GREGSON, Peter Noel 31 Northway, Maghull, Liverpool L31 7BG Tel: 0151 520 2488 Fax: 0151 531 1041; 1 Sandhurst Way, Lydiay, Liverpool L31 4DR — MB ChB Leeds 1969; MRCGP 1976; DCH RCP Lond. 1983; DObst RCOG 1976. GP Maghull. Socs: BMA. Prev: Ho. Phys. (Gen. Med. & Paediat.) S.port Gen. Infirm.; Ho. Surg. Providence Hosp. St. Helen's; SHO (O & G) Billinge Hosp. Wigan.

GREGSON, Raine Sara Irene Heathfielde Medical Centre, Lyttleton Road, London N2 0EE Tel: 020 8458 9262; 4 Francis Terrace, London N19 5PY Tel: 020 7272 6910 — MA Oxf. 1984, BM BCh 1983; DCH RCP Lond. 1986.

GREGSON, Mr Richard Michael Christopher 4 Francis Terrace, London N19 5PY Tel: 020 7272 6910 — BM BCh 1983 Oxf.; MA, DPhil Oxf. 1982, BM BCh 1983; FRCS Ed. 1988. Resid. Surg. Off. Moorfields Eye Hosp. Lond.

GREGSON, Roger Herald Salt Department of Radiology, Queens Med Cen, Nottingham NG7 2UH Tel: 0115 924 9924 Fax: 0115 970 9962 — MRCS Eng. LRCP Lond. 1974; BSc Lond. 1971, MB BS 1974; FRCR 1981; DMRD Eng. 1980; T(R)(CR) 1991. (St. Mary's) Cons. Radiol. Univ. Hosp. Nottm. Prev: Sen. Regist. & Regist. (Radiol.) St. Mary's Hosp. Lond.; SHO (Med.) Hammersmith Hosp. Lond.

GREGSON, Stephen Neil The Oaks, Nightingale Way, Swanley BR8 7UP Tel: 01322 668775 Fax: 01322 668010 — MB BS 1982 Lond.; MRCGP 1987; DCH RCP Lond. 1986; DRCOG 1986.

GREGSON, Susanna 4 Wheelwright Court, Walkhampton, Yelverton PL20 6LA Email: susiegregson@ntlworld.com — MB BS 1993 Lond.; DCH 1996; DRCOG 1997; BSc Lond. 1990. GP (Asst.) Kingskerswell & Ipplepen Med. Pract., Kingskerswell, Devon; Trainee GP Roy. Devon & Exeter Hosp. VTS.; CMO in Family Plann., S. Devon Healthcare Trust; GP Locum, S. & W. Devon. Socs: MRCGP.

GREIFF, Jonathan Miles Cameron Department of Anaesthesia, Leicester Royal Infirmary, Leicester LE1 5WW Tel: 0116 254 1414 Email: jgreiff@uhl.trent.nhs.uk; Prestlands, Ashby Road, Leicester LE17 5PZ Tel: 0116 247 8130 — MB BS 1985 Newc.; BMedSc (Hons.) Newc. 1982; FCAnaesth 1992; DA (UK) 1989. Cons. Anaesth. (Intens. Care) Leicester Roy. Infirm.; Hons. Clin. tutor, Uni. Of Leicester. Prev: Sen. Regist. (Anaesth.) Leicester Roy. Infirm.; Research Fell. & Regist. (Anaesth.) Leicester Roy. Infirm.; SHO (Anaesth.) Newc. HA.

GREIG, Adam Peter McGregor Sunny Meed Surgery, 15-17 Heathside Road, Woking GU22 7EY Tel: 01483 772760 Fax: 01483 730354; Chiltern Lodge, Station Road, Shiplake, Henley-on-Thames RG9 3JS — MB BS 1977 Lond.; DCH RCP Lond. 1981; DRCOG 1980.

GREIG, Agnes Isdale (retired) 21 Townsend Place, Kirkcaldy KY1 1HB Tel: 01592 260643 — MB ChB 1945 Ed. Prev: Ho. Surg. Simpson Memor. Pavilion, Roy. Infirm. Edin.

GREIG, Miss Aina Vibeke Hiller Chater's Cottage, Cranfield Road, Moulsoe, Newport Pagnell MK16 0HL — MB BChir 1994 Camb.; MA Camb. 1995; FRCS (Eng.) 1998. (Camb.)

GREIG, Anthony David The Bourne Valley Practice, 10-12 High St., Ludgershall, Andover SP11 9PZ Tel: 01264 400300 Fax: 01264 400310 Email: roskoff@msn.com; 11 Camomile Drive, Ludgershall, Andover SP11 9TA Tel: 01264 791985 — MB BS 1978 Lond.; MRCGP 1983. (St. Mary's Hosp. Lond.) Counc. Mem. Child Accid. Preven. Trust; Mem. Prescribine Policy Gp. Wilts. HA. Socs: GPs. in Asthma Gp. Prev: Mem. (Exec. Comm.) Wessex GP Educat. Trust; Mem. Fac. Bd. RCGP (Wessex Region); SHO (Obst.) Kingston Hosp. Kingston upon Thames.

GREIG, Anthony James 45 Weybourne Gardens, Southend-on-Sea SS2 4AU — MB ChB 1963 Liverp.; FFA RCS Eng. 1969; DA Eng. 1967. Sen. Regist. Liverp. Matern. Hosp.

GREIG, Charlotte Hutchison (retired) 7 Ancaster View, Leeds LS16 5HR Tel: 0113 278 6330 — MB ChB 1956 Aberd.; MFFP 1993. Locum Fam. Plann. Doctor Leeds Community and Ment. Health Trust. Prev: SCMO Leeds Community & Ment. Health Servs.

GREIG, David Charles (retired) Oldcart House, West Mains of Keithock, Brechin DD9 7QD Tel: 01356 622719 — MB ChB Ed. 1950.

GREIG, Douglas Graham Department of Anaesthesia, Wythenshawe Hospital, Southmoor Road, Manchester M23 9LT Tel: 0161 291 5710 — MB ChB 1987 Manch.; BSc St. And. 1984; FRCA 1994; DA (UK) 1991. (St. Andrews & Manchester) Cons.

(Anaesth.) S. Manch. Univ. Hosp. NHS Trust. Socs: BMA; Assn. Anaesth.; Manch. Med. Soc.

GREIG, Emma Rachel Royal Free Hospital, Pond St, London NW3 2QG Tel: 01282 613827, 020 794 0500 Fax: 01282 613827 — MB ChB 1992 Birm.; PhD 2000 Manc; MRCP (UK) 1995. (Birm.) Specialist Regist. (Gastroenterol. & Gen. internal Med.), N. E. Thames region. Prev: Roy. Lond. Hosp. Lond. Oct 2000-Sept 2001; DidCh. Hosp., Romford. Apr 1999 - Sept 2000; Clin. Research Fell. (Gastroenterol.) Hope Hosp. Salford.

GREIG, George Charles Trades Lane Health Centre, Causewayend, Coupar Angus, Blairgowrie PH13 9DP Tel: 01828 627312 Fax: 01828 628253; Beechbank, Forfar Road, Coupar Angus, Blairgowrie PH13 9AN — MB ChB 1978 Dundee; MRCGP 1982.

GREIG, Gordon Eric The Health Centre, Whyteman's Brae, Kirkcaldy KY1 2NA Tel: 01592 642178 Fax: 01592 644782 — MB ChB 1974 Ed.; BSc Ed. 1971, MB ChB 1974; MRCGP 1978; DRCOG 1978.

GREIG, Hamish David Brechin Health Centre, Infirmary Street, Brechin DD9 7AY Tel: 01356 624411 Fax: 01356 623259; Pearse Croft, 8-10 Pearse St, Brechin DD9 6JR Tel: 01356 622823 Fax: 01356 622823 — MB ChB 1978 Aberd.; MRCGP 1982; DRCOG 1981. Socs: Vice-Chairm. Scott. Assn. of Gen.Pract. Community Hosp.

GREIG, Henry Buer Wright Inversnaid, Martock Road, Long Sutton, Langport TA10 9HU — MB ChB 1945 Glas.; FRCPath 1963. Prev: Prof. Haemat. Univ. Natal.

GREIG, James Robertson, OBE (retired) 10 Cranfield Way, Brampton, Huntingdon PE28 4QZ Tel: 01480 383912 — MB ChB 1960 Aberd.; MSc (Occupat. Med.) Lond. 1973; MFOM RCP Lond. 1981; DIH Eng. 1973. Prev: Off. Commanding RAF Hosps. Ely & Wroughton.

GREIG, Jane Flat 6, 24 Queens Avenue, London N10 3NR — MB BS 1993 Lond.

GREIG, Jennifer Elizabeth Wood Alloa Health Centre, Marshill, Alloa FK10 1AB Tel: 01259 212088 Fax: 01259 724788; 31 Ramsey Tullis Drive, Tullibody, Alloa FK10 2UD Tel: 01259 720421 Email: brardwood@btinternet.com — MB ChB 1986 Ed.; MRCGP 1990; DCH RCP Lond. 1989; DRCOG 1988. GP Partner. Prev: Trainee GP Viewfield Med. Centre Stirling; Trainee GP/SHO (Gen. Med.) Stirling Roy. Infirm. VTS.

GREIG, Julia Margaret Department of Infectious Diseases, Birmingham Heartlands Hospital, Birmingham B9 5SS Tel: 0121 766 6611 Email: jmgreig@aol.com — MB BS 1991 Lond.; BSc (Hons.) Genetics Lond. 1988; MRCP (UK) 1994; DTM & H RCP 1998. Specialist Regist. (Infec. Dis. & gen. Med.) W. Midl. Region. Socs: Train. Grade Counc. Mem.; Brit. Infec. Soc. Prev: Trainee GP Camb.

GREIG, Kathleen 251 Bellahouston Drive, Mosspark, Glasgow G52 1QG — MB ChB 1996 Ed.

GREIG, Lynn Doreen 5 Shaw Road, Glasgow G62 6LU — MB ChB 1995 Glas.; MRCP (UK) 1998. Research Fell., W.ern Gen. Hosp. Prev: SHO (Gen. Med.) Glas. Roy. Infirm.

GREIG, Marjory Anne Department of Microbiology, St Richard's Hospital, Spitalfield Lane, Chichester PO19 4SE Tel: 01243 788122 Fax: 01243 831631 Email: marjory.greig@rws-tr.nhs.uk — MB ChB 1982 Glas.; MRCPath 1988; Dip. Hlth. Mgt. Keele 1994. (University of Glasgow) Cons. Microbiol. St. Richards Hosp. Chichester. Socs: Hon. Sec. Hosp. Infec. Soc. Prev: Sen. Regist. (Bacteriol.) W.. Infirm. Glas.; Regist. (Microbiol.) S.mead Hosp. Bristol.

GREIG, Mary McDonald Silvan House, Manor Farm Road, Waresley, Sandy SG19 3BX Tel: 01767 650494 — MB ChB 1945 Leeds; DPH Belf. 1962. (Leeds)

GREIG, Richard Anthony 7 Laburnum Grove, Dartington, Totnes TQ9 6EX Tel: 01803 862346 — MB BS 1955 Lond.; LMSSA Lond. 1955; DObst RCOG 1964. (St. Mary's) Prev: Ho. Surg. & Ho. Phys. Freedom Fields Hosp. Plymouth; Ho. Off. O & G Ronkswood Hosp. Worcester.

GREIG, Rupert Hector (retired) Flat 3, Abbeyfield Home, Camden Road, Brecon LD3 7RT Tel: 01874 623169 — MB ChB Ed. 1938.

GREISS, Gamal George 28 Whinney Heys Road, Blackpool FY3 8NP Tel: 01253 397056 — MB BCh 1981 Ain Shams; MRCOG 1992. Regist. (O & G) Blackpool & Wyre HA.

GREISS, Mr Magdi Ernest West Cumberland Hospital, Hensingham, Whitehaven CA28 8JG Tel: 01946 693181 Fax: 01946 523532 — MD 1982 Cairo; MB BCh (Hons.) Cairo 1972; FRCS Glas. 1978; MChOrth Liverp. 1981. (Cairo) Cons. Orthop. Surg. W. Cumbld. Hosp.; Vis. Hon. Lect. (Orthop.) Teesside Univ. Socs: Fell. BOA; Fell. Brit. Orthop. Foot Soc.; Mem. World Orthop. Concern. Prev: Temp. Cons. Orthop. Surg. & Hon. Fell. Rbt Jones & A Hunt Orth. Hosp. OsW.ry & Allied Hosps.; Orthop. Regist. OsW.ry; Orthop. Regist. Profess. Unit Roy. Liverp. Childr. Hosp.

GREISS, Michel Ayoub Mikhail Regional Blood Transfusion Centre, Royal Infirmary, Forest Hill, Aberdeen AB25 2ZW Tel: 01224 685685 Fax: 01224 695351/662200 Email: michaelgreiss@snbts.csa.scot.nhs.uk; 71 Beechgrove Terrace, Aberdeen AB15 5DS Tel: 01224 621459 — MB BCh 1971 Cairo; PhD Ed. 1984; BSc Cairo 1964; CTCM & H RCP Ed. 1993. Assoc. Specialist Regional Blood Transfus. Centre Aberd.; Hon. Lect. (Transfus. Med.) Aberd. Univ. Socs: Brit. Blood Transfus. Soc.; Brit. Soc. Immunol.; Assn. Clin. Path. Prev: Regist. Nat. Health Laborat. Khartoum; Regist. Edin. Blood Transfus. Serv.

GRELLIER, Leonie Frances Louise Worthing Hospital, Lyndhurst Road, Worthing BN11 2DH Tel: 01903 205111 Fax: 01903 285045 — MB BS 1988 Lond.; BSc Lond. 1985, MB BS 1988; MRCP (UK) 1991; MD London 1998. Cons. Gastroenterol.

GRENDER, Barbara Celia, Surg. Lt. RN 26 Penn Road, London N7 9RD — MB BCh BAO 1973 Dub.; BA Dub. 1971, MB BCh BAO 1973; CIH Dund 1975. (Tc Dub.) Med. Off. H.M. Dockyard Rosyth.

GRENFELL, Anasuya c/o Jeffrey Kelson Diabetic Centre, Central Middlesex Hospital, Acton Lane, London NW10 7NS Tel: 020 7453 2401 Fax: 020 7453 2415 Email: ana.grenfell@cmh-tr.nthames.nhs.uk — MB BS 1978 Lond.; MA Oxf. 1975; MD Lond. 1988; FRCP Lond. 1996; MRCP Lond. 1981. (Univ. Coll. Hosp.) Cons. Diabetes & Gen. Med. Centr. Middlx. Hosp. Prev: Sen. Regist. (Diabetes & Med.) Ipswich & Camb.; Regist. (Nephrol.) St. Paul's Hosp. Lond.; Regist. (Diabetes) King's Coll. Hosp. Lond.

***GRENFELL, Caroline Jane Pascoe** 31 Yester Road, Chislehurst BR7 5HN Tel: 07803 987524 (Mobile) — MB BS 1998 Lond.; BA Hons Cantab 1995; MB BS Lond 1998.

GRENFELL, Patricia Mary 5 Druid Road, Bristol BS9 1LJ Tel: 0117 968 3881 — MRCS Eng. LRCP Lond. 1951; MD Liverp. 1955, MB ChB 1951; DCH Eng. 1954; FRCOG 1974, M 1957, DObst 1954. (Liverp.) Prev: Assoc. Specialist (O & G) S.mead Hosp. Bristol; Regist. (O & G) United Bristol Hosps.; Resid. Obst. Off. Qu. Charlotte's Matern. Hosp. Lond.

GRENFELL, Rachel Catherine St Johns House, Sharow, Ripon HG4 5BN — MB ChB 1998 Dund.; MB ChB Dund 1998.

GRENFELL, Rowena Christine Kirkham Health Centre, Moor Street, Kirkham, Preston PR4 2DL Tel: 01772 683420 — MB ChB 1986 Sheff.; MRCGP 1992. Prev: SHO (A & E) Doncaster Roy. Infirm.; Ho. Phys. & Ho. Surg. Hallamsh. Hosp. Sheff.; Trainee GP Lancs. & Auckland, NZ.

GRENFELL-SHAW, Jennifer Mary Air Balloon Surgery, Kenn Road, St George, Bristol BS5 7PD Tel: 0117 909 9914 Fax: 0117 908 6660; 3 Great Brockeridge, Bristol BS9 3TY Tel: 0117 962 2693 — BM BCh 1989 Oxf.; MA Camb. 1989; MRCP (UK) 1992; MRCGP (Distinc.) 1996; DFFP 1995; DRCOG 1995. (Univ. Oxf.) p/t GP Princip. Socs: BMA. Prev: GP/Regist. Camberley; SHO (A & E) Frimley Pk. Hosp.; Regist. (Pub. Health Med.) S. & W. RHA.

GRENIER, Helen Patricia Mount View Practice, London Street Medical Centre, London Street, Fleetwood FY7 6HD Tel: 01253 873312 Fax: 01253 873130; 2 The Meadows, Thornton-Cleveleys FY5 2TL Tel: 01253 827841 — MB ChB 1981 Manch.; MRCGP 1985; DRCOG 1984; Cert. Family Plann. JCC 1984.

GRENNAN, David Michael Department of Rheumatology, Wrightington Hospital, Appley Bridge, Wigan WN6 9EP Tel: 01257 256420 Fax: 01257 256375; 7 Leaconfield Drive, Worsley, Manchester M28 2WE — MB ChB Liverp. 1969; PhD Strathclyde 1976; MD Liverp. 1977; FRCP Lond. 1986; FRCP Glas. 1982; MRCP (UK) 1972; T(M) 1991. (Liverp.) Cons. Rheum. Wrightington Hosp. Lancs. Prev: Prof. Rheum. Sydney Univ. 1992-1994; Reader (Rheum.) Manch. Univ.; Sen. Lect. (Med.) Univ. Otago, NZ.

GRENVILLE, John Stephen Macklin Street Surgery, 90 Macklin Street, Derby DE1 2JX Tel: 01332 340381 Fax: 01332 345387; Derbyshire LMC, 98 Eaton Bank, Duffield, Belper DE56 4BH Tel: 01332 842762 Fax: 01332 842762 Email: john.grenville@mail.sderby-ha.trent.nhs.uk — MB BChir 1978 Camb.; MA Camb. 1978; MRCGP 1981; DRCOG 1980. Sec. N. &

S.. Derbysh. LMC; Clin. Complaints Adviser to the MDU. Socs: BMA (Ex-Chairm. Derby Div.); Med. Defence Union. Prev: GP Adviser S.. Derbysh. HA.

GRENVILLE, Michai The Old Church Surgery, 99 Chingford Avenue, Chingford, London E4 6RG Tel: 020 8529 5543 Fax: 020 8559 4149 — MB BS 1972 Lond.; MRCS Eng. LRCP Lond. 1972.

GRENVILLE-MATHERS, Ann 1 The Marlins, Eastbury Avenue, Northwood HA6 3NP — MB ChB 1970 Baghdad; LMSSA Lond. 1974. (Baghdad) Med. Off. DSS Wembley. Socs: BMA. Prev: Regist. (Med.) N.wick Pk. Hosp. Harrow; SHO Colindale Hosp. Lond. & Highlands Hosp. Lond.

GRENYER, D R Churchtown Medical Centre, 137 Cambridge Road, Southport PR9 7LT Tel: 01704 224416 Fax: 01704 507168.

GRERO, Percy Shelton (retired) Laurentian, Radford Rise, Stafford ST17 4PS — MD 1959 Ceylon; MB BS 1953; FRCP Ed. 1983, M 1959. Cons. Phys. (Geriat.) Staffs. Gen. Infirm. Stafford. Prev: Cons. Phys. Gen. Hosp. Kurunegala & Gen. Hosp. Galle, Ceylon.

GRESHAM, Professor Geoffrey Austin, TD 18 Rutherford Road, Cambridge CB2 2HH Tel: 01223 841326 Fax: 01223 841326 — ScD Camb. 1968, MA 1949, MD 1957, MB BChir 1949; FRCP Ed. 1994; FRCPath 1973, M 1963. (Camb. & King's Coll. Hosp.) Prof. Morbid Anat. & Histol. Univ. Camb.; Hon. Cons. Addenbrooke's Hosp. Camb.; Home Office Path. E. Anglia; Lt.-Col. RAMC (V). Socs: Fell. Counc. on Arteriosclerosis, Amer. Heart Assn.; Internat. Soc. Mycol. Prev: Cons. Mem. Camb. Dist. Managem. Team; Ho. Phys. & Ho. Surg. King's Coll. Hosp. Lond.; Lect. (Path.) Univ. Camb.

GRESHAM, Gweneth Margery (retired) 18 Rutherford Road, Cambridge CB2 2HH Tel: 01223 841326 — MB BS 1950 Lond.; FRCPCH 1997. Prev: Princip. Clin. Med. Off. Camb. Health Dist. (T).

GRESPI, Lorenzo West End Community Mental Health Team, Soho Centre for Health and Care, 3rd Floor, 1 Frith Street, London W1D 3HZ Tel: 020 7534 6685 Fax: 020 7534 6643 Email: lorenzo.grespi@bkcw-tr.nhs.uk; 85 St. Augustine's Road, London NW1 9RR Tel: 020 7428 0284 Fax: 020 7267 3550 Email: l.grespi@btinternet.com — State DMS 1980 Catholic U Rome; MRCPsych 1997; Dip. Psychiat. Catholic U Rome 1984; Tavistock Qualification in Adult Psychother. 1993. (Catholic Univ. Med. Sch., Rome) p/t Cons. Psychother. (Psychiat.) Gordon & W. End Community Ment. Health Team Brent Kensington Chelsea & W.minster Ment. Health NHS Trust. Socs: Brit. Confederat. Psychother.; Tavistock Soc. Psychother.; Assn. Psychoanalyt. Psychother. NHS. Prev: Cons. Community Psychiat. Mantua, Italy; Cons. Adolesc. Psychiat. N.gate Clinic Lond.; Barnet Healthcare NHS Trust Lond.

GRETTON, Kate Louise 62 Sandleigh Road, Leigh-on-Sea SS9 1JU — BM BS 1998 Nottm.; BM BS Nottm 1998.

GREVESON, Gabrielle Constance Newcastle General Hospital, Westgate Road, Newcastle upon Tyne NE4 6BE Tel: 0191 273 8811 Fax: 0191 219 5049; Wansbeck House, Dogger Bank, Morpeth NE61 1RE — MB BS 1974 Newc.; FRCP Lond. 1996; MRCP (UK) 1977. Cons. Community Geriat. Newc. HA.; Train. Developm. Tutor Postgrad. Inst. Med. & Dent. Univ. Newc.-upon-Tyne. Prev: Cons. Gen. & Geriat. Med. S. Tyneside HA.

GREVILLE, Anne Catherine Dept. of Anaesthesia], UCLH NHS Trust, London W1N 4AA Tel: 020 7380 9013 Fax: 020 8693 6937 Email: 106367.2612@compuserve.com — MB BS 1982 Lond.; BSc (Hons.) Lond. 1979; FRCA. 1992. (Roy. Free) Cons. Anasth. UCLH NHS Trust, E.man Dent. Hosp. & Middl. Hosp. Lond. Socs: Fell. Roy. Soc. Med.; Assn. Anaesths. Prev: Sen. Regist. (Anaesth.) Middlx. Hosp. Lond.; Regist. (Anaesth.) Middlx. Hosp. & St. Bart. Hosp. Lond.; Regist. & SHO (Anaesth.) Whipps Cross Hosp. Lond.

GREVILLE, Elinor Margaret (retired) 8 Fir Tree Close, Elson Park, Ellesmere SY12 9PQ Tel: 01691 623873 — MRCS Eng. LRCP Lond. 1943; DPH Liverp. 1949. Prev: Med. Off. Powys AHA.

GREVILLE, Evan Andrew Meredith Little Crickett, Welsh Frankton, Ellesmere SY12 9HE Tel: 0169175 267 — MB ChB 1975 Bristol; DRCOG 1977.

GREVILLE, Nicholas Robert (retired) 58 Coast Road, West Mersea, Colchester CO5 8LS — MB BChir 1948 Camb.; MS Minnesota 1956; Dip. Amer. Bd. Orthop. Surg. 1963. Hon. Cons. Surg. (Orthop. Surg.) Basildon Hosp. Essex. Prev: Cons. Orthop. Surg. Basildon Hosp.

GREVILLE, William David Scourfield and Partners, The Surgery, Oakfield Street, Ystrad Mynach, Hengoed CF82 7WX Tel: 01443 813248 Fax: 01443 862283; Hên Berthlwyd, Pentwyn Road, Pentwyn, Bargoed — MB BCh 1976 Wales. GP Ystrad Mynach.

GREVITT, Mr Michael Paul Centre for Spinal Studies & Surgery, Queen's Medical Centre, Nottingham NG7 2UH Tel: 0115 924 9924 Fax: 0115 970 9991 — MB BS 1984 Lond.; BSc Lond. 1981; FRCS (Orth.) 1995, FRCS Lond. 1989; CCST 1997. ((St. Bart.)) Cons. Spinal Surg., Qu.'s Med. Centre, Nottm. Socs: Brit. Scoliosis Soc.; Brit. Assoc. Spinal Surg.; Spinal Soc. Of Europe. Prev: Sen. Regist. (Orthop.) St. Thos. Hosp. Lond.; BOA Nat. Spinal Fell. Qu. Med. Centre Nottm.; Regist. (Orthop.) Guy's Hosp. Lond.

GREW, Nicholas Roy 7 Tutbury Avenue, Perton, Wolverhampton WV6 7UR — MB ChB 1994 Birm.; BDS Birm. 1988; FDS RCS Eng. 1993. (Univ. Birm.)

GREW, Richard Charles Fern House Surgery, 125-129 Newland Street, Witham CM8 1BH Fax: 01376 502281; Warren Farm Barns, Faulkbourne, Witham CM8 1SP Fax: 01376 500309 Email: post@grew.keme.co.uk — MRCS Eng. LRCP Lond. 1971; BSc (Biochem.) (Hons.) Lond. 1968, MB BS 1972. (St Bartholomews) Sen. GP Partner Fern Ho. Witham Essex; Med. Adviser N. Essex HA. Socs: Assn. Clin. Biochem. & Essex LMC.; Assn. Primary Care Med. Advisers; Medico-Legal Soc. Prev: Sen. Regist. (Clin. Chem.) Chelmsford Hosp. Gp. & St. Bart. Hosp. Lond.; SHO (Med.) Rochford Gen. Hosp. S.end-on-Sea.

GREWAL, Mr Amarjit Singh c/o Mrs J. Gilchrist, 30 Merryston Court, Coatbridge ML5 1HB — LRCP 1987 Ed.; MB BS Madras,India 1980; FRCS Glas. 1987; LRCS Ed. 1987; LRCPS Glas. 1987; RCPS Glas. 1987.

GREWAL, Amrit Pal Singh Hirst Street Surgery, 9 Hirst Street, Cornholme, Todmorden OL14 8NX Tel: 01706 817474; 21 Thanet Lee Close, Cliviger, Burnley BB10 4TX Tel: 01282 414371 — MB BS 1969 Bihar; DTCH Liverp. 1979. (Bihar) GP Todmorden, Lancshire; Med. Off. c/o Eldery; Med. Off. Psychiat.; Med. Off. Benefits Agency.

GREWAL, Anthony The Medical Centre, 6 The Green, West Drayton UB7 7PJ Tel: 01895 442026 Fax: 01895 430753; 43 Langley Road, Slough SL3 7AH — MB BS 1977 Lond.; MRCS Eng. LRCP Lond. 1977. (Middlesex Hosp. Med. Sch.) Prev: Regist. (Surg.) Harefield Hosp. Lond.

GREWAL, Barender Singh 207 Horden Road, Wolverhampton WV6 0HA — BM 1992 Soton.

GREWAL, Gurmeet Kaur 51 Grove Road, Solihull B91 2AG Tel: 0121 711 7734 Fax: 0121 711 1881; 2 Birch Hollow, Edgbaston, Birmingham B15 2QE Tel: 0121 680 9084 — MB ChB 1976 Nairobi; MRCPsych 1982. Cons. Phys. Solihull Healthcare NHS Trust.

GREWAL, Gurmeet Kaur Stirling Royal Infirmary, Livilands, Stirling, Glasgow G51 4TF — MB BS 1979 Guru Nanak Dev, India; MRCOG 1992. Prev: Career Regist. (O & G) S.. Gen. Hosp. Glas.

GREWAL, Harkirat Singh 12 Taunton Av, Hounslow TW3 4AF — MB BS 1997 Lond.

GREWAL, Jasdev Singh 1 Langdale Close, Maidenhead SL6 1SY — MB BS 1993 Lond.

GREWAL, Manmohan Singh Department of Anaesthetics, Staffordshire General Hospital, Weston Road, Stafford ST16 3SA Tel: 01785 257731 Fax: 01785 245211; 2 Birch Hollow, Edgbaston, Birmingham B15 2QE — MB BS 1973 Poona; FRCA 1985. (Armed Forces Medical College, Poona, India) Cons. Anaesth. Stafford Dist. Gen. Hosp.

GREWAL, Nanu Avninder Singh 1 Langdale Close, Maidenhead SL6 1SY — BM 1992 Soton.

GREWAL, Nawkiran 32 Catherine Gardens, Hounslow TW3 2PR Tel: 020 8847 0191 — MB ChB 1991 Manch.; DRCOG 1995. Regist. (Anaesth.) St. Geo. Hosp. Tooting. Socs: Roy. Coll. Anaesth.; BMA; MDU. Prev: SHO (Paediat.) Kingston Hosp.; SHO (O & G) N.wick Pk. Hosp.; SHO (A & E) Middlx. Hosp.

GREWAL, Mr Nicholas, OBE (retired) 45 Pink Lane, Burnham, Slough SL1 8JP Tel: 01628 669226 Fax: 01924 410699 — MB BS 1945 Punjab; FRCS Ed. 1949; MCh Orth. Liverp. 1958. Prev: Cons. Orthop. Surg. Dewsbury Hosp. Gp.

***GREWAL, Pardeep Singh** 2 Jackson Close, Rainham, Gillingham ME8 0DN Tel: 01634 360407 — MB BS 1997 Lond.; BSc Lond. 1996.

GREWAL, Patricia Dolores Burnham Health Centre, Minniecroft Road, Burnham, Slough SL1 7DE Tel: 01628 605333 Fax: 01628 663743; 43 Langley Road, Langley, Slough SL3 7AH — MB BS 1976 Lond.; MRCS Eng. LRCP Lond. 1976; MRCP (UK) 1980; MRCGP 1984. GP Burnham Health Centre. Prev: Regist. (Med.) Wexham Pk. Hosp. Slough; SHO (Obst.) Centr. Middlx. Hosp. Lond.; SHO (Rheum.) N.wick Pk. Hosp. Harrow.

GREWAL, Perbinderpal Singh 11 The Mall, London W5 2PJ — MB BS 1998 Lond.; MB BS Lond 1998.

GREWAL, Rajvinder 48 Aragon Drive, Warwick CV34 6LR — MB ChB 1986 Birm.

GREWAL, Randeep Singh 11 Rees Drive, Finham, Coventry CV3 6QF — BChir 1990 Camb.

GREWAL, Sarbjit Singh Medical Centre, 2940 17th Avenue SW, Calgary AB T3E 0A9, Canada Tel: 00 1 403 249 5566 Fax: 00 1 403 249 1513 Email: sarb@home.com; 55 Dunstall Hill, Wolverhampton WV6 0SR — MB BCh BAO 1984 NUI; LRCPI LRCSI & LM 1984; DA (UK) 1988. GP Anaesth. Saskatchewan, Canada.; Emerg. Room Phys. Mercey Hosp. Williston, N. Daketa, Canada. Socs: Alberta Med. Assn. Prev: SHO (Paediat.) Lewisham Hosp. Lond.; SHO (Anaesth. & Obst. & Gyn.) Barnet Gen. Hosp.; SHO (Accid. & Emerg.) Stafford Dist. Gen. Hosp.

GREY, Arthur Cameron 76 Maryville Park, Belfast BT9 6LQ — MB BCh BAO 1989 Belf.

GREY, Isabella Elsbeth Mary Ferguson (retired) Llystyn Cottage, Brechfa, Carmarthen SA32 7QY Tel: 01267 202201 — MB ChB Aberd. 1950. Prev: Clin. Med. Off. Carmarthen HA.

GREY, Jeffrey c/o The Royal Bank of Scotland, 151 High St., Dumfries DG1 2RA — MB BS 1956 Lond.; LMSSA Lond. 1954; DPM Eng. 1961; DA (Eng.) 1957.

GREY, John Muir 15 Aashby Road, Burton-on-Trent DE15 0LA — LRCPI & LM, LRSCI & LM 1943; LRCPI & LM, LRCSI & LM 1943. (RCSI) Prev: Capt. RAMC 1951-53.; Ho. Surg. Fermanagh Co. Hosp. Enniskillen.

GREY, Joseph Edward Petravore, 2 Hollybush Road, Cyncoed, Cardiff CF23 6SX — MB BCh 1990 Wales.

GREY, Mark Robin Department of Pathology, Bury General Hospital, Walmerley Road, Bury BL9 6TD — MB ChB 1989 Manch.; MD 2000 Manch.; MRCP (UK) 1992; MRCPath 1999. (Manch.) Cons. Haematologist Bury & Rockdave NHS Trusts.

GREY, Paula 25 South Road, Grassendale Park, Liverpool L19 0LS Tel: 0151 427 0144 — MB ChB 1979 Liverp.; MFCM 1986. Dir. Pub. Health N. Chesh. HA. Prev: Sen. Regist. (Community Med.) Mersey RHA; SHO (Obst.) Liverp. Matern. Hosp.; SHO (Gyn.) Roy. Liverp. Hosp.

GREY, Philip Leslie 43 Perne Avenue, Cambridge CB1 3RY — MB BS 1984 Melbourne; FRACS 1993. Prev: Fell. Otoneurosurg. Addenbrooke's NHS Trust Camb.

GREY, Mr Rodney Humphrey Burchell 2 Clifton Park, Bristol BS8 3BS Tel: 0117 973 5904; The Old Rectory, Chelvey, Near Backwell, Bristol BS48 4AA Tel: 01275 462869 — MB BChir 1968 Camb.; FRCS Eng. 1974; MRCS Eng. LRCP Lond. 1967; FRCOphth 1987; DO Eng. 1971. (Lond. Hosp.) Cons. Ophth. Surg. Bristol Eye Hosp. Socs: (Pres.) S. W.. Ophth. Soc.; BMA; Macula Soc. Amer. Prev: Sen. Regist. Moorfields Eye Hosp. & W.. Ophth. Hosp. Lond.; Ho. Phys. & Ho. Surg. Lond. Hosp.

GREYWOODE, Godman Isaac Nathaniel Horton General Hospital, Department of Pathology, Banbury OX16 9AL Tel: 01295 229237 Fax: 01295 229225; 211 Bloxham Road, Banbury OX16 9JU Tel: 01295 257863 Email: godman.greywoode@virgin.net — MD 1978 Pecs, Hungary; FRCPath 1997; MRCPath 1989, D 1988. Cons. Histopath. Horton Gen. Hosp. Banbury; Clin. Director, Path. SDU (Serv. Delivery Unit). Socs: Internat. Acad. Path. (Brit. Div.); Brit. Soc. Clin. Cytol. Prev: Clin. Research Asst. Nuffield Dept. Path. John Radcliffe Hosp. Univ. Oxf.

GRIBBEN, Shona Catherine 111 Overton Crescent, East Calder, Livingston EH53 0RJ — MB ChB 1996 Ed.

GRIBBEN, Tania Marie 30 Meadowvale, Quarry Lane, Dungannon BT70 1QJ — MB BCh BAO 1990 Belf.

GRIBBIN, Clare Marretta 91 Woodbank Drive, Wollaton, Nottingham NG8 2QW — BM BS 1989 Nottm.; BMedSci Nottm. 1987; MRCOG 1994. Specialist Regist. Rotat. (O & G) Nottm. City Hosp. Prev: Cons. i/c O & G Aga Khan Health Servs. Karachi, Pakistan; Acting Regist. (O & G) Derby City Hosp.; SHO Rotat. (O & G) Qu. Med. Centre Nottm. & Nottm. City Hosp.

GRIBBIN, Guy Moncrieffe The Cardiothoracic Centre, Freeman Hospital, Newcastle upon Tyne NE7 7DN Tel: 0191 284 3111; 6 Wallace Terrace, Ryton NE40 3PL — BM BCh 1993 Oxf.; MRCP UK 1996. (Oxford) Specialist Regst. Cardiol.

GRIBBIN, Henry Robert Jamesbrook Univ. Hospital, Marton Rd TS4 3BW Tel: 01642 850850; 5 Fanacourt Road TS14 8BJ Tel: 01287 633835 — MB ChB 1972 Ed.; FRCP Lond. 1992; FRCP Ed. 1991; MRCP (UK) 1975. (Edin.) Cons. Phys. James Cook Univ. Hosp. MiddlesBoro.; Hon. Clin .Lect. Univ. Newc. u. Tyne 1997. Socs: Brit. Thoracic Soc. & Amer. Thoracic Soc.; Eur. Respirat. Soc. Prev: Sen. Regist. Univ. Coll. Hosp. Lond. & Lond. Chest Hosp.; Hon. Sen. Regist. Hammersmith Hosp. Roy. Postgrad. Med. Sch. Lond.; Regist. (Med.) Hammersmith Hosp. Roy. Postgrad. Med. Sch. Lond.

GRIBBIN, Nora Maria Annagh, Desertmartin, Magherafelt BT45 5NB Email: ngribbin@lineone.net — MB BCh BAO 1984 Belf.; MRCPsych 1994. (The Queen's University Belfast) Res. Fell. & Hon. Sen. Regist. Imperial Coll. Sch. of Med.; Cons. Psychiat. Springfield Hosp. Lond. SW17 7DJ. Prev: Sen. Regist. (Psychiat.) Manch. Roy. Infirm.; Regist. (Psychiat.) St. Geo.s Hosp. Lond.

GRIBBLE, Fiona Mary University Physiology Laboratories, Parks Road, Oxford OX1 3PT Tel: 01865 272456; 68 Stapleton Road, Headington, Oxford OX3 7LU Tel: 01865 750903 — BM BCh 1990 Oxf.; MA Camb. 1990; MRCP (UK) 1993. Research Scientist (Diabetes) Oxf. Univ. Prev: Research Fell. Diabetes Research Laborat. Radcliffe Infirm. Oxf.; SHO (Gen. Med.) John Radcliffe Hosp. Oxf.

GRIBBLE, Richard John Nigel Shatterwell House, North St., Wincanton BA9 9AZ — MB BS Lond. 1967; MRCP (UK) 1973; MRCS Eng. LRCP Lond. 1967; MLCOM 1994; DMS Med. Soc. Apoth. Lond. 1994. (St. Bart.)

GRICE, Alexander Stuart 7 Southwick Place, East Boscombe, Bournemouth BH6 5PX Tel: 0410 482495 Email: alex.grice@tesco.net; Nova, Rue Des Bergers, Catel, Guernsey GY5 7AP Tel: 01481 57749 — BM 1993 Soton.; BSc (Hons.) Soton. 1992; DCH RCP Lond. 1995; FRCA 1999. (Southampton) Specialist Regist Rotat. (Anaesth.). Socs: Train. Mem. Intens. Care Soc.; Train. Mem. Anaesth. Assn.; BMA. Prev: SHO (Paediat.) Roy. United Hosp. Bath; SHO (Anaesth.) Salisbury Dist. Hosp.; SHO (Anaesth.) Soton. Gen. Hosp.

GRICE, Craig Antony Flat 64, Lockyer House, The Platt, London SW15 1EE — MB ChB 1993 Glas.

GRICE, David John Preston Northgate Medical Practice, 1 Northgate, Canterbury CT1 1WL Tel: 01227 463570 Fax: 01227 786147 — BM 1979 Soton. (Southampton) GP. Socs: E. Kent LMC; Child Protec. Community; Kent Pharmaceutical Regulat.s Comm. Prev: Trainee GP Kent & Canterbury Hosp.; Ho. Surg. Dorset Co. Hosp.; Ho. Phys. (Gen. & Chest Med.) St. Martin's Hosp. Bath.

GRICE, Diana Margaret Berkshire Health Authority, 57-59 Bath Road, Reading RG30 2BA Tel: 0118 950 3094; Bowden End, Pangbourne, Reading RG8 8PT — MB BS 1982 Lond.; MSc (Credit) Community Med. Lond. 1986; BSc (Hons.) Lond. 1979; FPHM 1999. (King's Coll. Hosp. Med. Sch.) Dir. Pub. Health Med. Berks. HA. Prev: Dir. Pub. Health Med. Wycombe & S. Bucks. HA; Cons. Pub. Health Med. Milton Keynes & Oxf. RHA; Sen. Regist. & Regist. (Community Med.) Oxf. RHA.

GRICE, Edmund Radcliffe Scott 6 Waters Drive, Four Oaks, Sutton Coldfield B74 4TQ Tel: 0121 353 2919 — MB ChB 1937 Birm. (Birm.)

GRICE, Evan Gordon Old Orchard, Burnthorne Lane, Dunley, Stourport-on-Severn DY13 0TN — MB ChB 1940 Birm. (Birm.) Socs: BMA.

GRICE, Gail Clark The Cottage, 46 High St., Flitton, Bedford MK45 5DY — MB ChB 1978 Manch.; BSc (Med. Sci.) St. And. 1975; MB ChB (Hons.) Manch. 1978; MRCP Glas. 1981. Prev: Assoc. Dir. of Clin. Research Du Pont (UK) Ltd; Sen. Regist. (Genito-Urin. Med.) Roy. Hallamsh. Hosp. Sheff.

GRICE, Guinevere Lee 24 Lansdown Road, Redland, Bristol BS6 6NS — MB ChB 1998 Bristol.

GRICE, James Duff (retired) 1A Glebe Road, Cheam, Sutton SM2 7NS Tel: 020 8642 5570 — MB BS 1955 Lond. Prev: Ho. Surg. Roy. Sussex Co. Hosp. Brighton.

GRICE, Joanna Loiuse Timber Lodge, Queenborough Lane, Braintree CM7 8QE Tel: 01376 330310 — BM BCh 1998 Oxf.; BM BCh Oxf 1998; MA (Cantab) 1999.

GRICE, John Russell Grant (retired) Cornerstones, 17 Wood Top Avenue, Bamford, Rochdale OL11 4BD Tel: 01706 364718 — MB ChB 1942 Glas. JP. Prev: JP.

GRICE, Julie Ann 74 Framingham Road, Sale M33 3RJ — MB ChB 1997 Manch.

GRICE, Katherine BUPA Hospital, Heathbourne Road, Bushey, Watford WD2 1RD Tel: 020 8950 9090; St. John's Cottage, 87 South End Road, London NW3 2RJ Tel: 020 7435 5933 — MD Lond. 1967, MB BS 1950; DCH RCP Lond. 1954. Cons. Dermat. Watford Gen. Hosp., Shenley Hosp. & Napsbury Hosp. Socs: Fell. Roy. Soc. Med. & St. John's Hosp. Dermat. Soc.

GRICE, Margaret Joyce (retired) Nuthatch, Headley Hill Road, Arford, Bordon GU35 8DX Tel: 01428 712572 — MB ChB 1946 Birm. Prev: Clin. Med. Off. Notts. AHA (T).

GRICE, Stephen John The Old Court House, 4 Throwley Way, Sutton SM1 4AF Tel: 020 8643 8866; Furzewood House, Furze Hill, Tadworth KT20 6EP — MB BS 1985 Lond. (Middlx.) Prev: SHO (Geriat. & Psychiat.) Birch Hill Hosp. Rochdale; SHO (A & E) St. Mary's Hosp. Lond.

GRIER, Mr Arnold Macfarlane (retired) Elmbank, 68 Culduthel Road, Inverness IV2 4HH Tel: 01463 234682 — MB ChB Ed. 1955; FRCS Ed. 1962. Cons. ENT Surg. Highland HB (Inverness). Prev: Regist. (ENT) Roy. Infirm. Edin.

GRIER, David George 22 Lakelands, Craigavon BT64 1AW — MB BCh BAO 1993 Belf.

GRIER, David John Kingselm, Mead Road, Stoke Gifford, Bristol BS34 8PS — MB ChB 1983 Birm.; MRCP (UK) 1986; FRCR 1990. Cons. Radiol. Roy. Hosp. for Childr. St. Michael's Hill Bristol. Prev: Sen. Regist. (Radiodiagn.) S. W.. RHA; SHO Rotat. (Med.) E. Birm. Hosp.

GRIER, Ian William Eastleigh Surgery, Station Road, Westbury BA13 3JD Tel: 01373 822807 Fax: 01373 828904; 14 The Knoll, Westbury BA13 3UB Tel: 01373 858517 — MB BS 1971 Lond. Prev: SHO (Med.) Roy. United Hosp. Bath.

GRIER, Lynda Mary The Bridge Surgery, 8 Evesham Road, Headless Cross, Redditch B97 4LA Tel: 01527 550131 — BM BCh 1972 Oxf.

GRIERSON, Catherine Anne 12 St Edmunds Road, Ipswich IP1 3QZ — MB ChB 1997 Bristol.

GRIERSON, Mr David John 2 Speirs Road, Bearsden, Glasgow G61 2LU — MB ChB 1979 Ed.; FRCS Ed. 1987; FRCOphth 1988; DO RCS Eng. 1985.

GRIESE, Knut Armin 10B Cedar Court, North Tyneside General Hospital, Rake Hill, North Shields NE29 8NH — State Exam Med 1992 Freiburg.

GRIEVE, Alasdair Aitken Hume Denburn Health Centre, Rosemount Viaduct, Aberdeen AB25 1QB Tel: 01224 642757; Mill of Inver, Crathie, Ballater AB35 5TP — MB ChB 1965 Aberd.

GRIEVE, Alexander James Medical Centre, 12A Greggs Wood Road, Tunbridge Wells TN2 3JL Tel: 01892 541444 Fax: 01892 511157; The Old Bakery Surgery, Penshurst Road, Speldhurst, Tunbridge Wells TN3 0PQ Tel: 01892 863040 — MB BS 1972 Lond.; MRCP (UK) 1976; MRCS Eng. LRCP Lond. 1972. (King's Coll. Lond. & King's Coll. Hosp.) Princip. GP Tunbridge Wells Hosp. & Pract.(Gastroenterol.) Kent & Sussex Hosp. Tunbridge Wells. Socs: Brit. Diabetic Assn. (Med. & Scientif. Sect.); Primary Care Soc. Gastroenterol. Prev: Regist. (Med.) King's Coll. Hosp. Gp.; Ho. Phys. & Ho. Surg. King's Coll. Hosp.

GRIEVE, Alexander Millar GKN plc, PO Box 55, Redditch B98 0TL Tel: 01527 517715 Fax: 01527 517700 Email: alex.grieve@gknplc.com; Tyfield, 8 Kings Lane, Broom B50 4HB Tel: 01789 773813 Email: alex@grieve.co.uk — MB ChB Aberd. 1970; FFOM RCP Lond. 1993, MFOM 1985, AFOM 1982; FRCGP 1994, M 1975; DObst RCOG 1972. (Aberd.) Chief Med. Off. GKN plc Redditch. Socs: Fell. Roy. Soc. Med. (Ex-Pres. Occupat. Med. Sect.); Soc. Occupat.; BMA. Prev: Clin. Dir. BUPA Health Servs.; Chief Med. Off. Shell UK Ltd.; Asst. Sec. Med. Defence Union.

GRIEVE, Alexander Raeburn 4 Duchess Park, Helensburgh G84 9PY — MB ChB 1956 Ed.; DObst RCOG 1961. (Ed.)

GRIEVE, Annie Sheila (retired) — MB ChB 1960 Manch. Prev: Ho. Off. (Paediat.) Roy. Infirm. Bolton.

GRIEVE, Christine Drumchapel Health Centre, 80-90 Kinfauns Drive, Glasgow G15 7TS Tel: 0141 211 6110 Fax: 0141 211 6140 — MB ChB 1981 Glas.; MRCGP 1985.

GRIEVE, David Ian Clare House Practice, Clare House Surgery, Newport Street, Tiverton EX16 6NJ Tel: 01884 252337 Fax: 01884 254401 — MB ChB 1967 Ed.; MRCGP 1980; FFA RCS Eng. 1975; DA Eng. 1972; DObst RCOG 1970.

GRIEVE, David Kenneth Langsett, Woodside Hill, Chalfont St Peter, Gerrards Cross SL9 9TB — MB BS 1970 Lond.; MRCS Eng. LRCP Lond. 1969; FRCR 1980; DMRD Eng. 1979. (St. Bart.) Cons. Radiol. Wexham Pk. Hosp. Slough. Prev: Cons. Radiol. Brit. Milit. Hosp. Hong Kong & Qu. Eliz. Milit. Hosp.; Lond.

GRIEVE, David Rollo (retired) 4 Carnegie Gardens, Aberdeen AB15 4AW Tel: 01224 318316 — MB ChB 1958 Aberd.; MRCGP 1972.

GRIEVE, Douglas Clark 23 Barnton Gardens, Edinburgh EH4 6AE — MB ChB 1972 Ed.; FRCR 1978; DMRD Ed. 1976.

GRIEVE, Fiona Jane 12 Priestfield Road, Edinburgh EH16 5HJ — MB ChB 1993 Ed.

GRIEVE, James Henderson Kerr Department of Forensic Medicine, University Medical School, Foresterhill, Aberdeen AB25 2ZD Tel: 01224 681818; Wedderhill House, Maryculter, Aberdeen AB12 5YX Tel: 01224 861341 — MB ChB 1977 Aberd.; MRCPath 1984. Sen. Lect. (Forens. Med.) Univ. Aberd.; Cons. Path. Grampian HB. Prev: Med. Off. Roy. Army Med. Corps.

GRIEVE, Joan Patricia Atkinson Morley's Hospital, Copse Hill, Wimbledon, London SW20 0NE Tel: 020 8946 7711 Fax: 020 8947 8389; 83 Sutton Heights, Albion Road, Sutton SM2 5TD — MB BS 1990 Lond.; FRCS Eng. 1994. (St. Geo. Hosp. Med. Sch.) Regist. (Neurosurg.) Atkinson Morley's Hosp. Lond.

GRIEVE, John Michael Silvey (retired) Ashenhurst House, Todmorden OL14 8DS Tel: 01706 812086 — MRCS Eng. LRCP Lond. 1952; MA Camb. 1955, MB BChir 1952; MRCGP 1972; DObst RCOG 1956; Cert JCC Lond. 1977. Prev: GP Todmorden.

GRIEVE, Mary Gabrielle Dairy Cottage, Teffont Evias, Salisbury SP3 5RP Tel: 01722 716487 Email: ggrieve@lineone.net — MB BCh BAO NUI 1973; MRCGP 1981; T(GP) 1991.

GRIEVE, Nigel William Traquair Woking Nuffield Hosital, Woking GU21 4BY Tel: 01483 763511; 2 Oaklands Drive, Ascot SL5 7NE Tel: 01344 24544 — MB ChB 1954 Ed.; MA Camb. 1951; DMRD 1961; FRCR 1975; FFR 1964. Prev: Cons. Radiol. NW Surrey HA.; Regist. X-Ray Dept. Radcliffe Infirm. Oxf.; Sen. Regist. (Radiodiag.) St. Thos. Hosp. Lond.

GRIEVE, Philip Peter c/o Mr J.A. Grieve, 17 Windsor Avenue, Holywood BT18 9DG Tel: 01232 422141 — MB BCh BAO 1996 Belf. (Queens Univ. Belf.)

GRIEVE, Robert Culross Greenacre, White House Road, Stranraer DG9 0JB Tel: 01776 702954 Fax: 01776 702954 — MB ChB Glas. 1956; DObst RCOG 1960. (Univ. Glas.) Socs: BMA.

GRIEVE, Robert Gordon Health Centre, St. Marys Place, Townend, Kirkcudbright DG6 4BJ Tel: 01557 330755 Fax: 01557 330917 — MB ChB 1989 Ed. (University of Edinburgh)

GRIEVE, Robert Gordon Ross (retired) 3 Somerford Road, Bearsden, Glasgow G61 1AS Tel: 0141 942 7059 — M.B., Ch.B. Glas. 1925; F.F.A. R.C.S. Eng. 1953; D.A. Eng. 1951. Prev: Anaesth. Glas. Roy. Infirm.

GRIEVE, Robert James Department of Radiotherapy, Walsgrave Hospital, Clifford Bridge Road, Coventry CV2 2DY Tel: 024 76 602020; Ashfield House, Brooke Road, Kenilworth CV8 2BD Tel: 01926 856009 — MB ChB 1974 Birm.; FRCP 1998; FRCR 1983. Cons. Radiother. & Clin. Oncol. Walsgrave Hosp. Coventry & St Cross Hosp. Rugby. Socs: Brit. Oncol. Assn.; Brit. Inst. of Radiol.; Brit. Assn. Surg. Oncol. Prev: Sen. Regist. & Regist. (Radiother.) Christie Hosp. Manch.; CRC Fell. & Hon. Regist. (Med.) Qu. Eliz. Hosp. Birm.

GRIEVE, Rosemary Margaret Kerr 16 Maplebank Loaning, Calside, Dumfries DG1 4UJ Tel: 01387 69463 — MB ChB 1977 Aberd.; DRCOG 1980. Staff Grade (O & G) Cresswell Matern. Hosp. Dumfries.

GRIEVE, Susan Jayne 52 Holywell Hill, St Albans AL1 1BX Tel: 01727 841528 — MB BS 1980 Lond.; MSc 1995; MRCGP 1984; DRCOG 1983. GP Luton; Clin. Asst. St Albans Community Alcohol & Drug Team. Socs: RCGP; Fac. Family Plann. Prev: GP Lond.; GP Primary Care for Homeless People Camben & Islington.

GRIEW, Antony Russell Greenhill, Llangunnor, Carmarthen SA32 8EL Tel: 01267 237261; Centre for Health Informatics, University of Wales, Llanbadarn Fawr, Aberystwyth SY23 3AS Tel: 01970 622779 Fax: 01970 622578 — MB BS 1964 Lond.; MSc (Soc. Med.) 1973; MRCS Eng. LRCP Lond. 1963; FFPHMI 1995. Cons. Pub. Health Med. Dyfed Health; Med. Co-Ordinator Centre for Health Informatics. Prev: Cons. Pub. Health Med. E. Dyfed HA; Dist. Med. Off. Haringey HA; Lect. (Community Med.) Univ. Papua New Guinea.

GRIFFIN, Alfred James Graham (retired) 4 Elenors Grove, Quarr Hill, Ryde PO33 4HE Tel: 01983 882618 — MB BS 1953 Lond.; DObst RCOG 1959. Prev: Flight Lt. RAF Med. Serv.

GRIFFIN, Andrea Louise Postern Gate Surgery, Cinque Ports Street, Rye TN31 7AP Tel: 01797 223333/224924 Fax: 01797 226858; Lavender Cottage, Barnetts Hill, Peasmarsh, Rye TN31 6YJ Tel: 01797 230703 — MB ChB 1987 Manch. Clin. Asst. (Endoscopy) Conquest Hosp. Hastings. Prev: Trainee GP Hastings VTS; Ho. Off. (Med.) Qu. Pk. Hosp. Blackburn; Ho. Off. (Surg.) N. Manch. Gen. Hosp.

GRIFFIN, Ann Bernadette 104 Polsteads, Vange, Basildon SS16 4PL — MB BCh BAO 1992 NUI.

GRIFFIN, Ann Elizabeth 155 King Harolds Way, Bexleyheath DA7 5RB — MB BS 1985 Lond.

GRIFFIN, Anthea Jane Department of Rheumatology, Chase Farm Hospital, The Ridgeway, Enfield EN2 8JL Tel: 020 8366 6600 EXT 5608; 319 Cockfosters Road, Barnet EN4 0JY Tel: 020 8440 1519 — MB BS 1971 Lond.; FRCP Lond. 1995; MRCP (UK) 1973. (Middlesex) Cons. Rheum. Chase Farm Hosp. Enfield. Socs: Brit. Soc. Rheum.; MRCPCH (Rheum. Gp.); Fell. Roy. Soc. Med. Prev: Sen. Regist. (Rheum.) Guy's Hosp. Lond.; SHO (Med.) United Oxf. Hosps.; Ho. Phys. Middlx. Hosp. Lond.

GRIFFIN, Bernard Patrick (retired) Flat 15, Grangewood Hall, Cranfield Avenue, Wimborne BH21 1BZ Tel: 01202 840780 — MRCS Eng. LRCP Lond. 1941; MA Camb. 1941; MRCPsych 1971; DPM Eng. 1963. Prev: Cons. Psychiat. & Phys. Supt. Ely Hosp.

GRIFFIN, Brenda Joan 48 Leicester Road, Wigston, Leicester Tel: 0116 288 2566; 15 Sackville Gardens, Knighton, Leicester LE2 3TH — MB ChB 1984 Leic.; MRCGP 1988; DCH RCP Lond. 1990; DRCOG 1989.

GRIFFIN, Colette Maria 25 The Croft, Sudbury, Wembley HA0 3EQ Tel: 020 7837 3611 Email: c.griffin@ion.ucl.ac.uk — MB BS 1993 Lond.; MRCP 1997. (St Bartholomews) Research Fell. Inst. of Nerology Qu. Sqare Lond.

GRIFFIN, Cornelius Jeremiah (retired) 19 St Mary's Hall Road, Manchester M8 5DZ Tel: 0161 795 8700 — MB BS 1946 Lond.; MRCS Eng. LRCP Lond. 1939; DObst RCOG 1947.

GRIFFIN, Mr Damian Russel 13 Huntsmill, Fulbourn, Cambridge CB1 5RH — BM BCh 1989 Oxf.; MA Camb. 1986; FRCS Eng. 1993; FRCS (Orth.) Eng. 1998. Specialist Regist. Rotat. (Orthop. & Trauma Surg.) Camb.

GRIFFIN, David Robert Watford General Hospital, Vicarage Road, Watford WD18 0HB Tel: 01923 244366 — MB ChB Sheff. 1970; FRCOG 1992, M 1978. Cons. O & G Watford Gen. Hosp. Socs: Fell. Roy. Soc. Med.; Brit. Med. Ultrasound Soc. Prev: Research Fell. & Sen. Regist. Kings Coll. Hosp. Lond.; Regist. Roy. Berks. Hosp. Reading.

***GRIFFIN, Emma Louise** 35 Tilmore Road, Petersfield GU32 2HJ — MB BS 1996 Lond.; MBBS BSC (Aug 1993 Psychology with Basic Medical Sciences).

GRIFFIN, Professor George Edward Department of Infectious Diseases, St George's Hospital Medical School, Tooting, London SW17 0RE Tel: 020 8725 5827 Fax: 020 8336 0940 Email: ggriffin@sghms.ac.uk; 8 Buxton Drive, New Malden KT3 3UZ Tel: 020 8949 4953 Fax: 020 8336 0940 — MB BS 1974 Lond.; PhD (Physiol.) Hull 1974; BSc (Pharmacol.) Lond. 1968; FRCP Ed. 1994; FRCP Lond. 1988, M 1979; FRCPath 1998; F Med Sci 1998. (King's Coll. Lond. & St. Geo.) Prof. Infec. Dis. & Med. & Hon. Cons. Phys. (Head Div. Infec. Dis.) St. Geo. Hosp.; Hon. Prof. Med. Univ. of Michigan, USA; Chairm. Surveillance. Sub-Comm. UKXIRA. Socs: Med. Res. Soc.; Assn. Phys. Prev: Regist. (Med. & Gastroenterol.) Hammersmith Hosp. Lond.; SHO (Neurol.) Nat. Hosp. Nerv. Dis. Lond.; Harkness Fell. Commonw. Fund of New York Dept. Physiol. Harvard Univ.

GRIFFIN, Gerald Alipore (retired) 14 Holbrook Lane, Chislehurst BR7 6PF Tel: 0208 467 8338 Fax: 0208 249 3235 Email: gerald@birchcottages.fsnet.co.uk — MB BS Lond. 1944; MRCS Eng. LRCP Lond. 1943; FRCGP 1977, M 1968. Prev: Hosp. Pract. (Rheum. & Rehabil.) Qu. Mary's Hosp. Sidcup & Orpington Hosps.

GRIFFIN, Gilbert Vincent District Office, Union Lane, Rochford SS4 1RB — MB BS 1951 Durh.; DPH 1960; FFCM 1985, MFCM 1972. (Durh.) Dist. Med. Off. S.end HA. Socs: BMA. Prev: Dist. Community Phys. S.end Health Dist.; MOH S.end Co. Boro.; Sen. Med. Off. RAF Dishforth.

GRIFFIN, Jacqueline Mary Redwalls, School Lane, Bunbury, Tarporley CW6 9NR — MB ChB 1980 Birm.

GRIFFIN, Joan Campbell (retired) 14 Biddick Lane, Fatfield, Washington NE38 8AE — MB BS 1944 Durh. Prev: SCMO (Family Plann.) Sunderland AHA.

GRIFFIN, John Henry Lysaght (retired) Barton Lodge, Culmstock, Cullompton EX15 3JF Tel: 01884 840409 — MB ChB 1955 Bristol.

GRIFFIN, John Miles The Surgery, Harborough Road, Northampton NN2 8LL — MB BS 1976 Lond.; MRCS Eng. LRCP Lond. 1976. (Univ. Coll. Hosp.)

GRIFFIN, John Norman (retired) High Meadows, Tockholes Road, Darwen BB3 1JY — MB BS 1960 Lond. Prev: GP Darwen, Lancs.

GRIFFIN, John Parry Quartermans, Digswell Lane, Welwyn Garden City AL6 0SP Tel: 01438 714592 Fax: 01438 716029 — MRCS Eng. LRCP Lond. 1964; PhD Lond. 1961, BSc 1959, MB BS 1964; FRCP Lond. 1990, M 1980; FFPM RCP (UK) 1989; FRCPath 1986, M 1982. (Lond. Hosp.) Dir. John Griffin Assoc. Ltd.; Vis. Lect. Scripps Med. Clinic San Diego, Calif.; Edr.-in-Chief, Adverse Drug Reactions & Toxicol. Revs. Socs: Fell. Roy. Soc. Med.; Pharmacol. Soc. Prev: Dir. Assn. Brit. Pharmaceut. Industry; Sen. PMO & Profess. Head, Meds. Div. DHSS; Med. Assessor to Med. Commiss.

***GRIFFIN, Jonathan David** 17 Heol Derwen, New Inn, Pontypool NP4 0QS — MB ChB 1996 Birm.

GRIFFIN, Jonathan James Penistone Group Practice, High St., Penistone, Sheffield S36 6BR Tel: 01226 762257 — MB ChB 1991 Sheff.; MRCGP 1995. (Sheff.)

GRIFFIN, Liam Patrick Queens Park and Moredon Surgeries, 146 Drove Road, Swindon SN1 3AG Tel: 01793 487394 Fax: 01793 342011 — MB ChB 1973 Bristol; DCM Beijing 1998.

GRIFFIN, Lucy Jane 141 Ware Road, Hertford SG13 7EG — MB BS 1994 Lond.

GRIFFIN, Margaret Mary 48 Purley Bury Avenue, Purley CR8 1JD — MB BCh BAO 1977 NUI; MRCPI 1982; MRCPath 1988.

GRIFFIN, Marie Helen 2 Fryston Avenue, Croydon CR0 7HL Tel: 020 8654 7460 — MB BS 1964 Mandalay. (Inst. Med. Mandalay) Clin. Med. Off. (Child Health) Croydon HA.

GRIFFIN, Martin James Wesley 162 Station Road, Wylde Green, Sutton Coldfield B73 5LE — MB ChB 1995 Manch.

GRIFFIN, Mary Department of Family Planning, King's College Hospital, London SE5 9RS Tel: 020 7326 3421 — MB BS 1971 Lond.; MSc Lond. 1975; MRCS Eng. LRCP Lond. 1971; AHA 1964. (St. Thos.) SCMO Tower Hamlets Health Dist. (T). Prev: Ho. Surg. Birm. Accid. Hosp.; Ho. Phys. St. Thos. Hosp.; MRC Jun. Research Fell.

GRIFFIN, Michael The Cottage, 9 Arwenack Avenue, Falmouth TR11 3JW — MB BS 1984 Lond.; DFFP 1993. GP. Prev: Marina Indep. Med. Servs.; GP Milton Keynes; SHO (Paediat. & O & G).

GRIFFIN, Mona, MBE 156 Ashgrove Road W., Aberdeen AB16 5BD Tel: 01224 682602 — MB ChB 1943 Aberd.; DCH Eng. 1945; DPH Aberd. 1948. (Aberd.)

GRIFFIN, Nicholas Keeble Department of Paediatrics, General Hospital, Northampton NN1 5BD Tel: 01604 34700; Weston House, Weston Underwood, Olney MK46 5JZ Tel: 01234 713896 — MB BS 1969 Lond.; FRCP Lond. 1988; MRCP (UK) 1972; MRCS Eng. LRCP Lond. 1969. (Guy's) Cons. Paediat. Gen. Hosp. N.ampton. Prev: Resid. Asst. Phys. Hosp. Sick Childr. Lond.; Regist. (Paediat.) Radcliffe Infirm. Oxf.; SHO (Paediat.) Hosp. Sick Childr. Gt. Ormond St. Lond.

GRIFFIN, Nicholas Ronald Department of Histopathology, Airedale General Hospital, Skipton Road, Keighley BD20 6TD — MB ChB 1984 (Hons) Leeds; BSc (1st cl. Hons.) (Path.) Leeds 1981, MD 1992; MRCPath. 1992; 2000 FRCpath; MD 1992 Leeds. (Leeds) Cons. Histopath. Airedale Gen. Hosp. Socs: Path. Soc.; Assn. Clin. Pathologists; Brit. Div. Internat. Acad. Path. Prev: Cons. Histopath.

Univ. Hosp. NHS Trust Nottm.; Sen. Regist. (Histopath.) Notts.; Research Fell. (Path.) Univ. of Leeds.

GRIFFIN, Nicholas Vivian The Hatherton Centre, The Foundation NHS Trust, Corporation St., Stafford ST16 3AG Tel: 01785 221592 Fax: 01785 221371 — MB ChB 1975 Bristol; BSc Bristol 1973; FRCPsych 1995, M 1979. Dir. (Forens. Ment. Health Servs.) & Cons. Forens. Psychiat. The Hatherton Centre, Foundat. NHS Trust Stafford. Medic. Dir., Foundat. NHS Trust.; Hon. Sen. Lect. (Staffs. Univ.). Prev: Cons. Forens. Psychiat. Reaside Clinic Birm.

GRIFFIN, Miss Nyree 23 Highcroft, Woodthorpe, Nottingham NG3 5LP — MB ChB 1995 Bristol; MB ChB (Hons.) Bristol 1995; MCRS (Eng) (July 1999). (Bristol) (Surg.) Qu.s Med. Centre Nottingm.

GRIFFIN, Patrick John Moseley Avenue Surgery, 109 Moseley Avenue, Coventry CV6 1HS Tel: 024 7659 2201 Fax: 024 7660 1226 — MB BCh BAO 1978 NUI; MRCGP 1983; DRCOG 1982. (Galway) GP Coundon. Prev: SHO Geo. Eliot Hosp. Nuneaton; Ho. Off. Regional Hosp. Galway & Co. Hosp. Nenagh.

GRIFFIN, Mr Peter John Anthony 8 Panteg, Parc Saint Catwg, Pentyrch, Cardiff CF15 9TL — MB BCh 1970 Wales; FRCS Eng. 1976; FRCS Ed. 1976; DObst RCOG 1972. Assoc. Specialist (Transpl. Surg.) Cardiff Roy. Infirm.

GRIFFIN, Philip Leslie Lodge Surgery, Normandy Road, St Albans AL3 5NP Tel: 01727 853107 Fax: 01727 862657.

GRIFFIN, Richard George Rae Flat 6, 133 Princes Avenue, Hull HU5 3DT — BChir 1990 Camb.

GRIFFIN, Ronald Walter (retired) Colchester General Hospital, Turner Road, Colchester CO4 5JL Tel: 01206 853535 — MB ChB Birm. 1958; FFA RCS Eng. 1964; DA Eng. 1960. Prev: Cons. Anaesth. Essex Riverside Health Trust Colchester.

GRIFFIN, Ruth Amanda 6 Brewery Close, Wembley HA0 2XA Tel: 020 8908 6577 — MB BS 1985 Lond.; DA (UK) 1991; FRCA 1991. Cons. (Anaesth.) Centr. Middlx. Hosp. Lond. Socs: Intens. Care Soc.; Difficult Airway Soc. Prev: Sen. Regist. (Anaesth.) Hammersmith Hosp. Lond.; Sen. Regist. (Anaesth.) Char. Cross Hosp. Lond.

GRIFFIN, Professor Selwyn Michael Northern Oesophago-Gastric Cancer Unit, Royal Victoria Infirmary, Queen Victoria Road, Newcastle upon Tyne NE1 4LP Tel: 0191 282 0234 — MB BS 1978 Newc.; MD Newc. 1989; FRCS Eng. 1983; Hon. FRCS Ed. 1997; Hon. FCS (UK) 1995. (Newcastle upon Tyne) Cons. Surg. Upper GI Surg., Roy. Vict. Infirm. Newc.; Prof. Of Gastrointestinal Surg., Univ. of Newc.-Upon-Tyne. Socs: Brit. Soc. Gastroenterol.; Assoc. of Surg.s of GB & I; Assoc. of Upper GI Surg. Of GB & I. Prev: Sen. Regist. (Gen. Surg.) N.. RHA; Wellcome Surg. Fell.sh. 1984-85; Lect. (Gen. Surg.) Chinese Univ., Hong Kong.

GRIFFIN, Sharon 24 Cherry Gardens, Heathfield TN21 8XZ Tel: 01435 867637 Fax: 01435 867637 — MB ChB 1992 Manch. Specialist Regist. (O & G) S. Thames. Prev: SHO (O & G) S. Thames.

GRIFFIN, Sian Virginia Addenbrooke's Hospital, Level 5, Department Medicine, Hills Road, Cambridge CB2 2SP Tel: 01223 336742 Fax: 01223 411052 Email: svg20@medschl.cam.ac.uk; 92 Thoday Street, Cambridge CB1 3AX Tel: 01223 510895 — MB BChir 1991 Camb.; MA Camb. 1992; MRCP (UK) 1994. (Camb.) Research Fell. & Hon. Regist. (Med.) Addenbrooke's Hosp. Camb. Prev: SHO (Gen. Med.) Harold Wood Hosp. Romford & Roy. Lond. Hosp. Trust.

GRIFFIN, Simon James General Practice and Primary Care Research Unit, Department of Public Health and Primary Care, Inst. of Public Health, University Forvie Site, Robinson Way, Cambridge CB2 2SR Tel: 01223 330504 Fax: 01223 762515 Email: sjg49@medschl.cam.ac.uk; 17 Holland Street, Cambridge CB4 3DL Tel: 01223 369087 Fax: 01223 741023 — MB BS 1986 Lond.; DM 2001 Soton.; MSc (Pub. Health) Lond. 1995; DLSHTM Lond. 1995; MRCGP 1991. (London Hospital Medical College) Hon. Cons. Addenbrooke's NHS Trust; Hon. Cons. Lifespan NHS Trust. Socs: AUDGP; BMA; Diabetes UK. Prev: Wellcome Train. Fell. Primary Med. Care Gp. Univ. of Soton.; Lect. & Princip. GP (Primary Med. Care) Univ. Soton.; Trainee GP St. Mary's Hosp. Newport, I. of Wight VTS.

GRIFFIN, Stephen John Forrester, Bowman and Rowlandson, Berry Lane Medical Centre, Berry Lane, Longridge, Preston PR3 3JJ Tel: 01772 783021 Fax: 01772 785809 — MB ChB 1987 Manch.; MRCGP 1992.

GRIFFIN, Mr Steven Charles 20 Bryan Mere, Bishop Burton, Beverley HU17 8QW Tel: 01964 551852 Fax: 01482 623257; 20 Bryan Mere, Bishop Burton, Beverley HU17 8QW Tel: 01964 551852 — MB BS 1981 Lond.; MS Lond. 1995; FRCS (Cth.) 1993; FRCS Ed. 1985. (Middlesex Hospital London) Cons. Cardiothoracic Surg. Castle Hill Hosp. Cottingham; Hon. Sen. Lect. (Surg.) Univ. of Hull. Socs: Soc. Cardiothoracic Surgs. GB & Irel. Prev: Sen. Regist. (Cardiothoracic Surg.) SE Thames RHA; Regist. (Cardiothoracic Surg.) Freeman Hosp. Newc. u. Tyne & Harefield Hosp.

GRIFFIN, Susanne Tavistock Clinic, Child & Family Department, 120 Belsize Lane, London NW3 5BA; 35 Weavers Way, Elm Village, Camden, London NW1 0XF — MB BS 1984 Lond. SHO (Psychiat.) Roy. Free, Whittington & Friern Barnet VTS. Prev: SHO (Psychiat.) Carlton Hayes Hosp. Leicester.

GRIFFIN, Teresa Linda Station Medical Centre, Hohne BFPO 30 — BM 1979 Soton.; BSc (Hons.) Soton. 1974.

GRIFFIN, Thelma Doreen (retired) Birch Cottage, 14 Holbrook Lane, Chislehurst BR7 6PF Tel: 020 8467 8338 — MRCS Eng. LRCP Lond. 1946. Prev: Ho. Off. (Anaesth.) King's Coll. Hosp. Lond.

GRIFFIN, Thomas Martin Joseph Underwood, 18 Broomhill Road, Penicuik EH26 9EE — MB ChB 1982 Glas.; T(GP) 1994.

GRIFFIN, Yvette Stablehurst, 11 Bradgate Road, Altrincham WA14 4QU — MB ChB 1995 Manch.; MB ChB (Hons.) Manch. 1995. (Univ. Manch.) SHO (Gen. Med.) Nottm. City Hosp. Prev: Ho. Off. (Gen. Med.) Wythenshawe Hosp.

GRIFFITH, Aled Wyn Two Bridges, River Lane, Handbridge, Chester CH4 7JT — MB BS 1975 Lond.

GRIFFITH, Anthony Hugh 46 Woking Road, Parkstone, Poole BH14 0BZ — BM Soton. 1980; DCH RCP Lond. 1984. Trainee GP Poole. Socs: Assoc. MRCGP; BMA. Prev: SHO (A & E) Poole Gen. Hosp.; SHO (Paediat. & O & G) Poole Gen. Hosp.

GRIFFITH, Arlwyn Hughes (retired) 5 Ballantyne Drive, Kingswood, Tadworth KT20 6EA Tel: 017373 52943 — MB BS 1948 Lond.; MD Lond. 1964; MRCS Eng. LRCP Lond. 1944; FFCM 1976; DPH Lond. 1949. Prev: Cons. & Dep. Dir. Clin. & Applied Research Divis. Wellcome ResearchLaborat.

GRIFFITH, Barbara Ann Glannrafon Surgery, Glannrafon, Amlwch LL68 9AG Tel: 01407 830878 Fax: 01407 832512; Annedd Wen, Lon Goed, Bull Bay, Amlwch LL68 9SU — MB ChB 1987 Liverp.

GRIFFITH, Caradog (retired) Nevern, Ala Road, Pwllheli LL53 5BL Tel: 01758 613866 — MB ChB 1949 Liverp. Prev: GP.

GRIFFITH, Catherine Jane 33 Hall Dr, Wirral CH49 1RW — MB BCh 1997 Wales.

GRIFFITH, David Brian Erskine Health Centre, Bargarran, Erskine PA8 6BS Tel: 0141 812 4044 Fax: 0141 812 3053; Erraid, 179 Titwood Road, Pollokshields, Glasgow G41 4BL Tel: 0141 424 1562 — MB ChB 1978 Bristol; MRCGP 1982 DRCOG 1982. (Bristol) GP Princip. Prev: SHO (Anaesth.) Gt. Yarmouth Dist. Gen. Hosp.; Trainee GP Gt. Yarmouth; Ho. Surg. Roy. Devon & Exeter Hosp.

GRIFFITH, David Gavin Cooper (Surgery), 36 High St., Battle TN33 0EA Tel: 01424 772263 Fax: 01424 775569; Shrublands, 18 Hastings Road, Battle TN33 0TA Tel: 01424 772708 — MB BS 1955 Lond. (Char. Cross.)

GRIFFITH, David John Owen A.M.I. Unit, Bronllys Hospital, Bronllys, Brecon LD3 0LY Tel: 01874 711661; Holly Lodge, Lyonshall, Kington HR5 3JP Tel: 01544 340381 — MB BCh 1979 Wales; MRCGP 1986; DCH RCP Lond. 1985; DRCOG 1984. Staff Grade Community Psychiat. Ty Illtyd Ment. Health Resource Centre, Brecon. Prev: Surg. Lt. RN; Regtl. Med. Off. 45 Cdo. Gp RM.; Princip. in Gen. Pract., Kington, Heref.

GRIFFITH, David Norman Wynne Mayday University Hospital, London Road, Croydon CR7 7YE Tel: 020 8401 3615 Fax: 020 8401 3620; 11 Albany Mansions, Albert Bridge Road, London SW11 4PG — MD 1985 Camb.; MA Camb. 1972, MB 1972, BChir 1971; MRCP (UK) 1975; FRCP 1997. (Camb. & Univ. Coll. Hosp.) Cons. c/o Elderly Mayday Hosp. Croydon. Prev: Sen. Regist. Med. Unit Univ. Coll. Hosp. Lond.; Research Fell. Dept. Med. Roy. Free Hosp. Lond.; SHO Whittington Hosp. Lond.

GRIFFITH, Dewi Wyn 19 Vellacotts, Chelmsford CM1 7EA — LMSSA 1954 Lond. (Lond. Hosp.) Prev: Ho. Phys. & Ho. Surg. St. John's Hosp. Chelmsford.

GRIFFITH, Donald Horace Stewart (retired) 7/9 Bridgend, Aberfeldy PH15 2DF Tel: 01887 830375 — LRCP LRCS 1947 Ed.; LRCP LRCS Ed. LRFPS Glas. 1947; MFCM 1972; MRCGP 1965; DPH

(Distinc., Chadwick & Newsholme Prizes) Lond. 1955; DIH Eng. 1955; Cert. Health Plann. Johns Hopkins Univ. (USA) 1967. Prev: Cons. WHO Copenhagen.

GRIFFITH, Edmund Frederick Station Road Health Centre, 15-16 Station Road, Penarth CF64 3EP Tel: 029 2071 2118 Fax: 029 2071 2168; 7 The Paddocks, Penarth CF64 5BW Tel: 01222 70189 Fax: 01222 701897 — MB BCh Wales 1960; AFOM RCP Lond. 1981. Regional Med. Off. Merchant Navy Estab. Cardiff; Occupat. Phys. Cardiff Community Healthcare Trust; Med. Ref. Benefits Agency Cardiff; Med. Adviser Ch. in Wales. Socs: Soc. Occupat. Med.

GRIFFITH, Eirwen 306 Wigmore Road, Gillingham ME8 0LU Tel: 01634 376419 — MB BS 1954 Lond. (Roy. Free) Princip. Med. Off. (Paediat. Audiol.) Maidstone HA. Socs: BMA.

GRIFFITH, Enyd Bevan Daymer, Gayton Road, Heswall, Wirral CH60 8 — MB BCh 1958 Wales; MRCPsych. 1982. (Cardiff)

GRIFFITH, Fiona Mary 23 Coppice Avenue, Great Shelford, Cambridge CB2 5AQ Tel: 01223 843189 — MB BS 1972 Lond.; MRCS Eng. LRCP Lond. 1972; ECFMG Cert 1973; DO Eng. 1977. (Guy's) Clin. Asst. (Ophth.) Addenbrooke's Hosp. Camb. Prev: SHO (Cas. & Orthop.) & Ho. Surg. Roy. Surrey Co. Hosp. Guildford; Ho. Phys. (Neurol.) St. Lukes & Roy. Surrey Co. Hosps. Guildford.

GRIFFITH, Gary David William 24 Marshall House, Albert Road, London NW6 5DS — MB BS 1995 Lond.

GRIFFITH, Mr Gwilym Huw Argoed, 47 Fields Park Road, Newport NP20 5BH Tel: 01633 65394 — MB BS 1956 Lond.; FRCS Eng. 1962. (St. Mary's) Cons. Surg. Roy. Gwent Hosp. Newport. Socs: Welsh Surgic. Soc. Prev: Sen. Regist. Surg. United Cardiff Hosps.; Surg. Regist. St. Geo. Hosp. Lond.; Ho. Surg. St. Mary's Hosp. Lond.

GRIFFITH, Helen Elizabeth Employee Health Management, Glaxosmithkline, Cobden Street, Montrose DD10 8EA Tel: 01674 672606 Fax: 01674 666300 Email: heg35526@glaxowellcome.co.uk; Oakbank, Hillside by Montrose, Montrose DD10 9HY Tel: 01674 830237 Fax: 01674 830237 — MB ChB 1976 Aberd.; AFOM RCP Lond. 1997. (Aberdeen) Sen. Occupat.al health Phys., Employee Health Managem., Montrose; Sen. Occupat.al health Phys., Irvine. Socs: Assoc. Fac. Occupat. Med. Prev: SHO (Psychiat.) Sunnyside Roy. Hosp. Montrose; Ho. Off. (Thoracic Surg.) Roy. Infirm. Aberd.; Ho. Off. (Gen. Med.) City Hosp. Aberd.

GRIFFITH, Hugh Brynfor Chwaen Hen, Llantrisant, Holyhead LL65 4TN — MRCS Eng. LRCP Lond. 1974; BSc Lond. 1971, MB BS 1974; MRCOG 1979. (St. Bart.)

GRIFFITH, Mr Iolo Pyrs Hafod-y-Coed, Greenwood Lane, St Fagans, Cardiff CF5 6EL — MRCS Eng. LRCP Lond. 1959; PhD Lond. 1967, BSc 1956, MB BS 1959; FRCS Eng. 1970. (Univ. Coll. Hosp.) Cons. Surg.(ENT) Univ. Hosp. Wales, Cardiff. Socs: Fell. Roy. Soc. Med.; Pres. Otol. Sect. Roy. Soc. Med. Prev: Sen. Lect. (ENT) Welsh Nat. Sch. Med.; Hon. Cons. Univ. Hosp. of Wales, Cardiff; Sen. Regist. Middlx. Hosp. Lond.

GRIFFITH, James Francis 26 Corisande Road, Selly Oak, Birmingham B29 6RH Tel: 0121 472 6620 — MB BCh BAO 1983 NUI; MRCP UK 1988; FRCR 1992. Trainee Regist. in Radiol. W. Midl. Train. Scheme. Prev: Regist. Gen. Med. Doncaster Roy. Infirm.; SHO Gen. Med. Pilgrim Hosp. Boston.

GRIFFITH, Jannette Diana ap-Howell 27 Southway, Totteridge, London N20 8DD — MRCS Eng. LRCP Lond. 1945. (Royal Free Hospital) Prev: Phys. i/c NW Thames RHA Chest Radiog. Serv., St. Albans Units; Phys. Whittington Hosp. Chest Clinic Lond.; Phys. St. Alban's Chest Clinic.

GRIFFITH, John Lawrence Mary 25 Fulmar Drive, Sale M33 4WH — MB BS 1992 Lond.

GRIFFITH, John Morgan Townhead Surgery, Townhead, Murray Lane, Montrose DD10 8LE Tel: 01674 76161 Fax: 01674 673151; Oakbank, Hillside by Montrose, Montrose DD10 9HX Tel: 0167 483237 — MB ChB 1972 Dundee; MRCGP 1977; DCH Eng. 1975. Prev: SHO (Cas.) Roy. Infirm. Aberd.; SHO (O & G) Roy. Infirm. Stirling.

GRIFFITH, Kathryn Elizabeth University Health Centre, York University, Heslington, York YO10 5DD Tel: 01904 433290; Stanley House, 57 The Village, Osbaldwick, York YO10 3NP — BM BS 1978 Nottm.; MRCP (UK) 1982; MRCGP 1985. (Nottingham) Research Regist. (Cardiol.) York Dist. Hosp. Socs: Cardiac Soc. Prev: SHO & Regist. (Med.) Derbysh. Roy. Infirm.

GRIFFITH, Leslie Mercy Veronica (retired) Daws Hill, Powick, Worcester WR2 4RG Tel: 01905 830585 — MB ChB 1948 Aberd. Prev: GP Worcester.

GRIFFITH, Mr Maldwyn Jones, OBE West Wales General Hospital, Carmarthen SA31 2AF Tel: 01267 235151; Ael-y-Bryn, Dryslwyne, Carmarthen SA32 8RX Tel: 01558 668222 — MB ChB Liverp. 1963; MChOrth Liverp. 1972; FRCS Ed. 1970; FRCS Eng. 1970. Cons. Orthop. Surg. W. Wales Gen. Hosp. Carmarthen. Socs: Brit. Orthop. Research Soc. & Low Friction Arthroplasty Soc. Prev: Hunt. Prof. Roy. Coll. Surg. Eng.; Asst. Prof. Orthop. Surg. Albert Einstein Coll. Med., New York; Sen. Regist. Centre for Hip Surg. Wrightington Hosp.

GRIFFITH, Margaret Morris (retired) Nevern, Ala Road, Pwllheli LL53 5BL Tel: 01758 613866 — MB ChB 1952 Liverp.; DPH Eng. 1957. Prev: Sen. Med. Off. Gwynedd HA (Pwllheli).

GRIFFITH, Megan Eleri 85 Park Hill Road, Birmingham B17 9HH — MB ChB 1989 Birm.; MRCP (UK) 1992. Wellcome Research Fell. & Hon. Clin. Regist. Renal Unit Hammersmith Hosp. Lond.

GRIFFITH, Michael John 80 Sackville Road, Heaton, Newcastle upon Tyne NE6 5TA — MB BChir 1981 Camb.; MD Camb. 1990, MA 1981; MRCP (UK) 1984. (Camb.) Sen. Regist. (Cardiol.) Freeman Hosp. Newc. u. Tyne. Prev: Research Regist. (Cardiol.) St. Geo. Hosp. Lond.; Regist. (Cardiol.) St. Thos. Hosp. Lond.; Regist. (Med.) Poole Gen. Hosp.

GRIFFITH, Nia Wyn Anaesthesia Department, Southmead Hospital, Westbury-on-Trym, Bristol Tel: 0117 950 5050 — MB BCh 1987 Wales; FRCA 1994. (Univ. Wales Coll. Med.) Cons. Anaesth. N. Bristol NHS Trust Bristol. Socs: Roy. Coll. Anaesth.; Brit. Assoc.Of Day Surg.; Euro Soc Of Regional Anaesth. Prev: Regist. (Anaesth.) High Wycombe, Oxf. & Bristol; SHO (Anaesth.) N.ampton; Interne Anaesth. Cardiothoracic Hosp. Lym, France.

GRIFFITH, Olwen Rhiannon 325 St Margaret's Road, Twickenham TW1 1PW Tel: 020 8892 6031 Fax: 020 8892 6031 — MB BS 1981 Lond.; BSc Lond. 1978, MB BS 1981; MRCGP 1986. (St. Mary's Lond.)

GRIFFITH, Peter Crichton 159 Doncaster Road, Rotherham S65 2DQ Tel: 01709 364544 — MB ChB 1953 Sheff. (Sheff.) Prev: Ho. Surg. Doncaster Roy. Infirm.; Ho. Phys. Derbysh. Roy. Infirm.

GRIFFITH, Rebecca Jane 8 North Dr, Swanland, North Ferriby HU14 3QU — MB ChB 1997 Manch.

GRIFFITH, Richard Anthony Highbridge Medical Centre, Pepperall Road, Highbridge TA9 3YA Tel: 01278 783220 Fax: 01278 795486; Maple Tree House, Stretcholt, West Huntspill, Highbridge TA9 4SR Tel: 01278 685464 — MB BS 1988 Lond.; MRCGP 1994; DRCOG 1992. Prev: Trainee GP Som. VTS.

GRIFFITH, Rosa Anne Monica (retired) Delamere, 6 New Cross, Longburton, Sherborne DT9 6EJ Tel: 0196 321437 — LRCPI & LM, LRSCI & LM 1938; LRCPI & LM, LRCSI & LM 1938. Prev: GP Burnley.

GRIFFITH, Sarah Katherine Waldron The Health Centre, Iveldale Drive, Shefford SG17 5AD Tel: 01462 814899 Fax: 01462 815322; 15 Mill Lane, Campton, Shefford SG17 5NX — MB BS 1984 Lond.; MRCGP 1989; DRCOG 1987. (St. Bart.)

GRIFFITH, Shan 115 Gordon Road, Harborne, Birmingham B17 9EX — MB ChB 1981 Birm.

GRIFFITH, Sian Mererid Surrey and Sussex Healthcare Trust, Canada Avenue, Redhill RH1 5RH Tel: 01737 768511 Fax: 01737 761395 — MB ChB 1987 Sheff.; MD Sheff. 1996; MRCP (UK) 1990. p/t Cons. (Rheum), E. Surrey Hosp. Prev: Sen. Regist. (Rheum.) Staffs. Rheum. Centre Stoke-on-Trent; Hon. Lect. (Clin. Skills & Med. Informatics) Med. Coll. St. Bart. Hosp. Lond.; Regist. (Rheum.) Homerton Hosp. Lond.

GRIFFITH, Susan 156 Nine Mile Ride, Finchampstead, Wokingham RG40 4JA — MB BS 1980 Lond.; MFPM 1991; MRCGP 1985; Dip. Pharm. Med. RCP Lond. 1990; DRCOG 1986; DCH RCP Lond. 1984. (Middlx.) Therap. Area Head Boehringer Ingelheim, Germany.

GRIFFITH, Terence Paul The Cumbrian Clinic, West Cumberland Hospital, Whitehaven CA28 8JG Tel: 01946 523380 Fax: 01946 523506 — MB BS Lond. 1953; FRCOphth 1989; DO Eng. 1958. (St. Thos.) Cons. Ophth. Surg. Cumbrian Clinic W. Cumbld. Hosp. Socs: Fell. Roy. Soc. Med.; Oxf. Ophth. Cong. Prev: Cons. Ophth. Surg. W. Cumbria HA; Cons. Ophth. Irton Hall. Sch.; Sen. Regist.

Kent. Co. Ophth. Hosp. Maidstone & Corneoplastic Unit E. Grinstead.

GRIFFITH, Timothy Patrick Goldington Avenue Surgery, 85 Goldington Avenue, Bedford MK40 3DB Tel: 01234 349531 Fax: 01234 267455 Email: timgriffith@gp-e81047.nhs.uk; 28A Oakley Road, Bromham, Bedford MK43 8HZ Tel: 01234 823414 — MB BS 1974 Lond.; MRCGP 1978; DObst RCOG 1976. (Kings Coll Hosp.) Prev: Trainee Gen. Pract. Bedford Vocational Train. Scheme.

GRIFFITH, Professor Tudor Morley Deaprtment of Diagnostic Radiology, University of Wales College of Medicine, Heath Park, Cardiff CF14 4XN Tel: 029 2074 3070 Fax: 029 2074 3069 Email: griffith@cardiff.ac.uk; 3 St Edeyrns Close, Cyncoed, Cardiff CF23 6TH — MB BCh 1978 Wales; PhD Wales 1990; MA Camb. 1975, BA 1972; MRCP (UK) 1981; FRCR 1986. (University of Wales College of Medicine) Prof. (Radiol.) Univ. of Wales Coll. of Med. Prev: Reader & Sen. Lect. (Radiol.) & Brit. Heart Foundat. Research Fell. Univ. Hosp. Wales.

GRIFFITH, Vyvien Joan The White House, Lyth Hill Road, Shrewsbury SY3 0AU Tel: 01743 872512 — MB BCh 1951 Wales; BSc Wales 1948, MB BCh 1951. (Cardiff) Prev: Regist. (Gen. Med.) St. David's Hosp. Cardiff; Ho. Phys. (Child Health) Cardiff United Hosps.; Ho. Phys. Cardiff Roy. Infirm.

GRIFFITH, William Francis The White House, Lyth Hill Road, Bayston Hill, Shrewsbury SY3 0AU Tel: 01743 872512 — MB BS 1954 Lond.; DObst RCOG 1957. (Univ. Coll. Hosp.) Socs: BMA. Prev: Ho. Phys. & Ho. Surg. Univ. Coll. Hosp. Lond.; Ho. Surg. (Obst.) Cheltenham Matern. Hosp.

GRIFFITH-JONES, Martin David St James University Hospital, Beckett St., Leeds LS9 7TF Tel: 0113 243 3144; 77 Wike Ridge Avenue, Alwoodley, Leeds LS17 9NN Tel: 0113 269 6651 — MB BS 1984 Lond.; MRCOG 1989. Cons. O & G St. Jas. Univ. Hosp. Leeds.

GRIFFITHS, Adrian 4 Coastguard Cottages, Culvser Doen, Sandown PO36 8QT — MB BS 1987 Lond.; MRCP (UK) 1993. Regist. (Gastroenterol. & Gen. Med.) Bath Roy. United Hosp.

GRIFFITHS, Alan Paul 97 Lichfield Court, Sheen Road, Richmond TW9 1AX Tel: 0421 881652 — MB BCh 1990 Wales; MRCGP 1994. Prev: Trainee GP Ysbyty Gwynedd VTS; Ho. Med. (Med. & Surg.) Roy. Gwent Hosp. Newport.

GRIFFITHS, Alison Clare Treen, 1 Bittell Lane, Barnt Green, Birmingham B45 8NS Tel: 0121 445 4241; Churchfields Surgery, Recreation Road, Bromsgrove B61 8DT Tel: 01527 872163 — MB BS 1988 Lond.; MRGCP; DRCOG; DCH; DFFP. (The London Hospital)

GRIFFITHS, Alun Gwyn Rhys Cil y Coed, Llansadwrn, Menai Bridge LL59 5SE — MB BCh 1989 Wales; DRCOG 1996; DFFP 1996.

GRIFFITHS, Alun John Tenby Surgery, The Norton, Tenby SA70 8AB Tel: 01834 844161 Fax: 01834 844227 — MB BCh 1975 Wales.

GRIFFITHS, Alun Owen Little Horton Lane Surgery, 482 Little Horton Lane, Bradford BD5 0PA Tel: 01274 394277; 4 Wood Nook, Whalley Lane, Denholme, Bradford BD13 4LH Tel: 01535 272850 Email: aogriffs@gpiag-asthna.org — MB BCh 1980 Wales; MRCGP 1984; DRCOG 1984. (Welsh National School of Medicine) Prev: Trainee GP E. Glam. VTS; Ho. Phys. Neath Gen. Hosp.; Ho. Surg. P. Chas. Hosp. Merthyr.

GRIFFITHS, Alun Wynne (retired) 5 Albert Bridge Road, London SW11 4PX Tel: 020 7622 5171 — MRCS Eng. LRCP Lond. 1950; MA Oxf. 1949; MRCPsych 1971; DPM Eng. 1954. Prev: Sen. Off. Home Office.

GRIFFITHS, Amanda Gwyneth Royal Manchester Childrens Hospital, Hospital Road, Pendlebury, Manchester M27 4HA Tel: 0161 794 4696 Fax: 0167 727 2477 Email: mandy.griffiths@hotmail.com; Tel: 0161 790 5285 — MB ChB 1985 Bristol; FCAnaesth 1991. Cons. (Anaesth.) Roy. Manch. Childr.'s Hosp. Socs: Assn. Anaesth.; Assn. Paediat. Anaesth.; BMA. Prev: Sen. Regist. (Anaesth.) N.. W.. Region.

GRIFFITHS, Amanda Laurence Kincora, 40 St Edward's Drive, Sudbrooke, Lincoln LN2 2QR — MB ChB 1977 Sheff.; FRCR 1983; DMRD Eng. 1981. Cons. Radiol. Lincoln Co. Hosp.

GRIFFITHS, Andrew 172 High Street, Gilfach Goch, Porth CF39 8SH — MB BS 1991 Lond.

GRIFFITHS, Mr Andrew Brian Newcastle General Hospital, Newcastle upon Tyne NE4 6BE; 17 Albemarle Avenue, High West Jesmond, Newcastle upon Tyne NE2 3NQ Tel: 0191 285 8097 — MB ChB 1975 Bristol; PhD Lond. 1987; FRCS Eng. 1980. Cons. Gen. & BrE. Surg. Roy. Vict. Infirm. Newc.; Cons. Surg. BrE. Unit Newc. Gen. Hosp.; Arris & Gale Lect. RCS Eng. 1986. Socs: BASO. Prev: Lect. (Surg.) St. Geo. Hosp. Med. Sch. Lond.; Regist. (Surg.) N.. Gen. Hosp. Sheff.; Clin. Research Fell. ICRF Laborat. Lond.

GRIFFITHS, Andrew David 14 Haycroft Close, Bishops Cleeve, Cheltenham GL52 8SR — BM BS 1992 Nottm.

GRIFFITHS, Anna Leigh Lane End Cottage, Main Street, Cropwell, Butler, Nottingham NG12 3AB — MB BChir Camb. 1990; MA Camb. 1991; MRCGP 1994; DRCOG 1996. (Addenbrooke's Hosp. Camb.)

GRIFFITHS, Anne The Karis Medical Centre, Waterworks Road, Edgbaston, Birmingham B16 9AL Tel: 0121 454 0661 Fax: 0121 454 9104 — MB BS 1986 Lond.; DRCOG 1991; DCH RCP Lond. 1990.

GRIFFITHS, Anne Rhys Chippenham Surgery, Mouth Street, Monmouth NP25 3EQ Tel: 01600 713811 Fax: 01600 772652 — MB BCh 1983 Wales.

GRIFFITHS, Anthony David Linden Lea, 42 Avenue Road, Abergavenny NP7 7DB — MB BCh 1960 Wales; MD Wales 1971; FRCP Lond. 1994; FRCP Ed. 1972, M 1964; MRCP Lond. 1965; FRCPCH 1997, M 1996; DCH Eng. 1962. (Welsh Nat. Sch. Med.) Cons. Paediat. Nevill Hall Hosp. Abergavenny. Prev: Lect. (Child Health) Welsh Nat. Sch. Med.; Hon. Sen. Regist. United Cardiff Hosps. & Welsh Hosp. Bd.; Research Fell. (Child Health) Welsh Nat. Sch. Med.

GRIFFITHS, Anthony Evjen Manor Gwyn, Login, Whitland SA34 0XD — MB BChir 1989 Camb.; MA Camb. 1990, MB BChir 1989. SHO (Med.) Medway Hosp. Gillingham.

GRIFFITHS, Anthony Paul Department of Histopathology, Morriston Hospital NHS Trust, Morriston, Swansea SA6 6NL Tel: 01792 703040 Fax: 01792 703051 Email: paul.griffiths@morrnhst-tr.wales.nhs.uk — MB BS Lond. 1977; BSc Lond. 1974; MRCPI 1986; MRCPath 1992; FRCPath 2000. (Westm. Hosp. Lond.) Cons. Histopath. Neath Gen. Hosp. & Morriston Hosp. NHS Trust. Socs: Brit. Soc. Gastroenterol.; Assn. Clin. Path; Internat. Acad. Path. Prev: Sen. Regist. (Histopath.) Gen. Infirm. Leeds; Regist. (Endocrinol.) Leeds Gen. Infirm.; Med. Off. Brit. Antarctic Survey.

GRIFFITHS, Anthony Wayne Meddygfa Penygroes, Bridge Street, Penygroes, Llanelli SA14 7RP Tel: 01269 831193 Fax: 01269 832116; Y Wenallt, Drefach, Llanelli SA14 7BB Tel: 01269 841871 — MB BCh 1975 Wales; DCH Eng. 1978. (Univ. Wales Coll. Med., Cardiff) Clin. Asst. (Geriat. Med.) Dyfed; Med. Off. Common Wealth Games Counc. for Wales. Socs: (Treas.) Pub. Health Alliance, Wales. Prev: Clin. Asst. (Ment. Handicap) Med. Off. Commowealth Games Counc. for Wales; Non-Exec. Dir. Dyfed FHSA (Mem. Dist. Med. Comm.).

GRIFFITHS, Arthur Owen (retired) Joan Royd House, Joan Royd Lane, Cobley, Penistone, Sheffield S36 9DA Tel: 01226 765725 — MB ChB Manch. 1955. Prev: Ho. Phys. & Ho. Surg. Crumpsall Hosp. Manch.

GRIFFITHS, Belinda Jane 2 Alpha Cottages, 14 North End Lane, Sunningdale, Ascot SL5 0DZ Tel: 01344 622886 — MB BS 1981 Lond.; DRCOG 1984. (St. Marys, W2)

GRIFFITHS, Ben 38 Dutch Barn Close, Chorley PR7 1PR Tel: 01257 247159 Fax: 01257 247159 — MB ChB 1997 Manch.; BSc (Med Sci) 1994. SNO BST Surgic. Rotat., Chorley & S. Ribble D.G.H.

GRIFFITHS, Bernard Edmund Tynycoed Hir, Cwmynysminton Road, Llwydcoed, Aberdare CF44 0UT Tel: 01685 884203 — MB BCh 1974 Wales; MRCP (UK) 1977. Cons. Phys. & Cardiol. P. Chas. Hosp. Merthyr Tydfil. Prev: Lect. (Cardiol.) Univ. Hosp. Wales Cardiff; Regist. (Cardiol.) Papworth Hosp. Cambs.

GRIFFITHS, Brenda 86 King George V Drive, Cardiff — MB BS 1950 Lond.; MRCS Eng. LRCP Lond. 1949; DCH Eng. 1952. (W. Lond.)

GRIFFITHS, Brian John Waterside Primary Care, Combe Martin Health Centre, Castle Street, Combe Martin, Ilfracombe EX34 0JA Tel: 01271 882406 Fax: 01271 883821 Email: brian.griffiths@gp_l83017.nhs.uk; Holly Dene, King St, Combe Martin, Ilfracombe EX34 0AH — MB BS 1976 Lond.; DRCOG 1979. (St. Geo.) Gen. Practitioner. Prev: SHO (O & G) N. Devon Infirm/ Dist. Hosp.; SHO (A & E) Bristol Roy. Infirm.; Ho. Surg. St. Geo. Hosp. Lond.

GRIFFITHS, Bridget Level 2, Musculoskeletal Unit, Freeman Hospital, High Heaton, Newcastle NE7 7DN Tel: 0191 284 3111 Fax: 0191 223 1159; Tel: 01434 606779 — MB ChB 1988 Birm.; MD 1999; MRCP (UK) 1991. Cons. Rheum., Freeman Hosp., Newc.-upon-Tyne. Prev: Regist. (Gen. Med. & Rheum.) Dudley Rd. Hosp. Birm.; SHO (Med.) P.ss Roy. Hosp. Telford; Lect. (Rheum.) Univ. Leeds.

GRIFFITHS, Bryan Llewellyn (retired) Neath General Hospital, Neath SA11 2LQ Tel: 01639 641161 — MB BS 1956 Lond.; FRCP Ed. 1982, M 1966; FRCP Lond. 1979, M 1966; DCH Eng. 1960; FRCPCH. Cons. Paediat. Neath Gen. Hosp. Prev: Sen. Regist. (Child Health) Roy. Vict. Infirm. Newc.

GRIFFITHS, Mr Carl Lindsay Horton General Hospital, Oxford Radcliffe Trust, Banbury OX16 9AL; 6 Old Glebe, Tadmarton, Banbury OX15 5TH — MB BS 1976 Lond.; FRCS Eng. 1981; MRCS Eng. LRCP Lond. 1976. (Westm.) Cons. Surg. Horton Dist. Gen. Hosp. Banbury. Socs: Brit. Assn. Surg. Oncol.; Assn. Surg. Prev: Cons. Surg. Qu. Eliz. Milit. Hosp. Woolwich & Airborne Forces.; Cons. Surg. Camb. Milit. Hosp. Aldershot; Cons. Surg. 5 Airbourne Brig..

GRIFFITHS, Carol Ann Worcester Street Surgery, 24 Worcester Street, Stourbridge DY8 1AW Tel: 01384 371616 Fax: 01384 444310 Email: cagrifty@doctors.org.uk — MB ChB 1981 Leic.; MRCGP 1985; Dip. Pract. Dermat. Wales 1994; DRCOG 1985; DCH RCP Lond. 1984. Hon. Clin. Lect. (Gen. Pract.) Univ. Birm.; Clin. Sub Deen Univ. of Birm. Prev: Trainee GP Dudley VTS; Ho. Off. & Ho. Surg. Leic. Roy. Infirm.

GRIFFITHS, Carolyn Susan Apples Medical Centre, East Mill Lane, Sherborne DT9 3DG Tel: 01935 812633 Fax: 01935 817484; Half Acre, Horsecastles Lane, Sherborne DT9 6BH Tel: 01935 812063 — MB BS 1984 Lond.; BSc Lond. 1983; MRCGP 1988; DRCOG 1987.

GRIFFITHS, Cary Cantle Millbeck, Carding Mill Valley, Church Stretton SY6 6JF — MB ChB 1949 Birm.; DObst RCOG 1953. (Birm.) Prev: Ho. Surg. Gen. Hosp. Birm.; Ho. Phys. Dudley Rd. Hosp. Birm.; Paediat. Ho. Phys. S.mead Hosp. Bristol.

GRIFFITHS, Catherine Jane Swineshead Medical Group, The Surgery, Church Lane, Swineshead, Boston PE20 3JA Tel: 01205 820204 Fax: 01205 821034; Park House Farm, High St, Swineshead, Boston PE20 3LH Tel: 01205 820470 Fax: 01205 820470 — BM BCh 1987 Oxf.; BA Oxf. 1987. Prev: Asst. GP Grantham; Med. Advisor Total Purchasing Pilot Project, Latham Hse. Med. Pract. Melton Mowbray; Trainee GP Lincs. VTS.

GRIFFITHS, Charles Idris (retired) Ivy House, Shenstone, Lichfield WS14 0NF — MB ChB 1940 Birm.; DMRD Eng. 1949. Prev: Cons. Radiol. N. Birm. Gp. Hosps.

GRIFFITHS, Charles James Morgan 38 Broadmead, Killay, Swansea SA2 7EJ Tel: 01792 290575 — MB ChB 1971 Birm. Clin. Asst. Singleton Accid. Unit Swansea. Prev: Med. Supt. Kimdiawa Papua New Guinea; Resid. Med. Off. Rhodesian Light Infantry.

GRIFFITHS, Professor Christopher Ernest Maitland Dermatology Centre, University of Manchester, Hope Hospital, Salford M6 8HD Tel: 0161 787 4392 Fax: 0161 787 1095 Email: christopher.griff.ths@man.ac.uk; Brookheyes, Alan Drive, Hale, Altrincham WA15 0LR Tel: 0161 904 7006 — MB BS 1979 Lond.; MD Lond. 1991, BSc (Anat.) (1st cl. Hons.) 1976; FRCP Lond. 1995; MRCP (UK) 1983. (St. Thos.) Prof. Dermat. Univ. Manch. Sch. Med.; Hon. Cons. Dermat. Salford Roy. Hosps. NHS Trust. Socs: Brit. Assn. Dermat.; Eur. Soc. Dermat. Res.; (Past Chairm.) Brit. Soc. Invest. Dermat. Prev: Asst. Prof. Univ. Michigan Med. Center Ann Arbor, USA; Wellcome Research Fell. & Hon. Sen. Regist. (Dermat.) St. Mary's Hosp. Lond.; Regist. (Dermat.) St. Mary's Hosp. Lond.

GRIFFITHS, Christopher James 'Glentworth', Dalton Terrace, York YO24 4DB Tel: 01904 58542 — MB 1961 Camb.; BChir 1960. Prev: Ho. Phys. Sedgefield Gen. Hosp.; Ho. Surg. W. Kent Gen. Hosp.

GRIFFITHS, Christopher John Lower Clapton Health Centre, 36 Lower Clapton Road, London E5 0PQ; Department of General Practice & Primary Care, Medical & Dental School, St. Bartholomews & Royal London Hospital, London EC1M 6BQ Tel: 020 7982 6032 Fax: 020 7982 6103 Email: c.j.griffiths@mds.qmw.ac.uk — MB BS 1986 Lond.; MA, DPhil Oxf. 1984. Sen. Lect. (Gen. Pract.) St. Bart. & Roy. Lond. Hosp. Socs: RCP; Roy. Coll. Gen. Pract. Prev: SHO (Med.) Plymouth HA; Ho. Off. Gloucester Roy. Hosp.

GRIFFITHS, Claire Angela Glenfields, Sladacre Lane, Blagdon BS40 7RP Tel: 01761 463448; Glenfields, Sladacre Lane, Blagdon BS40 7RP Tel: 01761 463448 — MB ChB 1993 Bristol; DRCOG 2000; MRCP (UK) 1996. p/t GP VTS Scheme, Bristol. Prev: SHO (Paediat.) Roy. United Hosp. Bath; Ho. Off. (Surg.) Bristol Roy. Infirm.; Ho. Off. (Med.) Frenchay Hosp. Bristol.

GRIFFITHS, Constance Anne Southside Road Surgery, 43 Southside Road, Inverness IV2 4XA Tel: 01463 710222 Fax: 01463 714072; Windyridge, Drumchardine, Kirkhill, Inverness IV5 7PW — MB BS 1974 London; MB BS Lond. 1974. (London) GP Inverness.

GRIFFITHS, Mr David 31 Quarry Avenue, Hartshill, Stoke-on-Trent ST4 7EW Tel: 01782 744118; 6 Allthorpe Place, Newcastle under Lyme ST5 3TY Tel: 01782 621832 Fax: 0178 747193 Email: user@davidgriffith.u-net.com — MB BS 1984 Lond.; MA Camb. 1985, BA 1981; FRCS (Orth.) 1994; FRCS Eng. 1990; FRCS Glas. 1989. Cons. Orthop. Surg. N. Staffs. Roy. Infirm. Stoke on Trent. Socs: Brit. Orthop. Assn.; BMA; Fell.Brit. Orthopaedic Assoc. Prev: Sen. Regist. (Orthop.) N. Staffs. Roy. Infirm. & Robt. Jones & Agnes Hunt Orthop. Hosp. OsW.ry; Regist. Rotat. (Orthop.) OsW.ry; SHO Rotat. (Gen. Surg.) Bristol Roy. Infirm.

GRIFFITHS, Mr David Anthony Yeovil District Hospital, Higher Kingston, Yeovil BA21 4BE Tel: 01935 707252 Fax: 01935 410752 Email: hollm@gwise.esomerset-tr.swest.nhs.uk — MB ChB 1965 Bristol; MB ChB (Hons.) Bristol 1965; BSc (Anat., Hons.) Bristol 1962, MD 1970; FRCS Eng. 1971; FRCS Ed. 1971. (Bristol) Cons. Surg. E. Som. NHS Trust; Postgrad. Tutor Yeovil Hosp. Socs: Hon. Fell. Soc. M-C di Bologna.; Anat. Soc.; Brit. Assn. Urol. Surgs. (Counc. Mem.). Prev: Regist. (Surg.) Radcliffe Infirm. Oxf.; Demonst. (Anat.) Univ. Bristol; Vis. Prof. Anat. Dept. Anat. Coll. Med. Univ. Iowa, USA.

GRIFFITHS, David Francis Rees Department of Pathology, University of Wales College of Medicine, Heath Park, Cardiff CF14 4XN Tel: 029 2074 5316 Email: griffithsdfr@cf.ac.uk; 23 Church Road, Whitchurch, Cardiff CF14 2DX — MB BCh 1978 Wales; MRCP (UK) 1980; MRCPath 1985. Sen. Lect. (Path.) Univ. Wales Coll. Med. Cardiff.; Hon. Cons. in Histopath.

GRIFFITHS, David Gweirydd Denmead Health Centre, Hambledon Road, Denmead, Waterlooville PO7 6NR Tel: 023 9225 7111 Fax: 023 9225 7113; Mullions, Well Hill, Denmead, Waterlooville PO7 6HB Tel: 02392 255996 — MB BS Lond. 1969; MRCGP 1974; Cert JCC Lond. 1976; DA Eng. 1975; DObst RCOG 1972. (St. Bart.) Prev: Anaesth. Portsmouth Dist. Community Dent. Servs.; Trainee GP Oxf. VTS; Regist. (Anaesth.) Radcliffe Infirm. Oxf.

GRIFFITHS, David John (retired) Summerfield, Llandysul SA44 4DX Tel: 0155932 2374 — MB BCh 1956 Wales. Prev: GP.

GRIFFITHS, David John The Brown House, 12 Moor Hall Drive, Sutton Coldfield B75 6LP; 500 Brookline Avenue, Suite E, Boston MA 02115, USA Tel: 00 1 617 2786929 — MB ChB 1987 Leic.; MRCOG 1993. Specialist Regist. W. Mids Rotat. Prev: Clin. Research Fell. Brigham & Wom. Hosp. Harvard Med. Sch. Boston, MA, USA; Clin. Research Fell. St. Jas. Univ. Hosp. Leeds; Regist. Rotat. (O & G) W. Midl.

GRIFFITHS, Mr David Mervyn Wessex Regional Centre for Paediatric Surgery, Southampton General Hospital, Southampton SO16 6YD Tel: 02380 796489 Fax: 02380 794750 — BM BCh 1976 Oxf.; MA Camb. 1977; MCh Oxf. 1988; FRCS Eng. 1981; FRCS Ed. 1981. Cons. & Sen. Lect. (Neonat. & Paediat. Surg.) Soton. Gen. Hosp. Univ. Socs: Brit. Assn. Paediat. Surg.; Brit. Soc. Paediat. Gastroenterol. & Nutrit. Prev: Sen. Regist. (Paediat. Surg.) Soton. Gen. Hosp.; Clin. Research Fell. (Neonat. Surg.) Oxf.

GRIFFITHS, David Paul Geddes Carrick House, Resthonguet Point, Feock, Truro TR3 6RB — MB BS 1967 Lond.; MRCS Eng. LRCP Lond. 1967; FFA RCS Eng. 1971; DA Eng. 1969. (Guy's) Cons. Anaesth. Roy. Cornw. Hosp. (Treliske) Truro. Socs: Assn. Anaesths.

GRIFFITHS, David Roger Bronyn Farm, Ferryside SA17 5TW — MB ChB 1969 Liverp.

GRIFFITHS, Diane Elizabeth Nottingham City Hospital NHS Trust, Hucknall Road, Nottingham NG5 1PB Tel: 0115 969 1169; Blue Haze, Forest Road, Oxton, Southwell NG25 0TD Tel: 0115 965 3759 Fax: 0115 965 2272 Email: ajb_deg@compuserve.com — MB BCh 1983 Wales; FRCA 1989. Cons. Anaesth. Nottm. City Hosp. NHS Trust. Socs: Assn. Anaesth.; Obst. Anaesth. Assn.; Sec. SEMSA.

GRIFFITHS, Mr Donald Barry (retired) Convoy, Llanon SY23 5HS Tel: 01974 202295 — MB BS 1943 Lond.; MS Lond. 1959; FRCS Eng. 1952; MRCS Eng. LRCP Lond. 1943. Cons. Surg. Bronglais Hosp. Aberystwyth. Prev: John Marshall Fell. Univ. Lond.

GRIFFITHS, Donald Lawrence (retired) Crowndale, 90 Scatterdells Lane, Chipperfield, Kings Langley WD4 9EX Tel: 01927 764782 — MB BS 1946 Lond. Prev: Capt. RAMC.

GRIFFITHS, Donna Louise Bay Cottage, Kerry, Newtown SY16 4NU Tel: 01686 670412 Fax: 01686 670412 Email: stonegarden@compuserve.com — MB ChB 1992 Liverp.; DCH RCP Lond. 1996; DRCOG 1995.

GRIFFITHS, Dylan Chatham Forest House Adolescent Unit, Harperbury Hospital, Radlett WD7 9HQ Tel: 01923 427312 Fax: 01923 858158; 2 Darling Road, London SE4 1YQ Tel: 020 8691 7126 Email: drnhs.griff@btinternet.com — MB BS 1975 Lond.; MRCPsych 1979. (KCH) Cons. Adolesc. Psychiat. Forest Ho. Adolesc. Unit W. Herts Community Trust. Socs: Brit. Psychoanal. Soc. Prev: Sen. Regist. Adolesc. Unit Bethlehem Roy. & Maudsley Hosp.; Sen. Regist. (Child & Family Psychiat.) King's Coll. Hosp. Lond.; Cons. Bexley Clinic For Child & Family Psychiat.

GRIFFITHS, Edward Anthony Pen-y-Lan House, Pencoed, Bridgend CF35 6LT — MB BS 1954 Lond.; LMSSA Lond. 1952.

GRIFFITHS, Edward John Tel: 01983 295611 Fax: 01983 280815 — MB BS 1973 Newc.; Dip Pris Med 2000; MRCGP 1977. (Newc. Upon Tyne) Gen. Practitioner E. Cowes Health Centre E. Cowes, Isle of Wight. Prev: Sen. Med. Off. HMP Pk. Horst Isle of Wight; Head of Healthcare HMP Camphill Isle of Wight; GP Newport Isle of Wight.

GRIFFITHS, Elaine Mary Cardiothoracic Centre Liverpool, Thomas Drive, Liverpool L14 3PE Tel: 0151 228 1616, 0151 293 2397 Fax: 0151 293 2254 — MB BS 1979 Lond.; FRCS Ed. 1985; FRCS Eng. 1985. Cons. Cardiothoracic Surg. Cardiothoracic Centre Liverp.; Dir. (Cardiothoracic Studies) Liverp. Med. Sch.; Clin. Lect. Liverp. Med. Sch.; Dir. & Clin. Lect. (Cardiothoracic Studies) Liverp. Univ. Socs: Exec. Soc. Cardiothoracic Surg.s GB & Irel.

GRIFFITHS, Elisabeth Helen 23 Church Road, Whitchurch, Cardiff CF14 2DX — MB BCh 1982 Wales.

GRIFFITHS, Elizabeth Anne 59 Stockwood Road, Newcastle ST5 3LQ — MB ChB 1976 Liverp.; MA 1998. Clin. Asst. (Psychiat.) St. Geo. Hosp. Stafford. Prev: Clin. Asst. (Geriat. Med.) City Gen. Hosp. Stoke-on-Trent; Trainee GP N. Staffs. VTS; Ho. Off. (Surg. & Med.) City Gen. Hosp. Stoke-on-Trent.

GRIFFITHS, Mr Eurof (retired) Gelli Ceirios, Cwmaman, Aberdare CF44 6NG Tel: 01685 873121 — MB BCh Wales 1954; FRCSI 1976; DLO Eng. 1973. Prev: GP Aberdare.

GRIFFITHS, Frances Ellen Centre for Primary Health, Care Studies, University of Warwick, Coventry CV4 7AL Tel: 02476 524254 — MB BS 1982 Lond.; FRCGP 2001; PhD Durham 1988. Sen. Lect. 1998.

GRIFFITHS, Fred Vivian Coppers, New Polzeath, Wadebridge PL27 6UG Tel: 01208 862303 Email: vgriffi990@aol.com; Coppers, New Polzeath, Wadebridge PL27 6UG Tel: 01208 862303 — MB BS 1953 Lond.; MRCS Eng. LRCP Lond. 1953; MRCGP 1968; DObst RCOG 1955. (Middlx.) Socs: Fell. Roy. Soc. Med.; Brit. Soc. Med. & Dent. Hypn.; St. Thos. Obst. & Gyn. Comm. Prev: Ho. Surg. (Obst.) W. Middlx. Hosp.; Ho. Surg. Qu. Vict. Hosp. E. Grinstead; Cas. Off. S.lands Hosp. Shoreham-by-Sea.

GRIFFITHS, Frederick Douglas 51 Knightlow Road, Harborne, Birmingham B17 8PX — MB ChB 1942 Liverp.; MRCS Eng. LRCP Lond. 1943. (Liverp.) Prev: RN Med. Off.; Res. Med. Off. Smithdown Rd. Hosp. Liverp.

GRIFFITHS, Frederick John Alverton Cottage, Alverton Road, Penzance TR18 4TG Email: drjohn.griffiths@btinternet.com — MB ChB 1968 Liverp.; MRCS Eng. LRCP Lond. 1968; FFA RCS Eng. 1973. (Liverp.) Cons. Anaesth. Roy. Cornw. Hosps. NHS Trust. Prev: Cons. Anaesth. & Clin. Dir. St. Albans & Hemel Hempstead NHS Trust; Cons. Anaesth. Monklands Dist. Gen. Hosp. Airdrie; Cons. Anaesth. Gothenburg Childr. Hosp., Sweden.

GRIFFITHS, Mr Gareth David Department of Vascular Surgery, Manchester Royal Infirmary, Oxford Road, Manchester M13 9WL — MB ChB 1983 Manch.; FRCS Eng. 1987. Research Fell. (Gen. Surg.) Univ. Louisville, Kentucky, USA.

GRIFFITHS, Gareth Wyn (retired) Gorwelion, Penrhyn Geiriol, Trearddur Bay, Holyhead LL65 2YW Tel: 01407 860137 — MB ChB 1960 Liverp.; DObst RCOG 1963; AFOM RCP Lond. 1981. Prev: Ho. Phys. & Ho. Surg. Walton Hosp. Liverp.

GRIFFITHS, George Eamer (retired) 48 Strathspey Drive, Grantown-on-Spey PH26 3EY Tel: 01479 872663 — MB ChB 1943 Glas.; MRCGP 1954. Prev: GP Beauly & Glas.

GRIFFITHS, George Edward, TD (retired) Badger's Holt, The Kymin, Monmouth NP25 3SD Tel: 01600 713108 — MB BS 1945 Lond., DCH Eng. 1950; MRCGP 1960. Prev: Gp Monmouth.

GRIFFITHS, George Elmer Maghull Health Centre, Westway, Maghull, Liverpool L31 0DJ Tel: 0151 526 5453 Fax: 0151 531 7400; Meadowcroft, 2 Old Rectory Green, Sefton Village, Liverpool L29 6YD — MRCS Eng. LRCP Lond. 1978.

GRIFFITHS, Geraint Wyn, Maj. Medical Centre, Hammersmith Barracks, Great Sutton, Hereford BFPO 15 — MB ChB 1989 Liverp.; MRCGP 1996; DFFP 1995; DRCOG 1995. (Univ. Liverp.) Sen. Med. Off. Hereford Garrison Med. Centre, BFPO 15. Socs: BMA; RCGP. Prev: GP Catterick Garrison Med. Centre; SHO (O & G & Paediat.) BMH Rinteln, BFPO 31; SHO (Psychiat.) Qu. Eliz. Milit. Hosp. Lond.

GRIFFITHS, Glyn I T (retired) Dorset Lodge, Giggs Hill Road, Thames Ditton KT7 0BT Tel: 020 8398 1728 — MB ChB 1947 Liverp. Prev: Ho. Phys., Ho. Surg., & Jun. Regist. (Anaesth.) United Liverp. Hosps.

GRIFFITHS, Graham John Kingarth, Silver St., Branston, Lincoln LN4 1LR — MB BCh 1972 Wales; MRCPath 1979. Cons. Chem. Path. Lincs. AHA. Prev: Sen. Regist. (Chem. Path.) Manch. Roy. Infirm.; Regist. (Chem. Path.) Univ. Hosp. Wales Cardiff; SHO (Cardiorespirat. Med.) Cardiff Hosps.

GRIFFITHS, Gwenllian Branwen Iscoed, 64 Beulah Road, Rhiwbina, Cardiff CF14 6LY — MB BS 1946 Lond.; MRCS Eng. LRCP Lond. 1943; DMR Lond 1946. (Roy. Free) Cons. Radiol. Mid & S. Glam AHAs. Socs: BMA & Brit. Inst. Radiol. Prev: Ho. Phys. Roy. Free Hosp. Lond.; Ho. Surg. Roy. Cancer Hosp. Lond.; Regist. (Radiol.) Roy. Infirm. Cardiff.

GRIFFITHS, Gwyn Caesion Isaf, Carmel, Caernarfon LL54 7SN — MB ChB 1992 Liverp.

GRIFFITHS, Hamish Brantom Armour 50 Paddington Street, London W1 — MB BS 1977 Lond.; MRCS Eng. LRCP Lond. 1977; MRCP (UK) 1982; FFA RCS Eng. 1981. (Guy's)

GRIFFITHS, Hannah Mia 1 Eastcote Close, Roborough, Plymouth PL6 6JX Tel: 01752 701659 — BM BCh 1983 Oxf.; BA Oxf. 1980, BM BCh 1983; MRCGP 1987.

GRIFFITHS, Mr Harold Edward Dunstan, CBE, TD (retired) Royal Oak Lodge, Rudgeway, Bristol BS35 3RY Tel: 01454 612140 Fax: 01454 617796 — MB BS Lond. 1950; FRCS Eng. 1957; MRCS Eng. LRCP Lond. 1950. Prev: Cons. Orthop. Surg. S.mead, Frenchay & Winford Orthop. Hosps.

GRIFFITHS, Haydn Michael Haselour Cottage, Harlaston, Tamworth B79 9JT — MB ChB 1969 Liverp.; DPhysMed Eng. 1974.

GRIFFITHS, Heather Marie Scourfield and Partners, The Surgery, Oakfield Street, Ystrad Mynach, Hengoed CF82 7WX Tel: 01443 813248 Fax: 01443 862283 — MB BCh 1990 Wales.

GRIFFITHS, Helen 48 Gascoigne Way, Bloxham, Banbury OX15 4TL; Department Immunology, The Churchill Hospital, Old Road, Headington, Oxford OX3 7LE Tel: 01865 225995 Fax: 01865 225990 — MD Lond. 1981, MB BS 1970; FRCPath 1991. (University College Hospital London) Assoc. Specialist (Immunol.) John Radcliffe Hosp. Oxf. Prev: Sen. Regist. (Haemat.) Radcliffe Infirm. Oxf.; Regist. (Clin. Path.) Roy. Sussex Co. Hosp. Brighton.

GRIFFITHS, Helen Louise 24 Falkland St. (2nd Floor), Hyndland, Glasgow G12 9PR Tel: 0141 334 5676; 8 Newbyth Steading, East Linton EH40 3DU — MB ChB 1990 Glas.; BSc (Hons.) Glas. 1987; MRCP (UK) 1994. Specialist Regist. Rotat. (Radiol.) W. of Scotl. Prev: Regist. (Radiol.) S. Gen. Hosp. NHS Trust Glas.; SHO Rotat. (Gen. Med.) Aberd. Roy. Hosp. NHS Trust; Ho. Off. (Med. & Surg.) Gtr. Glas. HB.

GRIFFITHS, Horatio Jonathan The Old Rectory, 56 Hodge Bower, Ironbridge, Telford TF8 7QE Tel: 01952 432021 — MRCS Eng. LRCP Lond. 1951; DLO Eng. 1960.

GRIFFITHS, Hugh William St George's Hospital, Morpeth NE61 2NU Tel: 01670 512121 — MB BS 1980 Newc.; FRCPsych 1999; MRCPsych 1984. Med. Dir. & Cons. Psychiat. St. Geo. Hosp. Morpeth. Prev: Cons. Psychiat. Roy. Vict. Infirm. Newc. & St. Geo. Hosp. Morpeth; Sen. Regist. (Psychiat.) St. Geo. Hosp. Morpeth.

GRIFFITHS, Huw Swn-y-Nant, Pine Valley, Cwmavon, Port Talbot SA12 9NE Tel: 01639 896741 — MB BS 1992 Lond.; BSc Lond. 1989. (St. Thos. Hosp. Lond.)

GRIFFITHS, Huw 6 St Davids Place, Maesteg CF34 9LR — MB ChB 1993 Bristol.

GRIFFITHS, Huw 108 Long Lane, Honley, Huddersfield HD9 6EB — MB BS 1978 Lond.; MSc Surrey 1984; MRCPath 1990. (Char. Cross) Cons. (Chem. Path.) Huddersfield Roy. Infirm. Prev: Sen. Regist. (Chem. Path.) N.. Gen. Hosp. Sheff.; Regist. (Chem. Path.) Epsom Dist. Hosp. Surrey; Regist. (Anaesth.) Roy. Gwent Hosp. Newport.

GRIFFITHS, Ian David Department Rheumatology, Freeman Hospital, Newcastle upon Tyne NE7 7DN Tel: 0191 284 3111 Fax: 0191 223 1159; 181 Benfieldside Road, Shotley Bridge, Consett DH8 0RB — BSc (Hons.) Lond. 1966, MB BS 1969; FRCP Eng. 1984; MRCP (UK) 1971; MRCS Eng. LRCP Lond. 1969. (Char. Cross) Cons. (Rheum.) Freeman Hosp. Newc. & Roy. Vict. Infirm. Newc.; Hon. Sec. Clin. Lect. Univ. Newc. Socs: Brit. Soc. Rheum. & Assn. Phys. Prev: Sen. Regist. (Med.) Char. Cross Hosp. Lond.; Research Fell. Kennedy Inst. Rheum. Lond.; Regist. (Med.) Soton. Gen. Hosp.

GRIFFITHS, Ian Lee, Specialist Registrar Nottingham Occupational Health, Queens Medical Centre, Nottingham NG7 2UH Tel: 0115 970 9268 Fax: 0115 970 9704 — MB ChB 1992 Bristol; AFOM 2000; BSc (Microbiol.) Bristol 1989; MRCP (UK) 1997. (Bristol) Specialist Regist. (Occupat. Med.) Univ. Hosp. Nottm. Socs: Soc. of Occupat. Med. Prev: SHO (Neurol.) Radcliffe Infirm. Oxf.; SHO (Med.) Alexandra Hosp. Redditch; SHO (Med.) St. Mary's Hosp. Portsmouth.

GRIFFITHS, Iwan James Bro-Dawel, North Road, Whitland SA34 0AX — MB BS 1982 Lond.

GRIFFITHS, James Robert The Blackberry Orthopaedic Clinic, Blackberry Court, Walnut Tree, Milton Keynes MK7 7PB Tel: 01908 604666 Fax: 01908 692711; 33 Monnery Road, London N19 5SA Tel: 020 7263 6632 Fax: 020 7263 6632 — MRCS Eng. LRCP Lond. 1973; MLCOM 1994; DMS Med. Soc. Apoth. Lond. 1975. (St. Bart.) Specialist Osteop. Servs. (Rheum.) Homerton Hosp. Lond.

GRIFFITHS, Jane 40 Dunholme Road, Newcastle upon Tyne NE4 6XE — MB BS 1998 Newc.; MB BS Newc 1998.

GRIFFITHS, Janine Mary 17A Water Street, Crosby, Liverpool L23 1TB — MB BS 1997 Newc.

GRIFFITHS, Jeanette 23 Sunnybank Road, Wylde Green, Sutton Coldfield B73 5RE — MB ChB 1985 Birm. Term Time Staff Grade (Child Health) NBC Trust. Prev: Clin. Med. Off. (Child Health) Birm. HA.

GRIFFITHS, Jeremy Paul The Surgery, 152 Melton Road, West Bridgford, Nottingham NG2 6ER Tel: 0115 945 2656 Fax: 0115 923 5166; 8 Ashness Close, Gamston, Nottingham NG2 6QW Tel: 0115 981 8810 Email: jeremy.p.griffiths@talk21.com — BM BS 1989 Nottm.; BMedSci (Hons.) Nottm. 1987; DFFP 1997. (Nottm.) Princip. GP Ludlow Hill Surg. W. Bridford, Nottm.; Hon. Hosp. Pract./Research Asst. Dept. Neurol. Qu. Med. Centre Nottm. Socs: Nottm. M-C Soc.; Primary Care Cardiovasc. Soc. Prev: GP/Regist. Nottm.; Regist. (Neurol.) Qu. Med. Centre Nottm.; SHO (O & G) Kingsmill Centre Sutton in Ashfield.

GRIFFITHS, John Anthony 11 Eaton Drive, Baslow, Bakewell DE45 1SE Tel: 01246 582302 Fax: 01246 582302 — MB ChB Sheff. 1948; MD (Distinc.) Sheff. 1953; MRCS Eng. LRCP Lond. 1948; AFOM RCP Lond. 1983; FRCA 1953. (Sheff.) Med. Adviser Royston Lead plc & NBA Trent Centre; CMP UK Land Forces; Hon. Cons. (Anaesth.) Sheff. HA. Socs: Aesculapian Soc.; Soc. Occupat. Med. Prev: Cons. Anaesth. Sheff. HA; Hon. Clin. Lect. Univ. Sheff.; Nuffield Foundat. Med. Fell.

GRIFFITHS, John Bryn Thomas St Tysilio Nursing Home, Llanfairpwllgwyngyll LL61 5YR Tel: 01248 716400; Ty'n Ffridd, Brynsiencyn, Llanfairpwllgwyngyll LL61 6HQ Tel: 01248 430387 Fax: 01248 430387 Email: john.griffiths7@virgin.net — MB BCh 1958 Wales. (Cardiff) Mem. N. Wales LMC; Mem. Med. Pract. Comm. for Eng. & Wales (Mem. for Wales). Socs: BMA (Ex-Chairm. NW Wales Div.); Welsh Med. Soc. Prev: Ho. Phys. Med. Profess. Unit Cardiff Roy. Infirm.; Ho. Off. (Obst.) & SHO (Paediat.) St. David's Hosp. Bangor.

GRIFFITHS, John David Wadlerslade Surgery, Walderslade, 194 King Street, Hoyland, Barnsley S74 9LL Tel: 01226 743221 Fax: 01226 741100; 10 Kenwood Road, Sheffield S7 1NP Email: j.d.griffiths@btinternet.com — MB ChB 1975 Sheff.; MRCGP 1980. Adviser in Gen. Pract. Univ. of Sheff. Prev: SHO (Gen. Med.) Roy. Infirm. Sheff.; SHO (Neurol.) Roy. Hosp. (Fulwood Annexe) Sheff.; Ho. Phys. Roy. Infirm. Sheff.

GRIFFITHS, John Derek Vernon (retired) 74 Compit Hills, Roughton Road, Cromer NR27 9LP Tel: 01263 512126 — MA Camb. 1954; MRCS Eng. LRCP Lond. 1952. Prev: GP Birm.

GRIFFITHS, John James (retired) Morawel, Clarach, Aberystwyth SY23 3DP — MRCS Eng. LRCP Lond. 1949; TDD Wales 1953. Prev: Cons. Chest Phys. Powys AHA.

GRIFFITHS, John Lawson Penylan House, Pencoed, Bridgend CF35 6LT Tel: 01656 860343 — MRCS Eng. LRCP Lond. 1950. (St. Mary's)

GRIFFITHS, Mr John Michael Taylor General Surgical Unit, Western General Hospital, Crewe Road, Edinburgh EH4 2XV Tel: 0131 537 1000; 5 The Row, Ballencrieff, Longniddry EH32 0PJ Tel: 01875 870356 — MB ChB 1963 Ed.; FRCS Ed. 1967. (Ed.) Cons. Gen. & Urol. Surg. Lothian Univ Hosp NHS Trust. Socs: Surg. Research Soc.; Caledonian Soc. Gastroenterol.

GRIFFITHS, John Owen 72 Victoria Road, Fulwood, Preston PR2 8NJ — MB ChB Liverp. 1970; MRCS Eng. LRCP Lond. 1970; FFA RCS Eng. 1976. Cons. (Anaesth.) Preston HA. Socs: Obst. Anaesth. Assn.; Liverp. Soc. Anaesth.; Brit. Soc. of Orthopaedic Anaesth.s. Prev: Sen. Regist. (Anaesth.) Roy. Liverp. Childr. Hosp.; Sen. Regist. (Anaesth.) BRd.green Hosp. Liverp.; Sen. Regist. (Anaesth.) Whiston Hosp. Liverp.

GRIFFITHS, Professor John Richard Department Biochemistry & Immunology, St George Hospital Medical School, Cranmer Terrace, London SW17 0RE Tel: 020 8725 5811 Fax: 020 8725 2992 Email: sgbc100@sghms.ac.uk — MB BS Lond. 1969; Dip. Biochem. Lond. 1966; DPhil Oxon 1975. Prof. Med. Biochem.ry; Hon. Cons. Phys. Socs: Sec. Internat. Soc. Magnetic Resonance in Med.; Brit. Inst. Radiol.; Euro Soc. Magnetic Resonance in Med & Biol. (Counc. Mem.).

GRIFFITHS, Mr Jonathan David (retired) Breydon, 102 Broomfield Road, Bath BA2 2AP Tel: 01225 29221 — MB BCh 1962 Wales; FRC Ophth. 1988; FRCS Eng. 1968. Prev: Cons. Ophth. Bath Clin. Area.

GRIFFITHS, Jonathan James Bilbrook Medical Centre, Brookfield Road, Bilbrook, Wolverhampton WV8 1DX Tel: 01902 847313 Fax: 01902 842322 — MB ChB 1994 Manch.; MRCGP.

GRIFFITHS, Jonathan Mark 36 Moorhall Lane, Stourport-on-Severn DY13 8RB — BM 1994 Soton.

GRIFFITHS, Jonathan Stevenson, Flight Lt. RAF Med. Br. 3 Pinewood, Pontamman, Ammanford SA18 2QA Tel: 01269 594587 — MB BCh 1995 Wales; DRCOG 1997. (Wales) GP RAF.

GRIFFITHS, Jonathon James 50 Tewkesbury Street, Cardiff CF24 4QT — MB BCh Wales 1990; MRCGP 1994; DA (UK) 1995; FRCA (Lond.) 1998; FRCA 1998. Specialist Regist. Anaesth. Univ. Hosp. of Wales Cardiff. Socs: Assn. Anaesth.; BMA. Prev: Specialist Regist. Anaesth. Swansea; SHO Anaesth. Univ. Hosp. of Wales; SHO Anaesth. Roy. Gwent Hosp.

GRIFFITHS, Julia Marsden Breydon, 102 Bloomfield Rd, Bath BA2 2AP — MB BS 1997 Lond.

GRIFFITHS, Julie Maria Lilac Cottage, Cadley, Collingbourne Ducis, Marlborough SN8 3EA — MB ChB 1985 Birm.; FRCA 1994; DA (UK) 1987.

GRIFFITHS, Juniper Jane Old Post Office, East Road, East Mersea, Colchester CO5 8UN — MB BS Lond. 1964. (St. Mary's) Clin. Asst. (Ophth.) Essex Co. Hosp. Socs: MRCOphth.; Colchester Med. Soc.; Med. Wom. Federat. Prev: Asst. Med. Off. Lond. Boro. Redbridge; Ho. Phys. Roy. Devon & Exeter Hosp.; SHO (Neurol. & Neurosurg.) Plymouth Gen. Hosps.

GRIFFITHS, Katherine Ursula 23 Alma Road, Cardiff CF23 5BD — MB BCh 1985 Wales.

GRIFFITHS, Kathleen Greenacre, Snow Hill, Crawley Down, Crawley RH10 3EE — MB ChB 1983 Leeds; MRCGP 1987; DRCOG 1987.

GRIFFITHS, Kenneth John 402 Kingstanding Road, Great Barr, Birmingham B44 8LD — MRCS Eng. LRCP Lond. 1981; LLM 1996; BDS Birm. 1958; LDS RCS Eng. 1958; DFFP 1993.

GRIFFITHS, Kenneth Richard Llanfyllin Medical Centre, High Street, Llanfyllin SY22 5DG Tel: 01691 648054 Fax: 01691 648165;

The Old Rectory, Llanfihangel-Yng-Ngwynfa, Llanfyllin SY22 5JD Tel: 01691 648401 — BM BCh 1965 Oxf.; MA Oxf. 1966, BM Oxf. 1966; FRCP Canada 1972; MRCP (UK) 1970; MRCGP 1980; DObst RCOG 1974. (St. Thos.) Prev: Regist. (Med.) Sheff. Roy. Infirm.; Ho. Surg. St. Thos. Hosp. Lond.; Ho. Phys. Radcliffe Infirm. Oxf.

GRIFFITHS, Kenrick Philip David 52 Highcroft Lane, Horndean, Portsmouth — LMSSA 1939 Lond.

GRIFFITHS, Kevin Palmer Community Hospital GP Suite, Wear Street, Jarrow NE32 3UX Tel: 0191 451 6078 Fax: 0191 451 6088 — MB BS 1983 Newc.

GRIFFITHS, Lynn Kathleen 42 Church St., Ladybank, Cupar KY15 7LE — MB ChB 1983 Manch.

GRIFFITHS, Malcolm Department of Obstetrics & Gynaecology, Luton & Dunstable Hospital, Lewsey Road, Luton LU4 0DZ Tel: 01582 497459 Fax: 01582 497376 Email: malcolm.griffiths@udh-ts.anglox.nhs.uk — MB BS 1981 Lond.; MD Lond. 1993; MFFP 1993; MRCOG 1987. Cons. O & G Luton & Dunstable Hosp.; Vist. Lect. Univ. of Luton & Univ. of Herts.; Mem. Internat. Advis. Bd. Obgyn.net. Socs: Med. Soc. Study VD; Brit. Soc. Matern. & Fetal Med.; Medico-Legal Soc. Prev: Sen. Regist. (O & G) Reading & Oxf. Hosps.; Hon. Sen. Regist. & Regist. (O & G) Wexham Pk. Hosp. Slough.

GRIFFITHS, Mr Mansel Valmond 2 Clifton Park, Clifton, Bristol BS8 3BS Tel: 0117 906 4209 Fax: 0117 973 0887 — MB BCh Wales 1965; FRCS Ed. 1971; MRCS Eng. LRCP Lond. 1965; FRCS 1998. Head (Otolaryngol.) Univ. Bristol; Cons. Surg. Otolaryngol. United Bristol Healthcare Trust. Socs: Roy. Soc. Med.; BMA; Eur. Laryngol. Soc. Prev: Sen. Regist. (ENT Surg.) Avon AHA (T); Fell. (Laryng. Surg.) Univ. Toronto; Ho. Phys. & Ho. Surg. Morriston Hosp.

GRIFFITHS, Marcus Llewellyn Kingsbridge Medical Practice, Kingsbridge Avenue, Clayton, Newcastle ST5 3HP Tel: 01782 427361 Fax: 01782 427369; 59 Stockwood Road, Seabridge, Newcastle ST5 3LQ Tel: 01782 427 871 909 — MB ChB 1975 Liverp.; DRCOG 1983. GP Newc. Prev: Trainee GP N. Staffs. VTS; Ho. Off. (Surg. & Med.) David Lewis N.. Hosp. Liverp.

GRIFFITHS, Margaret Eileen Topfield House, 95 High St., West Wickham, Cambridge CB1 6SB Tel: 0122029 702 — MB BS 1965 Lond.; MRCS Eng. LRCP Lond. 1965. (Roy. Free) Prev: GP Hayling Is.; Regist. (Dermat.) Roy. Free Hosp.; Research Asst. Path. Roy. Free Hosp. Lond.

GRIFFITHS, Mark Paediatric X-Ray Department, Coutre Block, C Level, Southampton General Hospital, Tremona Road, Southampton SO16 6YD; 8 Cadland Court, Channel Way, Ocean village, Southampton SO14 3GP — MB BChir 1991 Camb.; MRCP (UK) 1995; FRCR 1999. Regist. (Radiol.) St. Bart. Hosp. Lond. & Cons. Paediat. Radiologist, Soton. Gen. Hosp. Soton.

GRIFFITHS, Mark Andrew First Floor Flat, 42 Great Eastern St., London EC2 3EP — MB BS 1992 Lond.

GRIFFITHS, Mark David Boughton Medical Group, Boughton Health Centre, Hoole Lane, Chester CH2 3DP Tel: 01244 325421; M, Station Road, Lea-by-Backford, Chester CH1 6NX Tel: 01244 851196 Email: mark@drgriffiths.prestel.co.uk — MB ChB 1983 Manch.; MRCGP 1988; Dip. Pract. Dermat. Wales 1995; DRCOG 1987; Cert Family Plann. JCC 1987. (Manch.) Socs: Chester & N. Wales Med. Soc.; (Chairm.) Chester Young Practs. Prev: Trainee GP Chester VTS.

GRIFFITHS, Mark James The Oaklands, Hollybush Lane, Clifton upon Teme, Worcester WR6 6HQ — MB BS 1969 Lond.; FDS RCS Eng. 1971; BDS Birm 1959; MRCS Eng. LRCP Lond. 1967. (St. Bart.) Cons. Oral Surg. & Oral Med. Bristol Dent. Hosp. Prev: Cons. & Lect. (Dent. Surg.) Univ. Bristol Dent. Sch.

GRIFFITHS, Mark Jonathan David Department of Anaesthetics & Intensive Care, Royal Brompton Hospital, Sydney St., London SW3 6NP Tel: 020 7352 8121 Fax: 020 7351 8524; 76 Bolingbroke Grove, London SW11 6HB Tel: 020 7350 1954 Email: mgriffi2@rpms.ac.uk — MB BS 1987 Lond.; BSc Lond. 1984; MRCP (UK) 1990; PhD 1995. (Charing Cross Westminster) Specialist Regist. in Critical Care Brompton Hosp.; Lect. (Med.) Char. Cross & W.m. Med. Sch. Socs: Brit. Assn. Lung Res.; Amer. Thoracic Soc.; Intens. Care Soc. Prev: Clin. Research Fell. Roy. Brompton Hosp. Lond.; Regist. (Med.) Medway Hosp.; SHO St. Thos. Hosp., Oxf. Renal Unit & Brompton Chest Hosp.

GRIFFITHS, Martin James Tyn y Pistyll, Carreg Heilin Lane, Dyserth, Rhyl LL18 6DA — MB ChB 1989 Liverp.

GRIFFITHS, Martin Patrick 4 Geoffrey Court, Geoffrey Road, London SE4 1NX — MB BS 1991 Lond.

GRIFFITHS, Martin Robert Wellington Street Surgery, 46 Wellington Street, Gorton, Manchester M18 8LJ Tel: 0161 223 1113 Fax: 0161 223 8639; 1 Oaklands Drive, Godley, Hyde SK14 3DD Tel: 0161 368 5015 — MB ChB 1982 Manch.; DRCOG 1985. GP Manch. Prev: SHO (A & E) Withington Hosp. W. Didsbury; Ho. Surg. Leighton Hosp.; Ho. Phys. Nobles Hosp. I. of Man.

GRIFFITHS, Mary Anne Child & Family Service, Salisbury District Hospital, Salisbury SP2 8BJ Tel: 01722 336262 Fax: 01722 341390 — MB BS 1974 Lond.; MRCPsych. 1983; DPM Eng. 1978. p/t Cons. Child & Adolesc. Psychiat. Salisbury Healthcare. Prev: Sen. Regist. (Child Psychiat.) SW Thames Regional Train. Scheme; Regist. (Child Psychiat.) Maudsley Hosp. Lond.; Ships Med. Off. NERC.

GRIFFITHS, Mary Carlyon Sunnybank, Plasmawr Road, Fairwater, Cardiff CF5 3XN Tel: 029 2056 1623 — MB BCh 1948 Wales; MRCS Eng. LRCP Lond. 1948. (Cardiff)

GRIFFITHS, Matthew Anders 379 Devon Mansions, Tooley St., Tower Bridge, London SE1 2XG Tel: 020 7407 0941 — MB BS 1996 Lond.; BMedSci. Lond. 1995. Ana. Demonst. Char. Cross & W.minster Med. Coll.; Resid. Med. Off. N. Lond. Nuffield Hosp. Enfield. Prev: SHO (A & E) The Roy. Lond. NHS Trust & Howerton Hosps.; Ho. Off. (Gen. Surg./Orthop.) The Roy. Lond. NHS Trust; Ho. Off. (Gen. Med./Cardiol.) Broomfield Hosp. Chelmsford.

GRIFFITHS, Meryl Helen Histopathology Department, Rockefeller Building, University College Hospital, University St., London WC1E 6JJ Tel: 020 7209 6041 Fax: 020 7387 3674 Email: meryl.griffiths@ucl.ac.uk — MB BS 1970 Melbourne; FRCPA 1980; FRCPath 1993, M 1981. (Melb.) Sen. Clin. Lect. & Hon. Cons. Univ. Coll. Lond. Hosps.

GRIFFITHS, Michael Nantgarw Road Surgery, 9 Nantgarw Road, Caerphilly CF81 3FA Tel: 029 2088 3174 Fax: 029 2086 6753; 6 Mountain Road, Caerphilly CF83 1HJ — MB BS 1983 Lond.; BSc Lond. 1979; DRCOG 1986; DCH RCP Lond. 1985. (St. Bart.)

GRIFFITHS, Michael Anthony The Armthorpe Surgery, Church Street, Armthorpe, Doncaster DN3 3AH Tel: 01302 831437 Fax: 01302 300623 — MRCS Eng. LRCP Lond. 1972.

GRIFFITHS, Mr Michael Frederick Peter, Col. L/RAMC Department of Ophthalmology, Frimley Park Hospital MoDHU, Camberley GU16 5UJ Tel: 01276 604516 Fax: 01276 604149; 3 Minorca Avenue, Deepcut, Camberley GU16 6TT Tel: 01252 837776 Fax: 0870 063 3012 Email: dcaophth@doctors.org.uk — MB ChB 1978 Sheff.; BSc Sheff. 1975; FRCS (Ophth.) Ed. 1986; FCOphth 1990; DO RCS Eng. 1985. Cons. Ophth. Frimley Pk. Hosp. MoD HU Camberley; Defence Cons. Adviser (Ophth).

GRIFFITHS, Michael John 14 Pendre Close, Brecon LD3 9EH — BM BS 1993 Nottm.

GRIFFITHS, Michael John Margaret Street Surgery, Margaret Street, Ammanford SA18 2PJ Tel: 01269 592477 Fax: 01269 597326; Y Mans, 4 Bryn Mawr Avenue, Ammanford SA18 2DA Tel: 01269 591315 — MB ChB 1975 Manch.; BSc Lond. 1969; MRCGP 1982. (Manch.) Clin. Asst. (Paediat.) Neath Gen. Hosp. Prev: Clin. Med. Off. W. Glam. HA; Regist. (Paediat.) Morriston Hosp. W. Glam.; SHO (Gen. Med.) Neath Hosp.

GRIFFITHS, Michael Paul 43 Falconhurst Road, Birmingham B29 6SB — MB ChB 1996 Birm.; ChB Birm. 1996.

GRIFFITHS, Miriam Margaret (retired) Ellisland, 13 Blundell's Avenue, Tiverton EX16 4DL — MB ChB 1943 Ed. Prev: O & G Ho. Surg. Simpson Pavil. Edin. Roy. Infirm.

***GRIFFITHS, Nia Gwyn** 52 Dol Elidir, Llanberis, Caernarfon LL55 4TN; 41 Rhosfryn, Penrhos Garnedd, Bangor LL57 2DL Tel: 01248 370670 — MB BCh 1995 Wales.

GRIFFITHS, Mr Nicholas John 9 North Road W., Hythe CT21 — MB BS 1967 Lond.; FRCS Eng. 1972; MRCS Eng. LRCP Lond. 1967. (St. Bart.) Cons. Surg. SE Kent Health Auth. Arris & Gale Lect. RCS Eng. 1977. Prev: Sen. Regist. St. Bart. Hosp. Lond.; Tutor in Surg. Hope Hosp. Salford; Demonst. Anat. St. Bart. Hosp. Med. Sch. Lond.

GRIFFITHS, Nicola Caroline Parkhouse Surgery, 1 Cavendish Road, Highams Park, London E4 9NQ Tel: 020 8523 1401; 21 Godwin Road, Forest Gate, London E7 0LE Tel: 020 8555 8359 — MB BS 1987 Lond.; BSc (Hons) Lond. 1984, MB BS 1987; MRCGP 1991; DRCOG 1990; Cert. Family Plann. JCC 1990.

GRIFFITHS, Norman Roby (retired) 41 The Row, Silverdale, Carnforth LA5 0UG — MB BS 1962 Durh.; DPM Eng. 1965. Clin. Med. Off. S. Cumbria HA. Prev: GP Bentham.

GRIFFITHS, Pamela Anne Brookside Clinic, Station Way, Aylesbury HP20 2SQ Tel: 01296 89951 Fax: 01296 398802; Wood End Farm, Nash, Milton Keynes MK17 0EL Tel: 01908 501860 Fax: 01908 501860 — MB ChB 1979 Liverp.; MRCGP 1984; Dip. Community Paediat. Warwick 1992. Assoc. Specialist (Community Child Health) Aylesbury. Socs: MRCGP; MCPCH. Prev: GP Kendal.

GRIFFITHS, Professor Paul David Department of Academic Radiology, Floor C, Royal Hallamshire Hospital, Sheffield — MB ChB 1983 Manch.; PhD Manch. 1988; FRCR 1991. (Manch.) Prof. of Radiol. Roy. Hallamsh. Hosp. Sheff. Socs: Amer. Soc. Paediat. Neuroradiol. Prev: Cons. Neuroradiol. Camb.; Sen. Regist. (Neuroradiol.) Newc. Gen. Hosp.; Sen. Regist. (Radiol.) Univ. Hosp. S. Manch.

GRIFFITHS, Professor Paul David Department of Virology, Royal Free and University College Medical School, Royal Free Campus,Rowland Hill St., London NW3 2PF Tel: 0207 830 2997 Fax: 0207 830 2854 Email: paulgrif@rfhsm.ac.uk — MB BS 1977 Lond.; DSc Lond. 1995; MD Lond. 1982, BSc 1974; MRCPath 1985; FRCPath 1996. (St Bartholomews) Prof. (Virol.) Roy. Free Hosp. Lond. Socs: Soc. Gen. Microbiol. (Counc. Mem.); Med. Research Club; Amer. Soc. For MicroBiol. Prev: Lect. (Virol.) St. Bart. Hosp. Lond.; Research Fell. Univ. Alabama, USA.

GRIFFITHS, Paul Justin Durnford Medical Centre, 113 Long Street, Middleton, Manchester M24 6DL Tel: 0161 643 2011 Fax: 0161 653 6570; Parkfield, 9 Polefield Road, Blackley, Manchester M9 6FN — MB ChB 1982 Manch.; AFOM 1995; MRCGP 1987; Dip. Pract. Dermat. 1991; DRCOG 1988; Cert. Fam. Plann. 1988. (Manch.) GP Princip. Durnford Med. Centre; Regional Occupat. Phys. Marks & Spencer plc, Manch. Socs: Assoc. Mem. Roy. Soc. Med. Prev: Ho. Surg. (Orthop.) Manch. Roy. Infirm.; SHO (Psychiat.) & Ho. Phys. Hope Hosp. Salford.

GRIFFITHS, Paul Robert 51 Douglas Avenue, Castle Bromwich, Birmingham B36 8EN — MB ChB 1977 Birm.

GRIFFITHS, Peter (retired) Sandy Lodge, 4 Castledon Road, Downham, Billericay CM11 1LD — MB BChir 1952 Camb.; MA Camb. 1953, MB BChir 1952; DObst. RCOG 1957. Prev: Clin. Asst. Varicose Veins Clinic Orsett Hosp. Grays.

GRIFFITHS, Peter The Orchard, Llanfabon Road, Nelson, Treharris CF46 6PG Tel: 01443 450336 — MB ChB 1952 Manch.; LMCC 1957. Mem. Disabil Living Allowance Advis. Bd. Prev: Sen. Med. Off. Benefits Agency Med. Serv. Wales & SW; Resid. Med. Off. Doctors' Hosp., New York City; Regist. (Surg.) Rookwood Hosp. Cardiff.

GRIFFITHS, Professor Peter Denham, CBE (retired) 52 Albany Road, West Ferry, Dundee DD5 1NW Tel: 01382 776772 Email: 100326.2775@compuserve.com — MB BS Lond. 1956; BSc Physiol. (1st cl. Hons.) Lond. 1953, MD 1964; MRCS Eng. LRCP Lond. 1956; FRCPath 1977, M 1965; FRCP Ed 1998. Prev: Prof. Biochem. Med. Univ. Dundee.

GRIFFITHS, Peter Derek Jones (retired) Ty Olwen Hospice, Morriston Hospital, Swansea SA6 6NL Tel: 01792 703414 Fax: 01792 703695 — MB BS 1956 Lond. Clin. Progr. Dir. & Cons. Palliat. Med. Morriston Hosp. Trust Swansea. Prev: Phys. St. Christopher's Hospice Sydenham.

GRIFFITHS, Peter Fairbairn Ivy House, Priors Norton, Gloucester GL2 9LT — MRCS Eng. LRCP Lond. 1973.

GRIFFITHS, Peter Hughes Gardd Wenyn Ty Capel, Llangefni LL77 7HP — MB BCh Wales 1949.

GRIFFITHS, Peter Martin Rutherford Medical Centre, 1 Rutherford Road, Mossley Hill, Liverpool L18 0HL Tel: 0151 722 1803 Fax: 0151 738 0083 — MB ChB 1978 Liverp.; MRCGP 1985; T(GP) 1991.

GRIFFITHS, Mr Philip Guy 37 Willerby Road, Woodthorpe, Nottingham NG5 4NZ — BM BS 1980 Nottm.; BMedSci Nottm. 1978, BM BS 1980; FRCS (Ophth.) Eng. 1985; DO 1984. Cons. Ophth. Newc. Gen. Hosp. Prev: Sen. Regist. (Ophth.) Newc. HA; Regist. Rotat. (Ophth.) Leeds HA.

GRIFFITHS, Philippa Katharine Lavender Cottage, 5 Station Road, Thames Ditton KT7 0NU — MB BS 1969 Lond.; MRCS Eng. LRCP Lond. 1969.

GRIFFITHS, Rebecca Louise 2 Pheabens Field, Bramley, Tadley RG26 5BX — MB ChB 1987 Sheff. Prev: SHO (A & E) S.end Gen. Hosp.; SHO (O & G & Med. for Elderly) Rochford Hosp. Essex.

GRIFFITHS, Richard Department of Anaesthesia, Peterborough District Hospital, Thorpe Road, Peterborough PE3 6PA Tel: 01733 874327 Fax: 01733 875684 Email: richard@wothorpe.com; Tel: 01733 874000 Fax: 01733 874001 — MB BS 1984 Lond.; MD Leic. 1995; FRCA 1990; DA (UK) 1986. (St. Thos.) Cons. Anaesth. P'boro. Hosps.; Asst. Prof. Dept. Anaesth. Univ. Calif., San Francisco. Socs: Assn. Anaesth.; Anaesth. Res. Soc.; Vasc. Anaesth. Soc. Prev: Lect. (Anaesth.) Univ. Leicester; Research Fell. Brit. Jl. Anaesth.

GRIFFITHS, Richard David Banc Cottage, Wernffrwd, Llanmorlais, Swansea SA4 3UE Tel: 01792 850403; (Surgery), 2 Calvert Terrace, Swansea SA1 6A — BM BCh 1963 Oxf.; DObst RCOG 1965. (Oxf.) Prev: Consult. (Matern. & Child Health & Family Plann.) Dominica Govt.

GRIFFITHS, Richard David Department of Medicine, University of Liverpool, PO Box 147, Liverpool L69 3BX Tel: 0151 706 4086 Fax: 0151 706 5802 Email: rdg@liverpool.ac.uk; 2 Westward Ho, Caldy, Wirral CH48 1QF Tel: 0151 625 6876 — MB BS 1977 Lond.; BSc Lond. 1974, MD 1986; FRCP Lond. 1993. (Univ. Coll. Hosp.) 1997 Reader in Med. (Intens. Care) Univ. Liverp..; Hon. Cons. Phys. IC Whiston Hosp. Prev: Research Fell. & Hon. Sen. Regist. (Med. & Child Health) Univ. Liverp.; Clin. Research Lect. (Med.) & Hon. Sen. Regist. Univ. Coll. Hosp.; Regist. (Paediat.) Middlx. Hosp. Lond.

GRIFFITHS, Richard Huw Psychiatric Unit, East Glamorgan Hospital, Church Village, Pontypridd CF38 1AB Tel: 01443 218218 Fax: 01443 218745 Email: huw.griffiths@btinternet.com — MB BCh 1980 Wales; MRCPsych 1990. (Welsh National School of Medicine) Cons. Psychiat. Gen. Adult Psychiat. with Liaison Pstchiatry; Clin. Dir., Ment. Health to Pontypridd & Rhondda NHS Trust; Mem., Ment. Health Act Commisioner.

***GRIFFITHS, Richard James** 61 Bluehouse La, Oxted RH8 0AP — MB BS 1997 Lond.; BSc (Hons) Lond.

GRIFFITHS, Richard Lanfear The Surgery, Ewyas Harold, Hereford HR2 0EU Tel: 01981 240320 Fax: 01981 241023; The Birches, Vowchurch Common, Hereford HR2 0RL Tel: 01981 550379 Fax: 01981 550379 — MB BS 1978 Lond.; MRCGP 1982; DRCOG 1981; DCH RCP Lond. 1981. (St. Mary's) Prev: Trainee GP Winchester VTS.

GRIFFITHS, Richard Wyn Cynefail, Y Glyn, Denbigh LL16 4NW — MB ChB 1998 Liverp.; MB ChB Liverp 1998.

GRIFFITHS, Mr Richard Wynn Northern General Hospital, Herries Road, Sheffield S5 7AN Tel: 0114 243 4343 Ext: 4763 — MB BS 1969 Lond.; MS Soton. 1982; FRCS Eng. 1974. (Lond. Hosp.) Cons. Plastic Surg. N. Gen. Sheff. Socs: Mem. Brit. Assn. Plastic Surgs.; BMA. Prev: Sen. Regist. (Plastic Surg.) Frenchay Hosp. Bristol; Lect. (Surg.) Univ. Soton. & Hon. Sen. Regist. Wessex RHA; Regist. Wessex Regional Plastic Surg. Centre Odstock Hosp. Salisbury.

GRIFFITHS, Robert Charles (retired) Potts Cottage, 45 Cambridge Road, Stansted CM24 8BX Tel: 01279 814816 Fax: 01279 814816 — MB BS 1967 Lond.; MRCS Eng. LRCP Lond. 1967; DObst RCOG 1970. Prev: GP Bishop's Stortford.

GRIFFITHS, Robert Lionel The White House, Aythorpe Roding, Great Dunmow, Dunmow CM6 1PD Tel: 01279 876358 — MB BS 1969 Lond. Prev: GP Epping.

GRIFFITHS, Robert Lyn Frome Medical Practice, Health Centre, Park Road, Frome BA11 1EZ Tel: 01373 301300 Fax: 01373 301313; 66 Goose Street, Beckington, Bath BA11 6SS Email: doctorbob@ukgateway.net — MB BS 1968 Lond.; MRCS Eng. LRCP Lond. 1968; MRCGP 1977; DA Eng. 1972; DObst RCOG 1971. (Lond. Hosp.)

GRIFFITHS, Robert Lyn Michael Warwick Street Surgery, 18 Warwick Street, Rugby CV21 3DH Tel: 01788 540860 Fax: 01788 560988 — MB BS 1976 Lond. Trainee Gen. Pract. Rugby Vocational Train. Scheme. Prev: Ho. Surg. St. Mary's Hosp. Lond.; Ho. Phys. St. Mary's Hosp. E.bourne; Resid. (A & E) King. Edwd. VII Memor. Hosp. Bermuda.

GRIFFITHS, Professor Roderic Keith NHS Executive West Midlands, Bartholomew House, 142 Hagley Road, Birmingham B16 9PA Tel: 0121 224 4682 Fax: 0121 224 4680; Stonebow Farm House, Worcester Road, Peopleton, Pershore WR10 2DY Email: rod@stonbow.demon.co.uk — MB ChB Birm. 1969; BSc Birm.

1966; FFCM 1986, M 1981; FRCP. (Birm.) Dir. Pub. Health W. Midl. Region; Prof. Pub. Health Pract. Univ. Birm. Socs: Internat. Epidemiol. Assn. Prev: Dist. Dir. Pub. Health Centr. Birm. HA; Lect. (Social Med.) Univ. Birm.; Lect. (Anat.) Univ. Birm.

GRIFFITHS, Ronald Malcolm, MBE (retired) Corner Ground, Norley Wood, Lymington SO41 5RS Tel: 01590 626202 Email: billgriffiths@easyner.co.uk — MB BS 1953 Lond.; FRCGP 1973, M 1963. Prev: GP. Newham, E. Lond.

GRIFFITHS, Rosalind Elaine Webb and Partners, Cox's Yard, West Street, Somerton TA11 7PR Tel: 01458 272473 Fax: 01458 274461 Email: elainegriffiths@gp-l85005.nhs.uk; Tol-Pedn House, New St, Somerton TA11 7NT Tel: 01458 272144 — MB ChB Sheff. 1970; DObst RCOG 1973. (Sheff.)

GRIFFITHS, Rosemary Jane Andover Health Centre, Charlton Road, Andover SP10 3AL Tel: 01264 365031 — MB ChB 1981 Leeds; MRCGP 1985; DRCOG 1983. GP Ref. DHSS (BAMS). Prev: GP Leeds; Ref. for DHSS.

GRIFFITHS, Rosentyl (retired) Shirley Road Health Centre, 20 Shirley Road, Cardiff CF23 5HN Tel: 029 2049 6339 — MB ChB Wales 1929; BSc Wales 1925; FRCGP 1975. Prev: Indep. GP Cardiff.

GRIFFITHS, Rowland Brian Carreg Wen Surgery, Church Road, Blaenavon NP4 9AF Tel: 01495 790264; Edlogan, Cwmavon Road, Blaenavon NP4 9LF Tel: 01495 790352 — MB BCh 1959 Wales. (Cardiff) Prev: Ho. Phys. Swansea Gen. Hosp.; Ho. Surg. E. Glam. Hosp. Ch. Village.

GRIFFITHS, Sara Sian 46 Hawthylands Road, Hailsham BN27 1HA — BM 1993 Soton.

***GRIFFITHS, Sarah Jane** Lower High Trees Farm, High Trees Lane, Greetland, Halifax HX4 8PP — MB ChB 1998 Birm.; BMedSc.

GRIFFITHS, Sheila Mary (retired) Corner Ground, Norley Wood, Lymington SO41 5RS Tel: 01590 626202 Email: billgriffiths@easyner.co.uk — MB BS 1951 Lond.; FRCGP 1973, M 1963. Prev: GP. Newham E. Lond.

GRIFFITHS, Sian Elin 11 Parc Thomas, Carmarthen SA31 1DP — MB BS 1998 Lond.; MB BS Lond 1998.

GRIFFITHS, Sian Meryl 13 Stratfield Road, Oxford OX2 7BG Tel: 01865 514855 Fax: 01865 311278 — MB BChir 1977 Camb.; MSc Lond. 1981; FFPHM RCP (UK) 1991; DRCOG 1979. Regional Dir. (Pub. Health & Health Policy) S.W. Thames RHA. Prev: Cons. Pub. Health Med. Oxf. RHA.

GRIFFITHS, Stephen Robert Feidrfair Health Centre, Feidrfair, Cardigan SA43 1EB Tel: 01239 612021 Fax: 01239 613373; Manor Gwyn, Login, Whitland SA34 0XD Tel: 01994 419372 — MB BS 1968 Lond.; MRCS Eng. LRCP Lond. 1968; DA Eng. 1970. (Univ. Coll. Hosp.) GP Trainer Course Organiser, Withybush Hosp. HaverfordW. VTS.

GRIFFITHS, Steven James Paget Old Mill Surgery, Stoke Road, Poringland, Norwich NR14 7JL Tel: 01508 492929; Old Mill Surgery, Stoke Road, Poringland, Norwich NR14 7JL Tel: 01508 492929 Fax: 01508 495371 — MB ChB Manch. 1971; DObst RCOG 1973. (Manchester) Med. Dir. S. Norf. Doctors on Call Co-op. Norwich. Socs: Brit. Med. Acupunct. Soc. Prev: SHO (Med.) Roy. Hosp. Sheff.; SHO (A & E) Roy. Hosp. Sheff.; Ho. Off. Withington Hosp. Manch.

GRIFFITHS, Mr Stewart John Long Valley, Dark Lane, Codicote, Hitchin SG4 8UZ — MB BS 1989 Lond.; BSc (Hons.) Lond. 1986; FRCS Eng. 1993. SpR (Neurosurg.) Morriston Hosp. Swansea. Prev: Career Regist. (Neurosurg.) Inst. Neurol. Sci. S.. Gen. Hosp. Glas.

GRIFFITHS, Susan Carol 19 Central Avenue, Eccleston Park, Prescot L34 2QL — MB ChB 1993 Ed.

GRIFFITHS, Susan Caroline Melville Street Surgery, 17 Melville Street, Ryde PO33 2AF Tel: 01983 811431 Fax: 01983 817215; Highclere, The Mall, Brading, Sandown PO36 0BU — MB ChB 1973 Liverp. Prev: Med. Off. I. of Wight AHA; Ho. Surg. St. Mary's Hosp. Newport, I. of Wight; Ho. Phys. Roy. I. of Wight Co. Hosp. Ryde.

GRIFFITHS, Susan Glenn 10 The Uplands, Radyr, Cardiff CF15 8BH — MD 1986 Lond.; MB BS Lond. 1967; FFPHM RCP (UK) 1997, M 1987. Cons. Pub. Health Med. Bro Taf HA Cardiff.

GRIFFITHS, Susan Jane Wessex Road Surgery, Wessex Road, Parkstone, Poole BH14 8BQ Tel: 01202 734924 Fax: 01202 738957 — MB BCh 1990 Wales; MRCPI 1993; MRCGP 1997; DRCOG 1996; DA (UK) 1995. GP Partner,. Socs: G. M. C.

GRIFFITHS, Susan Jane Fareham Health Centre, Osborn Road, Fareham PO16 7ER Tel: 01329 822111 Fax: 01329 286636; 42 Seamead, Stubbington, Fareham PO14 2NG Tel: 01329 667629 — MB BS 1982 Lond.; MRCGP 1986; DRCOG 1986. (Middlx. Hosp. Med. Sch.) Prev: Trainee GP Portsmouth VTS; Ho. Off. (Gen. Surg. & Urol.) Battle Hosp. Reading; Ho. Off. (Gen. Med. & Renal Med.) Kent & Canterbury Hosp.

***GRIFFITHS, Tami** 10 Willow Road, Bournville, Birmingham B30 2AU — MB ChB 1996 Birm.

GRIFFITHS, Mr Thomas Richard Leyshon 54 St Stephen's Road, Norwich NR1 3RE — MB BS 1989 Lond.; BSc (Hons.) Lond. 1986, MB BS 1989; FRCS Ed. 1993. SHO (Orthop.) Addenbrooke's Hosp. Camb. Prev: Ho. Off. (Surg.) St. Bart. Hosp. Lond.; Ho. Off. (Med.) Homerton Hosp. Lond.

GRIFFITHS, Timothy David Woodcott, Winton Hill, Stockbridge SO20 6HL — BM BCh 1988 Oxf.

GRIFFITHS, Timothy Leonard Section of Respiratory Medicine, University of Wales College of Medicine, LLandough Hospital, Penarth CF64 2XX Tel: 01222 716951 Email: griffithstl@cf.ac.uk — MB ChB 1981 Wales; PhD Soton. 1993; BSc (Hons.) Wales 1978; MRCP (UK) 1984. Sen. Lect. (Respirat. Med.) Univ. Wales Coll. Med.; Hon. Cons. Llandough Hosp. & Community NHS Trust. Socs: Brit. Thorac. Soc.; Eur. Respirat. Soc.; Amer. Thoracic Soc. Prev: Lect. (Med.) & Hon. Sen. Regist. St. Geo. Hosp. Med. Sch. Lond.; Lect. (Med.) St. Geo. Hosp. Med. Sch. Lond.; Regist. (Respirat. Med.) Freeman Hosp. Newc. u. Tyne.

GRIFFITHS, Tina Carol Shropshire Mental Health NHS Trust, Royal Shrewsbury Hospital, Shelton, Bicton Heath, Shrewsbury SY3 8DN Tel: 01743 261000 — MB ChB 1979 Manch.; 1998 Dip in Cognitive Analytil Ther.; MRCPsych 1985. p/t Cons. (Gen. Adult Psychiat.) Shrops. Ment. Health NHS Trust Shelton Hosp. Shrewsbury. Prev: Sen. Regist. Rotat. (Psychiat.) W. Midl. Train. Scheme.

GRIFFITHS, Trevor Neil Highlands Health Centre, Fore Street, Ivybridge PL21 9AE Tel: 01752 897111 Fax: 01752 691477; South Highlands, Blachford Road, Ivybridge PL21 0AD — MB BS 1977 Lond.; MA Oxf. 1974; MRCS Eng. LRCP Lond. 1977; MRCGP 1983; DRCOG 1982. (West.)

GRIFFITHS, Valerie Anne Mary 4 Queens Terrace, Wallsend NE28 7QU — MB ChB 1983 Dundee; BSc (Hons.) Dund 1979, MB ChB 1983; MRCGP 1987.

GRIFFITHS, William Andrew David Consulting Rooms King Edward VII Hospital, Emmanuel Kaye House, 37A Devonshire St, London W1G 6QA Tel: 020 7631 3459 Fax: 020 7631 3459 Email: andrew.griffiths@kcl.ac.uk; 56 Elliott Road, London W4 1PE Tel: 020 8994 7414 Email: wad.griffiths@btinternet.com — MB BChir 1966 Camb.; MD Camb. 1977; FRCP Lond. 1983, M 1968; MRCS Eng. LRCP Lond. 1965. (St. Thos.) Cons. Dermat. & Hon. Sen. Lect. St. John's Inst. Dermat. Lond.; Cons. Dermat. St. Thos. Hosp. & King Edwd. VII Hosp. Off.; Cons. Dermat. Dispensaire Français. Socs: Roy. Soc. Med. (Sect. Dermat.); Brit. Assn. Dermat. Prev: Civ. Adviser Qu. Alex. Hosp. Woolwich; Cons. Dermat. Liverp. HA; Ed. Clin. Experimen. Dermat.

GRIFFITHS, Mr William David The Old Parsonage, Warndon, Worcester WR4 0AB Tel: 01905 52384 — MB ChB 1960 Birm.; FRCS Eng. 1968; MRCOG 1970. Cons. (O & G) Worcester Roy. Infirm. Mem. BMA.

GRIFFITHS, William Edward Paradise Road Practice, 37 Paradise Road, Richmond TW9 1SA Tel: 020 8940 2423 Fax: 020 8332 6363; 37 Queen's Court, Liverpool Road, Kingston upon Thames KT2 7SY Tel: 020 8549 2080 — BM BCh 1978 Oxf.; MA Oxf. 1979; MRCGP 1986. (Oxford) Clin. Asst. (Genitourin. Med.) W. Middlx. Univ. Hosp. Isleworth. Socs: BMA & RCGP; Osler Club Lond. Prev: GP Tutor W. Middlx. Univ. Hosp. Isleworth; Med. Off. Lubwe Mission Hosp., Zambia; SHO (Med.) Univ. Coll. Hosp. Lond.

GRIFFITHS, Mr William Edward Granville Wayside, 139 Main Road, Emsworth PO10 8EY Tel: 01243 373151 Fax: 01243 373151 Email: weggriffiths@btinternet.com; Wayside, 193 Main Rd, Emsworth PO10 8EY Tel: 01243 373151 Fax: 01243 373151 Email: weggriffiths@btinternet.com — MB BS 1962 Lond.; FRCS Eng. 1968; FRCS Ed. 1967. (Westm.) Cons. Orthop. Surg. Portsmouth Hosp. NHS Trust. Socs: Brit. Scoliosis Soc.; Brit. Orthop. Assn. Prev: Sen. Regist. Lond. Hosp. Whitechapel; Assoc. Clin. Dir. (Orthop.) Qu. Alexandra Hosp. Portsmouth.

GRIFFITHS, William Gwyn, OBE Crofty, Salem Road, St Clears, Carmarthen SA33 4DD — MRCS Eng. LRCP Lond. 1952.

GRIFFITHS, William James Houghton 5 Towers Gardens, Havant PO9 1RZ — MB BChir 1994 Camb.

GRIFFITHS, William Satterlee Woodstock, 6 Regent St., Abergavenny NP7 Tel: 01873 4555 — MRCS Eng. LRCP Lond. 1950. (Camb. & Cardiff) Prev: Ho. Off. Obst. St. David's Hosp. Cardiff; Ho. Phys. Roy. Gwent Hosp. Newport.

GRIFFITHS, Yvonne Patricia (retired) 1 Northerwood House, Emery Down, Lyndhurst SO43 7DT Tel: 023 8028 4343 — MB 1959 Camb.; BChir 1958; DA Eng. 1960. Prev: GP Kent.

GRIGEREIT, Claudia Susanne 29 Carn Boasvern, St Just, Penzance TR19 9QX — State Exam Med 1991 Ulm.

GRIGG, Jonathan Marcus Department of Child Health, University of Leicester, PO Box 65, Leicester LE2 7LX Email: jg33@le.ac.uk; 15 Holmfield Road, Stoneygate, Leicester LE2 1SD Tel: 0116 270 6447 — MB BS 1982 Lond.; BSc (1st cl. Hons.) Lond. 1980; MRCP (UK) 1986; MD Lond. 1994. (Lond. Hosp.) Sen. Lect. (Paediat.) Thoracic Med. Prev: Thoracic Fell. Roy. Childr. Hosp. Melbourne, Austral.; Research Fell. (Paediat.) Roy. Postgrad. Med. Sch.; Regist. (Paediat.) John Radcliffe Hosp. Oxf.

GRIGG, Julie Alison Still Point, Cusop, Hay-on-Wye, Hereford HR3 5RQ — MB BS 1988 Lond.

GRIGGS, Nicolas John Oldbury Health Centre, Albert Street, Oldbury B69 4DE Tel: 0121 552 6665 Fax: 0121 544 8580; 15 Joinings Bank, Oldbury, Oldbury B68 8QJ Tel: 0121 552 7338 — BM 1979 Soton.

GRIGOR, Catriona Jane Department of Rheumatology, Northwick Park & St. Marks NHS Trust, Harrow HA1 3UJ — MB ChB 1995 Glas. Sen. Ho. Off., Dept. of Rheum., N.wick Pk., Harrow.

GRIGOR, Hilary Medwyn, 6 Barnton Gardens, Edinburgh EH4 6AF — MB ChB 1997 Glas.

GRIGOR, Jacqueline Community Child Health, 10 Chalmers Cres, Edinburgh EH9 1TS Tel: 0131 557 2100; 6 Barnton Gardens, Edinburgh EH4 6AF Tel: 0131 336 2824 Email: jackie.grigor@muttonhole.co.uk — MB ChB 1969 Glas.; DObst RCOG 1972; DCH RCPS Glas. 1972; MSC Audiological Med. Glas. SCMO Lothian HB. Socs: Brit. Assn. Community Drs in Audiol.; Brit. Soc. Audiol. Prev: Clin. Med. Off. Wandsworth & Merton AHA; Resid. (Obst.) Bellshill Matern. Hosp.; Resid. (Paediat.) Roy. Hosp. Sick Childr. Glas.

GRIGOR, Mr Kenneth Clark (retired) 31 Fairfax Avenue, Glasgow G44 5AL Tel: 0141 637 3760 — MB ChB 1937 Glas.; MD (High Commend.) Glas. 1952; FRCS Glas. 1970; FFA RCS Eng. 1953; DA Eng. 1940. Hon. Mem. Glas. & W. Scotl. Soc. Anaesth. Prev: Cons. in Admin. Charge Dept. Anaesth. Vict. Infirm. Glas. & Assoc. Hosps.

GRIGOR, Kenneth McNeill Department of Pathology, Edinburgh University, Teviot Place, Edinburgh EH8 9AG Tel: 0131 650 3001 Fax: 0131 650 6528 Email: ken.grigor@ed.ac.uk; 6 Barnton Gardens, Edinburgh EH4 6AF Tel: 0131 336 2824 Email: ken.grigor@muttonhole.co.uk — MB ChB 1969 Glas.; BSc Glas. 1967, MD 1980; FRCPath 1992, M 1980. (Glas.) Sen. Lect. (Path.) Edin. Univ.; Hon. Cons. Lothian Bd. Socs: Path. Soc.; Assn. Clin. Path.; Brit. Assn. Urol. Surgs. Prev: Lect. (Path.) Middlx. Hosp. Med. Sch.; Scientif. Asst. Chester Beatty Research Inst.; McGhie Schol. Glas. Roy. Infirm.

GRIGOR, Moray John Morven, Alarburn, Kiltarlity, Beauly IV4 7HG Tel: 01463 741540 Email: mjgrigor@aol.com — MB ChB 1991 Ed.; MRCGP 1996; DCCH 1994; DFFP 1997. (Edinburgh) GP Non-Princip. Socs: N. Scotl. Support Gp.

GRIGSON, Claudia Mary Beverley (retired) Lanlawren House, Trenewan, Looe PL13 2PZ — MB Camb. 1955, BChir 1954; MRCS Eng. LRCP Lond. 1954. Prev: Clin. Med. Off. (Child Health) N. Beds. HA.

GRILLAGE, Michael George Northbrook Health Centre, 93 Northbrook Road, Shirley, Solihull B90 3LX Tel: 0121 745 9181 Fax: 0121 733 6893; Toad Hall, 45 Mallards Reach, Mereside Way, Solihull B92 7BX Tel: 0121 706 3398 Fax: 0121 706 3398 Email: grilly@tinyworld.co.uk — MB ChB 1975 Birm.; BA (Hons.) (Physiol. Sc.) Oxf. 1972, MA 1976. Dir. Ethical Med. Research Assoc. Ltd. & EMI Audio-Visual Servs. Ltd.; Clin. Asst. (ENT) Solihull Hosp.; Clin. Asst. (Orthop.) E. Birm. Hosp. Socs: BMA. Prev: Ho. Surg. (Neurosurg.) Qu. Eliz. Hosp. Birm.; Ho. Phys. E. Birm. Hosp.

GRIMA, Francis Xavier, Group Capt. RAF Med. Br. Retd. 45 Triq Castro, Naxxar NXR03, Malta Tel: 00 356 471651 Fax: 00 356 311385; 45 Gowan Avenue, Fulham, London SW6 6RH Tel: 020 7384 3185 — MD 1959 Malta; MSc (Occupat. Med.) Lond. 1978; BPharm Malta 1955; MRCGP 1975; FFOM RCP Lond. 1993, M 1980; T(OM) 1991; DPH Eng. 1971. (Univ. Malta) Indep. Specialist (Occupat. Med.) Malta. Socs: Soc. Occupat. Med. Prev: Med. Adviser Hammersmith & Fulham Boro. Counc.; Occupat. Phys. Stoke Mandeville Hosp. Bucks.; Occupat. Phys. Atomic Weapons Estabm., Aldermeston.

GRIMALDI, Barry David Francis 49 Harley House, Marylebone Road, London NW1 5HG Tel: 020 7637 7989 Fax: 020 7935 0406 — MB BS 1971 Lond.; MRCP (U.K.) 1974; MRCS Eng. LRCP Lond. 1971. (St. Bart.) Indep. GP Lond.; Med. Cons. English Nat. Opera & English Nat. Ballet Sch.; Med. Adviser Sports Counc. Brit. Ballet Orgs. Socs: Fell. Med. Soc. Lond.; BMA. Prev: Research Regist. (Cardiol.) St. Bart. Hosp. Lond.; Med. Off. Lond. Clinic; SHO (Neurosurg.) St. Bart. Hosp. Lond.

GRIMALDI, Christopher Beaufort, MBE (retired) 160 Knole Lane, Brentry, Bristol BS10 6JR Tel: 0117 950 1735 — BM BCh 1940 Oxf.; MA; MRCGP 1968. Prev: Clin. Asst. (Growth) Bristol Childr. Hosp.

GRIMALDI, Mr Peter Martin Gort Beaufort Low Healthcare NHS Trust, Newport PO30 5TG Tel: 01983 524081 Email: peter.grimaldi@low.nhs.uk; Tyne Hall, Bembridge PO35 5NH Tel: 01983 872305 — MB BChir Camb. 1970; MA Camb. 1970; FRCS Eng. 1975. (Cambridge & St. Thomas') Cons. ENT. Surg. St. Mary's Hosp. NHS Trust I. of Wight; Hon. Cons. Qu. Alexandra's Hosp. Portsmouth. Socs: BAMM; HCSA; BAO - HNS. Prev: Sen. Regist. (ENT) St. Mary's Hosp. Lond.; Sen. Regist. (Head & Neck) Roy. Marsden Hosp. Lond.; Regist. (ENT) King's Coll. Hosp. Lond.

GRIMBALDSTON, Anne Heather Fern House, 7 Garstang Road, Bowgreave, Garstang, Preston PR3 1YD — MB ChB 1983 Manch.

GRIMBLE, Ian Turnbull Grimble and Partners, 20 Pepys Road, Raynes Park, London SW20 8PF Tel: 020 8946 3074/8249 Fax: 020 8296 0145; 41 Merton Hall Road, Wimbledon, London SW19 3PR — MB BS 1969 Lond.; MRCP (U.K.) 1974; MRCS Eng. LRCP Lond. 1969; DCH Eng. 1971. (Guy's) Princip. GP Med. Off. Pk.side Hosp. Prev: Med. Regist. Bolingbroke Hosp.; Ho. Phys. Paediat. FarnBoro. Hosp.; SHO Paediat. Qu. Mary's Hosp. Childr. Carshalton.

GRIMBLE, Sarah Amelia Jane 56 Shaftesbury Avenue, Southampton SO17 1SD Tel: 02380 583575 — MB ChB 1993 Leic.; FRCS Eng. 1997. SHO Rotat. (Surg.) Portsmouth Hosp. NHS Trust; Sen. (Gen. Surg.) SHO Roy. Hants. Co. Hosp. Winchester. Prev: Demonst. (Anat.) Char. Cross Hosp. Lond.; Cas. Off. Leicester Infirm.

GRIME, Ian David 254 Heaton Road, Heaton, Newcastle upon Tyne NE6 5QE Tel: 0191 265 9258 Fax: 0191 240 0334 Email: 100712.3331@compuserve.com — MB BS 1989 Newc.; BDS Sheff. 1981; LDS RCS Sheff. 1981; FDS RCS Sheff. 1984; DGDP 1996. (Newc.) Gen. Dent. Pract.; Assoc. Specialist (Oral Surg.) Dent. Sch. Univ. Newc. u. Tyne. Socs: Assoc. Mem. Brit. Assn. Oral & Maxillofacial Surg.; BMA; BDA.

GRIME, Lindsay Peter (retired) Hammerton, 132 Hollins Lane, Accrington BB5 2JS Tel: 01254 231427 Fax: 01254 399511 — LRCPI & LM, LRCSI & LM 1959; FFPHM RCP (UK) 1989; FFCM RCP (UK) 1981, M 1972; DPH Lond. 1963. Hon. Cons. Pub. Health Med. E. Lancs. DHA. Prev: Hon. Clin. Teach. Fac. of Med. Manch. Univ.

GRIME, Paul Robert Department of Occupational Health, King's College Hospital, Denmark Hill, London SE5 9RS Tel: 020 7346 3387 Fax: 020 7346 3261; 22 Haydens Mews, Tonbridge TN9 1PZ — MB ChB 1988 Leic.; MRCPI 1997; AFOM 1999. (Leic.) Specialist Regist. (Occupat. Med.) King's Coll. Hosp. Socs: Soc. Occupat. Med.; Brit. Thorac. Soc. Prev: Hon. Research Assoc. (Allergy & Respirat. Med.) Guy's Hosp.; Regist. (Gen. & Respirat. Med.) Cumbld. Infirm. Carlisle; SHO (Thoracic Med.) Lond. Chest Hosp.

GRIME, Mr Peter David 24 North Furzeham Road, Brixham TQ5 8BB — MB ChB 1985 Aberd.; BDS Bristol 1976; FDS RCS 1980; FRCS Ed. 1989.

GRIME, Mr Roland Thompson (retired) Trova Lon Bridin, Morfa Nefyn, Pwllheli LL53 6BY Tel: 01758 720501 — MB ChB 1939 Manch.; ChM 1955 Manch.; FRCS Eng. 1947. Mem. Med. Appeal

Tribunal; Hon. Cons. Surg. Stockport & Dist. Gp. Hosps. Prev: Cons. Surg. Ashton under Lyne Gp. Hosps.

GRIMER, Dominic Peter Henel Hempstead General Hospital, Hillfield Road, Hemel Hempstead HP2 4AD Tel: 01442 213141 Ext: 2337; Cobwebs, 24a Lattimore Road, Wheatampstead, Hatfield AL4 8QE — MB BS 1975 Lond.; FRCR 1982. (St. Geo.) Cons. (Radiol.) Hemel Hempstead Gen. & St. Albans City Hosp. Prev: Sen. Regist. (Radiol.) St. Geo. Hosp. Lond.

GRIMER, Mr Robert John Royal Orthopaedic Hospital, Bristol Road S., North Field, Birmingham B31 2AP Tel: 0121 685 4150 Fax: 0121 685 4146 Email: sarcomas@rohos.demon.co.uk; Pint Bar Cottage, Foredraught Lane, Tibberton, Droitwich WR9 7NH Tel: 0121 345601 Fax: 0121 345601 Email: grimer@pintbar.u-net.com — MB BS 1976 Lond.; FRCS (Orthop.) Ed. 1986; FRCS Eng. 1980. (Middlx.) Cons. Orthop. Surg. & Orthop. Oncol. Roy. Orthop. Hosp. Birm. Socs: Brit. Orthop. Assn.; Eur. Musculoskeletal Oncol. Soc.; Eur. Osteosarcoma InterGp.. Prev: Sen. Regist. Rotat. (Orthop.) W. Midl. RHA; Prosector (Anat.) St. Thos. Hosp. Lond.; Ho. Surg. Middlx. Hosp. Lond.

GRIMES, Conor Joseph New Cross Surgery, 48 Sway Road, Morriston, Swansea SA6 6HR Tel: 01792 771419; 67 Cecil Road, Gowerton, Swansea SA4 3DF — MB BCh BAO 1986 Dub.

GRIMES, David Stuart Blackburn Royal Infirmary, Bolton Road, Blackburn BB2 3LR Tel: 01254 687224 Fax: 01254 662043; 2 Lowerfield, Langho, Blackburn BB6 8HE Tel: 01254 240707 — MD 1994 Manch.; MB ChB 1966; FRCP Lond. 1985, M 1969. Cons. Phys. Roy. Infirm. & Qu. Pk. Hosp. Blackburn. Prev: Sen. Regist. (Med.) Manch. Roy. Infirm.; Regist.(Med.) St. Geo.'s Hosp. Lond.

GRIMES, Lee Karen Hallgarth Surgery, Cheapside, Shildon DL4 2HP Tel: 01388 772362 Fax: 01388 774150; 9 Vicarage Court, Heighington, Newton Aycliffe DL5 6SD — MB ChB 1981 Sheff.; MRCGP 1986; DRCOG 1985.

GRIMLEY, Mr Ronald Patrick Russells Hall Hospital, Dudley DY1 2HQ Tel: 01384 401401 — MB ChB 1970 Birm.; MD Birm. 1982, MSc (Anat.) 1972; FRCS Eng. 1975; FRCS Ed. 1975. (Birm.) Cons. Surg. (Gen. & Vasc.) Dudley HA. Socs: Fell. Assn. Surgs.; Brit. Melanoma Gp.; Brit. Assn. Surgic. Oncol. Prev: Lect. (Surg.) Univ. Birm.; Sen. Regist. (Surg.) W. Midl. RHA.

GRIMLEY EVANS, Professor Sir John The Radcliffe Infirmary, Oxford OX2 6HE Tel: 01865 224975 Fax: 01865 224815 Email: john.grimleyevans@geratology.ox.ac.uk — MB BChir Camb. 1962; MA Camb. 1962, MD 1985; DM Oxf. 1985; FRCP Lond. 1975, M 1963; FFPHM 1982, M 1978. (Oxf.) Prof. Clin. Geratol. Nuffield Dept. Med. Univ. Oxf.; Cons. Phys. (Geriat. & Gen. Med.) Oxf. Radcliffe Hosp. & Radcliffe Infirm. Oxf. Socs: Internat. Epidemiol. Assn.; Assn. Phys.; Brit. Geriat. Soc. Prev: Prof. Med. (Geriat.) Univ. Newc.; Lect. (Epidemiol.) Med. Statistics Lond. Sch. Hyg. & Trop. Med.; Research Fell. Clin. Epidemiol. Med. Unit Wellington, NZ.

GRIMM, Beate Waltraud The Hawthorn Surgery, 150 Hawthorn Avenue, Colchester CO4 3YA Tel: 01206 871157 Fax: 01206 869567 — State Exam Med 1986 Giessen.

GRIMMER, Claudia Royal Dundee Liff Hospital, Muirhead, Dundee DD2 5N Tel: 01382 660111; The Laurels, 64A Needless Road, Perth PH2 0LA Tel: 01738 621266 — State Exam Med 1991 Rostock. (Rostock)

GRIMMER, Philip Michael 44 Queens Road, Peterborough PE2 8BP — MB ChB 1995 Leic.

GRIMMER, Stephen Francis Martin The Ipswich Hospital, Ipswich IP4 5PD Tel: 01473 704135; Valley View, Main Road, Martlesham, Woodbridge IP12 4SF Tel: 01394 386971 — MB ChB 1973 Leeds; MD Leeds 1986, MB ChB 1973; MRCP (UK) 1977; FRCP 1995; MD 1986 Leeds. Cons. Phys.Gen. and Elderly Care Med. Heath Rd. Hosp. Ipswich. Socs: Brit. Pharm. Soc. & Brit. Hyperlip. Assn.; Brit. Geriat.s Soc. Prev: Sen. Regist. (Geriat. & Gen. Med.) Dudley Rd. Hosp. Birm.; Lect. (Clin. Pharmacol.) Univ. Liverp.; Regist. (Med. Cardiol.) Leeds Gen. Infirm.

GRIMMETT, Bernadette Mary Susan The Surgery, 98a Westbury Road, New Malden KT3 5AN Tel: 020 8949 6778 Fax: 020 8336 0103 — MB BS 1969 Lond.; MRCP (U.K.) 1973; MRCS Eng. LRCP Lond. 1969; DMRT Eng. 1973; DCH Eng. 1971. (Roy. Free) Med. Adviser Roy. Opera Hse. Orchestra; Sen. Clin. Med. Off. Roehampton CTPLD. Prev: SHO W.m. Hosp. Lond.; Regist. Hammersmith Hosp. Lond.

GRIMMETT, Brenda Myra (retired) Frogs Hall Cottage, Lower St., Cavendish, Sudbury CO10 8AG — MB BChir 1949 Camb.; DObst RCOG 1952. Prev: Gen. Pracitioner, Colchester Essex 1960-1986.

GRIMMOND, Linda Mabel Cummine 5 Church Street, Broughty Ferry, Dundee DD5 1EZ — MB ChB 1979 Dundee.

GRIMSELL, Clare Helen Wallis and Partners, The Health Centre, 5 Stanmore Road, Stevenage SG1 3QA Tel: 01438 313223 Fax: 01438 749734 — MB BS 1988 Lond.; BSc Lond. 1985, MB BS 1988; MRCGP 1992; DRCOG 1992.

GRIMSHAW, Bronwyn Sylvia MDS Harris, Sterling House, 20 Station Road, Gerrards Cross SL9 8EL Tel: 01753 893339 Fax: 01753 893239; 10 Church Road, Chavey Down, Ascot SL5 8RR Tel: 01344 882431 — MB ChB 1976 Sheff.; DCH Eng. 1979; DRCOG 1979; Dip. Occupat. Med. Lond. 1997. (Sheffield) Med. Adviser MDS Harris Gerrards Cross. Prev: Med. Adviser BAMS; GP Bracknell.

GRIMSHAW, Mr Clement 3 Wootton Road, Henley-on-Thames RG9 1QE — MB ChB 1938 Ed.; MA Oxf. 1970; FRCS Eng. 1970; FRCS Ed. 1944. (Univ. Ed.) Hon. Cons. Thoracic Surg. Oxf. RHB. Prev: Surg. Hope Hosp. Salford; Cons. Thoracic Surg. Oxf. RHA; Lect. (Clin. Surg.) Univ. Oxf.

GRIMSHAW, David Richard Langford Medical Practice, 9 Nightingale Place, Bicester OX26 6XX Tel: 01869 245665; 5 Church End Cottages, Bletchingdon, Kidlington OX5 3DU Tel: 01869 350820 — BM BCh 1987 Oxf.; MRCGP 1992; DRCOG 1991. (Oxf.) Med. Off. (Palliat. Med.) Katharine Hse. Hospice Adderbury. Prev: Trainee GP Oxf. VTS.

GRIMSHAW, Jeremy Michael Health Services Research, University of Aberdeen, Foresterhill, Aberdeen AB25 2ZD Tel: 01224 681818 Fax: 01224 663087 Email: j.m.grimshaw@abdn.ac.uk; North Lodge, Kinbroon, Inverurie AB51 8UE Tel: 01651 81371 — MB ChB 1984 Ed.; MRCGP 1993. Progr. Dir. & Sen. Lect. Health Servs. Research Unit. Prev: Sen. Lect. (Gen. Pract.) Aberd.; Wellcome Train. Fell. Health Servs. Research Univ. Aberd.; Trainee GP N.d. VTS.

GRIMSHAW, John Stuart The Orchard, Curdridge Lane, Curdridge, Southampton SO32 2BH Tel: 01489 782525 Fax: 01489 798592 — MB BChir Camb. 1959; MA Camb. 1959; FRCP Ed. 1977, M 1964; MRCS Eng. LRCP Lond. 1958; FRCPsych 1977, M 1971; DPM Eng. 1962. (Univ. Coll. Hosp.) Emerit. Cons. Psychiat. Soton. Univ. Hosp.; Mem. Ment. Health Review Tribunal Lond. S. & S. & W.; Ment. Health Act Commr. 2nd Opinion Apptd. Doctor; Edr.. MHRT Mems. Handbk. Socs: Fell. Roy. Soc. Med.; Worshipful Soc. Apoth. Liveryman. Prev: Sen. Regist. (Psychol. Med.) St. Thos. Hosp. Lond. & Knowle Hosp.; Maj. RAMC, Sen. Specialist Psychiat.; Ho. Surg. & Ho. Phys. Univ. Coll. Hosp. Lond.

GRIMSHAW, Katherine Margaret Nuffield Road Medical Centre, Nuffield Road, Chesterton, Cambridge CB4 1GL Tel: 01223 423424 Fax: 01223 566450 — MB BS 1972 Lond.; DCH Eng. 1973; DRCOG 1972. (St. Geo.) Med. Off. (Child Health) Camb. Health Dist.; SHO (Obst.) Soton. Gen. Hosp. Socs: BMA. Ho. Phys. & Ho. Surg. St. Geo. Hosp. Lond.

GRIMSHAW, Mahilradha Sharon 124 St Anthony Road, Sheffield S10 1SG — MB ChB 1994 Sheff.

GRIMSHAW, Margaret Edith 4 Back Millar, Barn Lane, Waterfoot, Rossendale BB4 7BQ Tel: 01706 215210 — MB ChB 1952 Manch. Prev: GP Waterfoot Health Centre; SHO (Paediat.) Wigan Infirm.; Ho. Phys. Dryburn Hosp. Durh.

GRIMSHAW, Robert John St Davids Surgery, Eryl Mor, 36 New Street, St. Davids, Haverfordwest SA62 6SS Tel: 01437 720303 Fax: 01437 721162 — MB BCh 1980 Wales; MA Camb. 1980; MRCGP (UK) 1988.

GRIMSHAW, Steven Leonard 139 Freedom Road, Sheffield S6 2XB — MB ChB 1994 Sheff.

GRIMSON, Thomas Arthur (retired) Pendine, 11 North Road, Chester-le-Street DH3 4AQ Tel: 0191 388 6396 — MB BS 1943 Lond.; MD Lond. 1949; FRCP Lond. 1970, M 1945. Cons. Phys. Durh. AHA. Prev: Chief Asst. Med. Profess. Unit St. Bart. Hosp. Lond.

GRIMSTON, Alison Jane Wellingham Vane, Wellingham Lane, Ringmer, Lewes BN8 5SN Tel: 01273 813251 Fax: 01273 814792 Email: grimston@globalnet.co.uk — MB BS 1994 Lond.; MPhil Lond. 1992, BSc (Hons.) 1988, MB BS 1994; DRCOG 1996; DFFP 1997. GP Regist. Haywards Heath W. Sussex.

***GRIMWADE, David James** 21 Mexfield Road, London SW15 2RG — MB BS 1987 Lond.; BA (Hons.) Oxf. 1984; MRCP (UK) 1990.

GRIMWADE, Peter Robert Windrush Health Centre, Welch Way, Witney OX28 6JS Tel: 01993 702911 Fax: 01993 700931 — MB BS 1990 Lond.; MRCGP 1995; DRCOG 1994; DCH RCP Lond. 1994. (Roy. Lond. Hosp. Med. Coll.)

GRINDEY, Caroline Ann 9 Chesterfield House, Henbury Hill, Bristol BS10 7AA — MB BS 1992 Lond.; BSc Basic Med. Sci. & Hist. Med. Lond. 1991. SHO (Neonat. Med.) St. Michael's Hosp. Bristol. Prev: Doctor Med. Emerg. Relief Internat.; SHO (A & E) W. Middlx. Univ. Hosp. Lond.

GRINDLAY, Dorothy Watson Spruell (retired) 37 Winchester Drive, Newcastle ST5 3JH Tel: 01782 617148 — MB ChB 1951 Glas. Prev: Ho. Off. (Midw.) Thornhill Matern. Hosp. Johnstone.

GRINDLAY, Walter (retired) 37 Winchester Drive, Newcastle ST5 3JH Tel: 01782 617148 — MB ChB 1951 Glas.; MRCGP 1962. Prev: GP Stoke-on-Trent.

GRINDLE, Mr Charles Frederic John 38 Devonshire Street, London W1G 6QB Tel: 020 7935 0884 Fax: 020 7935 0068 Email: j.grinolt@virgin.net; 11 Devonshire Mews W., Harley St, London W1G 6QE Tel: 020 7935 0068 Fax: 020 7935 0068 — MB ChB 1970 Ed.; BSc Ed. 1967; FRCS Eng. 1990; FCOphth 1990, M 1989; T(Ophth.) 1990; DO RCS Eng. 1989. (Paris, Harvard, Ed.) Cons. Ophth. Surg. Eye Acad. Lond. Socs: Fell. Roy. Soc. Med.; Indep. Doctors Forum; Fell. (Ex-Pres.) Roy. Med. Soc. Edin. Prev: Cons. Ophth. Surg. Refractive Centers Internat. Waltham, MA, USA; Research Fell. & Lect. Inst. Ophth. Moorfields & Lond. Hosps.; Carnegie Fell. Div. Med. Johns Hopkins Hosp.

GRINDROD, Roger Melvyn Cosham Health Centre, Vectis Way, Portsmouth PO6 3AW Tel: 023 9238 1117 Fax: 0223 9221 4266 — BM 1976 Soton.; MRCGP 1980.

GRINDULIS, Helen Sandwell General Hospital, Lyndon, West Bromwich B71 4HJ Tel: 0121 553 1831 Fax: 0121 607 3596; 68 Oakham Road, Harborne, Birmingham B17 9DG — MB ChB 1977 Birm.; FRCP Lond. 1995; MRCP (UK) 1981; DRCOG 1979. Cons. Community Paediat. Sandwell Gen. Hosp. W. Bromwich.

GRINDULIS, Karlis Armands Sandwell General Hospital, Lyndon, West Bromwich B71 4HJ Tel: 0121 607 3125 Fax: 0121 607 3580 — MB ChB 1977 Birm.; FRCP Lond. 1994; MRCP (UK) 1980. Cons. Phys. & Rheum. Sandwell Gen. Hosp. 1987.

GRINGRAS, Max Priorslegh Medical Centre, Civic Centre, Park Lane, Poynton, Stockport SK12 1GP Tel: 01625 872299; MGB Clinical Research, 32A Park Lane, Poynton, Stockport SK12 1RE Tel: 01625 875481 Fax: 01625 871321 — MB ChB 1960 Manch.; DObst RCOG 1962. (Manch.) GP Cheadle; Dir. MGB Clin. & Drug Research Stockport. Socs: Affil. RCPsych. Prev: Clin. Asst. (Psychiat.) Stepping Hill Hosp. Stockport; Med. Examr. Min. of Aviat.

GRINGRAS, Paul — MB ChB 1986 Leeds; MRCP (UK) 1991; ASc (Community & Developm. Paediat.) Univ. Coll. Lond. Cons. (Paediat. Disabil.) Harper Hse. Childr. Svcs.; Cons. (Paediat.) Multiple Birth Foundat. Qu. Charlotte's Hosp. Socs: BMA; RCPCH. Prev: Sen. Regist. (Paediat.) Univ. Coll. & Middlx. Hosp. Lond.; Regist. (Paediat.) Whittington Hosp. Lond.

GRINSTED, Robert Woden Road Surgery, Woden Road, Wolverhampton WV10 0BD Tel: 01902 608838 Email: robgrinsted@hotmail.com; 82 Coppice Farm Way, New Invention, Willenhall WV12 5YG Tel: 01922 710601 Email: robgrinsted@hotmail.com — MB ChB 1983 Leic.; MRCGP 1987; DRCOG 1985. GP Wolverhampton.

GRINT, Paul Charles Alexander Wellcome Research Laboratories, Department of Clinical Virology, Langley Court, Beckenham BR3 3BS Tel: 020 8658 2211 Fax: 020 8663 6341; 9 Acott Fields, Lees Road, Yalding, Maidstone ME18 6DQ Tel: 01622 814977 — MB BS 1982 Lond.; BSc Lond. 1979, MB BS Lond. 1982; MRC Path. 1988. Med. Adviser (Clin. Virol.) Wellcome Research Laborat. Beckenham Kent; Hon. Clin. Lect. (Virol.) St. Bart. Hosp. Lond. Socs: Internat. Soc. Antiviral Research; Europ. Gp. for Rapid Virus Diag. Prev: Clin. Lect. (Virol.) St. Bart. Hosp. Lond.; Regist. (Virol.) St. Bart. Hosp. Lond.; SHO Rotat. (Path.) St. Bart. Hosp. Lond.

GRINTER, Katherine Ruth 12 Cherington Close, Northenden, Manchester M23 0FE — BM 1979 Soton.

GRINYER, Sarah Anne Westfield Road Surgery, 11 Westfield Road, Bletchley, Milton Keynes MK2 2DJ Tel: 01908 377103 Fax: 01908 374427; The Hollies, 2 High St, Nash, Milton Keynes MK17 0EP — BM BCh 1990 Oxf.; MA Camb. 1991; DRCOG 1994; MRCGP 1996. (Oxf.) GP. Socs: BMA. Prev: SHO (Paediat.) Milton Keynes Hosp.; SHO (O & G) Milton Keynes Hosp.; SHO (Psychiat.) Milton Keynes Hosp.

GRIPPAUDO, Vincenzo Matteo Rylett Road Surgery, 45A Rylett Road, Shepherds Bush, London W12 9ST Tel: 020 8749 7863 Fax: 020 8743 5161 — MB BS 1990 Lond.; MRCGP 1995; DRCOG 1994; DFFP 1994. Prev: Trainee GP/SHO Hillingdon Hosp. Uxbridge VTS.

GRIPPER, Mark Bradley Cran, Gripper, Bolton and Evers, Health Centre, Chacewater, Truro TR4 8QS Tel: 01872 560346 Fax: 01872 561184; Windrush, Silver Hill, Perranwell Station, Truro TR3 7LP Tel: 01872 863833 — MB BS 1975 Lond.; DRCOG 1977.

GRIPPER, Susan Margaret Windrush, Silver Hill, Perranwell Station, Truro TR3 7LP — MB BS 1975 Lond.; MRCGP 1980; DRCOG 1978.

GRIPTON, Graham (retired) Church View Surgery, 239 Halesowen Road, Cradley Heath, Cradley Heath B64 6JE Tel: 01384 566929 — MB ChB 1957 Birm.; DObst RCOG 1959. GP(Retd.) Med. Adviser fro N.D.A. Prev: Ho. Surg. Profess. Unit, Qu. Eliz. Hosp. Birm.

GRISEWOOD, Helen Louise Merrow Park Surgery, Kingfisher Drive, Merrow, Guildford GU4 7EP; Petwood, Forest Road, E. Horsley, Leatherhead KT24 5BL Tel: 014865 4495 — MB ChB 1980 Liverp.; MRCS Eng. LRCP Lond. 1980; MRCGP 1986; DFFP 1994; DRCOG 1985. Socs: Assoc. Mem. BPA. Prev: GP Guildford & Esher; Civil. Med. Pract. HM. Forces The Med. Centre R.A.S.U. B.F.P.O.

GRISEWOOD, Margaret 2 Sydney Road, Guildford GU1 3LJ Tel: 01483 569005 — LRCP LRCS Ed. LRCPS Glas. 1966.

GRIST, Professor Norman Roy 5A Hyndland Court, 6A Sydenham Road, Glasgow G12 9NR Tel: 0141 339 5241 — MB ChB 1942 Glas.; BSc Glas. 1939; FRCP Glas. 1983, M 1980; FRCP Ed. 1957, M 1950; FRCPath 1967. (Univ. Glas.) Emerit. Prof. Infec. Dis. Univ. Glas. Socs: (Ex-Pres.) Brit. Soc. Study Infec.; Hon. Mem. Assn. Clin. Path. Prev: Prof. Infec. Dis. Univ. Glas.; Dir. Regional Virus Laborat. Glas.; Reader (Viral Epidemiol.) Univ. Glas. 1962-65.

***GRIST, Wendy Louise** 43 The Shires, Lower Bullingham, Hereford HR2 6EY — MB ChB 1994 Birm.

GRISTWOOD, Jacqueline Calcot Medical Centre, Gold Hill, Chalfont St Peter, Gerrards Cross SL9 9DT Tel: 01753 887311; 45 Baring Road, Beaconsfield HP9 2NF — MB BS 1978 Lond.; DRCOG 1990.

GROARKE, Alexander Warren West Gorton Medical Centre, 6A Wenlock Way, West Gorton, Manchester M12 5LH Tel: 0161 223 5226 Fax: 0161 230 6305; 32 Princes Road, Heaton Moor, Stockport SK4 3NQ Tel: 0161 442 1269 Email: warreng@g43.u-net.com — MB BS 1989 Lond.; MRCGP 1993; DCH RCP Lond. 1991. (UCL) Hon. Club Doctor Manch. City Football Club; LMC Exec. Socs: BMA. Prev: Manch. Doctor Co-Operat. Treas.

GROARKE, Mary Ita 23 New Park Croft, Farsley, Pudsey LS28 5TT — MB BCh BAO 1992 NUI.

GROARKE, Philip 38 All Saints Road, St Annes, Lytham St Annes FY8 1PL — LM 1955 Rotunda; MB BCh BAO NUI 1951, DCH 1955.

GROB, Paul Richard Crouch Oak Family Practice, 45 Station Road, Addlestone, Weybridge Tel: 01932 840123 — MRCS Eng. LRCP Lond. 1959; MD Lond. 1971, MB BS 1959; FRCGP 1977, M 1968; DObst RCOG 1961. (Guy's) Vis. Prof. Gen. Pract. & Epidemiol. Univ. Surrey; Hon. Dir. Epidemic Observat. Unit RCGP; Hon. Research Asst. Dept. Virol. Roy. Postgrad. Med. Sch. Lond.; Hon. Lect. (Infec. Dis. in Gen. Pract.) UCH Med. Sch. Lond; Hon. Lect. (Health Studies) Dept. Biol. Scs. Surrey Univ.; Adviser in Gen. Pract. to S.W. Metrop. Region. Socs: Fell. Roy. Soc. Med. Prev: Ho. Phys. Dept. Experim. Med. & Res. Med. Off. Nuffield Ho., Guy's; Hosp. Lond.; Res. Obstetr. FarnBoro. Hosp. Kent.

GROBBELAAR, Mr Adriaan Ockert 48 Wimpole Street, London W1G 8SF Tel: 020 7486 6388 Fax: 020 7486 7288; Fax: 020 7266 5030 — MB ChB 1984 Pretoria; MMEd (Plast.) Cape Town 1993; FRCS (Plast) 1997; FRCS Eng. 1997; FCS(SA) 1993. Cons. Plastic Surg. Mt. Vernon Hosp. N.wood; Hon. Sen. Lect. Univ. Coll. Lond. Socs: Brit. Soc. Surg. Hand; Brit. Assn. Plastic Surg.; Brit. Assn. Aesthetic Plastic Surg.

GROCK, Kenneth Karl Anthony 48 Green Street, Enfield EN3 7HW Tel: 020 8804 3200 — MB ChB 1949 Polish Sch. of Med. (Polish Sch. Med.) Prev: Surg. Regist. Watford Hosp. Gp.; Med. Off. Childs Psychiat. Clinic, New Jersey, U.S.A.

GROCOCK, John Howard The Surgery, 1 Rowner Road, Gosport PO13 9UA Tel: 023 9258 0093 Fax: 023 92 504060; 52 Weston Way, Alvestoke, Gosport PO12 2NQ — BM 1976 Soton.; DRCOG 1982.

GROCOTT, Anthony Edward Penkridge Medical Practice, St. Michael's Road, Penkridge, Stafford ST19 5AJ Tel: 01785 712300 Fax: 01785 713696; Woodlands Farm House, Ashflats Lane, Stafford ST18 9BP — MB ChB 1976 Birm.; MRCGP 1983; DCH Eng. 1979. Prev: Cas. Off. Stafford Gen. Infirm.; SHO (Paediat.) City Gen. Hosp. Stoke-on-Trent; SHO (Gen. Med.) Stafford Gen. Infirm.

GROCOTT, Mr Eric Cameron c/o Department of Vascular Surgery, The County Hospital, Union Walk, Hereford HR1 2ER Tel: 01432 355444 — MB BS 1985 West. Austral.; T(S) 1996. Cons. Surg. (Vasc. Surg.) Co. Hosp. Hereford; Cons. Vasc. Surg. Worcester Roy. Infirm. Worcester. Socs: Eur. Soc. Vasc. Surg.; Vasc. Soc. GB & Irel.; Internat. Soc. Endovasc. Surg. Prev: Sen. Regist. (Vasc. Surg.) Char. Cross Hosp.

GROCOTT, Michael Patrick William Kylemore, High Cote Lane, Slackhead, Milnthorpe LA7 7BD Email: 101321.2574@compuserve.com — MB BS 1989 Lond.; MB BS Lond. 1992; BSc (Biomed. Sc. & Immunol.) Lond. 1989; MRCP (UK) 1996. (St. Geo. Hosp. Med. Sch. Lond.) SHO (Anaesth. & ITV) Univ. Coll. Hosp. Lond. Socs: Roy. Coll. Phys.s; Fell.of Roy. Soc. of Med.; Train. Mem. RCA. Prev: SHO (Anaesth.) Chase Farm Hosp. Lond.; SHO (Infec. Dis. & Cardiol.) St. Geo. Hosp. Lond.; SHO (Neurol.) Atkinson Morley's Hosp. Lond.

GROCOTT-MASON, Richard Michael Hillingdon Hospital, Department of Cardiology, Pield Heath Road, Uxbridge UB8 3NN Tel: 01895 238282 — MB BS 1986 Lond.; MA Oxon 1983; MD Lond. 1995; MRCP (UK) 1989. (Jesus College, Oxford and St. Thomas' Hospital, London) Cons. Cardiol. Hillingdon Hosp., Uxbridge, Middlx. Socs: BMA; Brit. Cardiac Soc.; Brit. Soc. Echocardiogr. Prev: Lect. & Sen. Regist. (Cardiol.) Univ. Wales Coll. Med. Cardiff; Regist. (Cardiol.) Harefield Hosp. Middlx.; Brit. Heart Foundat. Research Fell. & Hon. Regist. (Cardiol.) Univ. Wales Coll. Med. Cardiff.

GROCUTT, Mandy Patricia Worthing & Southlands NHS Trust, A&E Dept Worthing Hospital, Lyndhurst Road, Worthing BN11 2 Tel: 01903 285189 — MB BCh 1987 Wales; FRCS Ed. 1994; FFAEM 1997. A & E Cons. Worthing Hosp. Socs: Fac.A&E med; BAEM. Prev: Regist. (A & E) Morriston Hosp. Swansea; SHO (Anaesth.) Roy. Gwent Hosp. Newport; Cas. Off. Glos. Roy. Hosp.

GROCUTT, Mark St John The Old Priory Surgery, 319 Vicarage Road, Kings Heath, Birmingham B14 7NN Tel: 0121 444 1120 — MB BChir 1985 Camb.; MRCGP 1992. (Cambridge)

GRODEN, Bernard Melville (retired) 7 Broom Road E., Newton Mearns, Glasgow G77 5RQ Tel: 0141 639 4432 — MB ChB 1957 Glas.; MD Glas. 1969; FRCP Ed. 1974, M 1962; FRCP Glas. 1972, M 1962; DPM Eng. 1960. Prev: Cons. Phys. (Cardiol.) CrossHo. Hosp. Kilmarnock.

GRODEN, Richard Elliot Tollcross Medical Centre, 1101-1105 Tollcross Road, Glasgow G32 8UH Tel: 0141 778 2717 Fax: 0141 778 6880; 12 Kenmure Road, Whitecraigs, Glasgow G46 6TU — MB ChB 1989 Glas.; DRCOG 1993.

GROEN, Bart Gerard Steven 30 Gracefield Gardens, London SW16 2ST — Artsexamen 1991 Rotterdam.

GROENENDIJK, Hans Woolhayes Farm, Cotleigh, Honiton EX14 9HR — Artsexamen 1982 Amsterdam.

GROENEVELD, Hugo 50 Aintree Close, Leegomery, Telford TF1 6UZ — MB ChB 1992 Pretoria.

GROENHUYSEN, Carole Fairfield Park Health Centre, Tyning Lane, Camden Road, Bath BA1 6EA Tel: 01225 331616 Fax: 01225 482932 — MB BS Lond. 1983; MRCGP 1988; T(GP) 1991; DRCOG 1987; DCH RCP Lond. 1986. (St. Mary's) GP Bath. Prev: Asst. GP Trowbridge; GP Retainer Leicester; Trainee GP Ealing Gen. Hosp. VTS.

GROGAN, Eleanor 22 Fosse Way, Garforth, Leeds LS25 2JE — MB BS 1998 Lond.; MB BS Lond 1998.

GROGAN, Jeremiah Christopher (retired) 80 Heaton Road, Solihull B91 2DZ Tel: 0121 705 1474 — LRCPI & LM, LRSCI & LM 1951; LRCPI & LM, LRCSI & LM 1951.

GROGAN, Richard James 33 Dalehouse Lane, Kenilworth CV8 2HW — BM BS 1992 Nottm.

GROGGINS, Robert Christopher County Hospital, Lincoln LN2 5QY; 217 Yarborough Road, Lincoln LN1 3NQ — MB BS 1974 Lond.; FRCP Lond. 1995; MRCP (UK) 1981; FRCPCH 1997. Cons. Paediat. Lincoln Co. Hosp. Prev: Sen. Regist. (Paediat.) S.mead Hosp. & Roy. Hosp. Sick Childr. Bristol; Regist. (Paediat.) City Hosp. Nottm.; Asthma Research Fell. Qu.s Med. Centre Nottm.

GROGONO, Geoffrey Russell Steele (retired) Alyerlea, 4 Longfield Rd, Weymouth DT4 8RQ Tel: 01305 786559 — MB BS Lond. 1945; DObst RCOG 1952. Prev: Ho. Surg. EMS Hosp. Horton.

GROGONO, Mr James Lyon The Garden House, Marlow Bridge Lane, Bisham, Marlow SL7 1RH Tel: 01628 484261 — MB BS Lond. 1961; FRCS Eng. 1967; MRCS Eng. LRCP Lond. 1960; DCH Eng. 1965. (Lond. Hosp.) Cons. Gen. Surg. S. Bucks NHS Trust; Chairm. Chiltern Med.Trust. Socs: (Pres.) St. Mark's Assn.; Grey Turner Surgic. Club; (Pres.) Chiltern Med. Soc. Prev: Sen. Regist. (Surg.) Lond. Hosp.; Resid. Surg. Off. Roy. Marsden Hosp. Lond. & St. Mark's Hosp.; Ho. Surg. Gt. Ormond St. Hosp.

GROGONO, Katharine Wyke Regis Health Centre, Portland Road, Weymouth DT4 9BE Tel: 01305 782226 Fax: 01305 760549; 2 Russell Avenue, Weymouth DT4 9RA Tel: 01305 773968 — MB BS 1979 Lond.

GROGONO, Roger Michael Mount Street Health Centre, Mount Street, Diss IP22 4WG Tel: 01379 642023 Fax: 01379 643320; The Friary, Snow Street, Roydon, Diss IP22 5SB Tel: 01379 643005 — MB BS 1974 Lond.; BSc Lond. 1971; MRCGP 1981. (Lond. Hosp.) GP Princip. Prev: SHO (Accid. Serv. & Neurol. Surg.) Addenbrooke's Hosp. Camb.; SHO (O & G) Ipswich Hosp.; Ho. Phys. Lond. Hosp.

GROM, Iain Andrew Peter Blantyre Health Centre, 64 Victoria Street, Blantyre, Glasgow G72 0BS Tel: 01698 826331 — MB ChB 1979 Glas.; BSc Pharmacol. Glas. 1976, MB ChB 1979; MRCGP 1988; BA (Hons.) Open Univ. 1998.

GRONOW, Rhian Elizabeth Kiklburn House, Ton Kenfig, Bridgend CF33 4PT — MB ChB 1993 Bristol; DFFP; MRCGP 1998. (Bristol University) Partner, Porthcawl. Socs: MDU. Prev: SHO (ENT) P.ss of Wales Hosp., Bridgend; SHO (Cas.) Morriston Hosp. Swansea; SHO (ENT, Ophth. & O & G) Singleton Hosp. Swansea.

GRONOW, Timothy Edward Ty Celyn, Mill-Lay Lane, Llantwit Major CF61 1QE — MB ChB 1991 Leeds.

GRONSKI, Michal Juliusz 7 Orwell Terrace, Apartment 1, Edinburgh EH11 2DU Tel: 0131 337 8501 — Lekarz 1988 Warsaw.

GROOM, Mr Alan Frederick Graeme King's College Hospital, Denmark Hill, London SE5 9RS Tel: 020 7346 3388; 65 Lee Road, Blackheath, London SE3 9EN Tel: 020 8852 9645 — MB BS 1977 Lond.; BA Camb. 1972, MA 1976; FRCS Ed. 1983; MRCS Eng. LRCP Lond. 1977. (Char. Cross) Cons. Orthop. Surg. King's Coll. Hosp. Lond.; Head Clinician/Sen. Cons. Orthop. Surg. KCH. Socs: Fell.BOA; Fell.RSM; Brit. Limb Reconstruction Soc. Prev: Train. Progr. Dir. KCH Rotating 1993-; Cons. Orthop. Surg. Qu. Eliz. Milit. Hosp. Lond.; Sen. Regist. (Orthop.) Qu. Med. Centre Univ. Hosp. Nottm.

GROOM, Alison Mary Clifden House, 24 Vauxhall St., St Helier, Jersey JE2 4TJ — MB BS 1978 Lond.; MRCGP 1982; DRCOG 1980.

GROOM, Corinne Elisabeth Medical Centre, Postmill Close, Wymondham NR18 0RF — MB ChB Sheff. 1965. Socs: Brit. Med. Acupunc. Soc.

GROOM, Fiona Hunter 7 The Farriers, Bramley, Guildford GU5 0HN — MB ChB 1985 Glas.; MRCGP 1990; DRCOG 1988.

GROOM, Helen Maria 7/8 Croxdale Terrace, Pelaw, Gateshead NE10 0RR Tel: 0191 469 2337 Fax: 0191 438 6132; 62A Fern Avenue, Jesmond, Newcastle upon Tyne NE2 2QY Tel: 0191 281 2003 — MB BS 1986 Newc.; MRCGP 1991. Socs: Med. Pract. Union (NE Represen. Nat. Counc.).

GROOM, Mark Richard, Surg. Lt.-Cdr. RN Woolcotts, Bourton, Gillingham SP8 5BS; Woolcotts, Bourton, Gillingham SP8 5BS — MB ChB 1986 Leeds; AFOM 1999; MRCGP 1996; DAvMed FOM RCP Lond. 1997. Socs: Fell. Roy. Soc. Med.; Soc. Occupat.al Med.

GROOM, Neville Harry The Medical Centre, Postmill Close, Wymondham NR18 0RF Tel: 01953 605313 — MRCS Eng. LRCP Lond. 1966; DObst RCOG 1969. (Sheff.) Socs: BMA. Prev: Ho. Surg.

Roy. Infirm. Sheff.; Ho. Phys. N.. Gen. Hosp. Sheff.; SHO Paediat. Jenny Lind Hosp. Childr. Norwich.

GROOM, Peter Ian 129 Osbourne Road, Newcastle upon Tyne NE2 2TB — MB BS 1991 Newc.

GROOM, Peter John Cyncoed Road Medical Centre, 350 Cyncoed Road, Cardiff CF23 6XH Tel: 029 2076 2514 Fax: 029 2076 4262; 9 Bryn Gwyn Road, Cyncoed, Cardiff CF23 6PQ Tel: 029 2075 1172 — BM BCh 1973 Oxf.; MA Oxf. 1970, BM BCh 1973; MRCP (U.K.) 1976; DCH Eng. 1975. (Oxford & St. Thomas's London) GP Partner Cyncoed Surg.; OHP Marks & Spencer plc; OHP Legal & Gen. Plc. Prev: Regist. Roy. Liverp. Childr. Hosp. & Alder Hey Childr. Hosp. Liverp.

GROOM, Raelene Vikki 23 Field End Road, Eastcote, Pinner HA5 2QQ — MB BS 1996 Lond.

GROOM, Ruth Lena Culmore, 47 Kennedy Road, Shrewsbury SY3 7AA; Directorate of Anaesthesic, City General, Newcastle Road, Stoke-on-Trent ST4 6QG — MB ChB 1990 Dundee; FRCA 1996. Regist. Rotat. (Anaesth.) Stoke-on-Trent.

GROOM, Sally Norah Public Health Laboratory, Department of Pathology, Dorset County Hospital, Williams Avenue, Dorchester DT1 2JY Tel: 01305 251150 Fax: 01305 251044; Shirley House, 5 West Walks, Dorchester DT1 1RE Tel: 01305 268702 Fax: 01305 268092 Email: rogo888@aol.com — MB BS 1977 Lond.; MSc (Microbiol.) Lond. 1986; MRCPath 1994. (St. Thos.) Cons. Microbiol. PHL Dorset Co. Hosp. Dorchester. Socs: Hosp. Infec. Soc. Ordinary Mem.; Brit. Infec. Soc.; Liveryman Worshipful Soc. Apoth. Prev: Sen. Regist. (Med. Microbiol.) Pub. Health Laborat. St. Luke's Hosp. Guildford; Lect. (Med. Microbiol.) The Roy. Lond. Hosp.

GROOM, Tamsin Mary 27 Norwich Common, Wymondham NR18 0SW — MB ChB 1993 Sheff.

GROOME, Jane Beatrice Ann 2 Bridhayes, Station Road, Bridstowe, Okehampton EX20 4EH — MB ChB 1975 Birm.; DRCOG 1979. Staff Grade in Psycohiatry, Plymouth Comm Servs. NHS Trust.

GROSART, Ann Katherine Camrose, Holly Hill Lane, Sarisbury Green, Southampton SO31 6AG Tel: 01489 574893 — MB ChB 1980 Manch.; MFFP 1993. SCMO (Family Plann.) Portsmouth & SE Hants. Prev: Clin. Med. Off. (Family Plann.).

GROSCH, Elizabeth Jane (retired) 7 Eastglade, Northwood HA6 3LD Tel: 01923 826523 Email: etothill@cs.com — MB BS Lond. 1963; FFR 1969; DMRT Eng. 1967. Prev: Sen. Regist. (Radiother.) Middlx. Hosp. Lond.

GROSE, Roderick Derwin 4 Station Rise, Lochwinnoch PA12 4NA — MB ChB 1987 Glas.

GROSS, Mr Errol Burnley General Hospital, Casterton Avenue, Burnley BB10 2PQ Tel: 01282 425071 — MB BCh 1967 Witwatersrand; FRCS Eng. 1974. (Witwatersrand) Cons. Surg. Burnley Health Care NHS Trust. Socs: Manch. Med. Soc.; Assn. of Surg.s of GB & Irel. Prev: Lect. (Surg.) Univ. Manch. & Hope Hosp. Salford.

GROSS, Grete 21 Walfield Avenue, Whetstone, London N20 9PS Tel: 020 8445 8275 — MB ChB 1963 Ed.; BA (Hons.) Lond. 1949; MRCPsych 1972; DPM Eng. 1969. Indep. Holistic Pract. Lond. Prev: Cons. Child Psychiat. Lister Hosp. Hitchin Child & Family Psychiat. Clinic; Cons. Child Psychiat. Stevenage; Regist. (Child Psychiat.) Univ. Coll. Hosp. Lond.

GROSS, Maurice 9 Devonshire Place, London W1N 1PB Tel: 020 7935 5205; 5 Sheen Common Drive, Richmond TW10 5BW Tel: 020 8876 7892 — MB BS 1957 Lond.; MB BS (Hons.) 1957; MD Lond. 1969; FRCP Lond. 1976, M 1960. (St. Thos.) Cons neurol. Kingston Hosp; Hon Cons. Neurol. St. Geo. & Atkinson Morley Hosps. Lond.; New Vict. Hosp. Kingston; Pk.side Hosp. Wimbledon. Socs: Fell. Roy. Soc. Med.; Assn. Brit. Neurols.; Medico-Legal Soc. Prev: Cons. Neurol. Ashford Hosp. Middlx.; Cons. Neurol. OldCh. Hosp. Romford & S.end & Basildon Hosps.; Sen. Regist. Nat. Hosps. Nerv. Dis. Lond. & Univ. Coll. Hosp. Lond.

GROSS, Michael Lester Phillip Division Neurological Science, Royal Surrey County Hospital, Egerton Road, Guildford GU2 7XX Tel: 01483 571122 Fax: 020 8954 7220 Email: michaelgross@hotmail.com; Green Waters, Green Lane, Stanmore HA7 3AF Tel: 020 8954 0987 Fax: 020 8954 7220 Email: michaelgross1@msn.com — MB BChir 1977 Camb.; MD Camb. 1987, MA 1977; FRCP Lond. 1995; MRCP (UK) 1979. Cons. Neurol. & Chairm. Div. Neurol. Sci. Roy. Surrey Co. Hosp. Guildford; Clin. Dir. Roy. & E. Surrey Neurol. Research Unit; Cons. Neurol. SW & E. Surrey HAs & Clementine Ch.ill Hosp. Harrow. Socs: Assn. Brit. Neurol. & Internat. Headache Soc.; Euro.Neurolog. Soc.; World Feder. Neurol. Prev: Sen. Regist. (Neurol.) Nat. Hosp. Nerv. Dis. & St. Mary's Hosp. Lond.; Regist. & Sen. Resid. (Neurol.) Nat. Hosp. Nerv. Dis. Lond.; Regist. (Neurol.) Roy. Free Hosp. Lond.

GROSSART, Kenneth William Macfarlane X-Ray Department, Ross Hall BMI Hospital, 221 Crookston Road, Glasgow G52 3NQ Tel: 0141 810 3151 Fax: 0141 882 7439; The Old Manse, Clachan of Fintry, Glasgow G63 0XG Tel: 01360 860203 — MB ChB 1950 Glas.; FRCR 1986; DMRD Ed. 1955. (Glas.) Cons. Neuroradiol. Ross Hall BMI Hosp. Socs: Brit. Soc. Neuroradiol. & Scott. Assn. Neurol. Sci. Prev: Cons. Neuroradiol. Inst. Neurol. Scs. S.. Gen. Hosp. Glas.; Cons. Radiol. Inst. Neurol. Scs. Killearn Hosp. Glas.

GROSSBERG, Mark (retired) — MB ChB Cape Town 1947; DA Eng. 1956. Prev: Anaesth. to Denatal Clinics in Lond. Area.

GROSSET, Donald Garry Department of Neurology, Southern General Hospital, Glasgow G51 4TF Tel: 0141 201 2486 Fax: 0141 201 2510 Email: d.grosset@clinmed.gla.ac.uk — MB ChB 1985 Glas.; MD 1992 Glas.; MRCP 1988 UK; BSc 1983 (Hons) Glas.; FRCP 1999. p/t Cons. Neurol. S.. Gen. Hosp. Glas. Socs: Movem. Disorder Soc.; Eur. Neurosonol Gp; Scot. Assn. Neurol. Sci. Prev: Sen. Regist. (Neurol. & Clin. Pharmacol.) & Lect. (Med. & Therap.) W.. Infirm. Glas.; Regist. (Neurol.) Inst. Neurol. Sci. Glas.

GROSSET, Katherine Anne Shettleston Health Centre, 420 Old Shettleston Road, Glasgow G32 7JZ Tel: 0141 531 6220 Fax: 0141 531 6206; 1A Grange Road, Bearsden, Glasgow G61 3PL — MB ChB 1985 Glas.; MRCGP 1989; DRCOG 1987.

GROSSMAN, Professor Ashley Barry Department of Endocrinology, St Bartholomew's Hospital, London EC1A 7BE Tel: 020 7601 8343 Fax: 020 7601 8505 Email: a.b.grossman@mds.qmw.ac.uk — MB BS 1975 Lond.; MB BS (Hons.) 1975; BSc Lond. 1971, BA 1969, MD 1987; FRCP (UK) 1990, M 1978. (UCHMS) Prof. Neuroendocrinol. St. Bartholomews & Roy. Lond. Hosp. Med. Sch. Lond.; Hon. Cons. Phys. St. Bart. & Roy. Lond. Hosps. Lond. Socs: Sec. Europ. Neuroendocrine Assoc.; Coun. Mem. Soc. Endocrinol.; Fell.Acad. Med. Sci.s. Prev: Regist. (Thoracic Med.) St. Thos. Hosp. Lond.; SHO Nat. Hosp. Nerv. Dis. Lond.; Ho. Phys. (Med.) Univ. Coll. Hosp. Lond.

GROSSMAN, Mark Laurence 37 Primrose Road, Calderstones, Liverpool L18 2HE — MB ChB 1998 Manch.; MB ChB Manch 1998.

GROSSMANN, Maria Elizabeth 11 Wimpole Street, London W1M 7AB Tel: 020 7580 1660; 13 Sheridan Walk, Temple Fortune Lane, London NW11 7UF Tel: 020 8455 5777 — MD 1936 Prague; MRCS Eng. LRCP Lond. 1942; DMRE Camb. 1942. Consg. Radiol. Univ. Coll. Hosp. Lond.; Consg. Radiol. Lond. Imaging Centre. Socs: Fell. Roy. Soc. Med.; FRCR; Brit. Inst. Radiol. Prev: Lect. (Dent. Radiol.) Univ. Coll. Hosp. Dent. Sch. & Hosp. Trop. Dis. Lond.; Regist. (Radiol.) Univ. Coll. Hosp. Lond.; Ho. Off. (Radiol.) Brit. Postgrad. Med. Sch. Hammersmith Hosp.

GROSSMARK, Karen Ruth Temple Fortune Health Centre, 23 Temple Fortune Lane, London NW11 7TE Tel: 020 8458 4431 Fax: 020 8731 8257 — MB BS 1987 Lond.; DRCOG 1987.

GROSSMITH, Cecilia Mary 4 Fordbridge Road, Ashford TW15 2SG; 2 Braddon Road, Richmond TW9 2HR — MB ChB 1982 Leic. GP Ashford Middlx.

GROSVENOR, Lisa Jane 23 Sheila Avenue, Wolverhampton WV11 3AJ — MB ChB 1995 Leeds.

GROTTE, Mr Geir Johan Manchester Heart Centre, Manchester Royal Infirmary, Oxford Road, Manchester M13 9WL Tel: 0161 276 4271 Fax: 0161 276 8522 Email: gjg.odin@man.ac.uk; Three Gables, 63 Bramhall Lane S., Bramhall, Stockport SK7 2EG Tel: 0161 440 9671 — FETCS 1998; MB BS Newc. 1969; FRCS Eng. 1975. (Newc.) p/t Cons. Cardiothoracic Surg. Manch. Roy. Infirm.; Vis. Cons. Rochdale Healthcare Trust, Rochdale Infirm. Socs: Europ. Soc. for Cardiothoracic Surg.; Soc. of Cardiothoracic Surg. of GB & N. Irel.; Brit. Cardiac Soc. Prev: Sen. Regist. (Cardiothoracic Surg.) Univ. Hosp. Wales Cardiff; Regist. (Gen. Surg.) Roy. Vict. Infirm. Newc.; Surg. Research Fell. Harvard Md. Sch. & Massach. Gen. Hosp. Boston.

GROUNDS, Adrian Thomas Institute of Criminology, 7 West Road, Cambridge CB3 9DT — BM BS 1977 Nottm.; DM Nottm. 1987, BMedSci 1974; MRCPsych 1981. Univ. Lect. Inst. Criminology Univ. Camb. & Hon. Cons. Forens. Psychiat. Addenbrooke's NHS

Trust. Prev: Lect. & Sen. Regist. (Forens. Psychiat.) Inst. Psychiat. & BRd.moor Hosp. Crowthorne; Regist. (Psychiat.) Bethlem. Roy. & Maudsley Hosps. Lond.

GROUNDS, John Grayson 6 Woodland Road, Weston Super Mare BS23 4HE — MB ChB St. And. 1948; MD St. And. 1961; DPH Lond. 1956; DTM & H Eng. 1952. (St. And.) Police Surg. Avon & Som. Constab. Socs: Mem. Assn. of Police Surg.s; Mem. Brit. Med. Assn. Prev: Sen. Med. Off. Kenya; Provin. Med. Off. Centr. Province Kenya; Med. Supt. Mombasa.

GROUNDS, Robert Michael Adult Intensive Care Unit, St Georges Hospital, Blackshaw Road, Tooting, London SW17 0QT Tel: 020 8672 1255 Fax: 020 8725 3195 — MB BS 1977 Lond.; MD Lond. 1988; MRCS Eng. LRCP Lond. 1977; FRCA Eng 1983; DA Eng. 1979. (University College Hospital London) Cons. Anaesth. & Intens. Care St Geo. Hosp. Lond.; Hon. Sen. Lect. Univ. Lond. Prev: Sen. Regist. (Anaesth.) Roy. Postgrad. Med. Sch. Hammersmith Hosp. Lond.

GROUNDWATER, Mr William (retired) Clowigar, Scapa, St Ola, Kirkwall KW15 1SD — MB ChB 1960 Ed.; FRCS Ed. 1966. Prev: Cons. Surg. Orkney Health Bd.

GROUT, Mr Paul 5 St Barnabas Drive, Swanland, North Ferriby HU14 3RL Tel: 01482 635165 Fax: 01482 635365 — BM 1986 Soton.; BM Soton. 1982; FRCS Ed. (A&E) 1988; FFAEM 1993; DA (UK) 1987; DCH RCP Lond. 1986; FFAEM 1993. Cons. (A & E) Hull Roy. Infirm.; Forens. Med. Examr. Humberside Police; Med. Dir. NEMHS Ltd; Mem. Resuc. Counc. UK.

GROUT, Philip Llys Meddyg Surgery, Llys Meddyg, 23 Castle Street, Conwy LL32 8AY Tel: 01492 592424 Fax: 01492 593068; Pen-y-Graig, Ty'n-y-Groes, Conwy LL32 8SZ — MB BS 1968 Lond.; MRCS Eng. LRCP Lond. 1968; MRCGP 1975; DObst RCOG 1970. (Westm.)

GROVE, Alison Jane 27 The Close, Norwich NR1 4DZ — MB BS 1978 Lond.; MRCS Eng. LRCP Lond. 1978; DA Eng. 1983; DCH RCP Lond. 1981; DRCOG 1980. (Char. Cross) GP Wimborne.

GROVE, Allison Margaret Pontefract General Infirmary, Friarwood Lane, Pontefract WF8 1PL Tel: 01977 606468 — MB BCh 1991 Wales; 1997 (MRCPCH); BSc Wales 1988; MRCP (UK) 1995. (Univ. Wales Coll. Med.) Cons. Paediat. Pindersfield & Pontefract NHS Trust, Pontefract Gen. Infirm.

GROVE, Clare Elizabeth York House Medical Centre, Heathside Road, Woking GU22 7XP — MB BS 1994 Lond.; BSc (Biochem.) Lond. 1991, MB BS 1994.

GROVE, Leslie Handel Clunbury, Victoria Road, Dodford, Bromsgrove B61 9BZ Tel: 01527 879593 Fax: 01527 879593 — MB ChB Birm. 1959; MRCS Eng. LRCP Lond. 1959; FFA RCS Eng. 1971; DA Eng. 1962; DObst RCOG 1961. (Birm.) Cons. Anaesth. Birm. HA (T). Socs: BMA. Prev: Hon. Anaesth. Wollongong Hosp., Austral.; Sen. Regist. (Anaesth.) Smethwick Neurosurg. Centre & United Birm. Hosps.

GROVE, Lucy Margaret Child Development Centre, Hospital Road, Bury St Edmunds IP33 3ND Tel: 01284 775112; Assington Hall, Assington, Sudbury CO10 5LQ Tel: 01787 211312 — MB BS 1986 Lond.; CH; MRCP; MRCP (UK) 1990; MRCGP 1992. (Roy. Free Sch. Med.) Cons. paediat. (Community) Child Developm. Centre Bury St. Edmundi. Socs: Roy. Coll. Paediat. & Child Health. Prev: Regist. (Paediat. & Child Developm.) Bury St. Edmunds.

GROVE, Lynn St Hilda's Surgery, 50 St Hilda's St., Sherburn, Malton YO17 8PH Tel: 01944 710226 Fax: 01944 710817; The Poplars, Rillington, Malton YO17 8LQ Tel: 01944 758325 — MB BS 1967 Lond.; MRCS Eng. LRCP Lond. 1967. (Royal Free Hospital)

GROVE, Madeleine Anne 65 Gipsy Lane, Wokingham RG40 2BW; 43 Route D'Ennezat, 63200 Riom, France — MB ChB 1993 Bristol. (Univ. Bristol) SHO (Oncol.) Plymouth Hosps. Trust. Socs: BMA & Med. Defence Union. Prev: SHO Rotat. (Med.) Havering Hosps.; Ho. Off. (Surg.) W.on Gen. Hosp. W.on-Super-Mare; Ho. Off. (Med.) N. Devon Dist. Hosp. Barnstaple.

GROVE, Matthew Lawrence North Tynside General Hospital, North Shields NE29 8NH Tel: 0191 293 4180 Fax: 0191 293 4180 Email: matthew.grove@northmbria-healthcare.nhs.uk; Caerleon, Middlestreads Farm, Morpeth NE61 6PT — MB BS 1992 Lond.; BSc Lond. 1989; MRCP (UK) 1995. (UMDS (Guy's)) Cons. Rheumatologist. Socs: Brit. Soc. Of Rheum.; Nat. Osteoporosis Soc.

GROVE, Richard Arthur Edward The Surgery, 3 St. John Street, Whithorn, Newton Stewart DG8 7JA Tel: 01988 500218 Fax: 01988 500737 — MB ChB 1977 Glas.; MRCGP 1981; DRCOG 1980.

GROVE, Steven John Holt Medical Practice, High Street, Holt NR25 6BH Tel: 01263 712461 Fax: 01263 713211; Eastcote Farm, Saxlingham Road, Field Dalling, Holt NR25 7LE — MB BChir 1987 Camb.; MA Camb. 1988; MRCP (UK) 1994; DCH RCP Lond. 1990. Clin. Asst. (Gastroenterol.) Qu. Eliz Hosp. King's Lynn. Prev: Trainee GP Qu. Eliz. Hosp. King's Lynn VTS.

GROVE-WHITE, Ion Greer Whitehouse, Lamondfauld Road, Hillside, Montrose DD10 9HY Tel: 01674 830466 Email: ion@grove-white.com; Department of Anaesthesia, Stracathro Hospital, Brechin DD9 7QA Tel: 01356 648165 Email: drgrove-white@angusnhs.finix.org.uk — MB 1966 Camb.; MA; BChir 1965; FFA RCS Eng. 1969. (Lond. Hosp.) Cons. Anaesth. Dundee Teach. Hosps. Trust & Angus NHS Trust; JP Angus Dist. Socs: Assn. Anaesths & Scott. Soc. Anaesth. Prev: Ho. Surg. Lond. Hosp.; Ho. Phys. City Hosp. Aberd.; Garden Research Fell. Univ. Aberd.

GROVER, Amanda Louise (Collins) Wessex Clinical Genetics Service, Princess Anne Hospital, Coxford Road, Southampton SO16 5YA Tel: 02380 796170 Fax: 02380 794346 Email: ac10@soton.ac.uk; Longwood, Hampton Hill, Swanmore, Southampton SO32 2QN — BM 1978 Soton.; FRCP 2001(UK); MRCP UK 1981. (Southampton) p/t Cons. In Clin. Genetics. Prev: Regist. (Paediat.) Soton. Gen. Hosp.; Sen. Regist. Clin. Genetics, Soton.; SHO (Paediat.) Brompton Hosp. Lond.

GROVER, Anil Barnsley Road Surgery, 899 Barnsley Road, Sheffield S5 0QJ Tel: 0114 245 6432 Fax: 0114 257 0895 — MB ChB 1983 Sheff.; MSc Sports Med. Nottm. 1993. Gen. Practitioner; Med. Mem. for Independant Tribute Serv.; Med. Examr. for Hand and Arm Vibration Syndrome for Definitech. Prev: Cliniocal Asst. in Orthop.

GROVER, Mr Deepak 24 Cliftonville Court, Northampton NN1 5BY — MB BS 1993 Delhi; FRCS Glas. 1993.

GROVER, Edwin Robert 5 Walkwood Rise, Beaconsfield HP9 1TX — MB BS 1985 Lond.; BSc Lond. 1982; FRCA 1991. (St. Bart.)

GROVER, Mr Martin Lewis Queen Alexandra Hospital, Cosham, Portsmouth PO6 3LY Tel: 023 92 286570; Longwood, Hampton Hill, Swanmore, Southampton SO32 2QN Fax: 01489 890702 Email: mlgrover@doctors.org.uk — MB BS 1974 Lond.; FRCS Eng. 1979; DObst RCOG 1976. (Char. Cross) Cons. Orthop. Surg. Qu. Alexandra Hosp. Portsmouth. Prev: Ho. Surg. & Ho. Phys. Kent & Canterbury Hosp.

GROVER, Munita 7 Heightside Avenue, Rossendale BB4 9HA — MB BS 1994 Lond.

GROVER, Neena Whitley Wood Road Practice, 257 Whitley Wood Road, Whitley Wood, Reading RG2 8LE Tel: 0118 931 3515 Fax: 0118 975 7065 — MB BS 1979 Meerut.

GROVER, Nikita Highgate Group Practice, 44 North Hill, London N6 4QA Tel: 020 8340 6628 Fax: 020 8342 8428; 9 Rotherwick Road, London NW11 7DG — MB BS 1990 Lond.; BSc (Hons.) Lond. 1987; MRCP (UK) 1995 MRCP (UK); MRCGP 1996; DRCOG 1994; DCH RCP Lond. 1993. (Univ. Coll. Middlx. Sch. Med.)

GROVER, Mr Rajiv 48 Wimpole Street, London W1G 8SF — MB BS 1989 Lond.; FRCS (Plast) 2000; BSc (1st cl. Hons.) Lond. 1986; FRCS Eng. 1993; MD Lond. 1996. Cons. plastic Surg., Mt. Vernon Hosp., Lond.; Hunt. Prof. RCS (Eng.). Prev: RCS Vis. Schol. in Plastic Surg., Harvard Med. Sch., Boston, USA; Specialist Regist. in Plastic Surg, Roy. Marsden Hosp. Fell.ship in Cosmetic Surg., Wellington Hosp., Lond.

GROVER, Sham Roop Lal 104 Woodfoot Road, Moorgate, Rotherham S60 3EG Tel: 01709 369333 — MB BS Agra 1956. (G.R. Med. Coll. Gwalior)

GROVER, Simon Paul 122 Chalkwell Avenue, Westcliff on Sea SS0 8HN Tel: 01702 343269 — MB BS 1988 Lond. Trainee GP/SHO Buckland Hosp. Dover VTS. Prev: SHO (Gen. Med.) Louth Co. Hosp.; Resid. Med. Off. BUPA S. Bank Hosp. Worcester; Ho. Phys. Kent & Canterbury Hosp.

GROVER, Vijay Paul Bob 45 Church Meadow, Long Ditton, Surbiton KT6 5EP; 45 Church Meadow, Long Ditton, Surbiton KT6 5EP — MB BS 1996 Lond.; BSc Lond. 1995. (Charing Cross & Westminster) SHO (ITU) Char. Cross Hosp., Lond. Socs: MPS. Prev: SHO (Med.) Chelsea & W.minster Hosp.; SHO (Med.) Mt. Vernon Hosp.; SHO (Med.) Watford Gen. Hosp.

GROVES, Alan Martin 33a Warren Road, Donaghadee BT21 0PD — MB ChB 1996 Ed.

GROVES, Andrea Helen Lansdowne Hospital, Sanatorium Road, Canton, Cardiff CF11 8PL — MB BS 1984 Newc.; MRCGP 1988; DRCOG 1987. (Newc.) Staff Grade (Community Child Health) S. Glam. HA. Prev: Community Med. Off. S. Glam HA; Trainee GP Whickham Gateshead.

GROVES, Mr Anthony Robert George Eliot Hospital, College St., Nuneaton CV10 7DJ Tel: 01203 351351; The Manor House, Nailstone, Nuneaton CV13 0QH — MB ChB 1964 Birm.; ChM Birm. 1973; FRCS Eng. 1969. Cons. Plastic Surg. Geo. Elliot Hosp. Nuneaton. Socs: Brit. Assn. Plastic Surg. Prev: Cons. Plastic Surg. Birm. Accid. Hosp.; Sen. Regist. (Plastic Surg.) Plastic & Reconstruc. Surg. Centre Chepstow.

GROVES, Ashley Mcallister 63 Abingdon House, Adrian Way, Cambridge CB2 2SA — MB BS 1993 Newc.; BSc. Newc. 1987; MRCP 1997. (Newc.) SHO (Rotat.) Leeds Gen. Infirm. Socs: Coll. Mem. Roy. Coll. Phys. Prev: Med. Residency Univ. of Pennsylvania, USA; Ho. Phys. Roy. Vict. Infirm., Newc.

GROVES, Betty (retired) 2/7 The Paragon, Blackheath, London SE3 0NY Tel: 020 8852 0479 — MB BS 1949 Lond.; MFCM 1971; DPH Eng. 1956. Princip. Phys. (Child Health) & Hon. Cons. in Community Paediat. Islington HA. Prev: Med. Off. Pub. Health Dept. LCC.

GROVES, Caroline Jane 42 Welbeck Close, Whitefield, Manchester M45 8PB — MB BS 1993 Lond.

GROVES, Charlotte Rebecca Flat 15, Mennie House, Royal Herbert Pavilions, Gilbert Close, London SE18 4PR — MB BS 1991 Lond.

GROVES, Christine Frances The Manor House, Nailstone, Nuneaton CV13 0QH — MB ChB 1970 Birm.; BSc Birm. 1967, MB ChB 1970.

GROVES, Christopher James 3 Grosvenor Court, Grosvenor Road, London W4 4EF — MB BS 1994 Lond.

GROVES, Clare Julia 14 Woodlea Croft, Meanwood, Leeds LS6 4SF — BMedSci Nottm. 1981, BM BS 1983; MRCGP 1990; DFFP 1993; DCH RCP Lond. 1986; DRCOG 1986. Specialist Regist. (Radiol.). Prev: Staff Grade Pract. (Minor Injuries) Halton Gen. Hosp.; GP Neston; Trainee GP Notts. VTS.

GROVES, Daniel Russell (retired) 80 Mahon Close, Enfield EN1 4DQ Tel: 020 8366 5497 — MB BS 1959 Lond.; MRCS Eng. LRCP Lond. 1959. Prev: Ho. Phys. & Ho. Surg. Whittington Hosp. Lond.

GROVES, David Hugh Manisty The Surgery, 1 Church St., Newtownards BT23 4FH Tel: 01247 816333 — MB BCh BAO 1967 Belf.; DCH RCPS Glas. 1969; DObst RCOG 1969.

GROVES, Elisabeth Ruth The Royal Hallamshire Hospital, Glossop, Sheffield S10 2JF Tel: 0114 271 1900 — MB BChir 1988 Camb.; MA Camb. 1989; FRCA 1993; DA (UK) 1990. Cons. Anaesth. Roy. Hallamshire Hosp. Prev: Lect. (Anaesth.) Roy. Hallamsh. Hosp. Sheff.; Regist. Rotat. Sheff. & Dist.

GROVES, Ian Paramabandhu 51 Roman Road, London E2 0HU — MB BS 1986 Lond.

GROVES, Jeremy Beaumont Chesterfield Royal Hospital, Calow, Chesterfield S44 5BL Tel: 01246 277271 — MB BS 1986 Lond.; BSc (1st cl. Hons.) Lond. 1983; FRCA 1992; DA (UK) 1988. Cons. Anaesth. & Intens. Care Chesterfield & Derbysh. Roy. Hosp. Prev: Sen. Regist. Rotat. Sheff. & Dist.; Post. Fell.sh. Regist. (Cardiothoracic Anaesth.) N.. Gen. Hosp. Sheff.; Regist. (ITU) Waikato Hosp. Hamilton, NZ.

GROVES, Mr John (retired) Flat 2, 7 The Paragon, Blackheath, London SE3 0NY — MB BS 1947 Lond.; FRCS Eng. 1953. Hon. Cons. ENT Surg. Roy. Free Hosp. Lond. Prev: Examr. FRCS (Otolarng.) Eng. & DLO Eng.

GROVES, Judith Anne (retired) 17 The Triangle, Paddock, Huddersfield HD1 4RN Tel: 01484 422509 — MB ChB 1966 Ed.; DObst RCOG 1968.

GROVES, Karen Elizabeth Queenscourt Hospice, Town Lane, Southport PR8 6RE Tel: 01704 544645 — MB ChB 1979 Liverp.; MSc Palliative Medicine (Bristol) 1999; Dip. Palliat. Med. Wales 1992; Dip. Ven. Liverp. 1988; MRCGP 1983; DRCOG 1981. (Liverp.) Med. Dir. (Palliat. Med.) Qu.sCt. Hospice S.port; Cons. Palliat. Med. N. Sefton & W. Lancs. NHS Trust. Prev: GP S.port.

GROVES, Lindsay Anne Department of Community Paediatrics, Colwyn Bay Hospital, Hesketh Road, Colwyn Bay LL29 8AY Tel: 01492 515218; Fedw Las, Bontuchel, Ruthin LL15 2BL Tel: 01824 710291 — MB ChB 1983 Cape Town; DCCH RCP Ed. 1996; DA (UK) 1991. Staff Grade (Community Paediat.) Clwyd Community Trust; Assoc. Specialist Clwyd Community Trust.

GROVES, Mary Clemitson Pattison (retired) 1 Becketts Avenue, St Albans AL3 5RT Tel: 01727 56474 — MB BS Durh. 1954; DObst RCOG 1962; DTM & H Liverp. 1959. Prev: GP Princip. Midway Surg. St. Albans.

GROVES, Nicholas Duncan c/o Department of Anaesthetics, University Hospital of Wales, Heath Park, Cardiff CF14 4XW Tel: 029 2074 7747 — MB ChB 1976 Bristol; MRCP (UK) 1980; FFA RCS Eng. 1983. (Bristol) Cons. (Anaesth.) Univ. Hosp. Wales; Clin. Teach. Univ. Coll. Med. Wales.; Assoc Med Dir Cardiff & Vale NHS Trust. Prev: Sen. Regist./Lect. (Anaesth.) Univ. Hosp. Wales; Regist. (Anaesth.) Radcliffe Infirm. Oxf.; Regist. (Med.) Morriston Hosp. Swansea.

GROVES, Patricia Hamilton BMJ Editorial, BMA House, Tavistock Square, London WC1H 9JR Tel: 020 7387 4499 Fax: 020 7383 6418; Marchfield, Flowers Hill, Pangbourne, Reading RG8 7BD Tel: 0118 984 5935 Fax: 0118 984 5966 — MB BS 1984 Lond.; MRCPsych 1988. (Roy. Free) Asst. Edr. BMJ. Prev: Hon. Research Fell. Sch. of Pub. Policy Univ. Coll. Lond.; SHO & Regist. (Psychiat.) Fair Mile Hosp. Wallingford Oxf.; SHO (Psychiat.) St. Bernard's Hosp. Ealing.

GROVES, Peter Howard Department of Cardiology, University Hospital Wales, Heath Park, Cardiff CF14 4XW Tel: 029 2074 3533 Fax: 029 2074 4473 Email: peter.groves@cardiffandvule.wales.nhsuk — MB BS 1984 Newc.; MB BS Newc. I984; MD Newc. 1994; MRCP (UK) 1987. (Newc.) Cons. Cardiol. Univ. Hosp. Wales. Socs: Cardiac Soc.; Med. Res. Soc.; Brit. Cardiac Interven. Soc. Prev: Sen. Regist. (Cardiol.) Roy. Brompton Nat. Heart & Lung Hosp. Lond.; Regist. (Cardiol.) Univ. Hosp. Wales, Cardiff; Regist. (Gen. Med.) Newc. Gen Hosp. & Freeman Hosp. Newc. u. Tyne.

GROVES, Philippa Ann Department of Anaesthesia, Kings College Hospital, Denmark Hill, London SE5 9RS Tel: 020 7346 3154 Fax: 020 7346 3632; 72 Croxted Road, West Dulwich, London SE21 8NP Tel: 020 8761 0622 — MB BS 1983 Lond.; FFA RCS Eng. 1988; DRCOG 1987. (Guy's Hosp. Med. Sch.) Cons. Anaesth. King's Coll. Hosp. Lond. Socs: Assn. Anaesth. Gt. Brit. & Irel.; Obst. Anaesth. Assn. Prev: Sen. Regist. (Anaesth.) Guy's Hosp. Lond.; Regist. (Anaesth.) St. Thos. & St. Bart. Hosps. Lond.; SHO (Anaesth.) St. Bart. Hosp. Lond.

GROVES, Richard Charles Cumming Brown Clee Medical Practice, Station Road, Ditton Priors, Bridgnorth WV16 6SS Tel: 01746 712672 Fax: 01746 712580 — MB ChB 1975 Liverp.; MRCGP 1980; DRCOG 1981.

GROVES, Richard William Department of Dermatology, Middlesex Hospital, Mortimer St., London W1T 3AA Tel: 020 7380 9224 Fax: 020 7380 9816 Email: r.groves@ucl.ac.uk — MB BS 1983 Lond.; MRCP (UK) 1986; FRCP 2000. (Guy's Hosp. Med. Sch.) Cons. & Sen. Lect. (Dermat.) Univ. Coll. Hosps. Trust Lond. Socs: Roy. Soc. Med.; Eur. Soc. Dermat. Res. Prev: Instruc. (Dermat.) Harvard Med. Sch. Boston, Mass., USA; Sen. Regist. & Regist. (Dermat.) Guy's Hosp. Lond.; Regist. (Gen. Med.) Lond. Hosp.

GROVES, Ruth (retired) Old Cote, Rag Clough Beck, Stairs, Oxenhope, Keighley BD22 9QY Tel: 01535 644180 — MB ChB 1947 St. And. Prev: GP Keighley.

GROVES, Ruth Marian 18 Sandhills Way, Calcot, Reading RG31 7PQ — MB BS 1998 Lond.; MB BS Lond 1998.

GROVES, Simon John Flat 3, 2 Kensington Place, Bath BA1 6AW Tel: 01225 337459 — BM 1982 Soton.; MRCPsych 1987. Sen. Regist. (Higher Rotat. Train. Scheme Psychiat.) Barrow Hosp. Bristol. Prev: SHO/Regist. (Psychol. Med.) St. Bart. Hosp. Rotat. Train. Scheme; Ho. Off. (Med.) Ryde I. of Wight Co. Hosp.; Ho. Off. (Surg.) St. Mary's Hosp. Newport I. of Wight.

GROVES, Thomas Kilwinning Medical Practice, 15 Almswall Road, Kilwinning KA13 6BO Tel: 01294 554591 Fax: 01294 557300; Almswall Road Surgery, Kilwinning Tel: 01294 54591 — MB ChB 1973 Birm.; MRCGP 1983; DObst RCOG 1975. Socs: BMA. Prev: Ho. Phys. Lewis Hosp. Stornoway; Ho. Surg. Staincliffe Hosp. Dewsbury; SHO (O & G) Staincliffe Matern. Unit Dewsbury.

GROVES-RAINES, Julia Caroline Main Street Surgery, 32 Main Street, Derrygonnelly, Enniskillen BT93 6HW Tel: 028 6864 1379 Fax: 028 6864 1832 — MB BCh 1970 Dublin; MB BCh Dub 1970. (Dublin) GP Enniskillen, Co. Fermanagh.

GRUBB, Alexander Blair Anderson (retired) Tor-na-Veen, Hillside, Montrose DD10 9HY — MB ChB 1960 St. And.; DPM Eng. 1965. Prev: Assoc. Specialist (Psychiat.) Sunnyside Roy. Hosp. Montrose.

GRUBB, Chandra 5 Abbey Road, London NW8 9AA Tel: 020 7289 0878 — MB BS 1949 Punjab; PhD Lond. 1965; MB BS East Punjab (India) 1949; MRCPath 1980. (Lady Hardinge Med. Coll.) Dir. Roy. Free & Univ. Coll. Hosps. Dept. Cytol. & Cytol. Train.; Fell. Internat. Acad. Cytol. Centre. Socs: Brit. Soc. Clin. Cytol. Prev: Brit. Empire Cancer Campaign Research Fell. (Cytol.) Roy. Free Hosp.; Regist. (Pathol.) Lond. Chest Hosp. & Stoke Mandeville Hosp.; Aylesbury.

GRUBB, Donald James 65 Pinkie Road, Musselburgh EH21 7EY — MB ChB 1956 St. And.; FFA RCS Eng. 1964. Cons. Anaesth. Roy. Hosp. Sick Childr. Edin. & Edin. Dent. Hosp.

GRUBB, Frederick (retired) 32 Harewood Avenue, Sale M33 5BY Tel: 0161 969 9647 — MB ChB St. And. 1961.

GRUBB, Harry Edward Stewart 54 Thornton Way, Girton, Cambridge CB3 0NJ — MB BS 1990 Lond.

GRUBB, Helen Ruth 3 Small Close, Smethwick B67 7RE — MB ChB 1996 Birm.; ChB Birm. 1996.

GRUBB, Mark Alister Durham Road Surgery, 25 Durham Road, Edinburgh EH16 4DT Tel: 0131 669 1153 Fax: 0131 669 3633; 5 Meadowfield Drive, Edinburgh EH8 7NX — MB ChB 1982 Ed.; MRCGP 1987; DCCH RCP Ed. 1988.

GRUBB, Neil Robert 16 Cameron Toll Gardens, Edinburgh EH16 4TG — MB ChB 1989 Ed.

GRUBB, (Pamela) Jane (retired) Garden Flat, 2 College Road, Clifton, Bristol BS8 3JB Tel: 0117 974 2736 Fax: 0117 974 2736 — MB ChB 1946 Ed. Prev: Research Assoc. (Child Health) Univ. Bristol.

GRUBIN, Professor Donald Harlan St Nicholas Hospital, Jubilee Road, Gosforth, Newcastle upon Tyne NE3 3XT Tel: 0191 223 2454 Fax: 0191 223 2241 Email: don.grubin@ncl.ac.uk — MB BS 1985 Lond.; BA Oxf. 1978; MD Lond. 1993; MRCPsych 1990. (King's Coll. Hosp. Lond.) Prof. Forens. Psychiat., Univ. Newc. u. Tyne; Hon. Cons. Forens. Psychiat., Newc., N. Tyneside and N.d. Ment. Health Trust. Prev: Sen. Lect. (Forens. Psychiat.) Univ. Newc.; Lect. (Forens. Psychiat.) Inst. Psychiat. Lond.

GRUBNIC, Sisa 19 Frank Dixon Way, London SE21 7ET — MB BS 1988 Lond.; MRCP (UK) 1991.

GRUCHY, Richard Ernest (retired) La Tour Du Nord, La Grande Route Des Sablons, Grouville JE3 9FQ Tel: 01534 853270 — MB BChir Camb. 1946; FRCP Lond. 1970, M 1953; MRCS Eng. LRCP Lond. 1945. Prev: Phys. Gen. Hosp. Jersey.

GRUDEN, Gabriella Division of Medicine, Floor 4 Hunt's House Guy's Hospital, St Thomas St., London SE1 9RT — State Exam Turin 1990.

GRUEBEL LEE, Mr David Mark Private Office, Aldershot NHS Outpatient Department, Cambridge Military Hospital, Hospital Road, Aldershot GU11 2AN Tel: 01252 310467 Fax: 01252 310481 Email: dglee@barclays.com; Woodburn, 2 Middle Bourne Lane, Farnham GU10 3ND Tel: 01252 712574 Email: dglee@barclays.com — MB BCh 1955 Witwatersrand; FRCS Eng. 1965; FRCS Ed. 1964. Indep. Cons. Orthop. Surg. Hants. Clinic Basingstoke; Hon. Cons. Orthop. Surg. Frimley Pk. Hosp., Camberly. Socs: Fell. BOA. Prev: Cons. Orthop. Surg. Frimley Pk. Hosp Camberley; Sen. Regist. (Orthop.) St. Thos. Hosp. Lond.; Assoc. Orthop. Surg. Albert Einstein Coll. of Med. New York.

GRUENEWALD, Peter Helios Medical Centre, 17 Stoke Hill, Stoke Bishop, Bristol BS9 1JN Tel: 0117 982 6060; 14 The Dell, Bristol BS9 3UD Tel: 0117 962 4840 — MD 1986 Vienna. Socs: Anthroposop. Med. Assn. Prev: Trainee GP/SHO (Psychiat.) Freiburg, Germany; Med. Off. Rehabil. & Assessm. Centre Delrow Hearts; Med. Off. Cottswold Clinic, Home Sch. Nailsworth, Glos.

GRUER, Laurence David, OBE Greater Glasgow Health Board, Dalian House, PO Box 15327, 350 St Vincent St., Glasgow G3 8FU Tel: 0141 201 4870 Fax: 0141 201 4949; 12 Kirkle Drive, Newton Mearns, Glasgow G77 5HA Email: ldgruer@aol.com — MB ChB 1978 Ed.; 1996 FFPHM RCP (UK) 1996; 1975 BSc (Med. Sci.) (Hons.) 1975Ed. 1975; 1986 MD Ed. 1986; 1993 FRCP Glas. 1993; 1981 MRCP (UK) 1981; 1989 MFPHM RCP (UK) 1989; 1986 MPH Glas. 1986. Cons. (Pub. Health Med.) Gtr. Glas. HB. Socs: Fell. Roy. Coll. Phys. & Surg. Glas.; Fell. Fac. Pub. Health Med.; Soc. Social Med. Prev: Clin. Dir. Gtr. Glas. Community & Ment. Health Servs. NHS Trust; Sen. Regist. (Community Med.) Gtr. Glas. HB; Roy. Soc. Research Fell.

GRUER, Nana Efua Mensiwa Royal Alexandra Hospital NHS Trust, Corsebar Road, Paisley PA2 9PN; 12 Kirkle Drive, Newton Mearns, Glasgow G77 5HA — MB BCh BAO 1979 Dub.; BA (Hons.) Dub. 1976, MRCP (UK) 1983. (Dub.) Staff Grade Phys. (Gastroenterol.) Roy. Alexandra Hosp. Paisley. Socs: BMA; Collegiate Mem. RCPS Glas.; Caledonian Soc. Gastroenterol. Prev: Clin. Asst. (Gastroenterol.) Roy. Alexandra Hosp. Paisley; Clin. Asst. (Dermat.) StoneHo. Hosp.; SHO (Dermat. & Gen. Med.) Wordsley Hosp.

GRUER, Rosamond (retired) 13 Winton Loan, Edinburgh EH10 7AN Tel: 0131 445 2841 — MB ChB 1950 Aberd.; MB ChB (Hons.) Aberd. 1950; FFCM 1977, M 1974; Dip. Soc. Med. Ed. 1968. Prev: SCM Lothian HB.

GRUFFUDD-JONES, David Martin 26 Merthyr Road, Abergavenny NP7 5BT — MB BCh 1984 Wales.

GRUFFYDD, D R Staffa Health Centre, 3 Waverley Street, Tibshelf, Alfreton DE55 5NU Tel: 01773 872252 Fax: 01773 591712 — MB BS 1971 London; MB BS 1971 London.

GRUFFYDD-JONES, Kevin The Surgery, London Road, Box, Corsham SN13 8NA Tel: 01225 742361 Fax: 01225 742646 — BM BCh 1979 Oxf.; MA Oxf. 1981; MRCGP 1983; Dip. Sports Med. Glas.1985; DRCOG 1981. (Oxford) Med. Off. Bath. RFC & Bath Sports Med. Clinc.; Nat. Steering Comm. GPs in Asthma Gp. Prev: Trainee GP Bristol VTS; Ho. Surg. Treliske Hosp. Truro; Ho. Phys. John Radcliffe Hosp. Oxf.

GRUMETT, Simon Aird 24 Showell Green, Droitwich WR9 8UE — MB ChB 1995 Birm.; MB ChB (Hons.) Birm. 1995; BSc (Hons.) Birm. 1990; MRCP (UK) 1998. (Birmingham) Cancer Research Campaign Lect. & Specialist Regist. in Med. Oncol., Univ. Hosp., Birm. Socs: Assoc. of Cancer Phys.s. Prev: SHO (Med.) Birm. Heartlands Hosp.; SHO (Med.) Kidderminster Dist. Gen. Hosp.

GRUMMITT, Celia Clare Health Care Centre, HMP Winchester, Romsey Road, Winchester SO22 5DF Tel: 01962 854494 Ext: 340; Popple Down Farm, Stockbridge Road, Lopcombe, Salisbury SP5 1BW Tel: 01980 863320 — MB BS 1982 Lond.; DFFP 1993; DCH RCP Lond. 1986. (Roy. Free) GP Winchester Prison.

GRUMMITT, Kris The Grange, 59 The Village, Strensall, York YO32 5XA Tel: 01904 491605 — BM BCh 1977 Oxf.; MRCGP 1986. Asst. GP York.

GRUMMITT, Richard Michael The Grange, 59 The Village, Strensall, York YO32 5XA — MB BS 1975 Lond.; MRCGP 1986; FFA RCS Eng. 1982. Cons. Anaesth. York.

GRUMMITT, William Morrow Cross Plain Surgery, 84 Bulford Road, Durrington, Salisbury SP4 8DH Tel: 01980 652221; Popple Down Farm, Stockbridge Road, Lapcombe, Salisbury SP5 1BW Tel: 01980 863320 — MB BS 1982 Lond.; MRCGP 1988; DRCOG 1987; Dip Occ. Med. 1997. Regtl. Med. Off. Devonsh. & Dorset Regtl. TA; Med. Adviser NAAFI.

GRUN, Lucia Mary 7C Cassland Road, London E9 7AL — MB BS 1984 Lond.; MRCGP 1992; DRCOG 1986.

GRUNDMAN, Michael John Chesterfield and North Derbyshire Royal Hospital, Chesterfield S44 5BL Tel: 01246 552198 Fax: 01246 552280; 60 Church Street, Matlock DE4 3BY Tel: 01629 56757 — BM BCh 1971 Oxf.; MA, DPhil Oxf. 1969; FRCP Lond. 1988; MRCP (UK) 1974. (Oxford) Cons. Phys. Chesterfield & N. Derbysh. Roy. Hosp. Socs: Brit. Soc. Gastroenterol. Prev: Lect. (Gastroenterol.) Univ. Manch. & Hope Hosp. Salford; Regist. (Med.) Ninewells Hosp. Dundee; Ho. Phys. Radcliffe Infirm. Oxf.

GRUNDY, Alan 110 Roseneath Road, London SW11 6AQ Fax: 020 8725 2936 Email: alangrundy@lineone.net — MB ChB 1974 Dundee; FRCR 1979; DCH Eng. 1976. Cons. & Sen. Lect. Diagnostic Radiol. St. Geo. Hosp. & Med. Sch. Prev: Sen. Regist. (Radiol.) St. Geo. Hosp. Lond.; SHO N. Middlx. Hosp. Lond.; Ho. Off. Ninewells Hosp. Dundee.

GRUNDY, Mr David James The Old Post Office, Besomers Drove, Lover, Redlynch, Salisbury SP5 2PN Tel: 01725 512905 Fax: 01725 512965 Email: digrundy@aol.com — MB BS Lond. 1961; FRCS Eng. 1970; FRCS Ed. 1969. (St. Geo.) Hon. Cons. Spinal Injuries Duke of Cornw. Spinal Treatm. Centre Salisbury Dist. Hosp. Prev:

Sen. Regist. (Spinal Injuries) Robt. Jones & Agnes Hunt Orthop. Hosp. OsW.ry; Regist. (Spinal Injuries) Stoke Mandeville Hosp.; Med. Supt. Wusasa Hosp., Nigeria.

GRUNDY, Ernest Michael Casula, Sarratt Lane, Rickmansworth WD3 4AS Tel: 01923 779472 — MB ChB 1970 Dundee; BSc St. And. 1967; MRCP (UK) 1979; MRCS Eng. LRCP Lond. 1970; FFA RCS Eng. 1974; DObst RCOG 1972. Cons. (Anaesth.) Middlx. & Univ. Coll. Hosp. Lond.

GRUNDY, Fiona Jane Montville House, Les Vardes, St Peter Port, Guernsey GY1 1BH — MB BS 1980 Lond.

GRUNDY, Gyl Valerie The Upper Surgery, 27 Lemon Street, Truro TR1 2LS Tel: 01872 74931 Fax: 01872 260339; Gloweth Barton, Truro TR1 3LT Tel: 01872 73948 — MB ChB 1968 Ed.; MRCGP 1975; DObst RCOG 1970. (Ed.) GP Truro.

GRUNDY, Howell Clive Microbiology Laboratory, Ashford and St Peter's Hospital NHS Trust, Guildford Road, Chertsey KT16 0PZ Tel: 01932 872000 Fax: 01932 875129; 21 High Garth, Esher KT10 9DN Tel: 01372 466349 — MB BChir 1977 Camb.; MSc (Clin. Microbiol.) Lond. 1984; MA Camb. 1980; FRCPath 1996; Dip. Clin. Microbiol. Lond 1983. Cons. Microbiol. St. Peter's Hosp. Chertsey Surrey. Prev: Sen. Regist. (Microbiol.) Qu. Mary's Hosp. Roehampton; Jun. Lect. (Microbiol.) W.m. Hosp. Lond.

GRUNDY, Julian Richard Brooks Gloweth Barton, Gloweth, Truro TR1 3LT — MB ChB 1997 Bristol.

GRUNDY, Keith Neville Church Walk Surgery, Metheringham, Lincoln LN4 3EZ Tel: 01526 320522; Abbots Grange, Nocton, Lincoln LN4 2BJ Tel: 01526 320522 — MB ChB 1963 Manch.; DA Eng. 1967. (Manch.) Hosp. Pract. (Anaesth.) Lincoln AHA. Socs: Fell. Manch. Med. Soc. Prev: Regist. (Anaesth.) Stockport & Buxton Hosp. Gp.; Ho. Off. (Med.) Oldham & Dist. Gen. Hosp.; Ho. Off. (Surg.) Hope Hosp. Salford.

GRUNDY, Mr Michael (retired) Rock Mount, 22 Whalley Road, Wilpshire, Blackburn BB1 9PJ Tel: 01254 248916 — MB ChB Ed. 1959; FRCS Ed. 1964.

GRUNDY, Mr Michael Francis Brooks (retired) Gloweth Barton, Truro TR1 3LT — MB BS 1964 Lond.; FRCS Ed. 1973; MRCS Eng. LRCP Lond. 1964; FRCOG, M 1971; DA Eng. 1968. Cons. (O & G) Cornw. AHA. Prev: Rotat. Sen. Regist. Centr. Middlx. Hosp. Lond. & Middlx. Hosp.

GRUNDY, Neil Jeffrey Westcotes Health Centre, Fosse Road South, Leicester LE3 0LP Tel: 0116 254 8568; 9 Grange Court, Church Lane, Desford, Leicester LE9 9ED — MB BChir 1979 Camb.

GRUNDY, Mr Paul Leslie Department of Neurosurgery, Frenchay Hospital, Frenchay, Bristol BS16 1LE Tel: 0117 970 1212 Fax: 0117 970 1161 Email: p.l.grundy@bristol.ac.uk; Walnut Cottage, Church Hill, Olveston, Bristol BS35 4BZ Tel: 01454 618878 — BM 1992 Soton.; BM (Hons.) Soton. 1992; FRCS 1996. Specialist Regist. (Neurosurg.) Frenchay Hosp. Bristol; RCS Research Fell. 1999-2000. Prev: SHO (Neurosurg.) Frenchay Hosp. Bristol; SHO (Gen. Surg.) Horton Gen. Hosp. Banbury; SHO (Trauma, Orthop., A & E & Cardiothoracic Surg.) John Radcliffe Hosp. Oxf.

GRUNDY, Peter Frederick Cardiff Road Medical Centre, Cardiff Road, Taffs Well, Cardiff CF15 7YG Tel: 029 2081 0260 Fax: 029 2081 3002 — MB BCh 1968 Wales; MD Wales 1980; MFCM 1979; DPM Eng. 1972. (Cardiff) Trainer (Gen. Pract.) E. Glam. VTS; Clin. Asst. (Psychol. Med.) Welsh Coll. Med.; Hon. Clin. Teach. (Gen. Pract.) Welsh Coll. Med. Prev: Lect. (Community Med. & Occupat. Health) Welsh Coll. Med.; SHO & Research Regist. (Psychol. Med.) Welsh Nat. Sch. Med.; Ho. Surg. Cardiff Roy. Infirm.

GRUNDY, Richard Guy Department of Paediatric Oncology, Birmingham Children's Hospital, Steelhouse Lane, Birmingham B4 6NH Tel: 0121 333 8243 Fax: 0121 333 8241 Email: r.g.grundy@bham.ac.uk — MB ChB 1988 Birm.; BSc (Hons. Physiol.) Lond. 1981; MB ChB (Hons. Paediat. & Child Health) Birm. 1986; MRCP (UK) 1989. Clin. Sen. Lect. in Paediat. Oncol.uni of Brimingham. Socs: Roy. Coll. of Paediat. and health. Prev: MRC & ICRF Research Fell. (Cell. & Molecular Biol.) Inst. Child Health Lond.; MRC & ICRF Research fell. (cell & molecular biol.) Inst. Child helath Lond., Full time.

GRUNDY, Robert (retired) The Medical Centre, Boyd Avenue, Padstow PL28 8ER Tel: 01841 532346 Fax: 01841 532602 — MB BS Lond. 1965; MRCP Lond. 1968; FRCGP 1983, M 1976. Prev: Lect. (Med.) Makerere Univ. Coll. Kampala, Uganda.

GRUNDY, Robert Errol The Surgery, 20 Low Road, Debenham, Stowmarket IP14 6QU Tel: 01728 860248 Fax: 01728 861300 Email: rob@grundipops.demon.co.uk; The Surgery, Chapel Road, Otley, Ipswich IP6 9NT Tel: 01473 890341 — MB ChB 1979 Birm.; BA (Hons.) Durham. 1968; MRCGP 1987. GP Vocational Trainer Suff. Prev: SHO (Neurosurg. & Neurol.) Midl. Centre Birm.; SHO (O & G) Dudley Rd. Hosp. Birm.; SHO (Paediat.) New Cross Hosp. Wolverhampton.

GRUNDY, Theodore Norsworthy (retired) 3 Sydnope Hall, Two Dales, Matlock DE4 2FN Tel: 01629 733734 Fax: 01629 733734 — MB BS Lond. 1936.

GRÜNEBERG, Anne Lillias (retired) 67 Cholmeley Crescent, London N6 5EX Tel: 020 8348 2372 — MB ChB 1959 Birm.; FFA RCS Eng. 1967. Prev: Cons. Anaesth. N.wick Pk. Hosp. Harrow.

GRÜNEBERG, Reuben Naphtali G.R.Micro LTD, 7-9 William Rd, London NW1 3ER Tel: 0207 388 7320 Email: rn.gruneburg@grmicro.co.uk; 67 Cholmeley Crescent, London N6 5EX Tel: 0208 8348 2372 — MD Lond. 1972, MB BS 1960; MRCS Eng. LRCP Lond. 1960; FRCPath 1980, M 1968. (Univ. Coll. Hosp.) Cons. Bacteriol. G. R. Micro Ltd., Lond. Socs: Brit. Soc. Antimicrob. Chemother. Prev: Sen. Regist. (Microbiol.) Univ. Coll. Hosp. Lond.; Cons. Bacteriol. Univ. Coll. Hosp. Lond.; SHO (Path.) Centr. Middlx. Hosp. Lond.

GRUNEWALD, Richard Adam Royal Hallamshire Hospital, Glossop Road, Sheffield S10 2JF Tel: 0114 276 6222 Email: r.a.grunewald@sheffield.ac.uk; 15 Mayfield Heights, Brookhouse Hill, Fulwood, Sheffield S10 3TT Tel: 0114 229 5418 Fax: 01433 613957 — BM BCh 1986 Oxf.; MA Oxf. 1985, DPhil 1983; MRCP (UK) 1989. (Univ. Oxf.) Cons. Neurol. Roy. Hallamsh. Hosp. Sheff.; Hon. Clin. Lect. Univ. Sheff. Prev: Lect. (Clin. Neurol.) Univ. Sheff.; Regist. Nat. Hosp. Neurol. & Neurosurg. Qu. Sq. Lond.; Research Fell. Inst. Neurol. Lond.

GRUNSHAW, Nigel David Airedale General Hospital, Skipton Road, STEETON, Keighley BD20 6TD — MB BS 1983 Newc.; MRCP (UK) 1986; FRCR 1991. Cons. Radiol. Darlington Memor. Hosp. Prev: Sen. Regist. (Radiol.) Yorks. RHA; Regist. (Med.) N.. Gen. Hosp. Sheff.; SHO (Med.) Hull HA.

GRUNSTEIN, John Albert Henry (retired) Queen Alexandra Hospital, Cosham, Portsmouth PO6 3LY Tel: 023 92 379451 — MB BS Lond. 1963; FRCP Lond. 1982, M 1968; MRCS Eng. LRCP Lond. 1963. Prev: Cons. Phys. (Geriat. Med.) Qu. Alexandra Hosp. Portsmouth.

GRUNSTEIN, Szlama, MBE (retired) 128 Birch Avenue, Chadderton, Oldham OL1 2QU Tel: 0161 624 8729 — M.B., Ch.B. Polish Sch. of Med. 1947.

GRUNWALD, Hermann (retired) 20 Sunnybank Road, Batley WF17 0LJ Tel: 01924 473765 — MD 1933 Vienna.

GRUSZECKA, Krystyna Ada Teresa Possilpark Health Centre, 85 Denmark Street, Glasgow G22 5EG Tel: 0141 531 6170 Fax: 0141 531 6177; 3 Victoria Park Corner, Glasgow G14 9NZ — MB ChB 1981 Ed.; BSc Ed. 1975, MB ChB 1981; MRCGP 1985; DRCOG 1984.

GRYF-LOWCZOWSKI, Mr Jan Victor Dobek Hinchingbrooke Hospital, Hinchingbrooke Park, Huntingdon PE29 6NT; 5 The Grove, Hartford, Huntingdon PE29 1YD — MRCS Eng. LRCP 1975 Lond.; MB BS Lond. 1977; FRCS Ed. 1982; MD Lond. 1996. (Guy's) Cons. Gen. Surg. Hinchingbrooke Hosp. Huntingdon. Prev: Sen. Regist. (Gen. Surg.) Luton & Dunstable Hosp.; Specialist Regist. 1996.

GRZYBOWSKA, Pola Helena Woodhill, Rhiwbina Hill, Cardiff CF14 6UP — MB BCh 1989 Wales; MRCGP 1993; Dip. Palliat. Med. Wales 1996; DRCOG 1992.

GUARASCI, Franco 48 Moor Road N., Newcastle upon Tyne NE3 1AD — MB ChB 1994 Sheff.

GUARD, Beverley Carol 47 Springfield Road, Bury St Edmunds IP33 3AS Tel: 01284 764094 — BM 1987 Soton.; MRCP (UK) 1990; FRCA 1994. Regist. (Anaesth.) Addenbrooke's Hosp. Camb.

GUARRO-MIRALLES, Mercedes E.E.T. Hospital, Murivance, Shrewsbury SY1 1JS Tel: 01743 55771; Viladomat 173, 08205 Sabddell, Barcelona, Spain — LMS 1988 U Autonoma Barcelona.

GUBAY, Angela 35 St Seiriol's Road, Llandudno LL30 2YT; Flat 2, 7 Lymington Road, West Hampstead, London NW6 1HX — MB BS 1990 Lond.; BSc Lond. 1986. Ho. Off. (Urol. & Gen. Surg.) City & Hackney HA, Homerton Hosp. Lond. Prev: Trainee GP Lond.; Ho. Off. (Gen. Med.) Harold Wood Hosp.

GUBBAY, Alan David 5 Wild Hatch, London NW11 7LD — BM BCh 1962 Oxf.

GUBBAY, Maurice 8 Ambrose Avenue, Golders Green, London NW11 9AN Tel: 020 8458 4656 — MB BS 1958 Calcutta; Mem. BMA. Prev: Ho. Phys. Lond. Jewish Hosp.; Ho. Surg. Nelson Hosp. Lond.

GUBBAY, Nicholas Histopathology Dept, Cheltenham Gen Hosp, Sandford Road, Cheltenham GL53 7AN Tel: 01242 274260 — MB BS 1967 Lond.; MRCS Eng. LRCP Lond. 1967; FRCPath 1989, M 1977. Cons. (Histopath.) Cheltenham Gen. Hosp.

GUCKENHEIM, Philip David Lloyd 24 Churchdown, Downham, Bromley BR1 5PT Tel: 020 8695 6575 Fax: 020 8695 0586; 24 Pound Court Drive, Orpington BR6 8AJ — MB BS Lond. 1978. (King's College Hospital)

GUCKIAN, Damian Michael Francis East Park Parade Surgery, 1 East Park Parade, Leeds LS9 9NQ Tel: 0113 248 2454 Fax: 0113 248 2454 — MB BCh BAO 1972 NUI; MRCP (UK) 1976; DCH RCPSI 1974. Prev: Regist. (Med.) Wharfedale Gen. Hosp. Otley; Regist. (Paediat.) Huddersfield Roy. Infirm.

GUDE, Rupert Adrian Abbey Surgery, 28 Plymouth Road, Tavistock PL19 8BU — MB BS 1971 Lond.; MRCP (UK) 1974; MRCGP 1982; DCH RCP Lond. 1977; FRCGP 1997. (Guy's) Socs: MEDACT. Prev: Princip. Med. Off. W.. Province, Solomon Is.s.

GUDE, Mr Somnath Jaivant Cross Gaits Cottage, Beverley Road, Blacko, Nelson BB9 6RF Tel: 01282 67163 — MB BS 1957 Bombay; FRCS Ed. 1961; FRCS Eng. 1961. (Grant Med. Coll.) Cons. (Otolaryngol.) Burnley Health Dist.

GUDGEON, Mr Andrew Mark Frimley Park Hospital NHS Trust, Portsmouth Road, Frimley, Camberley GU16 7UJ Tel: 01276 604236 Fax: 01276 604106 Email: mark.sudgeon@virgin.net; Dial Cottage, Hamlash Lane, Farnham GU10 3AZ Tel: 01252 795996 Email: mark.gudgeon@doctors.org.uk — MB BS 1980 Lond.; MS Lond. 1991; FRCS Eng. 1985; FRCS Ed. 1984; MRCS Eng. LRCP Lond. 1980. (Westm.) Cons. Gen. Surg. Frimley Pk. Hosp. NHS Trust. Socs: Roy. Soc. Med.; Assn. Coloproctol.; Brit. Soc. Gastroenterol. Prev: Cons. Gen. Surg. Derbysh. Roy. Infirm.; Sen. Regist. (Surg.) St. Geo. Hosp. Lond.

GUDGEON, Mr David Hugh (retired) Little Saltings, Ringmore, Shaldon, Teignmouth TQ14 0EX Tel: 01626 872491 — MB BS 1958 Lond.; FRCS Ed. 1967; FRCOG 1980, M 1966, DObst 1963. Prev: Cons. O & G S. Devon Healthcare Trust.

GUDGEON, Edmund Arthur 35 Ashwood Avenue, West Didsbury, Manchester M20 2YB — MRCS Eng. LRCP Lond. 1931. (St. Geo.)

GUDGEON, Judith Elizabeth Ann 15 Searle Road, Farnham GU9 8LJ — MB BS 1990 Lond.; BSc (Hons.) Pharmacol. Lond. 1987; MRCP (UK) 1993; FRCA 1994.

GUDGEON, Patricia Winifred The Beeches, 150A Shay Lane, Walton, Wakefield WF2 6LA — MB BCh BAO 1976 Belf.; FRCPath 1994, M 1982. Cons. Histopath. Dewsbury HA.

***GUDGIN, Emma Jane** 9 Frognal Court, Finchley Road, London NW3 5HL Email: egudgin@hotmail.com — MB BS 1998 Lond.; MB BS Lond 1998.

GUDI, Pratibha Vitthal The Surgery, 68 Hill Top, West Bromwich B70 0PU Tel: 0121 556 0455 Fax: 0121 556 8664 — MB BS 1974 Bombay.

GUELLARD, Paul Stanley 55 Meadow Court, Ponteland, Newcastle upon Tyne NE20 9RA Tel: 01661 25701 — MB BS 1974 Lond.; BDS 1969; MRCP (UK) 1979; MRCGP 1981; LDS RCS Eng. 1969; DRCOG 1980; DCH Eng. 1979. (St. Geo.) Socs: Colleg. Mem. Roy. Coll. Phys. Lond.; Soc. Occupat. Med. & BMA. Prev: Clin. Asst. (Occupat. Health) Roy. Vict. Infirm. Newc.; GP Sunderland.

GUERCKEN, Miss Nadejda 28 Sidmouth Road, London NW2 5HJ Tel: 020 8459 7100 Fax: 020 8830 2122 — MB BS Lond. 1969. Prev: Ho. Off. (Geriat. Med.), SHO (Dermat & Psychiat.) & Clin. Asst. (Psychiat.) Char. Cross. Hosp. Lond.

GUERCKEN, Tatiana P 28 Sidmouth Road, London NW2 5HJ Tel: 020 8459 2000 — MRCS Eng. LRCP Lond. 1945; LDS RCS Eng. 1927. Prev: Med. Supt. Univ. Coll. Hosp. Dent. Sch.; Jun. Anaesth. Univ. Coll. Hosp.

GUERENU CARNEVALI, Jose Antonio c/o Medical Staffing, Leighton Hospital, Crewe CW1 4QJ — LMS 1988 Oviedo.

GUÉRET WARDLE, David Francis Hemsley Flat 38, Harmont House, 20 Harley St., London W1G 9PJ Tel: 020 7631 1632 Fax: 020 7637 0043 Email: wardonc@dircon.co.uk — MB BS 1966 Lond.; PhD Lond. 1972; MRCP (UK) 1973; MRCS Eng. LRCP Lond. 1966; Specialist Accredit (Med. Oncol. & Gen. Internal Med.); MPS RCP Lond. 1978; FRCP1999. (Guy's) Hon. Cons. Phys. Hammersmith Hosp. Lond.; Cons. Med. Oncol. Lond. Oncol. & Marrow Transpl. Gp. Lond. Socs: Fell. Roy. Soc. Med. & Med. Soc. Lond.; (Ex-Counc. Mem.) BMA. Prev: Sen. Regist. (Oncol.) Sect. Clin. Research Centre N.wick Pk. Hosp.; Harrow; Res. Med. Off. Amer. Hosp. Paris, France; Clin. Lect. St. Bart. Hosp. Lond.

GUERET-WARDLE, Telesilla Christchurch Hall Surgery, 20 Edison Road, London N8 8AE Tel: 020 8340 2877 Fax: 020 8340 0896 — Laurea 1976 Rome; MRCS Eng. LRCP Lond. 1981. (University of Rome) Sen. Partner Med. Pract. Socs: Italian Med. Soc. GB. Prev: SHO (Renal Unit) St. Paul's & St. Philips Hosp.; SHO (Paediat.) Middlx. Hosp.; SHO (Endocrinol.) Roy. Free Hosp. Lond.

GUERIN, Mary Deirdre Department of Histopathology, St Thomas Hospital, London SE1 7EH — MB BCh BAO 1989 NUI; DRCPath 1994. Sen. Regist. (Histopath.) St Thos. Hosp. Lond.

GUERRERO, Karen Lesley 22 Springbank Rise, Farsley, Pudsey LS28 5LP; 423 Water Gardens, Waterport, Gibraltar — MB ChB 1995 Leeds. SHO (O & G) Bradford Roy. Infirm. Prev: Ho. Off. (Med.) Leeds Gen. Infirm.; Ho. Off. (Surg.) Bradford Roy. Infirm.

GUERRIER, Mr Hugh Philip (retired) Wood End, 9 King's Ride, Alfriston, Polegate BN26 5XP Tel: 01323 870020 — MB BS 1941 Lond.; MRCS Eng. LRCP Lond. 1940; FRCS Eng. 1947. Prev: Sen. Cons. Surg. Torbay & Newton Abbot Hosps.

GUERRIER, Mr Timothy Hugh Ingledene, 95 Andover Road, Winchester SO22 6AX Tel: 01962 882636 — MB BS 1966 Lond.; FRCS Eng. 1972; MRCS Eng. LRCP Lond. 1966. (Guy's) ENT Surg. Roy. Hants. Co. Hosp. Winchester.

GUERRIER DE GRAVILLE, Baron de Girecourt Conrad James William, RD Rowford Barton, Cheddon Fitzpaine, Taunton TA2 8JY Tel: 01823 451277 Fax: 01823 451322 — MB BS Lond. 1962; FRCP Lond. 1983, M 1968; MRCS Eng. LRCP Lond. 1962. (Guy's) Cons., W. of Eng. Laser Centre, Som. Nuffield Hosp., Taunton. Socs: Fell. Roy. Soc. Med.; Louis Rapkine Assn. Anglo-French Scientists. Prev: Regist. Radcliffe Infirm. Oxf.; Research, Fond. Ophth. Adolph de Rothschild Paris, France; Ho. Off. Guy's Hosp. Lond.

GUESS, Heather Marian Consignia EHS, Room 239, 2nd Floor, Royal Mail, Redstone Hill, Redhill RH1 1AA Tel: 01737 777141 Fax: 07737 777140 — MB BS 1970 Lond.; MFOM 2000 RCP Lond; MRCS Eng. LRCP Lond. 1970; AFOM RCP Lond. 1992; T(GP) 1991; Cert. Family Plann. JCC 1974; IUCD Cert. 1974; Dip. Travel. Med.Health 1999. (Roy. Free) Sen. Cons. Occ. Phys., Consignia Employee Health Serv. Redhill.; Area Med. Adviser Post Office EHS S. E. Socs: Fell. Roy. Soc. Med.; Epsom Med. Soc.; SOM (Ex Meetings Sec. & Counc. Mem.) Lond. Gp. Ex-Treas. & Ex-Gp. Rep. Prev: Med. Off. BR Occupat. Health Serv.; GP Ashtead & Nottm.; Clin. Asst. (O & G) Nottm. City Hosp.

GUEST, Catherine Sarah 26 Waterden Road, Guildford GU1 2AY — MB BS 1976 Lond.; MRCS Eng. LRCP Lond. 1976.

GUEST, Elizabeth Helen Little Thatch, Feiashill Road, Trysull, Wolverhampton WV5 7HN Tel: 01902 895570 — MB BS 1988 Lond.; BSc (Hons.) Lond. 1985; MRCGP 1993; DCH RCP Lond. 1991; DRCOG 1991.

GUEST, Elizabeth Lucy Henrietta 4 Perrin Springs Lane, Frieth, Henley-on-Thames RG9 6PD — BM BCh 1991 Oxf.

GUEST, Jane Elizabeth 3 Richmond Terrace, Buckland Monachorum, Yelverton PL20 7LU — MB ChB 1990 Bristol.

GUEST, John Martin American Medical Center, Janovskeho, 48, Prague 17000, Czech Republic Tel: (+422) 807756 Fax: (+422) 877973 Email: medical@amc.cz; 6 The Tyning, Widcombe, Bath BA2 6AL Tel: 01225 313974 — BM BCh 1970 Oxf.; BA Oxf. 1967; MRCP (UK) 1975; FRCS Ed. 1985. Med. Dir. Amer. Med. Centre Prague, Czech RePub. Socs: BMA; Anglo French Med. Soc. Prev: Med. Off. Hertford Brit. Hosp. Paris, France; Regist. (Cas.) Univ. Hosp. W. Indies Kingston, Jamaica; SHO (Gen. Med.) N. Devon Infirm. Barnstaple.

GUEST, Mr Jonathan Drystones, Dunces Houses, Hepscott, Morpeth NE61 6NU — MD 1984 Glas.; BSc (Hons.) Glas. 1971, MB ChB 1973; FRCS Glas. 1978. Cons. Surg. Wansbeck Gen. Hosp.; Cons. Surg. N.umbria Healthcare NHS Trust. Prev: Cons. Surg. Ashington Hosp. & N.d. HA; Hall. Fell. (Surg.) Univ. Glas.; Sen. Regist. Hammersmith Hosp. Lond. & N.ampton Gen. Hosp.

GUEST, Jonathan Air Balloon Surgery, Kenn Road, St George, Bristol BS5 7PD Tel: 0117 909 9914 Fax: 0117 908 6660; 5 Leigh Road, Clifton, Bristol BS8 2DA Tel: 0117 973 6701 Fax: 0117 973 6701 Email: jonathanguest@200.co.uk — MB BS 1975 Lond.; MRCP (UK) 1981; MRCS Eng. LRCP Lond. 1975; MRCGP 1985; DCH Eng. 1980. (Westm.) Socs: Bristol MIGO-CHI; Cossin. Med. Soc. Prev: Regist. (Paediat.) Freedom Fields Hosp. Plymouth; SHO (Neonat. Med.) Bristol Matern. Hosp.; GP Trainee Dartmouth.

GUEST, Karen Lindsay Ashworth Street Surgery, 85 Spotland Road, Rochdale OL12 6RT Tel: 01706 44582 Fax: 01706 346767; Inglemont, Buckley Hill Lane, Milnrow, Rochdale OL16 4BU — MB ChB 1989 Manch.; MRCGP 1993.

GUEST, Katherine Annabelle 15 Church Street, Hutton, Driffield YO25 9PR — MB ChB 1994 Glas.

GUEST, Mr Kenneth Edmund (retired) Thick Riggs, Portinscale, Keswick CA12 5RW Tel: 0176 87 72376 — MB BS 1938 Durh.; FRCS Ed. 1947. Prev: Cons. Orthop. Surg. Mearnskirk Hosp. Newton Mearns & Glas. Educat.

GUEST, Louise Sarah 9 Mayflower Close, Hartwell, Aylesbury HP17 8QH — MB BS 1990 Lond.

GUEST, Michael Arbury Medical Centre, Cambridge Drive, Stockingford, Nuneaton CV10 8LW Tel: 024 7638 8555 Fax: 024 7635 2396; Holly Cottage, 205 Plough Hill Road, Nuneaton CV10 9NZ — MB ChB 1984 Leic.; BSc Liverp. 1979.

GUEST, Mr Michael George 6 Sleepersdelle Gardens, Sparkford Road, Winchester SO22 4NU Tel: 01962 853514 Fax: 020 8846 7330 Email: m.guest@cxwms.ac.uk — BM BS 1992 Nottm.; BMedSci 1990; FRCS Eng. 1997. (Nottingham) Specialist Regist. (Gen. Surg.) Char. Cross Hosp. Lond. Socs: MDU; Roy. Coll. Surg.; BMA.

GUEST, Myrna (retired) Mayday University Hospital, Chemical Pathology Department, Mayday Road, Thornton Heath CR4 4YE Tel: 020 8684 6999 Fax: 020 8665 5106 — MRCS Eng. LRCP Lond. 1971; MRCPath 1980. Cons. Chem. Path. Mayday Hosp. Thornton Heath; Hon. Sen. Lect. (Chem. Path.) W.m. Med. Sch. Lond.

GUEST, Nigel David Hope Farm Medical Centre, Hope Farm Road, Great Sutton, South Wirral CH66 2WW Tel: 0151 357 3777 Fax: 0151 357 1444; 1 The Oaks Cottages, Badgers Rake Lane, Ledsham, South Wirral CH66 8PG — MB ChB 1981 Liverp.; DFFP 1997; DRCOG 1983. Med. Adviser to S. Chesh. HA; Sec. Chesh. Dist. LMC. Prev: Clin. Asst. (Cardiol.) Clatterbridge Hosp. Wirral.

GUEST, Patricia Anne 19 The Glade, Escrick, York YO19 6JH — MB ChB 1969 Manch.; DRCOG 1971. (Manch.) SCMO York. Health Servs. Trust.

GUEST, Peter James Department of Radiology, Queen Elizabeth Hospital, Birmingham B15 2TH Tel: 0121 627 2458 Fax: 0121 697 8290 Email: peter.guest@university-b.wmids.nhs.uk — BM BCh 1983 Oxf.; BA Oxf. 1980, BM BCh 1983; MRCP (UK) 1986; FRCR 1989; T(R)(CR) 1991. (Oxford) Cons. Radiol. Qu. Eliz. Hosp. Birm. Prev: Sen. Regist. (Radiol.) St. Geo. Hosp. Lond.; Regist. (Radiol.) St. Bart. Hosp. Lond.

GUEST, Mr Philip Gerard Department of Maxillofacial Surgery, Bristol Royal Infirmary & Bristol Dental School, Lower Maudlin St., Bristol BS1 2L Tel: 0117 928 4392 Fax: 0117 928 4222; Tel: 0117 973 0211 — MB ChB 1985 Dundee; FRCS Ed. 1990; FDS RCS Eng. 1988; BDS Wales 1979. Cons. Maxillofacial Surg. United Britsol Hosp. Trust. Socs: Fell. Brit. Assn. Oral & Maxillofacial Surg.; Eur. Assn. Cranio-Maxillo. Surg.; Eur. Assn. Facial Plast. Surg. Prev: Sen. Regist. Manch.; Regist. Oxf.

GUEST, Richard Michael 60 Foxes Dale, London SE3 9BQ — MB ChB 1995 Manch.

GUEST, Robert Ross House, Wickham Road, Grimsby DN31 3SW Tel: 01472 359111 Fax: 01472 240640; United Biscuits, Church Road, West Drayton UB7 7PR Tel: 01895 432016 — MB ChB 1978 Liverp.; MSc (Occupat. Med.) Lond. 1988; MRCGP 1983; MFOM RCP Lond. 1989, AFOM 1986; T(GP) 1991; T(OM) 1991; DIH Soc. Apoth. Lond. 1984. Med. Adviser United Biscuits; Asst. Sec. Soc. Occupat. Med. Prev: Cons. Occupat. Med. to RAF; Force Med. Adviser Brit. Forces Falkland Is.s; Wing Cdr. RAF Med. Br.

GUEST, Robert Stephen The Oaklands Practice, Yateley Medical Centre, Oaklands, Yateley GU46 7LS Tel: 01252 872333 Fax: 01252 890084; Gatekeepers, Beaver Lane, Yateley GU46 6XJ — MB BChir 1972 Camb.; MA, MB Camb. 1972, BChir 1971; DObst RCOG 1974. (Camb. & King's Coll. Hosp.) Prev: GP Trainee Dartford VTS.

GUEST, Sharon Portway Surgery, 1 The Portway, Porthcawl CF36 3XB Tel: 01656 304204 Fax: 01656 772605; 3 Beach Road, Newton, Porthcawl CF36 5NH Tel: 01656 788172 — MB BCh 1980 Wales; MRCGP 1986; DCH RCP Lond. 1987; DRCOG 1984. (Welsh National School of Medicine) GP Porthcawl.

GUEST, Toby Daniel Standard Lodge, Standard Drive, Crosland Hill, Huddersfield HD4 7AD — MB BS 1998 Lond.; MB BS Lond 1998.

GUEST, Victoria Joy Park Medical Centre, Shavington Avenue, Hoole, Chester CH2 3RD; 12 Whaddon Drive, Chester CH4 7ND Tel: 01244 681990 — MB BS 1987 Lond. Med. Off. RN Submarine Base.

GUETTE, Johannes Roslin Medical Practice, 6 Main St., Roslin EH25 9LE — State Exam Med. Hamburg 1989.

GUGENHEIM, John Michael Burnaston Medical Centre, 86 Heddon Court Avenue, Cockfosters, New Barnet, Barnet EN4 9NG Tel: 020 8449 4221 — MRCS Eng. LRCP Lond. 1969. (Lond. Hosp.) Clin. Asst. Barnet Gen. Hosp. Socs: BMA. Prev: SHO Hill End Hosp. St. Albans; Ho. Surg. Qu. Vict. Hosp. E. Grinstead; Ho. Phys. Buckland Hosp. Dover.

GUGENHEIM, Peter Simon Woodcroft Medical Centre, Gervase Road, Burnt Oak, Edgware HA8 0NR Tel: 020 8201 1812 Fax: 020 8201 1813; 2 Willow Court, Stonegrove, Edgware HA8 8AG Tel: 020 8958 6438 — MB BS 1967 Lond.; MRCS Eng. LRCP Lond. 1964. (Lond. Hosp.)

GUHA, Indra Neil 143 Jersey Road, Osterley, Isleworth TW7 4QL — MB BS 1996 Lond.

GUHA, Mrinal Kanti Kingsmead Healthcare, 4 Kingsmead Way, London E9 5QG Tel: 020 8985 1930 Fax: 020 8533 3951 — MB BS 1965 Calcutta. (N.R.S. Med. Coll.) Assoc. Specialist (Orthop.) Law Hosp. Carluke.

GUHA, Nabarun Secretary's Office, Department of Geriatric Medicine, Newcastle General Hospital, Westgate Road, Newcastle upon Tyne NE4 6BE Tel: 0191 273 8811; 70A Dilkhushast, Park Circus, Calcutta 700017, India Tel: 01 0 91 33 475974 — MB BS 1987 Calcutta; MRCP (UK) 1991. Regist. (Gen. & Geriat. Med.) Newc. Gen. Hosp.

GUHA, Parimal Kumar (retired) 2 Llanharry Road, Llanharan, Pontyclun CF72 9RN Tel: 01443 226323 — MB BS 1956 Calcutta; DTCD Wales 1962. Assoc. Specialist (Geriat. Med.) Dewi Sant Hosp. Pontypridd.

GUHA, Prithwis Kumar The Health Centre, 103 Brown Street, Broughty Ferry, Dundee DD5 1EP Tel: 01382 477310 Fax: 01382 737966 — MB BS 1963 Calcutta. (Calcutta) GP Dundee.

GUHA, Prosanto Kumar Nelson Health Centre, Leeds Road, Nelson BB9 9TG Tel: 01282 698036; Mercury Bungalow, Cuckstool Lane, Montford Fence, Burnley BB12 9NZ Tel: 01282 694225 — MB BS 1957 Calcutta; BSc (Hons.) Delhi 1951; MRCOG 1963, DObst 1962; DGO Calcutta 1959. (Calcutta Med. Coll.) Hosp. Pract. (O & G) Burnley Gen. Hosp.

GUHA, Shakunthala 1 Belstane Road, Carluke ML8 4BG Tel: 01555 751339 — MB BS 1967 Kerala. (Calicut Med. Coll.) Clin. Med. Off. Lanarksh. HB. Socs: Fac. Comm. Health.

GUHA, Sipra Conway Crescent Surgery, 2 Conway Crescent, Perivale, Greenford UB6 8HU Tel: 020 8997 2457 — MB BS 1969 Calcutta; FRCOG 1994.

GUHA, Tapas Walsgrave Hospital, Clifford Bridge Road, Walsgrave, Coventry CV2 2DX Tel: 024 76 538855 — MB BS Calcutta 1968; MD (Path.) Inst. Postgrad. Med. Educat. & Research Chandigarh 1973; FRCPath 1988, M 1977. (R.G. Kar Med. Coll.) Cons. Histopath. Walsgrave Hosp. NHS Trust.

GUHA RAY, Pulak Kanti The Nirmala Surgery, 112 Pedmore Valley, Bestwood Park, Nottingham NG5 5NN Tel: 0115 920 8501 Fax: 0115 966 6113; 121 Breckhill Road, Woodthorpe, Nottingham — MBBS 1967 Calcutta.

GUHADASAN, Rathi 47 North Way, London NW9 0RD — MB BS 1994 Lond. SHO (Paediat.) Roy. Berks. Hosp. Reading. Socs: BMA & Med. Defence Union. Prev: Ho. Phys. King's Coll. Hosp. Lond.; Ho. Surg. Conquest Hosp. Hastings.

GUHANIYOGI, Sakti Bhusan Ferndale Road Surgery, Ferndale Road, Tylorstown, Ferndale CF43 3HB Tel: 01443 730169 — MB BS 1969 Gauhati; T(GP) 1991.

GUHATHAKURTA, Sumit 23 Hewlett Road, Manchester M21 9WB — MB ChB 1997 Ed.

GUI, Mr Gerald PH Academic Surgery (Breast Unit), The Royal Marsden Hospital NHS Trust, Fulham Road, London SW3 6JJ Tel: 020 7808 2783 Fax: 020 7351 5410 Email: gerald.gui@rmh.nthames.nhs.uk; 48 Hartswood Road, London W12 9NF Tel: 020 87400900 Fax: 020 74875559 Email: ggui@cwcom.net — MB BS 1986 Lond.; MS Lond. 1996; FRCS Eng. 1991; FRCS Ed. 1990. Cons. Surg. Roy. Marsden Hosp. NHS Trust, Lond.; Hon. Sen. Lect. Inst. Cancer Research Lond. Socs: Brit. BrE. Gp.; Brit. Assn. Surgic. Oncol.- BrE. speciality grp Lond. Represen.; Surgic. Research Soc. Prev: Lect. & Sen. Regist. (Gen. Surg.) St. Geo. Hosp. Lond.; Regist. (Gen. Surg.) St. Bart. Hosp. Lond.; SHO (Gen. Surg.) St. Geo. Hosp. Lond.

GUIDER, Peter John Rood Lane Medical Centre, 10 Rood Lane, London EC3M 8BN Tel: 020 7283 4028 Fax: 020 7626 2184 Email: roodlane@aol.com; 17 Cleaver Square, London SE11 4DW — MB BChir 1980 Camb. (Cambridge & Barts) Socs: Soc. Occupat. Med.

GUILD, Malcolm Donald Glencorse Barracks Medical Centre, Penicuik EH26 0NP; 16 Cairns Place, Muckhart, Dollar FK14 7LH Tel: 01259 781435 — MB ChB 1973 Ed.; MFHom 1984; DObst RCOG 1975. (Edinburgh) Civil. Med. Pract. Glencorse Barracks Med. Centre Penicuik. Prev: Princip. GP E. Calder W. Lothian & Dollar, Clackmannansh.

GUILDER, Thomas Fergusson 3 Orchard Way, Send, Woking GU23 7HS Tel: 01483 223055 Email: user397695@aol.com; Riverbank Surgery, Westcott St, Westcott, Dorking RH4 3PA Tel: 01306 875577 Fax: 01306 883230 — MB ChB 1974 Aberd.; MRCGP 1978; DRCOG 1976. (Aberdeen)

GUILDFORD, Michael Andrew 1 Daisy Bank Drive, Sandbach CW11 4JR — MB ChB 1993 Liverp.

GUILDING, Anne Margaret Harboury, Marley Lane, Haslemere GU27 3PS Tel: 01428 651318 Email: anne.guilding@btinternet.com — MB BS 1972 Lond.; FRCR 1978. Roy. W. Sussex Trust, St. Richard's Hosp., Chichester; Cons. Radiol. King Edwd. VII Hosp. Midhurst & St. Richards Hosp. Prev: Sen. Regist. (Radiol.) St. Geo. Hosp. Lond.; SHO St. Geo. Hosp. Lond.; Ho. Off. St. Helier Hosp. Carshalton.

GUILDING, Richard Charles Eldene Surgery, Eldene Health Centre, Eldene Centre, Swindon SN3 3RZ Tel: 01793 480111; 2 Mill Lane, Old Town, Swindon SN1 4HG — MB BS 1982 Lond.; MRCGP 1986; DRCOG 1984. (Roy. Free) Prev: Trainee GP Swindon VTS; Ho. Surg. Roy. Free Hosp. Lond.; Ho. Phys. Swindon HA.

GUILDING, Teresa Mary 72 York Road, Montpelier, Bristol BS6 5QF — MB ChB Bristol 1994.

GUILLE, John Leonard The Surgery, Units 7-8, Crusader Bus Park, Stephenson Road West, Clacton-on-Sea CO15 4TN Tel: 01255 233850 Fax: 01255 233801; Bethel, 22 Alton Road, Clacton-on-Sea CO15 1LB — BM 1980 Soton.; MRCGP 1986; DRCOG 1985. GP Represen. Directorate O & G Colchester Hosp.

GUILLE, Susan 6 The Close, Winchester SO23 9LS Tel: 01962 863603 — BM 1979 Soton. Prev: Clin. Asst. (Psychiat.) Guernsey.

GUILLEBAUD, Professor John Margaret Pyke Centre, 73 Charlotte St., London W1T 4PL Tel: 020 7530 3620 Fax: 020 7530 3646; Whiteleaf Mead, 14 Hid's Copse Road, Cumnor Hill, Oxford OX2 9JJ Tel: 01865 863982 Fax: 01865 861953 Email: j.guillebaud@lineone.net — MB BChir Camb. 1965; MA Camb. 1965; FRCS Ed. 1969; FRCOG 1984, M 1972; MFFP 1993. (Camb. & St. Bart.) Med. Dir. Margt. Pyke Centre Lond.; Prof. Family Plann. & Reproduc. Health UCL Med. Sch. 1992; Hon. Cons. United. Eliz. Garrett Anderson Hosp. & Hosp. for Wom. Soho. Socs: BMA; Soc. for Advancem. of Contracep.; Brit. Menopause Soc. Prev: Lect. & Sen. Regist. Nuffield Dept. O & G John Radcliffe Hosp.; Med. Off. Roy. Soc. Roy. Geogr. Soc. Expedit. to Centr. Brazil; Ho. Phys. & Ho. Surg. St. Bart. Hosp. Lond.

GUILLEM, Albert William Countisbury Avenue Surgery, 152 Countisbury Avenue, Llanrumney, Cardiff CF3 5YS Tel: 029 2079 2661 Fax: 029 2079 4537; 16 Launcelot Crescent, Redholme Village, Thornhill, Cardiff CF14 9AQ — MRCS Eng. LRCP Lond. 1980. Med. Off. HM Prison Cardiff.

GUILLEM, Vincent Louis (retired) Ashurst, Hawkins Lane, West Hill, Ottery St Mary EX11 1XG Tel: 01404 815941 — MB BS Lond. 1945.

GUILLOCHON, Maurice Auguste Henri David Place Medical Practice, 56 David Place, St Helier, Jersey JE1 4HY Tel: 01534 33322 — MRCS Eng. LRCP Lond. 1964.

GUILLOU, Professor Pierre John Academic Surgical Unit, Level 8, Clinical Sciences Building, St James's University Hospital, Leeds LS9 7TF Tel: 0113 206 5281 Fax: 0113 244 9618; 20 Rose Croft, East Keswick, Leeds LS17 9HR Tel: 01937 574652 — MB ChB Leeds 1970; BSc (Hons.) Leeds 1967, MD 1975; FRCS Eng. 1976; FRCPS Glas. (Hon.) 1997; FAMS 1998. (Univ. Leeds) Prof. Surg. Univ. Leeds; Cons. Surg. St Jas. Univ. Hosp.; Prof. Surg. Univ. Leeds 1993. Socs: Surg. Research Soc. (Ex-Comm. Mem.); Brit. Oncol. Assn.; Fell. Acad. of Med. Sci. Prev: Prof. Surg. Imperial Coll. Sci. Technol. & Med. Univ. Lond.; Ethicon Trav. Fell.sh. Coll. of Surgs. Malaysia; Sims Commonw. Prof.ship Roy. Colls. 1996.

GUILMANT, Max Victor 44 Dudsbury Road, Ferndown, Wimborne Tel: 01202 573679 — MRCS Eng. LRCP Lond. 1945. (Guy's) Prev: Asst. Orthop. Consult. Halifax Roy. Infirm.; Orthop. Regist. Roy. Vict. Hosp. Boscombe; Orthop. Regist. & Res. Surg. Off. Bedford Co. Hosp.

GUILOFF, Roberto Jaime Charing Cross Hospital, Fulham Palace Road, London W6 8RF Tel: 020 8846 1196 Fax: 020 8746 8420 Email: rguiloff@cxwms.ac.uk; Chelsea & Westminster Hospital, 369 Fulham Road, London SW10 9NH Tel: 020 8746 8322 Fax: 020 8846 7872 Email: n.guiloff@ic.ac.uk — LMSSA 1978 Lond.; BSc (Biol.) Lond. 1960, MD 1967; FRCP Lond. 1987; MRCP (UK) 1975. (Univ. Chile, Santiago) Cons. Neurol. Char. Cross & Chelsea & W.m. Hosps. Lond.; Hon. Sen. Lect. Univ. Lond. Socs: Hon. Sec. Brit. Soc. Clin. Physiol.; Assn. Brit. Neurol.; Counc. Roy. Soc. Med. (Clin. Neurosci.). Prev: Sen. Regist. Univ. (Neurol.) Nat. Hosp. Lond. & King's Coll. Hosp. Lond.; Regist. (Neurol.) Nat. Hosp. Lond.

GUINAN, Ian 246 Bowerham Road, Lancaster LA1 4LR — LMSSA 1992 Lond.

GUINAN, John Stanislaus 3 Loughshinney Bay, Skerries, County Dublin, Republic of Ireland; 34 Crescent Court, Blackpool FY4 1ST — MB BCh BAO 1938 NUI. (NUI) Prev: RAMC 1940-5, Maj.

GUINAN, Kevin Thomas Lache Health Centre, Hawthorn Road, Lache, Chester CH4 8HX Tel: 01244 671991 Fax: 01244 680729 — MB ChB 1991 Leeds; MRCGP 1995; DRCOG 1994. Prev: Trainee GP Chester VTS.

GUINANE, Matthew James 73A New Park Road, Brixton Hill, London SW2 4EN Tel: 020 8671 6353 — MB BS 1990 Lond.; BSc Lond. 1986, MB BS 1990. SHO (Geriat.) Highlands Hosp. Enfield. Prev: SHO (Gen. Med.) Broomfield Hosp. Chelmsford; SHO (A & E) Brook Hosp. Lond.

GUINDI, George Guindi, 16 Nether Street, London N12 7NL Tel: 020 8445 6582 — MRCS Eng. LRCP Lond. 1976. GP N Lond.; Cas. Off. Finchley Memor. Hosp. Lond. Prev: Sen. Regist. Roy. Nat. Throat, Nose, & Ear; Regist. (Plastics) Hull Roy. Infirm.

GUINEY, Margaret 7 Boverton Street, Roath Park, Cardiff CF23 5ES — MB BCh 1980 Wales.

GUINNESS, Elizabeth Anne 1 Cherchefelle, Chart Lane, Reigate RH2 7RN Tel: 017372 22352 — MB 1966 Camb.; BA Camb. 1962, MB 1966, BChir 1965; MRCPsych. 1982; DRCOG 1968. Cons. Child & Adolesc. Psychiat. Redhill & E. Surrey Health Dist. Socs: Assn. Family Ther. Prev: Sen. Regist. Maudsley Hosp. Lond.; Regist. (Psychiat.) Netherue Hosp. Coulsdon; Govt. Psychiat. Ment. Health Serv., Swaziland.

GUINNESS, Lucian Francis 1 Cherchfelle, Chart Lane, Reigate RH2 7RN Tel: 01737 222352 — MB 1966 Camb.; BChir 1965; MRCOG 1981; Dip. GU Med. Soc. Apoth. Lond. 1988. Phys. (Genitourin. Med.) St. Heilier, E. Surrey & Crawley. Socs: Soc. Study VD. Prev: Specialist (O & G), Swaziland.

GUION, Andrew John Post Graduate Dean's Office, Medical School, Queen's Medical Centre, Nottingham NG7 2UH Tel: 0115 970 9377; 1 Churchill Close, Arnold, Nottingham NG5 6QG Email: guionajg@innotts.co.uk — MB ChB 1974 Ed.; BSc (Med. Sci.) Ed. 1971, MB ChB 1974; MRCGP 1979. (Edin.) Quality Assur. Co-ordinator (Post-Grad. GP) Nottm. Socs: BMA. Prev: Princip. GP; Trainee GP Nottm. VTS; SHO (Psychogeriat.) Coppice Hosp. Mapperley.

GUIRGIS, Rifky Rizk Maternity Unit, Obstetric Secretary's Office, St Mary's Hospital, Milton Road, Portsmouth PO3 6AD Tel: 023 92 822331 — MB BCh 1979 Cairo; FRCOG 1999; MRCOG 1986. Cons. O & G St. Mary's Hosp. Portsmouth; Hon. Clin. Teach. Soton.

Med. Sch. Socs: Brit. Fertil. Soc. & Internat. Soc. Ultrasound in Obst. & Gyn. Prev: Sen. Regist. (O & G) St. Mary's Hosp. Portsmouth; Clin. Research Fell. Reproduc. Med. Humana Hosp. & Lond. Fertil. Centre Lond.; Regist. (O & G) St. Mary's Hosp. Portsmouth & W.. Gen. Hosp. Edin.

GUIRGUIS, Amir Fouad Amin 36 Whinney Heys Road, Blackpool FY3 8NP — MB BCh 1981 Ain Shams; MRCPI 1991.

GUIRGUIS, Emil Guirguis Rezkalla Anaesthetics Department, Tudor Wing, Hemel Hempstead Hospital, Hillfield Road, Hemel Hempstead HP2 4AD — MB BCh 1979 Ain Shams; MB BCh Ains Shams 1979.

GUIRGUIS, Helmy Morcos The Surgery, 23 Showell Green Lane, Sparkhill, Birmingham B11 4NP Tel: 0121 766 8447 Fax: 0121 753 0543 — MB BCh Cairo 1970. Prev: GP Solihull.

GUIRGUIS, Mamdouh Maher Hanna 48 Mount Road, Tettenhall Wood, Wolverhampton WV6 8HW — MB BCh 1981 Cairo; MRCOG 1988. Assoc. Specialist (O & G) Wolverhampton.

GUIRGUIS, Matta Wissa 53 Almond Grove, Worksop S80 1AU Tel: 01909 81482 — MB BCh 1952 Cairo; DMR Cairo 1963. (Kasr-el-Aini) Cons. Radiol. Notts. AHA (T).

GUIRGUIS, Meranda 53 Almond Grove, Worksop S80 1AU — BM BS 1995 Nottm.

GUIRGUIS, Refaat Saad Flat 9 Block 'D', Burton Hospital Centre, Belvedere Road, Burton-on-Trent DE13 8BY Tel: 01283 66333 — MB BCh 1977 Cairo; MRCOG 1988.

GUIRGUIS, Roshdy Waguih 34 Stone Lodge Lane, Ipswich IP2 9PF Tel: 01473 690130; Flat 10, Latymer Court, Hammersmith Road, London W6 7JB Tel: 020 8741 5015 — MB BS 1996 Lond.; BSc 1993 (2nd cl. Hons.). (Charing Cross and Westminster) SHO (A & E) Centr. Middlx. Hosp. Acton Lond.; Demonst. Anat. Imperial Coll. Sch. of Med. (Aug 1997 - Feb 1998). Prev: Pre-Registration Ho. Off. (Med.) Colchester Gen. Hosp.; Pre-Registration Ho. Off. (Surg.) W. Middlx. Hosp. Isleworth.

GUIRGUIS, Saneya Awad (Suzanme) West Hertfordshire NHS Trust, Hemel Hempstead & St Albans City Hospitals, Hemel Hempstead HP2 4AD Tel: 01442 213141 Fax: 01442 287148 — MB BCh Cairo 1970; FFA RCS Eng. 1980; DA (UK) 1973. Cons. Anaesth. (Chronic Pain) Hemel Hempstead & St. Albans Hosp. Trust. Socs: BMA; MDU; Vict. Bd. of Anasthesia. Prev: Sen. Cons. Alfred Hosp. Melbourne, Austral.; Dir. Anaesth. & Sen. Cons. Melbourne, Austral.

GUIRGUIS, Waguih Roshdy 34 Stone Lodge Lane, Ipswich IP2 9PF Tel: 01473 690130 Fax: 01473 683898 Email: erguirguis@doctors.org.uk; Flat 10, Latymer Court, Hammersmith Road, London W6 7JB Tel: 020 8741 5015 Fax: 0208741 5015 Email: wrguirguis@doctors.org.uk — MB BCh 1963 Cairo; DM Cairo 1969; MRCPsych 1976(Elected Fellow FRCPsych1997); Dip. Human Sex Lond. 1983; DPM Cairo 1971. (Kasr-el-Aini) Cons. Psychiat.The Priory Hosp. Chelmsford; Cons. Psychiat. The Suff. Nuffield Hosp. Ipswich. Socs: Assn. Sexual & Marital Therapists; Eating Disorders Assn.; Amer. Psychiatric Assoc. Prev: Sen. Regist. (Family & Child Psychiat.) Inst. Family Psychiat. Ipswich; Cons. Psychiat. E.Suff. NHS Trust.

GUITE, Hilary Frances BBG Health Authority, Marloue House, 1st Floor, 109, Station Rd, Sidcup DA15 7EU Tel: 0208 298 6220; Tel: 020 8858 2522 Email: hilaryguite@hotmail.com — MB BS 1981 Lond.; MSc Lond. 1990; MRCGP 1987; MFPHM RCP (UK) 1993; T(PHM) 1994; T(GP) 1991; DCH RCP Lond. 1985. (St. Bartholomew's London) Cons. Pub. Health Med. Bexley, Bromley Greenwich Health Auth. Prev: research fell. (Health Servs.) King's Coll. Lond.; Sen. Regist. (Pub. Health Med.) S. E. Thames RHA; Hon. Lect. (Pub. Health Med.) UMDS Lond. 1993.

GUIVER, Ian Michael (retired) Crossways, The Street, Ardleigh, Colchester CO7 7LD — MRCS Eng. LRCP Lond. 1950; MA, MB BChir Camb. 1951; DObst RCOG 1956. Prev: Ho. Surg. Lond. Hosp.

GUJRAL, Hardarsh Kaur Cassio Surgery, 66 Merton Road, Watford WD18 0WL Tel: 01923 226011; 807 St. Alban's Road, Watford WD25 0LE Tel: 01923 671193 — MB BS 1952 Delhi; DObst RCOG 1971.

GUJRAL, Manoranjan Kaur Cassio Surgery, 62-68 Merton Road, Watford WD18 0WL Tel: 01923 226011 Fax: 01923 817342 — MB BS 1981 Lond.; DRCOG 1989. (Char. Cross) GP in Gp. Pract.; Examr. DCH. 1997. Socs: Fell. Roy. Soc. Med.; W Herts. & Watford Med. Soc. Prev: Clin. Med. Off. S.W. Herts. HA.

GUJRAL, Sandeep Singh Bristol Urological Institute, Southmead Hospital, Westbury-on-Trym, Bristol BS10 5NB Tel: 0117 959 5187; Tilil House, 10 Ferndale Close, Almondsbury, Bristol BS32 4NU Tel: 01454 619554 Fax: 01454 619554 Email: ssguj@aol.com — MB BS 1991 Lond.; BSc (1st cl. Hons.) Biochem. Lond. 1988; FRCS Eng. 1995. (Med. Coll. St. Bart. Hosp.) Specialist Regist. (Urol.) Taunton & Som. Hosp.; Hon Surgic. Tutor Univ. Bristol Med. Sch. Socs: Brit. Assn. Urol. Surg.; Bristol Urological Soc.; B.M.A. Prev: Research Regist. (Urol.) Bristol Urol. Inst.; SHO Rotat. (Surg.) Oxf. Univ. & Glos. Roy. NHS Trust; SHO (Trauma & Orthop.) Leicester Roy. Infirm.

GUL, Javed Westborough Road Surgery, 6 Westborough Road, Westcliff on Sea SS0 9DR Tel: 01702 349957 Fax: 01702 437048; 235 Maplin Way N., Thorpe Bay, Southend-on-Sea SS1 3NY — MB BS 1978 Lond.; DRCOG 1982. (St. Geo.) GP W.cliff-on-Sea.

GULAMALI, Imtiaz Haiderali Vange Health Centre, Southview Road, Vange, Basildon SS16 4HD Tel: 01268 533151 Fax: 01268 282059 — MB BS 1984 Karachi; MRCGP 1992; MRCPI 1991.

GULATI, Mr Bhim Sain (retired) The Sheilin, Lanark Road, Carluke ML8 4HD — MB BS 1957 Bombay; FRCS Ed. 1977; FRCS Eng. 1968. Prev: Cons. ENT Surg. Lanark Health Dist.

GULATI, Rajesh Kulbhushan The Brooke Surgery, 20 Market Street, Hyde OK14 1AT Tel: 0161 368 3312 Fax: 0161 368 5670 — MB ChB 1994 Manch.; DCH 1997; DRCOG 1997; MRCGP 1998; DFFP 1997. (Manchester) GP Princip. Socs: Med. Protec. Soc. Prev: GP Regist.; SHO (Paediat., O & G & Psychiat.) Roy. Oldham Hosp.; GP Non-Princip.

GULATI, Rajinder Kumar The Surgery, 119 Northcote Road, Battersea, London SW11 6PW Tel: 020 7228 6762 — MB BS 1963 Rangoon.

GULATI, Rajiv 9 Fern Close, Beeston, Nottingham NG9 3DF — MB ChB 1992 Birm.; ChB Birm. 1992.

GULATI, Rakesh c/o Miss N. Tayal, 4 Cheltenham Way, Southport PR8 5NP — MB BS 1984 Nagpur.

GULATI, Ramesh Chandra Shiv Lodge Medical Centre, 357-359 Dickenson Road, Longsight, Manchester M13 0WQ Tel: 0161 224 6522/9465 Fax: 0161 225 5366 — MB BS 1968 Lucknow.

GULATI, Mr Roy, Maj. RAMC (retired) Beaumont Hospital, Old Hall Clough, Chorely New Road, Lostock, Bolton BL6 4LA Tel: 01204 404604 Fax: 01204 404488 — MB BS 1956 Lond.; FRCS Eng. 1960; MRCS Eng. LRCP Lond. 1956. Cons. Traum. & Orthop. Surg. Bolton Hosp. Gp. Prev: Regist. (Orthop.) Char. Cross Hosp. Lond.

GULATI, Sanjay 13 Parliament Court, Parliament Hill, London NW3 2TS — MB ChB 1993 Glas.

GULATI, Varsha Viran Health Centre, 291 Hesketh Lane, Tarleton, Preston PR4 6RJ Tel: 01772 812207 Fax: 01772 816967; 242 Hesketh Lane, Tarleton, Preston PR4 6RH Tel: 01772 814346 Email: v@gulati.demon.co.uk — MB BS 1969 Delhi; MRCP (UK) 1978; DCH Eng. 1973; DCH Delhi 1971. (Lady Hardinge Med. Coll.) GP Viran Health Centre Tasleton Preston; Hosp. Pract. (Paediat.) Wigan Dist. Hosp.; Clin. Asst. (Rheum.) Wrightington Hosp. Wigan.

GULL, Mrs Sarah Elizabeth West Suffolk Hospital, Hardwick Lane, Bury St Edmunds IP33 2QZ Tel: 01284 713000 Fax: 01284 701993; South Hill, 42 Southgate St, Bury St Edmunds IP33 2AZ Tel: 01284 754838 — MB BS 1979 Lond.; FRCS Ed. 1983; MRCOG 1986. (Guy's) Cons. Gyn. W. Suff. Hosp. Bury St. Edmunds.; Grad. Course Supervisor Univ of Camb. Clin. Sch.; Governing Body Fell Lucy Cavendish Coll. Camb. Socs: BMA; BSCCP (coloscopy); BSSVD (Vulrai soc). Prev: Sen. Regist. (Obst. & Gyn) Addenbrooke's Hosp. Camb.

GULL, Sobbia Flat MC 30, Leighton Hospital, Middlewich Road, Crewe CW1 4QJ Tel: 01270 255141 — MB ChB 1998 Liverp.; MB ChB Liverp 1998; BSc (Hons) Anat & Human Biol, 1996. SHO A & E, Rotat., Leighton Hosp.

GULLAM, Joanna Elizabeth 1 Pembroke Close, The Mount, Par PL24 2BT — MB ChB 1998 Leic.; MB ChB Leic 1998.

GULLAN, Mr Richard Wilson Kings College Hospital, Denmark Hill, London SE5 9RS Tel: 020 7737 4000 Fax: 020 7346 3280 — MB BS 1977 Lond.; BSc 1978 (Hons. Physiol.) Lond.; FRCS Eng. 1983; MRCP (UK) 1982. (St. Bart.) Cons. Neurosurg. Kings Coll. Hosp. Lond.; Hon. Cons. Neurosurg. Maudsley Hosp. Lond. Socs: Fell. Med. Soc. Lond.; BMA; Soc. Brit. Neurol. Surgs. Prev: Sen. Regist. (Neurosurg.) Guy's, Maudsley & Brook Hosps. Lond.; Regist.

(Neurosurg.) W.. Gen. Hosp. & Roy. Infirm. Edin.; Ho. Surg. Surgic. Profess. Unit St. Bart. Hosp. Lond.

GULLICK, David Lionel (retired) 1 Heathbrow Road, Welwyn AL6 0QG Tel: 01438 714016 — MB BS Lond. 1943. Prev: Exec. Med. Adviser BUPA.

GULLIFORD, Catherine Jean Flat 4, 50/52 Woodside Road, Portswood, Southampton SO17 2GQ — BM 1998 Soton.; BM Soton 1998.

GULLIFORD, John Andrew Guy (retired) 20 St Michaels Road, Llandaff, Cardiff CF5 2AP — MRCS Eng. LRCP Lond. 1939; LMSSA Lond. 1936.

GULLIFORD, Martin Christopher Department Public Health Medicine, UMDS Guy's Hospital, Capital House, 42 Western St., London SE1 3QD Email: m.gullford@umds.ac.uk — MB BS 1980 Lond. Sen. Lect. (Pub. Health Med.) United Med. & Dent. Schs. Guy's Hosp. Lond.

GULLIFORD, Peter St Marys Surgery, Applethwaite, Windermere LA23 1BA Tel: 01539 488484 Fax: 01539 442838 — BM BCh 1984 Oxf.; MA MedSci. Camb. 1981 BM BCh Oxf. 1984; MRCGP 1989; DRCOG 1988; DCH RCP Lond. 1986. GP Windermere. Prev: Clin. Asst. (Geriat.) S. Cumbria HA.

GULLIFORD, Timothy John Godfrey 89 Melbourne Grove, London SE22 8RR — MB BS 1985 Lond.

GULLIVER, Simon Alistair 87 Ring Road, Cross Gates, Leeds LS15 7QB — MB BChir 1993 Camb.; MA Camb. 1994; MRCGP 1998; DRCOG 1997. (Camb.)

GULLY, Karen Sian — MB ChB 1986 Bristol; MRCGP 1990; DRCOG 1990; DCCH 1991. GP Retainer, Old Castle Surg. Bridgend.

GULY, Henry Raymund A&E Dept, Derriford Hospital, Derriford, Plymouth PL6 8DH Tel: 01752 777111 Email: henry.guly@phnt.swest.nhs.uk; The Shrubbery, Bedford Road, Horrabridge, Yelverton PL20 7QH — MB BS 1974 Lond.; MB BS (Hons.) Lond. 1974; FRCP Lond. 1994; MRCP (UK) 1977; FFAEM 1993; MRCGP 1978; DCH Eng. 1978; DRCOG 1977. (St. Mary's) Cons. A & E Derriford Hosp. Plymouth; Hon. Civil. Cons. A & E RN.; Hon. Sen. Lect. A&E Plymouth PostGrad. Med. Sch. Prev: Cons. A & E Roy. Hosp. Wolverhampton; Ho. Surg. St. Mary's Hosp. Lond. (Harrow Rd. Br.); Ho. Phys. Edgware Gen. Hosp.

GULY, John Kenelm 81 Shirley Avenue, Southampton SO15 5NH Tel: 02380 772507 — MB BS 1951 Lond.; DMJ Soc. Apoth. Lond. 1964. (St. Mary's) Socs: Brit. Acad. Forens. Sci.; Coroners' Soc. Prev: Ho. Surg. St. Mary's Hosp. & Colindale Hosp. Lond.

GULY, Olivia Claire Ruth Langdale Unit, Whittingham Hospital, Whittingham, Preston PR3 2JH Tel: 01772 865531 Fax: 01772 866133; Edenfield Centre, Prestwich Hospital, Bury New Road, Prestwich, Manchester M25 3BL Tel: 0161 773 9121 Fax: 0161 798 7877 — MB BS 1981 Lond.; MRCPsych 1986. Cons. Forens. Psychiat. N. W.. RHA.

GULYA'S, Larissa Magdalena 3 Granary Court, St Andrews Gate, York YO1 7JR — MB BS 1994 Lond.

GUMB, Jacqueline Patricia The Surgery, St. Mary Street, Thornbury, Bristol BS35 2AT Tel: 01454 413691 Fax: 01454 411141; Orchard House, Old Gloucester Road, Thornbury, Bristol BS35 3UG — MB ChB 1980 Bristol; MB ChB (Hons.) Bristol 1980; MRCP (UK) 1983; DCH RCP Lond. 1987; DRCOG 1987. (Bristol) Prev: SHO (Paediat.) Bristol; Regist. (Med.) Nottm. City Hosp.; SHO (Med.) Plymouth Gen. Hosps.

GUMBLEY, George Barrington Tel: 01792 850311; Scurlage Courtfarm, Scurlage, Reynoldston, Swansea SA3 1BA Tel: 01792 391500 Fax: 01792 391501 — MB ChB 1971 Birm.; MRCGP 1982. Medico-Legal Expert, Consg. Rooms in Bristol & Cardiff. Socs: BMA. Prev: Med. Off. (Occupat. Health) E. Birm. Hosp.

GUMBLEY, Michael Brook Cottage, Rooks Lane, Berkley, Frome BA11 5JD Tel: 01373 462072 Email: gumbley@rooks.demon.co.uk — MB BS 1984 Lond.; BSc Lond. 1981; MRCGP 1989; DRCOG 1988; DCH RCP Lond. 1986.

GUMBRIELLE, Thomas Paul Martin Department of Academic Cardiology, Freeman Hospital, Newcastle upon Tyne NE7 7DN — MB BCh BAO 1979 NUI; LRCPSI 1979.

GUMMERSON, Nigel William 10 Hillcroft Cl, Darrington, Pontefract WF8 3BD — BM BCh 1997 Oxf.

GUMMERY, Alan Roy The Surgery, Bridge St., Polesworth, Tamworth B78 1D Tel: 01827 892893; 90 Bedworth Road, Bulkington, Nuneaton CV12 9LL Tel: 01203 314042 — MB BS 1982 Newc.; MRCGP 1986; DRCOG 1985.

GUMPEL, James Michael Clementine Churchill Hospital, Sudbury Hill, Harrow HA1 3RX Tel: 020 8872 3872; 32 St Stephens Close, Avenue Road, London NW8 6DD Tel: 020 7722 2296 Fax: 020 7483 0194 Email: jmg@gumpel.co.uk — MA, BM BCh Oxf. 1960; FRCP Lond. 1979, M 1963. (St Thomas Hospital) Emerit. Phys. N.wick Pk. Hosp. Prev: Cons. Phys. N.wick Pk. Hosp. Harrow & Clin. Research Centre; Cons. Phys. MRC Rheum. Research Unit Taplow; Cons. Phys Mt. Vernon Hosp. N.wood.

GUMPEL, Shirley Martyn 43 Belsize Road, London NW6 4RX Tel: 020 7722 5680 — MB BS Lond. 1961; MSc Audiol. Med. 1991; RSCN 1956. Sen. Med. Clin. Off. (Paediat. & Audiol.) N. Paddington HA & St. Mary's Hosp. Lond. W2.; Paediat. Audiological Phys. Socs: Lond. Med. Soc.; FRCPCH. Prev: Ho. Surg. Middlx. Hosp. Lond.; Fell (Paediat.) Johns Hopkins Hosp. Baltimore, MD; MRC Research Fell. Hosp. Sick Childr. Gt. Ormond St.

GUMPERT, Ernest John Wallace Dane Hill Farmhouse, Kennett, Newmarket CB8 7QL Tel: 01638 751942 — MB BChir 1961 Camb.; MB Camb. 1961, BChir 1960; FRCP Lond. 1979, M 1967; MRCS Eng. LRCP Lond. 1961. (Camb. & Guy's) Emerit. Cons. Clin. Neurophysiol. & Neurol. Sheff. HA; Hon. Clin. Asst. (Applied Electrophysiol.) Nat. Hosp. Nerv. Dis. Qu. Sq. Lond.; Med. Mem. Pens. Appeal Tribunal; Examr. PLAB; Mem. Neurol. Comm. RCP Lond. Socs: Assn. Brit. Neurol. Prev: Acad. Regist. Univ. Dept. Clin. Neurol. Nat. Hosp. Qu. Sq.; Regist. (Neurol.) United Sheff. Hosps.; Ho. Surg. & Ho. Phys. Profess. Unit Guy's Hosp.

GUMPERT, Mr James Robert Wallace Royal Sussex County Hospital, Eastern Road, Brighton BN2 5BE Tel: 01273 696955; Park Gate, Ringmer, Lewes BN8 5RW Tel: 01273 813055 Email: robert.gumport@virgin.net — MB 1964 Camb.; BChir 1963 Camb.; FRCS Eng. 1969; FRCS Ed. 1966; MRCS Eng. LRCP Lond. 1962. (Camb. & Guy's) Cons. Gen. Surg., BrE. Surg. & Endocrinol. Brighton Healthcare Trust; Assit. Med. Director. Socs: Assn. Surg.; Brit. Assn. Surg. Oncol.; Brit. Assn. Of Endocrine Surg. Prev: Sen. Regist. (Surg.) Bristol Roy. Infirm.; Research Fell. & Regist. Rotat. (Surg.) Sheff. Roy. Infirm.; Surg. Resid. & Research Fell. (Surg.) Peter Bent Brigham, Boston, USA.

GUMPERT, Louise Charlotte Park Gate, Ringmer, Lewes BN8 5RW — MB BS 1993 Lond.

GUNARATNA, Ignatius Jayantha Care Perspectives, Burston House Hospital, Rectory Road, Burston, Diss IP22 5TU Tel: 01379 741562 Fax: 01379 740558 — MB BS 1980 Colombo; LLM 2001 Newc.; MRCPsych 1987. (Colombo, Sri Lanka) Cons. (Psychiat.) Care Perspectives Diss Norf. Socs: Roy. Coll. Psychiat.; Brit. Neuropsychiat. Assn.; BMA. Prev: Cons. (Psychiat.) Chesterfield; Sen. Regist. (Psychiat.) Brentry Hosp. Bristol; Regist. Rotat. (Psychiat.) Norwich Train. Scheme.

GUNASEKARA, Harsha Lankadari York Clinic, Guys Hospital, London SE1 3RR Tel: 020 7955 2804 — MRCS Eng. LRCP Lond. 1993. (UMDS Lond.) Regist. (Psychiat.) Guy's & St. Thos. Hosp. Lond.

GUNASEKARA, Kolita Vishvakeerthi 27 St George's Avenue, Grays RM17 5XB Tel: 01375 378840 — MB BS 1978 Sri Lanka.

GUNASEKARA, Ranjan Das 5 Ludham, Lismore Circus, London NW5 4SE — MB BS 1976 Colombo.

GUNASEKERA, Ananda Dias 19 Reynolds Road, New Malden KT3 5NG — MB BS 1964 Ceylon; MRCPI 1978; FFA RCS Eng. 1983.

***GUNASEKERA, Dushan S** 6 Goodrich HS, Sewardstone Road, London E2 9JN — MB BS 1997 Lond.; BSc Lond. 1995.

GUNASEKERA, Jude Bertram Laksiri 315 Canterbury Road, Westbrook, Margate CT9 5JA Tel: 01843 834956 — MB BS 1996 Lond.; BSc Lond 1993. (Kings' College, Lond)

GUNASEKERA, Kapila Dias 6 Beagles Close, Gosford, Kidlington OX5 2QJ — MB BS 1996 Lond.

GUNASEKERA, Nihal Prabhath Rohana Kettering General Hospital NHS Trust, Rothwell Road, Kettering NN16 8UZ Tel: 01536 492253 Fax: 01536 492296; 29 Poplars Farm Road, Barton Seagrave, Kettering NN15 5AE Tel: 01536 512303 — MB BS 1971 Ceylon; FRCP Lond. 1994; MRCP (UK) 1979; T(M) 1991. Cons. Phys. Kettering Gen. Hosp. Socs: Coun.(Oxf. Region) - Brit. Geriat.s Soc.

GUNASEKERA, Mr Wijitha Sri Lal 63 West Drive, Cheam, Sutton SM2 7NB — MB BS 1968 Ceylon; FRCS Eng. 1975.

GUNASINGHAM, Vimala Thameslink Healthcare Services NHS Trust, c/o Archery House, Bow Arrow Lane, Dartford DA2 6PB Tel: 01322 27211 Fax: 01322 223492 — MB BS 1965 Ceylon; MRCPsych 1984; DTM & H Liverp. 1980. Cons. Psychiat. Ment. Handicap Thameslink Healthcare Servs. NHS Trust.

GUNASINGHE, Nihal Upali 23 Kenton Court, Kenton Road, Harrow HA3 8AQ — MB BS 1971 Ceylon.

GUNASUNTHARAM, Thambirajah The Surgery, 31 Prentis Road, London SW16 1QB Tel: 020 8769 3308 Fax: 020 8769 4855; 48 Leigham Avenue, London SW16 2PZ Fax: 020 8769 4855 — MB BS Ceylon 1970; MRCP (UK) 1977; MRCGP 1981. (Ceylon) Examr. Med. Pract. DSS & The Doctors Chambers. Prev: Vis. Phys. HM Prison Wandsworth; Mem. Fell.sh. Course III Dept. Gen. Pract. St. Thos. Med. Sch.; GP Tutor St. Thos. Med. Sch. Lond.

GUNATHILAGAN, Gunaratnam Jeyasingham 99 Landseer Avenue, London E12 6HS — BM 1994 Soton.

GUNATHILAKA, Haupage Sushila 6 Charleston Close, Feltham TW13 7LJ — MB BS 1976 Sri Lanka; MRCS Eng. LRCP Lond. 1987; DA (UK) 1984; FFA RCSI 1991.

GUNATILLEKE, Andrew 30 Mill Green London Road, Mitcham Junction, Mitcham CR4 4JE — MB BS 1994 Lond.

GUNAWARDANA, Ariyawansa Abeyweera Pinfold Health Centre, Bloxwich, Walsall WS3 3JJ Tel: 01922 494949; 27 Redruth Road, Gillity Village, Walsall WS5 3EJ Tel: 01922 642447 — MB BS 1955 Ceylon; TDD Ceylon 1958. (Colombo) Family Pract. Comm. Walsall. Socs: Med. Protec. Soc. Prev: Regist. (Chest Med.) Oldham AHA.

GUNAWARDANA, Sunila Shanthi 24 Howton Place, Bushey Heath, Watford WD23 1HX — MB BS 1969 Ceylon; MRCP (UK) 1978.

GUNAWARDENA, Harsha 17 Kilncroft, Hemel Hempstead HP3 8HH — MB ChB 1997 Bristol.

GUNAWARDENA, Sayomi Abeysinghe 20 The Glade, Welshwood Park, Colchester CO4 3JD — MB BS 1996 Lond.

GUNAWARDENA, Shirani Mendis 9 Timothy Rees Close, LLandaff, Cardiff CF5 2RH Tel: 029 2056 2633 — MB BS 1975 Sri Lanka; DO RCPSI 1983. Clin. Asst. Roy. Hamadryad Hosp. Cardiff; GP Cardiff.

GUNAWARDENE, Kulasiri Abeyasingha Chiltern House, Bells Hill, Stoke Poges, Slough SL2 4EG Tel: 01753 642222 Fax: 01753 647030 Email: kulariri.gunawardene@clinic.chiltern.com; 2 Prides Crossing, Ascot SL5 7LP — MB BS 1971 Ceylon; MD Ceylon 1976; MRCP (UK) 1978; LRCP LRCS Ed. LRCPS Glas. 1979. Dir. (Clin. Research) Chilten Internat. Bucks.; Sen. Fell. (Med.) Heatherwood & Wexham Pk. Hosps. Trust. Socs: Brit. Thorac. Soc.; Eur. Respirat. Soc.; BMA. Prev: Cons. Respirat. & Gen. Med. Riyadh Milit. Hosp., Saudi Arabia.

GUNDA, Austin Faison 36 Biddall Drive, Manchester M23 1PF — MB ChB 1984 Manch.; MB ChB Manch. l984. SHO (Gen. Med.) Gwynedd HA. Socs: Med. Protec. Soc. Prev: SHO (Gen. Med.) Birch Hill Hosp. Rochdale & Halton Gen. Hosp. Runcorn.

GUNDKALLI, Abdulrazak Akbarsaheb (Surgery), 11 Market Place, South Normanton, Alfreton DE55 2BN Tel: 01773 810207 Fax: 01773 863653; 7 Copsewood, Broadmeadows, South Normanton, Alfreton DE55 3NQ Tel: 01773 811750 — MB BS 1965 Karnatak; DRCOG 1978. (Karnatak Med. Coll. Hubli) Socs: Med. Protec. Soc. Prev: GP Horsham; SHO (O & G) Leighton Hosp. Crewe; SHO (Obst.) St. David's Hosp. Bangor.

GUNDKALLI, Irfana 7 Copsewood, Broadmeadows, South Normanton, Alfreton DE55 3NQ — BChir 1996 Camb.

GUNDLE, Mr Roger Nuffield Orthopaedic Centre NHS Trust, Headington, Oxford OX3 7LD Tel: 01865 741155 Fax: 01865 742348 Email: roger.gundle@noc.anglox.nhs.uk; 5 The Green, Horton-cum-Studley, Oxford OX33 1AE Tel: 01865 358928 — BM BCh 1983 Oxf.; DPhil Oxf. 1995, MA 1989; MA Camb. 1984; FRCS (Orth.) 1994; FRCS Eng. 1988. Cons. Orthop. Surg. Nuffield Orthop. Centre Oxf.; Lect. In Human Anat. Univ Coll Oxf.; Hon. Sen. Clin. Lect. in Orthopaedic Surg., Univ. of Oxf. Socs: Brit. Orthopaedic Assoc. fell; Brit. Orthopaedic Research Soc. Mem.; Brit. Hip Soc. Mem. Prev: Clin. Lect. (Orthop. Surg.) Nuffield Orthop. Centre Oxf.; Regist. (Traum. & Orthop. Surg.) John Radcliffe Hosp. Oxf.; SHO (Gen. Surg.) Glos. Roy. Hosp.

GUNDLE, Valerie 69 Southernhay Road, Stoneygate, Leicester LE2 3TP — MB ChB 1982 Sheff. SCMO (Dermat.) Leicester.

GUNDRY, Alexandra Clare 20 Town End Street, Godalming GU7 1BH — MB BS 1991 Lond.

GUNDRY, David Roland Tyeth East Street Medical Centre, East Street, Okehampton EX20 1AY Tel: 01837 52233 Fax: 01834 54950 — MB 1973 Camb.; BChir 1972; MRCP (UK) 1975; MRCGP 1979; DRCOG 1979. (Camb. & St. Bart.) Community Hosp. Phys. Prev: Princip. Med. Off. E. Outer Is.s Province Solomon Is.s; Chief Med. Off. W.. Province Solomon Is.s.

GUNDRY, Mr Michael Francis Laurel House, Rectory Lane, Chart Sutton, Maidstone ME17 3AW Tel: 01622 844134 — MB BS 1963 Lond.; FRCS Eng. 1970; MRCS Eng. LRCP Lond. 1963; FCOphth 1990; DO Eng. 1967; T(Ophth) 1991. (St. Mary's) Cons. Ophth. Surg. Kent Co. Ophth. Hosp. Maidstone. Prev: Sen. Regist. Moorfields Eye Hosp. Lond. (City Rd. Br.); SHO W.. Ophth. Hosp. Lond.; SHO Guy's-Maudsley Neurosurg. Unit Lond.

GUNDUR, Mr Narayan Shambhurao E.N.T. Department, Royal Berkshire Hospital, London Road, Reading RG1 5AN — MB BS 1972 Karnatak; FRCS Ed. 1986; DLO Eng. 1979. (Karnatak Med. Coll. Hubli) Regist. (ENT) Roy. Berks. Hosp. Reading. Prev: SHO (Gen. Surg.) Rossendale Gen. Hosp.; SHO (ENT) Roy. Devon & Exeter Hosp. (W) Exeter; SHO (ENT) Roy. Hosp. Wolverhampton.

GUNETILLEKE, Lloyd Winstree Road Surgery, 84 Winstree Road, Colchester CO3 5PZ Tel: 01206 572372 Fax: 01206 764412; 42 Scythe Way, Prettygate, Colchester CO3 4SJ Tel: 01206 367171 — MB BS 1981 Sri Lanka; LRCS (Ed.); LRCP (Ed.); LRCPS 1986 (Glas.); DRCOG 1989. (Peradeniya, Sri Lanka) GP Princip. Socs: MDU. Prev: SHO (Gen. Neonat. & Community Paediat.) Wycombe Gen. Hosp.; SHO (A & E) Crawley Hosp.; Regist. (O & G) Crawley Hosp.

GUNJAL, Davinder 255 Bath Road, Hounslow TW3 3DA — MB ChB 1988 Dundee.

GUNN, Mr Alastair Woodside Cottage, West High House Farm, High House Road, Morpeth NE61 2YT Tel: 01670 503048 — MB BS 1961 Durh.; FRCS Eng. 1966. (Durh.) Hon. Cons. Surg. N.umbria Trust; Research Assoc. (Human Genetics) Univ. Newc. u. Tyne. Prev: Cons. Surg. N.d. AHA. Sen. Regist. Manch. Roy. Infirm.; Resid. Surg. Off. St. Marks Hosp. Lond.

GUNN, Alastair Turner Gray (retired) Home Farm, Wadenhoe, Peterborough PE8 5SX Tel: 01832 720769 — MB BChir 1951 Camb.; DObst RCOG 1955. Prev: Ho. Surg. (Obst.) Edgware Gen. Hosp.

GUNN, Mr Alexander Anton (retired) 17 Ravelston Gardens, Edinburgh EH4 3LE Tel: 0131 346 2664 — MB ChB Ed. 1950; ChM Ed. 1966; FRCS Ed. 1955. Prev: Cons. Surg. Bangour Hosp. Broxburn.

GUNN, Alexander Derek Gower, OBE (retired) Bulmershe Health Centre, University of Reading, Woodlands Avenue, Earley, Reading RG6 1HY Tel: 0118 931 4713 Fax: 0118 931 8847 — MRCS Eng. LRCP Lond. 1960; DPH Manch. 1964; DObst RCOG 1964. Med. Adviser Univ. Reading; Temporary Adviser Stud. Health WHO Geneva; Univ. Health. (Ex. Pres.).

GUNN, Andrew, RD (retired) Iatros Ltd, Prospect 2, Dundee Technology Park, Dundee DD2 1TY Tel: 01382 562111 Fax: 01382 561590 Email: iatrosltd@sol.co.uk — MB ChB 1959 Ed.; FRCS Ed. 1962. Scientif. Dir. Iatros Ltd. Dundee Technol. Pk. Prev: Cons. Surg. Dundee Teach. Hosps. NHS Trust.

GUNN, Andrew Christopher Milnrow Village Practice, 44-48 Newhey Road, Milnrow, Rochdale OL16 4EG; 32 Brookfield Drive, Littleborough OL15 8RH Tel: 01706 371309 Email: andrew.c.gunn@virgin.net — MB ChB 1988 Dundee. Socs: BMA. Prev: Trainee GP/SHO Rochdale VTS.

GUNN, Mr Andrew Livingston (retired) Christchurch Park Hospital, 57-61 Fonnereau Road, Ipswich IP1 3JN Tel: 01473 256071 — MB BChir 1956 Camb.; FRCS Eng. 1963; MRCS Eng. LRCP Lond. 1956. Active as Med. expert witness in personal injury. Prev: Cons. Orthop. Surg. Ipswich Hosps.

GUNN, Audrey Fraser Stonebow Unit, County Hospital, Union Walk, Hereford HR1 2ER Tel: 01432 355444; Beaulieu, Millway, Sutton St. Nicholas, Hereford HR1 3BQ Tel: 01432 880426 — MB ChB 1960 Aberd. (Aberd.) Assoc. Specialist (Psychiat.) Stonebow Acute Psychiat. Unit. Hereford. Prev: Regist. (Anaesth.) Derby Gp. Hosps.

GUNN, Catriona Jean — MB ChB 1988 Ed.; DFFP; MRCGP 1995; DRCOG 1993. (Edinburgh) p/t GP Fordingbridge Retainer Scheme; CMO Family Plann.

GUNN, Colin (retired) 12 Abbots Walk, Kirkcaldy KY2 5NL — MB ChB 1952 St. And.; DObst RCOG 1959. Clin. Asst. Roy. Infirm. Edin. Prev: Ho. Off. Vict. Hosp. Kirkcaldy.

***GUNN, Elizabeth Jane** 7 Aspen Fold, Oswaldtwistle, Accrington BB5 4PH Tel: 01254 239769 — MB ChB 1995 Manch.

GUNN, Mr Iain Gillies Ach-Na-Muilne, Sheriffmlll, Elgin IV30 6UH Tel: 01343 7447 — MB ChB 1975 Glas.; FRCS Glas. 1979; FRCS Ed. 1979. Cons. Surg. Dr. Gray's Hosp. Elgin. Prev: Sen. Regist. (Surg.) Glas. Roy. Infirm.

GUNN, Ian Robert Biochemistry Department, Law Hospital, Carluke Tel: 01698 361100 — MB ChB 1979 Dundee; MRCPath 1986. Cons. Biochem. Law Hosp. Lanarksh.

GUNN, James Castleiew, Roxburgh Road, Wick KW1 5HP — MB ChB 1991 Dundee.

GUNN, James Hamilton (retired) 34 Brookside, Tupsley, Hereford HR1 2RW — MRCS Eng. LRCP Lond. 1964. Assoc. Specialist Stonebow Unit Hereford. Prev: Med. Asst. St. Mary's Hosp. Hereford.

GUNN, Professor John Charles, CBE Institute of Psychiatry, Camberwell, London SE5 8AF Tel: 020 7919 3123 Fax: 020 7919 3754 Email: j.gunn@iop.bpmf.ac.uk — MB ChB Birm. 1961; MD Birm. 1969; FRCPsych 1980, M 1971; DPM Lond. 1966. (Birm.) Prof. Forens. Psychiat. Inst. Psychiat. Lond.; Hon. Cons. Bethlem Roy. & Maudsley Hosps. Lond. Socs: Fell. Roy. Soc. Med. Prev: Dir. Special Hosps. Research Unit. DHSS Lond.; Regist. Maudsley Hosp. Lond.; Ho. Off. Qu. Eliz. Hosp. Birm.

GUNN, John Fraser Mossbank Cottage, Bathgate EH48 1JX — MB ChB 1977 Ed.

GUNN, Julian Philip George Department of Cardiology, Northern General Hospital, Herries Road, Sheffield S5 7AU Tel: 0114 271 5814 Fax: 0114 261 9587 Email: j.gunn@sheffield.ac.uk; Old Mill House, Old Mill Lane, Thurgoland, Sheffield S35 7EG — MB BChir 1984 Camb.; MA Camb. 1984; MRCP (UK) 1988; MD 1999 Camb. Sen.Lect.& Hon Cons. (Cardiol) Univ. Sheff. Socs: Brit.Cardiac Soc.; Brit.Cardiac. Interven. Soc. Prev: Lllect & Hon Sen. Regist. (Cardiol) Univ. Sheff.

GUNN, June Mary Edinburgh Sick Children's NHS Trust, 10 Chalmers Crescent, Edinburgh EH9 1TS Tel: 0131 536 0470 Fax: 0131 536 0570; 43 East Trinity Road, Edinburgh EH5 3DL — MD 1955 Malta; MD Malta 1958; BPharm 1955. (Malta) Clin. Med. Off. (Community Paediat.) Edin. Sick Childr. NHS Trust. Prev: MRC Research Fell. (Radiat. Oncol.) W.. Gen. Hosp. Edin.; Ho. Off. Fulham Hosp.; Dept. Med. Off. (Pub. Health) W. Lothian CC.

GUNN, Karoline Liesel Trevilla Grange, Trevilla, Feock, Truro TR3 6QG — MB BS 1991 Melbourne.

GUNN, Kathleen London Road South Surgery, 366 London Road South, Lowestoft NR33 0BQ Tel: 01502 573333 Fax: 01502 581590 — MB ChB 1973 Manch.

GUNN, Kevin Paul 1 Queens Avenue, Broadstairs CT10 1EH — MB ChB 1979 Birm.; MSc (Neurochem.) Lond. 1984; MFPM 1990; MRCPsych 1985. Research Phys. Pfizer Centr. Research Sandwich. Prev: Regist. (Psychiat.) Newtown Hosp. Worcester; Wellcome Research Worker, Inst. Psychiat.

GUNN, Margaret Bernadette Quayside Medical Practice, 82-84 Strand Road, Londonderry BT48 7NN Tel: 028 7126 2790 Fax: 028 7137 3729; 66 Foreglen Road, Claudy, Londonderry BT47 4EB — MB BCh BAO 1982 Belf.; MRCGP 1987; DRCOG 1986; DCH RCP Lond. 1985. (Queen's University Belfast)

GUNN, Melanie Catherine Woodside Cottage, West High House Farm, High House Road, Morpeth NE61 2YT; 71 Woodbine Road, Gosforth, Newcastle-upon-Tyne NE3 1DE — MB ChB 1992 Leic.; MD 2001; MRCP 1996. Gastroenterol. Specialist Regist., Darlington Memor. Hosp./ Specialist Regist. Rotat. N.ern Deneary. Prev: research fell. August 1996 1998; Gastro SHO May 1996 July 1996; Dermat. SHO Feb 1996 April 1996.

GUNN, Mr Rodney Spencer Milton Keynes Hospital, Standing Way, Eaglestone, Milton Keynes MK6 5LD Tel: 01908 243005 Fax: 01908 243151 — MB BS 1970 Lond.; BSc 1967 Lond.; MRCS Eng. LRCP Lond. 1970 Lond.; FRCS Eng. 1975; MRCS Eng. LRCP Lond. 1970. (King's Coll. Hosp.) Cons. Orthop. Surg. Milton Keynes NHS Trust. Socs: Fell. BOA; Brit. Assn. Surg. Knee. Prev: Sen. Regist. (Orthop. & Trauma) Oxon. HA (T); Research Fell. Nuffield Dept. Orthop. Surg. Oxf. Univ.

GUNN, Sheila Catherine Saintfield Health Centre, Fairview, Saintfield, Ballynahinch BT24 7AD Tel: 028 9751 0575 — MB BCh BAO 1987 Belf.; MRCGP 1991; DCCH RCP Ed. 1992; DMH Belf. 1992. Socs: BMA.

GUNN, Stephen David Leak, Gunn, Fourie, Brennan and Roberts, Witton Medical Centre, 29-31 Preston Old Road, Blackburn BB2 2SU Tel: 01254 262123 Fax: 01254 695759 — MB ChB 1982 Manch.; BSc St. And. 1979; MRCGP 1986; DRCOG 1986. GP Blackburn.

GUNN, William James 140a Comiston Road, Edinburgh EH10 5QN; 12 Abbots Walk, Kirkcaldy KY2 5NL — MB ChB 1986 Aberd. SHO (Gen. Med.) Kirkcaldy. Prev: SHO (Chest Med.); SHO (Geriat. Med.) Kircaldy.

GUNNA, Mr Bhagavanth Reddy 68 Clevely Park, Belfast BT8 6NB — MB BS 1979 Kakaliya; FRCS Glas. 1987.

GUNNEBERG, Andar Department of Chemical Pathology, Morriston Hospital, Swansea SA6 6NL; Min y Mynydd, 92 Rhyddwen Road, Craig-Cefn-Parc, Swansea SA6 5RG — MB ChB 1982 Glas.; BSc Hons. Glas. 1979; MRCPI 1989; MRCPath 1995. (Glas. Univ.) Cons. Chem. Path. Morriston Hosp. Swansea. Prev: Sen. Regist. (Chem. Path.) S.mead Hosp. Bristol; Regist. (Chem. Path.) Univ. Hosp. Wales Cardiff; Regist. (Med.) Vale of Leven Hosp. Balloch.

GUNNEBERG, Christian T/R, 255 Wilton Street, Glasgow G20 6DE Tel: 0141 946 3738 — MB ChB 1985 Glas.; MSc Epidemiol. Lond. 1990; BSc (Hons. Immunol.) Glas. 1983; MFPHM RCP (UK) 1992; DTM & H Liverp. 1988. Cons. Pub. Health Argyll & Clyde HB Paisley; Hon. Sen. Lect. (Pub. Health) Univ. Glas.

GUNNEBERG, Nadja Endrick Hill, Main St., Drymen, Glasgow G63 0BG — MB ChB 1987 Glas.; MRCGP 1993; DRCOG 1992; Dip. GU Med. Soc. Apoth. Lond. 1991. Clin. Asst. (Genitourin. Med.) Alexandria. Prev: SHO (Psychiat.) Clackmannan Co. Hosp.; SHO (Ophth.) Glas. Roy. Infirm.; Trainee GP Birm.

GUNNELL, David John Department of Social Medicine, Bristol University, Canynge Hall, Whiteladies Road, Bristol BS8 2PR Tel: 0117 928 7253 Fax: 0117 928 7236 Email: d.j.gunnell@bristol.ac.uk — MB ChB 1984 Bristol; (Epidemology) PhD 1996; MSc Medical Statistics (Distinction) University of London 1997; MRCGP 1989; MFPHM 1993 (UK); DRCOG 1987; Cert. Family Plann. JCC 1987; FFPHM 2000 (UK). (Bristol Univ.) Sen. Lect. (Pub. Health Med. & Epidemiol.) Bristol Univ. Prev: Lect. in Publ. Health Med. Univ. Bristol; Sen. Regist. (Pub. Health Med.) Som. HA; SHO (Psychiat.) Bristol Train. Scheme.

GUNNER, Thomas (retired) Gable Crest, Stibbs Hill, Bristol BS5 8NA Tel: 0117 967 3509 — MB BCh Wales 1952. Prev: Cas. Off. Roy. Gwent Hosp. Newport.

GUNNING, Mr Alfred James Department of Cardiothoracic Surgery, Ward D27, Groote Schuur Hospital, Cape Town 7925, South Africa Tel: 404 9111; 386 Banbury Road, Oxford OX2 7PW Tel: 01865 58966 — MB ChB 1943 Cape Town; MA Oxf. 1964; FRCS Eng. 1949; FACS 1976; DLO Eng. 1950. Socs: Soc. Thoracic Surgs. Gt. Brit. Prev: Cons. Cardio-Thoracic Surg. Oxf. HA (T) Oxf. RHA; 1st Asst. Nuffield Dept. Surg. Radcliffe Infirm. Oxf.

GUNNING, Donald Peter Buchan Lodge, Pedwell Way, Norham, Berwick-upon-Tweed TD15 2LD — MB BS 1981 West. Austral.

GUNNING, Mr Keith Andrew Darlington Memorial Hospital, Hollyhurst Road, Darlington DL3 6HX Tel: 01325 743501 Fax: 01325 743044 — MB BS 1986 Newc.; FRCS 1999; FRCS Ed. 1992. (Univ. Newc. u. Tyne) Cons. Surg. Darlington Memor. Hosp., Darlington, Co. Durhum; Track Med. Off., Newc. Diamonds Speedway Team, Newc. upon Tyne. Socs: N. of Eng. Surg. Soc., Ungreyed Mem. 2000-2002. Prev: Trauma Fell. Liverp. Hosp. NSW, Australia.

GUNNING, Kevin Elwyn James Department of Anaesthesia, Addenbrooke's Hospital, Hills Road, Cambridge CB2 2QQ Tel: 01223 217434 Fax: 01223 217223 Email: kevin@kegunn.demon.co.uk — MB BS 1975 Lond.; FRCS Eng. 1980; FFA RCS Eng. 1985. ((St. Bart.)) Cons. Anaesth. & IC Addenbrooke's Hosp. Camb.; Assoc. Lect. (Med.) Univ. of Camb. Socs: Intens. Care Soc. & Europ. Intens. Care Soc.; Soc. Critical Care Med. Prev: Sen. Regist. (Anaesth.) St. Geo. & W.m. Hosps. Lond.;

Regist. (Anaesth.) Kings Coll. Hosp. Lond.; Regist. (Surg.) Kings Coll. Hosp. Lond.

GUNNING, Lucy Mary 3 Old Forge Manor, Upper Malone Rd, Belfast BT10 0HY — MB BCh BAO 1997 Belf.

GUNNING, Malcolm Paul 11 Ardent Close, Steynton, Milford Haven SA73 1AU Tel: 01646 695567 — MB BS 1989 Lond.

GUNNYEON, William James Liberty Occupational Health, Sunnybank Road, Aberdeen AB24 3NG Tel: 01224 492884 Fax: 01224 487812 Email: billigunnyeon@libertyhealth.co.uk; 10 Laverock Road, Newburgh, Ellon AB41 6FN Tel: 01358 789796 — MB ChB 1977 Dundee; FRCP (Lond.) 1999; FFOM RCP Lond. 1994, MFOM 1988, AFOM 1985; MRCGP 1983; DIH Eng. 1984. (Univ. Dundee) Dir. Occupat. Health Liberty Occupat. Health Ltd. Aberd.; Hon. Sen. Lect. (Environm. & Occupat. Med.) Univ. Aberd. Socs: Chairm. Assoc. Local Authorities Med. Advisers; Soc. Occup. Med. Prev: Princip. Med. Adviser Grampian Regional Counc. Aberd.; Sen. Med. Adviser OMS Ltd. Aberd.; Med. Off. RAF.

GUNPUT, Mitra Dave Glaxo Wellcome Research & Development, Clinical Pharmacology, Greenford Road, Greenford UB6 0HE Tel: 020 8966 2533 Email: mdg26058@ggr.co.uk; 14 Aspen Close, Ealing, London W5 4YG Tel: 020 8932 6651 — MB ChB 1984 Bristol; Dip. Pharm. Med. RCP 1997. (Univ. Bristol) Sen. Research Phys. (Clin. Pharmacol.) Glaxo Wellcome Research & Developm. Socs: Fell. RSM. Prev: Regist. St Bart. Hosp. Lond.; SHO Newham Gen. Hosp. Lond.; Resid. Med. Off. King Edwd. VII Hosp. for Offs. Lond.

GUNRAJ, David Reginald (retired) 23 Barnfield, New Malden KT3 5RH — MB BCh BAO 1957 Belf.; FRCP Ed. 1994; MRCP Ed. 1966; MRCP Lond. 1966; DTM & H Eng. 1961; DCH Eng. 1961; DPH Belf. 1960; DObst RCOG 1959.

GUNSON, Eilidh Jane 1 Dene Royd Close, Stainland, Halifax HX4 9QP — MB ChB 1995 Manch.

GUNSON, Harold Hastings, CBE (retired) North Western RHA, Gateway House, Piccadilly S., Manchester M60 7LP Tel: 0161 236 2263 — MD 1962 Manch.; DSc Manch. 1978, MD 1962, MB ChB 1952; FRCP Lond. 1985, M 1980; MRCP (UK) 1987; FRCPath 1974, M 1963. Prev: Reader Human Serol. Univ. Manch.

GUNSON, Oliver Stuart Beaufort Road Surgery, 21 Beaufort Road, Southbourne, Bournemouth BH6 5AJ Tel: 01202 433081; 18 Bronte Avenue, Christchurch BH23 2LY Tel: 01202 473038 Email: ok.gunson@cwcom.net — BM 1992 Soton.; 2001 Diploma in Therapeutics, University of Cardiff School of Medicine; MRCGP 1998; DRCOG 1999. GP Princip. Bournemouth. Prev: Regist. (Med.) Redcliffe Hosp. Qu.sland, Austral; SHO (Orthop.) Poole Hosp.; SHO (c/o Elderly) Soton. Gen. Hosp.

GUNSTON, Emma Louise 13 Steeple Close, Church Gate, London SW6 3LE — MB BS 1996 Lond. (Char. Cross & Westm.) SHO (Surg./A & E/O & G) MaryBoro. Base Hosp. Qu.sland, Australia. Prev: Ho. Off. (Med.) Char. Cross Hosp. Lond.

GUNSTON, Ina Kathleen (retired) — MB ChB Birm. 1961. Prev: Sen. Med. & Health Off. Hong Kong Govt.

GUNSTONE, Ann Jane Meadowsweet, 11 Freshfield Road, Formby, Liverpool L37 3JA Tel: 01704 872879 — MB ChB Liverp. 1969; MCommH Liverp. 1977; MRCS Eng. LRCP Lond. 1969; MFFP 1993; FFA RCS Eng. 1973. (Liverp.) Assoc. Specialist (Community Child Health) Roy. Liverp. Childr. NHS Trust; Community Doctor (Family Plann. & Reproduc. Health) N. Mersey Community NHS Trust. Prev: Sen. Regist. (Anaesth. & Community Med.) Mersey RHA.

GUNSTONE, Christopher Charles Gordon Street Surgery, 72 Gordon Street, Burton-on-Trent DE14 2JB Tel: 01283 563175 Fax: 01283 500638; South Bank, 18 Stapenhill Road, Burton-on-Trent DE15 9AF Tel: 01283 68450 — MB ChB 1982 Dundee; MRCGP 1987; DCH RCP Lond. 1986; DRCOG 1986.

GUNSTONE, Eileen Marie Gordon Street Surgery, 72 Gordon Street, Burton-on-Trent DE14 2JB Tel: 01283 563175 Fax: 01283 500638; South Bank, 18 Stapenhill Road, Burton-on-Trent DE15 9AF Tel: 01283 68450 — MB ChB 1982 Dundee; MRCGP 1986; DCH RCP Lond. 1987; DRCOG 1985.

GUNSTONE, Richard Frank (retired) Walsgrave Hospital, Coventry CV2 2DX Tel: 01203 602020 Fax: 01203 622197 — MB BS Lond. 1959; BSc Lond. 1956; FRCP Lond. 1980, M 1965; MRCP Ed. 1965; MRCS Eng. LRCP Lond. 1959. Prev: Med. 1st Asst. St. Geo. Hosp. Lond.

GUNTHER, Amanda Louise 7 Grimston Road, London SW6 3QR — BM BS 1993 Nottm.

GUNTHER, Hugh Neville Carr 2 Fir Tree Close, Ascot SL5 9LJ Tel: 01990 23518 — MB 1964 Camb.; BChir 1963; FRCP 1989, M 1973. (Univ. Coll. Hosp.) Cons. Psychiat. (Geriats. & G.I.M.) Ashford Hosp. Middlx. & W. Middlx. Univ. Hosp. Socs: Brit. Geriat. Soc. & Hosp. Cons. & Specialists Assn.; Fell.RSM; BMA. Prev: Ho. Phys. Hackney Hosp. & N. Middlx. Hosp.; Ho. Surg. Whittington Hosp.

GUNTHER, Mavis Hilda Dorothea 18 Clarefield Court, North End Lane, Ascot SL5 0EA Tel: 01344 28532 — MRCS Eng. LRCP Lond. 1928; MA Camb. 1940, MD 1945, MB 1935, BChir 1928. (Camb. & Lond. Sch. Med. Wom.) Hon. Mem. Neonat. Soc. Socs: Hon. Mem. Brit. Paediat. Assn. Prev: Clin. Asst. & Research Worker Obst. Paediat. Dept. Univ. Coll. Hosp.; Lond.; Ho. Phys. Roy. Free Hosp.

GUNTIS, Edmon 1 Steele Road, London W4 5AE — MB ChB 1994 Liverp.

GUNTON, Helen Jane Hastings House, Kineton Road, Wellesbourne, Warwick CV35 9NF Tel: 01789 840245 Fax: 01789 470993 — MB ChB 1988 Birm.; LF Hom (Med) 2001; MFFP 1994; DRCOG 1991.

GUPPY, Amy Elizabeth 33 Lyveden Road, London SE3 8TP — MB BS 1996 Lond.

GUPPY, John Michael Lutterworth Health Centre, Gilmorton Road, Lutterworth LE17 4EB Tel: 01455 553531; Little Bones, Welford Road, South Kilworth, Lutterworth LE17 6EA Tel: 01858 575261 — MB BS 1962 Durh.; DObst RCOG 1965. Socs: Leic. Med. Soc.

GUPTA, Ajay Department of Radiology, George Eliot Hospital, College St., Nuneaton CV10 7DJ; Greenacres, South Lane, East Boldon NE36 0SP Tel: 01783 368484 — MB BS 1967 Calcutta; FFR RCSI 1976; DMRD Eng. 1974. Cons. Radiol i/c Sunderland Roy. Infirm. Prev: Sen. Radiol. E. India Clinic Ltd. Calcutta; Sen. Regist. & Regist. Sheff. HA.

GUPTA, Alok Deep 45 Fox Hollies Road, Walmley, Sutton Coldfield B76 2RL — MB BS 1987 India; MRCP (UK) 1993.

GUPTA, Aman Prakash 4 Kingston Hill, Cheadle SK8 1JS — MB ChB 1998 Manch.; MB ChB Manch 1998.

***GUPTA, Andy Neil** 166 Princes Gardens, London W3 0LN Email: andy.gupta@virgin.net — MB BS 1994 Lond.; BSc (Hons) 1991.

GUPTA, Anil John H.M. Institution, Broadmoor, Crowthorne — MB BS 1973 Bangalor; MB BS Bangalore 1973.

***GUPTA, Anupam** Grove House, Grove Lane, Wightwick, Wolverhampton WV6 8NJ — MB ChB 1994 Birm.

***GUPTA, Arun** 38 St Stephens Road, Selly Oak, Birmingham B29 7RP — MB ChB 1994 Birm.

GUPTA, Arun Kumar Department Anaesthesic, Box 93, Addenbrooke Hospital, Cambridge CB2 2QQ Tel: 01223 217434 Fax: 01223 217223; 19 Tothill Road, Swaffham, Cambridge CB5 0JX Tel: 01638 743719 Email: akgo1@globalnet.co.uk — MB BS 1986 Lond.; FRCA 1991; DA (UK) 1988; MA 2000. (St. Mary's Hosp. Lond.) Cons. Anaesth. & Neuro Intens. Care Addenbrookes Hosp. Camb. Director NeuroIntens. care.; Assoc. Lect. Univ. Camb. Socs: Assn. Anaesth. Gt. Brit. & Irel.; Intens. Care Soc.; Soc. Neurosurg. Anaesth. Critical Care. Prev: Sen. Regist. Camb.; Asst. Prof., Richmond Va, USA; Regist. (Anaesth.) Leicester, Boston & Derby.

GUPTA, Mr Arun Kumar Tel: 01784 884155 Fax: 01784 884640; 86 The Avenue, Sunbury-on-Thames TW16 5EX Tel: 01932 782026 — MB BS 1979 All India Inst. Med. Sciences; FRCSI 1991; MRCOphth 1990; DO RCS Eng. 1987. Cons. Ophth. Ashford & St Peters Hosps NHS Trust. Socs: Roy. Coll. Opthamol.; Roy. Coll Surg. Irel.; Amer Aca of Opthamologists.

GUPTA, Arvind Kumar Department of Clinical Neurophysiology, City Hospitals NHS Trust, Dudley Road, Birmingham B18 7QH Tel: 0121 507 5443 Fax: 0121 602 1038; 110 Hamilton Avenue, Abbeyfields, Halesowen B62 8SJ Tel: 0121 503 0205 Fax: 0121 503 0205 — MD (Psychiat.) Lucknow 1973, MD (Med.) 1970, MB BS 1966. (King Geo. Med. Coll.) Cons. Clin. Neurophysiol. W. Birm. HA. Socs: Internat. League against Epilepsy; Brit. League against Epilepsy; Brit. Clin. Neurophysiol. (EEG Soc).

GUPTA, Avinash Rosewood Medical Centre, 1 Rosewood Avenue, Elm Park, Hornchurch RM12 5BU Tel: 01708 451295; 9 Hamilton Avenue, Ilford IG6 1AE — MB BS 1990 Lond.; BSc (Hons.) Biochem. Lond. 1987; MRCGP 1994; DCH RCP Lond. 1993; DRCOG 1993. Prev: Trainee GP Newbury Pk. Healthcentre & Kings Geo.

Hosp. VTS; Ho. Off. (Med.) Frimley Pk. Hosp.; Ho. Off. (Surg.) St. Bart. Hosp. Lond.

GUPTA, Bhgwan Krishan Arun 8 Malden Park, New Malden KT3 6AS — MB BCh BAO 1977 Belf.

GUPTA, Bibek 27 Heol Buckley, Felinfoel, Llanelli SA15 4LB — MB BS 1971 Calcutta; MRCPsych 1985.

GUPTA, Binay Kumar 55 Dinerth Road, Rhos-on-Sea, Colwyn Bay LL28 4YG Tel: 01492 546371 Fax: 01492 546371 — MB BS Patna 1966.

GUPTA, Mr Bisheshwar Nath Oakhurst, 20 St George's Road, Bickley, Bromley BR1 2AX — MB BS 1959 Bihar; BSc Banaras Hindu 1953; FRCS Ed. 1973. (Darbhanga Med. Coll.) Socs: BMA; Overseas Doctors Assn.

GUPTA, Chaman Lall The Surgery, 2 Falconwood Parade, Welling DA16 2PL Tel: 020 8304 7662; Nikraj, 15 Wansunt Road, Bexley Village, Bexley DA5 2DQ — MB BS 1961 Panjab; MB BS Panjab (India) 1961; Cert JCC Lond. 1979. (Amritsar Med. Coll.) Prev: Regist. (Psychiat.) St. Wulstan's Hosp. Malvern.

GUPTA, Chandra Prakash The New Surgery, 27 Stock Road, Billericay CM12 0AH Tel: 01277 633144 Fax: 01277 633374; 10 Lion Lane, Billericay CM12 9DL Tel: 01277 659995 — MB BS 1967 Lucknow; DTCD Lucknow 1968. (King Geo. Med. Coll)

GUPTA, Deepa 68 St George's Road W., Bromley BR1 2NP — MB BS 1989 Lond.; LMSSA Lond. 1988. Ho. Phys. (Gen./Respirat. Med.) Bromley Area HA. Prev: Ho. Surg. Joyce Green Hosp. Dartford.

GUPTA, Deepa Sarah 48 Queens Gardens, Eaton Socon, St Neots, Huntingdon PE19 8DN — MB BChir 1994 Camb.

GUPTA, Mr Deepak 21 Maesglasnant, Cwmffrwd, Carmarthen SA31 2LP — MB BS 1985 Aligarh; MB BS Aligarh Muslim U India 1985; FRCS Ed. 1993.

GUPTA, Deepti Flat 1/L, 14 Lawrence St., Glasgow G11 5HQ — MB ChB 1997 Glas.

GUPTA, Devinder Infirmary Street Practice, 106 Infirmary Street, Blackburn BB2 5HS Tel: 01254 674665 Fax: 01254 696252 — MB BS 1967 Jammu & Kashmir. (Govt. Med. Coll. Srinagar) GP Blackburn.

GUPTA, Devkishan Roshanlal Accident & Emergency Department, Alexandra Hospital, Woodrow Drive, Redditch B98 7UB Tel: 01527 503030 Fax: 01527 517432; 39 Durley Dean Road, Selly Oak, Birmingham B29 6SA Tel: 0121 471 1662 Fax: 0121 471 1662 — MB BS 1975 Nagpur; MS Bombay 1978; FRCS Ed. 1986; FRCS Glas. 1986. (Mahatama Gandhi Inst. Med. Sci. Sewagram, India) Staff Grade (A & E) Alexandra Hosp. Redditch. Socs: Assoc. Fell. Accid. & Emerg. Assn.; MDU; BMA. Prev: Staff Grade (A & E) Qu. Med. Centre Univ. Hosp. Nottm.; Resid. Surg. Off. (Surg. & A & E) Goole Dist. Hosp.; Regist. (Gen. Surg.) Benenden Hosp. Cranbrook & LLa.lli Gen. Hosp. Dyfed.

***GUPTA, Emma** 36 Bantock Gardens, Finchfield, Wolverhampton WV3 9LL — MB ChB 1995 Birm.; MBCLB (Hons) Distinc. in Medicine.

GUPTA, Girish Dept of Dermatology, Monklands Hospital, Monkscourt Avenue, Airdrie ML6 0JS Tel: 01236 712862 Fax: 01236 713196 — MB ChB 1990 Manch.; MRCP (UK) 1994. (Manchester) Cons. (Dermat.) Monklands Hosp. Lanarksh. Prev: SHO (Gen. Med.) Stepping Hill Hosp. Stockport; SHO (Gen. Med.) Glan Clwyd Hosp. Wales.; SPR (Dermat.), Glas.

GUPTA, Gulshan Rai Dipple Medical Centre, Wickford Avenue, Pitsea, Basildon SS13 3HQ Tel: 01268 555782 Fax: 01268 551362; 12 Srorhams, Langdon Hills, Basildon SS16 5TT Tel: 01268 413305 — LRCPI & LM, LRSCI & LM 1961; LRCPI & LM, LRCSI & LM 1961. Prev: Sen. Med. Off. i/c Curative & Preven. Health Servs. Nairobi City Counc., Kenya.

GUPTA, Hari Mohan Princess Margaret Hospital, Dept of Anaesthesia, Swindon SN1 4JU Tel: 01793 536231 — MB BS 1972 Agra; BSc Agra 1966; DA Agra 1982; DA (UK) 1989. Assoc.Special.P.ss Margt. Hosp. Swindon. Socs: Med. Defence Union. Prev: SHO & Regist. (Anaesth.) P.ss Margt. Hosp. Swindon; SHO (Anaesth.) Gen. Hosp. Bishop Auckland; SHO (A & E) Gen. Hosp. Milton Keynes.

GUPTA, Mr Janesh Kumar Birmingham Women's Hospital, Methley Park Road, Edgbaston, Birmingham B15 2TG Tel: 0121 607 4751 Fax: 0121 607 4795 Email: j.k.gupta@bham.ac.uk; 8 Greening Drive, Edgbaston, Birmingham B15 2XA Tel: 0121 455 0331 — MB ChB 1987 Leeds; MD 1999; MRCOG 1992; MSc Leeds 1991. (Leeds Med Sch.) Sen. Lect. O & G Univ. of Birm.; Hon. Cons. Birm. Wom. Hosp. Prev: Cons. O & G Ninewells Hosp. Dundee; Sen. Regist. (O & G) Ninewells Hosp. Dundee; Regist. (O & G) Yorks. RHA.

GUPTA, Jayanta Kumar Flat 1, Holmcroft House, Ormskirk District General Hospital, Wigan Road, Ormskirk L39 2AZ — MB BS 1982 Calcutta, India; MRCOG 1993.

GUPTA, Jayanti 11 South Royd Avenue, Halifax HX3 0BL — MB BS 1976 Calcutta.

GUPTA, Jyoti 141 Balmoral Road, Gillingham ME7 4QQ — MB BS 1998 Lond.; MB BS Lond 1998.

GUPTA, Kaushal Kumar Hunslett Health Centre, 24 Church St., Leeds LS10 2PE Tel: 0113 270 5620; Whitley Clinic for Healing, 12 Darfield St, Bradford BD1 3RU Tel: 01274 722335 — MB BS 1960 Agra; MD (Med.) Punjab (India) 1966; MD (Pharmacol.) Agra 1963; MRCP (UK) 1971. (S.N. Med. Coll. Agra) Healer Leeds. Socs: World Federat. of Healing; Yorks. Healers Assn. Prev: Sen. Research Fell. (Med.) Leeds Univ.; Regist. (Med.) Atkinson Morley's Hosp. Lond.; Tutor Experim. Med. Postgrad. Med. Inst. Chandigarh, India.

GUPTA, Kim John Royal United Hospital, Dept. of Anaesthesia & Intensive Care, Bath BA1 3NG Tel: 01225 825057 — MB ChB 1988 Bristol; FRCA 1994. Cons. in Anaesth. & Intens. Care, Roy. United Hosp., Bath.

GUPTA, Krishan Chandra The Surgery, 93 Richmond Road, London E8 3AA Tel: 020 7254 2298 — MB BS 1961 Vikram; DO Eng. 1968. (Gandhi Med. Coll. Bhopal) Prev: SHO (Ophth.) N. Staffs. Roy. Infirm. Stoke-on-Trent; Regist. (Ophth.) W. Wales Gen. Hosp. Carmarthen.

GUPTA, Laxmi 197 New North Road, Hainault, Ilford IG6 3AA Tel: 020 8501 0324 — MB BS 1965 Delhi; MRCOG 1973.

GUPTA, Madan Lal Resolven Health Centre, Resolven, Neath SA11 4LL Tel: 01639 710347 — MB BS 1968 Patna. (P. of Wales Med. Coll.)

GUPTA, Madan Mohan 818 Hollins Road, Oldham OL8 4SA Tel: 0161 681 9170 Fax: 0161 684 9299; 2 Woodside, Shaw, Oldham OL2 8LN Tel: 01706 849700 — MB BS 1958 Patna; MRCGP 1974; DIH Soc. Apoth. Lond. 1972; DIH Eng. 1972; DCH Eng. 1966; DTD Patna 1959. (P. of Wales Med. Coll.) GP Oldham; JP; Mem. Oldham LMC. Socs: Fell. Indian Acad. Med. Specialists.; Fell. Overseas Doctors Assn. (Pres. Oldham & Tameside Div.). Prev: Trainer GP Oldham.

GUPTA, Mamta The Lodge, 4 George Street W., Luton LU1 2BJ Tel: 01582 481577 Fax: 01582 412450; 44 Blandford Avenue, Luton LU2 7AY Tel: 01582 593404 Fax: 01582 593404 Email: mamta@clara.net — MB BS 1968 Lucknow; MFFP 1990; MRCPCH 1997. (G.S.V.M. Med. Coll. Kanpur, U.P., India) SCMO (Family Plann. & Reproduct. Health, Sexual DysFunc. & Developm. Paediat.) S. Beds. Community Health Trust. Socs: BMA; BASMT Fac. Family Plannning & Reproduct. Health.

GUPTA, Maureen Patricia 2a/2b Newton Road, Eastleigh Tel: 01903 620162; 159 Springvale Road, Headbourne Worthy, Winchester SO23 7LF Tel: 01962 883165 — MB BS 1975 Bangalor; MB BS Bangalore 1975. Clin. Med. Off. (Old Age Psychiat.) Winchester & E.leigh Healthcare NHS Trust. Prev: Regist. (Psychiat.) Garlands Hosp. Carlisle; SHO (Med. & Geriat.) Glas. Clwyd Hosp. Boddelwyddan, N. Wales.

GUPTA, Monica Flat 3/2 139 Broomhill Drive, Glasgow G11 7NB — MB ChB 1993 Liverp.; BSc Liverp. 1990. SHO (Gen. Med.) Freeman Hosp. Newc. u. Tyne.

GUPTA, Monica Flat 18, Exeter House, Putney Heath, London SW15 3SU Tel: 020 8789 3271 — MB ChB 1995 Leic. (Univ. Leic.) SHO (Paediat) King's Coll. Hosp., Lond. Socs: BMA. Prev: SHO (Paediat), Chelsea & W.minster, Lond.; SHO (Paediat.) St. Peter's Hosp. Chertsy, Surrey; SHO (A & E) Mayday Univ. Hosp. Thornton Heath.

GUPTA, Nagendra Kumar Mawney Road Surgery, 206 Mawney Road, Romford RM7 8BU Tel: 01708 739379 Fax: 01708 780457 — MB BS Allahabad 1968; MS; DCH.

GUPTA, Naraider Kumar Department of Nuclear Medicine, Manchester Royal Infirmary, Manchester M13 9WL Tel: 0161 276 4823 Fax: 0161 273 5248 Email: gupta@nucmed.cmht.nwest.nhs.uk; 1 Knightsbridge Mews, Didsbury, Manchester M20 6GX Tel: 0161 445 3933 — MB BS 1983 Delhi; MSc (Nuclear Med.) Lond. 1994; DRM 1987; FRCR.

Regist. (Radiol.) NWRHA. Socs: Brit. Nuclear Med. Soc.; Med. Counc. India; Assoc. Mem. Roy. Coll. Radiol. BrE. Gp. Prev: Sen. Regist. (Nuclear Med.) NWRHA; Regist. (Nuclear Med.) Middlx. Hosp. Lond.; Hon. Regist. (Radiol.) Sheff.

GUPTA, Niranjan 10 Fairway Close, Rowany, Port Erin IM9 6LS — MB BS 1951 Calcutta; DMRD Eng. 1958; DMRT Eng. 1956. (Calcutta) Cons. Radiol. Sunderland AHA. Socs: Roy. Coll. Radiol. Prev: Cons. Radiol. Min. of Health Doha Qatar & Min. of Health Accra Ghana; Cons. Radiol. Med. Diag. Centre Lusaka Zambia.

GUPTA, Nirmal Kumar Christie Hospital NHS Trust, Wilmslow Road, Withington, Manchester M20 4BX Tel: 0161 446 3000; 12 Old Broadway, Withington, Manchester M20 3DF Tel: 0161 445 6638 Fax: 0161 445 6638 — MB BS 1958 Calcutta; FRCR 1975; FFR 1973; DMRT Eng. 1971. (R.G. Kar Med. Coll.) Dep. Dir. (Radiother. & Oncol.) Christie Hosp. NHS Trust Manch.; Hon. Lect. (Radiother. & Oncol.) Univ. Manch. Socs: Fell. Roy. Soc. Med. Prev: Cons. Radiother. & Oncol. Christie Hosp. & Holt Radium Inst. Manch.

GUPTA, Nishi 38A Packington Street, London N1 8QB — MB BS 1991 Lond.; MRCP (UK) 1995. (Char. Cross & Westm. Med. Sch.) Regist. (Clin. Oncol.) Roy. Lond. Hosp.

GUPTA, Nityanand Dayanand Withybush general Hospital, Fishguard Road, Haverfordwest SA61 2PZ — MB BS 1986 Bombay.

GUPTA, Om Parkash Orsett Road Surgery, 126 Orsett Road, Grays RM17 5ET Tel: 01375 390717 Fax: 01375 383489; Sahayt, Homestead Road, Ramsden Bellhouse, Billericay CM11 1RP Tel: 01268 711374 — MB BS Punjabi 1967; AFOM RCP (UK) 1995; DTM & H Liverp. 1973. (Govt. Med. Coll. Patiala)

GUPTA, P Sandfield Medical Centre, 81 Liverpool Road, St Helens WA10 1PN Tel: 01744 22378.

GUPTA, Parveen Lata Derby Lane Surgery, 88 Derby Lane, Liverpool L13 3DN Tel: 0151 228 5868 Fax: 0151 259 6996 — MB BS 1975 Dehli.

GUPTA, Mr Pradip Kumar 11 South Royd Avenue, Halifax HX3 0BL — MB BS 1976 Calcutta; FRCS Ed. 1984.

GUPTA, Prashant 106 Sudbury Court Drive, Harrow HA1 3TG — MB ChB 1993 Manch.

GUPTA, Pratibha c/o Oldham District, General Hospital, Rochdale Road, Oldham — MB BS 1974 Agra. (S.N. Med. Coll.) GP Trainee Marjorie Lee Health Centre Oldham.

GUPTA, Purshotam Dass Netherton Surgery, 84 Halesowen Road, Netherton, Dudley DY2 9PS Tel: 01384 239657 Fax: 01384 458136; 4 Hazel Road, Dudley DY1 3EW Tel: 01384 258265 — MB BS 1971 Punjab; MRCP (UK) 1979; T(GP) 1991; FRCG (Glas); DFPP London. Clin. Asst. (Geriat. Med.) & Clin. Med. Off. (Family Plann.) Dudley; Mem. Disabil. Appeal Tribunal; Exam. Med. Off. Benefits Agency. Prev: Regist. (Geriat. Med.) W. Midl.

GUPTA, R L Camberley Medical Centre, 11b Camberley Drive, Halewood, Liverpool L25 9PS Tel: 0151 486 1178.

GUPTA, Rajat Tel: 01244 365000; 2 Woodside, Shaw, Oldham OL2 8LN — MB ChB 1992 Manch.; DCH RCP Lond. 1996; MRCPI (Eire) 1997. (Manchester) Specialist Regist. (Paediat.) Mersey Deanery. Socs: BMA; Dep. Sec., Overseas Doctors Assn. Prev: SPR (Paedriatrics), Alderhey Hosp., Liverp.; SPR (Paedriatrics) Arrowe Pk. Hosp., Wirral; SPR (Neonatology) Liverp. Wom.'s Hosp., Liverp.

GUPTA, Rajeev Laboratory of Eukaryotic Molecular Genetics, The National Institute for Medical Research, The Ridgeway, Mill Hill, London NW7 1AA Email: r.gupta@nimr.mrc.ac.uk — MB ChB 1990 Leeds; BSc (Hons.) Leeds 1987, MB ChB 1990; MRCP (UK) 1993; PhD Lond. 1998. MRC Research Fell. Laborat. of Eukaryote Molecular Genetics. Nat. Inst. for Med. Research Lond.; Specialist Regist. (Haemat.) NW Thames Region. Prev: SHO (Neurol.) Nat. Hosp. Lond.; SHO (Med.) Hammersmith Hosp. Lond.; SHO (Thoracic Med.) Roy. Brompton Hosp. Lond.

GUPTA, Rajen 50 Whitehall Drive, Dudley DY1 2RD Tel: 01384 353158 — BM BS Nottm. 1994.

GUPTA, Rajeshwar Chander 7 Grangewood Court, Outwood, Wakefield WF1 3SL — MB BS 1967 Punjab.

GUPTA, Rakesh The Surgery, 8 Shenfield Road, Brentwood CM15 8AB Tel: 01277 218393 Fax: 01277 201017; Hurstwood, Alexander Lane, Hutton, Brentwood CM13 1AG Tel: 01277 231345 — MB ChB 1972 Manch.

GUPTA, Rakesh Kumar 44 Blandford Avenue, Luton LU2 7AY Tel: 01582 593404 — MB BS 1964 Delhi; FFA RCS Eng. 1971; DA Eng. 1968. (Maulana Azad Med. Coll.) Cons. Anaesth. Luton & Dunstable Hosp. Socs: BMA. Prev: Sen. Regist. (Anaesth.) St. Mary's Hosp. Lond. & Assoc. Hosps.; Regist. (Anaesth.) Univ. Coll. Hosp. Lond. & Assoc. Hosps.; SHO (Anaesth.) Roy. Free Hosp. Lond.

GUPTA, Mr Ram Manohar The Surgery, 44 Sevenoaks Road, Orpington BR6 9JR Tel: 01689 821179 Fax: 01689 832579 — MRCS Eng. LRCP Lond. 1976; MS (Gen. Surg.) Jabalpur 1969, MB BS 1966; FRCS Eng. 1980. (Govt. Med. Coll. Jabalpur) Regist. (Orthop. & Gen. Surg.) Wycombe Gen. Hosp. Prev: Regist. (Orthop. Surg.) Raigmore Hosp. Inverness; Demonst. & Regist. (Surg.) Govt. Med. Coll. Hosps. Jabalpur, India; Asst. Surg. Vict. Hosp. Jabalpur, India.

GUPTA, Ram Prasad Newland Surgery, Newland Lane, Normanton WF6 1QD Tel: 01924 220256 Fax: 01924 220558; Half Moon Lodge, Kirkthorpe Lane, Heath, Wakefield WF1 5SY Tel: 01924 893031 — MB BS 1964 Lucknow. (G.S.V.M. Med. Coll. Kanpur) GP Wakefield. Prev: Regist. (Med.) Pinderfields Gen. Hosp. Wakefield.

GUPTA, Ram Prashad Dulwich Medical Centre, 163-169 Crystal Palace Road, London SE22 9EP Tel: 020 8693 2727 Fax: 020 8693 2121; 1 Dulwich Oaks, 92 College Road, London SE21 7NA Tel: 020 8693 1300 — MB BS Rajasthan 1957; Cert FPA 1976. (S.M.S. Med. Coll. Jaipur) Socs: MRCGP. Prev: SHO W. Kent Gen. Hosp. Maidstone; Regist. W. Hill Hosp. Dartford.

GUPTA, Mr Ramesh Department of Surgery, Southampton General Hospital, Floor F, Mail Point 816, Tremona Road, Southampton SO16 6YD Tel: 02380 777222; Flat 18, Locksley Court, 24-26 Archers Road, Southampton SO15 2LE — MB ChB 1984 Glas.; MD Glas. 1995; FRCS Ed. 1989. Lect. (Surg.) Soton. Gen. Hosp.

GUPTA, Ramesh Chander King Street Medical Centre, 43 King Street, Accrington BB5 1QE Tel: 01254 232435 Fax: 01254 394955 — MB BS 1972 Guru Nanak Dev U.; MB BS 1972 Guru Nanak Dev U.

GUPTA, Ravi 1 The Dulwich Oaks, 92 College Road, London SE21 7NA — MB BCh BAO 1990 NUI; LRCPSI 1990.

GUPTA, Ravindra Kumar Higham Hill Surgery, 258-260 Higham Hill Road, Walthamstow, London E17 5RQ Tel: 020 8527 2677 Fax: 020 8527 3636 — MB BS 1972 Jiwaji. (G.R. Med. Coll.)

GUPTA, Renu 21 Appledore, Shoeburyness, Southend-on-Sea SS3 8UW — MB BS 1992 Lond.

GUPTA, Richa 16 Rundle Road, Liverpool L17 0AG — MB ChB 1992 Liverp. SHO (Paediat.) Countess of Chester Hosp. NHS Trust. Prev: SHO (Paediat.) Neonat. Unit Liverp. Wom. Hosp. NHS Trust & Alder Hey Hosp. Liverp.; SHO (Med.) Whiston Hosp. St Helens & Knowsley Hosps. NHS Trust.

GUPTA, Robin St Bartholomew's Hospital, West Smithfield, London EC1 Tel: 020 7601 8888; 5 Belsize Avenue, Hampstead, London NW3 4BL Tel: 020 7794 6882 — MB BS 1992 Lond.; BSc (Hons.) Lond. 1991. SHO (Gen. Surg.) St. Bart. Hosp. Lond.

GUPTA, Mr Rohit Rattan 1 Exeter House, Putney Heath, London SW15 3SU — MB BS 1993 Lond.; BSc Lond. 1990; FRCS Eng. 1997. (UMDS Guy's and Thomas' Hospitals)

GUPTA, S K Stanley Medical Centre, 60 Stanley Road, Kirkdale, Liverpool L5 2QA Tel: 0151 207 3113 Fax: 0151 207 3800.

GUPTA, Sajiv Kumar The Surgery, 37 Waverley Crescent, Plumstead, London SE18 7QU Tel: 020 8317 7258 Fax: 020 8316 6353; 40 Middleton Avenue, Sidcup DA14 6JH Tel: 020 8300 0747 — MB BS 1977 Punjab; MB BS Punjabi 1977; LMSSA Lond. 1986. Socs: BMA & MPS.

GUPTA, Sandeep 26 Broomfield Avenue, Palmers Green, London N13 4JN — MB BS 1988 Lond.; MRCP (UK) 1991; MD (London) 1999. (St. Geo. Hosp.) Prev: Brit. Heart. Foundat. Research Fell. (Cardiol.) St. Geo. Hosp. Med. Sch. Lond.; Regist. (Cardiol.) King's Coll. Hosp. Lond.; Regist. (Med.) Conquest Hosp. Hastings & Frimley Pk. Hosp. Surrey.

GUPTA, Sanjay 11 Wellington Road, Hampton TW12 1JP — MB BS 1994 Lond.

GUPTA, Sapna 23 St Saviour's Road, Reading RG1 6EJ — MB BS 1993 Lond.

GUPTA, Satya Prakash Oldhill Medical Centre, 19-21 Oldhill Street, London N16 6LD Tel: 020 8806 6993 Fax: 020 8806 6008; The Medical Centre, 573 Green Lanes, Haringey, London N8 0RL — MB BS 1964 All India Inst. Med. Scs.; DTM & H Liverp. 1969; Cert. Family Plann. JCC 1968.

GUPTA, Shambhu Nath c/o Dr S. K. Singh, 1 Deepdale Drive, Burnley BB10 2SD — MB BS 1988 Patna.

GUPTA, Mrs Shashi Prabha 51 Aberdeen Park, London N5 2AZ Tel: 020 7226 2568 — MB BS 1961 Lucknow; BSc Agra 1956. (K.G. Med. Coll. Lucknow) Clin. Asst. (Geriat. Med.) E. Hosp. Lond.

GUPTA, Shiv Dutt Sunderland Royal Hospital, Kayll Road, Sunderland SR4 7TP Tel: 0191 565 6256 Ext: 42192 Fax: 0191 569 9219; 27 Dunelm Road, Elmtree Farm, Stockton-on-Tees TS19 0TS Tel: 01642 608629 — MB BS Jammu & Kashmir 1969; MRCPI 1980. Cons. Phys. Sunderland Roy. Hosp.

GUPTA, Shubh Shant Kumari Orsett Road Surgery, 126 Orsett Road, Grays RM17 5ET Tel: 01375 390717 Fax: 01375 383489; Sahayt, Homestead Road, Ramsden Bellhouse, Billericay CM11 1RP Tel: 01268 711374 — MB BS 1966 Punjab; DA Eng. 1972. (Govt. Med. Coll. Patiala)

GUPTA, Subash Chander (retired) 15 St John Street, Manchester M3 4DG Tel: 0161 834 2151 Fax: 0161 834 9294 — MB ChB 1964 East Africa; FRCP Ed. 1987; MRCP (UK) 1967; FRCR 1971; DMRD Eng. 1969. Cons. Radiol. Salford Gp. Hosps. Prev: Sen. Regist. (Med. Radiodiag.) Manch. Roy. Infirm.

GUPTA, Sudesh Kumari King Street Medical Centre, 43 King Street, Accrington BB5 1QE Tel: 01254 232435 Fax: 01254 394955 — MB BS 1974 Agra; MB BS 1974 Agra.

GUPTA, Sunil Kumar Rushbottom Lane Surgery, 91 Rushbottom Lane, Benfleet SS7 4EA Tel: 01268 754311 — MB BCh 1991 Wales; MRCGP 1995; DFFP 1994; DGM RCP Lond. 1994; DRCOG 1993; DCH RCP Lond. 1992.

GUPTA, Suraj Narain The Surgery, 7 Salisbury Avenue, Barking IG11 9XQ Tel: 020 8594 2023 Fax: 020 8594 1132; 96 Collinwood Gardens, Ilford IG5 0AN — MB BS 1968 Ranchi; DTCD Wales 1974; DTM & H Liverp. 1973. Socs: BMA; Overseas Doctors Assn. Prev: Clin. Asst. (Rheum.) Enfield AHA; Clin Asst. Minor Injury Unit City & Lond. Family Plann. Clinic.

GUPTA, Mr Suresh Kumar 37 Park Avenue, Worthing BN11 2HX — MB BS 1982 Delhi; FRCSI 1992.

GUPTA, Surya Rajni 204 Little Sutton Lane, Sutton Coldfield B75 6PH — MB BS 1997 Lond.

GUPTA, Suveer 63 Linden Avenue, Thornton Heath CR7 7DW — MB BS 1981 New South Wales; DRCOG 1984. Prev: Trainee GP Lower Broughton Health Centre Salford.

GUPTA, Trilokeshwar Nath The Lane Medical Centre, 52 Chesterton Rd, Sparkbrook, Birmingham B12 8HE Tel: 0121 442 4555 Fax: 0121 449 1907 — MB BS 1994 Lond.; 1997 Dip in Child Health; 1997 Dip Roy. Coll Obst & Gyn. Socs: Mem. of Roy. Coll. of Gen. Practitioners 2000.

GUPTA, Urmila Green Lane Surgery, 6 & 8 Green Lane, Lumb Lane, Bradford BD8 7SP Tel: 01274 724418; Hillcote, 11 Park Drive, Heaton, Bradford BD9 4DP Tel: 01274 541624 — MB BS Agra 1963. (S.N. Med. Coll.) GP Bradford. Socs: Fell. Roy. Soc. Med.; Pres. BMA Bradford Div. 1995-96; ODA. Prev: Ho. Surg. Oldham Roy. Infirm.; SHO (A & E) Bolton Roy. Infirm.; SHO (Orthop.) Bolton Dist. Gen. Hosp.

GUPTA, Usha Higham Hill Surgery, 258-260 Higham Hill Road, Walthamstow, London E17 5RQ Tel: 020 8527 2677 Fax: 020 8527 3636 — MB BS 1974 Calcutta.

GUPTA, Vijay Lakshmi 169 Kirkstall Lane, Leeds LS6 3EJ — MB BS 1979 Delhi; FCAnaesth. 1990.

GUPTA, Vinay Kumar 7 Strand Road, 2nd Bye Lane Kalitalla, Ramkristopore, Howrah, West Bengal, India; 4 Pen Y Ffridd Road, Penrhosgarnedd, Bangor LL57 2LZ — MB BS 1987 Calcutta; MRCP (UK) 1993.

GUPTA, Vineet Kishore c/o Dr V Mahajan, 11 Dickens Drive, Chislehurst BR7 6RU — MB BS 1969 Vikram.

GUPTA, Mr Vinod Kumar Security Forces Hospital, PO Box 3643, Riyadh 11481, Saudi Arabia Tel: 477 4480 Fax: 476 4757; 65 Queen Mary Avenue, Morden SM4 4JS Tel: 0208 540 6973 — MB BS 1974 Panjab; MB BS Panjab (India) 1974; FRCS Eng. 1981; FCOphth 1989; DO Eng. 1977; DO Delhi 1977. (Med. Coll. Rohtak) Cons. Ophth. Security Forces Hosp. Riyadh, Saudi Arabia.

GUPTA, Virender Kumar Sobell Medical Centre, 80 Hornsey Road, London N7 7NN Tel: 020 7609 3050 — LRCP LRCS 1982 Ed.; BSc Panjab 1973; MB BS Maharshi 1979; DRCOG 1986, M 1985. GP Lond.

GUPTA, Virendra Kumar Foxhill Medical Centre, 10-11 Foxhill, Peacehaven BN10 7SE Tel: 01273 583637 Fax: 01273 580586 — MB BS 1973 Patna. (Patna) GP Peacehaven, E. Sussex.

GUPTA, Vivek 68 Ravenswood Drive S., Solihull B91 3LP — MB BCh 1998 Wales.

GUPTE, Chinmay Madhukar 13 Vicarage Way, Harrow HA2 7JB Email: chimgup@aol.com — BM BCh 1996 Oxf.; BA (Hons.) Oxf. 1993. Research Fell. Imperial Coll. Lond. Prev: SHO Rotat. (Surg.) Hammersmith Hosp. Lond.; SHO (A & E) Guys Hosp. Lond.; Ho. Off. (Surg.) John Radcliffe Hosp.

GUPTHA, Soneil Medical Department, Merck Sharp & Dohme, Hertford Road, Hoddesdon EN11 9BU Tel: 01992 467272 Fax: 01992 451066; Flat 3, 56 Victoria Crescent, Upper Norwood, London SE19 1AE — MD 1980 Rajasthan; MB BS (Hons.) 1976; FCCP 1983. Pharm. Phys. (Cardiovasc.) Merck Sharp & Dohme Hoddesdon; Asst. Prof. Med. Cariol. Hoddesdon. Socs: BMA & Br. APP. Prev: Sen. Med. Off. Med. Control Agency.

GURA, Rowena Jane (retired) 3 Anson Walk, Northwood HA6 2LA Tel: 01923 821395 — MB BS 1981 Lond.; MA Camb. 1978. Prev: Clin. Asst. (Child Psychiat.) Roy. Free Hosp. Lond.

GURAM, Nardip Singh 20 Hayes Road, Bromley BR2 9AA — MB ChB 1983 Manch.

GURATSKY, Bernard Paul c/o Wirral Health Authority, District Headquarters, Clatterbridge Hospital, Clatterbridge Road, Bebington, Wirral CH63 4JY — MB ChB 1969 Liverp.; FFA RCS Eng. 1975.

GURBANNA, Bahlul Ahmed Cardiology Department, Victoria Infirmary, Queen's Park House, Langside Road, Glasgow G42 9TY — MB BCh 1984 Al Fateh; MRCP (UK) 1990. Staff Grade (Cardiol.) Vict. Infirm. Glas. Prev: Regist. (Gen. Med.) Torbay Hosp. Torquay.

GURD, Diane Elisabeth Penton 2 Ocean View Road, Bude EX23 8NW — MB ChB 1969 Bristol. Devon HA & Cornw. & Is. of Scilly HA Clin. Med. Off. (Family Plann.) N. Devon HA; SCMO. Socs: Inst. Psychosexual Med.

GURISIK, Ulku The Portman Clinic, 8 Fitzjohn Avenue, London NW3; 19 Abinger Mews, London W9 3SP — Tip Doktoru 1962 Istanbul; MD Ankara 1967; FRCPsych 1995, M 1980; Dip. Neurol & Psychiat. Ankara 1967. Cons. Psychother. Portman Clinic Lond. Socs: Brit. Psychoanal. Soc.; Internat. Psychoanal. Assn. Prev: Sen. Regist. Portman Clinic; Lect. Ankara Univ.

GURJAR, Ashalata Vasantrao 210 Whitton Ave E., Greenford UB6 0QA Tel: 020 8902 1142 — MB BS 1967 Nagpur; DObst RCOG 1974. (Nagpur Med. Coll.)

GURJAR, Pramod Yeshwantrao 8 Mayfields, Grays RM16 2XL — MB BS 1975 Nagpur; DRCOG 1984; DObst RCPI 1984. (Govt. Med. Coll. Nagpur) Prev: Regist. (O & G) Vale of Leven Hosp. Alexandria; Regist. (O & G) Sunderland HA.

***GURJAR, Shashank Vasantrao** 210 Whitton Avenue E., Greenford UB6 0QA Email: svgurjar@hotmail.com — MB BS 1997 Lond.; MBA Lond.; MA (Hons.) Camb.

GURJAR, Mr Vasant Ganpatrao 210 Whitton Avenue E., Greenford UB6 0QA — MB BS 1955 Nagpur; FRCSI 1965; DA Eng. 1957.

GURLING, Hugh Malcolm Douglas Department of Psychiatry, University College London Medical School, Riding House St., London W1P 7PN Tel: 020 7380 9474 Fax: 020 7436 5046 Email: hgurling@ucl.ac.uk — MB BS 1973 Lond.; MPhil Lond. 1981, MD 1989; FRCPsych 1995, M 1978. Prof. of Molecular Psychiat. Univ. Coll. Lond. Med. Sch.; Hon. Cons. Bloomsbury HA. Socs: Clin. Genetics Soc.; Amer. Soc. Human Genetics. Prev: Reader in Molecular Psychiat. UCL; Sen. Lect. Univ. Coll. & Middlx. Sch. Med. Lond.; Sen. Lect. Inst. Psychiat. & Hon. Cons. Psychiat. Maudsley Hosp. Lond.

GURLING, Kenneth John (retired) Greythorpe, Derby Road, Risley, Derby DE72 3SS Tel: 0115 9939 2352 Email: kmgurling@excite.co.uk — MB BS 1945 Lond.; MD Lond. 1949; FRCP Lond. 1969, M 1949; MRCS Eng. LRCP Lond. 1945. Prev: Postgrad. Dean Univ. Nottm. Med. Sch.

GURLING, Stephen Roy 8 Balmoral Drive, Cambuslang, Glasgow G72 8BG Tel: 0141 641 2558 — MB ChB 1993 Dundee; BMSc (Hons.) Clin. Psychol. Dund 1989. SHO (Psychiat.) Argyll & Bute Hosp. Lochgilphead. Prev: SHO (A & E & Orthop.) S.. Gen. Hosp. Glas.; Ho. Off. (Gen. Surg. & Gen. Med.) Perth Roy. Infirm.

GURM, Hitinder Singh 29 Bicknell Road, Camberwell, London SE5 9AU — MB BS 1992 Panjab; MRCP (UK) 1995.

GURMIN, Victoria Jane 2F1 4 Strathfillan Road, Edinburgh EH9 2AG — MB ChB 1997 Ed.

GURNANI, Helen Marie 1 Pickmere Lane, Wincham, Northwich CW9 6EB Tel: 01565 733662 — MB BS 1993 Lond.; BSc (Biomed. Sci. & Anat.) Lond. 1989, MB BS 1993. SHO (Geriat.) W. Morland Gen. Hosp. Kendal.

GURNELL, Eleanor May 22 County Road S., Willerby Road, Hull HU5 5LU — MB BS 1993 Lond.; MRCP (UK) 1997. (St. Bart.) Specialist Regist. Diabetes & Endocrinol, Addenbrooke's Hosp, Camb. Prev: SHO (Med) City Hosp NHS Trust Nottm; SHO (A & E) Kingsmill Centre for Healthcare Servs. Sutton in Ashfield; Ho. Off. (Surg.) York Dist. Hosp.

GURNELL, Mark University of Cambridge, Depatment of Medicine, Level 5, Box 157, Annesbrooke's Hospital, Cambridge CB2 2QQ Tel: 01223 245151 Fax: 01223 336846 — MB BS 1993 Lond.; PhD 2000 Cambridge; BSc Lond. 1990; MRCP (UK) 1996. (St. Bart. Hosp. Med. Coll.) Specialist Regist. & Research Fell. Socs: Medico-Legal Soc.; Med. Research Soc.; Soc. for Endocrinol. Prev: Wellcome Train. Fell. & Hon. Regist., Addenbrooke's Hosp., Camb.; Regist. & SHO (Med.) Qu. Med. Centre Univ. Hosp. Nottm.; Ho. Off. (Surg.) York.

GURNELL, Paul 22 County Road S., Willerby Road, Hull HU5 5LU — MB BS 1998 Lond.; MB BS Lond 1998.

GURNER, Angela Clare Cuckfield Medical Practice, Glebe Road, Cuckfield, Haywards Heath RH17 5BQ Tel: 01293 526881 — MB BChir 1982 Camb.; MA Camb. 1981; MRCGP 1989; DRCOG 1988; Dip. Pract. Dermat. Wales 1994; DCH RCP Lond. 1988; Cert. Family Plann. JCC 1988. (Univ. Camb.) p/t GP Non-Princip. Cuckfield Med. Pract.; GP Locum Leacroft Med. Centre Crawley. Prev: GP Leacroft Med. Centre Crawley; Clin. Asst. (Dermat.) Horsham, Crawley & Mid Sussex Hosps.; Clin. Research Fell. St. Mary's Hosp. Med. Sch. Lond.

GURNER, Ian Eric (retired) 39 Park Road, Wallington SM6 8AA — MB BS 1953 Lond. Prev: Regist. (Med.) Clare Hall Hosp. Dis. Chest.

GURNEY, Clair (retired) 3 Queen's Terrace, Jesmond, Newcastle upon Tyne NE2 2PJ Tel: 0191 281 1707 — MB ChB 1957 Ed.; FRCPsych. 1977, M 1971; DPM Durham. 1961. Prev: Sen. Research Off. Dept. Psychol. Med. Univ. Newc..

GURNEY, Ian 89A Bromsgrove Road, Romsley, Halesowen B62 0LE — BM BS 1998 Nottm.; BM BS Nottm 1998.

GURNEY, Jennifer Wolverhampton Health Care NHS Trust, Redhill Street Health Centre, Redhill St., Wolverhampton WV1 1NR Tel: 01902 444325 — MB ChB (Hons.) Bristol 1966; Dip. Community Paediat. Warwick 1988. (Bristol) SCMO Wolverhampton Healthcare Trust; Mem. Roy. Coll. Paediat. & Child Health. Socs: BMA; Foundat. for Study of Infant Deaths. Prev: Clin. Med. Off. Berks. HA.

GURNEY, Jill Diana White House, Wentnor, Bishops Castle SY9 5EJ Tel: 0158 861678 — MB ChB 1967 Aberd.

GURNEY, Katharine Jane Coleridge Medical Centre, Canaan Way, Ottery St Mary EX11 1EQ Tel: 01404 814447 — MB BChir 1988 Camb.; MRCGP 1992; T(GP) 1992; DRCOG 1991. (The London Hospital)

GURNEY, Margaret Fulton Dept. of Family Planning & Sexual Health, Nithbank, Dumfries DG1 2SO Tel: 01387 244593 Fax: 01387 244590 Email: mgurney@dg-primarycare.scot.nhs.uk; Tel: 01387 251232 — MB ChB 1984 Glas.; DFFP 1995; DA (UK) 1991. p/t Director of Family Plann. & Sexual Health. Socs: BMA; Fac. Fam. Plan. & Reproduct. Health (diplomate). Prev: SHO (A & E) Dumfries & Galloway Roy. Infirm.; Volunteer Work Romania.

GURNEY, Mr Michael James Tyson The Meads Surgery, Grange Road, Uckfield TN22 1QU Tel: 01825 765777 Fax: 01825 766220; The Hundred House, Pound Lane, Framfield, Uckfield TN22 5RU — MB BS 1966 Lond.; FRCS Eng. 1972. (Lond. Hosp.) Regist. (Orthop.) Bristol Roy. Infirm. Socs: Roy. Soc. Med. Prev: Regist. (Surg.) Cheltenham Gp. Hosps.; Ho. Surg. King Geo. Hosp. Ilford; Ho. Phys. Epsom Dist. Hosp.

GURNEY, Mr Peter William Valpy (cons. rooms), c/o A. J. Moore Ltd., 264 Castle St., Dudley DY1 1LQ Tel: 01384 252903 Fax: 01384 243121; Thet Lodge, 16 Richmond Road, Wolverhampton WV3 9HY Tel: 01902 420768 Email: pwvg@cwcom.net — MB ChB Bristol 1960; FRCS Eng. 1976; FRCOphth 1988; DO Eng. 1969; DObst RCOG 1969; DTM & H Liverp. 1963. (Bristol) Socs: BMA. Prev: Cons. Ophth. Sandwell Healthcare Trust & Dudley Gp of Hosps. Trust; Sen. Regist. (Ophth.) Roy. Berks. Hosp. Reading; Sen. Regist. (Ophth.) Moorfields Eye Hosp. Lond.

GURNEY, Sarah 1 Heath Villas, Halifax HX3 0BB — BM 1986 Soton.; MRCP (UK) 1990; FRCR 1994. Cons. Radiol. (p/t), Huddersfield Roy. Infirm., Huddersfield.

GURNEY, Valerie Phyllis (retired) Old Manor House, 1 Park Lane, Willingdon, Eastbourne BN21 2UT — MB ChB 1968 Bristol; MRCGP 1977; DCH Eng. 1970; DObst RCOG 1969. Prev: Gen.Prac. Snr. Partner. Drs. Gurney, Hamber, McCullough, Caroe, Prosser, Eyre, Stewart, Folwell & Evason. 6, Coll. Rd., E.bourne. BN21 4HY.

GURR, Jonathan Mark 7 Stonelea Drive, Brighouse HD6 3PT — MB ChB 1986 Leeds.

GURR, Mr Paul Andrew Northampton General Hospital, Cliftonville, Northampton NN1 5BD Tel: 01604 634700; 2 Stable Close, Finmere, Buckingham MK18 4AD — MB ChB 1982 Dundee; BMSc (Hons.) Pharmacol. Dund 1979; FRCS (ENT Surg.) Ed. 1989; FRCS (Gen. Surg.) Ed. 1987; FRCS (Orl.) 1996. Cons. (ENT), N.ampton Gen. & Milton Keynes Gen. Hosp.; Hon. Vis. Lect. Inst. of Otorhinolaryngol. UCL. Socs: F. Roy. Soc. Med.; Brit. Assn. Otol. Head & Neck Surg.; BMA. Prev: Clin. Lect. Roy. Nat. Throat, Nose & Ear Hosp. Lond.; Regist. (ENT) Exeter Dist. Hosp., S.mead Hosp. & Bristol Gen. Hosp.; Sen. Regist. (ENT) Roy. Berks. Hosp. & Roy. Nat. Throat Nose & Ear Hosp. Lond. & Gt. Ormond St. Lond.

GURRUCHAGA, Miren Queen Mary's Hospital, Frognal Avenue, Sidcup DA14 6LT; 11 Tilmans Mead, Farningham, Dartford DA4 0BY — LMS 1991 Basque.

GURRY, Brian Harvey Glenside Medical Centre, Glenside Rise, Plympton, Plymouth PL7 4DR Tel: 01752 341340 Fax: 01752 348913; Lower Lodge, Plympton, Plymouth PL7 5BL Tel: 01752 341153 — MB BS Lond. 1963; MRCS Eng. LRCP Lond. 1963; MRCGP 1970; Dip. Sports Med. Soc. Apoth. Lond. 1993; DCH RCP Lond. 1969; DObst RCOG 1965. (St. Bart.) p/t Hon. Specialist (Sports Med.) Derriford Hosp. Plymouth. Socs: Brit. Inst. Musculoskel. Med.; Brit. Assn. Sport & Med.; Brit. Med. Acupunct. Soc. Prev: Clin. Asst. (Orthop.).

GURTIN ZORKUN, Deniz Department of Paeditrics and Child Health, Homerton Hospital, Homerton Row, London E9 6SR Tel: 020 8510 7877 Fax: 020 8510 7171; 40 Kersley Road, London N16 0NH Tel: 020 7241 5300 — Tip Doktoru 1976 Hacettepe Univ. Turkey; MRCP (UK) 1993; DCH RCP Lond. 1992; MSc Lond. 1996; FRCPCH 1998. Cons. Paediat. Homerton Hosp. Lond.; Hon. Sen. Clin. Lect. Socs: RSM, Paediatric Sect. Counc. Mem.; BMA; RCPCH.

GURTLER, Christopher John Meridian Surgery, Meridian Way, Peacehaven BN10 8NF Tel: 01273 581999 Fax: 01273 589025 — MB BS 1990 Lond.; DFFP 1996; DRCOG 1993; DGM RCP Lond. 1992. (King's Coll. Lond.)

GURU-MURTHY, Krishnan (retired) Flat 8, Handel Mansions, Wyatt Drive, Barnes, London SW13 8AH Tel: 020 8748 7294 — MB BS 1961 Madras; DMRD Eng. 1971. Prev: Cons. Radiol. Burnley, Pendle & Rossendale HA.

GURURAJ PRASAD, Kasi Brahmanya Department of Child & Adolescent Psychiatry, Maiden Law Hospital, Howden Bank, Lanchester, Durham DH7 0QN — MB BS 1979 Bangalor; MB BS Bangalore 1979; MRCPsych 1986.

GURUSINGHE, Mr Nihal Trevor Department of Neurosurgery, Royal Preston Hospital, Sharoe Green Lane, Preston PR2 9HT Tel: 01772 710574 Fax: 01772 710093 Email: nihalg46@hotmail.com; Holmwood, 4 Beech Drive, Fulwood, Preston PR2 3NB Tel: 01772 862167 — MB BS Ceylon 1970; FRCS Ed. 1980. Cons. Neurosurg. Roy. Preston Hosp. Socs: Soc. Brit. Neurol. Surgs.; Chairm. BMA, Preston, Chorley, S. Ribble Div. 99/2000; Brit. Skull Base Soc. Prev: Sen. Regist. (Neurosurg.) Atkinson Morleys Hosp. Wimbledon, Nat. Hosp. for Nerv. Dis. Lond. & Hosp. for Sick Childr. Gt. Ormond St. Lond.

GURYEL, Enis Halil 17 Baldwyns Park, Bexley DA5 2BE — MB BS 1998 Lond.; MB BS Lond 1998.

GUSA LAVAN, Sathiaseelan 27 Wimberley Houses, Glamis Drive, Dundee DD2 1UP — MB ChB 1998 Dund.; MB ChB Dund 1998.

GUSE, Grace Elizabeth Wilson 94 Herries Road, Pollokshields, Glasgow G41 4AN Tel: 0141 423 8461 — MB ChB 1981 Glas. Sessional Med. Off. Blood Transfus. Serv. Glas. Prev: Regist. (Radiol.) W.. Infirm. Glas.

GUSE, Julian Victor Monklands Hospital, Monkscourt Avenue, Airdrie ML6 0JS Tel: 01236 748748 Email: julian.guse@laht.nhs.com; 145, Springkell Ave, Glasgow G41 4EY Tel: 0141 427 3518 — MB ChB 1982 Glas.; FRCR Lond. 1991. Cons. Radiol. Monklands Hosp. Airdrie.; Clin. Director (Imaging Servs.). Prev: Sen. Regist. & Regist. (Radiol.) Glas. Roy. Infirm.; SHO (Gen. Surg.) Monklands Dist. Gen. Hosp. Airdrie; SHO (Neurosurg.) Inst. Neurol. Scs. Glas.

GUSTAFSSON, Jane Veronica The Surgery, Marlborough, Seaham SR7 7TS Tel: 0191 581 2866 Fax: 0191 513 0393 — MB BS 1974 Lond.; MRCOG 1983. (St. Bart.)

GUSTAVSON, Mr Eric Harold (retired) (cons. rooms), Suite 2, 14 Queen Anne St., London W1M 9LD Tel: (20) 7636 4972 Fax: (20) 7580 5743 — MB BS 1964 Lond.; FRCS Eng. 1969, M 1964; LRCP Lond. 1964. Cons. Private Plastic Surg. Lond. Prev: Cons. Plastic Surg. Univ. Coll. Hosp. & Hosp. Sick Childr. Gt. Ormond St. Lond.

GUSTERSON, Professor Barry Austin Department Of Pathology, Western Infirmary, Glasgow G11 6NT Tel: 020 8643 8901 Fax: 020 8643 0238 Email: bag5@clinmed.gla.ac.uk; Oakhurst, Flat 3, 47 Dryden Road, Bearsden, Glasgow G61 2RN — MB BS 1975 Lond.; PhD Lond. 1980, BSc 1967, BDS 1972; FRCPath 1995, M 1983. Prof. Of Path., Univ. of Glas..

GUTHRIE, Alison Elizabeth Empingham Medical Centre, 37 Main Street, Empingham, Oakham LE15 8PR Tel: 01780 460202 Fax: 01780 460283 Email: guthrie_ae@gp-c82044.nhs.uk; Woodlands Farm House, Whitwell, Oakham LE15 8BW Tel: 01780 460213 — MB ChB 1985 Ed.; MFFP 1995; MRCGP 1990; DCH RCP Lond. 1991; DRCOG 1988. (Edinburgh) Prev: Clin. Med. Off. (Community Paediat.) P'boro.

GUTHRIE, Anne St Mary's Hospital, Newport PO30 5TG — MB ChB 1966 Glas.; MRCPsych 1972; DPM Ed. & Glas. 1969. (Glas.) Cons. Gen. Adult Psychiat. St Mary Hosp. Socs: BMA(Brit. Assoc. Behavioural & Cognitive Psychotherapists.); Int. Assn. Cognitive Psychother. Prev: Indep. Cons. Psychiat. Bermuda; Cons. (Psychiat.) St. Brendan's Hosp. Bermuda; Cons. Gen. Adult Psychiat. Crichton Roy. Hosp. Dulfries.

GUTHRIE, Bruce 27 Rankin Road, Edinburgh EH9 3AW — BChir 1988 Camb.

GUTHRIE, Christina Eleanor Anaesthetic Department, Vale of Leven Hospital, Alexandria Tel: 01389 754121; 57 St Germains, Bearsden, Glasgow G61 2RS Tel: 0141 942 8120 — MB ChB 1986 Dundee; DA (UK) 1989. Staff Anaesth. Vale of Leven Hosp. Alexandria.

GUTHRIE, Claire Elizabeth Mary 99/12 Easter Warriston, Edinburgh EH7 4QY — MB ChB 1967 Ed.; MRCGP 1974; DObst RCOG 1970. Clin. Asst. Cothian Memory Treatm. Centre, Roy. Edin. Hosp. Prev: GP Banff.; Research Clin. Asst. (Pychogeriats.) Roy. Edin. Hosp.

GUTHRIE, Colin Ivar Guthrie and Guthrie, 1448 Dumbarton Road, Glasgow G14 9DN Tel: 0141 959 2023 Fax: 0141 950 1822 — MB ChB 1978 Glas.

GUTHRIE, David Department of Clinical Oncology, Derbyshire Royal Infirmary, London Road, Derby DE1 2QY Tel: 01332 347141 Fax: 01332 254980; 587 Burton Road, Littleover, Derby DE23 6EJ Tel: 01332 271155 — PhD Newc. 1982; MB BS Durh. 1962; FRCOG 1988, M 1968; FRCR 1987; DObst RCOG 1964. (Durham University (King's College, Newcastle Upon Tyne)) Cons. Clin. Oncol. Derbysh. Roy. Infirm. Derby. Socs: Brit. Gyn. Cancer Soc.; Brit. Assn. Cancer Research; Brit. Soc. Colpos. & Cerv. Path. Prev: Regist. (Radiother.) Newc. Gen. Hosp.; Research Fell. Cancer Research Campaign Oncol. Centre, Radiother. Dept. Newc. Gen. Hosp.; Research Fell. Newc. RHB.

GUTHRIE, Eleanor Guthrie and Guthrie, 1448 Dumbarton Road, Glasgow G14 9DN Tel: 0141 959 2023 Fax: 0141 950 1822; 1448 Dumbarton Road, Scotstoun, Glasgow G14 9DN — MB ChB 1979 Glas.; MB ChB (Commend.) Glas. 1979; MRCGP 1983; DRCOG 1982.

GUTHRIE, Elizabeth Lindsay Brodick Medical Practice, Brodick Health Centre, Shore Road, Brodick KA27 8AJ Tel: 01770 302175 Fax: 01770 302040; Beinn Bharrain, Shiskine, Brodick KA27 8EW Tel: 01770 86 208 Fax: 01770 86 291 — MB ChB 1981 Aberd.; MRCGP 1985; DRCOG 1984. (Aberdeen) CMO Ayrsh. & Arran Community Trust. Prev: Med. Off. DHS; Trainee GP Inverclyde VTS.

GUTHRIE, Elspeth Anne Department of Psychiatry, Rawnsley Building, Manchester Royal Infirmary, Oxford Rd, Manchester M13 9BX — MB ChB 1981 Manch.; MSc Manch. 1990; MD Manch. 1990; MRC Psych 1986. Prof. of Psychol. Med. & Med. Psychotherary; Hon. Cons. in Liason Psychiat., Manch. Ment. Health Partnership. Prev: Sen. Lect. in Liason Psychiat. Univ. of Manch.; Regist. (Psychiat.) S. Manch. HA.

GUTHRIE, Gaynor Elizabeth Health & Safety Executive, Grove House, Skerton Road, Manchester M16 0RB; 10 Roundcroft, Romiley, Stockport SK6 4LL — MB ChB 1979 Manch.; MSc Manch. 1995; AFOM RCP Lond. 1994; MFOM RCP london 1997. Employm. Med. Adviser (Occupat. Med.) Health & Safety Exec. Manch. Socs: Soc. Occupat. Med. Prev: GP Tameside.

GUTHRIE, Giles Moir New House Surgery, 142A South Street, Dorking RH4 2QR Tel: 01306 881313 Fax: 01306 877305 — MRCS Eng. LRCP Lond. 1968. (King's Coll. Hosp.) Socs: BMA. Prev: SHO (O & G) Salisbury Gen. Infirm.; Ho. Phys. & Ho. Surg. Plymouth Gen. Hosp.

GUTHRIE, Gillian Margaret 11 Birks Court, Law, Carluke ML8 5HZ; 15 Haddon Road, Gannochy, Perth PH2 7JA — MB ChB 1985 Dundee.

GUTHRIE, Gordon Martin Emerald Bank, 32 North Deeside Road, Bieldside, Aberdeen AB15 9AB Tel: 01224 868440 — MB ChB 1986 Dundee; MRCGP 1994; DRCOG 1994; LLB Aberd. 1990.

GUTHRIE, Ida Mary Kirk (retired) 54 Craiglockhart Terrace, Edinburgh EH14 1XH — MB ChB 1943 Ed.

GUTHRIE, James Ashley Radiology Department, St James's University Hospital, Leeds LS9 7TF Tel: 0113 243 3144 Fax: 0113 283 6951 — MB BChir Camb. 1984; BA (Hons.) Oxf. 1981; MRCP (UK) 1987; FRCR 1992. Cons. Radiol. St. Jas. Univ. Hosp. Leeds; Hon. Clin. Sen. Lect. Univ. Leeds.

GUTHRIE, John 4 Walkers Lane S., Blackfield, Southampton SO45 1YN Tel: 023 8089 3258 — MB ChB (Commend.) 1946; MD (Commend.) Glas. 1967; FRCPath 1976, M 1964. (Univ. Glas.) Socs: BMA & Assn. Clin. Path.; Path. Soc. Prev: Cons. Path. Emerit. Soton. & SW Hants. HA; Sen. Lect. (Path.) Univ. Soton.; Lect. (Morbid Anat.) St. Mary's Hosp. Med. Sch. & Hon. Cons. Path. St. Mary's Hosp. Lond.

GUTHRIE, Katherine Anne Conifer House, 32-36 Prospect St., Hull HU2 8PX Tel: 01482 336336, 01482 336399; The Old Rectory, Rowley, Little Weighton, Cottingham HU20 3XR — MB ChB 1979 Dundee; FRCOG 2001; BSc (Hons.) St. And. 1976; MFFP 1994; MRCOG 1984. (St. And. & Dundee) Cons. Gyn. Hull and E. Yorks., Hosp's NHS Trust and Hull & E. Riding Comm. Health. Socs: Brit. Menopause Soc.; Soc. Cons.s Reproductive Health. Prev: Sen. Regist. St. Jas. Univ. Hosp. Leeds; Regist. Ninewells Hosp. Dundee.

GUTHRIE, Martin John 14 Garton Road, Loughborough, Leicester LE1 2DY — MB BS 1985 Lond.

GUTHRIE, Moyra Frances Ardbeg, 55 Brechin Road, Kirriemuir DD8 4DE — MB ChB 1983 Dundee.

GUTHRIE, Patricia Nell Health Centre, Balmellie Road, Turriff AB53 4DQ Tel: 01888 562323 Fax: 01888 568682 — MB ChB 1979 Glas.; DRCOG 1981.

GUTHRIE, Sylvia Kema (retired) 18 Rathen Road, Withington, Manchester M20 4GH Tel: 0161 445 2020 — MRCS Eng. LRCP Lond. 1920; MD (Commend.) Manch. 1926, MB ChB 1920; MRCP Lond. 1923. Prev: Cons. Paediatr. S. Manch. Gp. Hosps.

GUTHRIE, Trevor Riverbank Medical Centre, Dodsley Lane, Midhurst GU29 9AW Tel: 01730 812121 Fax: 01730 811400; Woodend, Church Road, West Lavington, Midhurst GU29 0EH Tel: 01730 812729 — MB BS 1966 Lond.; MRCS Eng. LRCP Lond. 1966. (St. Bart.) Prev: Ho. Surg. & Ho. Phys. Roy. W. Sussex Hosp. Chichester.; Ho. Off. (O & G) Soton Gen. Hosp.; Asst. Med. Off. King. Edwd. VII Hosp. Midhurst.

GUTHRIE, Victoria Janet Emerald Bank, 32 North Deeside Road, Bieldside, Aberdeen AB15 9AB Tel: 01224 868440 — MB ChB 1989 Aberd.; MRCGP 1993.

GUTHRIE, William Oldmore, 14 Strips of Craigie Road, Dundee DD4 7PZ Tel: 01382 42258 — MB ChB 1949 St. And.; FRCPath 1976, M 1964. Sen. Lect. in Path. Univ. Dundee; Hon. Cons. Path. Ninewells Hosp. Dundee; Hon. Treas. Forfarsh Med. Assn.

GUTIERREZ RODRIGUEZ, Ana 15/26 St Patrick Square, Edinburgh EH8 9EZ — LMS 1991 Acala de Henares.

GUTJAHR, Cornelia 4 Twitten Close, Southwick, Brighton BN42 4DY — State Exam 1986 Freiburg.

GUTMANN, Jacques Henry 33 Worchester Crescent, Woodford Green IG8 0LX — MB BCh 1973 Witwatersrand; T(R) (CR) 1995.

GUTOWSKI, Nicholas Jan Department of Neurology, Royal Devon and Exeter Hospital (Wonford), Barrack Road, Exeter EX2 5DW Tel: 01392 411611 Fax: 01392 402067 — MB ChB 1985 Birm.; BSc (Hons.) Physiol. Birm. 1982, MD 1996; MRCP (UK) 1989. Cons. (Neurol.) Roy. Devon & Exeter Hosp. Socs: Assn. Brit. Neurol.; Eur. Neurol. Soc.; Brit. Neuropathol. Soc. Prev: Sen. Regist. (Neurol.) Roy. Lond. & The Nat. Hosp. Lond.; Regist. (Neurol.) The Nat. Hosp. Lond. & N. Staffs. Roy. Infirm. Stoke-on-Trent; Clin. Research Fell. (Neurobiol.) Ludwig Inst. Cancer Research Univ. Coll. Lond.

GUTTERIDGE, Catherine Mary Derriford Hospital, Plymouth PL6 8DH; The Beeches, Walkhampton, Yelverton PL20 6JX Tel: 01822 853078 — MB ChB 1995 Birm.; MRCP (UK) 1999. SHO Rotat. (Med.). Prev: SHO (A & E) Nottm. QML; Ho. Off. (Surg.) Birm. Heartlands; Ho. Off. (Med.) Dudley Gp. of Hosps.

GUTTERIDGE, Charles Norman Department of Haematology, Royal London Hospital, Whitechapel, London E1 1BB Tel: 020 7377 7000 Email: cn.gutteridge@mds.qmw.ac.uk; 16 Ockendon Road, Islington, London N1 3NP — MB 1977 Camb.; BChir 1976; FRCP 1995, MR 1981; FRCPath 1996, MR 1986. Cons. Haemat. Newham Gen. Hosp. Lond.; Sen. Lect. Lond. Hosp. Med. Coll. Socs: Brit. Soc. Haematol.; Brit. Soc. Immunol. Prev: Chief Exec. Newham Healthcare Trust.

GUTTERIDGE, Eleanor Middle House, Box Drive, Nunthorpe, Middlesbrough TS7 0RH — BM BS 1995 Nottm.

GUTTERIDGE, Gary James Dept. of Anaesthesia, Bristol Royal Infirmary, Marlborough St., Bristol BS2 8HW Tel: 0117 923 0000; Flat 2, 68 Pembroke Road, Clifton, Bristol BS8 3ED Tel: 0117 973 5115 Email: gary.gutteridge@btinternet.com — BM BCh 1992 Oxf.; BA (Hons.) Oxf. 1989. (Oxford) Specialist Regist. in Anaesth. in Bristol Train. Deanery. Prev: Assn. Anaesth.; Mem. Roy. Coll. Anaesths.

GUTTERIDGE, Helen Jane 2 Malyon Court Close, Thundersley, Benfleet SS7 1TX — MB BS 1993 Lond.

GUTTERIDGE, Lisa Christine Donney Brook Medical Centre, Clarendon St., Hyde SK14 2AH Tel: 0161 368 4100; 13 All Saints Road, Heaton Norris, Stockport SK4 1QA Tel: 0161 477 5957 — MB ChB 1991 Manch.; BSc St. And. 1988; DRCOG. (St. Andrews Manch.) GP Princip.; Trainee GP Lond. Socs: BMA; Med. Wom. Federat.; Fac. Fam. Plann. Prev: Trainee GP Roehampton; SHO (Psychiat.) Qu. Mary's Univ. Hosp. Roehampton; SHO (O & G) St. Geo. Hosp. Lond.

GUTTERIDGE, William Harold Cooke Linden Medical Centre, 9A Linden Avenue, Maidenhead SL6 6HD Tel: 01628 20846 Fax: 01628 789318 — MB BS 1976 Lond.; MB BS (Hons.) Lond. 1976; MSc Lond. 1991; MA Camb. 1974; MRCGP 1981; MFPHM RCP (UK) 1993. (St. Bart.) GP; Cons. Pub. Health Med. Hillingdon HA. Prev: Cons. Pub. Health Med. Berks. Health Commiss.; Sen. Regist. (Pub. Health Med.) Oxon. RHA; GP Bourne End.

GUTTIKONDA, Anita 6 Whitebeam Close, Chelmsford CM2 8US — MB BS 1998 Lond.; MB BS Lond 1998.

GUTTIKONDA, Kishore Lal St John's Hospital, Wood St., Chelmsford CM2 9BG — MB BS 1972 Andhra; DLO RCS Eng. 1976. Assoc.Special (Otolaryngol.) St. John's Hosp. Chelmsford.

***GUTTIKONDA, Madhuri** 6 Whitebeam Close, Chelmsford CM2 8US Tel: 01245 358137 Email: maddi22@hotmail.com — MB BS 1998 Lond.; MB BS Lond 1998; BSc Lond. 1995.

GUTTING, Petra Andrea 5 Tai Caledffrwd, Clwt-y-Bont, Caernarfon LL55 3DU — State Exam Med 1992 Berlin.

GUTTMANN, Dennis (retired) 222 Thorpe Road, Peterborough PE3 6LW Tel: 01733 265526 — BM BCh 1954 Oxf.; BSc Oxf. 1952, MA 1954; FRCP Lond. 1979, M 1960. Phys. P'boro. Dist. Hosp. & Stamford & Rutland Hosp. Prev: Sen. Regist. (Med.) Addenbrooke's Hosp. Camb.

GUTTRIDGE, Brian The Old Manor, Mithian, St Agnes TR5 0QQ — MB BChir 1980 Camb.; MA, MB BChir Camb. 1980; MRCGP 1985; DRCOG 1985; MFCM 1988. (King's Coll. Hosp.) Cons. Pub. Health Med. Cornw. & I. of Scilly HA. Socs: BMA. Prev: Sen. Regist. (Community Med.) W. Midl. RHA; Regist. (Community Med.) W. Midl. RHA; Trainee GP I. of Wight VTS.

GUVENDIK, Mr Levent Hull& East Yorkshire Cardiothoracic Centre, Castle Hill Hospital, Castle Road, Cottingham HU16 5JQ Tel: 01482 623263 Fax: 01482 623257 — Tip Doktoru 1969 Istanbul; FRCS Eng. 1976; FRCS Ed. 1975. Socs: Soc. Cardiothoracic Surg. GB & Irel.; Parish Cardiac Soc.; Europ. Assn. for Cardiothoracic Surg. Prev: Sen. Regist. Cardio-Thoracic Surg. St. Geo. Hosp. Lond.; Sen. Regist. Cardio-Thoracic Surg. S.ampton Gen..; Sen. Regist. Cardio-Thoracic Surg. Hosp. S.ampton.

GUY, Mr Andrew John Leighton Hospital, Crewe CW1 4QJ — MD 1988 Newc.; BM BS Nottm. 1979; FRCS Eng. 1983.

GUY, Anna Dilys Church Plain Surgery, Church Plain, Loddon, Norwich NR14 6EX Tel: 01508 520222; Rose Cottage, Langley Road, Bergh Apton, Norwich NR15 1BY Tel: 01508 520527 — MB BS 1974 Lond.; BA (Hons.) Lond. 1967. (Middlx.) GP Loddon Norf.

GUY, Derek James Lakenham Surgery, 24 Ninham Street, Norwich NR1 3JJ Tel: 01603 765559 Fax: 01603 766790; Rose Cottage, Langley Road, Bergh Apton, Norwich NR15 1BY Tel: 01508 520527 — MB BS 1974 Lond.; DCH RCPS Glas. 1978. (Middlx.) Hosp. Pract. (Genitourin. Med.) Norf., Norwich.

GUY, Desmond David Bloomfield Surgery, 95 Bloomfield Road, Bangor BT20 4XA Tel: 028 9145 2426; 27 Downshire Road, Bangor BT20 3TN Tel: 01247 460839 — MB BCh BAO 1958 Belf.; DObst RCOG 1960. (Belf.)

GUY, Doreen Linton Mill, Mill Wynd, East Linton EH40 3AE Tel: 01620 860142 Fax: 01620 860142 Email: john.guy@lineone.net — MB ChB Ed. 1964. (Ed.) Co-Dir. Worcester Med. Videos. Socs: Exec. Comm. World Orthop. Concern (UK). Prev: GP Worcester; SHO (O & G) E. Gen. Hosp. Edin.; Regist. (Ophth.) Auckland Hosp., NZ.

GUY, Geoffrey William Le Manoir de Markham, Les Gravees, St Peter Port, Guernsey GY1 1RL — MRCS Eng. LRCP Lond. 1979; BSc (Hons.) (Pharmacol.) Lond. 1976, MB BS 1979; LMSSA Lond. 1979; Dip. Pharm. Med. RCP (UK) 1984. (St. Bart.) Chairm & Chief Exec. Ethical Holdings plc; Liveryman Soc. Apoth. Lond. Prev: SHO (Cas.) New Addenbrookes Hosp. Camb.; Ho. Surg. St. Bart. Hosp. Lond.; Ho. Phys. Soton. Gen. Hosp.

GUY, Ian Towers North Ormesby Health Centre, Elizabeth Terrace, North Ormesby, Middlesbrough TS3 6EN Tel: 01642 277000 Fax: 01642 281000; 14 North Terrace, Skelton-in-Cleveland, Saltburn-by-the-Sea TS12 2ES Tel: 01287 650309 Email: ian@refrain.dircoon.co.uk — MB BS 1970 Newc.; MSc Newc. 1989; MRCGP 1975; MFPHM 1990; DCCH Leeds 1987. (Newc.) GP Princip.; Hosp. Practitioner Drug & Alcohol Serv. Prev: Dir. Pub. Health Tees HA; Sen. Clin. Med. Off. S. Tees HA; GP Skelton-in-Cleveland.

GUY, Jacqueline Marie Wingate Medical Centre, 17 Glasven Road, Northwood, Kirkby, Liverpool L33 6UA; 14 Vulcan Street, Southport PR9 0TW Tel: 01704 33312 — MB ChB 1963 Liverp.

GUY, Jean Margaret (retired) The Radiology Department, West Suffolk Hospital, Bury St Edmunds IP33 2QZ Tel: 01284 712647 Fax: 01284 713108 — MB Camb. 1967, BChir 1966; FRCR 1975; FFR 1973; DHMSA 1980; DMRD Eng. 1970. Cons. Radiol. W. Suff. Hosp., Bury St. Edmunds. Prev: Cons. Radiol. Yeovil Dist. Hosp.

GUY, Joan (retired) Long Thatch, Pennington, Lymington SO41 8EB Tel: 01590 672092 — MB BCh 1945 Wales; BSc, MB BCh Wales 1945; FRCPath 1973; DCH Eng. 1947. Prev: Cons. Pathol. Hants. AHA (T).

GUY, John Towson and Partners, Juniper Road, Boreham, Chelmsford CM3 3DX Tel: 01245 467364 Fax: 01245 465584; Tavistock, Station Road, Hatfield Peverel, Chelmsford CM3 2DS Tel: 01245 380325 Fax: 01245 382430 Email: johnjuy@equip.ac.uk — MB BS 1975 Lond.; FRCGP 1991, M 1980. (Lond. Hosp.) Clin. Ldr. Equipm. (Primary Care Educat. & Quality) N. Essex. Prev: Trainee GP Chelmsford VTS.

GUY, Mr John Geraint Linton Mill, Mill Wynd, East Linton EH40 3AE — MB ChB Ed. 1963; FRCS Ed. 1967. (Edinburgh University) Hon. Cons. & Lect. (p/t); Founder Brit. Orthop. Assn. Videotape Library; Managing Dir. Worcester Med. Videos. Socs: BOA; Europ. Hip Soc.; Worcs. Medico-Legal Soc. (Chairm. Elect). Prev: Cons. Orthop. Surg. S. Bank Hosp. Worcester; Sen. Regist. (Orthop.) King's Coll. Hosp. Lond.; Chairm. World Orthop. Concern (UK).

GUY, Lesley Mary Towson and Partners, Juniper Road, Boreham, Chelmsford CM3 3DX Tel: 01245 467364 Fax: 01245 465584; Tavistock, Station Road, Hatfield Peverel, Chelmsford CM3 2DS Tel:

01245 380325 Fax: 01245 382430 — MB BS 1974 Lond. (Lond. Hosp.) Prev: Trainee GP Chelmsford VTS.

GUY, Margaret Anne Public Health Directorate, London Regional Office, NHS Executive, Department of Health, 40 Eastbourne Terrace, London W2 3QR; 77 Hornsey Lane Gardens, Highgate, London N6 5PA — MB BS 1980 Lond.; BSc (Hons.) 1976; DCH RCP Lond. 1982; MRCP (UK) 1984; DRCOG 1985; MSc (Distinc.) Community Med. Lond. 1988; MFPHM RCP (UK) 1991; FFPHM RCP (UK) 1997; FRCPCH 1999. (Univ. Coll. Lond.) Cons. Pub. Health Med. Lond. Regional Office of NHS Exec. Socs: Fell.Fac. of Pub. Health Med.; Brit. Diabetic Assn. (Med. & Scientif. Sect.); Fell.Roy. Coll. of Paediat. and Child Health. Prev: Cons. Pub. Health Med., Brent & Harrow HA; Cons. Pub. Health Med., N. W. Thames RHA; Sen. Med. Off., Dept. of Health.

GUY, Margaret Paula Phyllis Tuckwell Hospice, Waverley Lane, Farnham GU9 8BL Tel: 01276 729400; 3 Walkers Ridge, Camberley GU15 2DF Tel: 01276 503536 — MB ChB 1976 Birm.; MRCGP 1980; DCH Eng. 1979. (Birm.) Staff Grade Phyllis Tuckwell Memor. Hospice Farnham Surrey. Prev: SHO (Psychiat.) Centr. Hosp. Warwick; SHO (Paediat.) Warwick Hosp.; SHO (O & G) Warneford Hosp. Leamington Spa.

GUY, Michael John The Bondgate Practice, Bondgate Surgery, Infirmary Close, Alnwick NE66 2NL Tel: 01665 510888 Fax: 01665 510581; The Manse, Embleton, Alnwick NE66 3UW Tel: 01665 576220 Fax: 01665 510581 — MB BS 1975 Newc.; BSc (Anat.) Newc. 1972; MRCGP 1984. GP Tutor N. N.d.; Mem. N.d. LMC & Educat. Sub. Comm. Prev: Regist. (Surg.) Newc. AHA (T); SHO (Gen. Surg.) Newc. Gen. Hosp.; Demonst. (Anat.) Univ. Newc.

GUY, Patricia Margaret Mackenzie Drynoch, Glenburn Road, Ardrishaig, Lochgilphead PA30 8EU Tel: 01546 602947 — MB ChB 1975 Ed.; MRCGP 1981; DRCOG 1977.

GUY, Mr Patrick Robin Hope House, 19 Upper Town Lane, Felton, Bristol BS40 9YF — MB ChB 1986 Bristol; BSc (Biochem.) Bristol 1983; FRCS Eng. 1982; MRCGP 1996. (Bristol)

GUY, Mr Peter James, OBE Salisbury District Hospital, Odstock Road, Salisbury SP2 8BJ Tel: 01722 336262 Fax: 01722 414726 Email: pguy@aol.com; Jasmine Cottage, Church St, Bowerchalke, Salisbury SP5 5BH Tel: 01722 781077 — MB ChB 1974 Dundee; BSc St. And. 1971; FRCS Ed. 1980. Cons. Urol. Salisbury Dist. Hosp.; Cons.Urol. duke of Cornw. spinal Treatm. centre. Socs: Brit. Assn. Urol. Surgs.; BMA. Prev: Cons. Adviser Urol. to Army; Sen. Regist. (Urol.) Roy. Free & Middlx. Hosp. Lond.; Sen. Regist. (Surg.) Kent, Canterbury Hosp. & St. Peters Hosp. Chertsey.

GUY, Ralph Dunstan Cnoc An Torra, Kessock, Inverness IV1 3XB Tel: 01463 373487 — M.B., Ch.B. Ed. 1943. (Ed.)

GUY, Richard Charles North Manchester General Hospital, Delaunays Road, Manchester M8 5RB; Flat 3, 84 Great Bridgewater St, Manchester M1 5JG — MB BCh Witwatersrand 1993.

GUY, Robert Lawrence Dunluce Avenue Surgery, 1-3 Dunluce Avenue, Belfast BT9 7AW Tel: 028 9024 0884; 20 Olde Forge Manor, Upper Malone Road, Belfast BT10 0HY Tel: 01232 61790 — MB BCh BAO 1967 Belf.; DObst 1971. Socs: BMA.

GUY, Roland John Craig North Hampshire Hospital NHS Trust, Albermaston Road, Basingstoke RG24 9NA — MB BChir 1977 Camb.; MA, MB Camb. 1977, MD 1986, BChir 1976; MRCP (UK) 1980; DRCOG 1978. (Camb. & St. Thos.) Cons. Phys. N. Hants. Hosp. NHS Trust. Socs: Diabetes UK (Med. & Scientif. Sect.). Prev: Sen. Med. Regist. (Endocrinol. & Diabetes) Char. Cross Hosp. Lond.; Research Regist. (Diabetes) Kings Coll. Hosp. Lond.; Regist. (Diabetic Dept.) Kings. Coll. Hosp. Lond.

GUY, Rosemary Derbyshire Children's Hospital, Uttoxeter Road, Derby DE22 3NE; 125 Whitaker Road, Littleover, Derby DE23 6AQ — MB BS Lond. 1966; MRCS Eng. LRCP Lond. 1966; DCH Eng. 1968; MRCPCH 1997. (Roy. Free) Assoc. Specialist Derbysh. Childr. Hosp. Derby. Socs: Brit. Paediat. Assn. Prev: Med. Off. Dept. Community Health. Birm. AHA (T); Regist. (Paediat.) Gulson Hosp. Coventry; Ho. Off. (Surg.) Roy. Free Hosp. Lond.

GUY, Rosemary Lilian Conquest Hospital, The Ridge, St Leonards-on-Sea TN37 7RD Tel: 01424 755255; Tinkers Bar, The St, Sedlescombe, Battle TN33 0QJ — MB BS 1982 Lond.; BSc 1979 (Hons. Biochem.) Lond.; MRCP (UK) 1985; FRCR 1988. (St. Thos.) p/t Cons. Radiol. Conquest Hosp. Hastings. Socs: RCR; RSNA. Prev: Cons. Roy. Marsden Hosp. Sutton Surrey; Sen. Regist. & Regist. (Radiol.) St. Thos. Hosp. Lond.

GUY, Susanne Eluned 5/4 Hermitage Place, Leith, Edinburgh EH6 8AF Tel: 0131 555 0584 — MB ChB 1994 Birm.; ChB Birm. 1994; MRCP (UK) 1997. Specialist Regist. Rotat. (Radiol.) S. E. Scotl.. Prev: SHO (Rheum.) W.ern Gen. Hosp. Edin.; SHO Rotat. (Gen. Med.) S. E. Scotl..

GUY, Suzanne Elizabeth 11 Ardenlee Parade, Belfast BT6 0AL Tel: 01232 458291 — MB BCh BAO 1985 Belf.; MRCP (UK) 1988. Regist. (Gen. Med., Therap. & Pharmacol.) E. Health & Social Serv. DHSS. Prev: SHO (Gen. Med., Therap. & Pharmacol.) E. Health & Social Serv. DHSS.

GUYER, Barrington Michael 17 Gipsy Lane, Wokingham RG40 2BN Tel: 01734 785157 — MRCS Eng. LRCP Lond. 1962; MB Camb. 1963, BChir 1962; Dip Pharm Med RCP (UK) 1977; DObst RCOG 1965. (Camb. & Guy's) Dir. Med. & Regulat. Affairs Europe & Middle E. Allergan Pharmaceut. Inc. Socs: Fell. Roy. Soc. Med.; Portsmouth Med. Soc. Prev: Police Surg. Hants. Constab.; Med. Adviser WR Warner & Co. Ltd. E.leigh.

GUYER, Benjamin Seager 65 Glenapp Street, Glasgow G41 2LG — MB ChB 1941 Glas.

GUYER, Christopher Hugh 2 Larkspur Close, Swanmore, Southampton SO32 2RE Email: cguyer@doctors.org.uk — MB BS 1991 Lond.; MRCOG 1997.

GUYER, Martin Francis (retired) 4A West Hill Road, London SW18 1LN — MB BS 1974 Lond.; MRCS Eng. LRCP Lond. 1974; MRCGP 1978; DRCOG 1976. Prev: Trainee GP Lond. VTS:.

GUYER, Richard Jeremy (retired) L'Epine, rue de L'Epine, Trinity, Jersey JE3 5AU Tel: 01534 861052 — MB BS 1957 Lond.; FRCPath 1980. Prev: Cons. Haemat. Sheff. Childr. Hosp.

GUYLER, Christopher John Lucian The Surgery, 2 Nottingham Road, Burton Joyce, Nottingham NG14 5AE Tel: 0115 312929 — MB ChB 1968 Manch.; DObst RCOG 1971. (Manch.) Socs: Nottm. M-C Soc.; Assoc. Mem. RCGP.

GUYLER, Paul Christopher Coppins, 132 Lambley Lane, Burton Joyce, Nottingham NG14 5BN — MB BS 1997 Lond.

GUYLER, Roderick Michael 30 Marton Gill, Saltburn-by-the-Sea TS12 1QU — MB ChB 1986 Manch.

GUYMER, Robyn Heather Moorfields Eye Hospital, City Road, London EC1V 2PD — MB BS 1984 Melbourne.

GUYSTER, Bernard (retired) 13 Beresford Drive, Woodford Green IG8 0JH — MRCS Eng. LRCP Lond. 1926. Prev: Research Fell. Dept. Pathobiol. Johns Hopkins Hosp. Baltimore.

GUZ, Professor Abraham Room 11N19, Charing Cross Hospital, Fulham Palace Road, London W6 8RF Tel: 020 8846 7337 Fax: 020 8846 7326 Email: a.guz@ic.ac.uk; 3 Littleton Road, Harrow HA1 3SY Tel: 020 8422 2786 Fax: 020 8422 2786 — MB BS 1952 Lond.; MB BS (Hons. Med. & Surg.) Lond. 1952; MD Lond. 1967; FRCP Lond. 1969, M 1954. (Charing Cross Hospital) Prof. Emerit. Med. Char. Cross. & W.m. Med. Sch. Univ. Lond.; Hon. Cons. Char. Cross Hosp. Lond. Socs: Assn. Phys.; Physiol. Soc.; (Ex-Hon Sec.) Med. Research Soc. Prev: Prof. & Head Dept. Med. Char. Cross & W.m. Med. Schs. Lond.; Research Fell. Inst. Cardiovasc. Studies Univ. Cal. Med. Centre San Francisco; Research Fell. Harvard Med. Sch.

GUZDER, Purmaya Kaikhusroo (retired) The Firs, Blidworth Waye, Papplewick, Nottingham NG15 8GB Tel: 0115 963 5752 — MB BS 1966 Bombay.

GUZHAR, Anand Rangoji Ballycastle Health Centre, Dalriada Hospital, 1A Coleraine Road, Ballycastle BT54 6BA Tel: 028 2076 2684 Fax: 028 2076 9891; 12 Drumavoley Park, Ballycastle BT54 6PE Tel: 012657 62098 Fax: 012657 69891 — MB BS 1973 Mysore. (Mysore) Prev: SHO (Anaesth.) Craigavon Area Hosp.; SHO (Anaesth.) Roy. Vict. Hosp. Belf.

GWANMESIA, Ivo Langmia 6 Elmwood, Sale M33 5RN — MB ChB 1995 Manch.

GWILLIAM, Griffith Morgan Medical Centre, Heol-yr-Onnen, Pencoed, Bridgend CF35 5PF Tel: 01656 860270 Fax: 01656 861228; The Grange, 5 Felindre Road, Pencoed, Bridgend CF35 5PB Tel: 01656 860993 — MB ChB 1963 Birm.; DObst RCOG 1965.

GWILLIAM, Nicholas Joseph 13 Newport Court, Newport, Lincoln LN1 3DB — BM BS 1995 Nottm.

GWILT, David John 5 Rookery Lane, Stoke Bruerne, Towcester NN12 7SJ Tel: 01604 862007 — BM BCh 1972 Oxf.; DM Oxf.

1986, BM BCh 1972; FRCP Lond. 1991; MRCP (UK) 1978; FFA RCS Eng. 1977. Cons. Phys. Milton Keynes Gen. Hosp.

GWINNELL, Emily Frances 3 Almeida Street, London N1 1TA — MB BS 1997 Newc. SHO A&E Dryburn Durh.

GWINNER, Paul Dudley Valentine 17 Harley Street, London W1G 9QH Tel: 07831 872464; Crossways three leg Cross, Wadhurst TN5 7HH Tel: 01580 200675 — MRCS Eng. LRCP Lond. 1965; MRCPsych 1972; AFOM RCP Lond. 1993; DPM Eng. 1970. (St. Thos.) Occupat. Ment. Health Adviser & Occupat. Health Adviser. Socs: Soc. Occupat. Med. Prev: Med. Dir. Ticehurst Ho. Hosp.; Cons. Psychiat. i/c Armys Alcohol Treatm. Unit.; Occupat.al Health Adviser Allied Domecq Retailing ltd.

GWINNUTT, Carl Leonard 18 Stafford Road, Ellesmere Park, Eccles, Manchester M30 9HW Tel: 0161 789 0355 Fax: 0161 789 0355 — MB BS 1979 Lond.; MRCS Eng. LRCP Lond. 1979; FFA RCS Eng. 1983. (Guy's) Cons. Anaesth. Hope Hosp. Salford. Prev: Sen. Regist. N. W.. Region.

GWYNN, Alan Martin Brookfields Health Centre, Seymour Street, Cambridge CB1 3DQ Tel: 01223 723160 Fax: 01223 723089; Rydal House, 5 Bell Road, Cambridge CB5 9DF — MB BS 1987 Lond.; 2001 Diploma in Primary Care Diabetes, Bradford; MPH Leeds 1994; MRCGP 1992; DRCOG 1991; DCH RCP Lond. 1990. (Lond. Hosp. Med. Coll.) Princip. Police Surg. Camb.; Clin. Asst. (Geriat.) Camb. Socs: Assn. Police Surg.; Assn. Forens. Sci.s. Prev: Regional Train. Scheme (Pub. Health Med.) Yorks.; Trainee GP Lancaster VTS.

GWYNN, Mr Brian Rodney Stafford District General Hospital, Weston Road, Stafford ST16 3SA; Brook House, Allimore Green, Haughton, Stafford ST18 9JQ — MB ChB Birm. 1976; MD Birm. 1988; FRCS Eng. 1982; FRCS Ed. 1981. (Birm) Cons. Gen. Vasc. Surg. Mid. Staffs. HA; Assoc. Prof. St. Geo. Univ. Grenada. Socs: Vasc. Surg. Soc. GB. & Irel.; Brit. Assoc. of Surg. Onc.; Eur. Vasc. Soc. Prev: Sen. Regist. Rotat. (Surg.) W. Midl. RHA; Sheldon Vasc. Surg. Research Fell. W. Midl. RHA; Regist. (Surg.) Wolverhampton Roy. Hosp. & Selly Oak Hosp. Birm.

GWYNN, Charles Morgan, OStJ, TD (retired) Wordsley Green Health Centre, Wordsley Green, Wordsley, Stourbridge DY8 5PD Tel: 01384 277591 Fax: 01384 401156 — MB ChB Birm. 1965; MRCP (UK) 1971; DObst RCOG 1968; DCH Eng. 1967. Cons. Allergist Priory Hosp. Birm. Prev: Sen. Regist. (Paediat.) Birm. RHB.

GWYNNE, Bridget Mary Avenue Villa Surgery, Brynmor Road, Llanelli SA15 2TJ Tel: 01554 774401 Fax: 01554 775229; Wyfordby, 72 Rehoboth Road, Five Roads, Llanelli SA15 5DZ Email: wyford.by@virgin.net — MB BS 1981 Newc.; MRCGP 1986; Dip. Palliat. Med. Wales 1991; DCH RCPS Glas. 1985; Dip. Therp. 1997. (Newcastle) Clin. Asst. (Palliat. Med.).

GWYNNE, Edward Ieuan (retired) Angorfa, 60 Penrhys Road, Ystrad, Pentre CF41 7SW Tel: 01443 435342 — MB BCh 1949 Wales. Prev: GP Ferndale.

GWYNNE, Michael Vincent Peter 52 Jedburgh Road, Plaistow, London E13 9LG — MB BS 1986 Lond.

GWYNNE HUGHES, Linda Anne Intensive Therapy Unit, Morriston Hospital, Morriston, Swansea SA6 6NL Tel: 01792 702222; 31 Gelligaer Street, Catnays, Cardiff CF24 4LD Tel: 01222 341423 Email: linda-hughes@lineone.net — MB BCh 1990 Wales; MRCP (UK) 1994; FRCA (UK) 1997. Specialist Regist. (Anaesth.) Welsh Region. Socs: RCP; Assn. Anaesth.; FRCA. Prev: Regist. (Anaesth.) Oxf. Region; SHO (Anaesth. & Med.) Morriston Hosp. Swansea; Ho. Off. (Med.) Llandough Hosp. Cardiff.

GWYNNE-JONES, Mona (retired) 65 Ashley Gardens, London SW1P 1QG Fax: 020 7828 4654 — MB ChB Ed. 1944. Prev: Princip. Child Health Phys. Ealing, Hammersmith & Hounslow AHA (T).

GWYTHER, Mr Stephen James Ockley Lodge, Dukes Drive, Rusper Road, Newdigate, Dorking RH5 5BY — MB BS 1981 Lond.; FRCS Glas. 1985; FRCR 1989. (Westm.) Cons. Radiol. E. Surrey Hosp. Redhill. Prev: Sen. Regist. (Radiol.) Char. Cross Hosp. Lond.; Regist. (Radiol.) Char. Cross Hosp. Lond.; SHO (Gen. Surg.) Roy. Surrey Co. Hosp. Guildford & Hammersmith Hosp. Lond.

GYAWALI, Pranab 7 Amelia Close, Widnes WA8 9FR — MB BS 1997 Lond. SHO (Med.), Rotat., St. Geo.s.

GYDE, Oscar Humphrey Bohun Department of Haematology, Birmingham Heartlands Hospital, Birmingham B9 5SS Tel: 0121 766 6611 Fax: 0121 766 7530 Email: ogyde@cix.co.uk; 14 St. Bernards Road, Solihull B92 7BB Tel: 0121 706 0243 — MB BS Lond. 1961; MRCPath 1970. (Lond. Hosp.) Hon. Sen. Clin. Lect. Univ. Birm. Socs: Fell. Roy. Soc. Med.; (Chair.) Brit. Med. Informatics Soc.; Amer. Med. Informatics. Assoc. Prev: Sen. Regist. (Haemat.) King's Coll. Hosp. Lond.; Regist. (Clin. Path.) Univ. Coll. Hosp. Lond.; Asst. Lect. (Path.) St. Thos. Hosp. Med. Sch. Lond.

GYI KHIN MA, Dr Flat 6, Falcon House, 26 Morden Road, London SW19 3BJ — MB BS 1977 Med. Inst. Rangoon.

GYORFFY, Gita 33 Constantine Road, London NW3 2LN — MB BS 1998 Lond.; MB BS Lond 1998.

GYSELINCK, Pierre 25 Wimpole Street, London W1M 7AD Tel: 020 7637 7265 — MD 1951 Lille.

GYSIN, Jane Forest Lodge, Mabie, Dumfries DG2 8HB — MB ChB 1987 Aberd.; MRCGP 1994. Staff Grade Gen. Phys. Dumfries.

HA, Harold Cheung Yin Everest House Surgery, Everest Way, Hemel Hempstead HP2 4HY Tel: 01442 240422 Fax: 01442 235045; 3 Woodfield Gardens, Leverstock Green, Hemel Hempstead HP3 8LZ Tel: 01442 247748 — MB BS 1983 Lond.; BSc Lond. 1980; MRCGP 1991. (St. Mary's) Prev: Trainee GP Bracknell Berks.; Regist. (Med.) Luton & Dunstable Hosp.; SHO (Paediat.) Heatherwood Hosp. Ascot.

HA, Yvonne Woon Ming Maudsley Hospital, Denmark Hill, London SE5 8AZ Tel: 020 7703 6333 Fax: 020 7919 2171 Email: spjuywh@iop.bpmf.ac.uk — MB BS 1993 Lond.; MA Camb. 1994. (UMDS Lond.) Regist. (Psychiat.) Maudsley Hosp. Lond. Socs: Med. Wom. Federat. (Comm. Mem. Lond. Assn.); Wom. in Med. Soc. Prev: SHO (Psychiat.) Maudlsey Hosp. Lond.; Ho. Surg. Greenwich Dist. Gen. Hosp. Lond.; Ho. Phys. St. Thos. Hosp. Lond.

HA'ERI ZADEH, Hessameddine 3 Hart Hill, St John's Hill Road, St Johns, Woking GU21 1RG Tel: 01483 721450 — MD 1967 Tehran. Cons. Psychiat. Acad. Unit Psychiat. P.ss Alexandra Hosp. Harlow; Psychother. Barking Hosp. Essex. Socs: (Nat. Exec.) Hosp. Doctors Assn. Eng.; (Nat. Exec.) Brit. Hosp. Doctors Federat.; Amer. Med. Soc. Prev: Indep. Phys. & Psychiat., Tehran.

HAACKE, Mr Norman Patrick 234 Great Portland Street, London W1W 5QT Tel: 020 7630 9599 Fax: 070 9203 9266 Email: haacke@entfacialplastic.com; 2 Blackwater House, Blackwater, Lyndhurst SO43 7FJ Tel: 023 8028 2975 — BChir 1976 Camb.; MA (Hons.) Camb. 1976, MB Camb 1977; FRCS Eng. 1983; FRCSI 1982. (Camb. & St. Bart.) Cons. ENT & Facial Plastic Surg./Chalybeate Hosp., Chalybeate Cl., Tremonda Rd., Soton. Socs: Eur. Acad. Facial Plastic Surg.; Eur. Rhinol. Soc.; Am. Rhibol. Soc. Prev: Cons/ Sen Lect ENT Surg. Soton. Univ Hosp.; Sen. Regist. Roy. Infirm. Edin. & Hon. Clin. Tutor Univ. Edin.; Regist. Roy. Nat. Throat Nose & Ear Hosp. Lond.

HAAS, Andrea Jane Heatherals, Aston St., Aston Tirrold, Didcot OX11 9DQ — BM 1987 Soton.

HAAS, David Simon 7 Welbeck Street, London W1M 7PB Tel: 020 7935 1503 — MB ChB 1978 Cape Town.

HAAS, Dorothy Jean Newtown Health Centre, 171 Melbourne Avenue, Birmingham B19 2JA Tel: 0121 554 7541 — MB BS 1964 Lond.; MRCGP 1972. (Middlx.) Socs: BMA. Prev: Ho. Phys. & Ho. Surg. Mt. Vernon Hosp. N.wood; Ho. Phys. Chase Farm Hosp. Enfield.

HAAS, Joanna Marion Bridge House Healthcare Centre, 96 Umfreville Road, London N4 1TL Tel: 020 8482 9670 Fax: 020 8372 2096 — MB BS 1981 Lond.; DRCOG 1986. (St. Barts.) GP. Prev: GP Lond.; Trainee GP Newham VTS.

HAAS, Leonard (retired) Embemere, Watcombe Heights, Torquay TQ1 4SG Tel: 01803 327870 Fax: 01803 327870 — MA, MD Camb. 1955, MB BChir Camb. 1946; FRCP Lond. 1973, M 1952; DCH Eng. 1949. Prev: Cons. Paediatr. Torbay & Roy. Devon & Exeter Hosps.

HAAS, Peter Anthony The Electoral Reform Society, Mailing Department, Hope (Sufference) Wharf, St Mary Church St., London SE16 4JE — MB BS 1965 Lond.; MRCP (UK) 1973; FFA RCS Eng. 1970.

HAASE, Gerald Medicines Control Agency, Market Towers, 1 Nine Elms Lane, London SW8 5NQ Tel: 020 7273 0540/0458 Fax: 020 7273 0195 Email: gerald.haase@mca.gov.uk; 7 Riverside Court, River Reach, Teddington TW11 9QN Tel: 020 8977 7869 — MB ChB 1973 Glas.; FRCPath 1996; MFPM RCP (UK) 1991. Med. Assessor Meds. Control Agency.

HABASHI, Fawzy Ayad 9 Ivy Bank Close, Sharples, Bolton BL1 7EF — MB BCh 1973 Cairo.

HABASHI, Mr Sherif Department of Otolaryngology, Chase Farm Hospitals NHS Trust, The Ridgeway, Enfield EN2 8JL Tel: 020 8366 6600; Manor Barn, Hoddesdon Road, Stanstead St Margarets, Ware SG12 8EG Tel: 01920 872262 Fax: 01920 870178 Email: habashis@aol.com — MB BS 1984 Lond.; MA Camb. 1985; FRCS (Otol.) Eng. 1989. (Guy's) Cons. Otolaryngol. & Head & Neck Surg. Chase Farm Hosps. NHS Trust. Prev: Clin. Fell. Auckland, NZ; Sen. Regist. Manch. & Preston.

HABEL, Alex West Middlesex University Hospital, Isleworth TW7 6AF Tel: 020 8560 2121 Email: habel@wimbles.u-net.com — MB ChB 1967 Ed.; FRCP Lond. 1987; MRCP (UK) 1971; MRCPCH 1997. (Ed.) Cons. Paediat. W. Middlx. Univ. Hosp. Isleworth; Hon. Cons. Paediat. Cleft Lip & Palate Clinic Hosp. Childr. Gt. Ormond St. Lond.; Cons. Paediat., cleft lip and palate, Gt. Ormond St. Prev: Clin. Tutor W. Middlx. Univ. Hosp. Isleworth; Lect. (Child Life & Health) Edin. Univ.; Hon. Cons. Paediat. Cleft Lip & Palate Clinic Hosp. Childr. Gt. Ormond St. Lond.

HABER, Shraga Langworthy Medical Practice, 250 Langworthy Road, Salford M6 5WW Tel: 0161 736 7422 Fax: 0161 736 4816; 13 Vine Street, Salford M7 3PG Tel: 0161 708 8188 — MB ChB 1978 Manch.; MRCGP 1983. Hon. Clin. Lect. Univ. Manch.; Phys. Univ. Salford.

HABERMANN, Frank Friedrich West Eldon House, Kiltarlity, Beauly IV4 7BA — State Exam Med 1994 Dusseldorf.

HABERSHON, Richard Bryan 45-47 Ben Jonson Road, London E1 4SA — MB BChir 1965 Camb.; MRCP (UK) 1970; DRCOG 1977; DCH Eng. 1976; DTM & H Eng. 1968. (Lond. Hosp.)

HABERSHON, Robert Julian Linden Medical Centre, 9A Linden Avenue, Maidenhead SL6 6HD Tel: 01628 20846 Fax: 01628 789318 Email: julian.habershon@k81018-gp.nhs.uk; White House, Coronation Road, Littlewick Green, Maidenhead SL6 3RA Tel: 01628 822021 — MB BChir Camb. 1965; MA Camb. 1968, BA 1961; DObst RCOG 1967. (Camb. & St. Mary's) p/t Hosp. Pract. (Dermat.) E. Berks. Health Dist. Socs: Fell. Roy. Soc. of Med.; BMA.

HABESHAW, John Anthony 12 Wordsworth Road, Harpenden AL5 4AF — MD 1978 Ed.; PhD Ed. 1971, BSc 1964, MD 1978, MB ChB 1966; MRCPath 1985. (Ed.) Research Scientist MRC Clin. Research Centre Harrow. Prev: Sen. Research Fell. Med. Oncol. St. Bart. Hosp. Lond.; Lect. Dept. Path. Univ. Edin.; Ho. Phys. W. Cornw. Hosp.

HABESHAW, Margaret Joan Community Child Health, 10 Chalmers Crescent, Edinburgh EH9 1TS Tel: 0131 536 0477 Fax: 0131 536 0570; Damside, Romanno Bridge, West Linton EH46 7BY Tel: 01968 660887 Fax: 01968 660887 — MB ChB Ed. 1966. (Ed.) Clin. Med. Off. Edin. Sick Childr. NHS Trust. Socs: BMA & MEDACT. Prev: Clin. Med. Off. (Child & Adolesc. Psychiat.) Lothian HB; SHO (Child Psychiat.) Guy's Hosp. Lond.; SHO (Cas.) Hackney Hosp. Lond.

HABESHAW, Timothy 18A Winton Drive, Glasgow G12 9QA — MB ChB 1970 Ed.; FRCP Glas. 1986; MRCP (UK) 1973; FRCR 1977. Cons. Radiother. Inst. Radiother. Glas.

HABGOOD, Christine Marie Mile Oak Clinic, Chalky Road, Portslade, Brighton BN41 2WF — MB ChB 1984 Bristol; MRCGP 1989; DCH RCP Lond. 1987; DRCOG 1987. Prev: Trainee GP/SHO N. Devon VTS; Trainee GP Henfield Health Centre.

***HABIB, Ana Sufiza** 179 Denmark Road, Manchester M15 6JT; 42 Bellott Street, Cheetham hill, Manchester M8 0PP Tel: 0161 281 0326 Email: anasufiza@hotmail.com — MB ChB 1998 Manch.; MB ChB Manch 1998; BSc 1995.

HABIB, Mr Anjum Huddersfield Royal Infirmary, Lindley, Huddersfield HD3 3EA — MB BS 1981 Punjab; FRCS Ed. 1985.

HABIB, Fatima 12A Alma Court, Bristol BS8 2HQ — MB ChB 1992 Bristol.

HABIB, Mr Khurram A25 Northumberland Street, Liverpool L8 6TN — MB BS 1984 Punjab; FRCS Ed. 1990.

HABIB, Mohamed Jeilan Flat 6, Foyes Court, 205-223 Shirley Road, Shirley, Southampton SO15 3SJ — BM 1998 Soton.

HABIB, Mohammad 43 Harold Road, London NW10 7BG — MB BS 1970 Punjab; DO Eng. 1975; DOMS RCSI 1975. (King. Edwd. Med. Coll. Lahore) Regist. Ophth. Cumbld. Infirm. Carlisle.

HABIB, Mr Nabil Emil Nasry Royal Eye Infirmary, Aspley Road, Plymouth PL4 PL Tel: 01752 315123 Fax: 01752 254162 Email: nabil.habib@phnt.swest.nhs.uk — MB ChB 1985 Tanta; MB ChB Tanta, Egypt 1985; FRCS Ed. 1991; FRCOphth 1991. Cons. Ophth. Surg. Roy. Eye Infirm. Plymouth. Prev: Sen. Regist. (Ophth.) P.ss Alexandra Eye Pavil. Edin.; Regist. W. Midl. Train. Scheme; SHO St. Paul's Eye Hosp. Liverp.

HABIB, Nahed Kamel 1 Blacksmith Lane, Hockley Heath, Solihull B94 6QP — MB BCh 1972 Cairo.

HABIB, Said Basha Department of Diagnostic Radiology, Addenbrooke's Hospital, Hills Road, Cambridge CB2 2QQ Tel: 01223 245151 Email: said.habib@lineone.net — MB ChB 1982 Baghdad; MRCP Irel. 1997. (University of Baghdad) Specialist Regist. (Diagnostic Radiol.) Addenbrooke's Hosp. Hosp. Camb. Prev: Transpl. Phys. Harefield Hosp.; Regist. Chase Farm Hosp.; SHO Norf. & Norwich NHS Trust.

HABIB, Shereen 26 Cliff Road, Welton, Lincoln LN2 3JJ — MB BS 1997 Lond.; BSc 1996. (Guys) SHO Anaesth.Hitchingbrooke Hosp. Prev: Ho. Off. Horton Hosp.Banbury.

HABIB, Mr Sherif Emile St George House, 357 The Rowans, Milton, Cambridge CB4 6ZR Tel: 01223 440003 — MB ChB 1980 Tanta, Egypt; MRCS Eng. LRCP Lond. 1991; FRCS Ed. 1988.

HABIBA, Mawan Ali Hassan Clinical Sciences Building, Leicester Royal Infirmary, PO Box 65, Leicester LE2 7LX Tel: 0116 252 3170 Fax: 0116 252 3154 Email: mawan.habiba@which.net; 19 The Fairway, Oadby, Leicester LE2 2HN Tel: 0116 270 8788 Email: marwan.habiba@which.net — MB BCh 1982 Cairo; MSc Cairo 1986; MRCOG 1991; Phd 1998 Leicester University. (Univ. Cairo) Sen.Lec Univ of Leicester; Hon. Cons Univ. Hosps of Leicester, Leicester Roy. Infirm. Socs: Brit. Menopause Soc.; ESHRE. Prev: Clin. Research Fell. Leicester Univ.; Regist. (O & G) P.ss Margt. Hosp. Swindon.; Lect. & Regist. Leicester Univ & Leicester Roy. Infirm.

HABIBI, Parviz Paediatric Intensive Care Unit, St Mary's Hospital, South Wharf Road, London W2 1BL Tel: 020 7886 6077 Fax: 020 7886 6249 Email: p.habibi@ic.a.uk; 178 Raeburn Avenue, Berrylands, Surbiton KT5 9ED Tel: 020 8390 9500 Fax: 020 8390 3246 Email: p.habibi@ic.ac.uk — MB ChB 1980 Birm.; PhD Birm. 1980; BSc (Hons.) Aston 1973; MRCP UK 1983; FRCP Lond. 1995; FRCPCH 1997. (Birm.) Sen. Lect. (Paediat., Intens. Care & Respirat. Med.) St. Mary's Hosp. Lond. Socs: Brit. Paediat. Assn.; Intens. Care Soc.; Eur. Intens. Care Soc. Prev: Sen. Regist. Hosp. Sick Childr. Gt. Ormond St. Lond.

HABOUBI, Najib Yacoub 35 Green Pastures, Heaton Mersey, Stockport SK4 3RB Tel: 0161 291 3601 Fax: 0161 291 3594 Email: najhabpath@aol.com; 35 Green Pastures, Heaton Mersey, Stockport SK4 3RB Tel: 0161 431 6478 — MB ChB 1971 Baghdad; MRCPath 1979; DPath Baghdad 1974; FRCPath 1991. (Baghdad) Cons. (Path.) Withington Hosp. Manch.; Hon. Clin. Lect. Univ. of Manch. Socs: Assn. Clin. Path.; Founder Mem. Counc. Assn. Caloproctal.; BSG. Prev: Regist. (Path.) Manch. AHA; SHO (Path.) Gwent AHA; Lect. (Path.) Manch. Med. Sch.

HACK, Henrik Hermann Adrian 13 Tiverton Drive, London SE9 2DA — MB BS 1988 Lond.

HACK, Marianne Emma 13 Tiverton Drive, London SE9 2DA — MB ChB 1989 Leeds.

HACK, Melissa Anne St Charles Hospital, Exmoor St., London W10 6DZ — MB BS 1987 Lond.; BSc (Hons.) Infec. & Immunity Lond. 1983, MB BS 1987; MRCP (UK) 1991. Prev: SHO Rotat. (Med.) St. Mary's Hosp. Lond.; SHO (Intens. Ther. & Critical Care) Centr. Middlx. Hosp. Lond.

HACKETT, Claire Louise Linfield Surgery, 7 Belmont Road, Portswood, Southampton SO17 2GD Tel: 023 8058 5858 Fax: 023 8039 9858 — BM 1984 Soton.

HACKETT, David Ronald Cardiology Department, Hemel Hempstead General Hospital, Hillfield Road, Hemel Hempstead HP2 4AD Tel: 01442 287087 Fax: 01442 287091 — MB BCh BAO 1978 Dub.; BSc (Physiol.) Dub. 1975, MD 1989; FRCP Lond. 1996; MRCPI 1981; T(M) 1992. Cons. Phys. & Cardiol. Hemel Hempstead Gen. Hosp., St. Albans City Hosp. Herts. & St. Mary's Hosp. Lond. Socs: Fell. Europ. Soc. Cardiol.; Brit. Cardiac Soc.; Brit. Cardiovasc. Interven. Soc. Prev: Lect. (Cardiol.) & Hon. Sen. Regist. Roy. Postgrad. Med. Sch. Hammersmith Hosp. Lond.; Regist. (Cardiol.) Hammersmith Hosp. Lond.

HACKETT, Elizabeth Caroline 4 King Edward Road, Christ's Hospital, Horsham RH13 7ND — MB ChB 1994 Bristol; BSc (Hons.) Physiol. Bristol 1991; DCH 1996; DFCOG 1998; MRCGP 1998. (Bristol) GP. Socs: Med. Defence Union; BMA. Prev: Ho. Off. (Med.)

Frenchay Hosp. Bristol; Ho. Off. (Surg.) Taunton; Trainee GP Taunton.

HACKETT, Geoffrey Ian Langton Medical Group, St. Chads Health Centre, Dimbles Lane, Lichfield WS13 7HT Tel: 01543 258983 Fax: 01543 414776; Holly Cottage, Elford Road, Fisherwick, Lichfield WS14 9JL Tel: 01543 432757 — MB BS 1973 Lond.; MD 2000 Keele Univ.; MRCPI 1978; MRCGP 1981. Research Fell. Dept. Gen. Pract. Keele Univ.; Cons. in Sexual Func., Good Hope Hosp., Sutton Coldfield; BUPA Hosp., Little Aston, Sutton Coldfiled. Socs: Sec. of BSSIR (Brit. Soc. for Sexual and Impotence Research).

HACKETT, Gerald Anthony Rosie & Addenbrookes NHS Trust, Robinson Way, Cambridge CB2 2SW Tel: 01223 245151 Fax: 01223 216090 — MB BS 1980 Lond.; MD Lond. 1993; MRCS Eng. LRCP Lond. 1980; MRCOG 1987. Cons. O & G Addenbrooke's Hosp. Camb. Prev: Sen. Regist. Rotat. (O & G) St. Mary's Hosp. Lond. & Addenbrooke's Hosp. Camb.; Research Fell. (Obst.) Kings Coll. Hosp. Lond.; Regist. (O & G) King's Coll. Hosp. Lond. & Roy. Sussex Co. Hosp. Brighton.

HACKETT, Gillian Heather 29 Harewood Avenue, Marylebone, London NW1 6LE Tel: 020 7723 0893 Fax: 020 7258 1224 Email: mejh100@aol.com — MB BS 1973 Lond.; MRCS Eng. LRCP Lond. 1972; FFA RCS Eng. 1979. Cons. Anaesth. St. Bart. Hosp. Lond.

HACKETT, John Terence Aylmer (retired) 20 Cromer Road, Aylsham, Norwich NR11 6HE Tel: 01263 732448 — MB BS 1939 Lond.; MRCS Eng. LRCP Lond. 1939.

HACKETT, Joseph Scott 9A Lethamie Road, Strathaven ML10 6AD — MB ChB 1987 Dundee.

HACKETT, Keith (retired) 7 Waterdale, Compton, Wolverhampton WV3 9DY Tel: 01902 426562 — MB ChB 1955 Sheff.; DObst RCOG 1959.

HACKETT, Latha Child Mental Health Unit, Royal Oldham Hospital, Rochdale Road, Oldham OL1 2JH Tel: 0161 627 8080; Holly House, Gladstone Terrace Road, Greenfield, Oldham OL3 7HF — MB BS 1981 Calicut; BSc Calicut 1975; LRCP LRCS Ed. LRCPS Glas. 1983; MRCPsych 1987. Cons. Child & Adolesc. Psychiat. Roy. Oldham Hosp. Prev: Sen. Regist. (Child Psychiat.) N. W.. RHA; Regist. (Psychiat.) N.. Gen. Hosp. Sheff. & St. Crispin Hosp. N.ampton; SHO (Psychiat.) Tameside Gen. Hosp. Ashton-u-Lyne.

HACKETT, Matthew Thomas Christian Stanhope Health Centre, Dales Street, Stanhope, Bishop Auckland DL13 2XD Tel: 01388 528555 Fax: 01388 526122 — MB BS 1988 Lond.

HACKETT, Patrick Joseph Barrack Street Medical Centre, Barrack Street, Coalisland, Dungannon BT71 4LS Tel: 028 8774 7447; Gortin House, Dungannon BT71 6ET Tel: 018687 40208 — MB BCh BAO 1970 NUI.

HACKETT, Peter Leonard Beech House Surgery, Beech House, 69 Vale Street, Denbigh LL16 3AU Tel: 01745 812863 Fax: 01745 816574 — MB BS 1975 Lond. Retaines Occupat.al Gen. Practitioner,Warwick Int Chem. Co., Mostyn.

HACKETT, Richard Justin Department of Psychiatry, Withington Hospital, Manchester M20 2LR Tel: 0161 445 8111; 16 Ash Hill Drive, Mossley, Ashton-under-Lyne OL5 9PW — MB BS 1982 Lond.; BSc, MB BS Lond. 1982; MRCPsych 1988; DTM & H Liverp. 1983. Sen. Regist. (Psychiat.) Univ. Hosp. S. Manch.; Wellcome Research Fell. (Clin. Epidemiol.) Univ. Manch.

HACKETT, Robert 44 Greenfield Road, Little Sutton, South Wirral CH66 1QR; 343 Liverpool Street, Darlinghurst, Sydney NSW 2010, Australia Tel: 02 9380 6185 Email: robbielad@hotmail.com — MB ChB 1997 Sheff. Prev: RMO 1 (SHO) Emerg. Med.; RMO 1 (SHO Cardiol.

HACKETT, Roy Harold (retired) Whitewalls, 44 Greenfield Road, Little Sutton, Ellesmere Port CH66 1QR Tel: 0151 339 3536 — MB ChB Liverp. 1966; DObst RCOG 1971. Prev: Vis. Med. Off. Stanlow Oil Refinery Ellesmere Port.

HACKETT, Scott James 7 Isleham Close, Allerton, Liverpool L19 4XS Tel: 0151 494 2948 Email: scott.hackett@btinternet.com — MB ChB 1991 Liverp.; BSc (Hons.) Liverp. 1988; MRCP (UK) 1996. (Liverpool)

HACKING, Christopher Nigel Department of Clinical Radiology, Southampton General Hospital, Tremona Road, Southampton SO16 6YD Tel: 02380 796981 — MB BS 1980 Lond.; BSc Lond. 1977, MB BS 1980; MRCP (UK) 1985; FRCR 1988. Cons. Radiol. Soton. HA. Prev: Sen. Regist. (Radiol.) Soton. HA.

HACKING, Douglas Francis c/o Anne Ankew, Forrest House, Malting Close, Stewkley, Leighton Buzzard LU7 3HR — BM BCh 1994 Oxf.

HACKING, James Edward Greenacres, Haverbreaks Rd, Lancaster LA1 5BJ — BM BS 1996 Nottm.

HACKING, Jeremy Charles Department of Radiology, Yeovil District Hospital, Yeovil BA21 4AT Tel: 01935 475122 Fax: 01935 384572; West Winds, 90 Sheeplands Lane, Sherborne DT9 4BP — MB BChir 1984 Camb.; BSc (Hons.) Lond. 1982; MRCP (UK) 1987; FRCR 1990. Cons. Diag. Radiol. Yeovil Dist. Hosp.

HACKING, Joanna Frances Burchetts, Moushill Down, Milford, Godalming GU8 5JX — MB BS 1996 Lond.

HACKING, John Glen House, Wilsontown, Forth, Lanark ML11 8EP — MB ChB 1945 Glas. (Univ. Glas.)

HACKING, Linda C X-Ray, Law Hospital, Carluke ML8 5ER Tel: 01698 351100; 25 Athole Gardens, Glasgow G12 9BB — MB ChB 1983 Glas.; FRCR 1990. Cons. Radiol. Law Hosp. Carluke. Prev: Sen. Regist. & Regist. (Radiol.) S.. Gen. Hosp. Glas.

HACKING, Mary Wilson Glen House, Wilsontown, Forth, Lanark ML11 8EP — MB ChB 1944 Glas. (Glas.)

HACKING, Matthew Bruce 20 Crescent Court, 2 Park Hill, London SW4 8HR — MB BS 1993 Lond.

HACKING, Nicholas Mark The Beeches, Bullsnape Lane, Goosnargh, Preston PR3 2EF Email: nick@hacking.demon.co.uk — MB ChB 1988 Glas.; MSc Glas. 1991, MB ChB 1988; DA Lond. 1995. (Glasgow) Specialist Regist. (Anaesth. & ITU Med.) NW Region. Socs: SCATA; Assn. Anaesth.s. Prev: SHO (Anaesth. & IC Med.) Law Hosp. Carluke Scotl.

HACKING, Nicola Dicconson Terrace Surgery, Dicconson Terrace, Wigan WN1 2AF Tel: 01942 239525 Fax: 01942 826552 — MB ChB 1978 Leeds. p/t Princip. in Gen. Pract.; Vokuntary on Call Weekend Rota at Wigan and Leigh Hosp. Hindley Wigan. Prev: GP VTS Bolton Gen. Hosp.

HACKING, Peter Michael (retired) Holly House, 47 Main Road, Long Hanborough, Witney OX29 8BD Tel: 01993 882336 — MD 1962 Camb.; 1962 MD Camb.; 1960 FFR; 1958 DMRD Eng.; MB BChir 1953. Prev: Cons. Radiol. Roy. Vict. Infirm. Newc.

HACKING, Robert Stanley The Avenue Surgery, 1 The Avenue, South Moulsecoomb, Brighton BN2 4GF; 13 Cornwall Gardens, Brighton BN1 6RH — MB BS 1981 Lond.; DRCOG 1986.

HACKING, Stanley (retired) 6 Radinden Drive, Hove BN3 6LB Tel: 01273 508633 — MB BS 1950 Lond.; DObst RCOG 1952.

HACKMAN, Brian William Peterborough District Hospital, Thorpe Road, Peterborough PE3 6 Tel: 01733 67451 Fax: 01733 891082; Butts House, Church Road, Glatton, Huntingdon PE28 5RR Tel: 01487 830645 Fax: 01487 832949 Email: brianhackman@easynet.co.uk — MB ChB 1960 Bristol; FRCOG 1982, M 1969, DObst 1967; MFFP. (Bristol) Freelance Cons. O & G. Socs: Exec.Mem. Europ. Assn. Gyn. & Obst.; Internat. Soc. Gyn. Oncol. & Europ. Soc. Obst. & Gyn.; Med. Dir. Wom. Health Centre. Prev: Med. Aid Attache Brit. Embassy Laos; Cons. O & G P'boro Dis. Hosp.; WHO Advisor-outer Mongolia & Laos.

HACKMAN, Miriam Grace (retired) Butts House, Church Road, Glatton, Huntingdon PE28 5RR Tel: 01487 830645 Fax: 01487 832949 Email: brianhackman@easynet.co.uk — MB ChB 1962 Bristol; DCH Eng. 1966. Prev: Regist. (O & G) United Birm. Hosps.

HACKNEY, Julie Sian Manor Park Medical Centre, 204 Harborough Avenue, Sheffield S2 1QU Tel: 0114 239 8602 Fax: 0114 265 8010 — MB ChB 1990 Sheff.

HACKNEY, Juliet Helena 16 Ickworth Road, Sleaford NG34 7LJ Tel: 01529 303108 — MB ChB 1995 Sheff.; BMedSci. Sheff. 1992. (Sheff.) GP.

HACKNEY, Margaret Ann Ecclesfield Group Practice, 96A Mill Road, Ecclesfield, Sheffield S35 9XQ Tel: 0114 246 9151 — MB ChB 1986 Sheff.; DCH RCPS Glas. 1989. Prev: SHO (Cas.) Derbysh. Roy. Infirm.; SHO (Psychiat.) Tameside Gen. Hosp.

HACKNEY, Mr Roger Graham, Wing Cdr. RAF Med. Br. Retd. Consultant Orthopaedic Surgeon, Leeds General Hospital, Great George St, Leeds LS1 3EX Tel: 0113 392 6614 Fax: 0113 392 3770 Email: rghackney@lineone.net; Ashbridge, Main St, Linton, Wetherby LS22 4HT Tel: 01937 589665 Fax: 01937 589665 — MB ChB 1981 Birm.; FRCS (Orth.) 1995; FRCS Eng. 1989; Dip. Sports Med. Lond. 1987. (Univ. Birm.) Cons. Orthop. Surg. Leeds Gen. Inf. Socs: Brit. Orthop. Assn.; BMA; Brit. Assn. Sport and Med. (Chair

S.ern Region). Prev: Hon. Cons. Rheum. Research Unit Addenbrooke's Hosp. Camb.; Sen. Regist. (Orthop. Surg.) Qu. Med. Centre Nottm.; Sen. Regist. (Orthop. & Trauma) Black Notley Colchester & Roy. Lond. Hosp.

HACON, Deborah Susan The Coach House, Mill Lane, Bassingbourn, Royston SG8 5PR — MB ChB 1980 Bristol.

HACZEWSKI, Ian The Old Bakery, Little Dunham, King's Lynn PE32 2DG — MB BS 1983 Lond.; MRCGP 1987; Cert Family Plann JCC 1987; DRCOG 1987.

HACZKIEWICZ, Matthias Joseph (retired) 98 St Georges Avenue, Northampton NN2 6JF — MB ChB Ed. 1963; DObst RCOG 1966. Prev: Regist. (Geriat.) Stoke Mandeville Hosp. Aylesbury.

HADAWAY, Eric George 53 Hall Close, Kettering NN15 7LQ Tel: 01536 512335 — MB BS 1966 Lond.; FFA RCS Eng. 1972; DA Eng. 1968. (St. Mary's) Cons. Anaesth. Kettering Health Dist. Prev: Sen. Regist. (Anaesth.) Radcliffe Infirm. Oxf. & High Wycombe Gen. Hosp.; Regist. (Anaesth.) Hillingdon Hosp. & St. Geo. Hosp. Lond.

HADCROFT, Justine 2 The Anchorage, East Coburg Quayside, Liverpool L3 4DR — MB ChB 1992 Liverp.; MRCP (UK) 1996. Clin. Research Fell./Specialist Regist. (Thoracic Med.) Fazakerley Hosp. Liverp.

HADDAD, Ahmed Qais 14 Loxley Court, Rotherham District General Hospital, Moorgate Rd, Rotherham S60 2UD — MB ChB 1997 Sheff.

HADDAD, Diab Farhan St Peters Hospital, Guildford Road, Chertsey KT16 0PZ Tel: 01932 692986 Fax: 01932 875171 Email: dhaddad@dsk.co.uk — Vrach 1981 Karkov; MRCP (UK) 1991. (Khartov State) Cons. Paediat.St peters Hosp.Chertsey. Socs: RCPCH; BMA. Prev: Lect. (Child Health) & Sen. Regist. (Paediat.) Ninewells Hosp. Dundee; Sen.Reg.Ninewells hosp.

HADDAD, Mr Fares Sami Middlesex Hospital, Dept. of Orthopaedics, Mortimer St, London W1N 8AA Tel: 020 7380 9413, 020 7935 6083 Fax: 020 7935 6728 Email: fareshaddad@compuserve.com; 224 Belsize Road., London NW6 4DE Email: fareshaddad@compuserve.com — MB BS 1990 Lond.; BSc (Hons.) Lond. 1987; FRCS Lond. 1994; FRCS Ed. 1994; MCh 1997, MCh (orth.); FRCS (Orth.) 1997; Dip. Sports Med. 1998. (Univ. Coll. & Middlx. Hosp. Lond.) Cons. Ortho. Surg. Univ. Coll. & Middlx. Hosps. Socs: Brit. Orthopaedic Assn.; Brit. Hip Soc.; Brit. Assn. of Surg. of the Knee. Prev: Fell., Vancouver, Canada; Sen. Regist. Rotat. Roy. Nat. Orthop. Hosp. Lond.; Regist. Rotat. Roy. Free Hosp. Lond.

HADDAD, Mr Monther Jameel Yacoub Paediatric Surgery Department, Chelsea & Westminster Hospital, 369 Fulham Road, London SW10 9NH Tel: 0208 746 8885 Fax: 0208 746 8644 Email: m.haddad@ic.ac.uk — MB BCh 1973 Ain Shams; FRCS Glas. 1982; FRCPCH 1998. Cons. Paediat.Surg.Chelsea & W.minster Hosp.; Cons. Paediat. Surg. St Marys Hosp. Lond. Socs: Brit. Assn. Paediat. Surg.; Internat. Paediat. Endosurg. Grp. Prev: Asst.prof.Jordan univ.hosp.Amman.

HADDAD, Patricia Faith Tara Trout Rise, Loudwater, Rickmansworth WD3 4JY Tel: 01923 896625 — MD Sheff. 1984, MB ChB 1967; FRCOG 1989, M 1972. Cons. O & G Hosp. St. John & St. Eliz. Lond. Socs: Roy. Soc. Med.; Forum of Mat. and the Newborn - RSM Steering Comm.; Inst. Psychosexual Med. Prev: Lect. Char. Cross Hosp. Lond.

HADDAD, Peter Michael Cromwell House, Cromwell Rd, Eccles, Salford M30 0GT Tel: 0161 787 6007 Fax: 0161 787 6006 — MB ChB 1987 Manch.; BSc (Hons.) 1984; MRCPsych 1991; MSc Manch. 1993; MD 1995. (Manchester) Cons. Psychiat. Ment. Health Servs. of Salford; Hon. Clin. Lect. Univ. of Manch. Prev: Clin. Research Fell. Univ. of Manch.; Cons. Psychiat. Trafford Gen. Hosp.

HADDAD, Mr Salim Khalil Gwynfe, Caradoc Road, Aberystwyth SY23 2JY — MB BChir 1966 Camb.; FRCS Eng. 1972.

HADDAD, Stella Josephine 4 Barnstone Vale, Wakefield WF1 4TP — MB ChB 1993 Leeds.

HADDEN, Celia 24 South Inch Park, Perth PH2 8BU Tel: 01738 447544 — MB BCh BAO 1971 Belf. Staff Grade Comm Paediat., Rosewell Clinic, Lochore, Fife.

HADDEN, Professor David Robert Sir George E. Clark Metabolic Unit, Royal Victoria Hospital, Belfast BT12 6BA Tel: 02890 894798 Fax: 02890 310111 Email: david.hadden@royalhospitals.n-i.nhs.uk; 10 Mount Pleasant, Belfast BT9 5DS Tel: 02890 667110 Fax: 02890 667110 — MB BCh BAO 1959 Belf.; MB BCh BAO (Hons.) Belf. 1959; MD Belf. 1963; FRCP Lond. 1987; FRCP Ed. 1970, M 1962. (Belf.) Cons. Phys. Roy. Vict. Hosp. Belf.; Hon. Prof. (Endocrinol.) Qu. Univ. Belf. Socs: Assn. Phys.; (Pres.) Ulster Med. Soc.; Diabetes & Endocrine Socs. Brit., Europ. , US, Internat. Prev: Ho. Off. Roy. Vict. Hosp. Belf.; Fell. (Med.) Johns Hopkins Hosp. Baltimore, MD, USA & MRC Infant Malnutrit. Unit Mulago Hosp. Kampala, Uganda; Fell. (Med.) Dept. Experim. Med. Univ. Camb.

HADDEN, Diana Sheelah Mary 10 Mount Pleasant, Belfast BT9 5DS Tel: 01232 667110 — MB BCh BAO 1965 Belf.; DCH RCPS Glas. 1967. (Qu. Univ. Belf.) Assoc. Specialist (A & E) Roy. Vict. Hosp. Belf. Socs: Founder Fell. Fac. A & E Med.; Ulster Med. Soc.; Brit. Assn. Accid. & Emerg. Med. Prev: Resid. Med Off. Roy. Vict. Hosp. Belf. & Univ. Coll. Hosp. Kingston, Jamaica; SHO (Paediat.) Roy. Belf. Hosp. Sick Childr.

HADDEN, Fraser Marshall Suffolk HA, PO Box 55, Ipswich IP3 8NN Tel: 01473 323422 Fax: 01473 323420 Email: fraser.hadden@dial.pipex.com; 2 Lingside, Martlesham Heath, Ipswich IP5 3UT Tel: 01473 610434 — MB ChB 1979 Dundee; MSc Lond. 1990; MRCP (UK) 1988; MFPHM 1998; DLSHTM Lond. 1996. Cons. Communicable Dis. Control Suff. HA. Prev: Sen. Regist. Rotat. (Pub. Health) E. Anglian RHA; Med. Off. HM Ships & Submarines; SHO Rotat. (Med.) Cornw.

HADDEN, George Campbell (retired) Lawnside, Mucklow Hill, Halesowen B62 8BT Tel: 0121 550 1197 — MB ChB 1944 Aberd. Prev: GP Blackheath, W. Midl.

HADDEN, Ian James 2 Woodford Park, Somerset Road, Coleraine BT51 3LJ — MB BCh BAO 1992 Belf.; DCH RCPS Dub. 1996; DMH Belf. 1995; DGM RCP Glas. 1994; MRCGP RCGP Edin. 1997; DRCOG RCOG Glas. 1998. Socs: Roy. Coll. Gen. Pract.

HADDEN, Kathleen Murray (retired) 107 Winhill Gate, Aberdeen AB11 7WF Tel: 01224 314300 — MB ChB Aberd. 1945.

HADDEN, Nicholas David 24 Hill Rise, Potters Bar EN6 2RR Email: hillrise@clara.net — MB BS 1991 Lond.; FRCA 1997. (St. Geo. Hosp. Med. Sch.) Specialist Regist. (Anaesth.) UCL Hosp. Trust. Lond. Prev: Regist. (Anaesth.) Roy. Free Hosp. & Whittington Hosp. Lond.

HADDEN, Patricia (retired) Lawnside, 37 Mucklow Hill, Halesowen B62 8BT Tel: 0121 550 1197 — MB ChB 1953 Birm.; DObst RCOG 1956. Prev: Asst. Gen. Practioner.

HADDEN, Paul Ernest (retired) The Medical Centre, Adnitt Road, Rushden NN10 9TR Tel: 01933 412555 Fax: 01933 312666 — MB ChB 1957 Sheff. Hosp. Pract. (Dermat.) Rushden Memor. Hosp. Prev: Ho. Surg. Sheff. Roy. Infirm.

HADDEN, Robert David Martin Department of Neurology, Chelsea & Westminster Hospital, 369 Fulham Road, London SW10 9NH Tel: 0208 746 8000 Fax: 0208 746 7872 Email: rob.hadden@doctors.org.uk; 3 Butterworth Terrace, Sutherland Walk, London SE17 3EJ Tel: 020 7277 4400 — BM BCh 1992 Oxf.; PhD Lond. 2000; MRCP (UK) 1995; BA Camb. 1989, MA 1993. (Oxford) SpR. Neurol., W. Lond. Hosps. Rotat. Socs: Assoc. Mem. Assn. Brit. Neurol.; Europ. Assoc. Young Neurol. & Trainees, Treas.; Guillain Barre' Syndrome Supp. Gp. UK - Med. Advisery Comm. Prev: SHO Rotat. (Med.) Newc. 1993-1995; SpR (Neurol.) Nat. Hosp. Of Neurol. Lond. 2001-2002; Research Regist. (Neurol.: Guillain-Barré Syndrome) Dep. Neuroimmonol. Guy's Hosp. Lond. 1996-2001.

HADDEN, Mr William Alexander Highfield House, 30 Highfield Road, Scone, Perth PH2 6RN — MB BCh BAO 1969 Belf.; BAO 1972; FRCS (Orth.) Ed. 1982; FRCS Ed. 1976. Cons. Orthop. Surg. Tayside HB; Hon. Sen. Lect. Univ. Dundee.

HADDEN, William Edward (retired) Bamenda, Middle Road, Lytchett Matravers, Poole BH16 6HJ Tel: 01202 622362 — MB BS Lond. 1935; MRCS Eng. LRCP Lond. 1935; MFCM 1972; DTM & H Eng. 1938, DA 1940, DPH 1949. Prev: Sen. Med. Off. E. Dorset Health Dist.

HADDO, Omar 14 Wildcroft Manor, Wildcroft Rd, London SW15 3TS Tel: 020 8789 2437 — MB BS 1996 Lond.; BSc (Clin. Sci.) Lond. 1995. Surg. Rotat. Frimley Pk. Hosp. Camberley.

HADDOCK, Andrew Whyman 37 Turnstone Drive, Liverpool L26 7WP — MB ChB 1993 Liverp.

HADDOCK, Gail Kinmond The Surgery, 6 East Mount Road, York YO24 1BD Tel: 01904 646509 Fax: 01904 646743 — MB ChB 1985 Ed.; MRCGP 1993; DRCOG 1990; DA (UK) 1989. (Ed.) Prev:

SHO (Psychiat.) Harrogate Dist. Hosp.; Med. Off. Serabu Hosp., Sierra Leone.

HADDOCK, George David (retired) 4 Duncan House, 2 High St., Earith, Huntingdon PE28 3PP — MB ChB 1960 Sheff.; DObst RCOG 1962.

HADDOCK, Mr Graham Royal Hospital for Sick Children, Yorkhill, Glasgow G3 8SJ Tel: 0141 201 0000 Fax: 0141 201 0865 Email: ghaddock@udcf.gla.ac.uk; Flat 9, Whitegables, 116 St. Andrews Drive, Glasgow G41 4RB — MB ChB 1982 Glas.; MB ChB (Commend.) Glas. 1982; MD Glas. 1993; FRCS (Paediat.) 1995; FRCS Glas. 1986. (Univ. Glas.) Cons. Paediat. Surg. Roy. Hosp. Sick Childr. Glas.; Hon. Sen. Lect. Univ. Glas. Socs: Brit. Assn. Paediat. Surg. Prev: Sen. Regist. (Paediat. Surg.) Roy. Hosp. Sick Childr. Glas.; Clin. Fell. Hosp. for Sick Childr. Toronto, Canada.

HADDOCK, Jane Amanda Aldridge 62 Manchuria Road, London SW11 6AE; Royal Free NHS Trust, Pond St, London NW3 2QG Tel: 020 7830 2170 — BA Oxf. 1980; MB BS Lond. 1984; MRCP (UK) 1987; FRCR 1991. (Oxford/St Thomas' Londn) Cons. Roy. Free NHS Trust Hampstead.

HADDOCK, Katharine Mary (retired) 4 Duncan House, 2 High St., Earith, Huntingdon PE17 3PN — MB ChB 1960 Sheff.

HADDOCK, Raymond Community Health Sheffield, Specialist Psychotherapy Services, Brunswick House, 299 Glossop Road, Sheffield S10 2HL Tel: 0114 271 6894 Fax: 0114 271 6893 Email: rayhad@chsheff-tr.trent.nhs.uk — MB ChB 1982 Leeds; MMedSc (Clin. Psychiat.) Leeds 1988; MRCPsych 1987. Cons. Psychotherapist & Assoc. Med. Dir. Community Health Sheff. Socs: Inst. of Gp. Anal.; Brit. Assoc. of Med. Manag.

HADDON, Angela Lesley Dept of Clinical Biochemistry, Russells hall Hospital, Dudley DY1 2HQ — MB BCh 1989 Wales; BSc (Hons.) Wales 1984, MB BCh 1989. Chem. Path.

HADDON, Janice Elizabeth The Medical Centre, Church Field, Camelford PL32 9YT Tel: 01840 213894; Hawkmeade, 61 Valley Road, Bude EX23 8ES Tel: 01288 354602 — MB BS 1982 Lond.; MRCGP 1986; DRCOG 1986. (Kings Coll.) Prev: Clin. Asst. (Colposcopy) N. Devon Dist. Hosp. Barnstaple.

HADDON, Jeffrey The Health Centre, Bath Road, Buxton SK17 6HL Tel: 01298 24105 Fax: 01298 73227; 17 Birch Close, Buxton SK17 6FE — MB ChB 1991 Dundee.

HADDON, Philip Wright Stratton Medical Centre, Hospital Road, Stratton, Bude EX23 9BP Tel: 01288 352133; Hawkmede, 61 Valley Road, Bude EX23 8ES — MB BS 1982 Lond.; BSc Lond. 1979, MB BS 1982; MRCGP 1986; MRCOphth 1994; DRCOG 1985. (Kings Coll.)

HADDON, Richard William James, Surg. Lt.-Cdr. RN Anaesthetic Department, Royal Hospital Haslar, Gosport PO12 2AA Tel: 01705 584255; 2 Tawny Owl Close, Fareham PO14 3JB — MB BS 1980 Lond.; MRCS Eng. LRCP Lond. 1980; MRCGP 1990; AFOM RCP Lond. 1993; DAvMed FOM RCP Lond. 1992; T(GP) 1991. (St. Bart.) SHO (Anaesth.). Prev: Staff Med. Off. Flag Off. Sea Train.; Princip. Med. Off. HMS Sultan; Sen. Med. Off. HMS Glas.

HADDOW, Alison Marjory 264 Holburn Street, Aberdeen AB10 6DD — MB ChB 1988 Aberd.; MRCPsych 1993. Regist. (Psychiat.) Roy. Edin. Hosp.

HADDOW, Anne McLachlan 5 The Ridings, Ockbrook, Derby DE72 3SF Tel: 01332 662646 — MB ChB 1946 Glas.; MFOM RCP Lond. 1983. Cons. Occupat. Health. Socs: BMA & Soc. Occupat. Med. Prev: Sen. Med. Off. Ct.aulds; GP Sunthorpe.

HADDOW, Ian Forbes Gordon (retired) Causeway House, 4 Achany Road, Dingwall IV15 9JB Tel: 01349 861112 — MB ChB 1956 Birm.; MFPHM 1990; MFCM RCP Lond. 1974; DIH Dund 1968; DPH Glas. 1964. Prev: Cons. Pub. Health Med. Highland HB.

HADDOW, Kerry Adrienne Roper Top Left, 192 Hyndland Road, Glasgow G12 9ER — MB BS 1993 Lond.

HADDOW, Lewis John First Floor, 2 Buchanan Drive, Causewayhead, Stirling FK9 5HF — MB ChB 1998 Ed.; MB ChB Ed 1998.

HADDOW, Robert Alvey (retired) White Owl Cottage, Rectory Lane, Old Bolingbroke, Spilsby PE23 4EY Tel: 01790 763222 — MB ChB St. And. 1957; FRCP Ed. 1994; MRCP Ed. 1963; FFR 1966; FRCR 1975; DMRD Eng. 1964. Prev: Cons. Radiol. Pilgrim Hosp. Boston.

HADDOW, Thomas Gillespie (retired) 16 Netherlea, Scone, Perth PH2 6QA Tel: 01738 551182 Email: haddow@freeuk.com — MB ChB Glas. 1952. Prev: Resid. Ho. Phys. W.. Infirm. Glas.

HADDY, Caroline Edwina Louise The Surgery, 15 West Town Road, Backwell, Bristol BS48 3HA Tel: 0117 462026 Fax: 0117 795609 — MB ChB 1985 Bristol; MRCGP 1989; Cert. Family Plann. JCC 1988; DRCOG 1988. Prev: Trainee GP Backwell.

HADELMAYR-KUHN, Ilse Ruth (retired) 7 Barratt Close, Stoneygate, Leicester LE2 2AN — MD Vienna 1936; FFA RCS Eng. 1957; DA Eng. 1948. Prev: Cons. Anaesth. Oldham Gen. Gp. Hosps.

HADEN, Rachel 24 Gardner Road, Christchurch BH23 2DZ — BM 1991 Soton.; DCH RCP Lond. 1995. SHO (Anaesth.) Soton. Univ. Hosp. NHS Trust.

HADEN, Robert Myles 5 Regency Drive, Kings Coughton, Alcester B49 5QB — MB ChB 1976 Leeds; FFA RCS Eng. 1981; DRCOG 1978. Cons. Anaesth. BromsGr. & Redditch HA.

HADFIELD, Anne Amelia Mulberry House Surgery, 38 Highfield Road, Southampton SO17 1PJ Tel: 023 8055 4549 Fax: 023 8055 3151; 7 Meadowhead Road, Bassett, Southampton SO16 7AD Tel: 02380 760429 Email: kbs18@dial.pipex.com — MB BS 1970 Lond.; MRCGP 1982. (Lond. Hosp.)

HADFIELD, Caroline Sara Louise East Street Surgery, East Street, South Molton EX36 3BU Tel: 01769 573811 — BM BS 1991 Nottm.; BMedSci Nottm. 1989; MRCGP 1995; DRCOG 1993.

HADFIELD, David Anthony Glap Thurner Road, Oundle, Peterborough PE1 4JA Tel: 01832 273408; 69 Bengefield Road, Oundle, Peterborough — LMSSA 1972 Lond.; DPhil Oxf. 1972, BA 1970, BM ChB 1973; DRCOG 1974.

HADFIELD, Esme Victoria Ann Pickernell 29 Poynings Road, London N19 5LH — MB BS 1986 Lond.

HADFIELD, Mr Geoffrey John, CBE, TD (retired) Milverton House, 6 St Johns Close, Bishopsteignton, Teignmouth TQ14 9RT — 1946 MRCS Eng. LRCP Lond.; 1947 MB BS Lond.; 1954 MS Lond.; 1948 FRCS Eng. Hon. Col. City of Bath Gen. Hosp. TAVR; Hon. Fell. Coll. Phys. & Surgs., Pakistan, Liasion Off.; Hon. Vis. Prof. Sind. Inst. Of Urol. at Saw Med Coll. Karachi. Prev: Surg. Stoke Mandeville Hosp. & Hon. Tutor (Surg.) Univ. Coll. Hosp. Med. Sch. Lond.

HADFIELD, George Woods (retired) Fleet Rise, Fleet Hill, Finchampstead, Wokingham RG40 4LE Tel: 01734 733428 — MB BS 1949 Lond.; MRCP Lond. 1951; MRCS Eng. LRCP Lond. 1949; MRCGP 1958. Hon. Assoc. Prof. Dept. Community Med. Baylor Coll. Med. Texas Med. Center Houston USA. Prev: Chairm. Med. Staff. Comm. Yateley Hosp.

HADFIELD, Mr Gordon Berachah, Shores Road, Woking GU21 4HN Tel: 01483 773232 Fax: 01483 834032 — MRCS Eng. LRCP Lond. 1947; FRCS Eng. 1955. (King's Coll. Hosp.) Emerit. Cons. Orthop. Surg. NW Surrey; Hon. Med. Off. Brit. Motor Cycle Racing Club; Hon. Pres. Med. Panel Internat. Motorcycle Federat. Socs: Sen. Fell. BOA. Prev: Cons. Orthop. Surg. Rowley Bristow Orthop. Hosp. & St. Peters Hosp. Chertsey; Chief Asst. (Orthop.) St. Thos. Hosp. Lond.

HADFIELD, Gordon Trevor Salters Meadows Health Centre, Rugeley Road, Chase Terrace, Walsall WS7 8AQ Tel: 01543 682611 Fax: 01543 675391; Windmill Bank Cottage, Gentleshaw, Rugeley WS15 4NH Tel: 0154 36 72221 — MB BS 1969 Lond.; MRCS Eng. LRCP Lond. 1969; MFFP 1996; Cert Family Plann 1982; DCH Eng. 1972; DObst RCOG 1971; AKC Lond. 1969. (King's Coll. Hosp.) GP Princip., Salters Meadon Centre, Chase Terr., Staffs.; Partner-Prescription Free Pract., 152 Birm. Rd, Sutton Goldfield, W. Midl.s. Socs: Christ. Med. Fell.sh.; Nat. Assn. Family Plann. Doctors; Brit. Soc. Med. & Dent. Hypn. Prev: SHO (O & G) Pembury Hosp.; SHO (Paediat.) Roy. Manch. Childr. Hosp. Pendlebury; Med. Off. Vom Christian Hosp., Nigeria.

HADFIELD, Hugh Wollaston Mulberry House Surgery, 38 Highfield Road, Southampton SO17 1PJ Tel: 023 8055 4549 Fax: 023 8055 3151; 7 Meadowhead Road, Bassett, Southampton SO16 7AD Tel: 023 8076 0429 Email: kbs18@dial.pipex.com — MB BS 1970 Lond.; BSc Bristol 1964; MRCGP 1977; DObst RCOG 1973. (Lond. Hosp.) Socs: BMA.

HADFIELD, Ian (retired) 14A Crows Port, Hamble, Southampton SO31 4HG — BM BCh 1953 Oxf.; MRCPsych 1972; DPM Eng. 1957. Prev: Cons. Child & Family Psychiat. Wessex RHA.

HADFIELD, Mr James Irvine Havelock Bakers Barn, Stagsden West End, Bedford MK43 8SZ Tel: 01234 824514; Portheiddy Cottage, Berea, St. Davids, Haverfordwest SA62 6DR — BM BCh 1955 Oxf.; MA, BM BCh Oxf. 1955; FRCS Eng. 1960; FRCS Ed. 1960; FICS 1990. (Oxf. & St. Thos.) Anat. Tutor Jesus Coll. Camb.; Demonst. (Anat.) Camb. Univ.; Geo. Herbert Hunt Schol. Oxf. Univ.; Clin. Tutor Bedford Gen. Hosp.; Surg. Tutor Bedford Clin. Area; Chairm. Bedford Gen. Hosp. Med. Exec. Comm.; Examr. (Surg.) Univ. Camb.; Lect. (Anat. & Assoc. Teach Surg.) Univ. Camb.; Examr. RCS Ed. Socs: Fell. Roy. Soc. Med.; Fell. Assn. Clin. Anats.; Fell. Assn. Surgs. Prev: Cons. Urol. (Surg.) Bedford Gen. & Edgbury Hosps. & Med. Dir. Bedford Hosp. NHS Trust; Tutor (Surg.) Univ. Oxf. & Hon. 1st Asst. in Surg. Radcliffe Infirm. Oxf.; Sen. Regist. (Surg.) Leicester Roy. Infirm.

HADFIELD, John William 666 Chatsworth Road, Brookside, Chesterfield S40 3NU Tel: 01246 568843 — MB BS 1974 Lond.; FRCP Lond. 1994; MRCP (UK) 1977. Cons. Phys. (Gen. & Respirat. Med.) Chesterfield & N. Derbysh. Roy. Hosp. NHS Trust; Clin. Dir. of Med. Socs: Eur. Respirat. Soc.; Brit. Thorac. Soc.; BMA. Prev: Sen. Regist. (Med.) Derby Hosp.; Regist. (Med.) Papworth Hosp. Camb.

HADFIELD, Katharine Anastasia Mary FLeet Rise, Fleet Hill, Finchampstead, Wokingham RG40 4LE — MB BS 1975 Lond.; DA Eng. 1978; DCH Eng. 1978.

HADFIELD, Matthew Beecher 16 Millbrook Close, Shaw, Oldham OL2 8QA Tel: 01706 290633 — MB ChB 1990 Manch.; FRCS Eng. 1994. Specialist Regist. (Gen. Surg.) NW Region.

HADFIELD, Pandora Juliet King's College Hospital, Denmark Hill, London SE5 9RS — MB BS 1986 Lond.; MRCGP 1990. Trainee GP/SHO (O & G) St.Peter's Hosp. Chertsey.

HADFIELD, Peter Bernard 69 Benefield Road, Oundle, Peterborough PE8 4EU — MB BS 1997 Newc.

HADFIELD, Richard Jonathan Houghton 2nd & 3rd Floor Maisonette, 15 The Mall, Bristol BS8 4DS — MB BS 1989 Lond.

HADFIELD, Robert Noel (retired) Neath oak House, High pine Close, Weybridge KT13 9EA Tel: 01932 850360 Fax: 01932 850360 Email: alonoel@doctors.org.uk — MB BS Lond. 1950; MRCS Eng. LRCP Lond. 1944; FFA RCS Eng. 1954; DA Eng. 1953; FRCA. Prev: Cons. Anaesth. S.port & N. Liverp. Gps. Hosps.

HADFIELD, Sarah Caroline 666 Chatsworth Road, Brookside, Chesterfield S40 3NU Tel: 01246 568843 — MB BS 1974 Lond.; MRCGP 1979; DObst RCOG 1976. Staff Grade Sch. Health N. Derbysh. Community Health Care Servs.; Med. Adviser Adoption & Fostering N. Derbysh.

HADFIELD, Stephen John (retired) Port Na Mairt, Ganavan Road, Oban PA34 5TU — MB BChir 1934 Camb.; MA Camb. 1947; FRCP Ed. 1974, M 1969; MRCS Eng. LRCP Lond. 1933; DObst RCOG 1942. Prev: Scott. Sec. BMA.

HADI, Qusay Mossa Abdul Department of Child & Adolescent Psychiatry, Eaglestone Health Centre, Milton Keynes Hospital Campus, Standing Way, Eaglestone, Milton Keynes MK6 5AZ — MB ChB 1976 Baghdad.

HADIDA, Antoinette qThe Old Vicarage, Church Lane, Whaddon, Milton Keynes MK17 0LX — MB ChB 1998 Manch.; MB ChB Manch 1998.

HADJI, Farida 142 Bedford St S., Liverpool L7 7DB — MD 1990 Frankfurt; State Exam Med. Frankfurt 1990.

HADJI-STYLIANOU, Ronis RS Healthcare, PO Box 328, Enfield EN1 2HG — MB BS 1983 Lond. (Guy's) Head RS Healthcare.

HADJICHARITOU, Christos Grove Surgery, Charlotte Street, Wakefield WF1 1UJ Tel: 01924 372596 Fax: 01924 200913 — MRCS Eng. LRCP Lond. 1979. (Univ. Athens)

HADJIKAKOU, Mr Alexandros Pericles Doncaster Royal Infirmary, Doncaster DN2 5LT; 4 Mayfield Road, Sprotsbrough, Doncaster DN5 8AX — State Exam Med 1987 Saarland; FRCS Ed. 1993.

HADJIKOUMI, Irene Flat 5, Block 4, St Peter's Hospital, Chertsey KT16 0PZ — Ptychio Iatrikes 1991 Thessalonika.

HADJIKOUTIS, Savvas 23 Farm Drive, Cardiff CF23 6HQ — MB ChB 1994 Bristol.

HADJILOUCAS, Mr Ioannis Trafford General Hospital, Moorside Road, Davy Hulme, Manchester M41 5SL Tel: 0161 748 4022; 68 Fairholme Road, Manchester M20 4SB Tel: 0161 445 8309 Email: ioannis@clara.net — MB ChB 1992 Manch.; FRCS Ed. 1996. Research Fell.Surg. Prev: SSHO (Gen. Surg.) Barnsley Dist. Gen. Hosp.; SHO Centr. Manch. Surgic. Rotat.; SSHO (Gen. Surg.) Trafford Gen. Hosp.

HADJIMINAS, Mr Demetrios Breast Unit, 5th Floor, Stanford Wing, St Mary's Hospital, Praed St., London W2 1NY Tel: 020 8861 3143 Fax: 020 8861 3148 — Ptychio Iatrikes 1985 Athens; FRCS 1998 (Gen. Surg.); FRCS Eng. 1991; FRCS Ed. 1990; M.Phil Lond. 1998; MD Athens 1996. (Athens University) Cons. Surg.; Director of St. Mary's BrE. Unit, Lond. W2 1NY; Hon. Sen. Lect., Imperial Coll. Lond. Socs: BASO; BASO BrE. Gp.; BMA.

HADJINIKOLAOU, Leonidas Room 419, Salton House, St Mary's Hospital, Praed St., London W2 1NY — Ptychio Iatrikes 1985 Patras.

HADJIVASSILIOU, Marios Department of Neurology, The Royal Hallamshire Hospital, Glossop Rd, Sheffield S10 1HP; 11 Thomsett Road, Kenwood, Sheffield s7 1NB — MB ChB 1989 Sheff.; MRCP (UK) 1993; MD 1999. Cons. Neur. Dept. of Neur.Roy.Hallamshire.Hosps.heff. Prev: SHO (Neurol.) Roy. Hallamsh. Hosp. Sheff.; SHO Rotat. & Regist. (Med.) Chesterfield Roy. Hosp.; Research Regist. (Neurol.) Roy. Hallamsh. Hosp. Sheff.

HADKINS, Richard 14 Briar Rigg, Keswick CA12 4NN — MB ChB 1988 Manch.

HADLAND, Mark David 7 Hillcliffe Road, Walton, Warrington WA4 6NX — MB ChB 1998 Dund.; MB ChB Dund 1998.

HADLEY, Christopher Rhys The Surgery, High Street, Wombourne, Wolverhampton WV5 9DP Tel: 01902 892209 Fax: 01902 892441 — MB BS 1988 Lond.; BSc (Hons.) Lond. 1986; MRCGP 1992; DRCOG 1991. (Univ. Coll. Lond.)

HADLEY, David Allarton Consulting Rooms, 116 Heene Road, Worthing BN11 4PN Tel: 01903 200938; Glentham House, Binsted, Arundel BN18 0LP Tel: 01243 551238 Fax: 01243 555525 Email: dhadley107@aol.com — MB BS 1963 Lond.; FRCS Eng. 1971; FRCOphth 1989. (St. Bart.) Cons. Ophth. Surg. Gen. Hosp. Worthing & St. Richard's Hosp. Chichester. Prev: Sen. Regist. (Ophth.) St. Bart. Hosp. Lond.; Sen. Regist. Moorfields Eye Hosp.; Regist. (Ophth.) W.m. Hosp.

HADLEY, Dorothy Charlotte Gordon Mackay Orrin Lodge, 46 Culduthel Road, Inverness IV2 4HQ — MB ChB Ed. 1943. (Univ. Ed.) Prev: Med. Off. Matern. Unit, W.. Gen. Hosp. Edin.; Regist. Elsie Inglis Matern. Hosp. Edin.; GP Edin.

HADLEY, Elizabeth Mary 130 Blackbrook Lane, Bickley, Bromley BR1 2HP — MB BS 1998 Lond.; MB BS Lond 1998.

HADLEY, Ivor Maurice (retired) 6 Castle Bolton, Eastbourne BN23 8NU Tel: 01323 743187 — MB ChB 1954 Birm.; DMJ Soc. Apoth. Lond. 1973. Prev: Ho. Surg. Gen. Hosp. Birm.

HADLEY, Joanne Lesley Hadleigh Practice, 20 Kirkway, Broadstone, Poole BH18 8EE — MB BCh 1985 Wales; BSc Physiol. Wales 1982; DRCOG 1988. Gen. Practitioner with Hadleigh Pract. since 1991.

HADLEY, Mr John Maurice The Runnymede Hospital, Guildford Road, Ottershaw, Chertsey KT16 0RQ Tel: 01932 877836 Fax: 01932 254041 Email: johnsid@dial.pipex.com; 2 Willow Court, 98 Sidney Road, Walton-on-Thames KT12 3SA Tel: 01932 229157 Fax: 01932 254041 Email: hadley.family@ukgateway.net — BM BCh 1983 Oxf.; MA Camb. 1984; FRCS (Orl.) 1994; FRCS Eng. (Orl.) 1990; FRCS Eng. (Gen. with Orl.) 1990; FRCS Eng. 1988; MBA 1999. (Oxf. & Camb.) Cons. Ent. Surg. Ashford St. Peters Hosp. Trust & Roy. Surg. Co. Hosp. Guildford; Chairm., Med. Advisery Comm., Runnymede Hosp.; Chairm., Clin. effectiveness & audit Comm., ashford St. Peter's NHS Trust. Socs: Brit. Voice Assn.; Brit. Assn. Paediat. Otol.; Brit. Assn. Otolaryngol. Head & Neck Surg.s. Prev: Cons. Surg. (ENT) W. Middlx. Univ. Hosp. Trust Lond. & Ashford Hosp. Staines; Sen. Regist. (ENT) Roy. Lond. Hosp. Trust, N.wick Pk. & St. Mark's Hosp. Trust; Regist. (ENT) Roy. Nat. Throat, Nose & Ear Hosp. Lond.

HADLEY, John William 57 Senneleys Park Road, Northfield, Birmingham B31 1AE — MB ChB 1978 Birm.

HADLEY, Julia Susan 8 Fabricus Avenue, Droitwich WR9 8RR Tel: 01905 775503 — BM BS 1994 Nottm.; BMedSci Nottm. 1992. (Nottm.)

HADLEY, Katherine Mary 20 Roman Court, Bearsden, Glasgow G61 2HS — MB ChB 1972 Ed.; BSc (Med. Sci.) Ed. 1969, MB ChB 1972; MRCPath 1987. Lect. (Bact. & Immunol.) Univ. Glas. W.. Infirm. Prev: Sen. Regist. (Bact.) Univ. Aberd.; Clin. Med. Off. Grampian HB; Regist. (Obst.) Cresswell Matern. Hosp. Dumfries.

HADLEY, Lindsay Amy-Anne Old Town Surgery, 13 De la Warr Road, Bexhill-on-Sea TN40 2HG Tel: 01424 219323 Fax: 01424 733940; 35 South Cliff, Bexhill-on-Sea TN39 3EH — MB BS 1978 Lond.; BA Oxf. 1973; MRCGP 1984. Hosp. Pract. (Psychogeriat.) Dept. Med. for Elderly Bexhill; GP Ment. Health Facilitator, S. Downs Health Trust, Brighton; Clin. Governance Ldr., Bexhill & Rother Primary Care Trust. Prev: SHO (Med.) Whittington Hosp. Lond.

HADLEY, Montague Donald MacDonald 20 Roman Court, Bearsden, Glasgow G61 2HS — MB ChB 1974 Aberd.; PhD Aberd. 1980, MB ChB 1974; FRCR 1983; DMRD Aberd. 1981.

HADLEY, Montague William MacDonald (retired) Orrin Lodge, Culduthel Road, Inverness IV2 4HQ Tel: 01463 232564 — MD 1953 Ed.; MB ChB 1944; FRCP Ed. 1970, M 1949; FRCR 1984; DMRD Ed. 1955. Prev: Cons. Radiol. N.. RHB (Scotl.).

HADLEY, Nigel Stanley 3 Fernhill Close, Hawley Blackwater, Camberley GU17 9HD; 6 The Dingle, West Park, Gee Cross, Hyde SK14 5EP Tel: 0161 351 1859 Fax: 0161 351 1859 Email: valnigel95@aol.com — BM BS 1977 Nottm.; MRCP (UK) 1981; AFOM RCP Lond. 1991. Med. Adviser Med. Bd.ing Centre (Respirat. Dis.) Manch.

HADLEY, Mr Paul Alexander Victoria Surgery, Victoria Street, Bury St Edmunds IP33 3BD Tel: 01284 725550 Fax: 01284 725551; 17 Sharp Road, Bury St Edmunds IP33 2NB — MB BS 1978 Lond.; FRCS Ed. 1982. (St. Geo.)

HADLEY, Rebecca Sarah 21 Rosebank Road, London E17 8NH — MB BS 1997 Lond.

HADLEY, Robert John Riversdale Surgery, Riversdale House, Merthyrmawr Road, Bridgend CF31 3NL Tel: 01656 766866 Fax: 01656 668659; 16 Merthyr Road, Bridgend CF31 3NN Tel: 01656 768068 — MB 1977 Camb.; BChir 1976; MRCGP 1980. Princip. GP Course Organiser Bridgend VTS.

HADLEY, Mr Robert Martin 48 Crofton Lane, Orpington BR5 1HL Tel: 01689 833230 Email: robert.hadley@btinternet.com — MB BS Lond. 1960; FRCS Eng. 1970. (St. Bart.)

HADLEY, Susan Elisabeth Langton Hall, West Langton, Market Harborough LE16 7TY — BM BS 1984 Nottm.; BM BS Nottm. l984.

HADLEY BROWN, Martin School Lane Surgery, School Lane, Thetford IP24 2AG Tel: 01842 753115; 15 Hill House Lane, Thetford IP24 1UR Tel: 01842 753891 Email: hbthetford@aol.com — MB BS 1983 Lond.; MRCGP 1989. (St. Thos.) GP; Clin. Asst. Bertram Diabetes Unit W. Norwich Hosp. Socs: BMA. Prev: Trainee GP W. Dorset; SHO Renal Unit St. Thos. Hosp. Lond.

HADLINGTON, Kirsten Jane 50 Hyde Lane, Kinver, Stourbridge DY7 6AF — MB ChB 1991 Birm.; MRCGP 1996.

HADOKE, Joanna Katherine Rosyth Health Centre, Park Road, Rosyth, Dunfermline KY11 2SE Tel: 01383 418931 Fax: 01383 419007 — MB ChB 1991 Ed.

HADRILL, Katharine Clare Verney 120 Colleys Lane, Willaston, Nantwich CW5 6NT — MB ChB 1986 Manch.; DRCOG 1990. GP Nantwich.

HADWIN, Richard John 16A Semaphore Road, Guildford GU1 3PT — BM 1997 Soton.

HADZIC, Nedim Department of Child Health, King's College Hospital, Denmark Hill, London SE5 9RS Tel: 020 7346 3214 Fax: 020 7346 3564 Email: nedim.hadzic@kcl.ac.uk; Tel: 020 8761 1665 — MD 1979 Univ. Sarajevo, Bosnia; MSc Univ. Sarajevo, Bosnia 1987; FRCP 1998 CH. Cons. Paediat. Hepatologist King's Coll. Hosp. Lond. Socs: Fell. RCPCH; Amer. Assn. for Study of Liver Dis.; Europ. Assn. for Study of Liver Dis. Prev: Lect. (Paediat. Hepat.) King's Coll. Sch. Med. Lond.; Clin. Fell. (Immunol.) Inst. Child Health Lond.; Lect. (Paediat.) Univ. Hosp. Sarajevo, Bosnia.

HAEGER, Martin Peter Blackwater Medical Centre, Princes Road, Maldon CM9 7DS Tel: 01621 854204 Fax: 01621 850246 — MB BS 1981 Lond.; MRCP (UK) 1984; MRCGP 1988.

HAENEY, James Alexander 36 Church Barns, Church La, Marston, Oxford OX3 0PT — BM BCh 1997 Oxf.

HAENEY, Lynda Kay Danebridge Medical Centre, London Road, Northwich CW9 5HR Tel: 01606 01606 45786 Fax: 01606 331977 — MB BCh 1969 Wales; DObst RCOG 1971. (Cardiff) Gen. Practitioner.

HAENEY, Mansel Richard Department of Immunology, Clinical Sciences Building, Hope Hospital, Salford M6 8HD Tel: 0161 787 5572 Fax: 0161 789 0058 Email: mhaeney@fs1.ho.man.ac.uk; Nettlegate House, Colliers Lane, Aston-by-Budworth, Northwich CW9 6NF Tel: 01565 733526 — MB BCh 1969 Wales; MSc Birm. 1976; FRCP Lond. 1989; MRCP (U.K.) 1972; FRCPath 1990, M 1979. (Cardiff) Cons. Immunol. Hope Hosp. Salford. Prev: Sen. Regist. (Regional Immunol. Laborat.) E. Birm. Hosp.; MRC Clin. Research Fell. Dept. Experim. Path. Univ. Birm.; Regist. Metab. Research Unit E. Birm. Hosp.

HAERI, Mr Anthony D 73 Harley Street, London W1 Tel: 020 7935 5393; 29 Connaught Gardens, Muswell Hill, London N10 3LD Tel: 020 8883 1067 — MB BS 1964 Lond.; FRCS Eng. 1970; MRCS Eng. LRCP Lond. 1964; FRCOG 1984, M 1972, DObst 1966. (St. Bart.) Cons. O & G Ealing Hosp.; Examr. Mem. Roy. Coll. Obst. & Gyn.; Hon. Lect. Imperial Coll. Sch. of Med. Socs: Chelsea Clin. Soc. Prev: Lect. & Sen. Regist. (O & G) St. Bart. Hosp.; Resid. Surg. Off. Roy. Marsden Hosp. Lond.; Ho. Surg. Qu. Charlotte's Matern. Hosp. Lond.

HAETZMAN, Marisa Louise 13 Crown Terrace, Aberdeen AB11 6HE — MB ChB 1990 Glas.; MRCP (UK) 1993; FRCA 1997. (Univ. Glas.)

HAFEEZ, Abdul Plumstead Health Centre, Tewson Road, Plumstead, London SE18 1BB Tel: 020 8854 1898 Fax: 020 8855 9958 — MB BS 1981 Punjab; MB BS Punjab (Pakistan) 1981; MRCS Eng. LRCP Lond. 1989. (King Edwd. Med. Coll. Lahore, Pakistan) Prev: SHO (Rheum.) Harold Wood Hosp.; SHO (Geriat.) Brook Gen. Hosp. Lond.; Ho. Off. (Surg.) StoneHo. Hosp. Lanarksh.

HAFEEZ, Abdul The Surgery, 158 College Road, Moseley, Birmingham B13 9LH Tel: 0121 777 4040 Fax: 0121 778 6683 — MB BS 1967 Punjab. GP Birm. Prev: Regist. (Orthop.) W. Bromwich Hosp.; SHO (Cas.) E. Birm. Hosp.; Ho. Off. (Gen. surg.) & Ho. Phys. (Paediat.) Selly Oak Hosp. Birm.

HAFEEZ, Farhat The Surgery, 158 College Road, Moseley, Birmingham B13 9LH Tel: 0121 777 4040 Fax: 0121 778 6683 — MB BS 1964 Karachi; MB BS 1964 Karachi.

HAFEEZ, Irfan 63 Abbotts Park Road, Leyton, London E10 6HU — MB BS 1986 Punjab; MRCPI 1995.

***HAFEEZ, Uzma** 156 College Road, Moseley, Birmingham B13 9LH — MB ChB 1996 Birm.

HAFEJEE, Abdul 158 St Pauls Road, Preston PR1 1PX — MB ChB 1993 Manch.

HAFEZ, Mr Mahmoud Alm El-Din 1 Swithens Grove, Rothwell, Leeds LS26 0TL Tel: 0113 288 7843 Fax: 0113 288 7843 Email: mhafez@msn.com — MB BCh 1985 Cairo; MSc Cairo 1991; FRCS Ed. 1997. (Univ. Cairo) Specialist Registra Orthop., Leeds Teachg. Hosp. Leeds. Socs: Amer. Fract. Assoc.; BOA. Prev: Clin. Research Fell., Comuter Sci.s Dept., Univ. Hull.

HAFEZ AMIN, Hafez El Saied 22 Marlston Avenue, Chester CH4 8HF — MB ChB 1974 Alexandria.

HAFFENDEN, Deborah Kate Rowcroft Medical Centre, Rowcroft Retreat, Stroud GL5 3BE Tel: 01453 764471 Fax: 01453 755247; Cobwebs, Moor Court, Rodborough Common, Stroud GL5 5DA Tel: 01453 873429 — MB ChB 1987 Bristol; MRCGP 1994; DRCOG 1993. (Bristol) GP. Prev: SHO (Paediat.) Gloucestershire Roy. Hosp.; SHO (Psychiat.) Worcester Roy. Infirm.; SHO (O & G) Gloucestershire Roy. Hosp.

HAFFIZ, Tahir 76 Chairborough Road, High Wycombe HP12 3HJ — MB ChB 1990 Birm.; ChB Birm. 1990.

HAFIZ, Abdul Brierley Hill Health Centre, Albion St., Brierley Hill DY5 3EE Tel: 01384 77628; 10 Dingle Road, Stourbridge DY9 0RS — MB BS 1952 Punjab; MB BS Punjab (Pakistan) 1952; DObst RCOG 1963. (King Edw. Med. Coll. Lahore)

***HAFIZ, Riaz Mohamed** 374 Carter Knowle Road, Sheffield S11 9GD Tel: 0114 236 5858 — MB BS 1996 Lond.

HAFIZI, Sepehr 39 Windermere Avenue, London SW19 3EP Tel: 020 8542 4136 — MB BS 1995 Lond.; BSc (Hons.) Biochem. Surrey 1988. (Bart. Hosp. Lond.) SHO Rotat. (Psychiat.) Univ. Coll. Lond. Socs: Med. Protec. Soc.; BMA; Fell. Roy. Soc. Med. Prev: SHO (Neuro Psychiat.) Bethlem Roy. & Maudsley Hosp. Lond.; Ho. Surg. St. Bart. & Roy. Lond. Hosps.; Ho. Phys. Mayday Hosp.

HAFIZULLAH, Muhammad Deansgate Health Centre, Bolton BL1 1JE — MB BS 1951 Sind; LAH Dub. 1960. (Dow Med. Coll. Karachi) Clin. Asst. (ENT) Pk. Hosp. Davyhulme & Bolton Roy. Infirm. Socs: Fell. Manch. Med. Soc.; Assoc. N. Eng. Otolaryng. Soc. Prev: Regist. (ENT) Salford Roy. Hosp.

HAGAN, Christopher Mark 22 Polwarth Street, Glasgow G12 9TY — MB ChB 1990 Manch.

HAGAN, Gerald William Ernest Glaxo Wellcome UK Ltd, Stockley Park W., Uxbridge UB11 1BT Tel: 020 8990 9000 Fax: 020 8990 4328 Email: qwh75834@glaxowellcome.co.uk; 29 St John's Drive, Brandon Gate, Stone, Aylesbury HP17 8YJ — MB ChB 1972 Glas.; DObst RCOG 1974. Assoc. Med. Dir. Glaxo Wellcome UK; Clin. Asst. Chest Clinic Whipps Cross Hosp. Lond. Socs: Ord. Mem. Roy. Soc. Med. Prev: GP Rayleigh Essex.

HAGAN, Graham Clive Len Valley Practice, Tithe Yard, Church Square, Lenham, Maidstone ME17 2PJ Tel: 01622 858341 Fax: 01622 859659 — MB BS 1983 Lond.; MRCGP 1992; DA (UK) 1988; DCH RCP Lond. 1987; DRCOG 1986. (St George's Hosp. London) Prev: Clin. Asst. (Anaesth.) Maidstone Hosp.; Clin. Asst.(Rheum.) Maidstone Hosp.

HAGAN, Peter Martin 78 Mourne Crescent, Coalisland, Dungannon BT71 4LD Tel: 018687 48754; 16 Upton Aveue, Finaghy, Belfast BT10 0LU Tel: 01232 612383 — MB BCh BAO 1993 Belf.; BSc (Hons) Belf. 1990; DRCOG. GP Regist. Socs: MPS. Prev: SHO Lagan Valley Hosp. Lyburn.

HAGAN, Thomas John (retired) Loanda, 6 Dorwood Park, Newtownards BT23 7BE Tel: 01247 811769 — LM 1942 Rotunda; LRCPI & LM, LRCSI & LM 1940. Prev: PMO DHSS N.I. & Roy. Ulster Constab.

HAGARD, Professor Spencer London School of Hygience & Tropical Medicine, Keppel St., Mabledon Place, London WC1E 7HT Tel: 020 7612 7895 Fax: 020 7637 3238 Email: s.hagard@lshtm.ac.uk; 396 Milton Road, Cambridge CB4 1SU Tel: 01223 563774 Fax: 01223 423970 Email: spencer.hagard@dial.pipex.com — MB ChB 1968 St. And.; PhD Glas. 1977; MA Camb. 1977; FFPHM RCP (UK) 1989; FFCM 1981, M 1977; DPH Glas. 1973. (St. And.) Sen. Lect. Health Promotion Reserch Unit, Lond. Sch. of Hygeine & Trop. Med.; Vis. Prof. of Europ. Health Policy, Univ. of Bergen, Norway. Socs: BMA; Assn. Pub. Health; Pres. Internat. Union for Health Promotion & Educat. Prev: Chief Exec. Health Educat. Auth.; Dist. Med. Off. Camb. HA; Med. Supt. Kawolo Hosp. Lugazi, Uganda.

HAGDRUP, Nicola Anne 75 Oakley Road, London N1 3LW — MB BS 1987 Lond.

HAGE, Marinus Dirk The Surgery, 439 Beechdale Road, Nottingham NG8 3LF Tel: 0115 929 0754 Fax: 0115 929 6843.

HAGE, William Karim The Quarterdeck, Holywell, St Ives, Huntingdon PE27 4TG — BM BS 1998 Nottm.; BM BS Nottm 1998.

HAGEN, David Louis St Richards Hospital, Women & Children Block, Chichester PCG, Chichester PO19 4SE Tel: 01243 770772 Fax: 01243 770799 Email: david.hagen@wsha.nhs.uk — MRCS Eng. LRCP Lond. 1982; BSc (Hons.) Engin Illinois 1974, MD 1979. Cons. Pub. Health Med. W. Sussex HA; Assoc. Mem. Inst. Environm. Health Off. Socs: Fac. Pub. Health Med.; Soc. Social Med.; FRIPHH. Prev: Regist. & Sen. Regist. (Pub. Health Med.) Cheltenham; SHO P'boro. Dist. Hosp.; SHO Univ. & Gen. Hosp. Nottm.

HAGGAN, Robert Nicholas 3 Mount Pleasant, Bangor BT20 3TB — MB BCh BAO 1971 Belf.

HAGGART, Mr Brian Gerard (retired) 14 Furrocks Way, Ness, South Wirral CH64 4EW — MB ChB 1951 Liverp.; ChM Liverp. 1963, MB ChB 1951; FRCS Eng. 1960. Cons. Gen. Surg. Walton & Fazakerley Hosps. Liverp. Prev: Sen. Surg. Regist. Sefton Gen. Hosp. Liverp.

HAGGARTY, Elizabeth Gertrude (retired) 10 Carrick Street, Maybole KA19 7DN Tel: 01655 883078 — MB ChB 1951 Glas. Prev: GP Maybole.

HAGGER, Alan Owen 31 Stratton Road, Beaconsfield HP9 1HR Tel: 01494 673786 — MRCS Eng. LRCP Lond. 1949; MFOM RCP Lond. 1979. (King's Coll. Lond. & Char. Cross) Clin. Asst. Psychiat. Unit Char. Cross Hosp. Socs: Fell. Roy. Soc. Med. Prev: Chief Med. Off. Glaxo Laborats. Ltd. & Rockware Glas. Ltd.; Ho. Phys. Char. Cross Hosp.

HAGGER, Diana Clare Gurnett Cottage, Blakes Road, Wargrave, Reading RG10 8LA Tel: 0118 940 4820 — MB BS 1978 Lond.; MRCPath 1984. Lect. (Haemat.) Char. Cross Hosp. Med. Sch. Lond.; Assoc. Specialist (Haemat.) Char. Cross Hosp. Lond. Socs: Fell. Roy. Soc. Pathologists.

HAGGER, Mr Robert William 55 Heythrop Street, Southfields, London SW18 7SS — MB BS 1991 Lond.; BSc (Biomed. Sci.) Lond. 1988; FRCS Eng. 1995. (St. Geo. Hosp. Med. Sch. Lond.) Clin. Research Fell. (Colorectal Surg.) St. Geo. Hosp. Lond.

HAGGERTY, Gerard Central Avenue Health Centre, Central Avenue, Ardrossan KA22 7DX Tel: 01294 463838 Fax: 01294 462798 — MB ChB 1978 Glas.; MRCGP 1982; Dip. Sports Med. Scott. 1993; DRCOG 1980. (Univ. Glas.) Gen. Practitioner; Sen. Med. Off. Glas. Rugby; Med. Adviser Scott. Rugby Union.

HAGGERTY, Kenneth Andrew The Health Centre, 20 Duncan Street, Greenock PA15 4LY Tel: 01475 724477 — MB ChB 1975 Glasgow; MB ChB Glas. 1975. (Glasgow) GP Greenock, Renfrewsh.

HAGGERTY, Shona Roseanne Arolarich, 15 Culduthel Road, Inverness IV2 4AG — MB ChB 1985 Glas.; MRCGP 1992; Dip. IMC RCS Ed. 1995; DRCOG 1989; DCH RCPS Glas. 1987. (Glas.) Gen. Practitioner. Prev: Trainee GP Inverness; SHO (Psychiat.) Craig Dunain Hosp. Inverness; SHO (Obst.) Roy. Matern. Hosp. Glas.

HAGGERTY, Stephen John 48 Balshagray Drive, Glasgow G11 7DA — MB ChB 1988 Dundee.

HAGGETT, Matthew John 1 Croft Lane, Bromborough, Wirral CH62 2BX — MB BS 1996 Newc.

HAGGETT, Penelope Jane 16 Harlow Way, Old Marston, Oxford OX3 0QS — MB ChB 1987 Leeds; FRCR 1994. Sen. Regist. (Radiol.) John Radcliffe Hosp. Oxf.

HAGGETT, Timothy Ian 7 Redland Terrace, Redland, Bristol BS6 6TD Tel: 0117 973 7689 — MB BS 1985 Lond.

HAGGIE, Michael Henry Knox, OBE, MC (retired) The Tineings, Shucknall, Hereford HR1 3SR Tel: 01432 850520 — MB BChir 1940 Camb.; MD Camb. 1949; FRCP Lond. 1965, M 1947. Prev: Cons. Phys. SE Kent Gp. Hosps.

HAGGIE, Mr Stephen John 64 Alamein Avenue, Bedford MK42 0DF — MB BS 1968 Lond.; FRCS Eng. 1974.

HAGGIS, John Fabian Old Manor Hospital, Wilton Road, Salisbury SP2 7EP — MB ChB 1967 Glas.; MRCPsych 1977; DCH Eng. 1971; DObst RCOG 1972. (Glas.) Cons. (Adult Psychiat.) Old Manor Hosp. Salisbury. Prev: Sen. Regist. in Adult Psychiat. Knowle Hosp. Fareham & Roy. S. Hants.; Hosp. Soton.; SHO (Paediat.) Roy. Devon & Exeter Hosp.; Regist. (Psychiat.) Exe Vale Hosp. Exeter.

HAGGITH, Alison Katherine Fernbank Psychotherapy Clinic, Stobhill Hospital, 133 Balornock Road, Glasgow G21 3UW Tel: 0141 201 3936 — MB ChB 1986 Glas.; BA Camb. 1983; MRCPSych 1991. Cons. Psychotherepist, Fernbank Psychother. Clinic, Glas. Prev: Sen. Regist. (Psychother.) Claremont Hse. Newc.; Regist. & SHO (Psychiat.) S.. Gen. Hosp. Glas.; SHO (Med.) Freeman Hosp. Newc.

HAGLEY, Mandy Department of Genito-Urinary Medicine, Box 38, Addenbrookes NHS Trust, Hills Road, Cambridge CB2 2QQ Tel: 01223 217141, 01943 865087 — MB BChir 1992 Cambridge; MB BChir MA (Cantab.); MRCP; BA (Hons.) (Open). SpR in Genito-Urin. Med. Socs: Med. Soc. for the study of Venereal Dis.

HAGON, Jennifer Ann Arden Medical Centre, 1498 Warwick Road, Knowle, Solihull B93 9LE Tel: 01564 772010 Fax: 01564 771224; 146 Station Road, Knowle, Solihull B93 0EP — MB ChB 1978 Birm.; BSc Birm. 1975, MB ChB 1978; MRCGP 1982; DRCOG 1981.

HAGUE, David Edward Squires Lane Medical Practice, 2 Squires Lane, Finchley, London N3 2AU Tel: 020 8346 1516 Fax: 020 8343 2537 — MRCS Eng. LRCP Lond. 1975 London; MRCS Eng. LRCP Lond. 1975 London; MB BS 1975 London.

HAGUE, Gillian Frances 23 Buccaneer Close, Woodley, Reading RG5 4XP — MB BS 1982 Lond.; MSc Lond. 1986.

HAGUE, Mrs Greta Constance (retired) 10 Manor Court, Pinehurst, Grange Road, Cambridge CB3 9BE Tel: 01223 353430 — MRCS Eng. LRCP Lond. 1943; BA Camb. 1940, MB BChir 1946; MA 1999. Prev: CMS Med. Miss. Kweilin, China & Hong Kong.

HAGUE, Mr John Malcolm Seaforth (retired) Stonecourt, 3 & 5 Wellingborough Road, Great Harrowden, Wellingborough NN9 5AA Tel: 01933 678181 — MB BS 1953 Lond.; FRCS Ed. 1960; FRCS Eng. 1960. Prev: Traum. & Orthop. Surg. Kettering Gen. Hosp.

HAGUE, John Stuart Derby Road Practice, 52 Derby Road, Ipswich IP3 8DN Tel: 01473 728121 Fax: 01473 718810 Email: john.hague@gr-d83051.nhs.uk; Field End, Hemingstone, Ipswich IP6 9RR Tel: 01449 790619 — MB BS 1982 Lond.; DRCOG 1986.

Partner In Gen. Pract./Gen. Pract.; Ment. Health Lead; GP Mem. Socs: Ipswich Clin. Soc.

HAGUE, Julian Noel 6 Edgehill Chase, Adlington Road, Wilmslow SK9 2DJ — MB BS 1995 Lond.

HAGUE, Muhammad Ehsanul Claremont Medical Centre, 91 Claremont Road, Salford M6 7GP Tel: 0161 743 0453 Fax: 0161 743 9141.

HAGUE, Nigel John The Surgery, 143 Park Road, Camberley GU15 2NN Tel: 01276 26171 — MB BS 1978 Lond. (Guy's) GP Camberley.; Research Fell., Dept. of Gen.Pract., St. Geo.'s Hosp. Med. Sch., Lond.

HAGUE, Robert (retired) 1 Tintagel Court, Astley Road, Stalybridge SK15 1RA — MB BS 1976 Lond. Prev: GP Stalybridge.

HAGUE, Robert Victor Edgebrook Cottage, 2 Edgebrook Road, Nether Edge, Sheffield S7 1SG — MB ChB 1966 Bristol; FRCP Lond. 1986; MRCP (UK) 1970. (Bristol) Cons. Phys. Barnsley Dist. Gen. Hosp. Prev: Sen. Med. Regist. Sheff. Roy. Hosp.; Med. Regist. Manch. Roy. Infirm.; SHO (Paediat.) United Sheff. Hosps.

HAGUE, Rosemary Anne Yorkhill NHS Trust, Yorkhill, Glasgow G3 8SJ Tel: 0141 201 0598 Fax: 0141 201 0671 Email: rosie.hague@yorkhill.scot.nhs.uk; 23 Station Road, Bearsden, Glasgow G61 4AW Tel: 0141 942 2559 Email: william.spangler@virgin.net — MB ChB 1982 Ed.; MD Ed. 1993; MRCP (UK) 1985; FRCPCH 1997. Cons. Paediat. Infec. Dis. & Immunol. Yorkhill NHS Trust, Glas. Socs: BMA; Brit.Paediactric Infec., Immunol. & Allergy Gp.; Roy. Coll of Paediactrics & Child Health. Prev: Fell. Infec. Dis., Denver Childr. Hosp.; Sen. Regist. (Paediat.) Newc. Gen. Hosp.; MRC Research Fell. City Hosp. Edin.

HAGUE, Miss Susan, Surg. Cdr. RN Retd. Oxford Eye Hospital, Walton St., Oxford OX2 6UT Tel: 01865 228577 Fax: 01865 224515 — BM 1980 Soton.; FRCS Ed. 1986; FRCOphth 1993. (Soton.) Cons. Ophth. Surg. Oxf. Eye Hosp.; Hon Sen Lec Oxf. Univ. Socs: Fell. Roy. Soc. Med.; Amer. Acad. Ophth. Prev: Cons. Adviser Ophth. to MDG (N); Ocular Motility & Oculoplastic Fell.shs. Moorfields Eye Hosp.; Resid. Surg. Off. Moorfields Eye Hosp.

HAGYARD, Anne Hewitt Wiverton, Halifax Road, Heronsgate, Rickmansworth WD3 5DE — MB BS 1967 Newc. (Newc.) Clin. Asst. (Radiother.) Mt. Vernon Hosp. N.wood. Prev: Clin. Asst. (Psychiat.) Aylesbury & High Wycombe Health Dist.; Ho. Surg. Hexham Gen. Hosp.; Ho. Phys. Mt. Vernon Hosp. N.wood.

HAHN, Amanda Mary 37 Albert Road, Birmingham B17 0AP — MB ChB 1984 Birm.; FFA RCS Eng. 1988. Cons. Anaesth. City Hosp. NHS Trust. Prev: Sen. Regist. (Anaesth.) Midl. Anaesth. Train Scheme; Regist. (Anaesth.) Centr. Birm. HA; Research Fell. Flinders Med. Centre Adelaide, Austral.

HAHN, Mr David Michael Department of Orthopaedics, University Hospital, Queens Medical Centre, Nottingham NG7 2UH Tel: 0115 924 9924; Plum Tree House, 14 Moor Lane, Bunny, Nottingham NG11 6QX — MB ChB 1984 Birm.; FRCS (Orth.) 1994; FRCS Eng. 1988; FRCS Ed. 1988. Cons. Orthop. Surg. Univ. Hosp. Qu. Med. Centre Nottm.; Orthop. Trauma Fell., Charlotte N.C. USA. Prev: Sen. Regist. (Orthop.) Univ. Hosp. Nottm.; Orthopaedic Trauma Fell.. Carolinas Med. Centre, Charlotte, NC, USA.

HAHN, Mr Humphrey John Anthony, Surg. Capt. RN Retd. Lowlands, Wallington Shore Road, Wallington, Fareham PO16 8SG — MB BS 1948 Lond.; MB BS (Hnrs. Surg.) Lond. 1948; FRCS Eng. 1972; MRCS Eng. LRCP Lond. 1948; DO Eng. 1960. (St. Geo.) Ophth. Med. Pract. Wessex RHA. Socs: S.. Ophth. Soc. Prev: Cons. Ophth. RN Hosp. Haslar; Ho. Surg. St. Geo. Hosp.; Asst. Surg. St. John Ophth. Hosp. Jerusalem.

HAHN, Ines Rachel The Surgery, Chapel St., Shipdham, Thetford IP25 7LA Tel: 01362 820225; White House, Church St, Carbrooke, Thetford IP25 6SW — State Exam Med 1988 Mainz; MD Mainz 1989; T(GP) 1994.

HAHN, Stefan 26 Watling Road, Gillingham ME7 2YH — State Exam Med. Berlin 1991.

HAI, Syed Adel St Paul's Medical Centre, 248 St Paul's Road, Islington, London N1 2LJ Tel: 0207 226 6333 — MB BS 1989 Lond.; MRCGP 1996; DCH RCP Lond. 1993. (UCH & Middlx.) GP Islington; Gen. Practise Trainer. Prev: Acad. Fell. Dept. Primary Health Care Univ. Coll. Lond.

HAIDAR, Agha Brownlow Medical Centre, 140 Brownlow Road, Southgate, London N11 2BD Tel: 020 8888 7775 Fax: 020 8888 3450; Fernbank, 121 Powys Lane, London N13 4HJ Tel: 020 8886 1685 — MB BS 1962 Punjab; MB BS Punjab (Pakistan) 1962. (King Edwd. Med. Coll.) Gen. Pract. Wood Green & S.gate Hosp.; Med. Off. Occupat. Health Dept. E.. Gas; Metrop. Police Forens. Med. Examr. Socs: Roy. Soc. Med.; Soc. Occupat. Med. Prev: SHO Neasden Hosp. Lond. & St. Marys Hosp. E.bourne; Ho. Phys. St. Mary's Hosp. E.bourne.

HAIDAR, Anwar Fax: 01782 279047 — MB BS 1966 Punjab.

HAIDAR, Aqeel 47 Fatfield Park, Washington NE38 8BP — MB BS 1985 Punjab; PhD Lond. 1991, MSc 1988.

HAIDER, Agha Waqar Framingham Heart Study, Boston University School of Medicine, 5 Thurber St., Framingham MA 01701, USA Tel: 00 1 508 9353476 Fax: 00 1 508 6261262; Department Cardiology, Hammersmith Hospital, Du Cane Road, London W12 0NN Tel: 0208 743 2030 Fax: 0208 740 8373 — MB BS 1985 Karachi; PhD Lond. 1996; Dip. Cardiol. Lond 1987. (Sind Med. Coll. Karachi, Pakistan) Research Fell. & Hon. Regist. (Cardiol.) Roy. Postgrad. Med. Sch. Univ. Lond. & Hammersmith Hosp.; Fell. Boston Univ. Sch. Med. Boston, Mass., USA. Socs: BMA; Amer. Heart Assn.; Founder Mem. Internat. Soc. Holter Monitoring. Prev: Regist. Centr. Middlx. Hosp. Lond.; Regist. (Cardiovasc.) Roy. Postgrad. Med. Sch. Hammersmith Hosp. Lond.; Resid. Med. Off. Jinnah Postgrad. Med. Centre. Karachi, Pakistan.

HAIDER, Mrs Fatin Saleh The Surgery, 691 Coventry Road, Small Heath, Birmingham B10 0JL Tel: 0121 773 4931 Fax: 0121 753 2210; 33 Beachnut Lane, Solihull B91 2NN Tel: 0121 705 6119 Fax: 0121 705 6119 — MB ChB 1974 Baghdad; MRCOG 1982; MFFP. (Univ.Baghdad) GP; Sen. Clin. Med. Off. Socs: Fac. Fam. Plann. & Reproduc. Health Care; Brit. Menopause. Soc.

HAIDER, Mr Munawar 16 Broadacre, Stalybridge SK15 2TX — MB BS 1987 Karachi, Pakistan; FRCS Ed. 1992.

HAIDER, Rukn Uddin Hatfield Road Surgery, 61 Hatfield Road, St Albans AL1 4JE — MB BS 1959 Punjab; DTM & H 1962 Liverp. Socs: BMA. Prev: Clin. Asst. (Rheum.); Chase Farm Hosp., Enfield, Middex.; Assoc. Specialist (Gen. Med. & Geriat., S.port Gp. of Hosps., S.port.

HAIDER, Saad Mohamed Jawad The Surgery, 90 East Hill, London SW18 2HG Tel: 020 8874 1691 Fax: 020 8871 9132; 15 Mount Road, Wimbledon Park, London SW19 8ES Tel: 020 8946 7885 — MB ChB 1969 Baghdad; MRCPI 1983; DFFP 1993; DTM & H RCP Lond. 1976. Prev: Cons. Phys. Assalama Hosp. Alkhokar, Saudi Arabia.

HAIDER, Shabbir The Beeches, Henley St., Luddesdown, Cobham, Gravesend DA13 0XB Tel: 01474 813817 — MB BS 1959 Punjab; FRCP Lond. 1996; FRCP Ed. 1980. M 1966; FRCP Glas. 1979, M 1966; DCH Eng. 1971. (King Edwd. Med. Coll.) p/t Cons. Phys. Dartford & Gravesham Dist. Hosps. Socs: Brit. Soc. Study of Infec. Dis. Prev: Sen. Regist. Roy. Free Hosp. Lond.

HAIDER, Shehnaz Sami Corbets Tey Road Health Centre, 181 Corbets Tey Road, Upminster RM14 2YN Tel: 01708 225161 Fax: 01708 641477; The Pines, 33 Hall Lane, Upminster RM14 1AF — MB BS 1970 Karachi; MB BS Karachi (Pakistan) 1970; MRCS Eng. LRCP Lond. 1979; DA Eng. 1977.

HAIDER, Syed Ahsanuddin (retired) Charlecote, Cromwell Road, Whitefield, Manchester M45 7RS Tel: 0161 766 2364 — MB BS Punjab 1954; FRCP Ed. 1982, M 1968; DCH Eng. 1967. Cons. Paediat. Fairfield Gen. Hosp. Prev: Med. Supt. Al-Nahda Hosp. & Specialist Phys. MoH Muscat, Oman.

HAIDER, Syed Iftikhar Corbets Tey Road Health Centre, 181 Corbets Tey Road, Upminster RM14 2YN Tel: 01708 225161 Fax: 01708 641477; The Pines, 33 Hall Lane, Upminster RM14 1AF Tel: 01708 22069 — MB BS Karachi 1968. (Dow Med. Coll.) Princip. Med. Practitioner; Bd. Mem., Havering, Uppminster Primary Locality Care Trust. Socs: Fell. Overseas Doctors Assn.; Coll. Family Med. Karachi, Pakistan; (Lond. Regional Counseller) Nat. Advis. & Counselling Serv. Sick. Prev: Mem. Barking & Havering Local Med. Comm.

HAIDER, Mr Syed Imad Northwood Health Centre, Neal Close, Acre Way, Northwood HA6 1TH Tel: 01923 821821 Fax: 01923 820648 — MB BS 1964 Karachi; BSc Panjab Pakistan 1958; FRCS Ed. 1972. (Dow Med. Coll.)

HAIDER, Tanveer 35 Hardwick Green, Bramingham Park, Luton LU3 3XA — MB BS 1996 Lond. (St. George's Hospital Medical School) SHO (Gen. Psych.) St. Mary's Psychiat. Hosp., ScarBoro. Socs: Med. Protec. Soc. Prev: SHO Maidstone Hosp. A & E; Surg.

Ho. Off. James Paget NHS Trust, Gorleston; Med. Ho. Off. Luton & Dunstable NHS Trust Luton.

HAIDER, Yasser George Eliot Hospital, College St., Nuneaton CV10 7DJ Tel: 02476 351351 Fax: 02476 865377; 2 Surrey Close, Burbage, Hinckley LE10 2NY Tel: 01455 234501 Email: yhaider@doctors.org.uk — MB BS 1986 All India Inst. Med. Sciences; MB BS All India Inst. of Med. Sci. 1986; MRCP (UK) 1988. Cons. Phys. (Cardiol.) Geo. Eliot Hosp. Nuneaton.

HAIDER, Yussef 535 Barlow Moor Road, Chorlton-Cum-Hardy, Manchester M21 8AQ — MB ChB 1992 Dundee. Research Fell. in Respirat. & Transpl. Med. Socs: MPS; BMA; BTS. Prev: SHO Med. Rotat. 1995-1997 Salford Royakl Hosps. NHS Trust.

HAIDER, Zain Simon West Suffok Hospital, Harwick Lane, Bury St Edmunds IP33 2QZ Tel: 01284 713000 Email: z.s.haider@usa.net; 42 Farm Way, Northwood HA6 3EF Tel: 01923 821126 — LMSSA Lond. 1997. (St George's Hospital, London)

HAIDER, Zara Jane The Beeches, Henley St., Luddesdown, Gravesend DA13 0XB — MB BS 1994 Lond.

HAIDON, Joanne Lauren 36 West View, Darlington DL3 8BP Tel: 01325 485407 — MB ChB 1995 Glas. SHO (A & E Med.) Vict. Infirm. Glas.

HAIG, David Cameron (retired) 13 Abercromby Place, Stirling FK8 2QP Tel: 01786 74530 — MD 1942 Ed.; MD (High. Commend.) Ed. 1950. MB ChB 1942; FRCP Ed. 1962, M 1947. JP. Prev: Med. Regist. Deaconess Hosp. Edin.

HAIG, Gavin (retired) Hammett Square, Tiverton EX16 6LR.

HAIG, John Mill Street Clinic, 1 Wolseley Street, London SE1 2BP Tel: 020 7252 1817 Fax: 020 7394 6312 — MRCS Eng. LRCP Lond. 1978.

HAIG, Peter Stuart North Baddesley Health Centre, Norton Welch Close, North Baddesley, Romsey SO51 9EP Tel: 01703 743401 Fax: 01703 743428 Email: basicdrpn@aol.com — MB BS 1985 Lond.; MRCGP 1995. (St. Geo. Hosp. Med. Sch.) Hosp. Practitioner A&E Soton. Gen. Hosp. Socs: BASICS Mem. Prev: Clin. Asst. (A & E) St. Richards Hosp. Chichester; Clin. Asst. (Dermat.) St. Mary's Hosp. Portsmouth.

HAIG, Stephen Douglas 1 Wheeler Av, Oxted RH8 9LF — MB ChB 1997 Leic.

HAIG-FERGUSON, David Richard Rising Brook Surgery, Merrey Road, Stafford ST17 9LY Tel: 01785 251134 Fax: 01785 222441; 121 Baswich Lane, Stafford ST17 0BN Tel: 01785 257719 Email: haigferguk@aol.com — MB BS 1978 Lond.; DRCOG 1982. (St. Thos. Hosp. Lond.) Chairm. LMC. (Mid. Staffs Sub. Comm.); Sec. S. Staffs. LMC.

HAIGH, Adrian Blurton 33 Chiltern Road, Hitchin SG4 9PJ Tel: 01462 459307 — MB BS Lond. 1947; MRCGP 1963; DObst RCOG 1952. (St. Bart.) Prev: Hosp. Pract. (Neurol.) Lister Hosp. Stevenage; Ho. Surg. (O & G) N. Herts. & S. Beds. Hosp.; Ho. Surg. (Neurosurg.) St. Bart. Hosp. Lond.

HAIGH, Anne Caroline Honey Hill, Brighton Road, Hassocks BN6 9LY — MB BS 1987 Lond.; BSc Lond. 1982.

HAIGH, Anne Elizabeth Jessop 3/4 Blythfield Cottages, Bellsquarry, Livingston EH54 9AF Tel: 01506 410825 — MB ChB 1985 Dundee; MRCGP 1989; DRCOG 1991. p/t GP Broxburn Health Centre W. Lothian. Prev: Trainee GP Perth VTS; SHO (Cas., O & G & Paediat.) Perth Roy. Infirm.

HAIGH, Basil (retired) 28 Roman Hill, Barton, Cambridge CB3 7AX Tel: 01223 262391 — MB BChir Camb. 1943; MA Camb. 1943, MD 1975; MD Camb. 1958; MRCS Eng. LRCP Lond. 1943. Prev: Ho. Surg. & Regist. (Orthop.) Manch. Roy. Infirm.

HAIGH, Carola Seward The Surgery, 1 Manor Place, London SE17 3BD Tel: 020 7703 3988 Fax: 020 7252 4002; 50 Grove Lane, London SE5 8ST — BM BCh 1971 Oxf.; MA, BM BCh Oxf. 1969 DObst RCOG 1971; MRCGP 1975; DCH Eng. 1973. (Oxf. & Middlx.)

HAIGH, Christopher Roland 32Merchant's Quay, Salford M5 2XR Tel: 0161 876 0121 Email: chris@man36.freeserve.co.uk; Stones House, Stead Lane, Rishworth, Sowerby Bridge HX6 4ES Tel: 01422 823364 — MB BS 1991 Lond.; BSc (Hons.) Basic Med. Scs. & Pharmacol. Lond. 1988; MRCP (UK) 1994. (St. Geo. Hosp. Med. Sch. Lond.) Specialist Regist. Rotat. (Gastroenterol.) NW Region; Research.Fell.Univ.manch.

HAIGH, Colin Andrew Assheton (retired) 207 Ormskirk Road, Newtown, Wigan WN5 9DP Tel: 01942 494711 Fax: 01942 826240 — MB ChB Manch. 1955; DObst RCOG 1960. Prev: Ho. Surg. (Obst.) Billinge Hosp. Wigan.

HAIGH, David Paediatric Unit, St Luke's Hospital, Bradford BD5 0NA Tel: 01274 365453 Fax: 01274 365333; 40 Stapper Green, Wilsden, Bradford BD15 0HQ Tel: 01535 274225 Email: david@haigh.demon.co.uk — MB ChB 1968 Ed.; FRCP Eng. 1989; MRCP (UK) 1972; DCH RCPS Glas. 1971; DObst RCOG 1970; FRCPCH 1997. Cons. Paediat. St. Lukes Hosp. Bradford. Prev: Cons. Paediat. Bradford Childr. Hosp.

HAIGH, Deborah Judith Gillen 90 Windsor Road, London N7 6JH — MB ChB 1978 Sheff.; BSc Sheff. 1975, MB ChB 1978; DA Eng. 1982.

HAIGH, Elaine Haigh and Partners, 11 Church Street, Harston, Cambridge CB2 5NP Tel: 01223 870250 Fax: 01223 872741 — MB BChir 1978 Camb.; MBA (Health Serv. Plann. & Managem.) Keele 1994; MRCS Eng. LRCP Lond. 1978; DCH RCP Lond. 1982; DRCOG 1981. (Univ. of Cambridge) Prev: Trainee GP Cambs. VTS; Ho. Phys. Addenbrooke's Hosp. Camb.; Ho. Surg. Bedford Gen. Hosp.

HAIGH, Elizabeth Ruth (Robinson) Ramsey Health Centre, Mews Close, Ramsey, Huntingdon PE26 1BP Tel: 01487 812611 Fax: 01487 711801 Email: ramseyhc@gp-d81059.nhs.uk; 22 Brookfield Way, Bury, Huntingdon PE26 2LH Tel: 01487 813088 — MB BS 1978 Newc.; BMedSc Newc. 1975; MFFP 1992. p/t Princip. in Gen. Pract. Prev: Asst. GP Lancs.

HAIGH, Graham George, OStJ The Medical Centre, Caradon Ideal Ltd., PO Box 103, National Avenue, Hull HU5 4JN Tel: 01482 498443 Fax: 01482 597032; Birrabelle, 37 The Fairway, Westella, Hull HU10 7SA Tel: 01482 659291 — MB ChB 1954 Leeds; MRCGP 1968; AFOM RCP Lond. 1979. Med. Off. Caradon Ideal Ltd. Hull; Regional Med. Off. Rank Hovis McDougall Ltd.; Med. Adviser Glenrose (Fish Merchants) Ltd. Hull & W. H. Smith (Wholesale) Newsagents Hull; Med. Off. Stelrad Ideal Swinton, MexBoro.; EMO Benefits Agency Med. Servs.; Div. Surg. St. John Ambul. Brig.; Dept. Transport Approved Examr.; Approved Examr. Belgian Embassy; Mem. Disabil. Appeal Tribunals. Socs: Hull Med. Soc.; (Exec. Counc.) BMA (Ex-Pres. E. Yorks. Div.). Prev: Ho. Surg. & Ho. Phys. St. Jas. Hosp. Leeds; Chairm. Humberside LMC.

HAIGH, Jacqueline Sandra Elaine 33 Kensington Court, 20 Kensington Road, Glasgow G12 9NX — MB ChB 1984 Glas.; MB ChB Glas. l984.

HAIGH, Jonathan William Framfield House Surgery, 42 St. Johns Street, Woodbridge IP12 1ED Tel: 01394 382157 — MB BS 1976 Newc.; MRCP (UK) 1979; MRCGP 1984; DRCOG 1983. (Newc.)

HAIGH, Kathleen Maureen Clare St Hilary, 1 Sewell Road, Lincoln LN2 5RY Tel: 01522 545969 — MB ChB 1948 Leeds; DCH Ed. 1965; DCH Glas. 1965; DCH Eng. 1965; DPH Leeds 1957; DObst RCOG 1951. (Leeds) Assoc. Specialist (Geriat.) St. Geo. Hosp. Lincoln. Prev: Sen. Asst. Co. Med. Off. W. Riding CC. & Notts.; Asst. Med. Off. City Bradford.

HAIGH, Louise Isobel Gillen 32 Tredgold Avenue, Bramhope, Leeds LS16 9BU — MB ChB 1986 Leeds; MRCP (UK) 1989; FRCR 1993.

HAIGH, Paul Martin Croft Cottage, 124 Heath Lane, Lowton, Warrington WA3 2SJ — MB ChB 1989 Liverp.; FRCOphth 1993. Regist. (Ophth.) Manch. Roy. Eye Hosp. Prev: SHO St. Paul's Eye Unit Roy. Liverp. Univ. Hosp.

HAIGH, Philip 2 Graig Close, Bassaleg, Newport NP10 8PE — BM 1993 Soton.

HAIGH, Reginald Douglas South Lincolnshire Health Authority, Council Offices, Eastgate, Sleaford NG34 — MB ChB 1948 Leeds; DPH 1953; MFCM 1974; MMSA Lond. 1957; DCH Eng. 1957; DObst RCOG 1951. (Leeds) Dist. Med. Off. S. Lincs. Health Auth. Prev: Dist. Community Phys. N. Lincs. Health Dist.; MOH & Princip. Sch. Med. Off. Lincoln Co. Boro.; Dep. MOH Co. Boro. Bolton.

HAIGH, Rex Winterbourne House, 53-55 Argyle Rd, Reading RG1 7YL Tel: 0118 956 1250 Fax: 0118 956 1251 Email: rex.haigh@virgin.net; 15A Main Road, Castlehead, Paisley PA2 6AJ Tel: 0141 887 4823 — BM BCh 1982 Oxf.; Memb Inst Group Analysis 1995; MA Camb. 1983; MRCPsych 1989; MRCGP 1987; T(GP) 1991; DRCOG 1985. Cons. Psychiat. in Psychother. Berks. Healthcare Trust, Reading; Progr. Director, Oxf. Deaney Psychother. Higher Specialist Train.; Progr. Ldr. MDc in Psychodynamic Psychother. for Health Serv. Settings Oxf. Brookes Univ.; Series Edr.

Therapeutic Community Jessica Kingsley Publishers Lond.; Chairm. Assn. of Therapeutic Communities. Socs: Soc. for Psychother. Research (UK); Scientists and Med. Network; Mem. of Counc., Roy. Coll. of Psychiat.s. Prev: Higher Specialist Trainee, Birm. Psychother.; Trainee Psychiat. Oxf. RHA.; Trainee GP Cornw. VTS.

HAIGH, Richard Clive Auckland Hospital, Park Road, Private Bag 92024, Auckaland, New Zealand; 13 Simon Avenue, Margate CT9 3DT — BM BS 1989 Nottm.; BMedSci 1987. Regist. (Med.) Auckland Hosp., NZ. Prev: SHO (Gen. Med.) Frenchay Hosp. Bristol; SHO (Rheum.) Blackberry Hill Hosp. Bristol.

HAIGH, Robert Alexander St Richards Hospital, Spitalfields Lane, Chichester PO19 4SE Tel: 01234 831595 — MB BS 1981 Lond.; MRCP (UK) 1986. Cons. Phys. St. Richards Hosp., Chichester; Cons. Phys. and Clin. Director. Prev: Sen. Regist. (Med. Elderly) Leicester Gen. Hosp.; Cons. Phys., Roy. Bournmouth Hosp.

HAIGH, Sally Joanne 85 Totties Lane, Holmfirth, Huddersfield HD9 1UJ — MB ChB 1998 Dund.; MB ChB Dund 1998.

HAIGH, Steven John West Calder Medical Practice, Dickson Street, West Calder EH55 8HB Tel: 01506 871403; 3/4 Blythfield Cottages, Bellsquarry, Livingston EH54 9AF Tel: 01506 410825 — MB ChB 1985 Dundee; MRCGP 1989; DRCOG 1987. (Dundee) Trainee GP Perth VTS; Hosp. Practitioner (Geriat. Med.) Whitburn Day Hosp. Socs: BMA (Hon. Sec. Lothian Div.). Prev: SHO (O & G) Perth Roy. Infirm.; Ho. Off. (Gen. Med.) Perth Roy. Infirm. & ScarBoro. Hosp.

HAIGH, Susan Fiona Dept. of Radiology, Birmingham Childrens Hospital NHS Trust, Steelhouse Lane, Birmingham B4 6 Tel: 0121 333 9734 — MB BS 1981 Lond.; MRCP (UK) 1984; FRCR 1991; FRCPCH 1998. (St. Thos.) Cons. Radiol. Birm. Childr. Hosp. Prev: Sen. Regist. & Regist. (Radiol.) King's Coll. Hosp. Lond.; Sen. Regist. (Radiol.) Birm. Childr. Hosp.

HAIGNEY, Sean Arthur 4 Ashley Gardens, Omagh BT78 1JY — MB BCh BAO 1994 Belf.

HAIKEL, Mohamed Shaker Highland Hospital, Worlds End Lane, Winchmore Hill, London N21 1PN — MB ChB 1968 Alexandria; DLO Eng. 1978. Clin. Asst. Ear Nose & Throat Dept. Highland Hosp. Lond. Socs: BMA. Prev: Regist. (Ear Nose & Throat Surg.) Univ. Hosp. Wales Cardiff; Regist. (ENT) Norf. & Norwich Hosp. & Gt. Yarmouth Hosp.

HAIKEL, Sherif Mohammed Shaker 76 The Vale, Southgate, London N14 6AU — MB BS 1994 Lond. (Roy. Free Hosp. Sch. Med. Lond.) Sen. SHO in ENT, Chase Farm Hosp. Enfield. Prev: Demonst. (Anat.) Roy. Free Hosp. Sch. Med. Lond, SHO (Gen. Surg.) John Radcliffe Hosp. Oxf.; RMO Manor Hse. Hosp. Lond.; Ho. Off. (Gen. Surg. & ENT) Roy. Free Hosp. Lond.

HAILE, Arefaine 93 Upper Rushton Road, Bradford BD3 7LG — State Exam Med 1991 Berlin.

HAILEY, Jane Alison 112 Relugas Road, Edinburgh EH9 2LZ Tel: 0131 667 7718 — BM BCh 1989 Oxf.; MA Camb. 1990; MRCP (Paediat.) (UK) 1993; MRCPCH 1997; Cantab. Sen. Regist. (Paediat.) Edin. Socs: BMA. Prev: Regist. (Paediat.) Edin.; SHO III Rotat. (Paediat.) Edin.

HAILEY, Richard William Home Farm, Malthouse Bank, Little Wenlock, Telford TF6 5BN — MB BS 1977 Lond.

HAILEY, Stephen Robert Sand Farm, Sidbury, Sidmouth EX10 0QN — MB ChB 1994 Leeds.

HAILS, Andrew John 31 South View Drive, Upminster RM14 2LL — MB BS 1981 Lond.; MRCP (UK) 1987; FRCR 1992; T(R) (CR) 1993. Cons. Radiol. Basildon & Thurrock NHS Trust.

HAILSTONE, John Donovan Edward House, Charter Nightingale Hospital, 7 Lisson Grove, London NW1 6SH Tel: 020 7535 7900 — MB BS Lond. 1961; BSc Hons. (Psychol.) Nottm. 1952; MRCS Eng. LRCP Lond. 1961; FRCPsych 1979, M 1971; DPM Eng. 1965. (St. Geo.) Hon. Phys. (Psychol. Med. Roy.) Free Hosp. Lond. & Cons. Psychiat. Charter Nightingale Hosp. Lond.; Med. Mem., Ment. Health Review Triburals. Prev: Regist. Profess. Psychiat. Unit St. Geo. Hosp. Lond.; Res. Psychiat. Boston State Hosp., USA; Sen. Regist. St. Mary's Hosp. Lond.

HAILSTONE, Thomas Robert Markfield Surgery, The Green, Markfield LE67 9WU Tel: 01530 242313 Fax: 01530 245668 — MB BS Lond. 1959; MRCS Eng. LRCP Lond. 1960; FRCGP 1988, M 1969; DObst RCOG 1962. (Char. Cross)

HAILWOOD, Rhoswen Lynden 1 Church Close, Peterstone Wentloog, Cardiff CF3 2TP — MB BCh 1981 Wales.

HAILWOOD, Robert Anthony Market Surgery, 103 Chorley New Road, Horwich, Bolton BL6 5QF Tel: 01204 697696 Fax: 01204 699676 — MBBS 1973 Univ. of London; MRCGP 1981 London. (St. Mary's) p/t GP; Staff Grade, Suubstance misuse Serv.s in Wigan & Leigh; Examg. Practitioner, Disabil. Med. Serv.s. Prev: Chief Med. Off., Turks & Caicos Is.s, BWI 1984-88.

HAILWOOD, Sara Marguerite (retired) Chorley New Road Surgery, 103 Chorley New Road, Horwich, Bolton BL6 5QF Tel: 01204 697696 — MB BS 1973 Lond.; MRCS Eng. LRCP Lond. 1973. GP Bolton.

HAILWOOD, Sarah Jayne Dept Molecular medicine, University of Auckland, Auckland, New Zealand; 1A Warwick Street, Norwich NR2 3LD — MB BS 1991 Lond.; MRCP (UK) 1995. (St. Geo. Hosp. Med. Sch. Lond.) Research Reg. Univ.Auckland.NZ. Socs: Brit.Soc.Rheum; Brit.Paediat.Rheum.Gp. Prev: SHO (Gen. Med.) Norf. & Norwich Hosp.; SHO (Gen. Med. & c/o Elderly) Jersey Gen. & Overdale Hosps.; Regist. (Rheum.) Norf. & Norwich Hosp.

HAIMES, Gail Rebecca Lodge Barn, West Grinstead, Horsham RH13 8LN — MB BS 1997 Lond.

HAIMES, Paul Francis The Health Centre, Ash Meadow, High Street, Much Hadham SG10 6DE Tel: 01279 842242 Fax: 01279 843973; Health Centre, Ash Meadow, Much Hadham SG10 6DE Tel: 01279 842242 Fax: 01279 843973 — MB BS 1983 Lond.; MRCGP 1987; DRCOG 1986. (University College London) Prev: Trainee GP Reading VTS; Ho. Surg. Univ. Coll. Hosp. Lond.; Ho. Phys. Stoke Mandeville Hosp.

HAIN, Bethan 60 Harlow Terrace, Harrogate HG2 0PN Tel: 01423 858089 Email: john@hainjb.freeserve.co.uk — MB ChB 1992 Dundee; DFFP 1996; DRCOG 1995; DCH RCPS Glas. 1995. GP Retainee Alexandra Rd., Harrowgate. Socs: BMA.

HAIN, John Michael Henry Dacre House Farm, Harrogate HG3 4ES Tel: 01423 858089 Email: john@hainjb.freeserve.co.uk — MB ChB 1995 Dundee; MRCGP 2001; DFFP 2001; BSc (Hons.) Dund 1991. (Dundee) GP partner, Spring gables, Harrogate. Prev: SHO O & G Harrogate Dis.Hosp; GP Registar Moss& Ptnrs Harrogate; GP Regist. Green & Prtnrs Harrogate.

HAIN, Richard David William Dept of Child Health, WCM, Llandough Hospital, Penarth CF64 2XX Tel: 024 2071 6215 Fax: 029 2070 8064 Email: hainrd@cardiff.ac.uk; Robin Hill, Castle Court, Llandough, Cowbridge CF71 7LZ Tel: 01446 775048 Fax: 07092 202318 Email: richardhain@doctors.org.uk — MB BS 1986 Lond.; MSc Toronto 1993; MD 1996; MRCP (UK) 1990; Dip. Palliat. Med. Wales 1998; FRCPCH 2000. (Guy's Hosp.) Sen. Lec/ Hon Cons. Paedia Palliat. Care & Paediactric Oncol., Univ Wales Coll of Med. Socs: FellRoy. Coll. Paediat. & Child Health; Mem. Roy. Coll Phys.s. Prev: Specialist Regist. (Paediatric Palliat. Med.) Wales; Clin. Fell. (Palliat. Care) Univ. of Ottawa, Canada; Research Fell. (Paediat. & Palliat. Care) Inst. Cancer Research Surrey.

HAINE, Geoffrey Leonard (retired) 3 Stanier Road, Preston, Weymouth DT3 6PD Tel: 01305 832087 — MB BS 1939 Lond.; MRCS Eng. LRCP Lond. 1939. Prev: Vis. Anaesth. & Clin. Asst. Herrison Psychiat. Hosp. Dorchester.

HAINES, Professor Andrew Paul London School of Hygiene & Tropical Medicine, Keppal St., London WC1E 7HT Tel: 020 7927 2278 Fax: 020 7323 4562 Email: andy.haines@lshtm.ac.uk — MB BS Lond. 1969; MD Lond. 1985; FRCP Lond. 1993; MRCP (UK) 1971; FFPHM RCP (UK) 1992, M 1990; MFCM 1987; FRCGP 1991, M 1976. (King's Coll. Hosp.) Dean and Prof. of Pub. Health and Primary Care, Lond. Sch. of Hyg. & Trop. Med.; Hon. Cons. in Pub. Health Med., Camden & Islington NHS Community Trust. Socs: Roy. Soc. Med.; BMA; Founder Fell. Acad. of Med. Sci.s. Prev: Dir. Research & Developm. NHS Exec. N. Thames; Mem. Scientif. Staff MRC Epidemiol. & Med. Care Unit N.wick Pk. Hosp. Harrow; Sen. Lect. (Gen. Pract.) St. Mary's Hosp. Med. Sch.

HAINES, Ann Moore (retired) 5 Rectory Park, Pett, Hastings TN35 4EU Tel: 01424 812308 — MB ChB 1952 Bristol; DCH Eng. 1954, DA 1955; FFA RCS Eng. 1962. Cons. Anaesth. Hastings Health Dist. Prev: Ho. Phys. United Bristol Hosps.

HAINES, Anthony John, OBE (retired) The Old Rectory, St James, Shaftesbury SP7 8HG Tel: 01747 853658 — MA, MB Camb. 1956, BChir 1955; MRCPsych 1977; MFOM RCP Lond. 1984, AFOM 1983; MRCGP 1964; DPM Ed. 1972. Prev: Cons. Occupat. Phys. Hosp. For Sick Childr. Gt. Ormond St.

HAINES, Charles Ian 34 Greenhill, Blackwell, Bromsgrove B60 1BJ Tel: 0121 445 1729 — MB BS 1957 Lond.; FRCP Lond. 1984, M 1969; MRCS Eng. LRCP Lond. 1957; DCH Eng. 1965; DObst RCOG 1959. (St. Mary's) Emerit. Cons. Paediat. Alexandra NHS Health Care Trust Redditch. Prev: Sen. Clin. Lect. (Paediat.) Univ. Birm.; Sen. Regist. (Paediat.) Bristol Roy. Hosp. Sick Childr.; Surg. Lt. RN.

HAINES, Cicely Roffway (retired) 33 Park Lane, Norwich NR2 3EE — MD 1989 Sheff.; MB ChB 1956; MFCM 1972; DPH Manch. 1970; DObst RCOG 1959; FRCPCH 1997.

HAINES, Dr. Daniel Hugo, TD (Surgery), 58 Vesta Road, London SE4 2NH Tel: 07860 117758 Fax: 020 7358 9930; 56 Vesta Road, London SE4 2NH Tel: 020 7635 0305 — MRCS Eng. LRCP Lond. 1973; BDS Lond. 1968; LDS RCS Eng. 1968; DObst RCOG 1977; MRCGP 1997. Maj. RMO, 3 (V) Milit. Intelligence Bn. Socs: BMA; Fell. Roy. Soc. Med.; Police Surg.s Assoc. Prev: Sen. Med. Off. Govt. Falkland Is.s; Chief Med. Off. Usutu Pulp Co. Ltd. Swaziland; Govt. Med. Off. Cayman Is..

HAINES, David Alexander Swanage Health Centre, Railway Station Approach, Station Road, Swanage BH19 1HB Tel: 01929 422231 — MB BS 1982 Lond.; MRCGP 1987; DRCOG 1986. (King's Coll. Hosp.) Clin. Asst. Swanage Hosp. Prev: SHO (Paediat.) Lewisham Hosp. Lond.; SHO (Med.) The Mayday Hosp. Croydon; Ho. Surg. Kings Coll. Hosp. Lond.

HAINES, Derek Raymond 65 Davenport Avenue, Hessle HU13 0RN — MB ChB 1971 Ed.; BSc (Hons.) Ed. 1968, MB ChB 1971; FFA RCS Eng. 1977; DObst RCOG 1973. Cons. Anaesth. Hull & Beverley Health Dist. Hosps. Prev: Sen. Regist. (Anaesth.) Leicester Roy. Infirm.; Regist. (Anaesth.) Vict. Hosp. Kirkcaldy.

HAINES, Hilary Margaret Community Health South London NHS Trust, Priory Manor child Development Centre, 1 Blagdon Rd, London SE13 7HL Tel: 020 8690 3838 Fax: 020 7771 4540; 56 Vesta Road, London SE4 2NH Tel: 020 7635 0305 — MB BS 1969 Lond.; MRCS Eng. LRCP Lond. 1969; FRCPCH 1997; MFPHM 1989; MFCM 1980; DPH Eng. 1972. Cons. Community Paediat.Community Health S. Lond. NHS Trust. Socs: Fell. Roy. Soc. Med.; Fell. Roy. Inst. Pub. Health & Hyg. Prev: SCMO Lewisham & N. S.wark HA; Med. Off. Falkland I. Govt.; Med. Off. Usutu Pulp Company Swaziland.

HAINES, Jeremy Richard Liverpool Women's Hospital, Crown Street, Liverpool L7 8SS — MB ChB 1993 Liverp.

HAINES, Mr John Frederick 2 Betleymere Road, Cheadle Hulme, Cheadle SK8 5HT Tel: 0161 485 3238 — MB ChB 1974 Ed.; FRCS Eng. 1979.

HAINES, Lesley Joan John Elliott Unit, Birch Hill Hospital, Rochdale OL12 9QB Tel: 01706 755111 Fax: 01706 755098 Email: lesley.haines@zen.co.uk — MB ChB 1984 Manch.; MRCPsych 1989; MSc in Psychiatry Manchester 1998. Cons. Psychiat. Prev: Regist. (Geriat. Med.) St. Thos. Hosp. Stockport.

HAINES, Michael Edward Pine Trees, Mears Ashby Road, Earls Barton, Northampton NN6 0HQ — MB BS 1978 Lond.; BSc (1st cl. Hons. Biochem.) Lond. 1968, PhD 1971; MRCP (UK) 1982; FRCPath 1997. (Univ. Coll. Hosp.) Cons. Haemat. N.ampton HA. Prev: Sen. Regist. (Haemat.) Aylesbury & Oxon. HAs; Regist. (Haemat.) Hammersmith Hosp. Lond.; SHO Rotat. (Med.) Bath HA.

HAINES, Rebecca Mary 48 Beaumont Terrace, Gosforth, Newcastle upon Tyne NE3 1AS — MB ChB 1997 Sheff.

HAINING, Rose Elizabeth Brown 60 Seafield Road, Broughty Ferry, Dundee DD5 3AQ — MB ChB 1983 Ed. Research Regist. Univ. Dept. O & G Rosie Matern. Hosp. Camb. Prev: SHO Regist. Simpson Memor. Matern. Pavil. Edin.

HAINING, Mr William Moncrief — MB ChB 1952 Ed.; FRCS Ed. 1962; FRCOphth 1989. (Ed.) Socs: Counc. Mem. (Teas.) UK Intraocular Impl. Soc.; Internat. Intraocular Impl. Counc. Prev: Sen. Cons. Ophth. Ninewells Hosp. Dundee & Univ. Dundee Med. Sch.; Sen. Regist. (Ophth.) Roy. Infirm. Edin.; Vis. Prof. Univ. Coll. Hosp. Dub.

HAINSWORTH, Agnes Moira 107 Crawfordsburn Road, Bangor BT19 1BJ — MB BCh BAO 1958 Belf.; FFA RCSI 1971; FFA RCS Eng. 1965. Cons. Anaesth. Ulster Hosp. Belf.

HAINSWORTH, Mr Basil Hadi Amin The Parks Medical Centre, 340 Aikman Avenue, Leicester LE3 9PW Tel: 0116 287 1230 Fax: 0116 287 3724; 69 Main Street, Newton Linford, Leicester LE6 0AF — MB ChB 1972 Baghdad; FRCS Glas. 1983. Hosp. Pract. (Gen. Surg. & Gastroenterol.) Leicester. Socs: Leic. Med. Soc. Prev: Regist. (Neurosurg.) Hope Hosp. Manch.; Regist. (Surgic.) Bradford United Hosps.

HAINSWORTH, Eric (retired) Polbartha, Miners Way, Liskeard PL14 3ET Tel: 01579 347074 — MB BChir Camb. 1952; FRCGP 1980, M 1959; DObst RCOG 1955. Prev: Ho. Phys. Burton-on-Trent Gen. Infirm.

HAINSWORTH, Mark Tel: 01449 740254 Fax: 01449 740903; The Martins, Lindsey, Ipswich IP7 6PP — MB ChB 1984 Auckland; MRCGP 1991; DRCOG 1987. Socs: BMA.

HAINSWORTH, Mr Paul James 22 Montagu Avenue, Gosforth, Newcastle upon Tyne NE3 4JJ — MB BS 1982 Lond.; MD Melbourne 1992; FRCS Ed. 1986; FRCS Eng. 1987. Cons. Colorectal Surg. Freeman Hosp. Newc. u. Tyne. Prev: Sen. Regist. N.. RHA.

HAINSWORTH, Professor Roger Institute for Cardiovascular Research, University of Leeds, Leeds LS2 9JT Tel: 0113 233 4820 Fax: 0113 233 4803 Email: medrh@leeds.ac.uk — PhD Leeds 1969, DSc 1985, MB ChB 1962. Prof. Applied Physiol. & Hon. Cons. Clin. Physiol. Acad. Unit of Cardiovasc. Studies Univ. Leeds. Socs: Med. Res. Soc.; Physiol. Soc.; Clin. Autonomic Research Soc. (Treas.). Prev: Brit.-Amer. Heart Research Fell. Cardiovasc. Research Inst. Univ. Calif. Med. Centre, San Francisco, USA.

HAIR, Alan 21 Avondale Place, East Kilbride, Glasgow G74 1NU — MB ChB 1994 Glas.

HAIR, William Morton Flat 3, 197 Hart Road, Manchester M14 7BA — MB ChB 1993 Ed.

HAIRE, Angela Kathleen Lichfield Street Surgery, 19 Lichfield Street, Walsall WS1 1UG Tel: 01922 20532 Fax: 01922 616605; 9 Jesson Road, Walsall WS1 3AY Tel: 01922 626482 — MB ChB 1975 Birm.; MRCGP 1979; DRCOG 1977.

HAIRE, Anne Rosemary Department Child Health, Community Health South London NHS Trust, Elizabeth Blackwell House, Wardalls Gr., Aronley Road, London SE14 5ER Tel: 020 7635 5555 Fax: 020 7771 5119; 65 Lee Road, Blackheath, London SE3 9EN — MB BS 1977 Lond.; MRCS Eng. LRCP Lond. 1977; MRCCH 1997; DRCOG 1979; MRCGP 1981; Instruc. Doctor Cert. Family Plann. 1984; DCH 1982; MFFP 1978. (Charing Cross Hosp.) Assoc. Specialist (Child Health) Community Health S.Lond.NHS Trust. Socs: Fac. Fam. Plann.; RCPCH. Prev: Clin. Asst. (Ment. Handicap) Nottm.; GP, Hong Kong.; Trainee GP Char. Cross VTS Lond.

HAIRE, Kevin Martin 38 Blandfield Road, London SW12 8BG — MB BS 1983 Lond.

HAIRE, Margaret (retired) 4 Malone View Road, Belfast BT9 5PH Tel: 01232 615896 — MB BCh BAO Belf. 1943; MD Belf. 1966; FRCPath 1980, M 1972. Prev: Sen. Lect. (Microbiol. & Immunobiol.) Qu. Univ. Belf.

HAIRE, Thomas Raymond (retired) 'Wynbank', 9 Tyler Avenue, Limavady BT49 0DT Tel: 028777 63287 — MB BCh BAO 1933 Belf.; MD Belf. 1954, MB BCh BAO 1933; MRCPsych 1972; Dip. Psych. Ed. 1936. Prev: Cons. Psychiat. Gransha Hosp. Lond.derry.

HAITES, Professor Neva Elizabeth Medical Genetics Laboratories, Department of Molecular & Cell Biology, University of Aberdeen, Foresterhill, Aberdeen AB25 2ZD Tel: 01224 840749 Fax: 01224 685157 Email: n.haites@abdnac.uk; 32 Cairn Road, Bieldside, Aberdeen AB15 9AL Tel: 01224 868572 Email: n.haites@abdn.ac.uk — MB ChB 1980 Aberd.; PhD Queensland 1974; FRCP Ed. 1997; MRCPath 1996. Prof. Clin. Genetics Med. & Head Serv. Genetics Laborat. Univ. Aberd. Socs: Clin. Molec. Genetics Soc.; Clin. Genetics Soc.; BMA.

HAJARNAVIS, Jayashree 62 Parklands Avenue, Lillington, Leamington Spa CV32 7BE — MB BS 1972 Gujarat; MRCS Eng. LRCP Lond. 1978; Ahmedabad). (Smt. N.H. Lakhamichand Municip. Med. Coll.) Prev: SHO (Urol.) & SHO (Gen. Surg.) Walsgrave Hosp. Coventry; SHO (Orthop. & Cas.) Coventry & Warks. Hosp.

HAJAT, Cother 68 High Street, Nuneaton CV11 5DA — MB BS 1994 Lond.; BSc (Physiol.) Lond. 1991; MRCP Lond. (United Medical and Dental School)

HAJDU, Nicholas (retired) 3 Lurgan Mansion, Lower Sloane St, London SW1W 8BH Tel: 020 7730 3218 — MD Prague 1934; MRCS Eng. LRCP Lond. 1942; FRCR 1993; DMR Lond 1944. Hon. Cons. Radiol. St. Geo. Hosp. Lond. Prev: Cons. Radiol. St. Geo. Hosp. Lond.

HAJELA, Vijay Kumar University Hospital Lewisham, Lewisham High St., London SE13; 26 Fortisbridge Road, Clapham, London SW11 5NY Email: vijayhaj@aol.com — MB BS 1990 Newc.;

BMedSc (Hons.) Newc. 1989; MRCP Ed. 1992. Hon. Research Regist. (Cardiol.) Roy. Hallamsh. Hosp. Sheff.; Specialist Regist. Rotat. S.E. Trauma Gen. Med. & Rheumat. Socs: Clin. Autonomic Surg.; Med. Res. Soc.; Brit. Soc. of Rhumatology. Prev: Regist. (Med.) Middlemore Hosp. Auckland, NZ; SHO Rotat. (Med.) Roy. Hallamsh. Hosp. Sheff.

HAJELA, Vireshwar Prasad Hollydene, 1 Reedley Drive, Reedley, Burnley BB10 2QZ — MB BS 1955 Agra; FRCP Ed. 1977, M 1961; DTM & H Liverp. 1959. (Agra) Cons. Phys. (Geriat.) Burnley Hosp. Gp. Socs: Brit. Geriat. Soc. & BMA. Prev: Sen. Regist. Gen. Hosp. Sunderland; Ho. Phys. Med. Coll. Hosp. Agra, India.

***HAJI ABDUL HAMID, Mawarni** 59 Chamberlain Road, Southampton SO17 1PQ — BM 1988 Soton.

HAJI-MICHAEL, Philip George Intensive Care Unit, Withington Hospital, Nell Lane, West Didsbury, Manchester M20 2LR Tel: 0161 291 3966 Fax: 0161 291 3980 Email: with.ich@smht.nwest.nhs.uk — MB BS 1985 Lond.; MRCP (UK) 1988; FRCA 1994. Cons. Anaesth. & IC Withington Hosp. & Christies Hosp.

HAJI MISBAK, Noraini 62 Prince Edwin Street, Liverpool L5 3LW — MB ChB 1998 Liverp.; MB ChB Liverp 1998.

HAJI-SUHAILEE, Haji-Azlan 56 Church Street, Hyde SK14 1JJ — MB ChB 1998 Manch.; MB Ch Manch 1998.

HAJIANTONIS, Nicolas Constantinou The Surgery, 69 Bury Road, Gosport PO12 3PR Tel: 023 9258 0363 Fax: 023 9260 1346; 15 The Avenue, Gosport PO12 2JS — LMSSA 1976 Lond.; Med. Dipl. Athens 1965; MRCOG 1974. (Athens)

HAJIOFF, Daniel 505C Derwent Court, Melville Grove, Newcastle upon Tyne NE7 7DG Tel: 0191 284 3111; 1 Coutt's Crescent, St Albans Road, London NW5 1RF Tel: 020 7284 2702 — BM BCh 1994 Oxf.; BA Camb. 1991. Ho. Phys. Freeman Hosp. Newc. Prev: Ho. Surg. John Radcliffe Hosp. Oxf.

HAJIOFF, Jack 1 Coutts Crescent, St Albans Road, London NW5 1RF Tel: 020 7284 2702 Email: jackhajioff@doctors.org.uk — MB ChB 1957 Liverp.; MRCS Eng. LRCP Lond. 1957; MRCPsych 1971; DPM Eng. 1963. p/t Cons. Psychiat., Herts. Partnership NHS Trust; Home Office Vis. Psychiat. Prev: Cons. Psychiat. Hill End Hosp. St. Albans & Hemel Hempstead Gen. Hosp.; Sen. Regist. St. Bart. Hosp. Lond.

HAJIOFF, Steven Room 208A, New Science Block, St Bartholomew's Medical College, Charterhouse Square, London EC1M 6BQ Tel: 020 7982 6039 Fax: 020 7982 6013 Email: s.hajioff@mds.qmw.ac.uk; 135 Willifield Way, London NW11 6XY — MB BCh 1990 Wales; MRCGP 1996. Lect. (Gen. Pract.) St. Bart. Hosp. Med. Coll. Lond. Prev: SHO (Paediat.) Univ. Hosp. Wales Cardiff.

HAJIPOUR, Ladan c/o Students Cage - Level 6, Ninewells Hospital, Dundee DD1 9SY — MB ChB 1998 Dund.; MB ChB Dund 1998.

HAJIVASSILIOU, Mr Constantinos Argyrou Royal Hospital for Sick Children, Yorkhill, Glasgow G3 8SJ Tel: 0141 201 0000 Fax: 0141 201 0858 — MB ChB 1986 Ed.; FRCS Glas. 1990; FRCS Ed. 1990; FRCS (Paed.) 1997; MD Ed. 1998. Cons. Paediat. & Neonat. Surg. & Hon. Sen. Lect.; Wellcome Sen. Lect. Dept. of Surgic. Paediat. Roy. Hosp. Sick Childr. Glas. Socs: Fell. Roy. Soc. Med.; Brit. Assn. Paediat. Surg. Prev: Sen. Regist. (Paediat. Surg.) Roy. Hosp. for Sick Childr. Glas.; Regist. (Vasc. Urol.) Falkirk Dist. Roy. Infirm.; Regist. (Plastic & Cardiothoracic) Glas. Roy. Infirm.

HAK, Cornelis No 1 White Castle, Berkeley Heywood, Worcester WR4 0RA — MD 1992 Antwerp.

HAKEEM, Abdul G The Surgery, 95 Highfield Road, Alum Rock, Birmingham B8 3QE Tel: 0121 327 4939 — MB BS 1968 Med Inst (1) Rangoon; MB BS 1968 Med Inst (1) Rangoon.

HAKEEM, Azeem Abdul Harvest, 9 Bryn Twr, Abergele LL22 8DD — MB BS 1996 Lond.

HAKEEM, Javid Akther The Medical Centre, Tanhouse Lane, Church Hill, Redditch B98 9AA Tel: 01527 59192 Fax: 01527 597679 — MB BS 1970 Jammu & Kashmir. (Govt. Med. Coll. Srinagar) GP Redditch.

HAKEEM, Vaseem Fatima Department of Paediatrics, West Middlesex University Hospital, Isleworth TW7 6AF Tel: 020 8565 5365 Fax: 020 8321 6410 Email: vaseernhakeem@wmuh-tr.nthames.nhs.uk; 45 Draycott Avenue, Harrow HA3 0BL — MB BCh 1980 Wales; MRCP (UK) 1987; FRCPCH. Cons. Paediat. W. Middlx. Univ. Hosp. Isleworth.

HAKEEM-HABEEB, Quayyam Akinbode 7 Rosemoor Drive, Northampton NN4 0XD — MB BCh 1980 Cairo; MRCOG 1993.

HAKHAMANESHI, Dinyar (retired) X-Ray Department, Whittington Hospital, Highgate Hill, London N19 5NF Tel: 020 7288 5491 — MD 1956 Tehran; FRCR 1978; DMRD Eng. 1974. Prev: Cons. Radiol. Islington & Bloomsbury HA.

HAKIM, Alan James Queen Elizabeth, The Queen Mother Hospital, St Peter's Rd, Margate CT9 4AN Tel: 01843 225544 Email: alanhakim@aol.com — MB BChir 1992 Camb.; MA Camb. 1992; MRCP (UK) 1995. (University of Cambridge) Hon. Cons. in Rheum. and Gen. Med., Whipps Cross Univ. Hosp. Lond. E11 1NR; ARC Clin. Research Fell., St. Thomas' Hosp., Lond. EC1. Socs: Roy. Soc. Med.; Brit. Soc. Rheum.; Hunt. Soc.

HAKIM, Eluzai Abe St Mary's Hospital Newport, Newport PO30 5TG Tel: 01983 524081 Ext: 4871 Fax: 01983 534872 Email: eluzai-hakim@yahoo.co.uk; 15 Queens Road, Ryde PO33 3BG Tel: 01983 617261 Fax: 01983 534872 Email: rehab@soton.ac.uk — MB ChB 1976 Makerere, Uganda; MRCP (UK) 1989; DTM & H RCP Lond. 1982. (Makerere Univ. Med. Sch.) Cons. Phys. (Rehabil. Med.). Socs: Brit. Soc. Rehabil. Med.; BMA; Brit. Assn. of Stroke Phys.s. Prev: Sen. Regist. (Rehabil. Med.) Salisbury Dist. Hosp.; Sen. Regist. (Rehabil. Med.) Soton. Gen. Hosp.; Sen. Regist. (Rheumatol. & Rehabil.) Qu. Alexandra Hosp., Portsmouth.

HAKIM, Frank (retired) 26 Six Acres, Upton, St Leonards, Gloucester GL4 8AX Tel: 01452 617575 Fax: 01452 617575 — MD Tabriz 1960; FACS 1973; FICS 1969; Dip. Surg. Canada 1969; Cert. Family Plann. RCOG 1982. Prev: Cons. A & E W.on Gen. Hosp., W.on-super-Mare.

HAKIM, Mohammad-Shamim Mohammad-Hashim 1st Floor Flat, 22 Beaconsfield Road, London NW10 2JG Tel: 020 8459 3530 — MB BS 1965 Gujarat; BSc (Chem. & Physics) Gujarat 1959, MB BS 1965; DA Eng. 1981. (B.J. Med. Coll. Ahmedabad) Socs: Assn. Anaesth. Gt. Brit. & Irel.; Fac. Anaesth. RCS Eng. Prev: SHO (Anaesth.) S.mead Hosp. Bristol; Regist. (Anaesth.) Plymouth Gen. Hosp.; Regist. (Anaesth.) King Edwd. Memor. Hosp. Lond.

HAKIM, Mr Nadey, KStJ Transplant Unit, St Mary's Hospital, Praed St., London W2 1NY Tel: 020 7886 1852 Fax: 020 7886 1707 Email: nadey@globalnet.co.uk; 34 Hocroft Road, London NW2 2BL Tel: 020 7435 4021 Fax: 020 7431 8497 Email: nadey@globalnet.co.uk — MD 1984 Paris; PhD Lond. 1991; FRCS Eng. 1988; FRCSI 1987; FACS 1998; FICS 1987. (Cochin-Port Royal Paris) Cons. Gen. & Transpl. Surg. St. Mary's Hosp.; Surgic. Dir. Transport Unit; Edit. Bd. Transpl.ation Proc.; Edr. Internat. Surg. Edr in chi of; Edit. Bd. Graf; Prof of surg Univ of Aao Paulo; 1st Vice Pres Inter coll of surg 2000; Mem of counc Transpl. sect Roy. soc med. Socs: Fell. Roy. Soc. Med. (Gen. Surg. Sec.) Transpl. Sect.; Internat. Soc. Surg.; Fell. Internat. Coll. Surgs. (Sec. Brit. Sect.). Prev: Multiorgan Transpl. Fell.sh. Univ. Minnesota, Minneapolis, USA; Mayo Clinic Surgic. Fell., USA; Specialist Regist. Rotat. (Gen. Surg. & Transpl.) Guy's Hosp. Lond.

HAKIM, Samir Moussa Wemyss Grange, 5 East Fergus Place, Kirkcaldy KY1 1XT — MB BCh 1971 Ain Shams; DLO RCS Eng. 1981. Surg. (ENT) Vict. Hosp. Kirkcaldy.

HAKIN, Barbara Ann Moorside, Bank Nook, Denholme Road, Oxenhope, Keighley BD22 9SJ — MB ChB 1975 Leeds; MB ChB (Hons.) Leeds 1975; MRCP (UK) 1977; MRCGP 1980. GP Bradford.

HAKIN, Mr Kim Neal Taunton & Somerset Hospital, Musgrove Park, Taunton TA1 5DA Tel: 01823 333444 Fax: 01823 336877; Fosgrove House, Fosgrove, Taunton TA3 7BP Tel: 01823 421853 Email: kimhakin@aol.com — MB BS 1983 Lond.; FRCS Eng. (Ophth.) 1987; FRCOphth 1989; DO RCS Eng. 1987. Cons. Ophth. MusGr. Pk. Hosp. Taunton. Socs: (Elec.) Europ. Soc. Oculoplastic & Reconstruc. Surgs.; Eur. Soc. Cataract & Refractive Surgs. Prev: Fell. (Oculoplastic Surg.) Melbourne, Austral.; Sen. Regist. & Regist. Moorfields Eye Hosp.; SHO Soton. Eye Hosp.

HAKIN, Ronald Nigel Moorside, Banknook, Denholme Road, Oxenhope, Keighley BD22 9SJ — MRCS Eng. LRCP Lond. 1971; MRCP (U.K.) 1975. (Manch.) Cons. Neurol. St. Lukes Hosp. Bradford, Bradford Roy. Infirm. & Pinderfields Gen. Hosp. Wakefield.

HAKKAK, Maurice Steven 1 Canning Cross, London SE5 8BH — MB BS 1998 Lond.; MB BS Lond 1998.

HALABI, Sahar 92 Waterloo Warehouse, Waterloo Road, Liverpool L3 0BQ — LMSSA 1994 Lond.

HALAHAKOON, Wijesinghe Liyanarachchige Dona 15 Killynure Wood, Tempo Road, Enniskillen BT74 6FR — MB BS 1980 Sri Lanka; MRCP (UK) 1991.

HALAKA, Mr Ahmed Nageeb Ali Mohamed 9 Fulwith Close, Harrogate HG2 8HP Tel: 01423 872542 — MB BCh 1971 Cairo; PhD Leeds 1986; FRCS Ed. 1977. (Mansura) Cons. (Neurosurg.) Leeds HA (T). Socs: N. Eng. Neurol. Assn.; Soc. Brit. Neurol. Surgs.

HALAWA, Mr Maher Nuffield Hospital, Derriford Road, Plymouth PL6 8BG Tel: 01752 702096 Fax: 01752 702096; 10 Penlee Gardens, Stoke, Plymouth PL3 4AN Tel: 01752 568412 Email: mhalawa@aol.com — MB BCh 1966 Cairo; MChOrth Liverp. 1975; FRCS (Orth.) Ed. 1984; FRCS Eng. 1972; MRCS Eng. LRCP Lond. 1976; Dip. Orthop. Cairo 1970; Dip. Surg. Cairo 1969. (Cairo) Cons. Orthop. Surg. Nuffield Hosp. Plymouth & Derriford Gen. Hosp. Plymouth. Socs: Fell. BOA. Prev: Sen. Regist. (Orthop. Surg. & Trauma) P.ss Eliz. Hosp. Exeter & Roy. Devon & Exeter Hosps.; Regist. (Orthop.) Walton Hosp. Liverp. & (Orthop. Surg.) Univ. Liverp.; AO Fell. Kantonsspital Basel, CH.

HALBERSTADT, Imke Resident House 16, Social Centre, Newham General Hospital, Glen Road, London E13 8SL — MB ChB 1995 Stellenbosch.

HALCOX, Julian Patrick John 58 Shacklewell Lane, London E8 2EY Tel: 020 7249 4547 — MB BChir 1992 Camb.; MRCP (UK) 1994. (Univ. Camb. & Char. Cross & Westm. Hosp.) Regist. (Cardiol.) Lond. Chest Hosp. Prev: Regist. (Med. & Cardiol.) Homerton Hosp.; SHO Rotat. (Med.) St. Geo. Hosp.

HALCROW, John Sinclair West Linton Health Centre, West Linton EH46 7EX — MB ChB 1978 Dundee.

HALDANE, David John 12 Westside Gardens, 4 Partickhill Road, Glasgow G11 5BL — MB ChB 1991 Dundee.

HALDANE, Douglas Andrew, TD (retired) Limetrees, 9 Stanely Avenue, Paisley PA2 9LA Tel: 0141 884 4292 — MB ChB 1949 Glas.; FRCGP 1972. Prev: Assoc. Adviser (Gen. Pract.) & Hon. Clin. Lect. Dept. Postgrad. Med. Univ. Glas.

HALDANE, Grant James 2/L 54 Polwarth Street, Hyndland, Glasgow G12 9TL Tel: 0141 357 3478 — MB ChB 1989 Aberd.; FFA RCSI 1994; DA (UK) 1992. Specialist Regist. (Anaesth.) W.. Infirm. Glas. Socs: Fell. RCS Irel.; BMA; Assn. GB & Irel. Prev: SHO (Anaesth.) Paisley Roy. Alexandra Hosp. & Glas. Roy. Infirm.; SHO (A & E) Glas. Roy. Infirm.

HALDANE, Johnston Douglas, MBE (retired) Tarlogie, 54 Hepburn Gardens, St Andrews KY16 9DG Tel: 01334 473055 — MB ChB Ed. 1948; FRCP Ed. 1968; MRCP (UK) 1953; FRCPsych 1971; DPM Eng. 1954. Prev: Sen. Lect. (Ment. Health) Univ. Aberd.

HALDANE, Morgan Flat 31, Arthur Court, Queensway, London W2 5HW — MB BS 1997 Lond.

HALDAR, Ganeschandra c/o Mr. P.K. Basu, 55 Cambridge Road, Seven Kings, Ilford IG3 8LX Tel: 020 8597 3106 — MB BS 1971 Calcutta. (Nilratan Sircar Med. Coll.) SHO Burton Dist. Hosp. Centre Burton-on-Trent.

HALDAR, Gita The Surgery, 2A Berne Square, Dinnington Road, Woodsetts, Worksop S81 8RJ — MB BS 1974 Calcutta.

HALDAR, Mr Mukul Samuel (retired) Caerphilly District Miners Hospital, St Martin's Road, Caerphilly CF83 2WW Tel: 01222 882829 — MB BS 1959 Calcutta; BSc Calcutta 1953, MB BS 1959; FRCS Glas. 1967; FFAEM 1994; FICA 1980. Assoc. Specialist (A & E & Orthop.) Caerphilly Miners Hosp. Caerphilly.; Asst. GP. Prev: Cons. Orthop. Surg. US Army Hosp. Nuernberg, W. Germany.

HALDAR, Neil Anustup Plasmarl House, Cwmynysminton Road, Aberdare CF44 0UP — MB BS 1992 Lond.

HALDEN, Peter John 44 Burstow Road, London SW20 8SX — MB ChB 1978 Bristol.

HALDER, Bishnupada (retired) Ainsworth Road Surgery, 60 Ainsworth Road, Radcliffe, Manchester M26 4FA Tel: 0161 723 1859 — MB BS Calcutta 1963; MRCP (UK) 1972. Gen. Med. Practitioner.

HALDER, Dipti Lowestoft Hospital, Tennyson Road, Lowestoft NR32 1PT; 153 Colville Road, Lowestoft NR33 9RE — MB BS Calcutta 1967; DTM & H RCP Lond. 1988. (Nilratan Sircar Med. Coll.) Clin. Med. Off. (Community Health Serv.) LoW.oft. Prev: Clin. Med. Off. (Community Health Servs.) Bow Arrow Hosp. Dartford.

HALDER, Neel 48 Turks Road, Radcliffe, Manchester M26 4QB — MB ChB 1998 Manch.; MB ChB Manch 1998.

HALDER, Satya Ranjan 11 Norton Close, Avondale, Purewell, Christchurch BH23 3DY — MB BS 1967 Calcutta.

HALDER, Smita Luna Sudeshna Flat 2, A2 Atwood Road, Didsbury M20 6TD Email: smita@halder181.freeserve.co.uk — MB ChB 1994 Ed.; BA Camb. 1991; MRCP Ed. 1997. (Edin) Specialist Regist. Gastroent. N W. Rotat. Prev: Regist. (Gastroenterol.) RVI Newc.; SHO Rotat. (Med.) Edin.

HALDER, Mr Snehasish St Mary's Hospital, Newport PO30 5TG Tel: 01983 524081 — MB BS 1972 Calcutta; FRCS Ed. 1995; DO Lond. 1980. (Nat. Med. Coll. Calcutta) Assoc. Specialist Newport.

HALDER, Sudhir Ranjan Wheelwright Lane Surgery, 25 Wheelwright Lane, Coventry CV6 4HF Tel: 024 7668 8289; Anu Villa, 2 Roland Avenue, Coventry CV6 4HR Tel: 024 76 688289 — MB BS 1963 Dacca; Cert. Family Plann. JCC 1969. (Dacca) Prev: Clin. Asst. (Accid. Orthop. & Geriat.) St. Tydfil's Hosp.; SHO (Gyn. & Obst.) Neath Gen. Hosp.; SHO (Gen. Surg.) Merthyr Gen. Hosp.

HALDER, Tapan Kumar Wallington Medical Centre, 52 Mollison Drive, Wallington SM6 9BY Tel: 020 8647 0811/8659 2272 — MB BS 1974 Calcutta.

HALE, Alan Riverside Surgery, Le Molay Littry Way, Bovey Tacey, Newton Abbot TQ13 9QP Tel: 01626 832666 — MB ChB 1969 Manch.; MRCP (U.K.) 1972. Prev: Regist. (Gen. Med.) N.ampton Gen. Hosp.

HALE, Anthony Stephen Flat 7 Irving House, 5 Irving St., London WC2H 7AT — MB BS 1979 Lond.

HALE, Antony David 25D Lawford Road, London NW5 2LH — MB BS 1986 Lond.; MRCPath 1993.

HALE, Arthur James Garden House, Bolney Avenue, Shiplake, Henley-on-Thames RG9 3NP Tel: 0173 522 2572 — MB ChB 1949 Glas.; FRSE 1963; PhD Glas. 1954, DSc 1959, MB ChB 1949; FRCPath 1975, M 1963; FIBiol. 1971. (Univ. Glas.) Dir. Genzyme Corp. & Creative Biomolecules Boston; Dir. Biomed. Sensors High Wycombe; Dir. Efamol Holdings. Socs: Path. Soc. Prev: Chairm. G.D. Searle & Co. Ltd. High Wycombe; Sen. Lect. in Path. St. Thos. Hosp. Med. Sch. Lond.; Pathol. Imperial Cancer Research Fund Lond.

HALE, Barbara May (retired) Rose Farm, West End, Nailsea, Bristol BS48 4DE — MB ChB Bristol 1950; DObst RCOG 1953; DCH Eng. 1952.

HALE, Brendan Thornton (retired) Rose Farm, West End, Nailsea, Bristol BS48 4DE — MB ChB Bristol 1949; FFR 1964; DMRT Eng. 1953. Prev: Cons. Radiother. Centre Bristol & Roy. United Hosp. Bath.

HALE, Brian Clement (retired) Norris Wood, Baas Hill, Broxbourne EN10 7EP Tel: 01992 464195 — MB BS 1951 Lond.; MRCS Eng. LRCP Lond. 1950; DMRD Eng. 1953. Prev: Cons. Radiol. Colchester Hosp. Gp. & N. Middlx. Hosp. Lond.

HALE, Brian Edgar Corbyn Thorpes, Mill Hill, The Common, Galley Wood, Chelmsford CM2 8TN Tel: 01245 352620 — MB BChir Camb. 1960; MA Camb. 1960; MRCS Eng. LRCP Lond. 1961; MFHom 1980; MRCGP 1975; DObst RCOG 1965. (Westm.) Socs: BMA. Prev: GP Chelmsford; Ho. Phys. Edgware Gen. Hosp.; Ho. Surg. W.m. Childr. Hosp.

HALE, Christopher Woolsthorpe Surgery, Main Street, Woolsthorpe, By Belvoir, Grantham NG32 1LX Tel: 01476 870166 Fax: 01476 870560 — MB BS 1980 Lond.; BSc (Physiol.) Lond. 1977, MB BS 1980; MRCGP 1985. GP Grantham. Prev: Trainee GP Leicester VTS; Ho. Surg. & Ho. Phys. The Lond. Hosp.

HALE, Darren James 2 Malvern Villas, Witney Road, Freeland, Witney OX29 8HG — BM 1994 Soton.

HALE, Mr Ernest Graham The Manor House, Hemswell, Gainsborough DN21 5UN Tel: 01427 668393 — MB ChB 1968 Liverp.; PhD Liverp. 1974, MB ChB 1968; FRCS Ed. 1978; FRCOphth 1988. Cons. Ophth. Co. Hosp. Lincoln. Prev: Sen. Regist. (Ophth.) Hallamsh. Hosp. Sheff. Regist. (Ophth.) St. Paul's Eye Hosp. Liverp.; Lect. (Physiol.) Univ. Liverp.

HALE, Geoffrey, MBE (retired) 5 Perrywood, Walden Road, Welwyn Garden City AL8 7PZ Tel: 01707 329956 — MRCS Eng. LRCP Lond. 1930; MA (Nat. Sc. Trip.), MB BChir Camb. 1931. Prev: Med. Adviser Roy. Nat. Lifeboat Inst.

HALE, James Henry, OBE (retired) Chester Dene, Queens Road, Walbottle, Newcastle upon Tyne NE15 8JB — MD 1940 Birm.; MD Birm. 1951. MB ChB 1940; FRCP Lond. 1973, M 1955; FRCPath 1964. Prev: Prof. Bact. Univ. Malaya.

HALE, John Clinton Parker The Avenue Surgery, 71 The Avenue, Wivenhoe, Colchester CO7 9PP Tel: 01206 824447 Fax: 01206 827973 — MB BS 1978 Lond.; Dip. Pract. Dermat. Wales 1991; DRCOG 1982. (Westm. Hosp.) Prev: SHO (O & G) St. John's Hosp. Chelmsford; SHO (Gen. Med.) Essex Co. Hosp. Colchester; Ho. Surg. Roy. Surrey Co. Hosp. Guildford.

HALE, Mr John Edward East Surrey Hospital, Redhill RH1 2JX — MRCS Eng. LRCP Lond. 1960; MS Lond. 1976, MB BS 1960; FRCS Eng. 1966; T(S) 1991. (Westm.) Cons. Surg. Redhill Gen. Hosp. Socs: Fell. Assn. Surgs.; Brit. Assn. Surgic. Oncol. Prev: Sen. Regist. (Surg.) W.m. Hosp. Lond.; Clin. Asst. St. Mark's Hosp.

HALE, John Frank Trerice, Chamberlaines, Kinsbourne Green, Harpenden AL5 3PW Tel: 01582 460608 — BM BCh 1948 Oxf.; MA Oxf. 1954, DM 1964, BM BCh 1948; FRCP Lond. 1975, M 1953. (Oxf. & St. Bart.) Hon. Vis. Endocrinol. St. Bart. Hosp. Lond. Socs: Soc. Endocrinol.; Scientif. Sect. Brit. Diabetic Assn. Prev: Cons. Phys. Luton & Dunstable Hosp. & St. Mary's Hosp. Luton; Lect. Med. & Demonst. Physiol. St. Bart. Hosp. Med. Coll.; Res. Med. Off. Nat. Heart Hosp. Lond.

HALE, Julia Mary Greenwich Primary Care Trust, Vanburgh Health Centre, Vanburgh Hill, Greenwhich, London SE10 9HQ Tel: 020 8312 6232, 020 8312 6967 Email: julia.hale@greenwich-trust.org.uk — MB BS 1985 Lond.; MSc 1999; BSc (Hons.) Lond. 1982; MRCP (UK) 1994; MFFP 1995; DFFP 1994; T(GP) 1990; DCH RCP Lond. 1989; DRCOG 1988; MRCPCH 1996. (Lond.) Cons. Paediat. Greenwich Primary Care Trust, Greenwich, Lond. Prev: Sen. Regist. (Community Paediat.), Community Health, S. Lond. NHS Trust.

HALE, Juliet Patricia Paediatric Oncology, Royal Victoria Infirmary, Queen Victoria Road, Newcastle upon Tyne NE1 4LP — MB BChir 1983 Camb.; MA Camb. 1982, MB BChir 1983; MRCP (UK) Paediat. 1987. Cons. Paediat. Oncol. Roy. Vict. Infirm. Newc. u. Tyne. Prev: Sen. Regist. (Paediat. Oncol.) St. Jas. Hosp. Leeds; Leukaemia Research Fell. Childr. Hosp. Sheff.

HALE, Margaret Claire Cape Hill Medical Centre, 147 Cape Hill, Smethwick, Smethwick B66 4SH Tel: 0121 558 0871 — MB ChB 1978 Birm.; MRCGP 1982; DRCOG 1980; DTM & H 1980.

HALE, Margaret Clare Storer Road Medical Centre, 2A Storer Road, Loughborough LE11 5EQ Tel: 01509 212120; Church Cottage, 11 Church St, Hathern, Loughborough LE12 5LA Tel: 01509 843089 — MB ChB 1988 Leic. Gen. Practioner, Dr. Middleton & Partners, LoughBoro.

HALE, Michael Kelmestowe, Lawnswood Drive, Stourbridge DY7 5QW — MB BCh 1966 Wales; FFR 1973; DMRD Eng. 1970. Cons. Radiol. Wolverhampton HA.

HALE, Mr Peter Charles Royal Sussex County Hospital, Eastern Road, Brighton BN2 5BE Tel: 01273 696955; 55 New Church Road, Hove BN3 4BG — MB BS 1984 Lond.; MS Lond. 1993; MA Camb. 1983; FRCS (Gen.) 1995; FRCS Eng. 1988. (St. Bart. Hosp. Med. Coll.) Cons. Gen. Surg. (Gastroenterol.) Roy. Sussex Co. Hosp. Brighton. Socs: Fell. Roy. Soc. Med.; Brit. Soc. Gastroenterol.; Assoc of Upper GI Surg. Prev: Sen. Regist. (Gen. Surg.) Roy. Sussex Co. Hosp. Brighton; Lect. (Surg.) Guy's Hosp. Lond.; Regist. (Gen. Surg.) Greenwich Dist. Hosp. Lond. & Kent & Sussex Hosp.

HALE, Peter John Stepping Hill Hospital, Poplar Grove, Stockport SK2 7JE Tel: 0161 483 1010; 66 Bridge Lane, Bramhall, Stockport SK7 3AW — BM BCh 1975 Oxf.; BA (Hons. Sch. Natural Sc.) Oxf. 1971, MA 1975, DM 1986; MRCP (UK) 1979. (Oxf. & St. Bart.) Cons. Phys. Stepping Hill Hosp. Stockport. Socs: Diabetes UK; Europ. Assn. for Study of Diabetes.; Assn. of Brit. Clin. Diabetologists. Prev: Sen. Regist. (Med.) Gen. Hosp. Birm.; SHO (Med.) St. Bart. Hosp. Lond.; SHO (Med./Neurol.) Gen. Hosp. Nottm.

HALE, Richard John Department of Histopathology, Stepping Hill Hospital, Stockport SK2 7JE Tel: 0161 419 5615 Fax: 0161 419 5668; 8 Werneth Rise, Gee Cross, Hyde SK14 5ND — MD Manch. 1992, MB ChB 1983; MRCPath 1990. Cons. Histopath. Stepping Hill Hosp. Stockport.

HALE, Robert Blagden 138 Dukes Ave, London N10 2QB — MRCS Eng. LRCP Lond. 1970; FRCPsych 1990, M 1980. Cons. Psychother. Tavistock Clin. Lond.; Assoc. Mem. Brit. Psycho-Analyt. Soc. Prev: Cons. Psychiat. Portman Clin. Lond.

HALE, William Mark Lister House Surgery, Lister House, 53 Harrington Street, Pear Tree, Derby DE23 8PF Tel: 01332 271212 Fax: 01332 271939 — BM BS 1989 Nottm.

HALE-BROWN, Janine Ann 105 Belmont Road, Malvern WR14 1PN — MB BS 1987 Lond.

HALEEM, Mohammad Abdul 13 Chalfonts, Tadcaster Road, York YO24 1EX Tel: 01904 705585 — MB BS 1954 Karachi; MRCS Eng. LRCP Lond. 1962; DTM & H Eng. 1956. (Dow Med. Coll.) Asst. Phys. City & Dist. Hosp. York. Socs: Brit. Geriat. Soc.; York Med. Soc. Prev: Ho. Surg. Civil Hosp. Karachi; Med. Off. Internat. Karachi Airport.

HALEPOTA, Anwar Alam Springhill House, Springhill Lane, Lower Penn, Wolverhampton WV4 4TJ — MB BS 1980 Karachi; Dip. Psychiat. Lond. 1987.

HALEPOTA, Munawar Alam 153 Boundary Road., Woking GU21 5BT — MB BS 1977 Sind.

HALES, Alison Dorothy Margaret 217 Hubert Road, Birmingham B29 6ES — MB ChB 1992 Birm.

HALES, Professor Charles Nicholas Clinical Biochemistry Department, Addenbrookes Hospital, Hills Road, Cambridge CB2 2QR Tel: 01223 336787 Fax: 01223 762563 Email: cnh1000@cam.ac.uk; The Grange, The Lanes, Great Wilbraham, Cambridge CB1 5JN Tel: 01223 881906 — MB BChir Camb. 1959; PhD Camb. 1964, MA 1959, BA 1956, MD 1971; FRCP Lond. 1976, M 1971; FRCPath 1980, M 1971. (Camb. & Univ. Coll. Hosp.) Prof. Clin. Biochem. Addenbrooke's Hosp. Camb. Socs: Soc. Endocrinol.; Biochem. Soc.; Brit. Diabetic Assn. (Med. & Scientif. Sect.). Prev: Prof. Med. Biochem. Welsh Nat. Sch. Med. Cardiff; Lect. (Biochem.) Univ. Camb.; Ho. Surg. & Ho. Phys. Univ. Coll. Hosp.

HALES, David Simon Michael 17-19 Raise St, Saltcoats KA21 5LX Tel: 01294 605141 Fax: 01294 462828; 3 Kennedy Road, Saltcoats KA21 5NJ — MB BS 1980 Lond.; FRCS 1985 Glas.; FRCS Glas. 1985. (Lond. Hosp.) Princip. GP Saltcoats Ayrsh. Prev: Regist. Rotat. (Surg.) Glas. Teach. Hosp.; SHO (O & G) Lanarksh.

HALES, Diana Ann South Meadow Surgery, 3 Church Close, High Street, Eton, Windsor SL4 6AP; The Old School, Gorse Hill Road, Virginia Water GU25 4AU Tel: 01344 842878 — MB BS 1988 Lond.; MRCGP 1992; DRCOG 1993.

HALES, Heidi Joanna 19 Gladsmuir Road, London N19 3JY — MB BS 1996 Lond.; DCH 1998; PALS 1997. (UCH Oxford) SHO Paediat. N. Middlx. Hosp. Prev: PrHo (Med.) Hemel Hempstead; PrHo (Surg.) Edgeware Gen.

HALES, Paul Christopher 8 Willesden Lane, London NW6 7SR — MB BS 1994 Lond.

HALES, Sally Ann Pathology Laboratory, Macclesfield District General Hospital, Victoria Road, Macclesfield SK10 3BL Tel: 01625 421000 — MB ChB 1985 Sheff.; MA Camb. 1986, BA 1982; MRCPath 1991.

HALES, Samuel 1 Wickliffe Gardens, Wembley Park, Wembley HA9 9LG Tel: 020 8904 2567 — MRCS Eng. LRCP Lond. 1934. (Middlx.) Phys. Slim Centre Lond. Socs: Fell. Roy. Soc. Med. Prev: Asst. Phys. CharterHo. Rheum. Clinic; Asst. Clin. Path. Ct.auld Inst. Bio-chem. Middlx. Hosp.; Cas. Off. Nat. Temperance Hosp.

HALES, Timothy Bryan (retired) 57 Springcroft, Parkgate, South Wirral CH64 6SF Tel: 0151 336 1655 — MB 1957 Camb.; MA Camb. 1964, MB 1957, BChir 1956; FRCPath 1977, M 1966. Prev: Cons. Chem. Pathol. Clatterbridge Hosp. & Arrowe Pk. Hosp.

HALEY, Mr Arthur Heaton (retired) Llaindelyn, St Clears, Carmarthen SA33 4BB Tel: 01994 230364 — MB BCh 1954 Wales; BSc Wales 1954; FRCS Eng. 1985; DO Eng. 1956. Prev: Cons. Ophth. Dyfed AHA.

HALEY, Arthur John Lawrence (retired) 4 Vennwood Close, Wenvoe, Cardiff CF5 6BZ — MB BCh 1943 Wales; BSc Wales 1943; FFA RCSI 1959; DA RCPSI 1949. Prev: Cons. Anaesth. Dyfed & W. Glam. AHA's.

HALEY, Clifford John 18 Beverley Road, Liverpool L15 9HF — MB BCh BAO 1990 Belf.

HALEY, Peter Field 21 Wold Road, Hull HU5 5NJ — MB ChB 1975 Bristol.

HALFACRE, Julie Anne King Edward VII Hospital, Midhurst GU29 0BL; Three Anchor Bay, 2 Downview Road, Barnham, Bognor Regis PO22 0EE — MB BS 1984 Lond.; FRCA 1989. Cons. Anaesth. King Edwd. VII Hosp. Midhurst W. Sussex.

HALFHIDE, Antony William (retired) Kingswood, 23 Woodham Waye, Woking GU21 5SW — MA Camb. 1983; MRCS Eng. LRCP Lond. 1946; DLO Eng. 1952. Clin. Asst. (ENT Surg.) Qu. Mary's

Hosp. Roehampton; Cons. ENT Surg. Burwood Pk. Sch. for Deaf Walton-on-Thames. Prev: Sen. Regist. (ENT Surg.) Hosp. Sick Childr. Gt. Ormond St.

HALFHIDE, Clare Phyllis 31 Stanley Square, Carshalton SM5 4LX — MB ChB 1998 Manch.; MB ChB Manch 1998.

HALFORD, Claire Fiona Halesowen Medical Practice, 2 Quarry Lane, Halesowen B63 4WD Tel: 0121 550 1185 Fax: 0121 585 0699 — MB ChB 1987 Sheff.; MRCGP 1994; DFFP 1993; DRCOG 1993; DCH RCP Lond. 1991. (Sheffield) GP; Assessing Doctor BPAS; CMO Family Plann. Socs: MDU & BMA.

HALFORD, John Douglas 29 High Street, Ipswich IP1 3QH Tel: 01473 23224 — MB ChB Ed. 1942; MRCGP 1980; Dip Ven Soc. Apoth. Lond. 1978. (Ed.) Socs: Austral. Med. Assn.

HALFORD, Jonathan The Surgery, 114-116 Carden Avenue, Brighton BN1 8PD Tel: 01273 500155 Fax: 01273 501193 Email: jonathan.halford@gp-681014.nhs.uk — MRCS Eng. LRCP Lond. 1981. (University College Cardiffs The Middlesex Hospital)

HALFORD, Jonathan Grovenor Little Thatch, 5 The College, Ide, Exeter EX2 9RH — MB BS 1992 Lond.; DRCOG 1996; DFFP 1997; MRCGP 1997. (Roy. Lond. Hosp.) Prev: GP Regist. Mt. Pleasant Health Centre Exeter VTS; SHO (Paediat. & Med.) Roy. Devon & Exeter Hosp.

HALFORD, Judith Mary 20 Lime Grove, Alveston, Bristol BS35 3PN — BM BS 1994 Nottm.; BMedSci Nottm. 1991.

HALFORD, Malcolm Niels Grovenor (retired) 1 Peppers Lane, Burton Lazars, Melton Mowbray LE14 2XA Tel: 01664 569960 — MB ChB Leeds 1963; DA Eng. 1966. Prev: Med. Adviser Melton Total Purchasing Project.

HALFORD, Margaret The Loaning, New Road, Teignmouth TQ14 8UF Tel: 01626 772968 — MB BS 1961 Lond.; MRCS Eng. LRCP Lond. 1961. (Lond. Hosp.) Clin. Asst. (Radiother.) Torbay Hosp.; Med. Off. Med. Boading DSS. Prev: Clin. Asst. Sphincter Research Unit Roy. Devon & Exeter Hosp.; Ho. Surg. St. John's Hosp. Chelmsford; Ho. Phys. Roy. Portsmouth Hosp.

HALFORD, Martin Edward Honywood (retired) Fourstacks, 18 Druid Stoke Avenue, Stoke Bishop, Bristol BS9 1DD Tel: 0117 968 4449 — MD 1951 Lond.; MB BS 1944; MRCP Lond. 1949; FRCPath 1977, M 1965. Cons. Pathol. Bristol Clin. Area (W.on-super-Mare Gen. Hosp.); Clin. Teach. in Path. Univ. Bristol. Prev: Lect. Path. Univ. Bristol.

HALFORD, Michael Grovenor Teignbridge Medical Practice, 2 Den Crescent, Teignbridge, Teignmouth TQ14 8BG Tel: 01626 773729 Fax: 01626 777381; The Loaning, New Road, Teignmouth TQ14 8UF Tel: 01626 770297 — MB BS 1961 Lond.; MRCS Eng. LRCP Lond. 1961; DObst RCOG 1964; DA Eng. 1963. (Lond. Hosp.) Hon. Med. Off. Teignmouth Hosp. Prev: Ho. Off. (O & G, Gen. Med. & Surg.) & SHO (Anaesth.) S. Devon & E. Cornw. Hosp. Plymouth.

HALFORD, Neil William 124 Glenthorn Road, Jesmond, Newcastle upon Tyne NE2 3HJ — MB BS 1990 Newc.

HALFORD, Peter David 25 Newbridge Road, Llantrisant, Pontyclun CF72 8EX — MB BCh 1983 Wales; MRCPsych 1990. Cons. Child & Adolesc. Psychiat. Harvey Jones Adolesc. Unit. & Preswylfa Child & Family Centre Cardiff. Socs: BMA; Assn. Child Psychol. & Psychiat. Prev: Sen. Regist. Rotat. (Child & Adolesc. Psychiat.) S. Wales; Regist. (Psychiat.) Morgannwg Hosp. Bridgend; Ho. Off. (Neurol.) Univ. Hosp. of Wales.

HALFORD, Sarah Elizabeth Rosemary 3 Modbury Gardens, London NW5 3QE — MB BS 1990 Lond.; MRCP (UK) 1994.

HALFORD, Stephen Mark 65 Clarendon Road, Southampton SO16 4GD Tel: 01705 787679 — MB BS 1993 Lond.; MRCP. (UCL)

HALFPENNY, Deane Marc 1A Chatto Road, Battersea, London SW11 6LJ — MB BCh 1990 Witwatersrand.

HALFPENNY, Diana Valerie Allen Royal Surrey County Hospital, Egerton Road, Guildford GU2 7XX; Stapledowne, Maddox Lane, Little Bookham, Leatherhead KT23 3BS Tel: 01372 458852 — MB BS 1960 Lond.; DCH Eng. 1964; DObst RCOG 1964. (Middlx.) Assoc. Specialist (Paediat.) Roy. Surrey Co. Hosp. Guildford. Socs: BMA; Brit. Paediat. Assn.; MRCPCH. Prev: Ho. Surg. Middlx. Hosp.; Ho. Phys. Centr. Middlx. Hosp.; SHO (Paediat.) Radcliffe Infirm. Oxf.

HALFYARD, Andrea Ella Almuth Muxford, Lydeard St Lawrence, Taunton TA4 3SB — MB BS 1985 Lond.

HALFYARD, Ingrid Rhoda Mary Higher Tarr Cottage, Lydeard Street Lawrence, Taunton TA4 3RL Tel: 01984 7395 — MB BS 1982 Lond.; MA Camb. 1983; FFA RCS Eng. 1986. (Lond. Hosp.) Staff Grade (Anaesth. & Chronic Pain Managem.). Prev: Asst. GP Bishops Lydeard Health Centre Taunton VTS; Regist. (Anaesth.) MusGr. Pk. Hosp. Taunton; Med. Off. Tumu Tumu Hosp., Kenya.

HALHEAD, Gillian Elizabeth 38 High Mill Court, Dundee DD2 1UN — MB ChB 1995 Dundee.

HALIL, Ozay 70 Grange Park Avenue, Winchmore Hill, London N21 2LL Tel: 020 8360 4014 — MD 1969 Istanbul; DPath Eng. 1976; Univ. Istanbul).

HALILEH, Samieh Othman Mahmoud 9 Heath Royal, London SW15 3JN — MB ChB 1984 Sheff.; MRCP (UK) 1993; Dip. Community Paediat. Sheff. 1990. Regist. (Neonat.) Chelsea & W.m. Hosp. Prev: Regist. (Paediat.) Char. Cross Hosp. Lond.

HALIM, Abdul 17 Lexden Drive, Chadwell Heath, Romford RM6 4TJ — MB BS 1967 Punjab. (Nishtar Med. Coll.)

HALIM, Mohammed Abdul 50 whinfell Drive, Scotforth, Lancaster LA1 4PB Tel: 01524 62049 Fax: 01524 62049; 50 Whinfell Drive, Scotforth, Lancaster LA1 4PB Tel: 01524 62049 Fax: 01524 62049 — MB BS 1958 Dacca; FRCPS Glas. 1992; MRCP Glas. 1967; MRCP Lond. 1967; FRCPsych 1988, M 1972; DPM Eng. 1971. (Dacca Med. Coll.) Hon. Con. Psychiat.; Hon. Cons. Psychiat. Ridge Lea Hosp. Lancs. Socs: Mem., Brit. Med. Assn.; Mem. Bangladesh Med. Assn. Prev: SHO Neurol. & Psychiat. Midl. Nerve Hosp. Birm.; Regist. Psychiat. United Birm. Hosps.; Sen. Regist. (Psychiat.) St. And. & Hellesdon Hosps. Norwich.

HALKES, Matthew John Torbay Hospital, Torquay TQ2 7AA Tel: 01803 614567; Burleigh, Paignton Road, Stoke Gabriel, Totnes TQ9 6SJ Tel: 01803 782284 — MB BCh 1989 Wales; MRCP (UK) 1993. Med. Regist.

HALKETT, Seymour John (retired) 17 Malvern Drive, Leven Banks, Stokesley, Middlesbrough TS9 5NS Tel: 01642 712188 — LRCP LRCS 1943 Ed.; LRCP LRCS Ed. LRFPS Glas. 1943; DA Eng. 1954. Prev: Cons. Anaesth. N. & S. Tees-side Hosp. Gps.

HALL, Adrian David The Paddock, 210 Manor Lane, Halesowen B62 8RD; 14 Grove Gardens, Bromsgrove B61 0UG — MB ChB 1993 Birm.; FRCR 2000; MRCP (UK) 1996. Specialist Regist. Radiol. W. Midl.

HALL, Adrian Patrick Chestnuts Surgery, 70 East Street, Sittingbourne ME10 4RU Tel: 01795 423197 Fax: 01795 430179; 76 College Road, Sittingbourne ME10 1LD — MB BS 1982 Lond.; DRCOG 1986; DCH RCP Lond. 1986.

HALL, Alan Arthur (retired) 121 Grantham Road, Sleaford NG34 7NP Tel: 01529 302820 — MRCS Eng. LRCP Lond. 1946.

HALL, Alexander James MacDonald Cross Deep Surgery, 4 Cross Deep, Twickenham TW1 4QP Tel: 020 8892 8124 Fax: 020 8744 9801 — MB ChB 1968 Leeds; BSc (Hons.) Leeds 1965, MB ChB 1968. (Leeds) Socs: BMA. Prev: SHO (Anaesth.) Middlx. Hosp. Lond.; SHO (Paediat.) W. Middlx. Hosp.; SHO (Cas.) St. Marys Hosp. Lond.

HALL, Alfred Geoffrey (retired) 6 Birchall Park Avenue, Leek ST13 5SJ Tel: 01538 372294 — MRCS Eng. LRCP Lond. 1940. Prev: Med. Off. Assoc. Portland Cement Manufacturers Ltd. (Cauldon Fact.) & Tarmac Rd.stone Holdings Ltd. (Cauldon Quarry).

HALL, Alison Mary Woodlawn, 13 Hacketts Lane, Woking GU22 8PP — MB ChB 1997 Leic. SHO (O & G) All St.s Hosp., Chatham. Prev: Ho. Off. (Surg.) Kettering Gen. Hosp. Kettering.

HALL, Alistair Scott Department of Cardiovascular Studies, The University, Leeds LS2 9JT; 8 The Quarry, Leeds LS17 7NH — MB ChB 1983 Leeds.

HALL, Alyson Tel: 020 7515 6633 Fax: 020 7537 3770; Tel: 020 482 3163 — MB BS 1974 Lond.; FRCPCH 1997; MRCPsych 1979. (Middlx.) Cons. Child & Adolesc. Psychiat. E. Lond. and City Ment. Health Trust; Hon. Sen. Lect., St. Barts & Roy. Lond. Sch. of Med.; Hon. Cons., Barts Lond. Trust; Recognised Teach. Univ. Lond. Socs: Assn. Child Psychol. & Psychiat.; Brit. Assn. for Child Abuse and Neglect; Brit. Assn. for Adoption and Fostering. Prev: Med. Director, Tower Hamlets Healthcare Trust; Lect. (Psychiat.) St. Geo. Hosp. Med. Sch. Univ. Lond.; Regist. (Psychiat.) St. Geo. Hosp. Tooting.

HALL, Amanda c/o Salisbury District Hospital, Anaesthetics Department, Salisbury SP2 8BJ — MB BS 1992 West. Austral.

HALL, Amanda Mary Newcombes Surgery, Newcombes, Crediton EX17 2AR Tel: 01363 772263 Fax: 01363 775906; Taylors Farm, Brampford Speke, Exeter EX5 5HN Tel: 01392 841193 — MB BS 1985 Lond.; MRCGP 1990; DRCOG 1991; DCH RCP Lond. 1988; DGM RCP Lond. 1987. Prev: SHO (O & G) Edgware Gen. Hosp.

Lond.; SHO (Geriat. & Cas.) Univ. Coll. Hosp. Lond.; SHO (Paediat.) Llandough Hosp. S. Glam.

HALL, Andrew Graham Cancer Research Unit, Cookson Building, Medical School, Framlington Place, Newcastle upon Tyne NE2 4HH Tel: 0191 222 8711 Fax: 0191 222 7556 Email: a.g.hall@ncl.ac.uk; 8 Park Avenue, Hexham NE46 3EN — MB BS 1980 Newc.; PhD Newc. 1992; MRCP (UK) 1983. Reader in Experim. Oncol. Prev: Sen. Regist. (Haemat.) Roy. Vict. Infirm. Newc.

HALL, Andrew James London School of Hygiene & Tropical Medicine, Keppel St., London WC1E 7HT Tel: 020 7927 2272 Fax: 020 7436 4230 Email: ahall@lshtm.ac.uk; 60 Villiers Avenue, Surbiton KT5 8BD — MB BS 1973 Lond.; PhD Soton. 1986; MSc Lond. (Epidemiol.) 1982; FRCP Lond. 1995; MRCP (UK) 1976; FFPHM RCP (UK) 1996, M 1990. (Guy's) Reader (Epidemiol.) Lond. Sch. Hyg. & Trop. Med. Socs: Fell. Roy. Soc. Trop. Med. & Hyg.; Soc. Social Med. & IEA. Prev: Epidemiol. WHO/IARC Gambia; Clin. Scientist MRC EEU Soton.

HALL, Andrew Jonathan Tel: 01722 744775 Fax: 01772 746616 Email: andy.hall@gp-j83019.nhs.uk; Tel: 01722 744194 Fax: 01722 744194 Email: ajh.to the@virgin.net — MB BCh BAO 1979 Belf.; FRCGP 2000; MRCGP 1983; DCH RCP Lond. 1982; DRCOG 1981. Assoc. Dir. (Gen. Pract.) Wessex.

HALL, Andrew Peter Adult Intensive Care, Leicester Royal Infirmary, Leicester LE1 5WW Tel: 0116 258 5226 Fax: 0116 258 5026 — MB BChir 1989 Camb.; MA Camb. 1990; MRCP (UK) 1992; FRCA 1995. (Camb.) Cons. in Anaesth. & IC, Leicester Roy. Infiramry. Socs: Assn. Anaesth.; Intens. Care Soc.; Eur. Soc. Intens. Care Med. Prev: Lect. Univ. Dept. Anaesth. Leicester Roy. Infirm.

HALL, Mr Andrew William Department of Surgery, Glenfield Hospital NHS Trust, Groby Road, Leicester LE3 9QP Tel: 0116 287 1471 Fax: 0116 258 3950; 89 Kingsway Road, Stoneygate, Leicester LE5 5TU Tel: 0116 270 3963 — MB ChB 1968 Liverp.; FRCS Ed. 1973; FRCS Eng. 1973. (Liverp.) Cons. Gen. & Oesoph. Surg. Glenfield Hosp. NHS Trust Leicester; Hon. Lect. (Gen. Surg.) Univ. Leicester. Socs: BMA & Surgic. Res. Soc. Prev: Sen. Lect. (Gen. Surg.) Univ. Leicester; Sen. Regist. (Gen. Surg.) Dundee Health Dist.; Research Fell. & Instruc. (Surg.) Univ. Chicago, USA.

HALL, Angela Mary 4 Springford Gardens, Southampton SO16 5SW — BM 1991 Soton.; MRCGP 1996.

HALL, Angela Sara Paediatric Admissions Unit, The Leicester Royal Infirmary, Infirmary Square, Leicester LE1 5WW — MB ChB 1989 Sheff.; DCH RCP Lond. 1995. Staff Grade (Paediat.) Paediat. Admissions Unit The Leicester Roy. Infirm. Leicester. Socs: Assoc. Mem. BPA.

HALL, Ann Gillian (retired) Hall Place, Old Beaconsfield, Beaconsfield HP9 1NB Tel: 01494 673986 Fax: 01494 676710 — MB BS (Hons. Surg.) Lond. 1961; MRCS Eng. LRCP Lond. 1961. Prev: Ho. Surg. & Ho. Phys. King Edwd. VII Hosp. Windsor.

HALL, Anna Maude 2 Napier Road, Edinburgh EH10 5BD Tel: 0131 447 5688 — MB BCh BAO 1945 Dub. (T.C. Dub.)

HALL, Anne Denise South Kensington & Chelsea Mental Health Centre, 1 Nightingale Place, London SW10 Tel: 020 8846 6054 Fax: 020 8846 6119; 43a Elizabeth Avenue, London N1 3BW — MB BCh 1987 Wales; BA Oxf. 1984; MRCPsych 1992. Cons. Psychiat. Chelsea & W.m. Hosp. Lond. Prev: Sen. Regist. (Psychiat.) Hackney Hosp. Lond.; Sen. Regist. (Psychiat.) St. Ann's Hosp. Lond. & Severalls Hosp. Colchester; Regist. (Psychiat.) Char. Cross Hosp. Lond.

HALL, Anne Vilma Department of Microbiology, Harefield Hospital, Harefield, Uxbridge UB9 6JH Email: anne@rbht.demon.co.uk — MB BS 1985 Lond.; BSc (Hons.) Lond. 1982, MSc 1992; DRCPath 1993; MRCPath. 1997. (Char. Cross & Westm.) Cons. Microbiologist Harefield Hosp. Middlx. Socs: Fell. Roy. Soc. Med.; Hosp. Infec. Soc.; Assn. Med. Microbiologists. Prev: Sen. Regist. (MicroBiol.) St Bartholomews Hosp. Lond.; Regist. (Microbiol.) St. Geo. Hosp. Lond.; SHO (Med.) Char. Cross Hosp. Lond.

HALL, Anthony Bennett 12 Charlock Drive, Stamford PE9 2WP — MB ChB 1981 Zimbabwe; FCOphth 1991.

HALL, Mr Anthony John (retired) 126 Harley Street, London W1G 7JS Tel: 020 7486 1096 Fax: 020 7224 2520 Email: hall-aj@dircon.co.uk — MB BS 1962 Lond.; FRCS Eng. 1968; MRCS Eng. LRCP Lond. 1962; DObst RCOG 1964. Prev: Cons. Orthop. Surg. Chelsea & W.m. Hosp.

HALL, Anthony Kent Boehringer Ingelheim Limited, Ellesfield Avenue, Bracknell RG12 8YS Tel: 01344 424600 Fax: 01344 741150 Email: halla@bra.boehringer-ingelheim.com — MB BS 1991 Lond.; BSc Lond. 1986. (Roy. Free Hosp. Lond.) Sen. Med. Adviser (Pharmaceut. Med.) Boehringer Ingelheim Ltd. Bracknell. Prev: Regist. (Emerg.) ChristCh. Hosp. ChristCh., NZ.

HALL, Anthony William Inglis The Orchard, Arkholme, Carnforth LA6 1AX — MB BChir 1946 Camb. (Middlx.)

HALL, Bruce Ian East Anglian Neurosurgery & Head Injury Service, Addenbrooke's NHS Trust, Hills Road, Cambridge CB2 2QQ — MB BS 1984 Queensland.

HALL, Caroline Jane Darley Oaks Farm, Newchurch, Hoar Cross, Burton-on-Trent DE13 8RJ — MB ChB 1997 Bristol.

HALL, Carolyn Ann 80 Manor Road S., Esher KT10 0QQ — MB BS 1991 Lond.

HALL, Carolyn Joyce Crofton Health Centre, Slack Lane, Crofton, Wakefield WF4 1HJ Tel: 01924 862612 Fax: 01924 865519 — MB BS 1987 Lond.

HALL, Catherine Margaret The Endocrine Department, The Royal Manchester Children's Hospital, Hospital Rd, Pendlebury, Manchester M27 4HA Tel: 0161 727 2585 Fax: 0161 727 2583; Littlehill, 27 Clement Rd, Mellor, Stockport SK6 5AG Tel: 0161 427 4132 — MB ChB 1988 Manch.; BSc (Med. Sci.) St. And. 1985; MRCP (UK) 1992; MD 2000 Manchester. Cons. Paed. Endocrinologist, Roy. Manch. Childr.'s Hosp., pendlebury, Manch. Socs: RCPCH; Brit. Soc. of Paediatric Endocrinol. and Diabetes; Roy. Coll. Phys.s (Lond.). Prev: Regist. (Paediat., Endocrinol. & Metab.) Stepping Hill Hosp. Stockport & Gt. Ormond St. Hosp. Sick. Childr. Lond.; Regist. (Paediat.) Roy. Childr. Hosp. Melbourne, Austral.; Sen. Regist. (Paediat. Endocrinol.) Roy. Manch. Childr. Hosp. Pendlebury.

HALL, Catherine Melly Fishponds Health Centre, Beechwood Road, Fishponds, Bristol BS16 3TD Tel: 0117 965 6281 — MB BS 1972 Lond. (St. Geo.) GP Fishponds Health Centre.

HALL, Celia Margaret 433 Whirlowdale Road, Sheffield S11 9NG Tel: 0114 361141 — MB ChB 1968 Sheff.; MRCPsych 1973. Assoc. Specialist Psychiat. SE Sheff. Socs: Liverp. Med. Inst. Prev: Sen. Regist. (Psychiat.) United Liverp. Hosps.

HALL, Mr Charles Nicholas 4 Craddock Road, Sale M33 3QQ — MD 1986 Manch.; BSc (Anat.) Manch. 1972, MD 1986, MB ChB 1975; FRCS Ed. 1979. Cons. Gen. Surg. Wythenshawe Hosp. Manch.

HALL, Charlotte Emma 56 Main Street, Skidby, Cottingham HU16 5TG — MB ChB 1998 Sheff.; MB ChB Sheff 1998.

HALL, Cherry Ann Beatrice The Buthaye, Church End, Purton, Swindon SN5 4EB — MB ChB 1971 Manch. Asst. GP Chippenham Wilts. Prev: Sen. Regist. (Community & Gen. Paediat.) Lamia, Greece; Resid. (Paediat.) St Sophia's Childr. Hosp. Athens, Greece.

HALL, Christine 63 Thurlstone Road, Penistone, Sheffield S36 9EF — BM BS 1976 Nottm.; MRCGP 1983.

HALL, Christine North Staffordshire Hospital Centre, City General Hospital, Department of Surgery, Newcastle Tel: 01782 715444; 181 Broadway, Walsall WS1 3HD Tel: 01922 644269 — MB ChB 1980 Liverp.; ChM Liverp. 1992; FRCS Eng. 1985. Cons. Surg. (Coloproctol.) N. Staffs. Hosp. Centre Stoke-on-Trent. Prev: Sen. Regist. (Surg.) St. Marks Hosp. Lond., N. Staffs. Roy. Infirm. & Selly Oak Hosp. Birm.

HALL, Christine Margaret Dept. of Radiology, Gt. Ormond St. Hospital NHS Trust, London WC1N 3JH Tel: 020 7405 9200 Ext: 5269 Fax: 020 7829 8665; Apex Lodge, Fitzroy Park, Highate Village, London N6 6JA — MB BS 1968 Lond.; FRCR 1975; FFR 1974; DMRD Eng. 1972. (Univ. Coll. Hosp.) Cons. Radiol. Hosp. Sick Childr. Lond. Socs: Internat. Skeletal Dysplasia Soc.; Internat. Skeletal Soc.; Europ. Soc. of Paediatric Radiol. Prev: Sen. Regist. Radiol. Univ. Coll. Hosp. Lond.; Sen. Regist. Radiol. Nat. Heart Hosp. Lond.; Research Asst. Univ. Coll. Hosp. Med. Sch.

HALL, Christopher Basil 1 Ireton Road, Colchester CO3 3AT Tel: 01206 549444; 76 Ambrose Avenue, Colchester CO3 4LN Tel: 01206 549444 Fax: 01206 369910 — MB BChir 1963 Camb.; MB BChir Camb. 1964; MA Camb. 1963; MRCS Eng. LRCP Lond. 1963; MRCGP 1971; DCH Eng. 1968; DA Eng. 1967; DObst RCOG 1965. (St. Mary's) Socs: Fell. Roy. Soc. Med. Prev: Ho. Surg. Canad. Red Cross Memor. Hosp. Taplow & Watford Matern. Hosp.; Ho. Phys. Qu. Eliz. II Hosp. Welwyn Gdn. City.

HALL, Christopher John Orchardways, Main St., North Newington, Banbury OX15 6AE — MB BS 1975 Lond.; MSc Lond. 1980, MB BS 1975; FRCPath 1994, M 1982.

HALL, Christopher John West Common Lane Medical Centre, Dorchester Road, Scunthorpe DN17 1YH Tel: 01724 870414 Fax: 01724 280485 Email: a.lee@virgin.net; 91 Bushyfield Road, Scunthorpe DN16 1NA — MB ChB 1982 Sheff.; MRCGP 1987; DRCOG 1986; MBA 1999. CME Tutor Scunthorpe.

HALL, Claire Jean Haematology Department, Harrogate District Hospital, Lancaster Park Road, Harrogate HG2 7SX — MB BS 1985 Lond.; Dip RCPAth 1996; MRCP (UK) 1990. (St. Bart. Hosp.) Regist. (Haemat.) Harrogate Gen. Hosp. & Leeds Gen. Infirm. Prev: SHO (A & E) St. Jas. Hosp. Leeds; SHO (Med.) Harrogate Hosps.; SHO (Oncol.) St. Jas. Hosp. Leeds.

HALL, Clifford Emery (retired) 20 Cardy Road, Greyabbey, Newtownards BT22 2LT Tel: 0124 774442 — MB BCh 1961 Belf; MB BCh BAO Belf. 1961; FFPHMI 1985, M 1978; DObst RCOG 1963. Prev: Dep. Chief Med. Off. DHSS N. Irel.

HALL, Clive Leonard The School House, Lullington, Frome BA11 2PG Tel: 01373 830714 — MB ChB 1968 Birm.; BSc (1st cl. Hons.) Birm. 1965, MD 1975, MB ChB (1st cl. Hons.) 1968; FRCP Lond. 1988; MRCP (UK) 1971. (Birm.) Dir. of Med. & Cons. Phys. & Nephrol. Roy. United Hosp. Bath; Dir. Bath Mem.ship. Course & Bath Adv. Med. Course. Socs: Renal Assn. & Europ. Dial. & Transpl. Assn.; Wessex & S. W. Phys. & Kidney Clubs. Prev: Lect. (Med. & Nephrol.) Qu. Eliz. Hosp. Birm.; MRC Lilly Internat. Fell.sh. Mass. Gen. Hosp. & Havard Univ.; Nuff. Trav. Schol.sh. Trop. Med.

HALL, Colin Robert Hillview, Grove Road, Coombe Dingle, Bristol BS9 2RL — MB BS 1971 Lond.; FFA RCS Eng. 1978. Cons. Anaesth. S.mead Health Auth. Bristol. Prev: Regist. Nuffield Dept. Anaesth. Radcliffe Infirm. Oxf.; Sen. Regist. Anaesth. Bristol Roy. Infirm.; Vis. Asst. Prof. Anaesthesiol. Univ. Virginia Med. Center.

HALL, Daphne Jean (retired) 21 Duncombe Grove, Harborne, Birmingham B17 8SJ Tel: 0121 429 2978 — MB ChB 1953 Manch.; BSc (Hons.) Manch. 1950, MB ChB 1953; Dip. Community Paediat. Warwick 1987; DCH Eng. 1957. Prev: Clin. Med. Off. (Child Health) N. Birm. HA.

HALL, David James Greaves Accident & Emergency Dept., Pinderfields Hospital, Aberford Road, Wakefield WF1 4B9 Tel: 01924 212419 Fax: 01924 214840 Email: david.hall@panp-tr.northy.nhs.uk; 8 De Lacies Road, Woodlesford, Leeds LS26 8WH — MB ChB 1988 Leeds; FFAEM 1997; MRCP (UK) 1992. (Univ. of Leeds) Cons. In Accid. & Emerg. Med., Pinderfields and Pontefract NHS Trust. Socs: Mem. Brit. Accid. & Emerg. Med.; Fell. of The Fac. of Accid. and Emerg. Med. Prev: Specialist Regist. Yorks. Deanery.

HALL, David John Ground Floor Flat, 26 Sulloth, St Anniesland, Glasgow G13 1DF — MB ChB 1984 Glas.; MB ChB Glas. l984.

HALL, David Keith 29 Swift Cl, Crowborough TN6 1UN — MB ChB 1997 Leic.; DCH 2001; MRCOG 2001.

HALL, Professor David Michael Baldock Institute of General Practice, Northern General Hospital, Sheffield S5 7AU Tel: 0114 226 6729 Fax: 0114 242 2136 Email: d.hall@sheffield.ac.uk; Storrs House Farm, Storrs Lane, Sheffield S6 6GY Tel: 0114 285 3177 Fax: 0114 285 4054 Email: d.hall@sheffield.ac.uk — MB BS (Univ. Gold Medal) Lond. 1969; BSc (Pharmacol.) Lond. 1966; FRCP Lond. 1986; MRCP (UK) 1972; MRCS Eng. LRCP Lond. 1969; FRCPCH 1997; FFPHM (Hon.) 1999. (St. Geo.) Prof. Community Paediat. Comm. Health Sheff. & Sheff. Univ. Med. Sch. Socs: Pres. RCPCH 2000-2003. Prev: Cons. & Sen. Lect. (Paediat.) St. Geo. Hosp. Lond.; Sen. Regist. (Paediat.) Char. Cross Hosp. Lond.; Sen. Med. Off. Baragwanath Hosp., Johannesburg.

HALL, David Russell 5 Broughton Road, Ipswich IP1 3QR Tel: 01473 254265 Fax: 01473 702123 — MB ChB 1964 Liverp.; MD Liverp. 1976; FRCP Lond. 1985; MRCP (UK) 1970; DObst RCOG 1966. Cons. Phys. (Chest Dis.) Ipswich Hosp. Socs: Brit. Thorac. Soc.; BMA; Ipswich Medico Legal Soc.

HALL, David Sunderland (retired) 36 Crescent Road, Sidcup DA15 7HW Tel: 020 8300 3898 — MB BS Lond. 1957; MRCGP 1968; FRCGP 1991; DObst RCOG 1959. Prev: Ho. Phys. & Ho. Surg. Univ. Coll. Hosp.

HALL, Denise Mary 30 Mount Eden Park, Belfast BT9 6RB — MB BCh BAO 1949 Belf.

HALL, Mr Derek, Wing Cdr. RAF Med. Br. Orton Medical Practice, Orton Centre, Orton Goldhay, Peterborough PE2 5RQ Tel: 01733 238111 Fax: 01733 238236; Portadown Weg 20, 41179 Moenchengladbach, Germany Tel: 00 49 216 1559754 — MB ChB 1974 Birm.; FRCS (Otol.) Ed. 1986; MRCGP 1979; DRCOG 1978; Cert. Gen. Av Med. 1976. Socs: BAOL. Prev: Cons. Otorhinolaryng. Surg. RAF(H) Wegberg; Cons. Otorhinolaryng. PMH RAF Halton & TPOW RAF(H) Ely; Sen. Regist. Roy. Lond. Hosp.

HALL, Derek Geoffrey Forge Cottage, Newpcote Lane, Findon, Worthing BN14 0SE Tel: 01903 873018 — MRCS Eng. LRCP Lond. 1968; MB Camb. 1969, BChir 1968; FRCR Eng. 1976; DMRD Eng. 1973. (Camb. & St. Bart.) Cons. Radiol. Worthing Health Dist. Prev: SHO Gen. Hosp. Nottm.; Regist. Radiol. Gen Hosp. Nottm.; Sen. Regist. Radiol. Soton. Health Dist.

HALL, Desmond Laurence Hall Place, Beaconsfield HP9 1NB Tel: 01494 673986 Fax: 01494 676710 Email: desmond.lau@medix-uk.com — MB BS Lond. 1961; MRCS Eng. LRCP Lond. 1961; DObst RCOG 1963. (Guy's) Socs: Chiltern & Windsor Med. Socs.; Roy. Soc. Med. Prev: Ho. Phys. & Ho. Surg. King Edw. VII Hosp. Windsor; Ho. Surg. (Obst.) Old Windsor Hosp.

HALL, Donna Caroline Barts & London NHS Trust Tel: 01642 854600 — MB ChB 1989 Birm.; FRCA 1997. (Birm.) Cons. in Cardiothoracic Anaesth.

HALL, Duncan Philip Blackmore Health Centre, Blackmore Drive, Sidmouth EX10 8ET Tel: 01395 512601 Fax: 01395 578408; Clover Cottage, Boughmore Lane, Sidmouth EX10 8SJ Tel: 01395 512380 — MB BS 1983 Lond.; MRCGP 1989; DRCOG 1988; Cert. Family Plann. JCC 1988; DCH RCP Lond. 1988. Prev: SHO (Gen. Surg.) Whittington Hosp. Lond.; Demonstr. Anat. & Ho. Surg. The Lond. Hosp.

HALL, Edward Grindrod (retired) 2 Hatfield Road, Ainsdale, Southport PR8 2PE — MB ChB 1941 Manch.; BSc, MB ChB Manch. 1941; FRCPath 1972. Prev: Cons. Pathol. Alder Hey Childr. Hosp. Liverp.

HALL, Edward Joseph 22 Pegasus House, Beaumont Square, London E1 4NB Tel: 020 7791 2346 — MB BS 1998 Lond.; MB BS Lond 1998.

HALL, Elizabeth St helena Hospice, Barncroft Close, Eastwood Drive., Colchester CO4 4SF Tel: 01206 845566 Fax: 01206 842445 Email: ehall@sthelenahospice.org.uk; 1 Ireton Road, Colchester CO3 3AT Tel: 01206 570094 Email: elizahall@hotmail.com — MB BS 1963 Lond.; MRCS Eng. LRCP Lond. 1963; DObst RCOG 1965. (St. Mary's) Med. Dir. St. Helena Hospice Colchester; Clin. Asst. (Radiother. & Oncol.) Essex Co. Hosp. Colchester; Hon. Cons. Palliat. Med. Essex Rivers Heathcare. Prev: SCMO (Family Plann.) Essex HA; Ho. Surg. (Obst.) Qu. Eliz. II Hosp. Welwyn Garden City; Ho. Phys. Paddington Gen. Hosp.

HALL, Elizabeth Angela Forest House Surgery, 25 Leicester Road, Shepshed, Loughborough LE12 9DF Tel: 01509 508412 Fax: 01509 502229; Brookfield House, 35A Garendon Road, Shepshed, Loughborough LE12 9NU Tel: 01509 650663 — MB BS 1979 Lond.; BSc Lond. 1976; MRCGP 1983; DRCOG 1981; Joint Cert. Family Plann. & Contracep. 1981. (King's Coll. Hosp.) GP Shepshed Leics.; PHRO Educat.al Supervisor (Gen. Pract.) Shepshed. Socs: BMA. Prev: Lect. (Gen. Pract.) Dept. Community Health Leicester Univ.; SHO (O & G) City Hosp. Nottm.

HALL, Elizabeth Weir (retired) Stream Cottage, 16a The Street, Uley, Dursley GL11 5TB Tel: 01453 860417 Email: elizhopkins@lineone.net — MB BS 1954 Lond.; MRCS Eng. LRCP Lond. 1954; FRCPath 1976, M 1964. Prev: Cons. Histopath. Roy. United Hosp. Bath, NHS Trust.

HALL, Elspeth Jean Bryher, 11 Linwood Crescent, Ravenshead, Nottingham NG15 9FZ Tel: 01623 792899 — MB ChB 1963 Birm. (Birm.)

HALL, Emma Josephine Flat 9, Bracken House, Watts Grove, London E3 3RG Tel: 020 7515 6439 Email: emmaanddesi@hotmail.com; Storrs House Farm, Storrs Lane, Stannington, Sheffield S6 6GY Tel: 0114 285 3177 Fax: 0114 285 4054 — MB BS 1993 Lond.; MA Camb. 1994; MRCP (UK) 1996. (St. Geo. Hosp.) Specialist Regist. (Palliat. Med.) S. Thames. Prev: SHO (Palliat. Care) St. Joseph's Hospice, Hackney; SHO (Neurol.) Roy. Co. Surrey Hosp. Guildford Surrey; SHO Rotat. (Med.) St. Geo. Hosp. Lond.

HALL, Eric Glynn (retired) Little Meadow, Westlands, Birdham, Chichester PO20 7HJ Tel: 01243 512338 — MB BS Lond. 1947;

MRCS Eng. LRCP Lond. 1943; DObst RCOG 1947. Prev: GP Watford Herts.

HALL, Frances Clare Louise Rheumatology Unit, Department of Medicine, Hammersmith Hospital, Du Cane Road, London W12 0HS Tel: 020 8743 2030; 38 Hengrove Close, Headington, Oxford OX3 9LN — BM BCh 1989 Oxf.; MA 1992, BA Oxf. 1986; MRCP (UK) 1992. Regist. (Rheum.) Hammersmith Hosp. Lond. Socs: Roy. Coll. Phys. Lond. Prev: Regist. (Gen. Med.) Wexham Pk. Hosp. Slough; SHO (Gastroenterol. & Gen. Med.) Addenbrooke's Hosp. Camb.; SHO (Chest Med.) Papworth Hosp. Camb.

HALL, Francis Geoffrey Holly Cottage, E. Coker, Yeovil BA22 9LG — MB BS 1957 Lond.; FFA RCS Eng. 1968; DA Eng. 1961. (St. Bart.) Cons. Anaesth. S. Som. Clin. Area. Socs: Fell. Roy. Soc. Med.; Assn. Anaesths. Prev: Sen. Regist. Anaesth. Univ. Coll. Hosp. & Nat. Hosp. Nerv. Dis. Qu.; Sq.; Anaesth. Regist. St. Geo. Hosp. Lond.

HALL, Frederick John St Johns Surgery, 5 Kidderminster Road, Bromsgrove B61 7JJ Fax: 01527 576022; Robins Meadow, Hanbury Road, Stoke Prior, Bromsgrove Tel: 01527 835760 Fax: 01527 574527 Email: fjh999@aol.com — MB ChB 1977 Birm.; 2000 Dip IMC RCS (Ed); DRCOG 1981. Clin. Asst. (Orthop.) Alexandra Hosp., Redditch; Med. Adviser Hereford and Worcs. Amb. Serv.; Hon. Lect. in Emerg. Care, Dept. of Anaesthetics, Univ. of Birm. Socs: Brit. Assn. for Immediate Care. Prev: Div. Police Surg. B Div. W. Mercia Police.

HALL, Frederick Marcus (retired) 9 Whitehill Close, Nackington, Canterbury CT4 7AQ — MB ChB Birm. 1944; DMRT Eng. 1951. Prev: Cons. Radiotherap. & Nuclear Med. Canterbury & I. of Thanet Hosp. Gp.

HALL, Geoffrey David The Top Flat, 26 Cumberland Road, Headingley, Leeds LS6 2EF Tel: 0113 274 8429 — MB ChB 1990 Sheff.; MRCP (UK) 1993. ICRF Clin. Research Fell. ICRF Cancer Med. Research Unit, St. Jas. Univ. Hosp. Leeds. Prev: SHO Rotat. (Med.) St. Jas. Univ. Hosp. Leeds.

HALL, Geoffrey Ian Moorcroft Surgery, 646 King Lane, Leeds LS17 7AN Tel: 0113 295 2750 Fax: 0113 295 2761 — MB ChB 1983 Leeds. Clin. Asst. (Psychogeriat.) W. Yorks.

HALL, Geoffrey Peter Moorfield, Moor Lane, Burley-in-Wharfedale, Ilkley LS29 7AF Tel: 01943 863763 — MB ChB 1967 Leeds; MRCP (U.K.) 1972. (Leeds) GP Otley. Prev: Sen. Med. Regist. Leeds Hosp.; Med. Regist. Gen. Hosp. Nottm.; SHO (Neurol.) Hosp. Nerv. Dis. Qu. Sq.

HALL, George Felix Macdonald Cherry Cott, Maudlin Road, Totnes TQ9 5EX Tel: 01803 862005 — MD Bristol 1950, MB ChB 1942; FRCPath 1963. (Bristol) Cons. Pathol. Emerit. Nottm. Gen. Hosp. Socs: Path. Soc. & Internat. Acad. of Path. Prev: Sen. Lect. (Morbid Anat.) & Asst. Morbid Anatomist King's Coll. Hosp.; Surg. Lt. RNVR; Asst. Lect. (Pathol.) Univ. Bristol.

HALL, George Harry (retired) 87 Polsloe Road, Exeter EX1 2HW — MB BS (Hons. Med.) Lond. 1951; BSc Lond. 1948, MD 1961; FRCP Lond. 1972, M 1956; MRCS Eng. LRCP Lond. 1951. Chief Med. Off. Med. Sickness Soc. Exeter. Prev: Cons. Phys. Devon & Exeter HA.

HALL, George J Hird L (retired) 26 Victoria Gardens, Kilmacolm PA13 4HL Tel: 01505 872676 — MB ChB 1935 Glas.; DPH 1937; DCH Eng. 1949. Prev: Cons. Phys. & Geriat. St. Helier Gp. Hosps.

HALL, George Kenneth MacDonald (retired) St Ann's, 2 East Fergus Place, Kirkcaldy KY1 1XX Tel: 01592 260297 — MB ChB 1950 Ed.

HALL, George Martin St George's Hospital Medical School, Cranmer Terrace, London SW17 0RE Tel: 020 8725 2615 Fax: 020 8725 0256 — PhD Lond. 1976, MB BS 1967; MRCS Eng. LRCP Lond. 1967; FFA RCS Eng. 1971. (Univ. Coll. Hosp.) Prof. Anaesth. St. Geo. Hosp. Med. Sch. Lond. Socs: Anaesth. Res. Soc. & Assn. Anaesth. Prev: Prof. Clin. Anaesth, Hon. Cons., Reader & Sen. Lect. Roy. Postgrad. Med. Sch. & Hammersmith Hosp. Lond.

HALL, Georgina Wanda Paediatric Haematologist, John Radcliffe Hospital, Headley Way, Headington, Oxford OX3 9DU Tel: 01865 221066 Fax: 01865 221083 Email: georgina.hall@cellsci.ox.ac.uk — MB BS 1987 Lond.; PhD Lond. 1994; BSc Lond. 1984; MRCP (UK) 1990; MRCPath 1998. (Roy. Free Hosp.) Cons. Paediat. John Radcliffe Hosp. Oxon. Prev: Lec/Sen Reg Gt. Ormond St Hosp./ Roy. Free Hosp.; Regist. (Haemat.) Hammersmith Hosp. Roy. Postgrad. Med. Sch. Lond.; MRC Clin. Train. Fell. (Molecular Haemat.) John Radcliffe Hosp. Oxf.

HALL, Gerard Melville Department of Rheumatology, St Peters Hospital, Guildford Road, Chertsey KT16 0PZ Tel: 01932 872000; 41 Thurloe Square, London SW7 2SR — MB BS 1982 Lond.; MRCP (UK) 1988. Cons. Rheum. St. Peters Hosp. Chertsey. Prev: Sen. Regist. (Rheum.) St. Bart. Hosp. Lond.

HALL, Gillian Market St. Health Group, 52 Market St, East Ham, London E6 Tel: 020 8548 2200; Tel: 01708 724992 Email: cruzhall99@aol.com — MB BS 1990 Lond.; MRCGP 1994; DTM & H Liverp. 1995; DRCOG 1992. (Lond. Hosp. Med. Coll.) Salaried GP, Market St. Health Gp., E. Ham. Prev: GP Salaried - New Ham PCT; GP Locum; Head of HIV/Aids Dept-Sihanouk Hosp. Cnetre of Hope Phnom Penn, Cambodia.

HALL, Gillian Lesley 14 Moncrieff Avenue, Kirkintilloch, Glasgow G66 4NL Email: glh20@medschl.cam.ac.uk — BM BCh 1990 Oxf.; BSc (1st cl. Hons.) Immunol. Glas. 1986; MRCP (UK) 1993. (Oxf.) Research Regist. (Neurol.) Addenbrooke's Hosp. Camb. Prev: Regist. & SHO Rotat. (Med.) Addenbrooke's Hosp. Camb.

HALL, Glen Hedworth Strathallan, Todlaw Road, Duns TD11 3EW; Cluniter Farm, Cluniter Road, Innellan, Dunoon PA23 7SA Tel: 01369 830002 — MB ChB 1991 (Hons.) Ed.; Dip. in Advanced Obstetric Ultrasound RCR/RCOG 2000; BSc (Hons.) Ed. 1989; Dip. Of Fac. Of Family Plann. 1996; MRCPI 1997; MRCOG 1996; Dip. Ven. Liverp. 1994. GP Regist., Old Fire Station Surg., Albert Terr., Beverley. Socs: Brit. Med. Ultrasound Soc.; Brit. Soc. Colposc. & Cervic. Pathol.; Med. Soc. Study VD. Prev: Specialist Regist. (O & G) P.ss Roy. Hosp. Hull; Clin. Research Fell. (Gyn. Imaging) Univ. of Hull.; Specialist Regist. (O & G) York Dist. Gen. Hosp.

HALL, Graeme Douglas Frithwood Surgery, 45 Tanglewood Way, Bussage, Stroud GL6 8DE Tel: 01453 884646 Fax: 01453 731302; Peace Cottage, Beech Lane, Brownshill, Stroud GL6 8AJ Tel: 01453 885040 — MB ChB 1975 Glas.; MRCP (UK) 1978.

HALL, Mr Graham Sundown, Broadmayne, Dorchester DT1 2DT — MB ChB 1969 Manch.; LLM Cardiff Univ.; MD 1980; FRCS Eng. 1973. Cons. Traum. & Orthop. Surg. W. Dorset. Socs: Fell. Brit. Orthop. Assn. Prev: Sen. Regist. Bath & Wessex Orthop. Hosp.; Regist. (Orthop.) Soton. Univ. Hosps. & Lond. Mayor Treloar; Hosp. Alton.

HALL, Gregory John 13 Alberta House, Blackwall Way, London E14 9QH — MB BS 1991 Lond.

HALL, Haidri Isobel 8 Church Street, Baldock SG7 5AE — MB ChB 1947 Sheff. (Sheff.) Deptm. Med. Off. Herts. CC. Prev: Asst. Cas. Off. Roy. Hosp. Sheff.; Asst. Med. Off. Sheff. Co. Boro.

HALL, Harold Dearden 10 Cambridge Avenue, Crosby, Liverpool L23 7XW Tel: 0151 924 4448 — MB ChB 1940 Liverp. (Liverp.) Med. Off. Remploy; Med. Off. Mersey Mission to Seamen Liverp.; Med. Supt. Bibby Line. Socs: BMA & Liverp. Med. Inst. Prev: Regist. (Surg.) David Lewis N.. Hosp. Liverp.; Resid. Surg. Off. Qu. Mary's Hosp. Roehampton; Med. Off. RAF.

HALL, Hedley Walter (retired) Tudor Lodge, 8 Brightstowe Road, Burnham-on-Sea TA8 2HW Tel: 01278 783437 — MB BS 1933 Lond.; FRCS Eng. 1938; MRCS Eng. LRCP Lond. 1933. Prev: Cons. Orthop. Surg. Bath Clin. Area.

HALL, Helen Elizabeth George Street Surgery, 16 George Street, Alderley Edge SK9 7EP Tel: 01625 584545/6; 42 Knutsford Road, Wilmslow SK9 6JB Tel: 01625 536270 Email: helenehall@aol.com — MB BS 1979 Lond.; BA Oxf. 1976; MRCP (UK) 1982; MRCGP 1985; DRCOG 1983. (Oxford, Middlesex) p/t GP Chesh.

HALL, Henry Nicholas Parkfield Medical Centre, 255 Parkfield Road, Wolverhampton WV4 6EG Tel: 01902 342152 Fax: 01902 349411 — MB ChB 1976 Birm.; MRCGP 1982. PCG Chairm. Wolverhampton S. E.

HALL, Iain Munro Library House Surgery, Avondale Road, Chorley PR7 2AD Tel: 01257 262081 Fax: 01257 232114 — MB ChB 1969 Manch.; DObst RCOG 1975. (Manch.) Prev: Ho. Surg. Salford Roy. Hosp.; Ho. Phys. Stepping Hill Hosp. Stockport; SHO (Surg.) Hope Hosp. Salford.

HALL, Mr Iain Stuart, Squadron Ldr. RAF Med. Br. Department of Urology, Southampton General Hospital, Tremona Road, Southampton SO16 6YD Email: ishall@mcmail.com — MB BS 1987 Lond.; FRCS Eng. 1993. (Charing Cross and Westminster) Specialist Regist. (Urol.).

HALL, Ian Michael Health Centre, Newgate Street, Worksop S80 1HP Tel: 01909 500266 Fax: 01909 478014; 3 Blyth Grove,

Worksop S81 0JG — MB ChB 1982 Leeds; MRCGP 1987. Course Organiser Bassetlaw VTS.

HALL, Professor Ian Philip Division of Therapeutics, University Hospital, Nottingham NG7 2UH Tel: 0115 970 9905 Fax: 0115 942 2232 Email: ian.hall@nottingham.ac.uk — BM BCh 1982 Oxf.; BA Oxf. 1979; DM Nottm. 1990; FRCP Lond. 1995; MRCP (UK) 1985. Head. (Therap.) & Hon. Cons. (Therap.) Univ. Hosp. Nottm.; Dep. Dir., Inst. of Cell Signalling, Univ. of Nottm.; Dir. Of Research and Developm., NHS Trust, Univ. Hosp. Nottm. Socs: Assn. Phys.; Brit. Pharm. Soc. Prev: Lect. & Hon. Sen. Regist. (Therap.) Univ. Hosp. Nottm.; Clin. Research Fell. (Respirat. Med., Physiol. & Pharmacol.) Univ. Hosp. Nottm.; MRC Trav. Fell. Univ. Pennsylvania, USA.

HALL, Ian Robert Department of Cardiology, Stafford General Hospital, Weston Road, Stafford ST16 Tel: 01785 230457; 125 Lascelles Drive, Pontprennay, Cardiff CF23 8NP Tel: 029 2073 5380 Email: irhdoc@ianh29.freeserve.co.uk — MB ChB 1993 Manch.; BSc (Hons.) Leeds 1988; MRCP (UK) 1996. (Manch.) Specialist Regist. (Cardiol.) W. Midl. Rotat. Stafford Gen. Hosp., Stafford. Socs: BMA. Prev: Clin. Research Fell., Waled Heart Research Inst., Cardiff; Specialist Regist. Cardiol.,N. Staffs. Cardiothoracic Centre, Stoke on Trent.; Regist. (Cardiol.) Univ. Hosp. Wales Cardiff.

HALL, Ian Sebastian Islington Learning Disabilities Partnership, 1 Lowther Road, London N7 8US Tel: 020 7527 6600 Fax: 020 7527 6607 Email: ian.hall@cichs-tr.nthames.nhs.uk — MB BChir 1989 Camb.; MA (Hons.) Camb. 1991; MRCPsych 1993; MPhil 1999 London. (Camb. Univ. & Lond. Hosp. Med. Coll.) Cons. (Psychiat. of Learning Disabil.) Camden & Islington Ment. Health Servs. NHS Trust Lond.; Hon. Sen. Lect. (Psychiat. of Learning Disabil.)Roy. Free & Univ. Coll. Med. Sch. Lond. Socs: MRCPsych.; Penrose Soc.; Eur. Assn. Ment. Health in Ment. retardation. Prev: Sen. Regist. (Psychiat. of Learning Disabil.) St. Geo.'s Lond.; Research Fell. (Psychiat. of Disabil.) St. Geo. Hosp. Med. Sch. Lond.; Regist. (Psychiat.) St. Bart. Hosp. Lond.

HALL, Irene Anne 93 Northumberland Road, Leamington Spa CV32 6HQ Tel: 01926 427962 Fax: 01926 427962; Warwick Hospital, Lakin Road, Warwick CV34 5BW Tel: 01926 495321 — MB BS 1981 Lond.; MRCS Eng. LRCP Lond. 1981; FRCA 1989; DA (UK) 1985. (Char. Cross) Cons. Anaesth. Warwick Hosp. Prev: Sen. Regist. NW RHA; Regist. (Anaesth.) Char. Cross Hosp. Lond. & Harefield Hosp. Middlx.; SHO (Anaesth.) E.bourne Dist. Gen. Hosp.

HALL, Ivan Ross Frederick Place Surgery, 11 Frederick Place, Weymouth DT4 8HQ Tel: 01305 774411 Fax: 01305 760417; 11 Frederick Place, Weymouth DT4 8HN Tel: 01305 774411 Fax: 01305 760417 — MB BS 1988 Lond.; MRCGP 1992; DRCOG 1991. (St. Mary's Hosp. Lond.)

HALL, Miss Jacqueline Mary St Albans & Hemel Hempstead NHS Trust, Hemel Hempstead General Hospital, Hillfield Road, Hemel Hempstead HP2 4AD; 15 Gladstone Rise, High Wycombe HP13 7NW — MB BS 1980 Lond.; MRCOG 1986; RCR/RCOG Adv. Training in Obst. Ultrasound 1997. (Char. Cross) Cons. (O & G) St Albans & Hemel Hempstead NHS Trust. Prev: Sen. Regist. John Radcliffe Hosp. Oxf. Region Fexible Train. Scheme.

HALL, Mr James 133 Walkley Crescent Road, Sheffield S6 5BA Email: jandjhall@msn.com; 75 Linaker Road, Sheffield S6 5DS — MB ChB 1990 Sheff.; FRCS (Eng.) 1994; FRCS Urol 1998. (Sheffield) Specialist Regist. (Urol.) N. Trent Rotat.

HALL, James Anthony Department of Cardiology, The James Cook University Hospital, Marton Road, Middlesbrough TS4 3BW Tel: 01642 854609 Fax: 01642 854190; Busby Grange, Great Busby, Stokesley, Middlesbrough TS9 7AS — MB BChir 1980 Camb.; MA, MD Camb. 1990; MRCP (UK) 1983; FRCP (UK) 1997. Cons. Cardiol. Regional Cardiothoracic Unit James Cook Univ. Prev: Sen. Regist. (Cardiol.) Papworth Hosp. Cambs.; Regist. (Cardiol.) St. Thos. Hosp. Lond.; MRC Train. Fell. Addenbrooke's Hosp. Camb.

HALL, James Denis (retired) c/o National Westminster Bank, Station Place, Letchworth SG6 — MRCS Eng. LRCP Lond. 1951; MFCM 1972; DPH Sheff. 1958. Hon. Cons. WHO Copenhagen. Prev: DMO, DCP & MOH N. Herts. & DMO Barnsley.

HALL, James Desmond Ivoen 19 Harberton Drive, Belfast BT9 6PF — MB BCh BAO 1959 Belf.; MB BCh Belf. 1959.

HALL, James Gerald 36 Malone Heights, Belfast BT9 5PG Tel: 01232 618238 — MB BCh BAO 1957 Belf.; DObst RCOG 1959; FFOM RCP Lond. 1989, M 1983; FFOM RCPI 1985, M 1980; DIH Eng. 1980. Socs: Fell. Ulster Med. Soc.; Soc. Occupat. Med.

HALL, James Stuart, CBE (retired) 27 Okebourne Park, Swindon SN3 6AH Tel: 01793 539015 — MB BS 1955 Lond.; MSc (Occupat. Med.) Lond. 1980; FFOM RCP 1989, MFOM 1981; DAvMed Eng. 1973; DIH Eng. 1967. Prev: Med. Off. RAF.

HALL, James William Stones Throw, Brake Lane, Hagley, Stourbridge DY8 2XW Tel: 01562 884448 — MB BS Durh. 1936; MD Durh. 1938; DPH 1940. (Durh.) Socs: BMA & Leicester Med. Soc. Prev: Res. Med. Off. Devonsh. Roy. Hosp. Buxton; Med. Off. Health Barrow-upon-Soar RDC; Ho. Surg. (Orthop.) Roy. Vict. Infirm. Newc. u. Tyne.

HALL, Jane Pearce The Lodge, Newton Road, Emberton, Olney MK46 5JJ Tel: 01234 241925 — BM BS 1976 Nottm.; BMedSci Nottm. 1973, BM BS 1976; FFA RCS Eng. 1981. Cons. Anaesth. Milton Keynes Dist. Gen. Hosp.

HALL, Janet Gravesend Medical Centre, No 1 New Swan Yard, Gravesend DA12 2EN Tel: 01474 534123 Fax: 01474 333629; 1 Woodlea, Longfield DA3 7HX Tel: 01474 705380 Fax: 0870 063 7266 Email: janydoc@doctors.org.uk — MB ChB 1968 Aberd.; FRCGP 1993, M 1983. (Aberdeen) Princip. GP. Socs: Anglo-French Med. Soc.; Dispensaire francais. Prev: Regist. (Community Med.) SE Thames RHA; Clin. Med. Off. Bexley & Greenwich AHA; Research Fell. (Path.) Univ. Aberd.

HALL, Janet Aileen 132 Mealough Road, Carryduff, Belfast BT8 8LT Tel: 01232 826648 — MB BCh BAO 1976 Belf.; MRCGP 1981.

HALL, Janet Elizabeth 335 Millhouses Lane, Ecclesall, Sheffield S11 9HY Tel: 0114 236 6455 — MB ChB 1991 Sheff.; MB ChB (Hons.) Sheff. 1991; BMedSci Sheff. 1989; MRCP (UK) 1994; MRCGP 1996; DRCOG 1996; DCH RCP Lond. 1995. (Sheff.) SHO (A & E) Sheff.; GP Locum. Prev: SHO (Paediat.) Sheff. & Rotherham; Trainee GP Sheff.; SHO Rotat. (Gen. Med.) Freeman Hosp. Newc. u. Tyne.

HALL, Janine Heath (retired) Hooppells Torr, Kingston, Kingsbridge TQ7 4HA Tel: 01548 810560 — MB ChB 1965 Birm.; FFR 1972; DMRD Eng. 1970. Cons. Radiol. Derriford Hosp. Plymouth. Prev: Cons. (Radiol.) SHAPE Hosp. Belgium.

HALL, Jeremy Francis Pudsey Health Centre, 18 Mulberry Street, Pudsey LS28 7XP — MB ChB 1979 Leeds; MRCGP 1983.

HALL, Joanne Sarah Standish Medical Practice, Rodenhurst, Church Street, Standish, Wigan WN6 0JP Tel: 01257 421909 Fax: 01257 424259; 4 Brandreth Drive, Parbold, Wigan WN8 7HB — MB ChB 1985 Sheff.; MRCGP 1989; DRCOG 1988.

HALL, John Cedar Lodge, 34 Eastgate, Hornsea HU18 1DP Tel: 01964 532212 — MB ChB 1970 St. And.; MRCGP 1976.

HALL, John Daniel West Suffolk Hospital, Hardwick Ln, Bury St Edmunds IP33 2QZ — MB BS 1987 Lond.; FRCA 1994. Cons. Anaes. W. Suff. Hosp., Bury St. Edmunds. Prev: Regist. (Anaesth.) Roy. Marsden Hosp., Roy. Brompton & St Mary's Hosps. Lond.; Sen. Regist. (Anaesth.) Hammersmith Hosp. Lond.

HALL, John David Stockport Road Medical Practice, 50 Stockport Road, Marple, Stockport SK6 6AB Tel: 0161 426 0299 Fax: 0161 427 8112 — MB ChB 1988 Manch.; DRCOG 1991. Socs: BMA.

HALL, Mr John Hanson Quarry House, Walcot Road, Ufford, Stamford PE9 3BP Tel: 01780 740620 Fax: 01780 740537 Email: jhhsurg@supanet.com — MB BS 1961 Lond.; FRCS Eng. 1967. (St. Mary's) Cons. Surg. P'boro. & Stamford Gp. Hosps. Socs: Assn. Surg.; BMA; BASO. Prev: Sen. Regist. (Surg.) St. Thos. Hosp. Lond.; Regist. (Surg.) Peace Memor. Hosp. Watford; Cas. Off. St. Geo. Hosp.

HALL, John Innes (retired) 8 Pit Lane, Hough, Crewe CW2 5JQ Tel: 01270 841611 — MB ChB 1960 Ed.; PhD Ed. 1964, MB ChB 1960; FRCP Lond. 1990; FRCP Ed. 1977, M 1963. Prev: Cons. Phys. Gen. Med. (Heart Dis.) Leighton Hosp. Crewe.

HALL, John Lomas The Surgery, Field Road, Stainforth, Doncaster DN7 5AF Tel: 01302 841202 — MB BS 1964 Durh.; DObst RCOG 1967. Trainer Gen. Pract. Doncaster Vocational Train. Scheme.

HALL, Rev. John MacNicol HM Prison, Winson Green Road, Birmingham B18 4AS Tel: 0121 554 3838 Fax: 0121 515 3507 — M. Th. Nottm. 1988; MSc Loughborough 1993; MA Camb. 1975, BA (Hons.) 1973; BSc Glas. 1965, MB ChB 1969; MRCGP 1975; MMJ Soc. Apoth. Lond. 1996; Dip Ven Liverp. 1979. (Glas.) Sen. Med. Off. HM Prison Birm. Socs: Brit. Soc. Mycopathol.; Brit. Soc. Study Sexually Transm. Dis.; Brit. Assn. Police Surg. Prev: Sen. Regist. (Genitourin. Med.) Gtr. Glas. HB; Ho. Phys. W.. Infirm. Glas.

HALL, John Michael (retired) Fairmile, 27 Shirley Hills Road, Addington, Croydon CR0 5HQ Tel: 020 8654 1759 — MB BS 1947 Lond.; MRCS Eng. LRCP Lond. 1947; FFA RCS Eng. 1954; DA Eng. 1952. Prev: Cons. Anaesth. Guy's Hosp. & Thoracic Units, S.E. Metrop. RHB.

HALL, John Robert The Technology Centre, 40, Occam Rd, Surrey Research Park, Guildford GU2 7YG Tel: 01483 845 533 Fax: 01483 845 534 Email: john@jha.demon.co.uk; The Red House, Chatter Alley, Dogmersfield, Hook RG27 8SS Tel: 01252 810009 Fax: 01252 810019 Email: john@jha.demon.co.uk — MB ChB 1971 Birm.; DIH 1982 Eng; Dobst RCOG 1973; FFPM 1994 RCP, UK; AFOM 1982 RCP, Lond. (Birm.) Vice-Pres Clin. Operat.s & Managing Dir., Europe, Covalent Gp. Ltd, Guildford, Surrey. Socs: Fell. Roy. Soc. Med.; Counc. Mem. Pharmaceut. Med. & Research Roy. Soc. Med. Prev: Chief. Exec. & Princip. Cons. Doctor John Hall & Assocs. Ltd. Pharmacet. & He; Med. Dir. Allen & Hanburys (Glaxo Pharmaceuts.) Stockley Pk.; Assoc. Med. Dir. & Med. Adviser Lilly Indust. Basingstoke.

HALL, John Robert William Frimley Park Hospital, Portsmouth Road, Frimley, Camberley GU16 7UJ — MB BS 1979 Lond.; MRCP (UK) 1986; FRCR 1989. Cons. Clin. Radiol. Frimley Pk. NHS Trust. Socs: Brit. Soc. Interven. Radiol.; Roy. Coll. Radiol.; Brit. Nuclear Med. Soc. Prev: Sen. Regist. (Radiol.) Leeds.

HALL, Jonathan Christopher 51 Clevely Park, Belfast BT8 6NB — MB BCh BAO 1995 Belf.

HALL, Jonathan Michael Enville House, Warren Road, Newbury RG14 6NH — BM BS 1994 Nottm.

HALL, Professor Joseph Gustave 14 Banstead Road S., Sutton SM2 5LF Tel: 020 8642 4912 Email: joe@joeanddianahall.fsnet.co.uk — MB BS Lond. 1957; PhD Austral. Nat. Univ. 1965; DSc Lond. 1979; MRCS Eng. LRCP Lond. 1957; FRCPath 1979, M 1970. (Roy. Free) Emerit. Prof. Immunol. Lond. Univ. Prev: Chairm. Sect. Tumour Immunol. Inst. Cancer Research Roy. Marsden Hosps.Sutton; Reader (Experim. Path.) Univ. Birm. Med. Sch. & Hon. Cons. Path. United Birm. Hosps.; Flight Lt. RNZAF Med. Br. Wellington, NZ.

HALL, Judith Elizabeth University Hospital Wales, Heath Park, Cardiff CF14 4XW Tel: 029 2074 7747 — MB ChB 1989 Liverp.; MA Newc. 1983; BA (II(i)) Newc. Univ. 1981; FRCA 1994. Sen.Lect. Anaesth.Cardiff. Prev: Cons.Anaesth.N Tees Gen.Hosp; Lect. (Anaesth.) Cardiff.

HALL, Judith Mary Bassetts, 33 Baldock Road, Letchworth SG6 3JX — MB BS 1958 Lond.; MRCS Eng. LRCP Lond. 1958; DObst RCOG 1960. (Roy. Free) Socs: Fell. Roy. Soc. Med.; BMA. Prev: GP Stevenage, Herts.

HALL, Judith Rattray Apperley Dene, Stocksfield NE43 7SB Tel: 01661 842580 — MB BS 1969 Newc.; FRCR 1983; DMRD Eng. 1982. (Newc.) Cons. Radiol. Qu. Eliz. Hosp. Gateshead.

HALL, Julian Andrew The Paddock, 210 Manor Lane, Halesowen B62 8RD — MB ChB 1998 Liverp.; MB ChB Liverp 1998.

HALL, Julie Lyn 11 Aspin Way, Knaresborough HG5 8HL — MB BS 1991 Lond. Resid. Med. Off. Austral.

HALL, Julie Marie Links View, 48 Fall Birch Road, Lostock, Bolton BL6 4LG — MB ChB 1993 Manch. SHO (Palliat. Med.) St. Anns Hospice Worsley. Prev: GP Regist. Tottington HC Bury.

HALL, Karen Elaine 17 Westlands, Bransgore, Christchurch BH23 8BY — MB BCh BAO 1995 Belf.; BMedSci Nottm. 1993. (Nottm.) SHO (A & E) Wycombe Gen. Hosp. Prev: Ho. Off. (Med.) Nottm. City Hosp.; Ho. Off. (Gen. Surg.) Lincoln Co. Hosp.

HALL, Kathryn Claire 3 Halterburn Close, Kingsmere, Gosforth, Newcastle upon Tyne NE3 4YT — MB ChB 1994 Ed.

HALL, Keith 71 Kenton Road, Gosforth, Newcastle upon Tyne NE3 4NJ — MB BS 1967 Lond.; MRCS Eng. LRCP Lond. 1967; FRCR 1975; FFR 1974; DMRD Eng. 1972. (Westm.) Cons. Neuroradiol. Dept. Neuroradiol. Regional Neurol. Centre Newc.; Gen. Hosp. Prev: Sen. Regist. (Neuroradiol.) Regional Neurol. Centre Newc. Gen. Hosp.; Sen. Regist. & Trainee Regist. (Radiol.) Roy. Vict. Infirm.; Tyne.

HALL, Kenneth Henry 8 Dovecote Close, Wistaston, Crewe CW2 6TW — MB ChB 1985 Manch.

HALL, Kevin George Queens Park Medical Centre, Farrer Street, Stockton-on-Tees TS18 2AW Tel: 01642 679681 Fax: 01642 677124 — MB ChB 1981 Aberd.; MRCGP 1985; DRCOG 1985; DCH RCPS Glas. 1984. GP Stockton-on-Tees.

HALL, Lesley Katherine 34 Chapel Street, Warwick CV34 4HL Tel: 01926 499087 — MB ChB Birm. 1969. Clin. Med. Off. Solihull Healthcare; GP Asst.

HALL, Lewis The Health Centre, Bailey Street, Old Basford, Nottingham NG6 0HD Tel: 0115 978 1231 Fax: 0115 979 0419; 70 Wollaton Vale, Wollaton, Nottingham NG8 2PB Tel: 0115 922 8013 — BM BS 1977 Nottm.; MMedSci Nottm. 1991.

HALL, Lisa Ann 10 College Close, Rowlands Castle PO9 6AJ Tel: 01708 413970 — MB ChB 1990 Manch.; MRCGP 1994; DRCOG 1993.

HALL, Louise Mary Ivy Cottage, 448 Manchester Road, Heaton Chapel, Stockport SK4 5DL — MB ChB 1995 Manch. GP/Regist. Stockport VTS.

HALL, Malcolm Hedley (retired) Cantok, Church Road, Spaxton, Bridgwater TA5 1BZ Tel: 01278 671533 — MRCS Eng. LRCP Lond. 1942. Prev: Cons. Emerg. Accid. Dept. Roy. Preston Hosp.

HALL, Marcia Rosalind Mmount Vernon Centre for Cancer Treatment, Rickmansworth Rd,, Northwood HA6 2RN Tel: 01923 844579 Fax: 01753 636211 Email: marcia.hall@medix-uk.com; Hall Place, Beaconsfield HP9 1NB Tel: 01494 672525 Fax: 01494 676710 — MB BS 1986 Lond.; PhD Lond. 1997; MRCP (UK) 1990. (Guy's Hosp.) p/t Cons. (Med. Oncol.) Mt. Vernon Centre for Cancer Treatm. Middlx.; Lead Clinician, The Parpet, E. Berks BrE. Screening Progr., King Edwd. V11 Hosp., Windsor. Socs: Fell. Roy. Soc. Med. Prev: Sen. Regist. (Med. Oncol.) Roy. Free Hosp. Lond; Monut Vernon Centre for cancer Treatm., Middx.; Clin. Research Fell. (Med. Oncol.) ICRF Lond.; Regist. (Med. Oncol.) St. Bart. & Homerton Hosp. Lond.

HALL, Margaret (retired) Dale View, Castle Bolton, Leyburn DL8 4EX — MB BS Lond. 1962; MRCS Eng. LRCP Lond. 1962; MFFP 1993. Sen. Clin. Med. Off. Family Plann. Prev: Staff Grade (Demat.) York Hosps.

HALL, Margaret Ann Dunelm Cottage, 48 Hill Rise, Chalfont St Peter, Gerrards Cross SL9 9BQ Tel: 01753 886807 — MB BS Lond. 1963; FRCP Lond. 1967; FRCPCH 1997. (King's Coll. Hosp.) Cons. Rheum. Wexham Pk. Hosp. Slough.; Hon. Cons. Paediat. Rheum. John Radcliffe Oxf.

HALL, Margaret Jean Boundaries Surgery, 17 Winchester Road, Four Marks, Alton GU34 5HG Tel: 01420 562153 Fax: 01420 564172 Email: boundaries-surgery@dial.pipex.com — BM BCh 1973 Oxf.; MA Camb. 1974; MRCGP 1977. (Oxford) Prev: Trainee GP Aberd. VTS; Ho. Phys. Radcliffe Infirm. Oxf.; Ho. Surg. P.ss Margt. Hosp. Swindon.

HALL, Margaret Lucy Amersham plc, The Grove Centre, White Lion Road, Amersham HP7 9LL Tel: 01494 543973 Fax: 01494 545158 Email: margaret.hall@amersham.com — MB ChB 1984 Leic.; MSc Nuclear Med. Lond. 1990; MRCP (UK) 1987; FRCP 1999. Dir., Med. & Dis. Strategy Amersham plc; Hon. Cons. Nuclear Med. S.ampton Gen. Hosp. Socs: Eur. Assn. Nuclear Med. & Soc. Nuclear Med. Prev: Cons. Phys. Nuclear Med. St. Peters Hosp. Chertsey; Sen. Regist. & Clin. Lect. (Nuclear Med.) Inst. Nuclear Med. Univ. Coll. & Middlx. Sch. Med. Lond.; SHO Rotat. (Med.) St. Peter's Hosp. Chertsey.

HALL, Margaret Stobo (retired) 19 Belgrave Crescent, Edinburgh EH4 3AJ — MB ChB Ed. 1954; DCH Eng. 1959.

HALL, Professor Marion Harvey Aberdeen Maternity Hospital, Cornhill Road, Aberdeen AB25 2ZD Tel: 01224 681818 Email: marion.hall@arh.grampian.scot.nhs.uk; 90 Blenheim Place, Aberdeen AB25 2DY — MB ChB 1963 Aberd.; MD Aberd. 1971; FRCOG 1982, M 1968; DObst 1965. (Aberd.) Cons. O & G Grampian Univ. Hosps. Trust. Socs: Eur. Assn. Obst. & Gyn. & Perinatal Club. Prev: Lect. (O & G) Aberd. Univ.; Regist. (O & G) Aberd. Gen. Hosp. Gp.; Research Regist. (Obst.) Aberd. Special Hosps.

HALL, Mark Charles Scott Clow Cottage, Aldbrough St John, Richmond DL11 7TL — MB BS 1994 Newc.

HALL, Mark Foxley Russell Sedgwick Noble Lowndes Occupational Health Ltd., Washford House, Playbrook Drive, Redditch B98 0DU Tel: 01527 517747; 14 Barston Lane, Solihull B91 2SS Tel: 0121 711 7357 Fax: 0121 704 0696 — MB BS 1984 Lond.; AFOM RCP Lond. 1994; DRCOG 1988. (Middx Hosp) Occupat. Phys. Sedgewick Noble Lowndes Occupat. Health Ltd. Socs: Soc. Occupat. Med.; Fell.Roy.Soc.Med. Prev: GP. (Rotat.) N.

Middlx. Hosp.; Ho. Surg. Chase Farm Hosp. Enfield; Ho. Phys. N. Middlx. Hosp.

HALL, Mark James Kildonan House, Ramsbottom Road, Horwich, Bolton BL6 5NW Tel: 01204 468161 Fax: 01204 698186 — MB ChB 1986 Manch.; DRCOG 1990.

HALL, Martin Graham The Surgery, 578 Stratford Road, Sparkhill, Birmingham B11 4AN Tel: 0121 772 0392; 89 Monastery Drive, Solihull B91 1DP Tel: 0121 764 4575 — MB ChB 1978 Birm.; MRCGP 1983. GP Birm.

HALL, Martin William (retired) Measham Medical Unit, High Street, Measham, Swadlincote DE12 7HR Tel: 01530 270667 Fax: 01530 271433 — MB ChB 1968 Birm.; DObst RCOG 1970. Prev: SHO (Obst.) New Birm. Matern. Hosp.

HALL, Matthew Keith 47 Eccles Road, London SW11 1LZ — MB BS 1988 Lond.

HALL, Michael Histopathology Department, St Peter's Hospital, Chertsey KT16 0PZ Tel: 01932 872000 Fax: 01932 875129; 13 Hacketts Lane, Pyrford, Woking GU22 8PP — MB BS Lond. 1970; MRCS Eng. LRCP Lond. 1970; FRCPath 1988, M 1976. (Char. Cross) Cons. Histopath. St. Peter's Hosp. Chertsey. Prev: Sen. Lect. (Histopath.) St. Geo. Hosp. Med. Sch. Lond.; Sen. Regist. (Histopath.) Hammersmith Hosp.; Regist. (Path.) Char. Cross Hosp.

HALL, Michael Anthony Princess Anne Hospital, Coxford Road, Southampton SO16 5YA Tel: 02380 796007 — MB ChB 1974 Aberd.; FRCP Lond. 1991; MRCP (UK) 1978; DCH Eng. 1978. Cons. Paediat. P.ss Anne Hosp. Soton. & Soton. Gen. Hosp.; Hon. Sen. Lect. (Child Health) Univ. Soton. Prev: Lect. (Child Health) Univ. Soton. & Univ. Aberd.; Chief Resid. (Neonat.) Mt. Sinai Hosp., Toronto.

HALL, Michael Drummond Campbeltown Health Centre, Stewart Road, Campbeltown PA28 6AT Tel: 01586 552105 Fax: 01586 554997; Rockbank, Low Askomel, Campbeltown PA28 6EP — MB ChB 1973 Glas.

HALL, Michael George Tel: 01746 710223; 9 Wolverhampton Road, Pattingham, Wolverhampton WV6 7AF Tel: 01902 700462 — MB ChB 1975 Birm.; BSc (Hons.) Birm. 1969. Prev: Regist. (Paediat.) Univ. Aberd.

HALL, Mr Michael Henry (retired) South Green Lodge, 10 South Green, Southwold IP18 6ET — BM BCh 1948 Oxf.; MA Oxf. 1958, BM BCh 1948; FRCS Eng. 1952. Prev: Cons. Urol. Forest Gp. Hosps.

HALL, Michael Jackman (retired) Moorhill, 14 Uppermoor, Pudsey LS28 7SG Tel: 0113 257 0051 — MB ChB Ed. 1956; DObst RCOG 1960.

HALL, Michael Joseph County Hospital, Hereford HR1 2ER Tel: 01432 364064 Fax: 01432 364410 Email: michael.hall@hh-tr.wmids.nhs.uk; 64 Hafod Road, Hereford HR1 1SQ Tel: 01432 279943 — MB BS (Hons. Path.) Lond. 1972; MSc (Distinc.) Lond. 1986, MD London 1988; FRCP Lond. 1993; MRCP (UK) 1975. (Middlx.) Cons. Phys. & Gastroenterol. Hereford Hosps. NHS Trust. Socs: Brit. Soc. Gastroenterol.; Brit. Assoc. Parenteral & Enteral Nutrit.; Midl. Gastroenterol. Soc. Prev: Lect. (Med.) Univ. Bristol; Regist. (Med. & Gastroenterol.) Glas. Roy. Infirm.; Ho. Phys. Middlx. Hosp.

HALL, Professor Michael Robert Pritchard Peartree Cottage, Emery Down, Lyndhurst SO43 7FH Tel: 01703 282541 — BM BCh 1952 Oxf.; MA Oxf. 1957; FRCP Ed. 1971, M 1957; FRCP Lond. 1970, M 1957. Emerit. Prof. Geriat. Med. Univ. Soton.; Cons. Emerit. Soton & S. W. Hants. HA. Socs: BMA & Brit. Geriat. Soc.; Fell. Roy. Soc. Med. Prev: Cons. Phys. Newc. Gen. Hosp.; Sen. Regist. & Regist. (Med.) Radcliffe Infirm. Oxf.

HALL, Michael Stephen University of Exeter Institute of General Practice, Postgraduate School, Barrack Road, Exeter EX1 5DW Tel: 01392 403018 Fax: 01392 432223; Rose Cottage, Drewsteignton, Exeter EX6 6PG Tel: 01647 231634 — MB BS 1961 Lond.; BSc Lond. 1957; FRCGP 1977; DObst RCOG 1963. (Lond. Hosp.) Sen. Lect. (Gen. Pract.) Sch. Univ. Exeter. Socs: Brit. Diabetic Assn. (Chairm. Bd. Trustees). Prev: Med. Dir. Exeter & Dist. Community NHS Trust; GP Sussex & Devon; Vis. Fell. Univ. Sussex Centre for Continuing Educat. Brighton.

HALL, Molly (retired) 37 Palace Road, Llandaff, Cardiff CF5 2AG Tel: 02920 567689 — MB ChB Birm. 1955; FRCP Lond. 1975, M 1957; DObst RCOG 1957. Prev: Cons. Phys. Caerphilly Dist. Miners Hosp.

HALL, Neil Andrew 6 Duncombe Bank, Ferryhill DL17 8BP — MB ChB 1994 Leic.

HALL, Neil Lewis The Surgery Askeli Gate, Kirkby - in - Furness LA17 7TE Tel: 01229 889247 — MB ChB 1989 Manch.; MRCGP 1993.

HALL, Nicola Anne Merle 66 Forres Road, Sheffield S10 1WE — MB ChB 1994 Sheff.

HALL, Nicola Catherine 14 Haig Court, Bradford St., Chelmsford CM2 0BH — MB ChB 1975 Sheff. Regist. (Anaesth.) Norf. & Norwich Hosp.

HALL, Nigel Frederick Southampton Eye Unit, Southampton General Hospital, Tremona Road, Southampton SO16 6YD — BM 1985 Soton.; FRCOphth 1992. Regist. (Ophth.) Glas. Prev: SHO (Ophth.) Soton. Eye Hosp. & Basingstoke Dist. Hosp.; SHO (Urol. & Cas.) Roy. Liverp. Hosp.

HALL, Nigel Roger Station Drive Surgery, Station Drive, Ludlow SY8 2AR Tel: 01584 872461 Fax: 01584 877971 — MB ChB 1968 Birm. (Birm.) Prev: Resid. Med. Off. P.ss Margt. Hosp. Childr. Perth, Austral.; Ho. Phys. City Gen. Hosp. Stoke-on-Trent; Ho. Surg. Co. & Gen. Hosps. Hereford.

HALL, Mr Nigel Ruthven Box 201, Addenbrookes Hospital, Hills Rd, Cambridge CB2 2QQ Tel: 01223 586701 Fax: 01223 216015 Email: nigel.hall@addenbrookes.nhs.uk; 40 Duxford Road, Whittlesford, Cambridge CB2 4ND Tel: 01223 835039 Email: nigelrhall@email.msn.com — BM BCh 1985 Oxf.; BA Oxf. 1982; FRCS (Gen.) 1997; DM Oxf. 1996. (Oxf.) Cons. Colorectal & Gen. Surg., Addenbrookes Hosp. Prev: Sen. Regist. (Surgic.) Gen. Infirm. Leeds; Fell. in Colon and Rectal Surg., Univ. of Minnesota.

HALL, Mr Per Nicholas c/o Department of Plastic Surgery, West Norwich Hospital, Bouthorpe Road, Norwich NR2 3TU Tel: 01603 286286; 14 Eaton Road, Norwich NR4 6PY Tel: 01603 504880 — MB BChir 1984 Camb.; BSc (Anat.) Lond. 1981; FRCS Ed. 1988; FRCS Eng. 1988; FRCS (Plast) 1995. Cons. Plastic Surg. Addenbrooke's Hosp. Camb. Socs: Brit. Assn. Clin. Anat.; Brit. Melanoma Gp.; Brit. Assn. Plastic Surg. Prev: Sen. Regist. (Plastic Surg.) W. Norwich Hosp.; Regist. (Plastic Surg.) W. Midl. Regional Plastic Surg. Unit & RHA; SHO (Plastic Surg.) & Research Regist. Qu. Vict. Hosp. E. Grinstead.

HALL, Peter, Wing Cdr. RAF Med. Br. (retired) Woodbourne Priory Hospital, 21 Woodbourne Road, Edgbaston, Birmingham B17 8BY Tel: 0121 434 4343 Fax: 0121 434 3270 — MB ChB 1955 Birm.; PhD Sheff. 1962; FRCPsych 1973, M 1971; DPM Eng. 1959. Hon. Sen. Clin. Lect. Univ. Birm.; Hon. Vis. Research Fell. (Clin. Neurophysiol.) Univ. Aston. Prev: Med. Dir. Woodbourne Priory Hosp.

***HALL, Peter Andrew** Anaesth. Department, York District Hospital, Withington Road, York YO3 — MB BS 1986 Lond.; FRCA 1992.

HALL, Professor Peter Anthony Department of Molecular & Cellular Pathology, Ninewells Hospital & Medical School, University of Dundee, Dundee DD1 9SY Tel: 01382 632169 Fax: 01382 566933 Email: p.a.hall@dundee.ac.uk — MB BS 1982 Lond.; MB BS (Hons.) Lond. 1982; PhD Lond. 1993; BSc (Hons.) Lond. 1979, MD 1988; MRCPath 1990. (St. Bart.) Prof. Path. & Hon. Cons. Ninewells Hosp. & Med. Sch. Dundee. Socs: Path. Soc.; (Exec. Comm.) Brit. Assn. for Cancer Research. Prev: Prof. Histopath. & Hon. Cons. UMDS St. Thos. Campus; Sen. Lect. & Hon. Cons. Roy. Postgrad. Med. Sch. Hammersmith Hosp. Lond.; Research Fell. Histopath. Unit ICR Fund Lond.

HALL, Peter James 91H Wellhouse Lane, Mirfield WF14 0NS; Rookfield, 8 Huddersfield Road, Mirfield WF14 9HE — MB ChB 1993 Leeds; FRCA 2000; DA 1995.

HALL, Peter John 3 Newlyn Drive, Sale M33 3LF — MRCS Eng. LRCP Lond. 1971; FFA RCS Eng. 1976.

HALL, Peter Lawrence Pasque Hospice, Great Bramingham Lane, Luton LU3 3NT Tel: 01582 492339 Email: pasque@pasque.org; 91 Harlech Road, Abbots Langley, Watford WO5 0BE Email: phall@qn.apc.org — MB BS 1970 Lond.; MRCPI 1989; DGM RCP Lond. 1992. (St. Thos.) p/t Doctor Physical Health Care Needs (Learning Disabil.) Herts. Partnership Trust; Assoc. Specialist (Gastroentrol.) Herts. NHS Hosp. Trust; Med. Off. Palliat. Care, Pasque Hospice. Socs: Roy. Soc. Med.; BMA; Phys.s For Human Rights .uk. (Chairm.). Prev: Med. Regist., Watford Gen. Hosp. 73-77.

HALL, Petrina Renalda Honeysuckle Cottage, Colestocks, Honiton EX14 3JR — MB BCh BAO 1972 Dub.; BA Dub. 1970, MB BCh BAO 1972; MFFP 1993. (Trinity College Dublin) SCMO (Family Plann.) Margt. Jackson Ho. Exeter.

HALL, Philip Andrew Tel: 01823 259394; 1 Manor Farm, Chard, Somerset, Chard TA20 2EB Tel: 01460 61609 Email: hallpalg@yahoo.co.uk — MB ChB 1973 Bristol; MRCGP 1981; DRCOG 1977. Med. Off. Palliat. Care In-Pat. Unit, Taunton. Socs: BMA; Assoc. Palliat. Med.; Christ. Med. Fell.sh. Prev: Trainee GP Taunton VTS; Ho. Off. Bristol Roy. Infirm. & St. Martin's Bath; SHO (Med. & Geriat.) W.on-super-Mare.

HALL, Philippa Jane Inglis Green Close Surgery, Green Close, Kirkby Lonsdale, Carnforth LA6 2BS Tel: 015242 71210 Fax: 015242 72713; Lime Craggs, High Casterton, Kirkby Lonsdale, Carnforth LA6 2SF Tel: 01468 71429 — MB ChB 1981 Manch.; MRCGP 1986. GP Kirkby Lonsdale.

HALL, Rachel Louise 32 Kingsway, Eastleigh SO53 1EN — MB BS 1993 Lond.

HALL, Rachel Margaret Royal Berkshire & Battle NHS Trust, London Road, Reading RG1 5AN Tel: 0118 987 5111 Fax: 01734 987 7067; 32 Redlands Road, Reading RG1 5HD Tel: 0118 9867 855 — MB BS 1970 Lond.; MRCS Eng. LRCP Lond. 1970; FFA RCS Eng. (Prize) 1974. (Lond. Hosp.) Cons. Anaesth. Roy. Berks. & Battle Hosps. Reading. Prev: Sen. Regist. (Anaesth.) Middlx. Hosp.; SHO (Anaesth.) Lond. Hosp.; Sen. Resid. Med. Off. P.ss Alexandra Hosp. Brisbane, Austral.

HALL, Ralph David Burley Park Medical Centre, 273 Burley Road, Leeds LS4 2EL Tel: 0113 230 4111; The Old Forge, 78 Main St, Thorner, Leeds LS14 3BU Tel: 0113 289 2173 — MB ChB Leeds 1959; DPH Leeds 1965. (Leeds) Socs: BMA. Prev: Capt. RAMC; Asst. MoH City Leeds & W. Riding CC.

HALL, Rebecca Jane Peniston Royal Infirmary, Edinburgh EH3 9HB; 62 Montrose Terrace, Edinburgh EH7 5DP Tel: 0131 661 6689 Email: rebeccajphall@compuserve.com — MB ChB 1994 Ed.; BA Camb. 1991; DRCOG 1996; DFFP 1996; DTM & H 1997. (Cambridge and Edinburgh) SHO (GUM). Socs: Med. Wom. Federat. Prev: SHO (A & E & Orthop. Surg.); SHO (A & E) Edin. Roy. Infirm.; Med. Off. St. Francis Hosp. Katete, Zambia.

HALL, Rebecca Jayne Coppice Gate Farm, Tanners Hill, Bewdley DY12 2LP Tel: 01299 400614 — MB BS 1996 Lond. SHO (O & G) Ronkswood Hosp. Worcester. Prev: Ho. Off. (Med.) Alexandra Hosp. Redditch; Ho. Off. (Gen. Surg.) Kidderminster Gen. Hosp.; SHO (A & E) Kidderminster Gen. Hosp.

HALL, Reginald 2 Notting Hill, Malone Road, Belfast BT9 5NS Tel: 01232 666353 — MD 1940 Belf.; MD (Gold Medal) Belf. 1940, MB BCh BAO (Hnrs.) 1936; FRCP 1943, M 1940. (Qu. Univ. Belf.) Barrister-at-Law Hon. Soc. King's Inns, Dub.; Robt. R. Leathem Trav. Schol.; Dermatol. Roy. Vict. Hosp. Belf., Belf. City Hosp. & Ulster Hosp.; Dundonald; Fell. St. John's Hosp. Dermat. Soc. Socs: Brit. Assn. Dermat. Prev: Asst. in Med. Qu. Univ. Belf.; Ho. Phys. & Ho. Surg. Roy. Vict. Hosp. Belf.

HALL, Professor Reginald Ross Northern Cancer Network, Derwent Court, Freeman Hosp, Newcastle upon Tyne NE7 7DN Tel: 0191 223 1313; 77 Moorside North, Newcastle upon Tyne NE4 9DU — MRCS Eng. LRCP Lond. 1962; MS Lond. 1976, MB BS 1962; FRCS Eng. 1967. (Univ. Coll. Hosp.) Dir. N.ern Cancer Network; Vis. Prof. Univ. Newc. (1997). Socs: Brit. Assn. Urol. Surgs.; Eur. Org. Research & Treatm. Cancer; Genitourin. Gp. Prev: Cons. Urol. Newc.; Sen. Lect. Urological Surg., Newc. Univ.

HALL, Richard New Medical Centre, Crossley Street, Wetherby LS22 6RT Tel: 01937 543200 Fax: 01937 588689 Email: richard.hall@gp-b86033.nhs.uk; Tel: 01937 590408 — MB ChB 1985 Leeds; MRCGP 1989. GP Trainer; M.O. Leeds United Football Acad. Socs: BMA & Med. Protec. Soc.

HALL, Richard George Palmer (retired) 31 Crooksbarn Lane, Norton, Stockton-on-Tees TS20 1LR Tel: 01642 53210 — MB ChB 1961 Birm.; MPhil Leeds 1991; MRCP Lond. 1969. Prev: Clin. Asst. (Gastroenterol.) N. Tees Hosp.

HALL, Richard Gordon (retired) 46 Bank Fold, Barrowford, Nelson BB9 6JW Tel: 01282 692018 — MRCS Eng. LRCP Lond. 1945.

HALL, Mr Richard Iain Department of Surgery, Derby City General Hospital, Uttoxeter Road, Derby DE22 3NE Tel: 01332 625500 Fax: 01332 625696; Port Farm, Duck St, Egginton, Derby DE65 6HG Tel: 01283 733847 — MB BS 1976 (1st cl. Hons.) Newc.; MD Newc. 1985; FRCS Eng. 1980. Cons. Surg. Derby City Gen. Hosp. Socs: Brit. Soc. Gastroenterol. & Mem. Assn. Surgs.; Pancreatic Soc. of GB and N. Irel. Prev: Sen. Lect. (Surg.) St. Jas. Univ. Hosp. Leeds; 1st Asst. (Surg.) Newc. Univ.

HALL, Richard James 23 Blandy Road, Henley-on-Thames RG9 1QB; 29 Makins Road, Henley-on-Thames RG9 1PU — MB BS 1989 Lond. (St. George's Hospital Medical School)

HALL, Richard Scott (Surgery) 49-51 Leeds Road, Harrogate HG2 8AY — MB BS 1985 Lond.; MA Oxf. 1984; MRCGP 1990; DCH RCP Lond. 1990; Cert. Family Plann. JCC 1989; DRCOG 1987. GP Trainer. Prev: Trainee GP Harrogate VTS; SHO (Psychiat.) Clifton Hosp. York; SHO (Palliat. Med.) Wheatfields Hosp. Leeds.

HALL, Richard Stephen Group Practice Surgery, Middle Chare, Chester-le-Street DH3 3QD Tel: 0191 388 4857 Fax: 0191 388 7448; 34 Brackenbeds Close, Pelton, Chester-le-Street DH2 1XH Tel: 0191 370 1507 Fax: 0191 370 3121 Email: halldrrs@aol.com — MB ChB 1989 Manch. Prev: Trainee GP N.enden Gp. Pract.; Trainee GP Wigan VTS.

HALL, Richard William Corney Place Medical Group, The Health Centre, Bridge Lane, Penrith CA11 8HW Tel: 01768 245226 Fax: 01768 245229 — BM BCh 1984 Oxf.; MA Camb. 1985; MRCGP 1988; DRCOG 1988; DCH RCP Lond. 1987.

HALL, Mr Robert 79 Stockton Lane, York YO31 1JA Tel: 01904 423014 — MB BS 1961 Lond.; BSc Anat. (Hons.) Lond. 1958, MB BS 1961; FRCS Eng. 1966. (Middlx.) Cons. Gen. Surg. York Hosps.; Hon. Lect. (Surg.) Univ. Leeds; Assoc. Prof. Surg. Univ. Grenada Sch. Med. Socs: Vasc. Surg. Soc. GB & Irel.; (Pres.) 1921 Sug. Trav. Club of GB; (Pres.) York Med. Soc. Prev: Sen. Regist. (Surg.) Leeds RHB; Resid. Surg. Off. Cheltenham Gen. Hosp.

HALL, Robert Michael Stowmarket Health Centre, Violet Hill Road, Stowmarket IP14 1NL Tel: 01449 776000 Fax: 01449 776005; Hillcrest, Silver St, Old Newton, Stowmarket IP14 4HF Tel: 01449 673157 — MB ChB 1970 Manch.; MRCGP 1974; DObst RCOG 1972. (Manch.) Prev: Trainee GP Ipswich VTS; Ho. Surg. Univ. Hosp. S. Manch.

HALL, Robert William (retired) Chevins, The Green, Sarratt, Rickmansworth WD3 6BH Tel: 01923 268748 — MB BChir Camb. 1953; FFA RCS Eng. 1967; DA Eng. 1957. Cons. Anaesth. Harefield Hosp. Prev: Sen. Regist. (Anaesth.) Nat. Heart Hosp. & Univ. Coll. Hosp. Lond.

HALL, Robin Wakelin (retired) Eyles Cottage, Church St., St Mary Bourne, Andover SP11 6BL Tel: 01264 738387 — MB ChB Ed. 1952. Prev: SHO (O & G) & Cas. Off. St. Mary's Hosp. Newport, I. of Wight.

HALL, Mr Roger David (retired) Willow Hill, Stourport Road, Holt Heath, Worcester WR6 6TA — MB BS Durh. 1960; FRCS Eng. 1967; FRCOphth 1988; DO Eng. 1963. Prev: Sen. Regist. St. Paul's Eye Hosp. Liverp.

HALL, Professor Roger John Colchester Hammersmith Hospital, Du Cane Road, London W12 0NN Tel: 020 8383 3141 Fax: 020 8740 8373 Email: roghall@compuserve.com; Flat 14, 10-12 North Mews, London WC1N 2JN Tel: 020 7242 1109 Fax: 020 7242 1147 — MB BChir Camb. 1969; BA Camb. 1966, MD 1979; FRCP Lond. 1983; MRCP (UK) 1971. (St. Thos.) Socs: (Counc.) Brit. Cardiac Soc. Prev: Cons. Cardiol. Univ. Hosp. Wales Cardiff; Cons. Cardiol. Roy. Vict. Infirm. & Freeman Hosp. Newc.; Sen. Regist. (Cardiac) Brompton Hosp. Lond.

HALL, Rosamond Maria Kennington Health Centre, 200 Kennington Road, Kennington, Oxford OX1 5PY Tel: 01865 730911 Fax: 01865 327759; 56 Appleton Road, Cumnor, Oxford OX2 9QH Tel: 01865 863186 — BM 1984 Soton.; MRCGP 1988; DRCOG 1987. Prev: Asst. GP Titchfield & Oxf.

HALL, Rosemary Ann 11 Southdown Avenue, Lewes BN7 1EL Tel: 01273 476097 — MB BS 1967 Lond.; MRCS Eng. LRCP Lond. 1967; DObst RCOG 1969; DCH Eng. 1969. (Guy's) Hosp. Pract. (Endocrinol.) Roy. Sussex Co. Hosp. Socs: Brighton & Sussex M-C Soc.; Scientif. Serv. Brit. Diabetic Assn.; Counc. Mem. Med. Wom.'s Federat. Prev: Ho. Surg. Guy's Hosp Lond.; Ho. Surg. (O & G) Brighton Gen. Hosp.; Ho. Phys. (Paediat.) Roy. Alexandra Hosp. Brighton.

HALL, Rosemary Janet C/o Bradford Royal Infirmary, Duchworth lane, Bradford BD9 6RJ Tel: 0113 274 5468 — MB ChB 1980 Ed.; FRCOphth 1991; FRCS Ed. (Ophth.) 1985; Ed. p/t Clin. Asst.

(Ophth.) Bradford Roy. Infirm. Prev: Regist. (Ophth.) P.ss Alexandra Eye Pavil. Edin.

HALL, Russell Douglas The Surgery, 15 Almswall Road, Kilwinning KA13 6BL — MB ChB 1986 Glas.; MRCGP 1990; DFFP 1993; DCH RCP Lond. 1990; Cert. Family Plann. JCC 1988; DRCOG 1988. Prev: Ho. Off. (Surg.) W.ern Infirm., Glas.; Ho. Off. (Med.) Roy. Infirm., Glas.

HALL, Ruth National Assembly for Wales, Cathays Park, Cardiff CF10 3NQ Tel: 029 2082 3911 — MB BS Lond. 1970; MRCS Eng. LRCP Lond. 1970; FFPHM RCP (UK) 1994, M 1989; DCH Eng. 1973. (King's Coll. Hosp.) Chief Med. Off.Nat. Assembly for Wales. Prev: Dir. Pub. Health Clwyd.

HALL, Ruth Sian 7 Claughton Green, Birkenhead CH43 1YA — BM BCh 1992 Oxf.

HALL, Sally Ann Top Floor Flat, 28 Ennismore Avenue, London W4 1SF — MB BS 1996 Lond.

HALL, Sally Caroline Mary 6 Redcastke Road, Thetford IP24 3NF — MB ChB 1997 Birm.

HALL, Sally Elizabeth Compton Health Centre, High Street, Shaw, Oldham OL2 8ST Tel: 01706 842511 Fax: 01706 847106; 24 Oaklands Park, Grasscroft, Oldham OL4 4JY — MB ChB 1980 Manch.; MRCGP 1984; DRCOG 1982. (Manch.)

HALL, Mr Samuel James Craigavon Area Hospital, Lurgan Road, Craigavon BT63 5QQ Tel: 01762 334444; Trumra Villa, 19 Lisburn Road, Moira, Craigavon BT67 0JR Tel: 02892 619027 Fax: 02892 619027 Email: samhall41@hotmail.com — MB BCh BAO 1977 Belf.; FRCSI 1982. Cons. Otolaryngol. Craigavon Area Hosp. N. Irel. Prev: Resid. & Research Fell. Univ. Washington Seattle, USA.

HALL, Sara Jane Millstone, St Peter's Vale, Stamford PE9 2QT — MB ChB 1988 Leic.

HALL, Sara Louise 23 Blandy Road, Henley-on-Thames RG9 1QB — BM 1994 Soton.

HALL, Sharon Elizabeth 119 Farnaby Road, Bromley BR1 4BN — MB BS 1991 Lond.

HALL, Shaun William David (retired) Clover Cottage, Boughmore Lane, Sidmouth EX10 8SJ Tel: 01395 512380 — MA Dub. 1966, MB BCh BAO 1954; DObst RCOG 1960. Prev: Ho. Surg. Roy. Bucks. Hosp. Aylesbury.

HALL, Shirrin William The Old Stables, 9 Parkfields, Arden Drive, Dorridge, Solihull B93 8LL — MB ChB 1971 Sheff.; MRCOG 1977; FRCOG 1994. Cons. Obst. Gyn. Birm. Heartlands & Solihull NHS Trust.

HALL, Simon Anthony Links View, 48 Fall Birch Road, Lostock, Bolton BL6 4LG — MB ChB 1993 Manch.

HALL, Simon Jay The Rock Surgery, 50 High Street, Frodsham, Warrington WA6 7HG Tel: 01928 732110 Fax: 01928 739273 — MB ChB 1992 Manch.

HALL, Simon Kieran, Capt. RAMC Moresdale Lane Surgery, 95 Moresdale Lane, Leeds LS14 6GG Tel: 0113 295 1200 Fax: 0113 295 1210 — MB ChB 1990 Leeds; MRCGP 1994; DRCOG 1993; DEEP 1993. Army GP.

HALL, Sonia Rohini Haematology Department, Ipswich Hospital, Heath Road, Ipswich IP4 5PD Tel: 01473 712233; 27 Hasketon Road, Woodbridge IP12 4LD Tel: 01394 382937 — MB BChir 1957 Camb. (Lond. Hosp.) Clin. Asst. (Haemat.) Ipswich Hosp. Prev: Regist. Chest Unit Lond. Hosp.; Ho. Phys. Hosp. Sick Childr. Gt. Ormond St.; Regist. (Med.) S. Lond. Hosp.

HALL, Stephen 255 Maldon Road, Colchester CO3 3BQ — MB BS 1980 Lond.; MRCGP 1986.

HALL, Stephen Addison Grosvenor Medical Centre, 23 Upper Grosvenor Road, Tunbridge Wells TN1 2DX Tel: 01892 544777 Fax: 01892 511157; Whitehouse Cottage, Saxonbury Lane, Eridge, Tunbridge Wells TN3 9HX — MB BS 1973 Lond.; BSc (Pharmacol. & Therap.) Lond. 1970; MRCGP 1978; DRCOG 1978. Socs: Brit. Soc. Colpos. & Cerv. Path. Prev: Trainee GP Exeter VTS.

HALL, Stephen John Silksworth Health Centre, Silksworth, Sunderland SR3 2AN Tel: 0191 521 0252 — MB BS 1986 Newc. GP New Silksworth Health Centre Sunderalnd. Prev: SHO (O & G) Sunderland Dist. Gen. Hosp.; SHO (Geriat.) Sunderland Dist. Gen. Hosp.; Trainee GP Stafford VTS.

HALL, Stephen Leslie Marton Medical Centre, 1 Glastonbury Avenue, Blackpool FY1 6SF Tel: 01253 761321 Fax: 01253 792701 — MB ChB 1974 Manch.; BSc (Hons. Physiol.) Manch. 1971; MRCGP 1980; DCH Eng. 1978. GP Blackpool. Prev: SHO (Paediat.) Booth Hall Childr. Hosp. Manch.; Ho. Phys. Manch. Roy. Infirm.; SHO (Gen. Med.) Hope Hosp. Salford.

HALL, Steven Washington Burlington Road Surgery, 14 Burlington Road, Ipswich IP1 2EU Tel: 01473 211661 Fax: 01473 289187 — MB BS 1988 Lond.; T(GP) 1992.

HALL, Susan Marianne Department Paediatrics, Sheffield Children's Hospital, Sheffield S10 2TH Tel: 0114 271 7344 Fax: 0114 275 5364; Storrs House Farm, Storrs Lane, Sheffield S6 6GY Tel: 0114 285 3177 Fax: 0114 285 4054 Email: s.hall@sheffield.ac.uk — MB BS 1970; MB BS Lond. 1970; MSc (Soc. Med.) Lond. 1980; FRCP 1994; MRCS Eng. LRCP Lond. 1970; FFPHM 1988, M 1982; FRCPCH 1997. (King's Coll. Hosp.) Hon. Lect. (Paediat.) Univ. Sheff. Prev: Cons. Epidemiol. Communicable Dis. Surveillance Centre Colindale; Hon. Sen. Lect. (Epidemiol.) Inst. Child Health Lond.; Sen. Med. Off. Baragwanath Hosp., Johannesburg.

HALL, Thomas Flat 19, 5 Elm Park Gardens, Chelsea, London SW10 9QQ — MB BChir 1952 Camb.; MA Camb. 1952; MRCS Eng. LRCP Lond. 1952; FFPHM 1989; MFOM RCP Lond. 1978; FFCM 1982, M 1972; DIH Eng. 1967; DPH Lond. 1958. (Camb. & Westm.) Socs: Harv. Soc. & BMA. Prev: Head Med. Serv. ILEA; Med. Adviser GLC; Dep. MOH & Dep. Princip. Sch. Med. Off. Portsmouth.

HALL, Thomas Malcolm 32 Norfolk Road, Lytham St Annes FY8 4JG Tel: 01253 735712 Fax: 01253 795744 — MB ChB 1957 Leeds. (Leeds) Dir. Lancs. Lakeland Cancer Foundat. c/o Roy. Preston Hosp. Fulwood. Socs: Preston Medico Ethical Soc.; (Ex-Chairm.) Lytham Med. Soc.; Manch. Med. Soc. Prev: Clin. Asst. (ENT) Blackpool & Fylde Gp. Hosps.

HALL, Timothy John 138 Main Road, Wilford, Nottingham NG11 7AA — MB ChB 1991 Leeds; BChD Leeds 1981, MB ChB 1991; FDS RCPS Glas. 1987.

HALL, Timothy Noel 20 Huntly Street, Aberdeen AB10 1SH — MB ChB 1992 Aberd.; MRCP 1999. Path. Dept., Grampian Univ. Hosp. Prev: Emerg. Med. RMO Roy. Perth Hosp. W. Australia; Emerg. Med. Reg. Fremantle Hosp. W. Australia.

HALL, Toby Beresford 56 Nightingale Lane, London SW12 8NY Tel: 020 8673 8225 Email: tbh@gtobelnet.co.uk — MB BS 1990 Lond.; MRCP (UK) 1994; FRCR 1998. (Roy. Free Hosp. Sch. Med.) Regist. (Radiol.) St. Geo. Hosp. Lond. Socs: BMA & Med. Defence Union. Prev: Regist. (Med.) Chellenham Centr. Hosp. Glos.; Regist. (Med.) Freemantle Hosp., W. Austral.

HALL, Tony 5 Manland Avenue, Harpenden AL5 4RE Tel: 01582 712364 Fax: 01582 468091 Email: marva@cpoauk.com — MB BS 1958 Lond.; FRCP Lond. 1995; FRCP Ed. 1985, M 1962; FACP 1971. (Univ. Coll. Hosp.) Prev: Civil. Cons. Phys. MoD for Gulf War Veterans; Cons. Phys. Hosp. Trop. Dis. Lond.; Dir. Clin. Malaria Research Seato, Bangkok, Thailand.

HALL, Trevor Duke Forest House Surgery, 25 Leicester Road, Shepshed, Loughborough LE12 9DF Tel: 01509 508412; Brookfield House, 35A Garendon Road, Shepshed, Loughborough LE12 9NU Tel: 01509650663 Fax: 01509 502229 — MB ChB 1984 Leic.; MB ChB Leic. l984; MRCGP 1988; DRCOG 1986. (Leicester) Prev: SHO (Dermat.) & Ho. Off. Leicester Roy. Infirm.; SHO (A & E) Leic. Roy. Infirm.

HALL, Trevor John Oaklyn, 82 Bois Lane, Chesham Bois, Amersham HP6 6BZ Tel: 01494 433402 — MB BS Lond. 1957; MRCS Eng. LRCP Lond. 1957; DObst RCOG 1960. (St. Mary's) Locum work. Prev: Regist. (Gen. Med.) Amersham & High Wycombe Hosp. Gp.; SHO (Paediat.) Harold Wood Hosp.; Ho. Surg. (Gyn. & Obst.) Amersham Gen. Hosp.

HALL, Valerie Ann Prospect House Medical Group, Prospect House, Prospect Place, Newcastle upon Tyne NE4 6QD Tel: 0191 273 4201 Fax: 0191 273 0129; 77 Moorside N., Newcastle upon Tyne NE4 9DU — MB BS 1965 Lond.; MRCS Eng. LRCP Lond. 1965. (Univ. Coll. Hosp.) Prev: Med. Off. Community Health Newc. & Gateshead AHAs; Med. Off. Family Plann. Assn.; Ho. Surg. Surgic. Unit Univ. Coll. Hosp. Lond.

HALL, Mr Vincent 3 Edinburgh Close, Sale M33 4EZ Tel: 0161 905 1400 — MB ChB 1987 Manch.; BSc (Hons. Path.) Manch. 1985, MB ChB 1987; FRCS Ed. 1991; MRCOG 1993.

HALL, Virginia Louise Claramond House, 10 Clifton Road, Winchester SO22 5BP — MB BS 1968 Lond.; FRCR 1976; DMRT Eng. 1972. Cons. (Radiother. & Oncol.) Wessex Radiother. Centre Soton.

HALL, Wendy Lucy Walton and Partners, West Street Surgery, 12 West Street, Chipping Norton OX7 5AA Tel: 01608 642529 Fax: 01608 645066; 19 Litchfield Close, Enstone, Chipping Norton OX7 4LB Email: wendyhall@pgecc-horton.demon.co.uk — MB ChB 1992 Leic.; DRCOG 1997; DCH RCP Lond. 1996; DFFP 1998; MRCGP 1998. (Leicester) GP Princip. W. St. Surg. Chipping Norton, Oxon. Socs: BMA; RCGP. Prev: SHO (Dermat.) Ch.ill Hosp. Oxf.; SHO (A & E) Horton Gen. Hosp. Banbury; SHO (O & G) Horton Gen. Hosp.

HALL, William Gibson Court Medical Centre, Gibson Court, Boldon Colliery NE35 9AN Tel: 0191 519 0077 Fax: 0191 537 3559; 13 Station Road, East Boldon NE36 0LD Tel: 0191 519 3292 Fax: 0191 537 3559 — MB BS Durh. 1966; MRCGP 1974; DObst RCOG 1968. (Newc.)

HALL, William Barclay Bridge Street Medical Practice, 20 Bridge St., Loughborough LE11 1NQ Tel: 01509 263018 Fax: 01509 211427; Weavers Cottage, Main St, Long Whatton, Loughborough LE12 5DG Tel: 01509 842366 — MB ChB 1962 Glas. (Glas.) Prev: Ho. Off. Surg. & Med. S.. Gen. Hosp. Glas.

HALL, William David Brambles, 11 Southdown Avenue, Lewes BN7 1EL — MB ChB 1996 Birm.; ChB Birm. 1996; MBCHB Birm. 1996.

HALL, William John 86 Bootham Park Court, Wiggington Road, York YO31 8JT — MB ChB 1987 Leeds.

HALL, William Sidney (retired) 18 Stanley Park, Townsend Crescent, Kirkcaldy KY1 1DP Tel: 01592 264780 — LRCP LRCS 1947 Ed.; LRCP LRCS Ed. LRFPS Glas. 1947; DA Eng. 1954.

HALL, William Walton Townhead Surgeries, Settle BD24 9JA Tel: 01729 822611 Fax: 01729 892916 — MB ChB 1975 Birm.; MSc Gen. Pract. Lond. 1991; LMCC Canada 1979; MRCGP 1980; FRCGP 1998.

HALL, Zaida Mary East Lane, Ovington, Alresford SO24 0RA Tel: 0196 273 2515 — BM BCh 1948 Oxf.; MA Oxf. 1948, DM 1955; FRCP Lond. 1984; MRCP (UK) 1952; FRCPsych 1983, M 1971; DPM Eng. 1967; DCH Eng. 1951. (Oxf. & St. Geo.) Hon. Research Fell. Univ. Dept. Psychiat. & Hon. Cons. Psychother. Roy. S. Hants. Hosp.; Cons. Psycother. Marchwood Priory Hosp. Soton. Prev: Cons. Psychiat. & Psychother. Soton. Univ. & Roy. S. Hants. Hosp. Soton.

HALL-CRAGGS, Margaret Anne MR Unit, Department of Imaging, The Middlesex Hospital, Mortimer St., London W1T 3AA Tel: 020 7380 9067 Fax: 020 7323 6772; 134 Court Lane, London SE21 7EB — MB BS 1979 Lond.; BA Camb. 1976; MD Lond. 1993; MRCP (UK) 1981; FRCR 1987. (Univ. Coll. Hosp.) Cons. Radiol. Middlx. Hosp. Lond.

HALL-DAVIES, Geoffrey, CBE (retired) Park House, 463 Birmingham Road, Bordesley, Redditch B97 6RL — MB ChB Birm. 1956; FFA RCS Eng. 1967. Prev: Cons. Anaesth. United Birm. Hosps. & Birm. RHB.

HALL-JONES, Anthony Hugh The New Surgery, 106 High Street, Tring HP23 4AF Tel: 01442 890661; 2 Deer Park Walk, Lye Green, Chesham HP5 3LJ — MB ChB 1981 Birm.; MRCP (UK) 1984; MRCGP 1986; DRCOG 1985. Prev: Trainee GP Birm. VTS; SHO (Gen. Med.) Dudley Rd. Hosp. Birm.; Ho. Phys. Qu. Eliz. Hosp. Birm.

HALL-MATTHEWS, Patricia Noreen 42 Park Road E., Wolverhampton WV1 4QA — MB BS 1964 Lond.; MRCS Eng. LRCP Lond. 1964. (Guy's) Clin. Asst. Compton Hall Hospice Wolverhampton. Prev: Regist. St. Michael's Hospice Hereford; Clin. Asst. (A & E) Hereford Gen. Hosp.

HALL-SMITH, Alexander Michael (retired) The Limes Farm House, Elm, Wisbech PE14 0BQ Tel: 01945 587123 Email: am.hs@virgin.net — MB Camb. 1958, BChir 1957; MA Camb. 1958; MRCGP 1975; DObst RCOG 1965; DA Eng. 1959. Prev: Princip. GP N. Brink Pract. Wisbech.

HALL-SMITH, Hilda Agnes (retired) The Limes Farm House, Elm, Wisbech PE14 0BQ Tel: 01945 587123 Email: am.hs@virgin.net — MB BCh BAO Dub. 1957; DFFP 1993. Prev: Med. Off. Wisbech Family Plann. Clinic.

HALL-SMITH, Rupert Gerald Medical and Industrial Services Ltd., Mis House, 23 St Leonards Road, Eastbourne BN21 3PX Tel: 01323 724889 Fax: 01323 721161; 19 Mallory Road, Hove BN3 6TD Tel: 01273 558740 — MB BS 1982 Lond.; MRCGP 1986; D.Occ.Med. RCP Lond. 1996; DRCOG 1985; AFOM RLP Lond. 1999. (Lond. Hosp.) Med. Adviser Med. & Indust. Serv. Ltd E.bourne. Socs: Fell. Roy. Soc. Med.; Soc. Occupat. Med.; BMA. Prev: GP Hove, E. Sussex; Ho. Surg. Surg. Unit Lond. Hosp. Whitechapel; Ho. Phys. Lond. Hosp. Mile End.

HALL-SMITH, Sydney Patrick 30 The Drive, Hove BN3 3JD Tel: 01273 778123 Fax: 01273 776266; Noddings, 20 Wayland Avenue, Brighton BN1 5LW Tel: 01273 501227 — MB ChB 1942 Ed.; MD Ed. 1950; FRCP Lond. 1969, M 1951; FRCP Ed. 1963, M 1948. (Belf., Ed.) Hon. Cons. Dermat. Brighton Gen. Hosp. & Roy. Sussex Co. Hosp.; Vis. Fell. Univ. Sussex. Socs: Fell. Roy. Soc. Med. (Ex-Pres. Dermat. Sect., Mem. Counc.); Brit. Assn. Dermat.; BMA (Ex-Chairm. Dermat. Sub-Comm.). Prev: Cons. Dermat. Brighton Health Trust Hastings & Mid Sussex; Sen. Regist. (Dermat.) Lond. Hosp.; Maj. RAMC.

HALLAC, John Jossef (retired) Bannel Brow, Bannel Head, Windermere Road, Kendal LA9 5SA — LMSSA 1969 Lond. Prev: GP Wigan.

HALLACK, Ian Maurice (retired) 11A Warburton Drive, Hale Barns, Altrincham WA15 0SL Tel: 0161 980 6995 — MB ChB 1951 Cape Town; FFA RCS Eng. 1960; DA Eng. 1954. Cons. Anaesth. Salford AHA (T). Prev: Cons. Anaesth. Salford AHA (T).

HALLAM, Carl Samuel Milton Upper Eden Medical Practice, The Health Centre, Silver Street, Kirkby Stephen CA17 4RB Tel: 01228 71369 Fax: 017683 72385; Mossgill House, Crosby Garrett, Kirkby Stephen CA17 4PW Tel: 017683 71149 — MB BS 1969 Lond. (Roy. Free) Prev: Surg. Lt.-Cdr. RN, Med. Off. Roy. Marine Commando Gp.

HALLAM, Charles Philip Peelhouse Lane Surgery, 1 Peelhouse Lane, Widnes WA8 6TW Tel: 0151 424 6221 Fax: 0151 420 5436 — MB ChB 1982 Liverp.; DRCOG 1986. (Liverpool)

HALLAM, Christina Frances 184 Leicester Road, Mountsorrel, Loughborough LE12 7DE — MB ChB 1993 Sheff.

HALLAM, Claudia Ann Greyend, 11 Temple Road, Buxton SK17 9BA — MB ChB 1996 Liverp.

HALLAM, Diana Louise 22 Seggielea Road, Glasgow G13 1XJ — MB ChB 1992 Glas.

HALLAM, Duncan King Street Surgery, 38 King Street, Lancaster LA1 1RE Tel: 01524 32294 Fax: 01524 848412; 14 Bryn Grove, Hest Bank, Lancaster LA2 6EX — MB ChB 1987 Sheff.; MRCGP 1994; DRCOG 1993.

HALLAM, Louise 70 Waldegrave Road, Brighton BN1 6GE — MB BS 1992 Lond.

HALLAM, Rev. Nicholas Francis Regional Clinical Virus Laboratory, City Hospital, Greenbank Drive, Edinburgh EH10 5SB Tel: 0131 536 6329 Fax: 0131 536 6153; 11 Ravelrig Park, Balerno, Edinburgh EH14 7DL Tel: 0131 449 5341 — MB ChB 1981 Glas.; PhD Glas. 1976; MA Oxf. 1981, BA 1971; MRCPath 1991. Cons. Virol. City Hosp. Edin. Socs: BMA & Brit. Soc. Colposcopy & Cervical Path. Prev: Asst. Med. Microbiol: Virus Ref. Laborat. Centr. Pub. HA Lond.; Sen. Regist. (Colposcopy) & Regist. (Microbiol.) John Radcliffe Hosp. Oxf.

HALLAM, Patricia Louise c/o Mr. F. Hallam, 51 Penge Road, Upton Park, London E13 0SL — MB ChB 1982 Dundee.

HALLAM, Peter John Birks Carlton Gate, North Entrance, Saxmundham IP17 1AT — MB BS 1991 Lond.

HALLAN, Lesley Annette The Manor Street Surgery, Manor Street, Berkhamsted HP4 2DL Tel: 01442 875935 — MB BS 1983 Lond.; MRCGP 1988; DRCOG 1987. (St. Bart.) GP. Prev: GP Colchester; Trainee GP Gen. Hosp. VTS.

HALLAN, Priyanand Sidharth 145 Lodge Road, West Bromwich B70 8PJ — MB ChB 1996 Manch.

HALLAN, Mr Rodney Ingvar St Albans & West Herts NHS Trust Hemel Hempstead Hospital, Hillfield Road, Hemel Hempstead HP2 4AD Tel: 01442 287425 Fax: 01442 287422; 41 Ashlyns Road, Berkhamsted HP4 3BL — MB BS 1979 Lond.; BA Oxf. 1976; MS Lond. 1991; FRCS Eng. 1984; FRCS Ed. 1984. (St. Bartholomews) Cons. (Gen. Surg.) St Albans & Hemel Hempstead & W. Herts NHS Trust Hosp.s. Prev: Sen. Regist. (Gen. Surg.) Lond. Hosp. Whitechapel; Sen. Regist. (Gen. Surg.) St. Marks Hosp. Lond.; MRC Research Fell. (Anorectal Physiol. Surg. Unit) Lond. Hosp.

HALLAS, Clare Lynda 33 Hobby Close, East Hunsbury, Northampton NN4 0RN — MB BS 1996 Lond.

HALLAS, Shareen Farida The Poplars, Priory Road, Bowdon, Altrincham WA14 3BS — MB ChB 1990 Liverp.

HALLATT, Angela Mary 37 Berners Street, Ipswich IP1 3LN; South Park Farm House, Wherstead Vill., Ipswich IP9 2AF — MB ChB 1985 Sheff.; DObst. New Zealand 1987.

HALLATT, Brian Frank (retired) 89 Hemper Lane, Sheffield S8 7FA Tel: 0114 237 7109 — MB ChB 1953 Sheff.; DObst RCOG 1957. Prev: Cas. Off. & Ho. Phys. Sheff. Roy. Hosp.

HALLATT, Sandra Eunice The Surgery, South Hermitage, Belle Vue, Shrewsbury SY3 7JS Tel: 01743 343148 Fax: 01743 357772; Carmel House, 47 The Mount, Shrewsbury SY3 8PP Tel: 01743 361714 — MB ChB 1979 Sheff.; MRCGP 1985.

HALLE, Frances Mary (retired) Bramley Hollow, 8 Ford Road, Marsh Lane, Sheffield S21 5RE — BA Camb. 1943; MRCS Eng. LRCP Lond. 1946; MRCGP 1968. Prev: Ho. Phys. & Asst. Cas. Off. Roy. Infirm. Sheff.

HALLE, Hugh Max (retired) Bramley Hollow, 8 Ford Road, Marsh Lane, Sheffield S21 5RE Tel: 01246 434445 Fax: 01246 434445 — MRCS Eng. LRCP Lond. 1945; FRCGP 1984, M 1952. Prev: Orthop. Ho. Surg. Roy. Infirm. Manch.

HALLETT, Anna Maria Royal United Hospital, Coombe Park, Bath BA1 3NG Tel: 01205 428331 — MB ChB 1992 Bristol; DA (UK) 1995; DRCOG 1998. (Bristol) SHO (Anaesth.) Roy. United Hosp. Bath. Socs: Obst. Anaesth. Assn.; Assn. Anaesths. Prev: SHO (O & G) PMH Swindon; SHO (Gen. Med.) PMH Swindon; SHO (Anaesth.) PMH Swindon.

HALLETT, Caroline Louise Ophthalmology Department, Queen Alexandra Hospital, Cosham, Portsmouth PO6 3LY; Warringa, Forest Road, Denmead, Waterlooville PO7 6UE — MB BS 1993 Lond.; BSc Lond. 1990, MB BS 1993. SHO (Ophth.) Qu. Alexandra Hosp. Portsmouth. Prev: Ho. Off. (Ophth. & Gen. Surg.) St. Geo. Hosp. Lond.; Ho. Off. (Gen. Med.) Qu. Alexandra Hosp. Portsmouth.

HALLETT, Christopher Paul (retired) Maesbrook, Gwernaffield Road, Mold CH7 1RE Tel: 01352 758546 Email: chris.hallett@btinternet.com — MB ChB 1961 Bristol; FFPHM 1990, FFCM 1984, M 1972; Dip. Audiol. Soton. 1975; DPH Lond. 1968. p/t Cons. N. Wales H. A. Mold, Flintshire. Prev: Cons. Pub. Health Med. N. Wales HA Mold, Flintshire.

HALLETT, Mr Jeffrey Paul Orthopaedic Department, The Ipswich Hospital NHS Trust, Heath Road, Ipswich IP4 5PD Tel: 01473 702094 Fax: 01473 702094; The Laurels, The St, Pettistree, Woodbridge IP13 0HU Tel: 01728 746210 Email: 106206.3502@compuserve.com — BM BCh 1971 Oxf.; MA Oxf. 1971; FRCS Eng. 1976. (Univ. Coll. Hosp.) Cons. Orthop. Surg. The Ipswich Hosp. Socs: Fell. BOA; Sesamoid Soc.; Roy. Soc. Med. Prev: Regist. Rotat. (Surg. & Orthop.) W.m. Hosp. & Univ. Coll. Hosp. Lond.; SHO Roy. Nat. Orthop. Hosp. Stanmore.

HALLETT, Richard John Portsmouth Hospitals NHS Trust, Paediatric Department, St Mary's Hospital, Milton Road, Portsmouth PO7 6UE Tel: 023 92 866100 Fax: 023 92 866101 — MA, BM BCh Oxf. 1965; FRCP Lond. 1982; MRCP (U.K.) 1970; DCH Eng. 1968. (Oxf. & St. Thos.) Cons. Paediat. St. Mary's Hosp. Portsmouth. Socs: BMA. Prev: SHO Hosp. Sick Childr. Lond.; Sen. Regist. Soton. Univ. Hosp. Gp. Ho. Surg. Roy. Waterloo; Hosp. Lond.

HALLETT, Sandra Cogges Surgery, Cogges Hill Road, Witney OX28 3FP Tel: 01993 700505; Harcourt House, Church Road, North Leigh, Witney OX29 6TX — BM BCh 1985 Oxf.; BA Oxf. 1982; DRCOG 1990; DCH RCP Lond. 1990. Retainer GP; Family Plann. Prev: Trainee GP/SHO (Paediat.) Cheltenham VTS.; Ho. Surg. Gloucester HA.; Ho. Phys. Bath HA.

HALLEWELL, Christopher Leonard Garlands Hospital, Carlisle CA1 3SX Tel: 01228 31081 — MB 1983 Camb.; MA Oxf. 1980; BChir 1982; MRCP (UK) 1986; MRCPsych 1988. Cons. Old Age Psychiat. Garlands Hosp. Carlisle.

HALLEWELL, John Webb (retired) Field House, Wells Road, Healing, Grimsby DN41 7QQ Tel: 01472 884941 — MRCS Eng. LRCP Lond. 1952. Prev: ENT Ho. Surg. & Cas. Off. Roy. Devon & Exeter Hosp.

HALLEY, Paul Bernard South Lambeth Road Practice, 1 Selway House, 272 South Lambeth Road, London SW8 1UL Tel: 020 7622 1923 Fax: 020 7498 5530 — MB ChB 1989 Birm.

HALLGARTEN, Ruth Julia 47 Parliament Hill, London NW3 2TA; Holborn Medical Centre, 64 Lambs Conduit St, London WC1N 3NA — MB ChB 1992 Sheff. SHO (A & E) NE Thames RHA.

HALLIDAY, Alix Bruce Cochrane (retired) Strath-Urr, Dalbeattie DG5 4JB Tel: 01556 610220 — MB ChB 1959 Glas.; DCH RCPS Glas. 1966; DObst RCOG 1964. Regist. (Paediat.) Roy. Hosp. Sick Childr. Glas. Prev: Ho. Surg. Roy. Infirm. Glas.

HALLIDAY, Mr Andrew Edward Grant Beck Cottage, West Willoughby, Grantham NG32 3SN Tel: 01476 405804 Fax: 01476 405806 Email: handyhip@aol.com — MB BS 1981 Lond.; FRCS Eng. 1987. Cons. Orthop. & Trauma Surg. Grantham & Dist. Hosp. NHS Trust. Prev: Lect. (Orthop. Surg.) Univ. Newc. u Tyne; Regist. (Orthop. Surg.) Chelmsford & Colchester Hosps.

HALLIDAY, Anthony Martin (retired) 27 Chepstow Villas, London W11 3DR — MB ChB 1949 Glas.; BSc (Hons.) Glas. 1946; FRCP Lond. 1989; MRCP (UK) 1985. On Extern. Staff MRC Inst. Neurol. & Cons. Neurophysiol. Nat. Hosp. Qu. Sq. Prev: on Staff MRC Neurol. Research Unit Nat. Hosp. Qu. Sq.

HALLIDAY, Beth Louise 16 Sinnels Field, Shipton-under-Wychwood, Oxford OX7 6EJ — MB ChB 1998 Liverp.; MB ChB Liverp 1998.

HALLIDAY, Mr Brett Linsley The Coplow, Day Care Cataract Unit, Hampton Lane, Meriden, Coventry CV7 7JR Tel: 01676 521073 Fax: 01676 521074 Email: brett@thecoplow.co.uk; The Coplow, Hampton Lane, Meriden, Coventry CU7 7JR Tel: 01676 521073 Fax: 01676 521074 Email: brett@bretthalliday.co.uk — MB 1979 Camb.; BChir 1978; MA Camb. 1980; FRCS Eng. 1983; FRCOphth 1989; DO Eng. 1982. (Camb.) Indep. Cons. Ophth. Solihull. Prev: Cons. Ophth. Eye, Ear & Throat Hosp. Shrewsbry; Lect. Moorfield Eye Hosp. Lond.; Regist. Oxf. Eye Hosp.

HALLIDAY, Bruce William Greyfriars Medical Centre, 33-37 Castle Street, Dumfries DG1 1DL Tel: 01387 257752 Fax: 01387 257020 — MB ChB 1986 Ed.; MRCP (UK) 1990; MRCGP 1993; DRCOG 1989. (Ed.)

HALLIDAY, Catherine Cherryvalley Health Centre, Kings Square, Belfast BT5 7BP Tel: 028 9040 1744 Fax: 028 9040 2069; 541 Upper Newtownards Road, Belfast BT4 3LN Tel: 01232 483262 — MB BCh BAO 1965 Belf.; FRCGP 1992; DCH RCPS Glas. 1967. (Belf.)

HALLIDAY, Dorothy Jean 7 Kineton Road, Oxford OX1 4PG — MB BS 1991 Lond.; BSc Lond. 1989; MRCP Lond. 1996. (Char. Cross & Westm.) Jun. Research Fell. Univ. of Oxf. Socs: Brit. Soc. Human Genetics.

HALLIDAY, Eilidh Catriona (Renwick) Drs Burthwick, Harris, Shadbolt & Renwick, 24 Quarry St, Johnstone PA5 Tel: 01505 321733; 96 Southbrae Drive, Jurdanhill, Glasgow G13 1TZ Tel: 0141 959 1310 Email: c.renwick@btopenworld.com — MB ChB 1985 Glas. GP Princip.; Clin. Asst. (Learning Disabilities) Merchiston Hosp. Brookfield Johnstone. Prev: GP Maybole, Ayrsh.

HALLIDAY, Georgina Mabel (retired) 35 Carlogie Road, Carnoustie DD7 6ER Tel: 01241 55781 — MB ChB 1956 Glas.; DObst RCOG 1958. Prev: Med. Off. Fife HB Macmillan Serv.

HALLIDAY, Professor Henry Lewis Regional Neonatal Unit, Royal Maternity Hospital, Grosvenor Road, Belfast BT12 6BB Tel: 02890 894687 Fax: 02890 236203 Email: h.halliday@qub.ac.uk; 74 Deramore Park South, Belfast BT9 5JY Tel: 02890 662664 Email: henry.halliday@doctors.org.uk — MB BCh BAO 1970 Belf.; MD Belf. 1980; FRCP Lond. 1988; FRCP Ed. 1982; MRCP (UK) 1974; DObst RCOG 1972; DCH RCPS Glas. 1972; FRCPCH 1997. (Qu. Univ. Belf.) Cons. Neonat. Paediat. Roy. Matern. Hosp. Belf., Roy. Belf. Hosp. Sick Childr.; Hon. Prof. (Child Health) Qu. Univ. Belf. Socs: Past Pres. Eur. Soc. Paediat. Research; Past Pres. Irish & Amer. Pediatr. Soc.; Ulster Med. Soc. Prev: Neonat. Research Fell. Childr. Hosp. & the CVRI Univ. Calif. San Francisco, USA; Paediat. Case W.. Reserve Univ., Cleveland, Ohio.

HALLIDAY, Iain Macdonald Masterton Health Centre, 74 Somerville Street, Burntisland KY3 9DF Tel: 01592 872761; 19 Ramsay Crescent, Burntisland KY3 9JL — MB ChB 1973 Ed. GP Burntls., Fife.

HALLIDAY, Jennifer Campbell 92 Killermont Road, Bearsden, Glasgow G61 2NF — MB ChB 1992 Glas.

HALLIDAY, John Well Wynd Practice, Airdire Health Centre, Monkscourt Avenue, Airdrie ML6 0JU Tel: 01236 769333 Fax: 01236 748570; West Parkhill, North Biggar Road, Airdrie ML6 6EJ — MB ChB 1961 Glas.; MRCGP 1975; DObst RCOG 1963.

HALLIDAY, Mr John Agnew 154 Malone Road, Belfast BT9 5LJ Tel: 01232 668881 — MB BCh BAO 1962 Belf.; BSc Belf. 1959,

MB BCh BAO 1962; FRCS Ed. 1965; FRCS Eng. 1966. Orthop. Surg. Ulster Hosp. & Musgrave Pk. Hosp. Belf.

HALLIDAY, John James Plymouth Road Health Centre, Plymouth Road, South Brent TQ10 9HT Tel: 01364 72394 Fax: 01364 72922; Winsford, Totnes Road, South Brent TQ10 9JN — MB BChir 1968 Camb.; MA, MB Camb. 1968, BChir 1967; MRCP (UK) 1973. (Camb. & Guy's) Prev: Ho. Phys. Guy's Hosp. Lond.; Ho. Surg. Addenbrooke's Hosp. Camb.

HALLIDAY, Katharine Elizabeth 40 Canford Road, London SW11 6PD; Ashton, Countisbury, Lynton EX35 6NQ — MB ChB 1984 Manch.; MB ChB Manch. l984; FRCS Eng. 1989; FRCR 1994. Sen. Regist. (Radiol.) Qu. Med. Centre Nottm. Prev: Sen. Regist. (Radiol.) St. Mary's Hosp. Lond.; Regist. (Gen. Surg.) Ashford Gen. Hosp. & Hammersmith Hosp.; SHO (Surg.) Hammersmith Hosp. Lond.

HALLIDAY, Kenneth Charles Robertson Glenmarlin, New Galloway, Castle Douglas DG7 3RS Tel: 01644 420301 — MB ChB 1946 Ed. (Ed.)

HALLIDAY, Mr Mark William 48 Fairlawn Grove, Chiswick, London W4 5EH — MB BS 1985 Lond.; FRCS Eng. 1992. Specialist Regist. Vasc. Surg. St Marys Hosp. Lond. Prev: Specialist Regist. Surg.N.Wick Pk. hosp.; Specialist Regist. Surg. Watford Hosp.; Specialist Regist. Surg.hammersmith Hosp.

HALLIDAY, Maureen Elizabeth 8 St Julians Road, Omagh BT79 7HQ Tel: 01662 247728 — MB BCh BAO 1969 Belf.; MFFP 1993. (Belf.) SCMO (Family Plann.) Omagh Health Centre. Socs: BMA; Nat. Assn. Family Plann. Doctors; N. Irel. Assn. Family Plann. Doctors.

HALLIDAY, Nigel James Williton and Watchet Surgeries, Robert Street, Williton, Taunton TA4 4QE Tel: 01984 632701 Fax: 01984 633933 — MB ChB 1970 Bristol; DObst RCOG 1972; DCH Eng. 1973.

HALLIDAY, Norman Pryde, QHP Gurrs Farm, Crowborough Hill, Crowborough TN6 2SD Tel: 01892 669132 Fax: 01892 664389 Email: norman.halliday@btinternet.com — MB BS 1964 Lond.; MRCS Eng. LRCP Lond. 1964; DCH RCPS Glas. 1969. (King's Coll. Hosp.) Cons. Advisor MoH Saudi Arabia. Prev: Sen. PMO DoH; Regist. (Paediat.), Ho. Phys. & Ho. Surg. King's Coll. Hosp. Lond.

HALLIDAY, Mr Paul Department of Urological Surgery, Perth Royal Infirmary, Perth PH1 1NX Tel: 01738 623311 — MB ChB 1988 Glas.; BSc (Hons.) St. And. 1984; FRCS Glas. 1993; FRCS (Urol.) 1997. (Glas.) Cons. Urol. Surg. Perth Roy. Infirm. Perth. Socs: Brit. Assn. Urol. Surgs.; Eur. Assn. Urol.; Founder Mem. Brit. Soc. for Endourol. Prev: Sen. Regist. (Urol.) W. Gen. Hosp. Edin.; SHO (Orthop. Surg.) Aberd. Roy. Infirm.; SHO (Gen. Surg. & Urol.) Stobhill Gen. Hosp. Glas.

HALLIDAY, Rupert Michael Valkyrie Surgery, 20 Valkyrie Road, Westcliff on Sea SS0 8BX Tel: 01702 331255 Fax: 01702 437050 Email: Rupert.halliday@gp-f81097.nhs.uk — BM 1981 Soton.; MSc Lond. 1992; MFPHM RCP (UK) 1994; MRCGP 1985; DTM & H RCP Lond. 1996; DRCOG 1983; DFFP Lond. 1996. (Soton.) GP Princip. W.cliff on Sea; Clin. Governance lead. S.end on Sea; Pub. Health Professional, S. end On Sea. Prev: Cons. Pub. Health Med. S. Essex HA; GP Ramsgate.

HALLIDAY, Sheila Philomena Stormont, Dalbeattie Road, Dumfries DG2 7PL Tel: 01387 249481 — MB BCh BAO 1988 NUI; MRCGP 1994. GP Retainer, Greencroft Med. Centre (S.), Annan. Prev: GP retainer, Murrayfield Med. Centre Edin.; Area Med. Off., Mallow Co. Cork; GP Asst., Biggar Health Centre, Lanarksh.

HALLIDAY, Susan Elizabeth ACET Institute of Public Health, University Forvie Site, Robinson Way, Cambridge CB2 2SR Tel: 01223 762023 Fax: 01223 414036 Email: sueh@rdd.phru.cam.ac.uk; Meadow Farm, Broad End, Elsworth, Cambridge CB3 8JD Tel: 01954 268042 — MB ChB Liverp. 1980; MFPHM (RCP) UK 1991; MRCGP 1985; DCCH RCP Ed. 1987; DObst 1983. Cons. Pub. Health Med. Anglia Clin. Audit & Effectiveness Team. Prev: Cons. (Pub. Health Med.) Camb. & Huntingdon HA; Sen. Regist. (Pub. Health Med.) E. Anglia RHA; Regist. (Community Med.) Merton & Sutton HA.

HALLIDAY-BELL, Jacqueline Anthea Employee Health Services, 2nd Floor, 148 Old St., London EC1V 9HQ Tel: 020 7250 2153 Fax: 020 7250 2735; 10 Cuckoo Dene, Hanwell, London W7 3DP Fax: 020 8575 0070 — MB ChB 1988 Leic.; BSc Leic. 1985; MFOM 1999. Med. Adviser The Post Office Employee Health Serv. Lond. Socs: Soc. Occupat. Med.; Fell.. Roy. Soc. Med. Sect. Occupat. Med. Prev: EMAS Health & Safety Exec. Basingstoke; GP Lond.; SHO E. Birm. Hosp.

HALLIDAY-PEGG, Jacqueline Claire Eskdale, New Road, Ryhall, Stamford PE9 4HL — MB ChB 1990 Liverp.; MRCGP 1994.

HALLIDAY-PEGG, Sheila May Hereward Medical Centre, Exeter Street, Bourne PE10 9NJ Tel: 01778 394188 Fax: 01778 393966; Eskdale House, New Road, Ryhall, Stamford PE9 4HL Tel: 01780 64442 — MB ChB 1961 Liverp. (Liverp.) Occupat. Health Phys. NW Anglia Health.

HALLIFAX, Elizabeth Stewart (retired) 1 West Farm Close, Ashtead KT21 2LH Tel: 01372 275071 — MB ChB Ed. 1946. Prev: SCMO (Family Plann.) Kingston & Richmond, & Surrey HAs.

HALLIFAX, Linda Janet Langton Medical Group, St. Chads Health Centre, Dimbles Lane, Lichfield WS13 7HT Tel: 01543 258983 Fax: 01543 414776 — MB BS 1977 Lond.; MRCGP 1985; DRCOG 1979.

***HALLIGAN, Professor Aidan William Francis** University of Leicester, Clinical Sciences Building, Leicester Royal Infirmary, Leicester LE2 7LX Tel: 0116 252 3170 Fax: 0116 252 3154 Email: awfh1@le.ac.uk; 201B Swithland Lane, Rothley, Leicester LE7 7SJ Tel: 0116 252 3170 Fax: 0116 252 3154 — MB BCh BAO 1984 Dub.; MB BCh Dub. 1984; MD Dub. 1993; MRCOG 1991; MRCPI 1996.

HALLIGAN, Michael Stephen Francis 26 Harberson Road, London SW12 9QW — MB BS 1987 Lond.; MRCP (UK) 1990. Cons. (Radiol.) St. Mark's Hosp., Lond. Socs: Roy. Coll. Radiol. Prev: Regist. (Radiol.) St. Bart. Hosp. Lond.; SHO W.m. Hosp. Lond.; SHO (Radiother.) St. Bart. Hosp. Lond.

HALLIKERI, Chittaranjan Gudleppa c/o Dr S. B. Sanikop, No. 12A Llyn Berwin Close, Rogerstone, Newport NP1 — MB BS 1982 Karnatak, India.

HALLIKERI, Sangramsinha Gudleppa The New City Medical Centre, Tatham Street, Hendon, Sunderland SR1 2QB — MB BS 1969 Karnatak. (Karnatak) GP Sunderland, Tyne & Wear.

HALLIN, Rolf Gerhard Swedish Medical Centre, 15 Harley St., London W1N 1DA — Med Lic Umea 1967.

HALLINAN, John Alastair (retired) 52 Braithwell Road, Maltby, Rotherham S66 8JU Tel: 01709 813236 — MB BChir 1944 Camb.; MA Camb. 1944; MRCGP 1959. Prev: Ho. Surg. & Ho. Phys. Childr. Hosp. & City Gen. Hosp. Sheff.

HALLINAN, Margaret Joan (retired) 52 Braithwell Road, Maltby, Rotherham S66 8JU Tel: 01709 813236 — MRCS Eng. LRCP Lond. 1944.

HALLISSEY, Mr Michael Timothy Ward West 2, Queen Elizabeth Hospital, Edgbaston, Birmingham B15 2TH Tel: 0121 627 2278 Fax: 0121 627 2273 Email: mike.hallisey@university-b.wmids.nhs.uk; 24 Whitford Drive, Shirley, Solihull B90 4YG Tel: 0121 705 4910 — MB ChB 1979 Birm.; MD Birm. 1991; FRCS Eng. 1984; FRCS Ed. 1983; FRCS (Gen) 1993. (Birmingham) Cons. Gen. Surg. Qu. Eliz. Hosp. Birm.; Mem. Brit. Stomach Cancer Gp. Socs: Surg. Research Soc.; Assn. Surg. Prev: Sen. Lect. (Surg.) Qu. Eliz. Hosp. Birm.; Sen. Regist. (Gen. Surg.) Walsgrave Hosp. Coventry.

HALLIWELL, Anthony Clare Villa Surgery, 7 Clarendon Road, St Helier, Jersey JE2 3YS Tel: 01534 24256; Blanc Pignon, 2 St. Nicholas Drive, Mont Nicolle, St. Brelade, Jersey Tel: 01534 742622 — MRCS Eng. LRCP Lond. 1958; BA Camb. 1953; DObst RCOG 1961. (St. Thos.) Prev: Med. Off. Barbados Gen. Hosp. W. Indies; Sen. Ho. Off. (O & G) Dorking Gen. Hosp.; Ho. Phys. & Ho. Surg. E. Surrey Hosp. Redhill.

HALLIWELL, Emma Louise The Cottage, Pearse House, Parsonage Lane, Bishop's Stortford CM23 5BQ — BChir 1996 Camb.; MA 1998; MB B chir 1996. (University of Cambridge) SHO Gen. Med., Soton. Univ., NHS Trust - Soton.

HALLIWELL, Inderjit Kaur 27 East Meads, Guildford GU2 7SW — MB BS 1987 Lond.; DRCOG 1994; DCH RCP Lond. 1993. Trainee GP Guildford. Prev: Trainee GP/SHO (O & G) Frimley Pk. Hosp.

HALLIWELL, Mr Mark Christopher Warrington Hospital NHS Trust, Lovely Lane, Warrington WA5 1QG Tel: 01925 635911; 26 Chessington Close, Appleton, Warrington WA4 5HG — MB ChB 1987 Dundee; FCOphth 1992. Cons. Ophth., Warrington Hosp. NHS Trust. Socs: Coll. Ophthalmol. Prev: Regist. Rotat. (Ophth.) Lincoln & Leicester Lincoln Co. Hosp.

HALLIWELL, Roger Paul Sandhurst Group Practice, 72 Yorktown Road, Sandhurst GU47 9BT Tel: 01252 872455 Fax: 01252 872456 — MB BS 1974 Lond.; BSc Lond. 1971; MRCGP 1986; DRCOG 1978. (St. Geo.) Gen. Practitioner & GP Trainer Sandhurst Gp. Pract. Sandhurst, Berks.; PCG Bd. Mem. Bracknell PCG. Prev: SHO (Paediat., Med. & O & G) St. Lukes Hosp. Guildford.

HALLORAN, Mr Christopher Michael 233 Bills Lane, Shirley, Solihull B90 2PP Tel: 0151 227 3376 — MB ChB 1994 Liverp.; BSc (Hons.) Liverp. 1992; FRCS 1998. (Liverp) Demonst. (Anat.) & RMO Gr.snor Nuffield Chester; SHO (Surg.) Mersey Regional Rotat. Research. Reg. Prev: Ho. Off. Whiston Hosp.

HALLORAN, Eleanor Mary Dept. of Psychological Medicine, Western General Hospital, Crewe Rd, Edinburgh EH4 Tel: 0131 537 1834 Fax: 0131 537 1833 — MB BCh BAO 1987 NUI; MRCPsych 1994; MRCGP 1991; MICGP 1991; DCH RCPSI 1989; DObst RCPI 1989. (Univ. Coll. Cork, Irel.) Cons. Liaison Psychiat. W.ern Gen. Hosp., Edin. Prev: Research Fell. (Psychiat.) MRC Brain Metabol. Unit Edin.; Regist. (Psychiat.) Dingleton Hosp. Melrose; SHO (Psychiat.) Dingleton Hosp. Melrose.

HALLORAN, John Bradford Health, New Mill, Victoria Road, Saltaire, Shipley BD18 3LD Tel: 01274 366007 Fax: 01274 366060; 41 New Park Street, Morley, Leeds LS27 0PT Tel: 0113 252 8334 — BM BCh Oxf. 1969; BSc (Hons.) Leeds 1966; MRCGP 1975; DCH Eng. 1975; DObst RCOG 1974. (Oxf.) Med. Adviser Bradford HA; Medico-Legal Report Compiler (Claims for Damages) W. Yorks.

HALLORAN, Kathleen Mary South Cliff Surgery, 56 Esplanade Road, Scarborough YO11 2AU Tel: 01723 360451 Fax: 01723 353518 — MB ChB 1980 Leic.

HALLOTT, Deborah Elizabeth New Southgate Surgery, Buxton Place, off Leeds Road, Wakefield WF1 3JQ Tel: 01924 334400 Fax: 01924 334439 — MB ChB 1989 Leeds.

HALLOWAY, Angela Joy The Health Centre, Bow Street, Guisborough TS14 7AA Tel: 01287 634171 Fax: 01287 630963; 4 Little Crake, Guisborough TS14 8PL — MB ChB 1986 Manch.; DCH RCP Lond. 1989.

HALLOWS, Margaret Ruth 11 Nailers Close, Stoke Heath, Bromsgrove B60 3PL — MB BS 1987 Lond.; FRCS Eng. 1991.

HALLS, Geoffrey James Kent Elms Health Centre, Rayleigh Road, Leigh-on-Sea SS9 5UU Tel: 01702 522012 — MB BS 1960 Lond. (St. Bart.) Prev: Ho. Off. Dept. Endocrinol. New End Hosp.; Ho. Off. Surg. Unit, Med. Unit & Childr. Dept. St. Bart. Hosp.

HALLS, Geraldine Ann Old Bridge Surgery, Old Bridge, Newlyn, Penzance TR18 5PR Tel: 01736 351014; Lesingey Cottage, Lesingey, Penzance TR20 8TQ Tel: 01736 64841 — MB BS 1966 Lond. (King's Coll. Hosp.) Socs: W Penwith Med. Soc. Prev: Regist. (Psychiat.) Towers Hosp. Leicester; Regist. (Med.) St. Michael's Hosp. Hayle; Clin. Med. Off. Cornw. & I. of Scilly AHA.

HALLS, Patrick John Walsgrave Health Centre, 50 Hall Lane, Coventry CV2 2SW Tel: 024 7661 2004 — BM BCh 1978 Oxf.; MRCGP 1985; DRCOG 1983; DCH RCP Lond. 1984.

HALLUMS, Alexandra Louise Hanwell Health Centre, 20 Church Road, Hanwell, London W7 1DR Tel: 020 8579 7337 Fax: 020 8579 7337 — MB ChB 1990 Bristol; DRCOG 1994; MRCGP 1995. (Bristol)

HALLWARD, Colin Grenville The Red House, Bath Road, Devizes SN10 2AN Tel: 01380 722982 Fax: 01380 722982 — MB ChB 1963 Bristol; MRCS Eng. LRCP Lond. 1962; DA Eng. 1966. (Bristol) Socs: Fac. Anaesth. Prev: Med. Off. MarlBoro. Coll.

***HALLWARD, George Grenville** The Red House, Bath Rd, Devizes SN10 2AN Tel: 01380 722982 Fax: 01380 722982 — MB BS 1996 Lond.

HALLWOOD, Philip Malcolm Kite Consultancy, 2nd Floor, The Maltings, Bridge St., Hitchin SG5 2DE Tel: 01462 450777 Fax: 01462 450755 Email: phil@kite.ndirect.co.uk; 2 Hunts Barn, Green Tye, Much Hadham SG10 6LD Tel: 01279 841005 Fax: 01279 841233 — MB BS 1981 Lond.; MBA Lond. 1991; DPM Eng. 1986. Dir. Kite Consultancy. Socs: Fac. Pharmaceut. Med. Prev: Regional Med. Dir. Smith Kline & French Labs. Ltd. Welwyn Gdn. City.

HALLWORTH, David 54 Longview Drive, Huyton, Liverpool L36 6EF Tel: 0151 489 5405 — MRCS Eng. LRCP Lond. 1974; FFA RCS Eng. 1980.

HALLWORTH, Nigel Aston The Station House, Station Road, Perranporth TR6 0DD — MB ChB 1966 Leeds.

HALLWORTH, Stephen Phillip 49 Shipston Road, Stratford-upon-Avon CV37 7LN — BM BS 1990 Nottm.

HALLY, Mr Alistair Douglas (retired) 26 Campbell Road, Longniddry EH32 0NP Tel: 01875 852269 — MB ChB Glas. 1950; MD (Hons.) Glas. 1961; FRCS Ed. 1989. Prev: Reader (Anat.) Univ. Newc.

HALLY, Margaret Rose (retired) 26 Campbell Road, Longniddry EH32 0NP Tel: 01875 852269 — MB ChB 1950 Glas. Prev: Sen. Med. Off. Scott. Home & Health Dept. Edin.

HALMSHAW, Frank Raymond 10 Le Marchant Avenue, Lindley, Huddersfield HD3 3DF Tel: 01484 421916 — MB ChB 1955 Leeds; DO Eng. 1972. (Lond.)

HALNAN, Keith Edward (retired) 2 Wensleydale Gardens, Hampton TW12 2LU Tel: 020 8979 9320 — MB BChir 1950 Camb.; FRSE 1977; MA Camb. 1945, MD 1957; Hon. MD Gdansk 1976; FRCP Lond. 1973, M 1966; FRCP Glas. 1972; FRCR 1975; FFR 1957; DMRT Eng. 1954. Prev: Former Clin. Director, Hammersmith Hosp. Lond.

HALPE, Neil Lakshman Department of Obstetrics & Gynaecology, St James's' University Hospital, Beckett St., Leeds LS9 7TF — MB BS 1968 Ceylon; FRCOG 1989, M 1976.

HALPERN, Helen Sharon Addison Court Medical Centre, 4 Brondesbury Road, Kilburn, London NW6 6AS Tel: 020 7624 9853 Fax: 020 7372 3660 — MB BS 1981 Lond.; MRCGP 1986.

HALPERN, Ian Barry 7 Carrwood, Hale Barn, Altrincham WA15 0ED Tel: 0161 980 2021; 17 St. John Street, Manchester M3 4DR Tel: 0161 834 3660 — BM BCh 1975 Oxf.; MA Oxf. 1976; MRCGP 1980; ECFMG Cert 1975; DRCOG 1977; Cert JCC Lond. 1977.

HALPERN, Saul Maxim Department of Dermatology, Medway Hospital, Windmill Road, Gillingham ME7 5NY Tel: 01674 825014 Fax: 01634 825017; Whitefriars, Boley Hill, Rochester ME1 1TE — MB BS 1987 Lond.; BSc Lond. 1984; MRCP (UK) 1991. Cons. Dermatol. Prev: Sen. Regist. (Dermat.) Roy. Liverp. Univ. Hosp.; Regist. (Dermat.) St. Bart. Hosp. Lond.; Regist. (Gen. Med. & Toxicol.) Guy's Hosp. Lond.

HALPIN, David Charles Hollies Medical Practice, Tamworth Health Centre, Upper Gungate, Tamworth B79 7EA Tel: 01827 68511 Fax: 01827 51163; Coton Lodge, Lichfield Road, Tamworth B79 7SH Tel: 01827 310876 — MB ChB 1978 Manch.; BSc Manch. 1975, MB ChB 1978; MRCGP 1984; DCH Eng. 1980. Prev: SHO (O & G) St. Mary's Hosp. Manch.; SHO (Paediat.) Booth Hall Hosp. Manch.; Med. Off. Baglung MCH Clin., Nepal.

HALPIN, David Michael George Royal Devon & Exeter Hospital, Barrack Road, Exeter EX2 5DW Tel: 01392 411611 Email: d.m.g.halpin@ex.ac.uk — MB BS 1986 Lond.; MA, DPhil Oxf. 1983; FRCP 1999. Cons. Chest Phys. Roy. Devon & Exeter Hosp.; Sen. Lect. (Respirat. Med.) Univ. Exeter. Socs: Brit. Thorac. Soc. & Amer. Thorac. Soc. Prev: Sen. Regist. (Thoracic Med.) Roy. Brompton & W.m. Hosp. Lond.; Regist. (Chest Med.) St. Thos. Hosp. Lond.; SHO (Med.) Brompton Hosp. Lond.

HALPIN, Mr David Sydney Kiln Shotts, Haytor, Newton Abbot TQ13 9XR Tel: 01364661115 Email: sue.helpin@virgin.net — MB BS 1964 Lond.; FRCS 1969 Eng.; FRCS Eng. 1969. (St. Mary's) Socs: Fell. BOA. Prev: Cons. Orthop. & Trauma Surg. Torbay Hosp. & P.ss Eliz. Orthop. Hosp.; Sen. Regist. (Orthop. & Trauma Surg.) Exeter & Truro Gps. Hosps.; Research Fell. Mass. Gen. Hosp. Boston, USA.

HALPIN, Keith Gordon Health Centre, Poplar Avenue, Gresford, Wrexham LL12 8EP Tel: 01978 852208; Plas Goulbourne Farm House, Holt Road, Llan-y-Pwell, Wrexham LL13 9SA — MB ChB 1982 Manch.; MRCGP 1987; DRCOG 1985.

HALPIN, Kenneth Drummond Stonerunner Cottage, Rye Harbour, Rye TN31 7TT Tel: 01797 224351 — MB ChB 1957 Ed.

HALPIN, Mr Richard Michael Bestall Borders General Hospital, Melrose TD6 9BS Tel: 01896 754333 Fax: 01896 823476; Colemso, Weirhill Pl, Melrose TD6 9SF Tel: 01896 822527 Email: richard.halpin@btinternet.com — MB BS Lond. 1977; FRCS Ed. 1983; FRCS Glas. 1983; FRCPs Glas. 1983. (Lond. Hosp.) Cons. (Surg.) Borders Gen. Hosp. Melrose. Socs: Assn. Surg. GB & N Irel. Prev: Sen. Surg. Specialist Edendale Hosp. Pietermartizburg, S. Afr.; Sen. Regist. K. Edwd. VIII Hosp., Durban; Ho. Off. Surg. Unit Lond. Hosp.

HALPIN, Shawn Fergus Stanley 94 Westbourne Road, Penarth CF64 3HG — MB BS 1982 Lond.; MRCP (UK) 1986; FRCR 1988. Cons. Neuroradiol. Univ. Hosp. Wales. Socs: Brit. Soc. Neuroradiol.; World Federat. Interven. & Therap. Neuroradiol. Prev: Sen. Regist. (Reuroradiol.) Nat. Hosp. for Neurol. & Neurosurg. Atkinson Morley's Hosp. & Hosp. Sick Childr. Gt. Ormond St. Lond.
HALPIN, Sheila Community Child Health, 15-17 Carlton Terrace, Edinburgh EH7 5DD; 149 Baberton Mains Drive, Edinburgh EH14 3EA — MB ChB 1982 Ed.; MRCGP 1987; DCCH RCP Ed. 1989; DRCOG 1988. SCMO Edin.; Clin. Med. Off. (Community Child Health.) Edin. Prev: Clin. Med. Off. (Community Child Health) Lothian HB.
HALPIN, Simon Paul 22 School Lane, Lostock Grahlam, Northwich CW9 7PT — MB ChB 1989 Liverp. Clin. Asst. (Urol.) Whiston Hosp. Merseyside. Prev: SHO Rotat. (Surg.) Mersey RHA; SHO (Surg.) Whiston Hosp. & S.port Dist. Gen. Hosp.; SHO (Orthop.) Whiston Hosp.
HALPIN, William John (retired) Thrang Close, Chapel Stile, Great Langdale, Ambleside LA22 9JR Tel: 015394 37373 — MB ChB 1947 St. And.
HALSALL, Pamela Jane 17 North Park Grove, Leeds LS8 1JJ — MB ChB 1973 Manch.
HALSE, Gregory George 9 Aigburth Mansions, Mowll St., London SW9 0EP — MB BS 1983 Lond.; MRCPsych 1988. Prev: Sen. Regist. United Med. Dent. Sch. SE Thames Scheme.
HALSEY, Christina The Old Chapel, Mill Lane, Lower Heyford, Bicester OX25 5PG — BM BCh 1994 Oxf.; BA (Hons.) Physiol. Sci. Oxf. 1991; MRCP (UK) 1997. Specialist Regist. (Haemat.) N. Thames Deanery. Prev: SHO (Paediat.) Roy. Vict. Infirm. Newc.; SHO Rotat. (Gen. Med.) Roy. Infirm. of Edin.
HALSEY, Deborah Jane The Surgery, 139 Valley Road, London SW16 2XT Tel: 020 8769 2566 Fax: 020 8769 5301; 52 Marney Road, London SW11 5EP — MB BS 1976 Lond.; MB BS (Hons.) Lond. 1976; MRCP (UK) 1978; MRCGP 1984; DCH RCP Lond. 1983; DRCOG 1983. (King's Coll. Hosp.) Prev: Regist. King's Coll. Hosp. Lond.; SHO Roy. Devon & Exeter Hosp. Exeter; Ho. Phys. Brompton Hosp. Lond.
HALSEY, John Philip Graythwaite, Over Kellet, Carnforth LA6 1DG — MB BS 1972 Lond.; FRCP Lond. 1993; MRCP (UK) 1976. (St. Geo.) Cons. Rheum. Roy. Lancaster Infirm. Prev: Sen. Regist. (Rheum.) Lond. Hosp; Regist. (Med.) Norf. & Norwich Hosp.; Regist. (Med.) Soton. Gen. Hosp.
HALSON, Eve Renee (retired) 10 Ravelston Dykes, Edinburgh EH4 3ED Tel: 0131 332 5719 — MB BS 1949 Durh. Prev: Community Phys. Lothian HB.
HALSTEAD, Diane Elizabeth East Lynne Medical Centre, 3-5 Wellesley Road, Clacton-on-Sea CO15 3PP Tel: 01255 220010 Fax: 01255 476350 — MB BChir 1985 Camb.
HALSTEAD, Georgina Dawn Mayford House Surgery, East Road, Northallerton DL6 1NP Tel: 01609 772105 Fax: 01609 778553; The White House, Thirlby, Thirsk YO7 2DJ — MB ChB 1992 Leeds; DRCOG 1994; MRCGP 1996. GP.
HALSTEAD, Georgina Marie 18 Lower Alt Road, Liverpool L38 0BB — MB BS 1987 Newc.; MRCGP 1993; Dip. GU Med. Liverp. 1992. Clin. Asst. (Genitourin. Med.) S.port Dist. Gen. Hosp. Prev: Trainee GP S.port.
HALSTEAD, Gillian Anne Sanarima, Bolton Road, Anderton, Chorley PR6 9HN Tel: 01257 480900 — MB ChB 1986 Dundee; MRCP (UK) 1993. Sen. Regist. (Med. & Geriat.) Manch. Roy. Infirm. Socs: Brit. Geriat. Soc. Prev: Regist. (Med. & c/o Elderly) Stepping Hill Hosp. Stockport; Ho. Off. (Med. & Surg.) Ninewells Hosp. Dundee.
HALSTEAD, Helen Christine King Street Surgery, 38 King Street, Lancaster LA1 1RE Tel: 01524 32294 Fax: 01524 848412 — BM BCh 1981 Oxf.; MA Camb. 1990; DRCOG 1988; DCH RCP Lond. 1988. GP Lancaster.
HALSTEAD, Hilary Edith Abington Park Surgery, Christchurch Medical Centre, Ardington Road, Northampton NN1 5LT; 3 Greenway, Northampton NN3 3BW — MB BS 1979 Lond.; MRCGP 1983. (Roy. Free)
HALSTEAD, James Clifford 4 Cherry Grove, Cutgate, Rochdale OL11 5YT — BChir 1996 Camb.
HALSTEAD, Joan (retired) Gallery House, Glyn-Y-Mel Road, Lower Town, Fishguard SA65 9LY Tel: 01348 872005 — MB ChB 1939 Manch. Prev: Cons. Venereol. Croydon Gen. Hosp. & St. Helier Hosp. Carshalton.
HALSTEAD, John (retired) Glenoran, Lamlash, Brodick KA27 — MRCS Eng. LRCP Lond. 1939.
HALSTEAD, Karen Anne Wheeler Street Health Care, Wheeler St., Anlaby Road, Hull HU3 5QE Tel: 01482 853296; 15 Easenby Close, Swanland, North Ferriby HU14 3NP — MB ChB 1986 Liverp. Prev: Trainee GP Wirral VTS.
HALSTEAD, Linda Geraldine 16 Circular Road, Prestwich, Manchester M25 9WF — MB ChB 1983 Liverp.; MRCGP 1988.
HALSTEAD, Nicholas Anthony Holly Bank Farm, Huxley Lane, Tiverton, Tarporley CW6 9NB — MB ChB 1973 Liverp.; FRCPsych 1992, M 1978; DObst RCOG 1975. Cons. Psychiat. Countess of Chester Hosp.
HALSTEAD, Padma Enderby, Edwalton, Nottingham NG12 4BW; 121 Cranmer Court, London SW3 3HE — BSc Punjab 1948; MB BS Delhi 1953; FP Cert RCOG 1976. (Lady Hardinge Med. Coll.)
HALSTEAD, Peter James 129 Hazeldene Road, Northampton NN2 7PB; 3 Greenway, Northampton NN3 3BW Tel: 01604 406201 — MB BS 1977 Lond.; FRCGP 1999; DRCOG 1979; MRCGP 1981; DFFP 1998. Course Organizer N.ampton VTS. Prev: Trainee GP N.ampton VTS; Med. Off. Kandrian W. New Brit. Papua New Guinea.
HALSTEAD, Simon Care Principles Ltd, Ashley House, Ashley, Market Drayton TF9 4LX Tel: 01630 673800 Fax: 01630 673805 Email: simonhalstead@careprinciples.com; 97 The Lloyd, Hales, Northampton NN2 6JA Tel: 01630 654626 — MB BS 1984 Lond.; MRCPsych 1990. Cons. Psychiat. Care Principles Ltd; Hon. Sen. Lect. St. Geo. Hosp. Med. Sch. Prev: Cons. St. Andrews, N.ampton; Sen. Regist. (Psychiat.) Springfield Hosp. Lond.; Resid. (Psychol. Med.) Nat. Univ. Hosp., Singapore.
HALSTED, Clare June Pennine Drive Surgery, 6-8 Pennine Drive, London NW2 1PA Tel: 020 8455 9977; 46 Dartmouth Park Road, London NW5 1SN Tel: 020 7485 1498 Fax: 020 7681 9454 — MB BS 1980 Lond.; PhD Lond. 1973; BSc (Hons.) Bristol 1969; DRCOG 1986. (Roy. Free) GP Princip.; GP Tutor Roy. Free Hosp. Sch. of Med.
HALSTVEDT, Kirsten Annette 53 White Street, Glasgow G11 5EQ — MB ChB 1993 Aberd.
HALVORSEN, Richard Toralf Longdon Holborn Medical Centre, 64 Lambs Conduit Street, London WC1N 3NA Tel: 020 7405 3541 Fax: 02 7404 8198 — MB BS 1982 Lond. (Middlx.) Socs: PR Off. BMAS; Brit. Holistic Med. Assn. & BMA; Brit. Med. Acupunct. Assn. Prev: Community Med. Off. (Paediat.) Waltham Forest HA; SHO (Geriat.) Roy. Free Hosp. Lond.; SHO (Psychiat.) Friern Hosp. Lond.
HAM, Mr John Andrew Department of Ophthalmology, St George's Hospital, Blackshaw Road, London SW17 0QT Tel: 020 8672 1255; 112 Holly Lane E., Banstead SM7 2BE Tel: 020 8643 2588 — MB BS 1977 Lond.; BSc (Hons.) Lond. 1974; FRCS Eng. 1983; FCOphth 1988; DO Eng. 1980. (Univ. Coll. Hosp.) Assoc. Specialist (Ophth.) St. Geo. Hosp. Lond. Socs: Fell. Roy. Soc. Med.; BMA; Oxf. Ophth. Congr. Prev: Sen. Specialist (Ophth.) RAF; Regist. (Ophth.) Bristol Eye Hosp.; SHO (Ophth.) Univ. & Eye Hosps. Nottm.
HAM, John Clifford 99 Station Road, Llanishen, Cardiff CF14 5UW — MB BCh 1945 Wales; BSc Wales 1945; FRCGP 1977, M 1958. (Cardiff) Prev: Med. Regist. Llandough Hosp.; Med. Off. (Tuberc.) Sully Hosp.; RAF.
HAM, Mary Finlay Glenwood, Station Road, Llanishen, Cardiff CF14 5 — MB BCh BAO 1946 Belf. (Belf.) Prev: Ho. Surg. & Ho. Phys. Roy. Vict. Hosp. Belf.; Res. Surg. Off. E. Glam. Hosp. Ch. Village.
HAM, Mr Robert John The Royal London Hospital, London E1 1BB Tel: 020 7377 7695 Fax: 020 7377 7695; 8 Langton Way, London SE3 7TL — MB BS 1972 Lond.; BSc 1970 (Hons.) Lond.; FRCS Eng. 1977. (Lond. Hosp.) Cons. Vasc. Surg. Lond. Hosp. Prev: Research Fell. Thrombosis Research Unit King's Coll. Hosp. Lond.; Sen. Regist. Lond. Hosp.
HAM KOW BOON, Dr 69 Chatsfield, Peterborough PE4 5DL — MB BS 1991 West. Austral.
HAMA, Tariq Mahmood Hama Medical Centre, 11A Nottingham Road, Kimberley, Nottingham NG16 2NB Tel: 0115 938 2101 Fax: 0115 945 9208; Hama Lodge, 456 Arch Hill, Redhill, Nottingham NG5 8PF Tel: 0115 967 9600 — MB BS 1985 Newc.; MB BS Lond. 1985; BSc (Hons.) Newc. 1980; MRCPI 1987; Cert. Family Plann.

JCC 1993. Socs: BMA. Prev: Regist. (Med.) Univ. Hosp. Nottm.; Regist. (Med.) Glenfield Hosp. Leicester & Lincoln Gen. Hosp.

HAMA, Zahida Ansari Hama Medical Centre, 11A Nottingham Road, Kimberley, Nottingham NG16 2NB Tel: 0115 938 2101 Fax: 0115 945 9208; Hama Lodge, 456 Arch Hill, Redhill, Nottingham NG5 8PF Tel: 0115 967 9600 — MB BS 1982 Lond.; DFFP 1995; DCH RCP Lond. 1991; DRCOG 1990. (Roy. Free Hosp. Sch. Med.) GP 3/4 Time. Socs: BMA. Prev: SHO (Community Paediat.) Qu. Eliz. II Hosp.; SHO (Paediat.) Watford Gen. Hosp.; SHO (Obst.) Lister Hosp. Stevenage.

HAMAD, Mr Abdel Aziz Mohammed 135 Cliff Gardens, Scunthorpe DN15 7BL — MD 1979 Univ. Sarajevo; FRCSI 1990.

HAMAD, Mr Ahmed Hag 3 Angram Drive, Newminster Park, Ryhope Road, Sunderland SR2 7RD Tel: 0191 510 2008 — MB BS 1967 Khartoum; FRCS Ed. 1973.

HAMAD, Ghader Mohamed El-Solaih Ali The Surgery, 652 Preston Road, Clayton-le-Woods, Preston PR6 7EH Tel: 01772 323021 Fax: 01772 620078 — MB ChB 1984 Alexandria.

HAMAD, Hamdi Aziz Department of Dermatology, New Cross Hospital, Wolverhampton WV10 0QP Tel: 01902 307999 — MB ChB 1980 Mosul, Iraq; Dip. Ven. Liverp. 1989; Dip. Dermat. Sci. Wales 1988. (Univ. Mosul Med. Sch.) Assoc. Specialist (Dermat.) New Cross Hosp. Wolverhampton. Socs: BMA; Brit. Assn. Dermat.; Brit. Soc. Study VD. Prev: Regist. (Genitourin. Med.) Manch. Roy. Infirm.; SHO (Dermat.) New Cross Hosp. & Grimsby Dist. Gen. Hosp.

HAMAD, Mr Sabah Noori 2 Lamacraft Drive, Honeylands, Exeter EX4 8QS Tel: 01392 439815 — MB ChB 1973 Baghdad; FRCS Eng. 1988; FRCS Ed. 1983; LRCP LRCS Ed. LRCPS Glas. 1984. Assoc. Specialist (Gen. Surg.) Roy. Devon & Exeter Hosp. Socs: BMA. Prev: Regist. (Surg.) Hereford Co. Hosp. & Burnley Gen. Hosp.

HAMAD, Sayed Abdel Kader Mohamed Baycliffe Family Health Care Centre, Baycliffe Road, Liverpool L12 6QX Tel: 0151 228 4272 — MB BCh 1973 Cario.

HAMAD, Zakareia Mahmoud Saad Torbay Hospital, Lawes Bridge, Torquay TQ2 7AA Tel: 01803 64567 — MB ChB 1976 Alexandria; Dip. Clin. Path. Lond 1986; Dip. Haemat. Lond. 1985. Assoc. Specialist (Clin. & Laborat. Haemat.) Torbay Hosp. Torquay. Prev: Staff Grade Doctor & Regist. (Clin. & Laborat. Haemat.) Torbay Hosp. Torquay; Regist. (Clin. & Laborat. Haemat.) Walton Hosp. Liverp.

HAMADE, Prudence Marjorie Bryn Aber Hall, Llanrhaeaor Ym Mochnant, Oswestry SY10 0AJ — MB ChB 1968 Leeds. Community Med. Off. Salop HA.

HAMAL, Anokha 120 Hainault Road, Chigwell IG7 5DL — MB BS 1988 Lond.

HAMAL, Bobby Bikram Room 1, Flat 3, RMO Block, Hull Royal Infirmary, Anlaby Road, Hull HU3 2JZ — MB ChB 1995 Leeds.

HAMAL, Prem Bikram Pinderfields General Hospital, Aberford Road, Wakefield WF1 4DG Tel: 01924 375217; 9 Attlee Crescent, Sandal, Wakefield WF2 6RF Tel: 01924 258347 — MB BS 1960 Lucknow; MRCS Eng. LRCP Lond. 1975; FRCPath 1982, M 1970; DPath Eng. 1968. (King Geo. Med. Coll. Lucknow) Cons. Path. Pinderfields Gen. Hosp. Wakefield; Chairm. Wakefield Overseas Doctors' Assn.; Chairm. Nepalese Doctors' Assn.; Chairm. 'Yeti' Nepalese Assn. (Midl.s & N.). Socs: BMA; Assn. Clin. Pathologists. Prev: Sen. Regist. Med. Sch. & Dudley Rd. Hosp. Birm.; Regist. Birchall Hosp. Rochdale.

HAMAMI, Nabil Abdul Amir Jafar Cromwell Hospital, Cromwell Road, London SW5 0TU Tel: 020 7460 2000 Fax: 020 7460 5555 — MB ChB 1971 Baghdad; MSc Clin. Trop. Med. Lond. 1977; MRCPI 1984; MRCS Eng. LRCP Lond. 1985; DPH Baghdad 1973.

HAMANN, Ian David 39 Stirling Road, Edinburgh EH5 3JA Tel: 0131 552 0606 Fax: 0131 551 4901 — MB BS 1979 New South Wales.

HAMANN, Julian Christoph Horst 39 Avondale Road, Fleet GU51 3BS — MB BS 1997 Lond.

HAMANN, Wolfgang Christof Pain Management Unit, Department of Anaesthetics, New Guy's House, 2nd Floor, Guy's Hospital, St Thomas St., London SE1 9RT — PhD Ed. 1974; Dr. Med. Hamburg 1968; State Exam. Med. Hamburg 1967. (Hamburg) Prof. Physiol. Med. Fac. Chinese Univ. Hong Kong.

HAMAYUN, Mohammed Pervaiz Bridgeton Health Centre, 201 Abercromby Street, Glasgow G40 2DA Tel: 0141 531 6500 Fax: 0141 531 6505 — MB ChB 1976 Glas. Disabil. Analyst Sema, Benefits Agency, Glas.

HAMBER, Basil Hugh (retired) Dormers House, Upton Grey, Basingstoke RG25 2RH Tel: 01256 862454 — MB BS Lond. 1957.

HAMBER, George (retired) 29 Vicarage Drive, Eastbourne BN20 8AP — MB BChir 1961 Camb.; MA Camb. 1961; FRCS Ed. 1966; MRCS Eng. LRCP Lond. 1960; MRCGP 1979; DTM & H Liverp. 1965; DObst RCOG 1963. Prev: Med. Miss. Ruanda Mission CMS, Burundi.

HAMBER, Richard Claude (retired) 2 Bouverie Avenue, Salisbury SP2 8DT Tel: 01722 336500 — MB BS 1955 Lond.; MRCS Eng. LRCP Lond. 1955; FRCGP 1983, M 1964. Prev: GP Salisbury.

HAMBIDGE, David Michael 9 Weavervale Park, Warrington Rd, Bartington, Northwich CW8 4QU Tel: 01606 854523 — MB BS 1980 Lond.; BSc (Hons.) Lond. 1976; MRCPsych 1985; Specialist Regist. 1997. (St. Mary's Hosp. Med. Sch.) Indep. Cons. Psychiat.; Second Opinion Apptd. Doctoe (SOAD) Ment. Health Act Commiss. Prev: Cons. Psychiat. Mid Chesh. Hosp. Trust.

HAMBIDGE, Mr John Edward, Squadron Ldr. RAF Med. Br. Kings Mill Hospital, Mansfield Road, Sutton-in-Ashfield NG17 4JL Tel: 01623 22515; Hopkin Cottage, Hopyard, Lower Kirklington Road, Southwell NG25 0RT Tel: 01636 814559 — MB BS 1983 Lond.; FRCS (Orth.) 1993; FRCS Ed. 1988. (Lond. Hosp. Med. Coll.) Cons. Orthop. Surg. Kings Mill Hosp. Mansfield. Prev: Sen. Regist. (Orthop. Surg.) Harlow Wood Orthop. Hosp. & Qu. Med. Centre Nottm.; Sen. Regist. Roy. Lond. Hosp.

HAMBLEN, Professor David Lawrence University Department of Orthopaedic Surgery, Western Infirmary, Glasgow G11 6NT Tel: 0141 211 2678 Fax: 0141 339 0462 Email: dlhortho@netscapeonline.co.uk; 3 Russell Drive, Bearsden, Glasgow G61 3BB Tel: 0141 942 1823 — MB BS Lond. 1957; PhD Ed. 1975; FRCS Glas. 1976; FRCS Eng. 1963; FRCS Ed. 1962; MRCS Eng. LRCP Lond. 1957. (Lond. Hosp.) Prof. Orthop. Surg. Univ. Glas.; Hon. Cons. Orthop. Surg. to Army in Scotl.; Vis. Prof. Univ. Strathclyde; Chairm. Counc. Managem. Jl. Bone & Jt. Surg.; Chairm. Gt.er Glas. Health Bd. Socs: Fell. Roy. Soc. Med.; Fell. (Ex-Pres.) BOA. Prev: Sen. Lect. (Orthop.) Univ. Edin.; Lect. Nuffield Orthop. Centre Univ. Oxf.; Teach. & Clin. Fell. Harvard Univ. & Mass. Gen. Hosp. Boston, USA.

HAMBLET, Kathleen Mary Library Buildings, Lairg Road, Bonar Bridge, Ardgay IV24 3EA Tel: 01863 766383 Fax: 01863 766671; Carbisdale Farm House, Culrain, Ardgay IV24 3DW Tel: 01549 421225 Fax: 01549 421225 — MB ChB St. And. 1971. (St Andrews) Assoc. Gen. Pract. Bonar Bridge & Lairg Med. Pract.

HAMBLETON, David Hayward Building, Selly Oak Hospital, Raddlebarn Road, Birmingham B29 6JB; 4 Normans Cottages, Newtown, Little Neston, South Wirral CH64 4BP — MB ChB 1988 Manch.; MRCP (UK) 1993. Sen. Regist. (Geriat. & Gen. Med.) Selly Oak Hosp. Birm. Socs: Brit. Geriat. Soc.

HAMBLETON, Garry 8 Manor Close, Cheadle Hulme, Cheadle SK8 7DJ Tel: 0161 485 8852 — MA, BM BCh Oxf. 1965; FRCP Lond. 1980, M 1968; LMSSA Lond. 1965; FRCPCH 1997. (Oxf. & Guy's) Cons. Paediat. Cent, Manch. & Manch. Childr. Univ. Hosp. Trust; Assoc. Med Dir. Childr. Prev: Sen. Regist. (Paediat.) Hammersmith Hosp. Lond.; Cons. Paediat. Salford Roy. Hosp. Trust; Dyers' Company Research Fell. St. Thos. Hosp. Lond.

HAMBLETON, Karen Lesley The Surgery, 292 Derby Road, Lenton, Nottingham NG7 1QG Tel: 0115 947 4002 Fax: 0115 924 0783; 16 Varden Avenue, Lenton Abbey, Nottingham NG9 2SJ Tel: 0115 922 4713 Fax: 0115 924 0783 — BM BS 1986 Nottm.; BM BS Nottm.1986; BMedSci (Hons) Nottm. 1984; MRCGP 1991; DGM RCP Lond. 1989.

HAMBLETON, Mrs Kathleen Mary The Health Centre, Cheadle Hulme, Cheadle SK8 6LU Tel: 0161 485 7233; 8 Manor Close, Cheadle Hulme, Cheadle SK8 7DJ Tel: 0161 485 8852 — BM BCh 1964 Oxf.; MA Oxf. 1965, BM BCh 1964. (St. Thos.) Prev: Res. Clin. Pathol. St. Geo. Hosp. Lond.

HAMBLETON, Sophie Molecular Immunology Group, Institute of Molecular Medicine, The John Radcliffe, Oxford OX3 9DS Tel: 01865 222334 Email: shamblet@worf.molbiol.ox.ac.uk; 50 Hertford Street, Oxford OX4 3AL Tel: 01865 721760 — BM BCh 1991 Oxf.; BA Oxf. 1988; MRCP (UK) 1994. (Oxf. Univ.) MRC Clin. Train. Fell. Molecular Immunol. Gp. Inst. of Molecular Med. Oxf. Socs: Med.

Wom. Federat. Prev: Regist. Birm. Childr. Hosp.; Regist. (Neonat.) Birm. Matern. Hosp.; SHO Gt. Ormond St. Hosp. Lond.

HAMBLETT, Caroline Jane 52D Claxton Grove, London W6 8HF — MB BS 1994 Lond.

HAMBLETT, Eric Percival (retired) Tyn-y-Llan, Llanlleonfel, Llangammarch Wells LD4 4AN Tel: 01591 620415 — MB ChB Bristol 1952; MD Bristol 1969; MFOM RCP Lond.; MFCM RCP (UK) 1974; DIH Soc. Apoth. Lond. 1973; DPH (Distinc.) Bristol 1964; DTM & H Liverp. 1961; DCH RCP Lond. 1954. Prev: PMO Avon Co. Occupat. Health Serv.

HAMBLEY, Audrey Benita Langabridge, Burrington, Umberleigh EX37 9JT — MB BS 1970 Lond.; MRCS Eng. LRCP Lond. 1970. (Roy. Free) Socs: Fell. Hunt. Soc.; BMA. Prev: Ho. Surg. & Ho. Phys. Willesden Gen. Hosp. Lond.

HAMBLEY, Henry Department of Haematological Medicine, King's College Hospital, Denmark Hill, London SE5 9RS Tel: 020 7326 3570 Fax: 020 7326 3514; 40 Barnmead Road, Beckenham BR3 1JE — MB ChB 1974 Glas.; BSc (Hons.) Glas. 1972, MB ChB 1974; MRCPath 1983. Cons. Haemat. King's Coll. Hosp. Lond. Socs: Brit. Soc. Haematol. Prev: Sen. Regist. & Regist. (Haemat.) Roy. Infirm. Glas.

HAMBLEY, John Joseph 17 Burnside Grove, Tollerton, Nottingham NG12 4ET Tel: 0160 773674 — BM BS 1984 Nottm. Trainee GP Nottm. VTS.

HAMBLIN, Catherine Anne Munro Medical Centre, West Elloe Avenue, Spalding PE11 2BY Tel: 01775 725530 Fax: 01775 766168; 15 Farthingales, Spalding PE11 3AD Tel: 01775 710420 — MB ChB 1986 Leeds; BSc Leeds 1983; DRCOG 1991. Socs: MPS; BMA.

HAMBLIN, Christine Garda Mary Inglenook Cottage, Maidford Road, Farthingstone, Towcester NN12 8HE — MB BS 1964 Lond.; DCH Eng. 1969.

HAMBLIN, John Frederick (retired) — MB ChB Bristol 1966; DPH Bristol 1970. Prev: Med. Off. DSS Manch.

HAMBLIN, John Joseph 12 Chadwick Road, Westcliff on Sea SS0 8LS Tel: 01702 346728 — MB BS 1958 Lond.; FRCP Lond. 1977, M 1963. (Lond. Hosp.) Cons. Phys. S.end Hosp. Gp. Prev: Sen. Med. Regist. & Lect. in Med. Lond. Hosp.

HAMBLIN, Louise Grace Old Church, 146A Bedford Hill, Balham, London SW12 9HW Tel: 020 8675 2100 — BM 1982 Soton. Assoc. Specialist Pathfinder Ment. Health Trust. Socs: Roy. Coll. Psychiat.

HAMBLIN, Michael Thomas 77 Pentney Road, London SW12 0PA — MB BS 1989 Lond.; BSc (Hons.) Lond. 1986, MB BS 1989; MRCP (UK) 1992; MRCPath 1997. (London) Sen. Regist. Rotat. (Haemat.) SW Thames.

HAMBLIN, Professor Terence John Royal Bournemouth Hospital, Castle Lane E., Bournemouth BH7 7DW Tel: 01202 704790 Fax: 01202 300248; 15 Queens Park, South Drive, Bournemouth BH8 9BQ Tel: 01202 267156 Email: terjoha@aol.com — MB ChB 1967 Bristol; DM Soton. 1986; FRCP Lond. 1985; MRCP (UK) 1971; FRCPath 1985, M 1973. (Bristol) Cons. Haemat. Bournemouth; Prof. Immunohaemat. Univ. Soton. Socs: Brit. Soc. Haematol.; Amer. Soc. Haemat.; Brit. Soc. Immunol. Prev: Sen. Regist. Poole; MRC Research Fell. Med. Univ. Bristol; Regist. (Path.) S.mead Hosp. Bristol.

HAMBLING, Clare Elizabeth Watlington Medical Centre, Watlington, King's Lynn PL9 8UA Tel: 01553 481518 Fax: 01553 811629 — MB ChB 1990 Dundee; BMSc Dund 1987; MRCP (UK) 1995; DRCOG 1997; MRCGP 1998. GP Retainee; GP Regist. Prev: SHO (Gen. Med.) Portsmouth Hosps. Trust VTS; SHO Rotat. Tayside VTS.

HAMBLING, John Herbert (retired) Oxted Court, 33 Church Lane, Oxted RH8 9NB — MB ChB Birm. 1943; MD Flex 1977; FRCP Lond. 1973, M 1947. Hon. Med. Adviser, Sturt Hse. Priory Clinic, Walton on the Hill. Prev: Founding Med. Adviser, Stuart Ho. Clinic, Tadworth.

HAMBLING, Milton Herbert (retired) 2 Elmete Close, Wetherby Road, Leeds LS8 2LD Tel: 0113 265 9157 — MB BS 1951 Lond.; MD Lond. 1963; MRCS Eng. LRCP Lond. 1951; FRCPath 1976, M 1964; Dip. Bact. Lond. 1959; DObst RCOG 1953. Prev: Cons. Virol. Regional Pub. Health Laborat. Leeds.

HAMBLING, Simon Peter, Surg. Lt.-Cdr. RN RNSQ HMS Drake, Devonport, Plymouth PL2 2BG Tel: 01752 555186; 11 Carpenter Road, Plymstock, Plymouth PL9 8UA Tel: 01752 481518 Email: sphambling@aol.com — MB ChB Leeds 1988; MRCGP 1996; DRCOG 1995. (Leeds) Med Off. RN.

HAMBLY, Anthony Trevan The Upper Surgery, 27 Lemon Street, Truro TR1 2LS Tel: 01872 74931 Fax: 01872 260339; Bodrean Manor, St. Clements, Truro TR4 9AG Tel: 01872 75500 — MB 1973 Camb.; BChir 1972; MRCGP 1984; DObst RCOG 1975; DCH Eng. 1974.

HAMBLY, Elizabeth Mary (retired) Treharrock, 41 Long Grove, Seer Green, Beaconsfield HP9 2YN Tel: 01494 675917 — MRCS Eng. LRCP Lond. 1938. Prev: Clin. Asst. (Dermat.) Wycombe Gen. Hosp.

HAMBLY, John Collings Park Medical Centre, 57 Eggbuckland Road, Hartley, Plymouth PL3 5JR Tel: 01752 771500 Fax: 01752 787183 — MB BS 1980 Lond.; MRCGP 1987; DRCOG 1986; DCH RCP Lond. 1984. (St. Thos.) Princip. in Gen. Pract.

HAMBLY, John Francis Edward 58 Orchard Road, Seer Green, Beaconsfield HP9 2XU — MB ChB 1995 Bristol. Regist. (Critical Care Med.) Townsville, QLD, Australia. Socs: Australasian Coll. of Emerg. Med.

HAMBLY, Kenneth Norman High Street Health Centre, 45 High Street, Stewarton, Kilmarnock KA3 5BP Tel: 01560 482011 Fax: 01560 485483; Mains of Lochridge, by Stewarton, Kilmarnock KA3 5LH Tel: 01560 82521 — MB BCh BAO 1969 Belf.; DObst 1972. Socs: GP Writers Assn.

HAMBLY, Peter Robin Mes-y-Garreg, Penual Road, Pentyrch, Cardiff CF4 8QJ — MB ChB 1988 Bristol.

HAMBLY, Philip Brynmor Community Child Health Department, Princess of Wales Hospital, Coity Road, Bridgend CF31 1RQ; 10 Gower Street, Port Talbot SA13 1SL Tel: 01639 768220 Email: phillip.hambley@ntlworld.com — MB BS 1972 Lond.; FRCPCH 1997; MRCS Eng. LRCP Lond. 1972; MRCGP 1976; DCCH RCP & Ed. 1988; DObst RCOG 1975; FRCPCH 1997. Cons. Community Paediat. BRO Morgan & WG NHS Trust. Prev: SCMO (Child Health) W. Glam. HA.

HAMBLY, Trevan (retired) Mewstone, Oakhill Road, Springvale, Seaview PO34 5AP Tel: 01983 612358 — MRCS Eng. LRCP Lond. 1940. Prev: Res. Orthop. Ho. Surg. Gen. Hosp. Nottm.

HAMBLYN, Michael James 7 Walnut Close, Eynsford, Dartford DA4 0ES — MB BS 1998 Lond.; MB BS Lond 1998.

HAMBLYN, Norman Charles, MBE The Surgery, 42 High Street, Chislehurst BR7 5AX Tel: 020 8467 5551 Fax: 020 8468 7658; 7 Walnut Close, Eynsford, Dartford DA4 0ES Tel: 01332 861936 Fax: 01332 860198 Email: normandjan@nhamblyn.fsnet.co.uk — MRCS Eng. LRCP Lond. 1967; MB BS Lond. 1967; BSc Lond. 1964; DObst RCOG 1969. (Guy's)

HAMDALLA, Hisham Hamdalla Mohamed Department of Neurology, Royal Victoria Infirmary, Queen Victoria Road, Newcastle upon Tyne NE1 4LP Tel: 0191 227 5267 Fax: 0191 227 5267 Email: h.h.m.hamdella@ncl.ac.uk — MB BS 1984 Khartoum; MRCP (UK) 1993. (University ofKhartoum, Sudan) Clin. Research Fell. & Specialist Regist. Neurol. Roy. Vict. Infirm. Newc.; Hon. Research Assoc. Univ. Newc. u. Tyne. Socs: Gen. Sec. Sudanese Doctors Union UK & Irel.; BMA; Amer. Acad. Neurol. Prev: Regist. Neurol. St. James Univ. Hosp. Leeds & Leeds Gen. Infirm. & Pinderfields Hosp. Wakefield.

HAMDAN, Mr Nabil Mohammed Abdulla 41 Townsend Road, Ashford TW15 3PR — MB BCh 1972 Cairo; FRCS Ed. 1978.

HAMDI, Inaam Abdul Karem Majed Department of Clinical Biochemistry, Addenbrooke's Hospital, Hills Road, Cambridge CB2 2QR Tel: 01223 217155 — MB ChB 1970 Baghdad; PhD Wales 1979. Sen. Regist. Dept. Clin. Biochem. Addenbrooke's Hosp. Camb.

HAMDI, Mr Safa Sadi 33 Hurn Way, Christchurch BH23 2NU — MB ChB 1971 Mosul; FRCS Ed. 1983; FRCOphth 1989; DO RCS Eng. 1980. Clin. Asst. (Ophth.) Roy. Vict. Hosp. Bournemouth; Med. Pract. (Ophth.) Hants. & Dorset FPC.

HAMDY, Ahlam Ahmed Sello Al-Shaker 6 Mount Court, Crescent Road, Kingston upon Thames KT2 7RQ — MB ChB 1969 Mosul; FFA RCSI 1980.

HAMDY, Professor Freddie Charles University of Sheffield, Section of Urology, Royal Hallamshire Hospital, Glossop Road, Sheffield S10 2JF Tel: 0114 271 2154 Fax: 0114 271 2268 Email: f.c.hamdy@sheffield.ac.uk — MB ChB 1981 Alexandria; MD Sheff.

1992; LRCP LRCS Ed. LRCPS Glas. 1985; FRCS (Urol.) 1993; FRCS Ed. 1987. (Alexandria, Egypt) Prof. of Urol., Univ. of Sheff.; Cons. (Urological Surg.) Roy. Hallamshire Hosp. Sheff. Socs: Brit. Assn. Urol. Surgs.; Eur. Assn. Urol.; Amer. Urol. Assn. Prev: Sen. Lect. (Urol.) Univ. Newc.; Sen. Regist. (Urol.) Sheff.

HAMDY, Neveen Agnes Therese Charles 17 Endowood Road, Millhouses, Sheffield S7 2LY — MB ChB 1975 Alexandria; MB ChB (Hons.) Alexandria 1975; MRCS Eng. LRCP Lond. 1977; MRCP (UK) 1981. Clin. Research Fell. Renal & Metab. Units & Hon. Tutor Dept. Med. Roy. Hallamsh. Hosp. Sheff. Prev: Med. Regist. Profess. Unit Roy. Hallamsh. Hosp. Sheff.; Research Regist. Clin. Immunol. St. Thos. Hosp. Lond.; Med. Regist. Bromley AHA.

HAMDY, Rayan 25 Oriole Drive, Ellenbrook, Newearth Road, Worsley, Manchester M28 7XF — MB ChB 1987 Manch. SHO (Psychiat.) Birch Hill Hosp. Rochdale. Prev: SHO (A & E) Roy. Oldham Hosp.

HAMED, Mr Hisham Hilal Ahmed The Breast Unit, Guy's Hospital, St. Thomas' st., London SE1 9RT Tel: 020 7955 5000 Ext: 3776 Fax: 020 7403 8381 Email: hhamed@icrf.icnet.uk; 29 Bellamy's Court, Abbotshade Road, London SE16 5FJ — MB BCh 1975 Cairo; FRCSE Ed 1983; PhD Lond. 1995. (Cairo) Cons. BrE. Surg. - Guy's and St. Thomas' Hosps. Trust and Univ. Hosp. Lond. Socs: RSM; BASO; Roy. Coll. Surg. Edin. Prev: Sen. Regist. Br Surg. Guy's and St. Thomas' Hosps.; Reseach Fell. Br Surg. Guy's and St. Thomas' Hosps.; Reg. Br. Surg. Guy's and St. Thomas' Hosps.

HAMEED, Ashar 19 Longland Way, High Wycombe HP12 3UN — MB ChB 1996 Manch.

HAMEED, Farooq 27 Springdale Street, Huddersfield HD1 3NF — MB ChB 1997 Manch.

HAMEED, Muhammad Baber 28 Marriott Chase, Thorpe Marriott, Norwich NR8 6QQ — MB BS 1979 Karachi.

HAMEED, Mr Rafid Subhi Abdul 44 Thames Street, Windsor SL4 1PL — MB ChB 1976 Baghdad; FRCS Ed. 1990; FCOphth. 1991; DO RCS Eng. 1988.

HAMEED, Syed Abdul 63 Cresswell Road, E. Twickenham, Twickenham TW1 2EA — MB BS 1950 Punjab, Pakistan.

HAMEED-UD-DIN, Mr Syed Queen Elizabeth Queen Mother Hospital, Margate CT9 4AN Tel: 01843 225544; Little Acre, Woodland Way, Broadstairs CT10 3QD Tel: 01843 602400 — MB BS 1970 Karachi; F.F.A.E.M. R.C.S. London. (Dow Med. Coll.) Cons. (Trauma, A & E) Qu. Eliz. Qu. Mother Hosp. Margate; Cons. A&E. Kent & Canterbury Hosp. Socs: Fell. Roy. Soc. Med.; BMA (Vice-Chairm. SE Kent. Div.); Overseas Doctors Assn. (Gen. Sec. SE Kent Br.).

HAMELIJNCK, Jacobus Alphonse 1 Bron Derw, Penmaenmawr LL34 6TE — Artsexamen 1990 Amsterdam.

HAMER, Mr Andrew Jonathan 408 Brincliffe Edge Road, Banner Cross, Sheffield S11 9DB Email: ajhamer@medicine.demon.co.uk — MB ChB 1987 Bristol; FRCS Lond. 1991; FRCS (Orth) 1996; MD (Sheffield) 1997. Cons. N.ern Gen. Hosp. Sheff. Socs: Eur. Hip Soc.; BOA; Brit. Orthopaedic Research Assoc. Prev: Sen. Regist. Roy. Hallamsh. Hosp. & N.. Gen. Hosp. Sheff.; Career Regist. (Orthop. Surg.) Roy. Hallamsh. Hosp. Sheff.; SHO (Neurosurg.) Frenchay Hosp. Bristol.

HAMER, Angela Rosemary University Medical Practice, Elms Road, North Campus, Edgbaston, Birmingham B15 2SE; Hay Lane House, Shernal Green, Droitwich WR9 7JS Tel: 01905 776336 — MB ChB 1959 Birm. (Birm.) Med. Off. Univ. Birm. Health Serv.; Sch. Med. Off. King Edwd. Foundat. Edgbaston & Edgbaston High Sch. for Girls. Prev: Asst. to W. Midl. Occupat. Health Serv.; Ho. Phys. Childr. Hosp. Birm.; Ho. Surg. Gen. Hosp. Birm.

HAMER, Clare Elizabeth North Close, Blundells School, Blundells Road, Tiverton EX16 4DN — MB BS 1993 Lond. VSO, The Gambia.

HAMER, Mr David Buckley Nothampton General Hospital, Billing Road, Northampton NN1 5BD Tel: 01604 634700; Bramblewood House, 20 Yew Tree Lane, Spratton, Northampton NN6 8HL Tel: 01604 820935 — MB BS 1965 Lond.; FRCS Eng. 1970; MRCS Eng. LRCP Lond. 1965. (St. Mary's) Cons. Surg. N.ampton Gen. Hosp. Socs: Vasc. Soc. & Assn. Surgs.; Surgic. Club Gt. Brit. Prev: Sen. Surg. Regist. St. Mary's Hosp. Lond.; Surg. Regist. Roy. Postgrad. Med. Sch. Hammersmith Hosp. Lond.; Surg. Regist. Sheff. Roy. Infirm.

HAMER, David James 31 Dobbin Hill, Sheffield S11 7JA — MB ChB 1980 Liverp.; MRCPsych 1987. Prev: Regist. Rotat. (Psychiat.) Nottm. HA.

HAMER, Mr David Wayne Accident and Emergency Department, Leeds General Infirmary, Great George St., Leeds LS1 3EX Tel: 0113 292 6470 Fax: 0113 292 6470 — MB BCh 1983 Wales; BSc (Hons.) Wales 1981; FRCS (Eng.) 1991; MRCP (UK) 1988; FFAEM 1994. (Cardiff) Cons. & Hon. Sen. Lect. A & E Leeds Gen. Infirm. Prev: Sen. Regist. (A & E) Edin. Roy. Infirm.

HAMER, Fiona Charlotte Edith Watson Maternity Unit, Burnley General Hospital, Burnley BB10 2P; The Old Manse, Southview, Belmont, Bolton BL7 8AS — MB ChB 1985 Manch.; MRCOG 1991. Cons. O & G, Burnley Gen. Hosp. Prev: Regist. Wythenshawe Hosp. Manch.; Clin. Fell. IVF Unit St. Mary's Hosp. Manch.; SHO (Gen. Surg. & Urol.) Pilgrim Hosp. Boston.

HAMER, Heidi Marie Cranleigh Health Centre, Cranleigh GU6 8AE — MB BChir 1989 Camb.; MA Camb. 1990, BA 1986, MB BChir 1989. Trainee GP Cranleigh VTS. Prev: SHO (O & G & Paediat.) N.ampton Gen. Hosp.

HAMER, Ian Edward Kildonan House, Ramsbottom Road, Horwich, Bolton BL6 5NW Tel: 01204 468161 Fax: 01204 698186; The Old Manse, Southview, Belmont, Bolton BL7 8AS — MB ChB 1985 Manch.; MB ChB (Hons.) Manch. 1985; BSc (Hons.) Manch. 1982; MRCP (UK) 1988; MRCGP 1992; DRCOG 1991; Dip Occ Med 1998. Clin. Asst. (Diabetes) Chorley Gen. Hosp. Prev: Trainee GP Bolton Gen. Hosp.; Regist. (Cardiol.) Groby Rd. Hosp. Leicester; Regist. Rotat. (Gen. Med.) Trent RHA.

***HAMER, Joanne Elizabeth** 72 Cranbourne Drive, Otterbourne, Winchester SO21 2ET — MB ChB 1994 Birm.

HAMER, Mr John Drew Droitwich Private Hospital, St Andrews Road, Droitwich WR9 8DN Tel: 01905 794793; Hay Lane House, Shernal Green, Droitwich WR9 7JS Tel: 01905 776336 Fax: 01905 776336 Email: john-hamer@cinsil.msn.com — BM BCh 1960 Birm.; BM BCh. Birm. 1960; BSc Anat. (Hons.) Birm. 1957, ChM 1972; FRCS Eng. 1969; DObst RCOG 1962. (Birm.) Socs: Vasc. Surg. Soc. GB & Irel. & Moynihan Chirurgical Club. Prev: Cons. Surg. Qu. Eliz. Hosp. Birm.; Sen. Lect. (Surg.) & Lect. (Physiol.) Univ. Birm.; Ho. Surg. Profess. Unit & Ho. Phys. Qu. Eliz. Hosp. Birm.

HAMER, John Malcolm The Health Centre, Hawes DL8 3QR Tel: 01969 667200 Fax: 01969 667149; Sandford House, Hawes DL8 3NT Fax: 01969 667149 — MB ChB 1966 Liverp. (Liverp.) Socs: BMA. Prev: SHO (O & G) & Ho. Phys. & Ho. Surg. Walton Hosp. Liverp.

HAMER, Michelle Suzanne Fernande Department of Anaesthetics, William Harvey Hospital, Kennington Road, Ashford TN24 0LZ Tel: 01233 616041 Fax: 01233 616053; Sankey House, The St, Brook, Ashford TN25 5PG Tel: 01233 812744 Email: drmshamer@curcom.net — MD 1978 Montpelier; FFA RCS Eng. 1983. Cons. Anaesth. Intens. Therap. Unit William Harvey Hosp. Ashford, Kent. Socs: Assn. Anaesth.; Intens. Care Soc.; BMA. Prev: Cons. Anaesth. Intens. Therap. Unit Joyce Green Hosp. Dartford; Sen. Regist. (Anaesth.) Roy. Free Hosp. Lond.; Regist. (Anaesth.) W.m. Hosp. Lond.

HAMER, Neil Arthur John (retired) Selcroft, Woodmead Road, Lyme Regis DT7 3LJ Tel: 01297 443534 — MB BS 1951 Lond.; MB BS (Hons.) Lond. 1951; PhD Lond. 1965, MD 1959; FRCP Lond. 1969, M 1953; MRCS Eng. LRCP Lond. 1951. Prev: Asst. Dir. & Sen. Lect. Inst. Cardiol.

HAMER, Sonia Allis Towcester Medical Centre, Link Way, Towcester NN12 6HH Tel: 01327 359339; 5 Pigeon Hill, Tiffield, Towcester NN12 8AR Tel: 01327 351937 — MB ChB 1962 Manch.; Cert. Family Plann. JCC 1981. (Manchester)

HAMER, Vanessa Anne 36 Chepstow Road, Leicester LE2 1PA — MB ChB 1997 Leic.

HAMER-DAVIES, Elizabeth Ann Glannant, North St., Rhayader LD6 5BU — MB ChB 1989 Liverp.

HAMER-HODGES, Mr David William Western General Hospital, Crewe Road, Edinburgh EH4 2XU — MB BS Lond. 1967; MS Lond. 1978; MRCS Eng. LRCP Lond. 1967; FRCS Ed. 1981; FRCS Eng. 1971. (Univ. Coll. Hosp.) Cons. Surg. W.. Gen. Hosp. Edin. Prev: Sen. Regist. (Gen. Surg.) S. Grampian HB (Aberd.); Research Fell. (Surg.) Harvard Surg. Unit. Boston City Hosp.; Resid. Surg. Off. St. Mark's Hosp. Lond.

HAMER-PHILIP, John Malcolm, Brigadier late RAMC (retired) 4 Ludlow Gardens, Quadring, Spalding PE11 4QH Tel: 01775 821801 Fax: 01775 821801 — MB BCh Witwatersrand 1959; DA Eng. 1962. Prev: Comd. UK MoD Sangmed Team Riyadh, Saudia Arabia.

HAMERS, Raoul Henri Antoine Flat 11, 40 Lowndes St., London SW1X 9HX — Artsexamen 1989 Utrecht.

HAMERSLEY, Hugh Alan Noel Blue Orchard, Bosinner Lane, Polgooth, St Austell PL26 7BA Tel: 01726 65203 — MRCS Eng. LRCP Lond. 1944. (St. Mary's) Prev: Gp. Capt. RAF Med. Br. Dep. PMO Air Support Command.; OC RAF Hosp. Khormaksar Beach; Ho. Surg. Roy. Hants. Co. Hosp. Winchester.

HAMERTON, Robert Anthony Mountgarret (retired) New Buckenham, Norwich NR16 2AN Tel: 01953 860317 — MB ChB 1943 Ed.

HAMI, Faeqa 48 Rosebank Avenue, Wembley HA0 2TW — MB BS 1991 Lond.; MRCP (UK) 1996; DA (UK) 1994. (Roy. Free Hosp. & Sch. of Med.) Michael Sebel Ho., Mt. Vernon Hosp. Prev: SHO (Anaesth.) St. Mary's Paddington; Hon. Regist. (Palliat. Care) St. John's Hospice; SHO (Med.) Chelsea & W.m. Hosp. Lond. & Watford Gen. Hosp.

HAMID, Abdul Rahim Ahmed Said Church Lane Surgery, 1 Church Lane, Newsome, Huddersfield HD4 6JE Tel: 01484 514118 — MB BS 1979 Lond.

HAMID, Abdul Wajid 45 Warrington Avenue, Slough SL1 3BG — MB BS 1994 Lond.

HAMID, El Awad Hag Mohamed Green Lane Hospital, Devizes SN10 5DS Tel: 01380 731200 Fax: 01380 731308 — MB BS 1975 Khartoum; MRCPsych 1984. Cons. Psychiat. Old Age Green La. Hosp. Devizes Wilts. Socs: Clin. Soc. Bath; Brit. Assn. Psychopharmacol. Prev: Sen. Regist. (Psychiat.) Charter Nightingale Hosp. Lond.; Regist. (Psychiat.) Maidstone Hosp. Kent.

HAMID, Mariya Sithi Mirza Hampden Medical Centre, 22 Hampden Square, Southgate, London N14 5JR Tel: 020 8361 4403 — MB BS 1972 Sri Lanka; LMSSA Lond. 1987; DFFP 1990.

***HAMID, Mohammad Shoaib** 55 Northfield Park, Hayes UB3 4NU Tel: 020 8561 5083 — MB BS 1994 Lond.; BSc Lond. 1991, MB BS 1994.

HAMID, Saeed Sadiq 24 Watford Road, Northwood HA6 3NT Tel: 0192 74 27427 — MB BS 1981 Punjab; MRCPI 1988; MRCP (UK) 1988. Regist. (Gastroenterol.) Sunderland Roy. Infirm.

HAMID, Shahid Respiratory Medicine, Bromley Hospital, Bromley BR2 9AJ — MB BS 1985 Bahauddin Zakariya U Pakistan; MB BS Bahauddin Zakariya U, Pakistan 1985; MRCPI 1993.

HAMID, Shahida 28 Weymouth Street, London W1N 3FA; R17 Block No 6, Gulshan E Iqbal, Karachi, Pakistan — MB BS 1966 Karachi; MRCOG 1976, D 1969. (Dow Med. Coll. Karachi) Cons. O & G Lond. Prev: Cons. Gyn. & Obst. Zayed Milit. Hosp. Abu-Dhabi.

HAMID, Shahnaz Kausar Department of Anaesthetics, Royal Infirmary, Glasgow G4 0SF — MB ChB 1984 Glas.; FRCA 1989. Cons. Anaesth.

HAMID, Sinan Sabri Radiology Department, Homerton Hospital, Homerton Row, London E9 6SR — MB ChB 1976 Baghdad; FRCR 1984. (Univ. Baghdad) Cons. Radiol. Stracathro Angus. Socs: BMA; Brit. Med. Ultrasound Soc. Prev: Asst. Prof. Radiol. Univ. Jordan; Sen. Lect. (Radiol.) Univ. Baghdad.

HAMID, Zafar Abbots Wood Medical Centre, 12 Katherine Place, College Road, Abbots Langley WD5 0BT Tel: 01923 673060 Fax: 01923 681643; 94 Ridge Lane, Watford WD17 4TA Tel: 01865 435869 Email: oxford@doctors.org.uk — MB BS 1962 Lucknow. Socs: MPS. Prev: Clin. Asst. in Learning Difficulty & Anaesth.

HAMILL, Aileen M 8 Rossness Drive, Kinghorn, Burntisland KY3 9SE — MB ChB 1993 Aberd.

HAMILL, Angela Mary Murrayfield Medical Practice, 8 Corstorphine Road, Edinburgh EH12 6HN Tel: 0131 337 6151 Fax: 0131 313 3450; 8 Greenhill Place, Edinburgh EH10 4BR Tel: 0131 447 5912 — MB BCh BAO 1986 Dub.; MRCGP 1990; DObst. RCPSI 1989; MRCGP 1990.

HAMILL, Brigid Ann 23 Dub Lane, Upper Malone Road, Belfast BT9 5ND — MB BCh BAO 1990 Belf.; MRCGP 1994; DCH RCPSI 1993; DRCOG 1993; DGM RCP Lond. 1992. SHO (Psychiat.) Purdysburn Hosp. Belf. Socs: BMA.

HAMILL, Mr Derek Ian William Lisburn Health Centre, Linenhall Street, Lisburn BT28 1LU — MB BCh BAO 1969 Belf.; FRCS Ed. 1973; MRCGP 1979; DRCOG 1978.

HAMILL, Elizabeth Anne 34 Stewarton Drive, Cambuslang, Glasgow G72 8DG — MB ChB 1977 Glas.

HAMILL, Gregory 20 Lisboy Road, Downpatrick BT30 7LE — MB ChB 1997 Ed.

HAMILL, James Anthony Kildares Crew, 5 Crew Road, Ardglass, Downpatrick BT30 7UJ — MB BCh BAO 1962 Belf.; MRCGP 1976.

HAMILL, James Joseph Pasley Road Health Centre, Pasley Road, Eyres Monsell, Leicester LE2 9BU Tel: 0116 278 5182; 44 Linden Drive, Evington, Leicester LE5 6AH Tel: 0116 273 6377 Fax: 0116 273 6377 — MB BCh BAO 1960 NUI; DCH 1963; DObst RCOG 1962. (Univ. Coll. Dub.) Forens. Med. Examr. Leics. Constab.; EMO DHSS Birm. Socs: Leic. Med. Soc. & Assn. Police Surgs. Gt. Brit. & N. Irel. Prev: Ho. Phys. & Ho. Surg. Mater Miser. Hosp. Dub.; Clin. Asst. Nat. Matern. Hosp. Dub.; Ho. Phys. Our Lady's Hosp. Sick Childr. Dub.

HAMILL, James Patrick 5 Crew Road, Ardglass, Downpatrick BT30 7UJ — MB BCh BAO 1995 Belf.

HAMILL, Jonathan Samuel Vine Medical Centre, 69 Pemberton Road, East Molesey KT8 9LJ Tel: 020 8979 4200 Fax: 020 8941 9827 — MB BS 1975 Newc.; MRCGP 1981; DAvMed FOM RCP Lond. 1995; DRCOG 1980. Gen. Practitioner, The Vine Med. Centre, 69 Pemberton Rd. Socs: (Co-Operats.) Nat. Assn. GPs.; Nat. Assn. of GP Co-op.s. Prev: SHO Hexham Gen. Hosp.; Med. Off. RAF Med. Br. Germany & UK.

HAMILL, Mary (retired) 91 Kingsway Road, Leicester LE5 5TU Tel: 0116 270 3413 — MB BCh BAO NUI 1962. Cons. Community Paediat. Leics.

***HAMILL, Matthew Morgan** 81 Evenlode Crescent, Coundon, Coventry CV6 1BU Tel: 024 76 590 121 — MB ChB 1998 Bristol.

HAMILL, Samuel (retired) The White House, 36 Cornwall Gardens, Cliftonville, Margate CT9 2JE Tel: 01843 224212 — MB BCh BAO 1944 Belf.; MRCGP 1957. Prev: GP Margate.

HAMILL, Valerie Ann Kildares Crew, 5 Crew Road, Ardglass, Downpatrick BT30 7UJ — MB BCh BAO 1963 Belf.; MICGP 1987.

HAMILTON, Agnes Suzanne 41 Albyn Drive, Murieston S., Livingston EH54 9JN — MB ChB 1989 Ed.; MRCOG 1995. Specialist Regist. (O & G) Simpsons Memor. Matern. Hosp. Edin.

HAMILTON, Alan John Wynne Hill Surgery, 51 Hill Street, Lurgan, Craigavon BT66 6BW; 18 Tudor Lodge, Waringstown, Craigavon BT66 7SX — MB BCh BAO 1982 Belf.; MRCGP 1986; DRCOG 1985.

HAMILTON, Alan John Shepherd Spring Medical Centre, Cricketers Way, Andover SP10 5DE Tel: 01264 361126 Fax: 01264 350138; Douro House, Salisbury Road, Abbotts Ann, Andover SP11 7DL Tel: 01264 338787 — MB BS 1967 Lond.; MRCS Eng. LRCP Lond. 1967. (Guy's) Chief Med. Off. TSB Bank Insur. & Provident Capital Insur.

HAMILTON, Alexander Haldane Huddersfield Royal Infirmary, Acre St., Lindley, Huddersfield HD3 3AE Tel: 01484 342484 Fax: 01484 342121 Email: alex.hamilton@cht.nhs.uk; 87 Finkle Lane, Gildersome, Leeds LS27 7DR — MB ChB 1981 Ed.; MRCP (UK) 1984; FRCPCH 1997; FRCP Ed. 1998. (Edinburgh) Cons. Paediat. Huddersfield Roy. Infirm. Prev: Sen. Regist. Rotat. (Paediat.) Leeds & Bradford.

HAMILTON, Alison Fionn Margaret 64 Gillhurst Road, Harborne, Birmingham B17 8PB — MB ChB 1975 Aberd.; MFPHM 1990; DRCOG 1977; FFPHM 1999. (Aberd.) Dir. (Pub. Health) Dudley HA. Prev: Cons. Pub. Health Med. Dudley HA; Sen. Regist. (Pub. Health Med.) W. Midl. RHA; SCMO (Family Plann.) Birm. HA S. Dist.

HAMILTON, Alistair Byrne Marazion Surgery, Gwallon Lane, Marazion TR17 0HW Tel: 01736 710505 Fax: 01736 711205 — MB ChB 1979 Aberd.; MRCGP 1984; DRCOG 1982. (Aberd.) Socs: Penwith Med. Soc. Prev: Trainee GP Banbury VTS; SHO (Paediat.) Treliske Hosp. Truro; SHO (O & G) Wythenshawe Hosp. Manch.

HAMILTON, Amanda Jane 251 Church Road, Flixton, Urmston, Manchester M41 6EP — MB ChB 1985 Manch.

HAMILTON, Andrew Charles Edward Chesterton, Noads Way, Dibden, Purlieu, Southampton SO45 4PD — MB BS 1971 Lond.; MSc Occupat. Med. Lond. 1982; DObst RCOG 1973.

HAMILTON, Andrew Logan The Surgery, Nevells Road, Letchworth SG6 4TS Tel: 01462 683051 Fax: 01462 485650; 47 Pasture Road, Letchworth SG6 3LS Tel: 01462 671156 — MB ChB 1962 St. And.; DObst RCOG 1964.

HAMILTON, Mr Andrew Michael 149 Harley Street, London W1G 6DE Tel: 020 7935 4444 Fax: 020 7935 3061 Email: eyehamilton@msn.com; The Croft, 41 High St, Pinner HA5 5PJ Tel: 020 8866 6148 — MB BS Lond. 1964; FRCS Eng. 1970; MRCS Eng. LRCP Lond. 1964; FRCOphth 1988. (St. Mary's Hosp. Med. Sch. Univ. Lond.) Cons. Moorfields Eye Hosp. Lond.; Edit. Bd. Opthalmology. Socs: Macula Soc.; Amer. Acad. Ophth.; Gonin Club. Prev: Cons. Ophth. Middlx. Hosp.; Wellcome Lect. Inst. Ophth. Lond.

HAMILTON, Andrew Robert 13 Warrender Park Crescent, Edinburgh EH9 1EA; 7 Ross Road W., Stanley, Falkland Islands — MB ChB 1980 Ed.; BSc (Med. Sci.) Ed. 1977, MB ChB 1980. Chief Med. Off. King Edwd. VII Memor. Hosp. Stanley Falkland I.; Surg. Lt. Comm. HMS ClaverHo. Forth Div. RNR. Prev: Regist. (Med.) Roy. Infirm. Edin. & Regional Poisoning Treatm. Centre; SHO (Med.) Devizes & Dist. Hosp.; Regist. (Med.) Co. Hosp. Oban.

HAMILTON, Angela Geraldine Elm Tree Farm, Grove, Canterbury CT3 4BN Tel: 01227 722280 — MB ChB 1968 Aberd.; MB ChB (Hons.) Aberd. 1968; FFA RCS Eng. 1973. Prev: Cons. Anaesth. Roy. Berks. Hosp. & Battle Hosp. Reading; Sen. Regist. Anaesth. Soton. & Winchester Health Dist.; Regist. Anaesth. Hosp. Sick Childr. Gt. Ormond St. Lond.

HAMILTON, Angela Ida 2A Vicarage Gardens, London W8 Tel: 020 7229 7111 — MB BS 1954 Lond.; MRCS Eng. LRCP Lond. 1954. (Roy. Free) Prev: Obst. Ho. Surg. Eliz. G. Anderson Hosp.; Ho. Phys. S. Lond. Hosp. Wom. & Childr.; Asst. Lect. Roy. Free Hosp. Sch. Med.

HAMILTON, Anne 14 Craigrory, Kessock, Inverness IV1 3XH — MB BS Durh. 1962; DCH RCPS Glas. 1968; DObst RCOG 1967.

HAMILTON, Anne Mackenzie Stewart (retired) 152 Hillend Crescent, Clarkston, Glasgow G76 7XY Tel: 0141 639 5415 — MB ChB Glas. 1955; DObst RCOG 1963.

HAMILTON, Anne Shona Sneddon Bank House Medical Centre, East High Street, Airdrie ML6 6LF Tel: 01236 766983 Fax: 01236 750471; 4 Calderbankview, Hill Head Farm, Cairnhill Road, Airdrie ML6 9EU Tel: 01236 751201 — MB ChB 1983 Dundee. Prev: Regist. & SHO (Med.) Ninewells Hosp. Dundee.

HAMILTON, Mr Anthony John, TD 248 Old Bedford Road, Luton LU2 7EQ Tel: 01582 20881 — MB BS 1964 Lond.; FRCS Ed. 1971; FRCS Eng. 1972; MRCS Eng. LRCP Lond. 1964; FRCOG 1987, M 1974. (St. Geo.) Cons. (O & G) Luton & Dunstable Hosp. Socs: BMA & Nuffield Obst. & Gyn. Soc. Prev: Ho. Phys. Roy. Hants. Co. Hosp. Winchester; Ho. Surg. St. Geo. Hosp. Lond.; Asst. Lect. in Anat. Glas. Univ.

HAMILTON, Barbara 2 Kilbryde Court, Dunblane FK15 9AX — MB ChB 1992 Glas.

HAMILTON, Brian Anthony Redlands Surgery, 86 St. Johns Road, Stansted CM24 8JS Tel: 01279 813200 Fax: 01279 812426; The Pump House, Gilston Park, Gilston, Harlow CM20 2SF Tel: 01279 434000 — MB BS Lond. 1969; DFFP 1994. (Royal London)

HAMILTON, Brian Haley 23 De Pary's Avenue, Bedford MK40 2TX Tel: 01234 350022 — LMSSA 1959 Lond. (St. Mary's) Assoc. RCGP. Prev: SHO (Midw.) Orsett Hosp.; Ho. Surg. & Ho. Phys. Harold Wood Hosp.

HAMILTON, Charles Michie 5 King Street, Mirfield WF14 8AW — MB BS 1977 Lond.; MA Camb. 1977; DCH Eng. 1979; DRCOG 1979. (St. Geo.) SHO (Cardiol.) St. Geo. Hosp. Lond. Prev: Ho. Phys. Bolinbroke Hosp. Lond.; Ho. Surg. Ashford Hosp. Middlx.; SHO (Paediat.) St. Geo. Hosp. Lond.

HAMILTON, Charles Richard Wessex Radiotherapy Centre, The Royal South Hamts Hospital, Brinton's Terrace, off St. Mary's Rd, Southampton SO14 0YG Tel: 02380 634288; Heathdene, Hadrian Way, Chilworth, Southampton SO16 7HX Tel: 02380 769953 — MB BS 1977 Lond.; MRCP Lond. 1980; FRCR 1984; FRCP 1999. (St. Bart.) Cons. Radiother. & Oncol. Wessex Radiother. Centre. Prev: Regist. Dept. Radiother. St. Barts Hosp. Lond.; Leon V. Goldberg Fell. P.ss Margt. Hosp. Toronto; Lect. (Radiother.) Roy. Marsden Hosp.

HAMILTON, Colin Alexander 2 Rosswater, Londonderry BT47 6YR Tel: 01504 45556 — MB BCh BAO 1973 Belf.; MFCM 1982; MRCGP 1977; Dip Com. Med Ed. 1978; DCH RCPSI 1975; DObst RCOG 1975. Cons. Pub. Health Med. W.. Health & Soc. Servs. Bd. Lond.derry. Socs: BMA (Chairm. N. Irel. Comm. Pub. Health Med. & Community Health). Prev: SCM W.. Health & Social Servs. Bd. Lond.derry; Med. Off. DHSS Belf.

HAMILTON, David, SBStJ (retired) 17 Richmond Road, Brompton on Swale, Richmond DL10 7HF Tel: 01748 818578 — MB BChir 1946 Camb.; FRCP Lond. 1976.

HAMILTON, David Alexander 37 Selborne Road, Sheffield S10 5ND — MB ChB 1980 Ed.; MRCP (UK) 1983; FRCR 1990; DMRT Ed. 1986. Lect. & Hon. Sen. Regist. (Clin. Oncol.) W.on Pk. Hosp. & Univ. Sheff.; Research Regist. (Radiother. & Oncol.) Plymouth Gen. Hosp. Prev: Regist. (Radiat. Oncol.) Addenbrooke's Hosp. Camb. & W.. Gen. Hosp. Edin.

HAMILTON, David Allan William 175 Byres Road, Glasgow G12 8TS Tel: 0141 337 3930 Email: david.a.w.hamilton@talk21.com — MB ChB 1997 Glas. SHO (A&E) W.ern Infirm. Dumbarton Rd., Glas. Prev: SHO (Geriat.s) Ravenscraig Hosp., Greenock; Jun. Ho. Off. (Surgic.), Inverclyde Roy., Greenock; Jun. Ho. Off. (Med.) Storshill Hosp. Glas.

HAMILTON, David Charles Montgomery 2 Douro Road, Cheltenham GL50 2PQ; Ford Cottage, Stanford-in-the-Vale, Faringdon SN7 8LQ — MB BS 1986 Lond.; BA Oxf. 1983; DCH RCP Lond. 1991; DObst Otago 1988.

HAMILTON, David Cousin 50 School Lane, Fulbourn, Cambridge CB1 5BH — MB ChB 1991 Glas.

HAMILTON, David Geoffrey Boyd Como Villa Surgery, 7 Clarendon Road, St Helier, Jersey JE2 3YW Tel: 01534 870151 — MB BS 1981 Lond.; MRCP Eng. LRCP Lond. 1981. (Westm.)

HAMILTON, David Gilmour Regis Medical Centre, Darby Street, Rowley Regis, Warley B65 0BA Tel: 0121 559 3957 Fax: 0121 502 9117; Treetops Barn, Cashes Farm, Elmbridge, Droitwich WR9 0NQ Tel: 0121 427 3921 Email: hamiltons@treetopsbarn.freeserve.co.uk — MB ChB 1987 Birm.; MRCGP 1992; DCH RCP Lond. 1991; DRCOG 1989. GP; GP Tutor. Socs: RCGP; BMA.

HAMILTON, David Harvey Cul-Rathain, Milton, Crocketford, Dumfries DG2 8QT — MB BCh BAO 1989 Belf.; MRCGP 1994; DCH RCPS Glas. 1993; DRCOG 1992.

HAMILTON, Professor David Ian (retired) Links Cottage, 100 Meols Drive, West Kirby, Wirral CH48 5DB Tel: 0151 632 4481 — MB BS 1957 Lond.; FRCS Ed. 1989; FRCS Eng. 1961. Prev: Prof. Cardiac Surg. Univ. Edin. Roy. Infirm. & Roy. Hosp. Sick Childr. Edin.

HAMILTON, David Martin Mawney Road Practice, 34 Mawney Road, Romford RM7 7HD Tel: 01708 743627 Fax: 01708 738244 — MB BCh 1980 Wales. (University of Wales) Prev: GP Redbridge HA VTS; Ho. Off. Univ. Hosp. Wales.

HAMILTON, Mr David Ninian Hay (retired) Dalliefour, Barclaven Road, Kilmacolm PA13 4DQ — MB ChB Glas. 1963; PhD Glas. 1968, BSc 1960; FRCS Glas. 1974. Prev: Research Fell. Oxf. Univ.

HAMILTON, David Simpson (retired) Veran, Lyons Lane, Appleton, Warrington WA4 5JG Tel: 01925 265558 — MB BCh BAO 1955 Belf.; MRCGP 1962; DObst RCOG 1957. Prev: Ho. Surg. & Ho. Phys. Roy. Vict. Hosp. Belf.

HAMILTON, David Stewart Email: david.hamilton@rampton-hosp.trent.nhs.uk; Email: dav.dhamilton@doctors.org.uk — MB BCh BAO 1969 Belf.; MRCPsych 1979; DObst RCOG 1974. (Belf.) Nottm.shire Healthcare NHS Trust.

HAMILTON, David Valentine 219 Newmarket Road, Norwich NR4 7LA Tel: 01603 453859 Fax: 01603 504030 Email: david@hamilton219.freeserve.co.uk — MB BChir 1972 Camb.; MA Camb. 1972; FRCP Lond. 1992; MRCP (UK) 1975; MRCS Eng. LRCP Lond. 1972; FRCP 1992. (St.Thos.) Cons. Phys. Nephrol. Norf. & Norwich Hosp. Socs: Fell. RCP. Prev: Cons. Phys. Roy. Cornw. Hosp. Truro (Treliske); Sen. Regist. (Med.) Addenbrooke's Hosp. Camb. & Norf. & Norwich Hosp.

HAMILTON, Doreen 54 Holywood Road, Belfast BT4 1NT Tel: 01232 654668; 31 Earlswood Road, Belfast BT4 3DZ — MB BCh BAO 1963 Belf. (Belf.) Prev: SHO (Anaesth.) Belf. City Hosp. & Roy. Vict. Hosp. Belf.

HAMILTON, Duncan Lee 167 Cobbs Lane, Hough, Crewe CW2 5JL Tel: 01270 841308; 52 Hamilton Road, Wavell Heights, Brisbane Qld 4012, Australia Tel: 00 11 44 2566362 — BM BS 1992 Nottm.; BSc (Hons.) Leeds 1987; BMedSci (Hons.) Nottm. 1990. Regist. (Emerg. Med.) Roy. Brisbane Hosp. Qu.sland, Austral.; Regist. (IC) P. Chas. Hosp. Chermside, Qu.sland Austral. Prev: SHO (A & E) Roy. Lancaster Infirm.; Ho. Phys. (Cardiol. & Gen. Med.)

Derbysh. Roy. Infirm.; Ho. Surg. (Gen. & Vasc. Surg. & Urol.) Derbysh. Roy. Infirm.

HAMILTON, Edmund Monk, MBE (retired) 7 Pinecroft, St Georges Road, Weybridge KT13 0EN Tel: 01932 858507 — MB BCh BAO 1945 Belf.; DPH 1950; FFCM 1979, M 1972. Prev: DMO N.W. Surrey HA.

HAMILTON, Eleanor Maud (retired) 25 Weston Court, Burbo Bank Road S., Blundellsands, Liverpool L23 6SR Tel: 0151 924 4518 — MB ChB Liverpool. 1939; MRCS Eng. LRCP Lond. 1939. JP. Prev: Holt Research Fell. Physiol. Univ. Liverp. 1939-40.

HAMILTON, Eleanor May Greenock Health Centre, 20 Duncan St., Greenock PA15 4LY; Heywood Cottage, 13 Shore Road, Skelmorlie PA17 5EQ — MB ChB 1980 Glas.; MRCGP 1984.

HAMILTON, Elizabeth Findlay (retired) 2A Lennox Court, 22 Stockiemuir Avenue, Bearsden, Glasgow G61 3JN — MB ChB 1954 Aberd.; DO Eng. 1958. Prev: Assoc. Ophth. Specialist Glas. Roy. Infirm.

HAMILTON, Elspeth Mary The Firs, Tredunnock, Usk NP15 1LY — MB BCh 1981 Wales; DCH RCP Lond. 1987; DRCOG 1985. Clin. Med. Off. Gwent HA. Prev: Trainee GP Mid Glam. VTS; SHO (Paediat.) Roy. Gwent Hosp. Newport.

HAMILTON, Emily Coutts Beech House, 37 Station Road, Stone ST15 8ER — MB ChB 1969 Aberd. (Aberd.)

HAMILTON, Eric Brian Devon 11 Woodhall Drive, London SE21 7HJ Tel: 020 8693 2880; 152 Harley Street, London W1N 1HH Tel: 020 7935 3834 Fax: 020 7224 2574 — MA, MB BChir Camb. 1952; FRCP Lond. 1972, M 1957; DPhysMed. Eng. 1962. (Middlx.) Socs: Fell. Med. Soc. Lond. & Roy. Soc. Med. Prev: Cons. Phys. Rheum. & Rehabil. King's Coll. Hosp. Lond.; Regist. (Med.) Research Unit, Canad. Memor. Hosp. Taplow; Ho. Phys. Brompton Hosp. & Hammersmith Hosp.

HAMILTON, Ernest Anthony Gordon (retired) Thornfield Barn, Lancaster LA2 0QA — MB ChB 1956 Manch.; FRCR 1992; DMRD Eng. 1964. Prev: Cons. Radiol. & Clin. Dir. N. Lancs. BrE. Screening Servs.

HAMILTON, Evelyn Alison Cadogan Park Surgery, 34 Cadogan Park, Belfast BT9 6HH; 15 Broomhill Park, Belfast BT9 5JB Tel: 01232 667640 — MB BCh BAO 1983 Belf.; MRCGP 1988; DCH RCPI 1986; DRCOG 1985. Clin. Med. Off. S. Belf. Unit of Managem. E. HSSB. Prev: SHO (Paediat.) Roy. Belf. Hosp. Sick Childr.; SHO (O & G) Tyrone Co. Hosp. Omagh; SHO (Dermat.) Roy. Vict. Hosp. Belf.

HAMILTON, Fiona Locum Work Only; Easter Bodylair, Glass, Huntly AB54 4XR Tel: 01466 700375 — MB ChB 1982 Dundee; MRCGP 1986; DRCOG 1985. p/t Locum Work. Prev: GP Bedford & Edin.; Trainee GP/SHO Tayside HB VTS; GP Retainer Scheme Fife/Tayside.

HAMILTON, Fiona Jane Barnard Castle Surgery, Victoria Road, Barnard Castle DL12 8HT Tel: 01833 690707; Hilton Grange, Gainford, Darlington DL2 3JA — MB BS 1986 Newc.; MRCGP 1991. (Newc.) GP Princip. Socs: Roy. Coll. Gen. Pract.; BMA. Prev: Trainee GP/SHO Spennymoor Adan Hse.; SHO (O & G) Qu. Eliz. Hosp. Gateshead; SHO (ENT & Eyes) Sunderland.

HAMILTON, Fiona Louise 45A Yukon Road, London SW12 9PY — MB BS 1997 Lond. (UCL/Middx)

HAMILTON, Frank Archibald Edward (retired) Casita, Lawn Drive, Chudleigh, Newton Abbot TQ13 0LT Tel: 01626 852555 — MRCS Eng. LRCP Lond. 1946; MRCGP 1959. Prev: GP Chudleigh & Bovey Tracey Devon.

HAMILTON, Gary Walker 4 Maree Gardens, Bishopbriggs, Glasgow G64 1BX — MB ChB 1988 Glas.; MRCGP 1993.

HAMILTON, Mr George University Department of Surgery, Royal Free Hospital, Pond St., London NW3 2 Tel: 020 7830 2163 Fax: 020 7472 6278 Email: g.hamilton@rfc.ucl.ac.uk — MB ChB 1971 Glas.; FRCS Eng. 1977; DObst RCOG 1974. (University of Glasgow) Cons. Vasc. & Gen. Surg. Roy. Free Hosp. Lond.; Hon. Sec. Lect. Roy. Free Hosp. Sch. Med.; Clin Sub Dean and Site tutor Roy. Free & Univ Coll Sch. of Med UCL; Surg. to the Roy. Ho.hold. Socs: Eur. Vasc. Soc.; Coun. Mem. Internat. Soc. for Applied Cardiovasc. Biol.; Vasc. Advisory Comm. Prev: Hunt. Prof. 1997; Lect. & Sen. Regist. (Surg.) Roy. Free Hosp. Lond.; Clin. & Research Fell. (Vasc. Surg.) Mass. Gen. Hosp. Harvard Med. Sch. Boston, Mass. USA.

HAMILTON, Gerald Samuel David Leafield Cottage, Heathfield Drive, Blackwood, Lanark ML11 9SR — MB BCh BAO 1986 Belf.

HAMILTON, Gervase Robert (retired) 29 Elms Road, Clapham Common, London SW4 9ER — MB BS Lond. 1965; MSc (Community Med.) Lond. 1983; FFPHM RCP (UK) 1995; MFCM 1987; MRCGP 1970; DCH Eng. 1967; DObst RCOG 1967. Prev: Dir. (Pub. Health) Greenwich HA.

HAMILTON, Gordon James The Love Street Medical Centre, 40 Love Street, Paisley PA3 2DY Tel: 0141 889 3355 Fax: 0141 889 4785 — MB ChB 1973 Glasgow; MB ChB Glas. 1973. (Glasgow) GP Paisley, Renfrewsh.

HAMILTON, Gordon MacMillan Glasgow University Health Service, 63 Oakfield Avenue, Glasgow G12 8LP Tel: 0141 330 4538 Fax: 0141 330 3578; Gorrisholm, 2 Holm Road, Crossford, Carluke ML8 5RG Tel: 01555 860877 — MB ChB 1977 Glas.; MPhil Glas. 1994; DFM Glas. 1988. (Glas. Univ. Med. Sch.) Med. Off. Univ. Glas.; Med. Dir. Univ. Health Serv. Glas. Univ.; Hon. Sen. Lect. (Gen. Pract.) Glas. Univ. Socs: Soc. Occupat. Med.

HAMILTON, Guy Tancred Wolseys Farmhouse, Ingworth, Aylsham, Norwich NR11 6PH — MB BS 1957 Lond.; DObst RCOG 1967. (St. Thos.) Med. Examr. BAMS. Prev: Asst. Resid. (Med.) St. Eliz. Hosp. Youngstown, USA; Ho. Phys. St. Thos. Hosp. Hydestile; Ho. Off. (Obst.) St. Luke's Hosp. Guildford.

HAMILTON, Henry Clarke (retired) Whytelyons, 14 Primrose Hill, Brentwood CM14 4LT Tel: 01277 211342 — MD Lond. 1950, MB BS 1943; FRCP Lond. 1970, M 1947. Prev: Cons. Phys. Harold Wood Hosp., Brentwood Dist. Hosp. & Warley Hosp.

HAMILTON, Hilda Rose 12 Claremont Crescent, Edinburgh EH7 4HX Tel: 0131 558 3091 — MB ChB 1992 Ed.; BSc (Hons.) Heriot-Watt Univ. 1987. SHO (Genitourin. Med.) Roy. Infirm. Edin. Prev: Ho. Off. (Gen. Med. & Surg.) Roy. Infirm. Edin.

HAMILTON, Hyman (retired) 15 Manor Road N., Edgbaston, Birmingham B16 9JS Tel: 0121 454 4047 — MRCS Eng. LRCP Lond. 1924. Prev: Mem. Birm. Regional Hosp. Bd.

HAMILTON, Ian Alexander Harvey House Surgery, 13-15 Russell Avenue, St Albans AL3 5ES Tel: 01727 831888 Fax: 01727 845520 — MB BS 1988 Lond.; MSc (Sports Med.) Lond. 1995; MRCGP 1993. Clin. Asst. (Orthop.) St Albans City Hosp. St Albans. Socs: Brit. Assn. Sport & Med.

HAMILTON, Ian George (retired) 30 Kingsmoor Road, Harlow CM19 4HP — MB BS 1952 Lond.; DObst RCOG 1956. Prev: Ho. Phys. & Ho. Surg. Wembley Hosp.

HAMILTON, Mr Ian Jack Donald 19 St. James Street, Paisley PA3 2HQ Tel: 0141 889 5505; 34 Mansion Ho. Road, Paisley PA1 3RF Tel: 0141 889 1265 — MB ChB 1972 Glas.; MSc 1988 Glas.; FRCS Ed. 1978; MRCGP 1984. (Glas. Univ.)

HAMILTON, Ian Robert Grange Medical Group, 21A Kersiebank Avenue, Grangemouth FK3 9EL Tel: 01324 665533 — MB ChB 1982 Glas.; D.OCC.MED. 1999. Med. Off., Rohm & Hads, Grangemouth. Socs: Mem., Soc. Occupantional Med.

HAMILTON, Ian Samuel Kensington Medical Centre, 15A Donegall Road, Belfast BT12 5JJ Tel: 028 9032 5679 Fax: 028 9024 4267; Finaghy Health Centre, 13-25 Finaghy Road S., Belfast BT10 0BX Tel: 01232 628211 Fax: 01232 612210 — MB ChB 1976 Bristol; AFOM RCP Lond. 1992; MRCGP Lond. 1980; DRCOG Lond. 1980. Indust. Med. Off. Ulsterbus & Others. Socs: Fell. Ulster Med. Soc.; BMA; Soc. Occupat. Med. Prev: Trainee GP Cinque Ports VTS Dover; SHO W.on-super-Mare Hosps.; Ho. Surg. St. Martins's Hosp. Bath.

HAMILTON, Imogen Jane 12 Mason Street, Brunswick Village, Newcastle upon Tyne NE13 7EA — MB BS 1998 Newc.; MB BS Newc 1998.

HAMILTON, James Bruce Clifton Medical Centre, 571 Farnborough Road, Clifton, Nottingham NG11 9DN Tel: 0115 921 1288 — MB BS 1985 Lond.

HAMILTON, Mr James Bryan, TD 5 Mornington Villas, Bradford BD8 7JX Tel: 01274 44105 — MB BCh BAO 1963 Belf.; FRCS Ed. 1968. (Qu. Univ. Belf.) Socs: Brit. Orthop Assn.; Brit. Assoc Surg.Knee; Pres. Milit. Surg soc. Prev: Emerit. Cons. Surg. Orthop. Roy. Infirm. Bradford; Sen. Regist. (Orthop.) Leeds RHB.

HAMILTON, James Bryson (retired) Stromness, Dhailling Road, Kirn, Dunoon PA23 8EA Tel: 01369 703064 — MB ChB 1961 Glas.; DObst RCOG 1963. Anaesth. Dunoon Gen. Hosp.

HAMILTON, Mr James Gilmour (retired) 29 Hamilton Avenue, Birmingham B17 8AH Tel: 0121 429 1894 — MB BS Lond. 1947;

MD Lond. 1951; FRCS Eng. 1954; MRCP Lond. 1951. Prev: Cons. Neurosurg. Midl. Centre For Neurosurg. Smethwick.

HAMILTON, James Stanley Hunter Comely Bank, Rue du Vieux Moulin, Vallee Des Vaux, Trinity, Jersey JE3 5FD — MB ChB 1959 Glas.; DRCOG 1961.

HAMILTON, Janet Marion Isobel Well Lane House, Well Lane, Lower Froyle, Alton GU34 4LP — MB BS 1967 Lond.; MRCS Eng. LRCP Lond. 1967.

HAMILTON, Jennifer Doris 3R, 1 Grantley Gardens, Shawlands, Glasgow G41 3PY Email: jendh@msn.com — MB ChB 1989 Glas.; MRCP (UK) 1992. Sen. Regist. (Rheum.) Centre for Rheum. Dis. Glas. Roy. Infirm. Prev: Sen. Regist. (Gen. Med. & Rheum.) S.. Gen. Hosp. Glas.; SHO (Med.) W.. Infirm. Glas.; SHO (Geriat.) Vict. Geriat. Unit Glas.

HAMILTON, Jeremy William 40 Denorrton Park, Belfast BT4 1SF — MB ChB BAO 1991 Belf. SHO (Gen. Med.) Belf. City Hosp.

HAMILTON, Jessica Margaret Shadwell, TD 17 Bernard Terrace, Edinburgh EH8 9NU Tel: 0131 667 2836 — MB ChB 1947 Glas.; DA Eng. 1955. (Glas.) Asst. Anaesth. Edin. S.. Hosp. Gp.; Maj. RAMC TA. Prev: Jun. Hosp. Med. Off. E. Gen. Hosp. Edin; Regist. Anaesth. Glas. Roy. Infirm.; Ho. Phys. Roy. Hosp. Sick Childr. Glas.

HAMILTON, Jill Flat 8, 32 East Preston St., Edinburgh EH8 9QD Tel: 0131 662 4855 — MB ChB 1993 Aberd.; DFFP. (Aberdeen) GP Regist. Edin. Prev: SHO III (O & G) Simpsons Memor. Matern. Hosp. Edin.; SHO (O & G) St John's Hosp. Livingston; Trainee GP/SHO (O & G) Glas. Roy. Matern. Hosp. & Glas. Roy. Infirm.

HAMILTON, Jillian Gordon Top Left, 33 Victoria Park Drive S., Scotstown, Glasgow G14 9RH Tel: 0114 959 0446 — MB ChB 1995 Manch. SHO (Paediat.) Monklands Dist. Gen. Hosp. Airdrie. Socs: BMA; Med. Protec. Soc.; MSS. Prev: SHO (Paediat.) GRMH Glas.; SHO Paediat. RHSC Glasg. (Yorkhill); SHO A & E Roy. Lancaster Infirm.

HAMILTON, John (retired) 3 The Nurseries, Formby, Liverpool L37 4JG — MB ChB 1940 Glas.; MB ChB (Commend.) 1940; BSc Glas. 1937; FFA RCS Eng. 1954; DA Eng. 1947. Prev: Cons. Anaesth. Thos. Kt. Memor. Hosp. Blyth, Ashington Hosp., Morpeth Cott. Hosp., St. Geo. Hosp. Morpeth & N.gate & Dist. Hosp.

HAMILTON, Mr John Anthony (retired) 17 Kirklee Road, Glasgow G12 0RQ Tel: 0141 339 2051 Fax: 0141 357 0112 — MB ChB 1955 Glas.; FRCS Glas. 1985; FRCS Ed. 1961. Prev: Cons. Orthop. Surg. Roy. Infirm. Glas.

HAMILTON, John Cosbie Parkview Surgery, 28 Millfield Avenue, Hull Road, York YO10 3AB Tel: 01904 413644 Fax: 01904 431436; 8 Rawcliffe Lane, Clifton, York YO30 6NH Email: john@jhamilt.demon.co.uk — MB ChB 1977 Ed.; MRCGP 1981; DA Eng. 1983. Clin. Asst. Tang Hall Community Unit for Elderly. Socs: York Med. Soc. Prev: Clin. Asst. & SHO (Anaesth.) York Dist. Hosp.

HAMILTON, Mr John Robert Leslie Freeman Hospital, High Heaton, Newcastle upon Tyne NE7 7DN Tel: 0191 223 1331 Fax: 0191 213 2167 Email: leslie.hamilton@tfh.nuth.northy.nhs.uk; The Old Barn, Low Gosforth Home Farm, Bridle Path, Newcastle upon Tyne NE3 5EU Tel: 0191 285 0052 — MB BCh BAO 1977 Belf.; FRCS Ed. (Cth.) 1988; FRCS Eng. 1982. (Queen's Belfast) Cons. Cardiac Surg. (Paediat.& Adult) Freeman Hosp. Newc. u. Tyne. Socs: Soc. Cardiothoracic Surg. GB & Irel. - Cardiothoracic Dean; BMA; Brit. Paediat. Cardiac Assn. Prev: Sen. Regist. (Cardiothoracic Surg.) Yorks. RHA; Sen. Regist. (Cardiothoracic Surg.) Hosp. for Sick Childr. Gt. Ormond St. Lond.

HAMILTON, John Roger Queens Road Surgery, 10B Queens Road, Blackhill, Consett DH8 0BN Tel: 01207 502071 Fax: 01207 583717 — MB ChB 1965 Ed.

HAMILTON, John Winslow Fragaria, Lawrences Meadow, Gotherington, Cheltenham GL52 9UH — MB BChir 1985 Camb.

HAMILTON, Joseph Nevin 37 Rossdowney Road, Londonderry BT47 5PB — MB BCh BAO 1970 Belf.; FFA RCSI 1974. Cons. Anaesth. Altnagelvin Area Hosp. Lond.derry. Prev: Sen. Regist. (Anaesth.) Roy. Vict. Hosp. Belf.; Sen. Tutor Dept. Anaesth. Qu. Univ. Belf.

HAMILTON, Judith Ann Flat 2/2, 21 Lawrence St., Glasgow G11 5HF — MB ChB 1994 Aberd. SHO (Anaesth.) Stobhill Hosp. Glas. Prev: SHO (Geriat.) Vict. Infirm. Glas.; SHO (A & E) CrossHo. Hosp. Kilmarnock; Ho. Off. (Gen. Med.) The Ayr Hosp.

HAMILTON, Judith Anne 10 The Firs, Eaton Rise, Ealing, London W5 2HG — MB BS 1992 Lond.; BSc (1st cl. Hons.) Chem Path. Lond. 1989. Specialist Regist. Guy's & St. Thomas' Hosp., Lond. Prev: Research Regist. (O & G) Fertil Centre Roy. Hosps. NHS Trust.

HAMILTON, Judith Charlotte Chesterton, Noads Way, Dibden Purlieu, Southampton SO45 4PD — BM 1983 Soton.; MSc (Clin. Biochem.) Surrey 1974; BSc (Biochem.) Sussex 1971.

HAMILTON, Julia Ruth Whiteman's Surgery, Whitefriar's Street, Perth PH1 1PP Tel: 01738 627912 Fax: 01738 643969; 27 Torwoodlee, Perth PH1 1SY — MB BCh BAO 1990 Belf.; MRCGP 1994; DFFP 1996; DCH Dub. 1993. Socs: Med. & Dent. Defence Union. Scotl.; BMA. Prev: Trainee GP Perth.

HAMILTON, Kevin 4 Lorne Lane, Holywood BT18 0NW — MB BS 1997 Lond.

HAMILTON, Linda May Orkney Health Board, Health Centre, New Scope Road, Kirkwall KW15 1BX; Innistone, Dundas Crescent, Kirkwall KW15 1JQ — MB ChB 1970 Glas. SCMO Orkney HB. Socs: Brit. Assn. Community Child Health.

HAMILTON, Lorna Margaret Douglas Street Surgery, 1 Douglas Street, Hamilton ML3 0DR; 20 Invervale Avenue, Airdrie ML6 8NH — MB ChB 1988 Glas.

HAMILTON, Lyle William Eakin Camlet Lodge RSU, Chase Farm Hospital, Enfield EN2 8JL — MB BS 1982 Lond.; PhD Lond. 1977, BSc 1974; MRCPsych 1986. Cons. Forens. Psychiat. Camlet Lodge Secure Unit Chase Farm Hosp. Enfield. Prev: Sen. Regist. (Forens. Psychiat.) Roy. Free Hosp. Lond.

HAMILTON, Malcolm Seyton Department of Haematology, Good Hope Hospital, Rectory Road, Sutton Coldfield B75 7RR Tel: 0121 378 2211 Fax: 0121 311 1800 — MB ChB 1982 Bristol; MRCP (UK) 1985; MRCPath 1993. Cons. Haemat. Good Hope Hosp. Sutton Coldfield.; Dir. UKNEQAS Haematinics 1998-. Prev: Sen. Regist. (Haemat.) Univ. Coll. Hosp. Lond.; Leukaemia Research Fund Regist. Dept. Haemat. & Immunol. Qu. Eliz. Hosp. Birm.; Regist. (Haemat.) W.. Gen. Hosp. Edin.

HAMILTON, Margaret Alicia The Surgery, 8 Shenfield Road, Brentwood CM15 8AB Tel: 01277 218393 Fax: 01277 201017; 80 Park Road, Brentwood CM14 4TU — MB BS 1972 Lond. (London Hospital Medical School) Prev: SHO (Med.) Qu. Eliz. II Hosp. Welwyn Garden City; SHO (Cardiol.) St. Mary's Hosp. Lond.; Resid. Regina Gen. Hosp. Sascatchewan, Canada.

HAMILTON, Margaret Elizabeth Student Health Service, University of Aberdeen, Block E, Taylor Buildings, Old Aberdeen, Aberdeen AB24 3UB Tel: 01224 276655 Fax: 01224 272463 — MB ChB 1981 Ed.

HAMILTON, Margaret Hazel Fowey Health Centre, Rawlings Lane, Fowey PL23 1DT Tel: 01726 832451 — MB BCh BAO 1973 Belf.; MSc (Community Med.) Lond. 1979.

HAMILTON, Marjory Isabella Katherine (retired) St Aidans, Midmar, Inverurie AB51 7LX — MB ChB 1951 Aberd.; DObst RCOG 1957. SCMO (Community Health) S. Grampian Health Dist. Prev: JHMO (O & G) St. Albans City Hosp.

HAMILTON, Mark Andrew 6 Courtney Road, London SW19 2ED — MB BS 1994 Lond.

HAMILTON, Mark Ian Ravensworth 119 King Henry's Road, London NW3 3RB — MB BS 1987 Lond.; MRCP 1990.

HAMILTON, Mark Patrick Rogers Department of Obstetrics & Gynaecology, Aberdeen Maternity Hospital, Foresterhill, Aberdeen AB25 2ZL Tel: 01224 840567 Fax: 01224 684880 — MD 1989 Glas.; MB ChB 1978; MRCOG 1983; FRCOG 1996. Cons. (O & G) Aberd. Roy. Hosps. NHS Trust; Subspecialist in Reproduc. Med. (RCOG) 1990.; Deanery Coll. Adviser in Gyn. (N. Scotl.); Europ. Soc. for Human Reproductive & Embryology. Socs: Brit. Fertil. Soc.; Amer. Soc. Reproduc. Med.; Gyn. Vis. Soc. Prev: Lect. (O & G) Nat. Univ. Singapore.

HAMILTON, Mark Samuel 16 Gibson Pk Gardens, Belfast BT6 9GN — MB BCh BAO 1997 Belf.

HAMILTON, Martin Ian 96 Viewforth (3F1), Edinburgh EH10 4LG — MB ChB 1997 Ed.

HAMILTON, Mary Old Mill House, Old Mill Lane, Thurgoland, Sheffield S35 7EG — MB ChB 1986 Aberd.

HAMILTON, Mary Ligat (retired) 1 Alyth Road, Talbot Woods, Bournemouth BH3 7DF Tel: 01202 296600 — MB ChB 1924 Glas.

HAMILTON, Maurice James Hunt (retired) 20 Scotts Lane, Shortlands, Bromley BR2 0LH Tel: 020 8650 6094 — MB BCh BAO 1950 Dub.

HAMILTON, Maurice Julian Ambleside Road, Keswick CA12 4DB; 72 Blencathra Street, Keswick CA12 4HX — MB ChB 1967 Manch.; FRCGP 2000; MRCGP 1975; DObst RCOG 1969. (Manch.) Socs: Bd. Mem. Brit. Assn. Rally Doctors; BASICS. Prev: SHO (Obst.) H.M. Stanley Hosp. St. Asaph; Ho. Surg. & Ho. Phys. Cumbld. Infirm. Carlisle.

HAMILTON, Melinda 88 Cloverfield, Clayton-le-Woods, Chorley PR6 7RX — MB ChB 1995 Leic. SHO (Paediat.) Chelsea & W.minster Hosp. Lond.

HAMILTON, Michael, OBE (retired) 3 Barnfield, Feering Hill, Kelvedon, Colchester CO5 9HP Tel: 01376 571914 — MD 1949 Lond.; MB BS (Distinc. Path. & Obst.); FRCP Lond. 1966. M 1946. Hon. Cons. Phys. Mid. Essex HA. Prev: Cons. Phys. Chelmsford Hosp. Gp.

HAMILTON, Michael John 5 Lyneham Close, Blackpole Vill., Worcester WR4 9YY — MB ChB 1982 Birm.; ChB Birm. 1982; MRCP (UK) 1986; MRCGP 1990. Prev: Regist. (Gen. Med.) Hackney Hosp. Lond.; SHO (Gen. Med.) Good Hope Hosp. Sutton Coldfield; SHO (Neurol.) Pinderfields Gen. Hosp. Wakefield.

HAMILTON, Moira Anne Air Balloon Surgery, Kenn Road, St George, Bristol BS5 7PD Tel: 0117 909 9914 Fax: 0117 908 6660; 7 Napier Road, Redland, Bristol BS6 6RT Tel: 0117 973 6921 — MB ChB 1981 Bristol; MRCGP 1985; DRCOG 1983. GP Bristol.

HAMILTON, Muriel (retired) Thornfield Barn, Ellel, Lancaster LA2 0QA — MB ChB 1957 Manch. Prev: Clin. Asst. (Urol.) Lancaster Acute Hosps. NHS Trust.

HAMILTON, Neil William Orchard House Health Centre, Union Street, Stirling FK8 1PH Tel: 01786 50394 Fax: 01786 448284; Craigrossie, 15 Muiradam Villas, Newmarket, Bannockburn, Stirling FK7 8JB — MB ChB 1984 Glas.; MB ChB Glas. l984; MRCGP 1988.

HAMILTON, Pamela Gillian 50 Fordwich Rise, Hertford SG14 2BN — MB BS 1982 Lond.; MRCGP 1989; DCH RCP Lond. 1987; DRCOG 1986.

HAMILTON, Patricia Anne Department of Child Health, St Georges Hospital, Cranmer Terrace, London SW17 0RE Tel: 020 8725 2517 Fax: 020 8725 1933 Email: p.hamilton@sghms.ac.uk; 20 Bucharest Road, London SW18 3AR Tel: 020 8870 5822 Fax: 020 8870 5822 — MB ChB 1975 Bristol; MB ChB (Hons.) Bristol 1975; BSc (Anat.) Bristol 1972; FRCP Lond. 1993; MRCP (UK) 1978; DRCOG 1979; MRCPCH 1997; FRCPCH 1997. (Bristol) Cons. & Sen. Lect. Neonat. Paediat. St. Geo. Hosp. Lond.; Hon. Sec. Roy. Coll. of Paediat. Socs: (Treas.) Neonat. Soc.; Eur. Soc. Paediat. Research; Brit. Assn. Perinatal Med. Prev: Regist. (Paediat.) Hosp. Sick Childr. Bristol; SHO (Paediat.) Hosp. Sick Childr. Gt. Ormond St. Lond.; Clin. Lect. (Paediat.) Univ. Coll. Hosp. Lond.

HAMILTON, Paul Flat 1, Hamilton Lodge, 2 Cleveland Grove, Cleveland Way, London E1 4XH — MB BS 1998 Lond.; MB BS Lond 1998.

HAMILTON, Paul Gareth 1 Conway Road, London SW20 8PB — BM BS 1994 Nottm.

HAMILTON, Peter Gordon High Street Surgery, Cumberland House, 8 High Street, Stone ST15 8AP Tel: 01785 813538 Fax: 01785 812208; Beech House, 37 Station Road, Stone ST15 8ER Tel: 01785 817948 — MB ChB 1972 Aberd.; MRCGP 1976; MFFP 1993; DObst RCOG 1975. Socs: BMA & N. Staffs. Med. Inst. Prev: Trainee GP Aberd. VTS; Ho. Surg. Woodend Gen. Hosp. Aberd.; Ho. Phys. Aberd. Roy. Infirm.

HAMILTON, Peter John 143 Runnymede Road, Darras Hall, Ponteland, Newcastle upon Tyne NE20 9HN — BM BCh 1968 Oxf.; FRCP Lond. 1983; MRCP (U.K.) 1971; FRCPath 1987, M 1975. (Oxf.) Cons. (Haemat.) & Clin. Lect. Roy. Vict. Infirm. Newc. Prev: Sen. Med. Regist. & Lect. (Haemat.) Aberd. Teach. Hosps.; Intern. Dept. Path. Johns Hopkins Hosp. Baltimore, U.S.A; Resid. (Med. Surg. & Neurol.) United Oxf. Hosps.

HAMILTON, Philip Alexander Handsworth Wood Medical Centre, 110 Church Lane, Handsworth Wood, Birmingham B20 2ES Tel: 0121 523 7117 Fax: 0121 554 2406 — MB ChB 1966 Birm.; MRCS Eng. LRCP Lond. 1966. (Birm.) Socs: BMA & Soc. Occupat. Med. Prev: Ho. Surg. Gen. Hosp. Birm.; Ho. Phys. Qu. Eliz. Hosp. Birm.; SHO Birm. & Midl. Hosp. Wom.

HAMILTON, Rebecca Jane Farm View, 2 Spencers Lane, Berkswell, Coventry CV7 7BB — MB BS 1991 Newc.

HAMILTON, Rhys William Goring and Woodcote Medical Practice, Red Cross Road, Goring on Thames, Reading RG8 9HG Tel: 01491 872372 Fax: 01491 875908; Applegarth, Wantage Road, Streatley, Reading RG8 9LD Tel: 01491 872073 — BM BCh 1976 Oxf.; MA, BM BCh Oxf. 1976; MRCGP 1980; DRCOG 1981. GP Berks. AHA.

HAMILTON, Rita Ann Woodlands, Upper Lambourn Road, Lambourn, Hungerford RG17 8QG — MB BS 1991 Lond.

HAMILTON, Robin Douglas 1B Cleveland Square, London W2 6DH — MB BS 1994 Lond. (St. Mary's Hospital Medical School) SHO (Ophth.) Qu.'s Med. Centre Nottm.

HAMILTON, Robin William Archway Medical Practice, Francis St., Stornoway, Isle of Lewis HS1 2XB Tel: 01851 703588 Fax: 01851 706338 — MB ChB 1965 Glas.

HAMILTON, Roderick Malcomson 12 Lady Margaret Drive, Troon KA10 7AL — MB ChB 1998 Glas.; MB ChB Glas 1998.

HAMILTON, Ronald Joseph (retired) 15 Keel Point, Dundrum, Newcastle BT33 0NQ Tel: 0139 675375 — MB BCh BAO 1957 Belf.; DObst RCOG 1961. Prev: GP Belf.

HAMILTON, Rosemarie Joy Broom Close Farm, Pinfold Hill, Curbar, Hope Valley S32 3YL — BM 1984 Soton.; MRCOG 1991. Cons. O & G Rotherham Gen. Hosp. Prev: Sen. Regist. N. Staffs. Hosp NHS Trust Stoke-on-Trent; Ho. Surg. Roy. United Hosp. Bath; Ho. Phys. Soton. Gen. Hosp.

HAMILTON, Rosemary Ann Craigavon Area Hospital, 68 Lurgan Road, Portadown, Craigavon BT63 5QQ Tel: 01762 334444 — MB ChB 1978 Sheff.; MRCOG 1986. Cons. O & G Craigavon Area Hosp. Gp. Trust. Prev: Sen. Regist. (O & G) Belf. City Hosp.

HAMILTON, Ross Jamieson Royal Cornhill Hospital, Aberdeen AB25 3HG; 4 Kingshill Terrace, Aberdeen AB15 5JZ — MB ChB 1982 Aberd.; MRCPsych 1994; MRCGP 1986; DRCOG 1985. (Aberd.) Cons. Psychiat.; Hon. Sen. Lect. Ment. Health Univ. Aberd.

HAMILTON, Roy Mark 14 Tatton View, Withington, Manchester M20 4BU Email: sparky@mj-hamilton.demon.co.uk — MB ChB 1994 Manch. SHO (A & E) Manch. Roy. Infirm.

HAMILTON, Ruth Munro 18 Orchard Street, Motherwell ML1 3JD — MB ChB 1989 Glas.; BSc (Hons.) Physiol. Glas. 1987, MB ChB 1989.

HAMILTON, Ryan John 69 Moneymore Road, Cookstown BT80 8EH — MB ChB 1997 Glas.

HAMILTON, Samuel Gordon Ian (retired) Trevaunance, Comprigney Hill, Truro TR1 3EE Tel: 01872 272952 — MB BChir 1960 Camb.; MA Camb. 1961, BA 1956, MChir 1966; FRCS Eng. 1964; LMSSA Lond. 1959. Cons. Gen. Surg. Roy. Cornw. Hosp. (Treliske)(Urol.). Prev: Sen. Regist. (Surg.) Bristol Roy. Infirm.

HAMILTON, Sara Anne St Davids Surgery, Eryl Mor, 36 New Street, St. Davids, Haverfordwest SA62 6SS Tel: 01437 720303 Fax: 01437 721162; Treiago, St. David's, Haverfordwest SA62 6DB Tel: 01437 720348 — MB BS 1975 Newc.; Dip. Palliat. Med. Cardiff 1997.

HAMILTON, Sarah Ann 2 Gareth Close, Thornhill, Cardiff CF14 9AF — MB BS 1997 Lond.

HAMILTON, Sharon Anne 6 Anagach Hill, Old Speybridge, Grantown-on-Spey PH26 3NF; Elgin Community Surgery, Grampian Road, Elgin IV30 1XJ Tel: 01343 542234 — MB ChB 1991 Ed.; MRCGP 1995; DRCOG 1995. (Ed.) GP Elgin Community Surg. Elgin.

HAMILTON, Sharon Joan 13 Elm Way, London N11 3NP — MB ChB 1996 Birm.; ChB Birm. 1996.

HAMILTON, Sheila Christine Cavaye Burley Park Medical Centre, 273 Burley Road, Leeds LS4 2EL; 120 Adel Lane, Leeds LS16 8BX Tel: 674141 — MB ChB 1955 Glas.

HAMILTON, Shona Marie Calderdale Royal Hospital, Salter Hebble, Halifax HX3 0PW Tel: 01422 224131; 87 Finkle Lane, Gildersome, Leeds LS27 7DR — MB ChB Ed. 1982; MRCOG 1988. Cons. O & G Calderdale Roy. Hosp. Prev: Research Fell. (Clin. Audit) Roy. Coll. O & G Audit St. Mary's Hosp. Unit Manch.; Sen. Regist. (O & G) Bradford Roy. Infirm. & Leeds Gen. Infirm.; Regist. (O & G) N. Manch. Gen. Hosp.

HAMILTON, Sidney Gerrish 4 Grove Drive, Hope Corner Lane, Taunton TA2 7TD Tel: 01823 283028 — MRCS Eng. LRCP Lond. 1937; MA, MB BChir Camb. 1938; FRCGP 1972, M 1953; DCH Eng. 1946. (Lond. Hosp.) Socs: BMA. Prev: Ho. Phys. (Paediat.)

Lond. Hosp.; Surg. Lt.-Cdr. RNVR 1940-46; Med. Adviser Brit. High Commiss. Delhi, India 1972-76.

HAMILTON, Stephen Department of Orthopaedic Surgery, Victoria Infirmary, Langside Road, Glasgow G42 9TY — MB ChB 1991 Glas.

HAMILTON, Stephen Leonard Heaton Medical Centre, 2 Lucy St., Heaton, Bolton BL1 5PU Tel: 01204 843677 — MB BS 1990 Newc.; MRCGP 1995; T(G) 1995.

HAMILTON, Steven John Currie Woodend Hospital, Eday Road, Aberdeen AB15 6X6; 130 Kings Gate, Aberdeen AB15 4EQ — MB ChB 1978 Aberd.; FRCP Glas. 1992; MRCP (UK) 1982; MBA (Stirling)1999. Cons. Phys. & Hon. Clin. Sen. Lect. (Geriat. & Rehabil. Med.) Aberd.; Assoc. Med. Director. Prev: Sen. Regist. (Gen. Med. & Geriat. Med.) Oxf. RHA; Research Fell. Brit. Foundat. Age Research Univ. Oxf.

HAMILTON, Mr Stuart Andrew 47 Pasture Road, Letchworth SG6 3LS — MB ChB 1991 Glas.; FRCS Ed. 1996. (Glas. Univ.)

HAMILTON, Stuart John 9 Troon Close, Consett DH8 5XF — MB ChB 1998 Dund.; MB ChB Dund 1998.

HAMILTON, Susan Elizabeth 54 Asterfield Avenue, Bebbington, Wirral CH63 5JZ — MB ChB 1989 Liverp.; MRCGP 1995; DTM & H Liverp. 1996; DRCOG 1995; DCH RCP Lond. 1994; DFFP 1994; MRCPCH 1999. (Liverp) Staff Grade. Community. Paediat. Countess of Chester.Hosp. Socs: Liverp. Med. Inst.; Clin. Infec. Soc.; NW Epidemiol. Club. Prev: Staff Grade (A & E) Alder Hey Childr. Hosp. Liverp.

HAMILTON, Susan Henderson 2 Tylney Road, Oldhall, Paisley PA1 3JN — MB ChB 1980 Glas.; MFFP 1993; MRCGP 1985; DCH RCPS Glas. 1985; DRCOG 1982. SCMO (Primary & Community Care) Renfrewsh. NHS Healthcare Trust. Prev: Clin. Med. Off. (Primary & Community Care) Gtr. Glas. HB; Trainee GP Old Kirkpatrick; SHO Rotat. (Community Paediat.) Yorkhill Hosp. Glas.

HAMILTON, Thomas Jeffrey 87 The Thoroughfare, Woodbridge IP12 1AW — MB BS 1993 Lond. Prev: SHO (Anaesth.) The Roy. Hosps. Trust Whitechapel.

HAMILTON, Victoria Hazel Applegarth, Wantage Road, Streatley, Reading RG8 9LD — BM BCh 1976 Oxf.; MA Oxf. 1976, MSc 1974; MRCP 1980; MRCGP 1981. GP Prinicl.

HAMILTON, William (retired) 81 Woodend Drive, Glasgow G13 1QF Tel: 0141 954 9961 — MB ChB 1952 Glas.; MD Glas. 1967; FRCP Ed. 1969; FRCP Glas. 1968; MRCP (UK) 1962; MRCP (UK) 1959; FRFPS Glas. 1959; DPH Glas. 1954; DCH Eng. 1954. Sen. Lect. (Child Health) Univ. Glas.; Hon. Cons. Roy. Hosp. Sick Childr. Glas. Prev: Sen. Lect. (Child Health) Univ. Glas.

HAMILTON, William Donald Eric (retired) 67 Lower Road, Mackworth, Derby DE22 4NF — BM BCh 1950 Oxf.; MA Oxf. 1952; MCOphth 1990; DO Eng. 1957. Assoc. Specialist (Ophth.) St. Mary's Hosp. Paddington. Prev: Sen. Regist. King Edwd. VII Hosp. Windsor & St. Luke's Hosp. Maidenhead.

HAMILTON, William Farquhar Douglas Department of Anaesthesia, Ninewells Hospital & Medical School, Dundee DD1 9SY Tel: 01382 660111 Fax: 01382 644914; 54 Doocot Road, St Andrews KY16 8QP — MB ChB 1967 Aberd.; FRCA 1972; DA Eng. 1970. Cons. Anaesth. & Hon. Sen. Lect. (Anaesth.) Ninewells Hosp. & Med. Sch. Dundee; Cons. in Admi/c - Intens. Care Unit Ninewells Hosp. & Med. Sch. Dundee; Clin. Lead. ICU/HDU Dir.Critical Care. Socs: Assn. Anaesth. GB & Irel.; Intens. Care Soc.; Scott. Soc. Anaesth. Prev: Clin. Direct. Directorate Critical Care Med. Dundee Teach. Hosps NHS Trust; Sec. - Scott. Soc. of Anaesth.; Sec. Standing Comm. Scotl. Roy. Coll. Anaesth.

HAMILTON, William Marshall Orkney Health Board, Garden House, Kirkwall KW15 1BQ Tel: 01856 885400 Fax: 01856 885411; Innistore, Dundas Crescent, Kirkwall KW15 1JQ Tel: 01856 873007 — MB ChB 1965 Glas.; MB ChB (Commend.) Glas. 1965; BSc (Hons.) Glas. 1962; FFA RCS Eng. 1969; Dip. Soc. Med. Ed. 1974. (Glas.) Dir. (Pub. Health) Orkney HB. Prev: GP Kirkwall, Orkney; Fell. (Community Med.) Woodburn Ho. Edin.; Lect. (Anaesth) Univ. Nairobi, Kenya.

HAMILTON, William Trevor Barnfield Hill Surgery, 12 Barnfield Hill, Exeter EX1 1SR Tel: 01392 432761 Fax: 01392 422406 — MB ChB 1982 Bristol; MRCP (UK) 1986; MRCGP 1989. Research Fell., Univ. of Exeter.; Chief Med. Off. Liverp. Vict.

HAMILTON, Yvonne Margaret Hogg (retired) 9 Thistle Street, Dunfermline KY12 0JA — MB ChB 1949 Aberd.

HAMILTON-AYRES, Michele Jocelyn Jessica Cheltenham General Hospital, Sandford Road, Cheltenham GL53 7AN Tel: 01242 222222 Fax: 01242 273453 Email: michele.hamilton-ayres@egnhst.org.uk; Tel: 01242 236152 Fax: 01242 236152 — MD 1981 Louvain; MRCPI 1993; DCH Lond. 1997. (Université Catholique De Louvain, Belgium) Cons. Paediat. E. Glos. Trust. Socs: BAPM; Fell. Roy. Coll. Paediat. & Child Health; BMA.

HAMILTON-BELL, Patrick (retired) 214 Sheen Road, Richmond TW10 5AN Tel: 020 8940 3121 — MB ChB 1937 Aberd.

HAMILTON-DAVIES, Colin, Capt. RAMC 1 Grove Way, Esher KT10 8HH — MB BS 1986 Lond. Regtl. Med. Off. 3rd Bn. Parachute Regt. Aldershot. Prev: Med. Off. 23 Parachute Field Ambul.; Ho. Surg. (Urol. & Gen. Surg.) Middlx. & Univ. Coll. Hosps. Lond.; Ho. Phys. (Haemat. & Respirat. Med.) St. Albans City Hosp.

HAMILTON-DEANE, William Hart Hamilton (retired) 79 Middleton Road, Gorleston-on-Sea, Great Yarmouth NR31 7PN Tel: 01493 661482 Fax: 01493 441456 — MRCS Eng. LRCP Lond. 1955; LAH Dub. 1953. Prev: SHO (Obst.) Fulham Matern. Hosp.

HAMILTON-FAIRLEY, Diana 97 Drakefield Road, London SW17 8RS Tel: 020 8672 2341 — MB BS 1981 Lond.; MRCOG 1988.

HAMILTON-FARRELL, Martin Robert Department of Anaesthetics, Whipps Cross Hospital, London E11 1NR Tel: 020 8539 1222 Fax: 020 8539 1333 — MRCS Eng. LRCP Lond. 1977; BSc Lond. 1974, MB BS 1977; MRCP (UK) 1980; FFARCS Eng. 1984. (King's Coll. Hosp.) Cons. Anaesth. & Hyperbaric Med. Whipps Cross Hosp. Lond.

HAMILTON KIRKWOOD, Laurence John Brockweid, 99 Allt-yr-Yn Avenue, Newport NP20 5DE — MB BS 1984 Lond.; MSc (Community Med.) Lond. 1990; MFPHM RCP (UK) 1994; DGM RCP Lond. 1988. Commiss.ing Dir. Bro Taf HA; Cons. Pub. Health Med. M. Glam. HA. Prev: Sen. Regist. (Pub. Health Med.) Mid. Glam. HA; Med. Off. Welsh Off.

HAMILTON-PATERSON, John (retired) 36 Fourth Avenue, Frinton-on-Sea CO13 9DX — MRCS Eng. LRCP Lond. 1960; MRCGP 1987; DObst RCOG 1962.

HAMILTON-PATERSON, Ursula Ysabel (retired) Flat 36, Cloister House, 53 Griffiths Road, Wimbledon, London SW19 1SS Tel: 020 8543 2533 — MB BS 1932 Lond.; MRCS Eng. LRCP Lond. 1932; FFA RCS Eng. 1963; DA Eng. 1937. Prev: Cons. Anaesth. Battersea, Putney & Tooting, Sidcup & Swanley, & Dartford Hosp. Gps.

HAMILTON-SMITH, James Andrew Annie Prendergash Health Centre, Ashton Gardens, Romford RM6 6RT Tel: 020 8590 1461 Fax: 020 8597 7819; 9 St. Andrews Avenue, Elm Park, Hornchurch RM12 5DS Tel: 01708 478312 Email: james@ghazala.epulse.net — MB BCh BAO 1982 Belf.; DRCOG 1988; Cert. Family Plann. JCC 1988. (Queen's University of Belfast) GP Princip.; Private Pract. Socs: Med. Insur. Assn. Prev: SHO Rotat. (Paediat.) Essex; Trainee GP Essex.

HAMILTON-WOOD, Clive Department of Radiology, Royal Devon & Exeter Hospital, Barrack Road, Exeter EX2; Clystside, off Elm Grove Road, Exeter EX3 0BN Tel: 01392 877686 — MB ChB 1975 Aberd.; FRCP Lond. 1996; MRCP (UK) 1978; FRCR 1985. Cons. Radiol. Roy. Devon & Exeter Hosp. Wonford. Prev: Sen. Regist. & Regist. (Radiol.) Bristol Roy. Infirm.; Regist. (Med.) Bristol Roy. Infirm.; Lect. (Radiol.) Chinese Univ. Hong Kong.

HAMILTON-WRIGHT, Helena Mary 6 Raleigh Road, Southville, Bristol BS3 1QR — MB ChB 1986 Zimbabwe; MB ChB U Zimbabwe 1986; FRCR 1993.

HAMLET, George Wyndward, 1 Moadlock, Romiley, Stockport SK6 4QB Tel: 0161 430 5057 — LMSSA 1953 Lond.; MRCS Eng. LRCP Lond. 1958. (Manch.) Socs: BMA. Prev: GP Tameside; Ho. Surg. & Ho. Phys. Ashton-under-Lyne Gen. Hosp.; Capt. RAMC.

HAMLET, Mark Richard 94 Heythorp Street, London SW18 5BX — MB BS 1987 Lond.

HAMLET, Neil William — MB ChB 1982 Ed.; MRCGP 1986; DRCOG 1985. Regist. (Infec. Dis.) Ruchill Hosp. Glas. Prev: SHO (Med. Geriat.) Auchterarder VTS.

HAMLETT, John Watson (retired) 4 Niddries Court, Niddries Lane, Moulton, Northwich CW9 8RD Tel: 01606 559091 — MB BS Lond. 1951; MRCS Eng. LRCP Lond. 1951. Prev: Local Civil Serv. Med. Off.

HAMLIN, George William Anaesthetic Department, Blackburn Royal Infirmary, Blackburn BB2 3LR Tel: 01254 263555; 4

Rogersfield, Langho, Blackburn BB6 8HB — MB ChB 1977 Leeds; FRCA 1983 Eng.; 1980 DRCOG. Cons. Anaesth. Blackburn Roy. Infirm.; RCA Clin. Tutor Blackburn. Prev: Post Grad. Clin. Tutor Blackburn.

HAMLIN, Peter John 11 Weston Close, Blofield, Norwich NR13 4QN; 139 Main Street, Fulford, York YO10 4PP — MB ChB 1992 Leeds; MRCP (UK) 1995. SHO (Gastroenterol.) St. Jas. Hosp. Leeds. Prev: SHO Rotat. (Med.) York. Dist. Hosp.; Ho. Off. Seacroft Hosp. Leeds.

HAMLIN, Rosemary Ann The Oakwood Surgery, Masham Road, Cantley, Doncaster DN4 6BU Tel: 01302 537611 Fax: 01302 371804 — MB ChB 1977 Birm.; DRCOG 1980. Mem. (Sec.) Doncaster Area LMC; Med. Adviser Doncaster Health Auth.

HAMLING, Helen Marie-Claire 54 Midford Lane, Midford, Bath BA2 7DF — MB BS 1988 Lond.

HAMLING, Jonathan Brian Oldfield Surgery, 45 Upper Oldfield Park, Bath BA2 3HT Tel: 01225 421137 Fax: 01225 337808 — MB BS 1987 Lond.; BSc Lond. 1989, MB BS 1987; MRCGP 1992.

HAMLYN, Adrian Noel Department of Gastroenterology and Nutrition, Russells Hall Hospital, Dudley DY1 2HQ Tel: 01384 456111 Fax: 01384 244112; Email: anhamlyn@cs.comm — MB BS 1969 Lond.; FEBG; BSc (Hons.) Lond. 1966; FRCP Lond. 1986; MRCP (UK) 1972. (Middlx.) Cons. Phys. & Gastroenterol. Dudley Hosps. NHS Trust; Hon Reader in Gastroenterol. Sch. of Health Scis. Univ. of Wolverhampton. Socs: Brit. Soc. Gastroenterol.; Eur. Assn. Study Liver; Med Research Soc. Prev: Wellcome Trav. Research Fell. Univ. Tübingen, W. Germany; 1st Asst. Med. Univ. Newc.; Regist. (Med.) Roy. Free Hosp. Lond.

HAMLYN, Edward Cleveland Rutt House, Ivybridge PL21 0DQ — MB ChB Bristol 1944. (Bristol)

HAMLYN, Elizabeth Mary 11 Phillimore Terrace, Allen St., London W8 6BJ — MB ChB 1998 Bristol.

HAMLYN, Mr John Fromings Department Oral & Maxillo-Facial Surgery, Taunton & West Somerset Hospital, Musgrove Park, Taunton TA1 5DA Tel: 01823 342170 Fax: 01823 342169 — MB BS 1971 Lond.; BDS Lond. 1967; FRCS Ed. 1986; MRCS Eng. LRCP Lond. 1971; FDS RCS Eng. 1974. Cons. Oral & Maxillofacial Surg., Taunton And Som. Hosp. Socs: Fell. Brit. Assn. Oral & Maxillofacial Surg.; BMA. Prev: Sen. Regist. (Oral Surg., & Plastic & Jaw Surg.) Sheff. AHA (T).

HAMLYN, Mr Peter John Department of Neurological Surgery, Royal Hospitals NHS Trust, Whitechapel, London E1 1BB Tel: 020 7377 7209 Fax: 020 7377 7212; 30 Devonshire Street, London W4 Tel: 020 7935 3721 Fax: 020 7601 7130 — MB BS 1982 Lond.; MD Lond. 1994; BSc (1st cl. Hons.) Lond. 1979; FRCS Eng. 1987. Cons. Neurosurg. St. Bart. & Roy. Lond. Hosp. Socs: Vice-Chairm. & Founder Trustee Brit. Brain & Spine Foundat.; Mem. Roy. Soc Med. Neurosci.; Mem. Brit Med. Assn. & Sports Sect.s. Prev: Sen. Regist. & Research Fell. (Neurosurg.) Lond. Hosp.; Lect. (Neurosurg.) St. Bart. Hosp. Lond.

HAMM, Miss Rebecca Sansbury Bristol Royal Infirmary, Bristol BS2 8HW Tel: 0117 928 2281 Fax: 0117 928 2281 Email: rebecca.hamm@virgin.net; Tucker House, Bristol Royal Infirmary, Terrell St, Bristol BS2 8EE Tel: 0117 928 2281 Fax: 0117 928 2281 — MB ChB 1993 Liverp.; MB ChB (Hons.) Liverp. 1993; FRCS Eng. 1997. Urol. Research Fell.

HAMM, Richard Ernest Dunbar Promenade Medical Centre, Douglas IM1 2PX Tel: 01624 675490 Fax: 01624 676600; Apartment 2B, Milner Towers, Port Erin IM9 — MB ChB 1966 Liverp. (Liverp.) Socs: Undersea & Hyperbaric Med. Soc.; Soc. Occupat. Med. Prev: SHO (Med.) Noble's I. of Man Hosp.; SHO Alder Hey Childr. Hosp.; Ho. Surg. (Obst.) Maelor Gen. Hosp. Wrexham.

HAMMAD, Mr Abd-El-Kader Saleem Abd-El Kader 4 Greenfield Grove, Liverpool L36 0TA — MB BCh 1980 Ain Shams; FRCS Ed. 1991.

HAMMAD, Etedal Mohamed El Sayed Gwynfa Residential Unit, Pen Y Bryn Road, Colwyn Bay LL29 7BH Tel: 01492 532458 — MB ChB 1969 Alexandria.

HAMMAD, Gamal El-Dien Mohammad 24 Cassiobury Park Avenue, Watford WD18 7LB — MB BCh 1964 Ain Shams; MFPM RCP (UK) 1989; FFPM (RCPUK) 1998. (Ain Shams Med. Sch. Cairo) Cons. Psychiat. Hillingdon Hosp. Pembroke Centre, Pembroke Rd. Ruislip Manor, Middlx. HA4 8N6; Cons. Pharmaceutical Med. Lond.; Edit Bol mem Good Clin. Pract. Jl.; Edit. Bd. Mem. Curreur Research in Serotorin; Edit Bd mem Jl. of drug assessement. Socs: Brit. Assn. Pharm. Phys.; Internat. Federat. Pharmaceutical Phys. Assn. Prev: Cons. Psychiat. Fair Mile Hosp. Cholsey Oxon W. Berks. NHS Trust; Med. Dir. Middle & Far E. ICI (Zaneca Pharma) Macclesfield; Regional Med. Dir. Dupont Pharma Geneva Switz.

HAMMAD, Mahmoud Kamal Abdel Hady Hamid 83 Webheath Netherwood Street, London NW6 2SJ — MB BCh 1973 Cairo; PhD Dub. 1987; MRCOG 1981; DGO TC Dub. 1977; LM 1977.

HAMMAD, Mr Zaki Glan Clwyd Hospital, Bodelwyddan, Rhyl LL18 5UW Tel: 01745 534096 Fax: 01745 534160; 26 Crescent Court, Llandudno LL30 1AT Tel: 01492 878901 — MB ChB Alexandria 1968; FRCS Ed. 1976; DLO Alexandria 1971. (Alexandria) Cons. ENT Surg. Glan Clwyd Hosp. Bodelwyddan. Socs: BMA (Chairm. Rhyl Div.). Prev: Sen. Regist. (ENT Surg.) Leeds Gen. Infirm.; Tutor (Otolaryngol.) Univ. Leeds; Hon. Sen. Regist. (ENT Surg.) Leeds AHA.

HAMMAN, Marelise Medacs Professional Recruitment, High Street House, New Market St., Skipton BD23 2HY — MB ChB 1995 Stellenbosch.

HAMMANS, Simon Richard St Richard's Hospital, Chichester PO19 4SE Tel: 01243 831604 Fax: 01243 831599; Wessex Neurological Centre, Southampton General Hospital, Southampton SO16 6YD Tel: 01703 796780 Fax: 01703 794148 Email: srh@soton.ac.uk — MB BChir 1985 Camb.; MA Camb. 1985; MD Camb 1993; MRCP (UK) 1988; T(M) 1994; FRCP 1999. (Camb. Univ. & St. Thos. Hosp.) Cons. Neurol. St. Richards Hosp. Chichester & Wessex Neurol. Centre Soton. Socs: Assn. Brit. Neurols.; World Muscle Soc. Prev: Sen. Regist. Kings Coll. Hosp. Lond. & Nat. Hosp. for Neurol. & Neurosurg. Lond.; Research Regist. Inst. Neurol. Qu. Sq. Lond.; Regist. (Neurol.) Roy. Free Hosp. Lond.

HAMMATT, Mark David 33 Palmer Road, Bexleyheath DA7 4JS — MB ChB 1990 Leeds. Trainee GP/SHO Pontefract VTS. Socs: BMA. Prev: Ho. Off. (Surg. & Med.) Huddersfield Roy. Infirm.

HAMMER, Barbara Orchard Medical Centre, Macdonald Walk, Kingswood, Bristol BS15 8NJ Tel: 0117 980 5100 Fax: 0117 980 5104 — MRCS Eng. LRCP Lond. 1971.

HAMMER, Eve (retired) 12 Tedworth Square, Chelsea, London SW3 4DY Tel: 020 7352 0342 Fax: 020 7352 0435 — MRCS Eng. LRCP Lond. 1948; DA (UK) 1964; DCH Eng. 1950. Cons. Anaesth. St. Vincent's Orthop. Hosp. Pinner. Prev: Cas. Off. Evelina Hosp. Sick Childr.

HAMMER, Mr Harold Maurice Tennent Institute of Ophthalmology, Gartnavel Hospital, 1053 Great Western Road, Glasgow G12 0YN Tel: 0141 211 1041 Fax: 0141 211 2054 Email: harry@vitreous.freeserve.co.uk — MB ChB 1976 Glas.; FRCS Ed. (Ophth.) 1981; FRCOphth 1989. Cons. Ophth. Glas. Eye Infirm. & Gartnavel Gen. Hosp. Glas.; Hon. Clin. Sen. Lect. Univ. Glas. Prev: Sen. Regist. (Ophth.) Yorks. RHA.

HAMMER, Jacqueline Loraine Flat 48 - Block 3, Royal Bournemouth Hospital, Castle Lane E., Bournemouth BH7 7DW — MB ChB 1989 Aberd.; DCH RCP Lond. 1991. Prev: Clin. Research Phys. Roche Products Ltd. Welwyn Gdn. City; Trainee GP Maidstone; SHO (O & G, Gen. Med.) Maidstone Hosp.

HAMMER, Michael Russell Department of Chemical Pathology, North Manchester General Hospital, Manchester M8 5RB — MB BS 1976 Lond.

HAMMER, Peter Robert Charles 10 Chestnut Avenue, Chorleywood, Rickmansworth WD3 4HB — MB BS 1982 Melbourne; FRCA 1993; DObst 1985.

HAMMERSLEY, Andrew Giles Forde Grange, 42 Keyberry Park, Newton Abbot TQ12 1EA Tel: 01626 66316 — MB BS 1987 Lond.; MRCGP 1993.

HAMMERSLEY, Brian William Stenhouse Medical Centre, 66 Furlong Street, Arnold, Nottingham NG5 7BP Tel: 01159 673877 — BM BS 1977 Nottm.; BMedSci Nottm. 1975; MRCGP 1981. Socs: Nottm. M-C Soc.

HAMMERSLEY, Christopher Alan The Surgery, Greenwich Avenue, Hull HU9 4UX Tel: 01482 374415 Fax: 01482 786462; 4 Holmes Lane, Bilton, Hull HU11 4EY — BSc Lond. 1982, MB BS 1985; MRCGP 1989; DRCOG 1988. Prev: Trainee GP S. Cumbria VTS.

HAMMERSLEY, Daphne Yaxley Group Practice, Yaxley Health Centre, Landsdowne Road, Yaxley, Peterborough PE7 3JX Tel:

01733 240478 Fax: 01733 244645; Manor Farm, Wadenhoe, Peterborough PE8 5SX Tel: 01832 720002 Email: stephen.hall@farmline.com — MB BS 1984 Lond.; MRCGP 1988; DRCOG 1987; DCH RCP Lond. 1986. (St. Thos.) GP Yaxley Gp. Pract. PeterBoro.. Prev: Ho. Phys. Salisbury Gen Infirm.; Ho. Surg. St. Thos. Hosp. Lond.

HAMMERSLEY, Hugo Neville Beaumont Street Surgery, 27 Beaumont Street, Oxford City, Oxford OX1 2NR Tel: 01865 311500 Fax: 01865 311720; 27 Beaumont Street, Oxford OX1 2NR Tel: 01865 311500 Fax: 01865 311720 Email: beaudocs@oxongps.co.uk — MB ChB 1980 Birm.; MRCGP 1985; Cert. Family Plann. JCC 1985; DRCOG 1984; DA Eng. 1983. Socs: Oxf. Univ. Coll. Doctors Assn.; Assn. Police Surg. Prev: SHO (Paediat. & O & G) New Cross Hosp. Wolverhampton.

HAMMERSLEY, Kathryn Anne 4 Holmes Lane, Bilton, Hull HU11 4EY — MB BS 1985 Lond.; MA Camb. 1982. Community Med. Off. Hull. Prev: Asst. (Gen. Pract.) & Clin. Asst. (Colposcopy) Barrow-in-Furness.

HAMMERSLEY, Margaret Sinclair 283 Woodstock Road, Oxford OX2 7NY Tel: 01865 552608 Email: hammersleyfamily@cs.com — MB BCh 1978 Wales; 2000 FRCP; MRCP (UK) 1983. Cons. Phys., John Radcliffe Hosp.; Hon.Sen.Lect.Univ. of Oxf. Socs: Brit. Diabetic Assn.; Eur. Assn. Study Diabetes. Prev: Cons. Phys. Roy. Hants. Co. Hosp. Winchester; Sen. Regist. (Med.) John Radcliffe Hosp. Oxf.; Hon. Regist. & Research Fell. (Diabetes) Univ. Oxf. & (Med.) Soton. Univ.

HAMMERSLEY, Mr Nicholas Monklands Hospital, Monkscourt Avenue, Airdrie ML6 0JS Tel: 01236 748748 Fax: 01236 760015 Email: nicholas.hammersley@laht.scot.nhs.uk; 7 The Glebe, Bothwell, Glasgow G71 8AG Tel: 01698 853575 — MB BS 1979 Lond.; FRCS Ed. 1985; FDS RCPS Glas. 1990; FDS RCS Eng. 1974. Cons. Oral & Maxillofacial Surg. Monklands Hosp. Airdrie; Hon. Clin. Sen. Lect. Univ. Glas.

HAMMERSLEY, Rebecca Louise 110 Grange Road, Erdington, Birmingham B24 0EU — MB BS 1994 Newc.

HAMMERSLEY, Siobhan Elizabeth 9 Lumb Lane, Bramhall, Stockport SK7 2BA — BM 1989 Soton.

HAMMERSLEY, Stuart George (retired) Millrace Cottage, Manor Barton, Chiselborough, Stoke-sub-Hamdon TA14 6TZ — MB ChB 1960 Manch.; DObst RCOG 1963.

HAMMERTON, John (retired) Elm Tree, Handley, Clay Cross, Chesterfield S45 9AT Tel: 01246 862563 — MB ChB 1938 Glas.; FRCGP 1976, M 1957. Prev: Ho. Surg. Roy. Hosp. Sick Childr. Glas.

HAMMERTON, Marilyn Denise 8 Westgate Villas, Westgate, Bridgnorth WV16 4QX — MB ChB 1972 Ed.; BSc (Hons.) (Anat.) Ed. 1969, MB ChB 1972. Assoc. Specialist (Dermat.) Roy. Shrewsbury Hosp.

HAMMERTON, Simon Peter 22 Francis Gardens, Warfield Green, Bracknell RG42 3SX Tel: 01344 861918 Fax: 01344 861918 Email: simon.hammerton@virgin.net — MB BS 1993 Lond.; BA Camb. 1983; MA Camb. 1985; DCH RCP Lond. 1997; DRCOG 1996; MRCGP 1997. (St. Mary's Hosp. Med. Sch. Lond.) Trainee GP Oxf. VTS.

HAMMERTON, William Bridgnorth Medical Practices, Northgate House, 7 High Street, Bridgnorth WV16 4BU Tel: 01746 767121 Fax: 01746 765433 — MB ChB 1971 Ed.; MRCGP 1979; DObst RCOG 1975; DA Eng. 1974.

HAMMETT, Alistair Ian Downlands Medical Centre, 77 High Street, Polegate BN26 6AE Tel: 01323 482323/486449 Fax: 01323 488497 — MB BS 1977 Lond.; MRCGP 1982; DRCOG 1982.

HAMMETT, Peter John (retired) Corve Farmhouse, Corve Lane, Chale Green, Ventnor PO38 2LA Tel: 01983 551496 — MRCS Eng. LRCP Lond. 1950. Prev: Jun. Anaesth. & Cas. Off. King's Coll. Hosp.

HAMMETT, Rachel Jennifer Tel: 01962 856656 — BM 1991 Soton.; MRCPsych 2000; MRCGP 1995. G.P. Locum.

***HAMMETT, Rodney Brian** 4 Western Road, West End, Southampton SO30 3EL Tel: 02380 405170 — MB BS 1998 Lond.; MB BS Lond 1998.

HAMMILL, Rachel Mary 52 St David's Close, West Wickham BR4 0QZ — MB BS 1991 Lond.

HAMMOND, Anna 6A Briar Rigg, Keswick CA12 4NW — MB ChB 1994 Leeds.

HAMMOND, Anthony The Maidstone Hospital, Hermitage Lane, Maidstone ME16 9QQ Tel: 01622 224876 Fax: 01622 224876 Email: tony_hammond@online.regnet.co.uk — MB ChB 1980 Ed.; BSc (Hons.) Ed. 1977, MD 1991; FRCP Lond. 1996; MRCP (UK) 1983. Cons. Phys. & Rheum. Mid Kent Healthcare Trust Maidstone Hosp. Socs: Nat. Back Pain Assn.; Brit. Soc. Rheum.; Roy. Soc. Med. Prev: Sen. Regist. (Med. & Rheum.) St. Bart. & Whipp's Cross Hosps. Lond.; ARC Jun. Research Fell. (Rheum.) Roy. Postgrad. Med. Sch. Hammersmith Hosp. Lond.

HAMMOND, Arnold Ainsley (retired) 20 De Tany Court, St Albans AL1 1TT Tel: 01727 862437 Fax: 01727 862437 Email: arnoldh@tesco.net — MB ChB 1950 Manch.; LMC Canada 1967. Prev: Clin. Asst. Rheum. St. Albans City Hosp. & Qu. Eliz. II Hosp. Welwyn.

HAMMOND, Beatrice Odey (retired) 20 Laund Road, Salendine Nook, Huddersfield HD3 3TU — LRCPI & LM, LRSCI & LM 1971; LRCPI & LM, LRCSI & LM 1971; FRCR 1980; DMRD Eng. 1978. Prev: Cons. Radiol., Huddersfield NHS Trust.

HAMMOND, Catherine Mary 6 Cedar Grange, Harrogate HG2 9NY — BM BCh 1987 Oxf.; MA Oxf. 1989; MRCGP (Distinc.) 1993; DRCOG 1991. Hosp. Practitioner (Dermat.) Harrogate Healthcare Trust; Hosp. Practitioner (Dermat.) St. James & Seacroft Univ. Trust.

HAMMOND, Christopher John Department of Ophthalmology, St Thomas Hospital, Lambeth Palace Road, London SE1 7EH Tel: 020 7928 9292; Flat 2, 6 Great Ormond St, London WC1N 3RB — BM BCh 1988 Oxf.; MA Camb. 1989; MRCP (UK) 1991; FRCOphth 1993. Sen. Regist. (Ophth.) St. Thos. Hosp. Lond. Prev: Regist. (Ophth.) W.. Eye Hosp. St. Marys NHS Trust Lond.; SHO (Ophth.) Camb. & Brighton HA; SHO (Gen. Med.) N. Staffs. HA.

HAMMOND, Christopher John 2 Balmoral Terrace, Shaw Lane, Headingly, Leeds LS6 4EA — BM BCh 1996 Oxf.

HAMMOND, Christopher Robert 10 Harley Street, London W1N 1AA Tel: 020 7467 8374; 11 Westgate, Southwell NG25 0JN Tel: 01636 812912 — MB BS 1981 Lond. Homoeop. Pract. Notts.

HAMMOND, Clare 49 The Anchorage, Liverpool L3 4DX Tel: 0151 708 9385 Email: clareh@hotmail.com — MB ChB 1993 Birm.; MRCP (UK) 1996. Specialist Regist. (Cardiol.) Cardiothoracic Centre Liverp.

HAMMOND, David James 59 Brands Hill Avenue, High Wycombe HP13 5PY — MB ChB 1994 Leeds.

HAMMOND, Edward Joseph 50 Southfield Park, Bartlemans Close, Oxford OX4 2BA Tel: 01865 725198 Email: edyhammond@aol.com — BM BCh 1990 Oxf.; MA Camb. 1990, BA 1986; MRCP (UK) 1993; FRCA 1996; DA (UK) 1995; FRCA 1995. Regist. (Anaesth.) Soton. Gen. Hosp. Prev: SHO (Anaesth.) Oxf. Radcliffe Hosp.; Regist. & SHO (Med.) P.ss Margt. Hosp. Swindon; SHO (Med.) John Radcliffe Hosp. Oxf.

HAMMOND, Erika Lorraine 19 Hedgefield Road, Barrowby, Grantham NG32 1TA Tel: 01476 568523; 7 Stonelea Drive, Rastrick, Brighouse HD6 3PT Tel: 01484 714774 — MB ChB 1990 Leeds; MRCGP 1998. (Leeds) Socs: Assoc. Mem. RCGP. Prev: Trainee GP Bradford VTS; SHO (A & E) Rotherham Gen. Hosp.; SHO Rotat. (Med.) Lister Hosp. Stevenage.

HAMMOND, Francis Keith (retired) Charnwood Surgery, 5 Burton Road, Derby DE1 1TH Tel: 01332 737737 Fax: 01332 737738 — MB BChir Camb. 1963; MA Camb. 1963; DObst RCOG 1964.

HAMMOND, Mr Geoffrey Teall Erdely, Compton Down, Winchester SO21 2AL Tel: 01962 713213 — MB BS 1942 Lond.; MD Lond. 1952; LMSSA Lond. 1940; FRCOG 1963, M 1949. (Guy's Hosp. Lond.) Emerit. Cons. O & G Surg. Roy. Hants. Co. Hosp. Winchester & Andover Hosp.; Eminent Teach. Postgrad. Med. Sch. Budapest. Socs: SW Obst. Soc.; Hon. Mem. Hungarian Gyn. Soc. Prev: Sen. Obst. Med. Off Qu. Charlotte's Hosp.; Sen. Regist. (Obst.) Guy's Hosp.; Capt. RAMC, Surg. CMF, MEF.

HAMMOND, Ian Philip Larksmede, 101 Forest Road, Cuddington, Northwich CW8 2ED — MB BS 1976 Newc.

HAMMOND, James Stephen Ormskirk & District General Hospital, Wigan Road, Ormskirk L39 2AZ Tel: 01695 583621 Fax: 01695 583152; 11 Statham Way, Ormskirk L39 4XR — MB BS 1986 Newc.; FRCA 1992; DA (UK) 1988. Cons. Anaesth. W. Lancs. HA Ormskirk. Prev: Sen. Regist. (Anaesth.) NW Region; Instruc. Anesthesiol. Univ. Michigan.

HAMMOND, Janet Hermione 101 Forest Road, Cuddington, Northwich CW8 2ED — MB BS 1976 Newc.; DCCH RCP Ed. 1988. (Newc. u. Tyne) Assoc. Specialist (Community Paediat.) Chesh.

Community Healthcare Trust; Assoc. Specialist (Ophth.) Mid-Chesh. Hosps. Trust.

HAMMOND, Jennifer Mary (retired) Cuillins, Common Lane, Betley, Crewe CW3 9AL Tel: 01270 820390 — MB BS Lond. 1966; MRCS Eng. LRCP Lond. 1966. Prev: Ho. Surg. Vict. Hosp. Kirkcaldy.

HAMMOND, John David Symons (retired) let Wen, 2 Peterborough Road, Sheffield S10 4JE Tel: 0114 230 1789 — MD (Distinc.) Sheff. 1959, MB ChB (1st Cl. Hnrs.)1950; FRCP Lond. 1979, M 1954. Hon. Instruc. (Med.) Univ. Sheff. Prev: Lect. (Med.) Sheff. Univ.

HAMMOND, Josephine Elaine Child Development Centre, St George's Hospital, Tooting, London SW17 0QT Tel: 020 8725 1896; 5 Oaklands Avenue, West Wickham BR4 9LE — MB BS 1960 Lond.; FRCP Lond. 1989; FRCP Ed. 1981; MRCP (UK) 1967; MRCS Eng. LRCP Lond. 1960; T(M) (Paediat.) 1991; DCH Eng. 1963; DObst RCOG 1962. (Roy. Free) Cons. Paediat. St. Geo. Hosp. Lond. Prev: Cons. Paediat. Qu. Mary's Hosp. Childr. Carshalton; Sen. Regist. Hosp. Sick Childr. Gt. Ormond St.

HAMMOND, Justin The Medical Centre, The Household Cavalry Mounted Regiment, Hyde Park Barracks, Knightsbridge, London SW1 1SE Tel: 020 7414 2534 Fax: 020 7414 2515 — MB ChB 1992 Manch.; DRCOG 1996; Dip. Sports Med. Scotl. 1997. (Manchester) Med.Off.Ho.hold. Cavalry. Prev: SHO Accid & Emerg.; SHO Ent.; GP Regist. Ardesier Inverness.

HAMMOND, Kenneth Charles Princess Mary's RAF Hospital, Halton, Aylesbury HP22 5PS — MB BS 1967 Lond.; MRCP (UK) 1971; FRACP 1980. Sen. Specialist P.ss Mary's RAF Hosp. Halton. Prev: GP Robt.sbridge; Clin. Asst. (Cardiol.) Roy. E. Sussex Hosp. Hastings; Cons. Phys. Goulburn Med. Clinic NSW., Austral.

HAMMOND, Lisette Alexandra City Hospital NHS Trust, Dudley Road, Birmingham B18 7QH; 70 Woodgate Lane, Birmingham B32 3QY — MB BChir 1992 Camb. SHO (Histopath.) City Hosp. NHS Trust Birm. Socs: Train. Mem. Assn. Clin. Path. Prev: Ho. Off. (Med.) S.end Hosp. NHS Trust; Ho. Off. (Surg.) P.ss Alexandra Hosp. Harlow.

HAMMOND, Margaret Rhinedd (retired) let Wen, 2 Peterborough Road, Sheffield S10 4JE Tel: 0114 230 1789 — MB ChB Sheff. 1950. Prev: Fell. in Med. Johns Hopkins Hosp. Baltimore, U.S.A.

HAMMOND, Nicola Akuorko 30 Ivy lane Flats, Osler Road, Headington, Oxford OX3 9DY — MB ChB 1995 Bristol.

HAMMOND, Peter John Harrogate District Hospital, Lancaster Park Road, Harrogate HG2 7SX Tel: 01423 553747 Fax: 01423 874786; 6 Cedar Grange, Harrogate HG2 9NY Tel: 01423 872195 Email: peterkatehammond@cs.com — BM BCh Oxf. 1987; MA Camb. 1984; MD Camb. 1996; MRCP (UK) 1990; FRCP 2000. (Oxf.) Cons. Phys. (Diabetes & Endocrinol.) Harrogate Health Care NHS Trust; Dir., Postgrad. Med. Ed., Harrogate Health Care NHS Trust. Prev: Sen. Regist. (Gen. Med., Diabetes & Endocrinol.) Yorks. RHA; MRC Train. Fell. & Research Regist. (Endocrinol.) Roy. Postgrad. Med. Sch. Sch.; Regist. (Med.) Hammersmith Hosp. Lond.

HAMMOND, Philip James Email: drsansbury@aol.com — MB BChir 1987 Camb.; MRCGP 1993; DGM RCP Lond. 1989. p/t Clin. Asst. Genitourin. Med.; Hononary Lect. (Comm. Skills) Univ. Bristol. Prev: Lect. (Gen. Pract.) Univ. Birm.

HAMMOND, Philip John 89 Downs Road, Epsom KT18 5JT — MB ChB 1998 Ed.; MB ChB Ed 1998.

HAMMOND, Rachel Juliet 12 Akehurst Street, London SW15 5DR — MB BCh 1987 Wales. SHO (Paediat.) Glam. HAs.

HAMMOND, Richard James XRay Department, Dryburn Hospital, Durham DH1 5TW — MB ChB 1988 Liverp. Regist. (Radiol.) Roy. Liverp. Univ. Hosp. Trust. Socs: BMA; Assn. Roy. Coll. Radiol. Prev: Regist. (Med.) Wirral HA; SHO (Med.) Leicester HA; Ho. Off. Wirral HA.

HAMMOND, Richard Owen 2 Abingdon Mansions, Abingdon Rd, London W8 6AD — MB BS 1993 Lond.

HAMMOND, Mr Robert Henry The Red House, 3 Long Lane, Attenborough, Nottingham NG9 6BG Tel: 0115 943 6104 — MB ChB 1980 Sheff.; FRCS Ed. 1985; FRCOG 1997, M 1985. Cons. O & G Univ. Hosp. Qu. Med. Centre Nottm.

HAMMOND, Simon Jonathan St Osyths, Cuckoo Hill, Pinner HA5 2BA — MB BS 1984 Lond.

HAMMOND, Susan Ann 24 Renton Avenue, Guiseley, Leeds LS20 8EE Tel: 01943 875802 — MB ChB 1997 Manch. SHO Med. Elderly United Leeds Teach Hosp NHS Trust. Prev: Pre Registration Ho. Off.Wigan/Burnley Hosps.

HAMMOND, Terence Andrew Grant 62 New Road, Harmer Green, Welwyn AL6 0AN — MB BS 1986 Queensland.

HAMMOND, Terence John 13 Dulais Road, Seven Sisters, Neath SA10 9EL — MB BCh 1982 Wales; MRCP (UK) 1985; DRCOG 1984.

HAMMOND, Timothy John Parklands Surgery, 4 Parklands Road, Chichester PO19 3DT Tel: 01243 782819/786827; 6 Fordwater Road, Chichester PO19 4PR Tel: 01243 527147 — MB BS 1981 Lond.; MRCP (UK) 1986; MRCGP 1985; DCH 1984; DRCOG 1985.

HAMMOND, Timothy Marcus Long Lane Surgery, Beacon House, Long Lane, Coalville LE67 4DR Tel: 01530 831331 Fax: 01530 833985 — MB ChB 1983 Leic.; MRCGP 1992; Dip. Occ. Med. RCP Lond. 1996; DFFP 1996; DAvMed FOM RCP Lond. 1991; DRCOG 1988.

HAMMOND, Tobias Mark 29 Davenham Avenue, Northwood HA6 3HW — MB ChB 1998 Liverp.; MB ChB Liverp 1998.

HAMMOND, Mr Valentine Thomas (retired) Mill Farm, Park Lane, Heytesbury, Warminster BA12 0HE Tel: 01985 840997 Fax: 01985 841373 — MB BS Lond. 1953; FRCS Eng. 1957. Prev: Cons. ENT Surg. Roy. Masonic Hosp.

HAMMOND-EVANS, Mr John Michael 5 Burgess Close, Poughill, Bude EX23 9EB — MB ChB 1969 Bristol; FRCS Eng. 1977.

HAMMONDS, Geoffrey 2 Regency Chambers, Jubliee Way, Bury BL9 0JW — MB ChB 1972 Manch.

HAMMONDS, Mr John Christopher Strawberry Hill, Stoke Road, Noss Mayo, Plymouth PL8 1DZ Tel: 01752 872754 — MB BChir 1968 Camb.; MA, MB Camb. 1968, BChir 1967; FRCS Eng. 1972. (Camb. & St. Thos.) Cons. Urol. Derriford Hosp. Plymouth. Prev: Sen. Regist. (Urol.) Roy. Hosp. Sheff.; Cas. Off. & Ho. Surg. St. Thos. Hosp. Lond.

HAMMONDS, Richard Martin 4 Stevens Street, Alderley Edge SK9 7NL Tel: 01625 590162; 4 Stevens Street, Alderley Edge SK9 7NL Tel: 01625 590162 — MB ChB 1989 Leic.

HAMMOUDA, Mohammed 9 Cedar Court, North Tyneside General Hospital, Rake Lane, North Shields NE29 8NH — MB BS 1982 Garyounis, Libya; MRCOG 1995.

HAMNETT, Ewan Lordswood House, 54 Lordswood Road, Harborne, Birmingham B17 9DB Tel: 0121 426 2030 Fax: 0121 428 2658 — MB ChB 1980 Manch.; MRCGP 1984.

HAMON, Angela Marie 7 Ffordd Taliesin, Killay, Swansea SA2 7DF — MB ChB 1985 Bristol.

HAMON, Michael Douglas Department of Haematology, Royal Free Hospital & School of Med., London NW3 2QG; 61 Cranham Gardens, Cranham, Upminster RM14 1JQ — MB ChB 1983 Leic.; BSc Leic. 1981, MB ChB 1983; MRCP (UK) 1986; MRCPath 1990. Sen. Research Fell., Hon. Sen. Regist. & Hon. Lect. (Haemat.) Roy. Free Hosp. & Sch. Med. Lond.; Specialist Accredit. Haemat. JCHMT. Prev: Lect. (Haemat.) Lond. Hosp. Med. Coll.; Regist. (Haemat.) W. Midl. RHA.

HAMOUD, Hasiba Hanon Wylie House, 30 Kilmardinny Avenue, Bearsden, Glasgow G61 3NS — MB ChB 1980 Basrah.

HAMOUDI, Anam Harbi 2 Dumbrock Road, Milngavie, Glasgow G62 7RB — MB ChB 1976 Baghdad.

HAMOUR, Abu Obeida Abedel A'Al North Manchester General Hospital, Delaunays Road, Crumpsall, Manchester M8 5RB Tel: 0161 795 4567 — MB BS 1981 Khartoum; MSc Molecular Microbiol. Manch. 1993; DTM & H RCP Lond. 1993; MRCP (UK) 1989. Clin. Lect. (Infec. Dis.) Monsall Hosp. Univ. Manch. Socs: Roy. Colls. Lond. & Edin.; Brit. Soc. Study Infec. Prev: Regist. (Med.) Norwich Hosps.; SHO Norwich & Coventry Hosps.

HAMOUR, Mohammed Abdel A'Al Westbrook Centre, 150 Canterbury Road, Margate CT9 5DD Tel: 01843 255466 Fax: 01843 255473 — MRCS Eng. LRCP Lond. 1979; MB BS Khartoum 1962; DPM RCP Lond. 1975; DCS (UKC) 1991. (Univ. Khartoum) Cons. Gen. Psychiat. SE Thames RHA; Dip. Counselling Skill Univ. Kent.; Cons. Psychiat. Gen. Adult Psychiat., S. E. Community Nat. Health Trust, Canterbury, Kent. Socs: Roy. Soc. Med.; Roy. Brit. Assn. for Counselling; Roy. Assn. Family Therap.

HAMP, Florence Jane 2 Kings Drive, Gravesend DA12 5BG Tel: 01474 537123 — MB BS 1982 Lond. Prev: Trainee GP S. Glam. VTS.

HAMP, Ian Robert Albemarle Surgery, 27 Albemarle Crescent, Scarborough YO11 1XX Tel: 01723 360098 Fax: 01723 501546; 11 Holbeck Hill, Scarborough YO11 2XE Tel: 01723 373557 — MB ChB 1982 Leeds; MRCGP 1986; DRCOG 1985. GP ScarBoro..

HAMPAL, Mr Sucha 28 Meldyke Lane, Stainton, Middlesbrough TS8 9AU — MB ChB 1982 Bristol; FRCS Eng. 1987; FRCS Ed. 1987.

HAMPSHEIR, Richard Peter Thorpewood Surgery, Woodside Road, Norwich NR7 9OL Tel: 01603 701477; 13 Padgate, Thorpe End, Norwich NR13 5DG Tel: 01603 701360, 01793 731910 Fax: 01793 731319 — MB ChB 1990 Ed.; DRCOG 1995; DFFP 1997; MRCGP 1998. (Edinburgh) Partner Gen. Practitioner. Prev: Trainee GP & SHO MusGr. Pk. Hosp. Taunton VTS; SHO (Paediat.) Hammersmith Hosp. Lond.; SHO (Neonat.) City Hosp. Nottm.

HAMPSHIRE, Amanda Jayne 91A Imperial Road, Beeston, Nottingham NG9 1FE — BM BS 1986 Nottm.; BMedSci (1st. cl. Hons.) Nottm. 1984; MRCGP 1991; DRCOG 1991; DGM RCP Lond. 1988. Lect. (Gen. Pract.) Nottm. Univ. Med. Sch. Prev: Assoc. Acad. (Gen. Pract.) Nottm. Univ. Med. Sch.

HAMPSHIRE, Jane Catherine 19 Haredon Close, Forest Hill, London SE23 3TG — MB ChB 1990 Bristol.

HAMPSHIRE, Julia Elizabeth Dean Cross Surgery, 21 Radford Park Road, Plymstock, Plymouth PL9 9DL Tel: 01752 404743; Home Farm, Venn, Aveton Gifford, Kingsbridge TQ7 4NY — MB ChB 1985 Birm.; ChB Birm. 1985; DRCOG 1990.

HAMPSHIRE, Margaret Sybil Beryl Inshore, 2A Retreat Road, Topsham, Exeter EX3 0LF Tel: 01392 875498 — MB BS 1967 Lond.; LLM Cardiff 1995; DObst RCOG 1970. SCMO (Community Child Health) Roy. Devon & Exeter Healthcare NHS Trust. Socs: MRCPCH; Brit. Assn. Community Child Health; Brit. Assn. for Study & Preven. of Child Abuse & Neglect.

HAMPSHIRE, Peter Andrew 41 Heath Park Road, Romford RM2 5UL — MB ChB 1998 Liverp.; MB ChB Liverp 1998.

HAMPSON, Elizabeth Frances Rushey Mead Health Centre, 8 Lockerbie Walk, Leicester LE4 7ZX Tel: 0116 266 9616; 28 Woodfield Road, Oadby, Leicester LE2 4HP — MB BS Lond. 1969; MRCGP 1975; DObst RCOG 1972. (St. Mary's) GP Leic. Prev: SHO (Gen. Med.) City Hosp. Nottm.; SHO (Obst.) & Regist. (Geriat. Med.) N.. Gen. Hosp. Sheff.

HAMPSON, Emma Katharine Haste End, Hill Road, Haslemere GU27 2JP — MB BS 1997 Lond.

HAMPSON, Fay Graceley 1 Cranmer Road, Didsbury, Manchester M20 6AW — MB ChB 1995 Bristol.

HAMPSON, Jane Louise 6 Longton Cottages, Over Kellet, Carnforth LA6 1DB — MB BCh 1991 Wales; DCH RCP Lond. 1994. Trainee GP/SHO (A & E) Roy. Lancaster Infirm.

HAMPSON, John Martin 28 Woodfield Road, Oadby, Leicester LE2 4HP — MB BS 1969 Lond.; FFA RCS Eng. 1973. (St. Mary's) Cons. Anaesth. Leics. HA (T). Prev: Rotating Regist. (Anaesth.) & Sen. Regist. (Anaesth.) Sheff. AHA (T).

HAMPSON, John Roderick Greenmount Medical Centre, 9 Brandlesholme Road, Greenmount, Bury BL8 4DR Tel: 01204 883375 Fax: 01204 887431 — MB ChB 1984 Manch.; MB ChB Manch. l984; MRCGP 1988; DRCOG 1987.

HAMPSON, Joseph (retired) Gillside, Aldbrough St John, Richmond DL11 7TL Tel: 01325 374570 — MB ChB 1948 Ed.; FRCP Ed. 1967, M 1953; FRCP Lond. 1973, M 1956. Prev: Phys. N.allerton & Darlington Hosp. Gp.

HAMPSON, Lynn Alison Stonefield Street Surgery, 21 Stonefield Street, Milnrow, Rochdale OL16 4JQ Tel: 01706 46234 Fax: 01706 527946 — MB ChB 1984 Manch.; MRCGP 1988; DRCOG 1987; DCH RCPS Glas. 1986.

HAMPSON, Michele Elizabeth Rosebery House, Waterford St, Old Basford, Nottingham NG6 0DH Tel: 0115 916 9575 Fax: 0115 919 1994 — MB BS 1979 Lond.; MPhil Ed. 1985; BSc (Pharmacol.) Lond. 1976, MB BS 1979; MRC Psych. 1983. Cons. Psychiat. Nottm. HA. Prev: Sen. Regist. (Psychiat.) Newc. HA.

HAMPSON, Narainamah Department of Chemical Pathology, St Thomas's Hospital, Lambeth Palace Road, London SE1 7EH — MB ChB 1982 Manch.; MSc Birm.; MD Manch.; MRCPath. Sen. Lect. & Hon. Cons. (Chem. Pathol.).

HAMPSON, Rachael Sarah Chipping Surgery, 1 Symn Lane, Wotton-under-Edge GL12 7BD Tel: 01453 842214 — MB BChir 1992 Camb. (Cambridge) Socs: MRCGP; DRCOG; DFFP.

HAMPSON, Ralph Michael Alexandra Group Medical Practice, Glodwick Health Centre, Glodwick Road, Oldham OL4 1YN Tel: 0161 909 8350 Fax: 0161 909 8354 — MB ChB 1983 Leeds; DCH RCP Lond. 1987; DRCOG 1985.

HAMPSON, Shirley Whitworth Eye Clinic, Royal Surrey County Hospital, Egerton Road, Guildford GU2 7XX Tel: 01483 571122 Ext: 4641; 1 Woodmancourt, Godalming GU7 2BT Tel: 01483 423079 Fax: 01483 423079 Email: shirley.hampson@virgin.net — MB ChB Liverp. 1968; MRCOphth 1989; DO Eng. 1980; DPH Wales 1971. (Liverp.) Clin. Asst. (Ophth.) Roy. Surrey Co. Hosp. Guildford. Socs: BMA. Prev. SHO (Ophth.) Roy. Surrey Co. Hosp. Guildford; Med. Off. Cardiff City Counc.; Med. Off. W. Glam. Div. Glam. CC.

HAMPSON, Simon Carl Vale of The White Horse Community Mental Health Team, Abingdon Hospital, Marcham Road, Abingdon OX14 1AG Tel: 01235 205446 Fax: 01235 205448 Email: simon.hampson@omhc-tr.anglox.nhs.uk — MB BCh 1986 Wales; MB BCh (Hons.) Wales 1986; BSc (Hons.) Leeds 1980; MRCP (UK) 1989; MRCPsych 1991. Cons. Psychiat. Abingdon & Littlemore Hosp. Oxf. Prev: Sen. Regist. & Regist. (Psychiat.) Warneford Hosp. Oxf.; SHO (Med.) & Ho. Off. (Med. & Surg.) Univ. Hosp. Cardiff.

HAMPSON, Mr Simon Joseph (retired) 1 Oakhill Court, Edgehill, Wimbledon, London SW19 4NR Tel: 020 8947 2855 Email: sam.hampson@virgin.net — MB BChir 1981 Camb.; MA Camb. 1980, MChir 1991; FRCS (Urol.) 1992; FRCS Eng. 1984. Cons. Urol. St. Geo. Hosp. & Qu. Mary's Univ. Hosp. Lond.; Hon. Sen. Lect. St. Geo. Hosp. Med. Sch.; Asst. Tutor RCS Eng. Prev: Sen. Regist. (Urol.) St. Geo. Hosp. Lond.

HAMPSON, Suzanne Elizabeth 1 Woodman Ct, Godalming GU7 2BT — MB ChB 1997 Liverp.

HAMPSON, William Trevor 8 Alderwood Precinct, Sedgley, Dudley DY3 3QY Tel: 01902 885180 Fax: 01902 883615; 12 Oak Drive, Seisdon, Wolverhampton WV5 7ET Tel: 01902 897917 Fax: 01902 897917 — MB ChB 1979 Birm; MFFP; MRCGP 1984; DRCOG 1983. Clin. Asst. (Geriat. Med.) Dudley HA; Sen. Clin. Med. Off. (Family Plann.) Dudley HA.

HAMPSON-EVANS, Darryl Colin Dept. Of Anaesthetics, St George's Hospital, Blackshaw Road, London SW17 0BW Tel: 020 8672 1255 Ext: 3316 — MB BS 1990 Lond.; BSc (Hons.) Lond. 1987; FRCA 1996. (Char. Cross & Westm.) Cons. (Anaesth.) with interest in Paediatric Anaesth. Dept. Of Anaesth. St Geo.'s Hosp. Lond. Socs: Assn. Anaesth. GB & Irel. Prev: Regist. Rotat. (Anaesth.) St. Geo. Hosp. Lond., Ashford Hosp. Middlx. & Roehampton Univ. Hosp. Lond.; SHO (ICU) Addenbrooke's Hosp. Camb.; SHO (Anaesth.) W.m. Hosp., Char. Cross & Chelsea & W.m. Hosp. Lond.

HAMPTON, Aileen Mary Trefelwy, Mount Road, St Asaph LL17 0DF Tel: 01745 582593 — MB BS (Hons.) Lond. 1948; MRCS Eng. LRCP Lond. 1948. (Roy. Free) Socs: NW Soc. Cytol.; MDU; Welsh Hist. Med. Soc. Prev: Assoc. Specialist (Cytopath.) N. Clwyd Dist. Glan Clwyd Hosp. Bodelwyddan; Regist. (Path.) Liverp. Matern. Hosp.; Resid. Asst. Path. Roy. Free Hosp.

HAMPTON, Anne Caroline 169 Mayall Road, London SE24 0PR; 221 New Road, Ferndown BH22 8EF — BM BS 1990 Nottm.; BMedSci 1988. Trainee GP Lewisham VTS. Prev: SHO (Clin. Oncol.) Nottm. Gen. Hosp.; Ho. Off. (Med.) Roy. Infirm. Derby; Ho. Off. (Surg. & Urol.) Nottm. City Hosp.

HAMPTON, Caroline Danestone Medical Practice, Fairview Street, Danestone AB22 8ZP Tel: 01224 822866 Email: caroline.hampton@danestone.grampian.scot.nhs.uk — MB ChB 1980 Manch.; DFFP 2001; MRCGP 1985; DCH RCP Lond. 1983; DRCOG 1983. (St Andrews & Manchester) p/t GP Aberd.

HAMPTON, Fiona Jane Mount House Farm, Pinchin Thorp, Great Ayton, Middlesbrough TS9 6QX Email: clodbase@netcomuk.co.uk — BM BCh 1980 Oxf.; MD Leic. 1992; MRCP (UK) 1985. Cons. Paediat. S. Cleveland Gen. Hosp. Middlesbrough. Prev: Sen. Regist. & Lect. (Paediat.) Leicester Roy. Infirm.; Lect. (Paediat.) Univ. Sci. & Technol. Kumasi, Ghana.

HAMPTON, Geraldine Kensington Group Practice, Kensington Road, Road, Douglas IM1 3PF Tel: 01624 676774 Fax: 01624 614668 — MB ChB 1963 Liverp. (Liverp.) Socs: BMA; Isle of Man Med. Soc. Prev: SHO Nobles I. of Man Hosp.; SHO Alder Hey Childr. Hosp. Liverp.; Ho. Off. Sefton Gen. Hosp. Liverp.

HAMPTON, James St Michaels Surgery, Walwyn Close, Twerton-on-Avon, Bath BA2 1ER Tel: 01225 428277 Fax: 01225 338484; 2 Wingfield House, Wingfield, Trowbridge BA14 9LF Tel: 01225

775202 — MB BS 1980 Lond.; MRCS Eng. LRCP Lond. 1980; MRCGP 1987; DRCOG 1986. (Char. Cross Hosp. Med. Sch.)

HAMPTON, James Neil Seymour 24 Dark Lane, Wargrave, Reading RG10 8JU Tel: 0118 940 3080 Fax: 0118 940 2182 — MB BS 1994 Lond.; BSc Lond. 1993. (Char. Cross & Westm. Hosp. Lond.)

HAMPTON, Jennifer Amy Louise 34 Stella Street, Mansfield NG18 4AL — MB ChB 1989 Ed.

HAMPTON, Joanna Lucy 29 Oundle Dr, Nottingham NG8 1BN — BM BCh 1997 Oxf.

HAMPTON, Professor John Reynolds Division of Cardiovasc. Med. (South Block), Queen's Medical Centre, Nottingham NG7 2UH Tel: 0115 970 9346 Fax: 0115 970 9384 Email: john.hampton@nottingham.ac.uk; 29 Oundle Drive, Nottingham NG8 1BN Tel: 0115 978 3324 — DPhil Oxf. 1967, MA (1st cl. Hons. Animal); Physiol.) 1959, DM 1973, BM BCh 1962; FRCP Lond. 1975, M 1965; FESC 1996. Prof. Cardiol. Nottm. Univ.; Cons. Phys. Nottm. Univ. Hosp. Socs: Brit. Cardiac Soc.; Fell. Europ. Soc. Cardiac. Prev: Lect. (Med.) Oxf. Univ.; Radcliffe Trav. Fell.; Instruc. Med. Harvard Univ. Boston, USA.

HAMPTON, Kingsley Kevin Department of Haematology, Royal Hallamshire Hospital, Glossop Road, Sheffield S10 2JF Tel: 0114 271 2231 Fax: 0114 271 3996 Email: k.k.hampton@sheffield.ac.uk — MB ChB 1983 Leeds; BSc Leeds 1980; MD Leeds 1995; MRCP (UK) 1986; MRC Path. 1993. (Leeds) Sen. Lect. & Hon. Cons. Haemat. Roy. Hallamsh. Hosp. Sheff. Prev: Cons. Haemat. Univ. Hosp. of Wales Cardiff; Wellcome Research Train. Fell. (Med.) Gen. Infirm. Leeds.

HAMPTON, Mark Alan Malone Private Clinic, 93 Malone Rd, Belfast BT9 6SP Tel: 028 9038 6730 Fax: 028 9038 6733 Email: mark.hampton@nireland.com; 2 Upper Malone Road, Belfast BTP 5NA Tel: 028 9061 4667 Email: mark.hampton@nireland.com — MB BCh BAO 1989 Belf.; 1998 Membership of Soc. of Orthopaedic Med. (MSOM); 1998 Diploma Sports Med. (Royal Coll. of Scotland); MRCGP 1995; DCH RCP Dub. 1994; DMH Belf. 1994; DRCOG 1993. (Qu. Univ. Belf.) Orthopaedic & Sports Phys., Malone Private Clinic, Belf. Socs: BASEM; BIMM; MSOM.

HAMPTON, Naomi Rachel Elizabeth Department of Reproductive and Sexual Health Care, Wenlock House, 33 Eaton Road, Enfield EN1 1NJ Tel: 020 8370 2551 Fax: 020 8364 6691; 262 Leigh Hunt Drive, Southgate, London N14 6DS Tel: 020 8447 9722 Fax: 020 8447 9733 Email: nham@dircom.uk — MB BS 1986 Lond.; MFFP 1993; MRCOG 1992. (Jt. Sch. Med. Univ. Coll. & Middlx. Hosp.) Cons. Reproduc. Healthcare & Community Gyn. Enfield Community Care NHS Trust; Hon. Research Fell. Margt. Pyke Centre Lond.; Clin. Dir. (Reproduc. & Sexual Health Servs.) Enfield Community Care NHS Trust. Socs: (Hon. Sec.) Lond. Soc. Family Plann. Doctors; Chair.Heads of Serv.Forum.Lond.Soc.FP Docs. Prev: Research Regist. Margt. Pyke Centre.

HAMPTON, Philip Jeremy 50 Cavendish Place, Jesmond, Newcastle upon Tyne NE2 2NH — MB BS 1996 Newc.; B.Med. Sci. 1995. SHO (Med) RVI Newc. Prev: Ho. Off. (Med.) Roy. Vict. Infirm. Newc.; Ho. Off. (Surg.) Sunderland Hosp.; Ho. Off. (Med.) Wanganin Hsop. New Zealand.

HAMPTON, Richard William Dudley 69 Ashbourne Road, London W5 3DH — MB BS 1989 Lond.

HAMPTON, Robert Henry 75 South Knighton Road, Leicester LE2 3LS — MB ChB 1986 Leic. Trainee GP Leicester.

HAMPTON, Susanne Maria 2 Upper Malone Road, Belfast BT9 5NA — MB BCh BAO 1988 Belf.; FRCS Ed. 1992.

HAMPTON, Timothy John 56 Edward Road, Clevedon BS21 7DX — BM 1994 Soton.

HAMPTON, Trevor Richard Walker, CB, Surg. Rear-Admiral (retired) Coombe House, Latchley, Gunnislake PL18 9AX Tel: 01822 832419 — MB ChB Ed. 1954; FRCP Ed. 1975, M 1964. Prev: Surg. Rear Admiral (Operat. Med. Servs.).

HAMSHERE, Mr Richard John (retired) Seaton Cottage, Bradfield St George, Bury St Edmunds IP30 0AY Tel: 01284 386207 — MB BS 1964 Lond.; FRCS Eng. 1972; FRCS Ed. 1969; AFOM RCP Lond. 1991. Cons. Occupat. Health Bury St. Edmunds. Prev: Sen. Med. Off. Shell Centre Lond.

HAMWI, Mr Mohamed Walid Dewsbury District Hospital, Healds Road, Dewsbury WF13 4HS Tel: 01924 465105 Fax: 01924 450839 — MD 1984 Aleppo; FRCS Ed. 1992.

HAMZA, Pachery 114 Granville Drive, Kingswinford DY6 8LW — MB BS 1966 Kerala.

HAMZAH-SENDUT, Iean 1 Windsor Close, Finchley, London N3 3ST — MB BS 1985 Lond.

HAN, Calvert Francis Merrow Park Surgery, Kingfisher Drive, Merrow Park, Guildford GU4 7EP Tel: 01483 503331 — BSc 1992; MBBS 1996; MRCGP 1999 London; DCH; Dip. Family Planning; DRCOG. GP Princip.

HAN, Loong-Yuan 189 Bedford Hill, Balham, London SW12 9HQ Tel: 020 8675 1386; PO Box 272, Sandakan, Sabah 90703, Malaysia Tel: 00 60 89 216298 — BM BS 1980 Nottm.; BMedSci Nottm. 1978; MRCP (UK) 1986; DRCOG 1983. Cons. Phys. Roy.St Mary's Hosp Lond. Socs: Brit. Thorac. Soc. Prev: Sen. Regist. (Thoracic Med.) Roy. Free Hosp. Lond.; Research Fell. Cardiothoracic Inst. Brompton Hosp. Lond.; Regist. (Med.) Bradford Hosps.

HAN, Seong Won 40 Delaval Terrace, Gosforth, Newcastle upon Tyne NE3 4RT Fax: 0191 285 1653 — MB ChB 1993 Glas.; BSc (Hons.) Glas. 1990; MRCP (UK) 1996. (Univ. Glas.) Prev: SHO Rotat. (Gen. Med.) Newc.

HANA, Azad Babaka Llandudno General Hospital, Llandudno LL30 1LB — MB ChB 1976 Baghdad.

HANAFI, Zulkarnain Apartment 6, Archbishops House, Church Road, Woolton, Liverpool L25 5JF — MB ChB 1991 Liverp.

HANAFIAH, Siti Rukhani 109 Balsusney Road, Kirkcaldy KY2 5LQ — MB BCh BAO 1982 NUI; BSc (Hons.) Pharmacol. Lond. 1977; DCH RCPS Glas. 1988; MRCPCH 1999.

HANAFIAH, Zulkifli 56 Gilbey Road, London SW17 0QG — MB BCh BAO 1980 NUI; LRCPSI 1980; FFA RCSI 1990.

HANAFY, Mr Magdi Ezz El Din 39 Alfred Road, Birchington CT7 9NJ — MB BCh 1980 Al-Azhar, Egypt; FRCS Ed. 1987.

HANAGHAN, Jonathan Princess Elizabeth Hospital, Le Vauquiedor, St Martin's, Guernsey GY4 6UU Tel: 01482 725241 Fax: 01482 724272 Email: dnj.hanag@doh.org.uk — LRCPI & LRCSI 1976; FFR RCSI 1982. Cons. Radiol. P.ss Eliz. Hosp. Guernsey.

HANAK, Barbara Ann Garden City Practice, 11 Guessen Road, Welwyn Garden City AL8 6QW Tel: 01707 321166 Fax: 01707 391911; 76 Digswell Park Road, Welwyn Garden City AL8 7NS Tel: 01707 328684 Fax: 01707 322546 Email: mhanak@aol.com — MB BS 1984 Lond.; DRCOG 1988; DCH RCP Lond. 1986. (Roy. Free Hosp.) Prev: Trainee GP N.wick Pk. Hosp. Harrow.

HANAN, Peter Mark Grove House Surgery, 80 Pryors Lane, Rose Green, Bognor Regis PO21 4JB Tel: 01243 265222/266413 Fax: 01243 268693 — MB ChB 1977 Otago; DCH Lond 1981; DA Lond 1982; MRCGP London 1995. (Otago) GP Bognor Regis, W. Sussex.

HANBURY, Christopher Janson Spitalfields Practice, Spitalfields Health Centre, 9-11 Brick Lane, London E1 6PU Tel: 020 7247 7070 — MB BS 1979 Lond.

HANBURY, Mr Damian Capel Department of Urology, Lister Hospital, Stevenage SG1 4AB Tel: 01438 781268 Fax: 01438 781270; Howells Farm, Weston, Hitchin SG4 7DZ Tel: 01462 790226 Fax: 01462 790576 — MB BS 1980 Lond.; MS Lond. 1991; FRCS (Urol.) 1993; FRCS Eng. 1986; FRCS Ed. 1985. Cons. Urol. Lister Hosp. Stevenage.

HANBURY, Helen Ingrid Robin Hill, Hockett Lane, Cookham Dean, Maidenhead SL6 9UF — MB BS 1982 Lond.

HANBURY, William Janson (retired) Foxbury, The Ridge, Woldingham, Caterham CR3 7AT Tel: 01883 653234 — MRCS Eng. LRCP Lond. 1943; MD (Path.) Lond. 1950, MB BS 1943; FRCPath 1973, M 1963. Prev: Sen. Lect. Path. St. Bart. Hosp.

HANBURY-AGGS, Colina Ariane The Gatehouse, Merrywood Lane, Storrington, Pulborough RH20 3HE — MB BS 1985 Lond.; BSc Lond. 1982, MB BS 1985. Prev: Clin. Asst. St. Bart. Hosp. Lond.; SHO (Gen. Med.) OldCh. Hosp. Romford.

HANBURY-WEBBER, Raymond, MBE, TD 27 Prince of Wales Drive, London SW11 4SD Tel: 020 7223 6010 — MRCS Eng. LRCP Lond. 1939. (St. Bart.) Socs: Soc. Med. & Dent. Hypn.; BMA. Prev: Regt.. Med. Off. Bromley & Dist. Hosp.; Anaesth. E. Suff. & Ipswich Hosp.; Maj. RAMC DADMS Guards Armoured Div. (Mentioned in Despatches).

HANBY, Andrew Malcolm 40 St John's Road, Petts Wood, Orpington BR5 1HX — BM 1981 Soton.; MRCPath 1988. Sen. Lect. & Hon. Cons. United Med. & Dent. Sch. Div. Histopath. & Oncol.; Hon. Sen. Lect. Roy. Postgrad. Med. Sch.; Mem. Internat. Acad.

Path. (Mem. Brit. Div.). Socs: Path. Soc. Prev: Asst. Curator Gordon Museum Guy's Hosp. Lond.; Lect. & Hon. Sen. Regist. (Oncol. Path.) Hedley Atkins Path. Lab. Guy's Hosp. Lond.; Sen. Regist. (Histopath.) Lewisham & Guy's Hosps. Lond.

HANCE, Julian Richard 18 Green Lane, Shipston-on-Stour CV36 4HG — MB BS 1998 Lond.; MB BS Lond 1998.

HANCOCK, Amanda 10 Pytchley Way, Brixworth, Northampton NN6 9EF — BM BS 1993 Nottm.

HANCOCK, Andrea Louise 7 Byron Close, Windy Ridge, Yateley GU46 6YW — BM 1998 Soton.; BM Soton 1998.

HANCOCK, Anne Kathleen (retired) 50 Kepstorn Road, Leeds LS16 5HT Tel: 0113 275 1357 — MD Manch. 1972, MB ChB 1961; DObst RCOG 1963.

HANCOCK, Professor Barry William University Department of Clinical Oncology, Weston Park Hospital NHS Trust, Witham Road, Sheffield S10 2SJ Tel: 0114 226 5000 Fax: 0114 226 5511; Treetops, 253 Dobcroft Road, Sheffield S11 9LG Tel: 0114 235 1433 — MB ChB 1969 Sheff.; MB ChB (Hons.) Sheff. 1969; MD Sheff. 1977; FRCP Ed. 1995; FRCP Lond. 1985; MRCP (UK) 1973; FRCR 1995; DCH Eng. 1971. (Sheff.) YCR Prof. Of Clin. Oncol.Univ. Sheff. W.on Pk. Hosp.; Dir. Supraregional Gestational Trophoblastic Tumour Centre; Dir. Univ. Div. Oncol. Socs: Exec. Comm. Assn. Cancer Phys.; Brit. Oncol. Assn.; Amer. Soc. Clin. Oncol. Prev: Reader (Med.) Univ. Sheff.; Lect. (Med.) Roy. Hosp. Sheff.; Regist. (Med.) United Sheff. Hosps.

HANCOCK, Mr Brian David (retired) Laurel Bank, Yealand Coyers, Carnforth LA5 9SG Tel: 01524 730223 — MB ChB Manch. 1964; MD Manch. 1976; FRCS Eng. 1971; FRCS Ed. 1968. Prev: Cons. Surg. Wythenshawe Hosp. Manch.

HANCOCK, Caroline Anne Countisbury, Plain-an-Gwarry, Marazion TR17 0DR — MB BCh 1987 Wales.

HANCOCK, Christine Mayhill Surgery, 108 Pen-y-Graig Road, Mayhill, Swansea SA1 6JZ Tel: 01792 655667; Namaste, Rhyddwen Road, Craig Cefn Parc, Swansea SA6 5RG Tel: 01792 845886 — MB BCh 1982 Wales.

HANCOCK, Deborah Jayne 473 Tonbridge Road, Maidstone ME16 9LH Tel: 01622 721340 — MB BS 1992 Lond.; BSc (Hons.) Physiol. Lond. 1987; DFFP 1996; DCH RCP Lond. 1995. (Char. Cross & Westm. Med. Sch.) GP Regist. Maidstone.

HANCOCK, Mr Donald MacArthur (retired) Carradale, Glen Path, Sunderland SR2 7TU Tel: 0191 528 5249 Email: donald.hancock@virgin.net — MB ChB Ed. 1947; FRCS Ed. 1950. Prev: Cons. Surg. Sunderland HA.

HANCOCK, Fiona Byronny Lechlade Medical Centre, Oak Street, Lechlade GL7 — MB BChir 1989 Camb.; MA Camb. 1989; MRCGP 1992; DFFP 1993; DRCOG 1991; T(GP) 1993. p/t Retained GP; Clin. Asst. Gastroenterol., P.ss Margt. Hosp., Swindon.

HANCOCK, Gavin Dominic 31 St Davids Road, Hethersett, Norwich NR9 3DH — MB BS 1997 Lond.

HANCOCK, Jane Elizabeth Ground Floor Flat, 37 Cotham Vale, Cotham, Bristol BS6 6HS — MB ChB 1988 Bristol.

HANCOCK, John Henry Owen Royal Cornwall Hospital, Treliske, Truro TR1 3LJ Tel: 01872 252285 Email: john.hancock@rcht.swest.nhs.uk — BM 1986 Soton.; FRCS Eng. 1991; FRCR 1998. (Univ. Soton.) Cons. (Radiol.) Roy. Cornw. Hosp. NHS Trust. Socs: Brit. Soc. of Interven.al Radiol. Prev: Fell. in Interven.al. Radiol., Soton. Univ. Hosp. NHS Trust; Specialist Regist. (Radiol.) Soton. Univ. Hosps. NHS Trust; Higher Surg. Trainee SE Thames RHA.

HANCOCK, John Lovatt The Surgery, Mill Street, Harbury, Leamington Spa CV33 9HR Tel: 01926 612232 Fax: 01926 612991 — MB ChB 1967 Leeds; DObst RCOG 1969. Prev: SHO (Anaesth. & O & G) N.ampton Gen. Hosp.; Ho. Phys. Harrogate Gen. Hosp.

HANCOCK, John Mark Willow Barn, Parbrook, Glastonbury BA6 8PB — MB BS 1993 Lond.

HANCOCK, Jonathan Patrick 110 Parkfield Road, Pucklechurch, Bristol BS16 9PT — MB BS 1982 Lond.; MRCP (UK) 1988.

HANCOCK, Julian Martin 31 Wayneflete Tower Avenue, Esher KT10 8QQ — MB ChB 1982 Bristol; MRCGP 1987; DRCOG 1987; DA (UK) 1985; DCH RCP Lond. 1986. GP Surbiton. Prev: SHO (Paediat.) St. Geo. Hosp. Lond.; Trainee GP Kingston upon Thames VTS; SHO (Anaesth.) Salisbury HA.

HANCOCK, Karen Jane St Lawrence Surgery, 79 St Lawrence Avenue, Worthing BN14 7JL; 2 Brambles, Hassocks BN6 8EQ — MB BS 1989 Lond.; BSc Lond. 1986, MB BS 1989; MRCGP 1997; DCH 1993; DRCOG 1997; DFFP 1997. CMO (Family Plann. & Sexual Health) Centr. Clinic Worthing.

HANCOCK, Karl William (retired) 50 Kepstorn Road, Leeds LS16 5HT Tel: 0113 275 1357 — MB ChB Manch. 1957; FRCOG 1978, M 1966; DObst 1961.

HANCOCK, Keith Graham The Grayshott Surgery, Boundary Road, Grayshott, Hindhead GU26 6TY Tel: 01428 604343; Woodstock, 10 Ridgemoor Close, Hindhead GU26 6QX Tel: 01428 605792 — MB BS 1971 Lond.; MRCGP 1976; DObst RCOG 1975; Cert JCC Lond. 1976. (Univ. Coll. Hosp.) Prev: Trainee GP Lond. (Univ. Coll.) VTS; SHO Rotat. (Cas., Orthop. & Gen. Surg.) Leicester Roy. Infirm.; Ho. Surg. Univ. Coll. Hosp. Lond.

HANCOCK, Mr Kevin Mersey Regional Plastic Surgery & Burns Centre, Whiston Hospital, Prescot L35 5DR Tel: 0151 430 1664 Fax: 0151 430 1855; BUPA Murrayfield Hospital, Holmwood Drive, Thingwall, Wirral CH61 1AU Tel: 0151 648 7000 Fax: 0151 648 7684 — MB BS 1980 Lond.; FRCS (Plast) 1993; FRCS Ed. 1986. (St. Bart.) Cons. Plastic Surg. Mersey Regional Plastic Surg. & Burns Centre Whiston Hosp. Liverp.; Hon. Lect. Univ. Liverp. Socs: Brit. Assn. Plastic Surg.; BMA; Brit. Assn. Aesthetic Plastic. Surgs. Prev: Sen. Regist. W. Midl. Plastic Surg. & Jaw Unit Wordsley Hosp.; Sen. Regist. Head & Neck Unit Roy. Marsden Hosp.; Regist. UCH & Mt. Vernon Hosp.

HANCOCK, Marie-Claire 6 Pegwell Road, Ramsgate CT11 0HU — MB ChB 1997 Manch.

HANCOCK, Mark Roland 22 The Mead, Trentham, Stoke-on-Trent ST4 8DB — BM BS 1996 Nottm.

HANCOCK, Mary Sharon 32 Mill Street, Harbury, Leamington Spa CV33 9HR Tel: 01926 612860 — MB ChB 1967 Leeds. (Leeds) Clin. Med. Off. S. Warks. NHS Trust. Socs: Assoc. Mem. BPA. Prev: Ho. Phys. St. Jas. Hosp. Leeds; Ho. Surg. Harrogate Gen. Hosp.; Ho. Phys. (Paediat.) N.ampton Gen. Hosp.

HANCOCK, Nicola Jacqueline Almond The Surgery, Pleasant Place, Hersham, Walton-on-Thames KT12 4HT Tel: 01932 229033 Fax: 01932 254706 — MB ChB 1983 Manch.; Cert. Prescribed Equiv. Exp. JCPTGP 1989. GP Hersham. Prev: Trainee GP Epsom VTS; Regist. (Psychiat.) St. Thos. Hosp. Lond.

HANCOCK, Paul James 16 Rectory Field, Hartfield TN7 4JE — MB ChB 1998 Sheff.; MB ChB Sheff 1998.

HANCOCK, Robert Peter Dawbney Fordie House, 82 Sloane St., London SW1X 9PA Tel: 020 7235 3002 Fax: 020 7235 3721; 14 Gavden Road, Clapham, London SW4 6LT Tel: 020 7498 9972 — FRCS Eng. 1974; MRCS Eng. LRCP Lond. 1967; MRCGP 1977. (Guy's) Socs: Fell. Med. Soc. Lond.; Assn. Soc. of Occuptional Health. Prev: Surg. Specialist RAMC; Ho. Off. (O & G) Greenwich Dist. Hosp.; Hon. Clin. Asst. Dept. Psychiat. Guy's Hosp. Lond.

HANCOCK, Rev. Ronald Edward (retired) 9 Churchward Avenue, Preston, Weymouth DT3 6NZ Tel: 01305 832558 — MRCS Eng. LRCP Lond. 1949; MRCGP 1962. Prev: Med. Off. RAF Med. Rehabil. Unit, Chessington.

HANCOCK, Rosemary Jessica 48 Grafton Way, Northampton NN5 6NQ — MB BS 1997 Lond.

HANCOCK, Sally Margaret Queen's Medical Centre, Nottingham NG8 1GN Tel: 0115 924 9924 — MB ChB 1993 Manch.; FRCA 2000. Specialist Regist. Anaesth. Qu.s med. Centre. Notts. Socs: Train. Mem. Assn. Anaesth.; BMA; RSM. Prev: SHO (A & E) N. Manch. Gen. Hosp.; Ho. Off. (Gen. Surg.) Withington Hosp. Manch.; Ho. Off. (Gen. Med.) Vict. Hosp. Blackpool.

HANCOCK, Sheila Patricia 12 Burlington Road, Ipswich IP1 2EU Tel: 01473 211664 — MB ChB 1955 Birm.; MRCS Eng. LRCP Lond. 1955; MRCGP 1966; DObst RCOG 1957.

HANCOCK, Stephen William 494 New Hey Road, Huddersfield HD3 3XF Email: steve.hancock@ntl.net.com — MB ChB 1992 Leeds; MRCP (UK) 1995; DCH Leeds 1997. (University of Leeds) Specialist Regist. (Paediat.) Yorks. Deanery. Socs: Paediat. Intens. Care Soc. Prev: Clin. Fell. (Paediat. Intens. Care) Gen. Infirm. Leeds.

HANCOCK, Susan Amanda The Cabin Surgery, High Street, Rishton, Blackburn BB1 4LA Tel: 01254 884217 Fax: 01254 882899 — MB BS 1980 Lond.; MRCGP 1985; DRCOG 1984; DCH RCP Lond. 1983. (Univ. Coll.) Course Organiser Blackburn.

HANCOCK, Suzanne Elizabeth Student Health Service, High St., Aberdeen AB24 3UB Tel: 01224 276655; 79 Braemar Place,

Aberdeen AB10 6EQ — MB ChB 1986 Sheff.; DCH RCP Lond. 1989; DRCOG 1989.

HANCOCKS, Gerald Herbert John Warrengate Surgery, Upper Warrengate, Wakefield WF1 4PR — MRCS Eng. LRCP Lond. 1968.

HANCOCKS, Mark Edward 36 Highbury Avenue, Coutley, Doncaster DN4 6AJ — MB ChB 1983 Sheff. Trainee GP Doncaster VTS.

HANCORN, Mrs Marcia Kay Llanfyllin Medical Centre, High Street, Llanfyllin SY22 5DG Tel: 01691 648054 Fax: 01691 648165 — MB BCh 1983 Wales; MRCGP 1989; DRCOG 1989; DCH RCP Lond. 1988. Princip. GP Char.. Prev: Med. Ho. Off. Nevill Hall Hosp. Gwent.

HANCOX, Deborah Jane Claremont, Gloucester Road, Tutshill, Chepstow NP16 7DB — MB ChB 1983 Bristol; MRCGP Lond. 1988; DRCOG 1988; DCH RCP Lond. 1987.

HANCOX, Duncan 34 Palace Road, Southport PR8 2BY — MB ChB 1989 Manch.

HANCOX, Naomi 142 Bow Common La, London E3 4BH — MB BS 1997 Lond.

HAND, Anthony The Belmont Health Centre, 516 Kenton Lane, Harrow HA3 7LT Tel: 020 8863 0911 — M.B., B.S. Durh. 1947. (Newc.) Prev: Ho. Surg. Leazes Hosp. Roy. Vict. Infirm. Newc.; Capt. R.A.M.C.; Sen. Med. Off. Whittington Barracks.

HAND, Christopher Hillary The Beeches, 67 Lower Olland Street, Bungay NR35 1BZ Tel: 01986 892055 Fax: 01986 895519; Mettingham Pines, Bungay NR35 1TD Tel: 01986 892516 Fax: 01986 896692 — MB BChir 1971 Camb.; MSc Lond. 1993; MRCP (UK) 1973; FRCGP 1994, M 1987. (Middlx.) Regional Assoc. Adviser Anglia; Hon. Sen. Lect. UEA. Socs: BMA. Prev: SHO (O & G) Heath Rd. Hosp. Ipswich; SHO (Med.) Hammersmith Hosp. Lond.; Ho. (Phys.) Middlx. Hosp. Lond.

HAND, Mr Christopher John, Surg. Lt.-Cdr. RN St Mary's Hospital, Parkhurst Road, Newport PO30 5ST Tel: 01983 524081 Fax: 01983 534857; 12 Green Hollow Close, Fareham PO16 7XP — MB ChB 1988 Liverp.; FRCS (Eng.) 1996. (Liverp.) Specialist Regist. (Trauma & Orthop. Surg.) Wessex Rotat. Socs: Assoc. Mem. BOA.

HAND, Mr David Wilton (retired) Park Lodge, Cardew, Dalston, Carlisle CA5 7JQ Tel: 01228 710327 Fax: 01228 710327 — MB ChB 1959 Sheff.; FRCS (Orl.) Ed. 1968; FRCS (Orl.) Eng. 1968. Hon. Cons. ENT Surg. Carlisle Hosps. NHS Trust. Prev: Sen. Regist. (ENT) Leicester & Sheff. Roy. Infirms. & Sheff. Roy. Hosp.

HAND, George Campbell Ross — MB BS 1991 Lond.; FRCS Lond. 1996.

HAND, Joseph William Denis (retired) Kinnaird Castle, Kinnaird, Inchture, Perth PH14 9QY — LRCPI & LM, LRSCI & LM 1954; LRCPI & LM, LRCSI & LM 1954. Prev: Chief of Med. Serv. Bechtel Algeria.

HAND, Karen Wendy 26 Goddings Drive, Rochester ME1 3BA — MB BS 1994 Lond.

HAND, Malcolm Frank Department of Nephrology, North Staffordshire Royal Infirmary, Stoke-on-Trent ST4 7LN Tel: 01782 715444 Fax: 01782 745017; 3 College Fields, Yarnfield, Stone ST15 0TG Tel: 01785 760306 — MB ChB 1984 Liverp.; MRCP (UK) 1990. Sen. Regist. & Lect. (Nephrol.) N. Staffs. Roy. Infirm. Stoke-on-Trent. Prev: Postgrad. Research Fell. Univ. Edin.; Regist. (Renal, Transpl. & Gen. Med.) W.. Gen. Hosp. Edin.; Regist. (Med.) Roy. Berks. Hosp. Reading.

HAND, Margaret Mary Wheal Fortune Cottage, Cockwells Lane, Penzance TR20 8DB Tel: 01736 740908 Email: maggiehand@msn.com — MB ChB 1981 Glas.; MRCPsych 1986. (Glas.) Cons. Psychiat. (Community) Bellair Clinic Penzance.

HAND, Robert Wilton Rutherford House, Langley Park, Durham DH7 9XD Tel: 0191 373 1386 Fax: 0191 373 4288 — MB ChB 1985 Sheff.; MRCGP 1989.

HAND, Susan Elizabeth 3 College Fields, Yarnfield, Stone ST15 0TG — MB ChB 1984 Liverp.; MB ChB Liverp. I984; MRCP (UK) 1988; MRCGP 1994. (Liverpool) Socs: Collegiate Mem. RCP Lond.; NANP; RCGP. Prev: SHO (O & G) E.ern Gen. Hosp. Edin.; Trainee GP Ladywell Med. Centre Edin.; Regist. & Lect. (Haemat.) St. Thos. Hosp. Lond.

HANDA, Mr Ashok Inderraj Nuffield Department of Surgery, John Radcliffe Hospital, Headington, Oxford OX3 9DU Tel: 01865 741166 Fax: 01865 221117 Email: ashok.handa@surgery.ox.ac.uk; 48 East Field Close, Headington, Oxford OX3 7SH — MB BS 1987 Lond.; FRCS Eng. 1994; FRCS Ed. 1992. (St. Mary's Hosp. Med. Sch.) Clin. Lect. Vasc. Surg. Nuffield Dept. Surg. John Radcliffe Hosp. Oxf. Socs: Vasc. Surg. Soc.; Affil. Mem. Assn. Surgs. GB & Irel. Prev: Clin. Research Fell. Roy. Free Hosp. Lond.; Career Regist. Broomfield Hosp. Chelmsford & Whipps Cross Hosp. Lond.; Lect. (Transpl. Surg.) Lond. Hosp. Med. Coll.

HANDA, Mr Jawahar Lal 26 Locksley Crescent, Greenfaulds, Cumbernauld, Glasgow G67 4EL Tel: 0141 732300 — MB BS 1962 Panjab; MS (ENT) Kanpur 1969; MB BS Panjab (India) 1962; FRCS Eng. 1978; DLO Eng. 1971. (Govt. Med. Coll. Patiala) Cons. (ENT) Law Hosp. Carluke.

HANDA, Nita 143 Lonsdale Drive, Enfield EN2 7NB — MB BS 1976 Lond.

HANDA, Pratibha Brookwood Hospital, Knaphill, Woking GU21 2RQ; Heathermount, Station Road, Chobham, Woking GU24 8AZ — MB BS 1966 Punjab; MRCPsych 1974; DPM Eng. 1972.

HANDA, Sarjit Kumar 2B Pollards Hill N., London SW16 Tel: 020 8679 1700 — MB BS 1966 Jiwaji. (G.R. Med. Coll. Gwalior) Clin. Asst. (Dermat.) Lond.; Family Plann. Doctor Lond.

HANDA, Mr Satish Mohan Fartown Green Road Surgery, 34 Fartown Green Road, Fartown, Huddersfield HD2 1AE Tel: 01484 534386 — MB BS 1964 Agra; MS (Ophth.) Agra 1968, MB BS 1964.

HANDA, Sudhir Inderraj Leicester Street Medical Centre, Leicester Street, Wolverhampton WV6 0PS Tel: 01902 24118; Leicester Street Medical Centre, Whitmore Reans, Wolverhampton WV6 0PS Tel: 01902 24118 — MB ChB 1984 Ed.; MRCGP 1990. Socs: BMA.

HANDA, Sunil Inderraj Sandwell General Hospital, Lyndon, West Bromwich B71 4HJ Tel: 0121 607 3584 Fax: 0121 607 3253 Email: sunil.handa@swellhot.wmids.nhs.uk — MB ChB 1982 Leic.; MBA 1999; FRCP; FRCPath 2000; BMedSc (Hons.) Leic. 1980; FRCP Lond. 1997; MRCP (UK) 1986; MRCPath 1992; FRCP Ed. 1998. (Leic.) Cons. Haemat. Sandwell Healthcare NHS Trust, Sandwell. Socs: Brit. Soc. Haematol. (W. Midl. Regional Rep.). Prev: Sen. Regist. (Haemat.) NW RHA Manch.; Regist. (Haemat.) Roy. Infirm. Edin.

HANDA, Urmil Condorrat Health Centre, 16 Airdrie Road, Cumbernauld, Glasgow G67 4DN Tel: 01236 733221; Condorrat Health Centre, Airdrie Road, Cumbernauld, Glasgow G67 4DN Tel: 01236 732300 — MD (Obst. & Gyn.) Panjab (India) 1969; MB BS Calcutta 1965; DObst RCOG 1972. (Nat. Med. Coll . Calcutta) GP Cumbernauld.

HANDCOCK, Lisa Jane 5 Hill Side La, Arrington, Royston SG8 0DA — MB ChB 1997 Bristol.

HANDE, Mr Handattu Ravi Shankar 21 Mead Road, Cheltenham GL53 7DY — MB BS 1983 Madras; FRCS Ed. 1987.

HANDEL, Mr Bruno Mark (retired) Gimber Lodge, Thorndon Approach, Herongate, Brentwood CM13 3PA — MB BS Lond. 1963; FRCS Eng. 1972; MRCS Eng. LRCP Lond. 1964. Prev: Cons. Gen. Surg. Harold Wood Hosp. Essex.

HANDEL, Celia Christabel Gimber Lodge, Thorndon Approach, Herongate, Brentwood CM13 3PA — MB BS Lond. 1963; MRCS Eng. LRCP Lond. 1963. (Roy. Free) Community Med. Off. Barking, Havering & Brentwood HA.

HANDEL, Jeffrey Maurice Royal United Hospital, Coombe Park, Bath BA1 3NG — MB BS 1983 Lond.; FRCA 1991; MRCP (UK) 1987. Cons. Anaesth.

HANDELSMAN, Susan Merle 58 Loom Lane, Radlett WD7 8PA — MB BCh 1988 Witwatersrand.

HANDFIELD-JONES, Ranald Philip Clayton (retired) Tranters, Trelawney Road, St Mawes, Truro TR2 5BU Tel: 01872 270358 — BM BCh Oxon. 1946; MRCP Lond. 1951; FRCGP 1971; DObst RCOG 1952. Prev: Ho. Surg. Postgrad. Med. Sch. Lond.

HANDFIELD-JONES, Susan Elizabeth West Suffolk Hospital, Bury St Edmunds IP33 2QZ Tel: 01284 713404 — BM 1980 Soton.; FRCP (UK) 1987. (Soton.) Cons. Dermat. W. Suff. Hosp.

HANDFORD, David John (retired) 83 Ridgacre Road, Quniton, Birmingham B32 2TJ Tel: 0121 422 3111 — MB BS 1951 Lond.; DObst RCOG 1955. Prev: Obst. Ho. Surg. Mile End. Hosp. Lond.

HANDFORD, Michael Harold High Street, Ramsbury, Marlborough SN8 2QT — MF Hom 2000 Lond.; MB BChir Camb. 1970; MA Camb. 1970; DObst RCOG 1972; MRCGP 1974; LFHom

1998. (St. Thos.) Gen. Practitioner Ramsbury. Socs: BMA. Prev: Trainee GP Thanet VTS; Ho. Surg. St. Thos. Hosp. Lond.; Ho. Phys. Poole Gen. Hosp.

HANDFORTH, Jennifer 38A Lupus Street, London SW1V 3EB — MB ChB 1990 Cape Town.

HANDLER, Clive E Highgate Private Hospital, 1779 View Road, London N6 4DJ Tel: 020 8348 2129 Fax: 020 8341 9320 — MB BS 1977 Lond.; BSc (Hons.) (Pharmacol.) Lond. 1974, MD 1985; MRCP (UK) 1979; MRCS Eng. LRCP Lond. 1977; FESC 1994; FACC 1993. (Guy's) Socs: Fell. Amer. Coll. Cardiol.; Fell. Europ. Soc. Cardiol.; Brit. Cardiac Soc. Prev: Cons. Cardiol. N.wick Pk. Hosp. Harrow & St. Mary's Hosp. Lond.

HANDLER, Katherine Elisabeth The Waterhouse, Bollington Medical Centre, Bollington, Macclesfield SK10 5JH Tel: 01625 572481; 2 Pott Mill Cottages, Pott Shrigley, Macclesfield SK10 5RU — MB BS 1966 Lond.; MRCP (U.K.) 1973; MRCS Eng. LRCP Lond. 1966; DObst RCOG 1968; DCH Eng. 1970. (Roy. Free)

HANDLEY, Andrew Francis 35 Lea Road, Wolverhampton WV3 0LS Tel: 01902 423064 Fax: 01902 657800 Email: learoadpledialpractice@msn.com; 2 Sheringham Court, Winslow Drive, Wolverhampton WV6 0LJ — MB ChB 1961 Birm. Clin. Asst. Accid. Dept. Roy. Hosp. Wolverhampton. Socs: BMA. Prev: Surg. Regist. Corbett Hosp. Stourbridge; SHO (Orthop. & Cas.) Guest. Hosp. Dudley.

HANDLEY, Anna Katharine (Newhouse) 30 Kings Road, Harrogate HG1 5JP Tel: 01423 560261 — MB ChB 1994 Leeds; MRCGP 1999; DRCOG 1996; DFFP 1998. GP Non-Princip. Harrogate.

HANDLEY, Anthony James Turner Rise Consulting Rooms, 55 Turner Road, Colchester CO4 5JY Tel: 01206 752444 Fax: 01206 752116; 40 Queens Road, Colchester CO3 3PB Tel: 01206 562642 Fax: 01206 560910 Email: handley@essexambhq.demon.co.uk — MB BS Lond. 1965; MD Lond. 1975; FRCP Lond. 1985, M 1968; MRCS Eng. LRCP Lond. 1965; Dip. IMC RCS Ed. 1995. (Westm.) Cons. Phys. & Cardiol. Essex Rivers Healthcare; Chief Med. Adviser Roy. Life Saving Soc. UK; Hon. Clin. Tutor Char. Cross & W.m. Med. Sch. Lond.; Examr. RCP Lond.; Chairm., BLS SubComm. Internat. Liaison Comm.e on Resusc. Socs: Fell. Roy. Soc. Med.; Brit. Cardiac Soc. Prev: Sen. Regist. (Med.) Brompton Hosp.; Regist. Med. Profess. Unit W.m. Hosp.; Ho. Phys. (Neurol.) United Oxf. Hosps.

HANDLEY, Mr Christopher, Wing Cdr. RAF Med. Br. (retired) Blackgrove Farmhouse, Quainton, Aylesbury HP22 4AE — BM BCh 1974 Oxf.; MA Camb. 1975; FRCS Ed. 1979. Cons. Orthop. Surg. Bedford Hosp. NHS Trust. Prev: Cons. Orthop. Surg. P.ss Mary's RAF Hosp. Aylesbury.

HANDLEY, David The Surgery, Wellington Road, Newport TF10 7HG Tel: 01952 811677 Fax: 01952 825981; Aston Grove, Moorfield Lane, Newport TF10 9EH Tel: 01952 810592 — BSc (Med. Sci.) Ed. 1966, MB ChB 1969; DObst RCOG 1971.

HANDLEY, Derek Joseph The Surgery, The Coppice, Herne Lane, Rustington, Littlehampton BN16 3BE Tel: 01903 783178 Fax: 01903 859027 — BM 1980 Soton.

HANDLEY, Jennifer Brook House, Sugar St., Rushton Spencer, Macclesfield SK11 0SQ — MB BS 1961 Lond.; FRCPsych 1989, M 1972; DPM Eng. 1968. (Middlx.) Cons. (Psychiat.) N. Staffs. Hosp. Gp.

HANDLEY, Joan (retired) 7 The Coppice, Beardwood, Blackburn BB2 7BQ Tel: 01254 59174 — MB BS 1948 Durh. Prev: Anaesth. Blackburn Hyndburn & Ribble Valley HA.

HANDLEY, John Edward Craigshill Health Centre, Craigshill Road, Livingston EH54 5DY Tel: 01506 432621 Fax: 01506 430431 — MB ChB 1970 Edinburgh; MB ChB Edin 1970. (Edinburgh) GP Livingstone W. Lothian.

HANDLEY, Julian Marsham Department Dermatology, Ulster Hospital, Dundonald, Belfast Tel: 02890 484511 Ext: 2904; 10A Kincora Avenue, Belfast BT4 3DW Tel: 02890 655934 Fax: 02890 655934 Email: jules@doctors.org.uk — MB BS 1984 Lond.; MD Lond. 1992; FRCP Ed. 1996; MRCP (UK) 1987; FRCP 1996 Lond. (St. Thos. Hosp. Lond.) Cons. Dermat. Ulster Hosp. Belf.

***HANDLEY, Juliette Ann** 40 Queens Road, Colchester CO3 3PB — MB BS 1998 Lond.; MB BS Lond 1998; BSc 1992.

HANDLEY, Mr Robert Christopher Trauma Unit, John Radcliffe Hospital, Headington, Oxford OX3 9DU Tel: 01865 741166 — MB ChB 1978 Sheff.; BSc (Physiol.) Sheff. 1975; FRCS Ed. 1987. Cons. Trauma & Orthop. Surg. John Radliffe Hosp. Oxf. Socs: Brit. Orthop. Research Soc. Prev: Med. Off. Brit. Antarctic Survey.

HANDLEY, Simon Austyn James 40 Queens Road, Colchester CO3 3PB — MB ChB 1998 Bristol.

HANDLEY, Suzanne Marie 16 Chewter Lane, Windlesham GU20 6JP — BM 1998 Soton.; BM Soton 1998.

HANDOUSAH, Samir Mohamed Elalfy 5 Apers Avenue, Westfield, Woking GU22 9NB — MB ChB 1964 Alexandria; DLO Eng. 1976. (Alexandria) Clin. Asst. (ENT Surg.) St. Peter's Hosp. Chertsey. Prev: SHO (ENT) Poole Gen. Hosp.; SHO (ENT) St. Peter's Hosp. Chertsey; Regist. (ENT) Leighton Hosp. Crewe.

HANDS, Albert Henry (retired) 25 Waterloo Road, Birkdale, Southport PR8 2NA Tel: 01704 67136 — MB ChB 1940 Liverp.; MRCGP 1954. Prev: Chief Med. Off. Leyland Motor Corp.

HANDS, Alicia Joyce, MBE (retired) 25 Waterloo Road, Birkdale, Southport PR8 2NA Tel: 01704 67136 — MB ChB 1947 Liverp. JP. Prev: Med. Off. Brit. Red Cross Soc. (Lancs. Co. Br.).

HANDS, Brian Gerard Farrell and Partners, 4 Repton Road, Willington, Derby DE65 6BX Tel: 01283 703318 Fax: 01283 701457; The Lodge, Repton, Derby DE65 6GD Tel: 01283 703136 — MB BS 1971 Lond.

HANDS, Christopher Andrew Henry, Lt.-Col. RAMC Normandy Mess, Picton Barracks, Bulford Camp, Salisbury SP4 9NY — MRCS Eng. LRCP Lond. 1979; MSc Occupat. Med. 1992. (St. Bart.) Prev: Sen. Med. Off. SHAPE, BFPO 26.

HANDS, David Henry Haslington Surgery, Crewe Road, Haslington, Crewe CW1 5QY Tel: 01270 581259 Fax: 01270 257958; 1 Caernarvon Road, Wisaston, Crewe CW2 8JW Tel: 01270 69115 — MB ChB 1965 Birm.; PhD Birm. 1972, MB ChB 1965.

HANDS, Miss Linda Joan Nuffield Dept of Surgery, John Radcliffe Hospital, Oxford OX3 9DU Tel: 01865 221285 Fax: 01865 221117 — MB BS 1977 Lond.; MS Lond. 1987, BSc (Hons.) 1974; FRCS Eng. 1981. (Roy. Free) Clin. reader, Hon. Cons. Surg..Uni. Of Oxf. & John Radcluiffe Hosp. Oxf. Prev: Regist. (Surg.) John Radcliffe Hosp. Oxf.; Sen. Regist., John Radcliffe Hosp. Oxf.; Vasc. Fell., Univ. of Chocago Illinois.

HANDS, Sarah Jane Moss Street Surgery, Chadsmnoor, Cannock WS11 2DE Tel: 01543 504477 Fax: 01543 504636 — MB BS 1979 Lond.; M. Med. Sci. 1998. (Guys Hospital)

HANDSCOMBE, Marion Christine (retired) 4 Westwick Gardens, Hammersmith, London W14 0BU Tel: 020 7603 9992 — MB BS 1954 Lond.; FRCS Eng. 1962; FCOphth 1989. Course Co-ordinator, Maja Eye Hosp., Lagos. Prev: Cons. Ophth. Surg. Coventry & Warks. Hosp.

HANDSLEY, Robert David (retired) Moorcroft, 3 Kensington Road, Saville Park, Halifax HX3 0HN Tel: 01422 351242 Fax: 01422 351242 — MB ChB 1973 Leeds; MFPHM 1989. Prev: SCMO Huddersfield HA.

HANDSLIP, Peter Dermot Joseph Department of Thoracic Medicine, George Eliot Hospital, College St., Nuneaton CV10 7DJ Tel: 02476 865263 Fax: 02476 865263 Email: peter.handslip@geh-tr.wmids.nhs.uk — MB BCh 1973 Wales; FRCP Lond. 1993; MRCP (UK) 1976. Cons. Resp. Phys. Geo. Eliot NHS Trust; Med. Dir. Geo. Eliot NHS Trust. Socs: Brit. Thorac. Soc. (Regional Represen.); (Ex-Sec. & Mem. Counc.) Midl. Thoracic Soc.; BMA (Regional Cons.s & Specialist Comm.). Prev: Cons. Phys. Geo. Eliot Hosp. Nuneaton; Clin. Tutor Geo. Eliot NHS Trust; Lect. & Hon. Sen. Regist. (Gen. Med. & Thoracic) St. Thos. Hosp. Lond.

HANDY, Catherine Frances 34 Fairview Road, Istead Rise, Gravesend DA13 9DR Tel: 01474 355331; The Hoo, Wrotom Road, Meopham, Gravesend DA13 0HP — MB BCh BAO 1983 NUI; MRCGP 1987; DCH RCP Lond.1987; DRCOG 1988.

HANDY, John Lakshman (retired) Forest House, Twitty Fee, Danbury, Chelmsford CM3 4PF Tel: 01245 222654 Fax: 01245 227969 — MB BS 1964 Lond.; FFA RCS Eng. 1969. Cons. Anaesth. Mid Essex Hosps. NHS Trust. Prev: Sen. Regist. (Anaesth) United Bristol Hosps.

HANDY, Robert 8 Battenhall Road, Worcester WR5 2BH — MB BS 1949 Lond.; DPH Eng. 1954; MFCM 1973.

HANDY, Sumithra The Children's Hospital, Steelhouse Lane, Birmingham B4 6NH Tel: 0121 333 9183 Fax: 0121 333 9181 — MB ChB 1982 Zambia; BSc Zambia 1979; MRCPsych 1991; Dip. Psychother. 1990; Dip Social Learning Theory & Practice 1994.

(Univ. of Zambia) Cons. (Child & Adolesc. Psychiat.) Birm. Childr.s Hosp. NHS Trust Birm.; Hon. Sen. Clin. Lect. Univ. of Birm. 1998. Prev: Sen. Regist. (Child & Adolesc. Psychiat.) W. Midl. HA.

HANDYSIDE, Robert 100 South Gyle Gardens, Edinburgh EH12 7RZ — MB ChB 1975 Ed.

HANDYSIDE, William Bryan 41 Greencroft Road, Greencroft Close, Darlington DL3 8HW Tel: 01325 484618 — MB BS Durh. 1942. (Newc.) Prev: Ho. Phys. & Clin. Asst. City Hosp. Infec. Dis. Newc-on-Tyne.

HANDYSIDES, Julia Margaret 25 Fordwich Rise, Hertford SG14 2BW — MB BS 1988 Lond.; BSc Lond. 1983, MB BS 1988; MRC Psych 1996. Regist. (Psychiat.) P.ss Alexandra Hosp. Harlow.; Specialist Regist. (Child & Adolesc. Psychiat.) Roy. Lond. Hosps. Rotat. Prev: Ho. Off. N. Middlx. Hosp. Lond.

HANDYSIDES, Nigel Stuart Paul Orchard Surgery, Baldock Rd, Buntingford SG9 9DL Tel: 01763 272411; 25 Fordwich Rise, Hertford SG14 2BW Tel: 01992 587621 — MB BS 1983 Lond.; BSc Lond. 1980; MRCGP 1987; DRCOG 1986. (Univ. Coll. Lond.) Assoc. Managing Edr., ProMed Mail; GP Buntingford. Prev: Edit. Regist. BMJ Lond.; GP Hertford; Ed. Communicable Dis. Report Pub. Health Laborat. Serv. Lond.

HANEKOM, Wouter Van Heerden 7 Brayburne Avenue, London SW4 6AD — MB ChB 1988 Stellenbosch.

HANFORD, Francis William (retired) Kingscot, Ogbourne St George, Marlborough SN8 1SU — MRCS Eng. LRCP Lond. 1940. Prev: Chief Med. Off. Roan Consolidated Mines Ltd. Luanshya, Zambia.

HANGARTNER, John Robert Wilfred PPP healthcare PPP House, Vale Road, Tunbridge Wells TN1 1BJ Tel: 01892 505126 Fax: 01892 505027 Email: robert.hangartner@pppgroup.co.uk — MB BS 1979 Lond.; BSc (Hons.) Lond. 1976; MBA Open Univ. 1996; MRCS Eng. LRCP Lond. 1979; MRCPath 1988; FRCPath 1997. (Guy's) Sen. Med.Exec. PPP healthcare; Chief Med. Off. Guardian Health Ltd. Folkestone; Chief Med. Off.Bass Healthcare Trustee Ltd. Socs: Fell. Roy. Soc. Med.; BMA (Ex-Mem. Counc. & Chairm. HJSC). Prev: Sen. Princip. Med. Off. & Head Div. DoH Leeds; Princip. Med. Off. DoH Lond.; Lect. (Histopath.) St. Geo. Hosp. Med. Sch. Lond.

HANGER, Susan Jane 82 Oakland Avenue, Leicester LE4 7SF — MB BS 1992 Lond.

HANHAM, Iain William Ferguson Department of Radiotherapy & Oncology, Charing Cross Hospital, Fulham Palace Road, London W6 8RF Tel: 020 8746 8427 Fax: 020 8846 1603; 12 St Mary Abbot's Terrace, Kensington, London W14 8NX Tel: 020 7602 3439 Fax: 020 7602 3439 — MB BChir 1962 Camb.; MSc 2001 Imperial College London; MA Camb. 1962; FRCP Lond. 1995; MRCP Lond. 1967; MRCS Eng. LRCP Lond. 1960; FRCR 1975; FFR 1968; DMRT Eng. 1966. (Camb. & Guy's) Hon. Cons. Hammersmith Hosps. Trust, Clin. Onlogy; Cons. Radiother. Chelsea & W.m. Hosp. & Qu. Mary's Hosp. Roehampton; Cons. Cromwell Hosp. Lond.; Approved Teach. (Med.) Lond. Univ; Civil. Cons. Radiother. & Oncol. RAF. Socs: Fell. Roy. Soc. Med.; Brit. Assn. Oncol.; Amer. Soc. Clin. Oncol. Prev: Cons. Radiother. W.m. Hosp. Lond.; Sen. Regist. (Radiother.) & Resid. Med. Off. W.m. Hosp. Lond.; Cons. Radiother. & Clin. Oncol. Char. Cross Hosp. Hammersmith Hosps. Trust.

HANID, Mohamed Anwar 67 Sutton Lane, Hounslow TW3 4LA Tel: 020 8572 8483 — MD 1983 Wales; MB BCh 1972; MRCP (U.K.) 1974; FRCP 1998.

HANIEF, Mr Mohamed Rubnawaz 7 Ruskin Avenue, Kew, Richmond TW9 4DR — MB BS 1986 Bangalor; MB BS Bangalore 1986; FRCS Eng. 1993.

HANIF, Junaid ENT Department, University Hospital of Wales, Cardiff CF14 4XW; 71 Porthcawl Road, Cardiff CF4 6AQ — MB ChB 1988 Dundee; FRCS Ed. 1996. Specialist Regist. Rotat. (Ear, Nose & Throat) S. Wales. Socs: BMA; BAORL.

HANIF, Mohaammad 69 Severn Road, Heywood OL10 4SZ — MB BS 1966 Dacca.

HANIF, Mohammed 50 Hamstead Road, Birmingham B19 1DB — MB ChB 1991 Liverp.

HANIF, Rehana 364 Wellington Road S., Hounslow TW4 5JX — MB BS 1992 Lond.

HANIF, Shahed Mahmood 4 Second Avenue, Bradford BD3 7JQ — MB ChB 1993 Manch.

HANIF, Shahid Lypset Health Care, off Horbury Road, Wakefield WF2 8RE Tel: 01924 373377 — MB ChB 1995 Leeds; MRCGP 1999; BSc (Hons.) cl 1 1992; DRCOG 1999; DFFP 1998. (Leeds) Full-Time G.P; GP Regist. Prev: SHO (Paediat.) 1997-1998; SHO (A & E) 1996-1997; GP Regist. Dewsbury 1997.

HANIF, Shaista Tazayan 104 Chorley New Road, Bolton BL1 4DH — MB BS 1992 Lond.; MRCGP 1996. GP Bolton, Gtr Manch.

HANIFA, Yasmeen 68 Devonshire Way, Croydon CR0 8BR; 34 Scotforth Road, Lancaster LA1 4SB Tel: 01524 37511 — MB BS 1993 Lond.; MRCGP 1999; DRCOG 1996. (King's Coll. Lond.) Socs: BMA. Prev: GP/Regist. Gravesend.

HANINGTON, Edda Liselotte Ingeborg 9D Bedford Towers, Kings Road, Brighton BN1 2JG — MB BS 1948 Lond.; MD Lond. 1968; MRCP Lond. 1976; MRCS Eng. LRCP Lond. 1948. (Roy. Free) Socs: Fell. Roy. Soc. Med. & Med. Soc. Lond. Prev: Dep. Dir. Wellcome Trust; Hon. Cons. P.ss Margt. Migraine Clinic Lond.; Ho. Phys. Roy. Free Hosp. & Postgrad. Med. Sch.

HANINGTON, Sarah Joy Royal Devon and Exeter Health Care Trust, Newcourt House, Old Rydon Lane, Exeter EX2 7JU Tel: 01392 449837; Orchard Close, Belstone, Okehampton EX20 1RA — MB BS 1977 Lond. (Westminster Hospital) SCMO (Community Paediat.) Exeter.

HANKIN, Julie Elizabeth Reaside Clinic, Birmingham Great Park, Bristol Road S., Birmingham B45 9BE Tel: 0121 453 9630; 67 Neville Road, Shirley, Solihull B90 2QN — MB ChB 1995 Dundee. SHO (Psychiat.) Coventry & Warks. Train. Rotat.

HANKIN, Roland Gregory Trinity Street Surgery, 20 Trinity Street, Dorchester DT1 1TU Tel: 01305 251545 Fax: 01305 269707 — MB ChB 1972 Dundee; MRCGP 1976. Prev: Trainee GP Bournemouth/Poole VTS; Gen. Phys. Brit. Aircraft Corpn. Saudi-Arabia; Regist. (A & E) St. Albans City Hosp. Lond.

HANKIN, Terence 23 Melling Way, Liverpool L32 1TN; 3 Liverpool Road, Formby, Liverpool L37 4BN Tel: 01704 877454 Email: davros@hankin_t.demon.co.uk — MB ChB 1989 Liverp.; BSc (Hons.) Liverp. 1986, MB ChB 1989; FRCA 1994. (Liverpool) Cons. (Anaesth. & IC). Socs: Assn. Anaesth.; Intens. Care Soc.

HANKINSON, Christine Ann The Health Centre, 103 Brown Street, Broughty Ferry, Dundee DD5 1EP Tel: 01382 731331 Fax: 01382 737966 — MB ChB 1972 Glas.

HANKINSON, Professor John Mill Greens Hemmel, Angerton, Hartburn, Morpeth NE61 4EY Tel: 01670 772206 — MB BS Lond. 1946; FRCS Eng. 1950. (St. Mary's) Cons. Neurol. Surg. Roy. Vict. Infirm. Newc. & Regional Neurol. Centre Newc.; Emerit. Prof. Neurosurg. Univ. Newc. u. Tyne. Socs: (Ex-Pres.) Soc. Brit. Neurol. Surgs.; N. Eng. Surg. Soc. Prev: Sen. Regist. (Surg.) Nat. Hosp. Qu. Sq. Lond.; 1st Asst. Neurosurg. Dept. St. Geo. Hosp.; Ho. Surg. St. Mary's Hosp.

HANKS, Geoffrey Noel (retired) 33 Freston Gardens, Cockfosters, Barnet EN4 9LY Tel: 020 8449 9175 — MB BS 1952 Sydney. Prev: GP Barnet.

HANKS, Professor Geoffrey Warren Bristol Oncology Centre, Horfield Road, Bristol BS2 8ED Tel: 0117 928 3336 Fax: 0117 928 3865 — MB BS Lond. 1970; BSc (Hons. Anat.) Lond. 1967; FRCP Ed. 1991; FRCP Lond. 1990; FFPM RCP (UK) 1991; Dip Pharm Med RCP (UK) 1977. (Univ. Coll. Hosp.) Prof. Palliat. Med. Univ. Bristol; Hon. Cons. Phys. Utd. Bristol Healthcare Trust. Socs: WHO Expert Advis. Panel on Cancer; Bd. Managem. Cancer Relief Macmillan Fund; (Pres.) Europ. Assn. Palliat. Care. Prev: Prof. Palliat. Med. UMDS, Univ. Lond.; Cons. Phys. Roy. Marsden Hosp. Lond.; Hon. Sen. Lect. & Hon. Cons. St. Bart. Hosp. Med. Coll. Lond.

HANKS, Richard James Peel Medical Centre, Derby Road, Peel IM5 1HP — MB ChB 1991 Birm.; ChB Birm. 1991.

HANLEY, Mr David Jeffrey (retired) Nuffield Hospital, Derriford Road, Derriford, Plymouth PL6 8BG Tel: 01752 761835 Fax: 01752 768969 Email: david.hanley@lineone.net — MB BS Lond. 1965; FRCS Eng. 1972; MRCS Eng. LRCP Lond. 1966. Cons. Plastic Surg. Nuffield Hosp., Plymouth. Prev: Sen. Regist. (Plastic Surg.) Stoke Mandeville Hosp. Aylesbury.

HANLEY, Donal Aloysius (retired) 5 Westfield Avenue, Armley, Leeds LS12 3SJ Tel: 0113 263 0606 — MB BCh BAO NUI 1950; LM Coombe. Prev: Ho. Surg. & Ho. Phys. N.. Infirm. Cork.

HANLEY, John McDiarmuid (retired) 7 Langland, Springwood Est., King's Lynn PE30 4TH Tel: 01553 771925 — LRCP LRCS Ed. LRFPS Glas. 1947; DPH Glas. 1962. Prev: SCM (EnviroMent. Health) Walsall AHA.

HANLEY, John Patrick 23 Dunrobin Place, Stockbridge, Edinburgh EH3 5HZ — MB ChB 1987 Leic.; MRCP (UK) 1991; DRCPath 1993. Lect. (Haemat.) Edin. Univ.

HANLEY, Marie 112 Buxton Road, Hazel Grove, Stockport SK7 6AJ — MB ChB 1992 Manch.

HANLEY, Mary Lucia South Dene Surgery, The Shrubberies, George Lane, London E18 1BD Tel: 020 8530 3731 Fax: 020 8518 8157 — MB BCh BAO 1983 NUI.

HANLEY, Michael Timothy The Surgery, Cottage Hospital, Alston, Penrith CA9 3QY Tel: 01434 381214 Fax: 01434 382210 — MB BCh BAO 1980 NUI; MRCGP 1988; DObst RCSI 1982. (Univ. Coll. Dub.) Socs: Brit. Assn. Med. & Dent. Hypn.; Assn. Neurolinguistic Programming.

HANLEY, Neil Anthony 95 Bayswater Road, Newcastle upon Tyne NE2 3HP Tel: 0191 281 6005 — MB ChB 1993 Ed.; BSc (Med. Sci.) Hons. Pharmacol. Ed. 1991. SHO Rotat. (Gen. Med.) Freeman Hosps. Newc. u. Tyne.

HANLEY, Paul David Radiology Department, The Ulster Hospital, Dundonald, Belfast; 86 Osborne Park, Belfast BT9 6JQ Tel: 01232 661878 — MB BCh BAO 1982 Belf.; FRCR 1987. Cons. Radiol. Ulster Hosp. Dundonald & Ards Hosp. Newtownards. Prev: Sen. Regist. (Radiol.) Roy. Vict. Hosp. Belf.; Regist. Belf. City Hosp.; Ho. Off. Roy. Vict. Hosp. Belf.

HANLEY, Robert Ian Park Avenue Medical Centre, 9 Park Avenue, Stirling FK8 2QR Tel: 01786 473529 — MB ChB 1985 Ed.; BSc (Hons.) Biochem. Ed. 1982, MB ChB 1985; MRCGP 1989; DCCH RCP Ed. 1990; DRCOG 1988.

HANLEY, Ruth Carolyn Mary 38 Briony Avenue, Hale, Altrincham WA15 8QD — MB BCh BAO 1985 NUI.

HANLEY, Sally Ann Bank House, Belsay, Newcastle upon Tyne NE20 0EU — BM BS 1989 Nottm.

HANLEY, Simon Piers Chest Unit, 2nd Floor, Southern Offices, North Manchester General Hospital, Crumpsal, Manchester M8 5RB Tel: 0161 720 2042 Fax: 0161 7202741 Email: 100545.2712@compuserve.com; Tel: 0161 4069032 — MB BS 1973 Lond.; DM Nottm. 1985; FRCP Lond. 1994; MRCP (UK) 1975; MRCS Eng. LRCP Lond. 1973. Cons. Phycician, Gen. & Thoracic Med. Prev: Med. Direct. N. Manch. Gen. Hosp. 1995-1998.

HANLEY, Tracey-Anne 64 Garnie Avenue, Erskine PA8 7BE — MB ChB 1994 Liverp.

***HANLON, Charlotte Sophie** 28 Park Avenue, Duston, Northampton NN5 6QF — BM BCh 1998 Oxf.; BM BCh Oxf 1998; MA Cantab 1999.

HANLON, Geoffrey Peter Storer Road Medical Centre, 2A Storer Road, Loughborough LE11 5EQ Tel: 01509 212120 — MB ChB 1976 Birm.; FRCGP 2000; MA Oxf. 1979; MRCGP 1980; DRCOG 1979; DCH Eng. 1979. (Birmingham) GP LoughBoro..

HANLON, Lesley Christine Stevenson Russell Institute, Causey Side St., Paisley PA1 1UR Tel: 0141 889 8701; 17 Mansionhouse Road, Paisley PA1 3RG Tel: 0141 889 2835 — MB ChB Glas. 1980; MFFP 1993; MRCGP 1984; DRCOG 1982. p/t SCMO (Family Plann.) Renfrewsh. Prev: Clin. Med. Off. (Family Plann.) Argyll & Clyde HB.

HANLON, Margaret Edith (retired) 21 Broompark Drive, Newton Mearns, Glasgow G77 5DX Tel: 0141 639 8545 Fax: 0141 639 3028 — MB ChB Glas. 1958; DObst RCOG 1960. p/t The Appeal Serv. Prev: GP Glas.

HANLON, Professor Philip William Public Health Institute of Scotland, Clifton House, Clifton Place, Glasgow G3 7LS Tel: 0141 300 1011 Fax: 0141 300 1020 Email: p.hanlon@udcf.gla.as.uk; 17 Mansionhouse Road, Paisley PA1 3RG Tel: 0141 889 2835 Fax: 0141 889 0421 — MD 1988 Glas.; BSc Glas. 1975, MB ChB 1978; FRCP Glas. 1993; MRCP (UK) 1983; MPH Glas. 1988; MFPHM RCP Lond. 1988; MRCGP 1982; DRCOG 1980; FFPHM 1995. Prof. of Pub. Health Univ. of Glas. & Director Pub. Health Inst. of Scotl. Prev: Med. Dir. Roy. Alexandra Hosp. NHS Trust Paisley Scotl.; Hon. Sen. Lect. (Pub. Health) Univ. Glas.; Dir. of Health Promotion Gtr. Glas. HB.

HANLON, Rebecca 8 Liverpool Road, Aughton, Ormskirk L39 3LL — MB ChB 1993 Leeds. SHO (A & E) Bolton Roy. Infirm. Prev: Ho. Off. (Gen. Surg. & Gen. Med.) Halifax Roy. Infirm.

HANLY, Denis John Haslemere Health Centre, Church Lane, Haslemere GU27 2BQ; April Cottage, 3 Pk Road, Haslemere GU27 2NJ — MB BS 1977 Lond. (St. Geo.) Prev: Regist. (Histopath.) St. Geo. Hosp. Lond.; SHO (A & E) St. Stephens Hosp. Lond.; Regist. (Psychiat.) Hillingdon Hosp.

HANLY, James Francis 69 Andrewes House, Barbican, London EC2Y 8AY Tel: 020 7638 0071 — MB BCh BAO 1936 NUI; DPH 1939. (Univ. Coll. Dub.) Socs: Thoracic Soc. Wales & Brit. Thoracic Soc. Prev: Ho. Phys. St. Vincent's Hosp. Dub.; Asst. Med. Off. PeaMt. Sanat. Dub.; Cons. Phys. Mid Glam. AHA.

HANLY, Thomas Patrick Brandon Mental health unit, Leicester General Hospital, Leicester LE5 0TD Tel: 0116 225 6200; 105 Curzon Avenue, Birstall, Leicester LE4 4AG — MB BCh BAO 1986 NUI. Staff Grade Gen. Psych.Brandon Ment. health unit leics.

HANMER, Owen John Newham Community Health Services NHS Trust, Sydenham Building, Plaistow Hospital, Sampson St., London E13 9EH Tel: 020 8586 6306 Fax: 020 8586 6382 Email: owenhanmer@compuserve.com; 10c Glebe Avenue, Woodford Green IG8 9HB — MB ChB 1969 Manc.; MB ChB Manch. 1969; FRCP Lond. 1993; FRCP Ed. 1991; MRCP (UK) 1977; FRCPCH 1997; DCH Eng. 1972; DRCOG 1971. (Manch.) Med. Dir. & Cons. Paediat. Lond.; Regist. Adviser Paediat. (N. Thames E.); Chairm. Paediat. Specialist Train. Comm. Socs: Fell. Roy. Soc. Med.

HANMER, Rachel Louise 41 Clarence Place, Bristol BS2 8DD — MB ChB 1998 Bristol.

HANN, Gillian Sarah 22 Fareham Close, Fulwood, Preston PR2 8FH — MB ChB 1991 Sheff.

HANN, Helen Catherine Luis 38 Ferrers Road, Yoxall, Burton-on-Trent DE13 8PS — MB ChB 1998 Leic.; MB ChB Leic 1998.

HANN, Ian Malcolm Haematology Department, Great Ormond Street Hospital, for Children NHS Trust, London WC1N 3JH Tel: 020 7829 8831 Fax: 020 7813 8410 Email: hanni@gosh.nhs.uk; 1 Heathville Road, Crouch Hill, London N19 3AL Tel: 0207 263 7385 Fax: 020 7284 3664 Email: ian.jules@virginnet.co.uk — MB BS 1971 Lond.; MD Lond. 1980; FRCP Glas. 1993; FRCP Lond. 1989; MRCP (UK) 1974; MRCS Eng. LRCP Lond. 1971; FRCPath 1992; FRCPCH (UK) 1997; FRCP 2000 Edin.; FRCP 2000 Edin; FRCPI 2001. (St. Bart.) Trust Med. Director; Hon. Sen. Lect. Inst. Child Health Lond.; Med. Director, Gt. Ormond St. Childr.s Hosp. Lond. Socs: Brit. Soc. Haematol. Prev: Head Haemat. Dept. Roy. Hosp. Sick Childr. Glas.; Cons. Paediat. Haemat. Gt. Ormond St. Childr. Hosp. Lond.

HANN, Jeremy Christopher 22 Fareham Close, Fulwood, Preston PR2 8FH — MB BS 1992 Lond.; BSc Lond. 1987, MB BS 1992; MRCGP 1996; DRCOG 1994. (St. Bart.) GP Preston.

HANNA, Adel Rifaat Younan 19 Windsor Road, Poole BH14 8SF — MB ChB 1969 Alexandria; DPM Eng. 1980.

HANNA, Biatrice Wadie 56 St David's Crescent, Newport NP9 3AW — MB BCh 1978 Cairo; MRCOG 1994.

HANNA, Brendan Colmcille 3 Ashdale Gardens, Ardglass, Downpatrick BT30 7RZ — MB BCh 1998 Belf.; MB BCh Belf 1998.

HANNA, Carol Louise Velindre Hospital NHS Trust, Cardiff Tel: 029 2061 5888 — BM BCh 1989 Oxf.; MA Camb. 1990, BA 1986; MRCP (UK) 1993; FRCR 1998. p/t Cons. (Clin. Oncol.), Velindre Hosp. NHS Trust, Cardiff.

HANNA, Colin Martin Wheeler Street Health Care, Wheeler St., Hull HU3 5QE Tel: 01482 354933 — MB ChB 1988 Ed.; DFFP 1995; DRCOG 1993. (Edinburgh) GP Princip. Hull.

HANNA, Dalia 139 Horsenden Lane S., Perivale, Greenford UB6 7NS — MB BS 1996 Lond.; BSc (Psychol.) UCL 1993. SHO Psychiat., St Albans. Socs: MRCGP.

HANNA, Edith Mary 57 Hatherley Road, Cheltenham GL51 6EG Tel: 01242 22679 — MB BS 1960 Lond. (Univ. Coll. Hosp.)

HANNA, Elinor Violet Dept. Clinical Biochemistry, Kelvin Builiding, Royal Victoria Hospital, Grosvenor Rd, Belfast BT12 68A Email: elinor.hanna@bll.n-i.nhs.uk; 4 Mourne Grange, Dromore BT25 1BZ — MB BCh BAO 1995 Belf.; DipRCPath 2001; MRCP 1999; DMH 1999. (QUB) Specialist Regist. Chem. Path. Roy. Vict. Hosp. Belf.

HANNA, Frederick Alexander, OBE (retired) 57 Hatherley Road, Cheltenham GL51 6EG Tel: 01242 522679 — MB BCh BAO 1939 Dub.; FRCR 1980; DMRT Bristol 1948. Prev: Cons. Radiother. Glos. AHA Centre for Radiother. & Oncol.

HANNA, Mr George Bushra Dept. Surgery, Ninewells Hospital, Dundee DD2 9SY Tel: 01382 660111 — MB BCh 1987 Cairo; FRCS Ed. 1993; PhD Dundee 1998. Clin. Lect. in Surg. Univ. Hosp. Dundee; Hon. Specialist Regist. Tayside Univ. Hosps. Prev: Clin. Research Fell..

HANNA, Gerard Glynn 40 Tollymore Road, Newcastle BT33 0JN Tel: 0780 154 2098 Email: hanna@doctors.org.uk — MB BCh 1998 Belf.; MB BCh Belf 1998. SHO Med. RVH. Belf.

HANNA, Ghaly Farag Banoub Milton Keynes General Hospital, Standing Way, Eaglestone, Milton Keynes MK6 5LD Tel: 01908 660033 Fax: 01908 243172; 11 Crowborough Lane, Kents Hill, Milton Keynes MK7 6HE Tel: 01908 691774 — MB ChB 1981 Alexandria; MRCOG 1993. Assoc. Specialist Milton Keynes Gen. Hosp.; Research Fell. (Fetal Med.) Harris Birth Right Centre for Fetal Med. Kings Coll. Hosp. Socs: BMA; BMUS. Prev: Regist. & SHO (O & G) Milton Keynes Gen. Hosp. Trust; SHO (O & G) Darlington Memor. Hosp.

HANNA, Ghassan Salem Suleiman Hereford Hospitals NHS Trust, The County Hospital, Union Walk, Hereford HR1 2ER Tel: 01432 355444 — MB BCh 1973 Cairo; FRCS Eng. 1982. Cons. ENT Surg. Hereford Co. Hosp. Union Walk, Hereford, HR1 2ER. Prev: Regist. (ENT) Wexham Pk. Hosp. E. Berks.

HANNA, Hany Sadek Fahmi Hill Top Medical Centre, 15 Hill Top Road, Oldbury B68 9DU — MB BS 1972 Cairo; MB BS 1972 Cairo.

HANNA, Helen Mary Little Snakemoor, Sleepers Hill, Winchester SO22 4NA — MB BS 1972 Lond.; FRCR 1982; DMRD Eng. 1978; DObst RCOG 1975. (Middlx.) Assoc. Specialist (Radiol.) Soton. Gen. Hosp. Prev: Sen. Regist. (Radiol.) Soton. Gen. Hosp.; Regist. (Radiol.) Bristol Roy. Infirm.; Ho. Surg. Middlx. Hosp. Lond.

HANNA, James Alan Ramsay (retired) 2 Bowring Grove, Wellington, Telford TF1 2EG Tel: 01952 641094 — MB BCh BAO 1948 Dub.; LM Rotunda 1950; DObst RCOG 1950. Prev: Ho. Surg. Sir P. Dun's Hosp. Dub. & Wom. Hosp. Birm.

HANNA, Leila Stefanos Pine Lodge, Lodge Road, Sundridge Park, Bromley BR1 3ND Tel: 020 8460 6670 — MB ChB 1977 Ain Shams; MRCOG 1983; T(OG) 1991. Cons. (O & G) Qu. Mary's Hosp. Sidcup. Prev: Sen. Regist. (O & G) Hammersmith Hosp. Lond. & St. Heliers Hosp. Carshalton; Regist. (O & G) Hammersmith & Centr. Middlx. Hosp. Lond.; SHO (O & G) King's Coll. Hosp. Lond.

HANNA, Magdi Henein King's College Hospital, Denmark Hill, London SE5 Tel: 020 7346 3358 Fax: 020 7346 3632; 62 Park Road, Beckenham Tel: 020 8658 1147 — MB BCh 1972 Cairo; FFA RCSI 1979. Cons. Anaesth. & Dir. Pain Relief Unit King's Coll. Hosp. Lond.; Dir. Pain Research Unit Kings Coll. Sch. Med. Prev: Sen. Regist. (Anaesth.) King's Coll. Hosp., Brook Gen. Hosp. & Qu. Vict. Hosp. E. Grinstead.

HANNA, Maurice Iskander St Nicholas Health Centre, Saunder Bank, Burnley BB11 2EN Tel: 01282 422528 Fax: 01282 832834 — MB BCh 1965 Ain Shams.

HANNA, Nehad Philippe Mickleover Surgery, 10 Cavendish Way, Mickleover, Derby DE3 5BJ Tel: 01332 519160 Fax: 01332 523054 — LRCP LRCS 1978 Ed.; LRCP LRCS Ed. LRCPS Glas. 1978; MRCPI 1983.

HANNA, Nicola Jan Webster and Hanna, Newbury Park Health Centre, 40 Perrymans Farm Road, Ilford IG2 7LE Tel: 020 8518 2414 Fax: 020 8518 3194; 1 Davinia Close, Woodford Bridge, Woodford Green IG8 8DG — MB ChB 1983 Glas.; MRCGP 1990; DCH RCP Lond. 1986; DRCOG 1985.

HANNA, Patricia Ruth (retired) 8 Olde Forge Manor, Belfast BT10 0HY Tel: 02890 626331 — MB BCh BAO 1951 Dub. Prev: Clin. Med. Off. S. Belf. Dist. E. Health & Social Servs. Bd.

HANNA, Robert George John L'Aumone Medical Practice, Castel GY5 7RU Tel: 01481 56517 Fax: 01481 51190 Email: r.hanna@guernsey.net; Les Cambrees House, Rue Des Charrieres, St. Pierre Du Bois, Guernsey GY7 9JA Tel: 01481 65707 — MB BCh BAO 1985 Belf.; MB BCh BAO Belf. 1983; MRCGP 1988; DCH Dub. 1987; DRCOG 1986; DGM RCP Lond. 1986. Socs: Assoc. Mem. Brit. Med. Acupunc. Soc. Prev: SHO (Paediat.) Belf. City Hosp.; Trainee GP Rotat. Downpatrick Hosp.; SHO (Infec. Dis.) Belvoir Pk. Hosp. Belf.

HANNA, Sarah Julie Elisabeth Flat 1, 24 Kestrel Avenue, London SE24 0EB — MB BChir 1993 Camb.

HANNA, Selim Naguib Bradford Royal Infirmary, Duckworth Lane, Bradford BD9 6RJ Tel: 01274 42200 Ext: 514; 51 Kirklands Road, Baildon, Shipley BD17 6HT — MB BCh 1972 Cairo; MSc Clin. Chem. Surrey 1982; MRCPath 1985. Cons. Chem. Path. Bradford Roy. Infirm.

HANNA, Wade Jeffrey 11 Ramsden Close, Glossop SK13 7BB — MB ChB 1991 Manch.

HANNA, Mr William Alexander 14 Strathyre Park, Belfast BT10 0AZ — MB ChB 1950 Ed.; FRCS Ed. 1958.

HANNA, Wilma Jacqueline 18 Ballyardle Road, Kilkeel, Newry BT34 4JX Tel: 016937 62644 — MB BCh BAO Belf. 1964; DObst RCOG 1966. Well Woman Clin. Kilkeel. Prev: Med. Asst. (Geriat.) Mourne Hosp. Kilkeel.

HANNA, Winifred Elizabeth Margaret 1344 Evesham Road, Astwood Bank, Redditch B96 6BD — MB ChB 1980 Birm.

***HANNAFORD, Katie Louise** Dawn Cottage, Bridge St., Great Kimble, Aylesbury HP17 9TW — MB BS 1996 Lond.

HANNAFORD, Patricia Frances 29 Grange Road, Edinburgh EH9 1UQ Tel: 0131 225 6617 Fax: 0131 225 6617; 20 Howe Street, Edinburgh EH3 6TG Tel: 0131 225 6617 Fax: 0131 225 6617 Email: docph@aol.com — MB ChB 1977 Ed.; MRCGP 1982; MFHom 1979; DAvMed FOM RCP Lond. 1977; DCH RCPS Glas. 1982; DRCOG 1981. (Edinburgh) Cons. Homoeop. Med. Edin. & Midlothian NHS Trust; Homoeop. Pract. Edin. Prev: GP Lothian HB.

HANNAFORD, Professor Philip Christopher Department of General Practice and Primary Care, Foresterhill Health Centre, Westburn Road, Aberdeen AB25 2AY Tel: 01224 663131 Fax: 01224 84063 — MB ChB 1981 Aberd.; MD Aberd. 1995; MFFP 1994; FRCGP 1997, M 1985; DCH RCP Lond. 1985; DRCOG 1983. Prof. Grampian Health Care Chair of Primary Care; Dir. Roy. Coll. Gen. Pract. Centre for Primary Care Research & Epidemiol. Socs: Soc. Epidemiol. Research. Prev: Dir. Roy. Coll. Gen. Pract. Manch. Research Unit; Research Fell. Roy. Coll. Gen. Pract. Manch. Research Unit; GP Manch.

HANNAFORD, Robert William St Oswalds Surgery, The Parade, Pembroke SA71 4LD Tel: 01646 682374 Fax: 01646 622424; Avendale, Lower Lamphey Road, Pembroke SA71 4AF — MB BS 1976 Lond.; MRCS Eng. LRCP Lond. 1976; CIH Dund 1987; DRCOG 1979. (Guy's) p/t Med. Off. Texaco Oil Refinery Pembroke.

HANNAH, Adam Cook Fullarton Street Surgery, 24 Fullarton Street, Ayr KA7 1UB Tel: 01292 264260 Fax: 01292 283284; 46 Mount Charles Crescent, Doonfoot, Ayr KA7 4PA Tel: 01292 443648 — MB ChB 1974 Glas.

HANNAH, Andrew Hyndman 4 Boleyn Road, Glasgow G41 4NF — MB ChB 1992 Glas. Research Fell. W.. Infirm. Glas. Univ. NHS Trust.

HANNAH, Bernard Alexander Hannah and McGoldrick, Health Centre, Pound Lane, Downpatrick BT30 6HY; The Health Centre, Pound Lane, Downpatrick BT30 6HY Tel: 01396 612962 — MB BCh BAO 1974 Belf.; DObst RCOG 1976.

HANNAH, David William McNulty and Partners, Torkard Hill Medical Centre, Farleys Lane, Shieldfield, Nottingham NG15 6DY Tel: 0115 963 3676 Fax: 0115 968 1957 — MB ChB 1983 Dundee; MRCGP 1987; DRCOG 1987. (Dundee)

HANNAH, Elizabeth Gabrielle 75 St Brides Way, Bothwell, Glasgow G71 8QG — MB ChB 1998 Glas.; MB ChB Glas 1998.

HANNAH, George Downie Finlaggan Surgery, Finlaggan, Clachan Seil, Oban PA34 4TL Tel: 01852 300223 Fax: 01852 300392 — MB ChB 1980 Ed.; BSc Ed. 1977, MB ChB 1980; MRCGP 1985; DRCOG 1984; DA Eng. 1982. GP Easdale.

HANNAH, Helen Barbara (retired) 42 The Common, Bromham, Chippenham SN15 2JJ Tel: 01380 850589 — MB ChB 1965 Ed.; FRCA 1973; DA (UK) 1967. Prev: Sen. Cons. Anaesth. & Resusc. Camb. Milit. Hosp. Aldershot.

HANNAH, Jean Ann Ferness Road Surgery, 8 Ferness Road, Glasgow G21 3SH Tel: 0141 558 6178 Fax: 0141 557 3405 — MB ChB 1986 Glas.

HANNAH, John Alexander Matheson Douglas Street Surgery, 1 Douglas Street, Hamilton ML3 0DR Tel: 01698 286262; 25 Broughton Place, Hamilton ML3 9HJ — MB ChB 1985 Glas.; BSc Glas. 1980; MRCGP 1988; DRCOG 1988.

HANNAH, Julian Christopher Department of Public Health Medicine, Salford and Trafford Heath Authority, Albert St Eccles, Manchester M30 0NJ Tel: 0161 787 0292 Fax: 0161 787 0237 — MB ChB 1980 Manch.; BSc (Med. Sci.) St. And. 1977; MSc Community Med. Manch. 1988, MB ChB 1980; MFPHM 1989. Cons. Pub. Health Med. Salford & Trafford HA; Hon. Assoc. Lect. (Pub. Health Med.) Univ. Manch. Socs: Fell. Manch. Med. Soc.

HANNAH, Lesley Elizabeth Ground Right, 4 Boleyn Road, Glasgow G41 4NF — MB ChB 1992 Glas.

HANNAH, Margaret Clare Merton, Sutton & Wandsworth HA, The Wilson, Cranmer Road, Mitcham CR4 4TP Tel: 020 8648 3021; 27 Worlingham Road, London SE22 9HD — MB BChir 1986 Camb.; MFPHM RCP (UK) 1995. Sen. Regist. (Pub. Health Med.) Merton, Sutton & Wandsworth HA. Prev: Sen. Regist. Mid Surrey HA; Research Fell. (Community Med.), Hong Kong Univ.; Med. Off. Ruttonjee Sanat., Hong Kong.

HANNAH, Pamela Moira Flat 3, 3 Netherlee Place, Glasgow G44 3YL — MB ChB 1988 Glas.

HANNAH, Ramsay (retired) 2 Hillcrest View, Larkhall ML9 2HX Tel: 01698 882105 — MB ChB 1957 Glas.; MRCP Lond. 1965; MRCP Glas. 1962; DObst RCOG 1959. Prev: Sen. Med. Regist. S. Gen. Hosp. Glas.

HANNAH, Stanley Robert Hillbank Health Centre, Flat 1A, 1 Constitution Street, Dundee DD3 6NF Tel: 01382 221976 Fax: 01382 201980 — MB ChB 1986 Dundee.

HANNAH, Thomas (retired) 7 Glasclune Court, Greenheads Road, North Berwick EH39 4RD Tel: 01620 895910 — LRCP LRCS Ed. LRFPS Glas. 1948.

HANNAH, William Morrison (retired) Motherwell Health Centre, 138-144 Windmillhill St., Motherwell ML1 1TB — MB ChB 1961 Glas.; MRCGP 1975; DObst RCOG 1963. Prev: Ho. Phys. Vict. Infirm. Glas.

HANNAM, Ciara Rosemary 2 Strathleven Park, Holywood BT18 0NJ — MB BCh BAO 1997 Belf.

HANNAM, David Richard (retired) Department of Anaesthesia, Warrington Hospital NHS Trust, Lovely Lane, Warrington WA5 1QG — MB ChB 1971 Liverp.; FFA RCS Eng. 1978; FRCA. Prev: Cons. Anaesth.Warrington Hosp. NHS Trust.

HANNAM, Simon 17 Prospero Road, Adriway, London N19 3QX — MB BS 1988 Lond.; BSc (Hons.) Lond. 1985, MB BS 1988; MRCP 1992; MRCPCH 1998. (UCMMS) Sen. Regist. in Paediat. KCH Lond. Prev: SHO (Paediat.) Brighton & Kings. Coll. Hosp. Lond.; Hon. Regist. St Thomas' Hosp. Lond.

HANNAN, Amir Simon Market Street Surgery, Hyde SK14 2AF — MB ChB 1995 Manch.

HANNAN, Fadil Mohammed 16 Ospringe Road, Tufnell Park, London NW5 2JE — MB ChB 1996 Bristol.

HANNAN, Malcolm Charles Medical Centre, Derby Road, Peel IM5 1HP Tel: 01624 843636 Fax: 01624 844543; Brottby, Peveril Road, Peel IM5 1PJ Tel: 01624 842910 Fax: 01624 842910 Email: hannan@mcb.net — MB ChB 1970 Manch.; MA (Health Care Ethics) Manch. 1989; FRCGP 1990, M 1974; DObst RCOG 1974. (Manch.) Socs: I. of Man Med. Soc.; BMA. Prev: GP Postgrad. Tutor (IOM); Trainee GP Lancaster VTS; Ho. Off. (Surg.) Manch. Roy. Infirm.

HANNAN, Margaret Mary Flat 1, 263 Upper Richmond Road, London SW15 6SP — MB BCh BAO 1989 NUI.

***HANNAN, Shahla** 22 Lulworth Avenue, Hounslow TW5 0TZ — MB BS 1996 Lond.

HANNAY, David Rainsford Institute of General Practice and Primary Care, Community Sciences Centre, Northern General Hospital, Herries Road, Sheffield S5 7AU Tel: 0114 271 4302 Fax: 0114 242 2136; Kirkdale, Carsluith, Newton Stewart DG8 7EA Tel: 01557 840229 Fax: 01557 840229 — MB BChir Camb. 1965; PhD Glas. 1975; MA Camb. 1996, MD 1981; FRCGP 1988, M 1977; FFCM 1981, M 1974; DCH Eng. 1968. (St. Geo.) Asst Cairnsmore Med. Pract. Newton Stewart Wigtownsh.; Hon Sen. Research Fell. Glas. Univ.; Emerit. Prof. Sheff. Univ. Socs: Assn. Univ. Depts. Gen. Pract.; BMA. Prev: Prof. Gen. Pract. Sheff. Univ.; Sen. Lect. (Gen. Pract.) Glas. Univ.; Lect. (Community Med.) Glas. Univ.

HANNAY, Jonathan Alexander Forrest 3/3 18 Oban Dr, Glasgow G20 6AF — MB ChB 1997 Glas.

HANNAY, Patrick Wyattville (retired) 2 Deans Park, Caputh Road, Dunkeld PH8 0JH Tel: 01350 727530 — MB ChB 1937 Ed.; FRCP Ed. 1957, M 1948. Prev: Phys. Skin Dept. Roy. Infirm. Edin.

HANNAY, Walter Forrest The Health Centre, 20 Duncan Street, Greenock PA15 4LY Tel: 01475 724477 Fax: 01475 727140; Cherrytrees, 53 Cloch Road, Gourock PA19 1AT Tel: 01475 724477 Fax: 01475 731244 — MB ChB 1964 Glas.; FRCOG 1998; MRCOG 1969; DObst RCOG 1966. (Glas.) Socs: Glas. Obst. Soc. Prev: Hosp. Pract. (Obst. & Gyn.) Rankin Memor. Matern. Hosp. & Inverclyde Roy. Hosp.; Mem. Greenock & Dist. Fac. Med.

HANNAY, William Tully (retired) 9 Bonnington Avenue, Lanark ML11 9AL Tel: 01555 661785 — MB ChB 1966 Ed.; FRCOG 1986, M 1973; FRCP 1998 CH. Cons. O & G William Smellie Hosp. & Law Hosp. Lanarksh. Prev: Cons. O & G William Smellie Hosp. & Law Hosp. Lanarksh.

HANNER, Ian Edward The Surgery, 84 Ingleton Avenue, Welling DA16 2JZ Tel: 020 8303 1655 Fax: 020 8298 9228 — MRCS Eng. LRCP Lond. 1975; BSc (Hons.) (Pharmacol.) Lond. 1972, MB BS 1975. (Guy's) Prev: SHO (Gen. Med.) Brook Gen. Hosp. Lond.; Ho. Phys. Torbay Gen. Hosp. Torquay; Ho. Surg. St. Nicholas' Hosp. Lond.

HANNETT, Bernard Francis Middleway Surgery, Middleway, St. Blazey, Par PL24 2JL Tel: 01726 812019 Fax: 01726 816464 — MB ChB 1971 Leeds; BSc (Biochem. in Relation to Med.) (Hons.) Leeds 1967; MRCGP 1978; DRCOG 1977.

HANNEY, Ivan Paschal Gerard College Lane Surgery, Barnsley Road, Ackworth, Pontefract WF7 7HZ Tel: 01977 611023 Fax: 01977 612146; 24 Wenthill Close, Ackworth, Pontefract WF7 7LP Tel: 01977 611023 — MB BCh BAO 1979 NUI; MRCGP 1987; DCH RCP Lond. 1984; DRCOG 1983. Prev: SHO (Paediat.) Pinderfields Hosp. Wakefield; SHO (Gyn.) Clayton Hosp. Wakefield; Cas. Off. Pontefract Gen. Infirm.

HANNIFORD-YOUNGS, Simon James Royal Gwent Hospital, Cardiff Road, Newport NP9; Camden House, Duchess Road, Osbaston, Monmouth NP25 3HT — MB BS 1985 Lond.; MRCP (UK) 1989. Cons. Specialist Orthop. Med. Prev: Med. Regist. S. Beds. HA.

HANNIGAN, Barry FitzGerald Stainton Grange, Great Stainton, Stockton-on-Tees TS21 1NA — MB BCh BAO 1968 Dub.; MA Dub. 1968; FRCP Lond. 1991; MRCP (UK) 1977. (TC Dub.) Cons. Phys. N. Tees & hartlepool NHS Trust. Prev: Cons. Phys. Duchess of Kent's Milit. Hosp. & Camb. Milit. Hosp. Aldershot.

HANNIGAN, John Patrick Holmcroft Surgery, Holmcroft Road, Stafford ST16 1JG Tel: 01785 242172; Old Vicarage W., Castlebank, Stafford ST16 1DJ — BM BS 1985 Nottm.; MRCGP 1989; DRCOG 1988.

HANNING, Christopher Douglas Department of Anaesthesia, The General Hospital, Gwendolen Road, Leicester LE5 4PW Tel: 0116 249 0490; 7 Sanderson Close, Whetstone, Leicester LE8 6ER — MB BS 1972 Lond.; BSc Lond. 1969; MD Leic. 1996; MRCS Eng. LRCP Lond. 1972; FFA RCS Eng. 1976. (St. Bart.) Cons. Anaesth. Leicester Gen. Hosp.; Dir. Sleep Disorders Clinic Leicester Gen. Hosp. Prev: Sen. Lect. (Anaesth.) Univ. Leicester; Sen. Regist. W.. Infirm. Glas.; Regist. (Anaesth.) N.wick Pk. Hosp.

HANNINGTON-KIFF, John Garfield Winterstoke, Calthorpe Road, Fleet GU51 4LW Tel: 01252 617508 — MB BS Lond. 1960; BSc (Hons.) Lond. 1957; MRCS Eng. LRCP Lond. 1960; FFA RCS Eng. 1965. (Univ. Coll. Hosp.) Hon. Sen. Lect. (Anaesth.) St. Geo. Hosp. Med. Sch. Lond. Socs: Fell. Roy. Soc. Med.; Assn. Anaesth.; Founder Mem. Internat. Assn. Study Pain. Prev: Cons. Anaesth. & Dir. Pain Relief Centre Frimley Pk. Hosp.

HANNON, Cornelius 55 Thirsk Road, Northallerton DL6 1PP — MB BCh BAO 1973 NUI; MRCGP 1982; DRCOG 1980. (Univ. Coll. Galway)

HANNON, Damian Gerard Victoria House Surgery, Victoria Road, Bicester OX26 6PB Tel: 01869 248585 — MB BCh BAO 1983 Belf.; MRCGP 1991; T(GP) 1992; DRCOG 1990. (Queens University, Belfast)

HANNON, Mr Michael Aiden Orchard Lodge, Crossways, Thornbury, Bristol BS35 3UD — MB BCh BAO 1961 NUI; FRCS Eng. 1967. Cons. Orthop. Surg. Frenchay Hosp. Bristol & Winford Orthop. Hosp. Socs: Fell. Brit. Orthop. Assn.; Brit. Soc. Hand Surg. Prev: Regist. Nuffield Orthop. Centre Oxf.; Sen. Regist. St. Bart. Hosp. Lond.

HANNON, Monica Catherine 22 Bretby Lane, Burton-on-Trent DE15 0QN — MB BCh BAO 1977 NUI; DCH RCPSI 1980.

HANNON, Patricia Anne Cullen 7B Grosvenor Crescent, Edinburgh EH12 5EP — MB ChB 1965 Ed.

HANNON, Mr Raymond Joseph Department of Vascular and General Surgery, Level 5, Belfast City Hospital, Lisburn Road, Belfast BT9 7AB Tel: 02890 263752 Fax: 02890 263951 Email: ray.hannon@bch.n-i.nhs.uk — MD 1990 Belf.; MB BCh BAO 1981; FRCS Ed. 1985. Cons. Surg. Belf. City Hosp.; Dir. Of Surg., Belf. City Hosp. Socs: Assn. Surg.; Vasc. Soc. Prev: Sen. Regist. (Gen. Surg.) Belf. City Hosp.; Research Fell. Roy. Belf. Hosp. for Sick Childr.

HANOUKA, Allen 3 Carlyle Close, London N2 0QU — MB BS 1998 Lond.; MB BS Lond 1998.

HANRAHAN, John Michael Rainbow Medical Centre, 333 Robins Lane, St Helens WA9 3PN Tel: 01744 811211; 52 Brookside Avenue, St Helens WA10 4RL — MB ChB 1981 Manch.; MRCGP 1992.

HANRATH, Petrus Hendrikus Jozef Wallis Avenue Surgery, Wallis Avenue, Parkwood, Maidstone ME15 9JJ Tel: 01622 686963 Fax: 01622 695622 — Artsexamen 1989 Utrecht; MRCGP 1993; DRCOG 1991. GP; Cancer lead RCT.

HANRATTY, Barbara Dept. of Public Health, Whelan Building, University of Liverpool, Liverpool L69 3GB Tel: 0151 794 4780 Fax: 0151 794 5588 Email: barbara@hanratty.org.uk; 11 Livingston Drive, Liverpool L17 8XW Tel: 0151 727 7124 — MPH Leeds 1997; MRCGP 1993; DCH RCP Lond. 1991; DObst RCOG 1992; MFPHM 1999. (Bristol) Clin. Lect. Pub. Health Med., Univ. of Liverp.. Prev: SHO (Pub. Health Med.) Camden & Islington HA; Overseas Volun. Posts; Trainee GP Hull VTS.

HANRATTY, Brian 31 Ashwood, Lurgan, Craigavon BT66 8PF — MB BCh 1998 Belf.; MB BCh Belf 1998.

HANRATTY, Carl Michael Raymond 30 Towers Avenue, Newcastle upon Tyne NE2 3QE — MB BS 1976 Newc.; DRCOG 1978.

HANRATTY, Colm Gerard 31 Ashwood, Lurgan, Craigavon BT66 8PF — MB BCh BAO 1992 Belf.

HANRATTY, James Francis, OBE, KStG (retired) 44 Westminster Gardens, Marsham St., London SW1P 4JG Tel: 020 7834 4660 — MB ChB Leeds 1943; MRCGP 1953. Prev: Med. Dir. St. Joseph's Hospice Hackney.

HANRATTY, John Gerald 30 Towers Avenue, Jesmond, Newcastle upon Tyne NE2 3QE Tel: 0191 281 0988 — MB BCh BAO 1948 Belf.; DTM & H Liverp. 1952; DPH Belf. 1955. (Belf.) Dep. Sen. Med. Off. Univ. Health Serv. Newc. Prev: Med. Adviser Boots Pure Drug Co. Nottm.; Med. Off. Colon. Med. Serv. Tanganyika.

HANRATY, David Anthony Bridgeside Surgery, 1 Western Road, Hailsham BN27 3DG Tel: 01323 441234 Fax: 01323 440970 — MB BS 1971 Lond.; AKC 1968. (Kings Coll. Hosp. Lond.)

HANRETTY, Kevin Peter The Queen Mother's Hospital, Yorkhill, Glasgow G3 8SH; 5 Camphill Gardens, Bishopton PA7 5DQ — MD 1990 Glas.; MB ChB 1980; MRCOG 1985. Cons. O & G Qu. Mother's Hosp. & W.. Infirm. Glas. Prev: Lect. (Gyn. & Obst.) Univ. Dept. Midw. Univ. Glas.

HANROTT, Sarah Frances Coombe Down House, Salcombe Road, Malborough, Kingsbridge TQ7 3BX — MB BS 1993 Lond.; DPD 2001; DFFP 1996; MRCGP 1997. (UMDS (Guy's)) GP Princip. St. Albans; Clin. Asst. in Dermat. Hemel Hempstead. Prev: Trainee GP/SHO NW Herts. VTS.

HANS, Mr Stanley Frederick 60 Hoe Lane, Ware SG12 9NZ — MRCS Eng. LRCP Lond. 1942; MD Lond. 1947, MB BS 1943; FRCS Eng. 1952; FRCOG 1965, M 1948. (St. Bart.) Cons. O & G Harlow Hosp. Gp. Socs: Fell. Roy. Soc. Med. Prev: Ho. Phys. & Resid. Asst. O & G St. Bart. Hosp.; Sen. Resid. Med. Off. St. Mary's Hosp. Portsmouth.

HANSCHEID, Thomas 21 Park Hill, Clapham, London SW4 9NS — State Exam. Med. Frankfurt 1992.

HANSEL, Trevor Thomas Clinical Studies Unit, Royal Brompton Hospital, Fulham Road, London SW3 9HP Tel: 020 7351 8974 Fax: 020 7351 8973 Email: t.hansel@ic.ac.uk — MB BCh 1982 Wales; PhD 1993; BSc Liverp. 1977; MSc Birm. 1987; FRCPath 1989. (Welsh National School of Medicine) Med. Dir. & Hon. Cons. NHLI Roy. Brompton Clin. Studies Unit; Sen. Lect. Socs: Amer. Thoracic Soc. Prev: Asthma Drug Developm. Roche & Sandoz, Basel, Switz.; Sen. Regist. (Immunol.) E. Birm. Hosp.; Regist. (Immunol.) Univ. Hosp. of Wales Cardiff.

HANSELL, Anna Louise Small Area Health Statistics Unit, Imperial College Medicine at St Mary's, Norfolk Place, London W2 1PG Tel: 020 7594 3344 Fax: 020 7402 2150 Email: a.hansell@ic.ac.uk — MB BChir 1989 Camb.; MA Camb. 1989; MRCP (UK) 1993; MFPHM 1999. (Camb. Univ. & St. Geo's Hosp. Lond.) Regist. Rotat. (Pub. Health) N. Thames. Socs: Roy. Coll. Pract.; Roy. Soc. Med. (Hon. Sec. Epidemiol. & Pub. Health); Fac. Publ. Health Med. Prev: Regist. Rotat. (Chest Med.) St. Peter's Hosp. Chertsey; SHO (Renal Med.) Guy's Hosp. Lond.; SHO Rotat. (Med.) Worthing Hosp.

HANSELL, Barry (retired) Stockton House, Stockton, Worcester WR6 6UT Tel: 01524 881586 — MB ChB 1955 Birm. Prev: GP Stourbridge.

HANSELL, Professor David Matthew Royal Brompton Hospital, Sydney St., London SW3 6NP Tel: 020 7351 8034 Fax: 020 7351 8098 — MB BS 1981 Lond.; MD 1997; MRCP (UK) 1984; FRCR 1987; FRCP 1999. (Westm. Med. Sch.) Cons. Radiol. Roy. Brompton Hosp. Lond.; Prof. Thoracic Imaging, Nat. Heart & Lung Inst. and Div. of Investigative Sci.s, Imperial Coll. Scholl of Med., Lond. Socs: Fleischner Soc. Prev: Regist. & Sen. Regist. (Radiol.) W.m. Hosp. Lond.; Ho. Phys. & Surg. W.m. Hosp. Lond.

HANSELL, Mr Douglas Thomson 66 Monreith Road, Newlands, Glasgow G43 2PE — MD 1986 Glas.; MD (Hons) Glas. 1986, MB ChB 1977; FRCS Glas. 1981. Sen. Regist. (Gen. Surg.) Vic. Infirm., Glas. Socs: Surg. Research Soc. Prev: Regist. (Vasc. Surg. & Gen. Surg.) Roy. Infirm. Glas.; Research Regist. (Gen. Surg.) Roy. Infirm Glas.

HANSELL, Jean 5 Lansdown Place E., Bath BA1 5ET Tel: 01225 425516 — MRCS Eng. LRCP Lond. 1947. (W. Lond. & King's Coll. Hosp.) Prev: Sen. Regist. Dermat. Centr. Middlx. Hosp.; Sen. Ho. Off. W. Middlx. Hosp.; Edr. 'Modern Med. Gt. Brit.'.

HANSELL, Peter 5 Lansdown Place E., Bath BA1 5ET Tel: 01225 425516 Fax: 01225 425516 — MRCS Eng. LRCP Lond. 1944; FRCP Lond. 1981, M 1970. (Westm. & King's Coll.) Hon. Cons. Phys. W.m. Hosp. & Moorfields Eye Hosp. Lond.; Cons. Med. Photography, Television & Communication; Edr. Emerit. Jl. Audiovisual Media in Med. Socs: Hon. Fell. Inst. Med. Illustrators.; Fell. Biol. Photog. Assn.; Hon. Fell. Roy. Photog. Soc. Prev: Dir. Med. Audio-Visual Servs. W.m. Hosp. Med. Sch. & Inst. Ophth. (Univ. Lond.); Asst. Regist. (Med.) & Sen. Cas. Off. W.m. Hosp.

HANSELL, Robert Hawdon (retired) Sunningdale, Aldbrough St John, Richmond DL11 7SU Tel: 01325 374279 — MRCS Eng. LRCP Lond. 1945. Prev: RAMC.

HANSEN, Andrew Timothy The Medical Centre, 4 Craven Avenue, Thornton, Bradford BD13 3LG Tel: 01274 832110/834387 Fax: 01274 831694 — MB ChB 1989 Leeds; MRCGP 1995. GP Princip.

***HANSEN, Davina Jane** Ivy House, 4 Banbury Road, Ettington, Stratford-upon-Avon CV37 7TB Tel: 01789 740318 — MB BS 1998 Lond.; MB BS Lond 1998.

HANSEN, Lucinda Judy Department of Immunology, Clinical Sciences Building, Hope Hospital, Stott Lane, Salford M6 8HD — MB BS 1989 Lond.; MRCP (UK) 1994. (King's Coll. Lond.) Sen. Regist.in Clin. Immunol. & Internal Med Hope Hosp Salford; Mem. (Trainees Comm.) RCP; Trainee Mem of JCI & A RcPath.

HANSFORD, Neil George, Squadron Ldr. RAF Med. Br. 23 Northern Avenue, Henlow SG16 6ES — MB ChB 1988 Leic.; MRCGP 1994; DAvMed FOM RCP Lond. 1995. Med. Off. RAF.

HANSFORD, Paul Kenneth East Quay Medical Centre, East Quay, Bridgwater TA6 5YB Tel: 01278 444666 Fax: 01278 445448; 99 Durleigh Road, Bridgwater TA6 7JD — MB ChB 1975 Manch.; MRCGP 1979; DRCOG 1977; MSc Exeter 1997. (Manch.) GP Princip. Course Organiser Taunton VTS.

HANSLIP, Jennifer Louise Royal Victoria Hospital, Jedburgh Road, Dundee DD2 1SP Tel: 01382 423000 Fax: 01382 667685; 84 Blackness Avenue, Dundee DD2 1JL — MB ChB 1983 Dundee; MRCP (UK) 1986. Cons. Phys. Med. for Elderly Dundee; Hon. Sen. Lect. Dundee Univ.

HANSLIP, Judith Isabella 160B Murray Road, Ealing, London W5 4DA — MB ChB 1981 Dundee; MRCP (UK) 1985.

HANSLIP, Judith Mary 35 Brier Crescent, Nelson BB9 0QD — MB BS 1983 Lond.

HANSON, Audrey (retired) The Old School House, Dennys Lane, Kelsale, Saxmundham IP17 2PD Tel: 01728 602745 — MB BS Lond. 1946; MD Lond. 1949; FRCP Lond. 1973, M 1948; MRCS Eng. LRCP Lond. 1945. Prev: Cons. Chest Phys. E. Ham Chest Clinic.

HANSON, Barbara Chalmers 117 Braintree Road, Little Waltham, Chelmsford CM3 3NY — MB ChB 1949 Manch. (Manch.) Socs: Brit. Thoracic Soc.; BMA; Assn. Palliat. Med. Prev: Asst. Chest Phys. (Thoracic Med.) The Lond. Chest Hosp.

HANSON, Barbara Elizabeth Child Health Department, Bath & West Community NHS Trust, Newbridge Hill, Bath BA1 3QE Tel: 01225 313640; 5 The Butts, Steeple Ashton, Trowbridge BA14 6ES

Tel: 01380 870667 — MB BS 1968 Lond.; MRCS Eng. LRCP Lond. 1968; MFFP 1993; DCCH RCP Ed. 1988. (King's Coll. Hosp.) SCMO Bath DHA. Prev: Sen. Med. Off. Wilts. AHA; Ho. Surg. (ENT) King's Coll. Hosp.; Ho. Phys. (Paediat.) Belgrave Hosp. Childr.

HANSON, Carol Anne 17 Beech Close, Kinver, Stourbridge DY7 6LW — MB ChB 1981 Birm.

HANSON, Mr David Roland Outwood House, Outwood Lane, Horsforth, Leeds LS18 4HR Tel: 0113 258 2663 — MB 1964 Camb.; BA Camb. 1960, MB 1964, BChir 1963; FRCS Eng. 1972. (Westm.) Cons. Surg. (ENT) Gen. Infirm. Leeds & Wharfedale Gen. Hosp. Otley. Prev: Sen. Regist. & Clin. Tutor (ENT Surg.) Gen. Infirm. Leeds & Leeds Univ.; Regist. (ENT) Birm. & Midl. Ear & Throat Hosp.

HANSON, David Samuel (retired) Elmham Surgery, Holt Road, Elmham, Dereham NR20 5JS Tel: 01362 668215 Fax: 01362 668625 — MB BChir 1966 Camb.; MA, MB Camb. 1966, BChir 1965; MRCGP 1972; FRCGP 1997; DObst RCOG 1967; DCH Eng. 1968. Prev: Ho. Surg. Middlx. Hosp.

HANSON, George Hartley de Goldthorp Orchard House, Low Fell, Gateshead NE9 6DT — MB BS 1960 Durh.

HANSON, Gerald Ashleigh 102 Priestwood Avenue, Bracknell RG42 1XQ Tel: 01344 454269 Fax: 01344 454269 Email: g.hanson@doctors.org.uk — MB ChB 1991 Aberd.; MRCP 1998 - Paeqiatrics. (Gerald Hanson) Specialist Regist. (Paediat.) Roy. Berks. Hosp. Oxf. Socs: BMA. Prev: Locum Regist. (Paediat.); SHO (Paediat.) Ealing Hosp.; SHO (Neonatology) Hammersmith Hosp.f.

HANSON, Harry (retired) 8 Links Lodge, 9 Links Gate, Lytham St Annes FY8 3LF Tel: 01253 712629 — MB ChB Leeds 1946; MRCGP 1959; DObst RCOG 1949. Prev: Med. Off. DHSS.

HANSON, Helen Patricia 160 Meols Parade, Wirral CH47 6AN — MB ChB 1993 Leeds; DRCOG 1996; DTM & H 1997; MRCGP. (University of Leeds) GP Locum.

HANSON, Isabelle Marie 58 Moorgate, York YO24 4HR — MB ChB 1993 Manch.

HANSON, Jacqueline Mary Accident & Emergency Department, Royal Preston Hospital, Sharoe Green Ln, Preston PR2 9HT Tel: 01772 710383 Fax: 01772 716955; 1 The Oaks, St Michaels-on-Wyre, Preston PR3 0TF — MB ChB 1980 Leeds; BSc (1st cl. Hons. Microbiol.) Leeds 1980; FRCS Eng. 1990. Cons. A & E Med. Roy. Preston Hosp. Prev: Sen. Regist. Rotat. (A & E Med.) Hope Hosp. Manch. & Roy. Preston Hosp.; Tutor & Hon. Regist. (A & E Med.) St. Jas. Univ. Hosp. Leeds; SHO Rotat. (Surg.) Hope Hosp. Salford.

HANSON, John Roger High Street Surgery, 2 High Street, Macclesfield SK11 8BX Tel: 01625 423692 — MRCS Eng. LRCP Lond. 1976; BSc (Hons.) (Med. Physics) Lond. 1972. (Guy's) Prev: Trainee Gen. Pract. Macclesfield Vocational Train. Scheme; Ho. Surg. & Ho. Phys. Macclesfield Hosps.

HANSON, Jonathan Mark 62 Clayton Park Square, Jesmond, Newcastle upon Tyne NE2 4DP — MB BS 1992 Newc.

HANSON, Jonathan Richard Scissett Post Office, 3 Barnsley Road, Scissett, Huddersfield HD8 9HW — MB ChB 1997 Aberd.

HANSON, Judy Albion House Surgery, 22 Heneage Road, Grimsby DN32 9ES Tel: 01472 345411 Fax: 01472 269471 — MB ChB 1986 Sheff. Prev: SHO (Ophth.) Scunthorpe HA.; Ho. Phys. Hull HA; Ho. Surg. Lincoln HA.

HANSON, Julian Antony Department of Radiology, Austin & Repatriation Medical Centre, West Smithfield, Australia Tel: 00613 9496 5431 Email: julianhanson@netscape.net; 21 Treen Avenue, Barnes, London SW13 0JR Tel: 020 8876 0912 — BA 1986 Camb; MA Camb. 1990, MB BChir 1990; 2001 FRANZCR; MB BChir 1990 Camb.; FRCR 1996; MRCP (UK) 1993. Radiologist, Australia. Socs: Fell. Roy. Coll. Radiologists; Fell. Roy. Austral., New Zealand Coll. Radiol.; Radiol. Soc. N. America. Prev: Regist. (Radiol.) City & Hackney HA.; Fell. (Radiol.) Harborview Med. Centre, Seattle.

HANSON, Kate Elizabeth 39 Southfield Road, Burley in Wharfedale, Ilkley LS29 7PB — MB ChB 1998 Liverp.; MB ChB Liverp 1998.

HANSON, Katherine Jane Hassengate Medical Centre, Southend Road, Stanford-le-Hope SS17 0PH Tel: 01375 673064 — MB ChB 1986 Birm.; MRCGP 1990; DRCOG 1989. (Birmingham)

HANSON, Kathryn Barbara Louise Lindeem Medical Practice, 1 Cabourne Court, Cabourne Avenue, Lincoln LN2 2JP Tel: 01522 569033 Fax: 01522 576713; 82 Yarborough Crescent, Lincoln LN1 3LX — MB BS 1982 Nottm.; MRCGP 1986; DRCOG 1986.

HANSON, Mr Lionel Mark Halliday The BUPA Alexandra Hospital, Impton Lane, Chatham ME5 9PG Tel: 01634 864874 Fax: 01634 683426 Email: gillian.rolfe@ukgateway.net — MB BS Lond. 1976; BSc (Cellular Biol.) Lond. 1973; MRCS Eng. LRCP Lond. 1976; MRCOG 1982; T(OG) 1991. (St. Mary's) Cons. O & G Medway Maritime Hosp. Gillingham Kent. Socs: Brit. Soc. of Colposcopy; Brit. Soc. of Gyn. Endorcopy. Prev: Sen. Regist. Qu. Med. Centre Nottm & Derby Hosp.; Lect. (O & G) Univ. Nottm.; Regist. St Mary's & Samarotan Hosps.

HANSON, Lisbeth Grüner 22 Fairbridge Road, Ground Floor Flat, Archway, London N19 3HZ Tel: 020 8440 5111 — MD 1991 Copenhagen.

HANSON, Marguerite Elizabeth Langar House, Church Lane, Langar, Nottingham NG13 9HG Tel: 01949 860360 — MB ChB 1977 Leeds; MRCPsych 1984. Prev: Cons. Psychiat. S. Bucks. NHS Trust.

HANSON, Marion (retired) 15 Highmoor Walk, Baildon, Shipley BD17 5TT Tel: 01274 582641 — MB ChB Leeds 1950; DObst RCOG 1952.

HANSON, Mary Frances Department of Clinical Microbiology, Western General Hospital, Edinburgh EH4 2XU Tel: 0131 537 1934 Fax: 0131 537 1024; 20G Woodlands Terrace, Glasgow G3 2DF — MB ChB 1976 Glas.; MRCP (UK) 1980; FRCPath 1997. Cons. Med. Microbiol. Dept. of Clin. MicroBiol., Lothian Univ.

HANSON, Matthew Richard 15 Wood End Close, Halifax HX3 0JU — MB BS 1998 Lond.; MB BS Lond 1998.

***HANSON, Nicola** 13 Highbury Place, London N5 1QP Tel: 020 7359 5601 Fax: 020 7359 5601 — MB BS 1998 Lond.; MB BS Lond 1998.

HANSON, Peter John Vincent Princess Margaret Hospital, Okus Road, Swindon SN1 4JU Tel: 01793 536231 — MB BS 1982 Lond.; MA Camb. (Med. Sc.) 1982, MD 1991; FRCP. (Camb.) Cons. Phys. & Gastroenterol. P.ss Margt. Hosp. Swindon. Socs: Brit. Soc. Gastroenterol.; Fell. Roy. Coll. Phys. (Lond.). Prev: Sen. Regist. (Med. & Gastroenterol.) Guys's & Lewisham Hosp.; MRC Clin. Research Fell. Brompton Hosp. Lond.; Regist. (Med.) St. Stephens Hosp. Lond.

HANSON, Richard John Paradise Cottage, Hollington, Ashbourne DE6 3GA — BChir 1996 Camb.

HANSON, Robert de Goldthorp, Surg. Cdr. RN Retd. Boundary Cottage, Day Lane, Lovedean, Waterlooville PO8 0SH Tel: 02392 592044 — MB BCh BAO 1959 Dub.; PhD Soton. 1980; MD Dub. 1973; FFOM RCP Lond. 1993. (T.C. Dub.) Indep. Cons. Occupat Med. Hants. Prev: Civil. Princip. Med. Off. MoD; Sen. Med. Off. Civil Serv. Occupat. Health Serv.

HANSON, Sally Anne 3 The Mews, The Outwoods, Duffield, Belper DE56 4BP — MB BS 1994 Lond.

HANSON, Sally Marguerite Marlborough Medical Practice, The Surgery, George Lane, Marlborough SN8 4BY Tel: 01672 512187 Fax: 01672 516809 — MB BS 1983 Lond.; MRCGP 1987; DCH RCP Lond. 1987. (Westm.) GP Pricipal, MarlBoro. Prev: GP Lond.; Trainee GP Riverside HA VTS.

HANSON, Sian Deborah Warwick House Medical Centre, Holway Green, Upper Holway Road, Taunton TA1 2YJ Tel: 01823 282147 Fax: 01823 338181; 29 Shoreditch Road, Taunton TA1 3BU Tel: 01823 275570 Email: sianalbery@ukgateway.net — MB BS 1985 Lond.; MRCGP 1989; DRCOG 1991. p/t Gen. Practitioner; Clin. Asst. Gyn., MusGr. Pk. Hosp., Taunton.

HANSPAL, Judit Sarlay The Surgery, Waterfall House, 223 Tooting High Street, London SW17 0TD Tel: 020 8672 1327 Fax: 020 8767 5615 — MD 1980 Semmelweiss; MRCS Eng. LRCP Lond. 1984.

HANSPAL, Rajiv Singh (retired) The Hillindon Hospital, Pield Heath Road, Uxbridge UB8 3NN Tel: 01895 279964 Fax: 01895 279737 Email: rajiv.hanspal@228.hillingh-tr.nthames.nhs.uk — MB BS 1974 Calcutta; FRCS Eng. 1980; FRCS Ed. 1980; FRCP 1997; FRCP 1997 UK. Cons. Rehabil. Med. & Clin. Dir. Hillingdon Hosp.; Cons. Rehabil. Med. DSC Roy. Nat. Orthop. Hosp. Stanmore & United Pk. Hosp. Godalming. Prev: Sen. Med. Off. & Hon. Sen. Regist. NE Thames DSC & RHA.

HANSPAL, Roop Alfred Morris House, Taunton & Somerset Hospital, Musgrove Park, Taunton TA1 5DA Tel: 01823 333444 Fax: 01823 336877 — MB BS 1979 Calcutta; LRCP LRCS Ed.

LRCPS Glas. 1985; MRCP (UK) 1987; FRCP 1999. Cons. in Rehabil. Med. Prev: Sen. Regist. (Rehabil. Med.) Soton. Gen. Hosp.

HANSPAUL, Amrik Singh Rushden Medical Practice, Adnitt Road, Rushden NN10 9TU Tel: 01933 412666 Fax: 01933 317666 — MB BS 1975 Punjab; MB BS (Punjab) 1975; MRCS Eng. LRCP Lond. 1978; DRCOG Lond. 1980.

HANSTEAD, Barrie (retired) 115 Avon Road, Upminster RM14 1QX Tel: 01708 226364 — MB ChB Bristol 1961; DObst RCOG 1964.

HANUMANTHU, V R Causeway Medical Centre, 166-170 Wilderspool Causeway, Warrington WA4 6QA Tel: 01925 635024/630282 Fax: 01925 655113 — MB BS 1966 Andhra; MB BS 1966 Andhra.

HANUMARA, Surya Kumar Ward 4B, Pilgrim Hospital, Boston PE21 9QS Tel: 01205 364801 Fax: 01205 354395 — MB BS 1975 Osmania; FRCPCH; BSc Andhra 1968; MRCP (UK) 1989; MRCPI 1989; DCH RCPS Glas. 1980. Cons. Paediat. Pilgrim Hosp. Boston. Socs: Med. Protec. Soc.; BMA; RCPCH. Prev: SCMO Poole Hosp. Trust; Regist. (Paediat.) Lancaster & Chesterfield.

HANWELLA, Jinadasa Sunil Chesterfield and North Derbyshire Royal Hospital, Chesterfield S44 5BL Tel: 01246 277271; 21 Woodbridge Rise, Walton, Chesterfield S40 3LL Tel: 01246 230283 — MB BS 1972 Sri Lanka; MRCOG 1986.

HAPGOOD, Aled Iwan 28 Park Court Road, Bridgend CF31 4BW — MB BS 1996 Lond.

HAPGOOD, Debbie Simone Tudor Square Medical Practice, 1st Floor, Barclays Bank Chambers, Tudor Square, West Bridgford, Nottingham NG2 6BT Tel: 0115 914 3200 Fax: 0115 914 3201 — MB BS 1993 Lond.

HAPGOOD, Graham Clifford New Surgery, Victoria Street, Pontycymer, Bridgend CF32 8NW Tel: 01656 870237 Fax: 01656 870354; Gwerna, 28 Park Court Road, Bridgend CF31 4BW Tel: 01656 655058 — MB BCh 1964 Wales; DObst RCOG 1966. (Cardiff) Prev: SHO (Obst.) St. David's Hosp. Cardiff; SHO (Gyn.) Lansdowne Hosp. Cardiff; Ho. Surg. Gyn. Unit Llandough Hosp. Cardiff.

HAPGOOD, Rhydian Wyn 89 County Road, Gedling, Nottingham NG4 4JN — MB BS 1992 Lond.; B.Sc. (Hons) Lond. 1989; MRCGP 1997; DCH RCP Lond. (St. Mary's) Med. Advisor Notts. Hospice.

HAPPEL, John Short, OBE (retired) Little Barton, Ropley, Alresford SO24 0EE Tel: 01962 772212 Fax: 01962 772212 — MB ChB 1947 Glas.; FRCGP (Upjohn Fell. 1959) 1970; DObst RCOG 1951. Prev: Ch. Professional Standards Comm. GMC.

HAPPEL, Samuel (retired) 1 Churchill Close, Ashby-de-la-Zouch LE65 2LR Tel: 01530 412454 — MB ChB 1946 Glas.; FRCGP 1978. Prev: Ho. Surg. W.. Infirm. Glas.

HAPPEL, Susan Margaret Watercress Medical Group, Dean Surgery, Ropley, Alresford SO24 0BQ Tel: 01962 772340 Fax: 01962 772551 — MB BS 1977 Lond.; DCH RCP Lond. 1982; DRCOG 1981. (St Thomas)

HAPPOLD, Margaret Elfrieda 4 Lancelot Road, Peel Hall, Manchester M22 5JN Tel: 0161 437 2681 — BA (Nat. Sc.) Camb. 1951; MRCS Eng. LRCP Lond. 1955; DCH Eng. 1960. (Camb. & Leeds) Socs: Manch. Med. Soc.; Med. Wom. Federat.; BMA. Prev: Med. Off. (p/t) Sch. Health Serv. Manch. & Leeds Educat. Comms.; Ho. Phys. (Paediat.) St. Luke's Hosp. Bradford.

HAPUARACHCHI, Mr Joseph Sarath Antony 3 Wynstay Court, Clayton Village, Newcastle ST5 4HL Tel: 01782 632670 — MB BS 1981 Sri Lanka; FRCS Eng. 1989. Prev: Regist. (Orthop.) Stafford Dist. Gen. Hosp.; Regist. (Gen. Surg. & Orthop.) N. Staffs. Roy. Infirm. Stoke-on-Trent.

HAQ, Ahsanul 2 Howsin Street, Burnley BB10 1PZ — BChir 1992 Camb.

HAQ, Arfan-Ul X-Ray Department, Milton Keynes Hospital, Eaglestone, Milton Keynes MK6 5LD Tel: 01908 660033; Aaliya House, The High St, Great Linford, Milton Keynes MK14 5AX Tel: 01908 666037 — MB BCh 1976 Wales; FRCR 1983; Dip Health Mgt Keele. cons. Radio. Milton Keynes Hosp. Socs: Brit. Med. Assn.; Brit. Soc. of Interven.al Radiol.; Soc. Cardiovasc. & Interven.al Radiol. Prev: Trainee & Sen. Regist. (Radiol.) Nottm. Hosps.; SHO Tameside Gen. Hosp. Ashton-under-Lyne.

HAQ, Asif Israr 221 Upper Selsdon Road, Sanderstead, South Croydon CR2 0DZ — MB BCh BAO 1990 NUI; LRCPSI 1990.

HAQ, Hosne Ara Spitalfields Practice, Spitalfields Health Centre, 9-11 Brick Lane, London E1 6PU Tel: 020 7247 7070 — MRCS Eng. LRCP Lond. 1983. Prev: SHO (Gyn.) Newham Gen. Hosp. Lond.; SHO (Geriat. Med.) Hither Green Hosp. Lond.; SHO (A & E) Whittington Hosp. Lond. & N. Middlx. Hosp. Lond.

HAQ, Iftikhar Ul Department of Cardiology, Chesterman Wing, Northern General Hosp., Herries Road, Sheffield S5 7AU Tel: 0114 243 4343 Email: i.u.haq@sheffield.ac.uk; 6 The Beeches, 13 Montgomery Road, Nether Edge, Sheffield S7 1LN — MB ChB 1988 Manch.; MBA Open 1995; MRCP (UK) 1991. (Manch.) Specialist Regist. (Cardiol.) N. Gen. Hosp. Sheff. Prev: Research Fell. (Clin. Pharmacol. & Therap.) Roy. Hallamsh. Hosp. Sheff.; Regist. (Cardiol.) Nottm. City Hosp.

HAQ, Imran Ul The Surgery, 87 Kempson Road, Birmingham B36 8LR Tel: 0121 747 3586 — MB ChB 1994 Manch.

HAQ, Mr Khalid Saeed 63 Fairfield Drive, Burnley BB10 2PU — MB BS 1973 Peshawaar; FRCSI 1989.

HAQ, Mir Inamul 9 Forest Hill Road, London SE22 0SG — MB BS 1993 Lond.; BSc (Hons.) Lond. 1990. SHO Rotat. Guy's Hosp. Lond.

HAQ, Mohamed Fazlul Eastgate Surgery, Eastgate House, 28-34 Church Street, Dunstable LU5 4RR Tel: 01582 670050 Fax: 01582 607490; Asmaara, 13 Penrith Avenue, Dunstable LU6 3AN — MB BS 1976 Madras; LRCP 1981; DFFP 1994; DCCH RCP Ed. 1986; DCH (Madras) 1978. GP Dunstable. Socs: Fell. Roy. Soc. Health. Prev: Clin. Med. Off. (Child Health) & Acting SCMO (Audiol.) Merton & Sutton HA; Regist. St. Jas. Paget Hosp. Gorleston-on-Sea Norf.; SHO & Regist. (Neonat. Intens. Care) Qu. Charlotte Matern. Hosp. Univ.Lond.

HAQ, Mohammed Fazle 12 Parkstone Avenue, Emerson Park, Hornchurch RM11 3LU — MB BS 1967 Osmania.

HAQ, Muhammad Shamsul Health Clinic, Gardens Lane, Conisborough, Doncaster DN12 3JW Tel: 01709 862150 — MB BS 1961 Dacca.

HAQ, Muhammed Inam-ul Edenfield Road Surgery, Cutgate Shopping Precinct, Edenfield Road, Rochdale OL11 5AQ Tel: 01706 344044 Fax: 01706 526882; 24 Cranbourne Road, Bamford, Rochdale OL11 5JD Tel: 01706 43164 — MB BS 1958 Punjab; MB BS Punjab (Pakistan) 1958. (King Edwd. Med. Coll. Lahore)

HAQ, Mushfequr Raihan Guy's Hospital, St Thomas St., London SE1 9RT Tel: 020 7955 5000; Flat 9, 121 Alderney St, London SW1V 4HE — MB BS 1994 Lond. SHO (Paediat.) Guy's Hosp. Lond. Prev: SHO (Paediat.) Lewisham Hosp. Lond.; Ho. Off. (Surg.) P.ss Alexandra Hosp. Harlow; Ho. Off. (Med.) OldCh. Hosp. Romford.

HAQ, Rizwan Woodleigh Hall, Knott Lane, Rawdon, Leeds LS19 6JW — MB BCh BAO 1991 NUI; LRCPSI 1991.

HAQ, Shafi-Ul 14 Albemarle Road, Woodthorpe, Nottingham NG5 4FE.

HAQ, Shujina Hajira 65 Compton Road, London SW19 7QA — MB BS 1996 Lond.

HAQ, Syed Ebadat Ali National Heart and Lung Institute, And Royal Brompton Hospital, Dovehouse St., London SW3 6LY Tel: 020 7352 8121; 442 Lewisham High Street, London SE13 6LJ Tel: 020 8690 9198 Fax: 020 8690 2659 — MB BS 1993 Lond.; BSc (Hons) Lond. 1990; MRCP (UK) Lond. 1996. (Guy's Hosp., United Med. & Dental Schs Guy's & St. Thos. Hos) Hon. Regist. (Cardiol.) Nat. Heart & Lung Inst. & Roy. Brompton Hosp. Lond. Socs: BMA. Prev: SHO (Renal) Guy's Hosp., Hammersmith Hosp. & Roy. Brompton Hosp.

HAQ, Zelma 43 Bold Street, Blackburn BB1 7ES — MB BS 1991 Lond.; BSc (Hons.) Genetics Lond. 1989; MRCP (UK) 1995. SHO Rotat. (Med.) St. Bart. Hosp. Lond.

HAQQANI, Mohamad Riaz The Medical Centre, 39 Kenilworth Close, Crabbs Cross, Redditch B97 5JX Tel: 01527 402149 Fax: 01527 540183 — MB BS 1968 Jammu & Kashmir. (Med. Coll. Srinagar) GP Crabbs Cross Redditch. Prev: GP VTS Winyates Health Centre Redditch Worcs., SHO (Paediat.) N. Tees; Gen. Hosp. Stockton-on-Tees; SHO (Gen. Med., Nephrol. & Chest Med.) Rotat. Cleveland Gp. Hosp. (S.

HAQQANI, Moina Faizuddin Sohana, 2 Davies Way, Lymm WA13 0QW — MB BS 1969 Osmania; DMRT Eng. 1973. (Osmania Med. Coll. Hyderabad)

HAQQANI, Mustafa Tahseenuddin Department of Histopathology, Fazakerley Hosptial, Longmoor Lane, Liverpool L9 7AL Fax: 0151 529 3573; Sohana, 2 Davies Way, Lymm

WA13 0QW Tel: 01925 755231 Email: mhaqqani@aol.com — MB BS Osmania 1965; FRCPath 1986, M 1975; DPath Eng. 1969. (Osmania Med. Coll. Hyderabad) Cons. Histopath. Univ. Hosp. Aintree. Socs: Int. Acad. Pathol.; RSM; Assn. Clin. Pathologists. Prev: Sen. Demonst. (Path.) Roy. Vict. Infirm. Newc.; Sen. Regist. (Path.) Withington Hosp. & Roy. Infirm. Manch.

HAQUE, Abu Mohammad Zahurul (retired) 7 Penryn Close, Park Hall, Walsall WS5 3ET Tel: 01922 615811 Fax: 01922 615811 — MB BS Rajshahi 1965; DPM Eng. 1982. Locum Cons. Psychiat. Prev: S.C.M.O. N. Warks. NHS Trust.

HAQUE, Farhat Jehan Begum Nelson Health Centre, Leeds Road, Nelson BB9 9TG Tel: 01282 613592; 16 Willaston Avenue, Blacko, Nelson BB9 6LU — MB BS 1970 Punjab. (Fatima Jinnah Med. Coll. Lahore) Socs: Pakistan Med. Soc. & BMA.

HAQUE, Farida 116 Sutton Road, Maidstone ME15 9AP Tel: 01622 753211; 17 Lancet Lane, Loose, Maidstone ME15 9RY — MB BS 1968 Dacca. GP Maidstone. Prev: Regist. (Psychiat.) Bromley HA; SHO (Path.) Plymouth Gen. Hosp.; SHO (Psychiat.) Moorhaven Hosp. Ivybridge & FarnBoro. Hosp., Kent.

HAQUE, Iftikhar-ul Blackburn Street Health Centre, Blackburn Street, Radcliffe, Manchester M26 1WS — MB BS 1967 Punjab; MFFP; BSc; FRCOG Lond; MRCOG. Gen. Pract.; Clin. Assist. G.U. Med.; Obst. & Gynaecologist Locum. Socs: BSCCP; Fac. Of Family Plann. & Reproductive Health; MSSVD. Prev: Cons. (O&G), Gwynedd Hosp. Bangor (Locum) 1984-1996.

HAQUE, Imtiazi 47 Corringham Road, Wembley Park, Wembley HA9 9PX Tel: 020 8908 3045 — MB BS 1962 Punjab; MB BS Punjab (Pakistan) 1962; DObst RCOG 1968. Clin. Med. Off. Community Health, Wembley Hosp. Lond.

HAQUE, Khalid Mohammad 23 Becmead Avenue, Kenton, Harrow HA3 8HD — MB BS 1998 Lond.; MB BS Lond 1998.

HAQUE, Md Shamsul 42 Mount Stewart Street, Carluke ML8 5EB — MB BS 1966 Dacca; LRCP LRCS Ed. LRCPS Glas. 1988.

HAQUE, Mohammad Abrarul Flagg Court Health Centre, Flagg Court, South Shields NE33 2PG Tel: 0191 456 0463 Fax: 0191 454 5525 — MB BS 1947 Patna. (Patna) GP S. Shields, Tyne & Wear.

HAQUE, Mohammad Anwarul Flagg Court Health Centre, Flagg Court, South Shields NE33 2PG Tel: 0191 456 0463 Fax: 0191 454 5525 — MB BS 1961 Dacca. (Dacca) GP S. Shields, Tyne & Wear.

HAQUE, Mohammad Arshadul Nelson Health Centre, Leeds Road, Nelson BB9 9TG Tel: 01282 613592; 16 Willaston Avenue, Blacko, Nelson BB9 6LU Tel: 01282 612280 — MB BS 1966 Punjab; MB BS Punjab (Pakistan) 1966. (Nishtar Med. Coll. Multan) Socs: BMA; BMA. Prev: Cli.asst. A/E dept.

HAQUE, Mohammad Ehtesham Nasirul Market Place Health Centre, Market Place, Mossley, Ashton-under-Lyne OL5 0HE Tel: 01457 832561 Fax: 0161 330 6266; 39 Lodge Court Mottram, Hyde SK14 6LY — MB BS 1966 Karachi. (Dow Med. Coll.) Clin. Asst. (Geriat. Med.)Tameside Gen. Hosp. Ashton-under-Lyne.

HAQUE, Mohammad Ejazul 219 Woodlands Road, Batley WF17 0QS Tel: 01924 478015 — MB BS 1966 Bihar. (Darbhanga Med. Coll.)

HAQUE, Mohammed Anwarul The Surgery, Health Centre, St. John Street, Mansfield NG18 1RH Tel: 01623 622541 Fax: 01623 661313 — MB BS 1961 Dacca; MRCP Ed. 1964; DTM & H Ed. 1964. (Dacca Med. Coll.)

HAQUE, Mohammed Ehsanul (retired) 12 Arthur Road, Rainham, Gillingham ME8 9BT — MB BS 1959 Dacca; BSc Dacca 1953, MB BS 1959; FRCR 1974; FFR 1969; DMRT Eng. 1965. Prev: Cons. Radiother. & Oncol. Mid. Kent Oncol. Centre Maidstone Hosp.

HAQUE, Muhammad Ameerul 13 Cherry Holt Avenue, Stockport SK4 3PT — MB BS 1964 Rajshahi; MB BS Rajshahi Bangledesh 1964; MRCOphth 1968. Med. Pract. (Ophth.) Stockport.

HAQUE, Muhammad Azizul The Health Centre, Darenth Lane, South Ockendon RM15 5LP Tel: 01708 853113; 7 The Woodfines, Emerson Park, Hornchurch RM11 3HR Tel: 01708 471870 — MB BS 1961 Dacca; FRCOG 1995; MRCOG 1979; MFFP 1993; DObst RCOG 1966; DTM & H Univ. Ed. 1964.

HAQUE, Quazi Mohafuzal 2 Gardenia Grove, Liverpool L17 7HP — MB BS 1966 Rajshahi; FRCR 1978; DMRD Eng. 1974. (Rajshahi Med. Coll.) Cons. Radiol. Ormskirk & Dist. Gen. Hosp. W. Lancs. NHS Trust.

HAQUE, Quazi Shams Mahfooz 16 Colomb Street, London SE10 9EW — MB BS 1994 Lond.

HAQUE, Rubaiyat Aziz 1 Gernon Road, London E3 5DL — MB BS 1998 Lond.; MB BS Lond 1998.

HAQUE, Sadaf Jahan 56 Ashbourne Road, London W5 3DJ — MB BS 1996 Lond.

HAQUE, Seleena 18 Salford Close, Woodrow S., Redditch B98 7UN — BM 1998 Soton.; BM Soton 1998.

HAQUE, Serajul 91 Coventry Road, Bedford MK40 4EJ — LMSSA 1997 Lond.

HAQUE, Sirajam Munirul 6 Red Beck Vale, Bradford — MB BS 1972 Gauhati.

HAQUE, Syed Ekramul 133 Boundaires Road, London SW12 8HD — MB BS 1967 Dacca; DO Eng. 1972. (Dacca) Prev: SHO (Ophth.) Sussex Eye Hosp. Brighton, York Co. Hosp. & Sunderland; Eye Infirm.

HAQUE, Syed Quamrul Grove Park Surgery, 116 Sutton Road, Maidstone ME15 9AP Tel: 01622 753211 Fax: 01622 756722 — MB BS 1966 Dacca; DA Eng. 1972. (Dacca) GP Maidstone. Prev: Regist. Anaesth. Dept. FarnBoro. Hosp., Kent; SHO (Anaesth.) Plymouth Gen. Hosp. (Freedom Fields Br.); Regist. (Anaesth.) Torbay Hosp. Torquay.

HAQUE, Syed Tanvir Ariful 32 Benland, Bretton, Peterborough PE3 8EB — MB ChB 1998 Manch.; MB ChB Manch 1998.

HARAKE, Marie Desiree Janick 34 Linden Road, Boothstown, Worsley, Manchester M28 1JW — MB ChB 1989 Manch.; BSc (Hons.) Path. Manch. 1987; MRCP (UK) 1993. Regist. (Diag. Radiol.) NW RHA.

HARAN, Mary Philomena (retired) 26 Slieve Foy Place, Warrenpoint, Newry BT34 3NR Tel: 016937 73336 — MB BCh BAO NUI 1950; MFCM 1972; DPH Liverp. 1956. Prev: Clin. Med. Off. S.. Health & Social Serv. Bd. Co. Down.

HARAN, William John (retired) Russell Institute of Medicine, Causeyside St., Paisley PA1 1UR Tel: 0141 889 8701 — MB ChB 1958 Glas.; Spec. Accredit Paediat. JCHMT 1991. Prev: Dep. MOH I. of Lewis.

HARAR, Ravinder Pal Singh 152 Wellesley Road, Ilford IG1 4LJ — MB ChB 1991 Manch.

HARARI, Danielle St Thomas' Hospital, Elderly Care Unit, Lambeth Palace Road, London SE1 7EH Tel: 0207 922 8039 Fax: 0207 928 2339 Email: danielle.harari@kcl.ac.uk; 16 Lord Napier Place, London W6 9UB — MB BS 1982 Lond.; FRCP 2001; MRCP (UK) 1985. (St. Thos.) Sen Lec (Cons) in Elderly Med. St Thomas' Hosp Lond. Socs: Amer. Geriat. Soc.; BMA; BGS. Prev: Sen. Regist. (Geriat.) Univ. Coll. & Middlx. Hosps. Lond.; Clin. Dir Geriat. Dept Mass. Gen. Hosp Boston USA; Geriat. Fell., Harvard Med. Sch., Boston.

HARARI, Olivier Alfred 19 Mill Hill Road, London W3 8JE — BChir 1991 Camb.; MRCP (UK) 1994. Regist. (Rheum.) W. Middlx. Univ. Hosp. Lond. Prev: SHO Char. Cross Hosp., Whittington Hosp. & Hammersmith Hosp. Lond.

HARAZ, Mohamed Hanafi Bakri Abu 54 Brookshaw Street, Chesham, Bury BL9 6EB — MB BS 1980 Khartoum; MRCP (UK) 1992.

HARB, Maaly Mahmoud 26 Hallam Close, West Bromwich B71 4HU — MB ChB 1970 Alexandria; MRCOG 1993.

HARBAN, Fraser Mark John Mossdelph, Welsh Road, Offchurch, Leamington Spa CV33 9AH Email: fraser@tracle.screaming.net — MB BS 1994 Newc.; Dip. IMC RCs Ed 1999. SHO Anaesth. Roy.hosp.Haslar Gosport. Socs: RCA; Assoc.Anaesth; Brit.Assoc.Immediate Care. Prev: Regtl. Med. Off.; SHO A&E Palmerston N. Hosp.NZ.

HARBAN, John Lundwood Medical Centre, Penefract Road, Lindwood, Barnsley S71 5PN Tel: 01226 201737 Fax: 01226 731055 — MB ChB 1986 Sheff.; MRCGP 1990; T(GP) 1991.

HARBEN, Philip Ross (retired) Fengate, Church Walk, Mildenhall, Bury St Edmunds IP28 7ED Tel: 01638 713276 — MB BS 1948 Lond.; MRCS Eng. LRCP Lond. 1948.

HARBER, Mark Alan Altoona, Totnes Road, Ipplepen, Newton Abbot TQ12 5TD — MB BS 1990 Lond.

HARBIN, Leonard 87 Canterbury Road, North Harrow, Harrow HA1 4PD; 87 Canterbury Road, North Harrow, Harrow HA1 4PD — MRCS Eng. LRCP Lond. 1954; DMRD Eng. 1968. (Bristol) Prev: Specialist Med. Off. (Radiol.) Gen. Hosp. Port-of-Spain, Trinidad; Regist. Cas. Dept. Gen. Hosp. San Fernando, Trinidad.

HARBIN, Lucy Jane 5-16 Northwood Hall, Hornsey Lane, London N6 5PL — MB BS 1996 Lond.

HARBINSON, Helen Jessie Ards Hospital, Church St., Newtownards BT23 4AS — MB BCh BAO 1975 Belf.; M. Med Sci. 1996 Belf.; MD Belf. 1984, MMedSci 1992; MRCPsych 1979. (Belf.) Cons. Psychiat. Ards Hosp. Newtownards. Socs: Medico-Legal Soc.; Assoc. Mem. N.. Irel. Assn. Study of Psychoanal.

HARBINSON, Marcella Edith Elizabeth Cushleva, 124 Circular Road, Newtownabbey BT37 0RH — MB BCh BAO 1982 Belf.; DCH RCPS Glas. 1985; Cert. Family Plann. JCC 1985.

HARBINSON, Mark Thomas 16 Castlehill Drive, Belfast BT4 3GS — MB BCh BAO 1990 Belf.

HARBINSON, Michael John Tanfield View Surgery, Scott Street, Stanley DH9 8AD Tel: 01207 232384 — MB BS 1974 Lond.

HARBINSON, Nancy Kate (retired) Hillside, Bath Road, Norton St Philip, Bath BA2 7LW Tel: 01373 834445 — MB BS 1938 Lond.; MRCS Eng. LRCP Lond. 1938. Prev: Dep. Med. Supt. S. Middlx. Fev. Hosp.

HARBINSON, Patrick Liam 58 Crayford Road, London N7 0ND — MB BS 1986 Lond.; MRCP 1994. Sen. Reg.Geriats. Univ. Coll. Lond.Hosp.

HARBINSON, Robert Derek Manor Farm House, Kingham, Chipping Norton OX7 — MB BS 1956 Lond.

HARBINSON, Simon Adam 3 Lord Wardens Mews, Bangor BT19 1YH — MB ChB 1997 Aberd.

HARBORD, Kenneth William Morden Murragh, Ivy House Lane, Berkhamsted HP4 2PP Tel: 01442 865757 — MB BCh BAO 1951 Dub.; DPH Lond. 1961; MFOM RCP Lond. 1982. Socs: BMA. Prev: Sen. Med. Off. Kodak Ltd.; Asst. Co. Med. Off. Herts. CC & Dep. MOH Hemel Hempstead Boro. & RD; Sen. Med. Off. Ment. Health Herts. CC.

HARBORD, Marcus William Nixon 3 Palliser Court, Palliser Road, London W14 9ED Tel: 020 7386 7554 Email: doc@dircon.co.uk — MB BS 1992 Lond.; BSc (Hons.) Lond. 1989; MRCP (UK) 1995. (Imperial Coll. (St. Mary's)) Regist. (Gastro) Middlx. Hosp. Lond. Socs: BMA; Med. Protec. Soc.; (Sec.) Old Etonian Med. Soc. Prev: Regist. (Gastroenterol.) Roy. Free Hosp. Lond.; Regist. (Gastroenterol.) King Geo. Hosp. Ilford; SHO Rotat. (Med.) N.wick Pk. Hosp.

HARBORD, Peter Nicholas Brooklea Clinic, Wick Road, Bristol BS4 4HU Tel: 0117 971 1211; 95 Radnor Road, Horfield, Bristol BS7 8RA Tel: 0117 942 1367 — MB ChB 1984 Bristol. Prev: SHO (Psychiat.) Glenside Hosp. Bristol; Trainee GP Bristol.; SHO (O & G) Bristol Matern. Hosp.

HARBORD, Robert Braith Camden Road Surgery, 142 Camden Road, London NW1 9HR Tel: 020 7284 0384 Fax: 020 7428 0493; 8 Trinder Road, London N19 4QU Tel: 020 7284 0384 — MB ChB 1975 Bristol; DRCOG 1982.

HARBORNE, Mr Derek Jeremy Accident & Emergency, Royal Albert Edward Infirmary, Wigan Lane, Wigan WN1 2NN — MB BS 1981 Lond.; FRCS Ed. 1987; MRCS Eng. LRCP Lond. 1981; DA (UK) 1990. Cons. A & E Roy. Albert Edwd. Infirm. Socs: Brit. Assn. Accid. & Emerg. Med. Prev: Sen. Regist. (A & E) Basingstoke Dist. Hosp.; Regist. (A & E) Glos. Roy. Hosp.; SHO (Surg.) Worcester Roy. Infirm.

HARBORNE, Giles Christopher Department of Psychiatry, Wrexham Maelor Hospital, Wrexham LL13 7TD — MB ChB 1982 Liverp.; MMedSci (Clin. Psychiat.) Leeds 1988; MRCPsych 1990.

HARBOROW, Patrick William Waterloo Health Centre, 5 Lower Marsh, London SE1 7RJ Tel: 020 7928 4049 Fax: 020 7928 2644 — MB BS 1981 Lond.; MA Oxf. 1978; MRCGP 1987. GP Waterloo Lond.

HARBOROW, Peter Charles Ashberry House, The Nook, Eastbourne Road, Ridgewood, Uckfield TN22 5ST Tel: 01825 766009 Fax: 01825 766009 Email: pharborow@aol.com — MB BS Lond. 1969; MRCS Eng. LRCP Lond. 1970; DLO Eng. 1974; Dip. Counsel. 1994. (St. Thos.) p/t GP Tutor, V.T.S Organiser, Mentor, (KSS Deanery) CAA Med. Examr. Socs: Ass. Of Aviat. Med. Examr.s; Brit. Ass. For counselling; Assn. of Med. Educat. Prev: Regist. Ear, Nose & Throat Dept. Univ. Coll. Hosp. Lond.; SHO (Thoracic) Hosp. Sick Childr. Gt. Ormond St. Lond.; Ho. Surg. (ENT) St. Thos Hosp. Lond.

HARBOT, Philip William — MB ChB 1981 Manch.; BSc (Med Sci.) St And. 1978. Non. Princip. GP. Socs: BMA. Prev: Princip. GP Shap. Cumbria.

HARBOTT, Anthony James (retired) Twelve, Quarry Road, Winchester SO23 0JG Tel: 01962 865623 Fax: 01962 865623 — MB ChB 1955 Birm.; FRCPsych 1983, M 1971; DObst RCOG 1959; DPM Eng. 1968. Prev: Cons. Psychiat. Adolesc. & Childr. Wessex RHB.

HARBOTT, Elizabeth Joan (retired) Twelve, Quarry Road, Winchester SO23 0JG Tel: 01962 865623 Fax: 01962 865623 — MB BCh 1957 Wales; MRCPsych 1972; DObst RCOG 1959; DPM Eng. 1967. Prev: Assoc. Specialist (Psychiat.) Roy. S. Hants. Hosp. Soton.

HARBOTTLE, John Anthony Peel Health Centre, Angouleme Way, Bury BL9 0BT Tel: 0161 763 7613 Fax: 0161 763 9625 — MB ChB 1979 Manch.

HARBOTTLE, Timothy George The Surgery, Abbotswood Road, Brockworth, Gloucester GL3 4PE Tel: 01452 863200 Fax: 01452 864993 — MB BS 1969 Lond.; DObst RCOG 1973. (Univ. Coll. Hosp.) Mem. Disabil. Appeal Trib. Serv. Prev: Ho. Surg. Univ. Coll. Hosp. Lond.; SHO (Orthop.) Barnet Gen. Hosp.; SHO (O & G) Qu. Eliz. II Hosp. Welwyn Garden City.

***HARBURY, Richard Michael Charles** c/o 85 Ardrossan Road, Seamill, West Kilbride KA23 9NF; 27 Kerr Street, Charles Town NSW 2300, Australia Email: harbury@idl.net.au — MB ChB 1994 Dundee; FRCS 1998.

HARCHOWAL-MUIR, Vimty Swaranjit Kaur 58 Dowanside Road, Dowanhill, Glasgow G12 9DL — MB ChB 1989 Aberd.; FRCA 1995. Career Regist. (Anaesth.) Glas. Roy. Infirm.

HARCOMBE, Alun Andrew Cardiac Unit, Papworth Hospital, Cambridge CB3 8RE Tel: 01480 830541 Fax: 01480 831083; 26 Limes Park, St. Ives, Huntingdon PE27 5HA — MB ChB 1986 Ed.; MD Ed. 1995; MRCP (UK) 1989. Prev: MRC Internat. Fell. W.mead Hosp. Sydney, Australia; Regist. (Cardiol.) Papworth Hosp. Camb.; SHO (Med.) Nottm. City Hosp.

HARCOURT, Jane Elizabeth Whin Cottage, Ardoe, Aberdeen AB12 5XT — MB ChB 1983 Bristol; FRCS Eng. 1988; DO RCS Eng. 1988; FCOphth. 1989. Regist. (Ophth.) Oxf. Eye Hosp. Prev: SHO (Ophth) Bristol Eye Hosp.

HARCOURT, Mr Jonathan Philip 149 Harley St, London W1G 6DE Tel: 020 7486 0691 Fax: 020 7333 0340 Email: jh@harco.demon.co.uk — MB BS 1988 (Hons.) Lond.; MA Oxf. 1992, BA 1985; FRCS (Otol.) Eng. 1993; FRCS Eng. 1992. (Qu. Coll. Oxf. & St. Thos. Hosp. Med. Sch.) Cons. Otolaryngologist, Char. Cross & Chelsea & W.minster Hosp.s; Hon. Cons., Roy. Brompton Hosp. Prev: Regist. Roy. Nat. Throat, Nose & Ear Hosp. Lond.; Sen. Reg. Gt. Ormond St; Regist. Nat. Hosp. Neurol. & Neurosurg. Lond.

HARCOURT, William Gerard Vaughan The Old Vicarage, Benson, Oxford OX10 6SF; 143 Ellesmere Road, Shrewsbury SY1 2RA Tel: 01745 361706 — BChir 1990 Camb.; MA Camb 1993; MB BChir 1991; FRCS Eng. 1995. (Camb.) Regist. (Orthop.) OsW.ry Rotat. Prev: SHO Rotat. Stoke-onTrent.

HARCOURT-WEBSTER, Simon (retired) Fairlight Cottage, Fairlight Lane, Middle Rd., Tiptoe, Sway, Lymington SO41 6FX Tel: 01590 683939 Fax: 01590 681975 Email: 106205.1305@compuserve.com — MB BChir 1960 Camb.; MA, MB Camb. 1960, BChir 1959; DObst RCOG 1962; DA Eng. 1962. Prev: Assoc. Roy. Coll. Gen. Pract.

HARCUP, Dorothy Mary (retired) Triscombe, 17 Churchdown Road, Poolbrook, Malvern WR14 3JX Tel: 01684 574477 — MB ChB 1957 Leeds. Prev: SCMO Worcester HA.

HARCUP, John Winsor, OStJ (retired) Triscombe, 17 Churchdown Road, Poolbrook Common, Malvern WR14 3JX Tel: 01684 574477 Email: johnharcup@compuserve.com — MRCS Eng. LRCP Lond. 1958; MRCGP 1968; DObst RCOG 1961. Chairm. Med. Advis. Comm. Brit. Spas. Fed; Med. Comm. Internat. Spa Federat. Prev: SHO (Gen. Med.) Leicester Roy. Infirm.

HARCUS, Alfred Wilson Medicos Ltd., Medical & Scientific Services, Medicos House, 79 Beverley Road, Hull HU3 1XR Tel: 01482 320243 Fax: 01482 324304; Holly House, 10 Church St, Kirton Lindsey, Gainsborough DN21 4PN Tel: 01652 640626 — MB ChB 1959 Ed.; FFPM 1989; Dip. Occ. Med. RCP Lond. 1997; DObst RCOG 1961; DFFP 1998.

HARD, Peter Laurence Stanley Lower Street Surgery, 95 Lower Street, Pulborough RH20 2BP Tel: 01798 872305 — MB BS 1972

Lond.; DRCOG 1979. Prev: Ho. Phys. Roy. Cornw. Hosp. Treliske; Surg. Capt. The Blues & Roy.s; Maj. RAMC.

HARDAKER, Elizabeth Anne 3 Rathmore Close, Birkenhead CH43 2LP — BM BS 1991 Nottm.; MRCP Paediat. (UK) 1994.

HARDAKER, John Christopher Grange Lea, 23 Hollingwood Lane, Bradford BD7 2RE Tel: 01274 571437 Fax: 01274 571437 — MB ChB 1975 Liverp.

HARDAKER, John Michael Mildmay Court Surgery, Mildmay Court, Bellevue Road, Ramsgate CT11 8JX Tel: 01843 592576 Fax: 01843 852980 — MB BS 1972 Lond. (Middlx.)

HARDCASTLE, Mr Jack Donald, CBE University Hospital, Queens Medical Center, Nottingham NG7 2UH Tel: 0115 970 9245 Fax: 0115 970 9428; Goverton Heights, Goverton, Bleasby, Nottingham NG14 7FN Tel: 01636 830316 — MB BChir 1958 Camb.; MA, MChir (Distinc.) Camb. 1966; FRCP Lond. 1984, M 1961; FRCS Eng. 1962; MRCS Eng. LRCP Lond. 1958. (Lond. Hosp.) Prof. Surg. Univ. Nottm.; Cons. Surg. Univ. Hosp. Nottm.; Dir. Raven Dept. Educat. RCS Eng.; Dir. Overseas Off. RCS Eng.; Dir. Med. Protect. Soc. Socs: Surg. Research Soc.; Brit. Soc. Gastroenterol.; (Vice-Pres.) RCS Eng. Prev: Sen. Regist. (Surg.) St. Mark's Hosp. Lond.; Regist. & Sen. Lect. (Surg.) Surgic. Unit Lond. Hosp.; Sir Arthur Sims Commonw. Trav. Prof. 1985.

HARDCASTLE, Jacqueline Emma 12 Malden Road, Harrogate HG1 4SF — MB BS 1997 Newc.

HARDCASTLE, Margaret Elizabeth (retired) Homefield, Upper Minety, Malmesbury SN16 9PY Tel: 01666 860705 — MB Camb. 1960, BChir 1959; MRCPsych 1973; DPM Eng. 1971. Prev: Cons. (Child Psychiat. & Ment. Handicap) Wilts. AHA Swindon Health.

HARDCASTLE, Mr Paul Frederick The Westmorland Centre, 22 Railway Road, Leigh WN7 4AU Tel: 01942 679703 — MB ChB 1977 Manch.; FRCS 1982 (Orl.) Ed.

HARDCASTLE, Mr Philip Hobson c/o Surgicraft Ltd, Fishing Line Road, Redditch B97 6HF — MB BS 1974 Sydney; FRCS Ed. 1978; FRACS (Orthop.) 1981.

HARDCASTLE, Stephen James 5 Ashby Road, Twyford, Melton Mowbray LE14 2HN Tel: 01644 840733; Green Gate Medical Centre, 1 Green Gate Lane, Birstall, Leicester LE4 3JF Tel: 0116 267 7996 — MB ChB 1973 Leeds.

HARDEE, Mr Peter Sean George Fitzgerald St Bartholomew's & Royal London Hospital Maxillofacial Unit, Royal London Hospital, Whitechapel, London E1 1BB Tel: 020 7377 7299 Fax: 020 7377 7095 — MB BS 1992 Lond.; BDS Lond. 1985; FDS RCS Eng. 1992; FRCS Eng. 1995. (UMDS Guy's) Locum Cons. (Oral & Maxillofacial Surg.) Roy. Lond. Hosp. Whitechapel Lond.; Locum Cons (Oral & Maxillofacial Surg.) Whipp's Cross Univ. Hosp. Lond. Socs: Fell. in Train. Brit. Assn. Oral & Maxillofacial Surg.s; Fell. Brit. Assoc. Neck & Head Oncologists. Prev: Specialist Regist. (Oral & Maxillofacial Surg.) Roy. Lond. Hosp. Whitechapel, Lond.

HARDEMAN, Maureen Elisabeth (retired) 80 Ladbrook Road, Solihull B91 3RN Tel: 0121 705 1604 — MB ChB 1951 Birm.; FFA RCS Eng. 1960; DA Eng. 1956; DObst RCOG 1953. Prev: Cons. Anaesth. Selly Oak Hosp. Birm.

HARDEN, Mr Alec Frank Sussex Eye Hospital, Eastern Rd, Brighton BN2 5BF Tel: 01273 606126; 8 Withdean Road, Brighton BN1 5BL Tel: 01273 552627 — MB BCh BAO 1963 Dub.; MA Dub. 1966; FRCS Eng. 1971; FRCOphth 1989; DO RCPSI 1967. Hon. Cons Opthalmologist. Socs: MRCOphth. Prev: Cons. Ophth. Surg. Sussex Eye Hosp. Brighton; Sen. Regist. King's Coll. Hosp. & Moorfields Eye Hosp.; Demonst. (Anat.) T.C. Dub.

***HARDEN, Joanna Clare** 39 Elvaston Road, Wollaton, Nottingham NG8 1JU — MB ChB 1995 Birm.

HARDEN, Kenneth Alexander Milngavie Road Surgery, 85 Milngavie Road, Bearsden, Glasgow G61 2DN Tel: 0141 211 5621 Fax: 0141 211 5625 — MB ChB Glas. 1962; DObst RCOG 1964; FRCGP 1988, M 1974. Chairm. Scott. GP Comm.; Chairm. Anniesland, Bearside & Milngavie Local Health Care Co-Op. Socs: BMA. Prev: Ho. Surg. & Ho. Phys. W.. Infirm. Glas.; Ho. Surg. (Obst.) Stobhill Hosp. Glas.

HARDEN, Professor Ronald McGlashan 10 Guthrie Terrace, Broughty Ferry, Dundee DD5 2QX Tel: 01382 778130 Fax: 01382 774711 — MB ChB Glas. 1960; MB ChB Glas. 1960; MD Glas. 1971; MD Glas. 1971; FRCS Ed. 1994; FRCS Ed. 1994; FRCP Glas. 1975, M 1966; FRCP Glas. 1975, M 1966; FRCPC 1991; FRCPC 1991. Prof. Med. Educat.; Dir. Ed. Developm. unit. Scott. Counc. Postgrad. Med. Dent. Ed. Socs: (Sec. & Treas.) Assn. Med. Educat. Europe; (Sec. & Treas.) Assn. Med. Educat. Europe.

HARDEN, Stephen Philip Radiology Department, Southampton General Hospital, Tremona Road, Southampton SO16 6YD — MB BS 1993 Lond.; MA Camb. 1994; FRCS Eng. 1997. Specialist Regist. Radiol. Soton. Gen. Hosp. Prev: RSO Cardiothoracic Surg.Lond.Chest.Hosp; SHO (Cardiothoracic Surg.) Roy. Brompton Hosp. Lond.; SHO (Gen. Surg.) Kent & Canterbury Hosp.

HARDEN, Susan Victoria 3 Firbeck, Harden, Bingley BD16 1LP — BM BCh 1993 Oxf.

HARDENBERG, Janet Agnes (retired) 5 Farjeon House, Hilgrove Road, London NW6 4TL Tel: 020 7722 3949 — MB ChB 1938 Ed. Prev: Ho. Surg. Belgrave Hosp. Childr.

HARDIE, Alexander Waldie 51 Carbery Avenue, Southbourne, Bournemouth BH6 3LN Tel: 01202 432101 — MB ChB 1937 Aberd.; FFA RCS Eng. 1953; DA Eng. 1946. (Aberd.) Emerit. Cons. Anaesth. Roy. Surrey Co. Hosp. Guildford.

HARDIE, Andrew David The Surgery, 991 Bristol Road South, Northfield, Birmingham B31 2QT Tel: 0121 476 9191 — MB ChB 1977 Birm. GP Princip.; Clin. Asst. (Diabetic) Selly Oak Hosp. Prev: Clin. Asst. (Anticoagulant) Solihull Hosp.; Trainee GP Birm.; GP Shard End, Birm.

HARDIE, Charles John 35 Joe Connoly Way, Waterfoot, Rossendale BB4 9AT Tel: 01706 211714 — MB ChB 1949 Ed. (Ed.) Socs: BMA. Prev: Resid. Anaesth. Preston Roy. Infirm.; Ho. Surg. Sefton Gen. Hosp. Liverp.; Capt. RAMC.

HARDIE, Christine Jane Wallace 136 Archery Grove, Woolston, Southampton SO19 9EU Tel: 02380 441447 — MB ChB 1979 Dundee; DCH RCP Lond. 1985. SCMO Soton. HA. Socs: Brit. Paediat. Assn.; BMA; BACCH.

HARDIE, Claire Louise 29/2 Rankeillor Street, Edinburgh EH8 9JA — MB ChB 1998 Ed.; MB ChB Ed 1998.

HARDIE, Dean Malcolm Medical Centre, Queens Road, Skewen, Neath SA10 6UH Tel: 01792 812316 Fax: 01792 323208 — MB BCh 1982 Wales; MRCGP 1986. p/t Gen. Practitioner, Gen. Pract., Skewen; Hosp. Practitioner (Dermat.) Neath Gen. Hosp. Socs: BMA; MRCGP.

HARDIE, Isobel St Maur (retired) 28 Turnpike Road, Cumnor Hill, Oxford OX2 9JQ Tel: 01865 862880 — MB ChB Ed. 1938.

HARDIE, James Leslie (retired) Slack House, Embleton, Cockermouth CA13 9XP Tel: 017687 76663 — MB ChB Aberd. 1950. Prev: SHO Workington Infirm.

HARDIE, Joan Elizabeth Park Road Group Practice, The Elms Medical Centre, 3 The Elms, Dingle, Liverpool L8 3SS Tel: 0151 727 5555 Fax: 0151 288 5016 — MB ChB 1981 Aberd.; MSc 2001 Univ. Of Lond.; DFFP 1999 (RCOG:FFP); T(GP) 1993; MRCGP 1992; Cert. Family Plann. JCC 1990. Partner: Gen. Pract. Socs: BMA; Roy. Coll. Of Gen. Practitioners; Liverp. Med. Inst. Prev: Partner: Gen. Pract.: St. Stephen's Surg., Ashtead; GP Regist.: Sheen La. Health Centre, Lond. SW14; Regist. (Psychiat.): St Bart & Roy. Lond. Hosp. Lond.

HARDIE, Joanne Flat 3, Derwent House, 24A Aigburth Drive, Liverpool L17 4JH; 19 Cookson Road, Thornton-Cleveleys FY5 2RL — MB ChB 1993 Dundee; MRCP (UK) 1996. Specialist Regist. (Thoracic Med.).

HARDIE, Kenneth George 4 Newnham Road, Paisley PA1 3DY — MB ChB 1986 Glas. Trainee GP Stobhill Hosp. Glas. VTS. Prev: HO. Stobhill Hosp. & Glas. Roy. Infirm.

HARDIE, Lesley Anne Euphemia Rosemount, Riggs Place, Cupar KY15 5JA Tel: 01334 52537 — MB ChB 1962 St. And.; DObst RCOG 1964.

HARDIE, Lorraine 2 Broomfield Road, Heaton Moor, Stockport SK4 4ND Tel: 0161 432 9017 — MB ChB 1984 Manch.; MB ChB Manch. I984; DRCOG 1988. GP Stockport.

HARDIE, Lynsay 4 Newnham Road, Paisley PA1 3DY — MB ChB 1986 Glas.

HARDIE, Maryon Jean Flat E, 10 Grovepark Gardens, Glasgow G20 7JB — MB ChB 1998 Glas.; MB ChB Glas 1998.

HARDIE, Murray Robert William Kilsyth Medical Partnership, Kilsyth Health Centre, Burngreen Park, Kilsyth, Glasgow G65 0HU Tel: 01236 822081 Fax: 01236 826231; 4 Garrell Grove, Kilsyth, Glasgow G65 9PT — MB ChB 1980 Aberd.; MRCGP 1984; DRCOG 1982.

HARDIE, Rachel Mary 36 Muddelton Square, London EC1R 1YB Tel: 020 7833 5048 Fax: 020 7833 5049 Email: xeg52@dial.pipex.com — MB BChir 1989 Camb.; MRCP (UK) 1991; MSC 1993; MFPHM RCP (UK) 1994. (Camb.)
HARDIE, Richard Henry, OBE, Brigadier late RAMC Mains of Waterton, Auchmacoy, Ellon AB41 8JH Tel: 01358 721447 — MB ChB 1963 Aberd.; MSc. (Com. Med.) Lond. 1981. (Aberd.)
HARDIE, Richard James, TD Clinical Director, Wolfson Neuro-Rehabilitation Centre, Copse Hill, Wimbledon, London SW20 0NE Tel: 020 8725 4765 Fax: 020 8944 9927 Email: rhardie@sghms.ac.uk — MB BChir 1978 Camb.; MA Camb. 1979, MD 1985; FRCP Lond. 1996; MRCP (UK) 1981. (St. Thos.) Cons. Neurol. St. Geo.'s Hosp. Lond. & Atkinson Morley's Hosp. Lond.; Hon. Sec. UK Pk.inson's Dis. Research Gp. Socs: Brit. Soc. of Rehabil. Med.; Welf. Advis. Panel Pk.inson's Dis. Soc.; Brit. Neuropsych. Assn. Prev: Cons. Neurol. Roy. Devon & Exeter Healthcare NHS Trust; Sen. Regist. Rotat. (Neurol.) Nat. Hosps. for Nerv. Dis. & King's Coll. Hosp. Lond.; Regist. Rotat. (Med.) Univ. Coll. & Whittington Hosps. Lond.
HARDIE, Robert 7B Ardayre Road, Prestwick KA9 1QL — MB ChB 1971 Ed.; BSc (Med. Sci.) Ed. 1968, MB ChB 1971; FRCPath 1991, M 1979.
HARDIE, Robert Alastair Tel: 01225 791212; The Old Post Office, 134 Winsley, Bradford-on-Avon BA15 2LB Tel: 01225 722209 — MB BS 1972 Lond.; FRCS Eng. 1978. (Middlesex Hospital Med. School) Hon. Clin. Asst. Gen. Surg. RUH Trust, Bath; Mem. Edit. Bd. Catholic Med. Quar.; Wilts. RMC Bd. Mem. Socs: Fell. Roy. Coll. Surgs.; Chairm. Catholic Med. Miss. Soc.; (Counc.) Guild of Catholic Doctors. Prev: GP & Hosp. Pract. Swanage; Regist. (Surg.) Ipswich Hosp.; SHO (Plastic Surg.) Frenchay Hosp. Bristol.
HARDIE, Robin Allan Heathfield Clinic, Heathfield Road, Ayr KA8 9DZ Tel: 01292 614611 Fax: 01292 288021; Woodcroft, 23 Midton Road, Ayr KA7 2SF Tel: 01292 264383 — MB ChB 1971 Glas.; FRCP Glas. 1987; MRCP (UK) 1974. Cons. Dermat. Ayrsh. & Arran Acute Hosp.NHs.Trust. Prev: Sen. Regist. (Dermat.) Roy. Infirm. Edin.; Regist. (Dermat.) W.. Infirm. Glas.
HARDIE, Timothy James Hayes Wood, Pembury, Tunbridge Wells TN2 4BB — MB BS 1988 Lond.
HARDIMAN, Gaye Victoria Headley House, 55 Rayens Cross Road, Long Ashton, Bristol BS41 9DY Tel: 01275 392134 Fax: 01275 394576 — MB ChB 1976 Bristol.
HARDIMAN, Jacqueline Marguerite Ann The Field House, Knighton-on-Teme, Tenbury Wells WR15 8LT — MB ChB 1981 Sheff.; MRCGP 1987; DTM & H Liverp. 1987; DRCOG 1986. Prev: GP United Miss. Hosp. Tansen, Nepal.
HARDIMAN, James Henry (Surgery) Ruston Street Clinic, Bow, London E3 2LR Tel: 020 8980 1652 — MRCS Eng. LRCP Lond. 1964; DPM Eng. 1968. (Roy. Free) Socs: Fell. Roy. Soc. Med.
HARDIMAN, Maxwell Charles The Field House, Knighton-on-Teme, Tenbury Wells WR15 8LT — MB ChB 1981 Sheff.; MRCGP 1986; DTM & H Liverp. 1987; DRCOG 1986. Regist. (Pub. Health Med.) E. Anglian RHA. Prev: GP United Miss. Hosp. Tansen, Nepal.
HARDIMAN, Paul James Jean-Pierre Department of Obstetrics of Gynaecology, North Middlesex Hospital, Sterling Way, London N18 Tel: 020 8887 2622 Fax: 020 8887 2732 Email: hardiman@rfhsm.ac.uk; 13 Winscombe Crescent, London W5 1AZ Tel: 020 8997 2939 — MB BS 1980 Newc.; MD Newc. 1991; MRCOG 1986. Cons. N. Middlx. Hosp. Lond.; Sen. Lect. Roy. Free Hosp. Sch. Med. Lond. Socs: Fell. Roy. Soc. Med.; Brit. Fertil. Soc.; Soc. Study of Fertil. Prev: Sen. Regist. & Regist. (O & G) St. Bart. Hosp. Lond.; Research Fell. (Endocrinol.) Roy. Free Hosp. Lond.
HARDIMAN, Peter Malcolm (retired) Sungarth, 27 Chestnut Avenue, Barton-on-Sea, New Milton BH25 7BQ — LMSSA 1952 Lond.; DPH Leeds 1967. Prev: Sen. Med. Off. Gwent AHA.
HARDING, Alexander Macleod 2 Overland Road, Mumbles, Swansea SA3 4LS — MB BS 1991 Lond.
HARDING, Andrew Stephen, RD The Medical Centre, High Street, Lindfield, Haywards Heath RH16 2HX Tel: 01444 457666 — MB BS 1970 Lond.; MRCS Eng. LRCP Lond. 1970; DA Eng. 1976; DObst RCOG 1973. (Lond. Hosp.) Prev: Ho. Phys. King Edwd. VII Hosp. Midhurst.
HARDING, Brian Norman Department Histopathology, Great Ormond Street Hospital for Children NHS Trust, Great Ormond St., London WC1N 3JH Tel: 020 7405 9200 Fax: 020 7813 1170 Email: b.harding@ich.ucl.ac.uk — BM BCh 1976 Oxf.; MA Oxf. 1973, BA 1969, DPhil 1976; BM BCh Oxf, 1976; FRCPath 1995, M 1983. (St. Geo. Hosp. Lond.) Cons. Neuropath. Gt. Ormond St. Hosp. for Childr. Lond.; Hon. Sen. Lect. Inst. Neurol. Lond. Socs: Brit. Neuropath. Soc. (Ex-Comm. Mem.); Brit. Paediat. Neurol. Assn.; Amer. Assn. Neuropath. Prev: Sen. Lect. (Neuropath.) Inst. Neurol. & Inst. Child Health Lond.; Sen. Regist. (Neuropath.) Nat. Hosp. Nerv. Dis. Lond.
HARDING, Charles St James Ekundayo 12 Mountbaton Court, Mount Avenue, Ealing, London W5 2RF — MB BS 1950 Durh.; FRCOG 1976, M 1962.
HARDING, Christopher Karl Joyce Green Hospital, Dartford; 87 West Hill, Dartford DA1 2HJ Tel: 01322 293154 — BChir 1996 Camb.; BA Camb. 1994; BM Camb. 1997; MA Camb. 1998. (Cambridge) BST Surgic. Rotat. S. Thames Area. Prev: SHO (A & E) Middlesbrough Gen. Hosp.; PRHO (Surg.) Norf. & Norwich Hosp.; PRHO (Med.) S. Tees Hosp.
HARDING, Claire Myfanwy 23 Brookfield Rise, Whitley, Melksham SN12 8QP — MB BCh 1994 Wales.
HARDING, Clare Margaret Loddon NHS Trust, C/O Bridge Centre, New Road, Basingstoke RG21 7PJ — BM 1978 Soton.; MRCPsych. 1983. Cons Psychiat. Pk. Prewett Hosp. Basingstoke.
HARDING, Miss Claudia Lowood, Lymdinrst Road, Mossley hill, Liverpool L18 8AU Tel: 0151 724 1209 Fax: 0151 724 3242 Email: claudia.harding@ukgateway.net — MB ChB 1987 Ed.; FRCS Glas. 1994. Specialist Regist. (Surg.) Mersey Deamery. Socs: Manch. Med. Soc.; Liverp. Med. Inst.; WIST. Prev: Hon. Regist. (Surg.) Univ. Manch.; Regist. & SHO Bolton Gen. Hosp. & N. Manch. Hosps.
HARDING, Daniel George Royston 11 Blair Avenue, Esher KT10 8BQ — MB ChB 1980 Aberd.
HARDING, Daniel Richard Queen Marys Hospital, Sidcup DA14 6LT Tel: 020 8302 2678 Fax: 020 8308 3171 — MB BS 1987 Lond.; FRCA 1993. cons. anaesth. Qu.s. marys Hosp. Sidcup. Socs: Intens..Care.Soc.
HARDING, David PICU, Royal Liverpool Childrens NHS Trust, Alder Hey Hospital, West Derby, Liverpool L12 2AP — MB ChB 1993 Dundee.
HARDING, Elizabeth Muriel (retired) 75 Bryn Cwnin Road, Rhyl LL18 4UD Tel: 01745 350181 — MB ChB Liverp. 1926, DPH 1932; MB ChB 1926; DPH 1932. Prev: Asst. MOH (Matern. & Child Welf.) Liverp.
HARDING, Emma Victoria 12 Pilley Lane, Cheltenham GL53 9ER; 88 Claremont Road, Wavertree, Liverpool L15 3HL — MB ChB 1990 Liverp. SHO (Med.) Walton Hosp. Liverp. Prev: SHO (Med.) Whiston Hosp. Manch.
HARDING, Frank William Palatine Group Practice, Murray's Road, Douglas IM2 3TD Tel: 01624 623931 Fax: 01624 611712 — MB BS 1973 Newcastle; MB BS Newc. 1973. (Newcastle) GP Douglas, Isle of Man.
HARDING, Gillian Mary St John's Hospice, Weston Road, Balby, Doncaster DN4 8JS Tel: 01302 796666 Fax: 01302 796666 Email: gill.harding@dsh.nhs.net; Rockcliffe, 10 Regent Square, Doncaster DN1 2DS Tel: 01302 739339 — MB BS 1985 Lond.; Dip Palliat Med 1998; MA Camb. 1986; DRCOG 1989. p/t Macmillan director, St Johns Hospice, Doncaster Palliat. Care; Locum GP Doncaster; GP Med. Advisor to Macmillan Cancer Relief. Prev: Trainee GP Doncaster VTS; Ho. Phys. Whittington Hosp. Lond.; Ho Surg. N.ampton Gen. Hosp.
HARDING, Mr Ian James The Inch, Newport Road, Niton, Ventnor PO38 2DG — BM BCh 1994 Oxf.; FRCS Eng. 1998. (Oxford)
HARDING, Janet Anne 62 Bromborough Road, Bebington, Wirral CH63 7RH — MB BS 1991 Lond.; MRCP (UK) 1995; BSc (Hons.) 1998. (St Georges University of London)
HARDING, Jeremy William Dept. of Mental Health, Heatherwood Hospital, Ascot SL5 8AA Tel: 01344 877461 Fax: 01344 877443 — MB ChB 1975 Leeds; MRCPsych 1980. Cons. Psychiat. Heatherwood Hosp. Ascot. Prev: Sen. Regist. Warneford Hosp. Oxf.
HARDING, John Christopher Laverstock B, Boscombe Cliff Road, Bournemouth BH5 1JN Tel: 01202 398814 — MB BS 1961 Lond.; FRCP Lond. 1983; MRCP (U.K.) 1969; MRCS Eng. LRCP Lond. 1961. (Guy's) Cons. Rheum. & Rehabil. Bournemouth. Prev: Sen. Regist. (Physical Med. & Rheum.) Univ. Coll. Hosp. Lond.; SHO (Neurol.) Soton. Gen. Hosp.; Regist. (Med.) Univ. Coll. Hosp. Lond.

HARDING, John Richard Department of Clinical Radiology, St Woolos & Royal Gwent Hospitals, Newport NP9 4SZ Tel: 01633 238221 Fax: 01633 234324 Email: hardxray@gwent.nhs.gov.uk; Whitebrook Cottage, Llanvaches, Newport NP26 3BA Tel: 01633 400962 — MB BCh 1973 Wales; BSc (Hons.) Wales 1970; FRCR 1980; DMRD Eng. 1977. Cons. Radiol. Glan Hafren NHS Trust. Socs: FRCR; Thermology Soc. GB; Europ. Assoc. of Thermology Fell. (Counc. Mem.). Prev: Sen. Regist. & Regist. Univ. Hosp. Wales Cardiff.

HARDING, Karen Anne Frenchay Hospital, Bristol BS16 1LE Tel: 01179 701212 — MB ChB 1990 Bristol; MRCP (UK) 1995. Cons. Med.\c/o the Elderly, N. bristol NHS Trust, Frenchay. Socs: Nat. Osteoporosis Soc.; Brit. Ceriatice Soc.; Internat. Bone & Mineral Soc.

HARDING, Katherine Ruth 34 Milton Park Road, London N6 5QA; Department of Obstetrics & Gynaecology, St Thomas' Hospital, London E1 — MB BS 1986 Lond.; MRCOG 1992. (St Mary's Hosp.) Cons. Obst. Guy's & St Thos. Trust Lond. Socs: RSM.

HARDING, Kathleen Mary (retired) 34 Kingsfield Avenue, Ipswich IP1 3TA Tel: 01473 256006 — MB BS 1945 Lond.; MD Lond. 1952; MRCS Eng. LRCP Lond. 1939; MFCM 1972; DPH Lond. 1948. Prev: Asst. MOH & Sch. Med. Off. Co. Boro. Croydon.

HARDING, Professor Keith Gordon Wound Healing Research Unit, University Department of Surgery, University of Wales College of Medicine, Heath Park, Cardiff CF14 4XN Tel: 029 2068 2176 Fax: 029 2075 4217 Email: hardingkg@whrv.co.uk — MB ChB 1976 Birm.; MRCGP 1987; FRCS 1998. Dir. of Would Healing Research Unit & Prof. (Rehabil. Wound Healing) Univ. Wales Coll. of Med. Cardiff; Extern. Prof. Univ. Glam. Wales. Socs: Founder Mem. Europ. Wound Managem. Assn.; Eur. Tissue Repair Soc.; 1st Pres. Europ. Pressure Ulcer Advisery Panel. Prev: Lect. (Gen. Pract.) Univ. Wales Coll. Med. Cardiff; Research Fell. Univ. Dept. Surg. Univ. Wales Coll. Med.

HARDING, Miss Laura Denise 9 Timbrell Place, Silver Walk, London SE16 5HU; 25 Fishermans Drive, London SE16 6SG Tel: 020 7394 7331 — MB BS 1990 Lond.; FRCS Lond. 1996. (UMDS & St. Guy's Hosp. Lond.) Specialist Regist. ENT N. Thames Region Lond. Prev: SHO (ENT) Mayday Hosp. Croydon; SHO (ENT) Lewisham Hosp. Lond.; SHO (ENT) Roy. Nat. Throat, Nose & Ear Hosp. Lond.

HARDING, Leslie Keith Department of Physics & Nuclear Medicine, City Hospital NHS Trust, Dudley Road, Birmingham B18 7QH Tel: 0121 507 4430 Fax: 0121 507 5223 Email: l.k.harding@bham.ac.uk; Huntroyd, 27 Manor Road N., Edgbaston, Birmingham B16 9JS Tel: 0121 242 2497 Fax: 0121 242 2498 Email: keith@huntroyd.freeserve.co.uk — MB ChB 1963 Birm.; FRCP 1980 Lond.; BSc 1960 Birm.; FRCR 1990; MRCP 1967 Lond.; 2001 (FSRP). (Birm.) Cons. Nuclear Med. City Hosp. Birm.; Reader Med. Univ. Birm.; Mem. Ionising Radiat. Advis. Comm.; Mem. Article 31 Comm. (EC); Mem. (Sec.) Comm. 3. Internat. Commiss. Radiological Protec. Prev: Med Dir city Hosp Birm; Lect. (Med.) & Hon. Sen. Regist. Qu. Eliz. Hosp. Birm.; Regist. Cardiopulm. Bypass Team Qu. Eliz. Hosp. Birm.

HARDING, Liesel 23 Oakeshott Avenue, London N6 6NT Tel: 020 8348 0166 — MD 1935 Bonn; LRCP LRCS Ed. LRFPS Glas. 1939. (Univ. Bonn & Roy. Colls. Ed.) Prev: Capt. RAMC; Res. Med. Off. St. Mary's Hosp. Bellary.

HARDING, Lloyd James Eli Tair Ywen, Cherry Orchard Road, Lisvane, Cardiff CF14 0UE — MB BCh 1992 Wales.

HARDING, Louise 7 Ashlone Road, London SW15 1LS — MB BS 1990 Lond. Regist. (Anaesth.) Hillingdon Hosp. Uxbridge. Prev: SHO (Anaesth.) N.ants. Gen. Hosp.

HARDING, Mary Joy Peartree Lane Surgery, 110 Peartree Lane, Welwyn Garden City AL7 3XW Tel: 01707 329292 — MB BChir 1989 Camb.; MA Camb. 1991; MRCGP 1994. (Addenbrookes) GP Welwyn Gdn. City. Prev: Trainee GP Welwyn Gdn. City; SHO Qu. Eliz. II Hosp. Welwyn Gdn. City.

HARDING, Maura Josephine Manor Farm Medical Centre, Manor Farm Road, Huyton, Liverpool L36 0UB Tel: 0151 480 1244 Fax: 0151 480 6047 — MB ChB 1982 Liverp.

HARDING, Michael Jason 225 Springvale Road, Crookes, Sheffield S10 1LG Tel: 0114 266 1145 — MB ChB 1989 Sheff.; MRCGP 1996; Dip. Obst. Otago 1992.

HARDING, Michael John Harding 1 Park Close, Knightsbridge, London SW1X 7PQ Tel: 020 7589 1345 — MB BS 1966 Lond.; MRCS Eng. LRCP Lond. 1966; DObst RCOG 1968. (St. Mary's) Prev: on Staff Dept. Paediat. Univ. Cape Town.; Ho. Surg. St. Mary's Hosp. Lond.

HARDING, Mr Michael Leonard Dormer House, Brand Hill, Woodhouse Eaves, Loughborough LE12 8SX Tel: 01509 890490 — MB BS 1964 Lond.; MS Lond. 1981; FRCS Eng. 1971; MRCS Eng. LRCP Lond. 1964. (Char. Cross) Cons. Orthop. Surg. Leicester Gen. Hosp. Prev: Sen. Regist. Roy. Orthop. Hosp. Birm.

HARDING, Mr Montgomery George Beresford c/o 9 Redford Avenue, South Wallington, Wallington SM6 9DT — MB ChB 1978 Liverp.; BSc (Hons.) Sierra Leone 1973; FRCS Ed. 1984. Asst. Prof. Cons. Dept. of Orthop. & Trauma King Saud Univ. Saudi Ara bia. Prev: Cons. Orthop. Surg. King Faad Specialist Hosp. Saudi Arabia; Regist. (Orthop.) Whiston Hosp. Liverp.; Regist. (Orthop.) Chase Farm Hosp. Lond.

***HARDING, Neil John** 63 Crespin Way, Hollingdean, Brighton BN1 7FG — MB ChB 1998 Birm.

HARDING, Nicholas 23 South Drive, Wavertree, Liverpool L15 8JJ Tel: 0151 735 0409 — MB ChB 1977 Bristol; DRCOG 1980.

***HARDING, Nicholas John** 43 Hawthorne Road, Birmingham B30 1EQ — MB ChB 1994 Birm.; BSc Birm. 1991, ChB 1994.

HARDING, Professor Nigel Graham Lionel Health Systems Co-ordination, 82 Lime Walk, Oxford OX3 7AF — MB 1963 Camb.; DPhil Oxf. 1966; BA Camb. 1959, MB 1963, BChir 1962. (Camb.) SERC/BHF Fell. Dept. Clin. Biochem. Univ. Oxf.; Hon. Cons. Biochem. Oxf. RHA (T); Sen. Lect. Dept. Path. Biochem. Univ. Glas.; Mem. Staff. Med. Research Counc.; Radcliffe Prize Surg. Univ. Oxf.; Brian Johnson Prize Path. Univ. Oxf. Socs: Biochem. Soc.; Path. Soc. Prev: Asst. Dir. Research (Med. Research Counc.) Postgrad. Med. Sch.; Camb.; Dernham Fell. Amer. Cancer Soc.; Sir Henry Wellcome Fell. Med. Research Counc.

HARDING, Oliver John 21 Boxfield Green, Stevenage SG2 7DR Tel: 01438 759044 Email: o_e.harding@cableol.co.uk — MB ChB 1990 Glas.; T(GP) 1991; Msc 1997; LSHTM 1997. Sen.Reg.Pub.health.med S. thames.

HARDING, Penelope Brigid Prichard Dormer House, Brand Hill, Woodhouse Eaves, Loughborough LE12 8SX Tel: 01509 890490 — MB BS 1964 Lond.; MRCS Eng. LRCP Lond. 1964; DO Eng. 1976; DObst RCOG 1966. (Char. Cross) Assoc. Specialist Ophth. Dept. Leicester Roy. Infirm.

HARDING, Phillip John 9 Douglas Road, Aylesbury HP20 1ES — MB ChB 1988 Dundee; T(GP) 1994; DRCOG 1993.

HARDING, Rachel Ann The Surgery, Salisbury House, Lake St., Leighton Buzzard LU7 1RS — MB ChB 1992 Birm.

HARDING, Richard Dennis Flats 35 Rivers Street, Bath BA1 2QB Tel: 01225 462058; Higher Tale Farm, payenenbury, Honiton EX14 3HJ Tel: 01884 277344 — MB ChB 1969 Bristol; MRCS Eng. LRCP Lond. 1969; MRCGP 1979; DObst RCOG 1974. (Bristol) Hosp. Prac. Rhuem. Roy. Devon Exeter. Socs: York Med. Soc.; Roy. Soc. Med.; Devon & Exeter Med. Soc. Prev: GP Princip. York; Regist. (Med.) Bath Gp. Hosps.; SHO (Cardiol.) Newc. Gen. Hosp.

HARDING, Richard James 63 Trelawney Road, Bristol BS6 6DY — BM BS 1993 Nottm.

HARDING, Robert Joseph Patrick Park View Surgery, 24-28 Leicester Road, Loughborough LE11 2AG Tel: 01509 230717 Fax: 01509 236891; Havergal, 59 Pk Road, Loughborough LE11 2ED Tel: 01509 230251 — MB ChB 1966 Birm.

HARDING, Sally Elizabeth Priors Field Surgery, 24 High Street, Sutton, Ely CB6 2RB Tel: 01353 778208 Fax: 01353 777765; 17 Herford Close, Ely CB6 3QS — MB ChB 1976 Birm.; DRCOG Eng. 1980; DCH Eng. 1979.

HARDING, Sarah Louise 42 Trewhitt Road, Heaton, Newcastle upon Tyne NE6 5LU — BM 1989 Soton.

HARDING, Sian Rhiannon Galbraith Neonatal Unit, The Obstetric Unit, University College, Huntly St., London WC1E 6AU Tel: 020 7387 9300 Fax: 020 7380 9775 Email: sharding@academic.uclh.nlthames.nhs.uk; Amber House, Deepdene Pk Rd, Dorking RH5 4AW — MB BS 1984 Lond.; MRCP (UK) 1991. (King's Coll. Hosp. Med. Sch.) Cons. Neonat. Univ. Coll. Hosp. Lond. Prev: Wellcome Research Train. Fell. (Fetal Med.) Univ. Coll. Hosp. Lond.

HARDING, Mr Simon Peter St Pauls Eye Unit, Royal Liverpool Hospital, Prescot St., Liverpool L7 8XP Tel: 0151 706 3971 Fax: 0151 706 5861; 4 North Road, Grassendale Park, Liverpool L19 0LR Tel: 0151 427 8898 — MD 1990 Liverp.; MB ChB 1979;

FRCOphth 1989; FRCS (Ophth.) Eng. 1984. Cons. Ophth. Surg.; Hon. Clin. Lect. Dept. Med. Liverp. Univ. Prev: Cons. Ophth. Surg. & Clin. Dir. St. Pauls Eye Hosp. Liverp.; Lect. Ophth. Univ. Liverp.; Hon. Sen. Regist. St. Pauls Eye Hosp. Liverp.

HARDING, Steven Gareth 2 Desborough, 100 Bidston Road, Birkenhead CH43 6TW — MB BS 1986 Lond.; MRCOG 1992. Regist. (O & G) St. Bart. Hosp. Lond. Socs: RSM.

HARDING, Susan Claughton Medical Centre, 161 Park Road North, Birkenhead CH41 0DD Tel: 0151 652 1688 Fax: 0151 670 0565; 8 Kerris Close, Aigburth, Liverpool L17 5BY — MB ChB 1974 Liverp.; MRCGP 1982; DTM & H Liverp. 1986; DCH RCPS Glas. 1977; DObst RCOG 1976. (Liverpool) GP.

HARDING, Susan Alice Anaesthetic Department, Royal Lancaster Infirmary, Ashton Road, Lancaster LA1 4RP Tel: 01524 583517 Fax: 01524 583519; 2a Escowbeck House, Crook of Lune, Lancaster LA2 9HS Tel: 01524 770637 Email: sueandq@compuserve.com — MB BChir 1987 Camb.; FRCA 1992. Cons. Anaesth. Roy. Lancaster Infirm. Prev: Sen. Regist. Rotat. Roy. Free Hosp. Lond.; Regist. Rotat. (Anaesth.) St. Mary's Hosp. Lond.; SHO (Anaesth.) Roy. Free Hosp. Lond.

HARDING, Timothy Ambrose Challoner 45 London Road, Daventry NN11 4DT — MB BS 1991 Lond.; MRCP (UK) 1994. Specialist Regist. (Gastroenterol. & Gen. Internal Med.) W. Midl. Deanery.

HARDING, Timothy Michael 9 Birch Grove, Woking GU22 8NB — MB BS 1992 Lond.

HARDING, Vivienne Abbeywood, Abbey Lane, Delamere, Northwich CW8 2HW; Bentleys Cottages, Bentleys Farm Lane, Higher Whitely, Warrington WA4 4PZ — MB BCh 1979 Wales.

HARDING, Wilfrid G, CBE (retired) Bridge Cottage, High St., Farningham, Dartford DA4 0DW Tel: 01322 862733 — MRCS Eng. LRCP Lond. 1941; FRCP Lond 1972, M 1968; FFCM 1972; DPH Lond. 1949; Hon. FFCM 1986. Prev: Lt.-Col. (Hyg. Specialist) RAMC.

HARDING-JONES, Mr David (retired) Vermont, Wiseman's Bridge, Narberth SA67 8NX Tel: 01834 812527 — MB BS 1959 Lond.; FRCS Eng. 1964. Prev: Cons. Orthop. & Traum. Surg. W. Wales Gen. Hosp. Carmarthen NHS Trust.

HARDINGE, Frances Maxine Churchill Hospital, Headington, Oxford OX3 7LJ Tel: 01865 225236 Fax: 01865 225221; The White House, Thame Road, Stadhampton, Oxford OX44 7TP — MB ChB 1988 Bristol; MRCP (UK) 1991; MD 1998. Cons. (Gen & Respirat. Med.)John Radcliffe & Ch.ill Hosp. Oxf. Socs: BTS. Prev: Clin. Research Fell. Oxf.; Regist. (Med.) Soton. Gen. Hosp.

HARDINGE, Mr Kevin 10 St John Street, Deansgate, Manchester M3 4DY Tel: 0161 834 3588 Fax: 0161 839 2896; Thornfield, Legh Road, Knutsford WA16 8NR Tel: 01565 632399 Fax: 01565 632399 — MRCS Eng. LRCP Lond. 1962; MChOrth Liverp. 1969; FRCS Eng. 1967. (Liverp.) Cons. Orthop. Surg. Private Pract.; Hon. Lect. (Orthop.) Vict. Univ. Manch. Socs: Fell. BOA; Soc. Internat. Chir. Orthop. & Trauma; Brit. Assn. Surg. of the Knee. Prev: Cons. Orthop. Surg. Manch. Roy. Infirm.; Sen. Regist. & SHO (Orthop.) Liverp. Roy. Infirm.

HARDINGHAM, Charles Richard Malthouse Cottage, 1 Bell Lane, Wheatley, Oxford OX33 1XY — MB BS 1992 Lond.; BSc (Hons.) Lond. 1989; BA (Hons.) Oxf. 1981. (United Med. Dent. Sch. Lond.) Specialist Regist. (Radiol.) John Radcliffe Hosp. Oxf. Socs: RCP; Roy. Coll. Radiol. Prev: Specialist Regist. (Radiol.) Addenbrooke's Hosp. Camb.; SHO (Med.) Kent & Sussex Hosp. Tunbridge Wells; SHO (A & E) John Radcliffe Hosp. Oxf.

HARDINGHAM, Mrs Janet Elizabeth Dumbledore Surgery, High Street, Handcross, Haywards Heath RH17 6BN Tel: 01444 400243 Fax: 01444 401461; 5 Gander Hill, Haywards Heath RH16 1QU Tel: 01444 454693 — BM BS 1987 Nottm.; MRCGP 1992; DRCOG 1991. (Nottm.) Princip. in Gen. Pract., Balcombe & Handcross Country Pract., High St., Handcross, W. Sussex RH17 6BN. Prev: Trainee GP Midsussex VTS.

HARDINGHAM, Mr Michael The Winfield Hospital, Tewkesbury Road, Gloucester GL2 9WH Tel: 01452 331111 Fax: 01452 331200; Little Ashley, Ashley Road, Cheltenham GL52 6QE Tel: 01242 230300 — MB BS Lond. 1963; FRCS (Orl.) Eng. 1973; FRCS Ed. 1971; MRCS Eng. LRCP Lond. 1963. (St. Mary's) Cons. ENT Cheltenham & Gloucester Gp. Hosps.; Examr. FRCS (Otolaryngol. Edin.). Socs: Pres. S.W. Laryngol. Assn.; Pres. Midl. Inst. Otorhinolaryngol. Prev: Sen. Regist. (ENT) St. Mary's & Roy. Marsden Hosps. Lond.; Regist. (Paediat. Surg.) Childr. Hosp. Gothenburg, Sweden; SHO (Paediat. Surg.) Roy. Hosp. Sick Childr. Edin.

HARDISTY, Colin Arthur Northern General Hospital, Herries Road, Sheffield S5 7AU Tel: 0114 271 4976 Fax: 0114 256 0285; 125 Dore Road, Dore, Sheffield S17 3NF Tel: 01865 513851 — MB BS 1971 Lond.; MD Lond. 1981, BSc (Biochem. 1st cl. Hons.) 1968; FRCP Lond. 1987; MRCP (UK) 1974; MRCS Eng. LRCP Lond. 1971. (Kings Coll. Lond. & St. Geo.) Cons. Phys. (Diabetes & Endocrinol.) N. Gen. Hosp. Sheff.; Hon. Clin. Lect. Univ. Sheff.; Asst. Med. Dir. NHS Exec. Trent. Socs: Soc. Endocrinol.; Brit. Diabetic Assn. & Thyroid Club. Prev: Cons. Phys. S. Tees HA; Lect. (Med.) Univ. Sheff.; Med. Dir. N. Gen. Hosp.

HARDISTY, Paul Old Fire Station, Albert Terrace, Beverley HU17 8JW Tel: 01482 862236 Fax: 01482 861863; The Mill House, Mill Lane, Bishop Burton, Beverley HU17 8QT — MB ChB 1980 Leeds; MRCGP 1984; DRCOG 1983.

HARDMAN, Andrew Gatley Group Practice, Old Hall Road, Gatley, Cheadle SK8 4DG Tel: 0161 428 8484 Fax: 0161 428 6333 — MB ChB 1973 Manch.; DObst RCOG 1976. GP Gatley, Cheadle.

HARDMAN, Ann The Village Surgery, 5 Barrow Point Avenue, Pinner HA5 3HQ Tel: 020 8429 3777 Fax: 020 8429 4413; 5 South Cottage Gardens, Chorleywood, Rickmansworth WD3 5EH Tel: 01923 282521 Fax: 020 8429 4431 Email: ann@hardman.com — MB ChB 1976 Ed.; BSc (Hons.) Ed. 1973; MRCGP 1994; DRCOG 1985; DGM 1997. Clin. Asst. (Rheum.) N.wick Pk. Hosp. Harrow.

HARDMAN, Beaufort Maurice Hunt (retired) Doctors' Houses, Roadwater, Watchet TA23 0RP Tel: 01984 640823 — MB BChir 1951 Camb.

HARDMAN, Eric William (retired) 5 Carbis Close, The Green, Chingford, London E4 7HW Tel: 020 8559 4819 — MB ChB 1930 Manch.; MRCGP 1958. Prev: Hon. Phys. Chepstow & Dist. Hosp.

HARDMAN, Frederick Gordon, VRD (retired) 7 Ebberston Road W., Colwyn Bay LL28 4AP Tel: 01492 544374 Fax: 01492 544374 — MB ChB 1950 Manch.; MRCS Eng. LRCP Lond. 1950; BDS Manch. 1941; FDS RCS Eng. 1952, LDS 1941. Prev: Sen. Regist. (Oral) Inst. Dent. Surg. Lond.

HARDMAN, Gerard 6 Galtres Park, Off Kings Lane, Bebington, Wirral CH63 8RA — MB ChB Liverp. 1965; MRCGP 1974. Clin. Asst. in Dept. of Nuclear Med. Manch. Roy. Infirm. Manch.

HARDMAN, John Alexander Rupert Department Radiology, Royal United Hospital, Combe Park, Bath BA1 3NG; Sunnycroft, 37 Bloomfield Park, Bath BA2 2BX Tel: 01225 315463 — MB BS 1988 Lond.; MRCP (UK) 1992; FRCR 1995. Cons. Radiol. Roy. United Hosp. Bath.

HARDMAN, John Leslie Tonge Moor Health Centre, Thicketford Road, Bolton BL2 2LW Tel: 01204 521094; Harwood Health Centre, Hough Fold Way, Harwood, Bolton BL2 3HQ Tel: 01204 591526 Fax: 01204 53368 — MB ChB 1972 Manch.; MRCGP 1981; DObst RCOG 1974.

HARDMAN, Jonathan Grant 3A Clay Avenue, Mapperley, Nottingham NG3 6EN — BM BS 1990 Nottm.; BMedSci (Hons.) Nottm. 1988; FRCA 1994. Regist. (Anaesth.) Nottm.

HARDMAN, Michael 6 Hardwick Square W., Buxton SK17 6PX — MB ChB 1978 Sheff.; BSc Sheff. 1975; MD Sheff. 1988; MRCP (UK) 1981; Dip. Pharm. Med. RCP (UK) 1990. Med. Dir. Zeneza, Germany. Prev: Head of Performance Developm. Gp. Zeneca Alderley Pk. Macclesfield; Drug Team Ldr. Anh-Infectives Zeneca; Clin. Lect. (Clin. Pharmacol.) Radcliffe Infirn. Oxf.

HARDMAN, Paul Richard John Churchgate Surgery, 15 Churchgate, Retford DN22 6PA Tel: 01777 706661 Fax: 01777 711966; West Grove Farm, West Grove Road, Retford DN22 6HR — BM BCh 1984 Oxf.; BA Oxf. 1981, BM BCh 1984; MRCGP 1988.

HARDMAN, Peter Dudley John Department of Clinical Oncology, James Cook University Hospital, Middlesbrough TS4 3BW Tel: 01642 854616 Fax: 01642 854940; The Dower House, 41 Blackwell, Darlington DL3 8QT Tel: 01325 281067 — MD 1992 Leeds; FRCR 1986. (Leeds University Medical School) Cons. Clin. Oncol. James Cook Univ. Hosp. Middlesbrough. Prev: Sen. Regist. (Clin. Oncol.) W.. Gen. Hosp. Edin.; Clin. Fell. (Radiat. Oncol.) Cancer Control Agency BC, Vancouver, Canada.

HARDMAN, Richard George Heaton Norris Health Centre, Cheviot Close, Heaton Norris, Stockport SK4 1JX Tel: 0161 480

3338; Tudor Cottage, 17 Edmonton Road, Woodsmoor, Stockport SK2 7BG Tel: 0161 487 1928 — MB ChB 1970 Manch. Med. Ref. Stockport Crematorium.

HARDMAN, Roger J Whitevale Medical Group, 30 Whitevale Street, Glasgow G31 1QS Tel: 0141 554 2974 Fax: 0141 554 3979 — MB ChB 1979 Edinburgh; MB ChB 1979 Edinburgh.

HARDMAN, Susan Caroline 140 Church Road, Earley, Reading RG6 1HR — MB BS 1994 Lond.; MRCP 1997; BA Oxf. 1991. (UMDS)

HARDMAN, Susan Francoise 6 Hardwick Square W., Buxton SK17 6PX — MB ChB 1977 Sheff.

HARDMAN, Suzanna Marie Clarissa Department of Cardiovascular Medicine, St Mary's Wing, Whittington Hospital, Highgate Hill, London N19 5NF Tel: 020 7288 5292 Fax: 020 7288 5010; Academic & Clinical Departments of Cardiology, University College Hospitals, Grafton Way, London WC1E 6DB Tel: 020 7380 9888 Fax: 020 7388 5095 — MB BS 1980 Lond.; PhD Lond. 1992; MRCP (UK) 1983. (Univ. Coll. Hosp.) Sen. Lect. (Cardiol.) Univ. Coll. Lond. Med. Sch. & Hon. Cons. (Cardiol.) Univ. Coll. Lond. & Whittington Hosp. Socs: Brit. Cardiac Soc.; (Counc.) Brit. Soc. Cardiovasc. Research.; French Cardiac. Soc. Prev: BHF Intermediate Research Fell., Hon. Sen. Regist. & Lect. (Cardiol.) Univ. Coll. Lond. Hosps. & Med. Sch.; Garfield W.on Research Fell., Hon. Regist. & Lect. Char. Cross & W.m. Med. Sch. & Hosps.; Regist. Rotat. (Med.) Whittington Hosp., Univ. Coll. Hosp. & Chest Hosp.

HARDMAN LEA, Mr Simon John The Ipswich Hospital, Heath Road, Ipswich IP4 5PD — MB BS 1981 Lond.; FRCS Eng. 1986.

HARDO, Philippe 36 Clarendon Road, Leeds University, Leeds LS2 9NZ Tel: 01323 431751; 9 Far Moss, Leeds LS17 7NU Tel: 01323 673968 — MD 1978 Aleppo; MRCPI 1988; DTM & H Liverp. 1986. Sen. Regist. (Rehabil. & Gen. Med.) Leeds; Mem. Research Rehabil. N. Eng. Socs: Yorks. Gastroenterol. Soc. Prev: Regist. (Med.) Whiston & Arrowe Pk. Hosps. Wirral.

HARDSTAFF, Ruth Mary 1 Woodside Gardens, Gateshead NE11 9RB — MB BS 1994 Newc.

HARDWAY, Joan Maeve Kinmel Bay Medical Centre, Kinmel Bay, Rhyl LL18 5AU Tel: 01745 350348 Fax: 01745 356407 — MB ChB 1980 Manch.; MRCGP 1986; DFFP 1993; DRCOG 1985. GP Kinmel Bay Rhyl.

HARDWAY, Raymond Leonard (retired) Penlan, 6 Crugan Avenue, Kinmel Bay, Rhyl LL18 5DG Tel: 01745 350 1659 Email: ramonddway@beeb.net — MB BS 1952 Lond.; MRCGP 1974. Prev: Ho. Surg. Roy. Bucks. Hosp. Aylesbury & Harrow Hosp.

HARDWAY, Richard John Kinmel Bay Medical Centre, Kinmel Bay, Rhyl LL18 5AU Tel: 01745 35034 — MB ChB 1980 Liverp.; MRCGP 1986; DFFP 1993; DRCOG 1985.

HARDWICK, Bernard Raymond Heene and Goring Practice, 145 Heene Road, Worthing BN12 4PY Tel: 01903 235344 Fax: 01903 247099 — MB BS 1986 Lond.

HARDWICK, Christine Isobel Arrowside Unit, Alexandra Hospital, Woodrow Drive, Redditch B98 7UB — MB ChB 1979 Birm.; MRCGP 1983; DCH RCP Lond. 1988; DRCOG 1982; Dip. GU Med. 1993. Clin. Asst. Arrowside Unit Redditch.

HARDWICK, Christopher 8 Sondes Farm, Glebe Road, Dorking RH4 3EF Tel: 01306 882055 — MB BChir Camb. 1937; BA Camb. (Nat. Sc. Trip. Pts. 1 & 2), MA 1937, MD 1940; FRCP Lond. 1947, M 1937; MRCS Eng. LRCP Lond. 1935; DCH Eng. 1938. (Camb. & Middlx.) Prev: Phys. Emerit. Guy's Hosp. Lond.; Wing Cdr. RAFVR; Cons. Phys. Surrey AHA.

HARDWICK, Claire Elizabeth 15 Emmens Close, Checkendon, Reading RG8 0TU Tel: 01491 680346 — MB ChB 1989 Leeds; BSc (Hons.) Physiol. Leeds 1986; DRCOG 1995; DCH RCP Lond. 1994. (Univ. Leeds) Locum GP. Prev: GP/Regist. Bishops Waltham; SHO (Gen. Pract.) Roy. Hants. Co. Hosp. Winchester; Med. Pract. Goring on Thames.

HARDWICK, David John Department of Clinical Radiology, Borders General Hospital, Melrose Tel: 01896 4333; Kirkhope School House, Ettrickbridge, Selkirk TD7 5JJ — MB BCh 1975 Wales; BSc (Hons.) Physiol./Zool. Bristol 1970; FRCR 1982; DMRD Ed. 1980. Prev: Lead Cons. Radiol. Melrose; Clin. Dir. Radiol. Melrose; Cons. Radiol. Borders Gen. Hosp. Melrose.

HARDWICK, Elizabeth Top Farm, Grassthorpe, Newark NG23 6QZ Tel: 01636 821393 — MB ChB 1996 Sheff.

HARDWICK, James Christopher Henry Passfield Corner, Passfield, Liphook GU30 7RU — MB BChir 1993 Camb.; MRCP (UK) 1995.

HARDWICK, Joanne Lynne 35 Patterdale Avenue, Fleetwood FY7 8NW — MB ChB 1992 Leeds.

HARDWICK, John Christopher The Poplars, Briar Walk, Stockton-on-Tees TS18 5BQ — MB ChB 1992 Leic.

HARDWICK, Judith Mary Bellevue Medical Centre, 6 Bellevue, Edgbaston, Birmingham B5 7LX Tel: 0121 440 3197; 5 Antringham Gardens, Birmingham B15 3QL — MB ChB 1981 Birm.; MRCP (UK) 1985; MRCGP 1987; DRCOG 1986; Cert. Family Plann. JCC 1986. Med. Off. Family Plann. Prev: SHO (Anaesth.) Warwick Hosp.; SHO (Gen. Med.) Rotat. Dudley Rd. Hosp.; SHO (Paediat.) Good Hope Dist. Gen. Hosp. Sutton Coldfield.

HARDWICK, Linda Ann Elderly Mental Health Department, St James Hospital, Locksway Road, Portsmouth PO4 8LD Tel: 023 92 894463 Fax: 023 92 865750 — MB ChB 1976 Aberd.; MRCPsych 1981. Cons. Psychogeriat. St. Jas. Hosp. Portsmouth.

HARDWICK, Michael John Church Street Partnership, 30A Church Street, Bishop's Stortford CM23 2LY Tel: 01279 657636 Fax: 01279 505464; 5 Grange Park, Bishop's Stortford CM23 2HX — MB BS 1975 Lond.; MRCS Eng. LRCP Lond. 1975.

HARDWICK, Monica Anaesthetic Dept, Worcester Royal Infimary, Monkswood Branch, Newtown Road, Worcester WR5 1HN Tel: 01905 760637 Fax: 01905 760811 Email: monica.hardwick@worcsacute.wmids.nhs.uk; Walcot Farm, Drakes Broughton, Pershore WR10 2AL Tel: 01905 840606 Email: mhardwickwalco@aol.com — MB ChB 1977 Birm.; FFA RCSI 1982; FRCA 1999. Cons. Anaesth. Worcester Roy. Infirm.

HARDWICK, Nicholas Department of Dermatology, Stafford District General Hospital, Weston Road, Stafford ST16 3SA Tel: 01785 57731; High Oak, 15 Old Croft Road, Walton-on-the-Hill, Stafford ST17 0LS — MB ChB 1976 Cape Town; MMed (Dermat.) 1983; MRCP (UK) 1990; FRCP (Lond.) 1998. Cons. Dermat. Stafford Dist. Gen. Hosp. Socs: Brit. Assn. Dermatol. Prev: Sen. Regist. (Dermat.) Roy. Liverp. Hosp.; Cons. Dermat. Groote Schuur Hosp. & Lect. Univ. Cape Town, S. Afr.; Sen. Cons. Dermat. Kalafong Hosp. & Lect. Univ. Pretoria, S. Afr.

HARDWICK, Peter Bernard, QHP (retired) 72 Harley Street, London W1N 1AE Tel: 020 7436 3764 — MB BS 1958 Lond.; LRCP MRCS 1958; FFARCS 1996; DA 1960. Prev: Cons. Anaesth. & Cons. i/c Clinic for Pain Relief Roy. Free Hosp. Lond.

HARDWICK, Peter John Department of Child & Adolescent Psychiatry, Poole General Hospital, Poole BH15 2JB — MB ChB 1971 Bristol; BSc Bristol 1968; FRCPsych 1991, M 1976. Cons. Child & Adolesc. Psychiat. to E. Dorset. Socs: Inst. Family Ther. Lond.; Assn. Child Psychol. & Psychiat. & Assn. Family Ther.. Prev: Clin. Teach. Inst. Family Therap. Lond.; Sen. Regist. (Child & Adolesc. Psychiat.) Maudsley Hosp. Lond. & Dryden Clinic Exeter; Late Vis. Cons. State of Jersey.

HARDWICK, Rachel Jane Passfield Corner, Liphook GU30 7RU — MB BS 1996 Lond. (Cambs/Roy Lond) SHO Gen. Meds. St Geo.'s Hosp. Lond. Prev: SHO c/o the elderly Bolingbroke Hosp.Lond; SHO paediat.Ealing hosp.Lond; SHO A&E St thomas hosp.Lond.

HARDWICK, Richard Gerald (retired) Passfield Corner, Passfield, Liphook GU30 7RU Tel: 01428 751390 — MB BS Lond. 1949; MRCP Lond. 1956; MRCS Eng. LRCP Lond. 1949. Prev: Regist. (Med.) & Sen. Ho. Phys. (Neurol.) St. Thos. Hosp.

HARDWICK, Mr Richard Henry Cambridge Upper GI Unit, PO Box 201, Addenbrookes NHS Trust, Hills Road, Cambridge CB2 2QQ Tel: 01223 217421 Fax: 01223 216015 Email: richard.hardwick@addenbrookes.nhs.uk — MBBS 1981; MD 1995 University of Briton; FRCS Eng. 1991. (St. Thomas's Hospital, University of London) Cons. Upper Gastro-Intestinal and Laparoscopic Surg., Addenbrookes NHS Trust, Camb. Socs: BMA.; Assn. of Upper Gr. Surg.s; Assn. of Surg.s of Gt. Britian and Irel. Prev: Cons. Sen. Lect., Univ. Hosp. of Wales, Cardiff, 1999-2001; Lect. in Surg., Bristol Univ. , 1995-99.

HARDWICK, Robert Oswald Frederick (retired) Shenley House, Headcorn, Ashford TN27 9HX Tel: 01622 890307 — MB BS 1945 Lond.; FRCP Lond. 1973, M 1949; MRCS Eng. LRCP Lond. 1944; FRCGP 1969. Prev: Cons. Phys. (Gen. & Geriat. Med.) Maidstone & Dist. Hosp. Gp.

HARDWICK, Stephen Anthony Kirkham Health Centre, Moor Street, Kirkham, Preston PR4 2DL Tel: 01772 683420 — MB ChB 1988 Manch.; MRCGP 1993.

HARDWICK, Timothy John Adcote Mill Cottage, Adcote, Little Ness, Shrewsbury SY4 2JZ — MB BS 1990 Lond.

HARDWIDGE, Mr Carl Department of Neurosurgery, Hurstwood Park Neurosurgical Unit, Lewes Road, Haywards Heath Tel: 01444 441881; Tree Tops, Sussex Gardens, Lewes Road, Haywards Heath RH17 7SU Tel: 01444 440020 Fax: 01444 440020 — BM 1981 Soton.; FRCS Glas. 1986. Cons. Neurosurg. Mid. Downs HA. Socs: Brit. Base of Skull Soc.; Cervical Spine Soc.; Soc. Brit. Neurol. Surgs. Prev: Sen. Regist. (Neurosurg.) Midl. Centre for Neurosurg. Qu. Eliz. Hosp. & Childr. Hosp. Birm.; Regist. (Neurosurg.) Walton Hosp. Liverp.

HARDY, Alexander Bishops House, Eastgate, Lincoln LN2 1QQ — BM BCh 1998 Oxf.; BM BCh Oxf 1998.

HARDY, Charlotte Siordet 51 North Road, Whittlesford, Cambridge CB2 4NZ — MB BCh 1982 Wales. (Univ.Hosp.Wales) Clin. Asst. (A & E) Camb.; ATLS Camb. 1994; ACLS Oxf. 1993.

HARDY, Christine Isabel Tottering Brook House, Saccary Lane, Mellor, Blackburn BB1 9DW Tel: 0125 481 2919 — MB ChB 1967 Liverp.; MB ChB (1st cl. Hons.) Liverp. 1967; DObst RCOG 1969. (Liverp.) Staff Grade (A & E) Blackburn Roy. Infirm. Prev: Med. Off. (Occupat. Health) S. Manch. HA; SHO (Path. & Cas.) Roy. S.. Hosp. Liverp.

HARDY, Christopher Charles M6 Respiratory Unit, Manchester Royal Infirmary, Oxford Road, Manchester M13 9WL Tel: 0161 276 4322 Fax: 0161 276 4989; Carr End, 2 Carlton Road, Hale, Altrincham WA15 8RJ Tel: 0161 980 2280 Fax: 0161 980 2280 — MB BS 1977 Lond.; MD Soton. 1988; FRCP 1993; MRCP (UK) 1981. (London Hospital) Cons. Phys. Gen. & Respirat. Med. Manch. Roy. Infirm.; Hon. Lect., Manch. Univ. Socs: Brit. Thorac. Soc.

HARDY, Claire Louise 43 Ballyholme Esplanade, Bangor BT20 5NJ — MB BCh BAO 1997 Belf.

HARDY, David Gateshill The Health Centre, Bartholomew Avenue, Goole DN14 6AW — MB ChB 1945 Leeds. (Leeds) Clin. Asst. Anaesth. Bartholomew Hosp. Goole. Prev: Graded Surg. R.A.M.C., O.C. Milit. Hosp. Tobruk; Res. Surg. Off. Pub. Disp. & Hosp. Leeds; Ho. Surg. Leeds Gen. Infirm.

HARDY, Mr David Gordon Department of Neurosurgey, Addenbrooke's Hospital, Hills Road, Cambridge CB2 2QQ Fax: 01223 216302 — MB ChB 1965 Ed.; MA Camb. 1984; BSc (Hons.) Ed. 1962; FRCS Eng. 1971; FRCS Ed. 1970. (Ed.) Cons. Neurosurg. Addenbrooke's Hosp. Camb.; Assoc. Lect. Univ. Camb; Med. Dir. Addenbrooke's Hosp. NHS Trust. Socs: Roy. Soc. Med. (Sect. Neurol.); Soc. Brit. Neurosurgs. Prev: Sen. Lect. (Neurosurg.) Lond. Hosp. Med. Coll.; Hon. Cons. (Neurosurg.) Lond. Hosp.; Research Fell. (Neurosurg.) Univ. Florida, USA.

HARDY, Elizabeth Anne Corner Place Surgery, 46A Dartmouth Road, Paignton TP4 5AH Tel: 01803 557458; Wesley Manse, Station Road, Totnes TQ9 5HN Tel: 01803 862350 — MB ChB 1972 Birm. p/t Gen. Practitioner; Community Paediat., S. devon Healthcare Trust, Torquay. Socs: Roy. Coll. Gen. Pract.; Dipl. Fac. Family Plann. Prev: Clin. Med. Off. York Health Dist.; SHO Papworth Hosp. Camb & City Hosp. York; Clin. Med. Off. S. Devon Healthcare.

HARDY, Mr Eric Gordon (retired) Lowood House, 14 The Street, Surlingham, Norwich NR14 7AJ Tel: 01603 538174 Email: egh.surling@ukgateway.net — MB ChB (Hons.) Aberd. 1940; MD Aberd. 1954; FRCS Eng. 1958; FRCS Ed. 1948. Prev: Fell. & Instruc. (Surg.) Baylor Univ. Coll. of Med. Houston, Texas.

HARDY, Gregory Paul Stanford 1 Highbanks, Lydiate, Liverpool L31 2PJ Tel: 0151 520 1412 — MB ChB 1987 Liverp.; MRCGP 1992; DGM RCP Lond. 1991.

HARDY, Holly Deller Portishead Health Centre, Victoria Square, Portishead, Bristol BS20 6AQ Tel: 01275 847474 Fax: 01275 818250 — MB ChB 1988 Leeds; MRCGP 1993; DRCOG 1992; DCCH RCP Ed. 1991. (Leeds)

HARDY, Hugh Nevill (retired) 14 The Hooks, Henfield BN5 9UY Tel: 01273 495038 — BM BCh 1952 Oxf.; MA Oxf. 1960; DObst RCOG 1955. Prev: Ho. Phys. Profess. Med. Unit & Med. Off. (Cas.) Middlx. Hosp.

HARDY, Iain George 48 Craw Road, Paisley PA2 6AE — MB ChB 1995 Glas.; BSc (Hons.) Glas. 1992. Sen. Health Off. O & G S.ern Gen. Hosp., Glasgo. Socs: BMA. Prev: SHO Ear, Nose & Throat Roy. Alexander Hosp. Paisley; Sen. Health Off. Orthop. Roy. Alexander Hosp. Paisley; Sen. Health Off. Paediat. Surg., Roy. Hosp. for Sick Childr., Yorkhill, Paisley.

HARDY, Ian Lordship Farmhouse, 11 Broad End, Elsworth, Cambridge CB3 8JD Tel: 01954 267214 — MB BS 1971 Lond.; MA Camb. 1980; BSc Lond. 1965; FFA RCS Eng. 1976; DObst RCOG 1973. (Middlx.) Cons. Anaesth. Cardiothoracic Unit Papworth Hosp. Papworth Everard & Hinchingbrooke Hosp. Huntingdon. Prev: Sen. Regist. (Anaesth.) Addenbrooke's Hosp. Camb.

HARDY, James Patrick 54 Monthope Road, London E1 5LS Email: jim__hardy@hotmail.com — MB BS 1997 Lond.

HARDY, Janet Rea Department of Palliative Medicine, Royal Marsden NHS Trust, Downs Road, Sutton SM2 5PT Tel: 020 8661 3182 Fax: 020 8770 9297 Email: janet.hardy@rmh.nthames.nhs.uk — MB ChB 1981 Auckland; MD Auckland 1991; FRACP 1987. Cons. Phys. & Head Dept. Palliat. Med. Roy. Marsden NHS Trust Lond. Socs: Assn. Cancer Phys.; Assn. Palliat. Med.; BMA.

HARDY, Joan (retired) 16 Church Lane, Strensall, York YO32 5XU — MB BChir 1943 Camb.; MRCPath 1963. Prev: Specialist Pathol. Nigerian Govt.

HARDY, Joan Kathleen, CStJ (retired) Llangattock Manor, Monmouth NP25 5NQ Tel: 01600 712631 — MB ChB Leeds 1947. Prev: Nuffield Research Fell. Dept. Obst. Welsh Nat. Sch. Med. Cardiff.

HARDY, John (retired) Health Centre, Raulway View Road, Clitheroe BB7 2JG Tel: 01200 22674 Fax: 01200 442470 — MB BS 1957 Durh.; DObst RCOG 1959; FRCGP 1983, M 1969. Prev: Squadron Ldr. RAF Med. Br., Specialist in Obst.

HARDY, John Denis 6 Chesfield Close, Bishop's Stortford CM23 3PJ Tel: 01279 503106 — MB BS 1963 Lond.; FRCP Lond. 1985, MRCP (UK) 1970; MRCS Eng. LRCP Lond. 1963; DObst RCOG 1966; DCH Eng. 1968. (St. Bart.) Cons. Paediat. P.ss Alexandra Hosp., Harlow & Herts. & Essex; Hosp. Bishops Stortford. Socs: Neonat. Soc. Prev: Sen. Regist. (Paediat.) Roy. Free Hosp. Lond.; Leukaemia Research Fell. Hosp. Sick Childr. Lond.; Paediat. Regist. Addenbrooke's Hosp. Camb.

HARDY, Mr John Richard Wickham Avon Orthopaedic Centre, Southmead Hospital, Westbury-on-Trym, Bristol BS10 5NB Tel: 0117 959 5198 — MB BS 1984 Lond.; BSc Lond. 1981; FRCS (Orth.) 1996; FRCS Eng. 1989; FRCS Ed. 1989; MD 1997. (Westm.) Sen. Lect. (Orthop. & Trauma) Univ. Bristol; Hon. Cons. N. Bristol NHS Trust. Socs: Fell. Roy. Soc. Med.; Brit. Orthop. Research Soc.; Fell. BOA. Prev: Regist. Rotat. (Orthop. Surg.) Leicester Roy. Infirm.; Regist. (Gen. Surg.) N.ampton Gen. Hosp.; Demonst. (Anat.) Char. Cross & W.m. Med. Sch. Lond.

HARDY, Julia Elizabeth Hardelot, West End Road, Mortimer Common, Reading RG7 3TP — BM 1997 Soton.; BSc Psychol. (1st) Soton. 1995. (Southampton) SHO Psych. Som. NHS Trust. Prev: SHO Old Age Psych.Som.

HARDY, Julie Saxonhurst, School Lane, Seer Green, Beaconsfield HP9 2QJ — MB BS 1997 Lond.

HARDY, Kevin John Diabetes Centre, Whiston Hospital, Prescot L35 5DR Tel: 0151 430 1912 Fax: 0151 430 1900 Email: kev.hardy@bigfoot.com — MB ChB 1984 Liverp.; MD Liverp. 1994; MRCP (UK) 1988; FRCP 1999. (Liverp.) Cons. Phys. & Endocrinol. St. Helens & Knowsley Hosps. Trust Merseyside. Socs: Brit. & Amer. Diabetic Assn.; Eur. Assn. Study Diabetes. Prev: Sen. Regist. (Med.) Roy. Infirm. Edin.; Research Fell. (Med. & Endocrinol.) Univ. New Mexico Sch. Med., USA; Research Fell. Metab. Unit N. Staffs. Roy. Infirm. Stoke-on-Trent.

HARDY, Lucinda Ann 1 Ollerton Close, Manchester M22 4HG; 1 Ollerton Close, Manchester M22 4HG — MB BS 1990 Lond.; FRCA 1996; DA (UK) 1992. Cons. in Anaesth. & ICU, Stepping Hill Hosp., Stockport, Chesh. Socs: MMS; ANWICU; BASICS.

HARDY, Michael Terence 1 Park Terrace, Bratton Fleming, Barnstaple EX31 4RY — MB BChir 1965 Camb.; MRCP (UK) 1972; DCH RCPSI 1981. (Camb. & St. Thos.) Socs: BMA.

HARDY, Pamela Jane 2 Millstone Cottages, The Dale, Hathersage, Hope Valley, Sheffield S32 1AQ Tel: 01433 650435 — MB ChB 1988 Sheff.; MRCP (UK) 1994; Dip. IMC RCS Ed. 1998. Regist. (A & E) QMC Nottm. Socs: Fac. Pre-Hosp. Care; BASICS; Area Surg., St. John's Ambul., Nottm. City. Prev: Regist. (Paediat.) Nottm. City

Hosp.; Regist. (Paediat. Cardiol.) Killingbeck Hosp. Leeds; Regist. (Paediat. & A & E) Sheff. Childr. Hosp.

HARDY, Paul Andrew John Department of Anaesthetics, Gloucestershire Royal NHS Trust, Great Western Road, Gloucester GL1 3NN Tel: 01452 528555 Fax: 01452 394485 — MB ChB 1979 Manch.; BSc (Hons.) (Anat.) Manch. 1976, MD 1991; MA Wales 1993; FFA RCS Eng. 1984. Cons. (Pain Relief & Anaesth.) Gloucester Roy. Hosp.; Assoc. Prof. (Anesthesiology Pain Clinic) Univ. Wisconsin, Madison, USA; Cons. Pain Manag., Hereford. Socs: Eur. Soc. Regional Anaesth.; Internat. Assn. Study of Pain; Brit. Med. Acupunc. Soc. Prev: Specialist (Anaesth.) Univ. Hosp. Uppsala; Sen. Regist. (Anaesth.) Whiston Hosp.; Sen. Regist. (Pain Relief) Walton Hosp. Liverp.

HARDY, Paul Hartshorne Beaumont Villa Surgery, 23 Beaumont Road, Plymouth PL4 9BL Tel: 01752 663776 Fax: 01752 261520 — MB ChB 1980 Manch.; MRCGP 1993; Dip. Occ. Med. RCP Lond. 1995; DRCOG 1994; DFFP 1993; T(GP) 1993. (Manch.)

HARDY, Peter Gateshill Norwood Medical Centre, 360 Herries Road, Sheffield S5 7HD Tel: 0114 242 6208 Fax: 0114 261 9243; 622 Abbey Lane, Whirlow, Sheffield S11 9NA Tel: 0114 367639 — MB ChB 1976 Leeds; BSc (Hons.) Leeds 1973, MB ChB 1976; MRCGP 1983. (Leeds) Prev: Regist. (Med.) Lodge Moor Hosp. Sheff.; SHO (Med.) N.. Gen. Hosp. Sheff.; SHO (A & E) Leeds Gen. Infirm.

HARDY, Rebecca Louise Kings Cross Surgery, 199 King Cross Road, Halifax HX1 3LW Tel: 01422 330612 Fax: 01422 323740 — MB ChB Leeds 1982; MRCGP 1986. GP Halifax.

HARDY, Richard Graham Beau Lodge, Main St., Terrington, York YO60 6QB — MRCS Eng. LRCP Lond. 1955; DObst RCOG 1957. Prev: Ho. Phys. St. Luke's Hosp. Bradford; Cas. Off. Bradford Roy. Infirm.; Ho. Surg. Leeds Matern. Hosp.

HARDY, Mr Robert George Dept of Surgery, Queen Elizabeth Hospital, Birmingham B15 2TH Email: f.g.hardy@bham.ac.uk — MB ChB 1994 Birm.; ChB Birm. 1994; BSc Birm. 1993; FRCS (Eng.). Clin. Research Fell. Dept. Surg. Birm. Univ. Socs: BMA; MDU.

HARDY, Robert Michael (retired) The Surgery, King St., Burton-on-Trent DE14 3A Tel: 01283 568246 Fax: 01283 565657 — MB ChB 1965 Liverp.; DObst RCOG 1968.

HARDY, Rowan Peter Department of Anaesthetics, Princess Margaret Hospital, Okus Road, Swindon SN1 4JU; Broadley Cottages, 32 St. Martin's Lane, Marshfield, Chippenham SN14 8LZ — MB BS 1993 Lond.; MA Camb. 1990; MRCP (UK) 1997. SHO (Anaesth.).

HARDY, Sarah 9a Adelaide Crescent, Hove BN3 2JE — MB BS 1991 Lond.; BSc 1988; FRCA 1998. (Kings College London) Specialist Regist. in Anaesth. - S. E. Thames Rotat. KCH = base Hosp. Socs: RCA; Assoc. of Anaesth.s.

HARDY, Mr Simon Christopher Blackburn Royal Infirmary, Blackburn BB2 3LR Tel: 01254 263555; 47 Summerfield Road, Todmorden OL14 6AQ — MB ChB 1982 Leeds; MD Leeds 1992; FRCS Eng. 1987. Cons. Gen. Surg. Blackburn Roy. Infirm.

HARDY, Mr Stephen Kirk Tottering Brook House, Saccary Lane, Mellor, Blackburn BB1 9DW Tel: 01254 812919 — MB ChB 1967 Liverp.; FRCS Eng. 1973. (Liverp.) Cons. Orthop. Surg. Blackburn Health Dist. Socs: BMA; Fell. Brit. Orthop. Assn. Prev: Sen. Regist. (Orthop.) N. W.. RHA; Orthop. Regist. Wrightington Hosp.; Demonst. Anat. Dept. Univ. Liverp.

HARDY, Thomas James 2 Oakfield Park, Ballymoney BT53 6AS — MB BCh BAO 1989 Belf.

HARDY, Thomas Jonathan The Homeopathic Clinic, 13a North St., Havant PO9 1PW — BM 1984 Soton.; MA Oxf. 1978. Socs: Fac. Homeopathy.

HARDY, Thomas Kenneth (retired) Llwyn Celyn, Penrhos, Bangor LL57 2NL Tel: 01248 362724 Email: ken@hardt.prestel.co.uk — MB ChB 1950 Liverp.; MRCS Eng. LRCP Lond. 1950; FFA RCS Eng. 1960; DA Eng. 1956. Cons. Anaesth. Ysbyty Gwynedd Bangor. Prev: Sen. Regist. (Anaesth.) Welsh Nat. Sch. Med. Cardiff.

***HARE, Alison Sarah** High Trees Farm, Parkgate Road, Newdigate, Dorking RH5 5DZ Tel: 01306 631252 Fax: 01306 631252 — MB ChB 1997 Bristol; BSc (Hons.) Bristol 1994.

HARE, Angela Caroline 12 Thornleigh Drive, Lisburn BT28 2DA — MB ChB 1992 Birm.

HARE, Christopher Mark Bewley The Old Rectory, Exbury, Southampton SO45 1AH Tel: 02380 893127; 8 St. Simons Hall, Macroom Road, Maida Vale, London W9 3HY Tel: 020 8968 8876 — MB BCh 1989 Wales; MRCP (UK) 1992; FRCR 1994. Regist. (Radiol.) Middlx. Hosp. Socs: BMA & Med. Defence Union; Roy. Coll. Radiol.; Roy. Soc. Med.

HARE, Dennis Maxwell (retired) Cedar Lodge, Ashlake Farm Lane, Wootton Bridge, Ryde PO33 4LF Tel: 01983 882218 Fax: 01983 882218 Email: dennis@hare-cedar.freeserve.co.uk — MB BS Lond. 1943; MRCS Eng. LRCP Lond. 1942; DObst RCOG 1948; DA Eng. 1966. Prev: Sen. Obst. Ho. Phys. St. Thos. Hosp.

HARE, Elizabeth Helen Southfield House, Belhaven Road, Dunbar EH42 1NW — MB ChB 1977 Ed.; MPhil 1999 (Edin.); MRCPsych 1997. p/t SPR (Psychiat.) Roy. Edin. Hosp. Socs: MDDUS.

HARE, John Derek Northampton General Hopsital NHS Trust, Cliftonville, Northampton NN1 5BD Tel: 01604 545671 Email: john.hare@ngh-tr.anglox.nhs.uk; Email: drjdhare@cs.com — MB BS 1986 Lond.; FRCA 1995; DA (UK) 1993. (Roy. Free Hosp. Sch. Med.) Specialist Regist. (Anaesth.) Imperial Sch. of Anaesth. St. Mary's Hosp. Lond.; Cons. in Anaesth. and Critical Care, N.ampton Gen. Hopsital NHS Trust, N.ampton. Socs: Assn. of Anaesth.s of Gt. Britain & Irel.; Difficult Airway Soc. Prev: Specialist Regist. (Anaesth), Imperial Sch. of Anaesth, ST marys Hosp. Lond.

HARE, Jonathan Mark Stanley Mental Health Unit, Chase Farm Hospital, The Ridgeway, Enfield EN2 8JL — MB BS 1991 Lond.; BSc (Hons.) Physiol. Lond. 1988; MRCPsych 1996. (Guy's Hospital) Cons. Old Age Psychiat., Chase Farm Hosp. Prev: Sen. Regist. (Psychiat.) Roy. Free Hosp. NHS Trust Lond.; SHO Rotat. (Gen. Pract., Geriat. & Psychiat.) Roy. Free NHS Trust.

HARE, Joseph Francis (retired) 18 Kent Avenue, London W13 8BH — MB ChB 1947 N.Z.; FRCP Lond. 1977, M 1956; FRCP Ed. 1982, M 1956. Prev: Cons. Phys. Chest Clinic Upton Hosp., Heatherwood Hosp. Ascot & King Edwd. VII Hosp. Windsor.

HARE, Kenneth Malcolm East Linton Surgery, Station Road, East Linton EH40 3DP Tel: 01620 860204 Fax: 01620 860318; Southfield House, Belhaven Road, Dunbar EH42 1NW — MB ChB 1977 Ed.

HARE, Miss Liz Department Accident and Emergency, Bristol Royal Infirmary, Marlborough St., Bristol BS2 8HW; 187 Coldharbour Road, Westbury Park, Bristol BS6 7SX — MB ChB 1992 Liverp.; FRCSI. Clin. Fell.

HARE, Margaret Kathleen Buick (retired) 21 Raith Road, Fenwick, Kilmarnock KA3 6DB — MB BCh BAO 1948 Dub.; MD Dub. 1955; DCP Lond 1951. Prev: Cons. Bact. Roy. Infirm. Glas.

HARE, Michael Forsyth Colne Medical Centre, 40 Station Road, Brightlingsea, Colchester CO7 0DT Tel: 01206 302522 Fax: 01206 305131 — MB BS 1986 Lond.; DLO RCs Eng. (Lond. Med. Coll.)

HARE, Michael John The Manor House, 66 Main St, Hartford, Huntingdon PE29 1YA Tel: 01480 453172 Fax: 01480 451731 — MA Camb. 1977; MD Lond. 1971, MB BS 1964; MRCS Eng. LRCP Lond. 1964; FRCOG 1988, M 1973. (Lond. Hosp.) Cons. (O & G) In Indep. Medico-Legal Pract. Socs: RSM; Acad. of Experts. Prev: Cons. (O & G) Hinchingbrooke Hosp. Huntingdon; Lect. & Cons. (O & G) Univ. Camb.; Lect. (O & G) Roy. Free Hosp. Med. Sch. Lond.

HARE, Nicola Carol High Trees Farm, Parkgate Road, Newdigate, Dorking RH5 5DZ — MB ChB 1998 Bristol.

HARE, Tessa Monyca (retired) 18 Kent Avenue, Ealing, London W13 8BH Tel: 020 8998 4256 — MRCS Eng. LRCP Lond. 1956; BSc Lond. 1950, MB BS 1956. Prev: SHO & Med. Regist. St. Olave's Hosp. Lond.

HARES, Paul Stephen 7 Bignall Hill, Bignall End, Stoke-on-Trent ST7 8LS — MB BS 1972 Lond.; DRCOG 1978.

HARES, Robert Alan Drayton Medical Practice, Cheshire Street, Market Drayton TF9 3BS; Styche Hall, Market Drayton TF9 3RB — MB BS 1967 Lond.; DObst RCOG 1969. Clin. Asst. Dermat. Dept. Stafford Gen. Infirm.

HARFOOT, Deborah Anne The Towers Surgery, 163 Holton Road, Barry CF63 4HP Tel: 01446 734131 Fax: 01446 420002; 29 Highwalls Avenue, Dinas Powys CF64 4AP Tel: 01222 512953 — MB BS 1986 Lond.; MRCGP 1991; DGM RCP Lond. 1990. Socs: Barry Med. Soc.

HARFORD-CROSS, Elizabeth Shelagh Ashfield House Surgery, Main Street, Kirkby Malzeard, Ripon HG4 3SE Tel: 01765 658298 Fax: 01765 658846; Ashfield House, Kirkby Malzeard, Ripon HG4 3SE Tel: 01765 658795 Email: liz@kirkbym.demon.co.uk — MB BS 1971 Lond.; MRCS Eng. LRCP Lond. 1971; DObst RCOG

1973. (St. Bart.) Partner in Gen. Pract.; Clin. Asst. (Obst. & Gyn.) St. Jas. Univ. Hosp. Leeds. Socs: BMA. Prev: Clin. Med. Off. N. Yorks. Community Health Serv. York; Clin. Asst. (Med. Ultrasound) & SHO (Obst.) Matern. Hosp. Camb.

HARFORD-CROSS, Michael Ashfield House Surgery, Main Street, Kirkby Malzeard, Ripon HG4 3SE Tel: 01765 658298 Fax: 01765 658846 — MB BChir 1972 Camb.; MA Camb. 1972; FRCP Ed. 1990; MRCP (UK) 1978; DCH Eng. 1975. (St. Bart.) Hosp. Pract. (Dermat.) Harrogate Hosp. Prev: SHO (Dermat.) Addenbrooke's Hosp. Camb.; SHO (Neonat.) Matern. Hosp. Camb.; Ho. Off. (Gen. Paediat.) Addenbrooke's Hosp. Camb.

HARGADON, David John Dean Street Surgery, 8 Dean Street, Liskeard PL14 4AQ; Treweese Barn, Quethiock, Liskeard PL14 3SG Tel: 01579 346224 — MB BS 1981 Lond.; MRCGP 1985; Cert. Av. Med. 1997. (Westm.) Princip. Rosedean Surg. Liskeard; Course Organiser Plymouth VTS. Prev: Trainee GP Plymouth VTS; Ho. Phys. & Ho. Surg. Roy. Surrey Co. Hosp. Guildford.

HARGAN, Mrs Mary Helen (retired) Woodbank, Doncaster Road, Rotherham S65 1NN Tel: 01709 73943 — MB ChB 1933 Glas.

HARGATE, George Newlands Medical Centre, Borough Road, Middlesbrough TS1 3RX Tel: 01642 247401 Fax: 01642 223803 — MB BS 1975 Newc.

HARGEST, Emma Louise The Cockett, Llangorse, Brecon LD3 7UL — MB BS 1998 Lond.; MB BS Lond 1998.

HARGEST, Rachel Department of Surgery, Nevill Hall Hospital, Brecon Rd, Abergavenny W1P 7LD Tel: 01873 732843 Fax: 01873 732752 — MB BS Lond. 1988; MD Lond. 1996; FRCS Eng. 1992. Cons. Surg., Nevillhall Hosp., Abergavenny. Prev: Regist. (Surg.) Broomfield Hosp. Chelmsford; Regist. (Surg.) Univ. Coll. Lond. Med. Sch.

HARGRAVE, Catherine 6 Fitzjohns Road, Lewes BN7 1PS Tel: 01273 480607 — MB ChB 1976 Glas.; MRCGP 1980; DRCOG 1980.

HARGRAVE, Darren Russell 79 Aylesbury End, Beaconsfield HP9 1LS — MB ChB 1991 Leeds.

HARGRAVE, David Bowen Portland Group Practice, The Health Centre, Park Estate Road, Easton, Portland DT5 2BJ Tel: 01305 820422 Fax: 01305 824143 Email: postmaster@gp-j81009.nhs.uk; 6 Delhi Lane, Easton, Portland DT5 1JB Email: dbhargrave@supanet.com — MB BS 1976 Lond.; MRCS Eng. LRCP Lond. 1976; AKC. (Westm.) Princip. GP Portland. Prev: Trainee GP Luton & Dunstable Hosp. VTS; Ho. Surg. (Orthop.) Qu. Mary's Hosp. Roehampton; Ho. Phys. (Gen. Med.) W. Wales Gen. Hosp. Carmarthen.

HARGRAVE, Stuart Anthony 19 The Crest, Dinnington, Newcastle upon Tyne NE13 7LU — MB ChB 1968 Aberd.; FFA RCS Eng. 1974.

***HARGRAVES, Andrew** Crinkham Cottage, Upper Breinton, Hereford HR4 7PP — MB ChB 1998 Birm.

HARGREAVE, Mr Timothy Bruce Western General Hospital, Edinburgh EH4 2XU Tel: 0131 537 2578 Fax: 0131 537 1019 — MB BS 1967 Lond.; MS Lond. 1983; FRCS Ed. 1973; FRCS Eng. 1973; MRCS Eng. LRCP Lond. 1967; FEBU 1992; FRCP Ed. 1998. (Univ. Coll. Hosp.) Cons. Urol. W.. Gen. Hosp. NHS Trust; Mem. Scientif. & Ethical Review Gp. UNDP/UNFPA/World Bank/WHO; Special Progr. of Research, Developm. & Research Train. in Human Reproduc.; Sen. Lect. Univ. Edin. Socs: Brit. Assn. Urol. Surgs.; Deutschen Gesselbrhact fur Urologie (Hon. Corr. Mem.); (Pres.) Scott. Urological Soc.

HARGREAVES, Alfred John Maurice (retired) 8 New Cross, Longburton, Sherborne DT9 6EJ — MRCS Eng. LRCP Lond. 1942; MA Camb. 1976, BA 1939; DTM & H Eng. 1950. Prev: Sen. Med. Off. Dorset CC & AHA.

HARGREAVES, Allister David Falkirk and District Royal Infirmary, Major's Loan, Falkirk FK1 5QE Tel: 01324 624000 — MB ChB 1983 Ed.; BSc (Hons.) 1981; MRCP (UK) 1986; MD 1993. (Edinburgh) Cons. Phys. & Cardiol. Falkirk & Dist. Roy. Infirm. Prev: Sen. Regist., Manch. Roy. Infirm.; Lect. (Med.) Roy. Infirm. Edin.; Regist. (Cardiol.) Roy. Infirm. Edin.

HARGREAVES, Antony Grassmoor, Papcastle, Cockermouth CA13 0JT Tel: 01900 822087 — MB ChB 1955 Manch.; DPH 1962; MFCM 1974. (Manch.) Med. Off. (Environm. Health) Allerdale DC, Copeland Boro. Counc.; Specialist (Community Med.) W. Cumbria HA.

HARGREAVES, Mr Arthur Walsh Greenaways, Woodbourne Road, Brooklands, Sale M33 3SX Tel: 0161 973 7674 — MB ChB Manch. 1960; FRCS Ed. 1963; FRCS Eng. 1965; FRCS 1997 Glas. (Manch.) Socs: Fell. Manch. Med. Soc.; Moynihan Chirurgical Club. Prev: Cons. Surg. Hope Hosp. Salford & Salford Roy. Hosp.; Sen. Surg. Regist. Manch. Roy. Infirm.; Res. Surg. Off. Salford Roy. Hosp.

HARGREAVES, Caroline Diana The Surgery, Brede Lane, Sedlescombe, Battle TN33 0PW Tel: 01424 870225; Oxley Green Cottage, Brightling, Robertsbridge TN32 5HD Tel: 01424 838810 Email: carohargraves@hotmail.com — MB BS 1979 Lond.; MRCS Eng. LRCP Lond. 1979; MRCGP 1990; DCH Eng. 1981. (Char. Cross) Socs: BMA. Prev: Trainee GP Minehead; Clin. Med. Off. Wandsworth HA; SHO (Paediat.) W.m. Childr. Hosp. Lond.

HARGREAVES, Carolyn Mary Meadows Farm Cottage, Worlds End, Hambledon, Waterlooville PO7 4QU Tel: 01705 254459 — BM 1989 Soton. Staff Grade (A & E) Qu. Alexandra Hosp. Portsmouth. Prev: SHO (O & G) St. Mary's Hosp. Portsmouth; Clin. Asst. (Cardiac Measurem.) Roy. Hants. Co. Hosp. Winchester; Ho. Phys. & Ho. Surg. Roy. Hants. Co. Hosp. Winchester.

HARGREAVES, Christopher Graham Department Anaesthetics, The Whittington Hospital, Highgate Hill, London N19 5NF Tel: 020 7272 3070 — MB BS 1982 Lond.; BSc (Hons.) Lond. 1979; MRCP (UK) 1987; FRCA 1990. (St Mary's Hospital London) Cons. Anaesth. & Intens. Care Whittington Hosp. Lond. Prev: Sen. Regist. (Anaesth.) Middlx. Hosp.; Regist. (Anaesth.) Lond. Hosp.; Regist. (Med.) King Geo. Hosp. Ilford.

HARGREAVES, Christopher Sutherland Farnham Medical Centre, 435 Stanhope Road, South Shields NE33 4JE Tel: 0191 455 4748 Fax: 0191 455 8573 — MB BS Durh. 1964. (Newc.) Socs: Assn. Police Surg. Prev: SHO & Ho. Off. (O & G) Newc. Gen. Hosp; Surg. NZ Shipping Company.

HARGREAVES, Corinne Anne King George's Hospital, Barley Lane, Goodmayes, Ilford IG3 8YB — MB ChB 1983 Liverp.; MRCOG 1990; Dip. Ven. Liverp. 1985. (Liverpool University) Cons. (O & G) King Geo. Hosp.Goodmayes Essex. Socs: Brit. Fertil. Soc.; Roy. Soc. Med. Prev: SPR in (O&G) King Geo. Hosp.; Specialist Regist. (O & G) Whipps Cross Hosp. Lond.; Specialist Regist. in O & G S.end Hosp.

HARGREAVES, Craig 29 Kew Gardens Road, Kew, Richmond TW9 3HD — MB BS 1993 Flinders.

HARGREAVES, David Bruce 36 Park Road, Prescot L34 3LR Tel: 0151 426 6725 — MB ChB 1949 Liverp. (Liverp.) Mem. (Ex-Pres.) Whiston Postgrad. Med. Centre. Socs: (Ex-Pres.) St. Helens Med. Soc. Prev: Chairm. Merseyside LMC.

HARGREAVES, David Charles St Luke's Hospital, Blackmoorfoot Rd, Huddersfield HD4 5RQ Tel: 01295 768944, 01484 343575 Fax: 01295 768624 Email: caroline.rob@virgin.net, david.hargreaves@cht.nhs.uk — MB ChB 1990 Birm.; MMed Sc 1996 Leeds; MRCPsych 1995; BSc Birm. 1987. Cons. Forens. Psychiat., Calderdale & Huddersfield NHS Trust, Huddersfield; Vis. Sen. Research Fell., Sch Of Human & Health Sci. Univ. Of Huddersfield. Prev: Specialist Regist. Yorks. Regional Train. Scheme in Forens. Psychiat. 1995-1999; Leeds/Wakefield/Pontefract Regist. Train. Scheme in Psychiat. 1993-1995; Leeds SHO Train. Scheme in Psychiat. 1991-1993.

HARGREAVES, Mr David Gordon 15 Hillgate Place, London W8 7SL Tel: 020 7727 0059 — MB BS 1988 Lond.; FRCS Eng. 1992. Regist. (Orthop.) St. Mary's Hosp. Lond. Socs: Fell. Roy. Soc. Med.

HARGREAVES, David Michael Talma House, Giddylake, Wimborne BH21 2QU Tel: 01202 848683 — MB BS 1981 Lond.; FFA RCS Eng. 1986. (Char. Cross) Cons. Anaesth. Roy. Bournemouth Hosp. Prev: Sen. Regist. Poole & Soton. Hosps.; Regist. (Anaesth.) Char. Cross Hosp. & Nat. Hosp. Nerv. Dis. Lond.

HARGREAVES, Emma Jane 121 Dulwich Road, London SE24 0NG — MB BS 1989 Lond.

HARGREAVES, Emma Louise 18 Main Street, Calverton, Nottingham NG14 6FQ — MB ChB 1997 Sheff.

HARGREAVES, Fiona Margaret Valentine House, 1079 Rochdale Road, Manchester M9 8AJ Tel: 0161 740 2524 Fax: 0161 795 2531; 1 Woodlands Way, Accrington, Manchester M24 1WL — MB ChB 1986 Ed.; BSc (Med. Sci.) Ed. 1983; MRCGP 1990; DCH RCPS Glas. 1989; DRCOG 1988. GP Manch.

HARGREAVES, Frank Thomas Mather Avenue Practice, 584 Mather Avenue, Liverpool L19 4UG Tel: 0151 427 6239 Fax: 0151 427 8876; 203 Allerton Road, Mossley Hill, Liverpool L18 6JL Tel: 0151 724 5330 — MB BS 1982 Lond.; LMSSA Lond. 1982; MRCGP 1986; DRCOG 1984. (Roy. Free) Prev: Trainee GP Walton Hosp. VTS Liverp.

HARGREAVES, George Kenneth 19 St John Street, Manchester M3 4DS Tel: 0161 834 5649 Fax: 0161 834 4205 — MB ChB 1951 Ed.; FRCP Ed. 1971, M 1959. (Ed.) Socs: Brit. Assn. Dermat. Prev: Cons. Dermat. Skin Hosp. Univ. Manch. Stockport, Macclesfield & BuxtonHosps.; Cons. Dermat. Leighton Hosp. Crewe; Regist. (Dermat.) Gen. Infirm. Leeds.

HARGREAVES, Gordon Francis Little Garth, Woodlands Road W., Virginia Water GU25 4PL Tel: 01344 842121 — MB BChir 1950 Camb.; MA Camb. 1952. (Middlx.) Prev: Chairm. Boehringer Ingelheim Ltd. Bracknell; Cas. Med. Off. Middlx. Hosp.

HARGREAVES, Harriet Melinda Frenchay Health Authority, Community Services Unit, Wendover, Downend, Bristol BS16 5EB; 18 Camp View, Winterbourne Down, Bristol BS36 1BW — MB BChir 1967 Camb.; MRCP (UK) 1971; MRCPCH 1997. Cons. Paediat. Community Servs. Frenchay Healthcare Trust. Socs: BMA. Prev: Sen. Regist. & Cons. Ahmada Bello Univ. Hosp., Kaduna, Nigeria.

HARGREAVES, Jane 5 Coxswain Way, Selsey, Chichester PO20 0UA Tel: 01243 606809 — MB ChB Manch. 1954; MRCGP 1966; DCH Eng. 1967. (Manch.) Prev: SHO (Path.) Wythenshawe Hosp. Manch. & St. Martin's Hosp. Bath; Ho. Phys. Manch. Roy. Infirm.

HARGREAVES, John Bennett 151 redgate, Ormskirk L39 3NW Tel: 01695 77780 — MRCS Eng. LRCP Lond. 1938; FFA RCS Eng. 1965; DA Eng. 1946. (Liverp.) Cons. Anaesth. Roy. Liverp. United Hosp. & Walton Hosp. Liverp. Socs: Liverp. Soc. Anaesths. & Liverp. Med. Inst. Prev: Ho. Surg. & Res. Anaesth. Roy. S.. Hosp. Liverp.

HARGREAVES, John Neil Department Psychiatry, Eastbourne District General Hospital, Eastbourne BN21 2UD — MA, MB Camb. 1976, BChir 1975; MRCPsych 1983. Cons. Psychiat. E.bourne & Co. Healthcare NHS Trust. Prev: Cons. Psychiat. Hellingly Hosp. Hailsham.

HARGREAVES, Julian Nicholas Scott Newburn Road Surgery, 4 Newburn Road, Newcastle upon Tyne NE15 8LX Tel: 0191 229 0090 Fax: 0191 267 4830 — BM 1985 Soton.; MRCGP 1994; DRCOG 1995; DTM & H RCP Lond. 1991. GP Newc. Prev: SHO (O & G) Poole Hosp. NHS Trust; Dist. Health Off., Malawi; Trainee GP Bournemouth.

HARGREAVES, Kathleen Newburn Road Surgery, 4 Newburn Road, Newcastle upon Tyne NE15 8LX Tel: 0191 229 0090 Fax: 0191 267 4830 — BM 1985 Soton.; MRCGP 1995; DTM & H RCP Lond. 1991; DA (UK) 1991; DRCOG 1990. p/t GP Newc. Prev: Trainee GP Shirley Health Centre Soton.

HARGREAVES, Mark David The Surgery, 133 London Road, Cowplain, Waterlooville PO8 8XL; Meadows Farm Cottage, Worlds End, Hambledon, Waterlooville PO7 4QU — MB BS 1981 Lond.; BSc Lond. 1978; MRCGP 1990; DRCOG 1988. (Westm.) Prev: SHO (O & G) St. Mary's Hosp. Portsmouth; SHO & Clin. Med. Off. (Paediat.) Roy. Hants. Hosp. Winchester.

HARGREAVES, Mark Robert Rochdale Infirmary, Whitehall Street, Rochdale OL12 0NB Tel: 01706 517318 — MB ChB 1982 Dundee; FESC 2000; MD Dundee 1992; MRCP (UK) 1986; FRCP 1999 Lond. Cons. Cardiol. Rochdale Infirm., Rochdale; Assoc. Edr. Jl. Cardiovasc. Ris. Socs: BMA; RCP; Brit. Cardiac Soc. Prev: Research Fell. & Regist. (Cardiol.) John Radcliffe Hosp. Oxf.; Research Fell. (Cardiol.) Univ. Alberta Edmonton, Canada; Regist. (Med.) St. Stephens Hosp. Lond.

HARGREAVES, Martin James Parsons Heath Medical Practice, 35A Parsons Heath, Colchester CO4 3HS Tel: 01206 864395 Fax: 01206 869047; 171 St John's Road, Colchester CO4 4JG Tel: 01206 871665 — MB BS 1980 Lond.; Dip. IMC RCS Ed. 1991; DRCOG 1983. Socs: BMA & BASICS. Prev: ABS Health Project N. Yemen.

HARGREAVES, Melanie 6 Heath Mead, London SW19 5JP — MB BS 1996 Lond.

HARGREAVES, Michael Denham (retired) 150 Wigton Lane, Allwoodley, Leeds LS17 8RZ — MB ChB 1956 Leeds; FFA RCS Eng. 1961. Prev: Cons. Anaesth. United Leeds Hosps.

HARGREAVES, Michelle 53 Paddock Lane, Metheringham, Lincoln LN4 3YG — MB BS 1996 Newc.

HARGREAVES, Moira Joan Moorlands Surgery, 139A Willow Road, Darlington DL3 9JP Tel: 01325 469168 — MB ChB 1969 Liverp.; MRCS Eng. LRCP Lond. 1969. Clin. Med. Off. (Family Plann.) Co. Durh.

HARGREAVES, Neil Maples, Mowbray Drive, Burton-in-Kendal, Carnforth LA6 1NF — MB BS 1948 Durh. Med. Off. Libbys Milk Fact. Menthorpe.

HARGREAVES, Pamela Vine House Surgery, Vine Street, Grantham NG31 6RQ Tel: 01476 576851 Fax: 01476 591732; 41 Belton Lane, Great Gonerby, Grantham NG31 8NA Tel: 01476 76351 — MB ChB 1976 Rhodesia; LRCP LRCS Ed. LRCPS Glas. 1976.

HARGREAVES, Paul Ian Chelsea & Westminster Hospital, 369 Fulham Road, London SW10 9NH Tel: 020 8746 8000 Email: paul.hargreaves@chelwest.nhs.uk; 41 Enfield Road, Brentford TW8 9NY Tel: 020 8580 0960 Email: dr.paul@cableinet.co.uk — MB BS 1990 Lond.; MSc (Clin. Paed.) 2001 (Inst. Child Health, Lond.); MRCP, MRCPCH (Edin.) 1997. (Royal Free Hospital, University of London) Cons. in Paediat., Chelsea & W.m. Hosp., Lond. Prev: Regist. Rotat. (Paediat.) Wexham Pk. & Heatherwood Hosps.; SHO (Paediat.) Ealing Hosp., Lond.; SHO (Paediat.) Chelsea & W.m. Hosp. Lond.

HARGREAVES, Peter Nicholas Mount Edgcumbe Hospice, Porthpaen Road, St Austell PL26 6AB Tel: 01726 65711 Fax: 01726 66421; Churchtown Farm Barn, St Ewe, St Austell PL26 6EY Tel: 01726 844861 — MB ChB 1979 Liverp.; MRCS Eng. LRCP Lond. 1979; MRCGP 1987. Cons.Palliat. Med.Mt. Edgcumbe Hospice; Cons. Palliat. Med.Roy.Cornw..Hosp.Trust.

HARGREAVES, Peter Nicholas Health Centre, Bank Street, Cupar KY15 4JN Tel: 01334 654945 Fax: 01334 657306; Edenfield, East Road, Cupar KY15 4HQ Tel: 01334 655750 — MB ChB 1976 Dundee; DRCOG 1980. Clin. Asst. (Geriat. Med.) Fife.

HARGREAVES, Richard Jerry Anaesthetic Department, Darlington Memorial Hospital, Holly Hurst Road, Darlington DL3 6HX — MB ChB 1969 Liverp.; FFA RCS Eng. 1978; T(Anaesth.) 1991. Cons. Anaesth. S. Durh. Healthcare Trust Darlington Memor. Hosp. Darlington.

HARGREAVES, Roger James Burnham Market Surgery, Church Walk, Burnham Market, King's Lynn PE31 8DH Tel: 01328 737000 Fax: 01328 730104; The Old Norfolk Hero, Stanhoe, King's Lynn PE31 8PT Tel: 01485 518269 Email: rogerhargreaves@compuserve.com — MB BS Lond. 1966; MRCS Eng. LRCP Lond. 1966; DObst RCOG 1968. (Middlx.) Prev: Ho. Phys., Ho. Surg. & Ho. Off. (Obst.) Qu. Mary's Hosp. Sidcup.

HARGREAVES, Rosemary Elizabeth The Health Centre, Springs Lane, Ilkley LS29 8TQ Tel: 01943 602255 Fax: 01943 430005 — MB BS 1981 Lond.; BSc Lond. 1978, MB BS 1981; MRCGP 1987; DRCOG 1986.

HARGREAVES, Ruth Mary Medical Affairs, Pfizer Ltd, Ramsgate Road, Sandwich CT13 9NJ Tel: 01304 648533 Fax: 01304 655564 Email: ruth.hargreaves@pfizer.com; Bohemia, Downs Avenue, Epsom KT18 5HG — MB BCh 1980 Wales; MD Wales 1993; MRCP (UK) 1984; MRCPath 1993; MRCGP 1985. Cat. Med. Manager, Pfizer Ltd; Hon. Cons. Med. Microbiol., Brighton Health Care NHS Trust. Prev: Sen. Med. Adviser Pfizer Ltd.

HARGREAVES, Sally Ann 14 King Street, Cottingham HU16 5QE Tel: 01482 849580 — MB ChB 1982 Leic.

***HARGREAVES, Sally Jean** 5 Brooklyn Court, Ashtead Road, Brooklands, Sale M33 3PX — MB ChB 1996 Liverp.

HARGREAVES, Simon Alistair Mill Street Medical Centre, 2 Mill St., St Helens WA10 2BD Tel: 01744 23641 Fax: 01744 28398; 52 Layton Road, Woolton, Liverpool L25 9NF Tel: 0151 428 4439 — MB ChB 1989 Manch.; BSc St. And. 1986; MRCGP 1996; DCH RCP Lond. 1994; DFFP 1994. GP Mill St. Med. Centre St. Helens; Clin. Asst., Dematology, S.port Dist. Gen. Hosp. Socs: Liverp. Med. Inst.; Liverp. Med. Inst. Prev: GP/Regist. Pk. Med. Centre Chester; Trainee GP Lache Health Centre Chester; SHO (Community & Hosp. Paediat.) Countess of Chester Hosp.

HARGREAVES, Simon James Norton Brook Medical Centre, Cookworthy Road, Kingsbridge TQ7 1AE Tel: 01548 853551 Fax: 01548 857741; Crosslands, Towns Lane, Loddiswell, Kingsbridge TQ7 4QY — MB ChB 1979 Birm.; MRCGP 1984; DRCOG 1982.

HARGREAVES, Mr Simon Peter Royal Bolton Hospital, Minerva Rd, Farnworth, Bolton BL4 0JR; Dimple House, Cox Green Road, Dimple, Bolton BL7 9RA Fax: 01204 602869 Email: sphang@btinternet.com — MB ChB 1988 Birm.; BSc (Physiol.) Birm. 1985; FRCS Ed. 1994; FRCS 1995; FRCS 1998 ORL. Cons. Roy. Bolton Hosp., Minerva Rd, Farnworth; Cons. Otolaryngologist Beaumont Hosp., Old Hall Clough, Chorley New Rd., Bolt, Gtr. Manch. Socs: BMA; BAORLHNS; Manch. Med. Soc. Prev: SHO Rotat. (Surg.) N. Staffs. HA.; Regist. Rotat. (Otolaryngol.) Manch. Roy. Infirm.

HARGREAVES, Stephen James 27 Beech Avenue, Upton, Wirral CH49 4NJ Tel: 0151 677 5254 — MB ChB Liverp. 1952.

HARGREAVES, Thomas (retired) 42 High Street, East Budleigh, Budleigh Salterton EX9 7ED — MRCS Eng. LRCP Lond. 1955; PhD Lond. 1966, BSc 1952, MD 1963, MB BS 1955; FRCPath 1975, M 1963. Prev: Cons. Chem. Path. Exeter DHA.

HARGREAVES, Thornton Henry St Ives, 50 Penkett Road, Wallasey CH45 7QN Tel: 0151 639 1769; 9F Flat, 50 Penkett Road, Wallasey CH45 7QW Tel: 0151 639 1769 — MRCS Eng. LRCP Lond. 1943; MRS GRCP. (Liverp.) Socs: Brit. Med. Pilots Club & Wallasey Med. Soc.; Wallasey Med. Soc. Prev: Cas. Off., Ho. Surg. & Ho. Phys. David Lewis N.. Hosp. Liverp.; Temp. Surg. Lt. RNVR.

HARGREAVES, Una 10 Montacute Close, Farnborough GU14 7HG — MB BS 1944 Madras. Prev: Capt. IMS/IAMC 1944-8.

HARGREAVES, Valerie Seona Edenfield, East Road, Cupar KY15 4HQ — MB ChB 1979 Dundee.

HARGREAVES, Wanda Jane Heath Lane Medical Centre, Heath Lane, Chester CH3 5UJ Tel: 01244 348844 Fax: 01244 351057 — MB ChB 1987 Liverp.; MRCGP 1993. SHO Regist. (Med. Rotat.) & SHO (Cas.) Glan Clwyd Hosp. Bodelwyddan N. Wales. Socs: Med. Sickness Soc.; BMA. Prev: Pre. Regist. Countess of Chester Hosp.

HARGROVE, Richard Charles Andrew Flat 5, 72 Cornwall Gardens, London SW7 4BA — MB BS 1993 Lond.

HARGROVE, Rowland Leonard (retired) 172 Court Lane, Dulwich, London SE21 7ED Tel: 020 8693 4376 — MB BS 1955 Lond.; MRCS Eng. LRCP Lond. 1955; FRCA 1958; DA Eng. 1958. Prev: Cons. Anaesth. W.m. Hosp. Lond.

HARGROVES, David Robert 43 Clare Avenue, Darlington DL3 8SJ — MB BS 1996 Lond.; BSc Hons Psychology. SHO Barnet & Chase Farm NHS Trust. Prev: Transpl. SHO Roy. Brompton & Harefield NHS Trust; A&E Med. Univ. Coll. Hosp. Lond.; C of E SHO, E.bourne Hosp.

HARIHARAN, Mr Kartik 153 Bishop Hannon Drive, Cardiff CF5 3QU — MB BS 1986 Madras; FRCSI 1990.

HARIHARAN, Singaram 188 Middleton Road, Morden SM4 6RW — MB BS 1983 Colombo, Sri Lanka.

HARIHARAN, Thayumanavar Clifton House Surgery, 1 Church Street, Golcar, Huddersfield HD7 4AQ Tel: 01484 654100 — MB BS 1974 Madras. (Madras Med. Coll.) GP Huddersfield. Prev: GP Pontefract; SHO Castle Hill Hosp. Cottingham.

HARIHARAN, Vimalathevi Tel: 020 8539 3131 Fax: 020 8539 7875 — LRCP LRCS 1983 Ed.; LRCPS Glas. 1983. (Peradeniya Med. Sch. Kandy, Sri Lanka) SHO (Geriat.) Joyce Green Hosp. Dartford. Socs: Med. Inst. Tamil (1994-1996). Prev: SHO (A & E) W.hill Hosp. Dartford; SHO (Paediat.) Joyce Green Hosp. Dartford.

HARIKRISHNAN, Rangasamy Tel: 01207 215005 — MB BS 1974 Madras.

HARINDRA, Veerakathy St Mary's Hospital, Department Genitourinary Medicine, Milton Road, Portsmouth PO3 6AD Tel: 023 9286 6768 Fax: 023 92 866769 — MB BS 1981 Colombo; MRCP (UK) 1986; FRCP (UK) 1998. Cons. Genitourin. Med. St. Mary's Hosp. Portsmouth; Civil. Adviser in Genito-Urin. Med. to Roy. Navy; Hon Cons phys HIV Med. Socs: Soc. Study VD.; Assn. Genitourin. Med. & RCP Lond.

HARING, Sara Jane Northwood Health Centre, Neal Close, Acre Way, Northwood HA6 1TH Tel: 01923 829608 Fax: 01923 840593; 74 Moor Lane, Rickmansworth WD3 1LQ — MB BChir 1979 Camb.; MA Camb. 1976; MRCP (UK) 1982; MRCGP 1984.

HARINGTON, Judith Mary X-Ray Department, Royal Devon & Exeter Hospital (Wonford), Barrack Road, Exeter EX2 5DW Tel: 01392 402329; 8 Woodcote Court, Woodbury, Exeter EX5 1LZ — BM 1978 Soton.; Dip. Obst. Auckland 1980; FRCR 1986. (Soton.) Cons. Radiol. Roy. Devon & Exeter Hosp. Socs: Roy. Coll. Radiol.; Brit. Med. Ultrasound Soc.; Brit. Soc. of Paediatric Radiol. Prev: Cons. Radiol. Kingston Hosp. NHS Trust; Sen. Regist. (Radiol.) Wessex RHA Soton.; Regist. (Radiol.) ChristCh. Hosp., NZ.

HARINGTON, Michael (retired) 69 Waterford Road, Fulham, London SW6 2DT Tel: 020 7731 2572 — MB BChir 1947 Camb.; MA Camb. 1947; FRCP Lond. 1975, M 1953. Hon. Cons. Phys. St. Mary's Hosp. Lond.; Hon. Cons. Phys. St. Thos. Hosp. Prev: Cons. Phys. (Vasc. Disorders Med.) Ophth. Unit. St. Thos. Hosp. Lond.

HARIRAM, Premdat Mountbatten House Surgery, 1 Montgomery Close, North Springfield, Chelmsford CM1 6FF Tel: 01245 467750 Fax: 01245 466192 — MB ChB 1973 Glas.

HARIRI, Mohamed Ali — MD 1978 Damascus; MSc (Audiol. Med.) Manch. 1992; FRCS Ed. 1985; DLO RCS Eng. 1984. Cons. Audiol. Med. Char. Cross Hosp. Lond.; Clin. Tutor Univ. Manch.; Cons. Audiol. Med. The Portland Hosp. Socs: Brit. Assn. Audiol. Phys.; BMA; Internat. Assn. Phys. in Audiol. Prev: Sen. Regist. Manch. Roy. Infirm.

HARISH MALLYA, Kamalaksha Cripps Postgraduate Centre, Northampton General Hospital, Northampton NN1 5BD — MB BS 1990 Karnatak.

HARK, Alison Judith Danes Dyke Surgery, 463A Scalby Road, Newby, Scarborough YO12 6UB Tel: 01723 375343 Fax: 01723 501582; 11 Raincliffe Avenue, Scarborough YO12 5BU Tel: 01723 374953 — MB ChB 1977 Manch.; DRCOG 1981; DCH Eng. 1980.

HARKER, Clive Gerard The Biscuit Works, 54 Church St., Carlisle CA2 5TG; The School House, Faugh, Heads Nook, Carlisle CA8 9EG — MD 1990 Sheff.; MB ChB 1982; MFOM RCP Lond. 1994, AFOM 1990. Regional Med. Adviser United Biscuits. Socs: Soc. Occupat. Med. Prev: Lect. (Occupat. Med.) Aberd. Univ.

HARKER, Helen Anne Mid Sussex NHS Trust, The Princess Royal Hospital, Lewes Road, Haywards Heath RH16 4EX; Lower Flat, Brook House, Hammingden Lane, Ardingly, Haywards Heath RH17 6SR — MB BS 1994 Newc.

HARKER, Nicola Jane Parsonage Farmhouse, Hermitage, Dorchester DT2 7BB — MB ChB 1994 Birm.; ChB Birm. 1994. SHO GP VTS Dorset Co. Hosp. Dorchester Dorset. Prev: Pre Regist. Phys. Frenchay Hosp. Bristol.

HARKER, Noël Esmé Machell (retired) 63 Riverslea, Stokesley, Middlesbrough TS9 5DE Tel: 01642 710771 Email: nemh@globalnet.co.uk — MB BS Lond. 1967; MRCS Eng. LRCP Lond. 1967; BSc Lond. 1964; FRCPath 1986, M 1974. Prev: Med. Dir. St. Margt. Hospice Clydebank.

HARKER, Norrison Alexander (retired) 58 Somerford Road, Cirencester GL7 1TX Tel: 01285 653425 — MB BChir 1958 Camb.; MA Camb. 1958 MB 1959, BChir 1958; MRCS Eng. LRCP Lond. 1957; DObst RCOG 1959. Prev: Asst. Ho. Surg. & Cas. Off. & Childr. Ho. Phys. Guy's Hosp.

HARKER, Paul Parsonage Farmhouse, Hermitage, Dorchester DT2 7BB Tel: 01963 210450 — MB BS 1967 Lond.; MRCS Eng. LRCP Lond. 1967; FRCPCH 1997; FFCM 1985, M 1972; DPH Eng. 1971. (St. Bart.) Cons. Pub. Health, S. and E. Dorset, PC Trust. Prev: Dir. Health Promotion Research Dorset HA; Dir. Pub. Health Dorset HA; Cons. Pub. Health Dorset Healthcare NHS Trust.

HARKER, Richard Anthony Gerard (retired) Whinfield Surgery, Whinbush Way, Darlington DL1 3RT Tel: 01325 481321 Fax: 01325 380116 — MB ChB 1980 Liverp.; Diploma in Occupational Medicine 2000 Doncaster; MRCGP 1984; Dip. Ther. Newc. 1994; DRCOG 1984; DA RCS Eng. 1983. Police Surg. Darlington; Chair. PCG, Darlington Occupat.al Health Phys.

HARKER, Mr Richard Jason 9 St Marys Gardens, Kennington, London SE11 4UD Tel: 020 7820 8617 Email: r.harker@umds.ac.uk — MB BChir 1992 Camb.; MA Camb. 1993, BA (Hons.) 1989; FRCS Eng. 1996. (Univ. Camb.) Hon Research Fell. Orthop. Dept. Raine Inst. St. Thomas' Hosp. Lond.; Specialist Regist. Orthop. S. E. Thames Rotat. Socs: Brit.Orthop.Assoc.

HARKER, Rosemary Senior and Partners, Morrab Surgery, 2 Morrab Road, Penzance TR18 4EL Tel: 01736 363866 Fax: 01736 367809; Higher Porthcollum Farm, Porthcollum Lane, St. Erth, Hayle TR27 6EU — MB ChB 1972 Cape Town; DA Eng. 1977. (Cape Town) Prev: SHO (Psychiat.) Basingstoke Dist. Hosp.; SHO (Paediat.) Groote Schuur Hosp. Cape Town, S. Afr.; GP S.mead Health Centre Bristol.

HARKER, Ruth Jasmine Morris, Harker, Bleiker and Partners, Ivybridge Health Centre, Station Road, Ivybridge PL21 0AJ Tel: 01752 690777 Fax: 01752 690252 — MB ChB 1980 Bristol; BSc

Bristol 1974; MRCGP 1984; DCH RCP Lond. 1983; DRCOG 1983. (Bristol)

HARKER, Trevor Gareth Valley Medical Centre, Johnson Street, Stocksbridge, Sheffield S36 1BX Tel: 0114 288 3841 Fax: 0114 288 7897 — MB BS 1979 Newc.

HARKIN, Andrew John 33 Tobermore Road, Draperstown, Magherafelt BT45 7HG — MB BCh BAO 1990 NUI.

HARKIN, Catherine Bellevue Crescent Surgery, 26 Huntingdon Place, Edinburgh EH7 4AT Tel: 0131 556 8196 Fax: 0131 557 0535; 19 Craighall Gardens, Edinburgh EH6 4RH Tel: 0131 552 7529 Fax: 0131 552 0308 Email: boxking.bramble@cableinet.co.uk — MB ChB 1985 Ed.; BSc Biol. Sci. (Hons.) Ed. 1978; MSc Forens. Sci. Strathclyde 1979; DCCH RCP Ed. 1992. (Ed.) Prev: Trainee GP Glas. VTS.

HARKIN, Cyril Alexander High Street Medical Group Practice, 29 High Street, Draperstown, Magherafelt BT45 7AB Tel: 028 7962 8201 Fax: 028 7962 7523; 33 Tobermore Road, Draperstown, Magherafelt BT45 7HG — LRCPI & LM, LRSCI & LM 1960; MRCGP 1987.

HARKIN, Denis William 36 Irish Green Street, Limavady BT49 9AE — MB BCh BAO 1992 Belf.

HARKIN, Eithne Josephine 11 Bibsworth Lodge, Bibsworth Road, London N3 3RN — MB BCh BAO 1989 NUI; MRCP (UK) 1995.

HARKIN, Honor Mary 25 Linside Av, Paisley PA1 1SQ — MB ChB 1997 Glas.

HARKIN, Karen Anne 29 High street BT45 7AB — MB BCh BAO 1988 NUI; MRCGP 1992; DRCOG 1991.

HARKIN, Maire Siobhan 108 Upper Main Street, Maghera BT46 5AF; 99 Deramore Avenue, Ormean Road, Belfast BT7 3ES — MB BCh BAO 1993 Belf.; DCH Roy. Coll. Surg. Irel. 1997; DRCOG 1997; MRCGP 1998. GP Locum Belf.

HARKIN, Patrick James Robert Department of Pathology, University of Leeds, Leeds LS2 9JT Tel: 0113 233 3400 Fax: 0113 233 3404; 24 Woodbourne Avenue, Moortown, Leeds LS17 5PQ Tel: 0113 268 2401 — MB ChB 1981 Leeds; BSc (Hons.) Leeds 1978. Lect. (Path.) Univ. Leeds.

HARKINS, Clare Marie 7 Bellaire Drive, Greenock PA16 7UP — MB ChB 1985 Glas.

HARKINS, Francis Premier Brands UK Ltd., Pasture Road, Moreton, Wirral CH46 8SE Tel: 0151 678 8888 Fax: 0151 473 1678; 2 Roman Road, Storeton, Wirral CH63 6HS Tel: 0151 608 6945 — MRCS Eng. LRCP Lond. 1961; DObst RCOG 1963. Occupat. Health Dept. Premier Brands UK Ltd. Socs: BMA; Birkenhead Med. Soc.

HARKINS, Keith John Sherwood, Honeysgreen Lane, Liverpool L12 9EW — MB ChB 1990 Leeds; MRCP (UK) 1993.

HARKINS, Liam Hugh 235 Auchmead Road, Greenock PA16 0UP — MB ChB 1992 Glas.

HARKINS, Lynette Ashfield House Surgery, Ashfield House, 1 Ashfield Road, Milngavie, Glasgow G62 6BT Tel: 0141 956 1339 Fax: 0141 956 7098; 33H Herbert Street, Kelvinbridge, Glasgow G20 6NB — MB ChB 1989 Glas.; MRCGP 1993.

HARKINS, Michael 62 Fruin Avenue, Newton Mearns, Glasgow G77 6JB Tel: 0141 639 4134 — MB ChB 1988 Ed.; BSc (Med. Sci.) St. And. 1985.

HARKIS, Barbara Ann Northumberland Health Authority, E. Cottingwood, Morpeth, Newcastle upon Tyne NE20 9PD Tel: 01670 514331; 35 Darras Road, Darras Hall, Ponteland, Newcastle upon Tyne NE20 9PD — MB BS 1979 Newc.; MRCPsych 1983; MFPHM 1989. Cons. Communicable Dis. Control N.d. HA.

HARKNESS, Allan Clinical Research Initiative in Heart Failure, West Medical Building, University of Glasgow, Glasgow G12 8QQ Tel: 0141 330 4761 Fax: 0141 337 1651 Email: a.harkness@bio.gla.ac.uk; 20 St Boswells Crescent, Paisley PA2 9HX Tel: 01505 812092 — MB ChB 1994 Glas.; MRCP 1997. (Glasg.) Research Fell. Clin. Research Initiative in Heart Failure Univ. Glas. Prev: SHO II (Adult Med.) Roy. Alexandra Hosp. Paisley.

HARKNESS, David Gideon HM Prison Lincoln, Greetwell Road, Lincoln LN2 4BD Tel: 01522 533633 — MB BS 1965 Durh.; DPM Eng. 1980; DObst RCOG 1968. (Lond.) Sen. Med. Off. HM Prison Lincoln; Founder Mem. Prison Med. Assn. & Coll. Prison Med. Prev: Sen. Med. Off. HM Remand Centre Risley; Ho. Off., & Cas. & Ho. Surg. (Orthop.) Ashington Hosp.; SHO (ENT) Roy. Vict. Infirm. Newc u. Tyne.

HARKNESS, Graham John Mill View Court, Castle Hill Hospital, Cottingham HU16 5JQ Tel: 01482 622950 Fax: 01482 622923 — MB ChB 1987 Aberd.; MRCPsych 1991. Cons. Psychiat.Hull and E. Riding Community Health NHS Trust. Prev: Cons. Psychiat. Capital Coast Health Ltd. Wellington New Zealand; Regist. Bath Dist. HA.

HARKNESS, John (retired) Greenhayes, 49 Trull Road, Taunton TA1 4QN Tel: 01823 272517 — MB ChB 1936 Glas.; MB ChB (Hons.) Glas. 1936; BSc Glas. 1933, MD (Commend.) 1952; FRCPath 1963. Prev: Co-ordinator & Cons. Chem Path. Som. Area Path. Serv. at Dept. Clin. Path. MusGr. Pk. Hosp. Taunton.

HARKNESS, John The Surgery, Kings Road, Halstead CO9 1 Tel: 01787 475944; Wimbles, Great Maplestead, Halstead CO9 — MB ChB 1950 Ed.; MD Ed. 1962, MB ChB 1950; MFCM 1972; DObst RCOG 1957; DPH Leeds 1957; DIH Soc. Apoth. Lond 1957. (Ed.) Mem. Lincoln's Inn. Socs: Colchester Med. Soc. Prev: Asst. MOH Bradford; MOH Halstead UD & RD & Sen. Med. Off. Essex CC; Capt. RAMC.

HARKNESS, John Moore Sketty Surgery, De la Beche Road, Sketty, Swansea SA2 9EA Tel: 01792 206862 — MRCS Eng. LRCP Lond. 1973.

HARKNESS, John Noryl (retired) Stonewell, First Drift, Wothorpe, Stamford PE9 3JL Tel: 01780 52481 — MB BS 1953 Durh.; FRCGP 1978, M 1962; DObst RCOG 1954.

HARKNESS, Kirsty Annabel Cara Flat 7 St Ann's Tower, 214 Kirkstall Lane, Leeds LS6 3DS — MB ChB 1992 Sheff.

HARKNESS, Margaret Catherine Helen Henley Green Medical Centre, Henley Road, Coventry CV2 1AB Tel: 02476 602644 Fax: 02476 602699; Church Farm, Willey, Rugby CV23 0SH Tel: 01455 558662 Email: catherine-harkness@hotmail.com — MB ChB 1979 Bristol; MRCP (UK) 1984; DCH RCP Lond. 1984. Prev: Research Fell. Neonatol. Roy. Adelaide Childr. Hosp.; Regist. (Paediat.) E. Birm. Hosp.; SHO (Neonat. & Paediat.) Birm. Childr. Hosp.

HARKNESS, Michael Keith 13 Orchard View, Aughton, Ormskirk L39 5AD Tel: 01695 423755; 242 Low Lane, Horsforth, Leeds LS18 5QL Tel: 0113 258 9741 — MB ChB 1995 Leeds; MRCP UK April 1999. (Univ. Leeds Med. Sch.) SHO Rotat. (Med.) Leeds Gen. Infirm. Prev: SHO (A & E) St. Jas. Univ. Hosp. Leeds; SHO (Med. for Elderly) Leeds Gen. Infirm.; Ho. Off. Leeds Gen. Infirm. & Huddersfield Roy. Infrim.

HARKNESS, Mr Paul Andrew ENT Department, Rotherham District General hospital, Rotherham SU60 2UD Tel: 01709 304764 Email: harkness.secc@rgh-tr-trent.nhs.uk; Glebe Cottage, Retford Road, South Leverton, Retford DN22 0BY — BM BS 1985 Nottm.; FRCS (Oto.) Eng. 1991; FRCS (Otol.) Eng. 1997; BMedSci. 1983. Cons. Otor. Rotherham Gen. Hosp/Doncaster Roy.Infirm. Socs: BAOL-HNS.

HARKNESS, Robert Angus 41 Curriehill, Castle Drive, Balerno, Edinburgh EH14 5TA Tel: 0131 449 6598 — MB ChB 1955 Ed.; PhD Ed. 1962; FRCP Ed. 1970, M 1958; FRCPath 1978, M 1966. (Ed.) Hon. Research Fell. Univ. Edin. Socs: Hon. Mem. Soc. for the Study of Inborn Errors of Metab.; Biochem. Soc. Emerit. Mem.; Soc. for Endocrinol. Prev: Prof. Univ. Fed. Rio Grande do Sul Porto Alegre, Brazil; Sen. Lect. (Clin. Biochem.) Inst. Child Health Univ. Lond.; Scientif. Staff MRC Clin. Research Centre Harrow & Hon. Cons. N.wick Pk. Hosp. Harrow.

HARKNESS, Professor Robert Douglas Physiology Department, University College, Gower St., London WC1E 6BT Tel: 020 7387 7050; Rough Hey, Temple Wood Lane, Stoke Poges, Slough SL2 4AN Tel: 01753 663213 — MB BS 1942 Lond.; BSc Lond. 1939; MRCS Eng. LRCP Lond. 1942. (Univ. Coll. Hosp.) Prof. in Physiol. Univ. Lond. Socs: Physiol. Soc. & Biochem. Soc. Prev: RAMC 1943-46.

HARKNESS, Sally Marianne Inverurie Medical Group, Health Centre, 1 Constitution Street, Inverurie AB51 4SU Tel: 01467 621345 Fax: 01467 625374; 3 Jackson Street, Inverurie AB51 3QB Tel: 01467 621370 Fax: 01467 621370 Email: sally@inverurie.demon.co.uk — MB ChB 1984 Aberd.; MB ChB Aberd. l984; DCH RCP Lond. 1988; DRCOG 1987; FRCGP 1998.

HARKNESS, Veryan Innes Ker Silwood House, London Road SL5 7PU Tel: 01344 28576 Fax: 01344 628576; Silwood House, London Road, Sunninghill SL5 7PU Tel: 01344 628576 Email: veryanh@aol.com — MB BCh BAO 1972 Dub.; FFA RCSI 1978. (Trinity Coll. Dub.)

HARKNESS, Mr William Frederic James great Ormond St. Hospital, Great Ormond St, London WC1N 3JH Tel: 020 7405 9200 Ext: 8862 Email: harknw@gosh.nhs.uk — MB ChB 1979 Birm.; FRCS Eng. 1985; FRCS Ed. 1984. Cons. Neurosurg. Nat. Hosp. Neurol. & Neurosurg. Qu. Sq. & Hosp. for Childr. Gt. Ormond St. Lond.; Hon. Sen. Lect. Inst. Lond. Neurol. & Inst. Child Health. Socs: Fell. Roy. Soc. Med.; Brit. Soc. Neurol. Surgs.; Europ. Soc. of Paediatric Neurosurg. Prev: Sen. Regist. (Neurosurg.) Atkinson Morley's Hosp. & Qu. Sq. & Gt. Ormond St. Hosp. Lond.; Research Regist. (Neurosurg.) Radcliffe Infirm. Oxf.; Regist. (Neurosurg.) Qu. Eliz. Hosp. & Midl. Centre for Neurol. & Neurosurg. Birm.

HARLAND, Antoinette Imbert (retired) 123 Putnoe Lane, Bedford MK41 8LB Tel: 01234 45831 — MB BS 1950 Lond.; MRCS Eng. LRCP Lond. 1950; DObst RCOG 1952. Prev: Cas. Off. Roy. Free Hosp.

HARLAND, Christopher Charles Department of Dermatology, St Helier Hospital, Wrythe Lane, Carshalton SM5 1AA Tel: 020 8644 4343 Fax: 020 8296 2193; 83 Kenilworth Avenue, London SW19 7LP — MB BS 1983 Lond.; MA, BA(Hons) Camb. 1980; MRCP (UK) 1986. (St. Mary's) Cons. Dermat. St. Helier Hosp. Carshalton; Sen. Lect. (Dermat.) St. Geo. Hosp. Med. Sch. Lond. Prev: Sen. Regist. St. Geo. Hosp. Lond.; Regist. (Dermat.) Nottm. Univ. Hosp.; Regist. (Med.) Dudley Rd. Hosp. Birm.

HARLAND, Elizabeth Carolyn King Street Surgery, 84 King Street, Maidstone ME14 1DZ Tel: 01622 756721/756722/3; Tarn Hows, Sandy Lane, Ivy Hatch, Sevenoaks TN15 0PB Tel: 017323 811470 — MB ChB 1981 Bristol.

HARLAND, Mary East Street Medical Centre, 18-20 East Street, Littlehampton BN17 6AW Tel: 01903 731111 Fax: 01903 732295; St Andrews, King St, Weybread, Diss IP21 5TU Tel: 01508 855150 — BM 1983 Soton.; BA Open 1978; MRCGP 1987; DRCOG 1986. (Soton) Med.Off. Norwich Prison.

HARLAND, Noel Michael (retired) 18 Lime Crescent, Sandal, Wakefield WF2 6RY Tel: 01924 251899 — MB ChB 1956 Leeds. Prev: Lt. RAMC.

HARLAND, Philip Sydney Erasmus Gregory Cliff Grange, West Lane, Snainton, Scarborough YO13 9AR Tel: 01723 859549 — MRCP 1961 Lond.; BA Camb. 1959, MB 1962, BChir 1961; FRCP Lond. 1982; MRCP Lond. 1969 MRCS Eng. LRCP Lond. 1961. (Guy's) Cons. Paediat. W. La. Hosp. S. Tees. Socs: Fell. Amer. Acad. Paediat.; BMA & Brit. Paediat. Assn. Prev: Sen. Cons. Armed Forces Hosp. Riyadh; Prof. & Head. Dept. Child Health Univ. W. Indies, Kingston; Sen. Lect. (Paediat.) Univ. Dar es Salaam, Tanzania.

HARLAND, Rachel Frances Blackberry Hill Hospital, Stapleton, Bristol BS16 2EW Tel: 0117 965 6061 — MB BCh 1993 Wales; MSc 1999; MRCPsych 1998. (Cardiff) Specialist Regist. Adult Psych. Blackberry Hill Hosp. Bristol. Socs: BMA.

HARLAND, Richard David (retired) 13 Kingsley Road, Norwich NR1 3RB Tel: 01603 622830 — MRCS Eng. LRCP Lond. 1943; MFCM 1974; DTM & H Eng. 1955; DPH Lond. 1959. Prev: Sen. Med. Off. Norf. HA.

HARLAND, Mr Richard Nigel Leetall Royal Albert Edward Infirmary, Wigan Lane, Wigan WN1 2NN Tel: 01772 431704 — MB BS 1974 Lond.; 1985 MD Lond; 1978 FRCS Eng. (St Mary's Hospital Medical School, London) Cons. Gen. Surg. Wigan HA. Socs: Fell. Manch. Med. Soc.; Brit. Assn. Surg. Oncol. Prev: Lect. (Surg.) Univ. Manch.

HARLAND, Robert, Surg. Cdr. RN Retd. (retired) Fountain Hill House, Fountain Hill, Budleigh Salterton EX9 6BX Tel: 01395 442229 — MB ChB St. And. 1962; MRCGP 1971; DRCOG 1965. p/t Med.Mem. Pens. Appeal Tribunals.

HARLAND, Robert Wallace (retired) 6 Castlehill Road, Belfast BT4 3GL Tel: 02890 653682 Fax: 02890 473540 Email: r.harland@qub.ac.uk — MB BCh BAO Belf. 1948; FRCGP 1979, M 1962. Mem. of Senate, The Qu.'s Univ. of Belf. Prev: Sen. Med. Off. Univ. Health Serv. Qu. Univ. Belf.

HARLAND, Spencer Peter Department of Neurosurgery, Queen Elizabeth Hospital, Edgbaston, Birmingham B15 2TH; Oakleigh, 42 Broad Oaks Road, Solihull B91 1JB Tel: 0121 705 2678 — MB BS 1988 Lond.; BSc 1985; FRCS SN 1997. (Univ.Coll.Dub)

HARLAND, Stephen John Middlesex Hospital, Mortimer St., London W1T 3AA Tel: 020 7636 8333 Fax: 020 7436 0160; 3 Montana Road, London SW20 8TW — MB BS 1971 Lond.; MD Lond. 1986, MSc (Biochem.) 1979; FRCP Lond. 1994; MRCP (UK) 1975; MRCS Eng. LRCP Lond. 1971. Sen. Lect. (Med. Oncol.) Inst. Urol. & Nephrol. Univ. Coll. Lond.; Hon. Cons. Med. Oncol. Middlx. Hosp. & Edgware Gen. Hosp. Lond. Prev: Temp. Sen. Lect. (Med. Oncol.) Glas. Univ.; Sen. Regist. Roy. Marsden Hosp. Lond.

HARLAND, Timothy Gowan King Street Surgery, 84 King Street, Maidstone ME14 1DZ Tel: 01622 756721/756722/3; Tarn Hows, Sandy Lane, Ivy Hatch, Sevenoaks TN15 0PB Tel: 01732 811470 — MB BS 1975 Lond.; MRCS Eng. LRCP Lond. 1975. (Roy. Free) Prev: Med. Off. Kapenguria Dist. Hosp. Kenya.

HARLE, Christopher Coswald 12 Adey Road, Lymm WA13 9QX — MB ChB 1989 Stellenbosch.

HARLE, David George Corbridge Health Centre, Manor Court, Corbridge NE45 5JW Tel: 01434 632011 Fax: 01434 633878; Highfield, Sandy Bank, Riding Mill NE44 6HT — MB BS 1967 Newc. (Newc.) Prev: Med. Regist. Newc. Gen. Hosp.; Ho. Surg. & Ho. Phys. Roy. Vict. Infirm. Newc.

HARLE, Jane Highfield, Sandy Bank, Riding Mill NE44 6HT — MB BS 1972 Newc. (Newcastle-upon-Tyne) Clin. Med. Off. (Community Health) N.d. Community Health Trust; Med. Adviser N.d. Co. Counc. Adopt. & Fostering Agency; Clin. Asst. (Ophth.) Roy. Vict. Infirm. Newc. u. Tyne. Prev: Regist. (Anaesth.) Newc. Gen. Hosp.; SHO (Anaesth.) Newc. Gen. Hosp.; Ho. Phys. & Ho. Surg. Hexham Gen. Hosp.

HARLEY, Alexander Cardiothoracic Centre NHS Trust, Thomas Drive, Broadgreen, Liverpool L14 3PE Tel: 0151 228 1616 Fax: 0151 220 8573 Email: alex@harley4.freeserve.co.uk — MB 1960 Camb.; BChir 1959; FRCP Lond. 1976, M 1963; DObst RCOG 1961. (St. Mary's) Cons. Cardiol. Cardiothoracic Centre Liverp. Socs: Brit. Cardiac Soc. & Brit. Cardiovasc. Interven. Soc. Prev: Sen. Regist. Univ. Manch. Dept. Cardiol. Roy. Infirm. Manch.; Chief, Cardiol. Serv. Veterans' Admin. Hosp. Durh., U.S.A.; Fell. in Cardiol. Duke Univ. N. Carolina, U.S.A.

HARLEY, Angela Mary Walkergate Surgery, 117-119 Walkergate, Beverley HU17 9BP Tel: 01482 881298 — MB ChB 1988 Liverp. p/t Gen. Practitioner, Beverley; Clin. Asst., Dove Ho. Hospice, Hull. Socs: Local Med. Comm. Mem.

HARLEY, Clifford Elliott 62 Stockwell Park Road, London SW9 0DA Tel: 020 7274 7078 Fax: 020 7274 9773 — MB BS Lond. 1959; MRCS Eng. LRCP Lond. 1959; DPhysMed Eng. 1969; DObst RCOG 1961. (Guy's) Orth. Phys. Lond. Socs: Inst. Musculoskeletal Med.; Nat. Osteoporosis Soc.; SW Lond. Med. Soc. Prev: Research Asst. (Phys. Med.) Guy's Hosp. Lond.; Ho. Surg. (O & G) FarnBoro. Hosp. Kent; Clin. Asst. (Phys. Med.) Brook Gen. Hosp. Lond.

HARLEY, David Hugh 71 Paxton Road, Tapton, Chesterfield S41 0TL Tel: 01246 234898 Fax: 01246 552629 Email: dhh@globalnet.co.uk — MB ChB 1963 Sheff.; FFA RCS Eng. 1970; DA Eng. 1967. Cons. Anaesth. Chesterfield Gp. Hosps.

HARLEY, David Whitelaw Swyllmers Barn, The Lee, Great Missenden HP16 9NA — MB BChir 1963 Camb.; MA Camb. 1964, MB BChir 1963; MRCP Lond. 1966; MRCGP 1979. (St. Mary's) Hosp. Pract. (Neurol.) Oxf. & High Wycombe. Socs: Assoc. Mem. Assn. Brit. Neurol.; Movem. Disorder Soc. Prev: MRC Research Asst. (Investig. Med.) Camb. Univ.; Sen. Regist. (Med.) Addenbrooke's Hosp. Camb.

HARLEY, Dorothy Beatrix (retired) 3 Sutton Close, London Road, Macclesfield SK11 7RW — MB ChB 1945 Manch.; DA Eng. 1954; DObst RCOG 1948. Prev: Asst. Anaesth. Macclesfield Health Dist.

HARLEY, Ewen Cameron Keppoch Medical Practice, Possilpark Health Centre, 85 Denmark Street, Glasgow G22 5EG Tel: 0141 531 6170 Fax: 0141 531 6177; 44 Titwood Road, Glasgow G41 2DG Tel: 0141 632 1354 — MB ChB 1977 Ed.; DFFP 1983; DCH RCP Dub. 1982; DRCOG 1979. Prev: Med. Supt. Bamalete Lutheran Hosp. Ramotswa, Botswana; Regist. (Infec. Dis.) Monklands Dist. Gen. Hosp. Airdrie.

HARLEY, Harold Charles (retired) 15 Marston Ferry Road, Oxford OX2 7EF Tel: 01865 515681 — BM BCh 1930 Oxf.; MA Oxf. 1930. Prev: Hon. Phys. Evelina Hosp. Sick Childr.

HARLEY, Mr Hugh Rosborough Swanzy (retired) Flat 11 Kings Park, Kingswood Road, Tunbridge Wells TN2 4XF Tel: 01892 518053 — MRCS Eng. LRCP Lond. 1936; MS Lond. 1941, MB BS 1936; FRCS Eng. 1938. Prev: Cons. Cardiothoracic Surg. United Cardiff Hosps. & Welsh Hosp. Bd.

HARLEY, Ian James Graham 49 Cranmore Gardens, Belfast BT9 6JL Tel: 01232 669012 Fax: 01232 223061 — MB BCh BAO 1993 Belf.; BSc 1988. (Queens University Belfast) SHO (O & G) Craigavon Area Hosp. Prev: Route Hosp. Ballymoney; Ulster Hosp. Dundonald; Jubilee Matern. Hosp. Belf.

HARLEY, James Bernard Portstewart, Family Practice, 6 Lever Road, Portstewart BT55 7EF Tel: 028 7083 2149 Fax: 028 7083 3223; 75 Central Avenue, Portstewart BT55 7BT — MB BCh BAO 1975 NUI; MSc (Contemp. Biol.) Ulster 1986; MRCGP 1981; DRCOG 1977; Fell. Inst. Med. Laborat. Scs. 1968. (Galway) GP Portstewart. Prev: Trainee Gen. Pract. Lond.derry Vocational Train. Scheme; Intern (Surg.) Regional Hosp. Galway; SHO (Med.) Altnagelvin Hosp. Lond.derry.

HARLEY, Professor James MacDougall Graham, CBE 152 Malone Road, Belfast BT9 5LJ Tel: 02890 381511 Fax: 02890 381511 Email: graham.harley@net.ntl.com — MB BCh BAO 1953 Belf.; MD Belf. 1961; FRCPI 1986; FRCOG 1967, M 1958; DObst RCOG 1956. (Belf.) Hon. Prof. Clin. O & G Qu. Univ. Belf. Socs: Fell. Ulster Med. Soc.; N. Irel. Medico-Legal Soc.; (Vice-Pres.) Roy. Coll. Midw.. Prev: Cons. Roy. Matern., Roy. Vict., Samarit. & Jubilee Matern. Hosps. Belf.; Mem. N. Irel. Nat. Bd. Nurses, Midw. & Health Visitors; Chairm. Research Ethical Comm. Fac. Med. Qu. Univ. Belf.

HARLEY, James Sherrard 8 Montclair Dr, Liverpool L18 0HA — MB ChB 1997 Leeds.

HARLEY, Jane Elizabeth 52 Old Street, Fareham PO14 3HW — MB BS 1991 Lond.

HARLEY, John Joseph Woodlands Medical Centre, 106 Yarm Lane, Stockton-on-Tees TS18 1YE Tel: 01642 607398 Fax: 01642 604603; 58 High Street, Norton, Stockton-on-Tees TS20 1DR Tel: 01642 557565 — MB ChB 1978 Ed.; MRCGP 1983; Dip. Ther. Newc. 1994.

HARLEY, Mr John Michael Orthopaedic Department, Southampton General Hospital, Tremona Road, Southampton SO16 6YD Tel: 01703 796795; The Kestrels, Woodgreen, Fordingbridge SP6 2AJ Tel: 01725 512094 Fax: 01725 512094 Email: jmharley@beeb.net — MB ChB 1976 Ed.; FRCS Ed. 1981; FRCS Eng. 1981. (Edinburgh) Cons. Orthop. Surg. Soton. Gen. Hosp.

HARLEY, John Ralph Cadogan Place Practice, 29 Cadogan Place, London SW1X 9RX Tel: 020 7235 4842, 020 7235 5850 — MB BS 1985 Lond.; MRCGP 1995; DCH RCP Lond. 1988.

HARLEY, Karen Joy 43 Deerpark Drive, Arnold, Nottingham NG5 8SA Tel: 0115 967 6418; 43 Deerpark Drive, Arnold, Nottingham NG5 8SA Tel: 0115 967 6418 — MB ChB 1993 Sheff.; MRCGP 1997; DRCOG 1996. p/t New Princip. GP Old Station Surg. Ilceston Derbysh.; Clin. Asst. in Family Plann. S. Derbysh. H.A. Socs: BMA; RCGP; MDU. Prev: Trainee GP/SHO (Paediat.) Qu. Med. Centre Nottm.; SHO (Psychiat.) Gateshead Healthcare.

HARLEY, Noel Francis (retired) Medelpad, Ladywell, Barnstaple EX31 1QS — MB BS 1960 Lond.; MRCS Eng. LRCP Lond. 1960; FFA RCS Eng. 1966; DA Eng. 1963. Prev: Cons. Anaesth. N. Devon Dist. Hosp.

HARLEY, Oliver Jarvis Hamilton Havelock House, Ascot Road, Tidworth SP9 7AH — MB BS 1998 Lond.; MB BS Lond 1998.

HARLEY, Simon Clifford Llewelyn Deben Road Surgery, 2 Deben Road, Ipswich IP1 5EN Tel: 01473 741152 Fax: 01473 743237 — MB BS 1984 Lond.; MRCGP 1988; DGM RCP Lond. 1988. Orthop. Spinal Phys. Orthop. Spinal Clinic Ipswich Hosp. Trust. Socs: Brit. Inst. Musculo-Skeletal Med; Soc. Orthop. Med. Prev: Clin. Asst. (Orthop.) Heath Rd. Hosp. Ipswich.

HARLEY, Timothy Gerald Bere Regis Surgery, Manor Farm Road, Bere Regis, Wareham BH20 7HB Tel: 01929 471268 Fax: 01929 472098; Milborne Farm House, Milborne St Andrew, Blandford Forum DT11 0JF — MB BS 1980 Lond.; MRCS Eng. LRCP Lond. 1979; DRCOG 1984. GP Bere Regis.

HARLEY-MASON, Gillian Ruth The Karis Medical Centre, Waterworks Road, Edgbaston, Birmingham B16 9AL Tel: 0121 423 6300 Fax: 0121 454 9104; 148 Station Road, Knowle, Solihull B93 0EP — MB ChB 1988 Birm.; DRCOG 1992; DTM & H RCP Lond. 1991. (University of Birmingham) Salaried Partner. Prev: Trainee GP Birm.

HARLIN, Simon Jason 52 Bridgeman Road, Chester CH1 5LY — BChir 1995 Camb.

HARLING, Christopher Charles Bristol Royal Infirmary, Bristol BS2 8HW Tel: 0117 928 2276 Fax: 0117 928 3840 Email: kit.harling@ubht.swest.nhs.uk; 8 Burlington Road, Bristol BS6 6TL Tel: 0117 973 4023 Fax: 0117 973 9642 Email: kit.harling@virgin.net — MB BS 1975 Lond.; MA Oxf. 1977; FRCP Lond. 1995; FFOM RCP Lond. 1991, MFOM 1984, AFOM 1982; DAvMed FOM RCP Lond. 1988; DIH Eng. 1982; FFPHM 1999. (Oxford and UCH, London) Cons. Occupat. Phys. United Bristol Healthcare NHS Trust; Sen. Clin. Lect. (Occupat. Med.) Univ. Bristol. Prev: Cons. Occupat. Phys. Sheff. HA.

HARLING, David William 130 Dobbin Hill, Sheffield S11 7JD — MB ChB 1985 Leeds; MRCP (UK) 1998; FRCA 1993. Cons. Anaesth. Rotherham Dist. Gen. Hosp. Socs: Intens. Care Soc.; Assn. Anaesth.

HARLING, Douglas Simpson (retired) 105 Birkby Hall Road, Huddersfield HD2 2XE Tel: 01484 533505 — MD 1958 Ed.; MB ChB 1941; FRCP Ed. 1978, M 1948; FRCP Lond. 1984, M 1949; DTM & H Liverp. 1962. Prev: Consult. (Geriat.) St. Lukes Hosp. Huddersfield.

HARLING, Jill Diane Courtfield Medical Centre, 73 Courtfield Gardens, London SW5 0NL Tel: 020 7370 2453 Fax: 020 7244 0018; 36 Doneraile Street, London SW6 6EN — MB BS 1983 Lond.; BSc Lond. 1980; DRCOG 1988.

HARLING, Marianne Evelyn Flat 1, 24 Browning Avenue, Boscombe, Bournemouth BH5 1NN Tel: 01202 395149 — BM BCh Oxf. 1946; FFHom 1980, M 1958.

HARLING, Rachel Elizabeth The Acorns, Church Lane, Oakley, Bedford MK43 7RJ — BM BS 1995 Nottm.

HARLING, Richard Michael 4 St Nicholas Field, Berden, Bishop's Stortford CM23 1AX — MB BS 1994 Lond.

HARLOW, Eveline Dilys Southmead Health Centre, Ullswater Road, Bristol BS10 6DF Tel: 0117 950 7150 Fax: 0117 959 1110 — MB BChir 1964 Camb.; MRCGP 1978; Dip. Palliat. Med. Wales 1996; Dip. Scientif. Basis Dermat. Wales 1993; Dip. Pract. Dermat. Wales 1992. (Camb.) Hosp. Pract. (Dermat.) S.mead Hosp. Bristol.

HARLOW, Miss Francoise-Helene Dyer 168 Abbeyfields Close, Twyford Abbey Road, London NW10 7EJ Tel: 020 8961 7177 — MB BS 1989 Lond.; BSc Biochem. (1st cl. Hons.) Lond. 1986; MRCOG 1995. (Char. Cross & Westm.) SpR (O&G) Hillingdon Hosp. Uxbridge. Socs: Roy. Soc. Med.; BMA. Prev: Regist. (O & G) Chelsea & W.minster Hosp. & N.wick Pk. Hosp. & Watford Gen. Hosp.; Specialist Regist. Watford Gen. Hosp. (N. W. Thames Regional Rotat.).

HARLOW, Graham Robert (retired) 9 Lodge Close, Hamsterley Mill, Rowlands Gill NE39 1HB Tel: 01207 542731 — MB ChB 1963 Manch.; MRCP (U.K.) 1975. Prev: Cons. Phys. Sunderland Dist. Gen. Hosp.

HARLOW, Jane Margaret (retired) Westwood Farm, Edgeworth, Stroud GL6 7JF — MB BS 1954 Lond.; MRCS Eng. LRCP Lond. 1953; DObst RCOG 1955.

HARLOW, Paul Antony PO Box 17687, London N6 4WG — MRCS Eng. LRCP Lond. 1981.

HARLOW, Roger Anthony (retired) Chase Farm Hospital, The Ridgeway, Enfield EN2 8JL Tel: 020 8366 6600 — MB BS 1956 Lond.; LMSSA Lond. 1956; FRCOG 1981, M 1968, DObst. 1958. Cons. O & G Chase Farm Hosp. NHS Trust Enfield. Prev: Cons. Gyn. Manor Ho. Hosp. Lond.

HARLOW, Timothy Neal Tel: 01884 831300 Fax: 01884 831313; Whitley House, Hele Cross, Bradninch, Exeter EX5 4LA — MB ChB 1982 Birm.; DCH RCP Lond. 1985. GP Cullompton.

HARMAN, Amanda Nell Stoneham Lane Surgery, 6 Stoneham Lane, Swaythling, Southampton SO16 2AB Tel: 023 8055 5776 Fax: 023 8039 9723; Beech Cottage, Maurys Lane, West Wellow, Romsey SO51 6DB — BM 1978 Soton.; MRCGP 1982; DRCOG 1980.

HARMAN, Charles Owen Devereux (retired) Meadowbank, New Pond Hill, Cross-In-Hand, Heathfield TN21 0LX Tel: 01435 862819 Email: charles.harman@virgin.net — MA Camb. 1951; MB BS Lond. 1951.

HARMAN, Francesca Elizabeth Mary 14 Keymer Gardens, Burgess Hill RH15 0AF — MB ChB 1995 Leeds.

HARMAN, I Pamela Igbetti, 3 High St., Chew Magna, Bristol BS40 8PR Tel: 01275 332291 — MRCS Eng. LRCP Lond. 1961. (St.

Thos.) Prev: Gen. Med. Practitioner; Asst. Lect. in Haemat. Univ. Coll. Ibadan, Nigeria; Ho. Surg. Frenchay Hosp. Bristol.

HARMAN, Karen Elizabeth Marriage Hill Nurseries, 45 Salford Road, Bidford on Avon, Alcester B50 4EY — MB BChir 1992 Camb.; MRCP (UK) 1995.

HARMAN, Sarah Ann Marriage Hill Nurseries, 45 SAlford Road, Bidford on Avon, Alcester B50 4EY — BM BS 1993 Nottm.

HARMAN, William Benjamin 38 Buckingham Road, Edgware HA8 6LZ — LMSSA 1944 Lond. (Lond. Hosp.) Assoc. Phys. (Geriat.) Edgware Gen. Hosp. Socs: Brit. Geriat. Soc. Prev: Ho. Phys. & Cas. Off. St. And. Hosp. Bow.

HARMER, Clive Lucas The Royal Marsden NHS Trust, Fulham Road, London SW3 6JJ Tel: 020 7808 2591 Fax: 020 7808 2672 Email: clive.harmer@rmh.nthames.nhs.uk; 19 Sydney St, Chelsea, London SW3 6PU Tel: 020 7351 6621 Fax: 020 8672 8808 — MB BS 1963 Lond.; FRCP Lond. 1994, M 1968; MRCS Eng. LRCP Lond. 1963; FRCR 1968; DMRT Eng. 1966. (Westm.) p/t Cons. Radiother. & Oncol. St. Geo. Hosp. Lond. & Roy. Marsden Hosp. Lond. & Sutton; Sen. Lect. Univ. Lond. Socs: Brit. Nuclear Med. Soc.; Brit. Assn. Surg. Oncol.; Treas. Europ.Thyroid Cancer Research Network. Prev: Damon Runyon Fell. & Instruc. Div. Radiat. Ther. Stanford Univ. Med. Centre, USA; Regist. (Radiotherap.) W.m. Hosp. Lond.; Cons. Radiother. Guildford & Godalming Gp. Hosps.

HARMER, David Beech Haven, Nightingales Lane, Chalfont St Giles HP8 4SF — MB ChB 1975 Liverp.; MD Liverp. 1982; MRCP (UK) 1978; MFOM RCP Lond. 1988. (Liverp.) Internat. Med. Advisor ICI Paints. Prev: Med. Adviser ICI plc; Lect. (Med.) Liverp. Univ. & Roy. Liverp. Hosp.; Regist. (Med.) Roy. Liverp. Hosp.

HARMER, Professor Michael Department of Anaesthetics, University of Wales College of Medicine, Heath Park, Cardiff CF14 4XN Tel: 029 2074 3110 Fax: 029 2074 7203 Email: harmerm@cf.ac.uk; Tre Hir Farm, Llanbradach, Caerphilly CF83 3DZ Tel: 0292 862380 — MB BS 1974 Lond.; MRCS Eng. LRCP Lond. 1974; FFA RCS 1979; MD 1998. (St. Bart.) Prof., Dept. Anaesth. & Intens. Care Med. Univ. Wales Coll. Med. Cardiff. Socs: BMA; Assn. Anaesth. GB & Irel.(ED. Of Jl. & Off.); (Treas.) Obst. Anaesth. Assn. Prev: Sen. Lect. (Anaesth. & Intens. Care) Univ. Wales Coll. Med. Cardiff; Cons. (Anaesth.) Univ. Hosp. Wales Cardiff; Lect. (Anaesth.) Welsh Nat. Sch. Med. Cardiff.

HARMER, Rachel Helen Keldgate, Keldgate Road, Cottingham HU16 5TD — BChir 1995 Camb.

***HARMSTON, Christopher** 143 Tiverton Road, Selly Oak, Birmingham B29 6BS — MB ChB 1998 Birm.

HARMSWORTH, Neil John Bere Alston Medical Practice, Bere Alston, Yelverton PL20 7EJ Tel: 01822 840269 Fax: 01882 841104; St Aidans, 4 Long Orchard, Bere Alston, Yelverton PL20 7AS — BM BS 1981 Nottm.; BMedSci Nottm. 1979, BM BS 1981; MRCGP 1985; DRCOG 1984.

HARNDEN, Anthony Richard Morland House Surgery, 2 London Road, Wheatley, Oxford OX33 1YJ Tel: 01865 872448 Fax: 01865 874158; Spring House, Stanton St. John, Oxford OX33 1HF Tel: 01865 358947 Email: arharnden@dial.pipex.com — MB ChB 1983 Birm.; ChB Birm. 1983; MRCP (UK) 1990; MRCGP 1989; DCH RCP Lond. 1985. (Birm.) Princip. Gen. Pract.; Vice-Pres. Sect. Gen. Pract. Roy. Soc. Med.; Tutor (Gen. Pract.) Univ. Oxf.; Mem. Panel Examr. RCGP; Mem. Panel Examr. DCH. Socs: Fell. Roy. Soc. Med.; Green Coll. Common Room. Prev: Regist. (Paediat.) P.ss Mary Hosp. for Childr. Auckland, NZ; Trainee GP Oxf.; Regist. (Paediat.) Stoke Mandeville Hosp. Aylesbury.

HARNDEN, Christopher Edward Fishpool Cottage, Stanwardine-in-the-Fields, Baschurch, Shrewsbury SY4 2EU — MB ChB 1986 Manch.; MRCGP 1994; DRCOG 1993; DCH RCP Lond. 1993. Staff Grade (Cardiol.) Roy. Shrewsbury Hosp. Prev: Regist. (Med.) Roy. Shrewsbury Hosp.

HARNESS, Jonathan David 49 Greenhills, Killingworth, Newcastle upon Tyne NE12 5BA Tel: 0191 256 6096 Email: j.d.harness@argonet.co.uk — MB BS 1993 Newc. GP Regist. Prev: SHO (Gen. Paediat.) N. tyneside Gen.; SHO (Gen. Paediat.) Bishop Auckland Gen.; SHO (Child & Adolesc. Psychiat.) Prudhoe Hosp. N.umberland.

HARNETT, Adrian Nigel Beatson Oncology Centre, Western Infirmary, Dunbarton Road, Glasgow G11 6NT Tel: 0141 211 1742 Fax: 0141 211 6356 Email: qharnett@wghut-nhs.org.uk; Cheswood House, Moor Road, Strathblane, Glasgow G63 7EY Tel: 01360 770425 — MB BS 1978 Lond.; MRCP (UK) 1981; FRCR 1985. (Royal Free) Cons. & Hon. Clin. Lect. (Radiother. & Oncol.) Beatson Oncol.Centre W.ern Infirm. Glas. Socs: Brit. BrE. Gp.; BMA. Prev: Sen. Regist. (Radiotherpy) St. Bartholomews Hosp. Lond.; Regist. (Radiother. & Oncol.) Middlx. & Mt. Vernon Hosps.; Regist. (Gen. Med.) Lister Hosp. Stevenage.

HARNETT, Claire Louise Mannmead Surgery, 22 Egbuckland Road, Plymouth PL3 5HE Tel: 01752 223652 Fax: 01752 253875 Email: claire.harnett@virgin.net — MB BS 1992 Lond.; DRCOG 1994; MRCGP 1997. (Roy.Free) GP. Prev: Trainee GP/SHO Derriford Hosp. VTS.

HARNETT, Patrick Robert 14 Devas Road, London SW20 8PD — MB BS 1992 Lond.; BSc (Hons.) 1989 Lond.; MCP (UK) 1996.

HARNETT, Susan Janet Olive 16 Ravenscourt Walk, Shrewsbury SY3 8ZF — MB ChB 1995 Sheff.

HARNEY, Anne-Marie Stream Street Surgery, 40 Stream Street, Downpatrick BT30 6DE Tel: 028 4461 3029; 42 English Street, Downpatrick BT30 6AB Tel: 01396 615906 — MB BCh BAO 1983 Belf.; MRCGP 1989; DRCOG 1987.

HARNEY, Mrs Barbara Anna Gloucestershire Royal Hospital, Great Western Road, Gloucester GL1 3NN — MB ChB 1976 Bristol; PhD Bristol 1987, BSc 1973; FRCS Eng. 1980; FRCOphth 1989. Cons. Ophth. Glos. Roy. Hosp.& Cheltenham Gen Hosp. Prev: Cons. Ophth. Roy. United Hosp. Bath.

HARNEY, Edward James Stream Street Surgery, 40 Stream Street, Downpatrick BT30 6DE Tel: 028 4461 3029; 19 Orchard Crescent, Downpatrick BT30 6NY Tel: 01396 617232 — MB BCh BAO 1990 Belf.; MRCGP 1994; Cert. Prescribed Equiv. Exp. JCPTGP 1994; DMH Belf. 1993. GP Princip. Socs: BASM; BMA.

HARNEY, John Mary Vianney 2 Dig Lane, Frodsham, Warrington WA6 6UN — MB BCh BAO 1983 NUI.

HARNEY, Mark Anthony John Fron Road Surgery, 2 Fron Road, Connah's Quay, Deeside CH5 4PQ Tel: 01244 814272 Fax: 01244 821204 — MB ChB 1986 Manch.; BSc St. And. 1983; MRCGP 1990; DTM & H Liverp. 1992; DCH RCP Lond. 1990; DRCOG 1988. Med. Off. Kuluva Hosp. Arua, Uganda. Prev: Trainee GP Wrexham VTS.

HARNEY, Patrick Joseph Courthouse Practice, Ton-y-Felin Surgery, Bedwas Road, Caerphilly CF83 1XN Tel: 029 2088 7316 Fax: 029 2088 4445 — MB BCh BAO 1979 NUI; MRCGP 1984; DOBst RCPI 1982.

HARNEY, Peter James 26 Holywell Road, Norman Hill, Dursley GL11 5RS — MB ChB 1976 Bristol; BSc Bristol 1973; MRCP (UK) 1979; MRCGP 1982; DRCOG 1981.

HARNOR, Kirsti Jane Sacriston Surgery, Crossroads DH7 6LJ Tel: 0191 371 0232; Flat 3, 13 Haldane Terrace, Jesmond, Newcastle upon Tyne NE2 3AN Tel: 0191 281 7665 Email: kristi.harnar"virgin.net — BM BS Nottm.; BMedSci (Hons.) Nottm. 1990; Dip. Child Health 1997; Dip. IMC RCS Ed. 1995; DRCOG 1995; DFFP 1995; MRCGP 1997. (Nottm.) Salaried Gen. Pract. For Durh. And Chester-Le-St., PCG.; Locum Clin. Med. Off. - Familly Plann. + Repro. Health Care, QEH NHS Trust, Gateshead. Prev: GP Locum; GP Trainee, Pelaw; GP Career Start Scheme Salaried non Princip.

HAROLD, Richard St John The Health Centre, Leypark Walk, Estover, Plymouth PL6 8UE Tel: 01752 776772 Fax: 01752 785108; 26 Burnett Road, Plymouth PL6 5BH Tel: 01752 776915 — MB BChir 1971 Camb.; MA, MB Camb. 1971, BChir 1970.

HAROLD, Richard St John (retired) Bryher, 15 Tavistock Road, Manadon Hill, Plymouth PL5 3DG Tel: 01752 773285 — LRCPI & LM, LRCSI & LM 1940; DPH Dub. 1942. Prev: Cons. Dermat. Plymouth Gen. Hosp.

HAROON-UR-RASHID, Dr 46 Blondin Street, London E3 2TR — MRCS Eng. LRCP 1988 Lond.; MRCS Eng LRCP Lond. 1988.

HAROON, Agha Mohammad The Surgery, 1 Newport Road, Balsall Heath, Birmingham B12 8QE Tel: 0121 449 1327 — MB BS 1965 Peshawar. (Khyber Med. Coll. Peshawar) Prev: SHO Paediat. War Memor. Hosp. Scunthorpe; SHO Geriat. Moor Hosp. Lancaster; SHO Paediat. Gen. Hosp. Warrington.

HAROON, Mr Mallick Chestnut End, Lower Farm, Upton, Aylesbury HP17 8UA — MB BS 1976 Madras; FRCS Ed. 1982. Assoc. Specialist Trauma & Orthop. Surg. Stoke Mandeville Hosp. Aylesbury.

HAROON, Mohammad Munib 39 King George Avenue, Leeds LS7 4LN — MB ChB 1998 Leeds.

HAROON, Shameem Karim (retired) Westmoor Place, Moor St., Gillingham ME8 8QF — MB BS 1962 Karachi.

HARPALANI, Vijay Bharat 39 Crundale Avenue, Kingsbury, London NW9 9PJ Tel: 020 8204 6483; 25 Waltham Avenue, Kingsbury, London NW9 9SH Tel: 020 8206 0369 — MB BS 1981 Madras; LRCP LRCS Ed. LRCPS Glas. 1985; MRCGP 1988; DA Eng. 1984.

HARPER, Alastair Cant Baillieston Health Centre, 20 Muirside Road, Baillieston, Glasgow G69 7AD Tel: 0141 531 8040; 47 Camphill Avenue, Glasgow G41 3AX Tel: 0141 636 1494 — MB ChB 1978 Glas.; MSc Community Med. Lond. 1983. Socs: BMA.

HARPER, Professor Alexander Murray 2 Pollock Road, Bearsden, Glasgow G61 2NJ Tel: 0141 942 2510 — MB ChB 1957 Glas.; MD (Hons.) Glas. 1966. (Glas.) Socs: Hon. Fell. Amer. Heart Assn.; Internat. Soc. Cerebral Bloodflow & Metab. Prev: Emerit. Prof. Surgic. Research & Hon. Sen. Research Fell. Univ. Glas.; Prof. Surg. Reseach & Hon. Cons. Glasg. Roy. Inf.; Wellcome Sen. Research Fell. (Clin. Sc.).

HARPER, Alexander Stewart Bank Street Surgery, 46-62 Bank Street, Alexandria G83 0LS Tel: 01389 752650 Fax: 01389 752361; 15 Pladda Way, Helensburgh G84 9SE — MB ChB 1963 Glas.; Assoc. Fac. Occupat. Med. RCP Lond. 1980; DIH Soc. Apoth. Lond. 1977; DCH RCPS Glas. 1966; DObst RCOG 1965. (Glas.) Med. Off. Polaroid (UK) Ltd. Socs: BMA. Prev: SHO Cresswell Matern. Hosp. Dumfries & Seafield Sick Childr. Hosp. Ayr; Ho. Off. Glas. Roy. Infirm.

HARPER, Andrew David 41 Park Road, Buckden, St Neots, Huntingdon PE19 5SL — MB ChB 1997 Leeds.

HARPER, Caroline Amanda 25 Poplar Drive, Hutton, Brentwood CM13 1YU — MB BS 1988 Lond. Trainee GP Basildon.

HARPER, Caroline Louise Holmefield, Broomfleet, Brough HU15 1RJ — MB ChB 1987 Leic.; DRCOG 1991; MRCGP 1991; FRCA 1995. (Leicester Univ.) Specialist Regist. Train. Progr. Sheff./N. Trent. Socs: MRCAnaesth.; Assn. Anaesth.; BMA.

HARPER, Carolyn Valerie 83 Bushey Wood Road, Sheffield S17 3QD — MB BCh BAO Belfast; MRCGP; MFPHM 1995. (Queen's University Belfast)

HARPER, Catherine Anne Elmside, More Lane, Esher KT10 8AP Tel: 01372 463459 — MB BS Newc. 1969; DObst RCOG 1971. SCMO Kingston Hosp. Trust.

HARPER, Christina Mary Flat B, 28 Gray St., Glasgow G3 7TY — MB ChB 1995 Glas.

HARPER, Cynthia Margaret Alec Turnbull Clinic, East Oxford Health Centre, Cowley Road, Oxford OX4 1XD Tel: 01865 486123 Fax: 01865 486125; 10 Dale Close, Oxford OX1 1TU — MB ChB 1973 Birm.; MA Camb. 1973; MFFP 1993; Cert Contracep. & Family Plann. RCOG, RCGP &; Cert FPA 1975. (Cambridge/Birmingham) SCMO (Community Health Family Plann.) Oxf. RHA; Clin. Asst. (Colposcopy & Menopause) Dept. Obst. & Gyn. John Radcliffe Hosp. Oxf. Socs: BSCCP; BMS.

HARPER, David Gwynne 22 Roxby Court, Craiglee Drive, Atlantic Wharf, Cardiff CF10 4AG — MB BCh 1989 Wales; MRCGP 1993.

HARPER, David Richard The Surgery, 138 Beaconsfield Villas, Brighton BN1 6HQ Tel: 01273 552212/555401 Fax: 01273 271148; Birnam, South Bank, Hassocks BN6 8JP Tel: 01273 845042 — MB BS Lond. 1965; DCH Eng. 1970; DObst RCOG 1967. (St. Bart.)

***HARPER, Debra Anne** 5 Keswick Road, Fetcham, Leatherhead KT22 9HQ — MB BS 1996 Lond.

HARPER, Mr Douglas Ross Aberdeen Royal Infirmary, Day Surgery Unit, Aberdeen AB25 2ZN Tel: 01224 554794 Email: douglas.harper@arh.grampian.scot.nhs.uk; Boat Cottage, Monymusk, Inverurie AB51 7JA Tel: 01467 651800 Fax: 01467 651900 Email: douglasharper1@compuserve.com — MB ChB 1967 Aberd.; BSc Aberd. 1962, MD (Commend,) 1975; FRCS Glas. 1986; FRCS Eng. 1972; FRCS Ed. 1971. (Aberd.) Cons. Surg. Aberd. Roy. Infirm.; Dir. of Day Surg. Socs: Vasc. Soc. GB & Irel. & Assn. Surgs. GB & Irel.; BMA. Prev: Cons. Surg. (Vasc.) & Med. Dir. Falkirk & Dist. Roy. Infirm.; Ho. Off., Regist. (Surg.) & Fell. (Vasc. Surg.) Aberd. Roy. Infirm.

HARPER, Douglas Sloan 113 Jordanstown Road, Jordanstown, Newtownabbey BT37 0NT — MB BCh BAO 1983 Belf.; MRCGP 1987; DRCOG 1985; DCH RCPI & RCSI 1986. Socs: BMA.

HARPER, Edward North Farm, Aston, Bampton OX18 2DJ — BM BS 1992 Nottm.; BMedSci Nottm. 1990. SHO Rotat. (Surg.) SW Birm. HA. Prev: Ho. Off.(Med.) York. Dist. Hosp.; Ho. Off. (Surg.) Bradford Roy. Infirm.

HARPER, Elizabeth Frances Lincoln Lodge, Rayes Lane, Newmarket CB8 7AB Tel: 01638 663792 — MB BS 1972 Lond.; MRCP (UK) 1977; DObst RCOG 1974. (University College Hospital, London) Assoc. Specialist Neurol. W. Suff. Hosp. Trust.

HARPER, Elizabeth Mary (retired) 2 Osborne Court, 77 Prescot Road, Ormskirk L39 4SL Tel: 01695 573663 — MB ChB 1942 Liverp.; MRCS Eng. LRCP Lond. 1942; FRCOG 1989, M 1950. Chairm. Brandreth Club Ormskirk. Prev: Gyn. Regist. Roy. Liverp. United Hosp.

HARPER, Elizabeth Shearer 25 Stanley Court, 1 Woodfield Road, London W5 1SL — MB ChB 1959 Aberd.; MFCM 1972; DPH Lond. 1968; DCH Eng. 1964; DObst RCOG 1962. PMO Lond. Boro. Hounslow; Asst. Sen. Med. Off. Lond. Boro. Camden; Clin. Asst. Hosp. Sick Childr. Gt. Ormond St.

HARPER, Emma Elizabeth 24 Baronscourt Heights, Carryduff, Belfast BT8 8RS — MB BCh BAO 1989 Belf.

HARPER, Eric Imlay Health Centre, Milton Road, Swindon SN4 9LW Tel: 01793 22668 — MB ChB 1938 Aberd.; MA, MB ChB Aberd. 1938. (Aberd.)

HARPER, Esther Josephine Mary 404a Foreglen Road, Dungiven, Londonderry BT47 4LG — MB BCh BAO 1983 Belf.

HARPER, Fiona Victoria Louise 33 Delorme Street, London W6 8DS — MB BS 1990 Lond.; BSc (Hons.) Lond. 1985, MB BS 1990; FRCS 1995; MSc 1998. (St Thomas' Hospitas Medical School)

HARPER, Mr Gareth David Queen Alexandria Hospital, Portsmouth PO6 3LY Tel: 02392 286961 Email: g.d.harper@btinternet.co.uk — BM BCh 1988 Oxf.; MA Camb. 1988; FRCS (Orth.) 1996; FRCS Eng. 1992. (Cambridge) Cons. Orthop. and Trauma, Q.A. Hosp. Portsmouth. Socs: Seddon Soc. Prev: Fell. (Shoulder & Elbow Surg.) P. of Wales Hosp. Sydney; Lect. Roy. Nat. Orthop. Hosp. Lond.; Sen. Regist. (Orthop.) Roy. Nat. Orthop. Hosp. Lond.

HARPER, Gavin Kenneth 342 Belmont Road, Belfast BT4 2LA — MB BCh 1998 Belf.; MB BCh Belf 1998.

HARPER, Glen David Lemons Farm, Atherington, Umberleigh EX37 9HY Tel: 01769 560566 Email: glenharper@doctors.org.uk — MB BChir 1982 Camb.; MA Camb. 1983; FRCP (UK) 1986. Cons. Phys. (Special Responsibil. For Elderly) N. Devon Dist. Hosp.; Mem. Brit. Stroke Research Gp. Socs: Brit. Geriat. Soc. Prev: Sen. Regist. (Geriat. & Gen. Med.) Leicester Gen. Hosp.; Clin. Research Fell. Leic. Gen. Hosp.

HARPER, Gordon Leonard (retired) 28 Allanson Road, Rhos-on-Sea, Colwyn Bay LL28 4HL Tel: 01492 44570 — MRCS Eng. LRCP Lond. 1948; FCOphth 1989; DO Eng. 1953. Prev: Cons. Ophth. Gwynedd HA.

HARPER, Helen Margaret Bodowen Surgery, Halkyn Road, Holywell CH8 7GA Tel: 01352 710529 Fax: 01352 710784 — MB BS 1977 Lond.; BSc (Hons.) (Anat.) Lond. 1974; MRCGP 1981; DRCOG 1979.

HARPER, Helen Rosemary 5A Glenleigh Park, Havant PO9 2PH; 10 Elgar Close, Alverstoke, Gosport PO12 2LU Tel: 01705 589766 — MB BS 1988 Lond.; DA (UK) 1991.

HARPER, Ian Department of Anaesthesia, Doctor Grays Hospital, Elgin IV30 1SN Tel: 01343 543131 Email: ian.harper@mhs.grampian.scot.nhs.uk — MB ChB 1988 Ed.; FRCA 1994. Cons. anaesth. Dr Grays hosp. Elgin. Socs: Assn. Anaesth. Prev: Specialist Regist. Anaesth.Edin.Roy.Inf; Fell.Anaesth.Flindis.Adelaide.Aus; SHO (Anaesth.) Glas. Roy. Infirm.

HARPER, Ian Alexander (retired) 17 Rossie Avenue, Broughty Ferry, Dundee DD5 3ND Tel: 013827 37496 — MB ChB 1957 St. And.; FRCPath 1976, M 1964. Prev: Cons. Microbiol. & Hon. Sen. Lect. Univ. Dundee Med. Sch. & Perth Roy.Infirm.

HARPER, Ian Dominic Richard Queens Road Surgery, 27 Queens Road, Wimbledon, London SW19 8NW Tel: 020 8944 5916 Fax: 020 8947 8677 Email: ian.harper@gp-h85026.nhs.uk — MB BS 1983 Lond.; MRCGP 1989; MRCGP 1988; DRCOG 1988; DA (UK) 1985. (London Hospital)

HARPER, James, MBE (retired) 18A High Street, Kirkcudbright DG6 4JX Tel: 01557 330045 — MB ChB 1939 Ed.; FRCP Ed. 1958, M 1952; FRCPsych 1971; DPM Lond. 1947. Hon. Civil Cons. Psychiat. RAF. Prev: Lord Chancellor's Med. Visitor.

HARPER, James Walter Kirkwood (retired) Gara Lodge, Barking Road, Needham Market, Ipswich IP6 8EX Tel: 01449 720294 — MRCS Eng. LRCP Lond. 1936; DPH Eng. 1939.

HARPER, Janet Forsyth Watson (retired) 17 Rossie Avenue, Broughty Ferry, Dundee DD5 3ND Tel: 01382 737496 — MB ChB 1956 St. And. Prev: Clin. Med. Off. (Family Plann.) Perth & Kinross Dist. HealthBd.

HARPER, Janice Marian Department of Pathology, Tennis Court Road, Cambridge CB2 1QP Tel: 01223 333716 Fax: 01223 333914; 6 Greater Foxes, Fulbourn, Cambridge CB1 5EZ — MB BS 1985 Lond.; BSc Lond. 1981, MB BS (Hons.) 1985; MRCP (UK) 1988. Wellcome Train. Fell. (Immunol.) Univ. Camb. Prev: Hon. Regist. Addenbrooke's Hosp. Camb.; Regist. (Nephrol.) St Peter's Hosp. Chertsey; Regist. Middlx. Hosp. Lond.

HARPER, Joan 28 Allanson Road, Rhos-on-Sea, Colwyn Bay LL28 4HL Tel: 01492 544570 — MB ChB 1947 Birm.; DObst RCOG 1950. (Birm.) Prev: SCMO Gwynedd HA; Cas. Off. Guest Hosp. Dudley; Jun. Hosp. Med. Off. Birm. Blood Transfus. Serv.

HARPER, Joanne Ballymena Health Centre, Cushendall Road, Ballymena BT43 6HQ Tel: 028 2564 2181 Fax: 028 2565 8919 — MB BCh BAO 1986 Belf.; MRCGP 1991.

HARPER, John Albert (retired) Netherfield, Treviglas Lane, Probus, Truro TR2 4LH — MB BS 1959 Lond. Prev: SHO (Obst.) St. Jas. Hosp. Tredegar.

HARPER, John Irwin Great Ormond Street Hospital for Children, NHS Trust, London WC1N 3JH — MD 1985 Lond.; MB BS 1973; FRCP 1993; MRCP (UK) 1978. Cons. Paediat. Dermat. Gt. Ormond St. Hosp. Childr. Lond.

HARPER, John Murray (retired) Moor Croft, Helensburgh Tel: 01436 74812 — MB ChB 1946 Glas.

HARPER, John Reynolds 79 Sandmere Road, London SW4 7PT Tel: 020 7274 3790 — MB ChB 1993 Ed.; BSc Ed. 1991; MRCP (UK) 1996. (Ed. Univ. Med. Sch.) Prev: SHO Rotat. (Med.) York.

HARPER, John Richard The General Hospital, Northampton NN1 5BB Tel: 01604 34700; The White House, Guilsborough, Northampton NN6 8PY Tel: 01604 740040 — BM BCh 1958 Oxf.; MA, BM BCh Oxf. 1958; FRCP Lond. 1975, M 1964; DCH Eng. 1961. (St. Thos.) Cons. Paediat. N.ampton HA; JP. Socs: Fell. Roy. Soc. Med.; Brit. Paediat. Assn. Prev: Sen. Paediat. Regist. S. Warks. Hosp. Gp. & Birm. Childr. Hosp.; Ho. Phys. Hosp. Sick Childr. Gt. Ormond St.; Squadron Ldr. RAF Med. Br., Med. Specialist.

HARPER, Jonathan Richard 1 High Street, Bourton-on-the-Water, Cheltenham GL54 2AP Tel: 01451 20921 — MB ChB 1988 Leeds; BSc (Hons.) Leeds 1986, MB ChB 1988.

HARPER, Kay Louise Health Centre, Bridge Lane, Penrith CA11 8HW Tel: 01768 245200 — BM BCh 1984 Oxf.; 1985 MA Camb.; MRCGP 1988; DCH RCP Lond. 1988; DRCOG 1986. Gen. Practitioner; BrE. Phys. Diagnostic BrE. Clinic, Cumbld. Infirm., Carlisle.

HARPER, Kenneth Herbert, Col. late RAMC Retd. (retired) 18 Park Road, Beckenham BR3 1QD Tel: 020 8658 6898 — MRCS Eng. LRCP Lond. 1936; DMRD Eng. 1954.

HARPER, Kenneth James Sydenham House, Church Road, Ashford TN23 1RB Tel: 01233 645851; 4 John Newington Close, Kennington, Ashford TN24 9SG — MB BS 1982 Lond. Princip. GP Ashford Kent.

HARPER, Kenneth William Royal Victoria Hospital, Grovenor Road, Belfast BT12 6BA Tel: 01232 240503; 342 Belmont Road, Belfast BT4 2LA — MD 1986 Belf.; BSc Belf. 1971, MD 1986, MB BCh BAO 1976; FRCA 1981. Cons. Anaesth. Roy. Vict. Hosp. Belf.

HARPER, Lorraine 11 Ladyacre, Kilwinning KA13 7DW — MB ChB 1990 Ed.

HARPER, Louisa Bonthrone (retired) 38 Shandon Crescent, Edinburgh EH11 1QF Tel: 0131 337 5777 — MB ChB 1925 Ed. Prev: Dep. MOH Longbenton UDC.

HARPER, Margaret Ann Royal Maternity Hospital, Grosvenor Road, Belfast BT12 6BB Tel: 01232 263009 Fax: 01232 328247 Email: a.harper@qub.ac.uk; 96 Blaris Road, Lisburn BT27 5RA Tel: 01846 601592 — MB BCh BAO 1973 Belf.; MB BCH BAO (Hons.) Belf. 1973; MD Belf. 1987; FRCOG 1995, M 1978; DObst 1975. Cons. & Sen. Lect. (O & G) Roy. Matern. Hosp. Belf.

HARPER, Margaret Norah York Medical Practice, St John's Health Centre, Oak Lane, Twickenham TW1 3PA Tel: 020 8744 0220 Fax: 020 8892 6855 — MB BS 1973 Lond.; MRCP (UK) 1975; MRCS Eng. LRCP Lond. 1973; DCH RCP Lond. 1975. (St. Mary's Hospital Medical School) Prev: Sen. Regist. (Paediat.) St. Mary's Hosp. Lond.; Regist. (Paediat.) St. Mary's Hosp. Lond.

HARPER, Margaret Pollock (retired) 1 Whitehill Lane, Bearsden, Glasgow G61 4PY Tel: 0141 942 4639 — MB ChB 1947 Glas. Cytol. Stobhill Gen. Hosp. Glas.

HARPER, Matthew 68 Station Road, Llanishen, Cardiff CF14 5LU — BM 1993 Soton.

HARPER, Michael Edward Medical Research Council, PO Box 273, Gambia; 83 Parrys Lane, Bristol BS9 1AN — BM BCh 1969 Oxf.; MSc 2000; MRCGP 1975; DCH Eng. 1978. Epidemiological Research. Prev: SHO (O & G) & Ho. Phys. St. Martins Hosp. Bath; Ho. Phys. (Paediat.) Roy. United Hosp. Bath.; Gen. Practitioner, Whiteladies Health Centre, Bristol.

HARPER, Nicholas Charles 3 New End Square, London NW3 1LP — MB BS 1984 Lond.; FRCA 1994. Sen. Regist. Rotat. (Anaesth.) Roy. Free Hosp. Lond. & Harefield Hosp. Middlx. Prev: Regist. (Anaesth.) St. Bart. Hosp. Lond.

HARPER, Nicholas Gordon Blackpool Victoria Hospitals NHS Trust, Whinney Heys Road, Blackpool FY3 8NR Tel: 01253 303499; 1 Cheviot Avenue, The Belfry, Lytham St Annes FY8 4TE Tel: 01253 731551 — MB ChB 1989 Manch.; BSc St. And. 1986; FRCA 1995. (Manch.) cons. Anaesth. Blackpool Vict. Hosp. Socs: BMA; Assn. Anaesth.; Obst. Anaesth. Assn. Prev: Sen. Regist. Rotat. (Anaesth.) NW Region; Regist. (Anaesth.) Wigan, Blackpool & Bolton.

HARPER, Nigel Jeremy Nicholas Department of Anaesthesia, Manchester Royal Infirmary, Oxford Road, Manchester M13 9ES Tel: 0161 276 4551; Fuchsia Cottage, 15 Hough Lane, Wilmslow SK9 2LQ — MB ChB 1976 Birm.; FFA RCS Lond. 1980. Cons. Anaesth. & Intens. Care Manch. Roy. Infirm.; Hon. Assoc. Lect. (Anaesth.) Univ. Manch. Socs: Anaesth. Res. Soc.; Roy. Soc. Med. (Hon Sec. Sect. Anaesth.). Prev: Sen. Regist. (Anaesth.) Manch. Roy. Infirm.; Regist. (Anaesth.) Birm. Centr. Dist.

HARPER, Nigel Philip Adrian Lyddon Department Medicine for the Elderly, University hospital Aintree, Liverpool L9 7AL Tel: 0151 529 3695 Fax: 0151 529 3787; 11 Flaxfield Road, Formby, Liverpool L37 8BH Tel: 01704 879770 — MB BS Lond. 1961; FRCP Lond. 1987; MRCP (UK) 1970; MRCS Eng. LRCP Lond. 1961. (Guy's) Cons. Phys. & Geriat. Walton & Fazakerley Hosps. Liverp.; Clin. Lect. Univ. Liverp. Socs: Brit. Geriat. Soc.

HARPER, Norman Nigel Logan, Harper and Munslow, Castlefield Surgery, Castle Way, Stafford ST16 1BS Tel: 01785 223012; Rest Awhile, Holmcroft Road, Stafford ST16 1JB — MB ChB 1978 Manch.

HARPER, Patricia Isobel Clydebank Health Centre, Kilbowie Road, Clydebank G81 2TQ Tel: 0141 531 6475 Fax: 0141 531 6478; 101 Hyndland Road, Hyndland, Glasgow G12 9JD — MB ChB 1981 Dundee; MRCGP 1986.

HARPER, Paul Cedric William Lyddon Thorpe Wood Surgery, Woodside Road, Norwich NR7 9QL Tel: 01603 701477 Fax: 01603 701512; Dussindale Surgery, Pound Lane, Yarmouth Road, Norwich NR7 0SR Tel: 01603 700992 Fax: 01603 702348 — MB BS 1963 Lond.; DObst RCOG 1965. (Univ. Coll. Hosp.) Socs: BMA; Norwich M-C Soc.

HARPER, Peter George 149 Harley Street, London W1G 6DE Tel: 020 7935 6698 Fax: 020 7224 6504 Email: peter.harper@kcl.ac.uk; Castle Cottage, Bradenham, High Wycombe HP14 4HD Tel: 01494 563948 Fax: 020 7435 1801 — MB BS 1970 Lond.; FRCP Lond. 1988, M 1974; MRCS Eng. LRCP Lond. 1970. (Univ. Coll. Hosp.) Cons. Med. Oncol. Guy's Kings & St. Thomas' Cancer Centre; Hon. Sen. Lect. UMDS Guy's & St. Thos. Hosps. Lond. Socs: Internat. Assn. for the Study of lung cancer; UK Centr. Cancer Co-ordinating Comm.; UK Cancer Co-ordinating Comm. Cancer of the Elderly. Prev: Sen. Regist. (Med.) Univ. Coll. & Whittington Hosps. Lond.; Regist. (Med.) St. Mary's Hosp. Lond.

HARPER, Mr Peter Henry County Hospital, Union Walk, Hereford HR1 2ER Tel: 01432 364122; Overcourt, Sutton St. Nicholas, Hereford HR1 3AY Tel: 01432 880845 — MB ChB 1974 Oxford; BA Camb 1971; MA Camb. 1974; MCh Oxf. 1984; FRCS Eng.

1978. (Camb. & Oxf.) Cons. Gen. Surg. Co. Hosp. Hereford. Prev: Sen. Regist. (Surg.) Newc.; Fell. & Chief Resid. (Colon & Rectal Surg.) Cleveland Clinic Cleveland, Ohio.

HARPER, Peter Stanley Institute of Medical Genetics, University Hospital of Wales, Heath Park, Cardiff CF4 4XN Tel: 029 2074 4058 Fax: 029 2074 7603 — DM Oxf. 1972, MA, BM BCh 1964; FRCP Lond. 1978, M 1967. Prof. (Med. Genetics) Univ. Wales Coll. Med. Cardiff; Cons. Phys. (Med. Genetics) Univ. Hosp. Wales Cardiff. Socs: Genet. Soc.; Soc. Human Genetics. Prev: Research Fell. Med. Div. Med. Genetics Johns Hopkins Sch. Med. Baltimore USA; Edr. J. Med. Genetics, 1984-94.

HARPER, Raymond Henry Health Centre, Windmill Avenue, Hassocks BN6 8LY Tel: 01273 844242 Fax: 01273 842709; Tanners, Wickham Hill, Hassocks BN6 9NP Tel: 01273 845094 — BM BCh Oxf. 1969; MA Oxf. 1965. (Oxf.) Socs: BMA; W Sussex LMC; W Sussex HA Discipline Comm. Prev: Ho. Off. (O & G) Roy. Sussex Co. Hosp. Brighton; Ho. Phys. & Ho. Surg. Stoke Mandeville Hosp.

HARPER, Richard The White House, High St., Guilsborough, Northampton NN6 8PY — MB BS 1988 Lond.; MRCGP 1996.

HARPER, Richard John Market Street Practice, Ton-y-Felin Surgery, Bedwas Road, Caerphilly CF83 1PD Tel: 029 2088 7831 Fax: 029 2086 9037; 16 Orchard Castle, Thornhill, Cardiff CF14 9BA Tel: 029 2069 2248 — MB BCh 1988 Wales; MRCGP 1992. Prev: Trainee GP P.ss of Wales Hosp. Bridgend VTS.

HARPER, Robert Alexander Kemp (retired) 61 Vincent Drive, Westminster Park, Chester CH4 7RQ Tel: 01244 676670 — MD Ed. 1952, MB ChB 1929, DR 1932; FRCP Ed. 1950, M 1946; FFR 1954; FRCR 1977; FRCP Lond. 1963, M 1952; FRFPS Glas. 1947; FRCP Glas. 1964, M 1962. Prev: Dir. Diag. X-Ray Dept. St. Bart. Hosp.

HARPER, Rosalyn Denise 9 Compton Avenue, Aston-on-Trent, Derby DE72 2AU Tel: 01332 792610 — MB ChB 1988 Sheff.; FRCS Eng. 1992. Specialist Regist. Plastic Surg. W. Midl. Rotat.

HARPER, ROY Ulster Community Hospitals NHS Trust, Ulster Hospital, Dundonald, Belfast BT16 1RH Tel: 01232 484511 Fax: 01232 561396 Email: roy.harper@ida.n-i.nhs.uk — MB BCh BAO 1987 Belf.; BSc Belf. 1984, MD 1994; MRCP (UK) 1990. (QUB) Cons. Endocrinol. Ulster Comm. Hosp. Trust. Belf.

HARPER, Sarah Jane 34 Clifton Gardens, London NW11 7EL — MB ChB 1995 Bristol. (Univ. Bristol) SHO (Anaesth.) Roy. Free Hosp. Hampstead Lond. Socs: Train. Mem RCA; Train. Mem. Assn. AnE.h.

HARPER, Sharon 13 Hampton Drive, Bangor BT19 7GH Tel: 01247 473605 — MB BCh BAO 1997 Belf. SHO Antrim Area Hosp. Prev: Jun. Ho. Off. Ulster Hosp. Dundonald.

HARPER, Simon Heyworth Folly Cottage, Gollawater, Penhallow, Truro TR4 9LY — MB BS 1977 Lond.

HARPER, Steven James Richard Bright, Renal Unit, Southmead Hospital, Westbury-on-Trym, Bristol BS10 5UB — MD 1992 Manch.; FRCP 2001; BSc (Hons.) 1981 MB ChB (Hons.) 1984; MRCP (UK) 1987; MD 1991. Cons. (Nephrol.) S.mead Hosp. Bristol Wellcome Trust Research Leave Fell. Prev: Wellcome Trust Med. Grad. Advanced Train. Fell.; Research Regist. (Renal Med.) & Regist. (Renal & Gen. Med.) Leicester Gen.Hosp.; Regist. (Gen. Med.) Roy. Hallamsh. Hosp.

HARPER, Susan Jane Department of Anaesthetics & ITU, Royal Liverpool University, Liverpool L7 8XP Tel: 0151 706 3190; 18 Kirby Park, West Kirby, Wirral CH48 2HA Tel: 0151 625 9005 — BSc McGill, Canada 1975, MDCM 1979; FFA RCS Eng. 1985. Cons. Anaesth. & Intens. Ther. Roy. Liverp. Univ. Hosp. Prev: Sen. Regist. (Anaesth.) Mersey RHA.

HARPER, William David (retired) Clogwyn y Gwin, Rhyd Ddu, Caernarfon LL54 7YS Tel: 01766 890579 Fax: 01766 890569 Email: harperclogwyn@farming.co.uk — MB BChir 1962 Camb.; MA, MB Camb. 1962, BChir 1961. Prev: Mem. Wirral S.. Dist. Managem. Team.

HARPER, Mr William Farquharson (retired) 1 Whitehill Lane, Bearsden, Glasgow G61 4PY Tel: 0141 942 4639 — MB ChB 1940 Glas.; BSc Glas. 1936, MB ChB 1940; FRCS Glas. 1969; FRCOG 1964, M 1950. Prev: Cons. (O & G) Stobhill Hosp. Glas.

HARPER-SMITH, John Richard Old Mill House, Tetford, Horncastle LN9 6QA Tel: 01507 533233; Tetford Water Mill, Horncastle LN9 6PZ Tel: 01507 533355 — LRCPI & LM, LRCSI & LM 1956. (RCSI) Med. Off. Horncastle War Memor. Hosp. & Grace Swan Spilsby Hosp.; Chairm. & Co-Founder Lincs. Integr. Volun. Emerg. Servs. (L.I.V.E.S.). Socs: Lincoln Med. Soc. Prev: Ho. Surg. (Midw. & Gyn.) Roy. Devon & Exeter Hosp.; Res. Med. Off. Hulton Hosp. Bolton; Ho. Phys. Bolton Dist. Gen. Hosp. Farnworth.

HARPER-WYNNE, Catherine Linda 10 Langthorne St, Fulham, London SW6 6JY Tel: 020 7381 8140 Email: cwynne@icr.ac.uk; Mayhall Lodge, Oakway, Amersham HP6 5PQ — MB BS 1990 Lond.; MRCP 1996. (Charing Cross and Westminster) Research Fell The Roy. Marsden Hosp. Lond. Socs: BMA; MDU. Prev: Specialist Train. Regist. (Med. Oncol.) N. W. Thames.

HARPIN, Roderick Paul c/o Anaesthetic Department, Newcastle General Hospital, Newcastle upon Tyne NE4 6BE Tel: 0191 256 3198 Fax: 0191 256 3154 Email: r.p.harpin@ncl.ac.uk — MB BS 1978 Lond.; BA Oxon. 1975; MRCP (UK) 1980; FFA RCS Eng. 1983. (King's Coll. Hosp.) Cons. Anaesth. Newc. Gen. Hosp. Prev: Specialist Intens. & Anaesth. N.land Base Hosp. NZ.; Cons. Anaesth. & IC Newc. Gen. Hosp.; Sen. Regist. (Anaesth.) Newc. HA.

HARPIN, Valerie Anne Ryegate Childrens Centre, Tapton Crescent Road, Sheffield S10 5DD Tel: 0114 267 0273 Fax: 0114 267 8296; Riplingham, Sheffield Road, Hathersage, Sheffield S32 1DA Tel: 01433 650328 — MB BChir 1978 Camb.; 1980 MRCP (UK) 1980; FRCP; FRCPCH; 1987 MD 1987; 1974 BA Camb 1974. (Cambridge) Cons. Paediat. Sheff. Socs: (Paediat.) Research Soc. & Neonat. Soc.; MRCPCH. Prev: Cons. Community Paediat. Oxf.; Regist. (Paediat.) Leicester; Research Fell. (Paediat.) Nottm.

HARPUR, Jane Eleanor Gloucester Avenue Surgery, 158 Gloucester Avenue, Chelmsford CM2 9LG Tel: 01245 353182 Fax: 01245 344479; 9 Galleywood Road, Great Baddow, Chelmsford CM2 8DL — MB BS Lond. 1969; MRCS Eng. LRCP Lond. 1969; MRCGP 1975. (Roy. Free) Prev: Research Regist. Chelmsford & Essex Hosp. Chelmsford.

HARPUR, Nicholas Charles Wilfrid Ixworth Surgery, Peddars Close, Ixworth, Bury St Edmunds IP31 2HD Tel: 01359 230252 Fax: 01359 232586; 14 Common Lane, Troston, Bury St Edmunds IP31 1EY — MB BS 1983 Lond.; MRCGP 1989; DRCOG 1988.

HARRAD, John David 12 Cadogan Terrace, Victoria Park, London E9 5EG — MB BS 1989 Lond.

HARRAD, Mr Richard Anthony Bristol Eye Hospital, Lower Maudlin St., Bristol BS1 2LX Tel: 0117 928 4689 Fax: 0117 928 4686; 75 Kingsdown Parade, Bristol BS6 5UJ Tel: 0117 923 2168 — MB BS 1978 Lond.; MA Camb. 1978; FRCS Eng. 1985; FRCOphth 1988; MRCP (UK) 1981. (Camb. & Westm. Hosp.) Cons. Ophth. Bristol Eye Hosp.; Vis. Prof. in the Sch. of Life and Health Sci.s of Aston Univ. Prev: Sen. Regist. (Ophth.) Moorfield Eye Hosp. Lond.; Wellcome Vision Research Fell. Physiol. Laborat Camb.

HARRAN, Michael John York District Hospital, Wigginton Road, York YO31 8HE Tel: 01904 631313 Fax: 01904 453995 Email: michael.harran@excha.yhs-tr.northy.nhs.uk — MB ChB 1970 Liverp.; FRCP Lond. 1989; MRCP (UK) 1975; DCH Eng. 1972; FRCPCH 1997. Cons. Paediat. York Dist. Gen. Hosp.; Hon. Lect. (Child Health) Univ. Leeds. Socs: Brit. Assn. Perinatal Med.; Brit. Soc. Paediat. Endocrinol. Prev: Lect. (Child Health) Univ. Leicester; Tutor (Child Health) Univ. Manch.; Regist. (Paediat.) Roy. Liverp. Childr. Hosp.

HARRELL, Marise Elizabeth Ty Clyd, Govilon, Abergavenny NP7 9PS Tel: 01873 830072 — MB BCh 1956 Wales. (Cardiff) Clin. Med. Off. Gwent HA. Prev: Med. Off. Brompton Hosp. Sanat. Frimley; Ho. Surg. (Gyn.) Llandough Hosp. Cardiff; Med. Off. Sultan of Brunei.

HARRELL, Roydon Ty Clyd, Govilon, Abergavenny NP7 9PS Tel: 01873 830072 — MB BCh 1954 Wales; BSc Wales 1951. (Cardiff) Sen. Med. Off. Gwent HA. Prev: Med. Off. to Sultan of Brunei.

HARRETT, Douglas, QHP (retired) 119 Brandreth Road, Cardiff CF23 5LD Tel: 01222 754099 — MB BChir 1952 Camb.; MA Camb. 1952; FFPHM 1978, M 1972; DPH Wales 1958. Prev: Dir. Pub. Health Gwent HA.

HARRIES, Alison Jane (retired) Hillcrest, Midford Road, Bath BA2 5SB — MB BS 1980 Lond.; MRCP (UK) 1984; FFA RCS Eng. 1985; DCH RCP Lond. 1983.

HARRIES, Anabel Victoria Katharina The Finsbury Circus Medical Centre, 5 London Wall Buildings, Finsbury Circus, London EC2M 5NS Tel: 020 7638 0909 Fax: 020 7638 9211 Email: aharries@fcmc.co.uk; 137 Bearton Road, Hitchin SG5 1UB Tel: 01462 440056 — MB BS 1982 Lond.; DRCOG 1987. (St. Geo.

Hosp. Med. Sch. Lond.) Prev: GP Lond.; Research Fell. St. Peter's Hosp. Chertsey; SHO (Med.) St. Bart. Hosp. Lond.

HARRIES, Mrs Anne Madeleine 15 Kimbolton Avenue, Bedford MK40 3AA — MRCS Eng. LRCP Lond. 1952. SCMO N. Beds. HA.

HARRIES, Arthur Ieuan Old Road Surgery, Old Road, Llanelli SA15 3HR Tel: 01554 775555 Fax: 01554 778868 — MB BCh 1975 Wales.

HARRIES, Mr Bernard John (retired) 14 Stanton Drive, Chichester PO19 4QN Tel: 01243 528323 — MB BS 1947 Lond.; FRCS Eng. 1946; MRCS Eng. LRCP Lond. 1939. Prev: Cons. Surg. (Neurosurg.) Univ. Coll. Hosp. Lond.

HARRIES, Brian David John Dixton Surgery, Dixton Road, Monmouth NP25 3PL Tel: 01600 712152 Fax: 01600 772634; Cae Dee, Upper Ferry Road, Penallt, Monmouth NP25 4AN Tel: 01600 714899 — MB ChB 1982 Birm.; MRCGP 1990. Prev: Regist. (Med.) S.land Hosp. Invercargill, NZ.

HARRIES, Claire Pengarth Road Surgery, Pengarth Road, St Agnes TR5 0TN Tel: 01872 553881 Fax: 01872 553885 — MA, BM BCh Oxf. 1970; DCH Eng. 1977; DObst RCOG 1973. (Kings Coll. Hosp.)

HARRIES, Clive John 4 St Margaret's Grove, Leeds LS8 1RZ — MB ChB 1994 Leeds.

HARRIES, David Graham 24 South Eastern Road, Ramsgate CT11 9QF Tel: 01843 53252 — MB ChB 1959 St. And.; DObst RCOG 1961.

HARRIES, David James Windwhistle Cottage, Wittersham, Tenterden TN30 — MB BS 1976 Lond.; MRCP (UK) 1979; MRCS Eng. LRCP Lond. 1976.

HARRIES, David John 24-28 Leicester Road, Loughborough LE11 2AG Tel: 01509 230717; 32 Fairmount Drive, Loughborough LE11 3JR — MB ChB Manch. 1965; MFHom 1994; MRCGP 1980; DObst RCOG 1969. Socs: BMA. Prev: Med. Off. RAMC.

HARRIES, Mr David Kenneth Llys-y-Coed, Llanstephan Road, Johnstown, Carmarthen SA31 3NW Tel: 01267 234496 — MB BCh 1992 Wales; FRCS Ed. 1996. (Univ. Wales Coll. Med.) SHO (Gen. Surg.) Roy. Gwent Hosp. Newport.

HARRIES, Mr David Paul 3 Glendaruel Avenue, Bearsden, Glasgow G61 2PP — MB BCh 1986 Wales; FRCS Glas. 1990.

HARRIES, Eurig Wyn Meddygfa Rhiannon, Northfield Road, Narberth SA67 7AA Tel: 01834 860237 Fax: 01834 861625 — MB BCh 1993 Wales; DRCOG 1995; MRCGP 1998. (Univ. Wales Coll. Med. Cardiff) GP Princip. Narberth. Prev: GP/Regist. Carmarthen.

HARRIES, Helen Jane Lodgeside Surgery, 22 Lodgeside Avenue, Kingswood, Bristol BS15 1WW Tel: 0117 961 5666 Fax: 0117 947 6854; 77 Kenmore Crescent, Bristol BS7 0TP — MB ChB 1973 Bristol; MRCGP 1984. GP Bristol.

HARRIES, Iorwerth Geraint Countisbury Avenue Surgery, 152 Countisbury Avenue, Llanrumney, Cardiff CF3 5YS Tel: 029 2079 2661 Fax: 029 2079 4537 — MB BS 1978 Lond.; MRCGP 1982.

HARRIES, Jennifer Margaret Gwent Health Authority, Mamhilad House, Mamhilad Park Estate, Pontypool NP4 0YP Tel: 01495 765065 Fax: 01495 758593; Millwalk, Osbaston Road, Monmouth NP25 3AX Tel: 01600 713167 Fax: 01600 713167 Email: jenny_harries@inmoto.demon.co.uk — MB ChB 1984 Birm.; BSc (Hons.) Pharmacol. Birm. 1981. (Birm.) Regist. (Pub. Health Med.) Gwent Health Auth. Pontypool. Socs: BMA.

HARRIES, Jestyn Llwynbedw Medical Centre, 82/86 Caerphilly Road, Birchgrove, Cardiff CF14 4AG Tel: 029 2052 1222 Fax: 029 2052 2873; 4 Westbourne Crescent, Whitchurch, Cardiff CF14 2BL Tel: 029 2069 2137 — MB BCh 1966 Wales; MRCGP 1975. (Cardiff) GP Cardiff; Hosp. Pract. (Diabetes) Univ. Hosp. Wales Cardiff. Prev: SHO (Med.) Nevill Hall Hosp. Abergavenny; Ho. Off. (Surg.) Llandough Hosp. Penarth; Ho. Off. (Paediat.) Cardiff Roy. Infirm.

HARRIES, Joanna Mary Child Health Department, Bath & West Community NHS Trust, Newbridge Hill, Bath BA1 3QE Tel: 01225 313640; 16 Gloucester Walk, Westbury BA13 3XG — MB BS 1979 Lond.; MSc (Community Child Health) Warwick 1996; BSc Lond. 1976; MRCGP 1984; Dip. Community Paediat. Warwick 1992; DCH RCP Lond. 1983; DRCOG 1982. (Univ. Coll. Hosp. Med. Sch.) Staff Grade (Paediat.) Community Child Health Bath & W. Community NHS Trust. Socs: BACDA; BACCH.

HARRIES, John David Newton Surgery, Park Street, Newtown SY16 1EF Tel: 01686 626221/626224 Fax: 01686 622610; Cefnbrith Millfields, Milford Road, Newtown SY16 2JP — MB BS 1971 Lond. (Lond. Hosp.) GP Newtown; Hon. Clin. Teach. Dept. Gen. Pract. Univ. Wales Coll. Med. Cardiff.

HARRIES, Mark 41 Melville Road, Barnes, London SW13 9RH Tel: 020 8748 4268 — MB BChir 1991 Camb.; MRCP (UK) 1993. (Camb.) Regist. (Med. Oncol.) Roy. Marsden Hosp. Lond. Prev: Regist. (Gen. Med.) SW Thames RHA.; SHO Roy. Marsden Hosp., Lond. Chest Hosp. & Greenwich Dist. Hosp.

HARRIES, Mark Gwynne Clementine Churchill Hospital, Sudbury Hill, Harrow HA1 3RX Tel: 020 8422 3464; Northwick Park Hospital & St. Marks NHS Trust, Harrow HA1 3UJ Tel: 020 8864 3232 — MB BS 1968 Lond.; MD Lond. 1982; FRCP Lond. 1993; MRCP (UK) 1972; MRCS Eng. LRCP Lond. 1968. (King's Coll. Hosp.) Cons. Phys. N.wick Pk. Hosp. & St. Marks NHS Trust Harrow; Hon. Sen. Lect. (Gen. & Respirat. Med.) Imperial Coll. Sch. of Med.; Med. Adviser Brit. Olympic Assn., Brit. Amateur Gymnastics Assn., Surf Life Saving Assn & World Life Saving Assn; World Life Saving Assn.; Hon. Dir. (Clin. Servs.) Brit. Olympic Med. Centre; Mem. Resusc. Counc. (UK). Socs: Fell. Roy. Soc. Med. (Sec. Div. Sports Med.); Fell. Inst. Sports Med. Prev: Regist. (Med.) W.m. Hosp. Lond.; Hon. Sen. Regist. Guy's Hosp. Lond.; Lect. (Med.) Brompton Hosp. Lond.

HARRIES, Matthew John 32 Fairmount Drive, Loughborough LE11 3JR — MB ChB 1998 Leeds.

HARRIES, Mr Meredydd Lloyd The Ear, Nose and Throat Department, The Royal Sussex County Hospital, Eastern Road, Brighton BN2 5BE Tel: 01273 696955; The Malt House, 9 Cross Lane, Findon, Worthing BN14 0UQ Tel: 01903 873340 — MB BS Lond. 1983; BSc (Hons.) Lond. 1980; FRCS Ed. 1990; FRCS Eng. 1990. (St. Bart.) Cons. ENT Surg. Roy. Sussex Co. Hosp., Roy. Alexander Childr. Hosp. & Worthing Gen. Hosp. Socs: Brit. Assn. Performing Arts Med.; Brit. Voice Assn.; Brit. Assn. Otol. & Head & Neck Surg. Prev: Hon. Cons. Roy. Nat. Throat, Nose & Ear Hosp. Lond.; Fell. Phonosurg. Vancouver Gen. Hosp., Canada; Sen. Regist. Addenbrooke's Hosp. Camb.

HARRIES, Olwen (retired) 36 Nantyfelin, Efail Isaf, Pontypridd CF38 1YY Tel: 01443 204217 — MB BCh Wales 1961; FRCOG 1988, M 1974; DObst 1965. Prev: Cons. O & G Mid Glam HA.

HARRIES, Peter Gordon (retired) 42 Astra Court, Hythe, Southampton SO45 6DZ — MB BS 1955 Lond.; MD Lond. 1970; FRCP Lond. 1986, M 1972; FFOM 1979 MFOM 1978; MFCM 1974; DIH Soc. Apoth. Lond. 1965; DObst RCOG 1964. Prev: Chief Med. Off. Rank Hovis McDougall plc.

HARRIES, Philip Gerald 9A Cumnor Rise, Cumnor Hill, Oxford OX2 9HD — MB BS 1988 Lond.

HARRIES, Richard William James Department of Radiology, Diana Princess Of Wales Hospital, North Linncolnshire And Goole NHS Trust, Grimsby DN33 2BA Tel: 01472 875 560 Fax: 01472 875450; 75 Lansdowne Avenue, Grimsby DN32 0BX Tel: 01472 873389 Fax: 01472 875 450 Email: rwjharries@hotmail.com — MB BCh 1977 Wales; FRCR, Lond, 1982; MD 1999. (University Of Wales) Cons. Diagn. Radiol. N. Linncolnshire And Goole, NHS Trust, Grimsby. Socs: Roy. Coll. Radiol.; Brit. Med. Assn.; Brit. Inst. of Radiol. Prev: Sen. Regist. (Diagn. Radiol.) Univ. Hosp. Wales Cardiff.

HARRIES, Samantha Sharon Clare 32 Fairmount Dr, Loughborough LE11 3JR — MB BS 1997 Lond.

HARRIES, Sara Jeanette 23 Rhodesia Road, Brampton, Chesterfield S40 3AL — MB ChB 1959 Bristol; MB ChB (2nd Cl. Hons.) Bristol 1959.

HARRIES, Sarah Elizabeth Beryl Marle Farm, Llandissilio SA66 7JJ — MB BS 1961 Lond.

HARRIES, Sarah Elizabeth Mathias University Hospital, Wales, Heath Park, Cardiff CF14 4XW Tel: 01633 882645 Email: sarah.harries@lineone.net — MB BS 1991 Lond.; FRCA 1988. (Roy. Free Hosp.) Specialist Regist. Anaesth. Univ. Hosp. Wales Cardiff. Prev: SHO (Anaesth.) S.mead Gen. Hosp. Bristol; SHO (Intens. Care) Qu. Med. Centre Nottm.; Specialist Regist. (Anaesth.) Roy. Gwent Hosp. Newport.

HARRIES, Mr Simon Anthony Warwickshire Nuffield Hospital, The Chase, Old Milverton Lane, Leamington Spa CV32 6RW Tel: 01926 427971 — MB BS 1985 Lond.; MS Lond. 1995; FRCS Eng. 1989. (Roy. Free) Cons. Surg. (Gen. Surg.) Warwick Hosp. Socs: Brit. Assn. Surg. Oncol. Prev: Sen. Regist. (Gen. Surg.) Univ. Hosp. of Wales Cardiff; Clin. Lect. (Surg.) Univ. Coll. Hosp. Lond.; Regist. Rotat. (Surg.) Univ. Coll. Hosp. & Middlx. Hosp. Lond.

HARRIES, Simon Richard Dept of Radiology, Royal Devon & Exetor Hospital, Barrack Road, Exeter EX2; Rydon Mill, Rydon Lane, Woodbury FX5 1LB Email: simonrharries@hotmail.com — MB BS 1990 Lond.; FRCR 1997 (UK); MRCP (UK) 1993. Cons. Radiol. Roy. Devon & Exeter Hosp. Exeter Devon.

HARRIES, William Alan (retired) Broad Ash, Southgate, Gower, Swansea SA3 2BA — MB BS Lond. 1947; MRCS Eng. LRCP Lond. 1942. Prev: Ho. Phys. Morriston EMS Hosp.

HARRIES, Mr William James Lloyd, OBE, Group Capt. RAF Med. Br. Retd. Fairways, Butlers Cross, Aylesbury HP17 0TU — MB BS Lond. 1945; FRCS Eng. 1957; MRCS Eng. LRCP Lond. 1945. (Char. Cross) Cons. in Surg. RAF. Socs: Fell. Roy. Soc. Med. Prev: Cas. Off. W. Herts. Hosp. Hemel Hempstead; Ho. Phys. Char. Cross Hosp. (Ashridge EMS Hosp.).

HARRIES-BROWN, Rosemary Anne Andover Health Centre, Charlton Road, Andover SP10 3LD Tel: 01264 350270 Fax: 01264 336701 — MB BS 1981 Lond.; DRCOG 1985.

HARRIES-JONES, Richard Poole Hospital NHS Hospital, Longfleet Road, Poole BH15 2JB Tel: 01202 665511; 16 Chester Road, Branksome Park, Poole BH13 6DD Tel: 01202 762356 — MB BChir 1978 Camb.; MA, MD Camb. 1988, MB BChir 1978; FRCP (1997); MRCP (UK) 1981; LMSSA Lond. 1977. Cons. Phys. Health c/o the Elderly, Poole Hosp. Socs: Brit. Geriat. Soc.; Roy. Coll. Phys. (Ex-Comm. Mem. Neurol.). Prev: Sen. Regist. (Geriat./Gen. Med.) W. Midl. RHA; Regist. (Neurol.) Radcliffe Infirm. Oxf.; Acting Clin. Lect./MRC Research Fell. Univ. Dept. Clin. Neurol. Oxf.

HARRIGAN, Michael James 60 Parklands View, Sketty, Swansea SA2 8LT Tel: 01792 206014 — MB BS 1986 Lond.; MMedSci. (Occupat. Health) Birm. 1992; AFOM RCP Lond. 1992; DAvMed Lond. 1998. (St Bart. Hosp.) Socs: Soc. Occupat. Med.; Aerospace Med. Assoc.; Roy. Aeronautical Soc. (MRAeS).

HARRIGAN, Patrick North Tyneside General Hospital, Rake Lane, North Shields NE29 8NH Tel: 0191 259 6660; 20 Leslie Crescent, Newcastle upon Tyne NE3 4AN Tel: 0191 284 3431 Email: phamgian@blueyonder.co.uk — MB BS 1967 Newc.; FRCP Lond. 1988. Cons. Phys. (Community Geriat.s), N.umbria Healthcare NHS Trust. Prev: Cons. Phys. (Geriat. & Gen. Med.) Newc. Gen. Hosp.; Assoc. Postgrad. Dean Univ. Newc. N.. RHA.

HARRILL, John Guy Marcus The Whipton Surgery, 378 Pinhoe Road, Whipton, Exeter EX4 8EG Tel: 01392 462770 Fax: 01392 466220 — MB BS 1983 Lond.; MRCGP 1995; DRCOG 1987; Cert. Family Plann. JCC 1987.

HARRIMAN, Beatrice Phyllis (retired) Hunter's Moon, Hillcrest, Collingham, Wetherby LS22 5DN Tel: 01937 572316 Fax: 01937 572316 — MB BCh BAO Dub. 1949; MRCPsych 1973; DPM RCPSI 1963.

HARRIMAN, Denis Gaston Frederick (retired) Hunter's Moon, Hillcrest, Collingham, Wetherby LS22 5DN Tel: 01937 572316 — MB BCh BAO 1943 Belf.; DSc Belf. 1991. MD 1947; FRCP Lond. 1967, M 1949; FRCPath 1969, M 1964. Prev: Reader (Neuropath.) Univ. Leeds.

HARRINGTON, Albert Blair, CB (retired) 59 Lauderdale Drive, Petersham, Richmond TW10 7BS Tel: 020 8940 1345 — MD Aberd. 1944, MB ChB 1938; FFCM 1972. Prev: Med. Adviser Civil Serv. Dept.

HARRINGTON, Ashlin Kevin Employee health Services, Post office, 1 Kings Square, Gloucester GL1 1AD Tel: 01452 331981 Fax: 01452 331984; 5 Meadowfield, Bradford-on-Avon BA15 1PL Tel: 01225 862276 — MB ChB 1972 Dundee; MRCGP 1979; MFOM RCP Lond. 1992; Spec. Accredit. Occupat. Med. JCHMT 1994; DRCOG 1978. Cons. Occupat.al Phys., Employee Health Serv.s, W.ern Territory; Occupat. Health Phys. Wilts. CC. Socs: Soc. Occupat. Med.; BMA. Prev: Area Med. Advis. Post Off. Employee health serv.; Sen. Asst. Phys. Reading Univ. Health Serv.; SMO RAF Wattisham.

HARRINGTON, Brendan Edward John Department of Paediatrics, Wrexham Maelor Hospital, Croesnewydd Rd, Wrexham LL13 7TD Tel: 01978 725886 Fax: 01978 725188 Email: brendan.harrington@new-tr.wales.nhs.uk — MB ChB 1988 Bristol; MA Camb. 1981; MRCP (UK) 1992; MD Manchester 1998. (Bristol) Cons. Paediat., N. E. Wales NHS Trust, Wrexham, Wales.

HARRINGTON, Christine Ida Somersby, 3 Endcliffe Grove Avenue, Endcliffe, Sheffield S10 3EJ Tel: 0114 266 7201 — MD 1978 Sheff.; MD (Commend.) Sheff. 1978, MB ChB (Hons.) 1971; FRCP Lond. 1989; MRCP (UK) 1974. Cons. (Dermat.) Roy. Hallamshire Hosp. Sheff. Prev: Sen. Regist. (Dermat.) Roy. Hallamshire Hosp. Sheff.; Rotat. Regist. (Gen. Med.) Roy. Infirm. Sheff.; Ho. Phys. (Gen. Med. & Cardiol.) & Ho. Surg. N.. Gen. Hosp. Sheff.

HARRINGTON, David Anthony Victoria Health Centre, 5 Suffrage Street, Smethwick, Warley B66 3PZ Tel: 0121 558 0216 Fax: 0121 558 4732; 125 Court Oak Road, Harborne, Birmingham B17 9AA Tel: 0121 426 5540 — MB ChB 1981 Birm.

HARRINGTON, Dawn Samantha 1 Park Terrace, Stirling FK8 2NA — MB ChB 1987 Glas.; FFA RCSI 1991; MRCGP 1994.

HARRINGTON, Deborah Jane Queen Charlottes Hospital, Goldhawk Road, London W6 0XG; 3 Chatsworth Lodge, Bourne Place, Chiswick, London W4 2EE Tel: 020 8742 8327 — MB BS 1992 Lond.; BSc (Hons.) Lond. 1989; DFFP 1995. SHO (O & G) Qu. Charlottes Hosp. Lond. Prev: Clin. Research Fell. (O & G) John Radcliffe Hosp. Oxf.; SHO (O & G) John Radcliffe Hosp. Oxf.; SHO (A & E) High Wycombe Gen. Hosp. Bucks.

HARRINGTON, Deborah Kate 157 Cross Lane, Crookes, Sheffield S10 1WN — MB ChB 1995 Sheff.

HARRINGTON, Deirdre Mae Braeside, 1 Kynoch Terrace, Keith AB55 5FX Tel: 015422 2931 — MB ChB 1978 Aberd. Med. Off. (Well Wom. Clin.) Aberlour. Prev: SHO (Chest & Infect. Dis.) Culduthel Hosp. Inverness; SHO (O & G) Kilton & Vict. Hosp. Worksop; SHO (A & E) Stirling Roy. Infirm.

HARRINGTON, Derek William Malcolm Cardiac Department, Kent Sussex Hospital, Mount Ephraim, Tunbridge Wells TN4 8AT Tel: 01892 526111; Tel: 01892 526111 — MB BS 1988 Lond.; MD 1999; BSc Lond. 1985; MRCP (UK) 1991. Cons. Cardiol., Maidstone, Tunbridge Wells NHS Trust, Kent Sussex Hosp., Tunbridge Wells, Kent. Prev: Regist./ Specialist Regist. Roy. Brompton; Research Fell. Nat. Hearts Lung Inst.

HARRINGTON, Frances Mary University Hospital of North Tees, Hardwick, Stockton-on-Tees TS19 8PE — MB ChB 1989 Leic.; MRCP (UK) 1993. Cons. Phys. Univ. Hosp. of N. Tees, Stockton on Tees.

HARRINGTON, Jill 6 Pond Street, High Shincliffe, Durham DH1 2PS — MB ChB 1989 Leic.; MSc Sussex 1984; BSc (Hons.) Lond. 1983.

HARRINGTON, John Gerald 11 Western Avenue, Poole BH13 7AL; 17 Brittania Road, Lower Parkstone, Poole BH14 8AZ Email: jgharri@tesco.net — MB ChB 1995 Manch. SHO (Paediat.) Poole Gen. Hosp.

HARRINGTON, John Hendry Keith Medical Group, Health Centre, Turner St, Keith AB55 5DJ Tel: 01542 882244 Fax: 01542 882317; Braeside, 1 Kynoch Terrace, Keith AB55 5FX Tel: 01542 882931 — MB ChB 1981 Ed.; DRCOG 1986. Prev: Trainee GP Aultbea; SHO (A & E) Falkirk & Dist. Roy. Infirm.; Ho. Off. (Surg.) Raigmore Hosp. Inverness.

HARRINGTON, Professor John Malcolm, CBE Institute of Occupational Health, University of Birmingham, Edgbaston, Birmingham B15 2TT Tel: 0121 414 6022 Fax: 0121 414 2613 Email: j.m.harrington@bham.ac.uk — MB BS Lond. 1966; MSc (Occupat. Med.) Lond. 1970, BSc (Physiol.) 1963, MD 1976; FRCP Lond. 1982, M 1969; MRCS Eng. LRCP Lond. 1966; MFPHM RCP (UK) 1996; FFOM RCPI 1994; FFOM RCP Lond. 1982, M 1979; F Med.Sci 1998. (Westm.) Prof. Occupat. Health Univ. Birm.; Vice Pres. Internat. Commiss. on Occupat. Health. Socs: Soc. Occupat. Med.; Internat. Comm. Occupat. Health; Internat. Epidemiol. Assn. Prev: Sen. Lect. & Lect. (Occupat. Med.) Lond. Sch. Hyg. & Trop. Med.; Vis. Sci. (Environm. Med.) Center for Dis. Control US Pub. Health Serv. Atlanta, USA.

HARRINGTON, Justin Clive Clifton Lodge, 17 Cheddon Road, Taunton TA2 7BL Tel: 01823 282151 Fax: 01823 326755 — MB ChB 1985 Bristol.

HARRINGTON, Kevin Francis The Portland Hospital, 205-209 Gt Portland St, London W1N 6AH Tel: 020 73870022 Fax: 020 73870022 Email: kevin.harrington"gynaesurgeon.co.uk; Academic Department of Obstetrics & Gynaecology, St Bartholomews and the Homerton Hospital, London E9 6SR Tel: 020 85107544 Fax: 020 85107850 — MB BCh BAO 1982 NUI; LRCPI & LRCSI, RCSI 1982; MRCPI, RCPI 1985; DCH, RCSI 1987; MRCOG, RCOG 1989; MD, U of Lond. 1995. (Roy. Coll. of Surg. Irel.) p/t Cons. & Sen. Lec. St. Bart. & the Roy. Lond. Sch. of Med. & Dent., Dept. of O & G The

Homerton Hosp. Socs: Roy. Soc. Med.; Brit. Med Ultrasound Soc.; Internat. Soc. Ultrasound in Obst. & Gyn. Prev: Lect. Sen. Regist King's Coll. Hosp. Lond.; Regist. St. Geo.'s Hosp. Lond.; SHO The Hammeasmith Hosp. Lond.

HARRINGTON, Kevin Joseph Royal Marsden Hospital, Fulham Road, London SW3 6JJ Tel: 0207 808 2586 Fax: 0207 808 2235 Email: kevin.harrington@rmh.nthames.nhs.uk; Email: kevinh@icr.ac.uk — MB BS 1988 Lond.; FRCR 1994; BSc (Hons.) Lond. 1985, MB BS 1988; MRCP (UK) 1991. Cons. (Clin. Oncol.) Roy. Marsden Hosp. Lond. Prev: Regist. (Clin. Oncol.) Hammersmith Hosp. Lond.

HARRINGTON, Leslie Thomas Spires Medical Practice, St. Chads Health Centre, Dimbles Lane, Lichfield WS13 7HT Tel: 01543 258987 Fax: 01543 410162; Burntwood Health Centre, Hudson Drive, Burntwood, Walsall WS7 0EN Tel: 01543 682654 — MB ChB Birm. 1962; MRCGP 1974; DObst RCOG 1964. (Birmingham) Mem. Med. Staff Vict. & St. Michael's Hosps. Lichfield & Hammerwich Hosp; Mem. W. Midl. Inst. Psychother.; Mem. UKCP; Police Surg. Staffs. Div. Socs: Brit. Soc. Med. & Dent. Hypn.; W Midl. Inst. Psychother. Prev: Med. Superintendent Matern. Unit Vict. Hosp. Lichfield; Regist. (O & G) Walsall Hosp. Gp.

HARRINGTON, Mary Gabrielle Airedale General Hospital, Skipton Road, Steeton, Keighley BD20 6TD Tel: 01535 655207 — MB BS 1976 Lond.; MA Oxf. 1977; MRCP (UK) 1980. Cons. (Med. for the Elderly); Dir. of Postgrad. Educat., Airedale NHS Trust. Prev: Cons. & Hon. Sen. Lect. (Health c/o Elderly) King's Coll. Sch. Med. & Dent. Lond.; Sen. Regist. Middlx. & Univ. Coll. Hosps. Lond.; Sub-Dean for Curriculum King's Coll. Sch. Med. & Dent. Lond.

HARRINGTON, Michael (retired) Milnrow Health Centre, Stonefield St., Milnrow, Rochdale OL16 4HZ Tel: 01706 50355 — MB BCh BAO 1952 NUI; MRCGP 1969. Prev: Med. Off. S. Infirm. Cork, Roy. Infirm. Halifax, Birch Hill Hosp.

HARRINGTON, Monica Lelia 110 Pleckgate Road, Blackburn BB1 8PN — MB BCh BAO 1983 NUI.

HARRINGTON, Natalie Jane 51 Norwood Road, Effingham, Leatherhead KT24 5NU — MB ChB 1997 Liverp.

HARRINGTON, Professor Richard Charles Department Child & Adolescent Psychiatry, Royal Manchester Children's Hospital, Hospital Road, Pendlebury, Manchester M27 4HA Tel: 0161 794 4696 Fax: 0161 728 2294 Email: r.c.harrington@man.ac.uk — MB ChB 1980 Birm.; MD Birm. 1991; MPhil Lond. 1987; FCPsych 1996, M 1984. (Birm.) Prof. Child & Adolesc. Psychiat. Univ. Manch.

HARRINGTON, Richard Vincent Manley Thame Health Centre, East Street, Thame OX9 3JZ Tel: 01844 261066; 29 Croft Road, Thame OX9 3JF — MB BS 1985 Lond.; BA Exeter 1979; MRCGP 1989; DRCOG 1988; DCH RCP Lond. 1988; DGM RCP Lond. 1987.

HARRINGTON, Robert Francis Enright (retired) 11 Owarton Street, Lytham, St Annes Lanes — MRCS Eng. LRCP Lond. 1938; MRCGP 1953. Med. Ref., Lytham St Anne, Dep. Ref. Blackpool and Preston; Med. Ref. Lytham St. Anne's Crematorium. Prev: Police Surg. Lancs. Co. Constab.

HARRINGTON, Roger William Edward North End Surgery, High Street, Buckingham MK18 1NU Tel: 01280 818600 Fax: 01280 823449 — MB BS 1972 Lond.; MRCGP 1979; DFFP 1994; DObst RCOG 1975. (St. Geo.) Med. Off. Stowe Sch. & Buckingham Hosp. Socs: Immediate Past Pres. Med. Off.s of Sch.s Assn.; Sec. - Gen. Europ. Union of Sch. and Univ. Health and Med.. (Eusuhm); Fell.Roy. Soc. of Med. Prev: Cas. Off. St. Geo. Hosp. Lond.; SHO (O & G & Paediat.) Heatherwood Hosp. Ascot.

HARRINGTON, Yvonne Marie 2 Brook Road, Maghull, Liverpool L31 3EQ — MB ChB 1991 Sheff.

HARRIOTT, John Charles Robert Frew Medical Centre, Silva Island Way, Salcott Crescent, Wickford SS12 9NR Tel: 01268 578800 Fax: 01268 578825 — MB BS 1987 Lond.; DGM RCP Lond. 1990. Prev: Trainee GP Roy. Cornw. Hosp. (Treliske) VTS.

HARRIS, Adam Wayne Kent & Sussex Hospital, Mount Ephraim, Tunbridge Wells TN4 8AT Tel: 01892 526111 Fax: 01892 528381 Email: drawh1@aol.com — MB BS 1987 Lond.; FRCP 2001; BSc Lond. 1984, MD 1995; MRCP (UK) 1990. (Char. Cross & Westm. Hosp. Lond.) Cons. Phys. & Gastroenterol. Kent & Sussex Hosp. Socs: Brit. Soc. Gastroenterol.; Amer. Gastroenterol. Assn. Prev: Sen. Regist. (Gastroenterol. Med.) Centr. Middlx. Hosp. Lond.; Helicobacter Research Fell. Centr. Middlx. & St. Mary's Hosps. Lond.; Regist. Rotat. (Gen. Med. & Gastroenterol.) St. Geo. Hosp. Lond.

HARRIS, Professor Adrian Llewellyn ICRF Medical Oncology Unit, Churchhill Hospital, Headington, Oxford OX3 7LJ Tel: 01865 226184 Fax: 01865 226179; Institute of Molecular Medicine, John Radcliffe Hospital, Headington, Oxford OX3 9DS Tel: 01865 222457 Fax: 01865 222431 — DPhil. Oxf. 1979, MA 1989; BSc (Hons. Biochem.) Liverp. 1970, MB ChB (Hons.) 1973; FRCP Lond. 1986; MRCP (UK) 1975. ICRF Prof. Clin. Oncol. Univ. Oxf.; Dir. ICRF Clin. Oncol. Laborat. Inst. Molecular Med.; Profess. Fell. St Hugh's Coll. Oxf. Prev: Dir. CRC Laborat. Roy. Vict. Hosp. Newc.; Prof. Clin. Oncol. Univ. Newc.; Sen. Regist. (Med. Oncol.) Roy. Marsden Hosp. Lond.

HARRIS, Adrian Michael 11 Elm Grove, Forest Hall, Newcastle upon Tyne NE12 7AN — MB BS 1990 Newc.; FRCS Ed. 1996. Specialist Regist. (Gen. Surg.).

HARRIS, Mr Adrian Ralph Royal Devon & Exeter Hosp., Emergency Department, Barrack Road, Exeter EX2 5DW Tel: 01392 402170 Fax: 01392 402302 — MB BS 1986 Lond.; FRCS Ed. 1994; FFRAEM 1996; DCH RCP Lond. 1991; DIMC Ed. 1998. Cons. Emerg. Med. Roy. Devon & Exeter Hosp.

HARRIS, Alan Margeston Flat 10 Harmont House, 20 Harley St., London W1G 9PH Tel: 020 7637 3765 Fax: 020 7637 3765; Langridge Farm House, Hook Lane, West Hoathly, East Grinstead RH19 4PT Tel: 01342 810293 — MB BS (Hons. Distinc. Path., Surg., Midw. & Gyn. & Univ. Medal Med.) Lond. 1957; BSc (1st cl. Hons. Physiol.) Lond. 1955; MD Lond. 1965; FRCP Lond. 1976, M 1960; MRCS Eng. LRCP Lond. 1957. (St. Geo) Cons. Cardiol. Char. Cross Hosp. & Chelsea & W.m. Hosp. Lond.; Hon. Cons. Phys. Nat. Heart Hosp. Lond.; Phys. BUPA Med. Centre Lond. Socs: Fell. Europ. Soc. Cariol.; Brit. Cardiac Soc. & Med. Research Soc.; Fell. Roy. Soc. of Med. Prev: Hon. Cons. Phys. St. Geo. Hosp. Lond. & Sen. Lect. (Cardiol.) St. Geo. Hosp. Med. Sch. Lond.

***HARRIS, Alexandra Evelyn** Talwyn, Vicarage Lane, Lelant, St Ives TR26 3EA — BM 1995 Soton.

HARRIS, Alexandra Jane Greenwich Hospital, Greenwich, London SE10 9UG Tel: 020 8312 6489; 10 Kemsing Raod, Greenwich, London SE10 9UP — MB BS 1990 Lond.; BSc Lond. 1987; MRCP 1993. Cons. Dermatol. Greenwich Hosp. Lond. Socs: RSM; BAD.

HARRIS, Alison Rosemary Great Oakley Medical Centre, 1 Barth Close, Great Oakley, Corby NN18 8LU Tel: 01536 460046 Fax: 01536 461404; 79 Arden Way, Market Harborough LE16 7DB Tel: 01858 462956 — MB ChB 1990 Leic.; MRCGP 1995; DRCOG 1994; DCH RCP Ed. 1993. (Leic.) GP Asst.; Clin. Asst. (Genitourin. Med.). Prev: Clin. Asst. (Palliat. Care).

HARRIS, Allan Leonard Haxby - Wigginton Health Centre, 2 The Village, Wiggington, York YO32 9SL Tel: 01904 760125 Fax: 01904 750168; 11 Moor Lane, Haxby, York YO32 2PH Tel: 01904 768666 Email: allan@moor_lane.demon.co.uk — MRCS Eng. LRCP Lond. 1973. (Leeds) Socs: Assoc. Mem. Musculoskeletal Med.; York Med. Soc.; Primary Care Rheum. Soc.

HARRIS, Allan Richard Saint Chad Health Centre, Dimbles Lane, Lichfield WS13 7HT; 5 Leomansley Court, Lichfield WS13 8AT — MB BS 1991 Lond.

HARRIS, Alun Ap Gwilym Dyfed Road Health Centre, Dyfed Road, Neath SA11 3AP Tel: 01639 635331; Ty Caederwen, Penyralltwen, Alltwen, Pontardawe, Swansea SA8 3EA Tel: 01792 869673 — MB BCh 1981 Wales; DRCOG 1984; Dip. Occ. Med. 1996.

HARRIS, Andrew Furlong Medical Centre, Furlong Road, Tunstall, Stoke-on-Trent ST6 5UD Tel: 01782 577388 — MB ChB 1956 Manch. Socs: N. Staffs. Med. Soc.

HARRIS, Andrew John 40 Red Lion Road, Chobham, Woking GU24 8RG — MB BS 1988 Lond. (Univ. Coll. Hosp.) Occupat. Health Phys. Surrey.

HARRIS, Mr Andrew Michael Shaftesbury Medical Centre, 480 Harehills Lane, Leeds LS9 6DE Tel: 0113 248 5631 Fax: 0113 235 0658; Ingledew Cottage, Cross Ingledew Crescent, Leeds LS8 1BR Tel: 0113 266 0926 — MB ChB 1983 Leeds; FRCS Ed. 1988; MRCGP 1990; T(GP) 1991; DRCOG 1990.

HARRIS, Andrew Nigel Grahame Lambeth, Southwark & Lewisham, Family Health Services Authority, 1 Lower Marsh, London SE1 7RJ Tel: 020 7716 7000 Fax: 020 7716 7070; Bellevarde, 77 Underhill Road, Dulwich, London SE22 0QR Tel: 020 8693 1206

Fax: 020 8693 1206 — MB BChir 1977 Camb.; MA Camb. 1977; MRCP (UK) (Paediat.) 1980. (St. Thos.) Dir. Clin. Policy & Research Lambeth, S.wark & Lewisham FHSA; Hon. Lect. (Gen. Pract.) King's Coll. Eye Hosp. Lond. Socs: Fell. Roy. Soc. Med.; BMA. Prev: Sen. GP Lond.; SHO/Clin. Med. Off. (Child Health) Guy's Hosp. Lond.

HARRIS, Andrew Richard Birkbeck 116 St Gregory's Crescent, Gravesend DA12 4JW; 90 Darnley Road, Gravesend DA11 0SW Tel: 01474 355331 — MB BS 1976 Lond.; MRCS Eng. LRCP Lond. 1976; DRCOG 1980. (Guy's) Asst. Lions Hospice N.fleet; Mem. W. Kent LMC. Prev: Trainee GP Tunbridge Wells VTS.

HARRIS, Angus Seward, MC (retired) 50 Bath Road, Emsworth PO10 7ER Tel: 01243 372559 — MB BChir Camb. 1951; MA Camb. 1951; MFPHM 1981; DObst RCOG 1953. Prev: DMO Chichester HA.

HARRIS, Ann 11 The Halve, Trowbridge BA14 8SD; Church Farm, Bathford, Bath BA1 7RT — BM BCh 1955 Oxf.; DObst RCOG 1957; DCH Eng. 1957. (St. Geo.)

HARRIS, Anthony Paul Alvaston Medical Centre, 14 Boulton Lane, Alvaston, Derby DE24 0GE Tel: 01332 571322 — MB ChB 1978 Leeds; MRCGP 1982; DRCOG 1982.

HARRIS, Anthony Warren 519 Jockey Road, Sutton Coldfield B73 5DF Tel: 0121 354 1749; Smithy Hay, Longdon Green, Rugeley WS15 4QG Tel: 01543 490468 — MB ChB 1959 Birm.; MRCS Eng. LRCP Lond. 1959; DObst RCOG 1960. (Birm.) Med. Off. Remploy Ltd. Garretts Green La. Birm. Prev: Med. Off. Dunlop Co. Ltd. Birm.; Ho. Off. (Med.) Gen. Hosp. Birm.; Ho. Off. (O & G) St. Chad's Hosp. Birm.

HARRIS, Arthur Raymond (retired) Bodlondeb, Duffryn Terrace, Elliot's Town, New Tredegar NP24 6XJ Tel: 01443 834314 — MB BCh 1951 Wales; BSc Wales 1947. Med. Adviser Med. Ref. Serv. BAMS (DSS). Prev: SHO (Gen. Med.) & Ho. Off. (Paediat.) St. David's Hosp. Cardiff.

HARRIS, Benedict Robert Flat 12, 72 St Katherine's Way, London E1W 1UF — MB BS 1993 Lond.; DRCOG 1995. (St. Bart.) SHO (Paediat). James Paget Hosp. Gt. Yarmouth. Prev: SHO (A & E) Cumbld. Infirm. Carlisle; SHO (O & G) Doncaster Roy. Infirm.; Ho Off. Timaru Hosp., NZ.

HARRIS, Benjamin David Hospice Care (IoM), St Bridget's Hospice, Kensington Road, Douglas IM1 3PE Tel: 01624 626530 Fax: 01624 623846 Email: bdh@doctors.org.uk; Mona Cottage, Ballakilpheric, Colby, Castletown IM9 4BU Tel: 01624 834159 — MB ChB 1989 Liverp.; BSc (Hons.) Physiol. Liverp. 1986; MRCGP 1995; Dip. Palliat. Med. (Distinc.) Wales 1996; DRCOG 1992; Cert. Managem. Studies BTEC 1998. (Liverp.) Med. Dir. St. Bridgetis Hospice Douglas. I. of Man. Socs: I. of Man Med. Soc. Prev: Trainee GP Yorks. VTS.

HARRIS, Bernard Victor 1 Parklands, Whitefield, Manchester M45 7WY Tel: 0161 767 9665 — MB ChB Liverp. 1961; DCH Eng. 1964. Med. Examr. Benefits Agency Med. Serv.; GP Locum. Socs: Bolton Med. Soc.

HARRIS, Brian Benjamin 2 Chargot Road, Llandaff, Cardiff CF5 1EW Tel: 02920 563916 — MRCS Eng. LRCP Lond. 1963; BSc, MB BS Lond. 1963; FRCPsych 1991, M 1972; DPM Eng. 1968. (Westm.) Cons. In Gen. Psychiat., Powys NHS Trust, Bronllys, Hosp. Brecon LD3 0LU. Prev: Sen. Regist. (Psychiat.) Univ. Hosp. Wales; Sen. Regist. (Psychiat.) St. Thos. Hosp. Lond.; SHO (Psychiat. & Med.) United Bristol Hosps.

HARRIS, Brian Trevor 368-374 Commercial Road, London E1 0LR — MB ChB 1959 Liverp.; FRCGP 1980, M 1973. Socs: Fell. Roy. Soc. Med. Prev: Sen. Lect. (Gen. Pract.) Lond. Hosp. & St. Bart.; Dir. Centre for the Study of Primary Care Steel's La. Health Centre; Clin. Asst. (Rheum.) Lond. Hosp.

HARRIS, Carl Philip 85 Park Road, Prestwich, Manchester M25 0DX — MB BS 1985 Lond.; MRCOG 1991. (Lond. Hosp. Med. Coll.) Cons. O & G Billinge Hosp. Wigan; Chairm. of Clin. Effectiveness & Audit. Socs: Brit. Fertil. Soc.; Brit. Menopause Soc. Prev: Sen. Regist. (O & G) St. Mary's Hosp. Manch. & Billinge Hosp. Wigan; Clin. Research Fell. (Reproductive Med.) Withington Hosp.

HARRIS, Caroline Sara Hurstbourne Cottage, 1 Well Cross, Edith Weston, Oakham LE15 8HG Tel: 01780 721023 Fax: 01780 721023 — MA (Oxf.) 1980; MB BS Lond. 1980.

HARRIS, Charles 33 Hill Top, London NW11 6ED Tel: 020 8455 9184 — MRCS Eng. LRCP Lond. 1941. (Univ. Coll. Hosp.) Prev: Mem. City & W.m. Disablem. Advis. Comm.; Clin. Asst. Roy. Nat. Throat, Nose & Ear Hosp. Lond.; Capt. RAMC.

***HARRIS, Charles Rowland William** 11 St Audries Road, Battenhall, Worcester WR5 2AL — MB ChB 1995 Birm.

HARRIS, Charlotte Brigitte 59 The Avenue, Cheam, Sutton SM2 7QE — BChir 1995 Camb.

HARRIS, Christiane Gaye Maxine Bradley and Partners, 30 Woodland Avenue, Luton LU3 1RW Tel: 01582 572239 Fax: 01582 494227 — MB BS 1987 Lond.; BSc Lond. 1984; MRCGP 1995. Socs: BMA. Prev: Trainee GP Luton; Resid. (Surg.) King Edwd. VII Memor. Hosp., Bermuda; SHO (A & E) Luton & Dunstable Hosp.

HARRIS, Christopher Paul The Ridge Medical Practice, 3 Paternoster Lane, Great Horton, Bradford BD7 3EE Tel: 01274 502905 Fax: 01274 522060; 8 Grosvenor Avenue, Shipley BD18 4RR Tel: 01274 595881 — MB ChB 1987 Leeds; MRCP (UK) 1991; DRCOG 1992; DA (UK) 1991.

HARRIS, Claire 12 Harlech Cl, Blackwood NP12 1HJ — MB ChB 1997 Aberd.

HARRIS, Claire Agnes 2 Banks Terrace, Hurworth Place, Darlington DL2 2DE — MB BS 1980 Monash.

HARRIS, Claire Louise 48 Abbots Way, Morpeth NE61 2LZ — MB ChB 1998 Dund.; MB ChB Dund 1998.

HARRIS, Clare Jayne 52 padwell Road, Inner Avenue, Southampton SO14 6RA — BM BS 1995 Nottm.

HARRIS, Colin Albert 35 Parkinch EStreet, Erskine PA8 7HZ — MB ChB 1991 Glas.

HARRIS, Colin Calder Skene Medical Group, Westhill Drive, Westhill AB32 6FY Tel: 01224 742213 Fax: 01224 744664; Slack of Larg, Skene, Westhill AB32 6UB Tel: 01224 740965 — MB ChB 1974 Aberd.; FRCGP 1992, M 1978; DRCOG 1977. (Aberdeen) GP Dep. Trainer; GP Undergrad. Tutor.

HARRIS, Professor Conrad Michael Division of General Practice, 20 Hyde Terrace, Leeds LS2 9LN Tel: 0113 233 4180 Fax: 0113 233 4181; 4 Tudor House, Oakwood Grove, Leeds LS8 2PA Tel: 0113 265 0761 — MB ChB 1957 Liverp.; MEd Manch. 1974; FRCGP 1971, M 1964; DObst RCOG 1969. Prof. Dept. Gen. Pract. Univ. Leeds. Prev: Sen. Lect. & Head Dept. (Gen. Pract.) St. Mary's Hosp. Med. Sch. Lond.; Sen. Lect. (Gen. Pract.) Manch. Univ. Sch. Med.

HARRIS, Cyril The Medical Centre, 10A Northumberland Court, Shepway, Maidstone ME17 7LN Tel: 01622 753920; 14 Parkwood Parade, Maidstone ME15 9HJ Tel: 01622 56909 — MB ChB 1953 Glas.; LRCP LRCS Ed. LRFPS Glas. 1953; DMJ (Path.) 1980. (Glas.) Chief Med. Off. Kent Co. Constab.; Regional Med. Off. Navy, Army & Air Force Insts. Maidstone; Authorised Examr. Health & Safety Exec. Offshore Divers GB & Norway; Police Surg. Maidstone; Med. Assessor DHSS Reg. Med. Off. Treasury; DVLA Swansea Examr. Socs: Fell. Roy. Soc. Med. (Founder Mem. Forens. Sect.). Prev: SHO Ashford Hosp. Middlx.; Resid. Med. Off. Maidenhead Hosp.; Ho. Phys. Hairmyres Hosp. E. Kilbride.

HARRIS, David Auckland Medical Group, 54 Cockton Hill Road, Bishop Auckland DL14 6BB Tel: 01388 602728 — MB BS 1964 Durh.; BSc Durham. 1961.

HARRIS, Mr David Oswestry Orthopaedic Hospital, Oswestry SY10 7AG Tel: 01691 655311; Sandhurst, Port Hill Road, Shrewsbury SY3 8JF Tel: 01743 362694 Fax: 01743 362694 — MB BS Lond. 1958; FRCS Eng. 1966. (Univ. Coll. Hosp.) Sen. Orthop. Surg. Robt. Jones & Agnes Hunt Orthop. Hosp. OsW.ry. Socs: Brit. Soc. Surg. Hand; Brit. Microsurgic. Soc. Prev: Dir. (Hand & Microsurg. Serv.) & Resid. Surgic. Off. Robt. Jones & Agnes Hunt Orthop. Hosp. OsW.ry; Regist. (Orthop.) Centr. Middlx. Hosp. Lond.; SHO Roy. Nat. Orthop. Hosp.

HARRIS, David Ian 70 Hallam Road, Mapperley, Nottingham NG3 6HR — MB ChB 1994 Manch.; MB ChB (Hons.) Manch. 1994; PhD Aberystwyth 1988, BSc 1984; MRCGP 1999. GP. Socs: BMA. Prev: SHO (Internal Med.) Qu. Med. Centre Nottm.; SHO (O & G), Langsnell Hosp., Mansfield; SHO (Paediat.), City Hosp., Nottm.

HARRIS, Mr David Leslie The Nuffield Hospital, Derriford Road, Plymouth PL6 8BG Tel: 01752 707345 Fax: 01752 778421 — MB BS Lond. 1961; MB BS Lond. 1961; MS Lond. 1972; MS Lond. 1972; FRCS Eng. 1966; FRCS Eng. 1966; MRCS Eng. LRCP Lond. 1961; MRCS Eng. LRCP Lond. 1961. (Westm.) Sen. Cons. Plastic Surg. Plymouth Hosps. NHS Trust (1972-1998). Socs: (Pres.) Brit. Assn. Aesthetic Plastic Surgs. (1989 -1991); Brit. Assn. Plastic Surg.

Prev: Sen. Regist. & Hon. Lect. (Surg.) Makerere Univ. Kampala, Uganda; Sen. Regist. (Plastic Surg.) Univ. Hosp. S. Manch.; Regist. (Clin. Research) Roy. Marsden Hosp. Lond.

HARRIS, David Martin, Lt.-Col. RAMC Retd. Falkland Cottage, High St., Culworth, Banbury OX17 2BG Tel: 01295 760434 — MA Oxf. 1963, BM BCh 1965. (Oxf.) Occupat. Phys. Horton Gen. Hosp. NHS Trust & Littlemore & Warneford Hosps. Oxf.

HARRIS, David Melvyn (retired) 384 Whirlowdale Road, Sheffield S11 9NJ Tel: 0114 249 9863 — MB BS Lond. 1960; MD Lond. 1968; FRCPath 1980, M 1968. Hon. Clin. Lect. (Med. Microbiol.) Univ. Sheff. Prev: Cons. Microbiol. Centr. Sheff. Univ. Hosps.

HARRIS, David Nigel Fraser 2 Harewood Row, London NW1 6SE — MB ChB 1974 Bristol; FFA RCS Eng. 1984.

HARRIS, David Stephen 9 Willow Grove, Landare, Aberdare CF44 8BS — MB BCh 1991 Wales.

HARRIS, David William Simmons The London Clinic of Dermatology, The Hospital of St John & St Elizabeth, 60 Grove End Rd, London NW8 9NH Tel: 020 7431 2714 Fax: 020 7431 2714 Email: dharris@dircon.co.uk — MB BS 1981 Lond.; MRCP (UK) 1985; T(M) 1992; FRCP 1998. (Royal Free Hospital School of Medicine) Cons. Dermat. Whittington Hosp. Lond. Socs: Eur. Soc. Micrographic Surg.; Brit. Soc. Dermat. Surg.; Brit. Assn. Dermatol. Prev: Overseas Fell. (Dermat. Surg.) Univ. Minnesota, USA; Sen. Regist. (Dermat.) Roy. Free Hosp. Lond.

HARRIS, Dawn Elizabeth 7 Holly Street, Summerseat, Bury BL9 5PS — MB ChB 1990 Manch.

HARRIS, Dawn Elizabeth Royal Cornhill Hospital, 26 Cornhill Road, Aberdeen AB25 2ZH Tel: 01224 663131 Fax: 01224 646201; 74 Burns Road, Aberdeen AB15 4NS Tel: 01224 324895 Fax: 01224 324895 Email: dawn@deskjourno.demon.co.uk — MB ChB 1971 Aberd.; MSc (Pub. Health) Aberd. 1995. Med. Off. Roy. Cornhill Hosp. Aberd. Prev: Med. Off. (Occupat. Health) Aberd.; Clin. Asst. (Cardiol.) Aberd. Roy. Infirm.

HARRIS, Dean Anthony 27 Porter Road, Evesham WR11 6YA — MB BCh 1997 Wales.

HARRIS, Dean Mark Dullshot House Surgery, 12 The Parade, Epsom KT18 5DW Tel: 01372 726361 — MB BS 1984 Lond.; MRCGP 1988; DRCOG 1988.

HARRIS Diana Margaret 146 Lordswood Road, Harborne, Birmingham B17 9BT Tel: 0121 427 5904 Fax: 0121 428 1129; 2 Currie Hill Close, Wimbledon, London SW19 7DX Tel: 020 8946 6790 — MB ChB 1985 Birm.; MRCGP 1990; DTM & H 1990; DRCOG 1989. GP on Doctors Retainer Scheme. Socs: BMA. Prev: Trainee GP. Cent. Birm. HA. VTS; SHO (Paediat., O & G & Accid & Emerg.) Cent. Birm. HA.

HARRIS, Dominic James 53A West Street, Lilley, Luton LU2 8LH — MB BS 1994 Lond.

HARRIS, Dorothy Eileen (retired) 65 Ruddlesway, Windsor SL4 5SG — MB BS Lond. 1953; FFA RCS Eng. 1960. Prev: Cons. Anaesth. E. Berks. DHA.

HARRIS, Douglas Cameron Mackay Peterculter Health Service, Coronation Road, Peterculter AB14 0RQ Tel: 01224 733535 Fax: 01224 735662; The Glen, 1 Station Road E., Peterculter AB14 0PT — MB ChB 1984 Ed.; MRCGP 1992. Socs: BMA. Prev: Trainee GP Aberd. VTS.

HARRIS, Edward Annie Prendergash Health Centre, Ashton Gardens, Romford RM6 6RT Tel: 020 8590 1461 Fax: 020 8597 7819 — MB BCh BAO 1959 Dub.; DObst RCOG 1962. (T.C. Dub.)

HARRIS, Elizabeth Ann Evelyn (retired) 91 Minchenden Crescent, London N14 7EP — MB BS 1962 Lond.; MRCS Eng. LRCP Lond. 1962; MRCP UK 1980; FFCM 1987, M 1972; DCH Eng. 1977; DPH Eng. 1971. Prev: Dist. Med. Off. Gt. Yarmouth & Waveney DHA.

HARRIS, Elizabeth Erica 44 Marsite Mill Lane, Saltburn-by-the-Sea TS12 1HR Tel: 01287 623103 — MB ChB 1978 Sheff.

HARRIS, Ella Elizabeth Leonie Cae R'Odyn, 5 New Road, Rhos, Pontardawe, Swansea SA8 4PJ — MB ChB 1954 Birm.

HARRIS, Eric Holly Lane Clinic, Holly Lane, Smethwick, Warley B66 1QW Tel: 0121 558 5117 Fax: 0121 555 6938; 152 Newton Road, Great Barr, Birmingham B43 6BU Tel: 0121 357 1421 Email: eqls201@aom.com — MB BS Madras 1957; MFFP 1993. Manager Med. Dir. Family Plann. Serv. Sandwell W Midl.

HARRIS, Erika — MB ChB 1991 Sheff.; Clin Dip in Behaviourial Cognitive Ther St George's Hosp 1998; MRCPsych 1997. (Univ. Sheff.) p/t Specialist Regist. Child Psychiat. Socs: Assn. Child Psychol. & Psychiat.; Brit. Assn. of Behaviourial & Cognitive Psychother. Prev: SHO (Child Psychiat.) Horsham; SHO (Psychiat.) Springfield Tooting; SPR Maudsley Hosp.

HARRIS, Evan 32A North Hinksey Village, Oxford OX2 0NA Tel: 01865 250424 — BM BCh 1991 Oxf.; BA (Hons.) Oxf. 1988. MP. Socs: BMA. Prev: SHO (Gen. Med.) Oxf. Radcliffe Hosp.; Hon. Regist. (Pub. Health) & Regional Task Force Med. Off. Oxf. & Anglia RHA.

HARRIS, Fiona Ann Ruth Wheatfield Surgery, 60 Wheatfield Road, Lewsey Farm, Luton LU4 0TR Tel: 01582 601116 Fax: 01582 666421; 60 Station Road, Stanbridge, Leighton Buzzard LU7 9JF — MB BS 1987 Lond.

HARRIS, Fiona Elizabeth Division of Renal Medicine, St Georges Hospital Medical School, Cranmer Terrace, London SW17 0RE Tel: 020 8725 5310 Email: fharris@sghms.ac.uk; 5 Blenheim Close, Ashurst Bridge, Totton, Southampton SO40 2QR — BM 1990 Soton.; MRCP (UK) 1993. Clin. Research Fell. (Renal Med.) St. Geo. Hosp. Med. Sch. Lond. Prev: Regist. Rotat. (Med.) Greenwich Dist. Gen. Hosp. & King's Coll. Hosp. Lond.; SHO (ITU) Birm. Heartlands Hosp.; SHO Rotat. (Med.) St. Mary's Hosp. Portsmouth.

HARRIS, Fiona Ellen Springburn Health Centre, 200 Springburn Way, Glasgow G21 1TR Tel: 0141 531 9691 Fax: 0141 531 6705; 15 Tassie St, Glasgow G41 3QB — MB ChB 1991 Manch.; MRCGP 1996; DRCOG 1994. (Manch.)

HARRIS, Fiona Patricia 2 Swaledale Gardens, High Heaton, Newcastle upon Tyne NE7 7TA — MB ChB 1989 Glas.; MRCP (UK) 1995. Specialist Regist. (Clin. Oncol.).

HARRIS, Frances Eleanor The Centre Practice, Osborne Road, Fareham PO16 7EF Tel: 01329 823456 — MB BS 1989 Lond. (St. Geo. Hosp. Med. Sch.)

HARRIS, Francis Alan Sylvester (retired) Castleview, Park Barn Road, Broomfield, Maidstone ME17 1PN — MB BS Lond. 1954; DObst RCOG 1957. Prev: Med. Adviser Camb. & Huntingdon HA.

HARRIS, Francis Gordon (retired) 79 Sandy Lane, Hucknall, Nottingham NG15 7GN — MB ChB 1956 Leeds. Prev: GP Nottm.

HARRIS, Professor Frank, CBE University of Leicester Faculty of Medicine, and Biological Sciences, PO Box 138, Maurice Shock Medical Sciences Building University Road, Leicester LE1 9HN Tel: 0116 252 2962 Fax: 0116 252 5001 — MB ChB Cape Town 1957; MD Cape Town 1964, MMed 1963; FRCP Lond. 1982; FRCP Ed. 1975, M 1969; FRCPCH 1997. Dean. Fac. Med. & Biological Sci.s Univ. Leicester; Prof. (Paediat.) Univ. Leicester; Mem. Leics. DHA; Mem. ACMT. Socs: Assn. Phys.; Acad. of Med. Sci. Prev: Exec. Sec. Counc. of Deans of UK Med. Schs. & Faculties; Dean Fac. Med., Pro-Vice-Chancellor & Prof. Child Health Univ. Liverp.

HARRIS, Gareth Edward 17 Clarence Road, Harpenden AL5 4AJ — MB ChB 1997 Manch.

HARRIS, Gavin Charles Peak Cottage, Monyash Road, Bakewell DE45 1FG — BM BS 1993 Nottm.

HARRIS, Giles Malcolm Pamphilion, 46 Farleys Way, Peasmarsh, Rye TN31 6PZ — BM BS 1995 Nottm.

HARRIS, Gillian Pfizer Ltd, Ramsgate Road, Sandwich CT13 — MB ChB 1986 Glas.; AFOM (July) 2001; MSc Occ. Health (Birm.) 2000. p/t Occupat. Health Doctor Pfizer Sandwich Kent. Socs: Soc. of Occupat.al Med. Mem.

HARRIS, Gilmour 28 Hogback Wood Road, Beaconsfield HP9 1JT — MB ChB 1951 Glas.; FRFPS Glas. 1955; FRCP Glas. 1981, M 1962; MRCP Lond. 1957. Sen. Research Fell. Hon. Cons. Dept. Immunol., Lond. Hosp. Med. Coll. Socs: Brit. Soc. Immunol. & Brit. Soc. Haemat. Prev: Head Div. Experim. Path. Mathilda & Terence Kennedy Research Inst. Lond.; Sen. Lect. Immunol. & Hon. Cons. St. Mary's Hosp. Lond.

HARRIS, Gordon 38 Carmel Road S., Darlington — MB BS 1963 Durh.; FFARCS Eng. 1970. Cons. (Anaesth.) N. Tees Gen. Hosp. Socs: Assoc. Anaesth. & N.E. Soc. Anaesth. Prev: Cons. (Anaesth.) King Faisal Specialist Hosp. Riyadh Saudi Arabia, & Notre Dame De Fatima Hosp. Tehran; Capt. Specialist Anaesth. RAMC.

HARRIS, Graeme Kerr Quarry Street Surgery, 24 Quarry Street, Johnstone PA5 8ED — MB ChB 1981 Glas.; FRCP 1999 Glasgow; MRCP (UK) 1986; MRCGP 1985; DRCOG 1983. Prev: Hosp. Pract. Med. Clinic Roy. Alexandra Hosp. Paisley.

HARRIS, Guy (retired) The Medical Centre, Shipston-on-Stour CV36 4BQ Tel: 01608 61845 — BM BCh 1954 Oxf.; A, BM BCh Oxf. 1954; FRCGP 1980, M 1965; DObst RCOG 1956. JP.

HARRIS, Mr Guy Jonathan Charles The Coach House, Chestnut Road, Long Ashton, Bristol BS41 9HR Tel: 01275 392294 — MB BS 1991 Lond.; FRCS Eng. 1995. (St. Geo. Hosp. Lond.) Regist. (Gen. Surg.) Mayday Hosp. Croydon.

HARRIS, Gwendolen Ruth (retired) 6 Beacon Lane, Sedgley, Dudley DY3 1NB Tel: 01902 663134 — MB ChB Leeds 1956. Prev: GP Tipton.

HARRIS, Gwyn Peter Morgan 7 Crumpfields Lane, Webheath, Redditch B97 5PN — MB ChB 1990 Birm.

HARRIS, Professor Sir Henry Sir William Dunn School of Pathology, University of Oxford, South Parks Road, Oxford OX1 3RE Tel: 01865 275577 Fax: 01865 275501 — MB BS 1950 Sydney; FRS 1968; MA Oxf. 1963, DPhil 1954, DM 1979; BA Sydney 1944; FRCP Lond. 1976; FRCPath 1980. Regius Prof. Med. Emerit. Univ. Oxf. Prev: Prof. Path. Univ. Oxf.

HARRIS, Hilary Jean Brooklands Medical Practice, 594 Altrincham Road, Brooklands, Manchester M23 9JH Tel: 0161 998 3818 Fax: 0161 946 0716; The Cottage, Catherine Road, Bowdon, Altrincham WA14 2TD — MB ChB 1967 Liverp.; FRCGP 1997. (Liverp.) Research Asst. Dept. of Med. Genetics St. Marys Hosp. Manch. Socs: Manch. Med. Soc.; Brit. Soc. Human Genetics.

HARRIS, Hilary Margaret Burnhaies Farm, Butterleigh, Cullompton EX15 1PG — MB BS 1991 Newc.; DRCOG 1995; DCH RCP Lond. 1996; MRCGP 1997. (Newc. u. Tyne) GP Princip. Prev: GP Regist. Axminster; SHO (Gen. Med.) Roy. Devon & Exeter Hosp. Wonford.

HARRIS, Hilda Ruth (retired) The National Westminster Bank plc, Manchester Deansgate Br., PO Box 420, 11 Spring Gardens, Manchester M60 3NL Email: 7uth@ha771.fsbusiness.co.uk — MB ChB 1940 Manch.; MD Manch. 1958; FRCP Ed. 1982, M 1955; FRCPath 1973, M 1963; DPath. Eng. 1952. Prev: Cons. Histopath. Clwyd S. Health Dist.

HARRIS, Ian 7 Lancaster Road, Southport PR8 2LF — MB BS 1980 Lond.; MA Oxf. 1982; MRCP (UK) 1985.

HARRIS, Ian Martin The Surgery, 21 Queens Road, Brighton BN1 3XA Tel: 01273 328080 Fax: 01273 725209; Hangleton Manor Surgery, 96 Northease Drive, Hove BN3 8LH Tel: 01273 419628 Fax: 01273 423927 — BM BCh 1972 Oxf.; MA Oxf. 1972. Prev: Trainee GP Brighton VTS.

HARRIS, Israel Jacob (retired) 8 Linksway, Wallasey CH45 0NE Tel: 0151 638 2418 — MB ChB 1941 Liverp.

HARRIS, Jacqueline 5 Jolly Brows, Bolton BL2 4LZ — MB ChB 1990 Sheff.

HARRIS, Janet Directorate of Child Health, Royal Cornwall Hospitals Trust, Pendragon House, Gloweth, Truro TR1 3XQ — MB ChB 1966 Liverp.; BSc (Hons. Physiol.) Liverp. 1963, MB ChB 1966; FRCPCH 1997. (Liverp.) Cons. Community Paediat. Roy. Cornw. Hosps. Trust. Prev: SCMO Cornw. AHA; SHO (Paediat.) Roy. Cornw. Hosp. Truro; Clin. Med. Off. Cornw. AHA.

HARRIS, Janet Anne West House Farm, Llanmaes, Llantwit Major CF61 2XR — MB ChB 1980 Bristol; MRCGP 1985; DRCOG 1982. Staff Grade Med. Off. Bridgent & Dist. NHS Trust. Prev: Clin. Med. Off. Mid & S. Glam. Health Auth.; GP Budleigh Salterton Devon; Trainee GP Exeter VTS.

HARRIS, Jayne Elizabeth The Surgery, 1 Boxwell Road, Berkhamsted HP4 3EU Tel: 01442 863119 Fax: 01442 879909 — MB BS 1988 Lond.; MRCGP 1993. (St George's Hospital) GP Berkhamsted.

HARRIS, Jeanette Grayson 160 St Leonards Road, Windsor SL4 3DL — MB BS 1989 Lond.

HARRIS, Jeremy Nicholas The Groves Medical Centre, 72 Coombe Road, New Malden KT3 4QS Tel: 020 8336 2222 Fax: 020 8336 0297; 6 Corscombe Close, Kingston Hill, Kingston upon Thames KT2 7JS Tel: 020 8547 3434 Fax: 020 8549 2402 — MB BS 1985 Lond.; BSc (Therap. & Pharmacol.) Lond. 1982; MRCGP 1989; DRCOG 1988. (Lond. Hosp. Med. Sch.) Med. Dir. Kingston & Richmond; Mem. LMC; Mem. Kingston & Richmond Commiss.ing Gp.

HARRIS, Jessica Ruth 27 Rose Valley, Norwich NR2 2PX — MB BChir 1987 Camb.; MRCGP 1994; T(GP) 1993; Cert. Family Plann. JCC 1991; DRCOG 1990. Socs: Assn. Community Based Matern. Care.

HARRIS, Jessie Louise c/o Green Hedges, Chambers Green Road, Pluckley, Ashford TN27 0RH — MB ChB 1985 Manch.

HARRIS, Joanna Louise 80 Green Lane, Dronfield, Sheffield S18 2FH Tel: 01246 415404 — MB ChB 1992 Leeds.

HARRIS, Joanne Victoria Milburn House, 7 Colebrooke Avenue, London W13 8JZ Email: jomark5@epulse.net — MB BS 1988 Lond.; BSc (Anat.) Lond. 1985; MRCP (UK) 1992; MRCGP 1995.

HARRIS, John Bennett Spring Hill Medical Centre, Spring Hill, Arley, Coventry CV7 8FD Tel: 01676 540395 Fax: 01676 540760; The Birchleys, Birchley Heath, Nuneaton CV10 0QY — MB ChB 1972 Birm.

HARRIS, John Charles 63 Ramsden Road, Rotherham S60 2QN — MB ChB 1998 Glas.; MB ChB Glas 1998.

HARRIS, John Duncan Campbell 83 The Grove, Christchurch BH23 2EZ — BM 1981 Soton.

HARRIS, John Joseph The Oakwood Surgery, Masham Road, Cantley, Doncaster DN4 6BU Tel: 01302 537611 Fax: 01302 371804 — MB ChB 1974 (Hons.) Leeds; MRCGP 1978; DRCOG 1977.

HARRIS, John Kenneth (retired) 30 Park Road, Gatley, Cheadle SK8 4HW — MB ChB 1951 Manch. Prev: Sen. Cas. Off. & Asst. Orthop. Surg. Stockport Infirm.

HARRIS, John Langdon (retired) Hurst Lodge, Penshurst Road, Newton Abbot TQ12 1EN Tel: 01626 69013 — MB BChir Camb. 1947; MRCS Eng. LRCP Lond. 1946. Prev: Med. Off. Newton Abbot Hosp.

HARRIS, John Patrick Harris and Young, The Health Centre, Beam Street, Nantwich CW5 5NX Tel: 01270 610686 Fax: 01270 610511 — MB ChB 1966 Sheff. Prev: Med. Regist. United Sheff. Hosps.

HARRIS, John Paul 11 Ilkeston Road, Bramcote, Beeston, Nottingham NG9 3JP — MB BS 1988 Lond.; DCH June 1996. (Char. Cross) SHO (Anaesth.) Qu. Med. Centre Nottm.

HARRIS, John Robert William 77 Harley Street, London W1N 1DE Tel: 020 7486 4166; St. Mary's Hospital, Praed St, London W2 1NY Fax: 020 7725 6617 — MB BCh BAO Belf. 1967; FRCP Lond. 1985; MRCP (UK) 1970; DTM & H Liverp. 1971. (Belf.) Cons. (Venereol., Genitourin. Med. & Communicable Dis.) St. Mary's Hosp. Lond.; Teach. (VD) Univ. Lond. Socs: Assn. Phys.; Bd. Mem. (Vice-Pres.) Europ. Acad. Dermato Venerol.; Chairm. Assn. Genito Urin. Med. Prev: Phys. i/c Dept. Venereol. King's Coll. Hosp. Lond.; Vis. Consult. MoH Ont. Prov., Canada; Med. Dir. St. Marys Hosp. VD Control Div. Center Dis. Control Atlanta, USA.

HARRIS, John Roger Camberley Health Centre, 159 Frimley Road, Camberley GU15 2QA Tel: 01276 20101 Fax: 01276 21661 — MB 1974 Camb.; BChir 1973; MRCGP 1983. (Camb. & St. Bart.) Prev: Sen. Med. Off. Gilbert Isles, S. Pacific; Med. Regist. Wexham Pk. Hosp. Slough.

HARRIS, Professor John William Simmons Cranmers, Worships Hill, Riverhead, Sevenoaks TN13 2AS Tel: 01732 451167 — PhD Lond. 1961, MB BS 1949; FRCS Eng. 1985; MRCS Eng. LRCP Lond. 1949; FRCOG 1970, M 1953; DRCOG 1951. (St. Bart.) Emerit. Prof. Socs: Fell. Roy. Soc. Med.; Life Mem. Anat. Soc. GB. Prev: Prof. Anat. Roy. Free Hosp. Sch. Med. Lond.; Regist. (O & G) Luton & Dunstable & Luton Matern. Hosps.; Intern. Midw. Asst. St. Bart. Hosp.

HARRIS, Jonathan Neil 74 Hawkstone Avenue, Whitefield, Manchester M45 7PR Email: jnharris90@hotmail.com — MB ChB 1993 Manch.; BSc (Hons.) Manch. 1990; MRCP (UK) 1996; FRCR Part1 1998. (Manch.)

HARRIS, Jonathan Wintersgill Department of Anaesthesia, Northwick Park & St Marks Trust, Watford Road, Harrow HA1 3 Tel: 020 8864 3232; 20 Old Deer Park Gardens, Richmond TW9 2TL — MB BS 1979 Lond.; FFA RCS Eng. 1987; DRCOG 1982. (Univ. Lond.) Cons. Anaesth. & Pain Relief N.wick Pk. Hosp. Harrow. Socs: Pain Soc.; PANG; John Snow Soc. Prev: Sen. Regist. Rotat. (Anaesth.) St. Bart., Whipps Cross & Hosp. for Sick Childr. Lond.; Vis. Asst. Prof. Anesthesiol. Pk.land Memor. Hosp. Dallas, Texas, USA; Regist. St. Thos. Hosp. Lond.

HARRIS, Joshua (retired) 1 Beechfield Court, Holme Road, Didsbury, Manchester M20 2UA — MB ChB 1920 Manch.

HARRIS, Julia Ann Strawberry Place Surgery, 5 Strawberry Place, Morriston, Swansea SA6 7AQ; 57 Tyn yr Heol Road, Neath SA10 7EB — MB BCh 1986 Wales; MRCGP 1991. Socs: BMA.

HARRIS, Julia Elizabeth Department Diagnostic Radiology, St Mary's Hospital, Praed St., London W2 1NY; 32 Inglethorpe Street,

London SW6 6NT — MB BS 1992 Lond.; FRCR 2000; MRCP (UK) 1996. (Char. Cross & Westm.)

HARRIS, Julia Katherine Chelsea & Westminster Hospital, 369 Fulham Rd, London SW10 9NH Tel: 020 8746 8015 Fax: 020 8746 8121 Email: julia.harris@chelwest.nhs.uk; Tel: 020 8840 2542 — MB ChB 1988 (Hons.) Sheff.; FRCS Eng. 1992; FFAEM 1998. (Univ. Sheff.) Cons A & E Chelsea & W.minster Hosp. Prev: Regist. (Accid. & Emerg. Med.) Ealing Hosp.; Regist. & Lect. (Neurosurg.) Roy. Lond. Hosp.; SHO (Orthop.) Hammersmith Hosp. Lond.

HARRIS, Julie Claire Bourne Galletly Practice Team, 40 North Road, Bourne PE10 9BT Tel: 01778 562200 Fax: 01778 562207; Branksome, Stamford Road, Ryhall, Stamford PE9 4HB — MB ChB 1987 Leic.; MRCGP 1995; Cert. Family Plann. JCC 1993. Prev: Clin. Asst. (Obst.) P'boro. Dist. Hosp.

HARRIS, Justin Sebastian Eyre 44 Gunterstone Road, London W14 9BU — MB BS 1990 Lond.

HARRIS, Karen Ann 15 Pembroke Close, Morley, Leeds LS27 9SG Tel: 0113 238 3950 — MB ChB 1991 Leeds. GP Trainee Fountain Med. Centre Morley Leeds. Prev: SHO (Ophth.) Halifax Roy. Infirm.; SHO (O & G) ForthPk. Hosp. Kirkcaldy.

HARRIS, Katarzyna Joanna 27 Sutton Road, London N10 1HJ Tel: 020 8444 0479 Email: mike@torlonki.demon.co.uk; Dr. Katarina Harris, 10 Hertford Road, London N2 9BU — Lakarexamen Goteburg 1991. Specialist Regist. Chase Farm Hosp. Enfield. Socs: MRCP (UK). Prev: Ho. Off. Kiruna Hosp., Sweden.

HARRIS, Keith Isfryn Surgery, Isfryn, Ffordd Dewi Sant, Nefyn, Pwllheli LL53 6EA Tel: 01758 720202 Fax: 01758 720083; Gwynfryn, Ffordd Dewisant, Nefyn, Pwllheli LL53 6EA Tel: 01758 721026 — MB ChB 1981 Liverp.

HARRIS, Mr Keith Michael General Infirmary at Leeds, Great George St., Leeds LS1 3EP Tel: 0113 243 2799; East Wing, Highfield, Inholmes Lane, Tadcaster LS24 9JS — BM 1981 Soton.; FRCS Ed. 1985; FRCR 1991. Cons. Radiol. Leeds Gen. Infirm. Socs: Brit. Soc. Interven. Radiol.; Brit. Soc. Gastroenterol. Prev: Sen. Regist. (Radiol.) Cardiff; Regist. (Gen. Surg.) Nottm.

HARRIS, Kevin Paul 39 Pilgrims Way, Bisley, Woking GU24 9DQ — MB BS 1993 Lond.

HARRIS, Kevin Paul Gladstone Department of Nephrology, Leicester General Hospital, Gwendolen Road, Leicester LE5 4PW Tel: 0116 2584195 Fax: 0116 2584764 Email: kevin.harris@uhl-tr.nhs.uk; Woodlands, 21 Holmfield Road, Stoneygate, Leicester LE2 1SD — MB BS 1981 Lond.; MA Cantab. 1982; MD Leic. 1996; FRCP Lond. 1996; MRCP (UK) 1984. (King's Coll. Hosp. Lond.) Reader (Nephrol) Univ. Leci. & Hon. cons. Nephrologist Univ. hosp leci; Clin. director renal Serv.s and Urol., Univ. hosp. Of Leci. Socs: Renal Assn.; Internat. Soc. Nephrol.; Amer. Soc. Nephrol. Prev: Lect. (Med.) Leicester Univ.; Instruct. (Med.) Washington Univ., St. Louis MO, USA; Sen. Lect. (nephrol.) & honarary Cons. , leci.

***HARRIS, Laura Mary** 8 Powys Close, Dinas Powys CF64 4LQ — MB ChB 1998 Birm.

HARRIS, Lesley Jane Watson 35 Parkinch, Erskine PA8 7HZ — MB ChB 1991 Glas.

HARRIS, Liane Sarah Dawn 67 Upper Park Road, Salford M7 4JB — MB ChB 1989 Manch. Staff Grade Paediat. Mancunian Health Care NHS Trust. Socs: Med. Protec. Soc.; BMA. Prev: Princip. in Gen. Pract.; Trainee GP Unsworth Med. Centre; SHO (A & E) N. Manch. Gen. Hosp.

HARRIS, Linda Diane 7 The Ridings, Mansfield NG19 0QF — MB BS 1989 Lond.

HARRIS, Lindsey Jean Mary 24 Prospect Road, Hungerford RG17 0JL Tel: 01488 686512 — MB BS 1981 Lond. Indep. Healthcare Cons. Hungerford.

HARRIS, Lorna Mary (retired) 22 Roman Way, Ancaster, Grantham NG32 3PT Tel: 01400 230210 Fax: 01400 230210 — MB BS Lond. 1962; MRCS Eng. LRCP Lond. 1962; DObst RCOG 1964.

HARRIS, Luke 11 Broad Hey Close, Liverpool L25 5QQ — MB BS 1949 Lond.; FRCP Ed. 1982, M 1960. (Middlx.) Dir. Clin. Studies Sanofi Recherche Paris; Asst. Prof. Med. Coll. Med. & Dent. New Jersey, USA; Fell. Coll. Clin. Pharmacol. Prev: Sen. Med. Off. Meds. Div. DHSS; Exec. Dir. Clin. Pharmacol. CIBA-Geigy, U.S.A.; Cons. Chest Phys.; Liverp. Health Dist. & Clin. Lect. Geriat. Univ. Liverp.

HARRIS, Lynda Anne 15 Gelligeiros, Gellinedd, Pontardawe, Swansea SA8 3DZ — MRCS Eng. LRCP Lond. 1977.

HARRIS, Lynda Susanne St James's Practice, 138 Croydon Road, Beckenham BR3 4DG Tel: 020 8650 0568 Fax: 020 8650 4172; 17 Elm Road, Beckenham BR3 4JB Tel: 020 8658 0937 — MB ChB 1987 Birm.; DRCOG 1991. Prev: Trainee GP Bromley VTS; Ho. Phys. Orpington Hosp.; Ho. Surg. Mayday Hosp.

HARRIS, Professor Malcolm 95 Wood Vale, London N10 3DL Tel: 020 7915 1056 Fax: 020 7915 1259 Email: malcolm.harris@ucl.ac.uk — MD 1977 Lond.; MB BS (Lond.) 1963; BChD, LDS Leeds 1957; FFD RCSI 1983; FDS RCS Eng. 1964. (Lond. Hosp.) Prof. Maxillofacial Surg. E.man Dent. & Univ. Coll. Lond. Hosps. Socs: Fell. Brit. Assn. Oral & Maxillofacial Surg. & Roy. Soc. Med. Prev: Cons. Oral Surg. King's Coll. Hosp. Lond.; Vis. Lect. Harvard Sch. Dent. Med. & Mass. Gen. Hosp., USA.

HARRIS, Margaret Anne 34 Cartwright Road, Chorlton, Manchester M21 9EY Tel: 0161 860 7942 — BM BS 1994 Nottm.; BMedSci Nottm. 1992; MRCP (UK) 1997. Specialist Regist. Clin. Oncol. Christie Hosp. Prev: Ho. Off. (Surg.) Barnet Gen. Hosp.; Ho. Off. (Med.) Derbysh. Roy. Infirm.

HARRIS, Margaret Catherine Bolgoed Newydd Farm, Heol y Barna Pontlliw, Swansea SA4 1HG Tel: 01792 884050 Fax: 01792 783687 — MB BCh 1966 Wales; MRCPsych 1977; DPM Eng. 1977. Med. Advisor DVLA Swansea. Prev: GP Port Talbot; Clin. Asst. (Genitourin. Med.) Mt. Pleasant Hosp. Swansea; Sen. Regist. (Psychiat.) Cefn Coed Hosp. Swansea.

HARRIS, Margaret Cunningham Maryhill Health Centre, 41 Shawpark Street, Glasgow G20 9DR Tel: 0141 531 8800 Fax: 0141 531 8851; Underfell, 4 Mosspark Road, Milngavie, Glasgow G62 8NJ Tel: 0141 956 6277 Fax: 0141 956 6277 — MB ChB 1968 Glas.; DObst RCOG 1970. (Glas.) GP Trainer Glas. Socs: Sec. Scott. W.ern Assn. of MWF; Med. Wom. Federat. Prev: Regist. (Haematol.) Vict. Infirm. Glas.

HARRIS, Margaret Lois 27 Vaughan Road, Willenhall WV13 3TJ — MB BS 1973 Newc. SCMO Mid. Glam. HA. Prev: Clin. Med. Off. Mid. Glam. HA; Regist. (Psychol. Med.) S. Glam. HA.

HARRIS, Mark Nigel Edward 17 Wimpole Street, London W1G 8GB Tel: 020 7436 1991 — MB 1980 Camb.; MA MB Camb. 1980, BChir 1979; FFA RCS Eng. 1983. Indep. Cons. Anaesth. Lond. Prev: Cons., Sen. Regist. & Regist. (Anaesth.) St. Thos. Hosp. Lond.; Vis. Asst. Prof. Univ. Maryland Hosp., USA.

HARRIS, Professor Martin (retired) Department of Pathology, Christie Hospital & Holt Radium Institute, Withington, Manchester M20 4BX Tel: 0161 446 3273 Fax: 0161 446 3300 — MB ChB 1961 Manch.; MD Manch. 1988; FRCPath 1980, M 1968. Prev: Sen. Lect. (Geriat. Path.) Univ. Manch.

HARRIS, Martin Temple Fortune Health Centre, 23 Temple Fortune Lane, London NW11 7TE Tel: 020 8458 4431 Fax: 020 8731 8257; Tel: 020 8958 4879 — MB BS 1976 Lond.; BPharm. (Hons.) Lond. 1971; MRCS Eng. LRCP Lond. 1976; MRCGP 1981. (Lond. Hosp.) Clin. Lect. (Dept. of Primary Care & Populat. Sci.) Roy. Free & Univ. Coll. Med. Sch.; Hon. Clin. Asst. (Med.) Middlx. Hosp. Lond.; PCG Bd.; Hon. Clin. Asst. (Obst.) Roy. Free Hosp. Lond.; JCC Instruc. Doctor Well Wom. & Family Plann. Clin. Temple Fortune Health Centre; Med. Bd. Initiat. Soc. (Circumcision). Socs: Med. Bd. Initiation Soc. (Circumcision); Med. Ass. Soc.; BMA. Prev: Clin. Asst. (Diabetic Clinic) Edgware Gen. Hosp.; Regist. Rotat. (Med.) & SHO Lond. Hosp. & Enfield Dist. (Chase Farm) Hosps.; Ho. Phys. (Renal & Med.) Lond. Hosp.

HARRIS, Martin Andrew Michael Godswell Lodge, Church Street, Bloxham, Banbury OX15 4ES Tel: 01295 720347 — MB ChB 1971 Cape Town; DA Eng. 1979. Socs: BASM; Brit. Acupunc. Soc.

HARRIS, Martin Trevor Mundahl High Wray House, High Wray, Ambleside LA22 0JQ — MB BS 1984 Lond.; MA Camb. 1984, BA (Hons.) 1980; DCCH RCPGP 1994; DFFP 1994. Clin. Med. Off. (Child Health) Cumbria. Prev: Regist. (Community Med.) Mersey RHA.

HARRIS, Mary Isabel Peelview Medical Centre, 45 Union St., Kirkintilloch, Glasgow G66 1DN Tel: 0141 221 8270 Fax: 0141 221 8279; 608 Clarkston Road, Netherlee, Glasgow G44 3SQ Tel: 0141 637 4092 — MB ChB 1988 Glas.; MRCGP 1992. Locality Plann. Adviser.

HARRIS, Matthew James 5 Telegraph Hill, Platts Lane, London NW3 7NU — MB BS 1998 Lond.; MB BS Lond 1998.

HARRIS, Michael 96 Harley Street, London W1N 1AF — MB ChB 1970 Glas.; FRCA 1992; FFA RCS Eng. 1977; T(GP) 1982; DA (UK) 1973; Dip. Pharm .Med 1995. (Univ. Glas.) Med. Pract. Lond. Pain Phys. Musco-skeletal phys; Physch. Pyschol. Guys. Socs: Brit. Inst. Musculo-Skeletal Med. Prev: Pain & Musco-skelatal Phys. Lond .Roy. Homeopath.Hosp.; Pain & Musco-skelatal Phys. N. Middx.Hosp.

HARRIS, Michael David Hinchingbrooke Hospital, Department of Histopathology, Hinchingbrooke Park, Huntingdon PE29 6NT Tel: 01480 456131 Fax: 01480 434175; 5 Mead Close, Walton, Peterborough PE4 6BS — BM 1981 Soton.; MRCPath 1990. Cons. Histopath. Hinchingbrooke Hosp. Huntingdon.

HARRIS, Michael Frank Hope House Surgery, The Street, Radstock, Bath BA3 3PL; Gore Cottage, Old Gore Lane, Emborough, Bath BA3 4SJ Tel: 01761 241366 — MB BS 1980 Lond.; FRCGP 2001; MRCS Eng. LRCP Lond. 1980; MRCGP 1985. (Char. Cross) GP Course Organiser (Gen. Pract.) Roy. United Hosp. Bath.

HARRIS, Michael Gillis (retired) 63C Magdalen Yard Road, Dundee DD2 1AL Tel: 01382 644962 Fax: 01382 666254 Email: mikeharris@sol.co.uk — MB ChB 1960 Glas.; MRCGP 1971; AFOM RCP Lond. 1979. Prev: Med. Prescribing Adviser Primary Care Fife HB.

HARRIS, Michael Jeffrey St Andrews Hospital, Billing Road, Northampton NN1 5DG Tel: 01604 629696 Fax: 01604 616225 Email: meddir@standew.co.uk; 11A Breckhill Road, Woodthorpe, Nottingham NG5 4GP Tel: 01159522079 Fax: 0115 920 6091 Email: mikeharris@breathe.co.uk — MB BS 1973 Lond.; BSc Lond. 1969; MRCS Eng. LRCP Lond. 1973; FRCPsych 1995, M 1978. (Char. Cross.) Med. Dir. St. And. St. Andrews Hosp. N.ampton. Socs: FRSM; BMA (Hon. Treas. Nottm. Div.); Fell.ASM. Prev: Cons. Forens. Psychiat. & Med. Dir. Nottm. Healthcare; Cons. Psychiat. Mapperley Hosp. Nottm.; Lect. (Psychiat.) Nottm. Univ. Med. Sch.

HARRIS, Michael Leslie (retired) 15 Sandhurst Court, South Promenade, Lytham St Annes FY8 1LS — BM BCh 1952 Oxf.; MA Oxf. 1952.

HARRIS, Michael William (retired) — MB ChB 1968 Birm.; BSc Birm. 1965.

HARRIS, Miriam Benita Guy's Hospital, St Thomas St., London SE1 9RT Tel: 020 7955 5000; 8 Shawbury Road, London SE22 9DH — MB BS 1989 Lond.; MB BS (Lond.) 1989; BSc (Hons.) Lond. 1986; MRCP (UK) 1993. Specialist Regist. (A & E) Guy's Hosp. Lond.

HARRIS, Muriel Flower (retired) 18 West End, Witney, Oxford OX28 1NE Tel: 01993 704810 — MB BCh 1951 Witwatersrand. Prev: Colon. Med. Serv.

HARRIS, Myles Francis 51 Park Road, Chiswick, London W4 3 — MB ChB 1964 Manch.; DPH Eng. 1974.

HARRIS, Neil Michael 17 High Moors, Halton, Aylesbury HP22 5NY — MB ChB 1995 Leeds. SHO Plastic Surg. Stoke Mandeville Hosp. Aylesbury. Prev: Ho. Phys. St. Jas. Univ. Hosp. Leeds; Ho. Surg. Bradford Roy. Infirm.; Regt.. Med. Off. The Light Dragoons.

HARRIS, Neil Peter Poole General Hospital, Longfleet Road, Poole BH15 2SB — MB ChB 1984 Bristol; BA Oxf. 1981; MRCPsych. 1989.

HARRIS, Neville Laurence Boutet, Noctorum Lane, Birkenhead CH43 9UA — MB BCh BAO 1953 Dub.

HARRIS, Mr Nicholas John 62 Cranbourne Drive, Otterbourne, Winchester SO21 2EU Tel: 01962 712359 — MB ChB 1989 Aberd.; FRCS Ed. 1994; FRCS (Tr. & Orth) 1999.

HARRIS, Nicola Anne 45 Woodlawn Road, London SW6 6NQ — MB BS 1992 Lond.

HARRIS, Nicola Anne Apartment 10, Shotwick Park, Seahill Road, Saughall, Chester CH1 6BJ — MB ChB 1995 Birm.; ChB Birm. 1995.

HARRIS, Nicola Mary Catherine Paediatric Dept, Musgrove park Hospital, Taunton TA1 5DA Tel: 01823 342635 — MB ChB 1985 Bristol; MRCP (UK) 1990; M Med sci 1998. Staff Grade Paediat. Oncol. MusGr. Pk. Hosp. Taunton. Prev: Clin. Asst. (Paediat. Oncol.) MusGr. Pk. Hosp. Taunton.

HARRIS, Mr Nigel Henry 72 Harley Street, London W1N 1AE Tel: 020 7636 9112 Fax: 020 7636 4015; 14 Ashworth Road, London W9 1JY Tel: 020 7286 4725 — MB BChir 1948 Camb.; MA Camb. 1962, BA 1945; FRCS Eng. 1958. (Camb. & Middlx.) Hon. Cons. Orthop. Surg. NW (St. Mary's) Health Dist. (T). Socs: Fell. Roy. Soc. Med. & BOA. Prev: Sen. Regist. (Orthop.) Roy. Nat. Orthop. Hosp. Lond.; Regist. (Orthop.) Fulham Hosp.; Ho. Surg. (Orthop.) Middlx. Hosp. Lond.

HARRIS, Mr Nigel William Stewart Falkirk & District Royal Infirmary, Falkirk FK1 5QE Tel: 01324 24000; 40 Gartcows Crescent, Falkirk FK1 5QH Tel: 01324 623575 — MB ChB 1975 Ed.; FRCS Ed. 1979. Cons. Surg. Falkirk & Dist. Roy. Infirm. Socs: Surgic. Research Soc. Prev: Sen. Regist. (Surg.) Roy. Infirm. Edin.

HARRIS, Patricia (retired) Pontesbury Surgery, Pontesbury, Shrewsbury SY5 7JW Tel: 01743 790325 — MB BS 1958 Lond.; MRCS Eng. LRCP Lond. 1958. Prev: GP Shrewsbury.

HARRIS, Patrick 71 Weymoor Road, Birmingham B17 0RS — MB ChB 1986 Birm.

HARRIS, Paul Strawberry Place Surgery, 5 Strawberry Place, Morriston, Swansea SA6 7AQ Tel: 01792 522526 Fax: 01792 411020 — MB BCh 1983 Wales; LLM Wales 1996; MRCGP 1990; DRCOG 1993. (Welsh Nat. Sch. Med.)

HARRIS, Paul The Surgery, Highfield Road, North Thoresby, Grimsby DN36 5RT — MB ChB 1991 Leeds; MRCGP 1995.

HARRIS, Paul Burdwood Surgery, Wheelers Green Way, Thatcham, Newbury RG13 5AY Tel: 01635 868006; Rosewood, High St, Hermitage, Newbury RG18 9RE Tel: 01488 608302, 01635 200168 — MB BS 1982 Lond.; MB 1982; DFFP 1993; MRCGP 1986; DRCOG 1985; BSc 1979 Lond.; BSc (Hons.) Lond. 1979; MRCGP 1986; DFFP 1993; DRCOG 1985. (Roy. Free) Prev: Ho. Surg. Roy. Free Hosp. Lond.; Trainee GP/ SHO St. Bart. Hosp. VTS.

HARRIS, Paul Belmont Health Care Centre, Eastholme Avenue, Belmont, Hereford HR2 7UX Tel: 01432 354366 Fax: 01432 340434 — MB ChB 1984 Birm.; BSc Pharmacol. Birm. 1981; MRCGP 1992. Prev: SHO Rotat. (Gen. Med.) E. Birm. HA; SHO Rotat. Centr. Birm. HA VTS.

HARRIS, Paul Anthony The Medical Centre, Station Avenue, Bridlington YO16 4LZ Tel: 01262 670686 Fax: 01262 401685 — MB ChB 1983 Leeds; DRCOG 1987.

HARRIS, Mr Paul Anthony Dept. of Plastic & Reconstructive Surgery, St George's NHS Trust, BLAckshaw Rd, London SW17 0QT Tel: 020 8672 1255; 81 Disreali Road, Putney, London SW15 2DY Tel: 020 8780 5764 Email: paulharris@onet.co.uk — MB BS 1991 Lond.; BSc (Physiol.) Lond. 1988; FRCS Eng. 1995. (Char. Cross & Westm. Med. Sch.) Specialist Regist. (Palstic Surg.) Pan-Thames Train. Scheme. Socs: Roy. Soc. Med. Prev: Surg. Research Fell. RAFT Inst. Plastic Surg.; SHO (Plastic Surg.) Mt. Vernon Hosp.; SHO Rotat. (Surg.) Char. Cross Hosp. Lond.

HARRIS, Paul David 33 Sheraton Drive, Tilehurst, Reading RG31 5UZ — MB ChB 1996 Birm.; ChB Birm. 1996.

HARRIS, Paul Graham 20 Quarry Close, Chester CH4 7LG — MB ChB 1965 Manch. (Manch.) SHO (Psychiat.) W. Chesh. Hosp. Chester; Mem. Shrewsbury Hosps. Med. Inst. Prev: SHO (A & E) Putney Hosp. Lond.; Ho. Surg. St. Chas. Hosp. Lond.; Ho. Phys. Newmarket Gen. Hosp.

HARRIS, Paul Rupert Adelaide Street Health Centre, 19 Adelaide Street, Norwich NR2 4JL Tel: 01603 622044 — MB ChB 1979 Leeds. Prev: Trainee GP Bradford HA; SHO (Anaesth.) Bradford Roy. Infirm.

HARRIS, Pauline Louise West Gorton Medical Centre, 6A Wenlock Way, West Gorton, Manchester M12 5LH Tel: 0161 223 5226 Fax: 0161 230 6305; Tanglewood, 18 Park Lodge Close, Cheadle SK8 1HU Fax: 0161 491 4120 Email: grahamerose@msn.com — MB ChB 1978 Manch.; MRCGP 1983; DRCOG 1982; Cert. Family Plann. JCC 1981. (Manchester) Socs: BMA. Prev: GP Trainer W. Gorton; Trainee GP/SHO Stepping Hill Hosp. Stockport VTS.

HARRIS, Percy George Sunrise, 62 Beechill Park W., Newtownbreda, Belfast BT8 6ZZ Tel: 01232 703092 Email: percyharris@compuserve.com — MA, MD Dub. 1959, BA, MB BCh BAO (Hons.) 1943; MRCGP 1960. (T.C. Dub.) GP Belf.; Hon. Clin. Asst. (Cardiol.) Belf. City Hosp.; JP. Socs: Fell. Roy. Soc. Med. & Roy. Soc. Health.; Gen. Med. Servs. Comm. Prev: Phys. i/c Occupat. Health S. Belf. Health Dist.; Vice-Chairm. Area Med. Adviser Comm. EHSSB; Life Governor Purdysburn Hosp. Belf.

HARRIS, Mr Peter Alastair 22 Warrender Park Terrace, Edinburgh EH9 1EF Email: peteharris@cwcom.net — MB ChB 1987 Dundee; FRCS Eng. 1993; MRCOG 1999. Specialist Regist. Obs & Gynae Addenbrooke's Hosp.

HARRIS, Peter Anthony Amgen Ltd, Cambridge Science Park, 240 Milton Park Road, Cambridge CB4 0WD; 99 Duchess Drive, Newmarket CB8 8AL Tel: 01638 560228 — MRCS Eng. LRCP Lond. 1968; BSc (Hons.) Lond. 1965, MB BS 1968; MFPM 1990; DObst RCOG 1970; DPharmMed. 1980. (Lond. Hosp.) Dir. Clin. Research (Europe) Amgen Ltd. Camb.; Clin. Asst. (Gen. Med.) Stepping Hill Hosp. Stockport. Socs: Fell. Roy. Soc. Med.; Brit. Assn. Psychopharmacol. Prev: Head Med. Affairs ICI Pharmaceut. Plc. Macclesfield; Med. & Technical Dir. Rorer Health Care; Head Med. Affairs Roche.

HARRIS, Peter Charles (retired) National Heart & Lung Institute, Dovehouse St., London SW3 6LY — MB BS 1946 Lond.; PhD Lond. 1955, MD (Univ. Medal) 1951; FRCP Lond. 1965, M 1950. Prev: Simon Marks Prof. Cardiol. Univ. Lond.

HARRIS, Peter Christian 19 Boundary Drive, Crosby, Liverpool L23 7UY — MB ChB 1990 Liverp.

HARRIS, Peter John The Pool Medical Centre, Pool Road, Studley B80 7QU Tel: 01527 852133/853671 Fax: 01527 853072 — MB BS 1973 Lond.; Dip. Clin. Hypn. Sheff. 1993.

HARRIS, Peter John Stuart St Keverne Health Centre, St Keverne, Helston TR12 6PB Tel: 01326 280205 Fax: 01326 280710 — MB ChB 1966 Liverp. (Liverp.) Hosp. Pract. (Haemat.) Roy. Cornw. Hosp. Treliske. Prev: SHO (Obst.) & SHO (Paediat.) Roy. Cornw. Hosp. Truro; Ho. Surg. & Ho. Phys. Ormskirk & Dist. Gen. Hosp.

HARRIS, Mr Peter Lyon 88 Rodney Street, Liverpool L1 9AR Tel: 0151 709 0669 Email: 101617.2210@compuserve.com; Mayfield, 19 Ince Road, Thornton, Liverpool L23 4UE Tel: 0151 924 2311 — MB ChB 1967 Manch.; MD Manch. 1974; FRCS Eng. 1971. (Univ. Manch.) Cons. Vasc. Surg. Roy. Liverp. Univ. Hosp. Socs: (Sec.) Vasc. Surgic. Soc. GB & Irel.; Europ.Soc.Vasc..Surg; Internat.Soc.Endovasc.Special. Prev: Cons. Surg. (Gen. & Vasc.) BRd.green Hosp. Liverp.; Sen. Regist. (Gen. Surg.) Char. Cross Hosp. Lond.; Pres. Europ. Bd. Vasc. Surg.

HARRIS, Peter Walter Robert Farnborough Hospital, Farnborough, Orpington BR6 8ND Tel: 01689 53333 — MD 1972 Camb.; MB 1961, BChir 1960; FRCP Lond. 1980, M 1965; DObst RCOG 1961. (Guy's) Cons. Phys. Bromley Gp. Hosps. Prev: Sen. Regist. (Med.) Guy's Hosp. Lond.

HARRIS, Philip Edward Department of Medicine, King's College School of Medicine & Dentistry, Bessemer Road, London SE5 9PJ Tel: 020 7737 4000 Fax: 020 7346 3313 Email: philip.harris@kcl.ac.uk — MB BCh 1979 Wales; PhD Wales 1986, BSc (1st cl. Hons.) 1976; MRCP (UK) 1982; FRCP Lond. 1998. (Welsh National School of Medicine) Sen. Lect. (Endocrinol. & Gen. Med.) King's Coll. Sch. Med. & Dent. Lond.; Hon. Cons. Phys. KCH Lond.; Mem. Edit. Bd. CME Bull. Endocrinol. Socs: Soc. Endocrinol.; Endocrine Soc.; Eur. Neuroendocrine Assn. Prev: 1st Asst. (Endocrinol., Diabetes & Gen. Med.) Univ. Newc.; MRC Trav. Fell. Mass. Gen. Hosp., Boston, USA; Regist. (Endocrinol.) St. Bart. Hosp. Lond.

HARRIS, Professor Philip Frederick (retired) 41 Potters Lane, East Leake, Loughborough LE12 6NH Tel: 01509 852885 Fax: 01509 852 885 Email: pfharris27@yahoo.com — MD 1967 Bristol; MSc Manch. 1978; MB ChB Birm. 1950. p/t Teach. In Anat., Notts. Med. Sch. Prev: Prof. & Dir. Anat. Laborats. Univ. Manch.

HARRIS, Philip John Parkside Surgery, Tawney Street, Boston PE21 6PF Tel: 01205 365881 Fax: 01205 357583 — BM BS 1986 Nottm. (Nottm.) Med. Off. Norprint UK Boston, Lincs.

HARRIS, Philip Peter Fishponds Health Centre, Beechwood Road, Fishponds, Bristol BS16 3TD Tel: 0117 965 6281 — BM BS 1985 Nottm.; MRCGP 1995; DRCOG 1993; DCH RCP Lond. 1992.

HARRIS, Philip Rodney The Blofield Surgery, Plantation Road, Blofield, Norwich NR13 4PL Tel: 01603 712337 Fax: 01603 712899; The Grange, Doctors Road, Blofield, Norwich NR13 4LF Tel: 01603713656 Email: prodneyharris@netscapeonline.co.uk — MB BS 1966 Lond.; MRCS Eng. LRCP Lond. 1966; MRCGP 1974; DCH Eng. 1970. (St. Thos.) Prev: Ho. Off. (Med.) St. Luke's Hosp. Guildford; Ho. Off. (Paediat.) St. Jas. Hosp. Balham; Ho. Off. (O & G) City Matern. Hosp. Gloucester.

HARRIS, Philippa Jane Scott Bedlingtonshire Medical Group, Glebe Road, Bedlington NE22 6JX Tel: 01670 822695 — MB BS 1983 Lond.; MRCP (UK) 1986; MRCGP 1988. (St. Mary's)

HARRIS, Mr Phillip (cons. rooms), 14 Moray Place, Edinburgh EH3 6DT Tel: 0131 225 5320 — LRCP LRCS 1944 Ed.; LRFPS 1944 Glas.; FRS Ed.; FRCS Ed. 1948; FRCP Ed. 1959, M 1954; FRCS Glas. 1964. (Roy. Coll. Ed. & Ed. Univ.) Cons. Neurosurg. Execut. Memb. Neurotraum Ctc. World Fed. Neurosurg. Socs. Univ. Edin.; Cons. Neurosurg. Roy. Infirm. Edin., W.. Gen. Hosp. Edin. & Spinal Unit Edenhall Hosp. Musselburgh; Chairm. Profess. & Linguistic Assessm. Bd. GMC; Hon. Pres. Scotl. Sports. Ass. Disabled; Examr. RCS Ed., Roy. Colls. Ed. & Scott. Triple Qual.; Vis. Prof. & Guest Chief & Lect. various Foreign Univs., Hosps. & Med. Schs. Socs: Past Pres. Brit. Cervical Spine Soc.; Hon. Mem. Various Foreign Med. & Surg. Socs.; Founder Mem. And Fell. Int. Med.Soc. Paraplegia. Prev: Cons. Neurosurg. Roy. Inf. Edin. W.Gen. Hosp. Edin. & Spinal Unit Edenhall Hosp. Musselhead; Mem. MRC Brain Metab. Unit.Edinb. Univ.; Vis. Prof. Guest Chief Lect. Universities Hosps. & Med. Sch.

HARRIS, Queenie Woodbourne priory Hospital, 21 Woodbourne Rd, Edgbaston, Birmingham B17 8BY Tel: 0121 434 4343 Fax: 0121 434 3270; Parkview Clinic, 60 Queensbridge Road, Birmingham B13 8QE Tel: 0121 243 2000 Fax: 0121 243 2010 — MB BS Madras 1961; FRCPsych 1989, M 1973; DPM Eng. 1972. (Christian Medical College & Hospital Vellore S. India) Hon. Sen. Clin. Lect. (Psychiat.) Birm. Univ. Prev: Cons. Chilld and Adolesc. Psychiat., Pk.view Clinic, Birm.

HARRIS, Rachel Anne Millers Dale Surgery, 9 Ormesby Drive, Chandlers Ford, Eastleigh SO53 1SH Tel: 01703 262488; Highview, 1 Lower St, Braishfield, Romsey SO51 0PH Tel: 01794 367822 — MB BS 1986 Lond. SHO (Paediat.) Poole Gen. Hosp. Dorset. Prev: Trainee GP Romsey; SHO (Med. for Elderly) Dundee.

HARRIS, Rachel Christine Greystones, Over Lane, Hazelwood, Duffield, Belper DE56 4AG — MB ChB 1993 Manch.

HARRIS, Rachel Louise Browns Bensfield, Best Beech, Wadhurst TN5 6JR — BM 1997 Soton.

HARRIS, Rebecca Mary 668 Abbey Lane, Sheffield S11 9NB — MB ChB 1992 Sheff.; DCH RCP Lond. 1995; DRCOG 1994; MRCGP 1997. (Sheffield)

HARRIS, Richard The Health Centre, St. Peters Crescent, Selsey, Chichester PO20 0NN Tel: 01243 604321/602261 Fax: 01243 607996; Fairlight, 28 Clayton Road, Selsey, Chichester PO20 9DF Tel: 01243 604866 — MB BS 1973 Lond.; MRCS Eng. LRCP Lond. 1973. (Westm. Med. Sch.)

HARRIS, Richard David Highlands Practice, 3 Florey Square, Winchmore Hill, London N21 1US Tel: 0208 360 9044 Fax: 0208 306 2077 — MB ChB 1988 Manch.; DRCOG 1992. Gen. Med. Practitioner.

HARRIS, Richard Iliffe 41 Weston Lane, Bulkington, Nuneaton CV12 9RS Tel: 024 76 319872 Fax: 02476 732535 Email: rharris@doctors.org — MB BS 1969 Lond.; FRCP Lond. 1994; MRCP (UK) 1977; FRCPath 1992; MA 1998; Dip Psych 1997. (Westm.) Psychotherapist and Consg. trainer. Prev: Sen. Regist. (Haemat.) Qu. Eliz. Hosp. Birm.; Lect. (Path.) W.minster Med. Sch.; Regist. (Haemat.) United Birm. Hosp.

HARRIS, Mr Richard Paul 2A Vale Coppice, Horwich, Bolton BL6 5RP — MB ChB 1989 Manch.; FRCS Ed. 1993.

HARRIS, Richard William The Limes, 115 Dunstan Crescent, Worksop S80 1AG — MB BS 1977 Lond.; BSc Lond. 1974, MB BS 1977; FFA RCS Lond. 1982. Cons. Anaesth. Bassetlaw HA. Socs: Assn. Anaesth. Eng. & Irel. Prev: Sen. Regist. (Anaesth.) Sheff. Train. Scheme; Regist. (Anaesth.) Sheff. AHA (T); SHO E.bourne Dist. Gen. Hosp.

HARRIS, Robert Lyon 40 Greyhound Road, London W6 8NX — MB BS 1996 Lond. SHO (Orthop.) Ealing Hosp. Prev: SHO (Cardiothoracic) Hammersmith Hosp.; Ho. Off. (Med.) W. Middlx. Hosp.

HARRIS, Professor Rodney, CBE Genetics Enquiry Centre, St Mary's Hospital, Manchester M13 0JH Tel: 0161 276 6276 Email: rodney.harris@man.ac.uk; The Cottage, Catherine Road, Bowdon, Altrincham WA14 2TD Tel: 0161 928 8092 Fax: 0161 929 5170 — MB ChB (2nd cl. Hons.) Liverp. 1958; BSc (1st cl. Hons.) Liverp. 1955, MD 1961; FRCP Lond. 1974, M 1964; FRCPath 1980, M 1973; DTM & H Liverp. 1959. (Liverp.) Prof. Emerit.; Hon. Cons.; Lead BioMed. Research Gp. NW RO; Chairm. EU Concerted Action Genetic Serv. in Europ. Socs: (Ex-Chairm.) Clin. Genetics SAC JCHMT; (Pres.) Manch. Med. Soc. Prev: Prof. Med. Genetics Dir. Research & Developm. Centr. Manch. Healthcare NHS Trust; Cons. Adviser (Genetics) to Chief Med. Off. DHSS; Chair Clin. Gen. Comm RCP Lond.

HARRIS, Roger James The Childrens Department, The Royal London Hosptial, London E1 1BB Tel: 020 7377 7428 Fax: 020 7377 7759 Email: r.j.harris@mds.gmw.ac.uk; 5 Lake House Road, Wanstead, London E11 3QS Tel: 020 8989 9324 Email: r.j.harris@mds.qmw.ac.uk — MB ChB 1962 Bristol; MD Bristol 1970; FRCP Lond. 1986; MRCP (UK) 1970; DCH Eng. 1964; FRCP 1998 (CH). (Bristol) Cons. Paediat. Barts and the Lond. NHS Trust; Sen. Lect. (Child Health) Qu. Mary Coll., Univ. of Lond. Socs: Brit. Paediat. Assn. & Neonat. Soc. Prev: Sen. Regist. (Paediat.) Bromley Gp. Hosps. & King's Coll. Hosp. Lond.; Regist. (Med.) Hosp. Sick Childr. Gt. Ormond St. Lond.; Regist. (Neonat. Paediats.) Dept. Child Health United Bristol Hosps.

HARRIS, Rosemary Eileen (retired) The Dewerstone Surgery, Hampton Avenue, St Marychurch, Torquay TQ1 3LA Tel: 01803 323123/314240 Fax: 01803 322001 — MB ChB 1960 Birm.; DCH Eng. 1966. Prev: Clin. Asst. (Diabetes) & Hosp. Pract. (Paediat.) Torbay Hosp. Torquay.

HARRIS, Roy Francis, OBE Kings Mill Centre for Healthcare Services NHS Trust, Mansfield Road, Sutton-in-Ashfield NG17 4JL Tel: 01623 622515 Fax: 01623 672306 Email: royharris@kmc-tr.nhs.uk; 25 The Avenue, Mansfield NG18 4PD Tel: 01623 624593 — MB ChB 1966 Ed.; FRCP Ed. 1988; FRCP Lond. 1986, M 1973; FRCPCH 1997; DCH Eng. 1971. (Ed.) Cons. Paediat. King's MillCentre For Health Serv.Sutton inAshfield; Clin. Director Wom.'s and Childr.'s Div., Sherwood Forest Hosps. NHS Trust, Notts. Socs: Brit. Assn. Perinatal Med.; Brit. Assn. Med. Managers. Prev: Cons. Adviser Paediat. RAF; Hon. Cons. Dept. Child Health King's Coll. Hosp. Lond.

HARRIS, Rupert William Flat 4, 19 Kings Road, Richmond TW10 6NN — MB ChB 1996 Ed.; BSc (Hons.) Ed. 1994. (Edinburgh)

HARRIS, Russell Charles Ty'r Felin Surgery, Cecil Road, Gorseinon, Swansea SA4 4BY Tel: 01792 898844 — MB BCh 1982 Wales. (Welsh Nat. Sch. Med. Cardiff)

HARRIS, Russell Luke 83 Kingston Road, Oxford OX2 6RJ — MB BS 1989 Newc.

HARRIS, Ruth Abigail Macclesfield District General Hospital, Victoria Road, Macclesfield SK10 3BL Tel: 01625 421000 — MB ChB 1992 Manch.; MRCP (UK) 1995. Regist. (Med.) Macclesfield Dist. Gen. Hosp. Prev: SHO (Gen. Med.) Trafford Gen. Hosp. Manch.

HARRIS, Sally-Ann Saranade, The Street, Swallowfield, Reading RG7 1QY — BM BCh 1987 Oxf.

HARRIS, Sally Elizabeth 8 Tabley Road, Knutsford WA16 0NB — MB ChB 1994 Leic.

HARRIS, Sarah Jane Whiteoaks, 10 Fore St., Cornwood, Ivybridge PL21 9PY — MB ChB 1978 Bristol; MRCGP 1985; DRCOG 1983.

HARRIS, Sarah Jane dept Clinical Oncology, St thomas Hospital, lambeth Palace Road, London SE1 7EH Tel: 020 7928 9292 — MB BS 1989 Lond.; MRCP (UK) 1992; FRCR 1995. Cons. Clin. Oncol. St Thomas Lond. Prev: Regist. Rotat. (Radiother.) Soton. & Poole; Ho. Phys. (Radiother. & Oncol.) Kings Coll. Hosp.; Sen. Regist. (Radiother.) St. Bart. Hosp. Lond.

HARRIS, Sarah Joanne 57 Maple Way, Burnham-on-Crouch CM0 8DN — MB ChB 1994 Leic. (Leics) SHO Flex. Cardiovasc. Med. Leics. Roy. Infirm. Prev: SHO (Dermat.) Leicester Roy. Infirm.; SHO diabetes Leics Gen.Hosp; SHO (Intergrated Med.) Glenfield Hosp. Leicester.

HARRIS, Sheila Averina Scott (retired) 7 Heol Dinas, Box Lane Estate, Wrexham LL12 7RF Tel: 01978 352113 — MB ChB 1952 Manch.; MRCP Ed. 1968; DObst RCOG 1955; DCH Eng. 1954. Prev: Med. Asst. (Paediat.) Maelor Gen. Hosp. Wrexham.

HARRIS, Siân Jessica Anne Heron Practice, John Scott Health Centre, Green Lanes, London N4 2NU Tel: 020 7690 1172 Fax: 020 8809 6900; Flat 1, 103 Nelson Road, London N8 9RR — MB BS 1990 Lond.; BSc Lond. 1987; MRCGP 1996; DRCOG 1993. (Char. Cross & Westm.)

HARRIS, Sian Mererid 39 Mayals Avenue, Blackpill, Swansea SA3 5DB — MB ChB Bristol 1983; BSc (Pharmacol.) Bristol 1980; MRCP (UK) 1996; MRCGP 1989; DCH RCP Lond. 1988. Regist. (Paediat.) Treliske Roy. Corn. Hosp. Prev: Regist. (Paediat.) MusGr. Pk. Hosp. Taunton; SHO Rotat. (Med.) Treliske Roy. Cornw. Hosp., Truro.

HARRIS, Simon Mile Oak Clinic, Chalky Road, Portslade, Brighton BN41 2WF Tel: 01273 417390/419365 Fax: 01273 889192 — MB BS 1982 Lond. (Guy's Hosp.) Dep. Police Surg. Brighton & Hove. Socs: Brit. Assn. Sport & Med.; Brit. Med. Acupunct. Soc.; Soc. Orthop. Med.

HARRIS, Simon Andrew Bruce Sutton Place, Sutton Road, Maidstone ME15 9DU — MB BCh 1988 Wales.

HARRIS, Mr Simon Ashley 6 Epsom Lane S., Tadworth KT20 5SX Tel: 01973 408457 — MB BS 1990 Lond.; BSc Pharmacol. & Therap. Lond. 1987; FRCS Eng. 1995. Regist. (Gen. Surg.) St. Geo. Hosp. Lond.

HARRIS, Simon Grant 1 Claremont Gardens, Purbrook, Waterlooville PO7 5LL Tel: 023 9226 7408 — MB BS 1964 Lond.; MRCS Eng. LRCP Lond. 1964; MRCGP 1976; DObst RCOG 1967. (St. Bart.) Med. Adviser Zurich Financial Servs. Socs: BMA; Roy. Coll. Gen. Pract. Prev: Nuffield Trainee GP Wessex RHB; Ho. Surg. (ENT) St. Bart. Hosp. Lond.; Ho. Surg. & Ho. Phys. S.end Gen. Hosp.

HARRIS, Simon James Porch Farm, 229 Main Road, Clenchwarton, King's Lynn PE34 4AG — MB BS Lond. 1968; MRCS Eng. LRCP Lond. 1968; FFA RCS Eng. 1976; DObst RCOG 1972; DA Eng. 1973. (St. Bart.) Cons. (Anaesth.) King's Lynn & Wisbech NHS Health Trust. Prev: Sen. Regist. (Anaesth.) Addenbrookes Hosp. Camb.; Regist. (Anaesth.) Roy. Free Hosp. Lond.; Regist. (Anaesth.) Qu. Charlotte's Matern. Hosp. Lond.

HARRIS, Stanley James 1 Yew Close, Nottingham NG5 4EL Tel: 01159 605606 Fax: 01159 605606 — MB BS Lond. 1947; MRCS Eng. LRCP Lond. 1947. (Guy's) Mem. of Ct. Univ. Nottm. Socs: Nottm. M-C Soc. Prev: Hon. Med. Adviser Notts. Amateur Swimming Assn.; Cas. off., Orthop. & Ophth. Ho. Surg. Roy. Waterloo Hosp. Lond.; Cas. Off. Bromley & Dist. Hosp.

HARRIS, Stella Ann Mona Cottage, Ballakilpheric, Colby, Castletown IM9 4BU Tel: 01624 834159 — MB ChB 1989 Liverp.; MRCGP 1995; DRCOG 1992. Socs: I. of Man Med. Soc. Prev: Trainee GP Yorks VTS.

HARRIS, Stephen Clive Staffordshire Gen Hosp, Weston Road, Stafford ST16 3SA Tel: 01785 230783 Email: stephen.harris@msgh-trwmids.nhs.uk — MB BChir 1978 Camb.; MA, MB Camb. 1978, BChir 1977; MRCPath 1986. Cons. Histopath. Staffs. Gen. Infirm. Prev: Lect. Path. Sheff. Univ. Med. Sch.; Regist. (Histopath.) Roy. Hallamsh. Hosp. Sheff.

HARRIS, Stephen Clive Church Street Surgery, St Mary's Courtyard, Church Street, Ware SG12 9EF Tel: 01920 468941 Fax: 01920 465531; 15 Amberley Green, Ware SG12 0XX Tel: 01920 422360 Fax: 01920 421323 Email: stephen@relns.demon.co.uk — MB BS 1981 Lond.; MRCGP 1993; DCH RCP Lond. 1988; DRCOG 1984. (Char. Cross) Chairm. 'Hems' Co-op Herts. Emerg. Med. Serv. Ltd.

***HARRIS, Stephen John** 41 Inverary Road, Wroughton, Swindon SN4 9DH — MB ChB 1994 Birm.

HARRIS, Stephen William Glanvill and Partners, Springmead Surgery, Summerfields Road, Chard TA20 2HB Tel: 01460 63380 Fax: 01460 66483; Bartletts Cottage, Wambrook, Chard TA20 3DG — MB ChB 1980 Birm.; MRCGP 1990; DRCOG 1989; DA (UK) 1983. (Birmingham) GP Princip. Socs: BMA. Prev: Regist. (Med. & Paediat.) Tauranga Hosp., NZ; SHO (O & G) Yeovil Hosp.; SHO (Anaesth.) Taunton.

HARRIS, Susan Laundry Cottage, Brickendon Green, Hertford SG13 8NZ — MB BS 1990 Lond. SHO (Accid & Emerg.) Hull Roy. Infirm.

HARRIS, Susannah Rachel Hebden Bridge Health Centre, Hangingroyd Lane, Hebden Bridge HX7 6AG Tel: 01422 842333 Fax: 01422 842404; 6 Birchfield Villas, Hebden Bridge HX7 8DH — BM 1984 Soton.; DRCOG 1988. GP Prescriber. Socs: BMA; Med. Pract. Union. Prev: Trainee GP Burnley; SHO (A & E & Anaesth.) N. Middlx. Hosp. Lond.; SHO (O & G & Paediat.) Burnley.

HARRIS, Sylvia May 6 Ely Close, New Malden KT3 4LG Tel: 020 8942 8039 — MB BCh 1958 Wales. Med. Off. Kingston & Esher, Merton & Sutton HAs.

HARRIS, Teresa Jane 44 Burntwood, Grange Road, Wandsworth, London SW18 3JX Email: tharris@sghms.ac.uk — MB BS 1988 Lond.; MSc Epidemiol. Lond. 1994; BSc (Hons.) Lond. 1985; MRCGP 1992; DRCOG 1992; DCH RCP Lond. 1991; DGM RCP Lond. 1990. (St. Geo. Hosp. Med. Sch. Lond.) GP Lond.; Lect. St. Geo. Hosp. Med. Sch. Lond. Prev: Trainee GP/SHO Roy. Free Hosp. Lond. VTS.

HARRIS, Thomas Jeremy Britten Ysbty Gwynedd Hospital, Penrhosgarnedd, Bangor LL57 2PW — MB 1965 Camb.; BChir

1964; FFA RCS Eng. 1968. (Guy's) Cons. Anaesth. N. W. Wales NHS Trust.

HARRIS, Mr Thomas Martin Department of Otolaryngology Head & Neck Surgery, University Hospital Lewisham, Lewisham High St., London SE13 6LH Tel: 020 8333 3192 Fax: 020 8333 3333; 59 Southbrook Road, Lee, London SE12 8LJ Tel: 020 8473 1777 Fax: 020 8852 9629 Email: tom.harris@virgin.net — MB BChir 1972 Camb.; MA Camb. 1972; FRCS Otol. Eng. 1979. (St Marys Lond) Cons. ENT Surg. Lewisham & N. S.wark, Greenwich & Bexley HAs; Overseas Affil. Voice Center New York Eye & Ear Infirm. USA; Mem. UEP Commiss. on Voice. Socs: Fell. Collegium Medicorum Theatri; Fell. Roy. Soc. Med.; (Counc.) Brit. Voice Assn.

HARRIS, Timothy Easthope 64 Tinwell Road, Stamford PE9 2SD Tel: 01973 839836 — MB BS 1978 Lond.; BSc (Hons.) Lond. 1975; MRCS Eng. LRCP Lond. 1978; DRCOG 1981. (St. Mary's)

HARRIS, Timothy John Oldfield Surgery, 45 Upper Oldfield Park, Bath BA2 3HT Tel: 01225 421137 Fax: 01225 337808 — BM BCh 1977 Oxf.; MA Camb. 1978; MA Oxf. 1977; DRCOG 1979; MRCGP 1981; Cert. JCC 1980. (Oxford) Med. Off. Kingswood Sch.; Med. Off. King Edwd. Sch.; Med. Off. Cadburys. Prev: Stud. Health Off. Lond. Sch. Econ. & Pol. Sc.; Trainee GP Bath VTS.; Ho. Surg. & Ho. Phys. Radcliffe Infirm. Oxf.

HARRIS, Toba Elisabeth (retired) 7 Marlborough Court, Pembroke Road, London W8 6DE Tel: 020 7602 1752 — BM BCh Oxf. 1951; MA Oxf. 1952; MRCPsych 1972; DPM Eng. 1960. Prev: Cons. Psychiat. Earls Ct. Child Guid. Unit & Char Cross Hosp Lond.

HARRIS, Tom (retired) Blackbrook Surgery, Lisieux Way, Taunton TA1 2LB Tel: 01823 259444 Fax: 01823 322715 — MB BChir 1969 Camb.; MA, MB Camb. 1969, BChir 1968; DObst RCOG 1971; Cert. FPA 1971. Co. Surg. St. John Ambul. Prev: Ho. Off. W.m. Hosp. Lond.

HARRIS, Tristan John Nicholson Great Oakley Medical Centre, 1 Barth Close, Great Oakley, Corby NN18 8LU Tel: 01536 460046 Fax: 01536 461404; 79 Arden Way, Market Harborough LE16 7DB Tel: 01858 462956 — MB ChB 1990 Leic.; MRCGP 1994; DRCOG 1993; DCH RCP Lond. 1992. (Leicester) Clin. Asst. (Dermat.) Kettering.

HARRIS, Victor John Samuel Falk Centre, Birch Hill Hospital, Rochdale OL12 9QB Tel: 01706 377777 — MB BCh 1978 Wales; MRCPsych 1983; FRCPsych 1998. (Wales) Cons. (Psychiat.) Birch Hill Hosp. Rochdale.; Clin. Dir. (Psychiat.). Prev: Sen. Regist. (Psychiat.) Hope Hosp. Salford; Sen. Regist. (Psychiat.) Withington Hosp. Manch.; Sen. Regist. (Psychiat.) Prestwich Hosp. Manch.

HARRIS, Vivian Grant 14 Hayes Way, Beckenham BR3 6RL — MB BS 1971 Lond.; MRCS Eng. LRCP Lond. 1971; FRCOG 1990, M 1977. Cons. O & G Lewisham & Guy's Hosps. Lond.; Med. Off. 289 Commando Battery RA (V). Socs: (Sec.) SE Gyn. Soc.; Med. Chir. Soc.

HARRIS, Wallace Cyril (retired) 88 Brim Hill, London N2 0EY Tel: 020 8883 3730 — MB BS 1945 Lond.; FRCP Lond. 1972, M 1949; MRCS Eng. LRCP Lond. 1944. Mem. Cons. Phys. Edgware Chest Clinic, Edgware Gen. Hosp. & Colindale. Prev: Sen. Regist. Colindale Hosp.

HARRIS, William Evan 3 Cabin Hill Park, Belfast BT5 7AL Tel: 01232 656509 — MB BCh BAO 1980 Belf.

HARRIS, William Henry The Health Centre, Bridge St., Pontypridd CF37 4PF Tel: 01443 405996 Fax: 01443 485861; Fair View, Llanfabon, Nelson, Treharris CF46 6PG — BM BCh 1974 Oxf.; MA Oxf. 1974; MRCOG 1983.

HARRIS, Zoe Elizabeth (retired) 16 St Mary's Court, Sixpenny Handley, Salisbury SP5 5PH Tel: 01725 552430 — MB ChB 1939 Birm.

***HARRIS-DEANS, Ruth Anne** The Old Rectory, West Stourmouth, Canterbury CT3 1HT — MB ChB 1998 Leic.; MB ChB Leic 1998.

HARRIS-HALL, John James Mundesley Medical Centre, Munhaven Close, Mundesley, Norwich NR11 8AR Tel: 01263 724500 Fax: 01263 720165 — MB BS 1981 Lond.; BSc (Hons.) Mammalian Physiol. Lond. 1978, MB BS 1981; MRCGP 1990. (St. Bart.) Socs: Brit. Soc. Med. & Dent. Hypn. Prev: Trainee GP Norf. & Norwich Hosp. VTS; Ho. Surg. Prof.ial Surg. Unit St. Bart. Hosp. Lond.; Ho. Phys. Newmarket Gen. Hosp.

HARRIS HENDRIKS, Jean Mary Traumatic Stress Clinic, 73 Charlotte St., London W1T 4PC Tel: 020 7530 3666 Fax: 020 7530 3677 Email: rcs@ptsdclin.demon.co.uk; 13 Cunningham Hill Road, St Albans AL1 5BX Tel: 01727 812551 Fax: 01725 863523 — MB ChB Birm. 1958; FRCPsych 1985, M 1971; DPM Eng. 1960. (Birm.) p/t Hon. Cons. Psychiat. Trauma Stress Clinic Camden & Islington Community Servs. NHS Trust Lond.; Hon. Sen. Lect. UCL; Hon. Cons. & Hon. Sen. Lect. Roy. Free Hosp. Lond. Prev: Cons. Psychiat. Child & Family Psychiat. Clinic Dunstable; Cons. Psychiat. Hoxton Child Guid. Unit & Colebrook Sch.

HARRIS-JONES, Mr Richard David Lockhart Snow Hill Medical Centre, 1a Snow Hill Court, Snow Hill, London EC1A 2EJ Tel: 020 7236 2832 Fax: 020 7329 8297; 17 Harley Street, London W1N 1DA Tel: 020 7935 1928 — MB BS 1973 Lond.; FRCS Ed. 1981; MRCS Eng. LRCP Lond. 1973. (St. Bart.) Med. Adviser Assoc. Newspapers. Socs: Fell. Roy. Soc. Med.; Lond. Med. Soc.; InDepend. Doctors Forum. Prev: Regist. (Gen. Surg.) St. Helier Hosp. Carshalton; Regist. (Orthop.) Roy. Hants. Co. Hosp. Winchester; SHO (Path.) & Ho. Surg. St. Bart. Hosp. Lond.

HARRIS-LLOYD, Christine Margaret Whiteladies Health Centre, Wofinden Memorial Building, Bristol BS8 2PU Tel: 0117 973 1201; 63 Halsbury Road, Redland, Bristol BS6 7ST Tel: 0117 948388 — MB BS 1959 Durh.; DObst RCOG 1961.

HARRISON, Adele Marie 4 St Bernards Row, Edinburgh EH4 1HW — MB ChB 1990 Ed.

HARRISON, Adrian Philip Farfield Group Practice, St. Andrew's Surgeries, West Lane, Keighley BD21 2LD Tel: 01535 607333 Fax: 01535 611818; 8 High Croft Way, Farnhill, Keighley BD20 9AP — MB ChB 1964 Leeds. (Leeds) Socs: Keighley & Dist. Med. Soc. Prev: Ho. Phys. & Ho. Surg. St. Jas. Hosp. Leeds; Ho. Surg. (Obst.) St. Mary's Hosp. Leeds.

HARRISON, Andrew Jeffrey Todmorden Health Centre, Rose Street, Todmorden OL14 5AT Tel: 01706 815126 Fax: 01706 812693; Stoney Garth, 10 Lumbutts Road, Todmorden OL14 6PQ — MB ChB 1979 Manch.; MRCGP 1983.

HARRISON, Andrew Jeremy Heavitree Health Centre, South Lawn Terrace, Exeter EX1 2RX Tel: 01392 431355 Fax: 01392 498305 — MB ChB 1981 Bristol; MRCGP 1986; DRCOG 1985. Prev: Med. Adviser Aguaruna & Huambisa Counc., Amazonas, Peru.

HARRISON, Andrew Richard (retired) Junction House, Fradley Junction, Alrewas, Burton-on-Trent DE13 7DN Tel: 01283 791457 — MB BS 1972 Lond.; MRCS Eng. LRCP Lond. 1972; FFA RCS Eng. 1977. Prev: Cons. Anaesth. Centr. (Manch.) Health Dist. (T).

HARRISON, Andrew Thomas East Bridgford Medical Centre, 2 Butt Lane, East Bridgford, Nottingham NG13 8NY Tel: 01949 20216 Fax: 01949 21283 — MB ChB 1973 Leeds; MRCP (U.K.) 1976; MRCGP 1982. Princip. GP E. Bridford; Trainer Nottm. VTS.

HARRISON, Ann Margaret Urmston Group Practice, 154 Church Road, Urmston, Manchester M41 1DL — MB BS 1987 Lond.; DCH RCP Lond. 1992; DRCOG 1990.

HARRISON, Anne Margaret The Health Centre, 20 Cleveland Square, Middlesbrough TS1 2NX Tel: 01642 246138 Fax: 01642 222291; Old School House, Bentley Wynd, Yarm TS15 9BS Tel: 01642 788992 — MB ChB 1981 Manch. (Manchester)

HARRISON, Anne Patricia 11 Glebe Avenue, Woodford Green IG8 9HB — MB ChB 1981 Glas.; MRCP (UK) 1985.

HARRISON, Annette Theresa 21 Ridgewood Crescent, South Gosforth, Newcastle upon Tyne NE3 1SQ — MB BS 1993 Newc.; MRCP (UK) 1997.

HARRISON, Anthony Richard Sighthill Health Centre, 380 Calder Road, Edinburgh EH11 4AU Tel: 0131 537 7320 Fax: 0131 537 7005; 1F1 39 Merchiston Crescent, Edinburgh EH10 5AJ — BM 1985 Soton.; MRCGP 1992; DRCOG 1993; DFFP 1991; DCH Otago 1989.

HARRISON, Anthony Robert (retired) 73 Wolverhampton Road, Codsall, Wolverhampton WV8 1PL Tel: 01902 845820 — MB ChB 1950 Birm.; MRCGP 1971. Prev: Clin. Asst. Roy. Hosp. Wolverhampton.

HARRISON, Antony Julian Fitzalan Medical Centre, Fitzalan Road, Littlehampton BN17 5JR Tel: 01903 733288 Fax: 01903 733773 Email: antonyharrison@compuserve.com; The Willows, 48 Golden Avenue, East Preston, Littlehampton BN16 1QX Tel: 01903 775559 — MB BS 1987 Lond.; BSc (Hons.) Lond. 1984; MRCGP 1993; DRCOG 1992; DCH RCP Lond. 1990. (St George's) GP Trainer S. Thames; Arural PCG Bd. Mem.; Forens. Med. Off. Sussex Police; Clin. Asst. (Palliat. Care) St. Barnabas Hospice Worthing. Prev: SHO

(A & E & Paediat.) St. Richards Hosp. Chichester; SHO (Gen. Med.) Bristol Roy. Infirm.; SHO (O & G) S.lands Hosp. Shoreham-by-Sea.

HARRISON, Mr Barnard Joseph D Floor Firth Wing, Northern General Hospital, Herries Road, Sheffield S5 7AU Tel: 0114 271 4684 Fax: 0114 226 6986; 92 Tom Lane, Fulwood, Sheffield S10 3PD Tel: 0114 230 3717 — MB BS 1976 Lond.; MS Lond. 1988; FRCS Eng. 1980. (Westm.) Cons. Surg. N. Gen. Hosp. Sheff. Socs: Brit. Assn. Endocrin. Surgs.; Internat. Assn. Endocrine Surgs. Prev: Sen. Regist. (Surg.) Cardiff Roy. Infirm, Roy. Gwent Hosp & Univ. Hosp. Wales Cardiff.

HARRISON, Beth Diane Sheffield Teaching Hospital NHS Trust — BM BCh 1991 Oxf.; MRCPath 2000; MA Oxf. 1994, BA 1988; MRCP (UK) 1994; DRCPath 1996. (Oxford) Cons. Haematol., Univ. Hosp., Coventry and Warks. NHS Trust. Socs: Brit. Soc. for Haemat. Prev: Specialist Regist. (Haemat.) Sheff.; Clin. Research Fell. (Haemat.) Manch.

HARRISON, Mrs Betty (retired) 127 Cromwell Road, Fulwood, Preston PR2 6YE — MB ChB 1922 Ed.

HARRISON, Beverley Jane 40 Fordbank Road, Manchester M20 2TH Tel: 0161 445 7281 Email: bev@fs1.ser.man.ac.uk — MB ChB 1989 Manch.; BSc (Hons.) Experim. Immunol. & Oncol. Manch. 1986; MRCP (UK) 1993; MD 1998. (Univ. Manch.) Specialist Regist. (Rheum.) Hope Hosp. Salford; Hon. Lect. Univ. of Manch. Prev: Clin. Research Fell. Rheum. Dis. Epidemiol. ARC Epidemiol. Research Unit Manch.; Clin. Lect. (Rheum.) Manch. Roy. Infirm.

HARRISON, Brian David Walter Department of Respiratory Medicine, Norfolk & Norwich University Hospital, Colney Lane, Norwich NR4 7UY Tel: 01603 289642 Fax: 01603 289640 Email: brian.harrison@norfolk-norwich.thenhs.com; The White House, Church Avenue E., Norwich NR2 2AF Tel: 01603 456508 — MB BChir Camb. 1967; MA Camb. 1968; FRCP Lond. 1987; MRCP (UK) 1970; FCCP 1990; FRCP Ed 1998. (Camb. & Guy's) Cons. Phys. (Thoracic & Gen. Med.) Norf. & Norwich; Hon Sen Lec Sch. of Health Univ of E. Anglia. Socs: Brit. Thorac. Soc.; Eur. Respirat. Soc.; Amer. Thoracic Soc. Prev: Lect. (Thoracic & Gen. Med.) Middlx. Hosp. Lond.; Regist. (Med.) W.m. Hosp. Lond.; Regist. (Cardiol.) Guy's Hosp. Lond.

HARRISON, Carol 8 Mountague Place, Poplar, London E14 0EX — MB BChir 1989 Camb.

HARRISON, Carol Anne 92 Pen-y-Lan Road, Cardiff CF23 5HX — MB BCh 1979 Wales; BSc. MB BCh Wales 1979.

***HARRISON, Caroline Anne** 106 Little Barn Lane, Mansfield NG18 3JT Tel: 01623 635701 — MB ChB 1998 Sheff.; MB ChB Sheff 1998; BMedSci 1995.

HARRISON, Catherine Margaret 1 Dyke Nook, Clitheroe BB7 1JJ Tel: 01200 425353 — BM BS 1992 Nottm.; MRCP 1996. (Notts) Specialist Regist. Paediat. Sheff. Childr.s. Hosp. NHS Trust; Clinicou Research Fell. Neonatology, Jessop wing, Nicu Sheff.

HARRISON, Catherine Maria Sarah Riverdale, The Lendings, Barnard Castle DL12 9AB — MB BS 1990 Lond.

HARRISON, Cecil Ross Ghyll End, Beckermonds, Buckden, Skipton BD23 5JL — MRCS Eng. LRCP Lond. 1951. (Sheff.)

HARRISON, Chantelle Bridget 76 Wrysedale Road, Aintree, Liverpool L9 0JS — MB BS 1993 Lond.

HARRISON, Christine Jane Dept. of Child Health, Rotherham General Hospital NHS Trust, Moorgate Road, Rotherham S60 2UD Tel: 01709 304521 Email: christine.harrison@rgh-tr.trent.nhs.uk — MB ChB 1981 Birm.; BSc (Hons. Physiol.) Birm. 1978; MRCP (Paediat.) (UK) 1985. (Birm.) p/t Cons. Paediat. Rotherham Gen. Hosp. S. Yorks. Socs: Fell. Roy. Coll. Paediat. and Child Health; BMA. Prev: Sen. Regist. (Paediat.) Sheff. Hosps.

HARRISON, Christopher John Wesham Park, Derby Road, Wesham, Preston PR4 3AL Tel: 01253 306370; 61 Princes Reach, Preston PR2 2GB Tel: 01772 721051 Fax: 01772 721051 — MB ChB 1983 Manch.; MSc Manch. 1990; MFPHM 1991; DCH RCP Lond. 1987; DRCOG 1987; Cert. Family Plann. JCC 1986; FFPHM 1998. Dir. (Pub. Health) N. W. Lancs. Health Auth. Socs: Fell. Manch. Med. Soc.; Soc. Pub. Health. Prev: Dir. Pub. Health S. Lancs. HA; Sen. Regist. & Regist. (Pub. Health Med.) N. W.. RHA; SHO (A & E) Withington Hosp. Manch.

HARRISON, Christopher John Barlow Medical Centre, 8 Barlow Moor Road, Didsbury, Manchester M20 6TR Tel: 0161 445 2101 Fax: 0161 445 9560; 144 Chapel Lane, Hale, Altrincham WA15 0SS — MB ChB 1990 Manch.; MRCGP (Distinc.) 1994; DRCOG 1993; DGM RCP Lond. 1993. GP Barlow Med. Centre Didsbury; Lect. In Gen. Pract. Univ. of Manch. Prev: Trainee GP/SHO S. Manch. HA VTS; Ho. Surg. Stepping Hill Hosp. & Stockport Infirm.; Ho. Phys. Roy. Oldham Hosp.

HARRISON, Claire 22 Trigo Parade, Belfast BT6 9GA — MB BCh BAO 1995 Belf.

HARRISON, Claire Grace Top Flat 5 Nelson Street, Edinburgh EH3 6LF Tel: 0131 557 6505 — MB ChB 1997 Ed. (Edinburgh)

***HARRISON, Claire Margaret** 21 Hermit Lane, Higham, Barnsley S75 1PL — MB ChB 1997 Ed.; BSc Med. Sci. (Hons.) Pharmacology Ed. 1995.

HARRISON, Claire Nicola Dept pf Haematology, St Thomas' Hospital, Lambeth Palace Road, London SE1 7EI Tel: 020 7928 9292 Fax: 020 7928 7226 Email: clair.harrison@gstt.sthames.nhs.uk — BM BCh 1990 Oxf.; DM 1999; MRCPath 2000; BA (Hons.) Oxf. 1987; MRCP (UK) 1993. (Oxford) Regist. (Haemat.) Chase Farm Univ. Coll. Hosps.; Cons. Haematologist & Hon. Sen. Lect. St Thomas' Hosp. Prev: SHO Univ. Coll. Hosp.; SHO Watford Gen. Hosp.; SHO Chelsea & W.m. Hosp. Lond.

HARRISON, Clarice (retired) Pampus, 58 St Peter's Drive, Martley, Worcester WR6 6QZ Tel: 018866 532 — MB ChB 1935 Liverp. Prev: Asst. Co. Med. Off. Kent.

HARRISON, Dale 240 Common Edge Road, Blackpool FY4 5DH; St Brendan's Hospital, P.O. Box DV 501, Devonshire DVBX, Bermuda Tel: 00 1 809 441 236 3770 Fax: 00 1 809 441 236 9383 — MB ChB 1988 Dundee; MPhil Ed. 1995; MA Oxf. 1983, BA (Hons.) 1982; MRCPsych 1993. Chief of Psychiat.; Bermuda Hosps. Bd. Prev: Sen. Med. Off. (Forens. Psychiat. Servs.) Qu.sland, Austral.; Sen. Regist. Rotat. (Gen. Psychiat.) S. Wales; Regist. (Psychiat.) Roy. Edin. Hosp.

HARRISON, David Allan Department of Anaesthesia, Northern General Hospital NHS Trust, Herries Road, Sheffield S5 7AU Tel: 0114 243 4343 — MB ChB 1985 Dundee; BMSc Dund 1982; FRCA 1990. Cons. Anaesth. N. Gen. Hosp. NHS Trust Sheff. Prev: Sen. Regist. Rotat. (Anaesth.) Sheff.; Lect. (Anaesth.) Univ. Nottm.; Regist. Rotat. (Anaesth.) N. Trent.

HARRISON, David Anthony The White House, Ringsfield, Beccles NR34 8JU — MB ChB 1965 Manch.; BSc (1st cl. Hons. Anat.) Manch. 1962; FRCPath 1986, M 1973; DMJ (Path.) Soc. Apoth. Lond. 1972. Cons. Path. to Home Office. Socs: Assn. Clin. Pathols. & Brit. Assn. Foren. Med. Prev: Sen. Regist. (Morbid Anat.) Roy. Infirm. Sheff.; Hon. Clin. Tutor Univ. Sheff.; Regist. (Clin. Path.) Radcliffe Infirm. Oxf.

HARRISON, David Frederick The Medical Centre, Beech Grove, Sherburn-in-Elmet, Leeds LS25 6ED Tel: 01977 682208 Fax: 01977 681665 — MB ChB Leeds 1958; MRCGP 1972; DObst RCOG 1960. (Leeds)

HARRISON, Professor David James University Department of Pathology, Edinburgh University Medical School, Teviot Place, Edinburgh EH8 9AG Tel: 0131 650 2908 Fax: 0131 650 6840 Email: david.harrison@ed.ac.uk — MB ChB 1983 Ed.; BSc (Hons.) Ed. 1980, MD 1990; MRCPath 1990; FRCPath 1998. (Ed.) Prof/Head of Path.Dept. Univ.Edin; Hon. Cons. Lothian Univ. Hosp. NHS Trust.

HARRISON, Mr David John Royal National Orthopaedic Hospital, Brockley Hill, Stanmore HA7 4LP Fax: 0208 9095720; 1 Woodland Crescent, Farnborough GU14 8BF Tel: 01252 66182 — MB BS 1978 Lond.; BSc (Hons.) Physiol. Lond. 1975; FRCS Eng. 1983. (St. Geo.) Cons. Spinal Orthop., Roy. Nat. Orthopaedic Hosp. Stanmore; Orthop. Adviser Nat. Rett Syndrome Assn. & Child Growth Assn.; Hon. Cons. The Childr.s Trust, Tadworth, Surrey; Hon. Cons. Trezdars Sch. and Coll., Alton Hants. Socs: Fell. BOA; Internat. Soc. Orthop. & Trauma; Fell. Brit. Scoliosis Soc. Prev: Zimmer Internat. Research Fell. Inst. Orthop. Roy. Nat. Orthop. Hosp. Lond.; Sen. Regist. (Orthop.) King's Coll. Hosp. Lond.; Cons. Spinal Orthop. Frimley Pk. NHS Trust, Camberley Surrey.

HARRISON, Denise Margaret The Royal Hospital for Sick Children, Yorkhill NHS Trust, Yorkhill, Glasgow G3 8SJ — MB BS 1985 Lond.; MRCPsych 1990. Sen. Regist. (Child & Adolesc. Psychiat.) & Hon. Clin. Lect. Roy. Hosp. Sick Childr. & Univ. Glas.

HARRISON, Donald Alexander 1 Crossley Crescent, Hoole, Chester CH2 3EZ — MB ChB 1986 Liverp.

HARRISON, Sir Donald Frederick Norris Springfield, 6 Fishers Farm, Horley RH6 9DQ Tel: 01293 784307 Fax: 01293 784307 —

MB BS 1946 Lond; MB BS Lond. 1948; Hon. FRACS 1977; FRCS Eng. 1955; DLO Eng. 1951; Hon FRACS 1977; PhD Lond. 1983, MS 1959, MD 1960; Hon. FRCSI 1991; Hon. FRCS Ed. 1981; MRCS Eng. LRCP Lond. 1948; FRCOphth 1993; Hon. FRCR 1995; Hon. FACS 1990; Hon. FCA S. Afr. 1988. (Guy's) Emerit. Cons. ENT Surg. Moorfields Eye Hosp. Lond.; Emerit. Prof. Univ. Lond. Socs: Hon. Fell. RSM; (Ex-Pres.) Roy. Soc. Med.; Med. Soc. Lond. Prev: Hunt. Prof. RCS Eng.; Reader (Laryngol.) Inst. Laryngol. Lond.; Chief Asst. (ENT) Guy's Hosp. Lond.

HARRISON, Donald Tyson Somerstown Health Centre, Southsea PO5 2DS; 49 Stanley Street, Southsea PO5 2DS — MB BS 1955 Lond.; DObst RCOG 1958. (St. Thos.)

HARRISON, Dorothy Anne Longrigg Medical Centre, Leam Lane, Gateshead NE10 8QJ Tel: 0191 469 2173; Nunthorpe, Jesmond Park E., Newcastle upon Tyne NE7 7BT Tel: 0191 281 4063 — MB BS 1981 Newc.

HARRISON, Dorothy Jane The Health Centre, Bailey Street, Old Basford, Nottingham NG6 0HD Tel: 0115 978 1231 Fax: 0115 979 0419; Highbury Private Road, Wood Lane, Hucknall, Nottingham NG15 6PP Tel: 0115 964 1751 — BM BS 1977 Nottm.; MRCGP 1981. GP Nottm.

HARRISON, Edward Thomas 28 Traeth Melyn, Deganwy, Conwy LL31 9DP Tel: 01492 582302 — MB ChB 1943 Liverp.; FRCGP 1995, M 1961; AFOM RCP Lond.; DIH Eng. 1948. (Liverpool) Acupunc. Demonst. Brit. Acad. W.. Acupunc. Liverp. Socs: Colwyn Bay Med. Soc.; Fac.Bd Mem.N. Wales Coll Gps. Prev: Exam. Med. off. DHSS Cardiff; Lt.-Col. RAMC (TA); Ship's Surg., Roy. Fleet Auxil.

HARRISON, Elaine Lesley Oakwood, Lewins Rd, Chalfont St Peter, Gerrards Cross SL9 8SA — MB BS 1997 Lond.

HARRISON, Elinor Ann Depart. Of Anaesthesia, Leeds General Infirmary, Leeds — MB ChB 1989 Bristol; MRCP (UK) 1995; FRCA 1996. (Univ. Bristol) Cons., Paediatric Cardiac Anaesth/ICU, Leeds Gen. Infirm.; Hon. Sen. Clin. Lect., Univ. of Leeds. Socs: Assn. of Anaesth.s of Gt. Britain and Irel.; Paediatric Care Soc. Prev: Clin. Fell. (Anaesth/PICU) Hosp. Sick Childr., Toronto; Clin. Fell. PICU - Guy's Hosp.; Specialist Regist. (Anaesth) Gt. Ormond St. Hosp.

HARRISON, Elizabeth Hanham Surgery, 33 Whittucks Road, Hanham, Bristol BS15 3HY Tel: 0117 967 5201 Fax: 0117 947 7749 — MB ChB 1988 Bristol; BSc (Psychol.) Bristol 1985; MRCGP 1993; DRCOG 1991. Prev: Trainee GP Bristol VTS.

HARRISON, Elizabeth Ann St James House Surgery, County Court Road, King's Lynn PE30 5SY Tel: 01553 774221 Fax: 01553 692181 — MB BS 1965 Lond.; MRCS Eng. LRCP Lond. 1965; FRCGP 1989; MRCGP 1977; DCH Eng. 1967. (Roy. Free) Prev: Ho. Surg. Roy. Free Hosp. Lond.; Ho. Phys. St. Mary's Hosp. Portsmouth. SHO (Paediat.) Soton.; Childr. Hosp.

HARRISON, Elizabeth Mary The Village Green Surgery, The Green, Wallsend NE28 6BB Tel: 0191 295 8500 Fax: 0191 295 8519; 20 The Grove, Gosforth, Newcastle upon Tyne NE3 1NE Tel: 0191 285 5910 — MB BS 1978 Newc.

HARRISON, Elizabeth Mary Down End, Bourne Lane, Twyford, Winchester SO21 1NX — MRCS Eng. LRCP Lond. 1975; BSc Lond. 1972, MB BS 1975; DRCOG 1978; DCH Eng. 1977. (Roy. Free) Clin. Asst. (Diabetes Mellitus) Roy. Hants. Co. Hosp. Winchester. Prev: Trainee GP Twyford Surg. Winchester; Clin. Med. Off. (Child Health Serv.) Leeds AHA (T).

HARRISON, Enid Mary 19 Oak Tree Lane, Mansfield NG18 3HN Tel: 01623 653524 — MB ChB 1953 Sheff.; MFFP 1993. SCMO (Family Plann.) Centr. Notts. Health Care Trust. Prev: Med. Off. Mansfield & Dist. Hosp. Gp. Staff. Occupat. Health Serv.; Ho. Phys. (Paediat.) City Gen. Hosp. Sheff.; Ho. Surg. (O & G) Gen. Hosp. Wakefield.

HARRISON, Fiona Mary St.Andrews, Priory Park Hospital, Glastonbury Rd, Wells BA5 1TJ Tel: 01749 683366 Fax: 01749 683375 Email: fiona.harrison@sompar.nhs.uk — MB ChB 1979 Birm.; MRCPsych 1991. Cons. (Geriat. Psychiat.). Priory Pk. Hosp. Wells. Prev: Sen. Regist. (Psychiat) Cossham Hosp. Bristol.

HARRISON, Francis David Old Catton Surgery, 55 Lodge Lane, Norwich NR6 7HQ Tel: 01603 423341 Fax: 01603 486445 — MB BChir 1974 Camb.; MB Camb. 1974, BChir 1973; MRCGP 1980.

HARRISON, Gareth Luney 57 St Winifreds Avenue W., Harrogate HG2 8LS — MB ChB 1993 Leeds; MRCGP 1997; DRCOG 1995; DFFP 1997.

HARRISON, George Robert Pain Management Office, Selly Oak Hospital, Raddlebarn Rd, Birmingham B29 6JD Tel: 0121 627 8943 Fax: 0121 627 8944 Email: george.harrison@university_b.wmeds.nhs.uk; The Byre Moorfield, Lilley Green, Alvechurch, Birmingham B48 7HD Email: george@corgigas.demon.co.uk — MB BS 1977 Lond.; BSc Lond. 1974, MB BS 1977; FFA RCS Eng. 1981. (Univ. Coll. Hosp.) Cons. Anaesth. Qu. Eliz. Hosp. Birm. Prev: Clin. Lect. Univ. Birm.; Sen. Regist. Centr. Birm. HA.

HARRISON, Mr George Stuart Mark Down End, Bourne Lane, Twyford, Winchester SO21 1NX Tel: 01962 713282 — MB BChir 1973 Camb.; MA Camb. 1972; FRCS Eng. 1977. (Camb. & Middlx.) Cons. Urol. Surg. Roy. Hants. Co. Hosp. Winchester. Socs: Fell. Roy. Soc. Med.; Brit. Assn. Urol. Surgs. Prev: Sen. Regist. (Urol.) Leeds Gen. Infirm., St. Jas. Univ. Hosp. Leeds & Bradford Roy. Infirm.; Demonst. (Anat.) Univ. Camb.

HARRISON, Gillian Avondale Unit, Royal Preston Hospital, Sahroe Green Lane, Preston PR2 9HT Tel: 01772 710781 — MB ChB 1981 Aberd.; MRCPsych 1993. Cons. Gen. Adult Psychiat.

HARRISON, Gillian Margaret Meadow Cottage, Green Lane, Chieveley, Newbury RG20 8XB — MB BS 1976 Lond.; MRCS Eng. LRCP Lond. 1976. (Guy's) Clin. Asst. (Anaesth.) W. Berks. (Reading) Health Dist.

HARRISON, Glyn David 57 Bernard Street, St Albans AL3 5QL — MB BS 1994 Lond.

HARRISON, Professor Glynn Leslie Department of Psychiatry, Cotham House, Cotham Hill, Bristol BS6 6JL — MB ChB 1974 Dundee; MD Dundee 1990; FRCPsych 1996, M 1978. (Univ. Dundee) Norah Cooke Hurle Prof. Ment. Health Univ. Bristol. Prev: Prof. Community Ment. Health, Univ. Nottm.; Cons. Psychiat. Acad. Dept. Psychiat. Univ. Hosp. Nottm.; Lect. (Ment. Health) Univ. Bristol & Hon. Sen. Regist. (Psychiat.) Avon HA.

HARRISON, Graham Alan John Department Medical Microbiology, Prince Philip Hospital, Llanelli SA14 8QF Tel: 01554 756567; Public Health Laboratory, West Wales General Hospital, Carmarthen SA31 2AF Tel: 01267 237271 — MB ChB 1980 Bristol; MRCP (UK) 1986; MRCPath 1990; T(Path) 1990; DTM & H Liverp. 1988; FRCP 1998 (Path). Cons. Med. Microbiol. Pub. Health Laborat. Serv.

HARRISON, Herbert Percival Cooper (retired) Corrieknowe, Blanefield, Glasgow G63 9BW Tel: 01360 70088 — MB ChB 1940 Glas.; FRCGP 1977, M 1953. Prev: Surg. Regist. Dumfries & Galloway Roy. Infirm.

HARRISON, Mr Ian David 38 Grosvenor Road, Birkdale, Southport PR8 2ET Tel: 01704 565799 — MD 1977 Liverp.; MB ChB (Hons.) 1968; FRCS Eng. 1972. Cons. Surg. & Med. Director S.port & Ormskirk Hosp. NHS Trust; Clin. Lect. (Surg.) Univ. Liverp. Socs: Liverp. Inst. & Assn. Surg. Prev: Sen. Surg. Regist. Liverp. AHA (T); Wellcome Research Fell. Univ. Liverp.; Ho. Surg. BRd.green Hosp. Liverp.

HARRISON, Ian David Caradoc Surgery, Station Approach, Frinton-on-Sea CO13 9JT Tel: 01255 850101 Fax: 01255 851004; The Little House, 91 Polebarn Lane, Frinton-on-Sea CO13 9NQ — MB BS 1972 Lond.; MRCS Eng. LRCP Lond. 1972; MRCGP 1978; DObst RCOG 1974. (Guy's)

HARRISON, James 57 Woodpecker Mount, Pixton Way, Addington, Croydon CR0 9JB — MB BS 1954 Lond. (Westm.)

HARRISON, James Alastair Forth 6 Woodlands Drive, Penarth CF64 2EW — MB ChB 1995 Manch.

HARRISON, James Gordon Mark, Wing Cdr. RAF Med. Br. Retd. (retired) Jasmine Cottage, Church St., Crondall, Farnham GU10 5QQ Tel: 01252 850346 — MRCS Eng. LRCP Lond. 1950. Prev: GP Fleet Hants.

HARRISON, James Herbert Cheveley Park Medical Centre, Cheveley Park Shopping Centre, Belmont, Durham DH1 2UW Tel: 0191 386 4285 Fax: 0191 386 5934 — MB BS 1978 Lond.; MA Oxf. 1980; MRCGP 1983. (Oxf. & King's Coll.) GP Princip. Co. Durh.; GP Tutor Scheme Organiser GP Career Start Scheme Co Durh. Prev: SHO Roy. Hosp. Sick Childr. Bristol; SHO S.mead Gen. Hosp. Bristol; Ho. Phys. King's Coll. Hosp. Lond.

HARRISON, James Sydney 19 South Road, Twickenham TW2 5NU — MB BS 1990 New South Wales.

HARRISON, Mrs Jane Margaret Community Child Health, 10 Chalmers Crescent, Edinburgh EH9 1TS Tel: 0131 536 0473 Fax:

0131 536 0570 — MB ChB 1982 Ed.; MRCGP 1986; DCCH RCP Ed. 1987; DRCOG 1985. Staff Grade Clin. Med. Off. (Community Child Health) Edin. Sick Childr. NHS Trust.

HARRISON, Jean Florence National Blood Service, North London, Colindale Avenue, London NW9 5BG Tel: 020 8258 2723 Fax: 020 8258 2838 — BM BCh 1971 Oxf.; FRCP Lond. 1995; MRCP (UK) 1975; FRCPath 1991, M 1979. Cons. Transfus. Med. Nat. Blood Serv. N. Lond. Prev: Cons. Haemat. NE Thames Regional Transfus. Centre Brentwood; Sen. Regist. (Haemat.) Sheff. AHA; Regist. (Haemat.) Roy. Infirm. Sheff.

HARRISON, Jennifer 8 Lowstobhill, Morpeth NE61 2SG — MB ChB 1992 Liverp.

HARRISON, Jeremy Francis A & E Department, City Hospital NHS Trust, Dudley Road, Birmingham B18 7QH Email: jeremy@jeremyfh.demon.co.uk — MB ChB Manch. 1984; FRCA 1992. Specialist Regist. A & E Med. City Hosp. NHS Trust Birm. Socs: BMA; BAEM.

HARRISON, Joanne Margaret 120 Dorward Avenue, Glasgow G41 3SG — MB ChB 1991 Glas.; MRCP (UK) 1994.

HARRISON, John The Gables Health Centre, 26 St. Johns Road, Bedlington NE22 7DU Tel: 01670 829889 Fax: 01670 820841 — MB ChB 1982 Manch. GP Bedlington, N.d.

HARRISON, John Maples Family Medical Practice, 35 Hill Street, Hinckley LE10 1DS Tel: 01455 234576 Fax: 01455 250506; 17 Hurst Road, Hinckley LE10 1AB Tel: 01455 634064 — MB ChB 1978 Ed.; DRCOG 1982. Med. Off. Caterpillar UK Ltd. Leicester.

HARRISON, Sir John (Albert Bews), KBE, Surg. Vice-Admiral Retd. Alexandra Cottage, Lower Chase Road, Swanmore, Southampton SO32 2PB — MRCS Eng. LRCP Lond. 1947; FRCP Lond. 1982; FRCR 1976; DMRD Eng. 1955. (St. Bart.) CStJ. Socs: MRC Decompression Sickness Panel; Fell. Roy. Soc. Med. (Ex-Pres. Radiol. Sect.); Fell. (Ex-Pres.) Med. Soc. Lond. Prev: Med. Dir.-Gen. Navy; Dean Naval Med.; Hon. Phys. to HM the Qu..

HARRISON, John Conrad Meadend, 20 Meadway, Heswall, Wirral CH60 8PH — MB ChB 1984 Liverp.; MB ChB Liverp. l984; FRCA 1991. Cons. Anaesth. & Intens. Care Med. Aintree NHS Trust Liverp.

HARRISON, John Daniel Gable House Surgery, Malmesbury SN16 9AT Tel: 01666 825825 Fax: 01666 827515 — MB BS 1987 Lond.; MRCP (UK) 1991; MRCGP 1996. (St. Thos. Hosp. Med. Sch.)

HARRISON, John Ellis (retired) 36 Elmlea Avenue, Bristol BS9 3UU Tel: 0117 962 0375 — MB BChir 1964 Camb.; BA, MB Camb. 1964, BChir 1963; MRCS Eng. LRCP Lond. 1963.

HARRISON, John Ernest The Medical Health Centre, Gray Avenue, Sherburn, Durham DH6 1JE Tel: 0191 372 0441 Fax: 0191 372 1238; 9 Braidwood Drive, Durham DH1 3TD — MB BS 1968 Newc.

HARRISON, John Francis (retired) New Park, Bucknell SY7 0EW Tel: 01547 530380 Fax: 01547 530334 — MB BChir Camb. 1957; FRCP Lond. 1977, M 1961; DObst RCOG 1957. Prev: Cons. Phys. (Geriat.) S. Birm. Health Dist.

HARRISON, Mr John Martin 74 Suffolk Road, Cheltenham GL50 2SZ Tel: 01242 573058 Fax: 01242 575329; 7 Eldorado Road, Cheltenham GL50 2PU Tel: 01242 237463 — MB BS 1977 Lond.; BDS Liverp. 1967; FRCS Ed. 1988; FDS RCS Eng. 1980. Cons. Oral & Maxillofacial Surg. Cheltenham Gen., Glos. Roy. & Cirencester Hosps. Socs: Fell. Brit. Assn. Oral & Maxillofacial Surg. Prev: Sen. Regist. (Oral & Maxillofacial Surg.) Univ. Coll. Hosp. & Qu. Mary's Hosp. Lond.; Asst. (Maxillofacial Clinic) Univ. Münster, W. Germany.

HARRISON, John Myles The Old Bakehouse, Manor Road, Sulgrave, Banbury OX17 2RY — MB BS 1984 Lond.; MRCP (UK) 1989; MRCGP 1993; DFFP 1993; DRCOG 1992. Socs: Brit. Diabetic Assn. Prev: Regist. (Med.) St. Stephens Hosp. Chelsea & Char. Cross Hosp. Lond.; Research Fell. (Endrocrin.) St. Thos. Hosp. Lond.

HARRISON, John Robert sussex police headquarters, Malling House, Lewes BN7 2DZ Tel: 01273 404146 Fax: 01273 404283 Email: john.harrison@sussex.police.uk; 12 Crofton Way, Swanmore, Southampton SO32 2RF Tel: 01489 894932 Fax: 01489 894620 Email: john.r.harrison@lineone.net — MB BS 1966 Lond.; MSc (Occupat. Med.) Lond. 1971, BSc (Hons.) Physiol. 1962; MRCS Eng. LRCP Lond. 1965; FFOM RCP Lond. 1992, M 1979. (St. Bart.) Force med. Advis. Sussex Police; Hon. Sen. Clin. Lect. Birm. Univ. Med. Sch.; Vis. Lect. Surrey Univ., Soton. Univ. & St. Bart. Hosp. Med. Coll.; Examr. MFOM RCP; Med. Advis. NATO. Socs: Fell. Roy. Soc. Med.; Soc. Occupat. Med.; BMA. Prev: Hon. Phys. to HM The Qu. & Cons. Adviser Occupat. Med. RN; Head of Defence Radiol. Protec. Serv. MoD Gosport; Med.Advis.NRPB.

HARRISON, John Robert The Surgery, 12 The Green, Rowlands Castle PO9 6BN Tel: 023 9241 2846 — MB ChB 1984 Leeds; DFFP 1995; DRCOG 1988. Hosp. Pract. (Orthop.) Portsmouth.; Orthopaedic Specialist, Portsmouth. Prev: Med. Adviser (Audit) Portsmouth & S.E. Hants Health Auth.

HARRISON, John William Kenneth 251 Salters Road, Gosforth, Newcastle upon Tyne NE3 4HL — MB BS 1996 Newc.; BMedSci (Newc.) 1995.

HARRISON, Mr Jonathan David Harrogate District Hospitak, Lancaster Park Road, Harrogate HG2 Tel: 01423 553509; 8 Lancater Park Road, Harrogate HG1 7SW — MB ChB 1979 Leeds; DM Nottm. 1990; FRCS Eng. 1984. Cons Surg Surg. Harrogate. Socs: Surg. Research Soc. & Brit. Soc. Gastroenterol. Prev: Regist. (Surg.) Qu. Med. Centre Nottm.; SHO Rotat. (Surg.) Nottm.; SHO (Orthop.) ScarBoro..

HARRISON, Jonathan Michael Rolling Hills, Brandy Lane, Lerryn, Lostwithiel PL22 0QH — BM 1987 Soton.

HARRISON, Joyce (retired) Manor Farm Cottage, The Old Road, Felmersham, Bedford MK43 7JD — BSc (Special Hons.) Lond. 1949, MB BS 1952; MRCS Eng. LRCP Lond. 1952; Dip. Ven. Soc. Apoth. Lond. 1977. Prev: Sen. Med. Off. Beds. HA.

HARRISON, Judith Anne Manchester Royal Infirmary, Oxford Road, Manchester M13 9WL — BM BS 1985 Nottm.; MSc Manch. 1991, MD 1994; MRCPsych. 1990. Cons. Psychiat. Manch. Roy. Infirm.

HARRISON, Julian Francis Alder House, Sikeside, Kirklinton, Carlisle CA6 6DR — MB BS 1980 Lond.; FRCA 1985. (St. Bart.) Cons. Anaesthitics Carlisle Hosp. NHS Trust. Prev: Regist. (Anaesth.) Newc. Teach. Hosps.; SHO (Anaesth.) N. Tees Gen. Hosp.

HARRISON, Julie Michelle Portland Medical Practice, Anchor Meadow Health Centre, Aldridge, Walsall WS9 8AJ Tel: 01922 450950 Fax: 01922 450960 — MB ChB 1993 Liverp. GP Walsall.

HARRISON, Juliet Carleton (retired) St Piers Cottage, St Piers Lane, Lingfield RH7 6PN Tel: 01342 832773 — MB ChB 1946 Otago. Community Phys. (Child Health) Surrey AHA.

HARRISON, Justin Francis McKinnon Department of Haematology, Hemel Hempstead General Hospital, Hillfield Road, Hemel Hempstead HP2 4AD Tel: 01442 213141 Fax: 01442 260253 — MB BS 1983 Lond.; BSc Lond. 1980; MRCP (UK) 1987; MRCPath 1992; FRCP 1999; FRCPath 2000. (St Thomas's Hospital Medical School) Cons. Haemat. W. Herts Hosp.s NHS Trust. Prev: Lect. & Hon. Sen. Regist. (Haemat.) Univ. Coll. Hosp. Lond.; Clin. Research Off. (Haemat.) & Regist. Univ. Hosp. Wales. Cardiff; SHO (Gen. Med. & Haemat.) Mayday Hosp. Thornton Heath.

HARRISON, Kamal Majid Barnsley District General hospital, Gawber Road, Barnsley S75 2EP Tel: 01126 730000; 39 Heather Lea Avenue, Dore, Sheffield S17 3DL Tel: 0114 262 0106 — MB ChB 1956 Baghdad; FRCS Eng. 1968; LMSSA Lond. 1963; FFA RCS Eng. 1973. (Baghdad) Cons. (Anaesth.) Barnsley Dist. Gen. Hosp.; Hon. Clin. Lect. Sheff. Univ. Prev: Cons. Gastroenterol. Barnet & Edgware Gen. Hosp.; Resid. Surg. Off. Hosp. St. Cross Rugby; Sen. Regist. (Anaesth.) Sheff. AHA (T).

HARRISON, Kathleen Joy (retired) The Old Stables, Haycombe Lane, Englishcombe, Bath BA2 9DN Tel: 01225 319932 — MD Bristol 1961, MB ChB 1949; MRCS Eng. LRCP Lond. 1950; DObst RCOG 1951; DCH Eng. 1951; FRCPath 1977, M 1964. Prev: Cons. Pathol. Frenchay Hosp. Bristol.

HARRISON, Kathleen Muriel 6 Southcourt Avenue, Bexhill-on-Sea TN39 3AR — MB BS 1954 Lond.; FRCP Lond. 1990; MRCP (UK) 1972; FRCPath 1979, M 1967; DObst RCOG 1956. (Char. Cross) Prev: Cons. Haemat. Roy. E. Sussex Hosp. Hastings.

HARRISON, Keith Raymond The Market Surgery, 26 Norwich Road, Aylsham, Norwich NR11 6BW Tel: 01263 733331 Fax: 01263 735829; Hill House, Eagle Lane, Erpingham, Norwich NR11 7AD Tel: 01263 761698 — MB BS 1974 Lond.; MRCGP 1979; DRCOG 1978; DCH Eng. 1976. (St. Bart.) Prev: SHO (Paediat.) Derbysh. Childr. Hosp.; SHO (O & G & Cas.) Redhill Gen. Hosp.

HARRISON, Keith Richard Gloucester Royal Hospital, Great Western Road, Gloucester GL1 3NN — MB BCh 1984 Witwatersrand.

HARRISON, Kenneth Worsbrough Health Centre, Oakdale, Worsbrough, Barnsley S70 5EG Tel: 01226 204404; Fairfield, 2 Silkstone Lane, Cawthorne, Barnsley S75 4DX — MB ChB 1952 Birm.

HARRISON, Kevin The Surgery, Little London, Walsall WS1 3EP Tel: 01922 622898 Fax: 01922 623023; 9 Jesson Road, Walsall WS1 3AY — MB ChB 1981 Birm.; BSc Leic. 1971; MRCGP 1985; DRCOG 1983. (Birm.) GP.

HARRISON, Lesley Jane Paupers Cottage, 2389 Stratford Road, Hockley Heath, Solihull B94 6NW — MB ChB 1979 Birm.; MFPHM 1989.

HARRISON, Lorna Jane 2 West View, Eldwick, Bingley BD16 3ED — MB ChB 1994 Dundee. (Univ. Dundee) SHO (Paediat.) Bradford St Lukes Bradford W. Yorks.

HARRISON, Lorraine Wilhelmina Lagan Valley Hospital, Lisburn BT28 1JP; 15 Ballyworfy Road, Magheradartin, Hillsborough BT26 6LR Email: lorrwh@doctors.org.uk — MB ChB 1978 Ed.; FFA RCSI 1984 Dublin. (Edinburgh) Cons. Anaesth. Lagan Valley Hosp. Lisburn. Socs: Assn. Anaesth. GB & Irel.; BMA; Obst. Anaesth. Assn. Prev: Sen. Regist. (Anaesth.) Belf. City Hosp.; Regist. (Anaesth.) Roy. Vict. Hosp. Belf.; Ho. Off. (Orthop. Surg.) Vict. Hosp. Kirkaldy.

HARRISON, Louise Sommerville Westgate House, Southmead Hospital, Westbury-on-Trym, Bristol BS10 5NB Tel: 0117 959 5365; 2 Harley Place, Clifton Down, Bristol BS8 3JT — MB ChB 1974 Dundee. (Dundee) Staff Grade Community Paediat. S. Mead MHS Trust. Prev: Clin. Med. Off. (Child Health) Nottm. HA.; Ho. Phys. Ninewells Hosp. Dundee; Ho. Surg. Arbroath Infirm.

HARRISON, Lucy Elizabeth Red Oak Child & Family Services, Ashford Rd, Piccadilly, Scotforth, Lancaster LA1 Email: harrisonle@compuserve.com — MB ChB 1986 Birm.; MRCPsych 1991. Sen. Regist. N. W.. RHA. Socs: Manch. Med. Soc.; Soc. for Study of Behavioural Phenotypes; Assn. Child Psychol. & Psychiat. Prev: Regist. (Psychiat.) Leeds Gen. Infirm. & Centr. Hosp. Warwick; SHO (Psychiat.) Warwick.

HARRISON, Margaret Anne (retired) 33 High Street, Bishopton, Stockton-on-Tees TS21 1EZ — MB ChB 1954 Leeds; FFOM RCP Lond. 1991, MFOM RCP 1979; DIH Eng. 1963. Prev: Employm. Med. Adviser EMAS.

HARRISON, Margaret Anne Mackintosh Lockwood Surgery, 3 Meltham Road, Lockwood, Huddersfield HD1 3XH Tel: 01484 421580 Fax: 01484 480100; 13 Occupation Road, Lindley, Huddersfield HD3 3EE Tel: 01484 420404 — MB BS 1967 Lond.; BSc (Physiol.) Lond. 1964. (Lond. Hosp.) Prev: Ho. Phys. Lond. Hosp.; Med. Off. Lond. Boro. Islington; Ho. Phys. Lond. Chest Hosp.

HARRISON, Margaret Olivia Oak Tree, Hearns Lane, Faddiley, Nantwich CW5 8JL — MB ChB 1956 Liverp.; MD New York 1968; BCR Amer. Coll. Radiol. 1968; FRCR 1977.

HARRISON, Mrs Marianne Franziska (retired) 1 Wellbraes, Eyemouth TD14 5ET Tel: 018907 50520 — Dr. Med. Bonn 1950; LAH Dub. 1959; DA Ibadan 1972.

HARRISON, Mark Seaforth, Lon Isallt, Trearddur Bay, Holyhead LL65 2UP — MB BS 1985 Lond.; MRCP (UK) 1989; FRCR 1992. Clin. Research Fell. Imperial Cancer Research Fund Clare Hall Laborat. S. Mimms. Prev: Regist. (Clin. Oncol.) Hammersmith Hosp. Lond.

HARRISON, Mark Andrew 77 Harley Street, London W1N 1DE Tel: 020 7224 0030 Fax: 020 7224 2707 Email: harleystreetgroup@btinternet.com — BM 1988 Soton. MD of Harley St. Doctors Ltd.; MD of Harley St. Gp. of Companies.

HARRISON, Mark David Ian The Surgery, St. Mary Street, Thornbury, Bristol BS35 2AT Tel: 01454 413691 Fax: 01454 411141 — MB BS 1989 Lond.; MRCGP 1993; DRCOG 1995; DCH RCP Lond. 1994. (St. Mary's Hosp. Lond.)

HARRISON, Mark Llewellyn St Charles Hospital, Exmoor St., London W10 6DZ — MB BS 1989 West. Austral. SHO (Psychiat.) St. Chas. Hosp. Lond.

HARRISON, Martin David Fairwater Health Centre, Plasmawr Road, Fairwater, Cardiff CF5 3JT Tel: 029 2056 6291 Fax: 029 2057 8870; 19 Pencisley Crescent, Llandaff, Cardiff CF5 1DS — MB ChB 1979 Bristol; MRCGP 1983; DRCOG 1983.

HARRISON, Martyn Timothy East Farm, Thirlby, Thirsk YO7 2DJ — MB ChB 1975 Manch.; BSc (Hons.) Manch. 1972, MB ChB (Hons.) 1975. Pres. Manch. Med. Gp. & Tutor (Gen. Pract.) Leeds. Prev: SHO (Surg.) Leicester Gen. Hosp.; Ho. Phys. & Ho. Surg. Manch. Roy. Infirm.

HARRISON, Mary Ann Mackay St Mary's Hospice, 176 Raddlebarn Road, Selly Park, Birmingham B29 7DA Tel: 0121 472 1191; Laurel Cottage, Wrenbury Heath, Nantwich CW5 8EF Tel: 01270 780677 — MB ChB 1966 St. And.; BA Open 1980; FRCP Lond. 1989. Med. Dir. St. Mary's Hospice Birm. Prev: Cons. Geriat. Crewe & Gwynedd AHA; Research Asst. Dept. Investig. Med. Univ. Camb. & Hon. Med. Regist. United Camb. Hosps.

HARRISON, Matthew Norris (retired) 1 Cooper Hill Drive, Walton-le-Dale, Preston PR5 4HE — MRCS Eng. LRCP Lond. 1952. Prev: GP Walton-le-Dale.

HARRISON, Mr Max Henry Montague (retired) 25 Frederick Road, Edgbaston, Birmingham B15 1JN Tel: 0121 454 2776 Fax: 0121 454 2776 — MB ChB 1944 Leeds; MB ChB (Hons.) Leeds 1944; ChM Leeds 1953; FRCS Eng. 1950. Prev: Hillman Prize Clin. Med.

HARRISON, Melanie Jayne 61 Lorne Road, Clarendon Park, Leicester LE2 1YH Tel: 0116 270 9873; The Surgery, Mill Lane, Belton, Loughborough LE12 9UJ Tel: 01530 222368 — MB ChB 1992 Leic.; DRCOG 1995; MRCGP 1997. (Leicester) GP. Socs: MRCGP.

HARRISON, Michael, SBStJ 19 Sandles Close, The Ridings, Droitwich WR9 8RB Tel: 01905 798308 Fax: 01905 798307 — MB BS Lond. 1965; MRCS Eng. LRCP Lond. 1964; FFPHM 1980, M 1974; DPH Bristol 1969. (St. Mary's) Socs: Fell. Roy. Soc. Med.; Fell. Roy. Soc. of Health. Prev: Regional Dir. Pub. Health & Dep. Chief Exec. W. Midl. RHA; Dist. Gen. Manager & Dist. Med. Off. Sandwell HA; Vis.Fell.Univ.Aston.Bus.Sch.

HARRISON, Michael Charles 85 Kingswood Road, Bromley BR2 0NG Tel: 020 8464 0284 — MB BS 1978 Lond.; DRCOG Lond. 1981; MRCGP 1982. (Guy's)

HARRISON, Michael Craig Department of Paediatrics, Chelsea & Westminster Hospital, 369 Fulham Road, London SW10 9NH — MB ChB 1990 Cape Town.

HARRISON, Professor Michael John Gatfield Middlesex Hospital, Mortimer St., London W1T 3AA Tel: 020 7380 9431 Fax: 020 7380 9427 — BM BCh 1961 Oxf.; DM Oxf. 1968, MA, BM BCh 1961; FRCP Lond. 1977, M 1964. (Middlx.) Prof. Clin. Neurol. Univ. Coll. & Middlx. Sch. Med. Lond.; Hon. Cons. Neurol. Nat. Hosp. Nerv. Dis. Lond.; Dir. Research Dept. Neurol. Studies Middlx. Hosp. Med. Sch. Lond. Prev: Sen. Regist. & Resid. Med. Off. Nat. Hosp. Nerv. Dis. Lond.; Med. Regist. Dept. Regius Prof. Med. Oxf.

HARRISON, Michael Magnus 2 Frobisher Drive, Whitby YO21 1NX — MB BS 1993 Newc.

HARRISON, Michael Stephen 70 Rothwell Road, Gosforth, Newcastle upon Tyne NE3 1UA — MB BS 1988 Newc.

HARRISON, Nadine University Health Service, University of Edinburgh, Richard Verney Health Centre, 6 Bristo Square, Edinburgh EH8 9AL Tel: 0131 650 2777 Fax: 0131 662 1813; 16 Craiglockhart Terrace, Edinburgh EH14 1AJ Tel: 0131 443 1152 Email: nadine.harrison@ed.ac.uk — MB ChB 1973 Bristol; DRCOG 1976; Cert. Family Plann. JCC 1976. (Bristol) Med. Off. Univ. Health Centre, Edin. Prev: Regist. (Psychiat.) Roy. Edin. Hosp.; Clin. Asst. (Genitourin. Med.) Roy. Infirm. Edin.

HARRISON, Neil Andrew 93 Vanbrugh Court, Wincott St., London SE11 4NR — MB BS 1996 Lond.; BSc 1993. (Guys) SHO Neurol. Guys Hosp. Lond. Prev: Asst.Kantonspital.Basel.Switz.

HARRISON, Mr Neville Walter (retired) Kent, Surrey & Sussex Postgraduate Deanery, 20 Guildford Street, London WC1N DZ Tel: 0207 692 3178 — MB BS Lond. 1962; MD Lond. 1972; FRCS Eng. 1967; MRCS Eng. LRCP Lond. 1962; DObst RCOG 1964. p/t Assoc. PostGrad. Dean, Kent, Surrey & Sussex PostGrad. Deanery; Brighton Healthcare NHS Trust. Prev: Sen. Regist. (Gen. Surg.) Mulago Hosp. Kampala, Uganda.

HARRISON, Nicholas John Highcroft, Cotton, Stoke-on-Trent ST10 3DN — MB ChB 1997 Birm.; BSc Leeds 1992.

HARRISON, Nicholas Kim Morriston Hospital, Morriston, Swansea SA6 6NL Tel: 01792 702222 Fax: 01792 703845 Email: nkharrison@doctors.org.uk — MB BS 1979 Lond.; MA Camb. 1979, MD 1992; FRCP Lond. 1997; MRCP (UK) 1982. (University

College Hospital, Lodon) Cons. Phys. (Respirat. Med.) Morriston Hosp. Swansea. Socs: Brit. Assn. Lung Res.; Brit. Thorac. Soc.; Amer. Thoracic Soc. Prev: Sen. Regist. Roy. Brompton Hosp. Lond.

HARRISON, Nicholas Stanley Charles, Squadron Ldr. RAF Med. Br. Retd. The Surgery, 41 Lyndhurst Road, Barnehurst, Bexleyheath DA7 6DL Tel: 01322 525000 Fax: 03122 523123; 20 Dahlia Drive, Swanley BR8 7XS — MB ChB 1981 Leic.; MRCGP 1986.

HARRISON, Nicola Northern General Hospital, Sherries Rd, Sheffield S5 — MB ChB 1985 Dundee; FRCA 1991. Cons. Anaesth. N. Gen. Hosp. Trust Sheff. Prev: Sen. Regist. (Anaesth.) N. Trent, Sheff.; Regist. (Anaesth.) Nottm.; SHO (Anaesth.) Chesterfield & N. Derbysh. Hosp., Roy. Hallamsh. & N.. Gen. Hosps. Sheff.

HARRISON, Nigel Anthony Medical Department, Noble's Hospital, Douglas IM1 4QA Tel: 01624 642642 Fax: 01624 642527; Ballabunt Croft, The Cooil, Braddan, Douglas IM4 2AQ Tel: 01624 616682 Fax: 01624 670518 Email: nigel@ballabunt.demon.co.uk — MB BS 1979 Lond.; MMedSc Birm 1991; MRCP (UK) 1986; DAvMed FOM RCP Lond. 1994; DTM & H RCP Lond. 1989; T(M) 1991; FRCP 1996. (Charing Cross) Cons. Phys. (Cardiol.) Noble's Hosp. Douglas, I. of Man. Socs: Brit. Med. Acupunct. Soc.; Brit. Soc. Echocardiogr. Prev: Wing Cdr. RAF & Cons. Phys. RAF Hosp. Wegberg, Germany; Sen. Regist. (Med.) & Hon. Sen. Regist. (Infec. Dis.) E. Birm. Hosp.; Hon. Sen Regist. (Med. Cardiol.) John Radcliffe Hosp. Oxf.

HARRISON, Nigel Gregory Cornford House Surgery, 364 Cherry Hinton Road, Cambridge CB1 8BA Tel: 01223 247505 Fax: 01223 568187; 86 Mawson Road, Cambridge CB1 2EA Tel: 01223 321901 — MB BS 1979 Lond.

HARRISON, Pamela Fay Merriewood, 17 St Botolph's Road, Sevenoaks TN13 3AQ Tel: 01732 454491 — MB BS 1953 Lond.; LMSSA 1952. (Roy. Free)

HARRISON, Pamela Joy 94 Brackley Square, Woodford Green IG8 7LS — MB ChB Manch. 1967.

HARRISON, Pamela Susan The Albert Road Practice, Laurel House, 12 Albert Road, Tamworth B79 7JN Tel: 01827 69283; Shuttington House, Ashby Road, Statfold, Tamworth B79 0BT Tel: 01827 830633 — MB ChB 1970 Birm.; DObst RCOG 1972. (Birm.)

HARRISON, Paul dept of Haematology, Russells Hall Hospital, Dudley Dy1 2HQ Tel: 01384 456111 Fax: 01384 244258 Email: ph@haematology-rhh.demon.co.uk — MB BS 1987 Lond.; MRCP (UK) 1991; DRCPath 1995; MRCPath 1996. (UCL)

HARRISON, Paul David Angel Hill Surgery, 1 Angel Hill, Bury St Edmunds IP33 1LU Tel: 01284 753008 Fax: 01284 724744 — MB BS 1990 Lond.; BSc Lond. 1987; DRCOG 1993. (St. Geo. Hosp. Med. Sch.) Prev: Trainee GP Bury St. Edmunds.

HARRISON, Paul George William 2 Teawell Road, Newton Mearns, Glasgow G77 6SN — MB ChB 1998 Glas.; MB ChB Glas 1998.

HARRISON, Professor Paul Jeffrey University Department of Psychiatry, Neurosciences Building Warneford Hospital, Oxford OX3 7JX Tel: 01865 223730 Fax: 01865 251076 — BM BCh 1985 Oxf.; BA Oxf. 1982, DM 1991; MRCPsych 1989. Clin. Reader in Psychiat. Univ. of Oxf. Dept. of Psychiat. Warneford Hosp. Oxf. Prev: Wellcome Sen. Research Fell. (Clin. Sci.); Clin. Lect. (Psychiat.) Univ. Oxf. Warneford Hosp. Oxf.; MRC Train. Fell. St. Mary's Hosp. Med. Sch. Lond.

HARRISON, Paul Leslie Sefton House, 192B Burton Road, Ashby-de-la-Zouch LE65 2TF — MB ChB 1977 Liverp.

HARRISON, Peter Anthony (retired) The Surgery, 14 Front St., Acomb, York YO24 3BZ Tel: 01904 794141 Fax: 01904 788304 — MB BS Lond. 1964.

HARRISON, Peter Leslie (retired) (Surgery) 50 Stockport Road, Marple, Stockport SK6 6AB Tel: 0161 426 0299 — MB ChB 1965 Manch.; MRCGP 1975; DObst RCOG 1967; DA Eng. 1968. Lect. (Gen. Pract.) Manch. Univ. Prev: Clin. Asst. (Gastroenterol.) Stockport DHA.

HARRISON, Peter Richard James Paget Healthcare NHS Trust, Lowestoft Road, Gorleston-on-Sea, Great Yarmouth NR31 6LN Tel: 01493 452452 Fax: 01493 452421 Email: peter.harrison@jpaget.nhs.uk — MB BS 1971 Lond.; FRCP Lond. 1990; MRCP (UK) 1975. (Guy's) Cons. Phys. James Paget Hosp.; Clin Sub Dean Univ Camb; Assoc. Clin. Tutor. Socs: Renal Assn. & Brit. Transpl. Soc.; Internat. Soc. Hypertens. in Pregn.; Brit. Geriat.. Soc. Prev: Cons. Renal Phys. S.mead Hosp. Bristol; Clin. Dir. Med. & Sen. Regist. (Nephrol.) S.mead Hosp. Bristol; SHO (Renal) St. Thos. Hosp. Lond.

HARRISON, Philip Alan Hailwood Medical Centre, 2 Hailwood Court, Governors Hill, Douglas IM2 7EA Tel: 01624 675444 Fax: 01624 616290; Hillside, 43 Ballanard Road, Douglas IM2 5HB Tel: 01624 628565 Fax: 01624 628565 Email: philharrison@pastmaster.co.uk — MB ChB 1977 Dundee. Socs: Isle of Man Med. Soc. Prev: Police Surg. Isle of Man; SHO (Obst.) Vict. Hosp. Blackpool; Ho. Surg. & Ho. Phys. Noble's I. of Man Hosp.

HARRISON, Philip Albert (retired) 2a Preston Road, Southport PR9 9EG Tel: 01704 531202 Email: philah@premiumuk.com — MB ChB 1954 Liverp.; DObst RCOG 1957. Prev: GP S.port.

HARRISON, Philip James The Medicines Control Agency, Room 1534, Market Towers, 1 Nine Elms Lane, London SW8 5NQ Tel: 020 7273 0380 Fax: 020 7273 0493; North End House, 90 North End Road, London NW11 7SX Tel: 020 8201 8070 Fax: 020 8455 6122 — MB ChB 1973 Manch.; MRCP (UK) 1976; MFPM 1989. (St. And. & Manch.) Sen. Med. Off. Med. Control Agency DoH. Socs: Brit. Assn. Pharmaceut. Phys.; Soc. Pharmacuet. Med.

HARRISON, Philip Victor Royal Lancaster Infirmary, Ashton Road, Lancaster LA1 4RP Tel: 01524 583188 Fax: 01524 583166 — MB ChB 1973 Ed.; BSc 1971 Ed.; MD 2001 Ed.; FRCP Lond. 1993; MRCP (UK) 1975; FRCP Ed 1998. (Edinburgh) Cons. Dermat. Lancaster Acute NHS Trust.

HARRISON, Phillip MacDonald Institute of Liver Studies, King's College School of Medicine & Dentistry, Bessemer Road, London SE5 9PJ Tel: 020 7346 3169 Fax: 020 7346 3167; Weather Cock Barn, Little Linton, Cambridge CB1 6JD Tel: 01223 891990 Fax: 01223 891990 — MB BS 1984 Lond.; BSc Lond. 1981, MD 1992; MRCP (UK) 1987(St. Geo.); PhD Lond. 1997; FRCP 1998. (St. Geo. Hosp. Med. Sch. Lond.) Sen. Lect. (Inst. Liver Studies) King's Coll. Sch. Med. & Dent. Lond. Socs: Brit. Assn. Study Liver; A.M. Assn. Study of the Liver. Prev: Sen. Regist. (Hepatol.) Addenbrooke's Hosp. Camb.; MRC Train. Fell. Molecular Med. Unit. King's Coll. Hosp. Lond.; Regist. (Med.) Liver Unit King's Coll. Hosp. Lond.

HARRISON, Rachael Louise Department of Radiology, Addenbrookes Hospital NHS Trust, Hills Road, Cambridge CB3 7ND; 41 The Elms, Haslingfield, Cambridge CB3 7ND — MB BS 1991 Lond.; MRCP; FRCR. (Guy's and St. Thomas) Specialist Regist. (Radiol.). Prev: SHO (A & E) Norf. & Norwich Hosp.; SHO (Med.) Ipswich; SHO (Oncol. Radiother.) Norwich.

HARRISON, Rachel Elizabeth 1 Rosefield Place, Edinburgh EH15 1AZ — MB ChB 1985 Bristol; MRCGP 1989; MFHom 1992; DCCH RCP Ed. 1990; DRCOG 1988. Private Homeopathic Craniosacral Ther.

HARRISON, Rachel Elizabeth 21 Mile End Park, Pocklington, York YO42 2TH — BM BS 1996 Nottm.

HARRISON, Raymond 105 St James Road, Stockport SK4 4RE — MB ChB 1993 Sheff.

HARRISON, Rebecca Faith Department of Pathology, The Medical School, University of Birmingham, Edgbaston, Birmingham B15 2TT — MB ChB 1986 Birm.; BSc Birm. 1983; MRCPath 1992. (Birmingham) Cons. Path. Univ. Hosp. Birm. Socs: MRCPath. Prev: Cons. Path. S.mead Hosp. Bristol; Lect. (Path.) Univ. Birm.; Regist. (Path.) W. Midl. RHA.

HARRISON, Rex (retired) Brecken Ridge, Culgaith, Penrith CA10 1QF Tel: 01768 88451 — BA, MB BChir Camb. 1952; DLO Eng. 1966; DObst RCOG 1957. Prev: GP Clitheroe.

HARRISON, Mr Richard, TD, OStJ Furness General Hospital, Barrow-in-Furness LA14 4LF Tel: 01229 585396 Fax: 01229 585396 Email: hip.poc2@aol.com; Bank Hurst, Ulverston LA12 7PU Tel: 01229 583268 — MB BS 1944 Lond.; MB BS (Hons. Distinc. Obst. & Gyn.) Lond. 1944; FRCS Eng. 1952. (St. Bart.) Hon. Advis. Limbless Assn. & REACH. Socs: Osler Soc.; Milit. Surg. Soc.; Airbourne Med Off Soc. Prev: Maj. RAMC (T & AVR), Cons. Orthop.; Cons. Orthop. & Accid. Surg. SW Cumbria Health Dist.; Sen. Regist. (Orthop.) Roy. Free Hosp. Lond.

HARRISON, Richard Anthony Holly Lodge, Well End Road, Well End, Borehamwood WD6 5PR Tel: 020 8953 9409 Fax: 020 8953 4266 — MRCS Eng. LRCP Lond. 1972; MS Lond. 1987, MB BS (Hons. Surg., Med., Applied Pharmacol. &; Therap. Univ. Gold Medal) 1972; FRCS Eng. 1976. (St. Mary's) Cons. (Gen. Surg.) WellHo. NHS Trust Barnet Hosp. Prev: Lect. (Surg.) Univ. Coll. Lond.

HARRISON, Sir Richard John Downing College, Cambridge CB2 1DQ; 58A High Street, Barkway, Royston SG8 8EE — MB BChir 1944 Camb.; MB BChir Camb. 1945; FRS; DSc Glas. 1948; MA Camb. 1946, BA 1942, MD 1954; MRCS Eng. LRCP Lond. 1944. (Camb. & St. Bart.) Emerit. Prof. Anat. Univ. Camb. Socs: Hon. Mem. Amer. Assn. Anatomists. Prev: Prof. Anat. Univ. Lond. at Lond. Hosp. Med. Coll.; Fullerian Prof. Physiol. Roy. Inst.; Reader (Anat.) Char. Cross Hosp. Med. Sch.

HARRISON, Richard Kinder 12 Mostyn Road, Hazel Grove, Stockport SK7 5HL — BM BS 1997 Nottm.

HARRISON, Richard Neil North Tees General Hospital, Hardwick, Stockton-on-Tees TS19 8PE — MD 1984 Liverp.; MB ChB 1972; MRCP (UK) 1976. Cons. Phys. N. Tees Gen. Hosp.

HARRISON, Richard Thomas Scott Montalto Medical Centre, 2 Dromore Road, Ballynahinch BT24 8AY Tel: 028 9756 2929; 118 Magheraknock Road, Ballynahinch BT24 8UH Tel: 0184 663 8500 Fax: 01238 562065 — MB BCh BAO 1976 Belf.; DRCOG 1978. Socs: BMA & Assn. Forens. Med. Off.s N. Irel. Prev: Ho. Off. Roy. Vict. Hosp. Belf.

HARRISON, Richard Thomas Theodore (retired) Knowle, Bishops Lydeard, Taunton TA4 3LL — MB BS Lond. 1948; MRCGP 1960.

HARRISON, Richard William Medical Centre, Pinfold St., Howden, Goole DN14 7DD Tel: 01430 430318; Church Barn, Laxton, Goole DN14 7TS Tel: 01430 430827 — MB BChir 1983 Camb.; MA Camb. 1982, BA 1979; LMSSA Lond. 1982. (King's Coll. Hosp.)

HARRISON, Richard William Seymour Bensham Hospital, Saltwell Rd, Gateshead NE8 4YL Tel: 0191 403 6699 Fax: 0191 403 6685 — MB BS 1987 Newc.; MA Camb. 1988, BA 1984; MRCPsych. 1991. Cons. In Old Age Psychiat., Gateshead Health NHS Trust; Hon. Clin. Lect., Univ. of Newc. Upon Tyne. Prev: Regist. (Psychiat.) N.. RHA.; Lect. (Psychiat. Old Age) Univ. Newc. u. Tyne.

HARRISON, Professor Robert Frederick Academic Department of Obstetrics & Gynaecology, Royal College of Surgeons in Ireland, Rotunda Hospital, Dublin, Republic of Ireland Tel: 00 353 1 807 2696 Fax: 00 353 1 872 7831; 433 Aigburth Road, Liverpool L17 6BJ — LRCP 1967 Irel.; LM LRCPI, LM LRCSI 1967; MD NUI 1981; FRCPI 1980; FRCS Ed. 1971; FRCOG 1984, M 1972. Head Acad. Dept. Obst. & Gyn. Rotunda Hosp. Dub. Socs: (Pres.) Internat. Federat. Fertil. Soc.; Brit. Fertil. Soc. Prev: Prof. Obst. & Gyn. Trinity Coll. Rotunda Hosp. Dub.; Lect. & Sen. Regist. Inst. of Obst. & Gyn. Lond. Univ. & Qu Charlottes Hosp. Lond.

HARRISON, Robert Geoffrey 691 Coventry Road, Small Heath, Birmingham B10 0JL Tel: 0121 772 0845 Fax: 0121 753 2210; 195 Moor Green Lane, Moseley, Birmingham B13 8NT Tel: 0121 449 2770 — MB ChB 1958 Birm.; MRCGP 1973; DA Eng. 1961.

HARRISON, Robert William Swan Lane Medical Centre, Swan Lane, Bolton BL3 6TL — MB ChB 1982 Leeds.

HARRISON, Roger James 5 Birchley View, Moss Bank, St Helens WA11 7NT — MB ChB 1957 Liverp.; MD Liverp. 1967. p/t Phys. Billinge & Whelley Hosps. Socs: Fell of the Roy. Soc of Med; Pub.ations: Textbook of Med. 1977, 3rd Edition 1984. Hodder & Stoughton; The Causes and Preven. of Cancer 1991. Vantage Press. Prev: Assoc. Specialist St. Helens Hosp.

HARRISON, Miss Rosalind Joan Queens Hospital, Belvedere Road, Burton-on-Trent DE13 0RB Tel: 01283 566333 Fax: 01283 593014; Bretby House, Stanhope, Bretby, Burton-on-Trent DE15 0PT Tel: 01283 563427 Email: harrj@dircon.uk — MB BS 1971 Queensland; MB BS Queensland. 1971; FRCS Eng. (Ophth.) 1982; FRCOphth 1988; DO Eng. 1980; DTM & H Eng. 1976. (Queensld.) Cons. Ophth. Burton Hosp. NHS Trust. Socs: Fell. Roy. Soc. Med. Prev: Sen. Regist. (Ophth.) Bristol Eye Hosp. & Hon. Tutor Univ Bristol; Regist. Wolverhampton & Midl. Cos. Eye Infirm.; Jun. Resid. Med. Off. Roy. P. Albert Hosp. Sydney, Austral.

HARRISON, Rosalinde June (retired) 73 Wolverhampton Road, Codsall, Wolverhampton WV8 1PL Tel: 01902 845820 — MB ChB 1950 Birm.; FRCA 1955; DA Eng. 1952. Hon. Cons. Anaesth. Wolverhampton HA. Prev: Cons. Anaesth. Wolverhampton HA.

HARRISON, Rosaline Ann Royal Cornwall Hospitals, Treliske Hospital, Truro TR1 3LJ Tel: 01872 74242 Fax: 01872 40438 — MB ChB Manch. 1966; FFA RCS Eng. 1979; DA Eng. 1978. (Manch.) Cons. Anaesth. Roy. Cornw. Hosp. Trust Truro. Socs: Assn. Anaesth.; Soc. Anaesth. (SW Region); Difficult Airway Soc. Prev: Sen. Regist. (Anaesth.) Roy. Cornw. Hosp., Qu. Eliz. Hosp. Birm., Roy. Hosp. & New Cross Hosp. Wolverhampton.

HARRISON, Ruth Margaret Bolinbroke 55 The Whartons, Otley LS21 2AG — MB ChB 1962 Leeds; FFA RCS Eng. 1971. Assoc. Specialist (Anaesth.) Wharfedale Gen. Hosp. Otley. Prev: Cons. Anaesth. Dewsbury.

HARRISON, Sally Jane Woodcote, 1B Harmer Dell, Welwyn AL6 0BE; Flat 3, 121 Haverstock Hill, London NW3 4RS — MB BS 1991 Lond.; DA; MRCP. (RFHSM) Specialist Regist. Rotat. (Anaesth.) Whittington Hosp. Prev: SHO (Anaesth.) Barnet Gen. Hosp.; SHO (Med.) Lister Hosp.; SHO (IC) St Marys Hosp. Paddington.

HARRISON, Sara Katherine 39 Pen-Y-Lan Road, Cardiff CR23 5HZ Tel: 029 2049 2568; Dept. of Radiology, University Hospital of Wales, Health Park, Cardiff CF14 4XW Tel: 029 2074 5493 Fax: 029 2074 3029 — MB BCh 1987 Wales; MRCP (UK) 1991; FRCR (UK) 1995. Cons. Radiologist, UHW, Cardiff. Prev: Regist. (Diag. Radiol.) Cardiff.

HARRISON, Sarah Louise Public Health Medicine Department, South & West Devon Health Authority, Shinner's Bridge, Dartington, Totnes TQ9 6JE Tel: 01803 861836; 26 Church Street, South Brent TQ10 9AB — MB BS 1983 Lond.; MFPHM RCP (UK) 1994; MRCGP 1987; DRCOG 1986. Cons. Communicable Dis. Control S. & W. Devon HA. Prev: Princip. GP Taunton.

HARRISON, Sheila Carrick Radnor Street Surgery, 3 Radnor Street, Glasgow G3 7UA Tel: 0141 334 6111; 19 Strathblane Road, Milngavie, Glasgow G62 8DL — MB ChB 1974 Glas.; BSc Glas. 1970. Prev: SHO (Obst.) Cresswell Matern. Hosp. Dumfries; SHO (Paediat.) Falkirk Roy. Infirm. & (Psychiat.) Stobhill Gen. Hosp. Glas.

HARRISON, Simon Bernard Dalgregaig, Drumnadrochit, Inverness IV63 6TZ — BM BS 1983 Nottm.

HARRISON, Mr Simon Charles William Department of Urology, Pinderfields Hospital, Aberford Road, Wakefield WF1 4DG Tel: 01924 201688 Fax: 01924 212921; 11 Westfield Road, St. Johns, Wakefield WF1 3RB Tel: 01924 365274 — MB BS 1979 Lond.; MChir Camb. 1989, MA 1980; FRCS Eng. 1984. (Lond. Hosp.) Cons. Urol. with s/i in Spinal Inj. Pinderfields Hosp. Wakefield. Socs: Brit. Assn. Urol. Surgs. & Internat. Continence Soc. Prev: Sen. Regist. (Urol.) Bristol & Taunton Hosps.; Regist. (Urol.) Norf. & Norwich Hosp.; Surgic. Train. Progr. Addenbrooke's Hosp. Camb.

HARRISON, Simon James Haematology Department, Glasgow Royal Infirmary, 84 Castle St., Glasgow G3 0JE Tel: 0141 552 3535 — MB BS 1990 Newc. SHO (Haemat.) Glas. Roy. Infirm.

HARRISON, Simon Richard Barnard Woodgate-Jones and Partners, The Surgery, Mount Street, Bishops Lydeard, Taunton TA4 3LH Tel: 01823 432361 Fax: 01823 433864 — MB BS 1973 Lond.; MRCGP 1977; DCH Eng. 1977; DObst RCOG 1976. (Middlx.) Clin. Asst. (Learning Difficulties) Deane Barton Taunton. Prev: Trainee GP Nottm. VTS; Ho. Phys. (Gastroenterol.) Centr. Middlx. Hosp. Lond.; Ho. Surg. W.on-super-Mare Gen. Hosp.

HARRISON, Stanley (retired) Coleby, 14 Treeton Road, Howden, Goole DN14 7DQ Tel: 01430 430271 — MRCS Eng. LRCP Lond. 1941; DA Eng. 1956. Prev: Clin. Asst. (Anaesth. & Orthop.) Bartholomew Hosp. Goole.

HARRISON, Stephen John Department of Anaesthetics, West Middlesex University Hospital NHS Trust, Isleworth TW7 6AF Tel: 020 8565 5824; 20 Abbott Close, Hampton TW12 3XR — MB BS 1987 Lond.; FRCA 1994; DA (UK) 1990. (Lond. Hosp. Med. Coll.) Cons. Anaesth. W. Middlx. Univ. Hosp. NHS Trust. Prev: Sen. Regist. (Anaesth.) Roy. Hosp. NHS Trust, Lond; Regist. (Anaesth.) King's Coll. Hosp. Lond.; Regist. (Anaesth.) St. Thos. Hosp. Lond.

HARRISON, Steven Mark Flat D, St Judes Vicarage, 111 Mildmay Grove N., London N1 4PL — MB BS 1993 Lond.

HARRISON, Mr Stewart Hamilton (retired) Woodlands, Farnham Park Lane, Farnham Royal, Slough SL2 3LP Tel: 01753 643088 — LRCP LRCS Ed. LRFPS Glas. 1935; LDS RCS Ed. 1934; FRCS Eng. 1969; FRCS Ed. 1938. Hon. Cons. Plastic Surg. King Edwd. VII Hosp. Windsor; Hon. Cons. Plastic Surg. Mt. Vernon Centre Plastic Surg. & Jaw Injuries N.wood; Vis. Prof. Yale Univ. USA, Univ. Louisville, USA & Univ. Lisbon, Portugal. Prev: Surg. Plastic & Jaw Unit, Rooksdown Ho., Basingstoke.

HARRISON, Stuart Garth Collier (retired) Cedar House, Broad St, Orford, Woodbridge IP12 2NQ Tel: 01394 450892 — MB BS 1962 Lond.; FFA RCS Eng. 1970. Prev: Ho. Phys. Middlx. Hosp. Lond.

HARRISON, Sydney Hubert (retired) Forest Edge, 19 Oak Tree Lane, Mansfield NG18 3HN Tel: 01623 653524 Email: sydney.harrison4@which.net — MB ChB Sheff. 1953; DFFP 1993; FRCGP 1987. Prev: partner, Roundwood Surg., Wood St, Mansfield.

HARRISON, Thomas Alan (retired) 41 The Uplands, Loughton IG10 1NQ Tel: 020 8508 7834 Fax: 020 8508 7834 — MB BS Lond. 1946. Prev: GP W. Essex HA.

HARRISON, Mr Thomas Antony (cons. rooms) Blackheath Hospital, 40-42 Lee Terrace, Blackheath, London SE3 9UD Tel: 020 8463 1722 Fax: 020 8463 1707 Email: tonyharrison@hotmail.com; Tel: 020 8463 0851 — MB BS Lond. 1968; FRCS Eng. 1972. (Guy's) Cons. Gen. Surg. Greenwich Dist. Hosp. Lond. Socs: Grey Turner Surgic. Club; W Kent M-C Soc.; Hunt. Soc. Prev: Sen. Regist. (Surg.) Guy's Hosp. Lond.; Hon. Regist. Hosp. Sick Childr. Gt. Ormond St. Lond.; Regist. (Gen. Surg.) Lewisham Gen. Hosp.

HARRISON, Thomas Herbert (retired) 85 Buckingham Road, Shoreham-by-Sea BN43 5UD Tel: 0127 345 3550 — MRCS Eng. LRCP Lond. 1939; DPH Eng. 1946, DTM & H 1946. Med. Off. Shoreham Port Auth. Prev: MOH Shoreham-by-Sea UDC, S.wick UDC & Chanctonbury RDC & Asst. MOH.

HARRISON, Professor Thomas James (retired) 75 Hillside Road, Magheraknock, Ballynahinch BT24 8UL Tel: 028 9263 8339 — MB BCh BAO (Hons.) Belf. 1942; PhD Belf. 1957, MD (Commend.) 1949. Prev: Prof. Anat. Qu. Univ. Belf.

HARRISON, Thomas Michael Scarborough House, 35 Auckland Rd, Sparkbrook B11 1RH Tel: 0121 678 4204 Fax: 0121 678 4201 Email: medsec.scarboroughhouse@sbmht.wmids.nhs.uk; 146 Sandford Road, Moseley, Birmingham B13 9DA Email: thomas.harrison@virgin.net — MB ChB 1971 Birm.; MRCPsych. 1982; FRCPsych 1998. Cons. Psychiat. (Rehabil.) N. Birm. Ment. Health Trust. Socs: W Midl. Inst. Psychother. Prev: Cons. Psychiat. Hollymoor Hosp. Birm.

HARRISON, Timothy John Ryan 19 Fernwood, Marple Bridge, Stockport SK6 5BE — MB BS 1992 Lond.

HARRISON, Timothy Michael Tel: 01782 545444 Fax: 01782 570135 — MB ChB 1977 Leeds.

HARRISON, Victor Frederick (retired) Carriage House, Shaws Lane, Hexham NE46 3BN Tel: 01434 607136 — MB BS 1945 Durh.; MRCGP 1953. Prev: Ho. Phys. Roy. Infirm. Sunderland.

HARRISON, Vivienne Mary Avon Health Authority, King Square House, King Square, Bristol BS2 8EE Tel: 0117 976 6600 Email: viv.harrison@userm.avonhealth.swest.nhs.uk — MB ChB 1989 Bristol; MRCGP 1993; MFPHM 2000. (Bristol) Sen. Regist. (Pub. Health Med.) Bristol. Prev: Sen. Regist. (Pub. Health Med.) Som.; Trainee GP Bristol VTS.

HARRISON, Walford John (retired) 15A Hampstead Lane, Highgate, London N6 4RT Tel: 020 8340 3237 — BM BCh 1957 Oxf.; MA Oxf. 1958, BA 1954, DM 1966, BM BCh 1957; FRCPath 1978, M 1966. Prev: Lect. (Path.) Univ. Bristol & Hon. Cons. Path. United Bristol Hosps.

HARRISON, Wendy Anne 18 Brownlow Road, London N11 2DE — LRCPI & LM, LRSCI & LM 1975; LRCPI & LM, LRCSI & LM 1975.

HARRISON, Wendy Nicola Marylebone Road Health Centre, Marylebone Road, March PE15 8BG Tel: 01354 606300 Fax: 01354 656033 — MB ChB 1986 Sheff.; MRCGP 1990.

HARRISON, William (retired) 4 Morning Hill, Peebles EH45 9JS Tel: 01721 722748 Email: william@harcourt.freeserve.co.uk — MB ChB 1952 Ed.; DObst RCOG 1962. Prev: SHO Peel Hosp. Galashiels.

HARRISON, Mr William James — BM BCh 1990 Oxf.; MA Oxf. 1995; FRCS Eng. 1995. Career Regist. (Orthop.) N. Region. Prev: SHO Rotat. (Surg.) Newc.

HARRISON, William Paul (retired) 47 Palmers Road, Wootton Bridge, Ryde PO33 4NE Tel: 01983 883684 — MB BCh BAO Dub. 1956; BA Dub. 1954; DA Eng. 1965. Prev: Princip. GP, Isle of Wight.

HARRISON-HANSLEY, Ella Justine 64 Charlwood Road, London SW15 1PZ — MB BS 1994 Lond.

HARRISON-READ, Philip Ernest North Camden Mental Health Services, Royal Free Hospital, Pond St, London NW3 2QG Tel: 020 7794 0500 Ext: 5142 — MB BS 1975 Lond.; PhD 1978 Lond.; MRCPsych 1984; FRCPsych 1998. (Westm.) Cons. Psychiat. Roy. Free Hosp., Lond. Socs: Brit. Pharm. Soc. & Brit. Assn. Psychopharmacol. Prev: Lect. (Psychiat.) St. Mary's Hosp. Med. Coll. Lond.; Lect. (Pharmacol.) Med. Coll. St. Bart. Hosp. Lond.; Ho. Off. Profess. Med. Unit W.m. Hosp. Lond.

HARRISON-SMITH, Mark Keith Giffords Primary Care Centre, Spa Road, Melksham SN12 7EA Tel: 01225 703370 Fax: 01225 898200 — BM 1986 Soton.; BSc (Hons.) Biochem. Liverp. 1982; MRCGP 1995; DFFP 1994; DRCOG 1991. (Soton.) GP Partne, Giffords Primary Care Centre, Mecksham, Wilts.

HARRISON-WOOLRYCH, Mira Lesley Medicines Control Agency, Market Towers, 1 Nine Elms Lane, London SW8 5NQ Tel: 020 72730232/0024 Fax: 0207 273 0293 Email: mira.harrison-woolrych@mca.gov.uk — BM 1989 Soton.; DM Soton. 1995; MRCOG 1996; DFFP 1996. Med. Assessor Meds. Control Agency DoH. Prev: Regist. (O & G) ChristCh. Wom. Hosp., NZ; SHO (O & G) Rosie Matern. Hosp. Camb.; Research Fell. (O & G) Rosie Matern. Hosp. Camb.

HARRISS, Anthony Roger William Maes-y-Coed Doctors Surgery, Maes-y-Coed, Glandwr Park, Builth Wells LD2 3DZ Tel: 01982 552207 Fax: 01982 553826 — MB ChB 1960 Birm.; MRCP (UK) 1970; MRCS Eng. LRCP Lond. 1962; DTM & H Eng. 1963; DObst RCOG 1963. (Birm.) Prev: Gen. Duties Med. Off. Govt. of Uganda; Regist. Mpilo Centr. Hosp. Bulawayo, Rhodesia; Regist (Med.) Heref. Gp. Hosps.

HARRISS, Mr Duncan Ross 19 Magdala Road, Mapperley Park, Nottingham NG3 5DE Tel: 0115 962 3664 — MB BS 1986 Lond.; DM Nottm. 1994; FRCS (Urol.) 1996; FRCS Eng. 1990. (Guy's Hosp.) Sen. Regist. (Urol.) Nottm. City Hosp. Prev: Research Fell. Nottm. Univ. Med. Sch.; Regist. (Surg.) Nottm. Univ. Hosps.; SHO (Surg.) Oxf.

HARRISSON, Philippa Anne 2 Seymour Road, Clarendon Park, Leicester LE2 1TQ; 45 Quebec Road, Dereham NR19 2DR — MB ChB 1991 Birm. SHO (Orthop.) Leicester Gen. Hosp. Prev: SHO (O & G) Leicester Gen. Hosp.; SHO (Paediat.) Sandwell Gen. Hosp. Birm.; SHo (A & E) P.ss Roy. Hosp. Telford.

HARROCKS, Donald Raymond Manor Farm, Gaunts, Wimborne BH21 4JJ Tel: 01258 840520 Fax: 01258 840362 — MB BChir 1949 Camb.; MA Camb. 1949. (Middlx.)

HARROD, Robin Raymond Leckhampton Surgery, Lloyd Davies House, 17 Moorend Park Road, Cheltenham GL53 0LA Tel: 01242 515363 Fax: 01242 253512; Park Lawn, The Park, Cheltenham GL50 2SD Tel: 01242 269385 Email: rrharrod@aol.com — MB BS 1969 Lond.; BSc (Hons. Anat.) Lond. 1966; MRCS Eng. LRCP Lond. 1969. (Lond. Hosp.) Gen. Practitioner. Prev: Course Organiser Glos. VTS; Ho. Phys. Med. Unit & Ho. Surg. Surg. Unit Lond. Hosp.; Ho. Surg. (Obst.) Chester City Hosp.

HARROD, Simon Timothy Stewart-Clark 34 Milton Park, London N6 5QA — MB BS 1984 Lond.

HARROLD, Anthony John Assisted Conception Unit, Dept. of Obstetrics and Gynaecology, Ninewells Hospital, Dundee DD1 9SY Fax: 01382 633853; Eastfield House, Auchter House, Dundee DD3 0QP — MB ChB 1985 Dundee; MRCOG 1993.

HARROLD, Basil Philip (retired) Stockwell Farm, Fancott, Toddington, Dunstable LU5 6HT — MD 1968 Bristol; MB BS Lond. 1957; FRCP Lond 1979, M 1963. Prev: Cons. Phys. Luton & Dunstable Hosp. Luton.

HARROLD, Jane Alison 8 Lawers Place, Aberfeldy PH15 2BE — MB ChB 1986 Dundee.

HARROLD, Julian David Nightingales, Nightingale Lane, Maidenhead SL6 7QL — MB BS 1998 Lond.; MB BS Lond 1998.

HARROLD, Marianne 70 London Street, Reading RG1 4SL; Tel: 01491 874118 — MB BS 1982 Lond.; BSc (Hons.) Lond. 1979; MRCGP 1996; DCH RCP Lond. 1995; DRCOG 1994. (St. Geo. Hosp. Lond.) Trainee GP Lyndhurst; GP Partner since January 1996, 70 Lond. St., Reading. Prev: SHO (Paediat. & Community Paediat.) Heatherwood Hosp.; Regist. (Gen. & Geriat. Med.) Wexham Pk. Hosp. Slough; SHO Profess. Dept. Med. Char. Cross Hosp. Lond.

HARROLD, Patrick Francis Mary Drumclay Link, Enniskillen BT74 6DL — MB BCh BAO 1988 NUI.

HARRON, Joanne Camille 13 Curley Hill Road, Strabane BT82 8LP — BM BCh 1990 Oxf.

HARRON, Michael Eoin 13 Curleyhill Road, Strabane BT82 8LP — BChir 1992 Camb.

HARROP, Alison Jane Holly Bush Farm, Willow Pit Lane, Hilton, Derby DE65 5FN — MB ChB 1998 Sheff.; MB ChB Sheff 1998.

HARROP, Colin William The Grange, Kirby Hill, Boroughbridge, York YO51 9YB — MB ChB 1994 Glas.
HARROP, Francesca Mary Lynfield Mount Hospital, Heights Lane, Bradford BD9 6DP — BM BS 1979 Nottm.; MRCPsych 1986. Cons. Psychiat. Lynfield Mt. Hosp. Bradford.
HARROP, George Brian Clare 12 Oaklea Gardens, Leeds LS16 8BH Tel: 0113 673322 — MB ChB 1947 Leeds.
HARROP, Hilary Jill 16 Milton Avenue, Blackpool FY3 8LY — MB BCh 1975 Wales; MRCGP 1979; MFFP 1994.
HARROP, Jane Emily 100 Ferndale Road, Burgess Hill RH15 0EY — MB BS 1996 Lond.
HARROP, John Stanley Department of Pathology, Derby City General Hospital, Uttoxeter Road, Derby DE22 3NE Tel: 01332 340131 Fax: 01332 625672 Email: 100116.1047@compuserve.com — MB BS 1969 Lond.; MSc Surrey 1975; FRCPath 1988, M 1976. (St. Geo.) Cons. Chem. Path. Derby City Gen. Hosp. Prev: Sen. Regist. (Med. Biochem.) Univ. Hosp. Wales Cardiff.
HARROP, Mark Christopher Kensington Group Practice, Kensington Road, Road, Douglas IM1 3PF Tel: 01624 676774 Fax: 01624 614668 — MB ChB 1992 Manch.
HARROP, Meinir Cotswold, 22 Greet Road, Winchcombe, Cheltenham GL54 5JT Tel: 01242 602114 — MRCS Eng. LRCP Lond. 1947. (Liverp.) Prev: GP Liverp., Lond., Sheff. & Birm.; SCMO (Family Plann.) Birm. & Solihull HAs; Ho. Phys. & Ho. Surg. BRd.green Hosp. Liverp.
HARROP, Mr Stephen Nicholas 16 Milton Avenue, Blackpool FY3 8LY — MB ChB 1975 Manch.; MBA (Health Exec.) Keele 1994; FRCS Ed. (A&E) 1984; FRCS Eng. 1980. Cons. & Clin. Dir. A & E Vict. Hosp. Blackpool. Socs: Fell. Fac. Accid. & Emerg. Med. Prev: Sen. Regist. (A & E) Roy. Gwent Hosp. Newport; Regist. (A & E) Leicester Roy. Infirm.; Demonst. (Anat.) Univ. Manch.
HARROP-GRIFFITHS, Alan William 11 Rodway Road, London SW15 5DN — MB BS 1981 Lond.; MA Oxf. 1984, BA 1978; FFA RCS Eng. 1985. Cons. Anaesth. St. Mary's Hosp. Lond. Prev: Sen. Regist. (Anaesth.) St. Mary's Hosp. Lond.; Sen. Fell. (Anesth.) Univ. Washington USA; Regist. (Anaesth.) Edgware Gen. Hosp. & Hammersmith Hosp. Lond.
HARROP-GRIFFITHS, Mr Hilton (retired) Pantyddafad, Pontrhydygroes, Ystrad Meurig SY25 6DP Tel: 0197 422208 — MB BCh 1947 Wales; FRCS Eng. 1958. Cons. Orthop. Surg. Gwent HA. Prev: Regist. P. of Wales Orthop. Hosp. Rhydlafar.
HARROP-GRIFFITHS, Jane Louise Fulham Clinic, 82 Lillie Road, London SW6 1TN Tel: 020 7386 9299 Fax: 020 7610 0635; 11 Rodway Road, Roehampton, London SW15 5DN Tel: 020 8788 3931 Fax: 020 8788 9028 Email: whg@compuserve.com — MB BS 1982 Lond.; LMSSA Lond. 1982; MRCGP 1989; DRCOG 1985. (St Thos. Hosp. Med. Sch.) Socs: Fell. Roy. Soc. Med.; Roy. Coll. Gen. Pract. Prev: Trainee GP P.ss St. Gp. Pract. Lond.; Research Asst. (Psychiat. & Behavioural Sci.) Univ. Washington Seattle, USA; SHO (O & G) St. Thos. Hosp. Lond.
HARROP-GRIFFITHS, Katherine Nuffield Centre, Royal National Throat, Nose & Ear Hospital, Gray's Inn Road, London WC1X 8DA Tel: 020 7915 1641 Fax: 020 7915 1666 Email: katherine.harrop-griffiths@rfh.nthames.nhs.uk; 52 Champion Hill, London SE5 8BS Tel: 020 7733 3512 — MB BS 1977 Lond.; MSc (Audiol. Med.) Lond. 1991; FRCS Eng. 1981. (St. Thos.) p/t Cons. Audiol. Phys. Roy. Nat. Throat, Nose & Ear Hosp. Lond. Socs: Brit. Assn. Audiol. Phys.; Brit. Soc. Audiol. Prev: Sen. Regist. (Audiol. Med.) Roy. Nat. Throat, Nose & Ear Hosp. Lond.; SHO (Otorhinolaryngol.) Roy. Nat. Throat, Nose & Ear Hosp. & Roy. Marsden Hosp. Lond.; Regist. (Surg.) St. Thos. Hosp. Lond., St. Peter's Hosp. Chertsey & St. Helier's Hosp. Carshalton.
HARROP-GRIFFITHS, Wyndham 19 Radyr Avenue, Owls Lodge Lane, Mayals, Swansea SA3 5DU — MB BCh 1953 Wales.
HARROW, Alexander Kirklee, Elmton, Worksop S80 4LX Tel: 01909 721520 — MB ChB 1951 Glas.; MRCGP 1962. (Glas.) Police Surg. Derbysh. Constab. Socs: BMA; Assn. Police Surgs. Prev: GP Worksop.
HARROWER, Andrew David Burns Diabetes Centre, Monklands Hospital, Airdrie ML6 0JS Tel: 01236 712430 Fax: 01236 747018 Email: andrew.harrower@laht.swt.nhs.uk — MB ChB 1967 Ed.; FRCP Glas. 1987, M 1985; FRCP Ed. 1981; MRCP (UK) 1971. Cons. Phys. Monklands Hosp. Airdrie; Hon. Clin. Sen. Lect. Univ. Glas. Socs: Scott. Study Gp. for the Case of Young Diabetes; Europ. Assn. for the Study of Diabetes; Diabetes UK & Internat. Diabetes Federat. Prev: Sen. Regist. (Med.) Edin. Roy. Infirm.; Regist. (Diabetes & Med.) Edin. Roy. Infirm.
HARROWER, James Edward 50 Tintagel, Chapelhouse, Skelmersdale WN8 8PF Tel: 01695 27227; 22D Guildford Road, Tunbridge Wells TN1 1SW Tel: 01892 513708 — MB ChB 1993 Dundee. (Univ. Dundee) SHO (Gen. Med.) Kent & Sussex Hosp. Tunbridge Wells. Prev: Ho. Surg. (Cardiol., Renal & Psychiat.) Auckland Pub. Hosp., NZ.
HARROWER, Neil Alexander 5 Ochilview, Devonside, Tillicoultry FK13 6JD — MB ChB 1993 Aberd.; DRCOG 2000; MRCGP 2001; DFFP 2000; MRCP (UK) June 1998; MRCPH June 1998. GP N. Lond. Prev: Paediat. Regist., Roy. Hosp for Sick Childr., Yorkhill, Glas.
HARROWER, Richard Franklyn 46 Lady Byron Lane, Solihull B93 9AY; 2314 Coventry Road, Sheldon, Birmingham B26 3JS Tel: 0121 743 2154 Fax: 0121 743 9970 — MB ChB 1977 Birm.
HARROWER, Susan Irene 46 Lady Byron Lane, Solihull B93 9AY; 2314 Coventry Road, Sheldon, Birmingham B26 3JS Tel: 0121 743 2154 — MB ChB 1976 Birm.
HARROWER, Timothy Paul 12 Victoria House, Hinchingbrooke, Huntingdon PE18 8NS — MB ChB 1993 Cape Town.
HARROWER, Ulrike 66 Greystoke Road, Cambridge CB1 8DS Tel: 01223 500255 Fax: 01223 500255 — MB ChB 1987 Cape Town; BSc (Hons.) Med. Biochem. Cape Town 1989; DPhil Oxf. 1995; MRCP Lond. 1998. GP Regist., Linton Health Centre, Camb. Prev: SHO (Gen. Med.) Lister Hosp. Stevenage; SHO (O & G) Rosie Matern. Hosp. Camb.; SHO (O & G) Hinchingbrooke Hosp. Huntingdon.
HARRY, Amanda Jane West Hoe Surgery, 2 Cliff Road, Plymouth PL1 3BP Tel: 01752 660105 Fax: 01752 268992 — MB ChB 1989 Liverp.
HARRY, Carl Rosser 106 Newton Road, Mumbles, Swansea SA3 4SW — MB ChB 1978 Manch.
HARRY, Gaynor 19 Heol Gabriel, Whitchurch, Cardiff CF14 1JT — MB BCh Wales 1953; BSc Wales 1949. (Welsh National School of Medicine) Prev: Clin. Med. Off. Mid Glam. HA.
HARRY, John (retired) 21 Arley Road, Solihull B91 1NJ Tel: 0121 704 2638 — MB BCh 1956 Wales; BSc Wales 1952; FRCPath 1995, M 1983; FRCOphth 1988. Hon. Cons. Ophth. Path. Birm. Prev: Cons. Ophth. pathologist W. Midl.s regional health Auth.
HARRY, John David Coningsby, Macclesfield Road, Buxton SK17 9AH — MB BS 1964 Lond.; PhD Lond. 1963, BSc 1959; MRCS Eng. LRCP Lond. 1964. (St. Geo.) Dir. (Clin. Research & Developm.) Upjohn Laborats. Crawley. Socs: Brit. Pharm. Soc. (Comm. Mem. Clin. Sect.); Amer. Soc. Clin. Pharmacol. & Therap. Prev: Head, Clin. Pharmacol. Unit. Clin. Research Dept. ICI Ltd. Pharmaceut. Div. Alderley Edge; Lect. (Clin. Investig.) Cardiovasc. Unit. Univ. Leeds; Lect. (Physiol.) Univ. Coll. S. Wales & Mon. Cardiff.
HARRY, Lorraine Elizabeth Brunswick Health Centre, 139-140 St. Helens Road, Swansea SA1 4DE Tel: 01792 643001 / 643611; 13 Dover Street, Norwich NR2 3LG — BChir 1995 Camb.; MB Camb. (University of Cambridge) SHO (Surg.). Socs: MDU; MSS; Christ. Med. Fell.sh. Prev: SHO (A & E) Morriston Hosp.; Ho. Off. Norf. & Norwich Hosp.; Ho. Off. (Med.) Hinchingbrooke Hosp.
HARRY, Maria De Lourdes Goncalves Pereira 34 Gisburne Road, Wellingborough NN8 4EE — Lic Med Oporto 1976.
HARRY, Peter Ian (retired) Creystones, 1 Gilfach Road, Rhyddings, Neath SA10 8EH — MB BCh 1951 Wales. Prev: Regional Med. Off. to Welsh Office.
HARRY, Rachael Alexandra Institute of Liver Studies, Kings College Hospital, Bessener Road, London SE5 9RS — MB BS 1992 Lond.; BA (Hons.) 1989; MRCP (UK) 1995. Regist. Rotat. (Gastroenterol. & Gen. Med.) King's Healthcare Lond. Prev: SHO Rotat. (Med.) N.wick Pk. Hosp. Harrow; Ho. Surg. Whipps Cross Hosp. Lond.
HARRY, Robyn Mary Denmilne House, Newburgh, Cupar KY14 6HS — MB ChB Manch. 1992.
HARRY, Thomas Vernon Anthony (retired) 14 Howey Hill, Congleton CW12 4AF Tel: 01260 276207 — MB ChB 1951 Manch.; DPM Eng. 1960. Prev: assoc. Med. Dir. Wyeth Laboratories.

HARRY, Tubonye Clement Bure Clinic, James Paget Hospital NHS Trust, Lowestoft Road, Great Yarmouth NR31 6LA Tel: 01493 452747 Fax: 01493 452864 Email: tcharry@bureclinic.com — MB BS 1979 Lagos, Nigeria; MRCOG 1989; MFFP 1993; DObst RCPI 1989. (Univ. Lagos, Nigeria) Cons. Genitourin. Med. & HIV/AIDS Med. Jas. Paget Hosp. Gt. Yarmouth. Socs: Med. Soc. Study VD; Brit. HIV Assn.; Internat. AIDS Soc. Prev: Sen. Regist. (Genitourin. Med.) Sunderland Dist. Gen. Hosp.; Regist. (Genitourin. Med.) Newc. Gen. Hosp. & Sunderland Dist. Gen. Hosp.; Regist. (O & G) Fazakerley Hosp. Liverp.

HARRYMAN, Dr 39 Harold Road, Dartford DA2 7SA — MB ChB 1997 Bristol.

HARSE, John Benjamin 33 Heath Park Avenue, Cardiff CF14 3RF Tel: 029 2075 4390 — MB BCh 1969 Wales; MRCS Eng. LRCP Lond. 1969; DMJ (Path.) Soc. Apoth. Lond. 1973. (Cardiff) Pnuemoconiosis Med. Off. Dept. Health & Social Security. Socs: BMA. Prev: Lect. Foren. Med. Lond. Hosp.; Asst. Lect. in Path. Univ. Wales.

HARSHA, Mr Bdurga Shivarudrappa Darlington Memorial Hospital, Hollyhurst Road, Darlington DL3 6HX Tel: 01325 380100 — MB BS 1974 Bangalor; MB BS Bangalore 1974; FRCS Glas. 1988. Assoc. Specialist (Trauma & Orthop.) Darlington Memor. Hosp. Prev: Regist. (Orthop. & Trauma) Burnley Gen. Hosp.

HARSIANI, Seema 59 Anmersh Grove, Stanmore HA7 1NZ — MB BS 1996 Lond.

HARSTON, Antony Plumer Brunyee 6 Pickwick Crescent, Cotton Lane, Bury St Edmunds IP33 1XS Tel: 01284 766647 — MB ChB 1947 St. And.; MRCOG 1955; DObst 1949. Prev: Cons. Gynaecol. Milit. Hosp. Tidworth.

HARSTON, Philip John Richard Brundall Medical Partnership, The Dales, Brundall, Norwich NR13 5RP Tel: 01603 712255 Fax: 01603 712156 — MB BS 1976 Lond.

HART, Mr Alan John Lewington RoyalGlamorgan Hospital, Ynys Maerdy, Llantrisant, Pontyclun CF72 8XR Tel: 01443 443586 Fax: 01443 443678 Email: alanhart@pr.tr.wales.nhs.uk; 108 Heol ISAF, Radyr, Cardiff CF15 8EA Tel: 02920 842509 — MB ChB 1967 St. And.; FRCS Ed. 1972; FRCS 1997. (St. And.) Cons. Urol. Roy. Glam. Hosp., Llantrisant. Socs: (Ex-Pres.) Rhondda Med. Soc.; Welsh Surgic. Travellers. Prev: Sen. Regist. (Urol.) W.. Infirm. Glas.; Regist. (Urol.) Roy. Infirm. Edin.; Rotat. Regist. (Surg.) Dundee Hosp.

HART, Alexander Ethan Tudor (retired) 9 The Rookery, Kidlington OX5 1AW Tel: 0186 755870 — MRCS Eng. LRCP Lond. 1931. Prev: Ho. Phys. Hampstead Gen. Hosp.

HART, Amanda Jane 42 Rashleigh House, Thanet St., London WC1H 9ER; Top Flat, 201 Uxbridge Road, London W12 9DH Tel: 020 8742 9698 Email: amandahart@bt.com — MB BS 1996 Lond.

HART, Andrew Jonathan Greenview Surgery, 129 Hazeldene Road, Northampton NN2 7PB Tel: 01604 791002 Fax: 01604 721822 — BM BCh 1984 Oxf.

HART, Andrew McKay 29 Polwarth St. (T/L), Hyndland, Glasgow G12 9UD — MB ChB 1995 Glas.

HART, Andrew Robert School of Medicine, Health Policy & Practice, University of East Anglia, Norwich NR4 7TJ Tel: 01603 456161 Fax: 01603 593604 Email: a.hart@uea.ac.uk — MB ChB 1987 Leeds; BSc (Hons.) (Pharmacol.) Leeds 1984; MD Leic. 1996; MRCP (UK) 1991; (M Phil) Cambridge. (Leeds) Sen. Lect. In Gastroenterol., Univ. of E. Anglia; Hon. Cons. Gastroenterologist, Norf. & Norwich Univ. NHS Hosp. Trust. Socs: Brit. Med. Assn.; Brit. Soc. of Gastroenterol. Prev: Sen. Regist. (Gastroenterol. & Gen. Med.) Imperial Cancer Research Fund Leicester; Regist. (Med.) Leicester Gen. Hosp. & Peterboro. Dist. Gen. Hosp.; SHO (Gen. Med.) Leicester Gen. Hosp.

HART, Angela May Quenda, 34 Hill Rise, Gerrards Cross SL9 9BH Tel: 01753 891698 — MB BS 1988 Lond.; BSc Lond. 1985; MRCGP 1993; DRCOG 1991. Prev: SHO (A & E) Addenbrooke's Hosp. Camb.; SHO (O & G) Bedford Hosp.; SHO (Paediat.) P.ss Alexandra Hosp. Harlow.

HART, Anthony Maxwell 16 Clyst Heath, Exeter EX2 7TA — MB BS 1979 Lond.; BSc (Hons.) Lond. 1976. (Univ. Coll. Hosp. Lond.) Assoc. Specialist (Anaesth.) Roy. Devon & Exeter Hosp. Prev: Staff & Regist. (Anaesth.) Roy. Devon & Exeter Hosp.

HART, Benjamin Tudor 46 Albion Drive, London E8 4LX Email: bhart@blink.demon.co.uk — MB BS 1990 Lond.; BSc (Sociol. Applied to Med.) Lond., MB BS Lond. 1990; MRCGP. (Royal Free Hospital School of Medicine) Asst. in Gen. Pract. Prev: Regist. Lond. Acad. Train. Scheme; SHO (Oncol.) N. Middlx. Hosp. Lond.

HART, Brian Joseph 12 Havelock Street, (G/L), Glasgow G11 5JA — MB ChB 1990 Glas.

HART, Calum Duncan Caius Cottage, Bardwell Road, Barningham, Bury St Edmunds IP31 1DF — MB ChB 1988 Aberd.; DA (UK) 1994. (Aberd.) Sen. Med. Off. Kalgoorlie Base Roy. Flying Doctor Serv., Austral.; Designated Aviat. Med. Examr. Civil Aviat. Safety Auth., Austral.; ACCAM Melbourne 1996.

HART, Caroline Jane 25 The Drive, Cranleigh GU6 7LY — MB BS 1984 Lond.

HART, Professor Charles Anthony Department of Medical Microbiology & Genitourinary Medicine, University of Liverpool, PO Box 147, Liverpool L69 3BX Tel: 0151 706 4381 Fax: 0151 706 5805 Email: cahmm@liv.ac.uk; Holly Bank, 102 Barnston Road, Thingwall, Wirral CH61 1AT Tel: 0151 648 1491 — MB BS 1972 Lond.; PhD Lond. 1978, BSc 1970; FRCPCH 1997; MRCPCH 1996; FRCPath 1994, M 1982. (Roy. Free Hosp. Lond.) Prof. & Hon. Cons. Med. Microbiol. Univ. Liverp. & Alder Hey Childr. Hosp.; Vis. Prof. Univ. Santo Tomas, Manila, Philippines; Mem. Liverp. Med. Inst.; Pres. Liverp. Paediat. Club. Socs: (Counc.) Hosp. Infec. Soc.; (Counc.) Liverp. Sch. Trop. Med.

HART, Mr Charles Timothy Lansdown Lodge, Lansdown Road, Cheltenham GL51 6QL Tel: 01242 522475 — MB BS 1961 Lond.; FRCS Eng. 1965; MRCS Eng. LRCP Lond. 1961; DO Eng. 1964. (Middlx.) Cons. Ophth. Cheltenham Gen. Hosp. Socs: Internat. Mem. Amer. Acad. Ophth. & French Soc. Ophth. Prev: Lect. Univ. Sheff.; Regist. Bristol Eye Hosp.

***HART, Charlotte Nerys** 30 Greenway Avenue, Cherryfields, Stone ST15 0ER — MB ChB 1997 Birm.

HART, Cleone Louise The Rowan Centre, Dr Gray's Hospital, Elgin IV30 1SN Tel: 01343 558399 — MB ChB 1985 Aberd.; MRCPsych 1993; MRCGP 1990. Cons. (Child & Adolesc. Psychiat.) Dr Grays Hosp. Elgin; Hon. Sen. Lect. (Child Health) Univ. of Aberd. Prev: Sen. Regist. (Child & Adolesc. Psychiat.) Roy. Aberd. Childr.s Hosp.

HART, Colin Anthony 37 Crooked Usage, London N3 3EU — MB ChB 1998 Leic.; MB ChB Leic 1998.

HART, Cyril James Roy (retired) Goldthorns, Stilton, Peterborough PE7 3RH Tel: 01733 240447 — MB BS 1951 Lond.; DLitt Leic. 1975, MA 1958; FRCGP 1978, M 1958. Prev: GP Yaxley.

HART, Daniel Patrick Little Inchiquin, Tre-Graig, Bwlch, Brecon LD3 7SJ Tel: 01874 730308 — MB ChB 1995 Bristol; BSc (Hons.) Cell & Molec. Path. Bristol 1992. (Bristol) SHO (Cardiol./Haematol.) Glos. Roy. Hosp. Socs: BMA. Prev: SHO (A & E) Frenchay Hosp. Bristol; SHO (c/o Elderly) Bristol Roy. Infirm.; Ho. Off. (Gen. Surg.) Bristol Roy. Infirm. & S.mead Hosp.

HART, David Caithness Kerrsland Surgery, 169 Upper Newtownards Road, Belfast BT4 3HZ Tel: 028 9029 6600 Fax: 028 9047 1942; 5 Kensington Park, Belfast BT5 6NR — MB BCh BAO 1963 Belf.; DObst RCOG 1966. Socs: BMA. Prev: Ho. Off. & SHO (O & G) S. Tyrone Hosp. Dungannon.

HART, David Drummond, TD (retired) 31 Woodend Place, Aberdeen AB15 6AP Tel: 01224 34237 — MB ChB Glas. 1953; FFA RCS Eng. 1960; DA Eng. 1957. Prev: Cons. Anaesth. Aberd. Roy. Infirm.

HART, Mr David McKay Division Obstetrics & Gynaecology, Stobhill General Hospital, Glasgow G21 3UW; 7 Tweedsmuir Crescent, Bearsden, Glasgow G61 3LE — MD 1966 Glas.; MB ChB 1959; FRCS Glas. 1964; FRCOG 1976, M 1963.

HART, David Paul 19 Euan Close, Gillhurst Road, Birmingham B17 8PL — MB ChB 1976 Birm. GP Princip. Socs: BMA. Prev: Dep. Police Surg. N. Beds. & Mid-Beds; Head of Health Care HMP Bedford; Exam. Med. Off. DSS.

HART, Dominic John 15 Holly Lane, Newtownabbey BT36 5GU — MB BCh BAO 1995 Belf.

HART, Elaine Mary Pinderfields Hospital, Aberford Road, Wakefield WF1 4EE; Greenfields, 37 Shoreditch Road, Taunton TA1 3BX Tel: 01823 351071 — MB ChB 1995 Leeds. (Leeds) SHO (A & E) Pinderfields Hosp. Wakefield. Prev: Ho. Off. (Gen. Med.) Leeds Gen. Infirm.; Ho. Off. (Gen. Surg.) Pinderfields Hosp. Wakefield.

HART, Elizabeth Anne 16 Main Street, Oakthorpe, Swadlincote DE12 6PZ Tel: 01530 271295 — MB ChB 1994 Liverp.; BSc (Hons.) Chem. Nottm. 1989; DTM & H Liverp. 1998; MRCP (UK)

1998. Specialist Regist. Infect. Dis. & Trop. Med N. Manch. Gen. Hosp.

HART, Frances Joan 7 Lyndhurst Drive, Low Fell, Gateshead NE9 6BB — MB ChB 1953 Birm. (Birm.)

HART, Francis Dudley 19 Ranulf Road, London NW2 2BT Tel: 020 7794 2525 — MB ChB 1933 Ed.; MD Ed. 1939; FRCP Lond. 1949, M 1937. (Univ. Ed.) Hon. Cons. Phys. W.m. Hosp. & Hosp. St. John & St. Eliz. Lond.; Hon. Vice-Pres. Arthritis Research Campaign. Socs: Ex-Pres. Herberden Soc.; Hon. Fell. Roy. Soc. Med. & Brit. Soc. Rheum.; Hon. Mem. Ligue Francaise Contre le Rheum. & other Foreign Rheum. Socs. Prev: Phys. & Med. Off. i/c Rheum. Clinic W.m. Hosp.; Civil. Med. Cons. to Army; Med. Specialist & OC Med. Div. RAMC.

HART, Geoffrey Raymond Laynes Mead, West Drive, Angmering, Littlehampton BN16 4NL — MB BS 1955 Lond.; FRCR 1975; FFR 1968. (St. Geo.) Cons. Diagn. Radiol. Atkinson Morley's Hosp. Lond. Socs: Brit. Inst. Radiol. & Brit. Soc. Neuroradiol.

HART, Professor George Department of Medicine, University Clinical Departments, The Duncan Building, Daulby St., Liverpool L69 3GA Tel: 0151 706 4074 Fax: 0151 706 5802 Email: g.hart@liv.ac.uk — BM BCh 1975 Oxf.; MA Camb. 1976, BA (1st cl. Hons. Physiol.) 1972; DM Oxf. 1982, MA 1979; FRCP Lond. 1990; MRCP (UK) 1977. p/t David A. Price Evans Prof. of Med. Univ. of Liverp.; Hon. Cons. Cardiol. & Gen. Med. Roy. Liverp. Univ. Hosp. Socs: Brit. Cardiac Soc.; Physiol Soc.; (Ex-Chairm.) Brit. Soc. Cardiovasc. Research. Prev: Brit. Heart Foundat. Clin. Reader (Cardiovasc. Med.) Univ. Oxf.; Sen. Regist. (Cardiol.) Killingbeck & St. Jas. Univ. Hosps. Leeds; MRC Research Fell. Univ. Laborat. Physiol. Oxf.

HART, Mr Graeme Manson The Elms, 24 Hall Place Gardens, St Albans AL1 3SF Tel: 01727 865057; Sydenham House, Lewdown, Nr. Okehampton, Okehampton EX20 4PR Tel: 01822 860333 Fax: 01822 860300 Email: graemehart@hotmail.com — MB BS 1969 Lond.; FRCS Eng. 1974; MRCS Eng. LRCP Lond. 1969; DObst RCOG 1971. Cons. Orthop. Surg. St. Albans City Hosp. & W. Herts. Gen. Hosp. Socs: Fell. BOA; Fell. Roy. Soc. Med. Prev: Sen. Regist., Ho. Phys. & Ho. Surg. Roy. Free Hosp. Lond.; SHO Roy. Nat. Orthop. Hosp. Lond.

HART, Henry Chichester Vaughan Edward 30 Alberta House, Blackwall Way, London E14 9QH; 30 Alma Street, Chester CH3 5DF — MB BS 1990 Lond.; MRCGP 1995.

HART, Hilary Margaret Sydenham House, Lewdown, Okehampton EX20 4PR — MB BS Lond. 1970; MRCP (UK) 1973; DCH Eng. 1973. Edr. Developm. Med. & Child Neurol. Mackeith Press. Prev: Princip. Gen. Pract. Hemel Hempstead Herts; Hon. Lect. (Paediat.) St. Mary's Hosp. Sch. Med. Lond.; Ho. Phys. St. Mary's Hosp.

HART, Ian 4 Birch Grove, Barrow, Clitheroe BB7 9FE Tel: 01254 824183 — MB ChB 1985 Manch. Clin. Research Phys. Vict. Pk. Hosp. Manch.

HART, Ian James 21 Clinton Avenue, Rochester ME2 3TN — MB BS 1994 Lond.

HART, Ian John King's College School of Medicine & Dentistry, London SE5 9PJ — MB ChB 1987 Birm.; BSc Cell. Path. Bristol. 1982. Lect. (Immunol.) & Hon. Sen. Regist. King's Coll. Sch. Med. & Dent. Prev: SHO Rotat. (Med. & Histopath.) Soton. Univ. Hosps.; CRC Clin. Research Fell. & Hon. Regist. (Immunol.) Univ. Soton.

HART, Ian Kirkland Department of Neuroscience, University of Liverpool, Walton Centre, Lower Lane, Liverpool L9 7LJ Tel: 0151 529 5715 Fax: 0151 525 5465 Email: hart-i@wcnn.co.uk; 26 Leopold Street, Oxford OX4 1PU — MB ChB 1983 Glas.; PhD Lond. 1990; BSc (Hons.) Glas. 1981, MB ChB 1983; MRCP (UK) 1986; FRCP (G) 1997. Sen. Lect. (Neurol.) Univ. of Liverp.; Hon. Cons. Neurol., Walton Centre for Neurol. & Neurosurg., Liverp. Prev: MRC Clin. Sci. Neurosci. Gp. Inst. Molecular Med. John Radcliffe Hosp. Oxf.; Hon. Clin. Asst. Nat. Hosp. Nerv. Dis. Qu. Sq. Lond.; MRC Research Fell. Univ. Coll. Lond.

HART, Jacqueline Cecilia Clair Accident & Emergency Department, Royal Devon & Exeter Hospital, Barrack Road, Wonford, Exeter EX2 5DW Tel: 01392 411611; The Farm House, Little Houndbeare Farm, Aylesbeare, Exeter EX5 2DD Tel: 01404 812163 — MB BS 1987 Lond.; MRCGP 1994; DRCOG 1991. (Roy. Free Hosp. & Sch. Med. Lond.) Staff Grade (A & E). Socs: BMA. Prev: GP.

HART, Jacqueline Khadija 20B Campdale Road, London N7 0EB Email: paul.hart1@virgin.net — MB BS 1991 Lond.; BSc Lond. 1988. (Univ. Coll. & Middlx. Sch. Med. Lond.) SHO (Gyn.) Roy. Free Hosp. Lond.

HART, James Wheeler Cheriton House, Mill St., Houghton, Huntingdon PE28 2AZ — MB BS 1993 Lond.

HART, Janice Katharine Sullivan, Hart and Jones, Ringland Health Centre, Ringland Circle, Newport NP19 9PS Tel: 01633 277011 Fax: 01633 290706 — MB BCh 1988 Wales; DRCOG 1992.

HART, Jennifer Margaret St Margarets Hospital, Crossgate, Durham; West Winds, Elvet Moor, Durham DH1 3PR — MB BS 1967 Newc. (Newc.) Staff Grade Phys. Community Geriat. N. Durh. Community Health Care. Prev: Clin. Asst. (Staff Health) Dryburn Hosp. Durh.; Clin. Asst. (Child Welf. Clinics) Durh. AHA; SHO (Psychiat.) Darlington Memor. Hosp.

HART, Jerome Joseph 20 Hazel Gardens, Edgware HA8 8PB — MB BS 1979 Lond.; MRCPsych 1986; DRCOG 1982. (St. Geo.) Cons. Psychiat. Bowden Ho. Clininc Harrow-on-the-Hill. Prev: Sen. Regist. (Psychiat.) Lond. Hosp.; Ho. Surg. St. Geo. Hosp. Lond.; Ho. Phys. St. Helier Hosp. Carshalton.

HART, Mr John Christopher Dean Bristol Eye Hospital, Lower Maudlin St., Bristol BS1 2LX Tel: 0117 923 0060 Fax: 0117 928 4686; Litfield House Medical Centre, Clifton Down, Bristol BS9 3LS Tel: 0117 973 1323 Fax: 0117 973 3303 — MB BS Lond. 1961; BSc Lond. 1957; MD Bristol 1976; FRCS Eng. 1967; DO Eng. 1964; Hon FBCO 1996. (Middlx.) Cons. Surg. Bristol Eye Hosp.; Hon. Profess. Fell. Dept. Optometry Univ. Wales; Hon. Clin. Reader Univ Bristol. Prev: Sen. Lect. (Ophth.) & Head Dept. Univ. Bristol; Sen. Regist. (Ophth.) Nat. Hosp. Nerv. Dis. Lond.; Sen. Regist. (Ophth.) St. Mary's Hosp. Lond.

HART, John James Turner, Hart, Appleton and Briggs, Woodsend Medical Centre, School Place, Corby NN18 0QP Tel: 01536 407006 Fax: 01536 401711; Wantage Mews, Main St, Middleton, Market Harborough LE16 8YU Tel: 01536 771438 — MB ChB 1984 Leic.; MB ChB Leic. l984; MRCGP 1994; DRCOG 1991; DLO RCS Eng. 1989. Prev: SHO (Otolaryngol.) N. Riding Infirm. Middlesbrough & Qu. Med. Centre Nottm.; SHO (Neurosurg.) Roy. Preston Hosp.

HART, John Leslie Tel: 0115 963 3511 Fax: 0115 968 0947 — MB ChB 1976 Liverp.

HART, Jonathan Derek, Capt. RAMC Gainsborough Dairy House, Gainsborough Hill, Sherborne DT9 5NS — MB ChB 1985 Birm.; BSc (Hons.) Birm. 1980, ChB 1985. Regtl. Med. Off. 1st Bn. Duke of Wellington's Regt. Prev: Ho. Surg. Qu. Eliz. Milit. Hosp. Lond.; Ho. Phys. Yeovil Dist. Hosp.

HART, Judy Hyfield, Mill Lane, Ness, Neston, South Wirral CH64 8TP — MB BChir 1978 Camb.; DFPHM 2000; BSc St. And. 1975; Dip. Epidemiol. FPHM RCP (UK) 1995; Msc London 1998. p/t Specialist Regist. (Pub. Health) S. Chesh. HA. Prev: Specialist Regist. (Pub. Health) Bucks. HA; SHO (Pub. Health & Med.) Bucks. HA; SHO (Med.) Oxf. RHA.

HART, Julian Frank Queen Camel Health Centre, Queen Camel, Yeovil BA22 7NG Tel: 01935 850225 Fax: 01935 851247; Vine House, England's Lane, Queen Camel, Yeovil BA22 7NN Tel: 01935 850873 Fax: 01935 851247 — MB BS 1983 Lond.; DRCOG 1988. (Guy's) Prev: SHO (A & E) Kent & Canterbury Hosp.; Ho. Surg. Roy. Shrewsbury Hosp.; Ho. Phys. Hereford Co. Hosp.

HART, Julian Tudor (retired) Gelli Deg, Penmaen, Swansea SA3 2HH Tel: 01792 371314 Fax: 01782 371448 Email: crustyhard@aol.com — MB BChir Camb. 1952; FRCP Lond. 1987, M 1981; FRCGP 1974; DCH Eng. 1959. Sen. Research Fell Dept. of Health Sci.s, Univ. of Glam., Pontypridd; Hon. Research Fell. Glas. Univ. Med. Sch.; Mem. Sci. Staff MRC Epidemiol. & Med. Care Unit N.wick Pk. Hosp. Prev: GP Glyncorrwg.

HART, Lorraine Anne Cranborne Practice, Lake Road, Verwood Tel: 01753 842265 — BM BCh 1990 Oxf.; BA Camb. 1987; MRCP (UK) 1993; Phd 1998. (Cambridge?Oxford) Cons. Respirat. Phys. Heatherwood Hosp. Socs: Windsor Med. Soc. Prev: Regist. (Gen. Med.) Qu. Mary's Hosp. Lond.; SHO Rotat. (Med.) Ipswich Hosp.; SpR Respirat. Med. Char. Cross Hosp. Lond.

HART, Mrs Margaret Rachel Dalzell (retired) Craigton House, Bridge of Cally, Blairgowrie PH10 7LH Tel: 01250 882209 — MB ChB 1942 Birm. Prev: Asst. MOH Bucks. Co. Aylesbury.

HART, Mary Hilary 42 Picklers Hill, Abingdon OX14 2BB — MB 1969 Camb.; BA Camb. 1965, MB 1969, BChir 1968; MRCP (UK)

1972. (Lond. Hosp.) Clin. Asst. (Geratol.) Radcliffe Infirm. Oxf. Prev: Ho. Surg. Lond. Hosp. Annexe Brentwood; Ho. Phys. Lond. Hosp.

HART, Mary Winifred (retired) Howewath, Moorlands Road, Budleigh Salterton EX9 6AG Tel: 01395 443466 — MRCS Eng. LRCP Lond. 1947; MRCS Eng. LRCP Lond, 1947.

HART, Michael Thomas Wheeler Lower Badworthy, South Brent TQ10 9EG Tel: 01364 72440 — 1995 Dip Med. Acup.; MB BS Lond. 1967; MRCS Eng. LRCP Lond. 1967; MFHom 1982; MRCGP 1972; DObst RCOG 1970.

HART, Michael William The Medical Centre, Station Avenue, Bridlington YO16 4LZ Tel: 01262 670683 Fax: 01262 401685; Manor Farm Cottages, Grindale, Bridlington YO16 4XR Tel: 01262 400017 Email: michaelhart@doctors.org.net — MB ChB 1972 Leeds; MRCGP 1979; DObst RCOG 1976.

HART, Nicholas 111 Colwith Road, London W6 9EZ — MB BS 1993 Lond.

HART, Nicholas Marham Surgery, Marham, King's Lynn PE33 9HP Tel: 01760 337394 Fax: 01760 338319; Unicorn House, Shouldham, King's Lynn PE33 0BW Tel: 01366 347961 — MB BS 1981 Lond. (St. Thos.) Prev: Cas. Off. St. Mary's Hosp. Lond.; SHO (Geriat.) St. Thos. Hosp. Lond.

HART, Mr Nicholas Bernard Plastic Surgery Unit, Castle Hill Hospital, Cottingham HU16 5JQ Tel: 01482 622305 Fax: 01482 622353 — MB BS 1973 Lond.; FRCS Eng. 1979. (Middlx.) p/t Cons. Plastic Surg. Castle Hill Hosp., Hull. Socs: Brit. Assn. Plastic Surg.; Brit. Burns Assn.; Brit. Assn. Head & Neck Oncol. Prev: Sen. Regist. (Plastic Surg.) Ulster Hosp. Dundonald; Regist. (Plastic Surg.) W. Midl. Regional Plastic Surg. Unit.

HART, Nicola Janet 59 Rookery Lane, Rainford, St Helens WA11 8BL; Southwold, Holyhead Road, Bicton, Shrewsbury SY3 8EQ Tel: 01743 850870 — MB ChB 1993 Sheff.; DCH 1996; DRCOG 1998. SHO (Paediat.) Shrewsbury; GP Locum Shrops. Area. Prev: SHO (Med.) Shrewsbury.

HART, Patricia Margaret Anne Eye Department, Royal Victoria Hospital, Belfast BT12 6BA Tel: 01232 240503 Fax: 01232 330744 Email: pat.hart@qub.ac.uk; 24 Myrtlefield Park, Belfast BT9 6NE Tel: 01232 667107 — MB BCh BAO 1975 Belf.; FRCS Ed. 1979; FRCOphth 1989. (Qu. Univ. Belf.) Cons. Ophth. Roy. Vict. Hosp. Belf.; Sen. Clin. Fell. Qu.s Univ. Belf. Socs: BMA; ARVO. Prev: Cons. Ophth. Nat. Univ. Hosp. Singapore; Sen. Regist. (Ophth.) Roy. Vict. Hosp. Belf.

HART, Paul Edward 20B Campdale Road, London N7 0EB Email: paul.hart1@virgin.net — MB BS 1992 Lond.; BSc Lond. 1989; MRCP (UK) 1995. Regist. (Neurol.) Atkinson Morleys Hosp.

HART, Paul James 204/3140 Lakeside Road, Kelownia BC Y1W 3T1, Canada; 30 Golf Avenue, Dumfries DG2 9EW — MB ChB 1979 Glas.; DRCOG 1983.

HART, Paul Richard Birchgrove Surgery, 104 Caerphilly Road, Cardiff CF14 4AG Tel: 029 2052 2344 Fax: 029 2052 2487; 149 Heathwood Road, Heath, Cardiff CF14 4BL Tel: 029 2052 2344 — MB ChB 1972 Sheff.; MRCGP 1976; DObst RCOG 1975.

HART, Paul Simon 38 Juniper Heights, Canberra Close, Hendon, London NW4 4SZ — MB ChB 1985 Leic.; BSc (Hons.) Lond. 1980; FRCA 1996. Vis. Asst. Prof. Univ. Calif. San Francisco, USA; Pharmaceut. Phys. SmithKline Beecham. Prev: Regist. (Anaesth.) Hammersmith Hosp. Lond. & Edgware Gen. Hosp.

HART, Philip Charles Newtons, The Health Centre, Heath Road, Haywards Heath RH16 3BB Tel: 01444 412280 Fax: 01444 416943 — MB BS 1986 Lond.; MRCGP 1992; DRCOG 1988; Cert. Family Plann. JCC 1988. Trainee GP/SHO (Gen. Med. & Geriat.) Cuckfield Hosp. Haywards Heath VTS. Prev: SHO (Psychiat.) St. Francis Hosp. Haywards Heath; SHO (O & G & A & E) Cuckfield Hosp.; SHO (Paediat. Surg.) Roy. Alexandra Hosp. Brighton.

HART, Philip Montagu D'Arcy, CBE (retired) 37 Belsize Court, London NW3 5QN Tel: 020 7435 4048 — MB BChir Camb. 1925; BA Camb. (Nat. Sc. Trip. Pts. I & II) 1922, MA 1926, MD 1930; FRCP Lond. 1936, M 1926. Vis. Scien. Nat. Inst. for Med. Research. Prev: Grant Holder Nat. Inst. Med. Research.

HART, Raymond David Campbell (retired) Jimmers, St Neot, Liskeard PL14 6NG — MB BS 1948 Lond.; LMSSA Lond. 1947; MRCGP 1971; DObst RCOG 1949. Prev: Res. Obstetr., Outpats. Off. & Ho. Phys. Guy's Hosp.

HART, Richard 4 Norfolk Place, London W2 1QN Tel: 020 7723 7891 Fax: 020 7723 7891 Email: mobile 0956384667; 7 Holland Park Court, Holland Park Gardens, London W14 8DN Tel: 020 7603 8614 — MRCS Eng. LRCP Lond. 1950. (St. Mary's)

HART, Robert John, MBE St Margaret's Somerset Hospice, Heron Drive, Bishops Hull, Taunton TA1 5HA Tel: 01823 259394 Fax: 01823 345900 Email: hart @st-marg-hospice.demon.co.uk; 37 Shoreditch Road, Taunton TA1 3BX Tel: 01823 351071 — MB BS 1964 Lond.; FRCS Eng. 1972; MRCS Eng. LRCP Lond. 1964. Med. Dir. St. Margt. Som. Hospice Taunton; Hon. Cons. Palliat. Med. Taunton & Som. NHS Trust; Hon. Cons. Pall. Med. E. Som. NHS Trust. Socs: Assn. Palliat. Med. Prev: Med. Dir. St. Michael's Hospice St. Leonards-on-Sea; Sen. Regist. St. Josephs Hospice Hackney; Surg. Christian Hosp. & Leprosy Centre Chandraghona, Bangladesh.

HART, Robert Owen 32 Greenbank Avenue, Hall Green, Birmingham B28 8AR — MB BS 1983 Lond.

HART, Roger Brewer Street, 4 Brewer Street, Maidstone ME14 1RU Tel: 01622 755401/755402 Fax: 01622 695378; 30 Lord Romney's Hill, Ashford Road, Bearsted, Maidstone ME14 4LP Tel: 01622 37165 — MB BS 1967 Lond.; MRCS Eng. LRCP Lond. 1967; DObst RCOG 1971. (Univ. Coll. Hosp.) Prev: SHO (O & G) W. Suff. Gen. Hosp.; SHO Surg. Unit Addenbrook's & Newmarket Hosps.; Cas. Surg. Off. Univ. Coll. Hosp. Lond.

HART, Roger James 7 Balmoral Road, New Longton, Preston PR4 4JJ — MB BS 1989 Lond.; MRCOG 1994. Regist. (O & G) Roy. Free Hosp. Lond.

HART, Rosemarie Ann Millbarn Medical Centre, 34 London End, Beaconsfield HP9 2JH Tel: 01494 675303 Fax: 01494 680214 — MB BS 1987 Lond.; BSc (Hons.) Genetics & Microbiol. Lond. 1984; MRCGP 1992; DRCOG 1991. (Univ. Coll. Hosp. Lond.) Clin. Asst. (Diabetes) Hillingdon Hosp. Uxbridge.

HART, Ruth D'Arcy (cons. rooms) 35 Devonshire Place, London W1N 1PE Tel: 020 7486 5384; 37 Belsize Court, London NW3 5QN Tel: 020 7435 4048 — MRCS Eng. LRCP Lond. 1954. (Roy. Free) Socs: Inst. Psychosexual Med.; Fac. Fam. Plann. Prev: Sen. Med. Off. (Psychosexual & Family Plann.) Kentish Town & Finsbury Health Centre; Med. Asst. (Infertil.) Roy. N. Hosp. Lond.; Ho. Surg. & Ho. Phys. Fulham Hosp.

HART, Sally Anne Market Street Medical Centre, 112-114 Market Street, Hindley, Wigan WN2 3AZ Tel: 01942 256221 Fax: 01942 522479; 112 Market Street, Hindley, Wigan WN2 3AZ — MB ChB 1976 Liverp.

HART, Sarah Kathryn Flat C, 88 Walterton Road, London W9 3PQ — MB BS 1998 Lond.; MB BS Lond 1998.

HART, Sidney Samuel (retired) 8 Church Road, Kington HR5 3AG Tel: 01544 231231 — MRCS Eng. LRCP Lond. 1942; BA Camb. 1939. Prev: Clin. Med. Off. Glos. AHA.

HART, Simon Paul The Rayne Laboratory, Respiratory Medicine Unit, Medical School, Teviot Place, Edinburgh EH8 9AL Tel: 0131 650 6948 Fax: 0131 650 4384 Email: shart@srv1.ed.ac.uk; 56 Society Road, South Queensferry EH30 9RX — MB ChB 1991 Ed.; MB ChB (Hons.) Ed. 1991; BSc (Hons.) Ed. 1989; MRCP (UK) 1994. (Ed.) Research Fell. Rayne Laborat. Edin. Prev: SHO (Med.) Roy. Infirm. Edin. & Qu. Margt. Hosp. Dunfermline.

HART, Simon Rupert Laynes Mead, West Drive, Angmering, Littlehampton BN16 4NL — MB BS 1992 Lond.; BSc Lond. 1988; MRCP (UK) 1997. (Char. Cross)

HART, Stephanie Margaret Holywell Surgery, 83B Tolpits Lane, Holywell Estate, Watford WD18 6LL Tel: 01923 243130 — MB BS 1979 Lond.; MRCGP 1984. GP, Watford.

HART, Susan Mary 104 Caerphilly Road, Birchgrove, Cardiff CF14 4AG Tel: 029 2052 2344 Fax: 029 2052 2487; Tel: 029 2052 2344 — MB ChB 1972 Sheff.; DObst RCOG 1975. p/t GP; Clin. Asst. (Diabetes). Socs: Welsh Med. Soc. (Mem.ship secretary).

HART, Susanna Margaret Department of Paediatrics, Mayday University Hospital, London Road, Croydon CR7 7YE Tel: 020 8401 3399 Fax: 020 8401 3372 Email: susanna.hart@mhc-tr.sthames.nhs.uk; 15 Baskerville Road, Wandsworth, London SW18 3RJ Tel: 020 8870 2666 — MB BCh BAO 1972 Dub.; FRCP Lond. 1994; MRCP (UK) 1977; FRCP 1996; DCH Eng. 1974. (Trinity College Dublin) Cons. Paediat. Mayday Hosp. Croydon. Prev: Sen. Regist. (Paediat.) Kings Coll. Hosp. Lond.; Regist. (Paediat.) Brompton Hosp. Lond.

HART, Thomas (retired) Glengarth, Newcastle Road, Crossgate Moor, Durham DH1 4HZ Tel: 0191 384 4345 — MB ChB Glas. 1938. Clin. Asst. (Med.) Highfield Hosp. Chester-le-St.; Mem.

Indust. Injuries Bd.; GP NHS Meadowfield, Co. Durh. Prev: Maj. RAMC Specialist in Psychiat.

HART, Thomas Bernard 'The Roaches', June Lane, Midhurst GU29 9EW; 2 Avonside Way, Macclesfield SK11 8BY — MB BS 1976 Lond.; BSc (Hons.) Lond. 1973; MRCP (UK) 1979. Med. Adviser ICI Pharmaceut. Div. Macclesfield.

HART, Wendy Margaret 5 Bankhead Grove, Dalmeny, South Queensferry EH30 9JZ — MB ChB 1990 Ed.; MRCGP 1995; DFFP 1994; DRCOG 1994.

HART, William Alexander Brough and South Cave Medical Practice, 4 Centurion Way, Brough HU15 1AY Tel: 01482 667108 Fax: 01482 665090; Stone House, Low Road, Everthorpe, Brough HU15 2AD Email: hart@enterprise.net — BM BCh 1974 Oxf.; MA Oxf. 1974; DCH RCP Lond. 1978. Med. Examr. (Aviat.) Brit. Aerospace, Brough; Vice-Chairm. Yorks. E. Riding Volun. A & E Serv. Socs: BMA; Hull Med. Soc.; BASICS. Prev: GP Goroka, Papua New Guinea.

HART, Yvonne Mary Tel: 01865 224487 Fax: 01865 224303 — MD 1993 Lond.; MRCP (UK) 1983; FRCP 1998; MB BS 1979 Lond. (Royal Free Hospital School of Medicine) Cons. Neur. Radcliffe Infirm., Oxf. Prev: Sen. Regist. (Neurol.) Atkinson Morley Hosp. Lond.; Cons. Neurol. Kingston Hosp. Surrey & Atkinson Morley's Hosp. Lond.

HART PRIETO, Maria Consuelo 7 Tudor Drive, Hele Manor, Barnstaple EX31 2DR — MB BCh 1998 Wales.

HARTE, Barrie Dudley Middleton and Partners, Sele Gate Surgery, Hencotes, Hexham NE46 2EG Tel: 01434 602237 Fax: 01434 609496; Southside, Causey Way, Hexham NE46 2JQ Tel: 01434 603948 — MB BS 1974 Lond.; MRCS Eng. LRCP Lond. 1974; MRCGP 1988; DCH Eng. 1978; DObst RCOG 1976. (St. Mary's) GP. Prev: Dep. Police Surg. Hexham; Trainee GP Swindon & Cirencester VTS; Ho. Phys. Bedford Gen. Hosp.

HARTE, John Dudley (retired) 4 Fernville Road, Gosforth, Newcastle upon Tyne NE3 4HT Tel: 0191 285 2066 Fax: 0191 285 2066 Email: johnharte@lineone.net — MB BS Lond. 1952, CPH 1955; MRCS Eng. LRCP Lond. 1952; FFOM RCP Lond. 1986, MFOM 1982; FRCGP 1976, M 1961; DMJ Soc. Apoth. Lond. 1970; DIH Eng. 1957, DPH 1962; DObst RCOG 1954; FRIPHH; FRIPPH. Prev: HM Coroner Beds.

HARTE, Jonathan Henry Aspley Medical Centre, 511 Aspley Lane, Aspley, Nottingham NG8 5RW Tel: 0115 929 2700 Fax: 0115 929 8276; Flat 3, 1 Western Terrace, The Park, Nottingham NG7 1AF Tel: 0115 958 2519 — BM BS 1988 Nottm.; BMedSci (Hons.) Nottm. 1986, BM BS 1988; MRCGP 1992. (Nottm.) GP Princip. Nott. Socs: Chairm. Nottm. Local Med. Comm.

HARTE, Kathleen Mary 22 Virginia Road, London N21 1HJ — MB ChB 1983 Liverp.

HARTE, Margaret Rosarie 8 York Road, Rochester ME1 3DP — MB BCh BAO 1990 NUI.

HARTE, Nora Marianne 22 Overton Place, West Bromwich B71 1RL — MB BCh BAO 1992 NUI.

HARTEN-ASH, Vernon John The Harten Group, 7 Bennell Court, Comberton, Cambridge CB3 7DS Tel: 01223 264367 Fax: 01223 264370 Email: vha@hartengroup.co.uk — MB ChB 1981 Birm.; MBA Pennsylvania USA 1994; DCH RCP Glas 1987. (Birmingham) Med. & Managem. Cons. Harten Gp. Camb. Socs: Brit. Assn. Pharmaceut. Phys. (Exec.-Comm. Mem.). Prev: Head of Med. affiars. Asta Med. Ltd.; Surg. Lt. RN.

HARTER, Christina 126 Beedell Avenue, Westcliff on Sea SS0 9JP — State Exam Med 1986 Tubingen.

HARTFALL, Mr William Guy Christchurch Park Hospital, 57-59 Fonnereau Road, Ipswich IP1 3JW Tel: 01473 256071; Culpho End House, Culpho, Ipswich IP6 9EA Tel: 01473 785347 — MB BChir 1961 Camb.; BA Camb. 1957; FRCS Eng. 1964; MRCS Eng. LRCP Lond. 1961. (Camb. & Guy's) Socs: Fell. Roy. Soc. Med.; Brit. Assn. Urol. Surgs. Prev: Sen. Regist. (Surg. & Urol.) Guy's Hosp. Lond.; Cons. Urol. Surg. Ipswich Hosp. Gp.

HARTGILL, Mr John Clavering Bridge House Farm, Felsted, Dunmow CM6 3JF Tel: 01371 820349 Fax: 01371 821360 — MRCS Eng. LRCP Lond. 1951; FRCS Ed. 1962; FRCOG 1968, M 1958; DObst RCOG 1955. (Univ. Otago & Lond. Hosp.) Emerit. Cons. O & G Surg. Roy. Lond. Trust Hosp.; Sen. Lect. Lond. Hosp. Med. Coll.; Examr. Univ. Camb. & Lond., Roy. Coll. Obst. & Gyn.; Liveryman Worshipful Soc. of Apoth. & Freeman City Lond. Socs: Fell. Roy. Soc. Med.; Sydenham Med. Club; Fell. Assn. Lawyers. Prev: Asst. Dept. O & G Ulleval Hosp. Oslo, Norway; Sen. Regist. (O & G) & Sen. Resid. Accouch Lond. Hosp.

HARTGILL, Tom William Bridge House Farm, Felsted, Dunmow CM6 3JF — MB BS 1992 Lond.

HARTIKAINEN, Juha Erkki Kalle Department of Cardiological Sciences, St Georges Hospital Medical School, Cranmer Terrace, London SW17 0RE — Lic Med. Kuopio 1983.

HARTIKAINEN, Paivi Hillevi 173 Hillcross Avenue, Morden SM4 4AZ — Lic Med Kuopio 1984.

HARTILL, Sarah Ann Regional Medical Centre, RAF Cosford, Wolverhampton WV7 3EX Tel: 01902 377259 Fax: 01902 377681; Hallonsford Cottage, Worfield, Bridgnorth WV15 5LW Tel: 01746 716008 Fax: 01746 716002 Email: sahartill@aol.com — MB BS 1985 Lond.; MRCGP 1993; DFFP 1993; Cert. Av. Med. 1989; Cert. Family Plann. JCC 1987. (St Batholomew's Hospital London) Civil. Med. Pract. RAF Cosford; Clin. Asst. (Dermat.) New Cross Hosp. Wolverhampton; Clin. Med. Off. (Family Plann.) Wolverhampton & Staffs. HA; Civil Aviat. Examr. PPL & Commercial (Milit.). Prev: Civil Med. Pract. RAF Cosford; Trainee GP Albrighton VTS.

HARTINGTON, Katharine Garth Cottage, Weir Lane, Marshfield, Chippenham SN14 8NB — BChir 1991 Camb.

HARTLAND, Andrew John Department of Clinical Biochemistry, North Staffs Hospital NHS Trust, Stoke-on-Trent ST4 7PA Tel: 01782 554669 — MB ChB 1991 Birm.; DRCPath 1996. Sen. Regist. (Chem. Path.) N.Staffs.NHs Trust.

HARTLAND, Sophia Jane Psychotherapy Service, Sussex Weald and Downs NHS Trust, Chapel St. Clinic, 1 Chapel Street, Chichester PO19 1BX Tel: 01243 623400 Ext: 3410 Fax: 01243 623400 — BM BCh 1973 Oxf.; MA Camb. 1969; MRCPsych 1985. Cons. Psychother. Psychother. Serv. , Sussex Weald & Downs NHS Trust Chichester; Clin. Tutor in Psychiat., Sussex Weald & Downs NHS Trust, Chichester. Prev: Sen. Regist. (Psychother.) Nottm. Psychother. Unit; Clin. Asst. (Psychother.) Fairmile Hosp. Wallingford.

HARTLEY, Andrew Gerard John 35 Retford Drive, New Hall, Sutton Coldfield B76 1DG — MB ChB 1994 Dundee; MRCP (UK) 1997. Specialist Regist. Rotat. (Clin. Oncol.) W. Midl.

HARTLEY, Anthony William Buxton Medical Practice, 2 Temple Road, Buxton SK17 9BZ Tel: 01298 23298; 17 Dovedale Crescent, Buxton SK17 9BJ — MB ChB 1980 Manch.; MRCGP 1984; DRCOG 1983. Prev: SHO (Med.) N. Lonsdale Hosp. Barrow; Ho. Phys. Manch. Roy. Infirm.; Ho. Surg. Ancoats Hosp. Manch.

HARTLEY, Benjamin Ernest John Tomlinson Dept. of Otolaryngology, Great Ormond St. Hosptial for Children, Great Ormond St., London WC1N 3JH Fax: 020 7829 8644 — MB BS 1990 Lond.; BSc (Hons.) Lond. 1987; FRCS (Orl-Hns) 1999; FRCS Eng. 1995; FRCS Irel. 1995. Cons., Otolaryngol., Gt. Ormond St. Hosp. for Childr., Lond.; Cons. Otolaryngol., The Portland Hosp., Lond. Socs: Brit. Assn. Otolaryngol., Head and Neck Surg.; Brit. Associaton Paedatirc OtoLaryngol.

HARTLEY, Mr Charles Edwin (retired) Rosemerryn, Green Lane, Penryn TR10 8QQ — MA Camb. 1947, MB BChir 1944; FRCS Eng. 1951; DTM & H Eng. 1951. Sessional Med. Off. Nat. Blood Transfus. Serv. Prev: Med. Supt. & Surg. Vom Christian Hosp. Nigeria.

HARTLEY, Mr Christopher ENT dept, Royal Preston Hospital, Sharoe Green Lane, Fulwood, Preston PR2 9HT — MB BCh 1986 Wales; FRCS 1996 (ORL); BSc (Hons.) Wales 1983; FRCS Ed. 1992. Cons. Otolary Roy. Preston. Hosp. Prev: SHO (Cardiothoracic Surg. & ENT) Freeman Hosp. Newc. u. Tyne; Demonst. (Anat.) Med. Sch. Univ. Newc.; Sen. Regist. (ENT) Manch. Roy. Infirm.

HARTLEY, David Charles The Surgery, 6 East Mount Road, York YO24 1BD Tel: 01904 646509 Fax: 01904 646743; Park Farm, Askham Bryan, York DYO23 3QT — MB BS 1988 Newc.; MRCGP 1992; DCH RCP Lond. 1991.

HARTLEY, David Ian (retired) 32 Victoria Road, Salisbury SP1 3NG Tel: 01722 335140 Email: david-hartley@lineone.net — MB BS 1964 Lond.; MRCGP 1974; DObst RCOG 1966. Prev: Cdr. Med. 4 Div. Aldershot.

HARTLEY, Mr David Ronald Wallen (retired) Banff, Hillcote, Bleadon Hill, Weston Super Mare BS24 9JU Tel: 01934 813233 Fax: 01934 813233 — MB BS 1954 Lond.; FRCOG 1982, M 1969. Prev: Clin. Lect. Bristol Univ. & Cons. O & G W.on-Super-Mare & Bristol Matern. Hosp.

HARTLEY, Eleanor Dorothy Margaret (retired) Bwlch y Gwynt, 19 Marine Drive, Barry CF62 6QN Tel: 01446 732125 — LRCP LRCS Ed. LRFPS Glas. 1948; DPM 1972; MRCPsych 1973. Prev: Asst. Resid. (Neuropsychiat.) Albany Hosp., NY.

HARTLEY, Elizabeth Marguerite 2 Brickfields, Somerleyton, Lowestoft NR32 5QW — MB BS 1976 Lond.; MRCS Eng. LRCP Lond. 1976; MFFP 1995. SCMO (Family Plann.) Local Health Partnerships NHs Trust; Clin.Asst.Bure Clin.James paget Hosp.Gorleston. Prev: Clin. Med. Off. (Dent. Anaesth. & Family Plann.) Anglian Harbours NHS Trust.

HARTLEY, Geoffrey (retired) 135 Palatine Road, West Didsbury, Manchester M20 3YA Tel: 0161 445 0126 — MB ChB 1955 Manch.; FRCR 1975; FFR 1963; DMRD Eng. 1961. Prev: Cons. Radiol. Withington Hosp. Manch.

HARTLEY, Helen Marie St. George's Hospital, London SW17 0QT Tel: 020 8725 3316; 52 Corrance Road, London SW2 5RH Tel: 020 7274 6474 Email: helen.hartley@lineone.net — MB ChB 1992 Birm.; BSc Birm. 1991; FRCA 1997. p/t Specialist Regist. (Anaesth.) SW James.

HARTLEY, Herbert Anthony (retired) Tigh An Coileach, 18 Sconser, Sconser, Isle of Skye IV48 8TD Tel: 01478 650300 Fax: 01478 650433 — MB ChB Sheff. 1955; DObst RCOG 1959. Prev: GP Crewe.

HARTLEY, Ian Charles Rowley Grimble and Partners, 20 Pepys Road, Raynes Park, London SW20 8PF Tel: 020 8946 3074/8249 Fax: 020 8296 0145; Troon 59, Crossbush Road, Felpham, Bognor Regis PO22 7LY — MB BS 1975 Lond.; MRCP (UK) 1978; DRCOG 1982. (Lond. Hosp.) Clin. Asst. (Gastroenterol.) Roehampton; GP Tutor St. Geo. Hosp. Lond. Prev: Regist. (Gen. Med.) Whipps Cross Hosp. Lond.; Regist. (Rheum.) The Middlx. Hosp.

HARTLEY, Ishbel Mary Market Street Health Centre, Market Street, Ullapool IV26 2XE Tel: 01854 612015/612595 Fax: 01854 613025; 3 Broombank, North Road, Ullapool IV26 2XL — MB ChB 1982 Glas.; MRCGP 1987; DCH RCP Lond. 1986; DRCOG 1985.

HARTLEY, Janet Davina Ash Hill Cottage, The Green, Coleford, Bath — MB ChB 1978 Manch.

HARTLEY, Joanna Louise Flat 2, 23 Greenheys Road, Liverpool L8 0SX — BM 1993 Soton. SHO (Anaesth.) N. Hants. Hosp. Basingstoke.

HARTLEY, John Cecil Department of Microbiology, University College London, London WC1; 68 Meadow Road, London SW8 1PP — MB BS 1984 Lond.; BSc Lond. 1981, MB BS 1984; MRCP (UK) 1989; DTM & H Lond. 1991; MSc Lond. 1997; Dip RCPath 1998. (King's Coll. Sch. Of Med. & Dent.) Specialist Regist. (Med. MicroBiol.) Univ. Coll. of Lond. Hosps.

HARTLEY, Mr John Edward 7 Norfolk Street, Bishopthorpe Road, York YO23 1JY — MB BS 1990 Lond.; BSc (Hons.) Lond. 1987; FRCS Eng. 1994. (St. Mary's Hosp. Med. Sch.) Specialist Regist. (Gen. Surg.) N. & Yorks. Deanery. Prev: Research Fell. Univ. Hull Acad. Surgic. Unit; SHO St. Mary's Hosp. Lond.

HARTLEY, John Leonard George (retired) Rose Cottage, Manor Lane, Waddington, Lincoln LN5 9QD — MRCS Eng. LRCP Lond. 1941. Prev: Ho. Phys. & Ho. Surg. Joyce Green Hosp. Dartford.

HARTLEY, John Philip Rathbone Royal Sussex County Hospital, Brighton BN2 5BE Tel: 01273 696955; High Cross House, Henfield Road, Albourne, Hassocks BN6 9JH — BM BCh 1971 Oxf.; MA Oxf. 1972, DM 1983; FRCP Lond. 1989. (Univ. Coll. Hosp.) Cons. Phys. Brighton Health Care. Prev: Ho. Phys. (Med.) Unit Univ. Coll. Hosp. Lond.; Research Fell. (Hon. Sen. Regist.) & Sen. Regist. (Med.) Llandough & Sully Hosps. Cardiff.

HARTLEY, Kathryn Elizabeth Needham Market Country Practice, Barking Road, Needham Market, Ipswich IP6 8EZ Tel: 01449 720666; Little College Farm, Creeting St. Mary, Ipswich IP6 8PX Tel: 01449 720491 — MRCS Eng. LRCP Lond. 1974. (Camb.)

HARTLEY, Louise Mary 2 Hartington Grove, Cambridge CB1 7UE — BM BCh 1988 Oxf.; MRCP (UK) 1991. SHO (Intens. Care) Roy. Vict. Infirm. Newc. u Tyne.

HARTLEY, Lucy Anne Yew Tree Flat, Mayfair Mansions, Mersey Road, Didsbury, Manchester M20 2PY Tel: 0161 445 2167 — MB ChB 1992 Sheff.; FRCA 1999 Lond. SpR Anaesth., Manc. N.W. Deanery.

HARTLEY, Mr Mark Newton Royal Liverpool University Hospital Trust, Prescot St., Liverpool L7 8XP Tel: 0151 706 3450 — MB ChB 1981 Liverp.; MD Liverp. 1990; FRCS (S) 1994; FRCS Eng. 1985. Cons. Gen. Surg. Roy. Liverp. & BRd.green Univ. Hosps. Trust. Prev: Sen. Regist. (Gen. Surg.) Roy. Liverp. Univ. Hosp.

HARTLEY, Mary Jeannette (retired) Cottesmore, Grantham Avenue, Lower Walton, Warrington WA4 6PF — MB ChB Leeds 1946; FFA RCS Eng. 1954; DA Eng. 1951. Prev: Cons. Anaesth. St. Helens & Knowsley AHA.

HARTLEY, Michael 8 The Belfry, Lytham St Annes FY8 4NW — MB ChB 1984 Manch.; MB ChB Manch. l984; FRCA 1991. Cons. Anaesth. Blackpool Vict. Hosp. NHS Trust.

HARTLEY, Paul Christopher Yorkshire Street, 80 Yorkshire Street, Burnley BB11 3BT Tel: 01282 420141 Fax: 01282 832477; 2 Read Hall Cottages, Hammond Drive, Read, Burnley BB12 7RE Tel: 01282 778065 — MRCS Eng. LRCP Lond. 1978; MRCGP 1982. (Leeds.)

HARTLEY, Richard Barrie 7 Highmore Road, Blackheath, London SE3 7UA — MB BS 1980 Lond.; MRCS Eng. LRCP Lond. 1970; MRCPath 1979. Sen. Lect. (Path.) Guy's Hosp. Med. Sch. Lond.

HARTLEY, Mr Richard Cedric (retired) Lilac Cottage, Horrocks Fold, Bolton BL1 7BX Tel: 01204 301641 — MB ChB Birm. 1952; ChM Birm. 1965; FRCS Eng. 1959. Hon. Cons. Surg. N. Manch. Gen. Hosp.; Mem. PLAB Bd. GMC. Prev: Mem. Ct. Examrs. RCS Eng.

HARTLEY, Richard Craig 8 Vicarage Lane, Blackburn BB1 9HX — BM BS 1994 Nottm.

HARTLEY, Richard Howard Ronald (retired) 45 Shawfield Street, London SW3 4BA Tel: 020 7352 2334 — MRCS Eng. LRCP Lond. 1939; FRCP Lond. 1969, M 1945.

HARTLEY, Mr Richard Howarth Royal Bournemouth Hospital, Castle Lane East, Bournemouth BH7 7DW Tel: 01202 323606 Fax: 01202 885251 Email: rrhh.bmc@btinternet.com; 32 West Borough, Wimborne BH21 1NF Tel: 01202 884458 Fax: 01202 885251 Email: rrhh.bmc@btinternet.com — MB BS 1987 Lond.; FRCS (Orth.) Lond. 1997. Cons. Orthopaedic & Trauma Roy. Bournemouth Hosp Bournemouth. Prev: Sen. Regist. (Orthop.) Nottm.

HARTLEY, Richard William John South Tees Acute Trust, South Cleveland Hospital, Marton Road, Middlesbrough TS4 3BW Tel: 01642 850850; Richlieu House, 4 West Green, Stokesley, Middlesbrough TS9 5BB Tel: 01642 710080 — MB BS 1985 Newc.; MRCP (UK) 1988; FRCR 1993. (Newcastle upon Tyne) Cons. Radiol. S. Cleveland NHS Trust. Socs: BMA (Ex-Counc. Mem.); Brit. Soc. Interven. Radiol. Prev: Radiol. Trainee Manch. Hosps.; Sen. Regist. (Radiol.) Manch.; Regist. (Med.) Birm. Gen. Hosp.

HARTLEY, Robert David Chorley Health Centre, Collison Avenue, Chorley PR7 2TH Tel: 01257 265080 Fax: 01257 232285 — MB BS 1970 Lond.; MRCS Eng. LRCP Lond. 1970. (Guy's)

HARTLEY, Ruskin Howard 87 Oakshaw Drive, Norden, Rochdale OL12 7PF — MB ChB 1989 Leic.

HARTLEY, Sarah Louise Department of General Practice, St Mary's Hospital Medical School, 16 South Wharf Road, London W2 1PF Tel: 020 7594 3382/3380 Email: s.hartley@ic.ac.uk; 20 Cumberland Road, Kew, Richmond TW9 3HQ — BM BCh 1989 Oxf.; MRCGP 1995; DRCOG 1994. Clin. Lect. St. Mary's Hosp. Lond. Socs: BMA. Prev: GP Qu. Mary's Hosp. Roehampton VTS.

HARTLEY, Simon John Martyn 99 Western Road Medical Centre, Romford RM1 3LS Tel: 01708 748054 Fax: 01708 737936 — MB BS 1974 Lond.; MRCS Eng. LRCP Lond. 1974.

HARTLEY, Stephen 281 Main Street, Calverton, Nottingham NG14 6LT — MB ChB 1975 Ed.; MRCPath 1983.

HARTLEY, Stephen John 14 Hornby Street, Burnley BB11 3AS — MB ChB 1998 Manch.; MB ChB Manch 1998.

HARTLEY, Susan Mary Hanbury Community Project, 22A Hanbury St., London E1 6QR Tel: 020 7377 2497; 35 Buxton St, London E1 5EH — MB BS 1973 Newc.; MRCGP 1977. Hon. Med. Off. Hanbury Community Project Lond. Prev: Phys. Burrswood Christian Centre for Med. & Spiritual Care Kent; GP Rhyl.

HARTLEY, William Christian (retired) 42 New Walk, Beverley HU17 7DJ Tel: 01482 881388 — MB ChB 1955 Ed.; FRCP Ed. 1972, M 1962; FRCR 1975; FFR 1963. Cons. Radiol. Yorks RHA.

HARTLEY BOOTH, Adrianne Claire Hill House Consulting Rooms, Old Watton Road, Colney, Norwich NR9 4DB Tel: 01603 505011 — MB BChir 1976 Camb.; MB BChir Camb. 1977; MA Camb. 1977. (Westm.) Prev: Princip. GP Norwich.

HARTLEY-BREWER, Valerie Forbes 36 Combe Park, Bath BA1 3NR Tel: 01225 446089; Uplands, The Glen, Bristol BS31 3JP — MRCS Eng. LRCP Lond. 1979; MD Washington Univ. 1978;

MRCGP 1982; DRCOG 1981; FRCGP 1997. (Washington Univ. Med. School, St Louis) GP Bath.

HARTMAN, Jennifer Anne 48 Banks Road, Nottingham NG9 6HA — MB ChB 1987 Bristol.

HARTMANN, Dietmar Department of Anaesthetics, Ninewells Hospital, Dundee DD1 9SY Tel: 01382 660111 Email: dietmar.hartmann@bigfoot.com — State Exam Med 1989 Lubeck. (Medical University Lubeck) Socs: FRCA.

HARTNELL, Harry Roy, MBE (retired) 14 Lansdowne Square, Tunbridge Wells TN1 2NF — MRCS Eng. LRCP Lond. 1933. Prev: Lt.-Col. RAMC (Ret.) Sen. Surg. Specialist.

HARTNELL, Victoria Helen Horfield Health Centre, Lockleaze Road, Horfield, Bristol BS7 9RR Tel: 0117 969 5391 — MB BS 1987 Lond.; MRCGP (Distinc.) 1991; DRCOG 1990.

HARTNOLL, Gary 113 Overdale, Ashtead KT21 1PZ — MB BCh 1986 Wales; MA Camb. 1987; MRCP Paediat. (UK) 1991. Sen. Regist. (Paediat.) S.mead Hosp. Bristol. Prev: Research Fell. & Hon. Sen. Regist. Roy. Postgrad. Med. Sch. Hammersmith Hosp. Lond.; Regist. (Paediat.) St. Thos. Hosp. Lond. & Pembury Hosp. Kent; SHO Gt. Ormond St. Lond.

HARTOG, Martin (retired) Frenchay Lodge E., Beckspool Road, Frenchay, Bristol BS16 1NT Tel: 0117 956 9850 Fax: 0117 956 9850 Email: hartog@care4free.net — BM BCh 1954 Oxf.; BA (1st cl. Hons. Physiol.) Oxf. 1951, DM 1966; FRCP Lond. 1972, M 1957. Reader (Med.) Univ. Bristol; Hon. Cons. Phys. S.mead Health Dist. Prev: Sen. Regist. (Med.) Hammersmith Hosp.

HARTOPP, Ian Keith Penhallow, Eagley Bank, Sharples, Bolton BL1 7LF — MB ChB 1969 Manch.; FFA RCS Eng. 1978.

HARTOPP, Richard John Hall Gardens, Main St., Great Oxendon, Market Harborough LE16 8NE — MB BS 1994 Lond.

HARTREE, Colin James St Wilfrid's Hospice, Grosvenor Road, Chichester PO19 2FP; Sunny Mill, Mill Lane, Runcton, Chichester PO20 6PP — MB 1987 Camb.; BChir 1986; MRCGP 1991; Dip. Palliat. Med. Wales 1994. Cons. Palliat. Med. St. Wilfrid's Hospice Chichester.

HARTREE, Jane Fiona 2 Courtway Cottages, High Road, Fobbing, Stanford-le-Hope SS17 9JB Tel: 01375 360426 — MB BS 1990 Lond.; BA Oxf. 1987, MA 1992; DRCOG 1993. Trainee GP Basildon.

HARTREY, Rachel 20 Henry Street, Gloucester GL1 3DZ Tel: 01452 311943 — MB BCh 1986 Wales; FRCA 1993; DCH RCP Lond. 1990. (Univ. Wales Coll. Med.) Sen. Regist. (Anaesth.) Soton. Gen. Hosp. Socs: FRCA; Assn. Anaesth. GB & Irel.; BMA. Prev: Regist. (Anaesth.) Gt. Ormond St. Hosp. Childr. NHS Trust; Research Regist. Derriford Hosp. Plymouth; Regist. (Anaesth.) Cheltenham Gen. Hosp.

HARTRIDGE, Gerald Beech Cottage, Kedlock Feus, Cupar — MB BChir 1945 Camb.; MRCS Eng. LRCP Lond. 1944; DPM Eng. 1969.

HARTROPP, Philip Yaxley Group Practice, Yaxley Health Centre, Landsdowne Road, Yaxley, Peterborough PE7 3JL Tel: 01733 240478 Fax: 01733 244645 — BM 1976 Soton.; FRCGP 1992, M 1980. Macmillan GP Facilitator, P'boro. Prev: GP Adviser NW Anglia HA.

HARTSHORN, Clive Richard Alton Street Surgery, Alton Street, Ross-on-Wye HR9 5AB Tel: 01989 563646 Fax: 01989 769438; 4 The Orchard, Ross-on-Wye HR9 7BP Tel: 01989 564796 — BM BCh 1971 Oxf.; MA Oxf. 1971; MRCGP 1976; DObst RCOG 1974. (Oxford)

HARTSHORN, Julie 38 Linden Way, Boston PE21 9DS — MB BS 1988 Lond.

HARTSILVER, Emma Louise 39 Somerset Street, Kingsdown, Bristol BS2 8LY Tel: 0117 907 9007 Fax: 0117 904 0754 Email: emma.hartsilver@pointblank1.demon.co.uk — MB ChB 1991 Birm.; ChB Birm. 1991; DA (UK) 1995; FRCA 1997. (Univ. Birm.) Specialist Regist. (Anaesth.) S. W. Bristol Sch.; Clin. Research Fell. Univ. of Bristol Sir Humphry Davy Dept. of Anaesth.

HARTSTONE, Roger Eric 47 Pound Lane, Marlow SL7 2AZ Tel: 01628 483405 — BM BCh 1993 Oxf.; BA (Physiol. Sci.) Oxf. 1992, BM BCh 1993. Trainee GP E. Berks. VTS. Prev: Ho. Surg. Liver Unit. Qu. Eliz. Hosp. Birm.; Ho. Phys. Stoke Mandeville Hosp. Aylesbury.

HARTT, Antony Stedman Greenaway House, 76 Kingsgate Avenue, Broadstairs CT10 3LW Tel: 01843 224280 — MB BS (Hnrs. Obst. & Gyn.) Lond. 1958; DObst RCOG 1960. (St. Thos.) p/t Clin. Asst. Dept.Oncol.QEQM Hosp. Thanet. Prev: Ho. Surg. ENT & Ho. Phys. O & G St. Thos. Hosp. Lond.; Ho. Phys. St. Jas. Hosp. Balham.

HARTUNG, Thomas Kurt Orpington Hospital, New Flat 10, Sevenoaks Road, Orpington BR6 9JU — State Exam Med 1990 Gottingen.

HARTWELL, Mr Rudolf Thomas Rivers Medical Centre, High WychRoad, Sawbridgeworth CM21 0HH Tel: 01279 600282; Park House, 19 Pishiobury Drive, Sawbridgeworth CM21 0AD Tel: 01279 722435 — MB BS 1962 Lond.; FRCS Ed. 1972; MRCS Eng. LRCP Lond. 1962; FRCOG 1980, M 1967; T(OG) 1991. (King's Coll. Hosp.) Cons. O & G P.ss Alexandra Hosp. Harlow. Socs: Fell. Roy. Soc. Med. Prev: Regist. (O & G) Lond. Hosp.; SHO (Obst.) Qu. Charlotte's Hosp. Lond.; Ho. Off. (O & G) Radcliffe Infirm. Oxf.

***HARTWRIGHT, David** Gordons Farm, Church Lane, Tibberton, Droitwich WR9 7NW — MB ChB 1994 Birm.

HARTY, David Spencer Clipsley Lodge, Haydock, St Helens WA11 0ST — MB ChB 1966 Liverp.; DMRD 1969. (Liverp.) Cons. Radiol. Ashworth Hosp. Maghull; Locum Cons. Radiol. Univ. Hosp. Aintree. Socs: Roy. Coll. Radiol. Prev: Med. Off. Haydock Pk. Racecourse; Sen. Regist. (Radiol.) Roy. Infirm. Liverp.; Sen. Regist. (Neuroradiol. & Radiol.) Walton Hosp. Liverp.

HARTY, John Christian Renal Unit, Daisy Hill Hospital, 5 Hospital Rd, Newry BT35 8DR Email: penal.unit.edhh@ni.nhs.uk — MB BCh BAO 1987 NUI; MRCP Edin. 1990; MD NUI 1996. (Dublin) Cons. Nephzologist, Daisy Hill Hosp., Newry, Co. Down. Socs: Brit. Renal Assn.; Eur. Dialysis & Transpl. Assn.

HARTY, Mary Anne Bracton Teambase, Bexley Hospital, Old Bexley Lane, Bexley DA5 2BW Tel: 01322 294300 — MB BCh BAO 1989 NUI; MSc (Ment. Health Studies) NUI 1996; LRCPSI 1989; MRCPsych 1995; MRCGP 1994; DCH RCPI 1992; DRCOG 1992. Specialist Regist. (Forens. Psychiat.) Maudsley Higher Train. Scheme.

HARTY, Siobhan Marie Parkfield Health Centre, Sefton Road, New Ferry, Wirral CH62 5HS Tel: 0151 644 6665 — MB ChB 1990 Liverp.; MRCGP 1995. (Liverp)

HARUN, Shabbir 27 Windmill Lane, Epsom KT17 3AE Tel: 020 8393 6663 — MB BS 1991 Lond. (St. Bart.) SHO (Ophth.) Roy. Lond. & Moorfields Eye Hosp. Socs: Med. Protec. Soc. Prev: SHO (Neurosurg.) Roy. Lond. Hosp.; SHO (Cas.) Guy's Hosp. Lond.; Demonst. (Anat.) Qu. Mary & W.field Coll. Lond.

HARUNARASHID, Hanafiah 29A St Patricks Square, Edinburgh EH8 9EY — MB ChB 1993 Ed.

HARVAIS, Georges Roland Chamarel, Main St., Rhynie, Huntly AB54 4HB — MB ChB 1957 Aberd. Prev: Ho. Off. City Hosp. Aberd.; Ho. Surg. Aberd. Roy. Hosp. Sick Childr.

HARVATT, Celia (retired) 5 Knightsbridge Close, Tunbridge Wells TN4 9QN — BM BCh 1960 Oxf.; DObst RCOG 1962; DCH Eng. 1966. Prev: SCMO Tunbridge Wells HA.

HARVERD, Leora Batia Temple Fortune Health Centre, 23 Temple Fortune Lane, London NW11 7TE Tel: 020 8458 4431 Fax: 020 8731 8257 — MB BS 1992 Lond.

***HARVERSON, Andrew David** Applegate, 716 Galleywood Road, Chelmsford CM2 8BY; 716 Galleywood Road, Chelmsford CM2 8BY Tel: 01245 287366 — MB BS 1998 Lond.; MB BS Lond 1998.

HARVERSON, Angela Rosemary Victoria 716 Galleywood Road, Chelmsford CM2 8BY — MB BS 1969 Lond.; MRCS Eng. LRCP Lond. 1969; DRCOG 1970; DCH RCP Lond. 1971. Community Med. Off. Mid Essex HA.

HARVERSON, Godfrey X-Ray Department, Broomfield Hospital, Broomfield, Chelmsford CM1 7ET Tel: 01245 440761; Applegates, 716 Galleywood Road, Chelmsford CM2 8BY Tel: 01245 287366 — MB BS 1963 Lond.; MRCP Lond. 1968; MRCS Eng. LRCP Lond. 1963; FRCR 1975; FFR 1974; DTM & H RCP Lond. 1966. Cons. Radiol. Chelmsford Hosps. Gp. Socs: Brit. Inst. Radiol. & Brit. Nuclear Med. Soc. Prev: Med. Miss. Manorom Christian Hosp. Thailand; Sen. Regist. (Radiodiag.) United Bristol Hosp.; Regist. (Med.) Mt. Vernon Hosp. N.wood.

HARVEY, Mr Adam John The Old Vicarage, Main St., Newbold, Rugby CV21 1HH Tel: 01788 572192 — MB BCh 1994 Wales; FRCS (ED) 1999. (Univ. Wales Coll. Med.) SHO Orthop. - Shrewsbury.

HARVEY, Adrian Robert 8 Sandringham Close, Chandlers Ford, Eastleigh SO53 4LE — MB BS 1991 Lond.

HARVEY, Alexandra Claire — MB BS 1997 (Hons.) Lond.; DFFP 1999; DRCOG 2001; DCH 1999; MA Cantab. 1998. (Imperial Coll.

Sch. Med.) Gen. Practitioner, Lond.; Riverside Family Plann. Doctor, GP in St Mary's Paddington, A & E. Socs: BMA. Prev: GP Regist., Ashville Survey, Fulham Feb 2001- Sep 2001; SHO Obst. & Gynacology Aug 2000 - Feb 2001; SHO Accid. & Emerg. Feb 2000 - Aug 2000.

HARVEY, Alison Jane McIntosh, Trounce and Harvey, Health Centre, Orchard Way, Chillington, Kingsbridge TQ7 2LB Tel: 01548 580214 Fax: 01548 581080 — BM 1990 Soton.; MRCGP 1995.

HARVEY, Amanda Jane Manorside, Bosham Lane, Bosham, Chichester PO18 8HP — MB ChB 1991 Bristol.

HARVEY, Andrea Margaret Richmond Penthouse, 14 Crown Gardens, Glasgow G12 9HL — MB ChB 1990 Glas.

HARVEY, Andrew Mark AON Health Solutions, 2 Circus Place, London Wall, London EC2M 5RS Tel: 020 76280523 Fax: 020 76280498 Email: mark.harvey@aers.aon.co.uk; 13-15 High Street, Shipston-on-Stour CV36 4AB — MB BS 1983 Lond.; MRCGP 1990; FRCA 1988; Dip. Occ. Med. 1998. (LHMC) Regional Director, (S.) AON Health Solutions; Med. Adviser, Freshfields Bruckhaus Deringer; Med. Adviser, Allen & Overy; Med. Adviser, LinkLa.rs & Alliance. Socs: BMA; SOM; Indep. Doctors Forum. Prev: Trainee GP Shipston on Stour; Regist. (Anaesth.) Lond. Hosp.; Research Fell. Nuffield Dept. Anaesth. Oxf.

HARVEY, Andrew Roger Pontefract General Infirmary, Friarwood Lane, Pontefract WF8 1PL Tel: 01977 606137 Fax: 01977 606136 — MB ChB 1974 Sheff.; MD Sheff. 1989; FRCP Lond. 1994; MRCP (UK) 1979. Cons. Rheum. Pontefract. Gen. Infirm. NHS Trust. Prev: Cons. Rheum. & Rehabil. St. Jas. Hosp. Leeds & Leeds Community Health Trust.

HARVEY, Angela Marie 6 Thornhill Road, Leek ST13 8HN — MB ChB 1998 Leeds.

HARVEY, Ann Elizabeth (retired) 31 Brookfield Avenue, London W5 1LA — MB ChB 1960 Glas.

HARVEY, Ann Jill Nora Department of Anaesthesia, Royal Cornwall Hospital's Trust, Truro TR1 3LJ Tel: 01872 250000 — MB ChB 1987 Bristol; FRCA 1994; DCH. (Bristol) Cons. Anaesth.

HARVEY, Brian Robert 35 Hilderstone Road, Meirheath, Stoke-on-Trent ST3 7NU Tel: 01782 393026 — MB ChB Leeds 1958. (Leeds) Socs: BMA. Prev: Ho. Off. Gen. Surg. & Obst. St. Jas. Hosp. Leeds; Sen. Ho. Off. Orthop. Roy. Infirm. Huddersfield.

***HARVEY, Carl Jonathan** 54 Lady Byron Lane, Knowle, Solihull B93 9AY — MB ChB 1998 Birmingham.

HARVEY, Carol Lesley Tel: 0151 291 1357 — MB ChB 1983 Liverp.; MRCPsych 1987; MBA O.U. 1999. Prev: Cons. Psychiat. Learning Disabil. St. Helens & Knowsley Community Health NHS Trust.; Sen. Regist. Rotat. (Psychiat. of Ment. Handicap) Mersey RHA.; Clin. Dir.

HARVEY, Caroline Maria Doctors' Mess, Derbyshire Royal Infirmary N H S Trust, London Road, Derby DE1 2QY — BM BS 1998 Nottm.; BM BS Nottm 1998.

HARVEY, Christopher James Flat 5, Block J, Peabody Est., Horseferry Road, London SW1P 2EN Tel: 020 7799 1572; 68b winsham Grove, Clapham, London SW11 6NE — MB BS 1989 Lond.; BSc (Phys.) Lond. 1986; MRCP (UK) 1992; FRCR 1998. (Charing Cross/Westminster) Research.Fell.Hammersmith Hosp. Lond. Prev: SHO (Med.) St. Thos. Hosp. Lond., Hammersmith Hosp. Lond. & John Radcliffe Hosp. Oxf.; Reg.ITU St Thomas Hosp.Lond.

HARVEY, Claire Louise Denby, Cuckmere Road, Seaford BN25 4DE — MB BS 1998 Lond.; MB BS Lond 1998.

HARVEY, Mr Colum Francis Mater Hospital, Belfast; 56 Richmond Court, Lisburn BT27 4QX — MB BCh BAO 1975 Belf.; FRCS Ed. 1979; FRCS Irel. 1995; MA Belf. 1997. Cons. Surg. (Gen. & Vasc. Surg.) Mater Hosp. Belf.; Examr. Surg. QMB & RCS in Irel.; Hon.Clin.Lec. In Surg. QUB. Socs: Vasc. Surg. Soc. of GB & Irel.; Assn. Surg.; Med. Ethics Forum (NI). Prev: Clin. Dir. Surg. Mater Hosp.

HARVEY, David Cosmo Morris Department of Anaesthetics, Chase Farm Hospital, The Ridgeway, Enfield EN2 8JL Tel: 020 8366 9152; 52 Clay Hill, Enfield EN2 9AW — MB BS 1975 West Indies; FRCA 1982. Cons. Anaesth. Chase Farm Hosp. Middlx.

HARVEY, David John Department of Radiology, Singleton Hospital, Sketty, Swansea SA2 8QA Tel: 01792 285503 Fax: 01792 286088 Email: d.j.harvey@swan.ac.uk — BM BCh 1987 Oxf.; MSc Lond. 1984; MA Oxf. 1983; MRCP (UK) 1990; FRCR 1995. (Oxf.) Cons. Radiol. Swansea NHS Trust. Socs: Brit. Inst. Radiol. (Chairm. IT Comm.). Prev: Sen. Regist. (Radiol.) Welsh Train. Scheme Cardiff; Regist. (Radiol.) Univ. Hosp. Wales Cardiff; SHO Rotat. (Med.) Newc. HA.

HARVEY, Professor David Robert Dept of Paediatrics, Faculty of Medicine, Imperial College Hammersmith Hospital Campus, Du Cane Road, London W12 0NN Tel: 020 8383 3275 Fax: 020 8748 2378 Email: davidharvey@compuserve.com; 2 Lord Napier Place, Upper Mall, London W6 9UB Tel: 020 8748 7900 Fax: 020 8748 2378 — MB BS (Hons.) Lond. 1960; FRCP Lond. 1976, M 1963; MRCS Eng. LRCP Lond. 1960; DCH Eng. 1963; DObst RCOG 1962; FRCPCH 1996. (Guy's) Prof. Paediat. & Neonat. Med. Imperial Coll; Hon. Cons. Paediat. Qu. Charlotte's & Chelsea Hosp. & Hammersmith Hosp.; Edr. Matern. & Child Health & Postgrad. Doctor; Edr-in-Chief Early Human Developm. Socs: Neonat. Soc.; Brit. Paediat. Assn.; Eur. Soc. Paediat. Research. Prev: Ho. Phys. Hosp. Sick Childr. Gt. Ormond St. & Guy's Hosp. Lond.; Cons. Paediat. St. Mary's Hosp. Lond.

HARVEY, Mr David Robert North Devon District Hospital, Raleigh Park, Barnstaple EX31 4JB Tel: 01271 311672 Fax: 01271 311541; Tel: 01271 311672 Fax: 01271 311541 Email: david.harvey@ndevon.swest.nhs.uk — MB BS Lond. 1966; FRCS Eng. 1972; MRCS Eng. LRCP Lond. 1966. (Char. Cross) Cons. Surg. N. Devon Dist. Hosp.; Hon. Surg. Tutor Char. Cross & W.m. Med. Schs. Lond. Socs: Brit. Assn. Surg. Oncol.; Vasc. Surg. Soc. GB & Irel.; Assn. Surg. Gt Brit & Ire. Prev: Sen. Surg. Regist. & Hon. Surg. Tutor Char. Cross Hosp. & Med. Sch.; Clin. Research Fell. Char. Cross Hosp. Lond.; Sen. surg. Regist. W. Middlx. Hosp. Lond.

HARVEY, Deborah Jayne Willaston Surgery, Neston Road, Willaston, South Wirral CH64 2TN Tel: 0151 327 4593 Fax: 0151 327 8618 — MB BS 1992 Lond.; DRCOG 1996. (King's Coll. Lond.) Partner GP. Prev: SHO (Psychiat.) Clatterbridge Hosp.; SHO (Psychiat.) Fazaherley Hosp.; GP Trainee Chester.

HARVEY, Derek, OBE (retired) Lancefield House, St Saviours Lane, Padstow PL28 8EB Tel: 01841 532260 Fax: 01841 533130 — MB BS Lond. 1953; MRCS Eng. LRCP Lond. 1952; AFOM RCP Lond. 1982. Prev: Med. Dir. Jt. Oil Companies Clinic Sana'a, RePub. of Yemen.

HARVEY, Diane Mary Barnet Hospital, Wellhouse Lane, Barnet EN5 3DN Tel: 020 8216 4383 Fax: 020 8216 4509; 174 Harrow View, Harrow HA1 4TL — MD 1988 Leeds; MB ChB Leeds 1978; FRCP 1997; MRCP (UK) 1982; MRCPath 1989; FRCPath 1998. Cons. Haemat. WellHo. Trust Barnet.

HARVEY, Dolores Josefina 1 College Avenue, Melton Mowbray LE13 0AB Tel: 01664 68023 — MB ChB 1984 Leeds; DRCOG 1987. Prev: GP Syston, Leics. Retainer Scheme; GP Leicester; Trainee GP Mansfield VTS.

HARVEY, Elizabeth Margaret (retired) 11 Windsor Park, Dereham NR19 2SU Tel: 01362 693846 — MRCS Eng. LRCP Lond. 1939.

HARVEY, Emma Louise 51 Harding Road, Ryde PO33 1EQ Tel: 01983 563207 — MB BS 1996 Lond.; BSc (Physiol. with Basic Med. Sci) 1993. (St. Geo.) SO (Accd. & Emerg.) St Mary's Hosp. I. of Wight. Prev: Ho. Off. (Gen. Med.) Hants. Hosp. Basingstoke.

HARVEY, Felicity Ann Hope 45 Streathbourne Road, London SW17 8QZ Tel: 020 8682 3358 — MB BS 1980 Lond.; Dip. Clin. Microbiol. Lond 1983. (St. Bart.) Lect. Dept. Med. Microbiol.Kings Coll. Hosp. Lond. Prev: Ho. Surg. Essex Co. Hosp.; Lect. Dept. Med. Microbiol. Lond. Hosp.; Ho. Phys. St. Bart. Hosp.

HARVEY, Frances Margaret Keith 19 Hillview Terrace, Edinburgh EH12 8RB — MB ChB 1988 Aberd.

HARVEY, George Mackay Glebe Cottage, Manse Brae, Dalserf, Larkhall ML9 3BN — MB ChB 1971 Glas.; FFA RCS Eng. 1975.

HARVEY, Georgina Claire 22 Larkfield Close, Greenmount, Bury BL8 4QJ — MB ChB 1997 Manch. Ho. Off. (Orthop.) Manch. Roy. Infirm. Prev: Med. Ho. Off. Stepping Hill Hosp. Stockport.

HARVEY, Gillian Mary The Health Centre, High St., Dronfield S18 1PD Tel: 01246 412242; Norville, 9 Pk Avenue, Dronfield S18 2LQ Tel: 01246 417892 — MB ChB 1976 Sheff.; MA Oxf. 1981, BA 1973; MRCGP 1980; DRCOG 1979; Cert JCC Lond. 1979. Socs: Chesterfield Med. Soc. Prev: Trainee GP Chesterfield VTS; Ho. Phys. N.. Gen. Hosp. Sheff.; Asst. Cas. Off. Roy. Infirm. Sheff.

HARVEY, Graham Department of Medical Microbiology, Royal Liverpool University Hospital, Prescot St., Liverpool L7 8XP Tel: 0151

706 4410 Fax: 0151 706 5849; 20 Broadlake, Willaston, South Wirral CH64 2XB Tel: 0151 327 6066 — MB ChB 1983 Birm.; BSc (Cellular Path.) Bristol 1978; DRCPath 1994. Sen. Regist. (Med. Microbiol.) Mersey Region. Socs: Brit. Soc. Antimicrob. Chemother.; Brit. Soc. Study of Infec. Prev: Regist. (Clin. Microbiol.) Aberd. City Hosp.; Med. Off. Brit. Antarctic Survey.

HARVEY, Guy Thomas Priority Healthcare Wearside (NHS Trust), Cherry Knowle Hospital, Ryhope, Sunderland SR2 0NB Tel: 0191 569 9591 Fax: 0191 569 9593 — MB ChB Ed. 1988; MRCPsych 1992; Dip. Geriatric Med. 1993. (Edinburgh)

HARVEY, Harriet Riggall (retired) 15 Blueberry Gardens, Coulsdon CR5 2SX Tel: 020 8668 7094 — MB ChB 1953 Ed. Prev: GP Old Coulsdon.

HARVEY, Ian Rehabilitation Service, Springfield Hospital, 61 Glenurnie Road, London SW17 7DJ Tel: 0208 682 6692 Fax: 0208 682 6708 — MB ChB 1979 Ed.; MSc Manch. 1986; MD Ed. 1991; MRCPsych 1985. Cons. Psychiat.S W & St Geo.'s Ment. Health NHS Trust.

HARVEY, Mr Ian Alexander Countess of Chester Hospital NHS Trust, Liverpool Road, Chester CH2 1UL Tel: 01244 366288 — MB ChB 1981 Liverp.; MChOrth Liverp. 1989; FRCS (Orth.) Ed. 1993; FRCS Ed. 1985. Cons. Orthop. Surg. Countess of Chester Hosp. NHS Trust. Socs: Fell.of Brit. Orthopaedic Assoc.; Brit. Elbow & Shoulder Soc. Prev: Sen. Regist. (Orthop.) Mersey Region; Dow Corning Hand Fell. Wrightington Hosp. for Jt. Dis. Appley Bridge.

HARVEY, Professor Ian Morris School of Medicine, Health Policy and Practice, University of East Anglia, Norwich NR4 7TJ Tel: 01603 593605 Fax: 01603 593604 Email: ian.harvey@uea.ac.uk — MB BCh 1982 Wales; BA Camb. 1979; MRCP (UK) 1985; MFPHM 1989; FFPHM 1995; PhD Wales 1996; FRCP 1998. (University of Wales College of Medicine) Prof. Epidemiol. & Pub. Health Univ. of E. Anglia; Hon. Cons. Norf. & Norwich NHS Trust; Hon. Cons. E. Norf. HA. Socs: Internat. Epidemiol Assn.; Soc. Social Med., Treas.; Acad. Regist., Fac. of Pub. Health Med. Prev: Sen. Lect. (Pub. Health Med.) Univ. of Bristol; Wellcome Trust Lect. (Epidemiol.) Univ. of Wales Coll. of Med.; Sen. Lect. (Pub. Health Med.) Univ. of Wales Coll. of Med.

HARVEY, James Richard 46 Claremont Road, Newcastle upon Tyne NE2 4AN — MB BS 1998 Newc.; MB BS Newc 1998.

HARVEY, Jane Marie 1 Bank Street, Broadbottom, Hyde SK14 6AY Tel: 01457 766751 — MB ChB 1991 Manch.; BSc (Hons.) Manch. 1988, MB ChB 1991; DFFP 1993. Clin. Med. Off. (Family Plann. & Reproduc. Health) N. Mersey NHS Trust.; Researcher Postgrad. Dept. Manch. Univ. Prev: SHO (O & G) St. Mary's Hosp. Manch.

HARVEY, Janina Maria Falkirk & District Royal Infirmary NHS Trust, Major's Loan, Falkirk FK1 5QE Tel: 01324 624000 — MB ChB 1968 Glas.; FRCOG 1992, M 1977; DObst RCOG 1971. Cons. Genitourin Med. Forth Valley HB; Hon. Sen. Clin. Lect. Univ. Glas. Socs: Med. Soc. Study VD; Eur. Assn. Gyn. & Obst.; Assn. Genitourin. Med. Prev: Sen. Regist. (Genitourin. Med.) Gtr. Glas. HB; Regist. (O & G) S.. Gen. Hosp. Glas. & Glas. Roy. Matern. Hosp.

HARVEY, Mr Jason Roy 17 Wainwright Gardens, Hedge End, Southampton SO30 2NF Tel: 01489 797603 Email: jason@999harvey.freeserve.co.uk; 17 Wainwright Gardens, Hedge End, Southampton SO30 2NF Tel: 01489 797603 — MB BS 1992 Lond.; FRCS Ed. 1997. Specialist Regist. (Orthop.) Wessex. Prev: Ho. Phys. Ashford Hosp. Middlx.

HARVEY, Jo-Anne Elizabeth Grant 115 Dene Road, Wylam NE41 8EZ — MB BS 1983 Newc.

HARVEY, Joanne Elizabeth 11 Wellington Road, Pakstone, Poole BH14 9LF — MB BS 1989 Lond.; MRCGP 1994; DFFP 1994; DRCOG 1993; DCH RCP Lond. 1992. (King's Coll. Hosp.) GP; Clin. Asst. BrE. Clinic Poole Gen. Hosp.

HARVEY, John Anthony Dove River Practice, Gibb Lane, Sudbury, Ashbourne DE6 5HY Tel: 01283 812455 Fax: 01283 815187 — MB BS 1962 Lond.; MRCS Eng. LRCP Lond. 1962. (St. Bart.) Socs: BMA. Prev: Ho. Surg. & Ho. Phys. Roy. Berks. Hosp. Reading; Flight Lt. RAF Med. Br.

HARVEY, John Douglas States of Jersey Health Social services, Public Health Sevices Le Bas Centre, St Saviours Road, St Helier, Jersey JE1 4HR Tel: 01534 623708 Fax: 01534 623720 Email: j.harvey@gov.je — MB BChir 1971 Camb.; MSc Community Med. Lond. 1983. Dir. Pub. Health Serv.s/ Med. Off. of Health. Prev: Cons.Pub.Health.Med. States of Jersey HSS; Cons. Pub. Health Med. Newc. HA; Dir. (Pub. Health) Newc. & N. Tyneside HA.

HARVEY, John Ellis Department of Medicine, Southmead Hospital, Bristol BS10 5NB Tel: 0117 959 5284 Fax: 0117 959 6015 Email: harvey_j@southmead.swest.nhs.uk; 43 Florence Park, Bristol BS6 7LT Tel: 0117 942 1201 — MB BS 1971 Lond.; MD Lond. 1981; FRCP Lond. 1990; MRCP (UK) 1974; DObst RCOG 1975. (Middlx.) Cons. Phys. S.mead HA. Socs: Europ. Resp Soc.; BMA & Brit. Thoracic Soc. Prev: Sen. Regist. (Med.) Bath Health Dist. & Bristol Roy. Infirm.; Research Fell. Soton. Univ. Hosps.; SHO Middlx. Hosp. Lond.

HARVEY, John Michael Latham House Medical Practice, Sage Cross Street, Melton Mowbray LE13 1NX Tel: 01664 854949 Fax: 01664 501825; 1 College Avenue, Melton Mowbray LE13 0AB — MB ChB 1984 Leeds; MB ChB Leeds l984; MRCP (UK) 1987; MRCGP 1992. Prev: Regist. (Gen. Med. & Nephrol.) Leicester Gen. Hosp.; SHO (Gen. Med.) Dudley Rd. Hosp. Birm.

HARVEY, John Nigel Randall Diabetes Unit, Gladstone Building, Maelor Hospital, Wrexham LL13 7TD Tel: 01978 727107 Fax: 01978 727134; The Birches, 6 Westminster Avenue, Chester CH4 8JB — MB ChB 1976 Leeds; 1986 MD Leeds; 1981 MRCP (UK); 1996 FRCP. Sen. Lect. (Diabetes, Endocrinol. & Metab.) Univ. Wales Coll. Med. Maelor Hosp. Wrexham. Prev: Sen. Regist. St. Jas. Univ. Hosp. Leeds; Fell. (Endocrin. Med.) Univ. S. Carolina, Chas.ton, USA.

HARVEY, Mr John Scott 22 Mill Road, Dinas Powys CF64 4BU — MB ChB 1968 Leeds; MPhil Leeds 1976, MB ChB 1968; FRCS Eng. 1975. (Leeds) Cons. Surg. Llandough Hosp. Penarth. Socs: Assn. Surgs. Gt. Brit. & Irel.; BMA. Prev: Sen. Regist. (Surg.) S. Glam. AHA (T); Surg. Regist. Clatyon & Pinderfields Hosps. Wakefield; Asst. Lect. Dept. Physiol. Leeds Univ.

HARVEY, Judith Helen (retired) — BM BCh 1985 Oxf.; DPhil Oxf. 1972; DRCOG 1987. Chairm. Bucks. LMC.

HARVEY, Julia Rachel Lidden Vean, 12 Donnington Road, Penzance TR18 4PQ Email: dene.julia@btinternet.com — MB BCh 1994 Wales; MRCPCH 1999.

HARVEY, Kathleen Elizabeth (retired) 163A Bath Road, Atworth, Melksham SN12 8JR Tel: 01225 702811 — MB BCh BAO 1950 NUI; DObst RCOG 1956. Prev: Clin. Med. Off. (Child Health) Bristol Frenchay Dist. HA.

HARVEY, Kenneth Charles Haygarth Doctors, Cottage Lane Medical Centre, Cottage Lane, Talgarth, Brecon LD3 0AE Tel: 01874 713000 Fax: 01874 713016; Maesgwyn, Trefecca, Brecon LD3 0PW Tel: 01874 711309 — MB BCh 1968 Wales; FRCGP 1986, M 1974; DCH Eng. 1971; DObst RCOG 1970. (Cardiff) Mem. Powys LMC. Prev: SHO (O & G) Roy. Gwent Hosp. Newport; Ho. Phys. (Child Health) United Cardiff Hosps.; Ho. Surg. Llandough Hosp. Penarth.

HARVEY, Kerry Jane 1 Hamilton Drive, Kelvinbridge, Glasgow G72 8JG — MB ChB 1996 Glas.

HARVEY, Laura Jayne 93 Beccles Drive, Barking IG11 9HY — MB ChB 1998 Leeds.

HARVEY, Leonard Pathology Department, Rotherham District General Hospital, Moorgate Road, Rotherham S60 2UD; Cameroth, 3 Kelgate, Mosborough, Sheffield S20 5EJ — MB ChB 1976 Sheff.; BA Oxf. 1973, MA 1981; FRCPath 1992, M 1982. Cons. Path. Rotherham Dist. Gen. Hosp.; Special Lect. (Osteo-Articular Path.) Nottm. Univ. Med. Sch.; Hon. Lect. (Path.) Sheff. Med. Sch. Prev: Cons. & Sen. Lect. Univ. Nottm.; Lect. (Path.) Univ. Sheff.; Ho. Phys. & Ho. Surg. N.. Gen. Hosp. Sheff.

HARVEY, Leonard Paul (retired) The Old Vicarage, Main St, Newbold-on-Avon, Rugby CV21 1HH Tel: 01788 572192 Fax: 01788 572192 Email: leonardharvey@doctors.org.uk — MB ChB 1960 Birm.; MRCS Eng. LRCP Lond. 1960; LLM 1992; FRCOG 1978, M 1965 DObst 1962. Cons. Gyn. Private Pract.; Ex-Chairm. Subcomm. on Specialist Train. Standing Comm. Doctors; Vice-Pres Standing Comm. of Euro Doctors (CPME); Past-Pres. Europ. Union Of Specialist Doctors (UEMS); Past-Pres. Advis. Comm. Med. Train. EC Commiss. & Europ. Prev: Sen. Regist. United Birm. Hosps. & W. Midl. RHA.

HARVEY, Liela Elizabeth Anne Hurst Nook Farm Cottage, Derbyshire Level, Glossop SK13 7PR — MB ChB 1962 Ed.

HARVEY, Malcolm Philip Shere Surgery and Dispensary, Gomshall Lane, Shere, Guildford GU5 9DR Tel: 01486 202066 Fax: 01486 202761; Feldemore Cottage, Holmbury-St-Mary, Dorking RH5 6NH Tel: 01306 731071 — MB BS 1974 Lond.; MRCGP 1990. GP Trainer Shere.; Course Organiser Guildford & Chertsey VTS; Extern. Examr. Univ. of Oxf.

HARVEY, Malcolm Smith, OBE (retired) 14 Mulberry Court, Stour St., Canterbury CT1 2NT Tel: 01227 463391 — MB ChB 1935 Ed.; FFCM 1973; DPH Ed. & Glas. 1937. Prev: Dist. Community Phys. Canterbury & Thanet Health Dist.

HARVEY, Margaret Taylor (retired) 17 The Byeway, Rickmansworth WD3 1JW Tel: 01923 711499 — MB ChB 1950 Glas.; DObst RCOG 1953.

HARVEY, Martyn Cedric Hendon Health Centre, 74-75 Toward Road, Sunderland SR2 8JG; 10 Cedars Crescent, Ashbrooke, Sunderland SR2 7SY Tel: 0191 564 2007 — MRCS Eng. LRCP Lond. 1974.

HARVEY, Mr Michael Harold Broomfield Hospital, Court Road, Broomfield, Chelmsford CM1 7ET Tel: 01245 514447 Fax: 01245 515250; Ladyhope House, Mill Lane, Broomfield, Chelmsford CM1 7BQ Tel: 01245 443871 — MB BS 1977 Lond.; MS Lond. 1988; FRCS Eng. 1983; FRCS Ed. 1982; MRCS Eng. LRCP Lond. 1977. Cons. Surg. Broomfield Hosp. Chelmsford; Clin. Director in Surrey. Socs: Assn. Surg.. & Assn. Endoscopic Surgs.; Assn. Upper G.I. Surg. Prev: Sen. Regist. W.m. Hosp.; Regist. United Norwich Hosps.; Research Fell. Univ. Missouri., USA.

HARVEY, Michael Robert Cuckfield Medical Centre, Glebe Road, Cuckfield, Haywards Heath RH17 5BQ Tel: 01444 458738 Fax: 01444 416714; 33 Willow Park, Haywards Heath RH16 3UA Tel: 01444 417924 — MB BS 1972 Lond.; DObst RCOG 1974. (St. Thomas') Hosp. Pract. (Urol.) P.ss Roy. Hosp. W. Sussex.; Chairm. W. Sussex MAAG. Prev: Trainee GP Hereford VTS.

HARVEY, Michael Stafford (retired) 21 The Paddock, Eaton Ford, St Neots, Huntingdon PE19 7SA Tel: 01480 476805 — MB BS Lond. 1965. Prev: SCMO Hinchingbrooke Health Care Trust.

HARVEY, Miriam Ruth Fairway, The Green, Pitminster, Taunton TA3 7AX — BM 1983 Soton.; MRCGP 1987. Staff Grade-Med. Som HA.

HARVEY, Nicholas James 121 Carisbrooke Road, Leicester LE2 3PG — MB ChB 1989 Leeds. Prev: Ho. Off. (Med.) Pinderfield Gen. Hosp.; Ho. Off. (Surg.) Wharfedale Gen. Hosp.

HARVEY, Nigel Everard Tower Farm, Offwell, Honiton EX14 9TN — MRCS Eng. LRCP Lond. 1950. (St. Mary's) Prev: Med. Off. Roy. Milit. Acad. Sandhurst & Staff Coll. Camberley; Examr. to Army in Hyg.; Res. Med. Off., Putney Hosp.

HARVEY, Norman Stewart Waterlow Unit, Camden & Islington Community NHS Trust, Highgate Hill, London N19 5NF; Suite 101, Unit 5, 1000 North Circular Road, London NW2 7JP — MB ChB 1974 Cape Town; MRCPsych 1983; MD Sheff. 1991; T(Psych) 1991.

HARVEY, Paul Bennett Park Cottage, 13 Church Road, Plymstock, Plymouth PL9 9AJ — MB BS 1971 Lond.; MRCS Eng. LRCP Lond. 1971; FRCA Eng. 1978; DA Eng. 1975. Cons. Anaesth. Plymouth Health Dist. Socs: Obst. Anaesth. Assn.

HARVEY, Paul Ransome Devonshire Green Medical Centre, 126 Devonshire Street, Sheffield S3 7SF Tel: 0114 272 1626 — MB BS 1973 Newc.

HARVEY, Penelope Jane Devonshire Green Medical Centre, 126 Devonshire Street, Sheffield S3 7SF Tel: 0114 272 1626 — MB ChB 1976 Sheff.; MPH Nottm. 1995.

HARVEY, Peter Douglas (retired) Ivy Cottage, Naunton, Cheltenham GL54 3AD Tel: 0145 15 576 — MRCS Eng. LRCP Lond. 1951; LDS RCS Eng. 1943. Prev: Orthodont. Asst. Guy's Hosp.

HARVEY, Peter Kenneth Philip 134 Harley Street, London Tel: 020 7486 8005 Fax: 020 7224 3905; 11 Huddleston Road, London N7 0RE — MB BChir Camb. 1966; MA Camb. 1966; FRCP Lond. 1983, M 1969; MRCS Eng. LRCP Lond. 1966. (Camb. & Middlx.) Emerit. Cons. Neurol. Roy. Free & Chase Farm Hosp. NHS Trusts; Hon. Sen. Lect. Roy. Free Med. Sch. Lond.; Hon. Cons. Neurol. UCH Lond.; Hon. Sen. Lect. Med. UCL. Socs: Fell. Roy. Soc. Med.; Assn. Brit. Neurols.; Acad. of Experts. Prev: Cons. Neurol. Roy. Free Hosp. & Chase Farm Hosp. NHS Trust; Med. Dir. Roy. Free Hosp. NHS Trust; Sen. Regist. & Regist. Nat. Hosp. Nerv. Dis. Qu. Sq. Lond.

HARVEY, Peter Russell The Crouch Oak Family Practice, 45 Station Road, Addlestone, Weybridge Tel: 01932 840123 — MB BChir 1982 Camb.; MA, MB BChir Camb. 1982; MRCGP 1986; DRCOG 1987.

HARVEY, Mr Peter Thomas Holt Medical Prctice, Jacob's Place, Holt NR11 6LR Tel: 01263 712461 Email: harvey.nanp@paston.co.uk — MB ChB 1984 Dundee; BMSc (Hons.) Dund 1981, MB ChB 1984; FRCS Eng. 1989; MRCGP 1992; Cert. Family Plann. JCC 1991. GP Holt Med. Pract.; GP Asst. Socs: Nat. Assn. Non Princip.s (Sec.); GP Comm.'s Non Princip. SubComm. (Dep. Chairm.). Prev: Trainee GP Norwich HA; SHO (O & G) Heath Rd. Hosp. Ipswich; SHO Rotat. (Surg.) Norwich HA.

HARVEY, Peter Wynne, VRD (retired) Wynnecroft, Kirkbeck Close, Brookhouse, Lancaster LA2 9JN Tel: 01524 770250 — MB ChB 1945 Manch.; MSc Salford 1972; DPath Eng. 1953; FCPath 1966, M 1963. Prev: Cons. Path. Lancaster Health Dist.

HARVEY, Philip (retired) 28 Rodway Road, London SW15 5DS Tel: 020 8788 9778 — MB BS Lond, 1941; MD Lond. 1946; FRCP Lond. 1975, M 1943; MRCS Eng. LRCP Lond. 1940. Prev: Cons. Phys. St. Stephen's Hosp. Lond.

HARVEY, Philip Arthur Tel: 01773 852482 — BM BS 1983 Nottm.; BMedSci Nottm. 1981; FRCOphth 1992, M 1990; MRCGP 1988; DRCOG 1988; Cert. Family Plann. JCC 1987. Indep. Cons. Socs: Amer. Soc. of Cataract & Refractive Surg.s; Europ. Soc. of Cataract & Refractive Surg.s. Prev: Regist. (Ophth.) Trent RHA.

HARVEY, Philip Walter (retired) 25 Sycamore Avenue, Hatfield AL10 8LZ Tel: 0170 72 64788 — MB BChir 1961 Camb. Prev: Clin. Med. Off. E. Herts. Health Dist.

HARVEY, Richard Fenwick Cavendish Lodge, 7 Percival Road, Clifton, Bristol BS8 3LE Tel: 0117 973 9050; 7 Windsor Terrace, Clifton, Bristol BS8 4LW Tel: 0117 922 5393 — MB BS Lond. 1963; MD Lond. 1971; FRCP Lond. 1980, M 1966; MRCS Eng. LRCP Lond. 1963. (Middlx.) Cons. Phys. & Clin. Dean Frenchay Hosp. Bristol; Sen. Lect. (Med.) Univ. Bristol; Clin. Dean Frenchay Hosp. Bristol. Socs: Brit. Soc. Gastroenterol. (Mem. Counc.); Assn. Phys.; Cossham Med. Soc. Prev: Research Fell. MRC Gastroenterol. Research Unit Centr. Middlx. Hosp. & Regist. (Med.) Middlx. Hosp. Lond.; Regist. Inst. Nuclear Med. Middlx. Hosp. Med. Sch. Univ. Lond.

HARVEY, Richard James Dementia Research Group, National Hospital for Neurology & Neurosurgery, Queen Square, London WC1N 3BG Tel: 020 7829 8773 Fax: 020 7209 0182 Email: r.harvey@dementia.ion.ucl.ac.uk; Upper Flat, 127 Aldersgate St, London EC1A 4JQ — MB BS 1988 Lond.; MRCPsych 1993; MD 1998. (St Mary's London) Dir. Research Alzheimers Dis. Soc; Sen. Lect. Instit. Neurol; Sen. Lect. Imperial coll. Lond. Socs: Fell. Roy. Soc. Med.; Brit. Assn. Psychopharmacol.; Brit. Neuropsychiat. Assn. Prev: Clin. Research Fell. Dementia Research Gp. St. Mary's Hosp. & Nat. Hosp. Neurol. & Neurosurg. Lond.; Lect. (Psychiat.) St. Mary's Hosp. Med. Sch. Univ. Lond.; Regist. Rotat. (Psychiat.) St. Mary's Hosp. Lond.

HARVEY, Robert Alexander Hamilton Cuckfield Medical Centre, Glebe Road, Cuckfield, Haywards Heath RH17 5BQ Tel: 01444 458738 Fax: 01444 416714; Little Broomies, Holford Manor Lane, Lewes BN8 4DU — MB BS 1986 Lond.; BSc Lond. 1983, MB BS 1986; DRCOG 1989. GP Cuckfield.; Clin. Asst. (A & E) Cuckfield Hosp. Prev: Trainee GP Cuckfield VTS.

HARVEY, Robert Anthony Trevithick Surgery, Basset Road, Camborne TR14 8TT Tel: 01209 716721 Fax: 01209 612488; Penvu House, 39 Trevu Road, Camborne TR14 7AQ Tel: 01209 613195 — MB ChB 1978 Leeds; LMCC 1990; DRCOG 1988; DFFP 1998. (Leeds) Prev: Family Pract. Anaesth. Hanna Alberta; GP Darfield, NZ; Regist. (Microbiol.) York Dist. Hosp.

HARVEY, Mr Robert Anthony Arrowe Park Hospital, Arrowe Park Road, Upton, Wirral CH49 5PE Tel: 0151 604 7358 Fax: 0151 604 7078 — MB ChB 1982 Liverp.; FRCS (Orth.) 1995; FRCS Glas. 1987; MRCS Eng. LRCP Lond. 1982. (Liverpool Uni.) Cons. Orthop. Surg. Arrowe Pk. Hosp. Socs: Brit. Trauma Soc.; Liverp. Med. Inst.; BOA. Prev: Sen. Regist. (Orthop. Surg.) N. Manch. Gen. Hosp., Manch..; MRC Research Fell. NWIRC Manch.

HARVEY, Mr Robert Brian Torbay Hospital, Eye Department, Lawes Bridge, Torquay TQ2 7AA; Palm Trees, Hesketh Road, Torquay TQ1 2LN Tel: 01803 299267 — MB BS 1979 Lond.; BSc (Hons.) Lond. 1976; FRCS Ed. 1992; FRCOphth. 1992; MRCGP

1984; DRCOG 1982. Staff Grade(Ophth.) Torbay Hosp. Torquay; Managing Dir. Palmtrees Med. Informatics Torquay. Prev: SHO (Ophth.) Bath & Barnstaple.
***HARVEY, Robert Stephen** Abbey House, Ashow, Kenilworth CV8 2LE — MB BCh 1994 Wales.
HARVEY, Roderick David Raigmore Hospital, Inverness IV2 3UJ Tel: 01463 704000 Fax: 01463 705460 Email: roderick.harvey@haht.scot.nhs.uk; Balnaculloch House, Ardersier, Inverness IV2 7QN Tel: 01667 461029 Fax: 01667 461099 Email: rod.harvey@ntlworld.com — MB BS 1982 Newc.; MA Oxf. 1987, BA 1979; MD Aberd. 1991; MRCP (UK) 1985; FRCP Glas. 1998; FRCP 1999 Edin. (Oxford/Newcastle upon Tyne) Cons. Phys. in Remote & Rural Med. Enodcrinol. & Diabetes, Highland Acute Hosps. Trust Raigmore Hosp. Inverness. Socs: Soc. Endrocrinol.; Diabetes UK. Prev: Cons. Phys. (Diabetes & Endocrinol.) Grampian Univ. Hosps. Trust Dr. Gray's Hosp. Elgin; Cons. Phys. (Diabetes & Endocrinol.) Roy. Cornw. Hosp. (Treliske) Truro; Lect. (Med.) Univ. Aberd.
HARVEY, Roger William Seaford Health Centre, Dane Road, Seaford BN25 1DH Tel: 01323 490022 Fax: 01323 492156; Denby, Cuckmere Road, Seaford BN25 4DE — MB BS 1972 Lond.; MRCGP 1978. (Char. Cross) Prev: Med. Off. RN.
HARVEY, Rosemary Anne Dorothy pattinson Hospital, Alumwell Close, Walsall WS2 9XH Tel: 01922 858000; 29 Norman Road, Walsall WS5 3QL Tel: 01922 25377 — MB BS 1957 Durh. (Newc.) Clin. Asst. & Med. Off. Dorothy Pattison Hosp. Walsall.
HARVEY, Ruth Mary New Road Surgery, 109 York Road, Chingford, London E4 8LF Tel: 020 8524 8124 Fax: 020 8529 8655; 10 Bosgrove, Chingford, London E4 6QT — MB BS 1988 Lond.; MRCGP 1992; DRCOG 1991. Prev: Trainee GP St. Albans VTS.
HARVEY, Simon Charles Stonegarth, Church St., Broughton-in-Furness LA20 6HJ — MB ChB 1992 Manch.
HARVEY, Stephen George The Castle Medical Centre, 22 Bertie Road, Kenilworth CV8 1JP Tel: 01926 857331 Fax: 01926 851070; Abbey House, Ashow, Kenilworth CV8 2LE Tel: 01926 852543 — MB BS 1968 Lond. (Middlx.) Socs: BMA.
HARVEY, Timothy Corsellis 8 St Augustine's Road, Edgbaston, Birmingham B16 9JU Email: corsellis@aol.com — MB BS 1966 Lond.; FRCP Lond. 1983; MRCP (UK) 1970; MRCS Eng. LRCP Lond. 1966. (King's Coll. Hosp.) Cons. Phys. Walsall Hosp. Gp.; Research Fell. (Med.) Univ. Birm. Socs: Brit. Diabetic Assn. & Birm. Med. Research Expeditionary Soc. Prev: Lect. (Med.) Univ. Birm.; Regist. (Cardiol.) Radcliffe Infirm. Oxf.; Ho. Phys. Hammersmith Hosp. Lond.
HARVEY, Vincent Anderson Stanley Medical Centre, 60 Stanley Road, Kirkdale, Liverpool L5 2QA Tel: 0151 207 0126 — MB ChB 1969 Glas.
HARVEY, William James (retired) Old Mill Cottage, Cornhill-on-Tweed TD12 4RA Tel: 01890 883996 — MB ChB Ed. 1954.
HARVEY, William Richard Department of Anaesthesia, Royal Cornwall Hospital's Trust, Truro TR1 3LJ Tel: 01872 250000 Fax: 01872 252480 — MB ChB 1982 Cape Town; BSc (Zool.) Cape Town 1976; FRCA 1991. Lead Clinician Obst. Anaesth. Treliske Hosp. Truro. Socs: Underwater & Hyperbaric Med. Soc.; Assn. Anaesth.; BMA.
HARVEY, William Robert 32 Lislagan Road, Ballymoney BT53 7DD — MB BCh BAO 1968 Belf.; MRCOG 1972. (Belf.) Cons. (O & G) Route Hosp. Balleymoney. Prev: Sen. Tutor Roy. Matern Hosp. Belf.; Regist. (O & G) Route Hosp. Ballymoney & Mpilo African Hosp. Bulawayo, Rhodesia.
HARVEY-DODDS, Lucy Melissa 49 Woodfoot Road, Rotherham S60 3DZ — MB BS 1997 Newc.
HARVEY-HILLS, Mr Nicholas The Princess Margaret Hospital, Osborne Road, Windsor SL4 3SJ Tel: 01753 620116 Fax: 01753 620116 Email: harvey-hills@barclays.net; Withany, Heath Rise, Virginia Water GU25 4AX Tel: 01344 843979 — MB ChB 1966 Ed.; FRCS Eng. 1972. (Ed.) Cons. Urol. St. Peter's NHS Trust; Surgic. Tutor Guys & St. Thos. Med. Schs. Lond. Socs: Soc. Internat. D'Urlogie; Brit. Assn. of Urol. Surgs. Prev: Sen. Regist. & Research Sen. Regist. (Urol.) St. Thos.; Regist. (Gen. Surg.) St. Thos. Hosp. Lond.
HARVEY-SMITH, Edmund Andrew Hayes Grove Priory Psychiatric Hospital, Prestons Road, Hayes, Bromley BR2 7AS Tel: 020 8462 7722 Fax: 020 8462 5028; 33 Wolverton Avenue, Kingston upon Thames KT2 7QF Tel: 020 8546 5052 — MB BChir 1956 Camb.; MA Camb. 1956; MRCP Lond. 1962; FRCPsych 1982, M 1972; DPM Lond. 1966. (Westm.) The Priory Hosp. Hayes Gr., Preston's Rd., Hayes, Bromley; Chairm. Dist. Hosp. Med. Comm. Socs: Fell. BMA; Croydon Med. Soc.; Croydon Medico-Legal Soc. Prev: Sen. Regist. Maudsley Hosp.; Regist. W.m. Hosp. Lond. & Hammersmith Hosp. & Postgrad. Med. Sch. Lond.; Cons. Psychiat. Croydon & Warlingham Pk. Hosp. Gp., Portnalls Psychiat. Unit, FarnBoro. Hosp. & Hayes Gr. Priory Hosp. Kent.
HARVIE, Alison Kate The Health Centre, Byland Road, Skelton-in-Cleveland, Saltburn-by-the-Sea TS12 2NN Tel: 01287 650430 Fax: 01287 651268; 71 Roseberry Crescent, Great Ayton, Middlesbrough TS9 6EW Tel: 01642 722279 — MB ChB 1986 Aberd.; DRCOG 1990. Prev: Trainee GP Cleveland VTS.
HARVIE, Ann 21 Victoria Park Gardens N., Glasgow G11 7EJ Tel: 0141 339 1791 — MB ChB 1972 Glas.; MRCP (UK) 1978. Sen. Regist. (Paediat. & Community Child Health) Glas. Socs: MRCPCH; Scott. Paediat. Soc. Prev: Lect. (Paediat.); Regist. (Paediat.).
HARVIE, John Paul Aberdeen Royal Infirmary, Aberdeen AB25 2ZN Tel: 01224 681818 Email: j.harvie@abdn.ac.uk; 82 Burns Road, Aberdeen AB15 4NS Tel: 01224 318651 — MB ChB 1990 Glas.; MRCP (UK) 1993. Specialist Regist. Rheumat. & Gen. Med. Aberd. Roy. Infirm. NHS Trust.
HARVIE, Paul 15 Burgoyne Road, Sheffield S6 3QA — MB ChB 1997 Sheff.
HARWIN, Brian Gordon 6 Court Lane Gardens, Dulwich, London SE21 7DZ — MPhil Lond. 1970; MB ChB Birm. 1955; FRCPsych 1986, M 1973. p/t Cons. Psychiat. Hayes Gr. Priory Hosp. Hayes Kent. Prev: Cons. Psychiat. Ravensbourne Trust & Hon. Sen. Lect. Dept. of Psychiat. Med., Kings Coll. Hosp.; Sen. Lect. Inst. Psychiat; Hon. Cons. Bethlem & Maudsley Hosps.
HARWOOD, Anthony George, Col. late RAMC Lunesdale, Guildford Road, Woking GU22 7UT — MB BS 1957 Lond.; DTM & H Eng. 1959, DPH 1965, DIH 1966. (Char. Cross) Pk.es Prof. Preven. Med. RAMC; Cons. Adviser to Army in Occupat. Med. Prev: Head Army Occupat. Health Research Unit Apre FarnBoro..
HARWOOD, Catherine Anne 63 Sunnymede Drive, Ilford IG6 1JX — MB BS 1987 Lond.
HARWOOD, Daniel Michael James MAUDSLEY Hospital, London SE5 8AZ Tel: 020 7919 2195; 22 ONSLOW Drive, Thame OX9 3YY Tel: 01844 216570 — BM BS 1987 Nottm.; MRCPsych 1994. Specialist Regist. - Psychiat. Maudsley Hosp. Prev: Research Sen. Regist. (Psychiat.) Warneford Hosp. Oxf.; Regist. (Psychiat.) Haleacre Unit Amersham; SHO (Neurol.) St. Bart. Hosp. Lond.
HARWOOD, Elizabeth Jane Mooragh, Margaret Road, Blundellsands, Liverpool L23 6TR — MB ChB 1985 Liverp.; DFFP 1993; T(GP) 1991. GP Asst. Walton Liverp.; Family Plann. Clin. Med. Off. N. Mersey Community Trust. Socs: NW Soc. Family Plann. Prev: GP Asst. Aintree Liverp.; Trainee GP Alva Clackmannansh.; SHO (Paediat.) Birm. Childr. Hosp.
HARWOOD, George Neurosciences Unit, King's College Hospital, De Crespigny Park, Denmark Hill, London SE5 9RS — MB BS Lond. 1970; FRCP Lond. 1985, M 1975. (Middlesex Hospital) St. Bart. Hosp., Rochester & Medway Dist. Hosp. Gillingham & Neurosci. Unit King's Coll. Hosp. Lond. Prev: Cons. Neurol. Greenwich Dist Hosp. & Regional Neurol. Unit, Brook Hosp.; Sen. Regist. (Neurol.) Notts. AHA (T) & Neurol. Unit Derbysh. Roy. Infirm.; Regist. (Neurol.) Neurosci. Unit Brook Hosp. Woolwich.
HARWOOD, Janet Louise 10 Green Lane, Netherton, Wakefield WF4 4JD — MB ChB 1985 Leeds; DRCOG 1988; Cert. Family Plann. JCC 1989; T(GP) 1989. Clin. Med. Off. (Community Child Health) Huddersfield. Prev: Clin. Med. Off. (Child Health) Sheff. & Bradford; Trainee GP Bradford VTS.
HARWOOD, Jocelyn Mary The Folly, Folly Lane, Claxton, Norwich NR14 7AS — MB BS 1987 Lond.
HARWOOD, Paul John 52 Alder Drive, Hoghton, Preston PR5 0AD — MB ChB 1998 Leeds.
HARWOOD, Robert James The Folly, Folly Lane, Claxton, Norwich NR14 7AS — MB BS 1982 Lond.; DA 1987; FRCA 1990. (Middx) Cons. Anaesth. N+N Hosp. Socs: BMA; AAGBI.
HARWOOD, Rowan Harold Department Health Care of Elderly, A Floor East Block, University Hospital, Nottingham NG7 2UH Tel: 0115 924 9924 Ext: 42809 Fax: 0115 970 9947 Email: rowa.harwood@ntlworld.com — BM BCh 1985 Oxf.; MA Camb.

1986; MD Camb. 1996; MSc (Epidemiol.) Univ. Lond. 1993; MRCP (UK) 1988. (Oxf.) Cons. Phys. (Geriat.) Univ. Hosp. Nottm. Socs: Brit. Geriat. Soc.; Soc. Research in Rehabil.; Soc. Social Med. Prev: Hon. Sen. Regist. (Geriat.) & MRC Fell. Health Servs. Research Roy. Free Hosp. Lond.; Lect. (Health c/o Elderly) Lond. Hosp. Med. Coll.; Regist. (Gen. Med. & Health c/o Elderly) Univ. Hosp. Nottm.

HARWOOD-YARRED, Noel Henry 1 Fir Grove, Godalming GU7 1QX Tel: 01483 21122 — MRCS Eng. LRCP Lond. 1933; MA Camb., MB BChir 1933. (Camb. & St. Thos.) Local Treasury Med. Off. Socs: BMA. Prev: Clin. Asst. X-ray & Orthop. Depts. & Ho. Surg. ENT Dept. St. Thos.; Hosp.

HASAN, Abdul Kadir Hadi Department of Radiodiagnosis, Wycombe Hospital, High Wycombe HP11 2TT Tel: 01494 425195 Fax: 01494 425018; Tel: 01494 510317 Fax: 01494 510328 Email: kadirhasan@yahoo.co.uk — PhD Glas. 1989; MB ChB Mosul 1978; FRCR 1991 Lond. (Mosul. Univ.) Cons. Radiol. Wycombe Gen. High Wycombe; Cons. Radiol. childr. Hosp. Gt. Missenden; Manager, BrE. Screening, S. Bucks; Cons. Radiol. Shelbourne Hosp., High Wycombe. Socs: Brit. Inst. Radiol. & BMA; Europ. Soc. Uroradiol.; Radiol. Soc. of N. Amer. Prev: Cons. Radiol. Roy. Infirm. Dundee; Sen. Regist. (Radiodiagn.) Ninewells Hosp. Dundee; Regist. (Radiodiag.) Roy. Infirm. Glas.

HASAN, Abul High Road Surgery, 113 High Road, Loughton IG10 4JA Tel: 020 8508 9949 Fax: 020 8508 9961 — MB BS Rajshahi (Bangladesh) 1967. (Rajshahi) GP Loughton; Clin. Asst. (Orthop.) Whipps Cross Hosp. Socs: MDU. Prev: Regist. (Gen. Surg.) Bethnal Green Hosp. Lond.; Clin. Asst. (Vasc. Surg.) & Regist. (Orthop.) Roy. Lond. Trust.

HASAN, Ahmed Muzaffar (retired) 8 Grosvenor Road, South Shields NE33 3QQ Tel: 0191 455 5175 — MB BS 1951 Osmania; FRCP Glas. 1981, M 1964; MRCP Lond. 1968; MRCP Glas. 1964; LMSSA Lond. 1969. Prev: Cons. Phys. (Geriat. & Gen. Med.) S. Tyneside HA.

HASAN, Akhtar Ordsall Health Centre, Belfort Drive, Salford M5 3PP.

HASAN, Daulatun 25 Parkfields, Penyfai, Bridgend CF31 4NQ Tel: 01656 767328 — MB BS 1972 Dacca.

HASAN, Fadzilah Withington Hospital, Cavendish Road, Manchester M20 2LR — MB ChB 1993 Manch.

HASAN, Mr Faizul 24 Kensington Place, Newport NP19 8GP — MB BS 1986 Karachi; FRCS Ed. 1994.

HASAN, Mr Fazal Ali 43 Ridgmount Gardens, London WC1E 7AT — MB BS 1985 Lond.; MA Camb. 1986; FRCS Ed. 1989.

HASAN, Hasan Ilksen 122 Arcadian Gardens, London N22 5AE — MB BS 1993 Lond.

HASAN, Mr Husham Abdul Rezzak 2 Mount Road, London SW19 8ET — MB ChB 1968 Baghdad; FRCS Ed. 1983. Cons. Orthop Surg. Armed Forces Hosp. Saudi Arabia. Socs: FACS. Prev: Regist. (Orthop.) Vict. Hosp. Kirkcaldy & Mayday Hosp. Croydon.

HASAN, J R Handsworth Grange Medical Centre, 432 Handsworth Road, Sheffield S13 9BZ Tel: 0114 269 7505 Fax: 0114 269 8535.

HASAN, Kamrul 64 Settles Street, London E1 1JP — MB BS 1997 Lond.

HASAN, Khalid 280 Wigmore Road, Gillingham ME8 0LY — MB BS 1992 Lond.

HASAN, Khalida St Davids Court Surgery, 1 St. Davids Court, 68a Cowbridge Road East, Cardiff CF11 9DU Tel: 029 2030 0266 Fax: 029 2030 0273; 38 South Rise, Llanishen, Cardiff CF14 0RH Tel: 01222 756436 — MB BS 1969 Punjab; MB BS Punjab (Pakistan) 1969; LRCP LRCS Ed. LRCPS Glas. 1976. (Fatima Jinnah Med. Coll. Lahore) Prev: SHO (Med.) Derbysh. Roy. Roy. Infirm. Derby & Stobhill Gen. Hosp.; Glas.; Regist. (Geriat.) Profess. Unit Ruchill Hosp. Glas.

HASAN, Maan Abdul-Majid 107 Defoe House, Barbican, London EC2Y 8ND — MB ChB 1980 Baghdad; FRCA 1990.

HASAN, Mr Mahmud-Ul 5 Cromwell Crescent, Carlisle CA3 9NN — MB BS 1963 Punjab; FRCS Ed. 1973; FCOphth 1990; DO RCS Eng. 1966.

HASAN, Mehar Qamrul Jasmine, 32 Woodlands, Stalybridge SK15 Tel: 0161 338 4333 — MB BS 1956 Karachi; MRCOG 1964, DObst 1961; DTM & H Liverp. 1956. SCMO Manch. AHA(T).

HASAN, Meherunnisa 11 Cromwell Avenue, Cheshunt, Waltham Cross EN7 5DL Tel: 01992 24732 — MB BS 1962 Karachi; ECFMG Philadelphia 1977; DObst RCOG 1967; Assoc. Internat. Coll. Surgs. 1968. (Dow Med. Coll. Karachi)

HASAN, Merajuddin Child & Family Centre, Merthyr Road, Pontypridd CF37 4DD Tel: 01443 480540 Fax: 01443 480535; 38 South Rise, Llanishen, Cardiff CF14 0RH Tel: 01222 752942 — MB BS Peshawar 1969; LRCP LRCS Ed. LRCPS Glas. 1975; MRCPsych 1980; DPM Eng. 1975. (Khyber Med. Coll.) Cons. Child & Adolesc. Psychiat. Child & Family Centre Pontypridd; Asst. Med. Dir., Rhoudda Healthcare NHS Trust. Prev: Sen. Regist. (Child & Family Psychiat.) Roy. Hosp. Sick Childr. Glas.; Regist. (Psychiat.) Duke St. Hosp. Glas.; Med.dir.Rhonnda health Trust.

HASAN, Mr Mohammad Tahir Holmside House, 6 Holmside, Cumnock KA18 1AP — MB BS 1962 Karachi; FRCS Glas. 1969; FRCS Ed. 1969.

HASAN, Mohammed Ali Saddiquer Department of Ophthalmology, West Wales General Hospital, Carmarthen SA31 2AF Tel: 01267 235151; 9 Penybanc, Tanerdy, Carmarthen SA31 2HA — MB BS 1972 Rajshahi; MCOphth 1989; DO RCPSI 1979. Assoc. Specialist (Ophth.) W. Wales Gen. Hosp. Prev: Regist. (Ophth.) W. Wales Gen. Hosp.

HASAN, Muhammad Rizwan-Ul 2 Risedale House, Abbey Way, Barrow-in-Furness LA14 1BP Tel: 01229 832854 — MB BS 1985 Punjab, Pakistan; BSc Punjab, Pakistan 1988; FFA RCSI 1994. Staff Grade (Anaesth.) Furness Gen. Hosp. Prev: Regist. Rotat. (Anaesth.) St. Mary's Hosp. Lond.; SHO Walsgrave Hosp. Coventry; SHO Vict. Hosp. Blackpool.

HASAN, Mujtaba University Department of Geriatric Medicine, University of Wales, College of Medicine, Academic Centre, Llandough Hospital, Penarth CF64 2XX Tel: 01222 716986; 147 Cyncoed Road, Cyncoed, Cardiff CF23 6AG — MB BS 1982 Patna; MRCS Eng. LRCP Lond. 1988; MRCP (UK) 1988; MSc Wales 1998; MD Patna 1987. Sen. Lect. & Hon. Cons. Phys. (Geriat. Med.) Caerphilly Dist. Miner's Hosp. M. Glam.; Sen. Lect. Univ. Wales Coll. of Med. Prev: Sen. Regist. (Geriat. Med.) Glan Clwyd Dist. Gen. Hosp. NHS Trust; Regist. (Gen. Med.) Aberd. & Hon. Tutor Univ. Aberd.; SHO (Geriat. Med.) Burnley Gen. Hosp.

HASAN, Nadir Institute of Liver Studies, King's College Hospital, Denmark Hill, London SE5 9PJ Tel: 020 7737 4000 Fax: 020 8346 3167; 202 Casewick Road, West Norwood, London SE27 0SZ Tel: 020 7670 8031 — MB BS 1987 Karachi; MRCPath 1996; DRCPath 1994. (Dow Med. Coll. Karachi) Hon. Sen. Regist. & Clin. Lect. (Histopath.) Inst. Liver Studies King's Coll. Hosp. Lond. Socs: BMA; Path. Soc.; Assn. Clin. Path. Prev: Sen. Regist. & Regist. (Morbid Anat. & Histopath.) Roy. Lond. Hosp. & St. And. Hosp. Lond.; SHO (Histopath. & Clin. Path.) Lewisham Hosp. Lond.

HASAN, Noori Ubaid Department of Pathology, Whiston Hospital, Warrington Road, Prescot L35 5DR Tel: 0151 430 1190; 47 Wedgewood Gardens, St Helens WA9 5GA Email: n-hasan@hotmail.com — MB ChB 1981 Baghdad; MRCPath 1991. Cons. Histopath St Helen's & Knowsley NHS Trust. Socs: Internat. Acad. Path.; Overseas Doctors Assn.; Iraqi Med. Assn. Prev: Lect. (Histopath.) Univ. Aberd.; Regist. (Path.) Aberd. Roy. Infirm.

HASAN, Rafiq 58 Fieldend Road, London SW16 5SS — MB BS 1992 Lond.; BSc (Hons.) Lond. 1989, MB BS 1992. Ho. Phys. E. Birm. Hosp.

HASAN, Rumina Syeda 43 Rigmount Gardens, London WC1E 7AT — MB BS 1980 Lond.; PhD Lond. 1990; MSc Med. Microbiol. Lond. 1983; BSc Lond. 1977; MRCPth 1993. Cons. Microbiol. Aga Khan Univ. Karachi, Pakistan.

HASAN, Saadi Greyfriars Surgery, 25 St. Nicholas Street, Hereford HR4 0BH Tel: 01432 265717 Fax: 01432 340150 — MB BS 1985 Lond.; MRCGP 1990; DRCOG 1988; DCH 1989. Doctor attached to Hereford Drug Serv.; GP Tutor.

HASAN, Sabiha 35 Springhouse Lane, Ebchester, Consett DH8 0QF Tel: 01207 560488 — MB BS 1966 Bihar. (Darbhanga Med. Coll. Laheriasrai) SHO (Anaesth.) Shotley Bridge Gen. Hosp. Prev: SHO (Med.) Bideford & Dist. Hosp.; SHO (O & G) Hallam Hosp. W. Bromwich; SHO (Anaesth.) Stepping Hill Hosp. Stockport.

HASAN, Mr Shafqat 6 Gilbert Court, Upper Chaddlewood, Plympton, Plymouth PL7 2WW — MB BS 1987 Punjab; FRCS Ed. 1992.

HASAN, Sidra Qamar Saman Villa, 5 Cromwell Crescent, Carlisle CA3 9NN — MB ChB 1994 Dundee.

HASAN, Syed Keresley Road, 2 Keresley Road, Coventry CV6 2JD Tel: 024 7633 2628 Fax: 024 7633 1326 — MB BS 1962 Karachi. (Dow Med. Coll. Karachi) Late Med. Regist. Gen. Hosp. BromsGr.; Sen. Ho. Phys. Derbysh. Roy. Infirm. Derby; Sen. Ho. Phys. Coventry Hosps.

HASAN, Mr Syed Anees 44 Langley Crescent, Harlington, Hayes UB3 5HN — MB BS 1986 Punjab; FRCS Glas. 1993.

HASAN, Mr Syed Shabihul Royal Cornwall Hospital, Trelisek, Truro TR1 3LJ Tel: 01872 252736 Fax: 01872 252271 Email: syed.hasan@rcht.swest.nhs.uk; 22 Chainwalk Drive, Truro TR1 3ST Tel: 01872 240542 Email: syedhasan22@hotmail.com — MB BS Patna 1968; FRCS Glas. 1978. (Patna Med. Coll.) Cons. Thoracic Surg. Roy. Cornw. Hosp. (Treliske) Truro. Socs: Fell. Internat. Coll. Surgs.; Soc. Thoracic & Cardiovasc. Surgs. Gt. Brit.; Fell. Euro. Bd. of Cardiothoracic Surg. Prev: Sen. Regist. (Cardiothoracic Surg.) Gen. Infirm. & Killingbeck Hosp. Leeds.

HASAN, Syed Sibte Dept. of Neurosciences, York District Hospital, Wiggington Rd, York YO31 8HE Tel: 01904 454100 — MB BS 1980 Pakistan; MRCP (UK) 1990; MD 1998. Cons. (Clin. NeuroPhysiol.), York NHS Trust. Socs: Assn. of Brit. Clin. Neurophysiologists; Assn. of Brit. NeUrol.s; Internat. League Against Epilepsy. Prev: Research Fell. (Neurol.) Neuropsychiat. Unit. York Dist. Hosp.; Regist. Neurol., Leeds Teachg. Hosp.s.

HASAN, Mr Syed Tahseen Freeman Hospital, Newcastle upon Tyne NR7 7DN Tel: 0191 284 3111; 97 Jesmond Park West, Newcastle upon Tyne NE7 7BY — MB BS 1983 Karachi; FRCS Glas. 1988; FRCS (Urol.) 1996. Cons. Urol. Socs: MPS.

HASAN, Syeda Yasmin Husain 91 Eastwood Road, Leigh-on-Sea SS9 3AH — MB BS 1989 Lond.; MRCP Lond.1992; MRCPath. 1992. (King's College London) p/t Cons. Haematologist, Sandwell Hosp. W. Bromwich. Socs: Brit. Soc. of Haemat.; Roy. Coll. Pathologists.

HASAN, Y H Prescot Medical Centre, 4 Atherton Street, Prescot L34 5QN Tel: 0151 426 5277.

HASANIE, Naim Ul Haq Meltham Road Surgery, 9 Meltham Road, Lockwood, Huddersfield HD1 3UP Tel: 01484 432940 Fax: 01484 451423; 83 Lockwood Road, Lockwood, Huddersfield HD1 3QU — MB ChB 1990 Manch.; MRCP (UK) 1995; MRCGP 1995; DCH 1997; DRCOG 1998. (Manch.) GP Princip. Socs: MDU. Prev: Trainee GP/SHO (ENT & Paediat.) Huddersfield.

HASELDEN, Brigitte Marie Department of Allergy & Clinical Immunology, The National Heart & Lung Institute, Imperial College, Dovehouse St., London SW3 6LY Tel: 020 7351 8163; 60 Park Road, Hampton Wick, Kingston upon Thames KT1 4AY — MB BS 1990 Lond.; BSc (Hons.) Lond. 1987; MRCP (UK) 1993. (Univ. Coll. & Middlx. Hosp. Med. Sch. Lond.) Clin. Research Fell. & Hon. Regist. (Allergy & Clin. Immunol.) Nat. Heart & Lung Inst. & Roy. Brompton Hosp. Imperial Coll. Lond.

HASELDEN, Frank Gordon Depatment of Oral & Maxillofacial Surgery, Odstock Hospital, Salisbury SP2 8BJ Tel: 01722 336262 — MRCS Eng. LRCP Lond. 1963; FDS RCS Eng.1967; FFD RCSI 1966. (Middlx.) Cons. Oral Surg. Wessex Centre Plastic & Maxillofacial Surg. Odstock Hosp. Salisbury. Socs: BMA; Founder Mem. Europ. Assn. Maxillofacial Surg. Prev: Ho. Surg. (Gen. Surg.) Middlx. Hosp. Lond.; Sen. Regist. St. Thos. Hosp. Lond.; Cons. Maxillofacial Surg. Min. of Health Tripoli, Libya.

HASELDEN, James Benjamin York District General Hospital, Wigginton Road, York; Red Gables, The Avenue, Collingham, Wetherby LS22 5BU Tel: 01937 579135 — MB BS 1990 Lond.; MSc 1998; MRCP 1995; FRCR 1998. (Char. Cross & Westm.) Cons. Radiologist, York (Specialisation: BrE. Imaging). Socs: Roy. Coll. of Radiologists; Internat. Cancer Imaging Soc. Prev: Specialist Regist. Radiol. Leeds; Specialist Regist. (Radiol.) Edin.

HASELDEN, John Eric (retired) Bryher, Dorchester Road, Hook, Basingstoke Tel: 0125 672 762365 — MB BS 1961 Lond.; MRCS Eng. LRCP Lond. 1961; DObst RCOG 1964. Dep. Police Surg. Basingstoke. Prev: GP Basingstoke.

HASELDEN, Soraya Parvin The Surgery, 510 Hornsey Road, London N19 3QW Tel: 020 7272 0765; Ormelie, 20 Corstorphine Road, Edinburgh EH12 6HP Tel: 0131 337 2389 — MB BS 1992 Lond.; DRCOG 1994; DCH 1996; MRCGP 1996. (Charing Cross and Westminster) Clin. Res. MRC Environm. Epidemiol. Unit. Prev: GP/Regist. Sighthill Health Centre Edin.

HASELER, Anthony Richard Grange Street Surgery, 2 Grange Street, St Albans AL3 5NF Tel: 01727 833550 Fax: 01727 847961 Email: graye.surgery@gp-e82059.nhs.uk; 92 Harpenden Road, St Albans AL3 6DA Tel: 01727 850910 — MB BS Lond. 1969; DObst RCOG 1971. (Univ. Coll. Hosp.) Prev: SHO (Paediat. & O & G) Norf. & Norwich Hosp.; SHO (Med.) Perth Roy. Infirm.; SHO (O & G) Norf. & Norwich Hosp.

HASELER, Christine Mary St George's Surgery, St Pauls Medical Centre, 121 Swindon Road, Cheltenham GL50 4DP Tel: 01242 707755 Fax: 01242 707749 — MB ChB 1983 Birm.; MA Camb. 1984. Prev: GP Glos.; Sec. Glos. Doctors Co-op.; GP Ostende, Belgium.

HASENFUSS, Michael Frederick The Oakwood Surgery, Masham Road, Cantley, Doncaster DN4 6BU Tel: 01302 537611 Fax: 01302 371804; Lindsey House, Brethergate, West Woodside, Doncaster DN9 2AA — MB ChB 1970 St. And.

HASENSON, Benjamin Alexander (retired) Crouch End Health Centre, 45 Middle Lane, London N8 8PH — MB BS 1959 Lond.; MRCS Eng. LRCP Lond. 1959; DObst RCOG 1961. Prev: Ho. Surg. Bedford Gen. Hosp.

HASFORD, Christian St Charles Hospital, Nightingale House, Flat 1, Exmoor Street, London W10 6OZ Tel: 01206 844553 — State Exam Med 1991 Munich. (Ludwig - Maximilian Univ. Munich) Specialist Regist. Med. Socs: MDU; RCPHY; BMA.

HASHAM, Faiz Mahmud Ramzan Vali 11 Auckland Way, West Park, Hartlepool TS26 0AN Tel: 01429 266969 — MB BCh BAO 1981 NUI; LRCPSI 1981; FFA RCSI 1989. Research Fell. N. RHA. Socs: BMA & Assn. Anaesth. Prev: Regist. S. Tees HA; Regist. N. Tees Hosp.

HASHAM, Farida Mohamedali 32 Baroncroft Road, Woolton, Liverpool L25 6EH — MB ChB 1973 Liverp.; MRCP (Paediat.) (UK) 1978; DCH RCPS Lond. 1976; DRCOG 1975. SCMO Div. Community Child Health Liverp. HA; Sec. Div. Community Child Health Liverp. HA. Socs: Assn. Community Doctors in Audiol. Prev: Regist. (Paediat. Med.) Alder Hey Childr. Hosp. Liverp.; Clin. Research Fell. Respirat. Unit Alder Hey Childr. Hosp.

HASHAM, Nizar Ibrahim Tudor Lodge Health Centre, 3 Nithsdale Road, Weston Super Mare BS23 4JP Tel: 01934 622665 Fax: 01934 644332; Mulberry House, Bridgwater Road, Sidcot, Winscombe BS25 1NH Tel: 01934 843510 — MB ChB 1967 Bristol; MRCS Eng. LRCP Lond. 1965. (Bristol) Socs: BMA. Prev: Ho. Off. Ham Green Hosp. & P.ss Margt. Hosp. Swindon.

HASHAM, Saiidy Mulberry House, Bridgwater Road, Sidcot, Winscombe BS25 1NH — MB ChB 1998 Leeds.

HASHEMI, Mr Kambiz Accident & Emergency Department, Mayday University Hospital, London Road, Croydon CR7 7YE Tel: 020 8401 3015 Fax: 020 8401 3092 Email: yvone.woods@mayday.nhs.uk; 16 Rose Walk, Purley CR8 3LG — MB ChB 1973 Birm.; MD Birm. 1989; FRCS Eng. 1978; FFAEM 1993; T(S) 1991. Cons. A & E Servs. Mayday Hosp. Surrey; Regional Adviser A & E Med. Surrey; Chairm. Med. Commiss. for Accid. Preven. RCSE; Chairm. Regional Specialist Train. Comm. Socs: Roy. Soc. Med. (Pres. Accid. & Emerg. Sect.). Prev: Regist. (Cardiothoracic) E. Birm. Hosp. & Childr. Hosp. Birm.; Regist. (Surg.) E. Birm. Dist. Gen. Hosp.; SHO (A & E) Solihull AHA.

HASHEMI, Mr Majid The Gables, Peterborough Hospital, Thorpe Road, Peterborough PE3 6DA — MB ChB 1988 Manch.; FRCS Eng. 1993. Regist. (Gen. Surg.) P'boro. Dist. Hosp. Prev: SHO (Cardiothoracic) Roy. Postgrad. Med. Sch. Hammersmith Hosp. Lond.

HASHEMI, Mohammed Zubair 15 Wadebridge Drive, Ainsworth Chase, Bury BL8 2NN Tel: 0161 761 4770 Email: hashemi@globalnet.co.uk — MB ChB 1991 Dundee; BMSc (1st cl. Hons.) Dund 1988; FRCA - Lond 1996. Regist. (Anaesth.) Manch. Roy. Infirm, Cons., Anaesth. - Roy. Preston Hosp. Prev: SHO (Anaesth.) Stepping Hill Hosp. Stockport.

HASHEMI-NEJAD, Mr Aresh The Royal National Orthopaedic Hospital, Brockley Hill, Stanmore HA7 4LP Tel: 020 8954 2300 Email: areshnejad@rnoh-tr.org — MB BS 1985 Lond.; FRCS (Orth.) 1995; FRCS Eng. 1989. (Guy's) Cons. Orthop. Surg. Roy. Nat. Orthop. Hosp. Stanmore. Socs: Fell. BOA; Brit. Soc. Childr. Orthop. Surg.; BMA. Prev: Clin. Fell. The Hosp. for Sick Childr. Toronto; Sen. Regist. Rotat. (Orthop.) Roy. Nat. Orthop. Hosp. Stanmore; Regist. Rotat. (Orthop.) Roy. Free Hosp. Lond.

HASHEMIAN, Mr Hassan Agha 21 De Vere Gardens, Kensington, London W8 5NA — MB BS 1942 Lond.; FRCS Eng. 1964; FRCS Ed. 1945; MRCS Eng. LRCP Lond. 1941. Sen. Fell. Assn. Surg. Gt. Brit. & Irel. Socs: FICS. Prev: Prof. Surg. Teheran Univ.

HASHIM, Mr Adnan Abdul Amir 10 Larchwood Glade, Camberley GU15 3UW Tel: 01276 675386 Fax: 01276 675386 — MB ChB 1974 Baghdad; FRCS Ed. 1985; MRCS Eng. LRCP Lond. 1986; FRCOphth 1994. (Baghdad College of Medicine) Indep. Assoc. Specialist (Ophth.) Frimley Pk. Hosp. Camberley.; Fixed-Term Cons. Opthalmologist. Socs: S.. Ophth. Soc. UK; BMA; UKISCRS. Prev: Regist. (Ophth.) Raigmore Hosp. Inverness.

HASHIM, Hashim Flat 38, King Henrys Reach, Manbre Road, London W6 9RH — MB BS 1998 Lond.; MB BS Lond 1998.

HASHIM, Natasha Room 8, 99 Steps, Doctors Residence, Leeds General Infirmary, Great George St., Leeds LS1 3EX — MB ChB 1998 Leeds.

HASHIM-IQBAL, Humaira 44 Birdwood Road, Cambridge CB1 3SU Tel: 01223 573219 — MB ChB 1995 Leeds. SHO (Paediat.) N. Tyneside Gen. Hosp. Prev: GP/Regist. Walker, Newc.; SHO (Cas.) Roy. Vict. Infirm. Newc.

HASHMAT, Mr Iqbal 2 Micklemead, Highnam, Gloucester GL2 8NF — MB BS 1979 Karachi; FRCS Glas. 1986.

HASHMI, Arif Ahmad Friarwood Surgery, Carleton Glen, Pontefract WF8 1SU Tel: 01977 703235 — MB BS 1983 Peshawar. GP Princip.

HASHMI, Farrukh Siyar, OBE The Woodbourne Clinic, 21 Woodbourne Road, Edgbaston, Birmingham B17 8BZ Tel: 0121 434 4343 Fax: 0121 434 3270 — MB BS Punjab (Pakistan) 1953; FRCPsych 1979, M 1971; DPM Eng. 1965. (King Edwd. Med. Coll. Lahore) Vis. Psychiat. Woodbourne Clinic Birm. Socs: World Psychiat. Assn.; (Ex. Pres. & Patron) Overseas Doctor's Assn. (UK).; Medico-Legal Soc. Prev: Cons. Psychiat. All St.s' Hosp. Birm.; Mem. Gen. Med. Counc. & Parole Bd.; Commiss.er Commiss. for Racial Equality.

HASHMI, Mr Hasan Mushtaq 34 Grand Drive, Raynes Park, London SW20 0JT Tel: 020 8540 4054 — MB BS 1982 Karachi; FRCS (Ophth.) Ed. 1990; DO RCPSI 1985.

HASHMI, Khalida Zia The Surgery, 309 Evelyn Street, Deptford, London SE8 5RA Tel: 020 8469 3090 Fax: 020 8691 2525 — MB BS 1958 Punjab; MB BS 1958 Punjab.

HASHMI, Mahnaz 5 Woodbourne Road, Edgbaston, Birmingham B15 3QJ Tel: 0411 727121 Fax: 0121 455 0011 Email: manobillee50@hotmail.com — MB BCh 1996 Wales. (UWCM) SHO Psych. UCL Lond. Rotat.al. Train. Scheme. Socs: Mem. BMA; Inceptor RCS.

HASHMI, Mr Manzoor Shah Princess of Wales Hospital, Coity Road, Bridgend CF31 1RQ; 69 Priory Oak, Brackla, Bridgend CF31 2HZ Tel: 01656 658574 — MB BS 1965 Punjab; FRCS Ed. 1973; FRCOphth. 1988; T(Ophth.) 1991; DO Eng. 1970. (King Edwd. Med. Coll. Lahore) Cons. Surg. (Ophth.) P.ss Wales Hosp. Bridgend. Socs: MRCOphth.; Oxf. Ophth. Soc.; OGWR Med. Soc. Prev: Sen. Regist. (Ophth.) Univ. Hosp. Wales Cardiff & Singleton Hosp. Swansea; Regist. (Ophth.) Merthyr Gen. Hosp. Merthyr Tydfil.

HASHMI, Mr Syed Saeedul Hasan Department of Neurosurgery, Hope Hospital, Stott Lane, Salford M6 8HD — MB BS 1984 Karachi; FRCSI 1992.

HASHMI, Syed Shakil Javed Flat 1 Block 2, Victoria Residence, Memorial Avenue, Worksop S80 2BJ Tel: 01909 470598 Fax: 01909 470598 Email: shakil@hashmis.freeserve.co.uk — MB BS 1985 Karachi; MRCPI 1995; DCH 1995. (Dow Med. Coll. Karachi) Staff Grade (Paediat.) Bassetlow Hosp. Workshop. Prev: Regist. (Paediat.) P.ss Margt. Hosp.; Regist. (Paediat.) Salisbury Dist. Hosp.

HASHMI, Mr Syed Tanveer Ahmed 97 Longmead Avenue, Chelmsford CM2 7EZ — MB BS 1983 Karachi; FRCS (Ophth.) Glas. 1992.

HASHMI, Syed Zahid Ali 4 Claypits Road, Boreham, Chelmsford CM3 3BZ — MB BS 1961 Punjab; BSc Punjab (Pakistan) 1955, MB BS 1961; DTCD Wales 1969. (King Edwd. Med. Coll. Lahore) Assoc. Specialist (Gen. Med.) Colchester Health Dist. Socs: N.E. Thoracic Soc.

HASICI, Ersen 53 Capel Road, London E7 0JP Tel: 020 8519 3064 — MB BS 1992 Newc. SHO (Med.) Guy's Hosp. Lond.

HASKARD, Professor Dorian Oliver National Heart & Lung Institute, Imperial College of Science, faculty of Medicine., Hammersmith Hospital, Du Cane Road, London W12 0NN Tel: 020 8383 3064 Fax: 020 8383 1640 Email: dhaskard@ic.ac.uk — MB BS 1977 Lond.; BA (Psychol. & Physiol.) Oxf. 1973, DM 1989; FRCP Lond. 1994; 2001 F Med Sci. (Oxf. & Middlx.) Sir John McMichael Prof. of Cardiovasc. Med. Imperial Coll. Sci. Technol. & Med. Lond.; Hon. Cons. Phys. Hammersmith & Qu. Charlotte's SHA. Socs: Brit. Soc. Rheum.; Fell. Amer. Coll. Rheum.; Brit. Cardiac Soc. Prev: Wellcome Trust Sen. Research Fell. (Clin. Sci.) UMDS Guy's Hosp. Lond.; Arthritis & Rheum. Counc. Research Fell. Bone & Jt. Research Unit Lond. Hosp. Med. Sch.; Sen. Regist. (Med. & Rheum.) Guy's Hosp. Lond.

HASKAYNE, Leslie Frances Newton Lodge, Ouckthorpe Lane, Wakefield WF1 Tel: 01924 375217 — MD 1970 Alberta; BSc Alberta 1969, MD 1970; MRCPsych 1976. (Alberta) Assoc. Specialist Stanley Royd Hosp. Wakefield. Prev: Psychiat. Regist. Springfield Hosp. Lond.; Psychiat. SHO Joyce Green Hosp. Dartford; Cas. Off. Hammersmith Hosp. Lond.

HASKELL, Katherine Jane Western Road Medical Centre, 99 Western Road, Romford RM1 3LS Tel: 01708 746495 Fax: 01708 737936 — MB BS 1987 Lond.

HASKELL, Simon Jonathan Annie Prendergast Health Centre, Ashton Gardens, Chadwell Heath, Romford RM6 6RT Tel: 020 8590 1401 Fax: 020 8599 8499 — MB BS 1986 Lond.

HASKEW, Emma Elizabeth 89 Quarry Road, Ravenshead, Nottingham NG15 9AP — MB BS 1994 Newc.

HASKINS, Claire Louise 38 Carr Bottom Road, Greengates, Bradford BD10 0BB — MB ChB 1992 Leeds.

HASKINS, Henry William (retired) Primrose Bank, Ideford, Chudleigh, Newton Abbot TQ13 0BG Tel: 01626 853397 — MB ChB 1960 Bristol. Prev: Clin. Asst. (Venereol.) Freed Fields Hosp.

HASKINS, Nicholas Middleway Surgery, Middleway, St. Blazey, Par PL24 2JL — MB ChB 1969 Sheff. Socs: BMA.

HASKINS, Robert Henry The Medical Specialist Group, PO Box 113, Alexandra House, Les Frieteaux, St Martin's, Guernsey GY1 3EX; Le Bourg De Bas Farm, Forest, Guernsey — MB BCh 1970 Wales; FRCOG 1989, M 1975; DObst RCS Eng. 1972. (Cardiff) Specialist (O & G Med.) St. Sampsons Guernsey. Prev: O & G P.ss Eliz. Hosp. Guernsey; Squadron Ldr. RAF Med. Br., Specialist (O & G) P.ss Mary's RAF Hosp. Halton.

HASKINS, Tim David (retired) Cotswold, Fernhill Close, Upper Hale, Farnham GU9 0JL Tel: 01252 713251 Email: tdhaskins@aol.com — MB BS 1956 Lond.; DObst RCOG 1958. Prev: Hosp. Pract. (Geriat. Med.) Farnham Hosp.

HASLAM, Catherine Jane 98 Dundas Street, Edinburgh EH3 6RQ — MB BCh BAO 1986 Belf.

HASLAM, Professor David Antony Mews Close Health Centre, Mews Close, Ramsey, Huntingdon PE26 1BP Tel: 01487 812611 Fax: 01487 711801; 35 Biggin Lane, Ramsey, Huntingdon PE26 1NB Tel: 01487 813033 Fax: 01487 815944 Email: dhaslam@rcqp.org.uk — MB ChB 1972 Birm.; FRCGP 1989, M 1976; DObst RCOG 1974; DFFP 1998. (Birm.) GP; Chairm. of Counc. RCGP; Edit. Adviser The Pract.; Vice Pres. GP Writers Assn.; Vis. Prof. in Primary Health Care, de Montfort Univ. Leicester. Prev: Ho. Phys. Warneford Hosp. Leamington Spa; Chairm. Exam. Bd. RCGP; Trainee GP Birm. (Qu. Eliz. Hosp.) VTS.

HASLAM, David John Woodlands Park Surgery, 15 Woodlands Park Road, Maidenhead SL6 3NW Tel: 01628 825674 Fax: 01628 829036 — MB BS 1975 Lond. (Roy. Lond. Hosp.)

HASLAM, David William 137 Albert Road W., Bolton BL1 5EB — MB BS 1985 Lond.

HASLAM, Mrs Elizabeth Carolyn 19 Nursery Close, Tamerton Foliot, Plymouth PL5 4QG — MB BS 1988 Lond.

***HASLAM, George Mark** 130 Dorchester Road, Garstang, Preston PR3 1FE — BM BS 1997 Nottm.; BMedSci (Hons.).

HASLAM, Georgina Helen Priestthorpe Medical Centre, 2 Priestthorpe Lane, Bingley BD16 4ED Tel: 01274 568383 Fax: 01274 510788; Sefton Lodge, 49 Station Road, Baildon, Shipley BD17 6HS Tel: 01274 594802 — MB ChB 1977 Leeds; MRCOG 1982; DRCOG 1979.

HASLAM, Isobel Fiona (retired) 137 Albert Road W., Bolton BL1 5EB Tel: 01204 842354 — MB ChB Glas. 1955; PhD St. Andrews University 1982. Clin. Asst. Obst. Bolton Dist. Gen. Hosp. Prev: SCMO (Adult Health) Chorley & S. Ribble HA.

HASLAM, Mr James Duane Darlington Memorial Hospital, Darlington DL3 6YT — MB ChB 1976 Ed.; FRCS Ed. 1981; DO Eng. 1980. Cons. Ophth. Darlington Mem. Hosp. Prev: Sen. Regist. (Ophth.) Ninewells Hosp. Dundee; Regist. Tennent Inst. W.. Gen. Hosp. Glas.; SHO & Regist. S.. Gen. Hosp. Glas.

HASLAM, Jennifer Caroline The Meadows, Graig Road, Lisvane, Cardiff CF14 0UF; 14 Scotney Way, Pontprewau, Cardiff CF23 8PJ — MB ChB 1992 Bristol. Specialist Regist. Radiol. Univ. Hosp. Wales Cardiff. Socs: Roy. Coll. Phys.

HASLAM, Judith Sara 2 Forge House, High St., Ufford, Woodbridge IP13 6EN Tel: 01394 460789 Email: judedoc@aol.com — BChir 1996 Camb.; MB Camb. 1996; BDS Wales 1989. (Cambridge) SHO Basic Surgic. Rotat. Ipswich Hosp.

***HASLAM, Kirsty Emma** Whiteways, 556 Preston Rd, Clayton-Le-Woods, Chorley PR6 7EB Tel: 01772 323931 — BM BS 1997 Nottm.; BMedSci Nottm. 1995.

HASLAM, Laurence John Dundonald Medical Centre, 1 St. Johns Wood Park, Dundonald, Belfast BT16 1RS Tel: 028 9048 3100 Fax: 028 9041 9252 — MB BCh BAO 1983; MRCGP 1988; DCH RCP Lond. 1988; DRCOG 1987; DGM RCP Lond. 1986.

HASLAM, Loraine 117 Eton Close, Witney OX28 3GB — MB BS 1998 Newc.; MB BS Newc 1998.

HASLAM, Martin Brooke Tudor House Surgery, 43 Broad Street, Wokingham RG40 1BE Tel: 0118 978 3544 Fax: 0118 977 0420; 5 Tattersall Close, Wokingham RG40 2LP Tel: 01734 783565 — MB BS 1970 Lond.; MRCP (UK) 1977; DCH Eng. 1975.

HASLAM, Michael Trevor (retired) South Durham NHS Trust, Winterton Hospital, Sedgefield, Stockton-on-Tees TS21 3EJ Tel: 01740 620521 — MB BChir 1959 Camb.; MA Camb. 1959, MD 1971; FRCP Glas. 1979, M 1967; MRCS Eng. LRCP Lond. 1959; LMSSA Lond. 1958; FRCPsych 1980, M 1972; DMJ Soc. Apoth. Lond. 1972; DPM Eng. 1963. Chairm. Soc. Clin. Psychiat.; Adviser Gender Dysphoria Trust; Trustee, Beaumont Trust. Prev: Med. Dir. Harrogate Clinic.

HASLAM, Nathaniel 7 Percy Terrace, Gosforth, Newcastle upon Tyne NE3 1RS — MB BS 1996 Newc.

HASLAM, Neil 17 Norbury Grove, Bolton BL1 8SH — MB ChB 1988 Manch.

HASLAM, Nicholas Paul Hove Medical Centre, West Way, Hove BN3 8LD Tel: 01273 430088 Fax: 01273 430172; 6 Peacock Lane, Withdean, Brighton BN1 6WA — MB BS 1981 Lond. Prev: SHO (O & G, A & E Resp. Med., Geriat. & Paediat.); Lond. Hosp. VTS; Ho. Surg. & Ho. Phys. Lond. Hosp.

***HASLAM, Paul Gregory** 2 Marsden Drive, Timperley, Altrincham WA15 7XF — MB ChB 1994 Sheff.

HASLAM, Philip John 98 Manor House Road, Jesmond, Newcastle upon Tyne NE2 2LY — MB BS 1989 Newc.; MRCP (UK) 1992; FRCR 1996. Cons. (Interven.al Radiol.) Freeman Hosp., Newc. Prev: Regist. (Diagn. Radiol.) Newc. N.. RHA; Lect., Interven.al Radiol., Beaumont Hosp., Dub.

HASLAM, Richard George Edward 306 Knightsfield, Welwyn Garden City AL8 7NQ — MB BS 1992 Lond.

HASLAM, Richard Justin Maywood Cottage, 99A Manchester Road, Wilmslow SK9 2JH — MB ChB 1989 Manch.

HASLEHURST, Jillian Mary 21 Atwood Avenue, Kew Gardens, Richmond TW9 4HF — MB ChB 1975 Manch.; DIH Eng. 1982. Med. Off. Marks & Spencer Plc Lond.

HASLER, John Clendinnen, OBE Edgecumbe Consulting Ltd, 125 Pembroke Road, Richmond Hill, Clifton, Bristol BS8 3ES Tel: 0117 973 8899 Fax: 0117 973 8844 Email: jhasler@edgecumbe_health.demon.co.uk; Crossways, Peppard Common, Henley-on-Thames RG9 5LR Tel: 01491 628478 Fax: 01491 628747 Email: jhasler@edgecumbe-health.demon.co.uk — MB BS Lond. 1960; MD Lond. 1982; FRCGP 1975, M 1968; DCH Eng. 1965; DA Eng. 1963. (Middlx.) p/t Director Elgecombe Consg. Ltd; Chairm. Armed. Serv. Gen. Pract. Approval. Bd. Socs: Reading Path. Soc. Prev: Dir. Postgrad. Gen. Pract. Educat. Oxf. Univ. & Anglia Oxf. Region; Hon. Sen. Clin. Lect., Oxf. Univ.; Civil Cons. in Gen. Pract., Roy. air Force.

HASLER, Judith Carol Woodbourne Clinic, Woodbourne Road, Edgbaston, Birmingham B15 3Q; 41 Herbert Road, Bearwood, Smethwick B67 5DD — MB ChB 1983 Birm.; MRCPsych 1988. Staff Psychiat. Woodbourne Clinic Birm.; Clin. Asst. Highcroft Hosp. Birm. Prev: Regist. (Psychiat.) Kidderminster Dist. Gen. Hosp. & Reaside Clinic Birm.

HASLETON, Professor Philip Simon Department of Pathology, Regional Cardio Thoracic Centre, Wythenshawe Hospital, Southmoor Road, Manchester M23 9LT Tel: 0161 291 2144 Fax: 0161 291 2125 Email: phasle@fs1.scg.man.ac.uk — MB ChB 1964 Birm.; MD Birm. 1971; FRCPath 1987, M 1975. Cons. Histopath. & Prof. Pulm. Path. Univ. Manch. Socs: Pres. NW Thoracic Soc.; Assn. Clin. Path. Prev: Sen. Lect. Univ. Manch.; Lect. (Path.) Univ. Liverp.; Ho. Phys. Qu. Eliz. Hosp.

HASLETT, Christopher 12 The Ride, Brentford TW8 9LA — MB ChB 1977 Ed.; BSc (Med. Sci.) (1st cl. Hons. Path.) Ed. 1974; MB ChB (Hons.) Ed. 1977; MRCP (UK) 1979. Geo. Simon Award of Fleischmer Soc. 1985; Sen. Regist. Dept. Med. Roy. Postgrad. Med. Sch. Hammersmith Hosp. Lond. Prev: Research Assoc. Depts. Paediat. & Med. Nat. Jewish Center for Immunol.; & Respirat. Med. Denver Colorado, USA; Regist. Gen. Med. Rotat. Ealing & Hammersmith Hosps. Lond.; Ho. Phys. & Ho. Surg. Roy. Infirm. Edin.

HASLETT, Elizabeth Ann 14 Victoria Road, Poulton-le-Fylde FY6 7JA Tel: 01253 882974 Email: lizhaslett@yahoo.co.uk — MB ChB 1992 Manch.; MRCOG 2000; DRCOG 1996; DFFP 1995. (Manch.) SpR (O&G) E. Anglia Region; Sen. Regist. Obst. & Gyn., Monajn Med. Centre, Melbourne, Vict. 3184, Australia. Socs: BMA; Med. Protec. Soc. Prev: Specialist Regist. Obst & Gyn. Ipswich Hosp.; Specialist Regist. (Osbt. & Gyn.) Addenbrooke's Hosp. Camb.; Specialist Regist. Obst & Gyn. W. Suff. Hosp. Bury St Edmunds.

HASLETT, Michael Woods (retired) 14 Victoria Road, Poulton-le-Fylde FY6 7JA Tel: 01253 882974 — MB BChir Camb. 1957; DObst RCOG 1959. Prev: GP Poulton-le-Fylde.

HASLETT, Peter Jonathan The Stables, 36 East St., Alford LN13 9EH — BM BCh 1987 Oxf.

HASLETT, Roger Stephen Kilcullen, Vicarage Lane, Altrincham WA14 3AS Tel: 0161927 9316 — BM 1988 Soton.; MRCP (UK) 1991; FRCOphth 1993. Prev: SHO (Med.) Bolton Roy. Infirm. Lancs.; SHO (Infec. Dis.) Monsall Hosp. Manch.; SHO (Neurol.) N. Manch. Gen. Hosp.

HASLETT, Roisin Clare Kilcullen, Vicarage Lane, Altrincham WA14 3AS Tel: 0161 927 9316 — MB ChB 1989 Manch.

HASLETT, William Henderson Kevin, TD 30 Sheridan Drive, Helen's Bay, Bangor BT19 1LB — MB BCh BAO Belf. 1960; FFA RCSI 1969. Cons. in Anaesth. Ulster Hosp. Dundonald; Lt. Col., Cons. Anaesth. RAMC (TA). Socs: Assn. Anaesth.; Pres. NI Soc. Anaesth. 1997-1999; BMA. Prev: Res. Med. Off. Roy. Vict. Hosp. Belf.; Demonst. Anat. Dept. Anat. & Tutor & Regist. Dept. Anaesth. Qu. Univ.; Belf.

HASLEWOOD, Sally Mary St Nicholas Hospice, Bury St Edmunds IP33 2QY — MB BS 1967 Lond.; MRCS Eng. LRCP Lond. 1967; Dip. Palliat. Med. Wales 1993; DObst RCOG 1969. (Guy's) Clin. Asst. St Nicholas Hospice Bury St. Edmunds. Prev: GP Bury St. Edmunds.

HASLOCK, Professor David Ian The James Coolt University Hospital, Marton Road, Middlesbrough TS4 3BW Fax: 01642 854636 Email: ian.haslock@email.stahnhst.northy.nhs.uk; 95 The Larun Beat, Yarm TS15 9HX Tel: 01642 780580 — MB ChB 1965 Ed; MD 1972 Ed; FRCP 1997 lond.; MRCP 1996 UK. (Ed.) p/t Cons. Rheum. S. Tees Acute Hosps. Trust; Vis. Prof. Clin. Bioengin. Univ. Durh.; Hon. Clin. Lect. Univ. Newc.; Vis. Research Fell. & Hon. Lect. Teesside Univ. Socs: (Ex-Pres.) Brit. Soc. Rheum.; (Ex-Hon. Sec.) Brit. Health Profess. Rheum.; Brit. Assn. Med. Managers. Prev: William Hewitt Research Fell. Univ. Leeds; Med. Dir. S. Tees Acute Hosp. Trust; Regist. (Gen. Med.) Prof. Med. Unit Leeds Gen. Infirm.

HASNAIN, Naseem-Ul Group Practice Centre, Howard St., Glossop SK13 0DE Tel: 01457 854321 — MB BS 1961 Punjab; MB BS Punjab (Pakistan) 1961; DCH Eng. 1968. (Nishtar Med. Coll. Multan)

HASNAIN, Mr Rizvi Tehzib-ul Kos Clinic, Roydlands St., Hipperholme, Halifax HX3 8AF Tel: 01422 205154; Gulazma, 6 Ash Close, Lightcliffe, Halifax HX3 8PD Tel: 01422 205154 — MB BS 1958 Karachi; BSc (Hons.) Sind 1951; FRCS Ed. 1972. (Dow Med. Coll. Karachi) Clin. Asst. (Gen. Surg.) Roy. Halifax Infirm. Prev: SHO Jinnah Postgrad. Centre Karachi, Pakistan; Jun. Hosp. Med. Off. Warde-Aldam Hosp. S. Elmshall; Res. Surg. Off. Pontefract Gen. Infirm.

HASNAIN, Yasmeen Almas 64 Hughenden Avenue, High Wycombe HP13 5SJ Tel: 01494 536945 Fax: 01494 536945 Email: 106550.311@compuserve.com; A & E Department, Wycombe General Hospital, High Wycombe Tel: 01494 526161 — MB BS 1987 Karachi; FRCS Ed. 1994. (Univ. Karachi) Specialist Regist. (A & E) S. Oxf. Rotat.

HASSAAN, Mr Ali Mostafa Hassan 27 Cliff Road, Leigh-on-Sea SS9 1HJ Tel: 01702 470703 — MB BCh 1971 Cairo; FRCSI 1986.

HASSABO, Mohammed Samir Abdel-Aziz 252 Carlton Avenue E., Wembley HA9 8PZ Tel: 020 8904 8541 — MB BCh 1969 Ain Shams; FRCOG 1984, M 1981. Chairm. Hassahu Internat. Hosp., Cairo.

HASSALL, Christine Margaret Strahaven Health Centre, The Ward, Strathaven ML10 6AS Tel: 01357 522993; 14 Cullinpark Grove, Strathaven ML10 6EN — MB ChB 1986 Glas.; MRCGP 1991.

HASSALL, Dorothy Esther Nicholls Old Well Cottage, Petworth Road, Wormley, Godalming GU8 5TR Tel: 01428 684483 — MB ChB 1948 Manch.; FRCPsych 1984, M 1973; DPM Eng. 1972. Emerit. Cons. Psychiat. Frimley Pk. Hosp. Frimley. Socs: BMA. Prev: Cons. Psychiat. W. Surrey & NE Hants. Health Dist.; Cons. Psychiat. BUPA Hosp. Farnham; Sen. Regist. Graylingwell Hosp. Chichester.

HASSALL, Fiona 57 Millwood Street, Shawlands, Glasgow G41 3JS — MB ChB 1983 Glas.; MRCGP 1988; MPH Glas. 1992; DA (UK) 1985. Med. Off. Glas. Univ. Health Serv.; Clin. Asst. Glas. Drug Problem Serv. Prev: Regist. & Lect. (Pub. Health Med.) W.. Isles; Trainee Paediat. Edin.; Trainee GP Falkirk.

HASSALL, Mr Harold, OBE Rolland House, Mill Hill Lane, Sandbach CW11 4PN Tel: 01270 764357 — MB ChB (Distinc. Med.) Manch. 1940; FRCS Eng. 1949; MRCS Eng. LRCP Lond. 1943. (Manch.) Emerit. Cons. Surg. Mersey RHA & Leighton Hosp. Crewe. Socs: Fell. Manch. Med. Soc. Prev: Chief Asst. (Surg.) Roy. Infirm. Manch.; Surg. Regist. Withington Hosp. Manch.; Surg. Lt. RNVR (1941-6).

HASSALL, Janet Elaine Sarah 30 Moss View, Dumfries DG1 4LB — MB ChB 1994 Ed. Socs: Fell. Roy. Med. Soc. Edin.

***HASSAM, Farhannah** 8 Ampton Road, Edgebaston, Birmingham B15 2UH — MB ChB 1998 Birm.

HASSAM, Zehra 28A Yewtree Road, Streetly, Sutton Coldfield B74 3SJ — MB ChB 1970 East Africa; MRCPath 1977. (Makerere Med. Sch.) Cons. Manor Hosp. Walsall.

HASSAN, Abdel Ghani Luxor, Bressingham, Diss IP22 2AX Tel: 0195 381303 — MB ChB 1940 Ed. (Univ. Ed.) Socs: BMA. Prev: Clin. Asst. (Orthop.) Rochdale Infirm.; Cas. Ho. Surg. Kilmarnock Infirm.

HASSAN, Mr Adekunle Olubola 22 Enterprise Lane, Campbell Park, Milton Keynes MK9 4AP Tel: 07960 844077 Email: eyefoundation@hyperia.com, eyefoundationzozo@yahoo.com — MB BS 1976 Lagos; FRCS (Ophth.) Glas. 1985; DO RCPSI 1982; FCOphth 1990. Chief of Ophth. & Med. Dir. Eye Foundat. Hosp. & Lambo Eye Inst., Lagos, Nigeria; Dir. Post-Grad. Train., Lambo Eye Inst., 12 Sobo Arobiodu St., GRA Ikeja, Lagos, Nigeria. Socs: BMA.; Amer. Acad. of Ophth.; Guild of Med. Director, Nigeria. Prev: Sen. Cons. Ophth. Surg. New Jubail Hosp., Saudi Arabia; Cons. Ophth. Surg. King Khalid Nat. Guard Hosp. Jeddah, Saudi Arabia; Regist. (Ophth.) W.. Infirm. Glas.

HASSAN, Ahamad 71 Woodgrove Road, Burnley BB11 3EL — MB BS 1994 Lond.

HASSAN, Ahmed Hanafi Ahmed 148 The Quadrangle, Cambridge Square, London W2 2PL — MB BCh 1969 Ain Shams; MRCOG 1979.

HASSAN, Mr Ali Ibrahim Royal Preston Hospital, Sharoe Green Lane, Fulwood, Preston PR2 9HT Tel: 01772 710470; Woodland View, Fernyhalgh, Fulwood, Preston PR2 9NN Tel: 01772 797683 — MB ChB 1976 Baghdad; FRCS Ed. 1990; MSc Cardiff 1998. Cons. Orthop. Surg. Socs: BMA; Brit. Orthop. Assn.; SICOT.

HASSAN, Andrew Bassim Department of Zoology, University of Oxford, South Park Road, Oxford OX1 3PS; Rowan House, 7 Hurst Lane, Cumnor, Oxford OX2 9PR — BM BCh 1987 Oxf.; BSc Lond. 1984; DPhil Oxf. 1994; MRCP (UK) 1990. CRC Sen. Clin. Research Fell. (Hon. Cons.). Prev: Sen. Regist. (Med. Oncol.) Soton. Univ. Hosps.; Regist. (Gen. Med.) Addenbrooke's Hosp. Camb.; Wellcome Fell. Sir William Dunn Sch. Path. Oxf.

HASSAN, Andrew Gemmel — MRCS Eng. LRCP Lond. 1979. (Sheff.) GP Diss.

HASSAN, Batool Salman 88 St Albans Road, Arnold, Nottingham NG5 6GW — MB ChB 1989 Glas.

HASSAN, Claire Naheed 9 Douglas Road, Standish, Wigan WN6 0QT — MB BS 1996 Lond.

HASSAN, Ezzat Rageh Mahmoud 20 The Farthings, Washington NE37 1PG — MB BCh 1973 Cairo.

HASSAN, Fedaa Ali 1 Owen Court, Bingley BD16 4UL — MB BCh 1982 Ain Shams Egypt.

HASSAN, Gamal Ahmed El-Said Mohamed Ridgewood Centre, Old Bisley Road, Frimley, Camberley GU16 9QE Tel: 01276 692919; 7 Langley Avenue, Surbiton, Surbiton KT6 6QH Tel: 020 8399 1253 Fax: 020 8390 5174 — MB BCh 1973 Ain Shams; MRCPsych 1984. Cons. Psychiat. Surrey-Hants. Borders NHS Trust Ridgewood Centre Frimley Surrey.

HASSAN, Mr Hassan Mohammed Jawad Wolverhampton Eye Infirmary, Compton Road, Wolverhampton WV3 9QR Tel: 01902 307999; 6 Froyle Close, Tettenhall, Wolverhampton WV6 8XW Tel: 01902 756332 — MB ChB 1973 Basra; FRCS Ed. 1988; FCOphth 1989; DO RCS Eng. 1986. Assoc. Specialist (Ophth.) Wolverhampton HA. Prev: Regist. (Ophth.) Wakefield HA & Stonehome Hosp. Scotl.; SHO (Ophth.) St. Wooles Hosp. Newport.

HASSAN, Hesham Mohamed Gamal El Din Braeside, Pembury Hospital, Pembury, Tunbridge Wells Tel: 01892 823535 — MB ChB 1974 Cairo. (Ain Shams Cairo) SCMO Pembury Hosp.

HASSAN, Hussain Shames Alddin The Burrows, Hall Lane, Frampton, Boston PE20 1AB — MB ChB 1976 Baghdad.

HASSAN, Mr Ibrahim 7 Whitton Way Regent Farm, Gosforth, Newcastle upon Tyne NE3 3HY Tel: 0191 285 6176 — MB BS 1981 Ahmadu Bello, Nigeria; FRCS Ed. 1990. (Univ. Ahmadu Bello, Nigeria) Staff Grade (A & E Med.) Newc. u. Tune. Socs: FMCS (Nat. Postgrad. Med. Coll. Nigeria); BMA; BAEM. Prev: Vis. Regist. (Surg.) N. Tyneside Dist. Hosp.

HASSAN, Irfan-Ul Omagh Health Centre, Mountjoy Road, Omagh BT79 7BA Tel: 028 8224 3521; No 1 Lissan View, Dublin Rd, Omagh BT78 1TR Tel: 01662 241861 — LRCP LRCS 1979 Ed.; LRCP LRCS Ed. LRCPS Glas. 1979; MRCGP (UK); DRCOG (UK).

HASSAN, Isaac 9 Holden Road, Broughton Park, Salford M7 4NL — MB ChB 1973 Birm.; BSc (1st cl. Hons.) Birm. 1970, MB ChB 1973; DMRD Eng. 1978; FRCR 1983. Cons. (Radiol.) Bolton Roy. Infirm. & Bolton Gen. Hosp. Socs: Brit. Inst. Radiol.; BMA. Prev: Sen. Regist. (Radiol.) Qu. Eliz. Hosp. Birm.; Regist. (Radiol.) Notts. AHA (T); SHO (Med.) Soton. Univ. Hosps.

HASSAN, Jacob Hanover Close Health Centre, Hanover Close, Bar Hill, Cambridge CB3 8SE Tel: 01954 780442 Fax: 01954 789590; 2 Spens Avenue, Cambridge CB3 9LS — MB BChir 1979 Camb.; BA Camb. 1977, MA 1980, MB BChir 1979; Cert. Family Plann. JCC 1985.

HASSAN, Mr Karam Mohamed Rashad Royal Bournemouth Hospital, Castle Lane E., Bournemouth BH7 7DW Tel: 01202 303626 — MB BCh 1977 Cairo; FRCS Glas. 1986; FFAEM 1995. Cons. A & E Roy. Bournemouth Hosp. & Poole NHS Trust. Socs: BMA; BAEM; MDU.

HASSAN, Khalid Surgery, 75 Bank Street, Alexandria G83 0NB Tel: 01389 752626 Fax: 01389 752169 — MB ChB 1990 Dundee.

HASSAN, Kowthar Salman 66 Meadowburn, Bishopbriggs, Glasgow G64 3EZ — MB ChB 1991 Glas.

HASSAN, Mr M Hayder A&E Department, King's College Hospital, Denmark Hill, London SE5 9RS Tel: 020 7737 4000 Fax: 020 7346 3531 Email: hayder@doctors.org.uk; 55 Ravens Way, Lee Green, London SE12 8EY — MB ChB 1981 Baghdad; FRCS Eng. 1996. (Univ. Baghdad, Baghdad Med. Sch.) Specialist Regist. (A&E Med.) King's Coll. Hosp., Lond.; Instruc. PALS courses. Socs: BMA; RCS Eng.; Fac. Accid. & Emerg. Med. Prev: Specialist Regist. Rotat. A & E Med. Medway Hosp., King's Coll. Hosp. & St. Thos. Hosp. S. Thames E.; Regist. (Orthop.) Pilgrim Hosp. Boston.

HASSAN, Maha Kamal Central Pathology Laboratories, Department of Clinical Biochemistry, Hartshill Road, Hartshill, Stoke-on-Trent ST4 7PA Tel: 01782 716676 — MB ChB 1971 Baghdad; MSc (Clin. Biochem.) Lond. 1989; MSc (Path.) Baghdad 1977. Prev: Sen. Regist. (Chem. Path.) Qu. Eliz. Med. Centre Birm.

HASSAN, Mohammad Sabit Primary Care Health Care Centre, South Road, Chopwell, Newcastle upon Tyne NE17 7BU Tel: 01207

561736 Fax: 01207 563824; Hurtswood, 9 High Mill Road, Hamsterley Mill, Rowlands Gill NE39 1HE Tel: 01207 544424 — MB BS 1971 Bihar. (Darbhanga Med. Coll.) Clin. Asst. (A & E) Qu. Eliz. Hosp. Gateshead. Prev: Regist. (Orthop.) Monklands Dist. Gen. Hosp. Airdrie; Trainee GP Bolton Lancs.; SHO (Surg.) The Corbett Hosp. W. Midl.

HASSAN, Mohammed Shahbaz Ul 62 Dawlish Road, Selly Oak, Birmingham B29 7AE — MB BS 1996 Lond.

HASSAN, Mohammed Sultan Ul 62 Dawlish Road, Birmingham B29 7AE — MB ChB 1994 Leeds.

HASSAN, Mokhtar Amin 96 Dartmouth Road, London NW2 4HB — MB ChB 1964 Alexandria.

HASSAN, Nibras 22 Greystone Gardens, Harrow HA3 0EG — LRCP LRCS Ed. LRCPS Glas. 1997.

HASSAN, Paul Christopher Dunstable Health Centre, Priory Gardens, Dunstable LU6 3SU Tel: 01582 699622 Fax: 01582 663431; 4 Lancot Avenue, Dunstable LU6 2AW — MB BS 1976 Lond.; MRCGP 1983; DRCOG 1980.

HASSAN, Sami Nooh 158 Okus Road, Swindon SN1 4JY — MB ChB 1981 Basrah; PhD (UK); MRCP; MRCPCH; DCH RCPS Glas. 1987. Paediat. P.ss Margt. Hosp. Swindon. Socs: BMA.

HASSAN, Sobia 50 Hollybush Hill, London E11 1PX — BM BS 1998 Nottm.; BM BS Nottm 1998.

HASSAN, Stephen Peter Minfor Surgery, Park Road, Barmouth LL42 1PL Tel: 01341 280521; Allt Fechan, Barmouth LL42 1YG — MB BS 1977 Lond.; DRCOG 1983.

HASSAN, Mr Tajek Basheer Dept of Emergency Medicine, Leeds General Infirmary, Leeds LS1 3EX Email: thassan@ulth.northy.nhs.uk — MB BS 1986 Lond.; MD 2001; FRCS Ed. 1993; MRCP (UK) 1989; DA (UK) 1990; FFAEM 1996. (Charing Cross & Westminster Medical School) Cons., Emerg. Med., Leeds Gen. Infirm. Socs: Collegiate Fell. Roy. Coll. Surgs. Edin.; Collegiate Mem. Roy. Coll. Phys.; Fac. Accid. & Emerg. Med. Prev: Regist. (A & E Med.) Leicester Roy. Infirm.; SHO (Orthop.) Birm. Accid. Hosp.; SHO (Anaesth.) Qu. Med. Centre Nottm.

HASSAN, Professor Tarek Hassan Ali 6 Stanton Road, London SW13 0EX Tel: 020 8876 1404 Fax: 020 8876 5778 Email: agorinst@gn.apc.org; 18 Mohammad Saleh Street, Dokki, Cairo 12311, Egypt Tel: 00 20 2 3374311 Fax: 00 20 2 3491481 Email: tari@idsc.gov.eg — MB BCh 1959 Cairo; FRCP Ed. 1978, M 1964; MRCP Lond. 1965; LMSSA Lond. 1967. (Cairo) Prof. Endocrinol. & Chairm. Dept. Med. Specialities Al Azhar Univ., Cairo. Socs: Founding Mem. Egyptian Soc. Gp. Train. for Personal & Social Health.

HASSAN, Urfan Salim 24 Phillimore Road, Birmingham B8 1PR — MB BS 1994 Lond.

HASSAN, Wajahat University Hospital Leicester, Infirmary Square, Leicester LE1 5WW Tel: 0116 258 5652 Fax: 0116 258 5833 Email: wuhassaon@uhl.trent.nhs.uk — MB BS 1985 Punjab; MD (UK) 1997; MRCP (UK) 1989; FRCP Ed. 1998; FRCP London 2000. (King Edward Medical College, Lahore, Pakistan) Cons Rheumatologist Univ Hosp Leicester. Socs: Brit. Soc. of Sports Med.; Brit. Soc. Rheum. Prev: Sen. Regist. (Rheum. & Internal Med.) Leicester Roy. Infirm.; Cons Rheum City Hosp Sunderland.

HASSAN, William Ernest, Group Capt. RAF Med. Br. Retd. (retired) 12 Silverdale Road, St Annes, Lytham St Annes FY8 3RE Tel: 01253 720655 — MB BS Lond. 1945, DPH 1962; MFCM 1972. Prev: Sen. Med. Off. DHSS Blackpool.

HASSAN, Yunus Syston Health Centre, Melton Road, Syston, Leicester LE7 2EQ — MB ChB 1992 Aberd.

HASSAN, Zaki-Udin 9 Vigilant Close, High Level Drive, London SE26 6YA — MB BS 1990 Lond.

HASSAN-ALI, Rumina 142 Ashfield Avenue, Bushey, Watford WD23 4TE — BM 1994 Soton.

HASSANAIEN, Midhat Mohamed 25 St Dunston's Avenue, Acton, London W3 6QD Tel: 020 8723 6109 Email: mhassanaie@aol.com; The Old Police House, 49 Mulbany Green Road, Harlow CM17 0EZ Tel: 0976 401291 — MB ChB 1982 Alexandria; MRCOG 1995. (Alexanderia Med. Sch.) Specialist Regist. (O & G) w. Midl. Rotat. Socs: Colposcopy Soc. & Minimal Access Surg. Prev: Sen. Regist. O & G.

HASSANALLY, Delilah Abdulmohamed 102 Thetford Road, New Malden KT3 5DZ — MB BS 1993 Lond.; BSc (Hons.) Pharm. Brighton 1984; MSc (Biopharm.) Lond. 1986; MRPharmS 1985. (St. Geo. Hosp. Lond.) Specialist Regist. (Gen. Surg.) Old Ch. Hosp. Romford. Prev: SHO (Orthop.) Kingston Hosp.; SHO (Neurosurg.) Brook Hosp. Greenwich; SHO (A & E) St. Geo. Hosp. Tooting.

HASSANEIN, Mohamed Mahmoud Aly 17 Deva Lane, Chester CH2 1BN — MB ChB 1985 Alexandria, Egypt; MB ChB Alexandria Egypt 1985.

HASSANYEH, Fouad Khattar Department of Psychiatry, Royal Victoria Infirmary, Newcastle upon Tyne NE1 4LP; The Old Vicarage, High St, Newburn, Newcastle upon Tyne NE15 8LQ — MB BS 1971 Newc.; FRCPsych 1988, M 1975. Cons. Psychiat. Roy. Vict. Infirm. Newc.; Clin. Lect. (Psychiat.) Univ. Newc. u. Tyne. Prev: Cons. Psychiat. St. Mary's Hosp. Stannington; Lect. (Psychiat.) Univ. Newc. u. Tyne; Sen. Regist. (Psychiat.) Newc. AHA (T).

HASSARD, Jason Robert Arden House, Newton Blossomville, Bedford MK43 8AN Tel: 01234 888915 — MB BCh BAO 1941 Dub.; MA Dub. 1952, MD 1952. BA 1941; LM Rotunda 1946; FRCOG 1963, M 1948. (Dub.) Hon. Cons. O & G Bedford Gen. Hosp. Prev: Sen. Regist. W. Middlx. Hosp.; SHO (Surg.) Caern. & Anglesey Infirm. & Hampstead Gen. Hosp.

HASSELL, Andrew Brian 91 Lichfield Road, Stone ST15 8QD — MB ChB 1984 Manch.; MD Manch. 1993; MRCP (UK) 1988. Cons. Rheum. & Sen. Lect. Staffs. Rheuma. Centre Haywood Hosp. Stoke-on-Trent. Socs: Brit. Soc. Rheum.; Midl. Rhem. Soc. Prev: Sen. Regist. (Rheum.) Stoke-on-Trent; Research Fell. (Rheum.) Univ. Birm.; Tutor (Rheum.) Univ. Manch.

HASSETT, Mr Patrick Donal Ambrose Altnagelvin Area Hospital, Derry, Londonderry BT48 1SB Tel: 01504 345171 Fax: 01504 311020; 23 Gleneagles, Londonderry BT48 7TE — MB BCh BAO 1982 NUI; MSc NUI 1992; FRCS Glas. 1990; FRCOphth 1991. Cons. Ophth. Surg. Altnagelvin Area Hosp. Derry. Socs: Amer. Acad. Ophth.

HASSEY, Gerald Alan Fisher Medical Centre, Millfields, Coach Street, Skipton BD23 1EU — MB BS 1978 Ncle; MB BS 1978 Ncle.

HASSIM, Abubakr (retired) The Bwlch Cottage, Nr. Erwood, Builth Wells LD2 3TX Tel: 01982 560320 — MB BCh Witwatersrand 1955; BSc Witwatersrand 1955; FRCOG 1971, M 1961. Prev: Sen. Cons. O & G Wellcome NHS Trust Barnet.

HASSIM, Conan Eusuph 44A Richmond Avenue, London N1 0ND — MB BS 1993 Lond.

HASSIOTIS, Angeliki 2nd Floor, Wolfson Building, 48 Riding House St., London W1N 8AA Tel: 020 769 9451 Fax: 020 7679 9426 Email: a.hassiotis@ucl.ac.uk; Tel: 020 7482 6058 Fax: 020 7482 6058 — Ptychio Iatrikes 1987 Athens; MRCPsych 1992; MA (Med. Law & Ethics) 1997. (Nat. Univ. Athens) Sen. Lect. and Hon. Cons. Psychiat. Developm.al Disorders. Socs: BMA; MDU. Prev: Cons. Psychiat. & Hon Sen Lect. Psychiat. Developm Disorders & Learn. Disabil. Herts & Essex Community NHS Trust & UCL; Clin. Research Fell. St. Mary's Hosp. Lond.; Sen. Regist. (Learning Disabil.) Char. Cross Hosp. & Horizon NHS Trust.

HASSIOTOU, Anna The Surgery, 572 Green Lanes, Hornsey, London N8 0RP Tel: 020 8802 6250; 3 Francis Place, Holmesdale Road, London N6 5TQ — Ptychio Iatrikes 1976 Thessalonika. GP E & H Health Auth. Socs: BMA; MDU; LMC.

HASSLOCHER, Doris 24 Blake Hall Crescent, London E11 3RH Tel: 020 8989 6172 — MB BS 1986 Lond.; BSc (Pharmacol.) Lond. 1983; DTM & H RCP Lond. 1995. (St. Bart.)

HASSON, Fergal Prionsias 19 Hillview Avenue, Londonderry BT47 2NU — MB ChB 1994 Glas.

HASSON, Sayed Yaqub Rivergreen Medical Centre, 106 Southchurch Drive, Clifton, Nottingham NG11 8AD.

HASSOON, Abed Ali Majeed Department of Rehabilitation Medicine, Manchester Royal Infirmary, Oxford Road, Manchester M13 9WL Tel: 0161 276 4361 Fax: 0161 276 4188; 37 White Moss Avenue, Chorlton, Manchester M21 0XS Tel: 0161 881 0136 — MB ChB 1973 Baghdad; LMSSA Lond. 1988; MRCPI 1988; DMedRehab RCP Lond. 1998. Sen. Regist. (Rehabil. Med.) Manch. Roy. Infimary. Socs: Brit. Soc. Rehab. Med.; Soc. Res. Rehab. Prev: Staff Grade Phys. (Gen. Med. & Med. for Elderly) St. Richard's Hosp. Chichester; Staff Grade Doctor (Haemat. & Gen. Med.) Qu. Eliz. Hosp. King's Lynn; Regist. (Geriat. Med.) Sunderland Dist. Gen. Hosp.

HASSOON, Mohammed Majeed Pontefract General Infirmary, Friarwood Lane, Pontefract WF8 1PL Tel: 01977 600600 Fax: 01977 606468 — MB ChB Baghdad Iraq 1970; FRCP Ed. 1996;

MRCP (UK) 1982. (Baghdad Medical School) Cons. Paediat. Pontefract Gen. Infirm. Socs: BMA; MRCPCH; Yorks. Regional Paediat. Soc.

HASTE, Alan Richard 14 Broom Lane, Rotherham S60 3EL Tel: 01709 377257 — MB BS 1958 Lond.; FRCP Lond. 1979, M 1966. (Lond. Hosp.) p/t Cons. Phys. Rotherham AHA; Hon. Clin. Lect. Sheff. Med. Sch. Socs: BMA & Sheff. MC Soc. Prev: Sen. Regist. Leicester Roy. Infirm.; Regist. (Med.) Sheff. Roy. Infirm.; Ho. Surg. Lond. Hosp.

HASTIE, Anne Louise The Wrythe Green Surgery, Wrythe Lane, Carshalton SM5 2RE Tel: 020 8669 3232 Fax: 020 8773 2524; 55 The Avenue, Cheam, Sutton SM2 7QE Tel: 020 8661 9804 Fax: 020 8661 9804 — MB BS 1974 Lond.; FRCGP 1993, M 1979; DRCOG 1977. (St. Geo.) Assoc. Dean S. Thames Region (W.); Adviser for non-Princip. GPs. Socs: Sutton & Dist. Med. Soc. Prev: GP Trainer Surrey; Chairwom. SW Thames Career Advis. Subcomm.; GP Tutor St. Helier Hosp. Carshalton.

HASTIE, Gillian Sarah 1/R 5 University Av, Glasgow G12 8NN — MB ChB 1997 Glas.

HASTIE, Ian Robert Department of Geriatric Medicine, 3rd Floor, Lanesborough Wing, St George's Hospital, Blackshaw Road, London SW17 0QT Tel: 020 8725 3503 Fax: 020 8725 5325 Email: ihastie@sghms.ac.uk — MB BS 1973 Lond.; FRCP Lond. 1990; MRCP (UK) 1975. (St. Geo.) Cons. & Sen. Lect. (Geriat. Med.) St. Geo. Hosp. Lond.; Sec. (Geriat. Sect.) Europ. Union of Med. Specialist; Assoc. Dean Postgrad. Med.Lond. Deanery. Socs: Brit. Geriat. Soc.; BMA. Prev: Hon. Sec. Brit. Geriat. Soc.; Chairm. of B.G.S. Train. Comm.; Regional Clin. Tutor (Geriat. Med.).

HASTIE, John William Lincoln Road Surgery, 62 Lincoln Road, Peterborough PE1 2SN Tel: 01733 551008 Fax: 01733 345399; 1 Sunningdale, Orton Waterville, Peterborough PE2 5UB Tel: 01733 239028 — MB ChB 1978 Ed.; BSc Ed. 1975; D.Occ.Med. RCP Lond. 1996. (Univ. Ed. Med. Sch.) Socs: Soc. Occupat. Med.; Assn. Local Auth. Med. Advisors. Prev: SHO (Obst.) Bellshill Matern. Hosp.; SHO (Anaesth.) Roy. Infirm. Edin.; SHO (ENT) City Hosp. Edin.

HASTIE, Mr Kenneth John Royal Hariamrhine Hosp, Glossop Road, Sheffield S10 5SD Tel: 0114 271 3324 Fax: 0114 271 3425 — MB ChB 1979 Liverp.; MD Liverp. 1989; FRCS Ed. 1983. Cons. Urol. Surg. Roy. Hallamsh. Hosp. Sheff. Socs: Brit. Assn. Urol. Surgs.; Soc. Minimally Invasive Ther.; Brit. Soc. Endocrinol.

HASTINGS, Adrian Michael Saffron Group Practice, 509 Saffron Lane, Leicester LE2 6UL Tel: 0116 244 0888 Fax: 01162 831405; Department of General Practice & Primary Health Care, Leicester General Hospital, Gwendolen Road, Leicester LE5 4PW Tel: 0116 258 4622 Fax: 0116 258 4982 Email: ams@le.ac.uk — MB ChB 1976 Birm. Teachg. Co-ordinator (Gen. Pract.) Univ. Leicester. Socs: BMA; AGUDA (Co-ordinating Gp. Mem.). Prev: Dir. Agents de Medicina Course Maputo, Mozambique.

HASTINGS, Andrew Geoffrey Department of Pathology, Kings Mill Centre for Health Care Services, Mansfield Road, Sutton-in-Ashfield NG17 4JL Tel: 01623 622515 Ext: 3623; The Hurdles, Station Road, Rolleston, Newark NG23 5SE Tel: 01636 814961 — MB ChB 1976 Birm.; FRCPath 1996, M 1986; Dip. Med. Sci. Newc. 1997. Cons. Histopath., King's Mill Centre for Health Care Servs. NHS Trust. Socs: BMA; ACP. Prev: Cons. Histopath. N.d. HA; Sen. Regist. (Histopath.) United Bristol Hosps.; Regist. (Histopath.) Plymouth Gen. Hosp.

HASTINGS, Edith Marion (retired) 96 Main Street, Foxton, Market Harborough LE16 7RD — MB ChB 1967 Glas.; MRCPsych 1973; DPM Ed. & Glas. 1972. Prev: Cons. (Child Adolesc. Psychiat.) Leics. HA.

HASTINGS, James Liddell 13 Calside Avenue, Paisley PA2 6DD Tel: 0141 889 9018 — MB ChB 1951 Glas.; DPH 1957. Hosp. Pract. Darnley Hosp. Glas. Prev: Ho. Phys. Med. Unit Gartloch Hosp. Gartcosh; Ho. Surg. O & G Falkirk Roy. Infirm.; Dep. MOH Burgh of Paisley.

HASTINGS, John George Mark 184 Millhouses Lane, Sheffield S7 2HE — MD 1984 Lond.; MB BS 1976; MRCPath 1987. (Univ. Coll. Hosp.) Lect. (Med. Microbiol.) Univ. Sheff. Med. Sch.

HASTINGS, Linda Anne Basildon Primary Care Group, The Hatherley, Basildon SS14 2QJ Tel: 01268 441623 Fax: 01268 441621 Email: lindah@sessex-h.a.nthames.nhs.uk; 37 Tabors Avenue, Great Baddow, Chelmsford CM2 7EJ — MB ChB 1977 Liverp.; MRCGP 1989; DPH Camb. 1993; DRCOG 1980; MFPHM 1996. Chief Exec., Basildon Primary Care Gp. Prev: Indep. Med. Advisor & Policy Developm. Manager Enfield & Haringey FHSA; Cons. (Publ. Health Med.) N. Essex Health Auth.; Sen. Regist. Pub. Health Med., Oxf. & Anglia RHA.

HASTINGS, Lucy Irene 43 Wesley Road, Ironbridge, Telford TF8 7BD — MB BS 1997 Lond.

HASTINGS, Peter Douglas Newton Port Surgery, Newton Port, Haddington EH41 3NF; Cromdale, Victoria Road, Haddington EH41 4DJ — BSc (Med. Sci.) Ed. 1978, MB ChB 1981; T(GP) 1991; MRCGP 1985; DCH RCP Lond. 1983; DRCOG 1983. GP Princip.; GP Trainer. Socs: BMA. Prev: GP VTS Highland HB; Med. Off. Falkland I. Govt. Port Stanley; Ho. Off. (Gen. Med. & Gen. Surg.) Roy. Infirm. Edin.

HASTINGS, Stephen Craig 28 Moss Brow, Bollington, Macclesfield SK10 5HH — MB ChB 1992 Manch.

HASTLE, Janet Avril, Flight Lt. RAF Med. Br. RAF Headley Court, Epsom KT18 6JN Tel: 0372 378271; 9 Thorntree Green, Appleton Thorn, Warrington WA4 4QU Tel: 01925 602311 — BM BS 1992 Nottm.; BMedSci Nottm. 1990; DRCOG 1996. (Univ. Nottm.) SHO (Rheum. & Rehabil.) RAF Headley Ct. Epsom. Socs: Med. Protec. Soc. Prev: SHO (O & G) High Wycombe Hosp.; Med. Off. Akrotiri Cyprus; Ho. Off. (Med.) Torbay.

HATCH, Anna Louise 1 The Grove, Kings Avenue, Morpeth NE61 1HY — MB ChB 1987 Birm. Trainee GP Ashington; SHO (Psychiat.) St. Geo. Hosp. Morpeth. Prev: SHO (Paediat.) Wordsley Hosp. Stourbridge; SHO (O & G) Dudley Rd. Hosp. Birm.; Ho. Off. (Med.) E. Birm. Hosp.

HATCH, Professor David John Portex Department of Anaesthesia, Institute of Child Health, 30 Guilford St., London WC1N 1EH Tel: 020 79052382 Fax: 020 7829 8634 Email: d.hatch@ich.ucl.ac.uk; 6 Darnley Road, Woodford Green IG8 9HU Tel: 020 8504 4134 — MB BS 1961 Lond.; MRCS Eng. LRCP Lond. 1961; FFA RCS Eng. 1965. (Univ. Coll. Hosp.) p/t Prof. Paediat. Anaesth. Univ. Lond.; Professional Standards Adviser, Roy. Coll. of Anaesth.s. Socs: BMA; (Counc.) Roy. Coll. Anaeth.; AAGBI. Prev: Fell. (Anesth.) Mayo Clinic Rochester, Minn.; Regist. Char. Cross Hosp.; Ho. Phys. Univ. Coll. Hosp. Lond.

HATCH, Gordon Robert (Surgery) 1A Madeira Road, Parkstone, Poole BH14 9ET; 129 Dorchester Road, Oakdale, Poole BH15 3RY — LMSSA 1957 Lond. (St. Mary's) Prev: Ho. Phys. & Ho. Surg., SHO O & G & SHO Cas. Poole Gen. Hosp.

HATCH, John Windward, Langton Matravers, Swanage BH19 3HH — BM BCh 1966 Oxf.; BA; DCH Eng. 1973. Prev: Regist. (Paediat.) St. Peter's Hosp. Chertsey; Ho. Surg. Univ. Coll. Hosp. Lond.; Ho. Phys. St. James Hosp. Lond.

HATCH, Katharine May Susan 159 Verulam Road, St Albans AL3 4DW — MB BS 1987 Lond.

HATCH, Timothy Seaton Hirst Health Centre, Norham Road, Ashington NE63 0NG Tel: 01670 813167 Fax: 01670 523889; 1 The Grove, Kings Avenue, Morpeth NE61 1HY — MB ChB 1987 Birm.; MRCGP 1992. Prev: SHO (Psychiat.) St. Geo. Hosp. Morpeth; Trainee GP Birm.

HATCHER, Alexander Orchard House Surgery, Bleak Road, Lydd, Romney Marsh TN29 9AE Tel: 01797 320307; Popular House, Church Road, Lydd, Romney Marsh TN29 9DU Tel: 01797 321496 — MB BS 1967 Lond.; MRCS Eng. LRCP Lond. 1966. (St. Geo.) Prev: Maj. RAMC; Ho. Phys. & Ho. Surg. Sutton Gen. Hosp.

HATCHER, Geoffrey William (retired) 23 Bishops Road, Hove BN3 6PN Tel: 01273 555269 — MB BS 1956 Lond.; MA Oxf. 1952; FRCP Ed. 1974, M 1964; DObst RCOG 1957. Hon. Cons. Paediat. Brighton & Lewes, Mid Sussex Gp. Hosps. & Roy. Alexandra Hosp. Sick Childr. Brighton. Prev: Ho. Phys. Hosp. Sick Childr. Gt. Ormond St. Lond.

HATCHER, Graham Anthony 29 Queens Road, Wisbech PE13 2PE Tel: 01945 581111 — MB ChB 1977 Leeds; DRCOG 1981; DCH Eng. 1980.

HATCHER, Hilda Joan (retired) 4 Kerry Terrace, Summerside, Buckland, Faringdon SN7 8QZ — MB BS 1948 Lond.; MRCS Eng. LRCP Lond. 1948; DCH Eng. 1952. Prev: Ho. Phys. New Sussex Hosp. Brighton.

HATCHER, Ian Stuart 21 Tasker Road, Sheffield S10 1UY Tel: 0114 267 8154 Fax: 0114 267 8154 Email: ihatcher@msn.com — MB BS 1988 Lond.; FRCA 1994.

HATCHER, Luena Helen (retired) Suva, Cnwc Y Lili, New Quay SA45 9SH — MB BS 1951 Lond.; FFR 1974; MRCS Eng. LRCP Lond. 1951; DMRD Eng. 1969. Prev: Cons. (Radiol.) Newmarket Gen. Hosp.

HATCHER, Rowland Clifford Garden Cottage, Sydenham, Okehampton EX20 4PR — MB ChB 1924 Bristol; MRCS Eng. LRCP Lond. 1924.

HATCHER, Steven Michael Flat E, 3 Park Crescent, Leeds LS8 1DH — MB ChB 1995 Leeds.

HATCHICK, Bernard 2 Spanish Place, London W1 Tel: 020 7935 7676; 9 Albemarle Mansions, Heath Drive, London NW3 Tel: 020 7435 5336 — LMSSA 1953 Lond. (Univ. Coll. Lond. & Westm. Hosp.) Med. Off. Civil Serv. Dept.; Med. Adviser Arts Counc. of GB; Mem. Adviser Chartered Inst. of Managem. Accountants; Med. Adviser Design Counc. of GB. Socs: Fell. Roy. Soc. Med.; BMA. Prev: Sen. Cas. Off. Hampstead Gen. Hosp.; Ho. Phys. & Ho. Surg. Bethnal Green Hosp.; Ho. Phys. St. Jas. Hosp. Lond.

HATCHWELL, Eli Wessex Human Genetics Institute, Duthie Building (808), Southampton General Hospital, Tremona Road, Southampton SO16 6YD Tel: 02380 796424 Fax: 02380 794264 Email: eli@potsie.demon.co.uk; 26 Bye Road, Swanwick, Southampton SO31 7GX — MB BChir 1985 Camb.; MA Camb. 1985; DPhil Oxf. 1995; BA Open 1993. (University Cambridge) Hon. Cons. Wessex. Clin. Genetics Serv. P.ss Anne Hosp. Soton; Vis. Scientist Cold Spring Harbour Laborat. NY, USA. Socs: Clin. Genetics Soc. Prev: Sen. Regist. (Clin. Genetics) P.ss Anne Hosp. Soton.; Wellcome Clin. Research Fell. Genetics Laborat. Dept. Biochem. Oxf. Univ.; SHO (Gen. Paediat.) N.wick Pk. Hosp. Harrow.

HATELEY, Stuart James Knowle House Surgery, 4 Meavy Way, Crownhill, Plymouth PL5 3JB Tel: 01752 793383 Fax: 01752766510; Hagley, Spire Hill, Fairmead Rd, Burraton Coombe, Saltash PL12 4QE Tel: 01752 845617 — MB ChB 1986 Leeds. GP. Prev: SHO (Med. for Elderly) Greenbank Hosp. Plymouth; Trainee GP Saltash Health Centre; SHO (O & G) St. Jas. Hosp. Leeds.

HATELY, William (retired) 4 Hitherwood Drive, London SE19 1XB Tel: 020 8670 7644 Fax: 020 8670 9071 Email: williamhately@tinyonline.co.uk — MB ChB Ed. 1958; FRCP Ed. 1973, M 1965; FRCR 1975; FFR 1966; DMRD 1964. Prev: Cons. Radiologist, The Roy. Lond. Hosp., Whitechapel.

HATEM, Mohamed North Tees General Hospital, Hardwick Road, Stockton-on-Tees TS19 8PE Tel: 01642 617617; Newlands, 17 Dunottar Avenue, Eaglescliffe, Stockton-on-Tees TS16 0AB Tel: 01642 785180 — MB BCh 1976 Cairo; DM 1989; MRCOG 1983. Cons. O & G N. Tees Gen. Hosp. Stockton-on-Tees.

HATFIELD, Adrian Richard William Gastroenterology Department, The Middlesex Hospital, Mortimer St., London W1T 3AA Tel: 020 7380 9011 Fax: 020 7380 9162; Corfe House, 45 Arnison Road, East Molesey KT8 9JR Tel: 020 8941 0304 — MRCS Eng. LRCP Lond. 1969; MD Lond. 1984, MB BS 1969; FRCP Lond. 1989; MRCP (UK) 1972. Cons. Gastroenterol. Middlx. Hosp. & King Edwd. VII Hosp. for Offs.Lond. Prev: Cons. Gastroenterol. Lond. Hosp.

HATFIELD, Alison Geraldine Disablement Services Centre, St Mary's Hospital, Milton Rd, Portsmouth PO3 6BR Tel: 02392 286000 — MB BS 1989 Lond.; MRCP (UK) 1994. (St. Geo. Hosp. Med. Sch. Lond.) Cons. In Rehab. Med. Portsmouth Gen. Hosp. NHS Trust. Socs: Brit. Soc. Rehabil. Med.; Brit. Geriat. Soc.; BMA. Prev: Regist. (Gen. Med.) Stoke Mandeville Hosp. Aylesbury; SHO (Gen. Med.) Gt. Yarmouth & Waverly HA & Nottm. City Hosp.; Sen. Regist. (Rehabil. Med.Rivermead.Rehab.Centre.Oxf., Battle Hosp. Reading).

HATFIELD, Andrew David Hatters, Church Lane, Balsham, Cambridge CB1 6DS Tel: 01223 892961; 18 Heathfield Terrace, headingley, Leeds LS6 4DE Tel: 0113 275 7474 — BM BS 1990 Nottm.; BMedSci (Hons.) 1988. (Notts) Specialist Regist. Anaesth.

HATFIELD, Anita Clark NYCRIS, Arthington House, Hospital Lane, Leeds LS16 6QB Tel: 0113 392 4158 Fax: 0113 392 4132 Email: acrh@ulth.northy.nhs.uk; The Old Rectory, Cowthorpe, Wetherby LS22 5EZ Tel: 01423 358558 Fax: 01423 359280 Email: anita@cowthorpe.demon.co.uk — MB ChB 1979 Aberd.; MPH Leeds 1995; Cert. Family Plann. JCC 1984; Cert. Prescribed Equiv. Exp. JCPTGP 1981; MFPHM 1997. (Aberdeen University) Cons. Med. Care Epidemiologist Leeds Teachg. Hosps. Trust; Cons in Pub. health Med. N Yorks HA York. Socs: Fac. Pub. Health Med.; BMA. Prev: Sen. Regist. (Pub. Health Med.) N.. & Yorks. RHA; Princip. GP Broxburn Health Centre.

HATFIELD, Emma Christina Imogen Sherwood, Heronsgate, Rickmansworth WD3 5DE — MB BChir 1991 Camb.

HATFIELD, Frank Edward Stafford (retired) Ongar House, 212 High St., Chipping Ongar, Ongar CM5 9JJ Tel: 01277 363428 — MB BChir 1938 Camb.; MRCS Eng. LRCP Lond. 1936; FRCGP 1979, M 1957; DPM Eng. 1939.

HATFIELD, John Miles Richardson Manor Farm Medical Centre, Mangate Street, Swaffham PE37 7QN Tel: 01760 721786; Walnut Tree Farm, Drury Square, Beeston, King's Lynn PE32 2NA Tel: 01328 701560 — MB ChB 1980 Ed.; PhD Camb. 1971, BA 1966; MRCGP 1986. Foulkes Foundat. Fell.sh. 1978. Socs: Brit. Med. Acupunct. Soc. Prev: SHO Freeman Hosp. Newc.; Ho. Phys. Roy. Infirm. Edin.

HATFIELD, Michael (retired) Silverdene, Rushmere Lane, Orchard Leigh, Chesham HP5 3QY Tel: 01494 778606 — MB BS 1957 Lond.; MSc (Radiobiol.) Birm. 1963; MFOM RCP Lond. 1980. Prev: Surg. Capt. RN Retd.

***HATFIELD, Paul** 337 Coppice Road, Arnold, Nottingham NG5 7HH — MB ChB 1995 Birm.; ChB Birm. 1995.

HATFIELD, Penelope Anne 1 Slade Close, Ottery St Mary EX11 1SY — MB BS 1997 Lond.

HATFIELD, Mr Richard Herford Department of Neurosurgery, University Hospital of Wales, Heath Park, Cardiff CF14 4XW Tel: 029 2074 2733 Fax: 029 2074 2560 Email: hatfield@cardiff.ac.uk; 35 Victoria Road, Penarth CF64 3HY Tel: 029 2070 9473 Email: halfield@compuserve.com — MD 1991 Lond.; MA Camb. 1990; BSc (Hons.) Sussex Univ. 1972; MB BS Lond. 1980; FRCS Ed. 1984. (Roy. Free Hosp.) Cons. Neurosurg. Univ. Hosp. Wales Cardiff. Socs: Soc. Brit. Neurol. Surg.; Roy. Soc. Med. Prev: Clin. Lect. & Hon. Sen. Regist. (Neurosurg.) Addenbrooke's Hosp. Camb.

HATFIELD, Susanne Joy 102 Spen Lane, Cleckheaton BD19 4AA — MB ChB 1989 Leeds; MRCP (UK) 1993.

HATFIELD, Sylvia Annette Meakin (retired) Ongar House, 212 High St., Chipping Ongar, Ongar CM5 9JJ Tel: 01277 363428 — MB BS 1937 Lond.; MRCS Eng. LRCP Lond. 1935; MRCGP 1957.

HATFULL, Dean Mark 39 Swanbridge Road, Bexleyheath DA7 5BP — BM 1995 Soton.

HATHAWAY, Colin Coastal Villages Practice, Pippin Close, Ormesby St. Margaret, Great Yarmouth NR29 3RW Tel: 01493 730205 Fax: 01493 733120; The Retreat, Main Road, Ormesby St Michael, Great Yarmouth NR29 3LW Tel: 01493 731390 — MB BS 1968 Lond.; MRCS Eng. LRCP Lond. 1968. (Char. Cross) Prev: Regist. (Surg.) Roy. Masonic Hosp.; Cas. Off. St. Thos. Hosp. Lond.; SHO (Orthop.) Cromer Gen. Hosp.

HATHERELL, Margaret Jean Porch Surgery, Beechfield Road, Corsham SN13 9DL Tel: 01249 712232 Fax: 01249 701389 — MB BS 1990 Lond.; MRCGP 1996; DRCOG 1996; DFFP 1997. (St. Geo. Hosp.) Princip. GP. Prev: SHO (Geriat. & O & G) Stratton St. Margt. & P.ss Margt. Hosps. Swindon; Trainee GP Corsham VTS.

HATHERLEY, Candida Clare d'Arcy Manor Farm House, Heddington, Calne SN11 0PS — MB BS 1996 Lond.

HATHERLEY, Peter Richard The Retreat, Retreat Road, Wimborne BH21 1BU Tel: 01202 882861 Fax: 01202 883217 — MA Oxf. 1964; BM BCh Oxf. 1964; MRCGP 1972; DObst RCOG 1966. (Univ. Oxf.) Locum GP; Occupat. Phys. Flight Refuelling Ltd. Socs: Bournemouth & Poole Med. Soc. Prev: Sen. Partner Quarter Jack Surg., Wimbourne; Occupat. Phys. Flight Refuelling Ltd.; Sch. Med. Off. Carford Sch. & Dumpton Prep. Sch. Wimborne.

HATHI, Mohanlal Jivan (retired) 3 Carlina Gardens, Woodford Green IG8 0BP Tel: 020 8502 9674 — MB BS Bombay 1962.

HATHORN, Iain Andrew Greenhills Health Centre, 20 Greenhills Square, East Kilbride, Glasgow G75 8TT Tel: 01355 236331 Fax: 01355 234977 — MB ChB 1984 Glas.; MB ChB Glas. l984.

HATHORN, Michael Kenneth Shuldham Department of Physiology, Queen Mary & Westfield College, Mile End Road, London E1 4NS Tel: 020 7982 6374 Fax: 020 8983 0467 Email: m.k.s.hathorn@qmw.ac.uk; 112 Savernake Road, London NW3 2JR Tel: 020 7485 7843 Email: 100430.1547@compuserve.com — MB BCh 1950 Witwatersrand; PhD Lond. 1968. (Witwatersrand) Socs: Physiol. Soc.; Neonat. Soc. Prev: Emerit. Reader (Physiol.) Qu. Mary's & W.field Coll. Lond.; Hon. Sen .Lect. (Child Health) Lond. Hosp. Med. Coll.

HATHWAR, Vadiraj Billinge Hospital, Upholland Road, Billinge, Wigan WN5 7ET — MB BS 1974 Bangalore.

HATHWAY, Karen Louise 25 Ellesmere Road, West Bridgford, Nottingham NG2 7DE — MB ChB 1997 Bristol.

HATIMY, Umi Alhad 18 Southview Gardens, Schools Hill, Cheadle SK8 1PA — MB ChB 1993 Leeds.

HATJIOSIF, Rebecca Rutland House Surgery, 40 Colney Hatch, Muswell Hill, London N10 1DX; Oak Lodge, 70 Chandos Avenue, Whetstone, London N20 9DZ — MB ChB 1979 Leeds; DRCOG 1981; Cert. Family Plann. JCC 1981. Mem. Harangay Primary Care Trust Precribing Sub-Comm. Socs: BMA; Hellenic Med. Soc.

HATOUM, Mr Alaeddin Faris West Norwich Hospital, Norwich NR2 3TU Tel: 01603 286286, 01637 871445 Fax: 01603 288261; 77 High St, Thornhill Edge, Dewsbury WF12 0PS 9 Kingsley Meade, Trencreek, Newquay TR8 4PY Tel: 01603 250662, 01603 286286, 01637 871445, 01924 455082 Fax: 01603 250662, 01603 288261, alaeddinhatoum@hotmail.com — MD 1985 Damascus University; FRCS 1998 Edinburgh. (Damascus University) Staff Grade Opthalmology, W. Norwich Hosp., Norwich. Socs: Fell. of the Roy. Coll. of Surg., Edin.; BMA. Prev: Locum Regist., Opthalmology, Dudley Guest Hosp.; Sen. SHO Opthalmology, Dudley Guest Hosp., Dudley.

HATRICK, Andrew Graeme Tel: 01276 604604 Ext: 4370/4887 — MB BChir 1991 Camb.; FRCR 1997; MRCP (UK) 1994. Cons. Radiologist, Frimley Pk. Hosp. Prev: SHO (Med. & Endocrinol.) St. Mary's Hosp. Portsmouth; SHO (Geriat.) Qu. Alexandra Hosp. Portsmouth; SHO (Gen. & Thoracic Med.) St Mary's Hosp. Portsmouth.

HATRICK, Charlotte Mary The Surgery, The Street, Wonersh Tel: 01483 898123; Tel: 01483 839816 — MB BS 1991 Lond.; BA Oxf. 1988; MRCGP 1995; DRCOG 1993. GP Surrey Retainer Scheme. Prev: GP/Regist. Milford & Guildford Surrey; Trainee GP Soton. VTS.

HATRICK, Hugh The Knoll, Station Road, Duns TD11 3EL Tel: 01361 83322; Hardens Hill, Duns TD11 3NS Tel: 01361 83219 — MB ChB 1952 Glas.

HATRICK, John Alexander 11 Billings Hill Shaw, Hartley, Longfield DA3 8EU — MB BCh BAO NUI 1958; FRCPsych 1979, M 1971; LAH Dub. 1955. (Univ. Coll. Dub.) Emerit. Cons. Psychiat. Dartford & Gravesham HA. Socs: Fell. Roy. Soc. Med.; Soc. Clin. Psychiat. Prev: Postgrad. Clin. Tutor Univ. Lond. SE Thames RHA; Sen. Psychiat. St. And. Hosp. N.ants.; Regist. (Psychol. Med.) Univ. Glas. & S.. Gen. Hosp. Glas.

HATRICK, Mr Neil Cameron Th Lodge, Uplands Park, Sheringham NF26 8NE, 01273 696955 — MB BChir 1990 Camb.; MA Camb.1991; FRCS Eng. 1994; FRCS (Tr & Orth.) 1999. (Univ. Camb. (Clare Coll.) & St. Thos. Hosp. Lond.) Cons. Trauma, Orthopaedic Surg., Brighton Health Care NHS Trsut, Brighton. Prev: Hand & Shoulder Fell., Sydney,Australia; Regist. (Orthop.) Conquest Hosp., Hastings; Regist. (Orthop.) Brighton Health Care NHS Trust.

HATRICK, Robert Ian Eastwater House, Bramley, Guildford GU5 0DB Tel: 01483 893408 — MB BS 1996 Lond.; BSc (Hons) Lond. 1993. (UMDS Guy's & St. Tomas' Hospitals) SHO (Gen. Med.) Worthing Hosp. Worthing W. Sussex. Prev: SHO (A & E) St. Thomas' Hosp. Lond.

HATSIOPOULOU, Olga 1 Bentinek Terrace, Cambridge CB2 1HQ Tel: 01223 367229 — MB ChB 1997 Bristol. (Bristol University Medical School) SHO (O & G) Addenbrooke's Hosp. Camb.; PRHO (Diabetes) Gloucestershire Roy. Hosp. Socs: BMA; MPS. Prev: PRHO (Gen. Surg.) Bristol Roy. Infirm.

HATT, Heather Patricia Tel: 01928 733249 Fax: 01928 739367; 39 Grasmere Road, Frodsham, Warrington WA6 7LJ Tel: 01928 731318 — MB ChB 1978 Manch.; DRCOG 1981. Prev: Trainee GP Timperley Chesh.; Trainee GP Manch. VTS; Ho. Surg. Wythenshawe Hosp. Manch.

HATTAB, Mustafa Mohammed 5 St Augustine Road, Doncaster DN4 5LL — MB BCh 1975 Cairo.

HATTAM, Sarah Anna Louise Springfield Surgery, Park Road, Bingley BD16 4LR — MB ChB 1991 Leeds; MRCGP 1995. Retainer GP.

HATTAWAY, Benedick Matthew 4 Stalbridge Avenue, Liverpool L18 1EX — MB ChB 1998 Liverp.; MB ChB Liverp 1998.

HATTER, Tobias James Dept. of Forensic Medicine & Science, Glasgow University, Glasgow G12 8QQ Tel: 0141 330 4574 Email: thatter@formed.gla.ac.uk — MB BS 1996 Lond.; Dip FMS 2001; BSc 1989 (Hons). Lect. Fornsic Path.

HATTERSLEY, Professor Andrew Tym Department of Diabetes and Vascular Medicine, Postgraduate Medical School, Barrack Road, Exeter EX2 5AX Tel: 01392 403089 Fax: 01392 403027 Email: a.t.hattersley@ex.ac.uk — BM BCh 1984 Oxf.; MRCP (UK) 1987; DM Oxf. 1998. Cons. Phys. Roy. Devon & Exeter Healthcare NHS Trust; Prof. Molecular Med. Exeter Univ. Prev: Lect. (Med.) Qu. Eliz. Hosp. Birm.; MRC Research Fell. Diabetes Research Laborat. Radcliffe Infirm. Oxf.; Regist. (Med.) Hammersmith Hosp. Lond.

HATTERSLEY, Charlotte Louise 3 South View, Bramshall, Uttoxeter ST14 5BG — BM BS 1998 Nottm.; BM BS Nottm 1998. (Nottingham) SHO (Paediat.) Qu.'s Med. Centre, Nottm. Prev: Jun. Ho. Off. (Paediat./ Med./ Surg.) Qu.'s Med. Centre, Nottm.

HATTERSLEY, David Ashton Southea House, Main Road, Parson Drove, Wisbech PE13 4JA — MB 1972 Camb.; BChir 1971; MLCOM 1991; MRO 1991; DObst RCOG 1976. Indep. Phys. (Osteop.) Wisbech. Socs: Brit. Assn. of Manip. Med.; Brit. Osteop. Assn. Prev: GP Wisbech.

HATTERSLEY, Richard Wordsworth 15 Orchard Avenue, Lower Parkstone, Poole BH14 8AH Tel: 01202 232573 — MB BS 1987 Lond.; MRCGP 1995.

HATTERSLEY, Timothy Sherwood 9 Dyers Yard, Norwich NR3 3QY — MRCS Eng. LRCP Lond. 1959; MA, MB Camb. 1960, BChir 1959; DPhysMed Eng. 1970; MRCGP 1968. (St. Thos.)

HATTON, Catherine Taylor 45 Eastfield Crescent, Laughton, Sheffield S25 1YT — MB ChB 1993 Dundee.

HATTON, Christian Simon Ross Department of Haematology, Oxford Radcliffe Trust, Oxford OX3 9DU — MB BChir Camb. 1980; MRCP (UK) 1982; MRCPath 1989. Cons. Haemat. Wexham Pk. Hosp. Socs: Brit. Soc. Haematol. Prev: Sen. Regist. (Haemat.) John Radcliffe Hosp. Oxf.; Research Fell. (Med.) John Radcliffe Hosp. Oxf.

HATTON, Claire Elizabeth Fishponds Health Centre, Beechwood Road, Fishponds, Bristol BS16 3TD Tel: 0117 908 2365 Fax: 0117 908 2377 — MB BS 1992 Lond.; DRCOG 1996; MRCGP 1997. GP Regist. Surrey.

HATTON, Claire-Louise 43 Holmans, Church Road, Boreham, Chelmsford CM3 3EY Tel: 01245 462196 — MB BS 1996 Lond. (University College London) SHO (O & G) Qu.'s Med. Centre Nottm. Prev: SHO A & E Dryburn Hosp. Durh. City.

HATTON, Damian John 15 Watling Street Road, Fulwood, Preston PR2 8EA — MB ChB 1996 Manch.

HATTON, Emma Rebecca 45 Eastfield Crescent, Laughton, Sheffield S25 1YT — MB ChB 1998 Dund.; MB ChB Dund 1998.

HATTON, Jacqueline Anne The Old Dispensary, 8 Castle Street, Warwick CV34 4BP Tel: 01926 494137 Fax: 01926 410348; Avon Brook, Church Road, Sherbourne, Warwick CV35 8AN Tel: 01926 624348 — MB ChB 1979 Liverp.; DA (UK) 1986; DRCOG 1987.

HATTON, Margaret Ann 7 Acacia Grove, West Dulwich, London SE21 8ER — MB BS 1953 Lond.; FFA RCS Eng. 1965; DObst RCOG 1956. (Roy. Free)

HATTON, Marion Jennifer 214 Great Portland Street, London W1N 5HG Tel: 020 7383 2626 Fax: 020 7390 8428 — MRCS Eng. LRCP Lond. 1978; FRCOG 2000; 1978 MB BS Lond.; 1973 BSc (Hons.) Lond.; 1991 LLM; 1983 FRCS Ed.; 1978 MRCS Eng. LRCP Lond. (St. Bart.) Cons. O & G Lond. Prev: Sen. Regist. (O & G) Univ. Hosp. Wales Cardiff; Regist. (O & G) St. Bart. Hosp. Lond.; Ho. Surg. Profess. Surg. Unit St. Bart. Hosp. Lond.

HATTON, Mark Department of Orthopaedics, Queen's Medical Centre, Derby Road, Nottingham NG7 2; 24 Epperstone Road, West Bridgfprd, Nottingham NG2 7QF — MB ChB 1987 Ed.; FRCS Eng. 1994. (Edinburgh) Specialist Regist. (Orthop.) Mid Trent, Higher Surgic. Train. Progr.

HATTON, Matthew Quintin Fielding Weston Park Hospital, Whitham Lane, Sheffield S10 2SJ Tel: 0114 226 5000 — MB ChB 1986 Leeds; MSc Glos. 1994; FRCR 1995, M 1990. Cons. Clin. Oncol. W.on Pk. Hosp. Sheff.

HATTON, Michael (retired) 46 Aperfield Road, Biggin Hill, Westerham TN16 3LX — MRCS Eng. LRCP Lond. 1948.

HATTON, Paul Department of Public Health Medicine, Leeds HA, Blenheim House, West One, Duncombe St., Leeds LS1 4PL Tel: 0113 295 2040 Fax: 0113 295 2150 Email: paul.hatton@lh.leeds-ha.northy.nhs.uk — MB ChB 1982 Leeds; MB ChB (Hons.) Leeds 1982; BSc (Hons. Physiol.) Leeds 1979; MRCP (UK) 1986; MFPHM

RCP (UK) 1992; MPH Leeds 1988; FRCP 1998; FFPHM 1999. (Leeds) Cons. Communicable Dis. Control Leeds HA.; Cons. (Pub. Health Med.). Prev: Sen. Regist. (Pub. Health Med.) Leeds HA; Regist. (Community Med.) Leeds W.. HA; Regist. (Gen. Med.) Wharfedale Gen. Hosp. Otley.

HATTON, William James The Orchards, 1 Highway Lane, Keele, Newcastle ST5 5AN Tel: 01782 617403 — MB ChB Birm. 1948; MRCS Eng. LRCP Lond. 1948; MRCGP 1962. Med. Adviser Semma Gp. Festival Pk. Stoke-on-Trent. Socs: N. Staffs. Med. Soc. and Inst.

HATTON-ELLIS, Gerald Willmott Combe End, Daccombe, Newton Abbot TQ12 4ST — MB 1971 Camb.; BChir 1970.

HATTOTUWA, Karl Arjun Gampathi 428 Warwick Road, Solihull B91 1AQ — MB BS 1982 Colombo; MRCOG 1994.

HATTOTUWA, Keith Luxman 21 Bonar Place, Chislehurst BR7 5RJ Tel: 020 7515 7217 Fax: 020 7515 7217 Email: hattotuwa@aol.com — MB BS 1991 Sri Lanka; MRCS Eng. LRCP Lond. 1991; MRCP (UK) 1994.

HATTS, Robert Glentria, 6 Russell Field, Roman Road, Shrewsbury SY3 9AY — MRCS Eng. LRCP Lond. 1976; FFA RCS Eng. 1981. Cons. (Anaesth.) Roy. Shrewsbury Hosp. Shrewsbury.

HATTY, Sarah Rachel Lilly Reserach Centre, Erl Wood Manor, Windlesham GU20 6PH Tel: 01276 853214 Fax: 01276 853218 — MB BS 1980 Lond.; MRCP (UK) 1983. Dir. Europ. Early Oncol.Team. Prev: Europ. Dir. Clin. Developm. Shinix Pharmaceut. Corp.; Global Clin. Phys. Lilly Centre Windlesham.

HATZIS, Theodore Bristol Royal Infirmary, Department of Clinical Haematology, Marlborough St., Bristol BS2 8HW — Ptychio Iatrikes 1987 Thessalonika.

HAU, Ying Gate 148 Bunning Way, Frederica St., London N7 9UW — MB BS 1996 Lond.

HAUCK, Agnes, CBE (retired) Glenfrith Hospital, Groby Road, Leicester LE3 9QF Tel: 0116 287 2231 Fax: 0116 232 0441 — MB ChB 1963 Manch.; FRCPsych 1986, M 1976; DObst RCOG 1965; DPM Eng. 1968. Prev: Sen. Regist. (Ment. Handicap) Glenfrith Hosp. Leicester.

HAUER, Thomas Horton General Hospital, Oxford Road, Banbury OX16 9AL — State Exam Med 1991 Freiburg.

HAUGHEY, Fiona Anne Longreen Farm, South Keiss, Wick KW1 4XG Tel: 01955 631235 — MB ChB 1985 Ed.; BSc (Hons.) Pharmacol. Ed. 1983. Assoc. Camsbay, Caithness. Prev: SHO (ENT) City Hosp. Edin.; SHO (Geriat.) Roy. Vict. Hosp. Edin.; SHO (O & G) Dunfermline.

HAUGHEY, James Patrick 44 Northland Row, Dungannon BT71 6AP — MB BCh BAO 1966 NUI.

HAUGHEY, Nicola Margaret 12 Seymour Drive, Bromley BR2 8RE — MB BS 1991 Lond.

HAUGHEY, Sarah Josephine St Peters Street Medical Practice, 16 St Peters Street, London N1 8JG Tel: 020 7226 7131 Fax: 020 7354 9120 — MB BCh BAO 1975 NUI; MRCP (UK) 1981; MRCGP 1982; DCH Eng. 1978. (Univ. Coll. Dub.)

HAUGHIE, Robert Gascoine (retired) Leighton Villa, 50A Halifax Road, Batley WF17 7BH Tel: 01924 453358 Fax: 01924 453358 Email: gascoine@msn.com — MB ChB 1951 Glas.; DPH Glas. 1959.

HAUGHNEY, John Andrew Francis Alison Lea Medical Centre, Calderwood, East Kilbride, Glasgow G74 3BE Tel: 01355 261666; 5 Swanston Grove, Edinburgh EH10 7BN — MB ChB 1982 Aberd.; MRCGP 1987; DRCOG 1987.

HAUGHNEY, Michael Gerard Joseph 5 Swanston Grove, Edinburgh EH10 7BN — MB ChB 1980 Aberd.

HAUGHNEY, Robert Vincent Matthew Dept. of Obstetrics & Gynaecology, Kettering General Hospital, Rothwell Road, Kettering NN16 8UZ Tel: 01536 493349 — MB ChB 1990 Sheff.; DFFP 1995; MRCOG 1997. Cons. in Obst. & Gyn. (Lead Gyanecologist for Cancer Care), Kettering Genral Hosp. Socs: Brit. Gyn. Cancer Soc.; Birm. and Midl.s Obst. & Gyn. Soc.; Brit. Soc. for Colposcopy and Cervical Path. Prev: SHO (O & G) St. Mary's Hosp. Manch. & Jessop Hosp. for Wom. Sheff.; Regist. (O & G) St. Mary's Hosp. Manch.; Specialist Regist. Obst & Gyn Hope Hosps. Alford.

HAUGHNEY, Sarah Louise Chorley Road Surgery, 65 Chorley Road, Swinton, Manchester M27 4AF Tel: 0161 794 6287 Fax: 0161 728 3415 — MB ChB 1989 Sheff.; MRCGP 1994; DFFP 1993.

HAUGHTON, Neil Duncan L:ittle Venice Private Medical Practice, 3 Regent's Court, 92 Randolph Ave., Little Venice, London W9 1BG Tel: 020 7266 3037 — MB 1992 Camb.; BChir 1991; BSc (Hons.) St. And. 1989; MRCGP 1995; DFFP 1995; DCH RCP Lond. 1995; DRCOG 1994. (Cambridge) GP Medicentre, Lond. Socs: BMA. Prev: Princip. Med. Off. Lond. Light Ho.; GP Fell. (HIV/AIDS) St. Mary's Hosp. Lond.; GP Regist. Canterbury GPVTS.

HAUKE, Anne Hildegarde 30 Blaen-y-Coed, Radyr, Cardiff CF15 8RL Tel: 029 20843 140 — MB BCh 1980 Wales. (Welsh National School of Medicine - Cardiff)

HAUNSCHMIDT, Shirley Margaret Trenabie House Surgery, Trenabie House, Westray, Orkney KW17 2DL Tel: 01857 677209 Fax: 01857 617519; Hilldavale, Westray, Orkney KW17 2DW Tel: 01857 677294 — MB BS 1981 Lond.; MRCGP 1986; DCH RCP Lond. 1986; DRCOG 1984. (Roy. Free Hosp. Sch. Med.) GP Orkney. Socs: Roy. Coll. GPs.

HAUSSER, Beate Ingeborg Home 2, Flat 1, Victoria Hospital Residences, Whinney Heys Road, Blackpool FY3 8NR — State Exam Med 1992 Heidelberg.

HAUT, Fabian Franz Anton Teaching & Research Division, Royal Dundee Liff Hospital, Dundee DD2 5NF Tel: 01382 423080 Email: fhaut@ciff.finix.org.uk — State Exam Med 1990 Heidelberg; MRCPsych. Sen. Regist. Gen. Psychiat. (Learning Disabil.) Roy. Dundee Cliff Hosp.

HAVA, Mahmood Abdul Sattar Branch Surgery, 7 Raglan St., Hanson Lane, Halifax HX1 5QZ Tel: 01422 341957; The Gables, 161 Huddersfield Road, Halifax HX3 0AH Tel: 01422 354347 — MB BS 1955 Gujarat; FCCP 1969; TDD Madras 1963. (B.J. Med. Coll. Ahmedabad) Med. Assessor DHSS for Mobility Attend. Prev: Chief Med. Off. Chest Clinic & Hosp. Municip. Corpn. Ahmedabad India; SHO Maiden Law Hosp. Lanchester & P.ss Alice Memor. Hosp. E.bourne.

HAVARD, Amanda Caroline, Capt. Department of Radiology, Milton Keynes General NHS Trust, Standing Way, Eaglestone, Milton Keynes MK6 5LD Tel: 01908 660033 Fax: 01908 678545 Email: mandy.havard@mkg-tr.anglox.nhs.uk; Heronslea, 2 Little Horwood Manor, Little Horwood, Milton Keynes MK17 0PU Tel: 01296 713326 Fax: 01908 678545 Email: mandy.havard@mkg-tr.anglox.nhs.uk — MB BS 1980 Lond.; FLEX Lic (USA) 1984; VQE 1983; ECFMG 1982; T(R)(CR) 1991; FRCR 1988; ABR 1987. (Middlesex) Cons. Radiol. (Diag. Radiol.) Milton Keynes Gen. NHS Trust. Socs: BMA; Amer. Coll. Radiologists; Roy. Coll. Radiol. Prev: Sen. Regist. (Diag. Radiol.) Char. Cross Hosp. Lond.; Med. Fell. Specialist (Diag. Radiol.) Univ. Minneapolis, Minneasota, Minneapolis, USA; Resid. Internal Med. Abbott N. W.. Hosp. Minneapolis, USA.

HAVARD, Basil James (retired) 25 Christian Street, Maryport CA15 6HT — MB ChB 1963 St. And. Prev: Ho. Phys. & SHO (Paediat.) Dundee Roy. Infirm.

HAVARD, Mr Cyril The Pound, St Nicholas, Cardiff CF5 6TA Tel: 01446 760347 — MRCS Eng. LRCP Lond. 1947; BSc Wales 1944, MCh (Distinc.) 1956, MB BCh 1947; FRCS Eng. 1952. (Cardiff) Prev: Cons. Gen. Surg. Bridgend Gen. Hosp.; Hunt. Prof. RCS Eng. 1959; Sen. Surg. Regist. Cardiff Roy. Infirm.

HAVARD, Cyril William Holmes 8 Upper Wimpole Street, London W1M 7TD Tel: 020 7935 6297; 19 Park Lodge, St. John's Wood Park, London NW8 6QT — BM BCh 1952 Oxf.; MA Oxf. 1952, DM 1959; FRCP Lond. 1970, M 1955. Emerit. Cons. Phys. Roy. Free Hosp. Lond.; Sen. Examr. Univ. Lond.; Examr. MRCP; Censor RCP. Socs: Med. Res. Soc.; Eur. Thyroid Assn.; Assn. Phys. Prev: Cas. Phys. & Sen. Regist. (Med.) St. Bart. Hosp. Lond.; Ho. Phys. Postgrad. Med. Sch. Lond.

HAVARD, Elizabeth Mary Morgan (retired) The Pound, St Nicholas, Cardiff CF5 6SH Tel: 01446 760347 Fax: 01446 760347 — MB BCh 1952 Wales; BSc Wales 1949, MB BCh 1952. Regional Med. Off. Cardiff.

HAVARD, John David Jayne, CBE Commonwealth Medical Association, BMA House, Tavistock Square, London WC1H 9JP Tel: 020 7383 6095 Fax: 020 7383 6195; 1 Wilton Square, London N1 3DL Tel: 020 7359 2802 Fax: 020 7354 9690 — MB BChir Camb. 1950; LLB Camb. 1954, BA 1946, MD 1964, MA 1950; FRCP Lond. 1994; MRCP (UK) 1988; FRCGP (Hon.) 1987. (Camb. & Middlx.) Hon. Sec. Commonw. Med. Assn. Lond.; Barrister-at-Law Middle Temple 1954. Socs: (Pres. Advis. Bd.) Med. Protec. Soc.;

(Counc.) Brit. Acad. Forens. Sci. Prev: Sec. BMA; Presid. Brit. Acad. Forens. Sc.; Ho. Phys. Profess. Med. Unit Middlx. Hosp. Lond.

HAVARD, John Spencer The Surgery, Lambsale Meadow, North Entrance, Saxmundham IP17 1AS Tel: 01728 602022 — MB BS 1982 Lond.; MRCGP 1986; DRCOG 1985.

HAVARD, Lucy Katherine Sunnybrook Cottage, Hill Lane, Elmley Castle, Pershore WR10 3JA — MB ChB 1998 Leic.; MB ChB Leic 1998.

HAVARD, Mr Timothy John Dept of Surgery, Royal Glamorgan Hosp, Llantrisant, Pontyclun CF72 8XR Tel: 01443 443443; 24 Howells Crescent, Llandaff, Cardiff CF5 2AJ — MB BCh 1988 Wales; FRCS Ed. 1993; FRCS (Gen Surg) 1998; MD 1998. Cons. Roy. Glam. Hosp. Prev: Research Fell. & Hon. Regist. (Surg.) Soton. Gen. Hosp.; Regist. (Gen. Surg.) Univ. Hosp. Wales & E. Glam. Gen. Hosp.; Regist. (Gen. Surg.) Cardiff Roy. Infirm. & Roy. Gwent Hosp.

HAVARD-JONES, Mr Edward Llewelyn (retired) 6 Highcliffe Court, Langland, Swansea SA3 4TQ Tel: 01792 366509 — BM BCh 1942 Oxf.; FRCS Eng. 1949. Cons. Surg. Neath & Port Talbot Gen. Hosps. Prev: Sen. Surg. Regist. Radcliffe Infirm. Oxf. & Roy. Berks. Hosp. Reading.

HAVELOCK, Christine Margaret Department of Cytology, Division of Pathology, Wexham Park Hospital, Slough SL2 4HL Tel: 01753 01753 34567 — MB BS Lond. 1969; MD Lond. 1991; MRCS Eng. LRCP Lond. 1969. (St. Mary's) Cons. Cytopath. Wexham Pk. Hosp. Slough. Prev: Assoc. Specialist (Cytol.) Wexham Pk. Hosp. Slough; Ho. Surg. Surgic. Unit St. Mary's Hosp. Lond.; SHO (Path.) & Ho. Phys. Canad. Red Cross Memor. Hosp. Taplow.

HAVELOCK, Joyce Mary Wyle Cop, 41 The Avenue, Cheam, Sutton SM2 7QA Tel: 020 8642 3376 Fax: 020 8642 3376 — MB BS Lond. 1947; MRCS Eng. LRCP Lond. 1947; CPH Liverp. 1949. (Univ. Coll. Lond. & W. Lond.) Indep. Menopause Counsellor. Socs: Fell. Roy. Soc. Med.; Fell. RIPHH; Soc. Occupat. Med. Prev: Princip. Med. Off. (Adult Health) Merton & Sutton HA; Sen. Med. Off. & Clin. Med. Off. (Family Plann.) Merton, Sutton & Wandsworth AHA (T).

HAVELOCK, Peter Brian Pound House Surgery, 8 The Green, Wooburn Green, High Wycombe HP10 0EE Tel: 01628 529633 Fax: 01628 810963 — MB BS 1969 Lond.; MRCS Eng. LRCP Lond. 1969; FRCGP 1983, M 1975. (St. Mary's) Assoc. Advisor (Gen. Pract.) Oxf. Region; Co-Ldr. Wycombe Primary Care Prevent. Project. Prev: Tutor & Course Organiser High Wycombe Health Dist.; Examr. Roy. Coll. Gen. Practs.; Vice-Pres. Balint Soc.

HAVELOCK, Thomas Peter Hylands, Harvest Hill, Bourne End SL8 5JJ — BM BS 1998 Nottm.; BM BS Nottm 1998.

HAVERCROFT, Andrew Richard The Surgery, School Lane, Upton-upon-Severn, Worcester WR8 0LF Tel: 01684 592696 Fax: 01684 593122; The Leys, Birts Street, Birtsmorton, Worcester WR13 6AW Tel: 01684 833163 — MB ChB 1989 Sheff.; MRCGP 1995. (Sheff.) Clin. Asst. (Genitourin. Med.) Worcester Roy. Infirm.; PCG Mem.

HAVERKORN, Caroline Room 4A, Flat 4 Lakin House, Lakin Road, Warwick CV34 5BW — Artsexamen 1994 Rotterdam.

HAVERS, Andrew Ralph West View Surgery, 37 West View Road, Keynsham, Bristol BS31 2UB Tel: 0117 986 3063 Fax: 0117 986 5061; Shrublands, The Batch, Saltford, Bristol BS31 3EN Tel: 01225 872283 — MB BS 1985 Lond.; MRCGP 1989; DRCOG 1989. Prev: Trainee GP S. Clwyd VTS; Ho. Surg. St. Thos. Hosp. Lond.; Ho. Phys. Kent & Canterbury Hosp. Canterbury.

HAVERS, Christopher Ian Patrick Upper Deck, Captains Row, Lymington SO41 9RP Tel: 01590 673945 — MB BS 1968 Lond.; MRCS Eng. LRCP Lond. 1967; DObst RCOG 1969. (Guy's) Prev: SHO Farnham Hosp.; GP Wokingham; Reg. Med. Off. Surrey.

HAVERTY, Paul Francis 12 Second Avenue, London W3 7RX — MB BS 1998 Lond.; MB BS Lond 1998.

HAVES, Susan Elizabeth 48 Crimple Meadows, Pannal, Harrogate HG3 1EN — MB ChB 1996 Ed.; BSc Ed. 1994. (Ed. Univ.)

HAVINGA, Wouter Hindrik St Lukes Medical Centre, 53 Cainscross Road, Stroud GL5 4EX Tel: 01453 763755 Fax: 01453 756573 — Artsexamen 1990 Utrecht. (Utrecht) GP Stroud Glos.

HAW, Camilla Malyn St Andrews Hospital, Billing Road, Northampton NN1 5DG — MB BChir 1979 Camb.; MRCP (UK) 1982; MRCPsych 1985. Cons. Psychiat. St. And.Hosp., N.ampton (. Prev: Cons. Psychiat. Wallingford Fair Mile Hosp., Oxf.shire; Sen. Regist. (Psychiat.) Qu. Mary's Univ. Hosp. Roehampton.; Sen. Regist. (Psychiat.) Horton Hosp. Epsom.

HAW, David Stanley (retired) 2 The Green, Chapel Lane, Cleasby, Darlington DL2 2QZ — MB BS Durh. 1951. Prev: GP.

HAW, David William Martin (retired) East Court, Shipton-by-Beningborough, York YO30 1AR Tel: 01904 470324 — MB ChB 1951 Leeds; BSc (Anat.) Leeds 1948, MB ChB 1951; FRCS Eng. 1960. Hon. Demonst. Anat. Leeds. Med.Sch. Prev: Cons. Orthop. Surg. York Hosp. Gps.

HAW, Mr Marcus Peter Wessex Cardiothoracic centre, Southampton University Hospitals, Tremona Road, Southampton SO16 6YD Tel: 02380 794056 Email: marcushaw@hotmail.com; Arle Cottage, Arlesbury Park, Alresford SO24 9ES Tel: 01962 738490 Email: marcushaw@hotmail.com — MB BS 1982 Lond.; FRCS 1986; MS 1992; FECTS 2000. Cons. Cardio. Surg. Soton Gen. Hosp; Director S.ampton Homograft Heart bank valve bank; Vis. Prof., Vilnius Univ. Cardial Clinic, Lithuania; Trustar for Internat. integrated heal;thn Assoc.s (IIHA) Winchester. Socs: Euro. Assn. Cardiothoracic. Surg; Soc. Cardiothor. Surg.; Roy. Soc. Med. Prev: Sen.Lect.Cons.Cardio.Surg.Harefield.Hosp; Sen.Reg.Gt ormond St.Hosp.Lond.

HAW, Marjorie Elise (retired) East Court, Shipton-by-Beningborough, York YO30 1AR Tel: 01904 470324 — MB ChB 1950 Leeds MB ChB Leeds; 1969 FFA RCS Eng.; 1964 DA Eng.; 1998 BA (Hons) Hist. Leeds. Prev: Cons. Anaesth. Pinderfields Wakefield.

HAWA, Liyakat 7 Brambling Close, Southampton SO16 8HN — BM 1994 Soton.

HAWARD, Elaine Claire Stonebridge Surgery, Preston Road, Longridge, Preston PR3 3AP Tel: 01772 783271 Fax: 01772 782836; Lower Cockhill Farm, Hothersall Lane, Hothersall, Preston PR3 2XB — BM BS 1984 Nottm.; BMedSci Nottm. 1982; MRCGP 1988; DRCOG 1987; Cert. Family Plann. JCC 1987. GP Longridge. Prev: Trainee GP Lincoln VTS.

HAWARD, Michael Walter Ayton (retired) Mutton Row, Quethiock, Liskeard PL14 3SQ Tel: 01579 342606 — MB BChir 1952 Camb. Prev: GP Midsomer Norton.

HAWARD, Professor Robert Anthony, QHP NYCRIS, Arthington House, Cookridge Hospital, Leeds LS16 6QB Tel: 0113 392 4163 Fax: 0113 392 4178 Email: r.haward@ulth.northy.nhs.uk; 10 Wheatlands Road E., Harrogate HG2 8PX Tel: 01423 883586 — MB ChB Bristol 1968; FFCM 1981, M 1977; DPH Leeds 1971. (Bristol) Prof. Cancer Studies Centre for Cancer Research Univ. Leeds; Med. Dir. NYCRIS; Hon. Phys. to HM The Qu. Socs: Soc. Social Med.; Brit. Assn. Surg. Oncol. Prev: Regional Med. Off. & Dir. Pub. Health Yorks. RHA; Dist. Med. Off. Harrogate HA; Dist. Community Phys. Beverley Health Dist.

HAWAWINI, Alain 131 Gloucester Road, London SW7 4TH — MD 1975 Paris.

HAWBROOK, George William Johnson, OBE (retired) Westfield, 39 Breary Lane E., Bramhope, Leeds LS16 9EU — MB ChB 1945 Leeds. JP. Prev: Ho. Surg. Leeds Gen. Infirm.

HAWCO, Muriel Joan Croyard Road Surgery, Croyard Road, Beauly IV4 7DT Tel: 01463 782794 Fax: 01463 782111 — MB ChB 1977 Aberd.; MRCGP 1982.

HAWCROFT, Janet Chesham Hill Farm, Pinfold Lane, Inskip, Preston PR4 0UA — MB ChB 1959 Liverp.; DPH Liverp. 1971; DObst RCOG 1964. (Liverp.) Socs: BMA.

HAWDON, Jane Melinda Neonatal Unit, Obstetric Hospital, University College Hosp., Huntley St., London WC1E 6AU Tel: 020 7380 9875 Fax: 020 7380 9775 Email: j.hawdon@uclh.org; 4 Maiden Place, London NW5 1HZ Tel: 020 7281 7479 Fax: 020 7687 0470 — MB BS 1984 Newc.; MA Camb. 1985, BA (Hons.) 1981; DPhil Newc. 1995; FRCP Lond. 1997; MRCP (UK) 1987; FRCPCH 1997; FRCP Lond. 1997. Cons. Neonat. Univ. Coll. Hosp. Lond. Socs: BMA; MWF; ESPR. Prev: Lect. (Child Health) Univ. Liverp.; Research Regist. (Child Health) Med. Sch. Univ Newc. u Tyne; SHO (Paediat.) Hosp. Sick Childr. Gt. Ormond St. Lond.

HAWE, Brian Joseph (retired) 23 Aldford Close, Bromborough, Wirral CH63 0PT Tel: 0151 334 3357 — MB ChB Liverp. 1956. Prev: Ho. Phys. BRd.green Hosp. Liverp.

HAWE, Mr Mervyn John George Mid Ulster Hospital, 59 Hospital Road, Magherafelt BT45 5EX Tel: 028 7963 2124 Fax: 028 7563 2088 Email: ctsm2@aol.com; The Street, 65 Tobermore Road,

Magherafelt BT45 5EJ Tel: 02879632124 Email: ctsm2@aol.com — MB BCh BAO 1974 Belf.; FRCS Ed. 1978. (Qu. Univ. Belf.) Cons. Surg. Mid Ulster Hosp. Magherafelt. Socs: Fell. Ulster Med. Soc.; Assn. Surg.; Ulster Surgic. Club. Prev: Sen. Regist. Roy. Vict. Hosp. Belf.; Hon. Lect. (Surg.) Univ. Zambia; Ho. Off. Belf. City Hosp.

HAWE, Rosemary (retired) 31 Wetherby Road, Knaresborough HG5 8LH Tel: 01423 860705 — MB BCh BAO 1955 Belf.; DO Eng. 1957. Prev: Sen. Hosp. Med. Off. (Ophth.) Leeds Community & Ment. Health Servs.

HAWES, Barbara Mary Hallgarth, Durham Road, Easington, Peterlee SR8 3BA — MB ChB 1975 Manch.; MRCGP 1979.

HAWES, George Charles Barry (retired) 27 Green Lane, Coleshill, Warwickshire, Birmingham B46 3NE Tel: 01675 463010 Fax: 01675 463010 — MB BS Lond. 1955; MRCS Eng. LRCP Lond. 1955. Prev: Asst Co. Med. Off.

HAWES, Mr Stephen John Emergency Department, Wythenshawe Hospital, Southmoor Road,Wythenshawe, Manchester M23 9LT — MB ChB 1980 Bristol; FRCS Ed. 1988; FRCP (UK) 1999; FFAEM 1993. (Bristol) Cons. A & E Med. & Wythenshawe Hosp. Manch.; Hon. Clin. Lect. (A & E) Manch.; PostGrad. Clin. Tutor, Wythershawe Hosp. Socs: BMA; Brit. Assn. Accid. & Emerg. Med.; Fac. of Accid. & Emerg. Med. Prev: Sen. Regist. (A & E) Newham Gen., St. Bart., Univ. Coll. & Whipps Cross Hosps. Lond.; Regist. (A & E) Basingstoke Dist. Hosp.; Ho. Surg. Bristol Roy. Infirm.

HAWGOOD, Evelyn Anne 13 Ballbrook Avenue, Didsbury, Manchester M20 6AB Tel: 0161 445 5435 Fax: 0161 448 2314 — MB Camb. 1970. BChir 1969; MRCS Eng. LRCP Lond. 1968. (Univ. Coll. Hosp.) SCMO (Elderly & Stroke Rehabil.) Centr. Manch. Health Care Trust. Prev: Clin. Asst. Younger Disabled Unit Withington Hosp. Manch.; Lect. in Geriat. Med. Univ. Manch.; Regist. (Gen. Med.) Roy. Lancaster Infirm.

HAWK, Professor John Lyndon McLeod 47 Alma Road, Windsor SL4 3HH Tel: 01753 831254 Fax: 01753 858569 Email: john.hawk@kcl.ac.uk; East Lodge, Ridgemead Road, Englefield Green, Egham TW20 0YD Tel: 01784 433213 Fax: 01784 433213 — MB ChB Otago 1969; MD Otago 1992; BSc Auckland 1964; FRCP Lond. 1989; MRCP (UK) 1974; FRACP 1978, M 1975. (Otago) Prof. Dermat. Photo. St. John's Inst. Dermat. Lond.; Hon. Cons. Dermat. St. John's Inst. Dermaty St. Thos. Hosp. Lond. Socs: Fell. Roy. Soc. Med. & St. John's Hosp. Dermat. Soc.; Brit. Assn. Dermatol.mem; Amer Aca of Dermat. Prev: Sen. Regist. St. John's Hosp. Dis. Skin. Lond.; Fell. (Dermat.) Harvard Med. Sch. Mass. Gen. Hosp. Boston, USA; Regist. (Dermat). Guy's Hosp. Lond.

HAWK, Lorna Jean East Lodge, Ridgemead Road, Englefield Green, Egham TW20 0YD — MSc (Immunol.) Lond. 1988; BSc Ed. 1968, MD 1978, MB ChB 1970; MRCP (UK) 1974; FRCP Lond. 1997; FRCPCH 1997. (Ed.)

HAWKE, Catherine Isobel East Sussex Brighton And Hove Health Authority, 36-38 Friars Walk, Lewes BN7 2PB; Claphatch Farm, Claphatch Lane, Wadhurst TN5 7LH — MB BS 1983 Sydney; MFPhil 1999. (Sydney) Regist. (Pub. Health Med.) E. Sussex Brighton & Hove HA. Prev: Sen. Regist. (Pub. Health Med.) Oxon. HA.

HAWKE, Christopher Richard John Tel: 01362 668913 — BM BCh Oxf. 1959; MA Oxf. 1964; DObst RCOG 1969; DA Eng. 1962. (Oxf. & Lond. Hosp.) Prev: GP Fakenham; Ho. Phys., Ho. Surg. & Resid. Anaesth. Lond. Hosp.

HAWKEN, Michael John (retired) Wheathold House, Wolverton, Tadley RG26 5SA Tel: 01189 814461 — MB BS 1954 Lond. Prev: SHO Hosp. Sick Childr. Gt. Ormond St. & Roy. Nat. Orthop. Hosp. Lond.

HAWKEN, Richard Michael Avens Wheathold House, Wheathold, Ramsdell, Tadley RG26 5SA — BM 1997 Soton.

HAWKEN, William Joseph 23 Forest Close, Wendover, Aylesbury HP22 6BT — MB ChB 1979 Bristol; FFA RCS Eng. 1984; DA Eng. 1982.

HAWKER, Cathryn Frances Coopers Road Surgery, 51 Coopers Road, Handsworth Wood, Birmingham B20 2JU Tel: 0121 554 1812 — MB ChB 1971 Birm.; DA Eng. 1974.

HAWKER, Claire Elise 11 Scotland Street, Brighton BN2 2WA Tel: 01273 679283 — MB BS 1997 Lond. GP Train. Scheme.

HAWKER, David Bernard George Carraig, Craighouse, Isle of Jura PA60 7XG Tel: 01496 820388 Fax: 01496 820135; Carraig, Craighouse, Isle of Jura PA60 7XG Tel: 01496 820135, 01496 820388 — MB ChB Ed. 1967; FFA RCS Eng. 1974; DA Eng. 1970. (Ed.) p/t Locum Gen. Pract.; Med. Servs., Examinig Med. Practitioners, Galsgow. Socs: BMA; Christ. Med. Fell.sh.; Roy. Coll. Anaesth. Prev: Anaesth. Gandaki Zonal Hosp. Pokhara, Nepal; Med. Off. Shining Hosp. Pokhara, Nepal; Partner Dr Cheetham & Parnters Cornw.

HAWKER, Diana Judith Lucy Canbury Medical Centre, 1 Elm Road, Kingston upon Thames KT2 6HR Tel: 020 8549 8818; 107 Shortlands Road, Kingston upon Thames KT2 6HF — MB BS 1984 Lond.; MA Camb. 1985; MRCGP 1989; DCH RCP Lond. 1989.

HAWKER, Howard John Woodcote Group Practice, 32 Foxley Lane, Purley CR8 3EE Tel: 020 8660 1304 Fax: 020 8660 0721; No. 1 Stewart, Tadworth Park, Tadworth KT20 5TU Tel: 01737 370313 Fax: 01737 370313 Email: onestewart@talk21.com — BM BCh 1979 Oxf.; MA Oxf. 1979; MRCP (UK) 1983; MRCGP 1987; DRCOG 1986; Cert. Av. Med. 1991. ((Oxf.)) Asst. Med. Edr. Postgrad. Doctor Middle E. Prev: Trainee GP Croydon HA VTS; Regist. (Med.) Riyadh Armed Forces Hosp., Saudi Arabia.

HAWKER, Jeremy Ian CDSC (West Midlands), Lincoln House, Birmingham Heartlands Hospital, Birmingham B9 5SS Tel: 0121 773 7077 Fax: 0121 773 1407 — MB ChB Birm. 1985; BSc (Hons.) Birm. 1982; MFPHM RCP (UK) 1991; FFPHM 1999 UK. Regional Epidemiologist W. Midl.s PHLS Communicable Dis. Surveillance Centre, Birm.; Hon. Sen. Clin. Lect. Univ. of Birm. (since 1996). Socs: Fac. Pub. Health Med. R.C.P., UK (Fell.). Prev: Cons. in Communicable Dis. Control Birm. Health Auth.

HAWKER, Lesley Beryl Veor Surgery, South Terrace, Camborne TR14 8SN Tel: 01209 612626 Fax: 01209 612491; Leat House, 22 Trevu Road, Camborne TR14 7AD Tel: 01209 718436 — MB ChB 1969 Ed.; DCH RCP Lond. 1984. Prev: Trainee GP Bodriggy Clinic Hayle; SHO (Paediat.) & SHO (Cas.) Roy. Cornw. Hosp. Truro.

HAWKER, Peter Charles Warwick Hospital, Lakin Rd, Warwick CV34 5 Tel: 01926 495321; Rivendell Brook Ln, Newbold-on-Stour, Stratford-upon-Avon CU37 8UA — MB ChB 1971 Birm.; 1979 MD & MB ChB (1971) Birm.; 1974 MRCP (U.K.); FRCP 1994. (Birmingham) Cons. Phys. S. Warks. Hosp. Socs: Brit. Soc. Gastroenterol. & Mem. BMA.; BMA (Mem. Cons.s Specialist Comm.); Dep. Chairm. 1994-1998, BMA. Prev: Sen. Regist. (Med.) Gen. Hosp. Birm.; Research Fell. Hope Hosp. Salford.

HAWKER, Peter Gerald (retired) Tamar, St Johns Road, Hadleigh, Benfleet SS7 2PT Email: peter.hawker@btinternet — MB BS 1957 Lond.; MRCGP 1967; DObst RCOG 1959.

HAWKES, Mr Andrew Charles (retired) 63 Winifred Lane, Ormskirk L39 5DH — MB ChB 1974 Liverp.; FRCS Ed. 1980; MRCGP 1982. Prev: GP Maghull.

HAWKES, Barbara Lynne Burscough Health Centre, Stanley Court, Lord Street, Burscough, Ormskirk L40 4LA Tel: 01704 892254 Fax: 01704 897182; 63 Winifreds Lane, Aughton, Ormskirk L39 5DH Tel: 01695 72319 — MB ChB 1974 Liverp.; MRCGP 1987. Prev: SHO (Paediat. & Gen. Med. & O & G) & Ho. Phys. & Ho. Surg. Ormskirk & Dist. Gen. Hosp.

HAWKES, Christopher Hickman Essex Neuroscience Centre, Old Church Hospital, Romford RM7 0BE Tel: 01708 708055; 22 Heath Drive, Giden park RM2 5QJ — MB ChB 1963 Ed.; BSc (Hons.) Ed. 1965, MD (Commend.) 1970; BSc (Hons.) Liverp. 1960; FRCP Lond. 1994; FRCP Ed. 1985, M 1968. (Ed.) Cons. Neurol. OldCh..Hosp; Hon. Lect. (Neurol.) Inst. Neurol. Qu. Sq. Lond.; Hon. Cons. Nat. Hosp. for Neurol., Neurosurg., Qu. Sq. Lond. Socs: Brain Res. Assn. & Assn. Brit. Neurol.; Europ. Neurol. Soc.; Amer. Acad. of Neurol. Prev: Regist. (Neurol.) Qu. Eliz. Hosp. Birm.; Regist. (Clin. Neurophysiol.) Roy. Infirm. Edin.; Sen. Regist. (Neurol.) Wessex Neurol. Centre Soton. Gen. Hosp.

HAWKES, Davida Jane 17 Lomond Close, Stockport SK2 7DY — MB BCh 1992 Wales.

HAWKES, Diane Jennifer 26 Berwick Drive, Liverpool L23 7UH — MB ChB 1993 Liverp.

HAWKES, Fiona Anne The Health Centre, Hangingroyd Lane, Hebden Bridge — MB BS 1974 Lond.; MRCGP 1979; DObst RCOG 1976; DCH 1980. GP Todmorden & Hebden Bridge. Prev: Surg. P & O Cruises; SHO (Paediat.) St. Peter's Hosp. Chertsey; Clin. Med. Off. Kingston & Esher AHA.

HAWKES, Geoffrey Sherbourne Medical Centre, 40 Oxford Street, Leamington Spa CV32 4RA Tel: 01926 333500 Fax: 01926 470884 — MB ChB 1975 Leeds; MRCGP 1980; DRCOG 1979.

HAWKES, Georgina Ines Newton St Anns Hospital, St Anns Rd, Harringey, London N15 3TH Tel: 020 8442 6000; Langleys, Downham Rd, Stock, Ingatestone CM4 9RJ Tel: 01277 840868 — MB BS 1998 Lond.; MB BS Lond 1998; BSc Hons Lond. 1995. SHO Psychiat.

HAWKES, Mahboub 22 Heath Drive, Gidea Park, Romford RM2 5QJ Fax: 01708 731600 — MD 1973 Nat. Univ. Iran; MD (Hons.) Nat. Univ. Iran 1973, MB BS 1974; FRCS Ed. 1990; FCOphth 1990; DO Lond. 1977; MD Ophth 1979. Assoc. Specialist Whipps Cross Hosp Lond. Prev: Fell. Glaucoma Moorfields Eye Hosp.; Regist. (Ophth.) Norf. & Norwich Hosp.

HAWKES, Neil David 63 Bramcote Road, Brookside Court, Loughborough LE11 2SA — MB BCh 1992 Wales.

HAWKES, Nicola Mary West Suffolk Hospitals NHS Trust, Hardwick Lane, Bury St Edmunds IP33 2QZ Tel: 01284 713405 — MB ChB 1989 Manch. p/t GP Retainer. Prev: SHO (O & G) Gloucester; SHO (O & G) St. Mary's Hosp. Manch.; SHO (Paediat.) Brisbane, Austral.

HAWKES, Robert Andrew Limetree House, 63 Winifred Lane, Aughton, Ormskirk L39 5DH — MB ChB 1998 Sheff.; MB ChB Sheff 1998.

HAWKES, Roger Andrew Laurel House Surgery, 12 Albert Road, Tamworth B79 7JN Tel: 01827 69283 Fax: 01827 318029; 73 Wigginton Road, Tamworth B79 8RN Tel: 01827 62287 Fax: 01827 62287 — MB ChB 1976 Birm.; LMCC 1980; Dip. Sports Med. Scotl. 1995; DRCOG 1978. Med. Advisor PGA Europ. Golf Agency; Sports Phys. - BUPA Little Aslin Hosp. Socs: (Sec.) Tamworth Med. Soc.; Brit. Assn. Sport & Exercise Med. (BASEM). Prev: GP Goose Bay, Labrador, Canada; SHO (Paediat.) Blackburn Health Dist.; SHO (Anaesth.) Ealing Hosp. S.all.

HAWKES, Sarah Jane ICDDR, B (CHD), GPO Box 128, Dhaka 1000, Bangladesh Tel: 00 880 2 886050; 3 Edgecotts, Basildon SS16 5SN Tel: 01268 412792 — MB BS 1989 Lond.; DTM & H RCP Lond. 1991. Princip. Investigator Reproduc. Tract Infec. Study CHD Div. Internat. Centre Diarrh.l Dis. Research, Bangladesh. Prev: Clin. Research Fell. (Clin. Sci.) Lond. Sch. Hyg. & Trop. Med.

HAWKESFORD, Barbara The Quarry, 31 Batt House Road, Stocksfield NE43 7RA Tel: 01661 842338 — MB BS 1974 Lond.; MRCS Eng. LRCP Lond. 1974; MFFP 1994. (Roy. Free) SCMO Gateshead; Clin. Asst. BrE. Screening Dept. RVI Newc. upon Tyne.; SCMO Assn. Newc. upon Tyne. Socs: BMA; NAFFD.; Inst. Psychosexual Drs. Prev: SHO (Rheum. & Rehabil.) Nuffield Orthop. Centre Oxf.; Ho. Phys. Roy. Free Hosp. Lond.; Ho. Surg. Amersham Gen. Hospita.

HAWKESFORD, Linda Margery Manchester Brook Advisory Centre, Faulkner House, Faulkner St., Manchester M1 4DY Tel: 0161 237 3001 Fax: 0161 237 3003; The Hermitage, 26 Abbots Park, Chester CH1 4AN Tel: 01244 372187 — MB ChB 1971 Liverp.; MA Wales 1991; MFFP 1995. Sen. Doctor Manch. Brook Advis. Centre.

HAWKESWORTH, May Berti Tel: 0113 273 3733 Fax: 0113 232 2302; Kirby Hill House, Kirby Hill, Boroughbridge, York YO51 9DS Tel: 01423 323581 Fax: 01423 323588 Email: shawke4568@aol.com — MB BS 1976 Lond.; MD Lond. 1983; MRCP (UK) 1978; MRCS Eng. LRCP Lond. 1976. (The Royal Free Hospital School of Medicine) p/t GP Princip.; Clin. Asst. The Fridiage Hosp. N.allerton. Socs: BMA.

HAWKEY, Christopher John 12 Pelham Crescent, The Park, Nottingham NG7 1AW — BM BCh 1972 Oxf.; DM Oxf. 1983, BA 1969, BM BCh 1972; FRCP Lond. 1989; MRCP (U.K.) 1975. (Oxf. & Middlx.) Prof. Gastroenterol. Univ. Hosp. Nottm. Prev: Regist. (Med.) Nuffield Dept. Med. Radcliffe Infirm. Oxf.

HAWKEY, Professor Peter Michael Division of Immunity & Infection, The Medical School, University of Birmingham, Birmingham B15 2TT Tel: 0121 414 6955 — MB BS 1978 Lond.; BSc (Hons.) E. Anglia 1972; MD Bristol 1983; MRCPath 1984. (King's Coll. Hosp.) Med. Microbiol. & Pub. Health Bact., Univ. Birm. Med. Sch.; Hon. Cons. Med. Microbiol. Heartlands and Solihull NHS Trust. Socs: Amer. Soc. Microbiol; Hosp. Infec. Soc.; Brit. Soc. Antimicrob. Chemother. (Counc. Mem.). Prev: Reader (Med. Microbiol.) Univ. Leeds Med. Sch.; Lect. (Med. Microbiol.) Univ. Bristol Med. Sch.; Prof. Med. Microbiol. Univ. Leeds Med. Sch.

HAWKHEAD, Jacqueline Louise 133 Wakefield Road, Garforth, Leeds LS25 1AT — MB ChB 1996 Leeds.

HAWKING, Katherine Mary Kingsbury Court Surgery, Church Street, Dunstable LU5 4RS Tel: 01582 663218 Fax: 01582 476488; 28 Miletree Crescent, Dunstable LU6 3LS Tel: 01582 601289 — MB BS 1966 Lond.; Dip. Amer. Bd. Paediat. 1971. (St. Bart.) Prev: Resid. (Paediat.) New York Univ. Med. Centre USA; Fell. (Paediat. Nephrol.) Childr. Hosp. & Dept. Microbiol. State Univ. NY, USA.

HAWKINGS, John Manwell (retired) Willows, Yardley Close, Tonbridge TN9 1QA — MB BS Lond. 1960; MRCS Eng. LRCP Lond. 1960; DObst RCOG 1962. Prev: Ho. Phys. (Paediat.) Whipps Cross Hosp. Lond.

HAWKINGS, Martin Daunton 20 St Helens Close, Leeds LS16 8LS — MB ChB 1990 Leeds.

HAWKINS, Adam Lawrence Patwell Lane Surgery, Patwell Lane, Bruton BA10 0EG Tel: 01749 812310 Fax: 01749 812938 — MB ChB 1987 Sheff.; MRCGP 1996; DRCOG 1993. Socs: BMA. Prev: SHO (Neurol.) Roy. Surrey Co. Hosp. Guildford; SHO (Med. & Geriat.) Gen. Hosp. St. Helier Jersey; Ho. Off. (Surg.) W. Cornw. Hosp. Penzance.

HAWKINS, Allan Kenneth Ivor Bryn Road Surgery, 42 Bryn Road, Brynmill, Swansea SA2 0AP Tel: 01792 456056; 19 Royal Oak Road, Derwen Fawr, Swansea SA2 8ES Tel: 01792 229150 Fax: 01792 299150 — MB BCh Wales 1966. (Cardiff) Socs: BMA. Prev: Regist. (Med.) Neath Gen. Hosp.; SHO (Med.) St. David's Hosp. Cardiff.

HAWKINS, Amanda 14 Norton Road, Leeds LS8 2DE — MB ChB 1995 Leeds.

HAWKINS, Anne Elizabeth The Grange, Highfield Road, Hemsworth, Pontefract WF9 4DP Tel: 01977 610009 Fax: 01977 617182; Willow Cottage, Doncaster Road, Foulby, Wakefield WF4 1PY — MB ChB 1981 Leeds.

HAWKINS, Charlotte Elizabeth Anne Medicine Central Agency, Room 1026, Market Towers, 1 Nine Elms Lane, London SW8 5NQ Tel: 020 7273 0264; 83A Barnsbury Street, London N1 1EJ Tel: 020 7700 0610 — MB BS 1982 Lond.; MRCGP 1986; Dip. Pharm. Med. RCP (UK) 1996; DRCOG 1985. (Middlesex) Sen. Med. Assessor Meds. Control Agency Lond. Prev: Sen. Med. Adviser Pfizer Ltd. Sandwich; SHO (Ophth.) Edgware Gen. Hosp.; GP Markyate.

HAWKINS, Clare Jane Roseland, South St., South Molton EX36 4AE — MB ChB 1996 Birm.; ChB Birm. 1996.

HAWKINS, Clive Paul 'Hollybank', Heathcote Ave. (off Pinewood Road), Ashley Heath, Market Drayton TF9 4QQ — BM BS 1980 Nottm.; BMedSci 1978; DM Nottm. 1991; FRCP 1997; MRCP (UK) 1983. Cons. Neurol. N. Staffs. Roy. Infirm. Stoke-on-Trent; Reader (Neurol.) Sch. Med. Keele Univ. Socs: Roy. Coll. Phys.; Assn. Brit. Neurol. Prev: Research Regist. & Clin. Regist. (Neurol.) Nat. Hosp. of Neurol. & Neurosurg. Lond.; Sen. Regist. (Neurol.) Middlx. & Univ. Coll. Hosps.; Lect. (Clin. Neurol.) Inst. Neurol. & Nat. Hosp. Lond.

HAWKINS, Colette Sunderland Royal Hospital, Chester Rd, Sunderland SR4 7TP Tel: 0191 565 6256 — MB BS 1991 Lond.; BSc Lond. 1988; MRCP (UK) 1994. (Roy. Free Hosp.) p/t Cons.s (Palliat. Med) , Sunderland Roy. Hosp. Prev: Research Fell. (Palliat. Med.) Ealing; SHO (A & E) St. Thos. Hosp. Lond.; SHO (Infec. Dis.) Birm. Heartlands Hosp.

HAWKINS, David Arnold St Stephens Centre, Chelsea & Westminster Hospital, 369 Fulham Road, London SW10 9TH Tel: 020 8846 6158 Fax: 020 8846 6198 Email: dhawkins@crusaid-star.co.uk; 722 Fulham Road, London SW6 5SB Tel: 020 7736 9604 — MB BS 1977 Lond.; BSc (Hons.) Lond. 1973; FRCP Lond. 1994; MRCP (UK) 1981. (Univ. Coll. Hosp.) Cons. Phys. (Genitourin Med.) St. Stephens Centre & Chelsea & W.m. Hosp. Lond.; Hon. Sen. Lect. Imperial Coll. Lond. 1998-. Socs: Med. Soc. Study VD. Prev: MRC Clin. Sci. Div. Sexually Transm. Dis. Clin. Research Centre N.wick Pk. Hosp. Harrow; Hon. Sen. Regist. St. Mary's Hosp. Lond.

HAWKINS, David James Birmingham Heartlands NHS Trust, Bordesley Green E., Birmingham B9 5SS Email: hawkind@hearsol.wmids.nhs.uk; 44 Rothwell Drive, Prospect Grange, Solihull B91 1HG Email: d.j.hawkins@btinternet — MB ChB 1983 Ed.; FRCA 1990. Cons. Anaesth. Birm. Heartlands NHS Trust.

HAWKINS, Professor Denis Frank Blundel Lodge, Blundel Lane, Cobham KT11 2SP Tel: 01372 843073 Fax: 01372 377022 — MB BS Lond. 1955; PhD Lond. 1952, DSc 1967, BSc 1949; FRCOG 1970, M 1962, DObst 1957. (Univ. Coll. Hosp.) Cons Obster and

Gynae.; Emerit. Prof. Obst. Therap. Univ. Lond.; Consg. Edr. Jl. Obst. & Gyn. Socs: Fell. Amer. Coll. Obst. & Gyn. Prev: Lect. (O & G) Univ. Coll. Hosp. Lond.; O & G-in-Chief Univ. Hosp. Boston, Mass.; Prof. O & G Boston Univ. Sch. Med.

HAWKINS, Deric Bjorkman (retired) 28 Castellan Avenue, Gidea Park, Romford RM2 6EJ Tel: 01708 749064 — MB BS Lond. 1951; FRCGP 1975, M 1963; DCH Eng. 1955; DObst RCOG 1954. Prev: Ho. Off. (Obst.) & SHO Childr. Dept. St. Thos. Hosp.

HAWKINS, Doris Irene (retired) 5 The Genistas, Semley Road, Hassocks BN6 8PF Tel: 01273 842828 — MB BS 1957 Lond.; BSc Lond. 1947, MB BS 1957.

HAWKINS, Elizabeth (retired) Shal-Mai, Newry Road, Banbridge BT32 3NA Tel: 018206 22258 — MB BCh BAO 1950 Belf.; MFCM 1973; DPH Belf. 1956. Dist. Admin. Med. Off. Craigavon/Banbridge Health Dist. Prev: Asst. Chief Admin. Med. Off. S.. Area Bd.

HAWKINS, Fiona Jane St Davids Clinic, Bellevue Terrace, Newport NP20 2LB Tel: 01633 251133 — MB BCh 1972 Wales; MRCGP 1979; DObst RCOG 1975; DCH Eng. 1974. (Welsh National School of Medicine (Cardiff)) GP.

HAWKINS, Frances Deborah 1 Fairlea, Maidenhead SL6 3AS — MB BS 1974 Newc.

HAWKINS, Gerald Francis Caesar (retired) Newton Orchard, Pound Lane, Whitestone, Exeter EX4 2LJ — MRCS Eng. LRCP Lond. 1937; BM BCh Oxon. 1937. Prev: Maj. R.A.M.C.

HAWKINS, Ian Alexander (retired) 10 Lodway Gardens, Pill, Bristol BS20 0DL Tel: 01275 372125 — MB BS Lond. 1958; DObst RCOG 1964. Prev: Med. Off. Univ. Bristol.

HAWKINS, Jacqueline Ann Lorne House, 7 Swan St., Boxford, Sudbury CO10 5NZ — MB BS 1986 Lond.; MRCGP (Distinc.) 1992; DRCOG 1990; DCH RCP Lond. 1988.

HAWKINS, Jacqueline Lesley Cumming House, Gordonstoun School, Elgin IV30 5RQ — MB BS 1985 Lond.; MRCGP 1989; DRCOG 1988. (Charing Cross Hospital Medical School)

HAWKINS, James Wedderburn 78 Polwarth Terrace, Edinburgh EH11 1NJ Tel: 0131 337 8474 — MB 1976 Camb.; BChir 1975; Dip. Acupunc. China 1981.

HAWKINS, John Bernard Pear Tree Surgery, 28 Meadow Close, Kingsbury, Tamworth B78 2NR Tel: 01827 872755 Fax: 01827 874700; The Old Vicarage, Shustoke, Coleshill, Birmingham B46 2LA Tel: 01675 481331 Fax: 01675 481331 — MB ChB 1963 Birm.; FRCP Lond. 1979, M 1967; MRCS Eng. LRCP Lond. 1963; MRCGP 1994; DCH Eng. 1965. (Birm.) Socs: BMA, UK, & Europ. Renal Assns. Prev: Cons. Phys. (Renal Dis.) Birm. Heartlands Hosp.; Hon. Sen. Clin. Lect. Univ. Birm.; Resid. Med. Off. Birm. Childr. Hosp.

HAWKINS, Jonathon Michael Charles 5 Tidbury Close, Woburn Sands, Milton Keynes MK17 8QW — MB BS 1990 Lond.

HAWKINS, Julia Mary Woodside Health Centre, 3 Enmore Road, London SE25; 160 Farley Road, South Croydon CR2 7NH — MB BS 1982 Lond.; MRCGP 1986; DRCOG 1985. GP Woodside Health Centre Croydon.

HAWKINS, Julian Paul Justin 1 Stroud Road, Bisley, Stroud GL6 7BQ — MB BS 1990 Lond.

HAWKINS, Kathleen Marion (retired) 52 Clarendon Road, Sheffield S10 3TR — MB ChB Leeds 1942.

HAWKINS, Katy Abigail 22 Holt Lane, Kingsley, Stoke-on-Trent ST10 2BA — BM 1998 Soton.; BM Soton 1998.

HAWKINS, Kay Carolyn Manchester Children's Hospital NHS Trust, Royal Manchester Children's Hospital, Hospital Road, Pendlebury, Manchester M27 4HA Tel: 0161 794 4696 Fax: 0161 727 2198 Email: kay.hawkins@nessie.mcc.ac.uk; 4 Oakfield Road, Didsbury, Manchester M20 6XA Tel: 0161 445 2453 Fax: 0161 445 2453 — MB ChB 1982 Manch.; MRCP (UK) 1988; MRCGP 1988; FRCPCH 1997. (Manchester Medical School) Cons. (Paediat. Intens. Care) Manch. Childr. Hosp. NHS Trust; PostGrad. Clin. Tutor Roy. Coll. Paediat. & Child Health. Socs: Fell. Manch. Med. Soc. Prev: Cons. (Paediat.) Wythenshawe Hosp. Manch.; Sen. Regist. S. Cleveland Hosp.; Sen Regist. (PICU) Gt. Ormond St. Hosp. Lond.

HAWKINS, Margaret Jacqueline (retired) 7 Hunters Way, Chichester PO19 4RB Tel: 01243 539863 — MB ChB 1950 Birm. Prev: SCMO (Family Plann.) NW Herts. HA.

HAWKINS, Mark 31 Hereward Road, Cirencester GL7 2EH — MB BS 1997 Lond.

HAWKINS, Martyn Philip 86 Bwllfa Road, Cwmdare, Aberdare CF44 8UF; 28 Heathfield Road, Wavertree, Liverpool L15 9EZ Tel: 0151 738 0028 — MB BCh 1987 Wales; FRCA 1995. Clin. Research Fell. Aintree Hosps. NHS Trust Liverp. Socs: Anaesth. Res. Soc.; Assn. Anaesth.s.

HAWKINS, Michael John Queens Medical Centre, 6/7 Queens Street, Barnstaple EX32 8AY; Roseland, South St, South Molton EX36 4AE Tel: 01769 572039 Email: mikeandmin@roselandsm.fsnet.co.uk — MB BS 1970 Lond.; Dip Av Med 2000; MRCS Eng. LRCP Lond. 1970; MRCGP 1977; DObst RCOG 1972. (Guy's) Private Practitioner in Med. Acupunc., Qu.s Med. Centre; Clin. Asst., c/o the elderly, S. Molton Community Hosp.; Med. Acupunct., N. Devon Hospice. Socs: Accredit. Mem. of the Med. Acupunc. Soc. Prev: Gen. Practitioner Princip., E. St. Surg., S. Molton.

HAWKINS, Neil William 1 Rydelands, Cranleigh GU6 7DD — MB BS Lond. 1984; BSc (Basic Med. & Sci. & Neuroanat.) Lond. 1981; FRCA 1996; T(GP) 1990. (King's Coll. Hosp.) Regist. (Anaesth.) Qu. Med. Centre Nottm. Prev: SHO (O & G) Cuckfield Hosp. E. Sussex.

HAWKINS, Paul Mount Pleasant Practice, Tempest Way, Chepstow NP16 5XR Tel: 01291 636500 Fax: 01291 636518; Court Garden House, Itton, Chepstow NP16 6BR Tel: 01291 622150 — MB ChB 1965 Birm.; DObst RCOG 1971. (Birm.) Gen. Med. Practitioner. Socs: BMA. Prev: Police Surg. Chepstow; Capt. RAMC; Ho. Surg. Qu. Eliz. Hosp. Birm.

HAWKINS, Peter 306 Lynmouth Avenue, Morden SM4 4RS — MB BS 1990 Lond.; MRCP (UK) 1994.

HAWKINS, Philip Nigel Immunological Medicine Unit, Royal Postgraduate Medical School, Hammersmith Hospital, London W12 0NN Tel: 020 8383 3261 Fax: 020 8383 2118 — MB BS 1982 Lond.; MB BS (Hon. Med. & Clin. Pharmacol.) Lond. 1982; PhD Lond. 1990; FRCP Lond. 1994; MRCP (UK) 1985. Reader (Med.) Roy. Postgrad. Med. Sch. Lond. & Hon. Cons. Phys. Hammersmith & Ealing Hosp. Socs: Brit. Soc. Rheum.; Assn. Phys.; Internat. Soc. Amyloidosis.

HAWKINS, Richard Livingston Coull, 57 Brodrick Road, London SW17 7DX Tel: 020 8767 2730 — MB BS 1976 Lond.; FRCS Ed. 1982. (St. Thos.) Managing Dir. Hawker Pub.ats. Socs: Osler Club; Fell. Roy. Soc. Med. Prev: Edr. Brit. Jl. of Hosp. Med.; Clin. Edr. World Med.; Regist. Rotat. Soton Gen. Hosp.

HAWKINS, Richard Michael 2 Witham Lodge, Witham CM8 1HG — MB ChB 1997 Sheff.

HAWKINS, Richard Thomas Joseph Tamarisk, Breageside, Porthleven, Helston TR13 9JL Tel: 01326 574901 — MRCS Eng. LRCP Lond. 1962. (W. Lond.) Prev: GP Helston, Cornw.; Sessional Med. Off. MoD (PE) Helston; Local Treas. Med. Off. Penzance & Helston Area.

HAWKINS, Robert Edward Bristol Oncology Centre, Horfield Road, Bristol BS2 8ED Tel: 0117 928 4561 Fax: 0117 928 3865 — MB BS 1984 Lond.; PhD Lond. 1995; MA Camb. 1981; MRCP (UK) 1987. Prof. Oncol. Bristol Univ.; Hon. Cons. Med. Oncol. Univ. Bristol Health Trust; Clin. Edr. Brit. Jl. Cancer. Prev: CRC Sen. Clin. Research Fell. & Hon. Cons. Med. Oncol. Addenbrooke's Hosp. Camb.; MRC Recombinant DNA Fell. MRC Laborat. Molecular Biol. Camb.; Regist. (Med. Oncol.) Roy. Marsden Hosp. Lond.

HAWKINS, Sally Fiona St Clair 2 Woodside Road, Cobham KT11 2QR — MB ChB 1997 Sheff.

HAWKINS, Samantha Jane 3 Rosendene Close, Kirby Muxloe, Leicester LE9 2EZ — BM BS 1993 Nottm.

HAWKINS, Simon Shayle St Heller Hospital, Wrythe Lane, Carshalton SM5 1AA Tel: 0208 296 2444; 67 The Ridgeway, Sutton SM2 5JU Tel: 0208 642 3231 — MB BS 1975 Lond.; FFA RCS Eng. 1982; DRCOG 1980. (St. Thos.) p/t Cons. Anaesth. St. Helier Hosp. Carshalton Surrey. Socs: Fell. Roy. Soc. Med.; Assn. Anaesth. Prev: Sen. Regist. (Anaesth.) Middlx. Hosp. Lond.; Regist. (Anaesth.) Middlx. Hosp. Lond.; SHO (Paediat.) Roy. Shrewsbury Hosp.

HAWKINS, Stanley Arthur The National Hospital, Queen Square, London WC1N 3BG — MB BCh BAO 1972 Belf.; BSc Belf. 1969, MB BCh BAO 1972; MRCP (U.K.) 1975. Resid. Regist. Nat. Hosp. Qu. Sq.

HAWKINS, Stephen Jeremy The Upper Surgery, 27 Lemon Street, Truro TR1 2LS Tel: 01872 74931 Fax: 01872 260339; 39 Old Coach Road, Playing Place, Truro TR3 6ET — MB BS 1978 Lond.;

MRCP (UK) 1981. (St. Thos.) GP Truro; Hosp. Pract. Dept. Rheum. Roy. Cornw. Hosp. Prev: Regist. Roy. Nat. Hosp. Rheum. Dis. Bath; Regist. (Med.) Roy. Cornw. Hosp. Truro; SHO (Med.) Roy. Cornw. Hosp.

HAWKINS, Thomas Desmond (retired) Greyfriars, Little Wilbraham, Cambridge CB1 5LE Tel: 01223 811219 — MB BS 1949 Lond.; MPhil. Camb. 1989; MA Camb. 1977; FRCP Lond. 1979, M 1972; MRCS Eng. LRCP Lond. 1946; FRCR 1975; FFR 1959; DMRD Eng. 1957. Hon. Fell. Hughes Hall Camb. Prev: Pres. Hughes Hall Camb.

HAWKINS, Thomas James, TD (retired) Weatherbury, 119 Main St, Willoughby-on-the-Wolds, Loughborough LE12 6SY Tel: 01509 880912 Fax: 01509 880845 Email: thomas.hawkins@virgin.net — MB BS Lond. 1961; FFA RCS Eng. 1968; DA Eng. 1964. Prev: Sen. Resid. Anaesth. Roy. Free Hosp. Lond.

HAWKINS, Timothy Edward LRF Leukaemia Unit, Hammersmith Hospital, Du Cane Road, London W12 0NN — MB ChB 1984 Auckland.

HAWKINS, Timothy James 11 Rookery Road, Bristol BS4 2DS — MB ChB 1992 Birm.; BSc (Hons.) Pharmacol. Birm. 1989. Prev: SHO (Med.) City Hosp. Nottm.

HAWKINS, Victoria Jane Brook Cottage, Sheepstor, Yelverton PL20 6PF — MB ChB 1992 Birm.

HAWKINS, Warren (retired) 7 Hunters Way, Chichester PO19 4RB Tel: 01243 539863 — MB BS 1949 Queensland; FRCP Ed 1999; DCH RCP Lond. 1954.

HAWKINS, William John Staffordshire General Hospital, Intensive Care Unit, Weston Road, Stafford ST16 3SA Tel: 01785 230079 Email: john.hawkins@btinternet.com; Oak House, Lodge Gardens, Pool Lane, Brocton, Stafford ST17 0TY — BM BS 1986 Nottm.; FRCA 1992. (Nottingham) Cons. (Anaesth. & IC).

HAWKRIDGE, Helen Pontesbury Medical Practice, Pontesbury, Shrewsbury SY5 0RF Tel: 01743 790325 — MB ChB 1978 Bristol; DRCOG 1982.

HAWKS, Andrew Mosley Department of Clinical Chemistry, Bolton Royal Infirmary, Chorley New Road, Bolton BL1 4QS — MRCS Eng. LRCP Lond. 1965; PhD Lond. 1972, MSc 1968, MB BS 1965; FRCPath 1986, M 1975. (Middlx.) Cons. Chem. Path. Bolton Roy. Infirm. Prev: Sen. Lect. (Chem. Path.) St. Mary's Hosp. Med. Sch. Lond. & Hon. Cons. (Chem. Path.) St. Mary's Hosp. Lond.; Sen. Regist. (Clin. Biochem.) Roy. Vict. Infirm. Newc.

HAWKS, Anthony John Conroy (retired) — MB BS Lond. 1964; DCH Eng. 1967. Prev: Sen. Regist. (Haemat.) Cent. Laborat. St. Mary's Gen. Hosp. Portsmouth.

HAWKSWELL, Janet Christine 8 Littleworth Close, Rossington, Doncaster DN11 0HF — MB ChB 1981 Leic.

HAWKSWELL, John Anthony Lydgett Farm, Moor Lane, Netherthong, Holmfirth, Huddersfield HD9 3UW Tel: 01484 686497; Moss Lane Farm, Moss Lane, Moore, Warrington WA4 6XQ Tel: 01925 740434 Email: john@ahawkswell.freeserve.co.uk — MB ChB 1991 Dundee. (Dundee) GP Reg Runcorn. Socs: BMA. Prev: SHO (Neurol. & Orthop.) Hope Hosp. Salford; Demonst. & Cas. Off. Univ. Dundee.

HAWKSWORTH, Christopher Robert Ernest 74 Cairns Road, Cambuslang, Glasgow G72 8PZ — MB ChB 1985 Manch.; BSc (Hons.) St. And. 1982; FRCA 1993; DA (UK) 1992. Sen. Regist. Univ. Dept. Anaesth. W.. Infirm. Glas. Prev: Career Regist. (Anaesth.) Vict. Infirm. Glas.; Regist. Basic Surgic. Train. Scheme Lothian HB; SHO (Anaesth.) Hairmyres Hosp. Kilbride.

HAWKSWORTH, Mr Nicholas Robert Royal Glamorgan Hospital, Llantrisant, Pontyclun CF72 8XR Tel: 01443 443588; Email: n.r.hawksworth@btinternet.com — MB BS 1983 Lond.; FRCS Eng. 1987; FRCOphth. 1988; DO RCS Eng. 1987. (St. Bart.) Cons. Ophth. Roy. Glam., Llantrisant. Prev: Sen. Regist. Cardiff & Newport, Gwent; Regist. Rotat. Leeds & Bradford; SHO. (Ophth) Soton. Eye Hosp.

HAWKYARD, Mr Simon John Scarborough Hospital, Woodlands Drive, Scarborough YO12 6QL — MB ChB 1984 Liverp.; MD Liverp. 1992; FRCS (Urol.) 1994; FRCS Lond. 1988. Cons. Urol. ScarBoro. Hosp. W. Yorks.

HAWLEY, Alan, OBE, Col. L/RAMC 8 Minorca Avenue, Deepcut, Camberley GU16 6TT — MB ChB 1981 Birm.; DMCC Soc. Apoth 1996; Dip Occ Med. RCP 1997; MSc 1998 Birmingham; DPMSA 2000; MFOM 1999. Socs: Fell. Roy. Soc. Med.; Soc. Occupat. Med.; Fell. Roy. Inst. of Pub. Health & Hygeine.

HAWLEY, Anne Philippa Tel: 01206 824447 Fax: 01206 827973; 9 Beech Avenue, Wivenhoe, Colchester CO7 9AR — MB BS 1978 Lond.; DRCOG 1981. (St. Thos.) Princip. in Gen. Pract., Wivenhoe, Essex. Prev: Trainee GP Colchester VTS; SHO (Phys.) Croydon Gen. Hosp.; Ho. Phys. St. Thos. Hosp. Lond.

HAWLEY, Christopher John Queen Elizabeth II Hospital, Howlands, Welwyn Garden City AL7 4HQ Tel: 01707 365073 — MB BS 1982 Lond.; MRCPsych 1987. Cons. Psychiat. Qu. Eliz. II Hosp. Welwyn Gdn. City.; Vis. Prof. Fac. of Health and Human Sci., Univ. of Herts., Hatfield. Socs: Brit. Assn. of PsychoPharmacol.; Europ. Coll. of NeuropsychoPharmacol.

HAWLEY, Clare Louise 6 Brookfield Avenue, Brookside, Chesterfield S40 3NX — MB ChB 1986 Sheff.

HAWLEY, Ian Charles Conquest Hospital, The Ridge, St Leonards-on-Sea TN37 7RD Tel: 01424 744255 Ext: 6321 Fax: 01424 758121; 1 Beechfield, Main St, Northiam, Rye TN31 6LP — MB BS 1978 Melbourne; FRCPA 1993. (Melbourne) Cons. (Histopath.) Conquest Hosp. St. Leonards-on-Sea.

HAWLEY, Katherine Elizabeth 5 Paultons Square, London SW3 5AS Tel: 020 7352 6464 Fax: 020 7352 1617 — MD 1980 Univ. Calif. San Francisco; BA (Hons.) Washington DC 1968; MSc Univ. California Berkeley 1978; MSc 2000 Univ. London; MRCGP 1990; MACP 1983. (University of California San Fransisco) Prev: Clin. Lect. St. Geo.s' Hosp. Med. Sch.

HAWLEY, Mr Peter Robert 149 Harley Street, London W1N 2DE Tel: 020 7935 4444 Fax: 020 7486 1406 Email: prhawley1@aol.com; 35 Chester Close N., Regents Park, London NW1 4JE Tel: 020 7935 6788 Fax: 020 7935 6788 — MRCS Eng. LRCP Lond. 1956; MS Lond. 1970, MB BS 1956; FRCS Eng. 1960. (Univ. Coll. Hosp.) Cons. Surg. St. Marks Hosp. & King Edwd. VII Hosp. Offs. Lond.; Hon. Cons. Colon & Rectal Surg. to Army. Socs: Assn. Surg. & Brit. Soc. Gastroenterol.; Hon. Mem. Assn. Coloproct.(Past Pres); Roy Soc Med Coloproct Hon Mem.(Past Pres). Prev: Research Fell. Dept. Surg. Univ. Calif. Med. Center, San Francisco, USA; Sen. Regist. (Surg.) St. Mark's Hosp. Lond; Sen. Lect. Univ. Coll. Hosp. Med. Sch.

HAWLEY, Richard Martin Southmead Hospital, Westbury-on-Trym, Bristol BS10 5NB — MB ChB 1978 Birm.; FRCPsych 1996, M 1982. Cons. Psychiat. Avon & Wilts. Ment. Health Care NHS Trust.; Sen. Clin. Lect. Univ. Bristol. Prev: Cons. Psychiat. Barrow Hosp., Ham Green Hosp. & S.mead Hosp. Bristol; Clin. Lect. (Psychiat.) Univ. Birm.

HAWLEY, Richard Trevor Bryer Cottage, Hall Place, Cranleigh GU6 8LD Tel: 01483 273951 — MB BS 1958 Lond.; MRCS Eng. LRCP Lond. 1958. (Guy's)

HAWLEY, Susan Kay 7 Walton Close, Dronfield Woodhouse, Dronfield S18 8UB Tel: 0114 289 1493 — MB ChB 1978 Sheff.; MB ChB Sheff. 1983; BSc (Hons.) Physiol. & Zool. Sheff. 1978; FCAnaesth. 1988. Lect. & Hon. Sen. Regist. (Cardiothoracic Anaesth.) Cardiothoracic Centre Liverp.; Cons. Anaesth. N.. Gen. Hosp. NHS Trust Sheff. Prev: Sen. Regist. Rotat. (Anaesth.) Mersey; Regist. (Anaesth.) N.. Gen. Hosp. Sheff.; Research Fell. Roy. Hallamsh. Hosp. Sheff.

HAWLEY, Valerie Tindal House, Killingworth Vill., Newcastle upon Tyne NE12 6BL — MB BS 1960 Durh.

HAWLEY, William Lawrence Old Town Surgery, 13 De la Warr Road, Bexhill-on-Sea TN40 2HG Tel: 01424 219323 Fax: 01424 733940; Hurchington Manor, Little Common Road, Bexhill-on-Sea TN39 4JD Tel: 01424 845249 — MB BS 1978 Lond.; DRCOG 1983.

HAWNAUR, Jane Margaret Department of Diagnostic Radiology, University of Manchester, Oxford Road, Manchester M13 9PL Tel: 0161 275 5122 — MB ChB 1981 Manch.; MRCP (UK) 1984; DMRD 1987; FRCR 1987. Sen. Lect. & Hon. Cons. Univ. Manch. Prev: Research Fell. & Hon. Sen. Regist. (Radiol.) Univ. Manch.; Sen. Regist. (Diagn. Radiol.) N. Staffs. Roy. Infirm. Stoke-on-Trent.

HAWNEY, Eleanor Clare 2 Patrick Pl, Dundee DD2 1XB — MB ChB 1997 Dundee.

HAWORTH, Adam Ewart Dept of Dermatology, St Mary's Hsopital, Portsmouth PO3 6AD Tel: 0239 286 6073 Fax: 0239 286 6079 — MB BChir 1989 Camb.; MRCPI Dub. 1993. Cons. Derm. St Mary's Ports.

HAWORTH, Miss Catherine The Childrens Hospital, Leicester Royal Infirmary, Leicester LE1 5WW — MB BS 1972 Lond.; BSc (1st cl. Hons.) Lond. 1969; FRCP Lond. 1995; MRCP (UK) 1974; MRCS Eng. LRCP Lond. 1972; FRCPath 1991, M 1979. Cons Paediat. Haemat. Leicester Roy. Infirm. Prev: Sen. Lect. Char. Cross Hosp. Med. Schol. Christie Hosp. Manch.; Hon. Cons. Haemat. Char. Cross Hosp. & Hon. Cons. W.m. Hosp. Lond.; Research Sen. Regist. Paterson Laborat. Christie Hosp. Manch.

HAWORTH, Charles Mark Department of Anaesthesia, Castle Hill Hospital, Cottingham Tel: 01482 875875; 115 Woodhall Way, Beverley HU17 7JR Tel: 01482 863211 — MB ChB 1985 Leeds; DA (UK) 1990. Staff Grade (Cardiothoracic Anaesth.) Castle Hill Hosp. Cottingham; Advanced Trauma & Life Support Leeds 1992; Med. Off. Brit. Motorsport Marshals Club; Registered Doctor Motor Sports Assn., Colnbrooke. Prev: Regist. (Anaesth.) Hull Roy. Infirm.; SHO (Anaesth. & A & E) Vict. Hosp. Blackpool; SHO (Anaesth.) E. York. HA.

HAWORTH, Charles Stephen 9 Viceroy Court, Wilmslow Road, Didsbury, Manchester M20 2RJ — MB ChB 1993 Manch.; MRCP 1996. Specialist Regist. Resp & Gen.l nternal Med NW Thames. Prev: Research Fell.Manch Adult Cystic fibrosis unit.

HAWORTH, Damian John 66 Greys Road, Eastbourne BN20 8AZ — MB ChB 1992 Dundee.

HAWORTH, David Bennett Street Surgery, Bennett Street, Stretford, Manchester M32 8SG Tel: 0161 865 1100 Fax: 0161 865 7710 — BM 1979 Soton.; FFA RCS Eng. 1984.

HAWORTH, David Alan Layton Medical Centre, 200 Kingscote Drive, Blackpool FY3 7EN Tel: 01253 392403 Fax: 01253 304597 — MB ChB 1977 Manch.

HAWORTH, David Edward 62 Canning Street, Liverpool L8 7NR — MB ChB 1981 Liverp.

HAWORTH, David Gordon (retired) St Paul's Medical Centre, Dickson Road, Blackpool FY1 2HH Tel: 01253 623896 Fax: 01253 752818 — MB ChB 1966 Manch.

HAWORTH, Earl Top Flat, 1 Mossley Hill Drive, Liverpool L17 — MB ChB 1974 Liverp.; MRCP (UK) 1976.

HAWORTH, Fiona Landless Macgregor Department of Infection & tropical Medicine, Lister Unit, Northwick Park Hospital, Watford Road, Harrow, Harrow HA1 3UJ Tel: 020 8864 3232 Fax: 020 8869 2824 Email: fionalandless@hotmail.com; Flat 5, 565 Upper Richmond Road Wesr, East Sheen, London SW14 7ED Tel: 020 8876 5799 — BM BCh 1992 Oxf.; MA Oxf. 1993; MRCP (UK) 1996; DTM & H RCP Lond. 1996. (Oxf.) Specialist Train. Regist. (Infec. Dis.s & Gen. Med.) N.W. Thames. Prev: Regist. (Gen. Med. & Infec. Dis.) Ealing Hosp. & Hammersmith Hosp. Lond.; SHO (Trop. Med. & Genitourin. Med.) Univ. Coll. Lond. Hosp.; SHO Rotat. (Gen. Med.) Newc. u. Tyne.

HAWORTH, Gillian Margaret Otford Medical Practice, Leonard Avenue, Otford, Sevenoaks TN14 5RB Tel: 01959 524633 Fax: 01959 525086 — MB ChB 1982 Liverp.; MRCGP 1987; DRCOG 1986. p/t Gen. Practitioner, Sevenoaks, Kent. Prev: Trainee GP Paddock Wood; Trainee GP/SHO Wirral VTS; SHO Rotat. (Med.) Roy. Liverp. Hosp.

HAWORTH, Guy Turrett Medical Centre, Catherine St., Kirkintilloch, Glasgow G66 1JB; 69/71 Main Street, Torrance, Glasgow G64 4EW — MB ChB 1984 Glas.; MRCGP 1988; DRCOG 1987.

HAWORTH, Jennifer Isabel Bowland Road, 52 Bowland Road, Baguley, Manchester M23 1JX Tel: 0161 998 2014 Fax: 0161 945 6354; 4 Bancroft Avenue, Cheadle Hulme, Cheadle SK8 5BA — MB ChB 1974 Manch.; BSc Hons. Manch. 1972; DRCOG 1976. Hosp. Pract. (Obst. & Gyn.) Wythenshawe Hosp.; DFFP.

HAWORTH, John (retired) 40 Brampton Road, Carlisle CA3 9AT Tel: 01228 529213 — MB ChB St. And. 1966; FRCGP 1991, M 1974; DFFP 1993; DObst RCOG 1970. Med. Off. Carlisle United Assn. Football Club; JP. Prev: Scheme Organiser E. Cumbria GP VTS.

HAWORTH, John Leighton East Lancashire Health Authority, 31/33 Kenyon Road, Loneshaye Estate, Nelson BB9 5SZ Tel: 01282 610251 Fax: 01282 610223; Chapman Lodge, 54 Chapman Road, Fulwood, Preston PR2 8NX Tel: 01772 716270 Email: johnhaworth@msn.com — MB ChB 1975 Ed.; MRCGP 1979; DRCOG 1979; DCH Eng. 1978; Dip Prescribing Scheme Liverpool 1996. Med. Adviser E. Lancs. Health Auth.

HAWORTH, John Michael Hallenbrook House, Hallen Road, Hallen, Bristol BS10 7RH — MRCS Eng. LRCP Lond. 1974; BSc (Hons.) (Pharmacol.) Lond. 1971, MB BS 1974; FRCR 1981. (Guy's) Cons. Radiol. S.mead Hosp. Bristol.

HAWORTH, John Neil (retired) 10 Brunstock Close, Lowry Hill, Carlisle CA3 0HL Tel: 01228 31081 — MB ChB 1959 Birm.; FRCPsych 1986, M 1972; DPM Eng. 1968; DObst RCOG 1961. Prev: Cons. Psychiat. & Med. Dir. N. Lakeland Healthcare NHS Trust.

HAWORTH, Judith Margaret Alison Hallenbrook House, Hallen Road, Hallen, Bristol BS10 7RH — MRCS Eng. LRCP Lond. 1974; BSc (Hons.) (Pharmacol.) Lond. 1971, MB BS 1974. (Guy's)

HAWORTH, Karen Lesley Birling Avenue Surgery, 3 Birling Avenue, Rainham, Gillingham ME8 7HB Tel: 01634 360390/361843 Fax: 01634 264061; 9 Birling Avenue, Rainham, Gillingham ME8 7HB Tel: 01634 388549 Email: hawor123@aol.com — MB BS 1986 Lond. (St Georges) Prev: Trainee GP Medway VTS.

HAWORTH, Kathleen Shirley 9 Starkies, Manchester Road, Bury BL9 9QR Tel: 0161 761 2636 — MB ChB 1965 Manch.; FRCOG 1984, M 1970. Cons. (O & G) Fairfield Hosp. Bury.

HAWORTH, Mary Catherine 8 Lees Bank Hill, Cross Roads, Keighley BD22 9HA — MB ChB 1984 Dundee; MRCGP 1988; DRCOG 1987. SHO (Palliat. Med.) W. Yorks.

HAWORTH, Richard Edwin (retired) 314 Red Lees Road, Mereclough, Burnley BB10 4RQ — MB ChB 1950 Ed.

HAWORTH, Richard Noel The Health Centre, Coachmans Drive, Broadfield, Crawley RH11 9YZ Tel: 01293 531951 — MB BS 1976 Lond.; MRCGP 1982; DRCOG 1981; DCH Eng. 1978; FRCGP 1997. (Charing Cross) Course Organiser SW Thames RHA; Med. Stud. Local Area Organiser; Dep. Police Surg. Socs: Assn. Police Surg.; Assn. Course Organisers.

HAWORTH, Robert Airdrie Bryn Gelli, Barmouth LL42 1DE Tel: 01341 280734 — MRCS Eng. LRCP Lond. 1963; DA Eng. 1965. (Liverp.) Prev: SHO (Anaesth.) Liverp. Roy. Infirm.; SHO (Anaesth.), Ho. Surg. & Ho. Phys. Roy. Salop Infirm. Shrewsbury.

HAWORTH, Sheila Glennis 94 Clapham Common Northside, London SW4 9SG Tel: 020 7223 2384 — MRCS Eng. LRCP Lond. 1963; MD Lond. 1976, MB BS 1964; FRCP Lond. 1981, M 1969; FRCPath 1991, M 1983. Brit. Heart Foundat. Prof. Developm. Paediat. Cardiol. Inst. Child Health Univ. Lond.; Hon. Cons. Paediat. Cardiol. Hosp. Childr. Gt. Ormond St. Socs: Brit. Paediat. Assn. & Brit. Cardiac Soc. Prev: Sub-Dean Inst. Child Health; Sen. Lect. (Paediat. Cardiol.) Hosp. Sick Childr. Gt. Ormond St.; Fell. (Foetal Physiol. & Neonatol.) Columbia Univ. New York.

HAWORTH, Simon Charles Otford Medical Practice, Leonard Avenue, Otford, Sevenoaks TN14 5RB Tel: 01959 524633 Fax: 01959 525086 — BM BS 1981 Nottm.; BMedSci Nottm. 1979; MRCGP 1986; DRCOG 1984. Gen. Practioner, Otford, Sevenoaks, Kent. Prev: Cas. Off. Sevenoaks Hosp.; SHO Roy. Liverp. GP VTS; SHO (Gen. Med.) Whiston Hosp.

HAWORTH, Simon Richard Posterngate Surgery, Portholme Road, Selby YO8 4QH Tel: 01757 702561 Fax: 01757 213295; 1 Garrick Close, Brayton, Selby YO8 9RL Tel: 01757 210942 — MB ChB 1986 Leeds; MRCGP 1990.

HAWORTH, Mr Stephen Michael Department of Ophthalmology, Queen's Medical Centre, Nottingham NG7 2UH Tel: 0115 924 9924 Fax: 0115 970 9749; Wychwood, 18 Arlington Drive, Nottingham NG3 5EN Tel: 0115 960 6955 Fax: 0115 985 7586 — MB ChB 1960 Leeds; FRCS Eng. 1968; DO Eng. 1966. (Leeds) Cons. Ophth. Univ. Hosp. Nottm. Socs: Midl. Ophth. Soc. & N. Eng. Ophth. Soc.; (Ex-Pres.) UK & Irel. Soc. Cataract. & Refractive Surgs. Prev: Sen. Regist. (Ophth.) United Sheff. Hosps.

HAWRYCH, Alexander Bohdan X-Ray Dept., Crawley Hospital, West Green Drive, Crawley RH11 7DH — MB ChB 1980 Birm.; Spec. Accredit. Radiol. JCHMT 1987; FRCR 1987. (Birm.) Cons. Radiol. Crawley Hosp. & Horsham Hosp. Prev: Clin. Dir. (Clin. Support Servs.) Crawley Horsham NHS Trust.

HAWSON, David Stanton The Surgery, High Street, Kemnay, Inverurie AB51 5NB Tel: 01467 642289 Fax: 01467 643100; Paradise Cottage, Monymusk, Inverurie AB51 7JL Tel: 01467 651410 — MB BChir 1975 Camb.; MA Camb. 1975. (Camb. & St. Thos.)

HAWSON, John Philip Windermere Health Centre, Goodly Dale, Windermere LA23 2EG Tel: 015394 42496 Fax: 015394 48329 — MB BCh 1972 Oxf.; MRNZCGP 1981; DRCOG 1974.

HAWTHORN, Eileen Margaret Cranbrook, Lymington Road, Milford-on-Sea, Lymington SO41 0QN Tel: 01590 645307 — MRCS Eng. LRCP Lond. 1962. (Liverp.) Socs: BMA. Prev: Regist. (Electroenceph.) Dudley Rd. Hosp. Birm. & Midl. Centre; Neurosurg. & Neurol. Smethwick; Regist. Severalls Hosp. Colchester.

HAWTHORN, Mr Ian Eric Department of Surgery, University Hospital of North Durham, North Road, Durham DH1 5TW Tel: 0191 333 2664 Fax: 0191 333 2685; Heatherlea, Farnley Mount, Nevilles Cross, Durham DH1 4DZ Tel: 0191 384 7678 Fax: 0191 383 1487 — MB BS 1980 Lond.; FRCS Ed. 1986; MRCS Eng. LRCP Lond. 1980. (Char. Cross) Cons. Gen. & Vasc. Surg. N. Durh. Acute Hosps. NHS Trust; Clin. Director in Surg. & Urol. Socs: Vasc. Surg. Soc. GB & Irel.; Fell. Assn. Surgs. Prev: Hon. Sen. Regist. (Surg.) Roy. Hallamsh. Hosp. Sheff.; Wing Cdr. RAF Med. Br.

HAWTHORN, Robert James Seton Gamesland, 94 St Andrews Drive, Glasgow G41 4RX Tel: 0141 427 4235 — MB ChB Glas. 1981; MD Glas. 1989; MRCOG 1986. Cons. Gyn. & Obst. S.. Gen. NHS Trust Glas. Socs: (Sec.) Brit. Soc. Gyn. Endoscopy; Brit. Soc. Colpos. & Cerv. Path. Prev: Sen. Regist. Gtr. Glas. HB; Lect. & Hon. Sen. Regist. Qu. Mothers Hosp. Univ. Glas.

HAWTHORN, Sarah Jane 8 Alford Grove, Sprowston, Norwich NR7 8XB Tel: 01603 411394 — MB BS 1978 Lond.; MRCS Eng. LRCP Lond. 1978; FFA RCS Eng. 1983. (St. Bart.) Staff Grade Anaesth. Norf. & Norwich Hosp.

HAWTHORN, Tania Caroline 5 Eden Close, Stockport SK1 4ED — MB ChB 1994 Manch.

HAWTHORNE, Antony Barnabas 107 Cyncoed Road, Cyncoed, Cardiff CF23 6AD Tel: 029 2074 2183 Fax: 029 2074 5131 Email: barney.hawthorne@uhw-trwales.nhs.uk — BM BCh 1983 Oxf.; MA Camb. 1984; DM Nottm. 1992; FRCP (UK) 1986. (Oxford) Cons. Gastroenterol. Univ. Hosp. Wales Cardiff. Socs: Brit. Soc. Gastroenterol. & Cardiff Med. Soc. Prev: Sen. Regist. (Med.) Manch. Roy. Infirm.; Research Fell. (Gastroenterol.) & Regist. (Gen. Med.) Univ. Hosp. Nottm.

HAWTHORNE, Colin Thomas 18 Martello Park, Craigavad, Holywood BT18 0DG — MB BCh BAO 1986 Belf.

HAWTHORNE, Gillian Catriona Newcastle Diabetic Centre, West Gate Road, Newcastle upon Tyne Tel: 0191 273 6666 — MB BCh BAO 1978 Belf.; PhD Newc. 1990; MRCP (UK) 1980; FRCP (Lond) 1998. Cons. Diabetologist Newc. upon Tyne; Hon. Sen. Clin. Lect., Univ. of Newc. upon Tyne. Socs: Diabetes UK; EASD; Diabetes Assoc. Prev: Sen. Regist. (Diabetes, Endocrinol. & Gen. Med.) Freeman Hosp. Newc.; Med. Research Traing. Fell. & Hon. Sen. Regist. (Med.) Sch. Univ. Newc.; Smith & Nephew Trav. Fell. Rockefeller Univ. NY, USA.

HAWTHORNE, Kamila Four Elms Medical Centres, 103 Newport Road, Cardiff CF24 0AF Tel: 029 2048 5526 Fax: 029 2048 2871 — BM BCh 1984 Oxf.; MA Oxf. 1985; MRCP (UK) 1987; MRCGP 1988; DRCOG 1987; DCH RCP Lond. 1987; MD 1997. (Univ. Oxf.) Clin. Tutor & Hon. Lect. (Rheum.) Univ. Wales Med. Sch. Prev: GP Manch.; Hon. Lect. Diabetes Centre Manch. Roy. Infirm.; Research Train. Fell. Roy. Coll. Gen. Practs.

HAWTHORNE, Malcolm Edward Department of Psychological Medicine, Frimley Park Hospital, Portsmouth Road, Frimley, Camberley GU16 7UJ Tel: 01276 604604 Fax: 01276 604067 — BM BCh 1981 Oxf.; MA, MSc Oxf. 1981; MRCPsych 1988. Cons. Psychiat. with Special Responsibil. Liaison Psychiat. Surrey Hants. Borders NHS Trust. Socs: Roy. Soc. of Med. - Mem. Prev: Sen. Regist. (Psychiat.) St. Geo. Hosp. Lond.

HAWTHORNE, Mr Maurice Robert North Riding Infirmary, Newport Road, Middlesbrough TS1 5JE Tel: 01642 854040 Fax: 01642 854064; 4 Harewood Hill, Darlington DL3 7HY Tel: 01325 486807 Email: mhawthorne@enterprise.net — MB ChB 1977 Manch.; FRCS Eng. 1983; FRCS Ed. 1982. (Manch.) Cons. Otorhinolaryng. N. Riding Infirm. Middlesbrough; Hon. Sec. Inteercollegiate Speciality Bd. in OtoLaryngol. Socs: Fell. Roy. Soc. of Med.; Politzer Soc. Mem. Prev: Janet Nash Fell. (Otorhinolaryng.) Univ. Zürich, Switz.; Mem. Ct. Examr. RCS Eng., 1989-2001.

HAWTHORNE, Patricia Stewart Burrbanks, Nedderton Village, Bedlington NE22 6AS — MB BS 1951 Durh. (Newc.) Clin. Med. Off. (Child Health) N.d. AHA.

HAWTHORNE, Peter William 39A Sunningdale Park, Belfast BT14 6RW Tel: 01232 718979 — MB BCh BAO 1975 Belf.; 1998 DTM Dublin; MRCGP 1983; DPD Wales 1996; DRCOG 1984. (Queens Univ. Belf.) Ships Surg.s, Cunard, Soton. Prev: Med. Off. RAF; Flt. Surg. King Faisal Air Base Tabuk, Saudi Arabia.; Med. Off., Alscon, Nigeria.

HAWTHORNE, Sheelagh Elisabeth Didcot Health Centre, Britwell Road, Didcot OX11 7JH Tel: 01235 512288 Fax: 01235 811473; The Willows, Manor Road, Wantage OX12 8DW Tel: 0123 574619 — MB BS 1978 Lond.

HAWTHORNE, Stephan William Hawthorne, Myatts Field Health Centre, Foxley Square, London SW9 7RX Tel: 020 7411 3553 Fax: 020 7411 3557; 91 Milion Grove, London N16 8QX — MB ChB 1979 Dundee.

HAWTHORNTHWAITE, Ellen Mary Parkfield Health Centre, Sefton Road, New Ferry, Wirral CH62 5HS Tel: 0151 644 6665 — MB ChB 1980 Dundee.

HAWTING, Ruth Anne 13 Holmes Road, London NW5 3AA — MB ChB 1997 Manch.

HAWTON, Professor Keith Edward Warneford Hospital, Oxford OX3 7JX Tel: 01865 226262 Fax: 01865 793101 Email: keith.hawton@psychiatry.ox.ac.uk — MB BChir 1969 Camb.; MA, BA Camb. 1965; DM Oxf. 1980; FRCPsych 1990, M 1973; DPM Eng. 1972. (Cambs & Oxf) Cons. Psychiat. Warneford Hosp. Oxf.; Prof. Psychiat. Prev: Boerhaave Prof. Psychiat. Leiden Univ. Netherlands; Clin. Tutor (Psychiat.) Oxf. Univ.

HAWXWELL, Sarah Gail 1 Tivoli Road, London SE27 0ED — MB BS 1992 Lond.

HAXBY, Elizabeth Jane 53 Chestnut Road, London SE27 9EZ — MB BS 1985 Lond.; MB BS (Hons.) Lond. 1985; FRCA. 1992. Sen. Regist. (Anaesth.) SW Thames RHA; Cons. Cardiothoracic Anaesth. Roy. Brompton & Harefield NHS Trust. Prev: Regist. (Anaesth.) NW Thames RHA; SHO (Anaesth.) Hammersmith Hosp. Lond. & Edgware Gen. Hosp.; SHO (Cardiothoracic Surg. & Orthop. Surg.) Hammersmith Hosp. Lond.

HAXTON, Cyril Andrew (retired) 53 Deanhill Avenue, Clacton-on-Sea CO15 5BE — MB ChB 1944 Ed.; MRCOG 1950. Prev: Intermediate Regist. O & G City Hosp. Nottm.

HAXTON, Mr Herbert Alexander (retired) Strathisla, Kingarth Drive, Rosemount, Blairgowrie PH10 6TP — MB ChB 1937 St. And.; FRSE 1971; FRCS Eng. 1942; ChM St. And. 1944, MD 1946. Hon. Cons. Surg. Manch. N. Hosp. & Crumpsall Hosp. Manch.; Corresp. Fell. Brazilian Cardiovasc. Soc.; Hon. Mem. Cardiovasc. Soc. Chile. Prev: Hunt Prof. & Arris & Gale Lect. RCS Eng.

HAXTON, Michael John Department of Obstetrics & Gynaecology, Vale of Leven District General Hospital, Alexandria G83 0UA Tel: 01389 54121 Fax: 01389 55948 — MB ChB 1974 Ed.; BSc Ed. 1971; FRCOG 1992, M 1979. Cons. O & G Vale of Leven Dist. Gen. Hosp. Alexandria.

HAY, Alastair David 9 Woodfield Road, Oadby, Leicester LE2 4HQ — MB ChB 1991 Sheff.; MRCP (UK) 1995; DCH 1997; MRCGP 1997. (Sheff.) Clin. Lect. (Gen. Pract.) Univ. Leicester.

HAY, Alice Joan (retired) BUPA Alexandra Hospital, Impton Lane, Waldeslane, Medway, Chatham ME5 9PG Tel: 01634 813661 Fax: 01634 813661 Email: ajhay@waitrose.com — MB ChB Ed. 1962; DPM Ed. & Glas. 1972. Cons. Child & Family Psychiat. S.E. Thames RHA.

HAY, Alistair Gall Craig Dunain Hospital, Inverness IV3 8JR Tel: 01463 234101; Cradlehall Lodge, 1A Orchard Park, Inverness IV2 5TP Tel: 01463 794632 — MB ChB 1982 Aberd.; MRCPsych 1990; MRCGP 1987; DRCOG 1986. Cons. Psychiat. s/i Forens. Psychiat. Craig Dunain Hosp.

HAY, Andrew David Holburn Medical Group, 7 Albyn Place, Aberdeen AB10 1YE Tel: 01224 400800 Fax: 01224 407777 — MB ChB 1983 Aberd.; MRCGP 1993. Prev: Regist. (Anaesth.) Aberd. Roy. Infirm.

HAY, Andrew James Department of Medical Microbiology, Raigmore Hospital, Perth Road, Inverness IV2 3UJ Tel: 01463 704000 Email: andrew.hay@haht.scot.nhs.uk — MB ChB 1984 Ed.; MSc Lond. 1988; FRCPath 1990. Cons. Med. Microbiol. Raigmore Hosp. Highland acute Hosps NHS Trust. Prev: Cons. Med. Microbiol. King's Coll. Hosp. Lond.; Lect. (Med. Microbiol.) St. Bart. Hosp. Lond.

HAY, Mr Andrew MacPherson Dept of Urology, Royal Shrewsbury Hospital, Shrewsbury SY3 8XR Tel: 01743 261107; Upper Cound House, Cound, Shrewsbury SY5 6AX Tel: 01743 761247 Fax: 01743761071 Email: andrewhay@dial.pipex.com —

MB BS Lond. 1969; BSc (Physiol., 1st cl. Hons.) Lond. 1965; FRCS Eng. 1974; MRCS Eng. LRCP Lond. 1969. (St. Mary's) Cons. Surg. Urol. Roy. Shrewsbury Hosp. & P.ss Roy. Hosp. Telford; Founder MedIT Ltd. Socs: Roy. Soc. Med. Prev: Sen. Regist. & Regist. Hammersmith Hosp. & Roy. Postgrad Med. Sch. Lond.; Ho. Phys. St. Mary's Hosp. Med. Sch. Lond.

HAY, Arthur William (retired) 110 Glenridding Drive, Barrow-in-Furness LA14 4PA Tel: 01229 34152 — MB BS 1942 Durh.; MFCM 1973; DPH Durh. 1948. Prev: Dist. Community Phys. SW Cumbria Health Dist.

HAY, Catherine Joanne 24 Tennyson Road, Stockport SK5 6JQ — MB ChB 1995 Manch. SHO (Med.) Trafford Gen. Hosp. Manch.

HAY, Charles Richard Morris Department of Haematology, Manchester Royal Infirmary, Oxford Road, Manchester M13 9WL Tel: 0161 276 4727 Fax: 0161 276 4814 Email: haemophilia@man.ac.uk; Reddish House, Reddish Lane, Lymm WA13 9RY Tel: 01925 755173 Fax: 01925 755173 Email: haemophilia@mon.ac.uk — MB ChB 1976 Sheff.; MD Sheff. 1989; FRCP Lond. 1994; MRCP (UK) 1980; FRCPath 1996, M 1984. (Sheff.) Cons. Haemat. Manch. Roy. Infirm.; Dir. Manch. Roy. Infirm. Haemophilia Centre; Hon. Sen. Lect. (Med.) Manch.; Edit. Bd. Haemophilia. Socs: Brit. Soc. Haematol.; Internat. Soc. Thrombosis & Haemostasis.; Vice-Chairm. UK HCDO. Prev: Sen. Lect. (Haemat.) Liverp. Univ.; Sen. Regist. Rotat. (Haemat.) Sheff. HA; Regist. (Haemat.) N. Gen. Hosp. Sheff.

HAY, Colin Paterson (retired) High Meadow, Watermillock, Penrith CA11 0LR Tel: 017684 86248 — MB ChB 1948 Ed. Prev: Hosp. Pract. (ENT) Doncaster Roy. Infirm.

HAY, Daniel Perry Leakefield House, 24 Costock Road, East Leake, Loughborough LE12 6LY Tel: 01509 852899 — MB ChB 1989 Liverp.; BSc (Hons.) Liverp. 1987; MRCOG 1997. Specialist Regist. (O & G) Derby City Gen. Hosp. Prev: SHO (O & G) Univ. Hosp. Nottm.; SHO (Oncol.) Gen. Hosp. Nottm.; SHO (Genitourin. Med.) City Hosp. Nottm.

HAY, Mr David John Plas Craig, Marine Drive, Llandudno LL30 2QZ Tel: 01492 875702 Fax: 01492 878247 Email: dj.hay@glanclwyd-tr.wales.nhs.uk — MB ChB Manch. 1969; FRCS Eng. 1974; FACS 1998. (Manch.) Cons. Surg. Glan Clwyd Hosp. & Clwyd HA. Socs: Fell. Roy. Soc. Med. (Mem. Sect. Coloproctol.); St. Marks Assn.; (Counc.) Assn. Coloproctol. Prev: Cons. Surg. Gwynedd HA; Sen. Regist. Manch. Roy. Infirm. & St. Mark's Hosp. Lond.

HAY, Deirdre Jane Simpson Medical Group, Bathgate Primary Care Centre, Whitburn Road, Bathgate EH48 2SS Tel: 01506 654444 — MB ChB 1982 Edinburgh; MRCGP 1987. (Edinburgh) p/t GP Bathgate.

HAY, Douglas Middleton Gavin Brown Clinic, The Princess Royal Hospital, Saltshouse Road, Hull HU8 9HE Tel: 01482 676845 Fax: 01482 676558; 3 Ferriby High Road, North Ferriby HU14 3LD Tel: 01482 649903 Fax: 01482 649903 — MB ChB Aberd. 1964; MFFP 1993; FRCOG 1986, M 1973; DObst RCOG 1966. Cons. Hull & E. Yorks. Hosp.NHS Trust; Hon. Cons. Hull IVF Unit; Research Assoc. Univ. Hull; Divis. Clin. Dir. Wom. & Childr. Serv. Hull & E. Yorks Hosp. NHS Trust. Socs: Internat. Continence Soc. Prev: Sen. Regist. & Hon Lect. (O & G) Ninewells Hosp. Dundee; Regist. (O & G) S.. Gen. Hosp. Glas.; Med. Off. Sabah, Malaysia.

HAY, Douglas Scheiffler Lawn House, Marsh Lane, Bovey Tracey, Newton Abbot TQ13 9BS — MB BS 1994 Lond.

HAY, Edward Harvey The Health Centre, Shirebrook, Mansfield NG20 8AL Tel: 01623 742464 Fax: 01623 742558 — MB BCh BAO 1945 NUI; DCH RCPSI 1949. (Univ. Coll. Dub.) Prev: Asst. Res. Med. Off. Cork St. Fever Hosp. Dub.; Ho. Surg. Mater Miser Hosp. Dub.; Ho. Surg. Mater Miser. Hosp. Dub.

HAY, Elaine Margaret Staffordshire Rheumatology Centre, The Haywood, High Lane, Burslem, Stoke-on-Trent ST6 5AG Tel: 01782 835721 Fax: 01782 813419; Waterside Mews, 52 Cyril Bell Close, Lymm WA13 0JS Tel: 01925 759353 — MD 1993 Sheff.; MB ChB 1979; MRCP (UK) 1982; FRCP 1999 UK. Cons. Community Rheum. N. Staffs. Hosp. Trust; Sen. Lect. Keele Univ. Socs: Chairm. Arthritis Research Campaign Educat. Subcomm.; Vice-Chairm. Brit. Soc. Rheum. Train. & Research Comm. Prev: Sen. Clin. Research Fell. ARC Epidemiol. Research Unit Univ. Manch.; Sen. Regist. (Rheum.) Manch. Roy. Infirm.; Regist. (Med.) Roy. Hallamsh. Hosp. Sheff.

HAY, Elizabeth Jean 458 Clarkston Road, Glasgow G44 3QF — MB ChB 1977 Glas.; DCH RCPS Glas. 1979. GP Glas. Prev: Clin. Med. Off. Hamilton & E. Kilbride Health Dist; Trainee Gen. Pract.

HAY, Ewen David Agnew (retired) Stoke Hill Farm, Andover SP11 0LS Tel: 01264 738221 — BM BCh Oxf. 1956; MA Oxf. 1957; DCH Eng. 1962; DObst RCOG 1962. Prev: GP & Company Med. Off.

HAY, Fiona Alison Orchard House, Harley, Shrewsbury SY5 6LP Tel: 01952 510228 — BM BCh 1988 Oxf.; MA Oxf. 1992, BA 1985, BM BCh 1988; DRCOG 1991; MRCGP 1995. (Oxford) GP Retainer, Cressage Health Centre, Shrops. Socs: BMA. Prev: SHO (Obst.) Oxf.

HAY, Gail Catherine 79 Longdown Lane S., Epsom Tel: 0137 27 29061 — MB ChB 1968 Ed. (Ed.)

HAY, George Gordon 16 St John Street, Manchester M3 4EA Tel: 0161 834 8028 — MD 1967 Manch.; MB ChB 1958, DPM 1964; FRCPsych 1974, M 1971; DCH Eng. 1961. Hon. Cons. Psychiat. Univ. Hosp. S. Manch.; Hon. Lect. (Psychiat.) Univ. Manch. Prev: Cons. Psychiat. Univ. Hosp. S. Manch.; Lect. (Psychiat.) Univ. Manch.; Cons. Psychiat. Bolton & Dist. Hosp. Gp.

HAY, Gillian Colette 9 Woodfield Road, Oadby, Leicester LE2 4HQ — MB ChB 1992 Sheff.; DRCOG 1996. (Sheff.)

HAY, Graeme Ian Alva Medical Practice, West Johnstone Street, Alva FK12 5BD Tel: 01259 760331 Fax: 01259 769991 — MB ChB 1992 Ed.; BSc (Med. Sci.) Ed. 1990; MRCGP 1996; DRCOG 1994; DFFP 1994. Prev: Trainee GP Alva VTS.

HAY, Ian Fraser Colson Geriatric Medicine Department, Dumfries & Galloway Royal Infirmary, Bankend Road, Dumfries DG1 4AP Tel: 01387 241349 Fax: 01387 241361 — MB BChir 1980 Camb.; BA Camb. 1976, MA, MB 1980, BChir 1979; MRCP (UK) 1983. (King's Coll. Hosp.) Cons. Phys. Geriat. Med. Dumfries & Galloway Roy. Infirm. Prev: Sen. Regist. Rotat. (Gen. Chest & Geriat. Med.) Roy. Free Hosp. Lond.; Research Fell. & Regist. (Chest Med. incl. ITU) Addenbrooke's & Papworth Hosps. Camb.; SHO Rotat. (Endocrinol., Gastroenterol., Geriat.) John Radcliffe Hosp. Oxf.

HAY, Isabelle Cochrane 12 St Marys Place, Top Floor, Aberdeen AB11 6HL — MB ChB 1989 Glas.; BSc (Hons.) Microbiol. Glas. 1984. SHO (Med.) Aberd. Roy. Infirm.

HAY, Mr James Hugh 20 Urrdale Road, Glasgow G41 5DD Tel: 0141 427 6565 Fax: 0141 427 6969 Email: jameshlay@btinternet.com — MB ChB Glas. 1964; FRCS Glas. 1989; FRCS Ed. 1970. Consg. Hopitals, Ross Hall Hosp., 221 Crookston Rd, Glas. & HCI Internat. Med. Centre, Beardmore St., Clydebank. Socs: Fell. of Brit. Orthopaedic Assn.; Internat. Affil. Mem. of Amer. Acad. of Orthopaedic Surg.s. Prev: Cons. Orthop. Surg. Roy. Alexandra Hosp. Paisley.

HAY, James Leslie Surgery, 123 Victoria Road, Aberdeen AB11 9LY Tel: 01224 895116 Fax: 01224 891146; 14 Westholme Terrace, Aberdeen AB15 6AD Tel: 01224 319543 — MB ChB 1959 Aberd. Approved Maritime & Coastguard Agency Examr. N. Star Shipping (Aberd.) Ltd.

HAY, Jean Innes (retired) 17 Raleigh Way, Frimley, Camberley GU16 8RH Tel: 01276 676948 — MB ChB Aberd. 1940, DPH 1965. Prev: Med. Off. (Child Health) Grampian N. Area Health Bd.

HAY, Jochem Fritz 18 Kidbrooke Park Road, London SE3 0LW — State Exam Med. Marburg 1991.

HAY, Mr John Craig (retired) 18B Uigen, Isle of Lewis HS2 9HX Tel: 01851 672400 Email: vigean@globalnet.co.uk — MB ChB 1955 Glas.; MD Bangkok 1960; FRCS Ed. 1965; DObst RCOG 1958. Prev: GP I. of Lewis.

HAY, Professor John Duncan Oakenholt House, Eynsham Road, Farmoor, Oxford OX2 9NL Tel: 01865 863710 Fax: 01865 864831 — MB ChB Liverp. 1933; MB BCh Camb. 1935; MA Camb. 1934; MD Liverp. 1936; FRCP Lond. 1951, M. 1939; MRCS Eng. LRCP Lond. 1933; DCH Eng. 1939. (Camb. & Liverp.) Emerit. Prof. Univ. Liverp.; Hon. Cons. Paediat. Liverp. AHA (T). Socs: Hon. Mem. (Ex-Pres.) Brit. Paediat. Assn.; (Ex-Pres.) Liverp. Med. Inst. Prev: Cons. Paediat. Liverp. Educat. Comm.; Cons. Paediat. Liverp. RHB; Lt.-Col. RAMC, India Comm.

HAY, Mr Justin Mary The Psychiatric Unit, Derby City Hospital, Derby DE22 9ME — MB BCh BAO 1975 NUI; FRCS Ed. 1981; FRCS Eng. 1981; MRCPsych 1990. Cons. Psychiat. S.. Derbysh. Ment. Health Trust. Prev: Research Fell. & Hon. Sen. Regist. Profess. Unit Mapperley Hosp. Nottm.

HAY, Keith Wilson Carmondean Health Centre, Livingston EH54 8PY; 57 Calder Road, Bellsquarry, Livingston EH54 9AD — MB ChB 1975 Aberd.

HAY, Lesley Alison Midlock Medical Centre, 7 Midlock Street, Glasgow G51 1SL Tel: 0141 427 4271 Fax: 0141 427 1405 — MB ChB 1988 Glas.; MRCGP 1992.

HAY, Marion Hay Cochrane 6 Carlaverock Road, Glasgow G43 2SA Tel: 0141 649 3044 — MB ChB 1948 Glas.; DPH 1951. (Glas.) Prev: Asst. Co. MOH Dunbartonsh.; Ho. Surg. Stobhill Hosp. Glas.; Ho. Phys. Vict. Infirm. Glas.

HAY, Melissa Ann 15 Carlyle Square, London SW3 6EX — MB BS 1996 Lond.

HAY, Phillip Edward St George's Hospital Medical School, Cranmer Terrace, Tooting, London SW17 0RE Tel: 020 8725 3355 Fax: 020 8725 2736 Email: phay@sghms.ac.uk — MB BS 1983 Lond.; MRCP (UK) 1986. (St. Thos.) Sen. Lect. & Hon. Cons. Genitourin. Med. St. Geo. Hosp. Med. Sch. Lond. Socs: Brit. Soc. Study of Infec.; Med. Soc. Study VD. Prev: Clin. Scientif. Off. (Sexual Transm. Dis.) Clin. Research Centre Harrow; Hon. Sen. Regist. (Genitourin. Med.) St. Mary's Hosp. Lond.; Regist. Rotat. (Gen. Med. & Infect. Dis.) City Hosp., Edin. & Borders Gen. Hosp. Melrose.

HAY, Richard Norman Roysia Surgery, Burns Road, Royston SG8 5PT Tel: 01763 243166 Fax: 01763 245315; Churchfields, Vicarage Close, Melbourn, Royston SG8 6DY Tel: 01763 263457 — MB BS 1978 Lond.; DRCOG 1981.

HAY, Mr Robert Lawrie (retired) Hillfield House, Scragged Oak Road, Detling, Maidstone ME14 3HB — MB ChB Ed. 1962; FRCS Ed. 1966. Prev: Cons. Orthop. Surg. SE Thames RHA.

HAY, Professor Roderick James St John's Institute of Dermatology, St Thomas' Hospital, London SE1 7EH Tel: 020 7960 5802; 1 The Capol, 26 Cole Street, London SE1 4 YH — BM BCh 1971 Oxf.; MA Oxf. 1987, BA 1968, DM 1981; FRCP Lond. 1987; MRCP (UK) 1974; MRCPath 1982; FRCPath 1994, M 1982. (Oxf. & Guy's) Mary Dunhill Prof. Cutaneous Med. GKT Guy's Hosp. Lond.; Hon. Cons. Dermat. Guy's & St. Thos. Hosps. Lond.; Dean Extern. Affairs GKT. Lond.; VIS Prof. (Clin. Sci.) Lond. Sch. Hyg. & Trop. Med. Socs: Internat. Soc. Human & Animal Mycol.; Brit. Assn. of Dermatol.s; Europ. ConFederat. of Med. Mycology (PRES). Prev: Reader (Clin. Mycol.) Lond. Sch. Hyg. & Trop. Med.; Regist. & Hon. Phys. (Dermat.) Guy's Hosp. Lond.; Wellcome Fell. (Mycol.) Center for Dis. Control Atlanta, USA.

HAY, Mr Roger William Oxford Policy Management, 35 St. Aldates, Oxford OX1 1BN Tel: 01865 207300 Email: roger.hay@opml.co.uk; The Old Greyhound, Leckhampstead Road, Akeley MK18 5SS Tel: 01205 860260 Email: opirwh@sable.ex.ac.uk — MB ChB Otago 1962; FRCS Eng. 1969. (Otago) Health Policy Cons. Oxf. Policy Managem.; Sec. to the Tanelees Oxf. Policy Inst.

HAY, Rosalind Ann The Schoolhouse, Kirkton Manor, Peebles EH45 9JN — MB ChB 1965 Aberd.; DRCOG 1967; DCCH RCP Ed. 1986. Clin. Med. Off. Lothian Health Bd.

HAY, Ruth Elizabeth 45 Tenters Way, Paisley PA2 9HL — MB ChB 1997 Glas.

HAY, Samuel Richard Brunswick House Medical Group, 1 Brunswick Street, Carlisle CA1 1ED Tel: 01228 515808 Fax: 01228 593048; 61 Warwick Road, Carlisle CA1 1EB — MB ChB 1968 Ed.; MRCGP 1977. (Ed.)

HAY, Mr Stuart Martin The Robert James and Agnes Hunt Orthopaedic Hospital, Oswestry SY10 7AG Tel: 0161 404226 — MB ChB 1983 Ed.; FRCS Glas. 1989; FRCS (Orth.) 1996. (Edinburgh) Cons. Orthop. Surg., Specialist in Upper Limb Surg. & Sports Injuries The Robt. Jones & Agnes Hunt Hosp. OsW.ry. Socs: BMA; BOA; BESS. Prev: Lect. & Hon. Sen. Regist. Trauma & Orthop. Surg. Univ. of Sheff.; Regist. Trauma & Orthop. Surg. N. trent Progr.

HAY, Thomas Kerr (retired) 90 Links Road, Lundin Links, Leven KY8 6AU Tel: 01333 320367 — MB ChB 1955 Ed. Prev: Ho. Phys. Stoke Mandeville Hosp. Aylesbury.

HAY, Wallace McQueen 6 Carlaverock Road, Glasgow G43 2SA Tel: 0141 649 3044 — MB ChB 1952 Glas. (Glas.)

HAY, William (retired) 156 Findhorn, Forres IV36 3YL Tel: 01224 486371 — MB ChB 1933 Aberd.

HAY, William Irvine 6 Carlaverock Road, Glasgow G43 2SA — MB ChB 1982 Glas.; BSc (Hons.) Pharmacol. Glas. 1979, MB ChB 1982. Regist. Roy. Alexandra Infirm. Paisley. Socs: BMA. Prev: Jun. Ho. Off. Roy. Infirm. Glas.; Jun. Ho. Off. W.. Infirm. Glas.

HAY, William James, MC, TD (retired) Bridge End, Stainton, Kendal LA8 0LF Tel: 015395 60354 — MB BChir Camb. 1946; MA Camb. 1939; FRCP Lond. 1970, M 1947; MRCS Eng. LRCP Lond. 1938. Prev: Cons. Phys. Lancaster & Kendal Gp. Hosps.

HAYAT, F Abbotts Road Surgery, 9 Abbotts Road, Southall UB1 1HS Tel: 020 8843 9584 — MB BS 1967 Karachi; MB BS 1967 Karachi.

HAYAT, Mohammed 82 Llanthawey Road, Newport NP20 4LA Tel: 01633 250215 — MB BS 1966 Peshawar; LRCP LRCS Ed. LRCPS Glas. 1984; FACA 1992; FCPS Pakistan 1988; FCCP 1991; DTCD Wales 1978. (Khyber Med. Coll. Peshawar) Cons. Phys. Cheltenham Gen. Hosp. Socs: Med. Defence Union; Assoc. Mem. Brit. Thoracic Soc.

HAYAT, Mumtaz 429 Stanningley Road, Leeds LS13 4BL — MB BS 1988 Punjab; MRCP (UK) 1994.

HAYAT, Shaukat Shaftesbury Medical Centre, 39 Shaftesbury Pardae, South Harrow, Harrow HA2 0AH Tel: 020 8423 5500 — MB BS 1967 Patna.

HAYCOCK, Professor George Burdett Department of Paediatrics, Guy's Hospital, London SE1 9RT Tel: 020 7955 4018 Fax: 020 7357 6037; 55 Beaulieu Avenue, Sydenham, London SE26 6PW Tel: 020 8659 4417 — MB 1966 Camb.; BChir 1965; FRCP Lond. 1981, M 1968; DCH Eng. 1967. (St. Thos.) Prof. Paediat GKT sch of med.Lond. Socs: Brit. Paediat. Assn. & Brit. Assn. Paediat. Nephrol.; Europ.soc.Paediat.Nephrol.; Roy. Soc. Med. Prev: Cons. Paediat. Avon AHA (T); Fell. (Paediat. Nephrol.) Albert Einstein Coll. Med. Bronx, USA; Sen. Regist. (Paediat.) S.mead Hosp. Bristol.

HAYCOCK, Joanna Christa The Hedges, 4 Landmere Lane, Ruddlington, Nottingham NG11 6ND — MB ChB 1983 Birm.; FCAnaesth. 1991.

HAYCOCK, Karen Elizabeth 4 South Learmonth Avenue, Edinburgh EH4 1PE — MB ChB 1993 Ed.

HAYCOCK, Paul Cantab Pharmaceuticals PLC, 184 Cambridge Science Park, Wilton Road, Cambridge CB4 0GN — MB BS 1969 Lond. (Middlx.) Med. Dir. Novo Laborat. Socs: Fell. Roy. Soc. Med.

HAYDAR, Mr Ammar Abdulkareem Suleiman 45 Gorse Road, Blackpool FY3 9ED — MB ChB 1982 Baghdad; FRCS Ed. 1990; LRCP LRCS Ed. LRCPS Glas. 1984. Socs: BMA & ODA. Prev: Ho. Off. (Med.) Blackburn Qu. Pk. Hosp.; SHO (Neurosurg.) Salford HA; SHO (Cardiac. Surg.) Bristol Roy. Infirm.

HAYDEN, Anne, MBE Casa Velha, Ringwood Road, Three Legged Cross, Wimborne BH21 6RB — BM 1985 Soton.; BSc (Physiol. & Biochem.) Soton. 1975. Prev: SHO (A & E) Qu. Alexandra Hosp. Portsmouth; SHO (O & G) Roy. Vict. Hosp. Bournemouth; SHO (Psychiat.) St. Ann's Hosp. Poole.

HAYDEN, Brigid Eileen 56 Parsonage Brow, Upholland WN8 0JG Tel: 01695 622112 Email: brigid.hayden@doctors.org.uk; Dept. Obstetrics + Gynaecology, Fairfield Hospital, Bury Tel: 0161 764 6081 — MB ChB 1980 Bristol; 2000 Pg Cert. Clin. Teaching + Learning, Liverpool; MRCOG 1987. (Bristol) Cons. O+G Dept. Bury. Socs: N. of Eng. Obst. & Gyn Soc.; Brit. Soc. For colposcopy and cervical Path. Prev: Princip. (Gen. Pract.) Portsmouth; Specialist (O & G) Mauritius; Specialist Regist. (O & G) Mersey Region.

HAYDEN, Catherine Julia Rose Cottage, Taylor Lane, Barwick In Elmet, Leeds LS15 4LY — MB ChB 1993 Leeds.

HAYDEN, Professor Jacqueline Unsworth Medical Centre, Parr Lane, Unsworth, Bury BL9 8JR Tel: 0161 766 4448 Fax: 0161 767 9811; 12 Mercers Road, Heywood OL10 2NP Tel: 01706 625470 Fax: 01706 625593 — MB BS 1974 Lond.; FRCP Lond. 1996; MRCP (UK) 1976; MRCS Eng. LRCP Lond. 1974; FRCGP 1987, M 1979; DRCOG 1979; DCH Eng. 1977. (St. Geo. Lond.) Dean of Postgrad. Med. Studies Univ. Manch. NW Regional Office. Prev: Regional adviser (Gen. Pract.) NW Region Trainee GP Oxf. VTS.

HAYDEN, James Timothy 12 Lockington Cl, Tonbridge TN9 2RB — MB ChB 1997 Leic.

HAYDEN, Mr Jeremy David St James' University Hospital, Leeds LS9 7TE; Rose Cottage, Taylor Lane, Barwick-in-Elmet, Leeds LS15 4LY Tel: 0113 281 1028 — MB ChB 1993 Leeds; BSc 1990 (Hons.) Leeds; FRCS (Eng.) 1999; MD (Dist.) 1999. (Leeds) Prev: Research Fell. (Div. of Surg.) Leeds Gen. Infirm.

HAYDEN, John Thomas Dominic Eastfield Road Surgery, 4 Eastfield Road, Birchington CT7 9RH Tel: 01843 841128 Fax: 01843 846131 — MB BS Lond. 1962; MRCS Eng. LRCP Lond.

1962; MLCOM 1983. (Univ. Coll. Hosp.) Socs: BMA. Prev: Hosp. Pract. I. of Thanet, Kent & Canterbury Gps. Hosps.; Ho. Phys. W. Middlx. Hosp. Isleworth; Ho. Surg. Univ. Coll. Hosp. Lond.

HAYDEN, Mark John 78 Hardwick Lane, Bury St Edmunds IP33 2RA — MB ChB 1990 Sheff.; MRCP (UK) 1993. Research Fell. (Paediat.) P.ss Margt. Hosp. Perth. Prev: SHO (Paediat.) Rotherham Gen. Hosp. & Leeds Gen. Infirm.; SHO (Gen. Med.) N.ampton Gen. Hosp.

HAYDEN, Paul Graham 41 Norsey Road, Billericay CM11 1BG — MB BS 1997 Lond.

HAYDEN, Rex Bryan (retired) Forest Cottage, 29 Forest Glade, North Weald, Epping CM16 6LD Tel: 01992 573483 Fax: 01992 560543 — MB BS 1956 Lond.; MRCS Eng. LRCP Lond. 1956.

HAYDEN, Rosemary Juliet, MBE (retired) The Old Court House, Shillington, Hitchin SG5 3LY Tel: 01462 711672 Email: djhayden@talk21.com — MB BS 1946 Lond.; MRCS Eng. LRCP Lond. 1945; FFCM 1986, M 1982; DCH Eng. 1948. Prev: SCM (Child Health) N. & S. Beds. HA's.

HAYDN, Kathleen Frances University of East Anglia Health Centre, University of East Anglia, Earlham Road, Norwich NR4 7TJ Tel: 01603 592172; 3 Newmarket Road, Cringleford, Norwich NR4 6UE — MB ChB 1976 Sheff.

HAYDN SMITH, Peter Ashen Hill, The Drive, Hellingly, Hailsham BN27 4EP Tel: 01323 440022 Fax: 01323 847822 Email: peter@khrlewes.demon.co.uk — MB ChB 1978 Sheff.; BDS 1968; MRCPsych. 1982. Cons. Forens. Psychiat. Hellingly Hosp. Prev: Sen. Regist. (Forens. Psychiat.) & Regist. (Psychiat.) Bethlem Roy. & Maudsley Hosps. Lond.; Ho. Off. (Neurosurg.) Roy. Infirm. Sheff.

HAYDN TAYLOR, Derek (retired) La Cigale, Rue De Douet, St Ouen, Jersey JE3 2HN Tel: 01534 485095 Fax: 01534 482993 Email: bruin@itl.net — BM BCh Oxf. 1951; MA Oxf. 1956. Prev: Regist. (Cas.) Roy. Bucks. Hosp. Aylesbury.

HAYDOCK, Stephen Frederick Trevor Villa, 19 Histon Road, Cottenham, Cambridge CB4 8UF — MB 1986 Camb.; BChir 1985.

HAYDON, David Anthony (retired) Westwood, Devonshire Avenue, Amersham HP6 5JE Tel: 01494 726878 Fax: 01494 726878 — MB BS 1966 Lond.; DObst RCOG 1969. Prev: Med. Off. Amer. Internat. plc.

HAYDON, Eric Grigor (retired) Langleybury, 16 Waterford Gardens, Highcliffe, Christchurch BH23 5DP Tel: 01425 274034 — MB BS 1952 Lond.; MRCS Eng. LRCP Lond. 1952.

HAYDON, Geoffrey Harold Department of Medicine, University of Edinburgh, Royal Infirmary, Lauriston Place, Edinburgh EH3 9YW Fax: 0131 229 2294 Email: gh@srv2.med.ed.ac.uk; Flat 2F2, 25 Montpelier, Edinburgh EH10 4LY Email: geoffhay@msn.com — MB ChB 1990 Ed.; MRCP (UK) 1993. Career Regist. (Gastroenterol. & Gen. Med.) Univ. Glas. Roy. Infirm. Prev: Research Fell. (Med.) Univ. Edin.

HAYDON, John Ralph, Surg. Capt. RN Civilian Consultant, Occupational Health, Environment & Safety Group, HM Naval Base, Portsmouth PO1 3ND Tel: 02392 725489 Fax: 02392 725133; Field House, South Lane, Clanfield, Waterlooville PO8 0RB Tel: 02392 591963 Email: jrhaydon@doctors.net.uk — MRCS Eng. LRCP Lond. 1969; MSc (Occupat. Med.) Lond. 1979; FFOM RCP Lond. 1995, MFOM 1983; MRCGP 1976; DIH Eng. 1979; DObst RCOG 1970. (Middlx.) Civil. Cons., Occupat.al health, Environment & Safety Gp., HM Naval Base, Portsmouth. Socs: Fell. Roy. Soc. Med.; Fell. Med. Soc. Lond.; Soc. Occupat. Med. Prev: Asst. Dir. (Med. Policy) (Health & Research) Surg. Gen.s Dept.; Specialist Occupat.al Phys., BMI Health Serv.s; Asst. Chief of Staff (Med.) Fleet HQ, N.wood.

HAYDON, Sarah Catherine 165 Seaforth Gardens, Stoneleigh, Epsom KT19 0LW — MB BS 1991 Lond.; DRCOG 1996. (St. Geo. Hosp. Med. Sch. Lond.)

HAYE, Rashid (retired) 20 The Downs, Schools Hill, Cheadle SK8 1JL Tel: 0161 428 9861 — MB BS 1952 Punjab, Pakistan; MB BS Punjab (Pakistan) 1952; MD Birm. 1966. Prev: Assoc. Lect. Univ. Manch. Med. Sch.

HAYEK, Ann Hella Joyce 6 Baring Crescent, Beaconsfield HP9 2NG Tel: 01494 672451 — MB BS 1988 Lond. Trainee GP Hillingdon HA VTS.

HAYEK, Laurence Joseph Henry Eric 42 Huxhams Cross, Dartington, Totnes TQ9 6NT Tel: 01803 762693; 42 Huxhams Cross, Dartington, Totnes TQ9 6NT — MB 1961 Camb.; BChir 1960; MRCPath 1972; DObst RCOG 1963. (Middlx.) Cons. Locum. Prev: Lect. Bact. Wright-Fleming Inst. St. Mary's Hosp. Med. Sch. Lond.; Sen. Regist. Edgware Gen. Hosp.; Asst. Lect. Bland-Sutton Inst. Path, Middlx. Hosp. Med. Sch.

HAYES, Alan Kenneth The Surgery, 2 Yarborough Close, Godshill, Ventnor PO38 3HS; 2 Brook Farm Close, Brook, Newport PO30 4LD — MB BS 1979 Lond.; DObst. RCOG 1981; Cert Family Plann 1981. (Guys) GP Godshill.

HAYES, Alison Jane Tel: 020 8780 5770; Email: alisonhayes@btinternet.com — MB BS 1990 Lond.; MRCGP 1997. (King's College)

HAYES, Alison Margaret 11 Byron Place, Clifton, Bristol BS8 1JT — MB BS 1982 Lond.; MRCP (UK) 1988. Cons. Paediat. Cardiol. Roy. Hosp. Sick Childr. Bristol. Prev: Sen. Regist. (Paediat. Cardiol.) Roy. Brompton Nat. Heart & Lung Hosp.; Interven. Fell. (Paediat. Cardiol.) Hosp. Sick Childr. Toronto, Canada; Research Fell. & Hon. Regist. (Paediat. Cardiol.) Guy's Hosp. Lond.

HAYES, Anne Louise 26 Elliston Drive, Southdown Park, Bath BA2 1LU — MB ChB 1990 Bristol; FRCS Eng. 1994.

HAYES, Bernard 72 West Park Drive, Blackpool FY3 9HU Tel: 01253 761066 — MB BS Durh. 1947; DA Eng. 1954. (Newc.) Cons. Anaesth. Private Pract. Blackpool. Socs: Fac. Anaesth. RCS Eng.; Fell. Roy. Soc. Med.; BMA. Prev: Cons. Anaesth. Blackpool & Fylde Hosp. Gp.; Regist. (Anaesth.) Chester Roy. Infirm.; Anaesth. RAF Med. Br.

HAYES, Bernard (retired) 11 The Spinney, Handsworth Wood, Birmingham B20 1NR Tel: 0121 523 6328 — MB BS 1958 Lond.; MRCS Eng. LRCP Lond. 1958; FRCA 1967. Prev: Cons. Anaesth. City Hosp. Birm.

HAYES, Bramwell James 1 Richmond Way, Carbis Bay, St Ives TR26 2JY Email: bramwell.hayes@men.ac.uk — MB ChB 1995 Manch.; BSc St. And 1992; LFHom 1997. (Manchester) Socs: BMA.

HAYES, Mr Brian Robert Argoed Ganol Farm, Llanharry, Pontyclun Tel: 01443 225451 — MB BS 1955 Durh.; FRCS Ed. 1965; FRCS Eng. 1968. Cons. Surg. E. Glam. Hosp. Pontypridd; Hon. Teach. (Clin. Surg.) Univ. Hosp. Wales.

HAYES, Catherine 31 High Cross Drive, Highcross, Newport NP10 9AB — MB BCh BAO 1948 NUI.

HAYES, Claire Frances 25 Sefton Drive, Thornton, Liverpool L23 4TJ — BM BCh 1996 Oxf.

HAYES, Corinne Leigh Holt, The Crescent, Crapstone, Yelverton PL20 7PS Tel: 01822 855250 Fax: 01822 855512 — MB BS 1988 Lond.; BA (Hons.) Oxf. 1985; MRCP 1992. Sen. Regist. (Paediatris) Derriford Hosp. Plymouth. Prev: SHO (Paediat.) Bristol Childr. Hosp.

HAYES, Cyril Mary Joseph (retired) 3 Bowling Green Road, North Mount Vernon, Glasgow G32 0SR Tel: 0141 778 2005 — MB BCh BAO NUI 1947.

HAYES, David Frederick Grahame Treliske Hospital, Truro TR1 3LJ Tel: 01872 74242; White House, Wheal Damsel Road, Carharrack, Redruth TR16 5RU — MB ChB 1961 Manch.; FRCOG 1989, M 1970. (Manch.)

HAYES, Diana Gwyneth Brunswick House Medical Group, 1 Brunswick Street, Carlisle CA1 1ED Tel: 01228 515808 Fax: 01228 593048; The Old Rectory, Great Orton, Carlisle CA5 6NB — MB BS 1970 Lond.; MRCS Eng. LRCP Lond. 1970; MRCGP 1982; DObst RCOG 1972. (Roy. Free)

HAYES, Dorothy (retired) 10 Piney Way, Belfast BT9 5QT Tel: 02890661411 — MB BCh BAO 1957 Belf.; MD Belf. 1962; FRCPath 1979, M 1967. Prev: Cons. Histopath. Belf. City Hosp.

HAYES, Edna Mary (Dewar) Argoed Ganol Farm, Llanharry, Pontyclun CF72 9JX — MB ChB 1966 St. And.; MSc (Health Care) 1994 Wales; DA Eng. 1970. Med. Adviser Benefits Agency. Socs: Fac. Anaesth. & BMA. Prev: Med. Off.Dept. Social Security Cardiff; GP Pentwyn Cardiff; Regist. (Anaesth.) Univ. Hosp. Wales Cardiff.

HAYES, Elinor Jane 9 Torquay Avenue, Southampton SO15 5HA — MB ChB 1995 Leeds. SHO (Paediat.) Huddersfield Roy. Infirm. Socs: BMA. Prev: SHO elderly med.Huddesfield Roy.Infirm.

HAYES, Fiona Mary Student Health Service, 25 Belgrave Road, Bristol BS8 2AA Tel: 0117 973 7716 Fax: 0117 970 6804; 135 Howard Road, Westbury Park, Bristol BS6 7UZ Tel: 01179 424377 — MB BS 1985 Lond.; MRCGP 1991; DFFP 1993. (Guy's Hosp.) GP Stud. Health Serv. Bristol. Prev: Clin. Asst. (Dermat.) S.mead NHS Servs. Trust Bristol; McMillan Fell./SHO St. Peters Hospice Knowle Bristol; Trainee GP Exeter VTS.

HAYES, Gareth John Park Surgery, Park Road, Whitchurch, Cardiff CF14 7EZ Tel: 029 2062 3286 Fax: 029 2062 3839; 2 Queenwood Close, Cyncoed, Cardiff CF23 9JH — MB BCh 1982 Wales; BSc Wales 1979; MRCP (UK) 1986; MRCGP 1988. Med. Adviser (Gen. Pract.) Bro Taf HA; Clin. Asst. (Med. Probl. Pregn.) Univ. Hosp. Wales.

HAYES, Mr George (retired) 71 Thames Point, Fairways, Teddington TW11 9PP Tel: 020 8977 8138 — MB BS 1938 Durh.; FRCS Eng. 1958.

HAYES, Gillian Sandra St.Mary's Hospice, 176 Raddlebarn Road, Selly Park, Birmingham B29 7DA Tel: 0121 472 1191 Fax: 0121 472 4159; 55 Fiery Hill Road, Barnt Green, Birmingham B45 8JX Tel: 0121 445 1888 — MB ChB 1971 Birm. Staff Grade Phys. in Palliat. Care.

HAYES, Glyn Morgan AAH Meditel Limited, Orchard House, Newton Road, Bromsgrove B60 3EA Tel: 01527 579414 Fax: 01527 574061 Email: glyn@meditel.co.uk; 3 Beech Avenue N., Worcester WR3 8PX Tel: 01905 454705 Fax: 01905 456817 Email: glyn@conline.demon.co.uk — MB ChB 1971 Birm.; DObst RCOG 1973. Med. Dir. AAH Meditel BromsGr. Socs: Fell. Brit. Computer Soc.

HAYES, Gordon Claremont Surgery, 56-60 Castle Road, Scarborough YO11 1XE Tel: 01723 375050 Fax: 01723 378241 — MB ChB 1990 Ed.; MA Camb. 1990; MRCGP 1994; T(GP) 1994; DFFP 1993. Socs: BMA. Prev: Trainee GP York; SHO (Psychiat.) Bootham Pk. Hosp. York; SHO (O & G) York Dist. Hosp.

HAYES, Graham James Ashby Clinic, Collum Lane, Scunthorpe DN16 2SZ Tel: 01724 281552 Fax: 01724 822580; Swallow Eaves, 9 High St, Winterton, Scunthorpe DN15 9PU Tel: 01724 734807 — MB BS 1976 Lond.; MRCS Eng. LRCP Lond. 1976; MRCGP 1986; DFFP 1993; T(GP) 1991; DRCOG 1985. (St. Mary's) Dep. Forens. Med. Examr. Humberside Police.

HAYES, Gwilym Daniel Wathwood Hospital, Gipsy Green Lane, Wath upon Dearne, Rotherham S63 7TQ; 3 Bishopdale Court, Mosborough, Sheffield S20 5PD — MB ChB 1984 Liverp.; MB ChB Liverp. l984; MRCPsych 1988; Dip. Clin. Hypn. Sheff. 1992; MA (Criminology) Hull 1997. Cons. Forens. Psychiat. Wathwood Hosp. Rotherham. Prev: Cons. Psychiat. (Forens. Psychiat.) Sheff.; Cons. Psychiat. Chesterfield.; Sen. Regist. (Psychiat.) Sheff.

HAYES, Helen Joyce Powys Healthcare NHS Trust, Ynys-Y-Plant, Plantation Lane, Newtown SY16 1LH Tel: 01686 621209 Fax: 01686 629777 — MB ChB 1983 Sheff.; MRCPsych 1987. Cons. Child & Adolesc. Psychiat. Powys Health Care NHS Trust.

HAYES, Ian Paul Barn Cottage, Diseworth, Derby DE74 2QQ — MB BS 1987 Monash.

HAYES, Joanna Mary The Surgery, 5 Kensington Place, London W8 7PT Tel: 020 7229 7111 Fax: 020 7221 3069 — MB BS Lond. 1981; MRCGP 1985; DRCOG 1985. (Char. Cross)

HAYES, Joanne (Hughes) — MB BCh 1991 Wales; Dip Palliat Med 1999 Wales; MRCP (UK) 1996. (Wales) Specialist Regist. in Palliat. Med. All Wales Train. Progr. Socs: Assn. Palliat. Med. Prev: Regist. Gen. Med. Auckland Pub. Hosp. New Zealand; SHO Palliat. Med. Holme Tower Marie Curie Centre Penarth.

HAYES, John Charles 23 Paulsfield Drive, Wirral CH46 0UA — MB ChB 1992 Dundee.

HAYES, John Paul Leslie Adolph Medway maritime Hospital, Windmill Road, Gillingham ME7 5 Tel: 01634 830000 Fax: 01634 825182 — MRCS Eng. LRCP Lond. 1962; BSc Lond. 1959, MB BS 1962; FRCPath 1981, M 1969. (St. Thos.) Cons. (Haemat.) Medway Health Dist. Socs: BMA; Br. Soc. Haematol.; Fell. Roy. Soc. Med. Prev: Lect. Haemat. W.m. Med. Sch. Lond.; Regist. Path. & Res. Clin. Pathol. St. Geo. Hosp. Lond.

HAYES, John Randal 7 Alexandra Park, Holywood BT18 9ET — MD 1973 Belf.; MB BCh BAO 1968; FRCP Lond. 1985; FRCP Glas. 1983; FRCPI 1986, M 1985; MRCP (UK) 1971. Sen. Lect. Med. Qu. Univ. Belf.; Cons. Phys. Belf. City Hosp. Prev: Sen. Fell. Div. Endocrinol., Dept. Med. Univ. Washington, Seattle.

HAYES, John Stuart Geoffrey (retired) Norwood, Manor Road, Staple Grove, Taunton TA2 6EJ Tel: 01823 275739 — MB BS 1958 Lond.; MRCS Eng. LRCP Lond. 1958; FRCGP 1983, M 1973; MFFP 1993; DObst RCOG 1964. Prev: GP Taunton.

HAYES, Jonathan Richard Oldland Surgery, 192 High Street, Oldham Common, Bristol BS30 9QQ Tel: 0117 932 4444 Fax: 0117 932 4101 — BM 1995 Soton.

HAYES, Josephine Jill (retired) 87 Mile Oak Road, Portslade, Brighton BN41 2PJ Tel: 01273 412431 — MB ChB 1948 Leeds; Cert Contracep. & Family Plann. RCOG, RCGP &; Cert FPA 1975. Prev: Hon. Clin. Asst. Gen. Med. & Gyn. Maidenhead Hosp.

HAYES, Justin 139 Valley Road, London SW16 2XT Tel: 020 8769 2566 — MB BChir 1982 Camb.; MA Camb. 1983; MRCGP 1987. (Camb.) GP Princip., Streatham.

HAYES, Katherine Mary 67 High Beeches, Banstead SM7 1NW — BM 1995 Soton. Med. SHO diabetes.Roy.Hants Co. Hosp.winchester.

HAYES, Kevin Brian 33 Craven Avenue, London W5 2SY Tel: 020 7567 8391 — MB ChB 1992 Leic.

HAYES, Louisa Jane 4 Langhams Way, Wargrave, Reading RG10 8AX — BChir 1995 Camb.

HAYES, Louise Joy 24 Ramsdale Road, Carlton, Nottingham NG4 3JT — MB BS 1992 Lond.

HAYES, Lydia Margaret The Old Rectory, Kelston, Bath BA1 9AG Tel: 01225 425777 — MB BS 1959 Lond.; MRCS Eng. LRCP Lond. 1959; DO Eng. 1962. (King's Coll. Hosp.) Socs: Coll. Ophth. UK. Prev: Assoc. Specialist Bristol Eye Hosp., Frenchay Hosp., Tyndalls Pk. Childr. Assessm. Centre & S.mead HA Community Clinics; SCMO Moorfields Hosp. (High Holborn Br.) Lond. & Roy. Eye Hosp. Surbiton.

HAYES, Margaret Gwendoline Field Road Health Centre, Field Rd, Wallasey, Wirral CH45 5JP; 5 Market Street, Hoylake, Wirral CH47 2AD — MB ChB 1973 Leeds.

HAYES, Margaret Mary 27 Aldershot Road, Guildford GU2 8AE — MB BCh BAO 1989 NUI.

HAYES, Marie Loreto 3 Hall Gardens, Kildwick, Keighley BD20 9AF — MB BCh BAO 1978 Dub.; DObst RCPI 1982; DCH NUI 1979; Dip. Practical Dermatology 1996. (University of Cardiff) Prev: Med. Off. St. Lucy's Hosp. Transkei, S.. Afr.; Regist. (Psychiat.) St. Patrick's Hosp. Dub.; SHO (Geriat.) James Conolly Memor. Hosp. Blanchardstown.

HAYES, Mark Tadcaster Medical Centre, Crab Garth, Tadcaster LS24 8HD Tel: 01937 530082 Fax: 01937 530192 — MB ChB 1981 Sheff.

HAYES, Martin Edward Broughton 18 Crane Grove, London N7 8LE — MB BS 1956 Lond.; FFA RCS Eng. 1961.

HAYES, Martin John Manchester Road Surgery, 63 Manchester Road, Swinton, Manchester M27 5FX Tel: 0161 794 4343 Fax: 0161 736 0669 — MB ChB 1979 Manch.; DRCOG 1981.

HAYES, Mr Matthew Charles 9 Acorn Grove, Chandlers Ford, Eastleigh SO53 4LA — BM 1990 Soton.; DM 2000 Soton.; FRCS 2001 (urol); FRCS Eng. 1994. (Soton.) Specialist Regist. Rotat. (Wessex) Urol.; Paediat. Urol. at Soton. Gen. Hosp.; SpR in Urol., Roy. Marsden, Fulham Lond. Socs: Brit. Assn. Of Urologcal Surg.

HAYES, Michael Francis Bellevue Surgery, Courtybella Terrace, Newport NP20 2WQ; 6 Thornhill Gardens, Rogerstone, Newport NP10 9GA — MB ChB Bristol 1964. (Bristol) Prev: Med. Off. Fiji.

HAYES, Michael Graham Coldside Medical Practice, 129 Strathmartine Road, Dundee DD3 8DB Tel: 01382 826724 Fax: 01382 884129 — MB ChB 1983 Dundee; BMSc Dund 1980, MB ChB 1983; MRCGP 1987; DRCOG 1988. Regist. Dermat. Prev: Trainee GP Dundee VTS.

HAYES, Michael John 65 Kendall Avenue S., Sanderstead, Croydon — MB BS 1968 Lond.; MRCP (U.K.) 1971; MRCS Eng. LRCP Lond. 1968. (Westm.) Lect. in Med. Dept. Med. Nottm. Gen. Hosp.

HAYES, Michelle Amanda Downsleigh, 35 Barons Hurst, Woodcote, Epsom KT18 7DU — MB BS 1982 Lond.

HAYES, Michelle Frances Yorkley Health Centre, Bailey Hill, Yorkley GL15 4RS Tel: 01594 562437 Fax: 01594 564319; Tel: 01892 536913, 91514 530373 — MB ChB 1996 Birm.; MRCOG 2000 (Distinction) Lond.; DRCOG 1998 (RCOG); DFFP 1998. (Birmingham) GP Princip., Yorkley.

HAYES, Mr Nicholas 23 Archibald Street, Gosforth, Newcastle upon Tyne NE3 1EB — MB BS 1983 Newc.; FRCS Lond. 1987.

HAYES, Nicholas Richard Bath Lodge Practice, Bitterne Health Centre, Commercial Street, Bitterne, Southampton SO18 6BT Tel: 023 8044 2111 Fax: 023 8042 1316 Email: bathlodge@aol.com; 12 Western Road, West End, Southampton SO30 3EL Tel: 023 8047 4179 — MB BS 1973 Lond.; MRCGP 1984.

HAYES, Orleigh Mary 78 Belfast Road, Downpatrick BT30 9AY — MB BCh BAO 1993 Belf.

HAYES, Paul David 31 Church Hill, Spondon, Derby DE21 7LJ — MB ChB 1993 Aberd.

HAYES, Paula Marie Clinton Road Surgery, 19 Clinton Road, Redruth TR15 2LL Tel: 01209 216507 Fax: 01209 218262; Tel: 01209 821003 Fax: 01209 822320 Email: d.hayes8427@aol.com — MB BCh BAO 1972 Dub.; MA Dub. 1992. (Trinity College Dublin) Gen. Med. Practitioner, 19 Clinton Rd, Redruth. Socs: Cornw. Clin. Soc.; BMA.

HAYES, Professor Peter Clive Department of Internal Medicine, Royal Infirmary of Edinburgh, Edinburgh EH3 9YW Tel: 0131 536 2237; 2 Monteith Farm Steading, Mossend, Gorebridge EH23 Tel: 01875 822541 — MB ChB 1980 Dundee; PhD Ed. 1993; MD Dundee 1986, BMSc (Hons.) 1977; FRCP Ed. 1992; MRCP (UK) 1983. Prof. Of Hepat. & Hon.Cons.Phys. Roy. Infirm. Edin.; Director Wellcome Trust Clin. Research Facility, Lothian Univ. NHS Trust, Edin. Socs: Brit. Soc. Gastroenterol. & Scott. Soc. Phys.; Assn. Phys. Prev: Sen. Lect. Univ. Edin. & Hon. Cons. Phys. Roy. Infirm. Edin.; Lect. Univ. Edin.; Hon. Lect. Liver Unit King's Coll. Hosp. Lond.

HAYES, Peter John Blackpool Victoria Hospital NHS Trust, Whinney Heys Road, Blackpool FY3 8NR Tel: 01253 300000 Fax: 01253 303528 — MB ChB 1970 Liverp.; FRCP Lond. 1989; MRCP (UK) 1974. Cons. Phys. Vict. Hosp. Blackpool. Socs: Brit. Diabetic Assn. (Mem. Med. & Scientif. Sect.); NW Reproduc. & Edocrine Soc. Prev: Sen. Regist. (Med.) Liverp. Hosp.

HAYES, Philippa Ann Stowmarket Health Centre, Violet Hill Road, Stowmarket IP14 1NL — MB ChB 1981 Liverp.; DRCOG 1985; DTM & H Liverp. 1983. Trainee GP Cornw. VTS.

HAYES, Richard Anthony The Surgery, 18 Fouracre Road, Bristol BS16 6PG — MB ChB 1966 Bristol; DObst RCOG 1972.

HAYES, Sally Ann Ship House Surgery, The Square, Liphook GU30 7AQ Tel: 01428 723296 Fax: 01420 724022; Epstocks, Church St, West Liss, Liss GU33 6JY Tel: 01730 893626 — MB BS 1986 Lond.; MRCGP 1990; DRCOG 1989. (St. Geo. Hosp. Lond.) p/t Part time GP Princip. Socs: Haslemere Med. Soc. Prev: Trainee GP Chichester VTS.

HAYES, Sally Caroline The Group Practice, St Andrews Road, Tidworth SP9 7EP — MB ChB 1992 Birm.

HAYES, Sally Elizabeth 9 Torquay Avenue, Southampton SO15 5HA — MB ChB 1997 Manch. SHO (Med.) Countess of Chester Hosp., Chester.

HAYES, Sara Lindsey Iechyd Morgannwg Health, 41 High Street, Swansea SA1 1LT Tel: 01792 458066 Fax: 01792 607533 Email: sara.hayes@morgannwg-ha.wales.nhs.uk; 2 Queenwood Close, Cyncoed, Cardiff CF23 9JH Tel: 02920 473675 — MB BCh 1982 Wales; MPH Wales 1997; MFPHM 2000. (Wales) p/t Cons. (Pub. Health Med.) Iecwyd Morgannwg Health, Swansea. Socs: Brit. Med. Assn.; Fac. of Pub. Health Med. Prev: Community Med. Off. Cardiff.; Specialist Regist. (Pub. Health Med.) Gwent Health Auth.

HAYES, Sarah Joanne Inglenook, Easingwold Rd, Huby, York YO61 1HN — MB BS 1997 Newc.

***HAYES, Sarah Louise** 23 Highbury Street, Leeds LS6 4EZ — MB ChB 1994 Leeds.

HAYES, Stephen Francis White House Surgery, Weston Lane, Weston, Southampton SO19 9HJ Tel: 023 8044 9913; Email: stephen.hayes1@virgin.net — BM 1979 Soton.; 1990 Diploma of Practical Dermatology Cardiff. p/t GP W.on, Soton.; Primary Care Dermat. Practitioner, Roy. S. Hants Hosp., Soton. Socs: Primary Care Dermat. Soc.

HAYES, Susan Dorothy Alexina DHSS, Norcross, Thornton Cleveleys, Blackpool — MB ChB 1969 Liverp.; DObst RCOG 1971.

HAYES, Suzanne Clare 25 Sefton Drive, Thornton, Liverpool L23 4TJ — MB BS 1993 Lond.; MRCP (UK) 1996. Specialist Regist. (Gen. Internal Med. & Geriat.) NE Thames. Socs: Brit. Geriat. Soc. Prev: SHO Rotat. (Med.) Roy. Hosp. Trust Lond.

HAYES, Professor Tom Morgan School of Postgraduate Studies, University of Wales College of Medicine, Heath Park, Cardiff CF14 4XN Tel: 029 2074 3927 Email: hayestm@cf.ac.uk; 1 Amberheart Drive, Cardiff CF14 9HA — MB ChB 1959 Liverp.; FRCP Lond. 1977, M 1963. (Liverp.) Dir. & Dean Postgrad. Studies & Prof. Med. Educat. Univ. Wales Coll. Med. Cardiff; Hon. Cons. Phys. Univ. Hosp. Wales Cardiff & Mid Glam. HA. Socs: Assn. Study Med. Educat.; Assn. Med. Educat. Europ. Prev: Cons. Phys. Univ. Hosp. Wales Cardiff; Sen. Lect. in Med. Welsh Nat. Sch. Med.; Lect. in Metab. Med. Welsh Nat. Sch. Med.

HAYES-ALLEN, Martin Charles Broomhill & Crosspool Medical Centres, 183 Whitham Road, Sheffield S10 2SN Tel: 0114 266 5902 Fax: 0114 266 5902; Tithe Barn, Aston Lane, Thornhill, Hope Valley S33 0BR Tel: 01433 651767 — MB BChir Camb. 1969; MA Camb. 1969. (Univ. Coll. Hosp.) Socs: Fell. Roy. Anthropol. Soc.; Soc. Occupat. Med.; BSAENM. Prev: Hon. Teach. (Gen. Pract.) & Hon. Lect. (Cell Biol. & Anat.) Univ. Sheff.; Research Asst. Childr. Hosp. Sheff.; Ho. Phys. (Geriat. Unit) Univ. Coll. Hosp.

***HAYES-BRADLEY, Clare** Trinity Cottage, Coast Road, Bacton, Norwich NR12 0EY — MB BS 1998 Lond.; MB BS Lond 1998.

HAYFRON-BENJAMIN, John Mensah Sarbah 19 Telford Avenue, Streatham Hill, London SW2 4XJ — MB BS 1962 Lond.; MRCS Eng. LRCP Lond. 1962; DCH Eng. 1966. (Guy's) Clin. Asst. (Path.) Lewisham Hosp. Lond. Prev: Regist. (Med.) Med. Unit Univ. Coll. Hosp. Ibadan, Nigeria; Ho. Off. (Paediat.) St. Jas. Hosp. Balham; SHO (Gen. Med.) Middleton-in-Wharfedale Hosp.

HAYFRON-BENJAMIN, Terence Robert Mark 1 Bryburgh Crescent, Ham Estate, Plymouth PL2 2NU — MB BS 1996 Lond.

HAYHOE, Professor Frank George James 20 Queen Ediths Way, Cambridge CB1 7PN Tel: 01223 248381 — MRCS Eng. LRCP Lond. 1944; MD Camb. 1951, MB BChir. 1945; FRCP Lond. 1965, M 1949; FRCPath 1971; Hon. MD L'Auila 1992; Hon MD Montpellier 1993. (Camb. & St. Thos.) Emerit. Prof. Haemat. Med. Univ. Camb.; Emerit. Hon. Cons. Phys. Addenbrooke's Hosp. Camb. Socs: Fell. Internat. Soc. Haematol.; Brit. Soc. Haematol. Prev: Leukaemia Research Fund Prof. Haemat. Med. Univ. Camb.; Lect. (Med.) Univ. Camb.; Elmore Research Stud. Camb.

HAYHOE, Simon Hugh John Cherryfield, 249 Berechurch Hall Road, Colchester CO2 9NP Tel: 01206 575805 — MB BS 1970 Lond.; MRCS Eng. LRCP Lond. 1970; DA Eng. 1973. (St. Thos.) Community Dent. Anaesth. NE Essex HA; Clin. Asst. (Anaesth.) Essex Co. Hosp. Colchester. Socs: (Ex-Chairm.) Brit. Med. Acupunc. Soc.; Brit. Soc. Med. & Dent. Hypn. Prev: Regist. (Anaesth.) Gen. Hosp. Cheltenham; SHO (Anaesth.) St. Thos. Hosp. Lond.; SHO (Gyn.) W. Cumbld. Hosp. Whitehaven.

HAYHOW, Bryan Hardwicke House Surgery, Hardwicke House, Stour Street, Sudbury CO10 2AY Tel: 01787 370011 Fax: 01787 376521; The Old Rectory, Bulmer, Sudbury CO10 7TA — MB BS 1969 Lond.; MRCS Eng. LRCP Lond. 1969. (Guy's) Socs: Colchester Med. Soc. Prev: SHO (O & G) St. Margt. Hosp. Epping; Ho. Surg. & Ho. Phys. OldCh. Hosp. Romford.

HAYHURST, Valerie Centaur House, 33 Tower Road N., Heswall, Wirral CH60 6RS Tel: 0151 342 6100 — MB ChB 1985 Liverp.

HAYKAL, Najeeb Ghalib Ayoub 91 Avonside Drive, Leicester LE5 4LA — MB BCh 1971 Cairo.

HAYLE, Geoffrey Bowerbank Whitby Group Practice, 114 Chester Road, Ellesmere Port, South Wirral CH65 6TG Tel: 0151 355 6144 Fax: 0151 355 6843; 25 Liverpool Road, Chester CH2 1AB Tel: 01244 377912 — MB ChB (Hons.) Liverp. 1969; BSc (Hons.) Liverp. 1966; MRCP (UK) 1972. (Liverpool)

HAYLES, Shelley 3 Elmthorpe Road, Wolvercote, Oxford OX2 8PA — BM BCh 1993 Oxf.

HAYLETT, Anna Catherine Henfield Medical Centre, Deer Park, Henfield BN5 9JQ Tel: 01273 492255 Fax: 01273 495050; Little Lancasters, West End Lane, Henfield BN5 9RB Tel: 01273 493216 — MB BS 1972 Lond.; FRCP 1999; MRCP (UK) 1974; MRCS Eng. LRCP Lond. 1972. (King's College Hospital London) Socs: Brighton & Sussex M-C Soc. (Past Pres. -1998)); BMA. Prev: Asst. Phys. Univ. Coll. Health Centre Lond. 1975-1977.

HAYLEY, William David (retired) Ashdown, Sway Road, Brockenhurst SO42 7SG Tel: 01590 622952 — MRCS Eng. LRCP Lond. 1952; BM BCh Oxon. 1952; FRCP Lond. 1975, M 1958; DPhysMed. Eng. 1962. Prev: Cons. Rheum. & Rehabil. S.end Health Dist.

HAYMAN, Anne Woodburn (retired) 2 Upper Park Road, London NW3 2UP Tel: 020 7586 2424 Fax: 020 7586 2424 Email: ahayman@rmplc.co.uk — MB BCh 1947 Witwatersrand; FRCPsych 1991, M 1971; DPM Eng. 1959. Prev: Cons. Psychiat. & Research Psychoanalyst Hampstead Child-Ther. Clinic.

HAYMAN, Grant Raymond Top Floor Flat, 27 Mattock Lane, London W5 5BH — MB ChB 1989 Cape Town.

HAYMAN, Jonathan James Rock Barn, Sutton Bingham, Yeovil BA22 9QP — BM 1995 Soton.

HAYMAN, Laura Marian Hoddesdon Health Centre, High St., Hoddesdon EN11 8BQ — MB ChB 1984 Aberd.; MB ChB Aberd. l984.

HAYMAN, Matthew Robert 4 Redwoods, Welwyn Garden City AL8 7NR — BM BCh 1997 Oxf.

HAYNE, Dickon Forder Cottage, Forder LaA., Dartington, Totnes TQ9 6HT — MB BS 1994 Lond.

HAYNE, Peter Simon Quarry Ground Surgery, Broadway, Edington, Bridgwater TA7 9JB Tel: 01278 722077 Fax: 01278 722352; Little Kimble, Fulpitts Lane, Ashcott, Bridgwater TA7 9QR — MB ChB 1976 Birm. Prev: SHO Te Kuiti Hosp. New Zealand; Ho. Phys. Monkswood Hosp. Worcs.; Ho. Surg. Dudley Rd. Hosp. Birm.

HAYNES, Angela Anchorage, Sheeplands Lane, Sherborne DT9 4BW Tel: 01935 814418 Fax: 01258 473188 — MB ChB 1965 Sheff.; Cert. Family Plann. JCC 1973. (Sheff.) Clin. Med. Off., W. Dorset HA.; Sen. Clin. Med. Off. (Family Plann.) Som. AHA. Prev: Med. Off. (Family Plann.) Gloucester Health Dist.; Med. Off. (Family Plann. & Clin.) & Sch. Med. Off. Plymouth Health Dist.

HAYNES, Bernadette 44A Richmond Avenue, London N1 0ND — MB BS 1993 Lond.

HAYNES, David Ian 3M House, Morley St, Loughborough LE12 7RG Email: ian.haynes@cwcom.net — MB ChB 1994 Sheff.; DFFP (RCOG) 1998. (Sheff. Univ. Med. Sch.) Med. Adviser - 3M Health Care, LoughBoro. Socs: Med. Soc. for the study of Venereal Dis.s; Brit. Soc. for the Study of Vulual Dis. Prev: SHO (O & G) Jessop Hosp. Sheff.; SHO (O & G) N. Gen. Hosp. Sheff.; Specialist Regist. - N. Trent (O&G).

HAYNES, Mr Ian Gordon 3 Truro Close, Horeston Grange, Nuneaton CV11 6FQ — MB ChB 1972 Birm.; FRCS Eng. 1978.

HAYNES, Jeremy 1 Atcherley Close, Fulford, York YO10 4QF — MB ChB 1979 Bristol.

HAYNES, Joan Whitney 36 Linceslade Grove, Loughton, Milton Keynes MK5 8DT Tel: 01908 676428 — MB ChB 1968 Sheff.; Dip. Ven. Soc. Apoth. Lond. 1977. Cons. Venereol. Oxf. RHA & Milton Keynes HA. Socs: Med. Soc. Study VD. Prev: Sen. Regist. (Venereol.) Radcliffe Infirm. Oxf.; Regist. (Venereol.) Univ. Hosp. Wales Cardiff; SHO (Venereol.) Roy. Hosp. Sheff.

HAYNES, Joanna Claire The Granary, Low Park Farm, Chantry Lane, Hazelwood, Tadcaster LS24 9NH — MB ChB 1996 Liverp. SHO (Paediat.) Luton & Dunstable Hosp.

HAYNES, Katharine Gurney The Surgery, 81 Oxgate Gardens, London NW2 6EA Tel: 020 8208 0291 Fax: 020 8208 1753; 108 Mountview Road, London N4 4JX — BM BCh 1981 Oxf.; MRCGP 1985; DRCOG 1985. Prev: Trainee GP Lond. Hosp.; Ho. Phys. John Radcliffe Hosp. Oxf.; Ho. Surg. S. Lond. Hosp. For Wom.

HAYNES, Lucy Emma Ruth Trumpet Hill Lodge, Flanchford Road, Reigate RH2 8QY — BM BCh 1993 Oxf.; MA Camb. 1994.

HAYNES, Peter Anthony 24 Valley Drive, Ilkley LS29 8NN — MB ChB 1988 Manch.

HAYNES, Peter Joseph Saxon Clinic, Saxon St., Eaglestone, Milton Keynes MK6 5LR Tel: 01908 665533 Fax: 01908 608112; 36 Linceslade Grove, Loughton, Milton Keynes MK5 8DT Tel: 01908 676428 Fax: 0870 459 0127 Email: peterhaynes@aucom.net — MB ChB 1968 Sheff.; MD Sheff. 1981; FRCOG 1990, M 1973. Cons. O & G Oxf. RHA. Socs: Blair Bell Res. Soc.; Brit. Fertil. Soc. Prev: Sen. Lect. (O & G) Univ. Manch.; Lect. Nuffield Dept. O & G John Radcliffe Hosp. Headington; SHO (O & G) Jessop Hosp. Wom. Sheff.

HAYNES, Philip David Brookside Group Practice, Brookside Close, Gipsy Lane, Earley, Reading RG6 7HG Tel: 0118 966 9222 Fax: 0118 935 3174 — MB BS 1984 Lond. Trainee GP Reading.

HAYNES, Mr Richard John 23 Hollinwell Avenue, Wollaton, Nottingham NG8 1JY Tel: 0115 916 1319 Fax: 0115 470 9963 Email: richard.haynes@nottingham.ac.uk — MB BCh 1990 Wales; FRCOphth 1995. (Wales) Lect. & Regist. (Ophth.) Univ. Nottm. & Qu. Med. Centre. Socs: Med. Protec. Soc.; BMA. Prev: SHO (Ophth.) Aberd. Roy. Infirm.; SHO (A & E) Cardiff Roy. Infirm.; Ho. Off. (Med.) Singleton Hosp. Swansea.

***HAYNES, Shelley Victoria Zara** The Riddings, Crundalls Lane, Bewdley DY12 1NB Tel: 01299 402339 Email: shelleyhaynes@doctors.org.uk — MB ChB 1998 Manch.; MB ChB Manch 1998.

HAYNES, Simon Robert Department of Cardiothoracic Anaesthesia, Freeman Hospital, Newcastle upon Tyne NE7 7DN Tel: 0191 284 3111 Email: s.n.haynes@ncl.ac.uk — MB ChB 1983 Ed.; FRCA 1990. (Edinburgh) Cons. (Paediat. Cardiothoracic) Anaesth. & IC) Freeman Hosp. Newc. Socs: Assn. Paediat. Anaesth.; Assn. Anaesth. of GB & Irel.; Paediat. Intens. Care Soc.

HAYNES, Mr Stephen (cons. rooms), Cotswold Nuffield Hospital, Cheltenham GL51 6QA Tel: 01242 229616; Shornhill Farm, Withington, Cheltenham GL54 4BJ Tel: 01242 890339 — MB BS 1962 Lond.; FRCS Eng. 1965; MRCS Eng. LRCP Lond. 1961. (Guy's) Cons. Surg. N. Glos. Clin. Area Cheltenham Gen. Hosp. Prev: Sen. Regist. Middlx. Hosp. Lond.

HAYNES, Stephen Anthony West Bar Surgery, 1 West Bar Street, Banbury OX16 9SF Tel: 01295 256261 Fax: 01295 756848 — MB BS 1987 Lond.; MRCGP 1993; DFFP 1994.

HAYNES, Steven John Leslie Spindles, Gorsewood Road, Hartley, Longfield DA3 7DE Tel: 01474 707367 Email: steven_jl_haynes@hotmail.com — MB ChB 1991 Bristol; MRCP (UK) 1996; DA (UK) 1994; FRCA 1998. Specialist Regist. (Anaesth.) Roy. Cornw. Hosp., Truro, Cornw. Prev: Specialist Regist. (Anaesth.) Roy. Hobart Hosp., Tasmania; Specialist Regist. (Anaesth.) Taunton & Som. Hosp., Taunton.

HAYNES, Tonie Frances (retired) Moordown, 1 The Settlement, Ockbrook, Derby DE72 3RJ Tel: 01332 670492 — MB ChB 1952 Leeds; DPH 1963; FRCPCH Lond. 1997; MFPHM 1972; DCH Eng. 1965. Prev: Specialist (Pub. Health Med.) Wolverhampton HA.

HAYNES, Tracey Kathryn Department of Anaesthetics, Royal Gwent Hospital, Cardiff Road, Newport NP20 2UB Tel: 01633 234167; 7 Melin Dwr, Draethen, Newport NP10 8GL Email: tkhanes@btinternet.com — BM BS 1986 Nottm.; BMedSci Nottm. 1984; FRCA 1991; DA (UK) 1988. (Univ. Nottm.) Cons. Anaesth. Roy. Gwent Hosp. Newport. Socs: BMA; Assn. Anaesth.; Obst. Anaesth. Assn. Prev: Sen. Regist. & Regist. (Anaesth.) Univ. Hosp. Wales Cardiff; SHO (Anaesth.) Roy. Shrewsbury Hosp.

HAYNES, Valerie Kathleen (retired) Bradshaw Vicarage, Pavement Lane, Halifax HX2 9JJ Tel: 01422 244330 — MB ChB 1959 Manch.; BSc Manch. 1956; MRCOG 1969. Prev: SCMO Bradford HA.

HAYNES, William David Stafford Hadwen Medical Practice, Glevum Way Surgery, Abbeydale, Gloucester GL4 4BL Tel: 01452 529933 — MB BS 1989 Lond.; MRCGP 1994; DRCOG 1993; DCH RCP Lond. 1993; DFFP 1993. (St. Thos. Hosp. UMDS) GP Partner. Socs: BMA; MRCGP; Diplomate RCOG. Prev: Trainee GP/SHO (Gen. Med.) Bournemouth & Poole VTS; SHO (A & E) Basingstoke Dist. Hosp.; Ho. Phys. St. Thos. Hosp. Lond.

HAYS, Kathryn Jane William Brown Centre, Manor Way, Peterlee SR8 5TW Tel: 0191 554 4544 Fax: 0191 554 4552 — MB ChB 1973 Manch.; MRCGP 1977; DObst RCOG 1976.

HAYS, Peter Lyn Nicki West Memorial Surgery, The Health Centre, Vicarage Field, Hailsham BN27 1BE Tel: 01323 440202 Fax: 01323 847410; Shepnells, Ersham Road, Hailsham BN27 3LE Tel: 01323 842906 — MB ChB 1974 Liverp.; MRCGP 1980.

HAYSEY, Gordon Telford (retired) Belmont, Prospect Road, Market Drayton TF9 3BH Tel: 01630 652579 — BM BCh 1951 Oxf.; MA, BM BCh Oxf. 1951, DCH 1956; DObst RCOG 1957. Prev: Regist. (Paediat.) Luton & Dunstable Hosp.

HAYSOM, Mr Alfred Henry (retired) 7 The Close, Winchester SO23 9LF — MRCS Eng. LRCP Lond. 1942; FRCS Ed. 1948. Prev: Sen. Surg. Winchester & Centr. Hants. Health Dist.

HAYTER, Adrian Patrick 39 Warren Road, Leigh-on-Sea SS9 3TT — MB BS 1993 Lond.

***HAYTER, James Domisani** 12 Bucklands Lane, Nailsea, Bristol BS48 4PJ — MB ChB 1996 Birm.

HAYTER, James Meynell Ingram The Doctors House, Victoria Road, Marlow SL7 1DN Tel: 01628 484666 Fax: 01628 891206 — MB BS 1970 Lond.

HAYTER, Mr Jonathan Paul Maxillofacial Unit, Leicester Royal Infirmary, Leicester LE1 5WW Tel: 0116 258 5279 Fax: 0116 258 5205 — MB BS 1988 Lond.; BDS Bristol 1980; FRCS Ed. 1992; FDS RCS Eng. 1986. (St. Geo. Hosp. Med. Sch.) Cons. Oral & Maxillofacial Surg. Leicester Roy. Infirm. Prev: Sen. Regist. Rotat. (Oral & Maxillofacial Surg.) Mersey RHA.

HAYTER, Noel Patrick London Road Surgery, 1809 London Road, Leigh-on-Sea SS9 2ST Tel: 01702 559415 Fax: 01702 553685;

Greatwood, 39 Warren Road, Leigh-on-Sea SS9 3TT Tel: 01702 555366 — MB BS 1959 Rangoon; DTM & H Eng. 1962; DObst RCOG 1968. Socs: BMA.

HAYTER, Roger Clive City General Hospital, Newcastle Road, Stoke-on-Trent ST4 6QG Fax: 01782 275032 Email: roger@hayter.demon.co.uk; Email: 101554.3520@compuserve.com — BM BCh 1972 Oxf.; MA Oxf. 1977; MRCP (UK) 1977. (St. Thos.) Cons. Phys. (Geriat. Med.) N. Staffs. Hosp. & N. Staffs. Combined Healthcare Stoke-on-Trent. Socs: Fell. RCP.

HAYTHORNTHWAITE, Giles Edward 21 Stone Street, Boxford, Sudbury CO10 5NR — MB BS 1996 Lond.

HAYTHORNTHWAITE, Mary Jane (retired) Peel Gardens Nursing Home, Viviary Way, Colne BB8 9PR Tel: 01282 871243 — MRCS Eng. LRCP Lond. 1940. Prev: Ho. Surg. Vict. Hosp. Burnley.

HAYTON, Margaret Isabel (retired) The Cottage, 34 Church St., Littleover, Derby DE23 6GD — MB ChB 1952 Leeds.

HAYTON, Michael John 2 Tudor Close, Ashton-on-Ribble, Preston PR2 1YQ — MB ChB 1992 Liverp.

HAYWARD, Andrew Cunliffe division Of Public health & Epidemiology, School of Community Health Sciences, University of Nottingham Medical School, Nottingham NG7 2UH — MB BS 1990 Lond. Lect. Pub. Health & Epidemiol.

HAYWARD, Andrew Paul The Surgery, East Harling, Norwich NR16 2AD Tel: 01953 717204 Fax: 01953 718116 — MB BS 1983 Lond.; MRCGP 1988; DRCOG 1988. (St. Geo.)

HAYWARD, Angela Elizabeth 42 Church Way, London N20 0LA — MB BS 1998 Lond.; MB BS Lond 1998.

HAYWARD, Angus William 7 Beacon Way, Rickmansworth WD3 7PQ — MB BS 1979 Lond.; FFA RCS Eng. 1985. Cons. Anaesth. Mt. Vernon Hosp. N.wood Middlx. Prev: Sen. Regist. Rotat. Middlx. Hosp.

HAYWARD, Antony John Gables End, Church St., Ewell, Epsom Tel: 020 8394 1362 — BM BCh 1959 Oxf.; BA, BM BCh Oxf. 1959; DObst RCOG 1961. (Oxf. & St. Mary's) Prev: Ho. Surg. St. Mary's Hosp. Lond.; Ho. Surg. Obst. Hillingdon Hosp.; Sen. Ho. Off. Paediat. Kingston Hosp.

HAYWARD, Carolyn Jane The School House, Hillpooltop, Kidderminster DY10 4NL — MB ChB 1968 Liverp. Clin. Asst. (Anaesth.) Selly Oak Hosp. Birm.

HAYWARD, Charles Mark Church View Surgery, 30 Holland Road, Plymstock, Plymouth PL9 9BW Tel: 01752 403206 — BM BS 1983 Nottm.; MRCGP 1990; DRCOG 1986. Prev: Resid. Med. Off. Anzac Memor. Hosp. Katoomba NSW Australia.

HAYWARD, Christopher John Priory Medical Centre, Cape Road, Warwick CV34 4UN Tel: 01926 494411 — MB ChB 1960 Bristol. (Bristol) Socs: BMA & Med. Off. Schs. Assn. Prev: Regist. (Med.) St. Chad's Hosp. Birm.; Regist. Birm. Matern. Hosp.; Ho. Phys. Childr. Hosp. Bristol.

HAYWARD, Christopher Mark Morgan 5A Church Street, Ewell, Epsom KT17 2AU; 22 Overdale Road, Ealing, London W5 4TT Tel: 020 8579 5031 — MB BS 1986 Lond.; MSc Lond. 1993, MB BS 1986; MRCP Lond. 1989; DTM & H RCP Lond. 1993; PhD Lond. 1997. (St Mary's Hospital Medical School) Specialist Regist. (Gastroenterol.) Chelsea & W.minster Hosp. Lond.; Clin. Research Fell. (Communicable Dis.) St. Geo. Hosp. Med. Sch. Lond. Prev: Regist. Rotat. (Med.) St. Geo. Hosp. Lond.; SHO (Med.) W. Middlx. Hosp. Isleworth; SHO (Oncol.) Roy. Marsden Hosp.

***HAYWARD, Claire** New Cross Hospital, Wolverhampton WV10 6TL Tel: 01902 307999 — MB ChB 1997 Birm.

HAYWARD, Colin Richard William Flat 11, Park View, 30 West Drive, Brighton BN2 2GE — MB BS 1994 Lond. SHO (Anaesth.) P.ss Roy. Hosp. Haywards Heath.

HAYWARD, Daryl Margaret Copper Gate House, 132 Main St., Fulford, York YO10 4PS Tel: 01904 645649 — BM BS 1977 Nottm.; BMedSci Nottm. 1975, BM BS 1977; MRCGP 1983; DRCOG 1980; DA Eng. 1979. (Nottingham) GP Leeds.

HAYWARD, David 2 Swarthdale, Haxby, York YO32 3NZ — MB ChB 1987 Leeds; DA (UK) 1992.

HAYWARD, Dionne 123 Cartington Terrace, Heaton, Newcastle upon Tyne NE6 5SJ — MB BS 1989 Newc.

HAYWARD, Elizabeth Isla (retired) Heatherdene, Cricket Hill Lane, Yateley GU46 6BQ Tel: 01252 873542 — MB BS Lond. 1952; MRCS Eng. LRCP Lond. 1952; FFA RCS Eng. 1966; DA Eng. 1961. Prev: Sen. Regist. Anaesth. Roy. Free Hosp. Lond.

HAYWARD, Emma Louise 12 Knowsley Road, Chester CH2 3RL — MB ChB 1994 Liverp. GP Regist. Chester VTS. Prev: SHO (A & E Med.) Arrowe Pk. Hosp. Wirral.

HAYWARD, Helen Claire 176 Swanwick Lane, Swanwick, Southampton SO31 7GZ — MB BS 1998 Lond.; MB BS Lond 1998.

HAYWARD, Ian John 7 Greenwood Avenue, Lilliput, Poole BH14 8QD Tel: 01202 707851 — BM 1981 Soton.; MRCGP 1986; D.Occ.Med. RCP Lond. 1995; DRCOG 1983. (Southampton)

HAYWARD, Imogen Andrea Cruister, Dandwick, Shetland ZE2 9HN — MB BS 1998 Lond.; MB BS Lond 1998.

HAYWARD, James Douglas Ferry Road Health Centre, Ferry Road, Dingwall IV15 9QS Tel: 01349 863034 Fax: 01349 862022 — MB ChB 1986 Manch.; MRCOG 1994; MRCGP. (Manch.)

HAYWARD, Janet Mary Juniper Cottage, The Street, Redgrave, Diss IP22 1RY — MB ChB 1987 Manch.

HAYWARD, Jennifer Mary c/o 10 Branch Road, Lake Okareka, Rotorua N. Island, New Zealand Tel: 00 64 7 3628042; 4 Enderby Hall, Hall Walk, Enderby, Leicester LE9 5AH Tel: 0116 286 6054 — BM BS 1993 Nottm.; BMedSci Nottm. 1991; DRCOG 1995; DFFP 1995. SHO (Obst.) Nat. Wom. Hosp. Auckland, NZ; SHO (Obst. & Gyn.) Rotorua Hosp., NZ. Prev: Ho. Off. Rotorua, NZ; SHO (Obst. & Gyn.) City Hosp. NHS Trust Birm.; SHO (Accid. & Emerg.) Gen. Hosp. & Selly Oak Hosp. Birm.

HAYWARD, John Anthony Brent and Harrow Health Authority, Harrovian Business Village, Bessborough Road, Harrow HA1 3EX Tel: 020 8966 1063 Email: john.hayward@hbr.bah-ha.nthames.nhs.uk; 104 Culford Road, Hackney, London N1 4HN Tel: 020 7241 5468 Email: jhayward50@aol.com — MB BChir 1970 Camb.; MSc Lond. 1996; MRCP (UK) 1972; MRCGP 1975; MFPHM 1998. (St. Mary's.) Cons. Pub. Health, Brent & Harrow. Prev: Vist. Fell. Health Syst. Progr. King's Fund. Lond.; GP Princip. in Bristol and Lond. 1976- 1992; Med Dir Camden & Islington FHSA 1992 - 1995.

HAYWARD, Mr John Langford (retired) Bunces Farm, Birch Grove, Horsted Keynes, Haywards Heath RH17 7BT Tel: 01825 740301 Fax: 01825 740301 — MB BS 1947 Lond.; FRCS Eng. 1955. Prev: Skinner Lect. Roy. Coll. Radiol. 1987.

HAYWARD, Mr John Michael Eye Department, York District Hospital, Wigginton Road, York YO31 8HE Tel: 01904 631313 Fax: 01904 453397; Copper Gate House, 132 Main St, Fulford, York YO10 4PS — BM BS 1977 Nottm.; BMedSci Nottm. 1975; FRCS Eng. 1985; FRCOphth 1988; DO RCS Eng. 1984. Cons. Ophth. Surg. York Dist. Hosp. Prev: Sen. Regist. (Ophth.) Leeds Gen. Infirm.; Fell. Oculoplastic & Lacrimal Surg. Roy. Vict. Eye & Ear Hosp. Melbourne, Austral.; Med. Off. 40 Commando Roy. Marines.

HAYWARD, Jonathan McLean Thatcham Medical Practice, Bath Road, Thatcham RG18 3HD Tel: 01635 867171 Fax: 01635 876395; Littlecombe Cottage, Zin Zan, Turners Green, Upper Bucklebury, Reading RG7 6RE Tel: 01635 862778 Email: j.m.hayward@tesco.net — MB BS 1973 Lond.; MRCS Eng. LRCP Lond. 1976; MRCGP 1977; DRCOG 1976. (Char. Cross) Socs: Primary Care Spec. Gp. of Brit. Computer Soc.; VAMP User Panel.

HAYWARD, Lindsey 5 Shrigley Road N., Higher Poynton, Stockport SK12 1TE — MB ChB 1997 Manch.

HAYWARD, Mr Martin Paul 44 Petley Road, London W6 9ST — MB BS 1988 Lond.; MS Lond. 1997; FRCS Eng. 1992. Career Regist. (Cardiac Surg.) W. Lond. Rotat.

HAYWARD, Michael (retired) 6 Far Moss Road, Blundellsands, Liverpool L23 8TQ Tel: 0151 924 6939 — MB BChir Camb. 1961; MD Camb. 1976, MA 1961; FRCP Lond. 1976, M 1965. Prev: Cons. Neurophysiol. Walton Centre (Neurol. & Neurosurg.) Liverp.

HAYWARD, Michael George Alton Health Centre, Anstey Road, Alton GU34 2QX Tel: 01420 84676 Fax: 01420 542975; 54 Ackender Road, Alton GU34 1JS Tel: 01420 88925 — MB BS 1976 Lond.; BSc Lond. 1976; MRCP (UK) 1982; FRCGP; DRCOG 1984. (Lond. Hosp.) Trainer (Gen. Pract.) Hants.; Apoth. Worshipful Co. Ironmongers. Prev: Trainee GP MarlBoro. VTS; Regist. (Med.) Lond. Hosp. & Chelmsford Hosps.; Lect. (Physiol.) Lond. Hosp. Med. Coll.

HAYWARD, Michael John Silverdene, 11A Westminster Road, Branksome Park, Poole BH13 6JQ — MB BS 1969 Lond.; MRCP (U.K.) 1972. (St. Thos.) Cons. Phys. (Venereol.) Wessex RHA. Socs: Med. Soc. Study VD. Prev: Regist. (Med.) St. Nicholas' Hosp. Woolwich; Regist. (Haemat.) Roy. Infirm. Edin.; Sen. Regist. (Venereol.) E. Dorset. & Soton. Univ. Gp. Hosps.

HAYWARD, Michael John Medway Hospital, Windmill Road, Gillingham ME7 5NY Tel: 01634 830000; 3 Manwood Close, Sittingbourne ME10 4QL — BM 1981 Soton.; MRCP (UK) 1986; FRCP (UK) 1997. Cons. Phys. Med. c/o Elderly Medway HA. Prev: Sen. Regist. Rotat. (Geriat. Med.) Portsmouth & SE Hants. HA, Soton. &SW Hants. HA.

HAYWARD, Nicholas Simon Edward 22 Adderley Road, Leicester LE2 1WA — MB ChB 1998 Leic.; MB ChB Leic 1998.

HAYWARD, Paul Brian Lance Lane Medical Centre, 19 Lance Lane, Liverpool L15 6TS Tel: 0151 737 2882 Fax: 0151 737 2883; 7 Stonecrop, Liverpool L18 3LU — MB ChB 1977 Liverp. Prev: Cas. Off. BRd.green Hosp. Liverp.; SHO (Obst.) Mill Rd. Hosp. Liverp.; SHO (Paediat.) Alder Hey Childr. Hosp. Liverp.

HAYWARD, Peter John Sutton Park Surgery, 34 Chester Road North, Sutton Coldfield B73 6SP Tel: 0121 353 2586 Fax: 0121 353 5289 — MB ChB 1984 Birm.; MB ChB Birm. l984; MRCGP 1989.

HAYWARD, Peter John Department of Public Health, West Sussex HA, 1 The Causeway, Durrington, Worthing BN12 6BT Tel: 01903 708400 Fax: 01903 700981; 4 Church Grove, the Hollows, West Chiltington, Pulborough RH20 2QL Tel: 01798 813962 — MB BS 1979 Lond.; BSc (Hons.) Lond. 1975; FRCS Ed. 1983; MFPHM RCP (UK) 1990; FFPHM 1997. (Middlesex Hospital) Cons. Pub. Health Med. W. Sussex HA; Hon. Sen. Lect. (Pub. Health Sci.) St. Geo. Hosp. Med. Sch. Lond. Socs: Fell. Roy. Soc. Med. (Hon. Treas., Sect. Epidemiol. & Pub. Health). Prev: Regional Fac. Adviser (Pub. Health) S. Thames.

HAYWARD, Peter Michael (retired) Green Farm Clinic, Green Farm, Pettistree, Woodbridge IP13 0HU Tel: 01728 746558 Fax: 01728 747511 — MB BS Lond. 1961; DObst RCOG 1964. Prev: SHO (Obst.) Perivale Matern. Hosp. Greenford.

HAYWARD, Peter William (retired) Daru House, Northampton Lane, Dunchurch, Rugby CV22 6PR Tel: 01788 810449 — MB BChir 1953 Camb.; MA Camb. 1955, BA 1950, MB BChir 1953. Prev: Hosp. Pract. (Dermat.) Coventry & Warks. Hosp.

HAYWARD, Richard Andrew Higherland Surgery, 3 Orme Road, Poolfields, Newcastle ST5 2UE Tel: 01782 717044 Fax: 01782 715447; 19 Sneyd Avenue, Newcastle upon Lyme, Newcastle ST5 2PZ Tel: 01782 613330 — BM BS 1975 Nottm.; MA Keele 1990; BMedSci Nottm. 1973; DRCOG 1977; Cert Family Plann 1982; PHD 1998. GP; Comm. Mem. Newc. Shaffs PCG. Socs: BMA.

HAYWARD, Mr Richard David Department of Neurosurgery, Great Ormond Street Hospital for Children, Great Ormond St., London WC1N 3JH Tel: 020 7405 9200 Fax: 020 7242 5800 Email: haywar@gosh.nhs.uk; 23 Queen Square, London WC1N 3BG Tel: 020 7829 8792 Fax: 020 7833 8658 — MB BS 1966 Lond.; FRCS Eng. 1971. (St. Mary's) Cons. Neurol. Surg. Hosp. Sick Childr. Lond. & Nat. Hosp. for Neurol. & Neurosurg. Lond.; Hon. Cons. Neurol. Surg. King Edwd. VII Hosp. Offs. Lond.

HAYWARD, Richard James 7 Okell Drive, Fernbank Rise, Ross-on-Wye HR9 5QQ — MB ChB 1987 Sheff.

HAYWARD, Richard Laurence 16 Woodburn Terrace, Edinburgh EH10 4SJ — MB ChB 1989 Ed.

HAYWARD, Roger Philip Tel: 020 7806 4082 Fax: 020 7806 4002 — MRCS (LRCP); MB BS Lond. 1970; MD Lond. 1985; FRCP Lond. 1995; MRCP (UK) 1973; MRCS Eng. LRCP Lond. 1970. (St. Bart.) Hon. Cons. Hosp. Of St. John, St. Eliz.ondon; Hon. Cons. Heart Hosp., Lond. Socs: Brit. Cardiac Soc.; Brit. Pharm. Soc.; Eur. Soc. Cardiol. Prev: Sen. Regist. (Cardiol.) Middlx. Hosp. Lond.; Regist. (Cardiol.) Nat. Heart Hosp. Lond.; Ho. Phys. Med. Prof. Unit St. Bart. Hosp.

HAYWARD, Sally Ann Southmead Surgery, Southmead House, Blackpond Lane, Farnham Common, Slough SL2 3ER Tel: 01753 643195 Fax: 01753 642157 — MB BS 1988 Lond.; DRCOG 1991; DCH RCP Lond. 1990. Prev: Trainee GP Harrow HA VTS; Ho. Off. Whittington Hosp. & N.wick Pk. Hosp. Lond.

HAYWARD, Stephen John Department of Diagnostic Radiology, Royal United Hospital, Combe Park, Bath BA1 3NG Tel: 01225 824374; Roseland House, Greenway Lane, Bath BA2 4LN Tel: 01225 335955 — MB BS 1977 Lond.; BSc Lond. 1974,; FRCS Eng. 1981; FRCR 1988. (Middlx.) Cons. Diag. Radiol. Roy. United Hosp. Bath. Socs: Brit. Inst. Radiol.; Brit. Soc. Gastroenterol. Prev: Sen. Regist. (Diag. Radiol.) Char. Cross Hosp. Lond.; Regist. (Surg.) Hillingdon Hosp.; SHO (Surg.) N.wick Pk. Hosp. Harrow.

HAYWOOD, Gillian Sara 2 Yew Tree Cottages, Brighton Road, Coulsdon CR5 3ES — MB BS 1984 Lond.

HAYWOOD, Guy Anthony South West Cardiothoracic Centre, Derriford Hospital, Plymouth PL6 8DH Tel: 01752 777111 Fax: 01752 768976 — MD 1993 Camb.; MB BChir 1983; MRCP (UK) 1986. Cons. (Cardiol.) Derriford Hosp. Plymouth. Socs: Brit. Cardiac Soc.; Brit. Cardiovasc. Interven. Soc.; Brit. Pacing and Electrophysiol. Gp. Prev: Regist. (Cardiol.) St. Peters Hosp. Chertsey & St. Geo. Hosp. Lond.; Sen. Regist. Wessex Cardiothoracic Centre Soton.; Post Doctoral Fell. Dept. of Cardiol. Stanford Univ. Calif., USA.

HAYWOOD, Heather Alison Camelon Medical Practice, 3 Baird Street, Camelon, Falkirk FK1 4PP Tel: 01324 622854 Fax: 01324 633858; 20 Hodge Street, Falkirk FK1 1BN Tel: 01324 625921 — MB ChB 1986 Ed.; MRCGP 1993; DRCOG 1993; DCCH RCP Ed. 1993; DGM RCPS Glas. 1991; M Phil Glasgow 1996. (Edin.) Prev: Trainee GP/SHO Falkirk & Dist. Roy. Infirm.

HAYWOOD, James Andrew 18 Sycamore Grove, Eastburn, Keighley BD20 7SW — MB BS 1990 Lond.

HAYWOOD, Janice 25 Nursery Drive, Penkridge, Stafford ST19 5SJ — BM 1992 Soton.

***HAYWOOD, Jennifer Margaret** 5 Aycliffe Close, Bromley BR1 2LX — MB BChir 1994 Camb.; BA (Hons.) Camb. 1992.

HAYWOOD, Kathryn May 33 Beaumont Street, Oxford OX1 2NP — BM BCh 1998 Oxf.; BM BCh Oxf 1998.

HAYWOOD, Kenneth (retired) 17 Hope Lane, Baildon, Shipley BD17 5AS Tel: 01274 585071 — MB ChB Manch. 1958.

HAYWOOD, Paul Timothy Garden Flat, 39 Larkhall Rise, London SW4 6HU — MB BS 1987 Lond.

HAYWOOD, Rebecca Juliet Flitwick Surgery, The Highlands, Flitwick, Bedford MK45 1DZ Tel: 01525 712171 Fax: 01525 718756 — MB BS 1989 Lond.; MRCGP 1993; DRCOG 1991. Prev: Trainee GP N.ampton VTS; SHO (Dermat.) N.ampton.

HAYWOOD, Mr Richard Matthew 2 Chandos Road, Ampthill, Bedford MK45 2LF — MB BS 1992 Lond.; FRCS Eng. 1996. (St. Thomas') Specialist Regist. (Plastic Surg.) Nottm. City Hosp. Prev: SHO (Plastic Surg.) Lister Hosp.; Clin. Research Fell., Bedford Laser Dept.; SHO (Surg.) N.ampton Gen. Hosp.

HAYWOOD, Serena Flat 3, 18 Sussex Square, Kemptown, Brighton BN2 5AA Email: shaywo1@ibm.net — MB BS 1993 Lond.; BSc 1992; MRCP (UK) 1996. (St. Mary's Hospital London) Paediat. Neurol. Research Fell. Roy. Childr.'s Hosp. Melbourne Vict., Australia.

HAYWOOD, Stephen Clifford Adderlane Surgery, Adderlane Road, West Wylam, Prudhoe NE42 5HR Tel: 01661 836386 Fax: 01661 831353 — MB BS 1983 Newc.; MRCGP 1987. Clin. Asst. (Geriat.) Red Brick Hse. Prudhoe. Prev: Trainee GP N.umbria VTS.

HAYWORTH, Alistair Johnston Catto c/o 30 Craigiebuckler Terrace, Aberdeen AB15 8SX — MB ChB 1982 Aberd.; MRCGP 1986; DRCOG 1985.

HAZARIKA, Miss Emma Zircon Tel: 01392 874724 Fax: 01392 874724 Email: ezhazarika@btconnect.com — MB BS 1968 Gauhati; 1973 MAMS - NAMS (Nat. Acad. of Med. Sci.) New Delhi; MS - AIIMS, New Delhi 1972; FRCS Eng. 1976; FRCS Ed. 1976. (Guahati Medical College) Cons. Plastic Reconstruc. and Aesthetic Surg., Lond. and Exeter; Cons. Volun. Plastic and Reconstruc. Surg. Assam, India. Socs: BMA. Prev: Cons. Plastic Reconstruc. and Aesthetic Surg., Roy. Devon and Exeter Hosp., Exeter & Devon.

HAZARIKA, Podma Dhar Station Avenue Surgery, 60 Station Avenue, Coventry CV4 9HS Tel: 024 7646 6585 Fax: 024 7669 5944 — MB BS 1963 Gauhati.

HAZEL, Susan Penelope Curwen 31 Friars Road, Newbury RG14 7QU — MB BS 1993 Lond.

HAZELDEN, Audrey (retired) Harrycroft, Grasmere, Ambleside LA22 9RL Tel: 015394 35392 — MB BS 1945 Lond. Prev: Dep. Co. Med. Off. W.morland CC.

HAZELDINE, Richard Lawrence Westcotes Health Centre, Fosse Road South, Leicester LE3 0LP Tel: 0116 247 1949; 37 The Burrows, Narborough, Leicester LE9 5WS — MB ChB 1984 Leic.; MB ChB Leic. l984; MRCGP 1990; DGM RCP Lond. 1987.

***HAZELL, Joanne Louise** 51 Welbeck Road, Walkley, Sheffield S6 5AY — MB ChB 1997 Sheff.

HAZELL, Mr Jonathan Walter Peter 32 Devonshire Place, London W1G 6JL Tel: 020 7935 0328 Fax: 020 7486 2218 Email: j.hazell@ucl.ac.uk — MB BChir Camb. 1966; MA Camb. 1966;

FRCS Eng. 1974. (Middlx.) Sen. Lect. (Neuro-Otol.) UCL; Hon. Cons. (Audiol. Med.) Roy. Nat. Throat, Nose & Ear Hosp. Lond.; Vis. Prof. Univ. Maryland Sch. Med., USA. Prev: Hon. Cons. Neuro-Otol. Univ. Coll. Lond. Hosps.; Cons. Neuro-Otol. Roy. Nat. Inst. for Deaf Lond.; Sen. Regist. (ENT) Univ. Coll. Hosp. Lond.

HAZELL, Mark Jeremy Rutherford House, Langley Park, Durham DH7 9XD Tel: 0191 373 1386 Fax: 0191 373 4288; 14 Copperfield, Elvet Moor, Durham DH1 3QT — MB ChB 1978 Leeds; DRCOG 1981.

HAZELL, Michael Boundary Oaks, Carpenters Road, St Helens, Ryde PO33 1YG — MB ChB 1976 Sheff.; MRCP (UK) 1979. Cons. Dermat. Poole & Bournemouth. Socs: BAD; RSM. Prev: Sen. Regist. (Dermat.) Univ. Hosp. Wales, Cardiff; Regist. (Dermat.) Roy. Infirm. Edin.; SHO (Neurol.) Sheff. AHA.

HAZELL, Nicholas William Richard 58 Royston Park Road, Pinner HA5 4AF — MB BS 1998 Lond.; MB BS Lond 1998.

HAZELL, Yvonne Elizabeth Upper Green Road Medical Centre, Upper Green Road, St. Helens, Ryde PO33 1UG Tel: 01983 872772 Fax: 01983 874800 — MB ChB 1976 Sheff.; DRCOG 1980.

HAZELTON, David Christopher Queens Park Medical Centre, Farrer Street, Stockton-on-Tees TS18 2AW Tel: 01642 679681 Fax: 01642 677124 — MB BS 1983 Newc.; MRCGP 1987; DRCOG 1987.

HAZELTON, Trevor Lynn (retired) High Winds, 11 Kinnarchie Crescent, Methil, Leven KY8 3BB Tel: 01333 426122 — MB BCh BAO 1950 Belf. Prev: Ho. Phys. & Ho. Surg. Roy. Vict. Hosp. Belf.

HAZELWOOD, Simon Richard 46 Hillside Road, London N15 6NB — MB ChB 1993 Sheff.

HAZLE, Stuart Kenneth The Health Centre, Victoria Road, Hartlepool TS26 8DB Tel: 01429 262095 Fax: 01429 272374 — MB ChB 1980 Manch.; MBA Durham 1997; MRCGP 1984; DRCOG 1984; Cert. Family Plann. JCC 1983; DCH RCP Lond. 1983. (Univ. Manch.) Gen. Practitioner, Hartlepool; Trainer (Gen. Pract.) Cleveland VTS; Hartlepool PCT Exec. Comm. Bd. Mem.; Hartlepool Primary Care Developm. Lead GP.

HAZLEDINE, Claire 102 Muston Road, Filey YO14 0AN — MB ChB 1995 Manch.

HAZLEHURST, Dawn Elizabeth 8 Elizabethan Way, Northwich CW9 7UH Tel: 01606 42601 — MB ChB 1991 Manch.; BSc (Hons.) Physiol. Manch. 1988; MRCGP 1996. (Manch.) GP Princip. Prev: SHO (Psychiat.) Countess of Chester Hosp.; Trainee GP Tarporley, Chesh.; SHO (O & G) N. Manch. NHS Trust.

HAZLEHURST, Graham John Broom Leys Surgery, Broom Leys Road, Coalville LE67 4DE Tel: 01530 832095; White House, The Moor, Cole Orton, Coalville LE67 8GE — MB ChB 1982 Manch.; DRCOG 1985.

HAZLEHURST, Robert Vernon Dounby Surgery, Dounby, Orkney KW17 2HT Tel: 01856 771209 Fax: 01856 771320 — MB ChB 1973 Liverp.

HAZLEMAN, Brian Leslie Addenbrooke's Hospital, Hills Road, Cambridge CB2 2QR Tel: 01223 245151 Fax: 01223 217838 Email: brian.hazleman@msex.addenbrookes.nhs.uk; Church End House, Weston Colville, Cambridge CB1 5PE Tel: 01223 290543 Fax: 01223 290543 Email: brian.hazelman@which.net — MB BS 1965 Lond.; MB BS (Hons. Path.) Lond. 1965; MA Camb. 1977; FRCP Lond. 1980, M 1968; MRCS Eng. LRCP Lond. (Begley Prize RCS) 1965. (Lond. Hosp.) Cons. Rheum. Addenbrooke's Hosp. Camb.; Assoc. Lect. Univ. Camb; Dir. Rheum. Research Gp.; Fell. Corpus Christi Coll.; Mem. Edit. Bd. Jl. Orthop. Rheum. Inflammopharmacol. Socs: (Pres.) Brit. Soc. Rheum. Prev: Sen. Regist. (Med.) Radcliffe Infirm. & Nuffield Orthop. Hosp.; Regist. (Med.) Roy. Lond. Hosp.; Research Off. (Pharmacol. & Therap.) Lond. Hosp.

HAZLETT, James Joseph (retired) 58 Fornals Green Lane, Meols, Wirral CH47 9RL Tel: 0151 632 2713 — MB BCh BAO Dub. 1955; FFA RCS Eng. 1968; DA Eng. 1959. Prev: Cons. Anaesth. Arrowe Pk. & Clatterbridge Hosps.

HAZLEWOOD, Enid Beryl 7 Tennyson Drive, Attenborough, Beeston, Nottingham NG9 6BD Tel: 0115 925 6052 — MB BS 1956 Durh.; DCH Eng. 1965. (Newc.) Sen. Med. Off. Derbysh. AHA (Long Eaton). Socs: BMA. Prev: Sch. Med. Off. & Asst. MOH Derby; Ho. Surg. & SHO (Med.) Nottm. City Hosp.; SHO Derby Childr. Hosp.

HAZLEWOOD, Jane The Flop House, Manor Farm, Lower Chillington, Ilminster TA19 0PU — MB BS 1990 Lond.; BSc Lond. 1987, MB BS 1990. Trainee GP/SHO (A & E) Roy. Shrewsbury Hosp.

HAZLEWOOD, Janet Helen 2A Storer Road, Loughborough LE11 5EQ Tel: 01509 213002 — MB ChB 1976 Birm.; MRCGP 1980; DRCOG 1979; DCH Eng. 1979.

HAZLEWOOD, Judith Gilah 18 Westmoreland Terrace, London SW1V 4AL — BM BCh 1984 Oxf.; MBA Harvard 1988.

HAZRA, Dipti 33 Valley Road, Bromley BR2 0HB — MB BS 1974 Bombay; DCH RCPS Glas. 1983. (Topiwala Nat. Med. Coll.) Staff Grade (Child Health) Greenwich Health Care Trust. Socs: Med. Defence Union.

HAZZARD, Anthony John (retired) Redlands, 86 St John's Road, Stansted Mountfitchet, Stansted CM24 8JS Tel: 01279 813200 Fax: 01279 812426 — MB BS Lond. 1965; MSc (Psychol.) Lond. 1994; BA (Hons.) Open 1991; MRCS Eng. LRCP Lond. 1965; FRCGP 1996, M 1970; DObst RCOG 1968; AFBPsS 1996; Chartered Psychol. Brit. Psychol. Soc. 1993. Prev: Psychother. P.ss Alexandra Hosp. Harlow.

HEAD, Adrian Christopher Harold Road Surgery, 164 Harold Road, Hastings TN35 5NG Tel: 01424 720878/437962 Fax: 01424 719525; Rock Cottage, Toot Rock, Pett Level, Hastings TN35 4EN — MB BS 1971 Lond.; MRCS Eng. LRCP Lond. 1971. Med. Adviser RNLI Hastings.

HEAD, Amanda Jane 11 Lymore Terrace, Oldfield Park, Bath BA2 2JL — MB BCh 1989 Wales; DCH 1993; MRCP 1996. (Wales) Staff Grade (Paediat. A & E) Bristol Roy. Hosp. Sick Childr. Bristol. Prev: Trainee GP Bridgend VTS.

HEAD, Antony Charles Walsall Manor Hospital, Moat Road, Walsall WS2 9PS Tel: 0121 721172; 9 Wake Green Road, Moseley, Birmingham B13 9HB Tel: 0121 449 9834 — MB BCh 1976 Wales; MRCOG 1982; DRCOG 1978. Cons. O & G Walsall Manor Hosp. Prev: Sen. Regist. (O & G) Char. Cross W. Middlx. Hosp. Lond.; Regist. Rotat. United Birm. Hosp.

HEAD, Barbara Gillian 10 Parkview Avenue, Burley, Leeds LS4 2LH; 22 Greenhill, Burgot, Bromsgrove B60 1BJ — MB ChB 1964 Ed.; FFA RCS Eng. 1969. (Ed.) Retd. Del. 1999 From NHS APPT. Prev: Cons. Anaesth. Alexandra NHS Healthcare Trust.

HEAD, Catherine Elizabeth Saddleback, School Lane, Cookham Dean, Maidenhead SL6 9PQ Tel: 01682 488424 Fax: 01628 488424 — BM 1977 Soton.; MFPM RCP (UK) 1989; Dip. Pharm. Med. RCP (UK) 1986. (Southampton Univ.) Cons. Pharmaceut. Med. Socs: Fell. Roy. Soc. Med.; Brit. Assn. Pharmaceut. Phys.; BMA. Prev: Dir. Clin. Investig. Smithkline Beecham plc.; Med. Adviser Hoechst UK Ltd.; Regist. (Anaesth.) Char. Cross Hosp. Lond.

HEAD, Catherine Elizabeth Email: ceh14@mole.bio.cam.ac.uk — MB BChir 1993 Camb.; BA Oxf. 1988; MA Oxf. 1995; MRCP UK 1995. (Cambridge) Specialist Regist. Cardiol. Papworth Hosp. Camb.

HEAD, Christopher David 2 Coombe Drive, Cargreen, Saltash PL12 — MB ChB 1973 Sheff.

HEAD, Colin (retired) Home Lodge Surgery, Gloucester Road, Teddington TW11 0NS Tel: 020 8977 2516 Fax: 020 8977 3471 — MB BS 1974 Lond.

HEAD, Fiona Clare Watford General Hospital, Vicarage Road, Watford WD18 0HB; Fellow's Flat, Oak Hill Cottage, Southgate, London N14 4PS — MB BS 1993 Lond.; MA Camb. 1992, BA 1988. SHO (A & E Med.) Watford Gen. Hosp.

HEAD, Fiona Frances D.R A.J Raw & Partners, Farnham Health Care, Brightwells, East Street, Farnham GU9 7SA Tel: 01252 723122; Sunnyside House, 88 Farnborough Road, Heath End, Farnham GU9 9BE Tel: 01252 323586 Email: simon.head@ntlworld.com — MB ChB 1986 Bristol; Cert. Family Plann. JCC 1991. (Univ. Bristol) Retainee GP Farnham & Basingstoke Retainer Scheme. Prev: Asst. GP BromsGr.; Trainee GP BromsGr. & Redditch VTS; SHO (Geriat.,Paediat., O & G & Psychiat.) Alexandra Hosp. Redditch.

HEAD, Fraser Andrew Chestnut House, Saxthorpe, Norwich NR11 7BJ — MB ChB 1993 Ed. Clin. Asst. (Drugs Misuse) Bure Centre Norwich.

HEAD, Jacqueline Mary Southbourne Surgery, 17 Beaufort Road, Southbourne, Bournemouth BH6 5BF — MB BChir 1991 Camb.; DFFP 2000; MA Camb. 1991; DRCOG 1996; MRCGP 1997. p/t GP.

HEAD, Janice Elaine 30 Carnarvon Avenue, Enfield EN1 3DX; 30 Carnarvon Avenue, Enfield EN1 3DX — MB BS 1993 Lond.; DCH 1997; DRCOG 1997; DFFP 1998; MRCGP 1998. (The Royal London Medical College) Cruise Ship Doctor, P&O. Prev: GP Regist.; SHO (O & G, Paediat. & A & E).

HEAD, Jillian Elizabeth Health Centre, Wellington Avenue, Aldershot GU11 1DA; 8 Wilton Court, Farnborough GU14 7EL — MB BS 1984 Lond.; Dip. Ther. Lond. 1997; DRCOG 1988; Cert. Family Plann. JCC 1988. GP Aldershot Retainer Scheme. Prev: Civil. Med. Pract. Train. Bn. (ACC) Aldershot; Trainee GP Haywards Heath VTS; Med. Off. St. Catherine's Hospice Crawley.

HEAD, Laura Local Health Partnerships NHS Trust, Minsmere House, Heath Road, Ipswich IP4 5PD Tel: 01473 704202; Potters Farm, Mendlesham, Stowmarket IP14 5SR — MB BS 1980 Lond.; MRCPsych 1987; DGM RCP 1994 Lond. Cons. Psychiat. Prev: Sen. Regist. (Psychiat.) E. Anglian Rotat. Scheme; Regist. Fulbourne Hosp. Cambs.; Ho. Off. (Surg. & Phys.) Ipswich Hosp.

HEAD, Marcus Oliver Carter West End, 6 Mill Lane, Clanfield, Bampton OX18 2RT — MB BS 1998 Lond.; MB BS Lond 1998.

HEAD, Matthew Charles 47 The Drive, Bexley DA5 3DF Tel: 0208 6954 — MB BS 1948 Lond.; MRCS Eng. LRCP Lond. 1941; DOMS Eng. 1950. (St. Thos.) Sen. Hosp. Med. Off. Moorfields Eye Hosp.; Clin. Asst. Croydon Eye Unit. Socs: BMA & NOTB Assn. Prev: Ho. Surg. & Ho. Phys. St. Jas. Hosp. Balham; Squadron Ldr. RAF Med. Br. 1942-6; Sen. Ho. Surg. (Ophth.) St. Thos. Hosp. Lond.

HEAD, Nancy Eirwen Department Paediatric Audiology (Community), Cobtree, Preston Hall Hospital, Maidstone Tel: 01622 790696; East Weald, Ashford Road, Tenterden TN30 6LX Tel: 01580 765125 — MB BCh 1961 Wales. (Cardiff) SCMO (Paediat. Audiol.) Mid Kent Health Care Trust.

HEAD, Paul Harvey The Health Centre, Chapel Road, Mendlesham, Stowmarket IP14 5SQ Tel: 01449 767722; Potters Farm, Mendlesham, Stowmarket IP14 5SH Tel: 01449 767828 — MB BS 1980 Lond.; MRCGP 1994. Prev: Trainee GP Ipswich VTS; Ho. Surg. & Ho. Phys. The Ipswich Hosp.

HEAD, Mr Peter Warren, OBE, CStJ, Surg. Capt. RN Retd. (retired) Yew Tree Cottage, 7 Britten Road, Lee-on-the-Solent PO13 9JU — MB BS Lond. 1948; FRCS Eng. 1968; DLO Eng. 1954. Prev: Cons. ENT Brit. Milit. Hosp. Berlin, W. Germany.

HEAD, Stephen Middleton Lodge Surgery, New Ollerton, Newark NG22 9SZ Tel: 01623 860668 Fax: 01623 836073; Norwood, Church Lane, Boughton, Newark NG22 9JU Tel: 01623 863398 — MB ChB 1976 Dundee; FRCGP 1991, M 1980. Med. Adviser N. Derbysh. Health; Med. Writer. Socs: Assn. Primary Care Med. Advisers. Prev: Vice-Chairm. Vale of Trent Fac. RCGP; Train. GP VTS Course Organiser.

HEAD-RAPSON, Adrian Gilbert 110 Liverpool Road, Crosby, Liverpool L23 5TG Email: 100031.667@compuserve.com — MB ChB 1987 Liverp.; BSc Liverp. 1984; FRCA 1991. Cons. Anaesth. S.port & Formby NHS Trust. Socs: Anaesth. Res. Soc.; Assn. Anaesth. GB & Irel. Prev: Sen. Regist. Rotat. Mersey; Wellcome Research Fell. (Anaesth.) Roy. Liverp. Univ. Hosp.; Regist. Rotat. (Anaesth.) Mersey RHA.

HEADDEN, Elizabeth Anne 5 Dicks Park, Murray, East Kilbride, Glasgow G75 0DH — MB ChB 1990 Glas.

HEADDEN, Geoffrey Dewar The Surgery, Kearan Road, Kinlochleven PH50 4QU Tel: 01855 831225 Fax: 01855 831494 — MB ChB 1976 Manch.; BSc Hons. St. And. 1973; MRCGP 1982; DCH Lond. 1980.

HEADING, Carolyn Margaret Bedminster Rectory, 287 North St., Ashton Gate, Bristol BS3 1JP Tel: 0117 966 4025 — MRCS Eng. LRCP Lond. 1968; MFFP 1993; Cert. Family Plann. JCC 1978. Clin. Med. off. (UBHT in Child Health) Bristol; Sen. Clin. Med. Off. (Family Plann.) Frenchay Healthcare Trust. Socs: Foundat. Mem. Fac. Community Health; Assn. Doctors Gp. for Contracep. & Sexual Health. Prev: Clin. Med. Off. (Child Health & Family Plann.) Herefordsh. HA.

HEADING, Robert Campbell Centre for Liver & Digestive Disorders, Royal Infirmary, Edinburgh EH3 9YW Tel: 0131 536 2240 Fax: 0131 536 2197; 20 Frogston Road W., Edinburgh EH10 7AR Tel: 0131 445 1552 — MB ChB 1966 Ed.; BSc Ed. 1963; MD 1980; FRCP Ed. 1979; FRCP (Lond.) 1997; MRCP (UK) 1970. (Ed.) Reader (Med.) Univ. Edin.; Cons. Phys. Edin. Roy. Infirm. Socs: Brit. Soc. Gastroenterol.; Internat. Mem. Amer. Gastroenterol. Assn. Prev: Fell. (Gastroenterol.) Univ. Iowa Coll. Med., USA; Lect. (Therap.) Univ. Edin.

HEADLEY, Bevan Michael 63 Portland Road, West Bridgford, Nottingham NG2 6DN Tel: 0115 982 6098 — MB ChB 1991 Bristol; MRCP (UK) 1996. Specialist Regist. (Paediat.) Univ. Hosp. Nottm. Prev: SHO (Cardiol.) Gt. Ormond St. Lond.; SHO (Neonat. Med.) Rosie Matern. Hosp. Camb.; SHO (Paediat.) St. Thos. Hosp. Lond.

HEADLEY, Charles Arthur Jenner House Surgery, 159 Cove Road, Farnborough GU14 0HH Tel: 01252 548141 Fax: 01252 371516; 2 Trunk House, Trunk Road, Farnborough GU14 9SW Tel: 01252 515371 — MB BS 1973 Lond. (St. Geo.) Police Surg. Hants. N.. Div. Socs: Assn. Police Surg. Prev: SHO (O & G) St. Geo. Hosp. Lond.; Ho. Surg. St. Geo. Hosp. Tooting; Ho. Phys. Ashford Hosp. Middlx.

HEADLEY, Mary A T 8 Holly Blue Road, Wymondham, Norwich NR18 0XJ — MB BCh BAO 1978 Belf.; MRCPsych 1983. Cons. Gen. & Community Psychiat., Norf. Ment. Health Care Trust, 80 St. Stephens Rd, Norwich. Prev: Cons. Gen. Psychiat., Craigavon & Banbridge Community Trust, Craigavon Hosp.; Unit Gen. Manager Area Ment. Health Unit, Armagh; Cons. Psych. Of Old Age, St Luke's Hosp. Armagh.

HEADLEY, Philip Russell (retired) 42 Westerham Road, Bessels Green, Sevenoaks TN13 2PZ Tel: 01732 454640 — MA, MB BChir Camb. 1945; MRCS Eng. LRCP Lond. 1944; DCH Eng. 1946. Prev: Ho. Phys. Med. Profess. Unit & Childr. Dept. St. Bart. Hosp.

HEADLEY, Seton Robert Tristram, TD (retired) Vine Cottage, 2 Lancaster Gardens, Wimbledon, London SW19 5DG Tel: 020 8946 5866 Fax: 020 8946 5866 — MB BS 1939 Lond.; MRCS Eng. LRCP Lond. 1937; FRCA 1953; DA Eng. 1940. Prev: Cons. Anaesth. Roy. Masonic Hosp., St. Geo. Hosp. & Vict. Hosp. Childr.

HEADON, Mr Maurice Paul Eye Department, Royal Berkshire Hospital, London Road, Reading RG1 5AN Tel: 01734 875111 ext. 386; 14 Yew Lane, Coley Park Farm, Reading RG1 6DA Tel: 01734 576400 — MB BS 1978 Lond.; DPhil Lond., MA 1977, BA 1972, MB BS 1978; FRCS Glas. 1986; FCOphth 1988. (Oxf. & Middlx.) Sen. Regist. Oxf. RHA. Prev: Regist. Manch. Roy. Eye Hosp.; SHO Soton. Eye Hosp.; SHO King's Coll. Hosp. Lond.

HEADON, Olivia Therese The Health Centre, Crammavill Street, Stifford Clays, Grays RM16 2AP Tel: 01375 377127 Fax: 01375 394520 — MB BS 1980 Lond.; BSc Lond. 1977; MRCGP 1984; DRCOG 1984.

HEADS, Tracey Claire Flat 3, 255/257 St Margarets Road, Twickenham TW1 1NJ — MB ChB 1984 Otago.

HEAF, David Peter Respiratory Unit, Royal Liverpool Children's Hospital (Alder Hey), Eaton Road, Liverpool L12 2AP Tel: 0151 228 4811; 3 Graham Road, West Kirby, Wirral CH48 5DN Tel: 0151 632 5435 — MB BS 1974 Lond.; FRCP Lond. 1991; MRCP (UK) 1977. (Middlx.) Cons. Paediat. (Respirat. Med.) Roy. Liverp. Childr. Hosp. Liverp. Prev: Sen. Regist. Guy's Hosp. Lond.; Hon. Sen. Regist. The Hosp. for Sick Childr. Lond.; Sen. Research Childr. Hosp. Philadelphia, USA.

HEAF, Joanna Mary Gosford Hill Medical Centre, 167 Oxford Road, Kidlington OX5 2NS Tel: 01865 374242 Fax: 01865 377826; 23 Freeborn Close, Kidlington OX5 2BH — MB ChB 1976 Bristol; DRCOG 1979.

HEAF, Mary Margaret (retired) 24 Charlbury Road, Oxford OX2 6UU Tel: 01865 558356 — MB BCh BAO Dub.. 1953; BA Dub. 1951; DCH Eng. 1957. Prev: Sen. Med. Off. Oxf. HA.

HEAF, Peter Julius Denison (retired) Ferrybrook House, Chalmore Gardens, Wallingford OX10 9EP Tel: 01491 839176 Fax: 01491 839176 — MB BS 1946 Lond.; MD Lond. 1952; FRCP Lond. 1965, M 1954. Fell. UCL. Prev: Phys. Univ. Coll. Hosp. Lond.

HEAF, Rosemary (retired) Ferrybrook House, Chalmore Gardens, Wallingford OX10 9EP Tel: 01491 839176 — MB BS 1946 Lond.; LMSSA Lond. 1946. Prev: Cons. Cytol. Univ. Coll. Hosp. Lond.

HEAFIELD, Mark Thomas Eliot Consultant Neurologist, Queen Elizabeth Hospital, Edgbaston, Birmingham B15 2TH — MB BS 1984 Lond.

HEAFIELD, Richard John 45 Heatherdeane Road, Highfield, Southampton SO17 1PA — MB BS 1985 Lond.

HEAGERTY, Adrian Harding Department of Dermatology, The North Staffs Hospital Centre, Stoke-on-Trent Tel: 01782 716265 Fax: 01782 716646; The Oaks, Aston, near Pipe Gate, Market Drayton TF9 4JB — MB BS 1978 Lond.; MD Lond. 1990, BSc Lond. 1975; MRCP (UK) 1982. (Guy's) Sen. Regist. (Dermat.) W. Midl. RHA.

HEAGERTY, Antony Michael Manchester Royal Infirmary, Oxford Road, Manchester M13 9WL Tel: 0161 276 4575 Fax: 0161 274

4833 Email: tony-heagerty@manac.uk — MB BS 1977 Lond.; MD Leics. 1987; FRCP Lond. 1989; MRCP (UK) 1980; F Med Sci 1998. Prof. Med. Univ. Manch.; Sen. Research Fell. Brit. Heart Foundat. & Hon. Cons. Phys. Leicester; Roy. Infirm.

HEAL, Andrew John Sarum House Surgery, 3 St. Ethelbert Street, Hereford HR1 2NS Tel: 01432 265422 Fax: 01432 358440; Hill Cottage, Wellington, Hereford HR4 8BE Tel: 01432 830962 — MB BS 1985 Lond.; DA (UK) 1991; DRCOG 1990; DCH RCP Lond. 1989. Clin. Asst. & (Anaesth.) Hereford Hosp. NHS Trust.

HEAL, Carol Anne 6 Egerton Road, Monton, Eccles, Manchester M30 9LR Tel: 0161 789 3723 Email: chrisandcarrie@chrisandcarrie.freeserve.co.uk — MB ChB 1988 Manch.; MRCPI 1994; DCH RCP Lond. 1992; DRCOG 1992; DA (UK) 1990. (Manch.) Cons. Paeds. Roy. Albert Edwd. Infirm., Wigan. Prev: Sen. Regist. (Paediat.) N.W. Region.

HEAL, Christine Marina Queen's Hospital Burton on Trent, Belvedere Road, Burton-on-Trent DE14 0RB Tel: 01332 566333; 12 Bannels Avenue, Littleover, Derby DE23 7GG — MB ChB 1976 Sheff.; FRCA Eng 1980. Cons. Anaesth. Qu. Hosp. Burton on Trent. Prev: Cons. Anaesth. Burton Dist. Gen. Hosp.

HEAL, Clare Frances 4 Hazelbadge Close, Poynton, Stockport SK12 1HD — MB ChB 1990 Liverp.

HEAL, David Sutton 17 Rigden Road, Hove BN3 6NP Tel: 01273 504849 Fax: 01273 504849 Email: david.heal@dial.pipex.com — MB BS 1983 Lond.; MRCP Lond. 1987; MRCGP 1990.

HEAL, James Gordon Freeman (retired) 53 Ranelagh Road, Ealing, London W5 5RP Tel: 020 8840 2410 — MD CM 1915 Dalhousie; LMS Nova Scotia 1915; DOMS Eng. 1923. Prev: Clin. Asst. & Refrac. Asst. Roy. Lond. Ophth. Hosp.

HEAL, Katharine 8 Church Way, South Croydon CR2 0JQ — MB BS 1997 Lond.

HEAL, Mr Michael Richard Chapel House, Chapel Lane, Ravensmoor, Nantwich CW5 8PT Tel: 01270 624993 Email: mike@healhouse.freeserve.co.uk — MB BS 1957 Lond.; FRCS Eng. 1962; MRCS Eng. LRCP Lond. 1957. (Middlx.) Socs: Roy. Soc. Med.; (Ex-Counc.) BMA; (Ex-Counc.) Brit. Assn. Urol. Surgs. Prev: Emerit. Cons. Urol., S. Chesh. Hosp. Gp.

HEAL, Philip Carlton St Thomas Health Centre, Cowick St., Exeter EX4 1HJ — MB BChir 1958 Camb.; BA, MB Camb. 1958, BChir 1957; DObst RCOG 1963; DA Eng. 1963. (Camb. & St. Thos.) Prev: Ho. Off. Cas. & Surg. St. Thos. Hosp. Lond.; Med. Off. Dept. Techn. Cooperat. Uganda; Anaesth. Regist. Lambeth Hosp. Gp.

HEAL, Samuel William Peter Bay Tree Cottage, 19 Winchester St., Botley, Southampton SO30 2EB — MB BS 1990 Lond.

HEAL, Sarah Jane Victoria 23 Hillside Close, Hillam, Leeds LS25 5PB — MB BCh BAO 1997 Belf.

HEALD, Adrian Hugh Dept. of Endocrinology Hope Hospital, Salford M6 8MD Tel: 0161 787 5146 Fax: 0161 787 5989 — BM BCh 1988 Oxf.; DM 2002 Oxon; MRCP 1995; MA Oxf. 1987; MRCPsych 1992. Specialist Regist. (Endocrinol. & Diabetes) Hope Hosp. Salford. Socs: Brit. Endocrine Soc.; Amer. Endocrine Soc.; Fell. of Roy. Soc. of Med.

HEALD, Andrew Department of Neurosciences, York District Hospital, Wigginton Road, York YO32 8HE Tel: 01904 454161 Fax: 01904 453477; Fax: 01439 788313 — MB BS 1982 Newc.; MD Newc. 1994; MRCP (UK) 1985. Cons. Neurol. Dept of Neurosci.s,York Dist. Hosp.York; Pury list,Nuffield Hosp.,Precentors Ct.,York.; Cons.Neurol. Friarage Hosp.,N.Yorks.. Socs: Assn of Brit. Neurol.; N. of Eng. Neurol Ass. Prev: Sen. Registral.Roy.Vict.Infirm,Newc.; Research Sen. Regist. (Neurol.) Roy. Vict. Infirm. Newc.; Regist. (Med.) Newc. Gen. Hosp.

***HEALD, Corrie Anne** 43 Jubilee Close, Haywards Heath RH16 3PJ — MB BS 1998 Lond.; MB BS Lond 1998.

HEALD, Geoffrey Edward (retired) 17 Didsbury Park, Manchester M20 5LH Tel: 0161 445 0122 — MB BChir 1950 Camb.; MRCS Eng. LRCP Lond. 1949; MRCGP 1968; DObst RCOG 1965. Prev: Hosp. Pract. (Haemat.) Withington Hosp. Manch.

HEALD, Jane 72 Winchester Drive, Stockport SK4 2NU — MB ChB 1980 Manch.; BSc (Hons.) Manch. 1978, MB ChB 1980; MRCPath 1990.

HEALD, Professor Richard John, OBE Colo-rectal Research Office, Department of Surgery, Pelican Cancer Cnetre, North Hampshire Hospital, Basingstoke RG24 9NA Tel: 01256 328070 Fax: 01256 336556; Waytes, High St, Odiham, Hook RG29 1LE Tel: 01256 354747 Fax: 01256 818005 — MB BChir 1961 Camb.; MA, MChir Camb. 1965; FRCS Eng. 1966; FRCS Ed. 1965. (Camb. & Guy's) Prof. of Surg., Personal Chair., Univ. of Soton. Surgic. Director, Pelican Cancer Centre. Socs: Former Vice Pres., Roy. Coll. of Surg.s of Eng.; Ex-Pres. Assn. Coloproctol.; Ex-Pres. Sect.s Surg. and ColoprOtol., Roy. Soc. of Med. Prev: Cons. Surg. N. Hants. Hosp. Basingstoke; Hon. Mem. elect Swiss Surgic. Soc; Hon.Doct.Linkoping, Sweden.

HEALD, Spencer Charles Garden Flat, 524 Finchley Road, London NW11 8DD — MB ChB 1981 Otago; FRACP 1991.

HEALD, Suzanne Jayne Library House Surgery, Avondale Road, Chorley PR7 2AD Tel: 01257 262081 Fax: 01257 232114 — MB ChB 1988 Aberd.; DRCOG 1992. (Aberdeen) Clin. Asst. Derian Hse. Childr. Hospice Astley Vill. Chorley. Prev: SHO (Paediat.) Roy. Albert Edw. Infirm. Wigan; Cas. Off. Roy Albert Edw. Infirm. Wigan; SHO (O & G) Billinge.

HEALEY, Andrew Edward 4 Adamson Gardens, Manchester M20 2TQ — MB ChB 1996 Liverp.

HEALEY, Christopher John Airedale General Hospital, Skipton Road, Steeton, Keighley BD20 6TD Tel: 01535 651106 Fax: 01535 651172 Email: chrisjohn16@hotmail.com — MB ChB 1987 Sheff.; MRCP (UK) 1990. (Sheff.) Cons. Gastroenterol. & Gen. Phys. Socs: Full Mem. Amer. Gastroenterol. Assn. Prev: Sen. Regist. (Gen. Med. & Gastroenterol.) Addenbrooks Hosp. Camb.; Research Regist. (Gastroenterol.) John Radcliffe Hosp. Oxf.; Regist. Rotat. (Gastroenterol.) Gloucester & Bristol HAs.

HEALEY, David Guy Framfield House Surgery, 42 St. Johns Street, Woodbridge IP12 1ED Tel: 01394 382157 — MB BS 1969 Lond.; MRCP (UK) 1975; MRCS Eng. LRCP Lond. 1969; DTM & H Eng. 1971; DObst RCOG 1971. (Guy's) Prev: Ho. Phys. St. John's Hosp. Chelmsford; Dist. Med. Off. Papua, New Guinea; Sen. Ho. Phys. Roy. N.. Hosp. Lond.

HEALEY, Francis Bernard Till Valley Surgery, High St., Shrewton, Salisbury SP3 4BZ Tel: 01980 620259 Fax: 01980 620060 — MB BS 1976 Lond.; BSc (Hons.) Lond. 1973; MRCGP 1982; DRCOG 1979; DCH Eng. 1979.

HEALEY, Hilary Stonehill Medical Centre, Piggott St., Farnworth, Bolton BL4 9QZ Tel: 01204 73445; 18 Cornergate, Westhoughton, Bolton BL5 2SE — MB ChB 1976 Manch.

HEALEY, John Lychgate, Pollards Crescent, Norbury, London SW16 4NX — MB BS 1963 Lond.

HEALEY, John Charles Fleet Medical Centre, Church Road, Fleet GU51 4PE Tel: 01252 613327 Fax: 01252 815156 Email: bracken@globalnet.co.uk; Bracken, Waverley Avenue, Fleet GU51 4NN Email: bracken@globalnet.co.uk — MB BS 1968 Lond.; MRCP (U.K.) 1971; MRCS Eng. LRCP Lond. 1968; MRCGP 1987. (Univ. Coll. Hosp.) GP Fleet Med. Centre; Bd. Mem. Rushmoor & Hart PCG. Prev: Regist. (Med.) Univ. Coll. Hosp. Lond.; Sen. Ho. Phys. Univ. Coll. Hosp. Lond.; Ho. Phys. & Ho. Surg. Roy. N.. Hosp. Lond.

HEALEY, Norman John 16 Upper Wimpole Street, London W1G 6LT Tel: 020 7487 3162; Southgate, Whitchurch Road, Cublington, Aylesbury Tel: 01296 681394 — MRCS Eng. LRCP Lond. 1965; FLCOM 1979, M 1974; MRO 1975; DObst RCOG 1972; DA Eng. 1969. (Guy's) p/t Hon. Cons. St. Luke's Hosp. Lond. Socs: Brit. Inst. Musculoskel. Med.; Brit. Soc. Rheum.; (Ex-Hon. Sec.) Brit. Osteop. Assn. Prev: Counc. Mem. Brit. Assn. Manip. Med.; Clin. Asst. (Rheum. & Rehabil.) St. Mary's Hosp. Lond.; Surg. Lt. RN.

HEALEY, Philip David Market Harborough Medical Centre, 67 Coventry Road, Market Harborough LE16 9BX Tel: 01858 464242 — MB BS 1994 Lond.; MRCGP 1998; BA Oxf. 1991; DFFP 1997; DRCOG 1996; DCH 1998; DCCH 1998. (Lond. Hosp. Med. Coll.) GP Princip. Market HarBoro. Med. Centre. Prev: GP, Vivian Family Centre, Mouse Jaw, Sask, Canada; GP & Med. Represen., Mundubbera, QLD, Australia.

HEALEY, Ronald Jack (retired) North Hall Cottage, Launceston PL15 9JF Tel: 01566 773101 — MRCS Eng. LRCP Lond. 1938; MRCGP 1953. Prev: Med. Off. Launceston Hosp.

HEALEY, Susan 10 Roland Mews, Stepney Green, London E1 3JT — MB BS 1996 Lond. (LHMC) SHO Rotat. (Paediat.).

HEALEY, Tim (retired) Northfield, Salisbury St., Barnsley S75 2TL Tel: 01226 205348 Fax: 01226 205348 Email: tim.healey@chimera1935.freeserve.co.uk — MB ChB Sheff. 1959;

FRCR 1975; FFR 1966; T(R)(CR) 1996; DMRD Eng. 1963. Mem. Standards Comm. BSI, LEN, IEC & ISO. Prev: Cons. Radiol. Barnsley Hosp. Gp.

HEALICON, Jayne Elizabeth St George's Hospital, Morpeth NE61 2N — MB BS 1989 Newc.; BSc (Hons.) Wales 1980; PhD Lond. 1985; MRCPsych 1996. Cons. Gen. Adult Psychiat. St Geo.'s Hosp., Morpeth. Prev: Specialist Regist (Psychiat.) Newc. Gen. Hosp.

HEALICON, Richard Mark Department of Clinical Governance, 1st Floor Mezzanine, Milvain Building, Newcastle General Hospital, Westgate Road, Newcastle upon Tyne NE14 6BE Tel: 0191 256 3881 Email: richardhealic@doctors.nef — MB BS 1987 Lond.; PhD Lond. 1985, BSc (Hons.) 1981; DRCOG 1996; MRCGP 1997. (Guy's Hosp. Med. Sch.) Specialist Regist. Pub. Health Med. Prev: Med. Off. N.ern Regional Taskforce Newc.; GP Princip. Guide Post Med. Gp. N.umberland; Sen. Demonst. (Path.) Roy. Vict. Infirm. Newc.

HEALY, Andrew Aloysius Patrick 116 Court Lane, Dulwich, London SE21 7EA Tel: 020 8693 6944; 105 Bellenden Road, Peckham, London SE15 4QY Tel: 020 7639 9622 — LAH Dub. 1949. (RCSI)

HEALY, Anton Patrick 66 Church Road, Lower Bebington, Wirral CH63 3EB — MB BCh BAO 1960 NUI; LAH Dub. 1961; LDS RCSI. (Univ. Coll. Dub.) Prev: Ho. Off. St. Michael's Hosp. Dunleary, Clatterbridge Matern. Hosp. & Clatterbridge Gen. Hosp.

HEALY, Brendan James Linden House, Royal Liverpool University Hospital, Prescot St., Liverpool L7 8XP — MB ChB 1998 Liverp.; MB ChB Liverp 1998.

HEALY, Caitlin 66 Church Road, Bebington, Wirral CH63 3EB Tel: 0151645 1020 — LRCPI & LM, LRSCI & LM 1942; LRCPI & LM, LRCSI & LM 1942. (RCSI) Prev: Clin. Clerk Coombe Hosp. Dub.; Ho. Phys. St. Ultan's Hosp. Dub. & Heath Hosp. Dub.

HEALY, Christopher John The Market Place Surgery, Cattle Market, Sandwich CT13 9ET Tel: 01304 613436/612589 Fax: 01304 613877; Little Manwood, 25 Paradise Row, Sandwich CT13 9HU — MB BS 1982 Lond.; DRCOG 1988.

HEALY, Mr Ciaran Marion Joseph Flat 3, 52 Huntley St., London WC1E 6DD — MD Dub. 1993, MB BCh BAO 1981; FRCS Eng. 1986; FRCSI 1985; DCH Dub. 1983. Lect. Univ. Coll. Lond. Med. Sch. & Hon. Sen. Regist. Mt. Vernon Hosp. Lond. Socs: Fell. Roy. Soc. Med.; Brit. Assn. Plastic Surg.; Assoc. Mem. Brit. Soc. Surg. Hand. Prev: Regist. (Plastic Surg.) Addenbrooke's Hosp. Camb.; Assoc. Research Fell. (Neurol. Studies) Univ. Coll. & Middlx. Sch. Med. Lond.; Regist. Rotat. (Surg.) Swansea.

HEALY, David Thomas Mary Department of Psychological Medicine, Hergest Unit, Ysbyty Gwynedd, Bangor LL57 2PW Tel: 01248 384452 Fax: 01248 371397 — MB BCh BAO 1979 NUI; MD NUI 1986; MRCPsych 1985; FRCPsych 1996. Reader (Psychol. Med.) & Hon. Cons. Psychiat. Univ. Wales Coll. of Med.

HEALY, David William Christopher Cottage, Margaret St., Thaxted, Dunmow CM6 2QN Tel: 01371 830293 Email: dwhealy@msn.com — MB BS 1996 Lond; BSc (1st cl. Hons.) Physiol. Lond. 1993. (St. Bartholomew's and the Royal London) SHO Rotat. (Med.) St. Mary's Hosp. Lond. Prev: SHO (A & E) St. Mary's Hosp.; Ho. Off. (Med.) Roy. Hosps. NHS Trust.

HEALY, Ellen Teresa Our Lady of Apostles Convent, 2 Slyne Road, Lancaster LA1 2HU Tel: 01524 382919 — MB BCh BAO 1967 NUI; MRCPsych 1982; DTM & H Liverp. 1972. (Cork) Clin. Asst. (Psychiat.) Lancaster HA. Prev: Regist. (Psychiat.) Argyll & Clyde Health Bd.; Med. Off. Oke Offa Hosp. Ibadan, Nigeria & St. Mary's Hosp. Ogwashi-Uku, Nigeria; Chief Med. Off. Bacita Hosp. Nigeria.

HEALY, Eugene Pius Department of Dermatology, University of Newcastle upon Tyne, Royal Victoria Infirmary, Newcastle upon Tyne NE1 4LP — MB BCh BAO 1987 Dub.; MB BCh Dub. 1987; BA Dub. 1987; MRCPI 1989. (Trinity Coll.)

HEALY, James Maurice The Surgery, Station Lane, Farnsfield, Newark NG22 8LA Tel: 01623 882289 Fax: 01623 882286 — BM BS 1981 Nottm.; MRCGP 1985. GP Notts.

HEALY, Jeremiah Christopher 22 Grafton Square, London SW4 0DB — MB BChir 1986 Camb.; MA Camb. 1986; MRCP (UK) 1989; FRCR 1993. Cons. Radiol. Chelsea & W.m. Hosp. Lond. Prev: Clin. Lect., Sen. Regist. & Regist. (Diag. Radiol.) St. Bart. Hosp. Lond.

HEALY, Kate Marie 89 Norse Road, Glasgow G14 9EF — MB ChB 1992 Dundee.

HEALY, Kevin Joseph Cassel Hospital, 1 Ham Common, Richmond TW10 7JF Tel: 020 8940 8181 Fax: 020 8237 2996; 72 St. Albans Road, Kingston upon Thames KT2 5HH Tel: 020 8546 3259 — MB BCh BAO 1977 NUI; DCH NUI 1979; DObst. 1978. Cons. Psychother. Cassel Hosp. Richmond.; Dir. Cassell Hosp. Socs: MRCPsych.

HEALY, Marie Patricia National Blood Service, Midlands & South-West Zone, Southmead Road, Bristol BS10 5ND — MB ChB St. And. 1970; DObst RCOG 1973. Staff Grade Phys. (Code 480) Nat. Blood Serv. Bristol.

HEALY, Marie Therese Anaethetic Department, Royal London Hospital, Whitechapel Rd, London E1 1BB Tel: 020 7377 7793 — MB BCh BAO 1982 NUI; MRCPI 1986; FFA RCSI 1988. Cons. Anaesth. & Intens. Care Roy. Lond. Hosp.

HEALY, Maura Rosaleen Wilfrid Sheldon Centre, St Giles Rd, Camberwell, London SE5 7RN Tel: 020 7771 3456 Fax: 020 7771 3410 Email: ros.healy@chsltr.sthames.nhs.uk — MB BCh BAO 1985 (BA) Dub.; MRCPCH (UK) 1996; M. Sc (London)1998; MRCP (UK) 1991; DCH NUI 1987. (Dublin) Cons. Paed. (Comm. Child Health) Comm. Health, S. Lond. Prev: Sen. Regist. (Community Paediat.) S. Downs Health NHS Trust & Lambeth Healthcare NHS Trust; Lect. & Sen. Regist. (Community Paediat.) King's Coll. Sch. Med. & Dent. Lond.

HEALY, Maurice James Elms Farm, Stambourne Road, Toppesfield, Halstead CO9 4NB Tel: 01787 238510 Fax: 01787 238459 Email: timmacie99@hotmail.com — MB BS Lond. 1955; MRCGP 1965; DObst RCOG 1957. (St. Mary's) Socs: Cases Comm.; BMA; RSM. Prev: Ho. Off. (Gyn. & Obst.) St. Mary's Hosp. Lond. W2; Ho. Phys. St. John & St. Eliz. Hosp. Lond.; Jun. Specialist (O & G) Brit. Milit. Hosp. Hong Kong.

HEALY, Michael Denis 1 Woodchester, Hagley, Stourbridge DY9 0NF — MB BCh BAO 1986 NUI; MB BCh NUI 1986; LRCPSI 1986.

HEALY, Michael John Waterside Health Centre, Glendermolt Road, Londonderry BT47 6AU Tel: 028 7132 0100; 49 Trench Road, Londonderry BT47 3UD — MB BCh BAO 1984 Belf.; MB BCh BAO Belf. l984; MRCGP 1989; Dip. Palliat. Med. Wales 1993; DGM RCP Lond. 1985. (Qu. Univ. Belf.)

HEALY, Peter Michael (retired) 90 Coventry St, Southam, Leamington Spa CV47 0EA Tel: 01926 812662 — MB BS 1950 Lond.; LLM 1994 Cardiff; MA Keele 1991; FRCGP 1981, M 1966; MICGP 1986; DObst RCOG 1951. Hon. Tutor Dept. of Biomed. Sci. & Biomed. Ethics, Univ. Birm. Med Sch. Prev: Squadron Ldr. RAF Med. Br.

HEALY, Rosemarie Dukes Avenue Surgery, 1 Dukes Avenue, London N10 2PS Tel: 020 8883 9149 — MB BS 1978 Lond.; BSc (Pharmacol.) Lond. 1975; MRCGP 1986; MRCPsych 1984.

HEALY, Professor Thomas Edward John Department of Anaesthesia, Manchester Royal Infirmary, Manchester M13 9WL Tel: 0161 276 8650 Fax: 0161 273 5685 — MB BS 1964 Lond.; BSc (1st cl. Hons.) Lond. 1962, MD 1975; MSc Manch. 1984; MRCS Eng. LRCP Lond. 1963; FRCA 1968; DA Eng. 1967; LLM (Cardiff) 1999. (Guy's) Prof. Anaesth. & Hon. Cons. Univ. Manch. Socs: Chairm. Professional Standards Comm. Roy. Coll. Anaesth.; Former Counc. Mem. . RCAnaesth.; Fell. Roy. Soc. Med. (Ex-Hon. Ex pres. Sec. & Edit. Represen. Sect. Anaesth.). Prev: Reader (Anaesth.) & Hon. Cons. Univ. Nottm.; Regist. (Anaesth.), Ho. Surg. & Ho. Phys. Guy's Hosp. Lond.; Sen. Regist. (Clin. Invest. & Research) Dudley Rd. Hosp. Birm.

HEALY, Timothy James George Well Lane Surgery, Well Lane, Stow on the Wold, Cheltenham GL54 1EQ Tel: 01451 830625 Fax: 01451 830693; Tel: 01451 830009 — MB ChB 1976 Leeds; BSc (Hons.) Lond. 1973; MRCGP 1985; DRCOG 1980. Clin. Asst. (Gastroenterol. & Elderly Care Glos.

HEALY, Timothy John Southern Road Surgery, 26 Southern Road, East Finchley, London N2 9JG Tel: 020 8444 7478; 4 Abbots Gardens, E. Finchley, London N2 0JQ — MB BS 1971 Lond. (Roy. Free) Clin. Asst. (Venereol.) Roy. N. Hosp. Lond.; Cas. Off. Finchley Memor. Hosp.; Capt. RAMC (TVR). Socs: BMA. Prev: Ho. Phys. (Cardiol. & Gen. Med.) Roy. Free Hosp. Lond.; Ho. Surg. (Gen. Surg. & Orthop.) St. Stephen's Hosp. Lond.

HEAMES, Richard Mark, Surg. Lt.-Cdr. RN Department of Anaesthetics, Poole Hopsital NHS Trust, Longfleet Road, Poole BH15 2JB Email: rheames@globalnet.co.uk — BM 1993 Soton.;

2001 FRCA, Royal College Anaesthetists. (Southampton) Specialist Regist., Anaesthetics, Poole Gen. Hosp.. Socs: Train. Mem. Assn. AnE.h.; Soc. of Naval Anaesth.; Train. Mem RCA- Fell. Mem. RCA. Prev: SHO (Anaesth.), Portsmouth Hosps.; SHO (Anaesth.) Roy. Hosp. Haslar; SPR (Anaesth) Portsmouth Hosp.

***HEANEY, Anthony Patrick** 633 Antrim Road, Belfast BT15 4DY — MB BCh BAO 1987 Belf.; BSc (Hons.) Belf. 1985; MD Belf. 1995; MRCP (UK) 1991.

HEANEY, April Elizabeth 265 Newtownards Road, Bangor BT19 7PE — MB BCh BAO 1990 Belf.; MD Belf. 1997; MRCP Glas. 1994; DGM Glas. 1992. Specialist Regist. (Geriat. Med.) Ulster Hosp. Dundonald N. Irel. Socs: Brit. Geriat. Soc.; Roy. Coll. Lond.; Irish Gerontol. Soc. Prev: Research Fell. (Med.) Roy. Vict. Hosp. Belf.; SHO (Geriat. Med.) Belf. City Hosp.

HEANEY, Dominic Connell 365 Kettering Road, Northampton NN3 6QT Email: dheaney@ion.ucl.ac.uk — BM BCh 1993 Oxf.; MA, BM BCh Oxf. 1993; MRCP (UK) 1996. Research Fell. Epilepsy Research Gp. Nat. Hosp. for Neurol. & Neurosurg. Lond. Prev: SHO (Med.) Glas. W.. Infirm.

HEANEY, George Adair Hazelton (retired) 23A Wylde Green Road, Sutton Coldfield B72 1HD Tel: 0121 354 9972 — MB BCh BAO 1959 Belf.; FFA RCSI 1969; DA RCPSI 1968; DObst RCOG 1961; LMCC 1963. Prev: Cons. Anaesth. N. Birm. Gp. Hosps.

HEANEY, Gregory Laurence Limavady Health Centre, Scroggy Road, Limavady BT49 0NA Tel: 028 7776 6641 — MB BCh BAO 1975 Belf.; DRCOG 1977. Princip. Gen. Pract. Limavady.

HEANEY, Helen Antoinette 2 Dallan Road, Warrenpoint, Newry BT34 3PJ — MB BCh BAO 1994 Belf.

HEANEY, Henry Maurice (retired) 38 Poplar Court, King's Road, St Annes-on-Sea, Lytham St Annes FY8 1NZ Tel: 01253 722818 — MB BCh BAO 1943 NUI.

HEANEY, Liam Gabriel 16 Harberton Park, Balmoral, Belfast BT9 6TS — MB BCh BAO 1988 Belf.; MB BCh Belf. 1988; MD Belf. 1995; MRCP (UK) 1991.

HEANEY, Peter Connell Abington Park Surgery, Christchurch Medical Centre, Ardington Road, Northampton NN1 5LT Tel: 01604 630291 Fax: 01604 603524 — MB ChB 1967 Ed.; MRCGP 1987; Dip. Pract. Dermat. Wales 1991. (Ed.) Med. Adviser St. Francis' Childrs. Soc.; Med. Adviser N.ampton Town FC. Prev: VTS Trainer; SHO (Paediat. & O & G) N.ampton Gen.. Hosp.; Capt. RAMC, Garrison Med. Off. Dortmund.

HEANEY, Rebecca Irene 7 Craggyknowe, Washington NE37 1JY — MB ChB 1995 Manch.

HEANEY, Samuel John 37 Sinclair Drive, Largs KA30 9BL — MB ChB 1966 Glas. Site Med. Off. Scott. Nuclear Ltd. Hunterston Power Station W. Kilbride. Prev: GP Largs.

HEANLEY, Mr Charles Laurence, TD Studio Forge, Offham, Lewes BN7 3QD Tel: 01273 492947; St George Woodmancote, Brighton Road, Henfield BN5 9S Tel: 01273 492947 — MB BChir Camb. 1937; MA (Hons.) Camb. 1932; FRCS Eng. 1933; MRCP Lond. 1935; MRCS Eng. LRCP Lond. 1932. (Camb. & Roy. Lond. Hosp.) Hon. Emerit. Roy. Throat Nose Ear Hosp.; Hon. Emerit. Cons. Surg. Worthing Hosp. Socs: Brighton Med. Soc.; Hon Mem. Joseph Soc. Europ. Surg.; Hon. Mem. Brit. Soc. Plastic Surg. Prev: Cons. Surg. Lond. Hosp.; Cons. Plastic Surg. Qu. Vict. Hosp. E. Grinstead; Lt.-Col. RAMC, OC No. 3 Maxillofacial Surgic. Unit & Surgic. Div.

HEANLEY, Charles Peter Chieveley House, Little Coxwell, Faringdon SN7 7LW Tel: 01367 240017 Fax: 01367 240017 — MRCS Eng. LRCP Lond. 1961; MA Camb. 1964, BA 1958, MB BChir 1962. (Lond. Hosp.)

HEANLEY, Robert John Clews Farm, Clews Lane, Bisley, Woking GU24 9DY Tel: 01483 480066 — MB BChir 1972 Camb.; MB 1972 Camb.; MRCS Eng. LRCP Lond. 1971; DObst RCOG 1974. (St. Thos.) Prev: SHO (Med.) St. Peters' Hosp. Chertsey; Ho. Surg. (O & G) St. Thos. Hosp.; Ho. Surg. Lambeth Hosp.

HEAP, Alison Laura Leven Health Centre, Victoria Road, Leven KY8 4ET Tel: 01333 425656 Fax: 01333 422249 — MB ChB 1982 Dundee; MA (Hons.) St. And. 1974; DRCOG 1984. (Dundee) Prev: GP Tayside HB.

HEAP, Bevis Michael Manor House Medical Centre, Manor House, Mill Lane, Belton, Loughborough LE12 9UJ Tel: 01530 222368 Fax: 01530 224 2273; School Court, 99-101Main St, Stanton under Bardon, Markfield LE67 9TN — MB ChB 1981 Leic.; FRCGP 1995, M 1985; DRCOG 1986; Cert. Family Plann. JCC 1985. (Leic.) Socs: W Leic. Med. Soc.

HEAP, Bryan Jefferson Eastbourne & County Healthcare, Headquarters, Bowhill, The Drive, Hellingly, Hailsham BN27 4EP Tel: 01323 440022 Fax: 01323 842868 — MB BChir 1976 Camb.; MA Camb. 1977; MRCP (UK) 1982; DTM & H RCP Lond. 1985. Med. Dir. E.bourne & Co. Healthcare Trust. Prev: Cons. Communicable Dis. Control St. And. Hosp. Norwich; Hon. Lect. (Med.) Kenyatta Nat. Hosp. Nairobi, Kenya; Cons. Phys. BMH, Hong Kong & BMH Dharan, Nepal.

HEAP, Derek Clifford (retired) Marsic Mary Cottage, 269 Turleigh, Bradford-on-Avon BA15 2HF Tel: 01225 862002 — MB BChir 1955 Camb.; MA Camb. 1955; FFOM RCP Lond. 1986, M 1982; MRCGP 1968; DIH Eng. 1979; DObst RCOG 1959. Prev: Govt. Med. Off. Fed. Rhodesian Govt.

HEAP, Douglas Graham 30 Dunvan Close, Lewes BN7 2EY — MB ChB 1974 Manch.; FRCA 1980. Prev: Cons AnE.hetist, Geo. Eliot Hosp. Nuneaton.

HEAP, Emma Louise Flat 6, 19 Mercer St., London WC2H 9QR — MB BS 1991 Lond.; BSc (Hons.) Lond. 1988, MB BS 1991. SHO (Psychiat.) Camb. Univ. Teach Hosps.

HEAP, Kenneth Ingham (retired) 4 Keld Close, Pickering YO18 8NJ — MB ChB 1940 Leeds.

HEAP, Michael Jennings Department of Anaesthesia, Northern General Hospital, Herries Road, Sheffield S5 7AU Tel: 0114 243 4343; 62 Bushey Wood Road, Dore, Sheffield S17 3QB Tel: 0114 262 0131 — MB BS 1980 Lond.; MRCP (UK) 1986; FRCA 1991. Cons. Anaesth. N. Gen. Hosp. Sheff. Prev: Sen. Regist. (Anaesth.) N.. Gen. Hosp. Sheff.; Regist. (Anaesth.) Camb. & Norwich HA; SHO (Anaesth.) Camb. HA.

HEAP, Rachel 41 Tavistock Road, West Jesmond, Newcastle upon Tyne NE2 3HY — MB BS 1997 Newc.

HEAP, Ronald Eustace (retired) 91 Loughborough Road, Kirkcaldy KY1 3DD — LRCP LRCS Ed. LRFPS Glas. 1943. Prev: GP Fife.

HEAPPEY, Melvyn Hollybrook Medical Centre, Hollybrook Way, Heatherton Village, Derby DE23 7TU Tel: 01332 523300 — MB ChB 1986 Manch. Ho. Phys. Macclesfield Dist. Gen. Hosp. Prev: Ho. Surg. Macclesfield Dist. Gen. Hosp.

HEAPS, Edward Lionel (retired) 7 Arlington Court, Kenton Avenue, Newcastle upon Tyne NE3 4JR — MB ChB Leeds 1941.

HEAR, Gurdip Singh Crosby House Surgery, 91 Stoke Poges Lane, Slough SL1 3NY Tel: 01753 520680 Fax: 01753 552780; 118 Hammond Road, Southall UB2 4EH Tel: 020 8843 0864 — MB ChB 1992 Manch.; BSc (Hons.) Med. Biochem. Manch. 1989; MRCGP 1996; DFFP 1996; DCH RCP Lond. 1995; DRCOG 1995. Socs: BMA; MDU. Prev: GP/Regist. Wembley; Trainee GP/SHO Centr. Middlx. Hosp.

HEARD, Andrew Michael Bryan 135 Nursery Road, Sunderland SR3 1NU — MB ChB 1994 Dundee.

HEARD, Christopher Robert Lister House, 11-12 Wimpole St., London W1M 7AB Tel: 020 7436 2135; 17 Chatsworth Court, Pembroke Road, London W8 6DG — MB BS 1980 Lond. Indep. Pract. (Allergy & Nutrit. Med.) Lond. Socs: BMA; Brit. Soc. Allergy & Environm. Med.; Fell. RSM. Prev: Asst. Med. Dir. (Allergy & Environm. Med.) Breakspear Hosp. Hemel Hempstead; Regist. (Med.) Roy. Masonic Hosp.

HEARD, Dorothy Helen 19 The Green, Richmond DL10 4RG Tel: 01748 823262 — MB BS Lond. 1942; PhD Camb. 1953; FRCP Lond. 1976, M 1944; MRCS Eng. LRCP Lond. 1941; FRCPsych 1974, M 1971. (Roy. Free) Hon. Lect. & Cons. Dept. Psychiat. Univ. Leeds; Hon. Research Fell. (Psychol.) Univ. Leeds. Prev: Cons. Psychiat. Dept. Parents & Childr. Tavistock Clinic Lond.; Cons. Psychothe Addenbrooke's Hosp. Camb.; Fell. Dir. Studies in Med., & Lect. Path. & Physiol. Girton Coll.

HEARD, Mr Gordon Edyvean (retired) Woodcote, The Paddock, Penylan, Cardiff CF23 5JN Tel: 029 2048 3722 Fax: 029 2048 9504 Email: heardge@aol.com — MB BCh Wales 1949; BSc Wales 1946, MCh (Distinc.) 1960; FRCS Eng. 1954. Hon. Cons. Surg. Univ. Hosp. Wales Cardiff. Prev: Chairm. Ct. Examrs. RCS Eng.

HEARD, Jean The Laurels, 29 Camden Road, Brecon LD3 7RT — MRCS Eng. LRCP Lond. 1973; BSc Lond. 1964; MFFP 1993; DCH RCP Lond. 1975. SCMO (Family Plann. & Well Wom.) Powys Healthcare Trust.

HEARD, John Henry (retired) Sollien, Bradford Road, Sherborne DT9 6BP Tel: 01935 812366 — MB BS 1952 Lond.; DObst RCOG 1954. Prev: Cas. Off. & Ho. Phys. St. Thos. Hosp.

HEARD, Mr Michael John Department of Obstetrics and Gynaecology, Royal Hampshire County Hospital, Romsley Road, Winchester SO22 5DG Tel: 01962 863535 Fax: 01962 824228 Email: michael.heard@weht.swest.nhs.uk — MB BS 1980 Lond.; MRCP (UK) 1984; FRCOG 1999. (St. Thos.) Cons. Roy. Hants. Co. Hosp. Winchester. Prev: Sen. Regist. Univ. Coll. & Middlx. Hosp. Lond.; Regist. (O & G) St. Mary's Hosp. Lond.; SHO (Gyn.) Chelsea Hosp. for Wom. Lond.

HEARD, Robert Nigel Stewart 204 Banstead Road, Banstead SM7 1QG Tel: 020 8394 1401 — MB BS 1981 Lond.; BSc (Hons.) Lond. 1978, MB BS 1981; MRCP (UK) 1984. (Guy's) Regist. (Neurol.) Guy's Hosp. Lond. Prev: Research Regist. Roy. Postgrad. Med. Sch. Lond.; SHO Nat. Hosp. Nerv. Dis. Lond.; Ho. Phys. Guy's Hosp. Lond.

HEARD, Shelley Ray Postgraduate Medical Education, London Deanery, 20 Guilford Street, London WC1N 1DZ Tel: 020 7692 3396 Email: sheard@londondeanery.ac.uk — MB BS 1981 Lond.; PhD Lond. 1974, MSc 1971, BSc 1978; BA Wisconsin 1970; MSc Med. Microbiol. Lond. 1986; MHM 1993. (St. Bart.) Dean for PostGrad. Med., Univ. of Lond.; Hon. Cons. Med. MicroBiol. Socs: MRCPath.; Fell. of the Roy. Coll. of Pathologists (FRCPath). Prev: Sen. Regist. Hosp. Sick Childr. Gt. Ormond St. Lond.; Sen. Lect. & Hon. Cons. (Med. Microbiol.) St. Bart. Hosp. Med. Sch. Lond.; Cons. Microbiologist, Homerton Hosp., Lond.

HEARD, Wendy Elizabeth Swanage Medical Practice, Station Approach, Swanage BH19 1HB Tel: 01929 422231; 26 Moor Road, Swanage BH19 1RG Tel: 01929 422791 — BM 1989 Soton.; MRCGP 1996; DCH RCP Lond. 1994. Prev: SHO (O & G, Paediat. & c/o the Elderly) Poole NHS Trust.

HEARDMAN, Martin James West Road Surgery, 170 West Road, Fenham, Newcastle upon Tyne NE4 9QB Tel: 0191 273 6364; 7 The Poplars, Gosforth, Newcastle upon Tyne NE3 4AE Tel: 0191 213 5014 Fax: 0191 213 5014 Email: martin@jheardman.freeserve.co.uk — MB ChB 1987 Glas.; MRCGP 1992.

HEARING, Stephen David University Division of Medicine Level 5, Old Building, Bristol Royal infirmary, Bristol BS2 8HW Tel: 0117 923 0000 — MB BS 1990 Newc.; MRCP (UK) 1993. Lect. Gastroent. Med. Univ. Bristol. Prev: SHO Wythenshawe Hosp. Manch.; Specialist Regist. (Gen. Med.) SW RHA.

HEARMON, Christine Jane Harbinson House Surgery, Front Street, Sedgefield, Stockton-on-Tees TS21 3BN Tel: 01740 620300 Fax: 01740 622075 — MB BS 1985 Newc.; MRCGP 1989; DRCOG 1989. Prev: Trainee GP Cleveland VTS; SHO (Community Paediat.) Bishop Auckland.

HEARN, Mr Alan Raymond Royal Preston Hospital, Sharoe Green Lane, Fulwood, Preston PR2 9HT Tel: 01772 710372; 11 Moor Park Avenue, Preston PR1 6AS Tel: 01772 251507 Fax: 01772 558761 — MB ChB 1971 Bristol; MD Bristol, 1979; FRCS Eng. 1975. Cons. Gen. Surg. Roy. Preston Hosp.; Clin. Director of Surg., Preston Acute Hosp.s Trust. Socs: Assn. Coloproctol.; Assn. Surg. Prev: Sen. Regist. (Gen. Surg.) N. W.. RHA; Tutor (Surg.) Univ. Hosp. S. Manch.

HEARN, Andrea Jane 9 Windsor Terrace, South Gosforth, Newcastle upon Tyne NE3 1YL Tel: 0191 284 3221 — MB BS 1994 Newc.; BSc (Hons) Newc. 1984; PhD Newc. 1989; MRCPsych. SpR in Rehabil. Psychiat.

HEARN, Charles Edward Daniel (retired) Sapley Barn, Overton, Basingstoke RG25 3DN Tel: 01256 770692 — MB BS Lond. 1948; MD Lond. 1968; MRCS Eng. LRCP Lond. 1948; MFOM RCP Lond. 1978; MFCM 1974; DIH Eng. 1967. Prev: Cons. Med. Adviser Gillette UK Ltd.

HEARN, David Lloyd Camberley Health Centre, 159 Frimley Road, Camberley GU15 2QA Tel: 01276 20101 Fax: 01276 21661; The Hollies, 72 Frogmore Road, Frogmore, Camberley GU17 0DF Tel: 01276 20101 Email: davidhearn@compuserve.com — MB ChB 1980 Liverp.; MRCGP 1984; DRCOG 1984. Socs: BASM.

HEARN, Fiona Jane Frimley Park Hospital NHS Trust, Portsmouth Road, Frimley, Camberley GU16 7UJ Tel: 01276 604498 Fax: 01276 604546; Weir House, Hampton Court Road, Hampton Court, East Molesey KT8 9BP Tel: 020 8979 4873 Email: fiona@weirhouse.co.uk — MB BS 1979 Lond.; BSc (Biochem.) Lond. 1976; FRCR 1985. Cons. Radiol. Frimley Pk. Hosp. Camberley. Prev: Sen. Regist. (Radiol.) King's Coll. Hosp. Lond.

HEARN, Geraldine May Burnside Surgery, 365 Blackburn Road, Bolton BL1 8DZ Tel: 01204 528205 Fax: 01204 386409; 42 Albert Road W., Bolton BL1 5HG Tel: 01204 842282 — MB BChir 1968 Camb.; MA Camb. 1968.

HEARN, Hilary Jean Dr Nugent and Partners, 243 Abbey Road, Barrow-in-Furness LA14 5JY Tel: 01229 821599 — MB ChB 1977 Ed. GP Barrow-in-Furness. Prev: SHO (O & G) St. Mary's Hosp. Newport I. of Wight; Ho. Off. (Surg.) S.land's Hosp. Shoreham-by-Sea & Worthing Hosp.

HEARN, John Stephen Mill Bank Surgery, Water Street, Stafford ST16 2AG Tel: 01785 258348 Fax: 01785 227144 — MB BS 1988 Lond.; MRCS Eng. LRCP Lond. 1987.

HEARN, Kenneth Charles Royal Bolton Hospital, Minerva Road, Farnworth, Bolton BL4 0JR Tel: 01204 390351 — MB ChB 1965 Birm.; FRCP Lond. 1995; MRCP (UK) 1969. Cons. Phys. Roy. Bolton Hosp. Socs: Brit. Cardiac Soc. Prev: Lect. (Cardiol.) Univ. Manch.

HEARN, Kim Pauline Montpelier Health Centre, Bath Buildings, Bristol BS6 5PT Tel: 0117 942 6811 Fax: 0117 944 4182 — MB ChB 1980 Bristol; MRCGP 1984. (Bristol) Course Organiser Bristol Univ. VTS; Project Dir. Dept. Primary Care Univ. Bristol (primary healthcare reform Kazakstan).

HEARN, Melanie Torbay Hospital, Lawes Bridge, Torquay TQ2 7AA Tel: 01626 821851 Fax: 01803 614567; Valley Farm, West Ogwell, Newton Abbot TQ12 6EL Tel: 01626 52397 — MB BS 1982 Lond.; MRCP (UK) 1988; FFA RCS 1987; DA (UK) 1985. Cons. Anaesth., Torbay Hosp. Prev: Sen. Regist. (Anaesth.) S. W.. RHA.

HEARNDEN, Anthony John The Priors, Bishops Caundle, Sherborne DT9 5NE — MB BS 1995 Lond.

HEARNE, Maurice Joseph Patrick (retired) 4 Red Hill, Moor Court, Whitburn, Sunderland SR6 7JX Tel: 0191 529 3054 — MB BCh BAO 1948 NUI.

HEARNE, Michael James 34 Grenfell Road, Hereford HR1 2QR — MB BCh 1995 Wales.

HEARNS, Mr Stephen Thomas 56 Barns Street, Clydebank G81 1QY — MB ChB 1993 Glas.; FRCS Ed. 1998; Dip Immediate Medical Care Edin 1998 (DipIMCRCSED). Specialist Regist. W.ern Infirm. Dumbarton Rd. Glas.

HEARNSHAW, Cathryne Anne Sisson Glenlea Surgery, 703 Leeds Bradford Road, Stanningly, Leeds LS13 3HQ Tel: 0113 257 0313 — MB ChB 1984 Leeds; MB ChB Leeds l984; MRCGP 1988; DRCOG 1987.

HEARNSHAW, Dawn Rachelle Violet Locum GP — MB BCh BAO 1992 Belf.; DMH Belf. 1995; DRCOG 1994; DFP 1997. GP Locum. Prev: GP/Regist. Castlerock Rd. Health Centre Coleraine; SHO (Paediat. & Gen. Med.) Coleraine Hosp.; SHO (Psychiat.) Ross Thompson Unit Ballymoney.

HEARNSHAW, John Robert (retired) Main Street, East Langton, Market Harborough LE16 7TW — MB BS Lond. 1958; BSc Lond. 1955; FRCP 1976, M 1961. Prev: Ho. Phys., Resid. Med. Off. & Sen. Med. Regist. Middlx. Hosp. Lond.

HEARSEY, Julie Anne 3 Bracken Cottages, Calthwaite, Penrith CA11 9QS — MB ChB 1994 Leeds; DRCOG 1996; MRCGP 1998.

HEARTH, Matthew William 52 Suckling Green Lane, Codsall, Wolverhampton WV8 2BT — MB BS 1993 Lond.

HEARTY, Roisin Theresa 12 Fortfield, Dromore BT25 1DD — MB BCh BAO 1992 Belf.; MB BCh Belf. 1992.

HEASLEY, Richard Noel 1 Ballyhannon Grove, Portadown, Craigavon BT63 5SD Tel: 01762 337271 — MD 1984 Belf.; MB BCh BAO 1974; FRCOG 1993, M 1980. p/t Cons. O & G Craigavon Area Hosp. Prev: Sen. Lect. (O & G) Qu. Univ. Belf.

HEATH, Mr Alan Laurie Tel: 01553 692333 Fax: 01533 692555; 13 Valingers Road, King's Lynn PE30 5HD Tel: 01553 771504 — BM BCh 1970 Oxf.; MA Oxf. 1970; FRCS Eng. 1977; MRCGP 1984; DObst RCOG 1972. (Oxf.) Police Surg. King's Lynn; Clin. Asst. Gen. Surg. Prev: Research Regist. (Paediat. Surg.) Gt. Ormond Hosp. Sick Childr. Lond.; Regist. (Paediat. Surg.) Qu. Mary's Hosp. Childr. Carshalton; Lect. Surg. Unit Lond. Hosp.

HEATH, Andrena Claire 7 Oldicote Lane, Bretby, Burton-on-Trent DE15 0QH — MB ChB 1993 Liverp.

HEATH, Anne (retired) 62 Paddenswick Road, London W6 0UB Tel: 020 8743 0854 — MB BS 1955 Lond.; DCH Eng. 1958; DObst RCOG 1957.

HEATH, Mr Anthony David (retired) Southend Hospital, Prittlewell Chase, Westcliff on Sea SS0 0RY Tel: 01702 435555 — MB BS 1962 Lond.; FRCS Eng. 1968; FRCS Ed. 1967; MRCS Eng. LRCP Lond. 1962. Prev: Cons. Surg. S.end & Rochford Hosps.

HEATH, Caroline Marie Dept. of Primary Care & General Practise, The Medical School, University of Birmingham, Birmingham B15 2TT Tel: 0121 414 3354 Email: c.m.health@bham.ac.uk — MB ChB 1988 Birm.; MRCGR RCGP, 1996; DRCOG RCOG 1996. Clin. Research Fell., Dept. of Primary Care & Gen. Pract., Univ. of Birm.

HEATH, Catherine Mary Cookridge Hospital, Hospital Lane, Leeds LS16 6QB — MB ChB 1992 Sheff.; MB ChB (Hons.) Sheff. 1992; MRCP (UK) 1995; FRCR 1999. (Sheff) Regist. (Clin. Oncol.) Cookridge Hosp. Leeds.

HEATH, Cherry Diana (retired) 53 Canonbury Park S., London N1 2JL Tel: 020 7226 7734 — MB BS 1948 Lond.; MD Lond. 1952; MRCP Lond. 1954; MRCS Eng. LRCP Lond. 1948. Prev: Hon. Cons. Paediat. St. Thos. Hosp. Lond.

HEATH, Christopher David St Johns Surgery, 5 Kidderminster Road, Bromsgrove B61 7JJ Tel: 01527 871706 Fax: 01527 576022; North Barn, Monsieurs Hall Lane, Dodford, Bromsgrove B61 9AQ Tel: 01527 878653 — MB ChB 1982 Manch.; MRCGP 1988; DCH RCP Lond. 1988; Cert. Family Plann. JCC 1987; DRCOG 1987. Police Surg. W. Mercia Police B Div.; Mem. Advis. Comm. on Resource Allocation. Prev: SHO Regional Cardiothoracic Med. Unit Wythenshawe Hosp. Manch.

HEATH, Christopher James Holbrook Surgery, Bartholomew Way, Horsham RH12 5OL Tel: 01403 755901 Fax: 01403 755909 — MB BS 1975 Lond.; FRCP 2001; MRCP (UK) 1980; MSOM Lond. 1996; MRCGP 1989. (Middlx. Hosp. Lond.) GP; Occupat. Health Phys. Novartis. Prev: Occupat. Health Phys. Evans Med.; Lect. (Paediat.) Camb. Univ.; Regist. (Paediat.) St. Mary's Hosp. Portsmouth.

HEATH, Clare Penelope Margaret 1 Killyon Road, London SW8 2XS — MB BS 1983 Lond.; MA, MB BS Lond. 1983. Trainee GP Lond. VTS.

HEATH, Craig William 24 Harton Way, Birmingham B14 6PF — MB ChB 1993 Leic.

HEATH, David Arthur Univ Hosp Birm NHS Trust, Selly Oak Hospital, Raddlesbarn Road, Birmingham B29 6JD Tel: 0121 627 8287 Fax: 0121 627 8245 Email: david-b.wmids.nhs.uk; 11 Exmoor Court, Exmoor Drive, Bromsgrove B61 0TW Tel: 01527 577720 — MB ChB 1964 Birm.; FRCP Lond. 1979, M 1969. (Birm.) Cons. Phys., Selly Oak Hosp. Socs: Fell. Roy. Soc. Med.; Assn. Phys. Prev: Vis. Assoc. Nat. Inst. Health Bethesda, USA; Lect. & Sen. Lect. (Med.) Univ. Birm.

HEATH, Mr David Vincent Dryburn Hospital, North Road, Durham DH15 5TW Tel: 0191 333 2208 — MB BS 1965 Lond.; FRCS Eng. 1972; FRCS Ed. 1971. (Middlx.) Cons. Surg. (Orthop.) Dryburn Hosp. Prev: Cons. Surg. (Orthop.) W. Cumbld. Hosp.; Sen. Regist. (Orthop.) Leeds Gen. Infirm., St. Jas. Hosp. Leeds; Regist. & Sen. Regist. (Orthop.) Bradford Hosps.

HEATH, Dudley Fairman, VRD Glenberrow, Hollybush, Ledbury HR8 1EX Tel: 01531 650239 — MRCS Eng. LRCP Lond. 1934. (Birm. & Durh.) Socs: Fell. BMA. Prev: Ho. Surg. & Special Ho. Surg. Gen. Hosp. Birm.; Surg. Cdr. RNVR.

HEATH, Mr Dugal Ian West Middlesex University Hospital, Twickenham Road, Isleworth TW7 6AF; 107 Ullswater Crescent, Kingston Vale, London SW15 3RE Tel: 020 8549 2941 Email: dugalheath@compuserve.com — MB ChB 1982 Leic.; MD Leic. 1993; FRCS Eng 1987; FRCS Ed. 1986; FCS Hong Kong 1996; FRCS Pt. III 1996. (Leic.) Sen. Lect. Chas. Gairdener Hosp. Perth, W.ern Australia. Prev: Sen. Regist. NW Thames; Lect. (Surg.) Chinese Univ., Hong Kong.

HEATH, Edith (retired) The Cottage, Leybourn Road, Broadstairs CT10 1TE Tel: 01843 861618 Fax: 01843 862949 Email: rbheath@lineone.net — MB ChB 1954 Sheff.; MEd. (Audiol.) Manch. 1979.

HEATH, Emma Inneen 34 Arbery Road, London E3 5DD — MB BS 1994 Lond.; BSc Lond. 1988; MRCP (UK) 1997. (UCLMSM) Specialist Regist. Clin. Oncol. Bristol &Oncol.Centre. Socs: MBA; Med. Protec. Soc. Prev: Ho. Off. Whittington Hosp. Lond. & Basildon Hosp.

HEATH, Gabrielle Snowsfield, Stanhope in Weardale, Bishop Auckland DL13 2LN — MB ChB 1967 Birm.; DMRD Eng. 1973. Cons. Radiol. Darlington Mem. Hosp. Prev: Cons. Radiol. Bishop Aukland Gen. Hosp.

HEATH, Ian Douglas, TD (retired) 107 Ullswater Crescent, Kingston Vale, London SW15 3RE Tel: 020 8549 2941 — MB ChB Ed. 1954; FRCP Lond. 1982; MRCP (UK) 1965. Indep. Pract. Elland. Prev: Cons. Phys. Calderdale HA.

HEATH, Iona Caroline Caversham Practice, 4 Peckwater Street, London NW5 2UP Tel: 020 7530 6500 Fax: 020 7530 6530 — MB 1975 Camb.; BChir 1974; MRCP (UK) 1977.

HEATH, James Dominic 2 Parkland Drive, St Albans AL3 4AH — MB BS 1987 Lond.; MRCP (UK) 1990.

HEATH, James George Bewley Drive Surgery, 79 Bewley Drive, Liverpool L32 9PD Tel: 0151 546 2480 Fax: 0151 548 3474 — MB ChB 1983 Liverp.

HEATH, Jason Anthony St Andrews Surgery, The Old Central School, Southover Road, Lewes BN7 1US Tel: 01273 476216 Fax: 01273 487587 — MB BS 1990 Lond.; BSc (Hons.) Lond. 1987; MRCGP (distinct.) 1995; DRCOG 1994. (St. Bart. Hosp. Med. Coll.) GP St. Andrews Surg. Lewes; Hosp. Practitioner (Endoscopy) Dept. Gen. Surg. Roy. Sussex Co. Hosp. Brighton. Socs: BMA; E. Sussex LMC. Prev: Trainee GP Brighton VTS; Ho. Phys. Roy. Sussex Co. Hosp.; Ho. Surg. Roy. Hants. Co. Hosp.

HEATH, Mr Jonathan Charles David Dept. Of General Surgery, Blackpool Victoria Hospital, Whinney Heys Road, Blackpool FY3 8NR Tel: 01253 300000, 01483 224993 — MB ChB 1990 Liverp.; FRCS Ed. 1995. Regist. (Gen. Surg.) NW RHA. Socs: Manch. Med. Soc.; Assn. ColoProctol. Of Gt. Brit. & N. Ire.; Assn Of Surg. Gt. Brit. & N. Ire.

HEATH, Lorna 122 Houstoun Gardens, Uphall, Broxburn EH52 5PX — MB ChB 1993 Ed.; MB ChB Ed 1993.

HEATH, Margaret Queensway Health Centre, 75 Queensway, Southend-on-Sea SS1 2AB Tel: 01702 463 3333 Fax: 01702 603026; 3 Drake Road, Westcliff on Sea SS0 8LP Tel: 01702 340004 — MB BS 1962 Lond.; MB BS (Hons. Surg.) Lond. 1962; BA (Hons.) Open 1997; MRCS Eng. LRCP Lond. 1962. (St. Bart.) GP Princip. S.end. Socs: BMA. Prev: Regist. (Path.) Epsom Dist. Hosp.; Cas. Off. St. Bart. Hosp. Lond.; Ho. Phys. S.end Hosp.

HEATH, Margaret Longden Anaesthetic Department, Lewisham Hospital, London SE13 6LH Tel: 020 8333 3030 Fax: 020 8333 3333; 5 Orchard Drive, Blackheath, London SE3 0QP Tel: 020 8852 4804 Fax: 020 8297 2228 — MB BS 1960 Lond.; MB BS (Hons.) Lond. 1960; MRCS Eng. LRCP Lond. 1960; FRCA Eng. 1965; DA Eng. 1963. (St. Mary's) Cons. Anaesth. Lewisham NHS Trust; Chairm. Brit. Standards Inst. Automatic Tourniquet Comm. Prev: Chairm. S. Thames (E.) Regional Higher Awards Comm.; Vice-Pres. Assn. Anaesth. GB & Irel.; Chairm. Lewisham Acute Unit Managem. Bd.

HEATH, Martin John The Surgery, School Hill House, High Street, Lewes BN7 2LU Tel: 01273 474194 Fax: 01273 486368 Email: martin.heath@gp-g81021.nhs.uk — MB ChB 1977 Ed.; MRCGP 1981; DCH RCPS Glas. 1982; DRCOG 1981. (Univ. Ed.) GP, Lewes; Clin. Asst. in Dermat. (S. Downs NHS Trust), Vict. Hosp., Lewes. Socs: BMA (Pub. Affairs Off. Brighton Div.); Anglo-French Med. Soc.; Chairm., Med. Staff Comm., Vict. Hosp., Lewes. Prev: Trainee GP Brighton VTS; SHO (Paediat.) P.ss Alex. Hosp. Harlow.

HEATH, Maureen Teresa Windlestraws, Southfields Road, Woldingham, Caterham CR3 7BG — MB BS 1984 Lond.; BDS 1975; LDS RCS Eng. 1975. Regist. (Oral & Maxillofacial Surg.) St. Geo. Hosp. Lond.

HEATH, Michael John Medical Legal Centre, 8 Church Street, Harleston IP20 9BB Tel: 07973 553815 — MB BS 1975 Lond.; MRCPath 1990; DMJ(Clin) Soc. Apoth. Lond. 1981; DMJ(Path) Soc. Apoth. Clin. 1981.

HEATH, Patricia Kathleen Celltech R&D Ltd, 208 Bath Road, Slough SL1 3WE Tel: 01753 777166 Fax: 01753 777170 Email: pheath@celtechgroup.com — MB ChB 1979 Sheff.; MRCP (UK) 1989; Dip. Pharm. Med. RCP (UK) 1993; DCH RCP Lond. 1986; MFPM 1997. (Sheff.) Dir. Of Clin. Devel. Celltech R&D Ltd Slough. Socs: Fac. Pharmaceut. Med.; FRSM. Prev: Clin. Pharmacol. Hoechst UK Ltd. Milton Keynes; Regist. (Paediat.) Wexham Pk. Hosp. & Childr. Hosp. Sheff.; Clin. Asst. Paediat. Wexham Pk. Hosp. Slough.

HEATH, Paul Scartho Medical Centre, 26 Waltham Road, Grimsby DN33 2QA Tel: 01472 871747 Fax: 01472 276050; 26 Waltham Road, Grimsby DN33 2QA Tel: 71747 — MB ChB 1981 Manch.; MRCGP 1985; DRCOG & DCH 1985.

HEATH, Paul Trafford Dept. Child Health, St George's Hospital Medical School, Cranmer Terrace, London SW17 0RE Tel: 020 8725 3262 Fax: 020 8725 3262 Email: pheath@sghms.ac.uk — MB BS 1985 Monash; MB BS (Hons.) Monash 1985. (Monash University) Sen. Lect. (Paediat. Infec. Dis.s & Immunol.) Dept Child Health, St Geo.'s Med. Sch., Lond.; Hon. Cons., St. Geo. Med. Sch. Prev: research fell., Dept. Paediat., John Radcliffe Hosp., Oxf.

HEATH, Peter Desmond Department of Clinical Neurophysiology, North Staffordshire Hospitals, Princes Rd, Hartshill, Stoke-on-Trent ST4 7LN Tel: 01782 554554 Fax: 01782 555315; Little Paddock, 6 Friars Walk, Westlands, Newcastle-under-Lyme ST5 2HA Tel: 01782 660721 Email: peter.d.heath@talk21.com — MB BS 1977 Lond.; DM Oxf. 1988; FRCP 1997; MRCP (UK) 1980; MRCS Eng. LRCP Lond. 1977. (St. Mary's) Cons. Clin. Neurophysiol. N. Staffs. Roy. Infirm. Stoke-on-Trent; Regional Speciality Adviser, Clin. NeuroPhysiol., W. Midl.s; Clin. NeuroPhysiol. Represen., Specialist Advisery Comm., Roy. Coll. of Phys.s. Socs: Brit. Soc. of Clin. NeuroPhysiol.

HEATH, Richard Mark 12 Marple Hall Drive, Marple, Stockport SK6 6JN — BM BS 1994 Nottm.

HEATH, Robert William The Family Practice, Western College, Cotham Road, Bristol BS6 6DF Tel: 0117 946 6455 Fax: 0117 946 6410 — MB ChB 1972 Bristol; BSc Aston 1967.

HEATH, Rosamund Mary Church View Surgery, 30 Holland Road, Plymstock, Plymouth PL9 9BW Tel: 01752 403206 — BSc Lond. 1979, MB BS 1982; MRCGP 1986; DRCOG 1987; DCH RCP Lond. 1985.

HEATH, Rowan Caroline Manse Cottage, Rhynd, Perth PH2 8QG Tel: 01738 638438 — MB ChB 1996 Ed.; BmedSci. (Hons.) Edinburgh 1993. (Edinburgh) SHO (Paediat.) Roy. Hosp. for Sick Childr., Edin. Prev: Sen. Paediat. Ho. Off. York Dist. Gen. Hosp. York.

HEATH, Simon Timothy Wexford House, Wyre Lane, Garstang, Preston PR3 1JL — MB BS 1992 Lond.

HEATH, Susan (retired) Sibford Surgery, Sibford Gower, Banbury OX15 5RQ Tel: 01295 780213 — MB BS 1973 Lond.

HEATH, Timothy Ormond Tel: 01787 475944 Fax: 01787 474506 — MB BS 1989 Lond.; BSc Exeter 1977; MRCGP 1993; DRCOG 1992.

HEATH, Victoria Camilla Fleur 21 Fawe Park Road, Putney, London SW15 2EB Tel: 020 8874 4956 — BM BCh 1993 Oxf.; MA Camb. 1994. Research Regist. King's Coll. Hosp. Lond. Prev: SHO (Gyn.) Qu. Charlotte's & Chelsea Hosp. Lond.; SHO (Obst. & neonatol.) UCH, Lond.; SHO (Osbt. & Gyn.) Radcliffe Hosp. Oxf.

HEATHCOCK, John Philip The Tolsey Surgery, High Street, Sherston, Malmesbury SN16 0LH Tel: 01666 840270 Fax: 01666 841074; The Garden House, Twatley, Easton Grey, Malmesbury SN16 0RB Tel: 01666 829344 — MB ChB 1973 Bristol; BSc (Hons. Biochem.) Bristol 1969; DObst RCOG 1976; Cert JCC Lond. 1977. Teach. (Gen. Pract.) Univ. Bristol; Mem. Wilts LMC; Forens. Med. Off. Wilts. Police; Racecourse Med. Off. Chepstow & Bath Racecourse. Socs: BMA & Dispensing Doctors Assn.; Fell. RSM. Prev: SHO Manor Hosp. Walsall; Ho. Off. Frenchay Hosp. Bristol.

HEATHCOCK, Rachel Mary Lambeth Southwark lewisham HA, 1 Lower marsh, London SE1 7NT — MB BS 1986 Lond.

HEATHCOTE, Ian Trevor Rochdale Road Surgery, 48A Rochdale Road, Middleton, Manchester M24 2PU Tel: 0161 643 9131 — MB ChB 1972 St. And.

HEATHCOTE, James Anthony 55 Penerley Road, Catford, London SE6 2LH; South View Lodge, South View, Bromley BR1 3DR Tel: 020 8460 1945 — MB BS 1981 Lond.; MRCGP 1985; DRCOG 1984; FRCGP 1998. (King's Coll. Hosp.)

HEATHCOTE, Jennifer Anne 35 Black Road, Macclesfield SK11 7BZ — MB BS 1985 Newc.; MFFP 1993. Clin. Med. Off. Family Plann. & Well Wom. Servs.

HEATHCOTE, John Anthony 35 Bushey Wood Road, Sheffield S17 3QA — MB ChB 1971 Bristol; DCH RCPS Glas. 1977; DTM & H Liverp. 1985.

HEATHCOTE, Patricia Rhoda Mary Central Health Clinic, 1 Mulberry St., Sheffield S1 2PJ Tel: 0114 271 6790; 247 Carter Knowle Road, Sheffield S11 9FW Tel: 0114 258 5369 — MB ChB 1962 Sheff.; MFFP 1993; MFPHM RCP (UK) 1989; DObst RCOG 1965. (Sheff.) SCMO (Community Health) Sheff. Prev: Research Asst. Pre-Menstrual Syndrome Clin. Roy. Hallamsh. Hosp. Sheff.

HEATHCOTE, William 113 Melton Road, West Bridgford, Nottingham NG2 6ET Tel: 0115 923 2646 — MB ChB 1953 Sheff. Prev: Sen. Ho. Phys. Monkmoor Childr. Hosp. Shrewsbury & Highbury Hosp.; Nottm.; Asst. Cas. Off. & Ho. Phys. Roy. Hosp. Sheff.

HEATHER, Mr Brian Peter Gloucestershire Royal Hospital, Great Western Road, Gloucester GL1 3NN Tel: 01452 394663 Fax: 01452 381925; Westhall, 7 Lansdown Parade, Cheltenham GL50 2LH Tel: 01242 512450 — MB BS 1971 Lond.; MS Lond. 1985, BSc (Hons. Biochem.) 1968; FRCS Eng. 1976; MRCS Eng. LRCP Lond. 1971. (Westm.) Cons. Surg. Gloucester Roy. Hosp. Socs: Vasc. Soc. GB & Irel.; Assn. Surg.; (Hon. Sec.) Surgic. Club SW Eng. Prev: Sen. Regist. (Surg.) Char. Cross Hosp. Lond.; Regist. (Surg.) S.end-on-Sea Hosp.; Lect. (Surg.) Char. Cross Hosp. Lond.

HEATHER, John Derek Northdown Surgery, 12 Poplar Road, Ramsgate CT11 9SL; 15 Magnolia Avenue, Cliftonville, Margate CT9 3DS Tel: 01843 230665 — MB BS 1981 Lond.; DFFP 1994; DRCOG 1993; DCH RCP Lond. 1992.

HEATHER, John Douglas Riverside Surgery, Le Molay Littry Way, Bovey Tacey, Newton Abbot TQ13 9QP Tel: 01626 832666; Loganstones, Lustleigh, Newton Abbot TQ13 9SQ — MB BS 1986 Lond.; BSc Lond. 1985; MRCGP 1990.

HEATHERINGTON, Jane Emma 51 Highpoint, Richmond Hill Road, Birmingham B15 3RX — BM BS 1993 Nottm.

HEATHFIELD, Kenneth William Gordon (retired) Lynwood, Steeds Way, York Hill, Loughton IG10 1HX Tel: 020 8508 6739 — MD Lond. 1943, MB BS 1940; FRCP Lond. 1968, M 1947; MRCS Eng. LRCP Lond. 1940. Prev: Hon. Cons. Neurol. The Lond. Hosp. & Whipps Cross Hosp. Lond.

HEATLEY, Catherine Joyanna 173 Choumert Road, London SE15 4AW — MB BS 1997 Lond.

HEATLEY, Charles Thomas Birley Health Centre, 120 Birley Lane, Sheffield S12 3BP Tel: 0114 239 2541 Fax: 0114 264 5814; 24 School Green Lane, Sheffield S10 4GQ Tel: 0114 230 7568 — MB ChB 1986 Glas.; BA Camb. 1983; MRCP (UK) 1989; MRCGP 1992; DRCOG 1991.

HEATLEY, Professor Frederick William Orthopaedic Unit, Rayne Institute, St Thomas's Hospital, London SE1 7EH Tel: 020 7633 0964; Shenandoah, Aviary Road, Pyford, Woking GU22 8TH Tel: 020 7633 0964 — MB BChir 1965 Camb.; FRCS Eng. 1969. (St. Thos.) Prof. Orthop. Surg. United Med. & Dent. Schs. Guy's & St. Thos. Hosp. Lond.; Hon. Cons. Trauma & Orthop. Surg. Guy's & St. Thos. Hosp. Lond. Prev: Sen. Regist. (Trauma & Orthop. Surg.) St. Thos. Hosp. Lond.; Demonst. (Anat.) Univ. Camb.

HEATLEY, Ian Hugh Kinson Road Surgery, 440 Kinson Road, Bournemouth BH10 5EY Tel: 01202 574604 Fax: 01202 590029 — MB ChB Dundee 1983; DRCOG 1987; Cert. Family Plann. JCC 1986. Clin. Tutor Soton. Med. Sch.; Apptd. Doctor (Lead at Work Regulats.) Health & Safety Exec.; Edit. Bd. Mem. Telemed Med. TV Ltd. Socs: BMA. Prev: GP Poole; Trainee GP/SHO (Gen. & Neonat. Paediat. & O & G) Arrowe Pk. Hosp. Wirral VTS.

HEATLEY, Jonathan Patrick Holbrook Surgery, Bartholomew Way, Horsham RH12 5JB Tel: 01403 755900 Fax: 01403 755909; Murrayfield, Gordon Road, Horsham RH12 2EF Tel: 01403 260937 Email: jheatley@bigfoot.com — MB BS 1980 Lond.; MA Camb. 1977; MRCGP 1984; Dip. Pract. Dermat. Wales 1991; DGM RCP Lond. 1986; DCH RCP Lond. 1984; DRCOG 1982; Cert. Family Plann. JCC 1982. (Royal London) Socs: MRCGP. Prev: Trainee GP Reading VTS; SHO (Phys. & Homoeopathy Surg.) Homeopathy Norwich.

HEATLEY, Katrina Anne St Albans Medical Centre, 26-28 St. Albans Crescent, Bournemouth BH8 9EW Tel: 01202 517333; Beechwood House, 17 Rowlands Hill, Wimborne BH21 2QQ Tel: 01202 889660 — MB ChB 1982 Dundee; Cert. Family Plann. JCC 1984. (Dundee) GP Princip. Prev: GP Pk.stone Dorset; GP Wallasey.

HEATLEY, Mark Keith Department of Pathology, Royal Liverpool University Hospital, 5th Floor, Duncan Building, Prescott St., Liverpool L7 8XP — MB BCh BAO 1984 Belf.; MB BCh Belf. I984; MD Belf. 1992; MRCPath 1991; FRCP 1998 (Path). Cons. Gynaecoloogical Pathologist, St James' Hosp. Leeds. Socs: Treas.

Brit. Assn. of Gynaecol. Pathol.; Brit. Gyn. Cancer Soc. (Counc.); Internat. Acad. Path. Prev: Cons. Gyn. Pathologist, Roy. Liverp. Hosp.; Cons. Cell. Path. Taunton & Som. NHS Trust; NICPME Trav. Schol. Geo. Washington Univ. Med. Sch.

HEATLEY, Martyn Kenneth 73 Elm Street, Rhydyfelin, Pontypridd CF37 5DG — MB BCh 1985 Wales.

HEATLEY, Mercy Irene The Hazels, 12 Oxford Road, Old Marston, Oxford OX3 0PQ Tel: 01865 248588 — BM BCh 1947 Oxf.; MRCPsych 1971; DPM Lond. 1951. Cons. Psychiat. Oxon. Child Guid. Clinic. Prev: Jun. Regist. Warneford Hosp. Oxf.; Ho. Phys. Littlemore Ment. Hosp.

HEATLEY, Pamela Jean (retired) 11 Rossett Beck, Harrogate HG2 9NT — MB ChB 1956 Leeds.

HEATLEY, Paul Trevor Bennetts End Surgery, Gatecroft, Hemel Hempstead HP3 9LY Tel: 01442 63511 Fax: 01442 235419; 1 The Chestnuts, Beechwood Park, Hemel Hempstead HP3 0DZ Tel: 01442 260026 Fax: 01442 262413 Email: paul.heatley@btinternet.com — MB BS 1977 Lond.; MRCGP 1982; DRCOG 1982. (St. Marys) Jt. Course Organiser NW Herts GP VTS Train. Scheme.; Co. Chair of Dacorum PCG Exec.

HEATLEY, Richard Val Department Medicine, St James's University Hospital, Leeds LS9 7TF Tel: 0113 243 3144 — MD 1978 Wales; MB BCh 1971 Wales; FRCP Lond. 1989; MRCP (UK) 1974. (Cardiff) Hon. Cons. Phys. St. Jas. Univ. Hosp. Leeds. Socs: Brit. Soc. Gastroenterol. & Brit. Soc. Immunol. Prev: Sen. Lect. (Med.) Welsh Nat. Sch. Med. Cardiff; Clin. Fell. (Med.) McMaster Univ. Hamilton, Canada; Regist. (Med.) Nottm. Gen. Hosp.

HEATLEY, William Archibald Greer 76 Ballygroobany Road, Richhill, Armagh BT61 9NA — LRCPI & LM, LRSCI & LM 1944; LRCPI & LM, LRCSI & LM 1944. (RCSI)

HEATON, Alexander Norfolk & Norwich Hospital, Brunswick Road, Norwich NR1 3SR Tel: 01603 287076; The Rookery, Swainsthorpe, Norwich NR14 8PU Tel: 01508 471532 — MB BS Newc. 1976; MD Newc. 1987; FRCP Lond. 1994; MRCP (UK) 1979. Cons. Phys. i/c Renal Med. Norf. & Norwich Univ. Hosp. Healthcare Trust; Hon.Sen. Lect. Univ. E. Anglia Sch. Biol. Sci.and Sch. of Health.

HEATON, Alison Janette 44 Graham Road, West Kirby, Wirral CH48 5DW — MB BS 1991 Newc.

HEATON, Andrew Bronyffynnon, Bridge St., Denbigh LL16 3TH — MB ChB 1986 Sheff.; MRCGP 1991; T(GP) 1991.

HEATON, Catherine Helen Bridge Street Practice, 21 Bridge Street, Driffield YO25 6DB Tel: 01377 253441 Fax: 01377 241962; 24 St. Giles Croft, Beverley HU17 8LA — BM BS 1987 Nottm.; BMedSci Nottm. 1985; MRCGP 1993; DRCOG 1990. (Nottingham) Socs: Humberside MAAG. Prev: Trainee GP Hull VTS.

HEATON, David Charles Old Town Surgery, 10 Bath Road, Old Town, Swindon SN1 4BA Tel: 01793 616065 — MB ChB 1985 Manch. Clin. Asst. Drug & Alcohol Advis. Serv. Swindon. Prev: Trainee GP/SHO (A & E & Geriat.) VTS.

HEATON, Mr George Michael Andrew Department of Accident and Emergency Medicine, Whittington Hospital, Highgate Hill, London N19 5NF Tel: 020 7288 5699 Fax: 020 7288 5038; Newlands, 25 Grove Park, Wanstead, London E11 2DN Tel: 020 8925 2089 — MB BS 1971 Lond.; BSc Lond. 1968; FRCS Ed. (A&E) 1982; FRCS Eng. 1976; MRCS Eng. LRCP Lond. 1971; FFAEM 1993. (Guy's Hosp.) Cons. A & E Whittington Hosp. Lond. Socs: Brit. Assn. Accid. & Emerg. Med. Prev: Sen. Regist. (A & E) Whipps Cross Hosp. Lond., Univ. Coll. Hosp. Lond. & St. Bart. Hosp. Lond.; Regist. (Neurosurg.) Walsgrave Hosp. Coventry; Lect. (Anat.) St. Bart. Hosp. Med. Coll. Lond.

HEATON, Graham David St Nicholas Surgery, Queen Street, Withernsea HU19 2PZ Tel: 01964 613221 Fax: 01964 613960; Westerlies, 49 Greenshaw Lane, Patrington, Hull HU12 0RL Tel: 01964 631427 — MB ChB 1983 Leeds.

HEATON, John Moorhouse Top Flat, 41 Buckland Crescent, Swiss Cottage, London NW3 5DJ Tel: 020 7722 7428 — MB BChir 1951 Camb.; MA Camb. 1951; DO Eng. 1953. (Univ. Coll. Hosp.) Socs: Brit. Psychol. Soc. & Roy. Coll. Psychiat. Prev: Research Asst. Inst. Ophth. Univ. Lond.; Tutor (Ophth.) Univ. Bristol; Ophth. Specialist RAF.

HEATON, Josephine Charlotte Field House, E. Tytherton, Chippenham SN15 4LT — MB BS 1984 Lond.

HEATON, Miss Judith Mary ENT Department, Sunderland Royal Hospital, Kayll Road, Sunderland SR4 7TP Tel: 0191 565 6256 — BM BCh 1984 Oxf.; FRCS (Orl.) Eng. 1990. Cons. (ENT) Sunderland Roy. Hosp. Prev: Sen. Regist. Rotat. (ENT) Roy. Hallamsh. Hosp.; Regist. (ENT) Ninewells Hosp. & Med. Sch. Dundee.

HEATON, Juliet Mary (retired) Department of Pathology, Bassetlaw District Hospital, Worksop S81 0BD Tel: 01909 500990 Fax: 01909 502642 — MB BCh BAO 1965 Dub.; MA, MD Dub. 1972; FRCPath 1986. Cons. Histopath. Bassetlaw Dist. Hosp. Worksop. Prev: Sen. Lect. & Hon. Cons. Inst. Urol. Lond.

HEATON, Karen West Pottergate Health Centre, Norwich NR2 4BX Tel: 01603 628705 Fax: 01603 766789 — MB BS 1979 Newc.; MRCGP 1983; DRCOG 1983.

HEATON, Kenneth Willoughby (retired) Claverham House, Streamcross, Claverham, Bristol BS49 4QD Tel: 01934 832208 — MB BChir 1960 Camb.; MD Camb. 1968; FRCP Lond. 1974, M 1963; DSc 2000 Bristol. Sen. Research Fell. Univ. Bristol. Prev: Reader (Med.) Univ. Bristol.

HEATON, Mr Martin James 64 Winnipeg Quay, Salford M5 2TY Email: mjheaton@btinternet.com — BM BS 1992 Nottm.; FRCS Eng. 1996. (Notts) Clin. Research.Fell.Plastic Surg.Univ.sheff.

HEATON, Natalie Rachel 2 The Crescent, Richmond DL10 7BA — MB ChB 1998 Ed.; MB ChB Ed 1998.

HEATON, Mr Nigel David 53 Oakwood Avenue, Beckenham BR3 6PT — MB BS 1978 Lond.; FRCS Eng. 1982. (King's Coll. Hosp.) Cons. Surg. Liver Transpl. Surgic. Serv. King's Coll. Hosp. Lond.; Hon. Sen. Lect. Socs: Fell. Roy. Soc. Med.; Eur. Soc. Organ Transpl.; Brit. Soc. Gastroenterol. Prev: Sen. Regist. (Gen. Surg.) King's Coll. Hosp. Lond.; Regist. (Surg. & Urol.) King's Coll. Hosp. Lond.

HEATON, Richard Walter The Royal Infirmary, Lindley, Huddersfield HD3 3EA Tel: 01484 422191; Naskaupi, 73 Magdale, Honley, Huddersfield HD9 6LU Tel: 01484 661846 — BM BCh 1976 Oxf.; MA Oxf. 1978, DM 1989; FRCP Lond. 1994; MRCP (UK) 1980. Cons. Phys. The Roy. Infirm. Lindley, Huddersfield. Prev: Regist.(Med.) Ipswich Health Dist.; Phys. N.. Med. Servs. Internat. Grenfell Assn. NW River, Labrador; Sen. Regist. Char. Cross Hosp. Lond.

HEATON, Steven Gary 8 Smethurst Road, Billinge, Wigan WN5 7DW — MB ChB 1982 Leeds. GP Wigan.

HEATON, William Ralph (retired) 15 Glenway, Bognor Regis PO22 8BU Tel: 01243 822824 — MB BChir Camb. 1959; BA Camb. 1952; DO Eng. 1968; DObst RCOG 1960; DA Eng. 1960. Med. Pract. (Ophth.) W. Sussex Family Health Servs. Auth. Prev: Med. Pract. (Ophth.) W. Sussex Family Health Servs. Auth.

HEATON, Winifred Muriel Worston House, Worston, Clitheroe BB7 1QA — MRCS Eng. LRCP Lond. 1942.

HEATON-RENSHAW, John Squire Southbroom Surgery, 15 Estcourt Street, Devizes SN10 1LQ Tel: 01380 720909; The Dye House, Dyehouse Lane, Devizes SN10 2DF Tel: 01380 722030 — MB BS 1980 Lond.; MA Camb. 1981; MRCGP 1984; DRCOG 1983. (Guy's) Prev: Trainee GP Qu. Mary's Hosp. Roehampton VTS; Ho. Phys. Roy. Hants. Co. Hosp. Winchester; Ho. Surg. St. Stephens Hosp. Fulham.

HEATON-WARD, William Alan (retired) Bala Netty, 27 Withey Close W., Westbury-on-Trym, Bristol BS9 3SX Tel: 0117 968 1940 — MB ChB Bristol 1944; FRCPsych 1971; DPM Bristol 1948. Hon. Cons. Psychiat. Frenchay Health Dist. Prev: Lord Chancellor's Med. Visitor.

HEAVEN, Wayne Glyn 1 Meadowside, Sedbergh Road, Kendal LA9 6AF — MB ChB 1982 Manch.; DCCH RCGP & FCM 1988; Cert. Family Plann. 1988; DRCOG 1984; T(GP) 1991.

HEAVENS, Christopher Woodlands Surgery, 1 Greenfarm Road, Ely, Cardiff CF5 4RG Tel: 029 2059 1444 Fax: 029 2059 9204 — MB BCh 1985 Wales; MRCGP 1990. Prev: Trainee GP S. Glam. VTS.

HEAVENS, Michael Anthony Cyril Flat A, Linscott House, Russell Road, Buckhurst Hill IG9 5QE Tel: 020 8504 4791 Fax: 020 8504 4791 — MB ChB St. And. 1958. Psychoanalyst. Psychotherapist Essex. Socs: Assoc. Mem. Lincoln Inst. Psychother. Prev: GP Ilford; Clin. Asst. (Psychiat.) Whipps Cross Hosp. Lond.; Clin. Asst. (Psychogeriat.) Claybury Hosp. Woodford Bridge.

HEAVERSEDGE, Jon Townley Burnside House, Mill Rd, Meole Brace, Shrewsbury SY3 9JT Tel: 01743 364381 Fax: 01743 368488; 37 Aylesbury Road, Walworth, London SE17 2EQ Tel: 020 7701 5389 Email: jonty@jont.screaming.net — MB BS 1997 Lond.; MSc

(Men. Health) Lond. 1996; BSc (Psychol. & Basic Med. Sci.) Lond. 1993. (Roy. Free Hosp.)

HEAVEY, Anne Philomena Chiltern Wing, Sutton Hospital, Cotswold Road, Sutton SM2 5NF Tel: 020 8644 4343 Fax: 020 8770 7051 — MB BCh BAO 1976 NUI; MPhil NUI 1989, MB BCh BAO 1976; MRCP (UK) 1979; MRCPsych 1983. Cons. Psychiat. St. Helier NHS Trust Carshalton Surrey; Hon. Sen. Lect. (Psychiat.) Univ. Lond. Socs: Med. Interview Teach. Assn. & Assn. Family Ther. Prev: Sen. Regist. (Psychiat.) St. Geo. Hosp. Lond.; Clin. Research Fell. (Psychiat.) St. Geo. Hosp. Med. Sch. Lond.; Regist. (Psychiat.) Maudsley Hosp. Lond.

HEAVEY, Dennis John Mansell Road Surgery, 73 Mansell Road, Greenford UB6 9EJ Tel: 020 8575 0083; 181A Swakeleys Road, Ickenham, Uxbridge UB10 8DN — MB BS 1978 Lond.; BSc Lond. 1975; MRCP (UK) 1981; MRCGP 1996. (St. Mary's Hosp. Lond.) Socs: RCP; Roy. Coll. Gen. Pract. Prev: Research Fell. Harvard Med. Sch. Boston, USA; Research Fell. Roy. Postgrad. Med. Sch. Lond.; Hon. Sen. Regist. Hammersmith Hosp. Lond.

HEAVISIDE, David William Regional Cardiothoracic Centre, Freeman Hospital NHS Trust, Newcastle upon Tyne NE7 7DN — MB BS 1966 Durh.; FFA RCS Eng. 1972. Cons. Cardio-thoracic Anaesth. Newc. AHA (T); Clin. Lect. (Anaesth.) Univ. Newc. Socs: Intens. Care Soc. Prev: Sen. Regist. Newc. Univ. Gp. Hosps.; Resid. Helsinki Univ. Centr. Hosps.

HEAVISIDE, Victoria Alexandra 36 Oakfield Road, Gosforth, Newcastle upon Tyne NE3 4HS — MB BS 1996 Lond. (Char. Cross & Westm. Med. Sch.)

HEBBAR, Giridhar Kattingeri Ophthalmic Department, Warringhton Hospital NHS Trust, Warrington WA5 1QG; 26 Warrington Road, Lymm WA13 9EX Tel: 01925 753537 — MB BS 1982 Andhra; MRCOphth 1996. (Rangaraya Med. Coll., Kakinada, India) Staff Grade Practit. Socs: BMA.

HEBBAR, Indira Kattingeri Eye Clinic, University Hospital, Queens Medical Centre, Nottingham NG7 2UH Tel: 0115 924 9924; 32 Firth Drive, Chilwell, Beeston, Nottingham NG9 6NL — MB BS 1972 Andhra; MS (Ophth.) Andhra 1971, MB BS 1972; DO Lond. 1975; FRCS Ed. 1981; FRCOphth 1989. Assoc. Specialist (Ophth.) Univ. Hosp. Qu. Med. Centre Nottm. Socs: BMA; Fell. Roy. Coll. of Ophth.s; Oxf. Congr. of Ophthal. Prev: Assoc. Specialist Sunderland Eye Infirm.; Regist. (Ophth.) Qu. Eliz. Hosp. Kings Lynn; Regist. & SHO (Ophth.) Univ. Hosp. Cardiff.

HEBBERT, Francis John, ERD, OStJ (retired) 1 Russell Street, Wilton, Salisbury SP2 0BG Tel: 01722 744732 Fax: 01722 744732 Email: jsherbert@aol.com — MB ChB 1938 Glas.; MD Glas. 1947; FRCP Glas. 1972, M 1962. Prev: Cons. Phys. (Geriat.) W. Roding Dist. Hosps.

HEBBLETHWAITE, Neil Friarage Hospital, Northallerton DL6 1JG Tel: 01609 779911; The Cobbles, The Green, Brompton, Northallerton DL6 2QT — MB BS 1979 Lond.; MRCGP 1983; MRCOG 1988. (St Mary's) Cons. Obst. Gyn. N.allerton NHS Trust. Prev: Sen. Regist. Gen. Infirm. Leeds.

***HEBBLETHWAITE, Philippa Anne** 51 Chalky Road, Broadmayne, Dorchester DT2 8PJ Tel: 01305 852576 Fax: 01305 852576 — MB ChB 1998 Ed.; MB ChB Ed 1998.

HEBBLETHWAITE, Rodney Peter Everard 51 Chalky Road, Broadmayne, Dorchester DT2 8PJ Tel: 01305 852576 — MA, MB BChir Camb. 1969; FFA RCS Eng. 1974. Cons. (Anaesth.) W. Dorset Health Dist.

HEBDEN, Anna Louise Lynwood, 9 High St., Milton-under-Wychwood, Chipping Norton OX7 6LA — MB BS 1993 Lond.

HEBDEN, Mark William The Cot, Talygarn Estate, Pontyclun CF72 9JT — MB BS 1975 Lond.; FFA RCS Eng. 1980. (Univ. Coll. Hosp. Med. Sch.) ITU Dir. & Cons. Anaesth. Llandough Hosp. Cardiff.

HEBDEN, Stephen 10 Woodnook, Mereclough, Cliviger, Burnley BB10 4RL — MB ChB 1992 Liverp. Socs: Roy. Coll. Gen. Pract. Prev: Trainee GP/SHO Burnley Gen. Hosp. VTS.

HEBER, James William (retired) Ravenhurst, Knowbury, Ludlow SY8 3LG Tel: 01584 891434 — MB BS Lond. 1962; MRCS Eng. LRCP Lond. 1962; DA Eng. 1965; DObst RCOG 1965. Prev: Princip. in Beckington Family Pract., Som.

HEBER, Kenneth Reeve (retired) 2 Court Avenue, Old Coulsdon, Coulsdon CR5 1HF Tel: 0208 54721 — MB BS 1950 Lond.; DObst RCOG 1954. Prev: GP Old Coulsdon.

HEBER, Mary Elizabeth, TD Princess Royal Hospital, Apley Castle, Telford TF1 6TF Tel: 01952 641222 Fax: 01952 243405 Email: mary.heber@prh-tr.wmids.nhs.uk; Bernette, New Works Lane, Little Wenlock, Telford TF6 5BS Tel: 01952 505568 — MB BS 1977 Lond.; MD Lond. 1991; FRCP Lond. 1994; MRCS Eng. LRCP Lond. 1977. (Guy's) Cons. Phys. & Cardiol. P.ss Roy. Hosp. Telford. Socs: Brit. Cardiac Soc. Prev: Hon. Sen. Regist. (Cardiol.) N.wick Pk. Hosp.; Regist. (Cardiac.) Kings Coll. Hosp. & Roy. Sussex Co. Hosp. Brighton.

HEBER, Michael John Fax: 01424 850190, 01424 853888 Email: michael.heber@gp81105.nhs.uk — MB BS 1979 Lond.; MRCGP 1987; DFFP 1993; DRCOG 1986. (Guys Hopsital) Gen. Pratitioner, Ch.wood Med. Pract., St. Leonards-On-Sea; GP Trainer; Approved Under Sect. 12 (2) Ment. Health Act; Examr., Roy. Coll. of Gen. Practioners; Hon. Med. Adviser, RNLI Hastings Life Boat; Excutive Bd. Mem. and Clin. Governance Lead, Hastings and St. Leonards PCT. Socs: BMA Mem. Prev: Trainee GP Hastings VTS; Regist. (Med.) New E. Surrey Hosp.; SHO (Med.) Guy's Hosp. Lond.

HEBRERO MATOBELLA, Eva Doctor's Mess, St Helier Hospital, Carshalton SM5 1AA — LMS 1994 Valladolid.

HECKER, Katharine Victoria Regents Park Road Surgery, 99 Regents Park Road, London NW1 8UR Tel: 020 7722 0038 Fax: 020 7722 9724 — MB BS 1986 Lond.; MRCGP 1990; DRCOG 1990.

HECKMATT, John Zia Child Development Centre, Knutsford House, Peace Prospect, Watford WD17 3EW Tel: 01923 226436 Fax: 01923 248676 Email: yba04@dial.pipex.com; 3 Briants Close, Hatch End, Pinner HA5 4SY Tel: 020 8428 1679 — MB ChB Liverp. 1970; MD Liverp. 1985; FRCP Lond. 1996; MRCP (UK) 1973; FRCPCH. (Liverp.) Cons. Paediat. (Community) Child Developm. Centre Watford. Socs: Roy. Soc. Med.; Brit. Paediat. Neurol. Assn. Prev: Sen. Research Fell. (Paediat.) Roy. Postgrad. Med. Sch.; Tutor (Paediat. & Child Health) Univ. Leeds; Regist. Roy. Hosp. Sick Childr. Glas.

HECTOR, Mary Forrest (retired) 4 Montgomery Court, 110 Hepburn Gardens, St Andrews KY16 9LT Tel: 01334 473784 — MB ChB 1945 Aberd. Prev: Lect. Dept. Path. Univs. Aberd. & Edin.

HECTOR, Ralph Melville, CBE, Col. late RAMC Retd. Lyndhurst, Waverley Avenue, Fleet GU51 4NW Tel: 01252 613795 — MB ChB 1937 Aberd.; DMRD Eng. 1950. Mem. Fac. Radiol.

HEDAYATI, Bijan 51 Ullswater Crescent, Kingston Vale, London SW15 3RG — MB BS 1996 Lond.

HEDDERWICK, Sara Ann Email: shedderwick@which.net — MB BChir 1991 Camb.; MRCP (UK) 1993; DTM & H; RCP 1999. (Cambs) Cons. Infect. Dis. Roy. Vict. Hosp. Belf.

HEDDLE, Mr Robert Miller The Green, Ickham, Canterbury CT3 1QT — MB BS Lond. 1966; FRCS Eng. 1972; FRCS Ed. 1971; MRCS Eng. LRCP Lond. 1966. (Westm.) Cons. Surg. Kent & Canterbury Hosp. Prev: Sen. Regist. W.m. Hosp. Lond.; Research Fell. Harvard Med. Sch. U.S.A.

HEDGE, Chandralekha Vishweshwar 70 Moorfield Gardens, Cleadon, Sunderland SR6 7TP Tel: 0191 519 0298 — MB BS Bombay 1982, MD (Paediat.) 1984; MRCP (UK) 1990; DCH RCP Lond. 1990.

HEDGE, Ragchandra Naganna Riverside Centre for Health, Park Street, Liverpool L8 6QP Tel: 0151 706 8317 — MB BS 1973 Mysore.

HEDGER, James Roderick Buckfastleigh Medical Centre, 7 Bossell Road, Buckfastleigh TQ11 0DE Tel: 01364 42534 Fax: 01364 644057; Deancombe Farm, Dean Prior, Buckfastleigh TQ11 0LZ Tel: 01364 643794 — MB BS 1978 Lond.; DRCOG 1982. (Middlx.) GP Buckfastleigh; Clin. Asst. Torbay Hosp. Socs: Grad. Inst. Biol. Prev: SHO Torbay Hosp.; SHO Exminster Hosp.; Ho. Off. Kettering Gen. Hosp.

HEDGER, Neil Alexander, Surg. Cdr. RN Queen Alexandra Hosp, Cosham, Portsmouth PO6 3LY Tel: 01705 584255 Fax: 01705 762150; 1 Ellachie Gardens, Alverstoke, Gosport PO12 2DS Email: neil@ellachie.freeserve.co.uk — MB ChB 1982 Manch.; BSc St. And. 1979; MRCP (UK) 1990; AFOM RCP Lond. 1988. Cons. Phys.Nephrol. & Gen. Med. Qu. Alexandra Hosp. Cosham Hants; Hon. Cons. Phys. Wessex Renal & Transpl. Unit St Mary's Hosp. Portsmouth. Socs: Euro. Dialysis and Transpl. Assn. Prev: Hon. Sen. Regist. (Renal Med.) St. Mary's Hosp. Portsmouth; Sen. Regist. (Med.) RN Hosp. Haslar; Med. Specialist RN Hosp., Gibraltar.

HEDGES, Mr Anthony Richard Abernant, St Mary Church, Cowbridge CF71 7LT Tel: 01446 772786 Email: richard.hedges@btinternet.com — MB BS 1980 Lond.; MS Lond. 1989; FRCS Ed. 1984; FRCS Eng. 1984; MRCS Eng. LRCP Lond. 1980. (King's Coll. Hosp.) Cons. Surg. P.ss of Wales Hosp. Bridgend. Prev: Sen. Regist. (Surg.) Guy's Hosp. Lond.

HEDGES, Joan Isobel 6 Colworth Road, Sharnbrook, Bedford MK44 1ET — MB ChB 1943 St. And. (St. And.)

HEDGES, John Roderick, OStJ, TD The Health Centre, Melbourn Street, Royston SG8 7BS Tel: 01763 242981 Fax: 01763 249197; 59 Spring Lane, Bassingbourn, Royston SG8 5HT — MB BS 1972 Lond.; BSc (Hons. Pharmacol.) Lond. 1968; MRCP (UK) 1978; FRCGP 1995, M 1978; DRCOG 1979. (Univ. Coll. Hosp. Lond.) Prev: Cdr. Off. 254 Field Ambul. RAMC (V).

HEDGES, Kenneth Mark Templars Way Surgery, Templars Way, Sharnbrook, Bedford MK44 1PZ Tel: 01234 781392 Fax: 01234 781468; 86 High Street, Sharnbrook, Bedford MK44 1PE — MB ChB 1971 St. And.; MRCGP 1977. Socs: BMA. Prev: Ho. Phys. St. Luke's Hosp. Bradford; Ho. Surg. Maryfield Hosp. Dundee; SHO (Cas.) Altnagelvin Hosp. Lond.derry.

HEDGES, Peter James Devonshire House Surgery, 27 South Road, Birkenhead CH42 7JW Tel: 0151 653 7295; 72 Rodney Street, Liverpool L1 9AF Tel: 0151 707 0086 Fax: 0151 708 5525 — MB ChB 1990 Liverp.; Cert. Prescribed Equiv. Exp. JCPTGP 1995; DFFP 1994; DRCOG 1994. GP Princip. Wirral HA; Clin. Asst. Med. for the Elderly & Elderly Ment. Illness. Prev: Trainee GP/SHO Wirral Hosp.; SHO (A & E & Paediat.) Vict. Hosp. Blackpool; Ho. Off. (Surg. & Med.) Clatterbridge Hosp. Wirral.

HEDGES, Sarah Jane 59 Spring Lane, Bassingbourn, Royston SG8 5HT — MB BS 1996 Lond.; BSc (Hons) Lond. 1993. (King's Coll. Lond.) Med. Rotat. SHO Norf. & Norwich Hosp.

HEDLEY, David 67 Longmeadow Road, Knowsley, Prescot L34 0HW — MB ChB 1994 Liverp.

HEDLEY, Geoffrey Stuart, TD Church Street Practice, 8 Church Street, Southport PR9 0QT Tel: 01704 533666 Fax: 01704 539239; 33A Weld Road, Southport PR8 2DR — MB ChB 1974 Liverp.; DRCOG 1978.

HEDLEY, Kathlyn Rae Medical Centre, 12A Greggs Wood Road, Tunbridge Wells TN2 3JL Tel: 01892 541444 Fax: 01892 511157; Sutherland House, 40 Culverden Down, Tunbridge Wells TN4 9SE — MB BS 1972 Lond.; MRCS Eng. LRCP Lond. 1972; MRCGP 1976; DCH Eng. 1978. (Roy. Free) Prev: Ho. Off. (Surg.) Roy. Free Hosp. Lond.; SHO (Gen. Med.) & SHO (Obst.) S.mead Hosp. W.bury-on-Trym.

HEDLEY, Nicholas Edward Highfield Cottage, Ocker Hill, Randwick, Stroud GL6 6HY Tel: 01453 750131 — MB BS 1963 Lond. (St. Thos.) Private Psychother. Pract. Stroud. Prev: Sen. Research Asst. Univ. Coll. Hosp. Drug Addic. Unit; Ho. Surg. St. Peter's Hosp. Chertsey; Surg. Lt. RN.

HEDLEY, Nicholas Garth Thomas 16 Kingston Dr, Lytham St Annes FY8 4QS — MB ChB 1997 Leic.

HEDLEY, Patricia Jane The Congregational Hall, Town Street, Marple Bridge, Stockport SK6 5AA Tel: 0161 427 2049/1074 Fax: 0161 427 8389; 3 Whetmorhurst Lane, Mellor, Stockport SK6 5NZ — MB ChB 1980 Manch.; MRCGP 1984; DRCOG 1982.

HEDLEY, Robert Norman Medical School, Queens Medical Centre, Nottingham NG7 2UH Tel: 0115 970 9377 Fax: 0115 970 9716; Hopwell House, Hopwell, Ockbrook, Derby DE72 3RU Tel: 01332 872234 Fax: 01332 872234 — MB ChB Ed. 1962; BSc (Physiol., Hons.) Ed. 1958; FRCGP 1985, M 1977; DObst RCOG 1964. (Edinburgh) Regional Dir. Postgrad. Gen. Pract. Educat. Trent Region. Socs: (Ex-Pres.) Derby Med. Soc.; (Ex.-Chairm.) Derbysh. Obst. Gp.; Provost, Vale of Trent Fac. Prev: Course Organiser Derby Gen. Pract. VTS; Clin. Tutor (Gen. Pract.) Derby; Family Plann. Instruc. FPA.

HEDLEY, Russell Mark Bromley NHS Trust, Cromwell Avenue, Bromley BR2 9AJ Tel: 020 8289 7120; 7 Rodway Road, Bromley BR1 3JJ Tel: 020 8464 7999 — MB BS 1985 Lond.; FRCA 1990. (King's Coll. Hosp.) Cons. Anaesth. Bromley NHS Trust. Prev: Sen. Regist. (Anaesth.) St. Geo. Hosp. Lond.; Regist. (Anaesth.) St. Geo. Hosp. Lond.; SHO (Anaesth.) W.m. Hosp. Lond.

HEE, Christopher John 1 Greensleeves House, St Marys Avenue, Norwood Green, Southall UB2 4NL — MB BS 1987 Lond.

HEE, Michael 14 Alleyn Park, Norwood Green, Southall UB2 5QU Tel: 020 8574 4743 — MB BS 1963 Lond.; MRCS Eng. LRCP Lond. 1961. (Westm.) Med. Off. Crown Cork Co. Ltd. S.all; Examr. & Med. Off. Brit. Red Cross Soc. Socs: BMA. Prev: Cas. Off. St. Leonard's Hosp. Lond.; Ho. Surg. St. Chas. Hosp. Lond.; Ho. Phys. Lond. Jewish Hosp.

HEELAN, Bridget Theresa Royal Free Hospital, Pond St., London NW3 2QG Tel: 020 7830 2141 — MB BCh BAO 1985 NUI; BSc (Physiol.) NUI 1987, MB BCh BAO 1985; DPhil 1995; MRPM 1999. Specialist Regist. Immunol. Roy. Free. Hosp. Lond. Socs: MRCP; BTS; BSI.

HEELEY, Graham Martin The Wilton Health Centre, Market Place, Wilton, Salisbury SP2 0HT Tel: 01722 742404 Fax: 01722 744116 — MB BS Lond. 1966; MRCS Eng. LRCP Lond. 1965; DObst RCOG 1969. (Roy. Free) Mem. Wilts. Local Med. Comm. Socs: BMA & Salisbury Med. Soc. Prev: GP Mem. Salisbury HA; Clin. Asst. (Dermat.) Salisbury Gen. Infirm.; SHO (Paediat.) St. Helen's Hosp. Hastings.

HEELEY, Michael Edward Manor Road Surgery, 38 Manor Road, Deal CT14 9BX Tel: 01304 367495 Fax: 01304 239202; 144 Church Path, Deal CT14 9TU Tel: 01304 373727 — MB BS 1973 Lond.; DRCOG 1978. (Char. Cross) Socs: BMA. Prev: Sen. Resid. St. Vincents Hosp. Sydney, Australia, St. Margt. Hosp.; Wom. Sydney & Roy. Alexandra Hosp. Childr. Sydney.

HEELEY, Peter Joseph Marten Health Centre, Hurstpierpoint, Hassocks BN6 9UQ Tel: 01273 834388 Fax: 01273 834529; Washbrook Cottage, Brighton Road, Hurstpierpoint, Hassocks BN6 9EF — MB BS 1970 Lond.; MRCS Eng. LRCP Lond. 1970; DObst RCOG 1972; DCH Eng. 1973. Gen. Pract.

HEELIS, Graham Birchwood Surgery, 232-240 Nevells Road, Letchworth SG6 4UB Tel: 01462 683456 — MB BS 1978 Lond.; MRCS Eng. LRCP Lond. 1978; MRCGP 1982; DFFP 1996; DRCOG 1981.

HEENAN, Paul Nicholas Clapham Family Practice, 51 Clapham High Street, London SW4 7TL Tel: 020 7622 4455 Fax: 020 7622 4466 — MB BCh BAO 1984 NUI; DObst 1989. Socs: Med. Protec. Soc. & Pharmaceut. Soc.

HEENAN, Susan Deirdre Department of Diagnostic Radiology, St George's Hospital, Blackshaw Road, London SW17 0QT; Flat 2, 6 Douglas St, London SW1P 4PB — MB BChir 1989 Camb.; MA Camb. 1989, MB BChir 1989; MRCP (UK) 1991; FRCR 1994; MSc 1998. Cons.Radiol.St Geo.s Hosp. Lond.

HEEPS, Janet Margaret Mary The Grange, Moor Lane, Bunny, Nottingham NG11 6QX Tel: 0115 984 5591 — MB ChB 1975 Manch.; DCH. Eng. 1977. Prev: Clin. Med. Off. (Child Health) Notts. HA; SHO (Paediat.) Booth Hall Hosp. Manch.; Regist. (Paediat.) Odstock Hosp. Salisbury.

HEER, Amardeep Singh 18 Dewsbury Avenue, Styvechale, Coventry CV3 6NF — MB ChB 1998 Leic.; MB ChB Leic 1998.

HEER, Rakesh 1 Faldo Cl, Leicester LE4 7TS — BM BS 1997 Nottm.

HEERALALL, Dharmchand Chandos Medical Centre, 123 Lidgett Lane, Leeds LS8 1QR Tel: 0113 266 3384; Woodhouse Health Centre, Woodhouse St, Leeds LS6 2SF Tel: 0113 245 5989 — MB ChB 1959 Leeds. (Leeds) Socs: BMA. Prev: SHO (Neurosurg.) & Ho. Phys. (Paediat.) Gen. Infirm. Leeds; Ho. Surg. Vict. Hosp. Blackpool.

HEFFER, James Sidney Station Approach Health Centre, Station Approach, Bradford-on-Avon BA15 1DQ Tel: 01225 866611 — BM BCh 1981 Oxf.

HEFFERNAN, John (retired) 22 Cherry Garden Lane, Folkestone CT19 4AD Tel: 01303 275214 — MB BCh BAO 1951 NUI; DObst RCOG 1955; CPH 1954; DCH RCPSI 1954. Prev: Ho. Surg. Jervis St. Hosp. Dub.

HEFFERNAN, Susanne Burnside Surgery, 41 Connaught Road, Fleet GU51 3LR — MB BCh BAO 1981 NUI; LRCPI & LM, LRCSI & LM 1981.

HEFNI, Mohamed Ali Benenden Hospital Trust, Benenden, Cranbrook TN17 4AX Tel: 01580240333 Fax: 015802 20021 Email: mhefni@hotmail.com; Kaiainga Farm, Chalk Lane, Cranbrook TN17 2QB — MB BCh 1972 Cairo; FRCOG 1994, M 1981. Cons. Gyn. Benenden Hosp. Trust Kent.

HEGAN, Hugh (retired) Kirra, Lakewood Road, Chandler's Ford, Eastleigh SO53 5AA Tel: 02380 252605 Email: hegan@kissafsnet.co.uk — MB BCh BAO 1946 Belf.

HEGAN, Michael Colin 2 Mallusk Road, Newtownabbey BT36 4PP Tel: 028 9083 2188 Fax: 028 9083 8820; 15 Lenamore Avenue, Jordanstown, Newtownabbey BT37 0PF Tel: 02890 861638 Email: colin.hegan@btopenworld.com — MB BCh BAO 1981 Belf.; MRCGP 1985; DRCOG 1984. Prev: Research Asst. Diabetic Clinic Roy. Vict. Hosp. Belf.

HEGAN, Patricia Dorothy 4 Cranmore Avenue, Belfast BT9 6JH — MB BCh BAO 1985 Belf.; MRCGP 1989; DCH RCP Lond. 1988; DRCOG 1987; Dip. Occ. Med. (RCP Lond.) 1995; Cert. Family Plann. 1988. Socs: Soc. Occupat. Med. Prev: Med. Off., Harland & Wolff Shipbuilders, Belf.

HEGAN, Timothy John Michael North West Anglia Health Commission, St John's, Thorpe Road, Peterborough PE3 6JG; 1 Nelson Street, Hertford SG14 3AG — MB BChir 1988 Camb.; MA Camb. 1989. Regist. (Pub. Health Med.) NW Anglia Health Commiss.

HEGARTY, Bernadette Soubirous Mary Ardshiel, Lower Green, West Linton EH46 7EW — MB BCh BAO 1988 Belf.; MB BCh Belf. BAO 1988; Cert. Family Plann. JCC 1991; DRCOG 1991. Trainee GP W. Linton Health Centre Peebleseh. Prev: Trainee GP Waveney Hosp. Ballymena VTS.

HEGARTY, Daniel Donald Express Medicals Ltd, 16 City Business Centre, Lower Road, London SE16 2XB Tel: 020 7394 1788 Fax: 020 7394 1614; 121A Bromley Road, Catford, London SE6 2NZ Tel: 020 8244 4716 Email: dan.hegarty@centrenet.co.uk — MB BS 1985 Lond.; MA Oxf. 1978; MRCGP 1994; DCH RCP Lond. 1994; DRCOG 1993. (Guy's Hospital London) Chief. Med. Off. & Dir. Express Meds. Ltd. Lond.; Global Nutrit. Business. Prev: Trainee GP Lond.; SHO Rotat. (Gen. Surg.) King's Coll. Hosp. Lond.

HEGARTY, David Michael 149 Summerfields Av., Halesowen B62 9NT — MB ChB 1990 Birm.; ChB Birm. 1990.

HEGARTY, Declan Mary Haylodge Health Centre, Neidpath Road, Peebles EH45 8JG Tel: 01721 720380 Fax: 01721 723430; 11 Kingsmeadows Gardens, Peebles EH45 9LA Tel: 01721 721918 — MB BCh BAO 1987 Belf.; MRCGP 1992; DRCOG 1991.

HEGARTY, Helen Margaret Mary Swallowfield Medical Practice, The Surgery, Swallowfield, Reading RG7 1QY Tel: 0118 988 3134 Fax: 0118 988 5759; 52 Old Bath Road, Charvil, Reading RG10 9QL Email: hhegarty@aol.com — MB BCh BAO 1980 NUI; DCH Irel. 1983; DRCOG 1983. (Cork)

HEGARTY, Jennifer Deirdre 1 Steelstown Road, Londonderry BT48 8EU — MB BCh BAO 1990 Belf.

***HEGARTY, Joanne Elizabeth** 75 Richmond Court, Lisburn BT27 4QX Tel: 01846 677780 Email: jhegarty@doctors.net.uk — MB BCh 1998 Belf.; MB BCh Belf 1998.

HEGARTY, Joseph Eugene 75 Richmond Court, Lisburn BT27 4QX Tel: 01846 677780 — MB BCh BAO 1970 Belf.; FFA RCSI 1975. Cons. Anaesth. Belf. City Hosp.

HEGARTY, Karen Anne 149 Summerfields Avenue, Hurst Green, Halesowen B62 9NT — MB ChB 1993 Birm.

HEGARTY, Mary Katherina Iiewn House, 412 High Road, Harrow HA3 6HJ — MB BS 1994 Lond.

HEGARTY, Michael Anthony 14 St Augustine's Road, Edgbaston, Birmingham B16 9JU Tel: 0121 454 2388 — MB BCh BAO 1971 NUI; BSc NUI 1976, MB BCh BAO 1971. (Cork) Sen. Regist. (Microbiol.) Birm. AHA; Jun. Mem. Assn. Clin. Path. Socs: Brit. Soc. Hosp. Infec. Prev: Regist. (Microbiol.) W. Midl. RHA; Regist. (Microbiol.) W.. Health Bd. (Irel.); SHO (Path.) E.. Health Bd. (Irel.).

HEGARTY, William John (retired) Bankhead, South View Road, Pinner HA5 3YB Tel: 020 8866 9835 — MB BCh BAO 1948 NUI; FFA RCS Eng. 1961; DA Eng. 1956. Prev: Cons. Anaesth. Hillingdon Hosp.

HEGAZI, Mohamed Anwar c/o Royal College of Obstetrics & Gynaecology, 27 Sussex Place, Regents Park, London NW1 4RG — MB BCh 1983 Cairo; MB BCh Cairo, Egypt 1983.

HEGDE, Ayitha Kumar Kodyadke Galleries Health Centre, Washington Centre, Washington NE38 7NQ Tel: 0191 416 1841 — MB BS 1974 Mysore. (Mysore) GP Washington, Tyne & Wear.

HEGDE, Bakrabile Dinkar Grange Medical Group, 21A Kersiebank Avenue, Grangemouth FK3 9EL Tel: 01324 665533 Fax: 01324 665693 — MB BS 1967 Karntak; MB BS Karnatak 1967. (Karnatak) GP Grangemouth.

HEGDE, Rekha Flat1/1, 8 Highburgh Road, Glasgow G12 9YD — MB ChB 1998 Glas.; MB ChB Glas 1998.

HEGDE, Uday Mahabal Ealing Hospital, Uxbridge Road, Southall UB1 3HW Tel: 020 8967 5432 Fax: 020 8571 2617; 98 Moor Lane, Rickmansworth WD3 1LQ Tel: 01923 772608 — MB BS 1967 Bombay; FRCPath 1986, M 1975. (Grant Med. Coll. Bombay) Cons. Haemat. Ealing Hosp. Lond.; Sen. Lect. Roy. Postgrad. Med. Sch. Lond. & Hammersmith Hosp. Lond. Prev: Sen. Regist. Hammersmith Hosp. Lond.; Regist. N. Middlx. Hosp. Lond.; SHO (Haemat.) Hosp. Sick Childr. Lond.

HEGGARTY, Hugh Joseph (retired) 8 Hobgate, Acomb Road, York YO24 4HF — MB ChB Glas. 1961; FRCP Glas. 1975, M 1966; MRCP Lond. 1967; FRCPCH 1997. Assoc. Prof. Univ. St. Geo. Med. Sch. Grenada, W. Indies. Prev: Cons. Paediat. York Health Dist.

HEGGARTY, Paula Caroline 73 Ballymoney Road, Ballymena BT43 5BU — MB BCh BAO 1993 Belf.

HEGGESSEY, Louise Simone The Surgery, 2 Garway Road, London W2 4NH Tel: 020 7221 8803 020 8962 4400 Fax: 020 7792 9923; 16 Disraeli Road, Ealing, London W5 5HP Tel: 0182 567 9544 — MB BS 1984 Lond.; BSc (Hons.) Lond. 1981, MB BS 1984; MRCGP 1988; DRCOG 1987. (Westm.)

HEGGIE, Linda Jane Bonnyrigg Health Centre, High Street, Bonnyrigg EH19 2DA Tel: 0131 663 7272 Fax: 0131 660 5636; 3 St. Ninian's Terrace, Edinburgh EH10 5NL — MB ChB 1974 Ed.; DRCOG 1979; DCH RCPS Glas. 1978.

HEGGIE, Nicholas Maurice Foreberry House, The Green, Longfizamlington NE61 4NX — MB ChB 1977 Aberd.; FFA RCS Eng. 1981. Cons. Anaesth. Freeman Hosp., Newc. on Tyne.

HEGGS, Christopher George Bank House Surgery, The Health Centre, Victoria Road, Hartlepool TS26 8DB Tel: 01429 274800 — MB BS 1980 Lond.; FRCOG 1999; MRCGP 1989; MRCOG 1987; DLO RCS Eng. 1984. (St. Geo.) Socs: Anglo-French Med. Soc. Prev: Regist. (O & G) N. Tees Gen. Hosp.

HEHAR, Mr Sukhminderjit Singh 9 Southwood Road, St Michaels, Liverpool L17 7BG — MB BChir 1990 Camb.; FRCS Ed. 1994. SHO (Surg.) Qu. Med. Centre Univ. Hosp. Nottm.

HEHIR, Mr Michael Department of Urology, Royal Infirmary, Stirling FK8 2AU Tel: 01786 434000 Fax: 01786 450588; Allan Bank House, Mill Row, Dunblane FK15 0EL Email: mike.hehir@virgin.net.uk — MB BCh BAO 1973 NUI; FRCS (Urol.) Ed. 1987; FRCSI 1977. (Galway) Cons. (Urol.) Stirling Roy. Infirm. Falkirk & Dist. Roy. Infirm. Socs: Brit. Assn. Urol. Surgs.; Irish Soc. Urol. Prev: Sen. Regist. (Urol.) Meath, St. Vincents & Jervis St. Hosp. Dub.; Regist. (Urol.) St. Peters Hosps. Lond.; Regist. (Surg.) Regional Hosp. Galway.

HEHIR STRELLEY, Maureen Elizabeth Friendly Family Surgery, Welbeck Road, Bolsover, Chesterfield S44 6DE Tel: 01246 826815 Fax: 01246 559628; 8 Bryn Lea, Hady, Chesterfield S41 0EP Tel: 01246 559628 Fax: 01246 559628 Email: maureenstrelley@hotmail.com — BM BCh 1976 Oxf.; MRCP (UK) 1978; MRCGP 1986. Clin. Governance Lead N.E. Derbys; GP. Prev: Hosp. Pract. (Dermat.) & GP Tutor Mt. Vernon Hosp. N.wood.

HEIDARI-KHABBAZ, Nima 40 Newark Road, Croydon CR2 6HQ — MB BS 1993 Lond.; MB BS Lond 1993.

HEIDELMEYER, Carl Friedrich United Bristol Healthcare Trust, 41 Alfred Hill, Bristol BS2 8HN Tel: 0117 929 8879 Fax: 0117 929 8879 — State Exam Med 1979 Berlin; MD Munich 1982; T(Anaes) 1994. (LM Univ. Munich & Freie Univ. Berlin) Cons. Anaesth. Day Surg. Unit. Socs: Assn. Anaesth.; Deutsche Ges. Anaesth. und Intens. Med. Prev: Clin Dir. Critical Care Serv. S. Tyneside HCT; Obserarzt & HochschulAsst. Klinikum R. Virchow, Freie Univ., Berlin; Wiss Ass Klin Steglitz & Klin Charlottenburg Freie Univ., Berlin.

HEIDEMANN, Heinrich Bernhard 7 Trewhitt Road, Heaton, Newcastle upon Tyne NE6 5LT Email: b.heidemann@bigfoot.com — State Exam Med 1992 Dusseldorf; DA (UK) 1996. Specialist Regist. Rotat. Anaesth. - Edin. Socs: AAGBI; NESA; SCATA.

HEIGHT, Susan Elizabeth Department of Haematological Medicine, King's College Hospital NHS Trust, Denmark Hill, London SE5 9RS; 1 The Cottages, Manwood Road, London SE5 9RS Tel: 020 8314 5981 — MB BS 1985 Lond.; MD 1977 Lond.; MRCPath 2000; BSc (Hons) Lond. 1982; MRCP (UK) 1989. (St. Geo. Hosp. Med. Sch. Lond.)

HEIGHTON, David Robert Magnus (retired) Windyridge, 9 Kensington Close, Saxlingham Nethergate, Norwich NR15 1TR Tel: 01508 498284 Fax: 01508 498284 — MB ChB Bristol 1960; DCH Eng. 1962. Prev: Gen. Pract., Saxlingham.

HEIGHTON, Richard William 9 Kensington Close, Saxlingham, Nethergate, Norwich NR15 1TR — MB ChB 1991 Leeds; MRCGP 1995.

HEIGHWAY, John Dundas (retired) 15 Bolton Avenue, North Hykeham, Lincoln LN6 8JA Tel: 01522 824504 Email: jack@dundas19.freeserve.co.uk — MRCS Eng. LRCP Lond. 1948. Prev: Ho. Phys. Luton & Dunstable Hosp.

HEIJNE DEN BAK, Jan Beech House Group Practice, Beech House Medical Centre, St Bridget's Lane, Egremont CA22 2BD Tel: 01946 820692 Fax: 01946 820 372 — Artsexamen 1982 Free U Amsterdam; FRCGP 1995; MRCGP 1985. (Free Univ., Amsterdam) GP Princip.; Exec. Mem. W. Cumbria PCT. Prev: Scheme Organiser, W. Cumbria VTS; Chairm. W. Cumbria PCG.

HEIN, (Clare) Nicolette Department of Research & Development, Knightley Ward, Northampton General Hospital Trust, Cliftonville, Northampton Tel: 01604 34700; 6 Abington Park Crescent, Northampton NN3 3AD Tel: 01604 620295 — MB BS Lond. 1965; DA Eng. 1982. (Lond. Hosp.) Clin. Asst. (Research & Developm.) N.ampton Gen. Hosp. Prev: SHO (Anaesth.) Lond. Hosp. & Radcliffe Infirm. Oxf.; Regist. (Anaesth.) N.ampton Gen. Hosp.

***HEIN, Pierre Jules Dominic** 70 Rookery Road, Selly Oak, Birmingham B29 7DQ Tel: 0121 472 5780; 6 Abington Park Crescent, Northampton NN3 3AD Tel: 01604 20295 Fax: 01604 20295 — MB ChB 1995 Birm.; BSc (Hons.) Birm. 1992.

HEIN, Mr Pierre Louis Raymond (retired) Northampton General Hospital, Billing Road, Northampton NN1 3AD Tel: 01604 634700 — MA, BM BCh Oxf. 1964; FRCS Eng. 1974. Prev: Sen. Regist. Moorfields Eye Hosp. Lond. (City Rd. Br.).

HEINE, Bernard Edmund (retired) Willow Barn, Station Road, Pacham St Mary, Diss IP21 4QS Tel: 01379 608436 Fax: 01379 608747 — MB ChB 1953 N.Z.; FRCPsych 1979, M 1972; DPM Lond. 1965. Prev: Cons. Psychiat. Runwell Hosp., Wickford.

HEINERSDORFF, Nicoletta Ruth Victoria Place Surgery, 11 Victoria Place, Bethesda, Bangor LL57 3AG Tel: 01248 600212 Fax: 01248 602790; Ty'r Mynydd, Tan Y Bwlch Farm, Llanllechid, Bethesda, Bangor LL57 3HY — BM 1979 Soton. (Southampton) GP Bethesda.

HEINING, Edward Wilfrid (retired) 16 Leander Close, Wilford, Nottingham NG11 7BE — MB BChir 1949 Lond.; MB BChir Camb. 1949; MRCS Eng. LRCP Lond. 1944; MA Camb. 1949. Prev: Regist. St. Thos. Hosp.

HEINING, Mark Patrick Damian Dept of Anaesthesia, Nottingham City Hosp NHS Trust, Nottingham NG5 1PB — MB BChir 1977 Camb.; MA 1977 Camb.; FFA RCS Eng. 1980. Cons. Anaesth. City Hosp. Nottm.

HEININK, Paul Anton Five Elms Medical Practice, Five Elms Health Centre, Five Elms Road, Dagenham RM9 5TT Tel: 020 8517 1175 Fax: 020 8592 0114; 14 Grosvenor Gardens, Upminster RM14 1DJ Tel: 01708 227374 — MB BS 1977 Lond. (Char. Cross) Prev: Trainee GP S.end on Sea VTS; Ho. Phys. & Ho. Surg. Blackburn Health Dist.

HEINSHEIMER, Ruth Janet Chiswick Health Centre, Fishers Lane, London W4 1RX Tel: 020 8994 2465 Fax: 020 8994 9497 — MB ChB 1968 Birm.; DObst RCOG 1970.

HEITMANN, Marlies Ivy House, 1 School Lane, Kitts Green, Birmingham B33 8PD — State Exam Med. Berlin 1986; FRCS Eng. 1992.

HEIZMAN, Kerstin Pendrills, The Green, East Dean, Eastbourne BN20 0BY — State Exam Med. Gottingen 1990.

HELAL, Mr Basil (retired) Hackwoods, Baas Lane, Broxbourne EN10 7EL — MB BS Lond. 1951; MChOrth Liverp. 1962; FRCS Eng. 1978; FRCS Ed. 1960; MRCS Eng. LRCP Lond. 1951. Hon. Cons. Orthop. Surg. Lond. Hosp., Roy. Nat. Orthop. Hosp. & Enfield Hosp. Gp. Prev: Cons. Orthop. Surg. Roy. Lond. Hosp., Roy. Nat. Orthop. Hosp. Enfield GP. Hosps.

HELAN, Simon Anthony Uplands Surgery, 48 Sketty Road, Uplands, Swansea SA2 0LJ Tel: 01792 298554 / 298555 Fax: 01792 280416 — MB BS 1982 Lond.; MA Oxf. 1975; MRCGP 1986; DCH RCP Lond. 1985; DRCOG 1984. (Guy's)

HELBERT, David 7 Lowcross Drive, Great Broughton, Middlesbrough TS9 7EB — MD 1956 Liverp.; MB ChB 1953; MRCGP 1979; DCH Eng. 1962; DObst RCOG 1966. (Liverp.)

HELBERT, Matthew Reginald 35 Wesley Square, London W11 1TS Tel: 020 7727 4224 Email: mhelbert@dircon.co.uk — MB ChB 1982 Liverp.; PhD Lond. 1995; MRCP (UK) 1989; MRCPath 1997. Cons. (Clin. Immunol.) St. Bart. Hosp. Lond. Prev: Sen. Regist. (Immunol.) St. Helier Hosp. Surrey; MRC Research Fell. (Genitourin. Med.) Middlx. & Univ. Coll. Hosps. Lond.; Regist. (Med.) Edgware Gen. Hosp. Lond.

HELD, Ines 11 Park Crescent, Cardiff CF14 7AQ — State Exam Med 1988 Rostock.

HELENGLASS, Gilla Wishaw General Hospital, 50 Netherton Street, Wishaw ML2 0DP Tel: 01698 361100 Fax: 01698 376671 — MB ChB 1975 Glas.; FRCP (UK) 1999; M 1979; FRCPath 2000, M 1991. (Univ. Glas.) Cons. Haemat.Wishaw Gen. Hosp.

HELEY, Margaret Mary (retired) 169 Woodbridge Road, Ipswich IP4 2PE Tel: 01473 252947 Fax: 01473 252947 — MB BS Lond. 1953; MRCS Eng. LRCP Lond. 1953; DObst RCOG 1955. Prev: Ho. Surg. Hosp. Sick Childr. Gt. Ormond St.

HELIOTIS, Manolis Flat 2, 19 Morden Rd, Blackheath, London SE3 0AD — MB ChB 1996 Stellenbosch.

HELL, John Anthony 159 Russell Road, Moseley, Birmingham B13 8RR Tel: 0121 449 0895 — MB BS 1986 Newc.; DA (UK) 1991. SHO (Anaesth.) Cumbld. Infirm. Carlisle.

HELL, Suzanne Caroline 92 Lower Road, Gerrards Cross SL9 8LB — MB ChB 1984 Manch.; BSc St. And. 1981; MB ChB Manch. l984. Prev: Regist. (Anaesth.) Wythenshawe Hosp. Manch.

HELLAWELL, Mr Giles Oliver 6 Idris Terrace, Dolgellau LL40 1RT — BM BCh Oxf. 1994; FRCS 1998. (University of Oxford) SHO Surg. The Roy. Free Hosp., Lond.

HELLEN, Elizabeth Anne 16 Attlee Close, Northampton NN3 6FF — MB BS 1986 Newc.

HELLENDOORN, Jan Willem Rushey Mead Health Centre, 8 Lockerbie Walk, Leicester LE4 7ZX Tel: 0116 266 9616; 9 Barns Close, Kirby Muxloe, Leicester LE9 2BA Tel: 0116 239 3699 — MB ChB 1982 Leic.

HELLER, Andrew John Nunnery Fields Hospital, Canterbury CT1 3LP Tel: 01227 766877 — MB BS 1980 Lond.; FRCP Lond. 1996; MRCP (UK) 1983. (St. Mary's) Cons. Phys. (Geriat. Med.) Kent & Canterbury Hosp. Prev: Sen. Regist. (c/o Elderly) King's Coll. Hosp. Lond.; Regist. (Gen. Med.) S.mead Hosp. Bristol; Regist. (Neurol.) Frenchay Hosp. Bristol.

HELLER, Douglas Robert Email: doughelle@doctors.org.uk — MB BS 1976 Newc.; MSc Community Med. Lond. 1986; MRCP (UK) 1982; FRCPCH 1997; MFPHM 1988; DTM & H Lond. 1994.

HELLER, Eva Suthergrey House Surgery, 37A St. Johns Road, Watford WD17 1LS Tel: 01923 224424 Fax: 01923 243710 — MUDr 1977 Prague; LMSSA Lond. 1989. (Prague) Trainer (Gen. Pract.) Watford. Socs: Roy. Coll. Gen. Pract. Prev: Trainee GP Elstree.

HELLER, Keith Barry The Surgery, Lion Road, Glemsford, Sudbury CO10 7RF Tel: 01283 280484 — MB BS 1977 Lond.; BSc (Hons.) Lond. 1975, MB BS (Hons.) 1977; MRCP (UK) 1980; MRCGP 1984; DRCOG 1982; Cert. FPA 1982. (Lond. Hosp.) GP Glemsford. Prev: SHO (Med.) Rotat. & Regist. Leics. Roy. Infirm.; SHO (Med.) Leics. Gen. Hosp.; Trainee GP Syston Leics.

HELLER, Maxwell Henry 35 Wenthill Close, High Ackworth, Pontefract WF7 7LP — LRCPI & LM, LRSCI & LM 1955; LRCPI & LM, LRCSI & LM 1955; DA RCPSI 1960. (RCSI) Cons. Anaesth. Wakefield HA. Prev: Ho. Phys. Clayton Hosp. Wakefield; Ho. Surg. Kidderminster Gen. Hosp.

HELLER, Michael David Arthur Oak Trees, 6A Batchwood Gardens, St Albans AL3 5SE Tel: 01727 866115 — MB BS 1951 Lond.; FRCP Lond. 1982, M 1959; MRCS Eng. LRCP Lond. 1951; FRCPsych 1978, M 1971; DPM Lond. 1963. (St. Mary's) Prev: Cons. Psychiat. Roy. Alexandra Hosp. Brighton; Sen. Regist. Bethlem Roy. & Maudsley Hosps.; Cons. Psychiat. Colwood Hosp. Haywards Heath & Brighton Child Guid. Clinic.

HELLER, Simon Richard Clinical Services Centre, Northern General Hospital, Herries Road, Sheffield S5 7AU Tel: 0114 271 4160 Fax: 0114 256 0485 Email: s.heller@sheffield.ac.uk; 31 Parkers Road, Broomhill, Sheffield S10 1BN Tel: 0114 266 9382 — MB BChir 1977 Camb.; MA Camb. 1978, BA 1974; DM Nottm. 1989; FRCP Lond. 1994; MRCP (UK) 1980. (London Hospital) Sen. Lect. (Med.) & Hon. Cons. Phys. Univ. Sheff. & N. Gen. Hosp. Sheff.. Prev: Fell. (Endocrinol.) Washington Univ. St. Louis, USA; Sen. Regist. & Regist. (Med.) Univ. Hosp. Nottm.; SHO (Med.) Leicester Gen. Hosp.

HELLEWELL, David Robert Cos Lane Medical Practice, Woodside Road, Glenrothes KY7 4AQ Tel: 01592 752100 Fax: 01592 612692; 4 Laurel Bank Drive, Marinch, Glenrothes KY7 6DG — MB ChB 1990 Aberd.

HELLEWELL, Helen Elizabeth Victoria Road Surgery, 129A Victoria Road, Kirkcaldy KY1 1DH Tel: 01592 263332 Fax: 01592 644288; 4 Laurel Bank Drive, Markinch, Glenrothes KY7 6DG — MB ChB 1990 Aberd.

HELLEWELL, Jonathan Simon Edward Department of Psychiatry,Trafford Gerneral Hospital, Moorside Unit, Moorside Road, Daveyhume, Manchester M41 5SL Tel: 0161 746 2680 — MB ChB 1985 Manch.; MSc (Psychiat.) Manch. 1993; MRCPsych 1990. Cons. Psychiat. Trafford Gen. Hosp. Prev: Clin. Specialist Zeneca Pharmaceut.; Lect. (Psychiat.) Univ. Manch.; Sen. Regist. (Gen. Psychiat.) N. W.. Regional Train Scheme.

HELLEWELL, Simon Alistair 10 Roland Mews, 27a-33 Hayfield Passage, Stepney Green, London E1 3JT Email: sahellewell@hotmail.com — MB BS 1996 Lond. SHO (Anaesth.) Broomfield Hosp., Chelmsford. Prev: SHO (Med.) Old Ch. Hosp., Romford Essex; RMO Hornsby Ku-Ring-Gai Hosp. Hornsby, Sydney, NSW Australia.

HELLIAR, Nicholas Hares Mount Pleasant Health Centre, Mount Pleasant Road, Exeter EX4 7BW Tel: 01392 55262 Fax: 01392 270497 — MB BS 1982 Lond.; MRCGP 1987; DRCOG 1988; DCH RCPS Glas. 1985. Socs: BMA. Prev: Trainee GP Exeter VTS; SHO (O & G) Roy. Devon & Exeter Hosp.; Ho. Surg. & Ho. Phys. Lond. Hosp.

HELLIER, Janet Mary Prospect Hospice, Moormead Road, Wroughton, Swindon SN4 9BY Tel: 01793 813355; West Leaze, Aldbourne, Marlborough SN8 2LD Tel: 01672 540289 Fax: 01672 540289 — MB BS 1965 Lond.; DA Eng. 1968. (St. Thos.) Clin. Asst. (Palliat. Med.) Prospect Hospice Swindon. Prev: Clin. Asst. (Gastroenterol.) P.ss Margt. Hosp. Swindon; Med. Off. Wilts. HA; SHO (Anaesth.) Soton. Gen. Hosp.

HELLIER, Kate Dileas The Old Village Stores, The Street, Slinfold, Horsham RH13 7RP Email: kbridg@netcomuk.co.uk; 38a Ferry Road, Marston, Oxford OX3 0EU Email: kate.hellier@virgin.net — MB BS 1994 Lond.; MRCP (UK) 1997. (UMDS) Specialist Regist. (Geratology & Gen. Med.Wexham Pk. Hosps.lough. Socs: Brit. Geriat.. Soc. Prev: Specialist Regist. (Gen. Med.) John Radcliffe Hosp. Oxf.; SHO (Neurol.) Soton. Gen. Hosp. Soton.; SHO (Med.) Roy. Hants. Co. Hosp. Winchester.

HELLIER, Michael Denny Princess Margaret Hospital, Okus Road, Swindon SN1 4JU Tel: 01793 426325 Email: mikehell@epulse.net; West Leaze, Aldbourne, Marlborough SN8 2LD Tel: 01672 540289 Fax: 01672 541388 Email: mikehell@epulse.net — MB BChir 1966 Camb.; MA Camb. 1966, MD 1975; FRCP Lond. 1982, M 1969. (Camb. & St. Thos.) Cons. Phys. & Gastroenterol. P.ss Margt. Hosp. Swindon. Socs: Pres. Elect, Brit Soc. Gastroenterol.; Ex Vice-Pres. Brit. Soc. Gastroenterol. (Chairm. of Endoscopy); Ex Chairm. S.A.C. Gastroenterol. to JCHMT. Prev: Sen. Regist. (Med.) St. Thos. Hosp. Lond.; Lect. (Med.) St. Bart. Hosp. Lond.; Ho. Phys. St. Thos. Hosp. Lond.

HELLIER, Paul Andrew 12 Downs Cote View, Clifton, Bristol BS9 3TU — MB ChB 1983 Liverp.

HELLIER, Richard John Church Road Surgery, 261 Church Road, Stannes on Sea, Lytham St Annes FY8 1EH Tel: 01253 728911 Fax: 01253 732114 — MB BCh 1980 Liverp.

HELLIER, Simon Christopher West Leaze, Ogbourne Road, Aldbourne, Marlborough SN8 2LD; 38a Ferry Road, Marston, Oxford OX3 0EU — MB BS 1994 Lond.; MRCP Lond. 1998. Research Regist. John Radcliffe Hosp. Oxf. Prev: SHO Hepat. Soton.Gen.Hosp; SHO Nephrol. St marys Hosp. Portsmouth; SHO Med.Qu. Alex.Hosp.portsmouth.

HELLIER, Mr William Peter Laurence 27 Hanbury Road, Clifton, Bristol BS8 2EP — MB ChB 1990 Birm.; FRCS Eng. 1994.

HELLING, Jean Wyllie Fair Mile Hospital, Cholsey, Wallingford OX10 9HH Tel: 01491 651281; 16 Priory Avenue, Caversham, Reading RG4 7SE Tel: 01734 472933 — MB ChB 1976 Aberd.; MRCPsych. 1981; DPM Leeds 1979. Cons. Old Age Psychiat. W.. Berks. HA. Prev: Sen. Regist. (Psychiat.) Oxf. RHA.

HELLINGS, Pamela Mary (retired) 27 Lindfield Gardens, Hampstead, London NW3 6PX — MB ChB 1949 Bristol; FFA RCS Eng. 1954; DA Eng. 1952.

HELLINGS, Rona Mary Basement Flat, 15 Southleigh Road, Clifton, Bristol BS8 2BQ — MB ChB 1998 Bristol.

HELLIWELL, Cedric John Vincent Browe Cottage, Shamley Green, Guildford GU5 0TB Tel: 01483 892142 — MB BS Lond. 1947; MRCS Eng. LRCP Lond. 1944. (St. Mary's) Socs: BMA. Prev: SCMO Health Control Unit Lond. Airport Heathrow; Med. Adviser (Oncol.) Eli Lilly Ltd.; Ho. Off. (O & G) & Med. Off. Special Clinic St. Mary's Hosp. Lond.

HELLIWELL, Celia Dorothy Burn Brae Surgery, Hencotes, Hexham NE46 2ED Tel: 01434 603627 Fax: 01434 606373; Burnbrae, Hencotes, Hexham NE46 2ED Tel: 01434 603627 — MB BS 1978 Newc.; FRCS Ed. 1983; FRCGP 1995; MRCGP 1985.

HELLIWELL, Geoffrey Mark BMI Health Services, Elvet House, Hallgarth St., Durham DH1 3AT Tel: 0191 384 2422 Fax: 0191 386 4961 Email: ghelliwell@bmihs.co.uk; Roseneath, Redesmouth Road, Bellingham, Hexham NE48 2EH Tel: 01434 220791 Fax: 01434 220792 Email: geoff.hell@saqnet.co.uk — MB ChB 1981 Leeds; MFOM RCP Lond. 1992; T(OM) 1992; CIH Dund 1986; FFOM RCP London 1999. Dir. Occupat. Health Servs. (N.ern) BMI Health Servs. Socs: Soc. Occupat. Med. Prev: Regional Med. Off. (N.) Rolls-Royce plc; Med. Off. Boots Co. plc.; Med. Off. Roy. Navy.

HELLIWELL, John Russell St Michaels Vicarage, Lamphey Road, Pembroke SA71 4AY — MB ChB 1969 St. And.

HELLIWELL, Margaret Frances Ling House Surgeries, 130 Skipton Road, Keighley BD21 3AN Tel: 01535 605747 Fax: 01535 602901; 5 Greenhead Avenue, Keighley BD20 6EY Tel: 01535 602883 Email: margarethelliwell100610.3445@compuserve.com — MB BS 1973 Lond.; BSc Lond. 1970; MFPHM (Hon) 1999. (Westm.) Princip. in Gen. Pract.; Chairm. Airedale PCG.

HELLIWELL, Michael Charles John Stowmarket Health Centre, Violet Hill Road, Stowmarket IP14 1NL Tel: 01449 776000 Fax: 01449 776005; The Grange, Church Road, Old Newton, Stowmarket IP14 4ED Tel: 01449 673237 — MB ChB 1974 Bristol; MRCGP 1978. (Bristol) Course Organiser Ipswich VTS. Prev: Trainee Gen. Pract. Ipswich Vocational Train. Scheme.

HELLIWELL, Michael Graham Watergates House, Watergates Lane, Broadmayne, Dorchester DT2 8HA — MB BS 1975 Lond.; FRCP 1992; MRCP (UK) 1977. Cons. Phys. Rheum. W. Dorset Gen. Hosp. Trust. Socs: Brit. Soc. Rheum.& BMA. Prev: Sen. Regist. (Rheum.) E. Dorset Health Dist.; Regist. (Rheum. & Toxicol.) Guy's Hosp. Lond.

HELLIWELL, Philip Stephen Rheumatology Research Unit, 36 Clarendon Road, Leeds LS2 9NZ Tel: 0113 233 4935 Email: phelliwell@leeds.ac.uk; Lyndhurst, 5 Greenhead Avenue, Keighley BD20 6EY Tel: 01535 602883 — BM BCh 1972 Oxf.; PhD Leeds 1993; MA Oxf. 1985, BA 1969; DM Oxf. 1987; FRCP Lond. 1995; MRCP (UK) 1975; M. Erg. S. 1998. (Westm.) Sen. Lect. (Rheum.) Univ. Leeds; Hon. Cons. Rheum. Bradford Hosps. Trust. Socs: Brit. Soc. Rheum.; (Treas.) Soc. Back Pain Research; Ergonomics Soc. Prev: Princip. GP Keighley; Sen. Regist. (Med.) Palmerston N. Hosp., NZ; Regist. (Nuclear Med.) Flinders Med. Centre Bedford Pk., Austral.

HELLIWELL, Timothy Richard Department of Pathology, University of Liverpool, Duncan Building, Daulby St., Liverpool L69 3GA Tel: 0151 706 4492 Fax: 0151 706 5859 Email: trh@liverpool.ac.uk — MB BChir 1978 Camb.; MA, MD Camb. 1992; FRCPath 1997. (Lond. Hosp.) Reader (Path.) Univ. Liverp.; Hon. Cons. Histopath. Roy. Liverp. Univ. Hosps. Socs: Path. Soc.; Assn. Clin. Path.; Internat. Acad. Path. Prev: Sen. Lect. & Lect. (Path.) Univ. Liverp.; Ho. Phys. & Ho. Surg. Roy. Cornw. Hosp. (Treliske) Truro.

HELLIWELL, Vanessa Catherine Department of Anaethesia, Bristol Royal Infirmary, Marlborough Street, Bristol BS2 8HW — MB ChB 1994 Bristol.

HELLIWELL, William Eric 19 Lymewood Drive, Disley, Stockport SK12 2LD — MB ChB 1969 Manch.

HELLMANN, Kurt Windleshaw House, Withyham, Hartfield TN7 4DB Tel: 01892 770265 Fax: 01892 770265 — BM BCh 1958 Oxf.; DPhil Oxf. 1953, DM 1964. Cons. Windleshaw Healthcare Withyham E. Sussex. Socs: Roy. Soc. Med. (Ex-Pres. Oncol. Sect.); (Ex-Chairm.) Brit. Assn. Cancer Research. Prev: Hon. Vis. Prof. & Cons. Radiother. & Oncol. Dept. W.m. Hosp. Lond.; Head Dept. Cancer Chemother. ICRF Lond.

HELLYAR, Andrew George 12 King William IV Gardens, St Johns Road, London SE20 7EG — MB BS 1976 Lond.; MRCS Eng. LRCP Lond. 1975; MRCPath 1958.

HELLYAR, Elizabeth Anne Nelyn, Sandy Lane, Harlyn Bay, Padstow PL28 8SD — MB ChB 1988 Bristol.

HELM, Emma Elizabeth Fiona 22 Pickworth Close, Oakham LE15 6FL Tel: 01572 755470 Email: emma.dvis@lineone.net — MB ChB 1998 Leic.; MB ChB Leic 1998.

HELM, Emma Jane 50 Southbrook Road, London SE12 8LL — MB BS 1998 Lond.; MB BS Lond 1998.

HELM, Kathleen Mary (retired) Colchester House, 227 Whitegate Drive, Blackpool FY3 9HW Tel: 01253 761422 — MB ChB 1940 Liverp.

HELM, Matthew Rufus Dundas 7 Thornhill Grove, London N1 1JG — MB ChB 1988 Aberd.

HELM, Mr Roger Hargreaves Department Orthopaedic Surgery, Doncaster Royal Infirmary, Doncaster DN2 5LT; Austerfield Grange, High St, Austerfield, Doncaster DN10 6QS Tel: 01302 711780 — MB ChB Liverp. 1978; FRCS Ed. (Orth.) 1989; FRCS Eng. 1982. Cons. Orthop. Surg. Doncaster Roy. Infirm. Socs: Brit. Orthop. Assn.; Assoc. Mem. Brit. Soc. Surg. Hand. Prev: Sen. Regist. (Orthop.) Leeds & Bradford; Fell. Hand Surg. Roy. N. Shore Hosp. Sydney NSW, Austral.; Regist. (Orthop.) Roy. Vict. Infirm. Newc. u. Tyne.

HELM, Susan Mary Woosehill Practice, The Surgery, Emmview Close, Woosehill, Wokingham RG41 3DA Tel: 0118 978 8698 — MB ChB 1976 Manch.; BSc (Med. Sci.) St. And. 1973; DRCOG 1980; DCH Eng. 1979. Prev: SHO Centr. Middlx. Hosp. VTS; Ho. Phys. Birch Hill Hosp. Rochdale; Ho. Surg. Canad. Red Cross Hosp. Taplow.

HELM, W Harding (retired) Dalby Hall, Terrington, York YO60 6PF — FRCP Lond. 1971, M 1943; MRCS Eng. LRCP Lond. 1942. Cons. Phys. (Gen. Med. & Chest Dis.) York & Harrogate Areas. Prev: Med. Chief Asst. Brompton Hosp. Lond.

HELMAN, Cecil Gerald Department of Primary Care & Population Sciences, Royal Free & University College medical School, Holborn Union Building, Highgate Hill, London N19 3UA Tel: 0207 288 3249 Fax: 020 8208 2060 — MB ChB 1967 Cape Town; MRCGP 1989; Dip. Soc. Anthropol. Lond. 1972. Sen. Lect. (Primary Care & Populat. Sci.) Univ. Coll.Lond. Med. Sch.; Hon. Research Fell. (Anthropol.) UCL; Prof. Assoc. Human Sci. Brunel Univ. Socs: Fell. Roy. Anthropol. Inst. Prev: Vis. Fell. Soc. Med. & Health Policy Harvard Med. Sch., USA; Albert Wander Lect. Roy. Soc. Med. 1987.

HELMAN, Susan Catherine 14 Cowesby Street, Manchester M14 4UG — MB ChB 1998 Manch.; MB ChB Manch 1998.

HELME, Mark Medlicott Cantilupe Surgery, 49-51 St. Owen Street, Hereford HR1 2JB Tel: 01432 268031 Fax: 01432 352584 — MB BS 1978 Lond.; BA Oxf. 1975; MRCGP 1983; MRCP (UK) 1980.

HELME, Michael Antony 331 Shirland Road, Queen's Park, London W9 3JJ — MB BS 1996 Lond.

HELME, Vivien Phillips (retired) 18 Traherne Close, Lugwardine, Hereford HR1 4AF — MB ChB 1946 Liverp.; DObst RCOG 1949. Prev: Sen. Med. Off. (Audiol.) Heref. Health Auth.

HELMER, Mary (retired) Platts Orchard, Church St., Southwell NG25 0HQ Tel: 01636 813348 — MB BS Lond. 1947; MRCS Eng. LRCP Lond. 1945; DObst RCOG 1951. Prev: Ho. Phys. Eliz. G. Anderson Hosp. Lond.

HELMS, Professor Peter Joseph Department of Child Health, Foresterhill, Aberdeen AB25 2ZD Tel: 01224 404461 Fax: 01224 663658 Email: p.j.helms@abdn.ac.uk; 13 Beechgrove Lane, Aberdeen AB15 5HF Tel: 01224 630834 — MB BS 1972 Lond.; PhD Lond. 1982; FRCP Ed. 1992; FRCP Lond. 1991; MRCP (UK) 1975; FRCPCH 1997. (Roy. Free Lond.) Prof. Child Health Aberd.; Hon. Cons. Paediat. Roy. Aberd. Childr. Hosp. Prev: Sen. Lect. Inst. Child Health; Research Fell. & Hon. Sen. Regist. Brompton Hosp.; Sen. Regist. & SHO Hosp Sick Childr. Gt. Ormond St. Lond.

HELMY, Ahmed Hazem Ibrahim Ibrahim Friar's Nook, Pontefract General Infirmary, Pontefract WF8 1PL — MB BCh 1983 Ain Shams.

HELMY, Ezzat Latif 27 Reedings Road, Barrowby, Grantham NG32 1AU Tel: 01476 71482 — MB BCh 1968 Cairo; MRCP (UK) 1984. Staff Grade Phys. Newark Gen. Hosp. Prev: Regist. (Chest Med.) Walsall; Specialist (Gen. Med.) Saudi Arabia.

HELMY, Nassif Iskander (retired) Bro Gain, Meirion Lane, Bangor LL57 2BU Tel: 01248 370062 — MB BCh 1949 Cairo; LMSSA Lond. 1962; FRCOG 1984, M 1965. Prev: Cons. (Genitourin. Med.) Gwynedd Hosp. Bangor, Llandudno Gen. Hosp. & HM Stanley Hosp. St. Asaph.

HELPS, Catherine May County Practice, Barking Road, Needham Market, Ipswich IP6 8EZ Tel: 01449 720666 Fax: 01449 720030; Ivine Cottage, Nedging Road, Nedging Tye, Ipswich IP7 7HN — MB BS 1987 Lond.; DRCOG Lond. 1991. (St. George's Hosp. Med. Sch.)

HELPS, Edmund Peter Wycliffe Porch House, Coleshill, Amersham HP7 0LG Tel: 01494 727584 — MD 1947 Lond.; MD Lond. 1950 MB BS 1947; FRCP Lond. 1973, M 1950; MRCS Eng. LRCP Lond. 1944. (St. Bart.) Hon. Cons. Phys. Geriat. Dept. Char. Cross, W.m. Hosp. Gp. & Med. Sch. Socs: Fell. Roy. Soc. Med.; Brit. Geriat. Soc. Prev: Phys. (Geriat.) Char. Cross & W.m. Hosp. Med. Sch.; Regist. (Med.) Univ. Coll. Hosp.; Fell. (Med.) Johns Hopkins Hosp. & Univ. Baltimore, USA.

HELPS, Peter John The Surgery, 42 Upper Rock Gardens, Brighton BN2 1QF Tel: 01273 600103 Fax: 01273 620100 — MB BS 1971 Lond. Clin. Asst. (A & E) Roy. Sussex Co. Hosp. Brighton.

HELPS, Sarah Annabel Frida John Lewis Plc, 171 Victoria Street, London SW1E 5NN Tel: 020 7828 1000 — MB BS 1976 Lond.; MFOM RCP Lond. 1991, A 1991. Partnership Doctor John Lewis Plc Lond. Prev: Site Med. Off. Brit. Petroleum Sunbury Research Centre; Ho. Phys. & Ho. Surg. Char. Cross. Hosp. Lond.; Med. Off. Civil Serv. Occupat. Health Serv.

HELSBY, Joyce Coombe Farm, Goodleigh, Barnstaple EX32 7NB Tel: 01271 378824 — MB ChB Liverp. 1945; DObst RCOG 1947. (Liverp.) Prev: Ho. Phys. David Lewis N.. Hosp. Liverp.; Ho. Surg. (O & G) City Gen. Hosp. Leicester; Ho. Surg. (Obst.) S. Lond. Hosp. Wom.

HELSBY, Mary Rachel Glastonbury Health Centre, 1 Wells Road, Glastonbury BA6 9DD Tel: 01458 834100 Fax: 01458 834371 — BM 1978 Soton.

HELSBY, William George (retired) 25 The Rise, Llanishen, Cardiff CF14 0RB — MRCS Eng. LRCP Lond. 1941. Prev: Ho. Surg. King's Coll. Emerg. Hosp.

HELWA, Sanaa Ahmed Ibrahim 54 Osidge Lane, Southgate, London N14 5JG Tel: 020 8368 5995 Fax: 020 8368 5500 Email: shelwa@hotmail.com — MB BCh 1964 Cairo; LicAc 1981; FFA RCS Eng. 1974; FFA RCSI 1973; DPMSA 1980; DA Cairo 1967; Dip. Med. Cairo 1967. (Cairo) p/t Cons. Anaesth. Barnet & Chase Farm NHS Trust Hosp. Socs: Brit. Med. Assocation; Brit. Med. Acupunc. Soc.; Assn. of Anaesth.s of Britain and Irel.

HELY, Elisabeth Jane (retired) 37 Woodend Drive, Jordanhill, Glasgow G13 1QJ — MB ChB 1965 Edin.; MB ChB Ed Edin 1965; MRCGP; DRCOG.

HELYER, Kate Anne-Louise Little Langford Farm, Wylye Rd, Little Langford, Salisbury SP3 4NP — MB ChB 1997 Sheff.

HEMA KUMAR, Jadhav General Hospital, Bishop Auckland DL14 6AD Tel: 01388 604040 — MB BS 1969 Bangalor; MB BS Bangalore 1969; DA Eng. 1979. (Bangalore) Assoc. Specialist (Anaesth.) N. RHA. Prev: Regist. (Anaesth.) Co. Hosp. Hereford & E. Dorset HA; SHO (Anaesth.) Heref. & Worcs. HA.

HEMAN-ACKAH, Mr Christopher Asuaquarm Ground Flat, 21 Marlborough Road, London N19 4NA — MB ChB 1981 Ghana; MB ChB U Ghana 1981; FRCS Eng. 1989.

HEMANTHA KUMAR, Malur Lakshmana Reddy 28C Grangewood, Wexham, Slough SL3 6LP — MB BS 1976 Bangalor; MB BS Bangalore 1976; LMSSA Lond. 1984.

HEMBRY, Janet Nicola 60 Hambrook Lane, Stoke Gifford, Bristol BS34 8QD — MB BS 1997 Lond.

HEMING, Joseph Richard (retired) Littlecot, Cheriton Bishop, Exeter EX6 6HY — MRCS Eng. LRCP Lond. 1931. Prev: Asst. Pathol. City Hosp. Nottm.

HEMINGTON, Alun Blaenbarthen Cottage, Llangoedmor, Cardigan SA43 2LP — MB BCh 1998 Wales.

HEMINGWAY, Anne Patricia Department Radiology, Hammersmith Hospital, Ducane Road, London W12 0HS Tel: 020 8383 3121 Fax: 020 8743 5409 Email: ahemingway@hhnt.org — MB BS 1975 Lond.; FRCP Lond. 1989; MRCP (UK) 1978; MRCS Eng. LRCP Lond. 1975; FRCR 1982; DMRD Eng. 1981; T(R) (CR) 1991. (Guy's) p/t Sen. Research Fell. & Hon. Cons. Hammersmith Hosp. Imperial Coll. Sch. of Med. Prev: Sen. Lect. (Cons.) Diag.

Radiol. Roy. Postgrad. Med. Sch. Lond.; Regist. (Diag. Radiol.) Hammersmith Hosp. Lond.; Prof. Radiol. Sheff. Univ.

HEMINGWAY, Mr David Martin Leicester Royal Infirmary, Infirmary Square, Leicester LE1 5WW Tel: 0116 254 1414; 53 New Street, Oadby, Leicester LE2 4LJ Tel: 0116 271 4340 — MB ChB Liverp. 1983; MD Liverp. 1992; FRCS (Gen.) 1994; FRCS Eng. 1987. Cons. Colorectal Surg. Leicester Roy. Infirm. Socs: Assn. Coloproctol.; BMA. Prev: Sen. Regist. & Regist. (Gen. Surg.) Glas.; Regist. (Gen. Surg.) Liverp.

HEMINGWAY, Harry John Sealy Dept R & D, Kensington & Chelsea & Westminster HA, 50 Eastbourne Terrace, London W2 6LX Tel: 020 7725 3235 Fax: 020 7725 3259 Email: harryl@public-health.nd.ac.uk — MB BChir 1989 Camb.; MSc Lond. 1993; BA Camb. 1985; MRCP (UK) 1991; MFPM 1995. (Charing Cross & Westminster) Dir. Research & Developm., Cons. Kensington & Chelsea & W.m. Pub. Health Med. HA; Sen. Lect. (Epidemiol.) UCL Med. Sch. Prev: Sen. Regist. (Pub. Health Med.) E. Lond. & The City HA; Lect. (Epidemiol.) UCL Med. Sch.

HEMLOCK, Andrea Woodlands Surgery, 146 Halfway St., Sidcup DA15 8DF Tel: 020 8300 1680 Fax: 020 8309 7020; 7 Marlowe Close, Chislehurst BR7 6ND Tel: 020 8467 1312 Fax: 020 8467 1312 — MB ChB 1979 Birm.; MRCGP 1984; DRCOG 1983. (Univ. Birm. Med. Sch.)

HEMMAWAY, Claire Jane 21 Drybread Road, Whittlesey, Peterborough PE7 1XS Tel: 01733 202775 — MB BS 1996 Lond.; MRCP 1999. (Roy.Lond)

HEMMENS, Sally Ann 67 Coldharbour Lane, Bushey, Watford WD23 4NN Tel: 020 8950 1028 — MB ChB 1987 Manch.; MRCGP 1991; T(GP) 1991; DRCOG 1990; DCH RCP Lond. 1990. Trainee GP N.wick Pk. Hosp. Harrow VTS. Prev: Ho. Phys. Univ. Hosp. S. Manch.; Ho. Surg. Vict. Hosp. Blackpool.

HEMMING, Anne Elizabeth Flat 178, Goulden House, Bullen St., Battersea, London SW11 3HG Tel: 020 7223 8018 — MB BS 1986 Lond.; BSc Lond. 1983, MB BS 1986.

HEMMING, Charles Stanley Town View, Bank St., Bishops Waltham, Southampton SO32 1AE Tel: 01489 892104; Town View, Bank Street, Bishops Waltham, Southampton SO32 1AE Tel: 01489 892104 — MRCS Eng. LRCP Lond. 1937. (Lond. Hosp. Med. Coll.) GP Med. Asst., Spitfire Ct. Surg., Woolston. Socs: Soton. Med. Soc.; Hants. Med. Federat.; Lond. Hosp. Med. Club. Prev: O.C. Brit. Milit. Hosp. Juba & SDF Expansion 82 Gen. Hosp.; Clin. Asst. (Physical Med.) Roy. Hants. Co. Hosp. Winchester.

HEMMING, Clare Elizabeth 71 Peterswood, Harlow CM18 7RN — MB ChB 1998 Manch.; MB ChB Manch 1998.

HEMMING, Colin (retired) 2 Park Gardens, Blaenavon NP4 9AD Tel: 01495 790262 — MB ChB Bristol 1957. Prev: SCMO (Occupat. Health) Gwent AHA.

HEMMING, Janet Diane Tel: 0191 403 2535 Fax: 0191 403 6183 Email: diane.hemming@exchange.gatesh-tr.northy.nhs.uk; 12 Elvaston Road, Hexham NE46 2HD Email: hemrite@bigfoot.com — MB ChB 1980 Leeds; BSc (Hons.) Chem. Path. Leeds 1977; FRCPath 1987. (Leeds) Cons. (Histo Cytopath.), Qu. Eliz. Hosp., Gateshead. Socs: Assn. Clin. Path.; Brit. Soc. Clin. Cytol. Prev: Cons. (Histopath.) Hexham Gen. Hosp.; Cons. Cytopath. Newc. Gen. Hosp.; Sen. Regist. (Histopath.) Leeds Gen. Infirm.

HEMMING, Julian Charles King Edward VII Hospital, Midhurst GU29 0BL Tel: 01730 812341 Fax: 01730 816333; Frogmore, Garfield Road, Bishops Waltham, Southampton SO32 1AT Tel: 01489 893165 — MB BS 1998 Lond.; BSc Lond. 1995. Ho. Surg. King Edwd. VII Hosp. Midhurst W. Sussex.

HEMMING, Paul Anthony Lower Lane, Bishops Waltham, Southampton SO32 1GR Tel: 01489 892288 Fax: 01489 894402; Frogmore, Garfield Road, Bishops Waltham, Southampton SO32 1AT Tel: 01489 893165 — MB ChB 1971 Birm.; MRCGP 1987; DObst RCOG 1973. (Birmingham) Partner Gen. Pract., Dr P. A. Hemming and Partners, Bishops Waltham, Hants. Prev: SHO (Obst.) Birm. Matern. Hosp.; SHO (Psychiat.) Walsgrave Hosp. Coventry.

HEMMINGS, Colin Patrick 19 Cunningham Road, Tottenham, London N15 4DS Email: cph@talk21.com — MB BS 1994 Lond.; BSc (Hons.) Bristol 1989; MSc. Lond. 1988; MRCPsych 1998. (St. Bart. Hosp. Lond.) Specialist Regist. (Psych.) UMDS. Socs: BMA; MPU. Prev: Regist. Rotat. (Psychiat.) Univ. Coll. Lond.

HEMMINGS, Mary Anita 15 Kenmore Crescent, Filton Park, Bristol BS7 0TH Tel: 0117 969 3583 — MB ChB 1972 Birm. Med. Adviser Benefits Agency Med. Servs. Bristol. Prev: GP Bristol.

HEMMINGS, Patricia Mary Woodlands Park Surgery, 15 Woodlands Park Road, Maidenhead SL6 3NW Tel: 01628 825674 Fax: 01628 829036; Nyas, 56 Braywick Road, Maidenhead SL6 1DA — MB ChB 1974 Ed.; BSc MB ChB Ed. 1974.

HEMMINGS, Sebourne Clyde 48 Whinney Heys Road, Blackpool FY3 8NP — MB BS 1988 West Indies.

HEMPEL, Mr Arne Christoph Andreas 28 Rowney Gardens, Sawbridgeworth CM21 0AT — MD 1963 Dub.; MB BCh BAO 1955; FRCS Eng. 1969; DO Eng. 1958. (T.C. Dub.) Sen. Regist. Moorfields Eye Hosp.

HEMPENSTALL, Kathleen 13 Elmtree Road, Teddington TW11 8SJ — MB BS 1992 Lond.; FRCA 1999. (St. Bartholomews, London)

HEMPHILL, Barry Francis (retired) 10 Sandy Lane, Petersham, Richmond TW10 7EL — MB BS Lond. 1970; MRCS Eng. LRCP Lond. 1970; FRACDS 1965; FDS RCS Eng. 1963; MDS Sydney 1959, BDS 1956.

HEMPHILL, Peter Murray Richard (retired) Springhill, Kidmore Lane, Sonning Common, Reading RG4 9SH Tel: 0118 972 3200 — MB BChir 1946 Camb.; MA Camb. 1946; MRCS Eng. LRCP Lond. 1945.

HEMPLING, Stephen Michael 28 Tongdean Avenue, Hove BN3 6TN Tel: 01273 555382 Fax: 01273 556093 Email: hempling@cwcom.net; 7 Tithe Farm Close, South Harrow, Harrow HA2 9DP Tel: 01273 555382, 020 8933 2284 Fax: 01273 556093 Email: hempling@cwcom.net, renuga@lineone.net — MB ChB Manch. 1968; LLM Wales 1995; MRCS Eng. LRCP Lond. 1968; DMJ Soc. Apoth. Lond. 1977; DObst RCOG 1972. (Manchester University) Expert in Clin. Forens. Med. Socs: Brit. Acad. Forens. Sci.; Roy. Soc. Med.Counc. Mem. Forens. & Legal Med. Div.; Assoc. Mem. Assn. Police Surgs. Prev: GP Brighton & Hove; Med. Adviser Stiefel Laborat. (UK) Ltd.; GP Woking.

HEMPSALL, Victoria Jane Forest House, Fairlight Lane, Middle Road, Tiptoe, Lymington SO41 6SX — MB ChB 1978 Leeds.

HEMPSEED, George Drysdale 3 Derriman Grove, Sheffield S11 9LE Tel: 0114 236 4518 — MB ChB 1951 Sheff.

HEMPSHALL, Ian Noel River Lodge Surgery, Malling Street, Lewes BN7 2RD Tel: 01273 472233 Fax: 01273 486879; 44 Gundreda Road, Lewes BN7 1PU Tel: 01273 477366 Fax: 01273 480879 — MB BS 1975 Lond.; BSc Lond. 1972; MRCGP 1983. (St. Bart.) Prev: Trainee GP Hastings VTS; Ho. Surg. St. Bart. Hosp.; Ho. Phys. Metrop. Hosp. Lond.

HEMPSON BROWN, Jane Donnington Health Centre, 1 Henley Avenue, Oxford OX4 4DH Tel: 01865 771313 — MB BS 1976 Lond.; MRCGP 1984; DRCOG 1983.

HEMS, Richard Andrew Coastal Villages Practice, Pippin Close, Ormesby St. Margaret, Great Yarmouth NR29 3RW Tel: 01493 730205 Fax: 01493 733120; Hemsby Medical Centre, 1 Kings Court, Hemsby, Great Yarmouth NR29 4EW Tel: 01493 730449 Fax: 01493 384395 — MB BS 1987 Lond.; BSc Lond. 1984; DCH RCP Lond. 1991; DRCOG 1991. (Lond. Hosp.)

HEMS, Mr Timothy Edmund John Department of Orthopaedic Surgery, The Victoria Infirmary, Langside Road, Glasgow G42 9TY Tel: 0141 201 5436 Fax: 0141 201 5082 Email: t.e.j.hems@doctors.org.uk; 11 Oakridge Road, Drumpellier Lawns, Bargeddie G69 7TH — BM BCh 1985 Oxf.; MA Camb. 1986; DM Oxf. 1994; FRCS (Orth.) 1995; FRCS Eng. 1990; FRCS Ed. 1989; Europ. Dip. Hand Surg. 1997. (Univ. Oxf.) Cons. Hand & Orthop. Surg. Vict. Infirm. NHS Trust Glas.; Hon. Clin. Sen. Lect. Univ. Glas.; Hon. Fell. Univ. Edin.; Edit. Bd. Hand Surg. Socs: Brit. Orthop. Assn.; Brit. Soc. Surg. Hand; Girdlestone Orthop. Soc. Prev: Sen. Regist. (Orthop. Surg.) John Radcliffe Hosp. & Nuffield Orthop. Centre Oxf.; Wellcome Research Fell. (Anat.) Univ. Edin. Med. Sch.; Demonst. (Anat.) Univ. Camb.

HEMSI, David Nicholas Elms Medical Practice, 5 Stewart Road, Harpenden AL5 4QA Tel: 01582 769393 Fax: 01582 461735; Wood End House, Lime Avenue, Blackmore End, St Albans AL4 8LG Email: david.anne@tesco.net — MB BS 1984 Lond.; MRCGP 1988; DCH Otago 1991; DRCOG 1987. (St. Thos.) Ho. Off. (Surg.) St. Thos. Hosp. Lond. Prev: Trainee GP Kingston Hosp. VTS; SHO

(Paediat.) Derriford Hosp. Plymouth; Regist. (Paediat.) Taranaki Base Hosp., NZ.

HEMSLEY, Anthony Graham Dept elderly Med RoomG03, Royal Devon & Exeter Hospital, Barrack Road, Exeter EX2 5DW Tel: 01392 41611 Fax: 01392 402595 — BM BS 1994 Nottm.; BMedSci Nottm. 1992; MRCP (UK) 1998.

***HEMSLEY, Carolyn Joan** Springfield, 30 Frensham Vale, Lower Bourne, Farnham GU10 3HT — BM BCh 1994 Oxf.; MA Oxf. 1995, B 1991; MRCP 1997.

HEMSLEY, Debra Allyson Wye Valley Surgery, 2 Desborough Avenue, High Wycombe HP11 2RN; 42 The Chase, Tylers Green, Penn, High Wycombe HP10 8BA — MB BS 1987 Lond.; DRCOG 1991. Trainee GP Wycombe VTS.

HEMSLEY, Zoe Melissa 11 Borman Way, South Wonston, Winchester SO21 3EJ Tel: 01962 889120 Fax: 01962 889120 — MB ChB 1996 Birm.

HEMSTED, Edmund Henry (retired) Hermits Hill, Burghfield Common, Reading RG7 3BH Tel: 0118 983 2205 — BA (Hons.) Camb. 1936, MB BChir 1949; MRCS Eng. LRCP Lond. 1941; FRCPath 1969; DCP Lond 1948. Prev: Cons. Pathol. Roy. Berks. Hosp.

HEMSTED, Garnet Henry Midgley, MBE, Capt. RAMC (retired) 17 Priory Avenue, Kingskerswell, Newton Abbot TQ12 5AQ Tel: 01803 873305 — MRCS Eng. LRCP Lond. 1936. Prev: Asst. Rowcroft Hospice Torquay, 1992 -1994.

HEMY, Lindsay McDonald 2 Days Lane, Biddenham, Bedford MK40 4AD — MB ChB 1976 Ed.; DFFP 1995; MRCGP 1981; DRCOG 1979. Gen. Practitioner Asst., Bedford; Clin. Med. Off.; Family Plann.; Beds and Luton Community NHS Trust.

HEN, Biing Yuh 13 Churchill Road, Sheffield S10 1FG — MB ChB 1998 Sheff.; MB ChB Sheff 1998.

HENALLA, Girgis Abdel Shahid Tel: 01724 864426 — MB BCh Ain Shams University, Cairo. (AIN SHAMS University, Cairo) Dr Kafil & Partners, Gen. Pract., Scunthorpe; Clin. Asst., GUM Scunthorpe Gen. Hosp.; Hosp. Practitioner, Subst. Misuse Unit, Scunthorpe. Socs: MDU.

HENCHY, Michael Charles North Bretton Health Centre, Rightwell, Bretton, Peterborough PE3 8DT Tel: 01733 264506 Fax: 01733 266728 — MB BS 1974 Newc.; MRCGP 1978; DFFP 1993; Dip. IMC RCS 1989; DRCOG 1977.

HENCKEL, Johann University College London, Ramsay Hall, 20 Maple St., London W1T 5HB — MB BS 1998 Lond.; MB BS Lond 1998.

HEND, Magdy Fawzy Ahmed The British Fertility & Virility Centre, 10 Harley Street, London W1G 9PF Tel: 020 8446 0101 Fax: 020 8446 3262; 707 High Road Finchley, London N12 0BT Tel: 020 8446 6060 — MB BCh 1979 Cairo; LRCP LRCS Ed. LRCPS Glas. 1983; DRCOG 1987; FRSH 1996. Cons. Reproductive Endocrinol. & Infertil. Socs: Fell. Roy. Soc. Health; Egyptian Med. Soc.; ESHRE. Prev: Med. Dir. The Brit. Fertil. & Virility Centre.

HENDERSON, Adrian Scott Ystrad Mynach Surgery, Oakfield St., Ystrad Mynach, Hengoed CF82 7WX Tel: 01443 813248; 9 Gellideg Heights, Maesycwmmer, Hengoed CF82 7RL Tel: 01443 816871 — MB BS 1979 Lond.; BSc Lond. 1976, MB BS 1979; MRCGP 1985; DRCOG 1982. Prev: Ships Doctor RRS John Biscoe Brit. Antarctic Soc.; Med. Off. Brit. Antarctic Soc. Rothera Base.

HENDERSON, Alastair 8 Emery Street, Cambridge CB1 2AX; Flat 7, Cleveden House, 1A Ferry Road, Marston, Oxford OX3 0HA Tel: 01865 723985 Email: alihenderson@freenet.co.uk — MB BS 1996 Lond. (St Marys Hospital Medical School) SHO Gen. Surg. Swindon. Prev: Anat. Demonst. Oxf.; Med. Ho. Off. High Wycombe; Surgic. Ho. Off. St Mary's Hosp.

HENDERSON, Alexander George (retired) 62 Holywell Road, Studham, Dunstable LU6 2PD Tel: 01582 873303 — MB BS 1947 Lond.; MRCS Eng. LRCP Lond. 1947; FFA RCS Eng. 1954; DA Eng. 1953. Prev: Cons. Anaesth. Luton & Dunstable Hosp.

HENDERSON, Alexander John William Department of Child Health, University of Aberdeen, Foresterhill, Aberdeen AB25 2ZD Tel: 01224 681818 — MB ChB 1981 Manch.; MD Manch. 1991; MRCP (UK) 1986. Lect. (Child Health) Univ. Aberd. Prev: Fell. (Respitat. Med.) Univ. W. Austral.; Research Fell. Univ. Bristol.

HENDERSON, Alexander Leslie (retired) 114 Burges Road, Thorpe Bay, Southend-on-Sea SS1 3JL Tel: 01702 582333 — MB ChB 1941 Glas.; DMR Lond 1944. Hon. Cons. Gen. Hosp. S.end. Prev: Cons. Radiother. Gen. Hosp. S.end.

HENDERSON, Alexandra Dupen 73 Mendora Road, London SW6 7ND Tel: 020 7610 3739 — MB BS 1996 Lond. (Camb.) VTS SHO Ealing Hosp.

HENDERSON, Mr Alistair Andrew Department of Orthopaedics, Royal Bolton Hospital, Bolton; Fishbarn Farm, Back Lane, Heath Charnock, Chorley PR6 9DJ — MB ChB 1980 Manch.; MD Manch. 1989; FRCS (Orthop.) Ed. 1990; FRCS Glas. 1984; FRCS Ed. 1984. Cons. Orthop. Surg. Bolton HA. Socs: Brit. Orthop. Assn.; Trauma Soc.; Brit. Orthop. Foot Surg. Soc. Prev: Sen. Regist. NW Region; Tutor (Orthop.) Univ. Manch.; MRC Research Fell. Trauma Unit Hope Hosp. Salford.

HENDERSON, Allan Frank Lorn & Islands District General Hospital, Oban PA34 4HH Tel: 01631 567500 Fax: 01631 567510; Old Clachan Farm House, Clachan Seil, Oban PA34 4RH Tel: 01852 300493 Email: allanfhenderson@hotmail.com — MB BChir 1975 Camb.; MA Camb. 1978, BA 1972, MD 1987; FRCP Glas. 1991; MRCP (UK) 1978; FRCP Ed 1999; FRCP (Lond) 1999. Cons. Phys. Lorn & Is.s Dist. Gen. Hosp. Oban. Socs: Brit. Thorac. Soc.; Scott. Thoracic Soc.; Scott. Soc. Phys. Prev: Cons. Phys. Sunderland Health Dist.; Sen. Regist. (Med.) Glas. Roy. Infirm.; Research Fell. King's Coll. Hosp. Med. Sch. Lond.

HENDERSON, Amanda Jane 32 Gleggside, Wirral CH48 6DZ — MB ChB 1993 Manch.; DCH 1999; DRCOG 1999; Dipolma Family Planning. (Manchester) GP non-Princip. Prev: SHO Paeds - Chester; SHO O & G - Chester; SHO Anaesth. - Fazahertey.

HENDERSON, Andrea Jane 9 Moss Side Drive, Nairn IV12 5PN — MB ChB 1993 Aberd.

HENDERSON, Andrew Angus Phoenix Medical Practice, Allerton Health Centre, Bradford BD15 7PA; Oakwood Lodge, 23 Lady Lane, Bingley BD16 4AW — MB ChB 1974 Leeds; Adv. Dip. Occ. Med. 1999 Manch. Univ.; AFOM (RCP) 1999; BSc (Hons.) Leeds 1971.

HENDERSON, Professor Andrew Hurst (retired) Department of Cardiology, University of Wales College of Medicine, Heath Park, Cardiff CF14 4XN Tel: 01222 744430 Fax: 01222 761442 — MB BChir Ca,mb. 1957; BA Camb. 1958; FRCP Lond. 1977, M 1962; FESC 1988. Prev: Prof. & Cons. Cardiol. & Dir. Cardiovasc. Research Gp. Univ. Wales Coll. Med. Cardiff.

HENDERSON, Andrew John Spennymoor Health Centre, Bishops Close, Spennymoor DL16 6ED Tel: 01388 811455 Email: andrewjh@globalnet.co.uk; 38 Elton Road, Darlington DL3 8HS Tel: 01325 358145 — MB BS 1988 Lond.; MRCGP 1993; DRCOG 1993; DFFP 1993; Dip Ther 1997. (Univ. Coll. Lond.) Socs: Christ. Med. Fell.sh.

HENDERSON, Andrew John 12 Porlock Drive, Sherford, Taunton TA1 4HY Tel: 01823 286126 — MB ChB 1989 Bristol. Trainee GP/SHO (Paediat.) Som. FHSA. Prev: Trainee GP Burnham-on-Sea; Cas. Off. Yeovil Dist. Hosp.

HENDERSON, Andrew Kerr, MBE Lorn & Islands District General Hospital, Glengallan Road, Oban PA34 4H Tel: 01631 567500 Fax: 01631 567510 Email: andrewkhenderson@hemscott.net; Birkmoss, North Connel, Oban PA37 1RE Tel: 01631 710379 — MB ChB 1969 Glas.; FRCP Ed. 1989; FRCP Glas. 1983; MRCP (UK) 1973. Cons. Phys. Lorn & Is.s Dist. Gen. Hosp. Oban; Hon. Clin. Sen. Lect. Glas. Univ. Socs: Scott. Thoracic Soc.; Scott. Soc. Phys.; Scott. Cardiac Soc. Prev: Sen. Regist. (Med.) Roy. Infirm. Glas.; Regist. & SHO W.. Infirm. Glas.

HENDERSON, Andrew Michael 133 Higham Road, London N17 6NU — MB BS 1977 Lond.; BSc Lond. 1974, MB BS 1977; FFA RCS Eng. 1982. (Univ. Coll. Hosp.)

HENDERSON, Andrew Paul Kerr 12 Victoria Crescent, Kilsyth, Glasgow G65 9BJ Tel: 0141 821628 — MB ChB 1968 Ed.; MFOM RCP Lond. 1988, A 1982; DIH Soc. Apoth. Lond. 1981; DObst RCOG 1970.

HENDERSON, Angus 117 Great North Road, Potters Bar EN6 1JB — MB BS 1998 Newc.; MB BS Newc 1998.

HENDERSON, Anna Jane — BM BS 1996 Nottm.; MRCGP London 2001; B. Med. Sci Nottm. 1994; DCH Lond 1998. Locum Gen. Practitioner.

HENDERSON, Anne Frances Maidstone Hosp, Maidstone ME16 9QQ Tel: 01622 729000 — MB BChir 1986 Camb.; MA Camb. 1983; MRCOG 1994. Cons. Obst. & Gyn. Prev: Regist. (O &

G) St. Geo. Hosp. Lond.; SHO (O & G) King's Coll. Hosp. Lond.; Sen. Regist. Wessex HA.

HENDERSON, Betty Lorraine Clare Queens Road Surgery, 88A Queens Road, Nuneaton CV11 5QT Tel: 024 7664 2368 Fax: 024 7632 7204; 8 Rainsbrook Drive, Nuneaton CV11 6UE — MB BS 1972 Bangalor; MB BS Bangalore 1972.

HENDERSON, Bruce Colin East Lodge, Corraith, Symington, Kilmarnock KA2 9AT — MB ChB 1996 Dundee.

HENDERSON, Bruce Thomas Henry 70 Crosslees Drive, Thornliebank, Glasgow G46 7DT — MB ChB 1980 Dundee.

HENDERSON, Carol Ann Station Medical Group, Thoroton St., Blyth NE24 1DX Tel: 01670 353660 Fax: 01670 396540; 7 Westlands, Seaton Sluice, Whitley Bay NE26 4HL — MB ChB 1988 Leeds; MRCGP 1993. (Leeds) Prev: GP Jarrow; Trainee GP N.umbria & Pontefract VTS.

HENDERSON, Catriona Anne Department of Dermatology, Royal South Hants Hospital Brixtons Terrace, off St. Mary's Rd, Southampton SO14 0YG Tel: 02380 684288 Fax: 02380 825813 — MB ChB 1982 Sheff.; MRCP (UK) 1986; FRCP 1998. (Sheffield) Cons. Dermat. S.ampton Univ. Hosp. NHS Trust. Prev: Sen. Regist. (Dermat.) Coventry & Warks. Hosp.; Regist. (Dermat.) York HA.; Regist. (Med.) Lancaster HA.

HENDERSON, Claire Evelyn Ann 34 Blinkbonny Avenue, Edinburgh EH4 3HU — MB ChB 1997 Aberd.

HENDERSON, Clare Crown Street Surgery, 2 Lombard Court, Crown Street, Acton, London W3 8SA Tel: 020 8992 1963 — MB BS 1990 Lond.; DRCOG 1993; DCH RCP Lond. 1992. Trainee GP/SHO Riverside HA VTS.

HENDERSON, Clare Margaret 11 Bannachra Drive, Helensburgh G84 8DF — BSc (Hons) Biochem. Ed. 1985, MB ChB 1987; MRCGP 1991; DCH RCP Lond. 1990; DRCOG 1990. Prev: GP. Trainee S. Cumbria.

HENDERSON, Clive Anthony 4 Londesborough Road, Market Weighton, York YO43 3AY — BM BCh 1987 Oxf.; MA Oxf. 1988; MRCGP 1991; DRCOG 1991; DCH RCP Lond. 1990.

HENDERSON, David Cassie Pathology Labarotory, Friarage Hospital, Northallerton — MB ChB 1977 Aberd.; MRCPath 1984. Cons. Histopath. Friarage Hosp. N. Allerton.

HENDERSON, David John East Hill Surgery, 78 East Hill, Colchester CO1 2RW Tel: 01206 866133 Fax: 01206 869054; 61 Heath Road, Colchester CO3 4DJ Tel: 01206 562988 — MB BS 1986 Lond.

HENDERSON, David Paul 5 Pauline Avenue, Sunderland SR6 9JN — BM BS 1991 Nottm.

HENDERSON, David Stuart 5 The Sycamores, Guiseley, Leeds LS20 9EN — MB ChB 1964 Glas.; DPH Glas. 1971; DCH RCPS Glas. 1967. Community Phys. Bradford Health Dist.

HENDERSON, Dinah Constance Milne (retired) 10 Lawrence Court, Mill Hill, London NW7 3QP — MB ChB 1947 Ed.; DMRD Eng. 1952. Prev: Cons. Radiol. Edgware & Hendon Health Dist. & Wood Green & S.gate.

HENDERSON, Douglas Robert The Surgery, Alexandra Road, Lowestoft NR32 1PL Tel: 01502 574524 Fax: 01502 531526; 18/20 Gordon Road, Lowestoft NR32 1NL Tel: 4524 — MB ChB 1973 Glas.

HENDERSON, Duncan James Department of Anaesthesia, St John's Hospital, Livingston EH54 6PP Tel: 01506 419666 Fax: 01506 416182 — MB ChB 1988 Ed.; FRCA 1995. Cons. Anaesth. St Johns Hosp. Livingston.

HENDERSON, Edward Bell The Conquest Hospital, Dept. of Rheumatology, The Ridge, St Leonards-on-Sea TN37 7RD Tel: 01424 755255 Fax: 01424 757039 — MB BChir 1982 Camb.; BSc (Hons.) Lond. 1975; MRCP (UK) 1987; FRCP Lond. 1998. (Addenbroke's Hospital, Cambridge) Cons. Rheum. Conquest Hosp. Hastings; Cons. Rheum. BUPA Hosp. Hastings. Socs: (Hon. Sec.) Anglo-Amer. Med. Soc.; Fell. Med. Soc. Lond.; Fell. Roy. Soc. Med. Prev: Cons. Rheum. Roy. Hants. Co. Hosp. Winchester; Research Fell. ARC Bone & Jt. Research Unit Lond. Hosp. Med. Coll.; Regist. (Gen. Med. & Rheum.) The Lond. Hosp.

HENDERSON, Edward Ellice (retired) The Homestead, High St., Godshill, Ventnor PO38 3HZ — MB BS Lond. 1957; MFPHM RCP (UK) 1972; DPH Eng. 1961. Prev: Area Med. Off. I. of Wight AHA.

HENDERSON, Eileen Catherine Elizabeth (Surgery), 121 Theobald St., Borehamwood WD6 4PT Tel: 020 8953 3355; 20 Moreton Avenue, Harpenden AL5 2ET — MB ChB 1966 Glas.; MRCGP 1978.

HENDERSON, Eileen Margaret (retired) Claydon, Newtown Road, Carter's Clay, Lockerley, Romsey SO51 0GL Tel: 01794 340082 — MB ChB Glas. 1957; DA Eng. 1964. Clin. Asst. (Anaesth.) Soton. Gp. Hosps. Prev: Regist. (Anaesth.) Newc. Gen. Hosp. & Hartlepools Hosp. Gp.

HENDERSON, Elizabeth Ann 84 Sheerstock, Hadderham, Aylesbury HP17 8EX — MB ChB 1989 Birm.

HENDERSON, Elizabeth Phoebe (retired) 3 Garden Court, Cricket Field Lane, Budleigh Salterton EX9 6PN Tel: 01395 446147 — MB BS Lond. 1953. Prev: Clin. Med. Off. (Community Health) Bristol & W.on HA & Frenchay HA.

***HENDERSON, Elizabeth Tamasin** 12 Victoria Road, Harrogate HG2 0HQ — MB ChB 1996 Ed.; BSc Med. Sci. St. And 1993.

HENDERSON, Emma Jane Fairmile Hospital, Reading Road, Cholsey, Wallingford OX10 9HH; 27 Verlam Grove, Didcot OX11 7SW — MB ChB 1989 Otago; T (GP). (Otago Med. Sch. Dunedin, NZ) Staff Grade (Psychiat.); Clin. Asst. (Haemat.). Prev: GP Train. Reading VTS.

HENDERSON, Emma Ruth 37 Hardy Road, Wimbledon, London SW19 1JA — MB BS 1993 Lond.; DRCOG 1996. (UMDS Guy's & St. Thos. Hosps.)

HENDERSON, Eric Joseph David, Capt. RAMC Retd. The Surgery, 14 Burwash Road, Hove BN3 8GQ Tel: 01273 739271 Fax: 01273 727786 — MB BS 1965 Lond.; MRCS Eng. LRCP Lond. 1965; Cert. Av. Med. 1988; DObst RCOG 1971. Socs: BMA & Brighton & Sussex Med-Chir Soc.; Anglo-French Med. Assn. Prev: Ho. Phys. Hampstead Gen. Hosp. Lond.; Ho. Surg. Roy. E. Sussex Hosp. Hastings.

HENDERSON, Fiona 61 Ferry Road, Glasgow G3 8QD — MB ChB 1990 Glas.; FFA (RCSI) 1997. Socs: BMA; RCAnaesth.; Assn. Anaesth.

HENDERSON, Fiona Helen Mary 40 Lowden Close, Badger Farm, Winchester SO22 4EW — MB BS 1985 Lond.

HENDERSON, Fiona Judith Limes Surgery, 8-14 Limes Court, Conduit Lane, Hoddesdon EN11 8EP Tel: 01992 464533; 26 Rosehill Close, Hoddesdon EN11 8NH Tel: 01992 466012 — MB BS 1979 Lond.; MRCS Eng. LRCP Lond. 1978; DRCOG 1982. (Guy's)

HENDERSON, Forbes Wilson (retired) Albany House, 255 Loxley Road, Sheffield S6 4TG Tel: 0114 234 3264 — MB ChB 1943 Aberd.; DObst RCOG 1948. Prev: Clin. Asst. Middlewood Hosp. Sheff.

HENDERSON, Frances Bourne 23 Richards Way, West Harnham, Salisbury SP2 8NT — MB ChB 1937 Birm.; MB ChB (Hons. Gold Medal Surg.) Birm. 1937; MD Bristol 1951. (Birm.) Lect. (Med.) BromsGr. Coll. of Further Educat. Prev: Ho. Surg. Qu. Eliz. Hosp. Birm.; Resid. Surg. Off. Childr. Hosp. Soton. & Emerg. Hosp. Solihull.

HENDERSON, Francis Edwin (retired) Raffeen, 6 Regents Wood, Magheralin, Craigavon BT67 0RX Tel: 02892 611064 — MB BCh BAO 1945 Belf. Prev: Ho. Surg. Lurgan & Portadown Dist. Hosp.

HENDERSON, Gertrude Isabel Rome 17 Gartcows Crescent, Falkirk FK1 5QH Tel: 01324 23424 — MB ChB 1934 Glas.; MB ChB (Commend.) Glas. 1934, DPH 1936. (Univ. Glas.) Prev: Cytol. Stirlingsh. Area Laborat. Serv.; Asst. M.O.H. Perth & Kinross Jt. C.C.; Ho. Surg. Glas. Roy. Matern. & Wom. Hosp.

HENDERSON, Mrs Gertrude Mary (retired) 255 Loxley Road, Sheffield S6 4TG Tel: 01142 343264 — MB ChB Aberd. 1945. Prev: Clin. Asst. Chest Clinic Sheff.

HENDERSON, Gillian The Health Centre, 68 Pipeland Road, St Andrews KY16 8JZ Tel: 01334 477477 Fax: 01334 466512 — MB BS 1978 Newc. GP St Andrews, Fife.

HENDERSON, Graham Anthony Department of Public Health, East Surrey HA, West Park, Horton Lane, Epsom KT19 8PH Tel: 01372 731145 Email: grahamh@dsk.co.uk — MB BS 1984 Lond.; MSc Lond. 1990; MFPHM RCP (UK) 1992. Cons. Pub. Health Med. E. Surrey HA. Prev: Sen. Regist. (Pub. Health Med.) City & Hackney HA.

HENDERSON, Helen Richmond 4A Moss Park Road, Glasgow G62 8NJ — MB ChB 1968 Ed.

HENDERSON, Hilary Jane 7 Bensons Road, Lisburn BT28 3QX Tel: 01846 607761 — MB BCh BAO 1993 Belf.; DMH 1998; MRCPsych 1998. (Queen's University Belfast)

HENDERSON, Hilary Joyce Child & Family Consultation Service, 31 Woodward Road, Dagenham RM9 4SJ — MB ChB 1968 Liverp.; MRCPsych 1989; DObst RCOG 1973. Cons. Child & Adolesc. Psychiat. Child & Family Consult. Serv. Dagenham. Prev: Sen. Regist. (Child, Family & Adolesc. Psychiat.) Tavistock Clinic Lond.

HENDERSON, Hugh (retired) Feorlig, Church Terrace, Newtonmore PH20 1DT Tel: 01540 673448 — LRCP LRCS Ed. LRFPS Glas. 1935.

HENDERSON, Mr Hugh Peter Department of Plastic Surgery, Leicester Royal Infirmary, Leicester LE1 5WW Tel: 01162 585733 Fax: 01162 585852; Nether Hall, Snows Lane, Keyham, Leicester LE7 9JS Tel: 01162 595214 Fax: 01162 653679 — MB Camb. 1971, BChir 1970; FRCS Eng. 1975. (ST Thomas's Hospital London) Cons. Plastic Surg. Leicester Roy. Infirm. Socs: Brit. Assn. Plastic Surg.; Brit. Assn. Aesthetic Plastic Surgs.; Brit. Assn. Surg. Hand. Prev: Sen. Regist. (Plastic Surg.) Sheff. Health Dist. (T); Regist. (Plastic Surg.) Lond. Hosp. & St. And. Hosp. Billericay; Regist. (Gen. Surg.) Amersham Hosp.

HENDERSON, Hugo William Alexander Flat 2, 14 The Chase, London SW4 0NH — MB BS 1991 Lond.; FRCOphth 1997; BA Oxon. 1987. Specialist Regist. (Ophth.) N. Thames.

HENDERSON, Ian James McKenzie 26 Pentland Park, Loanhead EH20 9PA — MB ChB 1981 Dundee.

HENDERSON, Ian Roberton (retired) Kirkstane, Horsbrugh St., Innerleithen EH44 6LF Tel: 01896 831095 — MB ChB 1945 Ed.; LMCC 1955; DTM & H Liverp. 1984; DObst RCOG 1950.

HENDERSON, Isabel Mary 12 Woodhill Place, Aberdeen AB15 5LF — MB ChB 1982 Aberd.; MRCGP 1986; DRCOG 1985.

HENDERSON, Mr James (retired) 44 Oakland Road, West Jesmond, Newcastle upon Tyne NE2 3DR — MB BS 1924 Durh.; FRCS Eng. 1941; FICS 1953. Prev: Med. Off. Whipps Cross Hosp.

HENDERSON, James Cotton The Surgery, 29 Chesterfield Drive, Ipswich IP1 6DW Tel: 01473 741349; The Surgery, 29 Chesterfield Drive, Ipswich IP1 6DW Tel: 01473 741349 & 742661 — MB BCh 1974 Wales. Prev: Trainee Gen. Pract. Ipswich VTS; Ho. Surg. Univ. Hosp. Wales Cardiff; Ho. Phys. Roy. Gwent. Hosp. Newport.

HENDERSON, James Gordon (retired) Richmond, 36 Rubislaw Park Road, Aberdeen AB15 8DE Tel: 01224 313103 — MB ChB 1949 Aberd.; MD Aberd. 1970; FRCPsych 1971; Dip. Psych. Ed. 1954. Indep. Cons. Psychiat. Aberd.; Hon. Cons. (Psychiat.) Grampian Area HB; Lect. Robt. Gordon Univ. Aberd. Prev: Sen. Lect. (Ment. Health) Univ. Aberd.

HENDERSON, James Herd (retired) Ravenswood, 4 Victoria Road, Gourock PA19 1LD Tel: 01475 631645 — MB ChB 1951 Glas.; DPH Glas. 1952. Prev: Sen. Resid. Med. Off. Vict. Infirm. Glas.

HENDERSON, James Roger Health Clinic, Main Street, Lennoxtown, Glasgow G66 7DD Tel: 01360 310357 Fax: 01360 311740 — MB ChB 1978 Ed.; MRCGP 1983; DRCOG 1982.

***HENDERSON, Jane Elin** Keepers Cottage, St Andrews Major, Dinas Powys CF64 4HD — MB ChB 1997 Birm.

HENDERSON, Jane Elizabeth Abbey Rise, 24 Abbey Road, Bourne End SL8 5NZ — MB ChB Sheff. 1968; DCH Eng. 1972; DObst RCOG 1971. Prev: Clin. Med. Off. Berks. AHA; Lect. (Immunol.) Inst. Child Health Lond.; Research Regist. Qu. Eliz. Hosp. Childr. Lond.

HENDERSON, Jane Helen Top Floor Flat, 1 Harley Road, London NW3 3BX — BChir 1995 Camb.

HENDERSON, Janet Taylor Young (retired) Nether Dell, Nethy Bridge PH25 3DJ Tel: 01479 821244 — MB ChB 1946 Ed.; FRCGP 1979 M 1968. Prev: GP Grantown-on-Spey.

HENDERSON, Jean Elizabeth (retired) 6 Old Model Court, Coleraine BT51 3AR Tel: 02870 343517 — MB BCh BAO 1949 Belf.

HENDERSON, Jean Nisbet 20 Strathclyde Road, Motherwell ML1 3EE Tel: 01698 264408 — MB ChB 1944 Glas.; DPH 1947. (Univ. Glas.) Prev: Assoc. Specialist (Genitourin. Med.) Glas. Hosps.

HENDERSON, Joan Margaret Clements (retired) 17 Upper Malone Road, Belfast BT9 6TE Tel: 01232 660393 — MB BCh BAO Belf. 1957; DCH Eng. 1960. Prev: Assoc. Specialist (A & E) Belf. City Hosp.

HENDERSON, John Christopher (retired) 30 Goddard Avenue, Swindon SN1 4HR Tel: 01793 525856 Fax: 01793 525856 Email: jhender@rscm.u-net.com — MB BChir 1971 Camb.; MA Camb. 1971; MRCP (UK) 1973; DObst RCOG 1973; MRCGP 1974. Hosp. Pract. (Gastroenterol.) P.ss Margt. Hosp. Swindon. Prev: Ho. Off. Radcliffe Infirm. Oxf.

HENDERSON, John David, OBE (retired) 14 Old Coach Gardens, Belfast BT9 5PQ Tel: 02890 616110 — MB BCh BAO 1959 Belf.; DObst RCOG 1961. Prev: Ho. Off. Belf. City Hosp.

HENDERSON, John Dobie 14 Lake View, Powfoot, Annan DG12 5PG; 1 Dalziel Quadrant, Pollokshields, Glasgow G41 4NR Tel: 0141 427 0624 — MB ChB 1984 Ed.; AFOM; MRCGP; Dip Occ Med. (Edinburgh) Phys. (Occupat. Health) Stobhill NHS Trust Glas. Socs: Scot. Rep. Soc. Occup. Med.

HENDERSON, John Edward East Parade Surgery, East Parade, Harrogate HG1 5LW Tel: 01423 566574 Fax: 01423 568015; 12 Victoria Road, Harrogate HG2 0HQ — BM BCh 1973 Oxf.; MA Oxf. 1973; MRCGP 1978.

HENDERSON, John Hope (retired) 36 Long Cram, Haddington EH41 4NS Tel: 01620 829404 Fax: 01620 829405 Email: johnh@mhech.freeserve.co.uk — MB ChB 1954 Aberd.; FRCPsych 1976, M 1971; FFCM RCP (UK) 1982, M 1974; T(Psych) 1991; DPM Eng. 1960. Mem. WHO Expert Advis. Panel on Ment. Health. Prev: Med. Dir. & Cons. Psychiat. St. And. Hosp. N.ampton.

HENDERSON, John Jackson Anaesthesia Department, Western Infirmary, Dumbarton Road, Glasgow G11 6NT Tel: 0141 211 2069 Fax: 0141 211 1806; Loaningside, Balfron, Glasgow G63 0QF Tel: 01360 860361 Fax: 01360 860021 Email: john.henderson@dunellon.prestel.co.uk — MB ChB 1968 Glas.; FFA RCS Eng. 1973; DObst RCOG 1970. (Glas.) Cons. Anaesth. W.. Infirm. Glas. Socs: Difficult Airway Soc. Projects Manager; Assn. of Cardiothoracic Anaesth.; Amer. Soc. of Anaesth.s. Prev: Instruc. (Anaesth.) Harvard Med. Sch. & Assoc. Anaesthesiol. Peter Bent Brigham Hosp. Boston, USA.

HENDERSON, Mr John James Department of Orthopaedic Surgery, Royal Bolton Hospital, Minerva Road, Farnworth, Bolton BL4 0JR — MB ChB 1976 Manch.; FRCS Ed. 1982. Cons. Orthop. Surg. Roy. Bolton Hosp. Socs: Fell. BOA; Brit. Soc. Childr. Orthop. Surg. Prev: Sen. Regist. (Orthop. Surg.) N. W.. RHA; Sen. Regist. (Orthop. Surg.) Roy. N. Shore Hosp. Sydney; Tutor (Orthop. Surg.) Univ. Manch.

HENDERSON, John Lawrence Bassett Road Surgery, 29 Bassett Road, Leighton Buzzard LU7 1AR Tel: 01525 373111 Fax: 01525 853767; The White House, 10 Slicketts Lane, Edlesborough, Dunstable LU6 2JD Tel: 01525 222608 Email: 101572.4220@compuserve.com — MB BS 1984 Lond.; MSc (Pub. Health) Lond. 1989; MRCGP 1995; MFPHM RCP (UK) 1994. (Univ. Coll. Lond. Sch. Med.) Hon. Lect. Imperial Coll. Sch. of Med.

HENDERSON, John Michael (retired) 38 Brook Street, Warwick CV34 4BL Tel: 01926 491227 Fax: 01926 491227 Email: a-jhenderson@talk21.com — MB ChB 1959 Ed.; MRCGP 1968.

HENDERSON, John Richard Department of Physiology, St George's Hospital Medical School, London SW1 — BM BCh 1961 Oxf.; PhD Lond. 1969; MA, BSc, BM BCh Oxf. 1961. (Oxf. & Univ. Coll. Hosp.) Reader Physiol. St. Geo. Hosp. Med. Sch. Lond.; Ed. Bd. Quar. Jl. Physiol. Socs: Physiol. Soc.; Scientif. & Clin. Sect. Brit. Diabetic Assn. Prev: R.D. Lawrence Research Fell. Brit. Diabetic Assn.; Ho. Phys. Qu. Mary's Hosp. Sidcup; Ho. Surg. Whittington Hosp. Lond.

HENDERSON, Jon (retired) 33 Welbeck Avenue, Highfield, Southampton SO17 1ST Tel: 02380 555719 — MB BS 1955 Lond.; DO Eng. 1965; DTM Antwerp 1959; DObst RCOG 1958. Prev: Clin. Asst. Soton. Eye Hosp.

HENDERSON, Karen 68 Dukesmead, Fleet GU51 4HE — BM 1984 Soton.; BSc Leics. 1980; FRCA 1991. Cons. Anaesth. Roy. Sussex Co. Hosp. Brighton; Ho. Surg. Qu. Alexandra Hosp.; Ho. Phys. Roy. United Hosp. Bath. Prev: Sen. Regist. Rotat. (Anaesth.) W. Midl.; Lect. Univ. Ghana Med. Sch. Accra; Regist. Rotat. Centr. Birm.

HENDERSON, Katherine Isabella Murray 55 Mallard Point, London E3 3JF — BChir 1988 Camb.

HENDERSON, Kathleen Mary (retired) 36 Northampton Lane, Dunchurch, Rugby CV22 6PS Tel: 01788 810090 — MB ChB 1961

Ed.; Dip. Community Paediat. Warwick 1983; DObst RCOG 1966. Prev: SCMO Rugby NHS Trust.

HENDERSON, Keith James PO Box 28, Camborne TR14 0YD — MB ChB 1986 Birm.

HENDERSON, Kirsten 132 Greenbank Road, Edinburgh EH10 5RN — MB ChB 1997 Aberd.

HENDERSON, Kirsten Mairi Flat 1, 7 Glengyle Terrace, Edinburgh EH3 9LL — MB ChB 1998 Ed.; MB ChB Ed 1998.

HENDERSON, Lesley Marie 76 Osborne Avenue, Newcastle upon Tyne NE2 1JT — MB ChB 1992 Glas.

HENDERSON, Lesley Murray Department of Clinical Neurophysiology, University Hospital, Queens Medical Centre, Nottingham NG7 2UH Tel: 0115 970 9146 Fax: 0115 970 9196; Brandhill Cottage, Lower Brand, Griffy Dam, Coalville LE67 8HE Tel: 01530 222079 Fax: 01530 222079 Email: lesleyhenderson@compuserve.com — MB ChB Dundee 1981; MRCP (UK) 1985. Cons. Clin. Neurophysiol. Univ. Hosp. Nottm. Socs: Hon. Meetings Sec. Brit. Soc. Clin. Neurophysiol.; Roy. Coll. Phys. Edin. Prev: Sen. Regist. (Clin. Neurophysiol.) & Regist. (Neurol.) Inst. Neurol. Sci. S.. Gen. Hosp. Glas.

HENDERSON, Linda Joan A & E Department, Bradford Royal Infirmary, Duckworth Lane, Bradford BD9 6RJ Tel: 01274 542200; 22 Chapel Lane, Allerton, Bradford BD15 7RJ — MB ChB 1973 Leeds; Dip. IMC RCS Ed. 1992; DObst RCOG 1976. Hosp. Pract. (A & E Med.) Bradford Roy. Infirm.

HENDERSON, Lorna Kathryn 43 Fernleigh Road, Glasgow G43 2UD — MB ChB 1997 Glas.

HENDERSON, Lynda Margaret Wallacetown Health Centre, 3 Lyon Street, Dundee DD4 6RF Tel: 01382 459519 Fax: 01382 453110 — MB ChB 1990 Glas. Socs: Roy. Coll. Gen. Practs.; BMA. Prev: Asst. GP Birm.

HENDERSON, Lynn Forbes 6 Teviotdale Place, Edinburgh EH3 5HY — MB ChB 1998 Ed.; MB ChB Ed 1998.

HENDERSON, Lynne Little Court, Stone St., Seal, Sevenoaks TN15 0LT — MB BS 1969 Lond.

HENDERSON, Mabel Adams 4 West Mount, Sunderland SR4 8PY Tel: 0191 514 1758 — MB ChB 1938 Aberd.; DCH Eng. 1941. (Aberd.)

HENDERSON, Mark Edmund Limavady Health Centre, Scroggy Road, Limavady BT49 0NA Tel: 028 7776 6641 — MB BCh BAO 1984 Belf.; MRCGP 1989; DCH RCPS Glas. 1988; DRCOG 1987. Prev: GP Galashiels.

HENDERSON, Mary Kirkhope Pullar (retired) 29 Queensbury Avenue, Clarkston, Glasgow G76 7DU — MB ChB 1947 Glas.; FRCPsych 1981, M 1971; DPM Eng. 1957. Prev: Phys. Supt. Dykebar Hosp. Paisley.

HENDERSON, Mary Theresa Haydon Bridge Health Centre, North Bank, Haydon Bridge, Hexham NE47 6HG Tel: 01434 684216 Fax: 01434 684144 — MB BS 1986 Lond.; MRCGP 1993; DRCOG 1992; Dip. Ther. Newc. 1997. Prev: SHO (O & G) Camb. Milit. Hosp. Aldershot.

HENDERSON, Max Joseph 64a Hackford Road, London SW9 0RG Email: m.henderson@10p.kcl.ac.uk — MB BS 1994 Lond.; MRCP (UK) 1997. (St. Thomas') SHO Rotat. (Psychiat.) Maudsley Hosp. Lond. Socs: Fell. RSM. Prev: SHO Rotat. (Med.) OldCh. Hosp. Romford.

HENDERSON, Mr Michael Andrew 40 Rotchell Park, Dumfries DG2 7RJ Tel: 01387 5728 — MB ChB 1956 Ed.; FRCS Ed. 1960. (Ed.)

HENDERSON, Michael George The Health Centre, Mary Hill, Elgin IV30 1AT Tel: 01343 543141; Dunure, Duff Avenue, Elgin IV30 1QS — MB ChB 1970 Aberd.; MRCGP 1974. (Aberd.) Prev: Ho. Surg. Inverness Gp. Hosps.; Trainee Gen. Pract. Aberd. Vocational Train. Scheme; Civil. Med. Pract. BAOR.

HENDERSON, Michael John 112 Denison Street, Beeston, Nottingham NG9 1DQ — MB ChB 1981 Birm.; MRCP (UK) 1984.

HENDERSON, Minna Baillie Chisholm (retired) 10 Greencliffe Avenue, Baildon, Shipley BD17 5AF Tel: 01274 581514 Email: bhende@lineone.net — MB ChB 1940. Prev: Clin. Asst. Radioisotope Dept. Bradford Roy. Infirm.

HENDERSON, Moira Adelphi Room 612, 1 - 11 John Adam St, London WC2N 6HT Tel: 020 7962 8882 Fax: 020 7712 2330 Email: m.henderson@ms41.dss.gsi.gov.uk; 15 Sayers Gardens, Berkhamsted HP4 1BT Tel: 01442 871734 — MB BS 1971 Lond.; DDAM 2001; MRCGP 1979; DObst RCOG 1975. Sen. Med. Off. Dept. for Work and Pens. Lond. Prev: GP Reading.

HENDERSON, Moira Mary (retired) Treelands, 8 Castle Lane, Carisbrooke, Newport PO30 1PH Tel: 01983 526029 — MB BS 1958 Lond. SCMO (Community Paediat.) Health Care NHS Trust; Chief Med. Ref. I.W. Crematorium.

HENDERSON, Morag Hellen Royal Cornhill Hospital, Corhill Road, Aberdeen AB25 2ZH Tel: 01224 663131 — MB ChB 1990 Aberd.; MRCGP 1994; MRCPsych 1998. Specialist Regist. (Psychiat.) Grampian Healthcare NHS Trust. Prev: Trainee GP/SHO Aberd. Roy. Infirm. VTS.

HENDERSON, Neil Cowan 2FL/31 India Street, Edinburgh EH3 6HE — MB ChB 1997 Ed.

HENDERSON, Neil Derek The Surgery, Pengarth Road, St Agnes TR5 0TN Tel: 01872 553881; Pentlands, Wheal Butson Road, St Agnes TR5 0PP Email: neil.henderson@btinternet.com — MB ChB 1980 Aberd.

HENDERSON, Mr Nigel John Stoke Mandeville Hospital, Aylesbury HP21 8AL; Norstead House, Peters Lane, Whiteleaf, Princes Risborough HP27 0LQ — BM BCh 1975 Oxf.; FRCS Eng. 1979. Cons. Traum & Orthop. Surg. Stoke Mandeville Hosp. Aylesbury. Prev: Clin. Lect. (Orthop. Surg.) Nuffield Orthop. Centre, Oxf.

HENDERSON, Pamela Ann Louise 10 Greencliffe Avenue, Baildon, Shipley BD17 5AF Tel: 01274 587640 — MB ChB 1970 Liverp.; FFA RCS Eng. 1977; DObst RCOG 1972; DA Eng. 1973. Cons. Anaesth. Bradford Hosps. NHS Trust. Prev: Sen. Regist. (Anaesth.) Leeds AHA (T); Regist. (Anaesth.) & SHO (Paediat.) Bradford AHA.

HENDERSON, Patricia Mary Napier Doune Health Centre, Castlehill, Doune FK16 6DR Tel: 01786 841213, 01786 842053; 2 Low Town, Thornhill, Stirling FK8 3PX Tel: 01786 850602 — MB ChB Ed. 1970; B.Sc. Ed. 1967; DFFP. (Edinburgh) GP Partner Health Centre Doune; Clin. Med. Off. Family Plann. Clinic Grangemouth.

HENDERSON, Peter Alan, TD, OStJ (retired) 55 Pickwick Road, Corsham SN13 9BS Tel: 01249 712132 — MB BS 1952 Lond.; MRCS Eng. LRCP Lond. 1951; DObst RCOG 1955. Prev: Lt. Col. RAMC/TAVR.

HENDERSON, Richard Gordon Radiology Department, Memorial Hospital, Hollyhurst Road, Darlington DL3 6HX Tel: 01325 380100 Fax: 01325 743986; Ord House, Little Fencote, Northallerton DL7 0RR Tel: 01609 748284 Email: richardhenderson2@compuserve.com — MB BS 1978 Lond.; MB BS London 1978; BSc (Hons.) London 1975; MRCP (UK) 1982; FRCR 1986; FRCP Lond 1999. (Guy's) Cons. Radiol. Memor. Hosp. Darlington. Socs: Christ. Med. Fell.sh.; Brit. Inst. Radiol.; Fell. Roy. Soc. Med. Prev: Cons. Radiol. Friarage Hosp. N.allerton; Research Fell. NMR Unit Roy. Postgrad. Med. Sch. Lond.; SHO (Thoracic Med.) Brompton Hosp. Lond.

HENDERSON, Richard John Cantilupe Surgery, 49-51 St. Owen Street, Hereford HR1 2JB Tel: 01432 268031 Fax: 01432 352584; The Rock, Lugwardine, Hereford HR1 4AW Tel: 01432 850767 — MB BS 1971 Lond.; MRCGP 1978; DObst RCOG 1974. (St. Bart.)

HENDERSON, Richard Nichol 9 Brunton Place, Edinburgh EH7 5EG — MB ChB 1980 Ed.

HENDERSON, Robert Anthony Department of Cardiology, Nottingham City Hospital, Hucknall Road, Nottingham NG5 1PB Tel: 0115 969 1169 Ext: 45101 Fax: 0115 970 9384 Email: rhender1@ncht.org.uk — BM BS 1980 Nottm.; FESC 2000; DM Nottm. 1991; MRCP (UK) 1983; FRCP 2000. (Nottingham) Cons. Cardiol. Nottm. City Hosp. & Qu. Med. Centre Nottm. Socs: Brit. Cardiac Soc. Prev: Sen. Regist. (Cardiol. & Med.) Wythenshawe Hosp. Manch.; Research Regist. (Cardiol.) Guy's Hosp. Lond.; SHO (Gen. Med.) Ch.ill Hosp. & Radcliffe Infirm. Oxf.

HENDERSON, Robert Edwin Dispensary House, Finvoy, Ballymoney BT53 — MB BCh BAO 1971 Belf.; MB BCh BAO (Hons.) Belf. 1971; MRCGP 1976; DCH RCPSI 1974; DObst RCOG 1973.

HENDERSON, Robert George 7 Hilton Road, Fenstanton, Huntingdon PE28 9LJ — MB BS 1968 Lond.; MD Lond. 1980, MB BS 1968; MRCP (UK) 1970. (St. Geo.) Cons. Phys. (Gen. Med. & Nephrol.) Hinchingbrooke Hosp. Huntingdon & Addenbrooke's Hosp. Camb. Prev: Ho. Phys. St. Geo. Hosp. Lond.; Ho. Surg. Roy. Hants.

Co. Hosp. Winchester; Research Regist. (Nephrol.) United Oxf. Hosps.

HENDERSON, Robert Matthew 5 Castell Brychan, Aberystwyth SY23 2JD — MB BCh 1979 Wales.

HENDERSON, Robert Thomas Smith (retired) Creag Mhor, Bentlea Road, Gisburn, Clitheroe BB7 4EX Tel: 01200 445538 — MB ChB 1950 Aberd.; FFOM RCP 1989; DIH Eng. 1956; DPH Lond. 1956. Prev: Sen. Employm. Med. Adviser EMAS (Preston).

HENDERSON, Robert Walker (retired) 4 Easter Mews, Uddingston, Glasgow G71 7PJ — MB ChB 1952 St. And.; DObst RCOG 1956. Prev: Ho. Surg. Harrogate Gen. Hosp.

HENDERSON, Robert Warden (retired) Whitecraigs, 74 Pointon Road, Billingborough, Sleaford NG34 0LP Tel: 01529 240326 — MB ChB 1946 Glas. Prev: GP Sleaford.

HENDERSON, Robina Braidcraft Medical Centre, 200 Braidcraft Road, Glasgow G53 5QD Tel: 0141 882 3396 Fax: 0141 883 3224; 41 Buchanan Drive, Rutherglen, Glasgow G73 3PF — MB ChB 1977 Glas.; DRCOG 1980. Socs: BMA; Glas. S.. Med. Soc.

HENDERSON, Roger Julian Linden Hall Surgery, Station Road, Newport TF10 7EN — MB BS 1985 Lond.; LMSSA Lond. 1985. (St. Bart.) Clin. Asst. (Gastroenterol.) Stafford Dist. Gen. Hosp. Prev: Trainee GP Stafford VTS; SHO & Ho. Phys. Stafford Gen. Hosp.; Ho. Surg. W. Cumbld. Hosp. Whitehaven.

HENDERSON, Rosa (retired) 17 Brewhouse Lane, Hertford SG14 1TZ Tel: 01992 534672 — MB BS Lond. 1939; MRCS Eng. LRCP Lond. 1938; MRCOG 1948. Prev: Sen. Regist. (O & G) Postgrad. Med. Sch. Lond.

HENDERSON, Rosalind Claire Dept of Community Psychiatry, Institute of Psychiatry, De Crespigny Park, London SE5 8AF Tel: 020 7919 2610 Fax: 020 7277 1462 Email: iop@kcl.ac.uk; 30 Champion Grove, London SE5 8BW — BM BCh 1992 Oxf.; BA Physiol. Sci. Oxf. 1989; MPH Columbia Univ. NY 1995. MRC/Lond Region Train.Fell.Health Serv. Research; Specialist Regist.

HENDERSON, Rosalind Mary Rother House Medical Centre, Alcester Road, Stratford-upon-Avon CV37 6PP; 12 Waterloo Rise, Stratford-upon-Avon CV37 7HL — MB ChB 1990 Leeds; MRCGP 1996.

HENDERSON, Ruth Elizabeth Community Child Health, 10 Chalmers Crescent, Edinburgh EH9 1TS Tel: 0131 536 0460; 16B Morningside Place, Edinburgh EH10 5ER Tel: 0131 447 6566 — MB ChB 1986 Ed.; BSc Ed. 1984; MRCGP 1992; DCCH RCP Ed. 1993; DRCOG 1988. (Edinburgh) Staff Grade (Community Child Health) Edin. Sick Childr. NHS Trust.

HENDERSON, Ruth Lowson (retired) 20 Woodland Drive, Sandal, Wakefield WF2 6DD Tel: 01924 255496 — MB ChB Glas. 1941. Prev: GP Wakefield.

HENDERSON, Sarah Lee 9 Queens Terrace, Jesmond, Newcastle upon Tyne NE2 2PJ — MB ChB 1979 Liverp.; FFA RCSI 1989; FCAnaesth. 1989.

HENDERSON, Sarah Melanie Dermatology Department, Southend Healthcare Trust, Prittlewell Chase, Westcliff on Sea SS0 0RT Tel: 01702 435555 Fax: 01702 221467 — MB BS 1982 Singapore; FRCP 1999 Lond.; MRCP 1986 UK; 1986 MMed (Internal Med.) Singapore; FRCP 1999 Edin. (National University of Singapore) p/t Cons. Dermat. S.end Healthcare Trust. Socs: Brit. Assn. Dermatol.; Roy. Soc. Med.; Dowling club. Prev: Sen. Lect. (Dermat. & Internal Med.) Nat. Univ. Singapore; Regist. (Med.) & Med. Off. Tan Tock Seng Hosp. MUIII, Singapore.

HENDERSON, Sheila Campbell Croftfoot Road Surgery, 30 Croftfoot Road, Glasgow G44 5JT Tel: 0141 634 0431 Fax: 0131 633 5284; 64 Kelvingrove Street, Glasgow G3 7SA — MB ChB 1969 Glas. (Glas.)

HENDERSON, Mr Simon Alan Musgrave Park Hospital, Belfast BT9 7JB Tel: 02890 669501; Toorak, 21 Dromore Road, Hillsborough BT26 6HS Tel: 02892 689501 Fax: 02892 689501 — MB BCh BAO 1983 Belf.; BSc Belf. 1980, MD 1991; FRCS Ed. 1986. Cons. Orthop. Surg. MusGr. Pk. Hosp. Belf. Socs: Pres. Irish Orthop. Trainees Assn.; Brit. Orthop. Assn.; Irish Orthop. Assn.

HENDERSON, Mr Stanley (retired) Crantock, Moss Road, Alderley Edge SK9 7HZ Tel: 01625 582155 — MB ChB 1933 Liverp.; FRCS Ed. 1938; MRCS Eng. LRCP Lond. 1933; FRCOG 1956, M 1936; MMSA Lond. 1937. Prev: Cons. (O & G) Macclesfield Health Dist.

HENDERSON, Stella Dolores (retired) Virginia House, Langport TA10 9PW Tel: 01458 250522 — BM BCh 1941 Oxf.; MA Oxf. 1941. Prev: Res. Med. Off. Rycote Pk. Childr. Hosp. Oxf.

HENDERSON, Stephen James Fox How, 66 Burford Lane, Lymm WA13 0SJ — MB ChB 1978 Dundee.

HENDERSON, Steven Charles Health Centre, Balmellie Road, Turriff AB53 4DQ Tel: 01888 562323 Fax: 01888 568682 — MB ChB 1992 Aberd.

HENDERSON, Sunniva Camilla 2 Manor Walk, Newcastle upon Tyne NE7 7XX Tel: 0191 266 5246 — MB BCh BAO 1957 NUI.

HENDERSON, Theodore Lindsay, MBE (retired) Nether Dell, Dell Road, Nethy Bridge PH25 3DJ Tel: 01479 821244 — MB ChB 1946 Ed.; FRCP Ed. 1971, M 1950; FRCGP 1979, M 1968. Prev: GP Grantown-on-Spey.

HENDERSON, Thomas Eltringham (retired) 206 Coniscliffe Road, Darlington DL3 8PL Tel: 01325 63320 — M.B., B.S. Durh. 1935. Prev: GP Darlington.

HENDERSON, Thomas Frederick The Eastwood Centre, 38 Seres Road, Clarkston, Glasgow G76 7QF Tel: 0141 568 7531 — MB ChB 1986 Aberd.; MRCPsych 1993. Cons. Psychiat. (Gen. Psychiat.) Gt.er Glas. Community & Ment. Health Servs. NHS Trust. Prev: Sen. Regist. Gt.er Glas. Community & Ment. Health Servs. NHS Trust.

HENDERSON, Valerie Elizabeth 17 Stirling Way, Frome BA11 2XQ Tel: 01373 464625 — MB BS 1971 Newc. Clin. Asst. Bath & W. Community NHS Trust & Ment. Healthcare Trust.

HENDERSON, Walter (retired) The Post House, Farlington, York YO61 1NW Tel: 01347 810221 — MB ChB Ed. 1933; MD Ed. 1937; FRCP Ed. 1952, M 1946; DCH Eng. 1936. Prev: Lt.-Col. RAMC Off. i/c Med. Div. A Brit. Gen. Hosp.

HENDERSON, William Alexander (retired) 17 Cliff Terrace, Marske-by-the-Sea, Redcar TS11 7LX Tel: 01642 486352 — MB ChB 1949 St. And.

HENDERSON, William Austin 38 Cranagh Hill, Coleraine BT51 3NN — MB BCh BAO 1980 Belf.

HENDERSON, William Barber Greenock Health Centre, 20 Duncan Street, Greenock PA15 4LY Tel: 01475 724477; 43 Octavia Tce, Greenock PA16 7SR — MB ChB 1983 Glas.; Diploma in Occupational Medicine 2001 London; BSc (Hons.) (Physiol.) Glas. 1980; MRCGP 1987; DRCOG 1986. Med. Off. Alba Life Insur. Co. Glas.; Med. Off. Ferguson Shipbuilders, Greenock.

HENDERSON, William Benzie St Giles Road Surgery, St. Giles Road, Watton, Thetford IP25 6XG Tel: 01953 889134/881247 Fax: 01953 885167 — MB ChB 1982 Dundee.

HENDERSON, William Iain Fleming Kingsway Medical Practice, 12Kingsway Court, Glasgow G14 9SS Tel: 0141 959 6000 Fax: 0141 954 6971; 6 Durness Avenue, Bearsden, Glasgow G61 2AQ Tel: 0141 570 1366 Fax: 0141 570 1366 Email: ian.henderson@net.ntl.com — MB ChB 1980 Glas.; DRCOG 1985; DPD (S.E. Asia) Wales Coll. Med. (Glas. Univ.) Hosp. Pract. (Orthop.) W.. Infirm. Glas.; Hon. Lect. (Phys. & Pharmacol.) Univ. Strathclyde. Socs: Brit. Assn. Sport & Med.; Brit. Soc. Med. & Dent. Hypn.; Primary Care Dermat. Soc.

HENDERSON, William Kerr (retired) Greenbank, 21 Cherry Tree Park, Balerno EH14 5AQ Tel: 0131 449 3916 — MB ChB 1934 Ed.; MD (Commend.) Ed. 1942; FRCP Ed. 1963, M 1936; MFCM 1972. Prev: PMO Scott. Home & Health Dept.

HENDERSON SMITH, Richard 91 Nottingham Road, Long Eaton, Nottingham NG10 2BU Tel: 0115 973 3262 — MRCS Eng. LRCP Lond. 1975. (Liverp.) GP Long Eaton; Med. Adviser TecQuipment Ltd. Long Eaton. Socs: Nottm. Med. Chir. Soc. Prev: Med. Off. Chandraghona Christian Hosp. & Leprosy Centre Bangladesh; SHO Qu. Mary's Hosp. Sidcup; SHO (Ophth.) Guy's Hosp. Lond.

HENDLY, Anna Jean 31 Dublin Road, Omagh BT78 1HE Tel: 01662 42857 — MB BCh BAO 1950 Dub.; DPH Belf. 1958.

HENDOW, Gabriel Thomas Bransholme South Health Centre, Goodhart Road, Bransholme, Hull HU7 4DW Tel: 01482 825438; 2 Cavendish Road, Hull HU8 0JU — MB ChB 1968 Baghdad. Clin. Asst. (ENT) Hull. Prev: Trainee GP/SHO Sheff. VTS; SHO (Geriat., Med., O & G & Orthop.) Worksop; Regist. (Orthop. & Trauma) Worksop.

HENDRA, Deirdre Anne Jaunty Springs Health Centre, 53 Jaunty Way, Sheffield S12 3DZ Tel: 0114 239 9453 — MB BCh 1979 Wales.

HENDRA, Timothy James Dept. of Geriatric Medicine, Q Floor, Royal Hallamshire Hospital, Glossop Rd, Sheffield S7 2HD Tel: 0114 271 1773 Fax: 0114 271 3689 Email: tim.hendra@sth.nhs.uk; 111 Millhouse Lane, Sheffield S7 2HD Email: tim.hendry@btinternet.com — MB BCh 1980 Wales; BSc (Hons.) Wales 1977, MD 1992; FRCP Lond. 1996; MRCP (UK) 1984. Cons. Phys. Centr. Sheff. Teachg. Hosp. Trust Roy. Hallamsh. Hosps. Sheff.; Clin. Director (Med. Dir) Centred Univ. Hosp. Trust; Hon. Sen. Clin. Lect. (Health Care for Elderly) Univ. Sheff. Socs: Brit. Diabetic Assn. (Med. & Scientif. Sect.); Brit. Geriat. Soc. Prev: Sen. Regist. Frenchay Hosp. Bristol & Derriford Hosp. Plymouth; Research Fell. Acad. Unit Diabetes & Endocrinol. Univ. Coll. & Middlx. Sch. Med. & Whittington Hosp. Lond.

HENDRICK, Alex Margaret Haematology Department, South Tyneside District Hospital, Harton Lane, South Shields NE34 0PL Tel: 0191 454 8888 Fax: 0191 427 1426 Email: alex.hendrick@eem.sthct.northy.nhs.uk — MB BS Lond. 1968; FRCP Lond. 1996; MRCP (UK) 1972; MRCS Eng. LRCP Lond. 1968; FRCPath 1994, M 1982. (Guy's) Cons. Haemat. S. Tyneside Dist. Hosp.; City Hosp. Sunderland, Cons. Haematologist. Socs: Brit. Soc. Haematol.; Brit. Soc. Immunol.; Assn. Clin. Path. Prev: Asst. Prof. Med. W. Virginia Univ., USA; Asst. Prof. Med. TuLa. Univ., USA; Sen. Regist. (Haemat.) Newc. HA.

HENDRICK, David John Royal Victoria Infirmary, Queen Victoria Road, Newcastle upon Tyne NE1 4LP Tel: 0191 227 5278 Fax: 0191 227 5224 — MB BS 1966 Lond.; MD Lond. 1979; FRCP Lond. 1985, M 1969; FFOM RCP Lond. 1994, MFOM 1984. (Guy's) Cons. Phys. Newc. Univ. Med. Sch. Socs: Brit. Thorac. Soc.; Amer. Thoracic Soc.; Eur. Respirat. Soc. Prev: Assoc. Prof. of Med. TuLa. Univ., New Orleans; Asst. Prof. Med. W. Virginia Univ.; Sen. Regist. Oxf.

HENDRICKS, Monica Anne Dorchester Road Surgery, 179 Dorchester Road, Weymouth DT4 7LE Tel: 01305 766472 Fax: 01305 766499; 14 Mellstock Avenue, Dorchester DT1 2BE — MB ChB 1989 Birm.; MRCGP 1993.

HENDRICKS, Yvette Joyce Dalston Practice, 1b Madinah Rd, London E8 1PG Tel: 020 7275 0077 Fax: 020 8919 7314 — MB BS 1987 Lond.; DGM 1998; DFFP 1998; MRCP 1998; BSc Lond. 1984; Dip. Pharm. Med. RCP (UK) 1994; DRCOG 1997; DCH RCP 1998. p/t GP. Socs: BMA; Assoc. Mem. Fac. Pharmaceut. Med.; Dipl. Roy. Coll. Obst. & Gyn. Prev: GP Regist. Year Lawson Pract.; GP Rotat. Homerton Hosp.; Regist. (Gastroenterol., Cardiol. & Gen. Med.) Basildon Hosp.

HENDRICKSE, Adrian David, Lt.-Col. RAMC Frimley Park Hospital, Portsmouth Road, Frimley GU16 7UJ — BM 1987 Soton.; FRCA 1998; DA (UK) 1993. (University of Southampton Medical School) Cons. Anaesth. Frimley Pk. Hosp. Socs: Tri-Serv. Anaesth. Soc.; Assn. Anaesth.; Soc. of Educat. in Anaesth. Prev: Specialist Regist. John Radcliffe Hosp. Oxf.

HENDRICKSE, Mark Thomas Moorburn, New Lane, Thornton-Cleveleys FY5 5NH — MB ChB 1984 Sheff.; MD Sheff. 1992; MRCP (UK) 1987. (Sheff.) Cons. Phys. (Gastroenterol.) Vict. Hosp. Blackpool. Socs: N. Eng. Gastroenterol. Soc.; Brit. Soc. Gastroenterol. Prev: Sen. Regist. (Gastroenterol. & Gen. Med.) Leeds Gen. Infirm.; Lect. Univ. Sheff.; Regist. S.mead Hosp. Bristol.

HENDRICKSE, Professor Ralph George (retired) Beresford House, 25 Riverbank Road, Lower Heswall, Wirral CH60 4SQ Tel: 0151 342 5510 Fax: 0151 342 1312 — MB ChB 1948 Cape Town; MD Cape Town 1957; FRCP Lond. 1973, M 1966; FRCP Ed. 1963, M 1955; FMC (Hon. Foundat. Fell.) Nigeria 1970; Hon Dsc (Med.) Cape Town 1998; FRCPCH (Hon. Found. Fell)1998. Founder & Edr. in Chief Annals of Trop. Paediat. Prev: Prof. & Head of Dept. of Trop. Paediat., Uni. Of Liverp.

HENDRIE, Andrew 33 London Road, Bracebridge Heath, Lincoln LN4 2JW Tel: 01522 827458 — MB ChB Ed. 1975; MRCGP 1980; DRCOG 1988; DAvMed FOM RCP Lond. 1987.

HENDRIE, Gavin James 7 Kerse Gardens, Falkirk FK2 9DY — MB ChB 1996 Ed.

HENDRIE, Oliver Richard Stirling Meadow House, Norwich Road, Swaffham PE37 8DD — MB BS 1981 Lond.; DRCOG 1984. (Char. Cross) Prev: Research Asst. (Gastroenterol.) Qu. Eliz. Hosp. King's Lynn; Research SHO (Cardiol.) Norf. Norwich Hosp.; Ho. Surg. Prof. Dept. Surg. Char. Cross Hosp. Lond.

HENDRON, Joseph Gerard Albert Street Health Centre, Albert Street, Belfast BT12 4JR Tel: 028 9032 0777; 40 Bristow Park, Belfast BT9 6TJ Tel: 01232 665452 Fax: 01232 325196 — MB BCh BAO Belf. 1957, DPH 1961; FRCGP 1987, M 1971; DObst RCOG 1959. (Queens Unversity Belfast) Mem. of N.ern Irel. Assembly for W. Belf. Socs: Ulster Med. Soc. Prev: MP for W. Belf.

HENDRON, Mary Patricia Abbots Cross Medical Practice, 92 Doagh Road, Newtownabbey BT37 9QW Tel: 028 9036 4048 Fax: 028 9085 1804; 47 Derrykeeran Road, Portadown, Craigavon BT62 1UQ — MB BCh BAO 1988 NUI; MRCGP 1992; DCH Dub. 1991; DRCOG 1991; DGM Lond. 1990. Clin. Asst. Day Procedure Unit Whiteabbey Hosp. Newtownabbey. Socs: BMA.

HENDRY, Anne Law Hosp, Lanarkshire Auth Hosps NHS Trust, Carluke ML8 5ER — MB ChB 1984 Glas.; MB ChB Glas. l984; MRCP (UK) 1987; FRCP (Glas) 2000. Cons. Geriat. Med Lanarksh. Auth Hosps Trust. Socs: Brit.Geriat.s Soc.; Assoc for Palliat. Med. Prev: Sen. Regist. (Geriat. Med.) Gartnavel Gen. Hosp. Glas.; Regist. (Gen. Med.) Gartnavel Gen. Hosp. Glas.; Regist. (Med.) W.. Infirm. Glas.

HENDRY, Anthea Elizabeth Southview Surgery, Guildford Road, Woking GU22 7RR Tel: 01483 763186 Fax: 01483 821526; Penfield House, Mimbridge, Chobham, Woking GU24 8AR Tel: 01276 856235 — MB BChir 1980 Camb.; MA Camb. 1981; DRCOG 1985. (Univ. Camb. & St. Thos. Hosp. Lond.) p/t Princip. GP, S.view Surg., Guildford Rd, Woking; Bd. Mem. Woking PCG. Prev: Trainee GP Lightwater VTS.

HENDRY, Arthur Thomson (retired) Paxhill, 20 Links Road, Parkstone, Poole BH14 9QR Tel: 01202 707739 — MB ChB 1941 Glas.; FRCP Lond. 1980; FRFPS Glas. 1947; FRCP Glas. 1977, M 1962. Prev: Cons. Chest Phys. Roy. Nat. Hosp. Bournemouth.

HENDRY, Professor Bruce Melville Renal Medicine, King's College Hospital, Denmark Hill, London SE5 9RS Tel: 0207 346 3741 Fax: 0207 346 3742 Email: bruce.hendry@kcl.ac.uk — BM BCh 1980 Oxf.; PhD 1987, BA Camb. 1976, MA 1980, MD 1985; FRCP Lond. 1994; T(M) 1991. Prof. Renal Med. King's Coll. Lond. Socs: Physiol. Soc.; Eur. Dialysis & Transpl. Assn.; Amer. Soc. Nephrol. Prev: Dir. Renal Servs. King's Coll. Lond.; Tutor (Med.) Univ. Oxf.; MRC Train. Fell.sh. Physiol. Laborat. Camb. Univ.

HENDRY, Cara 31 Double Hedges Road, Neilston, Glasgow G78 3JQ — MB ChB 1997 Glas.

HENDRY, Charles MacKenzie Allan Square Surgery, Allan Square, Cromarty IV11 8YF Tel: 01381 600224 Fax: 01381 600223; Woodlands, Jemimaville, Dingwall IV7 8LU Tel: 01381 610243 — MB ChB 1969 Ed.; DObst RCOG 1974. Prev: Ho. Phys. & Ho. Surg. Stracathro Hosp. Brechin.

HENDRY, Claire Vivien Linley, East Road, Cupar KY15 4HR — MB ChB 1967 St. And.; DMRD Eng. 1972. Hosp. Specialist (Radiol.) Vict. Hosp. Kirkcaldy Fife.

HENDRY, Mr David Sutherland 19 Marlborough Court, 15 Dirleton Drive, Shawlands, Glasgow G41 3BG — MB ChB 1988 Glas.; BSc Glas. 1985, MB ChB 1988; FRCS Glas. 1993. Specialist Regist. W. of Scotl.

HENDRY, David William Weir (retired) 5 Eden Park, Cupar KY15 4HS Tel: 01334 653135 Email: david.hendry@dial.fifex.com — MB ChB 1944 Ed.; FRCGP 1978, M 1958. GP Cupar. Prev: GP Cupar.

HENDRY, Fiona 3 Peckfield, Ripon HG4 2SF — BM 1993 Soton.; DRCOG 1996; Mem. Royal College of General practitioners - Dec 1998. Hospice Doctor Palliat. Med. - Wakefield Hospice.

HENDRY, George Izatt Limebank, Charlestown, Dunfermline KY11 3EE — MB ChB 1952 Ed.

HENDRY, James Duncan Bangour Village Hospital, Broxburn EH52 6LW; 2B Abbotsford Crescent, Edinburgh EH10 5DY — MB ChB 1978 Aberd.; MRCPsych 1982. Cons. Psychiat. Bangour Village Hosp. Broxburn. Prev: Lect. (Ment. Health) Univ. Aberd.

HENDRY, James Gordon Brown 19 Islay Drive, Ryelands, Newton Mearns, Glasgow G77 6UD Tel: 0141 639 4353 — MB ChB 1959 Glas.; FFA RCS Eng. 1967. Sen. Partner Brown Hendry Assoc. Glas. Socs: Scott. Soc. Anaesth.; Glas. & W. Scotl. Soc. Anaesths. Prev: Med. Dir. Hosp. Managem. & Supplies Ltd. Glas.; Cons. Anaesth. Vict. Infirm. Glas.

HENDRY, Joseph McInnes (retired) 44 Dalziel Drive, Glasgow G41 4HY Tel: 0141 427 0481 — MB ChB 1942 Glas.; MA Camb.

1977, BA 1940. Cons. Orthop. Surg. Roy. Alexandra Infirm. Paisley. Prev: Sen. Regist. & Sen. Ho. Off. Orthop. Dept. Roy. Infirm. Glas.

HENDRY, Julie 27A Moseley Road, Cheadle Hulme, Cheadle SK8 5HJ — MB BS 1987 Newc.; MRCP (UK) 1990; MRCGP 1994.

HENDRY, Julie Ann 15 Pelhams Walk, Esher KT10 8QA Tel: 01372 464464 — MB BS 1989 Lond. Regist. (Child & Adolesc. Psychiat.) Chelsea & W.m. Hosp. Prev: SHO (Psychiat.) St. Bernard's Hosp. Ealing; SHO (Psychiat.) Mayday Hosp. Croydon & Qu. Mary's Univ. Hosp. Roehampton.

HENDRY, Leslie Robb Tel: 01625 532244 Fax: 01625 549024 — MB ChB 1978 Manch.; BSc St. And. 1975; MRCGP 1985; DRCOG 1983. Med. Adviser Kerry Foods Ltd. Prev: Med. Off. Brit. Nuclear Fuels Ltd.; SHO (Ophth., A & E Surg.) Newc. Gen. Hosp.; Ho. Surg. (Surg.) Manch. Roy. Infirm.

HENDRY, Margaret Jean 46 Baillieswells Drive, Bieldside, Aberdeen AB15 9AX Tel: 01224 868720 — MB ChB 1943 Aberd. (Aberd.) Med. Off. Aberd. & N.E. Scott. Blood Transfus. Serv. Prev: Ho. Phys. Roy. Hosp. Sick Childr. Aberd.; Cas. Med. Off. Roy. Infirm. Aberd.; Capt. R.A.M.C.

HENDRY, Mary Watson Limebank, Charlestown, Dunfermline KY11 3EE — MB ChB 1960 Ed.

HENDRY, Michael David, MBE Health Centre, Bank Street, Cupar KY15 4JN Tel: 01334 654945 Fax: 01334 657306 — MB 1972 Camb.; BChir 1971.

HENDRY, Peter John Department of Radiology, Raigmore Hospital NHS Trust, Perth Road, Inverness IV2 3UJ Tel: 01463 704000; The Pines, Feabuie, Culloden Moor, Inverness IV2 5EQ Tel: 01463 794838 — MB ChB 1981 Ed.; BSc Ed. 1978; MRCP (UK) 1984; FRCR 1988; DMRD Ed. 1986. (Univ. Ed.) Cons. Radiol. Raigmore Hosp. Inverness & Dir. N. of Scotl. BrE. Screening Centre; Hon. Sen. Lect. Aberd. Univ. Socs: Scott. Radiol. Soc.; FRCR; Fell. RCP Edin. Prev: Sen. Regist. & Regist. (Radiol.) Edin. Roy. Infirm.; Regist. (Med.) Aberd. Teach. Hosp.

HENDRY, Raymond Brown 70 Queens Drive, Glasgow G42 8BW Tel: 0141 423 1384; 14 Sandringham Court, Newton Mearns, Glasgow G77 5DT Tel: 0141 639 2557 — MB ChB 1946 Glas. Prev: Capt. RAMC; Ho. Surg. Lond. Homoeop. Hosp.

HENDRY, Robert Alexander — MB ChB 1981 Dundee; MRCGP 1985; DRCOG 1984.

HENDRY, Scott James 12A Royal Crescent, Edinburgh EH3 6PZ — MB ChB 1993 Dundee; BSc (Hons.) Dund 1988, MB ChB 1993; MRCP 1999. (University of Dundee Scotland) Research.Fell.A&E Roy.Hosps. Sick Childr. Edin. Prev: SHO (A & E) Roy. Hosp. Sick Childr. Edin.; SHO (Med. Paediat.) Roy. Hosp. Sick Childr. Edin.; Regist. (Paediat.) Sydney Childr.'s Hosp. Sydney, Australia.

HENDRY, Stuart William Lennox and Partners, 9 Alloway Place, Ayr KA7 2AA Tel: 01292 611835 Fax: 01292 284982; 5 Cunning Park Drive, Ayr KA7 4DT — MB ChB 1982 Glas.; DCH RCPS Glas. 1985; DRCOG 1984.

HENDRY, Mr William Forbes (retired) 107 Vanguard Building, 18 Westferry Road, London E14 8LZ — MB ChB 1961 Glas.; MD Glas. 1993, ChM 1971; FRCS Eng. 1966; FRCS Ed. 1966. Civil. Cons. Urol. Roy. Navy. Prev: Sen. Regist. (Surg.) St. Peter's Hosp. Lond.

HENDRY, Mr William Garden (retired) 47 Broad Walk, Winchmore Hill, London N21 3BL Tel: 020 8886 0773 — MB ChB 1936 Aberd.; FRCS Ed. 1944; FRCS Eng. 1947. Prev: Cons. Surg. Highlands Gen. Hosp. & Wood Green & S.gate Hosp. Lond.

HENDRY, William Thomson 46 Baillieswells Drive, Bieldside, Aberdeen AB15 9AX Tel: 01224 868720 — MB ChB 1944 Aberd.; MRCGP 1954. (Aberd.) Sen. Lect. Forens. Path. & Head Dept. Foren. Med. Univ. Aberd.; Hon. Cons. Forens. Path. Grampian HB. Socs: Fell. Brit. Assn. Forens. Med. Prev: Asst. Path. Univ. Aberd.; RAMC 1946-8, Graded Med. Specialist; Sen. Police Surg. Aberd.

HENDRY, Mr Wilson Stephen 15 Randolph Road, Stirling FK8 2AW Tel: 01786 473319 Fax: 01786 473319 — MB ChB 1975 Aberd.; MD Aberd. 1981; FRCS Glas. 1990; FRCS Ed. 1980. (Aberd.) Cons. Surg. Stirling Roy. Infirm. Prev: Sen. Regist. (Surg.) Grampian HB.

HENDY, Bernard (retired) 144 Church Road, Bolton BL1 6HJ Tel: 01204 841427 — MB ChB 1948 Manch. Prev: Ho. Phys. (Rheum. & Haemat.) Manch. Roy. Infirm.

HENDY, Charles The Halliwell Surgery, Lindfield, Halliwell, Bolton BL2 3DU Tel: 01204 23642; 87 Turton Heights, Bromley Cross, Bolton BL2 3DU — MB BS 1988 Lond.; MRCGP 1992.

HENDY, Michael Steven The Beeches, Roseacre Road, Elswick, Preston PR4 3UD — MB BS 1973 Lond.; BSc (Hons.) Lond. 1970, MB BS 1973; MRCP (UK) 1977. (St. Mary's) Cons. Phys. Vict. Hosp. Blackpool.

HENDY, Sophia Caroline Ley Farm, Diptford, Totnes TQ9 7NN — MB BS 1989 Lond.; MRCGP 1995. Prev: SHO Derriford Hosp.; Ho. Off. (Med.) St. Thos. Hosp. Lond.; Ho. Off. (Surg.) Stoke Mandeville Hosp. Aylesbury.

HENDY-IBBS, Mr Peter Michael Ormskirk General Hospital, Wigan Road, Ormskirk L39 2AZ Tel: 01695 577111 Fax: 01695 583062 Email: peter.hendry.ibbs@wlhs.nwest.nhs.uk; Church View, 5 Gorsey Lane, Mawdesley, Ormskirk L40 3TE — MB ChB 1980 Sheff.; MFFP 1993; MRCOG 1988. Cons. O & G Ormskirk Gen. Hosp. Socs: Brit. Soc. Colpos. & Cerv. Path.; Internat. Soc. Twin Studies; Brit. Assoc. of Perinatal Med. Prev: Lect. (O & G) Univ. Liverp.; Regist. (O & G) St. Bart's. Lond.; Research Fell. (Gyn. Oncol., Clin. Oncol. & Radiother.) Univ.

HENEBURY, Robert Emmett David Little Venice Medical Centre, 2 Crompton Street, London W2 1ND Tel: 020 7723 1314 Fax: 020 7723 8580 — MB ChB 1967 Birm.; DObst RCOG 1969. (Birm.) Socs: BMA. Prev: Ho. Surg. Worcs. Roy. Infirm. (Ronkshill Br.); Ho. Phys. & Ho. Surg. (O & G) Dudley Rd. Hosp. Birm.

HENEGHAN, Christopher Paul Hamilton Nevill Hall Hospital, Abergavenny NP7 Tel: 01873 852091; Hendre Cwrt, Llanellen, Abergavenny NP7 9LE — BM BCh 1973 Oxf.; BA Oxf. 1970, BM BCh 1973; FRCA 1978; Barrister Lincoln's Inn 1987. (Oxford and St. Bartholomews) Cons. (Anaesth.) Nevill Hall Hosp. Abergavenny. Prev: Cons. Dir. (Anaesth. & IC) Ealing Hosp.; Sci. Off. Div. Anaesth. Clin. Research Centre & Hon. Cons. Anaesth. N.wick Pk. Hosp. Harrow; Sen. Regist. Rotat. (Anaesth.) Brompton Hosp. Lond.

HENEGHAN, Frances Anne Tanybryn, Dewi Rd, Tregaron SY25 6JN Tel: 01974 298150 Email: daf@tanybryn.freeserve.co.uk — MB BCh 1997 Wales; BSc. Kings College Lond. 1992. (UWCM) GP Regist., VTS, Plymouth. Prev: SHO (Med.), Rookwood Hosp., Llandaff, Cardiff; Ho. Off. (Surg.), Bronglair Gen. Hosp., Aberystwyth; Ho. Off. (Med.), Llandough Hosp., Penarth, S. Glam.

HENEGHAN, Mark Bartholomew John Brecon Medical Group Practice, Ty Henry Vaughan, Bridge Street, Brecon LD3 8AH Tel: 01874 622121 Fax: 01874 623742; Glyngarth, Llanddew, Aberhonddu, Brecon LD3 9SY — MB BCh 1983 Wales; BSc (Hons.) Biochem. Wales 1980; MRCP (UK) 1987; DRCOG 1991; MRCGP 1998. (Cardiff) HP (Geriat.) Yshyt Coffa Aberhonddu; HP (Cardiol.) Yshyt Coffa Aberhonddu; PR (Endoscopy) Yshyt Coffa Aberhonddu. Prev: Clin. Asst. (Geriat.) Ysbyty Dewi Sant Llanfaes, Aberhonddu.; SHO (O & G) Withybush Gen. Hosp. HaverfordW.; Regist. (Gen. Med. & Gastro-Enterol.) Acad. Dept. Med. Roy. Free Hosp. Lond.

HENEGHAN, Noel David Hamilton (retired) Bartholomew's, Cwrtnewydd, Llanybydder SA40 9YH Tel: 01570 434308 — MRCS Eng. LRCP Lond. 1946. Prev: Ho. Phys. St. Bart. Hosp. Lond.

HENEGHAN, Sarah Jane Scourfield and Partners, The Surgery, Oakfield Street, Ystrad Mynach, Hengoed CF82 7WX — MB BCh 1984 Wales; BSc (Hons. Physiol.) Cardiff 1981. (Welsh Nat. Sch. Med.)

HENEGHAN, Thomas Terence Dufftown Medical Group, Health Centre, Stephen Avenue, Dufftown, Keith AB55 4FJ Tel: 01340 820888 Fax: 01340 820593 — MB ChB 1976 Aberd.; MRCGP 1985; DRCOG 1979.

HENEIN, Mr Reda Riad Manor Farm House, 29 Main St., Ledston, Castleford WF10 2AB — MB ChB 1967 Alexandria; FRCS Ed. 1976; DLO Alexandria 1970; Cert. Higher Surgic. Train. Ed. 1979. (Alexandria, Egypt) Cons. (ENT) Wakefield AHA.

HENFREY, Lisa Jayne 15 Melbourne Road, West Bridgford, Nottingham NG2 5BG — MB BS 1992 Lond.

HENK, John Michael 76 The Crescent, Sutton SM2 7BS Tel: 020 8643 2592 Email: mhenk@doctors.org.uk — MB 1960 Camb.; BChir 1959; FFR 1966; DMRT Eng. 1964. (Camb. & St. Geo.) Cons. Radiother. & Oncol. Roy. Marsden Hosp. Lond. Socs: Europ. Soc. of Therapeutic Radiol. and Oncol.; BMA & Brit. Oncol. Assn. Prev: Cons. Radiother. S. Glam. AHA (T); Ho. Phys. & Cas. Off. St. Geo. Hosp. Lond.

HENLEY, Mr Andrew John Teignbridge Medical Practice, 2 Den Crescent, Teignbridge, Teignmouth TQ14 8BG Tel: 01626 773729 Fax: 01626 777381; 2 Den Crescent, Teignmouth TQ14 8BG Tel: 0162 67 770297 — MB ChB 1976 Bristol; FRCS Eng. 1981. Clin.

Asst. (Gen. Surg.) Torbay HA. Prev: Regist. (Gen. Surg. & Orthop.) Newc. AHA (T).

HENLEY, Ann (retired) The Old Vicarage, Hambleton, Oakham LE15 8TH Tel: 01572 722053 Email: indi@rutnet.co.uk — MRCS Eng. LRCP Lond. 1960; DObst RCOG 1961. Prev: GP PeterBoro.

HENLEY, Brian (retired) Hangarfield, Dungells Lane, Yateley GU46 6EZ — MB ChB 1958 Birm.; MRCGP 1979; DObst RCOG 1965. Prev: Med. Off. RAF.

HENLEY, David Frederick (retired) 1 Greenacre Park, Gateshead NE9 6HF Tel: 0191 487 1724 — MB BS 1956 Durh.; FFCM 1980, M 1972; DPH Durh. 1964. Prev: DPH Gateshead HA.

HENLEY, Mr Francis Austin (retired) Flat 1, 29 Arlington Road, Eastbourne BN21 1DL — MB BS 1939 Lond.; FRCS Eng. 1949; MRCS Eng. LRCP Lond. 1939. Sen. Surg. & Consult. Centr. Middlx. Hosp. Lond.; Surg. & Hon. Demonst. Anat. Middlx. Hosp. Med. Sch. Lond.; Hon. Prof. Surg. Firusabadi Hosp. Teheran, Iran; Vis. Surg. Libyan Arab RePub. Govt.; Vis. Prof. & Examr. (Surg.) Univ. Caryounis, Benghazi. Prev: Chief Surg. Reza Shah Kabir Hosp. Tehran, Iran.

HENLEY, Grahame Duncan (retired) Rhodes, Harcombe Road, Raymond's Hill, Axminster EX13 5TB Tel: 01297 34926 Fax: 01297 34926 — MB ChB 1959 Bristol. Prev: GP Bristol.

HENLEY, Mr Mark Dept. of Plastic & Reconstructive Surgery, City Hospital NHS Trust, Hucknell Rd, Nottingham NG5 1PB Tel: 0115 962 7706 Fax: 0115 962 7706; 97 Torvill Drive, Nottingham NG8 2BR — MB ChB 1980 Birm.; FRCS Ed 1987; FRCS (Plast) 1993. (Birmingham) Cons. (Plastic, Reconstruc. & Hand Surg.) City Hosp. NHS Trust, Nottm.

HENLEY, Mr Michael Justin 48 Addison Street, Nottingham NG1 4HA — MB BS 1991 Lond.; FRCS Eng. 1995.

HENLEY, Peter Adrian 60 Hungate Street, Aylsham, Norwich NR11 6AA — MB ChB 1994 Manch.; FDS RCS Ed. 1990; DRCOG 1997; MRCGP 1998. (Manch) GP. Prev: GP/Regist. Gt. Witley Worcs.

HENLEY, Raymond Francis (retired) 29 Eccleston Gardens, St Helens WA10 3BL Tel: 01744 759999 — MB BCh BAO 1952 NUI. Prev: Regist. Liverp. ENT Hosp.

HENLY, John Gilbert (retired) 10 The Highfields, Wightwick, Wolverhampton WV6 8DW — MB Camb. 1964, BChir 1963; FFA RCS Eng. 1971; DObst RCOG 1967. Prev: Cons. Anaesth. Roy. Wolverhampton Hosps.

HENMAN, Mary Elizabeth The Great Holland Practice, The Great Hollands Health Centre, Great Hollands Square, Bracknell RG12 8WY Tel: 01344 786926 Fax: 01344 786910; 2 Kyle Close, Bracknell RG12 7DF Tel: 01344 451155 — MB ChB 1973 Manch. (Manch.) Prev: Clin. Med. Off. E. Berks. & NW Surrey HA.

HENMAN, Mr Philip David Orthopaedic Department, Dundee Royal Infirmary, Dundee Tel: 01382 60111; 4 Castle Terrace, Tayport DD6 9AG Tel: 01382 553043 — MB ChB 1987 Manch.; BSc (Med. Sci.) St. And. 1984; FRCS Ed. 1993. Career Regist. (Orthop.) Dundee Roy. Infirm. Prev: Demonst. (Anat.) Glas. Univ.; SHO (Orthop.) Norf. & Norwich Hosp.

HENN, Markus 9 Eton Grove, Nottingham NG8 1FT — State Exam Med. Essen 1991.

HENNAYAKE, Mr Supul Priyantha Room EG 228, Paediatric Surgery Department, Southampton General Hospital, Tremona Road, Southampton SO16 6YD — MB BS 1986 Colombo; FRCS Eng. 1993.

HENNEBRY, Mary Clare 52 Castlebar Road, Ealing, London W5 2DD — MB BS 1996 Lond.

HENNEBRY, Sheila (retired) 52 Castlebar Road, Ealing, London W5 2DD Tel: 020 8997 3100 — MB BS 1954 Lond.; DObst RCOG 1957.

HENNELL, Pauline Ann Send Surgery, 175 Send Road, Send, Woking GU23 7ET — MB ChB 1982 Ed.; BSc (Med. Sci.) Ed. 1979, MB ChB 1982; MRCGP 1987; DRCOG 1986. Prev: Trainee GP Cleveland VTS; SHO Rotat. (Med.) S. Tees DHA.

HENNELLY, Kieran Joseph 97 Weavers Way, London NW1 0XG — MB BS 1992 Lond.

HENNELLY, Michael Francis Riverside Close Surgery, Station Road, Liss GU33 7AD Tel: 01730 892412 Fax: 01420 476714; Stannards, Firth End, Bordon GU35 0QR Tel: 01420 473734 — MRCS Eng. LRCP Lond. 1968; DTM & H Eng. 1974. (Cardiff) Prev: PMO HMS Excellent; Sen. Med. Off. Brit. Servs. Clinic Naples, Italy; Med. Off. BJSTT, Accra, Ghana.

HENNESSEY, Christina Mary 35 The Downs, London SW20 8HG — MB ChB 1992 Ed.

HENNESSEY, Felicity Anne The Surgery, 57 Upper Tooting Park, London SW17 7SU Tel: 020 8673 5846; 35 The Downs, London SW20 8HG — MB ChB 1963 St. And. GP Lond. Prev: Ho. Surg. Maryfield Hosp. Dundee; Ho. Phys. Maidenhead Gen. Hosp.; Resid. (O & G) Doctors' Hosp. New York.

HENNESSEY, Terence David Ravens Oak, Davey Lane, Alderley Edge SK9 7NZ Tel: 01625 582148 — BM BCh 1959 Oxf.; DM Oxf. 1968, MA, BM BCh 1959. (Middlx.) Socs: Brit. Soc. Antimicrobiol. Chemother. & Amer. Soc. Microbiol. Prev: Research Asst. Dept. Bact. Roy. Postgrad. Med. Sch. Lond.; Asst. Pathol. Bland-Sutton Inst. & Ho. Phys. Profess. Med. Unit; Middlx. Hosp. Lond.

HENNESSY, Aisling Mary Walnut Tree Cottage, Cleeve Road, Goring on Thames, Reading RG8 9DA — MB ChB 1993 Bristol.

HENNESSY, Annabel Irene Morriston Hospital, Heol Maes Eglwys, Swansea SA6 6NL Tel: 01792 702222 — MB BCh 1979 Wales; FRCP (Lond.) 1997. Cons. Rehabil. Med. Swansea NHS Trust. Prev: Sen. Regist. (Rehabil. Med.) Roy. Nat. Orthop. Hosp. Stanmore.

HENNESSY, Mr Colm North Tees General Hospital, Hardwick, Stockton-on-Tees TS19 8PE Tel: 01642 624600 Fax: 01642 624978 Email: colmhennessy@nth.northy.nhs.uk; 6 Old Sunderland Road, Wolviston Village, Billingham TS22 5LZ Tel: 01740 644304 — MB BCh BAO 1981 NUI; MD Newc. 1993; FRCSI 1986. Cons. Surg. N. Tees Gen. Hosp. Stockton-on-Tees. Socs: BASO; Assn. Coloproctol.; Surgic. Research Soc. Prev: Sen. Regist. N.ern Region.

HENNESSY, Denise Mary Avenue Medical Centre, 51-53 Victoria Avenue, Blackley, Manchester M9 6BA Tel: 0161 720 8282 Fax: 0161 740 7991; 2 The Green, Greenmount, Bury BL8 4EQ — MB ChB 1983 Manch.; MRCGP 1987; DRCOG 1984; Cert. Family Plann. JCC 1984. Prev: Trainee GP N. Manch Gen. Hosp. VTS; Ho. Phys. N. Manch. Gen. Hosp.; Ho. Surg. Blackburn Roy. Infirm.

HENNESSY, Edmond Peter 35 Portman Road, Wavertree, Liverpool L15 2HH — MB ChB 1995 Liverp.

HENNESSY, Mr Jeremiah Dominick (retired) 36 Featherston Road, Sutton Coldfield B74 3JN Tel: 0121 353 1995 — MB BCh BAO 1945 NUI; MCh NUI 1952, MB BCh BAO 1945; FRCS Eng. (ad eund.) 1975; FRCS Ed. 1952. Cons. Gen. Surg. W. Bromwich Hosp. Gp. Prev: Sen. Surg. Regist. Coventry Hosp. Gp.

HENNESSY, Mr Michael John Department of Neurology, Morriston Hospital, Heol Maes Eglwys, Cwmrhydyceirw, Swansea SA6 6NL — BM BCh 1970 Oxf.; FRCS Eng. 1977.

HENNESSY, Mr Michael Sean Orthopaedic Dept., Wirral Hospitals NHS Trust, Arrowe Park Road, Upton CH49; 10 Fairfield Road, Scartho, Grimsby DN33 3DP Email: l1331c65@hotmail.com — MB ChB 1989 Liverp.; FRCS 1999 (Tr. Orth.); BSc (Hons.) Liverp. 1985; FRCS Ed. 1994. Cons. Orthopaedic-Trauma Surg. Socs: BMA; BOA; BOFSS.

HENNESSY, Niklas Liam Mark Southampton General Hospital, Tremona Road, Southampton SO16 6YD Tel: 02380 777222; 34 Northlands Road, Banister Park, Southampton SO15 2LF Tel: 02380 231108 — MB BS 1994 Lond.; BEng Soton. 1989. (United Med. & Dent. Schs. Guy's & St. Thomas' Hosp.) Specialist Regist. (Radiol.) Soton. Gen. Hosp. Prev: SHO (Med) King Edwd. VII Hosp. Midhurst.

HENNESSY, Rachel Elizabeth Abraham Cowley Unit, Holloway Hill, Lyne, Chertsey KT16 0AE Tel: 01932 872010 — MB ChB 1984 Leic.; MRCPsych 1988. Cons. Psychiat. Bournewood NHS Trust Chertsey; Clin. Dir. (Ment. Health). Prev: Hon. Sen. Regist. Springfield Hosp. Lond. & St. Peters Hosp. Chertsey; Lect. & Hon. Regist. Acad. Unit. Horton Hosp. Epsom Surrey.

HENNESSY, Thomas Daniel Silverdale Medical Centre, Mount Avenue, Heswall, Wirral CH60 4RH Tel: 0151 342 6128 Fax: 0151 342 2435; 5 Blair Park, Bebington, Wirral CH63 9FL — MB ChB 1975 Liverp.; MRCGP 1984. GP Wirral.

HENNIGAN, John Terence 9 St Johns Grove, London N19 5RW — MB ChB 1964 Glas. (Glas.)

HENNIGAN, Margaret (retired) Nether Pitlour, West Mill, Strathmiglo, Cupar KY14 7PU Tel: 01337 860203 Fax: 01337 860203 — MB ChB Glas. 1958; FFPHM RCP (UK) 1991; FRCOG 1982, M 1966; MFCM 1974. Prev: Princip. Med. Off. Scott. Home & Health Dept.

HENNIGAN, Mr Thomas William 119 Glentrammon Road, Orpington BR6 6DQ — MD 1993 Newc.; MB BS 1981; FRCS Eng. 1986; FRCS Ed. 1986. Sen. Regist. Chelsea & W.m. Hosp. Lond. Socs: Surgic. Research Soc. & Roy. Soc. Med. (Sec. Clin. Sect.). Prev: Lect. (Surg.) Char. Cross Hosp. & W.m. Med. Sch. Lond.; Regist. Rotat. (Surg.) Newc.

HENNING, Jeremy David Richard Dept of Anaesthesia, Bristol Royal Infirmary, Marlborough Street, Bristol BS2 8HW — MB BCh 1991 Wales. Specialist Anaest. Dept of Anaesth. Bristol Roy. Infirm. Prev: SHO (Anaesth.) Berks.

HENRICHSEN, Thore Andre PICU, Hospital for Sick Children, Great Ormond St., London WC1N 3JH — Canada Med. Oslo 1986.

HENRIKSEN, Peter Andrew 16 Redford Loan, Edinburgh EH13 0AX — MB ChB 1996 Ed.

HENRIQUES, Mr Cecil Q (retired) Potash Cottage, Great Glemham, Saxmundham IP17 2DE Tel: 01728 663604 — MA Camb. 1949, MChir 1956, MB BChir 1948; FRCS Eng. 1953. Cons. Surg. Ipswich & E. Suff. Hosp. Gp. Prev: Sen. Surg. Regist. & Research Fell. King's Coll. Hosp.

HENRY, Adam 21 Denham Avenue, Cramlington NE23 9FT — MB BS 1993 Newc.

***HENRY, Alison Patricia** 14 Whitely Lane, Fulwood, Sheffield S10 4GL — MB ChB 1996 Birm.

HENRY, Ann Marie 132 Tobermore Road, Desertmartin, Magherafelt BT45 5LF — MB ChB 1994 Liverp.

HENRY, Mr Anthony Patrick Joseph East Midland Nuffield Hospital, Rykneld Rd, Derby DE23 7SN Tel: 01538 304100 Fax: 01538 304100; Four Winds, Wagon Lane, Bretby, Burton-on-Trent DE15 0QF — MB BS Lond. 1962; FRCS Eng. 1971; MRCS Eng. LRCP Lond. 1962. (St. Thos.) Cons. Surg. (Orthop.) Derbysh. Roy. Infirm. & Derbsh. Child. Hosp.; Lect. (Anat.) Derby Sch. Occupat. Ther.; Examr. Surg. Coll. Occupat. Therapists Lond. Socs: Fell. BOA (Counc. Mem., 2000-2003); (Ex-Pres.) Naughton Dunn Club; (Ex Pres) Brit. Orthop. Foot Surg. Soc. Prev: Sen. Regist. (Orthop.) Harlow Wood Orthop. Hosp. Mansfield; Regist. (Surg.) King Edwd. VIII Hosp. Durban, S. Afr.; Lect. (Anat.) Univ. Alberta, Canada.

HENRY, Christine The Health Centre, Osborn Road, Fareham PO16 7ER Tel: 01329 823456 Fax: 01329 285772; 56 Southampton Road, Park Gate, Southampton SO31 6AF — MB ChB 1966 Liverp.

HENRY, Christopher Michael Thomas 7 Codrington Street, Newtown, Exeter EX1 2BU — MB BS 1984 Lond.

HENRY, Colm Nathy Mary 11 Glenisla Gardens, Edinburgh EH9 2HR — MB BCh BAO 1988 NUI; MRCPI 1991; MRCGP 1995; DObst 1994; DCH NUI 1992. Prev: Regist. (Diabetes & Endocrinol.) Mater Hosp. Dub.

HENRY, Denis Bernard 22 Sunningdale Close, Stanmore HA7 3QL Tel: 020 8954 6919 — MRCS Eng. LRCP Lond. 1949; Dip. Med. Acupunc. 1997 (BMAS). (Middlx.) Socs: BMA; Brit. Med. Acupunct. Soc. Prev: Ho. Surg. Willesden Gen. Hosp.

HENRY, Denise Olive (retired) 7 Morley Road, Farnham GU9 8LX Tel: 01252 716521 — MB BS 1940 Lond.; MRCS Eng. LRCP Lond. 1936; DCH Eng. 1946. Prev: Ho. Phys. Roy. Free Hosp. & Chelmsford & Essex Hosp.

HENRY, Donald James Tudor House Medical Practice, 138 Edwards Lane, Sherwood, Nottingham NG5 3HU Tel: 0115 966 1233 Fax: 0115 967 0017; York House, Burlington Road, Sherwood, Nottingham NG5 2GS Tel: 0115 960 3006 — MB ChB 1958 Ed.; DObst RCOG 1962. Lect. (Gen. Pract.) Nottm. Univ. Med. Sch. Prev: Sen. Cas. Off. Nottm. Gen. Hosp.

HENRY, Elaine Barbara Anderlea, Gulberwick, Shetland ZE2 9JX — MB ChB 1993 Aberd.; MRCP (UK) 1996. (Aberd.) Research Regist (Gastroenterol.) W.ern Infirm. Glas.; Specialist Regist. (Gastroenterol.) Ninewells Hosp. Dundee. Prev: SHO (Med.) Wythenshawe Hosp. Manch. & Aberd. Roy. Infirm.

HENRY, Garry Wayne Homeleigh, Broadhempston, Totnes TQ9 6BD Tel: 01803 813488 — MB ChB 1983 Bristol. Trainee GP St. MaryCh. Med. Centre Torquay. Prev: SHO Rotat. (Med.) Torbay Dist. Hosp.

HENRY, Gavin Philip 74 Partickhill Road, Glasgow G11 5AB Tel: 0141 339 5913 — MB ChB 1949 Glas.; DPH 1959. (Glas.) Prev: Ho. Phys. W.. Infirm. Glas.; Ship's Surg. Henderson, Glen & Booth Lines.

HENRY, George Francis James Craigelands Mill, Beattock, Moffat DG10 9RD — MB BS 1990 Lond. (St. Geo. Hosp. Med. Sch.) Med. Off. Mosvold Hosp. Kwazulu Natal S. Africa. Prev: GP/Regist. Old Cottage Hosp. Epsom.

HENRY, Geraldine Holywell Hospital, 60 Steeple Road, Antrim BT41 2RJ — MB BCh BAO 1980 Belf.

HENRY, Henry Christopher 12 Planetree Road, Hale, Altrincham WA15 9JL Tel: 0161 980 6392 — LRCPI & LM, LRCSI & LM 1952. (Roy.Coll.Surg.Irel) Prev: GP Manch.; Ho. Surg. (Obst.) Glam. Hosp. Pontypridd; Regtl. Med. Off. 41st Field Regt. Ra.

HENRY, Ian Brian Gault Comber Health Centre, Newtownards Road, Comber, Newtownards BT23 5BA Tel: 01247 878391; (resid.) Drumlin, 37 Coach Road, Comber, Newtownards BT23 5QX — LRCP LRCS 1971 Ed.; LRCP LRCS Ed. LRCPS Glas. 1971. Med. Off. Civil Serv. Med. Serv.; Fact. Med. Off. Flax Mills.

HENRY, Irene Johnston Abbey Medical Practice, The Health Centre, Merstow Green, Evesham WR11 4BS Tel: 01386 761111 Fax: 01386 769515; Stowick, Evesham Road, Broadway WR12 7HU Tel: 01386 01386 830858 Fax: 01386 830858 Email: irene@stowick.com — MB ChB 1978 Dundee; DRCOG 1981. Gen. Practitioner, Abbey Med. Pract., Evesham. Prev: Princip. GP N. Yorks., Sefton & Dudley FPC's.

HENRY, James 53 Compton Road, Canonbury, London N1 2PB Tel: 020 7226 6774 — MB BCh BAO 1948 Belf. (Belf.)

HENRY, James Alexander Department of Pathology, Wansbeck General Hospital, Ashington NE63 2NN Tel: 01670 521212 Fax: 01670 529719; 2 Monks Wood, Tynemouth, North Shields NE30 2UA Tel: 0191 257 2697 Email: jahenry@globalnet.co.uk — MB ChB 1984 Ed.; PhD Newc. 1992; BSc (Hons.) Ed. 1982; MRCPath (Histopath.) 1993. (Edinburgh) Cons. Histopath. Wansbeck Gen. Hosp. Ashington; Clin. Tutor Wanesbeck Gen. Hosp. Ashington. Socs: Assn. Clin. Path.; Path. Soc.; Internat. Acad. Path. Prev: Lect. (Path.) & Hon. Sen. Regist. Univ. Newc. u Tyne; Demonst. (Path.) Univ. Newc. u. Tyne; Clin. Research Assoc. Univ. Newc. u. Tyne.

HENRY, James Granville Shankill Surgery, 21 Fairlight Road, Hastings TN35 5ED Tel: 01424 421046 Fax: 01424 425177 — MB BCh BAO 1977 Belf. Prev: GP Port Glas.

HENRY, James Joseph (retired) c/o Barclays Bank, 112 Woodcote Road, Wallington SM6 0NF — MB BCh BAO 1944 NUI; DPH Belf. 1960. Prev: Gp. Capt. RAF Med. Br.

HENRY, Professor John Anthony Imperial College School of Medicine, St Mary's Hospital, London W2 1NY Tel: 020 7886 6187 Fax: 020 7886 6315 Email: j.a.henry@ic.ac.uk; 18 Netherhall Gardens, London NW3 5TH Tel: 020 7431 0074 Fax: 020 7433 1276 — MB BS 1965 Lond.; MRCP (UK) 1974; FRCP Lond. 1986; FFAEM 1997. (King's Coll. Hosp.) Prof. A & E Med. Imperial Coll. Sch. Med. Lond. 1997; Hon. Cons. St. Mary's NHS Trust. Socs: Brit. Pharm. Soc.; Eur. Assn. Poisons Control Centres & Clin. Toxicol.; Brit. Assn. for Accid. & Emerg. Med. Prev: Cons. Phys. Nat. Poisons Info. Serv. Guy's Hosp. Lond.; Hon. Sen. Lect. UMDS Univ. Lond.; Ho. Phys. King's Coll. Hosp. Lond.

HENRY, John Francis (retired) 2 Thornhill Malone, 117 Malone Road, Belfast BT9 6SP Tel: 02890 660235 — MB BCh BAO 1948 Belf.

HENRY, John Stewart Robert Lloyd Lisburn Health Centre, Linenhall Street, Lisburn BT28 1LU Tel: 028 9260 3111; 14 Elmwood Park, Lisburn BT27 4AX Tel: 01846 678100 — MB BCh BAO 1972 Belf.; MRCGP 1976; DObst RCOG 1974.

HENRY, Julian Kenneth Tudor House Medical Practice, 138 Edwards Lane, Sherwood, Nottingham NG5 3HU Tel: 0115 966 1233 Fax: 0115 967 0017 — MB ChB 1990 Leeds.

HENRY, Laurence Department of Pathology, University of Sheffield, Sheffield S10 — MRCS Eng. LRCP Lond. 1952; MD Birm. 1964, MB ChB 1952; FRCP Lond. 1979, M 1957; FRCPath 1978, M 1966. Prof. Path. Univ. Sheff.; Hon. Cons. Path. Sheff. AHA (T). Prev: Sen. Regist. (Path.) St. Bart. Hosp. Lond.

HENRY, Mary Elizabeth Curry 4 Bladon Court, Belfast BT9 5JP Tel: 028 669628 — MB BCh BAO 1947 Belf. (Qu. Univ. Belf.)

HENRY, Melvyn Jack Sheen Lane Health Centre, Sheen Lane, East Sheen, London SW14 8LP Tel: 020 8876 4086 Fax: 020 8878 9620 — MB BS 1961 Lond.; DObst RCOG 1964. (Middlx.) Tutor (Gen. Pract.) Roehampton.

HENRY, Mr Michael Meldrum 106 Harley Street, London W1N 1AF Tel: 020 7935 3889; 26 Langham Mansions, Earls Court Square, London SW5 9UJ — MB BS 1970 Lond.; FRCS Eng. 1975; MRCS Eng. LRCP Lond. 1970. (Guy's) Cons. Surg. Chelsea & W.m. Hosp. & Roy. Marsden Hosp. Lond.; Hon. Cons. Surg. St. Mark's Hosp. & Nat. Hosp. Nerv. Dis. Lond.; Hon. Sen. Lect. (Surg.) UCL; Tutor RCS Eng.; Hon. Sen. Lect. Imperial.Coll.Lond. Socs: Fell. Roy. Soc. Med. (Mem. Counc. Proctol. Sect.); Surg. Research Soc. Prev: Cons. Surg. Centr. Middlx. Hosp.; Sen. Regist. (Surg.) Middlx. Hosp. Lond.; Lect. (Anat.) Trinity Coll. Camb.

HENRY, Paul Gerard North Ireland Centre for Clinical Oncology, Belvoir Park Hospital, Hospital Road, Belfast BT8 8JR Tel: 02890 699069 Fax: 02890 492554; 15 Whitehall Road, Aghagallon, Lurgan, Craigavon BT67 0AE Tel: 02892 651736 — MB BCh BAO 1982 Belf.; DPhil Oxf. 1976; MA Camb. 1973; MB BCh Belf. 1982; FFR RCSI 1991; MRCP (UK) 1985. (Queen's Univ Belfast) Cons. Radiother. & Oncol. N. Irel. Radiother. Centre Belvoir Pk. Hosp. Belf. Socs: Fell. Fac. Radiol. Roy. Coll. Surg. Irel.; Roy. Coll. Phys.; Mem. Roy. Coll Radiol.

HENRY, Richard Aloysius 87 Whitehorse Road, West Croydon, Croydon CR0 2JJ — MB BCh BAO 1952 NUI. Prev: Ho. Phys. Co. Hosp. Mullingar.

HENRY, Mr Richard Cradock BUPA Alexandra Hospital, Impton Lane, Walderslade, Maidstone ME5 9PG Tel: 01634 662814; The Old Vicarage, Church Lane, Bearsted, Maidstone ME14 4EE Tel: 01622 737123 — MB BS 1966 Lond.; FRCS Eng. 1974. (Middlx.) Cons. Otolaryngol. Kent Co. Ophth. & Aural Hosp. Maidstone & Medway Hosp. Gillingham; Cons. Otolaryngologist, Sittingbourne Memor. Hosp. & Sheppey Gen. Hosp. Socs: Brit. Assn. Otol.; Mem. Europ. Acad. Facial Plastic Surg.; Fell., Roy. Soc. of Med. Prev: Sen. Regist. (Otolaryngol.) Univ. Hosp. S. Manch.; Sen. Regist. Manch. Roy. Infirm.; Sen. Regist. Manch. N. Health Dist.

HENRY, Richard Ian Faulkner Tudor House Medical Practice, 138 Edwards Lane, Sherwood, Nottingham NG5 3HU Tel: 0115 966 1233 Fax: 0115 967 0017 — MB ChB 1986 Sheff.; MRCGP 1991; T(S) 1991; Dip. Pract. Derm. Wales 1992. Clin. Asst. (Dermat.) King's Mill Hosp. Mansfield.; Police Surg. Notts. Constab. Socs: Nottm. Med. Clin. Prev: SHO (Cardiothoracic Surg. & O & G) Auckland, NZ; SHO (ENT) & Ho. Off. (Med. & Surg.) Barnsley Dist. Gen. Hosp.; SHO (Dermat.) Derby Roy. Infirm.

HENRY, Mr Richard John Wilson 1 Chaucer Road, Canford Cliffs, Poole BH13 7HB Tel: 01202 701122 Fax: 01202 701909 Email: rhengyn@aol.com — MB BS 1976 Lond.; FRCS Ed. 1983; FRACOG 1988; FRCOG 1995, M 1983. (St. Thos.) Cons. O & G Poole Gen. Hosp. & Roy. Bournemouth Gen. Hosp.; Hon. Lect. Univ. Soton. Socs: BMA; Blair Bell Res. Soc. Prev: Sen. Regist. (O & G) St. Thos. Hosp.; Regist. Ashford & St. Thos. Hosps.; Resid. Surg. Off. Roy. Marsden Qu. Charlottes & Chelsea Hosp. for Wom.

HENRY, Robert Welby Belfast City Hospital, Belfast BT9 7AB Tel: 01232 263815 Fax: 01232 263973; Kinelarty Stud, Ballynahinch BT24 8UR Tel: 01238 562020 Fax: 01238 562020 — MB BCh BAO 1970 Belf.; MD Belf. 1976; FRCP Lond. 1989; FRCP Glas. 1982; FRCPI 1986, M 1984; MRCP (UK) 1973. Cons. Phys. Belf. City Hosp. Socs: Brit. Diabetic Assn.; Eur. Assn. Study Diabetes. Prev: Sen. Lect. & Lect. (Med.), Sen. Regist. & Sen. Tutor (Med.) Qu. Univ. Belf.

HENRY, Seamus Ian The Surgery, Union Row, Margate CT9 1PP Tel: 01843 296980 — MB BCh BAO 1985 NUI; MRCGP 1989.

HENRY, Stephen Laurence Maidens Cottage, Watermeadow Lane, Bapton, Warminster BA12 0SD Tel: 01985 850722 Fax: 01985 850722 Email: s.henry@dochen.demon.co.uk — BM BCh Oxf. 1961; MA Oxf. 1961; MRCS Eng. LRCP Lond. 1961; FRCGP 1995, M 1973; DObst RCOG 1964. (Oxf. & Westm.) Advisor Primary Care Develop. The Henry Morris Partnership; Non Exec. Dir. - Bath & W. NHS Community Trust; Med. Off. Nestlé plc., N.ern Foods plc (Bowyers Ltd.) The Consortium for Purchasing & Wilts. Friendly Soc. Ltd; Trustee Help for Health Trust; Dir. Compete Co-Operat. Ltd. Socs: Assn. Community Based Matern. Care; Brit. Assn. Med. Managers. Prev: GP Trowbridge.

HENRY, Susan Jane (retired) 1 Manor Road, St Albans AL1 3ST Tel: 01727 859559 — MB BS 1962 Lond.; MRCS Eng. LRCP Lond. 1962. Prev: GP St. Albans.

HENRY, William Desmond (retired) 28 Hall Croft, Beeston, Nottingham NG9 1EL — MB BCh BAO 1959 NUI; MRCPsych 1972; DPM Eng. 1963. Prev: Assoc. Specialist (Psychiat.) Mapperley Hosp. Nottm.

HENRY, William Stuart Hathaway Surgery, 32 New Road, Chippenham SN15 1HR Tel: 01249 447766 Fax: 01249 443948; Badgers Green, Bremhill, Calne SN11 9LH — MB ChB 1967 Liverp.; DObst RCOG 1970. (Liverp.) Clin. Asst. (Geriat.) Bath HA; Clin. Asst. (Ment. Handicap) Bath HA. Prev: SHO (Obst.) Luton & Dunstable Hosp.; SHO (Anaesth.) Clatterbridge Gen. Hosp. Wirral.

HENRY, William Thomas (retired) Welwyn, Church Walk, Viney Hill, Lydney GL15 4NY Tel: 01594 516470 — MB BS 1954 Lond.; MRCS Eng. LRCP Lond. 1955. Prev: Med. Off. Lydney & Dilke Hosps.

HENRYK GUTT, Mrs Rita 79 West Heath Road, London NW3 7TH — MB BS Lond. 1955; MRCP Lond. 1964; MRCS Eng. LRCP Lond. 1955; FRCPsych 1988, M 1972; DPM Lond. 1968; DCH Eng. 1959; DObst RCOG 1957. (Roy. Free) Med. Mem. Ment. Health Rev. Trib. (Lond. N.). Prev: Cons. Psychiat. Centr. Middlx. Hosp. Lond.; Sen. Regist. (Psychol. Med.) St. Bart. Hosp. Lond.; Regist. (Psychol. Med.) Middlx. Hosp.

HENS, Martina Elmhurst Road, Aylesbury HP20 2AH — Artsexamen 1988 Nimegen; Artsexamen 1988 Niimegen.

HENSBY, Claire Montague Medical Centre, Fifth Avenue, Goole DN14 6JD Tel: 01405 767600 Fax: 01405 726126; Kiln House, Hoggard Lane, Adlingfleet, Goole DN14 8HU — MB ChB 1977 Leeds.

HENSEL, Christine Mary The Grange, Daggons Road, Alderholt, Fordingbridge SP6 3DN Tel: 01425 652606 — MB BS 1967 Lond.; MRCS Eng. LRCP Lond. 1967; MRCOphth 1990; DO Eng. 1969. (King's Coll. Hosp.) Staff Grade (Ophth.) Salisbury Dist. Hosp.; Clin. Asst. (Elderly Med.) Fordingbridge Hosp. Socs: Salisbury Med. Soc.; Soc. Ophth. Prev: Ho. Phys. (Diabetic) & Ho. Surg. (Ophth.) King's Coll. Hosp.

HENSEL, Elizabeth Ann 496 Crewe Road, Wistaston, Crewe CW2 6PZ — MB ChB 1978 Manch.

HENSEL, John Andrew (retired) The Surgery, Bartons Road, Fordingbridge SP6 1RS Tel: 01425 652123 — MB BS 1967 Lond.; MRCS Eng. LRCP Lond. 1967; DObst RCOG 1970. Prev: Ho. Phys. (Paediat.), Ho. Surg. (ENT) & SHO (A & E) King's Coll. Hosp. Lond.

HENSHALL, Anne Louise 2 Patina Close, Newcastle upon Tyne NE15 8TY — MB ChB 1992 Birm.

HENSHALL, Lucy Anne Helen Lattice Barn Surgery, 14 Woodbridge Road East, Ipswich IP4 5PA — MB ChB 1987 Sheff.; MRCGP 1991; DRCOG 1991; T(GP) 1991.

HENSHALL, Patricia Tameside & glossop C &PS Trust, Greenfield St., Hyde SK14 1EJ Tel: 0161 368 4242 Fax: 0161 366 0483 Email: pat.henshall@exchange.tgps-tr.nwest.nhs.uk; 61 High Grove Road, Cheadle SK8 1NW Tel: 01614282337 Email: pathenshall@aol.com — MB ChB Manch. 1963; DCH Eng. 1965. (Manch.) Cons. Paediat. Community Child Health Tameside & Glossop Community & Priority Servs. Trust; Cons. Paediat. Community Child Health Tameside & Glossop Community & Priority Servs trust; Med.Ref.Dukinfield Crem. Socs: BMA; Fell. Roy. Coll. Paed. & Child Health.

HENSHALL, Simon Mark Yardley Green Medical Centre, 73 Yardley Green Road, Birmingham B9 5PU Tel: 0121 773 3838 — MB ChB 1988 Birm.; DRCOG 1992; DCH RCP Lond. 1991; DTM & H RCP Lond. 1990.

HENSHALL, Tina Denise Valley View, Fenny Bentley, Ashbourne DE6 1LA — MB ChB 1992 Sheff.

HENSHAW, Carol Anne Department of Psychiatry, Keele University, Academic Unit, Harplands Hospital, Hilton Road, Hartshill, Stoke-on-Trent ST4 6RR Tel: 01782 441660 Fax: 01782 441650 Email: pcaoz@keele.co.uk — MB ChB 1984 Aberd.; MD 2000 Aberd.; MRCPsych 1988. (Aberd.) Cons. & Sen. Lect. Keele Univ. & Mid Chesh. Hosps. NHS Trust; Cons Psychiat. to Chesh. Relate Assoc. PostGrad. Clin. Tutor Mid Chesh. Hosps NHS Trust. Socs: Marce Soc Info. Edr. Prev: Lect. & Sen. Regist. Keele Univ. W. Midl. RHA; Research Fell. & Hon. Regist. (O & G) Univ. Keele N. Staffs. HA; Regist. & SHO (Psychiat.) Roy. Edin. Hosp.

HENSHAW, David James Edward 20A Harpenden Rise, Harpenden AL5 3BH — MB ChB 1991 Bristol.

HENSHAW, Michael Ekeng 57 Carr Lane, Willerby, Hull HU10 6JP — BM BCh 1977 Nigeria; MRCOG 1987. Assoc. Specialist (O & G) W.wood Hosp. Beverley. Socs: Brit. Soc. Colpos.

& Cerv. Path.; Brit. Menopause Soc.; Fac. Fam. Plann. Prev: Regist. (O & G) Dist. Gen. Hosp. Sunderland.

HENSHAW, Myra Beatrice Alice Glebe House, Firby Road, Bedale DL8 2AT Tel: 01677 422616 Fax: 01677 424507; Roomer Cottage, Back Lane, Kirkby Malzeard, Ripon HG4 3SH Fax: 01677 424596 — MB BS Durh. 1962. (Newc.) Clin. Asst. (Geriat.) Friarage Hosp. N.allerton. Socs: BMA. Prev: Ho. Phys. Sheriff Hill Infec. Dis. Hosp. Gateshead; Ho. Surg. & Clin. Asst. Gyn. Research Unit Qu. Eliz. Hosp. Gateshead.

HENSHAW, Richard Charles 6 Hollies Drive, Edwalton, Nottingham NG12 4BZ — MB ChB 1984 Leeds; MB ChB Leeds l984.

HENSHAW, Richard William Spires Medical Practice, St. Chads Health Centre, Dimbles Lane, Lichfield WS13 7HT; 76 Christchurch Lane, Lichfield WS13 8AL Tel: 01543 24460 — MB ChB 1970 Leeds; DCH Eng. 1975; DA Eng. 1973; DObst RCOG 1972. Socs: Christ. Med. Fell.sh. Prev: Med. Off. St. Mary's Hosp. Natal, S. Afr.; Med. Supt. Assisi Mission Hosp. Natal, S. Afr.

HENSHELWOOD, Julie Ann Torridon, Horton Road, Ringwood BH24 2EG — MB BS 1986 Lond.

HENSHER, Mr Robert William 11 Harcourt House, 19A Cavendish Square, London W1G 0PN Tel: 020 7499 0891 Fax: 020 7499 0889 Email: roberthensher@aol.com — MB ChB 1978 (Hons) Liverp.; BDS Liverp. 1972; FRCS Ed. 1985; MRCS Eng. LRCP Lond. 1978.; FDS RCS Eng. 1981; ATLS RCS Eng 1997. (Liverpool) Private practioner in oral & Maxillo-facial Surg.; Hon Cons Surg Univ coll Hosp Lond. Socs: Fell. Brit. Assn. Oral & Maxillofacial Surg.; Memb. Assn. Dent. Implantol.; Memb. Amer. Assn. T.M.J. Surg. Prev: Cons.(O & MF) Surg., Glos. Roy. Hosp.; Asst. Der Z-M-K Klinik Munster W. Germany; Sen. Resid. (Oral & Maxillofacial Surg.) Charity Hosp. New Orleans, USA.

HENSMAN, Edward Reginald 118 Beaver Lane, Ashford TN23 Tel: 01233 24917; 25 Malvern Road, Ashford TN24 8HX — MB BS 1946 Madras; DTM & H Eng. 1965. (Madras) Socs: BMA.

HENSMAN, Roger Humphrey (retired) Crosthwaite, 3 Sollershott W., Letchworth SG6 3PU Tel: 01462 683213 — MB BS Lond. 1962; DObst RCOG 1964. Prev: Med. Off. (Occupat. Health) Lister Hosp. Stevenage.

HENSON, Andrew Flat 3, 3 Malvern Place, Cheltenham GL50 2JN — MB BS 1990 Lond.

HENSON, Gaye Lesley Whittington Hospital, Highgate Hill, London N19 5NF — MD 1987 Lond.; MB BS 1974; MRCOG 1979; DA Eng. 1977; FRCOG 1993. Cons. O & G Whittington Hosp. Lond. Prev: Sen. Regist. (O & G) Univ. Coll. Hosp. Lond.

HENSON, Lisa Rosamund 136 Grimescar Road, Ainley Top, Huddersfield HD2 2EB — MB ChB 1993 Manch.; DRCOG 1998 Manch.; BSc St. And. 1990. Salaried GP.

HENSON, Sophie Elizabeth Woodside, Lon-y-Winci, Cardiff CF14 6UG — MB BCh 1995 Wales.

HENSTOCK-ZAPF, Cathryn Louisa Portree Medical Centre, Portree IV51 9BZ — MB BS 1992 Lond.

HENSTRIDGE, Victoria Jane 5 Rockleigh Avenue, Leigh-on-Sea SS9 1LA — MB BS 1997 Lond.

HENTON, Nicholas John 8 Ty Gwyn Crescent, Penylan, Cardiff CF23 5JL — MB BS 1996 Lond.

HENVILLE, John Davis Greystones, 13 Oxford Road, Woodstock OX20 1UN — MB BS 1964 Lond.; MRCS Eng. LRCP Lond. 1964; FFA RCS Eng. 1969; DA Eng. 1967. (Westm.) Cons. (Anaesth.) Nuffield Dept. Anaesth. Radcliffe Infirm. Oxf. Prev: Sen. Regist. Nuffield Dept. Anaesth. Radcliffe Infirm. Oxf. & St. Mary's Hosp. Portsmouth; Clin. Fell. (Anaesth.) Mass. Gen. Hosp. Boston, USA.

HENWOOD, Barry Perkins Albany Surgery, Albany Street, Newton Abbot TQ12 2TX Tel: 01626 334411 Fax: 01626 335663 — MB BS 1981 Lond.; MA Camb. 1982; MRCGP 1986; DRCOG 1984. (Guy's) GP Trainer Devon.

HENWOOD, Mark 55 Llewellyn Park Drive, Morriston, Swansea SA6 8PF — MB BCh 1993 Wales.

HENWOOD, Nicholas David c/o Interserve, 325 Kennington Road, London SE11 4QH Tel: 020 7735 8227; 35 Buxton Road, Norwich NR3 3HH Tel: 01603 631813 — BA Oxf. 1986, BM BCh 1989; MRCGP 1994; DCH RCP Lond. 1992. Socs: BMA & Christian Med. Fell.sh. Prev: Trainee GP/SHO Norwich; SHO King's Lynn; Ho. Off. York.

HEPBURN, Alastair Leonard Noble 11 Ferry Road, Teddington TW11 9NN Tel: 020 8977 5625 — MB BS 1993 Lond.; BSc (Hons.) Lond. 1990; MRCP (UK) 1997. (Lond. Hosp. Med. Coll.) Res. Fell. Rheum. Hammersmith Hosp. Socs: BMA; Brit. Soc. Rheum. Prev: Specialist Regist. Gen. Med. Rheum. Chelsea & W.minister Hosp.; Specialist Regist. (Rheum.) Watford Gen. Hosp.; SHO Rotat. (Med.) Roy. Lond. Hosp.

HEPBURN, Athol Noble, RD, OStJ (retired) Hylands, Ravensdale Road, South Ascot, Ascot SL5 9HL Tel: 01344 620307 — MB ChB Aberd. 1954; FFOM RCP Lond. 1982, MFOM 1978; DPH Lond. 1961. Prev: Dir. Civil. Med. Servs. Procurement Exec. MoD Lond.

HEPBURN, Beth Scapa Medical Group, Health Centre, New Scapa Road, Kirkwall KW15 1BQ Tel: 01856 885445 Fax: 01856 873556 — MB ChB 1985 Aberd.

HEPBURN, David Alexander Medical Division, Hull Royal Infirmary, Anlaby Road, Hull HU3 2JZ Tel: 01482 675369 Fax: 01482 675370 Email: david@hepburn.demon.co.uk; 71 Ferriby Road, Hessle HU13 0HU Tel: 01482 648530 — MB ChB 1984 Dundee; BMSc (1st cl. Hons.) Dund 1981; MRCP (UK) 1987; T(M) 1994; FRCP 2000. (Dundee) Cons. Phys. (Diabetes & Endocrinol.) Hull Roy. Infirm.; Clin. Dir. Med. Div., Hull & E. Yorks Hosp.s NHS Trust. Socs: Brit. Diabetic Assn. (Med. & Scientif. Sect.); Collegiate Mem. RCP Edin.; Soc. for Acute Med. Prev: Sen. Regist. Newc. Gen. Hosp. & Freeman Hosp.; Regist. (Diabetes) Edin. Roy. Infirm.

HEPBURN, Elspeth Leslie (retired) 3 Guildcroft, Epsom Road, Guildford GU1 2JU Tel: 01483 531542 — MB ChB Glas. 1959. Clin. Med. Off. Surrey Hants. Borders Community Health Unit. Prev: Clin. Med. Off. Ayrsh. & Arran HB.

HEPBURN, Gillian Esther 16 Littlefield, Bishopsteignton, Teignmouth TQ14 9SG — MB BS 1949 Durh.; MRCGP 1978; FFA RCS Eng. 1954; DA Eng. 1952; DCH Eng. 1962. Clin. Med. Off. Torbay Dist. Prev: GP Tiverton; Asst. Anaesth. Ulleval Sykehus Oslo; Anaesth. Regist. Wellington Hosp. N.Z.

HEPBURN, Hugh 6 Rubislaw Terrace, Aberdeen AB10 1XE — MB ChB 1974 Aberd.

HEPBURN, James Alastair Clark 5 Schooners Court, Shelly Road, Exmouth EX8 1XZ Email: jachepburn@msn.com — MB BS 1964 Durh.; MSc Glas. 1983; MRCGP 1983; T(GP) 1991. Cons. Regional Med. Adviser S. Thames RHA; Cons. Adviser States of Jersey. Prev: GP NW Durh.; Tutor (Family Med.) Univ. Newc.; Hosp. Pract. (Geriat.) Shotley Bridge & Maiden Law Hosps.

HEPBURN, John (retired) 18 Montgomerie Terrace, Skelmorlie PA17 5DT Tel: 01425 520070 — MB ChB 1954 Aberd.; MRCGP 1965.

HEPBURN, Julia Mary Family Planning Clinic, Health Centre, Newgate St., Worksop S80 1HP Tel: 01909 500512; Garden House, Burton-by-Lincoln, Lincoln LN1 2RD Tel: 01522 523787 — MB ChB 1985 Manch.; BSc St. And. 1982; MFFP 1995. SCMO (Family Plann.) Bassetlaw Hosp. & Community Servs. NHS Trust. Socs: BMA; N. InterBr. Doctors Gp. Prev: Clin. Med. Off. (Family Plann.) N. Downs Community Trust; Clin. Med. Off. (Family Plann.) Lothian HB & Session Family Plann. Doctor W. Surrey & NE Hants HA; Ho. Phys. Manch. Roy. Infirm.

HEPBURN, Mary Princess Royal Maternity Hospital, Alexandra Parade, Glasgow G31; 1 Huntly Gardens, Dowanhill, Glasgow G12 9AS — MB ChB Ed. 1973; BSc Ed. 1970, MD 1987; MRCGP 1977; FRCOG 1995, M 1981. (Ed.) Sen. Lect. (Wom. Reproduc. Health) Depts. O & G, Social Policy & Social Work Univ. Glas.; Hon. Cons. Obst. & Gyn. N. Glas. Trust. Prev: Hon. Cons. Obst. & Gyn. Gtr. Glas. HB.

HEPBURN, Maureen Elizabeth Shaftesbury Medical Practice, 1265 Dumbarton Road, Glasgow G14 9UU Tel: 0141 959 5500 Fax: 0141 954 4864; 33 Northland Drive, Scotstoun, Glasgow G14 9BE Tel: 0141 579 1813 Email: mohep@hepnet.demon.co.uk — MB ChB 1986 Glas.; DRCOG 1989. Clin. Asst. Glas. Drug Problem Serv.

HEPBURN, Neill Christopher Lincoln County Hospital, Greetwell Road, Lincoln LN2 5QY Tel: 01522 573412 Fax: 01522 573101 Email: neill.hepburn@ulh.nhs.uk; Garden House, Burton-by-Lincoln, Lincoln LN1 2RD Tel: 01522 523787 Fax: 01522 523787 Email: hepburn@btinternet.com — MB ChB 1984 Manch.; MB ChB (Hons.) Manch. 1984; BSc (Hons.) St. And. 1981; MD Ed. 1995; FRCP (UK) 1998; T(M) 1994. Cons. Dermat. United Lincs. Hosp NHS Trust; Cons. Dermat. Roy. Hallamshire Hosp.; Vis. Cons. Dermat.

Nobles Hosp. Isle of Man. Socs: Fell. Roy. Soc. Med.; Brit. Assn. Dermat. Prev: Cons. Dermat. MDHU Frimley Pk.; Hon. Sen. Regist. (Dermat.) Edin. Roy. Infirm.

HEPBURN, Paul Robert The Surgery, 227 Lodge Causeway, Fishponds, Bristol BS16 3QW Tel: 0117 965 3102; 1 Grove Bank, Riverwood, Frenchay, Bristol BS16 1NY — MB ChB 1971 Bristol; MRCP (UK) 1975. GP Bristol; Clin. Asst. (Chest. Med.) Frenchay Hosp. Bristol; GP Clin. Tutor Univ. Bristol. Prev: Regist. (Gen. Med.) Newc. AHA (T); SHO (Gen. Med.) Frenchay Hosp. Bristol; Ho. Phys. Profess. Med. Unit Bristol Roy. Infirm.

HEPBURN, Thomas West End Medical Practice, 21 Chester Street, Edinburgh EH3 7RF Tel: 0131 225 5220 Fax: 0131 226 1910 — MB ChB 1979 Ed.

HEPDEN, Mary 858 Woodborough Road, Mapperley, Nottingham NG3 5QQ Tel: 0115 948 3030 Fax: 0115 911 1074; 3 Roland Avenue, Nuthall, Nottingham NG16 1BB — MB BS 1972 Lond.; MRCP (UK) 1978; DCH Eng. 1976. Prev: Regist. (Paediat.) Childr. Hosp. Sheff.; Med. Off. Lesotho Flying Doctor Serv.

HEPPELL, Alison Clare Helen Lark Rise, Tidmarsh, Reading RG8 8ER — MB ChB 1994 Leic.

HEPPELL, David 69 Plantation Gardens, Leeds LS17 8SU — MB ChB 1994 Leeds.

HEPPELL, P Simon J 7 Rothley Way, Whitley Bay NE26 3EW — MB ChB 1993 Leic.

HEPPELL, Richard Mark 17 Victoria Row, Well St., Buckingham MK18 1ER — MB ChB 1988 Bristol.

HEPPENSTALL, Johanne Frances 19 St George's Court, Garden Row, Southwark, London SE1 6HD — BM BS 1986 Nottm.; MRCGP 1990; DRCOG 1989; DCH RCP Lond. 1989. SHO (Psychiat.) S.E. Lond. & Eng.

HEPPER, Felicity Jane Garden Flat, 61 Saltram Crescent, London W9 3JS — MB BS 1990 Lond.; MSc (Med. Anthropol.) Brunei 1995; BSc (Nutrit.) Lond. 1987. SHO (Psychiat.) St. Mary's Hosp. Lond. Train. Scheme. Prev: Ho. Off. (Med. & Surg.) Ealing Hosp.

HEPPLE, Jason Neil Magnolia House, 56 Preston Road, Yeovil BA20 2BN Tel: 01935 431725 Fax: 01935 411063 Email: jason.hepple@sompar.nhs.uk; Barrington House, Coldharbour, Sherborne DT9 4HP — BM BCh 1988 Oxf.; MA Oxf. 1990, BA (Physiol.) 1985; MRCPsych 1992. (Oxford) Cons. (Old Age Psychiat.) S. Som.; Hon. Fell., Exeter Univ. Socs: Assn. of Cognitive Analytic Therapists; Roy. Coll. of Psychiat.s. Prev: Sen. Regist. (Psychiat.) Oxf. Region Higher Train. Scheme.; Regist. Rotat. (Psychiat.) Oxf. VTS.

HEPPLE, Paul Alexander Muirhouse Medical Group, 1 Muirhouse Avenue, Edinburgh EH4 4PL Tel: 0131 332 2201 — MB BS 1992 Lond.; BSc Soton. 1984; MRCGP 1996; DCH RCP Lond. 1995; DRCOG 1994.

HEPPLE, Sophie Emma 42 Kersland Street, Glasgow G12 8BT — MB ChB 1992 Aberd.

HEPPLE, Stephen 186 School Road, Crookes, Sheffield S10 1GL Tel: 0114 268 6426 — MB ChB 1991 Sheff.

HEPPLESTON, John Dennis (retired) 108 Crewe Road, Nantwich CW5 6JS Tel: 01270 625691 — MB ChB Manch. 1944; DPath Eng. 1953; FRCPath 1966. Prev: Cons. Pathol. Crewe Health Dist.

HEPPLEWHITE, E A Whitwick Health Centre, North Street, Whitwick, Coalville LE67 5HX Tel: 01530 838866 Fax: 01530 810581 — MB BS 1978 Ncle. Gen. Practitioner.

HEPTINSTALL, Mrs Diana Philomena (retired) Toad Hall, Low Common, Deopham, Wymondham NR18 9DZ Tel: 01953 850803 — MB BS 1960 Lond. Prev: GP Hayling Is., Hants.

HEPTON, Sylvia Kathleen (retired) 34 Princes Way, Brentwood CM13 2JW Tel: 01277 227168 — MB BS 1955 Lond.; MRCS Eng. LRCP Lond. 1955; FRCA 1962; DA Eng. 1958. Prev: Cons. Anaesth. Rush Green & OldCh. Hosps. Romford.

HEPTONSTALL, Jonathan Marcus 5 Bunkers, Tunstead Lane, Greenfield, Saddleworth, Oldham OL3 7NY — MB ChB 1987 Manch.

HEPTONSTALL, Julia Martins, Knedlington Road, Howden, Goole DN14 7ER Tel: 020 7733 7323 — MB BS 1979 Lond.; MSc Lond. 1985, MB BS 1979; MRCP (UK) 1983; MRCPath 1986; DTM & H RCP Lond. 1985.

HEPWORTH, Mr Clive Charles 23 Friern Walk, Wickford SS12 0HZ — MB ChB 1986 Birm.; ChB Birm. 1986; BSc (Biochem.) Birm. 1983; FRCS Ed. 1992; FRCS (Gen Surg) 1999.

HEPWORTH, David Beech Tree Surgery, 68 Doncaster Road, Selby YO8 9AJ; Red Rose House, 29 Maypole Gardens, Cawood, Selby YO8 3TG — MB ChB 1977 Sheff.

HEPWORTH, David Martin Tayview Medical Practice, 16 Victoria Street, Newport-on-Tay DD6 8DJ Tel: 01382 543251 Fax: 01382 542052; 1 Linden Avenue, Newport-on-Tay DD6 8DU Tel: 01382 542423 Email: kaymarthep@netscapeonline.co.uk — MB ChB 1964 Sheff.; LMCC 1969; FRCGP 1997, M 1978; DA Eng. 1972; DObst RCOG 1967. (Sheff.) Prev: Regist. (Anaesth.) Lincoln Co. Hosp.; on Active Staff Lady Minto Hosp. Cochrane, Canada; SHO (Anaesth.) United Sheff. Hosps.

HERAPATH, Geoffrey Charles Kynaston (retired) 3 Cavendish Close, Saltford, Bristol BS31 3LH — MB ChB 1950 Bristol. Prev: RAF Med. Br.

HERATH, Nihal Lalendra Bandara 22 Chaffinch Crescent, Billericay CM11 2YX — MB BS 1979 Colombo; MRCS Eng. LRCP Lond. 1985; DRCOG 1992.

HERATH, Mr Samuel Navaratne Bandara 80 Sudbury Court Drive, Harrow HA1 3TF — MB BS 1967 Ceylon; FRCS Eng. 1976; DO Eng. 1976. (Ceylon) Regist. (Ophth.) N. Riding Infirm. Cleveland. Prev: Regist. (Ophth.) Norf. AHA.

HERBERG, Lewis Jacob (retired) Institute of Neurology, National Hospital, Queen Square, London WC1N 3BG Email: lherberg@ion.ucl.ac.uk — MB BCh 1954 Witwatersrand; DPhil Oxf. 1964. p/t Hon. Sen. Research Fell. (Neuropath.) Inst. Neurol. Lond. Prev: Reader (Experim. Psychol.) Inst. Neurol. Lond.

HERBERT, Amanda Dept of Histopathology, St Thomas Hospital, London SE1 7EH — MB BS Lond. 1968; MRCS Eng. LRCP Lond. 1968; FRCPath 1988, M 1976. CytoPath., Histopath., Guy's & St Thomas' Trust; Hon. Cons., CytoPath., Kings Healthcare Trust, Lond. Prev: Cons. Histopath. Cytopath. Soton. Gen. Hosp.

HERBERT, Anne Patricia Carlton House, Kirkby Fleetham, Northallerton DL7 0SJ Tel: 01609 748460 — MB BS 1967 Newc.; DCH RCPS Glas. 1969. Staff Grade (Paediat.) & Clin. Asst. (Diabetes) Friarage Hosp. N.allerton.

HERBERT, Asha Thomsett 127 London Road, Chatteris PE16 6LT — MB BS 1996 Lond.

HERBERT, Bethan Angharad Tel: 029 2034 1547 Fax: 029 2064 0499; Bryn-y-Wern, Maes-yr-Hafod, Creigiau, Cardiff CF15 9JU Tel: 01222 341547 — MB BS 1987 Lond.; MRCGP 1994; T(GP) 1992; DRCOG 1991; Dip. F. Hom. 1998. (St. Bartholomew's Medical School) Prev: Trainee GP Letchworth Herts.

HERBERT, Mr David Charles 9A Wilbraham Place, Sloane Square, London SW1X 9AE Tel: 020 7730 7928 Fax: 020 7823 5606; Ashdene, Halam, Southwell NG25 8AH Tel: 01636 812335 — MB BS Lond. 1961; FRCS Ed. 1966; FRCS Eng. 1966; MRCS Eng. LRCP Lond. 1961. (St. Bart.) Cons. Plastic & Cosmetic Surg. Cromwell Clinic Huntingdon, Cambs. & Broughton Pk. Hosp. Preston. Socs: (Vice-Pres.) Brit. Assn. Cosmetic Surgs.; BMA; Chelsea Clin. Soc. Prev: Sen. Regist. (Plastic Surg.) Liverp. Regional Plastic Surg. Unit Whiston Hosp. & Alder Hey Childr. Hosp. Liverp.; Regist. (Plastic Surg.) Birm. Regional Plastic Unit Wordsley Hosp.

HERBERT, David Laurence Alvanley, 160 Buxton Road, Heaviley, Stockport SK2 6HA — MB ChB Manch. 1963; MFOM RCP Lond. 1983, AFOM 1979. (Manch.) Employm. Med. Adviser Employm. Rehabil. Centre Denton; Med. Adviser CPC (UK) Ltd. Manch.

HERBERT, David Nicholas Tel: 01536 723566 Fax: 01536 420226 — BM BS 1985 Nottm.; MRCGP 1990.

HERBERT, Dennis William The Cambridge Medical Group, 10A Cambridge Road, Linthorpe, Middlesbrough TS5 5NN Tel: 01642 851177 Fax: 01642 851176 — MB BS 1975 Newc.; MRCGP 1979; DRCOG 1978. GP Middlesbrough; GP Tutor S. Tees; GP Trainer Cleveland VTS; Liaison Practitioner NoReN.

HERBERT, Mr Edward Nicholas — MB BChir 1994 Camb.; MA 1995 Cantab; FRCOphth 1997. (Camb.) Specialist Regist. (Ophth.) St. Paul's Eye Unit Liverp. Prev: SHO (Ophth.) Addenbrooke's Hosp. Camb.; SHO (Ophth.) Stoke Mandeville Hosp. Aylesbury; SHO (A & E) Whipps Cross Hosp.

HERBERT, Elizabeth Anne 54 School Lane, Manchester M20 6RT — MB ChB 1997 Manch.

HERBERT, Graham Norton Doctors Surgery, Sutherland House, 209 Mayburn Avenue, Loanhead EH20 9ER — MB ChB 1992 Aberd.

HERBERT, Helen Mary 91 St. Andrew Street, Liverpool L3 5XY — MB BS 1994 Lond.
HERBERT, Hugh, CStJ (retired) Tanyfron, South Road, Aberaeron SA46 0DP Tel: 01545 570459 Fax: 01545 571542 Email: hugh.herbert@tesco.net — MB BS Lond. 1948; MB BS Lond. 1948; MRCS Eng. LRCP Lond. 1947; FRCGP 1987. Prev: High Sheriff Cards. 1966.
HERBERT, Isabel 30 Garscube Terrace, Edinburgh EH12 6BN Tel: 0131 337 3634 — MB BS 1945 Durh. (Newc.)
HERBERT, James Mitchell 10 Newton Crescent, Dunblane FK15 0DZ Tel: 01786 822141 — MB ChB 1966 Glas.; DObst RCOG 1968.
HERBERT, Jeremy (Jay) John Francis Takeda Uk Limited, Takeda House, Mercury Park, Wycombe Lane, High Wycombe HP10 0HH Tel: 01628 537920 Fax: 01628 526617 Email: jayh@takeda.co.uk — MRCS Eng. LRCP Lond. 1975; MFPM 1990. (Char. Cross) Med. Dir. Roche Consumer Health Welwyn Garden City. Prev: Head Med. Servs. Hoechst Roussel Ltd.; Sen. Med. Off. Med. Control Agency DoH; Sen. Med. Adviser Bayer UK Ltd.
HERBERT, Joan Marguerite Tall Trees Surgery, Rectory Road, Retford DN22 7AY Tel: 01777 701637 Fax: 01777 710619; Blackstope Farm, Bracken Lane, Retford DN22 0PJ Tel: 01777 705238 — MB ChB 1956 Sheff. (Sheffield) Partner in GP.
HERBERT, John Charles 3 Lyndon Avenue, Shevington, Wigan WN6 8BT — MB ChB 1979 Liverp.; FRCR 1986; DMRD (Liverp.) 1983.
HERBERT, John Eifion (retired) 3 Harewood Avenue, Sale M33 5BX Tel: 0161 962 6420 — MRCS Eng. LRCP Lond. 1954. Prev: Ho. Surg. & Jun. Obst. Off. Moorgate Gen. Hosp. Rotherham.
HERBERT, John Lewis, OStJ, CStJ (retired) Sarn Helen, Peniel, Carmarthen SA32 7DJ Tel: 01267 237784 — MB BS 1948 Lond.; FRCGP 1993, M 1962. Prev: Capt. RAMC.
HERBERT, John Philip (retired) Dunanfiew, Corgarff, Strathdon AB36 8YP — MB BS 1966 Lond.; MRCGP 1976.
HERBERT, Joseph Department of Anatomy, University of Cambridge, Cambridge CB2 3DY Tel: 01223 333781 Fax: 01223 333786 — MB ChB 1960 Birm.; PhD Lond. 1965; MRCS Eng. LRCP Lond. 1960. Reader (Neuroendocrinol.) Camb. Univ.; Fell. & Dir. Studies in Med. Gonville & Caius Coll. Camb.
HERBERT, Juliet Rosalind 1 Beacon Close, Uxbridge UB8 1PX — MB BS 1997 Lond.
HERBERT, Kevin Charles Abbey House Surgery, Golding Close, Daventry NN11 5RA Tel: 01327 708570 Fax: 01327 708585 Email: kevin@davmed.com — MB ChB 1977 Birm.; Dip Av Med 1999 (Occupat. Med.) Roy. Coll. Of Physicians. p/t Gen. Practitioner, Abbey Ho. Surg., Deventry; Chairm. of Clin. Exec., Deventry and S. N.ants Primary Care Trust, Danetre Hosp., Deventry; Authorised Aviat. Med. Examr., Civil Aviat. Auth.
HERBERT, Margaret Helen Tanyfron Surgery, 7-9 Market Street, Aberaeron SA46 0AS Tel: 01545 570271 Fax: 01545 570136; Tanyfron, South Road, Aberaeron SA46 0DP Tel: 01545 570459 Email: hherbert@sagnet.co.uk — MB BS 1979 Lond.; FRCGP 1993, M 1986. (Guy's Hospital) GP Aberaeron; CME Tutor. Socs: SW Fac. RCGP Fac. Bd.; Welsh Counc. RCGP.
HERBERT, Mark Antony University Department of Paediatrics, John Radcliffe Hospital, Headington, Oxford Tel: 01865 221 1363 Fax: 07865 222626 Email: mherbert@molbiol.ox.ac.uk; 19 Green Ridges, Headington, Oxford OX3 8PL — MB ChB 1989 Bristol; BSc Bristol 1986; MRCP (UK) 1992. Clin. Lect. (Neonat. Paediat.), Univ. of Oxf. Socs: RCPCH; Brit. Paediatric Immunol. and Infect. Dis. Gp; Brit. Assn. Perinatal Med. Prev: MRC Clin. Research Tarining Fell., Inst. of Molecular Med., Oxf.; Research Regist. Oxf. Vaccine Gp. John Radcliffe Hosp. Oxf.; Regist. (Paediat.) Birm. Childr. Hosp.
HERBERT, Martha Eileen (retired) Studio Cottage, Lunces Common, Haywards Heath RH16 4QU — MB BCh BAO Belf. 1930; DPH Belf. 1932. Prev: SHMO St. Francis Hosp. Haywards Heath.
HERBERT, Murray MacRae Portland Park Medical Centre, 51 Portland Park, Hamilton ML3 7JY Tel: 01698 284353 Fax: 01698 891101 — MB ChB 1984 Glas.; MRCGP 1988; D.Occ.Med. RCP Lond. 1996; DRCOG 1987. Prev: Trainee GP Paisley VTS.
HERBERT, Myra Belmont Whipps Cross Hospital, Whipps Cross Road, London E11 1NR — MB BS 1992 Newc.
HERBERT, Orris Donald Ekundayo 38 Haversham Close, Benton Park Road, Newcastle upon Tyne NE7 7LR — LRCPI & LM, LRSCI & LM 1959; LRCPI & LM, LRCSI & LM 1959; BDS Durham. 1951; Cert JCC Lond. 1978. (RCSI) GP Newc.; Police Surg. Gosforth. Socs: BMA; NE Anaesth. Soc. Prev: Clin. Asst. Dept. Anaesth. Roy. Vict. Infirm. Newc.; Ho. Phys. & Ho. Surg. Tynemouth Vict. Jubilee Infirm.; SHO Plastic Surg. Newc. Gen. Hosp.
HERBERT, Pamela Margaret Louise 1 Yew Tree House, East Cross, Tenterden TN30 6AD — MB ChB 1991 Cape Town.
HERBERT, Paul Elliot Brindley Dene, Withernsea Rd, Hollym, Withernsea HU19 2QH — MB BS 1997 Lond.
HERBERT, Paul Martin Blackstopes Farm, Bracken Lane, Retford DN22 0PJ — MB BS 1996 Lond.
HERBERT, Peter Jeremy Temple Fortune Health Centre, 23 Temple Fortune Lane, London NW11 7TE Tel: 020 8458 4431 Fax: 020 8731 8257 — MB BS 1975 Lond.; FRCS 2000; MRCP (UK) 1979; Dip. Med. Acupunc. 1997. Socs: BMA; Brit. Med. Acupunc. Soc.
HERBERT, Richard Elkan Northumberland House Surgery, Northumberland House, 437 Stourport Road, Kidderminster DY11 7BL Tel: 01562 745715 Fax: 01562 863010; Pear Trees, Whitlenge Lane, Hartlebury, Kidderminster DY10 4HD Tel: 01299 250598 Fax: 01299 250598 Email: ric.doc@aol.com — MB ChB 1963 Birm.; MRCS Eng. LRCP Lond. 1963; DA Eng. 1967; DObst RCOG 1965. Clin. Asst. Anaesth. Kidderminster; Locum. Cons. Anaeseth. Dudley NHS Trust. Socs: Midl. Soc. Anaesth.; Brit. Assn. Immed. Care Schemes. Prev: SHO (Anaesth.) United Birm. Hosps.; Ho. Phys. & Ho. Surg. Qu. Eliz. Hosp. Birm.; Ho. Surg. Marston Green Matern. Hosp. Birm.
HERBERT, Rodney Lloyd (retired) Manderley, Rats Lane, High Beech, Loughton IG10 4AQ Tel: 020 8508 4920 Email: rodherb@dircon.co.uk — MB ChB 1963 Leeds; MRCS Ed. Surg. Whipps. Cross. Hosp. Prev: Tutor (Gen. Pract.) Roy. Free Hosp. Med. Sch.
HERBERT, Trefor John Westgate Practice, Greenhill Health Centre, Church Street, Lichfield WS13 6JL Tel: 01543 414311 Fax: 01543 256364; 64 Wentworth Drive, Lichfield WS14 9HN Tel: 01543 264416 — MB BChir 1972 Camb.; MA Camb. 1972; MRCGP 1976. Prev: SHO (Obst.) John Radcliffe Hosp. Oxf.; SHO (Gen. Med.) Roy. Lond. Hosp.; SHO (Paediat.) Radcliffe Infirm. Oxf.
HERBERTS, Patrick Joseph David Occupational Health Deparment, Adtranz, Litchurch Lane, Derby DE24 8AD Tel: 01332 251876 Fax: 01332 251771; 222 Musters Road, West Bridgford, Nottingham NG2 7DR Tel: 0115 981 2732 — BM BS 1983 Nottm.; BMedSci Nottm. 1979; AFOM RCP Lond. 1994. (Nottm.) Occupat. Health Phys. Adtranz Derby. Socs: Soc. Occupat. Med.; RSM; Roy. Soc. Med.
HERBERTSON, Michael Jonathan 2 Holbury View, East Dean Road, Lockerley, Romsey SO51 0JQ — MB BS 1982 Lond.
HERBERTSON, Rebecca Anne Cobden, Washington Rd, Storrington, Pulborough RH20 4BZ — BM BS 1997 Nottm.
HERBETKO, John c/o Department of Radiology, Poole Hospital, Longfleet Road, Poole BH15 2JB Tel: 01202 665511; 10 Forest Road, Branksome Park, Poole BH13 6DH Tel: 01202 752905 — MB ChB 1982 Bristol; BSc Bristol 1975, MB ChB 1982; MRCP (UK) 1985; FRCR 1988. Cons. Radiol. Poole Hosp. NHS Trust.
HERBISON, Jean Ward 5B, Royal Hospital for Sick Children, Yorkhill NHS Trust, Glasgow G3 Tel: 0141 201 9360 Fax: 0141 201 9228 — MB ChB 1983 Aberd.; MRCP; FRCPCH; DCCH.
HERBORN, Andrew 14 Mariners Drive, Backwell, Bristol BS48 3HT Tel: 01275 462058 — MB BS 1990 Lond.; MRCGP 1996; DRCOG 1994. (St. Bart. Hosp.)
HERCULES, Mr Brian Leslie c/o Consulting Suite, BUPA, Russell Road, Whalley Range, Manchester M16 8AJ Tel: 0161 232 2278 Fax: 0161 226 1187; c/o Department of Ophthalmology, Stepping Hill Hospital, Stockport SK7 2PE Tel: 0161 419 1094 Fax: 0161 483 8576 Email: judith.dingle@stockport-tr.nwest.nhs.uk — MB ChB 1969 Manch.; FCOphth 1980; FRCS Ed. 1976; MRCS Eng. LRCP Lond. 1969; FRCOphth 1989. (Victoria University) Cons. Ophth. Surg. Stockport Acute Servs. NHS Trust. Socs: Fell. Roy. Soc. Med.; Manch. Med. Soc.; Manch. Med. Ethical Soc. Prev: Cons. Ophth. Surg. Tameside Acute Servs. NHS Trust; Cons. Ophth. Surg. Roy. Devonshire Hosp. Burton.
HERD, Andrew Marshall Foleshill Road Surgery, 949 Foleshill Road, Coventry CV2 5HW Tel: 024 7668 8482/8230 Fax: 024 7663 8273; 22 Dove Close, Bedworth, Nuneaton CV12 0NN Tel: 024 76

310135 — MB ChB 1981 Glas.; DRCOG 1983. (Glas.) Socs: Fell. Roy. Soc. Med. (Paediat.).

HERD, Andrew Nicholas The Health Centre, Bishop's Close, Spennymoor, Durham DH6 6ED; 4 Goodwell Lea, Brancepeth, Durham DH7 8EN — MB BS 1982 Lond.; MRCGP 1989. (Middlx.) Med. Advisor Durh. Health Commiss. Socs: Fell. Med. Soc. Lond.; Harveian Soc.

HERD, Barbara Marion North Tees General Hospital, Hardwick, Stockton-on-Tees TS19 8PE — MB BS 1982 Lond.; MD Lond. 1992; MRCP (UK) 1985; FRCP Ed. 1997; FRCP Lond. 1998. (St. Thos.) Cons. Geriat. & Gen. Med. N. Tees Gen. Hosp. Socs: Harveian Soc.; Osler Club of Lond.

HERD, David Johnston Raigmore Hospital Trust, Perth Road, Inverness IV2 3UJ; 39 Oakdene Court, Culloden, Inverness IV2 7XL Tel: 01763 793757 — MB ChB 1968 Glas.; BSc Glas. 1966; MRCOG 1985; FFA RCS Eng. 1979; FRCOG 1999. (Glas.) Cons. O & G Raigmore Hosp. Trust. Prev: Cons. O & G Lewis Hosp. & W.. Isles Hosp. Stornoway.

HERD, Edmund Brian (retired) Shatton Hall, Lorton, Cockermouth CA13 9TL Tel: 01900 822349 Email: brian.herd@which.net — MB BS 1961 Lond.; MA Camb. 1959; FRCGP 1991, M 1979; DObst RCOG 1963. JP.; Chairm. & Med. Adviser W. Cumbria Hospice at Home. Prev: GP Cockermouth.

HERD, Elizabeth Jean Shawbirch Medical Centre, 5 Acorn Way, Telford TF5 0LW Tel: 01952 641555 Fax: 01952 260913; Sedgeford House, 27 Underdale Road, Shrewsbury SY2 5DW Tel: 01743 356924 — MB ChB 1977 Leeds; MRCP (UK) 1980. Socs: BMA. Prev: SHO (Paediat.) Maelor Gen. Hosp. Wrexham; SHO Rotat. (Gen. Med.) Roy. Shrewsbury Hosp.

HERD, Gordon James Christopher The Croft, Portway, Wantage OX12 9BU Tel: 01235 767111 — LRCP LRCS Ed. LRFPS Glas. 1948. Socs: Fell. BMA. Prev: Asst. Resid. Surg. Off. Stepping Hill Hosp. Stockport; Ho. Surg. & Ho. Phys. Roy. Infirm. Glas.

HERD, Gordon William Bank Street Medical Centre, 46-62 Bank Street, Alexandria G83 0LS Tel: 01389 756029 Fax: 01389 710049; 12 Hillside Road, Muirend, Dumbarton G82 5LX Tel: 01389 841607 Fax: 01389 841607 — MB ChB 1981 Glas.; BSc (Hons.) Glas. 1978; FRCP Glas. 1995; MRCP (UK) 1984; DRCOG 1987. (Univ. Glas.) Clin. Asst. (Gen. Med.) Dumbarton. Prev: GP Keith, Banffsh.; Regist. (Med.) Gartnavel Gen. Hosp.; Regist. (Med.) MRC Blood Pressure Unit Glas.

HERD, Gweneth Mary West End Medical Practice, 1 Heysham Road, Heysham, Morecambe LA3 1DA Tel: 01524 831931 Fax: 01524 832516; The Paddock, 151A North Road, Carnforth LA5 9LU Tel: 01524 736418 — MB ChB 1974 Manch.; MRCGP 1979. Prev: Course Organiser Lancaster GP VTS.; Occupat. Health Phys. Lothian HB.

HERD, James (retired) Edindoune, 26 Pine Field, Inchmarlo, Banchory AB31 4AF Tel: 01330 822777 — MB ChB Aberd. 1944, DPH 1948.

HERD, James Malcolm (retired) 49 Shawmoor Avenue, Stalybridge SK15 2RB — MB ChB Ed. 1944.

HERD, James Michael Rodger Stonehaven Medical Group, Stonehaven Medical Centre, 32 Robert Street, Stonehaven AB39 2EL Tel: 01569 762945 Fax: 01569 766552; Gleniffer, 15 Arduthie Road, Stonehaven AB39 2EH Tel: 01569 763286 — MB ChB 1978 Aberd.; BSc Aberd. 1973, MB ChB 1978; MRCGP 1982; DRCOG 1980. Prev: Trainee GP Dumfries & Galloway VTS.

HERD, Joanne Eastholme Surgery, 2 Heaton Moor Road, Stockport SK4 4NT Tel: 0161 443 1177 Fax: 0161 442 2521 — BM BS 1991 Nottm.; MRCGP 1995; DRCOG 1993.

HERD, Margaret Elizabeth 6 Guiseley Close, Walmersley, Bury BL9 5JR — MB ChB 1968 Aberd.

HERD, Robert Montgomery 82 Brunstane Road, Edinburgh EH15 2QR Tel: 0131 447 7552 — MB ChB 1984 Ed.; MSc Ed. 1977, BSc (Hons.) 1975, MB ChB 1984; MRCP (UK) 1988.

HERDMAN, Charlton Garth Rathmore Clinic, Cliff Road, Belleek, Enniskillen BT93 3FY Tel: 028 6865 8382 Fax: 028 6865 8124 — MB BCh 1983 Dublin; MB BCh Dub. 1983. (Dublin) GP Enniskillen, Co. Fermanagh.

HERDMAN, Clive Pearson Far Lane Medical Centre, 1 Far Lane, Sheffield S6 4FA Tel: 0114 234 3229 — MB ChB 1978 Sheff.; MRCGP 1984; DRCOG 1983. Prev: Capt. RAMC.

HERDMAN, Gareth 23 Standert Terrace, Seven Sisters, Neath SA10 9DF — MB BS 1984 Lond.

HERDMAN, Gawin Joseph Seaton (retired) Ty Cwmbeth, Crickhowell NP8 1SE Tel: 01873 810330 — MB ChB Bristol 1947; DObst RCOG 1951.

HERDMAN, Gregory John 36 Old Colin Road, Dunmurry, Belfast BT17 0NS — MB ChB 1997 Glas. SHO (Anaesth.) Mater hosp.Belf. Prev: SHO Anaesth.Roy.Vict. Hosp.Belf; Jun. Ho. Off. Surg.Stobhill Hosp.Glas.; Jun. Ho. Off. Med.RAH paisley.

HERDMAN, James Robin Elliot 5 Wick Hall, Radley, Abingdon OX14 3NF Tel: 01235 521934 — MB BChir 1982 Camb.; MA, MB BChir Camb. 1982; MRCPsych. 1990; MRCGP 1992. Prev: Hon. Sen. Regist. (Psychiat.) Littlemore Hosp. Oxf.; Trainee GP Abingdon; SHO (A & E) W.m. Hosp. Lond.

HERDMAN, Josephine Swallows Field, Tedburn St Mary, Exeter EX6 6BA — MB ChB 1982 Bristol; MRCGP 1989; DRCOG 1988. GP Exeter Retainer Scheme.

HERDMAN, Patricia 12 Goring Lodge, Pegasus Grange, White House Road, Oxford OX1 4QE — MRCS Eng. LRCP Lond. 1949.

HERDMAN, Mr Rory Charles Duddingstone Royal Berkshire Hospital, Reading RG1 5AN Tel: 01189 877136; Court End, 113 High St, Wargrave RG10 8DD — MB BS 1981 Lond.; FRCS Eng. 1987; FRCS Ed. 1986; FRCPS 1986. (Westminster) Cons. Surg. Otolaryngol. Roy. Berks. Hosp. Prev: Lect (Otolaryngol.) Manch. Univ.; Regist. (Otolaryngol.) St. Mary's Hosp. Lond.; SHO (Otolaryngol.) Radcliffe Infirm. Oxf.

HEREKAR, Sandip Ramkrishna The Surgery, 60 Market Square, Edmonton Green, London N9 0TZ Tel: 020 8807 7393 Fax: 020 8807 9247 — MB BS 1982 Lond.

HEREWARD, Anthony Charles Belmont Surgery, 12 Belmont Road, St Austell PL25 4UJ Tel: 01726 69444; Tarzell, Tregorrick, St Austell PL26 7AQ Tel: 01726 72946 Email: hereward@hereward.avel.co.uk — MB BS 1983 Lond.; BSc (Hons.) Aberd. 1978; MRCGP (Distinc) 1989; DFFP 1995; DTM & H Liverp. 1990; DCH RCP Lond. 1988. (Roy. Free Hosp. Lond.) Socs: Christian Med. Fell.sh.

HEREWARD, Janet Mary Family Health Practice, 20 Church Road, Hanwell, London W7 1DR Tel: 020 8579 7338 Fax: 020 8840 9928 — MB BS 1977 Lond.; MRCS Eng. LRCP Lond. 1977.

HEREWARD, Mr John Owen St Mellitus Vicarage, Church Road, London W7 3BA — MB BS 1977 Lond.; MRCS Eng. LRCP Lond. 1977; FRCS Ed. 1982.

HERFORD, Martin Edward Meakin, DSO, MBE, MC (retired) Tregithy Farm, Carne, Manaccan, Helston TR12 6ND Tel: 01326 231623 — MD Bristol 1955, MB ChB 1937; MFCM 1972; MRCGP 1965; DPH Lond. 1947. Prev: Rockefeller Research Fell. (Occupat. Med. & Hyg.) Harvard. USA.

HERFORD, Tamsin 52A Chelsea Park Gardens, London SW3 6AD — MB ChB 1998 Dund.; MB ChB Dund 1998.

HERIOT, Mr Alexander Graham 33 Glendarvon Street, Putney, London SW15 1JS Tel: 020 8785 0372 — MB BChir 1991 Camb.; MD (London) 1999; MA Camb. 1992; FRCS Eng. 1995; FRCS Ed. 1995. (Camb. & St. Thos. Hosp.) Specialist Regist., Frimley Pk. Hosp.; Specialist Regist. (Gen. Surg.) SW Thames. Socs: Roy. Soc. Med.

HERIOT, Jennifer Anne 28 Nightingale Lane, London SW12 8TD — MB BS 1985 Lond.; LMSSA Lond. 1984; FRCA 1993; MRCGP 1990; DRCOG 1990; DCH RCP Lond. 1989. (St. Thomas', London) Cons. Anaesth.

HERITAGE, Judith Helen The Harlequin Surgery, 160 Shard End Crescent, Shard End, Birmingham B34 7BP; Tel: 0121 354 3627 — MB BS 1984 Lond.; MRCGP 1988; DCH RCP Lond. 1986. Socs: Birm. Med. Inst.

HERITY, Niall Anthony Royal Victoria Hospital, Grosvenor Road, Belfast BT12 6BA Tel: 01232 240503 Fax: 01232 312907 Email: nherity@dial.pipex.com; 24 Baronscourt Heights, Carryduff, Belfast BT8 8RS Tel: 01232 815540 — MB BCh BAO 1988 NUI; MRCP (UK) 1991; MD Dub. 1996. Sen. Regist. (Cardiol.) Roy. Vict. Hosp. Belf. Prev: Sen. Regist. (Med. & Cardiol.) Antrim Hosp. Antrim; Regist. (Cardiol.) Belf. City Hosp.

HERMAN, Abraham Maurice 154 Marsham Court, Marsham St., London SW1P 4LB — LRCP LRCS 1944 Ed.; LRCP LRCS Ed. LRFPS Glas. 1944. (Durh.) Prev: Res. Ho. Surg. Luton Childr. Hosp.; Asst.

Med. Off. Preston Emerg. Hosp. N. Shields; Ho. Phys. Whipps Cross Hosp. Lond.

HERMAN, Christopher Robert 4 Linford Lane, Willen, Milton Keynes MK15 9DL — MB ChB 1977 Birm.

HERMAN, Jeanne Sibylla 2 Forlease Drive, Maidenhead SL6 1UD Tel: 01628 622437 — MB BS Ceylon 1958. (Ceylon) Clin. Asst. (Anaesth.) Wexham Pk. Hosp. Slough. Socs: BMA. Prev: Ho. Surg. N. Middlx. Hosp. Lond.; Ho. Surg. (Gyn.) Redhill Co. Hosp.; Ho. Off. De Soysa Hosp. Wom. Colombo.

HERMAN, Joanna Sarah 5 Jessel Mansions, Queens Club Gardens, London W14 9SH — MB BS 1990 Lond.

HERMAN, Jonathan Mark The Health Centre, Chapel Road, Mendlesham, Stowmarket IP14 5SQ Tel: 01449 767722; 20 Hall Farm Close, Melton, Woodbridge IP12 1RL Tel: 01394 384009 — MB BS 1989 Lond.; DFFP 1994; DRCOG 1994. Trainee GP Stowmarket. Prev: SHO (Paediat.) Ipswich Hosp.; SHO (O & G) Essex Co. Hosp. Colchester; SHO (Med. & Geriat.) Colchester Gen. Hosp.

HERMAN, Mary Joyce Georgia Willdock Cottage, Huntingdonsh. Close, Woosehill, Wokingham RG41 3BB — MB BS 1949 Lond. (W. Lond.)

HERMAN, Stephen Sydney 25 Wimpole Street, London W1M 7AD Tel: 020 7323 4959 Fax: 020 7636 3500; Barbary House, California Lane, Bushey Heath, Watford WD2 1EX Tel: 020 8950 1006 — MB BS 1965 Lond.; FRCP Lond. 1981, M 1969; FRCPCH 1997; DCH Eng. 1967. (St. Geo.) Cons. Paediat. Roy. Nat. Orthop. Hosp. NHS Trust. Socs: Neonat. Soc. & Brit. Paediat. Assn. Prev: Cons. Paediat. Centr. Middlx. Hosp.; Sen. Regist. (Paediat.) Univ. Coll., Edgware Gen. & Barnet Gen. Hosps.; Lect. (Paediat.) Dept. Physiol. Lond. Hosp. Med. Coll.

HERMANN, Josef 1 Lurgan Avenue, London W6 — MD 1986 Graz.

HERMANN-SMITH, Jacqueline Ann 104A Ryder Street, Cardiff CF11 9BU — MB BCh 1988 Wales.

HERMASZEWSKA, Elizabeth Jane 21 Burnham Drive, Bleadon Hill, Weston Super Mare BS24 9LN — MB ChB 1986 Bristol.

HERMASZEWSKI, Ryszard Andrzej 21 Burnham Drive, Bleadon Hill, Weston Super Mare BS24 9LN — MB ChB 1986 Bristol.

HERMITAGE, Alison Patricia Ship Street Surgery, 65-67 Ship Street, Brighton BN1 1AE — MB BS 1976 Lond. (King's Coll. Hosp.) Prev: GP Hove.

HERMON, Gail Adrienne 38 Wyeths Road, Epsom KT17 4EB — BA (Hons.) Dub. 1971; MB BS Newc. 1979. Clin. Med. Off. (Child Health) Newc. AHA. Prev: SHO (Anaesth.) Gateshead DHA.

HERMON-TAYLOR, Professor John Department of Surgery, St Georges Hospital Medical School, London SW17 0RE Tel: 020 8767 7631 Fax: 020 8725 3594 — MB 1961 Camb.; MB BChir Camb. 1961; BA Nat. Sci. Camb. 1957; MChir Camb. 1968; FRCS Eng. 1963. (Camb. & Lond. Hosp.) Prof. Surg. (Univ. Lond.) St. Geo. Hosp. Med. Sch.; Hon. Cons. Gen. Surg. to the RN. Socs: Biochem. Soc. & Brit. Soc. Cell. Biol. Prev: MRC Trav. Fell. Mayo Clinic Rochester, USA; Sen. Regist. & Reader (Surg.) Lond. Hosp.

HERN, Emma Elizabeth St Davids, Green West Road, Jordans Village, Beaconsfield HP9 2SY Tel: 01494 871336 Email: e-hern@hotmail.com — MB BS 1996 Lond.; BSc 1995. (Roy. Free) SHO Surg. Rotat. P.ss Margt.s Hosp. Swindon. Prev: Anat. Demonst., Oxf. Univ.

HERN, John Edwin Cornwall Woodside of Horner, Kintore, Inverurie AB51 0XT Tel: 01467 42536 — BM BCh 1962 Oxf.; BSc Oxf. 1960, DM 1971, MA 1962; FRCP Lond. 1979, M 1966. (Guy's) Cons. Neurol. Aberd. Roy. Hosps. Prev: Sen. Regist. Dept. Neurol. Guy's Hosp. Lond.; Sen. Res. Ho. Phys. Nat. Hosp. Nerv. Dis. Qu. Sq. Lond.

HERNANDEZ, Pauline Mary Baldwins Lane Surgery, 266 Baldwins Lane, Croxley Green, Rickmansworth WD3 3LG Tel: 01923 774732 Fax: 01923 711933 — MB BS 1992 Lond.

HERNANDEZ-MANSILLA PALUMBO, Jaime Mid Ulster Hospital, Bungalow 2, 59 Hospital Road, Magherafelt BT45 5EX — LMS 1933 U Complutense Madrid; LMS U Complutense Madrid 1993.

HERNON, Catherine Ann 10 Leegate Close, Stockport SK4 3NN — MB ChB 1995 Manch.

HERNON, James Martin 18 Whitton Drive, Greenford UB6 0QZ — BChir 1996 Camb.

HERNON, Mary 4 Rajar Cottages, Town Lane, Mobberley, Knutsford WA16 7ER — MB ChB 1994 Manch.

HERO, Isabelle Dept.of Cellular Pathology, Birmingham Medical School, Edgebaston, Birmingham B15 2TT — MRCS Eng. LRCP Lond. 1979; PhD Lond. 1990; FRCS (Ophth.) Eng. 1984; MRCPath 1993; FRCOphth 1989; DO RCS Eng. 1983. (Westm. Med. Sch.) Cons. Histo/Cytopathologist, Univ. Hosp., Birm. Prev: Lect. (Histopath.) Roy. Lond. Hosp.; Regist. (Ophth.) Oxf. RHA; SHO (Ophth.) King's Coll. Hosp. Lond.

HEROD, Jane Elizabeth 5 Dellfield Close, Radlett WD7 8LS — MB BS 1992 Lond.; BSc Lond. 1989, MB BS 1992.

HEROD, Jeremy Jonathan Owen 44 Crank Road, Billinge, Wigan WN5 7EZ — MB ChB 1987 Birm.; ChB Birm. 1987.

HEROD, Mrs Susan Jacqueline Dean Lane Family Practice, 1 Dean Lane, Bedminster, Bristol BS3 1DE Tel: 0117 966 3149 Fax: 0117 953 0699; Hollybush Barn, Main Road, Templecloud, Bristol BS39 5DQ Tel: 01761 452250 — MB ChB 1974 Bristol; DRCOG 1976.

HERODOTOU, Nicholas St Ann's Hospital, 69 Haven Road, Poole BH13 7LM — MB BS 1995 Lond.; BSc (Med. Sci.) (Hons.) St. And. 1991; DGM RCP Lond. 1997; DRCOG 1997; MRCOG 1999. (St. And. & St. Bart. Hosp. Med. Coll.) GP Regist. Bournemouth; Locum, H Spr, Psychiat. St Ann's Hosp., Poole; GP Non-Princip. Locum Out of Hours, Bournemouth; GP Locuming in Bournmouth, Dorset. Socs: Christ. Med. Fell.sh.; B.M.A.; Honary Med. Off., Moorlands Coll., Sopley. Prev: Ho. Off. (Med.) E. Surrey Hosp. Reigate, Surrey; Surg. Ho. Off. York Dist. Hosp. York; GPVTS Roy. Bournemouth Hosp. Bournemouth.

HEROLD, David Charles The Riverside Surgery, Waterside, Evesham WR11 6JP Tel: 01386 40121 Fax: 01386 442615; Elmbank House, Hill End Road, Twyning, Tewkesbury GL20 6JL — MB ChB 1991 Birm.; BSc Pharm. Dundee. 1986; MRCGP 1995; DFFP 1995; DRCOG 1994. Socs: Med. Protec. Soc.; BMA. Prev: Med. Off. (Palliat. Care) St. Michael's Hospice Hereford; GP/Regist. Moorfield Hse. Surg. Hereford; Trainee GP Hereford Co. Hosp. VTS.

HEROLD, Mr James Maxillofacial Department, Royal Sussex County Hospital, Eastern Road, Brighton BN2 5BE Tel: 01273 696955 Fax: 01273 628517 — MRCS Eng. LRCP Lond. 1987; BDS Bristol 1977; FRCS Eng. 1991; FRCS Ed. 1991; FDS RCS Eng. 1981. Cons. Maxillofacial Surg. Roy. Sussex Co. Hosp. Brighton; Cons. Maxillofacial Surg., P.ss Roy. Hosp., Haywards Heath. Socs: Fell.Brit. Assoc. Oral & Maxillofacial Surg.; BDA & BMA; Brit. Assn. Head & Neck Oncol. Prev: Sen. Regist. (Maxillofacial Surg.) Ulster Hosp. Belf.; Regist. (Maxillofacial Surg.) Roy. Surrey Co. Hosp. Guildford.

HERON, Ann Fionnuala (retired) Willowbrake, 6 Granville Avenue, Newcastle ST5 1JH — MB BS Lond. 1958; MRCS Eng. LRCP Lond. 1957; DA Eng. 1959. Prev: Assoc. Specialist (Dermat.) N. Staffs Hosp. Centre Stoke-on-Trent.

HERON, Anthony Turrettin (retired) 19A Derby Road, Risley, Derby DE72 3SY Tel: 0115 939 2163 — MB BCh BAO 1949 Belf. Maj. RAMC (Ret.). Prev: Ho. Off. Devizes & Dist. Hosp.

HERON, Christine Woodruff Radiology Department, St George's Hospital, Blackshaw Road, London SW17 0QT Tel: 020 8672 1255 — MB BS 1977 Lond.; MRCP (UK) 1980; MRCS Eng. LRCP Lond. 1977; FRCR 1985. (Roy. Free) Cons. Radiol. St. Geo. Hosp. Lond. Prev: Sen. Lect. (Radiol.) Roy. Marsden Hosp. Sutton; Sen. Regist. & Regist. (Radiol.) Middlx. Hosp. Lond.

HERON, Elizabeth Clare St Gabriels Medical Centre, Prestwich, Manchester M25 0HT Tel: 01782 617766; 42 Priory Street, Bowdon, Altrincham WA14 3BQ Tel: 0976 722006 — MB BS 1989 Lond.; BSc Lond. 1986; MRCGP 1995; DFFP 1995; DTM & H Liverp. 1994. (Roy. Free Hosp. Sch. Med.) GP. Socs: Med. Defence Union; BMA. Prev: Clin. Off. (Family Plann.) Sheff.; SHO (Genitourin. Med. & Infec. Dis.) Roy. Hallamsh. Hosp. Sheff.; GP/Regist. Shrewsbury.

HERON, Francis John The Quakers Lane Surgery, Quakers Lane, Richmond DL10 4BB Tel: 01748 850440 Fax: 01748 850802 — MB ChB 1964 St. And.; DCH RCPS Glas. 1967; DObst RCOG 1966; LM Rotunda 1966. Hosp. Pract. (Paediat.) Darlington Memor. Hosp. Prev: Ho. Phys. Dundee Roy. Infirm. & Roy. Hosp. Sick Childr. Edin.; Clin. Clerk Rotunda Hosp.

HERON, Ivan Douglas c/o Royal Cornwall Hospital (City), Truro TR1 — MB BCh BAO 1957 Belf.; FRCR 1975; FFR 1965; DMRD Eng. 1962. Cons. Radiol. Roy. Cornw. Hosp. City & Treliske. Prev: Sen. Regist. Radiol. Roy. Vict. Hosp. Belf.; SHO Radiol. Manch. Roy. Infirm.; Ho. Phys. Belf. City Hosp.

HERON, Professor James Riddick Willowbrake, Granville Avenue, Newcastle ST5 1JH Tel: 01782 617766 — MB ChB 1964 Birm.; MRCS Eng. LRCP Lond. 1958; FRCP Lond. 1980; FRCP Ed. 1971, M 1964. (Birm.) Emerit. Prof. Neurol. Univ. Keele. Socs: (Ex-Pres.) Assn. Brit. Neurol.; (Ex-Pres.) W. Midl. Phys. Assn.; Assn. Phys. Prev: Cons. Neurol. N. Staffs. Roy. Infirm. & City Gen. Hosp. Stoke-on-Trent; Sen. Regist. (Neurol.) United Birm. Hosps.; Regist. Nat. Hosp. Nerv. Dis. Qu. Sq. & Maida Vale.

HERON, Joseph Gerald Francis (retired) 23 Culverley Road, Catford, London SE6 2LD Tel: 020 8698 5526 — MB BCh BAO 1944 NUI; LM Nat. Matern. Hosp. Dub. 1944. Prev: Clin. Asst. (Ophth.) W. Hill Hosp. Dartford.

HERON, Judith Margaret (retired) 1 Greenacre, Burton Joyce, Nottingham NG14 5BT Tel: 0115 931 3771 — MB BS 1959 Durh.; FRCPsych 1985, M 1972; DPM Ed. 1970; DPM Eng. 1969; DCH Eng. 1961. Prev: Cons. & Sen. Lect. (Child Psychiat.) Notts. AHA (T).

HERON, Mark Oliver 18 Tobermore Road, Draperstown, Magherafelt BT45 7HG — MB BCh 1998 Belf.; MB BCh Belf 1998.

HERON, Mischa 10 Frognal Gardens, London NW3 6UX — MB BS 1994 Lond.

HERON, Richard James Lockhart Global SHE, Astrazeneca, Alderley House, Alderley Park, Macclesfield SK10 4TF Tel: 01625 512278 Fax: 01625 586912 Email: richard.heron@astrazeneca.com; Greenbank Cottage, 8 Scott Road, Prestbury, Macclesfield SK10 4DN — MB ChB 1985 Birm.; ChB Birm. 1985; MRCP (UK) 1989; MFOM RCP Lond. 1995; FFOM RCP Lond 1999. (Birmingham) Princip. Med. Off. Astrazeneca. Chesh. Socs: Soc. Occupat. Med. Prev: Occupat. Phys. ICI plc Huddersfield; Regist. (Med.) Burton-on-Trent & Dudley Rd. Birm.

HERON, Thomas Geoffrey 10 Rushmere Place, Marryat Road, London SW19 5RP Tel: 020 8944 6102 — MRCS Eng. LRCP Lond. 1947; DLO Eng. 1964. (St. Thos.) Prev: Cons. Audiol. Med. NW Thames RHA; Cons. ENT Surg. Johannesburg, S. Afr.

HERON, William Cecil West Winds, Exton, Exeter EX3 0PJ — MB BCh BAO 1950 Belf.; FRCR 1975; FFR 1958; DMRD Liverp. 1954; DMRD Eng. 1955. (Belf.) Cons. Radiol. Exeter Clin. Area. Socs: Brit. Inst. Radiol. & BMA. Prev: Asst. Radiol. Leicester Roy. Infirm. & Leicester Gen. Hosp.; Sen. Regist. Radiol. Belf. City Hosp.; Sen. Ho. Off. Roy. Vict. Hosp. Belf.

HERRAIZ MORILLAS, Raquel Kent & Canterbury Hospital, Ethelbert Road, Canterbury CT1 3NG Tel: 01227 766877; 17 Chaucer Court, New Dover Road, Canterbury CT1 3AU — LMS 1988 U Complutense Madrid. Trainee GP Canterbury & Thanet VTS. Prev: SHO (A & E) Roy. Albert Edwd. Infirm. Wigan.

HERREMA, Idse Harmen Department of Anaesthetics, Royal Victoria Infirmary, Queen Victoria Road, Newcastle upon Tyne NE1 4LP — MB BCh BAO 1982 Dub.; FFA RCS Eng. 1987; MBA 1999 Durham. Cons. Paediat. Anaesth. Roy. Vict. Infirm.

HERRERA VEGA, Leonor 45 Sydney Road, Sheffield S6 3GG — LMS 1993 Granada.

HERRERO, Jose Ramon 124 Empress Road, Kensington, Liverpool L7 8SF — LMS 1994 Saragossa.

HERRERO DIAZ, Miss Maite 31 Hanover Road, Norwich NR2 2HD; Brunswick Road, Norwich NR1 3SR — LMS 1985 Basque Provinces. Specialist Regist. (O & G) Norf. & Norwich NHS Health Trust Norwich.

HERRERO VELASCO, Leandro Eloy VP R & D Europe, Allergan Ltd., Crown Centre, Coronation Road, High Wycombe HP12 3SH Tel: 01494 427188 Fax: 01494 427181 Email: herrero_leandro@allergan.com — LMS 1973 Barcelona; Specialist in Psychiatry Barcelona 1995.

HERRICK, Angela Christine Britton and Partners, 10 Spencer Street, Carlisle CA1 1BP Tel: 01228 529171 — MB BS 1969 Lond.; MRCGP 1982; DRCOG 1981. (St. Thos.) Princip. GP Carlisle. Prev: SHO (Paediat. & A & E) Cumbld. Infirm. Carlisle.; Ho. Phys. Lambeth Hosp.

HERRICK, Ann Mary Chesterfield & North Derbyshire Royal Hospital, Calow, Chesterfield S44 5BL Tel: 01246 277271 Fax: 01246 553 2620; Tel: 01246 273354 Email: herrickga@aol.com — MB BCh 1980 Wales; MRCPI 1987. (Welsh National School of Medicine) Cons. Paediat. Chesterfield & N. Derbysh. Roy. Hosp. NHS Trust. Socs: FRCPCH; Brit. Assn. Perinatal Med. Prev: Sen Regist. (Paediat.) N. Staffs. Hosps; Regist. (Paediat.) Roy. Hosp. for Sick Childr. Glas. & Freedom Fields Hosp. Plymouth; SHO (Paediat.) Univ. Hosp. Wales, Cardiff.

HERRICK, Ariane Loraine Rheumatic Diseases Centre, Hope Hospital, Salford M6 8HD Tel: 0161 787 4367 Fax: 0161 787 4367 — MB ChB Aberd. 1981; MD Aberd. 1989; FRCP Glas. 1995; FRCP 1998 Lond. Sen. Lect. & Cons. Rheum. Univ. Manch. Rheum. Dis. Centre Hope Hosp. Salford. Prev: Lect. (Med.) W.. Infirm. Glas.

HERRICK, Erina Mary (retired) 64 Broomhill, Cookham, Maidenhead SL6 9LW — MB BS 1966 Lond.

HERRICK, Martin John Department of Anaesthesia, Box 93, Addenbrooke's Hospital, Cambridge CB2 2QQ — MB BChir 1972 Camb.; MA Camb. 1973; FFA RCS Eng. 1977. Cons. Anaesth. Addenbrooke's Hosp. NHS Trust Camb. Prev: Sen. Regist. (Anaesth.) Camb. & King's Lynn; Regist. (Anaesth.) Portsmouth; Sen. Med. Off. St. Luke's Hosp. Chilema Malawi.

HERRICK, Philip Richard The Surgery, 46 Annan Road, Gretna DG16 5DG Tel: 01461 338317 Fax: 01461 337180 — MB 1971 Camb.; BChir 1970; MRCGP 1975; DObst RCOG 1972. (St. Thos. & Camb.) Prev: SHO (Paediat.) Pembury Hosp.; SHO (O & G) Pembury Hosp.; Ho. Off. (Surg.) St. Thos. Hosp. Lond.

HERRIDGE, Colin Francis (retired) Landsview, Love Lane, Walton-on-the-Hill, Tadworth KT20 7QZ Tel: 01737 813284 Fax: 01737 813284 — MB BChir 1956 Camb.; MA Camb. 1956; FRCPsych 1980, M 1971; T(Psychiat.) 1991; DPM Eng. 1961. Cons. Mem Appeals Serv.; Hon. Cons. Psychiat. W. Middlx. Univ. Hosp. Prev: Sen. Cons. Psychiat. W. Middx. Univ. Hosp.

HERRIES, John W (retired) Elmfold, East End, Witney OX8 6PZ — MB ChB 1948 Ed.; MD 1968; DA Eng. 1955. Prev: USVA MA 01060 USA, Clin. Director.

HERRIN, Eleanor Joy (retired) 255 Woodstock Road, Oxford OX2 7AE Tel: 01865 515531 — BM BCh Oxon. 1940; DCH Eng. 1942.

HERRING, Agnes Jane (retired) Pine Grove Retirement Home, 334 Perth Road, Dundee DD2 1QE — MB ChB 1933 St. And.; BSc St. And. 1930, MB ChB (Distinc.) 1933; FRCS Ed. 1937; FRCOG 1951. Prev: Cons. O & G Maryfield Hosp. Dundee.

HERRING, Antony Babington (retired) Brentwood, 19 Penweathers Lane, Truro TR1 3PW Tel: 01872 273678 — BM BCh 1957 Oxf.; FRCP Lond. 1976, M 1959. Prev: Cons. Neurol. Cornw. & Plymouth Clin. Areas.

HERRING, Mr David William, QHS, TD 2 Barnstones, Plawsworth, Chester-le-Street DH2 3UZ Tel: 0191 3712700/0585 665561 — MB BS Durh. 1963; FRCS Eng. 1968. (Durham) Cons. Gen. Surg. & Urol. Dryburn Hosp. Durh. & Washington Hosp. Tyne & Wear; Col. L/RAMC (V). Prev: Demonst. (Anat.) Univ. Newc.; Sen. Regist. St. Mark's Hosp. Lond. & Roy. Vict. Infirm. Newc.

HERRING, Jeanne Kent House Surgery, Station Road, Longfield, Dartford Tel: 01474 702127 Fax: 01474 704735; Longview, Hartley Hill, Hartley, Longfield DA3 8LL Email: 106051.1713@compuserve.com — MB BS 1977 Lond.; BSc Lond. 1974, MB BS 1977; DMJ 1998. GP Longfield & New Ash Green; Princip. Forens. Med. Examr. W. Kent; Sector GP PCG. Socs: Assoc. of Police Surg.s; Roy. Soc. Med.; Medico Legal Soc.

HERRING, John Peter 41 Elms Avenue, Poole BH14 8EE — MB ChB 1997 Leeds.

HERRING, Sally Anne The Dye House, Thursley, Godalming GU8 6QL — MB BS 1978 Lond.; MRCS Eng. LRCP Lond. 1978; DCH RCP Lond. 1980. Clin. Med. Off. Guildford Surrey.

HERRINGTON, Professor Charles Simon Department of Pathology, Duncan Building, Royal Liverpool University Hospital, Liverpool L69 3BX Tel: 0151 706 4106 Fax: 0151 706 5859 Email: c.s.herrington@liv.ac.uk; 88 Cambridge Road, Crosby, Liverpool L23 7UA — MB BS 1985 Lond.; MB BS (Gold Medal) Lond. 1985; MA Camb. 1986; DPhil Oxf. 1990, MA 1990; MRCP (UK) 1988; MRCPath 1993. Prof. & Hon. Cons. Histopath. Roy. Liverp. Univ. Hosp. Socs: Path. Soc.; Internat. Soc. Gyn. Path.; Internat. Gyn. Cancer Soc. Prev: Clin. Tutor & Hon. Sen. Regist. (Histopath.) John Radcliffe Hosp. Oxf.

HERRINGTON, Lindsay Margaret St Johns Medical Centre, St. Johns Road, Altrincham WA14 2NW Tel: 0161 928 8727 Fax: 0161 929 8550; 23 Bankhall Lane, Hale, Altrincham WA15 0LA Tel: 0161 941 7138 — MB BS 1981 Lond.; BSc (Econ.) Lond. 1972; SRN Lond. 1975; MRCGP 1985. (Guy's) Prev: GP Whitburn Tyne & Wear; Trainee GP Newc. u. Tyne; Trainee GP Bath HA VTS.

HERRINGTON, Reginald Nicholas (retired) 9 Thorn Drive, Bearsden, Glasgow G61 4ND — MB ChB Birm. 1957; PhD Aberd. 1966 FRCPsych 1979; DPM Eng. 1960. Prev: Hon. Cons. Psychiat. Gartnavel Roy. Hosp. Glas.

HERRINGTON, Ruth Anne 19 Wynford Avenue, Leeds LS16 6JN Tel: 0113 275 7820; 6 Barnes Hall Road, Burncross, Sheffield S35 1RF Tel: 0114 236 0655 — MB ChB 1985 Dundee; MRCP (UK) 1989; MRCGP 1993; DPH Glas. 1994; DRCOG 1992; Dip. Ther. Newc. 1998. (Dundee) GP Princip.

HERRIOT, Bruce William Allan Cradley Surgery, Bosbury Road, Cradley, Malvern WR13 5LT Tel: 01886 880525 Fax: 01886 880630; Summerhayes, Bosbury Road, Cradley, Malvern WR13 5LT Tel: 01886 880207 Fax: 01886 880630 — MB ChB 1981 Manch.; BSc St. And. 1978; DCH RCP Lond. 1986; DRCOG 1986. Med. Dir. Herts. HA. Prev: SHO (Paediat. Surg.) Bristol Childr. Hosp.; SHO (Geriat. & Rheum.) Bristol Gen. Hosp.; GP Trainee Charlotte Keel, Bristol VTS.

HERRIOT, David Thompson The Bute Practice, The Health Centre, Townhead, Rothesay PA20 9JL; 6 Battery Place, Rothesay PA20 9DP Tel: 01700 3985 & 2388 — MB ChB 1957 Glas.

HERRIOT, Richard Pathology Department, Aberdeen Royal Infirmary, Foresterhill, Aberdeen AB25 2ZD Tel: 01224 681818 Fax: 01224 663002 Email: r.herriot@abdn.ac.uk — MB ChB 1982 Aberd.; BMedBiol Aberd. 1979; FRCP Ed. 1996; MRCP (UK) 1987; MRCPath 1993. Cons. Immunol. Aberd. Roy. Hosps. NHS Trust. Prev: Sen. Regist. (Clin. Immunol.) W.. Infirm. Glas.; Lect. (Path.) Aberd. Univ.; SHO (Gen. Med.) Grampian HB (S. Dist.) Aberd.

HERRIOT, Sarah Elizabeth Summerhayes, Cradley, Malvern WR13 5LT Tel: 0188 684207 — MB BS 1982 Lond.

HERRIOTT, Mary Longridge, Quakers Walk, London N21 2DE — MB BCh BAO 1947 Belf. (Belf.)

HERRIOTT, Sara Lucy The Wooda Surgery, Clarence Wharf, Barnstaple Street, Bideford EX39 4AU Tel: 01237 471071 Fax: 01237 471059; 4 Shepherds Meadow, Abbotsham, Bideford EX39 5BP — MB ChB 1987 Leeds; MRCGP 1992. (Leeds) Clin. Asst. (c/o the Elderly). Socs: Med. Protec. Soc.

HERRIOTT, Thomas Dunn Longridge, Quakers Walk, London N21 2DE — MB BCh BAO 1946 Belf. (Belf.)

HERRIOTT, Thompson Parker (retired) 2 Larch Hill, Craigavad, Holywood BT18 0JN — MB BCh BAO 1947 Belf.; MRCPsych 1972; DPM RCPSI 1968. Prev: Cons. Psychiat. Downshire Hosp. Downpatrick.

HERRMANN, Knut 16 Scotby Gardens, Botcherby, Carlisle CA1 2XH — State Exam Med 1992 Leipzig. (Univ. Leipzig, Germany) SHO (Gen. Surg.) Friarage Hosp. N.allerton. Prev: SHO (Orthop.) Friarage Hosp. N.allerton; SHO (Orthop.) Rehabil. Centre Spreewald Bürg, Germany; Ho. Off. (Orthop.) Orthop. Clinic Leipzig, Germany.

HERROD, Johanna Jane The Fermay Unit, Queen Elizabeth Hospital, King's Lynn Tel: 01553 613613; The Cottage, 32 Mill Hill, Swaffham Prior, Cambridge CB5 0JZ — PhD Camb. 1984, MB BChir 1990, MRC Psych1995; MRCPsych 1995. (Addenbrookes Hospital Univ. Cambridge) Cons. Psych. Qu. Eliz. Hosp., King's Lynn. Socs: Brit. Assn. Psychopharmacol.; Brit. Neuropsychiat. Assn.; BMA. Prev: Sen. Regist. Addenbrookes Hosp. Psychiat.

HERROD, Kathleen Elaine Whitethorn, Main St, Sicklinghall, Wetherby LS22 4BD — MB ChB Leeds 1957. (Leeds) Prev: Clin. Asst. St. Jas. Hosp. Leeds; Ho. Off. St. Jas. Hosp. Leeds; Cas. Off. Leeds Pub. Disp.

HERRON, Aine 188B Bush Road, Dungannon BT71 6EZ — MB BCh 1997 Belf.

HERRON, Bernard Michael 25 Sans Souci Park, Belfast BT9 5BZ — MB BCh BAO 1987 Belf.

HERRON, Christina Aitkenhead 51 Craw Road, Paisley PA2 6AE — MB ChB 1933 Glas.; DPH Glas. 1936. (Glas.) Socs: BMA. Prev: Sen. Med. Off. Argyll & Clyde HB; Asst. MOH Burgh Perth.

HERRON, Desmond Milburn Mulberry Cottage, The Street, Horringer, Bury St Edmunds IP29 5SA — MB ChB 1963 Cape Town.

HERRON, John James Govan Health Centre, 5 Drumoyne Road, Glasgow G51 4BJ Tel: 0141 531 8400 Fax: 0141 531 8404 — MB ChB 1981 Aberd.; BMedBiol Aberd. 1978, MB ChB 1981; MRCP (UK) 1984; MRCGP 1986.

HERRON, John Tristan 107 Park Av, Broadstairs CT10 2XL — MB BS 1997 Lond.

***HERRON, Julia Christine** 6 Virgina Close, Chipping Sodbury, Bristol BS37 6HN — BM BCh 1994 Oxf.; MRCP (UK) 1997.

HERRON, Kathleen (retired) 18 Rosepark, Belfast BT5 7RG Tel: 01232 483394 — MB BCh BAO 1940 Belf.; FRCGP 1976.

HERRON, Mark Laurence 6 Virginia Close, Chipping Sodbury, Bristol BS37 6HN — MB ChB 1991 Birm.; ChB Birm. 1991.

HERRON, Michael Joseph 188B Bush Road, Dungannon BT71 6EZ — MB BCh BAO 1989 Belf.

HERRON, Nicola Mary 10 Glebe Gardens, Newtownabbey BT36 6ED — MB BCh BAO 1989 Belf.

HERSANT, Michael Eric Henry Vellancoth, Trevedran, St Buryan, Penzance TR19 6DJ — MB BS Lond. 1963; MRCS Eng. LRCP Lond. 1963. (Lond. Hosp.)

HERSCH, Elizabeth (Glasby) St. Chad's Surgery, Gullock Tyning, Midsomer Norton, Bath BA3 2UH Tel: 01761 413334; Newlands, Claverton Down Road, Bath BA2 7AP — MB ChB 1993 Bristol; Dip Dermat; DRCOG. (Bristol) p/t GP Princip., Midsomer Norton, Som. Socs: BMA; FPA (Diplomat); RCGP. Prev: GP Princip., Newmarket, Suff.

HERSEY, Jeremy Adam (retired) 11 Whitethorn Lane, Letchworth SG6 2DN Tel: 01462 684478 — MRCS Eng. LRCP Lond. 1961. Mem. Appoint. Med. Mem. DLA Appeal Tribunals. Prev: GP Herts.

HERSEY, Nicholas Geoffrey Briscoe, Surg. Capt. RN Retd. 2 Great Churchway, Plymstock, Plymouth PL9 8JY Tel: 01752 405977 — MB BS 1951 Lond.; FFA RCSI 1962. (Middlx.) Socs: (Ex-Pres.) Soc. Anaesth. SW Region. Prev: Hon. Surg. to HM the Qu.; Cons. Anaesth. RN Hosp. Plymouth; Cons. Advis. (Anaesth.) RN.

HERSHMAN, Mr Michael Jeremy Royal Liverpool University Hospital, Prescot St., Liverpool L7 8XP Tel: 0151 706 3582 Fax: 0151 706 5827; Hersholme, 3 Merrilocks Rd, Blunderllsands, Liverpool L23 64J — MB BS 1980 Lond.; FRCS Irel., 1984; FICS 1989; DHMSA 1985; MSc (Hons.) Louisville 1988; MS (Hons.) Lond. 1990; FRCS Glas. 1984; FRCSEd 1984; FRCS Eng. 1984; FRCS (A&E Surg. & Med.) Ed. 1984; MRCS Eng. LRCP Lond. 1980. (St. Bart. Hosp.) Cons. Surg. Roy. Liverp. Univ. Hosp.; Lect. Univ. Liverp.; Hon. Sen. Lect. Univ. Liverp.; Hon Cons. Liverp. Wom.'s Hosp.; Hon. Cons. Alder Hay Hosp. Socs: Roy. Soc. Med. (Pres. Clin. Sect.); Assn. Surg.; (Counc.) Assn. Endoscopic Surg. Prev: Sen. Regist. St. Mary's, Hammersmith & Assoc. Hosps.; Resid. Surg. Off. St. Mark's Hosp. Lond.; Price Fell. Surg. Research Univ. Louisville, USA.

HERSHON, Andrew Lawrence Nigel Hugh 25 Hunters Crescent, Stalybridge SK15 2UH — MB ChB 1987 Manch. Regist. (Psychiat.) Gen. Hosp. St. Helier, Jersey CI.

HERSHON, Edgar 25 St John Street, Manchester M3 4DT Tel: 0161 907 3638 Fax: 0161 835 1413; 48 Rodney Street, Liverpool L1 9AA Tel: 0151 709 3580 Fax: 0151 709 2727 — MB ChB 1955 Liverp.; MSc Liverp. 1992, MA 1994; MRCGP (Henry Briggs Memor. Medal Obst. & Gyn.) 1965; Cert. Family Plann. RCOG & RCGP 1984. (Liverp.) p/t Admiralty Surg. & Agent; Local Med. Off. Civil Serv.; Flight Lt. RAF Med. Br. Res. of Offs. Socs: Liverp. Med. Inst. Prev: Clin. Asst. (Obst.) Mill Rd. Matern. Hosp. Liverp.; Clin Asst. Artific. Kidney Unit, Liverp. Urol. Centre; Hosp. Pract. (Surg.) Varicose Vein Injec. Clinic BRd.green Hosp. Liverp.

HERSHON, Howard Ivor (retired) c/o Bowden House Clinic, London Road, Harrow HA1 3JL Tel: 020 8966 7000 Fax: 020 8864 6092 — MD Sheff. 1974, MB ChB 1965; FRCPsych, M 1973; DPM Leeds 1969. Prev: Cons. Psychiat. Bowder Ho. Clinic, Harrow on the Hill.

HERST, Edward Richard 9 Fitzroy Road, Primrose Hill, London NW1 8TU Tel: 020 7722 1661 — MB BS 1952 Lond.; MD Lond. 1965; MRCS Eng. LRCP Lond. 1952; FRCPsych 1985, M 1971; MRCGP 1955; DPM Eng. 1967; DObst RCOG 1954; MA U Herts 1998. (Guy's) Vis. Cons. Psych. HMP Pentonville. Socs: Fell. Roy. Soc. Med.; Profess. Mem. Soc. Analyt. Psychol. Prev: Sen. Regist. (Psychol. Med.) Guy's Hosp. Lond.; Regist. Bethlem. Roy. & Maudsley Hosp.; Cons. Psychiat. Emerit. Bexley Hosp., Brook Gen. Hosp., Greenwich Dist. Hos.

HERTLEIN, Rufus Axel 6 George Street, Bath BA1 2EH — MB BS 1996 Lond.

HERTOGS, Drusilla (retired) The Chilterns, 211 Church Road, Earley, Reading RG6 1HW Tel: 0118 961 2141 Email: hertogs@ntlworld.com — MB ChB Cape Town 1948; MRCP (U.K.)

1976; DCH Eng. 1971. Prev: SCMO (Child Health) Tower Hamlets Health Dist. (T).

HERTZOG, Jeanne Lovell White Walls, Hollybank Lane, Emsworth PO10 7UE Tel: 01243 374538 Fax: 01243 379902 — MB ChB Birm. 1955; MRCPsych 1971; DPM Eng. 1962. (Birm.) Indep. Medicolegal Cons. Child & Family Psychiat.; Trustee & Counc. Mem. Pestalozzi Internat. Childr. Village. Socs: BMA. Prev: Cons. Child & Family Psychiat. City of Portsmouth Community Health Care Servs.; Cons. Child & Family Psychiat. Havant Child & Family Ther.; Cons. Child Psychiat. Redhill Gen. Hosp. Linden Bridge Sch. Worcester Pk.

HERVEL, Gino Maurice 17 Regent Gardens, Ilford IG3 8UL — MB BS 1986 Lond.; BSc (Hons.) Lond. 1982, MB BS 1986. (Middlx.) Proprietor of A1 Med. Agency Lond. Prev: Regist & SHO (Psychiat.) Univ. Coll. Hosp. Lond.; Ho. Phys. Middlx. Hosp. Lond.

HERVEY, Professor George Romaine c/o Department of Physiology, University of Leeds, Leeds LS2 9JT — MB BChir 1949 Camb.; PhD Camb. 1959, MA 1949. (King's Coll. Hosp.) Emerit. Prof. Phys. Univ. Leeds. Prev: Prof. & Head of Dept. Physiol. Univ. Leeds; Civil. Cons. (Physiol.) to RN; Surg. Lt. RNVR.

HERVEY, Morag Stuart (retired) Garth House, Beryl Lane, Wells BA5 2XQ Tel: 01749 670161 Fax: 01749 679549 Email: g.r.hervey@btinternet.com — MB ChB 1949 Ed.; MD Ed. 1959; DPM Eng. 1967; DCH Eng. 1955; DObst RCOG 1953. Prev: Assoc. Specialist Mendip Hosp. Wells.

HERVEY, Victoria Emma Johnanna Flat 5, 6 Portland St., Southampton SO14 7EB — BM 1997 Soton.; BSc 1996. SHO Med Rotat. Soton Gen.Hosp. Socs: BMA; MPS. Prev: SHO A & E Soton Gen.Hosp; PRHO Portsmouth Hosp.; PRHO Bournemouth Hosp.

HERXHEIMER, Andrew 9 Park Crescent, London N3 2NL Tel: 020 8346 5470 Fax: 020 8346 0407 Email: 101364.2017@compuserve.com — MB BS 1949 Lond.; FRCP Lond. 1977, M 1972. (St. Thos) p/t Emerit. Fell. UK Cochrane Centre, Oxf..; Cons. DIPEx Proj. Dept. of Prim. Health Care Univ. of Oxf. Socs: Brit. Pharm. Soc.; Internat. Soc. Drug Bull.; Health Action Internat. Prev: Cons. UK Cochrane Centre, Oxf.; Edr. Drug & Therap. Bull.; Sen. Lect. Clin. Pharmacol. & Therap. Char. Cross & W.m. Med. Sch.

HERXHEIMER, Johanna Christine Gabriele 9 Park Crescent, London N3 2NL Tel: 020 8346 5470 Fax: 020 8346 0407 — MD 1969 Berlin. (Free Univ. Berlin) Psychiat. Ref. German Embassy Lond. Socs: Assoc. Mem. Brit. Psychoanalyt. Soc. Prev: Psychoanal. & Psychiat. Stuttgart Germany.

HERZBERG, Joseph Larry East London & City Mental Health NHS Trust, The Royal London Hospital, Mile End, London E1 Tel: 020 7377 7848 Fax: 020 7377 7848; 82B Ashley Gardens, Thirleby Road, Westminster, London SW1P 1HG — MB BS 1978 Lond.; BSc (Hons.) Psychol. Lond. 1975, MPhil Psychiat. 1985; FRCPsych 1995, M 1983. (Lond. Hosp.) Cons. Old Age Psychiat. E. Lond. & City Ment. Health NHS Trust Roy. Lond. Hosp. (Mile End); Assoc. Dean. Postgrad. Med. (NE Lond.) Lond. Postgrad. Med. & Dent. Educat. (Univ. Lond.); Assoc. Med. Dir. E. Lond. & City Ment. Health NHS Trust. Socs: Fell. Roy. Soc. Med.; (Exec.) Assn. for Study of Med. Educat. (Roy. Coll. Psychiat. Represen.); Worshipful Soc. Apoth. Lond. (Mem. Yeomanry). Prev: Cons. Psychogeriat. Lewisham & Guy's NHS Ment. Health Trust, Guy's Hosp. Lond. & Sen. Lect. United Med. & Dent. Sch. Lond.; Sen. Regist. (Psychiat.) St. Mary's & The Maudsley Hosps. Lond.; SHO & Regist. (Psychiat.) Lond. Hosp.

HERZMARK, V J 1 Manor Place, London SE17 3BD — MRCGP 1989; MB BS 1984 London; MB BS 1984 London. (LCH London) GP Principle Lond.

HESELTINE, David 2 Station Road, Copmanthorpe, York YO23 3SX — MD 1991 Newc.; MB BS 1980; MRCP (UK) 1983. Cons. Geriat. Med. York Dist. Hosp. Socs: Brit. Geriat. Soc. & Med. Research Soc. Prev: Sen. Regist. (Geriat. Med.) Kingston Gen. Hosp. Hull; Hon. Research Assoc. (Med.) Newc. Univ.; Regist. (Gen. Med.) Middlesbrough.

HESELTINE, Jane Susan The Old Shippon, Damson Care, Mobberley, Knutsford WA16 7HY — MB ChB 1994 Manch.; BSc (Hons.) Manch. 1990.

HESFORD, Annabel Celia College Way Surgery, Taunton TA1 4TY Tel: 01823 259333; 8 Hine Road, Taunton TA1 4NE Tel: 01823 326247 Email: ahesford8@hotmail.com — MB BCh 1989 Oxf.; BA (Hons.) Physiol. Sci. Oxf. 1986; MRCGP 1995; DFFP 1994; DRCOG 1994; DCH RCP Lond. 1993. (Univ. Oxf.) GP Regist. Coll. Way Surg., Taunton; Clin. Asst. (Dermat.) Roy. Devon & Exeter Hosp. Socs: Primary Care Dermat. Soc. Prev: SHO (Dermat.) BRd.green Hosp. Liverp.; Trainee GP Taunton; SHO (Psychiat.) Tone Vale Hosp. Taunton.

HESFORD, Sharon Elizabeth 10 Greenhill, Leighton Buzzard LU7 3AE — MB ChB 1997 Birm. SHO Anaesth. Roy. Surrey Hosp. Socs: MDV. Prev: SHO A & E City Hosp.Birm.

HESKETH, Gillian Mary Ael-y-Bryn, Llandegfan, Menai Bridge LL59 5TH — MB BS 1984 Lond.; Cert. Prescribed Equiv. Exp. JCPTGP 1992; DA (UK) 1987.

HESKETH, John Christopher 297 Havant Road, Farlington, Portsmouth PO6 1DD Tel: 023 92 78836 — MB BS 1942 Lond.; MRCS Eng. LRCP Lond. 1942. (St. Thos.) Cons. Chest Phys. Portsmouth & S.E. Hants. Health Dist.

HESKETH, Mr Kenneth Thomas Sarum Road Private Hospital, Winchester SO22 5HA Tel: 01962 844555 Fax: 01962 842620; Wardour Castle, Tisbury, Winchester SP3 6RH Tel: 01747 871996 Fax: 01747 871996 — MB BS 1955 Lond.; FRCS Ed. 1959; MRCS Eng. LRCP Lond. 1956. (Char. Cross) Cons. Orthop. Surg. Roy. Hants. Co. Hosp. Winchester. Socs: Sen. Fell.Brit. Orthop. Assn.; Emerit. Fell. Soc. Internat. Chir., Orthop. & Traum.; World Orthopaedic Concern. Prev: Surg. Lt.-Cdr. RN, Cons. Orthop. Surg. RN Hosp. Haslar; Sen. Orthop. Surg. Brit. Milit. Hosp. Singapore; Clin. Teach. (Orthop.) Univ. Singapore.

HESKETH, Mary Lawton House Surgery, Bromley Road, Congleton CW12 1QG Tel: 01260 275454 Fax: 01260 298412 — MB ChB 1987 Manch.; MRCGP 1991; DRCOG 1990.

HESKETH, Susan Jane 14 Haroldston Cl, Haverfordwest SA61 1LP — MB ChB 1997 Liverp.

HESKETH, Therese Mary Institute of Child Health, University College London, London WC1H 1EH — MB ChB 1982 Bristol.

HESLING, Constance Mary (retired) 241 Didsbury Road, Heaton Mersey, Stockport SK4 3JG Tel: 0161 432 8348 — MB BS 1947 Lond.; FRCP Lond. 1974, M 1950. Prev: Cons. Phys. (Chest Dis.) Manch. AHA (T).

HESLIP, Mansell Roderick 32 Cantley Lane, Bessacarr, Doncaster DN4 6ND Tel: 01302 538504; Doncaster Royal Infirmary, Armthorpe Road, Doncaster DN2 5LT Tel: 01302 366666 — MB Camb. 1972, BChir 1971; FRCOG 1991, M 1979. Cons. O & G Doncaster Roy. Infirm.

HESLOP, Andrew James Orchard House, Sutton-on-the-Forest, York YO61 1DY — MB ChB 1996 Ed. SHO (Gen. Med.) Vict. Hosp. Kirkcaldy.

HESLOP, David Anthony Greensands Medical Practice, Brook End Surgery, Potton, Sandy SG19 2QS Tel: 01767 260260 Fax: 01767 261777 — MB ChB 1977 Ed.; BSc Hons Ed. 1974; MRCGP 1981; DFFP 1994.

HESLOP, Ian Hanson (retired) Millstone, 10 Beech Lane, Guildford GU2 4ES Tel: 01483 573141 Fax: 01483 573141 — MB BS 1951 Durh.; BDS 1946; FDS RCS Eng. 1952. Hon. Cons. Oral & Maxillofacial Surg. Roy. W. Sussex Hosp. Chichester (St. Richard's Br.) & Qu. Mary's Hosp. Roehampton. Prev: Cons. Oral Surg. Qu. Mary's Hosp. Roehampton, & Guildford, Holy Cross, Haslemere & Frimley Pk. Hosps.

HESLOP, John Victor Michael Oakenhayes, Calstock Road, Gunnislake PL18 9AA — MB ChB 1967 St. And.

HESLOP, Judith Margaret Northfield Health Centre, 15 St. Heliers Road, Northfield, Birmingham B31 1QT — BM 1982 Soton.; MRCGP 1988; DRCOG 1988; DCH RCP Lond. 1987.

HESLOP, Michael (retired) 2 Lanchester Road, Maiden Law, Lanchester, Durham DH7 0QS Tel: 01207 520908 — MB BChir 1953 Camb. Prev: Ho. Phys. & Ho. Surg. Newc. Gen. Hosp.

HESLOP, Richard William (retired) Eata House, Etton, Beverley HU17 7PQ Tel: 01430 810488 Email: rheslop@eidosnet.co.uk — MB ChB Birm. 1955; BSc (Hons.) Birm. 1952; FRCS Eng. 1962. Surg. to the Corpn. of Hull Trinity Ho. Prev: Cons. Urol. Surg. Hull Roy. Infirm.

HESSE, George William Austin 18 Scatcherd Grove, Morley, Leeds LS27 9LY — MB ChB 1965 Leeds.

HESSING, Randolph Factory Farmhouse, Nancekuke, Redruth TR16 4HX — State Exam Med 1988 Berlin.

HESSION, Mary Grace 16 Elmfield Grove, Gosforth, Newcastle upon Tyne NE3 4XA — MB BCh BAO 1986 NUI.

HESSION, Michael Anthony Dorstone House, Dorstone, Hereford HR3 6AW Tel: 01981 550300 Fax: 01981 550300 Email: mhession@bigfoot.com — MB Camb. 1964, BChir 1963; MA Camb. 1964; FRCPsych 1994, M 1973; DPM Eng. 1971. (Camb. & St. Bart.) Lord Chancellor's Reserve Visitor; Mem. Ment. Health Review Tribunal for Wales. Prev: Cons. Psychiat. Mid Wales Hosp. Talgarth & Hazel Centre Llandrindod Wells.

HESSION, Peter Thomas Mediplex Ltd, 48 Priest Avenue, Wokingham RG40 2LX Tel: 0118 978 5323 Fax: 0118 978 5323 Email: p.hession@mediplex.co.uk; 48 Priest Avenue, Wokingham RG40 2LX — MB BS 1986 Lond.; BA Oxf. 1983; Dip. Pharm. Med. Lond. 1993. (Oxford and Kings College) Dir. Mediplex Ltd. Socs: BMA; Brit. Assn. Pharmaceut. Phys.; Assoc. Mem. Fac. Pharmaceut. Med. Prev: Asst. Med. Dir. Med. Action Communications Ltd; Manager Med. Affairs & Med. Advisor BIOS Ltd. Bagshot; Med. Advisor Med. Tribune UK Ltd. Lond.

HESTEN, Fiona Jane Gordon St. Medical Centre, Mossley Road, Ashton-under-Lyne OL6 6PR Tel: 0161 330 5104 Fax: 0161 330 6266 — MB ChB 1987 Manch.; MRCGP 1991; DRCOG 1990.

HESTER, Joan Barbara District General Hospital, Kings Drive, Eastbourne BN21 2UD Tel: 01323 435855 Fax: 01323 414966 Email: john.hester@ed.esh-tr.sthames.nhs.uk; Tel: 01825 872279 Fax: 01825 872905 Email: hesroy@compuserve.com — MB BS Lond. 1969; MRCS Eng. LRCP Lond. 1969; FRCA Eng. 1973. (King's Coll. Hosp.) Med. Dir., E.bourne NHS Trust Hosps.; Vice-Pres. St. Wilfrid's Hospice E.bourne; Cons. In pain Managem., E.bourne Hosp.s NHS Trust. Socs: Brit. Med. Acupunct. Soc.; Internat. Assn. Study of Pain; Pain Soc. GB & Irel. Prev: Sen. Regist. (Anaesth) Hastings Gp. & Guy's Hosp. Lond. & Lewisham Hosp. Lond.

HESTER, Mr Kenneth Henry Clement (retired) Abberton Manor Nursing Home, Layer Road, Abberton, Colchester CO5 7NL Tel: 01206 735590 — MB BS 1932 Lond.; MB BS (Hons., Distinc. Med. & Midw.) Lond. 1932; FRCS Eng. 1936; MRCS Eng. LRCP Lond. 1932. Prev: Med. Off. Croydon Gen. Hosp.

HESTER, Nigel William Scobie The Surgery, Shaw Lane, Albrighton, Wolverhampton WV7 3DT Tel: 01902 372301 Fax: 01902 373807; Little Beamish, Beamish Lane, Albrighton, Wolverhampton WV7 3JJ Tel: 01902 372618 — MB ChB 1964 Leeds. (Leeds) Socs: GMSC 1996-97; Chairm. Shrops. LMC. Prev: Clin. Asst. (Geriat.) Pk. St. Hosp. Shipnal; Ho. Phys. (Paediat.) Leeds Gen. Infirm.; Clin. Asst. (Obst.) New Cross Hosp. Wolverhampton.

HESTER, Robert Ferguson The Hovel, Church Lane, Chichester PO20 6DE — MB BS 1989 Lond.

HESTON, John Patrick High Street Surgery, 117 High Street, Clay Cross, Chesterfield S45 9DZ Tel: 01246 862237 — MB ChB 1978 Sheff.

HETHERINGTON, Andrew Braeside Medical Group, Escomb Road, Bishop Auckland DL14 6AB Tel: 01388 663539 Fax: 01388 601847; 12 The Dell, Gib Chare, Bishop Auckland DL14 7HJ — MB BS 1984 Newc.; MB BS Newc. l984; MRCP (UK) 1987; MRCGP 1989; DRCOG 1989; Cert. Family Plann. JCC 1989. GP Trainer Cleveland VTS. Prev: Trainee GP N.d. VTS; SHO (Med.) Dryburn Hosp. Durh.; Ho. Off. (Med.) Freeman Hosp. Newc.

HETHERINGTON, Charles Henry Ray Main Street Surgery, 29 Main Street, Eglinton, Londonderry BT47 3AB Tel: 028 7181 0252 Fax: 028 7181 1347 — MB ChB 1976 Ed.; MB BS Ed. 1976.

HETHERINGTON, Dorothy Johnson 192 Tudor Drive, Kingston upon Thames KT2 5QH Tel: 020 8549 0061 — MB BS 1962 Durh.; MRCP (U.K.) 1971; DCH Eng. 1965; DObst RCOG 1964. Prev: SHO (Paediat. Cardiol.) Brompton Hosp. Lond.; Regist. (Paediat.) Hillingdon Hosp. Uxbridge; Research Regist. St. Mary's Hosp. Lond.

HETHERINGTON, Mr John William Department of Urology, Princess Royal Hospital, Saltshouse Road, Hull HU8 9HE Tel: 01482 676674 Fax: 01482 676635 Email: jwhurologist@yahoo.co.uk; 20 New Walk, Beverley HU17 7DJ — MB ChB 1974 Birm.; FRCS Eng. 1979; FRCS Ed. 1979. (Birmingham) Cons. Urol. Hull & E.Yorks NHS Trust, Hull, UK. Socs: EORTC GU; BAUS; Brit. Prostate Gp. Prev: Sen. Regist. (Urol.) Roy. Marsden Hosp. Lond.; Sen. Regist. (Urol.) Char. Cross Hosp. Lond.; Sen. Regist. St.Marys Hosp. Lond.

HETHERINGTON, Peter le Geyt Hungerford Surgery, The Croft, Hungerford RG17 0HY Tel: 01488 682507 Fax: 01488 681018; Buckland House, Oxford Street, Eddington, Hungerford RG17 0ET — MB BChir 1980 Camb.; MA Camb. 1980; MRCGP 1984; DRCOG 1982; Cert. Family Plann. RCOG & RCGP 1982. (Camb. & St. Thos.) Socs: Fell. Roy. Soc. Med. Prev: SHO (Oncol. & Paediat.) Roy. Berks. Hosp. Reading; SHO (O & G) St. Thos. Hosp. Lond.; SHO (Geriat.) P.ss. Margt. Hosp. Swindon.

HETHERINGTON, Robert John (retired) Coednewydd, Llanddewi, Llandrindod Wells LD1 6SE Tel: 01597 851286 — MB ChB 1950 Birm. Prev: Assoc. Specialist Geriat. Dept. Dudley Rd. Hosp. Birm.

***HETHERINGTON, Simon Lee** 15 Holly Court, Dadby, Leicester LE2 4EH Tel: 0116 271 1301 Email: simon.hetherington@virgin.net — MB ChB 1998 Leic.; MB ChB (Hons) Leic 1998.

HETIGIN, Amanda Jane (retired) 25 Chequer's Park, Wye, Ashford TN25 5BB Tel: 01233 812786 — MB BS 1968 Lond.; DCH Eng 1972.

HETREED, Michael Anthony Royal National Orthopaedic Hospital, Brockley Hill, Stanmore HA7 4LP Tel: 020 8954 2300 Fax: 020 8385 7639; 82 Cecil Park, Pinner HA5 5HH — LMSSA 1974 Lond.; BSc Lond. 1971, MB BS 1974; FFA RCS Eng. 1982. (St. Mary's) Cons. Anaesth. Roy. Nat. Orthop. Hosp. Stanmore. Socs: Assn. Anaesth. Gt. Brit. & Irel.; Brit. Scoliosis Soc.; Brit. Soc. Orthopaedic Anaesth., Exec. Comm. Mem. Prev: Sen. Regist. (Anaesth.) Hammersmith Hosp. Lond.; Vis. Asst. Prof. Anaesth. Univ. Maryland Med. Sch. USA; Regist. (Anaesth.) St. Thos. Hosp. Lond.

HETREED, Vincent William Joseph (retired) Coombe House, Coombe Keynes, Wareham BH20 5PS Tel: 01929 463459 — MB BS Lond. 1939; LMSSA Lond. 1939; MRCGP 1976; TDD Wales 1951; Cert. Av. Med. 1983. Prev: Sen. Med. Off. Yahya Costain Sult. of Oman.

HETT, Caroline Louise 47 Merceron House, Victoria Park Square, Bethnal Green, London E2 9PB — MB BS 1984 Lond.

HETT, David Anthony, Surg. Cdr. RN The University Hospital of North Tees and Hartlepool, Stockton-on-Tees TS19 8PE Tel: 01489 557160, 01642 617617 Fax: 01489 557158 Email: hetts@msn.com; Hook Park House, Hook Park Rd, Warsash, Southampton SO31 9LW Tel: 01489 557160, 01642 617617 Fax: 01489 557158 Email: hetts@msn.com — MRCS Eng. LRCP Lond. 1982; BSc Durham. 1977; FRCA 1992; DA (UK) 1986. (Guy's Hosp.) Cons. Anaesth. Soton. Gen. Hosp. Socs: Assn. Anaesth. Intens. Care Soc.; Assn. Cardiothoranie Anaesth.s. Prev: Sen. Regist. (Anaesth.) Soton. Gen. Hosp.; Sen. Regist. & Regist. (Anaesth.) RN Hosp. Haslar Gosport; Research Fell. (Cardiac) Soton. Gen. Hosp.

HETT, Walter John Bourdillon (retired) Herons, Higher Batson, Salcombe TQ8 8NF Tel: 01548 843331 — MRCS Eng. LRCP Lond. 1942; BA Oxf. 1938. Prev: GP Newbury, Berks.

HETTIARACHCHI, Charmila Dilini 18 Onslow Road, Sheffield S11 7AF — MB ChB 1997 Sheff.

HETTIARACHCHI, Jayasena Central Research Pfizer, Sandwich CT13 9NJ Tel: 01304 618572 Fax: 01304 616360; 26 Rochester Avenue, Canterbury CT1 3YE Tel: 01226 762348 — MD 1974 Ceylon; MB BS 1969; FRCP Lond. 1987; MRCP(UK) 1976. Clin. Project Manager Cardiovasc. Research Pfizer Centr. Sandwich. Prev: Prof. Med. Univ. Ruhuna, Sri Lanka; Vis. Prof. Univ. Sheff.

HETTIARACHCHI, Miss K D Manisha 33 Hallamshire Road, Fulwood, Sheffield S10 4FN Tel: 0114 263 0287 Email: mhetti@hotmail.com — MB BS 1996 Lond.; MB BS (Hons.) Lond. 1996; MRCS part I 1998; RCS eng. (UMDS) SHO Surg. Rotat.N.Gen.Hosps.heff; SHO Basic Surg. Train. Rotat. N. Gen. Hosp. Sheff. Socs: Med. Protec. Soc.; Roy. Coll. Surgs. of Eng. (Basic Surg. Trainee); Wom. Surg. Train. (WIST). Prev: Ho. Surg. St. Thos. Hosp. Lond.; Ho. Phys. Worthing Hosp. Worthing; Demonst. Anat. Dept. of Anat. UMDS - Guy's Hosp. Lond. Bridge.

HETTIARACHCHI, Seetha Padminie 26 Rochester Avenue, Canterbury CT1 3YE — MSc Lond. 1982; MB BS Ceylon 1969.

HETTIARATCHY, Pearl Daisy Jebaranee Winchester & Eastleigh Health Care NHS Trust, Melbury Lodge Mental Health Unit, Royal Hampshire County Hospital, Romsey Road, Winchester SO22 5DG Tel: 01962 825542 Fax: 01962 825528; Robin's Hill, 2 Olivers Battery Road N., Winchester SO22 4JA Tel: 01962 861287 Fax: 01962 867536 Email: pearlhet.@globalnet.co.uk — MB BS Ceylon 1965; FRCPsych 1986, M 1972; DPM Eng. 1970. (Univ. Colombo Fac. of Med., Sri Lanka) Cons. Psychiat. (Old Age Psychiat.) Winchester & E.leigh Healthcare NHS Trust; Clin. Tutor Univ. Soton.; Regional Cons. War Pens. Agency DSS; Second Opinion Apptd. Doctor; Hon. Cons. St. Luke's Hosp. for Clergy Lond.; Mem. (ex-Vice-Pres.) Roy. Coll. Psychiat.; Elected Mem. GMC Counc.; Med. Mem. Ment. Health Review Tribunal. Socs: Med. Protec. Soc.; Sri

Lankan Doctors Assn.; Roy. Soc. Med. Prev: Cons. Psychiat. (Psychogeriat.) St. Jas. Hosp. Portsmouth.

HETTIARATCHY, Mr Shehan Peter Dept of Plastic Surgery, Selly Oak University Hospital, Birmingham B29 6JD — BM BCh 1994 Oxf.; MA Oxf. 1995; FRCS Eng. 1998. Specialist Regist., W. Midl.s Regional Burns Unit. Socs: Founder Trinity Coll. Oxf. Med. Soc. Prev: Basic Surg. Trainee; Roy. Lond./St. Bart. Hosps.

HETTIARATCHY, Sidney Walter Surrey Hampshire Borders NHS Trust, Fairfields House, 8 Fairfields Road, Basingstoke RG21 3DR Tel: 01256 331468 Fax: 01256 359302; 2 Olivers Battery Road N., Winchester SO22 4JA Tel: 01962 861287 Fax: 01962 867536 — MB BS 1965 Ceylon; FRCPsych 1989, M 1972; DPM Eng. 1970. (Ceylon) Prev: Sen. Regist. Wessex Unit for Childr. & Parents Portsmouth; Sen. Regist. Leigh Hse. Adolesc. Unit E.leigh.

HETZEL, Martin Roger Department of Respiratory Medicine, Bristol Royal Infirmary, Bristol BS2 8HW Tel: 0117 928 3485 Fax: 0117 928 2921 Email: martin.hetzel@ubht.swest.nhs.uk; Church Farm, Church Road, Bitton, Bristol BS30 6LJ — MB BS 1970 Lond.; MD Lond. 1980; FRCP Lond. 1986; MRCP (UK) 1972; MRCS Eng. LRCP Lond. 1970. (Westm.) Cons. Phys. Bristol Roy. Infirm.; Sen. Clin. Lect. Resp. & Gen. Med. Bristol Univ. Socs: Brit. Med. Laser Assn.; Brit. Thorac. Soc. (Formerly Chairm. Research Comm.). Prev: Cons. Phys. Whittington Hosp. & The Univ. Coll. Lond. Hosps.; Hon. Sen. Lect. (Med.) Univ. Coll. Hosp. Lond.; Cons. Thoracic Phys. King Edwd. VII Hosp. Off. Lond.

HEUCHAN, Anne Marie c/o R W Heuchan, 15 Tower Drive, Gourock PA19 1LE — MB ChB 1989 Glas.

HEUSCHKEL, Robert Bailye 120E Brondesbury Park, Willesden Green, London NW2 5JR Tel: 020 8830 2243 — MB BS 1990 Lond.; MRCP (UK) 1994; DRCOG 1994. Regist. (Paediat.) St. Mary's Hosp. Lond. Prev: Lect. (Paediat. Gastroenterol.) Qu. Eliz. Hosp. Childr. Lond.

HEW, Wei-Shek Roger Department of Pathology, Ninewells Hospital and Medical School, Dundee DD1 9SY Tel: 01382 660111 Fax: 01382 640699 Email: w.s.r.hew@dundee.ac.uk; 42 Lister Court, Ninewells, Dundee DD1 9SY Tel: 01382 660111 Fax: 01382 640966 — BM BS 1992 Nottm.; BSc (Med. Sci.) Nottm. 1990. Specialist Regist. (Path.) Dundee Teach. Hosps. NHS Trust; Hon. Clin. Teach. Dundee univ. Prev: SHO (Path.) Dundee Teach. Hosps. NHS Trust; SHO (O & G) Qu. Med. Centre Nott.; SHO (O & G) Nottm. City Hosp. NHS Trust.

HEWARTSON, Rachel Mary 7 Pewsey Road, Upavon, Pewsey SN9 6DT Tel: 01980 630406 Fax: 01980 630888 Email: rachel@hewartson.demon.co.uk — MB BCh 1998 Wales; BSc 1992. (UWCM)

HEWAT-JABOOR, David Farris 2 St James' Way, Spalding PE11 2RR Tel: 01775 724686 Fax: 01775 724686 — MA, MB Camb. 1969, BChir 1968; MRCS Eng. LRCP Lond. 1968; MRCGP 1975; DCH Eng. 1971; DObst RCOG 1971. (Camb. & Guy's) Ref. Benefits Agency Med. Serv. Socs: BMA. Prev: Ho. Phys. New Cross Hosp. Lond.; Ho. Surg. (Obst.) Mile End Hosp. Lond.; Ho. Phys. (Paediat.) FarnBoro. Hosp.

HEWAVISENTI, Cuthbert 40 Viking Way, Brentwood CM15 9HX — MB BS 1954 Ceylon. (Ceylon) Asst. Psychiat. Warley Hosp. Brentwood.

HEWER, Professor Richard Langton Litfield House, Clifton, Bristol BS8 3LS Tel: 0117 973 1323 Fax: 0117 973 3303; Three Gables, Valley Road, Leigh Woods, Bristol BS8 3PZ Tel: 0117 973 2110 Fax: 0117 973 0071 — MB BS 1956 Lond.; FRCP Lond. 1975, M 1962. (St. Bart.) Hon. Prof. Neurol. Univ. Bristol; Emerit. Cons. N. Bristol NHS Trust; Sen. Research Fell. Dept. Social Med. Univ. Bristol; Lect. Green Coll. Oxf.; Vis. Prof. Univ. Amsterdam. Socs: Assn. Brit. Neurol.; (Ex-Chairm.) Brit. Soc. Rehabil. Med.; Soc.Research.Rehab. Prev: Cons. Neurol. Frenchay Health Care Trust Bristol; Sen. Regist. (Neurol.) Radcliffe Infirm. Oxf.; Ho. Phys. Nat. Hosp. Qu. Sq.

HEWERTSON, John Department of Paediatrics, Northampton General Hospital, Cliftonville, Northampton NN1 5BD Tel: 01604 545957 — MB ChB 1987 Bristol; MRCP (UK) 1991; MRCP (UK) 1991. Cons. (Paediat.) N.ampton Gen. Hosp. Socs: FRCPCH.

HEWES, Deborah Kathryn Mary 9 Elm Park, Brixton Hill, London SW2 2TX Tel: 020 8674 4893 — MB BS 1985 Lond.; MRCP (UK) 1988. SHO (Paediat.) Gt. Ormond St. Hosp. Lond.

HEWES, James Christian The A & E Department, Bristol Royal Infirmary, Marlborough St., Bristol BS2 8HW; 55 Lower Radley, Abingdon OX14 3AY — MB ChB 1995 Sheff.

HEWET, Mr John (retired) 29 Ladythorn Road, Bramhall, Stockport SK7 2EY Tel: 0161 439 1563 — MB ChB 1944 Manch.; BSc, MB ChB (Hons.) Manch. 1944; FRCS Eng. 1949. Prev: Cons. Surg. Stockport & Buxton Hosp. Gp.

HEWETSON, Christopher Tooth The Shaftesbury Practice, Abbey View Medical Centre, Salisbury Road, Shaftesbury SP7 8DH Tel: 01747 856700 Fax: 01747 856701; The House on the Green, Semley, Shaftesbury SP7 9AS Tel: 01747 830109 — MRCS Eng. LRCP Lond. 1964; DObst RCOG 1971. (St. Thos.) Med. Off. W.m. Mem. Hosp. Shaftesbury. Socs: BMA. Prev: Surg. Lt. RN; SHO (Paediat.) Ipswich & E. Suff. Hosp.; Ho. Phys. Roy. United Hosp. Bath.

HEWETSON, Helen Jane Tel: 0161 426 0299 Fax: 0161 427 8112 — MB ChB 1990 Manch.; BSc (Hons.) Manch. 1987; MRCGP 1994; DFFP 1994; DRCOG 1992; DCH RCP Lond. 1987. Clin. Asst. (Colposcopy) Stepping Hill Hosp. Stockport.

HEWETSON, Kathryn Ann Worcester Royal Infirmary, Ronkswood Branch, Newtown Road, Worcester WR5 1HN Tel: 01905 763333 — MB ChB 1979 Leeds; MRCP (UK) 1983; T(M) 1991. Occupat. Health Med. Adviser Worcester Roy. Infirm. Socs: Soc. Occupat. Med. Prev: Staff Geriat. Birm. Heartlands Hosp.; Sen. Regist. (Gen. & Geriat. Med.) W. Midl. RHA.

HEWETSON, Michael John Toppin (retired) Greytiles, Claypit Lane, West Hampnett, Chichester PO18 0NU — BA 1943, BM BCh Oxon. 1945; MRCS Eng. LRCP Lond. 1945; MRCGP 1960; DObst. RCOG 1949; DCH Eng. 1954. Prev: Capt. RAMC.

HEWETSON, Patrick Richard Tooth Bentley Surgery, Bentley Grove, Bentley, Ipswich IP9 2DD Tel: 01473 253384 Fax: 01473 310233; Bentley Grove, Ipswich IP9 2DD Tel: 01473 310295 Fax: 01473 311945 — MB BCh BAO 1973 Belf.; DRCOG 1977. (Queens University Belfast) Indep. GP Ipswich. Socs: BMA. Prev: Med. Off. Cunard Line Ltd.; Maj. RAMC; Ho. Phys. & Ho. Surg. P.ss Margt. Hosp. Swindon.

HEWETSON, Robert Philip Grove House Surgery, 18 Wilton Road, Salisbury SP2 7EE Tel: 01722 333034 Fax: 01722 410308 — MB BS 1982 Lond.; MRCP (UK) 1986; DRCOG 1985.

HEWETT, Beryl Mary (retired) Beech View, 2 Shenden Way, Sevenoaks TN13 1SE Tel: 01732 454631 — MB BS 1930 Lond.; DPH Eng. 1933. Prev: Asst. Co. Med. Off. Kent CC.

HEWETT, Helen Elizabeth St Peter's Road Surgery, 1 St. Peters Road, Cirencester GL7 1RF Tel: 01285 653184 Fax: 01285 655795 — MB ChB 1985 Bristol. Trainee GP Cirencester. Prev: SHO (Psychiat.) Worcester HA; SHO (Geriat., Trauma & Orthop.) Swindon HA.

HEWETT, Martyn Frank St Peter's Road Surgery, 1 St. Peters Road, Cirencester GL7 1RF Tel: 01285 653184 Fax: 01285 655795 — MB ChB 1983 Bristol; MRCGP 1988; DCH RCP Lond. 1986. Course Organiser Bath & Swindon VTS Day Release Course; Civil Serv. Local Med. Off. Prev: Trainee GP Swindon & Cirencester VTS; GP Adviser Glos. Health; SHO (Paediat.) P.ss Margt. Hosp. Swindon.

HEWETT, Nigel Collington The Croft Medical Centre, 2 Glen Road, Oadby, Leicester LE2 4PE Tel: 0116 271 2564 Fax: 0116 272 9000; 8 Guildford Road, Leicester LE2 2RB — MB ChB 1980 Birm.; MRCGP 1984; DCH RCP Lond. 1984; DRCOG 1982. (Birmingham) Vis. Med. Off. Medicare Centre for the Homeless & Rootless Leicester. Prev: Health Worker Brit. Volunteer Program in Peru; Gen. Pract. Leicester VTS.

HEWETT, Peter John Abbotsbury Road Surgery, 24 Abbotsbury Road, Weymouth DT4 0AE Tel: 01305 786257 — MB BS 1983 Lond.; BSc (Hons.) Lond. 1980; MRCGP 1995; DMJ(Clin) Soc. Apoth. Lond. 1994; DRCOG 1986. (Lond. Hosp. Med. Sch.) Sen. Police Surg. Weymouth. Socs: Assn. Police Surg.

HEWETT-CLARKE, Anthony Hugh Rowlands Trincomalee, Pevensey Bay, Pevensey BN24 6NG — LMSSA 1950 Lond.; MA Camb. 1954. (Camb. & Guy's) Prev: Ho. Surg. Roy. Berks. Hosp. Reading; Ho. Phys. St. Chas. Hosp. Lond.; Surg. Roy. Fleet Auxilary MoD.

HEWICK, Simon Alexander 17 Davidson Street, Broughty Ferry, Dundee DD5 3AT — MB ChB 1992 Dundee.

HEWIN, David Fitzgerald 3 Chudleigh Road, Exeter EX2 8TS — MB ChB 1989 Bristol; BSc Bristol 1986, MB ChB 1989.

***HEWINS, Peter** 171 Metchley Lane, Harborne, Birmingham B17 0JL — MB ChB 1994 Birm.; BSc Birm. 1991; MRCP (UK) 1997.

HEWINSON, Eric Elston (retired) 20 Oaklands, Ponthir, Newport NP18 1GS Tel: 01633 421487 — MB ChB Birm. 1963. Prev: partner Aldesgate Med. Pract. Tamworth.

HEWISH, Paul Anthony Fernando Dr Hewish, Dangare and Partners, The Health Centre, Bartholomew Avenue, Goole DN14 6AW Tel: 01405 767711 Fax: 01405 768212; High View, High St, Hook, Goole DN14 5PL Tel: 01405 760611 Fax: 01405 268212 — MB BS 1973 Lond.; BSc (Physiol. & Physics) Lond. 1970; MRCP (UK) 1978; MRCS Eng. LRCP Lond. 1973; FRCGP 1997, M 1981. (Guy's) Clin. Asst. (Subst. Misuse) Goole. Socs: Brit. Assn. of Sport & Med.; York Med. Soc.; Primary Care Cardiol. Soc. Prev: Regist. (O & G) Guy's Hosp. Lond.; Regist. (O & G) Canad. Rd. Cross Hosp Taplow; SHO (O & G) Qu. Charlotte's Hosp. Lond.

HEWISON, Richard Alan Carlin 39 Urquhart Terrace, Aberdeen AB24 5NG — MB ChB 1991 Aberd.

HEWITSON, Erica Helen Derby City General Hospital, Uttoxeter Road, Derby DE22 3NE — BM BS 1993 Flinders.

HEWITSON, Julianne Dorothy Parkview Surgery, 28 Millfield Avenue, Hull Road, York YO10 3AB Tel: 01904 413644 Fax: 01904 431436 — MB BS 1982 Lond.; MRCGP 1986; DRCOG 1985.

HEWITSON, Martha Wilhelmine Amalie 3 Seven Stones Drive, Broadstairs CT10 1TW Tel: 01843 862908 Fax: 01843 862908 — State Exam Med 1960 Hamburg; MD Hamburg 1963; DMRD Eng. 1972. (Hamburg) Prev: Sen. Regist. (Diag. Radiol.) Univ. Coll. Hosp. Lond.

HEWITSON, Mr William Andrew Hazelwood Villa, Akenside Terrace, Jesmond, Newcastle upon Tyne NE2 1TN — MB BS 1959 Durh.; FRCS Eng. 1964. (Newc.) Research Fell. Wellesley Hosp. Univ. Toronto. Socs: Fell. Roy. Soc. Med.; BMA. Prev: Sen. Regist. (Orthop. & Traum. Surg.) Univ. Coll. Hosp. Lond.; Orthop. Regist. St. Thos. Hosp. Lond.; Surg. Regist. W.m. Hosp. Lond.

HEWITT, Agnes Pollock Frew Terrace Surgery, 9 Frew Terrace, Irvine KA12 9DZ Tel: 01294 272326 Fax: 01294 314614 — MB ChB 1973 Glas.

HEWITT, Alan Ninian Murray The Long House, 73-75 East Trinity Road, Edinburgh EH5 3EL Tel: 0131 552 4919 — MB ChB 1972 Aberd.; MRCGP 1976; DObst RCOG 1974. Assoc. Adviser (Gen. Pract.) N. Lothian HB. Prev: SHO (Paediat.) St. Stephens Hosp. Lond.; SHO (Psychiat.) W.. Gen. Hosp. Edin.; SHO (O & G) St. Margt. Hosp. Epping.

HEWITT, Alfred (retired) 10 West Close, Carleton, Pontefract WF8 3NR Tel: 01977 703230 — MB BS 1954 Durh. Prev: GP Pontefract.

HEWITT, Caroline Ann Hughes Dept. Of Dermatology, St Mary's NHS Trust, Praed Street, London W2 1NY Tel: 0207 886 1083, 0207 886 1194 Fax: 0207 886 1134 Email: caro4line@aol.com; Tel: 0118 930 5846 Email: caro4line@aol.com — MB BS 1990 Lond.; MRCP 1993 UK; BSc 1985 (Hons) Lond.; DFFP 1993. (Char. Cross & Westm.) p/t Assoc. Specialist (Dermatol.) St Mary's NHS Trust, Lond. Socs: Application for Mem.ship of Brit. Assn. Of Dermatol. Submitted 02/02. Prev: Locum Cons. (Dermatol.), St Mary's, Lond.; Private Gen. Pract. SW3 1RJ Lond.; Regist. & SHO (Gen. Med.) Ealing Hosp. Lond.

HEWITT, Catherine Susan 6 Castilian Terrace, Northampton NN1 PLD Tel: 01604 250969 Fax: 01604 602457 Email: jryross@aol.com; 10 Weston Way, Weston Favell, Northampton NN3 3BL Tel: 01604 411821 — MB BS 1971 Lond.; BSc Lond. 1968; MRCGP 1977; DObst RCOG 1973. (St. Geo.)

HEWITT, Charles Mark Bolton Wadebridge and Camel Estuary Practice, Brooklyn, Wadebridge PL27 7BS Tel: 01208 812222 Fax: 01208 815907 — MB BS 1969 Lond.; MRCS Eng. LRCP Lond. 1969; DObst RCOG 1974.

HEWITT, Christopher David Long Lane Surgery, Long Lane, Coalville, Leicester LE67 4DR Tel: 01530 831331 Fax: 01530 833985 — MB ChB 1989 Birm.; MRCGP 1993; DRCOG 1992. Clin. Teach. Univ. Leic.

HEWITT, Craig Darren 26 Abbotswell Cres, Kincorth, Aberdeen AB11 5BL Tel: 01224 876000 — MB ChB 1992 Aberd.; MRCGP 1996. (Aberd.) Partner/GP Kincorth Med. Pract. Socs: BMA; Roy. Coll. Gen. Pract. Prev: GP Woodside Med. Gp Aberd. Infirm.

HEWITT, David Patrick Vaughan (retired) 17 Blackwood, Coalville LE67 4RG Tel: 01207 509047 — MB ChB 1961 Birm.

HEWITT, Dominic Bernard Vaughan Tel: 01773 822386 — MB BS 1985 Newc.; MRCGP 1989; DRCOG 1988. Prev: Trainee GP E. Cumbra VTS.

HEWITT, Dominic Brian Douglas 50 Garston Old Road, Liverpool L19 9AG — MB ChB 1994 Liverp.

HEWITT, Fred (retired) Croft Cappanach, Pitlochry PH16 5JT — MB ChB 1953 Liverp.; DObst RCOG 1956. Prev: Ho. Phys. Liverp. Roy. Infirm.

HEWITT, Mr Gareth Rodney Site 16 Royal Park Lane, Hillsborough BT26 6RG — MB BCh BAO 1985 Belf.; FRCSI 1989; FRCS Ed. 1989; FRCS (Gen.) 1998. Cons. (Gen. & Colorectal Surg.) Craigavon Area Hosp.

HEWITT, Horace Ronald, VRD (retired) The Manor House, Toot Baldon, Oxford OX44 9NG Tel: 01865 343398 Fax: 01865 343398 — MB BS Lond. 1950; MRCS Eng. LRCP Lond. 1950; DObst RCOG 1951. Prev: partner, Banbury Rd. Med. Centre, Oxf.

HEWITT, John Brian Albyne Hospital, 21-24 Albyne Place, Aberdeen AB10 1RW — MB BS 1985 Lond.; MRCP.

HEWITT, Jonathan 108 Loraine Mansions, Widdenham Road, London N7 9SH — MB BS 1994 Lond.

HEWITT, Jonathan The Liverpool Women's Hospital, Crown St., Liverpool L8 7SS; Netherby Chase, 11 College Avenue, Formby, Liverpool L37 3JL Tel: 017048 71922 — MB ChB 1978 Liverp.; FRCOG 1996, M 1983; ECFMG Cert. 1988; Dip. Venereol. Liverp. 1980. Cons. O & G Liverp. Wom. Hosp. & Lourdes Hosp. Socs: BMA; Brit. Fertil. Soc. Prev: Med. Dir. Wom. Hosp. Liverp. Assisted Conception Unit; Sen. Regist. (O & G) Liverp.; Research Fell. Bourn Hall IVF Clinic.

HEWITT, Kathleen Mary The Clayton Medical Centre, Wellington Street, Clayton le Moors, Accrington BB5 5HU Tel: 01254 383131 Fax: 01254 392261 — MB ChB 1979 Liverp.; MFFP 1994; DRCOG 1984; DCH RCP Lond. 1983.

HEWITT, Mark (retired) Belfield, The Avenue, Truro TR1 Tel: 01872 72058 — MB BS 1941 Lond.; FRCP Lond. 1970, M 1946; MRCS Eng. LRCP Lond. 1941. Prev: Cons. Dermatol. Cornw. Clin. Area.

HEWITT, Martin Department Child Health, Queens Medical Centre, Nottingham NG7 2UH Tel: 0115 924 9924 Fax: 0115 970 9763 Email: martin.hewitt@mail.qmcuh-tr.trent.nhs.uk — BM 1981 Soton.; BSc (Hons.) (Human Biol.) Surrey 1976; MD Bristol 1995; FRCP 1997; FRCPCH 1997; T(M) (Pediat.) 1992. (Soton.) Cons. Paediat. Med. & Oncol. Qu. Med. Centre Nottm. Prev: Sen. Regist. (Paediat.) Soton.; Research Fell. (Paediat. Oncol.) Roy. Hosp. Sick Childr. Bristol; Regist. (Paediat.) Bristol & Bath.

HEWITT, Mary Theresa — MB ChB Dundee 1987; MRCGP 1993; DCH RCP Lond. 1991. (Dundee University) p/t Locum Gen. Practitioner.

HEWITT, Maswyn Langston 32 Pinehurst Drive, Kings Norton, Birmingham B38 8TH — MRCS Eng. LRCP Lond. 1969.

HEWITT, Matthew John 24 Teal Wharf, Castle Marina, Nottingham NG7 1GW — BM BS 1993 Nottm. Research Fell. (O & G) Univ. of Nottm.; Hon. Regist. (Obst. & Gyn.) City Hosp. Nottm. Prev: SHO (O & G) City Hosp. Nottm.

HEWITT, Michael John West Calder Medical Practice, Dickson Street, West Calder EH55 8HB Tel: 01506 871403; 44 Spylaw Bank Road, Edinburgh EH13 0JG — MB ChB 1983 Ed.; MRCGP 1987.

HEWITT, Nicholas David Delapre Medical Centre, Gloucester Avenue, Northampton NN4 8QF Tel: 01604 761713 Fax: 01604 708589; 4 Daimler Close, Northampton NN3 5JT Tel: 01604 415458 Email: nick_hewitt@compuserve.com — MB BS 1975 Lond.; MRCS Eng. LRCP Lond. 1975; MRCGP 1985; MRCOG 1983, D 1978. Clin. Asst. (Urogin.) N.ampton Gen. Hosp.; GP Trainer N.ampton VTS. Socs: N.ampton Med. Soc. Prev: Regist. (O & G) Ealing Hosp.

HEWITT, Patricia Elizabeth National Blood Service, North London Centre, Colindale Avenue, London NW9 5BG Tel: 020 8258 2720 Ext: 8310 Fax: 020 8258 2965 Email: patricia.hewitt@nbs.nhs.uk; 32 Whittingstall Road, London SW6 4ED — MB ChB 1975 Leeds; FRCP Lond. 1996; MRCP (UK) 1979; FRCPath 1995. Lead Cons. Tranfus. Microbiol. Nat. Blood Serv.; Hon. Sen. Lect. (Haemat.) Roy. Free & Univ. Coll. Med. Sch. Socs: Brit. Blood Transfus. Soc.; Brit. Soc. Haematol.; Internat. Soc. Blood Transfus. Prev: Dep. Dir. &

Cons. Haemat. N. Lond. Blood Transfus. Centre; Lect. (Haemat.) Middlx. Hosp. Med. Sch. Lond.

HEWITT, Patricia Margaret 28 Buddon Drive, Monifieth, Dundee DD5 4TH — MB ChB 1977 Manch.; MRCGP 1982. Staff Grade (c/o Elderly) Dundee.

HEWITT, Penelope Boulton (retired) — MB BS 1961 Lond.; MRCS Eng. LRCP Lond. 1961; FRCA 1966; DA Eng. 1963. Cons. Anaesth. Guy's Hosp. & King's Neurosci. Centre; Hon. Sen. Lect. (Anaesth.) Guys, King's & St.Thos. Sch. Med. Lond.; Acad.ian and Senator Europ. Acad. Anaesth. Prev: Sen. Regist. (Anaesth.) Guy's Hosp. Lond.

HEWITT, Richard Samuel 52 Demesne Road, Holywood BT18 9EX — MB BCh 1998 Belf.; MB BCh Belf 1998.

HEWITT, Ruth Isobel Osmaston Road Medical Centre, 212 Osmaston Road, Derby DE23 8JX Tel: 01332 346433 Fax: 01332 345854 — BSc (Hons.) Agriculture & Environm. Sci. Newc. 1983, MB BS 1988; DRCOG 1992; Cert. Family Plann. JCC 1992.

HEWITT, Samuel John Whiteman's Surgery, Whitefriar's Street, Perth PH1 1PP Tel: 01738 627912 Fax: 01738 643969; 2 Corsie Avenue, Perth PH2 7BS Tel: 01738 631848 — MB ChB 1972 St. And.; DObst RCOG 1974.

HEWITT, Miss Susanne Margaret The Old Byre, Farmer St., Bradmore, Nottingham NG11 6PE — MB ChB 1987 Manch.; MB ChB (Hons.) Manch. 1987; FRCS Eng. 1991. Cons. A & E Derbysh. Roy. Infirm.

HEWITT, Victoria Anne, Capt. RAMC 57 Coniston Avenue, Newcastle upon Tyne NE16 4ER — BM BS 1995 Nottm.; BMedSci Nottm. 1993. SHO (A & E) S.mead Hosp. Bristol. Prev: Ho. Off. (Surg.) Qu. Hosp. Burton-on-Trent; Ho. Off. (Med.) Qu. Eliz. Hosp. Gateshead.

HEWITT, Wendy Elizabeth 62 Moss Lane, Churchtown, Southport PR9 7QS — MB ChB 1990 Liverp.

HEWITT, William (retired) Poyle Cottage, 2 The Brow, Friston, Eastbourne BN20 0ER Tel: 01323 423278 — MB BS Lond. 1945; MRCS Eng. LRCP Lond. 1942. Examr. (Anat. & Physiol.) Chartered Soc. Physiother. Prev: Reader (Anat. & Adviser Pre-Clin. Studies) St. Thos. Hosp. Med. Sch. Lond.

HEWITT-SYMONDS, Michael William Magnolia Cottage, 69 Whitbarrow Road, Lymm WA13 9AY Email: m.hewitt-symonds@fs1.ho.man.ac.uk — MB ChB 1987 Birm.; MRCP 1992; FRCA 1994. (Birm) Cons. IC & Anaesth. Hope Hosp. Salford.

HEWLETT, Anthony Maurice Department of Anaesthesia, Northwick Park Hospital, Watford Road, Harrow HA1 3UJ Tel: 020 8864 3232 Fax: 020 8869 3975 Email: tonygail.hewlett@btinternet.com; 29 West Drive, Harrow Weald, Harrow HA3 6TX Tel: 020 8954 0498 — MB ChB Otago 1964; FFA RCS Eng. 1970. (Otago) Cons. Anaesth. N.wick Pk. Hosp. Harrow; Hon. Sen. Lect. St. Mary's Hosp. Med. Sch. & Imperial Coll. Lond. Socs: Anaesth. Res. Soc. & Intens. Care Soc.; Vasc. Anaesth. Soc.

HEWLETT, Colin Frederick Mynnydd Llwyd, Llanvaches, Magor, Newport NP26 3AY — MB BCh 1968 Wales; MRCPath 1976. (Cardiff) Cons. (Haemat.) Roy. Gwent Hosp. Prev: Cons. (Haemat.) Whiston Hosp.

HEWLETT, Mr James Laurence Coles Lane Health Centre, Coles Lane, Linton, Cambridge CB1 6JS Tel: 01223 891456 Fax: 01223 890033; Chantry House, Walden Road, Hadstock, Cambridge CB1 6NX — MB BS 1972 Lond.; MRCS Eng. LRCP Lond. 1972; FRCS Eng. 1977. (Guys) Prev: Regist. (Surg.) Soton. Gen. Hosp.

HEWLETT, Patricia Mary Blue Hills, Tile Barn Lane, Brockenhurst SO42 7UE — MB ChB 1946 Ed.; FRCP Ed. 1980, M 1955; FFR 1968; DMRD Eng. 1964. (Ed.) Emerit. Cons. Radiol. Croydon HA. Socs: BMA. Prev: Cons. Radiol. Croydon & Warlingham Health Dist.; Sen. Regist. (Radiol.) Char. Cross Hosp. Lond.; Cons. Chest Phys. Wellington Pub. Hosp., NZ.

HEWLETT, Thomas Gordon Willingham Surgery, 52 Long Lane, Willingham, Cambridge CB4 5LB Tel: 01954 260230 Fax: 01954 206204 — MB 1961 Camb.; BChir 1960; DObst RCOG 1962. (Univ. Coll. Hosp.) Socs: BMA. Prev: Ho. Phys. & Ho. Surg. Univ. Coll. Hosp. Lond.; SHO. (Obst.) Poole Gen. Hosp.; Asst. Path. W.wood Hosp. Beverley.

HEWSON, Bernice 81 Edward Street, Hinckley LE10 0DH Tel: 01455 449291 — MB ChB 1990 Leic. Specialist Regist. (Anaesth.) Geo. Eliot Hosp. NHS Trust Nuneaton. Socs: Assn. Anaesth. GB & Irel. Prev: Specialist Regist. Walsgrave Hosp. Coventry; SHO (Anaesth.) Univ. Hosp. QMC Nottm.; SHO (Anaesth.) City Hosp. Nottm.

HEWSON, Finbar Patrick Barry (retired) (Surgery), 171 Bawtry Road, Brinsworth, Rotherham S60 5ND Tel: 01709 828806 — MB ChB 1966 Sheff.

HEWSON, Lesley Ann Child & Adolescent Service, Gieldhead House, 2-8 St Martins Avenue, Fieldhead Business Park, Listerhills, Bradford BD7 1LG Tel: 01274 770369 — MB ChB 1978 Leeds; MRCPsych 1982. Cons. Child & Adolesc. Psychiat. Bradford Community Health NHS Trust; Clin. Dir. Child & Adolesc. Ment. Health.

HEWSON, Margaret Josephine Parton Hall, Wigton CA7 0HE — MB ChB 1997 Dundee.

HEWSON, Morgan Wilson (retired) 3 Woodfield Road, Stevenage SG1 4BP — MRCS Eng. LRCP Lond. 1961; BSc (Hons. Anat.) Lond. 1958, MB BS 1961; DObst RCOG 1964. Prev: Ho. Surg. Whipps Cross Hosp. Lond.

HEWSON, Nicola 92 Industry Street, Sheffield S6 2WX; National Blood Service, Trent Centre, Longley Lane, Sheffield S6 2WX Tel: 0114 203 4800 — MB ChB 1994 Sheff. (Univ. Sheff.) Med. Off. Nat. Blood Trans. Serv., Trent Centre Sheff.

HEWSPEAR, David (retired) 56 Bennett Road, Four Oakds, Sutton Coldfield B74 4TH Tel: 0121 353 3378 — MRCS Eng. LRCP Lond. 1939; DA Eng. 1940; DPH Eng. 1943; DCP Lond 1952; FRCPath 1965. Hon. Cons. Path. Walsall. Prev: Cons. Path. Home Office.

HEXT, Jane Elizabeth 60 Sherwood Avenue, Poole BH14 8DL — MB ChB 1991 Leeds; DFFP 1995; DRCOG 1994; JCPTGP Reg. no. 34850 1995. Gen. Practitioner Locum, Poole, Dorset. Prev: GP, Qu.sland, Australia; SHO (O & G) Poole Gen. Hosp.; Wakefield GP VTS.

HEXTALL, Mr Andrew 38 Barnfield Avenue, Kingston upon Thames KT2 5RE Email: a.hextal@btinternet.com — MB ChB 1990 Birm.; MRCOG 1995. (Birmingham) Specialist Regist. Obst & Gyn. Hillingdon Hosp. Uxbridge. Socs: Internat.Continence.Soc. Prev: Regist. (O & G) The Hillingdon Hosp. Uxbridge Middlx, Qu. Charlotte's & Chelsea Hosp. Lond.; SHO (O & G) Qu. Med. Centre. & City Hosp. Nottm.; Research Regist. (Urogyn.) King's Coll. Hosp. Lond.

***HEXTALL, Justine Margaret** St John's Institute of Dermatology, St Thomas' Hospital Lambeth Palace Road, London SE1 7EH — MB BS 1994 Lond.; MRCP.

HEXTALL, Rachel Alexandra Lyndhurst, 109 Scalpcliffe Road, Burton-on-Trent DE15 9AD — MB ChB 1995 Leeds.

HEY, Edmund Neville (retired) 2 Tankerville Place, Newcastle upon Tyne NE2 3AT Tel: 0191 281 4856 — BM BCh 1962 Oxf.; MA, DPhil Oxf. 1960, DM 1969, BM BCh 1962; FRCP Lond. 1978, M 1971. Lect. Dept. Child Health Univ. Newc.

HEY, Graham Beresford The Surgery, 143 Park Road, Camberley GU15 2NN Tel: 01276 26171 — MB BS 1970 Lond.; MRCS Eng. LRCP Lond. 1970; DObst RCOG 1972. (Guy's) Authorised Med. Examr. Civil Aviat. Auth.; Clin. Asst. Endoscopy Frimley Pk. Hosp. Prev: Regist. (Med.) St. Luke's Hosp. Guildford; Ho. Phys. & Ho. Surg. Guy's Hosp. Lond.

HEY, Pauline Adele Bedfordshire and luton Community NHS Trust, Edwin Lobo Service, Liverpool Rd Health Centre, 9 Mersey Pl, Liverpool Rd, Luton LU1 1HH Tel: 01582 708100 Fax: 01582 708101; 14 Reach Green, Heath & Reach, Leighton Buzzard LU7 0AS Tel: 01525 237754 — MB ChB Ed. 1963; FRCPCH 1997. Cons. Community Paediat. Beds. And Luton Community NHS Trust, Luton. Socs: Assn. for Research in child Developm. (ARICD).

HEY, Ralph Stuart Tremearne (retired) 33 Falmouth Road, Truro TR1 2BL — MB ChB 1949 Birm.; MRCS Eng. LRCP Lond. 1949; DA Eng. 1954; DObst RCOG 1956.

HEYBURN, Gary 30 Browns Bay Road, Islandmagee, Larne BT40 3RX — MB BCh BAO 1989 Belf.

HEYBURN, Philip James South Bays, Norwich Road, Honingham, Norwich NR9 5BS — MD 1987 Leeds; MB ChB 1973; MRCP (UK) 1977. Cons. Phys. Norf. & Norwich Hosps. Norwich. Socs: Fell. Roy. Soc. Med.; Med. Research Soc. Prev: Sen. Regist. (Med.) Univ. Hosp. Wales, Cardiff; Hon. Sen. Regist. (Med.) MRC Mineral Metab. Unit Leeds.

HEYCOCK, Carol Rosemarie Queen Elizabeth Hospital, Sheriff Hill, Gateshead NE9 6SX — MB BS 1983 Newc.; FRCP 2000;

MRCP (UK) 1987. Cons. Rheum. Qu. Eliz. Hosp. Gateshead. Socs: Brit. Soc. for Rheum. (Ordinary Mem.); Fell. Roy. Coll. of Physicans of Lond.; RCP. Prev: Sen. Regist. (Rheum.) Freeman Hosp. Newc.

HEYCOCK, Elizabeth Gardner 1 Belle Vue Drive, Sunderland SR2 7SF — MB BS 1979 Lond.

HEYCOCK, Linda Jillian 12 Madeira Close, St Johns, Westerhope, Newcastle upon Tyne NE5 1YE Tel: 0191 267 3324 — MB BS 1985 Newc. (Newcastle-upon-Tyne) Trainee GP W.erhope Tyne & Wear VTS. Prev: SHO (Psychiat.) St. Geo. Hosp. Morpeth; SHO (Ophth., Ear, Nose & Throat & Dermat.) Roy. Vict. Infirm. Newc.

HEYCOCK, Mr Morris Hensman, RD (retired) Hope Lodge, Court Road, Newton Ferrers, Plymouth PL8 1DD Tel: 01752 872650 — MB Camb. 1956, BChir 1955; FRCS Eng. 1961. Prev: Cons. Plastic Surg. Hull Roy. Infirm. & Kingston Gen. Hosp.

HEYCOCK, Robert William 1 Belle Vue Drive, Sunderland SR2 7SF — MB BS 1989 Lond.

HEYDARI, Azarmidokht 5 Bonchurch Road, Ladbroke Grove, London W10 5SD — MB BS 1997 Lond.

HEYDERMAN, Eadie 4 Clarke's Mews, London W1G 6QN — MB BS Lond. 1958; MD Lond. 1985, BDS 1953; FRCPath 1991, M 1979; LDS RCS Eng. 1953. (Univ. Coll. Hosp.) Emerit. Reader (Histopath.) Univ. Lond. Socs: Roy. Soc. Med. Prev: Reader Histopath. & Hon. Cons. St. Thos. Hosp. Med. Sch. Lond.; Clin. Scientist & Hon. Pathol. Ludwig Inst. Cancer Research Sutton; Graham Schol. & Chas. Bolton Fell. Morbid Anat. Univ. Coll. Hosp. Med. Sch.

HEYDERMAN, Robert Simon Dept. of Pathology and Microbiology, School of Medical Sciences, University of Bristol, Bristol BS8 1TD — MB BS 1985 Lond.; BSc Lond. 1982, MB BS 1985; MRCP 1988. Sen. Lect., Dept. Path. & MicroBiol., Univ. Bristol. Prev: MRC Train. Fell. St. Mary's Hosp. Med. Sch.

HEYER, Elizabeth Janet Auckland Surgery, 84A Auckland Road, Upper Norwood, London SE19 2DF Tel: 020 8653 5146 Fax: 020 8653 1195; 99 Longton Avenue, London SE26 6RF Tel: 020 8699 7851 — MRCS Eng. LRCP Lond. 1968; PhD Lond. 1975, BSc 1965, MB BS 1968. (Westm.) Clin. Asst. New Cross Hosp. (Guy's) Lond. Prev: Proffit Stud. RCS Eng.

HEYES, Camilla Bridget Flat 1 Nightingale Walk, Royal Victoria Country Park, Netley Abbey, Southampton SO31 5GA — MB BS 1986 Lond.; MA Camb. 1987; MRCGP 1991; DRCOG 1989.

HEYES, Janet McRae, MBE (retired) 14 Adelaide Terrace, Waterloo, Liverpool L22 8QD Tel: 0151 928 3781 — MB ChB 1957 Glas.; FRCGP 1982, M 1978. Med. Mem.: InDepend. Tribunal Serv. Prev: Regist. Liverp. Psychiat. Day Hosp.

HEYES, Pamela Crompton Health Centre, High Street, Shaw, Oldham OL2 8ST Tel: 01706 842511 Fax: 01706 290751; 18 Whitebeam Close, Milnrow, Rochdale OL16 4ND — MB ChB 1982 Manch.; MRCGP 1986; DRCOG 1984. Princip. GP Oldham.

HEYES, Thomas George Darton Health Centre, Church Street, Darton, Barnsley S75 5HQ Tel: 01226 382420 Fax: 01226 213892 Email: thom.heyes@gp-c85614.nhs.uk; 130 Churchfield Lane, Kexborough, Barnsley S75 5DU Tel: 01226 386957 Email: tom.heyes@blueyonder.co.uk — MB BChir 1980 Camb.; MA Camb. 1981; MRCGP 1984; DRCOG 1983. (Univ. Camb.) GP, Dr Heyes & Cherry, Darton, Barnsley. Socs: Fac. Bd. Sheff. RCGP, Chairm.

HEYLEN, Josephine Clementine Maria 5 Carbone Hill, Northaw, Potters Bar EN6 4PJ Tel: 0170 787 2762 — MB BS Lond. 1952; MRCS Eng. LRCP Lond. 1952. (Guy's)

HEYLEN, Mrs Louise Alison Elisabeth — MB BChir 1993 Camb.; MA (Med. Sci.) Camb. 1993; FRCS (Irel) 1997. (Univ. Camb.) p/t Clin. Asst. (Locum) Accid. & Emerg., Hinchingbrooke Hosp., Huntingdon. Socs: BMA; Med. Defence Union. Prev: Specialist Regist. (LAT) Harlow(Orthop.); SHO (Orthop & Trauma) Hitchingbrooke Hosp; SHO (Paediat. Surg) Norf & Norwich Hosp.

HEYLEN, Victor Francis Maria 24A Pancroft, Abridge, Romford RM4 1BX Tel: 01992 812961; Roding House, Ongar Road, Abridge, Romford RM4 1UB Tel: 01992 812224 — MB BCh BAO 1957 NUI.

HEYLINGS, David John Agnew 127 Ballynahinch Road, Carryduff, Belfast BT8 8DP — MB BCh BAO 1979 Belf.; BSc (Hons) Belf. 1976, MB BCh BAO 1979. Sen.Lect. (Anat.) Qu. Univ. Belf.

HEYLINGS, Philip Newsome Keith 675 Holderness Road, Hull HU8 9AN Tel: 01482 74644; 'Janber', Benningholme Lane, Skirlaugh, Hull HU11 5EA Tel: 01964 562880 — MRCS Eng. LRCP Lond. 1954; MRCGP 1968. (Leeds) Socs: Accred. Mem. Brit. Soc. Med. & Dent. Hypn.; Brit. Assn. Med. Manip. Prev: Sen. Resid. Med. Off. St. Luke's Hosp. Huddersfield; Ho. Surg. (Thoracic Unit) Pinderfields Hosp. Wakefield; Ho. Phys. (Med. Unit) Halifax Gen. Hosp.

HEYLINGS, Ronald Taylor (retired) 56 Nursery Lane, Alwoodley, Leeds LS17 7HW — MB ChB 1948 Leeds; PhD Leeds 1969, MB ChB 1948, BChD 1939; LDS 1938. Prev: Sen. Clin. Lect. & Cons. Dent. Surg. Leeds Univ. Dent. Sch.

HEYMAN, Isobel Department of Child & Adolescent Psychiatry, Institute of Psychiatry, De Crespigny Park, London SE5 8AF — MB BS 1987 Lond.; MRCPsych 1991. Lect. (Child & Adolesc. Psychiat.) Inst. Psychiat. Lond.

HEYMAN, Josephine 3 Culford Grove, London N1 4HR — MB BS 1988 Lond.; BA Oxf. 1985; MRCP (UK) 1991.

HEYMANN, Klaus Guenter 10 Mercers Place, Brook Green, London W6 7BZ Tel: 020 7602 0484 — MB ChB 1953 N.Z.; BSc, MB ChB N.Z. 1953. (Otago) Prev: Med. Off. Qu. Eliz. Coll. Univ. Lond. & Wellington Pub. Hosp.

HEYMANN, Timothy Daniel 15 The Cresccent, London SW13 0NN Tel: 020 8878 0259 — MB Camb. 1987, BChir 1986; MBA Lond. 1991; MRCP (UK) 1990; DRCOG 1992. Cons. Phys. & Gastroenterol. Kingston Hosp. Kingston-upon-Thames. Prev: Sen. Regist. (Gastroenterol.) Roy. Lond. Hosp.; Hon. Regist. (Gastroenterol.) Char. Cross Hosp. Lond.; SHO (Cardiol.) Brompton Hosp. Lond.

HEYS, Michelle 14 Heathside Way, Hartley Wintney, Basingstoke RG27 8SG — BM BS 1996 Nottm.; BMedSci. Nottingham 1994; MRCPCH 1999. (Nottingham) SHO (Paediat.) Nottm.

HEYS, Robert Franklin (retired) 53 Bar Lane, Ripponden, Sowerby Bridge HX6 4EX Tel: 01442 824570 — MB ChB 1952 Manch.; FRCOG 1973, M 1960. Prev: Cons. O & G Halifax Gen. Hosp. & Roy. Infirm.

HEYS, Professor Steven Darryll Department of Surgery, University Medical Buildings, Aberdeen Royal Infirmary, Aberdeen AB15 Tel: 01224 681818 Fax: 01224 404417 Email: s.d.heys@abdn.ac.uk — MB ChB 1981 Aberd.; MB ChB (Hons.) Aberd. 1981; PhD Aberd. 1992, MD 1988, BMedBiol (Hons.) 1978; FRCS Glas. 1986; T(S) 1992; FRCS Eng. 1998; FRCS Ed. 1999. (Aberdeen University) Prof. of Surgic. Oncol. and Cons.Surg. Aberd. Roy. Infirm. Socs: Brit. Assn. Surg. Oncol.; Surgic. Research Soc.; Brit. Med. Assn. Prev: Cons. Surg. & Sen. Lect. (Surg.) Aberd. Roy. Infirm.; Lect. & Sen. Regist. (Surg.) Aberd. Roy. Infirm.; Wellcome Research Train. Fell.

HEYSE-MOORE, Mr George Henry 2 Station House, Station Road, Ellingham, Bungay NR35 2EW Tel: 01508 518501 Fax: 01508 518680 — MB BS Lond. 1970; FRCS Eng. 1975. Cons. Orthop. Surg. Dist. Gen. Hosp. Gorleston on Sea. Socs: Brit. Orthop. Assn.; Brit. Orthop. Research Soc. Prev: Sen. Regist. P.ss Eliz. Orthop. Hosp. Exeter.

HEYSE-MOORE, Joan Paula North London Blood Transfusion Centre, Colindale Avenue, Colindale, London NW9 5BG Tel: 020 8200 7777; 28 Goodwyns Vale, London N10 2HA Tel: 020 8444 8301 — MB BS 1973 Lond.; MRCS Eng. LRCP Lond. 1973. Clin. Asst. Lond. Blood Transfus. Centre Colindale. Prev: Clin. Asst. (Ophth.) Luton & Dunstable Hosp.; SHO (A & E & Orthop.) Barnet Gen. Hosp.; SHO (Path.) Roy. Free Hosp. Lond.

HEYSE-MOORE, Louis Henry St Joseph's Hospice, Mare St., London E8 4SA Tel: 020 8525 6000 Fax: 020 8533 0513 Email: l.heysemoore@sstjh.org.uk; Tel: 020 8444 8301 — MB BS 1973 Lond.; DM Soton. 1993; FRCP Lond. 1994; MRCP (UK) 1980; MRCGP 1978; T(M) 1991; DCH RCP Lond. 1975; DObst RCOG 1975. (Royal Free) Med. Dir. St. Joseph's Hospice Lond.; Hon. Lect. (Palliat. Care) Dept. Therap. Roy. Lond. Hosp. Trust; Hon. Cons. (Palliat. Care) Dept. Oncol. Roy. Lond. Hosp. Trust. Socs: Assn. Palliat. Med. & BMA. Prev: Med. Dir. (Palliat. Med.) Trinity Hospice Lond.; Sen. Lect. & Hon. Cons. Phys. (Palliat. Med.) Countess Mt.batten Hse. Soton.

HEYWOOD, Mr Anthony John Department of Plastic Surgery, Stoke Mandeville Hospital, Aylesbury HP21 8AL Tel: 01296 315000 Fax: 01296 315183 — MB 1981 Camb.; FRCS Ed. 1984; FRCS Plast 1994. Cons. Plastic Surg. Stoke Mandeville Hosp. & N.ampton Gen. Hosp.

HEYWOOD, Audrey Joan 24 Sion Hill, Bath BA1 2UL Tel: 01225 24403 — MB ChB 1949 Manch.

HEYWOOD, Brian Furley (retired) Humber Lodge, Whitton, Scunthorpe DN15 9LH Tel: 01724 732555 — MB ChB Ed. 1959; FRCOG 1980, M 1967. Cons. (O & G) Scunthorpe Gen. Hosp. Prev: Sen. Regist. (O & G) Roy. Vict. Infirm. & P.s Mary Hosp.

HEYWOOD, Diane Harewood, Burtons Lane, Chalfont St Giles HP8 4BA Tel: 01494 763553 — MB ChB 1965 Manch.

HEYWOOD, Edward Alan (retired) 12A Selby Terrace, Maryport CA15 8NF Tel: 01900 815544 Fax: 01900 816626 — MB BS 1962 Durh.

HEYWOOD, Helena Catherine Fairley Edefield, 127 High St., Odiham, Hook RG29 1NW Tel: 01256 702578; 38 Cammo Road, Barnton, Edinburgh EH4 8AP Tel: 0131 339 4931 — BM BCh 1988 Oxf.; MRCGP 1992. p/t GP Retainer, Odiham, Hants.

HEYWOOD, John David (retired) 40 Eastgate, Deeping St James, Peterborough PE6 8HJ Tel: 01778 342518 Fax: 01778 342518 Email: heywood4@supanet.com — MRCS Eng. LRCP Lond. 1960; DObst RCOG 1963. Prev: Princip. GP P'boro.

HEYWOOD, Linda Jane Fornham End, Sheepwash Bridge, Fornham St Genevieve, Bury St Edmunds IP28 6JJ Tel: 01284 769772 — MB ChB 1976 Leeds; Cert. Family Plann. JCC 1989. Barrister Inner Temple; Family Plann. Pract. Mid. Anglia Community Health Trust Bury St. Edmunds. Socs: Soc. Doctors in Law. Prev: Sen. Regist. (Radiol.) Addenbrooke's & Papworth Hosps.

HEYWOOD, Martin Furley (retired) 9 Tydd Low Road, Long Sutton, Spalding PE12 9AR — MB BS 1987 Lond. Medico-Legal Adviser Regional Medico Legal Serv. Anglia & Oxf. NHS Exec. PeterBoro. Dist. Hosp. Prev: SHO (Histopath.) Qu. Med. Centre Nottm. HA.

HEYWOOD, Matthew William 12 Lorraine Road, Timperley, Altrincham WA15 7NA — MB BS 1998 Lond.; MB BS Lond 1998.

HEYWOOD, Peter Department of Neurology, Frenchay Hsopital, Park Road, Bristol BS16 1LE — MB BChir 1988 Camb.; MA Oxf. 1985; LMSSA Lond. 1988; MRCP Lond. 1990. Cons. Neurol. Frenchay Hosp. Bristol; Hon. Sen. Lect. Univ. Bristol. Socs: Physiol Soc.; Assn. Brit. Neurol.; Movement Disorder Soc. Prev: Welcome Research Fell. & Hon. Regist. Profess. Med. Unit. Char. Cross Lond.; Regist. (Neurol.) Regional Neurol. Unit. Brook Hosp. Lond. & Guy's Hosp. Lond.; Ho. Phys. Hinchingbrooke Hosp. Huntingdon.

HEYWOOD, Peter John Tees Health Authority, Poole House, Nunthorpe, Middlesbrough TS7 0NJ; Tel: 01608 661755 — BM 1991 Soton.; 2001 DFPHM; MSc 2001; MRCGP 1995; DRCOG 1994; DTM &H 1999. p/t SPR Pub. Health. Prev: Trainee GP LLa.deryn Cardiff; SHO (Psychiat.) Gwent Community Trust; GP Middlesbrough.

HEYWOOD, Professor Philip Leslie Academic Unit of Primary Care, University of Leeds, 20 Hyde Terrace, Leeds LS2 9LN Tel: 0113 233 4183 Fax: 0113 233 4181 Email: p.l.heywood@leeds.ac.uk; 37 Flax House, Navigation Walk, Victoria Quays, Leeds LS10 1JH Tel: 0113 246 0499 — MB ChB Manch. 1966; FRCGP 1981, M 1971; DCH RCPS Glas. 1970; DObst RCOG 1969. Prof. of Primary Care Developm. & Dep. Dir. Centre for Research in Primary Care Univ. Leeds; Primary Care Adviser Leeds HA. Prev: Med. Adviser Yorks. Bank; Lect. (Gen. Pract.) Univ. Edin.; Course Organiser Leeds DHA.

HEYWOOD, Rebecca Louise 8 Dukes Ride, Gerrards Cross SL9 7LD — MB ChB 1998 Manch.; MB ChB Manch 1998.

HEYWOOD, Rosalyn Jill 16 Prospect Drive, Hest Bank, Lancaster LA2 6HX — MB ChB 1976 Bristol. (Bristol) Clin. Asst. (Ophth.) RLI Lancaster; Clin. Asst. Blood Transfus. Serv. Donor Suite.

HEYWOOD, Samuel Keith (retired) Fieldfares, 116 Chartridge Lane, Chesham HP5 2RG Tel: 01494 771272 — MB BS 1953 Lond.; MRCS Eng. LRCP Lond. 1949. Ref. DSS. Prev: Ho. Surg. St. Mary's Hosp.

HEYWOOD, Stephanie Ann Heywood and Partners, 119 Wren Way, Farnborough GU14 8TA Tel: 01252 541884 Fax: 01252 511410; Hollyhurst, 27 St. John's Road, Farnborough GU14 9RL — BM BCh 1977 Oxf.; MA Camb. 1978; MRCGP 1982; DCH Eng. 1980; DRCOG 1979. (Camb. & Oxf.) Prev: Ho. Surg. Canad. Red Cross Hosp. Taplow; Ho. Phys. Roy. Hants. Co. Hosp. Winchester; SHO Frimley Pk. Hosp. Camberley.

HEYWOOD, Timothy Richard Hagley Surgery, 1 Victoria Parsonage, Hagley DY9 0NH Tel: 01562 881700 Fax: 01562 887185 — MB BS; MRCGP 1999. (St Bartholomews Hosp. Lond.) Gen. Practitioner.

HEYWOOD, Warren c/o East Glamorgan Hospital, Church Village, Pontypridd CF38 1AB — MB BCh 1991 Wales.

HEYWOOD-WADDINGTON, Mr Michael Broke (retired) 184 New London Road, Chelmsford CM2 0AR Tel: 01245 256816 Fax: 01245 495790 — MB BChir 1953 Camb.; MA Camb. 1953; FRCS Eng. 1960. Cons. Surg. (Orthop. & Trauma) Chelmsford & Colchester Health Dists. Prev: Sen. Regist. Roy. Nat. Orthop. Hosp.

HEYWORTH, John Robert Charles Southampton General Hospital, Tremona Road, Southampton SO16 6YD Tel: 02380 794121 Fax: 02380 796297 Email: john.heyworth@suht.swest.nhs.uk; Dormers, 4 St. Mary's Avenue, Alverstoke, Gosport PO12 2HX Tel: 02392 581251 Fax: 023 8079 6297 — MB ChB 1976 Manch.; FRCS Eng. 1983; FFAEM 1993. Cons. Emerg. Med. Soton. Gen. Hosp. Prev: Cons. Qu. Alexandra Hosp. Portsmouth; Sen. Regist. (A & E) Hope Hosp. Salford.

HEYWORTH, Judith Anne (retired) Lindenthwaite, Beacon Edge, Penrith CA11 8BN Tel: 01768 890652 — MB ChB 1961 Liverp.; FFR 1972; DMRD 1969; DCH Eng. 1966; DPH Lond. 1965. Prev: Cons. Radiol. Univ. Hosp. S. Manch.

HEYWORTH, Robert Charles Frederick Park Lane House Medical Centre, 187 Park Lane, Macclesfield SK11 6UD Tel: 01625 422893 Fax: 01625 424870; Marsh House, Calrofold Lane, Rainow, Macclesfield SK11 0AA — MB ChB 1976 Manch.; BSc (Hons.) Salford 1967; MSc Manch. 1968, PhD 1971, MB ChB (Hons.) 1976; DRCOG 1978. Dir. Robt. Heyworth Gp. Ltd. Manch. Prev: SHO (O & G) Withington Hosp. Manch.; Ho. Phys. Renal Unit Manch. Roy. Infirm.; Ho. Surg. Stepping Hill Hosp. Stockport.

HEYWORTH, Stephen Peter St. Sampsons Medical Centre, Grandes Maisons Road, St Sampsons, Guernsey GY2 4JS Tel: 01481 243179, 01481 245915; Les Chandons, Le Hurel, Guernsey GY3 5AF — MB BS 1968 Lond.; MRCS Eng. LRCP Lond. 1968; DObst RCOG 1970. Prev: Ho. Phys. & Ho. Surg. Gen. Hosp. Jersey; Paediat. Ho. Surg. St. Mary's Hosp. Portsmouth.

HEYWORTH, Tessa Longmoor X-Ray Department, Stepping Hill Hospital, Poplar Grove, Stockport SK2 7JE Tel: 0161 483 1010 — MB BS 1969 Lond.; MRCS Eng. LRCP Lond. 1969; FRCR Eng. 1975; DMRD Eng. 1973. (King's Coll. Hosp.) Cons (Diag. Radiol.) Stepping Hill Hosp. Stockport. Prev: Sen. Regist. (Diag. Radiol.) Manch. Roy. Infirm.; Ho. Phys. (Paediat.) King's Coll. Hosp. Lond.; Ho. Surg. (Gen. Surg.) Nottm. Gen. Hosp.

HEYWORTH, Thomas IBH Berkshire Independent Hospital, Wensley Road, Coley Park, Reading RG1 6UZ Tel: 0118 956 0056 Fax: 0118 956 6333 — MB ChB St. And. 1962; FRCS Eng. 1969. Prev: Cons. ENT Surg. IBH Berks. Indep. Hosp. Reading.

HEZLETT, Hugh Alexander (retired) 53 St Mary's Avenue, Alverstoke, Gosport PO12 2HU Tel: 01705 528025 — MB BCh BAO 1931 Belf.; DObst RCOG 1946. Prev: Med. Miss. Presby. Ch. in Irel.

HEZSELTINE, Don Regent Square Group Practice, 8-9 Regent Square, Doncaster DN1 2DS Tel: 01302 819999 Fax: 01302 369204; 153 Thorne Road, Doncaster DN2 5BH Tel: 01302 323297 Email: donhezseltine@compuserve.com — MB ChB 1978 Sheff.; MRCGP 1982; DRCOG 1981. (Sheffield)

HIAM, Robert Charles Leacroft Medical Practice, Ifield Road, Ifield, Crawley RH11 7BS Tel: 01293 526441 Fax: 01293 619970 — MB ChB 1976 Bristol; BSc (Hons.) Bristol 1973, MB ChB 1976; MRCGP 1982.

HIBBARD, Professor Bryan Montague (retired) The Clock House, Cathedral Close, Llandaff, Cardiff CF5 2ED Tel: 012920 566636 Fax: 012920 566636 Email: bryanhibbard@compuserve.com — MB BS 1950 Lond.; PhD Liverp. 1967; MD Lond. 1960; MRCS Eng. LRCP Lond. 1950; FRCOG 1965, M 1956, DObst 1951; FRANZCOG (Hon) 1998. Prev: Prof. O & G Univ. Wales Coll. Med.

HIBBARD, Elizabeth Donald (retired) The Clock House, Cathedral Close, Llandaff, Cardiff CF5 2ED Tel: 012920 566636 Fax: 012920 566636 — MB ChB Aberd. 1951; MD Aberd. 1963; DObst RCOG 1954. Prev: Stud. Counsellor Univ. Wales Coll. Med. Cardiff.

HIBBERD, Margaret Louise 58 Stoke Green, Coventry CV3 1AN — MB BS 1959 Lond.; DA Eng. 1962.

HIBBERD, Simon Charles Elmham Surgery, Holt Road, Elmham, Dereham NR20 5JS Tel: 01362 668215 Fax: 01362 668625 — BM 1981 Soton.; MRCP (UK) 1984.

HIBBERT, Caroline Louise 64 Victoria Road, Beverley HU17 8PJ — MB ChB 1993 Birm.

HIBBERT, David John North Folly Farm, Noth Folly Road, East Farleigh, Maidstone ME15 0LT — MB BS Lond. 1969; FRCP Lond. 1988; MRCP (UK) 1972; MRCS Eng. LRCP Lond. 1969. (King's Coll. Hosp.) Cons. Phys. Maidstone Health Dist. Prev: Sen. Regist. & Regist. (Med.) & Ho. Phys. Kings. Coll. Hosp. Lond.

HIBBERT, David Louis St Gabriels Medical Centre, 4 Bishops Road, Prestwich, Manchester M25 0HT; 11 Moorside Road, Salford, Manchester M27 0EL Tel: 0161 792 2470 — MB ChB 1980 Manch.; BSc St. And. 1977; MRCGP 1984; DCH RCP Lond. 1983; DRCOG 1982; Cert. JCC Lond. 1982. Socs: BMA & MDU. Prev: SHO (Gen. Pract.) VTS Manch. AHA; Ho. Off. (Gen. Surg. & Med.) Manch. AHA.

HIBBERT, Geoffrey Stanley Charles (retired) 20 Kingswood Avenue, Bromley BR2 0NY — MB BS Lond. 1970; MRCS Eng. LRCP Lond. 1972; MRCGP 1981; DObst RCOG 1973. Prev: Sec. & Chairm. Bromley Div. BMA.

HIBBERT, George Andrew Tadpole Cottage, Tadpole Lane, Blunsdon SN25 2DY Tel: 01793 771991 Fax: 01793 770203 Email: george.hibbert@assessments_w_care.co.uk — MB BS 1977 Lond.; DM Oxf. 1990, MA 1979; MRCPsych. 1982. (Univ. Coll. Lond. / Oxf. Univ.) Cons. Psychiat.; Clin. Sen. Lect. Oxf. Univ.

HIBBERT, George Ralph Boon Cottage, 27 Linthurst Road, Barnt Green, Birmingham B45 8JL Tel: 0121 445 2564 — MB ChB 1966 Birm.; MRCS Eng. LRCP Lond. 1966; FFA RCS Eng. 1970. (Birm.) Cons. Anaesth. E. Birm. Hosp. Socs: Assn. Anaesths. Gt. Brit. & Irel.; BMA. Prev: Sen. Regist. (Anaesth.) Univ. Coll. Hosp. Lond. & Hosp. Sick Childr.; Gt. Ormond St.; SHO (Anaesth.) Roy. Hosp. Wolverhampton.

HIBBERT, Jane 27A Gardner Road, Guildford GU1 4PG Tel: 01483 577136 — BM BS 1989 Nottm.; MRCP Lond. 1992. Regist. (Radiol.) St. Thos. Hosp. Lond.

HIBBERT, Mr John Blencathra, Ockham Road N., West Horsley, Leatherhead KT24 6PF — MB 1969 Camb.; ChM Liverp. 1979; BChir 1968; FRCS Eng. 1974. Cons. ENT Surg. Guy's Hosp. Lond. Prev: Sen. Regist. ENT Infirm. Liverp.

HIBBERT, Rosemary Sabrina Ballards, Bury Lane, Bratton, Westbury BA13 4RD — MB BS 1981 Lond.; MA Camb. 1975; BSc Lond. 1978, MB BS 1981. (St. Bart.) Clin. Asst. (Psychiat.) Bath Ment. Health Care Trust. Socs: Assn. Fac. Homeop. Prev: SHO (Psychiat.) Roundway Hosp. Bath HA & Soton. HA; Clin. Asst. (Geriat.) Soton HA.

HIBBERT, Victoria Louise Garden Flat, 35 Cotham Road, Cotham, Bristol BS6 6DJ — MB ChB 1991 Bristol; MRCGP 1997; DRCOG 1996. Socs: BMA; MDU.

HIBBERT, William Keith Occupational Health Dept., University Hospital, Aintree, Longmoor Lane, Liverpool L9 7AL Tel: 0151 529 2353 — MB ChB 1973 Manch.; AFOM 2001. Director, Occupat.al Health, Univ. Hosp., Aintree, Liverp. L9 7AL.

HIBBLE, Arthur George New Sheepmarket Surgery, Ryhall Road, Stamford PE9 1YA Tel: 01780 758123 Fax: 01780 758102; Meadow Cottage, Water Furlong, Stamford PE9 2QL Tel: 01780 764991 Fax: 01780 482315 — MB BS Lond. 1969; MMedSci Leeds 1985; MRCP (UK) 1972; FRCGP 1987, M 1979. (St. Mary's) Dir. of Postgrad. GP Educat., E. Anglia. Prev: Chairm. Camb. MAAG.; Course Organiser P'boro. VTS; MRC Jun. Research Fell. & Ho. Phys. Profess. Med. Unit St. Mary's Hosp. Lond.

HIBBLE, Christine Jennifer Silver Lane Surgery, Suffolk Court, Yeadon, Leeds LS19 7JN; Netherleigh Cottage, Elmete Lane, Leeds LS8 2LN — MB ChB 1977 Leeds. GP Yeadon Retainer Scheme.

HIBBS, Helen Macpherson Parkfield Medical Centre, 255 Parkfield Road, Wolverhampton WV4 6EG Tel: 01902 342152 Fax: 01902 620868; 57 Showell Lane, Penn, Wolverhampton WV4 4TZ — BMedSci Nottm. 1981, BM BS 1983; MRCGP 1987; DCH RCP Lond. 1986; DRCOG 1986. Prev: Trainee GP Coventry.

HICHENS, Sarah Mariquita Bodrennick, Flushing, Falmouth TR11 5TP — MB BS 1996 Lond.

HICK, Arthur Geoffrey 18 Mauldeth Road, Heaton Mersey, Stockport SK4 3NG — LMSSA 1940 Lond.; MD Leeds 1946, MB ChB 1940; DIH Soc. Apoth. Lond. 1976; DIH Eng. 1976; DMJ Soc. Apoth. Lond. 1972; DPH Leeds 1942. Police Surg. Stockport.

HICK, Peter Geoffrey Eastholme Surgery, 2 Heaton Moor Road, Stockport SK4 4NT Tel: 0161 443 1177 Fax: 0161 442 2521; 65 Parsonage Road, Heaton Moor, Stockport SK4 4JW Tel: 0161 443 1888 Fax: 0161 442 2521 — MB ChB 1974 Leeds; MRCGP 1978; DRCOG 1977. (leeds) Primary Care Dermatol. Clinic. Prev: Trainee GP Banbury VTS.

HICKEN, Mr Gary James 25 Miller Close, Bromsgrove B60 3PG — MB ChB 1989 Birm.; FRCS Eng. 1993.

HICKEY, Bernadette Blanche 95 Ivy Lane, Headington, Oxford OX3 9DY — MB BS 1984 Monash.

HICKEY, Mr Brian Brendan, TD (retired) Llys Meddyg, 3 Llwynderw Drive, Blackpill, Swansea SA3 5AP Tel: 01792 404200 — MRCS Eng. LRCP Lond. 1935; BA (Hons. Physiol.) Oxon., MA 1941, MCh 1945, BM; BCh 1935; FRCS Eng. 1937. Prev: Cons. Surg. W. Glam. AHA.

HICKEY, Evelyn Maire (retired) 105 Blackheath Park, London SE3 0EX — LRCPI & LM, LRSCI & LM 1950; LRCPI & LM, LRCSI & LM 1950. Prev: Ho. Phys. & Ho. Surg. Waterside Hosp. Lond.derry.

HICKEY, Mr Fergal Gerald Edmund 1 Ferndale Road, West Knighton, Leicester LE2 6GN Tel: 0116 288 3397 — MB BCh BAO 1985 NUI; FRCS Ed. (A&E) 1991; FRCS Eng. 1990; DA (UK) 1990. Sen. Regist. (A & E) Leicester Roy. Infirm.

HICKEY, Hyacinthia Bridget Mary 2 Chelsea Embankment, London SW3 4LG Tel: 020 7352 7494 — MB BCh BAO NUI 1963; DO NUI 1965; DCH NUI 1964.

HICKEY, James Russell 8 Curzon Road, Lower Parkstone, Poole BH14 8BE Tel: 01202 740620 — MB BS 1996 Lond. SHO Med. Poole NHS Trust.

HICKEY, John Brendan The Surgery, 327D Upper Richmond Road, London SW15 6SU Tel: 020 8788 6002 Fax: 020 8789 8568; 19 Briar Walk, London SW15 6UD Tel: 020 8788 5585 Fax: 020 8785 4890 Email: putneydoc@aol_com — BM BCh Oxf. 1966; MA Oxf. 1966; MRCS Eng. LRCP Lond. 1966; FRCA 1972. (Oxf. & St. Thos.) GP Trainer Lond.; Hon. Cons. Anaesth. Hammersmith & Qu. Charlotte's Hosps. Lond. Prev: Cons. Anaesth. Chelsea Hosp. Wom. Lond.

HICKEY, John Dermot c/o Medical Protection Society, 33 Cavendish Square, London W1G 0PS Tel: 020 7399 1300 Fax: 020 7399 1301 Email: hickeyj@mps.org.uk; Bosworth Farm House, Draughton, Northampton NN6 9JQ Tel: 01604 686200 — MB BS 1977 Lond.; FFA RCS Eng. 1983.

HICKEY, John Joseph Mary Egremont Medical Centre, 9 King Street, Wallasey CH44 8AT Tel: 0151 639 0777 — MB BCh BAO 1982 NUI.

HICKEY, Kevin Eisner, Goldman and Ship, Shipley Health Centre, Alexandra Road, Shipley BD18 3EG Tel: 01274 589160; 13 Wilmer Drive, Heaton, Bradford BD9 4AR — MB ChB 1986 Leeds; MRCGP 1991.

HICKEY, Kim Marie The Anvil Centre, Parkhead Hospital, 81 Salamanca St., Glasgow G31 5ES Tel: 0141 211 8000 — MB ChB 1987 Dundee. Staff Grade (Psychiat.) Midsector Resource Centre Pk.head Hosp. Glas.

HICKEY, Malcolm Scott, Squadron Ldr. RAF Med. Br. Minfor Surgery, Park Road, Barmouth LL42 1PL Tel: 01341 280521 Fax: 01341 280912; Tyn Llwyn, Glandwr, Barmouth LL42 1DZ Tel: 01341 280282 Fax: 01341 280912 — MB BS 1982 Lond.; MRCGP 1989; DRCOG 1987.

HICKEY, Marie Caroline Agnes The Ulster Hospital, Dundonald, Belfast BT16 1RH; Craiglen, Sanquhar Road, Forres IV36 1DG — MB BCh BAO 1985 NUI. Regist. (Anaesth.) St. Jas. Hosp. Dub.

HICKEY, Mr Mark St John Glenfield Hospital, Groby Road, Leicester LE3 9QP Tel: 0116 287 1471; 222 Wintersdale Road, Evington, Leicester LE5 2GP — MB BCh BAO 1976 NUI; FRCSI 1980; FRCS 1998. (University college Dublin) Cons. Cardiothoracic Surg. Leics. HA.

HICKEY, Martha Department of Obs. & Gyn., Imperial School of Medicine, London W2 1PG — MB ChB 1990 Bristol; MSc Manch. 1986; BA (Hons.) Manch. 1981. Sen. Reg. Dept. of Obs. & Gyn. Imperial Sch. of Med., Lond. Prev: SHO (Gyn.) W.. Infirm. Glas.; SHO (O & G) Bristol. Matern. Hosp.

HICKEY, Mary Ursula Cardinal Hume Centre, 3-7 Arneway St., Horseferry Road, London SW1P 2BG Tel: 020 7222 8593 Fax: 020 7799 4222 — MB BS Newc. 1967; MRCOG 1974. (Newcastle upon Tyne)

HICKEY, Maurice Anthony Jerome Jenner Health Centre, 201 Stanstead Road, London SE23 1HU Tel: 020 8690 2231; 10

Braeside, Beckenham BR3 1SU — MB BCh BAO 1975 NUI; DCH NUI 1980.

HICKEY, Mr Nicholas Charles Department Surgery, Worcester Royal Infirmary, Ronkswood Branch, Newtown Road, Worcester WR5 1HN Tel: 01905 763333 — MB ChB Birm. 1984; MD 1991 Birm. 1991; FRCS Eng. 1988. Cons. Gen. & Vasc. Surg. Worcester Roy. Infirm. Socs: Eur. Soc. Vasc. Surg.; Vasc. Surg. Soc. GB & Irel. Prev: Lect. (Surg.) & Hon. Sen. Regist. Univ. Birm.; Career Regist. (Surg.) W. Midl. RHA; Vasc. Research Fell. Selly Oak Hosp. Birm.

HICKEY, Patricia Margaret (retired) Ennismore, 19 Thornholme Road, Sunderland SR2 7QF Tel: 0191 567 3366 — MB BS 1955 Durh. Prev: SHO Childr. Hosp. Sunderland.

HICKEY, Patrick Louis, CBE, Group Capt. RAF Med. Br. (retired) 15 Cranfield Way, Brampton, Huntingdon PE28 4QZ Tel: 01480 350832 Email: patrick@hickey93.freeserve.co.uk — MB BS 1968 Lond.; MSc (Pub. Health Med.) Lond. 1991; AFOM RCP Lond. 1983; DAvMed Eng. 1975; DObst RCOG 1972.

HICKEY, Robert Patrick, MC (retired) 9 Old Rectory Gardens, Thurlestone, Kingsbridge TQ7 3PD Tel: 01548 560632 — MB BS Lond. 1945; DPhysMed. Eng. 1956. Prev: Cons. Rheum. & Rehabil. Medway & Dartford & Gravesham HAs.

HICKEY, Mr Simon Alexander Ambrook Farm House, Torbryan, Newton Abbot TQ12 5UW — BM BCh 1983 Oxf.; MA Camb. 1984, BA 1980; FRCS (ENT) Eng. 1988. Cons. ENT Surg. Torbay Hosp. Torquay. Prev: Sen. Regist. Rotat. (ENT) Char. Cross Hosp. Lond.; Regist. (ENT Surg.) St. Thos. Hosp. Lond.

HICKEY, Sylvia Adelaide Medical Centre, 36 Adelaide Road, Andover SP10 1HA Tel: 01264 351144 Fax: 01264 358639 — MB ChB 1984 Liverp.

HICKIN, Lesley Ann Auckland Surgery, 84A Auckland Road, Upper Norwood, London SE19 2DF Tel: 020 8653 5146 Fax: 020 8653 1195 — MB BS 1974 Lond.; MRCGP 1980; DRCOG 1979.

HICKINBOTHAM, Mr Paul Frederick John 69 Main Street, Bushby, Leicester LE7 9PL Tel: 0116 243 1152 — MB ChB 1939 Birm.; ChM Birm. 1947; FRCS Eng. 1942. (Birm.) Emerit. Cons. Urol. Leics. DHA. Prev: Cons. Urol. Leics. AHA (T); Regist. (Surg.) Gen. Hosp. Birm.; Resid. Surg. Off. Roy. Infirm. Bradford.

HICKISH, Angus Edgar Burton Medical Centre, 123 Salisbury Road, Burton, Christchurch BH23 7JN Tel: 01202 474311 Fax: 01202 484412; Cedars, 111 Burley Road, Bansgore, Christchurch BH23 8AY Tel: 01425 72611 — MB BS 1976 Lond.; MRCP (UK) 1979; MRCGP 1985; DObst 1981; DCH RCP Lond. 1980. Health Safety Exec. Approved Diving Med. Examrs.; Hosp. GP (Neurol.) Poole Gen. Hosp. Socs: Assn. Aviat. Med. Examr.

HICKISH, Gordon Walter, VRD New Medical Centre, Ringwood Road, Bransgore, Christchurch BH23 8AD Tel: 01425 672857 Fax: 01425 674421 Email: gordon.hickish@lineone.net; Heather Cottage, Burnt House Lane, Bransgore, Christchurch BH23 8AL Tel: 01425 673484 Fax: 01425 673484 — MB ChB 1948 Ed.; FRCGP 1984, M 1972; DCH Eng. 1954. (Ed.) p/t GP, Bransgore; Health & Safety Exec. Approved Diving Med. Examr.; Approved Med. Examr. Civil Aviat. Auth., Federal Aviat. Admin. & Canad.Aviat Auth. Socs: Fell. Roy. Soc. Med.; Mem. of Roy. Med. Soc. Edin.; Mem. of Civil Aviat. Med. Assn. Prev: Regist. (Paediat.) Odstock Hosp. Salisbury; Regist. (Med.) P.ss Beatrice Hosp. Lond.; Hosp. Pract. (ENT) St. Bart. Hosp.

HICKISH, Tamas Frederick Gordon 204 Stanley Park Road, Beeches, Carshalton SM5 3JP — MD 1994 Lond.; BA Oxf. 1981; MB BS 1984; MRCP (UK) 1988.

HICKLIN, John Anthony Gatwick Park Hospital, Povey Cross Road, Horley RH6 0BB Tel: 01293 785511; (cons. rooms), Beauvoir Lodge, Effingham Lane, Crawley RH10 3HP Tel: 01342 712543 — MB BS 1957 Lond.; MB BS (Hons.) Lond. 1957; PhD Lond. 1962, BSc (Hons.) 1954; FRCP Lond. 1992; FRCP Ed. 1979, M 1965; DPhysMed. Eng. 1966. (Lond. Hosp.) Prev: Sen. Regist. (Physical Med.) Roy. Free Hosp. Lond.; 1st Asst. Med. Unit Research Asst. (Pharmacol.) & Ho. Phys. Lond. Hosp.

HICKLIN, Karen Lesley Charlotte 26 Warfield Road, Bracknell RG42 2JY Tel: 01344 642991 Email: jdhick@globalnet.co.uk — BM BCh 1985 Oxf.; MRCGP 1989; DRCOG 1988. (Oxford University) GP Lower Earley, Reading Retainer Scheme.; Clin. Asst. (Rheum.) Battle Hosp. Reading.

HICKLIN, Lucy-Anne Catherine 26A Albert Bridge Road, London SW11 4PY — MB BS 1988 Lond.

HICKLING, Christopher Bower Tel: 01223 723160 Fax: 01223 723089 — MB BS 1981 Lond.; DRCOG 1984. (Roy. Free) Prev: SHO (O & G) Newmarket Hosp.; SHO (A & E) Norf. & Norwich Hosp.

HICKLING, Deborah Jane South Manchester University Hospitals, NHS Trust, Southmoor Road, Wythenshawe, Manchester M23 9LT Tel: 0161 998 7070; 5 Royal Gardens, Bowdon, Altrincham WA14 3GX — MB BS 1982 Lond.; MRCOG 1988. (St. Geo.) Cons. O & G S. Manch. Univ. Hosps. NHS Trust. Socs: Brit. Fertil. Soc.; Eur. Soc. Human Reproduc. & Embryol. Prev: Cons. O & G Warrington NHS Trust Chesh.; Med. Dir. S. Manch. IVF Unit.

HICKLING, Elizabeth Jennifer 77 Avon Road, Worcester WR4 9AG — MB ChB 1985 Birm. Clin. Med. Off. Community Child Health.

HICKLING, James Alexander Killick Street Health Centre, 76 Killick Street, London N1 9RH Tel: 020 7833 9939 Fax: 020 7427 2740; 60A Trinity Church Square, London SE1 4HT — MB BS 1992 Lond.; BSc Lond. 1989; DFPM RCOG Lond. 1997; DCH RCP Lond. 1995. (King's Coll. Sch. Med. & Dent.) LIZEI Research Fell. (GP) Univ. Coll. Lond. Prev: GP/Regist. Lond.

HICKLING, John Bower (retired) Madingley Rise, Madingley Hill, Coton, Cambridge CB3 7PQ Tel: 01954 211232 Email: j.hickling@gtinternet.com — MB BS Lond. 1953; MRCS Eng. LRCP Lond. 1952; DObst RCOG 1953. Police Surg. Camb. Prev: Ho. Surg. & Resid. Obst. Asst. St. Geo. Hosp.

HICKLING, Peter Derriford Hospital, Plymouth PL6 8DH Tel: 01752 777111 Fax: 01752 768976 — MB ChB 1971 Bristol; BSc Bristol 1968; FRCP Lond. 1989; MRCP (UK) 1976; DObst RCOG 1973. Cons. Rheum. Derriford Hosp. Plymouth; Lect Univ. Plymouth Post. Grad. Sch. Prev: Sen. Regist. Rheum. Research Unit Leeds Univ. & St. Jas. Univ. Hosp. Leeds; Regist. (Rheum. & Gen. Med.) Univ. Hosp. Wales Cardiff.

HICKMAN, James Hickman and Hickman, The Health Centre, Greenway, North Curry, Taunton TA3 6NQ Tel: 01823 490505 Fax: 01823 491024; The Laurels, Meare Green, Stoke St Gregory, Taunton TA3 6HY Tel: 01823 490440 — MB BS 1989 Lond.; MRCGP 1995; DFFP 1993; DRCOG 1992; PHEC Cert 1998. (Lond. Hosp. Med. Coll.) GP Princip.; Hon. Teach. Gen. Pract. Bristol Univ. Socs: W Som. Med. Soc. (Sec.). Prev: Trainee GP Pontesbury Shrops.; SHO (A & E) Roy. Lond. Hosp.; SHO (Paediat.) P.ss Roy. Hosp. Telford.

HICKMAN, Lesley Jane York Street Medical Centre, 20-21 York Street, Stourport-on-Severn DY13 9EH Tel: 01299 827171 Fax: 01299 827910; Lowenva, Pensax, Abberley, Worcester WR6 6AG — MB ChB 1981 Birm. GP; Clin. Asst. (Ophth.) Worcester Roy. Infirm.

HICKMAN, Lucy 18 Onslow Road, Sheffield S11 7AF — MB ChB 1997 Sheff.

HICKMAN, Max Peter Ambrose Avenue Surgery, 76 Ambrose Avenue, Colchester CO3 4LN Tel: 01206 549444 Fax: 01206 369910; 97 Maldon Road, Colchester CO3 3AR Tel: 01206 549444 — MB BChir 1988 Camb.; BA (Med. Sci.) 1985; DCH RCP Lond. 1991. Asst. Police Surg. Colchester Div.; Bd. Mem. Colchester PCG. Socs: Colchester Med. Soc.; BMA & Anglo-French Med. Soc. Prev: Trainee GP Colchester VTS; Mem. Colchester GP Dist. Comm.

HICKMAN, Michael David 21 Selly Wick Road, Birmingham B29 7JJ Tel: 0121 472 0771 — MB BS 1953 Lond.; DObst RCOG 1958. (Univ. Coll. Hosp.) Chairm. Med. Bd. Min. Social Security. Prev: Ho. Surg. (O & G) Mayday Hosp. Croydon; Resid. Med. Off. Doctors Hosp. New York.

HICKMAN, Nicola Lilian Alice 332 Richmond Road, Kingston upon Thames KT2 5PP — MB ChB 1990 Leic.

HICKMAN, Mr Paul Doctors Surgery, 81 Prestwood Road W., Wolverhampton WV11 1HT — MB ChB 1983 Sheff.; FRCS Ed. 1989. GP Regist. N.umbria VTS. Prev: Regist. Rotat. (Surg.) Newc. Gp. Hosps. & Dundee Gp Hosps.; SHO Rotat. (Surg.) Dudley Gp. Hosps.; Ho. Surg. & Ho. Phys. Roy. Hallamsh. Hosp. Sheff.

HICKMAN, Peter James High Croft Surgery, 27 Thorley Hill, Bishop's Stortford CM23 3NE Tel: 01279 657684 Fax: 01279 653481; High Croft Surgery, 27 Thorley Hill, Bishop's Stortford CM23 3NE Tel: 01279 657684 Fax: 01279 506686 — MB BS 1975 Lond. (St Mary's) Police Surg. Stanstead Airporth.

HICKMAN, Philip (retired) — MB BS 1965 Lond.; MRCP (UK) 1970; MRCS Eng. LRCP Lond. 1966; MRCGP 1974; DObst RCOG

1967; DCH Eng. 1967. Prev: Regist. (Paediat.) Bristol Roy. Hosp. Sick Childr.

HICKMAN, Roger Charles The Medical Centre, 32 London Road, Sittingbourne ME10 1ND Tel: 01795 472109/472100; Deans Bank Farm, Bredgar, Sittingbourne ME9 8BG Tel: 01622 884394 — MB BChir 1966 Camb.; MA Camb. 1966; MRCP (UK) 1967; DObst RCOG 1973; DTM & H Eng. 1972. (Middlx.) Phys. i/c Somerfield Hosp. Med. Centre Maidstone. Socs: BMA. Prev: Sen. Med. Off. Save the Childr. Fund in E. Nigeria & W. Bengal; Regist. (Med.) Nat. Heart Hosp. Lond.; Ho. Phys. (Cardiol. & Neurol.) Middlx. Hosp.

HICKMAN, Rosemary Jane Dept Obstetrics & Gynaecology, Milton Keynes General Hospital, Standing Way, Milton Keynes MK6 5LD Tel: 01908 660033 — MB BChir 1994 Camb.; DFFP 1997; DCH 1998. SHO O & G. Prev: SHO O & G; SHO Paediat; GP Reg.

HICKMAN, Sarah Jane Deans Bank Farm, Deans Bottom, Bredgar, Sittingbourne ME9 8BG — MB BS 1997 Lond.; BA (Oxon.) 1994. (Roy. Lond. & St. Bart.) SHO Med. Rotat., N. Middlx. Hosp.

HICKMAN, Simon James Institute of Neurology, Queen Square, London WC1N 3BG — MB BChir 1994 Camb.; MB BChir Camb. 1993; MRCP 1997.

HICKMAN, Thomas Michael Pinkhill Farm, Eynsham, Witney OX29 4JQ — MB BS 1997 Lond.

HICKMOTT, Kenneth Charles Princess Royal Hospital, Apley Castle, Telford TF1 6TF Tel: 01952 641222; Treetops, The Rock, Telford TF3 5AA — MB ChB 1979 Liverp.; FFA RCS Eng. 1985; DRCOG 1982. Cons. Anaesth. P.ss Roy. Hosp. Shrops. Prev: Sen. Regist. (Anaesth.) NW RHA.

HICKS, Alan John Tel: 01473 289777 Fax: 01473 289545; 28 Kingsfield Avenue, Ipswich IP1 3TA Tel: 01473 252757 — MB BS 1984 Lond.; AFOM 2000 RCP Lond.; MSc 2001 Manchester Univ.; MRCGP 1988; Dip. Occ. Med. RCP Lond. 1996. (St. Bart.) Occupat. Health BOC Ipswich; Mem. Indep. Tribunal Serv.; Chief Med. Off. PPG, Europe; Dep. Chief Med. Off. RSPCA; Occupat.al Health ICI. Socs: Ipswich Clin. Soc.; Soc. Occupat. Health (Lond.); Fac. of Occupat.al Med. Prev: GP/Regist. Ipswich VTS; Ho. Phys. W. Norwich Hosp.; Ho. Surg. Norf. & Norwich Hosp. Norwich.

HICKS, Alaric John Birleywood Health Centre, Birleywood, Skelmersdale WN8 9BW Tel: 01695 723333 Fax: 01695 556193; Grange Farm, Higher Lane, Dalton, Wigan WN8 7TW — MB ChB 1982 Manch.

HICKS, Andrew Peter Stonebridge Surgery, Preston Road, Longridge, Preston PR3 3AP Tel: 01772 783271 Fax: 01772 782836; Countess Hey Barn, Elmridge Lane, Chipping, Preston PR3 2NY Tel: 01772 783413 Fax: 01772 783413 Email: a.hicks@btinternet.com — MB ChB 1973 Bristol; MRCGP 1977; DRCOG 1976; Cert JCC Lond. 1977. (Bristol) Prev: Trainee GP Clitheroe; Trainee GP Bristol VTS; SHO (Ophth.) Bristol Eye Hosp.

HICKS, Anne Adele Paterson Blackbrook Surgery, Lisieux Way, Taunton TA1 2LB Tel: 01823 259444 Fax: 01823 322715; Easter Cottage, Queen Square, North Curry, Taunton TA3 6LE Tel: 01823 490119 Fax: 01823 490119 — MB ChB 1984 Glas.; MB ChB Glas. l984; MRCGP 1989; BA Open Univ. 1996. (Glas.)

HICKS, Anne Elizabeth 21 Tintagel Crescent, East Dulwich, London SE22 8HT; 28 De Beauvoir Square, London N1 4LE Tel: 020 7923 1239 — MB BS 1994 Lond.; MRCPI 1999. (UMDS Lond.) Regist. (A & E) St. Thos. Hosp. Lond. Prev: SHO (Med.) Worthing Gen. Hosp.; SHO (A & E) St. Thos. Hosp. Lond.; Ho. Off. (Surg.) Portsmouth.

HICKS, Anne Grafton Countess Hey Barn, Elmridge Lane, Chipping, Preston PR3 2NY Tel: 01772 783413 Fax: 01772 783413 Email: a.hicks@btinternet.com — MB ChB 1976 Bristol; Cert. Family Plann. JCC 1979. Med. Adviser to SEMA Gp. plc on behalf of the Benefits Agency; Sect. Sec. Med. Sect. IPMS. Prev: GP Trainee Longridge; SHO (Haemat.) & Ho. Surg. Blackburn Roy. Infirm.; Ho. Phys. Frenchay Hosp. Bristol.

HICKS, Anne Louise Mary Tel: 02882 648216 Fax: 02882 250386 — MB BCh BAO 1984 NUI; DCCH 1993; MRCGP 1989; DRCOG 1987. Job Sharing Partner in Gen. Pract.

HICKS, Brendan Hamilton The KSS Deanery, 7 Bermondsey Street, London SE1 2DD Tel: 020 74153401; 60 Greenwich Park St, Greenwich, London SE10 9LT Tel: 020 8858 7363 Fax: 020 8293 3502 — MB BS Lond. 1965; BSc (Hons.) Lond. 1961, MD 1977; FRCP Lond. 1982. (Guy's) PostGrad. Dean for Kent Surrey and Sussex (NHS & Univ. of Lond.). Socs: Fell. Roy. Soc. Med.; Worshipful Soc. Apoth.; Assn. Study Med. Educat. Prev: Sen. Lect. (Med.) & Postgrad. Dean UMDS Guy's & St. Thos. Hosps. Univ. Lond. & Cons. Phys. & Endocrinol. Guy's & Lewisham Hosps. Lond.; Ho. Phys. Hammersmith & Brompton Hosps. Lond.; Internat. Research Fell. USA Pub. Health Serv.

HICKS, Carole Anne The Surgery, South Queen Street, Morley, Leeds LS27 9EW Tel: 0113 253 4863 Fax: 0113 238 3564 — MB ChB 1983 Leeds.

HICKS, Catherine Eryl 21 Llyswen Road, Cyncoed, Cardiff CF23 6NG — MB BCh 1977 Wales; FRCR Eng. 1982. Cons. (Radiol.) E. Glam. Gen. Hosp.

HICKS, Celia Rachel Trevilley, Sennen, Penzance TR19 7AH — MB BChir 1990 Camb.

HICKS, Mr David Arthur Central Sheffield University Hospitals Trust, Glossop Road, Sheffield S10 2JF Tel: 0114 270 0928 Fax: 0114 271 3408 Email: gum@extra_computers.co.uk; Kilbourne Villa, 32 Oakhill Road, Nether Edge, Sheffield S7 1SH Email: dahsheff@aol.com — MB ChB 1974 Liverp.; FRCOG 1994; MFFP 1993; MRCOG 1982; Dip Ven Liverp. 1979; DRCOG 1977. (Liverpool) Cons. Genitourin. Med. Centr. Sheff. Univ. Hosp. Trust & Barnsley Dist. Gen. Hosp. Trust; Hon. Sen. Lect. Univ. Sheff.

***HICKS, Derek** 316 Arnold Estate, Druid St., London SE1 2DR — MB BS 1998 Lond.; MB BS Lond 1998; BSc (Hons) Lond 1995.

HICKS, Elaine Mary 19 Ballyglighorn Road, Comber, Newtownards BT23 5SX — MB BCh BAO 1972 Belf.; FRCP Lond. 1994; DCH Eng. 1975. Cons. Paediat. Neurol. Roy. Hosps. Trust Belf. Socs: Brit. Paediat. Assn. & Brit. Paediat. Neurol. Assn. Prev: Clin. Fell. (Neurol.) Harvard Med. Sch. & Childr. Hosp. Med. Centre Boston, Mass; Sen. Regist. (Paediat.) Roy. Belf. Hosp. Sick Childr.

HICKS, Elizabeth Ann (retired) 56 Brigsley Road, Waltham, Grimsby DN37 0LA Tel: 01472 822651 — MB ChB St. And. 1954. Prev: GP Grimsby.

HICKS, Elizabeth Rosa (retired) Flat 5, 19 Park Lane, Bath BA1 2XH — MB BCh BAO 1956 Dub.; BA 1953. Prev: Hon. Cons. Path. Sutton & W. Merton Health Dist. (St. Helier) & Wandsworth Health Dist. (T) (St. Geo. Hosp. Lond.).

HICKS, Fiona Margaret 37 Kingsway Court, Harrogate Road, Moortown, Leeds LS17 6SS — BM BS 1986 Nottm.; BMedSci Nottm. 1984, BM BS 1986; MRCP (UK) 1989. SHO (Med.) Christie Hosp. Manch.

HICKS, Frederick Nathanael (retired) 30 Elm Park, Stanmore HA7 4BJ Tel: 020 8954 1677 — MRCS Eng. LRCP Lond. 1944; MA Camb. 1946, MB BChir 1948. Prev: Med. Adviser Nat. Skating Assoc.

HICKS, Gilbert Edward 33 Chancellor House, Mount Ephraim, Tunbridge Wells TN4 8BT Tel: 01792 526000 — MB BS 1954 Lond.; MRCS Eng. LRCP Lond. 1942; MRCGP 1968; DObst RCOG 1947. (St. Bart.) Med. Ref. Kent & Sussex Crematorium Tunbridge Wells. Prev: Jun. Res. Anaesth. St. Bart. Hosp.; Obst. Regist. W. Middlx. Co. Hosp.; Maj. RAMC.

HICKS, Ian Peter Bedford Hospital, Kempston Rd, Bedford MK42 9DJ Tel: 01234 792247; Wentworth House, Ravensden Rd, Renhold, Bedford MK41 0LA — MB BS 1980 Lond.; MRCP (UK) 1983; FRCR 1985. Cons. Radiol. Bedford Gen. Hosp. Socs: Fell. Med. Soc. Lond.; Brit. Inst. Radiol.

HICKS, Ian Roy Conquest Hospital, The Ridge, Hastings TN35 7RD Tel: 01424 755255; Gate End, Whatlington Road, Battle TN33 0NA Tel: 01424 775117 — MRCS Eng. LRCP Lond. 1980; LMSSA 1980; MRCGP 1987; FRCA 1992; FFA RCS Eng. 1988; DA (UK) 1985; DCH RCP Lond. 1983; DRCOG 1982. (King's) Cons. Anaesth. Conquest Hosp. Hastings. Socs: Intens. Care Soc. & Pain Soc. Prev: Sen. Regist. (Anaesth.) St. Geo. Hosp. Lond.; Regist. (Anaesth.) Brompton Hosp. Lond.; Regist. (Anaesth.) Nat. Hosp. Nerv. Dis. Lond.

HICKS, James Andrew Thorn Falcon, Glasllwch Lane, Newport NP20 3PR — MB BS 1994 Lond.

HICKS, Jane Amanda 5 Alexandra Park, Redland, Bristol BS6 6QB Tel: 0117 942 7373 — MB ChB 1987 Leic.; BSc (Hons.) Physiol. Lond. 1982; MRCPsych 1996; MRCGP 1992; Dip. Obst. Otago 1989. Specialist Regist. Rotat. (Psychiat.) Bristol. Prev: Research Fell. (Psychiat.) Univ. Toronto, Canada; Regist. (Psychiat.) Barrow Hosp. Bristol; SHO (Psychiat.) Bristol Gen. Hosp.

HICKS, Jennifer Susan 21 Cleasby Road, Menston, Ilkley LS29 6JE — BM BCh 1994 Oxf.; MA Camb. 1995. Demonst. & Anat. Prosector Sch. Molecular & Med. Biosci. Univ. Wales Coll. Cardiff.

HICKS, Miss Joanna Lynn Stonelea Cottage, 24 Whiston Road, Cogenhoe, Northampton NN7 1NL Tel: 01604 890637 — MB BChir 1993 Camb.; MA Camb. 1989; FRCS Eng. 1998. (St. Bart.) Specialist Regist. Orthop. & Trauma Oxf. Region.

HICKS, John Eightlands Surgery, Eightlands Road, Dewsbury WF13 2PA Tel: 01924 465929 Fax: 01924 488740; 4 Poplar Avenue, Wakefield WF2 9DG Tel: 01924 465929 Fax: 01924 488740 — MB ChB 1978 Leeds. Exec. Mem. Dewsbury GP Commiss. Gp.

HICKS, John Brian (retired) 22 Peacock Lane, Hest Bank, Lancaster LA2 6EN Tel: 01524 823150 — MB BS Lond. 1960; MRCS Eng. LRCP Lond. 1960; FFA RCS Eng. 1968; DA Eng. 1962. Prev: Cons. Anaesth. N. Lancs. & S. W.morland Hosp. Gp.

HICKS, Jonathan David 1 St Colme Drive, Dalgety Bay, Dunfermline KY11 9LQ — MB ChB 1994 Ed.; BSc Ed. 1992; MRCP (UK) 1998. (Edinburgh)

HICKS, Katrina Anne Suouthampton General Hospital, Tremona Road, Southampton SO16 6YB Tel: 02380 777222 — MB ChB 1988 Ed.; MRCP (UK) 1992. Cons. Geriat., Soton. Univ. Hosp. NHS Trust, Tremona Rd., Soton., SO16 6YB. Socs: Brit. Geriat. Soc. Prev: SHO (Med.) Stirling Roy. Infirm.; Ho. Off. (Med.) W.. Gen. Hosp. Edin.; Ho. Off. (Surg.) York Dist. Hosp.

HICKS, Kenneth Walter 18 Beltrim Crescent, Gortin, Omagh BT79 8NW — MB BCh BAO 1984 Belf.; MB BCh Belf. I984; MRCGP 1988; DGM RCP Lond. 1988; DRCOG 1987.

HICKS, Leopold (retired) Brigadoon, 6 Seamer Road, Hilton, Yarm TS15 9JH Tel: 01642 598433 — MB BS 1963 Durh. Prev: Ho. Off. (O & G) Roy. Lancaster Infirm.

HICKS, Louise Joy Hollow Way Medical Centre, 58 Hollow Way, Cowley, Oxford OX4 2NJ Tel: 01865 777495 Fax: 01865 771472; 2 Oakthorpe Road, Oxford OX2 7BE Tel: 01865 511353 — MB ChB 1987 Bristol. (Univ. Bristol) Prev: Trainee GP Oxf.; Trainee GP Avon VTS.

HICKS, Margaret Howson Murdoch (retired) Ataraxia, Church Road, Brean, Burnham-on-Sea TA8 2SF — MB ChB Glas. 1951. Prev: G.P. Burnham-on-Sea.

HICKS, Neville Charles 87 Carnreagh, Hillsborough BT26 6LJ — MB BCh BAO 1976 Belf.; ECFMG Cert 1976; MICGP 1987; DRCOG 1978. GP Princip. Dromara. Socs: BMA. Prev: Ho. Phys. & Ho. Surg. & SHO (O & G) Lagan Valley Hosp. Lisburn.

HICKS, Nicholas Julian Upper Dolcoppice Farm, Whitwell, Ventnor PO38 2PB — MB BS 1986 Lond.; BA Camb. 1983; MFPHM RCP (UK) 1995; MRCGP 1991; T(GP) 1991. Cons. Pub. Health Med. Portsmouth & SE Hants. HA. Prev: Sen. Regist. (Pub. Health Med.) Dudley; Dist. Med. Off. Grenfell Regional Health Servs. Labrador, Canada; Trainee GP Stafford Dist. Hosp. VTS.

HICKS, Nicholas Rooke Department of Public Health, Oxfordshire HA, Old Road, Headington, Oxford OX3 7LG Tel: 01865 226578 Fax: 01865 226824 Email: nicholas.hicks@dphpc.ox.ac.uk; Woodend, Shirvells Hill, Goring Heath, Reading RG8 7SP — BM BCh 1982 Oxf.; MA 1983; MRCP (UK) 1987; FFPHM RCP (UK) 1996; MRCGP 1986; DRCOG 1985; DCH RCP Lond. 1984; FRCP 1998. Cons. Pub. Health Phys. Oxon. HA; Hon. Sen. Clin. Lect. Oxf. Univ. (Pub. Health & Primary Care) Oxon. Prev: Lect. & Hon. Sen. Regist. (Epidemiol. & Pub. Health Med.) Univ. Bristol, Bristol & W.. HA; Harkness Fell. 1991; Trainee GP Bath VTS.

HICKS, Patricia Margaret Mary Sunnyside Surgery, Hawkins Road, Penzance TR18 4LT Tel: 01736 63340 — MB BS 1962 Lond.; MRCS Eng. LRCP Lond. 1962.

HICKS, Philip Yelverton (retired) Stable Cottage, Grays Farm, West End Lane, Henfield BN5 9RF Tel: 01273 492071 — MB BS 1930 Lond.; MRCS Eng. LRCP Lond. 1930. Hon. Clin. Asst. Finchley Memor. Hosp. Prev: Ho. Phys., Cas. Off. & Resid. Anaesth. St. Thos. Hosp.

HICKS, Robert Anthony Randolph Surgery, 235A Elgin Avenue, London W9 1NH Tel: 020 7286 6880 Fax: 020 7286 9787 — MB BS 1989 Lond. Trainee GP/SHO (O & G) Ashford Hosp. Middlx.

HICKS, Mr Robert Charles Jackson Integratey Surgery, Northampton General Hospital, Northampton NN1 5BD Tel: 01604 544353 Fax: 01604 544353; Belmont House, 6 High Street, Yardley Hastings NN7 1ER — MB BS 1989 Lond.; FRCS Eng. 1993; MS Lond. 1996; FRCS Gen. 1999. (St. Thos. Hosp. Lond) Cons. Vasc. & Gen. Surg. N.ampton Gen. Hosp.; Vasc. Fell.sh. Flinders Med. Centre S. Australia; Specialist Regist. (Vasc. Surg.) Char. Cross Hosp. Lond. Prev: Lect. (Surg.) Char. Cross & W.minster Med. Sch.

HICKS, Stephen Christopher Swindon Health Centre, Carfax Street, Swindon SN1 1ED Tel: 01793 692062; Caislean, South Farm, Draycott Foliat, Chiseldon, Swindon SN4 0JE Tel: 01793 741228 — LLM 1994 Wales; MB BCh 1978; MRCGP 1982. Medico-Legal Adviser for Med. Protec. Soc.; Dep. Police Surg. Wilts. Constab. Socs: Police Surgs. Assn.

HICKS, Thomas Michael The Forest Group Practice, The Surgery, Bury Road, Brandon IP27 0BU Tel: 01842 813353 Fax: 01842 815221; Clare House, 91 The Lammas, Mundford, Thetford IP26 5DS Tel: 01842 878176 — MB BChir 1976 Camb.; MA, MB Camb. 1976, BChir 1975.

HICKS, Trevor, Squadron Ldr. RAF Med. Br. Retd. Department of Psychiatry, Wonford House Hospital, Dryden Road, Exeter EX2 5; 55 Fore Street, Plympton St Maurice, Plymouth PL7 1NA Email: thicks484@aol.com — MB ChB 1985 Bristol; MRCGP 1989; DRCOG 1992. (Bristol) Socs: BMA. Prev: GP Princip. Plymouth; Med. Off. RAF Lyneham Chippenham; SHO/GP VTS Rotat. RAF Hosp. Ely.

HICKSON, Arthur Frederick The Health Centre, Kidsgrove, Stoke-on-Trent ST7 4AB Tel: 017816 4221; 47 Fields Road, Alsager, Stoke-on-Trent ST7 2NA Tel: 01270 872969 — MB ChB 1956 Bristol. Prev: O & G Ho. Surg. St. Mary's Hosp. Rugby; Ho. Surg. Gen. Hosp. W.on-super-Mare; Ho. Phys. Ham Green Hosp. Bristol.

HICKSON, Bryan David Place Surgery, 7 David Place, St Helier, Jersey JE2 4TD Tel: 01534 736666, 01534 768482; La Guilleaumerie Cottage, Rue De La Guilleaumerie, St. Saviour, Jersey JE2 7HQ Tel: 01534 862692 — MB ChB 1965 Aberd.; MRCP (U.K.) 1970. Phys. St. Helier, Jersey; Dep. Police Surg. States of Jersey, CI. Prev: Sen. Regist. (Gen. Med.) St. Bart. Hosp. Lond.; Regist. (Med.) Aberd. Gen. Gp. Hosps.; Ho. Surg. & Ho. Phys. Roy. Infirm. Aberd.

HICKSON, Caroline Katherine Rose Newport Pagnell Medical Centre, Queens Avenue, Newport Pagnell MK16 8QT Tel: 01908 611767 Fax: 01908 615099 — MB ChB 1977 Leeds; MRCGP 1981; DRCOG 1979.

HICKSON, David Edmund Graham The Medical Centre, Station Avenue, Bridlington YO16 4LZ Tel: 01262 670690; 148 Cavelingan Road, Bridlington YO15 3LK — MB BS 1986 Lond.; DRCOG 1990; Cert. Family Plann. JCC 1989; Dip. IMC RCS Ed. 1989. (London Hospital) GP; Clin. Asst. (Psychiat.) Bridlington; Police Surg. Humberside; Med. Off. Beverly Racecourse. Socs: ScarBoro. Medics Accid. Care Scheme; Yorks. E. Riding Volun. Accid. Scheme. Prev: Trainee GP ScarBoro.; Ho. Surg. Lond. Hosp.; Ho. Phys. Hull Roy. Infirm.

HICKSON, George Michael The Rowans, 2 Larches Road, Durham DH1 4NL — MB BS 1968 Newc.; DObst RCOG 1974.

HICKSON, Judith Deborah Cave PO Box 55314, Nairobi, Kenya Tel: 00 254 2 891578 Fax: 00 254 2 542782 Email: robshaw@net2000.ke.com; Debden, Edzell, Brechin DD9 7TE Tel: 01356 647189 — MB ChB 1985 Ed.; MRCGP 11990; DRCOG 1989. (Ed.) Med. Advisor United Nations, Nairobi; Vis. Staff Nairobi Hosp. Kenya.

HICKSON, Julie Ruth Malham House Day Hospital, 25 Hyde Terrace, Leeds LS2 9LN Tel: 0113 292 6716; 23 Valley Road, Harrogate HG2 0JQ Tel: 01423 568105 — MB ChB 1988 Sheff. Staff Grade (Acute Adult Psychiat.) Malham Ho. Day Hosp. Leeds. Prev: Clin. Med. Off. Rotherham.

HICKSON, Keith William, MBE (retired) 356 Bosty Lane, Walsall WS9 0QF Tel: 01922453201 Fax: 01922 453201 — MB BChir 1955 Camb.

HICKSON, Lucy Pamela Woolpit Health Centre, Heath Road, Woolpit, Bury St Edmunds IP30 9QV; The Old Shop, The Street, Pakenham, Bury St Edmunds IP31 2JU Email: lucy@roding.demon.co.uk — MB BS 1988 Lond.; BSc Lond. 1984; MRCGP 1995; DRCOG 1993; DCH RCP Lond. 1992. Employed Non-Princip. Prev: Locum.

HICKSON, Marcus John 3 Priory Lodge Close, Milford Haven SA73 2BZ — MB ChB 1997 Leeds.

HICKSON, Mary Sylvia Westbrook House, Vale View Drive, Beech Hill, Reading RG7 2BD — BM 1981 Soton.; AFOM RCP Lond.

1994. Occupat. Phys. Pruden. Assur. Company Ltd. Socs: Soc. Occupat. Med. Prev: Occupat. Phys. Pruden. UK Reading & W. Berks. Occupat. Health Reading; Occupat. Phys. Burmah Castrol, Castrol Internat., Marks & Spencer plc & Rutherford Appleton Laborat. Oxf.; GP Wootton Bassett.

HICKSON, Peter John Health Centre, High Street, Bedworth, Nuneaton CV12 8NQ Tel: 024 7631 5432 Fax: 024 7631 0038; 18 Withybrook Road, Bulkington, Nuneaton CV12 9SN Tel: 01203 319985 — MB ChB 1987 Birm.; BSc (Hons.) Birm. 1984; MRCGP 1993. Prev: Trainee GP Roy. Shrewsbury Hosp. VTS; Dist. Med. Off. Tennant Creek, Austral.

HICKSON, Rachel Mary La Guilleaumerie Cottage, Rue De La Guilleaumerie, St Saviour, Jersey JE2 7HQ — BM 1993 Soton.

HICKSON, Ruth Margaret (retired) 47 Fields Road, Alsager, Stoke-on-Trent ST7 2NA Tel: 01270 872969 — MB BS 1951 Lond.; FRCS Eng. 1956; MRCS Eng. LRCP Lond. 1951. Prev: Assoc. Specialist (Orthop.) W. Midl. RHA.

HICKSON, Veronica Mary Newport Divisional Office, 27 Clytha Park Road, Newport NP20 4PA Tel: 01633 435937 Fax: 01633 435934; New House Farm, Llangwm, Usk NP15 1HJ Tel: 01291 650279 Fax: 01633 861772 — MB BCh 1981 Wales; MSc (Audiol. Med.) Manch. 1997; MRCGP 1985; MRCPCH 1997. Assoc. Specialist (Child Health & Audiol.) Gwent Health Care NHS Trust. Socs: Brit. Assn. Community Drs in Audiol.

HIDALGO SIMON, Maria Ana Ground Floor Flat, 22 Castellain Road, London W9 1EZ — LMS 1989 Basque Provinces; MD Basque Provinces 1990; PhD Univ. Lond. 1995.

HIDE, David (retired) 23 Lavant Road, Chichester PO19 4RA Tel: 01243 527214 — MB BS Lond. 1954; MRCS Eng. LRCP Lond. 1954; MRCPsych 1972; DPM Eng. 1971. Prev: Cons. Psychiat. Ipswich HA.

HIDE, Emily Margaret Cross Green House, 25 Cross Green, Otley LS21 1HD — MB ChB 1987 Manch.; DRCOG 1991; DCH RCP Lond. 1989.

HIDE, Ian Geoffrey 9 Davenport Drive, Gosforth, Newcastle upon Tyne NE3 5AE — MB BS 1990 Newc.; MRCP 1993; FRCR 1997.

HIDE, Mr Thomas Armstrong Henry Department of Neurosurgery, Southern General Hospital NHS Trust, Glasgow Tel: 0141 201 2024 Fax: 0141 425 1442; Dunardrie, 15 Kilbarchan Road, Bridge of Weir PA11 3ET Tel: 01505 612366 — MB ChB 1960 Glas.; FRCS Eng. 1964; FRCS Glas. 1964. Cons. Neurosurg. Inst. Neurol. Sci. S.. Gen. Hosp. Glas. Socs: Pres. Soc. Brit. Neurol. Surg. Prev: Sen. Research Regist. Atkinson Morley's Hosp. Wimbledon; Sen. Regist. (Neurosurg.) Nat. Hosp. Nerv. Dis. Qu. Sq. Lond.; Sen. Regist. (Neurosurg.) Inst. Neurol. Sci. Glas.

HIDE, Yvonne Hainsworth (retired) The Old Vicarage, Shorwell, Newport PO30 3JL Tel: 01983 740863 — MB ChB 1960 Ed. Prev: Clin. Med. Off. St. Mary's NHS Trust I. of Wight.

HIDER, Calvin Fraser Marchwell Cottage, Penicuik EH26 0PX Tel: 01968 672680 — MB ChB 1954 Ed.; FFA RCS Eng. 1960. Prev: Cons. Anaesth. Edin. Roy. Infirm.; Hon. Sen. Lect. (Fac. Med.) Univ. Edin.; Surg. Lt.-Cdr. RNR.

***HIDER, James Daniel** 15 Station Road, North Ferriby, Hull HU12 8UT — BM BS 1996 Nottm.

HIDSON, Jeremy Martin Clach Mhile Surgery, Castlebay HS9 5XD Tel: 01871 810282 Fax: 01871 810333 — MB BS 1981 Lond.; MRCGP 1985. (Middlx.) GP I. of Barra. Prev: GP Greenlaw; Trainee GP Bronglais Hosp. VTS Aberystwyth; SHO (O & G) Sunderland Dist. Hosp.

HIDSON, Oliver James Rosebank Surgery, 153B Stroud Road, Gloucester GL1 5JQ Tel: 01452 522767; Drawdykes, The Leigh, Gloucester GL19 4AG — MB BS 1972 Lond.; MRCP (UK) 1978; MRCGP 1987. (Univ. Coll. Hosp.) Clin. Asst. (Rheum.) Gloucester Roy. Hosp. Socs: BMA.

HIEATT, Marilyn Susan Homhurst Medical Centre, 17 Hatchlands Road, Redhill RH1 6AA Tel: 01737 766602/761614 Fax: 01737 780608; 3 Wray Park Road, Reigate RH2 0DG Tel: 01737 221878 — MB BS 1972 Lond.; MRCS Eng. LRCP Lond. 1972. (Char. Cross Hosp.)

HIERONS, Audrey Mary 4 Adeline Gardens, Newcastle upon Tyne NE3 4JQ Tel: 0191 285 0667 — MB BS 1955 Durh.; DCH Eng. 1960; FRCPCH 1997. Prev: SCMO Gateshead HA.; Asst. Paediat. Qu. Eliz. Hosp. Gateshead; Regist. (Paediat.), Ho. Phys. & Ho. Surg. Roy. Vict. Infirm. Newc.

HIERONS, Mr Charles Douglas The Newcastle Clinic, 52 Mitchell Avenue, Jesmond, Newcastle upon Tyne NE2 3LA Tel: 0191 281 0193 Fax: 0191 281 7172; 4 Adeline Gardens, Newcastle upon Tyne NE3 4JQ Tel: 0191 285 0667 — MB BS Durh. 1954; FRCS Eng. 1963. (Durh.) Cons. Orthop. Surg. Qu. Eliz. Hosp. Gateshead. Prev: Regist. Roy. Vict. Infirm. Newc.; Ho. Surg. Birm. Accid. Hosp. & Hosp. Sick Childr. Gt. Ormond St.

HIEW, Stephen Chee Cheung Silver Street Medical Centre, 159 Silver Street, London N18 1PY Tel: 020 8807 1057 Fax: 020 8345 5259; 328 Alexandra Park Road, London N22 7BD Tel: 020 8364 0732 Fax: 020 8888 5654 Email: tame.elephant@virgin.net — MB BCh BAO 1983 NUI; LRCPI & LM, LRCSI & LM 1983. (Roy. Coll. Surgs. Irel.) Regional GP Tut. Thames Postgrad. & Dent. Educ. Univ. Lond.; Hon. Research Fell. Dept. of Primary Care, Roy. Free & Univ. Coll. Med. Sch., Lond. Socs: Fell. Roy. Soc. Med.; Fell. Roy. Soc. Health; BMA. Prev: Trainee GP Enfield; SHO (Paediat. & Neonat.) P.ss Alexandra Hosp. Harlow; SHO (Gastroenterol. & Haemat.) Chase Farm Hosp. Enfield.

HIFZI, Ozkan — MD 1959 Istanbul; MRCS Eng. LRCP Lond. 1975; FFA RCS Eng. 1972; DA Eng. 1969. (Istanbul) p/t Cons. Anaesth. Qu. Mary's Hosp. Sidcup. Socs: Assn. Anaesths.; Roy. Coll. Anaesth.; S. of Thames Soc. of Anaesth. Prev: Regist. (Anaesth.) Good Hope Hosp. Sutton Coldfield & St. Peter's; Hosp. Chertsey; Sen. Regist. (Anaesth.) W.m. Hosp. Lond.

HIGAB, Mohamed Goudat Bader 115 Belgrave Road, Darwen BB3 2SF — MRCS Eng. LRCP Lond. 1962.

HIGAZEY, Mahmoud Ahmed Mahmoud Department of Obstetrics & Gynaecology, Craigavon Hospital, 68 Lugen Road, Portadown, Craigavon BT63 5QQ — MB ChB 1974 Egypt; MRCOG 1994.

HIGENBOTTAM, Professor Timothy William Division of Clinical Science (CSUHT), Section of Respiratory Medicine, The Medical School, Beech Hill Road, Sheffield S10 2RX Fax: 0114 271 1711 Email: t.higenbottam@sheffield.ac.uk — MB BS 1971 Lond.; MA Camb. 1987; BSc (Biochem.) Lond. 1967, MD 1980; FRCP Lond. 1988; MRCP (UK) 1973; MRCS Eng. LRCP Lond. 1971; FCCP 1987. (Guy's) Prof. Respirat. Med. Roy. Hallamsh. Hosp. Sheff. Socs: Physiol. Soc.; Amer. Acad. Advancem. of Sci.; Eur. Respirat. Soc. Prev: Cons. Phys. Respirat. Physiol. Papworth & Addenbrooke's Hosp. Camb.; Sen. Regist. (Med.) Guy's Hosp. Lond.

HIGGENS, Clare Slade Northwick Park and St Marks Hospitals, Waford Road, Harrow HA1 3UJ Tel: 020 8869 2606 Fax: 020 8426 6357 Email: c.higgens@btinternet.co.uk; 25 Westmoreland Road, London SW13 9RZ — MB BS 1974 Lond.; MD Birm. 1981; FRCP Lond. 1992; MRCP (UK) 1977; MRCS Eng. LRCP Lond. 1974. (Lond. Hosp.) Cons. Phys. & Rheum. N.wick Pk. & St. Marks Hosps.; Hon. Cons. Rheum. Hammersmith Hosps. Lond. Prev: Cons. (Rheum.) Qu. Mary's Hosp. Roehampton; Regist. (Rheum.) The Lond. Hosp.; Regist. & Research Fell. & Hon. Sen. Regist. (Gastroenterol. & Gen. Med.) Gen. Hosp. Birm.

HIGGENS, Erica Woolliscroft West House, 7 Park Hill, Harlow CM17 0AE Tel: 01279 427279 — MRCS Eng. LRCP Lond. 1946; MA Camb. 1946, MB BChir 1946. (Camb. & Bristol) JP.

HIGGIE, Clement Baxter (retired) 26 Menlove Gardens S., Liverpool L18 2EL Tel: 0151 722 6015 — MRCS Eng. LRCP Lond. 1951; DPH Eng. 1957. Prev: Med. Off. Derwent Ho. Observat. & Assessm. Centre Liverp.

HIGGIE, Edith Jean (retired) Clare Cottage, Church St., Malpas SY14 8PF — MB ChB 1945 Bristol. Prev: Ho. Phys. Bristol Childr. Hosp.

HIGGIE, John Morris Munro Harley House Surgery, 2 Irnham Road, Minehead TA24 5DL Tel: 01643 703441 Fax: 01643 704867; Higher Moor, Moor Road, Minehead TA24 5RY Tel: 01643 706875 — MB ChB 1979 Birm.; BA Camb. 1976; MRCGP 1985; DCH RCP Lond. 1985; DRCOG 1981. Mem. Som. LMC.

HIGGIE, Mary Ruth 26 Menlove Gardens S., Liverpool L18 2EL Tel: 0151 722 6015 — LRCP LRCS 1952 Ed.; LRCP LRCS Ed. LRFPS Glas. 1952; DPH Liverp. 1960.

HIGGINBOTHAM-JONES, Kevin James Offerton Health Centre, 10 Offerton Lane, Offerton, Stockport SK2 5AR Tel: 0161 480 0324 — MB BS 1983 Newc.

HIGGINS, Adrian Peter 17 Hawes Close, Tottington, Bury BL8 1UH — MB ChB 1988 Manch.

HIGGINS, Amanda Suzanne West Walk Surgery, 21 West Walk, Yate, Bristol BS37 4AX Tel: 01454 272200; 6 Lime Grove, Alveston, Bristol BS35 3PN Tel: 01454 417756 — MB ChB 1984 Bristol; MB ChB (Hons.) Bristol 1984; MRCGP 1988; DRCOG 1986.

HIGGINS, Anthony 28 Thorniewood Road, Uddingston, Glasgow G71 5QG — MB ChB 1989 Glas.

HIGGINS, Anthony (retired) The Old Bakery, La Rue de la Pointe, St Peter, Jersey JE3 7AQ Tel: 01534 481815 — MB BS 1967 Lond.; MRCS Eng. LRCP Lond. 1962. Prev: Assoc. Specialist A & E Gen. Hosp. Jersey.

HIGGINS, Bernard (retired) 270 Rishton Lane, Bolton BL3 2EH Tel: 01204 400936 — MB ChB Manch. 1950. Prev: ENT Clin. Asst. Bolton & Dist. Hosp. Gp.

HIGGINS, Bernard Gerard Department of Respiratory Medicine, Freeman Hospital, Newcastle upon Tyne NE7 7DN — MD 1989 Manch.; MRCP (UK) 1983; FRCP. Cons. Phys. Freeman Hosp. Newc. u. Tyne. Prev: Sen. Regist. (Thoracic Med.) Hope Hosp. Salford & Wythenshawe Hosp. Manch.; Research Fell. (Respirat. Med.) Univ. Nottm.

HIGGINS, Brian Thomas Lowther Medical Centre, 1 Castle Meadows, Whitehaven CA28 7RG Tel: 01946 692241 Fax: 01946 590617; Retreat Farm House, High House Road, St Bees CA27 0BY Tel: 01946 822866 Fax: 01946 824640 — MB ChB 1961 Liverp.; DObst RCOG 1964. (Liverp.) Socs: BMA; Brit. Soc. Med. & Dent. Hypn. Prev: SHO (Paediat.) Alder Hey Hosp. Liverp.; Ho. Surg. (Obst.) Sefton Gen. Hosp. Liverp.; Ho. Surg. (Gen. Surg.) Roy. S.. Hosp. Liverp.

HIGGINS, Mrs Carol Jane Staunton Group Practice, 3-5 Bounds Green Road, Wood Green, London N22 8HE Tel: 020 8889 4311 Fax: 020 8826 9100 — MB BS 1968 Lond.; MRCS Eng. LRCP Lond. 1968. (Roy. Free) GP Lond. Prev: Ho. Phys. Hampstead Gen. Hosp.; Ho. Surg. Luton & Dunstable Hosp.

HIGGINS, Caroline Rose Department of Dermatology, Royal Berkshire NHS Trust, Reading RG1 5AN Tel: 01734 877417 — MB BS 1986 Lond.; MRCP (UK) 1989. Cons. Dermat. Roy. Berks. & Battle Hosps. NHS Trust. Prev: Sen. Regist. (Dermat.) Ch.ill Hosp. Oxf.; Regist. (Dermat.) Roy. Lond. Hosp.; Regist. (Med.) Battle Hosp. Reading.

HIGGINS, Catherine Mary 66 Surrey Drive, Kingswinford DY6 8HR — MB ChB 1991 Aberd.; MRCP (UK) 1995; DCH RCP Lond. 1995.

HIGGINS, Catherine Susan St Ann Street Surgery, 82 St. Ann Street, Salisbury SP1 2PT Tel: 01722 322624 Fax: 01722 410624; Hillside Cottage, The Hollows, Lower Woodford, Salisbury SP4 6NJ Email: khiggins@lwoodfordsp4.free — MB BS 1984 Lond.; MRCGP 1989; Cert Family Plann 1988; DRCOG 1988. GP Partner. Socs: BMA; BMAS. Prev: Clin. Med. Off. (Child Health) Soton.; Trainee GP/SHO Salisbury VTS; SHO (A & E) Yeovil Dist. Hosp.

HIGGINS, Charles Anthony (retired) Tall Trees, 87 Park Road, Buxton SK17 6SN Tel: 01298 26415 — MB BS 1951 Lond.; MRCS Eng. LRCP Lond. 1948. Prev: Ho. Surg. N. Staffs. Roy. Infirm. Stoke-on-Trent.

HIGGINS, Christopher John Charles Fleet Medical Centre, Church Rd, Fleet GU5 4PE Tel: 01252 613327 Fax: 01252 815156 — MB BS 1985 Lond.; MRCPI 1989; MRCGP 1994; DRCOG 1990; DCH RCP Lond. 1990. (St. Thomas' Hospital) Prev: Trainee GP Sandhurst Berks.; SHO (Gen. Med.) St. Peter's Hosp. Chertsey; Ho. Phys. St. Thos. Hosp. Lond.

HIGGINS, David Grahame Grange Medical Centre, Seacroft Crescent, Leeds LS14 6NX Tel: 0113 295 1801 Fax: 0113 295 1799; 9 North Lane, Leeds LS8 2QJ Tel: 0113 266 8797 — MB ChB 1982 Leeds; MRCGP 1989; Dip. Occ. Med. 1997.

HIGGINS, David John Department of Anaesthesia, Southend Hospital, Prittlewell Chase, Westcliff on Sea SS0 0RY — MB ChB 1984 Manch.; BSc (Hons.) Manch. 1981, MB ChB l984; FCAnaesth. 1989; DA (UK) 1987. Cons. Anaesth. & Intens. Care S.end Hosp. Prev: Sen. Regist. (Anaesth.) Univ. Coll. Hosp. Lond.; Post-Fell.sh. Regist. (Anaesth.) Hosp. for Sick Childr. Gt. Ormond St. Lond.; Regist. (Anaesth.) St. Bart. Hosp. Lond.

HIGGINS, Derek Alan Beckside House, East Woodside, Wigton CA7 8BB — MB ChB 1991 Aberd.

HIGGINS, Dorothy Ann Ashdene, Killinchy Road, Comber, Newtownards BT23 5SP — MD 1975 Malta; MRCS Eng. LRCP Lond. 1975; FFA RCS Eng. 1980. p/t Regist. (Oncol.) NICCO Belvoir Pk. Hosp. Belf.

HIGGINS, Eileen Margaret Heaton Road Surgery, 41 Heaton Road, Heaton, Newcastle upon Tyne NE6 1TP Tel: 0191 265 5509 Fax: 0191 224 1824; 31 West Farm Avenue, Longbenton, Newcastle upon Tyne NE12 8LS Tel: 0191 266 2215 Fax: 0191 266 4028 — MB ChB 1981 Leeds; DFFP 1996; DRCOG 1984; DCH RCP Lond. 1983. (Leeds) Prev: GP Hartlepool; SHO (O & G) Norwich HA; SHO (Paediat.) Shotley Bridge Gen. Hosp. Consett.

HIGGINS, Elisabeth Mary Department of Dermatology, King's College Hospital, London SE5 9RS — FRCP 1999; MB BS Lond. 1982; MA Camb. 1983, BA 1979; MRCP (UK) 1985. (Westm.) Sen. Lect. & Cons. Dermat. King's Coll. Hosp. Lond. Prev: Sen. Regist. (Dermat.) King's Coll. Hosp.

HIGGINS, Elizabeth Kirkwood Hospice, 21 Albany Road, Huddersfield HD5 9UY Tel: 01484 557900 Fax: 01484 557918; Old Water Hall, Mirfield WF14 8AE Tel: 01924 493465 — MB ChB 1959 Leeds; DObst RCOG 1961. (Leeds) Med. Dir. & Cons. Palliat. Med. Kirkwood Hospice Huddersfield. Socs: Hudds. Med. Soc. Prev: Clin. Asst. Huddersfield Roy. Infirm.

HIGGINS, Gordon Andrew 8 Lingard Drive, Astley, Tydesley, Manchester M29 7FD — MB ChB 1998 Manch.; MB ChB Manch 1998.

HIGGINS, Hilary Patricia 12 bankart Avenue, Oadby, Leicester LE2 2DB Tel: 0116 270 4030 — MB ChB 1971 Glas. (Glasg. Univ.) Staff Grade (Community Paediat.) Fosse Health Trust; Clin. Asst. (Paediat.) Leicester Roy. Infirm.; Clin. Asst. (Dermat.) Leicester Roy. Infirm. Socs: Leic. Med. Soc. Prev: Clin. Asst. Dermat. Leicester Roy. Infirm.f; SHO (Gyn. & Obst.) & Ho. Surg. Leicester Roy. Infirm.; Ho. Phys. Leicester Gen. Hosp.

HIGGINS, James Scott Clinic, Rainhill Road, St Helens WA9 5DR Tel: 0151 430 6300 Fax: 0151 430 8147 — MB ChB 1967 Glas.; FRCPsych 1984, M 1972; DPM Ed. & Glas. 1970. Cons. Forens. Psychiat. St. Helens & Knowsley Hosp. Trust & NW RHA; Hon. Clin. Lect. (Forens. Psychiat.) Univ. Liverp.; Assoc. Postgrad. Dean Univ. Liverp.

HIGGINS, Joan Carole (retired) 10 Lancaster Gardens, Penn, Wolverhampton WV4 4DN Tel: 01902 331601 — MB ChB 1961 Liverp.; MRCS Eng. LRCP Lond. 1961.

HIGGINS, Joanna Catherine 11 Moor Park Avenue, Leeds LS6 4BT — MB ChB 1998 Sheff.; MB ChB Sheff 1998.

HIGGINS, John Andrew Carrick Hill Medical Centre, 1 Carrick Hill, Belfast BT1 2JR Tel: 028 9043 973 — MB BCh BAO 1987 Dub.

HIGGINS, John Anthony Ferrybridge Medical Centre, 8-10 High Street, Ferrybridge, Wakefield WF11 8NQ Tel: 01977 672109 Fax: 01977 671107; Conifers, Rawfield Lane, Fairborn WF11 9LD Tel: 01977 671293 — MB ChB 1993 Leeds; MRCGP 1997; DRCOG 1996; Dip. Pract. Dermat. 1999. (Leeds) GP Ferrybridge; Clin. Asst. (Dermat.); Hon. Club Dir. Castleford RLFC.

HIGGINS, John Nicholas Peter Department of Radiology, Box 219, Addenbrooke's Hospital, Hills Road, Cambridge CB2 2QQ Tel: 01223 216910 — MB BS 1980 Lond.; BA Oxf. 1976, MSc 1996; MRCP (UK) 1984; FRCR 1990. Cons. Neuroradiol. Addenbrooke's Hosp. Camb. Prev: Hon Fell. (Interven. Neuroradiol.) Radcliffe Infirm. Oxf.; Sen. Regist. (Radiol.) Roy. Free Hosp. Lond.

HIGGINS, Mr Julian Richard Alexander 116 Vivian Road, Harborne, Birmingham B17 0DJ Tel: 0121 427 9326 — MB BS 1980 Lond.; ChM Manch. 1989; FRCS Eng. 1984; FRCS Ed. 1984. (Univ. Coll. Hosp.) Sen. Regist. (Urol.) Dudley Rd. Hosp. Birm. Prev: Regist. Rotat. (Surg.) Guy's Hosp. Lond. & Roy. Devon & Exeter Hosp.; Hon. Research Regist. (Urol.) Univ. Manch.; SHO (A & E) Guy's Hosp.

HIGGINS, June Margaret (retired) Glennie, Ramsden Road, Godalming GU7 1QE Tel: 01483 417383 — MB BS 1954 Lond.; MRCS Eng. LRCP Lond. 1954; DObst RCOG 1957. Prev: GP Godalming.

***HIGGINS, Katharine Susan** 402 Eccleshall Road, Sheffield S11 8PJ Tel: 01742 663775 — MB ChB 1994 Sheff.; PhD Sheff. 1994, MB ChB 1994, BMedSci 1991.

HIGGINS, Martin Timothy Christopher Vine House Surgery, Vine Street, Grantham NG31 6RQ Tel: 01476 576851 Fax: 01476 591732; 253 Barrowby Road, Grantham NG31 8NR — MB ChB 1975 Bristol.

HIGGINS, Miss Mary Ann Gerardine Emergency Unit, University Hospital of Wales, Heath Park, Cardiff CF14 4WZ Tel: 029 20748 086 Email: mary@cried.demon.co.uk — MB BCh BAO 1989 NUI; FRCSI 1993; DCH RCPI 1993. (Galway, Ireland) Specialist regist. (A&E), Univ. Hosp. of Wales. Prev: Fell. (Critical Care) N. Staffs Roy. Infirm.

HIGGINS, Mary Catherine 1 The Grange, Off Dobb Brow Road, Westhoughton, Bolton BL5 2AZ — MB ChB 1988 Leic.

HIGGINS, Mary Therese Allan Park Surgery, 19 Allan Park, Stirling FK8 2QD Tel: 01786 451375 — MB ChB 1972 Edinburgh. (Edinburgh) GP Stirling.

HIGGINS, Melanie Rose 737 Liverpool Road, Ainsdale, Southport PR8 3NS — MB ChB 1996 Liverp.

HIGGINS, Michael Joseph 17 Cranworth Street, Glasgow G12 8BZ — MB ChB 1981 Ed.; BSc (Hons.) (Physiol.) Ed. 1982, MB ChB 1981.

HIGGINS, Nicola Susan 22 St Francis Gardens, Copthorne, Crawley RH10 3JS — MB ChB 1998 Ed.; MB ChB Ed 1998.

HIGGINS, Norman Llewelyn (retired) The Chilterns, Hinderton Road, Neston, South Wirral CH64 9PG — MB BS 1949 Lond.; MRCS Eng. LRCP 1949; DObst RCOG 1953.

HIGGINS, Patricia Mary 12 Strandview Drive, Portstewart BT55 7LN — MB BCh BAO 1981 Belf.; FFR RCSI 1993; FRCR 1987. Cons. Radiol. Coleraine Hosp.

HIGGINS, Patrick The Laurels Medical Practice, 28 Clarendon Road, St. Helier, Jersey JE2 3YS Tel: 01534 733866 Fax: 01534 769597; 2 Jardin Du Mont A L'Abbe, La Grande Route De St. Jean, St. Helier JE2 3FN Tel: 01534 758325, 91534 758325 — MB ChB 1973 Glas.; DObst RCOG 1975; Dip. Pract. Dermat. Wales 1992. (Glas.) Socs: Assoc. Mem. RCGP. Prev: SHO /Regist. (Dermat.) Stobhill Hosp. Glas.; SHO (Obst & Gyn.) Qu. Mother's Hosp. Glas.; SHO (A & E) Glas. Roy. Infirm.

HIGGINS, Peter George (retired) Thornhedge, Ashbrook Lane, Poulton, Cirencester GL7 5JF Tel: 01285 851369 — MB BS 1950 Lond.; MD Lond. 1962; MRCS Eng. LRCP Lond. 1950; FRCPath 1977, M 1965; Dip. Bact. Lond 1958. Prev: Cons. Virol. Bristol Roy. Infirm. & Bristol Pub. Health Laborat.

HIGGINS, Peter Matthew, OBE (retired) Wallings, Heathfield Lane, Chislehurst BR7 6AH Tel: 020 8467 2756 — MB BS Lond. 1947; FRCP Lond. 1977, M 1953; FRCGP 1975. Prev: Bernard Sunley Prof. Gen. Pract. UMDS Lond.

HIGGINS, Mr Peter McRorie (retired) Windrush House, Aldsworth, Cheltenham GL54 3QY Tel: 01451 844734 Email: peterhiggins@onetel.net.uk — BM BCh 1955 Oxf.; MA Oxf. 1958, BA 1952, MCh 1967, BM BCh 1955; FRCS Eng. 1960. Prev: Cons. Urol. Surg. N. Staffs. Hosp. Centre.

HIGGINS, Philippa Caroline Wentworth Lodge, 40A Sea Avenue, Rustington, Littlehampton BN16 2DG Tel: 01903 783112 — MB BS 1994 Lond.; BSc (1st cl. Hons.) Lond. 1991, MB BS 1994. (St Barts) SHO Anaesth. Roy. Surrey Co. Hosp.Guildford. Socs: Mem. Assn. Anaesth.; Mem. BMA; MDU. Prev: SHO IC med.Qu. Alex hosp.Portsmouth.

HIGGINS, Raymond George Essex Lodge, 94 Greengate Street, Plaistow, London E13 0AS Tel: 0208 472 4888 Fax: 0208 472 5777; 173 Balaam Street, Plaistow, London E13 8AA Tel: 020 8470 3281 — MB BS 1974 Lond.; MRCS Eng. LRCP Lond. 1974. (Westm.) G.P. Princip.; GP Trainer Lond.; Co-Course Orgainser Newham VTS; Primary Care Tutor, Newham.

HIGGINS, Robert McRorie 53 Arch Road, Coventry CV2 5AD — MB BChir Camb. 1982; MA Camb. 1983, MD 1992; MRCP (UK) 1984. (Univ. Camb. & Lond. Hosp.) Cons. Renal & Gen. Med. Coventry; Mem. Edit. Bd. Transpl. Socs: Transpl. Soc.; Renal Assn.; Eur. Dialysis & Transpl. Assn. Prev: Sen. Regist. (Renal) & Hon. Lect. (Med.) Dulwich Hosp. Lond.; Research Fell. (Renal Transpl.) Oxf.; SHO Guy's Renal Unit.

HIGGINS, Robert Niel Twistington (retired) 7 Fairlawns, Cambridge Park, Twickenham TW1 2JY Tel: 020 8744 2409 — MB BChir Camb. 1949; DPM Eng. 1954. Vis. Lect. MA Art Psychother., Goldsmith's Coll.; Vis. Lect. MA Clin. PsychoAnal., Guild of Psychotherapists, Univ. of Herts. Prev: Vis. Lect. Laban Centre for Movement & Dance Lond.

HIGGINS, Robin Paul Three Villages Medical Practice, Audnam Lodge, Wordsley, Stourbridge DY8 4AL Tel: 01384 395054 Fax: 01384 390969 — MB ChB 1974 Birm.; DA Eng. 1979; DRCOG 1977.

HIGGINS, Sarah Jane Flat 2, 48 Kenilworth Road, London W5 3UH — MB ChB 1993 Sheff.

HIGGINS, Shane Patrick Joseph 24 South Erskine Park, Bearsden, Glasgow G61 4NA Tel: 0141 942 7316 — MB BCh BAO 1987 NUI; MRCOG 1996. (Univ. Coll. Cork) Specialist Regist. (O & G) S.. Gen. Hosp. Glas. Socs: Glas. Obst. & Gyn. Soc.

HIGGINS, Siobhan Maria 117 Osborne Park, Belfast BT9 6JQ — MB BCh BAO 1997 Belf.

HIGGINS, Stephen Peter 4 Brandreth Drive, Parbold, Wigan WN8 7HB Tel: 0161 720 2681 Email: gumed@compuserv.com — MB ChB 1981 Liverp.; MRCP (UK) 1990; DObst Auckland 1987. Cons. Phys. (Genitourin. Med.) N. Manch. Gen. Hosp.

***HIGGINS, Steven** 42 Stirling Way, Welwyn Garden City AL7 2QA — MB BS 1994 Lond.; BSc (Hons.) (Physiol.) Lond. 1991.

HIGGINS, Stewart Allen Cumberland House, Jordangate, Macclesfield SK10 1EG Tel: 01625 428081 Fax: 01625 503128 Email: stewart.higgins@gp-n81062.nhs.uk; Heylea, Yew Tree Way, Prestbury, Macclesfield SK10 4EX Tel: 01625 829049 — MB ChB 1975 Leeds; BSc (Hons.) (Physiol.) Leeds 1972; MRCGP 1979; Cert. Family Plann. JCC 1979; DRCOG 1978; Cert. Av. Med. 1988. (Leeds) Prev: Trainee GP Gatley Health Centre Chesh.; SHO (Gen. Med.) Stepping Hill Hosp. Stockport; SHO (O & G & Paediat.) St. Mary's Hosp. Manch.

HIGGINSON, Andrew George Rothschild House Surgery, Chapel Street, Tring HP23 6PU Tel: 01442 822468 Fax: 01442 825889 — MB ChB 1966 Birm.; MRCPath 1974; FRCPath 1986. GP Tring. Prev: Cons. Path. Horton Gen. Hosp.; Cons. Path. RAF Inst. Path. & Trop. Med. Halton; Wing Cdr. RAF Med. Br.

HIGGINSON, Antony Paul 52 Station Road, Tring HP23 5NW — MB ChB 1991 Bristol.

HIGGINSON, Brian Marshall Wellington Square Medical Centre, 45 Wellington Square, Hastings TN34 1PS Tel: 01424 722866 Fax: 01424 718385; Stalkhurst Barn, Ivyhouse Lane, Three Oaks, Hastings TN35 4NN Tel: 01424 751166 Email: bmhgginson@aol.com — MB BS Lond. 1971; MRCS Eng. LRCP Lond. 1970; DObst RCOG 1975; DO Eng. 1973. (St. Mary's) Primary Care Local R&D Off. Prev: Hosp. Med. Pract. (Ophth.) Roy. E. Sussex Hosp. Hastings HA.

HIGGINSON, Mr David William Orchard Cottage, Leighton Beck Road, Beetham, Milnthorpe LA7 7AX — MB ChB 1969 Birm.; FRCS Eng. 1978; FRCS Ed. 1977. Cons. Orthop. Surg. Lancaster & Kendal.

HIGGINSON, Ian Michael Dale House, Station Road, Tring HP23 5NW — BM 1990 Soton.

HIGGINSON, Irene Julie Department Palliative Care & Policy, King's College London and St Christopher's Hospice, 51-59 Lawrie Park Road, Sydenham, London SE6 6DZ Tel: 020 8778 9252 Fax: 020 8776 9345 Email: irene.higginson@kcl.ac.uk; Department of Palliative Care & Policy, Kings College School of Medicine & Dentistry, New Medical School, Bessemer Road, Denmark Hill, London SE5 9PJ Tel: 020 7346 3995 Fax: 020 7346 3864 — MB BS 1982 Nottm.; PhD Lond. 1992; BMedSci Nottm. 1980; FFPHM RCP (UK) 1997, M 1991. (Nottm.) Prof. (Hon. Cons.) Palliat. Care & Policy King's Coll. Lond. & St. Christopher's Hospice Lond.; Life Mem. Brit. Psychosocial Oncol. Gp. Socs: Assn. Palliat. Med.; Roy. Soc. Med.; BMA. Prev: Cons. & Sen. Lect. Lond. Sch. Hyg. & Trop. Med. & KCWHCA; Cons. Palliat. Med. Islington & Bloomsbury; Sen. Med. Off. DoH Lond.

HIGGINSON, John Christopher (retired) 1 Winkworth Road, Banstead SM7 2QJ Tel: 01737 354117 — MRCS Eng. LRCP Lond. 1944; MRCPsych 1973; DPM Eng. 1972. Prev: Assoc. Specialist (Psychiat.) Banstead Hosp. Sutton.

HIGGINSON, John David Stevenson Cardiology Department, Ulster Hospital, Dundonald, Belfast BT16 1RH Tel: 02890 484511 Fax: 02890 550438 Email: david.higginson@ucht.n-i.nhs.uk; The Willows, 62 Demesne Road, Holywood BT18 9EX Tel: 02890 424374 Email: dhiggi3551@aol.com — MB BCh BAO Belf. 1974; MD Belf. 1982; FRCP Lond. 1995; MRCP (UK) 1978; FESC 1996. (Qu. Univ. Belf.) Cons. Cardiol. Ulster Hosp. Belf., Ulster Community & Hosps. Trust; Bd. of Health Promotion Agency (DHSS) N. Irel. Socs: Brit. Cardiac Soc.; (Counc. & Ex-Sec.) Irish Cardiac Soc.; Fell.Europ. Soc. of Cardiol. Prev: Sen. Regist. (Cardiol. & Med.) &

Clin. Research Fell. Roy. Vict. Hosp. Belf.; Hon. Sen. Regist. (Clin. Cardiol.) Roy. Postgrad. Med. Sch. Hammersmith Hosp. Lond.; Calvert Lect. Roy. Vict. Hosp. Belf. 1981.

HIGGINSON, Richard The Bull Ring Surgery, 5 The Bull Ring, St. John's, Worcester WR2 5AA Tel: 01905 422883 Fax: 01905 423639; Porters Mill, Ladywood, Droitwich WR9 0AN Tel: 01905 58817 — MB BS 1962 Lond. (Middlx.) Prev: Ho. Phys./ Ho. Surg. (O & G) & Cas. Off. St. And. Hosp.; Billericay.

HIGGITT, Alan Carstairs (retired) 7 Perceval Avenue, London NW3 4PY Tel: 020 7435 0370 — MB BS 1942 Lond.; FRCS Eng. 1948; MRCS Eng. LRCP Lond. 1941; DOMS Eng. 1947. Hon. Cons. Ophth. Char. Cross Hosp. Prev: Regist. (Ophth.) Univ. Coll. Hosp.

HIGGITT, Allan The Clinic, Mount Street, Ruthin LL15 1BG Tel: 01824 703633 Fax: 01824 705503 — MB BS 1973 Lond.; DRCOG 1977.

HIGGITT, Anna Catherine St Charles Hospital, Exmoor St., London W10 6DZ Tel: 020 8969 2488 Fax: 020 8962 4302 Email: 100646.3627@compuserve.com — MB BS 1975 Lond.; BSc (Psychol.) Lond. 1972, MD 1987; FRCPsych 1997, M 1981. (Univ. Coll. Hosp.) Cons. Psychiat. St. Chas. & St. Mary's Hosp. Lond.; Hon. Sen. Lect. Imperial Coll. Sc. Technol. & Med.; Sen. Policy Adviser DoH. Prev: Research Worker (Psychopharmacol.) Inst. Psychiat. Univ. Lond.; Sen. Regist. Maudsley & Kings Coll. Hosp.; Regist. Bethlem Roy. & Maudsley Hosps. Lond.

HIGGS, Andrew George North Cheshire NHS Trust, Warrington Hospital, Warrington — MB ChB 1989 Liverp.; FRCA 1995; DA (UK) 1992. Cons. in Anaesth. and Intens. Care Med. Prev: Career Regist. (Anaesth.) Mersey; Sen. Regist. in Intens. Care Med., Alfred Hosp., Melbourne, Australia.

HIGGS, Barrie Denis Royal Free Hospital, Pond St., London NW3 2QG Tel: 020 7794 0500 Email: barrie.higs@rfh.nthames.nhs.uk — MB BS 1972 Lond.; FFARCS Eng. 1977; MSc Lond. 1997. Chairm. Med. Advis. Comm.

HIGGS, Mr Brian Millards Barn, Little Missenden, Amersham HP7 0QY; Mallards Barn, Little Missenden, Amersham HP7 0QY Tel: 01494 890487 — MChir Camb. 1966, MA, MB 1960, BChir 1959; FRCS Eng. 1962; MRCS Eng. LRCP Lond. 1959. (Westm.) Cons. Surg. Wycombe & Amersham Gen. Hosps.; Surg. Tutor RCS Eng. Socs: Brit. Assn. Urol. Surgs. & Chiltern Med. Soc. Prev: Sen. Regist. St. Thos. Hosp. Lond. & St. Peter's Hosp. for Stone; Research Asst. Mayo Clinic Rochester, U.S.A.

HIGGS, Christopher Michael Barton Dorothy House Hospice, Winsley, Bradford-on-Avon BA15 2LE Tel: 01225 722988 Fax: 01225 722907; 9 Cleveland Walk, Bath BA2 6JS — MB BChir 1976 Camb.; MA Camb. 1976, MD 1987; MRCP (UK) 1978; FRCP 1997. (Westm.) Med. Dir. Dorothy Hse. Hospice. Bath; Hon. Cons. Phys. (Palliat. Med.) Roy. United Hosp. Bath. Socs: Assn. Palliat. Med.; Brit. Thorac. Soc. Prev: Sen. Regist. (Gen. & Respirat. Med.) Bath; Carey Coombes Research Fell. Bristol Roy. Infirm.; SHO (Med.) Radcliffe Infirm. Oxf.

HIGGS, David Robert 69 Healey Avenue, High Wycombe HP13 7JR — BM 1994 Soton.

HIGGS, Deborah Sian 11 Larkspur Close, Leiros Park, Rhyddings, Neath SA10 7ER — MB BS 1998 Lond.; MB BS Lond 1998.

HIGGS, Douglas Roland 205 The Slade, Headington, Oxford OX3 7HR — MB BS 1974 Lond.; MRCP (UK) 1976; MRCPath 1982. Research Fell. & Hon. Cons. Nuffield Dept. Clin. Med. Univ. Oxf.; Jun. Research Fell. Wolfson Coll. Univ. Oxf. Socs: Brit. Soc. Haemat.; Assn. Phys.

HIGGS, Elizabeth Louise 21 Bamford Way, Rochdale OL11 5NA — BM BS 1993 Nottm.

HIGGS, Eluned Rachel Tel: 01225 824991 Fax: 01225 824529 Email: eluned@ruh.bath.swest.nhs.uk; 9 Cleveland Walk, Bath BA2 6JS — BM BCh 1976 Oxf.; DM Oxf. 1995; FRCP 1998. Cons. Phys. (Diabetes, Gen. Med. & Endocrinol.) P.ss Margt. Hosp. Swindon. Socs: Diabetes UK; Assn. of Brit. Clin. Diabetologist (ABCD). Prev: Sen. Regist. (Gen. Med., Diabetes & Endocrinol.) Roy. United Hosp. Bath; Regist. (Med.) Roy. United Hosp. Bath; Cons. Phys. (Diabetes & Gen. Med.).

HIGGS, Frederick David 1 Oak Cottages, Whitewell Lane, Cranbrook TN17 2PP Tel: 01580 715734 — BM BCh 1964 Oxf.; MA Oxf. 1964; MRCP Lond. 1969; MRCS Eng. LRCP Lond. 1967; DObst RCOG 1967. (Oxf. & Guy's) Prev: Specialist Phys. Solomon Is.s Govt.; Regist. (Paediat.) S.mead Hosp. Bristol; Ho. Phys. Guy's Hosp. Lond.

HIGGS, Janet Margaret 3 Buarthau, Blackmill, Bridgend CF35 6ER Tel: 01656 842038; 13 Avon Court, Cressex Close, Binfield, Bracknell RG42 4DR Tel: 01344 429514 — MRCS Eng. LRCP Lond. 1968; MD Lond. 1983, MB BS 1968; FRCS Eng. 1977. (Guy's) Cons. Gen. Surg. P.ss of Wales Hosp. Bridgend. Prev: Sen. Regist. Rotat. (Gen. & Vasc. Surg.) Roy. Marsden & St. Bart. Hosps. Lond.

HIGGS, John Forrester Child & Family Guidance Unit, Cherry Tree Hospital, Cherry Tree Lane, Stockport SK2 7DZ Tel: 0161 419 8130 — MB ChB 1973 Liverp.; MRC Psych. 1980. Cons. (Child & Adolesc. Psychiat.) Stockport HA. Prev: Tutor (Child & Adolesc. Psychiat.) Manch. Univ.; Regist. (Psychiat.) Withington Hosp. Manch.; SHO (Paediat.) Whiston Hosp.

HIGGS, Josephine Meadowgate, Chart Lane, Brasted, Westerham TN16 1LN Tel: 01959 562507 — MB ChB 1965 Bristol; DObst RCOG 1968. (Bristol)

HIGGS, Kenneth Peter (retired) 7 Church Street, Leintwardine, Craven Arms SY7 0LD — MRCS Eng. LRCP Lond. 1945. Prev: Ho. Surg. Roy. E. Sussex Hosp.

HIGGS, Michael James Edward Bodriggy Health Centre, 60 Queens Way, Bodriggy, Hayle TR27 4PB Tel: 01736 753136 Fax: 01736 753467 — MB BS 1979 Lond.; MRCS Eng. LRCP Lond. 1980; MRCGP 1985; DCH RCP Lond. 1983; DRCOG 1982. (Guy's)

HIGGS, Professor Roger Hubert, MBE Waltnut Road Practice, 1 Manor Place, London SE17 3BD Tel: 020 7703 3988 Fax: 020 7252 4002 Email: roger.higgs@kcl.ac.uk; 81 Brixton Waterlane, London SW2 1PH Tel: 020 7338249 Fax: 020 7336580 Email: roger.higgs@kcl.ac.uk — MA Camb. 1970; MB BChir Camb. 1969; FRCP Lond. 1991; MRCP (UK) 1972; FRCGP 1987, M 1981. (Camb. & Westm.) Prof. Gen. Pract. Guys Kings & St. Thomas Sch. of Med.Kings Coll. Lond.; Chair, Edr.al Bd., Jl. Med. Ethics; Vocational Train. Course Organiser and Trainer SLOVTS, Lond. Deanery. Socs: Institue of Med. Ethics. Prev: Chairm. Project Comm. Lambeth Community Care Centre; Case Conf. Edr. Jl. Med. Ethics; Mem. Comm. Use & Restriction of Barbiturates.

HIGGS, Sarah Anne Dept. of respiratory Medicine, Bristol Royal Hospital for Sick Children, Bristol BS2 8BJ Tel: 0117 928 5494 Fax: 0117 928 5693; 13 Sherbourne Avenue, Bradley Stoke, Bristol BS32 8BB — MB BS 1982 Lond. (Roy. Free Hosp. Sch. Med. Lond.) Cystic Fibrosis Fell. Prev: Clin. Asst. (Cystic Fibrosis) Community Based Research Fell. Glos.

HIGGS, Simon John Berkeley Health Centre, Marybrook Street, Berkeley GL13 9BL Tel: 01453 810228 Fax: 01453 511778; Tintock House, Abwell, Berkeley GL13 9RN Tel: 01453 810350 — MB BS 1979 Newc.

HIGGS, Stewart Ian Llewellyn London Lane Clinic, Kinnaird House, 37 London Lane, Bromley BR1 4HB Tel: 020 8460 2661 Fax: 020 8464 5041 — MB BS 1979 Lond.; BSc (Hons.) Lond. 1976, MB BS 1979; MRCGP 1983; DRCOG 1981. (St. Thos.) SHO (O & G) St. Thos. Hosp.; SHO (Psychiat.) Warlingham Pk. Hosp.; Ho. Phys. St. Thos. Hosp. Lond.

HIGGS, William Silvan (retired) Upper Digges Place, Barham, Canterbury CT4 6HH — MRCS Eng. LRCP Lond. 1939. Prev: Sen. Med. Off. Kent AHA.

HIGH, Janet Elizabeth Park Lodge Medical Centre, 3 Old Park Road, Palmers Green, London N13 4RG Tel: 020 8886 6866 Fax: 020 8882 8884; 76 Stapleton Hall Road, London N4 4QA Tel: 020 8348 1798 — MB BS 1980 Lond.; BSc (Hons.) Lond. 1977; MRCP (UK) 1983; DRCOG 1987; DCH RCP Lond. 1985. (Roy. Free) GP Princip.; Clin. Asst. Dermat. Middlx. Hosp. Lond. WC1; Tutor on Professional Developm. to PreClin. Stud.s UCL Med. Sch. Prev: Regist. (Med.) Newham Gen. Hosp. Lond.; SHO (Med.) Lond. Hosp. Whitechapel; Ho. Phys. Roy. Free Hosp. Lond.

HIGHAM, Andrew Damian Royal Lancaster Infirmary, Ashton Rd, Lancaster LA1 4RP Tel: 01744 26316 — MB ChB 1986 Liverp.; PhD Liverpool. 1998; BSc Liverp. 1984; MRCP (UK) 1990. Cons. Phys. With Interest In Gastroenterol. Socs: BMA; Brit. Soc. Of Gastroenterol. (ord.). Prev: Clin. Lect. Univ. Manch.; MRC Train. Fell. (Gastroenterol.) Univ. Liverp.; Temporary Sen. Lect. Roy. Liverp. Univ. Hosp.

HIGHAM, Mr Anthony Upper Holme House, Holme House Lane, Rishworth, Sowerby Bridge HX6 4PY — MB ChB 1962 Manch.; FRCS Eng. 1967; FRCS Ed. 1967.

HIGHAM, Catherine Pendennis, The Green, Theydon Bois, Epping CM16 7JH — BM BS 1996 Nottm. Derby VTS GP Regist. Year 2.

HIGHAM, Helen Elizabeth Nuffield Department of Anaesthetics, John Radcliffe Hospital, Headington, Oxford OX3 9DU — MB ChB 1990 Manch.; FRCA 1997.

HIGHAM, Miss Jennifer Mary Department of Obstetric & Gynaecology, St Mary's Hospital, Paddington, London W2 1PG Tel: 020 7886 1461 Fax: 020 7886 6054; Tel: 020 7837 6160 Fax: 020 7837 6160 — MB BS 1985 Lond.; MD Lond. 1993; MRCOG 1992. Sen. Lect./Hon. Cons. St. Mary's Hosp. Lond.; Dep. Head of Div. (Testing) for Paediat., Obst. and Gyn. Socs: Fell. Roy. Soc. of Med. Counc. Mem. Sect. of Obst. & Gyn.; Brit. Menopause Soc.; Mem. of Brit. Soceity for Gyn. Endoscopy. Prev: Sen. Regist. Rotat. Luton & St. Mary's Hosp. Lond.; SHO (Obst.) Qu. Charlotte's Hosp. Lond.; Research Fell. (O & G) Roy. Free Hosp. Lond.

HIGHAM, Lesley Jean Margaret Honor (retired) 48 Holm Park, Inverness IV2 4XU Tel: 01463 222647 — MB ChB 1970 Aberd.; DCCH RCP Ed. 1987. Prev: SCMO (Child Health) Highland HB.

HIGHAM, Paul Daniel Wansbeck Hospital, Woodhorn Lane, Ashington NE63 9JJ Tel: 01670 521212 Fax: 01670 529452 — MB BS 1985 Newc.; BMedSc (1st cl. Hons.) Newc. 1984; MRCP (UK) 1988. (Univ. Newc. u. Tyne) Cons. Cardiol. Phys. Wansbeck Hosp. N.d. Socs: BMA; Brit. Cardiac Soc. Prev: Sen. Regist. (Cardiol.) S. Cleveland Hosp.; Research Fell.sh. Brit. Heart Foundat. (Acad. Cardiol.) Freeman Hosp. Newc. u. Tyne.

HIGHCOCK, Martin Philip 3 Candelan Way, High Legh, Knutsford WA16 6TP — MB BS 1990 Newc.; MRCP (UK) 1994.

HIGHET, Allan Stewart York District Hospital, Wigginton Road, York YO31 8HE Tel: 01904 453547 Fax: 01904 750734; 7 Shilton Garth Close, Old Earswick, York YO32 9SQ Tel: 01904 763154 — MB ChB 1973 Glas.; BSc (Hons.) Glas. 1969; MRCP (UK) 1976; FRCP Lond. 1993. (Glasgow) Cons. Dermat. York Dist. Hosp. Socs: Brit. Assn. Dermatol. Prev: Sen. Regist. (Dermat.) Addenbrooke's Hosp. Camb.; Regist. (Dermat.) W.. Infirm. Glas.; Regist. (Med.) W.. Infirm. Glas.

HIGHLAND, Adrian Mark 66 Bankhouse Drive, Congleton CW12 2BL Tel: 01260 274052 — MB ChB 1994 Sheff. SHO (Med.) Wythenshawe Hosp. Manch. Prev: SHO (Cardiol.) Yorks. Heart Centre; SHO (Anaesth./Emerg. Med.) P.ss Alexandra Hosp. Brisbane, Australia.

HIGHLEY, David Anthony Oamaru, The Fosse, North Curry, Taunton TA3 6LN — MB ChB 1986 Leeds.

HIGHLEY, Martin Steven 92 Keighley Road, Illingworth, Halifax HX2 8HA — MB ChB 1984 Ed.

HIGHMAN, John Hirsch (retired) 50 Middleway, London NW11 6SG Tel: 020 8458 6424 — MB BS 1952 Lond.; FRCP Lond. 1978, M 1958; MRCS Eng. LRCP Lond. 1952; FRCR 1975; FFR 1963; DMRD Eng. 1960. Prev: Cons. Radiol. St. Mary's Hosp., St. Chas. Hosp. & Wellington Hosp. Lond.

HIGHMAN, Mr Vivian Neville Vahljon, Green Lane, Stanmore HA7 3AB — MB BS 1958 Lond.; FRCS Eng. 1970; MRCS Eng. LRCP Lond. 1958; DO Eng. 1965. (Westm.) Cons. in Ophth. Stoke Mandeville Hosp. Aylesbury. Socs: Fell. Roy. Soc. Med. Prev: Sen. Regist. (Ophth.) Char. Cross Hosp. Lond.; Research Asst. Inst. Ophth. Lond.; Regist. W.. Ophth. Hosp. Lond.

HIGHMAN, Wilma Joyce (retired) 50 Middleway, London NW11 6SG Tel: 020 8458 6424 — MB ChB 1955 Cape Town; FRCPath 1978, M 1966; DCH RCP Lond. 1958. Cons. Cytol. Middlx. Hosp. Lond. Prev: Cons. Cytol. St. Peter's Hosp. & Inst. Urol. Lond.

HIGHTON, Catherine Ruth The Surgery, 52B Well Street, London E9 7PX Tel: 020 8985 2050 Fax: 020 8985 5780 — MB BS 1988 Lond.; MRCGP 1992.

HIGHTON, Clare Lower Clapton Health Centre, 36 Lower Clapton Road, London E5 0PQ; 19 Navarino Road, London E8 1AD — MB 1978 Camb.; BChir 1977; MRCP (UK) 1980; MRCGP 1982.

HIGHTON, Roberta Sibyl Janette 19 Navarino Road, London E8 1AD — MB BChir 1946 Camb.; MRCS Eng. LRCP Lond. 1946.

HIGMAN, Mr Daniel James The Old Dairy, 4 Lewis Road, Radford Semele, Leamington Spa CV31 1UB — MB BS 1986 Lond.; MS Lond. 1994; FRCS Eng. 1990. Cons. (Gen. & Vasc.) Walsgrave Hosp., Coventry. Prev: Sen. Regist. (Surg.) Char. Cross Hosp. Lond.; Regist (Surg.) St. Albans City Hosp.; Lect. (Surg.) Char. Cross. Hosp. Lond.

HIGNELL, Antony Francis, OBE (retired) Red Braes, Redcliffe Road, St Marychurch, Torquay TQ1 4QG Tel: 01803 328599 — MA Camb. 1965, BA 1949, MB BChir 1953; MRCGP 1976; FFPHM RCP (UK) 1991; MFCM RCP (UK) 1974; DPH Bristol 1965. Prev: Dir. Pub. Health Torbay HA.

HIGNELL, Stephen Patrick Carnewater Practice, Dennison Road, Bodmin PL31 2LB Tel: 01208 72321 Fax: 01208 78478; Heather Ley, 45 St Nicholas St, Bodmin PL31 1AF — MB BS 1983 Lond.; MRCGP 1987.

HIGNETT, Andrew William High Street Medical Centre, 46-48 High Street, Newhall, Swadlincote DE11 0HS Tel: 01283 217092 Fax: 01283 551 9997 — BM BS 1984 Nottm.

HIGNETT, Catriona Louise Petersfield Medical Practice, Dr Farrant & Partners, 25 Mill Road, Cambridge CB1 2AB Tel: 01223 350647 Fax: 01223 576096; 21 Arbury Road, Cambridge CB4 2JB Tel: 01223 500869 — BM BCh 1989 Oxf.; MRCGP 1994; DRCOG 1994. (Oxford) GP Princip. Camb. Prev: SHO (Palliat. Med.) Camb.; Trainee GP Camb. VTS.

HIGNETT, Linda Hazel 57 Moorgreen, Newthorpe, Nottingham NG16 2FD — MB ChB 1972 Dundee; DCH RCP Lond. 1974. GP E.wood. Socs: Assoc. Mem. Fac. Homoeop.

HIGNETT, Rachel 3 Leawood Close, Hartford, Northwich CW8 3AS Tel: 01606 76122 — MB BChir 1994 Camb.; MA (Camb.) 1995; MRCP (UK) 1996. (Cambridge) SHO (Anaesth.) Chase Farm Middlx. & Whittington Hosps. Lond. Prev: SHO (ICU) Middlx. Hosp. Lond.; SHO (Med.) Middlx. Hosp. & Whittington Hosp. Lond.; Ho. Off. (Thoracic & Gen. Surg.) Norf. & Norwich Hosp.

HIGNEY, Mark Charles 125 Manse Road, Kilsyth, Glasgow G65 0BZ — MB ChB 1993 Glas.

HIGSON, Darrall Linton Glaxo Wellcome, Wilson House, Stockley Park W., Uxbridge UB11 1BU Tel: 020 8990 9000 Fax: 020 8990 8752 Email: dlh1202@glaxowellcome.co.uk — MB ChB 1971 Liverp.; FFPM RCP (UK) 1995, M 1989; DA Eng. 1974; DObst RCOG 1973. (Liverpool) Med. Dir.Self med Dir.ate. Socs: Fac. Anaesth. RCS Eng.; Brit. Assn. Pharmaceut. Phys. Prev: SHO (Anaesth.) St. Catherine's Hosp. Birkenhead; Ho. Off. & SHO (Obst.) BRd.green Hosp. Liverp.

HIGSON, Mark 5 Bowling Court, Brighouse HD6 2RL — MB ChB 1990 Leeds.

HIGSON, Nigel Goodwood Court Surgery, 52 Cromwell Road, Hove BN3 3ER Tel: 01273 328232/206911 Fax: 01273 207235; 5 The Heights, Brighton BN1 5JX Fax: 01273 207235 — BM BCh 1981 Oxf.; MA Oxf. 1982; DRCOG 1983; Cert. Family Plann. JCC 1983. (Oxf.) Socs: GP Writers Assn. Prev: Trainee GP Avon VTS; SHO Bristol Hosps.

HIGSON, Robert Sinclair Health Services Centre, Shelley Lane, Kirkburton, Huddersfield HD8 0SJ Tel: 01484 602040 Fax: 01484 602012; Dean House Farm, White Rock Road, Stainland, Halifax HX4 9LG Tel: 01422 377387 — MB ChB 1969 Leeds.

HIGSON, Roger Heyworth The Surgery, Masham, Ripon HG4 4DZ Tel: 01765 689317 Fax: 01765 689993 Email: rhigson@aol.com; Little Orchard, Mickley, Ripon HG4 3JE Tel: 01765 635244 — MB BChir 1971 Camb.; FRCS Eng. 1976. (Cambridge) Course Organiser N.allerton VTS; Clin. Asst. BrE. Clinic Friarage Hosp. N.allerton. Prev: Research Regist. (Urol.) & Regist. (Surg.) Radcliffe Infirm. Oxf.; SHO (Surg.) Manch. Roy. Infirm.; Demonst. (Human Anat.) Univ. Oxf.

HIGSON, Ronald James Pendleside Medical Practice, Clitheroe Health Centre, Railway View Road, Clitheroe BB7 2JG Tel: 01200 422674 Fax: 01200 443652; Riversdale, Waddington Road, Clitheroe BB7 2HN Tel: 01200 444322 — MB ChB 1985 Manch.; MRCGP 1989; DRCOG 1987. (St. And. Manch.) Clin. Asst. (Dermat.) Burnley NHS Trust. Socs: Primary Care Dermatol. Soc.; Blackburn & Dist. Med. & Dent. Soc.; Clitheroe & Whalley Med. Soc. Prev: Clin. Med. Off. Bolton; SHO (Dermat.) Salford Skin Hosp.

HIGSON, Vicki Louise 65 Linksway, Gatley, Cheadle SK8 4LA — MB ChB 1997 Leeds.

HIGSON, Wendy Anne Riversdale, Waddington Road, Clitheroe BB7 2HN Tel: 01200 444322 — MB ChB 1985 Manch.; MRCGP 1989; DRCOG 1988. (St. And. & Manch.) Asst. GP Whalley Retainer Scheme. Socs: BMA.

HIGTON, Charlotte Rose 14 The Chancery, Beeston, Nottingham NG9 3AJ — MB BS 1998 Lond.; MB BS Lond 1998.

HIGTON, Mr Desmond Ian Ralph (cons. rooms), Sloane Hospital, 125-133 Albemarle Road, Beckenham BR3 5HS Tel: 020 8466 6911 Fax: 01432 273985; (cons. rooms) Chelsfield Park Hospital, Bucks Cross Road, Chelsfield, Orpington BR6 7RG Tel: 01689 877855 — MB BS 1958 Lond.; FRCS Eng. 1963; MRCS Eng. LRCP Lond. 1958. (King's Coll. Hosp.) Cons. Gen. Surg. Sloane Hosp. Beckenham & Chelsfield Pk. Hosp. Orpington; Hon. Surg. Tutor Guy's Hosp. Med. Sch. Lond.; Recognised Teach. Univ. Lond. Socs: Fell. Roy. Soc. Med.; BMA. Prev: Cons. Gen. Surg. FarnBoro., Bromley & Beckenham Hosps.; Asst. Lect. (Anat.) Univ. Coll. Lond.; Sen. Regist. (Gen. Surg.) King's Coll. Hosp. Lond. & Woolwich Hosp. Gp.

HIJAB, Ahmed Rushdi Ahmed Stanley Health Centre, Clifford Road, Stanley DH9 0XE Tel: 01207 232696, 01207 232699 Fax: 01207 239066 — MB ChB 1970 Bagdad; MRCP 1978 UK. (Bagdad) GP Stanley, Co. Durh.

HIJAZI, Mr Ibraheem Saleh Abdel-Ghani 3A Windermere Avenue, Queens Park, London NW6 6LP Tel: 020 8968 5912 Email: ibraheemh@hot.mail.com — MB BS 1991 Lond.; FRCS Ed. 1996. (St. Mary's Hosp. Med. Sch.) Specialist Regist. Trauma & Orthop. Socs: BOA; BMA; BASK.

HIJAZI, Lina 65 Holly Road, Kings Norton, Birmingham B30 3AX — BM BS 1994 Nottm.

HIKMATULLAH, Syed 73 West Way, Edgware HA8 9LA — MB BS 1957 Karachi. (Dow Med. Coll. Karachi) Prev: Ho. Surg. St. Helen's Hosp. Hastings; SHO (Anaesth.) Sutton Gen. Hosp.; Regist. (Anaesth.) Orpington Hosp.

HIKMET, Sezar Atta Yiewsley Health Centre, High St., Yiewsley, West Drayton UB7 7DP Tel: 01895 435377; Harford, 53 The Drive, Harefield Place, Uxbridge UB10 8AG Tel: 01895 253414 — MB BS 1964 Lond.; MRCS Eng. LRCP Lond. 1962. (Lond. Hosp.) Med. Off. Home Off. Prison Serv. Socs: BMA. Prev: Ho. Phys. & Ho. Surg. (Orthop.) St. Bart. Hosp. Rochester.

HILARY-JONES, Evan Peter (retired) The Old Rectory, St Andrews Major, Dinas Powys CF64 4HD — MB BChir Camb. 1952; MA Camb. 1952; MRCS Eng. LRCP Lond. 1952; FRCPsych 1984, M 1972; DPM Eng. 1965; DObst RCOG 1957. Prev: Cons. Psychogeriat. Wexham Pk. Hosp. Slough.

HILBORNE, Frank Russell 6 Thorntree Drive, Newcastle upon Tyne NE15 7AQ — MB 1957 Camb.; BChir 1956; DObst RCOG 1960. (King's Coll. Hosp.)

HILBORNE, Jo Friarage Hospital, Northallerton DL6 1JG Tel: 01609 779911; Email: jo.obsngobs@doctors.org.uk — MB BS 1988 Newc.; MRCOG 2000; BMedSc Newc. 1985. Specialist Regist. (O & G) Yorks. Rotat. Socs: Brit. Soc. for Predictive ind Adolesc. Gyn.; Brit. Soc. for Colposcepy and Conical Path. Prev: SHO (O & G) S. Cleveland Hosp. Middlesbrough; SHO (O & G) Sunderland Gen. Hosp.; asst. Police Surg. Cleveland Constab.

HILDEBRAND, Ann Elizabeth Campbell 1 Lloyd Close, Heslington, York YO10 5EU Tel: 01904 411657 — MB BCh BAO 1973 Belf.; DCH Eng. 1976. (Qu. Univ. Belf.)

HILDEBRAND, Goran Darius Magdalen College, High St., Oxford OX1 4AU — BM BCh 1997 Oxf.

HILDEBRAND, Jonathan Morris Portsmouth & South East Hampshire HA, Finchdean House, Milton Road, Portsmouth PO3 6DP; Search's End, Beacon View Road, Elstead, Godalming GU8 6DT Tel: 01252 703948 — MB BS 1984 Lond.

HILDEBRAND, Perry Johnston 54 Ottoline Drive, Troon KA10 7AW — MB BCh BAO 1976 Belf.; FFA RCSI 1980. Cons. Anaesth. CrossHo. Hosp. Kilmarnock. Prev: Sen. Regist. (Anaesth.) Roy. Vict. Hosp. Belf.; Ho. Off. Roy. Vict. Hosp. Belf.

HILDEBRAND, Sarah Christine Tile House Surgery, 33 Shenfield Road, Brentwood CM15 8AQ Tel: 01277 227711 Fax: 01277 200649 — MB BS 1984 Lond.; DRCOG 1987. (King's Coll. Hosp.) Prev: Trainee GP Brentwood VTS; SHO (Paediat.) S.end Gen. Hosp.; SHO (O & G) Rochford Gen. Hosp.

HILDICK-SMITH, Bryony Anne Hilltops Medical Centre, Kensington Drive, Great Holm, Milton Keynes MK8 9HN Tel: 01908 568446 — MB BS 1987 Lond.; DRCOG 1994.

HILDICK-SMITH, David John Ryvet 13 The Causeway, Godmanchester, Huntingdon PE29 2HA — MB BChir 1989 Camb.; MA Camb. 1990; MRCP (UK) 1993; DA (UK) 1992. Regist. (Cardiol.) Papworth Hosp. Camb.; Regist. (Cardiol.) St. Geo. Hosp. Lond. Prev: SHO (Anaesth.) Roy. Lond. Hosp.

HILDICK-SMITH, Kathleen Wendy Ryvet Orpington Hospital, Sevenoaks Road, Orpington Tel: 01689 815056; Tel: 01689 851901 — MB BS 1985 Lond.; BA Camb. 1980; MRCP (UK) 1988; FRCP (UK) 2000. Cons. Phys. (Med. for Elderly) Bromley Hosps. NHS Trust. Socs: Brit. Geriat. Soc. Prev: Sen. Regist. King's Coll. Hosp. Lond. & St. Mary's Hosp. Sidcup; Sen. Regist. & Regist. (Med. & Med. for Elderly)) St. And. Hosp. & Newham Gen. Hosp.; SHO (Med. for the Elderly) Whipps Cross Hosp. Lond.

HILDICK-SMITH, Mrs Marion, CBE (retired) 9 The Crescent, Canterbury CT2 7AQ Tel: 01227 462582 — MD 1977 Camb.; MA Camb. 1956, MD 1977, MB 1955, BChir 1954; FRCP Lond. 1979, M 1957. Cons. Geriat. Kent & Canterbury Dept. Geriat. Nunnery Fields Hosp. Canterbury; Chairm. Edit. Bd. Age & Ageing 1988. Prev: Mem. Pneumoconiosis Med. Panel.

HILDICK-SMITH, Philippa Mary Royal Alexandra Hospital, Dyke Rd, Brighton BN1 3JN Tel: 01273 328145; Amberwood, Theobalds Rd, Burgess Hill RH15 0SS Tel: 01444 235029 — MB BS 1984 Lond.; MRCP (UK) 1990; DCH RCP Lond. 1989. Con. Paed. Roy. Alexandra Hosp., Brighton. Prev: Research Regist. (Paediat. Oncol.) & Regist. (Paediat.) Soton. Gen. Hosp.; SHO (Paediat.) Gt. Ormond St. Hosp. for Sick Childr. Lond.; SHO (Neonates) St. Geo. Hosp. Lond.

HILDITCH, Hugh (retired) 16 The Drive, Oakley, Basingstoke RG23 7DA — MB ChB 1946 Manch.

HILDITCH, Julie Southlea Surgery, 276 Lower Farnham, Aldershot GU11 3RB Tel: 01252 344868 Fax: 01252 342596; The Hollies, 72 Frogmore Road, Frogmore, Camberley GU17 0DF Tel: 01252 875215 Fax: 01252 664072 Email: davidhearn@compuserve.com — MB ChB 1980 Liverp.; MRCGP 1984; DRCOG 1983. (Liverpool) GP.

HILDITCH, Richard James 200 Daniells, Panshanger, Welwyn Garden City AL7 1QQ — MB ChB 1998 Sheff.; MB ChB Sheff 1998.

HILDITCH, William Graeme anaesthetic Dept Western infirmary, Dumbarton Road, Glasgow G11 6NT Tel: 0141 211 2069 Fax: 0141 211 1806 Email: wghilditch@yahoo.com — MB ChB 1993 Glas.; FRCA 1995. (Glasgow) Anaesth. Specialist Regist.

HILDORE, Lisa Margaret Posterngate Surgery, Portholme Road, Selby YO8 4QH Tel: 01757 700561 Fax: 01757 213295 — MB BS 1994 Newc.; DRCOG 1997. (Newcastle upon Tyne) GP Selby.

HILDRETH, Kathryn Anne 28 Grosvenor Drive, Whitley Bay NE26 2JS — MB BCh 1994 Wales.

HILDRETH, Victoria Anne The Moat House Surgery, Worsted Green, Merstham, Redhill RH1 3PN Tel: 01737 642207 Fax: 01737 642209 — BM BS 1983 Nottm.; MRCGP 1988. p/t GP Moat Hse. Surg. Merstham.

HILDREY, Andrew Charles Collingwood Freshwell Health Centre, Wethersfield Road, Finchingfield, Braintree CM7 4BQ Tel: 01371 810328 Fax: 01371 811282; Brook House, Great Bardfield, Braintree CM7 4RQ Fax: 01371 810904 — MB BS 1975 Lond. (Lond. Hosp.) Hosp. Pract. St. Michael's Hosp. Braintree; Police Surg. Essex Police; Div. Surg. St. John's Ambul. Socs: Fell. Roy. Soc. Med.; Mid Essex Doctor Immediate Care Scheme. Prev: Regist. (Med.) Chelmsford Health Dist.; SHO Div. Med. Lond. Hosp.

HILDYARD, Christine Louise 18 Chesterton Court, Benton Park, Horbury, Wakefield WF4 5QU — MB ChB 1993 Leeds.

HILDYARD, Kym Jane 241 Queens Road, Beeston, Nottingham NG9 2BB — BM BS 1991 Nottm.

HILES, Anita (Surgery) 467 Lytham Road, Blackpool FY4 1JH Tel: 01253 45086; 4 Headroomgate Road, Lytham St Annes FY8 3BD — MB BS 1963 Lond.

HILES, Richard Joseph Lambert Medical Centre, 2 Chapel Street, Thirsk YO7 1LU Tel: 01845 523157 Fax: 01845 524508; Brook House, 8 Ingram Gate, Thirsk YO7 1DD Tel: 01845 523882 — MB ChB 1984 Birm.; DRCOG 1989.

HILES, Mr Ronald William Up Yonder, Bury Hill, Hambrook, Bristol BS16 1SS Tel: 01179 560061 Fax: 01179 568763 — MB ChB Bristol 1957; FRCS Eng. 1966; FRCS Ed. 1965. p/t Indep. Cons. Plastic Reconstruc. & Hand Surg. Bristol. Socs: (Ex-Pres.) Brit. Assn. Plastic Surgs.; (Ex-Pres.) Brit. Soc. for Surg. Hand. Prev: Cons. Plastic Surg. Frenchay Hosp. Bristol & S. W.. RHB; Regist. (Surg.) Plymouth Gen. Hosp.; Med. Off. RAF.

HILEY, Anna Louise 241 Clarendon Park Road, Leicester LE2 3AN — MB ChB 1998 Leic.; MB ChB Leic 1998.

HILEY, Charles Arthur St Clair, Surg. Cdr. RN Retd. Collingtree Park Nursing Home, 110 Windingbrook Lane, Northampton NN4 0XN Tel: 01604 763623 — MRCS Eng. LRCP Lond. 1937. (Lond. Hosp.) Prev: Ho. Phys. & Ho. Surg. Lond. Hosp.

HILEY, Christopher David Ledbury Market Surgery, Market Street, Ledbury HR8 2AQ Tel: 01531 632423 Fax: 01531 631560 — MB BS 1987 Lond.; MRCGP 1993; DRCOG 1994; DCH RCP Lond. 1993. (Lond. Hosp. Med. Coll.)

HILEY, David Anthony Medical Advisory Service, Government Buildings, Gabalfa, Cardiff CF14 4YJ Tel: 029 2058 6753 — MB BCh 1966 Wales; DObst RCOG 1968. Med. Advisor.

HILEY, Debra Karen 131 Lavernock Road, Penarth CF64 3QG; 10 Biddulph Way, Ledbury HR8 2HN Tel: 01531 634873 — MB ChB 1992 Birm.; DRCOG 1996; DFP/Fplet 1996. GP Retainer.

HILEY, Dennis The Surgery, 45 Main St., Willerby, Hull HU10 6BP Tel: 01482 652652; 54 Tranby Lane, Anlay, Hull HU10 7DU Tel: 01482 652652 — MB BS 1958 Lond. (Lond. Hosp.)

HILEY, Neville Arthur (retired) 6 St Johns Close, Goring-by-Sea, Worthing BN12 4HX — MB BS Lond. 1952; MRCS Eng. LRCP Lond. 1952; DObst RCOG 1958. Prev: Obst. Ho. Surg. St. Luke's Hosp. Guildford.

HILEY, Paul Eugene 42 Melbourne Crescent, Stafford ST16 3SU Email: philey@compuserve.com — MB BS 1994 Lond. (Char. Cross & Westm.) Specialist Regist. Hist. W. Mids. Region. Rotat.

HILEY, Sharon Marie 42 Melbourne Crescent, Stafford ST16 3JU Tel: 01785 254777 Fax: 01785 254777 Email: 106075.1403@compuserve.com — MB BS 1994 Lond.; DCH RCP 1997; DRCOG- RCOG 1998. (Char. Cross & Westm. Med. Sch.) GP Asst. Burton on Trent.

HILL, Adam Charles 20 Harrisons Green, Edgbaston, Birmingham B15 3LH Tel: 0121 454 5682 — MB BS 1983 Lond.; FRCA 1991. Sen. Regist. (Anaesth.) Birm. Sch. Anaesth. Socs: BMA. Prev: Vis. Prof. Anesthesiol. Duke Univ. Med. Center Durh., NC, USA.

HILL, Adam Theo 21 Briar Close, Lickey End, Bromsgrove B60 1GE — MB ChB 1991 Glas.; MRCP (UK) 1994. Regist. (Chest Med.) Qu. Eliz. Hosp. Birm. Prev: SHO Rotat. (Med.) Vict. Infirm. NHS Trust Glas.

HILL, Professor Adrian Vivian Sinton Nuffield Department Medicine, John Radcliffe Hospital, Oxford OX3 9DU Tel: 01865 222301 Fax: 01865 222502; 20 St. Andrew's Road, Oxford OX3 9DL — BM BCh 1982 Oxf.; DPhil Oxf. 1986; DM Oxf. 1993; MRCP (UK) 1987; Fmed Sci 1999; FRCP 1999 (UK). Wellcome Princip. Research Fell. Univ. Oxf.; Prof. Human Genetics Univ. Oxf. 1996. Socs: Assn. Phys. Prev: Wellcome Sen. Research Fell. (Clin. Sci.) Inst. Molecular Med. Univ. Oxf.; Staines Med. Research Fell. Exeter Coll. Oxf.; MRC Train. Fell. Nuffield Dept. Med. Univ. Oxf.

HILL, Agnes Elizabeth 29 Malone Heights, Belfast BT9 5PG — MB ChB 1977 Bristol; MRCP (UK) 1980; DRCOG 1979. Cons. (Paediat.) E. Health & Social Servs. Bd.

HILL, Alan George Seymour, MC (retired) Coille Dharaich, Kilmelford, Oban PA34 4XD Tel: 01852 200285 — MB ChB 1939 Ed.; FRCP Lond. 1971, M 1966; FRCP Ed. 1953, M 1947. Prev: Cons. Phys. Rheum. Dis. Research Centre Stoke Mandeville Hosp. Aylesbury.

HILL, Alan Murray Moore Avenue Surgery, 7 Moore Avenue, South Shields NE34 6AA Tel: 0191 454 5380 Fax: 0191 427 9589 — MB BS 1970 Newc.; DA Eng. 1974; DCH RCPS Glas. 1973; DObst RCOG 1972. Dep. Med. Dir. (Palliat. Care) St. Clare's Hospice Jarrow. Prev: GP S. Shields; SHO (Anaesth.) Dryburn Hosp. Durh.; SHO (Paediat.) Sunderland Childr. Hosp.

HILL, Alison (retired) 4 The Dene, Canterbury CT1 3NW — MB BChir 1979 Camb.; MA Camb. 1980, MB BChir 1979; MRCGP 1983; DRCOG 1983. Prev: GP Shipston on Stour.

HILL, Alison Ann Llwynpatris, Bancffosfelen, Pontyberem, Llanelli SA15 5QR — MB ChB 1992 Leeds.

HILL, Alison Mary Olive 52 Merrick Avenue, Troon KA10 7BH — MB ChB 1993 Glas.

HILL, Alison Maynard Buckinghamshire Health Authority, Verney House, Gatehouse Road, Aylesbury HP19 8ET Tel: 01296 310000 Fax: 01296 318649 Email: alisonhill@cix.compulink.co.uk; 12 Apsley Road, Oxford OX2 7QY Tel: 01865 310350 Fax: 01865 310350 Email: alison.hill@dphpc.ox.ac.uk — MB ChB 1975 Bristol; MRCP (UK) 1977; MFPHM 1988; FRCP (UK) 1998; FFPHM (UK) 1996. Dir.Pub.Health.Resource.Unit.Instit.Health.Sci.s.Oxf. Prev: Cons. Pub. Health Med. Milton Keynes; Dir. Pub. Health Bucks. HA.; Med. Supt. All St.s Hosp. Transkei.

HILL, Alison Paice King's Fund, 11-13 Cavendish Square, London WC1 0AN Tel: 020 7307 2596 Fax: 020 7307 2810 Email: ahill@kenf.org.uk; 7 Alexandra Road, Reading RG1 5PE Tel: 01189 660047 — MB BS 1971 Lond.; BSc Lond. 1968; MRCP (UK) 1973; MRCS Eng. LRCP Lond. 1971; FRCGP 1997, M 1978; Msc Brunel 1998. (Guy's) Progr. Dir. Effective Pract. Kings Fund Lond. Prev: Sen. Lect. Dept Gen. Pract. & Primary Care, St. Bart. & Roy. Lond. Sch. Med. & Dent. Qu. Mary & W.field Coll.; 1994-96 Med. Advisor & Dep. Dir. of Primary Care (Provider Developm.) Ealing, Hammersmith & Hounslow Health Agency; Princip., Clin. Teach. & Clin. Dir. Dept. Primary Med. Care Univ. Soton.

HILL, Andrew Dereck 60 Tanners Street, Ramsbottom, Bury BL0 9ES — MB ChB 1994 Manch.

HILL, Andrew Stuart Benchill Medical Centre, 127 Woodhouse Lane, Wythenshawe, Manchester M22 9WP Tel: 0161 998 4305 Fax: 0161 945 4028 — MB ChB 1974 Manch.; MRCGP 1981.

HILL, Andrew William Botley Health Care Centre, Mortimer Road, Botley, Southampton SO32 2UG Tel: 01489 783422 Fax: 01489 781919; 38 Thistle Road, Hedge End SO30 0TT Tel: 01489 795736 — MB BChir 1976 Camb.; MA Camb. 1975; MRCGP 1982; DRCOG 1977. Prev: GP Lond.; Trainee GP/SHO Lond. Hosp. VTS; SHO (Anaesth.) Lond. Hosp. Whitechapel.

HILL, Ann Jacquelin (retired) Westgate Surgery, Dursley GL11 4AE Tel: 01453 542277 — MB BS 1959 Lond.; MRCS Eng. LRCP Long. 1959; DObst RCOG 1963.

HILL, Anne Shirley (retired) Goody Bridge House, Grasmere, Ambleside LA22 9QR — MB BChir 1958 Camb.; MA Camb. 1959; FRCP Ed. 1982, M 1963; FRCPath 1979, M 1967; FRCOG 1975, M 1962, DObst 1960. Prev: Cons. Path. Jessop Hosp. Sheff.

HILL, Anthony South Humber Health Authority, Wrawby Road, Brigg DN20 8GS Tel: 01652 601130 Fax: 01652 601160; 7 Caistar Lane, Tealby, Market Rasen LN8 3XN — MB ChB 1980 Dundee; MFPHM RCP Lond. 1989; MPH Dundee 1987; FFPHM RCP (UK) 1996; MFCM 1987; T(PHM) 1991. Dir. (Pub. Health) S. Humber HA; Hon. Sen. Lect. Postgrad. Med. Sch. Univ. Hull. Prev: Cons. Pub. Health Med. & Communicable Dis. Control Som. HA; Sen. Regist. Community Med. Tayside HB; Ho. Off. Profess. Surg. Unit Ninewells Hosp. Dundee.

HILL, Anthony Fenton 4J Portman Mansions, Chiltern St., London W1U 6NS Tel: 020 7935 3866 Fax: 020 7486 7258; Little Pittance, Smithwood Common, Cranleigh GU6 8QY Tel: 01483 272818 — MB BS 1952 Lond.; MRCS Eng. LRCP Lond. 1952; LMCC 1958. (St. Bart.) Med. Off. (Gastroenterol. & Food Intolerance) Chelsea & W.m. Hosp. Lond. Socs: Brit. Soc. Gastroenterol.; Med. Soc. Lond. Prev: Med. Resid. Hackensack Hosp. New Jersey, USA; Ho. Phys. German Hosp. Lond.; Ho. Phys. Seamen's Hosp. Greenwich.

HILL, Aubrey Norton 15 High Street, Holt NR25 6BN Tel: 01263 713974; 8 South Street, Sheringham NR26 8LL Tel: 01263 829805 Email: aubrey@aubcarforce9.com — LMSSA Lond. 1952. (St. Bart.)

HILL, Bede Martyn Department of Histopathology, New East Surrey Hospital, Canada Avenue, Redhill RH1 5RH Tel: 01737 768511 Fax: 01737 780396; 7 Redwood Mount, Reigate RH2 9NB Tel: 01737 247694 — MB BCh 1968 Wales; FRCPath 1991, M 1979. Cons. Histopath. E. Surrey Co. Hosp. Redhill.

HILL, Bernard Jonathan Bronllys hospital, Bronllys, Brecon LD3 0LS Tel: 01874 711661 Fax: 01874 712045 — MB BS 1981 Lond.; MRCPsych 1990. Cons. Psychiat. Mid Wales Hosp. Talgarth. Prev: Sen. Regist. St. Geo. Hosp. Lond.; Regist. WhitCh. Hosp. Cardiff; Regist. Mid Wales Hosp. Talgarth.

HILL, Brian (retired) 479 High Road, London E10 5EL — MB BCh BAO 1945 NUI; DPH Eng. 1955. Prev: Asst. Med. Off. Tate & Lyle Ltd. & Co-op. Flour Mills Silvertown.

HILL, Brian Andrew Orchard Croft Medical Centre, 2A Westfield Road, Horbury, Wakefield WF4 6LL Tel: 01924 271016 Fax: 01924 279459; 12 Kings Close, Ossett WF5 8QU Tel: 01924 270697 — MB ChB 1975 Leeds; MRCGP 1984.

HILL, Brian David Glenwood, Torton Lane, Hartlebury, Kidderminster DY10 4HX; 74 Grange Road, Dudley DY1 2A Tel: 01384 52729 — MB ChB 1960 Birm. (Birm.)

HILL, Brian William (retired) 23 Grange Park, Frenchay, Bristol BS16 2SZ Tel: 0117 956 8427 — MB ChB Bristol 1951, MRCS Eng. LRCP Lond. 1951; MRCGP 1962. Prev: Clin. Asst. in Dermat. Cossham Memor. Hosp.

HILL, Camilla Ann Louise Cutford House, Holyoakes Lane, Redditch B97 5SR — MB ChB 1990 Birm.; ChB Birm. 1990; DFFP 1994; DRCOG 1994.

HILL, Catherine 13 Yew Tree Avenue, Sheffield S25 4EW — MB ChB 1995 Leeds.

HILL, Catherine Mary 6 Glen Eyre Close, Bassett, Southampton SO16 3GB — BM 1987 Soton.; MRCP Paediat. (UK) 1992.

HILL, Charles Andrew MacKenzie The St Lawrence Surgery, 79 St. Lanewrence Avenue, Worthing BN14 7JL Tel: 01903 237346 — MB BS 1975 Lond.; MRCGP 1979; DRCOG 1977.

HILL, Charles Anthony (retired) Oakwood, Pelling Hill, Old Windsor, Windsor SL4 2LL Tel: 01753 865248 — MB BS 1963 Lond.; DObst RCOG 1965. Prev: GP Windsor.

HILL, Christina Margaret 31 Trelawney Road, Bristol BS6 6DY — BM 1987 Soton.

HILL, Christine Oakley Health Centre, Wardlaw Way, Oakley, Dunfermline KY12 9QH; Craigengar, Low Causeway, Culross, Dunfermline KY12 8HL — MB ChB 1986 Dundee; MRCGP 1990. Prev: Trainee GP Dundee VTS; SHO (Gen. Med., Psychiat. & O & G) Dundee.

HILL, Christine Margaret 12 Sutherland Close, Chipping Barnet, Barnet EN5 2JL Tel: 0 444818 — MB ChB 1978 Cape Town.

HILL, Christopher 36 Ballyholme Road, Bangor BT20 5JS Tel: 01247 473226 Fax: 01247 473226 Email: cmjhill@msu.com — MB BCh BAO 1991 Belf.

HILL, Claire Margaret 33 Waterloo Park N., Belfast BT15 5HW — MD 1977 Belf.; MB BCh BAO Belf. 1968; FRCPI 1985, M 1972; FRCPath 1992, M 1980. Sen. Lect. & Cons. Path. Qu.'s Univ. & Roy. Vict. Hosp. Belf. Socs: Renal Assn. & Path. Soc. Prev: Sen. Regist. (Histopath.) Roy. Vict. Hosp. Belf.; Research Fell. Roy. Vict. Hosp. Belf.; Regist. Renal Unit Belf. City Hosp.

***HILL, Clare Jessica** Merebrook Farm, Woodhouse Lane, Audlem, Crewe CW3 0DT — MB ChB 1996 Birm.

HILL, David Andrew 9 Kingscote Hill, Gossops Green, Crawley RH11 8PY — MB BS 1988 Lond.

HILL, David Arthur Department of Anaesthetics, Ulster Hospital, Dundonald, Belfast BT16 1RH Tel: 01232 484511 — MB BCh BAO 1986 Belf.; MD Belf. 1994; FFA RCSI 1992. (Qu. Univ. Belf.) Cons. Anaesth. & Pain Managem. Ulster Hosp. Belf.

HILL, David Hilary Department of Radiology, Antrim Hospital, 45 Bush Road, Antrim BT41; 19 Piney Lane, Belfast BT9 5QS — MB BCh BAO 1982 Belf.; FRCR 1989. Cons. Radiol. Antrim Hosp. Prev: Sen. Regist. (Radiol.) Roy. Vict. Hosp. Belf.

HILL, David Jesse Anaesthetic Department, Addenbrooke's Hospital, Hills Road, Cambridge CB2 2QQ Tel: 01223 245151 Fax: 01223 217223; The Old Post House, Eltisley, Huntingdon PE19 4TG Tel: 01480 880267 Fax: 01480 880267 — MB BS 1959 Lond.; MA Camb. 1977; FFA RCS Eng. 1966; DObst RCOG 1962; DA Eng. 1961. (Westm.) Hon.Cons. Anaesth. Addenbrooke's Hosp. Camb.; Clin. Lect. Univ. Camb. Med. Sch.; Vis. Cons. W.. Regional Hosp. Pokhara Nepal. Socs: Fell. Roy. Soc. Med.; FRCA; Assn. of Anaesth.s. Prev: Sen. Regist. (Anaesth.) King's Coll. Hosp. Lond.; Instruc. Dept. Anaesth. Univ. Washington, Seattle, USA; Regist. (Anaesth.) W.m. Hosp. & Roy. Marsden Hosp. Lond.

HILL, David John 5 Windsor Place, Stirling FK8 2HY — MB ChB 1998 Glas.; MB ChB Glas 1998.

HILL, David Jonathan The Health Centre, 10 Gresham Road, Oxted RH8 0BQ Tel: 01883 832850 Fax: 01883 832851 — MB BS 1985 Lond.; MRCGP 1991; DRCOG Lond. 1990. (King's Coll. Hosp. Med. Sch. Lond.) Clin. Asst., Dermat. Dept., E. Surrey Hosp., Redhill.

HILL, David McLeod Woodside, Barnetts Wood Lane, Bighton, Alresford SO24 9SF — MB ChB 1979 Dundee; BSc (Hons.) Surrey 1975. Vice-Pres. Matrix Pharmaceut. Ltd. Socs: Fac. Pharmaceut. Med. Prev: Managing Dir. Medeva Research Ltd Lond.; Med. Dir. Key Pharmaceut. (UK) Co.; Med. Advisor Sterling Winthrop Gp. Guildford.

HILL, David Mortimer Tel: 01386 553659 — BM BCh 1960 Oxf.; MA, BM BCh Oxf. 1960; FRCP Lond. 1977, M 1963. (Oxf. & Univ. Coll. Hosp.) Socs: BMA; (Ex-Hon. Sec.) BDA (Med. & Scientif. Sect.). Prev: Cons. Phys. Worcester Roy. Infirm.; Lect. (Med.) King's Coll. Hosp. Med. Sch.; Ho. Phys. Univ. Coll. Hosp. & Hammersmith Hosp.

HILL, David Rowland (retired) Hawthorns, 1 Studley Road, Ripon HG4 2BZ — MB BS 1956 Lond.

HILL, Mr David Spencer 151 Highgate Road, Kentish Town, London NW5 1LJ — MB BS 1987 Lond.; PhD CNAA 1992; FRCS Eng. 1995. Regist. (ENT) Univ. Coll. Lond. Hosp. Prev: SHO (ENT) Lewisham Dist. Hosp.; Med. Researcher Luding Inst. Cancer Research Lond.

HILL, Professor David William (retired) 28 Meadway, London NW11 7AY Tel: 020 8455 9617 — MB BS 1948 Lond.; FRCS Eng. 1959; FRCOphth. 1989; DO Eng. 1954. Hon. Cons. Ophth. Moorfields Eye Hosp. Prev: Research Prof. Ophth. RCS Eng. & Cons. Ophth. Moorfields Eye Hosp.

HILL, Debra Ruth Miriam Medical Centre, Laird Street, Birkenhead CH41 7AL Tel: 0151 652 6077 — MB ChB 1986 Sheff.

HILL, Denys Blethyn (retired) Woodlands, 38 Fakenham Road, Drayton, Norwich NR8 6PT Tel: 01603 867451 — MB BChir 1957 Camb.; MA Camb. 1957; MRCS Eng. LRCP Lond. 1956; MFCM 1972; DPH Eng. 1960. Prev: Cons. Pub. Health Med. Norwich HA.

HILL, Derek Aldwyn (retired) 280 Tubbenden Lane S., Farnborough, Orpington BR6 7DN Tel: 01689 858074 — MB BS Lond. 1953. Prev: Ho. Surg. & Ho. Phys. Whipps Cross Hosp. Leytonstone.

HILL, Derek Oscar (retired) 26 Guildford Drive, Chandlers Ford, Eastleigh SO53 3PT Tel: 023 8026 6536 — MB BS 1956 Lond.; FFA RCS Eng. 1970; DA Eng. 1965. Prev: Cons. Palliat. Med. St. Catherines Hospice Crawley.

HILL, Dorothy Ann (retired) 12 Brooklands Court, Brooklands Avenue, Cambridge CB2 2BP — MB BS 1953 Lond.; MRCS Eng. LRCP Lond. 1953; FFA RCS Eng. 1959. Prev: Sen. Anaesth. New Eng. Baptist Hosp. Boston, USA.

HILL, Edwin Benjamin Bernays & Whitehouse, 3 Grove Surgery, Solihull B91 2PG Tel: 0121 705 1105 Fax: 0121 711 4098; Grasmere, 222 Blossomfield Road, Solihull B91 1NT — MB ChB 1966 Birm.; BSc (Physiol.) Birm. 1962, MB ChB 1966; MRCGP 1974; MFFP 1993; DObst RCOG 1968. (Birm.) Med. Off. Marie Curie Foundat. Lond.; Cons. Palliat. Med. Pk.way & Priory Hosps.; Dep. Chairm. Solihull FHSA.

HILL, Edwin William 125 Barlaston Old Road, Trentham, Stoke-on-Trent ST4 8HJ Tel: 01782 643111 — MB 1969 Camb.; BChir 1968; FRCP Lond. 1989, MRCP (UK) 1974; DCH Eng. 1971; DObst RCOG 1970. (Univ. Coll. Hosp.) Cons. (Paediat.) N. Staffs. Hosp. Centre Stoke-on-Trent.

HILL, Eileen Elise (retired) Conygree, Wightfield Manor, Apperley, Gloucester GL19 4DP Tel: 01452 780870 — MD Glas. 1960, MB ChB (Commend.) 1950; FRCP Lond. 1973, M 1954; DCH Eng. 1956. Prev: Cons. Paediat. E. Birm. Dist. & Solihull Dist.

HILL, Elaine Louise 44 Leyson Road, The Reddings, Cheltenham GL51 6RX — MB ChB 1990 Liverp.

HILL, Elizabeth Austin Burnetts, Ticehurst, Wadhurst TN5 7HA — MB ChB 1979 Glas.

HILL, Elizabeth Bryce (retired) Wenden Place Cottage, Wendens Ambo, Saffron Walden CB11 4JX — MB ChB 1932 Glas.

HILL, Frank George Henry Department of Haematology, NHS Trust, Steelhouse Lane, Birmingham B4 6 Tel: 0121 333 9852 Fax: 0121 333 9841 Email: frank.hill@bhamchildren.worlds.nhs.uk — MB ChB 1967 Bristol; FRCPath 1987, M 1975; FRCPCH 1997. Cons. Haemat. Childr. Hosp. Birm.; Hon. Sen. Lect. Univ. Birm. Socs: Mem. BMA; Mem. Internat. Soc. Haomostasis & Thrombosis; BSM. Prev: Cons. Haemat. Qu. Eliz. Hosp. Birm.; Lect. (Haemat.) Inst. Child Health; Hon. Sen. Regist. Hosp. Sick Childr. Gt. Ormond St. Lond.

HILL, Gareth Nicholas 73B Gilbey Road, London SW17 0QH — MB BS 1998 Lond.; MB BS Lond 1998.

HILL, Gavin Macdonald Doncaster Royal Infirmary, Armthorpe Road, Doncaster DN2 5LT Tel: 01302 366666 Fax: 01302 320098; 39 Highfield Rise, Sheffield S6 6BS Tel: 0114 233 6669 — MB ChB 1995 Sheff. SHO (Gen. Med.) Doncaster Roy. Infirm.

HILL, Geoffrey William Roebuck Sinclair Pharmaceuticals Ltd, Borough Road, Godalming GU7 2AB Tel: 01483 426644; Longcroft, Pardown, Basingstoke RG23 7DY — MB ChB 1963 Manch.; FFPM RCP (UK) 1989. COO Sinclair Pharmaceut. Ltd. Socs: Fell. Roy. Soc. Med. Prev: Exec. Vice Pres. Cortecs plc.

HILL, Georgina Drumearl, 12 Glenkeen Avenue, Jordanstown, Newtownabbey BT37 0PH — MB BCh BAO 1939 Belf.; DPH Belf. 1941.

HILL, Glenda Mai Dermatology Department, Wrexham Maelor Hospital, Croesewewydd Road, Wrexham LL13 7TD Tel: 01978 291100 Fax: 01978 310326; Trem Berwyn, Garth Road, Garth, Llangollen LL20 7UR — MB ChB 1989 Liverp.; BSc Liverp. 1986; MRCGP 1993; Dip. Pract. Dermat. (Distinc.) Wales 1994; DRCOG 1992; DCH RCP Lond. 1992. (University of Liverpool) Staff Grade, Dermat. Socs: BMA; Assoc. Mem. of Bristol Assoc. of Dermatol.s. Prev: GP Princip.; Trainee GP/Sen. Health Off. (Gen. Med.) Wrexham Maelor Hosps. VTS; Hon. Off. (Med. & Surg.) Glan. Clwyd Hosp. Bodelwyddan.

HILL, Godfrey Garth (retired) 20 Bridgewater Road, Berkhamsted HP4 1HN Tel: 01442 862557 — MB BS 1953 Lond.; MRCS Eng. LRCP Lond. 1953; DObst RCOG 1957. Prev: Sen. Under Sec. Med. Defence Union.

HILL, Mr Graham Allen, Surg. Lt.-Cdr. RN 57A Oreston Road, Plymouth PL9 7JU Tel: 01752 480187 Email: graham@allenhill.freeserve.co.uk — MB ChB 1985 Manch.; FRCS Eng. 1992; FRCS 1999. (Univ. Manch.) Fell. at Melbourne Orthop. Gp. - Melbourne. Socs: Brit. Elbow & Shoulder Soc.; Girdlestone Soc. Oxf. Prev: Secialist Regist. (Orthop.) Nuffield Orthop. Centre, Oxf.; Specialist Regist. (Orthop.) John Rudcliffe Infirm. Oxf.; Regist. (Orthop.) P.ss Eliz. Orthop. Hosp. & Derriford Hosp. Plymouth.

HILL, Hannah Erica (retired) Whitestaunton, 7 Coleraine Road, Portrush BT56 8EA Tel: 01265 822242 — MB BCh BAO Dub. 1942.

HILL, Harry Fraser Bramhall Health Centre, 66 Bramhall Lane South, Bramhall, Stockport SK7 2DY Tel: 0161 439 8213 Fax: 0161 439 6398 Email: h.hill@which.net — MB ChB 1975 Manchester; BSc 1972 (Hons.Pharmacology) Manchester.

HILL, Helen Jane 7 Will Hall Close, Alton GU34 1QP — MB BS 1991 Lond.

HILL, Helen Sutherland (retired) Raymond Priestley House, 114 Bronford Lane, Erdington, Birmingham B24 8BZ — MB ChB 1924 Liverp.; MB ChB Liverp. (Hnrs.) 1924, DPH 1927. Med. Off. City of Birm. Prev: Med. Off. Matern. & Child Welf. Birm. & Lidcoln.

HILL, Henrietta Mary Anaesthetic Department, Luton & Dunstable Hospital, Dunstable Road, Luton LU4 0DZ Tel: 01582 491122 — MB BS 1980 Lond.; FFA RCS Eng. 1984. Cons. Anaesth. Luton & Dunstable Hosp.

HILL, Hilary Frances Hoyte (retired) Coille Dharaich, Kilmelford, Oban PA34 4XD Tel: 01852 200285 — MB ChB 1945 Ed.; MB ChB (Hons.) Ed. 1945; FRCP Ed. 1969, M 1948. Prev: Research Assoc. Rheum. Dept. Stoke Mandeville Hosp.

HILL, Ian Anderson (retired) Pullens, Burghfield Common, Reading RG7 3DR Tel: 01189 832626 — BM BCh 1952 Oxf.; DObst RCOG 1956. Prev: Ho. Phys. (Gen. Med. & Dermat.) Mt. Vernon Hosp. N.wood.

HILL, Mr Ian Macdonald (retired) Bracken Wood, Church Lane, Fernham, Faringdon SN7 7PB Tel: 01367 820475 — MB BS 1942 Lond.; MB BS (Hons., Distic. Path., Therap. & Applied Pharm.) Lond. 1942; MS Lond. 1945; FRCS Eng. 1944; MRCS Eng. LRCP Lond. 1942. Prev: Cons. Cardiothoracic Surg. St. Bart. Lond.

HILL, Ian Rowland, OBE Department of Aviation Pathology, RAF Centre of Avition Medicine, Henlow S916 6DN Tel: 01462 851515 Ext: 7733; Wesley House, Church Rd, Grafham, Huntingdon PE28 0BB — MB BChir 1972 Camb.; PhD Lond. 1989; MA Camb. 1972, BA (Med. Sc. Trip.) 1968, MD 1984; FRCPath 1995; LDS Sheff. Eng. 1963; MRAeS 1991. (Cambridge) Cons. Pathologist; Home Office Pathologist. Socs: Fell. Roy. Soc. Med.; Brit. Acad. Forens. Sci.; Brit. Assn. Forens. Med. Prev: Path. (Aviat. Path.) Inst. Path. RAF Halton; Pres. Internat. Organisation for Forens. Odontostomatol.; Ho. Surg. (Orthop. Rheum. & Gen. Surg.) King's Coll. Hosp.

HILL, Jacqueline Charlotte c/o 3 Doran Grove, London SE18 2LE — MB ChB 1990 Glas. SHO (Gyn.) St. Bart. Hosp. Lond. Prev: SHO (O & G & Paediat.) Newham Gen. Hosp. Lond.; SHO (A & E) Worthing Hosp.; Ho. Off. (Med. & Surg.) S.. Gen. Hosp. & Glas. Infirm.

HILL, Mr James Department of General & Colorectal Surgery, Manchester Royal Infirmary, Oxford Road, Manchester M13 9WL Tel: 0161 276 4286 Fax: 0161 276 4530; 34 Barlow Moor Road, Didsbury, Manchester M20 2GJ Tel: 0161 434 4055 — MB ChB 1984 Bristol; ChM Bristol 1992; FRCS Eng. 1988. (Bristol) Cons. Surg. (Gen. & Colorectal Surg.) Manch. Roy. Infirm. Socs: Assn. Coloproctol.; Amer. Soc. Colon & Rectal Surgs.; Roy. Soc. Med. Prev: Research Fell. Brigham & Wom.s Hosp. & Harvard Univ.

HILL, James David Plymouth Road Health Centre, Plymouth Road, South Brent TQ10 9HT Tel: 01364 72394 Fax: 01364 72922 — MB ChB 1979 Bristol. (Bristol)

HILL, James David Queens Hospital, Belvedere Road, Burton-on-Trent DE13 0RB Tel: 01283 566333; Yew Trees, 16 Main St, Egginton, Derby DE65 6HL — MB BS 1970 Lond.; DM Nottm. 1980; FRCP Lond. 1988; MRCS Eng. LRCP Lond. 1970. (Westm.) Cons. Phys. Burton-on-Trent. Prev: Sen. Regist. (Med.) Leeds AHA (T); Lect. (Med.) Nottm. Univ.; SHO (Med.) Roy. Vict. Infirm. Newc.

HILL, James David Howard Hawthorns, Studley Road, Ripon HG4 2BZ Email: jameshillgp@hotmail.com — MB BS 1994 Lond.; DCH 1998 Lond.; MRCGP 1999 (Merit) Lond.; DFFP 2000 Bath. (St. Mary's Lond.) GP Locum Princip., Kingston Upon Thames, Surrey.

HILL, James Ferguson SmithKline Beecham, New Horizons Court 1, Brentford TW8 9EP Tel: 020 8975 2612 Fax: 020 8975 2639 — MB BS 1969 Lond.; FRCP Ed. 1997; FRCP Lond. 1994; MRCS Eng. LRCP Lond. 1969; FFPHM RCP (UK) 1994. (Guy's) Dir. & Sen. Vice Pres. Corporate Affairs SmithKline Beecham. Socs: Fell. Roy. Soc. Med.; Fell. Inst. Dirs. Prev: Dir. & Sen. Vice Pres. Worldwide Strategic Product Developm. SmithKline Beecham; Vice-Pres. Cardiovasc. Product Plann. Squibb Inst. for Med. Research.

HILL, James Geoffrey Lanark Doctors, Health Centre, South Vennel, Lanark ML11 7JT Tel: 01555 665522 Fax: 01555 666857; The Priory, Friars Lane, Lanark ML11 9EL Tel: 01555 662190 Fax: 01555 666452 — MB ChB 1976 Birm.; BA Durham. 1970; DRCOG 1983. Prev: SHO (O & G) Vale of Leven Dist. Gen. Hosp.; SHO (Paediat.) Seafield Childr. Hosp. Ayr; Surg. Lt. RN.

HILL, Mr James Gordon (retired) Spring Glade, 94 Warwick Park, Tunbridge Wells TN2 5EN Tel: 01892 527898 Fax: 01892 513587 — MB ChB Glas. 1955; FRCS Glas. 1965; FRCOG 1976, M 1963, DObst 1957. Prev: Cons. O & G Tunbridge Wells Hosp. Gp.

HILL, James John The Surgery, Victoria Gardens, Lockerbie DG11 2BJ Tel: 01576 203665 Fax: 01576 202773; The Surgery, Lockerbie DG11 — MB ChB 1973 Glas.; MRCGP 1977; DObst RCOG 1975. Prev: Regist. (Psychiat.) Crichton Roy. Hosp. Dumfries; SHO (Paediat.) & SHO (Med.) Dumfries & Galloway Roy. Infirm.

HILL, James Justin 19 Meadvale Road, Croydon CR0 6JY — MB BS 1996 Lond. (St George's Hospital)

HILL, Mr James Thomas The Oaks, Middleton Road, Shenfield, Brentwood CM15 8D — MB BCh 1968 Wales; FRCS Eng. 1973. (Cardiff) Cons. (Urol.) OldCh. Hosp. Romford. Socs: Fell. Roy. Soc. Med.; Brit. Assn. Urol. Surgs. Prev: Sen. Regist. (Urol.) St. Peter's Hosp. Lond.; Sen. Regist. (Urol.) King's Coll. Hosp. Lond.; Regist. (Urol.) Norf. & Norwich Hosp.

HILL, Jane Muirhouse Medical Group, 1 Muirhouse Avenue, Edinburgh EH4 4PL Tel: 0131 332 2201 — MB ChB 1983 Leic.; DRCOG 1994. GP Princip.; Clin. Asst. (A & E) Edin. Prev: Trainee GP Falkirk; SHO (Psychiat.) Falkirk Roy. Infirm.; SHO (Paediat. Birm. Heartlands Hosp.

HILL, Jane Christina Newick Health Centre, Marbles Road, Newick, Lewes BN8 4LR Tel: 01825 722272 Fax: 01825 724391 — BM 1977 Soton.; DRCOG 1980.

HILL, Jane Roberta Flat 2, Avonmoore, Ray Park Road, Maidenhead SL6 8QX — MB BS 1986 Lond.; MRCGP 1990; DRCOG 1990. Prev: Trainee GP Windsor VTS.

HILL, Jason Grampian University hospitals NHS Trust, Aberdeen Roy.Infirmary, Forester hill, Aberdeen AB25 2ZN — MB ChB 1995 Leeds.

HILL, Jean Margaret 28 Meadway, Hampstead Garden Suburb, London NW11 7AY — MB BS 1954 Lond.; DObst RCOG 1958. (Roy. Free)

HILL, Jennifer Ann Holsworthy Health Centre, Welle Park, Holsworthy EX22 6DH Tel: 01409 253692 — MB ChB 1987 Bristol; DFFP 1995. p/t Gen. Practitioner (Retainer Scheme), Holsworthy, N Devon.

HILL, Jennifer Margaret 4 Dalchoolin, Holywood BT18 0HR Tel: 01232 424474 — BM BS 1988 Nottm.; MRCP Lond. 1991; DM Nottm. 1996. (Nottm.) Cons. (Respirat. Med.) N.ern Gen. Hosp.,

Sheff. Socs: BMA; Brit. Thorac. Soc.; Eur. Respirat. Soc. Prev: Sen. Registr. Respirat. Med. W.ern Infirm. Glas.

HILL, Jennifer Mary Salford & Trafford HA, Peel House, Albert St., Eccles, Manchester M30 0NJ Tel: 0161 787 0069 Fax: 0161 787 0003; 19 Taunton Road, Sale M33 5DD Tel: 0161 973 0961 — MB ChB 1969 Manch.; MSc Manch. 1976, BSc 1966, MB ChB 1969; DObst RCOG 1971. (Manch.) Cons. Communicable Dis. Control Salford & Trafford Health Auth. Socs: Ex-Pres. Manch. Med. Soc.; Brit. Infect. Soc.; Fell.Roy. Inst. Pub. Health and Hyg. Prev: Dir. Health Policy & Pub. Health Salford & Trafford Health Auth.

HILL, Jennifer Patricia 9 Darrell Road, London SE22 9NJ — MB ChB 1991 Liverp.

HILL, Jeremy Donald Tel: 01342 325959 — MB BS 1988 Lond.; MRCGP 1992; DCH RCP Lond. 1992; DRCOG 1991. G.P.; Organizer V.T.S; Course, Mid-Sussex, Hatwards Heath; Immediate Simcas Sussex; Care Doctor. Socs: Adviser in Primary Care Educat., Qu. Vict. Hosp., E. Grovstead, W. Sussex. Prev: SHO (Psychiat., O & G & Paediat.) E. Surrey Hosp. Redhill.

HILL, Jeremy Peter Jessop Medical Practice, 24 Pennine Avenue, Riddings, Alfreton DE55 4AE Tel: 01773 602707 Fax: 01773 513502 — MB ChB 1991 Birm.; MRCP 1994; MRCGP 1996; DCH 1994. GP Princip.

HILL, Joan Patricia (retired) Salmons Grange, 6 Salmons Lane, Whyteleafe CR3 0AL — MRCS Eng. LRCP Lond. 1959; MFFP 1993; FRCOG 1989, M 1966; DObst RCOG 1962. Prev: Assoc. Specialist (Obst., Gyn. & Family Plann.) St. Helier NHS Trust.

HILL, Mr John Freeman Hospital, Freeman Road, High Heaton, Newcastle upon Tyne NE7 7DN Tel: 0191 284 3111; 12 Brandling Park, Jesmond, Newcastle upon Tyne NE2 4QA Tel: 0191 281 3664 Fax: 0191 281 3664 Email: johnhillfrcs@compuserve.com — MB BS 1983 Lond.; FRCS (Otol.) Eng. 1990; FRCS Ed. 1990; FRCS Eng. 1987. Cons. Otolaryngol. Freeman Hosp. Newc. u. Tyne. Prev: Sen. Regist. (Otolaryngol.) Freeman Hosp. Newc.; Lect. (Otolaryngol.) P. of Wales Hosp. Chinese Univ. Hong Kong.

HILL, John Albert Pontardawe Health Centre, Pontardawe, Swansea SA8 4JU Tel: 01792 863103 Fax: 01792 865400; 58 Gwyn Street, Alltwen, Pontardawe, Swansea SA8 3AN Tel: 01792 863883 — MB BCh 1971 Wales; D.Occ.Med. RCP Lond. 1995; DAvMed Eng. 1974; DObst RCOG 1973. (Cardiff)

HILL, John Denby, TD 33 Forest Glade, Epping CM16 6LD — MB BS 1954 Lond.; FFA RCS Eng. 1961; DA Eng. 1959. (Char. Cross) Cons. Anaesth. St. Margt. Hosp. Epping & P.ss Alexandra Hosp. Harlow; Lt.-Col. RAMC, T & AVR. Socs: Assn. Anaesths. & BMA. Prev: Sen. Anaesth. Regist. & Ho. Surg. Char. Cross Hosp.; Regist. (Anaesth.) Fulham Hosp.

HILL, John Martyn Mary Health Centre, Great James Street, Londonderry BT48 7DH Tel: 028 7137 8500 — MB BCh BAO 1981 NUI; MRCGP 1989; DCH RCPS Glas. 1987.

HILL, John Stuart Crosby (retired) Dormans, Pretoria Road, High Wycombe HP13 6QW — MB ChB 1961 Ed.; DObst RCOG 1963. Prev: Chairm. Bucks. LMC.

HILL, Jonathan c/o Leighton Hospital, Middlewich Road, Crewe CW1 4QJ; c/o 8 Newgate Lane, Mansfield NG18 2LF — MB ChB 1990 Manch.

HILL, Jonathan Charles Royal Preston Hospital, Sharoe Green Lane, Fulwood, Preston PR2 9HT — MB ChB 1981 Liverp.; FRCR 1986; DMRD Liverp. 1985. Cons. Radiol. Roy Preston Hosp 1988.

HILL, Jonathan Henry Woodiwiss New Croft Surgery, 57 New Croft, Weedon, Northampton NN7 4RW Tel: 01327 340212 Fax: 01327 349728 — MB BS 1980 Lond. GP Weedon. Prev: Trainee GP Whittington & Univ. Coll. Hosps. Lond.

HILL, Jonathan Michael 7 Inglewood House, 281 West End Lane, West Hampstead, London NW6 1RB Tel: 020 7431 9490; Department of Cardiology, Royal London Hospital NHS Trust, Victoria Park Site, Bonner Road, London E2 9JX — MB ChB 1992 Ed.; MA Camb. 1993, BA (Hons.) 1989. SHO (A & E) St. Thos. Hosp. Prev: Ho. Phys. Roy. Infirm. & City Hosp. Edin.; Ho. Surg. Wycombe Gen. Hosp.

HILL, Jonathan William Department Child & Adolescent Psychiatry, Royal Liverpool Childrens Hospital, Eaton Road, Liverpool L12 2AP Tel: 0151 228 4811; Georgian House, Church St, Malpas SY14 8PD — MB 1975 Camb.; BChir 1974; MRCP (UK) 1977; MRCPsych 1979. Sen. Lect. (Child & Adolesc. Psychiat.) Liverp. Univ.

HILL, Joseph William (retired) 6 Paddock Way, Storth, Milnthorpe LA7 7JJ — MB ChB 1954 Liverp.; FFOM RCP Lond. 1980, M 1978; DIH Soc. Apoth. Lond. 1959.

HILL, Joshua Paul 80 Onslow Gardens, London N10 3JX — BM 1998 Soton.; BM Soton 1998.

HILL, Karen Elizabeth 16 Filton Avenue, Horfield, Bristol BS7 0AG — MB ChB 1995 Bristol; BSc (Hons.) Bristol 1984. GP Regist., Bristol. Prev: SHO on GP VTS Bristol.

HILL, Katherin Elizabeth New Croft Surgery, 57 New Croft, Weedon, Northampton NN7 4RW Tel: 01327 340212 Fax: 01327 349728; The Cottage, The Green, Everdon, Daventry NN11 3BL — MB BS 1978 Lond.; MRCS Eng. LRCP Lond. 1978; MRCGP 1983; DRCOG 1982; DCH RCP Lond. 1981. Prev: GP Trainee Whittington Hosp. VTS.

HILL, Katherine Sarah Wasps Nest Farm, Somerton TA11 7JH; 4 Shirebrook Close, Nottingham NG6 0JZ — BM BS 1988 Nottm.

HILL, Katherine Sheila Pring (retired) Shalom, 24 Blackbrook Drive, Sheffield S10 4LS Tel: 0114 230 5409 — MB BCh BAO 1947 Dub.; BA Dub. 1945; MA (Hon) 1992; MRCPI 1972; MFPHM 1989; MFCM 1973; DPH Manch. 1972. SCMO (Community Med.) Sheff. AHA (T); Chairm. Sheff. Div. BMA. Prev: Regist. (Neurol.) Unit Roy. Hosp. Annexe Fulwood.

HILL, Kathryn Emma 60 West Road, Pointon, Sleaford NG34 0NA — MB ChB 1994 Leic.

HILL, Kevin John 44 St Margarets Road, Whitchurch, Cardiff CF14 7AB Email: kevill@easynet.co.uk — MB BS 1991 Lond.; MRCGP 1996. (Lond. Hosp. Med. College)

HILL, Kevin John Willowbrook Medical Practice, Brook St., Sutton-in-Ashfield NG17 1ES Tel: 01623 440018; Longden House, Hermitage Lane, Mansfield NG18 5HA — MB BS 1979 Newc.; MRCGP 1986. Course Organiser Mansfield & Dist. VTS.

HILL, Kevin Paul 8 Kenmare Drive, Mitcham CR4 3JP — MB BS 1991 Lond.

HILL, Lawford Scott South Warwickshire Hospital, Lakin Road, Warwick CV34 5BW Tel: 01926 495321; Warwickshire Private Hospital, The Chase, Blackdown, Leamington Spa CV32 6RW Tel: 01926 427971 Fax: 01926 428791 — MB ChB 1971 St. And.; FRCP Lond. 1992; MRCP (UK) 1974. Cons. Phys. Warwick Hosp.

HILL, Leonard Frederick Radbrook Stables, Radbrook Road, Shrewsbury SY3 9BQ Tel: 01743 236863 — MB ChB 1963 Leeds; FRCP Lond. 1981 M 1967. (Leeds) Cons. Phys. Roy. Shrewsbury Hosp.; Clin. Director for Med. Servs. at Roy. Shrewsbury Hosp., NHS Trust. Prev: Lect. Med. & MRC Clin. Research Fell. Manch. Roy. Infirm.; Regist. Addenbrooke's Hosp. Camb.

HILL, Lisa Eva (retired) Saxons Tryst, Stoke Trister, Wincanton BA9 9PH Tel: 01963 32480 — MB BCh 1947 Bristol; MB ChB BRistol 1947; MD Bristol 1957; MRCP Lond. 1952; DCH Eng. 1951. Prev: Mem. Scientif. Staff MRC Tuberc. & Chest Dis. Unit Brompton Hosp. Lond.

HILL, Lorraine Denise 15 St Mary's Road, Poole BH15 2LQ Tel: 01202 660085 — MB ChB 1996 Birm.; ChB Birm. 1996; DRCOG 1998. SHO (O & G) Poole; SHO (A & E) Poole. Socs: MDU; MPS; MSS. Prev: SHO (c/o Elderly) Poole; Ho. Off. (Med.) Solihull; Ho. Off. (Surg.) Sutton Coldfield.

HILL, Louise Esther 21 Briar Close, Lickey End, Bromsgrove B60 1GE — MB ChB 1992 Glas. SHO Rotat. (Ophth.) Worcester Roy. Infirm.

HILL, Lydia Catherine Morden Hall Medical Centre, 256 Morden Road, London SW19 3DA Tel: 020 8540 0585 Fax: 020 8542 4480; St. Mawes, 1A The Warren, Carshalton SM5 4EQ Tel: 020 8661 1235 — MB BS Lond. 1967; MRCS Eng. LRCP Lond. 1967; MRCGP 1975; DObst RCOG 1973. (Roy. Free) Hon. Cons. Pub. Health Merton & Sutton HA; Hon. Sen. Lect. (Gen. Pract.) St. Geo. Hosp. Med. Sch. Lond. Socs: BMA. Prev: Chairm. Merton, Sutton & Wandsworth FPC.

HILL, Marguerite Elizabeth Wessex Neurological Centre, Southampton General Hospital, Tremona Road, Southampton SO16 6YD Tel: 02380 777222; 64 Rareridge Lane, Bishops Waltham, Southampton SO32 1DX Tel: 01489 893580 Email: marguerite@botwood.freeserve.co.uk — MB ChB 1990 Birm.; ChB Birm. 1990; BSc (Hons.) Birm. 1987; MRCP (UK) 1993; DPhil (Oxon) 1998. Specialist Regist. (Neurol.) Wessex Neurol. Centre Soton. Prev: MRC Fell. (Clin. Research Train.) Oxf.; Regist. (Neurol.) Qu. Eliz. Hosp. Birm.; SHO Rotat. (Med.) Centr. Birm.

*__HILL, Marina__ 7 Vane Close, London NW3 5UN — BM 1998 Soton.; BM Soton 1998.

HILL, Marion Kathleen Carisbrooke Health Centre, 22 Carisbrooke High Street, Newport PO30 1NR Tel: 01983 522150 — BM BS 1987 Nottm.; BMedSci Nottm. 1985; MRCGP 1992; DRCOG 1994; DGM RCP Lond. 1991. (Nottingham) Gen. Practitioner - Retainer Scheme. Prev: SHO Rotat. (Med.) Qu. Eliz. Hosp. Kings Lynn; SHO (A & E) Univ. Hosp. Nottm.; Ho. Phys. Canterbury Hosp. Bd. ChristCh., NZ.

HILL, Mark David 6 Farwell Road, Sidcup DA14 4LG — MB BS 1993 Lond.

HILL, Mark Edwin The Royal Marsden Hospital, Downs Road, Sutton SM2 5PT Tel: 020 8661 3582 Fax: 0208 661 3890 Email: mark.hill@rmh.nthames.nhs.uk; Email: markhill@lineone.com — MB BS 1986 Lond.; MD Lond. 1996; MRCP (UK) 1989. (St. Geo. Hosp. Univ. Lond.) Cons. (Med. Oncol.) Roy. Marsden Hosp., Sutton; Cons. (Med. Oncol.) Kent Cancer Centre, Maidstone. Socs: ACP; ASCO; ESMO. Prev: Sen. Regist. Roy. Marsden Hosp. Sutton & Lond.; CRC Fell. Inst. Cancer Research Lond.; Regist. Rotat. (Med.) Guy's Hosp. Lond.

HILL, Matthew Rhodri 29 The Cresecent, Solihull B91 1JR — BM BS 1994 Nottm.

HILL, Michael Arthur (retired) The Knowle, Shop Lane, Kirkheaton, Huddersfield HD5 0D — MD Liverp. 1972, MB ChB 1957; FRCPsych 1986, M 1972; DPH Leeds 1963; DPM Leeds 1967; Dip. Psychother. Leeds 1976. Prev: Cons. Psychiat. Huddersfield Hosp. Gp.

HILL, Michael David Hill and Partners, 36 Belmont Hill, London SE13 5AY Tel: 020 8852 8357 Fax: 020 8297 2011; 118 Eltham Hill, London SE9 5EF Tel: 020 8859 4990 — MB BS Lond. 1979; DCH RCP Lond. 1983. (Kings College, London)

HILL, Michael Graham (retired) Kirkdykes 11 St Colme Road, Dalgety Bay, Dunfermline KY11 9LH Tel: 01383 822405 — MB ChB St. And. 1963; FRCOG 1981, M 1968. Cons. BUPA Murrayfield Hosp. Edin. Prev: Sen. Regist. (O & G) Newc. Gen. Hosp.

HILL, Michael John Ballyclare Health Centre, George Avenue, Ballyclare BT39 9HL — MB BCh BAO 1957 Belf.; DObst RCOG 1959.

HILL, Moira Nancy Engleton House, 1A Engleton Road, Coventry CV6 1JF Tel: 024 7659 2012 Fax: 024 7660 1913; 488 Kenilworth Road, Balsall Common, Coventry CV7 7DQ Tel: 01676 532389 Email: m.hill@doctors.org.uk — MB BCh BAO 1974 Belf.; MRCGP 1978; DCH Eng. 1977; DRCOG 1976; FRCGP 1999. (Qu. Univ. Belf.) Prev: Sen. Clin Med. Off. (Family Plann.) Solihull HA.

HILL, Muriel Sheila (retired) 1 Apperley Park, Sawpit Lane, Apperley, Gloucester GL19 4EB — LRCP LRCS Ed. LRFPS Glas. 1949.

HILL, Nancy Alison Hallie (retired) 20 St Dionis Road, Parons Green, London SW6 4TT Tel: 020 7736 3130 — MB BS Lond. 1950; MRCS Eng. LRCP Lond. 1950; FRCPath 1976, M 1964. Prev: Cons. Haemat. Sutton & W. Merton Health Dist.

HILL, Nicholas Clive Woodiwiss Bromley Hospital NHS Trust, Cromwell Avenue, Bromley BR2 9AJ; Shire Cottage, Downe Road, Keston, Bromley BR2 6AD — MB BS 1981 Lond.; MD Lond. 1992; MRCOG 1986. Cons. O & G Bromley Hosp. NHS Trust. Prev: Lect. & Hon. Sen. Regist. (O & G) Roy. Free Hosp. Lond.; Clin. Research Fell. Nuffield Dept. (O & G) John Radcliffe Hosp. Oxf.; SHO (Gyn.) Chelsea Hosp. for Wom. Lond.

HILL, Oliver Jonathan Merebrook Farm, Woodhouse Lane, Audlem, Crewe CW3 0DT Tel: 01782 643111 — BM BS 1995 Nottm.; BMedSci Nottm. 1993. (Univ. Nottm.) SHO Rotat. (Anaesth.) S. Manch. Hosp. Withingshaw. Prev: SHO Paediat. Preston Roy. Hosp.; SHO (A & E) Blackpool Vict. Hosp.; Ho. Off. (Med.) Qu. Med. Centre.

HILL, Oscar William Tel: 020 8365 3592 — MB BChir 1956 Camb.; BA Camb.1956; FRCP Lond. 1974, M 1958; FRCPsych 1975, M 1972; DPM Lond. 1963. (Middlx.) Emerit. Cons. Psychiat. Middlx. Hosp. Lond.; Hon. Cons. St Luke's Hosp. for the Clergy. Socs: (Ex-Vice Pres.) Harveian Soc. of Lond.; Soc. for Psychosomatic Research; (Ex-Pres.) Fell. Roy. Soc. of Med. Prev: 1st Asst. Acad. Unit Psychiat. Middlx. Hosp. Med. Sch. Lond.; Regist.Prof. Med. Unit Middlx. Hosp. Lond.

HILL, Patricia Anne (retired) — MB ChB 1964 Leeds. GP Shrewsbury.

HILL, Paul Anthony 31 Thornhill Road, Derby DE22 3LX Tel: 01332 299256 — MB ChB 1990 Sheff.

HILL, Paul Rowland Department of Haematology, Princess Royal Hospital, Lewes Road, Haywards Heath RH16 4EX Tel: 01444 441881 Fax: 01444 443084; Bag End, Lower Station Road, Newick, Lewes BN8 4HT Tel: 01825 721129 — MB BS 1973 Lond.; FRCP Lond. 1996; MRCP (UK) 1976; FRCPath 1996, M 1984. (Middlx.) Cons. Haemat. P.ss Roy. Hosp. Haywards Heath. Prev: Lect. (Haemat.) & Regist. (Cardiol.) St. Geo. Hosp. Med. Sch. Lond.; Regist. (Haemat.) St. Geo. Hosp. Lond.

HILL, Pauline Jane 5 Ardmillan Gardens, Bangor BT20 4NF — MB BS 1998 Newc.; MB BS Newc 1998.

HILL, Penelope Jane 108 Portaferry Road, Newtownards BT22 2AH — MB BS 1987 Melbourne; FRACOG 1997; MRCOG 1997. (Univ. Melbourne (Aust.)) Regist. (Obst. & Gyn.).

HILL, Mr Peter The Basford Consulting Rooms, 540 Etruria Rd, Basford, Newcastle-under-Lyme ST5 0SX Tel: 01782 614419 Fax: 01782 630270 — MRCS Eng. LRCP Lond. 1959; MB Camb. 1960, BChir 1959; FRCS Eng. 1967; FRACS 1966. (Camb. & St. Mary's) Cons. Orthopaedic Surg. N. Staffordshire Nuffield Hosp. Socs: Brit. Orthop. Assn. Prev: Regist. (Gen. Surg.) Roy. Melb. Hosp., Australia; Regist. (Orthop.) Char. Cross Hosp. Lond.; Sen. Regist. (Orthop.) United Bristol Hosps.

HILL, Professor Peter David St Georges Hospital Medical School, London SW17 0RE Tel: 020 8725 5531 Fax: 020 8725 3592 Email: sallain@sghms.ac.uk — MB BChir 1970 Camb.; MA Camb. 1970; FRCP Lond. 1994; MRCP (UK) 1972; FRCPCH 1997, M 1996; FRCPsych 1987, M 1975. (St. Bart.) Prof. Child & Adolesc. Psychiat. Dept. Gen. Psychiat. & Hon. Cons. Child Psychiat. St. Geo. Hosp. Med. Sch. Lond.; Vis. Cons. Tadworth Ct. Childr. Hosp.; Cons. Civil. Adviser Brit. Army. Prev: Chairm. Child & Adolesc. Psychiat. Sect. Roy. Coll. Psychiat.; Adviser Health Comm. Ho. of Commons; Sen. Lect. (Child & Adolesc. Psychiat.) St. Geo. Hosp. Med. Sch. Lond.

HILL, Mr Peter Francis, Maj. RAMC Nuffield Orthopaedic Centre, Headington, Oxford OX3 7CD Tel: 01865 741155; 21 Stockhurst Close, Putney, London SW15 1NB Tel: 020 8780 9827 Email: pfhill@dial.pipex.com — MB BChir 1990 Camb.; M Chir. Camb. 2000; FRCS (Orth) 2002; BSc (Hons.) Lond. 1987; FRCS Eng. 1996. (Camb.) Specialist Regist. (Orthop.) Roy. Defence Med. Coll. Gosport, Hants; SPR (Orthop.) Nuffield Orthop. Centre Oxf. Socs: Fell. Roy. Soc. Med.; Assoc. Brit. Orthop. Assn.; Brit. Orthop. Res. Soc. Prev: Specialist Regist. Guy's Hosp. Lond.; Regtl. Med. Off. QRIH.

HILL, Peter John, Maj. RAMC Retd. Pyle Street Health Centre, 27 Pyle Street, Newport PO30 1JW Tel: 01243 670707 Fax: 01243 672808 — MB BCh 1982 Wales; MRCGP 1987; DRCOG 1989. Occupat. Phys. Marks & Spencer Newport.; Designated Phys. Austral. & Canad. Emigration Meds. Prev: SHO (Med.) BMH Munster; SHO (Dermat.) Camb. Milit. Hosp. Aldershot; SHO (O & G) BMH Hong Kong.

HILL, Professor Peter Michael Postgraduate Institute for Medicine and Dentistry, 10-12 Framlington Place, Newcastle upon Tyne NE2 4AB Tel: 0191 222 8928 Fax: 0191 222 8620 Email: peter.hill@ncl.ac.uk; Mill House, Mill Farm Road, Hamsterley Mill, Rowlands Gill NE39 1NW Tel: 01207 542981 Email: peterhill@fdn.co.uk — MB ChB 1968 Leeds; FFPHM RCP (UK) 1998; FRCGP 1986, M 1975; DObst RCOG 1970. (Leeds) Postgrad. Dean.

HILL, Peter Robert Bloomsbury Health Centre, 63 Rupert Street, Nechells, Birmingham B7 5DT Tel: 0121 678 3932 Fax: 0121 678 3925; 41 Heneage Street, Nechells, Birmingham B7 4NF Tel: 0121 359 1478 Fax: 0121 678 3925 — MB BS 1972 Lond.; BSc Lond. 1969; MRCS Eng. LRCP Lond. 1972; DObst RCOG 1976. Prev: GP Milton Keynes.

HILL, Phyllis Margaret (retired) Dr P Hill, Trewan Hall, St Columb TR9 6DB Tel: 01637 880261 — MB BS 1957 Lond.

HILL, Quentin Anthony 23 Belgrave Road, Edinburgh EH12 6NG — MB ChB 1997 Leeds; BSc (Hons) Anat Leeds 1995.

HILL, Mr Raymond Alwyn Holmewood, 27 Brudenell Avenue, Canford Cliffs, Poole BH13 7NW — MB ChB 1961 Ed.; FRCS Ed. 1966; FFR 1974; DMRD Ed. 1972; FRCR 1975. Cons. Radiol. E. Dorset Health Dist. Prev: Sen. Regist. & Clin. Tutor (Radiol.) Roy. Infirm. Edin.

HILL, Reginald Raymond Woodiwiss (retired) Fairfield, 25 The Twistle, Byfield, Daventry NN11 6UR Tel: 01327 262266 — MB BS 1950 Lond.; FFA RCS Eng. 1956. Prev: Cons. Anaesth. Stockport HA.

HILL, Richard Mark Fleming 27 Brudenell Avenue, Poole BH13 7NW — MB ChB 1991 Birm.; ChB Birm. 1991; FRCS Ed. 1997. Specialist Regist. (Orthop.) SE Scotl.

HILL, Mr Robert Aldwyn Hospital for Sick Children, Great Ormond St., London WC1N 3JH Tel: 020 7813 8240 Fax: 020 7813 8243 — MB BS 1980 Lond.; BSc Lond. 1977; FRCS Eng. 1985. (St. Bart.) Cons. Orthop. Surg. Hosp. Sick Childr. Gt. Ormond St. Lond.; Cons. Orthop. Surg. P.ss Alexandra Hosp. Harlow. Prev: Sen. Regist. (Orthop.) St. Bart. Hosp. Lond.; Regist. (Orthop.) St. Thos. Hosp. Lond.; SHO (Plastic Surg.) St. Thos. Hosp. Lond.

HILL, Robert Frank Wonford House Hospital, Dryden Road, Exeter EX2 5AF Tel: 01392 403463 — MB ChB 1972 Manch.; MRCPsych 1979; MRCGP 1976; DObst RCOG 1975. Cons. Psychiat. Exeter HA. Prev: Sen. Regist. St. Geo. Hosp. Lond.; Hon. Sen. Regist. Maudsley Hosp. Lond.; Research Asst. Dept. Experim. Psychopath. Inst. Psychiat. Lond.

HILL, Mr Robert Jonathan Dept. Ophthalmology, Singleton Hospital, Sketty, Swansea SA2 8QA Tel: 01792 205666 — MB BS 1988 Lond.; FRCOphth. 1992. Cons. (Ophth.) Singleton Hosp., Swansea. Prev: Sen. Regist. (Ophth.) Univ. Hosp. Wales Cardiff.

HILL, Robert Paul Villa Maria, Les Saules, 20 Seaward Drive, West Wittering, Chichester PO20 8LL — MB BS 1990 Lond.; FRCA. (St Georges)

HILL, Ronald David Marlow Grange, 20 Martello Road, Canford Cliffs, Poole BH13 7DH Tel: 01202 708917 Email: rhill73773@aol — MB BS 1960 Lond.; FRCP Lond. 1978, M 1965; MRCS Eng. LRCP Lond. 1960. (Guy's) Hon. Cons. Phys., Poole Hosp., poole, Dorset. Socs: Fell. Assur. Med. Soc.; Brit. Diabetic Assn. & Wessex Diabetes & Endocrinol. Assn. Prev: Cons. Phys. Diabetes Poole Gen. Hosp.; Sen. Regist. (Med.) Guy's Hosp. Lond.; Research Fell. (Med.) Guy's Hosp. Med. Sch.

HILL, Rosemary Ann 7 Murrayfield Road, St Andrews KY16 9NB — MB ChB 1994 Ed.

HILL, Rosemary Ann (retired) 85 Langley Park Road, Sutton SM2 5HF Tel: 020 8643 5056 — MB BS 1953 Lond.; DPH 1967; MFCM 1972; DObst RCOG 1956. Prev: Dist. Community Phys. Sutton & W. Merton Health Dist.

HILL, Rosemary Elizabeth Health Centre, Holme Lane, Cross Hills, Keighley BD20 7LG Tel: 01535 632147 Fax: 01535 637576 — MB ChB 1979 Bristol; MRCGP 1984; DRCOG 1982.

HILL, Rowena Mickleber House, Gargrave Road, Broughton, Skipton BD23 3AQ — BChir 1989 Camb.; MA Camb. 1990, BChir 1989.

HILL, Sarah 8 Aldwych Close, Nuthall, Nottingham NG16 1QH Tel: 01244 381128 — MB ChB 1992 Dundee; DRCOG 1996. Sen. SHO Kings Mill Hosp. Mansfield. Prev: SHO (Neonat. Paediat.) City Hosp. Nottm.; SHO (Neonat. Med.) St Mary's Hosp. Manch.; SHO (Paediat.) Countess of Chester Hosp.

HILL, Sarah Frances St Albans and Hemel Hempstead Trust, Hillfield Road, Hemel Hempstead HP2 4AD Tel: 01442 213141 Fax: 01441 287845; Scots Hill Cottage, Scots Hill, Croxley Green, Rickmansworth WD3 3AB — MB BS 1977 Lond.; FRCPath 1984. (Royal Free) Cons. Histopath. W. Herts Hosp.s Trust & Hemel Hempstead Hosp. Trust. Prev: Lect. (Histopath.) St. Bart. Hosp. Lond.; Regist. (Histopath.) & Ho. Surg. Roy. Free Hosp. Lond.

HILL, Sarah Jane — MB ChB 1994 Sheff. p/t GP Rotherham.

HILL, Sarah Rosemary Aven Paediatric Dept, St Lukes Hospital, Bradford PL8 1JG — MB ChB 1997 Leeds. SHO Paediat. Bradford.

HILL, Sian Elizabeth 1 Abbot's Barn, Vale Royal Courtyard, Whitegate, Northwich CW8 2BA — MB BCh 1982 Wales; BSc Wales 1979, MB BCh 1982; FFA RCS Eng. 1987. (Welsh National School of Medicine) Cons. Anaesth. Countess of Chester NHS Trust Chester. Prev: Sen. Regist. (Anaesth.) Mersey Region.

***HILL, Simon Alastair** 81 Shackstead Lane, Godalming GU7 1RL Tel: 01483 417093 Email: tarlyhill@hotmail.com — BM BCh 1997 Oxf.; MA (Oxon) 1997.

HILL, Simon Francis Public Health Laboratory, Poole Hospital NHS Trust, Longfleet Road, Poole BH15 2JB Tel: 01202 675771 Fax: 01202 665780 Email: sfhill@phls.nhs.uk; 14 Cogdean Close, Corfe Mullen, Wimborne BH21 3XA Email: simon.hill@care4free.net — MB BCh 1978 Wales; FRCPath 1996, M 1985. Dir. & Cons. Microbiol. Pub. Health Laborat. Serv. Poole; Clin. Dir. (Pathol.) Poole Hosp. NHS Trust.

HILL, Simon Nicholas Whitchurch Hospital, Whitchurch SY13 1NT Tel: 01948 660800 Fax: 01948 660803 Email: simon.hill@shropcomm.wmids.nhs.uk — MB BS 1978 Newc.; FRCP Lond. 1994; MRCP (UK) 1982. Cons. Geriat. Commun. Shrops. Commun. ment. Health Trust; Sen. Lect. (Geriat. Med.) Univ. Keele Postgrad. Med. Sch. Socs: Brit. Geriat. Soc. Prev: Lect. (Geriat. Med.) Univ. Dept. Selly Oak Hosp. Birm.; Sen. Regist. (Geriat. Med.) E. Birm. Hosp. & Walsgrave Hosp. Coventry.

HILL, Simon Owain 173 Heeley Road, Birmingham B29 6EJ — MB ChB 1991 Birm.; ChB Birm. 1991.

HILL, Simon Robert 142 Queens Drive, Liverpool L18 1JN — MB BS 1983 Lond.

HILL, Stanislaus George Bideford Medical Centre, Abbotsham Road, Bideford EX39 3AF Tel: 01237 476363 Fax: 01237 423351; Glenville, Orchard Hill, Bideford EX39 2RA Tel: 01237 474739 — MB BS 1964 Lond.; MRCP Lond. 1968; MRCS Eng. LRCP Lond. 1964; MRCGP 1974.

HILL, Stephen Alan The Health Centre, Manor Road, Beverley HU17 7BZ Tel: 01482 862733 Fax: 01482 864958; 22 York Road, Beverley HU17 8DP Tel: 01482 867649 — MB BS 1980 Newc.; MRCP (UK) 1983; MRCGP 1987; DRCOG 1987. Prev: Trainee GP Chalfont St. Peter; Regist. (Dermat. & Gen. Med.) Wycombe Gen. Hosp.; SHO (Med.) Soton Gen. Hosp.

HILL, Stephen Lionel Granville House, Hayesfield Park, Bath BA2 4QE — MB BS 1975 Lond.; FFA RCS 1981. Cons. Anaesth. Roy. United Hosp. Bath. Socs: SW Soc. Anaesth.; Anaesth. Research Soc. Prev: Clin. & Research Fell. Gen. Hosp. Mass., USA.

HILL, Steven Andrew 21 Millcroft Road, Streetly, Sutton Coldfield B74 2EE — BM BCh 1981 Oxf.

HILL, Susan Ann Department Anaesthesia, Southampton General Hospital, Tremona Road, Southampton SO16 6YD Tel: 02380 777222 Fax: 02380 794348; 60 Kingsgate Street, Winchester SO23 9PF Tel: 01962 860579 Email: sahneuro@aol.com — MB BChir 1984 Camb.; PhD Camb. 1982, MA 1982; LMSSA Lond. 1984; FCAnaesth 1989. (Univ. Camb.) Cons. Anaesth. Soton. Gen. Hosp. Socs: Intens. Care Soc.; Assn. Anaesth.; Neuroanesth. Soc. Prev: Sen. Regist. & Regist. (Anaesth.) Soton. Gen. Hosp.; Research Regist. (Intens. Care & Anaesth.) Addenbrooke's Hosp. Camb.

HILL, Susan Antonietta Crouch End Health Centre, 45 Middle Lane, London N8 8PH Tel: 020 8348 7711; 74 Station Road, West Wickham BR4 0PU — MB BS 1981 Lond.; MRCGP 1989; DRCOG 1986.

HILL, Susan Margaret Department of Gastroenterology, Great Ormond Street Hospital for, Children NHS Trust, London WC1N 3JH Email: susan.hill@gosh-tr.nthames.nhs.uk — BM 1980 Soton.; DM 1997; MRCP (UK) 1984; MRCPCH 1997; DCH RCP Lond. 1983. (Soton.) Cons. Paediat. (Gastroenterol.) Gt. Ormond St. Hosp. Childr. Lond.; Hon. Sen. Lect., Inst. of Child health, Lond. WC1.

HILL, Miss Susan Marion 54 South Croxted Road, West Dulwich, London SE21 8BD — MB BS 1985 Lond.; MA Oxf. 1987; MS Lond. 1995; FRCS Eng. 1989; FRCS Gen 1997. (Westminster Hospital) Cons. Surg. (Vasc.) Lewisham Hosp. Prev: Sen. Regist. (Vasc. Surg.) Hammersmith Hosp.; Sen. Regist. (Gen. Surg.) Chelsea & W.minster. Hosp.; Regist. (Gen. Surg.) Mayday Hosp. Croydon & Qu. Mary's Hosp. Roehampton.

HILL, Susanna Ruth Tel: 01271 812005 Fax: 01271 814768; The Granary, Spreacombe, Braunton EX33 1JA Tel: 01271 870873 — MB ChB 1982 Bristol; MRCGP 1988; Dip. Palliat. Med. Wales 1996; DCH RCP Lond. 1987. (Bristol) Gen. Practitioner Caem Med. Centre; Assoc. Specialist N. Devon Hospice. Prev: Regist. Rotat. (Surg.) Cardiff Hosp.; SHO (Paediat.) N. Devon Hosp. Barnstaple.

HILL, Timothy John Riverbank Medical Centre, Dodsley Lane, Midhurst GU29 9AW Tel: 01730 812121 Fax: 01730 811400 — MB BS 1990 Lond.; MRCGP 1996; DRCOG 1993; DFFP 1993. (St. Thos. Hosp. Lond.)

HILL, Timothy Roland Gray Field House, Field House Drive, Meole Brace, Shrewsbury SY3 9HL — BM BCh 1973 Oxf.

HILL, Virginia Ann GOSH NHS Trust, Great Ormond St., London; Tel: 0208 574 4381 — MB BS 1983 Lond.; MRCP (UK) 1992; MRCGP 1987; DCH RCP Lond. 1987; DRCOG 1986. (Guy's) p/t Spr Dermat. GOSH, Lond. Socs: Dowling Club; Brit. Assn. Dermat.;

BMA. Prev: GP FarnBoro.; SHO (Dermat.) St. Thos. Hosp. Lond.; SHO (Med.) Basingstoke Hosp.

HILL, William Edward 63 Saint Legers Crescent, Saint Thomas, Swansea SA1 8ET — MB BCh 1993 Wales.

HILL, William John Coleman (retired) Whitestaunton, 7 Coleraine Road, Portrush BT56 8EA — MB BCh BAO Dub. 1942; LM Rotunda 1946; MRCGP 1955. Prev: Gen. Practitioner, Portrush.

HILL, William Stanley, Capt. RAMC Retd. (retired) Derlwyn Isaf Cottage, Vicarage Road, Llanarthney, Carmarthen SA32 8HJ Tel: 01558 668624 — MB BCh 1942 Wales; BSc Wales 1939, MB BCh 1942; MRCGP 1969; DObst RCOG 1948. Prev: Chairm. Indust. Med. Bd. DHSS:.

HILL, William Tennison St Neots Surgery, 47 Wolseley Road, Plymouth PL2 3BJ Tel: 01752 561305 Fax: 01752 605565; 104 Looseleigh Lane, Crownhill, Plymouth PL6 5HH Tel: 01752 769172 Fax: 01752 721089 — MB ChB 1965 Bristol; DObst RCOG 1970. Hon. Treas. Devon LMC. Prev: SHO (Surg.) Leicester Roy. Infirm.; SHO (Obst.) Plymouth Gen. Hosp.; Ho. Off. Bristol Roy. Infirm.

HILL-COUSINS, Jeanette Lesley 1 Bramble Bank Cottages, Calshot Road, Calshot, Southampton SO45 1BR; 13 Hancroft Road, Hemel Hempstead HP3 9LJ Tel: 01442 55665 — BM 1984 Soton.; BSc (Hons.) Manch. 1977; DRCOG 1987. Trainee GP Soton. VTS.

HILL-COUSINS, Stephen Paul Adrian Forestside Medical Practice, Beaulieu Road, Dibden Purlieu, Southampton SO45 4JA Tel: 023 8087 7900 Fax: 023 8087 7909; 29 Sir Christopher Court, Hythe, Southampton SO45 6JR — BM 1984 Soton.; BM (Hons.) Soton. 1984; MRCGP 1989; FRCGP 1999. Hon. Clin. Tutor (Primary Care) & Trainer (Gen. Pract.) Soton. Univ.; Course Organiser Mid-Wessex Day Release Course, King Alfred Coll. Winchester; MAP Adviser for RCGP (Wessex Fac.). Prev: Hon. Med. Advisor RNLI Calshot.

HILL-SMITH, Ian Stopsley Group Practice, Wigmore Lane Health Centre, Luton LU2 8BG Tel: 01582 481294 Fax: 01582 456259; Hedgehogs, 35 Station Road, Ampthill, Bedford MK45 2QU Email: ian@azoth.demon.co.uk — MB BS 1980 Lond.; BSc (Anat.) Lond. 1977; MRCP (UK) 1986; MRCGP 1996. (Univ. Coll. Hosp.) GP Princip.; Hosp. Pract. (Diabetic Med.) Luton & Dunstable Hosp. Prev: Regist. (Med.) Luton & Dunstable Hosp.; SHO Nat. Hosp. Nerv. Dis. Lond.

HILLABY, Kathryn Julia Rowan House, Withington, Shrewsbury SY4 4PY Tel: 01743 709265 — MB BS 1998 Lond.; MB BS Lond 1998; BSc 1997. (Roy.Free.) SHO O & G Roy. Sussex Hosp. Brighton.

HILLAM, Andrew Clark Stokewood Surgery, Fair Oak Road, Fair Oak, Eastleigh SO50 8AU Tel: 023 8069 2000 Fax: 023 8069 3891 — MB BS 1987 Lond.; MRCGP 1992. Prev: Trainee GP Hastings VTS; Ho. Off. Newham Gen. Hosp. & St. Margt. Hosp. Epping.

HILLAM, Geoffrey Harold Health Centre, Osborn Road, Fareham PO16 7ER Tel: 01329 823456 Fax: 01329 285772; 53 Park Lane, Fareham PO16 7LE Tel: 01329 310352 — MB BChir 1960 Camb.; MB Camb. 1960, BChir 1959; DObst RCOG 1966. (Lond. Hosp.) Prev: Ho. Off. Lond. Hosp.; Maj. RAMC.

HILLAM, Jonathan Charles Chatterton House, Goodwins Road, King's Lynn PE30 5PD Tel: 01553 613613 Fax: 01553 613703 Email: jon.hillam@dial.pipex.com — MB BS Lond. 1986; BSc (Hons.) Lond. 1983; MRCPsych 1991. (Lond. Hosp. Med. Coll.) Cons. (Old Age Psychiat.) King's Lynn & Wisbech Hosp. NHS Trust. Socs: Brit. NeuroPsychiat. Assoc.; Internat. PsychoGeriat. Assn. Prev: Sen. Regist. (Psychiat.) Roy. Free Hosp. Lond.; Regist. (Psychiat.) St. Geo. Hosp. Train. Scheme Lond.; SHO (Psychiat.) N. Lond. Train. Scheme.

HILLAM, Sophie Joanna 139 Heavygate Road, Crookes, Sheffield S10 1PG — MB ChB 1995 Sheff.

HILLAN, Mr Kenneth John 1 Queen's Gate, 127 Dowanhill St., Glasgow G12 9DN — MB ChB 1983 Glas.; FRCS Glas. 1989.

HILLAN, Lila Russell Health Centre, Park Drive, Stenhousemuir, Larbert FK5 3BB Tel: 01324 554136 Fax: 01324 553622; 82 Franchi Drive, Dykes Park, Larbert FK5 4DY — MB ChB 1978 Glas.; MB ChB Glas.1978.

HILLARD, Kenneth Anthony (retired) North Chase, Salt Box Road, Worplesdon, Guildford GU3 3LH Tel: 01483 233383 — MB BS 1954 Lond. Prev: GP Guildford.

HILLARD, Timothy Charles Department of Obstetrics & Gynaecology, Poole Hospital NHS Trust, Longfleet Road, Poole BH15 2JB Tel: 01202 442511 Fax: 01202 448028 Email: thillard@poole-tr.co.uk; Fairlawn, 7 Belgrave Road, Branksome Park, Poole BH13 6DB Tel: 01202 763445 Fax: 01202 763693 — BM 1982 Soton.; DM Soton. 1994; MRCOG 1987; MFFP 1993. (Soton.) Cons. O & G Poole Hosp. NHS Trust. Prev: Sen. Regist. (O & G) King's Coll. Hosp. Lond.; Research Fell. Menopause Unit, King's Coll. Hosp. Lond.; Regist. (O & G) King's Coll. Hosp. Lond. & Basingstoke Hosp.

HILLARY, Andrew Guy Occupational Health Centre, NISZ PC623, Devonport Royal Dockyard, Plymouth PL1 4SD Tel: 01752 552338; Trappers Cottage, Reen, Perranporth TR6 0AJ — MB BChir 1984 Camb.; LMSSA Lond. 1984; AFOM RCP (UK) 1994; DAvMed 1989. Dep. Occupat. Phys. Occupat. Health Centre Plymouth. Socs: Soc. Occupat. Med.

HILLARY, Graham Malcolm Sunnybank House Medical Centre, 506 Huddersfield Road, Towngate, Wyke, Bradford BD12 9NG Tel: 01274 424111 Fax: 01274 691256 — MB ChB 1979 Leeds. GP Bradford. Prev: Ho. Surg. St. Jas. Hosp. Leeds; Ho. Phys. Airedale Gen. Hosp. Steeton.

HILLARY, Ian Alastair Henneth Annun, 351 Burton Road, Derby DE23 6AH Tel: 01332 344210 — MB ChB 1953 Leeds. (Leeds) Socs: Derby Med. Soc. Prev: Ho. Surg. & Ho. Phys. (Dermat.) St. Jas. Hosp. Leeds.

HILLAS, Clare Promenade Medical Centre, 46 Loce promenade, Douglas IM1 2LZ Tel: 01624 675490; Westwinds, Baldhoon Rd, Lonan IM4 7QH Tel: 01624 836119 — MB ChB 1989 Leeds; DRCOG 1994; MRCGP 1995; DFFP 19994. GP.

HILLEBRAND, Monika 45C Durham House, South Cleveland Hospital, Marton Road, Middlesbrough TS4 3ST — MD 1991 Gottingen; State Exam Med. 1991.

HILLEBRANDT, David Kenneth Holsworthy Health Centre, Western Road, Holsworthy EX22 6DH Tel: 01409 253692 Fax: 01409 254184; Derriton House, Derriton, Holsworthy EX22 6JX Tel: 01409 253814 — MB BS 1978 Lond.; MRCGP 1986; Dip. IMC RCS Ed. 1991; DRCOG 1983; Dip. Trav Med. (Glasgow) 1998. (Westm.) Socs: Brit. Assn. Travel Med.; Internat. Soc. Mt.ain Med. Prev: Trainee GP Truro VTS; Ho. Phys. & Ho. Surg. Penzance.

HILLEL, Moshi Daoud (retired) The Hollies, 22A Higham Lane, Gee Cross, Hyde SK14 5LX Tel: 0161 351 1991 — MB BS 1945 Lond.; MRCS Eng. LRCP Lond. 1944. GP Dukinfield. Prev: Surgic. Regist. War Memor. Hosp. Scunthorpe.

HILLEN, Heather Ann Old Catton Surgery, 55 Lodge Lane, Norwich NR6 7HQ Tel: 01603 423341 Fax: 01603 486445; 123 Newmarket Road, Norwich NR4 6SZ Tel: 01603 455946 Fax: 01603 507057 Email: h.a.roberts@btinternet.com — MB BS 1967 Lond.; MRCS Eng. LRCP Lond. 1967. (St. Bart.) Mem. Norf. LMC. Socs: (Ex-Pres.) Norwich M-C Soc.

HILLEN, Robert Samuel Somerton House Surgery, 79A North Road, Midsomer Norton, Bath BA3 2QE Tel: 01761 412141 Fax: 01761 410944 Email: robert.hillen@gp-l81101.nhs.uk — MB BS 1981 Lond.; DRCOG 1984. (St. Geo. Hosp. Med. Sch. Lond.) Gen. Practioner. Prev: SHO (Gen. Med.) Roy. United Hosp. Bath; SHO (O & G) P.ss Ann Hosp. Soton.

HILLENBRAND, Fritz Karl Michael (retired) 3 Elizabeth Court, Churchfields, South Woodford, London E18 2QX Tel: 020 8505 0619 — MD Rostock 1935; MB Berlin 1934; LAH Dub. 1956; DCH Eng. 1957. Prev: Med. Supt. Dr. Barnardo's Homes, Barkingside.

HILLENBRAND, Peter (retired) 85 Hollyfield Road, Sutton Coldfield B75 7SE Tel: 0121 378 0787 — MB BS 1962 Lond.; FRCP Lond. 1981 M 1967. Cons. Phys. Good Hope Hosp. Sutton Coldfield. Prev: Sen. Med. Regist. Lond. Hosp.

HILLER, Elizabeth Joan (retired) Whitegate, Tippings Lane, Farnsfield, Newark NG22 8EP — BSc, MB BS Lond. 1959; FRCP Lond. 1979, M 1966; DObst RCOG 1962; FRCPCH 1996. Prev: Cons. Paediat. City Hosp. Nottm.

HILLHOUSE, Professor Edward William Medical Research Institute, Department of Biological Sciences, The University of Warwick, Coventry CV4 7AL Tel: 024 76 524744 Fax: 024 76 523568; Department of Medicine, Walsgrave Hospital, Clifford Bridge Road, Coventry CV2 2DX Tel: 024 76 602020 Fax: 01203 622197 — MB BS 1981 Lond.; PhD Lond. 1975, BSc 1972; FRCP Lond. 1995; MRCP (UK) 1984. Prof. Med. MRI Univ. Warwick; Marjorie Robinson Memor. Fell. Soc. Endocrin. 1987. Socs: Soc. Endocrinol.; Brit. Diabetic Assn. Prev: Sen. Lect. (Med.) Univ. Bristol;

Sen. Lect. & Hon. Cons. Metab. Med. Univ. Newc.; Lect. (Med.) King's Coll. Hosp. Sch. Med. Lond.

HILLIARD, Andrew Keith 2 Wheelwright Court, Walkhampton, Yelverton PL20 6LA — MB ChB 1990 Leic.; AFOM 2001; DRCOG 1995; MRCGP 1996. (Leicester University) Specialist Regist.; Occupat. Health. Socs: Assn. Of NHS Occupat.al Health Phys.s; Soc. Of Occupat.al Med.. Prev: Non Princip. In Gen. Pract.; GP/SHO Derriford Hosp. VTS; SHO (A & E) Worcester.

HILLIARD, Jennifer Jane Talbot Lodge, Horton, Swansea SA3 1LB Tel: 01792 390442 — MB BS 1979 Lond.; MRCGP 1995. Prev: Trainee GP Swansea VTS; SHO (Paediat. & O & G) Morriston Hosp. Swansea.

HILLIARD, John Stephen Gower Medical Practice, Scurlage Surgery, Monksland Road, Scurlage, Swansea SA3 1AY Tel: 01792 390413 Fax: 01792 390093; Talbot Lodge, Horton, Swansea SA3 1LB Tel: 01792 390442 Fax: 01792 390093 — MB BS 1978 Lond.; MRCGP 1991. Prev: GP Trainee Swansea VTS; SHO (Gen. Med.) Luton & Dunstable Hosp.; Ho. Phys. W.m. Hosp. Lond.

HILLIARD, Olwyn Ruth 46 Grange Crescent, Bangor BT20 3QJ Tel: 01247 472198 — MB BCh BAO 1989 Belf.; DCH Dub. 1993; DMH Belf. 1992. Trainee GP Belf.

HILLIARD, Thomas Leonard (retired) Coed Deryn, 17 Cwn Lane, Rogerstone, Newport NP1 9AF Tel: 01633 894000 — MRCS Eng. LRCP Lond. 1939. Fell. Fell.sh. of Postgrad. Med. Prev: Cons. Chest Phys. Newport Chest Unit, Pontypool Chest Clinic & Mt.

HILLIARD, Thomas Norman Flat 19, Orchard Residence, Kent & Canterbury Hospital, Canterbury CT1 3NG Email: tom.hilliard4@virgin.net — BM BCh 1992 Oxf.; MA Camb. 1993, BA 1989; MRCP (UK) 1996. Paediat. Regist. Kent & Canterbury Hosp. Prev: Research Regist. Roy. Alexandra Hosp. Brighton; SHO (Paediat. Intens. Care) Guy's Hosp. Lond.; SHO (Cardiol.) Gt. Ormond St. Hosp. Lond.

HILLIER, Anthony Robert Park Slope Surgery, 32 Stoke Road, Blisworth, Northampton NN7 3BT Tel: 01604 858237 Fax: 01604 859437; Uplands, 15 Station Road, Blisworth, Northampton NN7 3DS Tel: 01604 858215 — MRCS Eng. LRCP Lond. 1974; BSc (Hons.) Lond. 1971, MB BS 1974; MRCP (UK) 1978; MRCGP 1979; DCCH RCP Ed. 1990; DObst RCOG 1976. (Univ. Coll. Hosp.) Hon. Med. Sec. N.ampton Local Med. Comm.

HILLIER, Charles Edward Montague 11 Grove Road S., Southsea PO5 3QR — MB BS 1991 Lond.

HILLIER, Edward Richard Countess Mountbatten House, West End, Southampton SO30 3JB Tel: 02080477414; The Cams, 11 Grove Road S., Southsea PO5 3QR Tel: 02392 643355 Fax: 02392 792263 — MB BS Lond. 1064; MD Lond. 1972; FRCP Lond. 1997; MRCP (UK) 1995; MRCGP 1972; DObst RCOG 1971. (St. Bart.) Sen. Lect. & Cons. Phys. Palliat. Med. Soton. Univ. Hosps. Trust; Chairm. Assoc. for Palliat. Med. (GB & Irel.). Socs: BMA & Internat. Assn. for Study of Pain. Prev: Med. Off. to Brit. Antarctic Survey.; Attached Worker Nat. Inst. Med. Research Lond.; Trainee GP Wessex VTS.

HILLIER, Ethel Weir The Milton Abbas Surgery, Catherines Well, Milton Abbas, Blandford Forum DT11 0AT Tel: 01258 880210 Fax: 01258 881252; The Corner House, Ansty, Dorchester DT2 7PJ Tel: 01258 880347 — MB ChB 1973 Aberd.; DRCOG 1977; DA Eng. 1976. Asst. GP Milton Abbas. Prev: SHO (O & G) Highland HB; SHO (Geriat.) Farnham Hosp.; SHO (Anaesth.) St. Bart. Hosp. Lond.

HILLIER, James Edward 123 Harvist Road, Queen's Park, London NW6 6HA Email: james-hillier@msn.com — MB BS 1994 Lond.; MA Camb. 1995. (Char. Cross. & Westm.) Regist. (Anciest) Hammersmith Hosp.

HILLIER, Janis Whitchurch Hospital, Whitchurch, Cardiff CF14 7XB Tel: 02920 693191 — MB BS 1984 Lond.; MRCPsych 1990. Cons. Gen Adult Psychiat. Cardiff & Vale NHS Trust WhitCh. Cardiff. Prev: Sen. Regist. (Psychiat.) Cardiff.

HILLIER, Mr Malcolm James Holman The Milton Abbas Surgery, Catherines Well, Milton Abbas, Blandford Forum DT11 0AT Tel: 01258 880210 Fax: 01258 881252; The Corner House, Ansty, Dorchester DT2 7PJ Tel: 01258 880347 Fax: 01258 881252 — MRCS Eng. LRCP Lond. 1969; FRCS Ed. 1976. (Guy's) Med. Manager of Dorset Doctors on Call Ltd.; Clin. Asst. (Diabetes) Blandford Community Hosp. Prev: Med. Adviser to W. Dorset Hospice MacMillan Serv.; Trainee GP Aldershot VTS; Med. Off. Duncan Hosp. Raxcul & Christian Hosp. Jhansi, N. India.

HILLIER, Mark James The Surgery, High Street, Rawmarsh, Rotherham S62 6LW Tel: 01709 522888 — BM BS 1986 Nottm.; MRCGP 1990.

HILLIER, Richard John c/o Annette Buckley, Psychiatric Training Schemes' Office, West London Healthcare Trust HQ, Uxbridge Road, Southall UB1 3EU Tel: 020 8967 5709; Flat 54, Barton Court, Barons Court Road, London W14 9EH Tel: 020 7381 9887 Fax: 020 7460 1182 Email: ursonet@demon.co.uk — MB ChB 1986 Birm.; PhD Sheff. 1993; MRCPsych 1998. Specialist Regist. Psych. Rotat. St Geo.s Hosp. Lond. Socs: Inceptorship Roy. Coll. Psych.; MDU. Prev: SHO Rotat. (Psychiat.) Char. Cross & W.minster Hosp. Train. Scheme.

HILLIER, Stephen John Lower Lane, Bishops Waltham, Southampton SO32 1GR Tel: 01489 892288 Fax: 01489 894402; Highfield Farm, Vicarage Lane, Upper Swanmore, Southampton SO32 2QQ — MB BS 1973 Lond.; BSc Lond. 1970; MRCP (UK) 1977; DRCOG 1978.

HILLIER, Thomas (retired) 2 Dunster Close, Park Lane, Harefield, Uxbridge UB9 6BS Tel: 01895 474552 — MB BS 1956 Lond.; MRCGP 1968; DObst RCOG 1962.

HILLING, Gareth Alun Lloyd 12 The Grange, Fairwater Road, Llandaff, Cardiff CF5 2LH — BM 1987 Soton.

HILLIS, Graham Scott 64 Watson Street, Aberdeen AB25 2SU Tel: 01224 635370 — MB ChB 1990 Aberd.; BMedBiol 1990.

HILLIS, Professor William Stewart Department of Medicine & Therapeutics, University of Glasgow, Gardiner Institute, Western Infirmary, Glasgow G11 6NT Tel: 0141 211 2897 Fax: 0141 211 1737 Email: w.s.hillis@clinmeed.gla.ac.uk; 20 Airthrey Avenue, Jordanhill, Glasgow G14 9LJ Tel: 0141 950 1268 — MB ChB 1967 Glas.; FRSC (Hon); Dip Sports Med; FRCP Glas. 1980; MRCP (U.K.) 1970. (Glas.) Prof. of CardiocVasc. & Exercise Med. Cons. Cardiol.; Vice Chairm., NEFA Med. Comm. Socs: Assn. Phys. & Brit. Cardiac Soc.; Brit. Assoc. of Sports Med. Prev: Sen. Lect. (Clin. Pharmacol.) & Hon. Cons. Cardiol. W.. Infirm. Glas.; Research Fell. (Cardiol.) Vanderbuilt Univ. Nashville Tennessee, USA; Cons. Cardiol. & Sen. Regist. (Cardiol.) Stobhill Gen. Hosp. Glas.

HILLMAN, Adrian Vaughan 79 College Road, Syston, Leicester LE7 2AQ; c/o 6 Manitoba Close, Corby NN18 9HX — BM BS 1990 Nottm.

HILLMAN, Audrey Ravenscraig Hospital, Inverkip Road, Greenock PA16 9H Tel: 01475 633777 — MB ChB 1989 Glas.; MRC Psych 1994. Cons. in Gen. Adult & Subst. Misuse Psychiat. Ravenscraig Hosp., Greenock.

HILLMAN, Barrie Swallownest Health Centre, Hepworth Drive, Aston, Sheffield S26 2BG Tel: 01142 872486 Fax: 01142 876045 Email: swallownest_hc@demon.co.uk; Patchways, 51 Oakwood Grove, Rotherham S60 3ES — MB ChB Bristol 1966; MRCP (U.K.) 1970. (Bristol) Prev: Regist. Profess. Med. Unit Roy. Hosp. Sheff.; Regist. (Cardiol. & Gen. Med.) N.. Gen. Hosp. Sheff.; Ho. Phys. Bristol Roy. Infirm.

HILLMAN, Beryl Shadwell Medical Centre, 137 Shadwell Lane, Leeds LS17 8AE Tel: 0113 293 9999 Fax: 0113 248 5888; 135 Wigton Lane, Leeds LS17 8SH Tel: 0113 268 9601 — MB ChB 1966 Liverp.; DObst RCOG 1968.

HILLMAN, Ferdinand (retired) 120 Appley Lane N., Appley Bridge, Wigan WN6 9DS Tel: 01257 254783 — MB BCh BAO 1950 Belf.; FRCPI 1969, M 1954; FRCPath 1972, M 1963; DObst RCOG 1952. Hon. Cons. Path. Roy. Albert Edwd. Infirm. Wigan. Prev: Cons. Path. Roy. Albert Edwd. Infirm. Wigan.

HILLMAN, Geoffrey 31 Devonshire Road, Horsham RH13 5EF — MB BS 1986 Lond.

HILLMAN, Graham William Tile House Surgery, 33 Shenfield Road, Brentwood CM15 8AQ Tel: 01277 227711 Fax: 01277 200649; Two Trees, 16 Crescent Drive, Brentwood CM15 8DS — MB BChir 1969 Camb.; MA Camb. 1970, MB BChir 1969; MRCP (U.K.) 1972. (Camb.) Hosp. Pract. Brentwood Chest Clin. Prev: Med. Regist. S.end Gen. Hosp.; SHO, Ho. Phys. (Cardiac Haematol.) & Ho. Surg. Thoracic Dept. Lond.; Hosp.

HILLMAN, Harold Unity Laboratory of Applied Neurbiology, 3 Merrow Dene, 76 Epsom Road, Guildford GU1 2BX Tel: 01483 568332 Fax: 01483 531110 Email: hillmanh@breathemail.net — MB BS Lond. 1956; PhD Lond. 1963, BSc (Physiol.) 1958; MRCS Eng. LRCP Lond. 1956. (Middlx. Hosp. Lond.) GP; Dir. Unity Laborat. Applied NeuroBiol.; Sec. Lond. Med. PostGrad. Assoc.;

Chairm. Freedom to Care. Socs: Physiol. Soc.; BMA (Sec. Phys. for Human Rights.); Chairm., Freedom to Care. Prev: Reader (Physiol.) Univ. Surrey; Med. Adviser Internat. Schizophrenia Centre, Bangor; Biochem. & Hon. Lect. (Applied Neurobiol.) Inst. Neurol. Lond.

HILLMAN, Mr Jeffrey Stuart 135 Wigton Lane, Leeds LS17 8SH Tel: 0113 268 9601 Fax: 0113 237 0884 — MB ChB 1964 Liverp.; FRCS Ed. 1973; MRCS Eng. LRCP Lond. 1964; FRCOphth 1988; DO Eng. 1969. p/t Cons. Ophth. Surg. St. Jas. Univ. Hosp. Leeds; Sen. Lect. (Ophth.) Univ. Leeds. Socs: Fell. Amer. Acad. Ophth.; Internat. Soc. Refractive Keratoplasty; Past Pres. N Engl. Ophth. Soc. Prev: Sen. Regist. (Ophth.) Birm. & Midl. Eye Hosp.; SHO (Ophth.) St. Paul's Eye Hosp. Liverp.; Ho. Surg. Profess. Unit BRd.green Hosp. Liverp.

HILLMAN, Jonathan Gill The Medical Centre, Station Avenue, Bridlington YO16 4LZ Tel: 01262 670690 — MB ChB 1978 Manch.; BSc St. And. 1975; MRCGP 1982; DRCOG 1980.

HILLMAN, June (retired) 37 Druids Park, Liverpool L18 3LJ Tel: 0151 738 0785 — LRCP LRCS Ed. LRFPS Glas. 1951.

HILLMAN, Katherine Anne 16 Baring Street, London N1 3DP — MB BChir 1993 Camb.; MA (Hons.) Camb. 1990; MRCP (UK) 1995. Regist. Rotat. (Nephrol. & Med.) S.end Hosp., Univ. Coll. Hosp. & Middlx. Hosp. Lond. Prev: SHO Rotat. (Med.) Whittington Hosp., Univ. Coll. Hosp. & Middlx. Hosp. Lond.

HILLMAN, Robert George Kilbirnie Medical Practice, 2 Kirkland Road, Kilbirnie KA25 6HP Tel: 01505 683333 Fax: 01505 683591 — MB ChB 1991 Glas.; MRCGP 1995.

HILLMAN, Roger Kingswood Surgery, Kingswood Avenue, Swindon SN3 2RJ Tel: 01793 534699 — MB ChB 1964 Birm.; FRCGP 1985, M 1971; DObst RCOG 1967.

HILLMAN, Ruth Anne The Surgery, Regal Chambers, 50 Bancroft, Hitchin SG5 1LL Tel: 01462 453232 — MB BS 1988 Lond.; DRCOG 1992.

HILLMAN, Samuel 37 Druids Park, Liverpool L18 3LJ Tel: 0151 738 0785 — LRCP LRCS Ed. LRFPS Glas. 1945; AFOM RCP Lond. 1980. Socs: Soc. Occupat. Med.; Liverp. Med. Inst. Prev: Regist. (ENT) Whipps Cross Hosp. Lond.; Regist. (Surg.) Glas. Roy. Infirm.; RAFVR Med. Br.

HILLMEN, Peter Dept. of Pathology, Pinderfields General Hospital, Aberford Road, Wakefield WF1 4DG Tel: 01924 212443 Fax: 01924 249462 Email: peter.hillmen@panp-tr.narthy.nhs.uk — MB ChB 1985 Leeds; MRCPath 1995; PhD 1995; MRCP (UK) 1988. Cons.in Clin. Haemat., Pinderfields Gen. Hosp.; Cons. Haem. Leeds Gen. Infirm.. Socs: Brit. Soc. of Haemat.; Amer. Soc. of Haemat.; Amer. Soc. of Clin. Oncol. Prev: Wellcome Trust Research Fell. Roy. Postgrad. Med. Sch. Lond.; Regist. (Haemat.) Hammersmith Hosp. Lond.; Sen. Regist. (Haemat.) Yorks. RHA.

HILLS, Ann-Mary Ewart (retired) 33 Yardley Park Road, Tonbridge TN9 1NB Tel: 01732 356570 — MB BS (Hons.) Lond. 1961; DRCOG 1962; BA Open U. 1988. Prev: Med. Off. DSS.

HILLS, Ann-Mary Ewart (retired) 33 Yardley Park Road, Tonbridge TN9 1NB Tel: 01732 356570 — MB BS (Hons. Distinc. Surg.) Lond. 1961; BA Open 1988; MRCS Eng. LRCP Lond. 1961; DObst RCOG 1962. JP. Prev: Med. Adviser Benefits Agency.

HILLS, David Graeme Muspratt, CB, OBE, Air Vice-Marshal RAF Med. Br. (retired) Heatherwell House, Lingfield RH7 6EF — MB BS 1949 Lond.; MFCM 1973; DPH Lond. 1961. Prev: Hon. Surg. to HM the Qu.

HILLS, Elizabeth Sarah Limes Medical Centre, Limes Avenue, Alfreton DE55 7DW Tel: 01773 833133 — MB BS 1989 Lond.; DFFP 1993. (Univ. Coll. & Middlx. Hosp. Sch. Med. Lond.) Prev: SHO (O & G, Med. & Paediat.) Chester.

HILLS, Horace Frank (retired) Parkstone Cottage, 27 Glyne Ascent, Bexhill-on-Sea TN40 2NX — MB BS Lond. 1944; MRCS Eng. LRCP Lond. 1944; MRCOG 1950. Prev: Regist. (O & G) Mayday Hosp. & Croydon Obst. Serv.

HILLS, Katherine Sarah 42 Teignview Road, Bishopsteignton, Teignmouth TQ14 9SZ — MB BS 1988 Lond.; MRCP (UK) 1992. Regist. (Med.) St. Albans City Hosp.

HILLS, Michael Marchant (retired) Cherry Court, Ashley Road, Battledown, Cheltenham GL52 6PJ Tel: 01242 514580 — MB ChB 1957 Birm.; FFA RCS Eng. 1964. Cons. Anaesth. Glos. Roy. NHS Trust. Prev: Sen. Regist. Hosp. Sick Childr. Gt. Ormond St. & Univ. Coll. Hosp. Lond.

HILLS, Michael William 2 Windsor Terrace, Clifton, Bristol BS8 4LW — MB ChB 1985 Bristol.

HILLS, Nigel David Orchard Surgery, Blackhorse Way, Horsham RH12 1SG Tel: 01403 253966/7 — MB BS 1986 Lond.; DRCOG 1990. Prev: Trainee GP Crawley & Horsham VTS.

HILLS, Richard Melvyn 17 Wadborough Road, Sheffield S11 8RF Email: drhillgp@onet.co.uk — MB ChB 1989 Sheff.; MRCGP 1996; DA (UK) 1994. (Sheffield) GP; Clin. Asst. in Epilepey & Movement Disorders. Prev: Trainee GP Sheff. VTS; Regist. & SHO Rotat. (Anaesth.) Sheff.

HILLS, Robert Christopher 12 Morrell Garth, Selby YO8 9XF — MB ChB 1984 Leeds; MB ChB Leeds l984.

HILLS, Russell Keith 11 West Park Lane, Worthing BN12 4EP — MB BS 1996 Lond.

HILLS, Suellen 21 Lomond View, Symington, Kilmarnock KA1 5QS — MB ChB 1990 Glas.; MRCP (UK) 1995; MRCPCH. (Glas.) SHO (Med. Paediat. & O & G) Glas. Prev: SHO (Med. Paediat.) S.. Gen. Hosp. & Roy. Hosp. Sick Childr. Glas.

HILLS, Susan Joan Robins, Paines Hill, Limsfield, Oxted RH8 — MB BS 1979 Lond.; MRCS Eng. LRCP Lond. 1979.

HILLS-WRIGHT, Paris Anne c/o Anaesthetic Department, Royal United Hospital, Combe Park, Bath BA1 3NG — MB BS 1990 West. Austral.

HILLSON, Rowan Mary The Hillingdon Hospital, Uxbridge UB8 3NN — MB BCh 1974 Birm.; MD Birm. 1983; FRCP Lond. 1994; MRCP (UK) 1976. Cons. Phys. Hillingdon Hosp. Uxbridge; Hon. Cons. Phys. Harefield Hosp. Prev: Sen. Regist. (Med. Diabetes & Endocrinol.) Radcliffe Infirm. Oxf.

HILLYARD, Andrew Charles 9 Northlands Gardens, Southampton SO15 2NL — MRCS Eng. LRCP Lond. 1971.

HILLYARD, Edgar Hugh, Lt.-Col. RAMC Retd. (retired) 11 Millbrook Dale, Axminster EX13 5EF Tel: 01297 34598 — BM BCh 1943 Oxf.; MA Oxf. 1991, BA 1938; DObst RCOG 1948.

HILLYARD, Mr Jeremy William PO Box 479, St Anthony NFLD A0K 4S0, Canada Tel: 00 1 709 4548596 Fax: 00 1 709 4542052 Email: jhillyar@nf.sympatico.ca; c/o 2 New Villas, Mumbles, Swansea SA3 4HT Tel: 01792 361492 — MB ChB 1974 Liverp.; FRCS Eng. 1981; LMCC 1990. Surg. Curtis Memor. Hosp. St. Anthony Newfld., Canada. Socs: Burke & Hare Soc. Prev: Research Regist. (Surg.) Welsh Nat. Sch. Med. Cardiff; Demonst. (Anat.) Univ. Liverp.; Ho. Off. Birkenhead Gen. Hosp.

HILLYEAR, Maureen Elizabeth Sunnyside Royal Hospital, Hillside, Montrose DD10 9JP Tel: 01674 830361 Fax: 01674 830361; Links Meadow, 26 Dorward Road, Montrose DD10 8SB Tel: 01674 675981 — MB ChB 1976 Aberd. Assoc. Specialist. (Psychiat.) Sunnyside Roy. Hosp. Montrose.

HILMAN, Serena Jayne 3 Rockmount Park, Saintfield, Ballynahinch BT24 7DQ — MB ChB 1997 Bristol.

HILMI, Fawaz Ghazi 26 Brookdale, Healey, Rochdale OL12 0SS — MB ChB 1969 Baghdad; DCP Lond. 1978. Socs: Med. Protec. Soc.; Internat. Acad. Path.; Assn. Clin. Path. Prev: Head (Path.) Al-Hammadi Hosp. Ryiadh, Saudi Arabia.

HILMI, Omar Jason 8 Upper Hill Rise, Chorleywood, Rickmansworth WD3 7NU — MB ChB 1993 Dundee.

HILMY, Hamdy Hussein Eaglestone Health Centre, Standing Way, Eaglestone, Milton Keynes MK6 5AZ Tel: 01908 679111 Fax: 01908 230601 — MB ChB 1980 Cairo.

HILMY, Naguib Mounir Halim The Surgery, 221 Whaddon Way, Bletchley, Milton Keynes MK3 7EA Tel: 01908 373058 Fax: 01908 630076; 8 Bartholomew Close, Walton Park, Milton Keynes MK7 7HH Tel: 01908 675054 Fax: 01908 630076 — MB BCh 1981 Cairo; MRCP (UK) 1987; DCH RCP Lond. 1991; DRCOG 1991; Cert. Family Plann. JCC 1991; Cert. Prescribed Equiv. Exp. JCPTGP 1991; MRCCP 1996. (Fasr El Aini Cairo) Hosp. Pract. (Gen. Med. & Cardiol.) Milton Keynes Gen. Hosp.; MAAG Co-ordinator for Milton Keynes. Prev: Regist. (Med.) Milton Keynes Gen. Hosp.

HILSDEN, Ewart Ian Spa Road Surgery, Spa Road East, Llandrindod Wells LD1 5ES Tel: 01597 824291 / 842292 Fax: 01597 824503; Hafod-y-Bryn, Llanyre, Llandrindod Wells LD1 6EA Tel: 015977 823374 — MB ChB 1968 Birm. (Birm.) Clin. Asst. Anaesth. Llandrindod Wells Hosp. Socs: BMA. Prev: Ho. Surg. Gen. Hosp. Hereford; Ho. Phys. Co. Hosp. Hereford.

HILSON, Andrew Joseph Walker Department Nuclear Medicine, Roy Free Hospital, London NW3 2QG Tel: 02077940500 Ext: 3215

Fax: 020 7472 6203 Email: a.hilson@rfc.ucl.ac.uk; 62 Ossulton Way, Hampstead Garden Suburb, London N2 0LB — MB BChir Camb. 1967; MSc (Nuclear Med.) Lond. 1976; MA Camb. 1968; FRCP Lond. 1989, M 1970. (Camb. & Westm.) Cons. Nuclear Med. Roy. Free Hosp. Lond. Socs: Brit. Inst. Radiol.; Brit. Nuclear Med. Soc.; Harv. Soc. (VP). Prev: Cons. Nuclear Med. Inst. Urol. & St Peter's Hosps.; Asst. Prof. (Nuclear Med.) Upstate Med. Center State Univ. New York Syracuse, USA; Sen. Regist. (Nuclear Med.) Guy's Hosp. Lond.

HILSON, Professor George Richard Forsyth St George's Hospital Medical School, Cranmer Terrace, London SW17 0RE Tel: 020 8725 5723 Fax: 020 8672 0234; 37 Wilderness Road, Reading RG6 7RU Tel: 01189 262718 — MB BS 1943 Lond.; MD Lond. 1950; FRCPath 1966, M 1963. (St. Geo.) Emerit. Prof. Bacteriol. Univ. Lond.; Hon. Cons. Bacteriol. St. Geo. Hosp. Lond. Socs: BMA. Prev: Prof. Bact. St. Geo. Hosp. Med. Sch. Lond.; Capt. RAMC.

HILTON, Alan Hugh Flat 9 Half Acre, 67/69 Woodford Road, London E18 2EX — MB BCh BAO Dub. 1954; MA Dub. 1955; LM Rotunda 1958. Chairm. Indust. Injury & War Pens. Bd. Prev: Ho. Surg. & Ho. Phys. Sir P. Dun's Hosp. Dub.; Ho. Phys. Whittington Hosp. Lond.; RAMC, Clin. Off. in Med. Brit. Hosp. Benghazi.

HILTON, Andrew 14 Glendale, Guisborough TS14 8JF — MB ChB 1997 Leic.

HILTON, Andrew Iain 68B Crayford Road, London N7 0ND — MB BS 1991 Lond.

HILTON, Bryony Anne Beresford Betton Grange, Betton Strange, Cross Houses, Shrewsbury SY5 6HZ — MB BS 1977 Lond.; MRCS Eng. LRCP Lond. 1977; FFA RCS Eng. 1983; T(Anaesth.) 1991. (Guy's) Prev: Cons. Anaesth. Raigmore Hosp. Inverness; Sen. Regist. (Anaesth.) E. Anglian HA; Regist. (Anaesth.) W.m. Hosp. Lond.

HILTON, Catherine (retired) 27 Fairkytes Avenue, Hornchurch RM11 1XS Tel: 01708 444331 Fax: 01708 444331 — MB ChB 1986 Manch.; BSc St. And. 1983. Trainee GP Havering HA VTS.

HILTON, Christopher Mark Betton Grange, Betton Strange, Cross Houses, Shrewsbury SY5 6HZ — MB ChB 1982 Birm.; MRCGP 1991; DA Eng. 1984. SHO (O & G) Salop. HA.

HILTON, Claire Fiona Dept. Old Age Psychiatry, Northwick park Hospital, Watford Road, Harrow HA1 3GJ Tel: 020 8869 2396 — MB BS 1983 Lond.; BSc Lond. 1980; MD Manch. 1996; MRCPsych 1992; MRCGP 1988; Cert IHSM 1997. Cons.(Old Age Psychiat.)Harrow & hillingdon healthcare NHS Trust.

HILTON, Mr Colin John Rodborough, 8 Westfield Grove, Gosforth, Newcastle upon Tyne NE3 4YA Tel: 0191 284 7394 — MB BS 1968 Newc.; FRCS Eng. 1973. Cons. Cardiothoracic Surg. Freeman Hosp. Newc.; Hon. Clin. Lect. Univ. Newc. Med. Sch.; Postgrad. Dean Soc. Cardiothoracic Surg. Gt. Brit. & Irel.; Regional Represen. (Cardiothoracic Surg.) RCS; Sec. Intercollegiate Exam. Bd. Cardiothoracic Surg. Socs: BMA & Soc. Thoracic & Cardiovasc. Surgs. Prev: Sen. Regist. Rotat. (Cardiothoracic Surg.) Papworth Hosp. & St. Bart. Hosp.; Research Fell. Brown Univ. Providence, USA; Regist. (Cardiac Surg.) Nat. Heart Hosp. Lond.

HILTON, David Andrew Department of Histopathology, Derriford Hospital, Plymouth PL6 8DH Email: david@hilton@phnt.swest.nhs.uk; Colcharton House, Gulworthy, Tavistock PL19 8HU — MB BCh 1984 Wales; MB BCh Wales l984; MRCP (UK) 1988; MD 1994; MRCPath 1996. Cons. Neuropath. Derriford Hosp. Plymouth.

HILTON, David Colin Wood Ide Lane Surgery, Ide Lane, Alphinton, Exeter EX2 8UP Tel: 01392 439868 Fax: 01392 493513; 14 Marlborough Road, Exeter EX2 4TJ Tel: 01392 437364 — MB ChB 1976 Bristol; MRCGP 1984; DRCOG 1981. (Bristol) Mem. (Chairm.) Exeter Non Fundlholders Gp. Socs: MEDACT (Chairm. Exeter Br.). Prev: Med. Off. Santa Ysabel Solomon Is.s; Chief Med. Off. Guadacanal Province Solomon Is.s.

HILTON, David Dawson (retired) 29 Middlefield Lane, Hagley, Stourbridge DY9 0PY Tel: 01562 883158 Fax: 01562 883158 — MB ChB Manch. 1956; FRCP Lond. 1978, M 1965. Prev: Cons. Phys. Dudley Gp. Hosps. NHS Trust.

HILTON, Denis Dewhurst Tokkos, 8 Festing Road, Southsea PO4 0NG Tel: 02392 733058 Fax: 023 9273 3058 — MB ChB 1947 Manch.; FFPHM RCP (UK) 1989; MFCM 1974, F 1981; DPH Lond. 1959; DTM & H Eng. 1955; DObst RCOG 1951. (Manch.) p/t Med. Ref. Portchester Crematorium. Socs: BMA & Portsmouth Med. Soc. Prev: Dist. Community Phys. Portsmouth & S.E. Hants. Health Dist.; Ho. Surg. Manch. Roy. Infirm.; Med. Off. N. Nigeria H.M. Oversea Civil Serv.

HILTON, Edward John — MB BS 1989 Lond. (St. Thos. Hosp. Lond.) p/t Gen. Pract. (Retainee), Grand Drive Surg., Raynes Pk., Lond. Socs: Med. Defence Union.

HILTON, Jacqueline Wendy 19 Springfield Road, Swindon SN1 4EP — BM 1984 Soton.; MRCGP 1991.

HILTON, Judith Alison Margaret Aviation House, 125 Kingsway, London WC2B 6NH Tel: 020 72768983 Fax: 020 72768910 Email: judith.hilton@foodstandards.gsi.gov.uk; 12 Church Hill Road, Walthamstow, London E17 9RX Tel: 020 8521 6740 Email: jamhilton@aol.com — MB BS 1976 Lond.; MRCPath 1985; FRCPath 1998. (Royal Free Hospital School of Medicine) Head of MicroBiol. and Foodbourne Dis. unit, Food Standards Agency, Lond. Socs: Hon.Se.Comparative Med.Sect.; Fell. Roy. Soc. Med. Prev: Sen. Regist. (Bacteriol.) St. Mary's Hosp. Lond.; Se. Med.off.DOH.

HILTON, Mr Malcolm Paul Southview, Catherine Hill, Olveston, Bristol BS35 4EN — BM BCh 1991 Oxf.; FRCS Eng. 1996; FRCS (Otol.) Eng. 1997. (Oxf.) Specialist Regist. (OtoLaryngol.) Roy. Devon & Exeter Hosp. Prev: SHO OtoLaryngol. Bristol.

HILTON, Nicola Jane 19 Creffield Road, Colchester CO3 3HZ Tel: 01206 570371 Fax: 01206 369908; The Rectory, 24 New Town Road, Colchester CO1 2EF Tel: 01206 530320 — MB ChB Birm. 1987; MRCGP 1991; DRCOG 1990. (Univ. Birm.) GP Retainee, Dr P. Marfleet and Partners, Colchester. Socs: Sands Cox Med. Soc. Birm. Prev: GP Trent Vale, Stoke-on-Trent; Trainee GP Stoke-on-Trent VTS; Ho. Surg. Good Hope Gen. Hosp. Sutton Coldfield.

HILTON, Paul Directorate of Women's Services, Royal Victoria Infirmary, Newcastle upon Tyne NE1 4LP Tel: 0191 282 5853 Fax: 0191 227 5173 Email: paul.hilton@ncl.ac.uk; 52 Reid Park Road, Newcastle upon Tyne NE2 2ES Tel: 0191 281 0004 Fax: 0191 281 0004 — MB BS 1974 Newc.; MD Newc. 1981; FRCOG 1996, M 1979. (Newc. u. Tyne) Cons. Gyn. & Urogyn. & Hon. Sen. Lect. (Urogyn.) Univ. Newc. Socs: Internat. Continence Soc.; Internat. Urogyn. Assn.; (Ex-Treas.) Blair Bell Research Soc. Prev: Sen. Lect. (O & G) Univ. Newc.; Clin. Research Fell. (Urodynamics) St. Geo. Hosp. Med. Sch. Lond.

HILTON, Peter John Pembury, 20 Elm Road, Tutshill, Chepstow NP16 7BX — MB BS 1976 Lond.; FFA RCS Eng. 1981. (Guy's) Regist. Anaesth. Bristol Roy. Infirm.

HILTON, Philip James 134 Harley Street, London W1N 1AH Tel: 020 7486 1042; 12 Imber Park Road, Esher KT10 8JB Tel: 020 8398 7903 — MD 1974 Camb.; MB 1964, BChir 1963; FRCP Lond. 1980, M 1967. (St. Thos.) Cons. Phys. St. Thos. Hosp. Lond.

HILTON, Rachel Brook Mill Medical Centre, College Street, Leigh WN7 2RB Tel: 01942 681880 Fax: 01942 262578 — MB ChB 1987 Leic.; MRCGP 1993; DRCOG 1992; DPD Wales 1998. p/t Clin. Asst. (Dermat.) Roy. Albert Edwd. Infirm. Wigan.

HILTON, Rachel Mary Guys Renal Unit Guys Hospital, St Thomas St., London SE1 9RT Tel: 020 7955 4158 Fax: 020 7955 4909 Email: rachel.hitton@gstt.sthames.nhs.uk — BM BCh 1988 Oxf.; BA Oxf. 1985, BM BCh 1988; MA Oxf. 1992; MRCP (UK) 1991. Cons. Nephrol. Guys Hosp. Lond. Prev: Research Fell. (Immunol.) Roy. Postgrad. Med. Sch. Lond.; Sen. Regist. (Renal) Guy's Hosp. Lond.

HILTON, Rebecca Mary 14 Ashworth Close, Bowden, Altrincham WA14 3AG — MB ChB 1995 Sheff.

HILTON, Roy Cheffins Hope Hospital, Eccles Old Road, Salford M6 8HD Tel: 0161 787 5161; 14 Ashworth Close, Bowdon, Altrincham WA14 3AG Tel: 0161 928 2095 — MD Manch. 1981, MB ChB 1964; FRCP Lond. 1983; MRCP (U.K.) 1970; DCH RCPS Glas. 1966. (Manch.) Cons. Rheum. Hope Hosp. Manch. Socs: Fell. Manch. Med. Soc.; Brit. Soc. Rheum. Prev: Sen. Regist. (Rheum.) Manch. Roy. Infirm.

HILTON, Royden Charles Flat 6, 75 Shrewsbury Road, Birkenhead CH43 8SS — MB ChB 1987 Liverp.

HILTON, Professor Sean Robert Canbury Medical Centre, 1 Elm Road, Kingston upon Thames KT2 6HR Tel: 020 8549 8818 Fax: 020 8547 0058; Division of General Practice & Primary Care, St. Georges Hospital Medical School, Cranmer Terrace, London SW17 0RE Tel: 020 8725 5423 Fax: 020 8767 7697 Email: shilton@sghms.ac.uk — MB BS 1974 Lond.; MD Lond. 1991; FRCGP 1990, M 1979; DRCOG 1977. Prof. Gen. Pract. & Primary Care St. Geo. Hosp. Med. Sch. Lond.; Dean of UnderGrad. Med. SGHMS 1999 -; Chairm. of Assoc. of Univ. Depts. of Gen. Pract.

1998-. Socs: Assoc. of Univ. Dept.s of Gen. Pract.; Med. Soc. Lond. Prev: Sen. Lect. (Gen. Pract.) St. Geo. Hosp. Med. Sch. Lond.; Clin. Research Fell. (Clin. Epidemiol.) Cardiothoracic Inst. (Path.) St. Geo. Hosp. Lond.; SHO (O & G) St. Helier Hosp. Carlshalton.

HILTON, Sidney Montague Glanrhyd, Llaneltyd, Dolgellau LL40 2TE; Glanrhyd, Llanelltyd, Dolgellau LL40 2TE Tel: 01341 422274 — MB BChir 1944 Camb.; PhD Camb. 1956, MA, MB BChir 1944. (Guy's) Emerit. Prof. Physiol. Univ. Birm. Socs: Physiol. Soc. Prev: Hon. Prof. Univ. Hong Kong 1987; Prof. & Head Dept. Physiol. Univ. Birm.; Bowman Prof. Physiol. Univ. Birm. 1965-86.

HILTON, Stephen Mark The Surgery, 7 Elvaston Road, Ryton NE41 3NT; 10 South View, Clara Vale, Ryton NE40 3SY Tel: 0191 413 9125 — MB BS 1983 Lond.; MRCGP 1991. GP. Prev: Regist. (Pub. Health Med.) N.. & Yorks. Region; Clin. Epidemiol. MRC Laborat., The Gambia; Dist. Med. Off. Menyamya, Papua New Guinea.

HILTON, Stephen Neil Cunliffe Medical Centre, 41 Cunliffe Street, Chorley PR7 2BA Tel: 01257 267127 Fax: 01257 234664; 135 Carr Lane, Chorley PR7 3JQ — MB ChB 1977 Liverp.

HILTON, Susan Rowena Upper Chorlton Road Surgery, 171 Upper Chorlton Road, Manchester M16 9RT Tel: 0161 881 4293 Fax: 0161 860 5265; 13 Morville Road, Chorlton-cum-Hardy, Manchester M21 0UG Tel: 0161 881 4318 Fax: 0161 881 4318 Email: morville13@cs.com — MB ChB 1972 Bristol; DObst RCOG 1974. (Bristol) Socs: BMA & MWF; Soc. Pub. Health; RCGP (Assoc.). Prev: Clin. Med. Off. S. Manch. HA; SHO Roan Consolidated Copper Mines Hosp. Mufulira, Zambia; SHO (Paediat.) Radcliffe Infirm. Oxf.

HILTON-JONES, David Milton Keynes NHS Trust Hospital, Standing Way, Eaglestone, Milton Keynes MK6 5LD Tel: 01908 660033 Fax: 01908 243205 Email: david.hilton_jones@clneuro.ox.ac.uk; Radcliffe Infirmary, Woodstock Road, Oxford OX2 6HE Tel: 01865 311188 Fax: 01865 790493 — MD 1987 Camb.; MA Camb. 1978, MD 1987, MB BChir 1977; MRCP (UK) 1979; FRCP Ed. 1994; FRCP 1997. (Cambridge) Cons. Neurol. Milton Keynes Hosp. NHS Trust & Radcliffe Infirm. NHS Trust Oxf. Socs: World Muscle Soc.

HIMAYAKANTHAN, Sivasithamparam General Hospital, St Helier, Jersey JE2 3QS Tel: 01534 622661 Fax: 01534 622669 — MB BS 1972 Sri Lanka; AMEC (Austr.) 1992; ESMO. Cert. (Euro) 1999; LRCP LRCS Ed. LRCPS Glas. 1984; FRCPI 1999; M.Med.Sci. (Birm.) 1996. (Fac. Med. Colombo, Ceylon) Assoc. Specialist (Oncol.) Gen. Hosp. St. Helier, Jersey. Socs: Med. Protec. Soc. Prev: Assoc. Specialist (Gastroenterol. & Oncol.) Gen. Hosp. St. Helier, Jersey; Regist. (Gen. Med. & Gastroenterol.) Jersey Gen. Hosp.; Regist. (Gen. Med. & Cardiol.) Maidstone & Guy's Hosp. Lond.

HIME, Martin Charles Health Centre, Old Street, Clevedon BS21 6DG Tel: 01275 871454; 26 Castle Road, Clevedon BS21 7DE — MB ChB 1971 Bristol; MRCP (UK) 1974; MRCGP 1979. (Bristol) Prev: Research Fell. Bristol Roy. Infirm.

HIMID, Khadija Ashraff Elizabeth Blackwell House, Avonley Road, London SE14 5ER; 65 Runnymede, London SW19 2PG — MD 1984 Dar-es-Salaam; MSc (Community Paediat.) Lond. 1993; DFFP 1995; DCH RCPS Glas. 1991; DTCH Liverp. 1988. Lect. (Community Paediat.) UMDS Lond. Socs: BMA. Prev: Regist. (A & E) & Clin. Med. Off. (Paediat.) (Guy's) Optimum Health Lond.; Regist. Argyle & Clyde HB; SHO Lanarksh. HB.

HIMSWORTH, Professor Richard Lawrence Institute of Public Health, University of Cambridge, Robinson Way, Cambridge CB2 2SR Tel: 01223 330360 Fax: 01223 330168 Email: himsworthr@rdd-phru.com.ac.uk; 39 High Street, Balsham, Cambridge CB1 6DJ Tel: 01223 893975 — MB Camb. 1962, BChir 1961; MD (Raymond Horton Smith Prize) Camb. 1971; FRCP Glas. 1989; FRCP Ed. 1988; FRCP Lond. 1977, M 1964. (Univ. Coll. Hosp.) Prof. Health Research & Developm. Univ. Camb.; Dir. Research & Developm., E.ern Region NHS Exec. Socs: Assn. Phys.; Med. Res. Soc. Prev: Regius Prof. (Med.) Univ. Aberd.; Hon. Cons. Phys. Aberd. Roy. Infirm.; Head Endocrinol. Research Gp. Clin. Research Centre Harrow.

HINCHCLIFFE, David Edward 160 Clifton Drive, Blackpool FY4 1RT — MB BS 1998 Lond.; MB BS Lond 1998.

HINCHCLIFFE, Martyn Gerard Department of Radiology, Worthing Hospital, Park Avenue, Worthing BN11 2DH Tel: 01903 205111 — BM 1979 Soton.; MRCP (UK) 1983; FRCR 1991. Cons. Radiol. Worthing Hosp. W. Sussex. Prev: Sen. Regist. (Radiol.) Univ. Hosp. Wales Cardiff; Regist. (Cardiol.) Cardiac Centre Riyadh Armed Forces Hosp.; SHO Rotat. (Med.) Univ. Hosp. Nottm.

HINCHCLIFFE, Robert John Billinghay Medical Practice, 39 High Street, Billinghay, Lincoln LN4 4AU Tel: 01526 860490 Fax: 01526 861860 — MB BS 1979 Newc.; MRCGP 1983; DRCOG 1983.

HINCHCLIFFE, Professor Ronald Institute of Laryngology & Otology, 330 Gray's Inn Road, London WC1X 8EE Tel: 020 7837 8855 Fax: 020 7278 8643; Hearing & Balance Centre, Portland Hospital, London W1N 6AH Tel: 020 7383 5870 Fax: 020 7631 1170 — MB ChB Manch. 1950; PhD Lond. 1965; BSc (1st cl. Hons.) Manch. 1947, MD 1955; FRCP Lond. 1982; FRCP Ed. 1976, M 1970; MRCS Eng. LRCP Lond. 1950; DLO Eng. 1957. (Manch.) Emerit. Prof. Audiol. Med. Inst. Laryngol. & Otol. Univ. Coll. Lond.; Cons. Audiol. Phys. Hearing & Balance Centre Portland Hosp. Lond.; Hon. Cons. Sixth People's Hosp. Shanghai, China; Mem. Coll. Otolaryngol. Amicitiae Sacrum.; Mem. WHO Expert Advis. Panel Preven. of Deafness & Hearing Impairment. Socs: Barany Soc.; (Ex-Pres.) Internat. Soc. Audiol.; (Ex-Pres.) Internat. Assn. Phys. Audiol. Prev: Vis. Assoc. Prof. Yale Univ., USA; Squadron Ldr. & Specialist Aviat. Physiol. RAF; Wernher Trav. Fell. in Otol. & Research.

HINCHLEY, Mr Geoffrey William Accident & Emergency, Chase Farm Hospital, The Ridgeway, Enfield EN2 8JL Tel: 020 8366 6600 Ext: 5008 Fax: 020 8967 5941 — MB BS 1983 Lond.; LLM Univ. Wales 1994; FFAEM 1996; FRCS Eng. 1987. (Char. Cross & Univ. Lond.) Cons. A & E Barnet & Chase Farm NHS Trust Enfield Middx. Prev: Sen. Regist. & Regist. (A & E) Poole, Bournemouth, Derby & Nottm.

HINCHLEY, Hazel Mary (retired) Kelloways Barn, Old Mill Lane, Donhead-St-Andrew, Shaftesbury SP7 9EF Tel: 01747 828708 — MB BS 1967 Lond.; MRCS Eng. LRCP Lond. 1967. Prev: Cons. (Pharmaceut. Med.).

HINCHLIFFE, Ann Catherine Evington Centre, Leicester General Hospital, Gwendolen Road, Leicester LE5 4PW Tel: 0116 225 5911; 26 Morland, Stoneygate, Leicester LE2 3PE — MB BS 1986 Lond.; MA Camb. 1986, BA 1983; MRCPsych 1991. Cons. (Psychiat. for the Elderly) Leicester. Prev: Sen. Regist. & Univ. Coll. & Middlx. Hosp. Train. Scheme.

HINCHLIFFE, Mr Anthony Banwell Court, Wolvershill Road, Banwell, Weston Super Mare BS29 6DJ Tel: 01934 822228 — MB ChB 1960 Bristol; ChM Bristol 1973; FRCS Eng. 1967; DObst RCOG 1963. Cons. Urol. W.on Area Health NHS Trust; Hon. Sen. Clin. Lect. Univ. Bristol. Socs: Brit. Assn. Urol. Surg. Prev: Cons. Surg. Bristol & W.on Health Dist. (T); Sen. Regist. Bristol Roy. Infirm.

HINCHLIFFE, Jack 5 Griffin House, Admiral Gardens, Cowes PO31 7XE Tel: 01983 294904 — MB ChB 1943 Manch. (Manch.)

HINCHLIFFE, Joan Betty (retired) 24 Saunders Green, Mottram Old Road, Stalybridge SK15 Tel: 0161 338 3335 — MB ChB Manch. 1951. Prev: SCMO (Child Health) Tameside AHA.

HINCHLIFFE, Marc St Saviours Surgery, Merick Road, Malvern Link, Malvern WR14 1DD Tel: 01684 572323 Fax: 01684 891067 — MB ChB 1983 Leeds; MRCGP 1987.

HINCHLIFFE, Mary Katherine (retired) Banwell Court, Wolvershill Road, Banwell, Weston Super Mare BS29 6DJ Email: maryhinchcliffe@llineone.nel — MB BS 1959 Lond.; FRCPsych 1996, M 1972; DPM Eng. 1965; DObst RCOG 1963; DCH Eng. 1961. Med. Mem. Ment. Health Review Tribunal. Prev: Sen. Regist. (Ment. Health) Bristol Health Dist. (T).

HINCHLIFFE, Michael David — MB ChB 1963 Manch.; DObst RCOG 1965. (Manch.) Clin. Asst. (Dermat.) Leighton Hosp. Crewe. Prev: SHO (Paediat.) Vict. Hosp. Blackpool; Ho. Phys. & Ho. Off. (O & G) Bolton Dist. Gen. Hosp.; Ho. Surg. Salford Roy. Hosp.

HINCHLIFFE, Robert Frederick Christopher Clifton Lane Health Centre, Clifton Lane, Doncaster Road, Rotherham S65 1DU Tel: 01709 382315 Fax: 01709 512646; Toll Bar House, Firsby Lane, Conisbrough, Doncaster DN12 2AZ — MB ChB 1965 Sheff.

HINCHLIFFE, William Stuart Rawtenstall Health Centre, Bacup Road, Rossendale BB4 7PL Tel: 01706 213060 Fax: 01706 213060 — MB ChB 1973 Manch.; MRCGP 1978; DRCOG 1977; DCH Eng. 1976.

HINCKS, Jonathan Richard Cheddar Medical Centre, Roynon Way, Cheddar BS27 3NZ Tel: 01934 742061 Fax: 01934 744374; Spring Field, 13 Barrows Road, Cheddar BS27 3AY Tel: 01934 742059 Fax: 01934 744374 — MB BS 1980 Lond.

HINCKS, Michael Edward, VRD (retired) The Coach House, Middle St., Ashcott, Bridgwater TA7 9QG Tel: 01458 210024 Fax: 01458 210024 — MB ChB Bristol 1951. Prev: Surg. Cdr. RNR.
HINCKS, Simon Sebastian Murray 43C Mitchell Street, London EC1V 3QD — MB BS 1988 Lond.
HIND, Alan Wheelton 17 Andrew Court, 68 Wickham Road, Beckenham BR3 6RG — MB BS 1947 Lond.; MRCS Eng. LRCP Lond. 1941; FFA RCS Eng. 1953; DA Eng. 1947. (Guy's) Socs: BMA. Prev: Cons. Anaesth. Roy. Masonic Hosp. Lond.; Sen. Med. Off. DHSS; Cons. Anaesth. Emerit. Guy's Hosp. Lond.
HIND, Charles Robert Keith The Cardiothoracic Centre, University of Liverpool, Liverpool L14 3FE Tel: 0151 293 2390 Fax: 0151 220 8573 Email: charles.hird@ccl-tr.nwest.nhs.uk; 45 Rodney Street, Liverpool L1 9EW Tel: 0151 708 0842 Fax: 0151 709 5679 — MB BS 1977 Lond.; BSc (Hons.) Lond. 1974, MD 1985; FRCP Lond. 1993; MRCP (UK) 1980; FRCP Edin 2000. (London Hospital) Cons. Phys. (Gen. & Respirat. Med.) Cardiothoracic Centre Univ. Liverp.; Censor & Dir. Pub.ations RCP Lond.; Pres.-Elect, Internat. Soc. of Med.; Clin. Lect. (Med.) and Sen. research Fell. Univ. Liverp. Prev: Edr. Postgrad. Med. Jl.; Censor & Dir. Pub.ations RCP Lond.
HIND, Edward Jonathan 10 Knowles Avenue, Crowthorne RG45 6DU — MB BS 1996 Lond.
HIND, Jesser Stewart (retired) Unthank's Pightle, Thurne, Great Yarmouth NR29 3BS Tel: 01692 670466 — MB BS 1945 Lond.; MRCS Eng. LRCP Lond. 1943; FFA RCS Eng. 1965; DA (UK) 1960; DTM & H Eng. 1952. Prev: Cons. Anaesth. Gt. Yarmouth & Gorleston & LoW.oft Gen. Hosps.
HIND, John West Wing, Esk Medical Centre, Ladywell Way, Musselburgh EH21 6AB Tel: 0131 665 2594 Fax: 0131 665 2428 — MB ChB 1980 Manch.; BSc St. And. 1978.
HIND, Jonathan Mark 76 Shields Road, Seaburn Dene, Sunderland SR6 8JN — BM BS 1996 Nottm.
HIND, Mr Richard Edward 20 Winthorpe Road, Newark NG24 2AB — MB ChB 1984 Sheff.; MB ChB Sheff. l984; FRCS Ed. 1989.
HIND, Simon Paul 55 Sutherland Avenue, Leeds LS8 1BY — MB ChB 1994 Manch.
HIND, Valerie Margaret Doris (retired) Strathview, Emma Terrace, Blairgowrie PH10 6JA Tel: 01250 872762 — MB ChB 1961 St. And.; PhD Birm. 1970; FRCS Glas. 1981; FRCS Ed. 1972; FRCOphth 1989. Hon. Sen. Lect. (Anat.) Univ. St. And. Prev: Cons. Ophth. Surg. Stobhill Gen. Hosp. Glas.
HINDE, Francis Ronald John Princess Royal Hospital, Telford TF1 6TF Tel: 01952 641222; Stevenshill Cottage, Harnage, Cressage TF2 0EA Tel: 01952 510218 — MB BChir 1975 Camb.; BA Camb. 1971, MD 1986; FRCP Lond. 1995; MRCP (UK) 1981; DCH Eng. 1976; FRCPCH 1997. Cons. Paediat. P.ss Roy. Hosp. Telford. Prev: Sen. Regist. (Paediat.) Bristol; Research Fell. Univ. Hosp. Nottm.; Ho. Off. Hosp. Sick Childr. Gt. Ormond St.
HINDE, Graham de Buckley, VRD (retired) Tynewydd, Westgate, Cowbridge CF71 7AQ Tel: 0144 632254 — MRCS Eng. LRCP Lond. 1941; MRCS Eng., LRCP Lond. 1941; FRCR 1978; DMRD Eng. 1948. Prev: Cons. Radiol. United Cardiff Hosps.
HINDE, Jean Mary (retired) The Old School, North Bovey, Newton Abbot TQ13 8RA Tel: 01647 440650 — MA, BM BCh Oxf. 1945; DObst RCOG 1948.
HINDER, Stephen Andrew John Solihull Primary Care Trust, Oliver House, 4 Ivy Lodge Close, Marston Green, Birmingham B37 7HL Tel: 0121 779 6302 — MB ChB 1988 Birm.; MRCPsych 1995. Cons. in the Psychiat. of Learning Disabilities Solihull Primary Care Trust. Socs: Soc. for Study of Behavioural Phenotypes. Prev: Sen. Regist. (Psychiat. of Learning Disabil.) W. Midl. Train. Scheme; Regist. Rotat. (Psychiat.) Coventry & Warks. Train. Scheme; Sen. Rotat. (CO Psychiat.) W. Midl.
HINDLE, Andrew Terence 315 Leigh Road, Leigh WN7 1TA — MB ChB 1987 Manch.
HINDLE, Catherine Mary Cadwgan Surgery, 11 Bodelwyddan Avenue, Old Colwyn, Colwyn Bay LL29 9NP Tel: 01492 515410 Fax: 01492 513270; The Old Vicarage, Trofarth, Abergele LL22 8BD — MB BS 1983 Lond.; MRCGP 1988; DRCOG 1987. (St. Mary's Hosp. Lond.) Prev: Med. Off. Clwyd HA; Trainee GP N. Humberside VTS.
HINDLE, David John Croft House Surgery, 5 Croft House, 114 Manchester Road, Slaithwaite, Huddersfield HD7 5JY Tel: 01484 842652 Fax: 01484 348223 — MB ChB 1991 Leeds; BSc (Hons.) Leeds 1988; MRCGP 1997; DRCOG 1996.
HINDLE, John Michael Warwick Road Surgery, 65 Warwick Road, Carlisle CA1 1EB Tel: 01228 36303 — MRCS 1973 Lond; MRCS Eng LRCP Lond 1973. (London) GP Carlisle.
HINDLE, John Vincent Llandudno General Hospital, Ffordd Ysbyty, Llandudno LL30 1LB Tel: 01492 862366 Fax: 01492 876973 — MB BS 1981 Lond.; MRCP (UK) 1986; MRCPsych 1988; FRCP 1995. Cons. Phys. Geriat. Med. Llandudno Gen. Hosp. Gwynedd; Hon. Sen Lect. Univ. Coll. of Wales, Bangor. Socs: Chairm. N. Wales Pk.inson's Dis. Forum.; Sec. Brit. Geriat. Soc.; s/i Gp. Pk.inson's Dis. Prev: Sen. Regist. (Gen. & Geriat. Med.) St. Geo. Hosp. Lond.; Regist. (Psychiat.) Bethlem Roy. & Maudsley Hosps. Lond.; Regist. (Gen. Med.) Hull HA.
HINDLE, Kirsten Sarah 8=97 Queens Drive, Berrylands, Surbiton KT5 8PP — MB BS 1996 Lond.
HINDLE, Thomas Stanley (retired) Crosshill, Kilmidyke Road, Grange-over-Sands LA11 7AQ Tel: 053 95 33525 — MB BChir 1942 Camb.; MA Camb. 1947, BA 1940, MD 1949; MRCS Eng. LRCP Lond. 1942. Prev: Ho. Surg. (Obst.) St. Luke's Hosp. Bradford.
HINDLE, Walter Joseph, TD Witches Green, 54 Mill Road, North Lancing, Lancing BN15 0PZ — LRCPI & LM, LRSCI & LM 1970; LRCPI & LM, LRCSI & LM 1970; DObst RCOG 1972. Hosp. Pract. (Orthop.) Worthing & S.lands Hosps.
HINDLE, Yvonne Anne 13 Talgarth Road, Manchester M40 7QA — MB ChB 1992 Liverp.
HINDLEY, Andrew Charles Lancashire and Lakeland Radiotherapy Unit, Royal Preston Hospital, Sharoe Green Lane, Fulwood, Preston PR2 9HT; Churchgate House, Church St, Churchtown, Preston PR3 0HT Tel: 01995 601970 — MB ChB 1977 Birm.; BSc (Physiol.) Birm. 1974, MD 1993, MB ChB 1977; FRCR Eng. 1989; MRCP (UK) 1980; FRACR 1995. (Birmingham) Cons. Clin. Oncol. Lancs. & Lakeland Radiother. Unit Roy. Preston Hosp. Prev: Cons. (Radiother.) Auckland Hosp. New Zealand; Sen. Registr. (Radiother.) Ch.ill Hosp. Oxf.; Regist. (Radiother.) Velindre Hosp. Cardiff.
HINDLEY, Christopher John Blackpool Victoria Hospital, Whinney Heys Road, Blackpool FY3 8NR Tel: 01253 303524 Fax: 01253 303546; Greenbank Cottage, 29 Ribby Road, Wrea Green, Preston PR4 2NA Tel: 01772 682323 — MB ChB 1977 Liverp.; MChOrth Liverp. 1985; FRCS Ed. 1983. Cons. Orthop. Blackpool Vict. Hosp. Socs: Brit. Soc. Surg. Hand. Prev: Sen. Regist. (Orthop.) Mersey RHA; Regist. (Hand Surg.) Wrightington Hosp.; Regist. (Orthop. Surg.) Walton Hosp. Liverp.
HINDLEY, Christopher Paton (retired) 11C Broadlands Road, Highgate, London N6 4AE Tel: 020 8348 2622 — MB BChir 1954 Camb.; MRCGP 1963; DGM RCP Lond. 1991; DCH Eng. 1958; DObst RCOG 1956. Asst. GP Qu.sbridge Gp. Pract. Lond.; Vis. Lect. Florence Nightingale Sch. of Nursing & Midw. Kings Coll. Lond. Prev: Clin. Asst. (Obst.) Whittington Hosp. Lond.
HINDLEY, Colin Boothman 37 Hardy Way, Enfield EN2 8NW — BSc (Psychol.) Lond. 1949, MB ChB Manch. 1946. (Manch.) Emerit. Prof. Child Developm. Univ. Lond. Inst. Educat. Socs: FBPsS; (Ex-Chairm.) Assn. Child Psychol. & Psychiat. Prev: Asst. Med. Off. Hope Hosp. Salford.
HINDLEY, Daniel Trevorrow 28 Walker Avenue, Whitefield, Manchester M45 6TP — MB BS 1985 Lond.; BSc (Immunol.) Lond. 1982; MRCP Paediat. (UK) 1991. Cons. Paediat. Fairfield Gen. Hosp. Bury. Prev: Sen. Regist. (Paediat.) St. Jas. Univ. Hosp. Leeds & St. Lukes Bradford; Regist. (Paediat.) NICU & Hope Hosp. Manch.; Regist. (Paediat. Neurol.) Roy. Manch. Childr. Hosp.
HINDLEY, David James Southview Surgery, Guildford Road, Woking GU22 7RR Tel: 01483 763186 Fax: 01483 821526; Nairn, Kettlewell Hill, Woking GU21 4JJ Tel: 01483 772460 — MB BS 1984 Lond.; DRCOG 1988. GP Woking.
HINDLEY, Frances Treloe, Bar Road, Helford Passage, Falmouth TR11 5LE — MB ChB 1957 Ed. Prev: Clin. Med. Off. (Community Med.) Bristol & W.on HA; Ho. Off. City Hosp. Edin. & Roy. Hosp. Sick Childr. Edin.
HINDLEY, Frank Ashton (retired) Fern Hill, Fern Road, Cropwell Bishop, Nottingham NG12 3BW Tel: 0115 989 3189 Email: fandj@connectfree.co.uk — MB ChB Manch. 1959. Prev: Gen. Pract. - Cropwall Bishop - Belvoir Health Gp., Nottm.
HINDLEY, John Sefton 42 Lugsmore Lane, St Helens WA10 3DL Tel: 01744 23131 — MB ChB 1939 Liverp. (Liverp.) Prev: Ho. Surg.

Stanley Hosp. Liverp.; Ho. Phys. Roy. Infirm. Blackburn; RAMC 1940-46.

HINDLEY, Jonathon Talbot The Vicarage, Lewes BN7 2JA — MB BS 1993 Lond.

HINDLEY, Judith Anne Andrew House Surgery, 2 South Terrace, Camborne TR14 8ST Tel: 01209 714876 — MB ChB 1983 Liverp.; MRCGP 1989; DTM & H Liverp. 1984.

HINDLEY, Mark Christopher Somerford Grove Practice, Somerford Grove Health Centre, Somerford Grove, London N16 7TX Tel: 020 7241 9700 Fax: 020 7275 7198; 31 Barrington Road, London N8 8QT — MB ChB 1987 Manch.; MRCGP 1991.

HINDLEY, Mark Olufisan Binrock Lodge, 454A Perth Road, Dundee DD2 1NG — BM BCh 1992 Oxf.; MA Camb. 1992.

HINDLEY, Peter Adrian Deaf & Child & Family Team, Springfield Hospital, 61 Glenburnie Road, London SW17 7DJ Tel: 020 8682 6925 Fax: 020 8682 6461 — MB BS 1981 Lond.; BSc Lond. 1978; MRCPsych 1987; CACPD (Pt III) 1994. Cons. Child & Adolesc. Psychiat. Pathfinder Community & Specialist Ment. Health Unit; Sen. Lect. (Child & Adolesc. Psychiat.) St. Geo. Hosp. Med. Sch. Socs: Brit. Soc. Ment. Health & Deafness (Exec. Comm.); Assn. Child Psychol. & Psychiat. Prev: Sen. Regist. (Child Psychiat.) Maudsley & Roy. Bethlem Hosps.; Research Fell. St. Geo. Psychiat. Train. Scheme.

HINDLEY, Richard Graham Flat 3, 1 Salisbury Road, Hove BN3 3AB — MB ChB 1991 Dundee; FRCS Lond. 1996. Specialist Regist. (Urol.). Socs: BAUS; RCS (Eng.); BMA.

HINDMARSH, Andrew Collingwood 10 Wilmot Street, London E2 0BS — MB BS 1997 Lond.

HINDMARSH, David John The Crane Surgery, Rectory Fields, Cranbrook TN17 3JB Tel: 01580 712260; Hazels, Bakers Cross, Cranbrook TN17 3NW Tel: 01380 712260 — MB BS 1982 Lond.; DCH RCP Lond. 1985; DRCOG 1985. Prev: GP Dover; Trainee GP Dover VTS.

HINDMARSH, Elizabeth Ann Yew Tree House, Bearstone Road, Norton in Hayes, Market Drayton TF9 4AP — MB ChB 1981 Liverp.; DRCOG 1986.

HINDMARSH, John Cowens Yew Tree House, Bearstone Road, Norton in Hales, Market Drayton TF9 4AP — MB ChB 1980 Liverp.; FFA RCS Eng. 1985.

HINDMARSH, Mr John Reed Croft House, Hurworth Place, Darlington DL2 2DQ Tel: 01325 721705 — MB BS Newc. 1968; MD Newc. 1981; FRCS Eng. 1975; FRCS Ed. 1975; FEBUrol 1996. (Newc.) Cons. Urol. S. Cleveland Hosp. Middlesbrough; Fell. Europ. Bd. Urol. 1996. Socs: Fell. Roy. Soc. Med.; Brit. Assn. Urol. Surgs. Prev: Sen. Lect. & Hon. Cons. Urol. Inst. Urol. Lond.; Sen. Regist. (Urol.) W.. Gen. Hosp. Edin.; Ho. Phys. & Ho. Surg. Roy. Vict. Infirm. Newc.

HINDMARSH, Joyce Heather 74 Moor Road N., Gosforth, Newcastle upon Tyne NE3 — MB BS 1951 Durh.; DPH 1956. (Newc.) Asst. Sch. Med. Off. City & Co. Newc. Socs: BMA; Fell. Soc. MOH. Prev: Ho. Phys. Roy. Vict. Infirm. Newc.

HINDMARSH, Peter Christopher 271 Kings Road, Kingston upon Thames KT2 5JJ — MB BS 1978 Lond.; BSc (1st cl. Hons.) Lond. 1975, MD 1989; FRCP Lond. 1993; MRCP (UK) 1982. Sen. Lect. (Med.) & Hon. Cons. Paediat. Endocrinol. Middlx. Hosp. Lond.; Hon. Sen. Lect. & Hon. Cons. Paediat. Endocrinol. Hosp. Childr. Gt. Ormond St. Lond.

HINDOCHA, Lucy Sarah 76 Monks Road, Lincoln LN2 5HU — MB ChB 1988 Sheff.; MRCGP 1992.

HINDOCHA, Sunil 34 Newland, Lincoln LN1 1XP — MB ChB 1986 Manch.; MRCGP 1990.

HINDS, Charles Johnston Department of Anaesthesia, St Bartholemeuis Hospital, Smithfield EC1A 7BE Tel: 020 7601 7526 — MB BS 1972 Lond.; FRCP Lond. 1990; MRCP (UK) 1979; MRCS Eng. LRCP Lond. 1972; FFA RCS Eng. 1977. (St. Bartholomew's) Cons. & Sen. Lect. (Anaesth. & IC) St. Bart. Hosp. Lond. Socs: (Ex-Chairm.) Intens. Care Soc.; Intercollegiate Bd. Train. Intens. Care Med.; Mem. of Counc., Europ. Soc. of Intens. Care Med.

HINDS, Gerald Eugene Department of Anaesthetics, Frenchay Hospital, Frenchay Park Road, Bristol BS16 1LE — MB BS 1985 West Indies.

HINDS, Gwyneth Miriam Elizabeth Begney Hill Road Surgery, Begney Hill Road, Dromara, Dromore BT25 2AT — MB BCh BAO 1986 Belf.; MRCGP 1993; DRCOG 1991. Socs: BMA.

HINDS, James Christopher Donald Croft House 6 Governors Road, Onchan, Douglas IM3 1AU — MB BS 1997 Lond.

HINDS, Michael Christopher Castledawson Surgery, Station Road, Castledawson, Magherafelt BT45 8AZ Tel: 028 7938 6237 Fax: 028 7946 9613 — MB BCh BAO 1980 Belf.; MRCGP 1989; DRCOG 1988. (Belfast) Gen. Practitioner, Castledawson Surg. Socs: BMA; MRCGP.

HINDS, Nigel Peter 73 Argyll Avenue, Southall UB1 3AT — MB BCh 1989 Wales.

HINDS, Mr Oliver 45 Coughey Road, Portaferry, Newtownards — MB BCh BAO 1972 Belf.; FRCS Ed. 1978.

HINDS, Philip Richard Marine Avenue Surgery, 49 Marine Avenue, Whitley Bay NE26 1NA Tel: 0191 252 4527 — MB BCh BAO 1987 Belf.; MRCGP 1991; DRCOG 1991; T (GP) 1991; DCH Dub. 1990. (Qu. Univ. Belf.) Princip. (Gen. Med.). Socs: BMA. Prev: Trainee GP Newtownards VTS; SHO Ards & Ulster Hosps.

HINDS, Priscilla Joy 83 Greenway, Monkton Heathfield, Taunton TA2 8NH — BM 1991 Soton.

HINDS, Robert Owen 3 Long Royd Cottages, Long Royd Road, Hubberton, Triangle, Sowerby Bridge HX6 1NX Tel: 01422 831728 — MB BS 1977 Lond. Med. Off. Benefits Agency Med. Servs. DSS.

HINDS, Rupert Michael 10 Templemere, Weybridge KT13 9PB — MB BS 1994 Lond.

HINDS, Sheldon Bloomfield Surgery, 95 Bloomfield Road, Bangor BT20 4XA Tel: 028 9145 2426 — MB BCh BAO 1981 Belf.; MRCGP 1985; DCH Dub. 1985; DRCOG 1984.

HINDS-HOWELL, Conrad Michael c/o National Westminster Bank Ltd., 87 High St., Sidcup DA14 6DL — MB BS 1968 Lond.; MRCS Eng. LRCP Lond. 1968.

HINDSON, Norman Alexander 78 Falkland Road, Hornsey, London N8 0NP — MB ChB 1972 Liverp.; MRCS Eng. LRCP Lond. 1972; DPM Eng. 1976. Sen. Med. Off. HM. Prison Holloway.

HINDSON, Thomas Colin Inchgarth, 369 Worcester Road, Malvern WR14 1AR Tel: 01684 568840 Fax: 01684 568840 — MB 1960 Camb.; MA Camb. 1956, MB 1960, BChir 1959; MRCP Lond. 1965; FRCP Ed. 1975, M 1964; FRCP Lond. 1989; DTM & H Lond 1964. (Camb. & St. Bart.) Cons. Skin Laser Ther. Lasercare Clinics Birm. Socs: Fell. Roy. Soc. Med.; Fell. Amer. Coll. Cryosurg. Prev: Cons. Dermat. Sunderland Roy. Infirm.; Cons. Adviser Dermat. MoD (Army).

HINDUSA, Kunal 6 Summerfield Place, Wilmslow SK9 1NE — MB ChB 1997 Manch.

HINE, Andrew Leonard Dept of Radiology, Central Middlesex Hospital, Acton Lane, London NW10 7NS; 34 Chartfield Avenue, Putney, London SW15 6HG — MB BS 1978 Lond.; MRCP (UK) 1980; FRCR 1985. (Middlx.) Cons. Radiol. Centr. Middlx. Hosp. Lond. Prev: Sen. Regist. (Radiol.) St. Geo. Hosp. Lond.; Regist. (Radiol.) Middlx. Hosp. Lond.

HINE, Christine Elizabeth Directorate of Public Health Medicine, Avon Health Authority, King Square House, King Square, Bristol BS2 8EE — MB ChB 1982 Bristol; MRCP (UK) 1985; MFPHM RCP (UK) 1989; FFPHM RCP (UK) 1999. (Bristol) Cons. Pub. Health Med. Avon HA. Prev: Cons. Pub. Health Med. Bath DHA; Sen. Regist. & Regist. (Pub. Health Med.) Bristol & W.on HA.

HINE, Dame Deirdre Joan, DBE (retired) Commission For Health Improvement, 103 Bunhill Rd, London EC1Y 8TE Tel: 020 7448 9246 — MB BCh Wales 1961; FRCP Lond. 1993; FFPHM RCP (UK) 1981, M 1974; DPH Wales 1964. Chair Commiss. Health Improvement, Finsbury Tower, 103 Bunhill Rd, Lond. EC1Y 8TG; Pres. Roy. Soc. Med.; Vice-Pres. Marie Curie Cancer Care; Chair Comm. Health Improvement. Prev: Chief Med. Off. Welsh Off.

HINE, Iain David Taylor and Partners, Shirehampton Health Centre, Pembroke Road, Shirehampton, Bristol BS11 9SB Tel: 0117 916 2233 Fax: 0117 930 8246; 1 Fremantle Square, Cotham, Bristol BS6 5TL — MB BS 1979 Lond.; MRCP (UK) 1983; MRCGP 1986. (Lond. Hosp.) Prev: Trainee GP Poole VTS; SHO (O & G) P.ss Anne Hosp. Soton.; Regist. (Med.) Univ. Hosp. Wales & Llandough Hosps. Cardiff.

HINE, Ian Peter Tel: 01432 275656 Fax: 0870 122 3554 Email: drhine@doctors.org.uk — MRCS Eng. LRCP Lond. 1967; MSc 2000 Univ. of Wales College of Medicine; FFA RCS Eng. 1974. (Guy's) p/t Asst. Med. Director, INPUT Pain Managem. Progr., Bronllys Hosp., Powys. Prev: Sen. Regist. (Dept. Anaesth.) St. Bart. Hosp. Lond.;

Anaesth. Regist. Salisbury Gp. Hosps.; Anaesth. Regist. Harold Wood Hosp.

HINE, James Leonard (retired) Hoy Cottage, Alde House Drive, Aldeburgh IP15 5EE Tel: 01728 452567 — MA Camb. 1950, MB BChir 1948; MRCGP 1960. Prev: GP Cambs.

HINE, Katy Louise The Paddock, Mersea Rd, Abberton, Colchester CO5 7NR — MB BS 1996 Lond.

HINE, Keith Richard Ashdown Nuffield Hospital, Burrell Road, Haywards Heath RH16 1UD Tel: 01444 456999 Fax: 01444 454111; Westerlands, 2 Clayton Road, Ditchling, Hassocks BN6 8UY Tel: 01273 843370 Email: keithrhine@mistral.co.uk — MB ChB 1973 Birm.; BSc (1st cl. Hons.) Birm. 1970, MD 1981; FRCP Lond. 1992; MRCP (UK) 1976; Euro.Dip.Gastroent 1999. (Birm.) Cons. Phys. P.ss Roy. Hosp. Haywards Heath. Socs: Brit. Soc. of Gastroenterol.; SW Thames Gut Club; Brighton & Sussex M-C Soc. Prev: Sen. Regist. (Med.) Univ. Hosp. Nottm.; Regist. (Med.) N. Staffs. Hosp. Centre Stoke-on-Trent; MRC Clin. Research Fell. (Immunol.) Univ. Birm.

HINES, Donald (retired) Thistlewood, Honicombe Road, St Anns Chapel, Gunnislake PL18 9HA — MB BS 1953 Lond.; MRCS Eng. LRCP Lond. 1950. Prev: Demonst. Anat. Lond. Hosp. Med. Coll.

HINES, Mr John Edward William Department of Urology, Whipps Cross University Hospital, Whipps Cross Road, Leytonstone, London E11 1NR Tel: 020 8535 6741 Fax: 020 8535 6741; 195 Whitehall Road, Woodford Green 1G8 0RG — MB ChB Liverp. 1985; FRCS Eng. 1991; FRCS Ed. 1991; FRCS (Urol) 1998. (Liverpool) Cons. Urol. Whipps Cross Hosp.; Hon. Sen. Lect. St. Barholomew's Hosp. Socs: BMA; BAUS; RSM. Prev: Sen. Regist. Rotat. in Urol. W. Lond. Scheme; Regist. Rotat. (Surg.) Hammersmith Hosp. & Roy. Postgrad. Med. Sch. Lond.

HINES, Kenneth Charles Eastwood Medical Centre, Eastwood Road, South Woodford, London E18 1BN Tel: 020 8530 4108 Fax: 020 8518 8728 — MB BS 1969 Lond. (Lond. Hosp.) Hon. Librarian Brit. Assn. Immediate Care; Hon. Tutor (Gen. Pract.) Roy. Free Hosp. Lond. Prev: Clin. Asst. (O & G) Whipps Cross Hosp. Lond.; Phys. to City Univ.; SHO Renal Dialysis & Transpl. Unit Lond. Hosp.

HING, Caroline Blanca 8 Meadow Way, Chigwell IG7 6LP — MB BS 1993 Lond.

HINGORANI, Aroon Dinesh 16 Princes Drive, Marple, Stockport SK6 6NJ Tel: 0161 449 9679 — MB BS 1989 Lond.; BA (Hons.) Physiol. Oxf. 1986; MRCP (UK) 1992. (Oxf. Univ. UMDS (Guy's) Lond.) Lect. & Sen. Hon. Regist. (Clin. Pharmacol.) Univ. Coll. Hosp. Lond. Socs: Med. Res. Soc. Prev: Hon. Sen. Regist. (Clin. Pharmacol.) Addenbrooke's Hosp. Camb.; Regist. Rotat. (Med.) St. Geo. Hosp. Lond.; SHO (HIV Med.) Middlx. Hosp. Lond.

HINGORANI, Kishin The Old Granary, North Brunton Farm, Gosforth, Newcastle upon Tyne NE3 5HD Tel: 0191 236 6442 Fax: 0191 236 6442 — MB BS 1953 Calcutta; FRCP Glas. 1984, M 1962; FRCP Ed. 1981, M 1960; DPhysMed. Eng. 1963. (R.G. Kar Med. Coll.) Cons. Rheum. BUPA Washington Hosp. Socs: Brit. Soc. Rheum. Prev: Cons. Rheum. Gateshead Hosp. Gp. & Regional Neurol. Unit Newc. Gen. Hosp.

HINGORANI, Tara Yvette 4 Well Road, Warrenpoint, Newry BT34 3RS — MB BS 1994 Lond.; Dip. Of Roy Coll Obst & Gyn 1997; Member of RCGP 1999.

HINGORANI, Mr Thakur Vasiomal 110 Bearwood Hill Road, Winshill, Burton-on-Trent DE15 0JW Tel: 01283 566899 Fax: 01283 515171 Email: hingoranitv@aol.com; Kedleston, 5 Brizlincote Lane, Burton-on-Trent DE15 0PR Tel: 01283 566900 Fax: 01283 515171 Email: hingoranitv@aol.com — MB BS 1952 Bombay; FRCS Glas. 1962; FRCS Ed. 1958; FRFPS Glas. 1958. (Grant Med. Coll. Bombay) Cons. ENT Surg., Burton-on-Trent. Socs: Life Fell. Roy. Soc. Med.; Midl. Inst. Otol. (Ex-Vice-Pres.); Life Mem. Brit. Assn. Otolaryngol. Head & Neck Surg. Prev: Sen. Regist. (Otolaryngol.) W.. Infirm. Glas.; Regist. (Surg.) Roy. Infirm. Blackburn; Resid. in Urol., Hosp. Of St. Raphael, New Haven, Connecticut, USA.

HINGSTON, Cecil Frank (retired) Coed Y Brenin, 14 Leaventhorpe Avenue, Bradford BD8 0ED — MB BChir 1947 Camb. Prev: Regist. (Med.) Maelor Gen. & War Memor. Hosps. Wrexham.

HINKES, Derrick Andrew Limpsfield Road Surgery, 515 Limpsfield Road, Warlingham CR6 9LF Tel: 01883 265262 Fax: 01883 627893; Malindi, 2 Westview Road, Warlingham CR6 9JD Tel: 01883 623712 — MB ChB 1977 Liverp.; DCH RCP Lond. 1982.

HINMAN, Margaret Maria Roseberry Centre, St Lukes Hospital, Marton Road, Middlesbrough TS4 3AF; 9 The Crescent, Carlton in Cleveland, Middlesbrough TS9 7BH — MB BS 1979 Newc.; MRCGP 1984.

HINNIE, John Department of Biochemistry, MacEwen Building, Glasgow Royal Infirmary, Glasgow G4 0SF; Flat S10, Clarendon Court, 9 Clarendon Place, St. George's Cross, Glasgow G20 7PZ — MB ChB 1987 Glas.; PhD St. And. 1978; BSc (Hons.) St. And. 1975; MRCP (UK) 1990; MRCPath 1996; Dip. Med. Sci. St. And. 1984. (Glas.) Lect. Univ. Dept. of Med. Glasg. Roy. Infirm.; Hon. Sen. Regist. Glas. Roy. Infirm.

HINSHAW, Mr Kim Sunderland Royal Hospital, Department of Obstetrics & Gynaecology, City Hospitals Sunderland NHS Trust, Kayll Road, Sunderland SR4 7TP Tel: 0191 565 6256 Fax: 0191 569 9218; 8 Beresford Park, Sunderland SR2 7JU Tel: 0191 567 2256 Email: kim.hinshaw@lineone.net — MB BS 1982 Newc.; MRCOG 1988. (Newc. u. Tyne) Cons. O & G City Hosps. Sunderland; Dist. Tutor (RCOG); Flexible Trainee Adviser (Obst. & Gyn.) N.ern Deanery; Vice Chairm. Regional speciality Train. Comm.; Chairm. Nat. Fac. Bd. ALSO (UK). Prev: Lect. & Hon. Sen. Regist. Univ. Aberd.

HINSHELWOOD, Barbara Gillian Medical Foundation for the Care of Victims of Torture, 96 - 98 Grapton Rd, London NW5 3EJ Tel: 020 7813 7777 Fax: 020 7813 0011; 24 Bramshill Gardens, London NW5 1JH Tel: 020 7272 1125 — MB BS 1963 Lond.; MRCS Eng. LRCP Lond. 1963. (Univ. Coll. Hosp.) Sen. Phys.,. Med. Foundat. for Care Victims of Torture, Lond. Socs: Brit. Stud. Health Assn.; Inst. Psychosexual Med.; Assoc. Mem. Brit. Psychoanalyt. Soc. Prev: Med. Dir. Coll. Health Serv. Lond.

HINSHELWOOD, Louise Sybil 1 Streatley Road, London NW6 7LJ — MB ChB 1989 Ed.; MRCGP 1996; DCH RCP Lond. 1994; DRCOG 1994. (Ed.) GP Asst. Lond.; Project Practitioner & Cancer LEAD Brent & Harrow Health Auth., Lond.

HINSHELWOOD, Professor Robert Douglas Centre for Psychoanalytic Studies, University of Essex, Colchester CO4 3SQ Tel: 01206 873745 Fax: 01206 872746 Email: rhinsh@essex.ac.uk; 18 Artesian Road, London W2 5AR Tel: 020 7229 2855 Email: 101364.2334@compuserve.com — MB BS Lond. 1965; BSc Lond. 1960; FRCPsych 1996, M 1990; DPM Eng. 1969. (Univ. Coll. Hosp.) Prof. Centre for Psychoanalytic Studies, Univ. Essex, Colchester; Founding Edr. Brit. Jl. Psychother. Socs: Brit. Psychoanal. Soc.; Fell. Roy. Coll. Psychiat.s. Prev: Clin. Dir. The Cassel Hosp. Richmond; Cons. Psychother. St. Bernard's Hosp. S.all; Clin. Asst. MarlBoro. Day Hosp. Lond.

HINSLEY, Anne Maureen The Surgery, 28 Claremont Road, Surbiton KT6 4RF Tel: 020 8399 2280 Fax: 020 8390 0371; 44 Gibbon Road, Kingston upon Thames KT2 6AB Tel: 020 8549 6598 — MB BS 1976 Lond.; MRCS Eng. LRCP Lond. 1976; DA 1980; DRCOG 1979; DCH Eng. 1978. (Char. Cross) Clin. Asst. (Anaesth.) Kingston Hosp.

HINSLEY, David Eric Maintop, Felden Lane, Felden, Hemel Hempstead HP3 0BE — MB ChB 1993 Leic.

HINSLEY, Susan Clare Maintop, Felden Lane, Felden, Hemel Hempstead HP3 0BE — MB ChB 1998 Liverp.; MB ChB Liverp 1998.

HINSON, David Stoakley (retired) 17 Muston Road, Hunmanby, Filey YO14 0JY Tel: 01723 890815 — MB ChB Leeds 1960. Prev: Ho. Phys. Leeds Gen. Infirm.

HINSON, Mr Frank Linden Storrsdale, Hawes Road, Ingleton, Carnforth LA6 3AN Tel: 015242 41843 — MB ChB 1981 Ed.; FRCS Eng. 1988.

HINTJENS, Kristien Laura Stockbridge Health Centre, 1 India Place, Edinburgh EH3 6EH — MB ChB 1988 Aberd.; DCH 1997; DFFP 1998. (Aberd.) GP Regist. Edin.; IPPNW Delegate to 9th World Congr. Japan 1989; IPPNW Delegate to 10th World Congr. Stockholm 1991. Socs: Internat. Phys. Preven. Nuclear War; MWF; BMA. Prev: SHO (Geriat.s) Liberton Hosp. E. & Midlothian NHS Trust; SHO (O & G) Roy. Infirm. Stirling; SHO (Paediat.) Roy. Infirm. Stirling.

HINTON, Anna Emily 13 Holly Lodge Gardens, London N6 6AA; 5 Cranebank mews, haliburton Road, Twickenham TW1 1PD — MB BS 1996 Lond.; MRCP 1999. (Middx) Med. SHO Rotat.N.wich Pk. Hosp.

HINTON, Catherine Ann Station Road Surgery, Station Road, Sowerby Bridge HX6 3AB Tel: 01422 831453/831457; 321 Holme Road, Warley, Halifax HX2 7RP — MB ChB 1972 Leeds; MRCGP 1976; DObst RCOG 1974.

HINTON, Christine Elizabeth Westholme, Bridge Bank, Telford TF8 7JT — MB ChB 1975 Bristol; MRCPath 1984.

HINTON, Mr Christopher Price The Princess Royal Hospital, Apley Castle, Telford TF1 6TF Tel: 01952 641222; Westholme, Bridge Bank, Telford TF8 7JT — MD 1988 Bristol; MB ChB 1974; FRCS Eng. 1980. Cons. Surg. P.ss Roy. Hosp. Telford. Socs: Surg. Research Soc. Prev: Sen. Regist. (Surg.) Trent RHA; Regist. (Surg.) Frenchay Hosp. Bristol; Surgic. Research Fell. (BrE. Screening) Nottm. HA.

HINTON, Mr Eamon Anthony St Georges Hospital, Blackshaw Road, Tooting, London SW17 0QT Tel: 020 8725 2054 Fax: 020 8725 3306 Email: ahinton@sghms.ac.uk; 107 Harley Street, London W1N 1DG Tel: 020 8336 1112 Fax: 020 8336 1112 — MB ChB 1984 Birm. Cons. Otolaryngologist St Geo.'s Hosp. Lond.; Cons. Otolaryngologist Kingston Hosp., Kingston Upon Thames. Socs: Eur. Acad. Facial Plastic Surg. (Asst. Sec.). Prev: Sen. Regist. (OtoLaryngol.) St. Geo.'s Hosp. Lond.; Regist. (Otolaryngologist) Manch. Roy. Infirm.

HINTON, Elizabeth Anne Flat 8, 12 Princes Ave, Muswell Hill, London N10 3LR — MB BS 1997 Lond.

HINTON, Hilary Anne 210 Queen's Road, Aberdeen AB15 8DJ — MB ChB 1974 Aberd.; DCH Dub. 1976.

HINTON, James Little Arden, Mount Park Road, Harrow on the Hill, Harrow HA1 3JZ — MB BS 1970 Lond.; MRCP (U.K.) 1973; MRCS Eng. LRCP Lond. 1970; FRCR 1977; DMRD Eng. 1975. Cons. Radiol. Roy. Free Hosp. Lond.

HINTON, John Mark Hillview, Higher Totnell, Leigh, Sherborne DT9 6HZ Tel: 01963 210271 — MB BS Lond. 1949; MD Lond. 1961; FRCP Lond. 1970, M 1954; FRCPsych 1971; DPM Lond. 1958. (King's Coll. Hosp.) Emerit. Prof. Psychiat. Univ. Lond. Socs: Fell. Roy. Soc. Med. (Ex-Pres. Psychiat. Sect.). Prev: Hon. Research Fell. St. Christopher's Hospice Sydenham; Prof. Psychiat. Middlx. Hosp. Lond.; Sen. Regist. Maudsley Hosp.

HINTON, John Michael King Edward VII Hospital, Midhurst GU29 0BL Tel: 01730 812341; Stoke Dorothy, West Burton, Pulborough RH20 1HD Tel: 01798 831237 — BM BCh 1958 Oxf.; MA Oxf. 1960; FRCP Lond. 1979, M 1963. (Univ. Coll. Hosp.) Emerit. Cons. Phys. & Gastroentrol. St. Richard's Hosp. Chichester; Cons. Phys. & Gastroenterol. King Edwd. VII Hosp. Midhurst. Socs: Brit. Soc. Gastroenterol.; Med. Soc. Lond. Prev: Cons. Phys. & Gastroenterol. Chichester Health Dist.; Sen. Regist. Univ. Coll. Hosp.; Research Fell. & Hon. Sen. Regist. (Med.) St. Mark's Hosp.

HINTON, Laura 37B Bedford Avenue, Aberdeen AB24 3YN; Kilmory, 25 Bridgend, Callender FK17 8AG Tel: 01877 330934 — MB ChB 1998 Aberd.; MB ChB Aberd 1998; BSc. (Aberd) SHO O & G Aberd. Prev: PRHO Surg.Raygmore Hosp.Inverness; PRHO med.ARI Aberd.

HINTON, Leslie The Health Centre, Sheen Lane, London SW14 Tel: 020 8876 0021 — MB BS 1950 Lond. (Middlx.) Prev: Ho. Surg. Middlx. Hosp.; Ho. Phys. Acton Gen. Hosp.; Capt. RAMC.

HINTON, Paul James Station Road Surgery, Station Road, Sowerby Bridge HX6 3AB Tel: 01422 831453/831457; 321 Holme Road, Warley, Halifax HX2 7RP Tel: 01422 831431 — MB ChB 1972 Leeds; MRCGP 1976; DCH Eng. 1975. (Leeds)

HINTON, Pauline Hazel (retired) 15 Chancery Court, Front St., Acomb, York YO24 3DP — MB ChB Leeds 1944.

HINTON, Richard Mark Hartley Corner, 51 Frogmore Road, Blackwater, Camberley GU17 0DB Tel: 01252 872791 Fax: 01252 878910; 82A Ellis Road, Crowthorne RG45 6PW Tel: 01344 751272 — MB BS 1984 Lond.; MRCGP 1988; DCH RCP Lond. 1987; DRCOG 1987. Prev: Trainee GP Reading VTS.

HINTON, Richard Montgomery (Surgery) Lansdowne, Priory Road, Hampton TW12 2PB Tel: 020 8979 5150; Tangley Medical Centre, 10 Tangley Pk Road, Hampton TW12 3YH Tel: 020 8979 5056 — MB BS 1981 Newc.; MSc (Community Med.) Lond. 1986; MRCGP 1988. Prev: Regist. (Community Med.) N.W. Thames RHA; SHO (Paediat.) Qu. Eliz. Childr. Hosp. Lond.; SHO (Geriat.) Bolingbroke Hosp. Lond.

HINTON, Rosalind Ann (cons. rooms) Tower House, Clifton Down Road, Clifton, Bristol BS8 4AG Tel: 0117 974 3846 Fax: 0117 974 3846 — MB BS 1954 Lond.; DObst RCOG 1955. (Roy. Free Hosp.) Emerit. Assoc. Specialist Sub-fertil. & Psychosexual Med. Reproduc. Med. Clinic Bristol; Teach. Bristol Univ. Socs: Brit. Fertil. Soc.; Accred. Mem. Brit. Soc. Med. & Dent. Hypn.; Roy. Soc. Med. (Pres. Elect. Sect. Hypn. & Psychosomatic Med.). Prev: Clin. Asst. (VD) Bristol Roy. Infirm.; Ho. Phys. Roy. Free Hosp.; Ho. Surg. Eliz. G. Anderson Matern. Home.

HINTON, Sheila Helen 7 Lynton Close, Liverpool L19 7NT — MB ChB 1987 Aberd.

HINVES, Mr Barry Leslie BUPA Hospital, The Ridge, St Leonards-on-Sea TN39 4QL Tel: 01424 757400 Fax: 01424 757424 — MB BS 1965 Lond.; FRCS Ed. 1972; FRCS Eng. 1972; MRCS Eng. LRCP Lond. 1965. (Westm.) p/t Cons. Orthop. Surg. Conquest Hosp, St. Leonards on Sea, E. Sussex. Socs: Fell. Roy. Soc. Med. (Counc. Mem.); Brit. Orthop. Assn. Prev: Sen. Regist. (Orthop.) Roy. Free Hosp. Lond. & Windsor Gp. Hosps.

HINWOOD, David Clive Radiology Department, Derbyshire Royal Infirmary, London Road, Derby DE1 2QY Tel: 01332 347141; 8 George Road, West Bridgford, Nottingham NG2 7PU Tel: 0115 981 4288 — MB ChB 1984 Birm.; MRCP (UK) 1988; FRCR 1992. Cons. Radiol. Derbysh. Roy. Infirm. Prev: Sen. Regist. (Radiol.) City Hosp. Nottm.; Regist. (Med.) Roy. Shrewsbury Hosp.

HINWOOD, Harry Clive Ramsay (retired) 351 Holyhead Road, Wellington, Telford TF1 2EZ Tel: 01952 641429 — MB ChB 1954 Ed. Prev: Sen. Ho. Off. ENT Dept. Roy. Infirm. Edin.

HIORNS, Melanie Patricia 58 Albert Road, Cheltenham GL52 2QX — MB BS 1990 Lond.; MRCP (UK) 1993.

HIORNS, Philip Edward The Chineham Medical Practice, Reading Road, Chineham, Basingstoke RG24 8ND Tel: 01256 479244 Fax: 01256 814190 — MB BS 1978 Lond.; BSc (Hons.) (Physiol.) Lond. 1975; MRCGP 1985; DRCOG 1984; DA Eng. 1981. (St. Bart.) Prev: Cas. Off. Roy. Berks. Hosp.; SHO (Anaesth.) Middl. Hosp.

HIPKIN, Leslie John, TD (retired) 3 Poplar Road, Prenton CH43 5TB Tel: 0151 652 2021 — MB ChB 1958 Liverp.; PhD Liverp. 1969, MD 1961; MRCS Eng. LRCP Lond. 1958; FRCP Ed. 1992; FRCPath 1982, M 1970. Hon Col. 208 (Liverp.) Field Hosp. (V). Prev: Sen. Lect. (Chem. Path.) Univ. Liverp.

HIPKINS, Amanda Mary 3 St James Terrace, Horsforth, Leeds LS18 5QT — MB BS 1983 Lond. (Char. Cross)

HIPKINS, Kevin Christopher (Surgery) Tithe Yard, Church Square, Lenham, Maidstone Tel: 01622 858341; Masons Farm, Grafty Green, Maidstone ME17 2AP Tel: 01622 858474 — MB BS 1974 Lond.; MRCGP 1979. (Univ. Coll. Hosp.)

HIPPISLEY-COX, Julia Orchard Medical Practice, Innisdoon, Crow Hill Drive, Mansfield NG19 7AE Tel: 01623 400100 Fax: 01623 400101 — MB ChB 1989 Sheff.; MB ChB (Hons.) Sheff. 1989; MRCP (UK) 1994; MRCGP (Distinc.) 1995; DRCOG 1991; DM 1998. (Sheff.) Lect. (Gen. Pract.) Univ. Nottm. Socs: Vale of Trent Fac. of the RCGP; RCGP (Vale of Trent Fac.).

HIPPLE, Laura Jeanette City General Hospital, Fusehill St., Carlisle CA1 2HG — MB BS 1986 Newc.; MRCOG 1992. Staff Grade (O & G) City Gen. & Matern. Hosp. Carlisle. Prev: Regist. (O & G) Hexham Gen. Hosp. N.d., City Gen. & Matern. Hosp. Carlisle.

HIPPS, George (retired) 75 Emm Lane, Bradford BD9 4JH Tel: 01274 543928 — MB ChB 1942 Leeds; MRCGP 1961.

HIPWELL, Michael Carl Peel House Medical Centre, Avenue Parade, Accrington BB5 6RD Tel: 01254 237231 Fax: 01254 389525 — MB ChB 1979 Liverp.; MRCS Eng. LRCP Lond. 1979.

HIPWELL, Penelope Monica Goldthorns, Stilton, Peterborough PE7 3RH — MB BS 1986 Lond.

HIRA, Jyostna Ramanlal 63 Uxendon Hill, Wembley Park, Wembley HA9 9SQ Tel: 020 8908 5341 — MB ChB 1987 Natal; BSc Witwatersrand 1984.

HIRA, Mr Naru, OBE (retired) 12 Elm Road, Delstar, Didsbury, Manchester M20 6XD Tel: 0161 445 1544 — MB BS 1953 Madras; FRCS Eng. 1961. Prev: Cons. Surg. Roy. Oldham Hosp.

HIRANANDANI, Mr Mukesh Rennie Eye Clinic, St Helens and Knowsley Hospital, Prescot L35 5DR Tel: 0151 426 1600 — MB BS 1981 Delhi; FRCOphth 1991; DO RCS Eng. 1990. Cons. Ophth. St. Helens & Knowsley Hosps. Socs: MDU & SWOS; BEAVRS; N. Eng. Ophth. Soc. Prev: Sen. Regist. Manch. Roy. Eye Hosp.

HIRANI, A East Park Road Medical Centre, 264 East Park Road, Leicester LE5 5FD Tel: 0116 273 7700 — MB BS 1967 Rajasthan; MB BS 1967 Rajasthan.

HIRANI, Nikhil Arjun 1 Farley Road, Leicester LE2 3LD — BM BS 1990 Nottm.; BMedSci Nottm. 1987, BM BS 1990; MRCP (UK) 1993.

HIRANI, Sacheen 1 Farley Road, Stoneygate, Leicester LE2 3LD — MB ChB 1996 Liverp.

***HIRD, Caroline Janet** 1 Fitzgerald Road, Crookes, Sheffield S10 1GX — MB ChB 1996 Sheff.

HIRD, Jayne Marion The Glebe, Naunton Beauchamp, Pershore WR10 2LQ Tel: 01386 462484 — MB ChB 1989 Leic.; DFFP 1993; DCH RCP Lond. 1992; MRCGP Lond. 1997. (Leicester) Asst. (Gen. Pract.) Kidderminster.

HIRD, Katherine Helen 9 Southwell Grove Road, Leytonstone, London E11 4PP Tel: 020 8539 7287 — BM 1994 Soton.

HIRD, Michael Fenton Department of Paediatrics, Royal London Hospital, Whitechapel, London E1 1BB Tel: 020 7377 7188 Fax: 020 7377 7712; 78 Overbury Avenue, Beckenham BR3 6PY — MB BS 1983 Lond.; BSc Lond. 1980; MRCPI 1990; DCH RCP Lond. 1987. Cons. Paediat. Roy. Lond. Hosp.

HIRD, Nicholas Edward 42 Adderley Road, Leicester LE2 1WB — MB ChB 1989 Leic.

HIRD, Victoria Department of Gynaecology Oncology, Samaritan Hospital for Women, Marylebone Road, London NW1; 23 Winterbrook Road, Herne Hill, London SE24 9HZ — MB BS 1982 Lond.; FRCS Ed. 1988; MRCOG 1988. Assoc. Specialist (Gyn. Oncol.) Samarit. Hosp. for Wom. Lond.

***HIREMATH, Kranti** 7 Gilmore Place, Edinburgh EH3 9NE — LRCP LRCS 1982 Ed.; LRCP LRCS Ed. LRCPS Glas. 1982.

HIRJI, Fatehali Merali Grove Hill Medical Centre, Kilbride Court, Hemel Hempstead HP2 6AD Tel: 01442 212038 — MB ChB 1972 Makere; MB ChB Makerere 1972; MRCS Eng. LRCP Lond. 1974; DFFP 1992; Dip. Pract. Dermat. Wales 1991; DCH Eng. 1975; DObst RCOG 1974. (Makerere) Socs: BMA. Prev: Trainee GP W. Bromwich VTS; Ho. Phys. Hosp. St. Cross Rugby.

HIRONS, James Michael Bexley Hospital, Old Bexley Lane, Bexley DA5 2BW; 1 Lavender Bank, Beesfield Lane, Farningham, Dartford DA4 0DA — MB BChir 1966 Camb.; MA, MB Camb. 1967, BChir 1966; MRCP (UK) 1971; MRCS Eng. LRCP Lond. 1966; MRCPsych 1976. (St. Thos.) Cons. Psychiat. Bexley Hosp.

HIRONS, Michael Norman (retired) St Peters Cottage, Lower Rowe, Holt, Wimborne BH21 7DZ Tel: 01202 882025 Fax: 01202 88025 — MB BS Lond. 1957; DObst RCOG 1959. Prev: SHO (Orthop. & Cas.) Roy. Vict. & W. Hants. Hosp. Bournemouth.

HIRONS, Ruth Margaret Mvieta Community Care NHS Trust, 35 Kings Hill Avenue, Kings Hill, West Malling ME19 4AX Tel: 01732 520400 Fax: 01732 520401; 1 Lavender Bank, Beesfield Lane, Farningham, Dartford DA4 0DA Tel: 01322 862629 — MB ChB 1969 St. And.; MRCPsych 1976; Mem.Brit.Assoc.Psycho.1983. (St. And.) Cons. Psychotheropist Mmvieta Community Care NHS Trust; Lect. Univ. Kent Canterbury. Socs: SE Psychother. Gp.; Brit. Confederat. Psychother.; UKCP. Prev: Regist. (Psychiat.) John Conolly Hosp. Birm.; Regist. (Psychiat.) Lond. Hosp. (Whitechapel); Clin. Asst. (Psychol. Med.) Nat. Hosp. Nerv. Dis. Lond.

HIRPARA, Ramjibhai Haribhai Timberley, 27 Madam Lane, Barnaby Dun, Doncaster DN3 1EW Tel: 01302 882277 — MB BS 1971 Gujarat; DAvMed FOM RCP Lond. 1987. (Smt. N.H.L. Municip. Med. Coll. Gujarat) Prev: OC Med. Wing Wegberg Hosp.; Sen. Med. Off. Waddington; Princip. Med. Off. & Aviat. Med. Adviser RAF of Oman.

HIRRI, Hussain Muter Haematology Department, Queen Alexandra Hospital, Portsmouth PO6 3LY — MB ChB 1977 Baghdad; MRCP (UK) 1988.

HIRSCH, Emil Arthur 61 Conifer Gardens, London SW16 2TY Tel: 020 8769 2416; 45 Woodfield Avenue, London SW16 1LE Tel: 020 8769 2626 — MD 1934 Munich; LRCP LRCS Ed. LRFPS Glas. 1938. (Munich, Berlin, Glas.) Socs: BMA. Prev: Res. Med. Off. Farnham Co. Hosp. Surrey CC; Ho. Phys. & Ho. Surg. W. End. Hosp. Nerv. Dis.; Hon. Capt. RAMC.

HIRSCH, Hans J (retired) Flat 14, St Elizabeths Court, Mayfield Avenue, London N12 9HZ — MB BCh Witwatersrand 1948; FRCPath 1968.

HIRSCH, Leonard Fairbrook Medical Centre, 4 Fairway Avenue, Borehamwood WD6 1PR Tel: 020 8953 7666; Beaulieu, Mildred Avenue, Borehamwood WD6 2DH — MB BS 1975 Lond.; DRCOG 1979; MFFP 1993. (Middlx.) Princip. in Gen. Pract.; Clin. Asst. (Surg.) Barnet Gen. Hosp.; Sen. Clin. Med. Off. Family Plann. Barnet Gen. Hosp. Prev: Ho. Surg. Middlx. Hosp. Lond.

HIRSCH, Mark Vincent Bellevue Medical Group Practice, 6 Bellevue, Edgbaston, Birmingham B5 7LX Tel: 0121 446 2000 Fax: 0121 446 2015 — MB ChB 1986 Birm.; MB ChB Birm. l986.

HIRSCH, Martha (retired) 8 March Road, Liverpool L6 4DA Tel: 0151 260 7901 — MD Toulouse 1976. Prev: Clin. Asst. (Psycho-Geriat.) Liverp. HA (T).

HIRSCH, Nicholas Paul The National Hospital for Neurology and Neurosurgery, Queen Square, London WC1N 3BG Tel: 020 7837 3611; 127 Woodwarde Road, Dulwich, London SE22 8UP — MB BS 1978 Lond.; FFA RCS Eng. 1982. (Guy's) Cons. (Anaesth.) Nat. Hosp. for Neurol. & Neurosurg.; Hon. Lect. Inst. Neurol. Lond. Prev: Sen. Regist. St. Mary's Hosp. Lond.; Ho. Phys. Guy's Hosp. Lond.; Ho. Phys. Lewisham Hosp.

HIRSCH, Paul Oscar Flat 5, Belvedere House, 115 High St., Esher KT10 9LG Tel: 01372 466719 — MB BS Lond. 1953; MRCS Eng. LRCP Lond. 1953; MRCGP 1966. (Guy's) Chief. Med. Adviser Combined Insur. Co. Amer. & Amer. Life Insur. Co. Socs: BMA. Prev: Clin. Asst. (Anaesth.) Kingston & Richmond AHA; Ho. Surg. St. Olave's Hosp.; Resid. Path. & Ho. Phys. (Med.) Guy's Hosp. Lond.

HIRSCH, Peter Joseph Withington Hospital, Nell Lane, Manchester M20 2LR Tel: 0161 291 4261 Fax: 0161 291 3087; Beeches Consulting Suite, Alexandra Hospital, Mill Lane, Cheadle SK8 Tel: 0161 428 4185 Fax: 0161 428 1692 — MD Lond. 1981, MB BS 1967; FRCOG 1988, M 1972, DObst 1969. (Westm.) Cons. O & G Hosp. Trust, Univ. S. Manch.; Hon. Lect. Univ. Manch; Postgrad Clin. Tutor, Withington Hosp. Socs: BMA; Roy. Soc. Med. Prev: Cons. O & G Stockport AHA; Lect. (O & G) Manch. Univ. Research Fell. ICRF.

HIRSCH, Professor Steven Richard Charing Cross & Westminster Medical School, Fulham Palace Road, London W6 8RF Tel: 020 8846 7390 Fax: 020 8846 7372 — LMSSA 1967 Lond.; BA Amherst 1959; MPhil (Psych.) Lond. 1969; MD Johns Hopkins Univ. 1963; FRCP Lond. 1983, M 1966; FRCPsych 1978, M 1972. Prof. Psychiat. & Hon. Cons. Char. Cross & W.m. Med. Sch. Lond.; Chairm. Assn. Univ. Teachs. Psychiat.; Chairm. Psychopharmacol. Sub-Comm. Roy. Coll. Psychiat.; Co-ordinator Psychiat. Subject Panel Lond. Univ. Socs: Fell. Roy. Soc. Med. (Ex-Pres. Psychiat. Sect.); BMA (Ex-Hon. Sec., Ex-Vice Pres. Med. Acad. Staff Comm.). Prev: Sen. Lect. W.m. Hosp. Med. Sch.; Lect. (Psychiat.) Inst. Psychiat.; Research Worker MRC Social Psychiat. Unit Inst. Psychiat.

HIRSCHFIELD, Gideon Morris 61 Beche Road, Cambridge CB5 8HX — BChir 1996 Camb.

HIRSCHOWITZ, Lynn Department of Cellular Pathology, Royal United Hospital, Combe Park, Bath BA1 3NG Tel: 01225 824722 Fax: 01225 824503 Email: lynn.hischowitz@ruh-bath.swest.nhs.uk — MB BCh 1978 Witwatersrand; MRCPath 1990. Cons. Histopath. & Cytopath. Roy. United Hosp. Bath.

HIRSCHOWITZ, Paul Mark Flat 1, 94 Street Lane, Leeds LS8 2AL — MB BS 1996 Newc.

HIRSH, Mr Anthony Victor The Surgery, 4 Lanark Road, London W9 1DA Tel: 020 7286 4200 Fax: 020 7289 6788; Andrology Clinic, Whipps Cross Hospital, Whipps Cross Road, Leytonstone, London E11 Tel: 020 8535 5650 — MB BS 1968 Lond.; FRCS Eng. 1973; MRCS Eng. LRCP Lond. 1968; DObst RCOG 1970; Cert. FPA 1973; Cert. Family Plann. JCC 1977. (Westm.) Cons. Androl. Lond. Wom. Clinic, Hallam Med. Centre, BUPA Roding Hosp.Redbridge, Whipps Cross Hosp. & Bourn Hall Clinic Camb.; Hon. Sen. Lect. St. Thos. & St. Geo. Hosps. Lond. Socs: BMA & Hunt. Soc.; Roy. Soc. Med. & Brit. Androl. Soc. Prev: Hon. Asst. (Androl.) King's Coll. Hosp. & St. Peter's Hosp. Lond.; Hon. Sen. Regist. King's Coll. Hosp. & Inst. Urol. Lond.; Ho. Surg. W.m. Hosp. Lond.

HIRSH, Julian (retired) 51 Oakleigh Park N., London N20 9AT — MB BS 1952 Lond.; FRCP Lond. 1980, M 1963. Prev: Cons. Phys. Barnet Gen. Hosp.

HIRSON, Richard Bernard East Street Surgery, East Street, Manea, March PE15 0JJ Tel: 01354 680774 Fax: 01354 688222; Church Farm, Horseway, Chatteris PE16 6XG Tel: 01354 694266 — MB BS Lond. 1980; BSc (Hons.) Lond. 1977; MRCGP 1984; DRCOG 1983; DCH RCP Lond. 1982. (Univ. Coll. Hosp.) Police Surg. Cambs. Prev: GP Lond.

HIRST, Anne Elaine Elizabeth (retired) Glebelands, 19 Bishopston Road, Bishopston, Swansea SA3 3EH Tel: 01792 232705 — MB BS

1941 Lond.; MRCS Eng. LRCP Lond. 1941. Prev: Sen. Med. Off. W. Glam. AHA.

HIRST, Anthony Michael Darwen Health Centre, Union Street, Darwen BB3 0DA Tel: 01254 778379 Fax: 01254 778372 — MB ChB 1978 Manch.; Dip Occ Med 1998.

HIRST, Christopher Ian Flat 2A3, 33 Ferndale, Tunbridge Wells TN2 3PD — MB BS 1990 Lond.

HIRST, David Kitson North Middlesex Hospital, Sterling Way, London N18 1QX Tel: 020 8887 2000 — MB ChB 1969 St. And.; MRCPsych 1976; DPM Leeds 1973. Chief Exec., N. Middlx. Hosp. NHS Trust. Prev: Cons. Psychiat. Goodmayes Hosp. Ilford; Sen. Regist. Middlx. & Maudsley Hosps. Lond.

HIRST, Geoffrey (retired) High Orchard, Beulah Hill, London SE19 3EL Tel: 020 8653 2987 — MB BChir 1951 Camb.; BA Camb. 1947, MA, MB BChir 1951; FRCGP 1975, M 1965. JP. Prev: Chief Med. Off. Internat. Computers Ltd.

HIRST, Geoffrey Brooke, MC (retired) Dinglebank Cottage, Bramhall Park, Bramhall, Stockport SK7 3NW Tel: 0161 485 1886 — MB ChB Leeds 1940. Prev: Capt. RAMC.

HIRST, Gillian Coltas White Cottage, Upcast Lane, Alderley Edge SK9 7SE Tel: 01625 586409 — MB ChB 1975 Manch.

***HIRST, Graham Robert** 36 Kingsley Drive, Birkenshaw, Bradford BD11 2NE Tel: 01274 872687 — MB ChB 1998 Dund.; MB ChB Dund 1998.

HIRST, John Michael 149-153 Chanterlands Avenue, Hull HU5 3TJ Tel: 01482 43614 — MB ChB 1950 Leeds. (Leeds)

HIRST, Jonathan The Surgery, Barmby Road, Pocklington, York YO4 2DN Tel: 01759 302500; The Coach House, Fangoss Hall Gardens, Fangoss, York YO4 5QH — MB ChB 1971 Ed.; BSc Ed. 1969, MB ChB 1971; T (GP) 1991; Cert. Family Plann. JCC 1976; DObst RCOG 1974. (Edinburgh)

HIRST, Julie Rachel Isabel Hospice, c/o QEII Hospital, Howlands, Welwyn Garden City AL7 1LT; 131 Whitehouse Avenue, Borehamwood WD6 1HB — MB BS 1989 Lond.; T(GP) 1993; DRCOG 1992. (Kings College School of Medicine London) Med. Off. Isabel Hospice QEII Hosp. Howlands, Welwyn Garden City. Prev: GP Borehamwood Retainer Scheme; SHO (Palliat. Med.) Hospice Care Serv. E. Herts.; Trainee GP/SHO (Gen. Pract.) Welwyn Gdn. City.

HIRST, Peter John 33 Rushton Drive, Middlewich CW10 0NJ Tel: 01606 737108 — MB ChB 1973 Manch.; BSc (Physiol.) Manch. 1970; MRCP (UK) 1976. Socs: Brit. Geriat. Soc. Prev: Lect. (Physiol., Therapeut. & Clin. Pharmacol.) Univ. Aberd.

HIRST, Mr Philip Fernleigh Consulting Centre, 77 Alderley Road, Wilmslow SK9 1PA Tel: 01625 536503 Fax: 01625 536516; White Cottage, Upcast Lane, Alderley Edge SK9 7SE Tel: 01625 586409 — MB ChB 1975 Manch.; FRCS Eng. 1980. Cons. Surg. Orthop. Manch. Roy. Infirm.

HIRST, Rachel Marian Oriel House, Peterchurch, Hereford HR2 0SQ — MB ChB 1985 Birm.; MB ChB (Hons.) Birm. 1985; DCH RCP Lond. 1987; DRCOG 1987.

HIRST, Rebecca Elizabeth 10 Golden Valley, Riddings, Derby — MB BS 1981 Lond.

HIRST, Robert Stafford Yealm Medical Centre, Yealmpton, Plymouth PL8 2EA Tel: 01752 880392 Fax: 01752 880582; Orchard Farm, Longbrook, Yealmpton, Plymouth PL8 2EH Tel: 01759 880567 Fax: 01752 860582 — MB BS 1984 Lond.; MRCGP 1992; MFFP 1994; DRCOG 1990; DCH RCP Lond. 1988. Sen. Clin. Med. Off. Plymouth.

HIRST, Stephen Leon Chiswick Health Centre, Fishers Lane, London W4 1RX Tel: 020 8321 3518/9 Fax: 020 8321 3568 — MB BS 1974 Lond.; MRCGP 1978; DCH Eng. 1977; DRCOG 1976. (Westm.) GP; Trainer in Gen. Pract.; Imperial Coll. Facilitator. Prev: SHO (Paediat.) Char. Cross Hosp. Lond.; SHO (O & G) W. Lond. Hosp.; SHO (A & E) Char. Cross Hosp.

HIRST, Stephen Nicholas New Hall Lane Practice, The Health Centre, Geoffrey Street, Preston PR1 5NE Tel: 01772 401730 Fax: 01772 401731 — MB ChB 1986 Liverp.; MRCGP 1991; DCH RCP Lond. 1991; DRCOG 1990. Prev: Trainee GP Preston VTS.

HIRST, Susan Gail Headache Clinic, Ipswich Hospital, Heath Rd, Ipswich IP4 5PD Tel: 01473 703188 Fax: 01473 702123; Barn House, 2 Otley Road, Cretingham, Woodbridge IP13 7DP — MB BS 1984 Lond.; FRCP (C) 1992. (Charing Cross, London) Resid. (Neurol.) Univ. Alberta, Edmonton, Canada. Prev: Cons. Neurol. Univ. of Alberta, Edmonton, Canada.

HIRST, William St John Barnby Hall Farm, Lane Head Rd, Cawthorne, Barnsley S75 4DT; 2Fl, 42 Argyle Place, Edinburgh EH9 1JT Tel: 0131 228 4950 Email: williamhurst@hotmail.com — MB ChB 1997 Ed. VT Tayside GP Train.Scheme.

HISCOCK, Bridget Mary Veronica Park Lane Surgery, 8 Park Lane, Broxbourne EN10 7NQ; 74 Station Road, Broxbourne EN10 7AN Tel: 01992 441074 — MB BS 1972 Lond.; DObst RCOG 1975. (Lond. Hosp.) Prev: SHO (Paediat.) P.ss Alexandra Hosp. Harlow; Cas. Off. King Geo. Hosp. Ilford; SHO (O & G) Ilford Matern. Hosp.

HISCOCK, Edward The Surgery, 160 Streetly Road, Erdington, Birmingham B23 7BD Tel: 0121 350 6668 Fax: 0121 382 1069; 304 King Edwards Wharf, Sheepcote Street, Birmingham B16 8AB Tel: 0121 643 1052 — MB ChB 1971 Birm.; Cert. (Train.) Family Plann. JCC 1973. Hosp. Pract. (Genitourin. Med.) Gen. Hosp. Birm. Socs: Assn. Genitourin. Med. (Non Career Grade Represen. Nat. Comm.). Prev: Clin. Asst. (A & E) Good Hope Hosp. Birm.; SHO (O & G) Good Hope Gen. Hosp. Sutton Coldfield; AIDS Counsellor N. Birm. HA.

HISCOCK, Ian Michael Kelvin The Surgery, 19 Amwell Street, Hoddesdon EN11 8TU Tel: 01992 464147 Fax: 01992 708698; 74 Station Road, Broxbourne EN10 7AN Tel: 01992 441074 — MB BS 1973 Lond.; BSc (Biochem.) Lond. 1970; MRCGP 1978; DObst RCOG 1976. (Lond. Hosp.) Socs: BMA; Roy. Soc. Med. (GP Div.). Prev: Ho. Phys. Lond. Hosp.; SHO (Obst.) St. John's Hosp. Chelmsford; Trainee GP Newc. VTS.

HISCOCK, Stephen Charles Rushbottom Lane Surgery, 91 Rushbottom Lane, Benfleet SS7 4EA Tel: 01268 754311; 8 Saxonville, Benfleet SS7 5TD Tel: 01268 754660 — MB BS 1981 Lond.

HISCOCKS, Emmeline Sarah High Street Surgery, 116-118 High Street, Hythe CT21 5LE; Shipley House, Mill Hill, Kingsworth, Ashford TN23 3EW — MB BS 1993 Lond.

HISCOTT, Mr Paul Stephenson Unit of Ophthamlmology, Department of Medicine, University of Liverpool, PO Box 147, Liverpool L69 3BX — MB BS 1977 Lond.; FRCPath 2000; PhD Lond. 1986; FRCS Glas. (Ophth.) 1988; MRCPath 1994; FRCOphth 1993; FCOphth 1989. Reader in Ophth. Path., Univ. of Liverp. Socs: Eur. Ophth. Path. Soc.(Sec., 1999-2002). Prev: Sen. Lect. (Ophth. Path.) Univ. Liverp.; Lect. (Ophth. Path.) Univ. Liverp.; Lect. (Ophth. Path.) & Research Fell. (Path.) Inst. Ophth. Lond.

HISCOX, Mr John Andrew c/o Accident & Emergency Department, Aberdeen Royal Infirmary, Foresterhill, Aberdeen AB25 2ZN Tel: 01224 681818 Email: jhiscox@abdn.ac.uk; 21 Hilltop Road, Cults, Aberdeen AB15 9RL Tel: 01224 861195 — MB ChB 1985 Aberd.; FRCS Ed. 1992; FRCS Glas. 1990; FFAEM 1996. (Aberd.) Cons. (A & E) Aberd. Roy. Infirm. & Roy. Aberd. Child. Hosp.

HISLOP, Edith Margaret (retired) 16 Forglen Road, Bridge of Allan, Stirling FK9 4BJ — MB ChB 1941 Ed.

HISLOP, Janet Elizabeth Pat Lewis Child Development Centre, Heath Lane Centre, Heath Lane, Hemel Hempstead HP1 1TT Tel: 01442 230861 Fax: 01442 219177; 10 Highclere Drive, Hemel Hempstead HP3 8BT Tel: 01442 244248 — MB BChir 1979 Camb.; MRCP (UK) 1982; FRCPCH 1997. Cons. Paediat. (Community Child Health) Herts. Partnership NHS Trust. Socs: Fell. Roy. Coll. Paediat. & Child Health; Brit. Assn. Community Child Health. Prev: Sen. Regist. (Community Paediat.) Harrow HA; Research Fell. (Paediat.) Roy. Postgrad. Med. Sch. Lond.

HISLOP, John Aitken (retired) Woodside, Broadgait, Gullane EH31 2DH Tel: 01620 843392 — MB ChB Ed. 1949; DPH Ed. 1965.

HISLOP, John McNeil Barony Practice, Northcroft Medical Centre, Northcroft St., Paisley PA3 Tel: 0141 889 3732 Fax: 0141 889 7502; 27 Cross Road, Paisley PA2 9QJ Tel: 0141 887 5685 — MB ChB 1979 Glas.; MRCGP 1986. Hosp. Practioner, Psychiat. Dykebar Hosp., Paisley.

HISLOP, Linda Jean Department of Accident & Emergency, Royal Alexandra Hospital, Paisley Tel: 0141 887 9111 Fax: 0141 887 1386; 53 Hamilton Avenue, Glasgow G41 4HB — MB ChB 1976 Glas.; FRCS Ed. 1992; Dip. IMC RCS Ed. 1991. Cons. A & E Roy. Alexandra Hosp. Paisley. Socs: Brit. Assn. Accid. & Emerg. Med.; Fell. Fac. Accid. and Emerg. Med. Prev: Hon. Clin. Lect. Aberd.

Univ.; Sen. Regist. (A & E) Aberd. Roy. Infirm.; Career Regist. (A & E) Vict. Infirm. Glas.

HISLOP, Rosalind Margaret Brookside Group Practice, Brookside Close, Gipsy Lane, Earley, Reading RG6 7HG Tel: 0118 966 9222 Fax: 0118 935 3174 — MB ChB 1984 Manch.; BSc (Hons.) Manch. 1981, MB ChB 1984. Prev: Regist. (Dermat.) Gtr. Glas. HB.

HISLOP, William Stuart Department of Medicine, Royal Alexandra Hospital, Paisley PA2 9PN Tel: 0141 887 9111 Fax: 0141 887 6701 — MB ChB 1973 Glas.; BSc (Hons.) Glas. 1971; FRCP Glas. 1985; FRCP Ed 1997; MRCP (UK) 1976; FACG 1996. Cons. Phys. Roy. Alexandra Hosp. Paisley. Socs: Brit. Soc. of Gastroenterol.; (Sec. & Treas.) Caledonian Soc. of Gastroenterol.; Scott. Soc. Phys.s. Prev: Sen. Regist. (Med. & Gastroenterol.) Ninewells Hosp. Dundee; Research Fell. (Med.) Ninewells Hosp. Dundee; Regist. W.. Infirm. Glas.

HISLOP, Mr William Stuart 44 Dundonald Road, Kilmarnock KA1 1RZ; 5 Burntbroom Gardens, Balliston, Glasgow G69 7NB — MB ChB 1987 Bristol; BDS Dundee 1978; FRCS Ed. 1991; FDS RCS Ed. 1982. Sen. Regist. Rotat. (Oral & Maxillofacial Surg.) W.. Scotl. Prev: Regist. Rotat. (Oral & Maxillofacial Surg.) W. Scotl. & Bristol; SHO (Otolaryngol.) Lancaster.

HITCH, Barbara Mary (retired) 73A Calderstones Road, Liverpool L18 3JA — MB ChB Liverp. 1952; DObst RCOG 1954. Prev: SCMO Liverp. HA.

HITCHCOCK, Andrew Departments of Histopathology & Cytology, Southampton General Hospital, Tremona Road, Southampton SO16 6YD Tel: 02380 794754; 240 Bassett Avenue, Southampton SO16 7FU — MB BS 1978 Lond.; MRCPath 1990. Cons. Histopath. & Cytopath. Soton. Gen. Hosp. Prev: Sen. Regist. (Histopath.) Nottm. City Hosp.

HITCHCOCK, Colin Tallis Great Shelford Health Centre, Ashen Green, Great Shelford, Cambridge CB2 5EY Tel: 01223 843661 Fax: 01223 844569 — MB BCh BAO 1983 NUI.

HITCHCOCK, Mark 49 Richmond Terrace, Carmarthen SA31 1HG — MB BS 1986 Lond.; BSc Lond. 1983, MB BS 1986.

HITCHCOCK, Robert Henry Rosemount Medical Practice, 52 Dean Road, Bo'ness EH51 9BB Tel: 01506 822556 Fax: 01506 828818; 20 Stoneyflatts, South Queensferry, Edinburgh EH30 9XT — MB BCh BAO 1982 NUI; MRCGP 1992; DObst RCPI 1989; DCH NUI 1988. (Univ. Coll. Galway Irel.) GP RoseMt. Med. Pract., Bo'ness, W. Lothian. Socs: BMA. Prev: GP, Kippen, Stirlingsh.

HITCHCOCK, Stephanie-Claire Millway Medical Practice, Hartley Avenue, Mill Hill, London NW7 2HX Tel: 020 8959 0888 Fax: 020 8959 7050 — MB BChir 1992 Camb.; MB BChir Camb. 1991; MA Camb. 1992; MRCGP 1995; DRCOG 1994. Partner.

HITCHENS, John Stockwell Group Practice, 107 Stockwell Road, London SW9 9TJ Tel: 020 7274 3225 Fax: 020 7738 3005 — MB BS 1970 Lond.

HITCHINGS, Miss Anne Elizabeth 123 Harvist Road, Queen's Park, London NW6 6HA Tel: 020 8968 5089 Email: james-hillier@msn.com — MB BS 1994 Lond.; MA Camb. 1995; FRCS CSIG 1998; FRCS Oto 1999. (St. Mary's Hosp. Med. Sch.) SHO Otolar,Audio. Gt. Ormond St Hosp.Lond.

HITCHINGS, Glenys Margaret Lawnswood, 169 Tettenhall Road, Wolverhampton WV6 0BZ — MB BCh 1968 Wales; FFA RCS Eng. 1975. (Cardiff) Cons. Anaesth. Roy. Wolverhampton Trust. Socs: Brit. Assn. Day Surg.; Assn. Anaesth.; BMA.

HITCHINGS, Norman Brian 92 Canford Cliffs Road, Canford Cliffs, Poole BH13 7AD Tel: 01202 707551 — LAH 1966 Dub. (Char. Cross & RCSI) Approved Examr. Dept. Transport. Prev: Surg. Lt.-Cdr. RN.

HITCHINGS, Professor Roger Alan 36 Devonshire Place, London W1G 6JR Tel: 020 7486 6987 Fax: 020 7487 5017; 5 Old Park Road, Enfield EN2 7BE — MB BS 1966 Lond.; FRCS Eng. 1972; MRCS Eng. LRCP Lond. 1966; FCOphth 1988; DO Eng. 1969. Cons. Ophth. Moorfields Eye Hosp. Lond. Socs: (Treas.) Europ. Glaucoma Soc.; Exec. Mem. Organising Comm. for Glaucoma Soc. Internat. Cong. Ophth. Prev: Sen. Lect. Dept. Clin. Ophth. & Res. Surg. Off. Moorfields Eye Hosp. Lond.; Clin. Fell. (Ophth.) Wills Eye Hosp. Philadelphia, U.S.A.

HITCHINGS, Samantha Renu 5 Old Park Road, Enfield EN2 7BE — MB BS 1992 Lond.

HITCHINGS, V Willow House Surgery, 285 Willow Road, Enfield EN1 3AZ Tel: 020 8363 0472 Fax: 020 8363 8936 — MB BS 1955 Punjab; MB BS 1955 Punjab.

HITCHINS, Jane Elizabeth Flat 25, Norman Court, Lordship Lane, London SE22 8JT — MB BS 1984 Lond.

***HITIRIS, Nikolas Gerasimos** 50 Moorgate, York YO24 4HR — MB ChB 1997 Birm.; BSc Birm. 1994.

HITMAN, Graham Alec 2 Yester Road, Chislehurst BR7 5LT — MB BS 1976 Lond.; FRCP Lond. 1991; MRCP (UK) 1981. (Univ. Coll. Hosp.) Asst. Dir., Reader (Med.) & Hon. Cons. Med. Unit Lond. Hosp. Socs: Brit. Diabetic Assn. & Amer. Soc. Human Genetics. Prev: Lect. & Hon. Sen. Regist. (Med.) Lond. Hosp.; Research Fell. Dept. Diabetes & Lipids St. Bart. Hosp. Lond.; SHO & Regist. (Med.) King's Coll. Hosp. Lond.

HIVEY, Sarah Elizabeth 48 Esslemont Avenue, Aberdeen AB25 1SQ — MB ChB 1998 Aberd.; MB ChB Aberd 1998.

HIWAIZI, Firiad Shafik 35 Gunenrsbury Avenue, London W5 3XD — MB ChB 1966 Baghdad; MRCP (UK) 1976. (Baghdad) Sen. Regist. (Haemat.) St. Geo. Hosp. Lond. Socs: BMA. Prev: Regist. (Haemat. & Gen. Med.) Walsgrave Hosp. Coventry; Regist. (Haemat.) Qu. Mary's Hosp. Roehampton.

HIXSON, Richard Charles 45 Waterside Drive, The Moorings, Market Drayton TF9 1HU Tel: 01630 653854 Fax: 01630 653854 Email: hixson@bigfoot.com — BM BS 1992 Nottm.; BMedSci Nottm. 1990; FRCA 1997; DA (UK) 1995. (Nottingham) Specialist Regist. (ITU) N. Staffs. Roy. Infirm. Socs: Assn. Anaesth.; Intens. Care Soc.; Fell. Roy. Coll. Anaesths. Prev: Specialist Regist. (Anaesth.) Roy. Shrewsbury; Specialist Regist. (Anaesth.) P.ss Roy. Telford; Specialist Regist. (Anaesth.) N. Staffs.

HJI YIANNAKIS, Pantelakis The Royal Marsden Hospital, Downs Road, Sutton SM2 5PT Tel: 020 8642 6011 — BM BS 1990 Nottm.; BMedSci 1988; MRCP (UK) 1993; FRCR 1997. Regist. (Clin. Oncol. & Radiother.) Roy. Marsden Hosp. Sutton. Socs: Roy. Coll. Phys. Lond. & Roy. Coll. Radiol. (Clin. Oncol. Sect.); BMA & Med. Defence Union. Prev: SHO (Radiother.) Roy. Marsden Hosp. Sutton; SHO (Med.) Sandwell Dist. Gen. Hosp. W. Midl. RHA.

HLA BU, Dr Tredegar General Hospital, Park Row, Tredegar NP22 3XP — MB BS 1982 Mandalay, Burma; DGM RCP Lond. 1994. Staff Grade Phys. (Geriat.) Tredegar Gen. Hosp. Gwent. Socs: BMA.

HLAING, Tun Tun 60 Campbell Street, Greenock PA16 8QP Tel: 01475 22735 — MB BS 1951 Rangoon; DTM & H 1956. Assoc. Specialist in Gen. Med. Argyll & Clyde Health Bd.

HNYDA, Bohdan Iwan Fleming Nuffield Unit, Burdon Terrace, Jesmond, Newcastle upon Tyne NE2 3AE Tel: 0191 219 6471 — MB BS 1989 Newc.; MRCPsych 1995. Sen. Regist. (Child & Adolesc. Psychiat.) Fleming Nuffield Unit. Newc. u Tyne. Prev: Sen. Regist. (Child & Adolesc. Psychiat.) Qu. Eliz. Hosp. Gateshead; Sen. Regist. (Child & Adolesc. Psychiat.) Young People's Unit Newc. Gen. Hosp.

HO, Alfred Kong-Meng 6 High Alder Road, Bessacarr, Doncaster DN4 7BB — MB ChB 1997 Sheff.

HO, Bobby Yin Man Dept. of Ansesthesia, Derby City General Hospital, Uttoxeter Road, Derby DE22 3NE Tel: 01332 340131 Email: bobbyho@sdah-tr.trent.nhs.uk — MB ChB 1984 Aberd.; FRCA 1994; DA (UK) 1989. Cons. Anaesth., Derby City Gen. Hosp. & Derbysh. Roy. Infirm. Socs: BMA & Assn. Anaesth. Prev: Specialist Regist. Nottm. & E. Midl. Sch. of Anaesth.; Research Fell. Anaesth. Nottm. City Hosp.; Regist. (Anaesth.) Nottm. City Hosp. & Derbysh. Roy. Infirm.

HO, Brian M L 93-107 Shaftesbury Avenue, 1st Floor, Wingate House, London W1V 8BT Tel: 020 7437 8525 Fax: 020 8731 9097 — MB BS 1980 Hong Kong; MSc (Audiol. Med.) Lond. 1995; DLO RCS Eng. 1985. (University of Hong Kong) Indep. Gen. Pract., Lond. Prev: Clin. Lect. (Audiol. Med.) Lond.; Cons. ENT Surg. Hong Kong.

HO, Chester Ho-Kai 183 Bridgewood Road, Worcester Park KT4 8XU — MB BChir 1993 Camb.; MA Camb. 1994, BA (Hons.) 1990, MB BChir 1993.

HO, Gigi Soke Wei 11 Willows Avenue, Morden SM4 5SG — MB BS 1997 Lond.

HO, Gwo-Tzer 1 (G/L) Fortingall Avenue, Glasgow G12 0LR — MB ChB 1997 Glas.

HO, John Tsun Fai Royal Hospital for Sick Children, Yorkhill, Glasgow G3 8SJ; 14 Ashwood Crescent, Bridge of Don, Aberdeen AB22 8XF — MB ChB 1993 Aberd.; DCH RCPS Glas. 1995. (Univ.

Aberd.) SHO The Roy. Hosp. Sick Childr. Glas. & Qu. Mothers Hosp. Glas. Prev: SHO (Paediat. & Neonat.) Ninewells Hosp. & Perth Roy. Infirm.; Ho. Off. (Gen. Surg., ENT & Gen. Med.) Aberd. Roy. Infirm.

HO, Kah Nai Victor The Grove Medical Centre, 103 The Grove, Isleworth TW7 4JE Tel: 020 8560 2069 Fax: 020 8560 1284 Email: victorho@grovemedcentre.demon.co.uk — MB BCh BAO 1980 NUI; LRCPI & LM, LRCSI & LM 1980; DRCOG 1985; DObst RCPI 1985; Dip. Primary Care Therap. Clin. Asst. (Obst. & Gyn.) Hillingdon Hosp. Socs: Fell. Roy. Soc. Med. Prev: SHO (O & G) N.wick Pk. Hosp. & Clin. Research Centre Harrow; SHO (Gen. Surg.) Profess. Surg. Unit Roy. S. Hants. Hosp. Soton.; SHO (O & G) Acad. Unit P.ss Anne Hosp. Soton.

HO, Kai Leung 3 Limewood Court, Newcastle upon Tyne NE2 4DB; 49 Tudor Drive, Princess Gardens, Hall Road, Hull HU6 9UF — MB BS 1988 Newc.

HO, Ki Wai Kevin 6 Bollington Close, Oxton, Wirral — MB ChB 1997 Manch.

HO, Mr Kossen Man Tzit 25 Warwick Mansions, Cromwell Crescent, London SW5 9QR — MB BCh 1988 Wales; FRCS Eng. 1992; FRCS Ed. 1992.

HO, Kuo Jong Flat 1, 13 Park Valley, Nottingham NG7 1BS — MB BCh BAO 1995 Belf.

HO, Lee 24 Leamington Road, Coventry CV3 6GG — MRCS Eng. LRCP Lond. 1961. (Birm.)

HO, Ling-Pei Osler Chest Unit, Churchill Hospital, Oxford OX3 7DS Email: ling-pei.ho@imm.ox.ac.uk — MB ChB 1991 Glas.; MD Glas. 2000; MRCP (UK) 1994. Specialist Regist. in Respirat. Med. Socs: Brit. Thoracic Soc.; Scott. Thoracic Soc. Prev: MRC Research Fell. (Respirat.) W.. Gen. Hosp. Edin.

HO, Luk Wai University of Cambridge, dept of Psychiatry, Box 189 Addenbrookes Hospital, Cambridge CB2 2QQ Tel: 01223 33695 Fax: 01223 336968 Email: luk.ho@whicj.net; 63 Blackthorn Close, Cambridge CB4 1FZ Tel: 01223 426296 — BChir 1992 Camb.; MB 1993; BA (Oxon) 1990; MRCPsych 1997. Specialist Regist. (Psychiat.) E. Anglian Train. Scheme. Prev: SHO Camb. Psychiat. Rotat. 1994-1997.

HO, Meilien 8A Traill Street, Broughty Ferry, Dundee DD5 3AX — MB ChB 1985 Glas. Lect. & Hon. Sen. Regist. (Rheum. & Gen. Med.) Ninewells Hosp. & Med. Sch. Dundee. Socs: RCP (UK); RCP Irel.

HO, Nicola Chuien Yheeg Flat 2, Saracen Court, Old Farm Avenue, London N14 5QR — MB ChB 1984 Sheff.; MB ChB Sheff. l984.

HO, Pauline Yuk Ping 4 Earlesfield Close, Sale M33 4UR — MB BCh 1995 Wales.

HO, Peter Ping X-Ray Department, St Peter's Hospital, Guildford Road, Chertsey KT16 0PZ Tel: 0193 287 2000; 54 Haven Lane, London W5 2HN — MB BS 1971 Lond.; MRCS Eng. LRCP Lond. 1970; FRCR 1978.

HO, Raymond Lei-Ming 111 Fellows Road, London NW3 3JS — MB BCh 1990 Wales.

HO, Sara Wei Ling 83 Scott Street, Dundee DD2 2BB — MB ChB 1997 Dundee.

HO, Selwyn Justin 51 Twyford Abbey Road, Park Royal, London NW10 7ET — MB BS 1994 Lond.; BSc (Hons.) Lond. 1991. (St. Mary's Hosp. Med. Sch.) Med. Advisor. Socs: Roy. Coll. Anaesth (Train.); BMA; BRAPP.

HO, Sheng-Ang 21 Disbrowe Road, London W6 8QG — MB ChB 1993 Leeds.

HO, Shu Fatt 80 Wenallt Road, Cardiff CF14 6SE — MB ChB 1989 Wales; MRCPI 1994.

HO, Simon Sze Ming 111 Fellows Road, London NW3 3JS Tel: 020 7722 9863 — MB BS 1992 Lond.; BSc (Hons.) Lond. 1989; MRCP (UK) 1996. (Roy. Free Hosp. Sch. Med.) Specialist Regist. (Radiol. & Imaging) Hammersmith Hosps. NHS Trust Lond. Socs: Collegiate Mem. RCP Lond.; Assoc. Mem. RCR. Prev: SHO (Med.) N.wick Pk. Hosp. Harrow; Ho. Phys. (Med.) Roy. Free. Hosp. Lond.; Ho. Surg. (Surg.) Edgware Gen. Hosp.

HO, Stanley Wang Tat Flat 26 Godolphin House, 76 Fellows Road, London NW3 3LG — MB BS 1989 Lond. SHO (Gen. Med.) Roy. Free Hosp. Lond.

HO, Thiam Hui Beth-Shalom, Laxton, Newark NG22 0PA — BM BS 1987 Nottm.; BMedSci (Hons.) 1985. Trainee GP/SHO (ENT Surg.) Leeds VTS.

HO, Thiam Poh The Residence, Bramble House, London Road, Retford DN22 7JG — MB BS 1997 Newc.

HO, Thiam Siew 32 Delmont Park, Belfast BT6 9RJ — MB BCh BAO 1986 Belf.

HO, Timothy Boon Leong 39 Hanworth Road, Hampton TW12 3DH Tel: 020 8979 2254 Email: t.ho@ic.ac.uk — MB BS 1991 Lond.; MB BS (Hons) Lond. 1991; MRCP (UK) 1994. (St. Geo. Hosp. Lond.) Wellcome Research Fell. Imperial Coll. Sch. of Med. Lond.; Regist. (Intens. Therap. Unit) St. Geo's. Hosp. Lond. Socs: Brit. Thorac. Soc.; Amer. Thoracic Soc. Prev: Regist. (Med.) St. Geo. Hosp. Lond.; SHO Rotat. (Med.) Leicester Teachg. Hosps.; Ho. Phys. Frimley Pk. Hosp. Surrey.

HO, Vicky Karen 51 Twyford Abbey Road, London NW10 7ET — MB BS 1998 Lond.; MB BS Lond 1998.

HO, Victor Chiuen Leey Saracen Court, Flat 2, Isabella Close, Old Farm Avenue, London N14 5QR — MB BCh BAO 1989 Belf.; MDS Singapore 1985, BDS 1980; MFHom 1994; FRACDS 1985; Dip. Derm. Wales 1994; LicAc 1993.

HO, Vinci Wan Che Old Swan Health Centre, St. Oswalds Street, Liverpool L13 2BY — LMSSA 1991 Lond.; MRCS Eng. LRCP Lond. 1991. Ho. Off. St. Helens & Knowsley Hosp. Prev: Ho. Off. Halton Gen. Hosp.

HO, Wai Tsun Vincent 52 Tyers Estate, Tyers Gate, London SE1 3HX — MB BS 1986 Lond.

HO, Mr Yew Ming Doctors' Residences, Coventry & Warwickshire Hospital, Stoney Stanton Road, Coventry CV1 4FH — MB BChir 1991 Camb.; MA Camb. 1992, BA (Path.) 1988; FRCS Eng. 1996. Specialist Regist. (Orthop. Surg.) Roy. Orthop. Hosp. Birm. Prev: Regist. (Neurosurg.) The Nat. Hosp. for Neurol. & Neurosurg. Lond.; SHO (Orthop. Surg.) Kingston Hosp.; SHO (Cardiothoracic Surg.) John Radclffe Hosp. Oxf.

HO-A-YUN, James Erwin Floyd Innerbuist, Stormont Field, Perth PH2 6BH — MB ChB 1965 St. And. Prev: Adviser (Rehabil. Servs.) Tayside HB.

HO-ASJOE, Mark Solomon Koon Wah Flat E, 32 Randolph Avenue, London W9 1BE — MB BCh BAO 1989 NUI; LRCPSI 1989.

HO BUU, Kim-Thuong c/o Royal Hospital for Sick Children, Yorkhill, Glasgow G3 8SJ — State Exam Med 1992 Saarland.

HO-YEN, Darrel Orlando Microbiology Department, Raigmore Hospital, Inverness IV2 3UJ — MB ChB 1974; DSc 2001; FRCPath 1997; MD Dundee 1983, BMSc (Hons.) 1971; MRCPath 1986. (Dundee) Cons. Microbiol. Raigmore Hosp. Inverness; Dir. Scott. Toxoplasma Ref. Laborat.; Hon. Clin. Sen. Lect. Univ. Aberd. Prev: Sen. Regist. (Haemat.) Ninewells Hosp. Dundee; Sen. Regist. Regional Virus Lab. Ruchill Hosp. Glas.

HO-YEN, Richard Gordon Westfield Road Surgery, 11 Westfield Road, Bletchley, Milton Keynes MK2 2DJ Tel: 01908 377103 Fax: 01908 374427; 8 The Bullfield, Watling St, Little Brickhill, Milton Keynes MK17 9NZ — MB ChB 1974 Birm.; MRCGP 1978; DRCOG 1977; DCH Eng. 1977.

HOAD, Christopher Frank (retired) 18 Oakdene, Rise Road, Sunningdale, Ascot SL5 0BU Tel: 01344 872069 — MB BS Lond. 1953. Prev: GP Brentford.

HOAD, Deborah Jane 20C Ardleigh Road, Islington, London N1 4HP Tel: 020 7254 1320 — MB BS 1976 Lond.; MRCS Eng. LRCP Lond. 1976; FFA RCS Eng. 1982. (Univ. Coll. Hosp.) Regist. (Anaesth.) St. Bart. Hosp. Lond.

HOAD, Nigel Anthony, Lt.-Col. RAMC Frimley Park Hospital, Camberley GU17 5UJ Tel: 01276 604179 — MB BChir 1980 Camb.; MB BChir Camb 1980; MA Camb. 1980; MRCP (UK) 1985; FRCP Lond. 1998. (St. Thos.) Cons. in Gen. Respirat. Med. Frimley Pk. Hosp. Camberley; Cons. in Respirat. Med. to the Army. Socs: Brit. Thorac. Soc. Prev: Cons. Chest Phys. Camb. Milit. Hosp. Aldershot; Regt. Med. Off. Coldstream Guards; Hon. Sen. Regist. Brompton Hosp.

HOAD-REDDICK, David Adam 30 Kingston Road, Manchester M20 2RZ — MB ChB 1994 Manch.

HOADLEY, Graham Martin Victoria Hospital, Whinney Heys Road, Blackpool FY3 8NR; 15 Bryan Road, Blackpool FY3 9BG — MB BS 1977 Lond.; BSc (Hons.) Lond. 1974; FRCR 1987. Cons. Radiol. Vict. Hosp. Blackpool. Socs: Brit. Inst. Radiol.; Brit. Med. Ultrasound Soc.; RCR BrE. Gp. Prev: Sen. Regist. W.m., Brompton & Roy. Marsden Hosps.

HOANG, Triet Minh 23 Taunton Dr, Southampton SO18 5BX — MB BS 1997 Lond.

HOAR, Amanda Caroline Deirdre St Ann's Hospital, St Ann's Road, London N15 3TH — MB BS 1983 Lond.

HOAR, Deborah Helen Mary Hollybrook, Pamber Heath Road, Basingstoke RG26 3TH Tel: 01734 700308 — MB ChB 1993 Birm. Demonst. (Anat.) Univ. Liverp. Prev: Ho. Off. (Thoracic & Gen. Surg.) Birm. Heartlands Hosp.; Ho. Off. (Gen. Med.) Good Hope Hosp.

HOAR, Fiona Jane 3 Firgrove Cottages, St Marks Road, Mount Ephraim, Tunbridge Wells TN4 8AT — BChir 1990 Camb.

HOARE, Antony Michael (retired) Wycombe General Hospital, High Wycombe HP11 2TT Tel: 01494 526161 — MA; MD Camb. 1979, MB 1969, BChir 1968; FRCP Lond. 1984; MRCP (U.K.) 1971. Prev: Cons. Phys. (Gen. Med. & Gastroenterol.) Wycombe Gen. Hosp. High Wycombe.

HOARE, Caroline Frankie (retired) The Surgery, Branksomewood Road, Fleet GU51 4JX Fax: 01252 816489 — MB BS 1962 Lond.; MRCS Eng. LRCP Lond. 1962; DCH Eng. 1966; DObst RCOG 1965. Locum GP. Prev: Princip. in Gen. Pract. at the Surg. Hants.

HOARE, David Martin The Medical Centre, 15 Cawley Road, Chichester PO19 1XT Tel: 01243 786666/781833 Fax: 01243 530042; The Laurels, Lagness Road, Runcton, Chichester PO20 6QA Tel: 01243 784949 Email: dave@hoares.freeserve.co.uk — MRCS Eng. LRCP Lond. 1970; BSc Lond. 1966, MB BS 1970; DObst RCOG 1976. (Lond. Hosp.) Police Surg. Chichester. Prev: Ho. Phys. & Ho. Surg. Lond. Hosp.; Cas. Off. St. Richard's Hosp. Chichester; SHO (Obst.) Zachary Merton Matern. Hosp. Rustington.

HOARE, Mr Edmund Martin Tel: 0161 434 2910; 91 Park Road, Hale, Altrincham WA15 9LE — BChir 1963 Camb.; MB BChir Camb. 1964; MChir Camb. 1980; FRCS Eng. 1968. (St. Bart.) Cons. Surg. Trafford Gen. Hosp. Davyhulme; Hon. Cons. Surg. Hope Hosp. Salford. Socs: Fell. Roy. Soc. Med.; Assn. Surg.; Brit. Assn. Surg. Oncol. Prev: Sen. Regist. Rotat. (Surg.) Manch. RHB; Regist. (Surg.) Roy. Free Hosp. Lond. & St. Bart. Hosp.

HOARE, Gillian Kate 103 Hillside Avenue, Bitterne Park, Southampton SO18 1JZ — MB BS 1988 Lond. SHO (Geriat.) E.bourne Dist. Gen. Hosp. Prev: SHO (Geriat.) St. Mary's Hosp. I. of Wight; Ho. Phys. Barking & King Geo. Hosps. Ilford; Ho. Surg. Crawley Hosp. W. Sussex.

HOARE, Gillian Louise Camden Cottage, Lewes Road, East Grinstead RH19 3TA Tel: 01342 328102 — MB BS 1971 Lond.; MRCS Eng. LRCP Lond. 1971. (Guy's.) Prev: Ho. Surg. Guy's Hosp. Lond.; Resid. Med. Off. Beckenham Hosp. & Guy's Hosp. (Nuffield Ho.).

HOARE, Mr Henry George Wishart (retired) Camtraf Home, 87 Bacon Road, Abergavenny NP7 7RD Tel: 01873 854657 — MA Camb. 1941. MB BChir 1938; FRCS Ed. 1939; MRCS Eng., LRCP Lond. 1937; FCOphth. 1989; DOMS Eng. 1944. Prev: Cons. Ophth. Surg. St. Woolos Hosp. Newport & Nevill Hall Hosp. Abergavenny.

HOARE, Jonathan Martin 2 Dinorben Beeches, Fleet GU52 7SR — MB BS 1993 Lond.

HOARE, Peter Department of Child & Family Psychiatry, Royal Hospital for Sick Children, 3 Rillbank Terrace, Edinburgh EH9 1LL Tel: 0131 536 0000 Fax: 0131 536 0545 Email: p.hoare@ed.ac.uk — BM BCh 1971 Oxf.; MA Oxf. 1971, DM 1983; FRCPsych 1996, M 1976. (Oxford) Sen. Lect. (Child & Adolesc. Psychiat.) Univ. Edin.; Hon. Cons. Child Psychiat. Roy. Hosp. for Sick Childr. Edin. Prev: Train. Fell. (Child & Adolesc. Psychiat.) Warneford Hosp. Oxf.

HOARE, Philip George Pond Close, Speldhurst Road, Langton Green, Tunbridge Wells TN3 0JF Tel: 01892 862853 Fax: 01892 863609 — MRCS Eng. LRCP Lond. 1957. (St. Mary's) Socs: BMA; Assoc. Mem. MRCGP. Prev: Ho. Off. (O & G & Gen. Med.& Gen Surg.) Lambeth Hosp. Lond.; Capt. RAMC.

HOARE, Richard John Selborne Road Medical Centre, 1 Selborne Road, Sheffield S10 5ND — MB ChB 1980 Sheff.; DPhil (Nat. Sc.) Oxf. 1969, BA (Hons.) 1966. Socs: BMA.

HOARE, Richard William The Surgery, 1 Crawley Lane, Pound Hill, Crawley RH10 7DX Tel: 01293 549916 Fax: 01293 615382; Brackenwood, West Pk Road, Copthorne, Crawley RH10 3HG — MB BS 1976 Lond.; DRCOG 1984.

HOARE, Simon Queen Elizabeth Hospital, Department of Paediatrics, Sheriff Hill, Gateshead NE9 6SX Tel: 0191 403 2190; Orchard Cottage, 26A Heddon Banks, Heddon-on-the-wall, Newcastle upon Tyne NE15 0BU — MB ChB 1980 Liverp.; MD 2001 Newc.; MRCP (UK) 1987; DCH Lond. 1985; FRCPCH 1997. (Liverpool) Cons. Paediat.; Hon. Lect. Univ. of Newc. Socs: Brit. Paediatric Immunol. and Infec. Dis.s Gp.; Europ. Soc. for Paediatric Infec. Dis.s; RCPCH.

HOARE, Mr Timothy James Bedford Hospital, Kempston Road, Bedford MK42 9DJ Tel: 01234 795950 Fax: 01234 795860 — MB BChir 1982 Camb.; BA Camb. 1979; FRCS (Orl.) 1996; FRCS (ENT) 1990; FRCS Eng. 1987. (Cambridge and Middlesex) Cons. ENT Surg. Bedford Hosp. Prev: Sen. Regist. & Regist. W. Midl.; Basic Surgic. Train. in Lond.

HOARE NAIRNE, James Edward Alexander Department of Ophthalmology, Gloucestershire Royal Hospital, Great Western Road, Gloucester GL1 3NN Tel: 01452 394910 — MB BChir 1977 Camb.; MA Camb. 1976; FCOphth 1988; FRACO 1983; FRACS 1983. Cons. Ophth. Glos. Roy.& Cheltenham Gen Hosp. Prev: Cons. Ophth. Singleton Hosp. Swansea; Sen. Regist. Bristol Eye Hosp. & W. Eng. Eye Infirm. Exeter; Regist. (Ophth.) Dunedin Hosp. Univ. Otago Med. Sch., NZ.

HOBAN, Benjamin Leon c/o 6 Musgrave Cr, London SW6 4PT — BM 1997 Soton.

HOBART, Mr Andrew George 21 The Lindens, Birmingham B32 2ER — MB BChir 1990 Camb.; FRCS Eng. 1994. Specialist Regist. (A & E) W. Midl. Specialist Train. Scheme. Socs: (Counc.) BMA.

HOBART, Jeremy Charles Institute of Neurology, Queen Square, London WC1N 3BG Tel: 020 7837 3611/3436 Fax: 020 7813 0924 Email: j.hobart@ion.ucl.ac.uk; Fax: 020 7628 3938 — MB BS 1987 Lond.; BSc Lond. 1984; MRCP (UK) 1990. (St. mary's Hospital, London) Clin. Lect. (Neurol.) & Hon. Sen. Regist. Inst. Neurol. & Nat. Hosp. for Neurol. & Neurosurg. Prev: Wellcome Clin. Research Fell. Inst. Neurol. & Lond. Sch. Hyg. & Trop. Med.; Regist. Rotat. (Med.) St. Richards Hosp. Chichester; Regist. (Neurol.) Atkinson Morley Hosp. Lond.

HOBBES, Caroline Janine Cameron Dudley Street Surgery, 11 Dudley Street, Grimsby DN31 2AW Tel: 01472 353303/4 — BM BS Nottm. 1987, BMedSci 1985; DCH RCP Lond. 1992.

HOBBIGER, Helen Elizabeth The Queen Elizabeth Hospital, Gayton Rd, King's Lynn PE30 4ET Tel: 01553 613613 Email: helen.hobbiger@rlshosp.anglox.nhs.uk; Tel: 01553 840296 — MB BS 1988 Lond.; BSc Lond. 1983; FRCA 1994; DA (UK) 1991. (Univ. Coll. & Middlx. Hosp. Sch. Med.) Cons. (Anaesth.) The Qu. Eliz. Hosp. Socs: Fell. Roy. Coll. Anaesths.; Assn. Anaesths. Prev: Clin. Fell. (Anaesth.) Papworth Hosp. Camb.; Regist. (Anaesth.) Qu. Eliz. Hosp. King's Lynn Norf.; Specialist Regist. (Anaesth.) Norf.&Norwich Hosp.

HOBBIGER, Stephen Franz NAPP Pharmaceuticals Research, Cambridge Science Park, Milton Road, Cambridge CB4 0GW — MB BS 1985 Lond.; BSc Lond. 1980; MRCP (UK) 1988; MFPM RCP (UK) 1994; Dip Pharmaceut Med RCP (UK) 1992. Dir Med. Research.

HOBBINS, Susan Margaret Childrens Department, Bromley Hospitals NHS Trust, Farnborough Hospital, Farnborough Common, Orpington BR6 8ND Tel: 01689 814188 — MB ChB 1973 Dundee; FRCPC 1978; FRCP 1993; FRCPCH 1997. Clin. Dir. of Paediat.; Cons. Paediat.; Div.al Dir. Wom. & Childr. Servs. Socs: RCPCH; BMA; RCP Lond.

HOBBIS, Joanne Mary Jackson, Knights, Richards and Hobbis, Thorney Medical Centre, Wisbech Road, Thorney, Peterborough PE6 0SA Tel: 01733 270219 Fax: 01733 270860 — MB ChB 1984 Leeds; MB ChB Leeds l984.

HOBBISS, Mr John Holland Royal Bolton Hospital, Minerva Road, Bolton BL4 0JR; Silver Birches, 110 Rawlinson Lane, Heath Charnock, Chorley PR7 4DE Tel: 01257480411 Email: john@hobbiss.freeserve.co.uk — MB ChB 1974 Bristol; MD Bristol 1987; FRCS Eng. 1980; MRCP (UK) 1977; DCH Eng. 1977. Cons. Gen. Surg. Bolton HA. Prev: Sen. Regist. (Gen. Surg.) NW RHA.

HOBBS, Adrian John Mingoose Farmhouse, Mount Hawke, Truro TR4 8BU — MB ChB 1979 Bristol; FFA RCS Eng. 1985. Cons. Anaesth. Roy. Cornw. Hosp. (Treliske) Truro.

HOBBS, Alison Clare 1 Cedar Close, Bickley, Bromley BR1 2NY — MB BS 1996 Lond.; BSc Lond. 1993. (King's Coll. Lond.) Prev: SHO (A & E).

***HOBBS, Alison Rosemary** 8 Glebe Road, Cheam, Sutton SM2 7NT — MB ChB 1996 Birm.

HOBBS, Andrew Michael Birkby The Doctors House, Victoria Road, Marlow SL7 1DN Tel: 01628 484666 Fax: 01628 891206 — MB BS 1991 Lond.

HOBBS, Anne 32 Braemar Crescent, Filton, Bristol BS7 0TD — BM 1979 Soton.

HOBBS, Mr Christopher Geoffrey Laurence The Royal Berkshire Hospital, London Road, Reading RG1 5AN Tel: 0118 987511 Email: chris.hobbs@lineone.net; Email: chris.hobbs@lineone.net — MB BS 1996 Lond.; MRCS 2000; DLO 2001; BSc Lond. 1995. (St Mary's) SPR in OtoLaryngol., Roy. Berks., hosp. Reading. Socs: Roy. Soc. of Med.; Brit. asso. Of Otorhinolaryngologists. and Head and Neck Surg. Prev: SHO (A & E) St Mary's Hosp. Lond.; RMO Wellington Hosp.Lond; Anat. Demonst. St marys hosp.

HOBBS, Christopher James St James (University) Hospital, Community Paediatrics, Leeds LS9 7TF Tel: 0113 206 4327 Fax: 0113 206 4877 Email: chrishobbs@netcom.uk.co.uk — MB BS 1970 Lond.; BSc Lond. 1967; FRCP Lond. 1993; FRCPCH 1997; DObst RCOG 1975. (Char. Cross & Leeds) Cons. Community Paediat. St. Jas. Univ. Hosp. Leeds; Sen. Clin. Lect. (Paediat. & Child Health) St. Jas. Univ. Hosp. & Univ. Leeds. Socs: Brit. Assn. Community Child Health. Prev: PMO Solomon Is.s.

HOBBS, Colin Bevan (retired) 4 Kingsdown House, Kingsdown, Corsham SN13 8AX — MB BChir 1953 Camb.; FRCPath 1976, M 1964. Prev: Cons. Chem. Pathol. Bath Clin. Area.

HOBBS, David Dickerson (retired) 18 St Charles Road, Spennymoor DL16 6JY Tel: 01388 815747 — MB BS 1950 Durh. Sen. Med. Off. (Child Health) S.W. Durh. HA. Prev: Sen. Partner Gen. Pract. Spennymoor.

HOBBS, Derek Joseph Dalkeith, Varteg, Pontypool NP4 — MB ChB 1971 Bristol.

HOBBS, Elizabeth Ann 4 Pitfield Drive, Meopham, Gravesend DA13 0AY — MB BS 1994 Lond. Specialist Regist. (A & E).

HOBBS, Professor Frederick David Richard Department of Primary Care and Genral Practice, Primary Care Clinical Services Building, University of Birmingham, Edgbaston, Birmingham B15 2TT Tel: 0121 414 3760 Fax: 0121 414 3050 Email: f.d.r.hobbs@bham.ac.uk; Bellevue Medical Centre, 6 Bellevue, Edgbaston, Birmingham B5 7LX Tel: 0121 446 2000 Fax: 0121 440 1028 — MB ChB 1977 Bristol; FRCP 2001; FRCGP 1990, M 1981. (Univ. Bristol) Mem. Birm. LMC; Mem. Sec. of States Advis. Gp. on SIFT; Mem. Culyer Implementation Gps. DH; Mem. NHS R & D HTA Progr. Socs: (Counc.) Med. Protec. Soc.; Midl. Fac. RCGP; Eur. Soc. Primary Care Gastroenterol. Prev: Sen. Lect. (Gen. Pract.) Birm. Univ.; Clin. Tutor (Gen. Pract.) Qu. Eliz. Hosp. Birm.; Assoc. Adviser (Gen. Pract.) W. Midl.

HOBBS, George Anthony, SBStJ (retired) The Abbey, Colonels Lane, Chertsey KT16 8RJ Tel: 01932 565588 — MB BChir Camb. 1960; Dip. Sports Med. Scotl. 1996; DCH Eng. 1966; DObst RCOG 1962. Sports Phys. Runnymede Hosp., Chertsey KT16 0RQ. Prev: Med. Supt. Ile Abiye Hosp. Ado Ekiti, W. Nigeria.

HOBBS, George Antony Talbot Ash Trees Surgery, Market Street, Carnforth LA5 9JU Tel: 01524 720000 Fax: 01524 720110; 35 St. Michaels Way, Bolton-le-Sands, Carnforth LA5 8JT Tel: 01524 824602 — MB ChB 1990 Ed.; MRCGP 1994. Socs: BMA. Prev: Trainee GP ScarBoro. VTS.

HOBBS, Gregory James 1 Rosthwaite Close, West Bridgford, Nottingham NG2 6RA — BM BS 1981 Flinders; FCAnaesth. 1990.

HOBBS, James Alfred (retired) Parkside Family Practice Green Road Surgery, 224 Wokingham Road, Reading RG6 1JS Tel: 0118 926 1590 Fax: 0118 926 3269 — MRCS Eng. LRCP Lond. 1977; DFFP 1993. Prev: Princip. in Gen. Pract., Reading 1981-1988.

HOBBS, James Ashworth (retired) 87 Whalley Drive, Bletchley, Milton Keynes MK3 6HX Tel: 01908 376962 — MB BS 1951 Lond.

HOBBS, James Henry Whitchurch Surgery, Bell Street, Whitchurch RG28 7AE Tel: 01256 892113 Fax: 01256 895610 — MRCS Eng. LRCP Lond. 1968. (St. Bart.)

HOBBS, James Joyce Ingledene Surgery, Ingledene, Wansbeck Road, Ashington NE63 8JE Tel: 01670 812305 — MB BS 1940 Durh.; FRCGP 1974. (Newc.)

HOBBS, Joanna Louise Graylings, Lower Budleigh, East Budleigh, Budleigh Salterton EX9 7DL; 66 East Grove Road, St Leonards, Exeter EX2 4LX — BM BS 1993 Nottm.; DRCOG 1998.

HOBBS, Joanna Rachel (Buxton) East Acre, Hatch Lane, Liss GU27 3JD — MB BS 1991 Lond.; DRCOG 1996. (St. Thos. UMDS Lond.) p/t GP Retainer Scheme Haslemere Surrey (Curr.ly on Matern. leave).

HOBBS, Professor John Raymond Whiteoaks, 5 Dormywood, Ruislip HA4 7UW Tel: 01895 673947 — MB BS 1956 Lond.; BSc (Hons.) Lond. 1953, MD 1963; FRCP Lond. 1972; MRCP (UK) 1958; MRCS Eng. LRCP Lond. 1956; FRCPCH 1997; FRCPath 1975, M 1963; DObst RCOG 1958. (Middlx.) Emerit. Prof. Immunol. Char. Cross & W.m. Med. Sch. Lond.; Chairm. COGENT Trust. Socs: Fell. Roy. Soc. Med. (Past-Pres.); Brit. Soc. of Immunol.; Assn. of Clin. Biochem.s. Prev: Sen. Lect. (Chem. Path.) Roy. Postgrad. Med. Sch. Lond.; Lect. (Chem. Path.) Roy. Free Hosp. Lond.; Regist. (Path.) Centr. Middlx. Hosp. Lond.

HOBBS, Mr John Thomas 4 Upper Wimpole Street, London W1M 7TD Tel: 020 7323 2830 — MD 1965 Lond.; MB BS 1954; FRCS Eng. 1963. (St. Bart.) Hon. Sen. Lect. Surg. St. Mary's Hosp. Med. Sch. & St. Geo. Hosp. Med. Sch. Lond.; Hon Cons. Surg. St. Mary's Hosp. Lond. Socs: Internat. Cardiovasc. Soc., Surg. Research Soc. & Assn. Surgs.; Vasc. Surg. Soc. of G. B.; Venans Forum, Roy. Soc. of Med. Prev: Cons. Surg. St. Geo. Hosp. Lond.; Lect. (Anat.) Birm. Univ. Med. Sch.; Research Fell. in Surg. Harvard Med. Sch. Boston, USA.

HOBBS, Professor Kenneth Edward Frederick (retired) The Rookery, Booseys Walk, New Buckenham, Norwich NR16 2AE Tel: 01953 860558 Fax: 01953 860558 Email: profkenhobbs@cs.com — MB BS Lond. 1960; ChM Bristol 1970; FRCS Eng. 1964; MRCS Eng. LRCP Lond. 1960. Prev: Sen. Lect. (Surg.) Univ. Bristol.

HOBBS, Leslie John (retired) Ramree, Forge Wood, Crawley RH10 3NH Tel: 01293 883234 — MB BS 1957 Lond.; MRCS Eng. LRCP Lond. 1957; DObst RCOG 1959. Prev: Ho. Surg. & Ho. Phys. Roy. Berks. Hosp. Reading.

HOBBS, Mark David Bedo The Cobham Health Centre, 168 Portsmouth Road, Cobham KT11 1HT Tel: 01932 867231 Fax: 01932 866874 — MB BS 1987 Lond.; MRCGP 1992; DRCOG 1991. (St. Thos. Hosp.) Prev: Trainee GP Portsmouth VTS.

HOBBS, Michael John Dannatt Warneford Hospital, Warneford Lane, Headington, Oxford OX3 7JX Tel: 01865 226330 Fax: 01865 223970 — MB BChir 1974 Camb.; MSc Lond. 1985; MA Oxf. 1989; BA Camb. 1970; FRCPsych 1993, M 1979; DCBT Oxford 1998. (Camb. & King's Coll. Hosp.) Cons. Psychother. Warneford Hosp. Oxf.; Hon. Sen. Clin. Lect. (Psychother.) Univ. Oxf.; Clin. Director, Oxf. City Locality. Prev: Sen. Regist. (Psychother.) St. Geo. Hosp. Lond.; Regist. (Psychiat.) Guy's Hosp. Lond.; Research Fell. (Psychiat.) Lewisham Health Dist.

HOBBS, Mr Nigel John, Maj. RAMC 61 Curie Court, Queens Medical Centre, Nottingham NG7 2UH — MB ChB 1977 Leeds; FRCS Eng. 1984. Sen. Specialist (Surg.) Duchess of Kent Milit. Hosp. Catterick.

HOBBS, Rebecca Jane Hillside Cottage, Flaxpool, Crowcombe, Taunton TA4 4AW Email: beccy@ukgateway.net — MB BS 1982 Lond.; MFHom 2000; 2000 (DIPM); DFFP 1993. (Roy. Free Hosp. Med. Sch.) p/t Lead Clinician, Contraceptive and sexual health Serv., Taunton; Clin. Assist. In Homeopathy, Bristol Homeopathic Hosp., Bristol.

HOBBS, Robert Charles Bennetts End Surgery, Hemel Hempstead HP3 9LY Tel: 01442 63511 — MB BS 1951 Lond.; MRCS Eng. LRCP Lond. 1951. (King's Coll. Hosp.)

HOBBS, Sarah Ann (retired) 8 West Cults Road, Cults, Aberdeen AB15 9HQ — MB ChB 1957 Leeds; MRCGP 1976. Prev: Ho. Surg. (Gen. Surg.) & Ho. Phys. (Gen. Med.) Morriston Hosp. Swansea.

HOBBS, Simon David Sundown House, 22 Deneside, East Dean, Eastbourne BN20 0JG — MB ChB 1998 Birm.; ChB Birm. 1998.

HOBBS, Mr Stephen John Frederick St Budeaux Health Centre, Stirling Road, St. Budeaux, Plymouth PL5 1PL Tel: 01752 361010 Fax: 01752 350675; 30 Whiteford Road, Mannamead, Plymouth PL3 5LX Fax: 01752 601707 — MB BChir 1976 Camb.; MA Camb. 1976; FRCS Eng. 1980.

HOBBS, William George Reginald c/o Prof. J. Hobbs, 5 Dormywood, Ruislip HA4 7UW — MB ChB 1956 Brist.

HOBBS, William Julian Caird 42 Whitehouse Lane, Liverpool L37 3LT — MB ChB 1991 Sheff.

HOBBY, Mr John Alan Elwyn Department of Plastic Surgery, Odstock Hospital, Salisbury SP2 8BJ — MB ChB 1965 Birm.; BSc (Hons.) (Physiol). Birm. 1962, MB ChB 1965; FRCS Eng. 1970. (Birm.) Cons. Plastic Surg. Odstock Hosp. Salisbury.

HOBBY, Mr Jonathan Leon Clinic 1, Addenbrooke's Hospital, Hills Road, Cambridge CB2 2QQ Tel: 01223 245151 Email: jlh@cam.ac.uk; 5 Beckett Close, Westley, Bury St Edmunds IP33 3RA Tel: 01284 760470 — MB BS 1989 Lond.; BSc (Hons.) Physiol. Lond. 1986; FRCS Eng. 1994; FRCS 1999; FRCS 1999 (Tr & Orth). (St. Thos.) Regist. (Orthop.) Addenbrooke's Hosp. Camb.; Hand Surg. Fell., St Andrews Centre, Broomfield. Socs: Assoc. Mem. BOA; Past Pres. Brit. Orthop. Train. Assn.; Assn. of Brit. Soc. for Surg. of the Head. Prev: SHO Rotat. (Surg.) St. Bart. Hosp. Lond.; SHO (Plastic Surg.) St. Thos. Hosp. Lond.; SHO (Orthop.) Roy. Nat. Orthop. Hosp. Stanmore.

HOBBY, Lucinda Jane Leighton 5 Bukett Close, Westley, Bury St Edmunds IP33 3RA Tel: 01284 760470 — MB BS 1992 Lond.; DRCOG 1996. (St. Thos. Hosp. Lond.) Trainee GP W. Suff. VTS. Prev: SHO (O & G) St. Thos. Hosp. Lond.

HOBDAY, Catherine Lucy 1 Newfield Court, Lymm WA13 9QU — MB ChB 1995 Sheff.

HOBDAY, David Ian 103 Welford Road, Shirley, Solihull B90 3HT — MB ChB 1991 Sheff.

HOBDAY, Paul Jeremy Sutton Valence Surgery, South Lane, Sutton Valence, Maidstone ME17 3BD Tel: 01622 842212 Fax: 01622 844396; 374 Loose Road, Maidstone ME15 9TT Tel: 01622 695240 Email: paulj@56.freeserve.co.uk — MB BS 1979 Lond.; MRCGP 1983; DRCOG 1982; Cert. FPA JCC 1982. (Guy's Hosp.) GP; Med. Manager Assn. Maidstone Doctors-on-Call; Med. Off. E. Sutton Pk. Prison. Prev: Trainee GP Maidstone VTS; Ho. Phys. & Ho. Surg. Lewisham Hosp. Lond.

HOBDAY, Sarah Ruth 7 Lavender Row, Darley Abbey, Derby DE22 1DF; Derbyshire Children's Hospital, Derby City General Hospital, Uttoxeter Road, Derby DE22 3NE Tel: 01332 340134 — MB ChB 1988 Bristol; MRCP (UK) 1994; DCH RCP Lond. 1993. Specialist Regist. (Paediat.) Derbysh. Childr.'s Hosp. Derby.

HOBDELL, Roger Allum 24 Oxford Road, London NW6 5SL — MB BS 1961 Lond.; MRCS Eng. LRCP Lond. 1961; DPM Eng. 1966. Train. Anal. & Profess. Mem. Soc. Anal. Psychol. Socs: Gp. Analyt. Soc. Prev: Med. Asst. MarlBoro. Day Hosp. Lond.; Regist. Claybury Hosp. Woodford Bridge; Regist. (Psychiat.) St. Clement's Hosp. Lond.

HOBDEN, Margaret Ann Burngreave Road Surgery, 5 Burngreave Road, Sheffield S3 9DA Tel: 0114 272 2858 — MB ChB 1979 Leeds.

HOBHOUSE, Penelope Margaret Tel: 01296 484054 Fax: 01296 397016 — MB ChB 1985 Liverp.; MRCGP 1990; Cert. Family Plann. JCC 1989; DCH RCP Lond. 1989. Clin. Asst., Neurol., Wycombe Gen. Hosp., Bucks. Prev: Trainee GP P'boro. Dist. Hosp. VTS.

HOBHOUSE, Sarah Lindsay Charlton Hill Surgery, Charlton Road, Andover SP10 3JY Tel: 01264 337979; Lake House, Norton, Sutton Scotney, Winchester SO21 3ND Tel: 01962 760003 — MB ChB Manch. 1989; MRCGP 1994; DRCOG 1991. GP Asst. Prev: Trainee GP Andover; SHO (Psychogeriat.) Andover War Memor. Hosp.; SHO (Geriat. Med.) Roy. Hants. Co. Hosp. Winchester.

HOBIN, David Anthony 22 Mayfield Road, Grappenhall, Warrington WA4 2NP — MB ChB 1991 Leic.; MRCP (UK) 1996.

HOBKINSON, Lucy Mary 6 Broughton Rise, Malton YO17 7BW — MB ChB 1994 Leic.

HOBKIRK, David William The Health Centre, Bow Street, Guisborough TS14 7AA Tel: 01287 634171 Fax: 01287 630963 — MB ChB 1973 Dundee; MRCGP 1977.

HOBMAN, Jonathan William Biscayne, Butts Lane, Lumby, South Milford, Leeds LS25 5JA — MB BS 1997 Lond.

HOBSLEY, Michael, TD Fieldside, Barnet Lane, Totteridge, London N20 8AS Tel: 020 8445 6507 Email: m.hobsley@ucl.ac.uk — MB BChir 1951 Camb.; PhD Lond. 1961, DSc (Med.) 1989; MChir Camb. 1963; FRCS Eng. 1958. (Middlx.) Emerit. Prof. Of Surg. UCL Med. Sch.; Chairm. Acad. Counc. Inst. Sports Med. Socs: Fell. Roy. Soc. Med. (Ex-Pres. Sect. Measurem. in Med.); (Ex-Pres.) Brit. Soc. Gastroenterol.; Sen. Mem. & Hon. Archiv. (Ex-Treas.) Surgic. Research Soc. Prev: David Patey Prof. Surg. Lond. Univ. Dept. Surg. Univ. Coll. Lond. Meds.ch.; Hon. Sec. Brit. Soc. Gastroenterol.; Asst., Depts. Surg. Studies & Physiol. Middlx. Hosp. Med. Sch. Lond.

HOBSON, Alexander Rowson Seaways, Lisle Court Rd, Lymington SO41 5SH — MB BS 1997 Lond.

HOBSON, Catherine Marie Hanley Street Medical Centre, Hanley Street, Hanley, Stoke-on-Trent ST1 3RX Tel: 01782 212305 Fax: 01782 201326; 8 The Parklands, Congleton CW12 3DS — BM BS 1988 Nottm.; BMedSci Nottm. 1986; DFFP 1993. (Nottingham) Prev: SHO Macclesfield Dist. Gen. Hosp.

HOBSON, David Godwin Ball Tree Surgery, Western Road North, Sompting, Lancing BN15 9UX Tel: 01903 752200 Fax: 01903 536983; 6 Pendine Avenue, Worthing BN11 2NB Email: davehobson@aol.com — MB BS 1982 Lond.; MA Camb. 1983; MRCGP 1986; DRCOG 1986. Course Organiser (Gen. Pract.) Worthing & Chichester VTS.

HOBSON, Emma Elizabeth University of Aberdeen, Dept. of Medicine and Therapeutics, Polworth Building, Foresterhill, Aberdeen AB25 2ZD Tel: 01224 681818 Email: e.e.hobson@abdn.ac.uk — MB BS 1993 Lond.; BSc Lond. 1990; MRCP (UK) 1996. (St. Bart.) MRC Clin. Train. Fell. Med. & Therap. Univ of Aberd. Prev: SHO (Gen. Med.) Aberd. Roy. Infirm.

HOBSON, Janet Elizabeth Foundry House, The Oval, Bedlington NE22 5HS Tel: 01670 536407 — MB BS 1985 Newc.; MMedSci. (Clin. Psychiat.) Leeds 1992; MRCPsych 1989. Cons. Old Age Psychiat. Newc., N. Tyneside and N.d. Ment. Health NHS Trust. Prev: Sen. Regist. (Psychiat. Old Age) N. Deanery N. & Yorks. HA.

HOBSON, Jeremy Graeme 11 B Beaufort Gardens, Ilford IG1 3DB Email: thehobsons@cwcom.net — MB BS 1996 Lond. (St. Bart.) Socs: Christ. Med. Fell.sh.

HOBSON, Joanne The Surgery, 152 Melton Road, West Bridgford, Nottingham NG2 6ER Tel: 0115 945 2656 Fax: 0115 923 5166; 70 Halllfields, Edwalton, Nottingham NG12 4AA — MB BS 1983 Lond.; DRCOG 1987. (St. Bart. Hosp.) Clin. Asst. PsychosexualMed.; Med. Adviser for Child Protec. (Primary Care). Socs: Media Medics; BMA; Coun. Mem. M-C Soc. Prev: GP Nottm.; Clin. Med. Off. (Family Plann. & Community Paediat.) Nottm.

HOBSON, John Andrew Devon House, 30 Shropshire St., Market Drayton TF9 3DD Tel: 01630 655988 — MB ChB 1985 Birm.; ChB Birm. 1985; MRCP (UK) 1989; MFOM RCP Lond. 1998. (Birmingham) Occupat. Phys. Michelin Stoke-on-Trent. Prev: Occupat. Phys. Nat. Power Rugeley.

HOBSON, John Barry Cardle Voar, 235 Huddersfield Road, Holmfirth, Huddersfield HD9 3TT Email: barry_hobson@talk21.com — MB ChB 1960 Manch.; DObst RCOG 1964. (Manch.) Socs: Hudds. Med. Soc. Prev: SHO (Obst.) Ashton-under-Lyne Gen. Hosp; SHO (Orthop.) Withington Hosp. Manch.; Course Organiser Huddersfield GP VTS.

HOBSON, John Frank (retired) c/o Lloyds Bank, Minster Place, Ely CB7 4EN — MB ChB 1949 Liverp.; MFOM 1981; MFCM 1973; DIH Eng. 1969; DPH Lond. 1961. Prev: Hon. Phys. to H.M. The Qu..

HOBSON, John Hay (retired) 9 Oxford Avenue, Southbourne, Bournemouth BH6 5HS Tel: 01202 420307 — MB BS Lond. 1946; DO RCS Eng. 1968; DTM & H RCP Lond. 1950. Prev: Med. Supt. BCMS Hosps. Kachwa, India & Mohnyin, Burma.

HOBSON, Lucinda Jane 92 Durnford Street, Stonehouse, Plymouth PL1 3QW — MB BS 1988 Lond. Trainee/SHO Plymouth VTS. Prev: SHO (A & E) Salisbury Gen. Infirm.; SHO (ENT) Greenbank Hosp. Plymouth.

HOBSON, Lynn Averell Moy Health Centre, 40 Charlemont Street, Moy, Dungannon BT71 7SL — MB BCh BAO 1976 Belf.

HOBSON, Mark Irving 11 Meddins Lane, Kinver, Stourbridge DY7 6BZ — MB ChB 1988 Ed.; FRCS (Plas.) 2001; BA (Physiol. Sci.) Oxf. 1985; FRCS Eng. 1992; DM Oxf. 1998. (Univ. Edin.) Specialist Regist. Rotot. (Plastic Surg.) W. Midl.

***HOBSON, Michelle** 41 Percivale Road, Chandler's Ford, Eastleigh SO53 4TS — MB ChB 1994 Birm.

HOBSON, Neil Andrew 14 Pingle Avenue, Sheffield S7 2LP — MB ChB 1992 Aberd.

HOBSON, Philip Joseph The Health Centre, Newgate St., Worksop S80 1HP Tel: 01909 500288 Fax: 01909 479564 — MB ChB 1964 Sheff.; DObst RCOG 1966. (Sheff.) Med. Off. Pandrol UK Ltd.; Dent. Anaesth. Worksop. Socs: BMA; Assn. Dent. Anaesthes. Prev: Cas. Off. Sheff. Roy. Infirm.; SHO (Obst.) Gen. Hosp. Bishop Auckland; Ho. Phys. N.. Gen. Hosp. Sheff.

HOBSON, Richard Patrick Department ofMolecular & cell Biology, Aberdeen University, Foresterhill, Aberdeen AB25 2zd Tel: 01224 273178 Email: r.p.hobson@abdn.ac.uk — MB BS 1988 Lond.; MRCP (UK) 1996; MRCpath, 1999. (St. Bart. Hosp. Med. Coll.) Clin.

research Fell., (molecular and Cell Biol.), Aberd. Univ. Socs: Brit. Soc. Med. Mycol; Assoc.Clin.Pathologists; ISHAM. Prev: Med. Off. Brit. Antarctic Survey Aberd.; Lond.; Spr Med. microbiollogy, Aberd. Roy. Univ.

HOBSON, Robert Peter The Tavistock Clinic, Adult Department, 120 Belsize Lane, London NW3 5BA Tel: 020 7435 7111; 24 Kingsbury Avenue, St Albans AL3 4TA — MB BChir 1976 Camb.; MB Camb. 1976, MA, BChir 1975; MRCPsych 1980. (Camb. & Univ. Coll. Hosp.)

HOBSON, Sarah Jane School Epidemiology & Public Health, Stopford Building, University of Manchester, Oxford Road, Manchester M13 9PL Email: mewxfsjh@fsi.ed.man.ac.uk; The Old Manse, 33 Caledonia Road, Batley WF17 5NS Tel: 01924 420234 — MB ChB 1983 Manch.; BSc St. And. 1980; MA Manch. 1988; MPH Leeds 1995; MRCGP 1987; DRCOG 1986. Sen. Regist. (Pub. Health) N. & Yorks. Region. Prev: GP Leeds.

HOBSON, Sweyn 335 Holyhead Road, Coventry CV5 8JQ Tel: 024 76 591598 — MB ChB 1927 Birm.; BSc Birm. 1925, MB ChB 1927. (Birm.)

HOCHHAUSER, Daniel 803 Finchley Road, London NW11 8DP — MB BS 1983 Lond.; DPhil Oxf. 1993; MRCP (UK) 1986. Sen. Lect./Hon. Cons. (Med. Oncol.) Roy. Free Hosp. Med. Sch. Prev: Fell. (Med. Oncol.) Memor. Sloan-Kettering Cancel Center, NY, USA; ICRF Fell. Dept. Molecular Oncol. Inst. Molecular Med. Oxf.; Regist. (Med.) Ch.ill & John Radcliffe Hosps. Oxf.

HOCK, Ye Lin Department of Histopathology, Manor Hospital, Moat Road, Walsall WS2 9PS Tel: 01922 656871 — MB BS 1985 Rangoon; MRCPath 1994. Cons. Histopath. Manor Hosp. Walsall. Socs: Roy. Coll. Pathol. (CPD Advisor for W Midl.). Prev: Sen. Regist. (Histopath.) Chase Farm Hosp. Enfield.

HOCK HENG THAM, Dr 6 Widford Grove, Chelmsford CM2 9AT — MB BS 1986 New South Wales.

HOCKADAY, Judith Mary (retired) The Mulberries, Main St., East Hanney, Wantage OX12 0JF — MB BChir 1953 Camb.; MD Camb. 1960; FRCP Lond. 1984, M 1955. Prev: Cons. Paediat. Neurol. John Radcliffe Hosp. Oxf.

HOCKADAY, Thomas Derek Ronald (retired) The Mulberries, Main St, East Hanney, Wantage OX12 0JF Tel: 01235 868231 Email: djhockaday@netscapeonline.co.uk — BM BCh 1955 Oxf.; DPhil (Biol. Sc.) Oxf. 1968, MA (1st cl. Hons. Physiol.), BSc 1952; FRCP Lond. 1971, M 1958. Hon. Cons. Phys. Oxf. HA (T). Prev: Cons. Phys. Radcliffe Infirm. Oxf.

HOCKEN, Mr David Brian Department of Surgery, Princess Margaret Hospital, Okus Road, Swindon SN1 4JU Tel: 01793 426627 Fax: 01793 426949; 4 Walcot Terrace, Bath BA1 6AB Tel: 01225 319336 Fax: 01225 471145 Email: david.hocken@virgin.net — MB BS 1979 Lond.; MS Lond. 1991; FRCS Eng. 1985. (St. Bart.) Cons. Gen. & Vasc. Surg. P.ss Margt. Hosp. Swindon & Savernake Hosp. MarlBoro.; Critical Prof. of Surg., St. Geo.s Univ. Sch. of Med., Grenada; Mem. of Fac., Train. the Trainers Course, Roy. Coll. of Surg.s. Socs: Surgic. Research Soc.; Vasc. Soc. GB & Irel.; Assn. Endoscopic Surgs. Prev: Lect. & Sen. Regist. (Gen. & Vasc. Surg.) St. Bart. Hosp. Lond.; Lect. & Research Fell. (Vasc. Surg.) Char. Cross & W.m. Med. Sch. Lond.; Regist. (Gen. Surg.) Roy. Devon & Exeter Hosp. Heavitree & Wonford.

HOCKEN, Paul Brooks (retired) Wood Cottage, Grennan, Drummore, Stranraer DG9 9HA — MB ChB 1961 Birm.; MRCGP 1980. Prev: Med. Off. Rolls Royce AED Scotl.

HOCKENHULL, Clara Helen Manor Farm, Kingsterndale, Buxton SK17 9SD — MB ChB 1992 Sheff. SHO (c/o Elderly) Stepping Hill Hosp. Stockport.

HOCKENHULL, Norman Joseph Boundary House, 462 Northenden Road, Sale M33 2RH Tel: 0161 972 9999; 2 Woodlands Drive, Brooklands, Sale M33 3PQ Tel: 0161 973 5521 — MB ChB 1964 Manch. (Manch.) Socs: BMA. Prev: Ho. Off. (Orthop.) Crumpsall Hosp. Manch.; Ho. Phys. & Ho. Surg. (O & G) Pk. Hosp. Davyhulme.

HOCKENHULL, Peter Darlington (retired) 6 Rhyd-y-Fawnog, Tregaron SY25 6JQ Tel: 01974 298791 — MRCS Eng. LRCP Lond. 1951; MA Camb. 1949. Clin. Asst. Tregaron Chest Hosp. Prev: Med. Off. Aberbargoed Hosp.

HOCKEY, Andrew James Sanofi-Synthelabo Ltd, One Oslow Street, Guildford GU1 4YS — MB BS 1989 Lond.; MSc 1999 London; FRCS Eng. 1994. Clin. ResearchPhys., Sanofi-Synthelabo, Guildford. Socs: Brit. Assn. of Pharmaceutical Phys.s; Brit. Med. Assn.

HOCKEY, Bryan John West Walk Surgery, 21 West Walk, Yate, Bristol BS37 4AX Tel: 01454 272200; Fading Cottage, Westend, Wickwar, Wotton-under-Edge GL12 8LD Tel: 01454 294814 — MA Camb. 1951, BA 1947, MB BChir 1949. (Camb. & Univ. Coll. Hosp.)

HOCKEY, Jane Agnes Hawthorn Surgery, Scotton Road, Scotter, Gainsborough DN21 3SB Tel: 01724 762204 — MB ChB 1978 Birm. GP Asst.

HOCKEY, Joanne Susan 5 Ambler Road, Finsbury Park, London N4 2QT — MB BS 1991 Lond.

HOCKEY, John Ronald (retired) Raggles, Noons Folly, Newmarket Road, Royston SG8 7NG Tel: 01763 244616 Fax: 01763 241343 Email: john.hockey@btinternet.com — MB BChir 1964 Camb.; MA Camb. 1964; MRCS Eng. LRCP Lond. 1963; MRCOG 1970; DObst RCOG 1967. p/t Clin. Governance Adviser, Uttlesford PCT. Prev: Regist. Middlx. Hosp. Lond.

HOCKEY, Mark Simon 6 Bingman Avenue, Poole BH14 8NE; Brackenhill, 6 Bingham Avenue, Poole BH14 8NE — MB ChB 1987 Bristol.

HOCKEY, Mr Michael Stanley Scunthorpe General Hospital, Cliff Gardens, Scunthorpe DN15 Tel: 01724 290184 Fax: 01724 290153 — MB BS 1973 Lond.; FRCS Eng. 1979; DA (UK) 1989; FFAEM 1993. (St. Geo.) Cons. A & E Scunthorpe Gen. Hosp.; Serv. Dir. Crit. Care. Prev: Sen. Regist. (A & E) Roy. Hallamsh. Hosp. Sheff.; Doctor i/c Kalene Hosp., Zambia.

HOCKING, Elizabeth Denison (retired) Croft Cottage, 2 Church Lane, Cricklade, Swindon SN6 6AD Tel: 01793 751331 — MB BChir 1956 Camb.; MA, MB BChir Camb. 1956; FRCP Ed. 1983, M 1962. Hon. Cons. Phys. (Geriat.) Swindon Health Dist. Prev: Cons. Phys. (Geriat.) Stockport & N. Derbysh. AHA.

HOCKING, Jeffrey Alan 13 Heol Gam, Pentyrch, Cardiff CF15 9QA — MB BCh 1997 Wales.

HOCKING, Miss Margaret Ann Accident & Emergency Department, Royal Cornwall Hospital (Treliske), Truro TR1 3LJ Tel: 01872 253203 Fax: 01872 253215; Bosrowynek, West Langarth, Threemilestone, Truro TR4 9AN — MB ChB (Hons.) Leeds 1971; BSc (Hons.) (Physiol.) Leeds 1968; FRCS Ed. 1976; FRCS Eng. 1976. Cons. A & E Roy. Cornw. Hosp. (Treliske) Truro. Socs: Fell. Fac. Accid. & Emerg. Med.; BMA & Brit. Assn. Accid. & Emerg. Med. Prev: Dir. of Emerg. Med. Qu. Eliz. II Jubilee Hosp. Brisbane, Austral.; Cons. A & E Lewisham Hosp.; Regist. (Surg.) Roy. Infirm. & Stobhill Hosp. Glas.

HOCKING, Mark Lawrence Dept. of Clinical Oncology, Walsgrave Hospital, Coventry CV2 2DX — MB ChB 1982 Leeds; MRCP (UK) 1986; FRCR 1994. Cons. Clin. Oncol. Walsgrave Hosp. Coventry.

HOCKING, Michael David Birmingham Childrens Hospital, Steelhouse Lane, Birmingham B4 6NH Tel: 0121 333 9999 — MB BS 1973 Lond.; MD Lond. 1991; FRCP Lond. 1995; MRCP (UK) 1979; MRCS Eng. LRCP Lond. 1973; DCH Eng. 1977; FRCPCH 1997. (Roy. Free) Cons. Paediat. Birm. Childr.s Hosp. & Birm. Womans Hosp.; Cons Paediat. Birm. Woman's Hosp. (Neonatology); Cons Paediat. Birm. Childr.'s Hosp. (Gen. Paediat.). Prev: Sen. Regist. Birm. Childr. Hosp. & New Cross Hosp. Wolverhampton.

HOCKINGS, Jane Elizabeth The Surgery, Mill Road, Ballasalla IM9 2EA Tel: 01624 823243 Fax: 01624 822947; 30 Selborne Drive, Douglas IM2 3NH Tel: 01624 671765 — MB ChB 1971 Glas.; DA Eng. 1974; DObst RCOG 1974. Asst. Hospice Doctor I. of Man. Socs: I. of Man Med. Soc. Prev: Clin. Asst. (A & E) Louth Co. Hosp. Lincs.; SHO (Anaesth.) Chelmsford Gp. Hosps.; Ho. Surg. & Ho. Phys. Chelmsford & Essex Hosp.

HOCKINGS, Michael 23 Princes Way, Fleetwood FY7 8PG — MB ChB 1992 Manch.

HOCKINGS, Neil Franklin Nobles Isle of Man Hospital, Douglas IM1 4QA Tel: 01624 642642; 30 Selborne Drive, Douglas IM2 3NH Tel: 01624 671765 — MB BS 1976 Lond.; FRCP Lond. 1993; MRCP (UK) 1979. Cons. Phys. Noble's I. of Man Hosp. Prev: Cons. Phys. Louth Co. Hosp.; Sen. Regist. (Mat. Med.) Stobhill Gen. Hosp. Glas.; MRC Research Fell. (Pharmacol. & Therap.) Univ. Dundee.

HOCKLEY, Mr Anthony David 19 Farquhar Road, Edgbaston, Birmingham B15 3RA Tel: 0121 454 4125 Fax: 0121 454 0460 — MB BS Lond. 1966; FRCS Ed. 1970; MRCS Eng. LRCP Lond. 1966. (Lond. Hosp.) Cons. Neurosurg. Qu. Eliz. & Childr. Hosps Birm.;

Hon. Sen. Lect. Univ. Birm. Socs: Soc. Brit. Neuro Surg.; Internat. Soc. Paediat. Neurosurg. (Exec. Comm.); BMA. Prev: Sen. Regist. (Neurosurg.) Addenbrooke's Hosp. Camb.; Chief Resid. (Neurosurg.) Hosp. Sick Childr. Toronto, Canada; SHO Inst. Neurol. Scs. Glas.

HOCKMAN, Nathaniel (retired) 27 Spencer Close, Finchley, London N3 3TX Tel: 020 8371 8781 — MB BS (Hnrs.) Lond. 1940; MRCS Eng. LRCP Lond. 1940. Prev: Cas. Off. & Ho. Phys. St. Mary Abbots (LCC) Hosp. Kens.

HOCKNELL, Joanna Margaret Loveday Nightingale MacMillan Unit, 117A London Road, Derby DE1 2QS Tel: 01332 254900 Fax: 01332 254984; The Malt House, Woodhouses, Melbourne, Derby DE73 1DN Tel: 01332 865492 — MB BS 1979 Lond.; MSc (Nuclear Med.) Lond. 1986; MRCP (UK) 1982; T(M) 1993; FRCP 1998. (St. Mary's Hosp. Med. Sch. Lond.) Cons. Palliat. Med. S.ern Derbysh. Acute Hosps. NHS Trust. Prev: Sen. Lect. Univ. Nottm.; Med. Dir. St. Michael's Hospice St. Leonards on Sea; Regist. (Nuclear Med.) Middlx. Hosp. Lond.

HOCKNEY, Elizabeth Anne Flood and Partners, Essex House Surgery, Station Road, Barnes, London SW13 0LW Tel: 020 8876 1033 Fax: 020 8878 5894; 64 East Sheen Avenue, London SW14 8AU Tel: 020 8876 4391 — BM 1986 Soton.; MRCGP 1990; DRCOG 1989. (Southampton) Prev: Trainee GP, Qu. Mary's Hosp., Roehampton; Ho. Phys., St. Peter's Chertsey; Ho. Surg. Mayday Hosp. Croydon.

HOCKRIDGE, Kevin Simon The Mumbles Medical Practice, 10 West Cross Avenue, Norton, Mumbles, Swansea SA3 5UA Tel: 01792 403010 Fax: 01792 401934; 57 Caswell Road, Caswell, Swansea SA3 4RH — MB BCh 1981 Wales; DRCOG 1984. Prev: Cas. Off. Singleton Hosp. Swansea; SHO (O & G) Mt. Pleasant Hosp. Swansea.

HODA, Alister Windle Ash Surgery, Chilton Gardens, Ash, Canterbury CT3 2HA — MB BS 1967 Lond.; DObst RCOG 1970.

HODA, Muhammad Qamarul c/o Mr M A Hashmi, 20 Helensburgh Close, Barnsley S75 2EU — MB BS 1985 Karachi.

HODDER, Katherine Mair Sycamore House, 11 Bell Crescent, Longwick, Princes Risborough HP27 9SE — MB BS 1998 Lond.; MB BS Lond 1998.

HODDER, Richard William Sycamore House, 11 Bell Crescent, Longwick, Princes Risborough HP27 9SE Tel: 01844 347535 — MB BS 1966 Lond.; MRCS Eng. LRCP Lond. 1967; MFPM RCP (UK) 1988; DObst RCOG 1972. (Univ. Coll. Hosp.) Socs: BMA.

HODDER, Rupert James Stonecroft House, Broadgreen Hospital, Thomas Drive, Liverpool L14 3LB; 23 Corndale Road, Liverpool L18 5HA — MB ChB 1992 Liverp.

HODDER, Sally Elizabeth Lanehouse Surgery, Ludlow Road, Weymouth DT4 0HB Tel: 01305 785681 Fax: 01305 760418; Villa Santander, 64 Budmouth Avenue, Preston, Weymouth DT3 6QJ Tel: 01305 834880 — MB ChB 1980 Birm.; MFPM RCP (UK) 1994; DRCOG 1994; DFFP 1994; T(GP) 1992. (Birm.) Prev: Med. Dir. Shire Pharmaceut. Developm. Ltd. Andover; Assoc. Europ. Med. Dir. Merrell Dow Research Inst. Winnersh; Med. Adviser Wellcome Internat. Trading Ltd. Berkhamsted.

HODDER, Mr Simon Charles Department of Maxillofacial Surgery, Morriston Hospital, Morriston, Swansea SA6 Tel: 01792 703063 Fax: 01792 703068 Email: simonhodder@swansea-tr.wales.nhs.uk; The Grange Farmhouse, Dyffryn, Neath SA10 7BQ — MB ChB 1991 Glas.; BDS Wales 1981; FRCS (Max Fac) 1997; FRCS Ed. 1994; Dip. Forens. Med. Glas 1991; FDS RCPS Glas. 1986. (Glasgow) Cons. Maxillofacial Surg. Morriston Hosp. Swansea; Clin. Tutour Swansea Med. Sch.; Lead Clin. Head and Neck Cancer Servs. S. W. Wales. Socs: BMA & Brit. Assn. Oral & Maxillofacial Surg.; Internat. Assn. Oral & Maxillofacial Surg.; Brit. Assn. Head & Neck Oncol. Prev: Specialis Regist. (Oral & Maxillofacial Surg.) Univ. Hosps. Wales Cardiff; Regist. (Oral & Maxillofacial Surg.) Morriston Hosp. Swansea; SHO (Gen. Surg.) Vict. Infirm. Glas.

HODDES, Colin Edward 9 St Andrews Road, Blundellsands, Liverpool L23 7UP — MB ChB 1986 Dundee; MRCGP 1990.

HODDES, Jane Ann 9 St Andrews Road, Blundellsands, Liverpool L23 7UP; St. Mary's Hospital, Praed St, Paddington, London W2 1PG — MB BCh 1992 Wales; MRCP (UK) 1996; MRCPCH 1996. Specialist Regist. (Paediat.) St. Mary's Hosp. Paddington. Prev: Specialist Regist. (Paediat.) Lister Hosp. Stevenage; SHO (Paediat.) Centr. Middlx. Hosp. Lond.

HODDES, Sidney Henry (retired) 9 St Andrew's Road, Blundellsands, Liverpool L23 7UP Tel: 0151 924 4986 — MB ChB Liverp. 1952. Hypnotherapist, Liverp. Prev: Princip. GP, Liverp. (Retd.).

HODDINOTT, Mr Huw Ceri Department of Orthopaedic Surgery, Morriston Hospital, Swansea — MB BS 1982 Lond.; BSc Lond. 1978; FRCS Ed. 1987; FRCS Eng. 1987. Cons. Orthop. Surg. Morriston Hosp. Swansea. Socs: Mem. Bristish Orthoptics Assn.; BMA; Brit. Elbow & Shoulder Soc. Prev: Sen. Regist. (Orthop.) Cardiff Roy. Infirm.; Regist. (Orthop.) Bristol Roy. Infirm.; Regist. (Surg.) Heath Hosp. Cardiff.

HODDINOTT, Patricia Mary Macduff Medical Practice, 100 Duff Street, MacDuff AB44 1PR Tel: 01261 833777 Fax: 01261 835100 — MB BS 1982 Lond.; BSc Lond. 1979; MRCGP 1986; DCH RCP Lond. 1986; DRCOG 1985; M Phil 1998. (St. Mary's) p/t GP; CSO Research Pract.; Hon. Clin. Research Fell. Dept. of Gen. Pract. Aberd. Prev: GP Lond.; Teachg. Fell. (Gen. Pract.) Lond.

HODDINOTT, Rebecca Elizabeth North Villa, 166 Fulford Road, York YO10 4DA — MB ChB 1998 Liverp.; MB ChB Liverp 1998.

HODDS, Elizabeth Jayne Brambles, 6 Campion Way, Rugby CV23 0UR Tel: 01788 338050 Fax: 01788 338090 Email: hodds@lizjames97.freeserve.co.uk — MB ChB 1991 Leic. GP. Prev: SHO (Med.) Walsgrave Hosp. Coventry.; GP Regist. Measham Med. Unit.

HODDY, Derek William (retired) 2 New Court, Allerby, Aspatria, Carlisle CA7 2NL Tel: 01900 816073 — MB ChB 1964 Birm.; DObst RCOG 1966. Prev: Ho. Phys. Qu. Eliz. Hosp. Birm.

HODELET, Nicola Patricia 1577 Great Western Road, Glasgow G13 1LS — MB ChB 1991 Aberd.

HODES, Cyril Bernard 1 Ashchurch Terrace, London W12 9SL Tel: 020 8743 2920; 10 St. Mary Abbot's Terrace, London W14 8NX Tel: 020 7602 3332 — MB BS 1952 Lond.; MRCS Eng. LRCP Lond. 1952; FRCGP 1980, M 1960. (Westm.) Private Pract. Socs: Fell. Roy. Soc. Med.; W Lond. Medico-Chir. Soc.

HODES, Deborah Tamara Child & Adolescent Services, St Leonards Primary Care, Nuttall St., Kingsland Road, London N1 5LZ Tel: 020 7301 3284 Fax: 020 7301 3270 — MB BS 1977 Lond.; BSc (Hons.) Lond. 1974; MRCP (UK) 1982; FRCPCH 1996; DRCOG 1985. p/t Cons. Community Paediat. City & Hackney Primary Care Trust. Prev: SCMO & Sen. Regist. Islington HA; Regist. (Paediat.) Whipps Cross Hosp. Lond.; SHO (Paediat.) Hammersmith Hosp. Lond.

HODES, Matthew Academic Unit of Child & Adolescent Psychiatry, Imperial College of Science, Technology & Medicine, St Mary's Campus, Norfolk Place, London W2 1PG Tel: 020 7886 1145 Fax: 020 7886 6299 Email: m.hodes@ic.ac.uk — MB BS 1980 Lond.; MSc Social Anthropol. Lond. 1982; BSc Lond. 1976; MRCS Eng. LRCP Lond. 1979; MRCPsych 1985. Cons. Child & Adolesc. Psychiat. St. Mary's Dept. Child & Adolesc. Psychiat. Lond. Prev: Research Worker & Hon. Sen. Regist. Inst. Psychiat. Lond.; Sen. Regist. (Child Psychiat.) King's Coll. & Maudsley Hosps. Lond.; Regist. (Psychiat.) Maudsley Hosp. Lond.

HODES, Philip Adam 14 Kirton Park Terrace, North Shields NE30 2BP — LMSSA 1983 Lond.

HODES, Robert Michael (retired) Berene, Prestwich Park Road Sth. M25 9PF Tel: 0161 773 7535 Fax: 0161 773 7535 Email: susan@hohes.demon.co.uk — MB ChB 1962 Manch.; AFOM 1981; DObst RCOG 1964; DIH Soc. Apoth. Lond. 1974. p/t Disabil. analyst, Manch. Prev: Ho. Surg. Manch. N. Hosp.

***HODES, Simon** 14 Ringley Road, Whitefield, Manchester M45 7LB — MB ChB 1996 Birm.; ChB Birm. 1996; MBChB Birmingham 1996.

HODGE, Adrian Laurence Hughes and Partners, 15 Dereham Road, Mattishall, Dereham NR20 3QA Tel: 01362 850227 Fax: 01362 858466 — MB ChB 1974 Glas.

HODGE, Bertrand Dennis (retired) 34 Caistor Lane, Tealby, Lincoln — MB ChB 1952 Birm. Prev: Capt. RAMC.

HODGE, Mr Colin Hedderwick (retired) 17 Kelvin Court, Glasgow G12 0AB Tel: 0141 339 0702 — MB ChB 1951 Glas.; FRCS Ed. 1960; FRCOG 1971, M 1958.

HODGE, Cyril Arthur (retired) Skipton Hall Retirement Home, Skipton-on-Swale, Thirsk YO7 4SB Tel: 01845 567457 — MRCS Eng. LRCP Lond. 1943. Prev: SCMO Cleveland AHA.

HODGE, Donald Galloway Flat 4, 23 Bainbrigge Road, Leeds LS6 3AD — MB ChB 1993 Leeds; BSc (Hons.) Leeds 1990; MRCP (UK) 1996. (Leeds) Regist. (Paediat.) Leeds Gen. Infirm.
HODGE, Grace Janet Kininmont (retired) 17 Kelvin Court, Glasgow G12 0AB Tel: 0141 339 0702 — MB ChB Glas. 1953; FRCPsych 1992, M 1976. Prev: Cons. Psychiat. Dykebar Hosp. Paisley.
HODGE, Ian Livingston Dingwall (retired) Upper Flat, 2 West Forth St., Cellardyke, Anstruther KY10 3HL — MB ChB Glas. 1947. Prev: Ho. Surg. & Sen. Ho. Phys. Horton Gen. Hosp. Banbury.
HODGE, Jennifer Clare 5 Church Close, Dolphinholme, Lancaster LA2 9AL — MB ChB 1997 Leeds.
HODGE, John-Charles 25 Glen Road, Leigh-on-Sea SS9 1EU — MB BS 1997 Lond.
HODGE, Keith Fernville Surgery, Midland Road, Hemel Hempstead HP2 5BL Tel: 01442 213919 Fax: 01442 216433 — MB BS 1981 Lond.; MA Camb. 1987; MRCGP 1985; DCH RCP Lond. 1985; DRCOG 1985. (Kings Coll. Hosp.) Prev: Trainee GP Greenwich & Brook VTS; Ho. Surg. (ENT) Kings Coll. Hosp. Lond.
HODGE, Michael George John Radcliffe Hospital, Headley Way, Oxford OX3 9DU Tel: 01865 221400 Fax: 01865 222040; 75 The Crescent, Mandelbrote Drive, Oxford OX4 4XQ Tel: 01865 776136 Fax: 01865 779771 — MB BS 1976 Lond.; BDS Lond. 1967; FDS RCS Eng. 1971. Cons. Oral & Maxillofacial Surg. Oxf. Radcliffe Hosps.
HODGE, Mr Raymond Carter Sigiriya, 7 Belgrave Close, Abergavenny NP7 7AP Tel: 01873 854797 Fax: 01873 856071; Sigiriya, 7 Belgrave Close, Abergavenny NP7 7AP Tel: 01873 854797 — MB ChB Bristol 1960; FRCS Ed. 1971; FRCSI 1971; FRCS Eng. 1968; MRCS Eng. LRCP Lond. 1960. (Bristol) Socs: Sen. Fell. BOA; Hosp. Cons. & Spec. Assn.; BMA. Prev: Cons. Orthop. Surg. Nevill Hall Hosp. Abergavenny; Sen. Regist. (Orthop. Surg.) P. of Wales Orthop. Hosp. Cardiff; Surg. Regist. Roy. Gwent Hosp. Newport.
HODGE, Robin James Abbey Road Surgery, 63 Abbey Road, Waltham Cross EN8 7LJ; 92A Turners Hill, Cheshunt, Waltham Cross EN8 8LQ — MB ChB 1972 Birm.
HODGE, Wendy Roser 49 Craigenbay Road, Lanzie, Glasgow G66 5JP; Interserve (Scotland), 12 Elm Avenue, Lanzie, Glasgow G66 4HJ Tel: 0141 776 2943 — MB ChB 1990 Dundee; MRCP (UK) 1993. Socs: Brit. Paediat. Assn. Prev: Sen. Regist. (Paediat.) Shaikh Zayed Hosp. Lahore, Pakistan; Regist. Craigavon Area Hosp. N. Irel.
HODGES, Alycen Elizabeth Josephine, Surg. Cdr. RN Retd. The Barn, Water St., Barrington, Ilminster TA19 0JR Tel: 01460 57195 Fax: 01460 55582 — MB 1977 Camb.; BChir 1976; MFOM RCP Lond. 1986, AFOM 1983; DAvMed Eng. 1980. Partner - Anton, Hodges & Goodman, Cons. Occupat.al Phys.s. Socs: BMA; SOM. Prev: Staff Med. Off. Flag Off. Portsmouth; Princip. Med. Off. HMS Heron Som.; Pres. Centr. Air Med. Bd. HMS Daedalus Hants.
HODGES, Ann Elizabeth Doctor Grays Hospital, Elgin IV30 1SN — MB BS 1985 Newc. cons. Psych.Elgin.
HODGES, Catherine 78 Wellington Hill W., Bristol BS9 4SN — MB ChB 1986 Manch.; MRCGP 1990; DRCOG 1988.
HODGES, Charlotte Barrett Lower Chapel House, Caldwell, Richmond DL11 7UQ — MB ChB 1995 Ed.
HODGES, Elizabeth Jane Red Roofs, 31 Coton Road, Nuneaton CV11 5TW Tel: 024 7635 7100 Fax: 024 7664 2036 — MB BCh 1995 Wales.
HODGES, Helen Christine 7 St John's Wood Court, London NW8 8QT Tel: 020 7286 7116 — MB BCh 1940 Wales; BSc Wales 1937; DMRT Eng. 1949. (Cardiff) Cons. Radiotherapist St. Mary's Hosp. Lond.; Mem. Brit. Inst. Radiol. Socs: Fell. Roy. Soc. Med. Prev: Cons. Radiotherapiast St. John's Hosp. Dis. of Skin Lond.; Asst. Lect. (Anat.) Univ. Coll. Cardiff; Regist. Postgrad. Med. Sch. Lond.
HODGES, Ian George Charles East Glamorgan General Hospital, Church Village, Pontypridd CF38 1AB Tel: 01443 218218 — MB BCh 1973 Wales; FRCP Lond. 1995; MRCP (UK) 1978. Cons. Paediat. E. Glam. Gen. Hosp. Pontypridd.
HODGES, Professor John Russell MRC Cognition & Brain Sciences Unit, 15 Chaucer Road, Cambridge CB2 2EF Tel: 01223 355294 Fax: 01223 359062 Email: john.hodges@mrc-apu.cam.ac.uk; Department of Neurology, Box 165, Addenbrooke's Hospital, Hills Road, Cambridge CB2 2QQ Tel: 01223 245151 Fax: 01223 415776 Email: jrh24@cus.cam.ac.uk — MD 1988 Lond.; MB BS (Hons.) (Distinc. Med.) Lond. 1975; FRCP Lond. 1993; MRCP (UK) 1977. (Lond. Hosp.) Prof. of Behaviour Nerol. & Hon. Cons. Neurol. Addenbrooke's Hosp. Camb. Socs: Assn. Brit. Neurols.; Internat. Neurophys. Soc.; Brit. Nemophys. Soc. Prev: Regist. (Neurol.) Oxf. Univ.; Lect. (Med. & Gastroenterol.) Soton. Univ.; Regist. (Med.) Profess. Unit Soton Gen. Hosp. & Roy. Vict Hosp. Bournemouth.
HODGES, Julia Marion The Surgery, 1 Richmond House, East Street, London SE17 2DU Tel: 020 7703 7393 Fax: 020 7708 3077 — MB BS 1981 Lond.
HODGES, Larissa Marie-Claire Rohan House, Willoughby, Rugby CV23 8BH — MB BS 1994 Lond.
HODGES, Mary Elizabeth Hamer 18 Wilberforce Road, Southsea PO5 3DR Tel: 01705 718532 Fax: 01705 718533 Email: maryhodges@doctors.org.uk — MB BS 1976 Lond.; DSc (Glas.) 1997; MRCP (UK) Paediat. 1981; VQE 1978; ECFMG Cert. 1977. (St. Bart.) Med. Dir. St. And. Clinic for Childr.; Staff Grade Paediat., Portsmouth Healthcare; Assoc. Paediat. Lect. Coll. Med. & Allied Health Sci. Univ. Sierra Leone; Hon. Sen. Research Fell. Fac. Biosci. Univ. Glas. Socs: Internat. Child Health Gp. Prev: Specialist Paediat. Sierra Leone Milit. Hosp.; Phys. i/c, Jt. Health Care Facility.
HODGES, Michael John Clayhall Clinic, 14 Clayhall Avenue, Ilford IG5 0LG Tel: 020 8550 5050 Fax: 020 8551 6393; West House, 2 Clarence Gate, Manor Road, Woodford Green IG8 8GN Tel: 020 8501 0815 Fax: 020 8501 0815 Mobile: 07050034125 Email: drmikehodges@hotmail.com — MB BS 1984 Lond.; BSc 1979 (Hons.) Lond.; DRCOG 1986. (Char. Cross) Phys. i/c BUPA Roding Hosp. / Med. Director of Private GP Serv.; Chairm. Mobile Doctors Ltd. (Medico-Legal Company); Director U-1st Healthcare Ltd.; Occupat.al Health Adviser to Tesco Plc. Socs: The St. Paul Insur. Co. Prev: Ho. Phys. Whipps Cross Hosp. Lond.; Ho. Surg. Char. Cross Hosp. Lond.; Trainee GP Ilford VTS.
HODGES, Michael Richard 3 The Courtyard, Staple Farm, Durlock Road, Staple, Canterbury CT3 1JX — MB BS 1985 Lond.; BSc Lond. 1982, MB BS 1985; MRCP (UK) 1988. Clin. Project Manager Pfizer Pharmaceut. Socs: Med. Soc. Study VD; Immunocomp. Host Soc. Prev: Regist. (Genitourin. Med. & Renal) St. Thos. Hosp. Lond.; SHO (Thoracic & Renal Med.) Roy. Free Hosp.
HODGES, Neville The White House, Treborth Road, Bangor LL57 2RJ Tel: 01248 355394 Fax: 01248 355394 Email: nefran@medix-uk.co; Ysbyty Gwynedd, Bangor LL57 2PW Tel: 01248 384327 Fax: 01248 385093 — MB BCh 1964 Wales; MD Wales 1981; FRCP Lond. 1981, M 1968. Cons. Phys.N. W. Wales NHS Trust; Cons. Phys. Private Med. & Medico Legal, Bangor. Prev: Sen. Regist. Soton Gen. Hosp.; Research Fell. United Manch. Hosp.
HODGES, Nicholas Adam The Health Centre, Moretonhampstead, Newton Abbot TQ13 8LW Tel: 01647 40591 — MB BS 1967 Lond.; DA Eng. 1969.
HODGES, Paul Steinhardt and Partners, The Surgery, 5A Brookfield Road, Hucclecote, Gloucester GL3 3HB Tel: 01452 617295 Fax: 01452 617296; 18 Twyver Close, Upton St. Leonards, Gloucester GL4 8EF — MB ChB 1987 Birm.; ChB Birm. 1987; MRCGP 1993; DRCOG 1991; DCH RCP Lond. 1990. (Birm.) SHO (O & G) Worcester; Clin. Asst. (Learning Disabil. & Haemat.) Glouc. Socs: BMA; RCGP; RCOG. Prev: SHO (Paediat.) Telford; Trainee GP Chester VTS.
HODGES, Roger Newton Yorkleigh Surgery, 93 St. Georges Road, Cheltenham GL50 3ED Tel: 01242 519049 Fax: 01242 253556 Email: rnhodges@doctors.org.uk; Email: rnhodges@doctors.org.uk — MB ChB 1967 Ed. (Ed.) Police Surg. Cheltenham Div. Glos. Constab.; Clin. Asst. (Ophth.) Cheltenham Gen. Hosp. Socs: Assn. Police Surg. Prev: SHO (Ophth.) Roy. Infirm. Edin.; Ho. Off. (Obst.) E.. Gen. Hosp. Edin.; Ho. Off. (Med.) Deaconess Hosp. Edin.
HODGES, Simon Richard St Thomas Court Surgery, St. Thomas Court, Church Street, Axminster EX13 5AG Tel: 01297 32126 Fax: 01297 35759 — MB BS 1975 Lond.; DRCOG 1979. (Westm.)
HODGES, Stephen Dept Child Health, Royal Victoria Infirmary, Newcastle upon Tyne Tel: 0191 232 5131; 31 Fenwick Terrace, Newcastle upon Tyne NE2 2JQ — MB ChB 1977 Sheff.; FRCP Lond. 1995; MRCP (UK) 1980; MRCGP 1985; DRCOG 1985; DCH RCP Lond. 1981. Cons Paediat Gastroenterologist, Roy. Vict. Infirm.,Newc. upon Tyne; Child Health Univ., Newc. upon Tyne.

Prev: Lect. (Child Health) Univ. Leic.; Cons Paediat. Qu. Eliz. Hosp, Gateshead.

HODGES, Walter Graham Woodstock, 346 Gower Road, Killay, Swansea SA2 7AE — MRCS Eng. LRCP Lond. 1950.

HODGES, Yvonne Maria Bukraba St Thomas' Court, Church St., Axminster EX13 5AG — MB BS 1976 Lond.; Cert. JCC Lond. 1979. (King's Coll. Hosp.)

HODGETTS, Professor Timothy John, OStJ, Lt.-Col. RAMC Accident & Emergency Department, Frimley Park NHS Trust, Camberley GU16 5UJ Tel: 01276 706263 Fax: 01276 604282 Email: tim@blenheim.softnet.co.uk — MB BS 1986 Lond.; MB BS (Hons.) Lond. 1986; MRCP (UK) 1990; FFAEM 1996; Dip. IMC RCS Ed. 1989; Dip. Med. Ed. 1998; FRCP 1999. (Westm.) Cons. A & E Frimley Pk. NHS Trust; Prof. (Emerg. Med. & Trauma) Univ. of Surrey 1998; Specialty Adviser (A & E) Defence Med. Serv.; Chairm. Edit. Bd. Pre-Hosp. Immediate Care Jl. Socs: BASICS (Mem. Ed. Bd.); Fac. Pre-Hosp. Care; Eur. Soc. Med. Edr.s. Prev: Hon. Trauma Fell. Liverp. Hosp., Sydney, Austral.; Sen. Regist. (A & E) Hope Hosp. Salford; Regist. (Med.) Qu. Eliz. Milit. Hosp. Woolwich.

HODGINS, Ian Robert 41 Peverell Terrace, Plymouth PL3 4JJ — MB BS 1990 Lond.

HODGINS, Priya Susan 16 Pelsall Road, Brownhills, Walsall WS8 7JE — MB ChB 1998 Liverp.; MB ChB Liverp 1998.

HODGKIN, John Eliot (retired) 4 The Crescent, Steyning BN44 3GD — BM BCh 1951 Oxf.

HODGKIN, Paul Keith Centre for Innovations in Primary Care, Walsh Court, Off Bell's Square, Trippet Lane, Sheffield S1 2FY Tel: 0114 220 2000 Fax: 0114 220 2001; 48 Montgomery Road, Sheffield S7 1LQ — MB ChB 1975 Manch.; MRCGP 1980; DCH Eng. 1978. Co-Dir. Centre for Innovations in Primary Care; Lect. Dept. of Gen. Pract. Univ. of Sheff.

HODGKINS, Mr John Darley Mount, 215 Duffield Road, Darley Abbey, Derby DE22 1JE Tel: 01332 552954 Fax: 01332 552954 Email: hodgkins@netcomuk.co.uk — MB ChB 1960 Manch.; FRCS Ed. 1970; FRCOG 1982, M 1968; DObst RCOG 1962. (Manch.) Cons. O & G Derby City Gen. Hosp. Socs: Fell. Birm. & Midl. Obst. & Gyn. Soc.; Founder Mem. Nuffield Visit. Soc.; Derby Med. Soc.

HODGKINS, Mr Peter Southampton Eye Unit, Southampton General Hospital, Tremona Road, Southampton SO16 6YD Tel: 02380 794645 Fax: 02380 794162 Email: peter.hodgkins@suht.swest.nhs.uk — MB ChB 1988 Birm.; BSc (Hons.); FRCS FRCOphth. (Birmingham) Cons. Ophth. Gen. Hosp. Soton.

HODGKINSON, Brian Raymond Mill Bank Surgery, Water Street, Stafford ST16 2AG Tel: 01785 258348 Fax: 01785 227144; The White Cottage, Seighford, Stafford ST18 9PQ Tel: 01785 282324 — MB ChB 1982 Birm.

HODGKINSON, Christopher Robert Sumner House, Over Wallop, Stockbridge SO20 8HT — BM 1981 Soton.; BSc (Eng.) Lond. 1970; MRCGP 1985. GP Trainer Soton.

HODGKINSON, Mr David William Ipswich Hospital NHS Trust, Heath Road, Ipswich — BM BS 1983 Nottm.; FRCS 1991 Ed.; MRCP 1987 UK; FFAEM 1994. Cons. A & E Med. Ipswich Acute Servs. Trust. Prev: Lect. (A & E) Hope Hosp. Salford.; Cons. A & E Stockport Acute Servs. Trust.

HODGKINSON, Mr John Pattison 76 Gartside Road, Manchester M3 3EL Tel: 0161 832 1741 Fax: 0161 839 1749; 50 Cross Lane, Bury BL8 4LY Tel: 01706 822333 — MB ChB 1977 Manch.; FRCS Eng. 1982. Socs: B.O.A.; Brit. Hip Sociaty; N.W. Orthopaedic Assn. (Sec.). Prev: Sen. Regist. NW RHA.; Cons. Orthop. Surg. N. Manch. Healthcare NHS Trust.

HODGKINSON, Nancy Bennett 169 Sir Williams Close, Aylsham, Norwich NR11 6AY Tel: 01263 734510 — MB ChB 1944 Manch.; MRCS Eng. LRCP Lond. 1944.

HODGKINSON, Nora Amy (retired) 12 Caledonian Road, Savile Town, Dewsbury WF12 9NT Tel: 01924 2871 — MRCS Eng. LRCP Lond. 1931. Prev: Asst. MOH Dewsbury.

HODGKINSON, Mr Peter David Dept. of Plastic Surgery, Royal Victoria Infirmary, Queen Victoria Rd, Newcastle upon Tyne NE1 4LP Tel: 0191 282 0195 Fax: 0191 227 5229 Email: peter@hodgkinson-plasticsurgery.co.uk — MB ChB 1985 Manch.; PhD Manch. 1982, BSc (Hons.) 1979; FRCS (Plast.) 1995; FRCS Eng. 1989. Cons. Plastic.surg.Roy.Vict..Infirm.Newc. Socs: Train. Mem. Brit. Assn. Plastic Surg.; Craniofacial Soc.; Brit. Assn. Anaesth. Plastic. Surg. Prev: Sen.Reg.plastic Surg.roy.Adelaide.Hosp.Adelaide; Sen. Regist. (Plastic Surg.) Morriston Hosp. Swansea.

***HODGKINSON, Polly Anne** Studio House, 43 Lovelace Road, Surbiton KT6 6NA Tel: 020 8390 1953 — MB BS 1998 Lond.; MB BS Lond 1998.

HODGKINSON, Vanessa Tyddyn Gwyn, 38 Bryn Tyddyn, Pentrefelin, Criccieth LL52 0PE — MB BS 1992 Lond.

HODGKISS, Andrew David Department of LiasonPsychiatry, St Thomas' Hospital, London SE1 7EH Tel: 020 7928 9292 — MB BS 1986 Lond.; BA Camb. 1983; MD Lond. 1997; MRCPsych 1991; DCP Lond 1993. Cons. Liaison Psychiat. St. Thos. Hosp. Lond.; Mem. Centre for Freudian Anal. & Research (Lacanian PsychoAnal.); Sen. Lect. (Liaison Psychiat.) GKT Lond.

HODGKISS, Rachel Victoria Church End, Hernhill, Faversham ME13 9JU — MB ChB 1998 Liverp.; MB ChB Liverp 1998.

HODGSON, Alfred Lewis, MBE (retired) La Colline, Swannells Wood, Studham, Dunstable LU6 2QB — MB ChB 1955 Liverp.; FRCGP 1987, M 1966; DObst RCOG 1959. Prev: Sen. Trainer & Partner, John Scott Health Centre, Lond., UK.

HODGSON, Andrew John 234A Otley Road, Leeds LS16 5AB — MB BS 1994 Lond.; BSc Lond. 1993. SHO (A & E) Centr. Middlx. Hosp. Lond.

HODGSON, Aruna Kay 31 Eden Road, West End, Southampton SO18 3QW — MB BChir 1989 Camb.; MRCGP 1993; DRCOG 1992.

HODGSON, Barbara (retired) 4 Welton Old Road, Welton, Brough HU15 1NT Tel: 01482 667273 — MB ChB Leeds 1947; DCH Eng. 1949.

HODGSON, Bernadette Hilary, Col. Head Quarters, British Forces Germany Health Service BFPO 40 Tel: 00 49 2161 908 2356 — MB ChB 1977 Manch.; FRCGP 2001; MRCGP 1982; DRCOG 1982; MSc Med. Lond. 1997.

HODGSON, Christine Anne University Hospital Aintree, Liverpool L9 7AL Tel: 0151 529 5152 — MB BS 1984 Lond.; BSc (Pharmacol.) Lond. 1981; FRCA 1990. (St. Mary's) Cons. Anaesth. Aintree Hosps. NHS Trust. Prev: Sen. Regist. (Anaesth.) Mersey RHA; SHO (Neonat. Paediat.) Liverp. Matern. Hosp.; Regist. (Anaesth.) Mersey RHA.

HODGSON, Christopher (retired) Hill House, 63 Anglesea Road, Ipswich IP1 3PJ Tel: 01473 211856 — MB BS Lond. 1964; MRCS Eng. LRCP Lond. 1964; FFA RCS Eng. 1968; DA Eng. 1966; Dip. Drug & Alcohol Studies Lond. Prev: Hon. Clin. Asst. NE Essex Drug & Alcohol Serv.

HODGSON, Christopher Charles Teacosy Cottage, The Green, Fornham All Saints, Bury St Edmunds IP28 6JX — MB BS 1980 Lond. GP Bury St Edmunds.

HODGSON, Colin William Laughton Incle Street Surgery, 8 Incle Street, Paisley PA1 1HR Tel: 0141 889 8809 Fax: 0141 849 1474; Meersbrook, 116 Corsebar Road, Paisley PA2 9PZ Tel: 0141 848 6676 Email: colin@colloquium.co.uk — MB ChB 1972 Glas.; DObst RCOG 1975. Assoc. Adviser (Gen. Pract.) Renfrew Dist; Assoc. Med. Dir. Renfrewsh. & Inverclyde PCT.

HODGSON, Courtney (retired) 134 Church Road, Moseley, Birmingham B13 9AA Tel: 0121 449 1908 Fax: 0121 449 1908 — MB ChB 1951 Birm.; MD Birm. 1965; MRCS Eng. LRCP Lond. 1951; FRCP Lond. 1978, M 1959. Prev: Cons. Dermat. Skin Hosp. & Selly Oak Hosp. Birm.

HODGSON, David Cullen 38 Lashford Lane, Dry Sandford, Abingdon OX13 6DY — MB BS 1951 Lond.; MA Oxf. 1963; FFA RCS Eng. 1957; DA Eng. 1955. (St. Bart.) Cons. Anaesth. United Oxf. Hosps. Socs: Thoracic Soc. Prev: Sen. Regist. (Anaesth.) Guy's Hosp. Lond.

HODGSON, David Iain 22 Capesthorne Close, Holmes Chapel, Crewe CW4 7EN — MB ChB 1991 Manch.

***HODGSON, Mr Dominic John** Beech nook, Thornthwaite, Keswick CA12 5SA Tel: 01768 778681 — MB ChB 1994 Sheff.; FRCSEA 1998.

HODGSON, Elaine Doctor's Residence, Manchester Royal Infirmary, Oxford Road, Manchester M13 9WL — MB ChB 1991 Manch.

HODGSON, Elizabeth Ann Lane Head Farm, Lane Head, Greenfield, Oldham OL3 7EZ — MB BS 1994 Lond.

HODGSON, Gail Iona Wotton Lawn, Horton Road, Gloucester GL1 3WL Tel: 01452 891500 Fax: 01452 891501 — MB ChB 1983 Ed.; PhD Bristol 1975, BSc (Hons. Biochem.) 1970; MRCPsych 1987. Cons. Psychiat. Glos. Prev: Sen. Regist. Rotat. (Psychiat.) Bristol.

HODGSON, Gillian Crossfell Health Centre, Berwick Hills, Middlesbrough TS3 7RL Tel: 01642 296777 Fax: 01642 296851 — MB BS 1981 Lond.; MRCGP 1985; DRCOG 1985. (St. Bart.) Gen. Practitioner; Assoc. Police Surg. Prev: SHO (Cas. &. O & G) Calderdale HA.

HODGSON, Gillian Ann Raiway View Medical Practice, The Health Centre, Clitheroe BB7 2JG Tel: 01200 422144; Croft House, West Lane, Sutton in Craven, Keighley BD20 7AS Tel: 01535 636101 — MB ChB Leeds 1979; MRCGP 1985. (Univ. Leeds) Asst. GP Clitheroe; Clin. Asst. (Diabetes & Rehabil. Med.) Airedale Gen. Hosp. Keighley; Clin. Med. Off. (Family Plann.) Airedale Gen. Hosp. Keighley. Prev: Asst. Cross Hills, Keighley Doctors Retainer Scheme.

HODGSON, Hilary Jane The Charter, Abingdon OX14 3JY; Thatched Cottage, 12 Kennel Lane, Abingdon OX13 6SB Tel: 01235 834725 — MB BS 1973 Lond.; Cert JCC Lond. 1977.

HODGSON, Professor Humphrey Julian Francis Department of Medicine, Imperial College School of Medicine, Hammersmith, London W6 Tel: 020 8383 3266 Fax: 020 8749 3436 Email: hhodgson@rpms.ac.uk; 40 Onslow Gardens, London N10 3JU Tel: 020 8883 8297 — BM BCh Oxf. 1970; MA Oxf. 1970, BA 1966, BSc 1969, DM 1977; FRCP Lond. 1983; MRCP (UK) 1972. (Oxf. & St. Thos.) Prof. Med. Imperial Coll. Sch. of Med.; Hon. Cons. Phys. Hammersmith Hosp. Lond. Socs: Assn. Phys. Prev: Vice-Dean Roy. Postgrad. Med. Sch. Lond.; Acad. Regist. Roy. Coll. Phys. Lond.; Prof. Gastroenterol. Roy. Postgrad. Med. Sch. Lond.

HODGSON, James Denis Kilmeny Surgery, 50 Ashbourne Road, Keighley BD21 1LA Tel: 01535 606415 Fax: 01535 669895; South Barn, Lees Farm, Haworth, Keighley BD22 9DL — BM BCh 1982 Oxf.; MA Camb. 1983; MRCGP 1986; DRCOG 1986; DCH Glas. 1986.

HODGSON, Jeffrey Mark Cumberland House, Jordangate, Macclesfield SK10 1EG Tel: 01625 428081 Fax: 01625 503128; 245 Kentwell Drive, Macclesfield SK10 2TR — MB ChB 1987 Liverp.; MRCGP (Distinc.) 1991; DRCOG 1990; DGM RCP Lond. 1990; DCH RCP Lond. 1989. Prev: Trainee GP Macclesfield Dist. Gen. Hosp. & Cumbld. Hse. Surg. VTS; SHO (O & G, A & E, Paediat. & Gen. Med.) Macclesfield Dist. Gen. Hosp.

HODGSON, John Ward End Medical Centre, 794A Washwood Heath Road, Ward End, Birmingham B8 2JN Tel: 0121 327 1049 Fax: 0121 327 0964; 5 Bishops Road, Sutton Coldfield B73 6HX Tel: 0121 354 8726 — MA Oxf. 1960; BM BCh Oxf. 1960; MRCGP 1984; DObst RCOG 1962. (Oxf.) Socs: BMA. Prev: Ho. Phys. & Ho. Surg. Radcliffe Infirm. Oxf.; Ho. Surg. (Obst.) Nuffield Matern. Hosp. Oxf.

HODGSON, John Garden Lane Medical Centre, 19 Garden Lane, Chester CH1 4EN Tel: 01244 346677 Fax: 01244 310094; Masons Cottage, Barton Road, Farndon, Chester CH3 6NL — MB ChB 1978 Manch. Chairm. Chester Gen. Pract. Locality Gp.

HODGSON, John David 5 Strathmore Drive, Baildon, Shipley BD17 5LP — LMSSA 1984 Lond.

HODGSON, John David Storey Maiden Law, 4 Cypress Close, Blackwell, Darlington DL3 8QR Tel: 01325 481422 Fax: 01325 243430 Email: lawmaid@aol.com — MB BS Durh. 1955; DA Eng. 1959. (Newc.) Ref. DSS. Socs: BMA.

HODGSON, Jonathan, Flight Lt. RAF Med. Br. 16 Bedeburn Road, Newcastle upon Tyne NE5 4JN Tel: 0191 286 0876 — MB ChB 1990 Sheff.

HODGSON, Judith 1 Farm Cottages, Ashington Farm Cottages, Wansbeck Road, Ashington NE63 8TN — MB BS 1970 Newc.; DCH RCPS Glas. 1972; DFFP (RCOG) 1996. (Newc.) Cons. Phys. Nat. Slimming Centres Newc. u Tyne; Locum GP N.. Newc. u Tyne & Tyne & Wear; Bank Family Plann. Doctor N.d. Community Health Morpeth, N.d. Socs: BMA. Prev: Princip. GP Waterloo Health Centre, Blyth; SHO (Paediat.) Darlington Memor. Hosp. & Cumbld. Infirm. Carlisle.

HODGSON, Keith George (retired) (Surgery) 1 Beeches Road, Bayston Hill, Shrewsbury SY3 0PF Tel: 01743 874565 Fax: 01743 873637 — MB ChB 1962 Manch. Med. Off. Condover Hall Sch. for Blind Childr. Shrewsbury. Prev: SHO (O & G& Surg.) Stepping Hill Hosp. Stockport.

HODGSON, Lesley Margaret High Point, Far Cl. Drive, Arnside, Carnforth LA5 0RG; 6 The Planters, Greasby, Wirral CH49 2QY Tel: 0151 606 1929 — MB ChB 1987 Sheff.

HODGSON, Louise Elizabeth Farmhouse Surgery, Christchurch Medical Centre, 1 Purewell Cross Road, Purewell, Christchurch BH23 3AF Tel: 01202 488487 Fax: 01202 486724 — MB BS 1976 Lond.; DRCOG 1980; Cert. Family Plann. JCC 1980; Cert. Av. Med. 1990. Prev: GP Benbecula; Civil. Med. Pract. Roy. Artillery Range Hebrides; Clin. Asst. (Obst.) Benbecula.

HODGSON, Mandell Coutier (Surgery) Poyle House, Poyle Road, Tangham, Farnham GU10 1BS; (surgery), Poyle House, Poyle Road, Tongham, Farnham GU10 1BS Tel: 0184 142846 — MB ChB 1939 St. And. Prev: RAMC.

HODGSON, Mark David Bridge House Surgery, Aldbrough St. John, Richmond DL11 7SU Tel: 01325 374332 Fax: 01325 374063; East Dilston House, Aldbrough St. John, Richmond DL11 7SZ Tel: 01325 374456 — MB ChB 1982 Manch.

HODGSON, Mary Eleanor 12 Maxwell Road, Bishopton PA7 5HE — MB ChB 1974 Glas.; DCH RCPS Glas. 1977.

HODGSON, Maureen Joyce (retired) Silverwood, 6 Brackendown, West Hill, Ottery St Mary EX11 1NT Tel: 01404 814205 — MB BS Lond. 1957; MRCS Eng. LRCP Lond. 1956; MFCM 1974; DCH Eng. 1959. Prev: SCM (Child Health).

HODGSON, Melanie Jane Larksfield Surrey, Arlesey Road, Stotfold, Hitchin SG5 4HE Tel: 01462 732200 Fax: 01462 383 2728; 28 Chiltern Road, Hitchin SG4 9PJ Tel: 01462 621693 Fax: 01462 621693 — MB BS 1982 Lond.; MRCGP 1986; DRCOG 1985; Cert. Family Plann. JCC 1985. (St. Bart.) Princip. in Gen. Pract., Stotfold, Hitchin, Hants; GP Tutor & Course Organiser Lister Hosp. Stevenage VTS. Prev: GP Hitchin.

HODGSON, Michael John (retired) 12 Old Barn Lane, Croxley Green, Rickmansworth WD3 3HU — MB BS 1953 Lond.; MB BS (Hnrs. Med.) Lond. 1953; MRCGP 1965; DObst RCOG 1957. Prev: Ho. Off. St. Bart. Hosp. Lond.

HODGSON, Monica Mary 84 Inverleith Place, Edinburgh EH3 5PA — MB ChB 1998 Aberd.; MB ChB Aberd 1998.

HODGSON, Oliver Ernest Fenner 49 Barrow Road, Cambridge CB2 2AR Tel: 01223 351079 — MB BChir 1948 Camb.; FRCPsych 1973, M 1972; DPM Eng. 1956. (St. Bart.) Prev: Cons. Psychiat. Fulbourn & Addenbrooke's Hosps.; Assoc. Lect. Univ. Camb.; Flight Lt. RAFVR.

HODGSON, Philip Edward 16 Shirlock Road, London NW3 2HS — MB BS 1986 Lond.

HODGSON, Rachel Elizabeth 9 North Parade, West Park, Leeds LS16 5AY — MB ChB 1996 Liverp.

HODGSON, Richard Edward Lymebrook MHC, Bradwell Hospital Site, Talke Road, Stoke-on-Trent ST5 7TL Tel: 01782 425560 — MB ChB 1986 Liverp.; MSc Keele 1993; MRCPsych 1991; MD Keele 1998. Cons. Psychiat. Lymbrook MHC Stoke-on-Trent; Sen. Lect. Univ. of Keele.

HODGSON, Richard John Kirton, Tamworth Road, Bassetts Pole, Sutton Coldfield B75 5RX — MB BS 1986 Lond.

HODGSON, Robert Michael Horsford Gorselands, Axtown, Yelverton PL20 6BU — MB BS 1964 Lond.; MRCS Eng. LRCP Lond. 1964; FFA RCS Eng. 1968; DA Eng. 1966. (King's Coll. Hosp.) Cons. Anaesth. Plymouth Gen. Hosp. Prev: Vis. Asst. Prof. (Anaesth.) Dept. Anaesth. Univ. Texas, Dallas U.S.A.; Sen. Regist. (Anaesth.) United Bristol Hosps. Bristol.

HODGSON, Ruth Sarah 7 Hillside Road, Harpenden AL5 4BS Tel: 01582 623117 Email: daltons@compuserve.com — MB BS 1989 Lond.; BA (Hons.) Oxf. 1986; MRCP (UK) 1992. Regist. (Gastroenterol.) Hemel Hempstead Hosp. (p/t). Socs: BMA; BSG. Prev: Regist. (Gastroenterol.) Roy. Devon & Exeter Hosp. - Devon; Regist. (Gen. Med.) St. Vincents Hosp. Sydney Australia.

HODGSON, Shirley Victoria Department of Medical & Molecular Genetics, 8th Floor Tower Block, UMDS, Guy's Hospital, London Bridge, London SE1 9RT Tel: 020 7955 4648 Fax: 020 7955 4644; 40 Onslow Gardens, London N10 3JU Tel: 020 8883 8297 Email: shirley.hodgson@kcl.ac.uk — BM BCh Oxf. 1969; DM Oxf. 1987; FRCP Lond. 1993; MRCP (UK) 1982; DCH Eng. 1972; DObst RCOG 1971. (Univ. Coll. Hosp. & Oxf.) Reader& Hon. Cons. (Clin. Genetics) Guy's Hosp. Lond. Socs: Brit. Soc. Human Genetics; Eur.

Soc. Human Genet.; ICG-HNPCC. Prev: Cons. Clin. Genetics Addenbrooke's Hosp. Camb.; Sen. Regist. (Clin. Genetics) Guy's Hosp. Lond.; Research Fell. & Hon. Sen. Regist. (Clin. Genetics) Guy's Hosp. Lond.

HODGSON, Shona 33 Ash Grove, Norwich NR3 4BE — MB ChB 1951 Otago; MFCM 1979; DPhysMed Eng. 1960. (Otago) Prev: Civil. Cons. Rheum. & Rehabil. Qu. Eliz. Milit. Hosp. Lond.; Area Specialist Community Med. (Social Servs.) Ealing, Hammersmith & Hounslow HA (T); Cons. Rehabil. & Rheum. Thames Gp. Hosp. & Newham Boro. Counc.

HODGSON, Mr Stephen Peter Royal Bolton Hospital, Minerva Road, Farnworth, Bolton BL4 0JR Tel: 01204 390343 Fax: 01204 390344; Washacre Barn, Anderton, Chorley PR6 9PH Tel: 01257 482526 — MB ChB 1981 Manch.; MD Manch. 1994; FRCS Ed. (Orth.) 1990; FRCS Eng. 1985. Cons. Orthop. Bolton Hosps. Trust. Prev: Sen. Regist. (Orthop.) NW RHA; Sir Harry Platt Research Fell. Univ. Manch.; Regist. (Orthop.) Salford HA.

HODGSON, Mr Timothy John Department of Radiology 'C' Floor, Royal Hallamshire Hospital, Glossop Road, Sheffield S10 2JF — MB ChB 1983 Sheff.; FRCS Ed. 1988; FRCR 1992. Cons. Neuroradiol. Roy. Hallamsh. Hosp. Sheff. Prev: Sen. Regist. (Neuroradiol.) Nat. Hosp. Neurol. Lond. & Gt. Ormond St. Lond.; Sen. Regist. (Diag. Radiol.) Trent RHA; SHO & Regist. Rotat. (Surg.) N.. Gen. Hosp. Sheff.

HODGSON, Mr Walter John Barry Montefiore Medical Park, 1575 Blondell Avenue, Bronx NY 10461, USA Tel: 00 61 718 405 8239 Fax: 00 61 718 405 8292 Email: wjbhodgson@aol.com; 65 South Hill, Catteshall Lane, Godalming GU7 1JU — MB BS 1964 Lond.; MS Lond. 1976; FRCS Eng. 1969; MRCS Eng. LRCP Lond. 1964. (Char. Cross Hosp. Med. Sch.) Dept. Surg. Montefiore Med. Center Bronx NY, USA; Prof. Surg. NY Med. Coll., USA; Clin. Prof. Surg. NYU, USA; Prof. Clin. Surg. Albert Einstein GU Med., USA. Socs: Brit. Soc. Gastroenterol.; Brit. Soc. Surg. Oncol.; Surgic. Research Soc. Prev: Chief of Gastrointestinal Surg. W. Chester Med. Center; Chief of Gastrointestinal and Colorectal Surg. Brooklyn Hosp. Centre NY, USA.

HODKIN, James Peter Gordon Birbeck Medical Group, Penrith Health Centre, Bridge Lane, Penrith CA11 8HW Tel: 01768 245200 Fax: 01768 245295 — MB BS 1988 Newc.; MRCGP 1992; DRCOG 1992. (Newc.) Prev: Trainee GP E. Cumbria VTS.

HODKINSON, Alice Clare 96A Savernake Road, London NW3 2JR — MB BS 1997 Lond.

HODKINSON, Cheow Khim Tavern House, Coedkernew, Newport NP1 9UD — MB BCh 1967 Wales.

HODKINSON, Edmund Henry 8 Georgian Villas, Omagh BT79 0AT — MB BCh BAO 1977 Belf.; FRCP Lond. 1994; MRCP (UK) 1982. Phys. i/c Elderly Tyrone Co. Hosp. Omagh.

HODKINSON, Professor Henry Malcolm (retired) Emerit. Professor of Geriatic Medicine, University College, London WC1H — BM BCh 1955 Oxf.; MA Oxf. 1957, DM 1975; FRCP Lond. 1974, M 1960. Vice-Pres. Research into Ageing. Prev: Barlow Prof. Geriat. Med. Univ. Coll. Middlx. Sch. Med.

HODKINSON, John Nigel Pain Relief Clinic, Furness General Hospital, Dalton Lane, Barrow-in-Furness LA14 4LF Tel: 01229 491013 Fax: 01229 431277 Email: hoddi@urswick.u-net.com; Weint End, Great Urswick, Ulverston LA12 0SP Tel: 01229 586502 — MB ChB 1968 Manch.; FFA RCS Eng. (Lond.) 1978; DA Eng. 1973; DObst RCOG 1972. (Manch.) Cons. Anaesth. & Pain Relief Furness Gen. Hosp. Socs: Assn. Anaesth.; Internat. Assn. Study of Pain; Pain Soc.

HODKINSON, Philip Simon 2 Linden Lea, Holly Tree Village, Blackburn BB2 5AG — MB ChB 1998 Ed.; MB ChB Ed 1998.

HODKINSON, Robert Stonebridge Surgery, Preston Road, Longridge, Preston PR3 3AP Tel: 01772 783271 Fax: 01772 782836; Springfield, Dilworth Lane, Longridge, Preston PR3 3ST Tel: 01772 782617 Email: rob.hod@virgin.net — MB ChB 1967 Ed.; MRCGP 1977; DObst RCOG 1971; FRCGP 1999. (Edinburgh, 1961-1967) Course Organiser Preston Postgrad Med. Centre VTS. Socs: Preston Medico Ethical Soc.; Brit. Med. Assn.; Roy. Coll. of Gen. Practitioners (Fell.). Prev: SHO (Paediat.) St. And. Hosp. Billericay; Ho. Surg. (Obst.) Dulwich Hosp. Lond.; Clin. Med. Off. (Psychosexual Counselling) Preston HA.

HODKINSON, Mr Simon Lloyd, Surg. Cdr. RN Retd. Queen Alexandra Hospital, Cosham, Portsmouth PO6 3LY Tel: 01239 664314 Fax: 01239 663765 Email: s.l.hodkinson@btinternet.com; 34 Tawny Owl Close, Fareham PO14 3JB Tel: 01705 584255 Email: s.l.hodkinson@btinternet.com — MB BS 1982 Lond.; FRCS (Orth.) 1994; FRCS Ed. 1989. (St. Bart.) Cons. Orthop. Surg. Qu. Alexandra Hosp. Portsmouth. Prev: Sen. Regist. (Orthop.) Roy. Naval Hosp. Haslar; Cons. Orth. Surg. Roy. hosp. Haslar.

HODNETT, Henry Thomas The Surgery, 6 Lower Brook St., Oswestry SY11 2HJ Tel: 01691 655844 — MB BS 1961 Lond. (Westm.)

HODNETT, Stephen Francis St James Surgery, Harold Street, Dover CT16 1SF Tel: 01304 225559 Fax: 01304 213070; 94 Minnis Lane, Dover CT17 0PT Tel: 01304 822026 — MB BCh BAO 1984 NUI.

HODSKINSON, Ruth 13 Ashtree Grove, Penwortham, Preston PR1 0XX Tel: 01772 745851 — MB ChB 1997 Manch. SHO Paediat. Qu.s Pk. Hosp. Blackburn. Prev: Ho. Off. (Gen. Med.) Qu.'s Pk. Hosp. Blackburn; Ho. Off. (Gen. Surg.) The Roy. Oldham Hosp. Oldham.

HODSMAN, Nadia Bridget Anne 5 Kirkstyle Avenue, Carluke ML8 5AQ; Department Anaesthesia, Law Hospital, Carluke ML8 5ER — MB ChB Glas. 1980; FFA RCS Eng. 1985. Cons. Anaesth. Law Hosp. Carluke.

HODSON, Andrew Christopher Middle Gingers, Cox Green, Rudgwick, Horsham RH12 3DD — MB BS 1997 Lond.

***HODSON, Daniel James** Apple Trees, Pettiford Lane, Wootton Wawen, Solihull B95 6ET — BM BCh 1998 Oxf.; BM BCh Oxf 1998; MA 1999.

HODSON, James Michael Middle Gingers, Cox Green, Rudgwick, Horsham RH12 3DD — MB BS 1994 Lond.

HODSON, Jane Mayfield Surgery, Mayfield, Buckden St. Neots, Huntingdon PE19 5SZ Tel: 01480 810216 Fax: 01480 810745; 28 London Road, Godmanchester, Huntingdon PE29 2JA Tel: 01480 454417 — MB BChir 1980 Camb.; MA Camb. 1981, MB BChir 1980; DRCOG 1984.

HODSON, Jean Patricia Anne Bridge House Medical Centre, Scholars Lane, Stratford-upon-Avon CV37 6HE Tel: 01789 292201 Fax: 01789 262087 — MB BS Lond. 1970; BSc (Hons.) (Pharmacol.) Lond. 1967; MMedSc Birm. 1995; MRCS Eng. LRCP Lond. 1970; DObst RCOG 1972. Res. Fell. Dept. O & G Leicester Univ.

HODSON, Margaret Ellen 21 Tibbet's Close, Inner Park Road, Wimbledon Parkside, London SW19 Tel: 020 8788 5468 — MRCS Eng. LRCP Lond. 1967; MSc (Immunol.) Lond. 1977; MD Leeds 1977, MB ChB (Hons.) 1967; FRCP Lond. 1983; MRCP (U.K.) 1971; DA Eng. 1969. (Leeds) Reader in Respirat. Med. Cardiothoracic Inst. Univ. Lond.; Hon. Cons. Brompton Hosp. Lond. Socs: Fell. Roy. Soc. Med.; Thoracic Soc. Prev: Med. Regist. Leeds Gen. Infirm.

HODSON, Michael John West Cumberland Hospital, Kirby Side, Pardshaw Hall, Cockermouth CA13 0SP Tel: 01900 827064 — MB ChB 1987 Aberd.; FRCA 1994. (aberd) Cons. Anaesth. W. Cumbld. Hosp. Cumbria. Socs: Intens. Care. Soc; Assoc.anaesth; Difficult Airway Soc.

HODSON, Neil James 3 Vincent Avenue, Carshalton Beeches, Carshalton SM5 4HZ Tel: 020 8642 2130 — MB ChB 1960 Bristol; MB ChB (Hons.) Bristol 1970; BSc (Hons.) (Biochem.) Bristol 1967; MRCS Eng. LRCP Lond. 1970; FRCR 1976. Sen. Lect. & Research Fell. Roy. Marsden Hosp. Lond. Prev: Sen. Regist. & Regist. Roy. Marsden Hosp. Lond.; Regist. Radiother. Dept. Bristol Roy. Infirm.

HODSON, Paul Brian Hodson and Partners, Park Farm Medical Centre, Allestree, Derby DE22 2QN Tel: 01332 559402 Fax: 01332 541001; Burley Lodge, 61 Burley Lane, Quarndon, Derby DE22 5JR Tel: 01332 840201 Fax: 01332 842879 Email: docgradon@aol.com — MB ChB Liverp. 1966; DTM & H Liverp. 1968; DObst RCOG 1968. (Liverp.) GP Tutor Univ. Nottm. Socs: (Ex-Sec. & Counc.) Derby Med. Soc.; (Ex-Sec., Chairm. & Comm. Mem.) Derby Obst. Gp. Prev: Dist. Med. Off. Karamoja Dist. & Med. Supt. Moroto Hosp. Uganda; SHO (Orthop.) Hope Hosp. Salford; Ho. Off. Sefton Gen. Hosp. Liverp.

HODSON, Rebecca Stacey Widcombe Surgery, 3-4 Widcombe Parade, Bath BA2 4JT Tel: 01225 310883 Fax: 01225 421600 — MB BS 1991 Lond. G.P.

HODSON, Simon Andrew 21 Westfield Road, Manchester M21 0SW — MB ChB 1993 Sheff.

HODSON, Susan Elizabeth Sunbury Health Centre, Green Street, Sunbury on Thames TW16 Tel: 01223 249773, 01932 713399 Email: ramez@kirollos.freeserve.co.uk; 3 Edenvale Close, Hills Avenue, Cambridge CB1 7XD Tel: 01223 249773, 01932 713399 Email: ramez@kirollos.freeserve.co.uk — MB BS 1988 Lond.; MRCGP 1992; DRCOG 1995; DCH RCP Lond. 1992; T(GP) 1992. (St. Geo.) GP Princip.

***HODSON, Zoe Louise** Boscobel, Sutherland Road, Longson, Stoke-on-Trent ST9 9QD — MB ChB 1996 Birm.

HODZOVIC, Iljaz Department of Anaesthetics, University Hospital of Wales, Heath Park, Cardiff CF14 4XW Email: hodzovic@cf.ac.uk; 32 Cefn Coed Gardens, Cynoed, Cardiff CF23 6AX — Lekarz 1986 Belgrade; Lekar Belgrade 1986; FRCA 1994. (Belgrade University) Clin. Sen. Lect./ Hon. Cons. Anaesth. Socs: RCA; Fell.Assoc. of Anaeshetists; PANG.

HOE, Mr Wilbert Kok-Chwan MCIndoe Surgical Centre, Holtye Road, East Grinstead RH19 3EB Tel: 01342 330300 Fax: 01342 330301 — MB BS 1971 Med. Inst. (I) Rangoon; FRCS Ed. 1987; FRCOphth. 1989; DO RCS Eng. 1983. Assoc. Specialist (Ophth.) Qu. Vict. Hosp. E. Grinstead. Prev: Regist. (Ophth.) Whittington & Roy. Free Hosps. Lond.; SHO (Ophth.) Cheltenham Gen. Hosp.; SHO (Ophth.) W. Middlx. Hosp.

HOEY, Anne Brigid Mataura, 696 Lightwood Road, Longton, Stoke-on-Trent ST3 7HE Tel: 01782 35547 — MB BCh BAO 1944 NUI; LM Rotunda 1945. (Univ. Coll. Dub.)

HOEY, Dermot Peter Wilfred Cherryvalley Health Centre, Kings Square, Belfast BT5 7BP Tel: 01232 401844 — MB BCh BAO 1968 Belf.

HOEY, Mr Moira June (retired) The Stables, Fernhill, Upper Brighton, Wallasey CH45 5AW Tel: 02920 752319 — MB ChB 1962 Liverp.; BSc (1st cl. Hons.) Liverp. 1959, MD 1968. Staff Grade Med. Off., Nat. Blood Serv.; Chair Bro Morgannw NHS. Prev: GP Wallasey, Merseyside.

HOEY, Penelope Roberta (retired) 1 Winscott Cottages, Newton St Cyres, Exeter EX5 5AJ Tel: 01392 851575 — MB BS 1967 Lond.; MRCS Eng. LRCP Lond. 1966; DObst RCOG 1969. Prev: Ho. Surg. (O & G) Roy. Vict. Hosp. Bournemouth.

HOEY, Rachel Clare O'Neil 10 Arden Mhor, Pinner HA5 2HR — MB ChB 1993 Bristol.

HOEY, Thomas Edwin 48 York Street, Norwich NR2 2AW — MB ChB 1995 Leic.

HOFFBRAND, Professor Allan Victor Department of Haematology, Royal Free Hospital, Pond St., London NW3 2QG Tel: 020 7435 1547 Fax: 020 7431 4537 Email: v.hoffbrand@rfc.ucl.ac.uk; 12 Wedderburn Road, London NW3 5QG Tel: 020 7435 9413 Fax: 020 7794 8329 — BM BCh Oxf. 1959; DSc Lond. 1987; MA Oxf. 1961, DM 1972; FRCP Ed. 1986; FRCP Lond. 1976, M 1962; FRCPath 1980, M 1972; DCP Lond 1963. Emerit. Prof. Haemat.Roy. Free Hosp. Sch. Med. Lond. & Hon. Consult. Roy. Free Hosp. Lond. Socs: Brit. Soc. Haematol.; Amer. Soc. Hemat.; Eur. Haematol. Assn. Prev: Hon. Cons. Hammersmith Hosp. Lond.; Sen. Lect. (Haemat.) Roy. Postgrad. Med. Sch. Lond.; Lect. (Haemat.) St. Bart. Hosp. Lond.

HOFFBRAND, Barry Ian Highgate Private Hospital, 17 - 19 View Rd, London N6 5ER Tel: 020 8348 7215 Fax: 020 340 5292 Email: bihoffbrand@talk21.com; 42 Cholmeley Park, London N6 5ER Tel: 020 8340 5063 Fax: 020 8340 5292 Email: 106032.1066@compuserve.com — BM BCh 1958 Oxf.; DM Oxf. 1971; FRCP Lond. 1976, M 1962. (Oxfrod/UCH) Socs: Sen. Vice-Pres. Roy. Soc. Med.; Brit. Soc. Hypertens.; Renal Assn. Prev: Edr. Postgrad. Med. Jl.; Cons. Phys. & Nephrol. Whittington Hosp. Lond.; Hon. Sen. Clin. Lect. (Med.) UCL.

HOFFBRAND, Caroline Ruth St Georges Medical Centre, 7 Sunningfields Road, Hendon, London NW4 4QR Tel: 020 8202 6232 Fax: 020 8202 3906 — MB BS 1990 Lond.; MRCGP (Distinc.) 1996; DGM RCP Lond. 1993. (Univ. Coll. & Middlx. Hosp. Sch. Med. Lond.) GP Princip. St. Geo.s Med. Centre, Sunningsfield, Lond. Prev: GP Regist. Lond.

HOFFBRAND, Sara Elizabeth Keats Group Practice, 1b Downshire Hill, London NW3 1NR Tel: 020 7435 1131 Fax: 020 7431 8501 — MB BS 1989 Lond.; BSc (Hons.) Lond. 1986; MRCP (UK) 1994; MRCGP 1996; DRCOG 1995. (Univ. Coll. & Middlx. Sch. Med.) GP Retainer (p/t).

HOFFENBERG, Sir Raymond, KBE Flat 5, 16 Davenant Road, Oxford OX2 8BX Tel: 01865 311512 Fax: 01865 302964 — MB ChB Cape Town 1948; PhD Cape Town 1968, MD 1957; FRCP Lond. 1971. Emerit. Prof. Univ. Birm. Socs: Endocrine Soc.; Amer. Thyroid Assn. Prev: Prof. Med. Univ. Birm.; Sen. Phys. & Sen. Lect. Groote Schuur Hosp. & Univ. Cape Town; Pres. Roy. Coll. Phys. Lond.

HOFFLER, David Evan 7 The Square, Countesthorpe, Leicester LE8 5RN Tel: 0116 277 2593 — MB BS 1974 Lond.; FFA RCS Eng. 1979. (Lond. Hosp.) Cons. Anaesth. & ITU Leicester; JP. Socs: Assn. Anaesth. Prev: Sen. Regist. (Anaesth.) Lond. Hosp., Gt. Ormond St. Hosp. & Lond. Chest Hosp.; Lect. (Anaesth.) Lond. Hosp. Med. Coll.; Regist. (Anaesth.) Lond. Hosp.

HOFFMAN, Ai-Ling 2 Cranleigh Gardens, Stoke Bishop, Bristol BS9 1HD Tel: 0117 968 2538 — MB BS 1976 Sri Lanka; MRCS Eng. LRCP Lond. 1979; DA Eng. 1980. Clin. Asst. (Haemat.) S.mead Hosp. Bristol.

HOFFMAN, Clare Lindsay 13 Normanton Road, Cliffton, Bristol BS8 2TY — MB ChB 1977 Birm.; MRCPsych 1984; DCH Eng. 1980.

HOFFMAN, Drummond Edgar Henry (retired) Honeysuckle Cottage, The Causeway, Tisbury, Salisbury SP3 6LB Tel: 01747 870532 — MRCS Eng. LRCP Lond. 1943. Prev: Cas. Off. & Ho. Surg. In-pats. St. Thos. Hosp.

HOFFMAN, James Nicholas (retired) 5 Abbey Road, Westbury-on-Trym, Bristol BS9 3QN Tel: 0117 962 4728 — MB BS Lond. 1951; MRCS Eng. LRCP Lond. 1946. Prev: Cons. Phys. Dis. of Chest Bristol Clin. Area.

HOFFMAN, Jeffrey 13 St Michael's Close, Ashby-de-la-Zouch, Leicester — MB ChB 1969 Leeds; MRCGP 1975; Dip. Sports Med. Lond. 1995; DCH Eng. 1979; DA Eng. 1972; DObst RCOG 1972.

HOFFMAN, Mr Martin Geoffrey Ashwell Surgery, Gardiners Lane, Ashwell, Baldock SG7 5PY Tel: 01462 742230 Fax: 01462 742764 Email: ashwellsurgery@compuserve.co; Chapel House, Hinxworth, Baldock SG7 5HN Tel: 01462 742567 — MB BS Lond. 1968; FRCS Eng. 1975; FRCS Ed. 1975; MRCS Eng. LRCP Lond. 1968; MRCOG 1978, DObst 1971. (King's Coll. Hosp.) GP Ashwell; Chairm. E. & N. Hants LMC; Bd. Mem. N. Herts PCG. Socs: BMA. Prev: Regist. (O & G) N. Herts. Matern. Unit Hitchin; Lect. (Anat.) King's Coll. Lond.; Ho. Surg. & Ho. Phys. King's Coll. Hosp. Lond.

HOFFMAN, Muriel Mary Delia c/o Cricketfield Road Surgery, Newton Abbot TQ12 2AS — MB BS 1970 Lond. (St. Geo.)

HOFFMAN, Nigel James 5 Abbey Road, Westbury-on-Trym, Bristol BS9 3QN Tel: 0117 962 4728 — MB 1977 Camb.; BChir 1976; MRCP 1980; MRCGP 1985. (Cambridge and St. Georges) Med. Superintendent Rietvlei Hosp. E.ern Cape, S. Africa.

HOFFMAN, Richard John Southmead Health Centre, Ullswater Road, Bristol BS10 6DF Tel: 0117 950 7100 Fax: 0117 959 1110; 19 Southmead Road, Henleaze, Bristol BS10 5D — MB 1979 Camb.; BA Camb. 1975, MB 1979, BChir 1978; MRCGP 1984; DRCOG 1982.

HOFFMAN, Ruth (retired) Flat E, 10 Regent's Park Road, London NW1 7TX Tel: 020 7485 8329 — MB ChB 1945 Glas.; MRCPsych 1971; DPM Roy. Med.-Psych. Assn. 1953. Prev: Cons. Child Psychiat. Waltham Forest Child Guid. Clinic.

HOFFMANN, Brad Robert Frederick 12 Hawthornbank Lane, Edinburgh EH4 3BH — MB BCh 1986 Witwatersrand.

HOFFMANN, Frank Balmoral Surgery, Victoria Road, Deal CT14 7AU; 138 Golf Road, Deal CT14 6RD — State Exam 1991 Hamburg; MD Hamburg 1992; DRCOG 1998.

HOFFMANN, Kathrin Anne Four Winds, Ford, Aylesbury HP17 8XA — MB BS 1986 Lond.

HOFINGER, Eva Department of Neurophsiology, Derriford Hospital, Plymouth PL6 8DH; Thorn House, Wembury, Plymouth PL9 0EQ — MD 1972 Vienna. Assoc Specialist (Neurophysiol.) Derriford Hosp. Plymouth.

HOFMANN, Hiltrud Agnes 24 Ravenshurst Road, Harborne, Birmingham B17 9SD Tel: 0121 427 8445 — State Exam Med. Heidelberg 1990.

HOFMEYR, John Adriaan 11 Roebuck Rise, Tilehurst, Reading RG31 6TP Tel: 0118 941 6610 — MRCS Eng. LRCP Lond. 1952. (St. Mary's) Louis Leipoldt Medal 1961. Socs: Fell. Roy. Soc. Med. Prev: Med. Supt. Mission Hosp. Nkandhla, Zululand; Regist. (Surg.) King Edwd. VIII Hosp. Durban; Ho. Phys. Addenbrooke's Hosp. Camb.

HOGAN, Anne Marie New House, Vinns Lane, Overton, Basingstoke RG25 3DB — MB BS 1988 Lond.
HOGAN, Mr Daniel John 78 Silhill Hall Road, Solihull B91 1JS — MB BS 1972 Lond.; FRCS Eng. 1978.
HOGAN, Geraldine Mary 25 Canadian Avenue, Hoole, Chester CH2 3HQ — MB BS 1984 Newc.
HOGAN, Helen Rosemarie Kensington, Chelsea & Westminster Health Authority, 50 Eastbourne Terrace, London W2 Tel: 0118 987 4551 — MB BS 1987 Lond.; MSc 2001 (Public Health) Lond.; DFPHM 2001; BSc Biochem. (Hon) Lond. 1987; MRCGP 1995; DRCOG 1992. Specialist Regist. Pub. Health. Prev: Gen. Practitioner, Th Univ. Health Centre, Reading, Berks.
HOGAN, James Patrick Rinaldo Lake Road Health Centre, Nutfield Place, Portsmouth PO1 4JT Tel: 023 9282 1201 Fax: 023 9287 5658 — MB BS 1982 Lond.; DRCOG 1986. Trainee GP Portsmouth.
HOGAN, John Westminster Medical Centre, Aldams Grove, Liverpool L4 3TT — MB ChB 1952 Liverp.; DTM & H 1957.
HOGAN, John Charles Cardiac Department, Whipps Cross Hospital, Leytonstone, London E11 1NR Tel: 020 8539 5522 — MD 1991 Manch.; BSc (Hons.) Manch. 1978, MB ChB 1981; FRCP Lond. 1997; MRCP (UK) 1984. Cons. Cardiol. Whipps Cross & St. Bart. Hosps. Lond.
HOGAN, Leonora Agnes 51 Lithgow Drive, Cleland, Motherwell ML1 5RD — MB ChB 1995 Manch.
HOGAN, Mary Martina 26B Lisburn Street, Hillsborough BT26 6AB — MB BCh BAO 1984 NUI; DCH NUI 1986; DObst RCPI 1987. Med. Regist. (Paediat.) Our Ladys Hosp. Dub.
HOGAN, Ruth Alexandra Julie 20 Leyland Green Road, North Ashton, Wigan WN4 0QJ; 7 Clifton Street, Alderley Edge SK9 7NW — MB ChB 1990 Birm.; ChB Birm. 1990; MRCGP 1996; DRCOG 1992. (Birm.) Assoc. GP Bootle. Prev: SHO (A & E) Alexandra Hosp. Redditch; SHO (Genitourin. Med.) Birm. Gen. Hosp.; SHO (O & G) Walsall Manor Hosp.
HOGAN, Simon Kevin Beeston Hill Health Centre, Beeston Hill, Beeston, Leeds LS11 8BS Tel: 0113 270 5131 Fax: 0113 272 0722 — MB ChB 1986 Leeds.
HOGARTH, Andrew Michael Harefield Health Centre, Rickmansworth Road, Harefield, Uxbridge UB9 6JY Tel: 01895 822 9441 — MB BS 1984 Lond.; MRCGP 1989; DCH RCP Lond. 1990. Prev: Trainee GP Otford; SHO (O & G) FarnBoro. Hosp.; SHO (Paediat.) Qy. Mary's Hosp. Lond.
HOGARTH, Euan Duncan Alexander 30 Anson Av, Falkirk FK1 5JB — MB ChB 1997 Glas.
HOGARTH, Margaret Christine 3 Oakwood, Hexham NE46 4LF Tel: 01434 602676 — MB ChB 1977 Leeds; MFFP 1993; DA (UK) 1980. (Leeds) SCMO (Family Plann.) Newc. City Health NHS Trust; Clin. Med. Off. (Family Plann.) N.d. Socs: Brit. Menopause Soc. Prev: SHO (O & G) Hexham Gen. Hosp.; SHO (Anaesth.) Roy. Vict. Infirm. Newc.; Ho. Off. (Surg. & Med.) Hexham Gen. Hosp.
HOGARTH, Maxine Beverley 21 Queen Anne's Gardens, Ealing, London W5 5QD Tel: 020 8579 1417 — MB ChB 1989 Liverp.; BSc (Hons.) Liverp. 1986; MRCP (UK) 1992. MRC Train. Fell. (Rheum.) Hammersmith Hosp. Roy. Postgrad. Med. Sch. Lond.
HOGARTH, Patricia Aileen 277 Mansfield Road, Redhill, Nottingham NG5 8LW Tel: 0115 926 5861 — MB BCh BAO 1949 Belf. Med. Mem. Indep. Tribunal Serv. Socs: Nottm. Med-Leg. Soc.; Nottm. MC Soc. Prev: SCMO (Child Health) Nottm. HA; Cas. Off. & Ho. Off. Gen. Hosp. Nottm.; Asst. Co. Med. Off. of Health Nottm. CC.
HOGARTH, Mr Thomas Burnett Elmcroft, Thurgarton, Nottingham NG14 7HA — MB ChB Leeds 1948; FRCS Ed. 1955. (Leeds) Cons. Emerit. Qu.'s Med. Centre Nottm. & Nottm. Educat. Comm. Socs: N. Eng. Otolaryng. Soc.; Brit. Assn. of Otolaryng. Prev: Cons. Otolaryngol. ScarBoro. Hosp. Gp.; Sen. Regist. ENT Dept. Leicester Roy. Infirm.; Regist. ENT Leeds Gen. Infirm.
HOGBEN, Monica Margaret (retired) 4 Cornford Court, Cornford Lane, Pembury, Tunbridge Wells TN2 4QX Tel: 01892 823527 — MB BS Lond. 1944; MRCS Eng. LRCP Lond. 1943. Prev: Resid. Phys. Home of Loving Faithfulness, Hong Kong.
HOGBEN, Richard Mark Oaklands Surgery, Birchfield Road, Yeovil BA21 5RL Tel: 01935 473068 Fax: 01935 412307; Abbey Manor Surgery, The Forum, Abbey Manor Park, Yeovil BA21 3TL Tel: 01935 433434 — MB BS 1981 Lond.; MRCGP 1986; DA Eng. 1983. (London Hospital) Prev: Clin. Asst. Yeovil Dist. Hosp.; SHO (Obst. & Anaesth.) Yeovil Dist. Hosp.; Ho. Phys. The Lond. Hosp.
HOGBEN, Mrs Rosalyn Katy Flint Frimley Park Hospital, Portsmouth Road, Camberley GU16 7UJ Tel: 01276 604604; Addison House, 6 Oxberry Avenue, Fulham, London SW6 5SS — MB BS 1993 Lond.; BSc Lond. 1990; FRCS Lond. 1997. (Roy. Lond. Hosp. Med. Coll.) Specialist Regist. S. W. Thames, Frisley Pk. Hosp. Socs: BMA; MDU; ASIT. Prev: SHO (Gen. Surg.) Roy. Marsden Hosp. Lond.; SHO Char. Cross Rotat.
HOGBIN, Mr Brian Martin (retired) Dingle Cottage, Trefonen, Oswestry SY10 9DQ Tel: 01691 653088 — MB BS 1961 Lond.; FRCS Eng. 1966; MRCS Eng. LRCP Lond. 1961; DObst RCOG 1963. Prev: Cons. Gen. Surg. Brighton Health Dist.
HOGBIN, Dorothy Jane (retired) Dingle Cottage, Trefonen, Oswestry SY10 9DQ Tel: 01691 653088 — MB BS 1960 Lond.; MRCS Eng. LRCP Lond. 1960; DObst RCOG 1962.
HOGBIN, Paul Anthony St Lawrence's Hospital, Bodmin PL31 2QT Tel: 01208 251339 Fax: 01208 251512 — MB BS 1976 Lond.; BSc (Hons.) (Physics in Med.) Lond. 1973; MRCS Eng. LRCP Lond. 1976; MRCPsych 1982. Cons. Old Age Psychiat. St. Lawrence Hosp. Cornw. Prev: Sen. Regist. Rotat. (Psychiat.) SW Thames RHA; Regist. (Psychiat.) Horton Hosp. Epsom; SHO & Regist. Rotat. (Psychiat.) Bath Hosps. Scheme.
HOGENBOOM VAN DEN EIJNDEN, Margaretha Geertruda Engelberta Camphill Rudolf Steiner Schools, Camphill Estate, Milltimber AB13 0AP Tel: 01224 734746; Camphill Medical Practice, Murtle Estate, Bieldside, Aberdeen AB15 9EP Tel: 01224 868935 — Artsexamen 1984 Utrecht; Cert. Anthopol. Med.1984. Ment. Handicap. Sch. Med. Off. Socs: Soc. Study Behav. Phenctype; Anthop. Med. Assn.
HOGEWIND, Georg Lukas 112A Harley Street, London W1N 1AN — MB ChB 1988 Pretoria.
HOGG, Claire Lillianne North Lodge, Syston, Grantham NG32 2BY — MB ChB 1990 Glas.
HOGG, David Christopher 33 Hill Crest Drive, Molescroft, Beverley HU17 7JL — MB ChB 1998 Liverp.; MB ChB Liverp 1998.
HOGG, David Cyril Oldland Surgery, 192 High Street, Oldham Common, Bristol BS30 9QQ Tel: 0117 932 4444 Fax: 0117 932 4101 — MB ChB 1970 Bristol; MRCGP 1976; DA Eng. 1972.
HOGG, Douglas William Bates, SBStJ 81 Whinfell Road, Darras Hall, Newcastle upon Tyne NE20 9ER — MB BS 1953 Durh. (Newc.) Prev: Ho. Off. Vict. Infirm. Newc. & Walkergate Hosp. Newc.; RAF Med. Br.
HOGG, Duncan Hywel 2 Muir Grove, Kinross KY13 8BS — MB ChB 1994 Aberd.
HOGG, Fiona Jacqueline St John Hospital, Howden Road W., Livingston EH54 6PP Tel: 01506 419666; 54 East Crates Rigg, Maybury Craigs, Corstorphine, Edinburgh EH12 8JA Email: fj.hogg@btinternet.com — MB ChB 1988 Glas.; FRCS Glas. 1993. Specialist Regist. (Plastic Surg.) SE Scotl. region, St. John's Hosp., Livingston. Prev: Hon. Regist. (Plastic Surg.) Qu. Vict. Hosp. E. Grinstead; SHO (Palstic Surg.) Canniesburn Hosp., Glas.; SHO (Plastic Surg.) Qu. Vict. Hosp. E. Grinstead.
HOGG, Geoffrey Peter 106 Redland Road, Redland, Bristol BS6 6QU Tel: 0117 914 3016 Fax: 0117 914 1705 Email: ghogg@bcf.kaliba.net — MB ChB 1987 Manch.; MRCP (UK) 1990; MRCGP 1993; DRCOG 1992; DCH RCP Lond. 1991.
HOGG, Hilary Anne 54 Benhill Avenue, Sutton SM2 6NS Tel: 020 8642 8011; 23 Chiddingstone Close, Sutton SM2 6NS — MB ChB 1978 Manch.; BSc St. And. 1975; MRCGP 1984. Edr. Help (Palliat. Care for GPs & Jun. Hosp. Doctors). Prev: Regist. GP VTS; Regist. (Paediat.) Duchess of York Hosp. Levenshulme & Wythenshawe Hosp. Manch.; Regist. (Psychiat.) Shelton Hosp. Shrewsbury.
HOGG, Hope Berthe Turner (retired) 7 Westside Gardens, Partickhill Road, Glasgow G11 5BL — MB ChB 1948 Glas.; DPH 1952. SCMO (Guardianship) Gtr. Glas. Health Bd. Prev: Asst. Sch. Med. Off. Glas.
HOGG, Iona Katherine Redriggs, Ceres, Cupar KY15 5LZ — MB ChB Glas. 1996.
HOGG, James Quintin Grantham Trower Inverlossie, 1 Scotland Place, Crescent Road, Nairn IV12 4ND Tel: 01667 456875 — BM BS 1990 Nottm.; BSc (Hons.) St. And. 1980; BMedSci 1988; Dip. Obst. Auckland 1992. Trainee GP Forres Moraysh. Prev: SHO (A & E & Orthop.) Raigmore Hosp. Inverness; SHO (Paediat.) Yorkhill Glas.

HOGG, James Renshaw Somercotes Medical Centre, 22 Nottingham Road, Somercotes, Derby DE72 3FL Tel: 01773 602141 — MB BS 1978 Lond.; BA Camb. 1975.

HOGG, Jeremy Ian Charles High Barn, Warnford, Southampton SO32 3LD Tel: 01730 829633 — MB BS 1976 Lond.; FRCR 1985; DMRD Eng. 1984. Cons. Radiol. Roy. Hants. Co. Hosp. Winchester.

HOGG, Joanne Heather 50 Portna Road, Rasharkin, Ballymena BT44 8SX — MB BCh BAO 1987 Belf.

HOGG, Joseph Sean 185 Teagues Crescent, Trench, Telford TF2 6RA — MB ChB 1994 Leeds.

HOGG, Kerry-Jane 8 Kensington Road, Dowanhill, Glasgow G12 9LF — MB ChB 1982 Glas.; MSc 1986; MRCP (UK) 1985. Doctor of Med.

HOGG, Kerstin Elizabeth Arcot, Pitcaple, Inverurie AB51 5HJ — MB ChB 1996 Ed.

HOGG, Leslie McArthur, MBE (retired) 13 Stuart Road, Gillingham ME7 4AA Tel: 01634 54734 — MB BS 1956 Madras. Prev: Sen. Med. Off. Medway Health Dist.

HOGG, Marjory Christin The Cedars Residential Home, 303 Perth Road, Dundee DD2 1LG — MB ChB 1938 Ed.; FRCGP 1972, M 1953.

HOGG, Martin Stuart 16 Kerscott Road, Northern Moor, Manchester M23 0FN Tel: 0161 976 2417 — MB BS 1993 Lond.; MA Oxf. 1994, BA 1990. Specialist Regist. in Clin. Oncol. Christie Hosp. Manch. Prev: Ho. Phys. St. Bart. Hosp. Lond.; Ho. Phys. S.end Gen. Hosp.

HOGG, Matthew John Home, Main St., Thorney, Newark NG23 7BS — MB ChB 1994 Manch.

HOGG, Nicholas James Thatched House, Bourn Road, Caxton, Cambridge CB3 8PP — MB BS 1992 Lond.

HOGG, Pauline 3 Ewing Walk, Milngavie, Glasgow G62 6EG — MB ChB 1969 Glas.

HOGG, Peter Frank, Wing Cdr. RAF Med. Br. Retd. Tel: 0117 932 4444 Fax: 0117 932 4101; 18 Back Lane, Marshfield, Chippenham SN14 8NQ Email: hoggies@madasafish.com — MB BS 1962 Lond.; MRCP (UK) 1970; MRCS Eng. LRCP Lond. 1962; DMRD Eng. 1975. (Lond. Hosp.) Sessional Phys., Health Call Servs., Bristol. Prev: GP Princip., Bristol; Sen. Med. Off. RAF St. Athan; Sen. Med. Of RAF Abingdon.

HOGG, Peter Scott 3 Parklands, Southampton SO18 1UE — MB BS 1967 Newc. (Newc.) Asst. Specialist Blood Transfus. Serv. Wessex RHA.

HOGG, Philip John Bilton East, Alnmouth, Alnwick NE66 2SU Tel: 01665 830424 — MB BS 1945 Durh. (Durh.) Lic. Fac. Osteop. Lond. 1957. Prev: Ho. Phys. Cardiovasc. Clinic Newc. Gen. Hosp.; Ho. Surg. Eye Dept. Roy. Vict. Infirm. Newc.

HOGG, Rachel Ann The Health Centre, Alfred Squire Road, Wednesfield, Wolverhampton WV11 1XU Tel: 01902 575033 Fax: 01902 575013 — MB BS 1994 Newc.

HOGG, Richard Brooke 3 Ewing Walk, Fairways, Milngavie, Glasgow G62 6EG — MB ChB 1969 Glas.; FRCP Glas. 1984; MRCP (U.K.) 1973; MRCPath 1977. Cons. Haemat. Gtr. Glas. Health Bd. & Postgrad. Tutor Univ. Glas.

HOGG, Richard Paul Great Gates, Main Road, Santon, Douglas IM4 1HS — MB ChB 1992 Bristol; BSc Bristol 1989, MB ChB 1992.

HOGG, Robert Anthony 27 Firs Road, Edwalton, Nottingham NG12 4BY — MB BS 1975 Newc.; MRCGP 1980.

HOGG, Stephen George Radiology Department, Lincoln County Hospital, Greetwell Road, Lincoln LN2 5QY; Orchard House, School Crescent, Scothern, Lincoln LN2 2UQ — MB BS 1982 (1st cl. Hons) Newc.; FRCR 1988. Cons. Radiol. Lincoln Co. Hosp. Prev: Sen. Regist. (Radiol.) Univ. Hosp. Nottm.

HOGG, Steven John Rushden Medical Centre, Parklands, Wymington Road, Rushden NN10 9EB; The Firs, 82 High Street, Broughton NN14 1NQ Email: stevenhogg@virgin.net — BM 1988 Soton.; DRCOG 1992; DCH RCP Lond. 1991.

HOGG, Susan Jane Huntsmoor, Stoney Lane, Bovingdon, Hemel Hempstead HP3 0DP Tel: 01442 832014 Fax: 01442 832369 — MB ChB 1979 Ed.; MRCP (UK) 1983; MRCGP 1983.

HOGG, Vera Jane The Surgery, Newton Port Surgery, Haddington EH41 3NF Tel: 01620 825497 Fax: 01620 824622 — MB ChB 1976 Ed.; FRCGP 2000; DRCOG 1980. (Edinburgh)

HOGG, William Antrim Health Centre, Station Road, Antrim BT41 4BS Tel: 028 9446 4938 Fax: 028 9446 4930; 55 Crosskennan Road, Antrim BT41 2RE — MB BCh BAO 1975 Belf. (Queens University Belfast)

HOGG, Wilma Jane High Street Surgery, 60 High Street, Newarthill, Motherwell ML1 5JU Tel: 01698 860246 Fax: 01698 861641 — MB ChB 1983 Glas.; MRCGP 1987; DRCOG 1986. Prev: Trainee GP Glas. VTS.

HOGGARD, Nigel 12 Laburnum Avenue, Gainsborough DN21 1ET — BChir 1990 Camb.

HOGGART, Barbara Department of Anaesthetics, Solihull Hospital, Lode Lane, Solihull B91 2JL Tel: 0121 711 4455; 38 Alderbrook Road, Solihull B91 1NN Tel: 0121 711 4078 — MB BS 1977 Lond.; FFA RCS Eng. 1981. (St. Mary's Hosp. Med. Sch. Lond.) Cons. Anaesth. Birm. Heartlands & Solihull NHS Trust (Teachg.). Prev: Sen. Regist. St. Mary's Hosp. Lond.

HOGGARTH, Caroline 14 Middlehey Avenue, Knowsley Village, Prescot L34 0HZ — MB BS 1996 Newc.

HOGGARTH, Catherine Elizabeth Dept. Haematology, Hinchingbrooke Hospital, Hinchingbrooke Park, Huntingdon PE29 6NT — MB ChB 1973 Sheff.; MRCPath 1979; DCH RCP Lond. 1974. Cons. Haemat. Hinchingbrooke Hosp. Huntingdon.

HOGGINS, Geoffrey Ross Buckley Health Centre, Padeswood Road, Buckley CH7 2JL Tel: 01224 550536; 184 Mold Road, Buckley CH7 2NT — MB ChB 1977 Manch.

HOGHTON, George Bruce Seymour St Mary's Surgery, James Street, Southampton SO14 1PJ Tel: 023 8033 3778 Fax: 023 8021 1894; Ingleford, Leigh Road, Southampton SO17 1EF Email: bhoghton@aol.com — MB BS 1989 Lond.; MRCGP 1993; DRCOG 1992. (St. Mary's Hosp. Med. Sch.) GP Princip. St. Mary's Surg. James St. Soton. Prev: Trainee GP Portsmouth & SE Hants. HA VTS.

HOGHTON, Matthew Anthony Richard The Surgery, 15 West Town Road, Backwell, Bristol BS48 3HA Tel: 0117 462026 Fax: 0117 795609 — MB ChB 1983 Bristol; MRCP (UK) 1987; MRCGP 1990; DRCOG 1989. GP Nailsea; Cons. Physical Healthin Learning Disabil. Bristol; Hon. Research Fell. Univ. Bristol; Mem. Avon DMAC; Mem. Avon Drugs & Therap. Comm. Prev: Sen. Regist. (Respirat.) Bristol Roy. Infirm.; Regist. (Cardiol. & Rheum.) Swindon HA; SHO (Neurol. & Gen. Med.) Frenchay Hosp. Bristol.

HOGSTON, Mr Patrick Department Obstetrics & Gynaecology, St Mary's Hospital, Portsmouth PO3 6AD Tel: 023 92 866510; 11 Brading Avenue, Southsea PO4 9QJ — MRCS Eng. LRCP Lond. 1979; MB BS Lond. 1979; BSc (Anat.) Lond. 1976; FRCS Eng. 1984; FRCOG; MRCOG 1986. (Char. Cross) Cons. Obst & Gyn. St. Mary's Hosp. Portsmouth. Socs: Brit. Gyn. Cancer Soc.; Brit. Soc. (Colposcopy & Cervical Path.). Prev: Sen. Regist. (O & G) S.mead Hosp. Bristol; Regist. (O & G) P.ss Anne Hosp. Soton.; SHO (Obst.) Qu. Charlotte's Hosp. Lond.

HOGWOOD, Frances Mary (retired) — MB BS 1978 Lond.; MRCS Eng. LRCP Lond. 1978.

HOH, Carmen Suet Li 10 Marchmont Terrace, Glasgow G12 9LS — MB ChB 1998 Glas.; MB ChB Glas 1998.

HOH, Hon Bing Department of Ophthamlology, Bristol Eye Hospital, Lower Maudlin St., Bristol BS1 2LX — BM 1988 Soton.; MCOphth 1991.

HOILE, Mr Ronald William Medway NHS Trust, Medway Maritime Hospital, Windmill Road, Gillingham ME7 5NY Tel: 01634 830000 Fax: 01634 815811 Email: rhoile@ncepod.org.uk; 6 Water Meadow Close, Hempstead, Gillingham ME7 3QF Tel: 01634 377070 Fax: 01634 377070 Email: ron.hoile@ukgateway.net — MB BS (Hons. Surg.) Lond. 1968; MS Lond. 1979; FRCS Eng. 1973; MRCS Eng. LRCP Lond. 1968. (Char. Cross) Cons. Surg. Medway NHS Trust; Princip. Surg. Co-Ordinator Nat. Confidential Enquiry PeriOperat. Death; Mem. GMC PCC; Mem. Educat. Fac. RCS. Socs: Vasc. Soc.; Assn. Surg.; Brit. Assn. Med. Managers. Prev: Sen. Regist. (Surg.) St. Stephen's Hosp. Lond.; Lect. (Surg.) & Hon. Sen. Regist. W.m. Hosp. Lond.; Clin. Research Fell. (Surg.) Char. Cross Hosp. Lond.

HOKAN, Radwan Cripps Postgraduate Centre, Northampton General Hospital, Northampton NN1 5BD Tel: 01604 34700; 57 Great Bowden Road, Market Harborough LE16 7DF — MD 1976 Aleppo; MSc (Orthop.) Lond. 1985. Sen. Regist. N.ampton Gen. Hosp.

HOLBOROW, Eric John 7 Northfield End, Henley-on-Thames RG9 2JG — MB BChir 1942 Camb.; MD Camb. 1953, MA, MB BChir 1942; FRCP Lond. 1978, M 1972; MRCS Eng. LRCP Lond. 1942; FCPath 1978, M 1968. (Camb. & St. Bart.) Emerit. Prof. (Immunopath.) Lond. Hosp. Med. Coll. Prev: Sen. Regist. in Path. Brit. Postgrad. Med. Sch.; Dir. MRC Rheum. Unit Taplow; Head MRC Immunol. Gp. Bone/Jt. Research Unit Lond. Hosp. Med. Coll.

HOLBOROW, Michael (retired) 38 Watford Road, Radlett WD7 8LE Tel: 01923 857289 — MB BS 1943 Lond.; MRCS Eng. LRCP Lond. 1943; FFA RCS Eng. 1954; DA Eng. 1945. Prev: Cons. Anaesth. Mt. Vernon Hosp. N.wood.

HOLBROOK, Mr Anthony George Windyridge, Cold Ashton, Chippenham SN14 8JT — MB ChB 1976 Bristol; FRCS Eng. 1980.

HOLBROOK, Brian William Castle Oak, Chilham, Canterbury CT4 8DE Tel: 01227 730571 — MB BS 1951 Lond.; MRCS Eng. LRCP Lond. 1951; DObst RCOG 1956. (St. Bart.) Prev: Ho. Surg. (O & G) Greenwich Dist Hosp.; Ho. Phys. & Ho. Surg. Metrop. Hosp. Lond.; Resid. Med. Off. W. End. Hosp. Neurol. & Neurosurg.

HOLBROOK, David Mark Anthony 14 Harrow View Road, London W5 1LZ — MB BS 1983 Lond.; LMSSA Lond. 1983. (St. Thos.) Prev: Ho. Phys. Medway Hosp. Gillingham; Ho. Surg. Plymouth Gen. Hosp.

HOLBROOK, George David North House Surgery, North House, Hope Street, Crook DL15 9HU Tel: 01388 762945 Fax: 01388 765333; Westholme, 22 St. Mary's Avenue, Crook DL15 9HY — MB ChB 1978 Leeds. Clin. Asst. (Geriat.) Homelands Hosp. Crook.

HOLBROOK, James David 61 Adderley Road, Clarendon Park, Leicester LE2 1WD Tel: 0118 270 8818 — MB ChB 1993 Leic. (Leic.) SHO Anaesth. Leic. Roy. Infirm.

HOLBROOK, Jonathan Bourne Hall Health Centre, Chessington Road, Ewell, Epsom KT17 1TG Tel: 020 8394 1362; 63 Beaconsfield Road, Surbiton KT5 9AW Tel: 020 8399 3891 — MB ChB 1983 Manch.; MRCGP 1996. (Manch.) GP Princip. Prev: GP Cheam; Trainee GP Leatherhead Surrey.

HOLBROOK, Judith Ann Patricia Red Lion House Surgery, 86 Hednesford Road, Heath Hayes, Cannock WS12 5EA Tel: 01543 502391 Fax: 01543 573424 — MB ChB 1987 Manch.; MRCGP 1992; DRCOG 1991.

HOLBROOK, Malcolm Charles Westmorland Centre, 22 Railway Road, Leigh WN7 4AU Tel: 01942 679703 Fax: 01942 262322; The Barn AT Hollins Head, Arley Lane, Haigh, Wigan WNI 2UQ Tel: 01942 830657 — MB BS 1969 Lond.; MS 1981 Lond.; MRCS 1976 Eng.; LRCP 1969 Lond. (St. Bart.) Cons. Gen. & Gastroenterol. Surg. Wrightington Wigan & Leigh NHS Trust; Tutor RCS; Examr. Surg. Univ. Manch.; Hon. Lect. Univ. Lond. Socs: Pres. Wigan Illeostomy Assn.; Suture Med. Soc. Prev: Tutor (Surg.) Univ. Manch. Roy. Infirm. Manch.; Regist. (Gen. Surg.) Windsor Gp. Hosps.; Regist. (Gen. Surg.) Watford Gen. Hosp.

HOLBROOK, Miles Rupert 63 Derby Road, Bramcote, Nottingham NG9 3GW Tel: 0115 925 9009 — BM BS 1993 Nottm.; BMedSci Nottm. 1991. Clin. Research Fell. (Clin. Immunol.) Univ. Hosp. NHS Trust Nottm. Prev: Ho. Off. (Gen. Med., Dermat., Gen. Surg. & Gyn.) Univ. Hosp. Nottm.

HOLBURN, Alexander McConnachie Wherrymans, Staithe Road, Barton Turf, Norwich NR12 8AZ — MB ChB 1963 Glas.; FRCPath 1986, M 1971. Prev: Cons. Haemat. & Dir. Blood Gp. Refer. Laborat. Radcliffe; Infirm. Oxf.; Scientif. Off. MRC Experim. Haemat. Unit St. Mary's; Hosp. Lond.; Sen. Lect. & Hon. Cons. St. Thos. Hosp. Lond.

HOLBURN, Colin James 70 Princess Crescent, Hawne Park, Halesowen B63 3QG — MB ChB 1981 Ed. Regist. (Surg.) Birm. Gen. Hosp. Prev: SHO (Surg.) N. Staffs. Roy. Infirm. Stoke on Trent; Ho. Off. G.I. Unit. W.. Gen. Hosp. Edin.; Ho. Off. Birm. Accid. Hosp.

HOLCOMBE, Mr Christopher Breast Unit 3rd Floor Linda McCartney Centre, Royal Liverpool University Hospitals, Liverpool L7 8XP Tel: 0151 706 3452 Fax: 0151 706 5875 Email: cholcombe@vlbuh-tr.nwest.nhs.uk; Heather Lea, 17 South Drive, Victoria Park, Liverpool L15 8JJ Tel: 0151 280 4570 — MB BS 1981 Lond.; MD Lond. 1992; FRCS Glas. 1985; DRCOG 1985. (Roy. Free Hosp. Sch. Med.) Cons. Surg. Roy. Liverp. Univ. Hosps.; Hon. Lect. Liverp. Univ. Socs: BMA; Brit. Assn. Surg. Oncol. Prev: Lect. Liverp. Univ.; Regist. Rotat. Char. Cross Hosp. Lond.; Lect. (Surg.) Univ. Maiduguri Nigeria.

HOLCOMBE, David Roderick The Health Centre, The Quay, Kingsbridge TQ7 1HR Tel: 01548 853551 Fax: 01548 857741 — MB BS 1962 Lond.; BSc (Hons. Physiol.) Lond. 1959; MRCS Eng. LRCP Lond. 1962; MRCGP 1978; MFHom 1978; DA (UK) 1966; DObst RCOG 1966; DCH Eng. 1964. (King's Coll. Hosp.) Clin. Homoeop. Phys. Vict. Cottage Hosp. Sidmouth Devon. Socs: Plymouth Med. Soc. & Dep. Vice Pres. for UK of Liga Medicorum Homoep. Internats; S. Hams Med. Soc. (Convenor). Prev: SHO (Anaesth. & Paediat.) Plymouth Gen. Hosp.; Ho. Phys. (Diabetic) King's Coll. Hosp.

HOLCOMBE, Elizabeth Louise Department Rheumatology, Battle Hospital, Reading RG30 1AG — MB BS 1986 Lond.; MRCGP 1991; DRCOG 1989. Clin. Asst. (Rheum.) Battle Hosp. Reading. Prev: Princip. GP Caversham, Berks.; Trainee GP Crowthorne, Berks.; SHO (Rheum.) The Battle Hosp. Reading.

HOLCROFT, Penelope Jayne Bilton Clinic, Bilton Road, Rugby CV22 7LU — MB ChB 1966 Birm.; MRCGP 1978; MFHom 1989. Prev: Ho. Phys. Ronkswood Hosp. Worcester; Ho. Surg. Childr. Hosp. Birm.

HOLDBROOK-SMITH, Mr Henry Andrew 24 Church Road, Frimley, Camberley GU16 7AE Tel: 01276 502625 Fax: 01276 26419 — MB ChB 1973 Ghana; FRCS Ed. 1986; FRCS Glas. 1986; LMSSA Lond. 1985; FWACS 1999. Chief Exec, Korlebu Teachg. Hosp. Kole Be Accra; Lect. & Cons. Orthop. Surg. Socs: Brit. Orthop. Assn. Prev: Cons. Orpthop. Surg.; Head of Trauma & Orthop. Dammam Centr. Hosp. Saudi Arabia.

HOLDCROFT, Anita 3 Regency Close, Ealing, London W5 2LP — MB ChB 1969 Sheff.; MD Sheff. 1983; FFA RCS Eng. 1973; FWACS 1981. Reader & Hon. Cons. Anaesth., Chelsea & W.minster Hosp. ICSM, Lond. Socs: Chairm., Roy. Soc. of Med., Forum on Matern. & Newborn. Prev: Prof. of Anaesth. Univ. of Jos Nigeria; Sen. Lect. & Hon. Cons. Char. Cross Med. Sch. Lond.

HOLDEN, Adrian Arthur 4 Hall Grove, Welwyn Garden City AL7 4PL Tel: 01707 328528 Fax: 01707 373139 — MB BS 1974 Newc.

HOLDEN, Adrian Paul 148 Halfway Street, Sidcup DA15 8DG — MB BS 1988 Lond.

HOLDEN, Andrew Francis Harold Swan Surgery, Swan Street, Petersfield GU32 3AB Tel: 01730 264011 Fax: 01730 231093 — MB BS 1988 Lond.; MRCGP 1997; DFFP 1994; DRCOG 1992. (St. Bart.) Princip. GP Petersfield; Hosp. Practitioner (Cardiol.) St. Mary's Hosp. Portsmouth. Socs: Med. Protec. Soc.; Roy. Coll. Obst. & Gyn.; Fac. Fam. Plann. Prev: Trainee GP Chichester VTS.

HOLDEN, Ann Marie 141 Childwall Valley Road, Childwall, Liverpool L16 1LA — MB ChB 1991 Liverp.; MB ChB Liverp. 1992; Dip. FRCA 1999. (Liverp.) Specialist Regist. Anaesth. Mersey Regional Rotat. (Mersey Deanery) Liverp. Sch. Anaesth. Socs: Liverp. Soc. Anaesth. Prev: SHO (Anaesth.) St. Helen's & Knowsley Hosps., Aintree Hosps. NHS Trust, Roy. Liverp. Univ. Hosp.

HOLDEN, Ann Melville West Leys, Bracondale, Esher KT10 Tel: 01372 466219 — MB BS 1961 Lond. (St. Bart.) SCMO (Child Health) Hounslow & Spelthorne Health Dist. Socs: BMA. Prev: Clin. Asst. (Paediat.) St. Peter's Hosp. Chertsey; Regist. (Paediat.) Qu. Eliz. II Hosp. Welwyn GC & St. Albans City Hosp.; Ho. Surg. St. Bart. Hosp. Lond.

HOLDEN, Anne Auckland Surgery, 84A Auckland Road, Upper Norwood, London SE19 2DF Tel: 020 8653 5146 Fax: 020 8653 1195; 40 Carson Road, West Dulwich, London SE21 8HU — MB BS 1978 Lond.

HOLDEN, Benedict Mark 37 Manor Street, Cardiff CF14 3PW — MB BCh 1993 Wales.

HOLDEN, Catherine Ann 1A Lightfoot Lane, Fulwood, Preston PR2 3LP — MB ChB 1995 Manch.

HOLDEN, Catherine Ruth 2 The Ridge, Redmires Road, Sheffield S10 4LL Tel: 0114 230 8531; 2 The Ridge, Redmires Road, Sheffield S10 4LL Tel: 0114 230 8531 — MB ChB 1987 Sheff.; MRCGP 1993; DFFP 1995; T(GP) 1993; Cert. Community Paediat. Sheff. 1992; DRCOG 1991. (Sheff.) p/t Staff Grade Dermatol., Sheff. Childr.'s Hosp.; GP Clin. Asst. (Dermat.) Sheff.; Roy. Hallanshire Hosp. Prev: GP N. Derbysh.- Health Auth. Employed Doctor,; Clin. Med. Off. (p/t) in Family Plann. & Reproductive Health Care, Sheff.; GP Sheff.

HOLDEN, Charles Leonard (retired) Ambleton, 23 Wyfordby Avenue, Blackburn BB2 7AR — MB ChB 1943 Manch.

HOLDEN, Mr Christopher Edward Aldridge Darby Green House, Stroud Lane, Blackwater, Camberley GU17 0BL Tel: 01252 861813 — MRCS Eng. LRCP Lond. 1956; MS Lond. 1970, MB BS 1956; FRCS Eng. 1964. (Guy's) Socs: Brit. Soc. Surg. Hand. Prev: Emerit. Cons. Orthop. Surg. King's Coll. Hosp. Lond.

HOLDEN, Christopher Gerard Park Lane Practice, 7-8 Park Lane, Swindon SN1 5HG Tel: 01793 523176 Fax: 01793 535080 — MB ChB 1977 Bristol; DRCOG 1981.

HOLDEN, Christopher James Spring Cottage, Church Lane, Errol, Perth PH2 7PX — MB ChB 1991 Dundee.

HOLDEN, Colin Arthur 40 Carson Road, West Dulwich, London SE21 8HU — MB BS 1977 Lond.; MD Lond. 1987, BSc (2nd cl. Hons.) 1974, MB BS 1977; MRCP (UK) 1979; MRCS Eng. LRCP Lond. 1977. Cons. Dermat. St. Helier Hosp. Carshalton; Hon. Sen. Lect. St. Geo. Hosp. Med. Sch. Lond. Prev: Sen. Regist. St. Johns Hosp. for Dis. of Skin Lond.; Dermat. Fell. Oregon Health Scs. Univ. Oregon, USA; Dermat. Sen. Regist. Guy's Hosp. Lond.

HOLDEN, Mr David 6 Buxton Old Road, Macclesfield SK11 7EL — MB BS 1976 Newc.; FRCS Eng. 1980. Cons. Urol. Surg. Macclesfield Dist. Gen. Hosp.

HOLDEN, David Ward Ribblesdale Place Surgery, 23 Ribblesdale Place, Preston PR1 3NA Tel: 01772 258474 — MB ChB 1959 Manch. (Manch.)

HOLDEN, Desmond Philip 10 Tolworth Park Road, Surbiton KT6 7RN — MB BS 1987 Lond.; BSc (1st cl. Hons) Lond. 1984, MB BS 1987; MRCOG 1994.

HOLDEN, Sir Edward (retired) Moorstones, Rueberry Lane, Osmotherley, Northallerton DL6 3BQ — MRCS Eng. LRCP Lond. 1942; FFA RCS Eng. 1958; DA Eng. 1946. Prev: Vis. Anaesth. Cumbld. Infirm. Carlisle.

HOLDEN, Fiona Miriam Jane Church Row, South Otterington, Northallerton DL7 9HG — MB BCh 1989 Wales.

HOLDEN, Geoffrey Creswick Aldridge (retired) Glebe Court NH, Glebe Way, West Wickham BR4 9QD Tel: 0208 462 6609 — MB BS Lond. 1951; MRCS Eng. LRCP Lond. 1950. Prev: Immunisation Med. Off. Brit. Airways Vict. Terminal Lond.

HOLDEN, George Radway Lodge, 52 Arlington Avenue, Gording-by-Sea, Worthing BN12 4SR — MB BChir 1950 Camb.; FRCP Ed. 1973, M 1961; DPhysMed. Eng. 1958. Emerit. Cons. Phys. Rheum. & Rehabil. Worthing HA. Prev: Sen. Regist. (Physical Med.) Guy's Hosp.

HOLDEN, Helen Mavis Broken Cross Surgery, Fallibroome Road, Macclesfield SK10 3LA Tel: 01625 617300 Fax: 01625 617300; Tel: 01625 434384 — MB ChB 1976 Liverp.; MB ChB 1974 Liverp.; DObst RCOG 1976. Asst. GP.

HOLDEN, Hyla Montgomery (retired) Westfield House, Clairmont House, Princes St., Bishop Auckland DL14 6AE — BM BCh Oxf. 1955; BA Durham. 1989; MA Oxf. 1949; MRCGP 1978; MRCPsych 1971; DPM Eng. 1961; DObst RCOG 1958. Supervisor N.ern Guild for Psychother. Prev: Vis. Assoc. Prof. Stanford Univ., USA.

HOLDEN, Jennifer Ruth (retired) Lister House, The Common, Hatfield AL10 0NL Tel: 01707 268822 Fax: 01707 263990 — MB BS 1972 Lond.

HOLDEN, John Duncan The Medical Centre, Station Road, Haydock, St Helens WA11 0JN Tel: 01744 734419 Fax: 01744 454875 — MB ChB 1976 Birm.; FRCGP 1993, M 1985; DTM & H Liverp. 1986. (Birmingham) GP; Vice Chairm. Fell.ship by Assessm. Nat. Gp., RCGP. Prev: Dep. Med. Supt. Mengo Hosp. Kampala, Uganda.

HOLDEN, John James (retired) 19 Hilder Gardens, Farnborough GU14 7BQ Tel: 01252 543205 — MB BS Lond. 1957; DObst RCOG 1959.

HOLDEN, John Michael Health Centre, Bridge Street, Rothwell, Kettering NN14 6JW Tel: 01536 418518 Fax: 01536 418373 — MB BS 1971 Lond. (Roy. Free) Prev: Med. Off. RAF Med. Br.

HOLDEN, John Stuart (retired) Beech House, Upper Lumsdale, Matlock DE4 5LB Tel: 01629 583794 — MB ChB 1946 Ed. Prev: Jun. Orthop. Regist. Preston Roy. Infirm.

HOLDEN, John Stuart Francis Quintins Medical Centre, Hawkswood Road, Hailsham BN27 1UG Tel: 01323 845669 Fax: 01323 846653 — MB BS 1984 Lond.; MRCGP 1990; DRCOG 1989; DCH RCP Lond. 1987. (King's Coll.) Socs: BMA. Prev: Trainee GP Lochmaddy I. of N. Uist; SHO (Neonat.) St. Geo. Hosp. Lond.; Ho. Surg. King's Coll. Hosp. Lond.

HOLDEN, Louise Gwendoline 24 Whitcliffe Grove, Ripon HG4 2JW — MB ChB 1988 Leeds; MMedSci Birm. 1993; AFOM RCP Lond. 1993. (Leeds)

HOLDEN, Mr Michael Preston 4 Holeyn Hall Road, Wylam NE41 8BB — MB ChB 1962 Leeds; FRCS Ed. 1967; DObst RCOG 1966. Cons. Cardiothoracic Surg. Newc. Health Dist. (T); Vis. Prof. & Head Dept. Cardiothoracic Surg. Mt. Sinai Med. Centre NY. Socs: Brit. Soc. Thoracic & Cardiovasc. Surgs. & Yorks. Thoracic Soc.; Fell. Amer. Coll. Nutrit. Prev: Asst. Lect. Dept. Anat. Univ. Glas.; Res. Surg. Off. St. Jas. Hosp. Leeds; Sen. Cardiothoracic Regist. Leeds Gen. Infirm.

HOLDEN, Neil Lindsay Department of Psychological Medicine, Queens Medical Centre, Nottingham NG7 2UH Tel: 0115 924 9924 Fax: 0115 849 3297 — MB BS 1978 Newc.; MA Camb. 1979; MRCP (UK) 1981; MRCPsych 1983; FRCP Ed. 1998; FRCPsych. 1998. Cons. Psychiat Nottm. Health Care Trust. Socs: Roy. Coll. Phys. Ed. & Roy. Coll. Psychiat. Prev: Sen. Lect. & Cons. Psychiat. Univ. Nottm. Med. Sch.; Clin. Lect. Inst. Psychiat. Lond.

HOLDEN, Norman Evan Samuel 14 Shapelands, Stoke Bishop, Bristol BS9 1AY — MRCS Eng. LRCP Lond. 1957; MB Camb. 1958, BChir 1957. (Westm.) Prev: Flight Lt. RAF Med. Br.

HOLDEN, Patrick James Surrey Docks Health Centre, Downtown Road, London SE16 6NP Tel: 020 7231 0207 Fax: 020 771 5650; 124 Redriff Road, London SE16 6QD — MB BS 1980 Newc.; MRCGP 1986; DRCOG 1988; DCH RCP Lond. 1987.

HOLDEN, Peter Edward Frome Medical Practice, Health Centre, Park Road, Frome BA11 1EZ Tel: 01373 301300 Fax: 01373 301313; 71 Forester Avenue, Bath BA2 6QB Tel: 01225 336826 Email: drpeterholden@yahoo.com — MB BS 1968 Lond.; MRCP (UK) 1971; MRCS Eng. LRCP Lond. 1968; MRCGP 1983.

HOLDEN, Peter John Pashley 8 Imperial Road, Matlock DE4 3NL Tel: 01629 583249 Fax: 01629 55708 Email: pjpholden@dial.pipex.com — MB ChB 1979 Sheff.; 2001 FIMCRCSEd; 1983 JCPTGP Certificate; Dip. IMC RCS Ed. 1991; DRCOG 1984. (Sheffield) GP Princip., Sen. Partner, Dr PJP Holden & Partners, Matlock; Med. Aircrew Lincs. & Notts Air Ambul.; Med. Staff. Whitworth Hosp. Matlock; Mem. Gen. Practitioners Comm., BMA (Negotiator); Mem. Advis. Comm., Air Ambul. Assn.; Extern. Assessor, The Health Serv. Ombudsman. Socs: (Counc.) BMA (Chairm. Professional Fees Comm.); (Hon Sec) Brit. Assn. Immediate Care. Prev: Trainee GP Chesterfield VTS; Ho. Surg. Barnsley Dist. Gen. Hosp.; Ho. Phys. Lodge Moor Hosp. Sheff.

HOLDEN, Raymond John Kynachan, Dullatur, Glasgow G68 0AW — MB BS 1968 Lond.; FRCP Glas. 1983; MRCP (UK) 1971; MRCS Eng. LRCP Lond. 1968; FRCP 1998 Edin. Cons. Phys. (Gastroenterol.) Monklands Dist. Gen. Hosp. Airdrie. Socs: Brit. Soc. Gastroenterol. Prev: Sen. Regist. (Gastroenterol. & Gen. Med.) Gtr. Glas. Health Bd.

HOLDEN, Roger Rehabilitation Unit, Dumfries & Galloway Royal Infirmary, Bankend Road, Dumfries DG1 4AP Tel: 01387 246246 — MB ChB 1982 Ed.; MSc Lond. 1997; MRCP (UK) 1986. (Ed.) Cons. Phys. Rehabil. Unit, Dumfries & Galloway Roy. Infirm.

HOLDEN, Roger Arthur (retired) 15 Sytche Close, Much Wenlock TF13 6JJ Tel: 01952 727870 — MRCS Eng. LRCP Lond. 1942; BA Camb. 1940, MA 1943, MB BChir 1942. Prev: Med. Ref. DHSS.

HOLDEN, Rosalind Elizabeth Mary Park Lane Practice, 7-8 Park Lane, Swindon SN1 5HG Tel: 01793 523176 Fax: 01793 535080; Trotter Cottage, Horpit, Lower Wanborough, Swindon SN4 0AT Tel: 01793 790578 Fax: 01793 790578 — MB ChB 1975 Birm. Med. Off. Lucent Technologies. Socs: Occupat. Health Soc.

HOLDEN, Ruth Margaret Kynachan, Dullatur, Glasgow G68 0AW — MB ChB 1972 Manch.; FRCP Glas. 1988; MRCP (UK) 1975; FRCR 1979; DMRD Eng. 1978. (Manch.) Cons. (Radiol.) Monklands NHS Trust Airdrie. Socs: Brit. Med. Ultrasound Soc.; Scott. Radiol. Soc. Prev: Sen. Regist. S.. Gen. Hosp. Glas.

HOLDEN, Samuel William Pear Tree Cottage, 27 Oulton Road, Stone ST15 8EB — MB ChB 1995 Leeds; DRCOG Birm. 1998; DFFP 1999. (Leeds)

HOLDEN, Mr Simon Timothy Rose Department of Urology, Gubbins Lane, Harold Wood Hospital, Romford Tel: 01708 345533; 107 Clifden Road, London E5 0LW Tel: 020 8533 0177 — MB BS Lond. 1990; BSc (Hons.) Lond. 1986; FRCS Eng. 1995. (Univ. Coll. & Middlx. Hosp.) Specialist Regist. Urol. Prev: Specialist Regist.

Urol., Whipps Cross Hosp., Leyton, Lond., E10; Research Fell. Urol., Roy. Free Hosp., Lond.

HOLDEN, Stephen Jeremy Portobello Medical Centre, 14 Codrington Mews, London W11 2EH Tel: 020 7727 5800/2326 Fax: 020 7792 9044; 39 Park View Road, London NW10 1AJ Tel: 020 8450 5295 — MB BS 1982 Lond.; DRCOG 1986. (St. Mary's Lond.)

HOLDEN, Susan Jane 77 Woodbury Avenue, Petersfield GU32 2EB — MB BS 1989 Lond.

HOLDEN, Victoria Anne Stonecroft Medical Centre, 871 Gleadless Road, Sheffield S12 2LJ Tel: 0114 398575 Fax: 0114 265 0001; 99 Millhouses Lane, Millhouses, Sheffield S7 2HD — MB ChB 1983 Leeds.

HOLDEN, Wendy Alison Sandalwood, Cock Lane, Southend Bradfield, Reading RG7 6HN — MB BS 1994 Lond.; MRCP 1997.

HOLDER, Belinda 48 Boyne Avenue, London NW4 2JN — MB BS 1990 Lond.

HOLDER, Elisabeth Helen (Hurter) Longacre, Kirkham Road, Horndon on the Hill, Stanford-le-Hope SS17 8QE Tel: 01268 545626 — MB BS 1986 Lond. (UCH) p/t GP Retainee, 63 Rowley Rd., Orsett, Essex. Prev: GP Laindon Health Centre Basildon; Trainee GP/SHO (Psychiat.) Orsett Essex.

HOLDER, Elizabeth Simone Law Hospital, Carluke ML8 5ER — MB BS 1995 W. Indies.

HOLDER, Paul Andrew 165 Cornhill Drive, Aberdeen AB16 5HN — MB ChB 1998 Aberd.; MB ChB Aberd 1998.

HOLDER, Mr Paul David 24 Highlands Park, Sevenoaks TN15 0AQ Fax: 070699 50236 Email: paul@holder.demon.co.uk; Tel: 01245 256896 — MB ChB 1980 Bristol; FRCS Glas. 1984; FRCR 1994. (Bristol University) p/t Cons. Radiol. Dartford & Gravesham NHS Trust; Cons. Radiologist, Fawkham Manor Hosp., Longfield, Kent; Cons. Radiologist, Chelsfield Pk. Hosp., Chelsfield, Kent. Prev: Sen. Regist. & Regist. (Radiol.) St. Thos. Hosp. Lond.; Regist. (Urol.) St. Mary's Hosp. Lond.

HOLDER, Susan Elizabeth 23 Balgowan Road, Beckenham BR3 4HJ — BM BS 1981 Nottm.; MSc (Med. Genetics) 1989; MRCP (UK) 1986. Sen. Regist. (Clin. Genetics) Hosp. Sick Childr. Gt. Ormond St. Lond. Socs: Clin. Genetics Soc. Prev: Research Regist. (Clin. Genetics) N.wick Pk. Hosp. Lond.

HOLDERNESS, Dinah Mary Harrowby Lane Surgery, Harrowby Lane, Grantham NG31 9NS Tel: 01476 579494 Fax: 01476 579694; 18 New Beacon Road, Grantham NG31 9JR — MB BChir 1975 Camb.; BA Camb. 1971, MB BChir 1975.

HOLDERNESS, Jane Alison Goyt Valley Medical Practice, Chapel Street, Whaley Bridge, High Peak SK23 7SR Tel: 01663 732911 Fax: 01663 735702; 22 Rock Bank, Whaley Bridge, High Peak SK23 7LE — MB ChB 1984 Manch.; MB ChB Manch. l984; MRCGP 1989. Prev: Trainee GP Wythenshawe VTS; SHO (Geriat.) Ladywell Hosp. Salford; SHO (A & E) Stockport Infirm.

HOLDERNESS, Michael Cautley (retired) 81 Weeping Cross, Stafford ST17 0DQ Tel: 01785 661046 — MB BChir 1960 Camb.; MA Camb. 1961; FFA RCS Eng. 1966; DA Eng. 1962. Prev: Cons. Anaesth. Mid Staffs. Health Dist.

HOLDERNESS, Yolanda Mary Chiswick Health Centre, Fishers Lane, London W4 1RX Tel: 020 8321 3518/9 Fax: 020 8321 3568; 98 Wellesley Road, Chiswick, London W4 3AL Tel: 020 8995 6023 — BM BCh 1988 Oxf.; MRCGP 1992; DRCOG 1991.

HOLDICH, Sally Yvonne Oakfield Surgery, Oakfield Road, Aylesbury HP20 1LJ Tel: 01296 423797 Fax: 01296 399246 Email: dr.holdich@gp-k82014.nhs.uk; The Well House, Burcott Lane, Bierton, Aylesbury HP22 5AS Tel: 01296 394330 Email: psyl@globalnet.co.uk — MB BS 1978 Lond.; MA Oxf. 1979, BA 1975; MRCGP 1982; DFFP 1993; DRCOG 1981. (St. Geo.) Princip. in Gen. Pract., Oakfield Surg., Aylesbury; Clin. Asst. (Genitourin. Med.), Brookside Clinic, Aylesbury. Socs: MSSVD. Prev: Trainee GP Enfield (Chase Farm) VTS; Ho. Phys. St. Helier Hosp. Carshalton; Ho. Surg. Ashford Hosp. Middlx.

HOLDICH, Thomas Alexander Hungerford Astra Charnwood, Bakewell Road, Loughborough LE11 5RH Tel: 01509 645117 Fax: 01509 645538 Email: tom.holdich@charwood.gb.astra.com; The Coach House, Reigate Hill, Reigate RH2 9PB — MB BS 1982 Lond.; MFPM 1990; Dip. Pharm. Med. RCP Lond. 1989. (Middlx.) Dir. Clin. Research Astra Charwood. Prev: Manager Medicial Dept. SmithKline Beecham Consumer Healthcare; Clin. Research Phys. Wellcome Research Laborat. Beckenham; Janssens Research Fell. St.James Hosp. Lond.

HOLDING, Barbara Elizabeth Netherfield House Surgery, Seghill, Cranhington NE23 7EF — MB BS 1979 Newc.; BA Newc. 1972; Dip. Ther. Newc. 1994. p/t Clin. Med. Off. Graingerville Family Plann. Clinic Newc. u Tyne.

HOLDING, Deirdre Janet Claymires House, Buchlyvie, Stirling FK8 3NR — MB ChB 1969 St. And.; FRCS Ed. 1975; FCOphth 1989; DO Eng. 1971. Cons. (Ophth.) Gtr. Glas. Health Bd.

HOLDING, James 1 Albert Street, Newtown, Exeter EX1 2BH — MB ChB 1998 Bristol.

HOLDING, Philip Kingsley Starboard Side, Kingsdown Close, Teignmouth TQ14 9AX — MB ChB 1941 Birm.; DObst RCOG 1944. (Birm.) Prev: Ho. Surg. Gen. Hosp. Birm.; Ho. Phys. Qu. Eliz. Hosp. Birm.; Ho. Surg. (Obst.) Dudley RD. Hosp. Birm.

HOLDING, Richard Spring Gardens Health Centre, Providence Street, Worcester WR1 2BS Tel: 01905 681781 Fax: 01905 681766; 14 Hallow Road, Worcester WR2 6BU Tel: 01905 422406 — MB ChB 1972 Birm. Prev: SHO (Gen. Med.), (O & G) & (Paediat.) Dudley Rd. Hosp. Birm.

HOLDING, Trevor Anthony Kneesworth House, Old North Road, Bassingbourn cum Kneesworth, Royston SG8 5JP Tel: 01763 255700 Fax: 01763 255718; 14 Sedley Taylor Road, Cambridge CB2 2PW Tel: 01223 247425 — MA, BM BCh Oxf. 1966; DM Oxf. 1976; FRCPsych 1983, M 1972; FRANZCP 1981, M 1979; DPM Eng. 1971; T(Psych) 1991. (Oxford/University College Hospital Medical School London) Cons. Psychiat. Kneesworth Hse. Hosp. Royston. Prev: Reader (Psychiat.) Univ. Tasmania; Lect. (Psychiat.) Edin. Univ.; Clin. Scientif. Off. MRC Unit for Epidemiol. Studies in Psychiat.

HOLDRIGHT, Diana Rosemary Tel: 020 7636 8333 Fax: 020 7573 8888 Email: diana.holdright@uclh.org; Tel: 01895 820578 — MB BS 1984 Lond.; MD Lond. 1994, BSc (Hons.) 1981; MRCP (UK) 1987; DA (UK) 1989; FRCP 2000. (UCH Lond.) Cons. (Cardiol.) Univ. Coll. Lond. Hosps. The Heart Hosp.; Hon Sen. Lect. Roy. Free & Univ. Coll. Med. Sch.; Hon Sen. Lect. Inst. of Neurol., UCL, Lond. Socs: BCS; BCIS; BMA. Prev: Sen. Regist. (Cardiol.) Univ. Coll. Lond. Hosps.; Research Regist. (Cardiol.) The Lond. Chest Hosp.; Research Fell. & Hon. Regist. (Cardiol.) Roy. Brompton Nat. Heart & Lung Hosp. Lond.

HOLDSTOCK, Douglas James (retired) 20 Tanglewood Close, Pyrford, Woking GU22 8LG Tel: 01483 768228 Fax: 01483 835087 Email: mary.holdstock@net.ntl.com — MB BS Lond. 1959; MSc Lond. 1956, MD 1971; FRCP Lond. 1979, M 1962. Prev: Phys. Ashford Hosp. Middlx.

HOLDSTOCK, Gregory Ernest Stoke End, West End Lane, Stoke Poges, Slough SL2 4NA Tel: 0175364 3457 — MB BS 1973 Lond.; DM Soton. 1981; FRCP Lond. 1993. Cons. Gastroenterol. Hillingdon & Mt. Vernon Hosp. Lond. Prev: Sen. Regist. Soton. Univ. Hosp.

HOLDSTOCK, Susan Fairholme, 24 Baring Road, Beaconsfield HP9 2NE — BM BS 1988 Nottm.

HOLDSWORTH, Anya Claire Cumberland Infirmary, Carlisle CA2 7HZ Tel: 01228 23444; 57 Coledale Meadows, Carlisle CA2 7NZ Tel: 01228 596323 — MB BS 1993 Newc.; DRCOG 1997; MRCGP 1998; DTM & H 1999. (Newcastle) Staff Grade (A & E), Cumbld. Infirm. Carlisle. Socs: BMA & Med. Protec. Soc. Prev: Trainee GP Cumbria; Ho. Off. Hexham Gen. Hosp.; Ho. Off. Cmbld. Infirm. Carlisle.

HOLDSWORTH, Mr Brian John 32 Victoria Crescent, Sherwood, Nottingham NG5 4DA Tel: 0115 960 4142 Fax: 0115 960 4142 Email: matt_holdsworth@msn.com — MB BS 1973 Lond.; BSc (Hons.) Lond. 1969; FRCS Eng. 1978; MRCS Eng. LRCP Lond. 1973. (Guy's) Cons. Orthop. Surg. Qu. Med. Centre & Nottm. Univ. Socs: Fell. Brit. Orthop. Soc.; (Sec.) Nottm. M-C Soc. Prev: Sen. Regist. Nottm.

HOLDSWORTH, Charles Derek (retired) 29 Clarendon Road, Fulwood, Sheffield S10 3TQ Tel: 0114 230 8042 — MB ChB 1957 Leeds; MB ChB (2nd cl. Hons.) Leeds 1957; MD Leeds 1965; FRCP Lond. 1974, M 1961; DObst RCOG 1959. Prev: Hon. Cons. Phys. Roy. Hallamsh. Hosp. Sheff.

HOLDSWORTH, Charles John Sergeant (retired) 4 Latimer Street, Oxford Mews, Southampton SO14 3EE — MRCS Eng. LRCP Lond. 1944. Prev: Cons. Venereol. Roy. Hants. Co. Hosp. Winchester Gen. Infirm. Salisbury & Special Treatm. Clinic Soton.

HOLDSWORTH, Clare Aurelie 48 Moor Road N., Newcastle upon Tyne NE3 1AD; 17 Grosvenor Gardens, Jesmond Vale, Newcastle upon Tyne NE2 1HQ Tel: 0191 281 9556 — MB ChB 1992 Sheff.

HOLDSWORTH, Faith Elizabeth Fern Hill Practice, Coxwell Road, Faringdon SN7 7ED Tel: 01367 242407; 57 Westland Road, Faringdon SN7 7EY Tel: 01367 243571 Email: faithholdsworth@compuserve.com — MB BS 1979 Lond.; BSc (Hons.) Lond. 1976, MB BS 1979; MRCGP 1984; DRCOG 1984. (Roy. Free) Prev: Trainee GP Harrow (N.wick Pk. Hosp.) VTS; SHO (Obst.) S. Lond. Hosp. Wom.

HOLDSWORTH, Gillian Margaret Claire Flat 2, 12-14 Monmouth Road, London W2 5SB Tel: 020 7229 4915 — MB ChB 1984 Bristol; MSc Lond. 1996; MSc Lond. 1990. Sen. Regist. (Pub. Health Med.) S. Thames; Cons. in Pub Health Med, Lambeth, Soutwark & Lewisham Health Auth. Socs: Mem. of Fac. of Pub. Health Med. Prev: Regist. (Pub. Health Med.) S. Thames; Progr. Manager Health UnLtd. Lond.; Overseas Developm. Admin. MoH Lesotho.

HOLDSWORTH, Jacqueline Ann 6 Telford Drive, Walton-on-Thames KT12 2YH Tel: 01932 253534 — MB BS 1983 Lond.; MRCGP 1987; DRCOG 1986; DCH RCP Lond. 1985.

HOLDSWORTH, John Derrick The Gables, Standingstine, Wigton CA7 9DP — MD 1984 Newc.; MB BS Lond. 1974; FRCS Eng. 1980. Cons. Surg. Carlisle. Prev: Cons. Surg. Wansbeck Hosp.; Sen. Regist. (Surg.) Newc. HA; Demonst. Anat. Leeds Univ. Med.

HOLDSWORTH, Jonathan Edward Gloucester Road Medical Centre, Tramway House, 1A Church Road, Horfield, Bristol BS7 8SA Tel: 0117 949 7774 Fax: 0117 949 7730; 27 Kings Avenue, Bishopston, Bristol BS7 8JL Tel: 0117 924 3616 — MB ChB 1990 Sheff.; DRCOG 1993; MRCGP 1996. Princip. Gen. Pract.

HOLDSWORTH, Mr Peter John Huddersfield Royal Infirmary, Acre St., Lindley, Huddersfield HD3 3EA — MB ChB 1980 Leeds; ChM Leeds 1993; FRCS Eng. 1985; FRCS Ed. 1984. Cons. Gen. Surg. Huddersfield Roy. Infirm.; Hon. Sen. Clin. Lect. Univ. Leeds.

HOLDSWORTH, Mr Richard Jeremy The Old Library, 6 Henderson Place, Dollar FK14 7EZ Tel: 01259 743186 Email: r.holdsworth@virgin.net — MB ChB 1981 Sheff.; MD Sheff. 1990; FRCS Ed. 1986. Cons. Vasc. Surg. Stirling Roy. Infirm. Socs: Surg. Research Soc.; Vasc. Surgic. Soc. GB & Irel. Prev: Sen. Regist., Regist. & Research Fell. (Surg.) Ninewells Hosp. Dundee.

HOLDSWORTH, Richard Killingbeck Whitehall Medical Practice, Lower Hilmorton Road, Rugby CV21 3AQ Tel: 01788 544264; 14 Sidney Road, Rugby CV22 5LB — BM BCh Oxf. 1964. (Oxf.) p/t Gen. Med. Pract.; Med. Adviser Coventry Univ. Socs: (Ex-Pres.) Brit. Assn. Health Servs. in Higher Educat.; Eur. Union of Sch. & Univ. Health & Med. Prev: Hosp. Pract. (Psychiat.) St. Cross Hosp. Rugby.

HOLDSWORTH, Sheila Nantwich Health Centre, Beam Street, Nantwich CW5 5NX Tel: 01270 610181 Fax: 01270 610511; Holly Lodge, 7 Audlem Road, Woore, Crewe CW3 9RJ Tel: 01630 647243 — MB ChB 1966 St. And. (St. And.) GP Trainer Nantwich VTS. Socs: Assoc. Mem. RCGP; BMA. Prev: Asst. Med. Off. Matern. & Child Welf. Stoke-on-Trent Pub. Health Dept.

HOLDSWORTH, Ursula Jean 32 Victoria Crescent, Sherwood, Nottingham NG5 4DA Tel: 0115 960 4142 Fax: 0115 960 4142; Nottingham Community Health NHS Trust, Carlton Clinic, 61 Burton Road, Carlton, Nottingham NG4 3DQ Tel: 0115 961 7616 Fax: 0115 961 3268 — MRCS Eng. LRCP Lond. 1976; BSc (Hons.) Lond. 1972. (Guy's) Staff Grade Community Paediat. Nott. Community Health NHS Trust. Socs: Assoc. Mem. Roy. Coll. Paediat. & Child Health; Brit. Assn. Community Child Health.

HOLDSWORTH, Mr William Goldthorpe 47 Angler's Reach, Grove Road, Surbiton KT6 4EX Tel: 020 8399 2766 — MB BS 1933 Melbourne; FRCS Ed. 1943; FRCS Eng. 1943. Emerit. Cons. (Plastic Surg.) St. Thos. Hosp. Lond. & W.m. Hosp. Lond.

HOLE, John Gregory Adcroft Surgery, Prospect Place, Trowbridge BA14 8QA Tel: 01225 755878 Fax: 01225 775445; 8 Budbury Ridge, Bradford-on-Avon BA15 1QP Tel: 01225 862769 — MB BS 1978 Lond. (St. Bart.)

HOLE, Mr Roger (retired) Wynd House, Hutton Rudby, Yarm TS15 0ES — MB 1957 Camb.; BChir 1956; FRCS Ed. 1960; FRCS Eng. 1964. Prev: Cons. Urol. S. Teeside & Darlington Health Dists.

HOLE, Sheila Georgina The Health Centre, Kings Road, Horley RH6 7DG Tel: 01293 772686 Fax: 01293 823950 — MB ChB 1976 Glas.

HOLEHOUSE, Geoffrey Douglas Thurston St Johns House Surgery, 28 Bromyard Road, St. Johns, Worcester WR2 5BU Tel: 01905 423612 Fax: 01905 740003 — MB BS 1971 Lond.; DObst RCOG 1974. (Univ. Coll. Hosp.) Socs: BMA. Prev: SHO (Paediat.) Worcester Roy. Infirm.; SHO (O & G) & Ho. Surg. Edgware Gen. Hosp.

HOLEMANS, John Alan Radiology Department, The Cardiothoracic Centre - Liverpool, Thomas Drive, Liverpool L14 3PE Tel: 0151 228 1616 Fax: 0151 293 2267 Email: johnholemans@ccl-tr.nwrst.nhs.uk; 2 South Bank, Oxton, Prenton CH43 5UP Tel: 020 8652 5150 Email: john@jaholemans.freeuk.com — MB BS 1989 Lond.; BSc (Hons.) Physiol. Lond. 1986; MRCP (UK) 1992; FRCR 1995. (Char. Cross & Westm.) Cons. Radiol. The Cardiothoracic Centre - Liverp. NHS Trust & Roy. Liverp. Univ. Hosp. Trust; Teach. Univ. of Liverp. Dept. of Med. Imaging. Socs: Eur. Congr. Radiol.; Amer. Rontgen Ray Soc.; UK Assn. of Chest Radiol. Prev: Sen. Regist. (Diag. Radiol.) Guy's & St. Thos. Hosp. NHS Trust Lond.; Regist. (Diag. Radiol.) Guy's Hosp. Lond.

HOLESH, Shura Alexandra 31 Princes Court, London SW3 1ES Tel: 020 7589 8624 — MB ChB 1944 Cape Town; FRCR 1975; FFR 1954; DMRD Lond 1951. Emerit. Cons. Radiol. Cromwell Hosp. Lond. Socs: Fell. Roy. Soc. Med.; Brit. Med. Ultrasound Soc.; Eur. Soc. Paediat. Radiol. Prev: Cons. Radiol. Kingston Hosp. Gp.; Sen. Regist. Diag. Radiol. Dept. W.m. Hosp. Lond.

HOLFORD, Mr Charles Peregrine Milton Keynes General Hospital, Standing Way, Eaglestone, Milton Keynes MK6 5LD; The Manor House, Bourne End, Cranfield, Bedford MK43 0AX — MRCS Eng. LRCP Lond. 1968; MS Lond. 1982, MB BS 1968; FRCS Eng. 1974. (St. Geo.) Cons. Surg. Milton Keynes Dist. Hosp. Prev: Lect. Surg. Profess. Unit & Hon. Sen. Regist. Char. Cross Hosp. Lond.; Sen. Surg. Regist. King Edwd. VII Memor. Hosp. Windsor; Surg. Regist. Hillingdon Hosp. Uxbridge.

HOLFORD, Lewis Charles Somerset Cottage, Otby Lane, Walesby, Market Rasen LN8 3UT — MB ChB 1995 Bristol.

HOLFORD, Stanley Arthur (retired) 13 Comilla Court, 17 The Avenue, Branksome Park, Poole BH13 6HD Tel: 01202 761988 — MRCS Eng. LRCP Lond. 1924; LDS RCS Eng. 1922. Consg. Dent. Surg. SS. John & Eliz. Hosp. St. John's Wood.

HOLGATE, Clive Schofield 2 St Margaret's Drive, Leeds LS8 1RU — MB ChB 1978 Leeds; BSc (Hons.) Leeds 1975, MB ChB 1978; MRCPath 1986. Lect. (Path.) Leeds Univ.

HOLGATE, Gail Parnell Oak Street Surgery, Oak Street, Cwmbran NP44 3LT Tel: 01633 866719 Fax: 01633 838208 — MB BCh 1978 Wales.

HOLGATE, Harold Woodlands, Stoke Park Avenue, Farnham Royal, Slough SL2 3BJ Tel: 01753 643279 — MB ChB 1951 Manch.; BSc Manch. 1940, MB ChB 1951; Dip. Biochem. Anal. 1943; Pharm. Chem. 1940. (Manch.) Socs: Fell. Roy Soc. Med.; Fell. Roy. Pharm. Soc. Prev: Demonst. Pharm. Chem. & Res. Tutor Dalton Hall Univ. Manch.

HOLGATE, John Aitken (retired) 3 The Fairway, Upper Chobham Road, Camberley GU15 1EF — MB ChB 1947 Leeds; MB ChB (1st cl. Hons.) Leeds 1947; MSc Leeds 1953. Prev: PMO DHSS.

HOLGATE, Nigel John Isca General Practice Unit, Cadoc House, High Street, Caerleon, Newport NP18 1AZ Tel: 01633 423886 Fax: 01633 430153 — MB BCh 1978 Wales; MRCP Lond. 1981. Gen. Practitioner (Principle).

HOLGATE, Paul Frederick Lund (retired) Beal Grange, Thornton Le St., Thirsk YO7 4DZ Tel: 01845 525370 — MB ChB 1967 Manch.; FRCP Lond. 1986, M 1973. Hon. Cons. Phys. Friarage Hosp. N. Allerton. Prev: Squadron Ldr. (Sen. Specialist Med.) RAF Med. Br.

HOLGATE, Paul Warren Queen's Hospital NHS Trust, Belvedere, Burton-on-Trent DE13 0RB Tel: 01283 511511; 4 Poplar Row, Darley Abbey, Derby DE22 1DU — BM BS 1989 Nottm.; BMedSci Nottm. 1987; FRCA Lond.

HOLGATE, Richard Stanley (retired) 26 Meadows Avenue, Thornton-Cleveleys FY5 2TS Tel: 01253 855977 — MB ChB 1938 Liverp.; BA (Hons.) Open 1980.

HOLGATE, Simon Keith High Street Family Practice, 37-39 High Street, Barry CF62 7EB Tel: 01446 733355 Fax: 01446 733489; 2 Castlewwod Cottages, Highwalls Road, Dinas Powys, Cardiff CF64 4AN Tel: 01222 512759 — MB BCh 1976 Wales. (Welsh National School of Medicine)

HOLGATE, Stephen Fairhurst House, Whalley Old Road, Billington, Clitheroe BB7 9LF — MB ChB 1977 Liverp.; FFA RCS Eng. 1983. Cons. Anaesth. Blackburn Roy. Infirm.

HOLGATE, Professor Stephen Townley Medical specialities Mailpoint 810 Level 1 Centre Block, Southampton General Hospital, Tremona Road, Southampton SO16 6YD Tel: 02380 796960 Fax: 02380 701771 — MB BS 1971 Lond.; BSc (1st cl. Hons. Biochem.) Lond. 1969, DSc 1992, MD 1979; FRCP Ed. 1995; FRCP Lond. 1984; MRCP (UK) 1973; CBiol, FIBiol 1999; FRCPath 1999; MBBS 1998; MBBS 1998. (Char. Cross) MRC Clin. Prof. Immunopharmacol. & Hon. Cons. Phys. Soton. Gen. Hosp. Roy.Bournemouth Hosps.; Assoc. Research & Developm. Dir. S. & W. RHA; Dorothy Temple Cross MRC Trav. Research Fell.sh.; Co-Edr. Clin. & Experim. Allergy; Sec. Thoracic Med. Comm. RCP; Philip Ellman Lect. RCP. Socs: Assn. Phys.; Amer. Thoracic Soc.; Brit. Thorac. Soc. Prev: Reader & Prof. (Med.) Soton. Gen. Hosp.; Vis. Scientist Harvard Med. Sch.

HOLIAN, Annette Coralie Children's Orthopaedic Unit, Robers Jones & Agnes Hunt Orthopaedic & District Hospital, Gobowen, Oswestry SY10 7AG Tel: 01691 655311 — MB BS 1981 Monash; FRACS 1990.

HOLIDAY, John Edward (retired) Leven House, High Spen, Rowlands Gill NE39 2BQ — MB ChB 1955 Aberd.; DA Eng. 1969. Hosp. Pract. (Anaesth.) Gateshead AHA. Prev: Med. Off. (Anaesth.) Newc. City Auth.

HOLKAR, Sandya Samantha 103 Goldstone Road, Hove BN3 3RG — BM 1993 Soton.

HOLKAR, Vasant Eaknath BUPA Hartswood Hospital, Warley Road, Brentwood CM13 3LE Tel: 01277 232525 Fax: 01277 200128; 2 Marden Ash Mews, Marden Ash, Stanford Rivers Road, Ongar CM5 9BT Tel: 01277 364395 — MB BS Bombay 1953; FFAEM 1993. Socs: Sen. Fell. BOA; Fell. Brit. Assn. Accid. & Emerg. Med.; Fell. Roy. Soc. Med. Prev: Cons. A & E Centre OldCh. Hosp. Romford.

HOLL, Cordelia Elizabeth Kidderminster General Hospital, Bewdley Road, Kidderminster DY11 6RJ; 56 Brindle Court, North Park Road, Erdington, Birmingham B23 7YQ Tel: 0121 356 1984 — MB ChB 1998 Dund.; MB ChB Dund 1998.

HOLL, Sally Gordon Burnham Medical Centre, Love Lane, Burnham-on-Sea TA8 1EU Tel: 01278 795445 Fax: 01278 793024; Somerdale, Burton Row, Brent Knoll, Highbridge TA9 4BW — MB BS 1978 Lond.

HOLL-ALLEN, Mr Robert Thomas James 1 Avenbury Drive, Solihull B91 2QZ Tel: 0121 704 4488 Fax: 0121 704 4488 — MB BS 1959 Lond.; MB BS (Hons. Obst. & Gyn.) Lond. 1959; BSc (Physiol., Hons.) Lond. 1956, MD 1972, MS 1971; FRCS Eng. 1963; MRCS Eng. LRCP Lond. 1959; FACS 1974; FICS 1973; DLO Eng. 1963. (Univ. Coll. Hosp.) Hon. Clin. Lect., Solihull.; Sen. Clin. Lect. Univ. Birm. Socs: Fell. Assn. Surgs.; Internat. Assn. Endocrine Surgs.; NY Acad. Sci. Prev: Cons. Surg. Birm. Heartlands & Solihull Hosps.; Peel Med. Trav. Fell. 1968-9; Research Fell. Harvard Med. Sch. & Peter Bent Brigham Hosp. Boston, USA.

HOLLAMBY, Mr Robert George Total Healthcare Solutions, Suites 6 & 7, 108 Point Pleasant, London SW18 1PP Tel: 020 8877 9876; 18 Beverley Gardens, Barnes, London SW13 0LX Tel: 020 8878 1116 — MB ChB Leeds 1983; FRCS Ed. 1988.

HOLLAND, Anthea (retired) Beggars Roost, Pool Hill, Newent, Gloucester GL18 1LL Tel: 01531 822024 — MB BS 1972 Lond.; BSc (Hons.) Lond. 1969, MB BS (Hons.) 1972; MRCP (UK) 1977; DCH Eng. 1976. Prev: GP Blakeney, Glos.

HOLLAND, Anthony John Section Developmental Psychiatry, 2nd Floor, Douglas House, 18B Trumpington Road, Cambridge CB2 2AH Tel: 01223 354978 Fax: 01223 324661; Orchard House, Station Road, Fulbourn, Cambridge CB3 8QU — MB BS 1973 Lond.; MPhil. Lond. 1987, BSc 1970, MB BS 1973; MRCP (UK) 1976; MRCPsych 1980. Univ. Lect. (Learning Disabil.) Camb.

HOLLAND, Barbara Mary Queen Mothers' Hospital, Dalnair St., Glasgow G3 8SH — MB BCh BAO 1969 NUI; FRCP Glas. 1988; MRCP (UK) 1973.

HOLLAND, Catherine Mary 18 Speedwell Close, Cambridge CB1 9YZ — BM BS 1992 Nottm.; BMedSci Nottm. 1990. SHO (O & G) Nottm. City Hosp. Prev: SHO (O & G) Derby City Hosp.; Ho. Off. (Med.) King's Mill Hosp. Mansfield; Ho. Off. (Surg.) Blackpool Vict. Hosp.

HOLLAND, Christopher David Sunderland Royal Hospital, Kayll Road, Sunderland SR4 7TP Tel: 0191 565 6256 Fax: 0191 569 9205; 24 Osbaldeston Gardens, Gosforth, Newcastle upon Tyne NE3 4JE — MB ChB 1972 Bristol; FRCP Lond. 1991; FRCP Ed. 1988; MRCP (UK) 1976. Cons. Rheum. Dist. Gen. Hosp. Sunderland.; Hon. Clin. Lect. (Med.) Newc. Univ. Socs: Brit. Soc. Rheum. Prev: Sen. Regist. (Rheum.) Manch.; Regist. (Med.) Torbay; SHO Rotat. (Med.) Bristol.

HOLLAND, Christopher George Causeway HSST, Mountsandal Road, Coleraine BT52 1JA; 5a St Patricks Avenue, Coleraine BT52 1HZ — MB BCh BAO Belf. 1997. SHO Gen. Med.

HOLLAND, Christopher John 12 Belton Close, Hockley Heath, Solihull B94 6QU — MB ChB 1989 Birm.; ChB Birm. 1989.

HOLLAND, Christopher John Stanley 16B Calton Hill, Edinburgh EH1 3BJ Tel: 0131 557 4285 Fax: 0131 557 4285; 213 Braid Road, Edinburgh EH10 6NY Tel: 0131 466 1714 Fax: 0131 466 1714 — MB ChB 1965 Ed.; BA (Nat. Sc. Trip.) Camb. 1962; MRCPsych 1974; DPM Ed. 1970. Psychoanalyst Edin.; Train. Analyst SIHR; Mem. Scott. Inst. Human Relations. Socs: Assoc. Mem. Brit. Psychoanalyt. Soc. Prev: Psychiat. i/c (Child Psychiat.) High Wick Hosp. St. Albans; Sen. Regist. (Child Psychiat.) Tavistock & Watford Clinics; Sen. Regist. (Ment. Handicap & Psychiat.) Gogarburn & Roy. Edin. Hosp.

HOLLAND, Clare Rhiannon The Pheasants, Winthill, Cradley, Malvern WR13 5NR; Pen y Banc House, 58 Gowerton Road, Three Crosses, Swansea SA4 3PX — MB BS 1992 Lond.; MRCGP 1998; DCH RCP Lond. 1997; DFFP 1996; DRCOG 1995. (Roy. Lond. Hosp. Med. Sch.) GP Princip. The Gower Med. Pract., Mt.sland Rd., Scurlage, Gower, Swansea; Pen y Banc Ho., 58 Gowerton Rd., Three Crosses, Swansea SA4 3PX. Tel: 01792 874124.

HOLLAND, Coryn Elka Trengweath Hospital, Penryn St, Redruth TR15 2SP; 7 Crown Close, Newquay TR7 2TR — MB BS 1987 Lond.; BSc (Hons.) Lond. 1984; MRCGP 1993. Clin. Asst., Subst. Misuse, Trewgweath Hosp., Redruth. Prev: GP Padstow, Cornw.; SHO (Psychiat.) St. Lawrence Hosp. Bodmin.

HOLLAND, David Douglas Blackwell Medical Centre, 6 Gloves Lane, Blackwell, Alfreton DE55 5JJ Tel: 01773 510065 Fax: 01773 563066; 95 Heanor Road, Smalley, Ilkeston, Derby DE7 6DX Tel: 01773 714016 — MB ChB 1973 Sheff.; MRCGP 1978; DRCOG 1977. (Sheffield) Prev: Trainee GP Sheff. VTS.; Ho. Phys. N.. Gen. Hosp. Sheff.; Ho. Surg. Doncaster Roy. Infirm.

HOLLAND, David Edward 11 Apsley Road, Clifton, Bristol BS8 2SH Tel: 0117 973 1411 — MB BS 1978 (Hons) Newc.; BMedSc (1st cl. Hons.) Newc. 1976, MB BS (Hons.) 1978; MRCP Ed. 1980; FFA RCS Eng. 1985. Cons. Intens. Care & Anaesth. S.mead Hosp. Bristol. Socs: Anaesth. Research Soc.; IC Soc. Prev: Regist. (Med.) Freeman Hosp. Newc.; Ho. Surg. & Ho. Phys. Roy. Vict. Infirm. Newc.

HOLLAND, Edwin Francis Nigel Warrington NHS Trust, Lovely Lane, Warrington WA5 1QG Tel: 01925 635911; Stretton Old School, Stretton Road, Stretton, Warrington WA4 4NT Tel: 01925 730787 Fax: 01925 730106 Email: efnholland@caraling.fsnet.co.uk — MB ChB 1984 Liverp.; FRCOG 2001; MD Liverp. 1994; MRCOG 1989; Dip. Venereol. Liverp. 1987. (Univ. Liverp.) Cons. O & G Warrington Gen. Hosp. Prev: Sen. Regist. (O & G) Yorks. RHA.

HOLLAND, Edwin Lionel (retired) Owenreagh, 24 Crieve Road, Newry BT34 2JT Tel: 028302 62571 — MB BCh BAO Dub. 1956; MA Dub. 1956; FRCOG 1974, M 1961; DObst RCPI 1959. Cons. O & G S. Down Gp. Hosps. Prev: Sen. Lect. (O & G) Qu. Univ. Belf.

HOLLAND, Elizabeth Joyce c/o 12 Owler Gate, The Foldrings, Oughtibridge, Sheffield S35 0DS — MB ChB 1956 Manch.; LMCC Canada 1981. (Manch.) Socs: Fell. Manch. Med. Soc.; BMA. Prev: Med. Off. Roy. Manch. Childr. Hosp.; Ho. Off. Manch. Roy. Infirm.; Asst. Co. MOH Chesh. CC.

HOLLAND, Hans-Christian 68 Merley Gate, Morpeth NE61 2EP Tel: 01670 504023 — State Exam Med 1986 Munich; AFOM RCP Lond. 1995. (Munich) Occupat. Health Phys. Indust. & Organisational Health Newc. u. Tyne. Socs: Soc. Occupat. Med. Prev: Trainee GP Manch.

HOLLAND, Henry Tudor Bron Seiont Surgery, Bron Seiont, Segontium Terrace, Caernarfon LL55 2PH Tel: 01286 672236 Fax: 01286 676404 — MB BS 1983 Lond.; MRCGP 1989; DRCOG 1987; DGM RCP Lond. 1985.

HOLLAND, Hilary Faith Anaesthetic Department, Hinchingbrooke Hospital, Huntingdon PE29 6NT — BM BS 1983 Nottm.; BMedSci Nottm. 1981, BM BS 1983; FRCA 1992; DA (UK) 1985. Cons. Anaesth. Hinchingbrooke Health Care NHS Trust. Prev: Sen. Regist. (Anaesth.) N.ampton & Oxf.; Regist. (Anaesth.) Milton Keynes HA; SHO (Anaesth.) Nottm. HA.

HOLLAND, Ian Mackay Department of Diagnostic Imaging, University Hospital, Queen's Medical Centre, Nottingham NG7 2UH Tel: 0115 924 9924 Fax: 0115 970 9962; 21 Marlborough Road, Woodthorpe, Nottingham NG5 4FG Tel: 0115 920 3499 Fax: 0115 920 3499 Email: ian@summerrose.freeserve.co.uk — MB ChB 1972 Manch.; FRCR 1979; DMRD Eng. 1977. Cons. Neuroradiol. & Dep. Med. Dir., Univ. Hosp. QMC Nottm.; Clin. Teach. Univ. Nottm.; Sec. Univ. Hosp. Ethics Comm.; Surveyor Health Serv. Quality; Mem. Trent MREC. Socs: BMA; Brit. Soc. Neuroradiol.; Eur. Soc. Neuroradiol. Prev: Cons. Neuroradiol. Leeds & Wakefield; Sen. Regist. (Neuroradiol.) Nat. Hosps. Nerv. Dis. Lond.; Sen. Regist. (Radiol.) Hammersmith Hosp. Roy. Postgrad. Med. Sch. Lond.

HOLLAND, Ian Stuart 79 Meldon Terrace, Heaton, Newcastle upon Tyne NE6 5XQ — MB BS 1993 Newc.; BDS 1985.

HOLLAND, Irene Frances (retired) Owenreagh, Crieve Road, Newry BT34 2JT — MB BCh BAO 1957 Dub.; BA Dub. 1957. Prev: SHO (Surg.) & Ho. Off. Lurgan & Portadown Hosps.

HOLLAND, Jacqueline Anne 7 Finney Terrace, Durham DH1 1RT — MB ChB 1989 Aberd.

HOLLAND, James 21 Lomond View, Symington, Kilmarnock KA1 5QS — MB ChB 1990 Glas.; MRCP (UK) 1995; MRCPCH. (Glas.) SHO (Med. Paediat. & Geriat.) Glas.

HOLLAND, Mr James Patrick Freeman Hospital, Newcastle upon Tyne NE7 7DN — MB ChB 1986 Birm.; FRCS Eng. 1991; FRCS (Orth.) 1996. Cons. (Orthop. & Trauma).

HOLLAND, Jane Elizabeth 68 Worsley Road, Worsley, Manchester M28 2SN; 22 Kempnough Hall Road, Worsley, Manchester M28 2GN Tel: 0161 703 8466 — MB ChB 1983 Manch.; BSc St. And. 1980; MRCGP 1988; DRCOG 1988; DCH RCP Lond. 1987. GP Manch. Prev: GP Sheff.

HOLLAND, Janice Kidsgrove Medical Centre, Mount Road, Kidsgrove, Stoke-on-Trent ST7 4AY Tel: 01782 784221 Fax: 01782 781703 — MB ChB 1978 Birm.

HOLLAND, Jayne Louise George Street Surgery, City Walls Medical Centre, St Martin's Way, Chester CH1 2NR Tel: 01244 357800 — MB ChB 1992 Birm.; MRCGP 1996; DFFP 1996; DRCOG 1995. (Birm.) GP. Socs: Med. Protec. Soc.; BMA. Prev: Trainee GP King's Norton; SHO (Paediat.) Birm. Childr. Hosp.

HOLLAND, Jennifer Jane Freeman Hospital, High Heaton, Newcastle upon Tyne NE7 7DN Tel: 0191 284 3111 Fax: 0191 213 1968; 68 Merley Gate, Morpeth NE61 2EP — MB ChB 1983 Manch.; FRCA. 1992; DA (UK) 1988; DCH RCP Lond. 1987. (Manch.) Cons. Anaesth. Freeman Hosp. Socs: Assn. Anaesth.; MDU; BMA. Prev: Sen. Regist. (Anaesth.) Wansbeck Hosp.; Sen. Regist. (Anaesth.) Roy. Vict. Infirm.

HOLLAND, John Walter (retired) 9 Park Road, Ketton, Stamford PE9 3SL Tel: 01780 720359 Fax: 01780 720359 — MB BS Lond. 1963; MRCS Eng. LRCP Lond. 1963. Prev: Course Organiser P'boro. VTS.

HOLLAND, John William 31 Teilo Street, Cardiff CF11 9JN — MB BCh 1994 Wales.

HOLLAND, Judith Anne (retired) 171 Croft Road, Swindon SN1 4DS Tel: 01793 514909 — MB ChB 1975 Ed.; BMedSc 1972. Clin. Asst. (Traum. & Orthop. Surg.) P.ss Margt. Hosp. Swindon.

HOLLAND, Mark Edward Homerton Hospital, Homerton Row, London E9 6SR; 10 Bryants Close, Shillington, Hitchin SG5 3PH — MB BS 1988 Lond.; MRCP (UK) 1993. Sen. Regist. (Gen. Internal Med.) Homerton Hosp. Lond. Socs: Brit. Geriat. Soc. Prev: Sen. Regist. (c/o Elderly & Gen. Internal Med.) Mile End. Hosp. Lond.; Research Regist. (Cardiol.) Luton & Dunstable Hosp.; Regist. (Gen. Med.) Roy. Preston Hosp.

HOLLAND, Mark James 11 Marine Crescent, Waterloo, Liverpool L22 8QP Tel: 0151 928 2281 Fax: 0151 474 5739; 29 Brooklands Road, Hall Green, Birmingham B28 8LA Tel: 0121 244 7849 Email: hollandmj@compuserve.com — MB BS 1993 Lond.; BSc Path. Sci. Lond. 1990, MB BS 1993. (Charing Cross and Westminster Medical School) Specialist Regist. W. Midl. Diagnostic Imaging Rotat. Prev: SHO (Infec. Dis.s & Trop. Med.) Birm. Heartlands Teachg. Hosp.; SHO (Haemato-Oncol.) Roy. Marsden; SHO (Med.) Conquest Hosp.

HOLLAND, Michael Anthony James 3 Little Crosby Road, Crosby Village, Liverpool L23 2TE Tel: 0151 924 2233 Fax: 0151 931 5063; 11 Marine Crescent, Waterloo, Liverpool L22 8QP Tel: 0151 928 2281 Fax: 0151 931 5063 — MB ChB 1962 Liverp.; DObst RCOG 1965. (Liverp.) GP Crosby. Prev: JP; Med. Off. Regional Med. Serv. DHSS.

HOLLAND, Michael William 11 Ennerdale Road, Richmond TW9 3PG Tel: 020 8940 4883 — BM BS 1994 Nottm.

HOLLAND, Patricia Anne Mary The Poplars, Hardy Barn, Shipley, Heanor DE75 7LY Tel: 01773 712552 — MB BS 1962 Lond.; MRCS Eng. LRCP Lond. 1961. (St. Bart.) Staff Grade (Surg.) Nottm. City Hosp. Socs: Fell. Roy. Soc. Med.; Nottm. M-C Soc. Prev: Clin. Asst. (Med.) Derbysh. Roy. Infirm.; Ho. Surg. & Ho. Phys. Essex Co. Hosp. Colchester.

HOLLAND, Peter X-Ray Department, Alexandra Hospital, Woodrow Drive, Redditch B98 7UB Tel: 01527 503030 Fax: 01527 512005; The Farm House, Morton Wood Farm, Abbots Morton, Worcester WR7 4LU Tel: 0831 548890 — BM 1981 Soton.; FRCR 1989; T(R) (CR) 1991. Cons. Radiol. Alexandra Hosp. Redditch. Prev: Sen. Regist. & Regist. (Radiol.) W. Midl. RHA; SHO (Med.) Dudley HA.

HOLLAND, Peter (retired) Ashen Wood House, West Tisted, Alresford SO24 0HJ Tel: 0173 088285 Fax: 01730 828383 Email: peter.holland@excite.co.uk — MB BS 1973 Lond.; MSc Lond. 1962; BPharm. (Hon.) Lond. 1957; MRCS Eng. LRCP Lond. 1965; FFPM RCP (UK) 1994. Pharmaceutical Cons Clin Research & Developm. Prev: Ho. Surg. Roy. N. Hosp. Lond.

HOLLAND, Peter Jonathon Pringle Eyre Crescent Surgery, 31 Eyre Crescent, Edinburgh EH3 5EU Tel: 0131 556 8842 Fax: 0131 557 2177 — MB ChB 1968 Ed.; MRCGP 1979; DObst RCOG 1970. (Ed.)

HOLLAND, Mr Philip Andrew 98 Causeway Head Road, Dore, Sheffield S17 3DW Tel: 0114 236 1796 Email: mrpaholl@aol.com — MB ChB 1988 Sheff.; FRCS Eng. 1992; MD 1999. (Sheff.) Lect. (Surg.) Roy. Hallamshire Hosp. Sheff.; Specialist Regist. Qu. Med. Centre, Nott. Prev: Lect. (Surg.) N.. Gen. Hosp. Sheff.; Hon. Regist. (Surg.) Withington Hosp. Manch.; SHO (Surg.) N.. Gen. Hosp. Sheff.

HOLLAND, Philip Cecil Department of Paediatrics, Clarendon Wing, Belmont Grove, The General Infirmary at Leeds, Leeds LS2 9NS Tel: 0113 243 2799; 26 North Parade, West Park, Leeds LS16 5AY Tel: 0113 274 6275 — MB BS 1973 Lond.; BSc (Hons.) Lond. 1970; FRCP Lond. 1994; MRCP (UK) 1979. Cons. Paediat. Gen. Infirm. Leeds; Hon. Sen. Lect. (Paediat., Med. & Dent.) Gen. Infirm. Leeds.

HOLLAND, Rachel Kirsten 9 Charis Avenue, Westbury on Trym, Bristol BS10 5JD — MB ChB 1995 Bristol.

HOLLAND, Richard Charles East Norfolk Health Authority, St Andrews House, Thorpe St Andrew, Norwich NR7 0HT Tel: 01603 300600; 11 Ennerdale Road, Kew, Richmond TW9 3PG Tel: 020 8940 4883 — BM BCh 1991 Oxf.; DA 1997. Specialist Regist. (Pub. Health Med.) E. Norf. Health Auth.

HOLLAND, Robert Leslie Zeneca Pharmaceuticals, Mereside Alderley Park, Macclesfield SK10 4TF Tel: 01625 515834 Fax: 01625 516904 Email: bob.holland@alderley.zeneca.com; 9 Kempton Way, Macclesfield SK10 2WB — BM BCh 1983 Oxf.; DPhil. Oxf. 1980, MA 1981; MFPM RCP (UK) 1991. (Oxf.) Head Global Project Ldr.ship Capability Med. Research & Communications Gp. Zeneca Pharmaceut. Prev: Dir. Clin. Research Upjohn Company, Brussels; Head Clin. Pharmacol. Solvay Duphar, Amsterdam; Clin. Research Phys. May & Baker Ltd. Lond.

HOLLAND, Sarah Jane 23 Burleigh Lane, Street BA16 0SH Tel: 01458 442396 — MB BCh 1990 Wales; MRCGP 1994; DFFP 1994; DRCOG 1993.

HOLLAND, Sharon Maria Ashling, 105A Hill St., Kingswood, Bristol BS15 4EZ Tel: 0117 961 6613; Brambles, Hill Road, Grayshott, Hindhead GU26 6HL Tel: 01428 605879 — BM BCh 1991 Oxf.; MRCP (UK) 1994. SHO (Anaesth.) Soton. Hosps. NHS Trust; Specialist Regist. (Anaesth.) Wessex Region (Portsmouth) Flexible Trainee. Socs: BMA; Med. Protec. Soc. Prev: SHO (Med.) Soton. Hosps. NHS Trust; SHO (ITU & Anaesth.) Portsmouth NHS Trust.

HOLLAND, Simon Oscar Miles (retired) Beggars Roost, Pool Hill, Newent GL18 1LL Tel: 01531 822024 Email:

holland@blakeney1.demon.co.uk — MB BS 1971 Lond.; DObst RCOG 1975. Prev: GP Glos.

HOLLAND, Sinclair 22 Union Street, Broughty Ferry, Dundee DD5 2AW — MB ChB 1993 Ed.; BSc (Hons.) Ed. 1991. SHO (Orthop.) CrossHo. Hosp. Kilmarnock; SHO ENT Surg. Roy. Infirm. Edin. Prev: SHO (Vasc. Surg.) Roy. Infirm. Edin.; Demonst. (Anat.) & Resid. Med. Off. Murrayfield Hosp. Edin.; Ho. Phys. Roy. Infirm. Edin.

***HOLLAND, Tamsin Mary** Catherine House, 136 Hinton Way, Great Shelford, Cambridge CB2 5AL Tel: 01223 842184 Email: tasminholland@hotmail.com; 40 Rydens Grove, Hersham, Walton-on-Thames KT12 5RU Tel: 01932 221025 — MB BS 1997 Lond.

HOLLAND, Professor Walter Werner, CBE LSE Health, London School of Economics, Aldwych, London WC2A 2AE Tel: 020 7955 6277 Fax: 020 7955 6803 Email: w.w.holland@lse.ac.uk; 11 Ennerdale Road, Kew, Richmond TW9 3PG Tel: 020 8940 4883 — MB BS (Hons.) Lond. 1954; BSc (Hons.) Lond. 1951, MD 1964; FRCP Ed. 1990; FRCP Lond. 1973, M 1971; FFPHMI (Hons.) 1993; FRCPath 1992; FFPHM 1989; FRCGP 1982, M 1978; FFCM 1974. (St. Thos.) Emerit. Prof. Pub. Health Med. Univ. Lond.; Vis. Prof. LSE Health Lond. Sch. Economics, 1998-; Fell. King's Coll. Lond. 1998-. Socs: Fell. (Ex-Pres.) Fac. Pub. Health Med.; Fell. Roy. Soc. Med.; Fell. (Hon.) (Ex-Pres.) Internat. Epidemiol. Assn. Prev: Prof. Pub. Health Med. United Med. & Dent. Sch. Lond.; Vis. Prof. Univ. Harvard & Case W.. Reserve, Austral.; Fogarty Schol.-in-Residence Nat. Inst. Health Bethesda MD, USA, 1984-85.

HOLLAND-ELLIOTT, Kevin St James' Building, 79 Oxford St., Manchester M60 1DA Tel: 0161 245 7251 Fax: 0161 245 7175; 12 West Drive, Gatley, Cheadle SK8 4JJ — MB ChB 1981 Manch.; LLB (Distinc.) Manch. 1992; LLB (Hon.) 1993; MRCGP 1986; MFOM RCP Lond. 1992; DRCOG 1984. Area Med. Adviser (N. W.) Occupat. Health Serv. The Post Office. Socs: Soc. Occupat. Med. & Roy. Soc. Med. Prev: Med. Advisor, GEC Alsthom; Princip. GP Salford; Clin. Asst. (Med. Clin.) Pk. Hosp. Davy Hulme Manch.

HOLLAND-GLADWISH, Julian Joseph Flat B1, 27 St Johns Park, Blackheath, London SE3 7TD — MB BS 1997 Lond.

HOLLAND-KEEN, Lance Barrington 35 Station Road, Healing, Grimsby DN41 7LX — MB ChB 1998 Dund.; MB ChB Dund 1998.

HOLLANDER, Rebecca 23C Huntingdon Street, London N1 1BS Tel: 020 7607 1072 Fax: 020 7607 1072 — MB BS 1993 Lond.; BSc Lond. 1990; DRCOG 1995; DCH 1996; DFFP 1997. (Royal London Hospital Medical College) Trainee GP/SHO Homerton Hosp. Lond. VTS.

HOLLANDERS, Frederick David Department Gastroenterology, Oldchurch Hospital, Romford RM7 0BE Tel: 01708 746090 Fax: 01708 708125 — MB BS 1968 Lond.; MSc Lond. 1964, BSc 1963; FRCP Lond. 1995; MRCP (UK) 1974; MRCS Eng. LRCP Lond. 1968; T(M) 1991. (Char. Cross) Cons. Phys. & Gastroenterol. OldCh. Hosp. Romford; Hon. Lect. (Med.) Roy. Lond. Hosp. Socs: Brit. Soc. Gastroenterol. Prev: Lect. (Med.) Univ. Hosp. S. Manch.

HOLLANDS, Jennifer Mary 14 Copt Elm Road, Charlton Kings, Cheltenham GL53 8AB — MB BS 1987 Lond.; MRCGP 1994.

HOLLANDS, Jeremy Jonathan de Carteret Hollands and Partners, Bridport Medical Centre, North Allington, Bridport DT6 5DU Tel: 01308 421896 Fax: 01308 421109 — MRCS Eng. LRCP Lond. 1975; DRCOG 1978. (St. Bart.) Prev: SHO (Paediat.) Roy. Berks. Hosp. Reading; Ho. Phys. (Endocrinol.) Roy. Devon & Exeter Hosp. Exeter; Ho. Surg. MusGr. Pk. Hosp. Taunton.

HOLLANDS, Mark Daniel The Medical Centre, 24-28 Lower Northam Road, Hedge End, Southampton SO30 4FQ Tel: 01489 785722 Fax: 01489 799414; 21 Cartref Close, Verwood, Wimborne BH31 6UT — BM 1988 Soton.; MRCGP 1995.

HOLLANDS, Robin Angus Bishton Manor, Albrighton, Wolverhampton WV7 3AY — MB ChB 1990 Birm.; ChB Birm. 1990.

HOLLANDS, Robin David Underwood Surgery, 139 St. Georges Road, Cheltenham GL50 3EQ Tel: 01242 580644 Fax: 01242 253519; 14 Copt Elm Road, Charlton Kings, Cheltenham GL53 8AB — MB BS 1987 Lond.; MRCGP 1992; DRCOG 1991.

HOLLE, Ian Stanley (retired) Willoughby Cottage, Patching, Worthing BN13 3XF Tel: 01903 871368 — MB BS 1951 Queensland; FRCP Ed. 1983, M 1982; FACOM 1984; FFOM RCP Lond. 1985, M 1981. Prev: Chief Med. Off. Brit. Petroleum Lond.

HOLLENBERG, Siri Block 3, Flat 1, DGH Residences, Weston Road, Stafford ST16 3RS — State Exam Med. Munchen 1989.

HOLLEY, Gillian Elizabeth Park Medical Centre, Shavington Avenue, Newton Lane, Chester CH2 3RD Tel: 01244 324136 Fax: 01244 317257; 27 Church Lane, Upton, Chester CH2 1DJ — MB BChir 1984 Camb.; MA Camb. 1986; MRCGP 1989; DRCOG 1986. Prev: Trainee GP Avon VTS; Ho. Off. (Med.) Qu. Eliz. Hosp. Kings Lynn; Ho. Off. (Surg.) Addenbrookes Hosp. Camb.

HOLLEY, Judith Mary Wallasey Village Group Practice, 50 Wallasey Village, Wallasey, Birkenhead CH45 3NL Tel: 0151 691 2088 Fax: 0151 637 0146 — BSc Lond. 1982, MB BS 1985; DCH RCP Lond. 1990; DRCOG 1989.

HOLLEY, Kenneth John Warwickshire Nuffield Hospital, Old Miverton Lane, Leamington Spa CV32 6RW Tel: 01926 436344 Fax: 01926 436334; Pine Trees, Dark Lane, Tiddington, Stratford-upon-Avon CV37 7AD Tel: 01789 266121 — MB BS (Hons. Surg.) Lond. 1958; MD Lond. 1969, BSc (Physiol.) 1955; FRCPath. 1981, M 1969. (St. Mary's) p/t Cons. Pathologist, Warks. Nuffield Hosp., Leamington Spa. Socs: Assn. Clin. Path. & Internat. Acad. Path. Prev: Sen. Regist. (Path.) St. Geo. & Roy. Marsden Hosps Lond. & Soton. Hosp. Gps.; Lect. (Morbid Anat.) Inst. Orthop. Roy. Nat. Orthop. Hosp. Lond.; Cons. Path. S. Warks. Gen. Hosps. NHS Trust Warwick.

HOLLEY, Peter James The Health Centre, Poundwell Meadow, Modbury, Ivybridge PL21 0QL; Widland Farm Cottage, Modbury, Ivybridge PL21 0SA — MB BS 1990 Lond.; MRCGP 1995; DRCOG 1995. (Univ. Coll. Lond.)

HOLLICK, Cyril Leslie (retired) 1 Honey Ditches Drive, Seaton Down Hill, Seaton EX12 2NU — MRCS Eng. LRCP Lond. 1944; LDS RCS Eng. 1937; FRCPath 1971, M 1963. Prev: Cons. Pathol. Withybush Gen. Hosp. HaverfordW..

HOLLICK, Emma Jane 30 Inkerman Road, Kentish Town, London NW5 3BT — BM BCh 1992 Oxf.; BA, BM BCh Oxf. 1992. SHO (Ophth.) Sussex Eye Hosp. Brighton.

HOLLICK, John Reginald (retired) Reynard's Close, Hall Bank, Hartington, Buxton SK17 0AT Tel: 01298 84215 — B.M., B.Ch. Oxf. 1935.

HOLLIDAY, Christopher Mason Somercotes Medical Centre, 22 Nottingham Road, Somercotes, Derby DE72 3FL; 25 Amber Heights, Ripley DE5 3SP — MB ChB 1979 Leeds; MRCGP 1984; DRCOG 1983.

HOLLIDAY, David Benjamin The Health Centre, Eastland Road, Thornbury, Bristol BS35 1DP Tel: 01454 412167; The Tynings, Oldbury Naite, Thornbury, Bristol BS35 1RH Tel: 01454 412040 — MB ChB 1961 Birm. (Birm.) Socs: Soc. Orthop. Med.; (Comm. Mem.) Brit. Med. Acupunc. Soc.; Brit. Inst. Musculoskel. Med. Prev: SHO (Obst.) Hallam Hosp. W. Bromwich; SHO (Anaesth.) Gravesend & N. Kent Hosp.; Ho. Surg. & Ho. Phys. Corbett Hosp. Stourbridge.

HOLLIDAY, Eric Eldene Surgery, Eldene Health Centre, Eldene Centre, Swindon SN3 3RZ Tel: 01793 522710 Fax: 01793 513217 — MB BS 1990 Newc.; BMedSci 1989. Trainee GP N.umbria VTS.

HOLLIDAY, George Maurice (retired) 3 Street Lane, Leeds LS8 1BW Tel: 0113 266 1033 — MB ChB 1930 Leeds; DPH 1933.

HOLLIDAY, Heather 25 Amber Heights, Ripley DE5 3SP — MB ChB 1979 Leeds; DRCOG 1981.

HOLLIDAY, Howard William Derby City General Hospital, Uttoxeter Road, Derby DE22 3NE Tel: 01332 340131 — MB BS 1973 Lond.; DM Nottm. 1983; FRCS Eng. 1978. (Guy's) Cons. Surg. Derby Hosp. Prev: Regist. (Surg.) Nottm.; Ho. Off. Surg. Pembury Hosp.; Ho. Off. Med. Lewisham Hosp.

HOLLIDAY, Joan Louise (retired) 7 The Knowe, Willaston, Neston, South Wirral CH64 1TA Tel: 0151 327 1681 — MB ChB 1947 Leeds. Prev: SCMO Wirral AHA.

HOLLIDAY, John David Penrose Doctors Surgery, Baugh House, Isle of Tiree PA77 6UN Tel: 01879 20323 Fax: 01879 220893 — MB BS 1980 Lond.; BA Camb. 1975; MRCGP 1985; DCH RCP Lond. 1984; DRCOG 1983. (King's Coll.) Princip. GP Is. of Tiree. Prev: Med. Off. Pintupi Homelands Health Serv. Kintore, Centr. Australia.

HOLLIDAY, John Robert (retired) 8 Aldwick Close, Leamington Spa CV32 6LP Tel: 01926 428132 Fax: 01926 428132 — MB ChB 1955 Birm.; DObst RCOG 1960. Prev: Gen. Practitioner (Retd.).

HOLLIDAY, Jonathan James Cornelius South Meadow Surgery, 3 Church Close, Eton, Windsor SL4 6AP Tel: 01753 833777 Fax:

01753 833689; The Coach House, Kings Road, Windsor SL4 2AS Tel: 01753 865203 — MB BS 1980 Lond.; MRCS Eng. LRCP Lond. 1980; MRCGP 1984; DFFP 1994; DRCOG 1985; DCH RCP Lond. 1984. (Char. Cross) Prev: SHO (Obst.) W. Middlx. Univ. Hosp.; SHO (Paediat.) Char. Cross Hosp.; SHO (Cardiol. & Gen. Med.) W. Middlx. Univ. Hosp.

HOLLIDAY, Mark Peter Department of Clinical Chemistry, Falkirk & District Royal Infirmary, Major's Loan, Falkirk FK1 5QE — MB ChB 1979 Bristol; MRCPath 1988.

HOLLIDAY, Michael Geoffrey Africa Cottage, Old Merrow St., Merrow, Guildford GU4 7BA Tel: 01483 35122 — MB BS 1975 Lond.; MRCS Eng. LRCP Lond. 1975; MFHom 1985. (Westm.) Socs: Accred. Mem. Brit. Med. Acupunc. Soc.

HOLLIDAY, Thomas Dean Stanley (retired) Netherleigh House, Eaton Road, Chester CH4 7EW Tel: 01244 675212 — MB BS 1942 Lond.; MD Lond. 1952; MRCS Eng. LRCP Lond. 1942; FRCPath 1965. Cons. Path. Chester Health Dist. Prev: Asst. Path. W. Cornw. Hosp. Gp.

HOLLIDAY-RHODES, Antony David Flat 1, 12 Park Avenue, Harrogate HG2 9BQ — MB ChB 1963 Liverp.; MRCP (UK) 1972.

HOLLIER, Geoffrey Paul Tamworth House Medical Centre, 341 Tamworth Lane, Mitcham CR4 1DL Tel: 020 8764 2666 Fax: 020 8679 3621; 20A Springfield Road, Wallington SM6 0BB Tel: 020 8647 2174 — MB BS 1978 Lond. (Char. Cross) Clin. Asst. (Diabetes) St. Geo. Hosp. Lond. Prev: SHO (Paediat. & A & E) Epsom Dist. Hosp.; SHO (Med.) Mayday Hosp. Croydon; Ho. Phys. St. Helier Hosp. Carshalton.

HOLLIER, Kevin Paul 29 South Road, Northfield, Birmingham B31 2QZ — MB ChB 1997 Bristol.

HOLLIER, Larry Harold Health Care International Ltd., Breadmore St., Clydebank G81 4DY — MD 1968 Louisiana State New Orleans.

HOLLIER, Pauline (retired) 23 Patch Lane, Bramhall, Stockport SK7 1HX Tel: 0161 439 6380 — MB ChB 1960 Birm.; DObst RCOG 1961. Prev: SCMO (Sch. Health) Mancunian Community Health NHS Trust.

HOLLIGAN, Estelle Marie The Surgery, Bellyeoman Road, Dunfermline KY12 0AE; 45 Couston Street, Dunfermline KY12 7QW Tel: 01383 723762 — MB ChB 1986 Glas.; MRCGP 1990.

HOLLIMAN, Richard Edward Department of Medical Microbiology, St George's Hospital and Medical School, Blackshaw Road, London SW17 0QT Tel: 020 8725 5673 Fax: 020 8725 5694 Email: nhollima@sgms.ac.uk; 11 Roxborough Avenue, Harrow HA1 3BT — MB BS 1981 Lond.; MSc Lond. 1986, BSc 1978, MD 1992; FRCPath 1997, M 1987. (St. Mary's) Cons. Med. Microbiol. St. Geo.'s Hosp. Lond.; Reader (Clin. Microbiol.) St. Geo. Hosp. Med. Sch. Univ. Lond. Prev: Sen. Regist. (Med. Microbiol.) Lond. Sch. Hyg. & Trop. Med. & St. Geo. Hosp. Lond.; Regist. (Med. Microbiol.) St. Geo. Hosp. Lond. & N.wick Pk. Hosp. Harrow.

HOLLIMAN, Susan Margaret Broomfield Cottage, Garfield Road, Camberley GU15 2JG Tel: 01276 25137 — MB BS 1984 Lond.; DRCOG 1989. (St. Bart.) Med. Advisor Benefits Agency Med. Serv. Lond. Prev: Trainee GP Tilehurst Reading; SHO (Anaesth. & O & G) Roy. Berks. Hosp. Reading; SHO (Paediat.) High Wycombe Gen. Hosp. Bucks.

HOLLINGDALE, Erika Elisabeth Community Health Services, 10 Chalmers Crescent, Edinburgh EH9 1TS Tel: 0131 536 0000; 7 Braid Avenue, Edinburgh EH10 4SL Tel: 0131 447 1542 — MB ChB 1961 Cape Town; DObst RCOG 1963. (Cape Town) SCMO (Community Health Serv.) Edin. Sick Childr. Hosp. NHS Trust.

HOLLINGDALE, Mr John Patrick Central Middlesex Hospital, Acton Lane, London NW10 7NS Tel: 020 8453 2416 Email: john.hollingdale@talk21.com — MB BS 1975 Lond.; FRCS Eng. 1979; MRCS Eng. LRCP Lond. 1975. (Westm.) Cons. Orthop. & Traum. Surg. Centr. Middlx. Hosp.; Hon. Sen. Lect. Char. Cross Hosp. Socs: Fell. Roy. Soc. Med.; BMA. Prev: Rotat. Sen. Regist. (Orthop.) Char. Cross Hosp. Lond.; Regist. (Orthop.) W.m. & Qu. Mary's Hosps. Lond.; Cons. Orthop. Surg. Kettering Gen. Hosp.

HOLLINGER, Mary Jemima 10 Knollwood Lurgan Road, Banbridge BT32 4PE Tel: 01820 623683 Fax: 01820 623683 — MB BCh BAO 1967 Belf.; FRCPCH 1997. (Belf.) Cons. Community Paediat. Newry & Mourne Health & Social Servs. Trust Newry. Prev: SCMO Child Health & Family Plann. Newry & Mourne Unit of Managem.

HOLLINGHURST, David 5 Peacock Close, Cams Bay, Fareham PO16 8YG — BChir 1995 Camb.

HOLLINGS, Alfred Harrison (retired) 9 The Rookery, Balsham, Cambridge CB1 6EU Tel: 01223 894299 — MRCS Eng. LRCP Lond. 1946. Prev: Ho. Surg. & Ho. Phys. Seacroft Emerg. Hosp. Leeds.

HOLLINGS, Andrew St John Yew Tree Farm, Ryton, Shrewsbury SY5 7LW Tel: 01743 73205 — MB ChB 1988 Manch.; BSc (Med.Sci) St. And. 1985; MRCGP 1993; DFFP 1994; DRACOG 1991. SHO (Anaesth.) Roy. Shrewsbury Hosp. Prev: Assoc. GP Takaka, S. Is. & Dargaville, NZ; SHO (A & E Whittington Hosp. Lond.; Trainee GP Bishops Castle, Shrops.

HOLLINGS, Anne Marie Shadbolt Park House, Salisbury Road, Worcester Park KT4 7BX Tel: 020 8337 3966 Fax: 020 8330 1928; Kimberley, 42 Grays Lane, Ashtead KT21 1BU Tel: 01372 273157 Fax: 01372 273157 Email: hollings@compuserve.com — MB ChB 1977 Manch. Audit Adviser E. Surrey HA.

HOLLINGS, Nicholas Paul The Paper Mill, Little Longnor, Shrewsbury SY5 7QF — MB BS 1991 Lond.; BSc (Hons. Chem. Path.) Lond. 1988; MRCP (UK) 1995; FRCR(I) 1996; FRCR II 1998. (St. Mary's)

HOLLINGSBEE, Edwin Reed 5 St Andrews Way, Tilmanstone, Deal CT14 0JH Tel: 0797 128 2712 Email: ecl@buzz174.freeserve.co.uk — MB ChB 1997 Bristol. (Bristol) GP Regist.Yeovil Som. Prev: SHO (A & E) Lincs.

HOLLINGSHEAD, John Fletcher Hollingshead, Brough, Waddington, Collins, Cave, Adler, Peters, Blandt, Newman & Rogan, Holmwood Health Centre, Franklin Avenue, Tadley RG26 4ER Tel: 01189 814166 Fax: 0118 811432; The Merse, Baughurst, Tadley RG26 5LP Tel: 01189 812976 — MB BChir Camb. 1968; MA Camb. 1968; MRCGP 1971; DObst RCOG 1969. (St. Bart.) Prev: GP Clin. Asst. St. Bart. Hosp. Lond.; SHO (Obst.) Roy. Berks. Hosp. Reading; Ho. Phys. Med. Profess. Unit St. Bart. Hosp.

HOLLINGSHEAD, Sheila Bodey Medical Centre, 363 Wilmslow Road, Fallowfield, Manchester M14 6XU Tel: 0161 248 6644 Fax: 0161 224 4228 — MB BChir 1970 Camb.; MA, MB Camb. 1970, BChir 1969. (Camb.)

HOLLINGSHURST, Grahame Gary (retired) Larkrise, Holmes Marsh, Lyonshall, Kington HR5 3JS Tel: 01544 340788 — MB BS Lond. 1963; DObst RCOG 1966. Prev: SHO (Cas.) Char. Cross Hosp. Lond.

HOLLINGSWORTH, Charles William (retired) 17 Mellish Road, Walsall WS4 2DQ Tel: 01922 625077 — MB BChir Camb. 1947. Prev: Hosp. Pract. (Dermat.) Walsall Manor Hosp.

HOLLINGSWORTH, Mr John David Kenneth Dyserth Hall, Dyserth, Rhyl LL18 6BW Tel: 01745 571386 — MB ChB 1991 Manch.; FRCS Ed. 1996. Specialist Regist. (A & E) Mersey Region. Prev: Regist. (A & E) Wythenshawe Hosp. Manch.; SHO (Gen. Med.) Wythenshawe Hosp. Manch.; SHO (A & E) Wythenshawe Hosp. Manch. & Countess of Chester.

HOLLINGSWORTH, Mr Robert Philip St Peters Hospital, Guildford Rd, Chertsey KT16 0PZ Tel: 01932 872 0000 Fax: 01932 872015 — MB BS 1963 Lond.; FRCS Eng. 1970; FRCS Ed. 1969; MRCS Eng. LRCP Lond. 1963. (Guy's) Cons. Orthop. Surg. Ashford & St.Peter's Hosp. NHS Trust; Med. Dir. Ashford & St. Peter's Hosp. Chertsey. Socs: Fell. BOA; BMA. Prev: Sen. Regist. (Orthop.) St. Geo. Hosp. & SW Thames Regional Orthop. Traine. Scheme; Regist. (Surg.) Roy. Hosp. Wolverhampton.

HOLLINGTON, Angela Marjorie Kingsway Medical Centre, 23 Kingsway, Narborough Road South, Leicester LE3 2JN Tel: 0116 289 5081 Fax: 0116 263 0145; East Leigh, Forest Drive, Kirby Muxloe, Leicester LE9 2EA Tel: 0116 289 5081 Fax: 0116 263 0195 — MB ChB 1977 Manch.; MRCGP 1982; DRCOG 1982. Dep. Police Surg. Leics. Police Force.

HOLLINGTON, Caroline Elizabeth 7 Britton Close, London SE6 1AP — MB ChB 1995 Aberd.

HOLLINGWORTH, Allen Vickers (retired) East Clock Lodge, Gordon TD3 6LY Tel: 01578 740254 — MB ChB Birm. 1954; MRCS Eng. LRCP Lond. 1954; MRCGP 1970. Prev: Sen. Med. Off. DSS.

HOLLINGWORTH, Mr Antony Arthur Department of Obstetrics & Gynaecology, University Hospital, Nottingham NG5 1PB; 101 Arnold Road, Basford, Nottingham NG5 1NG Tel: 0115 960 8008 — MB ChB 1977 Manch.; PhD Univ. Lond. 1991; FRCS Ed. 1982; MRCOG

1986; DHMSA 1988. Sen. Regist. (O & G) Nottm. Hosps. Prev: Clin. Research Fell. Imperial Cancer Research Fund Lond.; Regist. (O & G) Nat. Wom. Hosp. Auckland, NZ; SHO (Obst.) City Hosp. Nottm.

HOLLINGWORTH, Barbara Alicia The Margaret Pyke Centre, 73 Charlotte Street, London W1T 4PL Tel: 020 77530 3600 Fax: 020 7530 3646; 125 Princes Avenue, Watford WD18 7SQ Tel: 01923 254761 Fax: 01923 816065 Email: 100757.2664@compuserve.com — MB ChB 1977 Liverp.; MFFP 1993; DRCOG 1984. SCMO & Instruc. Doctor Family Plann. Margt. Pyke Centre Lond.; Clin. Asst. (Colposcopy) Luton & Dunstable Hosp.

HOLLINGWORTH, Hugh Caudwell The Manor Surgery, Chapel St., Redruth TR15 2BY Tel: 01209 212223 — MRCS Eng. LRCP Lond. 1957; MA Camb. 1958, MB BChir 1957; DObst RCOG 1959. (Camb. & Guy's) Fell. Assn. Certifying Fact. Surgs. Inc. Socs: BMA. Prev: Med. Miss. Ituk Mbang Hosp.; E. Nigeria; Obst. Ho. Surg. Marston Green Matern. Hosp. Birm.; Ho. Phys. S.. Gen. Hosp. Dartford.

HOLLINGWORTH, James Queens Hospital, Barton-on-Trent, Belvedere Rd DE13 0RB Tel: 01283 566333 Fax: 01283 593006 Email: james.hollingworth@btinternet.com; The Old Post Office, 2a Church Lane, Ticknall DE73 0RB Tel: 01332 865206 Fax: 01332 865206 Email: james.hollingworth@btinternet.com — MD 1994 Leicester; MB ChB Liverp. 1985; FRCS Eng. 1990; FRCS Ed. 1989; MRCOG 1997. Cons. Gynaecologist and Obst. with s/i in Gyn. Oncol. Socs: Brit. Cociety for Colposcopy and Genital Path. Prev: Specialist Regist. Leicester Train. Scheme.

HOLLINGWORTH, Kay Michelle 237 Oldfield Road, Stannington, Sheffield S6 6EA — MB ChB 1998 Leic.; MB ChB Leic 1998.

HOLLINGWORTH, Margaret Severn NHS Trust, Rikenel, Mount Pelner, Gloucester GL1 1LY — MB ChB 1978 Bristol; DRCOG 1981; Cert. Family Plann. JCC 1981; Vt GP cert 1983. Clin. Med. Off. Commun. Paediat. Severn NHS Trust. Gloucs. Prev: Princip. GP.

HOLLINGWORTH, Peter 14 Hope Square, Clifton, Bristol BS8 4LX Tel: 0117 930 0828 — MB ChB Bristol 1969; FRCP Lond. 1990; MRCP (UK) 1973. (Bristol) Cons. Rheum. S.mead Hosp. Bristol. Socs: Brit. Soc. Rheum.; Brit. Paediat. Assn. Rheum. Gp. Prev: Cons. Phys. Qu. Eliz. Hosp. Barbados; Sen. Regist. (Rheumat.) Char. Cross & W.m. Hosps. Lond.; Scientif. Off. Clin. Res. Centre Harrow, Middlx.

HOLLINGWORTH, Rebecca 12 Belle Gr W., Newcastle upon Tyne NE2 4LT — MB BS 1997 Newc.

HOLLINGWORTH, Terence 26 Norman Road, Northfield, Birmingham B31 2EW — MB ChB 1965 Birm.

HOLLINRAKE, Alan (retired) Bacton Grange, Bacton, Stowmarket IP14 4LE — MRCS Eng. LRCP Lond. 1932. Prev: Ho. Surg. Hounslow Hosp.

HOLLINRAKE, Michael Stuart Brighton Witton Street Surgery, 162 Witton Street, Northwich CW9 5QU Tel: 01606 42007 Fax: 01606 350659 — MB BCh BAO 1969 NUI; MB BCh BAO NUI 1969.; DObst RCOG 1971. Prev: SHO (Obst.) Birch Hill Hosp. Rochdale; Ho. Surg. Rochdale Infirm.; SHO (Path.) Withington Hosp. Manch.

HOLLINRAKE, Patricia Una 78 Forsyth Road, Newcastle upon Tyne NE2 3EU — MB BS 1998 Newc.; MB BS Newc 1998.

HOLLINS, Beren Jude 29 Westbourne Park, Scarborough YO12 4AS — MB ChB 1994 Dundee.

HOLLINS, Mr Graham William Department of Urology, The Ayr Hospital, Dalmellington Road, Ayr KA6 6DX Tel: 01292 615000 Fax: 01292 265265 Email: grahame.hollins@talk21.com; Essex Dene, 17 Greenfield Avenue, Alloway, Ayr KA7 4NW Tel: 01292 441249 Email: grahame.hollins@talk21.com — MB ChB 1987 Aberd.; MSc Lond. 1983; BSc (Hons.) Aberd. 1982; FRCS (Urol.) 1996; FRCS Ed. 1992; FEBU 1996. Cons. Upol. The Ayr Hosp. Ayr. Socs: Scott. Urol. Soc.Treas.; Scott. Urol. Oncol. Gp.; Full Mem. BAUS. Prev: Sen. Regist. & Regist. Rotat. (Urol.) W. Scotl. Higher Train. Scheme; Regist. Rotat. (Surg.) Aberd. Teach. Hosps.; SHO Rotat. (Surg.) Aberd. Roy. Infirm. Foresterhill Aberd.

HOLLINS, Kathryn Anne 3A Brookfield, Highgate West Hill, London N6 6AS — MB ChB 1995 Bristol; Msc Lond. 1997; MRCPsych (part 1 only) 1999. SHO (Child & Adolesc. Psych.) Tavistock Clinic & St. Anne's Hosp. Lond. Prev: SHO (NeuroPsychiat.) Nat. Hosp. for Neurol. & Neurosurg.; SHO (Adult Psych) St Annes Hosp., Lond.

HOLLINS, Michael Peter 1 Eton Avenue, Westlands, Newcastle under Lyme ST5 3JL Email: m_p_hollins@yahoo.co.uk; 1 Eton Avenue, Westlands, Newcastle ST5 3JL Email: m_p_hollins@yahoo.co.uk — MB ChB Sheff. 1969. p/t Examg. Med. Practitioner, Disabil. Med., Benefits Agency. Socs: Brit. Med. Acupunct. Soc.; Fell. Roy. Soc. Med. Prev: SHO (O & G) N. Staffs. Matern. Hosp. Stoke-on-Trent; Ho. Off. (Cas. & ENT Surg.) Roy. Infirm. Sheff.; Ho. Off. (Gen. Med.) City Gen. Hosp. Stoke-on-Trent.

HOLLINS, Peter Joseph Airedale House, Micklethwaite Lane, Micklethwaite, Bingley BD16 3HP Tel: 01274 565075 Email: peter.hollins@care4free.net — MB BS 1965 Lond.; BSc Lond. 1962; FRCP Lond. 1986, M 1968. (Univ. Coll. Hosp.) p/t Cons Community Diabetologist, Bradford. Prev: Lect. in Med. Univ. Coll. Hosp. Med. Sch. Lond.; Cons. Phys. Bradford Roy. Infirm. & St. Luke's Hosp. Bradford. Mem.; Hon. Sen. Med. Regist. Clin. Research Centre N.wick Pk. Hosp.Harrow.

HOLLINS, Professor Sheila Clare Department of Psychiatry of Disability, St Georges Hospital Medical School, Cranmer Terrace, London SW17 0RE Tel: 020 8725 5502 Fax: 020 8672 1070 — MB BS Lond. 1970; FRCPsych 1989, M 1977; MRCPCH 1997. (St. Thos.) Prof. & Hon. Cons. Psychiat. Learning Disabil. St. Geo. Hosp. Med. Sch. Lond.; Hon. Cons. Psychiat. Disabil. S.W Lond community Trust. Socs: Assn. for Psychoanal. Psychother. in NHS; Chairm. (Exec. Comm.) Roy. Coll. Psychiat. (Fac. Psychiat. Learning Disabil.). Prev: Sen. Policy Advisor, Dept. of Health; Sen. Lect. & Hon. Cons. Psychiat. Ment. Handicap St. Geo. Hosp. Med. Sch. Lond. & Richmond, Twickenham, Roehampton & Wandsworth HA; Sen. Regist. (Child & Family Psychiat.) Earls Ct. Child Guid. Unit & W.m. Childr. Hosp. Lond.

HOLLINSHEAD, James Francis Vance Lower Farm, Finney Green, Leycett, Newcastle ST5 6AB — MB BS 1994 Lond.

HOLLIS, Professor Christopher Peter Developmental Psychiatry Section University Hospital, Queen's Medical Centre, Nottingham NG7 2UH Tel: 0115 970 9946 Fax: 0115 970 9946 Email: chris.hollis@nottingham.ac.uk — MB BS 1984 Lond.; BSc (Psychol.) Lond. 1981; MRCPsych 1989; DCH RCP Lond. 1986. (Lond. Hosp.) Mem. Inst. Family Ther. Socs: Brit. Assn. Psychopharmacol.; Mem. Assn. Child Psychol.Psychiat. Prev: Lect. & MRC Train. Fell. Inst. Psychiat.; Sen. Regist. (Child Psychiat.), Regist. & SHO (Psychiat.) Bethlem Roy. & Maudsley Hosp.; Sen.Lect.Univ.Notts.

HOLLIS, Mr David George Hanbury (retired) 11 Court Lane Gardens, Dulwich, London SE21 7DZ Tel: 020 8693 6703 — MRCS Eng. LRCP Lond. 1947; FRCS Eng. 1959; DLO Eng. 1950. Prev: ENT Surg. Lewisham & N. S.wark HA & Greenwich HA.

HOLLIS, Helen Ruth Strelley Health Centre, 116 Strelley Road, Strelley, Nottingham NG8 6LN Tel: 0115 929 9219 Fax: 0115 929 6522 — BM BS 1987 Nottm. SHO (Psychiat.) Derby GP VTS.

HOLLIS, Henry (retired) 3 Hamilton Drive, Melton Mowbray LE13 0QY Tel: 01664 562298 — MB BS Lond. 1949; MRCS Eng. LRCP Lond. 1948; DTM & H Liverp. 1956. Prev: GP Melton Mowbray.

HOLLIS, John Nicholas Dorchester County Hospital, Dorchester DT1 2JY Tel: 01305 251150 — MB BS 1978 Lond.; FFA RCS 1982. (Lond. Hosp.) Cons. Anaesth. W. Dorset HA. Socs: IC Soc. Prev: Regist. (Anaesth.) Poole Gen. Hosp.; Regist. (Anaesth.) Dunedin Hosp. Otago, NZ; Sen. Regist. (Anaesth.) Nuffield Dept. Anaesth. John Radcliffe Hosp. Oxf.

HOLLIS, Mr Lance Julian 65 Eastern Cottages, Bishopstone, Aylesbury HP17 8SH — MB BS 1990 Lond.; FRCS Eng. 1995. (Guy's Hosp. Med. Sch. Lond.) Specialist Regist. (ENT-Head & Neck Surg.) Oxf. Deanery. Prev: SHO (ENT-Head & Neck Surg.) St. Mary's Hosp. Lond.; SHO (Head & Neck Surgic. Oncol.) Roy. Marsden Hosp. Lond.; SHO (ENT) Gt. Ormond St. Hosp. Lond.

HOLLIS, Michael Emeric (retired) 3 Cadogan Gardens, London SW3 2RJ — MB BChir 1945 Camb.; MA Camb. 1945; DOMS Eng. 1948; MRC Opth 1988. Prev: Assoc. Specialist Moorfields Eye Hosp.

HOLLIS, Michael John 63 Warblington Road, Emsworth PO10 7HG Tel: 01243 373669 — MRCS Eng. LRCP Lond. 1974; DRCOG 1977.

HOLLIS, Peter Child, Family & Adolescent Clinic, 28 Carlton Parade, Orpington, Bromley BR6 0JB Tel: 01689 829614 Fax: 01689 829577; Hayes Grove Priory Hospital, Prestons Road, Hayes, Bromley BR2 7AS Tel: 020 8769 4473 Fax: 020 8462 5028 — MB BS 1975 Lond.; MA (Hons.) Oxf. 1971; MRCPsych. 1981; T(Psych)

1992. (King's Coll. Hosp.) Cons. Psychiat. (Child & Adolesc. Psychiat.) Bromley Child, Family & Adolesc. Clinic Orpington, Kent; Vis. Cons. Hayes Gr. Priory Hosp.; Vis. Lect. Univ. Lond. & Univ. Sussex & Univ. Kent; Registered Psychother. UKCP; Mem. Inst. Gp. Anal. (Clin Trainer, Train. Comm., Counc. & Regional CCTE); Mem. Inst. Family Ther. (Clin. Trainer); Extern. Examr., Goldsmiths Coll., Lond. Univ.; Examr., Roy. Coll. of Psychiat.s; Hon. Cons. Psychiat., Maudsley Hosp., Psychother. Dept. Socs: Inst. of Family Ther.; Inst. of Gp. Anal.; Assn. Child Psychol. & Psychiat. Prev: Cons. Psychiat. SE Thames RHA; Sen. Regist. Tavistock Clinic Lond.; Sen. Regist. Guy's Hosp. Lond.

HOLLIS, Peter Robert The Surgery, 1 The Ridgeway, Woodingdean, Brighton BN2 6PE Tel: 01273 307555 Fax: 01273 304861; Flat 19, St Nicholas Lodge, Church St, Brighton BN1 3LJ — MB BS 1978 Lond.; LFHom. 2000; MRCGP 1986; Cert. Family Plann. JCC 1980; DRCOG 1980. (Middlx.) Socs: Sussex M-C Soc. Prev: Trainee GP Brighton VTS; SHO (O & G) & Ho. Surg. Middlx. Hosp. Lond.

HOLLIS, Sarah 4 Redford Neuk, Edinburgh EH13 0AW — MB ChB 1988 Manch.; MA Manch. 1991; MRCGP 1997; DRCOG 1995; DTM & H Liverp. 1992; FIMC RCS Ed. 2000. (Manch.) Civil. Med. Practitioner MOD. Prev: Med. Off. Vietnamese Refugee Camp, Hong Kong (Med. Sans Frontieres (Belgium).

HOLLIS, Yvonne Bailey Hill, Tilehouse Lane, Denham, Uxbridge UB9 5DD Tel: 01895 832955 — MB BS 1957 Adelaide; MFCM 1982; DPH Lond. 1965. Specialist in Community Med. Hillingdon Dist. HA.

HOLLMAN, Arthur Sea Bank, Chick Hill, Pett, Hastings TN35 4EQ — MB BS 1946 Lond.; MD Lond. 1950; FRCP Lond. 1967, M 1947; FLS 1984. (Univ. Coll. Hosp.) Socs: Soc. of Apoth. (Lect.); Brit. Cardiac. Soc. (Archiv.); Roy. Soc. Med. Prev: Hon. Sen. Lect. Univ. Coll. Lond. Med. Sch.; Emerit. Cons. Cardiol. UCL Hosps. Trust; Hon. Cons. Cardiol. Hosp. Childr. Gt. Ormond St. Lond.

HOLLMAN, Catharine Elizabeth (retired) Sea Bank, Chick Hill, Pett, Hastings TN35 4EQ Tel: 01424 813228 Fax: 01424 814228 — MB BS (Hnrs.) Lond. 1948, DPH 1961; MRCS Eng. LRCP Lond. 1948; MFCM 1972; DObst RCOG 1954. Prev: Area Med. Off. Hillingdon AHA.

HOLLMANN, Michaela Gisela 8 Regent Road, Wallasey CH45 8JU — State Exam Med. Heidelberg 1991.

HOLLOS, Roy Brearley (retired) 4 Sharon Avenue, The Park, Crasscroft, Oldham OL4 4HP Tel: 0145 774170 — MB ChB 1938 Manch.; LRCP LRCS Ed. LRFPS Glas. 1938.

HOLLOWAY, Allison Jane The Surgery, 79 Slateford Road, Edinburgh EH11 1QW Tel: 0131 313 2211 — MB ChB 1992 Manch. GP.

HOLLOWAY, Benjamin John 114 Wyre Hill, Bewdley DY12 2JA — MB ChB 1998 Sheff.; MB ChB Sheff 1998.

HOLLOWAY, Cynthia Muriel (retired) 90 Shirley Drive, Hove BN3 6UL Tel: 01273 553491 — MRCS Eng. LRCP Lond. 1945; FFA RCS Eng. 1955; DA Eng. 1950. Prev: Cons. Anaesth. Brighton & Lewes Hosp. Gp.

HOLLOWAY, Donald Edward (retired) Denholme, Bridekirk, Cockermouth CA13 0PE Tel: 01900 823575 — MB ChB (Commend.) St. And. 1964. Prev: Ho. Surg., Ho. Phys. & SHO Profess. Paediat. Unit Maryfield Hosp. Dundee.

HOLLOWAY, Elizabeth Anne 34A Walton Street, Oxford OX2 6AA — MB BS 1992 Lond.

HOLLOWAY, Frank Beckenham Royal hospital, Monks Orchard Rd, Beckenham BR3 3DX Tel: 020 8700 8510 Fax: 020 8700 8504 Email: f.holoway@iop.kcl.ac.uk; 77 The Crescent, West Wickham BR4 0HD Email: f.holloway@iop.kcl.ac.uk — MB 1978 Camb.; BChir 1977; MRCPsych 1982; FRCP. Cons. Psychiat. Bethlem & Maudsley NHS Trust. Socs: BMA; MDU; Fell. Roy. Coll. Psychiat. Prev: Cons. Psychiat. Camberwell HA; MRC Train. Fell. (Social Psychiat.) King's Coll. Hosp. Sch. Med. & Dent. Lond.

HOLLOWAY, Gail Hill and Partners, 36 Belmont Hill, London SE13 5AY Tel: 020 8852 8357 Fax: 020 8297 2011; 256 Court Road, Eltham, London SE9 4TY — MB ChB 1979 Wales; DRCOG 1984; DCH RCP Lond. 1982.

HOLLOWAY, Mr Graham Michael Noel Tel: 01793 814848; Lantern Cottage, Elcombe, Swindon SN4 9QL Tel: 01793 812359 Fax: 01793 812359 Email: gholloway@uk-consultants.co.uk — MB ChB 1969 Liverp.; FRCS Eng. 1977. Cons. Orthop. Surg. (Sports Injuries) Swindon & Lond. Socs: Fell. BOA; Roy. Soc. Med.; Brit. Assn. Sport & Med. Prev: Cons. Orthop. Surg. RAF; Sen. Regist. Harlow Wood Orthop. Hosp.; Sen. Regist. Qu. Med. Centre Univ. Hosp. Nottm.

HOLLOWAY, Guy John Temple 17 Harvest House, Cobbold Road, Felixstowe IP11 7SP Tel: 01394 274582; 16 Bangholm Loan, Trwity, Edinburgh EH5 3AH Tel: 0131 552 5196 — MB BS 1989 Lond.; MRCGP 1994. Specialist Regist. Old Age psychiat.

HOLLOWAY, Ian Ashwell Essex Way Surgery, 34 Essex Way, Benfleet SS7 1LT Tel: 01268 792203 Fax: 01268 759495 — MB BS 1962 Lond. (Lond. Hosp.)

HOLLOWAY, Ian Paul Flat 15, Chaucer Mansions, Queens Club Gardens, London W14 9RF — MB BS 1994 Lond.

HOLLOWAY, Joanne Peak Cottage, Monyash Road, Bakewell DE45 1FG — BM BS 1994 Nottm.

HOLLOWAY, John Barrie St Thomas's Hospital, Lambeth Palace Road, London SE1 7EH Tel: 020 7928 9292 Fax: 020 7960 5615; 78 Ditton Road, Surbiton KT6 6RH — MB BS 1990 Lond.; FRCA 1994. (King's Coll.) Lect. (Anaesth.) St. Thos. Hosp. Lond. Socs: BMA; MDU; Assn. Anaesth. Prev: Regist. (Anaesth.) St. Ormond St. Hosp. Lond.; Regist. (Anaesth.) Conquest Hosp. Hastings; SHO (Anaesth.) King's Coll. Hosp. Lond. & E.bourne Dist. Gen. Hosp.

HOLLOWAY, John Edward 9 Gloucester Row, Clifton, Bristol BS8 4AW — MB ChB 1991 Bristol.

HOLLOWAY, Josanne Edenfield Centre, Adult Forensic Mental Health Services, Prestwich Hospital, Bury New Road, Manchester M25 3BL Tel: 0161 772 3682 Fax: 0161 772 3446; 155 Brooklands Road, Sale M33 3PD Tel: 0161 976 1596 Fax: 0161 976 1596 Email: josanna@hozzer.freeserve.co.uk — MB ChB 1982 Sheff.; MRCPsych 1987. Cons. Forens. Psychiat. Adult Forens. Ment. Health Servs. Salford; Managing Cons.- Adult Forens. Ment. Health Serv.s, MHS, Salford. Socs: Internat. Assn. Forens. Psychother.; Manch. Med. Sch.; Manch. & Dist. Medico-Legal Soc.

HOLLOWAY, Joy Susan 7 Otterburn Terrace, Newcastle upon Tyne NE2 3AP — MB BS 1966 Lond.; MA (2nd cl. Hons. Physiol.) Oxf. 1969; MSc (Community Child Health) Newc. 1994; MRCS Eng. LRCP Lond. 1966; DPH Leeds 1968. (Guy's) Assoc. Specialist Paediat. & Med. Adviser Adoption & Fostering Unit Newc. u. Tyne. Socs: Soc. Pub. Health UK (Fac. Community Health).; Assoc. Mem. Roy. Coll. Paediat. & Child Health.

HOLLOWAY, Julia Ann Caroline 77 The Crescent, West Wickham BR4 0HD — MB 1978 Camb.; MSc Lond. 1982; BChir 1977; MRCGP 1981; DRCOG 1981.

HOLLOWAY, Katherine Jane Beaulieu, Goonbell, St Agnes TR5 0PH Tel: 01872 553809 — BM 1994 Soton.

HOLLOWAY, Kathleen Anne 90 Shirley Drive, Hove BN3 6UL Tel: 01273 553491 — MB BS 1978 Lond.; MSc (Pub. Health in Developing Countries) Lond. 1994; MRCP (UK) 1984; MRCS Eng. LRCP Lond. 1978; MRCGP 1982; DTM & H 1990; DRCOG 1981; DCH RCP Lond. 1980; Phd 1999. (Royal Free Hospital School of Medicine, London) Dr Publuic Health, Developing Countries. Prev: Dr. Pub. Health, Nepal; GP Nepal & SE Asia.; GP W. Malling.

HOLLOWAY, Michael Joseph Meadway Health Centre, Meadway, Sale M33 4PS Tel: 0161 905 2850; 155 Brooklands Road, Sale M33 3PD — MB ChB 1979 Dundee; MRCGP 1985; DRCOG 1984.

HOLLOWAY, Natalie Joy Dolphins Practice, Haywards Heath Health Centre, Haywards Heath RH16 3BB Tel: 01444 414767; Springmead House, Lindfield Road, Ardingly, Haywards Heath Tel: 01444 892303 — MB BS 1953 Lond.; MRCS Eng. LRCP Lond. 1952. (Lond. Hosp.) Prev: Path. Asst. Lond. Hosp.

HOLLOWAY, Paul Adrian Hunter Intensive Therapy Unit, John Radcliffe Hospital, Headington, Oxford OX3 9DU Tel: 01865 221815 Fax: 01865 220846 Email: paul.holloway@ndm.ox.ac.uk; Walnut Tree House, Old Marston, Oxford OX3 0PH — BM BCh 1985 Oxf.; PhD Soton. 1979; BSc St. And. 1972; MRCPath 1997. (Oxford) p/t Hon. Reader in Med. and Cons. Chem. Pathologist in Intens. Care, John Radcliffe Hosp.; Cons. Chem. Pathologist Ealing Hosp. S.all Middlx. Prev: Sen. Regist & Clin. Lect. (Clin. Biochem.) John Radcliffe Hosp. Oxf.

HOLLOWAY, Peter Burlington Road Surgery, 14 Burlington Road, Ipswich IP1 2EU Tel: 01473 211661 Fax: 01473 289187; 1 Blair Close, Ipswich IP4 5UN Tel: 01473 270273 Email: peteholl@oway.freeserve.co.uk — MB BChir 1984 Camb.; MA Camb. 1984, MB 1984, BChir 1983; DA (UK) 1987. GP. Prev:

Regist. (Anaesth.) Addenbrooke's Hosp. Camb. & Ipswich Hosp.; SHO (Psychiat.) St. Geo. Hosp. Lond.; Trainee GP Ipswich VTS.

HOLLOWAY, Richard The Surgery, 24 Pennine Avenue, Riddings, Derby DE22 2G — MD 1967 Witwatersrand; MB BCh 1959. (Witwatersrand) Prev: Sen. Phys. & Sen. Lect. Dept. Med. Univ. Natal Durban, S. Africa; Head Scientif. Worker Lung Func. Dept. Univ. Hosp. State Univ.; Groningen, Holland.

HOLLOWAY, Stuart Anthony Macklin Street Surgery, 90 Macklin Street, Derby DE1 2JX Tel: 01332 340381 Fax: 01332 345387 — MB BChir 1993 Camb.; BChir Camb. 1992 MB Camb 1993; MA Camb. 1994; DRCOG 1997; DFFP 1998; MRCGP 1998. (Camb.) GP Derby. Socs: BMA; MDU. Prev: GP/Regist. Derby VTS; SHO Rotat. (Med.) Derbysh. Roy. Infirm.

HOLLOWAY, Sylvia Mary (retired) 34 Radstock Lane, Earley, Reading RG6 5QL — MB ChB 1970 Bristol; MRCGP 1978; DObst RCOG 1972; Cert Contracep. & Family Plann. RCOG, RCGP &; Cert FPA 1975. Prev: SHO Psychiat. Barrow Hosp. Bristol.

HOLLOWAY, Victoria Joy 10 Aldwick Close, Leamington Spa CV32 6LP — MB ChB 1991 Sheff.

***HOLLOWBREAD, Andrew** 4 Cranham Gardens, Upminster RM14 1JG Tel: 01708 221364 — MB ChB 1994 Dundee; BSc (Phys. & Pharmacol.) Dund 1989.

HOLLOWOOD, Andrew David 14 Colleys Lane, Willaston, Nantwich CW5 6NS — MB ChB 1993 Birm.

HOLLOWOOD, Kevin 18 Rosehill Meadow, Banstead SM7 3DE — MB BS 1983 Lond.; BSc (Hons.) Lond. 1980, MB BS 1983; MRCP (UK) 1986; MRCPath 1993. Research Regist. (Histopath.) St. Thos. Hosp. Med. Sch. Lond.

***HOLLOWS, Karl Barry** 42 Avon Road, Kearsley, Bolton BL4 8PW — MB ChB 1998 Birm.; ChB Birm. 1998.

HOLLOWS, Mr Philip Flat 1, 9 Linden Road, Manchester M20 2QJ — MB ChB 1989 Manch.; BDS Sheff. 1980; FRCS Eng. 1993; FDS RCS Eng. 1986.

HOLLWAY, Jacqueline Fiona 1 Wadham Close, Wellington, Telford TF1 3PU — MB ChB 1989 Manch.; MRCGP 1993; DRCOG 1993; DCH RCP Lond. 1992. Retainee in Gen. Pract., Sutton Hill Surg.; Clin. Asst. (Rheum.) P.s Roy. Hosp.

HOLLWAY, Jocelyn Christine Drewitt Cottage, All Cannings, Devizes SN10 3PA — MB BS 1974 Lond.; MRCS Eng. LRCP Lond. 1974; FRCR 1982; DMRD Eng. 1978. Cons. Radiol. Qu. Charlotte's & Chelsea Hosp. Wom.

HOLLWAY, Meriel Caroline Northampton General Hospital, Cliftonville, Northampton NN1 5BD; 29 St Peters Way, Cogenhoe, Northampton NN7 1NU — MB BS 1978 Lond. (Guy's)

HOLLWAY, Thomas Edward Drewitt Cottage, All Cannings, Devizes SN10 3PA — MB BS 1974 Lond.; BA Camb. 1969; MRCS Eng. LRCP Lond. 1974; FFA RCS Eng. 1979; DRCOG 1977; DA Eng. 1977. Cons. Anaesth. St. Geo. Hosp. Lond.

HOLLWEY, Susan Jennifer L'Aumone and St. Sampsons Practice, L'Aumone Surgery, Castel, Guernsey GY5 7RU Tel: 01481 256517 Fax: 01481 255190; Les Fries, La Ruette Des Fries, Castel, Guernsey GY5 7PW — MB BCh BAO 1976 Dub.; MFHom. RCP Lond. 1984; MRCGP 1982; DRCOG 1981; DCH RCP Lond. 1981.

HOLLY, Hector Joseph Vernon Road Medical Centre, 12 Vernon Road, Greenmount, Bury BL8 4DD Tel: 01204 882256 Fax: 01204 883639; 562 Bolton Road, Bury BL8 2DU Tel: 0161 764 0700 — MB ChB 1967 Manch. (Manch.)

HOLLY, Louise Jane 1 Spinney Nook, Harwood, Bolton BL2 4BB Tel: 01204 531455 — MB BS 1994 Newc.; MRCPsych 1999. Specialist Regist. in Child & Adolesc. Pshchiarty - Manch.

HOLLY-ARCHER, Frances Katherine Mary The Grange, Church Road, Ellough, Beccles NR34 7TR — MB BCh 1976 Wales; FRCR 1983.

HOLLYHOCK, Vera Muriel Cicely (retired) Valmeon, Salisbury Road, Alresford SO24 9HG Tel: 01962 733824 — MRCS Eng. LRCP Lond. 1952; MA, MB BChir Camb. 1952; MFCM 1972; DPH Lond. 1967. Prev: Specialist in Community Med. Wessex RHA.

HOLLYHOCK, William Maxwell 40 Lakewood Road, Chandlers Ford, Eastleigh SO53 1EW Tel: 01703 252505 — MB BChir 1956 Camb.; MB Camb. 1956, BChir 1955. Prev: Sen. Med. Off. DHSS; Mem. Secretariat Comm. on Safety of Drugs; RN Specialist Physiol.

HOLLYMAN, Julie Anne Springfield University Hospital, 61 Glenburnie Road, London SW17 7DJ Tel: 020 8672 9911 — MB ChB 1976 Manch.; BSc Manch. 1973, MB ChB (Hons.) 1976; MRCPsych. 1981. Cons. (Psychiat.) & Hon. Sen. Lect. St. Geo. Hosp. Lond. Prev: Clin. Research Fell. & Hon. Sen. Regist. Acad. Dept. Psychiat. St.; Geo. Hosp. Med. Sch. Lond.; Sen. Regist. (Psychiat.) St. Geo. & Maudsley Hosp. Lond.; SHO (Neurol.) Hammersmith Hosp. Lond.

HOLLYOAK, Vivien Ann CDSC (Northern & Yorkshire), Leeds PHL, Bridle Path, York Road, Leeds LS15 7TR Tel: 0113 284 0603 Fax: 0113 284 0607 Email: cdcvholl@northy.phts.nhs.uk.ny@btinternet.com; 12 Rudby Close, Whitebridge Park, Gosforth, Newcastle upon Tyne NE3 5JF Tel: 0191 284 8469 — MB ChB 1978 Birm.; MSc Pub. Health Med. Newc. 1991; MFPHM RCP (UK) 1992; FFPHM RCP (UK) 1998. Cons. Epidemiol. (N. & Yorks.) CDSC. Prev: Cons. Communicable Dis. Control. Co. Durh. Health Auth.; GP Newbiggin By Sea, N.d.

HOLLYWOOD, Michelle Catherine 9 Glen Hill Park, Newry BT35 8BU — MB BCh BAO 1993 Belf.

HOLLYWOOD, Philip George Department of Anaesthesia, Southend General Hospital, Prittlewell Chase, Westcliff on Sea SS0 0RY — MB BS 1973 Lond.; FFA RCS Eng. 1978.

HOLMAN, Andrew James Leslie PO Box 5624, Billericay CM11 2SQ — MB BS 1992 Lond.

HOLMAN, Christopher John The Retreat, Heslington Road, York YO10 5BN Tel: 01904 412551 Fax: 01904 430828 Email: info@retreat-hospital.org — MB BS 1979 Lond.; MRCPsych 1985; MInst GA (Dip.) 1995. Cons. Psychiat. The Retreat, York. Prev: Cons. Psychiat. Trafford HA.

HOLMAN, Mrs Dorothea Stajkowa Department Psychology Medicine (Children), Clarendon Wing, Leeds General Infirmary, Belmont Grove, Leeds LS2 9NS Tel: 01132 926796 Fax: 01132 429775 — MB ChB Leeds 1970; FRCPsych 1995, M 1977; DPM Leeds 1974. (Leeds) Cons. Child & Adolesc. Psychiat. Leeds Community Ment. Health Teach. Trust; Sen. Clin. Lect. Univ. Leeds. Socs: Fell. Roy. Soc. Med.; Assn. Child Psychol. & Psychiat. Prev: Cons. Child & Adolesc. Psychiat. Airedale HA; Clin. Dir. Child & Adolesc. Servs. Leeds Community Ment. Health Teachg. Trust.

HOLMAN, Hazel Marie (retired) Denfield, 31 Denmark Road, Exeter EX1 1SL Tel: 01392 275757 — MB ChB Ed. 1950; DCH Eng. 1956, DA 1965. Assoc. Specialist (A & E) Roy. Devon & Exeter Hosp. Prev: Regist. (Path.) Roy. Devon & Exeter Hosp.

HOLMAN, Janet Elizabeth Forest Surgery, 2 MacDonald Road, Walthamstow, London E17 4BA Tel: 020 8527 5434; 24 Spareleaze Hill, Loughton IG10 1BT Tel: 020 8508 0550 — MB BS 1968 Lond.; MRCS Eng. LRCP Lond. 1968. (Roy. Free) Prev: Ho. Surg. New End Hosp. Hampstead; Ho. Phys. Eliz. G. Anderson Hosp. Lond.

HOLMAN, Jennifer Jane 3 Richmond Close, Chandlers Ford, Eastleigh SO53 5RA — MB BS 1991 Lond.; MRCP (UK) 1996. (Univ. Coll. & Middlx. Sch. Med. Lond.) Regist. (Paediat.) St. Mary's Hosp. Portsmouth.

HOLMAN, John George Scott, MC (retired) 28 Pulteney Mews, Bath BA2 4DS Tel: 01425 422950 — MRCS Eng. LRCP Lond. 1938; DPH Lond. 1951. Prev: Med. Off. Dept. Health & Social Security.

HOLMAN, Philip Lionel (retired) 3 Atwood Avenue, Kew, Richmond TW9 4HF Tel: 020 8876 8600 — MB BS Lond. 1949; MRCS Eng. LRCP Lond. 1948; MRCGP 1953. Prev: Ho. Surg. St. Geo. Hosp.

HOLMAN, Ralph Marcus 129 Wells Road, Malvern WR14 4PD Tel: 0168 45 74201 — MRCS Eng. LRCP Lond. 1957. (Leeds) Med. Off. St. Jas. & The Abbey Sch. Prev: Regist. Gen. Med. & Res. Med. Off. St. Jas. Hosp. Leeds; Capt. RAMC, Jun. Specialist Dermat.

HOLMAN, Reginald Albert (retired) Laylocks, Town Hill, Broadclyst, Exeter EX5 3EJ Tel: 01392 461388 — MD Leeds 1954, MB ChB 1947; FRCPath 1967. Hon. Cons. Clin. Bact. S. Glam. HA. Prev: Cons. Clin. Bact. S. Glam. HA.

HOLMAN, Richard Anthony Queens Medical Centre, 6/7 Queen Street, Barnstaple EX32 8HY Tel: 01271 372672 Fax: 01271 341902 — MRCS Eng. LRCP Lond. 1985; MRCGP 1992. (Char. Cross & Westm.) Prev: Trainee GP W. Middlx. Univ. Hosp. VTS; Ho. Surg. & Ho. Phys. W. Middlx. Univ. Hosp. Isleworth.

HOLMAN, Roy Arthur Edward Walnut House, 6A Brandy Hole Lane, Chichester PO19 4RJ — MB BS 1979 Lond.; MRCP (UK) 1982. Cons. Phys. Gen. Med. Geriat. & Gastroenterol. St. Richards Hosp. Chichester. Prev: Research Regist. Univ. Coll. Hosp. Lond.;

SHO & Regist. Rotat. Lond. Hosp.; Ho. Phys. & Ho. Surg. Lond. Hosp.

HOLMAN, Professor Rury Reginald Diabetes Trials unit, Radcliffe Infirmary, Woodstock Road, Oxford OX2 6HE — MB ChB 1973 Bristol; FRCP Lond. 1995; MRCP (UK) 1978. Hon. Cons. Phys. Radcliffe Infirm. Oxf.; Prof. (Diabetic Med.) Univ. Oxf.

HOLMBERG, Stephen Roger Mark Department of Cardiology, Royal Sussex County Hospital, Eastern Road, Brighton BN2 5BE Tel: 01273 696955 Fax: 01273 684554 — MB BChir 1981 Camb.; MB BChir (Hons.) Camb. 1981; MA Camb. 1982, BA 1978, MD 1990; FRCP Lond. 1996; MRCP (UK) 1984. (St. Thos.) Cons. Cardiol. Roy. Sussex Co. Hosp. Brighton. Socs: Brit. Cardiac Soc.; Brit. Cardiovasc. Interven. Soc.; BMA. Prev: Sen. Regist. (Cardiol.) Roy. Lond. Hosp.; Research Fell. Nat. Heart & Lung Inst. & Hon. Regist. (Cardiol.) Roy. Brompton & Nat. Heart Hosp. Lond.; Regist. (Med.) St. Thos. Hosp. Lond.

HOLME, Andrew David Lea 76 Hall Lane, Aspull, Wigan WN2 2SF — MB ChB 1993 Liverp.

HOLME, Anne Warr (retired) 76 Hall Lane, Hindley, Wigan WN2 2SF — MB ChB Liverp. 1961. Prev: SHO (Dermat.) Newsham Gen. Hosp. Liverp.

HOLME, Carole-Ann Greenway Street Medical Centre, Greenway Street, Handbridge, Chester CH4 7JS Tel: 01244 680169 Fax: 01244 680162; Rake Farm House, Rake Lane, Eccleston, Chester CH4 9JN Tel: 01244 671607 — MB ChB 1980 Manch.; MB ChB (Hons.) Manch. 1980; BSc St. And. 1977; DCH RCP Lond. 1984. Clin. Asst. (Colposcopy) Countess of Chester Hosp. NHS Trust; PCG Bd. Mem. Chester City. Socs: BMA; Brit. Menopause Soc.; (Comm.) Chester & N. Wales Med. Soc. Prev: SHO (O & G) W. Chesh. Hosp. Chester; SHO (Paediat.) Roy. Manch. Childr. Hosp. & Pk. Hosp. Manch.

HOLME, Catherine Anne Market Street Medical Centre, Hindley, Wigan WN2 3AY Tel: 01942 256221 Fax: 01942 522479 — MB ChB 1987 Liverp. Full Time Gen. Practitioner, Wigan Lancs.

HOLME, Charles Oliver Dept of Child health post Graduate medical School, Royal Devon & Exeter Hospital, Church Lane, Exeter EX2 5SQ Tel: 01342 403141 Fax: 01342 403158 Email: charles.holme@rdehc-t4.swest.nhs.uk; Old Park Farmhouse, Stockland, Honiton EX14 9BS Tel: 01404 881104 — MB 1970 Camb.; MA Camb. 1970, MD 1994, MB BChir 1971; MRCP (UK) 1974; FRCPCH 1997; DRCOG 1977; DCH Eng. 1972. Cons. s/i in Community Child Health Roy.devon & Exeter hosp. Prev: GP Wells, Som.; Lect. (Paediat.) Char. Cross. Hosp. Med. Sch. Lond.; Cons.paediat.Salisbury dis.Hosp.

HOLME, John David Lea Market Street Medical Centre, 112 Market St., Hindley, Wigan WN2 3AZ Tel: 01942 562 21/2 Fax: 01942 522479; 76 Hall Lane, Hindley, Wigan WN2 2SF Tel: 01942 55204 — MB ChB 1961 Liverp. (Liverp.) Prev: Ho. Surg., Ho. Phys. & Cas. Off. Liverp. Stanley Hosp.

HOLME, Pauline 15 Sedley Taylor Road, Cambridge CB2 2PW Tel: 01223 247475 — MB BS 1972 Lond.; MRCS Eng. LRCP Lond. 1972; MRCPsych 1977; DPM Eng. 1976.

HOLME, Sally Belinda Downlands Medical Centre, 77 High Street, Polegate BN26 6AE Tel: 01323 482323/486449 Fax: 01323 488497; 1 Hilary Close, Polegate BN26 5JH Tel: 0132 125234 — MB BS Lond. 1968; Cert Family Plannificate. (The Royal London) Clin. Asst. Pain Clinic.

HOLME, Stephen Alexander Dermatology Department, University Hospital of Wales, Heath Park, Cardiff CF14 4XN — MB ChB 1993 Ed.; BSc Med. Microbiol. Ed. 1992. Specialist Regist. Prev: Ho. Off. (Med. & Surg.) Edin. Roy. Infirm.

HOLME, Mr Thomas Camplin Department of Surgery, Lister Hospital, Coreys Mill Lane, Stevenage SG1 4AB Tel: 01434 314333; Saxon Rise, Millfield Lane, St Ippolyts, Hitchin SG4 7NH — MB ChB 1975 Dundee; MD (Commend.) Dundee 1986; FRCS Eng. 1982; FRCS Glas. 1982. Cons. Gen. Surg. Lister Hosp. Stevenage. Socs: Assn. of Surg.s of Gt. Britain & Irel.; Brit. Assn. of Surgic. Oncol., Nat. Comm. 1997 - 2000, Hon. Treas. Prev: Sen. Regist. (Surg.) Ninewells Hosp. Dundee; Bernard Sunley Research Fell. Hunt. Inst. Roy. Coll. Surg. Eng.; Regist. St. Thos. Hosp. & Rotat. Guy's Hosp. Lond.

HOLME, Vanessa Eileen 67 Woodcroft Road, Liverpool L15 2HG — MB ChB 1997 Liverp.

HOLME, Victoria Jane 8 The Meadows, Billington, Blackburn BB7 9LE — MB ChB 1991 Liverp.; MRCGP 1995; DRCOG 1993. Trainee GP/SHO Blackburn Roy. Infirm. & Qu. Pk. Hosp. VTS.

HOLMES, Alan Glenpark Medical Centre, Ravensworth Road, Dunston, Gateshead NE11 9AD Tel: 0191 460 4300 Fax: 0191 461 0106 — MB BS Newc. 1969. GP Dunston; Clin. Asst. (Endoscopy) Qu. Eliz. Hosp. Gateshead. Prev: Rotating Regist. (Orthop.) Roy. Vict. Infirm. Newc.; Regist. (Gen. Surg.) Eston Hosp. Teesside; Ho. Surg. & Ho. Phys. (Child Health) Roy. Vict. Infirm. Newc.

HOLMES, Mr Alec Edward (retired) The Old Vicarage, Great Shelford, Cambridge CB2 5EL Tel: 01223 842220 Email: alec-holmes@lineone.net — MB BChir Camb. 1958; MA Camb. 1958; FRCS Eng. 1966; FRCS Ed. 1965. Cons. Dept. Neurol. Surg. & Neurol. Addenbrooke's Hosp. Camb. Prev: Demonst. Anat. Dept. Lond. Hosp. Med. Coll.

HOLMES, Alison Helen Shell Cottage, Great Milton, Oxford OX44 7NF — MB BS 1985 Lond.; MA Camb. 1985; MRCP (UK) 1989. Regist. (Infec. Dis.) Ch.ill Hosp. Oxf.

HOLMES, Alistair Malcolm Westwood Selden Medical Centre, 6 Selden Road, Worthing BN11 2LL Tel: 01903 234962 — MB ChB 1983 Bristol.

HOLMES, Anna Eugenie 63 Connaught Street, London W2 2AE — MB BS 1990 Lond.

HOLMES, Anne Marie (retired) 5 Beechpark Avenue, Northenden, Manchester M22 4BL — MB ChB 1961 Manch.; BSc Manch. 1959; FRCP Lond. 1979, M 1965. Hon. Cons. Phys. Salford AHA (T). Prev: Sen. Regist. (Med.) Manch. Roy. Infirm.

HOLMES, Anne Rosemary Grange House Surgery, 22 Grange Road, Hartlepool TS26 8JB Tel: 01429 272679 Fax: 01429 861265; The Sycamores, 15 Serpentine Road, Hartlepool TS26 0HG Tel: 01429 274957 Email: anneholme@theholmes91.freeserve.co.uk — MB ChB 1978 Manch.; MRCGP 1982; DRCOG 1983; DCH Eng. 1980. (Manch.) GP; GP Tutor Hartlepool.

HOLMES, Barbara Janet Bloomfield Surgery, 95 Bloomfield Road, Bangor BT20 4XA Tel: 028 9145 2426 — MB BCh BAO 1987 Belf. SHO (Gen. Med.) Belf. City Hosp.

HOLMES, Bernard Martin Fisher Medical Centre, Millfields, Coach Street, Skipton BD23 1EU; Evergreens, Thorlby, Skipton BD23 3LL — MB ChB 1966 Liverp.; DObst RCOG 1971.

HOLMES, Brenda Joyce Farnham Health Centre, Brightwells, Farnham GU9 7SA Tel: 01252 723122 — MB ChB 1987 Glas.; BSc (Hons.) Aberd. 1981; DRCOG 1991.

HOLMES, Caroline Lesley The Maudsley Hospital, Denmark Hill, London SE5 8AZ Tel: 020 7703 6333 — MB BS 1991 Lond.; BSc (Hons.) Lond. 1988; MRCPsych 1996. Sen. Regist. (Gen. Adult Psychiat.) Maudsley Hosp. Lond.

HOLMES, Carolyn Jane 2 Baden Street, Chester-le-Street DH3 3JQ; 31 Harwood Drive, Simonside Park, Killingworth, Newcastle upon Tyne NE12 6FQ — MB ChB 1990 Liverp. Staff Grade (Community Paediat.) Palmers Hosp. Jarrow. Prev: Community Med. Off. (Paediat.) Longbenton Clinic N. Shields, Tyne & Wear; SHO (Community Paediat.) N. Tyneside; SHO (A & E) Roy. Vict. Infirm. Newc. u. Tyne.

HOLMES, Christopher Paul Austhorpe Road Surgery, 15 Austhorpe Road, Cross Gates, Leeds LS15 8BA Tel: 0113 295 1820 Fax: 0113 295 1822; Rosse Garth, 26 Park Drive, Heaton, Bradford BD9 4DT Tel: 01274 541526 — MB BS 1979 Lond. (Guy's) Occup. Health Phys. Vickers Defence Systems Leeds & Nat. Blood Serv. (Leeds Blood Centre).

HOLMES, Christopher Paul 24 Carlyle Place, Edinburgh EH7 5RY — MB ChB 1990 Ed.; MRCOG 1996. (Ed.)

HOLMES, David Albert 43 Waldbeck Road, London N15 3EL Tel: 020 8888 7245 — MB ChB 1968 Ed.

HOLMES, David Anthony New Sheepmarket Surgery, Ryhall Road, Stamford PE9 1YA Tel: 01780 758123 Fax: 01780 758102; The Limes, 23 The High St, Ketton, Stamford PE9 3TA Tel: 01780 721877 Fax: 01780 721270 Email: doc_holmes@email.msn.com — MB BS 1985 Lond. (St. Bart. Hosp. Med. Coll.) Clin. Tutor Camb. Med. Stud.s; Examg. Med. Phys. Midl. Benefits Agency; Surg. to Marie Stopes; Internat. Polic Surg. Prev: SHO (Surg.) P'boro. HA; SHO (Gen. Med. & O & G) P'boro. Dist. Gen. Hosp.; SHO (Geriat., Rheum. & Neurol.) Battle Hosp. Reading.

HOLMES, David John Ringmead Medical Practice, Great Hollands Health Centre, Great Hollands Square, Bracknell RG12 8WY Tel:

01344 454338 Fax: 01344 861050; Ringmead Practice, Great Hollands Health Centre, Bracknell RG12 Tel: 01344 454338 — MB ChB 1987 Birm.; DRCOG 1997; DFFP 1997; MRCGP 1997.

HOLMES, David McKenzie St Pauls Wing, Cheltenham General Hospital, Sandford Road, Cheltenham GL53 7AN Tel: 01242 273225 Email: david.holmes@egnhst.org.uk; Harvester's Barn, Upper Dowdeswell, Cheltenham GL54 4LU Tel: 01242 820185 — MB BCh 1979 Wales; BSc (Hons.) Chem. Engin. Ed. 1974; MD Wales 1987; FRCOG 1998. p/t Cons. O & G St. Paul's Wing Cheltenham Gen. Hosp.; Hon. Sen. Lect. Univ. of Bristol Med. Sch. Socs: Fell. Roy. Coll. Obst. & Gyn. Prev: Sen. Regist. (O & G) Ninewells Hosp. Dundee; Regist. (O & G) St. Geo. Hosp. Lond. & St. Peters Hosp. Chertsey; Clin. Research Fell. (O & G) St. Geo. Hosp. Med. Sch. Lond.

HOLMES, Donald Michael 51 Links Road, Parkstone, Poole BH14 9QS Tel: 01202 742942 Fax: 01202 742942 — MB BS Lond. 1960; LMSSA Lond. 1959. (Guy's) Socs: BMA; Med. Golf Soc. Prev: Ho. Surg. (O & G) St. Stephen's Hosp. Lond.; Ho. Phys. Lewisham Hosp.; Surg. Lt.-Cdr. RN.

HOLMES, Edward John Claypath Medical Practice, 26 Gilesgate, Durham DH1 1QW Tel: 0191 333 2830 Fax: 0191 333 2836; 9 Neville Drive, Durham DH1 4HY — MB BS 1970 Newc.; FRCGP 1993, M 1974; DObst RCOG 1973. (Newc.)

HOLMES, Eric (retired) St Brannocks Road Medical Centre, St. Brannocks Road, Ilfracombe EX34 8EG Tel: 01271 863840 — MB ChB Birm. 1968; DObst RCOG 1975.

HOLMES, Eric (retired) 5 The Meadows, Wittersham, Tenterden TN30 7NZ Tel: 01797 270114 — MB ChB 1954 Liverp.; FRCA 1993; FACA 1966; DA (UK) 1958; Dip. Amer. Bd. Anesthesiol. 1967. Prev: Cons. Anaesth. RN Hosp.

HOLMES, Erskine Joseph 41 Ashley Avenue, Lisburn Road, Belfast BT9 7BT — MB BCh BAO 1995 Belf.

HOLMES, Mr Frederick Joseph The Old House, 45 Front St., Tynemouth, North Shields NE30 4BX Tel: 0191 259 5278 — MB BS 1963 Lond.; FRCS Eng. 1974; FRCS Ed. 1973; MRCS Eng. LRCP Lond. 1963; DObst RCOG 1967. (Lond. Hosp.) Cons. Urol. N. Tyneside Dist. Gen. Hosp. N. Shields.; Cons. Urol. Freeman Hosp. , Newc. Upon Tyne. Prev: Surg. Edin. Med. Miss. Soc. Hosp. Nazareth, Israel; Regist. (Surg.) Romford Gp. Hosps.; Ho. Surg. Lond. Hosp.

HOLMES, Geoffrey Kenneth Towndrow Derbyshire Royal Infirmary, London Road, Derby DE1 2QY Tel: 01332 347141; 125 Whitaker Road, Derby DE23 6AQ — PhD Nottm. 1992; BSc Birm. 1963, MD 1974, MB ChB 1966; FRCP Lond. 1984; MRCP (UK) 1970. (Birm.) Cons. Phys. Derbysh. Roy. Infirm. Derby. Socs: Brit. Soc. Gastroenterol.; BMA. Prev: Sen. Regist. (Med.) Birm. HA; Regist. (Med.) Manor Hosp. Nuneaton; Research Regist. (Gastroenterol.) Gen. Hosp. Birm.

HOLMES, Geoffrey Wealbund (retired) 18 Hammondswick, Harpenden AL5 2NR — MB BS 1953 Lond.; DObst RCOG 1957.

HOLMES, Graham Michael 19 Lea Walk, Harpenden AL5 4NG — MB BS 1974 Lond.; T(GP) 1991.

HOLMES, Graham Paul 7 Twyford Cl, Widnes WA8 9RN — MB ChB 1997 Liverp.

HOLMES, Helen Philomena Preswylfa Child & Family Centre, Clive Road, Canton, Cardiff CF5 1GN Tel: 029 2034 4489 Fax: 029 2064 4993; Email: helen@magicwand.demon.co.uk — MB ChB 1984 Birm.; MRCPsych 1990. (Birmingham) Cons. Child & Adolesc. Psychiat. Cardiff.

HOLMES, Mr James Thornton Fitzwilliam Hospital, Milton Way, Bretton, Peterborough PE3 9AQ Tel: 01733 261717; Abbey House, The Green, Thorney, Peterborough PE6 0QD Tel: 01733 270318 Fax: 01733 271018 — MB BS Lond. 1961; FRCS Eng. 1966; MRCS Eng. LRCP Lond. 1961; T(S) 1991. (Univ. Coll. Hosp.) Cons. Surg. P'boro. HA; Arris & Gale Lect. Socs: Fell. Roy. Soc. Med.; Assn. Coloproctol.; Assn. Surg. Prev: Fell. Surg. Research Serv. Memor. Hosp. & Vis. Investig. Sloan Kettering Inst. NY, USA; Sen. Regist. (Surg.) Roy. Free Hosp. Lond.

HOLMES, James William Lawson 205 Marlborough Road, Swindon SN3 1NN — MB BS 1969 Lond.; FFA RCS Eng. 1973. (Univ. Coll. Hosp.) Cons. Anaesth. P.ss Margt. Hosp. Swindon. Prev: Sen. Regist. (Anaesth.) Addenbrooke's Hosp. Camb.; Regist. (Anaesth.) Univ. Hosp. Wales Cardiff.

HOLMES, Jane Elizabeth 18 Austen Court, Cubbington, Leamington Spa CV32 7LJ — MB ChB 1981 Birm. Clin. Asst. (Child & Adolesc. Psychiat.).

HOLMES, Jennifer Jane 20 Alderley Road, Wirral CH47 2AX — MB BS 1993 Newc.

HOLMES, Jeremy Alan North Devon District Hospital, Raleigh Park, Barnstaple EX31 4JB Tel: 01271 22666 Fax: 01271 311523 Email: j.a.holmes@btinternet.com — MB BChir Camb. 1969; MA Camb. 1965; MD Bristol 1995; MRCP (UK) 1971; FRCPsych 1986, M 1975. (Cambridge/UCH) Cons. Psychiat. & Psychother. N. Devon Dist. Hosp. Barnstaple; Hon. Cons. Psychotherapist. Tavistock Clinic Lond.; Chairm. Psychother. Fac. Roy. Coll. of Psychiat.; Hon. Sen Lect., Univ. of Exeter. Prev: Cons. Psychiat. Univ. Coll. Hosp. Lond.; Sen. Research Fell. Welcome Foundat.; Sen. Regist. Maudsley Hosp. Lond.

HOLMES, Joanne Ruth Croft Childrens Unit, Ida Darwin Site, Fulbarn, Cambridge CB1 5EE Tel: 01223 885800 Fax: 01223 885801 — BM 1988 Soton.; MRCPsych 1993. cons. Child. Psychiat. Lifespan NHS Trust Cambs. Prev: SHO (Psychiat.) St. John's Hosp. Aylesbury.

HOLMES, John Cecil Sidgwick (retired) Lowena, Liskeard PL14 6RD Tel: 01579 342026 — MRCS Eng. LRCP Lond. 1943.

HOLMES, John David University of Leeds, Academic Unit of Psychiatry, 15 Hyde Terrace, Leeds LS2 9LT Tel: 0113 233 2701 — BM BCh 1987 Oxf.; MA Oxf. 1988, BA 1984; MMedSc Leeds 1995; MRCP (UK) 1991; MRCPsych 1992; MD 1999 Leeds. (Oxf.) Sen. Lect. Old Age Psychiat., Univ. of Leeds; Hon. Sen. Clin. CMHT. Prev: Sen. Regist. (Old Age Psychiat.) Seacroft Hosp. Leeds; Cons. Old Age Psychiat. Aire Ct. Community Unit Leeds.

HOLMES, Mr John David Department of Plastic & Reconstructive Surgery, Ward 39, Aberdeen Royal Infirmary, Aberdeen AB25 2ZN Tel: 01224 681818; Mayfield House, Station Road, Cults, Aberdeen AB15 9NP Tel: 01224 867164 — MB BChir 1975 Camb.; MA Camb. 1976, MChir 1989; FRCS (Plast) 1993; FRCS Ed. 1980; FRCS Eng. 1980. Cons. Plastic Surg. Aberd. Roy. Infirm. Prev: Sen. Regist. (Plastic Surg.) Mt. Vernon & Char. Cross Hosp. Lond.

HOLMES, Joseph Masters (retired) Rede Farm House, Grove Road, Banham, Norwich NR16 2HG Tel: 0195 3887 230 — MB BS 1947 Lond.; MD Lond. 1952; FRCOG 1967, M 1953. Prev: Cons. Surg. (O & G) Univ. Coll. Hosp. Lond.

HOLMES, Katharine Mary Britton and Partners, 10 Spencer Street, Carlisle CA1 1BP Tel: 01228 529571 Fax: 01228 591472 — MA, MB Camb. 1977, BChir 1976; MRCP (UK) 1978. GP Carlisle.; Clin. Asst. in Diabetes; Clin. Asst. in Endoscopy. Prev: Regist. (Gen. Med.) Cumbld. Infirm. Carlisle.

HOLMES, Katherine Anne 17 Cooks Orchard, Gloucester GL1 3JY — MB ChB 1997 Bristol.

HOLMES, Kathleen Denise 11 Killure Road, Coleraine BT51 3SH — MB ChB 1997 Manch.

HOLMES, Kathryn Mariann The Firs, Northwick Road, Northwick, Pilning, Bristol BS35 4HE Email: sayeed-khan@msn.com — BM BS 1985 Nottm.; BMedSci Nottm. 1983. Clin. Med. Off. (Child Health) Bristol. Prev: Trainee GP Mansfield VTS.

HOLMES, Mr Keith Department of Paediatric Surgery, St Georges Hospital, London SW17 0QT Tel: 020 8725 2926 Fax: 020 8725 0711 Email: kholmes@doctors.org.uk; 66 Old Candle Factory, London SW11 3YS — MB ChB 1970 Liverpool; ChM Liverp. 1990; FRCS Eng. 1976; FRCS Ed. 1976; DRCOG 1972; DCH RCP Lond. 1972. Cons. Paediat. Surg. St. Geo. Hosp. Lond. & St Helier Hosp. Carshalton; Hon. Cons. Roy. Marsden Hosp. Sutton. Socs: Brit. Assn. Paediat. Surg.; Soc. Internat. Oncologie Paediatrique; Internat. Soc. Paediatric Surg. Oncol. Prev: Sen. Regist. Hosp. for Sick Childr. Gt. Ormond St. Lond.

HOLMES, Lorna Margaret Rosemary Bloomfield Avenue Surgery, 155 Bloomfield Avenue, Belfast BT5 5AB Tel: 028 9045 7677; 54 Martinez Avenue, Belfast BT5 5LY — MB BCh BAO 1982 Belf.; MB BCh Belf. 1982; MRCOG 1987; MRCGP 1989.

HOLMES, Mark Julian George Barton and Partners, Campingland, Swaffham PE37 7RD; Southacre House, Southacre, King's Lynn PE32 2AD — MB BS 1988 Lond.; BSc Lond. 1986; MRCGP 1995. Prev: Trainee GP W. Suff. Hosp. Bury St. Edmunds VTS; Ho. Phys. Lond. Hosp.; Ho. Off. (Surg.) Broomfield Hosp. Chelmsford.

HOLMES, Mark Richard 23 Ashchurch Terrace, London W12 9SL — MB BS 1991 Lond.

HOLMES, Matthew 28 Arkleston Road, Paisley PA1 3TF Tel: 0141 889 4292 — MB ChB 1954 Glas. Sen. Lect. Physiol. Univ. Glas.

HOLMES, Michael Bryan David Place Surgery, 7 David Place, St Helier, Jersey JE2 4TD Tel: 01534 736666 Fax: 01534 768482 Email: docholmes@jerseymail.co.uk — MB ChB 1967 Manch. Princip. Forens. Med. Examr. for States of Jersey Police.

HOLMES, Michael Edwin Princes Royal Hospital, Saltshouse Road, Hull HU8 9HE Tel: 01482 676624 Fax: 01482 656750; 1 Allanson Drive, Cottingham HU16 4PF — MB ChB 1971 Sheff.; FRCR 1980; DMRT Eng. 1978. Cons. (Clin. Oncol.) P.ss Roy. Hosp. Hull.

HOLMES, Michael John Ilchester Surgery, 17 Church Street, Ilchester, Yeovil BA22 8LN Tel: 01935 840207 Fax: 01935 840002 — MB ChB 1982 Birm.; DA (UK) 1984.

HOLMES, Michael John Flat 1, 21 Lymington Road, West Hampstead, London NW6 1HZ — MB BS 1990 Lond.; FRCS Lond. Specialist Regist. (Orthop.) Roy. Free/RNOH Rotat. N. Thames Region.

HOLMES, Nicholas Paul The Child & Adolesent Mental Health Service South Downs NHS Trust, The White House, 54 New Church Road, Hove BN3 4FL Tel: 01273 729365 Fax: 01273 728789; 23 Western Street, Brighton BN1 2PG Tel: 01273 776640 Fax: 01273 770054 — MB BS 1975 Lond.; PhD Lond. 1973, BSc 1969; MRCPsych 1980. Cons. Child & Adolesc. Psychiat. S. Downs Health NHS Trust Brighton. Socs: UKCP; Brit. Psychodrama Assn. Prev: Cons. Child & Adolesc. Psychiat. Wandsworth HA, Battersea Child Guid. Unit &. Adolesc. Community Team; Sen. Regist. (Child Psychiat.) Univ. Coll. Hosp., Roy. Free Hosp. & Holloway Child Guid.; Regist. Bethlem Roy. & Maudsley Hosps. Lond.

HOLMES, Nicola Karen Barton and Partners, Campingland, Swaffham PE37 7RD; Southacre House, South Acre, King's Lynn PE32 2AD — MB BS 1989 Lond.; MRCGP 1994; DCH RCP Lond. 1992. (St. Bart. Hosp)

HOLMES, Nigel, OStJ The Group Practice, Bengal Road, Bulford, Salisbury SP4 9AD Tel: 01980 672262 Fax: 01980 672101 — MB BS 1971 Lond.; MRCS Eng. LRCP Lond. 1971; FRCGP 1989, M 1976; DFFP 1993; DObst RCOG 1974; Cert. FPA 1974. (Lond. Hosp.) Assoc. Dir.(Gen. Pract.) to Dir. Army Gen. Pract.; Sen. Med. Off. (Civil.) Bulford Gp. Pract. Prev: Examr. RCGP; GP Horsham; Ho. Surg. Lond. Hosp.

HOLMES, Patrick John Lawrence Churchfields, Darley, Harrogate HG3 2QF — MB BS 1993 Lond.

HOLMES, Paul 43 Bedford Drive, Timperley, Altrincham WA15 7XB — MB ChB 1998 Ed.; MB ChB Ed 1998.

HOLMES, Paul Andrew 5 Upton Court, 3 The Downs, London SW20 8JB — MB BCh 1991 Witwatersrand.

HOLMES, Paul Christopher Brian Seaforth Farm Surgery, Vicarage Lane, Hailsham BN27 1BH Tel: 01323 848494 Fax: 01323 849316 — MB BS 1981 Lond. Prev: SHO (Paediat. & O & G) St. John's Hosp. Chelmsford.

HOLMES, Paul Michael 104 Langthorne Street, London SW6 6JX — MB BS 1996 Lond.

HOLMES, Peter Harry (retired) 11 Over Hall Park, Mirfield WF14 9JP Tel: 01924 494172 Fax: 01924 502506 — MB ChB 1957 Leeds; FRCGP 1988, M 1965.

HOLMES, Peter Raymond Stuart House Surgery, 20 Main Ridge West, Boston PE21 6SS Tel: 01205 362173 Fax: 01205 365710; 13 Rochford Tower Lane, Boston PE21 9RG Email: holmespr@compuserve.com — BM BS 1984 Nottm.; BMedSci Nottm. 1982, BM BS l984; MRCP (UK) 1988. (Nottingham) GP Boston Lincs.; Clin. Asst. (Diabetes).

HOLMES, Mrs Phyllis Christine Old School Medical Centre, School Lane, Greenhill, Sheffield S8 7RL; 87 Furniss Avenue, Dore, Sheffield S17 3QN — MB ChB Manch. 1966. (Manch.) GP Sheff. Prev: Clin. Med. Off. Sheff. AHA.

HOLMES, Raymond (retired) Withington Hospital, Manchester M20 2LR Tel: 0161 445 8111 — MB ChB 1958 Manch.; PhD Manch. 1955, MSc 1950; FRCP Lond. 1971, M 1962. p/t Cons. Phys. Manch. Roy. Infirm. Prev: Nuffield Med. Fell. Rutgers Med. Sch. New Jersey, USA.

HOLMES, Richard Ian Talbot Medical Centre, Stanley Street, South Shields NE34 0BX Tel: 0191 455 3867 Fax: 0191 454 3825; 11 Ravensbourne Avenue, East Boldon NE36 0EG — MB BS 1983 Newc.; MRCGP 1987; DRCOG 1986.

HOLMES, Richard James Lawson 205 Marlborough Road, Swindon SN3 1NN — BM 1995 Soton.

HOLMES, Robert Michael 79 Hunters Road, Spital Tongues, Newcastle upon Tyne NE2 4ND — MB BS 1998 Newc.; MB BS Newc 1998.

HOLMES, Robert Patrick Hunter The Health Centre, Beeches Green, Stroud GL5 4BH Tel: 01453 763980; c/o Ballygrot Cottage, 14 Kathleen Avenue, Helens Bay, Bangor BT19 1LF — MB ChB 1984 Bristol; MRCGP 1989; DCCH RCP Ed. 1993; DRCOG 1991. GP Stroud, Glos. Prev: GP Lond.

HOLMES, Sally Claire Tan y Graig, School Road, Pwll, Llanelli SA15 4AL Tel: 01554 759278 — MB BCh 1990 Wales; MRCGP 1994; DRCOG 1993.

HOLMES, Sandra Joan Fressingfield Medical Centre, New Street, Fressingfield, Eye IP21 5PJ Tel: 01379 586227 Fax: 01379 588265; Bridge House, Laxfield, Woodbridge IP13 8DW Tel: 01986 798232 — MB ChB 1974 Manch.; Cert. Family Plann. JCC 1978. Prev: Trainee GP Ipswich VTS.

HOLMES, Sarah Jane 27 Grenfell Road, Didsbury, Manchester M20 6TG — MB BS 1987 Lond.; MD Lond. 1995; MRCP (UK) 1990; MRCGP 1997; DCH RCP Lond. 1995.

HOLMES, Mr Simon Andrew Vaughton Department of Urology, St Mary's Hospital, Portsmouth PO9 6AE Tel: 023 9241 3560 — MB BS 1984 Lond.; MS 1993; FRCS 1994 UROL; FRCS Ed. 1989. Cons. Urol., St Mary's Hosp., Portsmouth. Socs: Roy. Soc. Med.; Brit. Assn. Urol. Surg. Prev: Sen. Regist. (Urol.) St. Bart. Hosp. Lond.; Regist. (Urol.) Portsmouth; Regist. (Surg.) S.end Hosp.

HOLMES, Simon Christopher 5A Cambrige Court, Twickenham TW1 2HT Tel: 020 8892 9315 Fax: 020 8892 9441 Email: drsimonholmes@aol.com — MB BS 1978 Lond.; MRCGP 1984; DRCOG 1983; DCCH RCP Ed, RCGP & FCM 1983. (Char. Cross) p/t Sen. Midico-Legal Adviser, The St. Paul Internat. Insur. Company Ltd., Redhill; Liveryman Soc. Apoth. Lond.; Freeman of City of Lond.

HOLMES, Stephanie Margaret 10 Cloverdale Crescent, Lambeg, Lisburn BT27 4LN — MB BCh BAO 1976 Belf.; MRCGP 1980.

HOLMES, Stephen George Thomas Edward Street Surgery, Edward Street, Earby, Barnoldswick BB18 6QT Tel: 01282 843407 Fax: 01282 844886; Newfield Edge House, Moorgate Road, Barnoldswick BB18 5SE — MB ChB 1984 Leic.; MB ChB Leic. l984; MRCGP 1988; DRCOG 1986; FRCGP 1996. (Leicester) Prev: Trainee GP N.ampton VTS; Ho. Phys. Leicester Gen. Hosp.; SHO (A & E) PeterBoro. Dist. Hosp.

HOLMES, Sue-Ella Jane Highways, 195 Shooters Hill, London SE18 3HP Tel: 020 8856 1584; 55/3 Blackfriars St, Edinburgh EH1 1NB Tel: 0131 557 6745 Email: lellie55@yahoo.co.uk — MB ChB 1994 Ed. SHO (Psychiat.) SE Scotl. Train. Scheme.

HOLMES, Susan Mary Lensfield Medical Practice, 48 Lensfield Road, Cambridge CB2 1EH Tel: 01223 352779 Fax: 01223 566930; 23 Humberstone Road, Cambridge CB4 1JD Tel: 01223 322881 — MB ChB 1981 Birm.; MRCGP 1988.

HOLMES, Victor Alan 6 Princess Royal Road, Ripon HG4 1TQ — MB BS 1979 Newc.

HOLMES, Walter, Lt.-Col. RAMC Retd. Rivendell, Over Silton, Thirsk YO7 2LJ — MB BS 1951 Durh.; MFCM 1974; AFOM RCP Lond. 1983; DIH Soc. Apoth. Lond. 1971; DTM & H Eng. 1970; DPH Glas. 1957. (Durh.) Fell. Roy. Inst. Pub. Health & Hyg. Socs: BMA. Prev: Sen. Lect. (Preven. Med.) RAM Coll. Lond.; Chief Med. & Health Off. Kuala Trengganu, Malaysia; Chief Med. Off. United Nations Force in Cyprus.

HOLMES, Wendy Patricia (retired) Spur House, Priory Lane, Lamberhurst, Tunbridge Wells TN3 8NA Tel: 01892 890313 — MB BCh BAO Dub. 1960; FRCPCH 1997; T(M)(Paed.) 1994; DPH Lond. 1963. Prev: Cons. Community Paediat. (Child Developm.) Weald of Kent Community NHS Trust Tunbridge Wells.

HOLMES, William 79 Woodland Park, Kilrea, Coleraine BT51 5SH — MB BCh BAO 1976 Belf.

HOLMES, William Francis Sherrington Park Medical Practice, 402 Mansfield Road, Nottingham NG5 2EJ Tel: 0115 985 8552 Fax: 0115 985 8553; 132 Nottingham Road, Ravenshead, Nottingham NG15 9HL Tel: 01623 797687 Fax: 01623 797923 — BM BS 1977 Nottm.; BMedSci (Hons.) Nottm. 1975; FRCGP 1996, M 1983; Joint Comm. Contracep. Lond. 1982; MRCP (London) 1998. (Nottm.) GP;

Special Lect. (Respirat. Med.) Univ. Nottm.; Tutor (Gen. Pract.) Univ. Nottm.; Hosp. Pract. (Respirat. Med.) City Hosp. Nottm.; Elect. Mem. GMC. Socs: Brit. Thorac. Soc.; Brit. Assn. Study Headache; Brit. Soc. Allergy & Clin. Immunol. Prev: GP Bingham.

HOLMES-MILNER, John Grahame Cotsall House, Leamington Road, Broadway WR12 7EQ Tel: 01386 854994 — MB BS 1956 Lond. (Char. Cross) Socs: BMA & Med-Leg. Soc. Prev: Mem. Vis. Staff Bexhill Hosp.; Hosp. Pract. (Dermat.) Hastings Hosp. Gp.; Ho. Phys. Char. Cross Hosp.

HOLMES-SIEDLE, Monica Winifred (retired) 64A Acre End Street, Eynsham, Oxford OX29 4PD Tel: 01865 880050 Fax: 01865 880030 — MB BCh BAO Dub. 1955; MA (Med. Ethics & Law) Lond. 1994; FRCPCH 1997. Prev: Assoc. Specialist Clin. Genetics Ch.ill Hosp. Oxf.

HOLMES-SMITH, John Graham, OStJ, OBE, Brigadier late RAMC Retd. The Frimley Childrens Centre, Church Road, Frimley, Camberley GU16 5AD Tel: 01483 782882 Fax: 01483 782999; 249 Vale Road, Ashvale, Aldershot GU12 5LA Tel: 01252 325469 Email: john_g.h@virgin.net — MB BS 1959 Lond.; FRCP Lond. 1984; MRCP (UK) 1975; MRCS Eng. LRCP Lond. 1959; MRCPCH 1996 FRCPCH 1996; DCH RCP Lond. 1966; DTM & H Eng. 1961; DObst RCOG 1960. (Guy's) Cons. Community Paediat.Surrey Hants. Borders NHS Trust; Chairm. - Hants. Child Protec. Comm. Socs: BMA; RCPCH. Prev: Cons. Adviser Paediat. MoD (A); Ho. Phys. Evelina Hosp. Lond.; Clin. Dir. (Paediat.) Frimley Pk. Hosp.

HOLMES-SMITH, Lawrence Ian (retired) Mullions, Market Hill, Whitchurch, Aylesbury HP22 4JB — MA Oxf. 1961, BM BCh 1954.

HOLMQUIST, Jennifer Caroline Church Street Surgery, 2 Church Street, Sutton, Hull HU7 4TT Tel: 01482 826457 Fax: 01482 824182; 74 Main Street, Cherry Burton, Beverley HU17 7RF Tel: 01964 551661 Fax: 01964 551772 Email: paul&jen@fastducati.freeserve.co.uk — MB ChB 1978 Manch.; MRCGP 1983; DRCOG 1982. Clin. Asst. (Gyn.) P.ss Roy. Hosp. Hull. Prev: Asst. GP Guernsey; GP Cockermouth; SHO (Anaesth.) Manch. Roy. Infirm.

HOLMS, Caroline McMillan 2R 50 Cranworth Street, Glasgow G12 8AG — MB ChB 1998 Glas.; MB ChB Glas 1998.

HOLMS, James Stuart Macpherson Fullarton Street Surgery, 24 Fullarton Street, Ayr KA7 1UB Tel: 01292 264260 Fax: 01292 283284; 23 Craigstewart Crescent, Doonfoot, Ayr KA7 4DB Tel: 01292 442772 — MB ChB 1968 Glas.; DObst RCOG 1970. Prev: SHO (Gen. Med.) S.. Gen. Hosp. Glas.; SHO (Obst.) Roy. Matern. Hosp. Glas.; Ho. Off. (Paediat.) Roy. Hosp. Sick Childr. Glas.

HOLMS, Lucy Frances Doctors Surgery, Dubbs Place, Port Glasgow PA14 5UD Tel: 01475 705604 Fax: 01475 701277 — MB ChB 1981 Manch.; BSc (Med. Sci.) St. And. 1978; MRCGP 1985; DRCOG 1983. Clin. Asst. gerito-Urin. Med. Socs: BMA; RCGP.

HOLMS, Mr William (retired) The Mornington Clinic, Cottingley Manor, Cottingley New Road, Bingley BD16 1TZ Tel: 01274 511133 Fax: 01274 511188 Email: billholms@haselhurst.junglelink.co.uk — MB BS 1959 Lond.; FRCS Eng. 1965; MRCS Eng. LRCP Lond. 1959. Hon. Cons. (Orthop. Surg.) Spastics Soc. Prev: Cons. Orthop. Surg. Bradford Roy. Infirm.

HOLOWKA, Karen Ann 3 Northwich, Woughton Park, Milton Keynes MK6 3BL — MB ChB 1979 Sheff.; BA Oxf. 1976; MRCGP 1984; DRCOG 1982. Asst. GP Newport Pagnell.

HOLOWNIA, Paul Julian 58 Outwoods Road, Loughborough LE11 3LY — BM BCh 1989 Oxf.

HOLROYD, Anastasia (retired) 13 Williamson Gardens, Ripon HG4 2QB — MB BS 1947 Durh.; MA Oxon. 1941.

HOLROYD, Benjamin James House, Jacks Lane, Marchington, Uttoxeter ST14 8LW — MB BS 1998 Lond.; MB BS Lond 1998.

HOLROYD, Mr John Brian Martin BUPA, Elland Lane, Elland HX5 9EB Tel: 01422 324000; 3 Ryleston Gardens, Halifax HX3 0JA Tel: 01422 351812 — MRCS Eng. LRCP Lond. 1961; FRCS Ed. 1971; FCOphth 1988; DO Eng. 1967. (King's Coll. Hosp.) Socs: Past Pres N. Eng. Ophth. Soc. Prev: Regist. Oxf. Eye Hosp.; Ho. Phys. King's Coll. Hosp. Lond.; Cons. Ophth. Surg. Roy. Halifax Infirm.

HOLROYD, John David Louis 4/200 Beach Street, Coogee NSW 2034, Australia Tel: 00 61 2 96659958 Fax: 00 61 2 96659958; 24 River Green, Hamble, Southampton SO31 4JA Tel: 01703 456329 Fax: 01803 843996 — MB ChB 1967 Bristol; DA Eng. 1971. Ships Med. Off. V-Ships Monaco; Chief Med. Off. MS Carousel, MS Sundream & MS Seawing. Prev: Ship's Princip. Med. Off. Cunard Line; Princip. Partner Double Bay Med. Cntr. NSW 2028, Australia; Sen. Ship's Surg. P & O Lines.

HOLROYD, Peter Bryan (retired) Ravenswood, Whitmore Lane, Sunningdale, Ascot SL5 0NS Tel: 01344 620941 Fax: 01344 620941 Email: peter.holroyd@cwcom.net — BM BCh 1958 Oxf.; MA Oxf. 1958; DObst RCOG 1963. Prev: GP Ascot.

HOLT, Alastair Keith Ian, Squadron Ldr. RAF Med. Br. Manchester Road Medical Centre, 27 Manchester Road, Knutsford WA16 0LZ Tel: 01565 633101 Fax: 01565 750135 — MB ChB 1985 Manch.; MSc Lond. 1980; BSc Manch. 1979; MRCGP 1990; T(GP) 1991; DRCOG 1991; Cert. Av. Med. 1986. (Manchester) GP Princip.; Hosp. Practitioner Medic/o the Elderly and Rehabil.; Cosmetic Dermat. Socs: Cosmetic Doctors Assn. 2001; Roy. Coll. of Gen. Practitioners; Brit. Cosmetic Doctors Assn.

HOLT, Alison Anne 1 Carr Hill Grove, Calverley, Pudsey LS28 5QB — MB ChB 1997 Leeds.

HOLT, Barbara Ann Ursula Department Urology, St Bartholomew's Hospital, West Smithfield, London EC1A 7BE — MB BChir 1988 Camb.; FRCS Eng. 1992. Regist. (Urol.) St. Bart. Hosp. Lond.

HOLT, Barbara Elizabeth Latham House Medical Centre, Sage Cross St., Melton Mowbray LE13 1NX Tel: 01664 60101; 2 Carnegie Crescent, Melton Mowbray LE13 1RP — MB ChB 1985 Manch.; BSc St. And. 1982; MRCGP 1989; DCH RCP Lond. 1988. Prev: SHO (Paediat.) St. Mary's Hosp. Manch.; SHO (Obst.& Gyn.) Bolton Gen. Hosp.; SHO (A & E) Crewe HA.

HOLT, Beverley Lee Deer Bield, Storrs Park, Windermere LA23 3LY — MRCS Eng. LRCP Lond. 1970.

HOLT, Caroline Sara Larch House, 1 Maltings Court, Bloxham, Banbury OX15 4TP — MB ChB 1976 Manch. Prev: Regist. (Anaesth.) Withington Hosp. Manch.

HOLT, Claire Martineo 10 Milton Close, Henley-on-Thames RG9 1UJ — BM 1998 Soton.; BM Soton 1998.

HOLT, Donald Ingram 20 Lancaster Avenue, Farnham GU9 8JY Tel: 01252 715689 — MB BS 1965 Durh.; MRCPsych 1973; DPM Eng. 1970. Cons. (Child Psychiat.) SW Thames RHA. Prev: Sen. Regist. (Child Psychiat.) Sheff. RHB; Hon. Clin. Tutor United Sheff. Hosps.

HOLT, Mr Edmund Michael Berkshire Independent Hospital, Wensley Rd, Reading RG1 6UZ Tel: 0118 902 8008; Frieze Farm, Crowsley, Henley-on-Thames RG9 4JL Tel: 01734 722275 Email: eddyholt@friezefm.freeuk.com — MRCS Eng. LRCP Lond. 1961; MB Camb. 1962, BChir 1961; FRCS Ed. 1967; FRCOG 1982, M 1968. (Camb. & Guy's) Prev: Res. Obstetr. Qu. Charlotte's Hosp. Lond.; Regist. (O & G) W.m. Hosp. Lond.; Regist. (O & G) St. Luke's Hosp. Guildford.

HOLT, Mr Edward Martin 14 Hillview Avenue, West Kirby, Wirral CH48 5EJ — MB BCh BAO 1983 NUI; LRCPI & LM, LRCSI & LM 1983; FRCS Ed. 1987; FRCS Ed (Orth) 1995. Cons. (Orthop. Surg.) S. Manch. Univ. Hosp. NHS Trust. Prev: Shoulder & Elbow Fell. Professional Upper Limb Unit Roy. Liverp. Univ. Hosp.; Sen. Regist. (Arthroplasty) Wrightington; Clin. Lect. & Trauma Sen. Regist. (Orthop.) Roy. Liverp. Univ. Hosp.

HOLT, Mr Gavin Montgomery 30 Botanical Road, Sheffield S11 8RP — MB ChB 1988 Aberd.; FRCS Eng. 1993.

HOLT, Geraldine Mary York Clinic, Guy's Hospital, London SE1 9RT Tel: 020 7955 4792 Fax: 020 7955 4232 — MB BS 1976 Lond.; BSc (Psychol.) Lond. 1973; MRC Psych. 1981. (Lond. Hosp.) Cons. Psychiat. & Sen. Lect.Psychiat. of Learning Disabilities, Lewisham & Guy's Ment. Health NHS Trust.

HOLT, Helen Bridget Queen Alexandra Hospital, Portsmouth PO6 3LY; 8 Handel Terrace, Southampton SO15 2FG — BM 1994 Soton.; MRCP 1998. (Southampton)

HOLT, Jacqueline Ann 11 Chelwood Avenue, Hatfield AL10 0RD — MB ChB 1973 Birm.

HOLT, Jane Allison Arden Medical Centre, 1498 Warwick Road, Knowle, Solihull B93 9LE Tel: 01564 739194 Fax: 01564 771224 — MB ChB 1980 Manch.; DFFP 2001 Fac. of Family Plann. p/t GP Partner, Arden Med. Centre 1498 Warwick Rd. Knowle. Socs: Christ. Med. Fell.sh. & BMA. Prev: GP Bury.; GP Retainer Scheme Shirley & Studley.

HOLT, Jane Louise 7 Elm Road, Hereford HR1 2TH — MB ChB 1993 Birm.

HOLT, Janina Marie 30 Rumbold Road, Huddersfield HD3 3DB Tel: 01484 451877 Email: nina_holt@yahoo.com — MB ChB 1997 Liverp. SHO Anaesth.Roy.Liverp.Univ.Hosp. Socs: BMA.

HOLT, John Michael Old Whitehill, Tackley, Kidlington OX5 3AB Tel: 01869 331241 — MB ChB 1959 St. And.; MSc Qu. Univ. Ontario 1963; MA Oxf. 1959; MD (High Commend.) St. And. 1964; FRCP Lond. 1975, M 1965. Emerit. Cons. Phys. John Radcliffe Hosp. Oxf.; Sen. Clin. Lect. Univ. Oxf.; Examr. Univ. Oxf., Univ. Hong Kong, Univ. Glas., Univ. Lond. & Dub. & RCP Lond.; Civil Cons. Med. to RAF; Censor RCP. Socs: Assn. Phys. Prev: Exec. Edr. Quar. Jl. Med.; Regional Adviser RCP; Dir. Clin. Studies & Mem. Counc. Univ. Oxf.

HOLT, Jonathan 35 Blenheim Drive, Oxford OX2 8DJ — MB ChB 1995 Manch. SHO Whangaret Hosp. New Zealand. Socs: MDU.

HOLT, Judith 28 West End, Wilburton, Ely CB6 3RE — MB BChir 1985 Camb.

HOLT, Judy Christine Department of Radiology, Queens Medical Centre, Nottingham NG7 2UH; 6 Elton Avenue, Barnet EN5 2EA — MB BCh 1990 Wales; MRCP Lond. 1993. Regist. (Radiol.) Qu. Med. Centre Nottm.

HOLT, Professor Kenneth Sunderland Nether Edge, 5 Walnut Close, Clifton, Banbury OX15 0PG Tel: 01869 338154 — MB ChB 1947 Manch.; MD Univ. Rochester, NY 1946; MD Manch. 1957; FRCP Lond. 1970, M 1949; Hon. FRCPCH 1997; DCH Eng. 1953. (Manch. & Rochester New York, USA) Emerit. Prof. Developm. Paediat. Inst. Child Health Lond. Prev: Dir. Wolfson Centre of Developm. Paediat. Inst. Child Health Lond.; Sen. Lect. (Child Health) Univ. Sheff.

HOLT, Kim Stonelaw Flat Farm, Eastmoor, Chesterfield S42 7DE Tel: 01246 583950 Email: kimmholt@netscape.net — MB ChB 1984 Manch.; MB ChB Manch. l984; MRCP (UK) 1987; DCH RCP Lond. 1987. Stud. Masters in Sci. Community Child Health. Socs: RCPCH; BAACH. Prev: Cons. Paediat. Community Child Health Roy. Manch. Childr. Hosp.; Sen. Regist. (Community Child Health) S. Manch.; Clin. Med. Off. Greenwich HA.

HOLT, Lennox Peter John Rheumatism Research Centre, The Royal Infirmary, Oxford Road, Manchester M13 9WL Tel: 0161 276 4272 Fax: 0161 275 8690 Email: l.holt@fs2-scgman.ac.uk; Linnet Hayes, Hough Lane, Wilmslow SK9 2LG Tel: 01625 522151 — MB ChB 1957 Manch.; FRCP Ed. 1975, M 1963; FRCP Lond. 1975, M 1964; MRCS Eng. LRCP Lond. 1957; MRCPCH 1996; DCH Eng. 1959; FRCPCH 1997. (Manch.) Reader (Rheum.) Manch. Med. Sch.; Cons. Phys. Manch. Roy. Infirm. & Booth Hall Childr. Hosp. Manch. Socs: Brit. Soc. Rheum.; Assn. Phys.; Amer. Rheum. Assn. Prev: Cons. Phys. Hammersmith Hosp. Lond.; Lect. (Med.) Roy. Postgrad. Med. Sch. Lond.; Research Fell. Arthritis & Rheum. Counc. & Hon. Sen. Regist. Qu. Eliz. Hosp. Birm.

HOLT, Lisa Wendy Jane 6 Viscount Close, London N11 3PX Tel: 020 8368 5264 Email: duncan@dtennent.freeserve.co.uk — MB BS 1996 Lond.; BSc (Hons.) Lond. 1993. (Royal Free Hospital) SHO (O & G), Univ. Coll. Hosps., Lond. Prev: SHO (A & E) Roy. Free Hosp. Lond.; SHO (Neurosurg.) Lond.

HOLT, Mark David 87 Beatty Avenue, Cardiff CF23 5QS — MB BChir 1987 Camb.

HOLT, Mr Martin Charles Whalley 3 Castledykes Road, Dumfries DG1 4SN Tel: 01387 257716 — MB ChB 1982 Aberd.; FRCS Ed. 1986. GP Trainee Dumfries & Galloway GP Train. Scheme. Prev: Resid. Surg. United Missions Hosp., Nepal.; Regist. (Surg.) Birch Hill Hosp. Rochdale; SHO (Surg.) Hope Hosp. Salford.

HOLT, Mary Elizabeth Rotherham District General Hospital, Rotherham S60 2UD Tel: 01709 820000; 37 Hallam Road, Moorgate, Rotherham S60 3ED — MD 1987 Glas.; MB ChB 1975; FRCP Glas. 1990; MRCP (UK) 1978. Cons. Rheum. Rotherham Dist. Gen. Hosp. Socs: Brit. Soc. Rheum. Prev: Sen. Regist. (Rheum.) Univ. Hosp. Wales Cardiff; Regist. & SHO Rotat. (Med.) W.. Infirm. & Gartnavel Gen. Hosp. Glas.

HOLT, Michael Frodsham East Borough Cottage, E. Borough, Wimborne BH21 1PA Tel: 01202 883888; 153 Cambridge Street, Pimlico, London SW1V 4QB — MB ChB 1947 Liverp.; MRCGP (Founder Mem.); DObst RCOG 1952. (Liverp.) Mem. Liverp. Med. Inst. Prev: Obstetr. Birkenhead Matern. Hosp.; Obst. Ho. Surg. Mill Rd. Matern. Hosp. Liverp. & Roy. S.. Hosp.; Liverp.

HOLT, Miles Charles Walsgrave Hospital, Coventry; Tel: 0208 642 5584 — BM 1992 Soton.; PG Dip Med Ed Dundee Univ.; FRCA 1998; DA (UK) 1995. (Southampton) Cons. Univ. Hosp. Coverntry & Warwich NHS Trust Coventry. Socs: Assn. Anaesth.; RCA. Prev: SHO (Anaesth.) Qu. Med. Centre Univ. Hosp. Nottm.; SHO (Anaesth.) Poole & Bournemouth Hosps.; Specialist Regist. (Anaesth.) Coventry Sch. Anaesth.

HOLT, Nicola Denise 3 North View, Mickley Square, Stocksfield NE43 7DA — MB BS 1990 Newc.; BMedSc (Hons.) Newc. 1987, MB BS 1990; MRCP (UK) 1993. Research Regist. (Cardiol.) Freeman Hosp. Newc. Prev: SHO (Med.) Freeman Hosp. & Newc. Gen. Hosp.

HOLT, Peter Geoffrey (retired) 9 Sharoe Green Park, Fulwood, Preston PR2 8HW Tel: 01772 719567 — MB ChB 1953 Liverp.; FFCM 1981, M 1972; DPH Liverp. 1957. Prev: Cons. Pub. Health Med. Preston HA.

HOLT, Peter Joseph Arthur 30 Llandennis Avenue, Cyncoed, Cardiff CF23 6JH Tel: 029 2075 2081 — MB ChB Sheff. 1969; FRCP Lond. 1987. Cons. Dermat. Univ. Hosp. Wales Cardiff. Prev: Sen. Regist. (Dermat.) Univ. Hosp. Wales Cardiff; Lect. (Dermat.) Univ. Oklahoma, USA.

HOLT, Philip Michael Hall Grove Surgery, 4 Hall Grove, Welwyn Garden City AL7 4PL Tel: 01707 328528 Fax: 01707 373139; 32 Carleton Rise, Welwyn AL6 9RF Tel: 01707 321258 Email: philholt9@cs.com — BM 1982 Soton.; MRCGP 1995. Clin. Asst. (Ophth.) E. Herts. NHS Trust. Prev: Trainee GP Aberystwyth VTS.

HOLT, Philip Ronald Astra Charnwood, Bakewell Road, Loughborough LE11 5RH Tel: 01509 644460 Fax: 01509 645558; 2 Whitehall Court, Radcliffe-on-Trent, Nottingham NG12 2NJ — MB ChB 1985 Manch.; BSc Manch. 1982; MRCP (UK) 1988; MFPM RCP (UK) 1992; Dip. Pharm. Med. RCP (UK) 1990. Project Dir. Astra Charnwood. Prev: Med. Dir. Leicester Clin. Research Centre; Sen. Clin. Pharmacol. Fisons Pharmaceuts. LoughBoro.; SHO (Med.) Roy. Liverp. Hosp.

HOLT, Phyllis Marie Maidstone Hospital, Hermitage Lane, Barming, Maidstone ME16 9 Tel: 01622 729000 Fax: 01622 224163; Longcroft, Windmill Park, Windmill Hill, Wrotham Heath, Sevenoaks TN15 7SY — MB ChB 1975 Manch.; MD Manch. 1984; FRCP Lond. 1993; MRCP (UK) 1978; FESC 1995; FACC 1997. Cons. Cardiol. Maidstone Hosp. & Guy's/St Thomas' Hosp. Lond. Socs: Brit. Cardiac Soc.; N. Amer. Soc. Pacing & Electrophys. Prev: Sen. Regist. (Cardiol.) Nat. Heart Hosp. Lond.; Regist. (Cardiol.) Guy's Hosp. Lond.

HOLT, Richard Charles Leonard — MB ChB 1994 (Hons.) Manch.; BSc (Hons.) Experim. Immunol. & Oncol. Manch. 1991; MRCP 1997. (Univ. Manch.) Specialist Regist. (Paediat. Med.) Roy. Manch. Childr.'s Hosp. Prev: SHO (Neonat. Med.) St. Mary's Hosp. Manch.; SHO (Paediat. Med.) Roy. Manch. Childr.'s Hosp.; SHO (Paediat. Med.) Booth Hall Childr.'s Hosp. Manch.

HOLT, Richard Ian Gregory 84 Babbacombe Road, Bromley BR1 3LS Tel: 020 8460 7543 — MB BChir 1989 Camb.; MRCP (UK) 1992. Lect. In Diabetes & Endocrinogy - St Thomas's Hosp. - UMDS - Lond. Socs: Brit. Endocrine Soc.; Brit. Diabetic Assn. Prev: MRC Clin. Train. Fell. King's Coll. Sch. Med. & Dent. Lond.; Regist. (Med.) King's Coll. Hosp. Lond.; Sen. regist. in Gen. Med. Diabetes & Endocrinol. E.bourne DGH.

HOLT, Samuel Nathan Brigstock Medical Centre, 141 Brigstock Road, Thornton Heath CR7 7JN Tel: 020 8684 1128 Fax: 020 8689 3647; 132 Llanrwst Road, Upper Colwun Bay, Colwyn Bay LL28 5UT — MB BS 1993 Lond.; DCH RCP Lond. 1995; DRCOG 1995. (King's Coll. Lond.) Trainee GP Brigstock Med. Centre Thornton Heath.

HOLT, Sasha Jane 2 Sunnywood Drive, Haywards Heath RH16 4PF — MB ChB 1992 Bristol.

HOLT, Sean Peter 1 Barn Meadow, Trowse, Norwich NR14 8UB — MB ChB 1995 Sheff.

HOLT, Shelagh Marie 29 Portland Street, Coatbridge ML5 3LH Tel: 01236 440995 — MB ChB 1994 Glas.

HOLT, Shirley (retired) 3 Holkham Rise, Whirlowdale Park, Sheffield S11 9QT Tel: 0114 235 0282 Fax: 0114 235 0282 — MD 1963 Manch.; MB ChB Manch. 1959. Prev: Cons. Path. N. Gen. Hosp. Sheff.

HOLT, Mr Simon David Henry Department of Surgery, Prince Philip Hospital, Llanelli SA14 8QF Tel: 01554 756567 Email: simon@holtsd.demon.co.uk — MB BChir 1976 Camb.; MA Camb. 1977; FRCS Ed. 1981. (Univ. Coll. Hosp.) Cons. Surg. P. Philip Hosp. LLa.lli; Cons. Surg. to BrE. Test Wales, Swansea. Socs: Assn.

Surgs.; Brit. Assn. Surgic. Oncol. Prev: Cons. Surg. RAF Hosp. Halton; Hon. Sen. Regist. St. Thos. Hosp. Lond.; Sen. Specialist (Surg.) P.ss Mary's RAF Hosp. Halton.

HOLT, Mr Stephen Chesterfield & North Derbyshire Royal Hospital, Chesterfield S44 5BL Tel: 01246 277271; Knoll Barn, The Knoll, Tansley, Matlock DE4 5FN Tel: 01629 580689 — MD 1985 Liverp.; MB ChB 1974 Liverp.; FRCS Eng. 1980. Cons. Gen. Surg. Chesterfield & N. Derbysh. Roy. Hosp.

HOLT, Stephen Geoffrey The Royal Free Hospital, Pond St., Hampstead, London NW3 2QG — MB BS 1990 Lond.; PhD 2000; BSc Lond. 1986; MRCP (UK) 1993. Cons. Nephrologist, Renal Unit, Roy. Sussex Co. Hosp., E.ern Rd., Brighton, E. Sussex BN2 5BE; Roy. Sussex Co. Hosp., E.ern Rd., Brighton, E. Sussex BN2 5BE. Tel: 01273 696955; Fax: 01273 664585; Email: steve.holt@brighton-healthcare.nhs.uk. Socs: Renal Assn.; Intens. Care Soc.

HOLT, Timothy Adrian Dale End Surgery, Danby, Whitby YO21 2JE Tel: 01287 660739 Fax: 01287 660069 — MB BS 1987 Lond.; FRCGP 2000; MRCP (UK) 1990; MRCGP 1993; DRCOG 1992. (St. Geo. Hosp. Med. Sch. Lond.) Gen. Pract. Princip. Prev: Med. Off. Pika Wiya Health Port Augusta, S. Austral.; Regist. (Gen. Med.) Roy. Gwent Hosp. Newport; SHO (Gen. Med. & Nephrol.) S.Cleveland Hosp.

HOLT, Victoria Janet Hoxton Health Collective Ltd, 12 Rushton Street, London N1 5DR Tel: 020 7739 8990 Fax: 020 7729 3197 — MB BS 1985 Lond.; BA (Hons.) Camb. 1982; MRCGP 1992. (The London Hospital)

HOLT, William John 16 Ashmere Grove, Ipswich IP4 2RE — MB BS 1978 New South Wales.

HOLT-WILSON, Mr Alexander Daniel Cefn Maen, Usk Road, Raglan NP15 2HR Tel: 01291 690428 — MB 1962 Camb.; BA 1958 Camb.; FRCOphth; BChir 1961 Camb.; FRCS Ed. 1975; FCOphth 1988; DO Eng. 1966. (St. Bart.) Cons. (Ophth.) St. Woolos Hosp. Newport. Socs: Ophth. Soc. UK. Prev: Ho. Surg. Eye Dept. St. Bart. Hosp. Lond.; Res. Surg. Off. Moorfields Eye Hosp. Lond.; Cons. (Ophth.) Dept. Pub. Health Kuwait.

HOLTBY, Ian Tees HA, District Offices, Poole House, Stokesley Road, Nunthorpe, Middlesbrough TS7 0NJ Tel: 01642 320000 Fax: 01642 304170 Email: ian.holtby@email.tees-ha.northy.nhs.uk; 62 Sandmoor Road, New Marske, Redcar TS11 8DJ Tel: 01642 486904 — MB ChB Leeds 1968; MFCM 1989; MRCGP 1976; DCCH RCP Ed. 1983; DObst RCOG 1972. (Univ. Leeds) Cons. Communicable Dis. Control Pub. Health Med. Tees HA; Med Off River Tees Port Health Auth. Socs: BMA; Fell. Roy. Inst. Pub. Health and Hyg.; Fell Fac. Pub. Health Med. Prev: Princip. GP Redcar; Regist. (Med.) Ahmadu Bello Univ. Zaria Nigeria.

HOLTBY, Vicki Clare 106 Southwood Lane, London N6 5SY — BM 1998 Soton.; BM Soton 1998.

HOLTERMAN, Katherine Anne 11 Fort Road, Belfast BT8 8LX — MB ChB 1998 Dund.; MB ChB Dund 1998.

HOLTHAM, Stephen John 20 Lansdowne Gardens, Newcastle upon Tyne NE2 1HE — MB BS 1993 Newc.

HOLTHAM-TAYLOR, Deborah Ann Jessop Medical Practice, 24 Pennine Avenue, Riddings, Alfreton DE55 4AE Tel: 01773 602707 Fax: 01773 513502; Hayes Farm, Main St, Ticknall, Derby DE73 1JZ Tel: 01332 862949 — MB BS 1981 Lond.; MRCGP 1985; Cert. Family Plann. JCC 1986. (Roy. Free Hosp. Med. Sch.) Socs: Derby & Ripley Med. Soc. Prev: Trainee GP Matlock & Crich; SHO (O & G) S. Derbysh. HA; SHO (Paediat. & A & E) S. Derbysh. HA.

HOLTI, Gillian Angela Zoe 211 Middle Drive, Darras Hall, Ponteland, Newcastle upon Tyne NE20 9LU Tel: 01661 22383 — MB ChB 1952 Leeds.

HOLTI, Gunter (retired) 211 Middle Drive, Darras Hall, Ponteland, Newcastle upon Tyne NE20 9LU Tel: 01661 822383 — MD Leeds 1955, MB ChB 1952; FRCP Lond. 1974, M 1964. Hon. Cons. Dermat. N.ern Regional & Yorks. HA. Prev: Pres. Brit. Microcirculat. Soc.

HOLTOM, Keith Oldbury Health Centre, Albert Street, Oldbury B69 4DE Tel: 0121 552 6747 Fax: 0121 552 2999; 6 Woodlands Avenue, Walsall WS5 3LN — MB ChB 1981 Birm.; MRCGP 1986; DRCOG 1983. Prev: SHO (Gen. Med.) & (Paediat.) Sandwell W. Bromwich.

HOLTOM, Nicola Catherine Eastrop, The Street, Stratfield, Mortimer, Reading RG7 3NR — MB ChB 1985 Liverp.; MRCGP 1990; DRCOG 1989; Dip. Palliat. Med. 1997; Univ. Wales Coll. Med.

HOLTON, Andrew Francis Department Paediatrics, Leicester Royal Infirmary, Leicester LE1 5WW Tel: 0116 254 1414 Fax: 0116 258 5631; 36 Almond Way, Lutterworth LE17 4XJ — MB ChB 1982 Leeds; PhD Leeds 1977, MB ChB Leeds 1982; BSc Hons. Lond. 1974; MRCP (UK) 1985; FRCPCH; FRCP. Cons. Paediat. Neurol. Leic. Roy. Infirm. Socs: Neonat. Soc.; Brit. Paediat. Assn.; Brit. Paediat. Neurol. Assoc. Prev: Lect. (Child Health) Char. Cross & W.m. Med. Sch. Univ. Lond.; Regist. (Paediat.) Soton. Gen. Hosp.

HOLTON, Anthony Richard Tolworth Hospital, Red Lion Road, Surbiton KT6 7QU — MB BS 1980 Newc.; MRCPsych 1985; T(Psychiat.) 1991.

HOLTON, Barbara Doreen (retired) 5 Yew Tree Close, Radcliffe-on-Trent, Nottingham NG12 2AZ — MRCS Eng. LRCP Lond. 1950. Prev: Head Clin. Investig. Research Dept. Boots Co. Nottm.

HOLTON, David William Ladywell Medical Centre (West), Ladywell Road, Edinburgh EH12 7TB Tel: 0131 334 3602 Fax: 0131 316 4816; 14 Succoth Avenue, Edinburgh EH12 6BT Tel: 0131 337 5805 — MB ChB 1970 Ed.; FRCGP 1983, M 1975; DCH RCPS Glas. 1974; DObst RCOG 1972. Assoc. Adviser (Community Paediat.) Edin. Prev: Regist. Paediat. E. Fife Health Dist.; SHO (Med.) E.. Gen. Hosp. Edin.

HOLTON, Diana Elizabeth Newton Port Surgery, Newton Port, Haddington EH41 3NF Tel: 01620 825497 Fax: 01620 824622; 30 Market Street, Haddington EH41 3JE Tel: 01620 810884 — MB ChB 1973 Ed.; BSc (Med. Sci.) Ed. 1970; FRCP Ed. 1995; MRCP (UK) 1976; MRCGP 1989. Hosp. Pract. (Diabetes & Gen. Med.) Roodlands Hosp. Haddington. Prev: Regist. (Gen. Med.) Roy. Infirm. Edin.; Ho. Off. (Gen. Med.) Roy. Infirm. Edin.; Ho. Off. (Gen. Surg.) Roy. N.. Infirm. Inverness.

HOLTON, Fiona Ann 14 Succoth Avenue, Edinburgh EH12 6BT — MB BS 1998 Newc.; MB BS Newc 1998.

HOLTON, Janice Lesley Department of Histopathology, Leicester Royal Infirmary, Leicester LE1 5WW — MB ChB 1983 Leeds; PhD Soton. 1991. Regist. (Histopath.) Leicester Roy. Infirm.

HOLTON, Kenneth Martin Holbrooks Health Team, 75-77 Wheelwright Lane, Coventry CV6 4HN Tel: 0247 636 6775 Fax: 0247 636 5793 Email: hht.admin@gp-m86032.wmids.nhs.uk; 55 Long Street, Bulkington, Nuneaton CV12 9JZ Tel: 024 76 640766 — MB ChB 1977 Liverp.; MMedSci Birm. 1994. Prev: SHO Huddersfield Roy. Infirm.; SHO (Rheum. & Rehabil.) Fazakerley Dist. Gen. Hosp. Liverp.; Ho. Off. Sefton Gen. Hosp. Liverp.

HOLTON, Thelma Shirley Erin House, Nightingales Lane, Chalfont St Giles HP8 4SR Tel: 01494 762278 — MB ChB 1961 Leeds; FFPHM RCP (UK) 1994; MFCM 1973; DPH Manch. 1968. (Leeds) Cons. Pub. Health Med. Bucks. Socs: Soc. Community Med.; BMA. Prev: SCM Rotherham HA; Dep. MOH & Dep. Princip. Sch. Med. Off. Rotherham Co. Boro.; Asst. Co. Med. Off. Derbysh. CC.

HOLTON, Wilfrid Roger 10 Marroway Lane, Witchford, Ely CB6 2HU Tel: 01353 662455 — MB BS 1965 Lond.; MRCS Eng. LRCP Lond. 1965. (Char. Cross) Socs: (Ex. Pres. & Ex.-Sec.) Camb. Med. Soc. Prev: GP Ely; Mem. Panel of Examrs. Dip. in Child Health; Med. Off. Palace Sch. for Severely Handicap. Childr.

HOLWEGER, Wlodzimierz Ireneusz Northbrook Health Centre, 93 Northbrook Road, Shirley, Solihull B90 3LX Tel: 0121 746 5000 Fax: 0121 746 5020; 41 Newton Road, Knowle, Solihull B93 9HL Tel: 01564 770217 — MB ChB 1963 Birm.; DObst RCOG 1966. (Birmingham) BUPA Health Screening. Prev: Regist. (Cas., Gen. Outpats. & O & G) P.ss Margt. Hosp. Nassau, Bahamas; Ho. Surg. Qu. Eliz. Hosp. Birm.

HOLWELL, Andrew David 71 Chantry Way E., Swanland, North Ferriby HU14 3QF — MB ChB 1992 Liverp.

HOLWELL, David William Park Surgery, Albion Way, Horsham RH12 1BG Tel: 01403 217100 — MB BS 1986 Lond.; BSc Lond. 1983, MB BS 1986; MRCGP 1990; DRCOG 1990.

HOLWELL, Ian Arthur Lyle and Partners, The Surgery, 4 Silverdale Road, Burgess Hill RH15 0EF Tel: 01444 233450 Fax: 01444 230412; Little Saffrons, Theobalds Road, Burgess Hill RH15 0SS — MB BS 1981 Lond.; MRCGP 1986; Dip. IMC RCS Ed. 1995; DRCOG 1985. (Char. Cross) Socs: Sussex & Surrey Immed. Care Scheme. Prev: Trainee GP Cuckfield VTS.

HOLWILL, Stephen David James 23 The Avenue, Liphook GU30 7QD — MB BS 1991 Lond.; PhD Lond. 1988.

HOLZEL, Frieda Bedriska (retired) The Elm, The Chase, Pinner HA5 5QP — MD 1933 Prague. Prev: Research Fell. Duchess of York Hosp. Babies Manch. & St. Mary's Hosp.

HOLZEL, Helen Sylvia 36 Harboro Road, Sale M33 — MD 1980 Manch.; MB ChB 1968; MSc Lond. 1977; MRCPath 1977.

HOLZER, Richard S (retired) 141 Mendip Road, Elvers Green, Halesowen B63 1JH Tel: 0121 550 8280 — MD 1938 Berne. Cons. Phys. City Hosp. Birm.

HOLZMAN, Richard Henry Andrew Medical Centre, Cleobury Mortimer, Kidderminster DY14 8QE Tel: 01299 270209 Fax: 01299 270482; 4 Lion Lane, Cleobury Mortimer, Kidderminster DY14 8QD Tel: 01299 270950 — MB ChB 1970 Ed.; MRCGP 1974; DObst RCOG 1974; Cert FPA 1975.

HOMA, Bernard 93 Princes Park Avenue, London NW11 0JS Tel: 020 8455 2901 — MRCS Eng. LRCP Lond. 1922. (King's Coll. & St. Bart.) Prev: Clin. Asst. P. of Wales Hosp. Tottenham; Hon. Anaesth. German Hosp. Dalston; Temp. Maj. RAMC.

HOMAPOUR, Babak 185 Moss Lane, Pinner HA5 3BE — MB ChB 1998 Dund.; MB ChB Dund 1998.

HOMBAL, Mr Johnson William Reuben (cons. rooms), 59 Cathedral Road, Cardiff CF11 9HE Tel: 029 2027 0007 Fax: 029 2038 3574; 110 Heol Isaf, Radyr, Cardiff CF15 8EA Tel: 02920 842574 — MB BS 1960 Bombay; MChOrth Liverp. 1967; FRCS Eng. 1964. Cons. Orthop. Surg. P. of Wales Orthop. Hosp. Cardiff; Cons. Orthop. Surg. P. Chas. Hosp. M. Glam.; Tutor (Surg.) RCS. Socs: Fell. BOA. Prev: Regist. Rotat. RJAH Orthop. Hosp. OsW.ry; Sen. Regist. (Orthop.) P. of Wales Orthop. Hosp. Cardiff.

HOME, Professor Philip David Freeman Diabetes Service, Freeman Hospital, Newcastle upon Tyne NE7 7DN Tel: 0191 284 3111 Fax: 0191 222 0723 Email: philip.home@ncl.ac.uk — BM BCh 1976 Oxf.; MA, DPhil Oxf. 1974, DM 1991, BM BCh 1976; MRCP (UK) 1978. Cons. Phys. Freeman Hosp. Trust; Prof. Univ. Newc. Socs: Fell. Roy. Coll. Phys. Lond.; Assn. Phys.; (Vice-Pres.) Internat. Diabetes Federat. Prev: Wellcome Sen. Research Fell. Clin. Sc. Univ. Newc.; Assoc. Ed. Diabetologia & Ed. Diabetic Med.; Research Fell. & Hon. Regist. Unit for Metab. Med. Guy's Hosp. Lond.

HOMER, Anne Charmaine Newcombes Surgery, Newcombes, Credition ex17 2ar Tel: 01363 772263 Email: a.c.homer@exeter.ac.uk; Email: a.c.homer@exeter.ac.uk — MB BS 1979 Lond.; MRCGP, 2000; FRCP; MRCP (UK) 1982. (Royal Free) GP Regist. Exeter. Socs: Mem. of Inst. of Learners and Teach.s, ILT(M). Prev: Cons. Phys. Edgeware Gen. Hosp.; Sen. Regist. (Geriat.) St. Geo. Hosp. Lond.; Regist. (Gen. Med.) Whittington Hosp. Highgate Lond.

HOMER, Deidre Elizabeth 1 Colinton Mains Loan, Edinburgh EH13 9AJ — MB ChB 1991 Ed.

HOMER, Jarrod James 9 Danford Lane, Solihull B91 1QA — BM BS 1991 Nottm.

HOMER, Joanna Rachel 5 Shelley Road, High Wycombe HP11 2UP — BM BCh 1998 Oxf.

HOMER, Lucinda Marie 77 Hyperion Road, Stourbridge DY7 6SJ — MB ChB 1992 Sheff.

HOMER, Patricia Mary 36 Whitelot Close, Southwick, Brighton BN42 4YQ; 60 Ladies Mile Road, Patcham, Brighton BN1 8TA — MB BCh 1980 Wales.

HOMER-WARD, Michael Dominic Disablement Services Centre, St. Mary's Hospital, Milton Road, Portsmouth PO3 6BR Tel: 02392 866976 Fax: 02392 866990 Email: mike.homer-ward@doctors.org.uk — BM BS 1992 Nottm.; BMedSci Nottm. 1990; MRCP (UK) 1996. (University Nottingham) Cons., Rehab. Med., St. Mary's Hosp., Portsmouth. Socs: Brit. Soc. Rehabil. Med.; Soc. For Res. In Rehabil. Prev: Clin. Lect. & Hon. Sen. Regist. (Rehabil. Med.) Univ. Nottm.

HOMEWOOD, Jill Mary Woodland View, Quarry Road, Frenchay, Bristol BS16 1LX — BChir 1990 Camb.; MB BChir Camb. 1990; MRCP UK 1994. Anaesth. Roy. United Hosp. Bath. Prev: Anaesth.Hope Hosp. Manachester.

HOMEWOOD, Lorna Inga Mackenzie (retired) Trees, Higher Broad Oak Road, West Hill, Ottery St Mary EX11 1XJ Tel: 01404 812928 — MD 1967 Lond.; MB BS 1956; FRCPsych 1989; MRCPsych 1973; DPM Lond. 1962. Prev: Ho. Phys. & Cas. Off. St. Geo. Hosp. Lond.

HOMFRAY, Tessa Frances Rose 56 Clancarty Road, London SW6 3AA — MB BS 1983 Lond.; MRCP (UK) 1986. SHO (Paediat.) King's Coll. Hosp. Lond. Prev: SHO (Med. Rotat.) St. Geo. Hosp. Lond.

HOMI, John 3 Mariteau House, German St., Winchelsea TN36 4ES — MB BS 1956 Lond.; MRCS Eng. LRCP Lond. 1956; FFA RCS Eng. 1977; FACA 1962; DObst RCOG 1958; Dip. Amer. Bd. Anaesth. 1964. (Char. Cross) Prof. Emerit. Univ. W. Indies; Hon. Research Fell. MRC Sickle Cell Laborats., Kingston, Jamaica. Socs: BMA & Roy. Soc. Med. Prev: Prof. & Head Anaesth. & Intens. Care Univ. Hosp. W. Indies, Jamaica; Vis. Prof. Lond. Hosp. Med. Coll.; Mem. Cons. Staff Cleveland Clinic Hosp., USA.

HOMMEL, Laurence Bacon Lane Surgery, 11 Bacon Lane, Edgware HA8 5AT Tel: 020 8952 5073 — MB ChB 1988 Manch.; MRCGP 1993; T(GP) 1992; DCH RCP Lond. 1992; DRCOG 1991; Cert. Family Plann. JCC 1990. (Univ. Manch.) GP Practitioner, Edgware, Middx; Clin. Asst. (Dermat.). Prev: SHO (O & G & A & E) Univ. Coll. Hosp. Lond.; SHO (Paediat.) Middlx. Hosp. Lond.

HOMMERS, Clare Elizabeth 1 Terrace Cottages, Oaken, Wolverhampton WV8 2AY — BM BS 1998 Nottm.; BM BS Nottm 1998.

HOMMERS, Marion (retired) Pentre Isaf, Cwmdu, Crickhowell NP8 1RT Tel: 01874 730360 — MB ChB 1954 Birm.; BA Open Univ. 1994. Prev: SCM (Child Health) Powys & Coventry HA.

HOMOLKA, Mark Patrick Paul 42 Allendale Close, London SE5 8SG — MB BS 1996 Lond.

HON, Edmund Hing Cheung 53 Norrice Lea, London N2 0RN — MB BS 1994 Lond.; BSc Lond. 1991, MB BS 1994.

HON, Jimmy Kim Fatt Dept. of Cardiothoracic Surgery, Royal Brompton Hospital, Sydney Street, London SW3 6NP — MB ChB Bristol. (Bristol Medical School) Surgic. Res. Fell. Dept. of Cardiothoracic Surg. Roy. Brompton Hosp. Lond.; Hon. Sen. Ho. Off., Roy. Brompton Hosp., Lond.

HON, Patricia Hing Tong 53 Norrice Lea, London N2 0RN — MB BChir 1991 Camb.; MA Camb. 1988, MB BChir 1991; MRCP (UK) 1994.

HONAN, William Phillips Royal Devon & Exeter Hospital (Wonford), Barrack Road, Exeter EX2 5DW — MB BS 1979 Lond.; MD Lond. 1988; MRCP (UK) 1982.

HONAVAR, Mrinalini Department of Neuropathology, Institute of Psychiatry, De Crespigny Park, London SE5 8AF — MB BS 1977 Bombay; MD All India Med Scs. 1980; MRCPath 1984; T(Path) 1991. Coins. Neuropath. & Hon. Sen. Lect. Inst. Psychiat. Lond. Prev: Sen. Lect. & Hon. Cons. Neuropath. St. Bart. Hosp. & Med. Sch. Lond.; Sen. Regist. (Morbid Anat.) Kings Coll. Hosp.; Sen. Regist. (Neuropath.) Maudsley Hosp. Lond.

HONE, Jane Helena 479 Gospel Lane, Acocks Green, Birmingham B27 7AR — BM BS 1991 Nottm.

HONE, Margaret Pollock Kneesworth House Hospital, Bassingbourn-cum-Kneesworth, Royston SG8 5JP Tel: 01763 242911 Fax: 01763 242011; Westwood House, Church St, Exning, Newmarket CB8 7EH Email: honemaggie@aol.com — MB BS 1980 Lond.; MRCS Eng. LRCP Lond. 1980; MRCPsych 1985. (Guy's Hospital) Cons. Psychiat. Kneesworth Hse. Hosp. Royston. Prev: Cons. Psychiat. W. Suff. Hosp. Bury St. Edmunds.

HONES, Hilary Jeanne Crofton Surgery, 109A Crofton Road, Orpington BR6 8HU Tel: 01689 822266 Fax: 01689 891790 — MB BS 1963 Lond.; BSc CP 1998; DObst RCOG 1965. (Char. Cross) Princip. GP; Clin. Asst. (Colposcopy) FarnBoro. Hosp. FarnBoro. Kent. Socs: BMA. Prev: Ho. Surg. Bromley Hosp.; Ho. Phys. S. Lond. Hosp.; Ho. Off. Beckenham Matern. Hosp.

HONEST, Dr Department of Oncology, Osborne Building, Leicester Royal Infirmary, Infirmary Square, Leicester LE1 5WW — MB ChB 1994 Dundee.

HONEY, Arthur Meadowside, Raby Road, Thornton Hough, Bebington, Wirral CH63 4JS — MRCS Eng. LRCP Lond. 1952.

HONEY, Cynthia Mary 375 High Road, Woodford Green IG8 9QJ Tel: 020 8504 0532 Fax: 020 8559 1503 — MB ChB 1974 Bristol; DCH Eng. 1977; DObst RCOG 1976. Prev: SHO (Cas. & Orthop.) St. Margt. Hosp. Epping; SHO (Paediat.) & SHO (O & G) Freedom Fields Hosp. Plymouth.

HONEY, Gerald Edward (cons. rooms), Abbey Park House Hospital, Park Road, Waterloo, Liverpool L22 3XE Tel: 0151 257 6702 Fax: 0151 928 7477; 50 Dowhills Road, Blundellsands,

Liverpool L23 8SW Tel: 0151 924 6875 — BM BCh 1947 Oxf.; DM Oxf. 1957, BM BCh 1947; FRCP Lond. 1970, M 1948. (Oxf.) Cons. Phys. BRd.green Hosp. Liverp. Socs: Med. & Scientif. Sect. Brit. Diabetic Assn. Prev: Cons. Phys. Walton Hosp. Liverp.; Sen. Med. Regist. United Oxf. Hosps.; Ho. Phys. Radcliffe Infirm. Oxf.

HONEY, Michael (cons. rooms), 148 Harley St., London W1N 1AH Tel: 020 7935 7591 Fax: 020 7224 1528; 58 The Knoll, Ealing, London W13 8HY Tel: 020 8997 0265 — MB BChir Camb. 1948; BA Camb. 1945; FRCP Lond. 1971, M 1952. (Cambridge University and Univ. Coll. Hosp.) Cons. Cardiol. Lond. Socs: Brit. Cardiac Soc. Prev: Phys. (Cardiol.) Brompton Hosp. Lond. & Lond. Chest Hosp.; Sen. Regist. (Cardiol.) St. Bart. Hosp. Lond.

HONEY, Susan Elizabeth The Medical Centre, 7E Woodfield Road, London W9 3XZ Tel: 020 7266 1449 Fax: 020 7451 8155 — MB BS 1982 Lond.; BSc Lond. 1979, MB BS 1982; MRCGP 1988.

HONEYBOURNE, David Department of Respiratory Medicine, Birmingham Heartlands Hospital, Bordesley Green E., Birmingham B9 5SS Tel: 0121 424 1734 Fax: 0121 772 0292 Email: honeybd@heartsol.wmids.nhs.uk — MB ChB 1974 Bristol; MSc 2002 Cardiff; MD Bristol 1982; FRCP Lond. 1993; MRCP (UK) 1977. Cons. Gen. & Respirat. Med., Birm. Heartlands Hosp.; Hon. Sen. Clin. Lect. (Med.) Univ. Birm.; Hon. Tut in Med. Educat., Univ. Cardiff; Hon. Clin. reader in biological Sci.s, univ Warwick. Socs: Amer. Thoracic Soc.; Eur. Respirat. Soc.; Brit. Thoracic Soc. Prev: Cons. Gen. & Thoracic Med. City Hosp. Birm.; Sen. Regist. (Gen. & Respirat. Med.) Hope & Wythenshawe Hosps. Manch.; Regist. (Med.) Kings Coll. Hosp. Lond.

HONEYBUL, Stephen 39 Nuns Road, Winchester SO23 7EF — BM 1995 Soton.

HONEYBUN, Jeremy Julian The Surgery, Kinmel Avenue, Abergele LL22 7LP Tel: 01745 833158 Fax: 01745 822490; Cerrig Gwynion, 10 Parc Glan Aber, Abergele LL22 7FA Tel: 01745 826044 Email: honeybun@tesco.net — MB BS 1993 Lond.; BSc Lond. 1990; MRCGP 1998; DFFP 1998. (Royal Free) Socs: Assoc. Mem. Assn. Palliat. Med.; BMA. Prev: Bangor VTS Ysbyty Gwynedd.

HONEYMAN, Alasdair Ewen 1 Rowan Court, 29 Dents Road, London SW11 6JA — MB BS 1993 Lond.

HONEYMAN, John Pattison Doctors Surgery, Half Moon Lane, Wigton CA7 9NQ Tel: 016973 42254 Fax: 016973 45464 Email: johnhoneyman@gp-a82045.nhs.uk; Stackyards, Curthwaite, Wigton CA7 8BG Tel: 01228 711181 Email: johnhoneyman@msn.com — MB ChB 1980 Ed.; MRCGP 1984; DObst 1984. (Edinburgh) Clin. Asst. (Elderly Care) Wigton Hosp.; GP Trainer E. Cumbria VTS. Prev: GP Adviser N. Cumbria Health Auth. 1994-1996.

HONEYMAN, Mary Margaret 59 Selly Park Road, Selly Park, Birmingham B29 7PH — MB BS 1978 Newc.; MRCP (UK) 1982; DCH RCP Lond. 1981; Dip. Human & Clin. Genetics Lond. 1984. Prev: Cons. Paediat. Selly Oak Hosp. Birm.; Sen. Regist. (Paediat.) W. Midl. RHA.

HONEYMAN, William Pattison (retired) 4 Marlborough Gardens, Carlisle CA3 9NW Tel: 01228 525072 — MB ChB 1951 Ed.; BSc St. And.

HONEYWILL, Miss Susan 2 Monica Drive, Cheltenham GL50 4NQ Tel: 01242 576505 Email: chan@chan.u-net.com; 12 Taylor Drive, Throop, Bournemouth BH8 0PZ Tel: 01202 527266 Fax: 01202 528494 Email: susan@chan-u-net.com — MB BS 1990 Lond.; FRCS (Eng.) 1997. (UMDS) Specialist Regist. Rotat. Wessex. Socs: Brit. Assn. Accid. & Emerg. Med.; Fac. Accid. & Emerg. Med; Roy. Soc. Med. Prev: SHO Rotat. (Surg.) Gloucestershire Roy. Hosp.

HONG, Mr Alvin Flat 2, 30 Pond Place, London SW3 6QP — MB BChir 1986 Camb.; MA Camb. 1986, MB BChir 1986; FRCS (SN) 1994; FRCS Ed. 1989. Sen. Regist. (Neurosurg.) Addenbrooke's Hosp. Camb.

HONG, Angela Swee Leng 15 St Johns Wood Park, London NW8 6QP Tel: 020 7722 3839 — MB ChB 1991 Bristol. SHO (Gyn.) Univ. Coll. Hosp. Lond. Prev: SHO (O & G) Whipps Cross Hosp. Lond.; Ho. Surg. Roy. Devon & Exeter Hosp.; Ho. Phys. Bristol Roy. Infirm.

HONG, Anne Exeter Oncology Centre, Royal Devon & Exeter Hospital (Wonford), Barrack Road, Exeter EX2 5DW Tel: 01392 402118 Fax: 01392 402112 — MB ChB 1976 Bristol; MRCP (UK) 1981; FRCR 1984; FRCP 1996. (University of Bristol) Cons. Clin. Oncol. Roy. Devon & Exeter Hosp. (Wonford); Cert. Health Economics Univ. Aberd. Prev: Hon. Cons. Radiother. & Oncol. Mt. Vernon Hosp. N.wood; Med. Advis. (Oncol.) Bristol-Myers Co. Ltd.

HONG, Vincent Tat Ee 6 The Spinney, Lancaster LA1 4JQ — MB BCh BAO 1991 NUI.

HONINGS, Franciscus Peter Gerardus Catharina 3 Macarthur Crescent, Stewartfield, east Kilbride, Glasgow G74 4TL — Artsexamen 1993 Maastricht.

HONNAPPA, Honnappa c/o York Medical Locums, 5 Middlebanks, Wiggington, York YO32 2ZF — MB BS 1975 Mysore.

HONNEYMAN, Forster Donald 58 Fleckers Drive, Cheltenham GL51 3BD Tel: 01242 234985 — MB BCh BAO 1945 Belf.; MD Belf. 1952; FRCPI 1986, M 1954; FRCP Ed. 1981, M 1960. (Belf.) Socs: Brit. Geriat. Soc. & Hosp. Cons. & Specialist Assn. Prev: Cons. Geriat. Phys. Delancey Hosp. Cheltenham; Cons. Geriat. Phys. Manor Hosp. Walsall & New Cross Hosp. Wolverhampton; Asst. Phys. Dept. Geriat. & Med. Sunderland Gen. Hosp.

***HONNOR, Sasha Elizabeth** 20 Eleanor Grove, Barnes, London SW13 0JN — MB BS 1994 Lond.

HOO, Carol Angeli 140 Kings Hall Road, Beckenham BR3 1LN — MB BS 1988 West Indies.

HOOD, Catherine Alexandra 53 Oakley Lane, Chinnor OX39 4HT — BM BCh 1994 Oxf.

HOOD, Catriona 44 Fitzjohn's Avenue, London NW3 5LX Tel: 020 7794 0317; 9 Lyndhurst Terrace, London NW3 5QA Tel: 020 7794 6434 — MB ChB 1953 Glas. (Glas.) Socs: Assoc. Mem. Brit. Psychoanalyt. Soc. Prev: Research Fell. (Paediat.) St. Mary's Hosp. Med. Sch. Lond.

HOOD, Christopher Allen Cross Keys Practice, The Surgery, Church Road, Chinnor OX39 4PG Tel: 01844 351584 Fax: 01844 354350; Garfields, Aylesbury Road, Asket, Princes Risborough HP27 9LY — MB BS Lond. 1961. (St. Bart.) Clin. Asst. Surg. Stoke Mandeville Hosp. Aylesbury; Med. Off. Vict. Hosp. Thame, Chilton Ho. Nursing Home & Watlington Cottage Hosp.; Div. Police Surg. Thames Valley; Med. Ref. DHSS; Apptd. Doctor (Fact. Act) Health & Safety Exec; Apptd. Doctor Dept. Vehicle Licencing; Chairm. Bucks/Berks Secretariat LMCs 1996-; Chairm. Bd. Ridgeway PCG. Socs: Assn. Police Surg. Prev: Ho. Off. Med. & Surg. Profess. Units & Intern. Dept. O & G St. Bart. Hosp. Lond.; Asst. Lect. (Anat.) Roy. Free Hosp. Med. Sch. Lond.; Dir. Aylesbury Multiple Sclerosis Clinic.

HOOD, Claire Margaret Benreay Surgery, Seaview Place, Buckie AB56 1JT Tel: 01542 831555 — MB ChB 1979 Aberd.; MRCGP 1983; DRCOG 1983. GP Retainer.

HOOD, David Andrew 38 Carclew St, Truro TR1 2DZ — MB ChB 1991 Birm.; MRCGP 1999; DRCOG Oct 1998. GP Princip., Newquay, Cornw.

HOOD, David Blair Inverurie Medical Group, Health Centre, 1 Constitution Street, Inverurie AB51 4SU Tel: 01467 621345 Fax: 01467 625374 — MB ChB 1977 Aberd.; BMedBiol. Aberd. 1974; MRCGP 1981.

HOOD, Diana Hilary Jacqueline Staithe Surgery, Lower Staithe Road, Stalham, Norwich NR12 9BU Tel: 01692 582000 Fax: 01692 580428 — MB BS 1982 Lond.; BSc Aberd. 1977; MRCGP 1986; DRCOG 1985. (Charing Cross)

HOOD, Diane Jane 41 Faroe Road, London W14 0EL — BM 1980 Soton.

HOOD, Enid Althea 36 West Leys Road, Swanland, North Ferriby HU14 3LX Tel: 01482 633470 — MB BS Durh. 1957; DObst RCOG 1959. (Newc.) Sessional Clin. Med. Off. E. Yorks. Community Healthcare Trust. Prev: SCMO E. Yorks. HA.

HOOD, Gillian 14 Glade Croft, Gleadless, Sheffield S12 2UZ — MB ChB 1980 Leeds; FFA RCS Eng. 1987. Cons. Anaesth. N. Gen. Hosp. Sheff. Prev: Sen. Regist. Anaesth. Sheff.; Regist. (Anaesth.) York HA.

HOOD, Graham James Alloa Health Centre, Marshill, Alloa FK10 1AQ Tel: 01259 216476 — MB ChB 1984 Aberd.; BMedBiol Commend. Aberd. 1981, MB ChB 1984; MRCGP 1988; DRCOG 1986.

HOOD, Hayley Louise Wickersley Health Centre, Poplar Glade, Wickersley, Rotherham S66 2JQ Tel: 01709 549610 Fax: 01709 702470; 24 Lindum Drive, Wickersley, Rotherham S66 1JW — MB ChB 1990 Sheff.; BMedSci Sheff. 1989; MRCGP 1995; DRCOG 1992. (Sheff.)

HOOD, James Alexander The Surgery, Newtown, St Boswells, Melrose TD6 0BJ Tel: 01835 22777 — MB ChB 1958 Ed. (Edin.)

HOOD, James Robertson 9 Lyndhurst Terrace, London NW3 5QA Tel: 020 7794 6434 — MB ChB Glas. 1950; MRCPsych 1971; DPM Eng. 1959. Socs: Brit. Psychoanal Soc. Prev: Cons. Child Psychiat. N.wick Pk. Hosp. & Clin. Research Centre Harrow; Regist. (Psychol. Med.) Hosp. Sick Childr. Gt. Ormond St. Lond.; Asst. Phys. Psychol. Dept. Paddington Green Childr. Hosp.

HOOD, John Flintfields, Sparepenny Lane, Eynsford, Dartford DA4 0JJ Tel: 01322 863215 — MB BS Lond. 1961; FRCP Lond. 1983; MRCP (UK) 1969; MRCS Eng. LRCP Lond. 1960; DCH Eng. 1967; FRCPCH 1997. (St. Mary's) Cons. Paediatr. Qu. Mary's Hosp. Sidcup & Erith Dist. Hosp. Socs: BMA. Prev: Sen. Regist. & Hon. Lect. (Paediat.) Middlx. & Centr. Middlx. Hosps.; Lond.; Regist. (Paediat.) Roy. Infirm. Dundee; SHO Hosp. for Sick Childr. Gt. Ormond St. Lond.

HOOD, John Department of Bacteriology, Glasgow Royal Infirmary, Glasgow G4 0SF Tel: 0141 211 4642 Fax: 0141 552 1524; 155 Cunningham Drive, Giffnock, Glasgow G46 6EW Tel: 0141 633 3785 — MB ChB 1978 Ed.; PhD Ed. 1991; BSc (Hons.) Ed. (Bacteriol.) 1975; MRCP (UK) 1982; FRCPath 1996, M 1985. Cons. Hon. Sen. Clin. Lect. (Bacteriol.) & Head NHS Dept. Glas. Roy. Infirm. Prev: Lect. (Bacteriol.) Univ. Edin.; SHO (Gen. Med.) N. Manch. Gen. Hosp.; SHO (Gen. Med.) Roy. Infirm. Edin.

HOOD, John Edwin Rothesay Surgery, 14 Rothesay Place, Bedford MK40 3PX Tel: 01234 271800 Fax: 01234 353722; Pippins, Brookside, Salph End, Renhold, Bedford MK41 0JL — MRCS Eng. LRCP Lond. 1972. (Roy. Free)

HOOD, John Stephen 10 Hunters Walk, Canal St., Chester CH1 4EB Tel: 01244 355007; Tel: 01244 355007 — MB ChB 1978 Manch.; BSc St. And. 1975; MRCGP 1982; DRCOG 1981. (Universities of St. Andrews and Manchester) Med. & Managing Dir. Border Med. Ltd. Chester; Forens. Med. Examr. Chester.

HOOD, Michael Patrick Health Centre, Prince Consort Road, Gateshead NE8 1NR Tel: 0191 477 2243 — MB BCh 1980 Wales; MRCS Eng. LRCP Lond. 1980; MRCGP 1987.

HOOD, Peter Alexander (retired) 18 Lansdowne Road, Yarm TS15 9NX Tel: 01642 785665 — MB ChB 1946 Glas.

HOOD, Stephen Victor 18 Chelmer Drive, Dunmow CM6 1HL — BM 1989 Soton.

HOOD, Valerie Davidson 123 Terregles Avenue, Glasgow G41 4DG Tel: 0141 423 7498 Fax: 0141 423 7498 — MB ChB 1973 Glas.; MRCOG 1978; FRCOG 1990. Cons. O & G S.. Gen. Hosp.; Hon. Clin. Lect. Glas.

HOOD, William Alistair Fenton Stokewood Surgery, Fair Oak Road, Fair Oak, Eastleigh SO50 8AU Tel: 023 8069 2000 Fax: 023 8069 3891 — MB BCh BAO 1976 Belf.

HOOD, William Goudielock Lintzford, Crown Point, Sprouston Road, Kelso TD5 Tel: 01573 24669 — MB ChB 1946 St. And.; DLO Eng. 1949. (St. And.) Cons. (ENT) W.. Infirm. Glas., Glas. Homoeop. Hosp. & Gartnavel; Gen. Hosp. Glas. Socs: Scott. Otolaryng. Soc. & Brit. Allergists Assn. Prev: Tutor Anat. Univ. St. And.

HOOD, William John Marshall (retired) 36 West Leys Road, Swanland, North Ferriby HU14 3LX Tel: 01482 633470 Email: billh@wjmh.karoo.co.uk — MB ChB 1959 Ed.; DA Eng. 1970; DObst RCOG 1961; Cert. Contracep. & Family Plann. RCOG, RCGP & Family Plann. Assn. 1976. Prev: GP Hull.

HOODBHOY, Abdullah Peermuhammed Riverside Health Centre, Station Road, Manningtree CO11 1AA Tel: 01206 396135 Fax: 01206 391570; Ashiana, Long Road W., Dedham, Colchester CO7 6EP Tel: 01206 322015 Fax: 01206 323645 Email: hoodbhoy@compuserve.com — MB BS 1968 Sind; Dip Ven Soc. Apoth. Lond. 1976; DTM & H Liverp. 1968. (Liaquat Med. Coll.) Hosp. Pract. (Venereol.) Ipswich Hosp. (Heath Rd. Wing). Socs: MSSVD. Prev: Hosp. Pract. (Geriat.) Heath Hosp. Tendring.; Regist. (Med.) Bournemouth & E. Dorset Gp. Hosps.; SHO (Med.) LoughBoro. Gen. Hosp.

HOODBOY, Shazia Abdullah Long Road W., Dedham, Colchester CO7 6EP — BM BS 1996 Nottm.

HOOFTMAN, Leonard Willem Frederik 17 Bellevue Road, London W13 8DF — Artsexamen 1985 Utrecht. Clin. Research Maidenhead UK & Palo Alto, USA. Prev: Regist. Hammersmith Hosp. Lond.; SHO Rotat. Plymouth; Resid. Orthop. Utrecht, Holland.

HOOGEWERF, Mary Hurst Place Surgery, 294A Hurst Road, Bexley DA5 3LH Tel: 020 8300 2826 Fax: 020 8309 0661; 5 Harley, Manor Park, Chislehurst BR7 5QQ Tel: 020 8467 0182 — MRCS Eng. LRCP Lond. 1957. (Roy. Free)

HOOGSTEDEN, Lucia St Mary's Hospital, Department of Anaesthesia, Praed St., London W2 1NY Tel: 020 7886 6666; 46 Kennet Street, London E1W 2JJ — Artsexamen 1986 Utrecht; FFARACS 1997.

HOOI, Yu Sing 3 Elwin Street, Bethnal Green, London E2 7BU — MB ChB 1975 Liverp.; MRCOG 1980. Cons. Genitourin. Med. Newham Gen. Hosp. Lond. & Barking Hosp. Essex.

HOOK, Alexandra Christian Philp 10 Granton Road, Edinburgh EH5 3QH — MB ChB 1966 Ed.; MRCGP 1990; DTM & H Liverp. 1992. Prev: Community Med. Off. W. Berks. HA; Med. Adviser MCOD; Med. Off. St. Mary's Hosp. Kwamagwaza, Zululand.

HOOK, Allen (retired) The Spinney, Teversal, Sutton-in-Ashfield NG17 3JN Tel: 01623 516122 — MB ChB 1955 Sheff. Prev: Med. Off. RAF.

HOOK, John Leslie Fax: 02380 825693; 54 Wilton Road, Shirley, Southampton SO15 5LB — MB BS 1978 Lond.; MSc Lond. 1991; MRCPsych 1983. (Middlx. Hosp.) Cons. Psychother. Roy. S. Hants. Hosp. Socs: M Inst. GA Lond. 1995. Prev: Sen. Regist. St. Geo. Hosp. Lond.(Psychother.).

HOOK, Mr Peter Charles Gordon Bluepot, Silver St., Culmstock, Cullompton EX15 3JE; P.O. Box 638, Crowsnest, Sydney NSW 2065, Australia Tel: 00 61 2 9906 2844 Fax: 00 61 2 9438 2374 — MB BChir 1983 Camb.; BDS Sydney 1976; FRCS Ed. 1988; LMSSA Lond. 1983; FFD RCSI 1984; FDS RCS Eng. 1986; T(S) 1991. (Camb.) Cons. (Maxillofacial Surg.) Crowsnest Sydney; Assoc. Mem. Brit. Assn. Oral & Maxillofacial Surgs. Prev: Sen. Regist. Maxillofacial Unit Walton Hosp. Liverp.; Regist. Maxillofacial Unit St. Richards Hosp. Chichester; Regist. Dept. Oral Surg. Qu. Vict. Hosp. E. Grinstead.

HOOK, Peter John 421 Banbury Road, Oxford OX2 8ED Tel: 01865 558184 — MB ChB St. And. 1959; DObst RCOG 1961. Med. Off. Bd. Inland Revenue. Socs: BMA; Fell. Roy. Soc. of Med. Prev: Sen. Med. Off. DHSS; Ho. Off. Craigtoun Matern. Hosp. St. And., Maryfield Hosp. Dundee & Bridge of Earn Hosp.

HOOK, Richard Alan Healdswood Surgery, Mansfield Road, Skegby, Sutton-in-Ashfield NG17 3EE Tel: 01623 513553 Fax: 01623 550753; Wharf Farm, Mansfield Road, Tibshelf, Alfreton DE55 5NG — MB ChB 1986 Birm. Gen. Pract.; Chairm. N. Notts CMC 1998; GP Occupat. Health Sutton-in-Ashfield; Occupat.al Health Phys. to Sherwood Forest Hosp.s NHS Trust; Exec. Bd. Mem. on Ashfeld Primary Care Trust. Prev: SHO (Paediat., O & G, Psychiat. & Cas.) Wolverhampton Gp. Hosps.; Ho. Off. (Surg.) Birm. Gen. Hosp.; Ho. Phys. Walsall Manor Hosp.

HOOK, Mr William Edwin Sarum Road Hospital, Sarum Road, Winchester SO22 5HA Tel: 01962 844555 — MB ChB 1973 Aberd.; MChOrth Liverp. 1983; FRCS Ed. 1977. Cons. Orthop. Surg. Roy. Hants. Co. Hosp. Winchester. Prev: Sen. Regist. (Orthop. Surg.) Mersey RHA; Regist. (Orthop. Surg.) S. Birm. HA.

HOOKE, Rachel Louise Derlett, 16 Longrood Road, Bilton, Rugby CV22 7RG — MB ChB 1994 Leic.

HOOKER, Alfred Gordon (retired) Brand House, Ludlow SY8 1NN Tel: 01584 872591 — MRCS Eng. LRCP Lond. 1940; MRCS Eng., LRCP Lond. 1940. Prev: Capt. RAMC.

HOOKER, Andrew Neil Towcester Medical Centre, Link Way, Towcester NN12 6HH Tel: 01327 359953 Fax: 01327 358929 — MB BChir 1971 Camb.; MA Camb. 1972; DObst RCOG 1973. (Camb. & Guy's) Prev: Trainee GP N.ampton VTS; SHO (Anaesth.) N.ampton Gen. Hosp.; Ho. Phys. N.wick Pk. Hosp. & Clin. Research Centre.

HOOKER, David (retired) Buckshead House, 195 Bodmin Road, Truro TR1 1RA Tel: 01872 272627 — MB BS 1952 Lond.; MRCGP 1967; DObst RCOG 1957. Med Ref. PenMt. Crematorium Truro. Prev: Capt. RAMC.

HOOKER, Mr Jonathan Gordon St Richard's Hospital, The Royal West Sussex Trust, Chichester PO19 4SE Tel: 01243 788122 Fax: 01243 831432; 19 The Avenue, Chichester PO19 4PX Tel: 01243 774857 — MB 1975 Camb.; BChir 1974; MRCOG 1982; DRCOG 1979. (Middlx.) Cons. O & G Chichester. Prev: Clin. Lect. (O & G) Univ. Coll. Lond.; Trainee Fell. (Perinatal Med.) Univ. Coll. Lond.; Regist. (O & G) Birm. HA.

HOOKER, Richard Chenoweth 2 Woodside Road, New Malden KT3 3AH — MB BS 1985 Lond.; MRCGP 1989; DCH RCP Lond.

1989. Asst. & Princip. (Primary Care Outreach) Lond. Outreach Project. Prev: Clin. Asst. (Hypertens. Clin.) Centr. Middlx. Hosp.; Clin. Asst. (Genitourin. Med.) Char. Cross Hosp.

HOOKS, Irene Catherine 55 Balmoral Avenue, Belfast BT9 6NX Tel: 01232 660655 — MB BCh BAO 1955 Belf.; DA Eng. 1958.

HOOKWAY, Kathryn Margaret Dr D J McNie and Partners, 4 St. Barnabas Road, Caversham, Reading RG4 8RA Tel: 0118 478123 — MB BS 1978 Newc.; MRCGP 1983; DRCOG 1981; DCH 1981.

HOOKWAY, Max Olof 1 Cranbury Court, 10 Cranbury Terrace, Southampton SO14 0LH — BM 1994 Soton.

HOOLE, Lady Eleanor Mary (retired) Yew Tree House, St Nicholas Hill, Leatherhead KT22 8NE Tel: 01372 373208 — MRCS Eng. LRCP Lond. 1947. Prev: Clin. Asst. Epsom Dist. Hosp.

HOOLE, Kathleen Community Child Health Department, Eastgate Ward, District Hospital, Peterborough PE3 6DA Tel: 01733 874914 Fax: 01733 562187 — MB ChB Manch. 1970; DCH RCP Lond. 1983; FRCPCH 1997. (Manch.) Cons. Community Paediat. S. PeterBoro. Primary Care Trust. Prev: SCMO P'boro. & N. Lincs. HA.

HOOLE, Philip Mark Shepherd Spring Medical Centre, Cricketers Way, Andover SP10 5DE Tel: 01264 361126 Fax: 01264 350138; Sarson Farm, Monxton Road, Amport, Andover SP11 8AQ — MB BS 1982 Lond.; MRCGP 1987.

HOOLE, Sarah Mary 1A Francis Avenue, St Albans AL3 6BL — MB ChB 1994 Leeds.

***HOOLE, Stephen Paul** 3 April Close, The marld, Ashtead KT21 1RE Tel: 01372 272206 Email: stevehoole@doctors.org.uk — BM BCh 1998 Oxf.; BM BCh Oxf 1998; BA 1995.

HOOPER, Alison Irene 9 Brymore Close, Bridgwater TA6 7PL — MB ChB 1981 Sheff.

HOOPER, Anita 14 Beaconsfield Road, Blackheath, London SE3 7LZ Tel: 020 8858 0716 — MB BS 1959 Bombay; FRCS Ed. 1962; MRCOG 1964, DObst 1961. (Topiwala Nat. Med. Coll. Bombay) SCMO (Community Health) Greenwich HA Lond. Prev: Regist. O & G Roy. N.. Hosp. Lond., City of Lond. Matern.; Hosp. & Highlands Gen. Hosp. Lond. & Kingston Hosp.; Kingston-on-Thames.

HOOPER, Mr Anthony Augustus 152 Harley Street, London W1N 1HH Tel: 020 7935 0444 Fax: 020 7224 2574; 209 Baring Road, Grove Park, London SE12 0PX Tel: 020 8857 7434 — MB BChir 1959 Camb.; MA Camb; FRCS Eng. 1969; MRCOG 1966, DObst 1963. (Westm.) Socs: Brit. Soc. Gastroenterol. & Brit. Assn. Surg. Oncol.; Assoc. Mem. BAUS. Prev: Sen. Regist. Roy. Marsden Hosp.; Resid. Surg. Off. Qu. Mary's Hosp. Stratford; Regist. (Surg.) Harold Wood Hosp.

HOOPER, Arthur John (retired) Quabbs House, Drybrook GL17 9JD — MB BCh Wales 1950. Prev: Anaesth. Dilke Memor. Hosp. Cinderford.

HOOPER, Blanche Margaret (retired) Swatchways, Farm End, London E4 7QS Tel: 020 8529 2242 — MB BS Lond. 1953; MRCS Eng. LRCP Lond. 1952. Prev: Clin. Asst. Wanstead Hosp. & Chingford Hosp. Lond.

HOOPER, Bryony Kate Aylmerton House, 8 Hitchin Road, Shefford SG17 5JA — BM 1986 Soton.; Dip. Public Health, Camb. 2000; MRCGP 1991; DRCOG 1988; LLM Cardiff, 1999. Specialist Regist. (Pub. Health Med.), E.ern Region. Prev: Trainee GP Soton. VTS; GP Partner Drs Townend, Littlejohn, Hooper & McDermott, Soton.

HOOPER, Carl Anthony Gorwelion, Llanbadarn Road, Aberystwyth SY23 1HB Tel: 01970 635410; 1 Dyfed Terrace, Swansea SA1 6NT — MB BS 1983 Lond.; MRCPsych 1988. Cons. Psychiat. Derwen NHS Trust.

HOOPER, Carol Louise 21 Carless Avenue, Harbourne, Birmingham B17 9BN — MB ChB 1989 Birm.

HOOPER, Catherine Ann Queens Medical Centre, 6/7 Queen Street, Barnstaple EX32 8HY Tel: 01271 372672 Fax: 01271 341902; Highbury, Long Lane, Diddywell, Bideford EX39 1NJ — MB ChB 1977 Leeds. GP Princip.; CMO Family Plann.; Clin. Asst. Ophth.

HOOPER, Charles Robert Byron Shenley, Stourbridge Road, Wombourn, Wolverhampton WV5 9BN Tel: 01902 2209 — MB ChB 1952 Birm. (Birm.) Prev: Ho. Surg. & Ho. Phys. St. Chad's Hosp. Birm.; Ho. Surg. O & G Dept. Lancaster Roy. Infirm.; Med. Off. Matern. Dept. David Bruce Memor. Hosp. Malta.

HOOPER, Daniel Keith Buchanan Milngavie Road Surgery, 85 Milngavie Road, Bearsden, Glasgow G61 2DN Tel: 0141 211 5621 Fax: 0141 211 5625 — MB ChB 1992 Aberd.

HOOPER, Deanne Margaret Whitley House Surgery, Moulsham Street, Chelmsford CM2 0JJ — MB BS 1996 Lond.; DCH 1999; DRCOG 1999. (Lond.) GP Regist.; Chelmsford GP VTS. Prev: Ho. Off. (Gen. Med.); Ho. Off. (Gen. Surg.).

HOOPER, Douglas Charles Old Station House, Ellerhayes, Hele, Exeter EX5 4PU — MB BS 1996 Lond.

HOOPER, Edgar Roy Sheerman, TD (retired) 125 Hill Village Road, Sutton Coldfield B75 5HU Tel: 0121 308 0407 — MB BS 1949 Lond.; MRCS Eng. LRCP Lond. 1949; FFA RCS Eng. 1954; DA Eng. 1951. Prev: Cons. Anaesth. Lichfield, Tamworth & Sutton Coldfield Hosp. Gp.

HOOPER, Evelyn Jean Lower Muckleford House, Dorchester DT2 9SW Tel: 01305 262753 — MB BS Lond. 1954. (Lond. Hosp.) Med. Asst. Geriat. Dorset Co. Hosp. Dorchester. Late Ho. Phys. Dorset Co. Hosp. Dorchester. Prev: Ho. Surg. S. Lond. Hosp. Wom. & Childr.

HOOPER, Fiona Dorothea Mary (retired) Wilton House, Upper High St., Taunton TA1 3PX — MB BS 1954 Lond. Prev: Clin. Med. Off. (Community Health) Norf. AHA.

HOOPER, Mr Geoffrey 27 Abercorn Terrace, Edinburgh EH15 2DF — MB ChB 1970 St. And. 1980; MMsc Dundee 1973; FRCS Eng. 1976; FRCS (Orthop.) Ed. 1980. Cons. Orthop. & Hand Surg. St. John's Hosp. Livingston & P.ss Margt. Rose Hosp. Edin.; Hon. Sen. Lect. (Orthop. Surg.) Univ. Edin. Socs: Fell. BOA; Brit. Soc. Surg. Hand.; Brit. Orthopaedic Research Soc.

HOOPER, Gerard Shepherd's Hey, Church Lane, Old Dalby, Melton Mowbray LE14 3LB — MB ChB 1964 Ed.; BSc Ed. 1962, MB ChB 1964; FFPM RCP (UK) 1991; Dip. Pharm. Med. RCP (UK) 1977. (Ed.) Dir. Clin. Progr. Clin. Research Internat. (Europe) Ltd. York; Clin. Research Phys. Pharmaceut. Profiles Ltd. Nottm.; Sec. Quorn Research Review Comm. Prev: Research & Developm. Dir. (Europe) Norwich-Eaton Pharmaceut.; Med. Adviser Wellcome Foundat. SE Asia & Japan; Lect. (Pharmacol.) Univ. Edin.

HOOPER, Henrietta Jane 13 Ivor Place, London NW1 6HS — MB BChir 1981 Camb.; MA Camb. 1982, MB BChir 1981. Prev: Ho. Phys. Lond. Hosp.; Ho. Surg. OldCh. Hosp. Romford.

HOOPER, John Morton Douglas (retired) Bakersbarn, Golford Rd, Cranbrook TN17 3NW Tel: 01580 713344 — BM BCh 1950 Oxf.; MA, BM BCh Oxf. 1950; DObst RCOG 1955; DCH Eng. 1956. Prev: Ho. Phys. Childr. Dept. Guy's Hosp.

HOOPER, Judith Mary Calderdale & Kirklees HA, St Lukes House, Blackmoorfoot Road, Huddersfield HD4 5RH Tel: 01484 466000 Fax: 01484 466111 — MB ChB 1978 Birm.; MSc Pub. Health Newc. 1991; MRCGP 1982; T(GP) 1991; DRCOG 1980; T(PHM) 1996; FFPHM 2000 RCP (UK). Cons. Pub. Health Med. Calderdale & Kirklees HA; GP Huddersfield. Socs: Brit. Med. Acupunct. Soc.; Soc. Social Med.; (Treas.) Pub. Health & Primary Care Gp. Prev: Lect. (Primary Health Care) Newc. Univ.; SCMO (Adult Health) Bury HA.

HOOPER, Kathleen Hope Childrens Hospital, Doncaster Royal Infirmary, Armthorpe Road, Doncaster DN2 5 Tel: 01302 36666; 1C Whin Hill Road, Bessacarr, Doncaster DN4 7AE Tel: 01302 537806 — MB ChB 1970 Sheff.; MSc (Audiol. Med.) Manch. 1996; DObst RCOG 1972. (Sheff.) Assoc. Specialist (Paediat.) Doncaster Roy. Infirm. Socs: MRCPCH; Brit. Audiol. Soc.; BACDA. Prev: SCMO Doncaster Roy. Infirm.; Clin. Med. Off. Doncaster AHA; SHO (Obst.) Doncaster Roy. Infirm.

HOOPER, Kathleen Margaret Easterhouse Health Centre, 9 Auchinlea Road, Glasgow G34 9HQ Tel: 0141 771 0781; Claddens House, Lindsaybeg Road, Lenzie, Glasgow G66 5LL Tel: 0141 776 6315 — MRCS Eng. LRCP Lond. 1964. (Manch.)

HOOPER, Lucy Anne Flat 3/2, 272 Crow Road, Glasgow G11 7LB — MB ChB 1995 Aberd.

HOOPER, Margaret (retired) 22 Washington Street, Chichester PO19 3BN — MB BS 1954 Lond. Prev: Med. Asst. Littlemore Hosp. Oxf.

HOOPER, Margaret Beryl The Surgery, 1536 Pershore Road, Stirchley, Birmingham B30 2NW Tel: 0121 458 1031 Fax: 0121 459 1182; 205 Pershore Road, Edgbaston, Birmingham B5 7PF — MB ChB 1969 Birm.; DObst RCOG 1971. Socs: BMA.

***HOOPER, Michael Crispin** 16 Troddi Close, Caldicot, Newport NP26 4PW — MB ChB 1998 Bristol; MA Cambridge 1998.

HOOPER, Michael David (retired) 287 New Mill Road, Brock Holes, Huddersfield HD9 7AL Tel: 01484 660535 — MB BCh BAO

1970 NUI; DObst RCPI 1986; Cert. Family Plann. JCC 1986; Dip. Sports Med. Lond. 1985; MICGP 1984. Prev: GP Huddersfield.

HOOPER, Nicholas Robert Joseph, RD Wrington Vale Medical Group, Station Road, Wrington, Bristol BS40 5NG Tel: 01934 862532 Fax: 01934 863568; Langford Place, Langford, Bristol BS40 5BT — MB ChB 1971 Bristol; DObst RCOG 1973.

HOOPER, Paul Arthur 5 West Heath Drive, London NW11 7QG Tel: 020 8455 1531 — MB BS 1982 Lond.; BDS Lond. 1976, MB BS 1982; FDS RCS Eng. 1984.

HOOPER, Paul Derek (retired) Selborne, Pyle Shute, Chale, Ventnor PO38 2LE Tel: 01983 551432 — MB ChB 1949 Birm.; FRCGP 1974; DObst RCOG 1957. Prev: Geo. Swift Lect.

HOOPER, Paul Julian Inwood Cottage, Inwood, All Stretton, Church Stretton SY6 6LA — MB ChB 1991 Liverp.

HOOPER, Rachel Ann 20 Radnor Green, Barry CF62 9AR — MB ChB 1993 Leeds.

HOOPER, Richard William Hedley 3 Manor Cottages, Westbrook, Blewbury, Didcot OX11 9QG — BChir 1984 Camb.; BChir Camb. l984.

HOOPER, Ronald James Loveluck Department of Clinical Biochemistry, Royal Brompton and Harefield NHS Trust, Sydney St., London SW3 6NP Tel: 020 7351 8414 Fax: 020 7351 8416 Email: j.hooper@rbh.nthames.nhs.uk; 70 Friars Walk, Southgate, London N14 5LN Tel: 020 8368 7489 — MB BS 1975 Lond.; BSc (Hons.) Lond. 1972, MD 1982; MRCS Eng. LRCP Lond. 1975; FRCPath 1997. (St. Mary's) Cons. Chem. Path. & Hon. Sen. Lect. Univ. Lond. Roy. Brompton Hosp.; Cons. Chem. Path. Roy. Marsden Hosp.; Clin. Dir. Laborat. Med. Roy. Brompton Hosp.; Hon. Research Fell. St. Mary's Hosp. Med. Sch. Lond.; Div.al Dir. Clin. Support Serv. Roy. Brompton Hosp.; Hon. Cons. Chem. Path. Roy. Lond. Hosp. Socs: Roy. Soc. Med. (Pres.-Elect); Assn. Clin. Biochem. (Nat. Mem. & Director Computer Aided Learning; Internat. Federat. Clin. Chem. (Chairm. Computer Aided Comm.). Prev: Sen. Regist. (Chem. Path.) Middlx. Univ. Coll. Hosp.; Wellcome Fell. Univ. Camb., St. Mary's Hosp. Med. Sch. & St. Bart. Hosp. Med. Coll. Lond.; Ho. Off. (Med. & Surg.) St. Mary's Hosp. Lond.

HOOPER, Ruth I 9 Brymore Close, Bridgwater TA6 7PL — MB ChB 1952 Glas. (Glas.) Med. Off. SW Region. Transfus. Serv. Prev: Med. Off. NE Metrop. Transfus. Servs.; on Staff Addington Hosp. Durban; Ho. Off. Roy. Alexandra Infirm. Paisley.

HOOPER, Susan Elizabeth 14 Beaconsfield Road, Blackheath, London SE3 7LZ — MB ChB 1990 Leeds.

HOOPER, Mr Timothy Lloyd Department Cardiothoracic Surgery, Wythenshawe Hospital, Southmoor Road, Manchester M23 9LT — MB ChB 1979 Manch.; BSc Manch. 1976, MD 1990; FRCS Ed. 1983; FRCS Eng. 1983. Cons. Cardiothoracic Surg. Wythenshawe Hosp. Manch.

HOOPER, Timothy Michael Castlehead Medical Centre, Ambleside Road, Keswick CA12 4DB Tel: 017687 72025 Fax: 017687 73862 — MB ChB 1988 Leeds; MRCGP 1994; DA (UK) 1992; DRCOG 1993.

HOOPER, William Laurence (retired) West Dene, 6A Cavendish Road, Bournemouth BH1 1RD Tel: 01202 555813 — MB BCh Wales 1957; BSc Wales 1953; FRCPath 1977, M 1965; Dip. Bact. Lond 1963. Prev: Cons. Microbiol. & Dir. Area Pub. Health Laborat. Poole.

HOOSEN, Yasmin 36 Eyebrook Road, Bowdon, Altrincham WA14 3LP — MB ChB 1997 Manch.

HOOSON, Timothy Kevin 7 Swift Street, Barnsley S75 2SN — MB ChB 1988 Sheff.; T(GP) 1993. SHO Barnsley Dist. Gen. Hosp.

HOOTON, Mr Norman Stanwell (retired) Almonds, Silverhill, Robertsbridge TN32 5PA Tel: 01580 880455 — MA, MB BChir Camb. 1944; FRCS Eng. 1949. Prev: Cons. Thoracic Surg. S.E. Thames Region.

HOPAYIAN, Kevork The Surgery, Main Street, Leiston IP16 4ES Tel: 01728 830526 Fax: 01728 832029 — MB BS 1980 Lond.; BSc (Hons.) Lond. 1976; FRCGP 1995, M 1984; DRCOG 1983; DCH RCP Lond. 1982. Prev: Trainee GP Redhill Surrey VTS; Clin. Asst. (Geriat.) Ipswich Hosp.; SHO (Paediat.) Bedford Gen. Hosp.

HOPCROFT, Joanne Paula Fern House Surgery, 125-129 Newland Street, Witham CM8 1BH Tel: 01376 502108 Fax: 01376 502281; 26 Augustus Way, Witham CM8 1HH — MB ChB 1986 Sheff.; DRCOG 1989.

HOPCROFT, John David The Health Centre, Dunning St., Stoke-on-Trent ST6 5AP Tel: 01782 577522; 22 Swettenham Close, Alsager, Stoke-on-Trent ST7 2XG Tel: 01782 577522 — MB ChB 1975 Birm. Clin. Asst. (Geriat.) W.cliffe & Stanfields Hosps. Stoke-on-Trent. Prev: Gp Wilmslow; Resid. Clin. Path. Manch. Roy. Infirm.; Trainee GP Cheadle Hulme VTS.

HOPCROFT, Keith Antony Laindon Health Centre, Laindon, Basildon SS15 5TR Tel: 01268 546411 Fax: 01268 491248 — MB BS 1984 Lond.; MRCGP 1988; DGM RCP Lond. 1987; DRCOG 1987. GP Laindon Health Centre, Basildon.

HOPCROFT, Mr Peter Wilson Kewyon Rooms, 7 Kewyon Rd, Wigan WN1 2DH Tel: 01942 679703 Fax: 01942 826580; Ashfield, 18 Tan House Lane Parbold, Wigan WN8 7HG Tel: 01257 462407 — MB ChB 1965 Ed.; MChOrth Liverp. 1976; FRCS Ed. 1973. (Ed.) p/t Cons. Orthop. & Traum. Surg. Wrightington, Wigan & Leigh Hosp. Trust. Socs: Brit. Orthop. Assn.; BMA.; Liverp. Med. Inst. Prev: Sen. Regist. (Orthop.) Preston Roy. Infirm., Wrightington Hosp.; Appley Bridge & Sen. Regist. (Orthop.) Withington Hosp. S. Manch.

HOPCROFT, Richard Wilson 18 Tan House Lane, Parbold, Wigan WN8 7HG — MB ChB 1993 Liverp.

HOPE, Alan Thomas 109 Southbrae Drive, Glasgow G13 1TU — MB ChB 1984 Ed.; DA UK 1986. SHO (Anaesth.) Freeman Hosp. Newc.

HOPE, Andrew Malcolm, TD St Johns Cross Farm, Marsh Lane, Sheffield S21 5RH — MB BS 1956 Lond. (Lond. Hosp.) Final Exam. Med. Off. RN & Roy. Marines Derby. Prev: Ho. Surg. Childr. Hosp. Sheff.; Ho. Phys. Doncaster Roy. Infirm.; Sen. Ho. Off. (O & G) W. Hosp. Doncaster.

HOPE, Brian MacDonald Road Medical Centre, MacDonald Road, Irlam, Manchester M44 5LH Tel: 0161 775 5421 Fax: 0161 775 2568 — MB ChB 1982 Dundee; MRCGP 1987; DRCOG 1986. Sec. Salford LMC.

HOPE, Mrs Bridget Margaret (retired) Stone Lea, The Street, Acton, Turville, Badminton GL9 1HH — MB ChB 1960 Ed.

HOPE, Christopher John (retired) Horseshoes, 15 Pynchon Paddocks, Little Hallingbury, Bishop's Stortford CM22 7RJ Tel: 01279 723258 Fax: 01279 723528 Email: chruzena@aol.com — MB ChB 1967 Liverp. Prev: GP Bishop's Stortford.

HOPE, David Alan 11 Inglefield Avenue, Heath, Cardiff CF14 3PY — BM 1984 Soton.

HOPE, Mr David Terence The Nunnery, Hemington, Derby DE74 2SQ Tel: 0115 970 9102; The Nunnery, Hemington, Derby DE74 2SQ Tel: 01332 811724 — MB ChB 1970 Liverp.; ChM Liverp. 1981; FRCS Eng. 1976. (Liverp.) Cons. Neurosurg. Qu. Med. Centre Nottm.; Examr. RCS Eng. & Intercollegiate (Neurosurg.). Socs: Soc. for Brit. Neurol. Surgs.; Nottm. M-C Soc. Prev: Sen. Regist. (Neurosurg.) Frenchay Hosp. Bristol; MRC Train. Fell. (Neurosurg.) Nat. Hosp. Nerv. Dis. Lond.; Sen. Regist. (Neurosurg.) Baptish Memor. Memphis, Tenn.

HOPE, Elizabeth Ann Marie 12 Cloonavon Park, Coleraine BT52 1RU — MB BCh BAO 1985 Belf.; MRCGP 1996. (Qu. Univ. Belf.)

HOPE, Mr Geoffrey Ardern (retired) 89 Stockton Lane, York YO31 1JA Tel: 01904 423188 — MB ChB 1960 Manch.; FRCS Eng. 1969; DObst RCOG 1962. Prev: Cons. ENT York Health Dist.

HOPE, George Malcolm The Old Manse, Ardeonaig, Killin FK21 8SX — MB ChB 1971 Glas.; MRCP (UK) 1977; Dip. Amer. Bd. Pediat. 1977; Dip. Amer. Bd. Emerg. Med. 1983.

HOPE, Humphrey Dugdale Astley (retired) The Bridge, Hungerford RG17 0DL Tel: 01488 682842 — MB BS 1948 Lond.; BDS Lond. 1954; LDS RCS Eng. 1954, DOrth 1961. Prev: Hon. Scientif. Adviser to BDJl.

HOPE, James Glen (retired) 18 Buckstone Wood, Edinburgh EH10 6QW Tel: 0131 445 3606 — MB ChB 1961 Ed.

HOPE, James Ian 45 Winterbourne Road, Solihull B91 1LX — MB ChB 1983 Leeds.

HOPE, Judith Alice 13 Ivy House Road, Lowton, Warrington WA3 2EX — MB ChB 1981 Otago; MRCPsych 1993.

HOPE, Katherine Mary 4 Beaumont Road, Windsor SL4 1HY Tel: 01753 855889 — MB BS 1972 Lond.; MRCS Eng. LRCP Lond. 1972; MRCGP 1981. (Roy. Free) Med. Advisor, BG Internat.; Cons. Med. Advis Medicom Excel Esher Surrey.

HOPE, Mildred Vivienne (retired) Garden House, Glen Andred, Colway Lane, Lyme Regis DT7 3HE Tel: 01297 443003 — MRCS Eng. LRCP Lond. 1951. Prev: SCMO (Ment. Health) E. Surrey HA.

HOPE, Mr Peter Gordon Department of Orthopaedics, Lister Hospital, Coreys Mill, Stevenage SG1 4AB Tel: 01438 781215 Fax: 01438 781274; Tel: 01462 441415 Fax: 01462 441415 Email: peter.hope@which.net — MB BS 1979 Lond.; BSc Lond. 1976; FRCS Eng. 1983. Cons. Orthop. Surg. Lister Hosp. Stevenage; Cons. Orthop. Surg. Pinehill Hosp., Hitchin. Prev: Sen. Regist. (Orthop.) St. Mary's Hosp. Lond.; Regist. N.. Gen. Hosp. Sheff.; Regist. (Accid. Serv.) John Radcliffe Hosp. Oxf.

HOPE, Ronald Anthony Ethox, Institute of Health Sciences, Old Road, Headington, Oxford OX3 7LF Tel: 01865 226936 Fax: 01865 226938 Email: tony.hope@ethox.ox.ac.uk; 45 Beech Croft Road, Oxford OX2 7AY Tel: 01865 316782 Fax: 01865 311860 — BM BCh 1980 Oxf.; PhD Lond. 1978; MA Oxf. 1977; FRCPsych 1997, M 1984. Reader (Med.), Univ. Lect. (Pract. Skills) & Hon. Cons. Psychiat. John Radcliffe Hosp. Oxf.; Inst. Med. Ethics (Edit. Asst. Jl. Med. Ethics.). Prev: Clin. Lect. (Psychiat.) Univ. Oxf.

HOPE, Sally Louise Park Lane Surgery, Park Lane, Woodstock OX20 1UD Tel: 01993 811452 — BM BCh 1981 Oxf.; MA Oxf. 1982, BM BCh 1981; MRCGP 1986; DRCOG 1986. (Oxford)

HOPE, Sarah Anne Rosemary Cottage, Offley, Hitchin SG5 3AG — MB ChB 1989 Ed.

HOPE, Steven Michael Bracondale House Medical Centre, 141 Buxton Road, Heaviley, Stockport SK2 6EQ Tel: 0161 483 2811 Fax: 0161 487 4221 — MB ChB 1973 Liverp.

HOPE-GILL, Benjamin David Michael Flat A, Sealyham Block, Fishguard Road, Haverfordwest SA61 2PY — MB ChB 1993 Sheff.; BMedSci Sheff. 1990; MRCP (UK) 1996. (Sheff.) Specialist Regist. (Thoracic & Gen. Med.) Penbrokeshire & Derwich NHS Trust HaverfordW. Socs: Roy. Free Coll. Phys.s Edin.; Brit. Thoracic Soc.; Welsh Thoracic Soc. Prev: Sen. SHO (Gen. Med.) Chesterfield & N. Derbysh. Roy. Hosp., Chesterfield.

HOPE-GILL, Michael Charles Bethany House Surgery, 85 Battle Road, Hailsham BN27 1UA Tel: 01323 848485 Fax: 01323 847988 — MB ChB 1984 Sheff.; PhD Camb. 1974, MA 1966. Prev: Regist. (Psychiat.) Middlewood Hosp. Sheff.; SHO (A & E) Childr. Hosp. Sheff. & Bassetlaw Dist. Gen. Hosp.

HOPE-ROSS, Miss Wanda Monica Birmingham & Midland Eye Centre, City Hospital NHS Trust, Dudley Road, Birmingham B18 7QU Tel: 0121 554 3801 Fax: 0121 507 6791 Email: chell-hope-ross@msn.com; Birchdene, 2 Kington Rise, Claverton, Warwick CV35 8PN Tel: 01926 843833 Fax: 01926 843833 — MB BCh BAO 1983 NUI; FRCS Eng. 1988; MRCPI 1985; FCOphth 1989; DO Dub. 1987. (Univ. Coll. Dub.) Cons. Ophth. Surg. Birm. & Midl. Eye Centre; Hon. Sen. Clin. Lect. Birm. Univ. Socs: Fell. Roy. Coll. Ophth; Midl. Ophthal. Soc. (Hon. Sec.); UK & Irel. Soc. Cataract & Refractice Surg. Prev: Sen. Regist. (Ophth.) Birm. & Midl. Eye Hosp. Birm.; Regist. (Ophth.) Roy. Vict. Hosp. Belf. & Roy. Vict. Eye & Ear Hosp. Dub.

HOPE-SIMPSON, Robert Edgar, OBE (retired) 46 Chesterton Park, Cirencester GL7 1XT Tel: 01285 654530 — MRCS Eng. LRCP Lond. 1932; FRCGP 1969. Prev: Dir. Epidemiol. Research Unit Cirencester.

HOPE-STONE, Harold Francis (retired) The Mallards, Littlebury Green, Saffron Walden CB11 4XB Tel: 01763 838461 — MB BS Lond. 1951; MRCS Eng. LRCP Lond. 1951; FRCR 1975; FFR 1959; DMRT Eng. 1957. Hon. Cons. Radiotherap. & Oncol. Lond. Hosp.; Hon. Cons. Radiother. Whipps Cross Hosp. & Harold Wood Hosp. Prev: Sen. Regist. (Radiother.) Lond. Hosp.

HOPEGOOD, Ursula Mary Priory Farm Barn, Halstead Road, Earls Colne, Colchester CO6 2LR Tel: 01787 222251 — MB BS 1952 Lond. (Roy. Free) Prev: Blood Transfus. Serv.

HOPES, David Robert 7 Rydal Street, Leicester LE2 7DS — MB ChB 1997 Leic.

HOPEWELL, Mr John Prince (retired) Old Vicarage, Langrish, Petersfield GU32 1QY Tel: 01730 261354 Fax: 01730 268317 Email: jhopewell@dial.pipex.com — MB BS Lond. 1943; FRCS Eng. 1950; MRCS Eng. LRCP Lond. 1943. Hon. Cons. Surg. Hosp. St. John & St. Eliz. Lond.; Hon. Cons. Surg. Roy. Free Hosp. Lond. Prev: Pres. Fell.sh. Postgrad. Med. & Urol. Sect. Roy. Soc. Med.

HOPEWELL, Rachel Elizabeth 12 Beresford Road, Wallasey CH45 0JJ — MB ChB 1998 Sheff.; MB ChB Sheff 1998.

HOPFORD, Rosemary Lowe Strathern 3 Brook Close, Charminster, Dorchester DT2 9RA — MB ChB 1969 St. And.; FFA RCS 1981; DA Eng. 1973. Assoc. Specialist Anaesth. W. Dorset Hosps.

HOPGOOD, Emma Louise Top Farm House, Sutton, Newport TF10 8DQ — MB ChB 1997 Birm.

HOPGOOD, Mr Philip 7 Edgeworth Drive, Fallowfield, Manchester M14 6RU Tel: 0161 224 7944 Email: pjhopgood@aol.com — MB ChB 1993 Manch.; FRCS Lond. 1997; FRCS Ed. 1997. (Manchester)

HOPKER, Stephen William Somerset House, Manor Lane, Shipley BD18 3BP; Somerset House, Manor Lane, Shipley BD18 3BP — BM BS 1979 Nottm.; MRCPsych 1985. Cons. Psychiat. For Adults, N. Bradford. Socs: BMA; MRCPsych. Prev: Sen. Regist. Midl. Nerve Hosp. Birm.; Cons. Psychiat. for Elderly Bierley Hall Hosp. Bradford.

HOPKIN, Deborah Joan 113 Wooton Road, King's Lynn PE30 4DJ Tel: 01553 772243 — MB BS 1975 Newc. (Newcastle)

HOPKIN, Janina Elizabeth 'HAFOD', Llanrhidian, Gower, Swansea SA3 1EH Tel: 01792 390033 — MB BCh 1973 Wales; MSc Ed. 1979; MB BCh (Hons.) Wales 1973. (Welsh National School of Medicine)

HOPKIN, Jennifer Ann (retired) 1 Birdhurst Avenue, South Croydon CR2 7DX Tel: 020 8686 2070 Fax: 020 8686 0824 — MB BS 1964 Lond.

HOPKIN, Jennifer Margaret 71 Rawcliffe Lane, York YO30 5SJ — MB ChB 1972 Aberd.

HOPKIN, Professor Julian Meurglyn The Cinical School, University of Wales Swansea, Swansea SA2 8PP Tel: 01792 513062 Fax: 01792 513054 Email: j.m.hopkin@swansea.ac.uk — MB BCh 1972 Wales; MA Oxf. 1992; MSc Ed. 1978; MD Wales 1981; FRCP Lond. 1987; MRCP (UK) 1974. Prof. Experim. Med. Univ. of Wales Swansea; Hon. Cons. Phys. Singleton Hosp. Swansea; Director. The Clin. Sch. Prev: Cons. Phys. Oxf. Radcliffe Hosp. Trust; Vis. Prof. Univ. Osaka, Japan; Fell. Brasenose Coll. Univ. Oxf.

HOPKIN, Mair Old School Surgery, School Street, Pontyclun CF72 9AA Tel: 01443 222567 Fax: 01443 229205; Trecastle Farm, Llanharry, Pontyclun CF72 9LY — MB BCh 1980 Wales; MRCGP 1993; DRCOG 1983. GP; VTS Course Organiser. Prev: Clin. Med. Off. S. Glam. HA.

HOPKIN, Mr Nicholas Buxton The Old Vicarage, Sydling St Nicholas, Dorchester DT2 — MB ChB 1968 Ed.; FRCS (Orl.) Eng. 1978; DLO Eng. 1972. Cons. ENT Surg. W. Dorset HA. Prev: Hon. Sen. Regist. Head & Neck Unit Roy. Marsden Hosp. Lond.; Surg. Cdr. RN (Cons. Otolaryngol.).

HOPKINS, Adrian Dennis 15 Essex Road, Gravesend DA11 0SL Email: kincbm@maf.org; 15 Essex Road, Gravesend DA11 0SL Email: adriandhopkins@compuserve.com — MB ChB 1971 St. And.; MRCOphth 1989; DO RCPSI 1989; DTM & H Liverp. 1975; DObst RCOG 1974. Director of Studies Opthalmology Train. Centre for Centr. African Kinshasa, Democratic RePub. of Congo; Technical Adviser Onchocerciasis Control, Democratic RePub. of Congo; Technical Adviser, Christian Blind Mission Internat. Centr. African Region. Socs: Roy. Soc. of Trop. Med. and Hyg. Prev: Technical Adviser (onchocerciasis Control and Blindness Preven.) M.O.H. Centr. African RePub.; Chief Med. Off. Pimu Rural Health Zone, Zaire.

HOPKINS, Alexander William (retired) 7 Rose Court, Easter Park Drive, Davidsons Mains, Edinburgh EH4 6SE Tel: 0131 336 6124 — MB ChB 1931 Ed.

HOPKINS, Brian James Whitehouse Surgery, 189 Prince of Wales Road, Sheffield S2 1FA Tel: 0114 239 7229 Fax: 0114 253 1650 Email: brian@maccinwhs.force9.co.uk — BM 1984 Soton.; MRCGP 1989; DRCOG 1988; DCH RCP Lond. 1987. (Southampton) Princip. in Gen. Pract. Sheff.; Hon. Teach. (Gen. Pract.); Med. Adviser to Sheff. Health Auth.; Clin. Lead for CHD S.E. Sheff. PCT. Socs: Chairm. of Sheff. Christian Med. Fell.sh. Prev: Vice-Chairm. Sheff. Med. Audit Advis. Gp.

***HOPKINS, Bridget Jane** Cresswell, Victoria Hill Road, Fleet GU51 4LG — MB BS 1996 Lond.; DRCOG 1998.

HOPKINS, Catherine 199 Millrose Close, Skelmersdale WN8 8QT — MB BS 1990 Newc.

HOPKINS, Charles Edward Oxley 26 Talbot Road, London W2 5LJ — BM BCh 1990 Oxf.

HOPKINS, Christopher John (retired) Ford House, Wangford, Beccles NR34 8RR Tel: 0150 278271 — MB BS Lond. 1952; DObst

RCOG 1958. Med. Off. Blythburgh & Dist. Hosp. & S.wold & Dist. Hosp. Prev: GP S.wold.

HOPKINS, Christopher Terence 156 Makepeace Road, Northolt UB5 5UH — MB BS 1994 Lond.

HOPKINS, Claire Louise 115 Higher Lane, Langland, Swansea SA3 4PS — MB BS 1994 Lond.; DRCOG 1998. (St. George's) Swansea Bay GP Train. Scheme. Prev: SHO (A & E) P. Philip Hosp. LLa.lli.

HOPKINS, Claire Louise 179 Cyncoed Road, Cardiff CF23 6AH — BM BCh 1996 Oxf.

HOPKINS, Colin Stirton Border Hall, Audley Road, Alsager, Stoke-on-Trent ST7 2UQ — MB ChB 1978 Liverp.; FFA RCS Eng. 1982. Cons. Anaesth. Leighton Hosp. Crewe. Socs: Liverp. Med. Inst., Assn. Anaesth. & BMA. Prev: Sen. Regist. Mersey RHA; Post-Fell.sh. Regist. Roy. Liverp. Hosp. & BRd.green Hosp.; SHO Walton & Fazakerley Hosps. Liverp.

HOPKINS, Colum (retired) Larne Health Centre, Gloucester Avenue, Larne BT40 1PB Tel: 028 2826 1924 Fax: 028 2826 1940 — MB BCh BAO 1965 Belf.; DObst RCOG 1967. Prev: Ho. Off., SHO (Surg.) & SHO (Obst.) Waveney Hosp. Ballymena.

HOPKINS, David Cleife Patrick (retired) Oriel llynfaes, Llynfaes, Tynlon, Holyhead LL65 3BJ Tel: 01407 720434 Fax: 01407 720037 — MRCS Eng. LRCP Lond. 1965; MA Oxf. 1960. Med. Advis.Benefits Agy. Prev: GP Wembley 1968-1997.

HOPKINS, David Frederick Charles Department of Medicine, King's College School of Medicine & Dentistry, Bessemer Road, London SE5 9PJ Tel: 020 7737 4000 Fax: 020 7346 3313; 21 Westpoint, Shortlands Grove, Bromley BR2 0ND — MB ChB 1987 Liverp.; MRCP (UK) 1991. Lect. (Med.) King's Coll. Sch. Med. Lond. Socs: Brit. Diabetic Assoc.; Soc. Endocrinol. & RSM. Prev: Lect. (Med.) Univ. Liverp.

HOPKINS, Mr David Julian (retired) The Yorkshire Clinic, Bradford Road, Bingley BD16 1TW Tel: 01274 560311 Fax: 01274 551247 — MB ChB Leeds 1962; FRCS Eng. 1968; FRCOphth 1989; DO Eng. 1965; T(Ophth.) 1991. Cons. Ophth. Surg., Yorks. Clinic, Bingley, W. Yorks. Prev: Tutor (Ophth.) Univ. Leeds.

HOPKINS, David Michael Corkran House, Golf Club Drive, Kingston upon Thames KT2 7DF — BM 1993 Soton.

HOPKINS, David Richard Victoria Road Surgery, 50 Victoria Road, Worthing BN11 1XB Tel: 01903 230656 Fax: 01903 520094; Hestia, 6 Palmers Way, High Salvington, Worthing BN13 3DP Tel: 01903 691412 — MB ChB 1976 Manch.; MRCP (UK) 1980; MRCGP 1982.

HOPKINS, David William John 144 Mason Road, Redditch B97 5DS — MB ChB 1992 Bristol.

HOPKINS, Denis Martin Ballymena Health Centre, Cushendall Road, Ballymena BT43 6HQ Tel: 028 2564 2181 Fax: 028 2565 8919; 83 Galgorm Road, Ballymena BT42 1AA — MB BCh BAO 1963 Belf.; DPM Eng. 1968.

HOPKINS, Donald Fraser (retired) 1 Graham Place, Ashgill, Larkhall ML9 3BA Tel: 01698 882831 — MRCS Eng. LRCP Lond. 1959; MD Lond. 1970, MB BS 1959. Prev: Cons. Scott. Nat. Blood Transfus. Serv. HQ Edin.

HOPKINS, Edward Adrian (retired) 91 East Street, Corfe Castle, Wareham BH20 5EE Tel: 01929 480551 — MRCS Eng. LRCP Lond. 1961.

HOPKINS, Edward Hector Benyon (retired) 23 Pontardulais Road, Llangennech, Llanelli SA14 8YE — MRCS Eng. LRCP Lond. 1937; DPH Wales 1953. Prev: RAF Med. Serv.

HOPKINS, Egbert Nathalan The Surgery, 30 Dudley Street, Grimsby DN31 2AB Tel: 01472 356832 — MB ChB 1973 Aberd.; DObst RCOG 1975. Prev: SHO (O & G) Cameron Matern. Hosp.; Resid. Ho. Off. (Surg.) Woodend Gen. Hosp. Aberd.; Resid. Ho. Off. (Med.) City Hosp. Aberd..

HOPKINS, Francis James 10 Eastbury Drive, Olton, Solihull B92 8TL Tel: 0121 684 5856 Email: frankhopkins@hotrail.com — MB ChB 1986 Birm.; MRCOG 1996; DRCOG 1990. Specialist Regist. (O & G) W. Midl.

HOPKINS, Graham Owen, Brigadier late RAMC Defence Services, Medical Rehabilitation Centre, Headley Court, Epsom KT18 6JN Tel: 01372 378271 Email: grahhopk@dsca.gov.uk — MB BS Lond. 1969; FRCP Ed. 1991; FRCP (Lond.) 1998; FISM 1995; DPhysMed Eng. 1975. (St. Bart.) Cons. Rheum. HM Forces; Edr. Jl. RAMC.; QHP. Prev: Cons. Rheum. & Rehabil. Qu. Eliz. Milit. Hosp. Woolwich; Sen. Specialist (Rheum. & Rehab.) Jt. Servs. Med. Rehabil. Unit Chessington; Med. Off. 3 Battn. Parachute Regt.

HOPKINS, Janet Patricia 142 Ballymoney Road, Banbridge BT32 4HN — MB BCh BAO 1981 NUI; MRCGP 1986; DRCOG 1985.

***HOPKINS, Jennifer Susan** c/o doctors mess, Ealing Hospital, Uxbridge Road, Southall UB1 3HW Tel: 020 8574 2444 Email: js.hopkins@doctors.org.uk — BM BS 1998 Nottm.; BM BS Nottm 1998; BMedSci.

HOPKINS, Joanne Firth Park Road Surgery, 400 Firth Park Road, Sheffield S5 6HH Tel: 0114 242 6406; 169 Oldfield Road, Stannington, Sheffield S6 6DX Tel: 0114 234 9022 — BM 1984 Soton.; MRCGP 1989.

HOPKINS, John Charles Purbeck Health Centre, Purbeck, Stantonbury, Milton Keynes MK14 6BL Tel: 01908 318989 Fax: 01908 319493; 48 Fairford Crescent, Downhead Park, Milton Keynes MK15 9AG — MB ChB 1974 Bristol; MRCGP 1980.

HOPKINS, John Stephen Parkgate Health Centre, Park Place, Darlington DL1 5LW Tel: 01325 359585 — MB ChB 1985 Manch.; MRCGP 1992. Prev: Trainee GP Cleveland VTS; SHO (O & G) S. Cleveland Hosp.

HOPKINS, Jonathan David 4 Appleton Court, Gilldown Place, Edgbaston, Birmingham B15 2LR Tel: 0121 440 0689 Email: jd_hopkins@hotmail.com — BM BS 1993 Nottm.; BMedSci (Hons.) Nottm. 1991. (Nottingham) Specialist Regist. (Radiol.), W. Midl. Scheme. Prev: SHO (Neurosurg.) Inst. of Neurosci.s Glas.; SHO (Cardiothoracic Surg.) Glas. Roy. Infirm.; SHO (Paediat. Surg.) Roy. Hosp. Sick Childr. Glas.

HOPKINS, Jonathan Price, Squadron Ldr. RAF Med. Br. Caer Ffynnon Surgery, Caer Ffynnon, Springfield Street, Dolgellau LL40 1LY Tel: 01341 422431 Fax: 01341 423717 — MB ChB 1976 Manch.; MRCGP 1989; DRCOG 1984; T(GP) 1991. Med. Off. RAF. Prev: GP Winsford.

HOPKINS, Katharine Jane Medical Research Department, ICI Pharmaceuticals Division, Alderley Park, Macclesfield SK10 4TE — MB ChB 1975 Manch.; FFA RCS Eng. 1982.

HOPKINS, Kirsten Isabel Vale View, Ham Lane, Marnhull, Sturminster Newton DT10 1JN — MB ChB 1981 Bristol; MRCP (UK) 1984.

***HOPKINS, Louise Nadia** Flat 7, 18 Moorland Road, Leeds LS6 1AL — MB ChB 1995 Leeds.

HOPKINS, Malcolm Kenneth Manselton Surgery, Elgin Street, Manselton, Swansea SA5 8QQ Tel: 01792 653643 / 642459 Fax: 01792 645257; 3 Millfield Close, Sketty, Swansea SA2 8BD Tel: 01792 299359 — MB BCh 1962 Wales. (Cardiff)

HOPKINS, Martin Patrick Larne Health Centre, Gloucester Avenue, Larne BT40 1PB Tel: 028 2826 1924 Fax: 028 2826 1940 — MB BCh BAO 1992 Belf.

HOPKINS, Michael John Lampier 'Hillside', Courtfield Road, Plymouth PL3 5BB Tel: 01752 229674 Fax: 01752 221920 Email: michael.hopkins@virgin.net; 'Hillside', Courtfield Road, Plymouth PL3 5BB — MRCS Eng. LRCP Lond. 1966; MRCGP 1977; DObst RCOG 1974. (St. Mary's) Med. Osteopath.; Rheum. Clin. Asst. Community Alute Back Pain Clinic Musculo / Skeletal Clinic. Socs: Brit. Osteop. Assn.; Primary Care Rheum. Soc.; BIMM. Prev: Ho. Surg. (Orthop.) St. Mary's Hosp. Lond.; Ho. Phys. (Med.) Mayday Hosp. Croydon; Med. Off. RN.

HOPKINS, Michael Patrick Meddygfa Minafon, Kidwelly, Kidwelly SA17 Tel: 01554 891240 — MB ChB 1988 Birm.; DGM RCP Lond. 1990.

HOPKINS, Millicent Ruth 35 Osborne Drive, Belfast BT9 6LH — MB BCh BAO 1944 Dub. (TC Dub.)

HOPKINS, Moira Ruth (retired) 39 Ballynahinch Road, Saintfield, Ballynahinch BT24 7ND — MB BCh BAO Belf. 1958. Prev: SHO Childr. Surg. Belf. City Hosp.

HOPKINS, Mr Nicholas Frederick Gowland Crawley Hospital, West Green Drive, Crawley RH11 7DH Tel: 01293 600300 Fax: 01293 600354; Cedar Cottage, Tremaines, Lewes Road, Horsted Keynes, Haywards Heath RH17 7EA Tel: 01825 791289 Fax: 01825 791289 Email: nfgowhopk.surgery@ic24.net — MB BS 1973 Lond.; MS Lond. 1989; FRCS Eng. 1978; MRCS Eng. LRCP Lond. 1973. (Guy's) Cons. Gen. & Vasc. Surg. Surrey & Sussex NHS Trust. Socs: Fell. Roy. Soc. Med. (Venous Forum); Fell. Surg. Research Soc.; Assn. Surg. Prev: Sen. Regist. (Surg.) Hammersmith Hosp. Lond.;

Regist. (Surg.) St. Thos. Hosp. Lond.; Res. Fell. Rotat. (Surg.) Roy. Postgrad. Med. Sch. Hammersmith Lond.

***HOPKINS, Nicola Thirza Anne** Addenbrookes Hospital, Hills Road, Cambridge CB2 2QQ; 32 Macclesfield Old Road, Buxton SK17 6TY — BM BS 1996 Nottm.; BMedSci. Nottm. 1993; DRCOG 1998.

HOPKINS, Patrick Adrian (retired) 17 Hillcourt Road, Romiley, Stockport SK6 4QD Tel: 0161 430 4365 — MRCS Eng. LRCP Lond. 1951; DObst RCOG 1955. Prev: GP Manch. 31 years.

HOPKINS, Patrick Noel The Surgery, Park Lane, Stubbington, Fareham PO14 2JP Tel: 01329 664231 Fax: 01329 664958; Amberley, 5 Fastnet Way, Stubbington, Fareham PO14 3QZ — MB BCh BAO 1985 NUI; MRCPI 1988; MRCGP 1993; DCH RCP Lond. 1991. Prev: Trainee GP Soton.; Regist. (Med. & Clin. Pharmacol.) Roy. Free Hosp. Lond.

HOPKINS, Philip (retired) 249 Haverstock Hill, Hampstead, London NW3 4PS Tel: 020 7794 3759 Fax: 020 7431 6826 — MRCS Eng. LRCP Lond. 1943; FRCGP 1969, M 1952. Indep. GP Lond. Prev: Mem. Standing Med. Advis. Comm. MoH.

HOPKINS, Philip Anthony Bedburn, Old Church Road, E. Hanningfield, Chelmsford CM3 8BG — MB BS 1992 Lond.

HOPKINS, Philip Morgan Academic Unit of Anaesthesia, St James's University Hospital, Beckett St., Leeds LS9 7TF Tel: 0113 206 5274 Fax: 0113 206 4140 Email: p.m.hopkins@leeds.ac.uk; 11 Pinewood Gate, Harrogate HG2 0JF — MB BS 1984 Lond.; MD Leeds 1996; FFA RCS Eng. 1988. (St Mary's Hosp.) Sen. Lect. (Anaesth.) Univ. Leeds; Hon. Cons. Anaesth. St. Jas. Univ. Hosp. Leeds. Socs: Hon. Sec. Anaesth. Research Soc. Prev: Lect. (Anaesth.) Univ. Leeds.

HOPKINS, Rachel Julia Killick Street Health Centre, 76 Killick Street, London N1 9RH Tel: 020 7833 9939 Fax: 020 7427 2740 — MB BS 1992 Lond.

HOPKINS, Richard John Ashburton Surgery, 1 Eastern Road, Ashburton, Newton Abbot TQ13 7AP Tel: 01364 652731 Fax: 01364 654273; Yarner, Netherton, Newton Abbot TQ12 4RW Tel: 01626 872438 Email: yarnet@aol.com — MB BChir 1980 Camb.; MB BChir Camb. 1979; MA Camb. 1980; MRCGP 1985; DRCOG 1983. (Camb. & St. Thos.) Clin. Asst. (Ophth.) Torbay Hosp.

HOPKINS, Richard Stanley 9 Rhuddlan Road, Buckley CH7 3QA — MB ChB 1990 Liverp.

HOPKINS, Robin John Haldon House Surgery, 37-39 Imperial Road, Exmouth EX8 1DH Tel: 01395 222777/222888 Fax: 01395 269769; White Craigs, 7 Merrion Avenue, Exmouth EX8 2HX — MB ChB 1975 Dundee; BSc Med. Sc. St. And. 1972; MPHil Exeter 1992; MRCGP 1981. Sen. Lect. (Gen. Pract.) Postgrad. Med. Sch. Univ. Exeter.

HOPKINS, Ronald Ernest 2 Woods Lea, Hillside, Chorley New Road, Bolton BL1 5DU Tel: 01204 840668 Fax: 01204 840668 Email: ronhopkins100705.66@compuserve.com — MB ChB 1973 Manch.; BSc Sheff. 1968; MRCOG 1978; MRACOG 1979; FRCOG 1990. (Manch.) Cons. (O & G) Bolton Dist. Gen. Hosp.; Hon. Clin. Teach. (Obst. & Gyn.) Univ. of Manch. Prev: Sen. Regist. (O & G) St. Mary's Hosp. Manch.; Sen. Regist. (O & G) Univ. Hosp. S. Manch.; Sen. Regist. (O & G) Wigan & Dist. Hosps.

HOPKINS, Russell, OBE (retired) Glamorgan House, BUPA Hospital, Pentwyn, Cardiff CF23 8XL Tel: 01222 736011 — MRCS Eng. LRCP Lond. 1964; BDS Durham. 1956; FDS RCS Eng. 1961. Chair Bro Morgannwe Trust. Prev: Chairm. Glan y Môr NHS Trust.

HOPKINS, Sandra Margaret Belmor, Hall Road, Winfarthing, Diss IP22 2EJ — BM 1980 Soton.

HOPKINS, Sarah Maria 11a Clifton Drive, Heald Green, Cheadle SK8 3UF — MB ChB 1997 Manch.

HOPKINS, Sharon Deborah Directorate of Public Health & Policy, Bro Taf Health Authority, Temple of Peace and Health, Cardiff CF10 3NW Tel: 029 2040 2477 Fax: 029 2040 2504 Email: charon.hopkins@bro-taf-ha.wales.nhs.uk; Tel: 029 2070 7573 — MB BCh BAO 1984 Dub.; BA Dub. 1984, MB BCh BAO 1984; FFPHM RCP (UK) 1993. (Trinity College Dublin) Dir. Publ. Health Policy. Bro Taf HA. Socs: Local Bd. Mem. Fac. PHM; Fac. Pub. Health Med. Prev: Cons. (Pub. Health Med.) S. Glam.; Sen. Regist. (Pub. Health Med.) S. Glam.; Regist. (Pub. Health Med.) Camb. HA.

HOPKINS, Sheila (retired) 17 Hillcourt Road, Romiley, Stockport SK6 4QD — MB ChB Manch. 1953. Prev: GP Manch. 25 years.

HOPKINS, Suzanne Elizabeth 49 Congleton Road N., Church Lawton, Stoke-on-Trent ST7 3AZ — MB ChB 1993 Birm.

HOPKINS, Thomas Price (retired) Bryn Wern, Northway, Bishopston, Swansea SA3 3JN Tel: 01792 232629 — MRCS Eng. LRCP Lond. 1939. Prev: Sen. Regist. (Orthop.) Morriston Hosp.

HOPKINS, Trevor North Road Medical Practice, 182 North Road, Cardiff CF14 3XQ Tel: 029 2061 9188 Fax: 029 2061 3484; 37 Caegwyn Road, Whitchurch, Cardiff CF14 1QN — MB BCh 1979 Wales; MSc Wales 1977, MB BCh 1979; MRCGP 1984.

HOPKINS, William Benedict Edgware Community Hospital, Edgware Road, Edgware HA8 0AJ Tel: 020 8732 6265 — MB BS 1987 Lond.; MRCPsych 1993. (University College London Middlesex Hospital) Cons. Psychiat. Barnet Healthcare NHS Trust; Lead Med Clinician; Princip. Psychiat.; Med. Foundat. for the c/o Victim of torture, Lond. Prev: Regist. (Child Psychiat.) Tavistock Clinic Lond.

HOPKINS, Mr William Desmond (retired) 46 Elizabeth Crescent, Queens Park, Chester CH4 7AZ Tel: 01244 675180 — MB BS 1952 Lond; MB BS Lond. 1952; FRCS Ed. 1962; MRCS Eng. LRCP Lond. 1950; DO Eng. 1955; FRCOphth 1993. Prev: Cons. Ophth. Surg. Chester Roy. Infirm. & Countess of Chester Hosp.

HOPKINS-JONES, Derek George Newham Walk Surgery, Wordsworth Grove, Cambridge CB3 9HS; 4 Ratfords Yard, Angle End, Great Wilbraham, Cambridge CB1 5JT — MRCS Eng. LRCP Lond. 1959; MA; BA Camb. (St. Thos.)

HOPKINS JONES, Katherine Mary The Keston House Medical Practice, 70 Brighton Road, Purley CR8 2LJ Tel: 020 8660 8292 Fax: 020 8763 2142; 24 Hawthorn Road, Wallington SM6 0SY — MB BS 1985 Lond.; MRCGP 1993; DRCOG 1988; Cert. Family Plann. JCC 1988. (Westm.) Prev: Trainee GP Mayday Hosp. VTS.

HOPKINSON, Professor Brian Ridley 32 Regent Street, Nottingham NG1 5BT Tel: 0115 947 2860; Lincolnsfield, 18 Victoria Crescent, Sherwood, Nottingham NG5 4DA Tel: 0115 960 4167 — MB ChB 1961 Birm.; ChM Birm. 1972; FRCS Eng. 1964. Prof. (Vasc. Surg.) & Cons. Surg. Univ. Hosp. Nottm.; Head (Vas. & Endovasc. Surg.) Univ. Nottm. Socs: BMA (Chairm. Annual Represen. Meeting) 1999-2001; Vasc. Surgic. Soc. GB & Irel. Prev: Lect. (Surg.) Qu. Eliz. Hosp. Birm.; Resid. Surg. Off. Hallam Hosp. W. Bromwich; SHO (Cas.) Gen. Hosp. Birm.

HOPKINSON, Professor David Albert Swan Cottage, 42 Church St., Great Missenden HP16 0AZ — MB BChir 1960 Camb.; MD Camb. 1966. (Lond. Hosp.) Dir. MRC Human Biochem. Genetics Unit Galton Laborat. Univ. Coll. Lond.

HOPKINSON, Mr David Nicholas Northern General Hospital, Herries Road, Sheffield S5 7AU Tel: 0114 271 4833; 22 John Hibbard Cresent, Woodhouse Mill, Sheffield S13 9UW Tel: 0114 288 9718 — MB ChB 1988 Manch.; FRCS 1999 (Cth); MD Manch. 1995; FRCS Eng. 1993; FRCS Ed. 1993. Cons. Cardiothoracic Surg. N.ern Gen. Hosp. Sheff. Socs: Soc. Cardiothor. Surg.; Internat. Soc. for Heart & Lung Transpl.ation. Prev: Clin. Lect. & Specialist Regist. (Cardiothoracic Surg.) Cardiothoracic Centre Liverp.; Clin. Fell. in Long Transpl.ation, Toronto Gen. Hosp. Canada; Specialist Regist. (Cardiothoracic Surg.)Manch. Roy. Infirm.

HOPKINSON, Mr Dick Anthony Walker (retired) Stable Court, Carlton Hall Lane, Carlton-in-Lindrick, Worksop S81 9EE Tel: 01909 732190 — MB ChB Leeds 1957; FRCS Ed. 1967. Prev: Cons. Surg. Bassetlaw Dist. Gen. Hosp. Worksop.

HOPKINSON, George Patrick The White House Surgery, 10-10A Market Place, Mildenhall, Bury St Edmunds IP28 7EF; Fox Cottage, Rhe Green, Risby, Bury St Edmunds IP28 6QH — MB BS 1985 Lond. Prev: Trainee GP Crawley.

HOPKINSON, George Robert The Surgery, 20-22 Westdale Lane, Carlton, Nottingham NG4 3JA Tel: 0115 961 9401 — MB ChB 1958 Ed. (Ed.)

HOPKINSON, Mr Gregory Bennett The Limes, Church Road, Ashley, Market Drayton TF9 4LU — MB ChB 1971 Manch.; MD Manch. 1983; FRCS Eng. 1978. Cons. Gen. & Vasc. Surg. N. Staffs Hosp. Stoke-on-Trent. Socs: Vasc. Surg. Soc.; Eur. Soc. Vasc. Surg.

HOPKINSON, Helen Elizabeth 15 Archer Crescent, Nottingham NG8 1HB Email: helen.hopkinson@nottingham.ac.uk — MB ChB 1989 Ed.; MRCP (UK) 1992; DRCOG 1991. (Ed.) Lect. (Med.) Div. of Therap. Univ. Nottm.; Hon. Sen. Regist. (Med.) Qu.s Med. Centre Nottm. Prev: Regist. (Gen. Med.) Qu.s Med. Centre Nottm.; MRC Clin. Train. Fell. Univ. of Nottm.

HOPKINSON, Ian Wound Healing Research Unit, University Department of Surgery, University of Wales College of Medicine, Heath Park, Cardiff CF14 4XN Tel: 029 2074 2893 Fax: 029 2076 1623 — MB ChB 1981 Manch.; PhD (Biochem. & Molec. Biol.) Manch. 1990, BSc (Hons.) Med. Biochem 1979. Lect. (Wound Biol.) & Dir. Wound Research Univ. Wales Coll. Med. Cardiff; Series Edr. Wounds. Socs: Brit. Connective Tissue Soc.; E. Coast Connective Tissue Soc. (USA). Prev: MRC Trav. Fell. & Research Fell. (Biochem. & Molec. Biol.) Thos. Jefferson Univ. Philadelphia PA; MRC Train. Fell. & Research Assoc. (Biochem. & Molec. Biol.) Univ. Manch. & ICI Pharm. Chesh.; Regist. (Path.) Kingston Hosp. Surrey.

HOPKINSON, James Richard 9 Morven Av, Hazel Grove, Stockport SK7 4QB — BM BS 1997 Nottm.

HOPKINSON, John Montgomery House Medical Centre, 83 Infirmary Road, Sheffield S6 3BZ — MB ChB 1967 Sheff.

HOPKINSON, John James (retired) Syke House, Broughton-in-Furness LA20 6ER Tel: 01229 716365 — MRCS Eng. LRCP Lond. 1946. Prev: GP.

HOPKINSON, John Michael (retired) Westfield Cottage, Kirk Hammerton, York YO26 8DU — MB ChB 1962 Leeds; FRCPath. 1982, M 1970. Prev: Cons. Path. York Dist. Hosp.

HOPKINSON, Jonathan Mark Royal Bolton Hospitals, Department of Anaesthetics, Minerva Road, Bolton BL4 0JR; 1 barn Acre, Blackrod, Bolton BL6 5BY Tel: 01204 691132 — MB ChB 1986 Manch.; FRCA 1993; DA (UK) 1988. Cons. Anaesthstist Bolton Hosp.s NHS Trust. Prev: Cons. (Anaesth.) Salford Roy. Hosps. NHS Trust; Sen. Regist. (Anaesth.) Wom. & Childr.'s Hosp., Adelaide, Australia; Sen. Regist. (Anaesth.) NW RHA.

HOPKINSON, Katherine Anne Stockwell Group Practice, 107 Stockwell Road, London SW9 9TJ Tel: 020 7274 3225 Fax: 020 7738 3005 — MB BCh 1990 Wales; BSc (Hons.) Bristol 1985; MRCGP 1994.

HOPKINSON, Margaret Elizabeth 27 Milbury Drive, Hollingworth Lake, Littleborough OL15 0BZ Tel: 01706 78495 — MB ChB 1963 Manch. SCMO Rochdale AHA; Clin. Asst. (Nephrol.) Manch. Roy. Infirm. Socs: BMA.

HOPKINSON, Maureen Claire (retired) Westfield Cottage, Kirk Hammerton, York YO26 8DU — MB ChB Glas. 1968.

HOPKINSON, Neil Andrew Clifton Lodge Surgery, 7 Clifton Lane, Meltham, Huddersfield HD9 4AH Tel: 01484 852073 Fax: 01484 854760; 8 Moor Lane, Netherton, Huddersfield HD4 7HA — MB BS 1986 Newc.; MRCGP 1991; DCH RCP Lond. 1991.

HOPKINSON, Neil David Royal Bournemouth Hospital, Castle Lane E., Bournemouth BH7 7DW — BM BS 1983 Nottm.; DM Nottm. 1992; MRCP (UK) 1986; FRCP Eng. 1997. Cons. Rheum. & Rahabil. Roy. Bournemouth & ChristCh. Hosps. Socs: Brit. Soc. Rheum. Prev: Sen. Regist. (Rheum.) Derby & Nottm. Hosp.; Regist. (Gen. Med. & Rheum.) N.wick Pk. Hosp. Harrow; Regist. (Gen. Med. & Neurol.) Walsgrave Hosp. Coventry.

HOPKINSON, Nicholas Shaun 10 Rotherham Walk, Nicholson St., Southwark, London SE1 0XE — MB BS 1993 Lond.; MA Camb. 1994, BA 1990; MRCP (UK) 1996. (Lond. Hosp. Med. Coll.) Specialist Regist. (Respirat. & Gen. Med.) S.W. Thames Rotat - St Geo.'s Hosp. - Lond. Socs: Brit. Thorac. Soc.

HOPKINSON, Nigel Robert Sea Dawn, Ballaragh, Laxey IM4 7PN — MB ChB 1987 Sheff.

HOPKINSON, Rowland Bennett Birmingham Heartlands Hospital, Bordesley Green E., Birmingham B9 5SS Tel: 0121 766 6611 Fax: 0121 685 5545 Email: gbf6fgbf; The Elms, 1405 Warwick Road, Copt Heath, Knowle, Solihull B93 9LR Tel: 01564 772091 — MB BS 1970 Lond.; FRCA 1974. (Univ. Coll. Hosp.) Med. Dir., Birm. Heartlands & Solihull NHS Trust (Teach.); Sen. Clin. Lect. Univ. Birm. Socs: BMA & W. Midl. Intens. Ther. Unit (ITU); Intens. Care Soc.; Brit. Assn. Med. Managers. Prev: Fell. Bowman Gray Sch. of Med. Winston-Salem, N. Carolina USA.

HOPKINSON, Zoe Elizabeth Clare University Department of Obstetrics and Gynaecology, Queen Elizabeth Building, Royal Infirmary, Glasgow G31 2ER — MB ChB 1995 Glas. Clin. Research Fell. (O & G) Glas. Roy. Infirm. Prev: Mem. Glas. O & G Soc.

HOPKINSON-WOOLLEY, Mr James Alexander The Ipswich Hospital, Heath Road, Ipswich IP4 5PD Tel: 01473 702095 Fax: 01473 702094 Email: hopkinson-woolley.sec@ipsh-tr.anglox.nhs.uk — MB BS 1989 Lond.; MSc Oxf. 1993; FRCS Eng. 1994. Cons. Orthop. & Hand Surg. The Ipswich Hosp. Prev: Career Regist. (Orthop.) E. Anglian Higher Surgic. Train. Progr.

HOPKIRK, John Andrew Cunningham King Edward VII Hospital, Midhurst GU29 0BL Tel: 01730 812341; Middle Bottingdean, Hollist Lane, Easebourne, Midhurst GU29 0QN Tel: 01730 812269 — MB BChir Camb. 1968; FRCP Lond. 1986; MRCP (UK) 1972. Cons. Phys. King Edwd. VII Hosp. Midhurst; Hon. Cons. Phys. Brompton Hosp. Lond.; Cons. Phys. to the Civil Aviat. Auth. Prev: Ho. Phys. Univ. Coll. Hosp. Lond.; Ho. Surg. Roy. Ear Hosp. Lond.

HOPKIRK, Timothy John c/o Scarborough Hospital, Scalby Road, Scarborough YO12 6QL — MB ChB 1988 Bristol; PhD Soton. 1980, BSc 1976; MRCP (UK) 1993; MRCPCH 1996. Staff Grade (Gen. Med. & Paediat.) ScarBoro. Hosp. Socs: Biochem. Soc.

HOPKISSON, Mr Bryan (retired) Boughton Green Farm, Moulton Lane, Boughton, Northampton NN2 8RF — MA, MB Camb. 1967, BChir 1966; FRCS Eng. 1975; DO Eng. 1972. Cons. Ophth. Surg. N.ampton Gen. Hosp.

HOPKISSON, James Frederick c/o 506 Wellingborough Road, Northampton NN3 3HX — MB BS 1991 Lond.

HOPMAN, Elizabeth Maria Flat 8-8 Frognal, London NW3 6AJ — MB BS 1994 Lond.

HOPPER, Adrian Harald 39 Huddleston Road, London N7 0AD — MD 1986 Lond.; MB BS 1978; MRCP (UK) 1980. Cons. Phys. St. Thos. Hosp. Lond. Prev: Sen. Regist. Tower Hamlets HA; Lect. (Med.) Univ. Leeds; Research Fell. (Med.) Univ. Leeds.

HOPPER, Andrew Derek 329 Springvale Road, Sheffield S10 1LL — MB ChB 1998 Sheff.; MB ChB Sheff 1998.

HOPPER, Christine Oliver Street Surgery, 57 Oliver Street, Ampthill, Bedford MK45 2SB Tel: 01525 402641 Fax: 01525 841107; 27 Russell Avenue, Bedford MK40 3TD — MB BS 1983 Lond.; MRCGP 1988; DRCOG 1987. (Middlx.) Prev: Trainee GP Stafford Dist. Gen. Hosp. VTS; Ho. Surg. Centr. Middlx. Hosp.; Ho. Phys. Roy. United Hosp. Bath.

HOPPER, Mr Colin Department of Maxillofacial Surgery, Eastman Dental Hospital, 256 Grays Inn Road, London WC1X 8LD Tel: 020 7915 1056 Fax: 020 7915 1012 Email: c.hopper@ucl.ac.uk — MRCS Eng. LRCP Lond. 1980; MB BS Lond. 1980; BDS Lond. 1976; FRCS Ed. 1987; FDS RCS Eng. 1987, LDS 1976. (Guys) Sen. Lect. & Cons. Maxillofacial Surg. E.man Dent. & Univ. Coll. Hosp. Lond. Hosps.; Sen. Research Fell. RCS Eng., Nat. Med. Laser Centre, Dept of Surg., Lond. Socs: Roy. Soc. Med. (Sec. Odontol. Sect.) (Former). Prev: Sen. Regist. (Oral & Maxillofacial Surg.) Qu. Vict. Hosp. E. Grinstead.

HOPPER, Derek Edward Field House Medical Centre, 13 Dudley Street, Grimsby DN31 2AE Tel: 01472 350327 — MB BS 1969 Lond.; MRCS Eng. LRCP Lond. 1969; DObst RCOG 1971. (King's Coll. Hosp.) Socs: Exec. Nat. Assn. Primary Care. Prev: Squadron Ldr. RAF Med. Br.; SHO (O & G) Farnham Hosp. Gp.; Ho. Surg. (Orthop. & Neurol.) King's Coll. Hosp.

HOPPER, Diane Lesley 46 Devon Street, Cottingham HU16 4LZ — MB BChir 1989 Camb.; MA Camb. 1990, MB BChir (Hons.) 1989. SHO (Paediat.) Nottm. Univ. Hosp. Prev: SHO Mater Adult Hosp. S. Brisbane, Austral.; Ho. Surg. Glos. Roy. Infirm.; Ho. Phys. W.m. Hosp. Lond.

HOPPER, Mr Ian (retired) 3 Corby Hall Drive, Sunderland SR2 7HZ Tel: 0191 522 7313 — MB ChB Sheff. 1961; FRCS Eng. 1991; FRCS Ed. 1967. Prev: Cons. ENT Surg. City Hosps. Sunderland.

HOPPER, Ian Philip Histopathol. Department, Derbyshire Royal Infirmary, London Road, Derby DE1 2QY; Holly Bush Lodge, Holly Bush Road, Newborough, Burton-on-Trent DE13 8SF — MB ChB 1972 Sheff.; MRC (Path.) 1979; FRCPath. 1991. (Sheff.) Cons. (Histopathol.) Derbysh. Roy. Infirm.

HOPPER, Jonathan Mark Room 1210, Hannibal House, Elephant & Castle, London SE1 6TQ Tel: 020 7972 8126 Fax: 020 7972 8103 Email: jon.hopper@doh.gsi.gov.uk — MB ChB 1987 Birm.; BSc (Hons.) Birm. 1984, MB ChB 1987; FRCS Ed. 1992; Dip. IMC RCS Ed. 1993. Sen. Med. Off. Med. Devices Agency (Lond.). Prev: Career Regist. (Trauma & Orthop. Surg.) W. Mild. Region; Sen. Regist. (Trauma & Orthop. Surg.) W. Midl.

HOPPER, Judith Margaret Holly Bush Lodge, Holly Bush Road, Newborough, Burton-on-Trent DE13 8SF Tel: 0128 375489 — MB ChB 1972 Sheff.; MRCGP 1978. GP Cannock, Staffs; Curr: Trainer (Gen. Pract.) Cannock.

HOPPER, Malcolm St Clair (retired) District General Hospital, Grimsby DN33 2BA Tel: 01472 74111 — MB ChB 1970 Manch.; FRCOG 1990, M 1975. Cons. (O & G) Yorks. RHA. Prev: Sen. Regist. (O & G) Yorks. RHA.

HOPPER, Melanie Ann 6 Hessary View, Saltash PL12 6HX — MB ChB 1996 Liverp.

HOPPER, Noel Brian 22 Arduthie Road, Stonehaven AB39 2DP — M.B., Ch.B. Aberd. 1950.

HOPPER, Paul Lindsay Western Hospital, Walnut Grove, Southampton SO16 4XE Tel: 02380 475413 — MB ChB 1992 Cape Town. Cons. Old Age Psychiat. Socs: MRCPsych.

HOPPER, Peter Kennedy (retired) Fairfield, 10 Lawrence Court, Mill Hill, London NW7 3QP Tel: 020 8959 7226 — MB BS 1947 Lond.; MRCS Eng. LRCP Lond. 1946; FRCPath 1982, M 1970. Cons. Pathol. Hackney Gp. Hosps. Prev: Sen. Lect. (Microbiol.) Roy. Free Hosp. Med. Sch.

HOPPER, Shirley Ann Department of Primary Health Care & General Practice, Imperial College School of Medicine, Chelsea & Westminster Hospital, 369 Fulham Road, London SW10 9NH Tel: 020 8746 8160 Fax: 020 8746 8151 Email: s.hopper@ic.ac.uk; Flat 5, 2 Dickenson Road, London N8 9EN Tel: 020 8340 8455 — MB BS 1991 Lond.; BA (Hons.) Oxf. 1988; MRCGP 1995; DRCOG 1993; DFFP 1996. (Univ.Coll.Middx) Clin. Lect. Gen. Pract. Socs: BMA; Med. Protec. Soc.; MRCGP. Prev: Lond. Acad. Trainee (GP) Char. Cross & W.m. Sch. Lond.

HOPSON, Andrew Sean Michael 21 Navarino Road, Hackney, London E8 1AD — MB BS 1996 Lond.; BSc (Hons) Lond. 1993. (Roy. Lond. Hosp.) SHO (A & E) Kings Coll. Hosp. Lond. Prev: SHO (Psychiat.) St. Clements Hosp. Lond.; Ho. Off. (Gen. Med.) Roy. Lond. Hosp.; Ho. Off. (Gen. Surg.) Newham Gen. Hosp. Lond.

HOPSON, Peter Raymond Roseberry, 9 Orchard Close, Ulgham, Morpeth NE61 3AP Tel: 01670 790836 — MB BS 1971 Newc.; MRCGP 1975.

HOPSTER, Deborah Jane Department Histopathology, King's College School of Medicine & Dentistry, Bessemer Road, London SE5 9PJ Tel: 020 7346 3023 Fax: 020 7346 3670 Email: debbie.hopster@kcl.ac.uk; 4a Patshill Road, Kentish Town, London NW5 2LB Tel: 020 7267 8627 — MB ChB 1990 (Hons) Manch.; BSc (Med Sci.) St. And. 1987; MRCPath 1996; DRCPath 1994. (St Andrews University & Manchester University) Cons. (Histopath.) King's Coll. Hosp.; Hon Sen. Lect. GKT Xchool of Med. & Dent. Prev: Sen. Regist. & Lect. (Histopath.) Lond. Hosp. Med. Coll. & Roy. Lond. Hosp.; Regist. (Histopath.) King's Coll. Hosp. Lond.; SHO (Histopath.) Roy. Liverp. Univ. Hosp.

HOPTON, Mr Barnaby Philip 11 Church Lane, Nether Poppleton, York YO26 6LB — MB ChB 1991 Bristol; FRCS Eng. 1996; FRCS Ed. 1996.

HOPTON, Christine The Pent House, Caythorpe Road, Caythorpe, Nottingham NG14 7EB — MB ChB 1969 Sheff.; MFCM 1982.

HOPTON, Mr David Samuel The Old Vicarage, 11 Church Lane, Nether Poppleton, York YO26 6LB Tel: 01904 794433 Fax: 01904 794433 Email: david@dhopton.freeserve.co.uk — MB ChB 1958 Manch; MD Manch. 1970; FRCS Eng. 1967; FRCS Ed. 1965. Mem., Pens. Appeals Tribunals. Prev: Cons. Surg. York Dist. Hosp. & Purey Cust Nuffield Hosp. York; Examr. RCS Edin.; Hon. Lect. Univ of Leeds.

HOPTON, Patrick Stephen 65 Tyndale Avenue, Bristol BS37 5EX — MB ChB 1989 Sheff.; FRCA 1994. Career Regist. (Anaesth.) Lothian HB.

HOPTON, Susan Stephanie 9 Ashton Close, Mickleover, Derby DE3 5QD; Quercy, The Broadway, Wickham Skeith, Eye IP23 8LT Tel: 01449 766626 Email: sue.hopton@virgin.net — MB ChB 1992 Sheff.; MRCP (UK) 1996; DRCOG 1997; DFFP 1998. (Sheffield) GP Reg. Socs: RCP Lond.; Roy. Soc. Med. Prev: SHO (O & G); SHO (Paediat.); SHO (Med.).

HOPWOOD, Beverley Carol 44 Fore Street, Bradninch, Exeter EX5 4NN — MB BS 1984 Lond.; DA (UK) 1987. Clin. Asst. (Anaesth.) Roy. Devon & Exeter Hosp. Prev: SHO (Anaesth.) Roy. Devon & Exeter Hosp.; SHO (A & E) Hartlepool Gen. Hosp.; Ho. Phys. Roy. United Hosp. Bath.

HOPWOOD, Bryan Burngreave Road Surgery, 5 Burngreave Road, Sheffield S3 9DA Tel: 0114 272 2858; 138 Chelsea Road, Sheffield S11 9BR — MB ChB 1974 Sheff.

HOPWOOD, David Pathology Department, Ninewells Hospital & Medical School, Dundee DD1 9SY Tel: 01382 60111 — MB ChB (Hons.) Leeds 1960; PhD St. And. 1967; BSc (Hons.) Leeds 1958, MD 1973; FRCPath 1982. (Leeds) Reader (Path.) Univ. Dundee; Asst. Edr. Histochem. Jl. Socs: Path. Soc. (Hon. Sec. Histochem. Sec.); Roy. Microscop. Soc.; Brit. Soc. Gastroenterol. Prev: Sen. Lect. (Path.) Univ. Dundee; Sen. Lect. (Human Morphol.) Nottm. Med. Sch.; Lect. (Path.) Univ. Dundee.

HOPWOOD, John Andrew 103 York Road, Bristol BS6 5QD — MB ChB 1995 Bristol.

HOPWOOD, Mark Edward Fraser 12 Kingfisher Crescent, Fulford, Stoke-on-Trent ST11 9QE — MB ChB 1984 Manch.; BSc St. And. 1981. Med. Adjudication Off. for Benefits Agency Stoke-on-Trent. Prev: GP Gt. Wyrley.

HOPWOOD, Penelope CRC Psychological Medicine Group, Christie Hospital NHS Trust, Withington, Manchester M20 4BX Tel: 0161 446 3682 Fax: 0161 448 1655; 5 Beech Mews, Davenport Park, Stockport SK2 6LB — MB ChB 1976 Manch.; MSc Manch. 1983; BDS Manch. 1969; FRCPsych. 1999. (Univ. Manch.) Sen. Research Fell. Hon. Cons. Psychiat. CRC Psychol. Med. Gp. Christie Hosp. Manch.; Mem. MRC Lung Cancer Working Party; Mem. CRC Psychol. & Educat. Research Comm. Socs: (Steering Comm.) Cancer Family Study Gp.

HOPWOOD, Philip Neil Alton Health Centre, Anstey Road, Alton GU34 2QX Tel: 01420 84676 Fax: 01420 542975 — MB ChB 1980 Birm.; DRCOG 1983.

HOPWOOD, Stephen 9 Dunkerry Road, Windmill Hill, Bristol BS3 4LD — MB ChB 1986 Bristol.

HOPWOOD, Sylvia Elaine Royal Dundee Liff Hospital, Dundee DD4 7PZ Tel: 01382 580441; 6 Strips of Craigie Road, Dundee DD4 7PZ Tel: 01382 462265 — MB ChB Leeds 1960; DPM Ed. 1965. (Leeds) Assoc. Specialist Roy. Dundee Liff Hosp.; Hon. Lect. Univ. Dundee.

HOQUE, Abu Taher Mohammed Mozammel The Surgery, 26 Westbury Avenue, Wood Green, London N22 6RS Tel: 020 8455 5880; 53 Harlech Road, London N14 7BY Tel: 020 8888 3227 — MB BS 1967 Dacca; MRCP (UK) 1976. (Dacca Med. Coll.) Regist. (Gen. Med.) Roy. Hosp. Chesterfield.

HOQUE, Mr Happy Mohammed Rezaul Surgical Directorate, Medway Maritime Hospital, Windmill Road, Gillingham ME7 5NY Tel: 01634 830000; 35 The Fairway, Bickley, Bromley BR1 2JZ — MB BS 1991 Lond.; BSc (Hons.) Lond. 1988; FRCS Eng. 1995. (King's Coll. Lond.) Specialist Regist. Rotat. (Gen. Surg.) SE Thames Regional HA.

HOQUE, Kowsor Ahmed 91 Valleyfield Road, Streatham, London SW16 2HX — MB BS 1996 Lond.

HOQUE, Leedy Anwara 91 Dhanmondi Residential Area, Road 11-A, Dhaka 9, Bangladesh; 3 Colless Road, Tottenham, London N15 4NR — BM BCh 1986 Oxf.; PhD Lond. 1981, BSc 1977. Prev: SHO (Geriat. Med.) N.ampton Gen. Hosp.

HOQUE, Mazedul 42 Fairfield, Arlington Road, London NW1 7LE Tel: 020 7209 3851 — LMSSA 1997 Lond.; DCP 1996; DTM & H 1991. (Guys) SHO VTS Doncaster. Socs: Roy. Soc. Trop. Med. Hyg.

HOQUE, Muhammad Sayeedul Shawbirch Medical Centre, 5 Acorn Way, Telford TF5 0LW Tel: 01952 641555 Fax: 01952 260913; Pinewoods, 3 College Lane, Wellington, Telford TF1 3DH Tel: 01952 641457 — MB BS 1962 Dhaka; DPhysMed Eng. 1971. (Dhaka Med. Coll.) GP. Socs: BMA; Assoc. Mem. BSR; FRSM.

HOQUE, Muhammed Hamidul Flat 2 Community Hospital, Sedgefield, Stockton-on-Tees TS21 3EJ — MB BS 1972 Dacca. (Dacca) Regist. S. W. Durh. Health Bd.

HOQUE, Selina Nahieed 37 Stansfield Road, Lewes BN7 2SL — MB BCh 1987 Wales.

***HOQUE, Shamili Rumathie** 17 Mill Lane, Great Warford, Alderley Edge SK9 7TY; 13 Belmont Road, Ilford IG1 1YW Tel: 020 8514 2490 — MB BS 1996 Lond.; BSc 1990.

HORA, Seema The Surgery, 67-69 Langley Crescent, Dagenham RM9 6TB Tel: 020 8592 5523 Fax: 020 8593 7235; 27 Parkstone Avenue, Emerson Park, Hornchurch RM11 3LN Tel: 01708 471677 Fax: 01708 430728 — MB BS 1965 Rajasthan; BSc Allahabad 1960. Socs: Med. Protec. Soc. Prev: Regist. (Psychiat.) SHO (O & G) & SHO (Accid. & Cas.) St. Edwds Hosp. Cheddleton.

HORA, Subhash Chandra The Surgery, 67-69 Langley Crescent, Dagenham RM9 6TB Tel: 020 8592 5523 Fax: 020 8593 7235 —

BSc Lucknow 1959, MB BS 1964; DCH RCP Lond.1967. (GSVM Med. Coll. Kanpur)

HORAK, Elisabeth Pasque Hospice, Great Bramingham Lane, Streatley, Luton LU3 3NT Tel: 01582 492339 Fax: 01582 564906; Frogmore, Little Milton, Oxford OX44 7QD Tel: 01844 278947 Fax: 01844 278228 — MD 1974 Budapest; DPhil Oxf. 1987.

HORAN, Mr Francis Thomas Providence, Plumpton, Lewes BN7 3AJ Tel: 01273 890316 Fax: 01273 890482 — MRCS Eng. LRCP Lond. 1959; MSc McGill 1975; FRCS Eng. 1966. (St. Mary's) Edr., Jl. Bone & Jt. Surg. (Brit. Volume). Socs: Fell. BOA; Soc. Internat. Chir. Orthop. Traumatol.; Ex-Pres. Brit. Orthop. Sports Trauma Assn. Prev: Med. Dir. & Cons. Orthop. Surg. P.ss Roy. Hosp. Haywards Heath; Sen. Regist. (Orthop.) St. Mary's Hosp. Lond. & N.wick Pk. Hosp. Harrow; Research Fell. Montreal Gen. Hosp. & McGill Univ., Canada.

HORAN, Marie 29 Oakfield Road, Hadfield, Hyde SK13 2BN — MB ChB 1990 Liverp.

HORAN, Michael Anthony 21 Church Place, Lurgan, Craigavon BT66 6EY Tel: 02838 326333 — MB BCh BAO 1944 NUI; MB BCh BAO NUI. 1944; LM Nat. Matern. Hosp. Dub. 1951. (NUI) Prev: Ho. Surg. & Ho. Phys. Centr. Hosp. Galway.

HORAN, Professor Michael Arthur University Hospital of South Manchester, Nell Lane, Manchester M20 2LR Tel: 0161 447 3851 Fax: 0161 447 3853; 77 Cheadle Old Road, Stockport SK3 9RH — MB BChir 1978 Camb.; PhD Utrecht 1985; MA, MB Camb. 1978, BChir 1977; FRCP Lond. 1992. (Camb.) Prof. Geriat. Med. Univ. Manch.; Research Fell. Inst. for Experim. Gerontol. Rijswijk. Socs: Assn. Europeen de Med. Intern d'Ensemble; Brit. Geriat. Soc. Prev: Sen. Lect. (Geriat. Med.) Univ. Manch.; Cons. Inst. for Experim. Gerontology Rijswijk.; Hon. Sen. Regist. & Tutor (Geriat. Med.) Univ. Manch. & Hope Hosp.

HORAN, Sarah 3 Cawcott Drive, Windsor SL4 5PU — MB BS 1993 Lond.

HORBY, Peter William 15 Norroy Road, Putney, London SW15 1PQ — MB BS 1992 Lond.

HORDEN, Peter Julian Village Surgery, 233 Village Street, Derby DE23 8DD Tel: 01332 766762 Fax: 01332 272084; Moorway Farm, 49 Moorway Lane, Littleover, Derby DE23 7FR — MB ChB 1971 Sheff.

HORDER, Elizabeth Anne Abbot House, Great Broughton, Cockermouth CA13 0YX — MB BS Lond. 1967; MRCS Eng. LRCP Lond. 1967. SCMO (Child Protec.) Cumbria; Asst. Police Surg. Cumbria.

HORDER, Elizabeth June (retired) 98 Regent's Park Road, London NW1 8UG Tel: 020 7722 3804 — BM BCh Oxf. 1945; BA Oxf. 1945. Volunteer for Med. Foundat. for c/o Victims of Torture. Prev: Counsellor for Child Line UK.

HORDER, Joan Margaret (retired) 313 Lauderdale Tower, Barbican, London EC2Y 8NA Tel: 020 7588 5434 — MB BS 1959 Lond.; MA Camb. 1965; FRCPath 1983, M 1971; DMJ Soc. Apoth. Lond. 1975. Prev: Cons. Histopath. Kettering & Dist. Gen. Hosp.

HORDER, John Plaistowe, CBE (retired) 98 Regent's Park Road, London NW1 8UG Tel: 020 7722 3804 — BM BCh Oxf. 1948; MA Oxf. 1948; Hon. MD Free Univ. Amsterdam 1985; FRCP Ed. 1981; FRCP Lond. 1972, M 1951; FRCGP 1970; FRCPsych 1980, M 1974. Pres. UK Centre for the Advance. of Interprofessional Educat. Prev: Pres. RCGP 1979-82.

HORDERN, Blanche Wellesley (retired) 15 Park Gate, Blackheath, London SE3 9XF Tel: 020 8852 0273 — MB ChB 1936 Birm. Med. Off. Lond. Boro. Greenwich & Inner Lond. Educat. Auth. Prev: Ho. Surg. Ear & Throat Dept. Gen. Hosp. Birm.

HORDON, Lesley Diane Dewsbury District General Hospital, Healds Road, Dewsbury WF13 4H Tel: 01924 465105 — MB ChB 1979 Manch.; MD (Commend.) Leeds 1991; BSc (Med. Biochem.) Manch. 1976; MRCP (UK) 1982; FRCP 1998. Cons. Rheum. Dewsbury Dist. Gen. Hosp.; Vis. Research Fell. Dept. of BioMed. Sci.s, Univ. of Leeds; Hon. Sen. Lect. Univ. of Leeds. Prev: Sen. Regist. (Rheum.) Leeds Gen. Infirm.

HORE, Angela Theresa Fern House Surgery, 125-129 Newland Street, Witham CM8 1BH Tel: 01376 502108 Fax: 01376 502281 — MB ChB 1982 Manch.; MRCGP 1986.

HORE, Brian David (cons. room), 17 St John St., Manchester M3 4DR Tel: 0161 834 5775 — MB BS Lond. 1962; MPhil Lond. 1970, BSc (Hons.) Physiol. 1959; FRCP Lond. 1982, M 1967; MRCS Eng. LRCP Lond. 1962; FRCPsych 1980, M 1971. (St. Bart.) Staff Cons. Psychiat. Priory Hosp. Altringham Chesh.; Hon. Cons. Psychiat. Univ. Hosp. & S. Manch. Trust; Hon. Lect. in Psychiat. Univ. of Manch. Socs: Hon. Vice Pres. Internat. Counc. for Alcohol and Addic.s; BMA; Soc. Study Addic. Prev: Sen. Regist. (Psychol. Med.) Hammersmith Hosp. Lond.; Regist. Maudsley Hosp. Lond.; Ho. Phys. St. Bart Hosp. Lond.

HORE, Ian David Banks 22 Handforth Road, Wilmslow SK9 2LU — MB BS 1992 Lond.

HORGAN, Mr Alan Frederick 1 Lorraine Gardens, Glasgow G12 9NY — MB BCh BAO 1988 NUI; FRCSI 1992.

HORGAN, Catherine Helena St Margarets Somerset Hospice, Heron Drive, Bishops Hull, Taunton TA1 5HA Tel: 01823 259394 Fax: 01823 345900 — MB BCh BAO 1980 NUI; MRCGP 1985; DCH NUI 1983; DObst RCPI 1982. Med. Off. St Margt.s Som. Hospice Taunton. Prev: GP New Ct. Surg. W.on Super Mare.

HORGAN, Dermot Finbarr Anthony Stockton Heath Medical Centre, The Forge, London Road, Stockton Heath, Warrington WA4 6HJ Tel: 01925 604427 Fax: 01925 210501 — MB BS 1982 Lond.; MRCGP 1988.

HORGAN, Jane Elizabeth May Oakley Bungalow, 15 Oakley Lane, Wimborne BH21 1SF — MB BCh BAO 1984 NUI; LRCPSI 1984.

HORGAN, Joanne Louise The Health Centre, Madeira Road, West Byfleet KT14 6DH Tel: 01932 336933 Fax: 01932 355681; 27 Jessamy Road, Weybridge KT13 8LB Tel: 01932 850728 — MB BS 1989 Lond.; BSc Lond. 1986. Prev: SHO (A & E) Basingstoke Gen. Hosp. & S. Hants. VTS.

HORGAN, John Timothy Christopher Health Centre, Darenth Lane, South Ockendon RM15 5LP Tel: 01708 853114 — MB BCh BAO 1951 NUI. (Cork)

HORGAN, Mr Kieran Department of Surgery, Leeds General Infirmary, Great George St., Leeds LS1 3EX Fax: 0113 392 3598 — MB BCh BAO 1979 NUI; MCh NUI 1987, MB BCh BAO 1979; FRCSI 1984. Cons. Surg. & Hon. Sen. Lect. (Surg.) Univ. of Leeds. Socs: Assn. Surg.; Surg. Research Soc.; Brit. Assn. Surg. Oncol.

HORGAN, Mr Liam Francis Mary University Department of Surgery, The Royal Free Hospital School of Medicine, Pond St., London NW3 2QG Tel: 020 7794 0500 Fax: 020 7431 4528 Email: liam@rfhsm.ac.uk; 15 Tarrant Drive, Harpenden AL5 1RP Tel: 01582 762639 — MB BCh BAO 1985 NUI; FRCS Eng. 1992; FRCSI 1992. Sen. Clin. Research Fell. & Hon. Sen. Regist. (Gen. Surg.) Roy. Free Hosp. Lond. Socs: ASIT; Affil. Mem. Assn. Surgs. GB & Irel.; SMIT.

HORGAN, Margaret Mary Flat 2 10 Middle House, Monks Orchard Road, Beckenham BR3 3BN — MB BCh BAO 1991 NUI.

HORGAN, Mary Patricia 12 Uddingston Road, Bothwell, Glasgow G71 8PH — MB BCh BAO 1991 NUI.

HORGAN, Mr Paul Gregory 37 Castlegate, Bothwell, Glasgow G71 7HU — MB BCh BAO 1982 NUI; FRCS Glas. 1987; FRCSI 1987.

HORGAN, Mr Simon Edward Royal Eye Hospital, Kington Hospital, Galsworthy Road, Kingston-upon-Thames KT2 7QB Tel: 8546 7711 — MB BS 1986 Lond.; FRCS Ed. 1991; FRCOphth 1991. Cons. Ophth., Kingston Hosp. NHS Trust; Cons. Ophth., St. Geo.'s NHS Healthcare. Socs: BMA; UK & Irel Soc. Cataract & Refractive Surg.; Brit. Diabetic Assoc. Prev: Regist. (Ophth.) Moorfields Eye Hosp. Lond.

HORKAN, Mary Carole 42 Woodlands, Harrow HA2 6EW — MB BS 1994 Lond.

HORLER, Gerald David (retired) 9 Ham Meadow, Marnhull, Sturminster Newton DT10 1LR Tel: 01258 820921 — MA Oxf. 1950, BM BCh 1952. Prev: Ho. Surg. St. Thos. Hosp.

HORLEY, John Fairbourne Pinelands, Sandy Lane, Henfield BN5 9UX — MB BS 1943 Lond.; FRCPath 1971. (Guy's) Socs: Assn. Clin Pathols. Prev: Res. Surg. Off. Roy. Hants. Co. Hosp. Winchester; Ho. Phys. Brompton Hosp. Sanat. Frimley; Haemat. Roy. Sussex Co. Hosp. Brighton.

***HORLOCK, Lucy** 30 Meadowfield, Springwell Village, Gateshead NE9 7QL — LMSSA 1997; LMSSA Lond. 1997; BA Oxf. 1993.

HORLOCK, Nigel Mark Brimfield Hall, Brimfield, Ludlow SY8 4NE — MB BS 1988 Lond.

HORMAN, Lisa Madeleine Boutport Street Surgery, 110 Boutport Street, Barnstaple EX31 1TD Tel: 01271 324106 Fax: 01271

347150 — MB BCh 1987 Wales; MRCGP 1991; DCH RCP Lond. 1990.

HORMBREY, Mrs Emma Léonie Common Farm, High St., Beckley, Oxford OX3 9UU; Common Farm, High St, Oxford OX3 9UU — MB BS 1994 Lond.; BSc (Hons.) Lond. 1990; FRCS (Eng.). (St. Bart. Hosp. Med. Sch.) SHO (Plastic Surg.) Stoke Mandeville Hosp. Aylesbury. Prev: SHO (Orthop.) Stoke Mandeville Hosp. Aylesbury.

HORMBREY, Mr Philip James Accident and Emergency Department, John Radcliffe Hospital, Headington, Oxford OX3 9DU Tel: 01865 741166 Fax: 01865 220220; Common Farm, High St, Beckley, Oxford OX3 9UU — MB ChB 1984 Liverp.; FRCS Ed. 1994; MRCP (UK) 1991; FFAEM 1996; DA (UK) 1992; Dip IMC RCS Ed. 1992. Cons. A & E Oxf. Radcliffe Hosp. Prev: Sen. Regist. (A & E) John Radcliffe Hosp. Oxf.; Regist. (A & E) St. Bart. Hosp. Lond.

HORMIS, Paul Birkwood, Mickledale Lane, Bilsthorpe, Mansfield Tel: 01623 870230; Birkwood, Bilsthorpe, Newark NG22 8QB Tel: 01623 870230 — MB BS 1970 Mysore. (Kasturba Med. Coll. Mangalore)

HORN, Alan Richard Flat 9, 41 Craven Hill Gardens, London W2 3EA — MB ChB 1988 Cape Town.

HORN, Andrew Charles Ombersley Medical Centre, Hastings House, Kidderminster Road, Ombersley, Droitwich WR9 0EL Tel: 01905 620202 Fax: 01905 621188 — MB BCh 1975 Wales; DRCOG 1979.

HORN, Christopher Ronald Dunbar Medical Centre, Abbey Road, Dunbar EH42 1JP Tel: 01368 862227 Fax: 01368 865646 — MB BS 1977 Lond.; MD Lond. 1988; MRCP (UK) 1980. (Middlx. Hosp. Med. Sch.)

HORN, Clare Katherine Dept. GU Medicine, Royal United Hospital, Combe park, Bath BA1 3NG Tel: 01225 825575 Email: kate.horn@ruh-bath.swest.nhs.co.uk — MB ChB 1988 Sheff.; MRCP (UK) 1991; DFFP 1994. (Sheff) Cons. (Genito-Urin. Med.), Roy. United Hosp., Bath. Socs: Med. Soc. Study VD; Assn. Genitourin Med.; BHIVA. Prev: Sen. & Career Regist. (Genitourin. Med.) Glas. Roy. Infirm.; Regist. (Med.) Pinderfields Hosp. Wakefield & Leeds Gen. Infirm. Yorks. RHA; Sen. Regist. (Genitourin. Med.) Roy. Infirm. Edin.

HORN, Mr David Nicholas Downlands, Pitcot Lane, Owslebury, Winchester SO21 1LR — MB BS 1983 Lond.; BSc (Hons.) Lond. 1980; FRCS Eng. 1988.

HORN, Elizabeth Helen Departments of Medicine & Haematology, University Hospital, Queens medical Centre, Nottingham NG7 2UH Tel: 0115 970 9446 Email: muzlh@mmnl.medical.nottingham.ac.uk; 53 Cranford Gardens, West Bridgford, Nottingham NG2 7SE — MB ChB 1980 Glas.; MD Glas. 1993; MRCP (UK) 1983; MRCPath 1992. Sen. Lect. (Haemat. & Med.) & Hon. Cons. Haemat. Univ. Hosp. Nottm.

HORN, Professor Gabriel Sidney Sussex College, Cambridge CB2 3HU Tel: 01223 338815 Fax: 01223 350869 Email: gh105@cus.cam.ac.uk; Jack of Clubs Barn, Fen Road, Lode, Cambridge CB5 9HE — MB ChB Birm. 1955; FRS 1986; ScD Camb. 1975, MA 1956; BSc (Hons. Birm). 1952, MD 1965; DSc 1999. (Birm.) Fell. Kings & Sidney Sussex Coll. Camb.; Sen. Scientist, Univ. Of Camb., Dept. of Behaviour. Socs: BMA; Physiol. Soc.; Eur. Neurosci. Assn. Prev: Prof. & Head of Dept. of Zool. Univ. Camb.; Prof. & Head of Dept. Anat. Univ. Bristol; Master Sidney Sussex Coll.Camb.

HORN, Helen Mary Department of Dermatology, Royal Infirmary of Edinburgh, Lauriston Place, Edinburgh EH3 9YW Tel: 0131 536 2057 Fax: 0131 229 8769 Email: hmhrda@hotmail.com; Balliol House, 1 The Doon, Spott, Dunbar EH42 1UX — MB BS 1977 Lond.; MRCP (UK) 1980.

HORN, Janet Sally MacRae Ysbyty Gwynedd, Bangor LL57 4AD Tel: 01248 384384 Fax: 01248 370629 — MB BS 1976 Lond.; MRCP (UK) 1980. Cons. Paediat. Gwynedd NHS Trust. Prev: Sen. Regist. Ealing Gen. Hosp.

HORN, Jill Alexandra 178 Wingrove Road, Newcastle upon Tyne NE4 9DA — MB BS 1990 Newc.

HORN, Kenneth William (retired) 45 Main Street, Irton, Scarborough YO12 4RJ — MB ChB 1941 Ed.

HORN, Mary Elizabeth Cathcart (retired) 6 Genoa Avenue, London SW15 6DY Tel: 020 8788 8398 — MB ChB 1951 Glas.; MA Glas. 1946, MB ChB 1951; DCH Eng. 1964. Lect. (s/i in Sickle Cell Dis.) Dept. Community Med. King's Coll. Hosp. Lond. Prev: Sen. Research Asst. Dept. Clin. Epidemiol. in Gen. Pract. & Hon.

HORN, Neil Richard 15 Daisy Bank, Lancaster LA1 3JW — MB ChB 1987 Cape Town.

HORN, Nicholas John Jubilee House, Ashford Hospital, King's Avenue, Ashford TN23 1LU Tel: 01233 204070 Fax: 01233 204071; 26 Canon Woods Way, Kennington, Ashford TN24 9QY Tel: 01233 634483 — BM BS 1981 Nottm.; BMedSci (Hons.) Nottm. 1979; DCH RCP Lond. 1993. (Nottm.) Assoc. SpecialistCommunity Child health E. Kent Hosp.NHs Trust. Prev: Clin. Med. Off. (Community Paediat.) Nottm. Community Health NHS Trust.

HORN, Nigel Mark Alistair 54 St Barnabus Road, Cambridge CB1 2DE — MB BS 1984 Lond.

HORN, Peter Alan 178 Wingrove Road, Newcastle upon Tyne NE4 9DA — MB BS 1990 Newc.

HORN, Peter Jeremy Bennetts Road North Surgery, 2 Bennetts Road North, Keresley End, Coventry CV7 8LA Tel: 024 7633 2636 Fax: 024 7633 7353; Nectans, Tamworth Road, Keresley End, Coventry CV7 8JJ Tel: 024 76 332195 — MB ChB 1985 Leic.; MRCGP 1990; DCH RCP Lond. 1988. Prev: GP Bottesford Lincs.; Trainee GP/SHO Nottm. VTS.

HORN, Robin Frank Holloway Simpson Centre, 70 Gregories Road, Beaconsfield HP9 1PS Tel: 0149 46 71571; 45 Hazlemere Road, Penn, High Wycombe HP10 8AF — MB BS 1950 Lond.; MRCS Eng. LRCP Lond. 1946. (Middlx.) Med. Off. Alfriston Sch. Prev: Ho. Phys. N.. Hosp. Lond. & Sutton & Cheam Hosp.; Capt. RAMC.

HORN, Sara Helen 26 Canon Woods Way, Kennington, Ashford TN24 9QY Tel: 01233 634483 Email: sara@docshorn.freeserve.co.uk; 26 Canon Woods Way, Kennington, Ashford TN24 9QY Tel: 01233 634483 Email: sara@docshorn.freeserve.co.uk — BM BS 1981 Nottm.; BMedSci Nottm. 1979. (Nottm.) GP/Regist. Ashford, Kent VTS. Prev: SHO Palliat. Med., Pilgrims Hospie, Hythe Rd., Ashford, Kent.

HORNBUCKLE, Janet Centre for Reproduction, Growth and Development, University of Leeds, 34 Hyde Terrace, Leeds LS2 9LN Tel: 0113 292 6240 Fax: 0113 292 6240 Email: j.hornbuckle@leeds.ac.uk; 200 Northfield Road, Sheffield S10 1QU Tel: 0114 268 7363 Email: j.hornbuckle99 @freeserve.co.uk — MB ChB 1990 Sheff.; MRCOG 1996. (Sheffield) Clin. Research Fell. Centre for ReProduc., Growth & Developm. Univ. of Leeds.

HORNBUCKLE, Joanne 35 Grove Road, Sheffield S7 2GY Tel: 0114 236 3481 Fax: 0114 236 3481 — MB BS 1989 Newc.; MRCP (UK) 1994.

HORNBY, Christopher John Charlbury Surgery, Spendlove Centre, Enstone Road, Charlbury, Chipping Norton OX7 3PQ Tel: 01608 810210 Fax: 01608 811636; Walton House, Southside, Steeple Aston, Bicester OX25 4RT — MB BChir 1989 Camb.; BA Oxf. 1983; MRCGP 1993; DRCOG 1991. Prev: Trainee GP Oxf.; Trainee GP Wessex VTS.

HORNBY, Judith Frances (retired) — MB ChB 1965 Manch.; FRCR 1983; DMRD Eng. 1981; DCH Eng. 1967. Prev: Sen. Regist. (Diag. Radiol.) Newc. AHA.

HORNBY, Richard Charles The Brow Medical Centre, The Brow, Burgess Hill RH15 9BS; Cambridge House, Cherry Lane, Bolney, Haywards Heath RH17 5PR — MB BS 1985 Lond.; MRCP (UK) 1989; DRCOG 1992. (Guy's) Prev: SHO (O & G) P.ss Roy. Hosp. Haywards Heath; Community Med. Off. (Palliat. Med.) Brighton.

HORNBY, Mr Roger Rosemount House, Eachwick, Dalton, Newcastle upon Tyne NE18 0AZ Tel: 01661 886389 Fax: 01661 886389; Rosemount House, Eachwick, Dalton, Newcastle upon Tyne NE18 0AZ Tel: 01661 886389 Fax: 01661 886389 — MRCS Eng. LRCP Lond. 1963; MD Manch. 1967, MB ChB 1963; FRCS Eng. 1985; FRCS Canada (Orthop.) 1971. (Manch.) p/t Cons. Surg. Nuffield. Hosp.Newc. upon Tyne; Sen. Med. Mem. InDepend. Tribunal Serv. Socs: Brit. Orthop. Assn. Prev: Sen. Lect. (Orthop.) Univ. Newc.; Asst. Lect. in Physiol. Univ. Manch.; Resid. Orthop. Surg. Univ. Toronto Hosps.

HORNBY, Miss Stella Jane Rosemount House, Eachwick, Newcastle upon Tyne NE18 0AZ Tel: 01661 886389 — MB BChir 1993 Camb.; MA Camb. 1994; FRCOphth 1997. (Univ. Camb.) Clin. Research Fell. Childh. Blindness Unit Dept. of Preven. Ophth. Inst. of Ophth. Lond. Socs: Fell. Roy. Coll. Ophth.s. Prev: SHO (Ophth.)

Oxf. Eye Hosp.; SHO (Ophth.) Carlisle & Roy. Berks. Hosp. Reading; SHO (Neurol.) Midl. Centre for Neurol. & Neurosurg.

HORNCASTLE, Rachel Anne 91 Sandwich House, Sandwich St., London WC1H 9PW — MB BS 1992 Lond.

HORNE, Alan Mclaren, TD (retired) 40 Cammo Gardens, Edinburgh EH4 8EG Tel: 0131 339 2665 — MB ChB 1954 Ed.; FRCGP 1996; MRCGP 1973. Prev: Med. Off. Scott. Home & Health Dept. Edin. Prison.

HORNE, Alexander Dewar Child & Family Consultation Service, Shernhall St., London E17 3EA Tel: 020 8509 0424; 76 Constantine Road, London NW3 2LX Tel: 020 7428 0355 — MB ChB 1979 Aberd.; MRCPsych 1984. Cons. Psychiat. (Child & Adolesc.) Child & Family Consult. Serv. Lond.

HORNE, Andrew Sutherland Broadmoor Hospital, Crowthorne RG45 7EG Tel: 01344 773111 Fax: 01344 754179 Email: 100532.1612@compuserve.com — MB ChB 1978 Bristol; MRCPsych 1983. (Univ. of Bristol) Cons. Forens. Psychiat. BRd.moor Hosp. Crowthorne. Prev: Sen. Regist. (Forens. Psychiat.) Pk. La. Hosp. Liverp.; Regist. (Psychiat.) Roy. Edin. Hosp.

HORNE, Andrew Wemyss Basement Flat, 15 Stonor Road, London W14 8RZ — MB ChB 1994 Ed. SHO (O & G) Roy. Infirm. Edin. Prev: Ho. Off. (Med.) E. Gen. Hosp. Edin.; Ho. Off. (Surg.) Falkirk & Dist. Roy. Infirm.

HORNE, Anthony Ronald London Road Surgery, 46-48 London Road, Carlisle CA1 2EL Tel: 01228 27559 Fax: 01228 594434 — MB BS 1969 Newcastle; MB BS Newc.1969. (Newcastle) GP Carlisle.

HORNE, Professor Charles Hugh Wilson, MBE Novocastra Laboratories, Balliol Business Park, Benton Lane, Newcastle upon Tyne NE12 8EW Tel: 0191 215 0567 Fax: 0191 215 1152 Email: chwhorne@compuserve.com; 7 Elmtree Grove, Gosforth, Newcastle upon Tyne NE3 4BG Tel: 0191 284 8803 Fax: 0191 284 8803 — MB ChB 1962 Glas.; DSc Aberd. 1979; MD (Hons.) Glas. 1973; FRCP Ed. 1994; FRCPath 1980, M 1968. Emerit. Prof. Path.; Chairm. & Managing Dir. Novocastra Laborat. Socs: Hon.Mem. Path. Soc. GB & Irel; Assn. Clin. Path. Prev: Prof. Path. Univ Newc.; Prof. Immunopath. & Hon. Cons. Univ. Aberd.; Lect. (Path.) Roy. & W.. Infirm. Glas.

HORNE, Christopher Richard Tel: 01353 778208 Fax: 01353 777765; 6 Main Street, Witchford, Ely CB6 2HG Tel: 01353 662492 — MB BS 1973 Lond.; DCH Eng. 1977. (Roy. Free) Clin. Asst. (Geriat.) P.ss of Wales Hosp. Ely. Prev: Trainee GP Hoddesdon, Herts; Regist. (Gen. Med. & Geriat.) E. Roding Dist. Ilford; SHO (Paediat.) Roy. Free Hosp.

HORNE, Clare Amanda 5 Ernicote Close, Ambrosden, Bicester OX25 2LG — MB BCh BAO 1993 Belf.; MRCP 1997. (Queens Univ. Belfast)

HORNE, David Kenneth Circuit Lane Surgery, 53 Circuit Lane, Reading RG30 3AN Tel: 0118 958 2537 Fax: 0118 957 6115 — MB BCh 1983 Wales; MRCP (UK) 1986; MRCGP 1988; DRCOG 1988. Hosp. Pract. (Endocrinol.) Roy. Berks. Hosp. Reading.

HORNE, Dominic Christopher 30 Dalmeny Road, Edinburgh EH6 4QY — MB BS 1991 Newc.

HORNE, Glenda May Department of bacteriology, Glasgow Royal Infirmary, 84 Castle St., Glasgow G4 0SF Tel: 0141 211 4640 Fax: 0141 552 1524; 19A Hughenden Gardens, Glasgow G12 9XZ Tel: 0141 357 0007 — MB ChB 1989 Aberd.; MRCP 1994; DTM & H 1996; Dip RCPath 1997. Specialist Regist. Med. Biol., Glas. Roy. Infirm. Socs: Hosp. Infec. Soc.; Brit. Soc. for the study of Infec.; Diplomate of RCPath.

HORNE, Helen Louise Department of Dermatology, South Cleveland Hospital, Marton Road, Middlesbrough TS4 3BW — MB BS 1975 Newc. Staff Grade (Dermat.) S. Cleveland Hosp. Middlesbrough. Socs: Assoc. Mem. Brit. Assn.Dermatol. Prev: Regist. (Histopath.) N. Tees Gen. Hosp. Stockton-on-Tees; Regist. (Geriat. & Gen. Med.) Dryburn Hosp. Durh.; Regist. (Community Med.) N.. RHA.

HORNE, James Hugh Macaliste Riverbank Medical Centre, Midhurst GU29 9AW Tel: 01730 812121 Fax: 01730 811400 — BM BCh 1973 Oxf.; MRCGP 1980; DCH Eng. 1975; DObst RCOG 1976. Prev: Trainee GP Chichester VTS; Ho. Phys. Radcliffe Infirm. Oxf.; Ho. Surg. Roy. United Hosp. Bath.

HORNE, Jean (retired) 12 West Avenue, Glasgow G33 6ES — MB ChB 1963 Glas.; DPH 1968.

HORNE, John Justin — MB BChir 1983 Camb.; BA Camb. 1979; MRCGP 1988. Prev: Trainee GP Tiverton Devon VTS; Regist. (Gen. Med.) Llandough Hosp. S. Glam.

HORNE, Margaret Marian Scotsburn Road, Tain IV19 — MB ChB 1937 Aberd.; MRCGP 1953. (Aberd.) Socs: B.M.A. Prev: Res. Med. Off. Ross & Cromarty Co. Hosp.; Ho. Surg. Childr. Hosp. Derby.

HORNE, Melanie Alexandra Macdonald London Road Medical Practice, 12 London Road, Kilmarnock KA3 7AD Tel: 01563 523593 Fax: 01563 573552; 4 Kay Park Grove, Kilmarnock KA3 7RA — MB ChB 1993 Glas.; DRCOG; DFFP; MRCGP. Socs: BMA. Prev: Trainee GP Paisley VTS.

HORNE, Michael 4 Linwood Place, Melton Park, Gosforth, Newcastle upon Tyne NE3 5TJ Tel: 0191 217 0088 — MB BS 1965 Durh.

HORNE, Michael Health Centre, Lower St., Tettenhall, Wolverhampton WV6 9LL Tel: 01902 751032 & 755631 — MB BS 1959 Lond.

HORNE, Morag Catherine 5 Falcon Close, Lightwater GU18 5NB Email: morag@levelgrove.demon.co.uk — MB ChB 1982 Aberd.; MSc Univ. Lond. 1989; MRCPath. 1992.

HORNE, Norman Wemyss (retired) 95/5 Grange Loan, Edinburgh EH9 2ED Tel: 0131 667 2149 — MB ChB 1940 Ed.; FRCP Ed. 1954, M 1947. Prev: Cons. Chest Phys. City Hosp. Edin.

HORNE, Pamela Mary 22 North Gyle Grove, Edinburgh EH12 8JZ — MB BS 1945 Lond.; MRCS Eng. LRCP Lond. 1945; DPM Ed. & Glas. 1966. (Roy. Free) Prev: Med. Off. Ment. Welf. Commiss. Scotl. Scott. Home & Health Dept.; Asst. Psychiat. Bangour Village Hosp. W. Lothian.; Cas. Off. & Resid. Anaesth. Roy. Free. Hosp. Lond.

***HORNE, Peter William** Ryefield, Packhorse Road, Sevenoaks TN13 2QP — MB ChB 1994 Bristol.

HORNE, Richard Alan Norton Medical Centre, Billingham Rd, Norton, Stockton-on-Tees TS20 2UZ Tel: 01642 360111 Fax: 01642 558672 — MB BS 1974 Newc.; FRCGP 1991, M 1978; DRCOG 1977. (University of Newcastle-upon-Tyne) GP Princip.; GP Trainer Cleveland VTS. Socs: (Hon. Treas.) RCGP; BMA. Prev: Med. Adviser Hoechst AG Pharma Div. Frankfurt am Main, W. Germany; Trainee GP Newc. u. Tyne VTS; Ho. Surg. & Ho. Phys. Roy. Vict. Infirm. Newc.

HORNE, Richard John 39 Sydney Avenue, Pennington, Leigh WN7 3LT Tel: 01942 681509 — LMSSA 1982 Lond. Clin. Anaesth. Specialist Chorley Dist. Hosp. Prev: Regist. Rotat. (Anaesth.) NW Region.

HORNE, Simon Thomas 18 Hart Synnot House, Leckford Road, Oxford OX2 6JL Tel: 01865 513756 Email: psihorne@hotmail.com — BM BCh 1996 Oxf.; BA Oxon. 1993. (Oxford) Med. Off. Roy. Army Med. Corps.

HORNER, Adam Scadding (retired) East Cottage, Beaminster DT8 3NE Tel: 01308 862929 — MB BS 1960 Lond.; MRCS Eng. LRCP Lond. 1960; DObst RCOG 1962. Prev: Ho. Phys. & Ho. Surg., Cas. Off. & Resid. Obst. Guy's Hosp. Lond.

HORNER, Anne Elizabeth, Squadron Ldr. RAF Med. Br. Retd. Regional Medical Centre, Rafc Cranwell, Sleaford NG34 8HB; 36 Salsbury Drive, Bracebridge Heath, Lincoln LN24 2SW — MB ChB 1989 Leic.; DRCOG 1995; DFFP 1995; MRCGP 1996. Civil. Med. Practitioner MOD (RAF Cranwell). Prev: GP Partner (p/t).

HORNER, Catherine 64 Trinity View, Caerleon, Newport NP18 3SU; 64 Trinity View, Caerleon, Newport NP18 3SU — MB BCh 1991 Wales. SHO (Anaesth.) Ipswich Hosp. Prev: Ho. Off. (Med.) Roy. Berks. Hosp.; Ho. Off. (Surg.) Ipswich Hosp.

HORNER, Daniel Richard Maxsted 95 Boundary Road, London SW19 2DE — MB BS 1996 Lond.

HORNER, George Frederick Brian 51 Rosetta Park, Rosetta, Belfast BT6 0DL — MB BCh BAO 1986 Belf.; DRCOG 1990; DCH RCPS Glas. 1990; DMH Belf. 1990.

HORNER, Glenda Rhianon Firlands, 10 Highdale Road, Clevedon BS21 7LR — MB BS 1986 Lond.; MRCGP 1990; DCH RCP Lond. 1989; DRCOG 1988.

HORNER, Gordon Lee (retired) Longridge House, Sheepscombe, Stroud GL6 7QU Tel: 01452 812128 — MB BS 1967 Lond.; MRCS Eng. LRCP Lond. 1967; DObst RCOG 1970.

HORNER, Jane Elizabeth Clinical Director Accident & Emergency Medical, Torbay Hospital, Lowes Bridge, Torquay TQ2 7AA Tel: 01803 654010 Fax: 01803 616331; Solsbro Court, Sosbro Rd,

Torquay TQ2 6PF Tel: 01803 690021 — MB ChB 1978 Liverp.; MRCP (UK) 1983; DTM & H Liverp. 1987; FFAEM 1998. (Liverpool) Cons. A & E Med. Torbay Hosp. Socs: BMA; BAEM. Prev: Sen. Regist. (A & E Med.) N.. RHA; Sen. Regist. (A & E Med.) Mersey Region; Regist. (Gen. Med.) Mersey Region.

HORNER, Joanna Caroline Pelynt House, Pelynt, Looe PL13 2LB — BM 1993 Soton.; BSc Physiol. 1989.

HORNER, John Lister 27 Carlton Gardens, Leeds LS7 1JL Tel: 0113 459415 — MB ChB 1957 Leeds; MA Camb. 1945; PhD Leeds 1953, MB ChB 1957; MRCGP 1968; DObst RCOG 1960.

HORNER, John Roydon Riverside Surgery, George Street, High Wycombe HP11 2RZ Tel: 01494 526500 Fax: 01494 450237 — MB BS 1971 Lond.; BSc (Microbiol.) Lond. 1968, MB BS 1971; MRCGP 1976. (St. Mary's)

HORNER, Professor John Stuart, CStJ (retired) Beth Shemesh, Spring Lane, Samlesbury, Preston PR5 0UX Tel: 01772 877600 Fax: 01772 877500 — MB ChB 1956 Birm.; MD Manch. 1995; FRCP Lond. 1996; FFPHM RCP (UK) 1990; FFCM 1975, M 1972; DIH Eng. 1961; DPH (Distinc.) Lond. 1960. Prof. (Med. Ethics.) Univ. Centr. Lancs.; Med. Ref. Preston Crematorium. Prev: Dir. Pub. Health Preston HA.

HORNER, Mr Joseph Ashford Hospital, Ashford TW15 3AA Tel: 01784 264313; The Yews, Woodlands Drive, Sunbury-on-Thames TW16 5JS Tel: 01932 788161 — MB ChB 1965 Cape Town; FRCS Ed. 1973; FCS(SA) 1972. (Cape Town) Cons. Surg. Ashford Hosp. Middlx. Prev: Sen. Surg. Regist. St. Mary's Hosp. Lond.

HORNER, Marilyn Elizabeth Anne 53 Borough Street, Castle Donnington, Derby DE74 2LB Tel: 01332 811480; The Hacklands, Woodhill Road, Collingham, Newark NG23 7NR Tel: 01636 892667 — MB BS 1979 Lond.; BSc Lond. 1974, MB BS 1979; MRCGP 1983. (St Geo. Lond.)

HORNER, Mark Stephen Middle Farm Surgery, 51 Main Street, Felton, Morpeth NE65 9PR Tel: 01670 787353 Fax: 01670 787353 — MB BS 1978 Newc.

HORNER, Olivia Jane 104 Wayland Road, Sheffield S11 8YE — MB ChB 1998 Sheff.; MB ChB Sheff 1998.

HORNER, Patrick Jacob Department of Genitourinary Medicine, Bristol Royal Infirmary, Bristol BS2 8HW Tel: 0117 928 3093 Fax: 0117 928 2385 Email: paddy.horner@bristol.ac.uk — MB BS 1986 Lond.; MA Camb. 1987; MRCP (UK) 1989. Cons. Genitourin. Med. Bristol Roy. Infirm.; Hon. Sen. Clin. Lect. (Genitourin. Med.) Univ. Bristol. Socs: Med. Soc. Study VD; Assn. Genitourin. Med.

HORNER, Ruth 50 Haven Green Court, Ealing Broadway, London W5 2UY Tel: 020 8998 6421 — MB ChB 1960 Cape Town; FRCPCH 1996. (Cape Town) Cons. Community Paediat. W. Lond. Healthcare NHS Trust. Socs: Roy. Coll. Paediat. & Child Health.

HORNER, Simon Scadding The Shaftesbury Practice, Abbey View Medical Centre, Salisbury Road, Shaftesbury SP7 8DH Tel: 01747 856700 Fax: 01747 856701 Email: simon-horner@gp-j81026.nhs.uk; Perrymead, Bedchester, Shaftesbury SP7 0JU — MB BS 1989 Lond.; BSc Lond. 1986; MRCGP 1994; DRCOG 1992. Prev: Trainee GP Dorchester, W. Dorset VTS.

HORNER, Susan Elizabeth 7 Teilo Street, Cardiff CF11 9JN — MB ChB 1989 Bristol; MRCGP 1993; DGM RCP Lond. 1994; DRCOG 1992. (Bristol) Staff Grade Phys. (c/o Elderly) Llandough Hosp. Penarth.

HORNER, William Maurice Leethem 11 Perry Close, Woodhouse, Eaves, Loughborough LE12 8SB — MRCS Eng. LRCP Lond. 1937. (St. Bart.) Prev: Cas. Off. & Res. Anaesth. Metrop. Hosp.; Ho. Phys. Haywood Hosp. Tunstall.

HORNETT, Graham Albert Wilfrid The Surgery, The Street, Wonersh, Guildford GU5 0PE Tel: 01483 898123 Fax: 01483 893104; Bay Cottage, Wonersh, Guildford GU5 0RU Tel: 01483 894349 Email: 106353.1144@compuserve.com — MB BChir Camb. 1963; MA Camb. 1963; MRCS Eng. LRCP Lond. 1962; FRCGP 1990, M 1979; DObst RCOG 1964. (St. Thos.) Dept. of Transport Med. Examr. for Seafarers; Hon. Fell. (Epidemiol. & Primary Health Care) Univ. Surrey; Mem. Panel Examrs. Roy. Coll. GPs; ACIArb 1995; MCIArb 1999. Socs: Fell. Roy. Soc. Trop. Med. & Hyg. Prev: Chairm. Med. Audit Advis. Gp. Surrey FHSA; Med. Off. Rd.s Nigeria Ltd.; Med. Adviser Sierra Leone Developm. Co.

HORNETT, John (retired) Portholme, 119 North Brink, Wisbech PE13 1LL Tel: 01945 584395 — MB BCh BAO 1966 Belf. Prev: Ho. Off. Ards Hosp. Newtownards.

HORNIBLOW, Philip James, OBE (retired) The Old Vicarage, Milton Clevedon, Shepton Mallet BA4 6NS Tel: 01749 830394 — MB BS Lond. 1954; FRCR 1975; FFR 1973; DMRD Eng. 1966. Prev: Last Appointment, cons. Radiologist, E. Som. NHS Trust.

HORNIBROOK, Sara Cathryn Leith Mount, 46 Ferry Road, Edinburgh EH6 4AE Tel: 0131 554 0558 Fax: 0131 555 6911 — MB ChB 1984 Birm.; MRCGP 1990; DCH RCPS Glas. 1988; Dip. Ther. Newc 1997. Socs: BMA; RCGP. Prev: Trainee GP Harrogate VTS.

HORNICK, Mr Philip Ian Department Cardiothoracic Surgery, Hammersmith Hospital, London W12 0NN; 66 Greenham Road, Muswell Hill, London N10 1LP Tel: 020 8883 9592 Email: phornick@rpms.ac.uk — MB BChir 1986 Camb.; BSc (Hons.) Lond. 1984; FRCS Eng. 1991. (London Hospital and Cambridge University) Specialist Regist. St. Geo.s Hosp. Lond.; Hon. Lect. Dept Cardiothoracic Surg. Imperial Coll. Sch. of Med. Hammersmith Hosp. Socs: Soc. Cardiothoracic Surgs. GB & Irel.; Brit. Transpl. Soc. Prev: Brit. Heart Foundat. Research Fell. 1994-1996; Roy. Coll. of Surgs. Research Fell. 1996-1997.

HORNIK, Rita Judith 2 Francklyn Gardens, Edgware HA8 8RX Tel: 020 8958 5630 Fax: 020 8958 8751 — MB BS Lond. 1959; MRCS Eng. LRCP Lond. 1959; DObst RCOG 1961. (Roy. Free)

HORNSBY, Arnold Hampshire Abbey Health Centre, East Abbey Street, Arbroath DD11 1EN Tel: 01241 870311 Fax: 01241 875411; 3 Lochlands Park, Arbroath DD11 3SR — MB ChB 1971 St. And. (St. And.)

HORNSBY, Charles Alistair Maryhill Practice, Elgin Health Centre, Maryhill, Elgin IV30 1AT Tel: 01343 543788 Fax: 01343 551604 — MB ChB 1986 Dundee; BMSc Dund 1983. Gen. Pract., Elgin Health Centr. Socs: BMA; Roy. Coll. Gen. Pract. Prev: SHO (Community Paediat. & Hosp. Paediat.) Raigmore Hosp. Inverness.

HORNSBY, Isobel Cleland Mallory, Aston Upthorne, Didcot OX11 9HQ — MB ChB 1945 Glas. (Glas.) Socs: Med. Wom. Federat.

HORNSEY, Jane Margaret 3 Deronda Road, Herne Hill, London SE24 9BQ — MB ChB 1982 Leeds; BSc Leeds 1979, MB ChB 1982.

HORNUNG, Elizabeth Anne (Surgery), Langley Corner, Ifield, Crawley RH11 0NF Tel: 01293 527114 Fax: 01293 553510; 205 Three Bridges Road, Crawley RH10 1LG Tel: 01293 528879 — MB BS 1986 Lond.; MA (Hons.) Oxf. 1989; MRCGP 1990; DRCOG 1990; DCH RCP Lond. 1989. (Oxford & Guy's.)

HORNUNG, Rimon Godfrey Medwyn, Moores Road, Dorking RH4 2BG Tel: 01306 882422 — LMSSA 1958 Lond.; MSc Lond. 1988, MB BS 1958; FRCGP 1981, M 1966; DObst RCOG 1961. (Guy's) Med. Off Starhurst Sch. Dorking & Boxhill Sch. Mickleham; Regional Adviser (Gen. Pract.) & Assoc. Dean Postgrad. Med. SW Thames RHA. Socs: Surrey Local Med. Comm.; BMA. Prev: Ho. Phys., Ho. Surg. & Res. Obst. Off. Guy's Hosp. Lond.

HORNUNG, Robert Samuel Aintree Cardiac Centre, University Hospital Aintree, Lower Lane, Liverpool L9 7AL Tel: 0151 529 2720 Fax: 0151 529 2724 — MB BS 1975 Lond.; BSc Lond. 1969; FRCP Lond. 1995; MRCP (UK) 1978. (St. Geo.) Cons. Phys. & Cardiol. Aintree Hosps. Trust Liverp. & Hon. Lect. Univ. Liverp. Prev: Sen. Regist. (Gen. Med. & Cardiol.) Vict. Infirm. & Roy. Infirm. Glas.; Regist. (Gen. Med. & Cardiol.) Dept. Mat. Med. Stobhill Gen. Hosp. Glas.; Research Regist. (Cardiol.) N.wick Pk. Hosp. Harrow.

HORNUNG, Timothy Scott Dept of paediatric Cardiology, Freeman Hospital, High heaton, Newcastle upon Tyne NE7 7DN — MB BChir 1990 Camb.; MA Camb. 1992; MRCP (UK) 1993. (Cambs) Specialist Regist. Paediat. Cardiol. Prev: Fell. Paediat. Cardiol. New Childr. Hosp. Sydney.AU; Regist. (Paediat.) Roy. Childr. Hosp. Melbourne, Austral.

HOROBIN, Roger Harold (retired) 30A Manor Road, Carlisle CA2 4LH Tel: 01228 23681 — MB ChB 1959 Birm. Prev: Ho. Phys. Manor Hosp. Walsall.

HOROBIN, Simon Roger 46 Woodway, Great Notley Garden Village, Braintree CM7 8JS — MB BS 1990 Lond.

HOROWITZ, Jack Israel The Old Vicarage, Melplash, Bridport DT6 3UD — LRCPI & LM, LRSCI & LM 1956; LRCPI & LM, LRCSI & LM 1956. (RCSI) Exam. Med. Off. Amateur Boxing Assn.; Lect. & Examr. St. John Ambul. Assn. & Brit. Red Cross Soc.; Examr. Standard Life Assur., Abbey Life Insur., Allied Dunbar Insur. & Permanent Insur. Socs: BMA; Anglo-Amer. Med. Soc. Prev: Ho.

Phys. Meath Hosp. Dub.; Ho. Surg. S.end Gen. Hosp.; Resid. (Obst., Gyn. & Path.) Sinai Hosp. Baltimore, USA.

HOROWITZ, Mr Martin (retired) 19 St Edmunds Green, Sedgefield, Stockton-on-Tees TS21 3HT Tel: 01740 622253 Fax: 01740 623490 — MB 1955 Camb.; BChir 1954; FRCS Eng. 1962; DLO Eng. 1957. Prev: Sen. Cons. ENT Surg. N. Riding Infirm. Middlesbrough.

HORROBIN, Anne Elizabeth 2 Curling Vale, Onslow Village, Guildford GU2 7PJ Tel: 01483 458969 — MB ChB 1994 Dundee; DCH RCP Lond. 1997; DRCOG 1998. GP Locum. Prev: SHO (O & G) Roy. Surrey Co. Hosp. Guildford; SHO (A & E) Roy. Surrey Co. Hosp. Guildford; SHO (Paediat.) Roy. Surrey Co. Hosp. Guildford.

HORROBIN, David Frederick Laxdale Limited, Kings Park House, Laurehill Business Park, Stirling FK7 9JQ Tel: 01786 476000 Fax: 01786 473137; Busk Cottage, Renwick, Penrith CA10 1LA Tel: 0176 883428 — BM BCh Oxf. 1968; DPhil Oxf. 1965, MA 1965. (Oxf. & St. Mary's) Chairm. Laxdale Research, Stirling; Dir. Efamol Research Inst. Nova Scotia. Socs: Fell. Roy. Soc. Med.; Physiol. Soc.; Soc. Endocrinol. Prev: Dir. Endocrine Pathophysiol. Laborat. Clin. Research Inst. Montreal, Canada; Reader (Physiol.) Newc. Univ. Med. Sch.; Chief Exec. Scotia Pharmaceut. Guildford.

HORROCKS, Andrew William Wythenshawe Hospital, Southmoor Road, Manchester M23 9LT — MB ChB 1975 Manch.; FRCR Lond. 1981; DMRD Lond. 1979. Cons. Radiol. Wythenshawe Hosp. S. Manch. Univ. Hosps. Trust. Socs: Chairm. Regional Radiol. Comm. Prev: Postgrad. Tutor Wythenshawe Hosp.

HORROCKS, Mrs Christine Tessa Wendover, 170 Downend Road, Downend, Bristol BS16 5EB Tel: 0117 957 3206 Fax: 0117 956 3472; 24 Cliff Court Drive, Frenchay, Bristol BS16 1LP Tel: 0117 956 9477 — MB ChB St. And. 1968. (St. And.) Head of Specialist Serv. & SCMO (Family Plann.)N. Bristol NHS Trust; Clin. Asst. (Genitourin. Med.) Bristol Roy. Infirm.; Profess.l Adviser Contracep & Sexual Health Serv. S. Mead NHS Trust; Mem. Fac. Family Plann. & Reproduc. Healthcare; Assoc. Mem. Inst. Psychosexual Med. Prev: Clin. Med. Off. Wilts. CC; Head of Fam.Plann.reproduct.Health.Frenchay Healthcare Trust.

HORROCKS, Claudine Lucy, Lt.-Col. RAMC ENT Department, Royal Hospital Haslar, Gosport PO12 2AA Tel: 01705 584255 — MB BS 1985 Lond.; FRCS (ORL-HNS) 2000. (Guy's) Specialist Regist. Rotat. (Otolaryngol.) Wessex. Prev: Regist Roy. Marsden Hosp. Lond.; Regist. (Otolaryngol.) Dist. Gen. Hosp. Sunderland; RMO 1st Bn. Green Howards.

HORROCKS, Frederick Arthur Ysbyty Maelor, Wrexham LL13 7TD — MB ChB 1974 Liverp.; MRCPsych 1986; AFOM 1980; DIH Lond. 1980. Cons. Psychiat. Ysbyty Maelor Wrexham. Socs: Welsh Psychiat. Soc. Prev: Sen. Regist. (Psychiat.) N. Wales Hosp. Denbigh.

HORROCKS, James Ernest Wellfield Surgery, 291 Oldham Road, Rochdale OL16 5HX Tel: 01706 355111; 1 Woodlands Way, Alkrington, Middleton, Manchester M24 1WL Tel: 0161 643 8371 — MB ChB 1979 Manch.; MRCGP 1985; DRCOG 1982.

HORROCKS, James Ewart (retired) Edgeside, Haggs Lane, Cartmel, Grange-over-Sands LA11 6HD — MB ChB 1939 Manch.; FRCPath 1963. Prev: Cons. Path. SW Cumbria Health Dist.

HORROCKS, Professor Michael Royal United Hospital, Combe Park, Bath BA1 3NG Tel: 01225 824761 Fax: 01225 825366 Email: m.horrocks@bath.ac.uk; Frenchay Common House, Frenchay, Bristol BS16 1LJ Tel: 0117 956 8945 Fax: 0117 956 4617 — MRCS Eng. LRCP Lond. 1970; MB BS Lond. 1970; MS Lond. 1982; FRCS Eng. 1974. (Guy's) Prof. Surg. Univ. Bath; Cons. Surg. Roy. United Hosp. Bath. Socs: Europ. Soc. Vasc. Surg.; Sec., Counc. Mem. Vasc. Surgic. Soc. of Gt. Gritain & Irel.; Past Counc. Mem. - Assn. of Surg.s of Gt. Britain & Irel. Prev: Sen. Regist. Bristol Roy. Infirm.; Research Fell. (Vasc. Surg.) King's Coll. Hosp. Lond.; Cons. Surg. (Gen. & Vasc. Surg.) Bristol Roy. Infirm.

HORROCKS, Peter (retired) 3 Langholm Close, Beverley HU17 7DH Tel: 01482 882390 Email: peter@minard.karoo.co.uk — MB ChB Manch. 1962; FRCP Lond. 1978, M 1967; MFPHM 1989. Prev: Cons. Phys. (Priority Servs. Developm.) Yorks. RHA.

HORROCKS, Peter Michael South Warwickshire Hospital, Lakin Road, Warwick CV34 5BW Tel: 01926 495321; Roseleigh, Barton Road, Welford on Avon, Stratford-upon-Avon CV37 8EY — MB BChir 1972 Camb.; BA Camb. 1968; MD Birm. 1987; FRCP Lond. 1994. (Camb. & King's Coll. Hosp.) Cons. Phys. S. Warks. Hosp. Warwick. Prev: Lect. (Clin. Med.) Dept. Med. Qu. Eliz. Hosp. Birm.; Sheldon Research Fell. Dept. Med. Qu. Eliz. Hosp. Birm.; Regist. N. Staffs. Roy. Infirm. Stoke-on-Trent.

HORROCKS, Sarah Noreen Foster Tel: 01745 343188 Fax: 01745 344574 Email: sarah.horrocks@vigin.net; 2 Tan Yr Ysgol, Sychdyn, Mold CH7 6SR Tel: 01352 753385 — MB ChB 1974 Liverp.; DCCH RCP Ed. 1988; DCH Eng. 1978. Cons. Paediat. (Community Child Health). Socs: Fac. Community Health; Fell. (Founder Mem.) Roy. Coll. of Paediat. and Child Health. Prev: SCMO (Community Child Health) Clwyd HA.

HORRY, George Malcolm (retired) 39 Grange Hill Road, King's Norton, Birmingham B38 8RE — MB ChB 1955 Sheff. Prev: GP Birm.

HORRY, Patricia Ann Health Centre, Old Street, Clevedon BS21 6DG Tel: 01275 871454; 2 St. John's Avenue, Clevedon BS21 7TQ — MB ChB 1982 Leic.; MRCGP 1986; DRCOG 1985.

HORRY, Pauline Elizabeth Hodson and Partners, Park Farm Medical Centre, Allestree, Derby DE22 2QN Tel: 01332 559402 Fax: 01332 541001; 16 Orpean Way, Beeston, Nottingham NG9 6LE Tel: 0115 946 4922 — MB BS 1990 Lond.; MRCGP 1995; DFFP 1994. (King's Coll. Hosp. Sch. Med. & Dent.) Prev: Asst. GP Friargate Surg. Derby; Trainee GP Derby; Trainee GP/SHO (A & E) Derby VTS.

HORSBURGH, Mr Andrew Gordon (retired) Little Waterdell House, Little Green Lane, Croxley Green, Rickmansworth WD3 3JH Tel: 01923 775177 — MB BS 1949 Lond.; FRCS Eng. 1957. Prev: Cons. Surg. Watford Gen. Hosp.

HORSBURGH, Ann (retired) Little Waterdell House, Little Green Lane, Croxley Green, Rickmansworth WD3 3JH Tel: 01923 775177 — MB BS 1955 Lond.; MRCS Eng. LRCP Lond. 1955; DObst RCOG 1957; DA Eng. 1957. JP. Prev: GP Watford.

HORSBURGH, Colin Broom Leys Surgery, Broom Leys Road, Coalville LE67 4DE Tel: 01530 832095 — MB ChB 1984 Ed.; DRCOG 1990; DCCH RCP Ed 1989; Dip. Med. Rehab. 1988. (Edinburgh) GP.

HORSBURGH, George (retired) 23 Cadogan Road, Edinburgh EH16 6LY Tel: 0131 664 3642 — MB ChB 1959 Ed.

HORSBURGH, James Donald (retired) 82 Brian Avenue, Cleethorpes DN35 9DG Tel: 01472 65861 — M.B., Ch.B. Ed. 1926.

HORSBURGH, Johann Catriona 8 Laverockbank Road, Edinburgh EH5 3DG Tel: 0131 552 5328 — MB ChB 1964 Glas.; DObst RCOG 1966.

HORSBURGH, Timothy Bremner Feldon Lane Surgery, Feldon Lane, Halesowen B62 9DR Tel: 0121 422 4703; 1 Woodgate Way, Belbroughton, Stourbridge DY9 9TL Tel: 01562 730507 — MB ChB 1986 Birm.; BSc Birm. 1983; MRCGP 1990; DRCOG 1990. (Birmingham) GP Princip.; Clin. Asst. The WareHo., Dudley Drugs Project. Prev: Trainee GP Walsall HA VTS.

HORSEWOOD-LEE, Susan Mary 34 Oakley Street, London SW3 5NT Tel: 020 7352 6748 Fax: 020 7352 0645 Email: drsusan@dircon.co.uk — MB BS 1972 Lond.; MRCGP 1978; Cert. JCC Lond. 1976. (Roy. Free Hosp. Sch. Med. Univ. Lond.) Indep. GP & Med. Gyn. Lond.; Spa Cons. Lond. Socs: Fell. Roy. Soc. Med.; Chelsea Clin. Soc.; Indep. Doctors Forum. Prev: GP Lond.; SHO Addenbrooke's Hosp. Camb. & Radcliffe Infirm. Oxf.; Sen. Med. Off. Baragwanath Hosp., S. Afr.

HORSEY, Peter John (retired) The Old Manor, Ashley, King's Somborne, Stockbridge SO20 6RH — MB BS 1947 Lond.; MRCS Eng. LRCP Lond. 1947; FFA RCS Eng. 1955; DA Eng. 1954. Prev: Cons. Anaesth. Soton. Univ. Hosps.

HORSFALL, Angela Tracey 2 Whitethorn Close, Marple, Stockport SK6 6XP — BM BS 1987 Nottm.; DRCOG 1992.

HORSFALL, Harold Ominini Pinderfields & Pontefract NHS Trust, Pontefract General Infirmary, Friarwood Lane, Pontefract WF8 1PL — MB BS 1985 Benin, Nigeria; FRCR 1997 Leeds. Cons. Radiol. With interest in Musculoskeletal Radiol., Pinderfields and Pontefract NHS Trust Wakefield, W. Yorks. Prev: Sen. Registra, United Leeds Teachg. Hosp. Leeds W. Yorks.; Registra, N.wick Pk. Hosp. Harrow, Lond.

HORSFALL, Helen Suzanne Coldwell Braids Medical Practice, 6 Camus Avenue, Edinburgh EH10 6QT Tel: 0131 445 5999; Torcraik House, North Middleton, Gorebridge EH23 4QX — BM 1985 Soton.; MRCGP 1990; Dip. Obst. Auckland 1988. Clin. Asst. Lothian

HB. Prev: Trainee GP Lothian VTS; Ho. Surg. S.land Hosp., NZ; Ho. Surg. Taraiaki HB, NZ.

HORSFALL, Thomas James Middlebrook (retired) 1 Rose Cottage, Lyndhurst Road, Brockenhurst SO42 7RL Tel: 01590 623566 — MB BChir Camb. 1968; MA Camb. 1967; MRCS Eng. LRCP Lond. 1967; MRCGP 1976; DObst RCOG 1970. Prev: Clin. Asst. (Palliat. Med.) Oakhaven Hospice Lymington & (ENT) Lymington Hosp.

HORSFIELD, Dorothy Holly Farm, New Brighton, Birds Edge, Huddersfield HD8 8XP Tel: 01484 608925 Fax: 01482 622923 — MB BS Lond. 1957; MRCS Eng. LRCP Lond. 1957; FRCPath 1984, M 1970. (Roy. Free) Emerit. Cons. Chem. Pathologist, Barnsley NHS Trust. Socs: Fell. Roy. Soc. Med. Prev: Cons. Chem. Path. Barnsley Dist. Gen. Hosp.; Sen. Regist. (Chem. Path.) Hammersmith Hosp. Lond.; Lect. (Chem. Path.) Inst. Neurol. Lond.

HORSFIELD, Keith (retired) Great Cragg, Clifford Hall, Burton in Lonsdale, Carnforth LA6 3LW Tel: 01524 262108 — MB ChB Manch. 1956; DSc Birm. 1982, PhD 1972, MD (Hons.) 1967; FRCP Lond. 1974, M 1961. Prev: Cons. King Edwd. VII Hosps. Midhurst.

HORSFIELD, Mary Fiona Annette Ripley Medical Centre, Derby Road, Ripley DE5 3HR; The Old School House, Lea, Matlock DE4 5AF — MB BS 1980 Lond.; BSc Lond. 1977; MRCGP 1984; DRCOG 1984. (Westm.) Gen. Practitioner-Ripley. Socs: Christ. Med. Fell. & Christians in Caring Professions. Prev: GP Reading; Trainee GP Bournemouth VTS; SHO (A & E) Poole Gen. Hosp.

HORSFIELD, Michael James 35 Hazel Beck, Bingley BD16 1LZ — MB BS 1996 Newc.

HORSFIELD, Nigel Orchard House, Slaidburn Road, Grindleton, Clitheroe BB7 4PT — MB ChB 1974 Birm.; FRCP 1993 Lond.; MRCP 1977 (UK); AFOM 1992 Lond. Cons. Phys. Chest Dis. Blackburn Roy. Infirm. Prev: Regist. Wythenshawe Hosp. Manch. & Qu. Eliz. Hosp. Birm.

HORSFIELD, Peter William 292 Derby Road, Lenton, Nottingham NG7 1Q — BM BS 1977 Nottm.

HORSFIELD, Philip 336 Fleetwood Road N., Thornton-Cleveleys — MB ChB 1972 Liverp.; MRCS Eng. LRCP Lond. 1972; DCH Eng. 1974.

***HORSLEY, Alexander Robert** 1 Little Withey Mead, Bristol BS9 3SY — MB ChB 1997 Ed.; MA Camb. 1994.

HORSLEY, Frank 72 Tettenhall Road, Wolverhampton WV1 4TB Tel: 01902 20420 — MB BCh 1954 Wales; BSc Wales 1951, MB BCh 1954. (Cardiff) Prev: Ho. Surg. & Ho. Phys. Swansea Hosp.

HORSLEY, Isobel Thomson Harold Road Surgery, 164 Harold Road, Hastings TN35 5NG Tel: 01424 720878/437962 Fax: 01424 719525 — MB ChB 1981 Leic.; DRCOG 1985. Prev: GP Reading.

HORSLEY, John Robert Southport and Ormskirk Hospital NHS Trust, Ormskirk & District General Hospital, Wigan Road, Ormskirk L39 2AZ Tel: 01695 656158 Fax: 01695 656484; The Gables, Ormskirk L39 2EE Fax: 01695 583888, 01695 696484 — MB ChB 1977 Liverp.; MSc (Experim. Med.) Alberta 1983; DM Soton. 1990; FRCP Lond. 1994; MRCP (UK) 1984; LMCC 1982; Cert. Managem. Manch. Metropol. Univ. 1995. (Liverp.) Cons. Phys. (Gen. & Geriat.w Med.) S.port & Ormskirk Hosp.; Trainer Advanced Cardiac Life Support (Resusc. Counc. U.K.); Vice Chairm. W. Lancs. Community Hospice Assoc.; Hon. Clin. Lect., Univ. of Manch. Socs: Hon. Life Mem. Liverp. Med. Studs. Soc.; Christ. Med. Fell.sh.; Brit. Geriat. Soc. Prev: Sen. Regist. (Geriat. Med.) Poole Gen. & Soton. Gen. Hosps.; Regist. (Med.) Walton Hosp. Liverp.; Chief Pulm. Resid. & Research Fell.sh. Univ. Alberta, Canada.

HORSLEY, Sarah Tweedvale, Holly Park, Huby, Leeds LS17 0BT Tel: 01423 734270 — MB ChB 1988 Leic.

HORSLEY, Professor Stephen Daril Firbank, Arrad Foot, Ulverston LA12 7SL; Morecambe Bay Health Authority, Tenterfield, Brigsteer Road, Kendal LA9 5EA Tel: 01539 735565 — MB BS 1971 Lond.; MBSc Manch Business Sch. 1985; FRCP Lond. 1988, M, 1976; MRCS Eng. LRCP Lond. 1971; FFCM RCP (UK) 1987, M 1979. (Guy's) Cons. (Pub. Health) Morecambe Bay HA; Dir. Pub. Health & Health Professional Developm. Unit Lancaster Univ.; Prof. (Pub. Health) Lancaster Univ. 1997. Socs: Counc. Manch. Med. Soc. Prev: Regional Med. Off. N. W.. RHA.; Specialist (Community Med.) Oxf. RHA; DMO S. Cumbria HA.

HORSMAN, Anne Margaret 77 Ware Road, Hertford SG13 7EE Tel: 01992 587961 — MB ChB 1972 Glas.; LF Hon 2000; MRCGP 1982. Asst. in Gen. Pract. Socs: RCGP; Fac. of Homeopaths. Prev: GP Lond.; Med. Off. Twba Hosp. Yemen Arab RePub.; SHO (Paediat.) Greenwich Dist. Hosp.

HORSMAN, Belinda Ann University of Bradford Health Centre, Laneisteridge Lane, Bradford BD5 0NH Tel: 01274 234979 Fax: 01274 235940 — MB BS 1988 Newc.; MRCGP 1993; DROCG 1992. (Newcastle upon Tyne) GP Princip. Prev: SHO (Med.) Newc.; Ho. Off. (Surg./Med.) Newc.

HORSMAN, David Colin 151 St. Helens Road, Swansea SA1 4DF Tel: 01792 476576 Fax: 01792 301136 — MB BS 1971 Lond.; MRCGP 1975; DObst RCOG 1973. (Roy. Free) Sen. Partner, St Helens Med. Centre, 151 St Helens Rd, Swansea. Prev: Trainee GP Swindon VTS; Ho. Surg. Roy. Free Hosp. Lond.; Ho. Phys. St. And. Hosp. Bow.

HORSMAN, Eileen Lesley 2 Shandon Avenue, Northenden, Manchester M22 4DP Tel: 0161 998 2009 — MB ChB 1968 Aberd.; FFA RCS Eng. 1975. Cons. Anaesth. Centr. Manch. Health Care Trust.

HORSMAN, Graham Salford Roayl Hospitals NHS Trust, Hope Hospital, Stott Lane, Salford M6 8HD Tel: 0161 789 7373 Fax: 0161 788 7443 Email: ghorsman@fsl.ho.man.ac.uk; 4 Maple Road W., Brooklands, Manchester M23 9HH Tel: 0161 976 6631 Email: grahamhorsman@mcmail.com — MB BS 1982 Newc.; MSc Lond. 1993; MRCP (UK) 1989; MRCPath 1997; DCH RCP Lond. 1990. (Newc. u. Tyne) Sen. Regist. (Clin. Biochem.ry) Roy. Bolton Hosp. Prev: Sen Regist. (Chem. Path.) S. Manch. Univ. Hosps. Trust; Sen Reg. (Che. Reg.) Roy. Bolton Hosp.; Sen. Reg. (Chem Path.) Salford Roy. Hosps. NHS Trust.

HORSNELL, Jane Margaret Hunters Way Medical Centre, Hunters Way, Kimbolton, Huntingdon PE18 0HY Tel: 01480 860205 Fax: 01480 861590; Little Owls, Staunch Hill, Leighton Bromswold, Huntingdon PE28 5BE Tel: 01480 891289 Fax: 01480 861590 — MB BS 1976 Lond.; MRCS Eng. LRCP Lond. 1976; MRCGP 1981; DCH Eng. 1979.

HORSNELL, Stephen Peter 20 Furnace Lane, Nether Heyford, Northampton NN7 3JT — MB ChB 1984 Leic.; MB ChB Leic. l984.

HORST, Cindy 15 St Dunstan Road, Leicester LE3 9DD Email: chorst@hotmail.com; 63 Nicholls Lane, Winterbourne, Bristol BS36 1NF — MB ChB 1992 Bristol; DA (UK) 1995. Specialist Regist. (Anaesth.) Leicester Roy. Infirm. Socs: Train. Mem. Assn. Anaesth.; Train. Mem. SW Assn. Anaesth. Prev: Clin. Fell. PICU Leeds Gen. Infirm. Leeds; SHO (Neonatology) St Michael's Hosp. Bristol; SHO (Anaesth.) Bri, Bristol.

HORTAS, Castor Grasmere, Rugby Road, Weston-under-Wetherley, Leamington Spa CV33 9BW Tel: 01926 632667 — LMS 1968 Santiago De Compostela.

HORTI, Jane Margaret Poppies, School Road, Kelvedon Hatch, Brentwood CM15 0DL — MB BS 1988 Lond.; BSc Lond. 1985. Prev: Community Child Health E. Herts. Trust.

HORTON, Alison Jane 2 Durham Road, Brancepeth, Durham DH7 8DQ Tel: 0191 378 2125 — MB ChB 1994 Leic.; DRCOG, 1998.

HORTON, Catharine Anne 19 Highfield Crescent, Wilmslow SK9 2JL — MB ChB 1991 Leeds. GP Burnage Healthcare Pract. Manch.

HORTON, David Department of Radiology, Hull Royal Infirmary, Anlaby Road, Hull HU3 2J2 Email: dhorton@doctors.org.uk; Email: dhorton@doctors.org.uk — MB BS 1986 Lond.; FRCR 1994. (St. Geo. Hosp. Lond.) p/t Cons. Paediat. Radiol. Hull Roy. Infirm. Socs: Brit. Inst. Radiol.; Brit. Med. Ultrasound Soc.; Brit. Soc. of Paediatric. Radiol.

HORTON, Denys Copperfield, Sibthorp Gardens, Canwick, Lincoln LN4 2RL Tel: 01522 21790 — MB ChB 1940 Birm.; MB ChB (2nd Cl. Hnrs.) Birm. 1940; MRCS Eng. LRCP Lond. 1940. (Birm.) Socs: Lincoln Med. Soc. & BMA. Prev: Ho. Phys. Gen. Hosp. Birm.; Temp. Surg. Lt. RNVR; Gyn. Ho. Surg. Hosp. Wom. Leeds.

HORTON, Eric William (retired) 16 Pashley Road, Eastbourne BN20 8DU — MB ChB 1955 Ed.; DSc Ed. 1968; PhD Ed. 1958; BSc Ed. (Hons.) 1953; MD Ed. 1980; FRCP Ed. 1970. Prev: Prof. Pharmacol. Univ. Ed.

HORTON, Evelyn Barbara Everglades, Willington Road, Findern, Derby DE65 6AS Tel: 01283 702298 Fax: 01283 702298 — MB ChB 1957 Bristol; MFFP 1993. Prev: Princip. Clin. Med. Off. Family Plann. S. Derbysh. Community Health Serv.; SHO (Obst.) Derby City Hosp.; Ho. Surg. S.mead Hosp. Bristol.

HORTON, G Frances (retired) 110 Riefield Road, Eltham, London SE9 2RA — MB BS 1949 London; BA Open Univ. 1989; MRCS Eng. LRCP 1949 London. Prev: Ho. Surg. & Ho. Phys. Whipps Cross Hosp. Leytonstone.

HORTON, Geoffrey Raymond Church Street Surgery, 30 Church Street, Dunoon PA23 8BG Tel: 01369 703482/702778 Fax: 01369 704502; 5 Commoncraig Place, Inverkip, Greenock PA16 0BE Tel: 01475 521416 — MB ChB 1958 Birm.; MRCS Eng. LRCP Lond. 1958; DObst RCOG 1959. Socs: Fell. BMA (Hon. Sec. Argyll & Bute Div.). Prev: GP S.end, Kintyre, Argyll.

HORTON, George Albert Neil (retired) 9 St Tysoi Close, Llansoy, Usk NP15 1EF — MRCS Eng. LRCP Lond. 1943; MA Camb. 1940.

HORTON, Graeme The Surgery, 352 College Road, Erdington, Birmingham B44 0HH Tel: 0121 373 1244 — MB ChB 1981 Leic.; DRCOG 1983.

HORTON, Ian Alfred 28 Halyards, Ferry Road, Topsham, Exeter EX3 0JU Tel: 01392 876518 — MB BS 1951 Lond.; BSc Lond. 1948, MB BS 1951; MRCP Lond. 1956; FRCPsych 1986, M 1971; DPM Eng. 1958. (St. Bart.) Prev: Cons. Psychiat. Exeter DHA; Sen. Regist. Maudsley & Bethlem Roy. Hosps.; Ho. Phys. St. Bart. Hosp. Lond.

HORTON, Jean Mary 18 Amhurst Court, Grange Road, Cambridge CB3 9BH Tel: 01223 364725 Fax: 01223 364725 Email: jeanhorton@tarrel.demon.co.uk — MB BS 1949 Lond.; MA Camb. 1977; MRCS Eng. LRCP Lond. 1948; FRCA 1988; FFA RCS Eng. 1958; DA Eng. 1953. (Univ. Coll. Lond. & W. Lond.) Socs: FHKCA; Fell. Roy. Soc. Med.; FHKAM. Prev: Sen. Lect. (Anaesth.) Chinese Univ. Hong Kong; Cons. Anaesth. Addenbrooke's Hosp. Camb.; Assoc. Lect. Fac. Clin. Med. Univ. Camb.

HORTON, Joan Nesta (retired) 1 Tyrone Drive, Bamford, Rochdale OL11 4BE Tel: 01706 360773 Fax: 01706 360773 — MRCS Eng. LRCP Lond. 1960. Prev: Sch. Med. Off. N. Dist. City of Manch.

HORTON, John Nicholas (retired) 11 Llwyn-y-pia Road, Lisvane, Cardiff CF14 0SX Tel: 029 2075 2303 Email: j.n.horton@btinternet.com — MB BS 1962 Lond.; MRCS Eng. LRCP Lond. 1962; FRCA 1967; DA Eng. 1964. Prev: Cons. Anaesth. Univ. Hosp. of Wales Healthcare Trust.

HORTON, John Paul The Park End Surgery, 3 Park End, South Hill Park, London NW3 2SE Tel: 020 7435 7282 — MB BS 1983 Lond.; MRCGP 1989. (Royal Free)

HORTON, Justine Louise 126 Greenhills Road, Eastwood, Nottingham NG16 3FR Tel: 01773 532016 — BM BS 1995 Nottm.; BMedSci Nottm. 1993 Nottingham. SHO O & G Derby City Gen. Hosp. NHS Trust. Prev: SHO Paediat. Derbsh. Childr. Hosp.; SHO A & E; SHO (Med.) Ct.ess of Chester.

HORTON, Leo Wyndham Lake Department of Cellular Pathology, Royal Berkshire Hospital, South Wing, Craven Road, Reading RG1 5AN Tel: 00189 877736 Fax: 01189 877913 Email: leo.horton@rbbh-tr.anglox.nhs.uk; Old Mill House, Mill Lane, Calcot, Reading RG31 7RS Tel: 01189 428398 Fax: 01189 414970 Email: leo-horton@virgin.net — BM BCh Oxf. 1969; MA Oxf. 1966; FRCP Lond. 1996; FRCPath 1989. (Westm.) Cons. Histopath. Roy. Berks. & Battle Hosp. NHS Trust Reading. Socs: Path. Soc.; Assn. Clin. Path.; Internat. Acad. Path. (Brit. Div.). Prev: Sen. Lect. & Lect. (Surg. Path.) St. Thos. Hosp. Lond.; Regist. (Med.) N.wick Pk. Hosp. Harrow.

HORTON, Professor Michael Anthony The Priory, Cambridge Road, Quendon, Saffron Walden CB11 3XJ Tel: 01799 543255 Email: m.horton@ucl.ac.uk — MB BS 1972 Lond.; FRCP 1995; BSc (1st cl. Hons.) Lond. 1969; FRCP Lond. 1996; MRCP (UK) 1975; FRCPath 1991, M 1987. (St. Bart.) Head, Bone & Mineral Centre & Prof. Med. UCL Med. Sch. Lond. Prev: ICRF Sen. Lect. & Hon. Cons. (Haemat.) St. Bart. Hosp. Lond.; Wellcome Trust Sen. Research Fell. (Haemat.) St. Bart. Hosp. Lond.; MRC Train. Fell. ICRF Tumour Immunol. Unit. Univ. Coll. Lond.

HORTON, Peter David (retired) Mont Royal, 117 Park Lane, Castle Donington, Derby DE74 2JG Email: pd.horton@virgin.net — MB ChB 1966 Birm.; BSc Birm. 1963, MB ChB 1966. Prev: Ho. Phys. & Ho. Surg. Dudley Rd. Hosp. Birm.

HORTON, Mr Peter John 27/49 Bettington Road, Oatlands NSW 2117, Australia Tel: 00 61 29 683 3230 Fax: 00 61 29 683 3230; Everglades, Willington Road, Findern, Derby DE65 6AS Tel: 01283 702298 — MB BChir 1986 Camb.; MA Camb. 1987; FRCS Eng. 1991. NH & MRC Research Fell. (Transpl.ation); Nat. Pancreas Transpl. Unit W.mead Hosp. W.mead, NSW Austral. Socs: Transpl. Soc. of Australia & NZ; New S. Wales Transpl. Soc. Prev: Career Regist. Rotat. Qu. Eliz. Hosp. Birm.f; SHO Rotat. (Surg.) Bristol Roy. Infirm.; Cas. Off. Whipps Cross Hosp. Lond.

HORTON, Richard Charles The Lancet, 42 Bedford Square, London WC1B 3SL Tel: 020 7436 4981 Fax: 020 7637 3265 Email: r.horton@elsevier.co.uk — MB ChB 1986 Birm.; BSc Birm. 1983. Edr. The Lancet. Prev: Clin. Research Fell. (Med.) Roy. Free Hosp. Lond.; SHO (Med.) Qu. Eliz. Hosp. Birm.; N. Amer. Edr. The Lancet.

HORTON, Richard Charles New Cross Hospital, Wolverhampton WV10 0QP Tel: 01902 307999; Wycott, Wightwick Bank, Wightwick, Wolverhampton WV6 8DR Tel: 01902 307999 — MB ChB 1984 Birm.; MRCP (UK) 1988; FRCP 2000. Cons. Cardiol. New Cross Hosp. Wolverhampton. Prev: Cardiac Transpl. Fell. Qu. Eliz. Hosp. Birm.

HORTON, Richard Jeremy The Health Centre, Worcester Street, Stourport-on-Severn DY13 8EH Tel: 01299 827141 Fax: 01299 879074 — MB ChB 1972 Birm.; DObst RCOG 1974. Prev: Ho. Off. (O & G) Good Hope Matern. Hosp. Sutton Coldfield; Ho. Surg. Good Hope Gen. Hosp. Sutton Coldfield; Ho. Phys. Kidderminster Gen. Hosp.

HORTON, Richard John SmithKline Beecham Pharmaceuticals, SB House, Great West Road, Brentford TW8 9BD Tel: 020 8975 3638 Fax: 020 8975 3514 Email: john.horton@sb.com; 24 The Paddock, Hitchin SG4 9EF Tel: 01462 624081 Email: hedgepigs@aol.com — MB Camb. 1969, BChir 1968; MRCS Eng. LRCP Lond. 1968; FFPM RCP (UK) 1994; MRCGP 1975. (Camb. & St. Bart.) Head of Therap. (Trop. Med.) SmithKline Beecham. Socs: Fell. Roy. Soc. Trop. Med. & Hyg.; Brit. Assn. Pharmaceut. Phys.; Amer, Soc. Trop. Med. & Hyg. Prev: Regional Med. Dir. Overseas Gp. SmithKline & French; Sen. Clin. Research Phys. SmithKline & French Research.

HORTON, Mr Robert Elmer, MBE 30 Stoke Hill, Bristol BS9 1LG Tel: 0117 968 3060 — MB BS Lond. 1939; MS Lond. 1952; FRCS Eng. 1947; MRCS Eng. LRCP Lond. 1939. (Guy's) Emerit. Cons. Surg. United Bristol Hosps. Socs: Surgic. Travellers; James IV Assn. Surg.s. Prev: Chairm. Ct. Examrs. RCS Eng.; Hunt. Prof. RCS Eng.; Exec. Edr. Annals RCS Eng.

HORTON, Robert Maxwell The Surgery, Exchange Road, Alrewas, Burton-on-Trent DE13 7AS Tel: 01283 790316 Fax: 01283 791863; Prospect House, 156 Main St, Alrewas, Burton-on-Trent DE13 7ED Tel: 01283 790085 — MB BS 1973 Lond.; MRCS Eng. LRCP Lond. 1973; DA Eng. 1975. (St. Mary's) Prev: SHO (Anaesth.) Basildon Gen. Hosp.; Ho. Phys. St. Mary's Hosp. E.bourne; Ho. Surg. King Edwd. VII Hosp. Windsor.

HORTON, Sarah Jane 10 Carters Close, The Forelands, Rock Hill, Bromsgrove B61 7HJ — MB BS 1989 Lond.

HORTON, Stephen John Robert Highfield Surgery, Garton Avenue, Southshore, Blackpool FY4 2LD Tel: 01253 345328 Fax: 01253 407801; 9 Thornycroft Close, Poulton-le-Fylde FY6 7PD — MB ChB 1977 Birm.; DRCOG 1981; MRCGP 1982.

HORTON, Tracy Claire University Hospital, Queen's Medical Centre, Nottingham NG7 2UH — MB ChB 1994 Sheff. Research Regist., Univ. Hosp. Qu.'s Med. Centre Nottm.

HORTON, Valerie Margaret O'Colmain and Partners, Fearnhead Cross Medical Centre, 25 Fearnhead Cross, Fearnhead, Warrington WA2 0HD Tel: 01925 847000 Fax: 01925 818650 — MB ChB 1985 Liverp. GP Fearnhead Cross Med. Centre Warrington.; Med. Off. St Roccus Hospice, Lockton La., Warrington, Chesh. Prev: Vis. Instruc. Family Pract. Oregon Health Sci.s Univ. Portland, USA; Trainee GP St. Helens & Knowsley HA; Ho. Phys. & Ho. Surg. St. Helens & Knowsley HA.

HORTON, Vanessa Clare Wake Green Surgery, 7 Wake Green Road, Moseley, Birmingham B13 9HD Tel: 0121 449 0300; Copper Beeches, Church Lane, Old Dalby, Melton Mowbray LE14 3LB Tel: 01664 823190 — MB ChB 1985 Liverp.; MRCP Ed. 1992; MRCGP 1994; DCH RCP Lond. 1990. Prev: Trainee GP Birm.; Regist. & SHO (Paediat.) Roy. Hosp. Sick Childr. Edin.; Resid. Amer. Hosp. Paris, France.

HORTON, William Anthony Deparment of Anaesthetics, University Hospital Aintree, Longmoor Lane, Liverpool L9 7AL Tel: 0151 529 2730 Fax: 0151 529 5155 — MB ChB 1980 Liverp.; BDS Liverp. 1973; FFARCS Eng. 1984. Cons. Anaesth. Univ. Hosp. Aintree. Prev: Clin. Dir. IC Servs. Aintree Hosps.; Vis. Asst. Prof.

Oregon Health Sci.s Univ. Portland USA; Sen. Regist. (Anaesth.) Mersey RHA.

HORTON-SZAR, Daniel Alfred James Kent & Canterbury Hospital, Ethelbert Rd, Canterbury CT1 3NG Tel: 01227 766877; 37 St Martin's Road, Canterbury CT1 1QP Tel: 01227 453398 Email: dan.norton-szar@virgin.com — MB BS 1998 Lond.; MB BS Lond 1998; BSc (Hons) Biochem & Microbiol Lond. 1991. (UMDS Guy's & St Thomas' Hospitals) SHO Kent & Canterbury Hosps. Prev: PRHO (Gen. Med.) St. Thomas' Hosp. Lond.; PRHO (Gen. Surg.) Kent & Canterbury Hosp.

HORTOP, Sarah Elizabeth 1 The Crescent, Pontypridd Road, Barry CF62 7LY — MB BS 1997 Lond.

HORVATH, Robert Stephen Waverley House CMCH, 1 St Luke's Road, Torquay TQ2 5NU Tel: 01803 214597 Fax: 01803 215981 — MB ChB 1985 Bristol; MRCPsych 1992. Cons. Psychiat. S. Devon Healthcare (NHS) Trust. Socs: BMA; MRCPsych. Prev: Sen. Regist. (Psychiat.) UMDS Guy's & St. Thomas' Hosps. Lond.; Regist., Research Fell. & SHO (Psychiat.) Barrow Hosp. Bristol; SHO (Med.) Torbay Hosp. Torquay.

HORWELL, Mr David Hugo 3 Jameson Road, Harpenden AL5 4HG Tel: 01582 460869 — MB BS 1970 Lond.; FRCS Ed. 1975; MFFP 1993; FRCOG 1990, M (Gold Medal) 1977. (Lond. Hosp.) Cons. O & G Luton & Dunstable Hosp. Socs: Brit. Soc. Colposc. & Cervic. Pathol.; Brit. Soc. Gyn. Endoscopy.; Brit Menopause soc. Prev: Lect. & Sen. Regist. (O & G) St. Mary's Hosp. Lond.; Rotat. Regist. (O & G) Brighton Health Dist. & Middlx. Hosp.; SHO Qu. Charlotte's Matern. Hosp. & Chelsea Hosp. Wom. Lond.

HORWICH, Professor Alan Royal Marsden Hospital, Downs Road, Sutton SM2 5PT Tel: 020 8642 6011 Fax: 020 8643 8809; Pond House, 1 Forest Road, East Horsley, Leatherhead KT24 5AZ — MB BS 1971 Lond.; PhD CNAA 1980; FRCP Lond. 1994; MRCP (UK) 1974; FRCR 1981. (Univ. Coll. Hosp.) Prof. Radiother. Lond. Univ.; Cons. Radiother. & Oncol. Roy. Marsden Hosp. Lond. Socs: Fell. Roy. Soc. Med. Prev: Sen. Lect. (Radiother. & Oncol.) Inst. Cancer Research; Fell. (Oncol.) Harvard Med. Sch., USA; Clin. Research Fell. Imperial Cancer Research Fund.

HORWITZ, Nicole Ilana 66 Woodcock Hill, Harrow HA3 0JF — MB BS 1997 Lond.

HORWOOD, Christiane Marianne P.O. Box 1540, Ballito 4420 K2N, South Africa Tel: 00 27 322 5259023 Email: chris@dham2.db.@heathlink.org.za; 63B Middle Lane, London N8 8PE Tel: 020 8 347 9678 — MB BS 1988 Lond.; MRCGP 1996; DRCOG 1995. (Roy. Free Hosp. Sch. of Med.) Sen. Med. Off. Kwazula - Natal. Dept. of Health Rep. S. Afr. Prev: Trainee GP Roy. Free Hosp. Lond. VTS.

HORWOOD, Emily 76 Copers Cope Road, Beckenham BR3 1RJ — MB BS 1998 Lond.; MB BS Lond 1998.

HORWOOD, Natalie 3 Trinity Grange, 319 Trinity Road, London SW18 3SL — MB BS 1994 Lond.; PhD Lond. 1992, BSc (Hons.) 1988. (St. Mary's Hosp.) SHO Med. Rotat. Char Cross Hosp. Lond.

HOSEGOOD, Janet Frances Bourne Hall Health Centre, Ewell, Epsom KT17 1TG; Moleside, 8 The Drive, Fetcham, Leatherhead KT22 9EN Tel: 01372 376642 — MB BS 1962 Lond.; MFFP 1993; DCH Eng. 1966; DObst RCOG 1965. (Roy. Free) Family Plann. Doctor Bourne Hall Health Centre Ewell Surrey & Ch. St. Epsom; Family Plann. Instruc. Doctor; Weybridge & Walton Family Plann. Clinics. Prev: SHO (Gen. Med.) Battersea Gen. Hosp.; SHO (Paediat.) Soton. Childr. Hosp.; Ho. Surg. (Obst.) Greenbank Matern. Hosp. Darlington.

HOSEN, Sally Clare Waters Edge, Mill Lane, Govilon, Abergavenny NP7 9SA — MB BCh 1985 Wales.

HOSIE, Cyril Carson (retired) The Cottage, Stanks Lane, London Heath, Worcester WR8 0QU — MB ChB 1950 Glas.; DPM Eng. 1966. Prev: Cons. Psychiat. Hartwood Hosp. Shotts.

HOSIE, Mr Gareth Peter 98 North Hill, Highgate, London N6 4RL Tel: 020 8341 1090 — MB ChB 1986 Manch.; FRCS Ed. 1991. Specialist Regist. (Paediat. Surg.) St Geo.'s Hosp. Lond. Prev: Clin. Research Fell. Inst. of Child Health Lond.; Regist. (Gen. Surg.) NW RHA.

HOSIE, Gillian Anne Crawford Great Western Medical, 1980 Great Western Road, Glasgow G13 2SW Tel: 0141 959 1196 Fax: 0141 950 1811; 31 Campbell Drive, Bearsden, Glasgow G61 4NF Tel: 0141 942 8622 — MB ChB Glas. 1966; Cert. JCC Lond. 1980; DA Eng. 1969. (Glas.) Pres. Primary Care Rheumatol. Soc.; Past Pres. Primary Care Rheum. Soc. Socs: Brit. Soc. Rheum. Prev: Hon. Clin. Research Fell. ARC Dept. Epidemiol. Univ. Manch.

HOSIE, Heather Elisabeth Tel: 0141 201 1658; St Ronans, 19 Dargarvel Avenue, Dumbreck, Glasgow G41 5LU — MB ChB 1980 Ed.; FFA RCS Eng. 1985. Cons. S.. Gen. Hosp. Gtr. Glas. HB. Prev: Sen. Regist. Gtr. Glas. HB; Sen. Regist. Trent RHA; Lect. Anaesth. Univ. Sheff.

HOSIE, James Great Western Medical, 1980 Great Western Road, Glasgow G13 2SW Tel: 0141 959 1196 Fax: 0141 950 1811 — MB ChB 1966 Glas.; MRCP (UK) 1972. (Glas.) Sen. partner, Gt. W.ern Med. Pract.; Vis. Prof. St. Geo. Univ. Grenada - May 1997. Socs: Brit. Hypertens. Soc. & Brit. Pharmacol. Soc.

HOSIE, Jane Edith 10 Ulster Terrace, Edinburgh EH8 7LH — MB ChB 1998 Aberd.; MB ChB Aberd 1998.

HOSIE, Kenneth Blamires Northern General Hospital, Sheffield S5 7AU Tel: 0114 271 5528; 2 Dalebrook Court, Belgrave Road, Sheffield S10 3LL — MB ChB 1982 Sheff.; BSc (Hons.) Sheff. 1977, MB ChB 1982; FRCS 1993; MD 1993. (Sheffield) Cons. (Gen. Surg.) N.ern Gen. Hosp. Sheff.

HOSKER, Harold Stephen Ronald Airedale Hospital, Skipton Road, Steeton, Keighley BD20 6TD Tel: 01535 652511 Fax: 01535 655129 — MB BS 1983 (Hons.) Newc.; MD Newc. 1990, BMedSci (Hons.) 1980; MD Newc. 1990, BMedSci (Hons.) 1980; MRCP (UK) 1986; FRCP 1998. (Newcastle upon Tyne) Cons. Gen. & Respiratry Med. Airedale Gen. Hosp. Prev: Cons. (Gen. & Respiratry Med.) Burnley Haelthcare Trust; Sen. Regist. (Gen. & Respiratry Med.) Leeds Gen. Infirm.

HOSKER, Helen Bridget Ashcroft Surgery, 803 Stockport Road, Levenshulme, Manchester M19 3BS Tel: 0161 224 1329 Fax: 0161 224 0094; 12 Bradwell Avenue, West Didsbury, Manchester M20 1JX Tel: 0161 445 2646 Email: helenhosker@compuserve.com — MB ChB 1982 Manch.; MFFP 1995; DRCOG 1987. Bd. Mem. E.Manch. PCG; Clin. Med. Off. (Family Plann. Instruc. Doctor) Mancunian Community NHS Trust; Clin. Asst. (Occupat. Health) N. Manch. Healthcare NHS Trust; Clin. Asst. (Genitourin. Med.) S. Manch. Univ. Hos. NHS Trust.

HOSKER, Ian Thomas Aran Deg, Banade Road, Aberystwyth SY23 1NA — MB ChB 1984 Sheff.; MB ChB Sheff. l984.

HOSKER, John Peter Diabetes Day Centre, Doncaster Royal Infirmary, Doncaster DN2 5LT Tel: 01302 366666 — MB BChir 1979 Camb.; MD Camb. 1985; FRCP Lond. 1996; MRCP (UK) 1981. Cons. Phys. (Endocrinol.) Doncaster Roy. Infirm. Prev: Sen. Regist. (Med.) Manch. Roy. Infirm.; Research Regist. (Diabetes) Radcliffe Infirm. Oxf.; Regist. (Gen. Med.) Roy. Hallamsh. Hosp. Sheff.

HOSKER, Kathryn Jane The Plane Trees Group Practice, 51 Sandbeds Road, Pellon, Halifax HX2 0QL Tel: 01422 330860 Fax: 01422 364830 — BM BS 1987 Nottm.; BMedSci Nottm. 1985; MRCGP 1991; DRCOG 1993.

HOSKIN, Peter John Mount Vernon Centre for Cancer Treatment, Mount Vernon Hospital, Rickmansworth Road, Northwood HA6 2RN Tel: 01923 844533 Fax: 01923 844167; Mayflower Cottage, Burtons Lane, Chalfont St Giles HP8 4BL — MB BS 1978 Lond.; BSc Lond. 1975, MD 1990; FRCP Lond. 1996; MRCP (UK) 1981; MRCS Eng. LRCP Lond. 1978; FRCR 1986. Cons. Clin. Oncol. Mt. Vernon Hosp. N.wood; Reader (Clin. Oncol.) UCL Med. Sch. Univ. Lond. Prev: Cons. Radiother. & Oncol. Roy. Lond. Hosp.

HOSKING, Alasdair Graham Fletcher Department of Child and Adolescent Psychiatry, 1 Randolph Road, Stirling FK8 2AJ Tel: 01786 450591 Fax: 01786 448980 — MB ChB 1986 Ed.; DRCOG 1988; MRCGP 1990; MRCPsych 1992. (Ed.) Cons. (Child & Adolesc. Psychiat.) Dept. Chld & Adolesc. Psychiat. Stirling.

HOSKING, Anthony John (retired) 60 Green End, Comberton, Cambridge CB3 7DY Tel: 01223 264324 — MB BChir 1957 Camb.; MRCS Eng. LRCP Lond. 1956.

HOSKING, David John Cowper House, 1242 Church Lane, Selston, Nottingham NG16 6 — MD 1972 Birm.; MB ChB 1966; FRCP (Lond.) 1981, M 1969. (Birm.) Cons. Phys. City Hosp. Nottm. Prev: Sen. Lect. & Hon. Cons. Phys. Dept. Med. Univ. Hosp. Nottm.; Wellcome Research Fell. & Hon. Cons. Phys. Gen. Hosp. Nottm.; MRC Trav. Fell. Dept. Endocrinol. Univ. Leiden Netherlands.

HOSKING, Emma-Jane Dept of Anaesthesia, Bristol Royal Infirmary, Bristol B52 8HW — MB ChB 1994 Liverp.

HOSKING, Granville Ernest (retired) Bel Air, 156 Manor Way, Whitchurch, Cardiff CF14 1RN Tel: 01222 612441 — MB BCh Wales 1939. Hon. Cons. Phys. W.m. Hosp. & Qu. Mary's Hosp. Roehampton.

HOSKING, Gwilym Penrose Integrated Neurocare Ltd., 234 Great Portland St., London W1W 5QT Tel: 020 7390 8286 Fax: 020 7390 8287 Email: admin@integratedneurocare.com; Upper Hurst, Gatehouse Lane, Outseats, Hope Valley S32 1BQ Tel: 01433 659918 Fax: 01433 659917 — MB BS 1969; FRCPCH 1997; FRCP Lond. 1990; MRCP (UK) 1972; MRCS Eng. LRCP Lond. 1969; FFPM RCP (UK) 1995; MFPM RCP (UK) 1994; Dip. Pharm. Med. RCP (UK) 1993; T(M) 1991; DCH Eng. 1972. (Char. Cross) Cons. Child Neurol. & Clin. Dir. Integrated Neurocare Ltd; Hon. Cons. Paediat. Neurol. Gt. Ormond St. Childr. Hosp.Trust Lond. & S.end NHS Trust; Hon. Cons. Paediat. Neurol. Char. Cross Hosp. Lond.; Vis. Child NeUrol., Supreme Headquaters Allied Powers Europe Belgium. Socs: Brit. Paediat. Neurol. Assn.; Assn. Brit. Neurol.; Euro Soc. For Paedia.Neurol. Prev: Cons. Paediat. Neurol. Amer. Hosp. Dubai; Sen. Clin. Research Phys. Wellcome Foundat. Beckenham; Cons. Paediat. Neurol.Ryegate Childr. Centre & Childr. Hosp. Sheff.

HOSKING, Lisa Annabel 3 Trerice Place, St Ives TR26 1AT — BM 1989 Soton.; MRCP (UK) 1995. Regist. (Med.) Roy. Cornw. Hosp. Treliske. Socs: Med. Protec. Soc.

HOSKING, Richard David Green Pastures, West View, Porthleven, Helston TR13 9LN — MB ChB 1997 Bristol.

HOSKING, Mr Shorland William Poole Hospital, Poole BH15 2JB Tel: 01202 665511; 20 Erpingham Road, Poole BH12 1EX — MB BS 1978 Lond.; MD 1988 Sheff.; FRCS 1983 Eng. (Char. Cross) Cons. Gen. Surg. Poole Hosp. Socs: Assn. Surg. Prev: Sen. Regist. Soton. Hosps.; Lect. (Surg.) Univ. Sheff.; Regist. (Surg.) Hammersmith Hosp. Lond.

HOSKINS, Ann Gateway House, Piccadilly S., Manchester M60 7LP Tel: 0161 237 2181 Fax: 0161 237 2808 Email: ann.hoskins@mchester-ha.nwest.nhs.uk — MB BCh BAO 1977 Belf.; MCommH Liverp. 1984; MFPHM RCP (UK) 1990; FFPHM (UK) 1997. (Belf.) Dir. Pub. Health Manch. HA; Hon. Lect. (Pub. Health Med.) Manch. Univ. Prev: Dir. Pub. Heath Wirral HA; Cons. Pub. Health Med. Liverp. HA; Sen. Regist. Mersey RHA.

HOSKINS, Elizabeth Ann 17 park Avenue, Bromley BR1 4EF — MB BS 1992 Lond.; DRCOG 1994; FRCA 1998.

HOSKINS, Evan Osmond Leyshon, TD The Old Stables, Taliaris Park, Llandeilo SA19 7NL Tel: 01558 823517 — MB ChB Ed. 1947; FRCP Ed. 1966, M 1953; FRCR 1975; FFR 1962; DMRD 1956. (Univ. Ed.) Teach. Radiol. Univ. Lond. Socs: Fell. Roy. Soc. Med. (Ex-Pres. Sect. Radiol.); Brit. Inst. Radiol.; Brit. Inst. Radiol. Prev: Emerit. Cons. Radiol. Guy's Hosp. Lond.; Sen. Regist. (Radiol.) Cardiff Roy. Infirm.; Regist. (Med.) Leic. Roy. Infirm.

HOSKINS, Margaretta Claire 16 Birkdale Gardens, Shirley, Croydon CR0 5HY — MB BS 1983 Lond.; BSc (1st. cl. Hons.) Anat. Lond. 1980, MB BS 1983; FRCR Eng. 1989; DCH RCP Lond. 1986. (Guy's) Cons. Mayday Univ. Hosp. Croydon. Prev: Sen. Regist. & Regist. (Radiol.) King's Coll. Hosp. Lond.; SHO W.m. Childr. Hosp. Lond.

***HOSKINS, Sarah Louise** 5 Cherry Orchard, Oakington, Cambridge CB4 5AY Tel: 01223 235272 Fax: 01223 235272 — MB BS 1997 Lond.; BSc Lond. 1994.

HOSKINS, Trevor Williams (retired) 16 Fen Street, Nayland CO10 5HL Tel: 01206 263309 — MB BChir Uni Cambridge; MRCS Eng. LRCP 1956; DCH 1961; Dobst RCOG 1958; MA 1958 Uni. Cambridge. Prev: Sen. Med. Off., Minbank Clinic, Lusaka, Zambia.

HOSKINSON, Mr James Mayfield Farm, Main St., Keyham, Leicester LE7 9JQ; Leicester Nuffield Hospital, Scraptoft Lane, Leicester LE5 1HY Tel: 0116 276 9401 Fax: 0116 246 1076 — MB ChB Liverp. 1965; FRCS Ed. 1971. (Liverp.) Cons. Orthop. Surg. Leicester Gen. Hosp. LoughBoro. Gen. Hosp.; Gen. Hosps. Socs: Brit. Orthop. Assn.; Brit. Orth. Foot Surg. Soc. Prev: Sen. Regist. Orthop. Surg. Nuffield Orthop. Centre Oxf. & Radcliffe; Infirm. Oxf.

HOSKISSON, David Martin Northgate Medical Centre, Anchor Meadow Health Centre, Aldridge, Walsall WS9 8AJ Tel: 01922 450900 Fax: 01922 450910; 21 Branton Hill Lane, Aldridge, Walsall WS9 0NR — MB ChB 1966 Birm.; MRCGP 1977; DObst RCOG 1968.

HOSKYNS, Edwyn Wren Department of Paediatrics, Leicester General Hospital, Gwendolen Road, Leicester LE5 4PW Tel: 0116 249 0490; Brooks Edge, 62 Main St, Cosby, Leicester LE9 1UU Tel: 0116 286 3129 — BM BS 1979 Nottm.; MRCP (UK) (Paediat.) 1984; FRCPCH 1996; FRCP 1997. Cons. Paediat. Leicester Gen. Hsop.

HOSKYNS, John Chandos 492 Main Road, Dovercourt, Harwich CO12 4ES — MB BS 1985 Lond.; DA (UK) 1988.

HOSNY, Amir Ahmed Fawkham Manor Hospital, Fawkham, Longfield DA3 8ND Tel: 01474 879900 Fax: 01474 703222 — MB BCh 1980 Cairo; FRCS Ed. 1992. Cons. ENT & Facial Plastic Surg. Fawkham Manor Hosp. Longfield Kent. Socs: Europ. Acad. - Facial Surg.; Europ. Acad. Of Cosmetic Surg.; Euro. Acad. of Cosmetic Surg.

HOSNY, Mr Mohammad Ahmed Borders General Hospital, Melrose TD6 9BS Tel: 01896 826000 Fax: 01896 826924 Email: mohammad.hosny@borders.scot.nhs.uk — MB BCh 1972 Cairo; FRCS Ed. 1978; FRCS Eng. 1978. (Cairo) Cons. Gen. Surg. Borders Gen. Hosp.; Hon. Surgic. Tutor, Edin. Med. Sch. Edin. Socs: MPS; BMA; Fell. Assn. Surgs. Prev: Cons. Gen. Surg. Gilbert Bain Hosp. Lerwick; Cons. Gen. Surg. King Fahd Milit. Med. Complex (Dhahran Armed Forces Hosp.) Kingdom Saudi Arabia; Sen. Regist. (Gen. & Renal Transpl. Surg.) Riyadh Armed Forces Hosp. Kingdom of Saudi Arabia.

HOSSACK, George Francis Wilkie Moorside Cottage, 154 Syke Road, Syke, Rochdale OL12 9TE Tel: 01706 42222 — LRCP LRCS 1947 Ed.; LRCP LRCS Ed. LRFPS Glas. 1947; FRCOG 1969, M 1956. Hon. Cons. O & G Birch Hill Hosp. Rochdale & Rochdale Infirm. Socs: Fell. Manch. Med. Soc. Prev: Sen. Regist. St. Mary's Hosps. Manch.

HOSSACK, Ian James 328 Nantwich Road, Crewe CW2 6PA Tel: 01270 68655 — MB BS 1969 Lond.; MRCS Eng. LRCP Lond. 1969. (Univ. Coll. Hosp.) SHO Univ. Coll. Hosp. Lond. Prev: Ho. Phys., Ho. Off. & SHO Univ. Coll. Hosp. Lond.

HOSSACK, William Strachan (retired) Kincraig, Skene St., Macduff AB44 1RP Tel: 01261 832099 Email: ws.hossack@ukonline.co.uk — MB ChB 1953 Aberd.; Cert. Av Med. MoD (Air) & CAA 1974; DObst RCOG 1955. Hon. Med. Off. RNLI Macduff. Prev: GP Banff & Hosp. Pract. Ladysbridge Hosp. Banff.

HOSSAIN, Abu Mohammad Motaher 5 Inett Way, Droitwich WR9 0DN — MB BS 1970 Dacca; DO RCP Eng. 1978; DO RCSI 1977.

HOSSAIN, Abu Tayeb Mohammad Amzad Hossain, 164 Lee High Road, London SE13 5PL Tel: 020 8852 0079 Fax: 020 8297 0763 — MB BS 1963 Karachi; MPH Johns Hopkins Univ. 1965; FICS 1973; FCGP Bangladesh 1987; DObst RCOG 1969; DMCH Univ. Punjab 1964. Socs: MRSH; FRIPHH. Prev: Regist. (O & G) W. Wales Gen. Hosp. Carmarthen; SHO (Obst.) Brit. Hosp. for Mothers & Babies.

HOSSAIN, Abul Basher Mohamed Mosharraf The Surgery, 263 Lavender Hill, London SW11 1JD Tel: 020 7223 5520 Fax: 020 7228 1067; 4 St. Michaels Close, Cleveland Road, Worcester Park KT4 7NA — MB BS 1968 Dacca.

HOSSAIN, Afzal 91 Mildmay Park, London N1 4NB Tel: 020 7226 6033 — MB BS 1982 Lond. (The Royal London Hospital)

HOSSAIN, Farhana 94 Falmouth Gardens, Ilford IG4 5JL — MB BS 1956 Punjab; LMSSA Lond. 1962; DPM Eng. 1964. Cons. Psychiat. Neuropsychiat. Lagos. Prev: Regist. (Psychiat.) Knowle Hosp. Hants.; Assoc. Prof. Psychiat. Dacca Med. Coll.

HOSSAIN, Jamal Dept of Gastroenterology, Chelsea & Westminster Hospital, 369 Fulham Road, London SW10 9NH Tel: 020 8746 8000 Fax: 020 8846 1073; 3 Partridge Road, Hampton TW12 3SB Tel: 020 8783 1313 Fax: 020 8783 1313 — MB BS 1971 Calcutta; MRCP (UK) 1979. Socs: Brit. Soc. Gastroenterol. & Saudi Gastroenterol. Assn. Prev: Cons. Phys. & Gastroenterol. Nat. Guard King Khalid Hosp., Jeddah; Sen. Regist. (Gen. Med. & Gastroenterol.) King Khaled Univ. Hosp., Riyadh; Regist. (Gen. Med.) Orpington Hosp. Kent.

HOSSAIN, Mr Jonathan Faisal Mahmood MacDonald General & Vascular Surgery, Pinderfields & Pontefract NHS Trust, Pontefract General Infirmary, Pontefract WF8 1PL Tel: 01924 606263; Email: johossain@arsenalfc.net — MB BS 1988 Lond.; FRCS 1999; FRCS Eng. 1992. Cons. Gen. Surg. with an interest in Vasc. Dis.; Specialist Reg. Gen. Sugery N. W. Thames. Socs: Federat. of Indep. Practitioners Organisation (FIPO); Vasucular Surgic. Soc. of Groit

Britian & Irel.; Assn. of Surg.s of Gt. Britian & Irel. (Counc. Mem.). Prev: Research Fell. (Vasc. Surg.) Hammersmith Hosp. Lond.; SHO Rotat. (Surg.) Kent & Canterbury Hosp.; Sen. Clincial Fell. Vasc. Surg., ST. Marys Hosp.

HOSSAIN, M M Bluebell Lane Surgery, 79 Bluebell Lane, Huyton, Liverpool L36 7XX Tel: 0151 489 2499.

HOSSAIN, Mahmood The Surgery, 12 Sternhall Lane, London SE15 4NT Tel: 020 7639 3553 Fax: 020 7639 0835; 18 Eynella Road, London SE22 8XF Tel: 020 8693 2455 — MB BS 1961 Dacca. (Dhaka Med. Coll.) Prev: Clin. Asst. (Rheum.) King's Coll. Hosp. Lond.; Regist. (Med.) Roy. Infirm. Bradford; Research Fell. Clin. Investig. Unit & Regist. (Med.) MRC Mineral Metab. Unit Leeds Gen. Infirm.

HOSSAIN, Marium 54 Basildon Avenue, Ilford IG5 0QE — MB BS 1998 Lond.; MB BS Lond 1998.

HOSSAIN, Modabbir The Limes, 755 Manchester Road, Over Hulton, Bolton BL5 1BA Tel: 01204 63432 — MB BS 1953 Calcutta; BSc, MB BS Calcutta 1953; TDD Wales 1958. Socs: BMA. Prev: Gp.; Regist. (Thoracic Med.) Welsh RHB & Manch. RHB.

HOSSAIN, Mohammad Altaf Folkestone Surgeries Group, 65-69 Guildhall Street, Folkestone CT20 1EJ Tel: 01303 851411 Fax: 01303 220443; 6 Avereng Gardens, Folkestone CT19 5HU Tel: 01303 42752 — MB BS 1964 Dacca. Clin. Asst.

HOSSAIN, Mohammad Musharraf 94 Falmouth Gardens, Redbridge, Ilford IG4 5JL — MB BS 1959 Dacca; MFOM RCP Lond. 1978; DIH Eng. 1964; DPH RCPS Eng. 1962. Med. Off. Lever Bros. (Nigeria) Ltd. Socs: Soc. Occupat. Med.; Exec. Mem. BMA (Redbridge & Stratford Div.).

HOSSAIN, Mohammed Abul (retired) 1 Britland Close, Pogmoor, Barnsley S75 2JP Tel: 01226 246985 — MB BS 1961 Dacca; FRCP Glas. 1993; FRCP Lond. 1992; FRCP Ed. 1988; MRCP (UK) 1972; DPhysMed Eng. 1973; Dip. Ven. Liverp. 1969; DTM & H Liverp. 1967; DCH RCPS Glas. 1967. Prev: Cons. Phys. Rheum. & Rehabil. Barnsley Dist. Gen. Hosp.

HOSSAIN, Mohammed Akter 36 Marvejols Park, Cockermouth CA13 0QR — MB BS 1967 Dacca.

HOSSAIN, Mohammed Anwar 52 Leegate Road, Heaton Moor, Stockport SK4 4AX Tel: 0161 432 4084 & profess. 061 336 3005 — MB BS 1967 Dacca. (Dacca Med. Coll.)

HOSSAIN, Mohammed Anwar Northumbria House, Lowland Road, Brandon, Durham DH7 8NN Tel: 0191 378 1397 — MB BS Dacca 1960; MRCP (UK) 1973; DTM & H Liverp. 1966; FRCP Lond.; FRCP Ed; FRCP Glas. (Dacca) Cons. Rheum. N. Durh. Health Care NHS Trust. Socs: BMA & Brit. Soc. Rheum.; BMA; BSR. Prev: Cons. Rheum. Durh. & NW Durh. Health Dists.; Sen. Regist. Roy. Free & Univ. Coll. Hosps. Lond.; SHO Char. Cross Hosp. Lond.

HOSSAIN, Mohammed Mehdi Killinghall Road Surgery, 308 Killinghall Road, Bradford BD2 4SE; New Court, 99 Crow Tree Lane, Bradford BD8 0AN Tel: 01274 546428 — MB BS 1964 Rajshahi; LMSSA Lond. 1976; DRCOG 1976; DObst RCPI 1976. (Rajshahi Med. Coll.) GP Bradford; Clin. Asst. & Hosp. Pract. (Obst.) Bradford Roy. Infirm. Socs: Chair, professional Comm., Bradford City Primary care (Teachg.) Trust. NHS; Mem. Bradford Local Med. Comm.; Mem. Bangladesh Med. Assoc. in the UK. Prev: Regist. (O & G) (Anaesth.) Burnley Gen. Hosp.; Chairm. Bradford City Primary Care Gp.

HOSSAIN, Mohammed Nazmul Mawney Medical Centre, 34 Mawney Road, Romford RM7 7HD Tel: 01708 743627 — MB ChB 1987 Leeds; BSc (Hons.) Leeds 1985; DRCOG 1992; Cert. Family Plann. JCC 1990.

HOSSAIN, Mohammed Nural Shahjalal Medical Centre, 44-56 Hessel Street, London E1 2LP Tel: 020 7265 9209; 31 Sotheby Road, London N5 2UP — MB BS 1953 Calcutta; LLB Calcutta 1959, MB BS 1953, DCH 1960. Socs: BMA. Prev: Regist. (Psychol. Med.) W. Pk. Hosp. & Hill End. Hosp.

HOSSAIN, Mosharraf The Surgery, Hill Street, Bradley, Bilston WV14 8SB Tel: 01902 491659; 6 Mayswood Drive, Wightwick, Wolverhampton WV6 8EF Tel: 01902 762491 — MB BS 1964 Dacca; DPM Eng. 1976; DTM & H Liverp. 1968. (Dacca Med. Coll.) Clin. Asst. (Learn. Disabil.) W. Midl. Socs: BMA.

HOSSAIN, Mustafa Omar Sharif Mabrouk 14 Rosebay Avenue, Blackburn BB2 5HT — MB ChB 1994 Manch.

HOSSAIN, Nilufa Akhtar Raj Mahal, Cwm Farm Road, Six Bells, Abertillery NP13 2PA — MB BCh 1993 Wales. Staff Grade Nevill Hall Hosp Abergavenny.

HOSSAIN, Shaheed 11 Nolton Place, Edgware HA8 6DL — MB ChB 1994 Manch.

HOSSAIN, Shaikh Ali (retired) 20 Elm Grove, Hornchurch RM11 2QX Tel: 01708 456553 — MB BS 1964 Karachi; MRCPsych 1976; DPM Eng. 1971. Prev: Cons. Psychiat. & Clin. Tutor (Ment. Handicap) S. Ockendon Hosp.

HOSSAIN, Shamim Akhtar Raj Mahal, Cwm Farm Road, Six Bells, Abertillery NP13 2PA — MB BS 1998 Lond.; MB BS Lond 1998.

HOSSAIN, Sharif Mohammad Shahadat 22 Lewis Road, Sutton SM1 4EQ Tel: 0182 643 7108 — MB BS 1968 Dhaka.

HOSSAIN, Suraiya 36 Marvejols Park, Cockermouth CA13 0QR — MB BS 1972 Dacca, Bangladesh.

HOSSAIN, Tanzeema 15 Burlington Avenue, Glasgow G12 0LJ — MB ChB 1991 Glas.

HOSSAIN, Upal 99 Crow Tree Lane, Bradford BD8 0AN — MB BS 1994 Lond.

HOSSAIN, Zahan Ara 164 Lee High Road, London SE13 5PL Tel: 020 8852 0079 — MB BS 1973 Dacca.

HOSSAIN-IBRAHIM, Mohammed Kismet 5 Woburn Court, 53/55 Bernard St., London WC1N 1LA Email: mkhi@hotmail.com — MB BS 1997 Lond.; BSc 1994. (UCL) SHO Neurosurg. Roy. Lond. Hosp. Socs: BMA; MPS.

HOSSEINI, Mr Massoud The White House, Rushmore Hill, Knockholt, Sevenoaks TN14 7NS — MB BCh BAO 1979 Belf.; MDS 1975, BDS 1970; FRCS Ed. 1987; FDS RCS Eng. 1975; FFD RCSI 1974; FDS RCPS Glas. 1974. p/t Cons. (Oral & Maxillofacial Surg.) Bromley & Greenwich Dists. Socs: Brit. Assn. of Oral & Maxillo Facial Surg.s-Fell.; Brit. Med. Assn. Prev: Sen. Regist. (Oral & Maxillofacial Surg.) Guy's Hosp. Lond.

***HOSTERT, Lutz** 73D Knatchbull Road, London SE5 9QR Tel: 020 7564 3092 — MB BS 1998 Lond.; MB BS Lond 1998; BSc Lond. 1995.

HOSTY, Gary Stephen 122 Alcester Road S., Kings Heath, Birmingham B13 8EE — BM BS 1984 Nottm.; BM BS Nottm. l984.

HOTCHIN, Ian Keith Southgates Medical Centre, 41 Goodwins Road, King's Lynn PE30 5QX Tel: 01553 692333 Fax: 01553 692555 — MB BS 1988 Lond.; MRCGP 1994; DCH RCP Lond. 1990.

HOTCHKIES, Iain Livingstone Mackay Mersey Bank Avenue Surgery, 38A Mersey Bank Avenue, Chorlton, Manchester M21 7NN Tel: 0161 445 5559 Fax: 0161 445 9725; Mountfield Cottage, 44 Mountfield Road, Edgeley, Stockport SK3 9RR Tel: 0161 480 0167 — MB ChB 1985 Manch.

HOTCHKIES, Susan Ann Cooper Trafford General Hospital, Moorside Road, Davyhulme, Manchester M41 5SL Tel: 0161 746 2537 Fax: 0161 746 2544 — MB ChB 1984 Manch.; MRCOG 1991. (Manchester) Cons. (O & G) Traffoed Gen. Hosp. Socs: Brit. Fertil. Soc. Prev: Specialist Regist. (O & G) Hope Hosp. - Salfurd; Clin. Fell. (Reproduc. Med.) IVF Unit. Manch.; Regist. (O & G) Burnley, St. Mary's Hosp. & Bolton Dist. Gen. Hosp.

HOTCHKIS, Betsy Dishington (retired) Ledaig, Kennedy Gardens, St Andrews KY16 9DJ — MB ChB Glas. 1946; DPH Glas. 1949.

HOTCHKISS, Carol McLeod Wishaw Health Centre, Kenilworth Avenue, Wishaw ML2 7BQ Tel: 01698 372201 Fax: 01698 371051 — MB ChB 1989 Glas.; MRCGP 1994; DRCOG 1993. GP Wishaw Lanarksh.

HOTH, Tariq Department of Anaesthetics, St Marys Hospital, Praed St., London W2 1NY — State Exam Med 1991 Munich.

HOTHAM, Deborah Sian New Road Surgery, 46 New Road, Bromsgrove B60 2JS Tel: 01527 872027 Fax: 01527 574516; 4 Bittell Lane, Barnt Green, Birmingham B45 8NS Tel: 0121 445 2930 — BSc (Hons.) Wales 1981, MB BCh 1986; MRCGP 1993; DCH RCP Lond. 1990. Prev: Trainee GP Wick VTS.

HOTHERSALL, Andrew Peter Ospadal nan Eilean, Stornoway HS1 2AF Tel: 01851 704704; 5 Stewart Drive, Stornoway HS1 2TU Tel: 01851 704816 — MB ChB 1971 Sheff.; FFA RCS Eng. 1975. Cons. Anaesth. Ospadal Nan Eilean Stornoway. Prev: Cons. Anaesth. W.. Infirm. Glas.

HOTHERSALL, Emma Louise Wynhill, Pope La, Whitestake, Preston PR4 4JR — MB BS 1997 Lond.

HOTHERSALL, Thomas Edward (retired) 540 Etruria Road, Basford, Newcastle ST5 0SX Tel: 01782 614419 Fax: 01782 630278 — MB ChB Ed. 1963; FRCP Lond. 1988; FRCP Ed. 1973,

M I968. Cons. Phys. Haywood N. Staffs. Hosp. Trust. Prev: Regist. (Rheum. Dis.) N.. Gen. Hosp. Edin.

HOTHI, Daljit Kaur 41 Rolvenden Road, Wainscott, Rochester ME2 4PF — MB BS 1996 Lond. (UMDS) SHO (Paediat.) Bedford Hosp. Bedford. Prev: SHO (A & E) Bedford Hosp.; Ho. Phys. Greenwich Hosp.; Ho. Surg. Frimley Pk. Hosp. Camberley.

HOTONU, Oluseyi Enitan Omorilewa 49 Birnam Road, London N4 3LJ — MB ChB 1987 Manch.; BSc (Hons.) Liverp. 1981.

HOTOPF, Matthew Hugo Guys King's St Thomas' School of Medicine, 103 Denmark Hill SE5 8AZ — MB BS 1989 Lond.; PhD 1999; BSc Lond. 1986; MRCPsych 1993; MSc 1996. Reader. Psych. Guys, Kings, St Thomas Hosps.; Hon. Cons. Psych.Maudsley Hosp. Prev: MRC Clin.Train.Fell; Regist. (Psychiat.) & SHO Maudsley Hosp. Lond.; Ho. Phys. St. Bart. Hosp. Lond.

HOTSON, Penny Anne 233 Richmond Road, Twickenham TW1 2NN — MB BS 1997 Lond.; BSc 1986. (UCL)

HOTSTON, Susan Jane Breast Test Wales - Velindre NHS Trust, North Wales Breast Screening Centre, Maesdu Road, Llandudno LL30 1QZ — MB ChB 1976 (Hons.) Liverp.; BSc 1971 (Hons.) Liverp.; MRCP (UK) 1978; FRCR 1984; DMRD Liverp. 1981. Cons. Radiol. BrE. Test Wale Llandudno. Socs: Roy. Coll. Radiol. BrE. Gp.; BMA; EUSOMA. Prev: Cons. (Radiol.) Glan Clwyd NHS Trust; Regist. (Radiol.) Mersey RHA; Regist. (Gen. Med. & Gastroenterol.) BRd.green Hosp. Liverp.

HOTTON, Mary Elizabeth Allum Medical Centre, Fairlop Road, Leytonstone, London E11 1BN Tel: 020 8539 2513 Fax: 020 8558 0525; 38 Marlborough Road, South Woodford, London E18 1AP Tel: 020 8668 0525 — MB BS 1988 Lond.; MRCGP 1992; DRCOG 1991; Cert. Family Plann. JCC 1990; DFFP 1994. (London University St Bartholomews Hospital) Prev: Trainee GP/SHO (A & E c/o Elderly & Obst. & Gyn.) Whipps Cross Hosp. VTS.

HOTTON, Thomas Howard Edward The New Surgery, River Street, Mevagissey, St Austell PL26 6UE Tel: 01726 843701 Fax: 01726 842565; 21 Lavorrick Orchards, Mevagissey, St Austell PL26 6TL — MB BS 1986 Lond.; DCH RCP Lond 1991; DGM RCP Lond. 1990. Clin. Asst. (Chest Med.) & Hosp. Pract. (c/o Elderly) Cornw.

HOU, David 29 Nightingale Road, Orpington BR5 1BH — BM 1997 Soton.

HOUANG, Elizabeth Tingsou 22 Horbury Crescent, London W11 3NF — MB ChB 1969 Bristol; FRCPath 1987, M 1976. Prof. (Med. Microbiol.) P. of Wales Hosp. Shatin, Kowloon, Hong Kong. Prev: Sen. Lect. & Cons. Dept. Med. Microbiol. Qu. Charlottes & Chelsea Hosp.

HOUCHIN, Pamela Joan (retired) 3 Rosewood, Park Road, Haslemere GU27 2NJ Tel: 01428 644224 — MRCS Eng. LRCP Lond. 1950; DCH Eng. 1952. Prev: Clin. Asst. Skin & Rheum. Depts. P. of Wales Gen. Hosp. Lond.

HOUFTON, Herbert Ernest (retired) Seven Acres, Upper Bentley, Redditch B97 5TA Tel: 01527 62897 — MRCS Eng. LRCP Lond. 1927. Prev: Surg. Smallwood Hosp. Redditch.

HOUGH, Allan (retired) Wilson Street Surgery, 11 Wilson Street, Derby DE1 1PG Tel: 01332 344366 Fax: 01332 348813 — MB ChB 1965 Leeds; DObst RCOG 1969; DA Eng. 1969. Prev: SHO (Obst.) Harrogate Gen. Hosp.

HOUGH, Caroline Frances Cable And Wireless, 26 Red Lion Square, London WC1R 4HQ Tel: 020 7528 1380 Email: caroline.hough@cwcom.co.uk; Flat 4, 57 Millbank, London SW1P 4RL — MB 1978 Camb.; BChir 1977; DRCOG 1981; DA Eng. 1979.

HOUGH, Cyril Thomas (retired) Nyhavn, Darrington Road, Carleton, Pontefract WF8 3RY Tel: 01977 702978 — MB ChB 1945 Leeds; DPH 1949; DObst RCOG 1951. Prev: Ho. Phys. Leeds Gen. Infirm.

HOUGH, Deborah Joy Church Road Surgery, 261 Church Road, Stannes on Sea, Lytham St Annes FY8 1EH Tel: 01253 728911 Fax: 01253 732114 — MB ChB 1988 Manch.

HOUGH, Jane Anne 9 Dellfield Lane, Liverpool L31 6AS — MB BS 1993 Lond.

HOUGH, Matthew 9 Springside View, Bury BL8 4LU — MB BS 1994 Newc.

HOUGH, Rachel Emma 35 Ranmoor Road, Sheffield S10 3HG — BM BS 1992 Nottm.

HOUGHTON, Adrian Mark Graystones Medical Centre, 33 Graystones Road, Sheffield S11 7BJ Tel: 0114 266 6528; 45 Crimicar Drive, Fulwood, Sheffield S10 4EF Tel: 0114 230 2162 — MB BS 1980 Lond.; MRCGP 1991; DA (UK) 1985; DCH RCP Lond. 1983; DRCOG 1982. (Char. Cross) Clin. Asst. (Dermat. Surg.) Roy. Hallamsh. Hosp. Sheff. Socs: Christian Med. Fell.sh.; Med. Protec. Soc. Prev: GP Sheff.; Regist. (Anaesth.) Worthing Hosp.; Staff (Paediat. & Anaesth.) Nazareth Hosp., Israel.

HOUGHTON, Alban Rose Cottage, Dundee Road, Letham, Forfar DD8 2PP — MB ChB 1968 Ed.; FFA RCS Eng. 1973; DObst RCOG 1970. (Ed.) Cons. Anaesth. Tayside Health Bd. Socs: Assn. Anaesths. & N. E. Scotl. Soc. Anaesths. Prev: Regist. Roy. Infirm. Edin.; Sen. Regist. Dundee Health Dist.; Fell. Roy. Vict. Hosp. Montreal, Canada.

HOUGHTON, Mr Andrew David Department of Surgery, Royal Shrewsbury Hospital, Mytton Oak Road, Shrewsbury SY3 8XQ Tel: 01743 261188; Crowmeole Farm House, Crowmeole Lane, Shrewsbury SY3 8AY Tel: 01743 366202 — MB BS 1980 Lond.; MS Lond. 1991; FRCS Ed. 1984; MRCS Eng. LRCP Lond. 1980. (Guy's) Cons. Gen. & Vasc. Surg. Roy. Shrewsbury Hosp. Socs: Vasc. Soc. & Surg. Research Soc.; Assn. Surg. Prev: Sen. Regist. (Surg.) Guy's & Lewisham Hosp. Lond.; Regist. (Surg.) Greenwich Dist. Hosp., W. Sussex Hosp. Tunbridge Wells& Guy's Hosp. Lond.

HOUGHTON, Andrew Robert Department of Cardiology, Glenfield Hospital NHS Trust, Groby Road, Leicester LE3 9QP Tel: 0116 287 1471 Fax: 0116 258 3950 Email: andrew.houghton@nottingham.ac.uk; 33 Dorset Gardens, West Bridgford, Nottingham NG2 7UH — BM BCh 1991 Oxf.; MA Oxf. 1992; MRCP (UK) 1994. (Univ. Oxf.) Specialist Regist. (Cardiol.) Glenfield Hosp. NHS Trust, Leicester. Socs: Brit. Soc. of Echocardiography; BMA; Founding Mem. Brit. Soc. Heart Failure. Prev: Specialist Regist. (Gen. Med. & Cardiol.) Pilgrim Hosp., Boston; Research Fell. (Cardiol.) & SHO (Gen. Med.) Qu. Med. Centre Nottm.; Ho. Off. (Gen. Med.) John Radcliffe Hosp. Oxf.

HOUGHTON, Anita Margaret London Postgraduate Medical & Dental Education, 20 Guildford St, London WC1N 3EJ Tel: 0207 692 3198 Email: ahoughton@londondeanery.ac.uk; 5 North Several, Orchard Drive, London SE3 0QR — MB BS 1981 Lond.; MSc Lond. 1986; MFPHM RCP (UK) 1987. Assoc. Postgrad. Dean for Flexible Train. TPMDE Lond. Prev: Sen. Research Fell. RCP; Cons. Pub. Health Med. City & Hackney HA; Cons. Pub. Health Med. Bexley & Greenwich HA.

HOUGHTON, Ann Louise Harden Medical Practice, 25 Sutton Road, Shrewsbury SY2 6DL Tel: 01743 241313; Crowmeole Farm House, Crowmeole Lane, Shrewsbury SY3 8AY Tel: 01743 366202 Email: adhoughton@aol.com — MB BS 1985 Lond.; MRCGP 1989; DRCOG 1989; DCH RCP Lond. 1988. (King's Coll. Sch. Med. & Dent.) GP Shrewsbury Retainer Scheme. Socs: BMA. Prev: GP Downham, Kent Retainer Scheme; Trainee GP Qu. Mary's Hosp. Sidcup VTS.

HOUGHTON, Anne Marie Grange Medical Centre, Seacroft Crescent, Leeds LS14 6NX Tel: 0113 295 1801 Fax: 0113 295 1799 — MB ChB 1977 Leeds; MRCGP 1981.

HOUGHTON, Anne Susan 225 Station Road, Knowle, Solihull B93 0PU — MB BS 1976 Lond.; MRCS Eng. LRCP Lond. 1976.

HOUGHTON, Mr Anthony Leon 7A Spen Road, West Park, Leeds LS16 5AL — MB BS 1964 Lond.; FRCS Eng. 1972; FRCR 1985. (St. Bart.) Cons. Clin. Oncol. N.ampton Gen. Hosp. Prev: Staff Radiat. Oncol. Lond. Cancer Centre, Ontario; Sen. Regist. (Radiother.) Regional Radiother. Centre Cookridge Hosp. Leeds; Lect. (Anat.) King's Coll. Lond.

HOUGHTON, Arnold Cecil, OBE, TD (retired) Grey Gables, 39 Fox Hollies Road, Acocks Green, Birmingham B27 7TH — MB ChB 1937 Birm.; MRCS Eng. LRCP Lond. 1936. Prev: Chairm. Midl. Regional Med. Comm. & Birm. Family Pract. Comm.

HOUGHTON, Barbara Lindsay 17 North Road, West Bridgford, Nottingham NG2 7NG; Services for People with Learning Difficulties, Central Nottinghamshire Healthcare, Southwell Road W., Mansfield NG18 4HH — BM BS 1981 Nottm.; MRCPsych 1990; MRCGP 1986; DRCOG 1984. Cons. Learning Disabil. Mansfield. Prev: Developm. Health Worker Ecuador, S. Amer.; SHO Rotat. (Psychiat.) Nottm. HA.

HOUGHTON, Brian John (retired) 113 Marlborough Crescent, Riverhead, Sevenoaks TN13 2HN Tel: 01732 455195 — MB BS

1952 Lond.; MRCS Eng. LRCP Lond. 1951; FRCPath 1985, M 1964. Hon. Cons. Chem. Path. Roy. Lond. Hosp.; Assoc. Mem. Clin. Biochem. Prev: Sen. Lect. (Clin. Biochem.) Lond. Hosp. Med. Coll.

HOUGHTON, Catherine Mary Manchester Royal Infirmary, Oxford Rd, Manchester M13; 6 Woodbank Cottages, Helmshore, Rossendale BB4 4NA — MB ChB 1992 Manch.; MRCP (UK) 1995. Specialist Regist. Respirat. & GIM. Prev: Regist. (Respirat. Med.) Luton & Dunstable NHS Trust.; SHO (Accid. & Emerg.) Watford Gen. Hosp.; Regist. (Med.) Ipswich Hosp. Qu.sland, Australia.

HOUGHTON, Christopher David 7 Elm Gardens, West End, Southampton SO30 3SA — MRCS Eng. LRCP Lond. 1974; FRCR 1984; T(R)(CR) 1991; DMRD Eng. 1980.

HOUGHTON, Christopher Stephen Kirkgate Surgery, 3 Kirkgate, Birstall, Batley WF17 9HE Tel: 01924 420242 Fax: 01924 423327; Ardwyn, Baghill Road, West Ardsley, Wakefield WF3 1DG Tel: 0113 253078 — MB ChB 1975 Sheff.; BMedSci. (Hons.) Sheff. 1972.

HOUGHTON, Cuthbert Colin (retired) Battridge House, Broadway WR12 7AE — MB ChB 1935 Birm.; MRCP Lond. 1945; MRCS Eng. LRCP Lond. 1935. Treasury Med. Off. Prev: Phys. Evesham Gen. Hosp.

HOUGHTON, David Jeremy 22 Dixon Avenue, Queens Park, Glasgow G42 8EE — MB ChB 1985 Manch.

HOUGHTON, Mr David John 8 Princes Way, Detling, Maidstone ME14 3LB Tel: 01622739373 — MB BS 1971 Lond.; FRCS Eng. 1976; FRCOG 1993; MRCOG 1980. (St. Thos.) Cons. O & G Medway HA. Socs: Hosp. Cons. & Spec. Assn.; BMA; Medway Surgic. Soc. Prev: Sen. Regist. (O & G) St. Barts. Hosp. Lond.; Resid. Med. Off. Qu. Charlotte's Matern. Hosp. Lond.; Gyn. Resid. Med. Off. Grosvenor Hosp. Wom. & St. Thos. Hosp. Lond.

HOUGHTON, Deborah Clare 192 Finchampstead Road, Wokingham RG40 3HB Tel: 01189 775530 — MB ChB 1995 Manch. SHO (Paediat.) Countess of Chester Hosp. Chester. Socs: Med. Protec. Soc.; BMA. Prev: SHO (O & G) Macclesfield DGH; SHO (A & E) Leighton Hosp. Crewe.

HOUGHTON, Debra Ann c/o S. Watson, Mangrove Hall Farm Cottage, Mangrove Green, Cockernhoe, Luton LU2 8QE — MB ChB 1988 Cape Town.

HOUGHTON, Elizabeth Scott Rose Cottage, 2 Dundee Road, Letham, Forfar DD8 2PP Tel: 0130 781302 — MB ChB 1970 Ed.; BSc Ed. 1967, MB ChB 1970; MCOphth 1990; DO Eng. 1974. (Ed.) Assoc. Specialist (Ophth.) Ninewells Hosp. Dundee. Socs: BMA & Scott. Opthal. Club.

HOUGHTON, Emma Jane 9 Carronhall, Stonehaven AB39 2QF — MB ChB 1997 Ed.

HOUGHTON, Harold John Kingland, Pioneer Avenue, Bath BA2 5QX Tel: 01225 832583 — MB BCh 1943 Wales; MRCS Eng. LRCP Lond. 1942. (Cardiff) Socs: BMA. Prev: Surg. Llandrindod Wells Hosp.; Cas. Regist. Cardiff Roy. Infirm.; Ophth. Regist. LLa.lly Hosp.

HOUGHTON, Ida 59 Geraint's Way, Cowbridge CF71 7AY — LRCP LRCS Ed. LRCPS Glas. 1995.

HOUGHTON, Ivan Timothy, QHS, Brigadier late RAMC Royal Hospital, Haslar, Gosport PO12 2AA Tel: 01705 762422 Fax: 01705 762555; c/o Lloyds Banks plc, 355 Stratford Road, Shirley, Solihull B90 3BP — MB BChir 1966 Camb.; MD Chinese Univ., Hong Kong 1993; MA Camb. 1967; LLB (Hons.) Lond. 1987; LMSSA Lond. 1966; FFA RCS Eng. 1970; Dip. Med. Care of Catastrophes Soc. Apoth. Lond. 1995; Dip. Med. Educat. Dund 1996. (Camb. & St. Thos.) Army Adviser (Anaesth. & Resusc.); Hon. Lect. (Anaesth. & IC) Chinese Univ., Hong Kong; Defence Cons. Advis. Anaesth. To Surg. Gen.; Defence Dir. Anaesth. To Defence Secon. Care Agency. Socs: BMA; Assn. Anaesth.; Medico-Legal Soc. Prev: Commanding Off. & Sen. Cons. Anaesth. Brit. Milit. Hosp. Rinteln BFPO 31; Sen. Regist. (Anaesth.) Liverp. RHB; Ho. Surg. Univ. Dept. Surg. & Ho. Phys. Addenbrooke's Hosp. Camb.

HOUGHTON, Jacqueline Ingrid Mill Street Medical Centre, 2 Mill Street, St Helens WA10 2BD Tel: 01744 23641 Fax: 01744 28398; 1 The Fairway's, Ashton Cross, Ashton-in-Makerfield, Wigan WN4 0YX Tel: 01942 723133 — MB ChB 1986 Sheff.; MRCGP 1990; DRCOG 1989. (Sheff. Univ. Med. Sch.) Princip. GP. Prev: SHO (O & G, Paediat. & A & E) Ormskirk & Dist. Gen. Hosp.; SHO (Psychiat.) Fazakerley Hosp. Liverp.

HOUGHTON, John Alexander, Wing Cdr. RAF Med. Br. 11 Mereworth, Wirral CH48 1QT Fax: 01923 217939 — MB BS 1987 Lond.; MRCGP 1994; DCH RCP Lond. 1992; DRCOG 1991. (Guy's) Sen. Med. Off. RAF AlderGr. Socs: BMA; MRCGP. Prev: SMO RAF Akrotin; SMO RAF AlderGr.; DSMO RAF Cottesmore.

HOUGHTON, John Benjamin Dept. Haematology, Hope Hospital, Salford M6 8HD Tel: 0161 787 4982 Email: j.houghton@hope.srht.nwest.nhs.uk — MB BChir 1974 Camb.; MA Camb. 1974; FRCP Lond. 1994; MRCP (UK) 1976; FRCPath 1989, M 1979. (Univ. Coll. Hosp.) Cons. Haemat. Hope Hosp. Salford. Socs: Camb. Univ. Med. Soc.; Brit. Soc. Haematol. Prev: Sen. Regist. (Haemat.) Nottm. Hosps.; Regist. (Haemat.) St. Geo. Hosp. Lond.

HOUGHTON, John Eric 1 Holbein Close, Handbridge, Chester CH4 7EU Tel: 01244 674576 — MB ChB 1965 Manch.; FRCR 1975; FFR 1972; DMRD Eng. 1970. Cons. Radiol. Chester Roy. Infirm. & Countess of Chester Hosp. Socs: Fell. Roy. Soc. Med.; Fell. Manch. Med. Soc.; Brit. Inst. Radiol.

HOUGHTON, Jonathan Mark 101a Bravington Road, London W9 3AA — MB BS 1996 Lond.

HOUGHTON, Joseph Plunkett 67 Fitzwilliam Street, Belfast BT9 6AX — MB BCh BAO 1997 Belf.

HOUGHTON, Josephine Bridget (retired) 19 The Dell, Gt. Baddow, Chelmsford CM2 7JY Tel: 01245 473078 — MB BChir 1962 Camb.; DO Eng. 1968; DCH Eng. 1965; DObst RCOG 1964. Prev: GP Chelmsford.

HOUGHTON, Karen Jayne St Martins Surgery, 378 Wells Road, Knowle, Bristol BS4 2QR Tel: 0117 977 5641 Fax: 0117 977 5490; 68 Lake Road, Westbury on Trym, Bristol BS10 5JF — MB ChB 1988 Liverp.; MRCGP 1996; DFFP 1996; DCH RCP Ed. 1993; DRCOG 1993.

HOUGHTON, Kerridwen c/o Day Surgery Unit, Torbay Hospital, Lawes Bridge Road, Torquay TQ2 7AA Tel: 01803 654043 Fax: 01803 654056 Email: kerri.houghton@sdevonhc-tr.swest.nhs.uk; Higher Tor House, East Ogwell, Newton Abbot TQ12 6BA Tel: 01626 332589 — MB ChB 1975 Bristol; FFA RCS Eng. 1984; DRCOG 1977. Cons. Anaesth. Torbay Hosp. Prev: Sen. Regist. SW Region.

HOUGHTON, Luke John 100 West Lane, Hayling Island PO11 0JN — MB ChB 1998 Manch.; MB ChB Manch 1998.

HOUGHTON, Lydia Moseley (retired) 38 Queen's Court, CLifton, Bristol BS8 1ND — MB BS 1923 Lond. Prev: Ho. Surg. & Ho. Phys. Bristol Roy. Infirm.

HOUGHTON, Maria 10 Manse Brae, Glasgow G44 5UG — MB ChB 1990 Glas.

HOUGHTON, Melanie Anne Herne Hill Group Practice, 74 Herne Hill, London SE24 9QP Tel: 020 7274 3314 Fax: 020 7738 6025; 26 Hyde Thorpe Road, Balham, London SW12 0HY Tel: 020 8673 7533 Fax: 020 8673 7531 — MB ChB Bristol 1986; BSc Bristol 1983; MRCGP 1993; DCH RCP Lond. 1992; DRCOG 1991; DTM & H Liverp. 1988. Clin. Asst. (Genitourin. Med.) KCH Lond. Prev: Regist. (Community Med.) Oxf. RHA.

HOUGHTON, Michael Ponting Brookside Surgery, Stretton-on-Dunsmore, Rugby CV23 9NH Tel: 024 7654 2525 Fax: 024 7654 5617; Harford Cottage, 25 Church Road, Church Lawford, Rugby CV23 9EG Tel: 01203 542255 — MB BChir 1979 Camb.; MA Camb. 1978, MB BChir 1979; MRCGP (Distinc.) 1986; DRCOG 1983; DCH Lond. 1982. (St. Thos.) Hon. Sen. Lect. Univ. of Warwich 1998; GP Tutor Rugby. Socs: BMA. Prev: GP. Walton Le Dale Preston, Lancs.; SHO (Neurol.) St. Thos. Hosp. Lond.; SHO Hammersmith Hosp. Lond.

HOUGHTON, Michael Wynn Keighley Road Surgery, Keighley Road, Illingworth, Halifax HX2 9LL Tel: 01422 244397/248308 Fax: 01422 241101; Thorn Lea, Upper Brockholes, Ogden, Halifax HX2 8XG Tel: 01422 244131 Fax: 01422 241101 Email: 113146.1554@compuserve.com — MB BS 1978 Lond.; MRCS Eng. LRCP Lond. 1978; DRCOG 1983. (Guy's) Socs: BMA. Prev: Maj. RAMC (Retd.); Ho. Surg. St. Olave's Hosp. Lond.; Ho. Phys. Joyce Green Hosp. Dartford.

HOUGHTON, Patrick Guy Greenbank Surgery, 1025 Stratford Road, Hall Green, Birmingham B28 8BG Tel: 0121 777 1490 Fax: 0121 778 6239; 39 Kineton Green Road, Olton, Solihull B92 7DX Tel: 0121 706 0165 Email: houghton@hsrc.org.uk — MB BChir 1972 Camb.; MA, MB Camb. 1972, BChir 1971; FRCGP 1989, M 1980; DObst RCOG 1973; Cert. FPA 1974; DFFP 1995. (Camb. & St. Thos.) Clin. Dir., Birm. HA Clin. Governance Unit; Assoc. Adviser Gen. Pract. W. Midl. Socs: BMA; Liveryman Worshipful Soc. Apoth.

Lond. Prev: Ho. Off. (O & G) Lambeth Hosp. Lond.; Ho. Surg. (ENT) St. Thos. Hosp. Lond.; Course organiser Cent. Birm. VTS.

HOUGHTON, Mr Paul William Jones Higher Tor House, E. Ogwell, Newton Abbot TQ12 6BA Tel: 01626 332589 — MB ChB 1973 Bristol; ChM Bristol 1987, MB ChB 1973; FRCS Eng. 1979. Cons. Gen. Surg. Torbay HA. Prev: Sen. Regist. S. W.. RHA; Maj. RAMC.

HOUGHTON, Mr Paul Winchester (retired) Yardway, Sinton Green, Hallow, Worcester WR2 6NW Tel: 01905 640271 — MB BS Lond. 1935; FRCS Eng. 1939; MRCS Eng. LRCP Lond. 1935. Prev: Cons. Surg. Worcester Roy. Infirm. & Ronkswood Hosp. Worcester.

HOUGHTON, Peter David 7 Howgill Way, Lytham St Annes FY8 4TA — MB BS 1974 Lond.; MRCS Eng. LRCP Lond. 1974; MRCGP 1986.

HOUGHTON, Robert James Park Road Medical Centre, 164 Park Road, Peterborough PE1 2UF Tel: 01733 52801; 24 Brookside, Peterborough PE4 6GL — MB ChB 1987 Liverp.; MRCGP 1994; DFFP 1994; DCH RCP Lond. 1993; DRCOG 1992. Prev: SHO (Psychiat.) Derby.; Trainee GP/SHO Derby.

HOUGHTON, Russell Patrick 9 Hathaway Road, Liverpool L25 4ST — MB ChB 1995 Leeds.

HOUGHTON, S Helga 67 Manor Way, Blackheath, London SE3 9XG Tel: 020 8852 4480 — MB ChB 1963 Birm.; BSc (Hons. Physiol.) Birm. 1960, MB ChB 1963; MRCS Eng. LRCP Lond. 1963; MFFP 1994; Dip. Ven. Soc. Apoth. Lond. 1978. SCMO (Family Plann. & Reproduc. Healthcare) Optimum Health Servs.; Assoc. Specialist (Genitourin. Med.) Homerton Hosp. Lond. Socs: Med. Soc. Study VD; Inst. Psychosexual Med.; Lond. Soc. of Family Plann. Doctors. Prev: Regist. (Genitourin. Med.) St. Thos. Hosp. Lond.

HOUGHTON, Sarah Rebecca Anne Cherry Orchard Surgery, Codford St Mary, Warminster BA12 0PN Tel: 01985 850298; Shepherds Cottage, High St, Berwick St James, Salisbury SP3 4TS Fax: 01722 790449 — BM Soton. 1983; DCH RCP Lond. 1986; DRCOG 1986.

HOUGHTON, Sasha Louise 101A Bravington Road, London W9 3AA — MB BS 1996 Lond.

HOUGHTON, Susan Jacqueline Chumleigh, Station Road, Ponthir, Newport NP18 1GU Tel: 01633 423136 — MB ChB 1991 Birm.; MRCOG 1998. Specialist Regist. O & G Walsall Manor Hosp. Prev: Specialist Regist. O & G New Cross Hosp.Wolverhampton; Specialist Regist. (O & G) N. Staffs. Hosp.; Research Fell. (O & G) Univ. Birm.

HOUGHTON, Thomas Ashley 63 Melbreck Road, Allerton, Liverpool L18 9SF — BM BCh 1984 Oxf.; LMSSA Lond. 1983.

HOUGHTON, Verna Patricia Woosehill Surgery, Wokingham RG41 3DA Tel: 01734 788689; Wargrave Court, Wargrave, Reading RG10 8EU Tel: 01734 402833 — MB BS 1955 Lond.; MB BS (Hons. Med.) Lond. 1955; MRCS Eng. LRCP Lond. 1955; MFFP 1994; DObst RCOG 1956. (Guy's) Socs: BMA.

HOUGHTON-CLEMMEY, Robert Sheridan Ashleigh 156 Westminster Way, Oxford OX2 0LR — MB BS 1997 Lond.; BSc 1994. (Roy.Free.Hosp.Lond) SHO Urol. Barnet. Gen. Hosp. Lond. Socs: La.Soc. Clinique Francaise. Lond. Prev: Ho. Off. Urol. Lister Hosp. Stevenage.

HOULAHAN, Diarmuid Patrick Joseph St Peters Surgery, 57 Leckie Road, Walsall WS2 8DA Tel: 01922 23755 Fax: 01922 746477 — MB BCh BAO 1980 NUI.

HOULBERG, Kristian Anthony Niels 32 Albert Street, Windsor SL4 5BU — BM 1993 Soton.

HOULDEN, Henry James The National Hospital for Neurology and Neurosurgery, Queen Square, London WC1N 3BG Tel: 020 7837 3611; The Nurseries, Bellamy Lane, West Walton, Wisbech PE14 7EY Tel: 01945 584225 — MB BS 1994 Lond.; BSc Lond. 1991; MRCP 1997; DHMSA 1991. (St. Mary's Hosp. Med. Sch.) SHO (Neurol.) The Nat. Hosp. for Neurol. Neurosurg. Socs: RCP (Coll.ate). Prev: SHO (Cardiol.) Lond. Chest Hosp.; SHO (Gastroenterol. & Haemat.) Hammersmith Hosp. Lond.; SHO (Respirat.) Roy. Brompton Hosp.

HOULDER, Mr Alexander Robert, Squadron Ldr. RAF Med. Br. Retd. The Surgery, Sandy Lane, Brewood, Stafford ST19 9ES Tel: 01902 850206 Fax: 01902 851360 — MB ChB 1983 Dundee; FRCS Ed. 1989; FRCS Eng. 1989; MRCGP 1994; DFFP 1993. CMP RAF Cosford Wolverhampton; SHO (Obst. & Gyn.) Shrewsbury Hosps. Prev: Sen. Specialist (Orthop.) RAF; Regist. (Surg. & Orthop.) Orsett Hosp. Grays; SHO (Surg.) Qu. Mary's Hosp. Carshalton.

HOULDER, Anne-Marie Teresa Wood Farmhouse, Wood Lane, Stretton, Stafford ST19 9LF Tel: 01902 851599 — MB BS 1987 Lond.; BSc (Hons.) Lond. 1984; MRCGP 1994; DFFP 1993. CMP RAF Stafford. Socs: Assn. Palliat. Med. Prev: SHO (Paediat.) Telford Hosp.; Trainee GP Orset Essex; Clin. Asst. (A & E) Roy. Shrewsbury Hosp.

HOULDSWORTH, Fiona Joy Borough Road Surgery, 167a Borough Road, Middlesbrough TS4 2EL Tel: 01642 243668 Fax: 01642 222252 — MB ChB 1988 Ed.; MRCGP 1993; DTM & H Liverp. 1994; DRCOG 1993. (Edinburgh) GP Tees HA.

HOULIHAN, John Francis 172 Oak Tree Lane, Bournville, Birmingham B30 1TX Tel: 0121 472 1647; 19 Corner Stone Country Club, Maryland Drive, North Field, Birmingham B31 2AT Tel: 0121 476 1647 — MB BCh BAO NUI 1937; LM Dub. 1937; DPH Lond. 1939. (Univ. Coll. Dub.) Prev: Ho. Phys. St. Vincent's Hosp. Dub.; Res. Med. Off. City Infec. Dis. Hosp. Birm.; Squadron Ldr. RAFVR.

HOULISTON, Mark David Elgin Community Surgery, Highfield House, Northfield Terrace, Elgin IV30 1NE Tel: 01343 542234 Fax: 01343 562101 — MB ChB 1987 Dundee; MRCGP 1994; DRCOG 1993; DFFP 1993; DCH Otago 1991. Chairm. Moray Docs. Out of Hours CoOperat.

HOULSBY, Wheldon Tinmouth Childrens Department, North Tyneside General Hospital, Rake Lane, North Shields NE29 8NH Tel: 0191 259 6660 Fax: 0191 293 2520 — BM BCh 1976 Oxf.; MA Camb. 1977; MD Sheff. 1986; FRCP Lond. 1994; FRCP Ed. 1993; MRCP (UK) 1979; FRCPCH 1997. Cons. Paediat. N.umbria Health Care; Clin. Lect. (Child Health) Univ. Newc. u. Tyne. Prev: Lect. & Hon. Cons. Paediat. Leeds Gen. Infirm.; Lect. & Hon. Sen. Regist. Sheff. Childr. Hosp.; Lect. & Hon. Regist. Roy. Aberd. Childr. Hosp. & Aberd. Matern. Hosp.

HOULSTON, Richard Somerset Section of Genetics, Institute of Cancer Research, 15 Cotswold Road, Sutton SM2 5NG Tel: 020 8643 8901 Fax: 020 8770 7876 Email: r.houlston@icr.ac.uk; 51 Adelaide Road, Surbiton KT6 4SR Tel: 020 8390 5636 — MB BS 1981 Lond.; PhD Lond. 1993, MSc (Neurochem.) 1985, BSc 1978, MD 1992; MRCP (UK) 1993; FRCPath 1997, M 1988; FRCP (UK) 1998. Sen. Lect. (Clin. Genetics) Inst. Cancer Research Roy. Marsden Hosp. Sutton; Hon. Sen. Lect. (Clin. Genetics) St. Geo. Hosp. Lond. Socs: Clin. Genetics Soc. Prev: ICRF Clin. Research Fell.

HOULT, Elizabeth Anne (retired) Arrowfields Barn, Grange Lane, Alvechurch, Birmingham B48 7DJ — MB ChB 1942 Birm.; MB ChB (2nd cl. Hons.) Birm. 1942; FFA RCS Eng. 1954; DA Eng. 1946. Prev: Cons. Anaesth. Dudley Rd. Hosp. Birm.

HOULT, Isobel Suzannah Leigh Bush Street Farm, North Nibley, Dursley GL11 6DQ — MB ChB 1995 Bristol; BSc (Hons.) Anat. Sci. Bristol 1989. SHO Gen. Surg. Gloucs Roy. Hosp. Socs: BMA; WIST. Prev: SHO A&E Frenchay Hosp; SHO (Orthop. & Trauma) Roy. United Hosp. Bath.

HOULT, John Edward c/o Waterlow Unit, Whittington Hospital, Highgate Hill, London N19 5NF — MB BS 1961 Sydney; FRANZCP 1974.

HOULT, Sarah Louise 26 Stratford Street, Oxford OX4 1SW Tel: 01865 723739 — MB BS 1989 Newc.; MRCGP 1994; DRCOG 1993. (Newc. u. Tyne) Prev: Acad. Regist. (Gen. Pract.) Univ. Coll. Lond. Med. Sch.

HOULTON, Peter Godfrey Pain Relief Clinic, St Peter's Hospital, Guildford Road, Ottershaw, Chertsey KT16 0PZ Tel: 01932 872000 Ext: 2599 Fax: 01932 692599; Willow House, Kemishford, Woking GU22 0RP Tel: 01483 232537 — MB BS 1971 Lond.; MRCS Eng. LRCP Lond. 1971; FFA RCS Eng. 1978; FFA RCSI 1977. (St. Bart. Med. Coll.) Cons. Anaesth. & Pain Managem. St. Peter's Hosp. Chertsey. Socs: Fell. Roy. Soc. Med.; Pain Soc.; (Comm.) Internat. Assn. Study of Pain. Prev: Staff Anaesth. & Asst. Prof. Dalhousie Univ. Halifax Nova Scotia, Canada.

HOULTON, Stephen Christopher 69A Hardy Barn, Shipley, Heanor DE75 7LY — MB BS 1986 Lond.

HOUNSFIELD, Victoria Oglanders, 1 Fairy Hill, Seaview Lane, Seaview PO34 5DG — BM 1998 Soton.; BM Soton 1998.

HOUNSLOW, Neil John Parke Davis Pharmaceutical research, Lamberly Court, Chestndy Avenue, Eastleigh SO55 3ZQ Tel: 0238 062 8902 Fax: 0238 062 9813 Email: neil.hounslow@wl.com; 71

Portchester Road, Fareham PO16 8AP — MB BS 1980 Lond.; BSc (Hons.) Lond. 1977, MB BS 1980; MRCP (UK) 1984; MFPM RCP (UK) 1993; Dip. Pharm. Med. RCP (UK) 1992. (Guy's Hospital Medical School)

HOUNSOME, Catherine Emma 8 Keepers Wood, The Drive, Chichester PO19 4XU; 8 Keepers Wood, The Drive, Chichester PO19 4XU — MB BS 1994 Lond.; MRCGP 2001; DFFP 2000. Socs: MPS; BMA.

HOURAHANE, Barbara Ethelreda 16 Lancaster Terrace, Merthyr Tydfil CF47 8SL — MB BCh 1989 Wales; DPM Wales 1996. Staff Grade Psychiat. Ment. Health Unit, E. Glam. Hosp. Prev: Ho. Off. (Surg.) Neath Gen. Hosp.; Ho. Off. (Med.) W. Wales Gen. Hosp.

HOURANI, Abdel Hafez Ibrahim 12 Grange Crescent, Rubery, Birmingham B45 9XB — LMS 1971 Seville.

HOURIHAN, Brendan Martin 158 Maes Glas, Caerphilly CF83 1JW Tel: 029 2088 2851 — BM BS 1986 Nottm.; BMedSci Nottm. 1984; MRCGP 1992; DFFP 1995; DCH RCP Lond. 1992; DRCOG 1992. Staff Phys. (Infec. & Immunol.) Roy. Lond. Hosp. Prev: Regist. (Genitourin. Med.) Roy. Lond. Hosp.; SHO Reading VTS.

HOURIHAN, Margaret Denise 27 Heol Wen, Rhiwbina, Cardiff CF14 6EG Tel: 029 2062 7729 Fax: 029 2074 3029 — MB BCh 1976 Wales; FRCR 1982. (Univ. Wales Coll. Med.) Cons. Neuroradiol. Univ. Hosp. of Wales Cardiff. Prev: Sen. Regist. (Neuroradiol.) Newc. Gen. Hosp.; Sen. Regist. (Radiol.) Univ. Hosp. of Wales Cardiff.

HOURIHANE, Brian Wombwell Medical Centre, George Street, Wombwell, Barnsley S73 0DD Tel: 01226 752363 — MB BCh BAO 1976 NUI; MRCS Eng. LRCP Lond. 1976; MRCGP 1980; DCH RCPSI 1979; DRCOG 1978.

HOURIHANE, Jonathan O'Brien Immunobiology Unit, Division of Cell & Molecular Biology, Institute of Child Health, 30 Guilford St., London WC1N 1EH; 59 Scholars Road, Balham, London SW12 0PF — MB BCh BAO 1987 Dub.; MRCPI 1991; DM Soton. 1996. Lect. (ImmunoBiol.) Inst. Child Health Gt. Ormond St. Lond. Socs: Brit. Paediat. Assn.; Paediat. Research Soc.; Brit. Soc. Allergy & Clin. Immunol. Prev: Lect. (Child Health) Soton.; Research Fell. (Child Health) Soton.; Regist. (Child Health) Soton.

HOURSTON, Austin James Daniel Flat F, 32 Richmond Walk, Aberdeen AB25 2YT — MB ChB 1997 Aberd.

HOURSTON, Ian Maurice, Air Commodore RAF Med. Retd. (retired) Carlton, Stromness KW16 3DZ Tel: 01856 850315 — MB ChB 1955 Ed.; MFOM 1980; DAvMed Eng. 1974. Prev: Dep. Princip. Med. Off. RAF Strike Command.

HOUSAM, Lt. Col. Graham Donald, CD, Lt.-Col. RAMC (V) Department of Anaesthetics, The Princess Mary's Hospital, Akrotiri BFPO 57, Cyprus; The Oaks, Llandewi, Llandrindod Wells LD1 6SL Tel: (01597) 851573 — MB ChB Birm. 1964; BA (Hons.) Toronto 1988; MRCS Eng. LRCP Lond. 1964; FRCPC 1972; FFA RCS Eng. 1969. (Birmingham) Cons. Anaesth, The P.ss Mary's Hosp., Akroitiri, BFPO 57. Socs: BMA. Prev: Col. TA 203 (Welsh) Field Hosp. RAMC (V); Cons. Anaesth. Joseph Brant Hosp. Burlington. Ontario, Canada; Resid. Anaesth. Hosp. Sick Childr. Toronto, Canada.

HOUSDEN, Mr Philip Lionel Kent & Canterbury Hospital, Ethelbert Road, Canterbury CT1 3NG Tel: 01227 766877 — MB BCh 1984 Wales; FRCS (Orth.) 1995; FRCS Ed. 1989; FRCS Eng. 1989. Cons. Kent & Canterbury Hosp. Prev: Sen. Regist. (Orthop.) Swansea & Cardiff; Regist. (Orthop.) Roy. Nat. Orthop. Hosp. Stanmore Middlx.

HOUSE, Alison Kathleen Arthington Medical Centre, 5 Moor Road, Hunslet, Leeds LS10 2JJ Tel: 0113 270 5645 Fax: 0113 270 0927 — MB BS 1973 Lond.; Dip. Ther 2001; DObst RCOG 1975. (St. Bart. Hosp. Med. Sch.)

HOUSE, Professor Allan Oliver Academic Unit of Psychiatry & Behavioural Sciences, 15 Hyde Terrace, Leeds LS2 9LT Tel: 0113 233 2725 Fax: 0113 243 3719 Email: a.o.house@leeds.ac.uk — MB BS 1974 Lond.; BSc (Hons.) Lond. 1971; DM Nottm. 1988; MRCP (UK) 1977; MRCPsych 1980. Prof. of liaison Psychiat. & Head of Acad. Unit of Psychiat. & Behavioural Sci.s; hon. Cons. Liaison Psych., United Leeds Teachg. Hosp.s NHS Trust. Prev: Research Off. Radcliffe Infirm. Oxf.; Lect. (Psychiat.) Qu. Med. Centre Nottm.; Regist. (Psychiat.) Mapperley Hosp. Nottm.

HOUSE, Catherine Anne 20A Church Street, Easton-on-the-Hill, Stamford PE9 3LL — BM 1979 Soton.; DFFP 1994. (Soton.) p/t Clin. Asst. (Gen. Pract.) Corby Glen Lincs.; Clin. Asst. (Genitourin. Med.). Prev: GP Asst. & Trainee GP Coningsby, Lincs.; Trainee GP Rotat. St. Geo. Hosp. Lond. VTS; Regist. (Anaesth.) Lincoln Hosp.

HOUSE, Charles Vernon 14 Dartford Road, Sevenoaks TN13 3TQ — MB BS 1992 Lond.; MRCP (UK) 1996.

HOUSE, David Allan (retired) 633 Scott Hall Road, Leeds LS17 5PD Tel: 0113 228 1954 — MB ChB 1957 Leeds; DObst RCOG 1962. Prev: GP Leeds.

HOUSE, Elizabeth Vaudrey, Squadron Ldr. RAF Med. Br. Retd. Beech Tree Surgery, 68 Doncaster Road, Selby YO8 9AJ Tel: 01757 703933; 16 The Paddock, Linton-on-Ouse, York YO30 2AD — MB BS 1990 Lond.; MRCGP 1995; DFFP 1995. (UMDS St. Thos. Hosp. Lond.) Retainer Scheme, Gen. Pract., Beech Tree Surg., Selby. Socs: RCGP; BMA; FFP. Prev: Milit. Off. RAF Linton-on-Ouse, York; Milit. Off. RAF Valley, Anglesey; Milit. Off. RAF Leuchars, Fife.

HOUSE, James Humphry The Health Centre, Kings Road, Horley RH6 7DG Tel: 01293 772686 Fax: 01293 823950 — MRCS Eng. LRCP Lond. 1975; MRCGP 1990; T(GP) 1991; DRCOG 1979; Dip Sports Med. (Ed.) 1998. (St. Bart. Hosp. Lond.) Socs: Brit. Med. Acupunct. Soc.; B.A.S.E.M. Prev: Trainee GP Epsom VTS; Ho. Off. Wanganui Base Hosp. Wanganui, NZ.

HOUSE, Julia Margaret Vietnam, c/o BP Exploration, Britannic House, 1-6 Finsbury Circus, London EC2M 7BA — MB BS 1985 Lond.; MRCGP 1990; DRCOG 1989; DCH RCP Lond. 1988.

HOUSE, Malcolm Lawrence (retired) 20 Pool Lane, Brocton, Stafford ST17 0TR — MB BChir 1951 Camb.

HOUSE, Michael John (retired) Breachfield, 35 Breach Lane, Shaftesbury SP7 8LD Tel: 01747 855814 — MB BS 1963 Lond.; MRCS Eng. LRCP Lond. 1962; FRCOG 1983, M 1969; T(OG) 1991. Prev: Hon. Cons. & Sen. Lect. Char. Cross & W. Lond. Hosps.

HOUSE, William St Augustines Medical Practice, 4 Station Road, Keynsham, Bristol BS31 2BN Tel: 0117 986 2343 Fax: 0117 986 1176 — MB BS 1971 Lond.; BSc (Hons.) Lond. 1968; MRCP (UK) 1974; DObst RCOG 1976. (Middlx.) Prev: Trainee GP Bath VTS; Regist. (Gen. Med.) St. Peters Hosp. Chertsey; SHO (Psychiat.) Barrow Hosp. Bristol.

HOUSEHAM, Elizabeth Ann 87 Grove Avenue, Costessy, Norwich NR5 0JA — MB BS 1993 Lond.

HOUSLEY, Edward Beechwood House, BUPA Murrayfield Hospital, 122 Corstorphine Road, Edinburgh EH12 6UD Tel: 0131 334 0363 Fax: 0131 334 9190 Email: ehousley@doctors.org.uk; 6 Kew Terrace, Edinburgh EH12 5JE Tel: 0131 337 5114 Fax: 0131 313 2757 — MB ChB 1957 Birm.; FRCP Lond. 1979, M 1963; FRCP Ed. 1975, M 1973. (Birm.) Socs: Fell. Roy. Soc. Med. (Hon. Sec. & Treas. Forum on Angiol.); Hon. Mem. Vasc. Surg. Soc. GB & Irel. Prev: MRC Clin. Research Fell.; Sen. Regist. (Med.) United Birm. Hosps.; Med. Specialist Armed Forces Scotl.

HOUSLEY, Lucy Elizabeth 33 Broomfield Road, Stockport SK4 4NB — MB ChB 1985 Manch.; BSc St. And. 1982. p/t GP Edgeley, Partner Edgeley Med. Pract. Prev: Trainee GP Stockport.

HOUSLEY, Russell Charles Edward 15 Warwick Road, Sidcup Hill, Sidcup DA14 6LJ — MB BS 1987 Lond.

HOUSSEMAYNE DU BOULAY, Professor Edward Philip George, CBE Institute of Neurology, National Hospital, Queen Square, London WC1N 3BG Tel: 020 7837 3611 Fax: 020 7278 5069; Old Manor House, Brington, Huntingdon PE18 0PX Tel: 01832 710353 — MB BS 1945 Lond.; DSc De Montfort Univ. 1992; FRCP Lond. 1973, M 1966; DMRD Eng. 1949; FFR 1952; Hon. FACR 1989. (Char. Cross) Emerit. Prof. Neuroradiol. Univ. Lond.; Hon. Vis. Prof. De Montfort Univ.; Hon. Mem. (Ex-Pres.) Brit. Inst. Radiol.; Mem. (Pres.) XIV Symp. Neuroradiol. Socs: (Hon. Pres.) Europ. Soc. Neuroradiol.; Hon. Research Fell. Zool. Soc. of Lond. Prev: Head of Radiol. Dept. Nat. Hosp. Nerv. Dis. Qu. Sq.; Ho. Phys. Char. Cross Hosp.; Head of Radiol. Inst. of Zool.

HOUSTON, Aileen Patricia Altries East, Kinnessburn Terrace, St Andrews KY16 9HA — MB ChB 1991 Manch.

HOUSTON, Alan Cromarty Quintiles (UK) Ltd, Ringside, 79 High St., Bracknell RG12 1DZ Tel: 01344 708456 Fax: 01344 708106 Email: ahouston@qred.quintiles.com — MB BS 1974 Lond.; MRCP (UK) 1978; FFPM RCP (UK) 1998. (Middlesex Hospital) Vice-Pres. Worldwide Phase I Serv. Socs: Fell. Roy. Soc. Med. Prev: Head Clin. Pharmacol. Internat. CIBA-GEIGY AG, Switz.; Vice-Pres. Clin. Research Besselaar, Europe; Managing Dir. Besselaar Clin. Research Unit Leeds.

HOUSTON, Brian David Department of Paediatrics, Luton & Dunstable Hospital, Lewsey Road, Luton LU4 0DZ Tel: 01582 497203 Fax: 01582 497280 Email: brian.houston@ldh-tr.anglox.nhs.uk; Mere Cottage, Tilsworth Road, Stanbridge, Leighton Buzzard LU7 9HY Tel: 01525 210122 Fax: 01525 210122 — MB BS 1972 Lond.; MRCP (UK) 1975; MRCS Eng. LRCP Lond. 1972; FRCPC 1984; LMCC 1983; DCH Eng. 1978. Cons. Paediat. Luton & Dunstable Hosp. Beds. Prev: Sen. Regist. (Paediat.) Roy. Berks. Hosp. Reading & Wolfson Centre Lond.; Regist. (Paediat.) Roy. Free Hosp. Lond.; Fell. (Neurol.) Hosp. for Sick Childr. Toronto, Canada.

HOUSTON, Brian Richard Mason Tel: 01702 710131 Fax: 01702 471154; 1643 London Road, Leigh-on-Sea SS9 2SQ Tel: 01702 710131 Fax: 01702 471154 — MB ChB 1977 Dundee; MRCGP 1981; DRCOG 1982. S.end PCT Bd. Mem., S.end PCT CHD lead; Director Neurologica (Memory Assessm. Clinic); Director Atrium (Counselling Company).

HOUSTON, David John Kerr 2 Southfield Avenue, Potterhill, Paisley PA2 8BY — MB ChB 1993 Aberd.

HOUSTON, David Ross Clydebank Health Centre, Kilbowie Road, Clydebank G81 2TQ Tel: 0141 531 6400 Fax: 0141 531 6336; 10 Park Crescent, Inchinnan, Renfrew PA4 9PW Tel: 0141 561 4604 — MB ChB 1977 Glas. Socs: BMA; Med. & Dent. Defence Union Scotl. Prev: SHO (Anaesth.) Vict. Infirm. Glas.; Ho. Surg. Greenock Roy. Infirm.; Ho. Phys. S.. Gen. Hosp. Glas.

HOUSTON, Diana Georgina 140 Main Street, Greyabbey, Newtownards BT22 2NG; 74 Manor Avenue, London SE4 1TE — MB BS 1992 Lond.

HOUSTON, Erika Christina 14 Whitechapel Street, Didsbury, Manchester M20 6UB — MB ChB 1990 Manch.; MRCP (UK) 1995.

HOUSTON, Fiona Margaret 48 Southbrae Drive, Glasgow G13 1QD — MB ChB 1970 Glas.

HOUSTON, Geraldine Leonie Nether Johnstone House, Johnstone PA5 8YP — MB ChB 1988 Glas.

HOUSTON, Helen Louise Ann Fairwater Health Centre, Plasmawr Road, Fairwater, Cardiff CF5 3JT Tel: 029 2056 6291 Fax: 029 2057 8870; 14 Bryn Rhosyn, Radyr, Cardiff CF15 8RN Tel: 029 2084 3872 Email: houston@cf.ac.uk — MD 1987 Wales; MB BCh Wales 1978; DCH RCP Lond. 1983; MRCGP 1982; DRCOG 1982; FRCGP 1996. Sen. Lect. Dept. of Gen. Pract., Cardiff. Prev: Gp.

HOUSTON, Iain Gibb (retired) Holmburn, Ormiston Terrace, Melrose TD6 9SW Tel: 01896 822425 — MB ChB 1966 Glas.; DMRD Eng. 1973; DObst RCOG 1967. Prev: Cons. Radiol. Borders Gen. Hosp., Melrose.

HOUSTON, Professor Ian Briercliffe (retired) Manor House, Wilderswood, Horwich, Bolton BL6 6SJ — MB ChB 1955 Manch.; MB ChB (Hons.) Manch. 1955; MD Manch. 1965; FRCP Lond. 1974, M 1958; DCH Eng. 1959; FRCPCH 1996. Prev: Dean Postgrad. Med. Studies Manch.

HOUSTON, Jacqueline Pamela X-Ray Department, Royal Berkshire Hospital, London Road, Reading RG1 5AN Tel: 01734 877930 — MB ChB 1983 Sheff.; BMedSci Sheff. 1980. p/t Assoc. Specialist (Radiol.) Roy. Berks. & Battle Hosps. Trust Reading. Socs: FRCR. Prev: Sen. Regist. (Radiol.) Roy. Berks. Hosp. Reading.; Regist. (Radiol.) Sheff.; SHO (Gen. Med.) Chesterfield & N. Derbysh. Roy. Hosp.

HOUSTON, James (retired) Flat 15, Westbury Court, Coten End, Warwick CV34 Tel: 01926 411425 — MB BCh BAO 1935 Belf.

HOUSTON, James Caldwell, CBE Discovery Cottage, 1 Mews St, London E1W 1UG Fax: 020 7481 8912 — MRCS Eng. LRCP Lond. 1939; MB BS Lond. 1940; MD Lond. 1946; FRCP Lond. 1956, M 1945. (Guy's) Cons. Phys. Emerit. Guy's Hosp. Socs: Fell. Med. Soc. Lond.; Assn. Phys. Prev: Dean United Med. & Dent. Sch. of Guy's & St. Thos. Hosps.; Clin. Tutor & Regist. (Med.) Guy's Hosp. Lond.; Maj. RAMC Med. Specialist.

HOUSTON, James Kenneth 12 Malone Hill Park, Belfast BT9 6RD Tel: 01232 666334 — MD 1968 Belf.; MB BCh BAO 1956; FRCOG 1974, M 1961, DObst 1958. (Qu. Univ. Belf.) Cons. (O & G) Belf. City Hosp. Socs: Ulster Obst. & Gyn. Soc. & Osprey Gyn. Soc. Prev: Cons. Gyn. Samarit. Hosp. Belf.; Cons. Lagan Valley & Musgrave Pk. Hosps.; Lect. (Midw. & Gyn.) Qu. Univ. Belf.

HOUSTON, James Richard Rosehall Surgery, 2 Mallusk Road, Newtownabbey BT36 4PP Tel: 028 9083 2188 Fax: 028 9083 8820; 1 Tudor Grove, Circular Road, Jordanstown, Newtownabbey BT37 0UX Tel: 01232 364098 — MB BCh BAO 1972 Belf.; MRCGP 1978; FRCOG 1997, MRCOG 1977. GP; Hosp. Pract. (Genitourin. Med.) Roy. Hosp. elf. Socs: BMA; BMA Genitourin Med.

HOUSTON, Janette Doreen Alanah Luing Cowley Centre, Milton Keynes Hospital, Standing Way, Milton Keynes MK6 5LD Tel: 01908 660033; 1 Vicarage Road, Yardley Gobion, Towcester NN12 7UN Tel: 01908 542657 — MB BCh BAO Belf. 1968; MFFP 1993; MRCGP 1972; DMJ (Clin.) Soc. Apoth. Lond. 1991; DObst RCOG 1970; DCH RCPS Glas. 1970. (Belf.) SCMO (Family Plann.) Milton Keynes Community Health Trust; Police Surg. Thames Valley; Sen. Clin. Med. Off. (Family Plann.) N.ampton HA. Socs: Assn. Police Surg.; BMA; RSM. Prev: GP N.ampton; Maj. RAMC, Princip. GP, Hong Kong; Trainee GP N.. Irel. VTS.

HOUSTON, John Clarence Steen (retired) 15 Skerries Fold, Portrush BT56 8PY Tel: 01265 824405 — MB BCh BAO 1945 Belf.

HOUSTON, John Finlay (retired) 38 Olinthus Avenue, Wednesfield, Wolverhampton WV11 3DH Email: jhouston@lineone.net — MB ChB 1948 Ed. Prev: Squadron Ldr. RAF Med. Br.

HOUSTON, John Graeme Radiology, Ninewells Hospital, 2 Medical School, Dundee DD1 9SY Tel: 01382 632651; Bishops House, Fairmount Road, Perth PH2 7AW Tel: 01738 621580 — MB BChir 1987 Camb.; MA Camb. 1983, MB BChir 1987; MRCP (UK) 1990; FRCR 1993. Cons. Radiol. Ninewells Hosp. Dundee. Socs: RCR; BSIR; CIRSE.

HOUSTON, Kathleen Elisabeth St Dunstan's Park Health Centre - , St Dunstan's Park, Melrose TD6 9RX Tel: 01896 822161 Fax: 01896 823151 — MB ChB 1965 Glas. (Glas.) GP Dingleton Hosp. Melrose; Partner Gen. Pract. Melrose Health Centre New Town St. Boswells Eildon HC. Prev: Clin. Med. Off. Borders HB; Med. Adoption & Fostering Panel Borders SWD 1990-97; Jun. Ho. Off. (Med.) & (Surg.) S.. Gen. Hosp. Glas.

HOUSTON, Kenneth Caldwell Lanehouse Surgery, Ludlow Road, Weymouth DT4 0HB Tel: 01305 785681 Fax: 01305 760418; 17 Bincleaves Road, Weymouth DT4 8RS Tel: 01305 779716 — MB BChir 1973 Camb.; DRCOG 1978; MA 1973 Camb.; MA Camb. 1973; DRCOG 1978. (Cambridge & St. Mary's Hospital London)

HOUSTON, Kerry Eileen 9 Orangefield Crescent, Belfast BT6 9GG — MB BCh BAO 1995 Belf.

HOUSTON, Matilda Elizabeth 11 Alexandra Road, Harrogate HG1 5JS — MB ChB BAO 1958 Belf.; MFFP 1993; DObst RCOG 1960. SCMO Harrogate; Instruc. Doctor Family Plann. Harrogate Health Dist. Prev: SHO Jubilee Matern. Hosp. Belf.; Ho. Surg. & Ho. Phys. Belf. City Hosp.

HOUSTON, Moira Elizabeth Chatsworth Clinic, 4 Chatsworth Rd, London NW2 4BN Tel: 020 563796 — MB ChB 1977 Bristol; MFHom 1988. p/t Homoeop. Pract. Chatsworth Clinic, Lond.; Homoeop. Pract. Letchworth Centre for Complementary Med. Socs: Fac. of Homeopathy. Prev: Clin. Asst. Roy. Lond. Homoeop. Hosp.; GP Trainee.

HOUSTON, Neil Mowat Dollar Health Centre, Park Place, Dollar FK14 7AA Tel: 01259 742120 Fax: 01259 743053; 19 Castle Road, Dollar FK14 7BE — MB ChB 1986 Dundee; MRCGP 1991; DRCOG 1991.

HOUSTON, Norma MC (retired) 7 Kyle Crescent, Loans, Troon KA10 7EZ — MB ChB 1950 Glas. Prev: Jun. Hosp. Med. Off. Blood Transfus.. Serv. (W. Scotl.).

HOUSTON, Richard John Tomnachadail, Glenborrodale, Acharacle PH36 4JP Tel: 01972 500251 Fax: 01967 421303 — MB BS 1971 Lond.; MRCS Eng. LRCP Lond. 1971; DObst RCOG 1974. (Roy. Free) Assoc. Pract. Salen & Lochaline. Socs: BMA; BASICS. Prev: SHO (Surg.) Dunoon Gen. Hosp.; SHO (Obst.) Vale of Leven Hosp.; Ho. Phys. (Paediat.) Hampstead Gen. Hosp.

HOUSTON, Robert Archibald (retired) Hillcrest, West Bay Road, Millport KA28 0HA Tel: 01475 553538 — MB ChB 1943 Glas.

HOUSTON, Ronald, OBE (retired) Braemar, 17 East Close, Middleton-on-Sea, Bognor Regis PO22 7RS Tel: 01243 586552 — MB ChB 1946 Ed.; FRCP Ed. 1977, M 1972; MFOM RCP Lond. 1978. Prev: Chief Med. Off. Shell UK Ltd. Lond.

HOUSTON, Rosamund Mary Hamilton West Manse, Taynuilt PA35 1JW — MB ChB 1947 Glas. (Glas.) Prev: GP Bonnyrigg Health Centre Midlothian; Med. Off. Family Plann. Clinics W. Lothian CC & Blood Transfus. Serv; Med. Regist. Stobhill Hosp. Glas.

HOUSTON, Russell Francis Belvoir Park Hospital, Belfast BT8 8JR Tel: 01232 491942; 90 North Circular Road, Belfast BT14 6TN — MB BCh BAO 1978 Belf.; MRCP (UK) 1981; FRCR 1985; FRCP Lond. 1998. (Queen's Belfast) Cons. N. Irel. Radiother. Centre Belf.
HOUSTON, Stephen John 5 Galbraith Gardens, Waringstown, Craigavon BT66 7QN — MB BCh BAO 1994 Belf.; FRCOphth Lond. 1997. (Qu. Univ. Belf.) Locum Regist., Ophth. Socs: MDU. Prev: SHO (Ophth.) Roy. Gp. Hosps. Belf.
HOUSTON, Thelma Cromarty Discovery Cottage, St Katharine-by-the-Tower, 1 Mews St., London E1W 1UG Tel: 020 7481 8912 — MB ChB 1943 Aberd. (Aberd.) Clin. Med. Off. Camden & Islington AHA (T). Prev: Ho. Phys. N.. Hosp. LCC; Ho. Surg. Chase Farm Hosp.; Capt. RAMC.
HOUSTON, Victoria 11 Roadside, Cumbernauld, Glasgow G67 2SS — MB ChB 1997 Glas.
HOUSTON, William Bernard 51 Fulwell Road, Peterlee SR8 5RD — MB ChB 1961 Aberd. Prev: GP Falkirk.
HOUSTON, William Lawrence John (retired) Lamellen, Trenshorne, Landons Shop, Launceston PL15 7PN — MB BCh BAO Dub. 1962; DObst RCOG 1964.
HOUTMAN, Peter Nicholas Department of Paediatrics, Leicester Royal Infirmary, Leicester LE1 5WW Tel: 0116 254 1414 Email: peter.houtman@dial.pipex.com; The Gables, Robert Hall Road, Amesby, Leicester LE8 5UX Tel: 0116 247 8243 — MB BS 1982 Lond.; BSc (Hons.) Lond. 1979; FRCP Lond. 1997; MRCP (UK) 1985; FRCPCH 1997. (Lond. Hosp.) Cons. Paediat. Leicester Roy. Infirm. Prev: Sen. Regist. Gt. Ormond St. Hosp. & Lond. Hosp.; Regist. (Paediat.) Childr. Hosp. Birm.; SHO (Paediat.) Hosp. for Sick. Childr. Gt. Ormond St. Lond.
HOVELL, Barry Colin 397 Beverly Road, Anlaby, Hull HU10 7BQ Tel: 01482 654295 — MB ChB 1960 Ed.; FFA RCS Eng. 1965. (Ed.) Cons. in Anaesth. Hull Roy. Infirm. Socs: Assn. Anaesths. Gt. Brit. & Irel. Prev: Lect. in Anaesth. Univ. Edin.; MRC Schol. Dept. Respirat. Dis. City Hosp. Edin.; Regist. Dept. Anaesth. Roy. Infirm. Edin.
HOVELL, Christopher John 38 Labrador Drive, Poole BH15 1UX — BM 1987 Soton.
HOVENDEN, Brian Jack (retired) Bolingbroke House, Old Bolingbroke, Spilsby PE23 4EY Tel: 01790 763484 — MB BS 1950 Lond.; MRCGP 1960; DObst RCOG 1959. Prev: Med. Off. Horncastle War Memor. Hosp.
HOVENDEN, Jonathan Lennox Pathology Department, Hartlepool General Hospital, Hartlepool TS24 9AH Tel: 01429 522414 Fax: 01429 274829 — MB BS 1985 Newc.; MRCPath 1992. (Newc. u. Tyne) Cons. Microbiol. Hartlepool Gen. Hosp. Cleveland. Socs: Brit. Soc. Study of Infec.; Assn. Clin. Path.; MRCPath. Prev: Sen. Regist. (Microbiol.) Ninewells Hosp. & Med. Sch. Dundee; Regist. (Microbiol.) Univ. Hosp. of Wales Cardiff.
HOVER, Evelyn Caroline 70 Lumbertubs Lane, Northampton NN3 6AH Tel: 01604 491059 — MB BS 1955 Lond.; MRCS Eng. LRCP Lond. 1955; DObst RCOG 1957. (Roy. Free)
HOVEY, Toni Madeline North Bristol NHS Trust, Westgate House, Southmead Hospital, Westbury-on-Trym, Bristol BS10 5NB Tel: 0117 959 5362 Fax: 0117 959 5363 Email: hovey_t@southmead.swest.nhs.uk; 19 Silver Street, Cheddar BS27 3LE Tel: 01934 743527 — MB BS 1984 Lond.; BSc Lond. 1981; MRCGP 1989; DFFP 1994; DCH RCP Lond. 1987; Cert. Family Plann. JCC 1988. (Guy's Hosp. Univ. Lond.) Staff Grade (Community Paediat.) N. Bristol. NHS Trust Bristol. Socs: Assoc. Mem. Roy. Coll. Paediat. Child Health; Roy. Coll. Gen. Pract.; Brit. Assn. Community Child Health. Prev: Asst. GP Swindon; Clin. Med. Off. (Child Health) Swindon HA.
HOVEYDA, Fatemeh 40 Garden Royal, Kersfield Road, London SW15 3HE — MB BS 1988 Lond.
HOVEYDA, Nourieh 40 Garden Royal, Kersfield Road, London SW15 3HE — MB BS 1989 Lond.
HOW, Gillian Carol Health Centre, Old Street, Clevedon BS21 6DG Tel: 01275 871454 — MB BS 1977 Lond.; MRCGP 1982; DRCOG 1981; MFHOM 1996. (King's Coll. Hosp.) GP; Clin. Asst. Bristol Homoeop. Hosp.
HOW, Norman Maurice (retired) Murcott House, Murcott, Long Buckby, Northampton NN6 7QR Tel: 01327 842293 Email: norman_how@hotmail.com — MB BS 1960 Lond.; FRCGP 1986, M 1973; DObst RCOG 1962. Prev: GP N.ampton.
HOWARD, Adam Quentin The White House, 3 Sandygate Park, Sheffield S10 5TZ — MB BS 1994 Lond.
HOWARD, Mr Andrew Corin Department of Orthopaedics, Northern General Hospital, Herries Road, Sheffield S5 7AU Tel: 0114 226 6197; Hollow Brook, Water Lane, Eyam, Hope Valley S32 5RG Tel: 01433 639203 — MB ChB 1985 Sheff.; FRCS (Orth.) 1995; FRCS Eng. 1991. Cons. Orthop. & Trauma & Spinal Surg., N. Gen. Hosp. Sheff.
HOWARD, Anthony John PHLS Wales, Department of Medical Microbiology & PHL, University Hospital of Wales, Heath Park, Cardiff CF4 4XN Tel: 029 2074 4515 Fax: 029 2074 6403 — MB BS 1972 Lond.; MSc Lond. 1977; LMSSA Lond. 1972; FRCPath 1990, M 1978. (St. Geo.) Gp. Dir. PHLS Wales. Socs: Brit. Soc. Antimicrob. Chemother.; Hosp. Infec. Soc. Prev: Dir. Bangor Pub. Health Laborat.; Cons. Med. Microbiol. Gwynedd Dist. Gen. Hosp. Bangor; Sen. Lect. & Lect. (Med. Microbiol.) Lond. Hosp. Med. Coll.
HOWARD, Caroline Grace 15 Oliver Close, Chatham ME4 5EF — MB BS 1996 Lond.
HOWARD, Catherine Mary Derby Medical Centre, 8 The Derby Square, Epsom KT19 8AG Tel: 01372 726361 — MB ChB 1976 Bristol; MRCGP 1987; DRCOG 1979. Prev: GP Purley Surrey.
HOWARD, Charles Vyvyan Fetal and Infant Toxico-Pathology, University of Liverpool, Liverpool L69 3BX Tel: 0151 794 3854 Fax: 0151 794 3854 Email: c.v.howard@liv.ac.uk; 38 Beresford Road, Oxton, Birkenhead CH43 1XJ Tel: 0151 652 2033 — MB ChB 1970 Liverp.; PhD Liverp. 1983; MRCPath 1995; FRCPath 1999. Sen. Lect. (Fetal & Infant Toxico-Path.) Univ. Liverp. Socs: Internat. Soc. Stereol.; Brit. Soc. Toxicol. Paths.; Fell. Roy. Microscopical Soc. Prev: Pres. Internat. Soc. Stereol.; Pres. Roy. Microscopical Soc.
HOWARD, Christine 14 St Andrews Road, Bebington, Wirral CH63 3DQ — MB ChB 1987 Sheff.; MRCP (UK) 1993.
HOWARD, Christopher Herbert 152 Harley Street, London W1G 7LH Tel: 020 7935 2477 — BM BCh 1971 Oxf.; BA Oxf. 1966; MPhil Lond. 1971; MRCS Eng. LRCP Lond. 1966; FRCPsych. 1982, M 1973. (Oxf. & Univ. Coll Hosp.) Prev: Hon. Cons. & Sen. Lect. (Psychiat.) Roy. Free Hosp. Sch. Med.; Regist. Maudsley & Bethlem Roy. Hosps.; Ho. Phys. Neurol. Unit Univ. Coll. Hosp. Lond.
HOWARD, Colin William Pond Tail Surgery, The Green, Godstone RH9 8DY Tel: 01883 742279 Fax: 01883 742913 — MB BChir 1974 Camb.; MA, MB Camb. 1974, BChir 1973; MRCP (UK) 1976. Prev: Sen. Regist. (Rheumatol.) St. Peter's Hosp. Chertsey; Regist. (Haemat.) Epsom Dist. Hosp.; Med. Regist. Groby Rd. Hosp. Leicester.
HOWARD, David Jameson Princess Margaret Hospital, Okus Road, Swindon SN1 4JU Tel: 01793 536231 Fax: 01793 437080; Bakers Farm House, Cerney Wick, Cirencester GL7 5QJ Tel: 01793 750288 Fax: 01793 751225 Email: 100750.2714@compuserve.com — MB ChB 1969 Bristol; BSc (Anat.) Bristol 1966; FRCP Lond. 1991; MRCP (UK) 1973. (Bristol) Cons. Phys. (Care Elderly) Swindon Hosps. Socs: Brit. Geriat. Soc. Prev: Sen. Regist. Rotat. (Geriat. & Gen. Med.) W. Midl.; Regist. (Med.) Bristol Roy. Infirm.; Vis. Instruc. Albert Einstein Coll. Med. New York, USA.
HOWARD, Mr David John Professorial Unit, Royal National Throat, Nose and Ear Hospital, 330 Grays Inn Road, London WC1X 8DA — MRCS Eng. LRCP Lond. 1972; BSc (Physiol.) Lond. 1968, MB BS 1972; FRCS Eng. 1978; FRCS Ed. 1980. (St. Geo.) Hon. Cons. Roy. Nat. Throat, Nose & Ear Hosp. Lond.; Sen. Lect. (Laryngol.) Inst. of Laryngol. & Otol. Socs: Roy. Soc. Med.; Brit. Assn. of Head & Neck Oncol. Prev: Sen. Regist. Sussex Throat & Ear Hosp. Brighton; Sen. Regist. Roy. Nat. Throat Nose & Ear Hosp. Lond.; Regist. (Accid. & Orthop.) St. Peter's Hosp. Chertsey.
HOWARD, David Jonathan Pemberley Avenue Surgery, 32 Pemberley Avenue, Bedford MK40 2LA Tel: 01234 351051 Fax: 01234 349246 — MB BS 1983 Lond.; MRCGP 1987. Trainee GP Warboys Huntingdon. Prev: SHO (Obst.) Lister Hosp. Stevenage; Ho. Phys. (Cardiol.) Roy. Free. Hosp. Lond.; Ho. Off. (Surg.) Lister Hosp. Stevenage.
HOWARD, David Michael Stonehaven Medical Group, Stonehaven Medical Centre, 32 Robert Street, Stonehaven AB39 2EL Tel: 01569 762945 Fax: 01569 766552 — MB ChB 1985 Aberd.; MRCGP 1991; DRCOG 1989. GP Stonehaven. Prev: Trainee GP Inverness.
HOWARD, Delyth Catrin Donald Winnicott Centre, Coate Street, London E2 9AG Tel: 020 7599 1005 Email:

delandalex@hotmail.com — MB BChir 1992 Camb.; MSc 2000; MRCP (UK) 1994. (Cambridge) Cons. Community Paediat. City & Hackney PCT, Hackney Lond. Socs: Mem. Of RCPCH & BACCH. Prev: Lect. (Community Child Health Roy. Free Hosp. Lond.).

HOWARD, Edward George (retired) 2 Netherby Cottages, Ladgate Lane, Middlesbrough TS5 7YZ Tel: 01642 318399 — MB ChB 1978 Ed.; MRCGP 1983; DCH RCPSI 1983; DRCOG 1982.

HOWARD, Professor Edward Richard Cromwell Hospital, Cromwell Road, London SW5 0TU; 5 High Standing, Chaldon Common Road, Chaldon, Caterham CR3 5DY Tel: 01883 349225 Fax: 020 7346 3438 Email: edwardrhoward@compuserve.com — MB BS 1960 Lond.; MS Lond. 1971; FRCS Ed. 1995; FRCS Eng. 1965; MRCS Eng. LRCP Lond. 1960. (King's Coll. Hosp.) Prof. Emerit. & Hon. Cons. Surg. Hepatobiliary & Paediatric Surg. King's Coll. Hosp. Lond. - Clin. Director, Paediatric Centre, Cromwell Hosp., Lond. SW5 0TU; Dir. Paediat. Unit Cromwell Hosp.Lond. Socs: Fell. Roy. Soc. Med. (Pres. Surg. Sect.); (Exec.) Brit. Assn. Paediat. Surgs.; Fell. Brit. Assn. Surgs. Prev: Cons. Surg. & Hon. Sen. Lect. King's Coll. Hosp. Lond.; Sen. Fulbright Schol.; Hunt. Prof. RCS Eng. 1970 & 1984.

HOWARD, Elizabeth Ann Walnut Tree Health Centre, Blackberry Court, Walnut Tree, Milton Keynes MK7 7NR Tel: 01908 691123 Fax: 01908 691120 — MB BS 1983 Newc.; MRCGP 1988; Dip. Obst. Otago 1987. (Newcastle upon Tyne) GP Princip. Milton Keynes. Socs: BMA; RCGP.

HOWARD, Elizabeth Clare University Hospital Aintree, Longmoor Lane, Liverpool L9 Tel: 0151 5295152/3 Fax: 0151 529 5155 Email: echoward@dial.pipex.com; Linnet Lodge, 29 Ince Road, Liverpool L23 4UE — MB ChB 1976 Liverp.; FFA RCS Eng. 1980. Clin. Director of Anaesth. & Theatres, Aintree Hosp.. Liverp. Socs: Liverp. Soc. Anaesth.; Linkman Assn. Anaesth.; Obst. Anaesth. Assn. Prev: Sen. Regist. Mersey RHA; Regist. Alder Hey Childr. Hosp.; Regist. (Anaesth.) Roy. Liverp. Hosp.

HOWARD, Frances Marianne Frimley Park Hospital Trust, Camberley GU16 5UJ Tel: 01276 604585 Fax: 01276 604307; Orchard House, Glaziers Lane, Normandy, Guildford GU3 2DE Tel: 01483 810972 Fax: 01483 810972 — MB BS 1970 Lond.; FRCPCH 1999; FRCP Lond. 1992; MRCP (UK) 1974; MRCS Eng. LRCP Lond. 1970; DCH Eng. 1973; DObst RCOG 1972. (Roy. Free) p/t Cons. Paediat. Frimley Pk. Trust Hosp.; Cons. Paediat. N.Downs Community Trust; Med. Advisor : CHASE; Med. Adviser: Marfans Assn, UK.; Med. Advisor: Make-a-wish Uk. Socs: RCPCH; Acad. Bd. Prev: Sen. Regist. (Paediat.) Roy. Free Hosp. Lond.; Scientif. Off. Clin. Genetics Unit Gt. Ormond St. Hosp. Sick Childr.

HOWARD, Frank Anthony 159 Armthorpe Road, Doncaster DN2 5PU Tel: 01302 367323; Holme Acre, Moss Lane, Trumfleet, Doncaster DN6 0DT Email: xqn09@ dial.pipe.com — MB ChB 1959 Liverp.; FRCOG 1983, M 1970, DObst 1966. (Liverp.) Cons. (O & G) Doncaster Roy. Infirm.; Maj. RAMC (RARO). Prev: Sen. Regist. (O & G) Univ. Hosp. S. Manch.; Clin. Tutor (Obst.) Manch. Univ.; Surg. Regist. Rochdale Infirm.

HOWARD, Grahame Charles William The Edinburgh Cancer Centre, The Western General Hospital, Crewe Road, Edinburgh EH4 2XU Tel: 0131 537 2211; 41A Argyle Crescent, Edinburgh EH15 2QE — MD 1986 Lond.; BSc Lond. 1973, MD 1986, MB BS 1976; FRCP Ed. 1993; MRCP (UK) 1979; FRCR 1984. (St Thomas') Cons. Clin. Oncologist W.. Gen. Hosp. Edin.; Hon. Sen. Lect. Univ. Edin.; Director The Edin. Cancer Centre. Prev: Sen. Regist. (Radiother. & Oncol.) Addenbrooke's Hosp. Camb.

HOWARD, Helen Louise National Blood Authority, Mersey & North Wales Blood Centre, West Derby St., Liverpool L7 8TW Tel: 0151 551 8800 Fax: 0151 551 8895; 3 Furrocks Close, Neston, South Wirral CH64 4EJ — MB BCh BAO 1966 Belf. (Queens Belf.) Staff Grade (Med. Audit) Mersey & N. Wales Blood Transfus. Serv. Liverp. Prev: Regist. MicroBiol. Qu. Eliz. Hosp. King's Lynn.

HOWARD, Ian Trevor Wonford Green Surgery, Burnthouse Lane, Exeter EX2 6NF Tel: 01392 250135 Fax: 01392 498572 — MB ChB 1979 Leeds; MRCGP 1983; DRCOG 1982; Cert. JCC Lond. 1982.

HOWARD, James Edward Australia Farmhouse, Twentypence Road, Wilburton, Ely CB6 3PX — BChir 1996 Camb.

HOWARD, Jane Elizabeth Woodchurch Road Surgery, 270 Woodchurch Road, Prenton, Birkenhead CH43 5UU Tel: 0151 608 3475 Fax: 0151 608 9535; 18 Claughton Firs, Oxton, Wirral L63 5TQ — MB ChB 1978 Manch.; MFFP 1981; DRCOG 1980. (St. And./Manch.) p/t Family Plann. Med. Off. Wirral. Prev: GP Trainee Timperley; SHO (O & G) Pk. Hosp. Davyhulme.; Ho. Phys. & Ho. Surg. Pk. Hosp. Davyhulme.

HOWARD, Jane Katherine Department of Endocrinology, Hammersmith Hospital, Du Cane Road, London W12 0NN Tel: 020 8383 3242 — MB BChir 1991 Camb.; BA Camb. 1988, MA 1992; MRCP (UK) 1993. (Camb.) MRC Clin. Train. Fell. & Hon. Regist. (Endocrinol.) Hammersmith Hosp. Lond. Prev: Regist. (Gen. Med. & Endocrinol.) Hammersmith Hosp. Lond.; SHO Hammersmith & Roy. Brompton Hosps. Lond. & Ch.ill Hosp. Oxf.

HOWARD, Jane Vivien Dept. of Anaesthesia, Charing Cross Hospital, Fulham Palace Rd, London W6 8RF Tel: 020 8846 7017 — MB BS 1985 Lond.; FRCA 1993; DA (UK) 1987. (Char. Cross) Cons. Anaesth. Char. Cross Hosp. Lond. Socs: BMA; Intens. Care Soc.; Assn. Anaesth. Prev: Sen. Regist. Rotat. (Anaesth.) Char. Cross, Chelsea & W.m. & Roy. Brompton Hosps.; Regist. Rotat. (Anaesth.) Char. Cross Hosp. Lond. & Watford Gen. Hosp.; SHO (Anaesth.) Kingston Hosp. Kingston u. Thames.

HOWARD, Janet Clare Westdown Cottage, Chalk Hill, Soberton, Southampton SO32 3PH Tel: 01489 877761 Fax: 01489 877761 — MB BS 1986 Lond.; MRCP (UK) 1992; MRCPCH 1997; DCH RCPS Glas. 1990. (Guy's Hosp. Med. Sch. Lond.) Sen. Regist. (Paediat.) Wessex. Prev: Regist. (Paediat.) Wessex RHA; SHO (Paediat.) Basingstoke Dist. Hosp. & St. Mary's Hosp. Portsmouth; SHO (Med.) St. Peter's Hosp. Chertsey.

HOWARD, Jennifer Alison Church Stretton Medical Practice, Easthope Road, Church Stretton SY6 6BL Tel: 01694 722127 Fax: 01694 724604; Ivy Cottage, Hope Bowdler, Church Stretton SY6 7DD Tel: 01694 722907 — MB ChB 1983 Birm.; DRCOG (RCOG) 1987. Prev: SHO (Psychiat.) Shrewsbury GP VTS.

HOWARD, Jillian Claire 2 Dunnes Close, Wedmore BS28 4BL — MB ChB 1993 Bristol.

HOWARD, Joanna 32 Larkhill, Wantage OX12 8HA — MB BChir 1993 Camb.

HOWARD, John Christopher Hungerford Medical Centre, School Crescent, Crewe CW1 5HA Tel: 01270 582534 Fax: 01270 216330; Warren House, Wybunbury Road, Willaston, Nantwich CW5 7ER Tel: 01270 669423 Email: jc.howard@dial.pipex.com — MB BS 1982 Lond.; BSc (Hons.) Lond. 1979; FRCGP 1996, M 1986; DRCOG 1987. (St. Mary's Lond.) Clin. Asst. (Psychiat.) Crewe; Trainer (Gen. Pract.) & GP Tutor Crewe. Prev: Trainee GP Melton Mowbray VTS; SHO (Gen. Med. & A & E) Leics. HA; SHO (O & G) Newc. Gen. Hosp.

HOWARD, John Dennis 120 Watermeadows, Worksop S80 3DB — MB ChB 1949 Sheff.; FFA RCS Eng. 1956; DA Eng. 1955. Cons. Anaesth. United Sheff. Hosps. & Sheff. RHB. Prev: Surg. Lt. RN; Sen. Anaesth. Ho. Off. United Liverp. Hosps.; Regist. Anaesth. United Sheff. Hosps.

HOWARD, John Richard The Health Centre, High Street, Arnold, Nottingham NG5 7BG Tel: 0115 926 7257; 63 Ribblesdale Road, Sherwood, Nottingham NG5 3GW Tel: 0115 926 2614 Fax: 0115 913664 Email: 106574.3722@compuserve.com — MB BS Durh. 1968; MRCGP 1976; DObst RCOG 1970; DFFP 1997. Undergrad. Tutor.

HOWARD, John Stephen Nocton, Old Avenue, Weybridge KT13 0PG Tel: 01932 43724 — MB BS 1959 Lond.; DO Eng. 1965. (Middlx.) Assoc. Specialist Eye Unit Roy. Kingston Hosp. Prev: Regist. St. Peter's Hosp. Chertsey; Med. Off. RAF Hosp. Nocton Hall; Ho. Off. Middlx. Hosp. Lond.

HOWARD, John Stewart 26 South Street, Cottingham HU16 4AS Tel: 01482 846147 — MB ChB 1981 Leic.

HOWARD, John Vincent Town End Surgery, 41 Town End, Caterham CR3 5UJ Tel: 01883 345613 Fax: 01883 330142 — MB BS 1972 Lond.; MRCS Eng. LRCP Lond. 1972; FRCGP 1993, M 1980. (Roy. Free) Assoc. Dean (Gen. Pract.) S. Thames (W.) Thames Postgrad. Med. & Dent. Educat.; RCGP Internat. Comm.; Dir., RCGP - Internat. Teachs. Course. Prev: Course Organiser Redhill GP VTS.

HOWARD, Judith 17 Blyth Grove, Worksop S81 0JG — MB ChB 1978 Sheff.; FRCR 1985; DMRD 1983. Cons. Radiol. Bassetlaw Dist. Gen. Hosp. Worksop.

HOWARD, Judith Catherine (retired) 44 Hartford House, Blount Road, Pembroke Park, Portsmouth PO1 2TW Tel: 02392 824136 —

MB BS Lond. 1955, DPH 1959; MRCS Eng. LRCP Lond. 1955; DObst RCOG 1960. Prev: Ho. Phys. Roy. Free Hosp.

HOWARD, Julian Mark Flat 5, 233 Camden Road, Islington, London N7 0HR — MB BS 1982 Lond.; MA Oxf. 1988, BA 1979; MRCP (UK) 1988; FRCA 1991; DA (UK) 1990. (Oxf.) Cons. (IC & Anaesth.) Roy. Free Hosp. Socs: Assn. Anaesth. & Intens. Care Soc.; Assn. Dent. Anaesth. Prev: Clin. Fell. IC W.mead Hosp., Sydney; Sen. Regist. (Anaesth.) Rotat. Char. Cross, Roy. Brompton, Roy. Marsden, Roy. Surrey Co. Hosp. & Chelsea & W.minster Hosp.

HOWARD, Kate 56 Toftwood Road, Crookes, Sheffield S10 1SJ — MB ChB 1998 Sheff.; MB ChB Sheff 1998.

HOWARD, Kerry Antoinette Chabuk, Kiln and Howard, 103a Rosendale Road, London SE21 8EZ Tel: 020 8670 3292 Fax: 020 8761 7310; 86 Idmiston Road, West Dulwich, London SE27 9HQ Tel: 020 8761 9926 — MB BS 1989 Lond.; DRCOG 1992. (Univ. Coll. & Middlx. Hosp. Sch. Med.) Prev: GP W. Midl.; GP E. Lond.; Trainee GP Paxton Green Health Centre Lond.

HOWARD, Linda Caroline Department of Genitourinary Medicine, Farnham Road Hospital, Guildford GU2 7LX Tel: 01483 537007 Fax: 01483 300129 — MB BS 1972 Lond.; MRCS Eng. LRCP Lond. 1972; FRCP Lond. 1995; MRCP (UK) 1984. (Roy. Free) Cons. Genitourin. Med. Surrey & Hants. Borders NHS Trust. Socs: Med. Soc. Study VD; Assn. Genitourin. Med.; BHIVA. Prev: Cons. Genitourin. Med. W.m. & St. Stephens Hosp. Lond.

HOWARD, Louise Michele The Institute of Psychiatry, De Crespigny Park, London SE5 8AF Email: spjelmh@iop.bpmf.ac.uk — MB BS 1988 Lond.; MPhil Lond. 1996; BSc Psychol. 1985; MRCP (UK) 1991; MRCPsych 1994. (Univ. Coll. Lond.) Wellcome Trust Research Fell. PT. Socs: Fell. Roy. Soc. Med. Prev: Sen. Regist. (Psychiat.) Maudsley Hosp. Lond.; Regist. Rotat. (Psychiat.) Maudsley Hosp. Lond.; SHO Rotat. (Psychiat.) St. Geo. Hosp. Lond.

HOWARD, Luke Sebastian Geoffrey Eliot 2 Clarendon Street, Cambridge CB1 1JU Email: lsgehoward@doctors.org.uk — BChir 1996 Camb.; MB BChir Camb. 1996; DPhil. Oxon. 1995, MA 1995. (Oxf. & Camb.) SHO (Nephrol.) Guy's Hosp. Prev: SHO (Cardiol.) St. Thomas'; SHO (Chest) Roy. Brompton.

HOWARD, Margaret Ann 63 Ribblesdale Road, Sherwood, Nottingham NG5 3GW Tel: 0115 926 2614 Fax: 0115 926 2614 — MB BS 1964 Lond.; MRCS Eng. LRCP Lond. 1964; DObst RCOG 1966. (Roy. Free) Cons. Community Paediat. Nottm. Community NHS Trust.

HOWARD, Martin Ronald Foss House, Main St., Wilberfoss, York YO41 5NN — MB ChB 1982 Leeds; FRCP 1999; FRCPath 2000; MD Leeds 1992; MRCP (UK) 1985; MRCPath 1992. (Univ. Leeds) Cons. Haemat. York Dist. Hosp.

HOWARD, Mary Elizabeth Department of Pathology, Law Hospital NHS Trust, Carluke ML8 5ER Tel: 01698 361100; 25 Invergarry Drive, Thornliebank, Glasgow G46 8UA — MB ChB 1976 Glas.; FRCPath 1994, M 1982. Cons. Histopath. Law Hosp. NHS Trust. Socs: Assn. Clin. Pathols.; Roy. M-C Soc. & BMA. Prev: Sen. Regist., Regist. & SHO (Histopath.) Gtr. Glas. HB.

HOWARD, Matthew Richard 23 Dean Road, Wilksden Green, London NW2 5AB Tel: 020 8459 8349 Email: mattoline@aol.com — MB BS 1990 Lond.; BSc Lond. 1987, MB BS 1990; MRCPsych 1995. (St. Georges)

HOWARD, Michael Robert Tel: 01403 264848 Fax: 01403 276386 — MB BS 1976 London. (London) GP Horsham, W. Sussex; Volun. Clin. Asst., St. Barnabas Hospice, Worthing, W.Sussex.

HOWARD, Neville 54 Cambridge Road, Southport PR9 9PP Tel: 01704 227535 Fax: 01704 227535 — MRCS Eng. LRCP Lond. 1952; DIH Eng. 1964; DPH Liverp. 1963. (Leeds) Prev: Indep. GP S.port; Med. Off. RAF; SHO (Dermat.) Dewsbury, Wakefield & Pontefract Hosp. Gps.

HOWARD, Nicola Margaret 115 Broad Lane, Hampton TW12 3BH — MB BS 1994 Lond.

HOWARD, Norman (retired) 5A Clarendon Road, London W11 4JA Tel: 020 7229 6704 — BM BCh Oxf. 1952; MA, DM Oxf. 1965; FRCR 1975; FFR 1958; DMRT Eng. 1956. Prev: Cons. Clin. Oncol. Cromwell Hosp. Lond.

HOWARD, Paul Woodlea, North Mead, Petworth GU28 9NJ — BM BS 1998 Nottm.; BM BS Nottm 1998.

HOWARD, Peter, CB, OBE, Air Vice-Marshal RAF Med. Br. (retired) 135 Aldershot Road, Church Crookham, Fleet GU52 8JU Tel: 01252 617309 Fax: 01252 816365 — MB BS 1949 Lond.; PhD Lond. 1964; FRCP Lond. 1977, M 1973; FFOM RCP Lond. 1981, M 1980; FRAeS. Prev: Regist. Fac. Occupat. Med.

HOWARD, Peter The White House, 3 Sandygate Park, Sheffield S10 5TZ Tel: 0114 230 2165 Fax: 0114 263 0139 — BM BCh 1960 Oxf.; BA (Physiol) Oxf. 1956, DM 1967; FRCP Lond. 1975; MRCS Eng. LRCP Lond. 1960. (Oxf. & Lond. Hosp.) Private Cons. in Respirat. Injury. Socs: Brit. Thorac. Soc.; Eur. Respirat. Soc. Prev: Reader & Sen. Lect. (Med.) Univ. Sheff.; Regist. (Gen. Med.) & Research Asst. (Med.) Roy. Hosp. Sheff.; SHO (Gen. Med. & Neurol.) Roy. United. Hosp. Bath.

HOWARD, Peter Alfred Old Orchard Cottage, Great Oak, Eardisley, Hereford HR3 6LU — MB BS 1991 Lond.; BDS Lond. 1983; LDS RCS Eng. 1983; MRCGP 1996; DFFP 1995; DRCOG 1994. (UMDS Lond.) GP Hay-on-Wye. Socs: BMA; Brit. Assn. Oral & Maxillofacial Surg.

HOWARD, Peter Basil 11 Willowfield, Randalstown, Antrim BT41 3AZ — MB BCh BAO 1993 Belf.

HOWARD, Mr Peter William Derbyshire Royal Infirmary, London Road, Derby DE1 2QY Tel: 01332 347141; Seven Spouts Farm House, Ingleby Lane, Ticknall, Derby DE73 1JQ Tel: 01332 864344 — MB ChB 1980 Leic.; FRCS Ed. 1984; FRCS Eng. 1984. (Leicester) Cons. Orthop. Surg. Derbysh. Roy. Infirm.; Clin. Dir. Prev: Sen. Regist. (Orthop. Surg.) W. Midl. HA; Regist. (Gen. Surg.) Nottm. Hosps.; Regist. (Orthop. Surg.) Derbysh. Roy. Infirm. Derby.

HOWARD, Philip John St Helier Hospital, Wrythe Lane, Carshalton SM5 1AA Tel: 020 8644 4343 Fax: 020 8644 9419; Division of Biochemical Medicine, St. George's Hospital, Cranmer Terrace, London SW17 0RE — MD 1987 Lond.; MA Oxf. 1984; MB BS 1978; MRCP (UK) 1983; FRCP Lond 1998; FRCP Ed 1997. (Guy's Hospital) Cons. Phys. St. Helier Hosp. Carshalton; Sen. Lect. (Med.) St. Geo. Hosp. Lond. Socs: Med. Res. Soc. & Brit. Soc. Gastroenterol. Prev: Lect. (Med.) Univ. Edin.

HOWARD, Rachel Elsa Canterbury Road Surgery, 186 Canterbury Road, Davyhulme, Manchester M41 0GR Tel: 0161 748 5559 Fax: 0161 747 1997; Tel: 01625 522676 — MB ChB 1989 Leeds; MRCGP 1994; DRCOG 1993. (Leeds) GP. Socs: BMA. Prev: Staff Grade Psychiat. Huddersfield.

HOWARD, Richard Francis 1 Frognal Mansions, Frognal, Hampstead, London NW3 — MB ChB 1980 Manch.

HOWARD, Richard John 29 Morgan Street, London E3 5AA — MB BS 1984 Lond.; MD Lond. 1997; MRCOG 1990. Cons. (O & G) King Geo. Hosp. Ilford Essex. Prev: Lect. & Hon. Sen. Regist. (O & G) Roy. Free Hosp. Lond.; Regist. (O & G) Roy. Free Hosp. Lond.

HOWARD, Robert Derek 11 Long Beach, Gorey, Grouville JE3 9DY Tel: 01534 22381 — MB BCh BAO 1957 Belf.; DCM (Dip. Chinese Med. Beijing Univ. of C.M.) 1998. (Qu. Univ. Belf.) Socs: Jersey Med. Soc. Prev: Ho. Surg. & Ho. Phys. Lagan Valley Hosp.; on GP Staff Qu. Vict. Hosp. E. Grinstead.

HOWARD, Robert John Michael Webster Section of Old Age Psychiatry, Institute of Psychiatry, Camberwell, London SE5 8AF Tel: 020 7848 0545 Fax: 020 7701 0167 Email: r.howard@iop.kcl.ac.uk; 77 Bushey Hill Road, London SE5 8QQ Tel: 020 7708 0457 — MB BS 1985 Lond.; MD Lond. 1996; MRCPsych 1990. Reader, (Psychiat. of Old Age) Inst. Psychiat. Lond. & Cons. Psychiat. Maudsley Hosp. Lond.; Vice Dean. Inst. Psychiat. Lond. Prev: Lect. Inst. Psychiat. Lond.; Regist. & Sen. Regist. (Psychiat.) Maudsley Hosp. Lond.; SHO (Med.) Selly Oak Hosp. & Midl. Centre for Neurosurg. & Neurol. Birm.

HOWARD, Robert Philip Whiston Hospital, Warrington Road, Prescot L35 5DR Tel: 0151 924 1715 Fax: 0151 430 1155; Linnet Lodge, 29 Ince Road, Thornton, Liverpool L23 4UE Tel: 0151 924 1715 Fax: 0151 924 1715 Email: rhoward@dial.pipex.com — MB ChB 1973 Liverp.; FFA RCS Eng. 1978. Cons. Anaesth. Whiston Hosp. Prev: Sen. Regist. (Anaesth.) Mersey RHA.

HOWARD, Robin Simon 18 Pages Hill, Muswell Hill, London N10 1QA — MB BChir 1980 Camb.; PhD Lond. 1989; MA Camb. 1981; FRCP Lond. 1995; MRCP (UK) 1983. (Middlx.) Cons. Neurol. St. Thos. Hosp. Lond. & Nat. Hosp. Neurol. & Neurosurg. Lond. Prev: Sen. Regist. & Regist. (Neurol.) Nat. Hosp. Nerv. Dis. Lond.; Regist. (Neurol.) St. Thos. Hosp. Lond.

HOWARD, Ronald George 7 Parkside Terrace, Edinburgh EH16 5BL — MB BS 1960 Sydney.

HOWARD, Simon Andrew The Health Centre, Pond Road, Shoreham-by-Sea BN43 5US Tel: 01273 440550 — MB BS 1988 Lond.; DRCOG 1991; MRCGP 1995. Trainee GP Huntingdon VTS.

HOWARD, Stephen Harry Fitzalan Locksley Cottage, North St., Burnham Market, King's Lynn PE31 8HG — MB BChir 1947 Camb.; MRCS Eng. LRCP Lond. 1942. (Lond. Hosp.) Prev: GP Barton-on-Humber.

HOWARD, Susannah Virginia Manor Road Surgery, 33 Manor Road, Caddington, Luton LU1 4EE Tel: 01582 25673 Fax: 01582 726672 — MB BS 1979 Lond.; MRCP (UK) 1982; MRCGP 1986; DRCOG 1986. Prev: GP Lond.

HOWARD, Timothy John 4 North Road, East Boldon NE36 0DL — BM BS 1980 Nottm.; MRCPsych 1987.

HOWARD, Timothy Robert Grenville Hadleigh House, 216A Wareham Road, Corfe Mullen, Wimborne BH21 3LN Tel: 01202 694721 Fax: 01202 658954; Woodside Farm, Brickyard Lane, Corfe Mullen, Wimborne BH21 3RJ Tel: 01258 857875 — MB BS Lond. 1969; MRCS Eng. LRCP Lond. 1969; MRCGP 1977; DObst RCOG 1972. (Guy's) Prev: Ho. Phys. (Med.) Guy's Hosp. Lond.; Ho. Surg. St. Luke's Hosp. Guildford; Trainee GP Wessex VTS.

***HOWARD, Tracey Elizabeth** Flat 4, Tudor Mews, Eastern Road, Romford RM1 3QF — MB BS 1995 Lond.; BSc (Basic Med. Scis. & Physiol.) Lond. 1991.

HOWARD, William Robert Grenville Woodside Farm, Brickyard Lane, Corfe Mullen, Wimborne BH21 3RJ — MB BS 1998 Lond.; MB BS Lond 1998.

HOWARD-ALPE, Georgina Mary West Carr Farm, West Carr Road, Attleborough NR17 1AN — MB BS 1998 Lond.; MB BS Lond 1998.

HOWARD-GRIFFIN, Julia Rose 77 Valley Road, Ipswich IP1 4NE Tel: 01473 216256 — BM 1976 Soton.; DO Lond. 1981. Clin. Asst. (Ophth.) Ipswich & Colchester Hosps. Socs: MRCOphth. Prev: Research Regist. (Ophth.) Oxf. Eye Hosp.; SHO (Ophth.) Soton. Eye Hosp.; SHO (Ophth.) & Cas. Off. Cornw. Regional Hosp., Jamaica.

HOWARD-GRIFFIN, Richard Michael 77 Valley Road, Ipswich IP1 4NE — BM 1976 Soton.; FFA RCS Eng. 1981. Cons Anaesth. Heath Rd. Hosp. Ipswich; Sen. Lect. Newham Gen. Hosp.; Lect. The Roy. Lond. Hosp. Whitechapel. Prev: Sen. Regist. (Anaesth.) Guy's Hosp. & Brighton Hosps.; Clin. Fell. (Anaesth.) Mt. Sinai Hosp. New York, USA; Regist. (Anaesth.) John Radcliffe Hosp. Oxf.

HOWARTH, Aileen Frances (retired) Copperas Lane, Haigh, Wigan WN2 1PA Tel: 01942 831098 — MB BCh BAO Dub. 1951. Prev: Med. Off. DHSS Manch.

HOWARTH, Alan John Fairfield Surgery, 1 Park Crescent, Llanelli SA15 3AE Tel: 01554 773133 Fax: 01554 777559; 3 Clos Y Ddraenen, Swiss Valley, Llanelli SA14 8ED Email: howartha@epulse.net — MB BCh 1976 Wales. (Cardiff) GP; JP. Prev: Regional Med. Off. (S. Wales) RAC Motor Sports Assn.; Chairm. Vale of Cothi Med. Comm. (Motor Sports); BMA Pl. of Work Accredit. Represen. for Bridgend Hosp. Area.

HOWARTH, Mr Anthony Edward 57 Dulwich Vill., London SE21 Tel: 020 8693 4498 — MRCS Eng. LRCP Lond. 1941; BA, MB BChir Camb. 1942; FRCS Eng. 1949. (St. Thos.) Cons. ENT Surg. Brook Gen. Hosp. Lond., Bromley Hosp., Beckenham; Hosp. & Childr. Hosp. Sydenham. Socs: Fell. Roy. Soc. Med.

HOWARTH, Antony James Chapel House, Chapel Lane, Threapwood, Malpas SY14 7AX — MB BCh 1998 Wales.

HOWARTH, Ben (retired) 1 Brayshaw Drive, Bradford BD7 4LY Tel: 01274 574704 — MRCS Eng. LRCP Lond. 1958; MRCGP 1972. Prev: GP W. Yorks.

HOWARTH, Brenda Elizabeth Flat 1 Beaufoy House, Regents Bridge Gardens, Rita Road, Vauxhall, London SW8 — MB BCh 1984 Wales; BSc (Hons.) Anat. St. And. 1981; MB BCh Wales l984.

HOWARTH, David Edward 18 Haigh Crescent, Chorley PR7 2QS — MB ChB 1993 Birm.; ChB Birm. 1993; MRCP Nov 1998 - Royal College of Physicians - Glasgow.

HOWARTH, David John Denton Turret Medical Centre, 10 Kenley Road, Slatyford, Newcastle upon Tyne NE5 2UY Tel: 0191 274 1840 — MB BS 1984 Newc.; MB BS Newc. l984; MRCGP 1988; DRCOG 1988.

HOWARTH, Edmund (retired) Yew Tree House, Martin Lane, Bawtry, Doncaster DN10 6NJ Tel: 01302 710269 — MB ChB 1952 Manch.; MD Manch. 1964; FRCPsych 1974, M 1971; DObst RCOG 1954; DPM Manch. 1957. Prev: Cons. Psychiat. Doncaster Roy. Infirm. & Loversall Hosp. Doncaster.

HOWARTH, Edmund Steven 2 Ridsdale Road, Nottingham NG5 3GQ — MB ChB 1986 Dundee.

HOWARTH, Francis Peter 38 Old Meldrum Road, Bucksburn, Aberdeen AB21 9DU Tel: 01224715146 Email: peter.howarth@rectory.grampian.scot.nhs.uk — MB ChB 1972 Aberd.; FRCGP 1992, M 1976. (Aberdeen) CAA Auth. Med. Examr.; Med. Adviser Grampian Primary Care Trust. Prev: GP Princip. Brimmond Med. Gp. Bucksburn, Aberd.

HOWARTH, Georgina Frances 67 St Bernards Road, Solihull B92 7DF — MB ChB 1993 Manch.

HOWARTH, John Arthur (retired) 36 Follyfield, Hankerton, Malmesbury SN16 9LA Tel: 01666 577462 — MB ChB 1948 Sheff. Prev: Mem. Pneumoconiosis Med. Panel DHSS.

HOWARTH, John Paul Fitz Road Surgery, 24 Fitz Road, Cockermouth CA13 0AD Tel: 01900 324124 Fax: 01900 324126 — MB BS 1983 Newc.; MRCGP (Distinc.) 1988; DTM & H Liverp. 1992. GP Cockermauth. Socs: Fell. Roy. Soc. Trop. Med. & Hyg. Prev: Princip. GP Cockermouth; Trainee GP Newc. VTS.

HOWARTH, Mrs Joyce Kathleen (retired) Yew Tree House, Martin Lane, Bawtry, Doncaster DN10 6NJ Tel: 01302 710269 — MB ChB 1951 Manch.; DCH Eng. 1954. Prev: SCMO Doncaster AHA.

HOWARTH, Kate Louise Gorsty Croft, Wood Lane, Mobberley, Knutsford WA16 7NJ — MB ChB 1995 Sheff.; MB ChB Manch. 1995.

HOWARTH, Lucy Joanna 73 Southmoor Road, Oxford OX2 6RE — BM 1997 Soton.

HOWARTH, Mark Walter The Health Centre, St. Peters Crescent, Selsey, Chichester PO20 0NN Tel: 01243 604321/602261 Fax: 01243 607996; Marigolds, Lewis Road, Selsey, Chichester PO20 0RQ Tel: 01243 603705 Fax: 01243 607335 Email: jillmark@compuserve.com — MB ChB 1975 Bristol. (Bristol) Clin. Asst. (Ophth.) St. Richards Hosp. Chichester. Prev: Refugee Camp Phys. Sudan; Trainee GP Perranporth; Med. Off. & Clin. Tutor Kainantu, Papua New Guinea.

HOWARTH, Nicholas John 16 Risborrow Close, Etwall, Derby DE65 6HY Tel: 01332 347141 — MRCS Eng. LRCP Lond. 1984. Staff Grade (A & E) Derbysh. Roy. Infirm.

HOWARTH, Nikolas James 225 Lutterworth Road, Nuneaton CV11 6PX — MB BCh 1974 Wales; MA 2000 University of Manchester; MRCGP 1978; DRCOG 1976.

HOWARTH, Patricia Jane 40 Heol-y-Pentre, Pentyrch, Cardiff CF15 9QE Tel: 029 2089 2344 — MB BCh 1979 Wales; MRCGP 1983. (Welsh Nat. Sch. Med.) Clin. Asst. (Geriat. Med.) Dewi Sant Hosp. Mid. Glam. HA. Prev: Clin. Asst. Community Memory Project Cardiff Roy. Infirm.; Clin. Med. Off. (Child Health & Family Plann.) Health Dist. M. Glam.

HOWARTH, Mr Paul Alexander Wrigley Accident & Emergency Department, Treliske Hospital, Truro TR1 3LJ Tel: 01872 253219 Fax: 01872 253215 — MB BS 1981 Lond.; FRCS Ed. 1987. Cons. A & E Roy. Cornw. Hosps. Trust. Socs: Fell. Fac. Accid. & Emerg. Med. Prev: Sen. Regist. (A & E) S. W.. RHA; Regist. (A & E) Frenchay Hosp. Bristol; Regist. (Surg.) Univ. Hosp. Wales Cardiff.

HOWARTH, Peter James Street Grove Practice, James Street, Workington CA14 2DF Tel: 01900 62241 Fax: 01900 603385; 71 High Street, Workington CA14 4EU — MB ChB 1978 Leeds. Prev: Trainee GP W. Cumbria Vocational Train. Scheme; SHO (ENT) Leeds Gen. Infirm.; Demonst. (Anat.) Univ. Leeds.

HOWARTH, Peter Edwin Holman Moorview, Lustleigh, Newton Abbot TQ13 9TL — MB ChB 1943 Sheff.; DA Eng. 1966. Prev: Ho. Surg. Roy. Hosp. Sheff.; Demonst. Anat. Univ. Sheff.

HOWARTH, Peter Hugo RCMB (MP810), Southampton General Hospital, Southampton SO16 6YD Fax: 02380 798492 Email: phh1@soton.ac.uk; Fax: 02380 796889 — MB BS 1976 Lond.; BSc Hons Lond. 1973; DM Soton 1988; FRCP Lond. 1993; MRCP (UK) 1979. Reader in Med. & Hon. Cons. Phys. Socs: Brit. Thorac. Soc.; Brit. Soc. Allergy & Clin. Immunol.

HOWARTH, Roderic Franklyn Burton (retired) Copperas Lane, Haigh, Wigan WN2 1PA Tel: 01942 831098 — MB BCh BAO Dub. 1953; MFOM RCP Lond. 1981; DIH Eng. 1976. Prev: Sen. Employm. Med. Adviser Health & Safety Exec. (Med. Div.).

HOWARTH, Roger Mervyn (retired) Winscombe Lodge, Station Road, Birch Vale, High Peak SK22 1BP Tel: 01663 746802 Fax: 01633 746802 — MB ChB 1973 Birm.; BSc (Hons.) (Anat.) Birm. 1970; MRCGP 1982. Examr. for Benefits Agency. Med. Servs. Prev: Regist. Rotat. (Med.) Glas. Roy. Infirm.

HOWARTH, Roy Victor 252 Ben Jonson House, Barbican, London EC2Y 8DL — MB ChB 1959 Leeds; FRCPsych 1983, M 1971; Acad. DPM Univ. Lond. 1966; DCH Eng. 1962. (Leeds) Prev: Cons. Child & Adolesc. Psychiat., Gt. Ormond St. Hosp; Sen. Regist. & Research Fell. Hosp. Sick Childr. Gt. Ormond St. Lond.; Regist. Roy. Bethlem & Maudsley Hosps.

HOWARTH, Stephanie Marjory Rose Bronwen 2 Oak Vale, Grampound, Truro TR2 4QY — MB BS 1983 Lond. Prev: SHO (O & G) & Regist. (Gen. Med.) Univ. Hosp. Wales Cardiff.

HOWARTH, Vicki Sharon 8 Moorfield Heights, Carrbrook, Stalybridge SK15 3RB — MB ChB 1997 Manch.

HOWAT, Alexander James Pathology Laboratory, Royal Preston Hospital, Preston PR2 4HG Tel: 01772 710141 Fax: 01772 710181; Fairfield House, Chatburn, Clitheroe BB7 4BB Tel: 01200 441335 Email: alec.howat@btinternet.com — MB BS 1978 Newc.; FRCPath 1995. (Newcastle) Cons. Histopath. Roy. Preston Hosp. Socs: Internat. Acad. Path. (Hon. Treas. & Mem.ship Sec. Brit. Div.); Brit. Soc. Clin. Cytol. (Meetings Sec.). Prev: Sen. Lect. (Path.) Univ. Sheff.; Sen. Regist. (Histopath.) Childr. Hosp. Sheff.; Regist. (Path.) Salisbury Gen. Infirm.

HOWAT, Alison Mary 98 (33) Clarence Drive, Hyndland, Glasgow G12 9RN — MB ChB 1995 Glas.

HOWAT, Anne McGillivray Old School House, North Moreton, Didcot OX11 9BA Tel: 01235 813228 — MB ChB Ed. 1951.

HOWAT, Colin Springburn Health Centre, 200 Springburn Way, Glasgow G21 1TR Tel: 0141 531 9641 Fax: 0141 531 9642 — MB ChB 1986 Glas.

HOWAT, Douglas Donald Currie (retired) Flat 10, 40 Wimpole St., London W1G 8AB Tel: 020 7935 6031 — MB BS Lond. 1943; FRCS Eng. 1984; FRCA 1953; DA Eng. 1946. Hon. Cons. Anaesth. St. Geo. Hosp. & Roy. Masonic Hosp. Lond. Prev: Vice-Pres. (Ex-Chairm. Exec. Comm.) World Federat. Socs. Anaesthesiols.

HOWAT, Isabel Mary Grace Free Church Manse, Kilberry Road, Tarbert PA29 6XX — MB ChB 1998 Dund.; MB ChB Dund 1998.

HOWAT, Jean McCurrach 22 Hove Park Road, Hove BN3 6LJ Tel: 01273 555465 — MB ChB 1958 Aberd.; DA Eng. 1960. (Aberd.)

HOWAT, John Gordon Munro Westminster House, 598 The Wells Road, Nottingham NG3 3AA Tel: 0115 969 1300 Fax: 0115 962 7889 — MB ChB 1969 Glas.; MRCPsych 1973; DPM Ed. & Glas. 1972. (Glas.) Clin. Dir. & Cons. Psychiat. Rehabil. & Community Care Servs. Nottm. Healthcare NHS Trust. Prev: Sen. Lect. (Psychiat.) Univ. Nottm. Med. Sch.; Research Fell. (Psychiat.) Univ. Nottm.; Regist. (Psychiat.) Stobhill Gen. Hosp. Glas.

HOWAT, Mr John Michael Taylor Department of Surgery, North Manchester General Hospital, Delaunays Road, Manchester M8 5RB Tel: 0161 795 4967 Fax: 0161 770 2228 — MB ChB 1969 Manch.; MD Manch. 1980; FRCS Eng. 1974. Cons. Surg. N. Manch. Gen. Hosp.; Hon. Clin. Lect. Univ. Manch. Socs: Manch. Med. Soc. (Mem. Surg. Sect.); Assn. Surg.; Assn. Coloproctol. Prev: Lect. (Surg.) & Hon. Sen. Regist. Univ. Hosp. S. Manch.; Research Regist. (Immunol.) Paterson Laborats. Christie Hosp. Manch.; Regist. (Surg.) Univ. Hosp. S. Manch.

HOWAT, Mr John Morton (retired) 22 Hove Park Road, Hove BN3 6LJ Tel: 01273 555465 — MB ChB 1958 Glas.; MB ChB (Commend.) Glas. 1958; FRCS Ed. 1965. Prev: Cons. Paediat. Surg. Brighton Health Dist.

HOWAT, Margaret Elizabeth (retired) 33 Holly Avenue, Newcastle upon Tyne NE2 2PU Tel: 0191 281 3798 — MB BS 1940 Lond.; MRCP Lond. 1943; MRCS Eng. LRCP Lond. 1940; DCH Eng. 1942. Prev: Med. Adviser Newc. Social Servs. Adopt. & Fostering Unit; Clin. Asst.

HOWAT, Robert Cunningham Lindsay (retired) 1 Coxdale Avenue, Kirkintilloch, Glasgow G66 1AR Tel: 0141 776 6828 — MB ChB Glas. 1962; FRCOG 1982, M 1969, DObst. 1964. Prev: Cons. (O & G) Roy. Infirm. & Roy. Matern. Hosp. Glas.

HOWAT, Rosaline (retired) 3 Brookdale Rise, 1 Hilton Road, Bramhall, Stockport SK7 3AG — MB ChB 1937 Manch. Prev: Sen. Med. Off. Manch. AHA (T).

HOWAT, Thomas Park 46 Norwood Park, Bearsden, Glasgow G61 2RZ — MB ChB 1957 Glas.; DPH 1962.

HOWAT, Mr Thomas Wood 2 Campsie Drive, Milngavie, Glasgow G62 8HY Tel: 0141 956 1196 — LRCP LRCS 1938 Ed.; LRCP LRCS Ed. LRFPS Glas. 1938; FRFPS Glas. 1945; FRCS Glas. 1962. (Anderson & St. Mungo's Colls. Glas.) Hon. Maj. RAMC. Socs: Sen. Fell. Brit. Orthop. Assn. Prev: Cons. Orthop. Surg. W.. Infirm. Glas. & Gartnavel Gen. Hosp.; 1st Asst. Surg. Birm. Accid. Hosp.

HOWATSON, Mr Allan George Department of Pathology, Royal Hospital for Sick Children, Yorkhill NHS Trust, Glasgow G3 8SJ Tel: 0141 201 0400 Fax: 0141 201 0397 — MB ChB 1976 Ed.; BSc (Med. Sci.) (Path.) Ed. 1973; FRCS Ed. 1980; MRCPath 1989. (Edinburgh) Cons. Paediat. & Prenatal Path. Roy. Hosp. Sick Childr. Glas.

HOWATSON, Susan Rosalind Department of Pathology, Monklands Hospital, Monkscourt Avenue, Airdrie ML6 0JS Tel: 01236 712080 Fax: 01236 770117 Email: ros.howatson@laht.scot.nhs.uk — MB ChB 1972 Aberd.; BMedBiol Aberd. 1969; FRCPath 1990; Dip. Forens. Med. Glas 1990. Cons. Histopath. Monklands Dist. Gen. Hosp. Airdrie.

HOWCROFT, Mr Andrew John Primrose Cottage, Garstang Road, Barton, Preston PR3 5AD — MB BS 1970 Lond.; BSc (Hons.) Anat. Lond. 1967, MB BS 1970; FRCS Eng. 1975. Cons. Plastic Surg. Preston Health Dist.; Surg. Lt. Cdr. Mersey Div. RNR. Socs: BMA & Brit. Assn. Plastic Surgs. Prev: Sen. Regist. (Plastic Surg.) Mersey Regional Burns & Plastic Surg.; Unit Whiston Hosp. Prescot; Regist. (Surg.) United Cardiff Hosps.

HOWCROFT, Kevin Michael Erw Vane Surgery, Penybont Road, Knighton LD7 1HB Tel: 01547 528330 Fax: 01547 520570; Hebron, Ludlow Road, Knighton LD7 1HP Tel: 01547 528330 — MRCS Eng. LRCP Lond. 1974.

HOWCUTT, Mark Trevor 156 Harrogate Road, Bradford BD2 3RH — BM BCh 1997 Oxf.

HOWD, Alison 5 Park Avenue, Dunfermline KY12 7HX — MB BS 1979 Newc.; FRCS Eng. 1985; FRCS Ed. 1983.

HOWD, Ronald James 8 Lambton Court, High Rickleton, Washington NE38 9HE — MB BS 1951 Durh. (Durh.)

HOWDEN, Margaret Doris Trafford General Hospital, Moorside Road, Davyhulme, Manchester M41 5SL Tel: 0161 748 4022; 33 Stonepail Close, Gatley, Cheadle SK8 4HX — MB ChB 1972 Liverp.; FRCR 1983; DMRD Eng. 1977. Cons. Radiol. Trafford HA. Prev: Sen. Regist. (Diag. Radiol.) Manch. AHA (T); Regist. (Diag. Radiol.) Manch. AHA (T); SHO (Geriat.) Withington Hosp.

HOWDEN, Paul Elliott, Surg. Lt.-Cdr. RN Gibraltar Services Medical and Dental Centre, Queensway BFPO 52 Tel: 00 350 55775 Fax: 00 350 55773 — MB BS 1990 Lond.; DRCOG 1997; DFFP 1997. (Char. Cross & Westm. Med. Sch.) GP Regist. Gibraltar Servs. Med./Dent. Centre.

HOWDEN, Paula Garden Surgery, 78A Osmondthorpe Lane, Leeds LS9 9BL Tel: 0113 248 2291 Fax: 0113 240 5362 — MB ChB 1976 Leeds; DA Eng. 1978; DRCOG 1980.

HOWDEN, Peter St James Surgery, 89 Wash Lane, Clacton-on-Sea CO15 1DA Tel: 01255 222121 — MB BS 1983 Lond.; DRCOG 1986. (Roy. Free)

HOWDLE, Professor Peter David Academic Medical Unit, St James's University Hospital, Leeds LS9 7TF Tel: 0113 206 5256 Fax: 0113 242 9722 Email: p.d.howdle@leeds.ac.uk — MB ChB 1972 Leeds; BSc Leeds 1969, MD (Distinc.) Leeds 1985; FRCP Lond. 1992; MRCP (UK) 1975. (Leeds) Prof. Clin. Educat. & Hon. Cons. Phys. & Gastroenterol. St. Jas. Hosp. Leeds. Socs: Brit. Soc. Gastroenterol.; Brit. Soc. Immunol. Prev: Sen. Lect. (Med.) St. Jas. Hosp. Leeds; Sub-Dean for Admissions & Overseas Stud. Leeds Med. Sch.; Reesearch Fell. & Lect. (Med.) St. Jas. Hosp. Leeds.

HOWDLE, Sarah Hardwick 18 Robin Lane, Edgemond, Newport TF10 8JN — MB ChB 1993 Leeds; FRCR 2000 Lond. Specialist Regist. Radiol., N. Satffordshire.

HOWE, Alison Mary 40 Priory Court Road, Westbury-on-Trym, Bristol BS9 4DE — MB BS 1989 Newc.; MA Camb. 1990, BA 1986. (Newc. u. Tyne)

HOWE, Alison Rosemary Clarendon Medical, 35 Northland Avenue, Londonderry BT48 7JW Tel: 028 7126 5391 Fax: 028 7126 5932; 2 Dunnwood Park, Victoria Road, Londonderry BT47 2NN Tel: 01504 312305 — MB BCh BAO 1964 Dub.; MA Dub. 1992; DFFP 1993; DA RCPSI 1967. (Dub.)

HOWE, Amanda Caroline University of East Anglia, Norwich NR4 7TJ; 261 Upperthorpe, Sheffield S6 3NG — MB BS 1979 Lond.; MA Camb. 1980; MRCGP 1983; DCH RCP Lond. 1983; DRCOG 1982. Prof. of Primary Care Univ. of E. Anglia Med. Sch.; Lect. (Gen. Pract.) Sheff. Univ.

HOWE, Andrew David Dyfed Road Health Centre, Dyfed Road, Neath SA11 3AP Tel: 01639 635331; 24 Gilfach Road, Rhyddings, Neath SA10 8EH — MB BCh 1985 Wales; MRCGP 1989; DRCOG 1987.

HOWE, Andrew David 91 Clent Avenue, Lydiate, Liverpool L31 0AU — MB ChB 1987 Leeds; MPH 1999; DFFP 1996; MRCP (UK) 1991; MRCGP 1996; DTM & H Liverp. 1997. Specialist Regist. Pub. Health Med. E. Lancs. Health Auth.

HOWE, Anita Nora Carmel 13 Lloyd Close, Hampton Magna, Warwick CV35 8SH Tel: 01926 407392 Email: anita_morgan@btinternet.com — MB BCh 1991 Wales; MRCP (UK) 1996; DCH RCP Lond. 1996. (University of Wales College of Medicine) Specialist Regist. (Paediat.) Sandwell Hosp. Prev: SHO (Community Paediat.) S. Warks. Healthcare Trust; SHO (Paediat.) Univ. Hosp. Wales Cardiff.

HOWE, Anthony Harry Mitchell Road Surgery, 9 Mitchell Road, Canferd Heath, Poole BH17 8UE Tel: 01202 672474 Fax: 01202 660926; Greenbank, 59 King's Avenue, Parkstone, Poole BH14 9QH Tel: 01202 743206 — MB BS 1973 Newc.; DRCOG 1976. Bd. Mem. Poole Centr. & N.PCG; Chairm. PCG Comissioning Sub Comm. Socs: Bournemouth & Poole Med. Soc. Prev: Trainee GP Wessex VTS; Ho. Phys. & Ho. Surg. Roy. Vict. Infirm. Newc.

HOWE, Carolyn Jane Fairbrook Medical Centre, 4 Fairway Avenue, Borehamwood WD6 1PR Tel: 020 8953 7666; The Old Rectory, 118 Wood St, Barnet EN5 4DA — MB BS 1984 Lond.; MRCGP 1988. GP Borehamwood.

HOWE, David Charles Kingsmoor, The Common, Mulbarton, Norwich NR14 8AE — MB ChB 1989 Ed.

HOWE, Mr David Thomson Wessex Fetal Medicine Unit, Princess Anne Hospital, Coxford Road, Southampton SO16 5YA Tel: 02380 794228 Fax: 02380 796207 Email: dth@soton.ac.uk; 1 Horseshoe Drive, Romsey SO51 7TP — MB ChB 1983 Bristol; 2001 FRWG; DM Soton. 1995; FRCS Ed. 1987; MRCOG 1989. Cons. Feto-Matern. Med. P.ss Anne Hosp. Soton. Prev: Sen. Regist. (Fetal Med.) Birm. Matern. Hosp.; Sen. Regist. (O & G) & Clin. Research Fell. P.ss Anne Hosp. Soton.

HOWE, Elaine Garvie 35 Forest Road, Aberdeen AB15 4BY — MB ChB 1989 Aberd.; MRCGP 1993.

HOWE, Graham Brian, Lt.-Col. MHHU, Wegberg Complex BFPO 40 Tel: 00 49 2161 9082273 Fax: 00 49 2161 9082246 — MB BS 1983 Lond.; MRCPsych 1988. (Middlx.) Clin. Director of Psychiat. Brit. Forces Germany. Prev: Cons. Psychiat. DK Hosp. Catterick Garrison; Regtl. Med. Off. 3rd. Bn. Roy. Anglian Regt.; Regist. (Psychiat.) Bootham Pk. Hosp. York.

HOWE, Gregor William Bell Victoria Street Medical Group, 7 Victoria Street, Aberdeen AB10 1QW Tel: 01224 641930 Fax: 01224 644081; 37 Hosefield Avenue, Aberdeen AB15 5NN — MB ChB 1989 Aberd.; MRCGP 1993.

HOWE, Ian Shire Pharmaceuticals PLC, East Anton, Andover SP10 5RG Tel: 01264 348569 Fax: 01264 348488; 1 Overhill, Homefield Road, Warlingham CR6 9JR — MB BS 1987 Lond.; MA, PhD Camb. 1970. Med. Dir. Shire Pharmaceut. PLC Andover, Hants.

HOWE, James Gordon c/o Airedale General Hospital, Skipton Road, Steeton, Keighley BD20 6TD Tel: 01535 651101 Fax: 01535 655129 — MB BCh BAO 1970 Belf.; FRCP Lond. 1991; MRCP (UK) 1973. (Qu. Univ. Belf.) Cons. Neurol. Airedale NHS Trust; Hon. Sen. Lect. Leeds Univ. Socs: Assn. Brit. Neurol.; Brit. Geriat. Soc. Prev: Cons. Phys. (Med. for the Elderly & Neurol. Rehabil.) Airedale NHS Trust; 1st Asst. (Neurol.) Univ. Newc. u. Tyne; Tutor (Neurol.) St. Jas. Univ. Hosp. Leeds.

HOWE, John Barry 33 Dundee Road, Hartlepool TS25 5DZ; 6 Raeburn St, Hartlepool TS26 8PT Email: j.b.howe@doctors.org.uk — MB ChB 1998 Dund.; MB ChB Dund 1998.

HOWE, John Leigh Apeldoorn, Moor Row, Wigton CA7 0DL — MB BS 1997 Newc.

HOWE, John Philip Belfast City Hospital, Belfast BT9 7AB Tel: 01232 329241 — MB BCh BAO Belf. 1973; MD Belf. 1981; FFA RCSI 1977.

HOWE, Mr John William Foxsteads, Tranwell Woods, Morpeth NE61 6AG Tel: 01670 503080 Fax: 01670 503080 — MB BS 1966 Newc.; FRCS Eng. 1971; FRCS Ed. 1971; FRCOphth. 1989; DO Eng. 1970. (Newc.) Cons. Ophth. Surg. Roy. Vict. Infirm. Newc.; Sen. Lect. (Ophth.) Univ. Newc. Socs: Ophth. Soc. UK & Internat. Soc. Electrophysiol. of Vision. Prev: Tutor (Ophth.) Univ. Leeds.

HOWE, Joy Gwendolen 62 Westmisnster Way, Lower Earley, Reading RG6 4BX Tel: 0118 921 2290 — MB BS Lond. 1961; MRCS Eng. LRCP Lond. 1961; DCH Eng. 1968. (Roy. Free) Asst. Phys. to Burrswood Christian Hosp., Greenbridge, Kent; Asst. G.P. to the Brookside Gp. Pract., Lower Early, Reading. Socs: Christians in Caring Professions. Prev: Gen. Pract.

HOWE, Kathryn Elizabeth Macgregor 22 Claremont Road, Headingley, Leeds LS6 4EB Tel: 0113 278 1085 — MB ChB 1987 Bristol; MRCP 1991.

HOWE, Kenneth John 5 Keep Hill Drive, High Wycombe HP11 1DU — MB ChB 1981 Manch.

HOWE, Linda Jane 2 Carlyle Mansions, Cheyne Walk, London SW3 5LS — MB BS 1987 Lond.; FRCOphth. 1991. Research Assoc. & Hon. Clin. Research Fell. UMDS St. Thos. Hosp. Lond. Socs: Fell. Roy. Soc. Med.

HOWE, Miles Coverdale 7 Trafalgar Place, Palatine Road, Manchester M20 3TF — MB ChB 1993 Manch.

HOWE, Peter Douglas 188 Baghill Lane, Pontefract WF8 2HE Tel: 01977 793112 — MB ChB 1963 Liverp.; MRCS Eng. LRCP Lond. 1964; FRCOG 1982, M 1969, DObst 1965. Cons. (O & G) Pontefract Hosp. Socs: BMA; Fell. N. Eng. Obst. & Gyn. Soc. Prev: Regist. (O & G) Warrington Gen. Hosp.; Regist. (O & G) United Liverp. Hosps.; Lect. in Obst. Univ. Liverp. at Liverp. Matern. Hosp.

HOWE, Peter John Challoner Latham House Medical Practice, Sage Cross St., Melton Mowbray LE13 1NX Tel: 01664 60101; 4 Hamilton Drive, Melton Mowbray LE13 0QY Tel: 01664 564380 Email: dphowe@globalnet.co.uk — MB BS Lond. 1955; MRCS Eng. LRCP Lond. 1955; DObst RCOG 1961. (St. Mary's) Prev: SHO (Paediat.) & SHO (Cas.) Harold Wood Hosp.; SHO (O & G) St. John's Hosp. Chelmsford.

HOWE, Rebecca Jane 309 Unthank Road, Norwich NR4 7QA — MB BS 1998 Newc.; MB BS Newc 1998.

HOWE, Robert William Lostwithiel Medical Practice, North St., Lostwithiel PL22 0EF — BM 1987 Soton.; MRCGP 1993; DRACOG 1991; DM Southampton 1998. GP; NHS R&D Pract. Prev: research fell., Univ. of Bristol.

HOWE, Robin Anthony 40 Priory Court Road, Westbury-on-Trym, Bristol BS9 4DE — MB BS 1989 Newc.; MA Camb. 1990, BA 1986; DRCPath 1996. (Newc. u. Tyne) Regist. (Microbiol.) Bristol Roy. Infirm.

HOWE, Tania Victoria Thomas Long Acres, Thursley, Godalming GU8 6QP — MB BChir 1976 Camb.

HOWE, Theresa Mary University Hospital of Wales, Heath Park, Cardiff CF4 4XN; 40 Maitland Street, Cardiff CF14 3JU — MB BCh 1997 Wales. (Cardiff) SHO (Med.). Prev: PRHO (Surg.) Univ. Hosp. of Wales; PRHO (Med.) Univ. Hosp. of Wales.

HOWE, Wilfred (retired) — MB BS 1969 Newc.; MRCGP 1977; FFOM RCP Lond. 1989, M 1985, A 1980; MFOM RCP Lond. 1985, A 1980; T(OM) 1991; DIH Lond. 1980; DA Eng. 1972. Prev: Manager, Med. Servs. Dupont & Conoco.

HOWELL, Annabel Paton 21 George Street, Bedford MK40 3RY Email: annabel.morrison@virgin.net — MB BS 1991 Lond.; DA (UK) 1994. Clin. Asst. The Pasque Hospice Streatley Luton; GP Locum Dr Aylward & Partners Ampthill Beds. Socs: MRCAnaesth. Prev: GP Regist. Dumbarton HC; SHO (Paediat. & Neonat.) Roy. Hosp. Sick Childr. Yorkhill Glas.; SHO Rotat. (Paediat. & Neonat.) St. Mary's Hosp. Lond.

HOWELL, Anthea 38 Kingswood Avenue, London NW6 6LS — MB BS 1962 Lond.; MRCP Lond. 1967; MRCS Eng. LRCP Lond. 1962. (St. Bart.) Assoc. Specialist (Rheum.) Edgware Gen. Hosp. Hosp. Socs: Brit. Assn. Rheum. & BMA. Prev: Sen. Regist. (Rheum. & Phys. Med.) Middlx. Hosp. Lond.

HOWELL, Anthony 14A Linden Road, Didsbury, Manchester M20 2QJ; 64 Wayland Avenue, Brighton BN1 5JN — MB BS Lond. 1968; MSc Lond. 1974, BSc (Hons.) 1965; FRCP Lond. 1986; MRCP (UK) 1971. (Char. Cross) Prof. (Med. Oncol.) Christie Hosp. & Holt Radium Inst. Manch.; Vis. Prof. Univ. of Toronto Nov 1998. Socs: BMA; Brit. Assn. Cancer Research; Chairm. UKCCCR BrE. Cancer

SubComm. Prev: Sen. Lect. (Red. Oncol.) Univ. Manch.; Mem. Scientif. Staff & MRC Research Fell. Clin. Research Centre Harrow; Sen. Lect. (Clin. Oncol.) Univ. Birm.

HOWELL, Catherine Margaret 3 Paddock End, Harpenden AL5 1JY Tel: 015827 67643 — MB BS 1992 Lond.; BSc Lond. 1989, MB BS 1992. SHO (Med.) Gold Coast Hosp. Austral.

HOWELL, Charlotte Janey Ridgwardine Manor, Market Drayton TF9 3TR — MB BChir 1981 Camb.; FFA RCS Eng. 1985; DRCOG 1991. Cons. Anaesth. N. Staffs. Hosp. Trust Stoke on Trent; Rev. Edr. Cochrane Centre Collabration Pregn. & Childbirth Module. Prev: Sen. Regist. (Anaesth.) W. Midl.; Sen. Regist. Univ. Cape Town; Lect. Kanti Childr. Hosp. Kathmandu, Nepal.

HOWELL, Mr Christopher John (cons. rooms), 34 Regent St., Nottingham NG1 5BT Tel: 0115 956 1300 Fax: 0115 956 1314; 22 Esher Grove, Mapperley Park, Nottingham NG3 5DR Tel: 0115 960 5405 — MB BS Lond. 1965; FRCS Eng. 1970; MRCS Eng. LRCP Lond. 1964. (St. Mary's) Cons. Orthop. Surg. Notts. HA. Socs: Fell. Brit. Orthop. Assn. Prev: Orthop. Lect. Soton. Univ.; Sen. Regist. (Orthop.) Hants. AHA.

HOWELL, Clifford Weston 64 Dulwich Village, London SE21 7AJ — MB BS 1966 Lond.; MRCS Eng. LRCP Lond. 1965; FFA RCS Eng. 1969. (Guy's) Cons. (Anaesth.) King's Coll. Hosp. Lond. Prev: Ho. Off. Roy. Sussex Co. Hosp. Brighton; Med. Off. RN Hosp. Bighi, Malta; Fell. Anaesth. Baylor Coll. Med. Houston. USA.

HOWELL, David Anthony Brookside Cottage, off Rectory Lane, Breadsall, Derby DE21 5LL Tel: 01332 831634 — MB BS 1948 Lond.; FRCPC 1972; MRCP Lond. 1948; MRCS Eng. LRCP Lond. 1942. (St. Thos.) Emerit. Cons. Neuropath. Derbysh. Roy. Infirm. Prev: Cons. Neuropathol. Nottm. HA; Asst. (Neurol.) Montreal Gen. Hosp.; Regist. (Neurol.) Postgrad. Med. Sch. Lond.

HOWELL, David Christopher John 70A Oakfield Road, London N14 6LS — MB BS 1994 Lond.

HOWELL, David Douglas 7 Malcolm Road, Wimbledon, London SW19 4AS Tel: 020 8946 7178 — MB BCh 1940 Wales; BSc Wales 1940; FRCPsych 1983, M 1973; DPM Lond. 1948. (Cardiff) Socs: Profess. Mem. Soc. Analyt. Psychol. Prev: Cons. Child Psychiat. St. Geo. Hosp.; Regist. Maudsley Hosp.; Psychiat. i/c Child Guid. Clinic, Kingston-on-Thames.

HOWELL, Doris Irene (retired) 1 Forty Hill House, Forty Hill, Enfield EN2 9EU — MRCS Eng. LRCP Lond. 1933. Prev: Med. Off. & Anaesth. Bermondsey Miss. Hosp.

HOWELL, Dorothy Stammers Vine Cottage, Hinton Martell, Wimborne BH21 7HD — MB ChB 1950 Birm. Prev: Cas. & Orthop. Ho. Surg. Gen. Hosp. Birm.; O & G Ho. Surg. St. Chad's Hosp. Birm.; Med. Res. St. Louis Univ. Mo., U.S.A.

HOWELL, Elizabeth Susan Chesterfield & North Derbyshire, Royal NHS Trust, Dept. of Anaesthesia, Chesterfield S44 5BL Tel: 01246 277271 — MB BS 1974 Newc.; FFA RCS Eng. 1980; DA Eng. 1977. Cons. Anaesth. Anaes. Dept. Chesterfield & N. Derbysh. Roy. Hosp.

HOWELL, Mr Francis Robin Hull Royal Infirmary, Anlaby Road, Hull HU3 2JZ; 27 Crawshaw Avenue, Beverley HU17 7QW — MB BS 1981 Lond.; MA Oxf. 1985; MS Lond. 1992, MB BS 1981; FRCS Ed. 1986. Cons. Orthop. Surg. Roy. Hull Hosp. & E. Yorksh. Trusts. Prev: Sen. Regist. (Orthop. Surg.) Yorksh. VTS.

HOWELL, Francis Roland (retired) Flat 6, Heron Way, 11 Deganwy Road, Deganwy, Conwy LL31 9DH Tel: 01492 592605 — MB ChB 1951 Liverp.; DPH 1958; MFCM 1972. Prev: Community Phys. (Environm. Health N. & S. Sefton Health Auth.

HOWELL, Mr Graham Peter Royal United Hospital Bath NHS Trust, Bath BA1 3NG Tel: 01225 824573 Fax: 01225 824192 — MB BS 1977 Lond.; FRCS (Urol.) 1994; FRCS Ed. 1984; LMSSA Lond. 1977. (St. Bart.) Cons. Urol. Roy. United Hosp. Bath. Prev: Cons. Surg. Urol. RAF; Sen. Regist. (Urol.) S.mead Hosp. Bristol & Glas. Infirm.; Sen. Regist. (Surg.) P.ss Alex. Hosp. RAF Wroughton & P'boro. Dist. Gen. Hosp.

HOWELL, Jacqueline Mary The Surgery, Hillsgarth, Baltasound, Unst, Shetland ZE2 9DY Tel: 01957 711318 Fax: 01957 711479 — MB ChB 1983 Sheff.; MRCGP 1995.

HOWELL, Jill Hilary 8 Smithfield Avenue, Hipperholme, Halifax HX3 8HZ Tel: 01422 201888 — MB BS 1969 Lond.; MRCP (UK) 1973; MRCS Eng. LRCP Lond. 1969; DCH Eng. 1971. (St. Thos.) Clin. Asst. (Diabetes) Halifax Roy. Infirm.; Hosp. Phys. (Diabetes) Pontefract Roy. Infirm. Prev: Regist. (Med.) Crumpsall Hosp. Manch.; Ho. Phys. & Ho. Surg. Essex Co. Hosp. Colchester.

HOWELL, John Arthur (retired) Apperley, 57 Rotchell Park, Dumfries DG2 7RZ Tel: 01387 65951 — MB ChB 1942 Ed.; MFCM 1972; DPH Eng. 1968. Prev: Surg. Lieut. RNVR.

HOWELL, John Barrie Grosvenor Street Surgery, 4 Grosvenor Street, St Helier, Jersey JE1 4HB Tel: 01534 30541 Fax: 01534 887948; Underwood, Rue des Bouillons, Trinity, Jersey JE3 5BB Tel: 01534 861227 — MB BS 1976 Lond.; MRCS Eng. LRCP Lond. 1977; MRCGP 1981; DCH 1980; DRCOG 1979. (St. Bart.) Prev: Ho. Surg. Devonport Hosp. Plymouth; Ho. Phys. St. Richard's Hosp. Chichester.; GP Train. Scheme St.Richards Hosp. Chichester.

HOWELL, Professor John Bernard Lloyd, CBE The Coach House, Bassett Wood Drive, Southampton SO16 3PT Tel: 01703 768878 Fax: 01703 768878 Email: jblhowell@aol.com — MB BS 1950 Lond.; PhD Lond. 1956, BSc 1947; DSc (Hon.) Soton. 1994; FRCP Lond. 1966, M 1954; Hon. FACP 1982. (Middlx.) Socs: (Ex-Pres.) BMA (Chairm. Bd. Sci. & Educat.); Med. Res. Soc.; (Ex-Pres.) Brit. Thoracic Soc. Prev: Dean & Prof. Med. Univ. Soton.; Cons. Phys. Manch. Roy. Infirm.; Chairm. Soton. & SW Hants. HA.

HOWELL, John Fleming 196 Mansefield Road, Murton, Swansea SA3 3AP — MB BCh 1972 Wales.

HOWELL, John Kelsey Caen Health Centre, Braunton EX33 1LR Tel: 01271 812005 Fax: 01271 814768; West Lodge, Lower Pk Road, Braunton EX33 2CQ Tel: 01271 813248 — MB ChB 1955 Bristol; MRCGP 1966; DObst RCOG 1969; DCH Eng. 1967. Prev: Wing Cdr. RAF Med. Br.

HOWELL, John Stanley Vine Cottage, Hinton Martell, Wimborne BH21 7HD — MD 1957 Birm.; MD (Hons.) Birm. 1957, MB ChB 1950; MCPath 1963. Prev: Sen. Lect. (Path.) Univ. Birm.; Hon. Cons. Path. United Birm. Hosps.; Fell. (Path.) St. Louis Univ. Sch. Med. USA.

HOWELL, Jonathan Richard 3 The Old School, New St., Chagford, Newton Abbot TQ13 8BB — MB BS 1991 Lond.

HOWELL, Jonathan Vere Public Health Medicine, South Staffordshire Health Authority, Mellor House, Corporation St., Stafford ST16 3SR Tel: 01785 252233 Fax: 01785 221131 Email: jonathon.howell@ssha.wmids.nhs.uk; Tel: 01785 662129 — MB BS 1977 Lond.; BA Oxf. 1974. (King's Coll. Hosp.) Cons. Pub. Health Med. & Med. Adviser, Pub. Health Med. Directorate S. Staffs. HA Stafford. Prev: Sen. Regist. (Pub. Health Med.) W. Midl. RHA; Regist. (Pub. Health Med.) N. Staffs. HA; GP W.bury Wilts.

HOWELL, Judith Elizabeth 98 Cambridge Road, Great Shelford, Cambridge CB2 5JS — MB BS 1977 Lond.

HOWELL, Mr Julian David Smith Kline Beecham Pharmaceuticals, UK Medical Department, Mundells, Welwyn Garden City AL7 1EY — MB BS 1990 Lond.; FRCS Eng. 1994.

HOWELL, Lisa Marie Flat 1, 3 Cavendish CrescentS., Nottingham NG7 1EN — BM BS 1993 Nottm.

HOWELL, Marianne Springfields Surgery, Durrington Health Centre, Durrington Lane, Worthing BN13 2RX Tel: 01903 843810 Fax: 01903 243801 Email: marianne.howell@gp-h82643.nhs.uk — MB BS 1986 Lond.; BSc Lond. 1983. p/t GP Princip. Socs: BMA.

HOWELL, Mark Edmund St Marys Surgery, St. Marys Close, Timsbury, Bath BA2 0HX Tel: 01761 470880 Fax: 01761 472492; The Old Coach House, Paulton, Bristol BS39 7RT Tel: 01761 413677 Fax: 01761 413677 Email: mhowell@wind_chimes.demon.co.uk — MB ChB 1975 Bristol; MRCGP 1981; DA Eng. 1982. (Bristol) Prev: Regist. (Med.) Auckland Hosp. Bd. NZ; SHO (O & G) Taunton & Som. Hosp. (MusGr. Pk. Br.); SHO (Anaesth.) Taunton & Som. Hosp.

HOWELL, Mark Edward 6 Stevenson Crescent, Parkstone, Poole BH14 9NU — MB ChB 1996 Birm.; ChB Birm. 1996; BSc Biochem. Birm. 1993.

HOWELL, Martin Lloyd Benefits Agency Medical Services, Sutherland House, Brighton Road, Sutton SM2 5AN Tel: 020 8652 6000; 14 Kingsmead Walk, Seaford BN25 2EX Tel: 01323 491661 — MB ChB 1973 Bristol; MRCGP 1979; DRCOG 1977. Med. Adviser Benefits Agency Med. Servs. Prev: GP Telscombe Cliffs E Sussex; GP Lond.; Trainee GP High Wycombe VTS.

HOWELL, Mr Michael Alfred, Surg. Cdr. RN A&E dept, Queen Alexandria Hospital, Portsmouth PO6 3LY Tel: 023 92 286367 Fax: 023 92 286937 — MB BS 1986 Lond.; MA Camb. 1986; FRCS Eng. 1992; FFAEM 1998. (Westminster) Cons. A&E

Qu..Alex.Hosp.Portsmouth; Cons. Adviser in Accid. and Emerg. Med. to Med. Director Gen. (Naval). Socs: BMA; Brit. Assn. Emerg. Med.; Roy. Coll. Surg. Eng. Prev: Sen.Reg.A & E Bristol.Roy.Infirm; Regist. (A & E Med.) Derriford Hosp. Plymouth.

HOWELL, Michael Richard Tel: 01983 551239 Email: mrhiow@aol.com — MB BS 1965 Lond.; MRCS Eng. LRCP Lond. 1965; DObst RCOG 1967. (King's Coll. Hosp.) p/t Hosp. Practitioner (Dermat.) St Mary's Hosp. Newport, I. of Wight. Prev: Ho. Phys. Roy. I. of Wight Co. Hosp. Ryde; SHO (O & G) Roy. United & St. Martin's Hosps. Bath; Ho. Phys. & Ho. Surg. King's Coll. Hosp.

HOWELL, Michelle-Clare 6 Stevenson Crescent, Parkstone, Poole BH14 9NU — MB ChB 1995 Birm.; ChB Birm. 1995.

HOWELL, Nicholas Charles Blake School House Lane Surgery, School House Lane, Bishops Castle SY9 5BP Tel: 01588 632285 — MB BChir 1971 Camb.; MA, MB Camb. 1971, BChir 1970; MRCGP 1981; DObst RCOG 1973. Prev: Ho. Surg. & Ho. Phys. (Paediat.) Guy's Hosp. Lond.; Sen. Ho. Surg. (Obst.) Dorset Co. Hosp.

HOWELL, Nicola Jane 11 Broad Walk, Buxton SK17 6JR — BM BS 1992 Nottm.; BMedSci Nottm. 1990. Prev: SHO Derby Roy. Infirm. & City Hosp. Nottm.

HOWELL, Paul Richard St Bartholomew's Hospital, West Smithfield, London EC1A 7BE Tel: 020 7601 7518 Fax: 020 7601 7520; Email: paul.howell@dial.pipex.com — MB ChB 1981 Manch.; BSc (Med. Sci.) St. And. 1978; FFA RCS Eng. 1987. Cons. Anaesth. St. Bart. Hosp. Lond.; Cons. Anaesth. Homerton Hosp. Lond. Socs: Comm. Mem. Obst. Anaesth. Assn. Prev: Regist. (Anaesth.) Baragwanath Hosp. Soweto, SA; (Anaesth.) Red Cross Surg. Team ICRC Hosp. Pakistan 1987 & 1992; Clin. Research Fell. (Anaesth.) Grace Hosp. Vancouver, Canada.

HOWELL, Penelope Jane East House, 10 Woodbridge Road E., Ipswich IP4 5PA Tel: 01473 727309 Fax: 01473 721146 — MB ChB 1976 Manch.; FFA RCS Eng. 1981. Cons. Anaesth. The Ipswich Hosp. Socs: Obst. Anaesth. Assn.; Assn. Anaesth. Prev: Cons. Anaesth. Barnsley Dist. Gen. Hosp.; Sen. Regist. (Anaesth.) Trent RHA; Regist. (Anaesth.) Newc. AHA.

HOWELL, Peter James Village Surgery, 233 Village Street, Derby DE23 8DD Tel: 01332 766762 Fax: 01332 272084 — MB ChB 1972 Manch.; DMRT Eng. 1977.

HOWELL, Richard David The Surgery, Commercial St., Abertillery NP3 — MRCS Eng. LRCP Lond. 1945. (King's Coll. Hosp.) Prev: Jun. Res. Med. Off. St. Mary's Hosp. Portsmouth.

HOWELL, Richard John Stammers 73 Harley Street, London W1N 1DE Tel: 020 7935 5098 Fax: 020 7224 6853; 50 Globe Wharf, 205 Rotherhithe St, London SE16 5XS Tel: 020 723211019 Email: r.j.s.h@btinternet.com — MB BS 1976 Lond.; BSc Lond. 1973; FRCOG 1995, M 1982. Cons. O & G Homerton Hosp. NHS Trust Lond. Prev: Lect. & Sen. Regist. (Reproduc. Physiol. & O & G) St. Bart. Hosp. Lond.

HOWELL, Richard Stanley Charles Keppel Gate Cottage, Frankton, Rugby CV23 9PB — MB BS Lond. 1968; FFA RCS Eng. 1973; DObst RCOG 1970. (St. Mary's) Cons. Anaesth. Walsgrave Hosp. Coventry; Hon. Sen. Clin. Lect. Univ. Birm. Socs: Fell. Roy. Soc. Med.; Neuroanaesth. Soc. Prev: Regional Adviser Roy. Coll. Anaesth.; Sen. Regist. (Anaesth.) Addenbrooke's Hosp. Camb.

HOWELL, Robert Duncan 9 Lanes End, Fareham PO14 2BH Tel: 01329 663518 — MB BS 1992 Lond.; BSc Lond. 1987, MB BS 1992. SHO (Orthop.) Roy. Bournemouth Hosp.

HOWELL, Ross Anderson 325 Muirfield Drive, Glenrothes KY6 2PZ — MB ChB 1989 Dundee.

HOWELL, Sacha Jon Flat 1, 3 Cavendish CrescentS., Nottingham NG7 1EN — BM BS 1993 Nottm.

HOWELL, Shirin Elizabeth 22 Shirley Avenue, Cheam, Sutton SM2 7QR — BChir 1994 Camb.

HOWELL, Sian Rowena St Stephens Health Centre, Bow Community Hall, William Place, London E3 5ED — MB BS 1992 Lond.; MRCGP 1996; DFFP 1996; DRCOG 1996. (Univ. Coll. & Middlx. Sch. Med.) GP Lond.

HOWELL, Simon Douglas 35 Crofters Mead, Court Wood Lane, Croydon CR0 9HS — MB BS 1998 Lond.; MB BS Lond 1998.

HOWELL, Simon James 1 Chantry Close, Nailsea, Bristol BS48 4FN — MB BS 1984 Lond.; BA Camb. 1981; MRCP (UK) 1987; FCAnaesth 1991.

HOWELL, Simon John 26 Westbourne Grove, Withington, Manchester M20 1JA — MB ChB 1991 Manch.

HOWELL, Stephen Dept. of Path., Nevill Hall Hospital, Brecon Rd, Abergavenny NP7 7EG; Email: sshowell@hotmail.com — MB BCh 1976 Wales; BSc (Hons.) Wales 1973; BSc 1973 (Hons.) Wales; MRCPath 1982. Cons. Path. Nevill Hall Hosp., Abergavenny, Mon. Prev: Cons. Path. Neath Gen. Hosp. W. Glam.; Sen. Lect. Univ. Wales Coll. Med. Cardiff.; Cons. Path. Swansea NHS Trust.

HOWELL, Stephen Alexander Young and Partners, The Ryan Medical Centre, St. Marys Road, Bamber Bridge, Preston PR5 6JD Tel: 01772 335136 Fax: 01772 626701 — MB ChB 1991 Manch. Socs: MDU. Prev: Trainee GP Preston HA VTS.

HOWELL, Stephen John Lamb Department of Neurology, Royal Hallamshire Hospital, Sheffield S10 2JF Tel: 0114 271 2942 Fax: 0114 271 3684 — BM BCh 1982 Oxf.; MA Camb. 1983, BA 1979; DM Oxf. 1993; MRCP (UK) 1985, FRCP. Cons. Neurol. Roy. Hallamsh. Hosp. Sheff. & Doncaster Roy. Infirm. Prev: Sen. Regist. (Neurol.) Roy. Hallamsh. Hosp. Sheff.; Regist. (Neurol.) Radcliffe Infirm. Oxf.

HOWELL, Tanya Katherine 9 Mafeking Road, Cardiff CF23 5DQ — MB BCh 1990 Wales.

HOWELL, Timothy John 27 Chapel Lane, Wymondham NR18 0DJ — MB ChB 1995 Bristol.

HOWELL, Tudor Morgan (retired) Ynyswen, Trefeglwys, Caersws SY17 5PH Tel: 01686 430633 — MB BChir 1950 Camb.; DObst RCOG 1954. Prev: Cas., Anaesth. Off. & Ho. Phys. (Childr.) St. Thos. Hosp. Lond.

HOWELL, Walter Ronald (retired) 9 Marjoram Close, East Hungbury, Northampton NN4 0SH — LMSSA Lond. 1952; DPH Lond. 1964. Prev: Ho. Surg. (O & G) & Ho. Phys. Dorset Co. Hosp. Dorchester.

HOWELLS, Barbara Jane 124 Sharps Lane, Ruislip HA4 7JB — MB ChB 1988 Glas.; MRCGP 1994. GP Trainee Hillingdon VTS. Prev: SHO (Anaesth.) Glas.

HOWELLS, Barbara Kaja (retired) The Forge, Totteridge Green, London N20 8PB Tel: 020 8445 1968 Fax: 0208 445 2700 — MB BS Lond. 1956; MRCS Eng. LRCP Lond. 1956; DCH Eng. 1959. p/t Med. Assessor Indep. Tribunal Serv. Prev: GP Lond.

HOWELLS, Bruce Richard (retired) 2 Sovereign Close, Kingsend, Ruislip HA4 7EF Tel: 0189 56 36233 — MA Oxf. 1957; MB BS Lond. 1962; MRCS Eng. LRCP Lond. 1962; DObst RCOG 1964. Prev: Ho. Surg. & Jun. Cas. Off. W.m. Hosp.

HOWELLS, Clifford John Health Care Centre, HMP Winchester, Winchester Tel: 01962 854494 — MB BS 1983 Lond. (St. Marys) Sen. Med. Off. HMP Winchester.

HOWELLS, Cyril Haydn Lewis (retired) 6 St Edeyrns Road, Cyncoed, Cardiff CF23 6TB Tel: 01222 764766 — BSc Oxf. 1955; MD Wales 1956, BSc, MB BCh 1947; FRCPath 1969, M 1964; FIBiol. 1980. Prev: Dir. Regional Pub. Health Laborat. Univ. Hosp. of Wales. Cardiff.

HOWELLS, David 44 Nanfawr Road, Cyncoed, Cardiff CF23 6JR — MB BCh 1990 Wales; FRCA, 1999. Specialist Regist. Anaesth.

HOWELLS, David Bernard Mervyn (retired) The Malt House, Frogmore, Kingsbridge TQ7 2PG — MB BS 1963 Lond.; MRCS Eng. LRCP Lond. 1962. Prev: SHO ENT Dept. United Birm. Hosps. Temp. Lect. in Physiol. Univ. Birm. Med Sch.

HOWELLS, David Philip Martin Pilsbury House, 1 Hall Lane, Willington, Derby DE65 6BZ Tel: 01283 703306 Fax: 01283 701515 Email: howells@howells76.freeserve.co.uk; Pilsbury House, 1 Hall Lane, Willington, Derby DE65 6BZ Tel: 01283 703306 Fax: 01283 701515 Email: howells@howells76.freeserve.co.uk — MB BS 1960 Lond.; FRCP Lond. 1979, M 1964; MRCS Eng. LRCP Lond. 1960. (St. Mary's) Indep. Cons. Phys. Derby; Med. Mem. Pens. Appeals Tribunals and Appeals Serv.; Director of Med. Educat., Armed Forces Hosps. S.. Region, Khamis Mushayt, Kingdom of Saudi Arabia; Head of Professional Developm., Healthcare Directorate, HM Prison Serv. Socs: BMA. Prev: Cons. Phys. Burton-on-Trent Gp. Hosps.; Sen. Regist. (Med.) & Sen. Tutor Univ. Hosp. of Wales Cardiff; Mem. Scientif. Staff MRC Laborat., The Gambia.

HOWELLS, Desiraie Marjorye Gwenllian, SSStJ (retired) 6 The Paddock, Ely CB6 1TP Tel: 01353 669882 — MRCS Eng. LRCP Lond. 1950; DPH Lond. 1960. Prev: Sen. Med. Off. Torbay HA.

HOWELLS, Edward Lynn Tel: 023 92 835095; Meadowview, Woodmancote, Emsworth PO10 8RF — MB BS 1963 Lond.; MRCS Eng. LRCP Lond. 1963; MFPHM 1974; DPH Eng. 1970. (Westm.) Cons. Pub. Health Med. Portsmouth (Retd.). Prev: Med. Off.

Portsmouth Co. Boro.; Asst. Co. Med. Off. Hants. CC; Resid. Med. Off. Childr. Hosp. Sydenham.

HOWELLS, Eirwyn Byron 11 Geraints Way, Cowbridge CF71 7AY Tel: 01446 773823 — MB BCh 1990 Wales; DA (UK) 1995. Regist. (Anaesth.) Roy. Gwent Hosp. Newport. Socs: BMA; Med. Protec. Soc. Prev: SHO (Anaesth., Gen. Med. & Paediat.) P.ss of Wales Hosp. Bridgend; SHO (A & E Med.) Cardiff Roy. Infirm.; SHO (Elderly Care) Morriston Hosp. Swansea.

HOWELLS, Enid Margaret Blewett Tel: 01792 582139; 15 Marine Walk, Maritime Quarter, Swansea SA1 1YQ Tel: 01792 458399 — MB BS 1955 Lond.; FRCPsych 1992, M 1976; DPM Eng. 1976. (St. Mary's) Cons. Child & Adolesc. Psychiat. W. Glam. HA. Prev: Consultatn in Child & Adolesc. Psychiat. Swansea NHS Trust.

HOWELLS, Gwyn, RD (Surgery) 151 St Helens Road, Swansea SA1 4DE Tel: 01792 476476; 15 Marine Walk, Maritime Quarter, Swansea SA1 1YQ Tel: 01792 458399 Fax: 01792 301136 — MB BCh 1954 Wales; BSc Wales 1954, MB BCh 1954; FRCGP 1991, M 1967; DCCH RCP Ed. RCGP & FCM 1983; DCH Eng. 1965. (Cardiff) Vis. Research Fell. (Community Med.) Univ. Melbourne, Vict., Austral.; Hon. Clin. Teach. (Psychol. Med.) Univ. Wales Coll. Med. Cardiff. Socs: Fell. Roy. Soc. Med.

HOWELLS, Huw Vivian 147 College Road, Kensal Rise, London NW10 5HB — MB BS 1984 Lond. Cons. (Anaesth.) Milton Keynes Gen. Hosp., Milton Keynes. Prev: SHO LLa.lli Gen. Hosp.; Sen. Regist. (Anaesth.) John Radcliffe Hosp. Oxf.

HOWELLS, Jane (Halina) The Health Centre, 280 Oakleigh Road North, Whetstone, London N20 0DH Tel: 020 8368 6550; Email: michael.pendock@btinternet.com — MB BS 1981 Lond.; MRCGP 1985; DCH RCP Lond. 1984. Socs: BMA.; Assoc. Mem. Inst. Psychosexual Med.

HOWELLS, John 2/L, 2 Garrioch Drive, Glasgow G20 8RP — MB ChB 1992 Dundee; BMSc (Hons.) Dund 1989; MRCP (UK) 1995.

HOWELLS, John Gwilym (retired) Hill House, Higham St Mary, Colchester CO7 6LD Tel: 01206 337333 Fax: 01206 337333 — MB BS Lond. 1943; MD Lond. 1951; MRCS Eng. LRCP Lond. 1943; FRCPsych 1971; DPM Eng. 1947. Prev: Mem. Fac. Bd. Clin. Med. Univ. Camb.

HOWELLS, John Howard Bournville Surgery, Sycamore Road, Bournville, Birmingham B30 2AA Tel: 0121 472 7231; 6 Elmdon Road, Selly Park, Birmingham B29 7LF — MB ChB 1970 Birm. Clin. Asst. (Obst. Ultrasound) S. Birm. HA. Socs: BMA. Prev: SHO (O & G) Birm. Matern. Hosp. & Birm. & Midl. Hosp. Wom.

HOWELLS, Julian Bruce 2 Sovereign Close, Kingsend, Ruislip HA4 7EF Tel: 01295 636233 — MB BS 1991 Lond.; MRCGP 1996; DCH 1995. (Lond. Hosp. Med. Coll.)

HOWELLS, Katherine Lucy 11 Geraints Way, Cowbridge CF71 7AY — MB BCh 1991 Wales; MRCGP 1995; DRCOG 1994. Staff Grade (Community Paediat.) S. Glam. Socs: Med. Protec. Soc. Prev: Trainee GP Bridgend VTS.

HOWELLS, Keith Arthur 17 Pinewood Drive, Morpeth NE61 3RS — MB BS 1976 Newc.; FRCR 1982; DMRD 1980. Cons. Radiol. Ashington Hosp.

HOWELLS, Kenneth Edwin (retired) 49 Oak Drive, North Bradley, Trowbridge BA14 0SW Tel: 01225 766576 — MB BS Lond. 1955; MFCM 1972; DPH Wales 1962. Prev: Specialist (Community Med.) Wilts AHA.

HOWELLS, Lisa 52 Westfield Road, Bishop Auckland DL14 6AE — MB ChB 1991 Leeds.

HOWELLS, Margaret Ruth Department of Obstetrics & Gynaecology, Withybush Hospital, Haverfordwest SA61 2PZ Tel: 01437 764545; Garlandstone, Dale Road, Haverfordwest SA61 1HZ — MB BCh 1975 Wales; FRCOG 1993, M 1980. Cons. & Clin. Dir. O & G Withybush Hosp. HaverfordW. Dyfed.

HOWELLS, Marion Lesley Hazel Court, Nicholaston, Penmaen, Swansea SA3 2HL — MB ChB 1969 Ed.; DO Eng. 1972. Clin. Asst. (Ophth.) Singleton Hosp. Swansea. Prev: Clin. Asst. (Ophth.) Brist. & W.on HA; Ophth. Med. Pract. Avon, Gwent & W. Glam. HAs.

HOWELLS, Mark 124b Marine Parade, Brighton BN2 1DD — MB BS 1995 Lond.

HOWELLS, Rachel Janet 25 Priory Gardens, Usk NP15 1AJ — BChir 1992 Camb.

HOWELLS, Rhys Meirion 14 Llanbleddian Gardens, Cardiff CF24 4AT — MB ChB 1996 Ed.

HOWELLS, Mr Robert Edwin John City Hospital, Dudley Road, Birmingham B18 7Q Tel: 0121 554 3801; 76 Marsh Avenue, Longmeadow, Worcester WR4 0HJ — MB BCh 1988 Wales; FRCS Ed. 1994. Regist. (O & G) City Hosp. Birm. Prev: Regist. (O & G) Walsall Manor Hosp.; SHO & Acting Regist. (Obst.) Birm. Matern. Hosp.; SHO (Gen. Surg.) E. Glam. Gen. Hosp.

HOWELLS, Roger Bruce Maudsley Hospital, Denmark Hill, London SE5 8AZ Tel: 020 7703 6333 Fax: 020 7919 2353 Email: roger.howells@drhowells.co.uk — MB BChir 1981 Camb.; BSc (Hons.) Lond.1978; MRCPsych 1988. (Univ. Camb. Sch. Clin. Med.) Cons. Psychiat. Maudsley Hosp. Lond. Socs: Brit. Neuropsychiat. Assn. Prev: Research Fell. & Lect. Inst. Psychiat. Lond.; Sen. Regist. Maudsley Hosp. Lond.; SHO Nat. Hosp. for Nerv. Dis. Lond.

HOWELLS, Thomas Hilary (retired) The Forge, Totteridge Green, London N20 8PB Tel: 020 8445 1968 Fax: 020 8445 2700 Email: bahil@ukgateway.net — MB ChB 1952 Birm.; FFA RCS Eng. 1960; DA Eng. 1957. Prev: Dir. (Anaesth.) Roy. Free Hosp. Lond.

HOWES, Alan Charles (retired) Copplestone, Oxenton, Cheltenham GL52 9SE Tel: 01242 672759 — MB BS 1962 Lond.; DObst RCOG 1965. Prev: Ho. Surg. & Ho. Phys. Cheltenham Gen. Hosp.

HOWES, Andrea Jane 35 Shorwell Close, Great Sankey, Warrington WA5 3JY — MB ChB 1994 Liverp.; DFFP 1996. SHO (O & G) Liverp. Wom. Hosp. Prev: Ho. Off. Roy. Liverp. Univ. Hosp.

HOWES, Christopher Malcolm Grove House Surgery, West Shepton, Shepton Mallet BA4 5UH Tel: 01749 342314 Fax: 01749 344016; Ashley House, Croscombe, Wells BA5 3QH Tel: 01749 342684 Fax: 01749 342684 Email: chowes@cwcom.net — MB BChir 1975 Camb.; MA Camb. 1975; MRCGP 1996; DRCOG 1978; DA Eng. 1977. (Camb. & Univ. Coll. Hosp.) Cas. Off. Shepton Mallet Community Hosp.; Company Med. Off. ICI Polyurethanes, Shepton Mallet; Med. Off. Glastonbury Festival of Contemporary Performing Arts; Med. Co-ordinator Festival Med. Servs. Socs: MRCGP; BMA. Prev: SHO (Anaesth.) Torbay Hosp.; SHO (O & G) Roy. Devon & Exeter Hosp.; SHO (Paediat.) Poole Gen. Hosp.

HOWES, David Mark 17 Abbey Road, Harborne, Birmingham B17 0JT Tel: 0121 426 4995 Email: dmhowes@netcomuk.co.uk — MB ChB 1977 Bristol; FRCA 1985. Cons. Anaesth. S. Birm. HA.

HOWES, David Thomas Laburnum House, Bridge End, Carlton, Bedford — MB ChB 1969 Manch.; MRCPath 1977. Cons. (Haemat.) Bedford Gen. Hosp.

HOWES, Douglas Ernest Leonard The Bovey Tracey & Chudleigh Practice, Tower House Surgery, Market Way, Chudleigh, Newton Abbot TQ13 0HL Tel: 01626 852379 Fax: 01626 853056 Email: doug.howes@gp-183045.nhs.uk; Princes, Bickington, Newton Abbot TQ12 6JZ Tel: 01626 824622 — MB BS 1968 Lond.; MRCS Eng. LRCP Lond. 1968; MRCGP 1979; DCH Eng. 1975; DObst RCOG 1970. (Univ. Coll. Hosp.) Socs: BMA. Prev: Med. Off. Brit. Solomon Is.s Protectorate.

HOWES, Helen Kathryn Practice A, Hinckley Health Centre, 27 Hill Street, Hinckley LE10 1DS Tel: 01455 635362 Fax: 01455 619797 — MB ChB 1991 Leic.; MRCGP 1995; DRCOG 1995; DGM RCP Lond. 1993. (Leicester)

HOWES, Jacqueline Ann Buachaille, Fortrose IV10 8SN — MB ChB 1984 Leeds; FRCA 1992; DA (UK) 1988. Cons. Raigmore Hosp. Inverness. Prev: Cons. Cumbld. Infirm. Carlisle; Sen. Regist. Roy. Vict. Infirm. Newc. u. Tyne.

HOWES, Jeremy Paul 57 Grafton Road, Acton, London W3 6PD — BSc (Psychol.) Lond. 1983, MB BS 1985; MRCGP 1991; DCH RCP Lond. 1990. Prev: Trainee GP Ealing Hosp. VTS.

HOWES, Marten Campbell — MB ChB 1993 Glas.; MRCP (UK) 1997. (Glasgow Univ.) Specialist Regist. (A&E) Roy. Preston Hosp. Preston. Socs: Conscious Sedation Soc. (Inaugural Mem.). Prev: SHO (Gen. Med.) Roy. Alexandra Hosp. Paisley; SHO (Gen. Med., Geriat. & A & E) Roy. Alexander Hosp. Paisley; Regist., A&E, Roy. Infirm., Edin.

HOWES, Nathan Robert 21 Peacock Avenue, Feltham TW14 8ET — MB ChB 1993 Liverp.

HOWES, Oliver David 45 New Road, Digswell, Welwyn AL6 0AQ — BM BCh 1997 Oxf.

HOWES, Paul Trevor Pendyffryn Medical Group, Ffordd Pendyffryn, Prestatyn LL19 9DH Tel: 01745 886444 Fax: 01745 889831; Hebron, 10 Clos Aberconwy, Prestatyn LL19 9HU — MB BCh 1969 Wales.

HOWES, Peter John Walter The Old Vicarage, Waresley, Sandy SG19 3DA — MB BS 1957 Lond.; BA (Hons.) Open Univ. 1997; MRCS Eng. LRCP Lond. 1957; DA Eng. 1964. (Westm.) Prev: Mem. Med. Bds. DHSS; Specialist (Anaesth.) Beds. AHA Community Dent. Serv.; Anaesth. Bedford Gen. Hosp. & RAF Hosp. Akrotiri, Cyprus.

HOWES, Timothy Quentin Department of Thoracic Medicine, Colchester General Hospital, Turner Road, Colchester CO4 5JL Tel: 01206 742179 Fax: 01206 742796 Email: angela.humphreys@erhc-tr.nthames.nhs.uk; Keepers, Newhouse Road, Earls Colne, Colchester CO6 2PE Email: tqhowes@talk21.com — MB BS 1984 Lond.; MA Camb. 1984; MRCPI 1988; MD London 1998. Cons. Respirat. & HIV Med. Colchester Gen. Hosp.; Hon. Sen. Lect. & Hon. Cons. Chest Phys. Lond. Chest Hosp. Socs: Brit. & Amer. Thoracic Socs.; Eur. Respirat. Soc. Prev: Sen. Regist. (Respirat. Med.) Roy. Brompton Hosp. & Nat. Heart & Lung Inst.; Lect. (Thoracic Med.) & Regist. (Chest Med.) Kings Coll. Hosp. Lond.

HOWES, Timothy Robert James French Weir Health Centre, French Weir Avenue, Taunton TA1 1NW Tel: 01823 331381 Fax: 01823 323689 — MB BS 1990 Lond.; MRCGP 1996; DRCOG 1996. (St. Bart. Hosp. Lond.) Princip. GP.

HOWGRAVE-GRAHAM, Antony John Howgrave-Graham and Partners, The Surgery, Moot Lane, Downton, Salisbury SP5 3QD Tel: 01725 510296 Fax: 01725 513119; The Cottage, Barford Lane, Downton, Salisbury SP5 3QA — MB BS 1967 Lond.

HOWGRAVE-GRAHAM, Tanya Ruth 33 Market Place, Melksham SN12 6ES — MB BS 1993 Lond.

HOWIE, Agnes Fulton Watt (retired) Craigellachie, Kirkhill, Inverness IV5 7PE Tel: 01463 831448 — MB ChB 1947 Glas. Prev: Gen. Practitioner.

HOWIE, Alastair Duncan Ardroy, 24 Keir St., Bridge of Allan, Stirling FK9 4AY — MB ChB 1971 Ed.; BSc (Hons.) Ed. 1968; FRCP Glas. 1992; FRCP Ed. 1985; MRCP (UK) 1974; DObst RCOG 1973. Cons. Phys. Roy. Infirm. Stirling. Socs: Scott. Thoracic Soc. & Brit. Thoracic Soc. Prev: Sen. Regist. (Gen. & Respirat. Med.) & Regist. Centre for Respirat.; Investig. Glas. Roy. Infirm.; Med. Regist. Dumfries & Galloway Roy. Infirm.

HOWIE, Alexander James Department of Pathology, The Medical School, Birmingham B15 2TT Tel: 0121 414 4001 — MD 1985 Birm.; MB ChB 1975; FRCPath. 1993. Sen. Lect. Path. Univ. Birm.

HOWIE, Anne Jardine 8 Travebank Gardens, Monifieth, Dundee DD5 4ET — MB ChB 1963 Glas. (Glas.)

HOWIE, Mr Colin Robert Princess Margaret Rose Hospital, Edinburgh EH10 7ED Tel: 0131 536 4661 Fax: 0131 536 4711 Email: colin.howie@ed.ac.uk; The Coach House, Glenbrook Road, Balerno EH14 7BE Tel: 0131 449 7864 — MB ChB 1977 Ed.; BSc (Med. Sci.) Ed. 1974; FRCS Glas. 1993; FRCS Ed. (Orth.) 1988; FRCS Ed. 1982. (Edinburgh) Cons. Orthop. Surg. P.ss Margt. Rose Hosp. Edin.; Hon. Sen. Lect. Univ. Edin. Socs: Europ. Rheumatoid Arthritis Surgic. Soc; Brit. Hip Soc; Brit. Knee Soc. Prev: Cons. Orthop. Raigmore Hosp. Inverness; Sen. Regist. (Orthop.) P.ss Eliz. Orthop. Hosp. Exeter; Demonst. (Anat.) Univ. Edin.

HOWIE, Constance Catherine Mary (retired) 9A Barnton Park, Edinburgh EH4 6JF Tel: 0131 312 8469 — MB ChB 1952 Ed.; FFA RCS Eng. 1964; DA Eng. 1957. Prev: Cons. Anaesth. St. John's Hosp. Livingston.

HOWIE, Eleanor Margaret 40 Wellhall Road, Hamilton ML3 9BN — MB ChB 1953 Glas. (Glas.) Assoc. Specialist (Cytopath.) Monklands Dist. Gen. Hosp. Airdrie.

HOWIE, Elizabeth Anne (retired) 2 Albany Terrace, Rothesay PA20 9LD Tel: 01700 502898 — MB ChB 1955 Glas. Prev: Ho. Phys. (Paediat.) Geo. Eliot Hosp. Nuneaton.

HOWIE, Ellen Baird 54 Whittinghame Drive, Glasgow G12 0YQ Tel: 0141 334 7991 — MB ChB 1969 Glas.; FFA RCS Eng. 1973. (Glas.) Cons. Anaesth. W.. Infirm. Glas. Socs: BMA & W. Scotl. Soc. Anaesth. Prev: Cons. Vict. Infirm. Unit Glas.; Sen. Regist. (Anaesth.) Stobhill Hosp. Glas.; Regist. (Anaesth.) W.. Infirm. Glas.

HOWIE, Fiona Mary Crawford Hairmyres and Stonehouse NHS Trust, Hairmyres Hospital, East Kilbride, Glasgow G75 8RG Tel: 014120292; Hazelden Mains Farm, Hazelden Rd, Mearnskirk, Glasgow G77 6RR Tel: 01416391522 — MB ChB 1980 Glas.; FRCR 1987. (Glas.) Cons. Radiol. Hairmyres Hosp. E. Kilbride. Socs: BMA; Roy. Coll. Radiol. (BrE. Gp.); Scott. Radiological Soc. Prev: Cons. Radiol. Vict. Infirm. Glas.

HOWIE, Francis James Thomas Shankill Surgery, 21 Fairlight Road, Hastings TN35 5ED Tel: 01424 421046 Fax: 01424 425177; 8 Laton Road, Hastings TN34 2ET Tel: 01424 426685 Email: frank.howie@btinternet.co — MB BCh BAO 1978 Belf.; MICGP 1987. (Qu. Univ. Belf.) Prev: GP Lond.derry N. Irel.

HOWIE, George Francis Andrew (retired) 21 Station Crescent, Invergowrie, Dundee DD2 5DT Tel: 01382 562543 — MB ChB 1950 Ed.; MD Ed. 1968; FRCP Ed. 1969, M 1954; FRCR 1974, FFR 1959; DMRD Ed. 1956. Cons. Radiol. Dundee Teach. Hosps. Prev: Sen. Regist. (Diag. X-Ray) W.m. Hosp. Lond.

HOWIE, Gillian Margaret 9 Brunton Place, Edinburgh EH7 5EG Tel: 0131 557 5545; Torwood, Mayfield Terrace, Newington, Edinburgh EH9 1RH Tel: 0131 668 1123 — MB ChB 1983 Glas.; MRCGP 1987; DRCOG 1986. Prev: Trainee GP Stirling VTS; SHO (O & G) Stirling Roy. Infirm.; Ho. Off. (Med.) Gartnavel Gen. Hosp. Glas.

HOWIE, Graham MacDonald North Lodge, Duncow, Dumfries DG1 1TA — MB ChB 1980 Aberd.; LMCC 1990; MRCGP 1984; DRCOG 1989; DA (UK) 1987; Dip. Med. Acupunc. GP Locum BC, Canada; Cert. Progr. in Med. Acupunc. Univ. Alberta, Canada 1994. Socs: MRCAnaesth.; Brit. Med. Acupunct. Soc.; BMA. Prev: Dent. Anaesth.Peffermill Dent. Anaesth. Clinic Edin.; GP & Anaesth. Quesnel Brit. Columbia, Canada.

HOWIE, Helen Cynthia Grampian Health Board, Summerfield House, 2 Eday Road, Aberdeen AB15 6RE — MB BCh 1978 Wales; MRCGP 1983; T(GP) 1991; MRPHM 2000; MFPHM 2000; MSc 1996. p/t Cons. (Pub. Health Med.) Grampian HB.

HOWIE, Jane Helen Meopham Medical Centre, Wrotham Road, Meopham, Gravesend DA13 0AH Tel: 01474 814811/814068 Fax: 01474 814699 — BM 1980 Soton.; MRCGP 1985; DRCOG 1983; DO Eng. 1982.

HOWIE, Professor John Garvie Robertson, CBE McKenzie Medical Centre, 20 West Richmond Street, Edinburgh EH8 9DX Tel: 0131 667 2955; 4 Ravelrig Park, Balerno, Edinburgh EH14 7DL Tel: 0131 449 6305 Email: John.Howie2@btopenworld.com — MB ChB Glas. 1961; PhD Aberd. 1974; MD Glas. 1967; FRCP Ed. 1989, M 1985; FRCGP 1981; MRCGP 1974; F Med.Sci 1998. (Glasg.) Prof. Gen. Pract. Univ. Edin. Prev: Sen. Lect. (Gen. Pract.) Univ. Aberd.

HOWIE, Karen Lesley North Oxford Medical Centre, 96 Woodstock Road, Oxford OX2 7NE Tel: 01865 311005 Fax: 01865 311257 — BM BCh 1985 Oxf.; MA Camb. 1986; MRCGP 1989; DCH RCP Lond. 1989; DGM RCP Lond. 1988; DRCOG 1987. (Oxford) GP Princip.

HOWIE, Maureen Beryl Altnagelvin Hospital, Londonderry BT47 6 Tel: 01504 45171; 50 Carmoney Road, Coolafinney, Eglinton, Londonderry BT47 3PH Tel: 01504 810488 — MB BCh BAO 1968 Belf.; MFFP 1993; DA Eng. 1972. Assoc. Specialist (Anaesth.) Altnagelvin Hosp. Lond.derry; Sen. Clin. Med. Off. & Instruc. Doctor (Family Plann.) Limavady. Socs: Fac. Anaesth.; Brit. Soc. Experim. & Clin. Hypn.

HOWIE, Peter Galloway Health Centre, Stewarton, Kilmarnock KA3 5BP Tel: 01560 482011 Fax: 01560 485483; The Steading, High Peacock Bank, Stewarton, Kilmarnock KA3 5JG Tel: 01560 482145 — MB ChB St. And. 1964; DObst RCOG 1970. (St. And.) Socs: BMA. Prev: Capt. RAMC.

HOWIE, Peter Kelvin Larne Health Centre, Gloucester Avenue, Larne BT40 1PB Tel: 028 2826 1919 Fax: 028 2827 2561; 97 Glenarm Road, Larne BT40 1DY Tel: 01574 270808 — MB BCh BAO 1980 Belf.; MRCGP 1984; DFFP 1993; DRCOG 1982.

HOWIE, Professor Peter William Department of Obstetrics & Gynaecology, Ninewells Hospital & Medical School, University of Dunee, Dundee DD1 9SY Tel: 01382 632147 Fax: 01382 633847 Email: b.c.charnley@dundee.ac.uk; 8 Travebank Gardens, Monifieth, Dundee DD5 4ET Tel: 01382 534802 — MB ChB 1963 Glas.; FRSE 1991; MD Glas. 1974; FRCP Glas. 1994; FRCOG 1981, M 1968. Prof. O & G Dundee; Dep. Princip. Univ. Dundee; Chairm. Scott. Counc. Postgrad. Med. & Dent. Educat. Socs: BMA; Ed. Obst. Soc. Prev: Dean Fac. Med. & Dent. Univ. Dundee.

HOWIE, Ronald McNab 40 Wellhall Road, Hamilton ML3 9BN — MB ChB 1953 Glas. (Univ. Glas.) Local Civil Serv. Med. Off.; Mem. Med. Bd.ing Panel DHSS. Prev: Ho. Phys. & Ho. Surg. Vict. Infirm. Glas.; Capt. RAMC.

HOWIE, Stephen Murray 2 Macdonald Road, London E17 4AZ — MB ChB 1978 Glas.

HOWIE, Susan Patricia 10-14 Frazer Street, Largs KA30 9HP; 12 Glen Road, Fairlie, Largs KA29 0DJ — MB ChB 1979 Glas.

HOWIE, Theresa (retired) Dunvorist, Brae St., Dunkeld PH8 0BA — MB ChB 1951 Glas. Prev: Med. Off. (Geriat.) Morningfield Hosp. Aberd.

HOWIE, Thomas James Gordon (retired) 2 Albany Terrace, Rothesay PA20 9LD Tel: 01700 502898 — MB ChB Glas. 1950; MFPHM 1989; MFCM 1972; MRCGP 1966; DPH Glas. 1956; DTM & H Liverp. 1956; DObst RCOG 1956. Prev: Med. Off. of Health, Co. of Bute.

HOWIS, Alexander Penton House, Queen Anne St., Shelton, Stoke-on-Trent ST4 2EQ Tel: 01782 48642 Fax: 01782 747617; Barri, Winghouse Lane, Tittensor, Stoke-on-Trent ST12 9HW Tel: 01782 372846 — MB ChB 1962 Liverp.; DTM & H Eng. 1967. (Lond.) Socs: BMA & N. Staffs. Med. Inst. Prev: Ho. Off. Liverp. Roy. Infirm. & BRd.green Hosp. Liverp.

HOWITT, Alistair John Warders Medical Centre, 47 East Street, Tonbridge TN9 1LA Tel: 01732 770088 Fax: 01732 770033 — MB ChB 1978 Birm.; MRCP (UK) 1982; MRCGP 1983; DFFP 1996; Msc 1998. (Birmingham) Mem. Panel Examrs. RCGP. Socs: Ex-Chairm. Kent MAAG. Prev: Clin. Asst. Diabetic Clinic Kent & Sussex Hosp. Tunbridge Wells.

HOWITT, Gertrude Blima 6 High Sheldon, Sheldon Avenue, Highgate, London N6 4NJ Tel: 020 8348 7754 — MB ChB Manch. 1963; MRCP (UK) 1970. Prev: Sen. Geriat. Shaare Zedek Med. Centre Jerusalem, Israel; Hon. Cons. Phys. (Geriat. Med.) & Sen. Lect. Roy. Postgrad. Med. Sch. Hammersmith Hosp. Lond.; Cons. Phys. (Med. for Elderly) Ealing Hosp. Lond.

HOWITT, John Stafford, AFC, Group Capt. RAF Med. Br. Retd. Nags Head Cottage, Littlewick Grove, Maidenhead SL6 3RF — MRCS Eng. LRCP Lond. 1939.

HOWITT, Josephine Burnell 20 Streatham Common S., London SW16 3BU Tel: 020 8679 1039 Fax: 020 8679 1073 — MB BS Lond. 1966; MRCS Eng. LRCP Lond. 1966; DMJ (Clin.) Soc. Apoth. Lond. 1992. (Roy. Free) Princip. Forens. Med. Examr. Metrop. Police; Hon. Lect. (Clin. Forens. Mewd.) Monash & Melbourne Univs. in Clin. Forens. Med. 1993-94. Socs: Fell. Roy. Soc. Med.; Assn. Police Surg. (Vice-Chairm. Exec. Metrop. & City Gp.).; Founding Mem. Expert Witness Inst. Prev: Ho. Surg. Roy. Free Hosp. Lond.; Intern Sydney Hosp., Austral.; GP Streatham.

HOWITT, Lewis Finnigan (retired) 27 Cluny Drive, Edinburgh EH10 6DT Tel: 0131 447 5849 — MB ChB 1951 Aberd.; FRCP Glas. 1985, M 1983; FFCM 1983, M 1972; DPH 1955. Prev: Cons. Pub. Health Med. Lothian HB.

HOWITT, Marion Jill Village Medical Centre, 400-404 Linthorpe Road, Middlesbrough TS5 6HF Tel: 01642 851234 Fax: 01642 820821; 120 Rockliffe Road, Linthorpe, Middlesbrough TS5 5DG Tel: 01642 876998 — MB BCh BAO 1971 Belf.; DObst RCOG 1973. (Qu. Univ. Belf.) Prev: Trainee GP Cleveland VTS; SHO (Gen. Med.) N. Tees Gen. Hosp. Stockton-on-Tees; SHO (Paediat.) Newc. Gen. Hosp.

HOWITT, Rachel Jane Department of Pathology, Royal Liverpool University Hospital, Daulby St., Liverpool L69 3GA; 86 Phillips Lane, Formby, Liverpool L37 4BQ — MB ChB 1991 Dundee; BMSc (Hons.) 1988; Dip RCPath 1996. Specialist Regist. (Histopath.) Roy. Liverp. Univ. Hosp. Prev: SHO (Path.) Ninewells Hosp. Dundee.

HOWITT, William Peter Fowler Pembroke House Surgery, 1 Fortescue Road, Paignton TQ3 2DA Tel: 01803 553558 Fax: 01803 663180 — MB ChB 1982 Birm.; DCH RCPS Glas. 1986. GP Devon; Hosp. Practitioner (Ophth.) S. Devon HA.

HOWITT WILSON, Michael Bernard Woking Nuffield Hospital, Shores Road, Woking GU21 4BY Tel: 01483227800 Fax: 01483 227830; Bull Lane Cottage, Sutton Park, Sutton Green, Guildford GU4 7QW Tel: 01483 453661 — MB BS Lond. 1962; MRCS Eng. LRCP Lond. 1962; DObst RCOG 1964; Dip. Chiropract. Anglo-Europ. Coll. Chirop 1975. (Westm.) Indep. Special. Muscoskeletal Med. Chiropractic; Chairm. World Federat. Doctors who Respect Human Life (Brit. Sect.). Socs: Brit. Inst. Musculoskeletal Med.; Fell. Roy. Soc. Med.; Guild Catholic Doctors. Prev: GP Woking; Ho. Surg. (O & G) FarnBoro. Hosp. Kent; Ho. Surg. Hosp. SS John & Eliz. Lond.

HOWKINS, Mr John (retired) Caen Hen, Abercegir, Machynlleth SY20 8NR — MB BS 1933 Lond.; MD (Gold Medal) Lond. 1937; MS 1936; FRCS Eng. 1936; MRCS Eng. LRCP Lond. 1932; FRCOG 1948. Hon. Cons. Gyn. Hampstead Gen. & St. Bart. Hosp. Lond. Prev: Gyn. Surg. Roy. Masonic Hosp.

HOWL, Elizabeth Mary Caroline (retired) 8 Broxwood Park, Tettenhall Wood, Wolverhampton WV6 8LZ Tel: 01902 746470 — BM BCh Oxon. 1947; DCH Eng. 1951; DObst RCOG 1955. Prev: Ho. Phys. (Paediat.) Ch.ill Hosp. Oxf.

HOWL, Matthew October House, 5 Drayton La, Fenny Drayton, Nuneaton CV13 6AY — MB ChB 1997 Leic.

HOWLAND, Christopher Emlyn Lighfoot Hall, Manresa Road, Chelsea, London SW3 6LX — MB BS 1996 Lond.

HOWLAND, Elizabeth Jane Lightfoot Hall, Manresa Road, London SW3 6LX — MB BS 1998 Lond.; MB BS Lond 1998.

HOWLAND, Nicola Jane Park Street Surgery, 6 Park Street, Falkirk FK1 1RE Tel: 01324 623577 Fax: 01324 633636; 17 Craighorn Drive, Falkirk FK1 5NS — MB ChB 1989 Aberd.; DRCOG 1992; DCH RCPS Glas. 1991.

HOWLETT, Alan John 26 Taw Meadow Crescent, Fremington, Barnstaple EX31 2QA — MB ChB 1987 Bristol; MRCGP 1992.

HOWLETT, Christopher Ross Tilehurst Surgery, Tylers Place, Pottery Road, Tilehurst, Reading RG30 6BW Tel: 0118 942 7528 Fax: 0118 945 2405 — MB BS 1972 Lond.; Dip Dermat 1993; MRCGP 1978.

HOWLETT, David Crispin 30 Woodcote Park Road, Epsom KT18 7EX Tel: 01372 727651 — MB BS 1988 Lond.; MRCP (UK) 1991; FRCR 1995. (King's Coll. Hosp. Sch. Med. Lond.) Specialist Regist. (Radiol.) Guy's & St. Thos. NHS Trust Lond. Socs: Roy. Coll. Radiol.; BMA. Prev: Regist. (Radiol.) St. Thos. Hosp. Lond.; SHO (Gen. Med.) Brook Hosp.; SHO (Cardiol.) King's Coll. Hosp.

HOWLETT, Diana Mary Child Health Department, Bath and West Community NHS Trust, Newbridge Hill, Bath BA1 3QE — MB BS 1992 Lond.; BSc 1989; MRCP (UK) 1996. (St. Bart.) Specialist Regist. (Paediat.). Socs: MRCPCH.

HOWLETT, Kenneth Arthur, TD (retired) 30 Woodcote Park Road, Epsom KT18 7EX Tel: 01372 727651 — MB BS 1959 Lond.; MRCS Eng. LRCP Lond. 1959; FRCR 1975; FFR 1969; DMRD 1965; DCH Eng. 1962. Lt.-Col. RAMC (TA). Prev: Cons. Radiol. Char. Cross Hosp. Gp.

HOWLETT, Nicholas David 22B Priory Crescent, Milton, Southsea PO4 8RL Tel: 01705 734576 — MB ChB 1991 Sheff.; DCH Lond. 1994; DRCOG 1995; DFFP 1996. Out of Hours Gen. Pratitioner Hobalt, Tasmania. Socs: Roy. Coll. Gen. Pract. Prev: Expedition Doctor Operat. Raleigh, Chile 1997; SHO (Dermat.) Qu. Vict. Hosp. Morecombe 1996; SHO (Rhaumatology) Roy. Lancaster Infirm. 1995.

HOWLETT, Robert William The Surgery, Margaret Street, Thaxted, Dunmow CM6 2QN Tel: 01371 830213 Fax: 01371 831278; Gobions, Dunmow Road, Great Bardfield, Braintree CM7 4SA Tel: 01371 831278 — MB 1984 Camb.; MA Camb. 1985, MB 1984, BChir 1983; MRCGP 1987; Cert. Family Plann. JCC 1987; DRCOG 1987.

HOWLETT, Rosemarie Ann Child Health Bureau, PO Box 115, Chichester PO19 4YT Tel: 01243 815400; Clovelly, Newells Lane, West Ashing, Chichester PO18 8DF Tel: 01243 575659 — MB BS 1976 Lond.; MRCS Eng. LRCP Lond. 1976; DCCH RCP Ed. 1992.

HOWLETT, Ruth Mary Medical Centre, Barker Barracks BFPO 22; 2 Southgreen Hill, Mansfield NG18 4PU — MB BS 1989 Lond.; MRCGP 1994; DRCOG 1992. Civil. Med. Pract. MoD Germany.

HOWLETT, Sean Frederick Joseph Glebelands Avenue Surgery, 2 Glebelands Avenue, South Woodford, London E18 2AD Tel: 020 8989 6272 Fax: 020 8518 8783; 66 Queen's Road, Loughton IG10 1RS Tel: 020 8508 2444 — MB BS 1978 Lond.; MRCS Eng. LRCP Lond. 1978; MRCGP 1983; DRCOG 1982. (St. Bart) GP Woodford; GP Mem. Acute Servs. Unit Waltham Forest HA. Socs: BMA & Redbridge Local Med. Comm. Prev: SHO Rotat. (GP Trainee) Whips Cross Hosp.; SHO (O & G) Whipps Cross Hosp.; SHO (Radiother. & Gen. Med.) OldCh. Hosp.

HOWLETT, Trevor Anthony Leicester Royal Infirmary, Leicester LE1 5WW Tel: 0116 254 1414 — MB BChir 1977 Camb.; BA Camb. 1974, MD 1988, MA 1978; FRCP Lond. 1992; MRCP (UK) 1979. (Camb. & King's Coll. Hosp.) Cons. Phys. & Endocrinol. Leic. Roy. Infirm. Socs: Soc. Endocrinol. Prev: Lect. (Endocrinol.) St. Bart. Hosp. Lond.; Regist. (Med.) Frimley Pk. Hosp.; SHO (Med.) Centr. Middlx. Hosp. Lond.

HOWLETT, William Patrick c/o Centre for International Health, Armauer Hansen Building Haukeland Hospital, N-5021 Bergen N-5021, Norway; 95 Land Croft Road, East Dulwich, London SE22 9PJ Tel: 020 8693 1080 — MB BCh BAO 1970 NUI; FRCPI 1988, M 1977; DTM & H RCP Lond. 1981; DObst RCOG 1973; DCH NUI 1973. (Univ. Coll. Dub.) Phys. Kilimanjaro Christian Med. Center Moshi, Tanzania; Research Fell. Univ. Bergen Norway. Prev: Resid. (Internal Med.) St. Mary's Hosp. Rochester, USA; Intern Mater Miser. Hosp. Dub., Coombe Matern. Hosp. Dub. & Our Lady's Hosp. Sick Childr. Crumlin.
HOWLEY, Helen Maria Taliesin Surgery, Taliesin, Lampeter SA48 7AA Tel: 01570 422665 Fax: 01570 423810 — MB BCh BAO 1991 NUI.
HOWLIN, Stephen Graham 135B Eastgate, Deeping St James, Peterborough PE6 8RB — MB ChB 1980 Sheff.
HOWLING, Sarah Jane 14A Almedia Street, Islington, London N1 1TA Tel: 020 7359 7479 — MB BS 1989 Lond.; MRCP (UK) 1992.
HOWLING, Thomas David 81 Loghurst Lane, Mellor, Marple Bridge, Stockport SK6 5AH — BM BCh 1996 Oxf.; BA Oxf. 1993, BM BCh. 1996. (Oxf.) SHO VTS for GP.
HOWMAN, Elizabeth Mary 55 Thoresby Road, Beeston, Nottingham NG9 3EP — BM BS 1989 Nottm.
HOWORTH, Irene Elsie, OBE (retired) 4 Yewlands Avenue, Fulwood, Preston PR2 9QR Tel: 01772 717536 — BSc Manch. 1937, MB ChB 1940, DPH 1954; DObst. RCOG 1943; DCH Eng. 1948; MFCM 1972. Prev: 2nd Dep. Co. MOH Lancs. CC.
HOWORTH, Paul c/o P.J. Watkins, 20 Moorfield Avenue, Stalybridge SK15 2SP — MB ChB 1982 Manch.; MSc Trop. Med. Liverp. 1996; DRCOG 1986; DTM & H Liverp. 1988. (Manchester) GP Kijabe Med. Centre, Kijare, Kenya. Prev: Med. Supt. Kagando Hosp., Kasese, Uganda.
HOWORTH, Peter James Nicholas, TD (retired) Prospect House, Greenhead, Brampton CA8 7HN — MB Camb. 1960, BChir 1959; MSc Lond. 1967; MA Camb. 1960, MD 1970; FRCPath 1980, M 1968. Prev: Cons. Chem. Path. Vict. Hosp. NHS Trust Blackpool.
HOWORTH, Peter Willis Dept. of Psychiatry, University Hospital Of North Tees, Stockton-on-Tees TS19 8PE Tel: 01642 624327 — MB BS 1991 Newc.; MRC Psychb. 1996. Cons. in Old Age Psychiat. Univ. of N. Tees Stockton-on-Tees TS19 8PE.
HOWS, Professor Jill Moira Department of Transplantation Sciences, Paul O'Gorman Lifetime Centre, Southmead Hospital, Westbury on Trym, Bristol BS10 5NB Tel: 0117 9596233 Fax: 0117 9696342 Email: jill.hows@bristol.ac.uk; The Old Manse, 12 The Parade, Chipping Sodbury, Bristol BS37 6AT — MB BS 1972 Lond.; MSc (Immunol.) Lond. 1983, MD 1984; FRCP Lond. 1990; MRCP (UK) 1975; FRCPath 1991, M 1979. (St. Thomas' Hospital London) Cons. Haematologist & Dir. of Avon Haemat. Unit United Bristol Healthcare Trust; Dir. Stem Cell Research Progr., Paul O'Gorman Lifetime Centre, Univ. of Bristol. Socs: Amer. Soc. Haemat.; Brit. Soc. Haematol.; Internat. Soc. Experim. Haematol. Prev: Cons. Haemat. S.mead Hosp. Bristol; Sen. Lect. (Immunohaemat.) Roy. Postgrad. Med. Sch. Lond.
HOWSAM, Sally Elizabeth 42 Kilmaine Road, London SW6 7JX — MB ChB 1984 Liverp.; MB ChB Liverp. l984; FRCA 1993. Cons. Anaesth., Kingston Hosp., Lond.
HOWSE, Mr Alan Justin Greenway 40A Green Lane, Northwood HA6 2QB Tel: 01923 828898 Fax: 01923 828790 — MB BS Lond. 1955; FRCS Eng. 1962; DObst RCOG 1956. (Middlx.) Dir. RDC Physiother. Clinic Lond.; Emerit. Cons. Orthop. Surg. Centr. Middlx. Hosp. Lond.; Cons. Orthop. Roy. Acad. Dancing, Roy. Ballet Schs. Lond., Roy. Soc. Musicians. Prev: Cons. Orthop. Surg. St. Vincent's Orthop. Hosp. Pinner; Sen. Regist. (Orthop) Middlx. Hosp.; Regist. (Orthop.) St. Bart. Hosp. Lond.
HOWSE, Matthew Lewis Peter 5 Lyngarth Drive, Kendal LA9 4JA Tel: 01539 722114 — MB BS 1993 Newc.; MRCP 1996. Specialist Regist. Nephrol. Gen. med. Arrow Pk. Hosp. Birkenhead.
HOWSE, Michael Lewis The James Cochrane Practice, Maude Street, Kendal LA9 4QE Tel: 01539 722124 Fax: 01539 734995; Linthwaite, Lyngarth Drive, Kendal LA9 4JA Tel: 01539 722114 — MB BS 1970 Lond.; MRCGP 1979; DCH RCPSI 1978; DRCOG 1975. (Westm.) Princip. Gen. Pract.
HOWSE, Nicole Lyn Grosvenor Medical Centre, 26 Grosvenor Place, Bath BA1 6BA Tel: 01225 484748 Fax: 01225 789022 — MB BS 1983 Sydney; MRCGP 1991; DGM RCP Lond. 1988. (Sydney) GP; Clin. Asst. (ENT) Roy. United Hosp. Bath.
HOWSE, Patricia Margaret (retired) Fir Tree Cottage, 73 York Road, Haxby, York YO32 3EF — MB BS Lond. 1962; FRCP Lond. 1987; MRCP (UK) 1971; MRCS Eng. LRCP Lond. 1962; DCH Eng. 1965. Prev: Cons. Paediat. Manor Hosp. Walsall.
HOWSON, Anthony Neville 58 Chatham Road, Kingston upon Thames KT1 3AA — MB ChB 1973 Sheff.; MRCP (UK) 1978.
HOWSON, Beverly Edwina The Evelyn Medical Centre, Marsh Avenue, Hope, Hope Valley S33 6RJ — MB ChB 1985 Sheff.; MFFP 1995; DRCOG 1988. Prev: Trainee GP Chesterfield VTS.
***HOWSON, Jane Emma** 21 Benlaw Grove, Felton, Morpeth NE65 9NG — MB BS 1998 Newc.; MB BS Newc 1998.
HOWSON, Simon Duncan Upper Smithy Clough Farm, Smithy Clough Lane, Ripponden, Sowerby Bridge HX6 4LG — MB ChB 1981 Manch.; DRCOG 1985.
HOWSON, William John Dryden Paddock House, Queensway, Netheravon, Salisbury SP4 9QQ — MB BS 1976 Melbourne.
HOWTON, Derek Harry (retired) 36 Coldermeadow Avenue, Corby NN18 9AJ Tel: 01536 460830 — MB ChB 1958 Bristol.
HOXEY, Katharina Louisa Ann 8 Sandy Lane, Fareham PO14 4ER — MB BS 1992 Lond.
HOY, Andrew Martin The Princess Alice Hospice, West End Lane, Esher KT10 8NA Tel: 01372 468811 Fax: 01372 469329 Email: andrewhoy@princess-alice-hospice.org.uk; Rapallo, Epsom Road, Epsom KT17 1LB Tel: 020 8393 9053 Email: ahoy@lineone.net — MB BS 1973 Lond.; BSc Lond. 1970; FRCP Lond. 1994; MRCP (UK) 1976; MRCGP 1995; FRCR 1983; DMRT Eng. 1983. (Westminster) Cons. in Palliat. Med. Epsom and St Helier Healthcare Trust; Med. Dir. P.ss Alice Hospice Esher; Hon. Cons. (Radiother. & Oncol.) St. Thos. & Guy's Hosps. Lond. & Kingston Hosp. Socs: (Director) Help the Hospices; Exec. Mem. Assn. Palliat. Med. Prev: Sen. Regist. (Radiother. & Oncol.) St. Thos. Hosp. Lond.; Regist. St. Christophers Hospice Lond.; Ho. Phys. W.m. Hosp. Lond.
HOY, Antony Nicholas Bunbury Medical Practice, The Surgery, Bunbury, Tarporley CW6 9PJ Tel: 01829 260218 Fax: 01829 260411; 7 Dysart Buildings, Nantwich CW5 5DW Tel: 01270 625001 Fax: 01829 260411 Email: ahoy162758@aol.com — MB ChB 1976 Liverp.; MRCS Eng. LRCP Lond. 1976; FRCGP 1993, M 1983; Dip. Pract. Dermat. Wales 1990; DRCOG 1978; D. Occ. MED 1998. (Liverp.) Clin. Asst. (Dermat.) Countess of Chester Hosp.
HOY, Mr Campbell Henry Alfred Laconia, Lowicks Road, Rushmoor, Tilford, Farnham GU10 2EZ — MB BS 1945 Lond.; FRCS Ed. 1959; MCRS Eng. LRCP Lond. 1945.
HOY, Christine Muriel The Lodge, South Bramwith, Doncaster DN7 5SJ — MB ChB 1982 Aberd.
HOY, Gregory Alexander 42 The Avenue, Windsor SL4 2RS — MB BS 1981 Monash; FRACS (Orth.) 1991.
HOYAL, Robin Hugo Austen The Princess Royal Hospital, Mid Sussex NHS Trust, Lewes Road, Haywards Heath RH16 4EX Tel: 01444 441881; The Friary, South St, Cuckfield, Haywards Heath RH17 5LB Tel: 01444 440964 Fax: 01444 441955 — MB ChB 1973 Leeds; BSc Leeds 1970, MB ChB 1973; FFA RCS Eng. 1978; DA Eng. 1975. (Leeds) Cons. Anaesth. Mid Downs NHS Trust. Socs: Assn. Anaesth.; BMA; HCSA. Prev: Sen. Regist. (Anaesth.) Oxf. AHA (T); Regist. (Anaesth.) Bristol Health Dist. (T).
HOYEN-CHUNG, Eustace Garvin 8 Gardenia Grove, Riverside Gardens, Liverpool L17 7HP — MB BCh 1959 Wales; BSc Lond. 1955; MRCS Eng. LRCP Lond. 1959; DObst RCOG 1960. (Cardiff) Socs: BMA. Prev: SHO (Cas. & Orthop.) & Ho. Surg. Surgic. Unit, Cardiff Roy. Infirm.
HOYES, Shirley Eileen (retired) Old Coach House, 4 Listers Court, Cunliffe Road, Ilkley LS29 9DZ Tel: 01943 436802 — MRCS Eng. LRCP Lond. 1952; MRCPsych 1971; DPM Leeds 1968; DPH Leeds 1963. Cons. Child Psychiat. Child & Family Psychiat. Dept. Doncaster Gate Hosp. Rotherham. Prev: Asst. MOH Lincs. Sch.
HOYLAND, Hugh James (retired) The Surgery, Hoyland House, Gyde Road,Painswick, Stroud GL6 6RD — MB BChir 1957 Camb.; MRCS Eng. LRCP Lond. 1956; FRCGP 1981, M 1965; DObst RCOG 1958. Prev: Ho. Phys. Roy. Devon & Exeter Hosp.
HOYLE, Andrew 74 Chelsea Road, Southsea PO5 1NJ — MB BS 1996 Lond.
HOYLE, Andrew Nicholas 46 Southdown Avenue, Brighton BN1 6EH — MB ChB 1984 Ed.; MRCP (UK) 1988.

HOYLE, Christine Florence Dept of Haematology, Guy's Hosp, St Thomas' St, London SE1 9RT Tel: 0207 955 4003 Fax: 0207 955 4002 Email: chrishoyle@pawling.freeserve.co.uk; Tel: 0207 627 1979 — MB ChB 1977 Sheff.; MRCP (UK) 1980; MRCPath 1989; FRCPath 1998. Cons Haemotologist Guy's & St Thomas' NHS Trust Guy's Hosp St. Thomas' St Lond. Socs: Brit. Soc. Haematol.; Amer. Soc. Haematol. Prev: Vis. Instruc. (Med.) BMT Program Stanford Univ. Med. Center Calif., USA; Clin. Research Fell. (Leukaemia Research) Hammersmith Hosp. Lond.; Sen. Regist. (Haemat.) Hammersmith & N. Middlx. Hosp. Lond.

HOYLE, Derek (retired) The Doctors' House, Aysgarth, Leyburn DL8 3AB Tel: 01969 663222 — MB ChB Leeds 1959. Prev: Med. Off. for Staff Health Doncaster Hosp. Gp.

HOYLE, Greville (retired) 12 Selbourne Road, Bishops Cleeve, Cheltenham GL52 8BT Tel: 01242 676747 — MB ChB Birm. 1945. Prev: GP Tamworth.

HOYLE, Harry Vickerstaff (retired) 30 Warren Road, Blundellsands, Liverpool L23 6UE Tel: 0151 924 6905 — MB BS 1951 Lond.; MRCS Eng. LRCP Lond. 1951. Prev: ENT Ho. Surg. Guy's Hosp.

HOYLE, Helen Margaret (retired) The Doctors House, Aysgarth, Leyburn DL8 3AB Tel: 01969 663046 — MB ChB 1959 Leeds; MB ChB (Hnrs. Cl. II) Leeds 1959; DObst RCOG 1961. Prev: GP Leyburn.

HOYLE, James Thomas Edward 49 Main Street, Costock, Loughborough LE12 6XD — MB ChB 1998 Sheff.; MB ChB Sheff 1998.

HOYLE, Jennifer Louise — MB ChB 1993 Leeds; MRCP (Ed.) 1997. Regist. Thoracic Med. NW Rotat. Socs: BMA. Prev: SHO, N. Manch. Gen. Hosp.; SHO, Huddersfield Roy. Infirm.

HOYLE, John Anthony (retired) 78 Cammo Grove, Edinburgh EH4 8HB — MB ChB 1971 Ed.; DObst RCOG 1973; AFOM RCP 1980. Prev: Med. Off. Scott. Prison Serv. HMP Edin.

HOYLE, John Rosewarne (retired) 4 Boscombe Cliff Road, Bournemouth BH5 1JL Tel: 01202 397561 Fax: 01202 397561 Email: john@noni-hoyle.fsnet.co.uk — MB Camb. 1959, BChir 1958; FFA RCS Eng. 1963; DA Eng. 1961. Prev: Cons. Anaesth. Poole Gen. Hosp.

HOYLE, Martin John (retired) The Surgery, Rockleigh Court, 136 Hutton Road, Shenfield, Brentwood CM15 8NN Tel: 01277 223844 Fax: 01277 230136 — MB BS 1965 Lond.; MRCS Eng. LRCP Lond. 1965. Prev: Ho. Phys. E. Surrey Hosp.

HOYLE, Martin Kitson Oakworth Health Centre, 3 Lidget Mill, Oakworth, Keighley BD22 7HY Tel: 01535 643306 Fax: 01535 645832; 9 Gledhow Drive, Oxenhope, Keighley BD22 9SA — MB ChB 1978 Liverp.

HOYLE, Mr Michael David c/o Orthopaedic Department, Stafford District General Hospital, Weston Road, Stafford ST16 3SA Tel: 01785 57731 — MB ChB 1972 Sheff.; MB ChB 1972 Sheff; FRCS Eng. 1978.

***HOYLES, Rachel Kate** The Quillets, Lees Lane, Little Neston, South Wirral CH64 4DH — BChir 1996 Camb.

HOYSAL, Nagpal 161 East Dundry Road, Bristol BS14 0LS — MB ChB 1995 Manch.

HOYTE, Christine Alice Elizabeth Corbett House Surgery, Avondale Road, Bristol BS5 9QX Tel: 0117 955 7474 Fax: 0117 955 5402 — MB ChB 1974 Bristol; MRCGP 1979.

HOYTE, David Augustus Noel (retired) The Barn, 4 Village Farm Close, West Leake, Loughborough LE12 5RF Tel: 01509 672666 — MB ChB 1946 Manch.; MB ChB (Hons.) Manch. 1946; MD (Gold Medal) Manch. 1959; FRCGP 1992, M 1978. Prev: Sen. Lect. (Human Morphol.) Univ. Nottm.

HOYTE, Patrick John Tel: 020 7202 1500; Brook House, Thornley, Preston PR3 2TN Tel: 01995 61547 — MRCS Eng. LRCP Lond. 1966; MA (Distinc.) (Med. Ethics) Keele 1993; MRCGP 1972; DCH Eng. 1971; DObst RCOG 1970; DLDS (Lancaster) 1996. (St. Mary's) Sen. Research Fell. Secretariat Med. Defence Union. Socs: BMA; BASPCAN. Prev: Maj. RAMC, Obst. Louise Margt. Matern. Hosp. Aldershot; GP Clitheroe; SHO (Paediat.) St. Peter's Hosp. Chertsey.

HRABOVSKY, Anton 118 Pond Park Road, Lisburn BT28 3RE Tel: 01846 601261 — MUDr 1971 Komensky Univ. Czech.; MUDR Komenskeho Czechoslovakia 1971; FFR RCSI 1985; DMRD Eng. 1984. (Bratislava) Cons. Radiol. Whiteabbey Hosp. Belf., Waveney Hosp. Ballymena & Carrickfergus Hosp. Socs: Ulster Radiol. Soc.; Brit. Med. Acupunct. Soc. Prev: Regist. (Radiol.) Roy. Vict. Hosp. Belf.; Regist. (Orthop. Surg. & Traumat.) Roy. Vict. Hosp. Belf. & Ulster Hosp. Dundonald; Regist. (Gen. Surg.) Lagan Valley Hosp. Lisburn.

HRBACEK, Franck Josef (retired) 131 Stafford Road, Croydon CR0 4NN Tel: 020 8686 7319 — MD 1937 Brno.

HRISHA, Mr Giamal Sadeg 46 Smith Drive, Elgin IV30 4NE — MB BCh 1983 Al-Fateh; MD Ed. 1994; FRCS Ed. 1991. Staff Surg. Dr. Gray's Hosp. Elgin. Prev: Regist. Poole Hosp. Roy., Shrewsbury Hosp. & Countess of Chester Hosp.

HRONIS, Vassilios Georgios 5 Juniper Croft, Clayton-le-Woods, Chorley PR6 7UF — Ptychio Iatrikes 1984 Athens.

HROUDA, David Charing CrossHospital, Fulham Palace Road, London W6 8RF Tel: 020 8846 1234 Fax: 020 8846 1757; 112 Chadacre Road, Epsom KT17 2HF Tel: 020 8393 4450 Email: davidhrouda@compuserve.com — MB BS 1989 Lond.; 1989 MB BS Lond.; 1986 BSc Lond.; 1993 FRCS Eng.; FRCS 2000 Urol.; MD 2000 Lond. specialist Regist. Urol., Char. Cross Hosp. Socs: Fell. Roy. Soc. Med.; Brit. Assn. Urol. Surg.; Brit. Prostate Gp. Prev: Sen. Regist. (Urol.) Roy. Surrey Co. Hosp. Guildford; Sen. Regist. (Urol.) St Geo.'s Hosp., Lond.; Sen. Regist. (Urol.) The Inst. of Urol., Lond.

HROUDA, Denise Radiotherapy Department, Churchill Hospital, Oxford Tel: 01865 741841; Malthouse Cottage, 1 BellLane, Wheatley, Oxford OX33 1XY — MB BS Lond. 1992. (St. Thos. Hosp. Med. Sch.) Specialist Regist. (Clin. Oncol.) Ch.ill Hosp. Oxf. Socs: RCP. Prev: SHO (Gen. Med.) Essex & Sussex Hosp.; SHO (Oncol.) Essex Co. Hosp. Colchester; Ho. Off. (Surg.) St. Thos. Hosp. Lond.

HRYCAICZUK, Walter The Old School Medical Centre, Horseman Lane, Copmanthorpe, York YO23 3UA Tel: 01904 706455 — MB BS 1982 Lond.; BSc 1979 Lond.; DCH RCP Lond. 1986; DRCOG 1985. (St. Geo.)

HRYNASZKIEWICZ, Anthony The Medical Centre, Church Field, Camelford PL32 9YT Tel: 01840 213894 Fax: 01840 212276 Email: tony@cammedcentre.demon.co.uk; Trelowen, Rosecare, St. Genny's, Bude EX23 0BE Tel: 01840 230775 — MB BS 1976 Lond.; Dip. IMC RCS Ed. 1989. (King's Coll.) GP; Hosp. Pract. (Cardiol.) Derriford Hosp. Plymouth.

HSIN, Michael Kuan-Yew 5E Cliveden Place, Belgravia, London SW1W 8LA — MB BChir 1992 Camb.

HSU, Pon Poh Flat 3/2, 22 Rosefield St., Dundee DD1 5PS — MB ChB 1993 Dundee.

HSU, Ronald Te-Hsin Department of Epidemiology & Public Health, University of Leicester, 22 -28 Princess Road West, Leicester LE1 6TP Tel: 0116 252 3205 Fax: 0116 252 3272 — MB ChB 1983 Leeds; MFPHM 1995; MRCGP 1990; DGM RCP Lond 1988; DRCOG 1987; DCH RCP Lond. 1986. (University of Leeds)

HTAY NYUNT KYI, Dr 36 Sundridge Street, Addiscombe, Croydon CR0 6RH — MB BS 1981 Med. Inst. (I) Rangoon.

HTAY WIN, Dr Flat 8 Wakefield House, Warrington Hospital NHS Trust, Loverly Lane, Warrington WA5 1QG — MB BS 1978 Med. Inst. (II) Rangoon.

HTIN AUNG, Dr 25 Lavender Road, Up Hatherley, Cheltenham GL51 3BN — MB BS 1982 Med. Inst. Rangoon.

HTUN NYUNT, Richard 20 Broadmeadows, Darlington DL3 8SP — MB BS 1959 Rangoon; DTM & H Eng. 1962. (Rangoon) Med. Off. St. John of God's Hosp. Scorton. Socs: Burma Med. Soc. Prev: SHO Roy. Vict. Hosp. Belf.; 1st Asst. to Phys. Rangoon Gen. Hosp.; Asst. Lect. Med. Inst. Med. (2) Mingaladon, Burma.

HU, Michele Tao-Ming 26 Honor Oak Road, Forest Hill, London SE23 3SB; Department of Neurology, King's College Hospital, Mapother House, Decrespigny Park, London SE5 8AF Tel: 020 7346 5319 Fax: 020 7346 5332 — MB BS 1993 Lond.; MRCP 1996. (King's College Hospital London) Research Regist. (Neurol.) Dept. of Neurol. King's Coll. & Imperial Coll. Sch. of Med.; Action Research Train. Fell.sh. Hammersmith Hosp. Lond. Socs: Fell. Roy. Soc. Med.; Assoc. Mem. Assn. Brit. Neurol.

HU, Shan 5 Cross Lane, Dundee DD1 1NQ — MB ChB 1998 Dund.; MB ChB Dund 1998.

HU, Yu Jen 130 Knights Hill, London SE27 0SR — MB BChir 1975 Camb.; DRCOG 1979.

HUANG, Andrew 40 York Terrace E., Regent's Park, London NW1 4PT Tel: 020 7486 0885 Fax: 020 7486 0883 Email: 101652.1757@compuserve.com — MB ChB 1992 Manch.; MB ChB

(Hons.) Manch. 1992; BSc (Hons.) Manch. 1989; FRCS Eng. 1996. (Manch.) Specialist Regist. (Gen. Surg.) Oxf. Regional Train. Progr. Socs: Assn. Surg.; Assn. Surg. Train.; Assn. Coloproctol. Prev: Specialist Regist. (Gen. Surg.) Wycombe Hosp. Bucks.; Demonst. (Anat.) Univ. Oxf.; SHO (Vasc.) St. Mary's Hosp. Lond.

HUANG, Charles Paul 2 Papillons Walk, Blackheath Park, London SE3 9SF — MB BS 1994 Lond.

HUANG, Christopher Li-Hur New Hall, Cambridge CB3 0DF — BM BCh 1977 Oxf.; ScD Camb. 1995; PhD Camb. 1980, MA 1979, MD 1986; MA Oxf. 1978, BA 1974, DSc 1995, DM 1985. (Oxf.) Univ. Reader (Cellular Physiol.) Camb.; Fell. & Dir. of Med. Stud. New Hall. Camb.; Chairm. Edit. Bd. for Monographs of the Physiol. Soc. 1994; Edr. Jl. Physiol. 1990; Hon. Research Fell. St. Geo. Hosp. Med. Sch. 1991. Socs: (Edr. Jl. Physiol.) Phys. Soc.; USA Biophys. Soc.; Soc. Gen. Physiol. USA. Prev: Univ. Demonst. (Physiol.) Camb.; Univ. Lect. (Physiol.) Camb.; Ho. Phys. Nuffield Dept. Med. Oxf.

HUANG, David Ching Siang c/o Hudgell, Yeates & Co., 2 Charlton Road, London SE3 7EX — MB BS 1985 Lond.; MRCP (UK) 1989. (Roy. Free.) Clin. Research Fell. & Hon. Lect. Walker & Eliza Hall Inst. Med. Research Roy. Melbourne Hosp. Melbourne, Austral. Prev: Clin. Research Fell. & Hon. Lect. Acad. Dept. Haemat. Roy. Free Hosp. Lond.; SHO & Regist. (Haemat.) Roy. Free Hosp. Lond.; SHO (Oncol.) Roy. Marsden Hosp. Surrey.

HUANG, Dean Yi-Hsiang 68 Runswick Drive, Wollaton, Nottingham NG8 1JB — BM BS 1998 Nottm.; BM BS Nottm 1998.

HUANG, Djoni Sian Wei Flat 6, Rosebank Mews, Rosebank St., Dundee DD3 6PS — MB ChB 1998 Dund.; MB ChB Dund 1998.

HUANG, Mr Joseph Kwang Chi 102 The Sanctuary, Reardon Path, London E1W 2PP — MB ChB 1990 Bristol; FRCS Eng. 1995. (Univ. Bristol) Specialist Regist. in Gen. Surg. Anglia Region. Prev: Hon. Research Fell. Univ. Dept. Surg. Roy. Free Hosp. Lond.; SHO (Surg.) Whipps Cross Hosp. Lond.

HUANG, Yung Lung Eric The Surgery, 2 Garway Road, London W2 4NH Tel: 020 7221 8803 020 8962 4400 Fax: 020 7792 9923 — MB BS 1989 Lond.; Dip. Derm. Lond. 1992; DFFP London 1993. (U.C.L.) Prev: GP Regist. Lond.

HUANG YUN PUI, Beatrice 32 Spencer Walk, London NW3 1QZ — BM BS 1992 Nottm.

HUARTE PANO, Juan Ignacio Semor Flat 1, Crawley Hospital, West Green Drive, Crawley RH11 7DH — LMS 1988 Basque Provinces. SHO (ENT) Frimley Pk. Hosp. Surrey. Prev: SHO (ENT) Poole Hosp.; SHO (Neurosurg.) Preston Roy. Hosp.; SHO (A & E) Arrowe Pk. Hosp.

HUBBARD, Alan David 122 Corbyn Street, London N4 3DB — MB BS 1991 Lond.

HUBBARD, Alice Patricia 65 Daniells, Welwyn Garden City AL7 1QT — BM 1998 Soton.; BM Soton 1998.

HUBBARD, Alison Judith 23 Swan Crescent, Olive Mount, Liverpool L15 8AL — MB ChB 1995 Liverp.

HUBBARD, Barbara Mary DA1 1QY; Sedges, Cooper St., Ashford CT3 9NW Tel: 01304 814110 — MB BS 1962 Lond. (Univ. Coll. Hosp.) Prev: Regist. St. Chas. Hosp. Lond.; Demonst. (Path.) Camb. Univ.; Asst. Med. Off. Family Plann. Assn. Clinic Gravesend.

HUBBARD, Catherine Stella ffolliot Department of Radiology, Hinchingbrooke Hospital, Huntingdon PE29 6NT Tel: 01480 416132; The Old Recory, Main Street, Cambridge CB3 7NU Tel: 01223 264138 — MB BS 1978 Lond.; FRCR 1983. Cons. Radiol. Hinchingbrooke Hosp. Huntingdon. Prev: Sen. Regist. (Radiol.) Roy. Free Hosp. Lond.; Regist. (Radiol.) St. Mary's Hosp. Lond.

HUBBARD, Daniel John 21B Pincroft Wood, New Barn, Longfield DA3 7HB — MB BS 1996 Lond.

HUBBARD, Dudley Charles, OStJ City Way Surgery, 67 City Way, Rochester ME1 2AY Tel: 01634 843351 Fax: 01634 830421; The Pines, 7 Shaws Way, Rochester ME1 3DY Tel: 01634 848444 Fax: 01634 327048 Email: dudleyhull@aol.com — MB ChB Birm. 1966; DObst RCOG 1969. (Birm.) Prev: SHO (Med.) Wordsley Hosp.; Ho. Surg. Qu. Eliz. Hosp. Birm.; Ho. Off. (O & G) Qu. Eliz. Hosp. Birm.

HUBBARD, Graham Hamilton Ponteland Medical Group, Thornhill Road, Ponteland, Newcastle upon Tyne NE20 9PZ Tel: 01661 825513 Fax: 01661 860755; 5 Edgewood, Darras Hall, Ponteland, Newcastle upon Tyne NE20 9RY Tel: 01661 860401 — MB BS 1964 Durh.; FFA RCS Eng. 1972; FRCGP 1986, M 1972; DA Eng. 1971; DObst RCOG 1969. (Newc.) Hosp. Pract. (Anaesth.) Roy. Vict. Infirm. Newc. Prev: Regist. (Anaesth.) Roy. Vict. Infirm. Newc.; Ho. Surg. & Ho. Phys. Shotley Bridge Gen. Hosp.; Flight Lt. RAF Med. Br. Med. Div. RAF Hosp. Wegberg.

HUBBARD, Hilary Constance North Devon District Hospital, Raleigh Park, Barnstaple EX31 4JB — MB BS 1970 Lond.; FRCP Lond. 1994; MRCP (UK) 1975; MRCS Eng. LRCP Lond. 1970. (Roy. Free) Cons. Dermat. N. Devon Dist. Hosp. Prev: Sen. Regist. Skin Hosp. Manch.; Ho. Phys. Med. Unit Roy. Free Hosp.

HUBBARD, Mr Ian Hamilton Nettleslack Farm, Broughton Beck, Ulverston LA12 7PN — MB BS 1966 Lond.; FRCS Ed. 1977; MRCS Eng. LRCP Lond. 1965; DO Eng. 1971. (St. Geo.) Cons. (Ophth.) SW Cumbria Health Dist. Prev: SHO (Ophth.) & Regist. (Ophth.) Lond. Hosp.; Ho. Off. (Ophth.) St. Geo. Hosp. Tooting.

HUBBARD, Irene Margaret Dept of medicine, Leicester General Hospital, Gwendolen Road, Leicester LE5 4PW — MB ChB 1987 Leic.; MRCP (UK) 1995; MRCGP 1991; DRCOG 1992; FRCA. (Leics Univ.) Specialist Regist. Gen. Med. Leics. Gen. Hosp. Prev: Specialist Regist. Anesth.Leicester Roy.Infirm; Regist. (Gen. Med.) Leicester Roy. Infirm.; SHO ITV Derby.Roy.Infirm.

HUBBARD, Mr Johnathan Guy Hamilton 109 Middle Drive, Darras Hall, Ponteland, Newcastle upon Tyne NE20 9DS — MB BS Newc. 1991; FRCS Glas. 1996. Specialist Regist. (Gen. Surg.) N. Deanery. Prev: Research Fell. Univ. Newc. u. Tyne.

HUBBARD, Karin Elisabet The Surgery, 64 Victoria St., Blantyre, Glasgow G72 0BS Tel: 0141 823260 Fax: 0141 712948; 5 Reay Avenue, East Kilbride, Glasgow G74 1QT — MB ChB 1987 Aberd.; MRCGP 1994; DFFP 1993.

HUBBARD, Melissa 122 Corbyn Street, London N4 3DB — MB BS 1991 Lond.; BSc Lond. 1989, MB BS 1991; MRCP (UK) 1994. Prev: SHO Gt. Ormond St. Hosp. for Childr. Lond. & Alder Hey Childr. Hosp. Liverp.

HUBBARD, Mr Michael John Stewart Glan Clwyd Hospital, Bodelwyddan, Rhyl LL18 5UJ; Pendyffryn, Clip Terfyn, Llanddulas, Abergele LL22 8EH — MChir Camb. 1979, MA, MB 1963, BChir 1962; FRCS Ed. 1967; FRCS Eng. 1967. (Middlx.) Cons. Orthop. & Traum. Surg. i/c Problem Knee Clinic Robt. Jones & Agnes Hunt Orthop. Hosp. OsW.ry & Clwyd N. Health Dist. Socs: Assoc. Surg. of Knee; Fell. Brit. Orthop. Assn. Prev: Sen. Regist. (Orthop. Rotat.) King's Coll. Hosp. Lond.; Regist. (Orthop.) Robt. Jones & Agnes Hunt Orthop. Hosp. OsW.ry; Ho. Surg. Roy. Nat. Hosp. Lond.

HUBBARD, Michael Patrick 2 Abbots Row, Durham DH1 1HE — MB BS 1987 Lond.

HUBBARD, Peter John Egerton (retired) 8 Pluck Row, Docking Road, Burnham Market, King's Lynn PE31 8DN Tel: 01328 738433 — MB BChir 1956 Camb.; MRCS Eng. LRCP Lond. 1955; DObst RCOG 1958.

HUBBARD, Richard Brian 44 Patterdale Road, Nottingham NG5 4LQ Email: richard.hubbard@nottingham.ac.uk — MB BS 1989 Lond.; BSc Lond. 1986; DM Nottm. 1996; MRCP (UK) 1992. (St. Thos. Hosp. Med. Sch.) Lect. & Hon. Sen. Regist. (Respirat. Med.) Nottm.

HUBBARD, Ruth Eleanor Llandough Hospital, Penlan Road, Penarth CF64 2XX — MB BS 1994 Lond.

HUBBARD, St Clair Mark L'Amie 9 Home Close, Histon, Cambridge CB4 9JL — MB BS 1950 Lond.; MRCS Eng. LRCP Lond. 1950. (King's Coll. Hosp.) Cas. Off. Bridgwater Gen. Hosp. Prev: Ho. Pathol. Taunton & Som. Hosp.; Ho. Surg. Gyn. & Obst. Dept. & Urol. Dept. King's Coll. Hosp.

HUBBARD, William Nickles Royal United Hospital, Combe Park, Bath BA1 3NG Tel: 01225 428331; Hillcrest, Midford Road, Bath BA2 5SB — MB BS 1980 Lond.; MA Camb. 1981, BA 1977; FRCP Lond. 1995; MRCP (UK) 1983. Cons. Phys. & Cardiol. Roy United Hosp. Bath. Prev: Sen. Regist. Nat. Heart Hosp. Lond.

HUBBERT, Catherine Marian The Orrell Park Surgery, 46 Moss Lane, Orrell Park, Liverpool L9 8AL Tel: 0151 525 2736 Fax: 0151 524 1037 — MB ChB 1978 Liverp.; MRCGP 1983; Dip. Paliat. Med. Wales 1997; DRCOG 1981. (Liverp.) Primary Care Clin. Cancer Lead Alt Valley PCG. Socs: Assn. Palliat. Med.

HUBBLE, Dominique 47 St Peters Close, College Gardens, London SW17 7UH — MB BS 1987 Lond.

HUBBLE, Mr Matthew Jonathon Wakelin University Department of Orthopaedic Surgery, Bristol Royal Infirmary, Bristol BS2 8HW Tel: 0117 928 2658; Manor View Cottage, Manor Lane, Abbots Leigh, Bristol BS8 3RY — MB BS 1989 Lond.; FRCSI 1993; FRCS Eng. 1993; FRCS (Tr. & Ortn.) 1999. (St. Thos. Hosp. Univ. Lond.) Lect. &

Hon. Regist. (Orthop. Surg.) Bristol Roy. Infirm. Socs: BOA; BOTA; BORS. Prev: SHO (Plastic Surg.) Chepstow; SHO Rotat. (Surg. & A & E) Bristol Roy. Infirm.; Demonst. (Anat.) Qu. Mary & W.field Coll. Univ. Lond.

HUBER, Mr Christopher Peter Paul 46 St Stephen's Road, Cheltenham GL51 3AD — MB BS 1991 Lond.; BSc Lond. 1990; FRCS Eng. 1996. (St. Geo. Hosp. Med. Sch.) Specialist Regist. (Orthop. Surg.) N. Thames (W.) Train. Progr. Socs: Brit. Orthopaedic Assn.; Brit. Orthopaedic Trainees Assn.; Seddon Soc. Prev: Specialist Regist. (Orthop.) Chelsea & W.minster Hosp.; SHO (Orthop.) Roy. Nat. Orthop. Hosp. Stanmore & Hammersmith Hosp. Lond.

HUBER, Joseph Pius Ambrose Avenue Surgery, 76 Ambrose Avenue, Colchester CO3 4LN Tel: 01206 549444 Fax: 01206 369910; Kirton Wood, Kingsford, Colchester CO2 0HT — MRCS Eng. LRCP Lond. 1978.

HUBER, Mary Jean Elizabeth 11 Derby Street, Cambridge CB3 9JE — MB BChir 1979 Camb.; MA Camb. 1980, MB BChir 1979; FRCS Eng. 1984; MRCP (UK) 1981; FCOphth. 1989.

HUBERT, Helen Mary Old Denshott, Flanchford, Leigh, Reigate RH2 8RD — MB BCh BAO 1970 Dub.; BA, MB BCh BAO Dub. 1970; DObst RCOG 1973; DA Eng. 1972. (Tc Dub.) Prev: Ho. Phys. Roy. City of Dub. Hosp.; GP Bristol Area; Trainee Gen. Pract. Wessex (Portsmouth) Vocational Train. Scheme.

HUBERT, Slawa Jadwiga (retired) 52 Cleveleys Avenue, Leicester LE3 2GG Tel: 0116 289 8447 — Med. Dipl. Warsaw 1934.

HUBNER, Peter John Benedict Glenfield Hospital NHS Trust, Groby Road, Leicester LE3 9QP Tel: 0116 256 3877 Fax: 0116 232 0368 Email: p.hubner@uhl-tr.nhs.uk; Barncroft, Stamford Road, Kirby Muxloe, Leicester LE9 2ER Tel: 0116 239 5322 Fax: 0116 238 8398 Email: phubner@btinternet.com — MB BS 1965 Lond.; FRCP Lond. 1986, M 1967; MRCS Eng. LRCP Lond. 1965; DCH Eng. 1971. (Middlx.) Cons. Cardiol. Glenfield Hosp. NHS Trust; FACC; FESC. Socs: Brit. Cardiovasc. Interven. Soc.; Brit. Cardiac Soc. Prev: Cons. Cardiol. Groby Rd. Hosp. Leicester; Sen. Regist. (Med. & Cardiol.) Middlx. Hosp. Lond.; Regist. Hammersmith Hosp. Lond. & Hosp. Sick Childr. Gt. Ormond St.

HUBNER, Richard Anthony Barncroft, Stamford Road, Kirby Muxloe, Leicester LE9 2ER — BM BCh 1998 Oxf.; BM BCh Oxf 1998.

HUBREGTSE, Geer 4 Simmons Yard, Harberton, Totnes TQ9 7SQ Tel: 01803 865674 Email: geer@compuserve.com — MB ChB 1990 Stellenbosch; FRCA 1998.

HUBSCHER, Agnes Maria 27 Arlington Drive, Nottingham NG3 5EN Tel: 0115 960 8034 — State Exam. Med. Marburg 1953. (Mainz & Marburg) Regist. Nottm. Eye Hosp.; Assoc. Specialist (Ophth.) Univ. Hosp. Nottm.

HUBSCHER, Isac 122 Sussex Way, London N7 6RR; 38 Ringwood Avenue, London N2 9NS Tel: 020 8883 9033 — MD 1939 Paris.

HUBSCHER, Stefan Georg Department of Pathology, University of Birmingham, Birmingham B15 2TT Tel: 0121 414 4005 Fax: 0121 414 4019 Email: s.g.hubscher@bham.ac.uk — MB ChB 1979 Birm.; MRCPath 1985. Reader (Path.) Univ. Birm.

HUBY, Christopher Land Dalkeith Road Medical Practice, 145 Dalkeith Road, Edinburgh EH16 5HQ Tel: 0131 667 1289; 57 Morton Street, Edinburgh EH15 2HZ Tel: 0131 657 4238 — MB ChB 1972 St. And.; MSc (Social Med.) Lond. 1980. Prev: Sen. Regist. (Community Med.) N.E. Thames RHA.

HUCHZERMEYER, Philippa Margaret 68 Burleigh Park, Cobham KT11 2DU — MB ChB 1987 Cape Town.

HUCK, Jonathan David The Pool House, Kimpton Bottom, Harpenden AL5 5EA — MB ChB 1980 Bristol.

HUCK, Patrick (retired) 26 Whirlowdale Crescent, Millhouses, Sheffield S7 2NA — LRCP LRCS 1942 Ed.; LRCP LRCS Ed. LRFPS Glas. 1942; FRCR 1967; DMRT Eng. 1948. Prev: Cons. Radiotherap. W.on Pk. Hosp. Sheff.

HUCK, Stephen Upper Eden Medical Practice, The Health Centre, Silver Street, Kirkby Stephen CA17 4RB Tel: 01228 71369 Fax: 017683 72385; Rosecote, Winton, Kirkby Stephen CA17 4HS Tel: 017683 71341 — MB ChB 1981 Leeds; MRCGP 1985; DRCOG 1983. Prev: SHO (Gen. Med., Paediat. & O & G) Airedale Gen. Hosp.

HUCKER, Mr Jeremy Charles Department of Orthopaedics, Charing Cross Hospital, Fulham Palace Road, Fulham, London W6 8RF Tel: 020 2246 1234 Fax: 020 8846 1439; 6 Pumping Station Road, Chiswick, London W4 2SN — MB BS 1979 Lond.; MS Lond. 1994; FRCS (Orth.) 1996; FRCS Ed. 1988; MRCS Eng. LRCP Lond. 1979. (Westm.) Cons. Orthop. Surg. Char. Cross Hosp. Fulham; Hon. Sen. Lect. Imperial Coll. Sch. of Med. Lond.; Cons. Orthop. Surg. Cromwell Hosp., Kensington, Lond. SW5 0TU. Socs: Brit. Hip Soc.; BMA; Brit. Orth. Assn. Prev: Sen. Regist. (Orthop.) Char. Cross Hosp.; Regist. (Orthop.) W. Middlx. Hosp. Isleworth, Hammersmith Hosp. Lond. & Mayday Hosp. Croydon.

***HUCKER, Timothy Robert** 14 Grosvenor Place, Vale Road, Weybridge KT13 9AG Email: timh@doctors.org.uk — MB BS 1998 Lond.; MB BS Lond 1998.

HUCKETT, Edward Charles Arthur (retired) 124 Thorne Road, Edenthorpe, Doncaster DN3 2JA Tel: 01302 882122 — MB ChB 1955 Ed. Prev: Capt. RAMC, Regtl. Med. Off. HQ 1 (BR) Corps.

HUCKLE, John Anthony Croft Hall Medical Practice, 19 Croft Road, Torquay TQ2 5UA Tel: 01803 298441 Fax: 01803 296104; Holmwood, Lincombe Drive, Torquay TQ1 2LP Tel: 01803 292030 — MB BS 1969 Lond.; DObst RCOG 1971. (Univ. Coll. Hosp.) Socs: Torquay & Dist. Med. Soc. Prev: Cas Med. Off. & Ho. Phys. Univ. Coll. Hosp.; Ho. Surg. & Ho. Surg. (Obst.) Barnet Gen. Hosp.

HUCKLE, Philip Lee Partnerships in Care, Llanarth Court Hospital, Raglan NP5 2UD Tel: 01873 840555 — MB BCh 1984 Wales; MB BCh Wales l984; MRCPsych 1990. (Welsh National School of Medicine) Sen. Regist. (Forens. Psychiat.) S. Wales. Socs: Wales Medico-Legal Soc.; NOTA; Brit. Assoc. of Law & Ment. Health. Prev: Sen. Regist. (Adult Psychiat.) S. Wales; Inceptor Regist. (Psychiat.) WhitCh. Hosp.

HUCKSTEP, Christopher 170A Dyke Road, Brighton BN1 5AA Tel: 01273 270963 — MB BS 1987 Lond.; DCH RCP Lond. 1992; DRCOG 1991. (St George's Hospital Medical School) Prev: GP Princip. Horsham 1993-1997; Trainee GP Guildford; Trainee GP/SHO Roy. Free Hosp. Lond.

HUCKSTEP, Mark Reinhardt Kendall Crescent Health Centre, Templer Road Estate, Oxford OX2 8NE Tel: 01865 512288 — BM BCh 1986 Oxf.

HUCKVALE, Bertha Fiona The Surgery, 21 North Bar Without, Beverley HU17 7AQ Tel: 01482 882546; 21 East Dale Road, Melton, North Ferriby HU14 3HS Tel: 01482 634402 — MB ChB 1972 Aberd.; BMedBiol 1969. (Aberdeen) GP Princip.; Asst. Forens. Med. Examr. Humberside Police.

HUDA, Abul Hasnat Mohammed Qamrul 22 Wilton Drive, Darlington DL3 9PS — MB BS 1973 Dacca; MRCPI 1987; LRCP LRCS Ed. LRCPS Glas. 1983. Cons. Gen. Phys. Walsgrave Hosp. Coventry. Prev: Cons. Internist Armed Forces Hosp. Tabuk, Saudi Arabia.

HUDA, Ahmed Samei 29 Goukscroft Park, Ayr KA7 4DS — MB ChB 1992 Glas.

HUDA, Mohammed Fakhrul 56 Hale End Road, Walthamstow, London E17 4BQ — MB BS 1996 Lond.

HUDA, Qudsia Ailsa Hospital, Dalmellington Road, Ayr KA6 6AB Tel: 01292 610556; 29 Goukscroft Park, Doonfoot, Ayr KA7 4DS Tel: 01292 443018 — MB BS 1962 Karachi; DObst RCOG 1968. (Dow Med. Coll.) Staff Psychiat. Ailsa Hosp. Ayr. Prev: Clin. Asst. Ailsa Hosp. Ayr.

HUDA, Shahzya Shahnaz 29 Goukscroft Park, Doonfoot, Ayr KA7 4DS — MB ChB 1997 Glas.

HUDA, Uzma Flat 2, 59 Marlborough Park N., Belfast BT9 6HL — MB BCh BAO 1993 Belf.

HUDA, Zamir-ul (retired) 50 Killyman Road, Dungannon BT71 6DE Tel: 01868 722082 Fax: 01868 722082 — MB BS 1964 Punjab; MB BS Punjab (Pakistan) 1964; DCH RCPS Glas. 1973. Prev: Airport Health Off. Lahore Airport Pakistan.

HUDD, Mr Charles Alan Maurice 53 Oxhey Lane, Hatch End, Pinner HA5 4AY — MB BS 1976 Lond.; MS Lond. 1990, MB BS 1976; FRCS (Urol) Eng. 1991; FRCS Eng. 1981. (St. Geo.)

HUDD, Nicholas Payne Benenden Hospital, Cranbrook TN17 4AX Tel: 01580 242426 Fax: 01580 240021 Email: nphudd@compuserve.com; 54 Wimpole Street, London W1G 8YJ Tel: 020 7935 6863 Fax: 01580 240021 — MB BChir 1971 Camb.; MA Camb. 1971; FRCP Lond. 1995; MRCP (UK) 1976. (Westm.) Cons. Phys. Benenden Hosp. Cranbrook. Socs: Fell. Roy. Soc. Med.; Brit. Diabetic Assn.; BMA. Prev: Sen. Regist. (Med.) Manch. Roy. Infirm.; Regist. (Med.) Basildon Hosp.; Ho. Phys. P.ss Alexandra Hosp. Harlow.

HUDDART, Julia Elizabeth Kenmore Medical Centre, 60-62 Alderley Road, Wilmslow SK9 1PA Tel: 01625 532244 Fax: 01625 549024 — MB ChB 1979 Manch.; MRCGP 1984; DRCOG 1981; DCH RCP Lond. 1982. (Manchester) Clin. Asst. E. Chesh. Hospice.

HUDDART, Martin James Lea Bridge Road Surgery, 454 Lea Bridge Road, Leyton, London E10 7DY Tel: 020 8539 3246 Fax: 020 8556 9082 — MB BS 1980 Lond.; MRCGP 1988; DRCOG 1983. (Univ. Coll. Hosp.) Med. Adviser, Healthcal. Prev: Part0time Hosp. Practitioner Dry Dependency Unit Hemerton Hosp.; Ho. Off. (Paediat.) Univ. Coll. Hosp. Lond.

HUDDART, Robert Anthony c/o Royal Marsden Hospital, Downs Road, Sutton SM2 5PT Tel: 020 8661 3457 Fax: 020 8643 8809 Email: roberth@icr.ac.uk; Beacon Hill, The Drive, Banstead SM7 1DN Tel: 01737 350252 — MB BS 1986 Lond.; PhD 2001; BA Oxf. 1983; MRCP (UK) 1989; FRCR 1992. Sen. Lect. (Clin. Oncol.) Roy. Marsden Hosp. Sutton; Chairm., NCRI teshs Study Gp. Prev: Sen. Regist. & Regist. (Radiother.) Roy. Marsden Hosp. Sutton; CRC Clin. Research Fell. Inst. Cancer Research Sutton; SHO Rotat. (Med.) Addenbrooke's Hosp. Camb.

HUDDART, Mr Simon Neil University Hospital of Wales, Heath Park, Cardiff CF14 4XW Tel: 029 207 45342 Fax: 029 207 46322 Email: huddartsn@msn.com — MB BS 1982 Lond.; BA Oxf. 1979, MA 1992; FRCS Eng. 1994; FRCS Eng. 1987. Cons. Paediat. Surg. Univ. Hosp. Wales Cardiff. Prev: Sen. Regist. (Paediat. Surg.) Manch.; Fell. (Neuroblastoma) Birm.; Regist. (Paediat. Surg.) Birm.

HUDDLESTON, Iain (retired) Fern Bank, Emma Terrace, Blairgowrie PH10 6JA Tel: 01250 872670 — MB ChB 1957 St. And.; DObst RCOG 1962.

HUDDLESTON, Robert Everett Granton Medical Centre, 114 Middleton Hall Road, King's Norton, Birmingham B30 1DH Tel: 0121 459 9117 Fax: 0121 486 2889; 117 Selly Park Road, Selly Park, Birmingham B29 7HY Tel: 0121 472 1800 — MB ChB 1972 Birm.; DA Eng. 1975; DObst RCOG 1974. Prev: SHO (Anaesth.) Gen. Hosp. Birm.; SHO (Obst.) Prof. Unit New Matern. Hosp. Birm.

HUDDLESTON, Sarah 42 Duke Street, Settle BD24 9DJ — MB ChB 1998 Manch.; MB ChB Manch 1998.

HUDDLESTONE, Leslie Apartment 10, Chomlea, Devisdale Road, Bowdon, Altrincham WA14 2AT Tel: 0161 928 8625 Fax: 0161 928 8625; Apartment 10, Chomlea, Devisdale Road, Bowdon, Altrincham WA14 2AT Tel: 0161 928 8625 Fax: 0161 928 8625 — LRCP LRCS Ed. LRFPS Glas. 1950. (Roy. Colls. Ed. & Anderson Coll. Glas.) Socs: Social Sec. (Ex-Pres.) Sale Med. & Dent. Soc. Prev: Clin. Med. Off. Paediat. Clinics Salford & Trafford HA.

HUDDY, Charlotte Lucy Jane Univ. Hosps. of Leicester NHS Trust, Leicester Gen. Hospital, Gwendolen Rd, Leicester LE5 Fax: 0114 271 7000 — MB BS 1986 Lond.; MRCPCH; BSc Lond. 1983; MRCP (UK) 1991. Cons. Neonatologist. Socs: Mem. of Neonat. Soc. and Brit. Assn. of Pevinatal Med. Prev: Sen. Regist. (Paediat.) Roy. Berks. Hosp. Reading & John Radcliffe Hosp. Oxf.

HUDDY, Ernest Charles Hotten c/o Barclays Bank plc, Sturminster Newton DT10 1BW — MRCS Eng. LRCP Lond. 1927; MD Lond. 1940, MB BS 1929, DPH 1939. (Guy's) Socs: BMA. Prev: Co. Med. Off. Berks.; Cas. Off. & Ho. Phys. Miller Gen. Hosp. For S.E. Lond.

HUDDY, Francis William Avalon Mews, North End IG9 5RA Tel: 0208 504 8711 — MB BChir 1950 Camb.; MA Camb. 1952. (St. Thos.) Hosp. Pract. ENT Dept. St. Bart. Hosp. Lond. Prev: Ho. Surg. St. Thos. Hosp. Lond.; Surg. Lt. RN.

HUDDY, James Edward 119 St Jospeh's Vale, London SE3 0XQ Tel: 0208 318 0440 Email: jimhuddy@hotmail.com; 119 St Josephs Vale, London SE3 0XQ Tel: 0208 318 0440 — MB BS 1995 Lond. (St Barts, Lond.)

HUDDY, Joanna Margaret Mary The Bush Doctors, 16-17 The Links, Shepherds Bush Centre, London W12 8PP Tel: 020 8749 1882 Fax: 020 8749 4278 — MB BChir 1989 Camb.; MRCGP 1993.

HUDDY, Nicholas Charles Anaesthetic Department, Broomfield Hospital, Court Road, Broomfield, Chelmsford CM1 7ET Tel: 01245 514080 Fax: 01245 514079 Email: nick.huddy@meht.nhs.uk — MB BS 1980 Lond.; FRCA Eng. 1985. (Lond. Hosp. Med. Coll.) Cons. Anaesth. Broomfield Hosp. & St. John's Hosp. Chelmsford. Prev: Sen. Regist. (Anaesth.) Univ. Coll. Hosp., Gt. Ormond St. & Whittington Hosps. Lond.; Sen. Regist. (Anaesth.) Roy. Brisbane Hosp. Austral.

HUDDY, Mr Philip Edward (retired) Brick House, Axford, Marlborough SN8 2EX Tel: 01672 514686 — MB BChir 1950 Camb.; MChir Camb. 1965, MA 1950; FRCS Eng. 1957; MRCS Eng. LRCP Lond. 1950. Prev: Hon. Surg. Querns Hosp. Cirencester.

HUDDY, Richard Bernard (retired) 21 St John Street, Manchester M3 4DT — MRCS Eng. LRCP Lond. 1959; MA Oxf. 1959, BM BCh 1958; FRCP Lond. 1983, M 1962. Prev: Cons. Phys. N. Manch, Gen. Hosp.

HUDDY, Mr Simon Philip John The Ipswich Hospital, Heath Road, Ipswich IP4 5PD Tel: 01473 712233 — MB BChir 1978 Camb.; MA, MChir Camb. 1988, MB 1978, BChir 1977; FRCS Eng. 1983; FRCS Ed. 1982. Cons. Surg. Ipswich Hosp. NHS Trust. Prev: Sen. Regist. (Gen. Surg.) SW Thames.

HUDDY, Mrs Vaneeta Jayne Broomfield Hospital, Court Road, Broomfield, Chelmsford CM1 7ET Tel: 01245 440761 — MB BS 1981 Lond.; FRCS Eng. 1990. (St Georges' Hosp med school) Assoc spec(Urol.) Broomfield Hosp. Chelmsford. Prev: Regist. (Gen. Surg.) S.end; SHO (Gen. Surg.) Plymouth; SHO (Gen. Surg.) Ham Green Hosp. Bristol.

HUDECEK, Ivan Peter 20 Orwell Road, Walsall WS1 2PJ Tel: 01922 649053 — MRCS Eng. LRCP Lond. 1973; MD Charles Univ. 1969; FFA RCS Eng. 1978; DA Eng. 1974. (Charles Univ. Prague) Cons. Anaesth. Walsall DGH. Prev: Regist. (Anaesth.) Roy. Free Hosp. Hampstead.; SHO (Anaesth.) St. Stephen's Hosp. Chelsea; Cas. Off. Centr. Middlx. Hosp. Lond.

HUDGINS, David 54 Royal Hill Road, Spondon, Derby DE21 7AG — MB ChB 1968 Liverp.; MRCP (UK) 1973; FFOM RCP Lond. 1994, MFOM 1983; DIH Soc. Apoth. Lond. 1978; DCH Eng. 1970; DObst RCOG 1971. (Liverp.) Sen. Med. Off. The Boots Co. Ltd. Nottm. Prev: Sen. Regist. (Med.) Sefton Gen. Hosp.; Regist. (Med.) Roy. Liverp. Hosps.; Ho. Off. Clatterbridge Hosp.

HUDGSON, Margaret Jean 36 Elmfield Road, Gosforth, Newcastle upon Tyne NE3 4BA — MB BS 1962 Durh.; DA Eng. 1966; DObst RCOG 1964.

HUDGSON, Peter, Lt.-Col. RAMC Retd. 36 Elmfield Road, Gosforth, Newcastle upon Tyne NE3 4BA — MB BS 1958 Melbourne; FRCP Lond. 1978, M 1970; FRACP 1971, M 1963. (Melb.) Cons. NeUrol., Newc. Nuffield Hosp. Socs: Assn. Phys. (Sen. Mem); Assn. Brit. Neurols. (Sen. Mem). Prev: Sen. Lect. (Neurol.) Univ. Newc.; Cons. Neurol. Newc. HA; 1st Asst. (Neurol.) Dept. of Med. Univ. Newc.

HUDSMITH, Jonathan Guy White Gates, 12 Whitehall Road, Sittingbourne ME10 4HB Tel: 01795 423940 — BM 1995 Soton.

HUDSON, Alison Jane Renowden Heavitree Health Centre, South Lawn Terrace, Exeter EX1 2RX Tel: 01392 431355 Fax: 01392 498305 — MB BS 1983 Lond.; MRCGP 1988.

HUDSON, Andrea Jane 31 Houstead Road, Sheffield S9 4BX — MB ChB 1996 Sheff.

HUDSON, Andrew Bernard Medical Centre, Derby Road, Peel IM5 1HP Tel: 01624 843636 Fax: 01624 844543; Red House, Peveril Avenue, Peel IM5 1QA Email: dr.hudson@advsys.co.uk — MB ChB 1988 Manch.

HUDSON, Angeline Dodsley Lane, Midhurst GU29 9AW; New Barn Cottage, Bepton, Midhurst GU29 0HY Tel: 01730 812902 — MB ChB 1965 Leeds. (Leeds)

HUDSON, Anne Bernadette 33 Horseshoe Road, Pangbourne, Reading RG8 7JQ — MB BS 1990 Lond.; BSc (Hons.) Nutrit. Lond. 1987; MRCGP 1997; DRCOG 1995; DFFP 1995. (King's Coll. Hosp. Lond.) GP Reading. Prev: SHO (O & G) Withybush Hosp. HaverfordW.; Resid. Paediat. & Gen. Med. King. Edwd. VII Memor. Hosp., Bermuda.

HUDSON, Anthony John 8 Monmouth Avenue, Exeter EX3 0AF — MB BS 1987 Lond.

HUDSON, Aubrey John Rees, VRD c/o Welsh Office, Grove House, Grove Place, Swansea SA3 5HL — MRCS Eng. LRCP Lond. 1943; MA Camb. 1945, BA 1939. (Camb.) Regional Med. Off. Welsh Office; Hon. Med. Off. Mumbles RNLI. Socs: Assoc. MRCGP; BMA. Prev: Surg. Cdr. RNR (Ret.); Fact. Med. Off. Aluminium Wire & Cable Co.; Cas. Off. P. of Wales's Hosp. Plymouth.

HUDSON, Ben Kirton Lodge, Main Road, Elm, Wisbech PE14 0AB — MB BS 1998 Newc.; MB BS Newc 1998.

HUDSON, Brendan The Surgery, 83 Grove Road, Sutton SM1 2DB Tel: 020 8642 1721/643 9366; White Rose Cottage, 84 Banstead Road, Carshalton Beeches, Carshalton SM5 3NH Tel: 020 8770

9523 — MB ChB 1977 Birm.; MRCGP 1982; DRCOG 1981; DCH Eng. 1980. Socs: Sutton Med. Soc. Prev: Police Surg. S. Yorks. Police; GP & Trainer Rotherham; Course Organiser Rotherham VTS.

HUDSON, Carol The Vicarage, Church Lane, Mellor, Blackburn BB2 7JL — MB BS 1970 Newc.; MRCGP 1980. Med. Off. DHSS.

HUDSON, Cedric Frank Estcourt Cedric Frank Estcourt, Meadow View, Yockleton, Shrewsbury SY5 9PA — LRCPI & LM, LRSCI & LM 1967; LRCPI & LM, LRCSI & LM 1967.

HUDSON, Charles Keith (retired) Fox End, Wolverton Road, Baughurst, Tadley RG26 5JH Tel: 0118.9.814815 Fax: 01189821181 — MB BS 1952 Lond.; MRCP Lond. 1957; FRCGP 1982; MRCS Eng. LRCP Lond. 1952. Prev: GP Hants.

HUDSON, Professor Christopher Neville St Bartholomew's Hospital, London EC1A 7BE Tel: 020 76 1 7180 — MB BChir Cantab. 1956; MChir Cantab. 1967; FRCS Eng. 1960; FRFPS Glas. 1960; FRCOG 1972; FRACOG 1979. (Univ. Camb. & St. Bart.) Emerit. Prof. O & G St. Bart. Hosp. & Roy. Lond. Sch. Med. & Dent. Lond. Socs: Fell. Roy. Soc. Med.; Life Mem. Aust. Soc. Gyn. Ouc; RCOG Visitor Santha Molten Project (FIGO), Lahore, Pakistan. Prev: Prof. O & G Univ. of Sydney & W.mead Hosp., Austral.; Reader (O & G) Med. Coll. St. Bart. Hosp. Lond.; Sen. Lect. O&G, St. Bart's Hosp. Lond.

HUDSON, Christopher Nigel Singleton Hospital, Sketty, Swansea SA2 8QA Tel: 01792 285042 Fax: 01792 285042 — MB BCh 1986 Wales; MRCP (UK) 1990; FRCP 2000 UK. (Welsh Nat. Sch. Med.) Cons. Gen. & Geriat. Phys. Singleton Hosp. Swansea. Socs: Fell.. RCP Lond.; Brit. Geriat. Soc.; Brit. Assn. Stroke Phys. Prev: Sen. Regist. (Geriat. & Gen. Med.) Ysbyty Gwynedd Bangor; Regist. (Geriat.) Univ. Hosp. Wales, Llandough Hosp. & Morriston Hosp. Swansea.

HUDSON, Chrysanthi 1 Briardale, Dinnington, Newcastle upon Tyne NE13 7JD Tel: 01661 821458 — MB BS 1993 Newc.

HUDSON, Darren Roger St Oswalds Surgery, The Parade, Pembroke SA71 4LD Tel: 01646 682374 Fax: 01646 622424; 11 Wades Close, Holyland Road, Pembroke SA71 4BN — MB ChB 1989 Manch.; MRCGP 1993.

HUDSON, David Jeffrey Ashworth Street Surgery, 85 Spotland Road, Rochdale OL12 6RT Tel: 01706 346767 Fax: 01706 346800; 33 Nordale Park, Norden, Rochdale OL12 7RT — MB BS 1979 Lond.; MRCGP 1983; DRCOG 1982. (St. Thomas's Hospital Medical School, London) Partner, Ashworth St. Surg., Rochdale.

HUDSON, David Michael Tarleton Health Centre, Gorse Lane, Tarleton, Preston PR4 6UJ Tel: 01772 812205 Fax: 01772 814934; 27 The Beeches, Hesketh Lane, Tarleton, Preston PR4 6EL — MB ChB 1987 Liverp.; MRCGP 1991; DRCOG 1990. GP Adviser Health Auth. Purchasing Team. Prev: Trainee GP W. Lancs.; Clin. Med. Off. & SHO (Community Paediat.) Vict. Gen. Hosp.; SHO (A & E) Ormskirk Gen. Hosp.

HUDSON, Donald Campbell (retired) Beechwood, 105 Ruff Lane, Ormskirk L40 6HA Tel: 01695 572572 — MB ChB 1949 Ed.; MRCGP 1963; DObst RCOG 1954. Prev: Obst. Ho. Surg. Heathfield Matern. Hosp. Birm.

HUDSON, Mrs Elisabeth (retired) Celfan, 9 Eastcliff, Southgate, Swansea SA3 2AS Tel: 01792 233151 — MB ChB 1943 Bristol. Prev: SCMO W. Glam. AHA.

HUDSON, Elizabeth Anne (retired) Fox End, Wolverton Road, Baughurst, Tadley RG26 5JH Tel: 0118 981 4815 Fax: 0118 982 1181 Email: ahudson@doctors.org.uk — MB BS 1955 Lond.; MD Lond. 1974; MRCS Eng. LRCP Lond. 1955; FRCPath 1992, M 1980; DObst RCOG 1956. Prev: Cons. Cytopath. N.wick Pk. Hosp. NHS Trust Harrow.

HUDSON, Professor George Box Cottage, Hill Bottom, Whitchurch Hill, Pangbourne, Reading RG8 7PU Tel: 0118 984 2671 — MB ChB 1949 Manch.; DSc Bristol 1966, MD 1959; MSc Manch. 1962, BSc 1945; Hon. LLD Sheff. 1993; FRCP Lond. 1988, M 1984; FRCPath 1975, M 1970. (Manch.) Emerit. Prof. Univ. Sheff. Socs: Anat. Soc.& Brit. Soc. Haemat. Prev: Regional Postgrad. Dean Univ. Sheff.; Prof. & Head Dept. Haemat. Univ. Sheff.; Administ. Dean. Fac. Med. Univ. Sheff.

HUDSON, George Russell 61 Oakdale Drive, Heald Green, Cheadle SK8 3SN Tel: 0161 437 1632 — MB ChB 1969 Birm.; DObst RCOG 1971.

HUDSON, Mr Horace Noble Guthrie 80 Hillway, Highate, London N6 6DP — MB BS 1937 Lond.; MB BS (Hnrs.) Lond. 1937; FRCS Eng. 1942; MRCS Eng. LRCP Lond. 1937. (Middlx.) Sen. Surg. Regist. N.E. Metrop. RHB. Socs: Fell. Roy. Soc. Med.; Assoc. Mem. Brit. Assn. Urol. Surgs. Prev: Sen. Surg. Regist. W.m. Hosp. (All St.s' Urol. Centre) & Metrop.; Hosp. Lond.; Surg. Regist. W. Lond. Hosp.

HUDSON, Ian Department of Cardiology, Glenfield Hospital, Groby Road, Leicester LE3 9QP Tel: 0116 287 1471 Fax: 0116 287 5792 Email: ih9@le.ac.uk; 7 Burley Rise, Kegworth, Derby DE74 2DZ Tel: 01509 673125 Fax: 01509 673125 — MB ChB 1988 Dundee; BMSc (Hons.) Gen. Path. Dund 1985; MRCP (UK) 1991. (Dundee) Research Regist. (Cardiol.) Glenfield Hosp. Leceister; Clin. Lect. Univ. Leicester. Prev: Regist. (Cardiol. & Gen. Med.) Derby Roy. Infirm.; Regist. (Cardiol.) Glenfield Hosp.; Regist. (Gen. Med.) Airedale Gen. Hosp.

HUDSON, Ian Norman, RD Royal Hospital for Sick Children, Sciennes Road, Edinburgh EH9 1LF Tel: 0131 667 1991 — MB ChB 1970 Ed.; BSc Ed. 1967, MB ChB 1970; FFA RCS Eng. 1977; DObst RCOG 1974. Cons. Anaesth. Roy. Hosp. Sick Childr. Edin. Socs: Assn. Anaesths.; Assn. Paediat. Anaesth. Prev: Regist. & Sen. Regist. (Anaesth.) Roy. Infirm. Edin.

HUDSON, Ian Robert Burton Marsworth, Monk St., Thaxted, Dunmow CM6 2NR — MD 1992 Lond.; MB BS Lond. 1982; BSc Lond. 1979, MD 1992; MRCP (UK) 1985; MFPHM RCP (UK) 1993; Dip. Pharm. Med. RCP (UK) 1991; DCH RCP Lond. 1985. Dir. & Vice-Pres. Clin. Investig. SmithKline Beecham Pharmaceut. Prev: Research Fell. (Child Health) Univ. Glas.

HUDSON, Mr Ivan Ipswich Hospital, Heath Road, Ipswich IP4 5PD Tel: 01473 712233 — MB BS 1980 Lond.; FRCS Eng. 1985. (Char. Cross) Cons. Orthop. Surg. Ipswich Hosp. Socs: Fell. BOA; Roy. Soc. Med.; Brit. Soc. Childr.s' Orthopaedic Surg. Prev: Sen. Regist. (Orthop.) Char. Cross Hosp. Lond.; Regist. (Gen. Surg.) Wexham Pk. Hosp. Slough; SHO Roy. Nat. Orthop. Hosp. Lond.

HUDSON, Mr James Ralph, CBE (retired) 17 Montagu Square, London W1H 2LE Tel: 020 7487 2680 — MB BS Lond. 1940; FRCS Eng. 1949; MRCS Eng. LRCP Lond. 1939; FRACO (Hon.) 1978, M 1970; FRCOphth 1988; Hon. FRCOphth 1990; DOMS Eng. 1948. Hon. Civil Cons. (Ophth.) RAF; Hon. Ophth. Surg. Moorfields Eye Hosp. Lond. Prev: Hon. Ophth. Surg. K. Edwd. VII Hosp. for Off. Lond.

HUDSON, Jane Margaret Sandy Lane Surgery, Sandy Lane, Leyland, Preston PR25 2EB Tel: 01772 909915 Fax: 01772 909911 — MB ChB 1987 Liverp.; MRCGP 1993.

HUDSON, Jocelyn Marsh Street Surgery, 25A Marsh Street, Rothwell, Leeds LS26 0AG Tel: 0113 282 1571 Fax: 0113 282 4720; 135 Mangates Lane, Sandal, Wakefield WF2 7DS Tel: 01924 249280 — MB ChB 1981 Leeds; MRCGP 1986. GP Oulton Health Centre Leeds.

HUDSON, John Govan 78 Egerton Road, Bristol BS7 8HP; 64 West Green, Stokesley, Middlesbrough TS9 5BD — MB BS 1983 Lond.; MRCP (UK) 1988. Research Fell. (Haemat.) SW Regional Transfus. Centre Bristol.

HUDSON, John Harral (retired) The Pippins, Rays Hill, Horton Kirby, Dartford DA4 9DB — MB ChB Leeds 1933; BSc Leeds 1929; MRCS Eng. LRCP Lond. 1934; MFCM 1972; DTM & H Eng. 1935, DPH 1947. Prev: MOH Dartford Boro. & RD & N.fleet & Swanscombe UDs.

HUDSON, Mr John Marshall (retired) — MB ChB 1959 Sheff.; FRCS Ed. 1971; FRCOphth 1989; DO Eng. 1967; FRCS 1971 Edin. Cons. Ophth. (Hon.) N. Riding Infirm. Middlesbrough; Hon. Cons. Ophth. (Retd.) N. Riding Infirm., MiddlesBoro. Prev: Sen. Regist. Birm. & Midl. Eye Hosp. & Wolverhampton & Midl. Cos. Eye Infirm.

HUDSON, Jonathan David Piers 3 Guilder Lane, Salisbury SP1 1HW Tel: 01722 326066 — MB ChB 1994 Sheff. GP Salisbury Wilts. Socs: Med. Defence Union; BMA. Prev: SHO (Paediat.) Salisbury Dist. Gen. Hosp.; SHO (Psychiat.) Old Manor Hosp. Salisbury; SHO (A & E) Doncaster Roy. Infirm.

HUDSON, Julie Claire Flat 5, 139 Osborne Rd, Newcastle upon Tyne NE2 2TB — MB BS 1997 Newc.

HUDSON, Kenneth David The Surgery, Richmond House, Fore St., St James Precinct, Teignmouth TQ14 8DZ Tel: 01626 773339; Redsands, Torquay Road, Shaldon, Teignmouth TQ14 0BQ Tel: 01626 872555 — MB BS 1962 Lond.; MRCS Eng. LRCP Lond, 1962; MRCGP 1970; DRCOG 1975. (St. Mary's) Med. Off. Teignmouth Hosp.; Clin. Asst. (Radiother.) Torbay Hosp. Socs: Torquay & Dist. Med. Soc.; Roy. Soc. Med. (Assoc. Study Obesity).

Prev: SHO (O & G) Luton Matern. Hosp.; Ho. Phys. W. Suff. Gen. Hosp. Bury St. Edmunds; Ho. Surg. St. John's Hosp. Lewisham.

HUDSON, Margaret Mary Theresa Medicines Control Agency, Market Towers, 1 Nine Elms Lane, London SW8 5NQ Tel: 020 7273 0710 Fax: 020 7273 0554; 12 Molewood Road, Hertford SG14 3AQ — MB BS 1989 Lond.; BSc Lond. 1986; MRCP (UK) 1992; DFFP 1995. (Guys and St Thomas) Trainee Med. Assessor Meds. Control Agency Lond. Socs: Med. Soc. Study VD; Brit. Soc. Colpos. & Cerv. Path. Prev: Sen. Regist. (Genitourin. Med.) Roy. Hallamshire Hosp. Sheff.; Regist. (Genitourin. Med.) St. Bart. & Homerton Hosps. Lond.; Regist. (Med. Microbiol. & Virol.) Pub. Health Laborat. Serv. Manch.

HUDSON, Mark 6 Woodbine Avenue, Gosforth, Newcastle upon Tyne NE3 4EU — MB ChB 1982 Aberd.; FRCP Ed. 1996; MRCP (UK) 1986. Cons. Phys. (Gastroenterol.) Gastrointestinal & Liver Unit Freeman Hosp. Newc. u. Tyne. Socs: Fell. Roy. Coll. Edin.; Brit. Soc. Gastroenterol. Prev: Hon. Sen. Regist. Liver Failure Unit King's Coll. Hosp. Lond.; Sen. Regist. Freeman Hosp. Newc. u. Tyne; Research Fell. Roy. Free Hosp. Lond.

HUDSON, Martin Frederic Grasmere Medical Services, Grasmere, 7 Swanwick Close, Crewe CW4 8NU Email: martin-hudson@lineone.net, www.grasmere-medical-services.co.uk; Grasmere, 7 Swanwick Close, Goostrey, Holmes Chapel, Crewe CW4 8NU — MB BS Lond. 1965; MRCP (UK) 1971; MRCS Eng. LRCP Lond. 1965; FRCP Ed 1998; Royal College of Physicians of Edinburgh. (St. Bart. Hosp. Lond.) Authorised. Med. Examr. Civil Aviat. Auth & Fed. Aviat. Auth. UK; Adviser Airtours Internat. Airlines and Airtours Sun Cruises; Authorised Med. Examr. Civil Aviat. Auth. & Federal Aviat. Admin. (USA); Authorised Med. Examr. Austral. Civil Aviat. Safety Authoriy. Socs: Brit. Hypertens. Soc.; Hon Treas Assn. Authorised Aviat. Med. Examrs. Prev: Princip. in Gen. Pract., Holmes Chapel Health Centre; Squadron Ldr. RAF Med. Br., Med. Specialist; Ho. Phys. St. Bart. Hosp.

HUDSON, Maurice Cedric (retired) 91 Old Orchard, Haxby, York YO32 3DS — MB BS Lond. 1958; FFA RACS 1969.

HUDSON, Michael Gray Springfield Surgery, Elstead, Godalming GU8 6EG Tel: 01252 703122; Hurst Farm Surgery, Chapel Lane, Milford, Godalming GU8 5HU Tel: 0148 685885 — MB BCh BAO 1963 Dub.; DObst RCOG 1966.

HUDSON, Michael Kenneth George (retired) 6 Whitcombe Road, Beaminster DT8 3NB Tel: 01308 862262 — MB BS (Hnrs. Surg.) Lond. 1960; MRCS Eng. LRCP Lond, 1960; DObst RCOG 1964. Prev: Ho. Surg. Roy. Free Hosp. Lond. & Portwey Matern. Hosp. Weymouth.

HUDSON, Nicholas GI Unit, Leicester Royal Infirmary, Leicester WR5 1NH Tel: 01905 760623; 11 Emerson Road, Harborne, Birmingham B17 9LT — MB ChB 1984 Birm.; DM Nottm. 1995; FRCP 1999. Cons. Phys. (Gastroenterol.) City Hosp. Birm. Prev: Sen. Regist. (Gastroenterol.) Roy. Infirm. Edin.; Hon. Research Fell. (Therap.) Qu. Med. Centre Nottm.; Regist. (Gastroenterol.) Dudley Rd. Hosp. Birm.

HUDSON, Nicholas William 100 Glendale Road, Middlesbrough TS5 7NL — MB ChB 1990 Sheff.

HUDSON, Norah Marion Glenfield Hospital, Leicester LE3 9QP; Deene Cottage, E. Langton, Market Harborough LE16 7TB Tel: 01858 545360 — MB BS 1962 Lond.; MRCS Eng. LRCP Lond. 1962; FFR 1972; DMRD Eng. 1969. (Roy. Free) Hon. Cons. Radiol.Glenfield Hosp. Socs: BNMS; Brit. Inst. Radiol.; BMA. Prev: Clin. Research Fell. Univ. S. Calif. USA.

HUDSON, Patrick Timothy Pilkington Four Trees, Hookley Lane, Elstead, Godalming GU8 6JD — MB BS 1989 Lond.; DCH RCP Lond. 1993; DObst. RCOG 1992.

HUDSON, Paul Christopher 89 Fieldhead Avenue, Bury BL8 2LZ Tel: 0161 764 8616 — MB ChB 1993 Liverp. GP Regist. Lancs.

HUDSON, Peter McKenzie Windrush, Stamford Road, Ufford, Stamford PE9 3BP — MRCS Eng. LRCP Lond. 1969; MB Camb. 1970, BChir 1969; FRCP Lond. 1987; MRCP (U.K.) 1972. (Camb. & Guy's) Cons. Dermat. PeterBoro. Dist. Hosp. Prev: Sen. Regist. (Dermat.) St. Thos. Hosp. Lond.; Regist. (Dermat.) Univ. Coll. Hosp.; Jun. Med. Regist. Guy's Hosp.

HUDSON, Richard Callander (retired) Callanders, Ferry Road, fingringhoe, Colchester CO5 7BX Tel: 01206 570371 — MB BS 1957 Lond. Prev: Hosp. Pract. (Chest Dis.) NE Essex HA.

HUDSON, Robert Basil Spencer 22 Ilkley Road, Morton Banks, Keighley BD20 5PU — MB BCh BAO 1965 Dub.; FFA RCS Eng. 1973.

HUDSON, Robin Mulroy 149 Simonside Terrace, Heaton, Newcastle upon Tyne NE6 5LF — MB BS 1993 Newc.

HUDSON, Sally Lynn Tadworth Farm Surgery, 1 Troy Close, Tadworth KT20 5JE Tel: 01737 362327 — MB BS 1983 Lond.

***HUDSON, Sonia Jane** 5 Hillside Gr, Chelmsford CM2 9DA Tel: 01245 354612 Email: sonia@sjhudson.freeserve.co.uk — MB BS 1997 Lond.

HUDSON, Stephen William South Ham House, 96 Paddock Road, Basingstoke RG22 6RL Tel: 01256 324666 Fax: 01256 810849 — MB ChB 1974 Bristol; MRCGP 1978.

HUDSON, Stuart James Forestside Medical Practice, Beaulieu Road, Dibden Purlien, Southampton SO45 4JA; 25 Lambourne Road, West End, Southampton SO18 3LS Tel: 01703 477044 Email: hudsail@aol.com — MB ChB 1988 Birm.; DRCOG.

HUDSON, Susan Jane Microbiology Department, Queen Elizabeth Hospital, Sherriff Hill, Gateshead NE9 6SX Tel: 0191 487 8989 — MB BS 1979 Lond.; MRCPath 1986. Cons. Microbiol. Gateshead HA & Freeman Hosp. Newc.; Clin. Lect. Univ. Newc.

HUDSON, Timothy Ian 8 Tennyson Street, Pudsey LS28 9HA Email: dr.tim@currantbun.com — MB ChB 1993 Leeds; BSc (Hons.) Leeds 1990. Prev: SHO (Paediat.) Whiston Hosp.

HUDSON, Trevor Gordon 25 Cadogan Place, London SW1X 9SA Tel: 020 7730 3737 — MB BChir 1963 Camb.; BA Camb. 1958; LMSSA Lond. 1962; MRCGP 1973. (St. Bart.) Hunt. Soc. Gold Medal 1974. Prev: Ho. Phys. St. Bart. Hosp. Lond.; Resid. Med. Off. King Edwd. VII Hosp. Offs. Lond.

HUDSON, William Alan (retired) The Walk House, Walk Lane, Wombourne, Wolverhampton WV5 9HL Tel: 01902 892344 — MB ChB 1951 Sheff.; FRCP Lond. 1972, M 1955. Hon. Cons. Phys. & Cardiol. Roy. Hosp. Wolverhampton. Prev: Sen. Regist. (Med.) Qu. Eliz. Hosp. Birm.

HUDSON, William Francis Metcalfe 7 Beechcroft Flats, Kenton Road, Gosforth, Newcastle upon Tyne NE3 4NB — MB BS 1945 Durh.; MRCGP 1953. (Newc.) Med. Ref. DoH. Prev: Regional Med. Off. N.E. Div. DHSS; Ho. Phys. & Ho. Surg. Accid. Room Roy. Vict. Infirm. Newc.

HUDSON, William Stanley The Surgery, Reading Road, Hook, Basingstoke RG27 9ED Tel: 01256 762125 Fax: 01256 760608 — MB BS 1964 Lond.; MRCGP 1983; DCH Eng. 1968; DObst RCOG 1967. (King's Coll. Hosp.)

HUDSON-JESSOP, Pamela Courtyard Apartment, 30 Royal Crescent, Bath BA1 2LT — MB ChB 1991 Bristol.

HUDSON-PEACOCK, Alice Sau-Chun Flat 2, 1 North Terrace, Newcastle upon Tyne NE2 4AD — MB BCh 1987 Wales; DRCOG 1990.

HUDSON-PEACOCK, Mark John FLat 2, 1 North Terrace, Newcastle upon Tyne NE2 4AD — MB BCh 1987 Wales; BSc (Hons.) Cardiff 1984; MRCP (UK) 1990.

HUDSPITH, Michael Julian Anaesthesia, Norfolk & Norwich University Hospital NHS Trust, Norwich NR1 3SR Tel: 01603 287086 Fax: 01603 287886 — MB BS 1989 Lond.; FRCA 1993; PhD Lond. 1988, BSc 1983. Cons. Anaesth. & Pain Managem., Norf. & Norwich Univ. Hosp., NHS Trust. Prev: Clin. Lect. (Anaesth.) Univ. Camb.; Regist. (Anaesth.) Addenbrooke's Hosp. Camb.; SHO (Anaesth.) King's Coll. Hosp. Lond. & Surrey Hosp. Redhill.

HUEBNER, Rurik 75A Penn Hill Avenue, Poole BH14 9LY — State Exam Med 1993 Technical U Munich.

HUEHNS, Professor Ernst Reinhard 18 Crundale Avenue, London NW9 9PL Tel: 020 8204 7369 — MB BS 1950 Lond.; PhD, MD Lond. 1962, MB BS 1950; MRCS Eng. LRCP Lond. 1950; FRCP Lond. 1983; MRCPath 1963. (Univ. Coll. Hosp.) Emerit. Prof. Haemat. Univ. Coll. Hosp. Lond. Prev: Rockefeller Trav. Fell. in Med. Dept. Med. Seattle, USA; Sen. Beit. Memor. Fell. Univ. Coll. Hosp. Med. Sch.; Ho. Phys. Univ. Coll. Hosp. Lond.

HUELSER, Ruth Eva Edgware General Hospital, Edgware HA8 0AD — State Exam Med 1993 Cologne.

HUENGSBERG, Maria Department of Genitourinary Medicine, Whittall Street Clinic, Birmingham B4 6DH Tel: 0121 237 5721 Fax: 0121 237 5729; Jelanda, Wyndley Drive, Sutton Coldfield B73 6EU — MB BS 1982 New South Wales; MD 1999 Birmingham, UK.

Cons. Genitourin. Med. Whittall St. Clinic. Birm.; Hon. Sen. Lect. Birm. Univ.

HUEY, Brian Robert Thomas Lisburn Health Centre, Linenhall St., Lisburn BT28 1LU Tel: 01846 665181 — MB BCh BAO 1961 Belf.

HUEY, David Millar Oakeswell Health Centre, Brunswick Park Road, Wednesbury WS10 9HP Tel: 0121 556 2114 Fax: 0121 505 1843; 11 Elizabeth Road, Brookhouse, Walsall WS5 3PF Tel: 01922 629372 — MB BCh BAO 1968 Dub.

HUEY, Kathleen Anne Frambury Lane Surgery, Frambury Lane, Newport, Saffron Walden CB11 3PY Tel: 01799 540570 Fax: 01799 542126 — MB BCh BAO 1967 Dub.; DCH Eng. 1970.

HUEY, Michael John Main Street Surgery, 11 Main Street, Loughbrickland, Banbridge BT32 3NQ Tel: 028 4066 2692 Fax: 028 4066 9517 — MB BCh BAO 1982 Belf.

HUEY, Susan 37 Main Street, Castlerock, Coleraine BT51 4RA — MB BCh BAO 1980 Belf.; MRCGP 1984; DRCOG 1984.

HUEY, Timothy David Scott 17 Blackthorn Way, The Brambles, Newtownabbey BT37 0GW — MB BCh BAO 1995 Belf. SHO (O & G) Antrim Hosp.

HUFF, Anthony George Mayfield Surgery, 246 Roehampton Lane, Roehampton, London SW15 4AA Tel: 020 8780 5650; 35 Crestway, Roehampton, London SW15 5DB Tel: 020 8789 6050 — MB BS Lond. 1962; MRCGP 1977; DObst RCOG 1965. (Westm.) Prev: Ho. Surg. King Edwd. VII Hosp. Windsor; Obst. Ho. Surg. St. Alfege's Hosp. Greenwich; SHO (Path.) Qu. Mary's Hosp. Roehampton.

HUFTON, Barrie Richard Audlem Medical Practice, 16 Cheshire Street, Audlem, Crewe CW3 0AH Tel: 01270 811440 Fax: 01270 812382; Ash Tree House, 31 Stafford St, Audlem, Crewe CW3 0AR Email: dachufaud@netscapeonline.co.uk — MB BS 1974 Lond.; MRCP (UK) 1978.

HUGGAN, David Kerr Kilwinning Medical Practice, 15 Almswall Road, Kilwinning KA13 6BO Tel: 01294 554591 Fax: 01294 557300; 24 Carrick Road, Ayr KA7 2RB Tel: 01292 267225 Fax: 01292 267225 Email: cd.huggan@dial.pipex.com — MB ChB 1969 Glas. (Glas.) GP Kilwinning; Clin. Asst. (Psychogeriat. Med.) Ravens Pk. Hosp. Socs: Assn. Neurolinguistic Programming; Scott. Soc. Med. & Dent. Hypn.; Ment. Hypn. Soc.

HUGGAN, Mr John David Eye Department, Royal Infirmary, Stirling FK8 2AU Tel: 01786 434000 Fax: 01786 450588; 13 Randolph Road, Stirling FK8 2AJ Tel: 01786 461193 Email: david.huggan@virgin.net — MB ChB 1971 Ed.; FRCS Ed. 1976; FRCOphth 1988; DO Eng. 1974. (Edinburgh) Cons. Ophth. Stirling Roy. Infirm. NHS Trust. Prev: Sen. Regist. (Ophth.) SW RHA; Hon. Tutor (Ophth.) Bristol Univ.

HUGGARD, Susan Emily Rainworth Health Centre, Warsop Lane, Rainworth, Mansfield NG21 0AD — MB ChB 1983 Manch.; Cert Family Planning; BSc (Med. Sci.) St. And. 1980; DRCOG 1986. Socs: BMA & Mansfield Med. Soc.

HUGGETT, Andrew Martin The Surgery, 69 Stockingate, South Kirkby, Pontefract WF9 3PE Tel: 01977 642251 Fax: 01977 645515 — MB ChB 1977 Sheffield; MB ChB Sheff. 1977. (Sheffield) GP Pontefract, W. Yorks.

HUGGETT, Isabel Mary Westmorland General Hospital, Kendal LA9 7RG Tel: 01539 732288 Fax: 01539 795312; Greenfield House, Aynsome Road, Cartmel, Grange-over-Sands LA11 6PS Tel: 01539 536378 Fax: 015395 36378 — MB BS 1977 Newc.; FRCP Lond. 1995; MRCP (UK) 1980. Cons. Phys. Geriat. Med. W.morland Gen. Hosp. Kendal & Roy. Lancaster Infirm. Prev: Cons. Phys. Geriat. Med. Kendal Green Hosp. Cumbria & Roy. Lancaster Infirm.; Sen. Regist. (Geriat. Med.) St. Geo. Hosp. Lond.

HUGGETT, Robert John Fancy Dale Huse, Clearbrook, Yelverton PL20 6JB — MB BS 1997 Lond.

HUGGINS, Anne Glebe House, 51 Church Lane, Old Marston, Oxford OX3 0PT — MB ChB Bristol 1966; DMRT Eng. 1970. (Bristol) Asst. GP Oxf. Prev: Prog. Manager & BrE. Phys. Oxf. BrE. Care Progr.; Dep. Dir. SE Scotl. BrE. Screening Centr.

HUGGINS, Claire Louise 2 Belah Crescent, Carlisle CA3 9TX — MB ChB 1994 Leic.

HUGGINS, David Anthony Peter Highfield, 103 Brookhill St., Stapleford, Nottingham NG9 7GJ Tel: 0115 939 7792 Email: huggins@argonet.co.uk — MB BS 1973 W. Indies. (W. Indies) private Pract. in Med.Acupunct. Socs: BMA; Accred. Mem. Brit. Med. Acupunc. Soc. Prev: Regist. (Radiol.) Nottm. Gen. Hosp.; Regist. (Orthop. Surg.) Bridge of Earn Hosp. Perth; Regist. (Gen. Surg.) W.ern Isles HB.

HUGGINS, Eleanor Maria Flat 3, 22 Fairmile Avenue, London SW16 6AG — MB BS 1992 Lond.

HUGGINS, Kathleen (retired) 138 Westbury Road, Westbury-on-Trym, Bristol BS9 3AL — MB ChB 1946 Bristol; FFA RCS Eng. 1954; DA Eng. 1950. Prev: Anaesth. S.mead Hosp. Bristol.

HUGGINS, Linda Jane 19 Shenley Fields Road, Birmingham B29 5AG — MB ChB 1991 Aberd.; FRCA 1996. Specialist Regist. (Anaesth.) Univ. Hosp. Wales Cardiff. Socs: Assn. Anaesth. Prev: Specialist Regist. (Anaesth.) Newport Gwent; SHO (Anaesth.) St. Bart's & Whipps Cross Hosps. Lond.

HUGGINS, Nigel John Featherstone Department of Anaesthesia, Queen Elizabeth Hospital, Edgbaston, Birmingham B15 2TH Tel: 0121 627 2395 Fax: 0121 697 8340 Email: nigelhuggins@cucom.net; Email: nigelhuggins@curcom.net — MB ChB 1980 Birm.; FRCA 1987; FFA RCSI 1986. (Birmingham) Cons. NeuroAnaesth. Qu. Eliz. Hosp. Birm.; Hon. Sen. Lect. Univ. Birm. Socs: Fell. Roy. Soc. Med.; Neuroanaesth. Soc.; Assn. Anaesth. Prev: Lect. (Neuroanaesth. & IC) Nat. Hosp. Neurol. & Neurosurg. Qu. Sq. & Maida Vale Lond.; Sen. Regist. (Anaesth.) W. Midl. RHA.

HUGGINS, Sheldon Tarquin Victor 106 Kingsbridge Road, Morden SM4 4QB Tel: 020 8337 4277 Email: stvhuggins'yahoo.com — MB BS 1992 West Indies; MRCOG1 1997. (West Indies) Socs: BMA; Med. Protec. Soc. Prev: Sen.SHO.Kingston.Hosp; SpR (O & G) Guy's & St. Thomas', Lond.; SpR (O & G) Lewisham Hosp.

HUGGON, Anne-Marie Lewisham Hospital, Lewisham High St., London SE13 6LH — MB ChB 1986 Leeds; MRCP (UK) 1990; DRCOG 1992; DCH RCP Lond. 1991. Sen. Regist. (A & E) Lewisham Hosp.

HUGGON, Ian Charles Fetal Cardiology Unit, Fetal Medicine, 9th Floor, Ruskin Wing, King's College Hospital, Denmark Hill, London SE5 9RS Tel: 020 7734400003040 Email: ian.huggon@kcl.ac.uk — MB ChB 1983 Leeds; BSc (Hons.) Leeds 1980, MB ChB (Hons.) 1983; MRCP (UK) 1986; MD Leeds 1997. Cons. Neonat. & Fetal Cardiol. King's Coll. Hosp.; Cons Paediactric Cardiol. Guy's and St Thoma's Hosp Lond. Socs: BMA; Roy. Coll Paediat. & Child Health. Prev: Sen. Regist. (Paediat. Cardiol.) Guy's Hosp. Lond.

HUGH, Alan Edward Cornwall House Clinic, Sandy Lane, Newcastle ST5 0LZ Tel: 01782 714600 Fax: 01782 714609; The Old Hall, Poolside, Madeley, Crewe CW3 9DX Tel: 01782 750209 — MB BCh 1955 Wales; MB BCh Wales, 1955; FRCP Ed. 1967, M 1957; FRCR 1975; FFR 1962; DMRD Eng. 1960. (Cardiff) Dir. & Cons. Radiol. Instant X Rays plc Cornw. Ho. Clinic Newc. Prev: Cons. Radiol. Stoke-on-Trent Hosp. Gp.; Research Fell. (Radiodiag.) Univ. Leeds.

HUGH, David John 148 Harley Street, London W1N 1AH Tel: 020 7935 1900 Fax: 020 7928 1702; 24 Blenheim Road, St Albans AL1 4NR Tel: 01727 860387 — MRCS Eng. LRCP Lond. 1982; T(GP) 1992. (Manch.) Police Surg. Lond.; Asst. Coroner W. Herts.; Local Med. Off.

HUGH, Duncan Graham Road Surgery, 22 Graham Road, Weston Super Mare BS23 1YA Tel: 01934 62811 Fax: 01934 645842 — MB ChB 1991 Manch.; BSc Bristol 1981; MSc Univ. Surrey 1983. (Manchester) GP W.on Super Mare. Socs: Assoc. Mem. Roy. Coll. Path.; Roy. Coll. Gen. Pract. Prev: SHO (O & G) St. Pauls Hosp. Cheltenham; Trainee GP/SHO Cirencester Hosp.; SHO P.ss Margt. Hosp. Swindon.

HUGH, Mr Ivan Anthony 36 Buckthorne Drive, East Ardsley, Wakefield WF3 2LP — MB BS 1978 West Indies; FRCS Ed. 1988.

HUGH, James Edwin Elizabeth Place Surgery, 8 Elizabeth Place, St Helier, Jersey JE2 3PN Tel: 01534 723718; Mid Bay, St Aubin's Road, Bel Royal, St Lawrence, Jersey JE3 1LN Tel: 01534 879747 — MB ChB 1958 Ed.; LRCP LRCS Ed. LRFPS Glas. 1958. (Univ. Ed.) Princip. GP. Prev: Late Ho. Surg. (O & G), Ho. Phys. & Ho. Surg. Stirling Roy. Infirm.

HUGH, Stephen Edward John Stirchley Medical Practice, Stirchley Health Centre, Stirchley, Telford TF3 1FB Tel: 01952 660444 Fax: 01952 415139; 43 Darby Road, Coalbrookdale, Ironbridge, Telford TF8 7EW Tel: 01952 433540 — MB ChB 1982 Birm.; Dip. Primary Med. Care Keele 1993. (Birmingham) Med. Manager Shrops. Doctors Co-op. Ltd; GP Trainer Advanced Train. Pract. Prev: Regist. (Radiol.) Univ. Manch.

HUGH-JONES, Jean Alison (retired) 36 Laurel Drive, St Helens WA10 5JD Tel: 01744 29962 Email: jeanhj@jeanhj.demon.co.uk — M.S.C, History of Science & Tech, Liverpool Univ.; MB ChB St. And. 1949. Prev: GP St. Helens.

HUGH-JONES, Katy Tel: 0208 321 3844 Fax: 0208 321 3862 — MB ChB 1987 Sheff.; MRCGP 1992; DCH RCP Lond. 1991. (Univ. Sheff.) p/t GP. Prev: Trainee GP Kentish Town Lond.; SHO (Paediat.) Whittington Hosp. Lond.; SHO (O & G) Auckland Hosp., NZ.

HUGH-JONES, Kenneth (retired) The Court House, Pyrton, Watlington OX49 5AP Tel: 01491 612283 Fax: 01491 612283 — MB BS 1946 Lond.; MD Lond. 1952; FRCP Lond. 1971, M 1952; FRPCH 1997. Cons. Paediat. W.m. Childr. Hosp. Lond. & St. Albans City Hosp. Prev: Chief Asst. Childr. Dept. St. Bart. Hosp. Lond.

HUGH-JONES, Mary Christine The Laurels Surgery, 20 Newmarket Road, Cambridge CB5 8DT Tel: 01223 350513 Fax: 01223 300445 — MB 1985 Camb.; PhD (Social Anthropol.) Camb. 1977; BSc (Sociol.) Lond. 1968; BChir 1984; MRCGP 1989; DRCOG 1989. Socs: BMA. Prev: Trainee GP Bury St. Edmunds VTS; SHO (A & E, O & G, Paediat., Psychiat. & Gen. Med.) W. Suff. HA.

HUGH-JONES, Philip 167 Camberwell Grove, London SE5 8JS Tel: 020 7274 3040 Fax: 020 7274 2633; Amberleaze Farm, Semley, Shaftesbury SP7 9AP Tel: 01747 830574 — MB BChir 1942 Camb.; MA Camb. 1943, BA (1st cl. Nat. Sc. Trip.) 1938; MD Camb. 1949; FRCP Lond. 1959, M 1950. (Camb., Univ. Coll. Hosp. & Ed.) Hon. Consg. Phys. King's Coll. Hosp. Lond.; Philip Elman Lect. RCP Lond.; Sydney Watson-Smith Lect. RCP Ed.; Waring Vis. Prof. Med. Colorado Univ. Sch. Med. & Stanford Univ. Socs: Assn. Phys.; Brit. Thorac. Soc.; Eur. Respirat. Soc. Prev: Cons. Phys. Dir. Chest Unit King's Coll. Hosp. Lond.; Cons. Phys. & Direct. of MRC Clin. Resp. Phys. Unit Hammersmith Hosp. Lond.; Cons. Phys. & Sen. Lect. Med. Univ. Coll. of W. Indies.

HUGH-JONES, Simon Fosse Medical Centre, 344 Fosse Road North, Leicester LE3 5RR Tel: 0116 253 8988 Fax: 0116 242 5178 — MRCS Eng. LRCP Lond. 1988; BDS Lond. 1980.

HUGHAN, Isabelle Catherine Flat 91, 29 Abercorn Place, St John's Wood, London NW8 9DT Tel: 020 7625 4621 — MB BS 1996 Lond.; BMedSci. Lond. 1995. SHO (A & E/Anat.) Roy. Free Hosp. Lond. Socs: BMA. Prev: Med. Ho. Off. Roy. Hosps. Trust N.ampton Gen. Hosp.

HUGHES, Adam John Elmcroft, Crab Hill Lane, South Nutfield, Redhill RH1 5NR — MB ChB 1995 Birm.; ChB Birm. 1995.

HUGHES, Adrian Paul Wirral Hospital NHS Trust, Arrowe Park Rd, Upton, Wirral CH49 5PE Tel: 0151 678 5111 Fax: 0151 604 7206 — MB ChB 1986 Manch. Cons. Paediat., Wirral Hosp. NHS Trust, Upton, Wirral. Prev: Regist. Rotat. (Paediat.) Roy. Liverp. Childr. NHS Trust Alder Hey.; Sen. Regist. Rotat. (Paediat.) Mersey Region.

HUGHES, Alan Mackenzie Rossendale, Main Road, Langbank, Port Glasgow PA14 6XP — MB ChB 1979 Glas.

HUGHES, Alexa Jane Baddidarroch, Lochinver, Lairg IV27 4LP Tel: 01571 844750; Flat 1, 4 Infirmary St, Edinburgh EH1 1LT Tel: 0131 556 6439 — MB ChB 1997 Glas. (Glasgow) SHO (c/o the Elderly) Roodlands Hosp. Haddington. Prev: Pre-regist. Ho, Off. (Med.) Glas. Roy. Infirm.; Pre-regist. Ho. Off. (Surg.) Dumfries & Galloway Roy. Infirm.

HUGHES, Alison Frances Ann 17 Queens Gate Terrace, South Kensington, London SW7 5PR — MB BS 1978 Lond.

HUGHES, Alison Jane The Old School House, Rosehill Road, Stoke Heath, Market Drayton TF9 2LF — MB BCh 1991 Wales; MRCGP 1996; Dip. Obst. NZ 1994. (Cardiff) Prev: GP Acting as Med. Off. Hospice of the Good Shepherd Chester; SHO (O & G & Med.) Auckland, NZ.

HUGHES, Alison Jane 154 Bond Street, Macclesfield SK11 6RE — MB ChB 1989 Birm.; MRCGP 1993; DRCOG 1991. Staff Grade Dr A & E E. Chesh. NHS Trust.

HUGHES, Alun 36 Coed y Canddo Road, New Inn, Pontypool NP4 0RA — MB BCh 1980 Wales.

HUGHES, Alun David National Heart and Lung Institute Imperial College, St marys Hospital, South Wharf Road, London W2 1BL Tel: 020 7886 1117 Fax: 020 7886 6145 Email: a.hughes@ic.ac.uk — MB BS 1983 Lond.; PhD Lond. 1988, BSc (Hons.) 1980. (St. Mary's Hosp. Med. Sch.) Reader. Clin Pharm.Imperial. Coll. Lond. Socs: Brit. Hypertens. Soc.; Brit. Pharm. Soc.; Amer. Heart. Assn. Prev: Brit. Heart Foundat. Intermediate Fell. & Lect. (Clin. Pharmacol.) St. Mary's Hosp. Med. Sch. Lond.; MRC Train. Fell. St. Geo. Hsop. Med. Sch. Lond.

HUGHES, Amanda Jane Hafan, Llanddoged, Llanrwst LL26 0AJ — MB ChB 1994 Liverp.; MRCP Lond. 1997. Specialist Regist. (Gastroenterol. & Gen. Med.).

HUGHES, Andrew Charles 31 Green Close, Stannington, Morpeth NE61 6PE — MB BS 1988 Newc.; MRCGP 1992. Cons. (Palliat. Med.) St Oswalds Hospice Newc.

HUGHES, Andrew Mark Zeneca Pharmaceuticals, Mereside, Alderley Park, Macclesfield SK10 4TG Tel: 01625 512092 Fax: 01625 583074; 128 Plant Lane, Moston, Sandbach CW11 3QD — MB ChB 1991 Manch.; MB ChB (Hons.) Manch. 1991; PhD Camb. 1988, MA 1985; MRCP (UK) 1994; AFPM RCP Lond. 1996. (Camb. & Manch.) Clin. Pharm. Zeneca Pharmaceut. Chesh.; Clin. Asst. (Gen. Med. & Cardiol.) Withington Hosp. Manch. Socs: Med. Protec. Soc. Prev: SHO & Clin. Asst. (Gen. Med.) Withington Hosp. Manch.; SHO (Cardiothoracic Med.) Wythenshawe Hosp. Manch.

HUGHES, Andrew Noel Northern Centre For Cancer Treatment, Newcastle General Hospital, Westgate Road, Newcastle upon Tyne NE4 6BE Email: andrew.hughes@newcastle.ac.uk — MB BS 1990 Newc.; MRCP (UK) 1995. (Newcastle upon Tyne) Cons. Med. Oncologist, Newc. Gen. Hosp. Socs: Mem. of ASCO. Prev: Clin. Research Assoc. & Hon. Regist. (Med. Oncol.) Univ. Newc.; Specialist Regist. (Med. Oncol.) Newc. Gen. Hosp.

HUGHES, Andrew Simon 1 Beaumont Lodge, 16 Ford Park, Newton Abbot TQ12 1DD — MB ChB 1983 Birm.; MRCGP 1993.

HUGHES, Andrew Stanley Barton Department of Haematology, Harold Wood Hospital, Gubbins Lane, Harold Wood, Romford RM3 0BE Tel: 01708 345533 Fax: 01708 708442; 17 Weald Close, Brentwood CM14 4QU Tel: 01277 224722 Email: asbh47@aol.com — BM BCh 1972 Oxf.; MRCP (U.K.) 1975; MRCPath 1981; FRCP 1997; FRCPath 1991; MA 1972 Oxon. (Oxford University) Cons. Haemat. Havering Hosp. Romford. Socs: Brit. Soc. Haematol. & Roy. Soc. Med. Prev: Cons. Path. Roy. Vict. Hosp. Banjul, The Gambia; MRC Train. Fell. Roy. Free Hosp. Lond.; Sen. Regist. (Haemat.) Univ. Coll. Hosp. Lond.

HUGHES, Mr Angus William Department of Trauma and Orthopaedics, The Horton Hospital, Oxford Road, Banbury OX16 9AL Tel: 01295 275500/229169 Fax: 01295 229670 — MB BCh 1974 Wales; FRCS Ed. 1979.

HUGHES, Anne Court Road Surgery, 29 Court Road, Barry CF63 4YD Tel: 01446 733181 Fax: 01446 420004 — MB BS 1982 Lond.; MRCGP 1987. (Westm.) Prev: GP Driffield E. Yorks.

HUGHES, Anne Hilary Department of Psychiatry, Royal South Hampshire Hospital, Brintone Terrace, Southampton SO14 0YG — BM 1980 Soton.; MRCPsych 1985. Staff Grade (Psychiat.) Roy. S. Hants. Hosp. Soton.

HUGHES, Anne-Marie Therese 8 Brookhill, Culmore Road, Londonderry BT48 7RJ — MB BCh BAO 1984 Belf.

HUGHES, Anthony Bradford Royal Infirmary, Duckworth Lane, Bradford BD9 6RJ Tel: 01274 364065 Fax: 01274 366548 Email: ahughes@doctors.org.uk; Turf House, Turf Lane, Cullingworth, Bradford BD13 5EJ Tel: 01535 274665 Email: ahughes@doctors.org.uk — MB BS 1981 Nottm.; FRCA 1989. (Nottm.) Cons. Anaesth. (Intens. Care) Bradford Roy. Infirm. Socs: Intens. Care Soc.; Yorks. Soc. Anaesth.; Assn. Anaesth. GB & N.. Irel.

HUGHES, Anthony Francis Rippon Ground Floor Consulting Suite, Princess Grace Hospital, 42/52 Nottingham Place, London W1M 7 FD Tel: 020 7935 2230; 15 Ashington Road, London SW6 Tel: 020 7736 9090 — MB ChB 1976 Birm.; Cert. Family Plann. JCC 1981. Socs: Chelsea Clin. Soc. & Med. Assur. Soc.; Interpendant Doc. Forum. Prev: SHO (Psychiat.) Sir Chas. Gairdner Hosp. W. Australia; SHO (O & G) W.m. Hosp. Lond.; Resid. Med. Off. Cromwell Hosp. Lond.

HUGHES, Anthony Geoffrey Exwick Health Centre, New Valley Road, Exeter EX4 2AD Tel: 01392 270063 Fax: 01392 431884; Barton House, Newton St Cyres, Exeter EX5 5DA Tel: 01392 851301 — MB BS Lond. 1970; DObst RCOG 1972. (St. Thos.) Prev: SHO Paediat. MusGr. Pk. Hosp. Taunton; SHO Obst. Yeovil Matern. Unit.; Ho. Phys. Roy. Devon & Exeter Hosp. S.ernhay.

HUGHES, Anthony Raymond 44 Windmill Rise, Kingston upon Thames KT2 7TU — MB BCh 1991 Wales; DRCOG 1995; DGM RCP Lond. 1994. (Wales) Socs: BMA. Prev: GP/Regist. Middlx.

HUGHES, Arthur Colin Park Medical Centre, Shavington Avenue, Newton Lane, Chester CH2 3RD Tel: 01244 324136 Fax: 01244 317257; 100 Hoole Road, Chester CH2 3NU Tel: 01244 312703 — MB ChB 1964 Manch.

HUGHES, Arthur Swindale 72 Hadrian Way, Sandiway, Northwich CW8 2JT Tel: 01606 888604 — MB BS 1945 Durh. (Newc.) Med. Assessor DHSS Attend. Allowance Claims. Prev: GP Durh.

HUGHES, Barbara Anne Coed y Glyn Surgery, Coed y Glyn, Church Street, Llangefni LL77 7DU; Bryn-Y-Gwynt, Greenfield Avenue, Llangefni LL77 7NU Tel: 01248 722114 Fax: 01248 750551 Email: postdoc@lineone.net — MB ChB 1969 Leeds. Med. Manager (MENAI Doctors) ,G.P out of hours loop, Sanglesei/Gwynedd.

HUGHES, Beatrice Margaret (retired) Broomfield, 8A Station Road, South Queensferry EH30 9HY Tel: 0131 331 2829 — MB ChB 1939 Ed. Prev: Res. Med. Off. Emerg. Hosp. Bridge of Earn.

HUGHES, Beatrix l Ince Avenue, Crosby, Liverpool L23 7XE Tel: 0151 924 9396 — MB ChB 1943 Birm.

HUGHES, Bridget Claire 40B Lawford Road, London NW5 2LN — MNB BCh BAO 1988 NUI.

HUGHES, Bronwyn Ruth Milford Dermatology Unit, St Mary's Hospital, Portsmouth PO3 6AD; Manor House, Cot Lane, Chidham, Chichester PO18 8SX — MB ChB 1980 Bristol; MD Bristol 1991; MRCP (UK) 1983. Cons. Dermat. St. Mary's Hosp. Portsmouth. Prev: Sen. Regist. (Dermat.) Roy. Lond. Hosp. & Gen. Infirm. Leeds; Research Regist. (Dermat.) Gen. Infirm. Leeds.

HUGHES, Bruce Davey 3 Trelawny Road, Saltash PL12 4DB — MB BS 1993 Lond.

HUGHES, Bryan James 39 Portfield, Haverfordwest SA61 1BN — MB BCh 1994 Wales.

HUGHES, Carly Anna Tel: 01328 851321 Fax: 01328 851412 — MB BS 1985 Lond.; BA (Med. Sci.) Camb. 1982; MRCGP (Distinc.) 1995; DCH Lond. 1991; MSc Health Sciences 2000. (Lond. Hosp. Med. Coll.) Gen. Practitioner, Fakenham. Socs: Worshipful Soc. Apoth.; Roy. Coll. of Gen. Practitioners.

HUGHES, Catherine Coila Mary Daleswood Farm Cottage, Shut Mill Lane, Romsley, Halesowen B62 0LY Tel: 01562 711053 Email: paul.m@dial.pipex.com — MB BS 1992 Lond.; BSc (1st cl. Hons.) Biomed. Sci. with Physiol. Lond. 1989; MRCPI 1997; DRCOG 1998. (St. Geo. Hosp. Med. Sch. Univ. Lond.) Assoc. Gen. Pract. Dudley HA.

HUGHES, Catherine Mair Health Centre, Village Road, Llanfairfechan LL33 0NH Tel: 01248 680021 Fax: 01248 681711 — MB BS 1986 Lond. Prev: Trainee GP Gwynedd VTS.

HUGHES, Ceri Wyn Flat 2, 8 Clifton Park, Bristol BS8 3BU — MB ChB 1998 Bristol; BDS 1990; FDS RCS 1996. (Bristol) Socs: Brit.Assoc.Oral.Max.Surg.

HUGHES, Charles Patteson The Medical Centre, Reading Road, Wallingford OX10 9DU Tel: 01491 835577 Fax: 01491 824034 Email: charles.hughes@gp-k84037.nhs.uk; Herries, Reading Road, Wallingford OX10 9DT Tel: 01491 32387 Email: charles.hughes@ntlworld.com — MB BS 1982 Lond.; MRCGP 1988; DCH RCP Lond. 1987; DRCOG 1985. Prev: Trainee GP Reading VTS; Ho. Off. Univ. Coll. Hosp. Lond.; Ho. Off. Edgware Gen. Hosp.

HUGHES, Christine Mary 50 Portrush Road, Portstewart BT55 7DE — MB BCh BAO 1997 Belf.

HUGHES, Christine Tillott Taylor (retired) 15 Slades Road, St Austell PL25 4HA Tel: 01726 66631 — MB BS Lond. 1955; MFFP 1993.

HUGHES, Christopher Alon The Moat House Surgery, Worsted Green, Merstham, Redhill RH1 3PN Tel: 01737 642207 Fax: 01737 642209; 82 Monson Road, Redhill RH1 2EZ Tel: 01737 773122 — MRCS Eng. LRCP Lond. 1968; MSc Lond. 1974, MB BS 1968; MRCP (UK) 1971; MRCGP 1986; DCH Eng. 1972. (Univ. Coll. Hosp.)

HUGHES, Christopher Harwood The Health Centre, Leypark Walk, Estover, Plymouth PL6 8UE Tel: 01752 788778 Fax: 01752 779905 — MB ChB 1975 Manchester; MB ChB 1975 Manchester.

HUGHES, Christopher John (retired) Loddon Vale Practice, 1 Hurricane Way, Woodley, Reading RG5 4UX Tel: 01734 691360 & 691932 — MB BS 1961 Lond.; MRCS Eng. LRCP Lond. 1961; DObst RCOG 1971. Prev: GP Loddon Vale Pract. Reading.

HUGHES, Claire Alison 2 Myln Meadow, Stock, Ingatestone CM4 9NE — MB BS 1998 Lond.; MB BS Lond 1998.

HUGHES, Claire Margaret 68 Stapleton Road, Headington, Oxford OX3 7LU — BM BCh 1989 Oxf.

HUGHES, Damien Anthony 24 Hawthorn Manor, Carryduff, Belfast BT8 8SR — MB BCh BAO 1991 Belf.

HUGHES, Damien Martin 46 Dorchester Park, Belfast BT9 6RJ — MB BCh BAO 1992 Belf.

HUGHES, Daniel Francis Ballywalker Health Clinic, Ballywalter, Newtownards BT22 2PY Tel: 012477 58292 Fax: 012477 58540 Email: danielhughes@postmaster.co.uk; 75 Grangewood Road, Dundonald, Belfast BT16 1GB Tel: 01232 410240 — MB BCh BAO 1991 Belf.; MRCP (UK) 1995; MRCGP 1996; DMH Belf. 1994; DRCOG 1993. (Queens University, Belfast) GP.

HUGHES, Daniel Joseph Elmcroft, Crabhill Lane, South Nutfield, Redhill RH1 5NR — MB ChB 1998 Leic.; MB ChB Leic 1998.

HUGHES, Daniel Myfyr Evans (retired) 10 Caswell Drive, Mumbles, Swansea SA3 4RJ — MB BS 1961 Lond.

HUGHES, David Alexius Alder Hey Children's Hospital, Eaton Road, Liverpool LI2 2AP Fax: 0151 252 5928 Email: david.hughes@rlch-tr.nwest.nhs.uk — FRCP; MB ChB 1983 Aberd.; FRCPCH; MRCP (UK) 1986. Cons. Paediatric Nephrologist, Alder Hey Hosp. Prev: Sen. Regist., Paediat., Roy. Hosp. for Sick Childr., Glas..

HUGHES, David Chester Cranmer Ringwood Health Centre, The Close, Ringwood BH24 1JY Tel: 01425 478901 Fax: 01425 478239; Linmoor Cottage, Highwood, Ringwood BH24 3LE — MB BChir 1970 Camb.; MA, MB Camb. 1970, BChir 1969; MRCS Eng. LRCP Lond. 1969; Dobst RCOG 1972; DA Eng. 1971. (Camb. & Guy's) Prev: SHO (Obst.) Torbay Hosp. Torquay; SHO (Paediat. & Anaesth.) Torbay Hosp. Torquay.

HUGHES, David Christopher (retired) Ash Tree Cottage, Carlton in Cleveland, Stokesley, Middlesbrough TS9 7DB Tel: 01642 712901 — MB BS Lond. 1950; FFA RCS Eng. 1956; DA Eng. 1954. Prev: Cons. Anaesth. NW Surrey Health Dist.

HUGHES, David Edward Department of Pathology, Chesterfield & North Derbyshire, Royal Hospital, Carlow, Chesterfield S44 5BL Tel: 01246 277271 Ext: 2540 Fax: 01246 552536 Email: david.hughes@cndrh-tr.trent.nhs.uk; 210 Baslow Road, Sheffield S17 4DS Tel: 0114 236 1265 — MB ChB 1989 Sheff.; PhD Sheff. 1988, BMedSci 1985; MRCP 1995. Cons. Histopath., Chesterfield and N. Derbysh. Roy. Hosp. NHS Trust. Socs: Path. Soc.; Assn. Clin. Path.; Bone and Tooth Soc. Prev: Lect. in Path., Univ. of Sheff..; Vis. Asst. Prof. in Path., Univ. of Texas Health Sci. Center, San Antonio; Lect. (Path.) Univ. Edin.

HUGHES, David Gary Meddygfa Tywyn Bach, Parc-y-Minos Street, Burry Port SA16 0BN Tel: 01554 832240 Fax: 01554 836810; 19 Parc Tyisha, Burry Port SA16 0RR Tel: 01154 834512 — MB BCh 1984 Wales; DRCOG 1987. (Wales) GP Meddygfa Tywyn Bach, Burry Port. Prev: Trainee GP W. Wales Gen. Hosp. Carmarthen VTS; Ho. Off. (Gen. Med.) Neath Gen. Hosp.; Ho. Off. (Gen. Surg.) & (Traum. & Orthop. Surg.) Cardiff Roy. Infirm.

HUGHES, David Gerard 49 Whitechapel Street, Manchester M20 6TX — MB ChB 1986 Leeds; MMedSci 1992; MRCPsych 1991. Sen. Regist. (Psychiat.) Manch. Roy. Infirm.

HUGHES, David Graham Bristol Royal Hospital for Children, St Richars Hill, Bristol BS2 8BJ Tel: 0117 928536 Fax: 0117 928 5820; Grove House, 13 Grove Rd, Coombe Dingle, Bristol BS9 2RQ — MD 1975 Liverp.; MB ChB 1969; FFA RCS Eng. 1977; FRCA 1977; FRCP 1998 CH. (Liverp.) Cons. Paed. Anaesth. United Bristol Healthcare Trust; Clin. Director, Bristol Roy. Hosp. for Childr., St Michaels Hill, Bristol. Socs: Assn. Paediat. Anaesth. Prev: Sen. Regist. (Anaesth.) Adelaide Childr. Hosp., Australia; Med. Off. Brit. Antarctic Survey.

HUGHES, David Gruffydd Department Radiology, Hope Hospital, Salford; Yealand House, 81 Pk Road, Hale, Altrincham WA15 9LQ — MB BS 1979 Lond.; MRCP (UK) 1982; FRCR 1986. Cons. Neuroradiol. Hope Hosp. Salford. Prev: Sen. Regist. (Neuroradiol.) Manch. Roy. Infirm.; Sen. Regist. (Radiol.) Oxf. RHA.

HUGHES, David Gwyn 27 Adeline Gardens, Gosforth, Newcastle upon Tyne NE3 4JQ — MB BS 1978 Newc.; FFA RCS Eng. 1983. Cons. Anaesth. Newc. HA.

HUGHES, David Hywel Moorland Medical Centre, Dyson House, Regent Street, Leek ST13 6AU Tel: 01538 399008 Fax: 01538

398228 — BM BS 1980 Nottm.; BSc Birm. 1974; BMedSci 1978; MRCGP 1989.

HUGHES, David James, Surg. Lt. RN Department of Anaesthetics, Derriford Hospital, Plymouth PL6 8DH Tel: 01752 777111 Fax: 01752 763287; 7 Warren Park, Woolwell, Plymouth PL6 7QR Tel: 01752 774698 Email: djhughes@lineone.net — MB ChB 1993 Dundee. Surg. Lt. RN; SHO (Anaesth.) Derriford Hosp. Socs: MDU; BMA. Prev: SHO (A & E) Roy. Hosp. Haslar; Ho. Off. Roy. Naval Hosp. Plymouth; Ho. Off. W. Cumbld. Hosp. Whitehaven.

HUGHES, David Lloyd Bron-y-Gocyd, Capel Llanilltern, Cardiff CF5 6JH — MB BCh 1966 Wales. (Cardiff) Prev: Ho. Surg. Cardiff Roy. Infirm.; Ho. Phys. St. David's Hosp. Cardiff; SHO (O & G) Co. Hosp. Hereford.

HUGHES, David Morgan Elmwood Health Centre, Huddersfield Road, Holmfirth, Huddersfield HD9 3TR Tel: 01484 681777 Fax: 01484 689603; Malkin House, Brow Lane, Holmfirth, Huddersfield HD9 2RJ Tel: 01484 683935 Email: malkin.house@dial.pipex.com — MB BS 1982 Lond.; BSc Lond. 1979, MB BS 1982. (University College Hospital) GP Holmfirth. Prev: Trainee GP VTS Friarage Hosp. N.allerton; Ho. Surg. Whittington Hosp. Lond.; Ho. Phys. Friarage Hosp. N.allerton.

HUGHES, David Mortimer Sandibank, Channel Road, Blundellsands, Liverpool L23 6TA — MRCS Eng. LRCP Lond. 1963.

HUGHES, David Owen (retired) 12 Roehampton Drive, Liverpool L23 7XD Tel: 0151 924 8108 Email: 100644.65@compuserve.com — MB ChB Liverp. 1951; MRCP (U.K.) 1973; MRCS Eng. LRCP Lond. 1952; DCH Eng. 1969. Prev: Cons. Paediat. Ormskirk & N. Sefton Dist.

***HUGHES, David Peter** 20 Windlehurst Drive, Worsley, Manchester M28 1HL — MB ChB 1997 Liverp.

HUGHES, David Putt St Thomas Surgery, Ysyol Street, St. Thomas, Swansea SA1 8LH Tel: 01792 653992; 19 Caswell Avenue, Caswell, Swansea SA3 4RU Tel: 01792 368454 — MB BCh 1983 Wales; BSc (Hons.) Wales 1976, MB BCh 1983; MRCGP 1988; Cert. Family Plann. JCC 1987. (WNSM) Clin. Asst. (Dermat. & A & E). Prev: SHO Rotat. (Cardiopulm.) Univ. Cardiff Hosp. Wales.

HUGHES, David Russell The Pain Clinic, Addenbrooke's Hospital, Hills Road, Box 215, Cambridge CB2 2QQ Tel: 01223 217796 Fax: 01223 247063; 22 Mill Road, Impington, Cambridge CB4 9PE — BM BCh 1972 Oxf.; MA Oxf. 1972; FRCA 1977. (St. Bart. Hosp. Lond.) Cons. Anaesth. Prev: Cons. Anaesth. Roy. Surrey Co. Hosp. Guildford; Sen. Regist. (Anaesth.) Univ. Coll. Hosp. Lond.; Foundat. Fell. in Anaesthiol. Mayo Clin. Rochester Mn, USA.

HUGHES, David Scott 23 Nelson Way, Muxton, Telford TF2 8QA — MB ChB 1997 Birm.

HUGHES, Mr David Stanley E Block, Royal Gwent Hospital, Newport NP20 2UB Tel: 01633 238443; 2 Rectory Road, Penarth CF64 3AN — MB ChB 1981 Bristol; FRCS Glas. 1986; FCOphth 1988; DO RCS Eng. 1986.

HUGHES, David Treharne Dillon (retired) 94 Overbury Avenue, Beckenham BR3 6PY Tel: 020 8650 3983 Fax: 020 8650 3983 — BM BCh Oxf. 1957; BSc Oxf. 1954, MA 1957; FRCP Lond. 1972, M 1959. Hon. Cons. Phys. Roy. Lond. Hosp.; Cons. Phys. Lond. Indep. Hosp. Prev: Eli Lilly Research Fell. Univ. Calif., San Francisco.

HUGHES, David Vaughan 11 Baslow Road, Eastbourne BN20 7UL — MB BS 1984 Lond.

HUGHES, David Wyn Long Lane Medical Centre, Aintree, Liverpool L9 6DQ Tel: 0151 530 1009/1069 — MB ChB 1968 Birm.; BSc Birm. 1965, MB ChB 1968. (Birm.)

HUGHES, Declan Michael 73 The Beeches, Crumlin BT29 4FH — MB BCh BAO 1989 Belf. Staff Grade (A & E) Roy. Vict. Hosp. Belf.

HUGHES, Denise Dib Lane Practice, 112A Dib Lane, Leeds LS8 3AY Tel: 0113 295 4650 Fax: 0113 295 4663 — MB ChB 1984 Leeds; BSc (Hons.) Leeds Med. Microbiol. 1981; MRCGP 1988; DRCOG 1988.

HUGHES, Derek William Millview Surgery, 1A Goldsmith St., Mansfield NG18 5PF Tel: 01623 649528; Meadow Cottage, Mansfield Road, Farnsfield, Newark NG22 8HG Tel: 01623 882450 — MB ChB Manch. 1970; MMedSc (Gen. Pract.) Leeds 1988; MRCGP 1979. Course Organiser Mansfield & Dist. VTS. Prev: Trainee GP Lancaster VTS; SHO (Gen. Med.) Birch Hill Hosp. Rochdale.

HUGHES, Dermot Francis Altnagelvin Area Hospital, Londonderry BT48 8PH Tel: 01504 45171; 6 Clarence Avenue, Londonderry BT48 7NH Tel: 01504 377068 — MB BCh BAO 1982 Belf.; MRCPath 1989. Cons. Path. Altnagelvin Area Hosp. Lond.derry.

HUGHES, Dermot Joseph Department of Anaesthesia, University Hospital of Wales, Heath Park, Cardiff CF14 4XW — MB BCh BAO 1985 NUI.

HUGHES, Derralynn Arlene 78 Balcarres Avenue, Whelley, Wigan WN1 3UT — BM BCh 1997 Oxf.; MA Oxf. 1996, DPhil 1994. (Oxf.) Pre-registration Ho. Off. (Acute Gen. Med.) John Radciffe Hosp. Oxf.; PRHO Surg. Hereford; SHO Hammersmith Hosp.; SHO Roy.Brompton.Hosp. Socs: BMA; Soc. for Gen. Microbiol.; Brit. Soc. Immunol.

HUGHES, Diane Marie Flat 3 Newstead Court, 41 Newstead Road, Bournemouth BH6 3HL — MB BS 1988 Lond.

HUGHES, Dyfed Wyn Princess of Wales Hospital, Coity Road, Bridgend CF31 1RQ Tel: 01656 752752; 6 Melrose Court, Penhill Road, Cardiff CF11 9PS Tel: 01222 231219 — MB BCh 1993 Wales; BMedSci Wales 1993. SHO (Med.) P.ss of Wales Hosp. Bridgend. Prev: SHO (Med.) Llandough Hosp. Cardiff; SHO (A & E Med.) Morriston Hosp. & Ysbyty Treforys NHS Trust Swansea; Ho. Off. (Med.) P.ss of Wales Hosp. Bridgend.

HUGHES, Edward Williams (retired) Drym House, Praze, Camborne TR14 0NU Tel: 01209 831400 — MD 1952 Lond.; MB BS 1945; FRCP Lond. 1973, M 1953. Prev: Sen. Phys. Cornw. & I. of Scilly DHA.

HUGHES, Elaine Frances 149 Verdant Lane, London SE6 1JA — MB BS 1982 Lond.; MRCP (UK) 1985.

HUGHES, Elis Owain The Old School House, Rosehill Road, Stoke-on-Tern, Market Drayton TF9 2LF — MB BCh 1991 Wales; FFAFRCSI Dublin 1999; FRCA Lond. 1999; Dip. Paediat. Auckland, NZ 1994. Specialist Regist. (Anaesth.) Stoke Rotat. Prev: SHO (Anaesth.) Countess of Chester Hosp.

HUGHES, Elizabeth Ann Department of Clinical Biochemistry, Sandwell General Hospital, Lyndon, West Bromwich B71 4HJ Tel: 0121 607 3426 Fax: 0121 607 3253; Email: eahughes@doctor.org.uk — MB ChB 1983 Birm.; BSc (Hons.) Wales 1979; MRCP (UK) 1986; FRCP 1999. (Birmingham) Cons. Chem. Pathologist; Postgrad. Clin. Tutor & Dir. Of Med. Educat.; Hon. Sen. Clin. Lect. Dept. Med. Univ.Birm.; Acad. Sub-Dean for Roy. Soc. Of Med. Lon. (For W. Midl.s); Med. Adviser Family Health Assn. Maidenhead. Socs: Eur. Atherosclerosis Soc.; BAPEN; FRSM. Prev: Sen. Regist. (Chem. Path.) E. Birm. Hosp. & Qu. Eliz. Hosp. Birm.; Regist. (Chem. Path.) Qu. Eliz. Hosp. Birm.

HUGHES, (Elizabeth) Judith Bluegates Hole, Mill Lane, Byfleet, Weybridge KT13 Tel: 01932 342573 — MB ChB 1950 Liverp.; BDS 1955. (Liverp.)

HUGHES, Elwyn Meddygfa Pengorof, Gorof Road, Ystradgynlais, Swansea SA9 1DS Tel: 01639 843221 Fax: 01639 843790 — MB BCh 1976 Wales; MRCP (UK) 1981.

HUGHES, Elwyn Trefor (retired) Llys Maelog, Penglais Road, Aberystwyth SY23 2EU Tel: 01970 624525 — MB BS 1948 Lond.; MB BS (Hnrs.) Lond. 1948; MRCS Eng. LRCP Lond. 1949; FRCP Ed. 1983, M 1958. Prev: Assoc. Specialist (Gen. Med.) Bronglais Hosp. Aberystwyth.

HUGHES, Eric Glyn (retired) 6 The Bramleys, Shepreth, Royston SG8 6PY Tel: 01763 260973 — MRCS Eng. LRCP Lond. 1952; FFOM RCP Lond. 1986, MFOM 1978. Prev: Med. Dir. Harlow Occupat. Health Serv.

HUGHES, Ernest Philip Celynog, 153 Llanelian Road, Old Colwyn, Colwyn Bay LL29 8UW Tel: 01492 516160 — MB ChB 1967 Ed.; DObst RCOG 1970.

HUGHES, Eugene Joseph Esplanade Surgery, 19 Esplanade, Ryde PO33 2EH Tel: 01983 813600 Fax: 01983 813609 — MB BS 1979 Lond.; MRCGP 1984; DRCOG 1984; DCH RCP Lond. 1983; DA 1981. (Guy's)

HUGHES, Gaenor Kathryn 4 Welbeck Rise, Harpenden AL5 1SL — MB ChB 1997 Birm.

HUGHES, Gareth Tel: 01534 728777 Fax: 01534 788977 Email: ivyhouse@itl.net — MB ChB 1976 Manch.; Cert Av Med. GP, Jersey, C.I.

HUGHES, Gareth (retired) Coetmor, Talybont SY24 5DY Tel: 01970 832365 Fax: 01970 832365 Email: garfeddyg@aol.com — MB ChB Liverp. 1956; FRCP Lond. 1980; FRCP Glas. 1977. Prev: Ch.ill Fell. 1970.

HUGHES, Gareth John Bro Hafren, Back Lane, Newtown SY16 2NG Tel: 01686 623364 Fax: 01686 623364 Email: garhughes.org.uk; Email: garhughes@doctors.org.uk — MB BS 1977 Lond.; BSc Lond. 1974; MRCPsych 1982. (Guy's) Cons. Psychiat. Bro Hafren Resource Centre Newtown.

HUGHES, Gareth Robert Rosewell, St Johns Close, Scampton, Lincoln LN1 2SU — MB BS 1994 Newc.

HUGHES, Gareth Wynne Cefn Coed Hospital, Swansea SA2 0GH Tel: 01792 561155 Fax: 01792 580740; 3 Ridge Acre, Derwen Fawr, Swansea SA2 8AP Tel: 01792 207216 — MB BCh Wales 1971; MD Wales 1985; FRCPsych 1999, M 1976; DPM Eng. 1974. (Univ. Wales Coll. Med.) Cons. Psychiat. Cefn Coed Hosp. Swansea. Prev: Sen. Regist. Rotat. (Psychiat.) Bath & Bristol; Regist. (Psychiat.) S. Glam. AHA (T).

HUGHES, Geoffrey Bristol Royal Infirmary, Bristol BS2 8HW Tel: 0117 928 2713 Fax: 0117 928 2334; Hawthorne House, Silver St, Chew Magna, Bristol BS40 8RE — MB BS 1978 Lond.; FRCP Lond. 1994; MRCP (UK) 1982; DRCOG 1983. Cons. A & E Med. Bristol Roy. Infirm.; Sen. Clin. Lect. (A & E) Univ. Bristol. Socs: Fell. Fac. Accid. & Emerg. Med. Prev: Sen. Regist. Char. Cross Hosp. Lond. & St. Richards Hosp. Chichester.

HUGHES, Geoffrey William 2 Queensgate Mews, Greenbank, Plymouth PL4 7PH — MB ChB 1983 Auckland; MRCOG 1990.

HUGHES, George (retired) Aravon, 30 Belfast Road, Antrim BT41 1PB Tel: 01849 462232 — MB BCh BAO Belf. 1947. Prev: Med. Off. i/c Robt.s Hosp. Borsad, India.

HUGHES, George Hamilton (retired) Broomfield, 8A Station Road, South Queensferry EH30 9HY Tel: 0131 331 2829 — MB ChB Ed. 1937; MRCGP 1953. Prev: Regional Med. Off. Scott. Home & Health Dept.

HUGHES, Geraint Brierley Clinton Road Surgery, 19 Clinton Road, Redruth TR15 2LL Tel: 01209 216507 Fax: 01209 218262; 19 Clinton Road, Redruth TR15 2LN Tel: 01209 218262 — MB BS 1977 Lond.; MB BS Lond. 1977 MRCS Eng. LRCP Lond. 1977; MRCGP 1984. (Roy. Free) Socs: BMA; Cornw. Clin. Soc. Prev: SHO (Cas.) Roy. Cornw. Hosp. Truro; SHO (Psychiat.) Roy. Cornw. Hosp. Truro; Trainee GP Penryn.

HUGHES, Gerard Michael 6 The Maltings, West Ilsley, Newbury RG20 7AX — MB BS 1993 Lond.

HUGHES, Gillian Mary Combined Health Care, 79 London Road, Stoke-on-Trent ST4 7PZ Tel: 01782 744444; 31 Redhills, Eccleshall, Stafford ST21 6JW Tel: 01785 850815 — MB ChB 1966 St. And. (St. And.) Clin. Med. Off. N. Staffs. HA.

HUGHES, Graham John 29 Elfindale Road, Herne Hill, London SE24 9NN — MB BS 1986 Lond.

HUGHES, Graham Robert Vivian Lupus Research Unit, Rayne Institute, St Thomas Hospital, London SE1 7EH Tel: 020 7928 9292 Fax: 020 7633 9422 — MD Lond. 1973, MB BS 1964; FRCP Lond. 1978, M 1967; MRCS Eng. LRCP Lond. 1964. (Lond. Hosp.) Cons. Phys. Rheum. Dept. St. Thos. Hosp. Lond.; Head Lupus Arthritis Research Unit; Hon. Cons. Rheum. RAF; Life Pres. Lupus UK. Socs: Heberd. Soc.; Brit. Soc. Immunol. & Amer. Rheum. Assn.; Assn. Phys. Prev: Cons. Phys. & Reader Roy. Postgrad. Med. Sch. Lond.; Sen. Regist. (Med.) Hammersmith Hosp. Lond.

HUGHES, Graham Victor Chiswick Health Centre, Fishers Lane, London W4 1RX Tel: 020 8321 3518 Fax: 020 8321 3568; 23 Staveley Road, Chiswick, London W4 3HU Tel: 020 8994 0158 Email: g.vhuges@doctors.org.uk — MB BS Lond. 1960; MRCS Eng. LRCP Lond. 1960; MRCGP 1977; Dip. Pract. Dermat. Wales 1994; DObst RCOG 1962. (King's Coll. Lond. & St. Geo.) Gen. Med. Pract.; AKC; Vis. Med. Off. John Aird Hse. Brentford. Socs: BMA. Prev: Ho. Off. (Surg.) St. Geo. Hosp. Tooting; Ho. Off. (Med.) & Resid. (Obst.) St. Geo. Hosp. Lond.

HUGHES, Griffith Edward (retired) Medway House, 199 Wigmore Rd, Rainham, Gillingham ME8 0TN Tel: 01634 233892 — MRCS Eng. LRCP Lond. 1943. Prev: Cas. Off. & Ho. Surg. St. Bart. Hosp. Rochester.

HUGHES, Gwilym 69 Love Lane, Pinner HA5 3EY Tel: 020 8866 7098 Fax: 020 8868 7244 — MB BS 1961 Lond.; MRCS Eng. LRCP Lond. 1961; FRCP Lond. 1990; FFOM RCP Lond. 1987, M 1983, A 1978; FACOEM 1991. (King's Coll. Hosp.) Med. Dir. OH Servs. Lond.; Asst. Clin. Prof. Dept. Occupat. Health Univ. Utah; Mem. Ho. of Delegates Amer. Coll. Occupat. & EnviroMent. Med.; Med. Adviser Kodak Ltd; Med. Adviser Synpac Pharmaceut. Ltd. Socs: SOM (Ex-Chair. Lond. Gp.); Vice-Chairm. Internat. Occupat.al Med. Gp; Fell.Roy. Soc. of Med. Prev: Chief Med. Off. Brit. Telecom PLC Occupat. Health Serv.; Occupat. Health Adviser Pruden. Assur. Co. Ltd; Med. Off. Kodak Ltd.

HUGHES, Hannah Eirlys 45 Wellington Square, Hastings TN34 1PN Tel: 01424 722166 — MB BS 1982 Lond.; DRCOG 1986. GP Hastings.

HUGHES, Helen Jane 3 Barrow Road, Quorn, Loughborough LE12 8DH — MB ChB 1988 Leic.

HUGHES, Helen Mary 332 Priory Road, Shirley, Solihull B90 1BQ — MB ChB 1980 Leeds; MRCGP 1991.

HUGHES, Helena Everard (retired) The Penthouse, 10 Savoy Ct., Racecourse Road, Ayr KA7 2XP Tel: 01292 281876 — MB ChB Manch. 1952; FRCPath 1975, M 1964; FRCOG 1971, M 1958; DObst RCOG 1954. Prev: Cons. Exfoliative Cytol. Glas. Roy. Infirm.

HUGHES, Henry Pierce (retired) 45 Benscliffe Drive, Loughborough LE11 3JP Tel: 01509 263382 — MB ChB 1942 Liverp. Prev: Ho. Surg. Birkenhead Gen. Hosp.

HUGHES, Hugh PenY Coed, Llangollen LL20 8LR — MB ChB 1944 Birm.

HUGHES, Hugh John (retired) The Brae, 29 Well Lane, Gayton, Heswall, Wirral CH60 8NQ — MB BCh Wales 1953; FRCR 1963; DMRT Liverp. 1957. Cons. Radiotherap. Liverp. Regional Radiotherap. Centre Clatterbridge Hosp. Bebington; Lect. in Clin. Radiotherap. Liverp. Univ. Prev: Sen. Regist. Liverp. Radium Inst.

HUGHES, Hugh Owen, OBE (retired) 4 Wood Lane, Scarcliffe, Chesterfield S44 6TF — MRCS Eng. LRCP Lond. 1939. Prev: Ho. Phys. Middlx. Hosp.

HUGHES, Hugh Vickers (retired) Brimstry, Shaw Lane, Albrighton, Wolverhampton WV7 3DT Tel: 01902 372338 Fax: 01902 373331 — MB BS Lond. 1956; MRCS Eng. LRCP Lond. 1956; DObst RCOG 1961. Prev: Ho. Surg. King's Coll. Hosp.

HUGHES, Mr Hywel Accident & Emergency Department, Wrexham Maelor Hospital, Wrexham LL13 7TD Tel: 01978 725519; Chaple House, Golly, Rossett, Wrexham LL12 0AL Tel: 01244 571303 — MB ChB 1987 Manch.; Dip Sports Med 1998 Edinburgh; 1999 Dip (A & E) Edinburgh; MRCGP 1993; DRCOG 1992; DCH RCPS Glas. 1990. Staff Grade (A & E) Wrexham Maelor Hosp. Prev: Trainee GP Llangollen & Overton on Dee Wrexham; SHO (A & E, Med. & O & G) Wrexham Maelor Gen. Hosp.

HUGHES, Ian Mark Cumberland House, 58 Scarisbrick New Road, Southport PR8 6PG Tel: 01704 501500 Fax: 01704 549382; 64 Grange Road, Southport PR9 9AD Tel: 01704 538020 — MB ChB 1981 Liverp.; MRCGP 1990; Dip. Pre. Sci. Liverp. 1996; DRCOG 1985. Prev: Clin. Asst. (O & G) S.port Gen. Infirm.

HUGHES, Professor Ieuan Arwel Department of Paediatrics, Addenbrooke's Hospital, Level 8, Box 116, Hills Road, Cambridge CB2 2QQ Tel: 01223 336885 Fax: 01223 336996 Email: iah1000@cam.ac.uk; 4 Latham Road, Cambridge CB2 2EQ Tel: 01223 356892 — MB BCh Wales 1968; MA Camb. 1990; MD Wales 1978; FRCP Lond. 1984, M 1971; FRCPC 1975; FRCPCH 1997; F Med Sci 1998. (Univ. Wales Coll. Med. (formerly Welsh Natl. School of Med.) Prof. & Head of Dept. Paediat. Univ. Camb. Sch. of Clin. Med.; Hon. Cons. Paediat. Addenbrooke's NHS Trust; Hon. Cons. Paediat. Endrocrinol. Hosp. for Sick Childr. Gt. Ormond St. Lond. Socs: 1942 Club; Eur. Soc. Paediat. Endocrinol.; Endocrine Soc. Prev: Reader. (Paediat. Endocrinol.) Dept. Child Health Univ. Wales Coll. Med.; Regist. (Med.) Univ. Coll. Hosp. Lond.; Sen. Resid. (Paediat.) Childr. Hosp. Winnipeg, Canada.

HUGHES, Isabelle Lois City Walls Medical Centre, St. Martin's Way, Chester CH1 2NR Tel: 01244 357800 — MB ChB 1977 Birm.; MRCGP 1984; DCH Eng. 1981. GP Chester.

HUGHES, Ivor William, OStJ Eastview Surgery, 81-83 Crosby Road North, Liverpool L22 4QD Tel: 0151 928 8849 Fax: 0151 928 2090; Northwood, 29 Far Moss Road, Blundellsands, Liverpool L23 8TG Tel: 0151 924 2044 Fax: 0151 928 2090 — MB ChB 1960 Liverp. (Liverp.) Prev: Clin. Asst. (Psychiat.) Walton Hosp. Liverp.; SHO (Obst.) Qu. Vict. Hosp. Morecambe; SHO (Orthop.) & Ho. Phys. (Med.) Walton Hosp. Liverp.

HUGHES, Iwan Elfan (retired) — BM BCh 1953 Oxf.

HUGHES, Jacqueline Ann Department of Radiology, Guy's & St Thomas' Hospitals NHS Trust, London SE1 — MB BS 1991 Lond.; MRCP (UK) 1994. (King's College London) Specialist Regist. (Radiol.) Guy's & St Thomas Hosps.

HUGHES, Jacqueline Mary Maypole Health Centre, 10 Sladepool Farm Road, Kings Heath, Birmingham B14 5DJ Tel: 0121 430 2829 Fax: 0121 430 6211 — MB BS 1989 Lond.; MRCGP 1995.
HUGHES, Mr James 17 Station Road, Corstophine, Edinburgh EH12 7AA — MB ChB 1947 Ed.; FRCS Ed. 1956; DO Eng. 1952. (Ed.) Ophth. Surg. Roy. Infirm. Edin. & Leith Hosp. Socs: Scott. Ophth. Club & Ophth. Soc. U.K. Prev: Ophth. Surg. Bangour Gen. Hosp. Broxburn; Asst. Ophth. Surg. Glas. Eye Infirm.; Flight Lt. RAF Med. Br.
HUGHES, James Andrew 34 Rhosfryn, Penrhosgarnedd, Bangor LL57 2DL — MB BCh 1994 Wales; MRCPsych. (Cardiff) Psychiat. Praist. Hergest Unit, Bangor Gwynedd.
HUGHES, James I — MB BCh BAO 1988 Belf.; MRCP (UK) 1993; DCH. (QUB) Cons. Paediat. Socs: MRCPCH.
HUGHES, Jane Elizabeth 165 Sanderstead Road, South Croydon, Croydon CR2 0PH — MB BS 1986 Lond.; MRCGP 1992; DRCOG 1991; DCH RCP Lond. 1991.
HUGHES, Janet, OStJ 14 Spenbeck Drive, Allestree, Derby DE22 2UH Tel: 01332 552403 — MB ChB 1970 Sheff. Phys. (Occupat. Health) Derbysh. CC. Prev: Med. Asst. (Psychiat.) Pastures Hosp. Derby.
HUGHES, Janet Marie West Wirral Group Practice, 33 Thingwall Road, Irby, Wirral CH61 3UE Tel: 0151 648 1846 Fax: 0151 648 0362 — MB ChB 1987 Manch.; MRCGP 1991; DCH 1990; DRCOG 1992. (Manch.) GP Princip.
HUGHES, Jayne Elizabeth Medical Microbiology, University of Edinburgh, Teviot Place, Edinburgh EH8 9AG Tel: 0131 650 3162; 99 Avontoun Park, Linlithgow EH49 6QQ — MB ChB 1992 Ed.; BSc (Hons.) Med. Sci. Ed. 1990; PhD Univ of Edin 1998. (Edinburgh) Research Fell. (Microbiol.) Univ. Edin.
HUGHES, Jean Doreen (retired) The Brae, 29 Well Lane, Heswall, Wirral CH60 8NQ Tel: 0151 342 4722 — MB ChB Liverp. 1961, DMRD 1964. Assoc. Specialist (Radiol.) Chester Roy. Infirm.
HUGHES, Jean Innes 18 Miller Terrace, St Monans, Anstruther KY10 2BB Tel: 01333 730919 — MB ChB 1961 St. And.; DPH St. And. 1965. Staff Grade Paediat. Community Child Health Dundee Health Care Trust; DCH Coll. Med. SA. 1982. Prev: Med. Off. Baragwanata Hosp. & Soweto Comm. Clinics; GP Zambia; Med. Off. Pub. Health Newfld. & Labrador.
HUGHES, Jennifer 34 Westwood Road, Southampton SO17 1DP Tel: 02380 582688 — MB BS 1966 Lond.; DO Eng. 1970. (St. Mary's)
HUGHES, Jennifer Margaret (retired) Cambria House, Sutton, Ely CB6 2RB Tel: 01353 778692 — MB BS 1962 Lond.; DObst RCOG 1965; Cert. FPA 1965. Prev: Clin. Asst. (O & G) Maelor Gen. Hosp. Wrexham.
HUGHES, Jennifer Sarah 29 Micawber Way, Chelmsford CM1 4UG — MB ChB 1992 Manch.
HUGHES, Jenny Rosanne Department of Dermatology, Royal Free Hospital, London NW3 2QG Tel: 020 7794 0500; 42 Brewster Gardens, London W10 6AJ Tel: 020 8969 8664 — MB ChB 1986 Bristol; MRCP (UK) 1990. Sen. Regist. (Dermat.) Roy. Free Hosp. Lond. Prev: Sen. Regist. & Regist. (Dermat.) King's Coll. Hosp. Lond.; Aid Worker Health UnLtd. S.., Sudan; SHO (Gen. Med.) City Hosp. Nottm.
HUGHES, Joanna Margaret Birtley Medical Group Practice, Birtley Medical Group, Durham Road, Birtley, Chester-le-Street DH3 2QT Tel: 0191 410 3421 Fax: 0191 410 9672 — MB ChB 1986 Leeds; MRCGP 1990; DRCOG 1990; DCH RCP Lond. 1988. Prev: Trainee GP Airedale VTS.
HUGHES, John Alistair 30 St Stephens Hill, Canterbury CT2 7AX — MB BCh 1983 Wales; FFA RCS Eng. 1989.
HUGHES, John Anthony Kent & Sussex Hospital, Tunbridge Wells TN4 8AT Tel: 01892 618093 Fax: 01892 618093; Email: ja.hug@virgin.net — MB ChB 1973 Manch.; FRCP Lond. 1993; MRCP (UK) 1978. Cons. Phys. (Gen. & Thoracic Med.) Kent & Sussex Weald NHS Trust; Dep. Regional Adviser (SE Thames), Roy. Coll. of Phys.s. Socs: Amer. Thoracic Soc.; Eur. Respirat. Soc.; Brit. Thorac. Soc. Prev: Sen. Regist. (Gen. Med. & Chest Dis.) Lodge Moore Hosp. Sheff.; Sen. Regist. (Gen. Med.) Brighton AHA; Clin. Research Fell. Chest Unit King's Coll. Hosp. Lond.
HUGHES, John David Whitchurch Road Medical Centre, 210-212 Whitchurch Road, Heath, Cardiff CF14 3NB Tel: 029 2062 1282 Fax: 029 2052 0210; 107 King George V Drive, Cardiff CF14 4EH Tel: 029 2075 4665 — MB BCh 1965 Wales. Socs: Cardiff Med. Soc. Prev: SHO A & E Unit & SHO Urol. Dept. Cardiff Roy. Infirm.; SHO (Gen. Surg.) Llandough Hosp. Cardiff.
HUGHES, John Edward 22 Spinney Green, Eccleston, St Helens WA10 5AH — MB ChB 1985 Liverp.
HUGHES, John Elfed (retired) Pennant, LLanfair Caereinion, Welshpool SY21 0BH Tel: 01938 810546 — BA Sheff. 1974, MB ChB 1957; MRCGP 1975; Dip. Pract. Dermat. Wales 1991; DRCOG 1962. Med. Off. Family Plann. Clinic Welshpool. Prev: GP Welshpool.
HUGHES, John Francis (retired) 10 Rowley Crescent, Stratford-upon-Avon CV37 6UT Tel: 01789 297106 — MB BS 1963 Lond.; DObst RCOG 1965.
HUGHES, John Gerard 25 Old Market Street, Blackley, Manchester M9 8DX Tel: 0161 721 4865 Fax: 0161 740 6532 Email: hughesj@manchester.nwest.nhs.uk — MB BCh BAO 1983 Belf.; DFFP 1996; MICGP 1993. p/t GP Pricipal, Blackley, Manch.; C.M.O. Family Plann., Palatine Centre, Manch.; Hosp. Practitioners Headache Clinic Neurol. Dept., Manch. Roy. Infirm., Manch. Socs: Manch. Locum Med. Comm.; Primary Care Rheum. Soc. Prev: SHO (Accid.& Emerg.) Mater Hosp. Belf.; Trainee GP Bath VTS; SHO (Surg., A & E, O & G) Mid-Ulster Region.
HUGHES, John Gwilym 24 Chatsworth Road, Croydon CR0 1HA; 27 Upper Brighton Road, Surbiton KT6 6QX — MB BCh 1975 Wales; BSc (Hons.) Human Anat. Wales 1972; MSc Occupat. Health Birm. 1991; MRCGP 1980; MFOM RCPI 1992; MFOM RCP Lond. 1996, AFOM 1991; DCH RCP Lond. 1979; DRCOG 1977. Occupat. Med. Advisor Croydon. Socs: Soc. Occupat. Med. Prev: Sen. Regist. (Occupat. Health) King's Coll. Hosp. Lond.; Med. Off. Bechtel Corpn..
HUGHES, John Hamilton South Cleveland Hospital, Marton Road, Middlesbrough TS4 3BW Tel: 01642 850850 — MB BS 1986 Lond.; FCAnaesth 1991. (St. Thos. Hosp. Med. Sch.) Cons. Anaesth. Pain Managem. S. Cleveland Hosp. Socs: Fell. Roy. Soc. Med.; Assn. Anaesth.; Internat. Assn. Study of Pain. Prev: Sen. Regist. (Anaesth.) N.. RHA; Vis. Assoc. Prof. Univ. Maryland Med. Center, USA; Regist. (Anaesth.) Qu. Mary's Hosp. Roehampton.
HUGHES, John Haydn, BEM (retired) 24 North Parade, Aberystwyth SY23 2NF Tel: 01970 612983 — MB BCh Wales 1953; LLM Wales 1990; BSc Wales 1950; DObst RCOG 1955; PhD Wales 1997. Hon. Lect. (Med. Law) Univ. Wales Aberystwyth. Prev: Clin. Asst. (O & G) Aberystwyth Hosp.
HUGHES, Mr John Howell, CBE 28 Rodney Street, Liverpool L1 Tel: 0151 709 7578; Pennant, Newcroft Road, Woolton, Liverpool L25 6EP Tel: 0151 428 1485 — MRCS Eng. LRCP Lond. 1931; MD Liverp. 1933, ChM 1936, MB ChB 1931; FRCS Eng. 1937. (Liverp. & Guy's) Emerit. Cons. Surg. Roy. Liverp. Hosp. Socs: Fell. Assn. Surgs.; Soc. Thoracic Surgs. Prev: Thoracic Surg. King Edwd. VII Welsh Nat. Memor. Assn.; Lect. in Applied Surg. Anat. & Lect. Surg. Path. Liverp. Univ.; Res. Surg. Off., Surg. Tutor & Regist. & Ho. Surg. Liverp. Roy.
***HUGHES, John Hugh** 13 Bemersyde Drive, Newcastle upon Tyne NE2 2HL — MB BS 1988 Newc.
HUGHES, John Humphreys (retired) Fron, Llangefni LL77 7HB Tel: 01248 722178 — MB ChB 1941 Liverp. Prev: GP Llangefni.
HUGHES, Mr John Hunter (retired) Princess Margaret Hospital, Osbourne Road, Windsor SL4 3SJ Tel: 01753 868750 — MB BCh 1952 Wales; FRCS Ed. 1966; FRCOG 1977, M 1961. Prev: Cons. (O & G) Wexham Pk. Hosp. Slough.
HUGHES, John Laurence Flat 2, 186 St. Johns Street, London EC1V 4JZ — MB BChir 1992 Camb.; MD Manchester 1998; BA Camb. 1989; MRCOG 1998. SpR Radiol., Guy's & St. Thomas' Hosps., Lond. Prev: SpR (O & G) Rose Matern. Hosp., Camb.; Research Fell. (Child Health) St. Mary's Hosp. Manch.; SHO (O & G) John Radcliffe Hosp. Oxf.
HUGHES, John Lloyd 25 Clodien Avenue, Cardiff CF14 3NL — MB BCh 1993 Wales.
HUGHES, John Martel, TD, OStJ The Laurels, Westfield Road, Newport NP20 4ND Tel: 01633 262449 — MB BCh 1946 Wales; BSc Wales 1943, MB BCh 1946; FRCP Ed. 1971, M 1958; FRCPsych 1972, M 1971; DPM Eng. 1955; BA 2000 Wales. (Cardiff) Cons. Psychiat. St. Cadoc's Hosp. Newport. Socs: BMA (Treas. Gwent Div.). Prev: Hon. Phys. to HM the Qu.; Col. late

RAMC, T & AVR, CO 203 (W.) Gen. Hosp.; Hon. Col., 203 (W) Gen. Hosp. RAMC T & Avr.

HUGHES, John Meredith Irwell Springs, Bishop's Wood, Cuddesdon, Oxford — MB BChir 1963 Camb.; MA, MB BChir Camb. 1963; MRCS Eng., LRCP Lond. 1962; DObst RCOG 1964. (Guy's) Prev: SHO Amer. Red Cross Hosp. Paris; Surg. Union Castle Line; Ho. Surg. & Ho. Phys. Pembury Hosp.

HUGHES, Professor John Michael Barton National Heart and Lung Directorate, Imperial College School of Medicine, Hammersmith Hospital Campus, London W12 0NN Tel: 020 8383 3269 Fax: 020 8743 9733 Email: mike.hughes@ic.ac.uk; 4 Cedars Road, London SW13 0HP Tel: 020 8876 6822 Fax: 020 8878 9681 Email: mike.hughes@ic.ac.uk — BM BCh Oxf. 1963; DM Oxf. 1973; FRCP Lond. 1979, M 1965. (Oxford) Prof. Emerit. Imperial Coll. Sch. of Med.; Hon. Cons. Phys. Hammersmith Hosp. Lond. Socs: Assn. Phys.; Physiol. Soc.; Brit. Thorac. Soc. Prev: MRC Research Fell. Harvard Sch. Pub. Health, USA; Respirat. Research Regist. Hammersmith Hosp.; Ho. Phys. & Ho. Surg. Lond. Hosp.

HUGHES, John Neville Phillips, OBE (retired) 204 Lake Road E., Cardiff CF23 5NR Tel: 02920751526 — MB BCh Wales 1960; FFPHM 1980, M 1974; DPH 1964. Prev: Chief Admin. Med. Off. Mid. Glam. HA.

HUGHES, John Philip (retired) 1 Bury Road, Harlow CM17 0ED — MB BS 1960 Lond.; DObst RCOG 1963.

HUGHES, John Rhydwen The Surgery, Recreation Drive, Billinge, Wigan WN5 7LY Tel: 01744 892205 Fax: 01744 895796; 189 Higher Lane, Rainford, St Helens WA11 8NF — MB ChB 1967 Liverp.; DObst RCOG 1970.

HUGHES, John Richard Havant Health Centre Suite B, PO Box 43, Civic Centre Road, Havant PO9 2AQ; 37 Portsdown Hill Road, Bedhampton, Havant PO9 3JU — MB BS 1971 Lond.; MRCGP 1983; DObst RCOG 1974; DCH Eng. 1973.

HUGHES, John Trevor (retired) No 2 Bishop Kirk Place, Oxford OX2 7HJ Tel: 01865 316669 Fax: 01865 576021 — MB ChB 1951 Manch.; DPhil Oxf. 1968, MA 1970; MD Manch. 1961; FRCP Lond. 1981, M 1980; FRCP Ed. 1971, M 1956; MRCS Eng. LRCP Lond. 1951; DCP Lond 1954; DPath Eng. 1956; FRCPath 1978 M 1974. Prev: Warden acting Green Coll Univ Oxf.

HUGHES, John William (retired) The Skerries, High Street, Guilsborough, Northampton NN6 8PU — MB BS 1950 Lond.; MRCS Eng. LRCP Lond. 1950. Prev: Resid. Surg. Off. Brompton Hosp. Lond.

***HUGHES, Jon** The Glebe House, Claverton Village, Bath BA2 7BG — MB ChB 1996 Birm.; ChB Birm. 1996.

HUGHES, Jonathan Charles Dept. of Anaesthetics, Princess of Wales of Wales Hospital, Coity Rd, Bridgend CF31 1RQ Tel: 01656 752361 Fax: 01656 752365 Email: jolly.jon@lineone.net — MB BCh 1989 Wales; FRCA 1994; DA (UK) 1991. Sen. Regist. (Anaesth.) Univ. Hosp. Wales. Socs: Assn. Anaesth.; Assn. Obst. Anaesth.; BMA. Prev: Sen. Regist., P.ss of Wales Hosp., Bridgend; Sen. Regist. (Anaesth.) P. Chas. Hosp., Merthyr Tydfil; Regist. (Anaesth.), neath Gen. Hosp. & Univ. Hosp., Wales.

HUGHES, Josephine Anne Frances 21 Slemish Way, Belfast BT11 8GW — MB BCh BAO 1992 Belf.

HUGHES, Judith Deborah 20 Waldershare Avenue, Sandwich Bay, Sandwich CT13 9PL — MB ChB Leic. 1986; FRCOphth 1993; MBA 1998. Sen. Med. Advisor Pfizer Ltd, Sandwich. Socs: Fell. Roy. Soc. Med.; Fell. Roy. Coll. Ophth.; BrAPP.

HUGHES, Julian Christopher Gibside Unit, Newcastle General Hospital, Westgate Road, Newcastle upon Tyne NE4 6BE Tel: 0191 256 3300 Fax: 0191 219 5065 Email: jchughes@doctors.org.uk — MB ChB 1988 Bristol; MA Oxf. 1982; MRCPsych 1994. Cons. Old Age psychiat; Research Fell. Ethox Inst. of Health Scis. Oxf. Prev: Sen. Regist. (Old Age Psychiat.) Fair Mile Hosp.; Sen. Regist. (Old Age Psychiat.) Ch.ill Hosp. Oxf.; Sen. Regist. (Community Psychiat.) Warneford Hosp. Oxf. & RAF Wroughton.

HUGHES, June Maureen (retired) Whittericks, Feock, Truro TR3 6SA Tel: 01872 862273 — MB BS Lond. 1944; MRCS Eng. LRCP Lond. 1944. Prev: GP Cornw.

HUGHES, Justine Claire 12 Stonecroft Gardens, Haydon Grange, Little Benton, Newcastle upon Tyne NE7 7GD — MB BS 1992 Newc.; MRCGP 1997; DRCOG 1997; DFFP 1997.

HUGHES, Karen Sian Division of Obstetrics & Gynaecology, The Southern General Hospital, Glasgow G51 4TF Tel: 0141 332 0044; 7 Kirklee Gardens, Glasgow G12 0SG Tel: 0141 337 2150 — MB ChB 1986 Aberd.; MRCOG 1992. Career Regist. (O & G) Gtr. Glas. HB. Prev: Regist. (O & G) Odstock Hosp. Salisbury.

HUGHES, Kathleen Isobel (retired) 1/116 Homeross House, Mount Grange, Strathearn Road, Edinburgh EH9 2QY Tel: 0131 447 0964 — MB ChB 1939 Ed.

HUGHES, Kathryn Anne Hamlet, Holton, Oxford OX33 1PS Tel: 01865 872541 — MB BCh 1981 Wales; DCH RCP Lond. 1984; DRCOG 1983.

HUGHES, Kay Alyson Fax: 01554 752570 — MB ChB 1988 Bristol; MRCGP 1992; DRCOG 1992; DFFP 1995; DCH 1996. (Bristol) GP. Prev: Community Paediat. Swansea; Clin. Asst. (Gerontology) P. Philip Hosp. LLa.lli; PHO Nambour Qu.sland, Australia 1993.

HUGHES, Keith Meddygfa Pengorof, Gorof Road, Ystradgynlais, Swansea SA9 1DS Tel: 01639 843221 Fax: 01639 843790; Llysycoed, Ynisuchaf, Ystradgynlais, Swansea SA9 1RP — MB 1975 Camb.; BChir 1974; MRCGP 1978; DRCOG 1976; Cert JCC Lond. 1978. Clin. Asst. (Geriat.) Ystradgynlais Community Hosp.

HUGHES, Mr Keith Basil Shelton House, 4 Bennetthorpe, Doncaster DN2 6AD Tel: 01302 323489 Fax: 01302 323489 Email: hughes.keith@virgin.net; The Old Rectory, Low Lane, Kirk Bramwith, Doncaster DN7 5SW Tel: 0302 843285 — MB BS 1964 Lond.; FRCS Eng. (ENT) 1973; MRCS Eng. LRCP Lond. 1964; DLO Eng. 1971. (Guy's) Cons. ENT Doncaster Roy. Infirm.; Trent Regist. Specialist Advis. Socs: Roy. Soc. Med. (Mem. Sects. Otol. & Laryngol.); Regional Speciality Advisor (ENT); Brit. Assn. Otorhinol. Head & Neck Surg. Prev: Cons. (ENT) Qu. Eliz. Milit. Hosp. Woolwich & Brit. Milit. Hosp. Hong Kong/Münster; Research Asst. Head & Neck Unit Roy. Marsden Hosp. Lond.

HUGHES, Kenneth Monklands Hospital, Monkscourt Avenue, Airdrie ML6 0JS Fax: 01236 713085, 01236 748748 Ext: 2170; Hill House, 11 Locksley Place, Greenfaulds, Cumbernauld, Glasgow G67 4BL — MB ChB 1975 Glas.; FRCR Lond. 1981; DMRD (Eng.) Lond. 1979; DRCOG Lond. 1977. (Univ. Glas.) Cons. Radiol. Monklands Hosp. Airdrie Lanarksh. HB. Socs: Fell. Roy. Coll. Radiologists. Prev: Sen. Regist. (Radiol.) S.. Gen. Hosp. Glas.; Regist. (Radiol.) W.. Infirm. Glas.; SHO (Paediat.) Roy. Hosp. Sick Childr. Glas.

HUGHES, Kim Rosemary 30 Shandon Road, London SW4 9HR — MB BS 1981 Lond.; FFA RCS Eng. 1987. Cons. Anaesth. Mayday Hosp. Prev: Sen. Regist. St. Thos. Hosp. Lond.; Regist. (Anaesth.) Middlx. & Univ. Coll. Hosp.; Regist. (Anaesth.) Whipps Cross Hosp. Lond.

HUGHES, Professor Leslie Ernest 14 Millwood, Lisvane, Cardiff CF14 0TL Tel: 01222 752451 — MB BS Sydney 1955; DS Queensld. 1975; FRCS Eng. 1959; FRACS 1959. Emerit. Prof. Surg. Univ. Wales Coll. Med. Socs: (Ex-Pres.) Surgic. Research Soc.; (Ex-Pres.) Welsh Surgic. Soc.; (Ex-Chairm.) Brit. Melanoma Study Gp. Prev: Hunt. Prof. Roy. Coll. Surgs. Eng. 1987; Reader (Surg.) Univ., Qu.sland; Eleanor Roosevelt Cancer Fell. Roswell Pk. Memor. Inst. Buffalo, NY 1969-70.

HUGHES, Liam Oisin Norfolk & Norwich Hospital, Norwich NR1 3SR Tel: 01603 286286 — MB BS 1980 Lond.; MD Lond. 1989; MRCP (UK) 1983; MRCS Eng. LRCP Lond. 1979. (Guy's) Cons. Cardiol. Norf. & Norwich Hosp. Socs: Brit. Cardiac Soc. Prev: Sen. Regist. (Cardiol.) St. Bart. Hosp. Lond.; Regist. & Research Regist. (Cardiol.) N.wick Pk. Hosp. Harrow; Regist. (Gen. Med.) Roy. Surrey Co. Hosp. Guildford.

HUGHES, Linda Sian Miles House, Dunsford Place, Bathwick Hill, Bath BA2 6HF Tel: 01225 423272; 17 Bennett Street, Bath BA1 2QL Tel: 01225 338002 — MB ChB 1991 Bristol. SHO (Psychiat.) Bath Ment. Health Care NHS Trust.

HUGHES, Louis 99 Harley Street, London W1G 6AQ Tel: 020 7935 9004 Fax: 020 7935 6494 Email: lhughes@louishughes.demon.co.uk; Beechwood, Burton's Lane, Chalfont St Giles HP8 4BA Tel: 01494 762297 Fax: 01494 766624 — MB BCh Wales 1959; DObst RCOG 1964. (Cardiff) Socs: Fell. Roy. Soc. Med.; Brit. Fertil. Soc.; Brit. Andrology Soc. Prev: Med. Off. (Infertil.) Qu. Charlotte's Hosp. Lond.; SHO (Obst.) Monmouth Gen. Hosp.; Ho. Phys. Bridgend Gen. Hosp.

HUGHES, Mair Eluned (retired) Fron, Llangefni LL77 7HB Tel: 01248 722178 — MB ChB 1941 Liverp. Prev: GP Llangefni.

HUGHES, Marcus Wyndham The Maudsley Hospital, Denmark Hill, London SE5 8AZ Fax: 020 7919 2171 Email: marcus@balham.u-net.com — MB ChB 1993 Ed.; DTM & H Liverp. 1994. (Ed.) Regist. (Psychiat.) Maudsley Hosp. Lond. Prev: Head of Health Sector Samuha, Raichur & Karnataka India.

HUGHES, Margaret Elizabeth Saint Vincent Medical Centre, 77 Thorne Road, Doncaster DN1 2ET Tel: 01302 361318; 62 St. Wilfrids Road, Doncaster DN4 6AD Tel: 01302 536977 — MB ChB 1972 Birm.

HUGHES, Margaret Pat (retired) 35 Dunraven Road, Sketty, Swansea SA2 9LG — MB BCh 1955 Wales. Prev: Med. Off. W. Glam. AHA.

HUGHES, Marian (retired) 14 Millwood, Lisvane, Cardiff CF14 0TL Tel: 01222 752451 — MB BS Sydney 1956. Prev: Assoc. Specialist (Child & Adolesc. Psychiat.) Mid Glam. HA.

HUGHES, Marie Jane Ground Left, 61 Lymburn St., Glasgow G3 8PD — MB ChB 1997 Glas.

HUGHES, Marie Louise 23 Woodbreda Drive, Belfast BT8 7HZ — MB BCh BAO 1992 Belf.

HUGHES, Mark Ivor Eastview Surgery, 81-83 Crosby Road North, Liverpool L22 4QD Tel: 0151 928 8849 Fax: 0151 928 2090 — MB ChB 1984 Liverp.

HUGHES, Mark Lewis Royal Victoria Hospital, Edinburgh EH4 2DN; 19 Comiston Dr, Edinburgh EH10 5QR — MB ChB 1997 Ed. SHO I (IC of the Elderly), Roy. Vict. Hosp. Edin. Prev: Jun. Ho. Off. (Med.) W.ern Gen. Hosp., Edin.; Jun. Ho. Off. (Med.) E.ern Gen. Hosp., Edin.; Jun. Ho. Off. (Surg.) Dumfries & Galloway Roy. Infirm.

HUGHES, Mark Lloyd Email: mark.hughes@rlbuh-tr.nwest.nhs.uk — MB BChir 1989 Camb.; MA Camb. 1990; MRCP (UK) 1992; FRCR 1996; DMRD Liverp. 1995. (Camb.) Cons. Radiol. Roy. Liverp. Univ. hosp. Prev: Lect.Dept.med.image.univ.Liverp.

HUGHES, Mark Peter 78 Belmont Road, Wealdstone, Harrow HA3 7PN — MB BS 1986 Lond.

HUGHES, Mark Philip North Devon District Hospital, Barnstaple EX31 4JB Tel: 01271 378980 Fax: 01271 311541 — BSc (Hons.) Soton. 1982, BM 1986; MRCP (Lond.) 1991. (Southampton) Cons. Paediat. N. Devon Dist. Hosp. Prev: Sen. Regist. (Paediat.) Guy's Hosp. Lond.

HUGHES, Mark William 30 Sanders Road, Quorn, Loughborough LE12 8JN — MB ChB 1996 Liverp.

HUGHES, Martin 121 Terregles Avenue, Glasgow G41 4DG — MB ChB 1990 Glas.; BSc Glas. 1987; MRCP Glas. 1993; FRCA Lond. 1997. Specialist Regist. (Anaesth.) Glas. Roy. Infirm.

HUGHES, Martin Red House Surgery, 96 Chesterton Road, Cambridge CB4 1ER Tel: 01223 365555 Fax: 01223 356848; 234 Milton Road, Cambridge CB4 1LQ Tel: 01223 501069 Fax: 01223 501068 — MB BChir 1979 Camb.; MB BChir (Hons.) Camb. 1979; PhD Camb. 1975; BSc Lond. 1972. (Camb.) Clin. Asst. (Geriat. Med.) Camb. HA; Clin. Asst. (Clin. Pharmacol.) Camb.; Examr. DGM. RCP Lond.; Med. Correspondent BBC Radio Camb.; Lect. Magdalene Coll. Camb.; Affil. Lect. (Clin. Pharmacol.) Camb; Mem. Cambs. LMC; Mem. E. Anglian Regional Manpower Comm. Socs: (Chairm.) Assn. BRd.casting Doctors. Prev: Clin. Asst. (Gen. Med.) NW Thames HA; Ho. Phys. & Ho. Surg. Addenbrooke's Hosp. Camb.

HUGHES, Martin Christopher Talbot Medical Centre, 63 Kinson Road, Bournemouth BH10 4BX Tel: 01202 523059 Fax: 01202 533239; 23 Cassel Avenue, Poole BH13 6JD Tel: 01202 769870 — MB BS 1983 Lond.; BSc Lond. 1980; MRCGP 1988; DRCOG 1987. (St. Geo.) Prev: Trainee GP Avon VTS; SHO (Gen. Med.) Centr. Middlx. Hosp. Lond.; Ho. Phys. St. Geo. Hosp. Lond.

HUGHES, Martin David White House Surgery, Weston Lane, Weston, Southampton SO19 9HJ Tel: 023 8044 9913 Fax: 023 8044 6617 — BM 1984 Soton.; MRCGP 1988. GP Soton. Prev: SHO (Gen. & Geriat. Med.) Barnet HA; SHO (Gen. Med. & Radiother.) N.W. Thames RHA; SHO (O & G) Soton. HA.

HUGHES, Martyn Wayne 236 Station Road, Rolleston-on-Dove, Burton-on-Trent DE13 9AD; 12 Wetmore Road, Burton-on-Trent DE14 1SN Tel: 01283 64848 — MB ChB 1979 Bristol; DCH RCP Lond. 1982; DRCOG 1981.

HUGHES, Mary The Malthouse Surgery, The Charter, Abingdon OX14 3JY Tel: 01235 524001 Fax: 01235 532197 — MB ChB 1983 Aberd.; MRCGP 1989; DCH RCP Lond. 1989.

HUGHES, Mary Elizabeth Rosemary (retired) Killevey Cottage, Mill Hill Lane, Burton-on-Trent DE15 0BB Tel: 01283 568272 — MB ChB Ed. 1949. Prev: SCMO S. Derbysh. HA.

HUGHES, Mary Imelda Royal Manchester Children's Hospital, Hospital Road, Manchester M27 4HA Tel: 0161 727 2555 Fax: 0161 727 2185 — MB BCh BAO 1983 Belf.; MRCP (UK) 1986; DCH RCPSI 1985; FRCP CH. Cons. Paediat. Neurol. Roy. Manch. Childr. Hosps. Trust. Socs: MRCPCH; Brit. Paediat. Neurol. Assn.; BMA. Prev: Lect. (Paediat. Neurol.) Univ. Soton.; Sen. Regist. (Paediat.) Roy. Belf. Hosp. for Sick Childr.

HUGHES, Mary Rowland Trevor House, Chirk, Wrexham LL14 5HD Tel: 01691 772444 — MB ChB 1940 Liverp.; DOMS Eng. 1944. (Liverp.) Ophth. Co. Denb. Socs: N. Eng. Ophth. Soc.; Assoc. Mem. Fac. Ophthalmols. Prev: Clin. Asst. in Ophth. Maelor Hosp. Wrexham; Clin. Asst. Ophth. Preston Roy. Infirm.; Ophth. Lancs. CC.

HUGHES, Mervyn Stephens (retired) Brook Cottage, Cerney Wick, Cirencester GL7 5QJ Tel: 01793 750760 — MRCS Eng. LRCP Lond. 1944; DMRD Eng. 1965. Prev: Cons. Radiol. Gloucester Roy. & Cheltenham Gen. Hosps.

HUGHES, Meurig (retired) Tan Y Pentre Mawr, Llangoed, Beaumaris LL58 8RY Tel: 01248 490212 — MB ChB 1964 Liverp.; FRCPath 1983, M 1971. Prev: Cons. Histopath. Ysbyty Gwynedd, Bangor.

HUGHES, Mr Michael X-Ray Department, South Warwickshire Hospital, Lakin Road, Warwick CV34 5BW — MB BS 1980 Lond.; FRCS Ed. 1984; FRCR 1990. (St. Geo.) Cons. Radiol. S. Warks. Hosp. Prev: Sen. Regist. Rotat. (Diag. Radiol.) Manch. HA; Regist. Rotat. (Diag. Radiol.) Manch. HA; Regist. Rotat. (Surg. & Orthop.) Wolverhampton HA.

HUGHES, Mr Michael Anthony 10 Metchley Park Road, Edgbaston, Birmingham B15 2PG Tel: 0121 454 1007 Fax: 0121 605 5596 — MB ChB Birm. 1967; FRCS Eng. 1973. (Birm.) Cons. Urol. Surg. Qu. Eliz. Hosp. Birm. Prev: Sen. Urol. Regist. Qu. Eliz. Hosp. Birm.; Ho. Surg. Hallam Hosp. W. Bromwich; Surg. Regist. United Birm. Hosps.

HUGHES, Michael John Manorlands, Sue Ryder Palliative Care Home, Hebden Road, Oxenhope, Keighley BD22 9HS Tel: 01535 642308 — MB BS 1988 Lond.; MRCGP 1992. Cons. Phys. Pallab. Med. Airedale Gen. Hosp. & Moorlands Sue Ryder Palliat. Care Home.

HUGHES, Michael John Hill House, Hill Waye, Gerrards Cross SL9 8BH; 54 Barton House, Addenbrooke's Hospital, Cambridge CB2 2SB — BChir 1995 Camb. (Addenbrooke's)

HUGHES, Michael John Minto Old Brandon Road Surgery, Old Brandon Road, Feltwell, Thetford IP26 4AY Tel: 01842 828481 Fax: 01842 828172; The Rectory, Main St, Little Downham, Ely CB6 2ST Tel: 01353 699237 — MB ChB 1974 Liverp.; MTh Oxf. 1994; DGM RCP Lond. 1989; DRCOG 1987. GP Feltwell. Prev: Trainee Seascale W. Cumbria VTS; SHO (O & G) Hartlepool; Ho. Off. (Med. & Surg.) Fazakerley Hosp. Liverp.

HUGHES, Michael Stephen 154 Bond Street, Macclesfield SK11 6RE — MB ChB 1991 Liverp.

HUGHES, Moira 58 Monkhams Drive, Woodford Green IG8 0LD — MB ChB 1964 Manch. Assoc. Specialist (Psychiat.) Claybury Hosp. Prev: Regist. (Psychiat.) & Clin. Asst. (Anaesth.) Claybury Hosp.; Regist. (Anaesth.) N. Manch. Hosp. Gp.

HUGHES, Moran Sidney Treetops, Hascombe Road, Southern Munstead, Godalming GU8 4AB — MB BS 1960 Lond.; MSc Lond. 1978; MRCS Eng. LRCP Lond. 1960; MFOM RCP Lond. 1979; DIH Eng. 1970; DAvMed Eng. 1970. (St. Geo.) Chief Occupat. Phys. Beecham Pharmaceut. Ltd. Socs: Soc. Occupat. Med. Prev: Res. Obst. Asst. St. Geo. Hosp. Lond.; Med. Off. Unilever Ltd.

HUGHES, Mureen (retired) Orchard Dale, Church St., Storrington, Pulborough RH20 — MB BS 1953 Lond.; MRCS Eng. LRCP Lond. 1953; DObst RCOG 1956. Prev: Clin. Asst. (Physical Med.) Worthing Hosp.

HUGHES, Muriel Mallalieu (retired) 86 Tan y Bryn Road, Colwyn Bay LL28 4TU Tel: 01492 44610 — MB ChB 1948 Manch.; DObst RCOG 1954.

HUGHES, Neil 16 Hillcrest Road, Bramhall, Stockport SK7 3AE — MB ChB 1978 Leeds; MRCGP 1982.

HUGHES, Neill Rowland 12 Whitchurch Road, Withington, Manchester M20 1FX — MB ChB 1998 Manch.; MB ChB Manch 1998.

HUGHES, Nicholas Charles St Georges Hospital, Blackshaw Rd, Tooting, London SW17 0QT Tel: 020 8672 1255 — MB BS 1990 Lond.; FRCR 2000; MRCP (UK) 1995. (St. Geo. Hosp. Med. Sch.) Specialist Regist., Dept. of Radiol., St Geo.s Hosp., Lond. Prev: Regist. Renal Med., Univ. Hosp. Birm. NHS Trust, Birm.

HUGHES, Nicholas John Milestone Surgery, 208 Farnborough Road, Farnborough GU14 7JN Tel: 01252 545078 Fax: 01252 370751; 71 Park Road, Camberley GU15 2SW Tel: 0468 497593 Email: nickhu02@globalnet.co.uk — MB ChB 1984 Liverp.; MRCGP 1994; DCH RCP Lond. 1990. (Liverpool) GP Princip.

HUGHES, Nigel John Longview Adolescent Unit, 216 Turner Road, Colchester CO4 5JR Tel: 01206 228745 Fax: 01206 843702 — MB BCh BAO 1984 Belf.; MRCPsych 1989. Cons. Adolesc. Psychiat. N. E. Ment. Health Partnership NHS Trust.

HUGHES, Owen David Marshall 4 Gelligaer Gardens, Cardiff CF24 4LT — BM BS 1990 Nottm.; DM 2000; FRCS 2001; FRCS 1994; FRCS Ed 1994. (Nottingham) Specialist Regist. urol. Socs: BAUS; RCS Eng.

HUGHES, Patricia 19 Silverknowes Avenue, Edinburgh EH4 5HG — MB ChB 1982 Liverp.; MRCGP 1990; DRCOG 1989.

HUGHES, Patricia Anne Commonfield Road Surgery, 156 Commonfield Road, Woodchurch, Birkenhead CH49 7LP Tel: 0151 677 0016; 84 Cavendish Drive, Rock Ferry, Birkenhead CH42 6RQ — MB ChB 1976 Liverp.; DRCOG 1978.

HUGHES, Patricia Mary Dept. of Psychiatry, Jenner Wing, St George's Medical School, Cranmer Terrace, London SW17 0RE Tel: 020 8994 8102 — MB ChB 1970 Glas.; MSc Lond. 1985; FRCPsych 1995; DObst RCOG 1972. (Glas.) Sen. Lect. & Cons. Psychother. St. Geo. Hosp. Lond. Socs: Inst. Gp. Anal. & Assoc. Mem. Brit. Psychoanal. Soc.

HUGHES, Patrick Bernard 6 The Green, Woolley, Wakefield WF4 2JG Tel: 01226 388288; 6 The Green, Woolley, Wakefield WF4 2JG Tel: 01226 388288 — LMSSA 1950 Lond.; MA Camb. 1946.

HUGHES, Paul Antony, Surg. Lt.-Cdr. RN GSMDC, Queensway BFPO 52 — MB BS 1985 Lond.; MRCGP 1992; DRCOG 1993; DFFP 1993. (St. Thos.) GP RN. Socs: BMA. Prev: Ho. Surg. Kingston Hosp. Surrey; Ho. Phys. St. Thos. Hosp. Lond.

HUGHES, Paul James, RD Hurstwood Park Neurological Centre, Lewis Road, Haywards Heath RH16 4EX Tel: 01444 441881 Fax: 01444 417995 — MB BCh Wales 1979; MD Wales 1988; MRCP (UK) 1982; FRCP 1999. (Cardiff) Cons. Neurol. Hurstwood Pk. Neurol. Centre Sussex.; Surg. Cdr. RNR; PMO HMS King Alfred. Socs: Brit. Neurol. Assn. Prev: Sen. Regist. (Neurol.) Wessex Neuro-Centre Soton.; Regist. (Neurol.) Char. Cross Hosp. Lond.; Research Regist. (Neurol.) Univ. Hosp. Wales.

HUGHES, Paul Richard, Squadron Ldr. RAF Med BR 16 Parlington Villas, Aberford, Leeds LS25 3EP Email: drprhughes@aol.com — MB ChB 1992 Manch.; MB ChB Mar 1992; FRCA 1998. (Manchester)

HUGHES, Peter (retired) 3 Holkham Rise, Whirlowdale Park, Sheffield S11 9QT Tel: 0114 235 0282 Fax: 0114 235 0282 — MD 1969 Manch.; MB ChB Manch. 1959; FRCP Ed. 1982, M 1964; FRCP Lond. 1979, M 1964. Prev: Hon. Cons. Phys. N.. Gen. Hosp. Sheff.

***HUGHES, Peter George** 108 Galgorm Road, Ballymena BT42 1AE Tel: 01766 41406; 5 Wilton Drive, Flat G/R, Glasgow G20 6RW Tel: 0141 945 5081 — MB ChB 1996 Glas.

HUGHES, Mr Peter James 159 Thingwall Road, Wavertree Garden Suburb, Liverpool L15 7JY — MB ChB 1991 Liverp.; BSc (Hons.) Appl. & Human Biol. Birm. 1986; FRCS Eng. 1996. Specialist Regist. (Orthop.) Mersey Region. Prev: SHO Rotat. (Surg.) Merseyside.

HUGHES, Mr Peter Leslie 36 Gregstown Park, Newtownards BT23 8GW — MB BCh BAO 1962 Belf.; FRCS Ed. 1974; DO RCPSI 1972; DObst RCOG 1964. (Belf.) Cons. A & E Dept. Craigavon Area Hosp. Prev: Resid. (Ophth.) St. Joseph's Hosp. Toronto, Canada; Med. Miss. Irish Baptist Foreign Miss. Peru; Regist. (Ophth.) Eye & Ear Clinic Roy. Vict. Hosp. Belf.

HUGHES, Peter Lloyd 3 Sandown Court, Dartmouth Road, London SE26 4RT Tel: 020 8291 2688 Email: petehughes@aol.com — MB BS 1994 Lond.

HUGHES, Peter Lyndon Stable End, Scarisbrick Park, Scarisbrick, Ormskirk L40 9RZ — MB ChB 1980 Liverp.; MRCS Eng. LRCP Lond. 1980; FRCR 1986; DMRD Liverp. 1985. Sen. Regist. (Radiol.) Liverp. HA.

HUGHES, Philip Daniel Derriford Hospital, Derriford Road, Plymouth PL6 8DH Tel: 01752 777111 — MB BS 1989 Lond.; MD 1999; MRCP (UK) 1992. Regist. (Med.) Derriford Hosp. Plymouth./Cons. Respirat. Phys., Derriford Hosp. Plymouth.

HUGHES, Philip Mark 32 Westminster Road, Ellesmere Park, Eccles, Manchester M30 9EA — MB BS 1983 Lond.; MRCP (UK) 1986.

HUGHES, Phillppa Jane 52 Rosefield Road, Staines TW18 4NB — MB BS 1984 Lond.

HUGHES, Polly Nicola — MB ChB 1994 Bristol; BSc MB ChB. (University of Bristol) SpR (O & G) May Univ. Hosp.

HUGHES, Ralph Anthony Penistan and Partners, Cordell Road, Long Melford, Sudbury CO10 9EP Tel: 01787 378226 Fax: 01787 311287 — MB BS 1990 Lond.; MRCGP 1994; T(GP) 1994. (Char. Cross and Westm.)

HUGHES, Rebecca Jane Green Garth, 14 Park Crescent, Pontyclun CF72 9BR — MB BS 1998 Lond.; MB BS Lond 1998.

HUGHES, Rhona Grace Simpson Memorial Maternity Pavilion, Lauriston Place, Edinburgh EH3 9EF Tel: 0131 536 1000; 4 Abbotsford Park, Edinburgh EH10 5DX — MB ChB 1989 Ed.; MB ChB Ed. 1983; BSc (Hons. Med. Sci.) Ed. 1980, MD 1989; MRCOG 1990. Cons. O & G Simpson Memor. Matern. Pavil. Edin.; Hon. Sen. Lect. Univ Edin. Prev: Sen. Regist. (O & G) Simpson Memor. Matern. Pavil. Edin.

HUGHES, Professor Richard Anthony Cranmer Department of Neurology, Guy's Hospital, London SE1 9RT Tel: 020 7955 4500 Fax: 020 7378 1221; 2 Onslow Gardens, London N10 3JU Tel: 020 8444 5200 — MA, MD Camb. 1973; FRCP Lond. 1980; MRCP (UK) 1970. (Camb. & Guy's) Prof. Neurol. Head of Dept. Clin. Neurosci.s Guy's, King's & St. Thomas' Sch. of Med. King's Coll.; Hon. Cons. Neurol. Guy's Hosp. Lond.; Edr. Jl. Neurol., Neurosurg. & Psychiat.; Co-ordinating Ed. Cochrane Neuromuscular Dis. Review Gp.; Chairm. Med. & Dent. Advis. Comm. Guy's & St Thos. Hosp. Trust. Socs: Fell. Roy. Soc. Med.; Assn. Phys.; Assn. Brit. NeUrol.s. Prev: Sen. Regist. Univ. Coll. Hosp. Lond.; Regist. Nat. Hosp. Nerv. Dis. Qu. Sq. Lond.; Ho. Phys. Hammersmith Hosp.

HUGHES, Richard Curtis 169 Heathwood Road, Heath, Cardiff CF14 4BN Tel: 02920754817 — MB BCh 1987 Wales; FRCA 1995. (Wales) cons. Anaesth. UHW NHS Trust Cardiff. Prev: Clin. Fell. (Critical Care Med.) Toronto Hosp. Canada; Regist. (Anaesth.) Univ. Hosp. Wales Cardiff; SHO (Paediat. Surg. Neonatol. & Anaesth.) Univ. Hosp. Wales Cardiff.

HUGHES, Richard David 6 Gisburn Dr, Bury BL8 3DH — MB ChB 1997 Birm.

HUGHES, Richard Glyn Moore 31 Harrow Place, Stone ST15 8ST Tel: 01785 811117 Email: rgmhughes7@yahoo.co.uk — BM BS 1992 Nottm.; FRCS Eng. 1997. Regist. Rotat. (Otolaryngol.) W. Midl. Socs: BMA.

HUGHES, Richard John Rippon Hughes and Partners, 15 Dereham Road, Mattishall, Dereham NR20 3QA Tel: 01362 850227 Fax: 01362 858466; Vine Lodge, Hardingham, Norwich NR9 4AE Tel: 01953 850460 — MB ChB 1971 Leeds. Prev: Ho. Phys. Chapel Allerton Hosp. Leeds; Ho. Surg. Clayton Hosp. Wakefield; Ho. Off. (Obst.) Manygates Hosp. Wakefield.

HUGHES, Richard Mark Glastonbury Surgery, Feversham Lane, Glastonbury BA6 9LP Tel: 01458 833666; Mascot House, Chapel Lane, Butleigh, Glastonbury BA6 8TB Tel: 01458 850896 — MB BS 1991 Lond.; BSc (1st cl. Hons.) Clin. Sci. Lond. 1990; MRCGP 1997.

HUGHES, Richard Michael 19 Wild Ridings, Fareham PO14 3BS — MB BS 1977 Lond.; MRCS Eng. LRCP Lond. 1977; MRCGP 1982; DRCOG 1986; DCH Eng. 1979. (Guy's)

HUGHES, Mr Robert Royal Preston Hospital, Sharoe Green Lane N., Fulwood, Preston PR2 9NT Tel: 01772 710224 Fax: 01772 710190 Email: gwylan@hotmail.com; Inglewood, Fern Road, Burnley BB11 4NN Email: robert.hughes@btinternet.com — MA Camb. 1970; FRCS Eng. 1975. (Westm.) Cons. Surg. Roy. Preston

Hosp. Socs: Fell. Roy. Soc. Med.; Vasc. Soc.; Manch. Med. Soc. Prev: Cons. Surg. Burnley Pendle & Rossendale Hosps.; Sen. Regist. (Surg.) N. Manch. Roy. Infirm.; Sen. Regist. (Surg.) Birch Hill Hosp. Rochdale.

HUGHES, Robert Andrew 1 Boghall Park, Biggar ML12 6EY — BM BS 1975 Nottm.

HUGHES, Robert Emrys Maurice The Caxton Surgery, Oswald Road, Oswestry SY11 1RD Tel: 01691 654646 Fax: 01691 670994 — MB ChB 1965 Liverp.; DObst RCOG 1967. (Liverp)

HUGHES, Robert George Department of Haematology, West Middlesex University Hospital, Twickenham Rd, Isleworth TW7 6AF Tel: 020 8565 5844 Fax: 020 8565 5516 Email: tobeert.g.hughes@questdiagnostics.com — MB ChB 1970 Glas.; FRCP Lond. 1993; MRCP (UK) 1975; FRCPath 1994, M 1982. (Glas.) Cons. Haemat. W. Middlx. Univ. Hosp. Isleworth. Prev: Sen. Regist. Roy. Marsden Hosp. Lond.; Clin. Sci. Med. Research Counc.; Regist. Hammersmith Hosp. Lond.

HUGHES, Mr Robert Gwilym 5 St Johns Court, Ditton Priors, Bridgnorth WV16 6TQ Tel: 01746 712419 — MB BCh 1944 Wales; BSc Wales 1941; FRCS Ed. 1947. (Cardiff) Socs: Fell. Roy. Soc. Med. (Ex-Pres. Sect. Laryngol.). Prev: Cons. ENT Surg. Wolverhampton & Dudley Gp. Hosps.; Sen. Regist. Cardiff Gp. Hosps. & Roy. Nat. Throat, Nose & Ear Hosp. Lond.; Regist. (Ear, Nose & Throat) Roy. Vict. Hosp. Newc. u. Tyne.

HUGHES, Robert Ian 146 Vicarage Road, Morriston, Swansea SA6 6DR — MB BS 1998 Lond.; MB BS Lond 1998.

HUGHES, Robert John Mid-Cheshire Homeopathic Group, 2 Watling Street, Northwich CW9 5EX Tel: 01606 42445 — MB ChB 1969 Liverp.

HUGHES, Robert John 18 Maplehatch Close, Godalming GU7 1TH — MB BS 1996 Lond.

HUGHES, Robert Kendrick George 2 Wellmeadow Drive, Copthorne, Shrewsbury SY3 8UW Tel: 01743 246759 — MB ChB 1969 Birm.; FRCPsych 1991, M 1976. Cons. Psychiat. Shelton Hosp. Shrewsbury; Clin. Dir. EMI Serv.

HUGHES, Robert Kieron Frederick Ferryview Health Centre, 25 John Wilson Street, Woolwich, London SE18 6PZ Tel: 020 8319 5400 Fax: 020 8319 5404 — MB BS 1983 Lond.; MRCGP 1988. (Univ. Coll. Hosp.) Nat. Co-ordinator Med. Pract. Union; Vice-Pres. Med. Pract. Union; MAAG Mem. Greenwich & Bexley. Prev: Trainee GP Croydon VTS; Ho. Surg. (Acad. Unit) Whittington Hosp. Lond.; Ho. Phys. Chase Farm Hosp. Enfield.

HUGHES, Mr Robin Gwynedd Torbay Hospital, Lawes Bridge, Torquay TQ2 7AA Tel: 01803 654840 — MS Lond. 1983, MB BS 1969; FRCS Eng. 1974. (St. Thos.) Cons. Surg. Torbay Hosp. Prev: Sen. Surg. Regist. Bristol Health Dist. (T); Surg. Regist. Nottm. Gen. Hosp.; SHO (Surg.) Sheff. Roy. Hosp.

HUGHES, Roderick Carl (cons. rooms), Flat 2, 94 Tettenhall Road, Wolverhampton WV6 0BP Tel: 01902 423888 Fax: 01902 717120; Holly Cottage, Upper Farmcote, Bridgnorth WV15 5PS Tel: 01746 710716 — MB ChB 1960 Birm.; FRCP Ed. 1982, M 1967; FRCP Lond. 1980, M 1967. Locum Cons. Neurol. New Cross Hosp. Wolverhampton. Socs: N. Eng. Neurol. Assn.; Assn. Brit. Neurols. Prev: Sen. Regist. (Neurol.) Newc. Regional Neurol. Centre; Regist. (Neurol.) Derbysh. Roy. Infirm. Derby; SHO (Neurol.) Regional Neurol. Centre Newc.

HUGHES, Roderick Carson Watcyn (retired) Frome Valley Medical Centre, 2 Court Road, Frampton Cotterell, Bristol BS36 2DE Tel: 01454 772153 Fax: 01454 250078 — MB ChB 1961 Bristol; DObst RCOG 1963; FRCGP 1981. Assoc. Med. Postgrad, Dean; Regional Adviser. GP.

HUGHES, Rodney Andrew 11 Westcroft Square, London W6 0TB Tel: 020 8748 0035 — MB BS 1982 Lond.; MA Oxf. 1979; MD Lond. 1995; MRCP (UK) 1985; FRCP (UK) 1998. (Lond. Hosp. Med. Coll.) Cons. Rheum. & Gen. Med. St. Peters Hosp. Chertsey. Socs: (Vice Pres.) Roy. Soc. Med.; Brit. Soc. Rheum. Prev: Sen. & Research Regist. (Rheum.) W.m. Hosp. Lond.; Regist. (Rheum. & Immunol.) Char. Cross Hosp. Lond.

HUGHES, Roger Llewellyn Stobhill Hospital, 133 Balornock Rd, Glasgow G21 3UW Tel: 0141 201 3003 Fax: 0141 201 3007; 7 Ballaig avenue, Bearsden, Glasgow G61 4HA Tel: 0141 942 5626 Fax: 0141 942 5626 Email: roger@saintronanas.freeeserve.co.uk — MD 1980 Glas.; MB ChB 1970; FRCP Glas. 1985; MRCP (UK) 1973; FFA RCS Eng. 1974. Cons. Anaesth. Stobhill Gen. Hosp. Glas.; Hon. Sen. Lect., Univ. of Glas. Socs: BMA. & Assn. Anaesth. Prev: Lect. Univ. Dept. Anaesth., Sen. Regist. & Regist. Dept. Anaesth.; Glas. Roy. Infirm.

HUGHES, Rosemary (retired) Long Meadow, Ballylesson, Belfast BT8 8JU — MB BCh BAO 1945 Belf. SCMO (Family Plann.) E.ern Health & Social Servs. Bd. Prev: Ho. Surg. Roy. Vict. Hosp. Belf.

HUGHES, Rowland Tudor 61 Marlborough Hill, Harrow HA1 1TX — MB BCh 1981 Wales; MRCP (UK) 1985.

HUGHES, Ruth Caroline Elizabeth Nant-y-Graean, Hendurnpike, Tregarth, Bangor LL57 4NS — MB BCh 1995 Wales.

HUGHES, Ruth Eva Emily (retired) 16 The Beeches, Holywell CH8 7SW Tel: 01352 713197 Email: holywllrath@aol.com — MB ChB 1954 St. And.; MRCPsych 1973; DObst RCOG 1956; DPM Eng. 1972. Cons. Child Psychiat. Merseyside AHA. Prev: Cons. Child Psychiat. Clwyd AHA. Psychiat. Regist. N. Wales Hosp.

HUGHES, Ruth Mary Maes-y-Gynesh, Garth Road, Machynlleth SY20 8HQ Tel: 01654 702224 Fax: 01654 703688 — MB BCh 1966 Wales. (Cardiff) Prev: SHO Radiother. Dept. Singleton Hosp. Swansea.

HUGHES, Sarah Cherry Hill, 16 Storeborough Lane, Budleigh Salterton EX9 6HL — MB BS 1988 Lond.

HUGHES, Sarah Anne 69 Edward Road, West Bridgford, Nottingham NG2 5GE — MB BCh 1987 Wales. SHO (Geriat. Med.) St. Woolas Hosp. Newport. Prev: Ho. Off. (Med./Respirat. Med.) Llandough; Ho. Off. (Surg.) Morriston Hosp.

HUGHES, Sarah Frances Southend Hospital, Prittlewell Chase, Westcliff on Sea; 48 Aviary Road, Armley, Leeds LS12 2NS — MB BS 1988 Lond.; MS 1998 University of London; FRCS 1999 (Gen. Surg.); FRCS Eng. 1992. Cons. Surg., S.end Hosp., Wescliff on Sea. Socs: Assoc. of Surg.; Assoc. of Coloproctologists; Assic, if Upper GI Surg.s.

HUGHES, Sean Michael St Mary's Hospital, Manchester M13 0JH; 253 Beesley Green, Worsley, Manchester M28 2QW Tel: 0161 799 1893 — MB ChB 1983 Leic.; MRCOG 1989. Research Regist. (In Vitro Fertilisation) St. Mary's Hosp. Manch.

HUGHES, Professor Sean Patrick Francis Department Orthopaedic Surgery, Charing Cross Hospital, Fulham Palace Road, London W6 8RF Tel: 020 8846 1477 Fax: 020 8383 0468 Email: shughes@ic.ac.uk; 24 Fairfax Road, London W4 1EW Tel: 020 8995 2039 Fax: 020 8742 8465 — MB BS 1966 Lond.; MS Lond. 1976; FRCS Ed. (Orth.) 1984; FRCSI 1972; FRCS Eng. 1972; FRCS Ed. 1971; MRCS Eng. LRCP Lond. 1965; T(S) 1991. (St. Mary's) Prof. Orthop. Surg. Imperial Coll. Sch. Med. Lond.; Clin. Dir. Surg. & Anaesth. Hammersmith Hosps. NHS Trust; Chairm. & Head of Div. Surg. Anaesths. & Intens. care (Imperial Coll Sch Med; Hon. Cons. Orthop. Surg. Hammersmith Hosps. Lond.; Hon. Cons. Nat. Hosp. Nerv. Dis. Qu. Sq.; Hon. Civil. Cons. (Orthop.) RN; Hon. Cons. Orthop. Surg. Ealing Hosp. Lond.; Hon. Cons. Nat. Hosp. Nerv. Dis. Qu. Sq.; Hon. Civil. Cons. (Orthop.) RN. Socs: (Pres.) Brit. Orthop. Research Soc.; Internat. Soc. Study Lumbar Spine; Fell. BOA. Prev: Prof. Orthop. Surg. Univ. Edin.; Research Asst. Mayo Clinic; Sen. Regist. (Orthop.) Middlx. Hosp. Lond.

HUGHES, Sian Ty Cerrig, 6 Gwyllt Cottages, 3 Gwyllt Road, Llanfairfechan LL33 0EE; Hergest Unit, Ysbyty Gwynedd, Penrhosgarnedd, Bangor LL57 2PW — MB ChB 1993 Bristol.

HUGHES, Sian Elisabeth St Thomas' Hospital, Department of Histopathology, Lambeth Palace Road, London SE1 7EH; 58 Finsen Road, Camberwell, London SE5 9AW — MB BS 1989 Lond.; MSc (Distinc.) Lond. 1991, MB BS 1989; PhD Lond. 1995. (King's College Hospital School of Medicine and Dentistry) Clin. Lect. (Histopath.) St. Thomas's Hosp. Lambeth Palace Rd. Lond.; Sen. Lect. Cardiovasc. Path. St Geo. Hosp. Lond. Socs: Brit.Cardiovasc.Soc. Prev: Clin.Lect.Histopath.St thomas Hosp.

HUGHES, Simon John 1 Kingsfort Crescent, Culmore Road, Londonderry BT48 7TB — MB BS 1993 Lond.

HUGHES, Simon Nicholas 53 Crosby Hill Drive, Camberley GU15 3TZ Tel: 01276 28133 — MB BS 1997 Lond.; BSc 1994. (St Barts) RAF Med Off; SHO Anaesth.

HUGHES, Simon Porteous Taylor and Partners, The Surgery, Hexton Road, Barton-le-Clay, Bedford MK45 4TA Tel: 01582 882050 Fax: 01582 528714; Tel: 01582 882640 — MB BS 1985 Lond.; BSc Lond. 1982; MRCGP 1992; T(GP) 1992; DA (UK) 1988. (Lond. Hosp.)

HUGHES, Simon Richard Laurel Bank, Sandy La, Lyndhurst SO43 7DN — MB BS 1997 Lond.

HUGHES, Sinead 211 Annagher Road, Dungannon BT71 5DA — MB BCh 1998 Belf.; MB BCh Belf 1998.

HUGHES, Stephen Department of Medicine, Southmead Hospital, Westbury-on-Trym, Bristol BS10 5NB Tel: 0117 950 5050; The Oaklands, 43 Kellaway Avenue, Henleaze, Bristol BS6 7XS Tel: 0117 924 6584 — MB ChB 1974 Leeds; MD Leeds 1987; FRCP Lond. 1995; MRCP (UK) 1976. Cons. Phys. & Gastroenterol. S.mead Hosp. Bristol. Socs: Brit. Soc. Gastroenterol. Prev: Sen. Regist. (Med. & Gastroenterol.) BRd.green Hosp. Liverp.; Tutor (Med.) Univ. Manch. Med. Sch. Hope Hosp. Salford.

HUGHES, Mr Stephen Anthony Rose Cottage, Church End, Stebbing, Dunmow CM6 3SW Email: shughes736@aol.com — MB BS 1990 Lond.; BSc Lond. 1987; FRCS Ed. 1994. Specialist Regist. (A & E) P.ss Alexandra Hosp. Harlow.

HUGHES, Stephen Miles 13 Linnell House, 50 Folgote St., London E1 6UP Tel: 020 7377 5063 Fax: 020 7375 2182 Email: shug@holyrood.ed.ac.uk; 50 Burgoyne Road, London SW9 9QJ Tel: 0207 787 8132 Email: s.hughes@bigfoot.com — MB ChB 1994 Ed.; BSc Ed. 1991; MRCP (UK) 1997; MRCPCH 1998; DTM & H 1999. (Ed.) Reg. Paediat.N.wick Pk. Hosp. Lond. Prev: Visit.Lect.Paediat.univ.Sci. & Tech.Kumasi Ghana.

HUGHES, Stephen Paul The Deepings Practice, Godsey Lane, Market Deeping, Peterborough PE6 8DD Tel: 01778 579009 — MB ChB 1986 Leic.; MRCGP 1991; DGM RCP Lond. 1990; DRCOG 1988. (Leic.)

HUGHES, Steven 20 Orchard Grove, Manchester M20 2LB — MB ChB 1994 Liverp.

HUGHES, Steven George 18 Maidenshaw Road, Epsom KT19 8HE Email: s.hughes@cwcom.net — MB BS 1991 Lond.; BSc (Hons.) Lond. 1988; MRCP (UK) 1996; Dip. Health Managem. Lond. 1998. (St. Mary's Hosp. Med. Sch.) Med. Dir. HPRU Med. Research Centre Univ. of Surrey Guildford. Socs: BMA; Med. Protec. Soc.; Roy. Coll. Phys.s. Prev: Med. Adviser Sanofi Winthrop Ltd Guildford; Sen. Regist. Rotat. (Gen. Med. & Geriat.) St. Geo. Hosp. Lond.; Regist. (Gen. Med.) Mayday Hosp. Lond.

HUGHES, Mr Steven James Birmingham Heartlands Hospital, Bordesley Green E., Birmingham B9 5SS Tel: 0121 424 2315 Fax: 0121 424 1318 Email: steven.hughes@virgin.net; 15 Pembridge Road, Dorridge, Solihull B93 8SA Tel: 01564 739305 Fax: 01564 770660 Email: steven.hughes@virgin.net — MB BS 1980 Lond.; FRCS (Orth.) 1995; FRCS Eng. 1987; MRCS Eng. LRCP Lond. 1980. (Char. Cross) Cons. (Trauma & Orthop. Surg.) Birm. Heartlands Hosp. & Solihull Hosp. NHS Trust. Socs: Fell. BOA; Girdlestone Orthop. Soc.; E. Assn. Surg. of Trauma. Prev: Trauma Fell. Univ. Tennessee at Knoxville; Sen. Regist. (Orthop.) Oxf.; RMO 2nd Bn. The Parachute Regt.

HUGHES, Susan Claire Osborne Road Surgery, 17 Osborne Road, Newcastle upon Tyne NE2 2AH Tel: 0191 281 4588 Fax: 0191 212 0379; 32 Hollywood Avenue, Gosforth, Newcastle upon Tyne NE3 5BQ Tel: 0191 285 0417 — MB BS 1989 Newc.; MRCGP 1993; DRCOG 1992. GP Partner. Prev: Locum GP.

HUGHES, Susan Diane 41 Elms Road, Stoneygate, Leicester LE2 3JD — MB ChB 1982 Leic. Clin. Med. Off. Child Health Leic. HA.

HUGHES, Tanya Gail St. Mark's Dee View Surgery, Church Street, Connah's Quay CH5 4AD Tel: 01244 812003 — MB ChB 1988 Liverp.; MRCGP 1994; DRCOG 1992. (Liverp.) GP Retainee, St. Mark's Dee View Surg., Connah's Quay. Prev: GP Hawarden Health Centre Hawarden; Clin. Med. Off. (Child Health) Clwydian Community Care; Trainee GP/SHO Ormskirk & Dist. Gen. Hosp.

HUGHES, Terence John Morris (retired) 14 Delphfields Road, Appleton, Warrington WA4 5BY Tel: 01925 262403 — MB ChB 1948 Liverp.; MRCS Eng. LRCP Lond. 1949. Prev: Sen. Ho. Off. Alder Hey Childr. Hosp. Liverp.

HUGHES, Terry Owen (retired) Field End, Pleck Lane, Higher Ansty, Dorchester DT2 7PT Tel: 01258 880049 — MB BS Lond. 1954; DObst RCOG 1956. Prev: GP Basingstoke 1961-1989.

HUGHES, Thomas Aquinas High Royds Hospital, Menston, Ilkley LS29 6AQ Tel: 0113 305 6114 — MB ChB 1984 Birm.; MRCPsych 1991; MD 2000 Leeds. (Birmingham) Cons. Psychiat. High Royds Hosp. Menston W. Yorks. Prev: Lect. (Psychiat.) Univ. of Leeds; Sen. Regist. (Gen. Psychiat.) Yorks. Higher Train. Scheme.

HUGHES, Thomas Arthur Tudor Department of Neurology, University Hospital of Wales, Heath Park, Cardiff CF14 4XW Tel: 029 20742835/743798; 11 Beulah Road, Rhiwbina, Cardiff CF14 6LT Tel: 029 2061 8782 — MB BS 1987 Lond.; MRCP (UK) 1991; MD (Lond.) 1999. Cons. Neurol. Univ. Hosp. Wales; Cons. NeUrol., Rookwood Hosp., Llandaff, Cardiff. Prev: Regist. (Med.) Glan Clwyd Hosp.

HUGHES, Thomas Benjamin John South Warwickshire General Hospitals NHS Trust, South Warwickshire Hospital, Lakin Road, Warwick CV34 5BW — MB ChB 1967 Birm.; BSc Birm. 1964, MB ChB 1967; FRCOG 1987, M 1972. (Birm.) Cons. O & G Warks. AHA. Socs: N. Eng. Obst. & Gyn. Soc. Prev: Lect. (Obst.) Univ. Liverp.; Regist. (Obst. & Gyn) & Ho. Off. O & G Warneford Hosp. Leamington Spa.

HUGHES, Thomas Collingwood The Berristead, Station Road, Wilburton, Ely CB6 3RP — MB ChB 1991 Sheff.

HUGHES, Thomas Meirion Holly Lodge, Coed-y-Paen, Pontypool NP4 0TH — MB BCh 1975 Wales; Dip. Pract. Dermat. Wales 1996. p/t Hosp. Practitioner Occupat. Skin Dis. Gwent NHS Trust, Newport; Med Examr. Benefits. Agency. Med. Serv; Med Mem. Appeals Serv. Socs: Soc. of Occupat.al Med.; Brit. Contact Dermatitis Gp. Prev: GP.

HUGHES, Thomas Owen (retired) Cynlas, Tycroes LL63 5SP Tel: 01407 810294 — MB ChB 1941 Liverpool; 1949 BDS Liverp.; 1949 LDS RCS Eng.

HUGHES, Timothy James 62 St Wilfrids Road, Doncaster DN4 6AD — MB ChB 1972 Birm.; FFA RCS Eng. 1979; DA Eng. 1977. (Birm.) Cons. Anaesth. Doncaster Roy. Infirm.

HUGHES, Timothy John The Old Priory Surgery, 319 Vicarage Road, Kings Heath, Birmingham B14 7NN Tel: 0121 444 1120; Oak Tree Cottage, Aqueduct Lane, Alvechurch, Birmingham B48 7BP — MB BCh 1981 Wales.

HUGHES, Timothy Philip 51 Starfield Road, London W12 9SN — MB ChB 1986 Bristol.

HUGHES, Timothy Richard John The Kirkbymoorside Surgery, Tinley Garth, Kirkbymoorside, York YO62 6AR Tel: 01751 431254 Fax: 01751 432980; The Cedars, Main St, Wombleton, York YO62 7RX — MB BS 1984 Lond.; MRCGP 1990; DGM RCP Lond. 1989. (St Bartholomew's Hospital London) Bd. Mem. & Clin. Governance Lead, ScarBoro., Whitby & Rycdale PCG.

HUGHES, Tracey 15 Beech Gardens, Gateshead NE9 5TQ — MB BCh BAO 1987 NUI.

HUGHES, Trevor Richard Thornton Lygon, Mill Lane, Buckley CH7 3HB Tel: 01244 550069 — MB ChB 1954 Liverp. Prev: Ho. Surg. Trevalyn Manor Matern. Hosp. Rossett; Ho. Surg. & Ho. Phys. Wrexham War Memor. Hosp.

HUGHES, Mr Tudor Hesketh Department of Radiology, Christchurch Hospital, Christchurch, Private Bag 4710, Canterbury, New Zealand; c/o 88 Blacketts Wood Drive, Chorleywood, Rickmansworth WD3 5QD — MB BS 1984 Lond.; FRCS Ed. 1988; FRCR 1991; T(R) (CR) 1993. Dept. Radiol. ChristCh. Hosp. NZ. Prev: Musculoskeletal Radiol. Univ. Calif., San Diego; Sen. Regist. (Radiol.) Bloomsbury & Islington HA.

HUGHES, Valerie Charlotte IDA Darwin Hospital, Fulbourn, Cambridge CB1 5EE Tel: 01223 248074; 9 Crossways House, Anstey Way, Trumpington, Cambridge CB2 2JZ Tel: 01223 844472 — MB ChB 1959 Bristol; MRCPsych 1982. Cons. Psychiat. Ment. Handicap. Camb. HA.

HUGHES, Vivienne Emma Beatson Oncology Centre, Western Infirmary, Glasgow G11 6NT; 7 Ballaig Avenue, Bearsden, Glasgow G61 4HA — MB ChB 1995 Aberd. SHO (Med.) Hairmyres Hosp. Glas. Prev: SHO (Med.) Hairmyres Hosp. Glas.; SHO (Med. Elderly) Stobhill Hosp. Glas.; SHO (Surg.) Stobhill Hosp. Glas.

HUGHES, Wendy Yvonne 21 Valley Road, Barlow, Dronfield S18 7SL — MB ChB 1992 Sheff.; DRCOG 1995.

HUGHES, William Charles Norfolk Mental Health Care (NHS) Trust, Drayton Old Lodge, 146 Drayton High Road, Norwich NR8 6AN — MB BS 1968 Lond.; MRCS Eng. LRCP Lond. 1968; FRCPsych 1995, M 1976. (Guy's Hosp. & Postgrad. St. Thos. Hosp. Lond.) p/t Cons. Psychiat. & Psychother. Norf. Ment. Health Care NHS Trust; Hon. Sen. Lect. Health Scis. UEA. Socs: M-C Soc. Norwich. Prev: Cons. Ment. Illness David Rice Hosp. Drayton; Sen. Regist. Moorhaven Hosp. Bittaford; Sen. Regist. & Research Regist. (Psychol. Med.) & Regist. (Neurol.) St. Thos. Hosp. Lond.

HUGHES, William Edgar The Surgery, The Norton, Tenby SA70 8AB — MB BCh 1961 Wales; MRCGP 1973; DObst RCOG 1964. (Cardiff)

HUGHES, William Lloyd Cossington House Surgery, 51 Cossington Road, Canterbury CT1 3HX Tel: 01227 763377 Fax: 01227 786908 — MB BS 1981 Lond.; DA (UK) 1987; MRCGP 1985; DRCOG 1985. Regist. (Anaesth.) Canterbury & Thanet HA. Prev: Trainee GP Canterbury VTS; SHO (Anaesth.) Canterbury & Thanet HA; SHO (ENT Surg.) Canterbury & Thanet HA.

HUGHES, Zoe Louise 8 Tarrant Walk, Coventry CV2 2JJ — MB BS 1992 Lond.

HUGHES-DAVIES, David Ifan Pen Dinas, Van Diemens Lane, Lansdown, Bath BA1 5TW Tel: 01225 312230 — MB BS 1956 Lond.; MRCS Eng. LRCP Lond. 1956; FFA RCS Eng. 1967; DIH Eng. 1966; DObst RCOG 1958. (Westm.) Prev: Ho. Surg. W.m. Childr. Hosp.; Ho. Phys. Highlands Gen. Hosp. Lond.; Obst. Ho. Surg. Mile End Hosp.

HUGHES-DAVIES, Thomas Hugh, OBE (retired) Slades Cottage, Breamore, Fordingbridge SP6 2EJ Tel: 01725 512493 — BM BCh Oxf. 1953; MA (1st cl. Hons.) Oxf. 1950; FRCP Lond. 1973, M 1957. Prev: Cons. Paediat. Ealing, Soton & Salisbury Hosps.

HUGHES-GAMES, John Stephen 22 Duchess Road, Clifton, Bristol BS8 2LA Tel: 0117 973 5966 Fax: 0117 973 5966; 22 Duchess Road, Clifton, Bristol BS8 2LA Tel: 0117 973 5966 Fax: 0117 973 5966 — MB ChB 1954 Bristol; FFHom 1985, M 1973. Socs: BMA; Roy. Soc.

HUGHES-GUY, Lynne Idle Medical Centre, 440 Highfield ROAd, Idle, Bradford BD10 8RU Tel: 01274 771999 Fax: 01274 772001 — MB BS 1986 Lond.; PhD Exeter 1981, BSc 1974; MRCGP 1991; DRCOG 1988.

HUGHES HALLETT, Ian (retired) White Gates, Elmswell Road, Great Ashfield, Bury St Edmunds IP31 3HH Tel: 01359 240040 — MB ChB Ed. 1954; FFOM RCP Lond. 1988, MFOM 1978; DIH Eng. 1966. Prev: Princip. Med. Adviser Unilever.

HUGHES JONES, Nevin Campbell (retired) 65 Orchard Road, Melbourn, Royston SG8 6BB Tel: 01763 260471 Fax: 01763 260471 Email: nch1001@hermes.com.ac.uk — BM BCh 1947 Oxf.; FRS 1985; PhD Lond. 1957; MA Oxf. 1951, DM 1966; FRCP Lond. 1986, M 1973. Prev: Scientif. Staff MRC molecular ImmunoPath. Gp. Camb.

HUGHES-NURSE, Jennifer (retired) The Gables, 12A Rectory Lane, Glinton, Peterborough PE6 7LR — MB ChB 1967 (Hons. Dist. In O&G) Liverp.; FRCOG 1984, M 1972, DObst 1969. Gyn. (FT Private Pract.). Prev: Sen. Regist. Jessop Hosp. for Wom. Sheff.

HUGHES-ROBERTS, Huw Elfyn Bodfaen, Bishopswood Road, Prestatyn LL19 9PL Tel: 01745 852585 — MB BCh 1955 Wales; BSc Wales 1952; FRCPsych 1989, M 1971; DPM Eng. 1961. (Cardiff) Socs: Welsh Psychiatric Soc. (Ex-Chair). Prev: Cons. Psych.; Cons. Psychiat. N. Wales Hosp. Nerv. & Ment. Dis. Denbigh.; Cons. Psychiat. Ballamona Hosp. Braddan, I. of Man.

HUGHESDON, Anthony Geoffrey Veor Surgery, South Terrace, Camborne TR14 8SN Tel: 01209 712208 — MB BS 1953 Lond. (Lond. Hosp.) Prev: Ho. Surg. Neurosurg. Unit, Lond. Hosp.; SHO O & G St. John's Hosp. Chelmsford; Med. Off. Basutoland Med. Serv.

HUGHSON, Andrew Vincent Mark 1 Cleveden Gardens, Glasgow G12 0PU — MB ChB 1970 Glas.; MD Glas. 1989; FRCPsych 1996, M 1975; DPM Ed. & Glas. 1973. (Glas.) Cons. Psychiat. Leverndale Hosp. Glas.; Hon. Clin. Sen. Lect. (Psychol. Med.) Univ. Glas. Socs: BMA. Prev: Cons. Psychiat. Dykebar Hosp. Paisley; Ho. Off. (Med.) & Regist. (Psychiat.) S.. Gen. Hosp. Glas.

HUGHSON, David Richard (retired) 15/9 Rothesay Terrace, Edinburgh EH3 7RY — MB ChB 1968 Edin; MB ChB Ed. 1968; MRCGP 1978. Prev: Sen. Partner, Gen. Pract.

HUGKULSTONE, Mr Charles Ewing Department of Ophalmology, Queen Mary's Hospital, Sidcup DA14 6LT Tel: 020 8302 2678 — MB BS 1980 Lond.; FRCS Ed. 1989; FRCOphth. 1989; DO RCS Eng. 1988. Cons. Ophth. Qu. Mary's Hosp. Sidcup.

***HUGMAN, Andrew Jack** 347 Winslow Road, Bromyard HR7 4TX Email: andrewhugman@bigfoot.com — MB BS 1997 Lond.

HUGO, Anthony Brian (retired) Trillinghurst Barn, Goudhurst, Cranbrook TN17 1HL Tel: 01580 211064 — MB BS 1954 Lond.; MRCS Eng. LRCP Lond. 1954; MRCGP 1968; DObst RCOG 1956. Prev: Ho. Phys. St. Martin's Hosp. Bath.

HUGO, Philippa Jane St George's Hospital Medical School, Department of Mental Health Sciences, Tooting, London SW17 Tel: 020 8725 5525 Email: phugo@sghms.ac.uk; 46 Haverhill Road, Balham, London SW12 0HA Tel: 020 8675 8637 — MB ChB 1985 Cape Town; MRCPsych 1994. Lect. (Gen. Psychiat.) St. Geo. Hosp. Med. Sch. Lond. Socs: Roy. Coll. Psychiat. Prev: Regist. & SHO (Psychiat.) St. Geo. Hosp. Lond.

HUI, Eugene Hoong Kwong 44B Hague Street, Glossop SK13 8NS — MB BChir 1976 Camb.; MA Camb. 1976; MRCP (UK) 1982; MFOM RCP Lond. 1993, A 1986. (Camb. & Univ. Coll. Hosp.) Prev: Sen. Regist. Rotat. (Occupat. Med.) NW RHA.

HUI, Fong Chung 3 Winterdown Gardens, Esher KT10 8NB — MB ChB 1980 Sheff.

HUI, Keen Wei 43 Russell Road, Northolt UB5 4QS — MB BS 1998 Lond.; MB BS Lond 1998.

HUI, Wai Ling 8A Grange Road, Billericay CM11 2RB — MB BS 1998 Lond.; MB BS Lond 1998.

HUI, Yui 27 Southernhay Road, Leicester LE2 3TN — BChir 1993 Camb.; BA 1991; MB BChir (Camb.) 1993.

HUINS, Simon James Queen Camel Health Centre, Queen Camel, Yeovil BA22 7NG Tel: 01935 850225 Fax: 01935 851247 — MB BS 1989 Lond.; MRCGP 1994; DFFP 1994; DRCOG 1993; DCH RCP Lond. 1993. (Guy's Hosp. (UMDS)) Prev: Trainee GP Yeovil Dist. Hosp. VTS; Ho. (Surg.) Guy's Hosp. Lond.; Ho. (Med.) Roy. Hants. Co. Hosp.

HUINS, Timothy James Berinsfield Health Centre, Fane Drive, Berinsfield, Wallingford OX10 7NE Tel: 01865 340558 Fax: 01865 341973; Oaktrees, Warborough, Wallingford OX10 7DH Tel: 01865 858242 Fax: 01865 858242 — MB BS Lond. 1969; MRCS Eng. LRCP Lond. 1964; FRCGP 1980, M 1973; DObst RCOG 1967. (Guy's) Assoc. Adviser (Gen. Pract.) Oxf. Region. Prev: SHO (Paediat.) Plymouth Gen. Hosp.; Ho. Surg. Gloucester Matern. Hosp.; Ho. Phys. Roy. Hants. Co. Hosp. Winchester.

HUISH, Christopher Charles Nattore Lodge, West Hill, Budleigh Salterton EX9 6BT; 12 Clover Rise, Woolwell, Plymouth PL6 7TB — MB ChB 1989 Aberd. SHO (Anaesth.) Derriford Hosp. Plymouth.

HUISH, Emma Frances Central Milton Keynes Medical, 1 North Sixth Street, Central Milton Keynes, Milton Keynes MK9 2NR Tel: 01908 605775 Fax: 01908 676752 — MB BS 1988 Lond. Trainee GP Stony Stratford, Bucks. Prev: SHO (Paediat., O & G & Med.)) Milton Keynes Dist. Gen. Hosp.

HUISH, Robert Anthony Guy (retired) 12 Friars Walk, New Milton BH25 7DA — MB ChB 1958 Bristol; DObst RCOG 1965. Prev: GP New Milton.

HUISH, Zoe Kate Russells Halls Hospital, Pensnett rd, Dudley DY1 2HQ Tel: 01384 456111; 32 Wynchall Road, Northfield, Birmingham B31 3AA Tel: 0121 608 5372 — MB ChB 1997 Birm.

HUISMAN, Alida Natascha 18 Hyndland Avenue, G/R, Glasgow G12 9UP — Artsexamen 1991 Groningen.

HUISMAN, Gerrit Boudewijn Spires Medical Practice, St. Chads Health Centre, Dimbles Lane, Lichfield WS13 7HT Tel: 01543 258987 Fax: 01543 410162; 14 Gaiafields Road, Lichfield WS13 7LT — Artsexamen 1986 Nijmegen; MRCGP 1991.

HUISSOON, Aarnoud Pieter Department of Immunology, Queen's Medical Centre, Nottingham NG7 2UH Tel: 0115 924 9924 Email: aarn. huissoon@nottingham.ac.uk — MB BCh BAO 1987 Dub.; PhD Birm. 1996; MRCPI 1989; DCH RCPI 1990. Sen. Regist. (Immunol.) Qu. Med. Centre Nottm. Prev: Research Fell. (Rheumat.) Univ. of Birm.; Med. Regist. St. Vincent's Hosp. Dub., Irel.

HUKIN, Amanda Joy 25 Sharmans Cross Road, Solihull B91 1RG — MB ChB 1987 Aberd.

HUKIN, Sarah Louise 90 Kerr Street, Glasgow G40 2QP Tel: 0141 531 3300 Fax: 0141 531 3302 — MB ChB 1988 Glas.; MRCPsych. 1993. Cons (Child & Adolesc. Psychiat.) GTR Glas Primary Care NHS Trust Glas. Prev: Regist. (Psychiat.) Gtr. Glas. HB; Sen. Regist. (Child & Adolesc. Psychiat.) Gtr. Glas. HB.

HULANDS, Godfrey Howard (retired) Howefield, Moorfoot Lane, Cononley, Keighley BD20 8LX Tel: 01535 633055 — MB ChB. Bristol 1958; FFA RCS Eng. 1966. Prev: Cons. Anaesth. N.wick Pk. Hosp. Harrow.

HULBERT, Christopher Courtenay Hulbert, Price, Hulbert and Davies, Laurel Bank Surgery, Old Hall Street, Malpas SY14 8PS Tel: 01948 860205 Fax: 01948 860142; Dyers Farm, Edge, Malpas SY14 7DN — MB ChB 1973 Bristol; MRCP (UK) 1978; MRCGP

1995. Hon. Research Fell. Dept. Prim. Care Univ. Liverp. Prev: Regist. (Geriat. Med.) United Bristol Hosps.; Ho. Surg. Cosham Hosp. Bristol; Ho. Phys. S.mead Hosp. Bristol.

HULBERT, Miss Diana Catherine 72 Kingsway, Chandlers Ford, Eastleigh SO53 1FJ Tel: 02380 253757 — MB BS 1988 Lond.; BSc Lond. 1985; FRCS Glas. 1993; FFAEM 1997. (Char. Cross. & Westm. Hosp. Lond.) Cons. A & E S.ampton. Socs: RSM (Fell.); BAEM (Fell.); FAEM (Fell.). Prev: Cons. A 7 E W. Middx Univ Hosp; Sen. Regist. (A & E) NW Thames.

HULBERT, Grace Miriam Hulbert, Price, Hulbert and Davies, Laurel Bank Surgery, Old Hall Street, Malpas SY14 8PS Tel: 01948 860205 Fax: 01948 860142 Email: grace.hulbert@gp-n81038.nhs.uk; Dyers Farm, Edge, Malpas SY14 7DN Tel: 01829 250205 Email: grace.hulbert@btinternet.com — MB ChB 1975 Bristol.

HULBERT, John Kenneth Macdonald Terra Nova House Medical Practice, 43 Dura Street, Dundee DD4 6SW Tel: 01382 451100 Fax: 01382 453679; Wayside, Castle Road, Longforgan, Dundee DD2 5HA Tel: 01382 360294 — MB ChB Ed. 1964; MD Ed. 1971. (Ed.) Socs: BMA. Prev: Lect. (Bact.) Univs. Dundee & Aberd.

HULBERT, Mr Kenneth Frederick Timberden Farm Cottage, Shacklands Road, Shoreham, Sevenoaks TN14 7TX — MB BS Lond. 1936; FRCS Eng. 1945; MRCS Eng. LRCP Lond. 1936; DA Eng. 1938. (Middlx.) Socs: Fell. Brit. Orthop. Assn.; Fell.Roy.Soc.Med. Prev: Cons. Orthop. Surg. Dartford Gp. Hosps., Sydenham Childr. Hosp. & Chailey Heritage; Regist. Roy. Nat. Orthop. Hosp.

HULBERT, Mr Mark Faraday George Dept Ophthamolgy, St Bartholomews' Hosp, London EC1A 7BE Tel: 07050 605615 Fax: 020 7601 7863 — MB ChB 1986 Bristol; FRCOphth 1992. Cons (Ophth) St Bart. Hosp Lond. Prev: Fell in Neuro-Ophthamology Nat. Hosp. for Neurol. & Neurosurg. Qu. Sq. Lond.; Fell in Ophthamology Moorfields Eye Hosp Lond.; Sen Regist Ophthaology St Bart. Hosp Lond.

HULF, Judith Ann 47 Alleyn Park, London SE21 8AT Tel: 020 8670 6105; Department of Anaesthesia, The Middlesex Hospital, Mortimer St., London W1T 3AA Tel: 020 7380 9013 — MB BS Lond. 1969; MRCS Eng. LRCP Lond. 1969; DObst RCOG 1971; FFA RCS Eng. 1974. (Roy. Free) Cons. (Anaesth.) Middlx. Hosp. Lond.; Regional Adviser Anaesth. N. Thames (Centr.) 1998. Prev: Sen. Regist. (Anaesth.) King's Coll. Hosp.; Ho. Surg. Hampstead Gen. Hosp.; Ho. Phys. St. Mary Abbots Hosp. Kensington.

HULIN, Sally Jane Forest House Adolescent Unit, Harperbliry Hospital, Harper Lane, St Albans WD7 9HQ Tel: 01923 427312 Fax: 01923 858158 — MB BS 1980 Lond.; BSc Lond. 1977; MRCPsych 1994. Cons. Child & Adolesc. Psychiat. Forest Ho. Regional Adolesc. Unit St. Albans; Cons. Child & Adolesc. Psychiat., Harper Ho. Childr.s Serv. (Paediatric NeuroDisabil. Serv.), Harper La., Radlett, Herts WD7 9HQ.

HULIN, Sarah Jane 12 Ribston Avenue, Exeter EX1 3QE — BChir 1994 Camb.

HULINE-DICKENS, Sarah Jane Ashhurst B, Littlemore Hospital, Oxford OX4 4XN Tel: 01865 778911; 8 St Peters Avenue, Waltham Forest, London E17 3PU — BM BCh 1990 Oxf.; BSc (Lond.) 1990. SHO (Psychiat.) Oxf. HA.

HULKS, Geoffrey Chest Unit, Raigmore Hospital, Inverness IV2 3UJ Tel: 01463 704364 Fax: 01463 705358 Email: geoffrey.hulks@raigmore.scot.nhs.uk — MB ChB 1982 Dundee; BSc (Hons.) Dund 1978, MD (Hons.) 1993; MRCP (UK) 1987; FRCP (Glas) 1997; FRCP Ed 1999. (Dundee) Cons. Phys. Chest Unit Raigmore Hosp. Inverness. Prev: Sen. Regist. (Respirat. Med.) Lothian HB; Regist. & Wellcome Grad. Fell. (Respirat. Med.) W.. Infirm. Glas.; Regist. (Respirat. Med.) Kt.swood Hosp.

HULL, Caroline Ann Beech House Group Practice, Beech House, Beech Avenue Hazel Grove, Stockport SK7 4QR Tel: 0161 483 6222 Fax: 0161 419 9244 — MB ChB 1990 Leeds; BSc Leeds 1987; MRCGP 1994; DRCOG 1993.

HULL, Professor Christopher James Quarry Cottage, Red Barns, Bamburgh NE69 7AZ Email: christopherhull@doctors.net.uk — MB BS Lond. 1961; MRCS Eng. LRCP Lond. 1961; FRCA 1966; DA Eng. 1963. (St. Thos.) Emerit. Prof. of Anaesth. Univ. Newc.; Emerit.d Cons. Anaesth. Roy. Vict. Infirm. Newc. Socs: Anaesth. Res. Soc.; (Ex-Pres.) N. Eng. Soc. Anaesth.; Fell., Roy. Coll. Anaesthetics, ex-vice Pres. Prev: Prof. of Anaesth. Univ. Newc.; Sen. Lect. & 1st Asst. (Anaesth.) Univ. Newc.

HULL, Professor Sir David 3 Lanark Close, Wollaton Park, Nottingham NG8 1BQ Tel: 0115 978 3479 — MB ChB 1956 Liverp.; BSc (Hons.) Liverp. 1953; FRCP Lond. 1974, M 1961; Hon. FRCPCH 1997, M1967, P 1991; DObst RCOG 1958; DCH Eng. 1958. Emerit. Prof. Child Health Med. Sch. Univ. Nottm. Socs: Neonat. Soc.; Brit. Assn. of Perinatal Med. Prev: Lect. (Paediat.) Univ. Oxf.; Cons. Phys. Hosp. Sick Childr. Gt. Ormond St. Lond.; Sen. Lect. Inst. Child Health Lond.

HULL, David Hugill, Air Vice-Marshal RAF Med. Br. (retired) 20 Chedworth Gate, Broome Manor, Swindon SN3 1NE Tel: 01793 496922 Email: davidhretd@aol.com — MB BChir 1957 Camb.; MA Camb. 1956; FRCP Lond. 1974; MRCP (UK) 1961. Prev: Clin. Dir. & Dean Air Force Med.

HULL, Dearbhla Anne Flat 1, 7 Macaulay Road, London SW4 0QP Email: dearbhlahull@hotmail.com — MB BS 1994 Lond.; BSc (Med. Informatics & Managem.) City Univ. 1993. Specialist Regist. (Histopath.), Roy. Lond. Hosps. NHS Trust; Specialist Regist. (Histopathol.), Roy. Brompton Hosp. & Roy. Marsdon Hosp. Prev: SHO (Med.) Whittington Hosp.; SHO (Med.), Hammersmith Hosp.; SHO (Histopath.), Roy. Lond. Hosp.

HULL, Donald Richard 1 Bryansford Meadow, Bangor BT20 3NX — MB BCh BAO 1987 Belf.

HULL, Frank Martin (retired) West Carnliath, Strathtay, Pitlochry PH9 0PG Tel: 01887 840380 Fax: 01887 840380 Email: robin@strathtan.fsbusiness.co.uk — MB BS 1955 Lond.; FRCGP 1974; DObst RCOG 1961. Prev: Prof. Gen. Pract. Vrije Univ., Amsterdam.

HULL, Jacqueline Anne 55 Pebworth Road, Harrow HA1 3UE — MB ChB 1993 Manch.; BSc (Hons.) Manch. 1991, MB ChB 1993; Dip. Child Health 1996; MRCGP 1997.

HULL, Jeremy Department of Paediatrics, John Radcliffe Hospital, Oxford OX3 9DU; 51 Langley Close, Headington, Oxford OX3 7DB — BM BCh 1987 Oxf.; DM Oxf. 1995; MRCP (UK) 1990; MRCPCH 1994. (Oxf.) Clin. Lect. (Paediat.).

HULL, Mr Jonathan Barry, Lt.-Col. RAMC Frimley Park Hospital, Camberley GU16 7UJ Tel: 01276 604583; Email: jbh4lah@aol.com — MB ChB 1983 Birm.; MD Birm. 1995; FRCS (Orth.) 1995; FRCS Ed. 1989. Cons. Orthop. Surg. Frimley Pk. Hosp. Camberley. Socs: Combined Servs. Orthop. Soc.; Brit. Trauma Soc.; Brit. Orthop. Assn. Prev: Sen. Regist. (Orthop.) N.. Gen. Hosp. Sheff.; Trauma Fell. R. Adams Cowley Shock Trauma Center Baltimore, USA; Sen. Specialist Surg. 23 Para Field Ambul. Aldershot.

HULL, Julian Michael Pear Tree Cottage, Foul End, Hurley, Atherstone CV9 2JW — MB 1983 Birm.; MB, ChB Birm. 1983; FRCA 1990. (Birm.) Cons. Anaesth. & Intens. Care; Good Hope Hosp. NHS Trust Sutton Coldfield. Socs: BMA; Intens. Care Soc.

HULL, Keren Elizabeth St John's Hill Surgery, 39 St. John's Hill, Sevenoaks TN13 3NT Tel: 01732 747202 Fax: 01732 747218; Gospel Hall, Weald, Sevenoaks TN14 6PH — MB 1979 Camb.; BChir 1978; DRCOG 1980; MRCGP 1982.

HULL, Louise Elizabeth Great House Farm, Llangeview, Usk NP15 1EN — MB BS 1987 Lond.

HULL, Mark Arthur Division of Medicine, St James' University Hospital, Leeds LS9 7TF Tel: 0113 206 5251 Fax: 0113 242 9722 Email: medmah@stjames.leeds.ac.uk — BM BCh 1988 Oxf.; MRCP (UK) 1991; PhD (Nottm.) 1997. (Oxf.) Lect. (Gen. Med.) St. James' Univ. Hosp. Leeds. Prev: Research Regist. (Gastroenterol.) Qu. Med. Centre Nottm.; Regist. (Gen. Med.) Qu. Med. Centre Nottm.; SHO (Clin. Therap. & Gastroenterol.) Qu. Med. Centre. Nottm.

HULL, Martyn Robert Philip Ivy Cottage, Baldersby Park, Rainton, Thirsk YO7 3PQ; The hatchery, Little Fencote, Northallerton DL7 0RR — MB ChB 1996 Birm.; ChB Birm. 1996. (Birm) SHO Paediat.

HULL, Professor Michael George Raworth University of Bristol, Department Obstetrics & Gynaecology, St Michael's Hospital, Bristol BS2 8EG Tel: 01179 285293 Fax: 01179 272792 Email: m.g.r.hull@bristol.ac.uk; 12 Westbury Park, Bristol BS6 7JA Tel: 01179 730999 — MB BS Lond. 1962; MB BS Lond. 1962; MD Lond. 1984; MD Lond. 1984; MRCS Eng. LRCP Lond. 1962; MRCS Eng. LRCP Lond. 1962; FRCOG 1980, M 1968; FRCOG 1980, M 1968. (Lond. Hosp.) Prof. Reproduc. Med. & Surg. Univ. Bristol Dept. O & G St. Michael's Hosp.; Cons. (Obst. & Gyn.) United Bristol Healthcare Trust. Socs: (Ex-Comm.) Brit. Fertil. Soc.; (Ex-Comm.) Europ. Soc. Human Reproduc. Embryol.; (Ex-Comm.) Soc.

Study Fertil. Prev: Lect. (O & G) St. Mary's Hosp.; SHO Wom. Hosp. Liverp. & Qu. Charlotte's Hosp. Lond.

HULL, Moira Geraldine 26 Salterton Road, Exmouth EX8 2ED Tel: 01395 263730 — LRCPI & LM, LRSCI & LM 1951.

HULL, Peter Jonathan Abbotsbury Road Surgery, 24 Abbotsbury Road, Weymouth DT4 0AE Tel: 01305 786257 — MB BS 1973 Lond.

HULL, Rachel Elizabeth Lomabard Street Surgeries, Lombard St., Newark NG24 1XG Tel: 01636 702363 — MB ChB 1991 Bristol; BSc (Hons.) Cell Path. Bristol 1988; DCH RCP, Lond. 1995; MRCGP Lond. 1996. p/t GP Princip. Prev: Trainee GP Nottm. VTS.

HULL, Richard George Queen Alexandra Hospital, Cosham, Portsmouth PO6 3LY Tel: 023 92 286332 Fax: 023 92 286862 Email: richard.hull@qmail01.porthosp.swest.nhs.uk — MB ChB 1975 Birm.; FRCP Lond. 1994; MRCP (UK) 1980; FRCPCH 1997. (Birm.) Cons. Rheum. Cons. Rheumatologist Qu. Alexandra Hosp. Portsmouth; Hon. Clin. Tutor, Univ. of Soton. Med. Sch.; Examr. RCP of Lond.; Mem. Brit. Paediat. Rheum. Gp.(Convener Elect); Trustee, Arthritis Care (Vice-Chairm., Med. Advis. Comm.). Socs: Brit. Soc. Rheum. (Clin. Affairs Comm.); Brit. Soc. Rehabil. Med.; Educat. Sub-Comm. Arthritis Research Campaign. Prev: Research Fell. & Hon. Sen. Regist. (Rheum & Rehabil.) N.wick Pk. Hosp. Harrow; Regist. & Research Fell. Hammersmith Hosp. Lond.; Hon. Sec. The Garrod Club 1984-88.

HULL, Sarah Ann Steels Lane Health Centre, 368-374 Commercial Road, London E1 0LS Tel: 020 7335 4900 Fax: 020 7335 4901; Tel: 020 7833 4529 Fax: 020 7713 5343 — MB BChir 1975 Camb.; MSc Pub. Health Med. Lond. 1993; MA Camb. 1976; MRCP (UK) 1979; FRCGP 1994, M 1980. (St. Thos.) Princip. in Gen. Pract., Lond.; Sen. Lect. (Gen. Pract.) Lond. Hosp. Socs: Fell. Roy. Soc. Med.; Balint Soc; AUDGP. Prev: Non-Exec. Mem. E. Lond. & The City DHA; Clin. Asst. (Rheum.) Lond. Hosp.

HULL, Susan Elizabeth Totteridge, 195 Bell's Lane, Hoo, Rochester ME3 9JD Tel: 01634 252761; 31 Chessington Mansions, Colworth Road, Leytonstone, London E11 1HZ Tel: 020 8539 0241 — MB BS 1993 Lond. SHO (Gen. & Geriat. Med.) Bedford Hosp. NHS Trust.

HULL-DAVIES, Joanne Margaret 19 Boot Brow, Distington, Workington CA14 5XR Tel: 01946 833289 — MB ChB 1989 Leic.; DRCOG 1992. (Leic.)

HULLAH, Graham John Church Grange Health Centre, Bramblys Drive, Basingstoke RG21 8QN Tel: 01256 329021 Fax: 01256 817466; 30 Marsh Court, Lychpit, Basingstoke RG24 8UY Tel: 01256 26023 — MB BS 1988 Lond.; MRCGP 1993; DRCOG 1993. (St George's London) Prev: Trainee GP Basingstoke Dist. Hosp. VTS.

HULLAND, Nigel William RNSQ, HMS Neptune, Faslane, Helensburgh; 108 Park Avenue, Ashbourne DE6 1GB Tel: 01335 45058 — MB ChB 1981 Birm. Med. Off. RN Hosp. Haslar Gosport. Prev: Med. Off. HMS Renown RN Hosp. Haslar; Med. Off. Vale of Leven Gen. Dist. Hosp.; Med. Off. Med. Centre Helensburgh.

HULLEY, Catherine Mary 82 Rosemary Road, Wickersley, Rotherham S66 2DE — MB ChB 1991 Birm.; ChB Birm. 1991. Specialist Regist. (Gastroenterol. & Gen. Med.). Socs: MRCPI; MRCP (Lond.).

***HULLEY, Rachel Grace** 28 Aberbran Road, Gabalfa, Cardiff CF14 2SP — MB BCh 1996 Wales.

HULLIN, Mr Michael Gareth Southern General Hospital, 1345 Govan Road, Glasgow G51 4TF Tel: 0141 445 2466; 31 Pendicle Road, Bearsden, Glasgow G61 1DY — MB BS 1979 Lond.; BA Camb. 1976, MD 1993; FRCS Eng. 1984. Cons. Orthop. Sothern Deneral Hosp. NHS Trust Glas.

HULLY, Robert The Health Centre, Dunning St., Tunstall, Stoke-on-Trent ST6 5AP Tel: 01782 577522; The Health Centre, Chapel Lane, Burslem, Stoke-on-Trent ST6 2AD Tel: 01782 577344 — MB ChB 1951 Birm.; DLO Eng. 1953.

HULMAN, Geoffrey Department of Histopathology, King's Mill Centre, Mansfield Road, Sutton-in-Ashfield NG17 4JL Tel: 01623 622515 Fax: 01623 626575; 28 Tunstall Road, Woodthorpe, Nottingham NG5 4JZ Tel: 0115 952 5770 — MRCS Eng. LRCP Lond. 1980; MD Sheff. 1993, MB ChB 1980; MRCPath 1987. Cons. Histopath. King's Mill Hosp. Sutton-in-Ashfield. Prev: Sen. Regist. (Histopath.) St. Geo. Hosp. Lond.; Regist. (Histopath.) Leic. Roy. Infirm.;'An Accurate, Simple & Rapid Test for Detecting Elevated Levels of C-reactive Protein in Serum' Clin.

HULME, Alan 46 Beck Crescent, Mansfield NG19 6SY — MB ChB 1968 Birm.; BSc Birm. 1965, MB ChB 1968; MRCP (U.K.) 1971.

HULME, Alan William The Health Centre, 20 Duncan Street, Greenock PA15 4LY Tel: 01475 724477 Fax: 01475 727140; Aman, 120 Finnart St, Greenock PA16 8HU Tel: 01475 794783 Email: hulme.kerr@cableol.co.uk — MB ChB 1979 Dundee. Prev: Regist. (Geriat. Med.) Roy. Vict. Hosp. Dundee; SHO (O & G) Ninewells Hosp. Dundee; SHO (Neurol. & Gen. Med.) Dundee Roy. Infirm.

HULME, Alison Leigh Chelsea & Westminster Hospital, 369 Fulham Road, London SW10 8RH; 163 Abbeville Road, London SW4 9JJ Tel: 020 7622 5138 — MB BS 1984 Lond.; FRCS (Orth.) 1995; FRCS Eng. 1988. (King's Coll. Hosp. Sch. Med. & Dent. Lond.) Cons. Orthop. Surg. Chelsea & W.m. Hosp. Lond. Socs: Brit. Limb Reconstruction Soc.; Fell. BOA; Fell. Roy. Soc. Med. Prev: Sen. Regist. Rotat. St. Bart. Hosp. Lond.; Regist. Rotat. W.m. Hosp. Lond.; Peri Fell.sh. Rotat. Univ. Coll. & Middlx. Hosps.

HULME, Mr Allan (retired) Broomfield, Balquhidder, Lochearnhead FK19 8NY Tel: 01877 384600 — MB BChir 1942 Camb.; FRCS Eng. 1947. Prev: Cons. Neurosurg. S. W.. RHA & Bristol Health Dist. (T).

HULME, Angela Verity Lytham Road Health Centre, Lytham Road, Blackpool Tel: 01253 401261; 48 Hodderway, Poulton-le-Fylde FY6 8AQ Tel: 01253 896694 — MB ChB 1987 Liverp.; DCH RCP Lond. 1991. Staff Grade (Community Paediat.) Blackpool, Wyre & Fylde HA. Socs: BMA. Prev: Trainee GP/SHO (Paediat., O & G, Orthop. & Psychiat.) Bronglais Hosp. Aberystwyth; SHO (Paediat.) Vict. Hosp. Blackpool.

HULME, Barry The Renal Unit, St Mary's Hospital, Praed St., London W2 1NY Tel: 020 7725 1217; Wingrove House, Winkers Lane, Chalfont St Peter, Gerrards Cross SL9 0AL Tel: 01753 886293 — MB ChB 1961 Birm.; BSc (Hons.) Birm. 1958, MD (Hons) 1968; FRCP Lond. 1975, M 1963. (Birm.) Cons. Nephrol. St. Mary's Hosp. Lond. Socs: Renal Assn. & Brit. Transpl. Soc.

HULME, Mr Christopher Edward 4 Allerford Grove, Gilwern, Abergavenny NP7 0RP Tel: 01873 830877; 6 Heathfield Road, Keston BR2 6BQ Tel: 01689 862418 — MB BS 1992 Lond.; BSc Lond. 1989, MB BS 1992; FRCS (Eng.) 1998. (King's College School of Medicine and Dentistry) Specialist Regist. St Geo.s S. E. Thames Rotat.

HULME, Gillian 7 Wroxham Drive, Wirral CH49 0TS — MB ChB 1992 Manch.

HULME, Henry Kennedy (retired) Little Chambersbury, Bedmond Road, Leverstock Green, Hemel Hempstead HP3 8LJ Tel: 01442 251848 — MB BS Lond. 1947. Prev: Hosp. Pract. Bennetts End Hosp. Hemel Hempstead.

HULME, Ian Stanley Heather Croft, Mount Av, Heswall, Wirral CH60 4RH — MB ChB 1997 Birm.

HULME, John Michael (retired) Chesnut Croft, Carlton, Goole DN14 9LY Tel: 01405 860214 — MB ChB 1955 Leeds. Prev: Indep. Med. Adviser N. Yorks. FHSA.

HULME, Kathryn Bernadette — MB ChB 1986 Liverp.; MRCGP 1991; T(GP) 1991; DRCOG 1989. GP W.way Med. Centre Maghull. Prev: Trainee GP Carnforth; SHO (O & G) Warrington Dist. Gen. Hosp.; SHO (Paediat.) Whiston & St. Helens.

HULME, Lynne Veronica Hednesford Street Surgery, 60 Hednesford Street, Cannock WS11 1DJ Tel: 01543 503121 Fax: 01543 468024 — MB BS 1970 Lond.; MRCS Eng. LRCP Lond. 1970.

HULME, Sara-Louise 147 Portsmouth Road, Horndean, Waterlooville PO8 9LQ Tel: 01705 593968 — MB BS 1993 Lond.; MRCPCH 1999. (Guy's & St. Thos.) SHO (Paediat.) Guy's & St. Thos. Hosp. Trust; Regist. (Neonatol.) St. Thos Hosp. Lond. Prev: SHO (Genitourin. Med.) King's Coll. Hosp. Lond; SHO (Neonat.) St. Thos. Hosp. Lond.; SHO (O & G) Guy's & St. Thos. Hosp. Lond.

HULME, Shirley Ann Swanley House, Swanley Lane, Burland, Nantwich CW5 8QB; 417 London Road, Appleton, Warrington WA4 5DP Tel: 01925 262117 Fax: 01925 262117 — MB ChB 1996 Liverp.; MRCP 1999. (Liverp) Specialist Regist. Diabetes & Endocrin. Mersey Region.

***HULME, Simon Nicholas** Wingrove House, Winkers La, Chalfont St Peter, Gerrards Cross SL9 0AL; 39 Saumoale Road, Ossett WE5 8BA Tel: 01924 274365 Email: drsimonhulme@hotmail.com — MB ChB 1997 Leeds.

HULME, Sophie Louise — MB ChB 1996 Birm.; DFFP 1999; DRCOG 2000. (Birm.) GP, Pirbright, Surrey. Prev: Ho. Off. (Med.) Salisbury Dist. Hosp.; Ho. Off. (Surg.) W. Dorset Co. Hosp.

HULSE, Eustace Valentine (retired) Bedecote, 9 Priory Orchard, Wantage OX12 9EL — MB ChB 1946 Manch.; MD (Commend.) Manch. 1959; FRCPath 1972, M 1963. Prev: Head Path. Sect. MRC Radiobiol. Unit Harwell.

HULSE, John Anthony The Maidstone Hospital,Maidstone & Tunbridge Wells NHS Trust, Hermitage Lane, Barming, Maidstone ME16 9QQ Tel: 01622 224203 Fax: 01622 224495; Costens, Carpenters Lane, Hadlow, Tonbridge TN11 0EY Tel: 01732 851404 — MB BChir 1974 Camb.; MD Camb. 1983; FRCP Lond. 1994; MRCP (UK) 1976; FRCPCH 1997. Cons. Paediat. Maidstone Hosp.; Hon. Cons. Paediat. St. Thos. & Guys Hosps. Lond. Socs: Fell. Roy. Soc. Med.; Wilkins Paediat. Endocrine Soc. (USA); Fell. Roy. Coll. Paediat. & Child Health. Prev: Sen. Regist. (Paediat.) St. Thos. Hosp. Lond.; Fell. (Endocrinol.) Univ. Calif. San Francisco, USA; Research Regist. (Endocrinol.) Hosp. Sick Childr. Gt. Ormond St.

HULSE, Mr Michael (retired) Auld Petty, Dalcross, Inverness IV2 7JH Tel: 01463 790030 — BM BCh 1968 Oxf.; MA Oxf. 1968; FRCS Eng. 1977; FRCOG 1992, M 1979. Cons. (O & G) Raigmore Hosp. Inverness. Prev: Sen. Regist. (O & G) S. Grampian (Aberd.) Health Dist.

HULSE, Michael Graham Ditton Lea, Love Lane, Long Ditton, Surbiton KT6 5EB — MB BS 1973 Lond.; BSc Lond. 1970, MB BS 1973; FFA RCS Eng. 1978. (Univ. Coll. Lond. & St. Geo.) Cons. Anaesth. St. Geo. Hosp. Lond. Prev: Sen. Regist. St. Geo. Hosp. & Hosp. Sick Childr. Gt. Ormond St. Lond.; Research Fell. Respirat. Unit Gt. Ormond St. Lond.

HULSE, Patricia Geraldine (retired) — MB ChB 1980 Manch.

HULSE, William Harrogate District Hospital, Lancaster Park Road, Harrogate HG2 7SX Tel: 01423 553302 Fax: 01423 888337 Email: bill.husle@hhc-tr.northy.nhs.uk; Email: billhulse@aol.com — MB ChB 1979 Leeds; MRCP (UK) 1984; FFAEM 1993; FRCP Lond 1997. Cons A & E Med. Harrogate. Prev: Sen Regist. (A & E) Yorks. Region.

HULTEN, Maj Anita Regional Genetic Services, Birmingham Heartlands Hospital, Birmingham B9 5PX Tel: 0121 766 6611 Fax: 0121 766 5681; 22 Mayfield Road, Moseley, Birmingham B13 9HJ Tel: 0121 449 5164 — BSc, PhD Stockholm 1974, Med. Lic. 1966; FRCPath 1992, M 1980. (Lund & Stockholm) Cons. Clin. Cytogeneticist Birm. AHA (T); Hon. Profess. Cytogenetics Dept. Clin. Genetics. Univ. Birm.

HULTON, Sally-Anne Department of Nephrology, Children's Hospital NHS Trust, Steelhouse Lane, Birmingham B4 6NH Tel: 0121 333 9225 Fax: 0121 333 9231 — MB BCh 1982 Witwatersrand; FRCPCH 1998; MD Birm. 1996; MRCP (UK) 1992; FCP(SA) 1989. Cons. Paediat. & Paediat. Nephrol. Childr.'s Hosp. NHS Trust Birm. Socs: Fell. Roy. Coll. Paediat. & Child Health.; Eur. Soc. Paediat. Nephrol.; Brit. Assn. Paediat. Nephrol. Prev: Sen. Regist. Birm. Childr.'s Hosp.; Sen. Regist. & Research Fell. Gt. Ormond St. Hosp. NHS Trust.

HULYER, Mark Charles Glyn North Tyneside General Hospital, Rake Lane, North Shields NE29 8NH; 5 Reivers Gate, Long Horsley, Morpeth NE65 8LA — MB BS 1991 Newc. Ho. Phys. N. Tees Gen. Hosp. Stockton. Socs: BMA. Prev: SHO (Psychiat.) St. Mary's Hosp. Stannington; SHO (O & G) Ashington; Trainee GP Berwick upon Tweed.

HUMAN, Mark Scott Welcome Hill, Shebbear, Beaworthy EX21 5SN — BM 1992 Soton.

HUMAN, Sarah Jane Oxenpark, Gidcott, Holsworthy EX22 7AS — MB ChB 1992 Bristol.

HUMAYUN, Mr Mohammad Sajjad PO Box 24241, Safat 13103, Kuwait; 12 Okehampton Close, Montgomery Park, Radcliffe, Manchester M26 3LT Tel: 0161 724 7775 — MB BS 1965 Punjab; FRCS Ed. 1970; FRCS Eng. 1970. Cons. Surg. Min. Pub. Health Kuwait. Prev: Gen. Surg. Combined Milit. Hosp. Iranian Airforce Iran; Asst. Prof. Gen. Surg. Fatima Jinnah Med. Coll. Lahore; Sen. Regist. (Surg.) Nishtar Med. Coll Multan.

HUMBER, John Colin 18 Rosebury Avenue, Blackpool FY4 — MB ChB 1948 Liverp.; MRCS Eng. LRCP Lond. 1948.

HUMBER, Sarah Anne 15 Denby Grange, Church Langley, Harlow CM17 9PZ — MB BS 1996 Lond.; BA Camb. 1993. (Camb. St. Geos.) Nat. Train. Scheme, Roy. Berks. Hosp., Reading. Prev: SHO Paediat. Wexham Pk. Hosp. Slough; SHO Paediat. Chelsea & W.minster.

HUMBERSTONE, Ian Philip 22 St Mary's Lane, Louth LN11 0DT — MB BS 1993 Lond.

HUMBERSTONE, Miles Richard Lane End Cottage, Main St., Cropwell Butler, Nottingham NG12 3AB — MB BChir 1990 Camb.; MRCP (UK) 1994. (Addenbrooke's Hosp. Camb.)

HUMBLE, Richard David 67 Drumsmittal Road, North Kessock, Inverness IV1 3JU Email: richard@humble29.freeserve.co.uk; 18/5 Balfour Place, Leith, Edinburgh EH6 5DW Tel: 0131 554 0968 Fax: 0131 554 0968 Email: richard.humble@lineone.net — MB ChB 1992 Ed. (Edinburgh University) GP VTS Raigmore Hosp. Inverness. Socs: BMA; Highland Med.Soc. Prev: Regist. (Respirat. Med.) Waikato Hosp. Hamilton, NZ; Clin. Research Fell. (Respirat. Med.) W.. Gen. Hosp. Edin.; SHO Rotat. (Gen. & Respirat. Med.) W.. Gen. Hosp. Edin.

HUMBY, Ellinor Mary Balmer Lawn Cottage, Balmer Lawn Rd, Brockenhurst SO42 7TT — MB ChB 1997 Liverp.

HUMBY, Frances Claire 13 The Grove, Doncaster DN2 5SA — MB BS 1997 Lond.

HUMBY, Mr Martin Douglas Department Surgery, Lymington Hospital, Lymington SO41 9ZH Tel: 01590 644011; Balmer Lawn Cottage, Brockenhurst SO42 7TT Tel: 01590 622371 — MB BS 1971 Lond.; FRCS Eng. 1979. (Univ. Coll. Hosp.) Assoc. Specialist (Gen. Surg.) Lymington Hosp. Socs: BMA; Assn. Surg. Prev: Regist. Rotat. (Surg.) Dorset & Hants. (T) AHAs; Demonst. (Anat.) Soton. Univ.; SHO (Surg.) Salisbury Gen. Infirm.

HUME, Alison Julia The Barn, Hone Court, Pooles Lane, Charlbury, Oxford OX7 3TF — MB BS 1989 Lond.

HUME, Anna Margaret Rose Cottage, Finchdean, Waterlooville PO8 0AU — MB BS 1983 Lond. (St. Geo.) GP Finchdean.

HUME, Mr Arthur Christopher (retired) 136 Lexden Road, Colchester CO3 4BL Tel: 01206 578328 — MB BS 1948 Lond.; FRCS Eng. 1959. Hon. Cons. Orthop. Surg. Colchester Gp. Hosps. Prev: Sen. Regist. (Orthop.) Addenbrooke's Hosp. Camb.

HUME, Daniel Christian Millview Hospital, Neville Avenue, Hove BN3 7HZ Tel: 01273 696011 — MB ChB 1997 Leic. (Leics)

HUME, David Douglas 27 Bredbury Green, Romiley, Stockport SK6 3DN Tel: 0161 494 2175 — MB ChB 1991 Manch.; BSc (Hons.) St And. 1988; FRCA 1996.

HUME, Edward Martyn 253 Ongar Road, Writtle, Chelmsford CM1 3NT Tel: 01245 420700; Clovers, Victoria Road, Writtle, Chelmsford CM1 3PB Tel: 01245 420288 — MRCS Eng. LRCP Lond. 1950; MRCGP 1959. (Guy's) Socs: Chelmsford Med. Soc. Prev: Mem. Bd. Managem. Harlow Indust. Health Serv.; Asst. Chest Phys. Colchester Chest Clinic; Jun. Med. Specialist RAMC.

HUME, Ian Martyn Mount Street Health Centre, Mount Street, Diss IP22 4QG Tel: 01379 642023 Fax: 01379 643320 — MB BS 1984 Lond.; MRCGP 1990. Socs: Norf. LMC. Chairm. Prev: GP Chelmsford; SHO (Paediat.) W. Suff. Hosp. Bury St. Edmunds; SHO (Geriat. Med.) Qu. Eliz. Hosp. King's Lynn.

HUME, Michelle Jean Woodhouse Health Centre, Woodhouse Street, Leeds LS6 2NS — BM BS 1992 Nottm. p/t GP Princip.

HUME, Morag Ann 29a Thorn Drive, Bearsden, Glasgow G61 4ND Tel: 0141 334 9417 — MB ChB 1986 Glas.; MRCGP 1990; FRCA 1993; DA (UK) 1991; DRCOG 1989. Cons. (Anaesth.) S. Gen. Hosp Glas. Prev: Sen. Regist. (Anaesth.) Vict. Infirm. Glas.; Regist. & SHO (Anaesth.) W. Infirm. Glas.

HUME, Nigel Scott St Marys Medical Centre, Wharf Road, Stamford PE9 2DH Tel: 01780 64121 Fax: 01780 756515; Branksome, Stamford Road, Ryhall, Stamford PE9 4HB — MB ChB 1986 Leic.; MRCGP 1990; Cert. Family Plann. JCC 1990. Clin. Asst. Ophth. Stamford Hosp. Prev: Trainee GP Leic. VTS.

HUME, Raymond Clive 1 Woodberry Avenue, London N21 3LE Tel: 020 8886 2751 Fax: 020 8882 2891; 21 Stonehall Road, London N21 1LR Tel: 020 8360 9797 — MB BS 1970 Lond.; BSc (Hons.) Lond. 1967; MRCS Eng. LRCP Lond. 1970; FRCGP 1984, M 1976. (King's Coll. Lond. & St. Geo.) GP Tutor Enfield. Prev: Sen. Lect. (Gen. Pract.) Roy. Free Hosp. Sch. Med. Lond.; Ho. Phys. St. Geo. Hosp. Lond.; Ho. Surg. & Cas. Off. Highlands Hosp. Lond.

HUME, Professor Robert University of Dundee, Ninewells Hospital & Medical School, Dundee DD1 9SY Tel: 01382 60111 Fax: 01382 632597 Email: r.hume@dundee.ac.uk — MB ChB 1972 Ed.; PhD Ed. 1980, BSc (Hons.) 1969, MB ChB 1972; FRCP Ed.

1986; MRCP (UK) 1980; FRCPCH 1996. Prof. (Developm. Med.) Univ. Dundee; Cons. Paediat. Ninewells Hosp. & Med. Sch. Dundee. Prev: Sen. Lect. (Child Life & Health) Univ. Edin.; MRC Fell. Univ. Edin.; Lect. Univ. Edin.

HUME, Robert (retired) 6 Rubislaw Drive, Bearsden, Glasgow G61 1PR Tel: 0141 586 5249 — MB ChB 1953 Glas.; Hon. FCM (SA) 1992; Hon. FACP 1991; Hon. FRACP 1991; DSc Glas. 1986, MD (Commend.) 1968; FRCPI 1993; FRCS Ed. 1992; FRCP Ed. 1969, M 1959; FRCP Glas. 1968, M 1962; FRFPS 1959; Hon. FRCPS (Canada) 1992; FRCPath 1992. Cons. Phys. S.. Gen. Hosp. Glas.; Clin. Sub Dean Univ. Glas.; Bd. Mem. Healthcare Int. Clydebank. Prev: Hutcheson Schol. & Hall Tutorial Fell. Roy. Infirm. Glas. & Univ. Glas.

HUME, Susanne Margaret Young Peoples Unit, Royal Edinburgh Hospital, Tipperlin Road, Edinburgh EH10 5HF Tel: 0131 537 6000; 111 Avalon Gardens, Lochmill, Linlithgow EH49 7PL Tel: 01506 845353 — MB ChB 1992 Ed.; MRCPsych 1997. (Edinburgh) Specialist Regist. Roy. Edin. Hosp. Prev: SHO Roy. Edin. Hosp.; SHO Doncaster Roy. Infirm.; SHO Craig Dunain Hopsital Inverness.

HUME KENDALL, Julia Anne 15 Pickering Road, Broughton Astley, Leicester LE9 6WA — MB BS 1985 Lond.

HUME-SMITH, Helen Vivien Weathervane, Sarum Road, Winchester SO22 5QE — MB BS 1998 Lond.; MB BS Lond 1998.

HUMM, Tracy Elizabeth 67 Erlanger Road, Telegraph Hill, London SE14 5TQ — MB BS 1983 Lond.; DA (UK) 1986. Prev: Regist. (Anaesth.) W.m., St Stephens & Roy. Brompton Hosps. Lond.

HUMMEL, John Paul Frobisher Frobisher's Rest, Victoria Quay, Salcombe TQ8 8DB Tel: 0154 884 2433 — MRCS Eng. LRCP Lond. 1939; DTM & H Eng. 1947. (Leeds) Prev: Clin. Asst. in Psychiat. Moorhaven Hosp. Ivybridge; Temp. Surg. Lt. RNVR.

HUMPHERSON, Claire Elaine 18 Featherston Road, Sutton Coldfield B74 3JN — BM BCh 1997 Oxf.

HUMPHERSON, John Richard School of Biological Sciences, Box 3.239, Stopford Building, University of Manchester, Manchester M13 9PT Tel: 0161 275 5248 Fax: 0161 275 5661 Email: j.r.humpherson@man.ac.uk; 11 Aspenwood Close, Marple, Stockport SK6 6NU — MB ChB 1964 St. And. (St. And.) Sen. Lect. (Anat.) Univ. Manch. Socs: Anat. Soc. & Brit. Assn. Clin. Anat.

HUMPHREY, Adele Mackeith Centre, c/o RACH, Dyke Road, Brighton BN1 3JN Tel: 01273 328145; 59A Tisbury Road, Hove BU3 3BL Tel: 01273 381167 Email: humphrey@smile.swinternet.co.uk — MB BS 1993 Lond.; BSc Physiol. 1990; MRCP (Paeds) UK 1998. (King's Coll. Hosp.) Specialist Regist. Community Paediat. (Brighton). Socs: MRCPCH; BAACH. Prev: SHO (Paediat.) Soton. Gen. Hosp.; SHO (Paediat.) Poole Gen. Hosp.; SpR (Paediat.) Pembury Hosp.

HUMPHREY, Mr Alan William Broadford Medical Practice, High Road, Broadford, Isle of Skye IV49 9AA Tel: 01471 822460 Fax: 01471 822860; Corriegorm, Broadford, Isle of Skye IV49 9BD Tel: 01471 822515 Fax: 01471 822860 — MB ChB 1963 St. And.; MLitt (Health Care Resource Managem.) St. And. 1996; FRCS Ed. 1969; FRCGP 1993, M 1971; DA Eng. 1965. (St. And.) Socs: Scott. Soc. Anaesth.; BMA; RGCPs. Prev: SHO (Cardiothoracic Surg.) Hammersmith Hosp. Lond.; Ho. Surg. Dundee Roy. Infirm. & Birm. Accid. Hosp.

HUMPHREY, Mr Anthony Richard Oak House, Old Grammar School, Scorton, Richmond DL10 6DS Tel: 01748 812440 — MB BS 1989 Lond.; BSc Lond. 1985; FRCS Ed. 1994. (St. Geo. Hosp. Lond.) Clin. Research Fell. Cleveland Back Care Project Middlesbrough. Prev: Regist. (Neurosurg.) Middlesbrough Gen. Hosp.

HUMPHREY, Caroline Anne 360 Upper Ballynahinch Road, Lisburn BT27 6XL — MB ChB 1977 Liverp.; MRCPath 1985. Cons. Haemat. Craigavon Area Hosp.

HUMPHREY, Cecilia Ann Aquhythie Croft, Kemnay, Inverurie AB51 5NY Tel: 01467 643662 — MB ChB 1979 Aberd.

HUMPHREY, Mr Christopher Stuart Rochdale Infirmary, Whithall Street, Rochdale OL12 0NB Email: aquinas@btinternet.com; 30 Tong End, Whitworth, Rochdale OL12 8BJ Tel: 01706 852640 — MD 1981 Leeds; BA Open. 1991; MB ChB 1968; FRCS Eng. 1974. (Leeds) Cons. Gen. Surg. Rochdale Healthcare Trust. Socs: Brit. Assn. Surg. Oncol. (Past Mem. Counc.); Europ. Soc. Of Mastology; Europ. Sch. of Oncol. Prev: Lect. (Surg.) St. Jas. Hosp. Leeds; Clin. & Research Fell. Dept. Surg. Mass. Gen. Hosp. & Harvard Univ.

HUMPHREY, Edward Guy 26 Bisham Drive, Abbey Park, West Bridgford, Nottingham NG2 6LT — MB BS 1969 Lond.; MRCS Eng. LRCP Lond. 1969.

HUMPHREY, Janet Rumney 34 Gayton Road, London NW3 1TY Tel: 020 7431 0815 — MRCS Eng. LRCP Lond. 1941; MRCPsych 1973. (Univ. Coll. Hosp.) Socs: Brit. Psychoanal. Soc. Prev: Psychoanalyst Hampstead Child Ther. Clinic; Med. Off. Shenley Hosp.; Clin. Asst. Portman Clinic.

HUMPHREY, Julian Alan 14 Church Heights, Hoylandswaine, Sheffield S36 7LX — MB ChB 1995 Sheff.

HUMPHREY, Karen Faye 10 Hangerfield Close, Yateley GU46 6HR — BM BS 1992 Flinders; BSc 1998.

HUMPHREY, Martin Eric Denwood Psychother. Department, Harewood Ho., Springfield Hospital, 61 Glenburnie Road, London SW17 7DJ — MB BS 1991 Lond.; MRCPsych; Diploma Forens. Ment. Health St. George's Hosp. Med. Sch.; BSc Lond. 1988; BA Oxon. 1983. (University College London) Specialist Regist. (Forens. Psychiat. and Physiother.) S. W. Lond. St. Geo.s NHS Ment. Health Trust.

HUMPHREY, Peter Ronald David Department of Neurology, Walton Neurosciences Centre, Walton Hospital, Lower Lane, Liverpool L9 7LJ Tel: 0151 529 5717 Fax: 0151 529 5512 Email: humphr-powcnn-tr.nwest.nhs.uk; The Chart, Croft Drive E., Caldy, Wirral CH48 2JR — BM BCh 1972 Oxf.; MA, DM Oxf. 1980; FRCP Lond. 1989; MRCP (UK) 1975. Cons. Neurol. Walton Hosp. Liverp.; Dir. of Research & Educat., Waton Neurosci.s Centre. Prev: Sen. Regist. Nat. Hosp. Nerv. Dis. & St. Bart. Hosp.; MRC Fell. Nat. Hosp. Nerv. Dis.; Regist. (Neurol.) Wessex RHA Neurol. Centre.

HUMPHREY, Sara Helen Westcliffe Medical Centre, Westcliffe Road, Shipley BD18 3EE Tel: 01274 580787 Fax: 01274 532210; Low House Farm, Stocks Lane, Clayton Heights, Bradford BD13 2RW — MB ChB 1990 Leeds; MRCGP Lond. 1995; DFFP 1996. (Leeds) GP Princip.; Hosp. Pract. Shipley Hosp. Prev: Trainee GP Shipley; SHO (Gerait.) Bradford Roy. Infirm.

HUMPHREY, Sarah Jane 37 Cavendish Road, London NW6 7XR — MB BS 1992 Lond.

HUMPHREY, Susan Marie 2 Mill House Cottages, Cambridge Road, Quendon, Saffron Walden CB11 3XJ — MB ChB 1986 Sheff.

HUMPHREY, Timothy Simon 11 Lower Orchard, Tibberton, Gloucester GL19 3AX Tel: 01452 790790 — MB ChB 1989 Birm.; T(GP) 1993; DFFP 1993. Civil. Med. Practitioner MoD Bath. Prev: Regist. (A & E) Hornsby Hosp. Sydney, Austral.; Regist. (Psychiat.) Jersey Gen. Hosp.; Trainee GP Staunton, Glos.

HUMPHREY EVANS, Ian Rhodri (retired) Cartref, Pant Erwyn Road, Dyserth, Rhyl LL18 6DF Tel: 01745 570847 — MB BS Lond. 1955. Prev: Regist. (Med.) Llandudno Gen. Hosp.

HUMPHREYS, Alison Claire Dept Medical Oncology, St james University Hospital, Beckett Lane, Leeds LS9 7TF Tel: 0113 243 3144 Fax: 0113 242 9886 Email: medach@concerned.leeds.ac.uk — BM BCh 1990 Oxf.; MA Camb. 1991; MRCP (UK) 1993. (Camb. & Oxf.) Specialist Regist. Med. Oncol. St James Univ. Hosp. Leeds. Socs: Assn. Cancer Phys.

HUMPHREYS, Ann Judith Lifespan Healthcare, Community Child Health, Ida Darwin, Fulbourn, Cambridge CB1 5EE Tel: 01223 884160 Fax: 01223 884161; 21 Cow Lane, Fulbourn, Cambridge CB1 5HB — MB ChB 1981 Bristol; BSc Bristol 1978; MRCGP 1986; DRCOG 1986. Staff Grade (Community Paediat.) Lifespan Healthcare Camb.; Clin. Asst., Neonat. Paediat., Addenbrookes Hosp., Camb.

HUMPHREYS, Daphne Margaret The Ivy House, Charlbury, Oxford OX7 3PX Tel: 01608 810242 — MB BS 1960 Lond.; MRCP Lond. 1966; DCH Eng. 1965. (St. Bart.) Socs: BMA. Prev: Assoc. Specialist (Gastroenterol.) Roy. Berks. Hosp. Reading; Sen. Regist. Roy. Berks. Hosp. Reading; Regist. Slade Hosp. Oxf.

HUMPHREYS, David Michael Ranworth, 4 Portsmouth Road, Camberley GU15 1LA Tel: 01276 685022 — MB ChB 1965 St. And.; MB ChB St And. 1965; FFPM RCP (UK) 1993, M 1989. Med. Dir. Boehringer Ingelheim Ltd. UK Bracknell. Socs: BMA. Prev: Dir. Clin. Research (Europe) Cyanamid Internat. Research Centre Richmond; Assoc. Dir. Clin. Research (Europe) Cyanamid Overseas Corp. Rome.

HUMPHREYS, David Ridley (retired) Knill Court, Knill, Presteigne LD8 2PR Tel: 01544 267379 Email: humulus@btinternet.com — MB ChB 1938 Birm.; MB ChB (2nd cl. Hons.) Birm. 1938; MD

(Hons.) Birm. 1943; FRCP Lond. 1963, M 1940. Prev: Phys. United Birm. Hosps. & Mid-Worcs. Hosp. Gp.

HUMPHREYS, Eifion William 6 Watkin Avenue, Old Colwyn, Colwyn Bay LL29 9NN — MB ChB 1961 Liverp.; DMJ (Clin.) Soc. Apoth. Lond. 1972. (Liverp.)

HUMPHREYS, Frances Warwick Hospital, Lakin Road, Warwick CV34 5BW Tel: 01926 495321 Fax: 01926 482664 — MB BS 1980 Newc.; MRCP (UK) 1983; FRCP Lond 2000. p/t Cons. Dermatol. Warwick Hosp. Socs: Ordinary Mem. Brit. Assn. of Dermatol.; BMA; Brit. Soc. Paediactric Dermat. Prev: Sen. Regist. (Dermat.) Roy. Infirm. Edin.; Clin. Research Fell. Dermat. Dept. Univ. Ed.; Regist. (Dermat.) Roy. Vict. Infirm. Newc.

HUMPHREYS, Helen Christine (retired) Knill Court, Knill, Presteigne LD8 2PR Tel: 01544 267379 — MB BChir 1943 Camb.; BA Camb. 1940, MB BChir 1943; DCH Eng. 1947. Prev: Ho. Phys. Birm. Childr. Hosp.

HUMPHREYS, Huw Idris (retired) Bod heullog, Gellifor, Ruthin LL15 1SB Tel: 01824 790176 Fax: 01492 543829 — MB BCh 1955 Wales; FRCGP 1983, M 1965; DObst RCOG 1960. Prev: GP Llandudno.

HUMPHREYS, Joanne 9 Orchard Street, West Didsbury, Manchester M20 2LP — MB ChB 1998 Manch.; MB ChB Manch 1998.

HUMPHREYS, Mr John, TD, Lt.-Col. (retired) 24 Waterloo Road, Birkdale, Southport PR8 2NF Tel: 01704 568261 — MB ChB 1948 Liverp.; ChM Liverp. 1959; FRCS Eng. 1955; FRCS Ed. 1955; MRCS Eng. LRCP Lond. 1948. JP; Clin. Lect. (Surg.) Univ. Liverp.; Surg. Tutor RCS Eng.; Surg. Cons. RAMC TA; Examr. FRCS Ed.; Regional Adviser RCS Edin. Prev: Cons. Surg. N. Sefton S.port.

HUMPHREYS, John Richard Humphrey (retired) Anchor House, Church Plain, Mattishall, Dereham NR20 3QE — MB BS 1955 Lond.; DPH 1962.

HUMPHREYS, Lyster Mervyn, TD (retired) The Old School House, 87 London St., Faringdon SN7 8AA Tel: 01367 240025 — BM BCh 1961 Oxf.; MRCP (UK) 1969. Prev: Clin. Asst. (Radiother.) P.ss Margt. Hosp. Swindon.

HUMPHREYS, Martin Sydney Reaside Clinic, Birmingham Great Park, Rubery, Birmingham B45 9BE Tel: 0121 453 6161 Fax: 0121 627 8424 Email: martin.humphreys@sbmht.wmids.nhs.uk — MB BS 1986 Newc.; BDS Lond. 1978; MRCPsych 1990. Sen. Lect. (Forens. Psychiat.) Univ. Birm. & Hon. Cons. Forens. Psychiat. S. Birm. Ment. Health NHS Trust. Prev: Lect. (Forens. Psychiat.) Univ. Edin.; Regist. (Psychiat.) Roy. Edin. Hosp.

HUMPHREYS, Mary Doreen (retired) 204 Colchester Road, London E10 6HQ Tel: 020 8539 0985 — MB ChB Liverp. 1955; DA Eng. 1959; DObst RCOG 1958. Prev: Asst. MOH Lond. Boro. Waltham Forest.

HUMPHREYS, Michael Frederick Community Mental health Team, 68b Junction Road, Andover SP10 3QX Tel: 01264 358180 Fax: 01264 335372; 43 Hulse Road, Salisbury SP1 3LU Tel: 01722 320968 Fax: 01722 414783 — MB BS Newc. 1967; MRCPsych 1975; DPM RCPSI 1973. Cons. Psychiat. Roy. Hants. Co. Hosp. Winchester; Cons. Psyiniatrist, Clouds Ho., E. Knoyle, Wilts SP3 6BE. Socs: Wessex Psychother. Soc.

HUMPHREYS, Nigel 13 Willoughby Road, Horfield, Bristol BS7 8QX Tel: 0117 924 1983 Email: nigel@humphreys.mildram.co.uk — MB ChB 1995 Bristol; BSc (Hons) (Chemistry) Bristol 1982; MB ChB (Hons) Bristol 1995; MRCP (UK) 1998. (Bristol) Specialist Regist. (Paediat.) Roy. United Hosp., Bath. Prev: SHO (Neonat. Med.) Soutmead Hosp.; SHO (Neonat. Med.) St. Micheals Hosp., Bristol.

HUMPHREYS, Richard Cenric, OBE (retired) Tan-y-Bryn, Greenhill Way, Crickhowell NP8 1AF Tel: 01873 810263 — MB ChB 1946 Ed.; MD (High Commend.) Ed. 1953; FRCGP 1974, M 1956; DObst RCOG 1949. Prev: Chairm. Welsh Counc. Roy. Coll. Gen. Pract.

HUMPHREYS, Robert Anthony Kirkcaldy Chiropractic Clinic, 42 Townsend Place, Kirkcaldy KY1 1HB Tel: 01592 260791; Leven Health Centre, Victoria Road, Leven KY8 4ET Tel: 01333 425656 — MB BCh BAO 1984 NUI; MRCGP 1991; MFHom 1994; DCCH RCP Ed. 1991; DRCOG 1990; Dip. Med. Acupunc. 1997. (Univ. Coll. Dub.) Clin. Med. Off. (Community Child Health) Fife Healthcare NHS Trust; Indep. Homoeop. & Acupunc. Kirkcaldy Chiropractic Clinic; Undergrad. Tutor Tayside Centre for Gen. Pract. Socs: Accred. Mem. Brit. Med. Acupunc. Soc.; Brit. & Scott. Assn. Community Child Health; Assoc. Mem. Roy. Coll. Paediat. & Child Health. Prev: GP Fife HB; SHO (Surg. Paediat.) & Clin. Asst. (Cas.) Roy. Hosp. Sick Childr. Glas.

HUMPHREYS, Ruth Olivia 94 Ulsterville Avenue, Lisburn Road, Belfast BT9 7AR — MB BCh 1998 Belf.; MB BCh Belf 1998.

HUMPHREYS, Sharon Anita Broadmoor Hospital, Crowthorne RG45 7EG Tel: 01344 773111 Fax: 01344 754179 — MB BS 1983 Lond.; 2000 BAP Certificate in Psychophormacology; MRCPsych 1992; MRCGP 1987; DRCOG 1986. (St. Geo.) p/t Cons. Forens. Psychiat., BRd.moor Hosp. Socs: Fell. Roy. Soc. Med.; Mem. Brit. Assn. Psychopharmacol.; Mem. CINP. Prev: Sen. Regist. (Psychiat.) Old Manor Hosp. Salisbury; Sen. Regist. (Psychiat.) Roy. S. Hants. Hosp.; Clin. Research Asst. (Tranquilliser Dependency & Mood Disorders) Char. Cross Hosp. Lond.

HUMPHREYS, Shaun Wallace Ystwyth Medical Group, Ystwyth Primary Care Centre, Parc Y Llyn, Llanbadarn Fawr, Aberystwyth SY23 3TL Tel: 01970 613500 Fax: 01970 613505 — MB BCh 1984 Wales; MB BCh Wales l984; MRCGP 1988.

HUMPHREYS, Stephen Cellular Pathology Department, Preston Hall Hospital, Aylesford ME20 7NH Tel: 01622 224059 Fax: 01622 224061; 21 Holter's Mill, The Spires, Canterbury CT2 8SP Tel: 01227 455868 Email: stephen.humphreys7@btinternet.com — MB BS 1979 Lond.; BSc Lond. 1976; MRCPath 1986; FRCPath 1996. Cons. Cellular Path. Mid Kent Healthcare Trust Maidstone Kent; Hon. Sen. Lect., Univ. of Kent at Canterbury. Prev: Lect. (Histopath.) St. Thos. Hosp. Med. Sch. Lond.; Cons. Histopath. & Cytologist King's Coll. Hosp. Lond.

***HUMPHREYS, Susan Rosemary** 24 Ballymacormick Road, Dromore BT25 1QR; 2 Village Green, main St, Moira, Craigavon BT67 0TN — MB ChB 1995 Dundee.

HUMPHREYS, Thomas Victor, OBE, OStJ, Col. late RAMC Retd. Powderham House, Powderham, Exeter EX6 8JJ Tel: 01626 890536 — MB BCh BAO Belf.; MB BCh BAO (Hons. Forens. Med. & Hyg.) Belf. 1945. (Qu. Univ. Belf.) Socs: Fell. (Ex-Pres.) Milit. Med. Soc. SHAPE (Belgium); (Pres. Emerit.) Berlin Internat. Med. Soc. Prev: Cdr. Army Med. Servs. HQ Lond. Dist. Horse Guards Lond.; Cdr. Army Med. Servs. & CO. BMH, Berlin; Med. Off. HM Embassy, Moscow with Diplomatic Rank 1st Sec. of Embassy.

HUMPHREYS, Mr William George Antrim Hospital, 45 Bush Road, Antrim BT41 2RL Tel: 01849 424125 Fax: 01849 424519 Email: george.humphreys@uh.n.i.nhs.uk; 1 Rossland Park, Knowehead Road, Broughshane, Ballymena BT43 7LG Tel: 01266 861702 Email: 100645.2131@compuserve.com — MB BCh BAO 1968 Belf.; MD Belf. 1976; FRCSI 1994; FRCS Ed. 1972. (Belf.) Cons. Surg. (Gen. Surg.) Antrim Hosp.; Hon. Sen Lect. (Surg.) Qu. Univ. Belf. Socs: Fell. Roy. Soc. Med. (Coloproctol. Div.); Assn. Surg.; BMA.

HUMPHREYS, William Heber (retired) Glebe Garden, Montgomery SY15 6QA — MB BS 1943 Lond.; MRCS Eng. LRCP Lond. 1943. Prev: Surg. RNVR.

HUMPHREYS, Mr William Vowell Ael Y Bryn, Llandegfan, Menai Bridge LL59 5PH — MD 1975 Manch.; MB ChB 1968; FRCS Ed. 1972. (Manch.) Cons. Surg. Gwynedd Hosp. Bangor. Prev: Lect. Surg. Univ. Manch.; Ho. Surg. & Regist. Gen. Surg. Manch. Roy. Infirm.

HUMPHREYS-DAVIES, William Peter Crompton (retired) Saddlers Cottage, 43 London Road, Horndean, Waterlooville PO8 0BW — BM BCh 1962 Oxf.; MA, BM BCh Oxf. 1962. Prev: Obst. Ho. Phys. St. Thos. Hosp. Lond.

HUMPHREYS JONES, Mair (retired) Ystrad Awel, Brynsiencyn, Llanfairpwllgwyngyll LL61 6HX — M.B., Ch.B. Liverp. 1948, C.P.H. 1949. Prev: Ho. Phys. Caern. & Anglesey Infirm. Bangor.

HUMPHRIES, Alexander Bromley Devere 40 College Road, Clifton, Bristol BS8 3HX — MB BS 1992 Lond.

HUMPHRIES, Angela Marie 7 Glas Efail, Cardiff CF14 4SQ — MB BCh 1997 Wales.

HUMPHRIES, Carl Andrew Blackpool Victoria Hospital, Whinney Heys Road, Blackpool FY2 8NR Tel: 01253 303499; 4 Norfolk Road, Lytham St Annes FY8 4JG Tel: 01253 730612 — MB ChB 1988 Dundee; BMSc Dund 1985; FRCA 1994. (Dundee) Cons. Anaesth. Blackpool Vict. Hosp. Prev: Sen. Regist. (Anaesth.) NW Region; Regist. (Anaesth.) NW Region; SHO (Neonat. Paediat.) Walsgrave NHS Trust Coventry.

HUMPHRIES, Charles Peter Huntlyburn, Melrose — MB BS 1967 Lond.; MRCPsych 1977. Cons. Psychiat. Borders Primary Care NHS Trust.

HUMPHRIES, Elaine Ann Mary 1 Milton Avenue, Bath BA2 4QZ — MB ChB 1983 Leic.; MRCPsych 1988. Clin. Med. Off. (Child Psychiat.) W.on Gen. Hosp. W.on-super-Mare. Prev: Regist. (Child Psychiat.) Cardiff.

HUMPHRIES, Enid Elaine (retired) The Woodlands, 22 Chantry Road, Stourton, Stourbridge DY7 6SA Tel: 01384 390016 Fax: 01384 444724 Email: elainhumphries@talk21.com — MB ChB 1968 Sheff.; Dip. Community Paediat. 1990; DObst. RCOG 1971. Prev: Clin. Med. Off. Dudley Priority Health NHS Trust.

HUMPHRIES, John Michael The Leicester Nuffield Hospital, Scraptoft Lane, Leicester LE5 1HY Tel: 0116 276 9401 Fax: 0116 246 1076; 8 Blackthorn Road, Glenfield, Leicester LE3 8QP Tel: 0116 291 8867 Fax: 0116 224 0364 Email: john.humpries@tn.ntl.com — MB BS 1961 Durh.; MSc Pharmaceutical Medicine Surrey 1998. (Durh.) Medico-Legal Assessor; Med. Mem., DAT Tribunals. Prev: Clin. Research Phys. Pharmceut. Profiles Nottm.

HUMPHRIES, Mrs June Ann Wake Green Surgery, 7 Wake Green Road, Moseley, Birmingham B13 9HD Tel: 0121 449 6370; 48 Billesley Lane, Moseley, Birmingham B13 9QS — MB ChB 1960 Birm. Prev: Asst. Sch. Med. Off. Birm.

HUMPHRIES, Paul David 35 Phillimore Gardens, London NW10 3LL — MB BS 1998 Lond.; MB BS Lond 1998.

HUMPHRIES, Samantha Anne 6 Ridgeway Walk, Eastleigh SO53 2LT — MB BS 1993 Lond.

HUMPHRIES, Thomas Alan Welbeck Road Surgery, 1A Welbeck Road, Bolsover, Chesterfield S44 6DF Tel: 01246 823742; Grove Farm, Loads Road, Holymoorside, Chesterfield S42 7HW — MB BS 1984 Lond.; MRCGP 1989.

HUMPHRIS, Stephen Daniel Meanwood Group Practice, 548 Meanwood Road, Leeds LS6 4JN Tel: 0113 295 1737 Fax: 0113 295 1736 — MB ChB 1987 Leeds; BSc (Hons.) Physiol. Leeds 1984; MRCGP 1991; T(GP) 1991; DRCOG 1990; Cert. Family Plann. JCC 1990. (Leeds) Socs: BMA. Prev: Trainee GP Leeds E. VTS; Ho. Surg. Leeds Gen. Infirm.; Ho. Phys. Huddersfield Roy. Infirm.

HUMPHRISS, Bryan Eric (retired) 27 Hightor Road, Woolton, Liverpool L25 6DJ Tel: 0151 428 2861 — MB ChB 1956 Liverp.; FRCGP 1986, M 1965. Prev: GP Liverp.

HUMPHRISS, David Bryan The Medical Diagnostic Unit, Scarborough Hospital, Woodlands Drive, Scarborough YO12 6QL Tel: 01723 342036 Email: david@dthumphries.demon.co.uk — MB ChB 1985 Liverp.; BSc (Hons.) Liverp. 1982; MRCP (UK) 1988. Cons. Phys. (Diabetes & Endocrinol.) ScarBoro. Hosp. Prev: Clin. Research Assoc. (Med.) Univ. Newc.; Regist. (Med.) Mersey Region HA; SHO (Med.) S. Sefton HA.

HUMPHRY, Nicholas John Craig Sleaford Medical Group, Riverside Surgery, 47 Boston Road, Sleaford NG34 7HD Tel: 01529 303301 Fax: 01529 415401; Angel Barn, Main St, Ewerby, Sleaford NG34 9PH Tel: 01529 461662 — MB BS 1986 Lond.; MRCGP 1990. (St. Bart. Hosp. Med. Coll.) Socs: Primary Care Rheum. Soc. Prev: Trainee GP E.bourne VTS.

HUMPHRY, Robert John Health Centre, Lake Lock Road, Stanley, Wakefield WF3 4HS Tel: 01924 822328 Fax: 01924 870052 — MRCS Eng. LRCP Lond. 1971; MRCGP 1975; DObst RCOG 1973.

HUMPHRY, Mr Roger Christopher Department of Ophthalmology, Salisbury District Hospital, Salisbury SP2 8BJ Tel: 01722 336262 Fax: 01722 425155 Email: mr.r.humphry@shc-tr.swest.nhs.uk — MB BS 1977 Lond.; MD Lond. 1988; FRCS Eng. 1984; FRCOphth 1988; DO Eng. 1982. (St Barth.) Cons. Ophth. Salisbury Dist. Hosp. Socs: Coun. Mem. UKIIS; Hon. Sec. Ophth. Sect. Roy. Soc. Med.; Sec. S.. Ophth. Soc. Prev: Sen. Regist. Bristol Eye Hosp.; Fell. Smith Kettlewell Eye Research Inst. San Francisco, Calif.

HUMPHRY, Terence Murchison (retired) 34 Torton Hill Road, Arundel BN18 9HL Tel: 01903 882395 — MRCS Eng. LRCP Lond. 1944. Prev: Clin. Med. Off. W. Sussex HA.

HUMPHRYS, Mrs Catharine Mary Shere Surgery and Dispensary, Gomshall Lane, Shere, Guildford GU5 9DR Tel: 01486 202066 Fax: 01486 202761; 29 Wolseley Road, Godalming GU7 3EA — MB BS 1985 Lond.; MA Camb. 1986; MRCGP 1989; DRCOG 1988.

HUMPSTON, David Joseph Occupational Health Department, Pfizer Ltd., Sandwich CT13 9NJ Tel: 01304 643230 Fax: 01304 656500 Email: davidhumpston@lineone.net; High Barn, Brookestreet Farm, Ash, Canterbury CT3 2NP Tel: 01304 813599 — MB ChB Birm. 1962; AFOM RCP Lond. 1983. (Birm.) Sen. Occupat. Health Phys. Pfizer Ltd. Sandwich, Kent. Socs: Fell. Roy. Soc. Med.; Soc. Occupat. Med.; Inst. Occupat. Safety & Health. Prev: Regist. (Neurol.) Midl. Centre Neurosurg. & Neurol. Warley; Regist. (Med.) Bath Hosp. Gp.; Ho. Surg. (Cas.) Gen. Hosp. Birm.

HUMZAH, Mr Muhammed Dalvi Department of Plastic Surgery, Radcliffe Infirmary, Woodstock Road, Oxford OX2 6HE Tel: 01865 311188 — MB BS 1988 Lond.; MB BS (Hons.) Surg. Lond. 1988; BSc (Hons.) Lond. 1985; FRCS Glas. 1992; AKC 1988; FRCS (Plast.) 1997. (King's College) Cons. Plastic Surg. Radcliffe Infirm. Oxf. Prev: Regist. (Plastic Surg.) St. John's Hosp. Edin.; SHO (Plastic Surg.) St. Thos. Hosp. Lond.; SHO Rotat. (Surg.) St. Geo. & Roy. Marsden Hosps.

HUNDAL, Kulwinder Singh 209 Ealing Road, Northolt UB5 5HS — MB BS 1997 Lond.

HUNDAL, Lorna Margaret 8 James Street, Newport-on-Tay DD6 8BB — MB ChB 1986 Dundee.

HUNDAY, Deb Sankar Bradford Street Surgery, 54 Bradford Street, Walsall WS1 3QD — MB BS 1961 Calcutta; MB BS Calcutta, 1961; FRSH 1984. (Nat. Med. Coll.) JP; Mem. Exec. Copmm. Citizens Advis. Bureaux Halsall; Mem. Primary Health Care Specialist Gp. Socs: Fell. Roy. Soc. Med.; BMA (Ex-Chairm. Walsall Div.). Prev: Res. Med. Off. Newark Hosp.; Ho. Surg. Roy. Infirm. Greenock; Ho. Phys. Larkfield Hosp. Greenock.

HUNDLE, Bhagwant Singh 54 Waterslea Drive, Heaton Chase, Bolton BL1 5FJ — MB ChB 1993 Manch.; FRCA 1999; DRCOG 1996. (Manch.) Specialist Regist. Anaesth. N. W. Rotat. Prev: SHO (Anaesth.) City Hosp. Birm.

HUNG, Cheung Tsui 14 Faulkner Close, Milton, Cambridge CB4 6EF — BChir 1996 Camb.

HUNG, Chi Chuen 27 Keybank Road, West Derby, Liverpool L12 5JH — MB ChB 1986 Dundee; MRCP (UK) 1991.

HUNG, Ivan Fan-Ngai 3 Woodland Court, Knoll Hill, Bristol BS9 1NR — MB ChB 1996 Bristol.

HUNG, Liang Choo 44/1 Glenfrith Close Residence, Leicester Glenfield District Hospital, Leicester LE3 9QQ; Flat 44, Room 1, Glenfrith Close Residences, Leicester LE3 9QQ Tel: 0116 287 1471 — MB BS 1986 Malaya; MRCP (UK) 1991. Regist. (Paediat. Cardiol.) Glenfield Gen. Hosp. Leicester.

HUNG, Terry Che-Wai 16 St Clements Mansions, Lillie Road, Fulham, London SW6 7PG Tel: 020 7381 8432 — MB BChir 1994 Camb.; MA Camb. 1995. (Camb.) Basic Surg. Rotat. SHO The Hammersmith Hosp. NHS Trust; SHO Otolar. St Geo. Hosp. Lond. Socs: Fell. Roy. Soc. Med. Lond.; BMA; MDU. Prev: SHO (A & E) Char. Cross Hosp. Lond.; SHO (Renal Transpl. & Urol.) Hammersmith Hosp. Lond.; SO (Otolaryngol). Roy. Infirm. Edin. NHS Trust.

HUNG, Wellington Yu-Chin Abraham Cowely Unit, Holloway Hill, Lyne, Chertsey KT16 0AE Tel: 01932 872010 Fax: 01932 875128 — MB BChir 1974 Camb.; MA, BA Camb. 1970; MRCPsych 1978. (Camb. & King's Coll. Hosp.) Cons. Psychiat. Abraham Cowley Unit Chertsey. Prev: Sen. Regist. (Psychiat.) Nat. Hosp. Nerv. Dis. & Maudsley Hosp. Lond.; Regist. (Psychiat.) Maudsley Hosp. Lond.

HUNG KWOK CHOI, Marie Josephe Annielle 2/R, 44 Grandtully Drive, Kelvindale, Glasgow G12 0DS — MB ChB 1987 Glas.; MRCP (UK) 1992; DRCPath 1995; MRCPath 1998. Career Regist (Haemat.) Glas. W.. Infirm. Prev: SHO (Haemat.) Glas. Roy. Infirm.; SHO (Gen. Med.) Law Hosp. Lanarksh. HB.

HUNGERFORD, Mr John Leonard 114 Harley Street, London W1N 1AG Tel: 020 7935 1565 Fax: 020 7224 1752; Kingswood Hanger, Gomshall, Guildford GU5 9QB Tel: 01483 202212 Fax: 01483 202694 — MB BChir Camb. 1970; FRCOphth 1988; FRCS Eng. 1978; DO RCS Eng. 1973. Cons. Surg. Oncol. Clinic Moorfield Eye Hosp. & Cons. Ophth Surg. St. Bart. Hosp. Lond. Prev: Sen. Lect. (Ophth.) Inst. Ophth. Med. Coll., St. Bart. Hosp. Lond.; Sen. Regist. Univ. Coll. Hosp. & Moorfields Eye Hosp. Lond.; Resid. Surg. Off. Moorfields Eye Hosp. Lond.

HUNGIN, Professor Amritpal Singh The Health Centre, Sunningdale Drive, Eaglescliffe, Stockton-on-Tees TS16 9EA Tel: 01642 780113 Fax: 01642 791020; 4 Butts Lane, Egglescliffe, Stockton-on-Tees TS16 9BT Fax: 01642 791629 — MB BS 1975

Newc.; MD Newc. 1996; FRCGP 1991, M 1979; DRCOG 1979. Prof. (Gen. Pract.) Centre for Health Studies Univ. of Durh. GP (Gen. Pract.) Centre for Health Studies Univ. of Durh.; Hosp. Pract. (Gastrointestinal Endoscopy) Middlesbrough Gen. Hosp.; Research Assoc. (PHC) Univ. Newc. u. Tyne; Dir. N.. Research Network (NOREN). Socs: Primary Care Soc. Gastroenterol. (Mem. Steering Comm.).; Comm. Mem. Europ. Primary Care Soc. (Gastroenteroly). Prev: Research Fell. RCGP; Treas. Cleveland Med. Soc.; Treas. N. Fac. Bd. RCGP.

HUNJAN, Arvinder Singh 85 Sudbury Court Drive, Harrow HA1 3SS — MB BS 1998 Lond.; MB BS Lond 1998.

HUNJAN, Mohinder Singh Kings Avenue Medical Centre, 18 Kings Avenue, Greenford UB6 9BZ Tel: 020 8578 6016 Fax: 020 8575 1141; 85 Sudbury Court Drive, Harrow HA1 3SS Tel: 020 8904 6112 — MB BS 1967 Bombay; MCPS Bombay 1967.

HUNJIN, Manjit Singh Newton Surgery, 305 Chapeltown Road, Leeds LS7 3JT Tel: 0113 295 3737 Fax: 0113 295 3738 — MB ChB 1983 Sheff.

HUNN, Martin Kent The Walton Centre for Neurology & Neurosurgery, Rice Lane, Liverpool L9 1AE — MB ChB 1985 Otago.

HUNNAM, Geoffrey Robert Rose Garth, 89 Station Road, Great Massingham, King's Lynn PE32 2JQ Tel: 01485 520392; Mimm's Farm Barns, Priory Road, Castle Acre, King's Lynn PE32 — MB BChir 1979 Camb.; MA Camb. 1979; MRCP (UK) 1980; FRCR 1986. Cons. Radiol. King's Lynn & Wisbech Hosps. NHS Trust. Prev: Sen. Regist. & Regist. Addenbrookes Hosp. Camb.; Regist. Qu. Mary's Hosp. Roehampton.

HUNNIFORD, Yvonne Edna The Medical Centre, 15 Cawley Road, Chichester PO19 1XT Tel: 01243 786666/781833 Fax: 01243 530042 — MB BCh BAO 1984 NUI; DRCOG 1989.

HUNNINGHER, Anne 10 Canning Road, London N5 2JS — MB ChB 1998 Manch.; MB ChB Manch 1998.

HUNNYBUN, Jennifer Margaret (retired) 14 Harestone Valley Road, Caterham CR3 6HB Tel: 0208 42831 — MB BS 1955 Lond.

HUNNYBUN, John (retired) 14 Harestone Valley Road, Caterham CR3 6HB Tel: 01883 342831 — MB BS 1955 Lond.; DObst RCOG 1957. Prev: GP Caterham.

HUNSLEY, David Cherry Knowle Hospital, Ryhope, Sunderland SR2 0NB Tel: 0191 565 6256 — MB BS 1980 Newc.; BSc Newc. 1966, PhD 1971, MB BS 1980; MRCPsych 1984. (Newcastle) Cons. Psychiat. of Old Age N. RHA Sunderland. Socs: Internat. PsychoGeriat. Assn.; Europ. Assoc. for Geriat. Psychiat.; BMA. Prev: Cons. Adult Psychiat. Lothian HB; Sen. Regist. (Adult Psychiat.) Roy. Edin. Hosp.; Regist. (Psychiat.) N.. RHA Newc.

HUNSLEY, John Edmund Northern General Hospital, Herries Road, Sheffield S5 7AU Tel: 0114 271 4818 Fax: 0114 256 0394; 129 Knowle Lane, Ecclesall, Sheffield S11 9SN Tel: 0114 236 3621 Email: j.e.hunsley@sheffield.ac.uk — MB ChB 1975 Sheff.; FFA RCS Eng. 1979. Cons. Anaesth. N. Gen. Hosp. Trust. Socs: Assn. Anaesth.s of GB & Irel.; Assn. Cardiothoracic Anaesth. Prev: Sen. Regist. (Anaesth.) Leeds; Regist. (Anaesth.) Alder Hey Childr. Hosp. Liverp.; SHO & Regist. (Anaesth.) Sheff.

HUNT, Alan James Dewhurst Terrace Surgery, 8 Dewhurst Terrace, Sunniside, Gateshead NE16 5LP Tel: 0191 496 6477 Fax: 0191 488 2800; 59 Peareth Hall Road, Springwell Village, Gateshead NE9 7N — MB BS 1982 Newc.; MRCGP 1986; DRCOG 1986.

HUNT, Albert Charles (retired) Barronhall, George Terrace, St Monans, Anstruther KY10 2AY Tel: 01333 730249 Email: ahunt@ahunt.screamingnet.co.uk — MB BS Lond. 1949; MD Lond. 1952; MRCS Eng. LRCP Lond. 1949; FRCPath 1971, M 1963. Prev: Cons. Path. Plymouth Gen. Hosp.

HUNT, Anita Bernadette Devon Road Surgery, 32 Devon Road, South Darenth, Dartford DA4 9AB Tel: 01322 862121 Fax: 01322 868794; The Old Parsonage, High St, Otford, Sevenoaks TN14 5PG Tel: 01959 524014 — MB BS 1982 Lond.; DObst 1985.

HUNT, Ann Cecilia (retired) — MB ChB 1966 Sheff. Staff Grade Paediat. Soton. NHS Community Trust. Prev: Clin. Med. Off. Reading Community Health Scheme.

HUNT, Anne Elizabeth 65 Manor Road, Clayton-Le-Woods, Chorley PR6 7JR — MB ChB 1989 Liverp.

HUNT, Anthony Charles Flat 5 Moorcourt, Moorcourt Close, Sidmouth EX10 8SU — BM 1977 Soton.; MRCP (UK) 1983.

HUNT, Austin Lawrence Seymour 160 South Mossley, Hill Road, Garston, Liverpool L19 9BD — MB BS 1996 Lond.

HUNT, Barbara Jean 4 St Edmunds, 86 Christchurch Road, Winchester SO23 9TE Tel: 01962 850844 — MB ChB 1956 Aberd.; MB ChB (Hons. Med.) Aberd. 1956; MSc (Biochem.) Toronto 1971. (Aberd.) Med. Adviser Benefits Agency Med. Servs.; Sen. Research Fell. (Pharmacol.) Univ. Bath. Socs: Fell. Roy. Soc. Med.; BMA. Prev: Dir. Health Studies Unit Univ. Sussex; Specialist in Community Med. (Plann. & Info.) Brighton HA; Mem. DHSS Comm. Safety of Meds.

HUNT, Bernadette Mary Anne Northamptonshire Health Authority, Highfield, Cliftonville Road, Northampton NN1 5DN; Flat 16, Ascot House, Buckingham Square, North Third St, Milton Keynes MK9 3LZ — MB ChB 1988 Dundee; BSc (Econ.) Wales 1978. Sen. Regist. (Pub. Health Med.) Anglia & Oxf. RHA. Prev: Regist. (Pub. Health Med.) Oxf. RHA; GP Perth, W.. Austral.

HUNT, Bernard Peter Saddlers Mead, Northlands, Sibsey, Boston PE22 0UA Tel: 01205 750165 Email: huntbernard@hotmail.com — MB BChir 1974 Camb.; MA Camb. 1974; FRCP Lond. 1993; MRCP (UK) 1976. (Camb. & Univ. Coll. Hosp.) Cons. Rheum. United Lincs. Hosp.s Trust. Socs: Brit. Soc. Rheum. Prev: Tutor (Rheum.) Univ. Manch.; Regist. (Med.) Hull & Beverley Dist. Hosps.

HUNT, Bernard Wallis (retired) 1 Fisherton Island, Salisbury SP2 7TG — MB BS Lond. 1937; MRCS Eng. LRCP Lond. 1936. Prev: Surg. Lt.-Cdr. RNVR.

HUNT, Beverley Jane Department Haematology, St Thomas' Hospital, London SE1 7EH Tel: 020 7928 9282 Fax: 020 7928 5698 Email: beverley.hunt@gstt.sthames.nhs.uk; Woodhall House, 23 Woodhall Drive, College Road, Dulwich, London SE21 7HJ — MB ChB 1979 Liverp.; MD (Liverp.) 1997; MRCS Eng. LRCP Lond. 1979; FRCP UK 1997; MRCP 1984; FRCPath 1996, M 1987; FRCP 1996; MD 1997. Cons. Haemat. & Rheum. & Hon. Sen. Lect. Guy's & St. Thos. Trust Lond.; Hon. Lect. Nat. Heart & Lung Inst. Imperial Sch. Med.; Hon. Sen. Lect. (Cardiothoracic Surg.) Nat. Heart & Lung Hosp.; Research Cons. Haemat. Harefield Hosp. Middlx. Socs: Internat. Soc. Thrombosis & Haemostasis; Brit. Soc. Haematol.; Brit. Soc. Thrombosis & Haemostasis. Prev: Research Sen. Regist. (Haemat.) Harefield Hosp.; Sen. Regist. Rotat. Middlx. & Univ. Coll. Hosps. Lond.; Regist. Rotat. (Haemat.) Hammersmith & Ealing Hosps. Lond.

HUNT, Cain Rohan Milton Surgery, Coles Road, Milton, Cambridge CB4 6BL Tel: 01223 420511 Fax: 01223 425078 — BChir 1988 Camb.; LMSSA Lond. 1988; MRCGP 1992. Prev: Trainee GP Huntingdon HA VTS.

HUNT, Carol Mary Histopathology Department, Scunthorpe General Hospital, Cliff Gardens, Scunthorpe DN15 7BH Tel: 01724 282282; 6 Park Close, Lea, Gainsborough DN21 5JE — MB BS 1976 Lond.; MRCPath 1992. Cons. Histopath. Scunthorpe & Goole Hosps. Trust.

HUNT, Caroline Beatrice Maria The Green Street Clinic, 120 Green St., Eastbourne BN21 1RT Tel: 01323 722908 Fax: 01323 723136 — MB BS 1976 Lond.; MRCS LRCP 1976; DMRD 1980; DRCOG 1978; Dip. Palliat. Med. 1998. (Roy. Free) Prev: Trainee GP Newhaven VTS; Regist. (Radiol.) Guy's Hosp. Lond.

HUNT, Charles Peter (retired) 5 Daisy Bank Crescent, Audlem, Crewe CW3 0HD Tel: 01270 811951 — MB BS 1951 Lond. Prev: Ho. Phys. & Ho. Surg. W. Suff. Gen. Hosp. Bury St. Edmunds.

HUNT, Christine Frances Harley House Surgery, 2 Irnham Road, Minehead TA24 5DL Tel: 01643 703441 Fax: 01643 704867 — MB BS 1991 Lond.

HUNT, Christopher Roger Department of Pathology, Stepping Hill Hospital, Stockport SK2 7JE Tel: 0161 419 5600 Fax: 0161 419 5668 Email: roger.hunt@stockport.tr-.nwest.nhs.uk — MB BS 1989 Lond.; MRCPath 1996; DRCPath 1995. (St. Thos. Hosp. (UMDS)) Cons. Histopath. Roy. Oldham Hosp. Socs: Manch. Med. Soc. Prev: Sen. Regist. Rotat. (Histopath.) N. W.. RHA.

HUNT, Christopher Simon Cleveland House, 16 Spital Terrace, Gainsborough DN21 2HF Tel: 01427 613158 Fax: 01427 616644 — MB BS 1975 Lond.; MRCGP 1980; DRCOG 1978.

HUNT, David Alan Gloucestershire Health Authority, Victoria Warehouse, The Docks, Gloucester GL1 2EL Tel: 01452 300222 Fax: 01452 318803 Email: david.hunt@glosha.swest.nhs.uk; Silverstone, Vicarage Lane, Brockworth, Gloucester GL3 4EY Tel: 01452 862086 Email: huntda@doctors.org.uk — MB BS 1976 Lond.; MA Camb. 1980; MFPHM RCP (UK) 1989; T(PHM) 1991; MFCM 1986; FFPHM 1999. Cons. Pub. Health Med. Glos. HA. Prev:

Sen. Regist. (Community Med.) S. W.. RHA; Regist. (Psychiat.) Hackney Hosp.

HUNT, David Charles Edward Eastfield House, Cheselbourne, Dorchester DT2 7NP; 25 Peal Gardens, Ealing, London W13 0BA — MB BS 1994 Lond. (Lond. Hosp. Med. Coll.) Clin. Fell. Health Serv. Elderly People Roy. Free. Hosp; Resusc. Counc. (UK). ALSL Instruc. Socs: BMA; Brit. Geriat.. Soc; Fell.roy.coll.Med. Prev: SHO med Rotate Barnet/Edgeware/harefield hosps.; SHO Haem.Hillingdon.Hosp; LAS Reg.c/o the Elderly.Barnet.Gen.hosp.

HUNT, David James White House, Morton, Derby DE65 5AU — MB BS 1958 Lond.; MRCS Eng. LRCP Lond. 1958; MRCGP 1977. (Lond. Hosp.) Clin. Asst. (Psychiat.) Chesterfield Hosp. Prev: Ho. Phys. & Ho. Surg. Harold Wood Hosp.; SHO King Geo. V Hosp. & Matern. Hosp. Ilford.

HUNT, David John Department of Psychiatry, St James Hospital, Leeds — MB ChB 1989 Leeds; MRCPysch. 1997. Specialist Regist. (Psychiat.) St. James Hosp. Leeds. Prev: Regist. (Psychiat.) Doncaster Roy. Infirm.; Regist. (Psychiat.) Wathwood RSU Rotherham; Regist. (Psychiat.) Barnsley Dist. Gen. Hosp.

HUNT, Mr David Maitland 106 Harley Street, London W1G 7JE Tel: 020 7935 6347 Fax: 020 7935 2788 Email: davidhunt@uk-consultants.co.uk — MB BS 1971 Lond.; FRCS Eng. 1978; FRCS Ed. 1978; MRCS Eng. LRCP Lond. 1971. (Guy's) Cons. Orthop. Surg. St. Mary's Hosp. Lond. Socs: Fell. Roy. Soc. Med. & BOA; Brit. Soc. Childr. Orthop. Surg. Prev: Sen. Regist. St. Mary's Hosp. & Roy. Nat. Orthop. Hosp. Lond.

HUNT, Edward John St Helens & Knowsley Health Authority, Cowley Hill Lane, St Helens WA10 2AP Tel: 01744 33722 Fax: 01744 457339; 2 Brookfield, Parbold, Wigan WN8 7JJ Tel: 0125 76 462649 — MB BS 1962 Lond.; FFPHM RCP (UK) 1989, M 1972; DPH 1965. (Univ. Coll. Hosp.) Dir. Pub. Health St. Helens & Knowsley DHA.

HUNT, Elaine Rosemary Bretton Health Centre, Rightwell, Bretton, Peterborough PE3 8DT Tel: 01733 264506 Fax: 01733 266728; 2 Mickle Gate, Longthorpe, Peterborough PE3 6SU Tel: 01733 265953 — MB BS 1967 Lond.; MRCS Eng. LRCP Lond. 1967. GP P'boro.

HUNT, Elizabeth 78B Blenheim Road, Moseley, Birmingham B13 9TZ — MB ChB 1992 Sheff. SHO (Anaesth.) Centr. Sheff. Hosp. Trust. Prev: SHO (Anaesth.) N.ern Gen. Hosp. Sheff.

HUNT, Ernest Thirugnanaselvam (retired) 15 Bryan Road, Edgerton, Huddersfield HD2 2AJ — MB BS 1956 Ceylon; MRCP Lond. 1964; MRCP Ed. 1963. Prev: Cons. Phys. Huddersfield Roy. Infirm.

HUNT, Gillian Agnes Luz Maria (retired) Nags Head Farmhouse, Mappowder, Sturminster Newton DT10 2EW Tel: 01258 817314 — MB BS 1957 Lond. Prev: Clin. Asst. A & E Essex Co. Hosp. Colchester.

HUNT, Gillian Mary (retired) 65 Grantchester Street, Cambridge CB3 9HZ Tel: 01223 358537 Email: jill.poulton@comnews.net — MB BChir 1946 Camb.; MA (Nat. Sc. Trip.) Camb. 1949; DCH Eng. 1950. Prev: Clin. Asst. (Urol.) Addenbrooke's Hosp. Camb.

HUNT, Graham Bernard (retired) Hardwicke, 20 Mallory Road, Hove BN3 6TD Tel: 01273 506717 — MB ChB 1958 Birm.; MRCS Eng. LRCP Lond. 1958; DObst RCOG 1960. Prev: Surg. Lt. RN.

HUNT, Harry Halesowen Health Centre, 14 Birmingham St., Halesowen B63 3HL Tel: 0121 550 4917/1185 — MB BS 1958 Lond.; LMSSA Lond. 1958. (Guy's) Prev: Clin. Asst. Corbett Hosp. Stourbridge; Cas. Off. & Ho. Surg. & Ho. Phys. Guy's Hosp. Lond.; Res. Obstetr. Torbay Hosp. Torquay.

HUNT, Harry Atkinson Meadow Farm, East Chisenbury, Pewsey SN9 6AQ Tel: 01980 670428 Email: huntha@meadowfarm.u-net.com — MB ChB Leeds 1957; FRCGP 1977, M 1972; DObst RCOG 1970; DCH Eng. 1969. (Leeds) Prev: Adviser in Gen. Pract. RAF; Gp. Capt. RAF Med. Br.

HUNT, Ian John 1 Church Lane, Kislingbury, Northampton NN7 4AD — MB BS 1996 Lond.

HUNT, Jacqueline Patricia GU Clinic, Warren HilCentre, Kettering General Hospital, Rothwell Road, Kettering NN16 8UZ Tel: 01536 410647 Fax: 01536 492223 — BM BS 1979 Nottm.; MFFP 1994; MRCGP 1983; DRCOG 1982; Memberof the Institute of Pyscosexual Medicine June 1999. Assoc. Specialist (Genitourin. Med.) Kettering; Instruc. Family Plann. Doctor Kettering; Sen. Clin. Med. Off. (Psychosexual Med.) Bedford; Audit Facilitator Inst. Psychosexual Med. Socs: Med. Soc. Study VD. Prev: GP WellingBoro., N.ants.

HUNT, Jane Louise 21 Higher Greenfields, Ingol, Preston PR2 3ZX — MB BS 1990 Lond.

HUNT, Jayne Sara 35 Moreton Drive, Staining, Blackpool FY3 0DR Tel: 01253 886468 — MB BCh 1992 Wales. SHO (Anaesth.) Gloucester Roy. Hosp. Prev: SHO (Anaesth.) P.ss Roy. Hosp. Telford NHS Trust; Regist. & SHO (ICU) Mackay Base Hosp. Qu.sland, Austral.; SHO (A & E) & Ho. Off. (Gen. Med.) Morriston Hosp. Swansea.

HUNT, John Bernard Bromley NHS Trust, Cromwell Avenue, Bromley BR2 9 — MB BS 1979 Lond.; MD Lond. 1991; MRCP (UK) 1983; FRCP 1999. (Kings College Hospital) Cons. Phys. King's Coll. Hosp. & Bromley Hosp. Socs: Brit. Soc. Gastroenterol.; Fell of the Roy. Coll of Phys; Fell of the Roy. Soc of Med. Prev: Research Regist. St. Bart. Hosp. Lond.; Lect. (Med.) St. Mary's Hosp. Med. Sch. Lond.

HUNT, John Leslie, OBE (retired) 109 Northcote Road, London SW11 6PN Tel: 020 7738 0843 Email: huntjohn1@talk21.com — MB ChB 1951 NZ; MRCP Lond. 1972; FFCM 1979, M 1974; FFPHM 1989. Prev: PMO Dept. Health & Social Security.

HUNT, John Stanley Martin (retired) The Annexe, Shaw Wood, Court Drive, Hillingdon, Uxbridge UB10 0BW Tel: 01895 813974 — MB BS 1959 Lond. Hon. Master Brunel Univ. Prev: Med. Off. Univ. Health Serv. Brunel Univ. Uxbridge.

HUNT, John William St James Surgery, Wash Lane, Clacton-on-Sea CO15 1DA Tel: 01255 222121; 16 Albert Gardens, Clacton-on-Sea CO15 6JA — MB BS 1956 Lond.; DCH Eng. 1962; DObst RCOG 1959. (Middlx.)

HUNT, The Hon. Jonathan Philip Henderson 82 Sloane Street, London SW1X 9PA Tel: 020 7245 9333 Fax: 020 7245 9232; 29 South Terrace, London SW7 2TB Tel: 020 7584 2158 Fax: 020 7225 3136 — BM BCh 1972 Oxf.; MA, BM BCh Oxf. 1972. (Oxf. & St. Thos.) Br. Med. Off. Min. of Defence; Phys. Smiths Indust. plc EMI plc; Governor Sutton's Hosp. CharterHo. Socs: Fell. Med. Soc. Lond. & Roy. Soc. Med. Prev: Resid. Med. Off. King Edwd. VII Hosp. Offs. Lond.; Demonst. & SHO St. Thos. Hosp. Lond.

HUNT, Judith Ann Whitefields Surgery, Hunsbury Hill Road, Camphill, Northampton NN4 9UW Tel: 01604 760171; 45 High Street, Bugbrooke, Northampton NN7 3PG Tel: 01604 830004 — MB ChB 1974 Manch.

HUNT, Kanageswary Mathuramanie (retired) 15 Bryan Road, Edgerton, Huddersfield HD2 2AJ Tel: 01484 429552 — MB BS 1956 Ceylon; FRCPath 1981, M 1969, D 1966. Prev: Cons. Haemat. Bradford Hosps.

HUNT, Katharine Dorothy The Garden Flat, 18B Ranelagh Road, London W5 5RJ — MB BS 1994 Lond.

HUNT, Katherine Alison 38 Edderston Road, Peebles EH45 9DT — MB ChB 1997 Birm.

HUNT, Kathleen Mary (retired) 57 Pledwick Lane, Sandal, Wakefield WF2 6EA Tel: 01924 255810 — MB BS 1961 Lond.; MRCS Eng. LRCP Lond. 1961; FRCOG 1980, M 1967, DObst 1963. Cons. O & G Wakefield Gp. Hosps. Prev: Regist. (O & G) Hammersmith Hosp.

HUNT, Kevin Peter Riverside Surgery, Water Street, Port Talbot SA12 6LF Tel: 01639 891376 Fax: 01639 870163; 85 The Meadows, Cimla, Neath SA11 3XF Tel: 01639 638260 Email: kph@meadows.demon.co.uk — MB ChB 1981 Wales; DRCOG 1983.

HUNT, Leonard Bryan (retired) 19 Queen's Gardens, London NW4 2TR Tel: 020 8202 9241 — MB BChir 1949 Camb.; MA Camb. 1949; FFPHM 1989, M 1981; DHMSA 1980; DPH Lond. 1957. Prev: Cons. Pub. Health Med. Barnet HA.

HUNT, Lesley Margaret 48 Latimer Road, Cropston, Leicester LE7 7GN — MB ChB 1985 Sheff.; FRCS Ed. 1989.

HUNT, Louise Elizabeth 20 Louvain Terrace, Ebbw Vale NP23 5AF Email: louisehunt5@hotmail.com — MB BS 1991 Lond.; FRCS Ed. 1997. (St. Bartholomew's Hospital Medical School) Research Regist. Dept. of Surg. Univ. of Louisville Kentucky, USA.

HUNT, Margaret Olwen (retired) The Meadows, Peterston-super-Ely, Cardiff CF5 6NE Tel: 01446 76036 — MRCS Eng. LRCP Lond. 1949; DA Eng. 1954. Prev: Cons. Anaesth. Centr. Middlx. Hosp. Lond.

HUNT, Marilyn Jane 64 London Road, Wickford SS12 0AH Tel: 01268 765533 — MB BS 1985 Lond. GP Partner Wickford.
HUNT, Mark Atkinson Frome Medical Practice, Health Centre, Park Road, Frome BA11 1EZ Tel: 01373 301300 Fax: 01373 301313 — MB ChB 1983 Birm.; MBA Manch. 1989; MRCGP 1987; DRCOG 1986; DCH RCP Lond. 1985. Chair PCG, Mendip.
HUNT, Martin Somerfield 12 Beacon View, Dartington, Totnes TQ9 6HH Tel: 01803 864231 — MB BS 1969 Lond.; MSc (Community Med.) Manch. 1979; DObst RCOG 1972. Indep. Med. & Paediat. Cranial Pract. Devon.
HUNT, Mr Martin Thomas Whipps Cross Hospital, Whipps Cross Road, Leytonstone, London E11 1NR; 14 Durham Way, Rayleigh SS6 9RY — MRCS Eng. LRCP Lond. 1978; MB BS 1978; FRCS Ed. 1984; DA (UK) 1986 (St. George's. Hosp.). (St Georges HMS) Cons. A & E Whipps Cross Hosp. Hosp. Socs: Founding Fell. Fac. of A & E Med.; Roy. Soc. Med. Prev: Cons. A & E Basildon Hosp.; Sen. Regist. (A & E) King's Coll. Hosp. & Roy. Sussex Co. Hosp.
HUNT, Mathew John Nicholas The Hollies Surgery, The Green, Great Bentley, Colchester CO7 8PJ Tel: 01206 250691 Fax: 01206 252496 — MB BS 1984 Lond.
HUNT, Matthew Noel Seyfang Victoria Cross Surgery, 168-169 Victoria Road, Swindon SN1 3BU Tel: 01793 535584 Fax: 01793 497526 — BM BCh 1985 Oxf.; MA Camb. 1986; MRCGP 1989; DRCOG 1988; DCH RCP Lond. 1987. (Camb. & Oxf.) Prev: Trainee GP Swindon VTS; Ho. Surg. Qu. Eliz. Hosp. Birm.; Ho. Phys. John Radcliffe Hosp. Oxf.
HUNT, Neil 9 Sedgefield, Longton, Preston PR4 5ZP — MB BS 1993 Lond.
HUNT, Neil Arthur (retired) White Lodge Cottage, Eastbourne Road, Blindley Heath, Lingfield RH7 6LG Tel: 01342 837067 — MB BS 1965 Lond.; BSc Lond. 1962, MB BS 1965; MRCS Eng. LRCP Lond. 1965; DObst RCOG 1967.
HUNT, Neil John Fulbourn Hospital, Cambridge CB1 5EF Tel: 0123 218807 Fax: 01223 218817 Email: nh212@cam.ac.uk — MD 1993 Lond.; MB BS 1983; MA Camb. 1984; MRCPsych 1987. Cons. Psychiat. Fulbourn Hosp. Camb. Prev: Sen. Regist. Rotat. (Psychiat.) Oxf. RHA; Hon. Lect. Unit of Human Psychopharmacol. St. Bart. Hosp. Lond.; SHO & Regist. (Psychiat.) St. Bart. Hosp. Lond.
HUNT, Nigel Guy Rivermead Gate Medical Centre, 123 Rectory Lane, Chelmsford CM1 1TR Tel: 01245 348688 Fax: 01245 458800; 158 Wood Street, Chelmsford CM2 8BN Tel: 01245 354732 Fax: 01245 344562 Email: nigel.hunt@dial.pipex.com — MB ChB 1981 Liverp.; MSc (Gen. Pract.) Lond. 1994; FRCGP 1995, M 1985; DFFP 1996; DCH RCP Lond. 1985; DRCOG 1984; DPD 1999. (Liverp.) Vis. Fell. Anglia Polytechnic Univ.; Tutor (Gen. Pract.) Essex. Socs: Roy. Coll. Gen. Pract. (Essex Fac. Bd.). Prev: Chairm. Essex Fac. Roy. Coll. Gen. Practs.; Hon. Sec. Essex Fac. Roy. Coll. Gen. Practs.; GP Tutor Mid. Essex.
HUNT, Norman Graham Health Centre, Barrett Way, Wroughton, Swindon SN4 9LW Tel: 01793 812 2211; 1 Inverary Road, Wroughton, Swindon SN4 9DH — BM BS 1975 Nottm.; DRCOG 1982.
HUNT, Paul Chestnut House, 10 Northgate, Hunmanby, Filey YO14 0NT — MB ChB 1981 Bristol.
HUNT, Peter Frederick Whitstable Health Centre, Harbour Street, Whitstable CT5 1BZ Tel: 01277 263033 Fax: 01277 771474; Robinshatch, The Drove, Chesgfield, Whitstable CT5 3NY Tel: 01227 792023 — MRCS Eng. LRCP Lond. 1964; MB Camb. 1966, BChir 1965; MRCGP 1980; DObst RCOG 1967. (Camb. & Westm.)
HUNT, Peter Geoffrey Merryfield, 54 Marldon Road, Shiphay, Torquay TQ2 7EJ — MB BS 1978 Lond.; BSc (Pharmacol.) Lond. 1975; DRCOG 1982.
HUNT, Peter Geoffrey The Rothbury Practice, 3 Market Place, Rothbury, Morpeth NE65 7UW Tel: 01669 620339 Fax: 01669 620583; Ballachan, Hillside Road, Rothbury, Morpeth NE65 7YD — MB BS 1988 Newc.; BA Camb. 1985; MRCGP 1993; DRCOG 1993.
HUNT, Mr Peter Woodland (retired) Les Capucines, Venelle Du Val Du Sud, Alderney GY9 3TT Tel: 0148 13101 — MRCS Eng. LRCP Lond. 1939; MB BS Lond. 1947; FRCS Eng. 1948; MB BS 1947 Lond. Prev: Cons. Surg. Rokana Corp. Kitwe, Zambia.
HUNT, Philip Charles William Hollow View, The Drift, Wittering Road, Barnack, Stamford PE9 3EY — MB BS 1977 Lond.; MRCS Eng. LRCP Lond. 1977; FFA RCS Eng. 1981. Cons. Anaesth. PeterBoro. Dist. Hosp.
HUNT, Richard 77 Lydgate Lane, Sheffield S10 5FN; 77 Lydgate Lane, Sheffield S10 5FN — MB ChB 1983 Sheff.
HUNT, Richard Joseph 48 Julian Road, West Bridgford, Nottingham NG2 5AP — MB BS 1998 Lond.; MB BS Lond 1998.
HUNT, Robert Alan The Halliwell Surgery, Lindfield Drive, Bolton BL1 3RG Tel: 01204 523716; 7 Coverdale Avenue, Heaton, Bolton BL1 5HX — MB ChB 1977 Manch.; MRCGP 1981. (Manchester) Med. Off. St. Ann's Hospice Worsley.; Bd. Mem. Bolton N. E. PCG. Prev: Ho. Off. Bolton Gen. Hosp.; Trainee GP Bolton VTS.
HUNT, Rodney Wayne c/o Flat 107, Ivy Lane, Headington, Oxford OX3 9DY; 82 Torres Avenue, Flinders Park SA5025, Australia — BM BS 1992 Flinders; MRCP (UK) 1995; DCH RCP Lond. 1994.
HUNT, Roger Fenton (retired) The Surgery, Greencliff Farm, Abbotsham, Bideford EX39 5BL Tel: 01237 424674 — MB BS 1957 Lond.; DA Eng. 1959. Med. Off. The Roy. Smithfield Club; Exec. on Med. Counc. on Alcoholism. Prev: Ho. Surg. & Sen. Res. Anaesth. St. Thos. Hosp. Lond.
HUNT, Sally Jane Litchdon Medical Centre, Landkey Road, Barnstaple EX32 9LL Tel: 01271 23443 Fax: 01271 25979; Rock Hill House, Rock Hill, West Down, Ilfracombe EX34 8NH — MB BS 1986 Lond.; DRCOG; DGM; MRCGP. (The Royal London Hospital) GP Barnstaple. Prev: Ho. Surg. & Ho. Phys. Harold Wood Hosp. Essex.
HUNT, Samantha Jane 50A Grafton Terrace, London NW5 4HY — MB BS 1993 Lond.
HUNT, Sarah Joanna Whickham Health Centre, Rectory Lane, Whickham, Newcastle upon Tyne NE16 4PD Tel: 0191 488 5555 Fax: 0191 496 0424; 12 Whaggs Lane, Whickham, Newcastle upon Tyne NE16 4PF — MB BS 1981 Newc.; MRCGP 1988; DCCH RCP Ed. 1988.
HUNT, Sarah Rosamund 38 Hamilton Terrace, London NW8 9UJ — MB BS 1972 Lond.; MRCS Eng. LRCP Lond. 1972.
HUNT, Sheila Moira Grave Park Surgery, 95 Burlington Lane, Chiswick, London W4 3ET Tel: 020 8747 1549 Fax: 020 8400 1092; 16 The Butts, Brentford TW8 8BL — MB BS 1980 Lond.
HUNT, Sian Carreg Wen, West Farm Road, Ogmore by Sea, Bridgend CF32 0PU — MB BCh 1988 Wales; MRCGP 1992; DRCOG 1992. (UWCM) Prev: Community Med. Off. Bridgend & Dist. NHS Trust; Clin. Fell. (Gen. Pract.) Univ. Wales Coll. Med.
HUNT, Stephen James Waterside Primary Care, Combe Martin Health Centre, Castle Street, Combe Martin, Ilfracombe EX34 0JA Tel: 01271 882406 Fax: 01271 883821 — MB BS 1984 Lond.; MRCGP 1988.
HUNT, Susan Teresa Goodinge Health Centre, Goodinge Close, North Road, London N7 9EW Tel: 020 7530 4940; 124 Glyn Road, London E5 0JE — MB ChB 1978 Birm.
HUNT, Theresa Margaret 27 West Square, London SE11 4SP — MB BS 1970 Lond.; MRCP (UK) 1974; FFA RCS Eng. 1975. Cons. Anaesth. St. Thos. Hosp. Lond.
HUNT, Timothy John Arthur Rank House, Brookfields Hospital, Cambridge CB1 3DF Tel: 01223 245926 Fax: 01223 415701; Farm Lodge, Hildersham, Cambridge CB1 6BU — MB BChir 1978 Camb.; PhD Ed. 1966, DSc 1975, MD 1985; LRCP LRCS Ed. LRCPS Glas. 1978; MRCP (UK) 1981. Cons. Phys. & Dir. Arthur Rank Hse. Addenbrooke's Hosp. Camb.; Hon. Lect. Camb. Univ. Prev: Scientif. Staff MRC Human Physiol.; Cons. to Dir. of Army Health; Staff Imperial Cancer Research Fund.
HUNT, Mr Trevor Millman Royal Shrewsbury Hospitals NHS Trust, Mytton Oak Road, Shrewsbury SY3 8XQ Tel: 01743 261000; Clonard, 100 Roman Road, Shrewsbury SY3 9AL — MB BS 1981 Lond.; MS Soton. 1989; FRCS Eng. 1986. (Westm.) Cons. Surg. (Gen. & Colorectal) Roy. Shrewsbury Hosps.; Lead Colorectal Cancer Clinician; Roy. Shrewsbury Hosp. NHS Trust. Socs: Assn. Coloproctol. GB & I; Assoc. Of Surg.s GB & I. Prev: Sen. Regist. (Gen. Surg.) Trent RHA; Resid. Surg. Off. St. Mark's Hosp. Lond.; Research Fell. (Surg.) Soton. Univ.
HUNT, Ursula Mary (retired) 2 Shadwell Walk, Leeds LS17 6EG Tel: 0113 268 6746 — MB ChB 1943 Leeds. Prev: Clin. Med. Off. (p/t) Leeds AHA (T).
HUNT, Victoria Jane 1F2, 168 Blackness Road, Dundee DD1 5PQ — MB ChB 1997 Dundee.
HUNT, Warwick John Northants Health Authority, Highfield, Cliftonville Road, Northampton NN1 5DN Tel: 01604 615392 Fax: 01604 615010 Email: warwick.hunt@northants-ha.anglox.nhs.uk —

BM BS 1979 Nottm.; BMedSci 1977 Nothingham; MRCGP 1986; DRCOG 1983. (Nottingham) p/t Head of Clin. Governance and Quality Deveopment. Prev: GP Kettering, N.ants.

HUNT, Wendy Graeme 36 Old Bath Road, Charvil, Reading RG10 9QR — MB ChB 1967 Bristol. Assoc. Specialist (Haemat.) Wycombe Gen. Hosp. Prev: Med. Off. Path. Dept. Wycombe Gen. Hosp. Ho. Phys. Bristol; Gen. Hosp.; Ho. Surg. Roy. S. Hants. Hosp. Soton.

HUNTBACH, Julie Anne, Flight Lt. RAF Med. Br. 1 Cedar Court, Hills Road, Cambridge CB2 2QJ — BChir 1995 Camb.; MA (Cantab.) Camb. 1997; BSc (Hons.) Sheff. 1990; MB BChir Camb. 1995. Jun. Med. Offic. RAF Laarbruch. Prev: Jun. Med. Off. RAF Wittering; Ho. Off. (Surg.) Norf. & Norwich Hosp.; Ho. Off. (Med.) Norf. & Norwich Hosp.

HUNTER, Abigail Ruth Alexander Leewood, Roslin EH25 9PZ — MB ChB 1995 Manch.

HUNTER, Aine Marie 9 Torr Road, Ballycastle BT54 6RB — MB BCh BAO 1988 Belf.

HUNTER, Alan Marshall 31 Hillcrest Avenue, Nether Poppleton, York YO26 6LD — MB ChB 1971 Ed.; FRCP Lond. 1990; FRCP Ed. 1988, M 1974. Cons. Phys. (Gen. & Respirat. Med.) York Dist. Hosp.

HUNTER, Alice Isabel 15 Drydales, Kirkella, Hull HU10 7JU — MB BS 1997 Newc.

HUNTER, Alison Christine Child Health Medical Services, 55 Osborne Road, Sheffield S11 9BF Tel: 0114 271 6636 Fax: 0114 271 6619 — MB BCh BAO 1980 Belf.; MRCP Ed. 1984; DCH RCPI 1983. SCMO (Child Health) Sheff. HA. Socs: BPA. Prev: Regist. Roy. Belf. Hosp. Sick Childr.

HUNTER, Alison Elizabeth Downland Practice, East Lane, Chieveley, Newbury RG20 8UY Tel: 01635 248251 Fax: 01635 247261; The Lodge, Curridge Road, Curridge, Thatcham RG18 9DL Tel: 01635 202056 — MB BS Lond. 1983; MRCGP 1987; DCH RCP Lond. 1987; DRCOG 1986. (Middlx. Hosp. Univ. Lond.)

HUNTER, Alison Jane Wenlock Terrace Surgery, 18 Wenlock Terrace, York YO10 4DU Tel: 01904 646861 — MB ChB 1988 Dundee; BMSc Dund 1985; MRCGP 1993; Dip. Pract. Dermat. Wales 1996; DRCOG 1992. (Dundee) G. P.

HUNTER, Alison Jean Catherine Whin Park Medical Centre, 6 Saughton Road, Edinburgh EH11 3RA Tel: 0131 455 7999 Fax: 0131 455 8800; 3 King Malcolm Close, Edinburgh EH10 7JB Tel: 0131 445 7771 Fax: 0131 445 7772 — MB ChB 1975 Ed.; MRCGP 1979; DRCOG 1978. (Edinburgh) p/t GP.

HUNTER, Alistair Top Flat, 4 Orchard Road, Aberdeen AB24 3DP — MB ChB 1997 Aberd.

HUNTER, Alyson Julie Department Obstetrics and Gynaecology, ICS, Queen's University Belfast, Grosvenor Road, Belfast BT12 6BJ Tel: 01232 894600 Email: ahunter.qub.ac.uk; 21 Belvedere Manor, Windsor Park, Belfast BT9 6FT Tel: 01232 874959 — MB BCh BAO 1991 Belf.; MRCOG 1996. (Queen's University of Belfast) Research Regist. (O & G) Roy. Mat. Hosp. QUB Belf.; Mem. N.. Irel. Regional Trainees Comm.; Research Regist. Obst. & Gyn. Roy. Matern. Hosp. Belf. Socs: Ulster Obst. & Gyn. Soc.; Reg. Trainees Comm. Prev: Regist. (O & G) Craigavon Hosp.; Regist. (O & G) Roy. Matern. Hosp.; SHO (O & G) Belf. City Hosp., Roy. Matern. Hosp. & Ulster Hosp.

HUNTER, Andrew Nicol (retired) Lilac Dene, High Green, Brooke, Norwich NR15 Tel: 01603 550321 — MB ChB 1949 Glas.; DPH 1955; MFCM 1974. Med. Adviser Norwich City. Prev: SCM (Child Health) Norf. AHA.

HUNTER, Andrew Stone (retired) Longview, 40 Abden Avenue, Kinghorn, Burntisland KY3 9TE Tel: 01582 891073 — MB ChB Glas. 1941. Admiralty Surg. & Agent.

HUNTER, Ann Elizabeth Leicester Royal Infirmary, Leicester LE1 5WW Tel: 0116 258 6602 Fax: 0116 258 5093 Email: ahunter@uhl.trent.nhs.uk; 576 Derby Road, Adam's Hill, Nottingham NG7 2GZ — MB BS 1982 Lond.; 1982 MB BS Lond; 1987 MRCP (UK); 1992 MRCPath; 1998 FRCP; FRCP 2001 (Path). (University College London) Cons. Haemat. Leicester Roy. Infirm. Prev: Cons. Haemat. City Hosp. Nottm.

HUNTER, Anne Luise, OBE (retired) Orchard Rise, Bunch Lane, Haslemere GU27 1ET Tel: 01428 3829 — MRCS Eng. LRCP Lond. 1950; DObst RCOG 1952. Prev: Med. Asst. (Neurol.) SW. Thames RHA.

HUNTER, Archibald Stewart Regional Cardiothoracic Unit, Freeman Hospital, Freeman Road, High Heaton, Newcastle upon Tyne NE7 7DN Tel: 0191 284 3111 Fax: 0191 213 2167; 29 Moor Crescent, Gosforth, Newcastle upon Tyne NE3 4AQ Tel: 0191 285 2782 — MB ChB 1960 Aberd.; FRCP Ed. 1981, M 1966; FRCP Glas. 1981, M 1966; DCH RFPS Glas. 1962. (Aberd.) Cons. Paediat. Cardiol. Newc. HA; Hon. Sen. Lect. (Child Health) Univ. Newc. Socs: (Counc.) Brit. Cardiac Soc.; (Ex-Pres. Counc.) Brit. Paediat. Cardiac Assn.; (Ex-Pres.) Brit. Soc. Echocardiography. Prev: Hon. Med. Regist. Thoracic Unit Hosp. Sick Childr. Gt. Ormond St. Lond.; Sen. Regist. (Paediat. Cardiol.) SE RHB (Scotl.).

HUNTER, Beatrix Joan 8 Russell Place, Southampton SO17 1NU — MB BS 1993 Lond.

HUNTER, Bridgid Jane (retired) 9 Cricket Close, Newton Solney, Burton-on-Trent DE15 0RZ Tel: 01283 703596 — MB BCh BAO Belf. 1955. Prev: GP Burton-on-Trent.

HUNTER, Cameron John 3 Woodside Avenue, Bridge of Weir PA11 3PQ — MB ChB 1988 Ed.

HUNTER, Mrs Carol Community Child Health, Wembley Hospital, Wembley HA0 4UH Tel: 020 8903 1323 Fax: 020 8451 8369; 21 Langmead Drive, Bushey Heath, Watford WD23 4GD Tel: 020 8950 6007 — MB BS 1969 Newc. SCMO Pk.side Community NHS Trust. Socs: Fac. Community Health; Roy. Coll. Paediat. & Child Health.

HUNTER, Caroline Mila 25 Downshire Park, Hillsborough BT26 6HB — MB BS 1978 Lond.

HUNTER, Catherine Barbara 70 White Street, Partick, Glasgow G11 5ED Tel: 0141 337 3004 — MB ChB 1991 Ed.; FRCS Glas. 1996. SHO (Anaesth.) Glas. Roy. Infirm. Prev: SHO (A & E) W.. Infirm. Glas.; SHO (Gen. Surg.) Roy. Alexandra Hosp. Paisley; SHO (Surgic. Specialities) W.. Infirm. Glas.

HUNTER, Catherine Frances 7 Riverdale, Dungannon BT71 6PZ — MB BCh BAO 1987 Belf.; MRCGP 1991; DRCOG 1993. (Qu. Univ. Belf.)

HUNTER, Charles Christopher Caswell Clinic, Glanrhyd Hospital, Bridgend CF31 4LN Tel: 01656 662179 Fax: 01656 662157 — MB BS 1973 Lond.; MRCS Eng. LRCP Lond. 1973; FRCPsych 1994, M 1980; DPM Eng. 1979. (Guy's) Cons. Forens. Psychiat. Glanrhyd Hosp. Bridgend; Clin. Dir. S. Wales Forens. Psychiat. Serv.; Co-ordinator All-Wales Forens. Psychiat. Serv.; Adviser Forens. Psychiat. Nat. Assembly for Wales; Med. Mem. Ment. Health Review Tribunal; Mem. Parole Bd. for Eng. & Wales. Prev: Cons. Forens. Psychiat. Pk. La. Hosp. Maghull; Specialist in Psychiat. RN; Sen. Regist. (Forens. Psychiat.) Knowle Hosp. Fareham.

HUNTER, Christine Anne Perry Bank Street Surgery, 46-62 Bank Street, Alexandria G83 0LS Tel: 01389 752650 Fax: 01389 752361; Ronachan, Drumore Road, Killearn, Glasgow G63 9NX Tel: 01360 550711 Email: rjahunter@compuserve.com — MB ChB 1980 Glas.; MRCGP 1984; DRCOG 1982. (Glas.) GP. Socs: BMA; RCGP. Prev: Trainee GP Milngavie Glas. VTS; SHO (Obst.) Roy. Matern. Hosp. Rottenrow, Glas.; SHO (Paediat.) Stobhill Gen. Hosp. Glas.

HUNTER, Christine Bryden Johnson St Thomas Road Health Centre, St. Thomas Road, Newquay TR7 1RU Tel: 01637 878599; 16 Dukes Way, Newquay TR7 2RW — MB ChB 1981 Aberd.; BMed Biol. Aberd. 1978, MB ChB 1981. GP Newquay.

HUNTER, Christine Mary Bryson Street Surgery, 115 Newtownards Road, Belfast BT4 1AB Tel: 028 9045 8722 Fax: 028 9046 6766 — MB BCh BAO 1979 Belf.; MRCGP 1984; DRCOG 1983. Socs: Ulster Med. Soc. & Brit. Med. Soc.; RCGP; ICGP.

HUNTER, Christopher James Hook and Hartley Wintney Medical Partnership, 1 Chapter Terrace, Hartley Wintney, Hook RG27 8QJ Tel: 01252 842087 Fax: 01252 843145; 9 Hawkes Close, Hartley Wintney, Hook RG27 8SD — MB BS 1978 Lond.; MA Camb. 1979; MRCGP 1985; DRCOG 1984. (King's Coll. Hosp.) Bd. Mem., Hart PCG. Prev: Clin. Asst. (Dermat.) Basingstoke Dist. Hosp.; Trainee GP Frimley Pk. Hosp. VTS; SHO (Surg.) Portsmouth Gp. Hosps.

HUNTER, Colin John Kirkwood Twelve Hand Cottage, West End, Goldsithney, Penzance TR20 9LN — MB ChB 1985 Glas.; Cert. Family Plann. JCC 1989; Cert. Prescribed Equiv. Exp JCPTGP 1990. Specialist Regist. Carrick CMHT City Hosp. Truro. Prev: SHO (Psychiat.) Trengweath Hosp. Redruth.; Special Regist. Glenbourne Unit Plymouth.

HUNTER, Colin Moffat Skene Medical Group, Westhill Drive, Westhill AB32 6FY Tel: 01224 742213 Fax: 01224 744664 Email: colin.hunter@skene.grampion.scot.nhs.uk; 1 Craigston Gardens,

Westhill AB32 6NL Tel: 01224 742594 — MB ChB 1981 Aberd.; FRCP 2000 Ed.; FRCGP 1993, M 1985; DRCOG 1983. GP (Gen. Pract.) Univ. Aberd.; Nat. Co-ordinator Primary Care, Scott. Counc. PostGrad. Med. & Dent. Educat. Edin.; Clin. Sen. Lect., Nat. Specialty Adviser (Gen. Pract.), Scott. Office. Socs: Hon. Fell. Inst. Healthcare Managem. Prev: Chairm. Roy. Coll. of Gen. Practitioners (Scotl.) 1996-2000.

HUNTER, Constance Mary Chapeltown Road Surgery, 178 Chapeltown Road, Leeds LS7 4HR Tel: 0113 262 1239 Fax: 0113 262 1239; 28 Hawkstone Avenue, Guiseley, Leeds LS20 8ET — MB ChB 1959 Leeds; DFFP 1993. (Leeds)

HUNTER, David, TD Priory Fields Surgery, Nursery Road, Huntingdon PE29 3RL Tel: 01480 52361 Fax: 01480 434640; The Nook, The Green, Houghton, Huntingdon PE28 2AX — MB ChB 1963 Sheff.; DObst RCOG 1967.

HUNTER, David Archibald (retired) Westlea, Glaitness Road, Kirkwall KW15 1BA Tel: 01856 873474 — MB ChB Ed. 1963.

HUNTER, David Charles 36 Wandsworth Road, Belfast BT4 3LT — MB BCh BAO 1992 Belf.; MRCOG 1998. (Queen's University Belfast) Regist. (O & G) Ulster Hosp. Dundonald, Belf. Socs: Roy. Coll. Obst. & Gyn.

HUNTER, Mr David Cubbon Three Shires Hospital, Cliftonville, Northampton NN1 5DR Tel: 01604 620311 Fax: 01604 629066; Grove Farm, West Haddon, Northampton NN6 7AS Tel: 01788 510525 — MB ChB 1981 Aberd.; ChM Aberd. 1991; FRCS (Gen.) 1993; FRCS Ed. 1985; FRCS Eng (ad eundem) 1996. Cons. Gen. Surg. N.ampton Gen. Hosp. Socs: Sen. Sec. Fell. (Counc.) Hunt. Soc.; Fell. Roy. Soc. Med.; Fell. Assn. Surgs. Prev: Sen. Regist. (Surg.) W.m. Hosp. Lond.; Clin. Fell. (Surg.) Harvard Med. Sch. New Eng. Deaconess Hosp. Boston Mass.; USA Regist. (Surg.) Aberd. Roy. Infirm.

HUNTER, David Ian (retired) 43 Norfolk Road, Aberdeen AB10 6JR Tel: 01224 311405 — MB ChB 1954 Aberd. Prev: GP Aberd.

HUNTER, Mr David Laing Ridge House, Chelsfield Lane, Orpington BR6 7RP Tel: 01689 873888 Email: hunterstz@aol.com — MB BS 1964 Lond.; FRCS Eng. 1975; FRCOphth 1988. Prev: Cons. Ophth. Surg. Bromley Hosp. & Qu. Mary's Hopsital Sidcup; Cons. Ophth. Surg. Tanzania.

HUNTER, David Neville Anaesthetic Department, St Thomas's Hospital, Lambeth Palace Road, London SE1 7EH Email: david.hunter@gstt.sthames.nhs.uk; 40 Therapia Road, London SE22 0SE — MB BS 1980 Lond.; MD Lond. 1991; MRCS Eng. LRCP Lond. 1980; FFA RCS Eng. 1986; FRCA Eng 1986. (Guy's) Cons. Anaesth. St. Thos. Hosp. Lond. Prev: Sen. Regist. (Anaesth.) St. Thos. Hosp. Lond.; Lect. Nat. Heart & Lung Inst. Lond.; Regist. (Anaesth.) Univ. Coll. Hosp. Lond.

HUNTER, Denise Marie Brownlow Health Centre, 1 Legahory Centre, Legahory, Craigavon BT65 5BE Tel: 028 3834 1431 Fax: 028 3834 5983 — MB BCh BAO 1987 Belf.; DRCOG 1989; DME Belf. 1990; MRCGP 1991. (Qu. Univ. Belf.) GP Craigavon. Socs: Roy. Coll. Gen. Pract.

HUNTER, Donald McAllan School Lane Surgery, School Lane, Thetford IP24 2AG Tel: 01842 753115; Balquholly, Blacksmith Lane, Barnham, Thetford IP24 2NE Tel: 01842 890478 — MB BS 1960 Lond.; MRCS Eng. LRCP Lond. 1960; DObst RCOG 1963. (St. Mary's) Socs: BMA.

HUNTER, Dorothy Wilkie (retired) Invertay, Fearnan, Aberfeldy PH15 2PF Tel: 01887 830433 Fax: 01887 830433 — MB ChB Glas. 1950. Prev: Sen. Med. Off. (Clin. Servs.) Lanarksh. HB.

HUNTER, Ernest Kennedy Mid Ulster Hospital, Magherafelt BT45 5EX Tel: 028 7963 1031 — MB BCh BAO 1976 Belf.; FRCP Lond. 1994; MRCP (UK) 1979. (Queens University, Belfast) Cons. Phys. Mid Ulster Hosp. Magherafelt. Socs: BMA; Fell. Ulster Med. Soc.; Ulster Soc. Internal Med.

HUNTER, Euphan Maria Montserrat Church Grange Health Centre, Bramblys Drive, Basingstoke RG21 8QN Tel: 01256 329021 Fax: 01256 817466; The Old School, Basingstoke Road, Ramsdell, Tadley RG26 5RB — MB BS 1987 Lond.; MRCGP 1991; DGM RCP Lond. 1989; DRCOG 1990. (Guy's Hosp.) Prev: Trainee GP Bath VTS.

HUNTER, Frances Margaret Lowfield Medical Centre, 65/67 Lowfield Street, Dartford DA1 1HP Tel: 01474 855000 Fax: 01474 855001 — MB BS 1976 Lond.; MRCGP 1980; DCH Eng. 1979; DRCOG 1979. (King's Coll. Lond.)

HUNTER, Frederick George (retired) The White House, 15 Old Camp Road, Eastbourne BN20 8DH Tel: 01323 730950 — MB BS Lond. 1956. Prev: Ho. Phys. St. Mary's Hosp. Lond.

HUNTER, Graham 13 Franciscan Road, Tooting Bec, London SW17 8EA — MB BS 1974 Lond.

HUNTER, Graham Martin 39 Sea Road, Bexhill-on-Sea TN40 1JJ Tel: 01424 211616 Fax: 01424 733950; Graythwaite, 65 Hastings Rd, Bexhill-on-Sea TN40 2NH Tel: 01424 219653 — MB ChB 1955 Manch.; MRCS Eng. LRCP Lond. 1956. (Manch.) Socs: BMA & Roy. Coll. GPs. Prev: Capt. RAMC; Resid. Clin. Path. Brit. Milit. Hosp. Munster, Germany; Ho. Surg. & Ho. Phys. Manch. Roy. Infirm.

HUNTER, Graham William Galloway Regional Medical Office, Corunna House, Cadogan St., Glasgow G2 7; The Cottage, Dumfries Est., Cumnock KA18 2NJ Tel: 01290 21322 — MB ChB 1955 Aberd.; DPH Ed. 1961; DTM & H Eng. 1963.

HUNTER, Harold Stanley Adams and Partners, The Health Centre, Tavanagh Avenue, Portadown, Craigavon BT62 3BU Tel: 028 3835 1393 — MB BCh BAO 1972 Belf.

HUNTER, Helen Stuart 12 London Road, Kilmarnock KA3 7AE Tel: 01563 523593; 11 Racecourse View, Ayr KA7 2TX — MB ChB 1984 Glas.; MFFP 1995; MRCGP 1988; DRCOG 1987.

HUNTER, Henry (retired) Minster Lodge, Church St., Southwell NG25 0HQ — MB BS 1951 Lond.; MD Lond. 1967; MRCS Eng. LRCP Lond. 1951; FRANZCPsych. 1983; FRCPsych 1974, M 1971; DPM Eng. 1961. Adviser on Ment. Disorder Notts. CC; Special Lect. & Clin. Teach. Univ. Nottm. Med. Sch.; Extern. Examr. Dept. Educat. Nottm. Univ.; Cropwell Fell.sh. Inst. Criminol. Camb. 1977. Prev: Med. Dir. E.dale Special Hosp. Rehabil. Unit.

HUNTER, Iain Andrew 8 Snydale Avenue, Normanton WF6 1SS — BM BS 1994 Nottm.

HUNTER, Iain Morton 14 Rocklands, Annahilt, Hillsborough BT26 6NU — MB BCh BAO 1994 Belf.; Dip. Ment Health QUB 1999.

HUNTER, Iain Paterson 72 Cadzow Street, Hamilton ML3 6DA — MB ChB 1973 Glas.; BDS Glas. 1969; FDS RCPS Glas. 1973. Vis. Asst. Prof. Dept. Oral Path. Univ. Illinois, USA. Prev: Resid. Glas. W.. Infirm. & Roy. Hosp. Sick Childr. Glas.; Ho. Off. Glas. Dent. Sch.

HUNTER, Ian Meadowbank Health Centre, 3 Salmon Inn Road, Falkirk FK2 0XF Tel: 01324 715446 Fax: 01324 717986; Tel: 01324 716758 — MB ChB 1978 Ed.

HUNTER, Ian 41 Kilmany Road, Wormit, Newport-on-Tay DD6 8PG Tel: 01382 541490 — MB ChB 1990 Dundee; MRCP (UK) 1994. Regist. (Paediat.) Ninewells Hosp. Dundee. Prev: SHO (Paediat.) Ninewells Hosp., Simpson Memor. Matern. Pavil. & Roy. Hosp. Sick Childr. Edin.

HUNTER, Ian Flat 2F2, 2 Boroughloch Square, Edinburgh EH8 9NJ — MB ChB 1998 Ed.; MB ChB Ed 1998.

HUNTER, Ian William Elmer Craigavon Area Hospital, Lurgan Road, Portadown BT63 5QQ Tel: 028 3833 4444 Fax: 028 3861 2788; Cohannon Lodge, 38 Bovean Road, Dungannon BT71 6HR Tel: 01868 727070 — MB BCh BAO Belf. 1968; FRCOG 1989, M 1974; DObst RCOG 1971. Cons. O & G Craigavon Area Hosp. Craigavon Co. Armagh BT63 5QQ. Prev: Cons. O & G S. Tyrone Hosp. Dungannon Co. Tyrone BT71 4AV.

HUNTER, James Merrydown, Rushfield, Helens Bay, Bangor BT19 1JZ; Merrydown, Rushfield, Helens Bay, Bangor BT19 1JZ — MB BCh BAO 1956 Belf.; FRCPI 1973, M 1959; FRCPath 1976, M 1964. (Belf.) Socs: BMA & Assn. Clin. Pathols. Prev: Cons. Clin. Pathol. Ulster & N. Down Hosp. Gps.

HUNTER, James 43 Cadogan Park, Belfast BT9 6HH — MB BCh BAO 1988 Belf.; MRCGP 1992; DGM RCP Lond. 1991; DCH Dub. 1991; DRCOG 1991. Socs: Ulster Med. Soc. Prev: Trainee GP Belf. VTS.

HUNTER, Mr James Bowman Queen's Medical Centre, Nottingham NG7 2UH Tel: 0115 924 9924; Kenwood, 576 Derby Road, Nottingham NG7 2GZ — MB BS 1984 Lond.; BA (Hons) Oxf 1981; FRCS (Orth.) 1994; FRCS Ed. 1988. (King's College Hospital Medical School) Cons. Orthop. Surg. Qu. Med. Centre Nottm. Prev: Fell. (Paediat. Orthop.) Sheff. Childr. Hosp.

HUNTER, James Brian 110 Crankill Road, Glarryford, Ballymena BT43 5NW — MB BCh BAO 1986 Belf.

HUNTER, James Douglas 106 Moorside N., Fenham, Newcastle upon Tyne NE4 9DX Tel: 0191 273 9976 — MB ChB 1949 Aberd.; FFA RCS Eng. 1964; DA Eng. 1956. (Aberd.) Emerit. Cons. Anaesth. Newc. GP Hosps. Socs: BMA. Prev: Sen. Regist. (Anaesth.) Newc. Hosp. Gp.; Regist. (Anaesth.) Co. Hosp. Lincoln; RAF Med. Br. Flight Lt.

HUNTER, James More 8 Davie Street, Edinburgh EH8 9EB Tel: 0131 668 3933; 7 Craigmillar Park, Edinburgh EH16 5PF — MB ChB 1961 Aberd. (Aberd.) Socs: BMA.

HUNTER, Mr James Wood Glamorgan House, Bupa Hospital, Croescadarn Road, Pentwyn, Cardiff CP23 7XL Tel: 029 2073 6011 Fax: 029 2054 9930 — MB ChB 1959 Aberd.; FRCS Ed. 1974. Cons. Ophth. Surg. Univ. Hosp. Wales Cardiff; Hon. Clin. Tutor Welsh Nat. Sch. Med. Cardiff. Socs: Fell. Roy. Soc. Med.; Ophth. Soc. U.K.; United Kingdom & Irel. Soc. of Cataract and Refractive Surg.s. Prev: Sen. Regist. Birm. & Midl. Eye Hosp.

HUNTER, Jane Elizabeth 4D Reres Road, Broughty Ferry, Dundee DD5 2QA Tel: 01382 775021 — MB ChB 1988 Ed.; BSc Hons. (Med. Sci.) Ed. 1986; MRCGP 1995. SHO (A & E) Dundee Roy. Infirm. Prev: Trainee GP Carnoustie, Angus; SHO (O & G) Vict. Infirm. Glas.; Resid. Med. Off. Kempsey Hosp. NSW, Austral.

HUNTER, Janet Elsie Global House, 10 Station Approach, Hayes, Bromley BR2 7EH Tel: 0208-315 8355 Fax: 020 8462 6767 Email: janet.hunter@bromley-ha.sthames.nhs.uk; Ridge House, Chelsfield Lane, Orpington BR6 7RP Tel: 01689 873888 Email: hunterstz@aol.com — MB BS 1964 Lond.; MRCS Eng. LRCP Lond. 1964; FFA RCS Eng. 1969; MFCM 1989; DA Eng. 1967; DObst RCOG 1966; FFPHM 2000. (St. Bart.) p/t Cons. Pub. Health Med., Bexley, Bromley & Greenwich HA. Prev: Head of Community Health Dept, Kilimanjaro Christian Med. Centre Moshi, Tanzania.

HUNTER, Janet Latta Picken, OBE (retired) 59 Lansdowne Avenue, Grimsby DN32 0BX Tel: 01472 878558 — MB ChB Glas. 1949; FRCP Ed. 1969, M 1952; DCH Eng. 1951. Prev: Cons. Paediat. Grimsby Hosp. Gp.

HUNTER, Jean Oxley (retired) Willishayes, Dulverton TA22 9LJ Tel: 01398 23318 — BM BCh 1954 Oxf. Prev: SCMO W. Lambeth Health Auth.

HUNTER, Professor Jennifer Margaret Banavie, Spital Heyes, Spital, Wirral CH63 9NF Tel: 0151 334 6557 Fax: 0151 706 5884 Email: jennie@liv.ac.uk — MB ChB 1971 St. And.; PhD Liverp. 1995; FFA RCS Eng. 1975. Prof.(Anaesth.) Univ. Liverp.; Edr. in Chief Brit. Jl. Anaesth.

HUNTER, Jill Vanessa 77 Theberton Street, London N1 0QY — MB BS 1975 Lond.; MRCP (UK) 1978; FRCR 1986. (St. Bart.) Sen. Regist. (Radiol.) Nat. Hosp. for Nerv. Dis. Lond.

HUNTER, Joan Stella (retired) 2 Bellevale Avenue, Ayr KA7 2RP — MB ChB 1948 Ed.

HUNTER, Joanne White Medical Group, Thornhill Road, Ponteland, Newcastle upon Tyne NE20 9PZ Tel: 01661 822222; 16 Lyndhurst Drive, Gateshead NE9 6BB — MB ChB 1994 Sheff.; MB ChB (Hons.) Sheff. 1994; MRCGP 1998. GP White Med. Gp. Ponteland. Prev: Trainee GP Newc.; Ho. Off. (Surg.) Qu. Eliz. Hosp. Gateshead; Ho. Off. (Med.) Wansbeck Gen. Hosp. Ashington.

HUNTER, John Airlie (retired) Dunchurch Surgery, Dunsmore Heath, Dunchurch, Rugby CV22 6AP Tel: 01788 522448 Fax: 01788 814609 Email: jairlie_hunter@lineone.net — MB BS 1960 Lond.; MRCS Eng. LRCP Lond. 1960; DObst RCOG 1964.

HUNTER, John Andrew Gartnavel General Hospital, Floor 7, 1053 Great Western Road, Glasgow G12 0YN Tel: 0141 211 3253 Fax: 0141 211 0239; 5 Richmond Drive, Cambuslang, Glasgow G72 8BH — MB ChB 1975 Aberd.; BMedBiol Aberd. 1972, MB ChB 1975; MRCP (UK) 1978. (Aberdeen) Cons. (Physiother. & Rheum.) W.ern Infirm. & Gartnavel Gen. Hosp. Glas.; Hon. Clin. Sen. Lect. Univ. Glas. Socs: Brit. Soc. of Rheum.; BMA. Prev: ARC Lect. (Gen. Med. & Rheum.) Centre Rheum. Dis. & Roy. Infirm.; Glas.; Regist. (Gen. Med.) W.. Infirm. Glas.; SHO (Gen. Med.) W.. Infirm. Glas.

HUNTER, Professor John Angus Alexander, OBE Department of Dermatology, University of Edinburgh, Lauriston Building, Royal Infirmary, Lauriston Place, Edinburgh EH3 9YW Tel: 0131 536 2041 Fax: 0131 229 8769 Email: john.hunter@ed.ac.uk; Leewood, Rosslyn Castle, Roslin EH25 9PZ Tel: 0131 440 2181 — MB ChB Ed. 1963; BA Camb. 1960; MD Ed. 1977; FRCP Ed. 1978, M 1967. (Camb. & Ed.) Prof. Dept. Dermat. Univ. Edin.; Hon. Cons. Dermat. Roy. Infirm. Edin. NHS Trust. Socs: (Ex-Pres) Brit. Assn. Dermat.; Assn. Phys.; (Ex-Pres.) Scott. Dermat. Soc. Prev: Cons. Dermat. Roy. Infirm. Edin.; Research Fell. (Dermat.) Univ. Minesota; Research Fell. Inst. Dermat. Lond.

HUNTER, John David Department of Radiology, Bristol Royal Infirmary, Marlborough St., Bristol BS2 8HW — MB ChB 1986 Dundee; MRCP (UK) 1990; FRCR 1995. Sen. Regist. (Radiol.) Bristol Roy. Infirm.

HUNTER, John Douglas Dept. of Anaesthesia, Aberdeen royal Infirmary, Aberdeen AB25 2ZN Email: j.d.hunter@abdn.ac.uk; 17 Ashwood Mews, Bridge of Don, Aberdeen AB22 8XS Tel: 01224 706325 — MB ChB 1990 Aberd.; FRCA 1994. Specialist Regist. In Anaesth. & IC. Socs: Intens. Care Soc. Prev: Specialist Regist. (Intens. Care Med.) Aberd.

HUNTER, John Ian Wadsley Bridge Medical Centre, 103 Halifax Road, Sheffield S6 1LA Tel: 0114 234 5025 — MB ChB 1974 Sheff.

HUNTER, John Langwill Orchardleigh, Off Archers Way, Boraston Lane, Burford, Tenbury Wells WR15 8AL Tel: 01584 810000 — MB ChB 1952 Ed.; DA Eng. 1959. (Ed.) Mem. Fac. Anaesths. Prev: Vis. Anaesth. Worcester Roy. Infirm.; Anaesth. Regist. W. Norf. & King's Lynn Gen. Hosp.

HUNTER, John Oakley Dept. of Gastroenterology, Box201A, Addenbrookes Hospital, Cambridge CB2 2QQ Tel: 01223 217469 Fax: 01223 217443; Bridge House, Hiddersham, Cambridge CB1 6BU Tel: 01223 890376 Fax: 01223 890377 Email: johunter@uk-consultants.co.uk — MB BChir Camb. 1965; MA Camb. 1974, BA 1961, MD 1974; FRCP Lond. 1981, M 1968. (Camb. & St. Mary's) Cons. Phys. Addenbrooke's Hosp. Camb.; Assoc. Lect. Univ. Camb. Socs: Fell. Amer. Coll. Gastroenterol.; Fell. Roy. Soc. Med.; Nutrit. Soc. Prev: Research Fell. Liver Unit King's Coll. Hosp. Med. Sch. Lond.; Sen. Reg. Addenbrookes Hosp.

HUNTER, John Raymond Fax: 028 3834 5983 — MB BCh BAO 1981 Belf.; MSc Lond. 1989; BSc (Hons.) Belf. 1978; MRCGP 1985; DRCOG 1984. (Queen's University Belfast) Sen. Partner GP. Socs: Ulster Med. Soc.; Alum. Sch. Hyg. & Trop. Med. Lond.

HUNTER, Joy Thomson Acreswood Surgery, 5 Acreswood Close, Coppull, Chorley PR7 5EJ Tel: 01257 793578 Fax: 01257 794005 — MB ChB 1981 Manch.; MRCGP 1985; DRCOG 1983.

HUNTER, June Daphne Stockton Heath Medical Centre, The Forge, London Road, Stockton Heath, Warrington WA4 6HJ Tel: 01925 604427 Fax: 01925 210501 — MB BS 1966 Lond.; MRCS Eng. LRCP Lond. 1966. (Roy. Free)

HUNTER, Kenneth Ross Derriford Hospital, Plymouth PL6 8DH; 104 Molesworth Road, Plymouth PL3 4AQ Tel: 01752 568985 — LRCP 1963 Lond.; MB 1964 (& MA) Camb.; FRCP 1983 FRCP Lond. M 1967; MB BChir 1964 Camb.; MD 1975 Camb; BChir 1963; MRCS 1963 Eng. (Univ. Coll. Hosp.) Hon. Cons. Phys., Plymouth Hosp.s NHS Trust, Derriford Hosp., Plymouth. Socs: Fell. Roy. Soc. Med.; Mem., Brit. Pharm. Soc. Prev: Cons. Phys. Derriford Hosp. Plymouth.

HUNTER, Kenneth William (retired) Health Centre, Park Place, Dollar FK14 7AA Tel: 01259 742120 Fax: 01259 743053 — MB ChB 1971 Glas.; DObst RCOG 1973. Prev: Trainee GP Glas. (W. Infirm.) VTS.

HUNTER, Kim Brae House, 3 Port Davey Road, Whitehead, Carrickfergus BT38 9LU — MB BCh BAO 1993 Belf.

HUNTER, Linda Christine Larkhall Health Institute, Low Pleasance, Larkhall; 8 Cherryhill View, Larkhall ML9 1BD — MB ChB 1982 Aberd.; DFFP 1993; DRCOG 1984. Clin. Med. Off. Lanarksh. HB.

HUNTER, Linda Christine Horning Road Surgery, Horning Road West, Hoveton, Norwich NR12 8QH Tel: 01603 782155 Fax: 01603 782189 — MB BS 1988 Lond. SHO (ENT) Lewisham Univ. Hosp.; Trainee GP Norf. & Norwich Hosp VTS.

HUNTER, Margaret Godfrey (retired) Auld Licht Manse, 16 Brechin Road, Kirriemuir DD8 4BX Tel: 01575 572362 — MB ChB Ed. 1951.

HUNTER, Marion Davidson (retired) 2 Lindsay Avenue, Cheadle Hulme, Cheadle SK8 7BQ Tel: 0161 485 5688 Fax: 0161 485 4552 Email: docmhunter@aol.com — MB ChB 1969 Ed. Prev: GP Asst. Cheadle Heath Stockport.

HUNTER, Mark de Gay and Partners, The Surgery, 50 Barnaby Gate, Newark NG24 1QD Tel: 01636 704225 Fax: 01636 613044

— MB BS 1979 Lond.; BSc Lond. 1976; MRCP (UK) 1982; MRCGP 1986. (Lond. Hosp. Med. Sch.)

HUNTER, Mark Andrew 23 Gardenside Avenue, Uddingston, Glasgow G71 7BU — MB ChB 1997 Glas.

HUNTER, Mark Frederick Community Paediatrics, Horton General Hospital, Oxford Road, Banbury OX16 9AL Tel: 01295 229510 Fax: 01295 229603 Email: mark.hunter@orh.anglox.nhs.uk; Hazel Barn, 4 Rectory Farm Court, Shennington, Banbury OX15 6NQ Tel: 01295 670051 Email: mfhunt@globalnet.co.uk — MB BS 1985 Lond.; MA Camb. 1986; MRCP (UK) 1989; FRACP 1996; DCCH RCP Ed. 1988; DCH RCP Lond. 1987. (Lond. Hosp.) Cons. Community Paediat. Horton Gen. Hosp. NHS Trust. Prev: Regional Paediat. Roy. NZ Plunket Soc.; Cons. Paediat. Coast Health Care, NZ.

HUNTER, Mark Robert Alfred 7 Elm Park Mansions, London SW10 0AN — MB BS 1985 Lond.

HUNTER, Mary Adams 3 Raikes Avenue, Skipton BD23 1LP Tel: 01756 2900 — MB BCh BAO 1945 Dub.; BA, MB BCh BAO Dub. 1945. (TC Dub.)

HUNTER, Mary Georgina Catherine Ann (retired) 9 Ennismore Avenue, Guildford GU1 1SP Tel: 01483 66755 — MB BS 1950 Lond.; MRCS Eng. LRCP Lond. 1950; DA Eng. 1956. Prev: Med. Asst. (Anaesth.) S.W. Surrey Health Dist.

HUNTER, Mrs Mary Margaret (retired) 68 Springfield Road, Aberdeen AB15 7RS Tel: 01224 316089 — MB ChB 1936 Aberd.; DPH 1947. Prev: Asst. Med. Off. Matern. & Child Welf. Servs. Corp. Sheff.

HUNTER, Matthew, MBE (retired) 3 Raikes Avenue, Skipton BD23 1LP Tel: 01756 792900 — MD 1947 Ed.; MB ChB 1935; DPH Eng. 1940. Prev: MOH & Div. Med. Off. No. 1 Div. W. Riding CC.

HUNTER, Michael Charles Cassels Robinscroft, 14 Main St., Rempstone, Loughborough LE12 6RH Tel: 01509 880259 Email: michael@robinscroft.demon.co.uk — MRCS Eng. LRCP Lond. 1972. Med. Cons. Supporting Implementation of Read Codes.

HUNTER, Michael David, MBE Levenwick Medical Practice, Gord, Levenwick, Shetland ZE2 9HX Tel: 01950 422240 Fax: 01950 422201 Email: levenwick.surgery@shetland-hb.scot.nhs.uk; Iolaire, South Punds, Levenwick, Shetland ZE2 9HX Tel: 01950 422357 Email: iolaire@lineone.net — MB ChB 1974 Dundee. Socs: Chairm. Scot. Assn. Aviat. Med. Examr.s; Mem. of the Internat. Acad. of Aviat. & Space Med.

HUNTER, Michael David 140B Chester Road, Streetly, Sutton Coldfield B74 2HS — MB ChB 1995 Sheff.

HUNTER, Monica Patricia (retired) 39 Ridgeway Crescent, Tonbridge TN10 4NR Tel: 01732 358756 Fax: 01732 771170 Email: monica@mmenzies.demon.co.uk — MB BS Lond. 1960; DObst RCOG 1962. JP. Prev: Med. Director Weald of Kent NHS Trust Tunbridge Wells.

HUNTER, Neil Oliver Greenhill Orchard, Greenhill Road, Kingerswell, Newton Abbot TQ12 3BD Tel: 01803 872342 — MB BS Lond. 1956; MRCS Eng. LRCP Lond. 1956. (Char. Cross) Socs: Torquay & Dist. Med. Soc. Prev: GP Torquay; Clin. Asst. (Dermat.) Torbay Hosp. Torquay; Ho. Surg. & Cas. Off. Char. Cross Hosp.

HUNTER, Nicholas John Fraser 32 Gilmour Road, Edinburgh EH16 5NT — MB ChB 1990 Bristol.

HUNTER, Oliver Gerard (Surgery) 115 Newtownards Road, Belfast BT5 Tel: 028 58722 — LRCPI & LM, LRSCI & LM 1958; LRCPI & LM, LRCSI & LM 1958; FRCGP 1987, M 1971. (RCSI) GP Med. Off. Purdysburn Ment. Hosp. Belf.; Med. Dir. Glendale Nursing Home Belf.

HUNTER, Pamela Holmdale, Aldborough, Boroughbridge, York YO51 9ES Tel: 0190 12 322104 — MB ChB 1963 Ed. (Ed.) Prev: GP Hartlepool; Ho. Phys. City Hosp. York; SHO (O & G) St. Helen Hosp. Barnsley.

HUNTER, Pamela 46 Nursey Avenue, Coleraine BT52 1LP — MB BCh BAO 1988 Belf.

HUNTER, Pamela Joan Leywood, West Leys Road, Swanland, North Ferriby HU14 3LX Tel: 01482 632173 — MB BS 1960 Lond.; MRCS Eng. LRCP Lond. 1960; FFA RCS Eng. 1979; DA Eng. 1964; DObst RCOG 1962. (Roy. Free) Assoc. Specialist (Anaesth.) Hull & E. Yorks. Gps. Prev: Ho. Surg. (O & G) Huddersfield Roy. Infirm.; Ho. Phys. Bradford Roy. Infirm.

HUNTER, Patricia Anne 96 Main Road, Wybunbury, Nantwich CW5 7LS — MB ChB 1982 Leeds.

HUNTER, Patricia Jean Cathays Surgery, 137 Cathays Terrace, Cardiff CF24 4HU Tel: 029 2022 0878 Fax: 029 2038 8771; Henstaff Court Lodge, Llantrisant Road, Pontyclun CF72 8NG — MB BCh 1988 Wales; MRCGP 1994; DRCOG 1995. (Univ. Wales Coll. Med.)

HUNTER, Paul Oriel Surgery, 31 Oriel Road, Antrim BT41 4HR Tel: 028 9446 4936 Fax: 028 9446 1316; 3 Eskylane Road, Antrim BT41 2LL — MB BCh BAO 1983 Belf.; MRCGP 1988. Socs: BMA.

HUNTER, Mr Paul Anthony 148 Harley Street, London W1G 7LG Tel: 020 7935 1207 Fax: 020 7935 6860 — MB BChir Camb. 1970; MA Camb. 1970; FRCS Eng. 1978; FRCOphth. 1988; DO Eng. 1974. (Middlx.) Cons. Ophth. Surg. King's Coll. Hosp. Lond. Socs: (Pres.) S.. Ophth. Soc. (Ex-Mem. Counc.).; Pres. Roy. Coll. of Ophth. (2000 - 2003). Prev: Sen. Regist. Middlx. Hosp. & Moorfields Eye Hosp. Lond.; Ho. Off. (Surg.) Middlx. Hosp. Lond.

HUNTER, Paul Raymond Public Health Laboratory, Countess of Chester, Heath Park, Liverpool Road, Chester CH2 1UL Tel: 01244 366770 Fax: 01244 366770 — MD 1990 Manch.; MB ChB 1979, Dp Bact. 1983; MRCPath 1985; DHMSA 1989; MBA 1996; FRCPath 1995; MFPHM 1999. Dir. Chester Pub. Health Laborat.; Hon. Cons. (Med. Microbiol.) Chester HA; Hon. Cons. (Communicable Dis. Control) Chester HA; Hon. Regional Epidemiol. (CDSC-NW). Prev: Sen. Regist. (Med. Microbiol.) Div. Hosp. Infec. Centr. Pub. Health Laborat. Lond.; Sen. Regist. (Med. Microbiol.) Cardiff Pub. Health Lab.; Regist. (Med. Microbiol.) Manch. Pub. Health Lab.

HUNTER, Rachel Charlotte Alice (retired) 32 Oaklands, Bulmershe Road, Reading RG1 5RW Tel: 01734 68793 Fax: 01189 268793 — MB BChir 1945 Camb.; MRCS Eng. LRCP Lond. 1944. Prev: Gyn. & Obst. Ho. Surg. King Edwd. VII Hosp. Windsor.

HUNTER, Richard Frizzell Cullyhagan House, Lislea, Kilrea, Coleraine BT51 5SL — MB BCh BAO 1987 Belf.

HUNTER, Robert Research & Development Directorate, Gartnavel Royal Hospital, 1055 Gt Western Rd, Glasgow G12 0XH Tel: 0141 211 3706 Fax: 0141 211 3814 Email: roberthunter@gartnavel.glacomen.scot.nhs.uk — MB ChB 1975 Glas.; MB ChB Glas. 1980; MD Glas. 1992; BSc (Hons. Molecular Biol.) Glas. 1975; MRCPsych 1985. (Univ. Glas.) Cons. Psychiat. & Sen. Lect. Univ. Dept. Psychol. Med. Gartnavel Roy. & Gen. Hosps. Glas.; Dir. Research & Developm. Gtr. Glas. Community Ment. Health Trust; Adviser to Alzheimer Scotl. Charity. Socs: Scott. Health Advis. Serv.; CINP & ECNP; BMA & Brit. Assn. for Psychopharmacol. Prev: Clin. Servs. Manager Gartnavel Roy. Hosp. Glas.; Clin. Sci. MRC Brain Metab. Unit Roy. Edin. Hosp.; Regist. (Psychiat.) S.. Gen. & Leverndale Hosps. Glas.

HUNTER, Mr Robert Douglas (retired) 395 Albert Drive, Glasgow G41 4JS — MB ChB 1952 Glas.; FRCS Glas. 1964; FRCS Ed. 1963; DO Eng. 1961. Prev: Cons. Ophth. Glas. Roy. Infirm.

HUNTER, Robert James (retired) 8 Eastfield Road, Thurmaston, Leicester LE4 8FP Tel: 0116 220 7237 — MB BS Lond. 1954.

HUNTER, Mr Robert William Tel: 01904 725545 Fax: 01904 454848; Thornhill Farm, Stearsby, York YO61 4SB Tel: 01347 888685 — MB BS 1981 Lond.; FRCS Eng. 1986; FRCOG 2000; MRCOG 1988. (Middlx.) Cons. O & G York Health Servs. Trust. Socs: Brit. Gyn. Cancer Soc.; York Med. Soc.; Brit. Soc. Colpos. & Cerv. Path. Prev: Sen. Regist. (O & G) Hammersmith & St. Mary's Hosp. Lond.; Fell. (Gyn. Oncol.) King Edwd. Memor. Hosp., Perth, W. Australia.

HUNTER, Robert Wilson 31 Honeybourne Drive, Whiston, Prescot L35 7NB — MB BCh 1989 Wales.

HUNTER, Robin West End Surgery, 19 Chilwell Road, Beeston, Nottingham NG9 1EH Tel: 0115 925 4443 Fax: 0115 922 1255 — MB BS 1981 Newc.; MRCGP 1986; DCCH RCP Ed. 1985; DRCOG 1984. (Newcastle Upon Tyne)

HUNTER, Rosemary Leila (retired) 32 Mayflower Drive, Yateley GU46 7RR Tel: 01252 873301 — MB BS Lond. 1955; MRCS Eng. LRCP Lond. 1955; FFPHM RCP Lond. 1986, M 1977; DPH Eng. 1969; DObst RCOG 1959. Prev: Dir. of Pub. Health NW Surrey DHA.

HUNTER, Ruth Elizabeth 21 Cherry Garth, Beverley HU17 0EP; Dove House Hospice, Chamberlain Road, Hull HU8 8DH Tel: 01482 784343 — MB BS 1988 Newc.; Dip. Palliat. Med. Wales 1997; Lett. Competence Intrauterine Techniques Fac. Fam. Plann. & Reprod. Health Care; Roy. Coll. Obst. & gyn. 1996; Cert. Family Plann. JCC 1993; Cert. Prescribed Equiv. Exp. JCPTGP 1992. Med.

Off. (Palliat. Care) Dove Hse. Hospice; Clin. Asst. Centre for Metab. Bone Dis. Hull Roy. Infirm.

HUNTER, Ruth Marian (retired) 83 Hanover Terrace, Brighton BN2 2SP Tel: 01273 692163 — MB ChB 1940 Bristol. Prev: Med. Asst. Bevendean Hosp. Brighton.

HUNTER, Sally Ann 8 Bateson Street, Bradford BD10 0BE — MB ChB 1991 Leeds.

HUNTER, Mr Sam Graham Castleton, Gloddaeth Avenue, Llandudno, Conwy LL30 2AH Tel: 01492 860800 Fax: 01492 860890 — MB ChB 1970 Manch.; MSc (Mech. Engineering) Salford 1983; FRCS Ed. 1975. (Manchester) Cons. Orthop. Surg. Gwynedd Hosp. Trust. Prev: Cons. Orthop. Surg. Trent.

HUNTER, Samuel Andrew Coates (retired) Willow Croft, 97 Raglan Road, Reigate RH2 0ES Tel: 01737 245355 — MB BCh BAO 1938 Belf.; MD Belf. 1942. Prev: Cons. Chest Phys. Epsom Dist. Hosp. & Dorking Hosp.

HUNTER, Sarah Jane Stringer Walkley House Medical Centre, 23 Greenhow Street, Sheffield S6 3TN Tel: 0114 234 3716 — MB ChB 1984 Birm.; MRCGP 1988. Prev: Trainee GP Birm. FPC; SHO (Psychiat., O & G, Paediat. & A & E) Centr. Birm. HA.

HUNTER, Sarah Ruth The Green Surgery, 1B The Green, Twickenham TW2 5TU Tel: 020 8894 6870 — MB ChB 1990 Manch.; BSc (Med. Sci.) St. And. 1987. Prev: SHO (Med.) Basildon Hosp.; SHO (A & E & Med.) Basildon & Thurrock HA; SHO (c/o Elderly) Orsett Hosp.

HUNTER, Sheila Sarah Dunnikier Day Hospital, Whytemans Brae Hospital, Kirkcaldy KY1 2ND Tel: 01592 643355; 6 Lomond House, Glenlomond, Kinross KY13 9HF Tel: 01592 840859 — MB ChB 1990 Dundee. Staff Grade, Adult Psychiat. Fife Primary Care Trust. Socs: Affil. Mem. Roy. Coll. of Psychiat.s. Prev: SHO Rotat. (Psychiat.) Fife HB; Ho. Off. (Gen. Med.) Perth Roy. Infirm.; Ho. Off. (Surg.) Gilbert Bain Hosp. Lerwick.

HUNTER, Simon, Capt. RAMC The Wardroom, HMS Drake, Plymouth PL2 2BG — MB ChB 1992 Manch.; BSc (Med. Sci.) St. And. 1989. (Manchester) SHO Gen. Surg - Derriford Hosp. Plymouth. Prev: SHO Orthop. - Plymouth; SHO Neuro Surg - Plymouth; SHO Gen. Surg - Catterick.

HUNTER, Simon Charles Hill Lane Surgery, 162 Hill Lane, Southampton SO15 5DD Tel: 023 8022 3086 Fax: 023 8023 5487 — MB ChB 1992 Sheff.; MRCGP 1996; DRCOG 1995; DCH 1995; DFFP 1996.

HUNTER, Simon Lindsay Testvale Surgery, 12 Salisbury Road, Totton, Southampton SO40 3PY Tel: 023 8086 6999/6990 Fax: 023 8066 3992 — MB ChB 1981 Bristol; MSc 2000; MRCGP (Distinc.) 1985; DRCOG 1984; DCH RCP Lond. 1983.

HUNTER, Stephen Gwent Healthcare NHS Trust, Grange House, Llanfrechfa Grange, Cwmbran NP44 8YN Tel: 01633 623840 Fax: 01633 623836 Email: stephen.hunter@gwent.wales.nhs.uk — MB ChB 1982 Glas.; MRCPsych 1987; FRCP 2000 (Psych). Med. Dir. Gwent Healthcare NHS Trust. Socs: Fell. Roy. Soc. Arts; Internat. Assn. Study of Pain; Inst. Health Servs. Man. Prev: Lect. (Psychol. Med.) Univ. Wales Cardiff.

HUNTER, Stephen John Yeovil District Hospital, Higher Kingston, Yeovil BA21 4AT Tel: 01935 475122 — MB BS 1978 Lond.; BSc (Hons.) Lond. 1975; FRCA 1985. (St. Bart.) Cons. Anaesth. & Pain Managem. Yeovil Dist. Gen. Hosp.; Clin. Tutor E. Som. NHS Trust. Socs: Assn. Anaesth. Prev: Cons. Anaesth. P.ss Alexandra RAF Hosp. Wroughton; Sen. Regist. RAF & Hon. Sen. Regist. Frenchay Hosp. Bristol; SHO (Renal Med.) Guy's Hosp. Lond.

HUNTER, Mr Steven Cardiothoracic Unit, South Cleveland Hospital, Marton Road, Middlesbrough TS4 3BW Tel: 01642 854242 Fax: 01642 854613 Email: steve.hunter2@virgin.net — BM BS 1986 Nottm.; FRCS Eng. 1990; FRCS CTH 1996; B.Med. Sci. Nottm. 1984. Cons. cardiothoracic Surg. Socs: BMA; Roy. Soc. Med.; Fell. Roy. Coll Surg. Lon. Prev: Sen. Regist., Papworth Hosp., Camb.; Regist., St Geo.'s Hosp., Lond.

HUNTER, Steven John Regional Centre for Endocrinology and Diabetes, Level 1, Royal Victoria Hospital, Grosvenor Rd, Belfast BT12 6BA Tel: 0289 089 4798 Fax: 0289 031 0111 — MB BCh BAO 1989 Belf.; MRCP (UK) 1992; MD Belf. 1996. Cons. Phys. Endocrinol. & Diabetes, Roy. Vict. Hosp. Belf. Socs: Diabetes UK. Prev: Specialist Regist. Roy. Vict. Hosp. Belf.

HUNTER, Susan Margaret Department of Cytopathology, Ninewells Hospital, Dundee DD1 9SY Tel: 01382 660111; Kirktonshade, East Hillbank, Kirriemuir DD8 4GQ Tel: 01575 573557 — MD 1988 Manch.; MB ChB 1977. Assoc. Specialist (Cytopath.) Ninewells Hosp. Dundee.

HUNTER, Suzanne 7 Liddel Way, Valley Park, Chandlers Ford, Southampton SO53 4QF — MB ChB 1992 Sheff.; MRCGP 1996; DRCOG 1995; DCH 1995; DFFP 1996.

HUNTER, Thomas Walter Barns Street Surgery, 3 Barns Street, Ayr KA7 1XB Tel: 01292 281439 Fax: 01292 288268; 11 Racecourse View, Ayr KA7 2TX Tel: 01292 610395 Email: thunter@stranleur.freeserve.co.uk — MB ChB 1984 Glas.; MRCGP (Distinc.) 1988; DRCOG 1986.

HUNTER, Wendy Jane St Katherines Surgery, High Street, Ledbury HR8 1DZ Tel: 01531 633271 Fax: 01531 632410; Barnfold House, Redhill, Ross-on-Wye HR9 5AU — BM BCh 1985 Oxf.; MRCGP 1989; DRCOG 1990; DCH RCP Lond. 1987. (Oxford) Prev: Trainee GP Oxf VTS.

HUNTER, William (retired) Renagour, Canalside, Fort Augustus PH32 4BA — MB ChB 1937 Ed.; MRCP Ed. 1947. Prev: Chief Med. Off. Rank Hovis McDougall Ltd. & NAAFI.

HUNTER, William Taylor (retired) Beech House, Egremont Tel: 01946 820692 — MB ChB 1957 Ed.; DObst RCOG 1959. Prev: Ho. Surg. Peel Hosp. Galashiels.

HUNTER-BROWN, Isobel Henderson (retired) 8 Rectory Lane, Kibworth Beauchamp, Leicester LE8 0NW — MB ChB Glas. 1953; MA (Hons.) Glas. 1940; MRCPsych 1972; DPM Eng. 1957. Prev: Cons. Psychiat. & Psychother. Health Serv. Univ. Leicester.

HUNTER-CAMPBELL, Paul 9 Shakespeare Road, St Ives, Huntingdon PE27 6TR — MB BS 1994 Lond.

HUNTER-CRAIG, Colin James Crawley Hospital, West Green Drive, Crawley RH11 7DH Tel: 01293 600300; 16 Marlowe Court, Lymer Avenue, Dulwich, Wood Park, London SE19 1LP Tel: 020 8670 3580 — MB BChir Camb. 1959; MA Camb. 1964; FRCPath 1985, M 1968. (Camb. & Guy's) Cons. Histol. Surrey & Sussex Healthcare NHS Trust. Prev: Cons. Histol. & Cytol. Mid Downs HA Crawley; Sen. Regist. (Path.) Roy. Marsden Hosp. Lond.; Ho. Off. & Lect. (Forens. Med.) Guy's Hosp. Lond.

HUNTER-CRAIG, Mr Ian Douglas (retired) Pittyfield House, Wray Lane, Reigate RH2 0HU Tel: 01737 247949 — MB BChir 1958 Camb.; MA Camb. 1964, MChir 1967, MB BChir 1958; FRCS Eng. 1964. Prev: Cons. Surg. E. Surrey HA.

HUNTER-ROWE, Caroline Katherine Anne 5 Courtney Road, Newton Abbot TQ12 1HW — MB BCh BAO 1980 NUI; LRCPI & LM, LRCSI & LM 1980; DRCOG 1984. GP Kingskeeswell Health Centre.

HUNTING, John Basil, TD (retired) Moor Farm, Ruddington, Nottingham NG11 6JX Tel: 0115 921 5887 Fax: 0115 921 5887 — MB ChB 1955 Leeds. Med. Off. Notts. ACF; Sen. Med. Off. Med. Centre Chilwell Garrison; Med. Off. 38 Signals Regt. (V); Hon. Med. Off. S. Notts. Hussars Yeomanry. Prev: Ho. Surg. & Ho. Phys. Derbysh. Roy. Infirm.

HUNTLEY, James Seymour Boxwell Farm, Tetbury GL8 8UG — BChir 1996 Camb.

HUNTLEY, John Nicholas Fairhaven, 2 Fosse Lane, Thorpe on the Hill, Lincoln LN6 9BE — MB ChB 1971 Manch.

HUNTLEY, Laurence Stephen Radiology Department, West Cumberland Hospital, Hensingham, Whitehaven CA28 8JG Tel: 01946 693181; High Bank, Low Lorton, Cockermouth CA13 0RQ — MB BCh 1981 Wales; FRCR 1991. Cons. Radiol. W. Cumbld. Hosp. Whitehaven, Cumbria. Prev: Cons. Radiol. P.ss Alexandra Hosp. RAF Wroughton Swindon; Sen. Specialist (Radiol.) Ch.ill & John Radcliffe Hosps. Oxf.; Specialist (Radiol.) Middlx. Hosp. Lond.

HUNTLEY, Louise Elizabeth 11 The Beeches, Belfast BT8 6PP — MB BChir 1993 Camb.

HUNTLEY, Stuart 15 Glendale Avenue, Whitley Bay NE26 1RX — MB BS 1991 Newc.; MRCP (Roy. Coll. Phys. & Surg. Glas.) 1995. Specialist Regist. (Geriat. & Gen. Med.) Freeman Rd. Hosp. Newc. Prev: Specialist Regist. (Geriat.s & Gen. Med.) S. Tyneside DH; Specialist Regist. (Geriat. Med.) Sunderland Roy. Hosp.

HUNTLY, Brian James Patrick 53 Comely Bank Road, Edinburgh EH4 1EJ — MB ChB 1990 Ed.; MRCP (UK) 1993. Regist. (Haemat.) Ninewells Hosp. Dundee.

HUNTON, John 17 North Road, Stokesley, Middlesbrough TS9 5DY Tel: 01642 712791 Fax: 01642 713826 — MB BS 1967 Newc.; FFA RCS Eng. 1975; DA Eng. 1973. (Newc.) Indep. Pract.

MiddlesBoro.; Cons. Anaesth. S. Tees Community & Ment. Health NHS Trust. Prev: Cons. Anaesth. S. Cleveland Hosp. Middlesbrough; Sen. Regist. (Anaesth.) Nuffield Dept. Anaesth. Radcliffe Infirm. Oxf. & P.ss Margt. Hosp. Swindon; Anaesth. RAF.

HUNTON, Mollie Worcester Street Surgery, 24 Worcester Street, Stourbridge DY8 1AW Tel: 01384 371616; 21 Pargeter Street, Stourbridge DY8 1AU Tel: 01384 373111 — MB BS 1965 Newc.; FFHom 1990; DObst RCOG 1967. (Newc.) GP & Homoep. Phys. W. Midl.; Tutor Midl. Br. Fac. Homoeop.

HUNUKUMBURE, S B Long Lane Surgery, 15 Long Lane, Liverpool L19 6PE Tel: 0151 494 1445.

HUNYI, Steven Joseph 5 Sandpiper Court, 1 Shellduck Close, Booth Road, Hendon, London NW9 5DW Tel: 020 8203 5589; 130 Dale Avenue, Edgware HA8 6AF Tel: 020 8952 6932 — MB BS 1990 Lond.; BSc (Anat.) Lond. 1987; MRCGP 1996; MFFP 1995; DRCOG 1995. (Univ. Coll. & Middlx. Hosp. Med. Sch.) SHO (Psychiat.). Socs: BMA; Roy. Coll. Psychiat. Prev: GP/Regist. Welwyn.

HUPPERTZ, Richard Clemens Maria 34 Columbia Drive, Worcester WR2 4DB — Artsexamen 1987 Maastricht. SHO (A & E) Russells Hall Hosp. Dudley.

HUQ, Anowarul St Audry's Hospital, Melton, Woodbridge; 2 Bridport Avenue, Ipswich IP3 8QA Tel: 01473 73621 — MB BS 1968 Dacca; MB BS Dacca Bangladesh 1968; DPM Eng. 1980. (Sir Salimullah Med. Coll.) Med. Asst. St. Audry's Hosp. Woodbridge. Prev: Regist. St. Clements Hosp. Ipswich & St. Audry's Hosp. Woodbridge.

HUQ, Mrs Hasna Hena 10 Fairmount Road, Swinton, Manchester M27 0EP — MB BS 1970 Dacca; DObst RCPI 1978. Clin. Asst. (Health Care for Elderly) Ladywell Hosp. Salford. Prev: Regist. (Geriat. Med.) Hope & Ladywell Hosps. Salford.; SHO (O & G) City Hosp. Derby.

HUQ, Kazi Kilsum 38 Eversley Crescent, London N21 1EJ — MCRS Eng. LRCP 1983 Lond.

HUQ, Mr Mominul (retired) 14Himepont House, Hoghton St, Southport PR9 0PY Tel: 01704 530517 — MB BS 1951 Dacca; FRCS Ed. 1959. Prev: Prof. Surg. Gen. & Chest Surg. Dacca Univ., Bangladesh.

HUQ, Rabiul (retired) Hulton District Health Centre, Haysbrook Avenue, Worsley, Manchester M28 0AY Tel: 0161 790 3276 Fax: 0161 703 7948 — MB BS 1958 Dacca.

HUQ, Sabih Momenul 41 Welldon Crescent, Harrow HA1 1QP — MB BS 1997 Lond.

HUQ, Zahirul 47 Albion Street, Old Trafford, Manchester M16 9LZ — MB ChB 1998 Manch.; MB ChB Manch 1998.

HURDING, Roger Frederick (retired) 12 Fircliff Park, Portishead, Bristol BS20 7HQ Tel: 01275 843413 — MB BChir Camb. 1960; DObst RCOG 1961. Prev: Med. Off. Univ. Bristol.

HURDING, Simon Bartholomew The Surgery, Tigh-Na-Mara, Glenelg, Kyle IV40 8ST Tel: 01599 522272 — MB ChB 1989 Sheff. Socs: MDU. Prev: SHO (O & G, Community Paediat. & Paediat.) N.. Gen. Hosp. Sheff.

HURDLE, Anthony David Frederick (retired) Cootamundra, Wonham Way, Gomshall, Guildford GU5 9NZ — MB BS 1955 Lond.; MD Lond. 1967; MRCP Ed. 1962; FRCPA 1969; FRCPath 1977, M 1965. Hon. Cons. (Haemat.) St. Thos. Hosp. Med. Sch.; Hon. Cons. Haematol. Epsom & W. Pk. Gp. Hosps. Prev: Regist. (Haemat.) Postgrad. Med. Sch. Lond.

HURFORD, Wallace Eric 24 Rectory Road, Gosforth, Newcastle upon Tyne NE3 1XP — MB BS 1948 Durh. (Durh.) Socs: BMA. Prev: Ho. Phys. Neuro-Surgic. Unit, Newc. Gen. Hosp.; Maj. RAMC (TA).

HURLE, David Edward Charles Saundersfoot Medical Centre, Westfield Road, Saundersfoot SA69 9JW Tel: 01834 812407 Fax: 01834 811131 — MB BS 1969 Lond.; MRCS Eng. LRCP Lond. 1968; DObst RCOG 1974. (St. Mary's) Prev: Surg. Specialist RAF Cosford; Unit Med. Off. RAF Manby; Jun. Med. Off. i/c RAF Gan.

HURLE, Rhidian Ashley 71 Heathfield Road, Gabalfa, Cardiff CF14 3JX Tel: 029 2061 4752 — MB BCh 1995 Wales. (University of Wales College of Medicine) Socs: BMA (Welsh Jun. Represen.).

HURLEY, Alexander Victor Alfred, Wing Cdr. RAF Med. Br. RAF Centre of Aviation Medicine, RAF Henlow S916 6DN; Aylmerton House, 8 Hitchin Road, Shefford SG17 5JA Tel: 01462 812883 Email: hurley@beeb.net — BM 1986 Soton.; Dip Av Med 2000; Dip Occ Med 1998; BA (Hons.) (Open) 1990, BA 1977. Cheif Instruc. Centre of Aviat. Med., RAF Henlow. Socs: Roy. Aeronautical Soc. Prev: Trainee GP RAF; Regist. (Forens. Psychiat.) Knowle Hosp. Fareham; Rotat. Psychiat. Roy. S. Hants. Hosp. Soton.

HURLEY, Denis 11 Lyneside Road, Knypersley, Stoke-on-Trent ST8 6SD — MB BCh BAO 1952 NUI.

HURLEY, Emmanuelle Nightingale Centre, Withington Hospital, Nell Lane, Manchester M20 0PT — MB BCh BAO 1983 NUI; MRCP (UK) 1986; FRCR 1990. Cons. Radiol S. Manch. Univ Hosps spec; brE. Radiol., ENT imaging. Prev: Cons. Radiol. Roy. Liver. Univ. Hosp.

HURLEY, Jill Elizabeth North Hampshire Hospital, Basingstoke RG24 9NA Tel: 01256 314762 Fax: 01256 332660 Email: jill.hurley@bas.swest.nhs.uk; Greensleeves, Bentworth, Alton GU34 5JT — MB ChB Manch. 1968; FFA RCS Eng. 1973; DA Eng. 1971; DObst RCOG 1970. p/t Cons. Anaesth. & Pain Managem. N. Hants. Hosp. Trust Basingstoke. Socs: Pain. Soc. And Assn. Anaesth. Prev: Med. Off. Anaesth. Unit Qu. Eliz. Hosp. Hong Kong.

HURLEY, John David (retired) Dove House, Vicarage Lane, Ropley, Alresford SO24 0DU Tel: 01962 773521 — MB BS 1956 Lond. Prev: GP Winchester.

HURLEY, Maeve Mary 15 St Peters Way, Chorleywood, Rickmansworth WD3 5QF — MB BCh BAO 1982 NUI; MRCGP 1986; DRCOG 1987; DCH RCP Lond. 1986. GP Retainers Scheme Hemel Hempstead.

HURLEY, Michael Brendan 3 Grange Court, North Grange Mount, Leeds LS6 2BZ — MB BCh BAO 1975 NUI.

HURLEY, Patricia Anne 15 Cameron March, Edinburgh EH16 5XG — MB ChB 1994 Ed.

HURLEY, Patrick Daniel 125 Woodlands Avenue, Wanstead, London E11 3RB — MB BCh BAO 1951 NUI.

HURLEY, Patrick John Regent Square Group Practice, 8-9 Regent Square, Doncaster DN1 2DS Tel: 01302 819999 Fax: 01302 369204; Earlwood, Beech Tree Close, Old Cantley, Doncaster DN3 3QY — MB BCh BAO 1986 NUI.

HURLEY, Mr Paul Richard Druids Cottage, Druids Close, Ashtead KT21 2UH — MB BS 1978 Lond.; MS Lond. 1989, MB BS 1978; FRCS Eng. 1983. Cons. Gen. Surg. Mayday Univ. Hosp. Croydon. Prev: Sen. Regist. SW Thames.

HURLEY, Pauline Anne John Radcliffe, Headley Way, Oxford OX3 9DU; Royston, Church Lane, Islip, Kidlington OX5 2TA — BM BS 1980 Nottm.; MRCOG 1986. Cons. O & G Special Responsibil. Subspeciality Fetal Med. John Radcliffe Hosp. Oxf.

HURLEY, Professor Dame Rosalinde, DBE 2 Temple Gardens, 4th Floor, Temple, London EC4Y 9AY Tel: 020 7353 0577 Fax: 020 8740 3923; 42 Squirrels Heath Road, Harold Wood, Romford RM3 0LJ Tel: 017083 71454 — MB BS 1955 Lond.; LLB Lond. 1959, MD 1961; MRCS Eng. LRCP Lond. 1955; FRCOG 1993; FFPM RCP (UK) 1989; FRCPath 1975, M 1963; Hon. FRSM 1995; L.D. Univ. Surrey 1984; Hon. F.I Biol 1998. (Char. Cross) Barrister-at-law Inner Temple; Mem. Managem. Bd. Europ. Med. Eval. Agency; Prof. Emerit. Imperial Coll. Sch. Med. Socs: (Ex-Pres.) Assoc. Clin. Path.; Roy. Soc. Med. (Ex-Sen. Sec. & Ex-Pres. Sec. Pathol.); Chairm. Ther. Research & Educat. Organisation. Prev: Cons. MicroBiol. Qu. Charlotte's Matern. Hosp. Lond.; Prof. MicroBiol. Inst. O & G Univ. Lond. Roy. Postgrad. Med. Sch.; Chairm. Med. Commiss. & Comm. on Dent. & Surg. Materials.

HURLEY, Ruth 14 Greenwood Road, Llandaff, Cardiff CF5 2QD — MB BS 1990 Lond.

HURLEY, Shirley Yorke (retired) Dove House, Vicarage Lane, Ropley, Alresford SO24 0DU Tel: 01962 773521 — MB BS 1956 Lond.; MRCS Eng. LRCP Lond. 1956.

HURLOW, Dorothy The Surgery, Kingswood Road, Tunbridge Wells TN2 4UJ Tel: 01892 511833; 9 Calverley Park, Tunbridge Wells TN1 2SH Tel: 01892 532184 — MB BS 1965 Lond.; MRCS Eng. LRCP Lond. 1965; MFFP 1993. (Roy. Free) Med. Off. (Family Plann.) Tunbridge Wells. Prev: Ho. Off. Roy. Free Hosp. Lond., Putney Hosp. & Brook Gen. Hosp. Lond.

HURLOW, Mr Robert Anthony The Old Rectory, Rodington Heath, Rodington, Shrewsbury SY4 4QX Email: robert.hurlow@talk21.com — MB BS Lond. 1967; FRCS Eng. 1972; MRCS Eng. LRCP Lond. 1967. (Univ. Coll. Hosp.) Cons. Surg., Roy. Shrewsbury Hosp. NHS Trust. Socs: Assn. of Surg.s of GB & Ire; Mem. BASO. Prev: Sen. Lect. Dept. Surg. Univ. Birm.; Hon. Cons.

Surg. Birm. AHA (T) Research Fell. (Surg.) Dept. Surg. Char. Cross Hosp. Lond.; Cons. Surg. Salop AHA & Powys AHA.

HURLSTONE, David Paul 27 Northfield Drive, Biddulph, Stoke-on-Trent ST8 7DU — MB ChB 1995 Sheff.

HURLY, Kathleen (retired) 17 Dunelm Court, South St., Durham DH1 4QX — MB BCh Witwatersrand 1953.

HURMAN, David Charles Department of Clinical Oncology, Aberdeen Royal Infirmary, Foresterhill, Aberdeen AB25 2ZN Tel: 01224 681818 Ext: 59570 Fax: 01224 404495 Email: david.hurwan@arh.grampian.scot.nhs.uk; 15E St Swithin Street, Aberdeen AB10 6XB Tel: 01224 323406 — MB ChB 1975 Liverp.; Hon. MD Manitoba 1987; FRCR 1985; DMRT Liverp. 1981; DTM & H Liverp. 1977. (Univ. Liverp.) Clin Oncol. Grampian Univ Hosps NHS Trust; Vis. Cons. Shetland HB; Hon. Clin. Sen. Lect. Univ. Aberd.; Hon. Cons. & Expert Advisor Bhaktapur cancer care centre Kathmandu Nepal. Socs: Med.-Chir. Soc.; UKCCSG; Scott. Radiol. Soc. Prev: Clin. Research Fell. (Radiat. Oncol.) Cross Cancer Inst. Univ. Alberta, Canada; Sen. Regist. Mersey Regional Centre for Radiother. & Oncol. Clatterbridge Hosp. Bebington; Med. Off. Trans-Borneo Expedition 1978.

HURN, Barry Anthony Lincoln (retired) 3 Beck River Park, Beckenham BR3 1HT Tel: 020 8650 4966 — MB BS 1955 Lond.; MB BS (Hons.) Lond. 1955; MD Lond. 1964; FRCPath 1976, M 1965. Prev: Head Clin. Safety Surveillance Serv. Wellcome Research Laborat. Beckenham.

HURN, Juliet Diana 22 Sandy Lane, Charlton Kings, Cheltenham GL53 9BZ — MB ChB 1990 Manch.

HURRELL, Frederick Charles, CB, OBE, Air Vice-Marshal RAF Med. Br. (retired) Hale House, 4 Upper Hale Road, Farnham GU9 0NJ Tel: 01252 714190 Email: f.hurrell@ntlworld.com — MB BS Lond. 1952; MRCS Eng. LRCP Lond. 1952; FFOM RCP 1986; DAvMed Eng. 1972. Prev: Dir. Gen. RAF Med. Serv.

HURRELL, George David (retired) Stoneycroft, Hawkwell, Stamfordham, Newcastle upon Tyne NE18 0QT Tel: 01661 886463 — MB BS 1955 Durh.; DObst RCOG 1958. Prev: GP Newc.

HURRELL, Kevin John The Surgery, 50 The Glade, Furnace Green, Crawley RH10 6JN Tel: 01293 612741 — MB BS 1980 Lond.; MRCGP 1984; Cert. Family Plann. JCC 1984. (St. Thos.)

HURRELL, Leonard Henry (retired) Peverell Park Villa, 201 Outland Road, Plymouth PL2 3PF Tel: 01752 771837 — MB BChir 1955 Camb.; MA Camb. 1955; MRCS Eng. LRCP Lond. 1954. Prev: Res. Obst. Ho. Surg. & Res. Paediat. Ho. Phys. Edgware Gen. Hosp.

HURREN, Claire Magdalene 73 Southbourne Coast Road, Bournemouth BH6 4DX; 10 Buckfast Road, Lincoln LN1 3JS — BM BS 1997 Nottm. GP VTS Reg. Lincoln Co. Hosp.

HURREN, Mr Jeremy Simon Deepfield, Westwood Road, Windlesham GU20 6LT Tel: 01344 24492 Email: jetahurren@ad.com — MB BS 1987 Lond.; BSc Lond. 1984; FRCS Eng. 1991; FRCS Plast 1998. Regist. (Plastic Surg.)Norwich health care NHS Trust.

HURREN, Samuel Richard Strahan (retired) Adeline Road Surgery, 4 Adeline Road, Boscombe, Bournemouth BH5 1EF Tel: 01202 309421 — BM BCh 1971 Oxf. Princip. Police.Surg.Dorset.

HURRI, Heikki Olavi The Department of Rheumatology, Clinical Sciences Building, Hope Hospital, Eccles Old Road, Salford M6 8HD — Lic Med 1978 Kuopio.

HURRY, Roderick Alfred Alva Health Centre, West Johnstone St., Alva FK12 5BD Tel: 01259 760331 Fax: 01259 769991; Jinglebank, Back Road, Alva FK12 5LH Tel: 01259 760174 — MB ChB 1978 Aberd.; MRCGP 1982; DRCOG 1981. Occupat. Health Med. Off. Stirling Roy. Infirm.

HURST, Abigail The Brant Road Surgery, 291 Brant Road, Lincoln LN5 9AB Tel: 01522 722853 Fax: 01522 722195 — MB ChB 1991 Leic.; MRCGP 1995; DFFP 1995. (Leic.) GP Lincoln.

HURST, Graham Leslie Tel: 01298 84315 Fax: 01298 84899 — MB ChB 1980 Leeds; MRCGP 1996; DFFP 1995; DCH RCP Lond. 1986. (Univ. Leeds) Prev: Trainee GP/SHO Huddersfield VTS; Med. Off. Brit. Antarctic Survey; Ho. Off. Wharfedale Gen. Hosp. Otley.

HURST, Graham Richard 448 Unthank Road, Norwich NR4 7QJ — MB BS 1976 Newc.; MRCP (UK) 1978; FRCR 1981.

HURST, Helen Barbara 7 Dale Cl, Orton Waterville, Peterborough PE2 5HB; 23 Travers Street, Middleport, Stoke-on-Trent ST6 3PG — MB ChB 1997 Dundee. SHO Psych. Leighton Hosp. Crewe.

HURST, James Robert Blackford House Medical Centre, 137 Croft Lane, Hollins, Bury BL9 8QA Tel: 0161 766 6622 Fax: 0161 786 2748; 28 Bloomfield Drive, Unsworth, Bury BL9 8JX — MB ChB 1973 Manch. Prev: SHO (Paediat.) SHO (Gen. Med.) & SHO (O & G) Bolton Dist. Gen.; Hosp.

HURST, Jane Bedford Hospital, (Sth. Wing.), Kempston Road, Bedford MK42 9DJ Tel: 01234 355122; 22 Amberley Gardens, Bedford MK40 3BT — MB ChB 1974 Liverp.; FFA RCS Eng. 1978. Cons. Anaesth. Bedford Gen. Hosp.

HURST, Jane Alison Department of Clinical Genetics, Oxford Radcliffe Hospital, The Churchill, Oxford OX3 7LJ Tel: 01865 226020 — MB BS 1980 Lond.; MRCP (UK) 1984; FRCP 1996. (St. Mary's) Cons. Clin. Genetics Ch.ill Hosp. Oxf. Prev: Sen. Regist. Hosp. for Childr. Gt. Ormond St. Lond.

HURST, John (retired) 22 Poplar Road, Bearwood, Smethwick B66 4AW Tel: 0121 429 7319 — MB ChB Birm. 1960; FRCPsych 1986, M 1971; DPM Eng. 1968. Prev: Cons. Psychiat. Lea Castle Hosp. Kidderminster & Lea Hosp. BromsGr..

HURST, John (retired) 7 Somerville Road, Sutton Coldfield B73 6JD Tel: 0121 354 6052 — MB BChir 1954 Camb.; MRCS Eng. LRCP Lond. 1951.

HURST, John Robert Flat 6/5 South Clerk Street, Edinburgh EH8 9JD — MB ChB 1997 Ed.

HURST, Julian Richard Townsend House, 49 Harepath Road, Seaton EX12 2RY Tel: 01297 20616 Fax: 01297 20810 — MB BS 1983 Lond.; MA Camb. 1984; MRCGP 1987; DRCOG 1987. (St. Mary's) Gen. Practitioner Townsend Ho. Seaton. Prev: Trainee GP Oxf.

HURST, Leslie (retired) 16 Bryn Coed, St Asaph LL17 0DQ — MB ChB 1947 Polish Sch. of Med.

HURST, Lindsay Cameron 120 Fore Street, Kingsbridge TQ7 1AW Tel: 01548 852420 — 1949 M.A., M.B., B.Chir. (Camb.); FRCPsych 1979, M 1971; DPM Eng. 1958. (Camb. & Univ. Coll. Hosp.) Emerit. Cons. Psychiat. Plymouth Hosps. NHS Trust. Socs: Fell. Roy. Soc. Med.; Plymouth Med. Soc. Prev: Vis. Prof. Rochester State Hosp. NY, USA; Cons. Psychiat. Mapperley Hosp. & Gen. Hosp. Nottm.; Sen. Regist. (Psychiat.) St. Bart. Hosp. Lond.

HURST, Mark Haslemere Health Centre, Church Lane, Haslemere GU27 2BQ Tel: 01483 783023 Fax: 01428 645065 — MB BS 1978 Lond.; MRCS Eng. LRCP Lond. 1977. (Char. Cross)

HURST, Nigel Peter Rheumatic Diseases Unit, Western General Hospital, Crewe Road, Edinburgh EH4 2XU Tel: 0131 537 1806 Fax: 0131 537 1051 Email: n.hurst@ed.ac.uk; Flat 49, The Park, 89 Holy Rood Road, Edinburgh EH8 8BA Tel: 0131 556 0123 — MB BS 1975 Lond.; PhD Ed. 1983; BSc Bristol 1967; FRCP Ed. 1991; MRCP (UK) 1977. (St. Mary's Hosp. Lond.) Cons. Rheum. W.. Gen. Hosp. Edin.; Sen. Lect. (Med.) Univ. Edin. Prev: Sen. Staff. Rheum. Qu. Eliz. Hosp, Adelaide, S. Austral.; Hon. Sec. Lect. (Med.) Univ. Adelaide, S. Austral.

HURST, Mr Paul Anthony Edmund Royal Sussex County Hospital, Eastern Road, Brighton BN2 5BE Tel: 01273 696955 — MB BS 1970 Lond.; MRCS Eng. LRCP Lond. 1970; BSc (Hons.) (Physiol.) Lond. 1967, MS 1979; FRCS Eng. 1974; MRCP (UK) 1974. (St. Mary's) Cons. Surg. Roy. Sussex Co. Hosp. Brighton. Socs: Fell. Roy. Soc. Med. (Vice-Pres. Surgic. Sect.); Vasc. Surgic. Soc.; Eur. Soc. Vasc. Surg. Prev: Lect. & Sen. Regist. (Surg.) St. Thos. Hosp. Lond.; SHO (Cas.) St. Mary's Hosp. Harrow Rd.; Ho. Surg. (Urol. & Gen. Surg.) St. Mary's Hosp. Paddington.

HURST, Paul Laurence 3 Delph Lane, Aughton, Ormskirk L39 5EB — MB ChB 1981 Liverp.; DRCOG 1983.

HURST, Philip 82 Cooper Lane, Laceby, Grimsby DN37 7AS; 17 Chantry Lane, Grimsby DN31 2LP — MB ChB 1976 Birm.

HURST, Robert Kenneth Grosvenor Street Surgery, 4 Grosvenor Street, St Helier, Jersey JE1 4HB Tel: 01534 30541 Fax: 01534 887948; Kimberley, Bagatelle Road, St Saviour, Jersey JE2 7TX Tel: 01534 872326 Fax: 01534 876928 — MB ChB 1973 Aberd. GP Jersey. Prev: Regist. (Gen. Med. Jersey Gen. Hosp. St. Helier; SHO (Gen. Med.) & Ho. Off. (Med.) Qu. Mary's Hosp. Sidcup.

HURST, Timothy Joseph Anthony 65 Harp Hill, Charlton Kings, Cheltenham GL52 6PR — MB ChB 1990 Liverp.

HURST, Zuzanna Helena Bennetts End Surgery, Gatecroft, Hemel Hempstead HP3 9LY Tel: 01442 63511 Fax: 01442 235419 Email: zunia.hurst@rapidial.co.uk; Tel: 01442 262413 Fax: 01442 260026

Email: zunia.hurst@rapidial.co.uk — MB BS 1977 Lond.; MRCGP 1995.

HURT, Mr Raymond Lambert (retired) The White House, 8 Loom Lane, Radlett WD7 8AD Tel: 01923 855248 — MB BS Lond. 1944; FRCS Eng. 1950; MRCS Eng. LRCP Lond. 1944; DHMSA 1993. Examr. RCS Eng. Prev: Cons. Thoracic Surg. N. Middlx. & St. Bart. Hosps. Lond.

HURTADO CASANOVA, Alfonso 171 Church Lane, Scunthorpe DN15 7HD — LMS 1982 Cadiz.

HURTER, David Garnett (retired) High Bank, Pembury Road, Tonbridge TN9 2JJ Tel: 01732 352104 — MB BS 1950 Lond.; FFA RCS Eng. 1956; DA Eng. 1955. Prev: Cons. Anaesth. Orpington & Sevenoaks, & Dartford Hosp. Gps.

HURTER, Lois Edythe (retired) Chilver Cottage, Downsview Lane, East Dean, Eastbourne BN20 0DS — MRCS Eng. LRCP Lond. 1944; MD Lond. 1948; MB BS 1944; FRCOG 1960, M 1947. Prev: Cons. (O & G) St. Thos. Hosp. & Lambeth Hosp. Lond.

HURTER, Michael David The Health Centre, Crammavill Street, Stifford Clays, Grays RM16 2AP Tel: 01375 377127 Fax: 01375 394520; Longacre, Kirkham Road, Horndon on the Hill, Stanford-le-Hope SS17 8QE Tel: 01268 545626 — MB BS 1978 Lond.

HURTON, Patricia Bernadette 115 Olympic Way, Greenford UB6 8NJ — MB BS 1992 Lond.

HURWITZ, Brian Simon The Surgery, 2 Mitchison Road, London N1 3NG Tel: 020 7226 6016 — MB BS Lond. 1977; MA (Med. Law & Ethics) Lond. 1993; MD Univ. Lond. 1994; MSc Community Med. Lond. 1983; BA Camb. 1974; FRCP Lond. 1996; MRCP (UK) 1981; MRCGP 1982. (Univ. Coll. Hosp.) Sen. Lect. (Primary Health Care) Imperial Coll. Sch. Med. Lond. Prev: Sen. Lect. (Primary Health Care) Univ. Coll. Sch. Med. Lond.; Hon. Sen. Lect. (Primary Health Care) Univ. Coll. Lond.; Trainee GP Lond. VTS.

HURWITZ, Daniel Clive The Dekeyser Group Practice, The Fountain Medical Centre, Little Fountain, Leeds LS27 9EN Tel: 0113 295 1600 Fax: 0113 238 1901 — MB ChB 1979 Leeds; MRCP (UK) 1985; MRCGP 1987.

HURWITZ, David Stanley 1 Malone Hill Park, Belfast BT9 6RD — MB BCh BAO 1970 Belf.; FFA RCSI 1974. Prev: Asst. Prof. Anaesth. Univ. Texas Health Sc. Centre San Antonio; U.S.A.

***HURWITZ, Jane Louise** 1 Malone Hill Park, Belfast BT9 6RD — MB ChB 1998 Manch.; MB ChB Manch 1998; BSc 1995.

HURWITZ, Natalie Antoinette (retired) — MB ChB 1958 St. And.; PhD Belf. 1968. Prev: Research Fell. WHO Dept. Therap. Qu. Univ. Belf.

HURWITZ, Mrs Ruth (retired) 2 Bentcliffe Drive, Leeds LS17 6QX — MB BS 1960 Durh.

HURWOOD, David Sells (retired) Hebden House, 50A Syston Road, Queniborough, Leicester LE7 3FX Tel: 0116 260 7533 — MRCS Eng. LRCP Lond. 1949; FRCGP 1984, M 1965. Prev: Clin. Teach. (Gen. Pract.) Fac. Med. Univ. Leicester.

HURWOOD, Hubert Anthony (retired) 54 Woodland Rise W., Sheringham NR26 8QL Tel: 01263 824332 — MB BS 1949 Lond.; DObst RCOG 1954. Prev: GP Waltham Forest, Lond.

HURWOOD, Richard Sells The Health Centre, Syston, Leicester LE7 2EQ Tel: 0116 260 9161 Fax: 0116 269 8388; The Red House, 50 Syston Road, Queniborough, Leicester LE7 3FX Tel: 0116 260 6580 — MB BS 1977 Lond.; MRCGP 1983; DRCOG 1986; FRCGP 1998. (Guy's) Clin. Teach. (Gen. Pract.) Univ. Leic. Med. Sch.; PEC Mem. milton Rutland HarBoro. PCT. Socs: Rutland Accid. Care Scheme. Prev: SHO (Cas.) & Ho. Surg. Guy's Hosp. Lond.; Ho. Phys. Orpington Hosp.; Maj. RAMC.

HUSAIN, Aftab 289 Birmingham Road, Walsall WS5 3QA — MB BS 1965 Punjab; MRCPsych 1973.

HUSAIN, Akhtar James Cook University Hospital, 1 Marton Road, Middlesbrough TS5 3 BW Fax: 01642 282636 — MB BS 1983 Karachi, Pakistan; MRCPath 1997; DRCPath 1996; Dip. Clin. Path. Lond 1986.

HUSAIN, Asfar The Health Centre, Crane Street, Cefn Mawr, Wrexham LL14 3AB Tel: 01978 822341 Fax: 01978 824660 — MB BS 1971 Patna.

HUSAIN, Farhat (retired) 4 Marshall Close, Sanderstead, South Croydon CR2 9ED Tel: 020 8657 7676 Fax: 020 8407 3087 Email: fhusain@doctors.net.uk — MB BS 1955 Lucknow; MRCGP 1975.

HUSAIN, Fatimeh Asma — MB BS 1986 Lond.; MRCOG 1993; MRCGP 1992. (King's College London) Specialist Regist. (O & G) S. W. Thames Region. Socs: Brit. Fertil. Soc.; BMA. Prev: Specialist Regist. (O & G) Crawley, Redhill and St Geo.'s Lond..

HUSAIN, Mr Huned Muzaffer Department of Accident & Emergency, Queen Elizabeth II Hospital, Howlands, Welwyn Garden City AL7 4HQ Tel: 01707 328111 Fax: 01707 391228; 16 Beehive Lane, Welwyn Garden City AL7 4BA Tel: 01707 395430 Email: huned@msn.com — MB BS 1988 Osmania Univ. India; FRCS Glas. 1998. Staff Grade Doctor (A & E) E. Herts. NHS Trust Welwyn Garden City. Socs: Assoc. Mem. Brit. Assn. Accid. & Emerg. Med. Prev: SHO Rotat. (Surg.) Univ. Hosps. NHS Trust S. Manch.

HUSAIN, Masud Division of Neuroscience & Psychological medicine, Imperial Colllege School of Medicine, 10 East, Charing Cross Hospital, Fulham palace Road, London W6 8RF Tel: 020 8846 7383 Fax: 020 8846 7715 Email: m.husain@cxwms.ac.uk — BM BCh 1991 Oxf.; DPhil Oxf. 1987, BA 1984; MRCP (UK) 1994. Hon. Regist. (Neurol.) Char. Cross Hosp. Lond.; Wellcome Trust Advanced Train. Fell. Prev: Regist. (Med.) St. Peter's Hosp. Chertsey; SHO (Med.) ITU St. Thos. Hosp. Lond.

HUSAIN, Mohammed Hamid, OBE Greasbrough Medical Centre, Munsbrough Rise, Greasbrough, Rotherham S61 4RB Tel: 01709 559955 Fax: 01709 740483; Barbot Hall, Carr Hill, Rotherham S61 4QL — MB BS 1962 Osmania; FRCP Glas. 1982, M 1967; MRCGP 1993; AFOM RCP Lond. 1980. (Osmania Med. Coll.) GP, Greasbrough Med. Centre, Rotherham; Mem. Med. Advis. Comm.; Mem. Sec. of State for Health (Panel of Apptd. Persons for Oral Hearing); Adviser. & Extern. Assessor to NHS Commr (Ombudsman for Inplan.). Socs: Fell. (Ex-Counc.) BMA. Prev: Mem. GMSC & Occupat. Health Comm. & Counc. BMA; Mem. Rotherham FPC & DHA; Chairm. Trent Regional Counc. BMA.

HUSAIN, Oliver Anthony Nasseem (retired) 42 Oakhill Court, Edgehill, Wimbledon, London SW19 4NR Tel: 020 8947 3405 Fax: 020 8946 2880 — MB BS 1947 Lond.; MB BS (Hons.) Lond. 1947; MD Lond. 1950; MRCS Eng. LRCP Lond. 1948; FRCOG 1980; FRCPath 1970. Consg. Appt. Chelsea & Kensington & Char. Cross Hosps. (Imp. Coll. Med.). Prev: Cons. Path. Cytol. Dept. Char. Cross Hosp. & Regional Cytodiag. Unit St. Stephen's Hosp.

HUSAIN, Rehana Aijaz 55 The Broadway, Dudley DY1 4AP — MB ChB 1972 Manch.

HUSAIN, Shahid Masud Homerton University Hospital, Homerton Row, London E9 6SR Tel: 020 8510 7544 Fax: 020 8510 7850 Email: s.m.husain@qmul.ac.uk; Flat 3, 1 Frognal, Hampstead, London NW3 6AL — MB ChB 1979 Manch.; FRCPCH; MD Manch. 1997; MRCP (UK) 1987. Sen. Lect. & Hon. Cons. St. Bart. & Lond. Sch. Of Med. & Dent.; Cons. Neonatol. Homerton Hosp. Lond.

HUSAIN, Shaikh Muhammed Shahadat 7 Cotswold Close, Ashford TN24 8HT — MB BS 1970 Dacca.

HUSAIN, Sheikh Yawar 16 Marsden Drive, Timperley, Altrincham WA15 7XF Tel: 0161 980 2873 — MB BS 1964 Sind; MRCGP 1977; DCH Dub. 1984. (Liaquat Med. Coll. Hyderabad)

HUSAIN, Mr Syed Abrar 35 Beechwood Gardens, Clayhall, Ilford IG5 0AE Tel: 020 8550 0970 — MB BS 1951 Sind; FRCS Ed. 1968; LRCP LRCS Ed. LRFPS Glas. 1954; FCOphth 1989; DO Eng. 1956. (Dow Med. Coll. Karachi) SHMO S.E. Essex Gp. Hosps. Socs: Ophth. Soc. UK & Ophth. Soc. Pakistan. Prev: Regist. (Ophth.) Nottm. Eye Hosp.; Asst. Prof. Ophth. & Prof. Ophth. Nishtar Med. Coll.

HUSAIN, Syed Amjad 16 Lazenby Grove, Darlington DL3 9QD — MB ChB 1997 Dundee. Ho. Off. (Med.) Friarage Hosp. N.allerton. Socs: MPS. Prev: Ho. Off. (Surg.) S. Cleveland Hosp. Middlesbrough.

HUSAIN, Syed Sharkir Flat 6, Regents Court, 26 Orwell Terrace, Edinburgh EH11 2DT Tel: 0131 313 2561 Email: syed@saira73.freeserve.co.uk — MB ChB 1994 Glas. SHO (Gen. Adult Psychiat.) Roy. Edin. Hosp. Prev: SHO (Gen. Adult Psychiat.) Falkirk & Dist. Roy. Infirm.; SHO (Psychogeriat.) Bannockburn Hosp.; SHO (Gen. Adult Psychiat.) Stirling Roy. Infirm.

HUSAIN, Syed Sheher-Yar 22 Altyre Way, Beckenham BR3 3HA — MB BS 1997 Lond.

HUSAIN, Mr Syed Tauseef 151 Gladstone Park Gardens, London NW2 6RN — MB BS 1984 Karachi; FRCS Ed. 1993.

HUSAIN, Tajammul Bewbush Medical Centre, Bewbush Place, Bewbush, Crawley RH11 8XT Tel: 01293 519420; 4 Sommerville Drive, Crawley RH10 3TF — MB BS 1968 Jabalpur. GP Crawley, W. Sussex.

HUSAIN-QURESHI, Sharafat 144 Nabwood Drive, Shipley, Bradford BD18 4EW Tel: 01274 532851 — MB BS Karachi 1956;

MFCM 1974; DPH Manch. 1964; DTM & H Eng. 1958. Chief Med. Refree Bradford Metrop. Counc. Socs: Fell. Roy. Inst. of Pub. Health & Hyg.; Fell. Fac. Community Health; Fell. Roy. Soc. Trop. Med. & Hyg. Prev: Community Phys. Bradford HA; Asst. MoH Basildon UD; Regist. (Geriat. Med.) St. Tydfil's Hosp. Merthyr Tydfil.

HUSAINI, Hassan Murtaza Department of Anaesthesia, North Tyneside General Hospital, Rake Lane, North Shields NE29 8NH — MB BS 1985 Newc.

HUSAINI, Murtaza Husain Tameside & Glossop Acute NHS Trust, Ashton-under-Lyne OL6 9RW Tel: 0161 331 6369 Fax: 0161 331 6610; 2 Sharon Avenue, Grasscroft, Oldham OL4 4HP Tel: 01457 872808 Email: murtazahusain@msn.com — MB BS Karachi 1956; BSc (Hons.) Sind 1951; FRCP Lond. 1984, M 1966; FRCP Ed. 1980, M 1962; TDD Wales 1960; DTM & H Eng. 1958. (Dow Med. Coll. Karachi.) Cons. Phys. Cardiol. Tameside Gen. Hosp. Ashton-under-Lyne. Socs: Internat. Soc. Internal Med.; Brit. Cardiac Soc.

HUSAINI, Tahir Ali Joyce Green Hospital, Dartford DA1 5PL Tel: 01322 227242 — MB BS 1958 Karachi; FRCPath 1986, M 1974. (Dow Med. Coll. Karachi) Cons. Pathol. Dartford & Gravesham Health Dist. Socs: Assn. Clin. Pathols.; Internat. Acad. Path. Prev: Sen. Regist. Morbid Anat. Lewisham Hosp.; Regist. Path. Chelsea Hosp. Wom. Lond.; Regist. Path. Frenchay Hosp. Bristol.

HUSBAND, Mr Andrew David 26 Withy Close, Romsey SO51 7SA Email: ahusband@doctors.org.uk — BM 1990 Soton.; FRCS 2001 (ORL-HNS); FRCS Eng. 1995. Regist. (ENT) Hants. Socs: Brit. Assoc. Otolaryngologists, Head & Neck Surg.s.

HUSBAND, David John Clatterbridge Centre for Oncology, Clatterbridge Road, Bebington, Wirral CH63 4JY Tel: 0151 334 1155 Fax: 0151 334 0882 — MB ChB 1977 Leeds; BSc Leeds 1974, MB ChB 1977; MRCP (UK) 1980; FRCR 1990. (Leeds) Cons. Clin. Oncol. Clatterbridge Centre Oncol.; Hon. Lect. Univ. Liverp.

HUSBAND, Professor Janet Elizabeth Siarey Department of Diagnostic Radiology, The Royal Marsden NHS Trust, Downs Road, Sutton SM2 5PT Tel: 020 8642 6011 Fax: 020 8770 1643 Email: j.husband@icr.ac.uk; 38 The Mansion House, Kingston Hill Place, Kingston upon Thames KT2 7QY — MB BS Lond. 1964; FRCP Lond. 1987; MRCS Eng. LRCP Lond. 1964; FRCR 1976; DMRD Eng. 1974; DObst RCOG 1967; DCH Eng. 1966. (Guy's) Prof. Diagn. Radiol. & Cons. Radiol. Roy. Marsden Hosp. Lond. & Sutton & Clin. Dir. Lond. Clinic Scanning Servs.; Co-Dir. Cancer Research Campaign Clin. Magnetic Research Gp. Socs: Amer. Soc. Computed Body Tomography; Pres. Internat. Cancer Imaging Soc.; (Bd. Fac.) Roy. Coll. Radiol. Prev: Research Fell. (Radiol.) Roy. Marsden Hosp. Sutton; Sen. Regist. MRC, Div. Radiol. N.wick Pk. Hosp. Harrow; Regist. (Diag. Radiol.) King's Coll. Hosp. Lond.

HUSBAND, Peter (retired) 36 Rose Square, The Bromptons, Fulham Rd, London SW3 6RS Tel: 020 7584 0487 — BM BCh 1960 Oxf.; FRCP Lond. 1980, M 1966; MRCP Ed. 1965; DCH Eng. 1965; DObst RCOG 1966. Prev: Cons. Paediat. Ashford & W. Middlx. Univ. Hosps.

HUSBAND, Peter Robin Stonyford Hill, Holbury, Southampton SO45 2HD Tel: 023 8089 2579; Stonyford Hill, Holbury, Southampton SO45 2HD Tel: 023 8089 2579 — MB BS 1966 Lond.; MLCOM 1999 Lond.; MRCS Eng. LRCP Lond. 1965. (St. Bart.) p/t Private Pract. at Home; Osteop. Practitioner at Lond. Col. of Osteop. Med., 8-10 Boston Pl., Lond. NW1 6QH; Centre for Study of Complementary Med., 51 Bedford Pl., S.ampton SO15 2DT. Socs: Brit. Soc. Allergic & Environm. Med.; Brit. Inst. Musculoskel. Med. Prev: Regist. & Clin. Asst. Rheumatol. Dept. Nuffield Orthop. Centre Oxf.; SHO Rheum. Research Unit, Canad. Red Cross Memor. Hosp. Taplow; Rotating SHO (Med.) N. Staffs. Hosp. Centre Stoke-on-Trent.

HUSBAND, R G Amherst Medical Practice, 21 St. Botolphs Road, Sevenoaks TN13 3AQ Tel: 01732 459255 Fax: 01732 450751 Email: richard.husband@btinternet.com — MB ChB 1978 Cape Town; DRCOG 1983.

HUSBAND, Valentine Margaret (retired) Flat 8, 83-85 Onslow Gardens, London SW7 3BU Tel: 020 7244 7702 — MB ChB 1943 Aberd.; FRCOG 1971, M 1953; DObst 1950. Cons. O & G City & E. Lond. AHA (T). Prev: Regist. (O & G) St. Mary Abbots Hosp. Lond. & Paddington Gen. Hosp.

HUSBANDS, Sandra Diane 79 Rymer Road, Croydon CR0 6EF — MB BS 1987 Lond.

HUSEIN, Yusuf Ali 42 Meadow Waye, Heston, Hounslow TW5 9EZ — MB BS Peshawar 1966. (Khyber Med. Coll.)

HUSEMEYER, Roy Patrick 88 North Parade, Grantham NG31 8AU Tel: 01476 576328 Fax: 01476 576328; The Old Vicarage, Church Drive, Norton Disney, Lincoln LN6 9JX Tel: 01522 789278 Email: roy@husemeyer.freeserve.co.uk — MB BCh Witwatersrand 1969; PhD (Med.) Witwatersrand 1986; MFFP 1995; FRCOG 1988, M 1975. (Witwatersrand) Cons. O & G United Lincs. Hosp.s NHS Trust. Prev: Mem. Clin. Scientif. Staff Med. Research Counc.; Hon. Sen. Regist. (O & G) N.wick Pk. Hosp. & Clin. Research Centre; Regist. & Tutor Hammersmith Hosp. & Roy. Postgrad. Med. Sch. Lond.

HUSEYIN, Turan Suavi 280 Malden Way, New Malden KT3 5QS — MB BS 1993 Lond.

HUSIEN, Mr Amjad Mohammad Ali Radiology Department, The North Middlesex Hospital NHS Trust, Sterling Way, Edmonton, London N18 1QX Tel: 020 8887 2000 Fax: 020 8887 2270; 76 Vera Avenue, Grange Park, Winchmore Hill, London N21 1RR — MB ChB 1977 Baghdad; FRCS Ed. 1984; LRCP LRCS Ed. LRCPS Glas. 1982; FRCR 1989; ECFMG Cert. 1982. Cons. Radiol. The N. Middlx. Hosp. NHS Trust. Socs: Roy. Coll. Radiol. BrE. Gp.; Kettering & Dist. Med. Soc. Prev: Cons. Radiol. Kettering & Dist. Gen. Hosp.; Sen. Regist. (Radiol.) N. Staffs. HA; Regist. (Radiol.) W. Midl. RHA.

HUSKISSON, Edward Cameron 14A Milford House, 7 Queen Anne St., London W1G 9HN Tel: 020 7636 4278 Fax: 020 7323 6829 — BSc Lond. 1961, MD 1974, MB BS 1964; FRCP Lond. 1980, M 1967; MRCS Eng. LRCP Lond. 1964. (Westm.) Cons. Phys. & Sen. Lect. St. Bart. Hosp. Lond.; Cons. Rheum. King Edwd. VII Hosp. Lond.

HUSKISSON, Lucinda Jane Dept. Paediatric Surgery, Bristol Royal Hospital for Sick Children, St Micheal's Hill, Bristol BS2 8BJ; Rambler Cottage, Church Hill, Sheepscombe, Stroud GL6 7RE — MB BS 1984 Lond.; FRCS Eng. 1988; FRCS (Paed) 1997.

HUSON, Anne Sybil Pendleside Medical Practice, Clitheroe Health Centre, Railway View Road, Clitheroe BB7 2JG Tel: 01200 422674 Fax: 01200 443652; Stonehill House, Grindleton, Clitheroe BB7 4QT — MB ChB 1976 (Hons.) Manch.; BSc St. And. 1973; FRCGP 1997; DRCOG 1979.

HUSON, Susan Mary Department of Clinical Genetics, Oxford Radcliffe Hospital, Oxford OX3 7LJ — MB ChB 1978 Ed.; MD Ed. 1989; FRCP Lond. 1997, MR (UK) 1981; FRCP Ed. 1998. (Ed.) Cons. Clin. Geneticist Oxf. Radcliffe Hosp.; Hon. Clin. Sen. Lect. Nuffield Dept. Med. Univ. Oxf. Prev: Sen. Regist. Kennedy Galton Centre N.wick Pk. Hosp. Middlx.; Clin. Research Off. (Med. Genetics) Univ. Wales Coll. of Med. Cardiff.

HUSS, Brian Kenneth David 13 Magheralavae Park N., Lisburn BT28 3NL — MB BCh BAO 1970 Belf.; FFA RCS Eng. 1975; DObst RCOG 1972. Cons. Anaesth. Lagan Valley Hosp. Lisburn. Prev: Sen. Regist. Roy. Vict. Hosp. Belf.

HUSSAIN, A Teehey Lane Surgery, 68 Teehey Lane, Bebington, Wirral CH63 2JN Tel: 0151 608 2519.

HUSSAIN, Abid 191 St Saviours Road, Saltley, Birmingham B8 1HW — MB ChB 1982 Birm.

HUSSAIN, Abid Central Sheffield University Hospital, Glossop Road, Sheffield S10 2JF Tel: 0114 276 6222 Fax: 0114 279 8314 — MB ChB 1983 Ed.; FRCA 1988; DA (UK) 1989. Sen. Regist. (Anaesth.) Trent RHA; Hon. Lect. Univ. Sheff. Prev: Research Fell. (Intens. Ther.) Roy. Hallamsh. Hosp. Sheff.; Regist. (Anaesth.) Sheff. HA; SHO (A & E) Manch. Roy. Infirm.

HUSSAIN, Aga Wajahat Anlaby Road Surgery, 263 Anlaby Road, Hull HU3 2SE; 20 Sorrel Drive, County Meadows, Hull HU5 5GD Tel: 01482 569230 Fax: 01482 569230 — MB BS Madras 1960; FRCP Ed. 1994; MRCP Ed. 1968; Cert. Family Plann. JCC 1983; DTM & H Liverp. 1961. (Madras Med. Coll.) Dir. Humberside Med. Servs. Ltd.; GP & i/c Drug Misuse Rehabil. Unit. Socs: Hull Med. Soc.; FRS Lond. 1997. Prev: Chief Med. Off. Sierra Rutile Ltd., Sierra Leone; Regist. Profess. Unit Hosp. Trop. Dis. Lond.; Regist. (Med. & Cardiol.) Leeds RHB.

HUSSAIN, Aisha 93 Goldington Avenue, Huddersfield HD3 3PZ — MB BS 1998 Newc.; MB BS Newc 1998.

HUSSAIN, Ajmal 58 Chiltern Crescent, Earley, Reading RG6 1AN — MB ChB 1992 Leeds; DRCOG 1996.

HUSSAIN, Mr Akhtar 186 Compstall Road, Romiley, Stockport SK6 4JF — MB BS 1978 Peshawar; FRCS Ed. 1986.

HUSSAIN, Ali Arshad 11 Gladstone Avenue, London E12 6NR — LMSSA 1997 Lond.

HUSSAIN, Mr Altaf Prince Charles Hospital, Merthyr Tydfil CF47 9DT Tel: 0117 923 0000; 20 Plas Tymawr, Pen-y-Fai, Bridgend CF31 4NH Tel: 01656 660483 — MB BS 1967 Jammu & Kashmir; MChOrth Liverp. 1982. Cons. Osth. Surg. P. Chas. Hosp. Merthyr & Tyafil. Socs: Fell. BOA; BMA; Mem. World Osthopaedic Concern (WOC).

HUSSAIN, Ashar 8 Felixstowe Drive, Newcastle upon Tyne NE7 7JY — MB BS 1994 Newc.

HUSSAIN, Ashiq Walderslade Medical Centre, Princes Avenue, Chatham ME5 7PQ Tel: 01634 668160; 43 Barleymow Close, Chatham ME5 8JZ Tel: 01634 660735 Fax: 01634 660735 — MB BS Karachi 1962; BSc Karachi 1955; DA Eng. 1967. (Dow Med. Coll.) Prev: GP Oxf.

HUSSAIN, Emad Salman Hesketh Centre, 51-55 Albert Road, Southport PR9 0LT Tel: 01704 547471 Fax: 01704 502014; 19 Blundell Drive, Birkdale, Southport PR8 4RG Tel: 01704 563979 — MB ChB 1976 Baghdad; MPsychMed Liverp. 1986; MRCPsych 1982; DPM Eng. 1982; FRCPsych 1997. Cons. Psychiat. & Lead. Cons. N. Sefton & W. Lancs Community NHS Trust; Med. Dir /Cons. Psychiat. Florence Nightingale Hosp Liverp. Socs: S.port Med. Soc. & BMA; Fell.Roy.Coll.Psychiat. Prev: Sen. Regist. (Psychiat. of Old Age) Roy. Liverp. Hosp.; Sen. Regist. (Gen. Psychiat.) Sefton Gen. Hosp. & Winwick & WarringtonDist. Gen. Hosps.; Med Dir S.port & Formby Comm Health Serv.s NHS Trust.

HUSSAIN, Faisal Manzoor 29 Stratford Way, Watford WD17 3DL — MB BS 1993 Lond.

HUSSAIN, Faizi Nauman 49 Ashford Drive, Ravenshead, Nottingham NG15 9DE — MB ChB 1987 Manch.

HUSSAIN, Farah Farhat 13 Elgin Avenue, Harrow HA3 8QW — MB BS 1996 Lond. (St. Mary's Hospital)

HUSSAIN, Farzana Iffat 49 Queens Dr, Fulwood, Preston PR2 9YL — MB BCh 1997 Wales.

HUSSAIN, Ferida Khanam 37 Geneva Drive, Newcastle ST5 2QQ — BM BS 1993 Nottm.

HUSSAIN, Fuad Faruque 53 Brantwood Road, London SE24 0DH — MB BS 1994 Lond.

HUSSAIN, Hasina Mehdi The Surgery, 295 Brownhill Road, London SE6 1AG Tel: 020 8698 1837; 3 Bennetts Copse, Chislehurst BR7 5SG Tel: 020 8467 8067 Fax: 020 8467 8067 — MB BS Punjab (Pakistan) 1964; MRCOG 1974, DObst 1969. (King Edwd. Med. Coll. Lahore) Socs: Pakistan Med. Soc. (Lond.); Muslim Med. Inst. (Lond.).

HUSSAIN, Hero Kamal 20 Copper Beeches Court, Witham Road, Isleworth TW7 4AW — MB ChB 1986 Baghdad.

HUSSAIN, I Stansfield House Surgery, 305 Skircoat Green Road, Halifax HX3 0NA Tel: 01422 353517 Fax: 01422 380799 — MB BS 1969 Bihar; MB BS 1969 Bihar.

HUSSAIN, Iftikhar Kings Avenue Surgery, 23 Kings Avenue, Buckhurst Hill IG9 5LP Tel: 020 8504 0122 Fax: 020 8559 2984 — MB BS 1988 Lond.; DFFP 1993; MRCGP 1994; DRCOG 1993; DCH 1995. (Royal London Hospital) GP Princip.; GP Trainer; Clin. Asst. Dermat., Whipps Cross Hosp., Lond. Prev: SHO (Psychiat.) Claybury Hosp. Woodford Green.; Trainee GP Buckhurst Hill.

HUSSAIN, Iftikhar Balayogi, Hussain and Sreenivasan, Doctors Surgery, 76 Market Street, Droylsden, Manchester M43 7UD Tel: 0161 370 2626 Fax: 0161 371 3577; 7 Ralphs Lane, The Lakes, Dukinfield SK16 4UZ Tel: 0161 339 4355 — MB BS 1967 Punjab; MB BS Punjab (Pakistan) 1967; DTM & H Liverp. 1977. (Nishtar Med. Coll. Multan) Med. Off. (Family Plann.) Tameside & Glossop HA. Prev: Regist. (Infec. Dis.) Monsall Hosp. Manch.

HUSSAIN, Ilyas 47 Craven Terrace, Halifax HX1 4DY — MB ChB 1998 Dund.; MB ChB Dund 1998.

HUSSAIN, Mr Imran 101 Glandon Drive, Cheadle Hulme, Cheadle SK8 7HD — MB BS 1980 Peshawar; FRCS Ed. 1989. SHO & Regist. (Ophth.) Roy. Preston Hosp. Prev: Ho. Off. (Gen. Surg.) Khyber Teach. Hosp., Pakistan; SHO (Gen. Med.) Khyber Teach. Hosp., Pakistan; Med. Off. Pakistan Army.

HUSSAIN, Imran Raza 163 Black Shaw Road, Tooting, London SW17 0BU Email: imran@imrach.freeserve.co.uk — MB BS 1990 Lond.; BSc (Hons.) Lond. 1987; MRCP (UK) 1993; DTM & H RCP Lond. 1993. (St. Geo. Hosp. Med. Sch.) Clin. Research Fell. Univ. Soton. Prev: Regist. Rotat. (Gen. Med.) St. Geo. Hosp. Lond.; SHO Rotat. (Med.) E. Birm. Hosp.

HUSSAIN, Iqbal Biscot Road Surgery, 21 Biscot Road, Luton LU3 1AH Tel: 01582 732697 Fax: 01582 402554; 5 Conway Road, Luton LU4 8JA Tel: 01582 454690 — MB ChB 1984 Sheff.; MRCGP 1990. Trainer (Gen. Pract.) Luton. Prev: GP Rotherham.

HUSSAIN, Mr Iqbal Faruque Pharmacia Ltd, Hillbotton Road, High Wycombe HP12 4PX Tel: 01494 613157 Email: iqbal.hussain@pharmacia.com — MB BS 1991 Lond.; BSc Lond. 1987; FRCS Eng. 1995; MSc 1999. (St. Thos. Hosp. Med. Sch.) Assoc. Director Uro - Gyn. & Wom.'s Health; Higher Surg. Trainee (Urol.) N. Thames Rotat. Socs: EUA Europ. Urological Assoc.; ICS Internat. Contience Soc.; Brit. Med. Assn. Prev: Regist. (Gen. Surg.) Qu. Hosp. Burton on Trent; Research SHO (Urol.) Roy. Berks. & Battle Hosp. NHS Trust Reading; SHO Rotat. (Surg.) Frimley Pk. Hosp. NHS Trust Camberley.

HUSSAIN, Irshad 19 Maytree Crescent, Watford WD2 6BN Tel: 01923 662263 — MB BS 1986 Madras; MRCP (UK) 1990.

HUSSAIN, Jameel Ahmed 18B Albert Street, Liverpool L7 3EJ — MB ChB 1997 Liverp.

HUSSAIN, Karamat 158 Hairault Road, Leytonstone, London E11 1EW — MB BS 1974 Punjab, Pakistan; MRCPI 1985.

HUSSAIN, Mr Karim Department of Oral & Maxillofacial Surgery, Guy's Hospital, London SE1 9RT; 19 Frank Dixon Way, Dulwich, London SE21 7ET — MB BS 1988 Lond.; BDS Liverp. 1981; FRCS Eng. (Max Fac) 1995; FRCS Eng. 1992; FDS RCS Eng. 1989; FFD RCSI 1988. Cons. Oral & Maxillofacial Surg. Guy's Hosp. Lond. & Qu. Mary's Hosp. Sidcup. Socs: Brit. Assn. Oral & Maxillofacial Surg.; BMA. Prev: Sen. Regist. (Oral & Maxillofacial Surg.) St. Geo. Hosp. & Guy's Hosp. Lond.; Regist. (Oral & Maxillofacial Surg.) Birm. Gen. Hosp.

HUSSAIN, Khadim Roundwell Day Hospital, Roundwell St., Tunstal, Stoke-on-Trent ST6 5JJ Tel: 01782 425740 Fax: 01782 825741; 37 Geneva Drive, Westlands, Newcastle ST5 2QQ — MB BS Punjab 1962; MRCPsych 1973; DPM Eng. 1971. (Nishter Med. Coll. Multan) Cons. Pychiat. St. Edwd. Hosp. Cheddleton, City Gen. Hosp. Stoke-on-Trent & N. Staffs. Hosp. Centre.

HUSSAIN, Khalid 3 Cowley Road, Ilford IG1 3JL — MB ChB 1988 Glas.

HUSSAIN, Latif Mohammed Castletown Surgery, 123 Liverpool Road, Cross Heath, Newcastle ST5 9ER Tel: 01782 637082 Fax: 01782 710421; The White Swan, 6 Elder Road, Cobridge, Stoke-on-Trent ST6 2HD Tel: 01782 823669 — MB ChB 1983 Manch.; MRCGP 1987; DRCOG 1986. Prev: Clin. Asst. (A & E) N. Staffs. Roy. Infirm. Stoke on Trent; SHO (Paediat.) Roy. Manch. Childr. Hosp. Pendlebury; SHO (Gen. Med.) Ladywell Hosp. Salford.

HUSSAIN, Mahbuba 3 Fort Road, Northolt UB5 5HH — MB BS 1969 Dacca; MRCOG 1980.

HUSSAIN, Mahreen 1 Pear Tree Close, Slough SL1 5EZ — MB BS 1997 Lond.

HUSSAIN, Malik Javed Hillfields Health Centre, 1 Howard Street, Coventry CV1 4GH Tel: 024 7622 2527 — MB BS 1964 Punjab; MB BS Punjab (Pakistan) 1964. (King Edwd. Med. Coll. Lahore) Prev: SHO (Paediat.) Buckland Hosp. Dover & Gen. Hosp. Ashton-under-Lyne; SHO (Gen. Med. & Paediat.) Herts & Essex Hosp. Bishop's Stortford.

HUSSAIN, Matlub 48 Queens Road E., Beeston, Nottingham NG12 1DJ — MB BS 1994 Lond.

***HUSSAIN, Mazzar** 19 Curzon Avenue, Coventry CV6 5LF — MB ChB 1994 Leeds.

HUSSAIN, Mian Farrukh Chaucher Hospital, Nackington Rd, Canterbury CT4 7AR Tel: 01227 455466; 6 Cadnam Close, St. Stephens, Canterbury CT2 7SD Tel: 01227 762267 Fax: 01227 455799 Email: drmfhussain@hotmail.com — MB BS 1966 Karachi; MRCPsych 1972; DPM RCPSI 1971; DPM Eng. 1971; FRCPsych 1998. (Dow) p/t Cons. Psychiat., Chaucer Hosp., Canterbury, Kent; Hon. Mem. Keynes Coll. Kent Univ.; Hon. Clin. Tutor St.Geo. Univ. Socs: Fell. Roy. Asiatic Soc.; Treas., SAARC Foundat. UK; Fell. Roy. Soc. Med. Prev: SHO (Psychiat.) Long Gr. Hosp. Epsom.; Regist. (Psychiat.) St. Geo.'s Hosp. Lond.; Sen. Regist. (Psychiat.) Univ. Sheff. Dept. Psychiat. Whiteley Wood.

HUSSAIN, Mir Sahidul Concord Way Surgery, Concord Way, Jarrow NE32 5BB Tel: 0191 489 7232 — MB BS 1965 Gauhati. GP Jarrow, Tyne & Wear.

HUSSAIN, Mohammed Abul 120 Cavendish Meads, Ascot SL5 9TQ — MB BS 1965 Dacca; DCH RCP Glas. 1971.

HUSSAIN, Mohammed Abul Royal Infirmary, Castle St., Worcester WR1 3AS Tel: 01905 763333; 11 Millbrook Close, Northwick, Worcester WR3 7BJ Tel: 01905 457345 — MB BS 1968 Dacca; DLO RCS Eng. 1989.

HUSSAIN, Mudassar 35 Eton Hall, Eton College Road, London NW3 2DP — MB BS 1994 Lond.

HUSSAIN, Muzammal 25 Sudbury Court Road, Harrow HA1 3SD — MB BS 1997 Lond.

HUSSAIN, Najabat Park View Group Practice, 2 Longford Road West, Stockport SK5 6ET Tel: 0161 431 9339 — MB ChB 1985 Manch.

HUSSAIN, Nasir 7 Inch Garvie, St Leonards, E. Kilbride, Glasgow G74 2JY — MB ChB 1991 Glas.

HUSSAIN, Noor (retired) The Health Centre, Magna Lane, Dalton, Rotherham S65 4HH Tel: 01709 851414 — MB BS 1962 Peshawar; BSc Peshawar 1955, MB BS 1962.

HUSSAIN, Nowshaba 3 Spires View, Stapleton, Bristol BS16 1UR — MB BS 1998 Lond.; MB BS Lond 1998.

HUSSAIN, Rashid Iqbal Treetops, Bryn Rhedyn, Llanfrechan, Cwmbran NP44 8UB — MB BCh 1988 Wales.

HUSSAIN, Saadi Abdul Jalil Al-Roumani North Cheshire BUPA Hospital, Warrington WA4 4LU Tel: 01925 265000 Fax: 01925 604469; 26 Easby Close, Poynton, Stockport SK12 1YG — MB ChB 1969 Baghdad; MRCP (UK) 1979. Resid. Med. Off. BUPA N. Chesh. Hosp.

HUSSAIN, Saira 100 Harpenden Lane, Redbourn, St Albans AL3 7PD — MB BCh 1998 Wales.

HUSSAIN, Sajidah Asmat 12 Faraday Road, Lenton, Nottingham NG7 2DU — BM BS 1993 Nottm.

HUSSAIN, Saniya Marriam 5 Elphinstone Street, London N5 1BS — MB BS 1996 Lond.

HUSSAIN, Sarah Maryyum c/o The Royal Bank of Scotland plc, 1 Dale St., Liverpool L2 2PP — MB ChB 1993 Liverp.

HUSSAIN, Shabina 7 Lynton Drive, Bradford BD9 5JH; University College London, Bloomsbury Rheumatology Unit, Arthur Starley House, 40-50 Tottenham St., London W1P 9PG Tel: 020 7380 9230 — MB ChB 1993 Leeds; MRCP (UK) 1997. Clin. Research Regist. (Rheum.) Univ. Coll. Lond. Prev: SHO (Rheum.) Univ. Coll. Lond.; Med. Rotat. Pinderfields Gen. Hosp. Wakefield W. Yorks.

HUSSAIN, Shafqat Plumstead Health Centre, Tewson Road, Plumstead, London SE18 1BB Tel: 020 8854 1898 Fax: 020 8855 9958; 9 Goddington Chase, Orpington BR6 9EA Tel: 020 8854 1898 — MB BS 1963 Punjab; MSc (Med.) Lond. 1988; DCH RCP Lond. 1971; DCH RCPS Glas. 1967. (Nishtar Med. Coll.)

HUSSAIN, Shahnaz Akhtar 6 Cadnam Close, St Stephens, Canterbury CT2 7SD Tel: 01227 762267 — MB BS 1968 Punjab.

HUSSAIN, Sharafat Child & Family Psychiatry, Albion Road Clinic, Albion Road, North Shields NE29 0HG Fax: 0191 219 6650 Email: sharafat-hussain@hotmail.com; 32 Rothwell Road, Gosforth, Newcastle upon Tyne NE3 1TY — MB BS 1975 Punjab; MRCPsych 1984; DPM Eng. 1982. (KEMC Lahore, Pakistan) Cons. Child & Adolesc. Psychiat., N.umbria Healthcare NHS Trust.

HUSSAIN, Sharif Mohamed Anwar Bassetlaw District General Hospital, Worksop S80 0BD Tel: 01909 500990; 5 Sparken Dale, Crabtree Park, Worksop S80 1BL Tel: 01909 475416 Fax: 01909 502984 — MB BS 1962 Dacca; FRCP Lond. 1993; FRCP Ed. 1987; FRCP Glas. 1981; MRCP (UK) 1970. (Dacca Med. Coll.) Cons. Phys. Bassetlaw Dist. Gen. Hosp. Prev: Cons. Phys. Geriat. Basset Law Health Dist. Nott.; Cons. Phys. Geriat. Worksop & Retford Health Dist.

HUSSAIN, Shehriar Abdullah 5 Princess Way, Euxton, Chorley PR7 6PL — MB ChB 1992 Manch.

HUSSAIN, Shezad 53 St Peters Road, Reading RG6 1PA — MB ChB 1995 Leeds.

HUSSAIN, Simin 4 Broughton Road, Thornton Heath, Croydon CR7 6AL — MB BCh 1998 Wales.

HUSSAIN, Smaila 12 Winchester Close, Woolton, Liverpool L25 7YD — MB ChB 1994 Liverp.

HUSSAIN, Sumera Khanam 37 Geneva Drive, Newcastle ST5 2QQ — MB ChB 1990 Liverp. Regist. (Anaesth.) Nottm. Socs: Fell. Roy. Coll. Anaesth.; Assn. Anaesth.; BMA. Prev: SHO (A & E) St. Jas. Hosp. Leeds; SHO (Anaesth.) Nottm. & Derby.

HUSSAIN, Syed Anwar The Surgery, 36 Harvey Road, Leytonstone, London E11 3DB Tel: 020 8539 7414 Fax: 020 8518 7977 — MB BS 1964 Punjab; BSc Punjab (Pakistan) 1958, MB BS 1964; DO Eng. 1967. (King Edwd. Med. Coll. Lahore) Clin. Asst. Ophth. Whipps Cross Hosp. Lond.

HUSSAIN, Syed Asad 57 Hemwood Road, Windsor SL4 4YX — MB BS 1995 Lond.; MRCP Lond. 1998. (Char. Cross & Westm. Med. Sch. Lond.) Specialist Regist. Rheum. Gen. Med. Mersey Deanery. Socs: BMA; Med. Defence Soc.; Brit. Soc. Rheum. Prev: SHO (A & E) Char. Cross Hosp. Lond.; SHO (med.) Wycombe Hosp.

HUSSAIN, Syed Mazhar Newland Avenue Surgery, 239-243 Newland Avenue, Hull HU5 2EJ Tel: 01482 448456 Fax: 01482 449536 — MB BS 1967 Osmania.

HUSSAIN, Mr Syed Rahmath 7 Brantingham Close, The Dales, Cottingham HU16 5JW Tel: 01482 849612 — MB BS 1962 Osmania; MS (ENT) Osmania 1967, MB BS 1962. (Osmania Med. Coll.)

HUSSAIN, Mr Syed Shah Musheer Department of Otolaryngology, Ninewells Hospital and Medical School, Dundee DD1 9SY Tel: 01382 660111 Fax: 01382 632816 Email: musheerh@tuht.scot.nhs.uk; 6 Norwood Terrace, Dundee DD2 1PB — MB BS 1977 Karachi; MSc (Audiol. Med.) Manch. 1990; FRCS Ed. 1986; DLO RCS Eng. 1983; Intercollegiate Board in Otolaryngology 1995. (Dow) Cons. ENT Surg. Ninewells Hosp. Dundee & Hon. Sen. Lect. Med. Sch. Univ. of Dundee.; TWJ Fell. (Otol. & Neurotol.) Univ. Michigan, Ann Arbor, USA; Cons. Temporal Bone Laborat.. Minewells Hosp. & Med. Sch. Dundee; ir. Post Grad meetings (otoLaryngol.) Minewells Hosp. Socs: Fell. Roy. Soc. Med. (Mem. Sect. Otol., Laryngol. & Rhinol.); Brit. Soc. Audiol.; Acoustical Soc. Amer. Prev: Sen. Regist. (Otolaryngol.) St. Jas. Univ. Hosp., Gen. Infirm. Leeds. & Bradford Roy. Infirm; SHO (ENT & Plastic Surg.) King's Coll. Hosp. Lond.; SHO (Surgic. Neurol.) Proffesoral Unit, Roy. Infirm. of Edin. and W.ern Gen. Hosp., Edin.

HUSSAIN, Mr Syed Tahir 171 Milton Avenue, East Ham, London E6 1BN; 99 Wellesley Road, Ilford IG1 4LJ — MB BS 1987 Lond.; MS Lond. 1996; FRCS Eng. 1991. (St. Geo. Med. Sch. Lond.) Specialist Regist. Milton Keynes Hosp. Socs: Physiol. Soc. Prev: Lect. St. Bart. Hosp. Lond.

HUSSAIN, Tanveer Hawthornden Surgery, Wharf Lane, Bourne End SL8 5RX Tel: 01628 522864 Fax: 01628 533226 — MB BS 1983 Punjab; MB BS 1983 Punjab.

HUSSAIN, Tanweer 48 Queen's Road E., Beeston, Nottingham NG9 2GS — MB ChB 1994 Liverp.

HUSSAIN, Mr Tariq 69 Helen Avenue, Feltham TW14 9LA — MB BS 1990 Karachi; FRCSI 1994.

HUSSAIN, Tokeer 125 Salisbury Road, Watertree, Liverpool L15 2HU — MB ChB 1991 Liverp.

HUSSAIN, Wajid Imperial College of Science, Technology & Medicine, 10th Floor QEQM Wing, St. Marys Hospital, South Wharf Road, London W2 1NY Tel: 0207 886 6293 — MB ChB 1993 Birm.; MB ChB Birm. (Hons.) 1993; BSc (Hons.) Physiol. 1990; MRCP (UK) 1996. (Birm.) Clin. Research Fell., Imperial Coll. Socs: Assn. Study Med. Educat.; Brit. Cardiac Soc. Prev: SpR Cardiol., St. Bartholomews Hosp.; Spr Cardiol., Lond. Chest Hosp.; Regist. (Cardioogy & Gen. Med.) Colchester Gen. Hosp.

HUSSAIN, Zaheer 9 Turnberry Drive, Wilmslow SK9 2QW — MB ChB 1993 Ed.

HUSSAIN, Zaheer Lillie Road Surgery, 322 Lillie Road, Fulham, London SW6 7PP Tel: 020 7385 1964 Fax: 020 73816 1071 Email: dezeehussain@hotmail.com; 330 Lillie Road, Fulham, London SW6 7PP — MB BS 1964 Punjab; MRCP (UK) 1974; LicAc 1988. (King Edwd. Med. Coll. Lahore) GP Lond. Socs: BMA & Roy. Coll. Phys. Prev: SHO (Med.) Vict. Hosp. Blackpool; Regist. (Med.) E. Glam. Gen. Hosp. Pontypridd; Regist. (Geriat.) Qu. Alex. Hosp. Cosham.

HUSSAIN, Zahid Moss Side Health Centre, Monton Street, Moss Side, Manchester M14 4GP Tel: 0161 226 1849 Fax: 0161 226 1849 — MB BS 1972 Peshawar; MRCS Eng. LRCP Lond. 1981.

HUSSAIN, Zahid Marine Medical, Blyth Health Centre, Thoroton Street, Blyth NE24 1DX Tel: 01670 396520 Fax: 01670 396537 — MB BS 1988 Newc.; MRCP (UK) 1991; MRCGP 1993; DCH RCP Lond. 1992. GP Blyth, N.d.; Clin. Asst. (Rheum.) N. Shields. Prev:

SHO (Med.) Newc. Teachg. Hosps.; SHO (Paediat.) S. Tyneside Gen. Hosp.; SHO (O & G) N. Tyneside Gen. Hosp.

HUSSAIN, Zahid 6 Ffordd Mon, Wrexham LL11 2LH — MB BS 1982 Punjab.

HUSSAIN, Zia 35 Kingslynn Drive, Glasgow G44 4JB — MB ChB 1988 Glas.

HUSSAIN, Zia-Ul The Consulting Rooms, Oxhey Drive, South Oxhey, Watford WD1 6RU Tel: 020 8428 2292 — MB BS 1972 Osmania; DCH 1974. Prev: Trainee GP Watford Gen. Hosp. VTS; SHO (Paediat.) Roy. Albert Infirm. Wigan; SHO (Paediat.) Vict. Hosp. Blackpool.

HUSSAINI, Syed Abdul Aziz (retired) birchdene, 19 Longley Drive, Worsley, Manchester M28 2TP Tel: 0161 794 0666 Email: aziz@longley.freeserve.co.uk — MB BS 1956 Karachi; DA Eng. 1965. Prev: GP Manch.

HUSSAINI, Syed Hyder Royal Cornwall Hospitals (Treliske), Truro TR1 3JW Tel: 01872 252717 Email: hussaini@rcht.swest.nhs.uk; By the Way, Mingoose Vale, Mount Hawke, Truro TR4 8BY — MB BS 1984 Lond.; MD 1996; MRCP (UK) 1988; MD London 1996. (St. Thomas London) Cons. Phys. & Gastroenterol. Treliske Hosp. Truro Cornw. Socs: Brit. Soc. Gastroenterol.; Brit. Assn. for the study of Liver Dis. Prev: Lect. (Med.) & Hon. Sen. Regist. (Gastroenterol.) St. James Univ. Hosp. Leeds.

HUSSEIN, Ali Moh'd Moh'd Khalil Winwick Hospital, Winwick, Warrington WA2 8RR Tel: 01925 655221; 4 Hankelow Close, Northgate Village, Chester CH2 2DZ Tel: 01244 399348 — MB BS 1983 Jordan; Irish Dip. Psychiat. 1997. (Univ. Jordan) Staff Grade (Gen. Adult Psychiat.) Warrington Community Health Care (NGS) Trust. Prev: Clin. Asst. (Gen. Adult Psychiat.) Chesh.

HUSSEIN, Ammar Abdel Gadir 29 Northview, Tufnell Park Road, London N7 0QB — MRCS Eng. LRCP Lond. 1984; MB BS Khartoum 1981.

HUSSEIN, Jasmin Ramzi 16 Draycott Place, London SW3 2SB Tel: 020 7589 7446 — MB BChir 1993 Camb.; MSc. Med. Parasitol. Lond. 1990. (St. Thos. & Camb.) Clin. Research. Fell. Neurosurg. Nat. Hosp. Nerol & Neuro. Lond.

HUSSEIN, Julia Lillian Pension Hall, Talbot Square, London W2 1TT; Flat 8 Lamerton Lodge, 228 Kew Road, Kew, Richmond TW9 3JX — MB BCh BAO 1986 Dub.; MRCOG 1991.

HUSSEIN, Kudair Ali Department of Pathology, Poole Hospital NHS Trust, Longfleet Road, Poole BH15 2JB — MB ChB 1978 Baghdad; MRCPath 1987. Cons. Histopath. & Cytol. Dundee Roy. Infirm. Prev: Lect. (Pathol.) Ninewells Hosp. Dundee.

HUSSEIN, Osama Taher Mohamed Khalil X-Ray Department, Prince Charles Hospital, Merthyr Tydfil CF47 9DT Tel: 01685 728107 Fax: 01685 387475 — MB ChB 1981 Mansoura; FRCR 1990; T(R) (CR) 1992; DMRD Ed. 1989. Cons. Radiol., Price Chas. Hosp.

HUSSEIN, Mr Reda Salem Ahmed West Lodge, Ruyton Road, Baschurch, Shrewsbury SY4 2BA Tel: 01939 260025 — MB ChB 1973 Cairo; MD Banha Egypt 1985; FRCS Glas. 1984.

HUSSEIN, Shabir Palms Medical Centre, 97-101 Netley Road, Newbury Park, Ilford IG2 7NW Tel: 020 8554 9551 Fax: 020 8518 2045 — MB BCh BAO 1991 NUI.

HUSSEIN, Shuman Ejaj Knightsbridge Medical Centre, 71-75 Pavillion Road, London SW1X 0ET Fax: 0208 237 2626 Email: shumanhussein@hotmail.com; 19 Chetwode Roade, London SW17 1RF Tel: 020 8693 0970 Email: pdhadly@aol.com, shumanhussein@hotmail.com — MB BS 1994 Lond.; DFFP 2001 Roy. Coll. Of Obstetriciates & Gynaecologists; MRCGP 2001 Roy. Coll. Of Gen. Pract.; BSc (Hons.) Lond. 1991; MRCP (UK) 1998; Dip. IMC 1999. (St. George's Hospital Medical School) GP Sen. Regist., Kt.sbridge Med. Centre, Lond.; Primary Care Practitioner, Accid. & Emerg., St Geo.s Hosp. Lond. Socs: Roy. Coll. Phys.; Roy. Coll. Of Gen. Practitioners; Fac.Pre Hosp.Care.Roy.Coll.Surg. Prev: Specialist Regist. A&E Med. S. W. Thames Reg. Train. Progr.

HUSSELBEE, Andrew James The Surgery, Sandy Lane, Brewood, Stafford ST19 9ES Tel: 01902 850206 Fax: 01902 851360; Gunstove House, 13 Stafford Street, Brewood, Stafford ST19 9DX Tel: 01902 851744 — BM BCh 1986 Oxf.; BA Oxf. 1983; MRCGP 1994; DRCOG 1989; DA (UK) 1989. (Oxf.) Princip. in Gen. Pract.

HUSSELBEE, Kirsten Marie 4 Mallaig Avenue, Gowrie Park, Dundee DD2 4TW — MB ChB 1996 Dundee.

HUSSELL, Mr John Gavin Owls Oast, Lossenham Lane, Newenden, Hawkhurst, Cranbrook TN18 5QQ — MB BS 1987 Lond.; FRCS Eng. 1991.

HUSSELL, Thomas Anthony (retired) Owls Oast, Lossenham Lane, Newenden, Hawkhurst, Cranbrook TN18 5QQ — MRCS Eng. LRCP Lond. 1958; MA Camb.; DA Eng. 1960. Prev: Chest Hosp. Kent.

HUSSEY, Andrew Stephen The Queen Edith Medical Practice, 59 Queen Ediths Way, Cambridge CB1 8PJ Tel: 01223 247288 Fax: 01223 213459 — MB BS 1987 Lond.; MA Camb. 1988, BA 1984; MRCGP 1993; Cert. Family Plann. JCC 1992. Clin. Asst. (Ophth.) Addenbrookes Hosp. Camb. Prev: SHO (Psychiat. & Geriat.) W. Suff. Hosp. Bury St. Edmunds; SHO (Ophth.) Addenbrooke's Hosps. Camb.

HUSSEY, Jacqueline Sally Fair Mile Hospital, Reading Road, Cholsey, Wallingford OX10 9HH Tel: 01491 651281; 12 Church Street, Twyford, Reading RG10 9DR Tel: 0118 934 4925 — MB BCh 1988 Wales; BSc (Hons.) Physiol. Wales 1983; MRCPsych 1993. p/t Cons. in Old Age Psychiat.,Berks. HealthCare NHS Trust. Socs: Roy. Coll. of Psychiat.s. Prev: Sen. Regist. (Psychiat.) Oxf. RHA.

HUSSEY, Jefferey Keith Seronok, Sunnyside Farm, Newmachar, Aberdeen AB21 7PH — MB ChB 1975 Aberd.; FRCR 1982. Cons. Radiol. Aberd. Roy. Infirm. Socs: Brit. Soc. Intervent. Radiol.

HUSSEY, John Anthony Park Road Group Practice, The Elms Medical Centre, 3 The Elms, Dingle, Liverpool L8 3SS Tel: 0151 727 5555 Fax: 0151 288 5016 — MB ChB 1980 Liverp.; MRCS Eng. LRCP Lond. 1980; MRCGP 1986; DRCOG 1984. Prev: GP (Rotat.) Liverp. HA; Regist. (Gen. Med.) Derby City Hosp.; SHO (Med.) Whiston & St. Helen's Hosps. Merseyside.

HUSSEY, Martin Henry Poole Hospital NHS Trust, Longfleet Road, Poole BH15 2JB Tel: 01202 665511 — MB ChB 1982 Leic.; DCH RCP Lond. 1995. Staff Grade (Paediat.) Poole Hosp. NHS Trust. Prev: Regist. (Paediat.) Poole Hosp. NHS Trust; SHO (Paediat. Oncol.) Roy. Marsden Hosp. Sutton.

HUSSEY, Olivia Jane Chatham House, Curry Rivel, Langport TA10 0EZ — MB BS Lond. 1996; BSc Lond. 1993. (Royal Free Hospital School of Medicine)

HUSSEY, Philip Graham Roper and Partners, Syston Health Centre, Melton Road, Syston, Leicester LE7 2EQ Tel: 0116 260 9111 Fax: 0116 260 9055; 67 Broad Street, Syston, Leicester LE7 1GH Tel: 0116 260 0889 — MB ChB 1981 Leic.; MRCGP 1987. Prev: Trainee GP Leicester VTS.

HUSSEY, Ruth Mary Liverpool HA, Hamilton House, 24 Pall Mall, Liverpool L3 6AL Tel: 0151 285 2338 Fax: 0151 285 2357 Email: ruth.hussey@liverpool_ha.nwest.nhs.uk; 11 The Serpentine, Grassendale, Liverpool L19 9DT — MB ChB 1979 Liverp.; MSc Manch. 1987; FFPHM RCP (UK) 1995; MFCM 1987; DRCOG 1983. Dir. (Pub. Health) Liverp. HA; Hon. Prof. (Pub. Health) Univ. Liverp. 1997; Hon. Prof. Pub. Health John Moores Univ. Liverp. 1992. Prev: Sen. Lect. (Pub. Health) Univ. Liverp.

HUSSEY, Susan Rurki, 53 High St., Cromarty IV11 8YR — MB BS 1981 Lond.; PhD Ed. 1990. (St. geo. Hosp. Med. Sch.)

HUSSIEN, Mr Ahmed Medhat Mohammed Ahmed 64 Bloomfield Road, Woolwich, London SE18 7JH Tel: 020 8854 7043 — MB BCh 1983 Cairo; FRCS RCPS Glas. 1993.

HUSTON, Carolyn Avenue Surgery, 24 The Avenue, Alwoodley, Leeds LS17 7BE Tel: 0113 267 9703 — MB ChB 1973 Birm.; MRCGP 1984. (Zimbabwe) Prev: SHO Nottm. Gen. Hosp. & W.m. Childr. Hosp. Lond.; Med. Resid. McMaster Med. Center Hamilton Canada.

HUSTON, Gareth James Seacroft Hospital, York Road, Leeds LS14 6UH Tel: 0113 264 8164 — MB BS 1969 Lond.; MD Lond. 1979; FRCP Lond. 1991; MRCP (UK) 1972. (St. Bart.) Cons. Phys. Rheum. Seacroft Hosp. Leeds & Hon. Sen. Lect. Univ. Leeds. Prev: Sen. Regist. (Rheum.) Guy's Hosp. Lond.; Chief Resid. & Teach. Fell. (Med.) McMaster Univ. Canada; Lect. (Clin. Pharmacol.) St. Bart. Hosp. Lond.

HUSTON, Robert Black 165 Ilford Lane, Ilford IG1 2RS — MB ChB 1943 Ed. (Ed.) Socs: BMA. Prev: Ship's Surg. Ellerman & Bucknall Lines; Ho. Phys. & Sen. Ho. Surg. Bridge of Earn Hosp. Perthsh.

HUTCHBY, John Peter (retired) West End Manor, West End, Northwold, Thetford IP26 5LG Tel: 01366 728555 Email: p.hutchby@ukgateway.net — MB BCh BAO NUI 1958; FFPHM

1981, M 1972; DIH Soc. Apoth. Lond. 1968; DPH Lond. 1967. Prev: DMO Heref. HA.

HUTCHCROFT, Bruce John Department of Respiratory Medicine, Northern General Hospital, Herries Road, Sheffield S5 7AU Tel: 0114 271 4646 Fax: 0114 271 5745 Email: brucehutchcroft@northngh-tr.trent.nhs.uk; Glenwood, 14 Dore Road, Dore, Sheffield S17 3NB Tel: 0114 236 1517 Fax: 0114 236 1517 Email: emp96bjh@sheffied.ac.uk — MB BS Lond. 1968; MD Lond. 1977; FRCP Eng. 1991; MRCS Eng. LRCP Lond. 1968. (Char. Cross) Cons. Phys. N. Gen. Hosp. Trust Sheff.; Hon. Lect. Univ. Sheff. Socs: Med. Res. Soc.; Brit. Thorac. Soc.; Chair. IM&T Gp. BAMM. Prev: Cons. Phys. Lodge Moor Hosp. Sheff.; Lect. (Med.) Manch. & Hon. Sen. Regist. Manch. Roy. Infirm.; Clin. Research Fell. Hosp. Sick Childr. Toronto, Canada.

HUTCHEON, Andrew William Moreseat, 159 Mid Stocket Road, Aberdeen AB15 5LU Tel: 01224 637204 — MB ChB 1968 Aberd.; MD Aberd. 1977; FRCP Lond. 1991; FRCP Ed. 1989; FRCP Glas. 1983; MRCP (UK) 1971. Cons. Phys. S. Grampian Health Dist.; Hon. Sen. Lect. (Med.) Grampian Health Dist. Socs: BMA; Amer. Soc. Clin. Oncol. Prev: Ho. Phys. (Gen. Med.) Aberd. Roy. Infirm.; Ho. Surg. Balfour Hosp. Kirkwall.

HUTCHEON, Mary Hosie (retired) 4 Byron Court, Beech Grove, Harrogate HG2 0LL Tel: 01423 504813 — MB ChB Aberd. 1944; FRCOG 1976, M 1957, DObst 1949. Prev: Cons. Obstetr. & Gynaecol. Harrogate Health Dist.

HUTCHEON, Stuart David 35A Ireland Street, Carnoustie DD7 6AS — MB ChB 1994 Dundee.

***HUTCHESON, Nicola Mary** Stoke Mandeville Hospital, Aylesbury HP21 8BD — MB BS 1997 Lond.

HUTCHESON, Patricia Margaret Whitegate, Broadwath, Heads Nook, Carlisle CA8 9BA Tel: 01228 560051 — MB ChB 1983 Aberd.; DCCH RCP Ed. 1989; DCH RCP Lond. 1989; DRCOG 1985. Staff. Grade (Community Paediat. Child Health) Dumfries & Galloway Community Health Trust.

HUTCHESON, Robert Bennett (retired) 1 Burnet Close, Robinswood, Gloucester GL4 6YS Tel: 01452 305841 — MB BS 1963 Lond.; BA McGill 1956; MRCS Eng. LRCP Lond. 1970; FRCOG 1983, M 1970; DObst RCOG 1969. Prev: Cons. O & G Glos. Roy. Hosp.

HUTCHESSON, Andrew Christopher Jolyon Department of Clinical Biochemistry, Royal Bolton Hospital, Bolton BL4 0JR Tel: 01204 390422 Fax: 01204 390464; 12 Bilsby Road, Alford LN13 9EW Tel: 01507 466655 Email: keith.dunnett@which.net — MB BChir 1982 Camb.; MA Camb. 1983, BA (Physiol. & Psychol.) 1979; MRCP (UK) 1986; MRCPath 1994. (Camb. & King's Coll. Hosp.) Cons. Chem. Path. Roy. Bolton Hosp. Prev: Lect. (Med.) Birm. Univ.; Sen. Regist. (Chem. Path.) W. Midl. Regional Train Scheme; Regist. (Chem. Path.) Roy. Hallamsh. Hosp. Sheff.

HUTCHESSON, Elizabeth Anne C/o Freshfields Mental, Health Unit, Brighton General Hospital, Elm Grove, Brighton TN2 3EW Tel: 01273 696011 Ext: 3190 — MB ChB 1977 Birm.; BSc (Med. Biochem.) Birm. 1974; MRCPsych 1986; T(GP) 1991; T(Psychiat.) 1991; Cert. Family Plann. JCC 1980; DRCOG 1979. Cons. Gen. Psychiat. W.bourne and Millview Hosps., Brighton; Hon. Cons. Burrswood, Groombridge, Kent. Socs: Roy. Soc. of Med. Prev: Sen. Regist. (Psychiat.) United Sheff. Hosps.; Regist. (Psychiat.) Guy's Hosp. Lond.

HUTCHIN, Alister Kenneth Mackinlay Victor Street Surgery, Victor Street, Shirley, Southampton SO15 5SY Tel: 023 8077 4781 Fax: 023 8039 0680; The Oaks, 2 Peterscroft Avenue, Ashurst, Southampton SO40 7AB Tel: 02380 292925 — MB BS 1965 Lond.; MRCS Eng. LRCP Lond. 1965; MRCGP 1976. (Univ. Coll. Hosp.) Socs: Fell. Roy. Soc. Med. Prev: Sen. Med. Off. Celle Stn., W. Germany (Min. of Defence).

HUTCHINGS, Adrian 38 King Richard Drive, Bearwood, Bournemouth BH11 9PE — MB BS 1978 Lond.; BSc (Hons.) Lond. 1976.

HUTCHINGS, Anthony High Street Surgery, 26 High Street, Wanstead, London E11 2AQ Tel: 020 8989 0407 Fax: 020 8518 8435; 20 Fairlands Avenue, Buckhurst Hill IG9 5TF Tel: 020 8505 1979 — MB BCh 1984 Wales; MRCGP 1989; DCH RCP Lond. 1988. Prev: SHO (O & G) Univ. Hosp. Wales; Community Paediat. Hillingdon HA; SHO (Paediat.) Hillingdon Hosp.

HUTCHINGS, Caroline Jane Southampton General Hospital, Mailpoint 874, Victoria House, Southampton SO16 6YD Tel: 02380 777222 — MB BS 1988 Lond.; MRCP (UK) 1991. Cons. (Rehabil. Med.) Soton. Gen. Hosp. Prev: Sen. Regist. (Rehabil. Med.) Salisbury Dist. Hosp.; Lect. (Rehabil. Med.) Soton. Gen. Hosp.; Regist. (Med.) Kent & Canterbury Hosp.

HUTCHINGS, Catherine Mary Rosemead Surgery, 8A Ray Park Avenue, Maidenhead SL6 8DS Tel: 01628 622023 Fax: 01628 639495 — MB BS 1985 Lond.; MRCGP 1989; DCH Lond. 1989; DRCOG 1987. GP Maidenhead.

HUTCHINGS, Charlotte Anne Farthings, Church Lane, Ewshot, Farnham GU10 5BD — BM BS 1993 Nottm.; DRCOG 1997. GP Regist. Altou Health Centre, Altou. Prev: SHO (Med.) Roy. Hants. Co. Hosp. Winchester.

HUTCHINGS, Douglas Gilbert (retired) 34 South Street, Wells BA5 1SL — MB ChB 1947 Ed.

HUTCHINGS, Gina Michele 8 Wallace Avenue, Worthing BN11 5RA — MB ChB 1995 Manch. (Manchester University) SHO Rotat. (Gen. Med.) Worthing Hosp. Prev: SHO (A & E) Preston.

HUTCHINGS, Graham Richard 118 Howard Road, Leicester LE2 1XJ — MB ChB 1995 Leic.

HUTCHINGS, Mr Henry Quartus, OStJ, Col. late RAMC Retd. Mulberry, Hazelwood Close, Storrington, Pulborough RH20 3HX Tel: 01903 742546 Fax: 01903 742566 Email: henry@llatchings.freeserve.co.uk — MB BCh BAO 1952 Dub.; BA Dub. 1950; FRCS Ed. 1968; T(S) 1991. Prev: Asst. Med. Dir. & Cons. Gen. & Cosmetic Surg. Al Zahra Hosp. Sharjah, Arab Emirates; Cons. Surg. RAMC; Regist. (Surg.) St. Nicholas' Hosp. Lond.

HUTCHINGS, Kim Nicolette Gowrie House, Chelmsford Road, Hatfield Heath, Bishop's Stortford CM22 7BH — MB BS 1988 Lond.; DRCOG 1993.

HUTCHINGS, Margaret Susan 31 Shirehampton Road, Stoke Bishop, Bristol BS9 1BL; 4 Ipswich Road, Elmsett, Ipswich IP7 6NY — BM 1985 Soton.; FRCPA 1995.

HUTCHINGS, Michael William (retired) 11 Clymping Dene, Feltham TW14 0JA Tel: 020 8890 3906 — MB ChB 1941 Liverp.; FRCPath 1966. Hon. Cons. Haemat. Paddington & N. Kensington Health Dist. Prev: Cons. Path. St. Chas. Hosp. Lond.

HUTCHINGS, Paul Jeremy George Department of Anaesthetics, Norfolk & Norwich Hospital, St Stephen's Road, Norwich NR1 3SE Tel: 01603 287086 Fax: 01603 287886 Email: paul.hutchings@norfolk-norwich.thnhs.com; Email: pjghutch@aol.com — MB BS 1978 Lond.; MRCS Eng. LRCP Lond. 1978; FFA RCSI 1986; FFA RCS Eng. 1987. (Guy's) Cons. Anaesth. Norwich HA. Socs: Assn. Anaesth. Prev: Sen. Regist. (Anaesth.) W. Midl. RHA.; Regist. (Anaesth.) Sheff. HA.

HUTCHINGS, Peter Treleven Meadowfield House, The Lane, West Deeping, Peterborough PE6 9HS — MB ChB 1994 Leeds.

HUTCHINGS, Steffan Lyn 25 Lancaster Grove, London NW3 4EX — MB BS 1997 Lond.

HUTCHINGS, Warwick (retired) Bitternsdale Farm, Lower Leigh, Stoke-on-Trent ST10 4PE — MRCS Eng. LRCP Lond. 1955; BSc. (Engin.) Lond. 1949, MB BS 1955; Dip. Loughborough Coll. 1948; FFA RCS Eng. 1965; DA Eng. 1961. Cons. Anaesth. City Gen. Hosp. Stoke-on-Trent. Prev: Cas. Surg. Off. Middlx. Hosp.

HUTCHINS, Mr Christopher John (retired) Nuneaton Private Hospital, 132 Coventry Road, Nuneaton CV10 7AD — MB ChB 1971 Liverp.; FRCS Ed. 1976; T(OG) 1991; FRCOG 1989, M 1976. Prev: Cons. O & G Geo. Eliot Hosp. Nuneaton.

HUTCHINS, Kenneth John Windmill Lodge Centre for Children's Services, Hownlslow & Speltnorwe Community & Mental Health NHS Trust, Uxbridge Road, Southall UB1 3EU Tel: 020 8867 5447 Fax: 020 8967 5248; 37 Kings Road, Uxbridge UB8 2NW Email: johnh@jags.co.uk — MB BS 1985 Lond.; MRCP (UK) 1990. Cons. Community Paediat. Hownlslow & Speltnorwe Community & Ment. Health NHS Trus; Hon. Cons. Paediat. Ealing Hosp. Trust.

HUTCHINS, Mr Philip Michael Royal Cornwall Hospital (City), Truro TR1; 28 Haddon Way, Carlyon Bay, St Austell PL25 3QG — MB ChB 1972 Bristol; FRCS Eng. 1978; FRCS (Orthop.) Ed. 1985. (Bristol) Cons. (Orthop.) Roy. Cornw. Hosp. Truro; Cons. (Orthop. s) St Michaels Hosp. Hayle. Socs: RASS; BESS. Prev: Sen. Regist. & Regist. (Orthop.) P.ss Margt. Rose Hosp. Edin.; Med. Off. Internat. Grenfell Assn. N. W. River, Canada.

HUTCHINS, Mr Robert Rayner 4 Edwards Mews, Islington Park St., London N1 1SG — MB BS 1988 Lond.; FRCS Eng. 1993.
HUTCHINSON, Alan Frederick 1 Downshire Gardens, Larne Road, Carrickfergus BT38 — MB BCh BAO 1975 Belf.; DRCOG 1977.
HUTCHINSON, Alison Ross Howden Health Centre, Howden West, Livingston EH54 6TP Tel: 01506 423800 Fax: 01506 460757 — MB ChB 1991 Ed. GP Livingston, W. Lothian.
HUTCHINSON, Professor Allen University of Sheffield, Scharr Regents Court, 30 Regents St., Sheffield S1 4DA Tel: 0114 222 0811 Fax: 0114 222 0791 Email: allen.hutchinson@sheffield.ac.uk — MB BS 1970 Newc.; FRCGP 1986, M (Distinc.) 1974; FFPHM RCP (UK) 1996, M 1991; DObst RCOG 1973; DCH Eng. 1972. (Univ. Newc. u. Tyne) Prof. Pub. Health Med. Univ. Sheff; Hon. Cons Community health Sheff.NHS.Trust. Prev: Trainer Div. Gen. Pract. N.. Region Postgrad. Inst.; GP Ashington N.d.; Sen.Lect.Health serv.Research Univ.Newc.
HUTCHINSON, Andrew Town End Surgery, 41 Town End, Caterham CR3 5UJ Tel: 01883 345613 Fax: 01883 330142 — MB BS Lond. 1970; MRCS Eng. LRCP Lond. 1970.
HUTCHINSON, Andrew 14 Lily Grove, Beeston, Nottingham NG9 1QL — MB BS 1979 Lond.; FFA RCS Eng. 1984. (St. Bart.) Cons. Anaesth. ICU Qu.'s Med. Centre Nottm. Prev: Sen. Regist. (Anaesth.) Nottm. HA; Regist. (Anaesth.) Leeds Gen. Infirm.; SHO (Anaesth.) Roy. Free Hosp. Lond.
HUTCHINSON, Brian Robert Galt 78 Strensall Road, Huntington, York YO32 9SH Tel: 01904 769245 Email: g3vgh@clara.net; Windward, 78 Strensall Road, Huntington, York YO32 9SH Email: g3vgh@clara.net — MB ChB 1950 Leeds. (Leeds) Prev: Mem. N. Yorks LMC & York DMT.; Receiv. Room Off. Leeds Gen. Infirm.; Hosp. Pract. (Med.) York Dist. Gen Hosp.
HUTCHINSON, Caroline Jane Ambrose King Centre, Department of Genitourinary Medicine, Royal London Hospital, Whitechapel, London E1 Tel: 020 7377 7000; 47 Merrow Woods, Guildford GU1 2LQ — MB ChB 1994 Birm.; ChB Birm. 1994; PhD Lond. 1992; BA (Hons.) Camb. 1984; MRCP 1997. (Univ. Birm. Med. Sch.) Specialist Regist. (Genitourin. Med.). Prev: SHO (Gen. Med.) Newham Health Care NHS Trust Lond.; SHO (Gen. Med.) P.ss Alexandra Hosp. Harlow; SHO (HIV & Genito Urin. Med.) St Mary's Hosp. Lond.
HUTCHINSON, Catherine Mary 123 Hall Gate, Cottingham HU16 4DA; 47 Priory Road, Cottingham HU16 4RR — BM BS 1984 Nottm. Prev: Fell. (Infec. Dis.) John's Hopkins Hosp. Baltimore, USA.
HUTCHINSON, Charles Edward Department of Diagnostic Radiology, University of Manchester, Stopford Building, Oxford Road, Manchester M13 9PT Tel: 0161 275 5114 Email: chutchin@fs1.sdr.man.ac.uk; 34 Heaton Road, Withington, Manchester M20 4PU — MB ChB 1980 Birm.; BSc Birm. 1977; FRCR 1990; FFR RCSI 1990; MD 1998. Sen. Lect. Univ. Manch.; Hon. Cons. Hope Hosp. Salford. Socs: Internat. Soc. MRI; MRCRadiol.; RCR Postgrad. Educ. Advis.NW region. Prev: Research Fell. & Hon. Sen. Regist. (Diagn. Radiol.) Univ. Manch.; Sen. Regist. (Radiol.) W. Midl. RHA.
HUTCHINSON, Christopher Tom Gurney Surgery, 101-103 Magdalen Street, Norwich NR3 1LN Tel: 01603 448800; 31 Oakfields Road, Cringleford, Norwich NR4 6XF Tel: 01603 502094 — MB BChir 1980 Camb.; MA Oxf. 1983; MRCGP 1985; DRCOG 1984; DCH RCP Lond. 1983. Socs: (Hon. Treas.) Norwich M-C Soc. Prev: SHO (O & G & Geriat.) Leeds E. HA; SHO (Paediat.) Leeds W. HA.
HUTCHINSON, Claire Victoria 27 Oakside Crescent, Evington, Leicester LE5 6SL Tel: 0116 243 2958 — BM BS 1996 Nottm.; BMedSci. II (I) Nottm. 1994. (Nottingham) Med. SHO (Gen. Med.) Palmerston N. Hosp. New Zealand. Prev: SHO (Emerg. Med.) Roy. Brisbane Hosp. Australia; Jun. Ho. Off. (Med.) Qu.s Med. Centre Nottm.; Jun. Ho. Off. (Surg.) W.ern Isles Hosp. Stornoway Isle of Lewis.
HUTCHINSON, Clare 42A Park Lane, Norwich NR2 3EF Tel: 01603 765146 — MB BS 1992 Lond.; MRCP Lond. Specialist Regist. Resp. & Gen. Med. Anglia Rotat.
HUTCHINSON, Mr Colin Hugh 11 Heath Villas, Free School Lane, Halifax HX3 0BB Tel: 01422 366293 — MB BChir 1979 Camb.; BA Camb. 1976; FRCS Eng. (Ophth.) 1984; FRCOphth 1991; DO RCS Eng. 1984. Cons. Ophth. Roy. Halifax Infirm.Huddersfield Roy. Infirm. Prev: Cons Opthamologist Aberd. Roy. Infirm.; Sen. Regist. (Ophth.) Aberd. Roy. Infirm.; Regist. (Ophth.) Leeds Gen. Infirm., St. Jas. Univ. Hosp. Leeds & Bradford Roy. Infirm.
HUTCHINSON, David Brian Ashton Wellcome Research Laboratories, Beckenham BR3 3BS Tel: 020 8658 2211; Betsoms Farm House, Pilgrims Way, Westerham TN16 2DP Tel: 01959 563487 — MB BS 1962 Lond.; DTM & H Liverp. 1971; DObst RCOG 1965. (St. Bart.) Clin. Pharmacol. Wellcome Research Laborat. Beckenham. Socs: Roy. Soc. Trop. Med. & Hyg. Prev: Ho. Phys. & Ho. Surg. Roy. Berks. Hosp. Reading.
HUTCHINSON, David Giles 28 St Catherine Drive, Hartford, Northwich CW8 2FF — MB ChB 1991 Leic.
HUTCHINSON, David Ian Evelyn Medical Centre, Marsh Avenue, Hope, Sheffield S30 2RJ Tel: 01433 621557 — MB ChB 1986 Sheff.; BSc Sheff. 1981, MB ChB 1986.
HUTCHINSON, David Noel (retired) 6 Meins Croft, Blackburn BB2 6QH Tel: 01254 262695 — MB ChB 1958 Manch.; MD Manch. 1969; Dip. Bact. Lond 1964. Prev: Cons. Microbiol. Preston Health Dist. & Pub. Health Laborat. Serv.
HUTCHINSON, David Robert 18 Shanreagh Park, Limavady BT49 0SF — MB BCh BAO 1988 Belf.; MRCGP 1992; DMH RCP Lond. 1993; DRCOG 1991. GP Co. Antrim. Prev: Trainee GP/SHO Rotat. Altnagelvin Hosp. Lond.derry VTS; Ho. Off. Coleraine Hosp.
HUTCHINSON, Deborah Department of Psychiatry, Royal South Hants Hospital, Brintons Terrace, Southampton SO14 0YG Tel: 02380 825527 Fax: 02380 825693 — MB BS Newc. 1968; MRCPsych 1986. Cons. Psychother. Roy. S. Hants. Hosp. Prev: Cons. Psychiat. (Learning Disabil.) Lifecare NHS Trust Surrey; Cons. Psychother. Warlingham Pk. Hosp. Surrey.
HUTCHINSON, Diana Joy Bleak Hey Road Surgery, 2 Bleak Hey Road, Peel Hall, Manchester M22 5ES Tel: 0161 437 2661 Fax: 0161 437 8332; 34 Heaton Road, Withington, Manchester M20 4PU — MB ChB 1979 Birm.; MRCGP 1983; DFFP 1993; DCH RCP Lond. 1982; DRCOG 1981. GP; Clin. Asst. in Gen. Med., Manch. Roy. Infirm.
HUTCHINSON, Diana Ruth 23 Bayswater Road, Jesmond, Newcastle upon Tyne NE2 3HR — BM BS 1992 Nottm.; MRCGP 1997; DRCOG 1996; DCH RCP Lond. 1995. GP Asst. Claypath Med. Pract. Durh.
HUTCHINSON, Doreen (retired) Barley Croft, Oakamoor, Stoke-on-Trent ST10 3AN Tel: 01538 702478 — MB ChB 1951 Birm.; MRCPsych 1972; DPM Eng. 1959. Prev: Cons. Child Psychiat. N. Staffs. Hosp. Centre.
HUTCHINSON, Edward Charles (retired) Ankerton Cottage, Slindon, Stafford ST21 6LX — MD 1954 Manch.; MD (Commend.) Manch. 1954, MB ChB 1945; FRCP Lond. 1962, M 1949. Prev: Cons. Neurol. N. Staffs. Hosp. Centre.
HUTCHINSON, Elizabeth Ann Salop Road Medical Centre, Salop Road, Welshpool SY21 7ER Tel: 01938 553118 Fax: 01938 553071; Brookland Hall, Welshpool SY21 9BU Tel: 01938 552230 — MB BS 1961 Lond.; BSc Lond. 1958, MB BS 1961. (St. Thos.) Prev: Ho. Phys. Roy. Waterloo Hosp.; Ho. Surg. Soton. Gen. Hosp.
HUTCHINSON, Felicia Dolores, MBE 45 Mornington Road, Woodford Green IG8 0TL Tel: 020 8504 1451 Fax: 020 8504 1451 Email: fay1@woodfordo.freeserve.co.uk — MB BS Lond. 1950; LMCC 1953. (King's Coll. Hosp.) Sen. Med. Off. Lond. Brook Advis. Centres; Seminar Ldr. Inst. Psychosexual Med.; Rep. Know How Fund DFID WHO Task Force to limit spread of STDs in E. Europe & the Former Soviet Union. Socs: Inst. Psychosexual Med.; Lond. Soc. Family Plann. Doctors; Forum Mem. Roy. Soc. Med. Prev: Ho. Surg. (O & G) & Ho. Phys. (Paediat.) King's Coll. Hosp. Lond.; Resid. Paediat. Kingston Gen. Hosp., Canada.
HUTCHINSON, Fiona Helen 21 Fenhall Park, Lanchester, Durham DH7 0JT — MB ChB 1990 Leeds.
HUTCHINSON, Geoffrey Over Wyre Medical Centre, Pilling Lane, Preesall, Poulton-le-Fylde FY6 0EX Tel: 01253 810722 Fax: 01253 812039; Farefield, Sower Carr Lane, Hambleton, Poulton-le-Fylde FY6 9DJ Tel: 01253 700599 — MB ChB 1966 Manch. (Manch.)
HUTCHINSON, Geoffrey Edward (retired) Seawards, 7 Fisherman's Avenue, Bournemouth BH6 3SQ Tel: 01202 418628 — MB BS 1962 Lond.; DObst RCOG 1965. Prev: SHO (Cas. & Orthop.), Ho. Off. (O & G) & Ho. Surg. & Ho. Phys. Roy. Vict. Hosp. Bournemouth.

HUTCHINSON, Mr Geoffrey Henry BUPA North Cheshire, Stretton, Warrington WA4 4LU; Kingswood Lodge, Kingswood, Warrington WA6 6JQ Tel: 01928 740538 — MB ChB 1974 Manch.; MD Bristol 1984; FRCS Eng. 1979; FRCS Ed. 1979. Cons. Surg. Halton Dist. Gen. Hosp. Runcorn; Hon. Lect. (Surg.) Univ. Liverp. Socs: BSG; BASO; BSI. Prev: Sen. Regist. (Surg.) N.. RHA; Wellcome Surg. Fell. Dept. Surg. Univ. Bristol; Regist. (Surg.) N. Manch. Gen. Hosp.

HUTCHINSON, Gerard Anselm The Maudsley Hospital, Denmark Hill, London SE5 8AZ — MB BS 1987 West Indies; DM West Indies 1993. Clin. Research Worker & Clin. Acad. Lect. (Psychiat.) Inst. Psychiat. Lond.

HUTCHINSON, Hamish Torrie Department of Anaesthetics, Kent & Sussex Hospital, Mount Ephraim, Tunbridge Wells TN4 8AT Tel: 01892 526111 Ext: 2530 Fax: 01892 513467 Email: hthutch@aol.com; Stitches Farm Barn, Eridge Green, Tunbridge Wells TN3 9JB Tel: 01892 853496 Fax: 01892 853496 Email: hthutch@aol.com — MB BS 1973 Lond.; MRCS Eng. LRCP Lond. 1972; FRCA 1976; DA Eng. 1975. (King's Coll. Hosp.) Maidstone & Tunbridge Wells NHS Trust; Trust Dep. Med. Dir. Socs: Pain Soc.; Assn. Anaesth.; (Div. Sec.) BMA. Prev: Sen. Regist. (Anaesth.) Soton. Gen. Hosp. & Basingstoke Dist. Hosp.; Regist. (Anaesth.) King's Coll. Hosp. Lond.; Cons. Anaesth. Tunbridge Wells HA.

HUTCHINSON, Helen Christine Family Planning Clinic, Auckland Road, Cambridge CB5 8DW Tel: 01223 533320; 60 Windsor Road, Cambridge CB4 3JN Tel: 01223 364705 Fax: 01223 364705 — MB BS Lond. 1969; MFFP 1993; DObst RCOG 1972; DCH Eng. 1971. (Univ. Coll. Hosp.) SCMO (Family Plann. & Psychosexual Med.) Addenbrooke's NHS Trust. Socs: Inst. Psychosexual Med.

HUTCHINSON, Mr Ian Fraser Cherry Tree House, Maxwell Road, Ben Rhydding, Ilkley LS29 8RP — MD 1984 Glas.; MB ChB 1974; FRCS Glas. 1978. Cons. Surg. Airedale Gen. Hosp. Keighley.

HUTCHINSON, James Anthony (retired) Barley Croft, Oakamoor, Stoke-on-Trent ST10 3AN Tel: 01538 702478 — MB ChB Birm. 1950; FRCPsych 1986, M 1971; DPM Eng. 1956. Cons. Psychiat. N. Staffs Hosp. Centre, St. Edwd. Hosp. Cheddleton & Lodge Day Hosp.; Sen. Clin. Lect. (Psychiat.) Univ. Keele. Prev: Postgrad. Clin. Tutor (Psychiat.) Univ. Birm.

HUTCHINSON, James Edmunds MacDonald (retired) 44 Northumberland Avenue, Gosforth, Newcastle upon Tyne NE3 4XH Tel: 0191 285 3192 — MB BS 1949 Durh. Prev: Sen. Med. Off. Dept. Health & Social Security Newc.

HUTCHINSON, James Robert McFarlane Woodside, Felixstowe Road, Nacton, Ipswich IP10 0DE — MB BS 1993 Lond.

HUTCHINSON, Mr James Ross (retired) Waulkmill House, Minnigaff, Newton Stewart DG8 6AF — MRCS Eng. LRCP Lond. 1944; FRCS Ed. 1949; FRCS Glas. 1962; FRFPS Glas. 1948. Prev: Cons. Orthop. Surg. Burnley Gp. Hosps.

HUTCHINSON, Mr James William 85 Almshouse Lane, Newmillerdam, Wakefield WF2 7ST — MB BChir 1990 Camb.; FRCS Eng. 1994.

HUTCHINSON, John Duncan Collingwood, Aylstone Grange Close, Alestone Hill, Hereford HR1 1GJ Tel: 01432 273133 — MB BS 1979 Lond.; MRCS Eng. LRCP Lond. 1978; FFA RCS Eng. 1984. (St. Bart.) Cons. Anaesth. Hereford HA. Prev: Sen. Regist. (Anaesth.) Midl. Train. Scheme.

HUTCHINSON, Katherine Frances Clare Laburnum Cottage, Peckforton Mall Lane, Spurstow, Tarporley CW6 9TG — MB BS 1981 Lond.; MRCGP 1986.

HUTCHINSON, Keith 49 Back Lane, Guiseley, Leeds LS20 8LS — MB ChB 1967 Leeds.

HUTCHINSON, Lilian (retired) 38 The Pastures, Kirkhill Est., Morpeth NE61 2AH Tel: 01670 514858 — MB BS Durh. 1940; DPM Eng. 1970. Prev: Med. Asst. St. Mary's Hosp. Stannington.

HUTCHINSON, Linda Ruth Department of Child Health, St George's Hospital Medical School, Cranmer Terrace, London SW17 0RE Tel: 020 8725 2203 Fax: 020 8725 2858 Email: l.hutchinson@sghms.co.uk — MB BS 1984 Lond.; MRCP (UK) 1989; DCH RCP Lond. 1987. Sen. Regist. (Paediat.) St. Geos. Hosp.

HUTCHINSON, Margaret Esther Jill (retired) The Oaks, 27 Clantilew Road, Portadown, Craigavon BT62 1RE — MB BCh BAO Belf. 1968; FRCP Ed. 1983; MRCP (UK) 1973; DCH RCPS Glas. 1970. Prev: Cons. Paediatr. Craigavon Area Hosp.

HUTCHINSON, Mark Ridley Redstacks, Shilburn, Hexham NE47 9LG — MB BS 1988 Newc.

HUTCHINSON, Mervyn John North Bristol NHS Trust, Frenchay Hospital, Bristol BS16 2EW — MB BCh BAO 1987 Belf.; MMedSci Keele 1997; FRCS Eng. 1992; FRCS 1997. Cons. in Orthop. Socs: BOA; BSS; BASS.

HUTCHINSON, Michael (retired) 23 Beech Avenue, Worcester WR3 8PZ Tel: 01905451314 — MB ChB 1943 Leeds; DObst RCOG 1945. Prev: Sen. Med. Off DHSS.

HUTCHINSON, Michael Charles Ekins 1 Town Place, Freshfields Lane, Scaynes Hill, Haywards Heath RH17 7NP — MRCS Eng. LRCP Lond. 1968; MB BS Lond. 1968, BDS 1963; LDS RCS Eng. 1963.

HUTCHINSON, Nevil Peter 6 Somerton Road, London SE15 3UG Email: 106643.2562@compuserve.com — MB BChir 1993 Camb.; MA Camb. 1993. Specialist Regist. Anaesth. Greenwich Dist. Hosp. Lond.

HUTCHINSON, Nicholas Jason 29 Manthorpe Crescent, Sherwood Vale, Nottingham NG5 4EF Tel: 0115 952 5605 — BM BS 1991 Nottm.; MRCGP 1996. Princip. GP Nottm. Prev: GP/Regist. Derby; SHO (O & G) Derby City Hosp.

HUTCHINSON, Nicolette Anne 60 Hackford Road, London SW9 0RG Tel: 020 7820 0883 — MB BS 1986 Lond.; MSc (Med. Microbiol.) Lond. 1990; MRCPath 1993. Sen. Regist. Rotat. (Med. Microbiol.) St. Geo. Hosp. Lond. Prev: Regist. (Med. Microbiol.) W.m. & St. Stephens Hosps.

HUTCHINSON, Patricia Lilian (retired) Long Meadow, Inval, Haslemere GU27 1AH Tel: 01428 644170 — MB BS 1945 Lond.; MRCS Eng., LRCP Lond. 1944.

HUTCHINSON, Patricia Mary Brownhills, Dockray, Matterdale, Penrith CA11 0JY — MB BS 1945 Durh.

HUTCHINSON, Patrick Dermott Lisburn Health Centre, Linenhall Street, Lisburn BT28 1LU Tel: 028 9260 3111; 25 Glenavy Road, Lisburn BT28 3UT — MB BCh BAO 1978 Belf.; MRCGP 1982.

HUTCHINSON, Paul Franklin Old Mill Surgery, 19 Old Mill Road, Chelston, Torquay TQ2 6AU Tel: 01803 605939 Fax: 01803 606525 Email: paul.hutchinson@gp-183667.nhs.uk — BM 1980 Soton.; MRCGP 1985; DRCOG 1982. (Southampton) GP.

HUTCHINSON, Pauline Grace (retired) Kingswood Lodge, Kingswood, Warrington WA6 6JQ — MB ChB 1974 Manch.

HUTCHINSON, Mr Peter John Ashton Academic Department of Neurosurgery, Addenbrooke's Hospital, University of Cambridge, Cambridge CB2 2QQ Tel: 01223 245151 Fax: 01223 216926 Email: peter.hutchinson@dial.pipex.com; 29 Mariner's Way, Cambridge CB4 1BN Tel: 01223 302995 — MB BS 1990 Lond.; BSc (Hons.) Pharmacol. 1987; FRCS Eng. 1994. (St. Bart.) Regist. (Neurosurg.) Addenbrooke's Hosp. Camb.; Research Fell. Brit. Brain & Spine Foundat. Prev: SHO (Surg.) St. Bart. Hosp. Lond.; SHO (Neurosurg.) Nat. Hosp. Neurol. & Neurosurg. Qu. Sq. Lond.; SHO (A & E) John Radcliffe Hosp. Oxf.

HUTCHINSON, Peter Julian Bidford Health Centre, Bidford on Avon B50 4BQ — MB BS 1983 Newc.; BA Oxf. 1980; MRCGP 1988; DRCOG 1987.

HUTCHINSON, Rachael Claire Betsoms Farmhouse, Pilgrims Way, Westerham TN16 2DP — MB BS 1992 Lond.; BSc 1989; FRCA 1997. (St. Bartholomew's)

HUTCHINSON, Richard 27 Claremont Avenue, Bramcote, Nottingham NG9 3DG Tel: 0115 925 1073 — MB ChB 1950 Ed.

HUTCHINSON, Robert Michael Department Haematology, Leicester Royal Infirmary NHS Trust, Leicester LE1 5WW Tel: 0116 254 1414 Fax: 0116 258 5772; 24 Stoughton Road, Stoneygate, Leicester LE2 2EA Tel: 0116 221 7885 Email: drhutch@msn.com — BM BCh Oxf. 1965; MA, BSc Oxf. 1965; FRCP Lond. 1989; FRCPath 1986, M 1975. (St. Mary's) Emerit. Cons. Clin. Haemat. Leicester Roy. Infirm. Hon. NHS Trust; Reviewer Brit. Jl. Haemat. & Jl. Clin. Path. Socs: Brit. Haemat. Soc.; Amer. Soc. Haemat.; Eur. Blood & Marrow Transpl. Prev: Sen. Regist. (Haemat.) Bristol; Regist. (Med.) Hillingdon Hosp. & Hammersmith Hosp.

HUTCHINSON, Mr Roderic Department of Surgery, Staffordshire General Hospital, Weston Road, Stafford ST16 3SA Tel: 01785 257731 Fax: 01785 245211; The Rookery, 40 St John's Road, Rowley Park, Stafford ST17 9AP Tel: 01785 246025 Email: rodhutchinson@lineone.net — MB BS 1984 Lond.; FRCS Eng. 1988. Cons. Gen. Surg. Staffs. Gen. Hosp. Socs: Assn. Coloproctol.;

W Midl. Surgic. Soc.; Midl. Gastroenterol. Soc. Prev: Sen. Regist. (Surg.) N. Staffs. Hosp.; Career Regist. Rotat. (Surg.) W. Midl. Hosp.

HUTCHINSON, Sarah 1 Carey Avenue, Wirral CH63 8LU — MB ChB 1993 Leic.

HUTCHINSON, Sarah Ashford, 138 Harrogate Road, Yeadon, Leeds LS19 6AH — MB ChB 1994 Sheff.; DRCOG 1997; MRCGP 1998. GP Regist. Leeds Gen. Infirm.; Clin. Asst. Leeds Gen. Infirm. A & E. Prev: SHO (A & E & O & G) Leeds Gen. Infirm.; SHO (c/o Elderly) Wharfedale Gen. Hosp.; SHO (Paediat., A&E, O & G) Leeds Gen. Infirm.

HUTCHINSON, Sheila Marjorie (retired) 38 Upper Brook Hill, Woodstock, Oxford OX7 1VA — LRCP LRCS 1948 Ed.; LRCP LRCS Ed. LRFPS Glas. 1948; MFCM 1972; DPH Manch. 1954; DObst RCOG 1950. Prev: Sen. Div. Med. Off. Lancs. CC.

HUTCHINSON, Shirley Elizabeth Hadleigh Lodge Surgery, 216A Wareham Rd, Corfe Mullen, Wimborne BH21 3LN Tel: 01202 694721; Hillview, Broadmoor Road, Corfe Mullen, Wimborne BH21 3RA Tel: 01202 694369 — MB BCh BAO 1976 Belf.; DRCOG 1978.

HUTCHINSON, Simon Patrick 114 Shankbridge Road, Kells, Ballymena BT42 3NJ — MB BCh BAO 1995 Belf.

HUTCHINSON, Sonya Jane 27 Bushtown Road, Somerset Forest, Coleraine BT51 3QP — MB BCh BAO 1981 Belf.; MRCGP 1986; DCH RCP Lond. 1986; DRCOG 1985. Clin. Med. Off. Dermat. Belf. Prev: Trainee GP Newtownabbey; SHO (O & G) Route Hosp. Ballymoney; SHO (Med. Rotat.) Roy. Vict. Hosp. Belf.

HUTCHINSON, Stephen Peter The Walled Gardens, Maynard Road, Grindleford, Hope Valley S32 2JD Tel: 01433 30649 — MB ChB 1990 Leeds; BSc Leeds 1987, MB ChB 1990. SHO (A & E) Leeds Gen. Infirm.

HUTCHINSON, Stuart Granville 30 Angerstein Road, Portsmouth PO2 8HN — MB BChir 1989 Camb.

HUTCHINSON, Susan Elizabeth Dept Of Anaesthesia, St George's Healthcare NHS Trust, Blackshaw Road, London SW17 0QT Tel: 0208 725 3316; 43 Earlsfield Road, London SW18 3DB Tel: 0208 870 7834 — MB BS 1983 Lond.; FCAnaesth. 1990. (Char. Cross) p/t Cons. Anaesth. Director of Day surg. St Geo.s Healthcare NHS Trust. Socs: Brit. Assn Day Surg.; Coll. Of Anaesth.s; assn. Of anaesth. Prev: Regist. (Anaesth.) Char. Cross & Harefield Hosps. Lond.; SHO (Gen. Med./Endocrinol., IC & Anaesth.) Whittington Hosp. Lond.; SHO (Anaesth.) W.m. Hosp. Lond. & St. Helier Hosp. Carshalton.

HUTCHINSON, Talia Ruth 16 Vardon Drive, Wilmslow SK9 2AQ — BM BS 1993 Nottm.

HUTCHINSON, Ursula Margaret Arthur Street Surgery, 47 Arthur Street, Brierfield, Nelson BB9 5RZ Tel: 01282 614599 — MB BCh BAO 1981 NUI.

HUTCHINSON, Victor Hugh (retired) 45 Mornington Road, Woodford Green IG8 0TL Tel: 020 8504 1451 — MB BS 1952 Lond.; DMRD Eng. 1958; LMCC 1953. Prev: Cons. Radiol. P.ss Alexandra Hosp. Harlow.

HUTCHINSON, William Armitage The Surgery, 29 High Stile, Leven, Beverley HU17 5NL Tel: 01964 542155 Fax: 01964 543954; 86 West Street, Leven, Beverley HU17 5LR Tel: 01964 542592 — MB ChB 1965 Leeds; DA Eng. 1969; DObst RCOG 1968. (Leeds)

HUTCHINSON, William David Antrim Health Centre, Station Road, Antrim BT41 4BS Tel: 028 9446 4937 Fax: 028 9446 4930 — MB BCh BAO 1974 Dub.; BA Dub. 1973. (Trinity Coll. Dub.) Socs: BMA. Prev: SHO (Anaesth.) Roy. Vict. Hosp. Belf., Belf. City Hosp., Craigavon Area Hosp. & Co. Dub. Infirm.

HUTCHINSON, William Fleury 8 Down Road, Rodwell, Weymouth DT4 0SB Tel: 01305 782924 Email: freewill@zetnet.co.uk — BChir 1980 Camb.; MB BChir Camb. 1981; MA Camb. 1980; FFA RCSI 1987. (Cambs. & Middlx. Hosp. Med. Sch. Lond.) Assoc. Specialist (Anaesth.) W. Dorset Hosps. Prev: Regist. (Anaesth.) Roy. Nat. Throat, Nose & Ear Hosp. Lond.; Regist. & SHO (Anaesth.) St. Geo. Hosp. Lond.; Ho. Off. (Med.) St. Helier Hosp. Carshalton.

HUTCHISON, Alan Simpson Biochemistry Department, Southern General Hospital, Glasgow G51 4TF Tel: 0141 201 1100 Fax: 0141 201 1698 Email: alan.hutchison@sgh.scot.nhs.uk; 52 Stamperland Gardens, Clarkston, Glasgow G76 8HG Tel: 0141 644 3537 — MB ChB 1977 Glas.; BSc (Hons.) Glas. 1973; FRCP Glas. 1991; MRCP (UK) 1980; FRCPath 1997, M 1986. Cons. Clin. Biochem. S.. Gen. Hosp. Glas.; Hon. Clin. Sen. Lect. Univ. Glas.; Hon. Club Doctor Qu. Pk. Football Club Ltd. Glas.

HUTCHISON, Alastair James Manchester Royal Infirmary, Oxford Road, Manchester M13 9WL Tel: 0161 276 4488 Fax: 0161 276 8022 Email: ahutchison@renal.cmht.nwest.nhs.uk; 14 The Mount, Altrincham WA14 4DX Tel: 0161 928 1940 — MB ChB 1983 Birm.; MD Birm. 1993; MRCP (UK) 1986; FRCP 1999. Cons. Renal Med. Manch. Roy. Infirm.; Hon. Clin. Lect. (Med.) Univ. of Manch. Socs: Eur. Dialysis & Transpl. Assn.; Internat. Soc. Peritoneal Dialysis; Manch. Med. Soc. Prev: Sen. Regist. & Hon. Regist. (Renal Med.) Manch. Roy. Infirm.; Lect. (Med.) Char. Cross & W.m. Med. Sch.

HUTCHISON, Andrew Fleming (retired) 4 North East Circus Place, Edinburgh EH3 6SP Tel: 0131 226 6451 — MB BS 1939 Durh.; MFCM 1974; DPH Ed. 1961; DTM & H Ed. 1954. Prev: Med. Off. Min. of Health & Environm. Control Kingston, Jamaica.

HUTCHISON, Andrew George Knockin Surgery, Knockin, Oswestry SY10 8HL Tel: 01691 682203 Fax: 01691 682700 — MB ChB 1969 Birm.; MRCS Eng. LRCP Lond. 1969; MRCGP 1976.

HUTCHISON, Mr Archibald Gardner (retired) 2 Letham Drive, Glasgow G43 2SL Tel: 0141 633 1388 — MB ChB 1953 Glas.; FRCS Ed. 1960; FRFPS Glas. 1961. Cons. Urol. Vict. Infirm. Glas. Prev: Regist. Gen. Surg. & Ho. Surg. Vict. Infirm. Glas.

HUTCHISON, Benjamin Stewart Kildary House, Kildary, Invergordon IV18 0NW — MB ChB 1944 Ed.; FRCGP 1996, M 1954. (Ed.) Prev: Surg. Lt. RNVR; Ho. Surg. Dumfries & Galloway Roy. Infirm.

HUTCHISON, Benjamin Torquil Neilson Pendleside Medical Practice, Clitheroe Health Centre, Railway View Road, Clitheroe BB7 2JG Tel: 01200 425201 Fax: 01200 442470; Cibola, Pendleton, Clitheroe BB7 1PT Tel: 01200 422394 — MB BChir 1976 Camb.; BChir Camb. 1975; MA Camb. 1976; MRCGP 1980; DCH RCP Lond. 1981; DRCOG 1978.

HUTCHISON, Mr Bruce McLaughland 597 Kilmarnock Road, Newlands, Glasgow G43 2TH Tel: 0141 637 4882 — MB ChB 1986 Glas.; FRCS Glas. 1991. Sen. Regist. (Ophth.) W.. Infirm. Glas.

HUTCHISON, Christopher Richard The Avenue Surgery, 1 The Avenue, Cirencester GL7 1EH Tel: 01285 653122 Fax: 01285 650098; High Tun House, Itlay, Daglingworth, Cirencester GL7 7JA Tel: 01285 651960 Fax: 01285 651960 Email: hutchtunc@aol.com — MB 1975 Camb.; MA Camb. 1971, MB 1975, BChir 1974; MRCP (UK) 1976. (St. Mary's) Hosp. Pract. (Gastroenterol.) P.ss Margt. Hosp. Swindon & Cheltenham Gen. Hosp.; Hosp. Pract. (Geriat.) Querns Hosp. Cirencester. Socs: BMA; RCP (Lond.). Prev: Regist. (Gen. Med.) St. Mary's Hosp. Lond.

HUTCHISON, Douglas Anderson Merrylee Medical Centre, 142-144 Clarkston Road, Glasgow G44 4EG Tel: 0141 633 2345 Fax: 0141 633 5262 — MB ChB 1977 Glas.

HUTCHISON, Duncan Charles Seton Department of Respiratory Medicine, King's College Hospital, London SE5 9PJ Tel: 020 7346 3166 Fax: 020 7346 3589; 39 Arlington Avenue, London N1 7BE Tel: 020 7226 9858 Fax: 020 7226 9858 — BM BCh 1956 Oxf.; FRCP Glas. 1981, M 1968. (Guy's) Sen. Lect. & Cons. Dept. Respirat. Med. Guy's Kings & St. Thomas' Sch. of Med. Socs: Brit. Thoracic Soc.; Europ. Repiratory Soc.; Assn. for Respirat. Technol. & Physiol.

HUTCHISON, Ewan James 1F1, 14 Roseburn Place, Edinburgh EH12 5NN — MB ChB 1992 Aberd.

HUTCHISON, Frances Catherine Edith 82 Townhead Road, Coatbridge ML5 2HU Tel: 01236 423557 — MB ChB 1941 Ed.; DA Eng. 1956. (Univ. Ed.) Prev: Regist. (Anaesth.) King Edwd. Memor. Hosp. Ealing & Gen. Hosp. Shotley Bridge.

HUTCHISON, George Bell (retired) 1 Charlotte Street, Dumfries DG1 2AQ Tel: 01387 67626 — MB ChB 1954 Ed. Police Surg. Dumfries & Galloway Constab. Prev: Surg. Lt. RNR.

HUTCHISON, Gillian Jane 54 Torridon Road, Broughty Ferry, Dundee DD5 3JH — MB ChB 1995 Manch.

HUTCHISON, Graham 147 Sharrowval Road, Sheffield S11 8ZA — MB ChB 1985 Glas.

HUTCHISON, Grant Leslie Department of Anaesthesia, Ninewells Hospital, Dundee DD1 9SY — MB ChB 1980 Dundee; FFA RCS Eng. 1985. Cons. Anaesth. Tayside HB Dundee.

HUTCHISON, Mr Iain Louis Oral and Maxillofacial Surgery, Royal London Hospital, Whitechapel, London E1 1BB Tel: 020 7377 7299

Fax: 020 7377 7095; 2 Eton Road, Hampstead, London NW3 4SP — MB BS 1980 Lond.; BDS 1973; FRCS Eng. 1984; FRCS Ed. 1984; FFD 1985. Cons. (Oral & Maxillofacial Surg.) St. Bart. Hosp. Lond., Roy. Lond. Hosp. & Homerton Hosp. Socs: Brit. Assn. Oral & Maxillofacial Surg.; Brit. Assn. Head & Neck Oncol.; Brit. Oncol. Assn.

HUTCHISON, Professor James Douglas Cowiehillock Cottage, Echt, Westhill AB32 6XD Tel: 01330 860716 — MB ChB 1979 Dundee; PhD Aberd. 1988; FRCS Ed. 1984. Prof. Orthop. Surg. Univ. Aberd.; Hon. Cons. Orthop. Surg. Grampian HB.

HUTCHISON, James Graham Pinney (retired) 38 Chantry Road, Moseley, Birmingham B13 8DJ Tel: 0121 449 1535 Email: jimhutchison@jamhut.dircon.co.uk — MB BS Lond. 1946; MD Lond. 1957; FRCP Glas. 1967, M 1963; FRCPath 1973, M 1963. Prev: Dir. Pub. Health Laborat. Birm. & Cons. Bacteriol. E. Birm. Hosp.

HUTCHISON, James Tudhope (retired) 20 Perton Grove, Wightwick, Wolverhampton WV6 8DH — MB ChB 1945 Glas.; FRFPS Glas. 1949; FRCP Glas. 1975, M 1962. Prev: Cons. Chest Phys. & Med. Dir. Chest Radiol. Serv. Wolverhampton.

HUTCHISON, Janet Katharine Newnham Surgery, Newnham on Severn, Gloucester; The Vicarage, Viney Hill, Lydney GL15 4NA — MB BS 1983 Lond.; LMSSA Lond. 1982. (St. Bart.) Socs: Christ. Med. Fell.sh. Prev: GP Retainer Scheme Newnham on Severn; Trainee GP Friarage Hosp. VTS; Civil. Med. Pract. Med. Centre Tofrek Barracks.

HUTCHISON, John Blundell Cerebrus Ltd, 613 Reading Road, Winnersh, Wokingham RG41 5UA Tel: 0118 977 3133 Fax: 0118 989 9300 — MB ChB 1985 Leic.; PhD Physiol. Liverp. 1980, BSc (Hons.) Physiol. 1977; MRCP (UK) 1988; MFPM RCP (UK) 1992. (Leic.) Med. Dir., Cerebrus Ltd. Prev: Dir. of Experim. Med., Astra Pharmaceut. Ltd.

HUTCHISON, Mr John Douglas (cons. rooms) The Physiotherapy Clinic, Nut Bush Lane, Torquay TQ2 6LF Tel: 01803 616050 Fax: 01803 616056; 35 Shiphay Avenue, Torquay TQ2 7ED Tel: 01803 613874 Email: jhutch@eurobell.co.uk — MB ChB Birm. 1965; FRCS Eng. 1974. (Birm.) Cons. ENT Surg. Torbay Hosp. Torquay. Prev: Sen. Regist. Sussex Throat & Ear Hosp. Brighton; Sen. Regist. Roy. Nat. Throat, Nose & Ear Hosp. Lond.; Lect. Dept. Surg. Univ. W. Indies Kingston.

HUTCHISON, Julie Kedie Flat 3F2, 28 Strathearn Rd, Edinburgh EH9 2AB — MB ChB 1997 Ed.

HUTCHISON, Katherine Rae Inverisla, Seafield Avenue, Keith AB55 5AS — MB ChB 1975 Aberd.

HUTCHISON, Peter George Greyfriars Medical Centre, 33-37 Castle Street, Dumfries DG1 1DL Tel: 01387 257752 Fax: 01387 257020; Lynford, 47 Nunholm Road, Dumfries DG1 1JW Tel: 01387 261611 — MB ChB 1977 Dundee; MRCGP 1981; Cert. Av Med. 1983. GP Princip. Dumfries; Authorised Med. Examr. Civil Aviat. Auth.; GP Trainer Dumfries. Prev: Trainee GP Dumfries & Galloway VTS.

HUTCHISON, Robert Brown Keith Medical Group, Health Centre, Turner St, Keith AB55 5DJ Tel: 01542 882244 Fax: 01542 882317 — MB ChB 1976 Aberd.

HUTCHISON, Mr Robert Stewart 88 The Grove, Marton-in-Cleveland, Middlesbrough TS7 8AP Tel: 01642 325555 — MB ChB 1971 Glas.; FRCOG 1991, M 1979. Cons. O & G S. Tees Hosp. NHS Trust.

HUTCHISON, Sallyanne Regional Medical centre, RAF Kinloss, Forres IV36 3UH — MB ChB 1992 Manch.; BSc (Med. Sci.) St. And. 1989; DRCOG 1996; MRCGP 1997. (St Andrews/Manchester) Civil. Med. Pract. Raf Kinloss. Prev: SHO (Cas.) Dryburn Hosp. Durh. & St. Helier Hosp. Jersey.; Trainee GP/SHO S. Cumbria VTS.

HUTCHISON, Stephen James Ross Nevill Hall Hospital, Abergavenny NP7 7EG Tel: 01873 732097, 01873 732100 Fax: 01873 732836; 8 Belmont Road, Abergavenny NP7 5HN Tel: 01873 857467 Email: stephen.hutchison@btinternet.com — MB ChB 1979 Aberd.; FRCP Glas. 1993; MRCP (UK) 1981; FRCP 2000 Lond. (Aberdeen) Cons. Phys. Nevill Hall Hosp.; Clin. Director (Med.), N. Hall Hosp. Prev: Lect. (Cardiol.) Univ. Wales Coll. Med.

HUTCHISON, Stephen Michael William Highland Hospice, 1 Bishop's Road, Inverness IV3 5SB Tel: 01463 243132 Fax: 01463 242758 — MB BCh BAO 1979 Belf.; MD Belf. 1990; FRCP Glas. 1995; MRCP (UK) 1983. (Belf.) Cons. Palliat. Med. & Med. Dir. Highland Hospice Inverness. Prev: Sen. Regist. St. Columba's Hospice Edin.; Lect. (Med.) Univ. Edin.; Regist. (Med.) Edin. Roy. & Stirling Roy. Infirms.

HUTCHISON, Stuart Rankine Jesmond House Practice, Chance Street, Tewkesbury GL20 5RF Tel: 01684 292813 Fax: 01684 274910; 3 Cotswold Close, Bredon, Tewkesbury GL20 7QW Tel: 01684 773095 — MB ChB 1985 Birm.; T(GP) 1991.

HUTCHISON, Susan Jane Cibola, Pendleton, Clitheroe BB7 1PT Tel: 01200 422394 Fax: 01200 425124 Email: hutchi@zetnet.co.uk — MB BS 1977 Newc.; MRCGP 1986. (Newc.) GP Clitheroe; Mem. Lancs. Family Pract. Comm. Prev: GP Blackburn.

HUTCHISON, Thelma Helen (retired) 28 Bristow Park, Belfast BT9 6TH — MD 1980 Belf.; MB BCh BAO 1959. Prev: Assoc. Specialist (Dermat.) Belf. City Hosp.

HUTCHON, David James Riddell St Cuthberts Consulting Rooms, St Cuthberts Way, Darlington DL1 1GB Tel: 01325 364624 Fax: 01325 364624; 9 Farr Holme, Blackwell, Darlington DL3 8QZ Tel: 01325 358134 — MB ChB Ed. 1970; BSc Ed. 1967; FRCOG 1990, M 1978. (Univ. Ed.) Cons. O & G Memor. Hosp. Darlington. Socs: Fell. Edin. Obst. Soc. Prev: Sen. Regist. (O & G) E. Gen. Hosp. Edin.; Regist. (O & G) Ninewells Hosp. Dundee; Regist. N.wick Pk. Hosp. & Clin. Research Centre Harrow.

HUTCHON, Susan Patricia 28 Breckhill Road, Woodthorpe, Nottingham NG5 4GP — MB ChB 1987 Aberd. Regist. (O & G) Soton.

HUTHART, Patricia Anne Lowcroft, Pinfold Lane, Romiley, Stockport SK6 4NP Tel: 0161 430 4071 — MB ChB 1964 Manch.

HUTSON, Andrew Massey Kentelms Health Centre, Rayleigh Road, Eastwood, Leigh-on-Sea SS9 5UU Tel: 01702 522012 — MB BChir 1978 Camb. GP Leigh-on-Sea.

HUTSON, Anne Jacqueline The Dairy House, Easton Royal, Pewsey SN9 5LZ — MB ChB 1986 Bristol; MRCPsych 1994; DRCOG 1991. Regist. Rotat. (Psychiat.) Oxf.

HUTSON, Carl Andrew Arundel Street Surgery, 10 Arundel Street, Treeton, Rotherham S60 5PW Tel: 0114 269 2600 Fax: 0114 269 3296; Robins Hill, Hooton Lane, Slade Hooton, Sheffield S25 1YQ — MB ChB 1984 Sheff.

HUTSON, Holly Sarah Florence Whitewell, Burry, Reynoldston, Swansea SA3 1BH — MB BS 1994 Lond.; BA Oxf. 1991. SHO (Med.) Leicester NHS Trust. Prev: Ho. Off. (Gen. Surg.) Brighton; Ho. Off. (Gen. Med.) King's Coll. Hosp. Lond.

HUTSON, Michael Alexander The Park Row Clinic, 2 Regent St., Nottingham NG1 5BQ Tel: 0115 941 1544 Fax: 0115 950 8174 Email: parkrow@aol.com; Village House, Cotgrave Road, Owthorpe, Nottingham NG12 3GE — MB 1967 Camb.; BChir 1966; MA Camb. 1967; DObst RCOG 1969. (St. Thos. Hosp. Lond.) Phys. (Orthop.) Pk. Row Clinic Nottm. & Wakefield Primary Care NHS Trust; Chairm. Policy Comm., Internat. Federat. Manual Med.; Pres. Intern. Federat. Musculo-Skeletal Med.; Extern. Examr. Dip. Sports Med. Lond. Univ.; Examr. Dip. Sports. Med. Soc. Apoth.; Examr. Dip. Musculo-Skeletal Med. Soc. Apoth. Socs: Medico-Legal Soc.; Brit. Inst. Musculoskel. Med.; Acad. Experts. Prev: Phys. (Orthop.) Leeds Gen. Infirm.; Dir. Sports & Fitness Assessm. Ltd. Lond. Bridge Clinic Lond.; Special Lect. (Orthop.) Nottm. Univ. Fac. Med.

HUTSON, Richard Challenor 26 East Causeway Vale, Adel, Leeds LS16 8LG Tel: 0113 230 0185 Email: rhh5@aol.com — MB ChB 1985 Leic.; MRCOG 1993. Sen. Regist. (O & G) The Gen. Infirm. at Leeds; Research Regist. Asst. Conception Unit Leeds Gen. Infirm. Socs: Brit. Gyn. Cancer Soc.; Brit. Soc. Colposc. & Cervic. Pathol. Prev: Regist. Rotat. (O & G) Dewsbury; SHO (Gyn.) Leeds W.. HA; SHO (Obst.) Bradford Roy. Infirm.

HUTT, Anne Francis (retired) Haulfryn, Terrace Walk, Llanfairfechan LL33 0EW Tel: 01248 680073 — MB BS 1953 Lond.; DA Eng. 1958. Prev: Gen. Practitioner.

HUTT, Nicholas Charles The Surgery, 52B Well Street, London E9 7PX Tel: 020 8985 2050 Fax: 020 8985 5780; 52B Well Street, London E9 Tel: profess. 020 8 985 2050 — MB BChir 1975 Camb.

HUTT, Miss Renata 4 Oldbury Close, Horsham RH12 5JZ Tel: 01403 272588 Email: renata@hutt84.freeserve.co.uk — MRCS Eng. LRCP Lond. 1990; MRCOG. Regist. Rotat. (O & G) St. Geo. Hosp. Lond. Socs: Med. Defence Union; BMA; MDU. Prev: Regist ESH Redhill; Regist. St. Helier Hosp. Carshalton; Regist. St. Richard's Hosp. Chichester.

HUTT, Richard Samuel Allen 30 Colville Terrace, London W11 2BU Tel: 020 7229 7107 Fax: 020 7229 7107 Email:

samhutt999@aol.com — MB BChir Camb. 1967; MA Camb. 1967; Cert. Family Plann. JCC 1971; MFFP 1993. (St George's Hospital London) SCMO Margt. Pyke Centre Lond. Socs: Inst. Psycho-Sexual Med.; Assoc. Fac. Homoeop.

HUTTER, Anton Woodlands Cottage, Brownshill, Stroud GL6 8AJ — Artsexamen 1989 Amsterdam; T(GP) 1994.

HUTTER, Christopher Duncan Denys 32 Fellows Road, Beeston, Nottingham NG9 1AQ — MB BS 1967 Lond.; MRCS Eng. LRCP Lond. 1967; FFA RCS Eng. 1972. (St. Mary's)

HUTTER, Mr Jonathan Alec Department of Cardiac Surgery, Bristol Royal Infirmary, Bristol Tel: 0117 928 3835; 23 Grange Park, Westbury-on-Trym, Bristol BS9 4BU Tel: 0117 962 1076 — MB BS 1976 Lond.; BSc Lond. 1973; FRCS Eng. 1981; MRCS Eng. LRCP Lond. 1976. (St. Geo.) Cons. Cardiac Surg. Bristol Roy. Infirm. Socs: Fell. (Transpl.) Papworth Hosp. Cambs.; Soc. Cardiothoracic Surg.; Internat. Transpl. Soc. Prev: Sen. Regist. (Cardiothoracic Surg.) Bristol Roy. Infirm. & Frenchay Hosp.; Regist. St. Thos. & Guy's Hosp. Lond.

HUTTER, Uwe Christian Southchurch Boulevard Surgery, 27 Southchurch Boulevard, Southend-on-Sea SS2 4UA Tel: 01702 468443 Fax: 01702 603281 — MD 1970 Vienna; LMSSA Lond. 1977.

HUTTERER, Marion Nikola Stepping Hill Hospital, Poplar Grove, Stockport SK2 7JE; 12 Warwick Road, Romiley, Stockport SK6 3AX Tel: 0161 494 9515 — State Exam Med 1992 Giessen; State Exam Med. Giessen 1992; MD Univ. Giessen 1994. (Univ. Giessen) Clin. Asst. (A & E) Stepping Hill Hosp. Stockport. Prev: SHO (Surg.) Grimsby Dist. Gen. Hosp.; SHO (Anaesth.) ScarBoro. Dist. Gen. Hosp.; SHO (A & E) Grimsby Dist. Gen. Hosp.

HUTTON, Alison Jane Fletcher Mount Road Surgery, 110 Mount Road, Gorton, Manchester M18 7BQ Tel: 0161 231 4997 Fax: 0161 230 6227; 51 Fullerton Road, Stockport SK4 4EN — MB BCh 1976 Wales; MRCGP 1984; DRCOG 1984.

HUTTON, Andrew John Chapel Street Medical Centre, Chapel Street, Ashton-under-Lyne OL6 6EW Tel: 0161 339 9292 Fax: 0161 339 7808 — MB ChB 1981 Manch.; MRCGP 1985; DMJ (Clin.) Soc. Apoth. Lond. 1991; DRCOG 1983. Police Surg. Gtr. Manch.

HUTTON, Charles William Department Rheumatology, Derriford Hospital, Plymouth PL6 8DH Tel: 01752 777111 — MB ChB 1976 Bristol; FRCP Lond. 1994; MRCP (UK) 1980. Cons. Rheum. Plymouth Gen. Hosp. Socs: Brit. Soc. Rheum. Prev: Cons. Rheum. Mt. Gould Hosp. Plymouth; Sen. Regist. (Rheum. Dis.) Bristol Roy. Infirm. & Roy. Nat. Hosp. Rheum. Dis.

HUTTON, Claire Louise 1A Clarence Street, Edinburgh EH3 5AE Tel: 0131 556 6064 Email: clair@buj.freeserve.co.uk — MB ChB 1996 Ed.; DFFP Glasg. & Newc. 1998. (Edinburgh) SHO (O & G) Falkirk & Dist. Roy. Infirm. Prev: SHO (Reproductive Med.), Internat. Centre for UGE, Newc.; SHO (O & G), Roy. Infirm. of Edin.; SHO (O & G), Falkirk.

HUTTON, Derek Alan Collingham Health Centre, High Street, Collingham, Newark NG23 7LB Tel: 01636 892156 Fax: 01636 893391; Westfield House, Westfield Lane, Collingham, Newark NG23 7LN Tel: 01626 892915 — MB ChB 1970 Manch.; FRCGP 1989, M 1982. GP Notts.

HUTTON, Donald Stuart Anaesthetic Department, Scunthorpe General Hospital, Scunthorpe DN15 7BH Tel: 01724 843481 — MB BS 1953 Lond.; FRCP Ed. 1994; MRCP Ed. 1966; MRCS Eng. LRCP Lond. 1953; FFA RCS Eng. 1960; DHMSA 1982; DA Eng. 1956, DTM & H 1959. (King's Coll. Hosp.) Cons. Anaesth. Scunthorpe Gen. Hosp. Socs: Fell. Roy. Soc. Med.; Assn. Anaesths. Prev: Cons. Anaesth. Qu. Eliz. Milit. Hosp. Woolwich; Cons. Anaesth. ANZUK Hosp. Singapore; Sen. Anaesth. Brit. Milit. Hosps. Hannover & Singapore.

HUTTON, Ellen Margaret Calderstones Hospital, Whalley, Blackburn BB7 9PE — MB BCh BAO 1971 NUI; DPH NUI 1979; DCH NUI 1972.

HUTTON, Francoise Marie (retired) The Priory Clinic, 14 - 18 New Church Road, Hove BN7 4FH — LRCP LRCS 1967 Ed.; LRCPS Glas. 1967; MRCPsych 1972; DPM Eng. 1972. Prev: Cons. Psychiat./Psychotherapist E.bourne.

HUTTON, Ian Dept. of Medical Cardiology, Royal Infirmary, 10 Alexandra Parade, Glasgow G31 2ER Tel: 0141 211 4723 Fax: 0141 211 4245 — MB ChB Glas. 1964; MD Glas. 1975; FRCP Lond. 1985, M 1968; FRCP Glas. 1978, M 1968; FACC 1982. Reader Univ. Glas. & Hon. Cons. Cardiol. Roy. Infirm. Glas. Prev: SHO (Med.) Glas. Roy. Infirm.; Research Asst. Cardiol. Dept. W.. Infirm. Glas.; Research Fell. Brit.-Amer. Heart Assn. Univ. Texas Dallas, USA.

HUTTON, Mr Ian Michael Heighington Hall, Potterhanworth Road, Heighington, Lincoln LN4 1RJ — MRCS Eng. LRCP Lond. 1967; MB BS Lond. 1967; BSc (Special Physiol.) Lond. 1964; FRCS Eng. 1972; LRCP Lond. 1967. (St. Mary's) p/t Cons. Gen. Surg. Lincoln Hosps. Prev: Sen. Regist. (Surg.) Hammersmith Hosp. & Roy. Postgrad. Med. Sch. Lond. & Reading Gp. Hosps.; Regist. (Surg.) United Norwich Hosps.

HUTTON, James (retired) 101 Copeland Drive, Parkstone, Poole BH14 8NP Tel: 01202 744140 — MD Ed. 1938, MB ChB 1934; MFCM 1971; DPH Ed. & Glas. 1937. Prev: MOH Boro. & Port Poole.

HUTTON, James Frederick c/o The Robertson Health Centre, Alness IV17 0UN; Flat 2 Right, 167 Hyndland Road, Glasgow G12 9HT — MB ChB 1986 Glas.

HUTTON, John Frederick Kilpatrick (retired) 25 Bushell Drive, Solihull B91 2QU — MB ChB 1939 Glas.; MA Camb. 1948; DMRD Eng. 1948; FRCR 1975; FFR 1953. Prev: Cons. Radiol. United Birm. Hosps.

HUTTON, John Neville Thomas (cons. rooms), 152 Harley St., London W1N 1HH — MB BS 1939 Durh.; FFA RCS Eng. 1954; DA Eng. 1947. (Univ. Durh.) Hon. Cons. Anaesth. Roy. Nat. Throat, Nose & Ear Hosp. Lond.; Teach. (Anaesth.) Univ. Lond. Socs: Fell. Roy. Soc. Med.; Assn. Anaesths. Gt. Brit.

HUTTON, Mr Kim Alexander Ramsay University Hospital of Wales, Heath park, Cardiff CF14 4XW Tel: 02920 743361 Fax: 02920 746322; The Old School House, 27 Palace Road, Cardiff CF5 2AG Tel: 02920 901920 — MB ChB 1983 Leeds; ChM Leeds 1995; FRCS Eng. 1988; FRCS Paediat 1996. Cons. Paediat.Surg.&urol.Univ.Hosp.Wales Cardiff. Socs: Brit. Assn. Paediat. Surg.; Assoc. Mem. Brit. Assn. Urol. Surg; Brit. Assn. of Paediatric Urol.s. Prev: Clin. Fell.sh., Paediatric Urol., UCLA Med. Sch. Los Angeles, Calif., USA.

HUTTON, Lynne Stewart 26 Wallfield Crescent, Rosemount, Aberdeen AB25 2JX — MB ChB 1995 Glas. SHO Rotat. (Med.) Aberd. Roy. Infirm. Prev: Ho. Off. (Surg.) Hairmyers Hosp. E. Kilbride; Ho. Off. (Med.) W.. Infirm. Glas.

HUTTON, Margaret McPhedran (retired) Ashdene, 108 Strathblane Road, Milngavie, Glasgow G62 8HD Tel: 0141 956 2975 — MB ChB 1962 Glas.; MA Hons. Glas. 1997; FRCPath 1983, M 1972; M.Phil 1999. Prev: Macmillan Sen. Lect. (Palliat. Med.) Univ. Glas.

HUTTON, Michael David Charles 3 Home Farm House, 6 Home Farm Close, Esher KT10 9HA — MB BS 1993 Lond.

HUTTON, Peter Department of Anaesthesia & Intensive Care, University of Birmingham, Queens Elizabeth Hospital, Edgbaston, Birmingham B15 32H Tel: 0121 627 2060 Fax: 0121 627 2062 — MB ChB 1978 Birm.; PhD Birm. 1973, BSc 1969, MB ChB 1978; FFA RCS Eng. 1982. Prof. Anaesth. Univ. Birm.

HUTTON, Mr Peter Andrew Noel Parkside Hospital, 53 Parkside, London SW19 5NE Tel: 020 8971 8000 Fax: 020 8971 8002 — MB BS 1974 Lond.; FRCS Eng. 1978; MRCS Eng. LRCP Lond. 1974. (Guy's) Cons. Orthop. Surg. Qu. Mary's Univ. Hosp. Roehampton & W.m. Hosp. Lond. Socs: Fell. Roy. Soc. Med.; Fell. BOA. Prev: Sen. Regist. (Orthop.) Univ. Coll. Hosp. & W.m. Hosp. Lond.; Regist. (Gen. Surg.) W.m. Hosp. Lond.; Ho. Off. & Cas. Off. Guy's Hosp. Lond.

HUTTON, Philip William (retired) Long Acre, Beckbury, Higford Lane, Shifnal TF11 9DL Tel: 01952 750248 — MB 1935 Camb.; BChir Camb. 1932, MB 1935; MD Camb. 1948; FRCP Lond. 1960, M 1936; DTM & H Eng. 1937. Prev: Cons. Phys. (Geriat.) Wolverhampton & Walsall Hosp. Gps.

HUTTON, Richard Adrian White House Surgery, 10/10A Market Place, Mildenhall, Bury St Edmunds IP28 7EF Tel: 01638 718177 Fax: 01638 718901 — MB BCh BAO 1976 Belf.

HUTTON, Richard David Welsh Blood Service, Ely Valley Road, Talbot Green, Pontyclun CF72 9WB Tel: 01443 622027 Fax: 01443 622028 Email: dave.hutton@wbs.wales.nhs.uk; Bryn Lodge, St. Lythans, Cardiff CF5 6BQ Tel: 02920 598627 Fax: 02920 596216 Email: hutton@stlythans.freeserve.co.uk — MB ChB 1972 Bristol; MRCS Eng. LRCP Lond. 1971; FRCPath 1991, M 1979. (Bristol)

Cons. Haemat. Welsh Blood Serv. Prev: Cons. Palliat. Med. Marie Curie Foundat.; Sen. Lect. (Haemat.) Univ. Wales Coll. Med.; Hon. Cons. Haemat. Cardiff Roy. Infirm.

HUTTON, Roger Malcolm PHLS, Coventry & Warwickshire Hospital, Stoney Stanton Road, Coventry CV1 4FH Tel: 024 76 844124 Fax: 024 76 220081; 24 The Fairways, Leamington Spa CV32 6PR — MB ChB 1969 Ed.; FRCPath 1988, M 1976. Cons. Microbiol. Pub. Health Laborat. Serv. Area Laborat. Coventry; JP Coventry.

HUTTON, Sarah Anne 2 Drax Avenue, Wareham BH20 4DJ — BM 1996 Soton. Sen. Lect., Keele Univ., Staffs. Research Fell. in Gen. Pract., Regional GP Unit, Birm.; Med. Adviser to C.E. andersons & Sons Ltd., Barclays Bank Ltd. & other Cos.; Primary Care Phys. (UK & abRd.); Vis. Cons. Learning Assessm. Centre, Horsham, W. Sussex; HP. Rshit S.port; HS RSCH Guildford; RAF Med. Pract.

HUTTON, Susan Jane Mediscreen, Trust Headquarters, West Holme Avenue, Oldham Tel: 0161 627 8093 — MB ChB 1982 Manch.; AFOM 2000; DRCOG 1984. SPR Occupat.al Med. Oldham The Roy. Oldham Hosp. Prev: Gen. Practitioner.

HUTTON, William Noel (retired) Mill House, 6 Redbeck Cottages, Woodbottom, Horsforth, Leeds LS18 4EQ — MB BChir 1962 Camb.; MA Camb. 1962; FRCP Lond. 1981, M 1965. Prev: Cons. Phys. Wharfedale Gen. Hosp. Otley, Coronation Hosp. Ilkley, High Royds Hosp. Menston.

HUTTON, William Woodman (retired) 4 Elderslie Road, Eltham, London SE9 1UE — MB ChB 1939 Ed.; MA Ed. 1934; DPH Ed. 1946.

HUTTON-TAYLOR, Ms Sonia Diana Medical Forum, Greyhound House, 24 George St., Richmond TW9 1HY — MB BS 1982 Lond.; FRCS Glas. 1987; FRCOphth. 1989; DO 1986. Indep. Specialist in Career Guid. within Med. Educat. Founder of Med. Forum (www.Med.forum.com). Prev: Cons. Career Guid., Human Resources, Med. Educat. Med., Surrey.

HUWEZ, Farhad Umer — MB ChB 1975 Mosul; PhD Glas. 1991; MRCP (UK) 1990; MRCPI 1988. (Mosul, Iraq) Cons Phys. Basildon Hosp. Orsett Hosp; Phys. i/c of stroke Serv.s. Socs: BMA; Roy. Coll. Phys.s; Brit. Geriat.s Soc. Prev: Research Fell. & Hon. Regist. Univ. Dept. Med. Cardiol. Roy. Infirm. Glas.; Staff Cardiol. Scott. CardioPulm. Transpl. Unit Roy. Infirm. Glas.; Sen Med Regist at Chelsea and W.minster Hosp.

HUWS, Anita Maria Grove Medical Centre, 6 Uplands Terrace, Uplands, Swansea SA2 0GU Tel: 01792 643000 Fax: 01792 472800; Southfield, 14 Cwmbach Road, Llanelli SA15 4EP — MB BCh 1987 Wales. (Cardiff) Clin. Asst. P. Phillip Hosp. LLa.lli.

HUWS, Dafydd John Lewys (retired) Ffwrnes Blwn, Caerphilly CF8 1NF Tel: 01222 884587 — MB BCh 1960 Wales; FRCPsych 1988, M 1971. Prev: Cons. Psychiat. S. Glam. HA.

HUWS, Nia Owain Bron Seiont Surgery, Bron Seiont, Segontium Terrace, Caernarfon LL55 2PH Tel: 01286 672236 Fax: 01286 676404; Rhedynog Felen, Llanwnda, Caernarfon LL54 5U Tel: 01286 830365 — MB BCh 1989 Wales; BSc Wales 1986; MRCGP 1993. (Univ. Coll. Wales) Socs: Y Gymdeithas Feddygol Genedlaethol.

HUWS, Rhodri Wyn St Georges Community Health Centre, Winter St., Sheffield S6 2WT Tel: 0114 271 8930 Fax: 0114 273 9129 Email: r.huws@sheffield.ac.uk; Email: r.huws@sheffield.ac.uk — MB ChB 1981 Liverp.; MRCPsych 1988; UKCP Accredited Therap. 1997; MBA 2000 Keele. (Liverpool) Cons. Psychiat. Community Health Sheff.

HUWS, Rhys Gwyn Ty-Elli Group Practice, Ty Elli, Llanelli SA15 3BD Tel: 01554 772678 / 773747 Fax: 01554 774476; Southfield, 14 Cwmbach Road, Llanelli SA15 4EP — MB BCh 1983 Wales.

HUXHAM, Christine Dorothy 15 Watermill Way, South Darenth, Dartford DA4 9BB — MB BS 1987 Lond.

HUXHAM, Kenneth Guy (retired) Chelmsley, Stones Lane, Catterall, Preston PR3 0HA Tel: 01995 602593 — LRCP LRCS Ed., LRFPS Glas. 1940. Prev: GP Preston.

HUXLEY, Caroline Ann 5 Lethbridge Road, Old Town, Swindon SN1 4BY Tel: 01793 488965 — MB ChB 1995 Manch.; DCH 1997; DRCOG 1998. (Manchester) Trainee GP/SHO Swindon VTS.

HUXLEY, Joanna Charlotte Airedale Hospital, Skipton Road, Steeton, Keighley BD20 6TD — MB ChB 1991 Leeds. GP Regist. Airedale Hosp.

HUXLEY, Philip Alexander The Surgery, Edward St., Earby, Barnoldswick BB18 6QT Tel: 01282 843407 — MB ChB 1991 Leeds; DA; MRCGP 1999. (Leeds) GP.

HUXTABLE, Christine Anne Milton Keynes General Hospital, Department of Anaesthetics, Eaglestone, Milton Keynes MK6 5LD — MB BS 1991 Adelaide.

HUYNH, Philip Sanh Nhut Lister Health Centre, Camden Square, London SE15 5LW Tel: 020 7277 4198 Fax: 020 7771 3810; 606 Streatham High Road, London SW16 3QJ Tel: 020 8764 9601 — MRCS Eng. LRCP Lond. 1981; Dip. Med. Saigon 1964. Socs: BMA.

HUYTON, Alison Judith 16 Adel Vale, Adel, Leeds LS16 8LF Tel: 01132610238 Fax: 01132610238 Email: drshep1@msn.com — MB ChB 1995 Leeds. (Leeds) GP Regist. Leeds VTS. Prev: Ho. Off. (Surg.) Airedale Gen. Hosp.; Ho. Off. (Med.) N. Allerton Hosp.

HUYTON, Catherine Susan Beech House, Fleetwood Road, Esprick, Preston PR4 3HJ — MB BS 1993 Lond.

HUYTON, Margaret Clare East Cheshire NHS Trust, Macclesfield District General Hospital, Macclesfield SK10 3BL Tel: 01625 421000; 2 Lindop Close, Knutsford WA16 8AY — MB ChB 1974 Manch.; MFFP 1993; DCH Eng. 1976. (Manch.) Assoc. Specialist (Community Paediat.) E. Chesh. NHS Trust; Clin. Med. Off. (Family Plann.) E. Chesh. NHS Trust; Assoc. Specialist David Lewis Centre for Epilepsy, Alderley Edge. Prev: Clin. Med. Off. (Family Plann.) Highland HB (N. Dist.).

HUZZEY, Reginald Hopkin (retired) 4 Woodchurch, Crapstone, Yelverton PL20 7UX — BM BCh 1955 Oxf.; MRCS Eng. LRCP Lond. 1955; MA Oxf. 1951; DObst RCOG 1958. Prev: Ho. Surg. (ENT) King's Coll. Hosp. Lond.

HVIDSTEN, Sasha Jane 58 Barnes Hill, Birmingham B29 5UW — MB ChB 1996 Birm.; ChB Birm. 1996.

***HWANG, Cheng-Yang** Flat 20, Carrington House, 39 Westwood Road, Southampton SO17 1DH; 77 Duchess Road, Singapore 269007, Singapore Fax: 65 468 5027 — BM 1998 Soton.; BM Soton 1998.

HWANG, David Tah Wee 123 Rectory Lane, London SW17 9PX Email: dtwh@hotmail.com — MB ChB 1995 Manch.; BSc (Hons.) 1993; MRCP (UK) 1999. (Manchester)

HWONG, Ming-Tak 11 The Avenue, Harrow HA3 7DB — MB ChB 1993 Ed.

HYAMS, Anne Barbara 24 Gorham Avenue, Rottingdean, Brighton BN2 7DP — BM 1980 Soton.; DTM & H Liverp. 1990; DRCOG 1984. Prev: GP Peacehaven; Trainee GP Hastings VTS.

HYAMS, Gillian Margaret 100 Station Road, Harpenden AL5 4TU — BM BS 1983 Nottm.; MRCPsych 1987. Socs: Roy. Coll. Psychiat. Prev: Staff Grade (Subst. Misuse) Community Subst. Misuse Team Blyth N.umberland; Sen. Regist. (Psychiat.) & Lect. (Drug Dependence) SE Thames Region.

HYAMS, Nigel Aubrey Hodge Road Surgery, 2 Hodge Road, Worsley, Manchester M28 3AT Tel: 0161 790 3615 Fax: 0161 703 7638 — MB ChB 1989 Liverp.; Cert. Family Plann. JCC 1993; T(GP) 1993; DRCOG 1992; DGM RCP Lond. 1991; DFFP 1999. (Liverpool) Socs: LMC Memb. Worsley constituent. Prev: Trainee GP/SHO (Psychiat.) Whiston Hosp.; Trainee GP St. Helens & Fazakerley; SHO (Paediat.) Whiston & St. Helens.

***HYARE, Harpreet Kaur** 70 Halford Lane, Coventry CV6 2GW Tel: 024 76 333543 — MB BS 1997 Lond.; BA Camb. 1994; MA Cambridge 1998.

HYATT, Mr Derek Wellesley 99 Harley Street, London W1N 1DF Tel: 020 7935 5944 — MB BS Lond. 1961; FRCS Ed. 1967; MRCS Eng. LRCP Lond. 1961; FRCOG 1989, M 1972. (Westm.) Cons. O & G Ashford/St. Peter's NHS Trust; Assoc. Prof. Clin. St. Geo. Univ. Sch. Med; Hon. Clin. Lect. St. Thos. Hosp. Med. Sch. Lond; Examr. Profess. Linguistics Assessm. Bd.; Examr. Roy. Coll. Obst. & Gyn. Socs: Blair Bell Res. Soc.; Brit. Menopause Soc. Prev: Sen. Regist. King's Coll. Hosp. Gp.; Regist. (O & G) St. Thos. Hosp. Lond.; Regist. Hosp. Wom. Soho Sq. Lond.

HYATT, Martin Frank (retired) — MB BS 1959 Lond.; MRCS Eng. LRCP Lond. 1959. GP Lond.

HYATT, Penelope Joan 4 Woolstone Road, London SE23 2SG — MB BS 1990 Lond.; MRCP Lond. 1994. (University College London) Prev: Sen. Regist. Univ. Coll. Hosp. Lond.; Sen. Regist. N. Middlx.

HYATT, Raymond Harvey Burnley General Hospital, Casterton Avenue, Burnley BB10 2P Tel: 01282 474592 — MB ChB 1976 Manch.; FRCP Lond. 1995; MRCP (UK) 1981. Cons. Phys. & Geriat.iian Burnley Healthcare NHS Trust. Socs: Brit. Geriat. Soc. Prev: Cons. Phys. Health c/o Elderly Sandwell Healthcare NHS Trust.

HYATT WILLIAMS, Mary Geraldine Corinthian Surgery, St Paul's Medical Centre, 121 Swindon Road, Cheltenham GL50 4DP Tel: 01242 707777 Fax: 01242 707776; Maiden House, Oxenton, Cheltenham GL52 9SE — MD 1972 West. Ontario; BSc (Hons.) Lond. 1965; MFFP 1992; MCPS Manitoba 1978. (Univ. West. Ontario, Canada) Hosp. Pract. (Gyn.) Cheltenham Gen. Hosp.; Sen. Clin. Med. Off. (Family Plann. & Menopause) Glos. HA; Hosp. Pract. Rheum. Cheltenham. Gen. Hosp. Socs: Brit. Menopause Soc.; Primary Care Rheum. Soc. Prev: Hosp. Practitioner Psychiat.

HYATT WILLIAMS, Robert The Royal Well Surgery, St Pauls Medical Centre, 121 Swindon Road, Cheltenham GL50 4DP Tel: 01242 707701 — MRCS Eng. LRCP Lond. 1967; LMCC 1969. Socs: BMA & Assoc. Fac. Homeop. Prev: Sen. Resid. Montreal Neurol. Inst., Canada; Cons. Neurol. Chas. Lemoyne Hosp. Montreal, Canada.

HYBEL, Anthony Peter 8 Richmond Av, London E4 9RS — MB BS 1997 Lond.

HYDE, Andrew John Alexander 52 Newton Crescent, Rosyth, Dunfermline KY11 2QW Tel: 01383 415552 — MB ChB 1986 Glas. SHO (Paediat.) Roy. Hosp. Sick Childr. & Stobhill Hosp. Glas. Prev: Trainee GP Irvine Ayrsh.; SHO (Paediat.) CrossHo. Hosp. Ayrsh.

HYDE, Bryan John 63 Newland Street, Eynsham, Oxford Tel: 01865 881206 — MB BChir 1961 Camb.; MB BChir Camb. 1962; MRCS Eng. LRCP Lond. 1961. (Camb. & Lond. Hosp.) Prev: Sen. Resid. Obst. Bristol Matern. Hosp.; SHO (Paediat.) All St.s' Hosp. Chatham; Ho. Phys. (Dermat.) Lond. Hosp.

HYDE, Caroline Susan Dept. of Child and Adolescent Psychiatry, Thelma Golding Centre, 92 Bath Road, Hounslow TW3 3FZ — BSc (Hons.) Lond. 1973, MB BS 1982; MRCPsych 1988; DCH RCP Lond. 1985. Cons. Child & Adolesc. Psychiat. Hounslow & Spelthorne.; Hon. Clin. Sen. Lect., Imperial Coll. Sch. of Med. (St. Mary's Campus). Prev: Sen. Regist. (Psychol. Med.) Gt. Ormond St. Hosp. Lond.

HYDE, Christopher John ARIF, Department of Public Health & Epidemiology, University of Birmingham, Edgbaston, Birmingham B15 2TT Tel: 0121 414 7870 Fax: 0121 414 7878 Email: c.j.hyde@bham.ac.uk; 1 Evendine Corner, Colwall Green, Malvern WR13 6NT Tel: 01684 541631 — MB BS 1986 Lond.; MRCP (UK) 1989; MFPHM RCP (UK) 1994. Sen. Lect. in Pub. Health, Univ. of Birm. Prev: Sen. Regist. (Pub. Health Med.) Anglia & Oxf. RHA.; Sen. Regist. (Pub. Health Med.) W. Suff. HA & Norwich; SHO (Med.) Qu. Mary's Hosp. Sidcup.

HYDE, Elizabeth Anne Mackintosh (retired) Greenbank, 15 The Firs, Bowdon, Altrincham WA14 2TG Tel: 0161 928 3545 — MB ChB 1956 Manch.; DObst RCOG 1957.

HYDE, Mr Ian David Lindisfarne, Burton, Lincoln LN1 2RD — MB BS 1963 Lond.; FRCS Eng. 1972; MRCS Eng. LRCP Lond. 1963. Cons. Orthop. Surg. N. Lincs. & S. Lincs. HAs. Prev: Sen. Regist. (Orthop.) Bath Health Dist.; Research Fell. (Orthop.) Hosp. Sick Childr. Toronto, Canada; Orthop. Regist. Dundee Roy. Infirm.

HYDE, Ivan (retired) Chapel Lane, Lyndhurst SO43 7FG Tel: 023 8028 2810 — MB ChB 1949 Birm.; FRCP Ed. 1971, M 1958; FRCR 1975; FFR 1964; DMRD Eng. 1960; DCH RCP Lond. 1951. Prev: Radiol. Soton. & SW Hants. HA.

HYDE, James (retired) The Paddock, Caldwell, Richmond DL11 7QA Tel: 01325 718177 Email: james.hyde@which.net — MB BS 1958 Lond. Prev: Ho. Surg. & Cas. Off. Char. Cross Hosp. Lond.

HYDE, Jean Lesley Wirksworth Health Centre, St. Johns Street, Wirksworth, Matlock DE4 4DT Tel: 01629 822434 — MB ChB 1972 Ed.; MRCP (UK) 1978.

HYDE, Jeffrey (retired) Sparrow's Nest, Amroth Road, Amroth, Narberth SA67 8QJ Tel: 01834 831156 Fax: 01834 831156 Email: hydeanguilla@yahoo.com — MB ChB Bristol 1964; FRCS Ed. 1972; DO Eng. 1971; DObst RCOG 1966; PhC Ed. 1957. Prev: Cons. Ophth. W. Wales Gen. Hosp. Carmarthen.

HYDE, John Broadhurst 6 Pettit's Close, Fulbourn, Cambridge CB1 5BH Tel: 01223 880559 — MB ChB 1971 Liverp.; MRCGP 1977; DCH Eng. 1976; DObst RCOG 1974. Psychiat. Regist. Fulbourn Hosp. Cambs. Prev: Med. Regist. Newmarket Hosp.

HYDE, John Cyril Lister Hospital, Stevenage SG1 4 — MB BCh 1966 Witwatersrand; MRCP (UK) 1972; FRCPCH 1997. Cons. Paediat. Lister Hosp. Stevenage.

HYDE, John Michael English (retired) 101 Barnt Green Road, Rednal, Birmingham B45 8PH Tel: 0121 447 7767 — MB BCh Wales 1948; MRCS Eng. LRCP Lond. 1949; LMCC 1951. Prev: on Active Staff Qu.sway Gen. Hosp. Toronto.

HYDE, John Nicholas Worcester Road Surgery, 74A Worcester Road, West Hagley, Stourbridge DY9 0NH Tel: 01562 882474 Fax: 01562 887185; The Grove, 7 Mill Lane, Blakedown, Kidderminster DY10 3ND — BM BCh 1980 Oxf.

HYDE, Mr Jonathan Andrew Jeremy 65 Metchley Lane, Harborne, Birmingham B17 0HT Tel: 0121 605 1800 Email: j.a.j.hyde@bham.ac.uk — MB BS 1989 Lond.; BSc Lond. 1986; FRCS Ed. 1993; FRCS Eng. 1993. (Univ. Coll. Hosp. Lond.) Specialist Regist. (Cardiothoracic Surg.) Qu. Eliz. Med. Centre Birm. Socs: Soc. Cardiothoracic Surg. GB & Irel. Prev: Regist. (Cardiothoracic) Roy. Lond. Hosp.

HYDE, Judith Pamela Ground Floor Flat, 13 Cornwallis Crescent, Clifton, Bristol BS8 4PJ Tel: 0117 973 2080 — MB ChB 1992 Aberd. SHO (O & G) S.mead Hosp. W.bury on Trym Bristol.

HYDE, Keith Robin Webb House, Victoria Avenue, Crewe CW2 7SQ Tel: 0161 773 9121 Email: khyde@webbhouse.mhss-tr.nwest.nhs.uk — MB BS 1971 Lond.; FRCPsych 1993, M 1975. (King's Coll. Hosp.) Cons. Psychother. Webb Ho. Ment. Health Serv.s of Salford NHS Trust; Clin. Dir. Webb Ho. Ment. Health Serv.s of Salford NHS Trust. Socs: Inst. Gp. Anal. Prev: Med. Dir. Meal Health Servs. Salford Trust; Sen. Regist. (Psychiat.) St. Geo. Hosp. Lond.; Cons.Psycho.Red Ho. Salford.

HYDE, Maria Frances St Marys Road Surgery, St. Marys Road, Newbury RG14 1EQ Tel: 01635 31444 Fax: 01635 551316; Drumragh, 1 Speen Lane, Newbury RG14 1RW Tel: 01635 40513 — MB BS 1979 Lond.; BSc (Pharm.) Lond. 1976, MB BS 1979; DRCOG 1983. (Univ. Coll. Hosp.)

HYDE, Marie Therese 14 Maldon Road, Standish, Wigan WN6 0EX — BA, MB BCh BAO Dub. 1952; DCH RCPSI 1955; DPH Liverp. 1957. (T.C. Dub.)

HYDE, Nicholas Charles Clockhouse, Stichens Green, Streatley on Thames, Reading RG8 9DU Tel: 01491 873826 — MB BS 1993 Lond.; LDS RCS Eng. 1984; BDS Lond. 1984; FDS RCS Eng. 1992; FRCS 1996. (The London Hospital Medical College) Specialist Regist. (Maxillo-Facial Surg.) UCH/GOS Lond. Prev: SHO (A & E) St. Geo.'s; SHO (Gen. Surg.) St. Helier Hosp.; Specialist Regist. (Maxillo-Facial) Qu. Mary's Roehampton.

HYDE, Paula Jane Courtlands, Wellow, Bath BA2 8PU — MB ChB 1986 Birm.; ChB Birm. 1986; DRCOG 1991; DA (UK) 1990; MRCGP (UK) 1994.

HYDE, Penny 7 Glanfield Road, Beckenham BR3 3JS — MB ChB 1992 Leic.; DRCOG 1995; DCH RCP Lond. 1994; MRCGP 1996. (Leicester University) Socs: MRCGP. Prev: GP Locum; GP Regist.

HYDE, Peter Rodney Hawthorn Surgery, Scotton Road, Scotter, Gainsborough DN21 3SB Tel: 01724 764641 Fax: 01724 764265; Highfield House, Scotton Road, Scotter, Gainsborough DN21 3SB Tel: 01724 764102 — MB BS 1971 Lond. Bd mem. N.W. Links PCG prescribing Lead PCG. Prev: Med.Advis. Lincs HA.

HYDE, Robin Fellows Watcombe Hill House, Teignmouth Road, Torquay TQ1 4SQ Tel: 01803 558257 — MB ChB 1974 Liverp.; MRCGP 1979; DGM RCP Lond. 1986; DRCOG 1976.

HYDE, Ronald Dennis 3 The Puddledocks, Sutton Poyntz, Weymouth DT3 6LZ Tel: 01305 834409 — MB BChir 1955 Camb.; MD Camb. 1963; FRCP Lond. 1980, M 1958; FRCPath 1976, M 1964. (St. Thos.) Hon. Emerit. Cons. Haemat. Soton. Univ. Hosps. NHS Trust. Socs: Assn. Clin. Path.; Brit. Soc. Haematol. Prev: Lect. (Clin. Path.) St. Thos. Hosp. & Med. Sch. Lond.; Resid. Pathol. Sen. Med. Cas. Off. St. Thos. Hosp. Lond.; Clin.Teach. (Haemat). Univ.Soton.

HYDE, Rowa Ann 3 Rubislaw Drive, Bearsden, Glasgow G61 1PR; 2 Sunscales House, lorton Road, Cockermouth CA13 9DU — MB ChB 1983 Manch.; BSc St. And. 1980; FRCA 1992; DCH RCP Lond. 1988. Research Asst. (Anaesth.) Vale of Leven Dist. Gen. Hosp. Alexandria. Prev: Staff Grade (Anaesth.) Blackburn, Hyndburn & Ribble Valley NHS Trust.

HYDE, Shona Louise 57 Bernard Street, St Albans AL3 5QL Tel: 01727 857743 — MB BS 1993 Lond.; MRCP 1996. (UCH/Middx.)

HYDE, Simon Edward c/o 8 Billy Lows Lane, Potters Bar EN6 1XN — MB BS 1987 Melbourne.

HYDE, Susan Margaret Bowland Road, 52 Bowland Road, Baguley, Manchester M23 1JX Tel: 0161 998 2014 Fax: 0161 945 6354; Newlands, Stenner Lane, Didsbury, Manchester M20 2RQ — MB ChB 1990 Manch.; BSc St. And. 1986; MRCGP 1996. (St Andrews & Manchester) GP Wythenshawe, Manch. Prev: SHO (A & E) Bolton Roy. Infirm.; Trainee GP Wythenshawe Hosp. Manch. VTS; SHO (Med.) Amer. Hosp., Paris.

HYDE, Susan Wendy 3 Tyberton Place, Hunts Cross, Liverpool L25 0PL Tel: 0151 486 3788 — MB ChB 1989 Liverp.; MRCGP 1993; DCH RCP Lond. 1992; DRCOG 1991. Prev: Trainee GP Liverp.; SHO (A & E & Geriat.) Liverp.

HYDE, Thomas Alexander 48A Lancaster Road, London W11 1QR — MB BS 1993 Lond.

HYDE, Trevor William Wirksworth Health Centre, St. Johns Street, Wirksworth, Matlock DE4 4DT Tel: 01629 822434; High Meadows, 51 Summer Lane, Wirksworth, Derby DE4 4EB Tel: 01629 823329 — MB BS 1974 Lond.; BA (Hons.) Cardiff 1968; MRCGP 1978; DObst RCOG 1976. (Middlx. Hosp. Med. Sch.)

HYDE-FORSTER, Isatou South Downs Health NHS Trust, School Clinic, Morley St., Brighton BN2 2RA Tel: 01273 267300 — State Exam Med 1980 Ulm. Staff Grade Commun. Child health.

HYDER, Chaudry Kamruz Zaman Ightenhill Medical Centre, Tabor Street, Burnley BB12 0HL Tel: 01282 424464 Fax: 01282 416327 — MB BS 1972 Poona.

HYDER, Mohammed Nisar London Road Practice, 84-86 London Road, Bedford MK42 0NT Tel: 01234 266851 Fax: 01234 363998; Tel: 01234 309830 — MB BS 1972 Osmania. Prev: Hosp. Pract. (Geriat. Med.) Clapham Hosp. Bedford; SHO (Geriat. & Chest Med.) Burton Dist. Hosp. & Bedford Gen. Hosp.

HYDER, Mohammed Tajuddin 121 Whitburn Road, Cleadon, Sunderland SR6 7QX — MB BS 1968 Dacca; MB BS Dacca Bangladesh 1968; DA Eng. 1977 Dacca. Assoc. Specialist (Anaesth.) Gen. Hosp. S. Shields.

HYDER, Mr Nasiruddin 12 Laurel Close, Middlewich CW10 9QL — MB BS 1984 Karachi; FRCS Ed. 1989. Regist. (Orthop.) Airedale Gen. Hosp. Prev: Regist. (Orthop.) N. Tyneside Gen. Hosp.; SHO (Orthop.) Roy. Preston Hosp.; SHO (Gen. Surg.) Grimsby Dist. Gen. Hosp.

HYDER, Sabiha Launceston Close Surgery, Winsford Tel: 01606 861200; 12 Laurel Close, Middlewich CW10 9QL — MB ChB 1988 Manch.; BSc St. And. 1985; MRCGP 1996. GP Retainer. Socs: BMA; NANP. Prev: GP Retainer Silsden; GP Trainee Bingley; GP Trainee Silsden.

HYDES, Ciaran Elizabeth — BM 1994 Soton.; DFFP 1998; MRCGP 1998; DCH 1997; DRCOG 1996. GP W. Sussex.

HYER, Stephen Laurence St Helier Hospital, Wrythe Lane, Carshalton SM5 1AA Tel: 020 8644 4343 Fax: 020 8644 4377; 51 The Drive, Wallington SM6 9ND Fax: 020 8647 1076 Email: shyer@sthelier.sghms.ac.uk — MB BS 1976 Lond.; MBA 1996; MB BS (Hons.) Lond. 1976; MD Lond. 1990; MRCP (UK) 1979; FRCP Lond. 1997; DTM & H Liverp. 1980. (Univ. Coll. Hosp. Lond.) Cons. Phys. St Helier Hosp.; Hon. Cons. Phys. Roy. Marsden Hosp. Sutton; Sen. Lect. St. Geo. Hosp. Med. Sch. Prev: Sen. Regist. St. Geo. Hosp. Lond.; Research Regist. Hammersmith Hosp. Lond.; Regist. (Med.) Walsgrave Hosp. Coventry.

HYER, Warren Frank Northwick Park Hospital, Watford Road, Harrow HA1 3UJ Tel: 020 8869 2644 Fax: 020 8869 2927 Email: warrenhyer@aol.com; 16 Pikes End, Pinner HA5 2EX Tel: 0208 866 5598 — MB ChB 1988 Manch.; MRCP (UK) 1992. Cons. Paediat. Socs: Brit. Soc. Paediat. Gastroenterol.; MRCPCH; Roy. Coll. Phys. Prev: Sen. Regist. (Paediat.) N.wick Pk. & St. Marks NHS Trust; Regist. & Lect. (Child Health) St. Bart. Med. Sch. Lond.; Regist. (Neonat.) Homerton Hosp. Lond.

HYETT, Anthony Roy (retired) The Old Manor, Plaxdale Green, Stansted, Sevenoaks TN15 7PE — BSc (Hons. Anat.) Lond. 1953, MB BS 1956; MRCS Eng. LRCP Lond. 1956. Treas. Med. Off. Guild Freemen City of Lond. Prev: Med. Off. Bromley HA.

HYETT, Catherine Ann Meddygfa Llwyncelyn Practice, Park Road, Whitchurch, Cardiff CF14 7EZ Tel: 029 2035 7602 Fax: 029 2062 3839 — MB BCh 1987 Wales; MRCGP 1991.

HYETT, Elaine Louise 4 Kip Avenue, Inverkip, Greenock PA16 0DX — MB ChB 1997 Aberd.

HYETT, Mr Jonathan Anthony 18 Eton Place, Eton College Road, London NW3 2BT Tel: 020 7722 4679 Email: jon_hyett@compuserve.com — MB BS 1991 Lond.; MRCOG 1997. (Kings College London) Specialist Regist. (O & G) Whittington Hosp. Lond.

HYKIN, Jonathan Leslie 1 Main Street, Eastwell, Melton Mowbray LE14 4EH — MB BS 1990 Lond.

HYKIN, Lynnette Ruth 1 Main St, Eastwell, Melton Mowbray LE14 4EH — MB BS 1991 Lond.; BSc Lond. 1988, MB BS 1991.

HYKIN, Mr Philip George 149 Harley Street, London W1N 2DE Tel: 020 7935 4444 Fax: 020 7935 3061; Moorfields Eye Hospital, City Road, London EC1V 2PD Tel: 020 7566 2599 Fax: 020 7566 2608 — MB BS 1984 Lond.; BSc Lond. 1981; FRCS (Ophth.) Eng. 1989; FRCOphth 1989; DO RCS Eng. 1989. (St. Mary's Hosp. Med. Sch.) Cons. Ophth. Surg. Moorfields Eye Hosp. Lond. Socs: Assn. Research Vision & Ophth.; Oxf. Ophth. Congr.; Brit. Diabetic Assn. Prev: Fell. Retina Serv. Wills Eye Hosp. Philadelphia, USA; Sen. Regist. Moorfields Eye Hosp. Lond.; Research Fell. Inst. Ophth. Lond.

HYLAND, Catharine Guardian Street Medical Centre, Guardian Street, Warrington WA5 1UD Tel: 01925 650226 Fax: 01925 240633; The Grange, Reed Lane, Antrobus, Northwich CW9 6JL Tel: 01565 777243 — MB ChB 1983 Liverp.; MRCGP 1988; DCH RCP Lond. 1987; DRCOG 1986. Prev: Trainee GP Frodsham.

HYLAND, Jacqueline Mary Department of Public Health Medicine, Fife Health Board, Springfield House, Cupar KY15 5UP Tel: 01334 656200 Fax: 01334 657579 Email: jackie.hyland@fifenhsboard.scot.nhs.uk — MB ChB 1987 Ed.; MFPHM RCP (UK) 1998. (Edinburgh) p/t Cons. (pub. Health med.) fife Hb. Prev: Project Doctor Roy. Infirm. Edin. & W.. Gen. Hosp. Edin.; Trainee GP N. Lothian Scheme; Trainee (Pub health med) Fife HB.

HYLAND, John Biska, Spernen Wyn Road, Falmouth TR11 4EH Tel: 01326 314551 — BA; MB BCh BAO Dub. 1954; DA Eng. 1958; FFA RCS Eng. 1968. (T.C. Dub.) Socs: Assn. Anaesth. Gt. Brit. & Irel. & Soc. Anaesth. S. W. Region. Prev: Sen. Cons. Anaesth. Cornw. & Isles of Scilly HA; SHO Anaesth. S. Teesside Hosp. Gp.; Regist. Anaesth. Barrow & Furness Hosp. Gp.

HYLAND, Michael Adrian 20 Grahamsbridge Road, Dundonald, Belfast BT16 2DB — MB BCh BAO 1985 Belf.

HYLAND, Peter Nigel 40 Upper Malone Gardens, Belfast BT9 6LY; 85 Baronscourt Road, Carryduff, Belfast BT8 8BQ — MB BCh BAO 1989 Belf.

HYLAND, Reginald Keith (retired) Rosegarth Surgery, Rothwell Mount, Halifax HX1 2HB Tel: 01422 53450 — MB BS 1953 Lond. Assoc. RCGP; Hosp. Pract. (Dermat.) Halifax Gen. Hosp. & Roy. Halifax Infirm.; Corps. Surg. St. John Ambul. Assn. Prev: Ho. Phys. & Ho. Surg. Metrop. Hosp. Lond.

HYLAND, Stephen Colm Causeway Place Surgery, Causeway Place, Newcastle BT33 0DN; 78 Churchtown Road, Strangford, Downpatrick BT30 7AN — MB BCh BAO 1986 Belf.; MRCGP 1992; DRCOG 1993; DMH Belf. 1993; DCH Dub. 1991. Socs: BMA; Diplomates Assn. Prev: SHO (O & G) Route Hosp. Ballymoney.

HYLAND, Veronica Mary Egerton Croft Medical Centre, Calder Walk, Leamington Spa CV31 1SA Tel: 01926 421153 Fax: 01926 832343; 2 Stuart Close, Warwick CV34 6AQ — MB ChB (1st.cl. Hons.) Liverp. 1966. Socs: BMA.

HYLAND-MCGUIRE, Mr Patrick Accident & Emergency Department, Plymouth Hospitals, Derriford Hospital, Derriford Road, Plymouth PL6 8DH — MB BCh BAO 1984 NUI; FRCSI 1991.

HYLTON, Lorna Christine (retired) 16 Madeira Road, Clevedon BS21 7TJ Tel: 0117 987 3714 — MRCS Eng. LRCP Lond. 1939; MRCS Eng., LRCP Lond. 1939; DCH Eng. 1941. Prev: Res. Med. Off. Duchess of York Hosp. Babies Manch. & Halifax Gen.

HYLTON, Susan Mary Farm Cottage, 38 Greenfield Road, Harborne, Birmingham B17 0EE Tel: 0121 427 5037 — MB ChB Leeds 1970; FFA RCS Eng. 1975. Trust Anaethetist Univ. Hosp. Birm. NHS Trust. Prev: Sen. Regist. Birm. AHA.

HYMAN, Adrian Oscar 39 Tuffnells Way, Harpenden AL5 3HA — MB BCh BAO 1948 Belf.

HYMAN, Barry Martin Colston Health Centre, 10 Bath Row, Lee Bank, Birmingham B15 1LZ Tel: 0121 622 1446 — MB ChB 1982 Birm.

HYMAN, Harry Benny (retired) 3 Edinburgh House, Tenterden Grove, Hendon, London NW4 1TL Tel: 020 8203 0377 — MRCS Eng. LRCP Lond. 1941. Prev: Resid. Med. Off. City Gen. Hosp. Gloucester.

HYMAN, Jonathan Geoffrey Wood Street, Middleton, Manchester M24 5QL — MB BS 1981 Newc.

HYMAN, Nigel Montague Haycroft, The Slade, Upper Bucklebury, Reading RG7 6TL — MD 1984 Sheff.; MB ChB 1971; MRCP (U.K.) 1974; FRCP. Cons. Neurol. W. Berks. AHA & Oxf. AHA (T) Roy. Berks. Hosp.; Neurol. Radcliffe Infirm. Oxf. Socs: Assn. Brit. Neurol.; Movem. Disorder Soc. Prev: Sen. Regist. Dept. Neurol. Radcliffe Infirm. Oxf. MRC Train. Fell.; (Neuropath.) Radcliffe Infirm. Oxf.; Regist. Dept. Neurol. Ch.ill Hosp. Oxf.

HYMAN, Samuel (retired) 13 Bracknell Gate, Frognal Lane, London NW3 7EA Tel: 020 7435 4769 — MB BCh BAO Dub. 1940; DPH Lond. 1947.

HYMAN, Vivian Colman Wembley Park Medical Centre, 21 Wembley Park Drive, Wembley HA9 8HD Tel: 020 8902 4411 Fax: 020 8795 2987 — MB BS 1959 Lond. (Westm.) Clin. Asst. (O & G) N.wick Pk. Hosp. Prev: Ho. Surg. Ophth. & Ho. Phys. Paediat. & Dermat. King Geo. Hosp.; Ilford; SHO O & G Ilford Matern. Hosp.

HYMANSON, Elise Natasha Flat 4, 98 Fellows Road, London NW3 3JG — MB ChB 1996 Birm.; ChB Birm. 1996.

HYMAS, Nigel Francis Sénac 4 Guest Road, Cambridge CB1 2AL — MB BChir 1974 Camb.; MA Camb. 1974; MRCP (UK) 1980; MRCPsych 1984.

HYNAM, Paul 24 Deanery Road, Warmley, Bristol BS15 9JB — MB BS 1996 Lond.

HYND, Andrew Tel: 01371 872105 Fax: 01371 873679; Pingles, Chelsmford Road, Felsted, Dunmow CM6 3ET — MB BS 1973 Lond.; BDS 1969; LDS RCS Eng. 1970; MRCGP 1980; DRCOG 1980. (St. Bartholomews) Prev: Regist. (Med.) Barnet Gen. Hosp.; SHO (Oncol.) Roy. Marsden Hosp.; Ho. Surg. St. Bartholomews Hosp. Lond.

HYND, Iain Macgregor (retired) 10 Millar Place, Stirling FK8 1XD Tel: 01786 474568 — MB ChB Glas. 1958. Prev: Assoc. Spec. W. of Scotl. Blood Transfus. Serv.

HYNDMAN, Alexander McInnes Watergall, High Askomil, Campbeltown PA28 6EN — MB ChB Glas. 1943.

HYNDMAN, Niall (retired) 4 Shoreham Avenue, Moorgate, Rotherham S60 3DB — MB ChB 1943 Glas.

HYNDMAN, Niall Campbell Cos Lane Medical Practice, Woodside Road, Glenrothes KY7 4AQ Tel: 01592 752100 Fax: 01592 612692; 4 Shoreham Avenue, Moorgate, Rotherham S60 3DB — MB ChB 1982 Sheff.; MRCGP 1986; DRCOG 1985; DCH RCP Lond. 1984.

HYNDMAN, Robert Wilson Crumlin Medical Practice, 5 Glenavy Road, Crumlin BT29 4LA Tel: 028 9442 2209 Fax: 028 9442 2233; Inishowen, 5 Glenavy Road, Crumlin BT29 4LA — MB BCh BAO 1972 Belf.; MICGP 1984; DObst RCOG 1975.

HYNDS, William Robert George Brielands, Kendal Avenue, Epping CM16 4PL — MB BChir 1994 Camb.; DCH 1998; DRCOG 1998; MRCGP 1999. (Addenbrooke's)

HYNE, Susan Jean Thew Surgery, Chapel Howe Lane, Halesowen — BM BS 1987 Nottm.; DRCOG 1991.

HYNES, Anthony Noel Rossmoor Lodge Farm, General Lane, Melbourne, York YO42 4SZ — MB BCh BAO 1977 NUI.

HYNES, Bartholomew (retired) Middle Cherubeer, Dolton, Winkleigh EX19 8PP Tel: 01805 804434 — MRCS Eng. LRCP Lond. 1932.

HYNES, Christina Jane Great Eccleston Health Centre, Raikes Road, Great Eccleston, Preston PR3 0ZA Tel: 01995 670066 Fax: 01995 671054 — MB ChB 1989 Liverp.; MRCGP 1993; DRCOG 1994.

HYNES, Donal Morley Redgate Medical Centre, Weston Zoyland Road, Bridgwater TA6 5BF Tel: 01278 444411 Fax: 01278 446816; Oakford House, Nether Stowey, Bridgwater TA5 1LJ Tel: 01278 732409 — MB BCh BAO 1979 NUI; MSC Exeter 1991; MRCP (UK) 1987; DGM RCP Lond. 1987. Chairm. Sommerset Coast PCG; Clin. Asst. (Rheum.) Taunton & Som. NHS Trust. Socs: (Nat. Chairm.) Primary Care Rheum. Soc. & Brit. Geriat. Prev: Regist. Bristol & W.on HA; SHO St. Thos. HA.

HYNES, Mr Eamonn Francis 9 Bowness Close, Holmes Chapel, Crewe CW4 7JX — MB BS 1980 Lond.; MA Camb. 1981; FRCSI 1991.

HYNES, Joanne Maria 25 Sans Souci Park, Malone Rd, Belfast BT9 5BZ — MB BCh BAO 1997 Belf.

HYNES, John Benjamin Paul Castle Place Surgery, Park Hill, Tiverton EX16 6RR — MB BCh BAO 1988 NUI; LRCPSI 1988.

HYNES, John Eugene 79 Folly Lane, Swinton, Manchester M27 0DB — MB BCh BAO 1984 NUI; MRCPI 1989; FRCR 1990. (Univ. Coll. Dub.) Sen. Regist. Rotat. (Radiol.) Manch. Socs: BMA.

HYNES, Jonathan Mark The Croft, Longtail Hill, Bowness-on-Windermere, Windermere LA23 3JD — BM BS 1996 Nottm.

HYNES, Kilian Anthony 55 Quarrendon Road, Amersham HP7 9EH — MB BCh BAO 1990 NUI.

HYNES, Matthew Christopher 7 Watford Road, St Albans AL1 2AA — MB ChB 1994 Bristol.

HYNES, Philomena Costello Deepdale, 9 Young St., Strathaven ML10 6LH — MB ChB 1958 Glas.; DA Eng. 1962.

HYPHER, Mr Terence Joseph, OStJ (retired) 46 Hendrefoilan Road, Sketty, Swansea SA2 9LT Tel: 01792 203312 Fax: 01792 203312 — MB BCh BAO 1959 NUI; FRCS Ed. 1974; FRCOphth 1988; DO Eng. 1964. Prev: Cons. Ophth. Singleton Hosp. Swansea & Neath Gen. Hosp.

HYSLOP, Alan Rutherford (retired) Welgarth, 14 Welburn Avenue, West Park, Leeds LS16 5HJ Tel: 0113 275 5655 — MB ChB 1943 Leeds. Prev: Sch. Med. Off. Leeds Grammar Sch.

HYSLOP, Carolyn Bell — MB ChB 1992 Glas.; DRCOG 1994; MRCGP 1996; DFFP 1996. p/t GP. Prev: Trainee GP Glas. VTS.

HYSLOP, David Alan Windrush Surgery, 21 West Bar, Banbury OX16 9SA Tel: 01295 251491; Callaly Cottage, Tanners Lane, Adderbury W., Banbury OX17 3ET Tel: 01295 811433 — MB BS 1958 Lond.; MRCGP 1971. (Middlx.) Prev: Ho. Surg. & Ho. Phys. Kettering Gen. Hosp.; Med. Off. Uganda Civil Serv.

HYSLOP, John Stuart Elstow, The Avenue, Truro TR1 1HR — MB BS 1977 Lond.; MRCS Eng. LRCP Lond. 1976; FRCR 1983; DMRD Eng. 1982. (Roy. Free) Cons. Radiol. Duchy & Roy. Cornw. Hosps. Truro & W. Cornw. Hosp.; Penzance. Socs: Brit. Med. Ultrasound Soc. Prev: Sen. Regist. (Radiol.) Yorks. RHA; Regist. (Radiol.) Plymouth HA.

HYSLOP, Richard Neil The Old Cole House, 41 Park Road, Bedworth, Nuneaton CV12 8LH Tel: 024 7631 1200 Fax: 024 7631 2311 — MB ChB 1986 Liverp.

HYSON, George Edmund 7 Town Mill, Marlborough SN8 1NS Tel: 01672 515258 — MRCS Eng. LRCP Lond. 1940; MA Camb. 1945. (Camb. & St. Mary's) Prev: Surg. Lt. RNVR; Ho. Phys. & Ho. Surg. EMS Hosp. Pk. Prewett, Basingstoke.

HYTTEN, Frank Eyvind (retired) Blossoms, Cobblers Hill, Little Hampden, Great Missenden HP16 9PW Tel: 01494 863140 Fax: 01494 863140 — MB BS 1948 Sydney; PhD Aberd. 1954; MD Sydney 1962; FRCOG 1970. Prev: Head Div. Perinatal Med. Clin. Research Centre Harrow.

HYZLER, Adrian Hugh 2 Maxwell Drive, Dartnell Park, West Byfleet KT14 6PZ Tel: 01932 51599 Fax: 01932 402466 Email: adehyzler@aol.com — MB ChB 1990 Sheff.

HYZLER, Caroline Alexandra 14 Widcombe Crescent, Widcombe Hill, Bath BA2 6AH — MB BS 1994 Lond.; MA Camb. 1992.

IACOPONI, Eduardo Sherwood, Heronsgate, Rickmansworth WD3 5DE — Medico Santa Casa de Sao Paulo Brazil 1980; MRCPsych 1994.

IACOVOU, Mr John William Princess Margaret Hospital, Okus Road, Swindon SN1 4JU Tel: 01793 426370; The Old Vicarage, East Kennett, Marlborough SN8 4EY Tel: 01672 861327 — BM BS 1980 Nottm.; DM Nottm. 1984, BMedSci (Hons.) 1978; FRCS Ed. 1986. Cons. Urol. P.ss Margt. Hosp. Swindon. Prev: Sen. Regist. & Research Regist. (Urol.) City Hosp. Nottm.; Regist. Rotat. (Surg.) Nottm. Hosps.

IADEVITA, Giovanni 25A Amberland Road, London SW18 1PX — State Exam Siena 1978.

IAFELICE, Elaine Damasceno 24 Ramblers Way, Welwyn Garden City AL7 2JX — MB ChB 1998 Leic.; MB ChB Leic 1998.

IBBITSON, David John Bishops Waltham Surgery, Lower Lane, Bishops Waltham, Southampton SO32 1GR Tel: 01489 892288 Fax: 01489 894402; Red Hill, Vernon Hill, Bishops Waltham,

Southampton SO32 1FH — MB BS 1971 Lond.; BSc (Hons. Physiol.) Lond. 1968. (Char. Cross) Prev: Trainee GP Norwich VTS; Ho. Surg. (Orthop.) & Ho. Phys. (Renal & Gen. Med.) Fulham Hosp.

IBBOTSON, Geoffrey Peter The Surgery, Mark St., Rochdale OL12 9BE Tel: 01706 43183; Stubley House, 166 Featherstall Road, Littleborough OL15 8NZ Tel: 01706 373825 — MB BS 1971 Lond.; BSc (Physiol., Hons.) Lond. 1968; DObst RCOG 1973. Socs: Brit. Soc. Med. & Dent. Hypn.; Chesh. Br.). Prev: Ho. Off. (Med. & Surg.) & SHO (O & G) Birch Hill Hosp. Rochdale.

IBBOTSON, Ian James Castle Medical Group, Clitheroe Health Centre, Railway View Road, Clitheroe BB7 2JG Tel: 01200 421900 Fax: 01200 421900; 2 Shays Drive, Clitheroe BB7 1LL Fax: 01200 426163 Email: ian.ibbotson@virgin.net — MB ChB 1988 Leic.; Dip. Occ. Med. RCP Lond. 1996; DRCOG 1994; DFFP 1994. (Leic.) Princip. in Gen. Pract. - Castle Med. Gp., The Health Centre; Med. Office In Occupat.al Health. Prev: Trainee GP/SHO (Psychiat. & O & G) Qu. Pk. Hosp. Blackburn.

IBBOTSON, Richard Benjamin Oakdene, Stag Hill, Yorkley, Lydney GL15 4TD — MB BChir 1983 Camb.

IBBOTSON, Richard Neville (retired) 6 Brafferton Hall Gardens, Brafferton, York YO61 2NW Tel: 01423 360843 Email: nchard.tbbotson@virgin.net — MB BS 1951 Lond; MD Adelaide 1962; MB BS Lond. 1951; FRCPA 1964; MRCPath 1963. Prev: Dep. Dir. Nat. Blood Transfus. Serv. W. Midl. Region.

IBBOTSON, Robert Michael Hollyend, Aston Lane, Aston, Stone ST15 0BW — MB BS 1968 Lond.; MRCP (U.K.) 1971; MRCS Eng. LRCP Lond. 1968; FRCPath 1986, M 1974; Dip. Gen. Biochem. (Distinc.) Univ. Lond. 1968. (Guy's)

IBBOTSON, Sally Helen photobiology Dept University dept of Dermatology, Ninewells Hospital & Medical School, Dundee DD1 9SY Tel: 01382 425717 Fax: 01382 646047 Email: s.h.ibbotson@dundee.ac.uk; 21 Hartside Gardens, Jesmond, Newcastle upon Tyne NE2 2JR Tel: 0191 281 3889 — MB ChB 1986 Leeds; MB ChB (Hons.) Leeds 1986; BSc (Hons.) Leeds 1983; MD (Commend.) Leeds 1994; MRCP (UK) 1989; CCS7 Derm 1997. Clin. Sen. Lect/Photobiol./Hon.Cons. Derm. Ninewells Hosp. Dundee. Socs: Brit. Assn. Dermat.; Brit. Soc. Investig. Dermat.; Brit. Photodermatol. Gp. Prev: Regist. (Dermat.) Roy. Vict. Infirm. Newc.; Research Regist. (Gen. Med.) Leeds Gen. Infirm.; Teachg. Fell. Med. Profess. Med. Unit Leeds Gen. Infirm.

IBBOTSON, Susan Louise Grimsby & Scunthopre Health Authority, Wrawby Road, Brigg DN20 8GS Tel: 01652 659659 — MB BChir 1986 Camb.; MA Camb. 1986; MFPHM RCP (UK) 1993; MPH Leeds 1991; DRCOG 1988. Cons. Pub. Health Med. United Health Grimsby & Scunthorpe HA. Socs: BMA & MDU.

IBBOTT, James Martin Dunelm Medical Practice, 1-2 Victor Terrace, Bearpark, Durham DH7 7DF Tel: 0191 373 2077 Fax: 0191 373 6216; 9 Nickleby Chare, Merryoaks, Durham DH1 3QX Tel: 0191 383 0854 — MB BS 1981 Lond.; DRCOG 1985. (St. Geo.)

IBBOTT, Naomi Elizabeth Sanderson and Partners, Adan House Surgery, St. Andrews Lane, Spennymoor DL16 6QA Tel: 01388 817777 Fax: 01388 811700; 9 Nickleby Chare, Merryoaks, Durham DH1 3QX — MB BS 1981 Lond.; DCH RCP Lond. 1984. GP; Police Surg. Prev: Community Med. Off. Chester-le-St.; Trainee GP Redhill Gen. Hosp. VTS.

IBISON, Judith Margaret Camden & Islington Health Authority, 110 Hampstead Road, Camden, London NW1 Tel: 020 7383 4888; 2 Pretoria Road, Streatham, London SW16 6RP — MB BS 1985 Lond.; MB BS Lnd. 1985; MSc Epidemiol. Lond. 1993; MRCGP 1989; DCH RCP Lond. 1988; DRCOG 1987. (Royal London Hospital) Specialist Regist. (Pub. Health); GP Asst. Prev: Lect. (Pub. Health & Epidemiol.) Lond.

IBOJIE, Joseph Omoike Graceland, 245 Midstocket Road, Aberdeen AB15 5PH — MB BS 1978 Benin; MRCPath 1986.

IBRAHEEM, Yasin Abdul 59 Farley Road, Catford, London SE6 2AA Tel: 020 8461 2111 — MB ChB 1970 Mosul; Dip. Neurol. 1983. (Institute of Neurology, London University) Staff Grade. Socs: BMA. Prev: Regist.; SHO.

IBRAHIM, Agnes Jean Farnham Health Centre, Brightwells, Farnham GU9 7SA Tel: 01252 712572 Fax: 01252 716336 — MB ChB 1973 Aberd.; DObst RCOG 1975. Sen. Partner, Drs Ibrahim, Sturdy & Dempster, Farnham Health Centre.

IBRAHIM, Ahmad Fadzli 74 Humphrey Road, Old Trafford, Manchester M16 9DF — MB ChB 1998 Manch.; MB ChB Manch 1998.

IBRAHIM, Asiah 15 Shrubland Road, Walthamstow, London E17 7QH — MB BS 1984 Malaya.

IBRAHIM, Atef Tawfik 145 Upper Clapton Road, London E5 9JZ Tel: 0208 806 7735 Fax: 0208 806 2991 — MB ChB 1973; 1986 (Dip.th.Med.) Univ. of London; MRCGP 1985 UK -Royal College of GPs; MRCPI 1990 Royal College of Physicians of Ireland. (Mansoura, Egypt) Gen. Practitioner. Prev: Cons. Family & Community Med. Riyadh Milit. Hosp. Riyahd, Saudi Arabia.

IBRAHIM, Ayoub Mohammed 10A Grosvenor Road, Whalley Range, Manchester M16 8AF — MB ChB 1979 Manch.

IBRAHIM, Fairol Huda Victoria Infirmary, Langside Rd, Glasgow G42 9TY — MB ChB 1996 Dundee.

IBRAHIM, Farid Isaid 7 Bron-y-De, Bangor LL57 4TL — Vrach 1978 Kiev Med. Inst. USSR; FFA RCSI 1993.

IBRAHIM, Farouk Riskalla North Street Surgery, 2 North Street, Littleover, Derby DE23 6BJ Tel: 01332 332812; 82 Muirfield Drive, Mickleover, Derby DE3 5YF — MB BCh 1962 Cairo.

IBRAHIM, Fatima Flat 9, Riverside Drive, 300 Golders Green Road, London NW11 9PU — MB ChB 1993 Leics. (Leicester) SHO (Elderly Care Med.) Lister Hosp. Stevenage. Prev: SHO (Med.); SHO (A & E) Watford Gen. Hosp.

IBRAHIM, Furhana Kausor 34 Sefton Avenue, Heaton, Newcastle upon Tyne NE6 5QR; 11 Redcar Road, North heaton, Newcastle upon Tyne NE6 5UE — MB BS 1995 Newc. SHO. Child & Adolesc. psychiat.Fleming Nuffield Unit. Newc. Prev: Psychiat. of Old Age N.umberland Ment. Health Trust; Adult Psychiat.

IBRAHIM, Gihan Mohamed Abd El-Moneim Aly 22 Warren Road, Gorleston, Great Yarmouth NR31 6JT Tel: 01493 445648 — MB ChB 1981 Alexandria; MRCOphth Bristol 1996. Staff Grade (Ophth.) James Paget Hosp. Gorleston Gt. Yarmouth. Prev: SHO Roy. Eye Infirm. Plymouth; SHO James Paget Hosp. Gt. Yarmouth; SHO York Gen. Hosp.

IBRAHIM, Mr Ibrahim Farid Long Grove Lodge, 32 Sutton Spring Wood, Calow, Chesterfield S44 5XF — MB BCh 1965 Cairo; FRCS Ed. 1977. (Cairo) Accid. Surg. Roy. Hosp. Chesterfield.

IBRAHIM, Ibrahim Habib Horsefair Practice, Horse Fair, Rugeley WS15 2EL Tel: 01889 582244 Fax: 01899 582244; The Oracle, Wolseley Bridge, Colwich, Stafford ST17 0XJ Tel: 01889 883003 — MB ChB 1976 Assiut; MRCPI 1990; MRCS Eng. LRCP Lond. 1986. (Assiut, Egypt) GP Princip.; Med. Adviser Benefits Agency Birm. Socs: BMA. Prev: Regist. (Geriat.) Kingsmead Hosp. Stafford; Regist. (Geriat.) Monklands Hosp. Airdrie.

IBRAHIM, Ibrahim Kamel Abbots Thatch, Botany Hill, The Sands, Farnham GU10 1LZ Tel: 01276 604693 Fax: 01276 604862; Frimley Park Hospital, Portsmouth Road, Frimley, Camberley GU16 7UJ Tel: 01276 604693 Fax: 01276 604862 — MB ChB 1965 Cairo; FRCP Lond. 1991; FRCP Ed. 1985; MRCP (UK) 1973; LMSSA Lond. 1976. (Cairo) Cons. Phys. (Geriat.) Frimley Pk. Hosp. Camberley. Socs: Brit. Geriat. Soc. Prev: SHO (Gen. Med.) York Co. Hosp.; Regist. (Gen. Med.) Bradford Roy. Infirm.; Sen. Regist. (Geriat. Med.) Univ. Soton. Hosps.

IBRAHIM, Kemal 7 Hartington Park, Bristol BS6 7ES — MB ChB 1992 Bristol.

IBRAHIM, Mahmoud Nabil X-Ray Department, Southend Hospital, Prittlewell Chase, Westcliff on Sea SS0 0RY — MB BCh 1961 Cairo; FRCR 1978; Dip. Med. Alexandria 1970; DMRD Alexandria 1969. (Cairo) Cons. Radiol. N.E. Thames RHA.

IBRAHIM, Muhammad 66 Charles Crescent, Bathgate EH48 1JG — MB BS 1968 Punjab.

IBRAHIM, Nassif Bekhit Nakhla South Lodge, Beckspool Road, Frenchay, Bristol BS16 1NT Tel: 0117 956 2254 — MB BCh 1970 Cairo; FRCPath 1990, M 1978. Cons. Histopath. Frenchay Hosp. Bristol; Clin. Teach. Path. Univ. Bristol. Socs: Internat. Acad. Path.; Assn. Clin. Path. Prev: Sen. Regist. Histopath. Manch. AHA (T).

IBRAHIM, Pamela Ibrahim, St. Anns Health Centre, St. Anns, Well Road, Nottingham NG3 3PX Tel: 0115 950 1883; 2 Loughborough Road, West Bridgford, Nottingham NG2 7QQ — MB ChB 1972 Sheff.

IBRAHIM, Seyed Mohammed Yoosuf Mumtaz Medical Centre, 42 Pembridge Road, London W11 3HN Tel: 020 7727 6135 Fax: 020 7221 9556; 140 Reynolds Drive, Queensbury, Edgware

HA8 5PY Tel: 020 8952 9116 — MRCS Eng. LRCP Lond. 1979; MD Moscow 1973; MRCP UK 1981; DGM RCP Lond. 1985. GP Lond.; Med. Off. Community Geriat. Assess. Centre St. Bart. Hosp. Lond. Prev: Regist. (Gen./Chest Med.) Springfield Hosp. Grimsby; Hosp. Pract. (Geriat. Med.) Hollymoor & Solihull Hosp. Birm.

IBRAHIM, Sherine Amin Hendawy 18 Gledhow Gardens, London SW5 0AZ Tel: 020 7373 9164 — LMSSA 1990 Lond.; FRCS 2000; FRCS 1 2000. (Guy's Hosp. Med. Sch.) SHO.Gen.Surg. Univ. Hosp. Liverp. Socs: BMA; MDU. Prev: SHO (Orthop. & Trauma) Chelsea & W.m. Hosp. Lond.; SHO (Cardiothoracic Surg.) Guy's Hosp. Lond.; SHO, Ho. Surg. & Ho. Phys. (A & E) Roy. Surrey Co. Hosp. Guildford.

IBRAHIM, Sonya 12 Woodwarde Road, London SE22 8UJ — MB BS 1994 Lond.

IBRAHIM, Tarek Shoucry 3 Briarly, Ashfield Park, Standish, Wigan WN6 0BY — MB ChB 1979 Alexandria; MS (Anaesth.) Alexandria 1983; FFA RCSI 1996; DA (UK) 1994. Staff Grade (Anaesth.) Wigan & Leigh NHS Trust; Locum Cons. (Anaesth.) Wigan & Leigh NHS Trust. Socs: Assn. Anaesth.; Med. Protec. Soc.; Assn. Obst. Anaesth. Prev: SHO (Anaesth.) Wigan & Leigh NHS Trust; Regist. (Anaesth.), Kuwait.

IBRAHIM, Zaky Henry Zaky 29 Meadow Rise, Woodbrooke Road, Birmingham B30 1UZ — MB BCh 1979 Ain Shams; MRCOG 1986.

IBRAHIMI, Ghulam Sarwar 23 Capel Road, East Barnet, Barnet EN4 8JD Tel: 020 8440 9019 — MD 1962 Kabul; FRCPsych 1987, M 1974; DPM Eng. 1971. (Kabul Med. Sch.) Cons. Psychiat. with s/i in Old Age Friern Hosp. Lond.; Hon. Sen. Lect. Roy. Free Hosp. Lond.; Vis. Cons. Gr.lands Priory Hosp. Lond. Prev: Cons. Psychiat. N.. & NE Thames RHAs.

IBRAHIMI, Mohammad-Qasim The Medical Centre, 144-150 High Road, London NW10 2PT Tel: 020 8459 5550 Fax: 020 8451 7268 — State Exam Med 1983 Berlin.

IBRECK, Robert Frederick 5 South Bank Road, Liverpool L19 9AR — MB BCh BAO 1970 NUI.

ICETON, Norma May The Surgery, 28 Holes Lane, Woolston, Warrington WA1 4NE Tel: 01925 653218 Fax: 01925 244767 — MB ChB 1984 Liverp.; MRCGP 1990; DRCOG 1988. GP Warrington. Prev: SHO (Psychiat.) Countess of Chester Hosp.; SHO (O & G) Warrington Dist. Gen. Hosp.; SHO Rotat. (Med.) Roy. Liverp. Hosp.

ICKERINGILL, Mathieu Guy 58 Ainsworth Avenue, Brighton BN2 7BG — MB BS 1992 Lond.; BSc (Hons.) Lond. 1989; MRCP (UK) 1996. (St Bartholomews) SHO (Anaesth.) Roy. Devon & Exeter Hosps. Prev: Specialist Regist. (Cardiovasc. Med.) W. Dorset Hosp.; SHO (Med.) Treliske Hosp. Truro.

ICKRINGILL, John Charles Wilson 28 Deena Close, Queens Drive, London W3 0HR — LAH Dub. 1964. (RCSI) Prev: Surg. Resid. Knickerbocker Hosp. New York City, U.S.A.; SHO (Radiol.) Centr. Middlx. Hosp. Lond.; Ho. Phys. St. Luke's Hosp. Bradford.

IDAMA, Tennyson Ohwo 18 Beaverdyke, York YO30 5ZG — MB BS 1987 Lagos.

IDDENDEN, David Antony 58 Selworthy Drive, Hillcroft Park, Stafford ST17 0PP — MB ChB 1975 Manch.; BSc (1st cl. Hons.) Manch. 1972, MB ChB 1975. Asst. Prof. O & G Univ. Pennsylvania, USA. Prev: Dir. (O & G) Presbyt. Univ. Pennsylvania, USA.

IDDLES, Andrew John Magpies, Bankside, Gosport PO12 2NH Tel: 01705 503373 — MB BS 1974 Lond.; MRCS Eng. LRCP Lond. 1974. (St. Mary's) Sen. Ship's Doctor, P & O/P.ss Cruises, Soton. & Los Angeles. Prev: Ho. Surg. St. Mary's Hosp. Lond.; Ho. Phys. St. Richard's Hosp. Chichester.

IDDON, Jonathan Newton Eastgate Surgery, 31B York Place, Knaresborough HG5 0AD Tel: 01423 557202 Fax: 01423 860446 — MB ChB 1973 Liverp.; MRCS Eng. LRCP Lond. 1973.

IDDON, Miss Julie North West Regional Health Authority, Gateway House, Picadilly, Manchester M20 2PL; Email: julie.iddon@virgin.net — MB ChB 1991 Manch.; FRCS Eng. 1995.

IDDON, Peter William The Vernon Street Medical Centre, 13 Vernon Street, Derby DE1 1FW Tel: 01332 332812 Fax: 01332 202698; Tel: 01332 602785 — MB ChB 1984 Liverp.; DA (UK) 1992; DTM & H Liverp. 1992.

IDE, Christopher William Medical Suite, Strathclyde Fire Brigade Headquarters, Bothwell Road, Hamilton ML3 0EA Tel: 01698 300999 Fax: 01698 338444; 25 Riverside Road, Waterfoot, Eaglesham, Glasgow G76 0DQ Tel: 0141 644 3739 Email: ide@lineone.net.uk — MB ChB 1974 Dundee; MFOM RCP Lond. 1987, AFOM 1986, FFOM 1997; MRCGP 1979; CIH Dund 1985; Cert. Family Plann. JCC 1982; DRCOG 1980. (Dundee) Brig. Med. Advis. Strathclyde Fire Brig.; Hon. Sen. Clin. Lect. (Pub. Health Med.) Univ. Glas.; Tutor Centre for Occupat. Health Distance Learning Course, Univ. Manch. Socs: (ex-Chairm., ex-Treas.) Soc. Occupat.al Med.; Assn. Local Auth. Med. Advisors. Prev: Sen. Employm. Med. Adviser. Scotl. W.. Area Health & Safety Exec.; Maj. RAMC, SHO (ENT) Camb. Milit. Hosp. Aldershot; Sen. Med. Off. Herford Garrison BFPO 15.

IDE, Joanna Elizabeth Station Road Surgery, 11 Station Road, Loughton IG10 4NZ Tel: 020 8508 3818 Fax: 020 8508 2539; North Farm House, Loughton IG10 4JJ Tel: 020 8508 3021 Fax: 020 8508 2539 — MB BS 1971 Lond.; MRCS Eng. LRCP Lond. 1971. Clin. Asst. (Neurol.) St. Margt. Hosp. Epping; Med. Off. (Physically Handicap.) W. Essex HA. Prev: Med. Off. Harlow Health Dist.; Clin. Asst. (Migraine) St. Bart. Hosp. Lond.

IDIA, Togunde Imoafe Joyce 249 Summerwood Road, Isleworth TW7 7QW — MUDr 1978 Komensky Univ. Czech.; MUDr Komensky U, Czech. 1978.

IDOO, Jaweeda 3 Lowland Road, Stockport SK2 7EG — MB ChB 1991 Dundee.

IDOWU, Mr Akinyemi Olaoye — MB BS 1973 Lond.; FRCS Eng. 1985; MRCS Eng. LRCP Lond. 1973. (St. Mary's London) Cons. A & E Med. Havering Hosps. NHS Trust. Socs: BMA; Brit. Accid. & Emerg. Med. Soc.; Roy. Soc. Med. Prev: Sen. Regist. (A & E) Centr. Middx. Hosp.; Regist. (A & E) Kings Coll. Hosp.

IDOWU, Oladapo Abiodun 28 Middle Close, Swadlincote DE11 0EF — MB BS 1986 Ibadan.

IDOWU, Oluyinka Lola 91 Rodney Court, 6-8 Maida Vale, London W9 1TJ; 17 Alverstone Road, Wembley HA9 9SD — MB BS 1997 Lond. VTS Welwyn Garden City QE2 Hosp. SHO psychiat. Socs: BMA; Roy. Coll. Med. Prev: PRHO Gen.med.Barnet Gen.hosp; PRHO Gen.Surg.& orthop.Lisks hosp.Stevenage.

IDREES, Faisal 11 Paddock Close, Leigh-on-Sea SS9 5QP Tel: 01702 421226 Fax: 01702 421226 — MB BS 1993 Lond. (St. Geo. Hosp. Med. Sch. Lond.) SHO Rotat. (Ophth.) SW Thames (Kingston/Frimley Pk./St. Geo.'s Hosp.). Socs: Fell. Roy. Soc. Med. Prev: SHO (Neurosurg.) Atkinson Morley's Hosp. Lond.; SHO (A & E) St. Geo. Hosp. Lond.; SHO (Med.) King Edwd. VII Hosp. Midhurst W. Sussex.

IDREES, Farah 11 Paddock Close, Leigh-on-Sea SS9 5QP — MB BS 1989 Lond. Regist. (Anaesth.) Roy. Surrey Co. Hosp. Guildford. Prev: SHO (Anaesth.) S.end Hosp. & King's Coll. Hosp. Lond.; Ho. Off. (Surg.) King's Coll. Hosp. Lond.

IDREES, Foozia Richmond Group Medical Centre, 1 Albion Street, Ashton-under-Lyne OL6 6HF Tel: 0161 214 8717 — MB ChB 1992 Manch.; MRCGP 1996; DRCOG 1995. (Manchester) GP. Socs: BMA. Prev: Trainee GP/SHO Hope Hosp. Salfrord VTS.

IDRIS, Iskander Rauf Dukeries Pigeon Hole, Kings Mill Hospital, Mansfield Road, Sutton-in-Ashfield NG17 4JL — BM BS 1994 Nottm.

IEVINS, Frank Andris University Hospital Birmingham NHS Trust, Selly Oak Hospital, Raddlebarn Road, Selly Oak, Birmingham B29 6JD Tel: 0121 627 1627 — MB BS 1979 Lond.; FFA RCS Eng. 1987; DRCOG 1982. Cons. Anaesth. & Intens. Care Univ. Hosp. Birm. NHS Trust. Socs: Intens. Care Soc.; Age Anaethesia Assn. Prev: Cons. Anaesth. & Intens. Care Selly Oak Hosp. Birm.

IEVINS, Rachel Ann c/o Parkview Clinic, Queensbridge Road, Kings Heath, Birmingham B13 8QE — MB ChB 1979 Birm. Clin. Asst. (Child Psychiat.) Pk.view Clinic Birm.

IFE, Sharon Patricia Mount Edgcumbe Hospice, Porthpean Road, St Austell PL26 6AB Tel: 01726 65711; 24 Ridgewood Close, Porthpean, St Austell PL26 6AT — MB BS 1985 Lond.; BSc Lond. 1982; MRCGP 1989; Dip. Palliat. Med. Wales 1997; Cert Family Plann. JCC 1988. (Univ. Coll. Lond.) Cons. Palliat. Med. Mt. Edgcumbe Hospice Cornw.; Hon. Cons. Palliat.Med.Roy.Cornw. Hosp.Trust. Socs: BMA; Assn. Palliat. Med.; Roy. Coll. Gen. Pract. Prev: Trainee GP Huntingdon VTS; Regist. (Palliat. Med.) P.ss Alice Hospice Esher; SHO St. Joseph's Hospice E. Lond.

IFFLAND, Miss Claire Adele The North Hampshire Hospital, Aldermaston Road, Basingstoke RG24 9NA Tel: 01256 473202 Fax: 01256 313164; Tel: 01635 278153 Email: clansley@email.msn.com — MB BS 1982 Lond.; FRCOG 2001; MRCOG 1989. p/t Cons. O & G N. Hants. Hosp. Basingstoke. Prev: Sen. Regist. (O & G) Chelsea

& W.m. Hosp. & N.wick Pk. Hosp. Harrow; Regist. (O & G) Hillingdon Hosp. Middlx.

IFTIKHAR, Muhammad Dorset County Hospital, Dorchester DT1 2YJ Tel: 01305 254248 Fax: 01305 254155; Winterbourne Hospital, Dorchester DT1 2DR Tel: 01305 263252 — MB BS 1979 Punjab; MFFP 1994; MRCOG 1988. (Nishtar Med. Coll. Multan, Pakistan) Cons. O & G W. Dorset Gen. Hosp. Dorchester.

IFTIKHAR, Mr Syed Yusuf 11 Snelston Crescent, Littleover, Derby DE23 6BL; Department of Surgery, Derbyshire Royal Infirmary, London Road, Derby DE1 2QY Tel: 01332 254878 Fax: 01332 295652 — MB BS 1980 Karachi; DM Nottm. 1991; FRCS Ed. 1985. (Dow Med. Coll. Karachi, Pakistan) Cons. Gen. Surg. (Gastroenterol.) Derbysh. Roy. Infirm.; Postgrad. Clin. Tutor Derby. Socs: Brit. Soc. Gastroenterol.; Assn. Surg.; E. Midl. Surg. Soc. Prev: Sen. Regist. & Regist. Rotat. (Surg.) Univ. Hosp. Nottm.; SHO (Gen. Surg.) Centr. Notts. HA.

IGBASEIMOKUMO, Usiakimi 76 Old Run Road, Leeds LS10 3AU; 2 longhill Road, London SE6 1TU Email: usiakimi@aol.com — MB BS 1985 Ibadan; FRCS Ed. 1993.

IGBOAKA, Gilbert Ukokweluchukwu Agwunedu Department of Cellular Pathology, Central Middlesex Hospital, Action Lane, Park Royal, London NW10 7NS Tel: 020 8453 2174 Fax: 020 8453 2532 Email: gilbert.igboaka@cmh-tr.nthames.nhs.uk; Homestead, 91 Brownlow Road, New Southgate, London N11 2BN Tel: 020 8888 0482 Fax: 020 8889 5600 — MB BS 1975 Ibadan; FRCPath 1995; MRCPath 1985; DMJ (Path.) Soc. Apoth. Lond. 1982. Cons. Histopath. & Cytopath. Centr. Middlx. Hosp. Lond. Socs: Brit. Acad. Forens. Sci.; BMA; Brit. Soc. Clin. Cytol. Prev: Lect. (Path.) & Hon. Sen. Regist. (Histopath.) Univ. Bristol & S. W.. RHA.

IGGO, Neil Christopher Trafford Dept of Renal Medicine, Royal Sussex County Hospital, Eastern Rd, Brighton BN2 5BE — BM BCh 1982 Oxf.

IGIELMAN, Farrel Ian Paul 13 Morley Street, Whitefield, Manchester M45 6GF — MB ChB 1992 Leeds.

IGLESIAS ALVAREZ, Maria 16 Plover Drive, Broadneath, Altrincham WA14 5NW — LMS 1986 Cadiz.

IGNOTUS, Mr Paul Imre Kent and Sussex Hospital, Mount Ephraim, Tunbridge Wells TN4 8AT Tel: 01892 526111; The Red House, Bordyke, Tonbridge TN9 1NN Tel: 01732 369437 Email: paul-ignotus@bigfoot.com — MB BS 1983 Lond.; FRCS Ed. 1987; FRCR 1991. (Westm.) Cons. Radiologist Tunbridge Wells Hosp.s; Sen. Lect. ChristCh. Coll. Canterbury. Socs: Radiological Soc. of N. America; Soc. of Cardiovasc. & Interven.al Radiologists.; Roy. Coll. of Surg.s of Edin. Prev: Cons. Diagnostic & Interven. Radiol.William Harvey Hosp. Ashford Kent; Sen. Regist. (Diagn. Radiol.) St. Geo. Hosp. Lond.; Clin. Fell. Univ. Toronto, Canada.

IGWE, Udho Christiana Janice 147 Upperton Road, Leicester LE3 0HF — LRCP LRCS 1982 Ed.; LRCP LRCS Ed. LRCPS Glas. 1982. (Middlx.) SCMO Plasmapheresis Unit Leics. HA.

IGWILOH, Mr Chukwudi Obinna Kingsley 51 Woodfield Road, Coventry CV5 6AJ — MB BS 1986 Nigeria; MB BS Univ. Nigeria 1986; FRCS Glas. 1993; FRCS Ed. 1993. Regist. (Gen. Surg. & Urol.) P.ss Margt. Hosp. Swindon.

IHAMAH, Felix Emwinghama 14 Shelbourne House, New Orleans Walk, London N19 3UQ Tel: 020 7561 1063 — MB BS 1977 Ibadan; MRCPI 1985. Prev: SHO (Med.) Preston Roy. Hosp.

IHARA, Tetsujiro London Iryo Centre, 234-6 Hendon Way, Hendon Central, London NW4 3NE Tel: 020 8202 7272 Fax: 020 8202 6222 — MB BS 1983 Lond. Socs: Roy. Soc. Med.; BMA; Indep. Doctors Forum.

IHEANACHO, Ikechukwu Ogadinma 43 Mantilla Road, London SW17 8DY — MB BS 1988 Lond.

IHEKWABA, Mr Frank Nwabueze The Willows, 2 Relugas Road, Edinburgh EH9 2NE — MB ChB 1968 Ed.; FRCS Ed. 1973.

IHENACHO, Augustine Okechuku Flat 6, Brewers Buildings, Rawstorne St., London EC1V 7NB — MB BS 1997 Lond.

IHENACHO, Professor Hdede Nlem Chukwu Department of Medicine, University of Nigeria, Enugu Campus, Enugu, Nigeria Tel: (00 234) (42) 450365; 15 Leam Green, Canon Park, Coventry CV4 7DG — MB BS Lond. 1963; FRCP Lond. 1988. (Univ. Coll. Ibadan) Cons. Cardiol. Univ. Nigeria Teach. Hosp. Enugu.; Prof. Med. Univ. Nigeria 1993. Socs: BMA; Brit. Cardiac Soc; Nigerian Cardiac Soc. Prev: Hon Cons. Cardiol. Dudley Rd. Hosp. Birm.; Regist. (Med. & Cardiol.) Qu. Eliz. Hosp. Birm.; Sen. Research Regist. & Hon. Sen. Med. Regist. Dept. Cardiol. Childr. Hosp. Birm.

IHSAN, Fouzia 162 Salt Street, Bradford BD8 8BQ — MB ChB 1997 Manch.

IJAZ, Qasim 25 Porthyfelin, Holyhead LL65 1AY — MB BS 1981 Peshawar; MRCPsych 1989.

IJAZ, Samia Flat 2, 10A Airlie Gardens, London W8 7AL — MB BS 1997 Lond.

IJOMAH, Geoffrey Chikwuma Nicholas 12 Clairmont Gardens, Kelvingrove, Glasgow G3 7LW — MB ChB 1989 Aberd.

IKEAGWU, Ejitu Okorafor Kalu 344 Old Bedford Road, Luton LU2 7EJ — MB BS 1997 Lond.

IKEAGWU, Okorafor Kalu 344 Old Bedford Road, Luton LU2 7EJ Tel: 01582 484072 Email: okorafor@ntlworld.com; 344 Old Bedford Road, Luton LU2 7EJ Email: okorafor@ntl.world.com — MB BS 1973 Ibadan; BSc (Hons.) Lond. 1964; FRCOG 1996, M 1981. (Univ. Ibadan) Cons. O & G King Fahad Hosp., Jeddah. Prev: Regist. (O & G) Luton & Dunstable Hosp.; Regist. (O & G) Lister Hosp. Stevenage; Sen. Regist. (O & G) King Fahad Hosp., Jeddah.

IKHENA, Eseroghene Ituehan Grantham Health Clinic, St Catherine's Road, Grantham NG31 6TT; Tel: 01843 225544 — MB BS 1987 Ibadan; MB BS Ibadan, Nigeria 1987; MRCP (UK) 1992; FRCPCH 1997. Cons community Paediat. Prev: Cons. Canterbury & Thanet Community Health Care Trust Ramsgate; Cons Thanet & NHS Trust Margate.

IKHENA, Sunday Ederibhor 28 Shakespeare Road, Birchington CT7 9ET — MB BS 1982 Ibadan; MRCOG 1992.

IKIN, Peter Nicholas 121 The Meadows, Cherry Burton, Beverley HU17 7SD — MB BS 1982 Tasmania.

IKKOS, George Edgware Postgraduate Centre, Edgware Hospital, Burnt Oak Broadway, Edgware HA8 0AD Tel: 020 8732 6693 Fax: 020 8952 7113 — LMSSA 1981 Lond.; BSc Toronto 1978; MRCPsych 1985; MInst GA 1992; T(Psychiat.) 1991. (Middlesex) Cons. Psychiat., Barnet, Enfield and Haringly Ment. Health NHS Trust; Head Med. Educat. Barnet, Enfield and Haringly Ment. Health NHS Trust. Socs: Assoc. Psychoanal. Psychother. in NHS; Assoc for Ment. health law; Soc for Interpersonal Theory & Research. Prev: Hon. Clin. Lect. Univ. Coll. & Middlx. Hosp. Sch. Lond.; Sen. Regist. (Psychiat.) Univ. Coll. Hosp. Lond.; Cons. Psychiat. Barnet Healthcare NHS Trust & Roy. Nat. Orthop. Hosp. Trust.

IKOGHO, Mr Oyaberbe Okpako 42 Alloa Road, London SE8 5AJ — MB BS 1978 Ibadan; FRCS Ed. 1991.

IKOMI, Amaju Eyitomi Abayomi 31 Hatherleigh Close, Morden SM4 5AD — MB BS 1985 Lond.

IKPEME, Mr James Onoyom 4 Hookstone Oval, Harrogate HG2 8QE Tel: 01423 883231 Email: jikpeme@aol.com — MB BS 1959 Lond.; FRCS Ed. 1967. (Newc.) Assoc. Specialist (Orthop. Surg.) Harrogate Dist. Hosp. Socs: Fell. BOA; BMA. Prev: Demonst. (Path.) Univ. Newc.; Cas. Off. Gen. Hosp. ScarBoro.; Regist. (Orthop.) Gen. Hosp. Harrogate.

IKPOH, Anthony Chukwuemeka Akukalia 15 St Andrews Road, Croydon CR0 1AB — LRCPI & LM, LRSCI & LM 1974; LRCPI & LM, LRCSI & LM 1974. Clin. Asst. (Psychiat.) Ticehurst Ho. Hosp. Ticehurst. Socs: IMA & BMA. Prev: SHO St. Columcille' Hosp. Loughlinstown; Intern. Jas. Connolly Memor. Hosp. Blanchardstown.

IKRAM, Mr Khalid 37 Kingsley Avenue, Hounslow TW3 4AE; 14 Dorchester Close, Old Road, Headington, Oxford OX3 8SS Email: khalid.ikram@ikram.demon.co.uk — MB BS 1991 Lond.; FRCOphth 1995. (Char. Cross & Westm.) Specialist Regist. (Ophth.) Oxf. Deanery; Corneal Fell., Ophth., Roy. Eye Hosp., Manch. Prev: SHO (Ophth.) Soton. Eye Unit.; SHO (Ophth.) Qu. Eliz. II Hosp. Welwyn Gdn. City; Demonst. (Anat.) St. Geo. Hosp. Med. Sch.

IKRAM, Shahid 37 Kingsley Avenue, Hounslow TW3 4AE — MB BCh 1979 Wales.

IKWUEKE, Jerome Kaine The Surgery, 1 Grove Road, Tottenham, London N15 5HJ Tel: 020 8800 9781 Fax: 020 8800 3196; 125 Audley Road, Hendon, London NW4 3EN Tel: 020 8202 0304 — MB BS 1974 Ibadan; MRCP (UK) 1979. Socs: BMA. Prev: Assoc. Prof. Med. & Cardiol. Univ. Jos, Nigeria; Sen. Lect. (Med.) Univ. Jos, Nigeria.

ILANGARATNE, Jayantha Bandara 8 Megson Way, Walkington, Beverley HU17 8YA — MB BS 1981 Colombo; LMSSA Lond. 1986.

ILANGOVAN, Chelliah Kumaresan 1 Clos du Parcq, Richmond Road, St Helier, Jersey JE2 3GL — MB BS 1975 Madras; FFA RCSI 1987.

ILANGOVAN, Pryadarsani Bruhathambal Child Health Services, Loddon NHS Trust, G Floor, North Hampshire Hospital, Basingstoke RG24 9NA Tel: 01256 314797 Fax: 01256 314796; 2 Beckett Close, Basingstoke RG23 8HS — MB BS 1982 Lond.; MRCP (UK) 1991; DCH RCP Lond. 1986. (Roy. Free) Cons. N. Hants. Hosp. Prev: Sen. Regist. (Paediat.) St. Mary's Hosp. Portsmouth & Soton. Gen. Hosp.; Research Regist. (Paediat.) Guy's Hosp. & Brompton Hosp. Lond.; Regist. (Paediat.) Soton. Gen. Hosp.

ILANKOVAN, Mr Velupillai Poole General Hospital NHS Trust, Longfleet Road, Poole BH15 2JB Tel: 01202 442576 — MB BCh 1984 Wales; BDS Ceylon 1974; FRCS Ed. 1988; FDS RCS Ed. 1977. Cons. Maxillofacial Surg. Poole Gen. Hosp. Prev: Sen. Regist. N. RHA; Regist. Cannesburn Hosp. Glas..

ILARI, Luca 277 Golders Green Road, London NW11 9JJ Tel: 01622 673444 — State Exam 1990 Pisa. SHO (Ophth.) Kent Co. Ophth. & Aural Hosp. Maidstone.

ILBERT, Robin Charles HM Prison Service Headquarters, Cleland House, Page St., London SW1P 4LN Tel: 020 7217 6550 Fax: 020 7217 6412; 2 Summerfield Terrace, Liss GU33 7LF Tel: 01730 895218 — BM BCh 1953 Oxf.; MA Oxf. 1953; MRCGP 1966; DObst RCOG 1959. (Oxf. & St. Thos.) Sen. Med. Off. Home Off. Prison Serv.; Chairm. Coll. Prison Med. Prev: Cas. Off. &c. St. Thos. Hosp.; Capt. RAMC, Jun. Specialist in Med.; Ho. Surg. (Obst.) St. Luke's Hosp. Guildford.

ILCHYSHYN, Andrew Department of Dermatology, Walsgrave Hospital, Clifford Bridge Road, Coventry CV2 2DX Tel: 024 76 602020 Fax: 024 76 622197; 29 Asthill Grove, Coventry CV3 6HN Tel: 024 76 503092 — MB ChB 1975 Liverp.; FRCP Lond. 1994; MRCP (UK) 1980. (Univ. Liverp.) Cons. Dermat. Univ Hosps Coventry & Warks. NHS Trust. Socs: Fell. Roy. Soc. Med.; Brit. Assn. Dermat.; Midl. Dermat. Soc. Prev: Sen. Regist. (Dermat.) N. Staffs. Hosp. Centre Stoke-on-Trent; Regist. (Dermat.) Roy. Liverp. Hosp.; Regist. (Med.) Clatterbridge Hosp. Bebington.

ILES, David John Barry 23 Jenner Way, Halterworth, Romsey SO51 8PD — BM 1994 Soton.; BSc 2nd cl. Hons. Soton. 1993.

ILES, Elizabeth Ann The Willows, 2 Trem-y-Nor Forest Road, Llanharry, Pontyclun CF72 9JW — MB ChB 1988 Dundee; DRCOG 1991. Trainee GP Lincoln. Prev: SHO (A & E) Lincoln Co. Hosp. & Leicester Roy. Infirm.

ILES, Peter Bernard City Hospital NHS Trust, Dudley Road, Birmingham B18 7QH Tel: 0121 507 4576 Fax: 0121 523 6125; 9 Richmond Hill Gardens, Birmingham B15 3RW Tel: 0121 454 8217 — MB BS 1971 Lond.; DM Nottm. 1978; FRCP Lond. 1989; MRCP (UK) 1973; MRCS Eng. LRCP Lond. 1971. (Westm.) Cons. Phys. Gen. & Respirat. Med. City Hosp. NHS Trust Birm.& Cons Respiral Med Birm Chest Clinic; Hon. Sen. Clin. Lect. Univ. Birm.; Examr. Mem.ship. RCP. Socs: Brit. Thorac. Soc. & Midl. Thoracic Soc.; Eur. Respirat. Soc. Prev: Hon. Sen. Regist. (Med.) Nottm. Univ.; Sen. Regist. (Med.) Liverp. Hosp.; Regist. W.m. Hosp. Lond.

ILES, Philip John Shaw House, 11 Shaw Lane, Headingley, Leeds LS6 4DH Tel: 0113 278 4914 Fax: 0113 274 5822; 10 North Parade, West Park, Leeds LS16 5AY Tel: 0113 278 8753 Fax: 0113 274 5822 Email: philip@iles100.freeserve.co.uk — MB BS 1983 Lond.; MRCGP 1989; DRCOG 1988. (Char. Cross) Med. Adviser Yorks. TV plc Leeds. Prev: Trainee GP Harrogate VTS; SHO (Paediat.) Gen. Infirm. Leeds; SHO (Palliat. Care) Wheatfields Hospice Leeds.

ILES, Rachael Elizabeth 41 Chough Crescent, St Austell PL25 3AY — MB BS 1992 Lond.

ILES, Richard Arthur (retired) Hazelbrook, 4 Rectory Gardens, Henbury, Bristol BS10 7AQ Tel: 0117 959 0850 — MB ChB Bristol 1952; DTM & H Eng. 1960. Prev: GP Bristol.

ILES, Richard Wentworth Box 181, Addenbrooke's NHS Trust, Cambridge CB2 2QQ Tel: 01233 216020 Email: richard.iles@msexc.addenbrookes.anglox.nhs.uk — MB BS 1985 Lond.; MRCP (Paediat.) Ed. 1990; FRCP Ed.; FRCPCH. (St Thomas's) Cons. Respirat. Paediat. Addenbrooke's NHS Trust Camb. Prev: Sen. Regist. Alder Hey Hosp. Liverp.; Research Fell. - Sick Child. Hosp. Toronto, Canada.

ILES, Stephen 9 Redland Park, Bristol BS6 6SA — BM 1993 Soton.

ILES, Susan Angela Broadmoor Hospital, Crowthorne RG45 7EG Tel: 01344 773111 — MB BCh 1973 Oxf.; BM BCh Oxf. 1973; MA, DPhil Oxf. 1973; MRCPsych 1983. Cons. Forens. Psychiat. BRd.moor Hosp. Crowthorne. Prev: Sen. Regist. (Forens. Psychiat.) Oxf.; Wellcome Research Fell. (Ment. Health); Regist. Rotat. (Psychiat.) Oxf. VTS.

ILES, Susan Elizabeth Walderslade Village Surgery, 62A Robin Hood Lane, Walderslade, Chatham ME5 9LD Tel: 01634 685681; Pemberth Lodge, Spekes Road, Hempstead, Gillingham ME7 3RT Tel: 01634 235909 — BM 1980 Soton. Prev: Trainee GP Strood Health Centre; SHO (Neonat.) Univ. Coll. Hosp. Lond.; SHO (Paediat.) N.wick Pk. Hosp. Harrow.

ILESLEY, Ian Charles Department of Pathology, North Hampshire Road, Basingstoke RG26 9NA — MB BS 1979 Newc.; FRCPath 1997.

ILETT, Rebecca Jane America Farm, Woodcotes Lane, Darlton, Newark NG22 0TJ — MB ChB 1998 Dund.; MB ChB Dund 1998.

ILETT, Susan Jean Airedale General Hospital, Skipton Road, Steeton, Keighley BD20 6TD Tel: 01535 652511; 5 Skibeden Court, Skipton BD23 6AY — MB BS 1971 Newc.; MRCP (UK) 1975; DCH RCPS Glas. 1973. Cons. Community Paediat. Airedale NHS Trust.

ILIFF, Anne Marie The Halliwell Surgery, Lindfield Drive, Bolton BL1 3RG; 16 Whitsters Hollow, Smithills Croft Road, Smithills, Bolton BL1 6TY — MB ChB 1981 Leic.; MRCGP 1985.

ILIFFE, Ann Louise 20 Marchhall Crescent, Edinburgh EH16 5HL — MB BS 1981 Lond.; MRCP (UK) 1985; MRCGP 1986; DRCOG 1983.

ILIFFE, Stephen Roger Lonsdale Medical Centre, 24 Lonsdale Road, London NW6 6RR Tel: 020 7328 8331 Fax: 020 7328 8630 Email: s.iliffe@pcps.ucl.ac.uk — MB BS 1974 Lond.; MRCS Eng. LRCP Lond. 1974; MRCGP 1979; DCH Eng. 1978; DRCOG 1977. p/t Reader (Gen. Pract.) Roy. Free & Univ. Coll. Med. Sch.

ILKIW, Philip Steven John 4 Golden Sands Residential Park, Brighton Road, Lancing BN15 8LW — MB BS 1988 Lond.

ILLIDGE, Timothy Martin Wessex Cancer Centre, Royal South Hants Hospital, off Brunton's Terrace, Southampton SO14 0YG; Rivers Edge, West Park Lane, Damerham SP6 3HB Tel: 01725 518651 Email: tmi@soton.ac.uk — MB BS 1988 Lond.; BSc Lond. 1985; MRCP (UK) 1993; FRCR 1996; DRCOG 1990; Phd 1999. (UMDS Guy's Hosp. Lond.) Sen. Lect. Cons.Oncol.Soton. Univ. Hosp; Sen. Clin. Research Fell. CRC Soton.

ILLING, Richard Cruttwell (retired) Central Surgery, Corporation Street, Rugby CV21 3SP — MB BS Lond. 1969; BA Open 1988; MRCS Eng. LRCP Lond. 1969. Prev: Hosp. Pract. (Gastroenterol.) Walsgrave Hosp. Coventry & Geo. Eliot Hosp. Nuneaton.

ILLING, Rowland Oliver 3 Longwater Lane, Old Costessey, Norwich NR8 5AH — BM BCh 1998 Oxf.; BM BCh Oxf 1998; MA 1999. A & E SHO St Thomas Hosp. Lond.

ILLINGWORTH, Charlotte Sarah 10 Priors Wood, Crowthorne RG45 6BZ — MB ChB 1992 Bristol.

ILLINGWORTH, Mr Christopher David Flat 2, 38 Kidbrooke Park Road, London SE3 0DU — MB ChB 1987 Leic.; FRCS Glas. 1994.

ILLINGWORTH, Cynthia Mary 8 Harley Road, Sheffield S11 9SD Tel: 0114 236 2774 — MB BS 1942 Durh.; MB BS (2nd cl. Hons.) Durh. 1942; FRCP Lond. 1976, M 1945; Hon. FCPCH 1996. Prev: Cons. A & E Childr. Hosp. Sheff.; Tutor (Child Health) Univ. Sheff.; Regist. (Med.) Roy. Vict. Infirm. Newc.

ILLINGWORTH, David Gordon, LVO, CVO (retired) 19 Napier Road, Edinburgh EH10 5AZ Tel: 0131 229 8102 — MB ChB 1943 Ed.; MD (Commend.) Ed. 1963; FRCP Ed. 1965; MRCP (UK) 1949; AFOM RCP Lond. 1980; FRCGP 1970. Mem. (Life Govenor) ICRF. Prev: Surg. Lt. RNVR (2nd Escort Gp).

ILLINGWORTH, David Marshall Dundonald Medical Practice, 9 Main Street, Dundonald, Kilmarnock KA2 9HF Tel: 01563 850496 Fax: 01563 850426; 20 Fullarton Drive, Troon KA10 6LE — MB ChB 1990 Glas.; MRCGP 1994. (Glas.) Socs: Med. & Dent. Defence Union Scotl.; BMA.

ILLINGWORTH, Mr Geoffrey (retired) 10 Lawhead Road West, St Andrews KY16 9NE Tel: 01334 478946 — MB ChB 1957 St. And.; FRCS Ed. 1965. Prev: Cons. Orthop. Surg. Stobhill Gen. Hosp. & Glas. Roy Infirm.

ILLINGWORTH, John Basil (retired) Fair Mead, Hindon, Salisbury SP3 6DJ Tel: 01747 820328 — MB BS Lond. 1956; MRCS Eng. LRCP Lond. 1956. Prev: GP Hindon.

ILLINGWORTH, Karen Anne Accident & Emergency Depsrtment, St James's University Hospital, Beckett St., Leeds LS9 7TF; 69 Old Park Road, Leeds LS8 1JB — MB ChB 1975 Liverp.; FRCA 1980. Train. Manager (Resusc.) St. Jas. & Seacroft Univ. Hosps. Trust; Clin. Asst. St. Jas. Univ. Hosp. Leeds.

ILLINGWORTH, Michael John (retired) 34B Ochil Road, Alva FK12 5JT Tel: 01259 760256 — MB ChB 1957 St. And. Prev: Ho. Phys. & Ho. Surg. Roy. Infirm. Dundee.

ILLINGWORTH, Mr Robert David (retired) Department of Neurosciences, Charing Cross Hospital, Fulham Palace Road, London W6 8RF Tel: 020 8846 1186 Fax: 020 8846 7487 — MB BS Lond. 1958; FRCS Eng. 1964. Hon. Cons. Neurosurg. Char. Cross Hosp. Lond. Prev: Cons. Neurosurg. Middlx. Hosp. Lond.

ILLINGWORTH, Robin Nigel Accident & Emergency Department, St James's University Hospital, Leeds LS9 7TF Tel: 0113 243 3144 — BM BCh 1974 Oxf.; MA Camb. 1975, BA 1971; FFAEM 1994; FRCP Lond. 1994; MRCP (UK) 1977; FRCP Ed. 1997. Cons. A & E Med. St. Jas. Univ. Hosp. Leeds; Sen. Clin. Lect. Univ. Leeds. Socs: Fell. Fac. Accid. & Emerg. Med. Prev: Sen. Regist. (A & E) Leeds Gen. Infirm. & St. Jas. Univ. Hosp. Leeds; Regist. (Med.) Regional Poisoning Treatm. Centre Roy. Infirm. Edin.

ILLINGWORTH, Stephen Charles Hanham Surgery, 33 Whittucks Road, Hanham, Bristol BS15 3HY Tel: 0117 967 5201 Fax: 0117 947 7749 — MB 1976 Camb.; MA; BChir 1975; MRCP (UK) 1978; MRCGP 1981. Princip. GP Bristol.

ILLINGWORTH, Stephen George Martin Bruntsfield Medical Practice, 11 Forbes Road, Edinburgh EH10 4EY Tel: 0131 228 6081 Fax: 0131 229 4330; 6 Bonaly Terrace, Edinburgh EH13 0EL — MB ChB 1973 Aberd.; DRCOG 1977.

ILLIS, Léon Sebastian Editor, Spinal Cord, Wessex Nuffield Hospital, Chandlers Ford, Eastleigh SO53 2DW Tel: 02380 275353 Fax: 02380 275354 Email: spinal.cord.@vigin.net; Pond House, Sowley, East End, Lymington SO41 5SQ Tel: 01590 626351 Fax: 01590 626749 — MB BS Lond. 1957; BSc Lond. 1954, MD 1964; FRCP Lond. 1975, M 1963. (Univ. Coll. Hosp.) Edr. Spinal Cord; Clin. Sen. Lect. Univ. Soton. Med. Sch.; Trustee Internat. Spinal Research Trust; Emerit. Cons. Neurol. Wessex Neurol. Centre Soton. Univ. Hosp. Gp. Socs: Fell. Roy. Soc. Med.; Scientif. Fell. Zool. Soc.; (Pres.) Internat. Neuromodulation Soc. Prev: Vis. Prof. of Neurol. Univ. Sri Lanka & Univ. Wisconsin, USA; Sen. Regist. & Resid. Med. Off. Nat. Hosp. Nerv. Dis. Qu. Sq. Lond.

ILLSLEY, Kathryn Margaret Allenfield, 71 High St., Workington CA14 4EU — MB ChB 1985 Dundee.

ILO, Olumuyiwa Ayodapo 33 Albemarle Park, Albemarle Rd, Beckenham BR3 5XG — MB BS 1996 Lond.

ILSLEY, Charles Duke Jesse Department of Cardiology, Harefield Hospital, Harefield, Uxbridge UB9 6JH Tel: 01895 828603 Fax: 01895 825503; 36 Kewferry Road, Northwood HA6 2PB Tel: 01923 827402 — MB BS 1973 Lond.; MB BS Univ. Lond. 1973; FRCP Lond. 1992; MRCP (UK) 1975; FRACP 1986. Cons. Cardiol. Harefield Hosp., Hillingdon Hosp. Middlx. & Lister Hosp. Stevenage. Prev: Cons. Cardiol. Dunedin Hosp. & Clin. Lect. Univ. Otago NZ; Regist. (Gen. Med.) St. Mary's Hosp. Lond.; Hon. Regist. Nat. Heart Hosp. Lond.

ILSLEY, David William 152 Woodsley Road, Leeds LS2 9LZ Tel: 0113 234 7431 — MB ChB 1990 Leeds. SHO (Surg.) Leeds.

ILSLEY, John Kevin Nunwell Surgery, 10 Pump Street, Bromyard HR7 4BZ Tel: 01885 483412 Fax: 01885 488739; Rowden Mill House, Winslow, Bromyard HR7 4LS Tel: 01885 483577 — MB BS 1974 Lond.; FRCGP 1994, M 1981; DRCOG 1980. (St. Thos.) Assoc. Adviser (Gen. Pract.) W. Midl. Socs: BMA Herefod Div. (Hon Press Off.).

ILSLEY, Mark Dorian Edenbridge Medical Practice, West View, Station Road, Edenbridge TN8 5ND Tel: 01732 864442 Fax: 01732 862376; Oak Tree House, Crouch House Road, Edenbridge TN8 5EL Tel: 01732 862000 — MB ChB 1987 Bristol; BSc Bristol 1984; MRCGP 1991; DRCOG 1990. Prev: Trainee GP N. Wilts. VTS.

ILVES, Annabel Clare 10 Wincanton Road, London SW18 5TY — MB BS 1990 Lond.

ILVES, Peter Julien Melbourne Grove Medical Practice, Melbourne Grove, London SE22 8QN Tel: 020 8299 0499 Fax: 020 8299 1954 — MB BS 1989 Lond. GP.

ILYAS, Mohammad 19 Kirkburn Place, Bradford BD7 2BZ — MB ChB 1986 Manch.

ILYAS, Mohammad 58 Stamford Street, Ashton-under-Lyne OL6 6QH — MB ChB 1988 Bristol.

ILYAS, Mohammed Gateshead Health Centre, Prince Consort Road, Gateshead NE8 1NR Tel: 0191 478 3678 Fax: 0191 477 1211 — MB BS 1969 Ranchi. GP Gateshead, Tyne & Wear.

ILYAS, Nasreen Prestwood Road West Surgery, 81 Prestwood Road West, Wednesfield, Wolverhampton WV11 1HT Tel: 01902 721021 Fax: 01902 306225 — MB ChB 1990 Bristol.

ILYAS, Nohaid 86 Glapton Road, Nottingham NG2 2FG — MB BS 1992 Lond. SHO (A & E) Roy. Free Hosp. Lond.

ILYAS, Sabina 76 Chairborough Road, High Wycombe HP12 3HJ — MB BS 1998 Lond.; MB BS Lond 1998.

IMAM, Mr Atique 48 St James Terrace, Boundaries Road, London SW12 8HJ — MB BS 1992 Lond.; FRCS (Eng.) 1997. (St Georges Hospital Medical School) Research Fell.St Geo.s Hosp. Lond. Prev: SHO (Gen. Surg. & Urol.) Frimley Pk. Hosp. Surrey; SHO Surg. Rotat. St Geo.'s Hosp. Lond.

IMAM, Nilufar Byron House Surgery, 30 Byron Road, Gillingham ME7 5QH Tel: 01634 576347 — MB BS 1962 Dacca; MB BS (Gold Medal) Dacca 1962; FRCS Ed. 1971; MFFP 1993; FRCOG 1989, M 1968. (Dacca) Sen. Partner Gen. Pract.; Sen. Instruc. Family Plann. Doctor Medway HA. Socs: BMA. Prev: Regist. (O & G) Roy. Hanmshire Co. Hosp. Winchester; Hosp. Off. (Radiother.) Ch.ill Hosp. Oxf.; Hosp. Surg. Nuffield Deptartment O & G Oxf.

IMAM, Shah Hassan Whittle Surgery, 199 Preston Road, Whittle-le-Woods, Chorley PR6 7PS Tel: 01257 262383 Fax: 01257 261019 — MB BS 1969 Dacca. (Dacca Med. Coll.)

IMAM, Syed Bizaat Buteland Terrace Health Centre, Buteland Terrace, Newbiggin-by-the-Sea NE64 6NS Tel: 01670 816996 Fax: 01670 816946; Lelant House, Stakeford, Choppington NE62 5UR Tel: 01670 813436 — MB BS 1965 Karachi; BSc Karachi 1958; DTM & H Eng. 1967. (Dow Med. Coll.) Socs: Pakistan Med. Soc. (Gen. Sec. NE Br.). Prev: SHO (Paediat.) Bridgend Gen. Hosp. & Neath Gen. Hosp.

IMAM, Syed Masroor 5 Walker Terrace, Gateshead NE8 1HX Tel: 0191 477 2033 Fax: 0191 478 2083 — MB BS 1978 Karachi. GP Gateshead, Tyne & Wear.

IMBER, Charles Jason 39A Prince of Wales Road, London NW5 3LJ — BChir 1992 Camb.

IMESON, Jennifer The Surgery, 114 Walm Lane, London NW2 4RT Tel: 020 8452 0366 Fax: 020 8450 3816 — MB BS 1972 Newc.; DObst RCOG 1974; DCH Eng. 1975. Clin. Med. Off. Harrow HA.; Clin. Asst. (Paediat.) N.wick Pk. Hosp. Harrow. Prev: SHO (Obst.) P.ss Mary Matern. Hosp. Newc.; SHO (Gyn.) Roy. Vict. Infirm. Newc.; SHO (Paediat.) N.wick Pk. Hosp. Harrow.

IMISON, Christopher Lancaster 87 Heath Road, Widnes WA8 7NU — MB ChB 1954 Liverp. (Liverp.) Prev: Ho. Surg. O & G, Ho. Phys. & Orthop. Ho. Surg. Whiston Hosp.

IMLACH, Audrey Ann 7 Gatcombe Close, Chatham ME5 7RD — BSc West. Ontario 1980; MB BS W. Indies 1985.

IMLACH, Marie 411 Clifton Road, Aberdeen AB24 4EB — MB ChB 1994 Aberd.

IMLAH, Mary Medical Centre, The Grove, Rowlands Gill NE39 1PW Tel: 01207 542136 Fax: 01207 543340 — MB ChB 1981 Aberd.; MRCGP 1988; Cert. Family Plann. JCC 1988.

IMLAH, Norman William 17 Leasowes Road, Birmingham B14 7AU Tel: 0121 449 1166 — MB ChB 1955 Ed.; Dipl. Psych. 1958; FRCPsych 1977, M 1971. (Univ. Ed.) p/t Sen. Staff Cons. Woodbourne Priory Hosp. Birm. Socs: BMA; Brit. Assn. of PsychoPharmacol. Prev: Med. Dir. Alcohol Progr. Manor & Woodbourne Clinic Birm.; Med. Dir. & Cons. Psychiat. All St.s' Hosp. Birm.; SHO Roy. Edin. Hosp. Ment. & Nerv. Disorders.

IMLAY, Joice Margaret Wimborne House, 155 Wellington Road, Oldham OL8 4DD Tel: 0161 624 4114 — MB ChB 1944 Aberd.; MRCGP 1953.

IMM, Nicholas David Harvey Hardingstone, Renney Road, Heybrook Bay, Plymouth PL9 0BG Email: imm-nick@hotmail.com — BM 1993 Soton. GP Reg. Prev: Unit Dr.Beach Film Produc.; Regist. (Med.) Jersey Gen. Hosp.; Expedition Medic Raleigh Internat.

IMMACULATE, Mary Burton Road Surgery, 140 Burton Road, Lincoln LN1 3LW Tel: 01522 520155 Fax: 01522 537565.

IMMELMAN, Robert Edward 5 Bournemouth Gardens, Folkestone CT19 5BB — MB ChB 1990 Cape Town.

IMMS, Frederick John 135 Albert Road, Epsom KT17 4EN Tel: 01372 720590 Fax: 020 7848 6302 Email: fred.imm@kcl.ac.uk — MB BS Lond. 1963; PhD Lond. 1963, BSc 1958. (Univ. Coll. Hosp.) Sen. Lect. (Physiol.) Sch. BioMed. Sci.s, Sheperd's Ho., GKT Sch. Med. Lond. SE1 7EN. Socs: BMA; Physiol. Soc. Prev: Scientif. Off MRC Environm. Physiol. Unit Lond. Sch. Hyg. Trop. Med.; Sen. Lect. (Physiol.) St. Thos. Hosp. Med. Sch. Lond.; Ho. Surg. (Obst.) Univ. Coll. Hosp. Lond.

IMMS, Jeremy Macmillan 23 Shelley Road, Worthing BN11 4 Tel: 01903 234844 — MB BS 1990 Lond.; MRCGP 1994. (St. Thos.) Prev: Trainee GP Bournemouth & Poole VTS.

IMPALLOMENI, Mario Giuseppe Charing Cross Hospital, Fulham Palace Road, London W6 8RF Tel: 020 8383 0004 Fax: 020 8846 1307 Email: m.impallomeni@ic.ac.uk; 20 Southway, Hampsthead Garden Suburb, London NW11 6RU Tel: 020 8455 3007 Email: m.impallomeni@ic.ac.uk — MD 1961 (Hons.) Florence; MD (Hons.) Florence 1961; FRCP Lond. 1985, M 1969. (University of Florence medical school. Italy) Cons. Gen. & Geriat. Med. Hammersmith & Char. Cross Hosps; Phys. Saracens RFU Football Club Lond.; Hon. Sen. Lect. Fac. of Med., Imperial Coll. of Sci. Technol. and Med., Hammersmith Hosp. Campus. Socs: Fell. Roy. Soc. Med.; Brit. Geriat. Soc.; Amer. Geriat. Soc. Prev: Cons. Phys. (Geriat.) N. Middlx. & St. Ann's Hosps. Lond.; Sen. Regist. (Geriat.) St. Thos. Hosp. Lond.; Hon. Cons. Phys. Italian Hosp. Lond.

IMPEY, Jacqueline Anne Elms Medical Practice, 5 Stewart Road, Harpenden AL5 4QA Tel: 01582 769393 Fax: 01582 461735; 22 Manland Avenue, Harpenden AL5 4RF — MB ChB 1981 Birm.; DRCOG 1988; DCH RCPS Glas. 1983. Clin. Asst. (Dermat.) Luton & Dunstable Hosp.

IMPEY, Mr Lawrence William Mellanby The Women's Centre, John Radcliffe Hospital, Headington, Oxford OX3 9DU Tel: 01865 221625 Email: lawrence.impey@orh.nhs.uk — MB BS 1988 Lond.; BA Oxf. 1985; MRCOG 1993. Cons. in Obst. & Feto-Matern. Med., John Radcliffe Hosp. Oxf. Prev: Regist. (O & G) John Radcliffe Hosp. Oxf.

IMRAN, Mr Sikander Khan 8 Duchess Drive, Seaford BN25 2XL — MB BS 1982 Punjab; FRCS Glas. 1990.

IMRAY, Mr Christopher Henry Ernest 11 Dalton Road, Earlsdon, Coventry CV5 6PB Tel: 02476 677443, 02476 677444 Email: chrisimray@aol.com; Email: chrisimray@aol.com — MB BS 1983 Lond.; FRCS Eng. 1987. Cons. Surg. Walsgrave Hosp. NHS Trust. Socs: BMA; Med. Protec. Soc.; Birm. Med. Research and Expeditionary Soc.

***IMRAY, Elizabeth Anderson** 209 Springfield Road, Aberdeen AB15 8JN Tel: 01224 317727 — MB ChB 1994 Aberd.

IMRAY, James McGregor 209 Springfield Road, Aberdeen AB15 8JN — MB ChB 1957 Aberd.; FFA RCS Eng. 1969; DA Eng. 1963. Cons. (Anaesth.) N.E. RHB (Scotl.).

IMRIE, Alastair Harris The Princess Royal Hospital, Hull HU8 9HE — MB ChB 1958 St. And.; FRCOG 1981, M 1965.

IMRIE, Alexander Henderson (retired) Braehead, Academy St., Fortrose IV10 8TW Tel: 01381 20312 — MB ChB 1930 Glas.; MD (High. Commend.) Glas. 1948. MB ChB (Commend.); FRFPS Glas. 1933; FRCP Glas. 1962; FRCP Lond. 1951, M 1933; FRCP Ed. 1976, M 1965. Hon. Cons. Phys. Roy. Infirm. Glas. Prev: Phys. i/c Wards & Diabetic Clinic, Roy. Infirm. Glas.

IMRIE, Professor Clement William 11 Penrith Avenue, Giffnock, Glasgow G46 6LU Tel: 0141 638 0055 Fax: 0141 211 4991 — MB ChB 1967 Glas.; BSc (Physiol.) (Hons.) Glas. 1964; FRCS Glas. 1972. (Glas.) Cons. Surg. Glas. Roy. Infirm.; Hon. Apptd. Prof. Univ. Glas. Socs: Brit. Soc. Gastroenterol.; (Ex-Pres.) Europ. Pancreatic Club; (Ex-Pres.) Internat. Assn. Pancreatol.

IMRIE, Fiona Jane 45 Eldon Terrace, Windmill Hill, Bristol BS3 4PA Tel: 0117 949 4481 — BM 1990 Soton.; DRCOG 1995. Prev: GP Reg.Malago Surg.Bedminster; SHO O & G St michaels Bristol; SHO ENT S.mead hosp.Bristol.

IMRIE, Fraser Robert Dept of Ophthalmology, Glasgow Royal Infirmary, Castle St., Glasgow G4 0SF — MB ChB 1995 Glas.; BSc (Hons.) Molecular Biol. Glas. 1992. (Univ. Glas.) SHO Ophth Glas. Roy. Infirm. Prev: Ho. Off. W.. Infirm. Glas.; SHO Gold Coast Hosp. Qu.sland, Austral.

IMRIE, Gregor John 11 Penrith Avenue, Giffnock, Glasgow G46 6LU — MB ChB 1991 Glas.

IMRIE, Jean Mary Stoney Bank, Long Preston, Skipton BD23 4PF Tel: 01729 840355 — MB ChB 1953 Leeds; MFFP 1994. (Leeds) Prev: Ho. Surg. Hosp. for Wom. Leeds; Ho. Phys. (Med. & Paediat.) Gen. Hosp. Otley.

IMRIE, Jocelyn Elizabeth Anne, OBE Pathology Department, Monksland District General Hospital, Monkscourt Avenue, Airdrie ML6 0SF Tel: 0123 64 69344 — MB ChB 1973 Glas.; FRCPath 1995; MRCPath 1983. Cons. Cytopath. Monklands Dist. Gen. Hosp. Airdrie.; Quality Assur. Adviser to the Scott. Cervical Screening Progr.

IMRIE, Michael John (retired) 2 Foldyard Cottage, North St., Leven, Beverley HU17 5NF Tel: 01964 543890 — MB ChB 1959 Manch.; MSc Manch. 1962; DMRD Liverp. 1964. Prev: Clin. Dir. Humberside BrE. Screening Serv.

IMRIE, Michael Murdoch Vikings, Danes Hill, The Hockering, Woking GU22 7HQ — MB BS 1978 Lond.; BSc Lond. 1975, MB BS 1978; FFA RCS Eng. 1985. Cons. Anaesth. St. Peters Hosp. Chertsey.

IMRIE, Wai Lan 44 Braidpark Drive, Giffnock, Glasgow G46 6LY — MB ChB 1991 Glas.

IMTIAZ, Fawzia 105 Millway, London NW7 3JL — MB BS 1993 Lond.

IMTIAZ, Shah Mohammad Health Centre, High St., Aberdare CF44 7DD — MB BS 1964 Bihar. (Darbhanga Med. Coll.)

INADA-KIM, Matthew 38 Raisins Hill Road, Pinner HA5 2BS — MB BS 1993 Lond.

INAYAT, Dr 43 Tomswood Road, Chigwell IG7 5QR — MB BS 1968 Peshawar.

INAYAT, Mohammad The Lodge, 25 Bedfordwell Road, Eastbourne BN21 2BQ Tel: 01323 412280 Fax: 01323 416054 — MB BS 1985 Punjab; DPM RCPSI 1994. (Allama Iqbal Med. Coll. Lahore, Pakistan) Staff Grade Psychiat. Community Drugs Team & Adult Psychiat. E.bourne & Co. Healthcare NHS Trust. Socs: Life Mem. Pakistan Psychiat. Soc.; Coll. Phys. & Surgs. Pakistan; MDU. Prev: SHO (Psychiat.) William Harvey Hosp. Ashford & E.bourne Hosp.; SHO (Adult Psychiat.) Canterbury & Thanet HA; SHO Rotat. (Psychiat.) E.bourne Hosp.

INCE, Anne Helen Auchtermuchty Health Centre, 12 Carswell Wynd, Auchtermuchty, Cupar KY14 7AW; Glassarts Cottage, Newburgh Rd, Auchtermuchty, Cupar KY14 7EF Tel: 01337 828618 — MB ChB 1975 Dundee; MRCGP Edin. 2001; DRCOG 1978.

INCE, Colin Stuart Critical Care Directorate, Whiston Hospital, St Helen's & Knowsley Trust, Prescot L35 5DR Tel: 0151 430 1329 Fax: 0151 430 1341 Email: cince18270@aol.com; 73 St.James Road, Rainhill, Prescot L35 0PE Email: cince18270@aol.com — MB ChB 1968 Liverp.; FRCA 1972. (Liverp.) Cons. Anaesth. St. Helens & Knowsley Hosps. Trust. Socs: Assn. Anaesth.; BMA; Sec. Plastic Surg. & Burns Anaesths. Prev: Sen. Regist. (Anaesth.) Alder Hey Childr. Hosp. Liverp.; Sen. Regist. (Anaesth.) Whiston Hosp. Prescot; Regist. (Anaesth.) Walton Hosp. Liverp.

INCE, David Andrew James Bas de L'Allee, La Rue de la Fontaine de Colard, Trinity, Jersey JE3 5DR — MB BS 1998 Lond.; MB BS Lond 1998.

INCE, Gregory James Grosvenor Street Surgery, 4 Grosvenor Street, St Helier, Jersey JE1 4HB Tel: 01534 730541 Fax: 01534 887948; Bas De L'Allee, Trinity, Jersey JE3 5DR Tel: 01534 861106 — MB BS 1971 Lond.; MRCS Eng. LRCP Lond. 1971; FRCGP 1995, M 1977; DFFP 1995; DObst RCOG 1973. (Westm.) Socs: BMA; Jersey Med. Soc. Prev: SHO (Gyn.), Ho. Surg. & Resid. Obst. Asst. W.m. Hosp. Lond.

INCE, Maureen Margaret (retired) Cuil Gorm, Duncrievie Road, Glenfarg, Perth PH2 9PA Tel: 01577 830227 — MB ChB Liverp. 1946. Prev: Ho. Surg. Roy. Infirm. Liverp.

INCE, Professor Paul Geoffrey Neuropathology, E floor, Royal Hallamshire Hospital, Glossop Road, Sheffield S10 2JF Tel: 0114 271 2949 Fax: 0114 271 2200 Email: p.g.ince@shef.ac.uk — MB BS 1978 Newc.; BSc (Anat.) Newc. 1975, MD 1990; MRCPath 1987; FRCPath 1997. (Newcastle) Prof. Neuropath. Sheff. Univ.; honourary Cons. Newcatle CA; honourary Cons. neuropath CSHH trust Sheff. Socs: Newc. u. Tyne Path. Club; Sec. Brit. NeuroPath. Soc. Prev: MRC Clin. Sci. MRC Neurochem. Path. Unit. Newc. Gen. Hosp.

INCEMAN, Hubert 3 The Brooklands, Heywood OL10 1HB — MB BS 1954 Lond.; MRCS Eng. LRCP Lond. 1954; MRCPsych 1971.

INCH, Douglas Dick (retired) 6 North Park Avenue, Leeds LS8 1DN — MB ChB 1942 St. And.; FRCGP 1978, M 1953. Prev: Maj. RAMC.

INCH, Heather Margaret 69 Onslow Road, Endcliffe, Sheffield S11 7AG; Bassetlaw Hospital and Community Services, NHS Trust, Worksop — MB ChB 1988 Sheff.; MRCPsych 1992. Cons. Psychiat. Socs: Roy. Coll. Psychiat.

INCH, Philip John The Health Centre, Viewley Centre, Hemlington, Middlesbrough TS8 9JQ Tel: 01642 590500 Fax: 01642 591721; 4 Rothbury Close, Ingleby Barwick, Stockton-on-Tees TS17 0YR — BM BS 1983 Nottm.; BMedSci Nottm. 1981; MRCGP 1987; DRCOG 1987. (Nottm.) Socs: Christian Med. Fell.sh.; Med. Protec. Soc.; BMA. Prev: SHO Cleveland VTS.

INCHLEY, David Charles Upton Village Surgery, Wealstone Lane, Upton, Chester CH2 1HD Tel: 01244 382238 Fax: 01244 381576 — BM BS 1994 Nottm.; DRCOG 1998. GP Regist. Wrexham.

INCHLEY, Joanne Patricia 99A Kenyon Street, London SW6 6LA — MB BCh 1990 Wales. GP Regist. Aylesbury VTS. Prev: SHO (Oncol.) Mt. Vernon Hosp. Middlx.; SHO (Oncol.) Char. Cross Hosp.; SHO (Haemat.) Univ. Hosp. of Wales.

INCHLEY, Sarah Jane Cape Road Surgery, 3 Cape Road, Warwick CV34 4JP Tel: 01926 499988 Fax: 01926 498956; 31 Guys Cliffe Villas, Hyde Place, Leamington Spa CV32 5BT — MB ChB 1985 Manch.; MRCGP 1990; DRCOG 1989. Trainee GP Bicester Oxon. VTS.

IND, John Edgar 51 Sloane Street, London SW1X 9SW Tel: 020 7235 5151 Fax: 020 7823 1499 Email: drjohnind@msn.com — MB BS Lond. 1962; Dip Occ Med 1998. (St. Bart.) Occupat. Health Cons. C&A Ltd., MSD Recruitment, Maersk Co., Niarchos Lond. Internat., Planned Parenthood Federat., Safinvest etc; Sen. Aviat. Med. Exam. Fed. Aviat. Admin. USA. Socs: Fell. Roy. Soc. Med. (Mem. Sect. Occupat. Med.); Soc. Occupat. Health; Med. Soc. Lond. Prev: Regist. (Path. & Med.) St. Bart. Hosp. Lond.; Ho. Surg. St. Bart. Hosp. Lond.; Ho. Phys. N. Middlx. Hosp. Lond.

IND, Philip Waterloo Respiratory Medicine, Hammersmith Hospital, Du Cane Road, London W12 0NN Tel: 020 8383 3077 Fax: 020 8743 9733 Email: pind@rpms.ac.uk; 35 Kenilworth Road, London W5 5PA Tel: 020 8567 9107 — MB BChir 1975 Camb.; MA Camb. 1975; FRCP Lond. 1991; MRCP (UK) 1976. (Univ. Coll. Hosp.) Sen. Lect. & Hon. Cons. Phys. (Respirat. Med.) Hammersmith Hosp. Prev: Cons. Phys. & Hon. Sen. Lect. (Respirat. Med.) Hammersmith Hosp. & Ealing Hosp. Lond.; Sen. Regist. (Respirat. Med.) Hammersmith Hosp. Lond.; Hon. Sen. Regist. (Clin. Pharmacol.) Roy. Postgrad. Med. Sch. Lond.

IND, Sally Hutcheon North End Medical Centre, 211 North End Road, West Kensington, London W14 9NP Tel: 020 7385 7777 Fax: 020 7386 9612 — MB ChB 1973 Ed.; DObst RCOG 1975.

IND, Thomas Edward James Department Gynaecology, St Bartholomew's Hospital, West Smithfield, London EC1A 7BE Tel: 020 7601 8951; Flat 1, 51 Sloane St, London SW1X 9SW Tel: 020 7601 8951 Fax: 020 7823 1499 — MB BS 1990 Lond. Research Fell. (Gyn.) St. Bart. Hosp. Lond. Socs: Fell. Roy. Soc. Med.; BMA.

INDAPURKAR, Narayan Rao 10 Canonbury Park N., London N1 2JT — MB BS 1970 Jiwaji.

INDAR, Mr Rupert 15 Clanricarde Gardens, Flat 7, London W2 4JJ Tel: 020 7792 0650; 87 Mc Lelland Street, St Joseph Village, San-Fernando, Trinidad & Tobago Tel: 1 868 652 0780 Fax: 1 868 652 4874 — MD 1957 Dub.; MB BCh BAO 1952; FRCS Eng. 1959.

INDAR, Rupert Arjoon Flat 3, 66 Sotheby Road, London N5 2UT — MB BS 1995 Lond. (london Hosp) Socs: MDU; MPS.

INDER, Graham Malcolm Cliff Road Health Centre, 4 Cliff Road, Welton, Lincoln LN2 3JH Tel: 01673 860203 Fax: 01673 862888; Stonewell, Church St, Scothern, Lincoln LN2 2UA — BM BS 1975 Nottm.; BMedSci 1973. Socs: BMA; Assoc. Mem. RCGP. Prev: Trainee Gen. Pract. Humberside Vocational Train. Scheme.

INDRA KUMAR, Kathiraveloe Weller Wing, Bedford General Hospital (South Wing), Bedford MK42 9DL Tel: 01234 55122 — MB BS 1972 Ceylon.

INDRASENAN, Natheera 21 St Johns Way, Rochester ME1 3NT — MB BS 1993 Lond.

INDWAR, Anil Chandra 19 Walford Street, Tividale, Oldbury B69 2LD Tel: 0121 557 1328 Fax: 0121 557 2274; 75 Moorcroft Road, Moseley, Birmingham B13 8LS — MB BS 1971 Ranchi. (Rajendra Med. Coll.) Socs: BMA; MPS; ODA.

INDWAR, Chhaya 75 Moorcroft Road, Moseley, Birmingham B13 8LS Tel: 0121 557 1328 — MB BS 1971 Ranchi. (Rajendra Med. Coll.) Sen. Med. Off. Sandwell HA.

***INDWAR, Sheena** 75 Moorcroft Road, Moseley, Birmingham B13 8LS Tel: 0121 449 2105; Cambridge University Department of Anatomy, Downing St, Cambridge CB2 3DY — BChir 1996 Camb.; MB Camb. 1996; MA Camb. 1998.

***INESON, Christopher Malcolm** Newham General Hospital, Glen Road, London E13 8SL Tel: 020 7476 4000; 21 Highwood Avenue, Cheltenham GL53 0JJ Tel: 01242 523804 — MB BS 1997 Lond.

INESON, Neil, Col. late RAMC Frimley Park Hospital, Portsmouth Road, Frimley, Camberley GU16 7UJ Tel: 01276 692777 — MB BS 1978 Newc.; FRCP Lond. 1995; MRCP (UK) 1980. Cons. Phys. Army Cardiac Unit Camberley; Assoc. Dean Defence Med. (Army). Socs: Brit. Cardiac Soc.

INESON, Nigel Richard Leavesden Road Surgery, 141A Leavesden Road, Watford WD2 5EP Tel: 01923 225128; Wentworth, 30 Green Lane, Oxhey, Watford WD19 4NH Tel: 01923 233992 Fax: 01923 443143 Email: nigelineson@msn.com — MB BS 1977 Lond.; DFFP 1993; FRCGP 1992, M 1985; T(GP) 1991; DRCOG 1982. (Guy's) Prev: Trainee GP Watford VTS; SHO Rotat. (Surg.) Medway Hosp. Gp.

INFANTONE, Lorena 16 Norfolk House, Restell Close, London SE3 7UW — State DMS 1992 Catania.

INFELD, David Ashley 50 Yellowhammer Court, Kidderminster DY10 4RR — MB BS 1981 Melbourne.

INFIELD, Jean Augusta (retired) 79 Harley Street, London W1N 1DE Tel: 020 7486 1586 — MRCS Eng. LRCP Lond. 1947; MFFP 1993; FFFP 1999. Prev: SCMO Family Plann. Unit Qu. Charlotte's Matern. Hosp. Lond.

***ING, Alison Catriona** 4 Park Walk, Easton on the Hill, Stamford PE9 3LW — MB ChB 1998 Dund.; MB ChB Dund 1998.

ING, Richard Peregrine CAMHS, St Stephens House, 45 Borough St., Brighton BN1 3BG Tel: 01273 327221 Fax: 01273 202312 Email: richard.ing@southdowns.nhs.uk — MRCS Eng. LRCP Lond. 1982; MRCPsych 1988. Cons. Child & Adolesc. Psychiat. S. Downs NHS Trust. Prev: Sen. Regist. Rotat. (Child & Adolesc. Psychiat.) Yorks. RHA; Regist. (Psychiat.) Walsgrave Hosp. Coventry & Centr. Hosp. Warwick; Ho. Off. (Med. & Surg.) Hosp. of St. Cross Rugby.

INGAMELLS, Susan Obstetrics & Gynaecology, Princess Anne Hospital, Coxford Road, Southampton SO16 Tel: 02380 777222 Email: si@soton.ac.uk; Kite Lodge, 15 Ardnave Crescent, Southampton SO16 7FL Tel: 02380 766387 Email: si@soton.ac.uk — BM 1990 Soton.; PhD Soton. 1986; BSc (Hons.) Physiol. & Biochem. Soton. 1982; MRCOG 1995. (Soton.) p/t Specialist Regist. In Reproductive Med. P.ss Anne Hosp. Soton.

INGE, Kelvin Shing-Kon Flat 2, 113 Cheyne Walk, London SW10 0ES — MB BChir 1988 Camb.; MA Camb. 1989; MRCP (UK) 1992. Socs: Brit. Cardiac Soc. Prev: Regist. (Cardiac) John Radcliffe Hosp. Oxf.; SHO (Med.) St. Bart. Hosp. Lond.; SHO (Cardiol.) Roy. Free Hosp. Lond.

INGHAM, Barry 3 Weeford Road, Sutton Coldfield B75 6LY Tel: 0121 308 6311 — MB ChB 1952 Birm.; DObst RCOG 1956. (Birm.) Prev: Ho. Surg. Birm. Matern. Hosp.

INGHAM, Douglas Gibson 7 Turnberry Road, Glasgow G11 5AF — MB ChB 1990 Glas.

INGHAM, Elizabeth Joan Nuffield House Surgery, The Stow, Harlow CM20 3AX Tel: 01279 425661 Fax: 01279 427116; 4 Watlington Road, Harlow CM17 0DX — MB ChB 1980 Manch.; BSc St. And. 1977; DCH RCP Lond. 1985.

INGHAM, Fraser Emrys 10 Monks Close, Dorchester-on-Thames, Wallingford OX10 7JA — MB BS 1996 Lond.; BSc (Hons.) Lond. 1993, MB BS Lond. 1996. (UCL)

INGHAM, Horace (retired) Briar Hill, 5 Pembroke Close, Belgrave Park, Chester CH4 7BS Tel: 01244 678618 Email: h.ingham@btinternet.com — MB ChB 1939 Liverp.; FRCPath 1963. Prev: Cons. Path. Chester Health Dist.

INGHAM, Jane Stella St James (University) Hospital, Becket St., Leeds LS9 7TF Tel: 0113 243 3144; The Turnings, Woodacre Crescent, Bardsey, Leeds LS17 9DQ Tel: 01937 72673 — MB ChB 1967 Manch.; DA Eng. 1970. (Manch.) Clin. Asst. (Anaesth.) St. Jas. (Univ.) Hosp. Leeds. Socs: Pain Soc.; Brit. Med. Acupunct. Soc.

Prev: Regist. (Anaesth.) Wycombe Gen. Hosp. High Wycombe; Ho. Surg. & Ho. Phys. Ancoats Hosp. Manch.

INGHAM, John Frank 78 New Park Road, Cranleigh GU6 7JN — MB BS 1996 Lond.

INGHAM, Jonathan Edward The Surgery, The Doctors House, Tarrington, Hereford HR1 4HZ Tel: 01432 890218 Fax: 01432 890722 — MB BS 1972 Lond.; MRCS Eng LRCP Lond. 1971.

INGHAM, Jonathan Neil Bluebell Cottage, Cott Road, Dartington, Totnes TQ9 6HD — BM BCh 1989 Oxf.

INGHAM, Linda Jean 5 Edinburgh Road, Tranent EH33 1BA Tel: 01875 613841 — MB 1974 Camb.; BChir 1973; MRCGP 1978; DCH RCPS Glas. 1975. Clin. Asst. Psychiat. of Old Age E. & Midlothian NHS Trust Edenhall Hosp. Musselburgh; Med. Adviser, Benefits Agency Med. Servs. Prev: GP E. Wing, Esk Med. Centre, Musselburgh.

INGHAM, Margaret (retired) Woodlands, 434 Penn Road, Wolverhampton WV4 4DH Tel: 01902 620243 — MB ChB Birm. 1940; MFCM 1973; DCH Eng. 1947. Prev: Sen. Med. Off. Wolverhampton AHA.

INGHAM, Mary Constance (retired) 10 Stiles Avenue, Marple, Stockport SK6 6LR — LRCPI & LM, LRCSI & LM 1959. Prev: Assoc. Specialist Psychiat. Salford HA.

INGHAM, Peter John Ashfurlong Health Centre, 233 Tamworth Road, Sutton Coldfield B75 6DX Tel: 0121 308 6311; 3 Weeford Road, Sutton Coldfield B75 6LY — MB ChB 1985 Birm.; ChB Birm. 1985.

INGHAM, William Geoffrey York Bridge Surgery, 5 James Street, Morecambe LA4 5TE Tel: 01524 831111 Fax: 01524 832493 — MB ChB 1971 Manch. Clin. Asst. (Genitourin. Med.) Lancs.

INGHAM, William Norman (retired) 4 Lismore, Hollington Park Road, St Leonards-on-Sea TN38 — MB BChir 1948 Camb.; MB BChir. Camb. 1948; MRCS Eng. LRCP Lond. 1943; DCH Eng. 1949. Prev: Supernum. Chief Asst. & Ho. Surg. St. Bart. Hosp.

INGHAM CLARK, Celia Louise Department of Surgery, Whittington Hospital Trust, Highgate Hill, London N19 5NF Tel: 020 7272 3070 Email: celia.inghamclark@whittington.thenhs.com — MB BChir 1984 Camb.; MChir Camb. 1992; FRCS (Gen.) 1995; FRCS Eng. 1987. (Camb. & Middlx.) Cons. Surg. Whittington Hosp. Trust Lond. Socs: Fell. Roy. Soc. Med.; Assn. Coloproctol.; Assn. Surg. Prev: Resid. Surgic. Off. St. Mark's Hosp.; Lect. & Sen. Regist. N. Thames.

***INGLE, Gordon Thorpe** Lilybank, Leny Road, Callender FK17 8AJ Tel: 01877 330380 — MB ChB 1994 Ed.; BSc (Hons.) Neurosci. Ed. 1992, MB ChB 1994.

INGLE, Mr Hemant Trimbak 5 Priory Gardens, Stamford PE9 2EG — MB BS 1979 Poona; FRCS Glas. 1987. Assoc. Specialist (Gen. Surg. & Urol.) Lincs. Socs: BMA.

INGLE, John Howard Narrowcliff Surgery, Narrowcliff, Newquay TR7 2QF Tel: 01637 873363 Fax: 01637 850735 — MB ChB 1978 Bristol.

INGLE, Prabhakar Rangnath Quarry Road Surgery, 10 Quarry Road, Dudley DY2 0EF Tel: 01384 569050 Fax: 01384 350321 — MB BS 1966 Poona; DA Eng. 1971. (B.J. Med. Coll.) Community Med. Off. Child Health W. Midl. Prev: GP St. Nicholas Health Centre Burnley; GP Pudsey W. Yorks.; Clin. Asst. Anaesth. Burnley Hosp.

INGLE, Urmila Prabhakar Quarry Road Surgery, 10 Quarry Road, Dudley DY2 0EF Tel: 01384 569050 Fax: 01384 350321 — MB BS 1970 Poona. (B.J. Med. Coll.) Clin. Asst. (Ophth.) Guest Hosp. Dudley. Prev: GP Burnley; SHO (Ophth.) Darlington Hosp.

INGLE-FINCH, Fiona Marjory Ivy Court Surgery, Recreation Ground, Tenterden TN30 6RB; Maynes, Stone-in-Oxney, Tenterden TN30 7HA — MB ChB 1978 Dundee. GP Asst. Socs: BMA.

INGLEBY, Isadore 14 Arlington Road, Cheadle SK8 1LW Tel: 0161 428 2162 — MRCS Eng. LRCP Lond. 1954; MA Manch. 1992, MB ChB 1954.

INGLEDEW, Derek Charlton Kirkleatham Street, Redcar TS10 1UA, USA Tel: 01642 471388 Fax: 01642 488701; 27 Reighton Drive, York YO30 5QP — BA Oxf. 1963, BM BCh 1966; MRCGP 1979. (Middlx.) Prev: Trainee Gen. Pract. Teesside Vocational Train. Scheme; SHO (Obst.) N. Tees Gen. Hosp. Stockton-on-Tees; SHO (Paediat.) Childr. Hosp. Stockton-on-Tees.

INGLEDEW, Margaret Elizabeth Tayview Medical Practice, 16 Victoria Street, Newport-on-Tay DD6 8DJ Tel: 01382 543251 Fax: 01382 542052 — MB ChB 1990 Dundee; BA Open 1989; BSc (Med. Sci.) St. And. 1987; DRCOG 1993.

INGLES, Elizabeth Mary (retired) Flat 2, 60 York Place, Harrogate HG1 5RH Tel: 01423 567237 — MB ChB Ed. 1948, DPH 1961.

INGLESBY, Mr David Valentine Sunderland Eye Infirmary, Queen Alexandra Road, Sunderland SR2 9HP Tel: 0191 528 3616; Tel: 0191 523 6326 — MB BS 1979 Lond.; BSc (Hons. Physiol.) Lond. 1976; FRCS Eng. 1985; FRCOphth 1988. (St. Bart.) Cons. Ophth. Sunderland Eye Infirm.; Cons. Ophth., Hartlepool Gen. Hosp. Socs: The Vitreous soc. Prev: Sen. Regist. Moorfields Eye Hosp. & St. Thos. Hosp. Lond.; Research Fell. Roy. Postgrad. Med. Sch. Lond.; Ho. Surg. St. Bart. Hosp. Lond.

INGLIS, Alexander (retired) The Orchard, Houghton House, Houghton, Carlisle CA6 4DX Tel: 01228 674615 — MB ChB St. And. 1942; MD St. And. 1955; FCRPath 1964. Prev: Hon. Cons. E. Cumbria Health Dist.

INGLIS, Alistair (retired) Baile Mhuilinn, Lawers, Aberfeldy PH15 2PA Tel: 01567 820876 — MB BS 1963 Lond.; AFOM Lond. 1986; DObst RCOG 1966. Prev: GP Market HarBoro.

INGLIS, Andrew Cleland 79 Randolph Road, Glasgow G11 7DU — MB ChB 1993 Glas.

INGLIS, Andrew Erskine Tadcaster Medical Centre, Crab Garth, Tadcaster LS24 8HD Tel: 01937 530082 Fax: 01937 530192 Email: andrew@coughsandsneezes.com — MB BS 1990 Lond.; MRCGP 1994; DFFP 1994; DRCOG 1993. (Univ. Lond. & Char. Cross & Westm.) Chairm., Local Diabetes Serv. Advis. Gp. (LDSAG). Prev: Trainee GP/SHO St. Richard's Hosp. Chichester VTS; SHO (Paediat.) S. Cleveland Acute Hosps. NHS Trust; Clin. Asst. (Diabetes Centre) York Dist. Hosp.

INGLIS, Andrew Iain Intensive Care Unit, Southern General Hospital, 1345 Govan Road, Glasgow G51 4TF Tel: 0141 201 1658 — MB ChB 1987 Glas.; DTM & H 2001 Royal College of Physicians of London; FRCA 1992 London; MRCP 1999 Glasgow. (Glasgow) Cons. Intens. Care & Anaesth., S. Glas. Hosp.s. Prev: Sen. Regist. (Anaesth.) Vict. infirm. Glas.; Sen. Regist., Intens. Care, Royla Brisbane Hosp.,Brisbane; Sen. Regist.,Intens. Care, W. of Scotl., Glas.

INGLIS, Andrew Ronald Sutton Hill Medical Practice, Maythorne Close, Sutton Hill, Telford TF7 4DH Tel: 01952 586471 Fax: 01952 588029; The Orchard, 27 Church Hill, Ironbridge, Telford TF8 7PZ Tel: 01952 432791 — MB ChB 1987 Glas.; BSc Birm. 1976; MRCGP 1991; DRCOG 1989; DCH RCPS Glas. 1989.

INGLIS, Edward Marine Avenue Surgery, 49 Marine Avenue, Whitley Bay NE26 1NA Tel: 0191 252 4527 — MB ChB 1970 St. And.

INGLIS, Fraser George Crosshome Hospital, Kilmarnock KA2 0BE Tel: 01563 577078 Fax: 01563 577369 — MB ChB 1987 Dundee; BMSc (Hons.) (Anat.) 1984; MRCP (UK) 1992. (University of Dundee) Cons. Phys. (Geriat. Med.) CrossHo. Hosp. Kilmarnock. Prev: Lect. (Geriat. Med.) Ninewells Hosp. Dundee.

INGLIS, Gary Scott Staff Residences, Battle Hospital, Oxford Road, Reading RG30 1AG — MB ChB 1994 Ed.

INGLIS, Iain Moir Bewdley Medical Centre, Dog Lane, Bewdley DY12 2EG Tel: 01299 402157 Fax: 01299 404364; Brackenhills, 10 Clarence Way, Bewdley DY12 1QE Tel: 01299 404730 — MB ChB 1983 Dundee; MRCGP 1988; DRCOG 1987; MSc Glasg. 1998MSc Glas. 1998. GP Princip. Socs: BMA. Prev: SHO (O & G) Warneford Hosp. Leamington Spa.; Trainee GP Stratford-on-Avon.

INGLIS, James 50 Riverhead, Sprotbrough, Doncaster DN5 7QR — MB ChB 1970 St. And.; MRCP (UK) 1975. Cons. Paediat. Doncaster Roy. Infirm. Socs: Brit. Paediat. Assn. Prev: Sen. Regist. (Paediat.) Newc. Gen. Hosp. & Sunderland Childr. Hosp.; Regist. (Paediat.) Roy. Hosp. Sick Childr. Glas.; Regist. (Paediat.) Ninewells Gp. Hosps.

INGLIS, Mr James Douglas Angus Abbey Health Centre, East Abbey Street, Arbroath DD11 1EN Tel: 01241 870307 Fax: 01241 431414 — MB ChB 1968 St. And.; FRCS Glas. 1975; Dip. Sports Med. (Scott. Roy. Coll.) 1992. GP Arbroath; Med. Adviser Dundee Sports Med. Centre. Socs: (Comm.) Brit. Assn. Sports Med. Prev: Regist. Rotat. (Surg.) Dundee Health Dist.; SHO Birm. Accid. Hosp.; Med. Off. Globe Universal Scs., Algeria.

INGLIS, James Hans Christian 79 Bruntsfield Place, Edinburgh EH10 4HG — MB ChB 1980 Ed.; BSc Ed. 1977, MB ChB 1980.

INGLIS, James McNaught, Squadron Ldr. RAF Med. Br. (retired) 5 Chester Road, Streetly, Sutton Coldfield B74 2HP Tel: 0121 353 6817 — MB ChB 1945 Leeds; FRCA 1994; FFA RCS Eng. 1954; DA Eng. 1946. Prev: Cons. Anaesth. Birm. Centr. Health Dist.

INGLIS, Mr John Alexander 53 Wergs Road, Wolverhampton WV6 9BN — MD 1992 Ed.; MB ChB 1975; FRCS (Urol) 1992; FRCS Eng. 1981. Cons. Urol. New Cross Hosp. Wolverhampton. Prev: Sen. Regist. (Urol.) Roy. Liverp. Hosp.

INGLIS, Kenneth Thomas 8A Montague Street, Barnhill, Dundee DD5 2RB Tel: 01382 477446 Fax: 01382 477446 Email: kinglis@sol.co.uk — MB ChB St. And. 1966; AFOM RCP Lond. 1983; CIH Dund 1977. Prev: Staff Grade Roy. Vict. Hosp. Dundee.

INGLIS, Margaret Elizabeth 50 Buchanan Drive, Rutherglen, Glasgow G73 3PE — MB ChB 1939 Glas. Prev: Asst. Dermatol. Roy. Hosp. Sick Childr. Glas. & S.. Gen. Hosp.; Glas.; Surgic. Resid. Stobhill Hosp. Glas.

INGLIS, Margaret Rose (retired) Upper Reigate, Park Terrace, Ayr KA7 2AN Tel: 01292 267707 — MB ChB 1948 Aberd.; MRCPsych 1971; DPM Eng. 1955. Prev: Cons. Psychiat. Ailsa Hosp. Ayr.

INGLIS, Michael D Monklands Hospital, Department Anaesthesia, Monkscourt Avenue, Airdrie ML6 0JS Tel: 01236 748748; 50 Sherbrooke Avenue, Pollokshields, Glasgow G41 4SB Tel: 0141 427 1368 — MB ChB 1975 Glas.; FFA RCS Eng. 1980. Cons. Anaesth. Monklands & Bellshill Trust.

INGLIS, Michael Scade The Ashtead Hosp, The Warren, Ashtead KT21 2SB Tel: 01372 276161 Email: jaspie@aol.com; Email: jaspie@aol.com — MB ChB 1975 Glas.; FRCA 1984 Eng; FFA RCSI 1984. (Univ. Glas.) Cons. Anaesth. Ashted Hosp. Socs: Brit. Assn. Day Surg.; Soc. Computing & Technol. in Anaesth.; Assn. of Anaesth.s of Gt. Britain and Irel. Prev: Sen. Regist. (Anaesth.) Hammersmith Hosp., Roy. Postgrad. Med. Sch. Lond., Roy. Nat. Orthop. Hosp. Stanmore & Qu. Charlottes Hosp.; Regist. (Anaesth.) St. Thos. Hosp. Lond.; Regist. (Anaesth.) Poole Gen. Hosp., Roy. Vict. Hosp. Bournemouth & ChristCh. Hosps.

INGLIS, Peter Malcolm Keepers Cottage, Farthing Common, Lyminge, Folkestone CT18 8DQ — MRCS Eng. LRCP Lond. 1951. (Lond. Hosp.) Socs: Whipps Cross Hosp. Med. Soc. Prev: 3rd Field Ambul. El Balah; Med. Off. BMH Fahid & BMH Benghazi.

INGLIS, Peter Railton Rye Bank House, 2 Whins Lane, Wheelton, Chorley PR6 8HN — MB ChB 1974 Aberd.

INGLIS, Sarah Ann 4 Sycamore Gardens, Edinburgh EH12 7JJ Tel: 0131 334 8882 — MB ChB 1998 Aberd.; MB ChB Aberd 1998. SHO Med. Falkirk Roy. Infirm.

INGLIS, Sheila Ann The Petersgate Medical Centre, 99 Amersall Road, Scawthorpe, Doncaster DN5 9PQ Tel: 01302 390490; 100 Amersall Road, Scawthorpe, Doncaster DN5 9PH — MB ChB 1972 St. And.; DObst RCOG 1974; Cert FPA 1973. Approved Instruc. Doctor (Family Plann.) Jt. Comm. Contracep. Lond.; Clin. Med. Off. (Family Plann.) Doncaster HA. Prev: Regist. (Psychiat.) Doncaster Roy. Infirm.; Trainee GP Doncaster VTS; Clin. Med. Off. Sunderland HA.

INGLIS, Sylvia Lorraine 23 Hylands Close, Hornchurch RM11 1DX — MB BS 1967 Lond. SCMO Barking & Havering AHA.

INGLIS, Timothy Christopher McNaught Dudley Hill House, Whins Lane, Read, Burnley BB12 7RB — MB ChB 1971 Birm.; FRCOG 1990, M 1978. Cons. O & G Burnley Health Care Trust. Socs: BMA; BMOGS; BSCCP.

INGOLD, Sylvia Ray (retired) Edberry, Main Road, Woodham Ferrers, Chelmsford CM3 8RW Tel: 01245 320308 — MB BS 1950 Lond.; MRCS Eng. LRCP Lond. 1950; FRCOG 1986, M 1958, DObst 1954; DCH Eng. 1961. Prev: GP Chelmsford.

INGOLDSBY, Beverley Jean Fore Street Surgery, 26 Fore Street, Totnes TQ9 5DX Tel: 01803 862671; Heathfield, Weirfields, Totnes TQ9 5JS Tel: 01803 866510 — MB ChB 1984 Sheff.; MB ChB Sheff. l984; MRCGP 1990; DCH RCPS Glas. 1987. GP Totnes. Prev: Trainee GP/SHO Torbay Hosp. VTS.

INGRAM, Alexander (retired) Kirklands, Lane Side, Kirkheaton, Huddersfield HD5 0ES Tel: 01484 420549 — LRCP LRCS Ed. LRFPS Glas. 1945; DObst RCOG 1954. Prev: Ho. Surg. Samarit. Hosp. Glas.

INGRAM, Alexis Stacey 80 Dyke Road Avenue, Brighton BN1 5LF — MB ChB 1993 Leeds.

INGRAM, Alistair James 7-8 Park Street, Ripon HG4 2AX Tel: 01765 692337; Clandfield House, Galphay, Ripon HG4 3NJ — BM BS 1989 Nottm.; MRCGP 1993; DRCOG 1993. GP Trainer, Dales GPEC, N. Allerton. Prev: Trainee GP Lincoln VTS.

***INGRAM, Anne Louise** 25 Glynn Road, Peacehaven BN10 8AT — MB BS 1998 Lond.; MB BS Lond 1998.

INGRAM, Anne Tait Beaumont Park Surgery, 35 Hepscott Drive, Beaumont Park, Whitley Bay NE25 9XJ Tel: 0191 251 4548; 47 Western Way, Whitley Bay NE26 1JE — MB BS 1971 Newc.; MRCGP 1981. (Newcastle upon Tyne) GP Princip.

INGRAM, Charles Greig 17 Huntly Place, St Andrews KY16 8XA Tel: 01334 76472 — MB ChB 1951 Aberd.; DA Eng. 1956. (Aberd.) Sen. Lect. Physiol. Dept. Univ. St. And. Prev: RAF; Regist. (Anaesth.) Roy. Infirm. Aberd.; Research Assoc. Univ. Michigan, USA.

INGRAM, Christine Elizabeth 6 Cliffe Farm Drive, Sheffield S11 7JW — MB BChir 1979 Camb.; MRCP (UK) 1982; FRCR 1985. (Camb. & Lond. Hosp. Med. Coll.) Cons. Radiol. W. Suff. Hosp. Bury St. Edmunds. Prev: Sen. Regist. (Radiol.) St. Geo. Hosp. Lond.

INGRAM, David Alastair 85 Martin Lane, Bilton, Rugby CV22 7RF — MB ChB 1970 St. And.; Assoc. Fac. Occupat. Med. RCP Lond. 1979. Cons. Occupat. Health Warks. Socs: Soc. Occupat. Med. Prev: Gp. Med. Off. Automotive Products plc; Med. Off. Midl. Chrysler UK Ltd.

INGRAM, David Arthur Department of Clinical Neurophysiology, The Royal London Hospital, Whitechapel, London E1 1BB Tel: 020 7377 7239 Fax: 020 7375 2103 — MB BS 1974 Lond.; BSc (Hons.) Lond. 1971, MB BS 1974. (Westm.) Cons. Clin. Neurophysiol. Lond. Hosp. Whitechapel. Socs: Fell. Roy. Soc. Med.

INGRAM, David Frank Bank House, Oakes Corner, Hatherton, Nantwich CW5 7PQ Tel: 01270 842432 Fax: 01270 842432 Email: davidfingram@doctors.net.uk — MB BS Lond. 1963; BSc (Hons.) Lond. 1961; MRCS Eng. LRCP Lond. 1963; Dip. Pharm. Med. RCP (UK) 1976. Cons. Pharmaceut. Industry. Socs: Fell. Fac. Pharmaceut. Med. 1989; BMA; Brit. Assn. Pharm. Phys. Prev: Hon. Clin. Asst. Roy. Free Hosp. Lond.; Ho. Phys. St. Paul's Hosp. Hemel Hempstead; Flight Lt. RAF Med. Br., Specialist Aviat. Physiol.

INGRAM, David Longden North Street House Surgery, 6 North Street, Emsworth PO10 7DD Tel: 0143 373538 — MB BS Lond. 1968; MRCS Eng. LRCP Lond. 1966; DObst RCOG 1968. (Guy's)

INGRAM, Mr David Vernon (retired) Claremont House, 4 Lodge Green, Burton Park, Duncton, Petworth GU28 0LH Tel: 01798 342272 — MB BChir Camb. 1965; MA Camb. 1965; FRCS Eng. 1969; MRCS Eng. LRCP Lond. 1964; FRCOphth. 1988; DO Eng. 1967; MB BChir 1965 Camb. Cons. Ophth. Sussex Eye Hosp. Brighton. Prev: Sen. Regist. (Ophth.) St. Geo. Hosp. Lond.

INGRAM, Dominic James The Strawberry Gardens Medical, 377 Heysham Road, Morecambe LA3 2BP Tel: 01524 850999 Fax: 01524 855688; 4 Cartwright Court, Doverbreaks, Lancaster LA1 5XA Tel: 01524 383144 — MB ChB 1991 Manch. (Manch.)

INGRAM, Mr Edward Alexander, MBE 104 Whitehall Place, Aberdeen AB25 2RZ Tel: 01224 639737; Lerwick Health Centre, Lerwick ZE1 — MB ChB 1942 Aberd.; FRCS Ed. 1958. (Aberd.) Prev: Sen. Surg. Regist. Roy. Infirm. Aberd.; Surg. Tutor, Christian Med. Coll. Ludhiana; Temp. Maj. RAMC.

INGRAM, Elizabeth Ruth Garden Street Surgery, 29 Garden Street, Magherafelt BT45 5DD Tel: 028 7938 6237 Fax: 028 7930 1302 — MB BCh BAO 1977 Belf.; MRCGP 1981; Dip. Ther. Wales 1996; DCH CPSI 1979; DRCOG Eng. 1980. (Qu. Univ. Belf.) Socs: BMA; Mid Ulster Clin. Soc. Prev: Clin. Med. Off. N.. HSSB Ballymena; Princip. GP Dromore Co. Down.

INGRAM, Geoffrey 6 Coach Drive, London Road, Hitchin SG4 9AP — MB ChB 1952 Liverp.; Dip. Obst. Auckland 1967. Prev: Ho. Surg. & Ho. Phys. St. Catherine's Hosp. Birkenhead.

INGRAM, Mr Geoffrey (retired) 11 St John Street, Manchester M3 4DW Tel: 0161 832 9999 — MB ChB 1960 Manch.; FRCS Eng. 1966. Cons. Surg. Hope Hosp. Salford. Prev: SHO Thoracic Surg. Baguley Hosp. Manch.

INGRAM, George Stuart 12 Park House, 123/125 Harley St., London W1G 6AY Tel: 020 7935 6053 Fax: 020 7935 6053 Email: stuart_ingram@msn.com — MB BS Lond. 1967; MRCS Eng. LRCP Lond. 1967; FFA RCS Eng. 1971. (St. Thos.) Cons. Anaesth. Univ. Coll. Lond. Hosps. Trust (Middlx. Hosp. & Nat. Hosp. Neurol. & Neurosurg.); Anaesth. Clinc. Co-ordinator, Nat. Confidential Enquiry into PeriOperat. Deaths (NCEROD). Socs: (Pres.) Neuro Anaesth.

Soc. GB & Irel.; Counc. Mem. Roy. Coll. of Anaethetists. Prev: Sen. Regist. (Anaesth.) St. Thos. Hosp. Lond.

INGRAM, Gillian Elizabeth 9 Sandfield Drive, Lostock, Bolton BL6 4DU — MB BS 1991 Newc. Specialist Regist. (Med./Elderly Care) N.ern Region.

INGRAM, Graham Richard 48 Lower Road, Beeston, Nottingham NG9 2GT — MB ChB 1992 Birm.

INGRAM, Howard John c/o The Howe, Crook, Kendal LA8 8LH — MB BS 1988 Newc.

INGRAM, Iain James Barkwood Surgery, Birkwood, 31-33 Laceby Road, Grimsby DN34 5BH Tel: 01472 879529 Fax: 01472 278817 — MB ChB 1978 Glas.

INGRAM, Ian Malcolm (retired) 7 Bishopsgate, Thorntonhall, Glasgow G74 5AX Tel: 0141 644 4331 Email: malcolmi@compuserve.com — MB ChB 1951 Ed.; MD Ed. 1958; FRCPsych 1974, M 1972; DPM Eng. 1956. Prev: Cons. Psychiat. S.. Gen. Hosp. Glas. & Hon. Clin. Lect. Univ. Glas.

INGRAM, Joseph Christopher 13 Alder Drive, Timperley, Altrincham WA15 7YG Tel: 0161 903 9507 — MB ChB 1994 Sheff.

INGRAM, Karin Sonja 3 Dawson Place, Allendale, Hexham NE47 9PP — MB ChB 1988 Glas.; FRCA 1993. Cons. (Anaesth.) N. Tyneside Dist. Gen. Hosp.

INGRAM, Katharine Lisette 36 Salisbury Avenue, St Albans AL1 4TU Tel: 01727 865949; 22 Village Road, Clifton Village, Nottingham NG11 8NE Tel: 0115 921 4460 — BM BS 1995 Nottm.; BMedSci. 1993. (Nottingham) SHO Anaesth. Derbys.Acute hosp.NHS Trust. Prev: P.ss Alexandra Hosp. Brisbane Australia; SHO (A & E) Kingsmill Hosp. Nottm.; Jun. Ho. Off. Qu.s Med.Centre.Notts.

INGRAM, Lewis Charles Princess Royal Hospital, Apley Castle, Telford TF1 6TF — MB ChB 1977 Brist.; FRCPCH UK; PhD, MA (1st Cl. Hons. Nat. Sc. Trip.) Camb. 1969; FRCPC 1993; MRCP (UK) 1981. (Bristol) Cons. Paediat. P.ss Roy. Hosp. Telford; Roy. Coll. of Paediat. & Child Health, tutor; Assoc. Prof. of Paediat., St Geo.'s Univ. Usa & Paediatric Course Dir. Socs: Brit. Paediat. Assn.; Amer. Soc. Haemat.; Fell. of Roy. Coll. of Phys.s (Canada). Prev: Sen. Regist. (Paediat.) King's Coll. Hosp. Lond.; Special Clin. Fell. St. Judes Memphis Tenn., USA.; Assoc. Prof. In Paediatric Haemat. & Oncol., Memor. Univ. Canada ('90-'95).

INGRAM, Michael, Maj. RAMC — MB ChB 1995 Sheff. SHOPaediat., Frimley Pk. Hosp. Prev: Med. Off. 2nd Roy. Tank Regt.

INGRAM, Michael Jeremy Red House Surgery, 124 Watling Street, Radlett WD7 7JQ Tel: 01923 855606 Fax: 01923 853577; 22 Aldenham Avenue, Radlett WD7 8HX Tel: 01923 857340 Fax: 01923 469363 Email: mike@conferenceplus.co.uk — MB BS 1981 Lond.; MRCS Eng. LRCP Lond. 1981; MRCGP 1985; DRCOG 1984; DCH RCP Lond. 1984. (Charing Cross) Prev: Trainee GP Reading VTS.

INGRAM, Mr Nicholas Paul The Little Grove Clinic, Rue De Haut, St Lawrence, Jersey JE3 1JZ Tel: 01534 639500 Fax: 01534 610116; Two Steeples, Route Des Augerez, St Peter, Jersey JE3 7DS Tel: 01534 483075 — MRCS Eng. LRCP Lond. 1974; MS Lond. 1986, MB BS 1974; FRCS Eng. 1979. (Char. Cross) Cons. Surg.& Urol. States of Jersey. Socs: Fell. Roy. Soc. Med.; BMA; Assoc. Mem. BAUS. Prev: Sen. Regist. (Surg.) Char. Cross Hosp. Lond., W. Middlx. Hosp. & King Edwd. VII Hosp., Windsor; Clin. Research Fell. Transpl. Roy. Hallamsh. Hosp. Sheff.; Regist. (Surg.) St. Geo. Hosp. Lond. & St. Jas. Balham.

INGRAM, Peter Jonathan 27 Woodfield, Jordanstown, Newtownabbey BT37 0ZH — MB BCh BAO 1993 Belf. Specialist Regist. Forens. Med. State Path Dept. Instit. Forens. Med. Belf.

INGRAM, Reginald Keith Surrey Hampshire Borders Trust, Community Learning Disability Team, 11 Church Road, Frimley, Camberley GU16 5AD Tel: 01483 782940 Fax: 01483 782830 Email: kingram3@compuserve.com — MB BCh BAO 1984 NUI; MRCPsych 1992. Cons. Psychiat. (Psychiat. of Learning Disabilities).

INGRAM, Richard Michael 10 Killyleagh Road, Finnebrogue, Downpatrick BT30 9BL — MB BCh BAO 1986 Belf.; MRCPsych 1990; DMH Belf. 1989. Sen. Regist. & Research Fell. (Ment. Health) Qu. Univ. Belf.

INGRAM, Robert Meynell (retired) 118 Northampton Road, Kettering NN15 7LA Tel: 01536 514196 Email: robertingramrara@lineone.net — MA Oxf. 1956, DM 1965, BM BCh 1955; FRCOphth. 1988; DO Eng. 1959. Cons. Ophth. Surg. Kettering & N.ampton Gen. Hosps. Prev: Ho. Surg. (Ophth.) St. Thos. Hosp.

INGRAM, Roger Martin The Portmill Surgery, 114 Queen Street, Hitchin SG4 9TH Tel: 01462 434246; The Cottage, Upper Green, Ickleford, Hitchin SG5 3YF Tel: 01462 58688 — MB ChB 1980 Liverp.

INGRAM, Mr Roland Ralph Department of Orthopaedics, Royal Infirmary, Castle St., Glasgow G4 0SF Tel: 0141 211 4605 Email: eliz@gowen@northglasgow.scot.nhs.uk; 1 Chesters Road, Bearsden, Glasgow G61 4AF Tel: 0141 563 8688 — MB ChB 1981 Glas.; FRCS (Orth.) 1993; FRCS Glas. 1985. Cons. Orthop. Roy. Infirm. Glas.; Hon. Clin. Sen. Lect. Univ. Glas.

INGRAM, Sheila Elaine Whitelums, Keithhall, Inverurie AB51 0LN — MB ChB 1981 Aberd.

INGRAM, Stella Mary 4 Tongdean Road, Hove BN3 6QB Tel: 01273 552305 Fax: 01273 553038 — MB ChB 1963 Manch.; DObst RCOG 1965; DCH Eng. 1966. Prev: Regist. (Paediat.) Centr. Middlx. Hosp.; SHO Qu. Eliz. Hosp. Childr. Lond.; Ho. Phys. Manch. Roy. Infirm.

INGRAM, Stephen David Yew Tree Cottage Surgery, 15 Leyton Road, Harpenden AL5 2HX Tel: 01582 712126 Fax: 01582 462414 — MB ChB 1982 Liverp.; MRCGP 1986; DRCOG 1986.

INGRAM, Susan Marianne Department of Radiology, Royal Infirmary of Edinburgh, Lauriston Place, Edinburgh EH3 9YW Tel: 0131 536 2900; 8 Suffolk Road, Edinburgh EH16 5NR — MB ChB 1982 Glas.; MRCP (UK) 1986; FRCR 1990. Cons. Radiol. Roy. Infirm. Edin.

INGRAM, Suzanne Mary Yalbury Lodge, Fromewhitfield, Dorchester DT2 7SE — MB BChir 1990 Camb.

INGRAM, Wendy Ann 42 Lan Street, Morriston, Swansea SA6 7AY — MB BS 1997 Lond.

INGRAMS, Mr Duncan Richard Royaal Gwent Hospital, Cardiff Road, Newport NP20 2UB Tel: 01633 234234; Email: duncan.ingrams@lineone.net — BM BCh 1987 Oxf.; MA Oxf. 1990; MA Camb. 1988, BA 1984; FRCS (Otol.) 1993; FRCS Eng. 1992; FRCS (ORL-HNS) 1998. (Camb. & Oxf.) Cons. ENT Surg., Roy. Gwent Hosp. Socs: Brit. Assn. Otorhinol. Head & Neck Surg.; Otorhinolaryng. Research Soc.; BMA. Prev: Sen. Regist. (ENT) Roy. Berks. Hosp. Reading; Sen. Regist. (ENT) Roy. Nat. Throat, Nose & Ear Hosp. Lond.; Regist. (ENT) Whittington Hosp. Lond.

INGRAMS, Grant Jonathan 1 Malham Close, Nuneaton CV11 6WW — MB ChB 1989 Birm.

INGS, Margaret Eleanor — MB BS 1973 Lond.; DObst RCOG 1975. (St. Geo.) p/t Non Princip. GP; Facilitator for the Dyfed Non-Princip.s.

INKSTER, Clare Frances 19 Hawthorn Grove, Bramhall, Stockport SK7 1EF — MB ChB 1990 Liverp.

INKSTER, Graeme David George 241 Munster Court, Liverpool L7 3QH — MB ChB 1987 Liverp.

INKSTER, Janet Emily Greenmoss, Kinellar, Aberdeen AB21 0SE — MB ChB 1978 Aberd.

INKSTER, John Scott (retired) Briar Cottage, Bridge Park, Gosforth, Newcastle upon Tyne NE3 2DX Tel: 0191 285 1937 Email: jinks@briarcotlage70.freeserve.co.uk — MB ChB 1946 Aberd.; FFA RCS Eng. 1954; DA Eng. 1951; FRCA FRCA Eng. Cons. Anaesth. Roy. Vict. Infirm. & Hosp. Sick Childr. Newc. Prev: 1st Asst. Dept. Anaesth. Univ. Durh. Newc.

INKSTER, Teresa Jane 6 Manse Road, Thrumster, Wick KW1 5TQ — MB ChB 1997 Aberd.

INMAN, Alison Joy Saint Vincent Medical Centre, 77 Thorne Road, Doncaster DN1 2ET Tel: 01302 361318; 3 Armthorpe Lane, Wheatley Hills, Doncaster DN2 5LZ Tel: 01302 349395 — MB ChB 1974 Sheff.

INMAN, Charles David Carey Rookery Farm, Well Lane, Manley, Warrington WA6 9JG; 41 Henbank Road, Redland, Bristol BS6 6PX — MB ChB 1994 Bristol. SHO (Respirat.) S.mead Hosp. Prev: SHO (Renal) S.mead.

INMAN, Mr Clive Gordon Rookwood Hospital, Llandaff, Cardiff CF5 2YN Tel: 0292 031 3702 Fax: 0292 057 6144 Email: clive.inman@uhw-tr.wales.nhs.uk; Hen Ysgol, Llansilin, Oswestry SY10 7QB Tel: 01691 791497 — MB ChB 1970 Birm.; BA Birm. 1981; FRCS Ed. 1977; MPhil Birm. 1997. (Birmingham) Cons. Spinal Injuries Univ Hosp of Wales & Llandough NHS Trust, Cardiff. Socs:

Internat. Med. Soc. Paraplegia; Brit. Soc. Rehabil. Med.; Brit. Cervical Spine Soc. Prev: Lect. Univ. Coll. & Middlx. Sch. Med. Lond.; Resid. Surg. Malawi Against Polio, Malawi; Sen. Regist.Midl.Centre for spinal Injury Robt.Jones & Agnes Hunt Orthop& Dist Hosp OsW.ry.

INMAN, George Kingsley Edwin (retired) 4 Banff Close, Oakham LE15 6JJ Tel: 01572 757250 Fax: 01572 757250 — MB ChB Sheff. 1944; DMRD Eng. 1949. Prev: Cons. Radiol. P'boro. & Dist. Memor. Hosp. & Stamford & RutlandHosp.

INMAN, John Kingsley Roper and Partners, Syston Health Centre, Melton Road, Syston, Leicester LE7 2EQ Tel: 0116 260 9111 Fax: 0116 260 9055; 41 Six Hills Road, Walton Le Wolds, Loughborough LE12 8JF Tel: 01509 881566 Fax: 01509 881576 — MB ChB 1978 Leeds; DRCOG 1982. Prev: Hon. Sec. Med. Equestrian Assn.

INMAN, Michael Thomas, RD (retired) Department of Anaesthetics, Derriford Hospital, Plymouth PL6 8DH Tel: 01752 792692 Fax: 01752 763287 Email: mike@inman.force9.co.uk — MB BS Lond. 1956; MRCS Eng. LRCP Lond. 1956; FFA RCS Eng. 1966; DA (UK) 1963; DCH Eng. 1962; DObst RCOG 1961. Hon. Cons. Anaesth. Derriford Hosp. Plymouth. Prev: Cons. Anaesth. Plymouth Hosp.

INMAN, Nicola Jill Sunbury Health Centre, Green St., Sunbury-on-Thames TW16 6RH Tel: 01932 787861; 39 Wensleydale Road, Hampton TW12 2LP — MB BS 1986 Lond.; MRCGP 1990; DRCOG 1990.

INMAN, Mr Richard Dominic 79 North End, Meldreth, Royston SG8 6NU Tel: 01763 260416 — BM BS 1990 Nottm.; BMedSci. (Hons.) 1988; FRCS Eng. 1994. Prev: SHO Rotat. (Surg.) Canterbury & Thanet.

INMAN, Shirley Margaret 2 Jasper Road, Oakham LE15 6UN Tel: 01572 757046 — MRCS Eng. LRCP Lond. 1953. (Sheff.) Prev: Asst. Cas. Off. Roy. Hosp. Sheff.; Ho. Phys. Roy. Infirm. Derby; Gyn. Ho. Surg. Roy. Salop Infirm.

INMAN, Stephen Eric Folly Hill House, Farnham GU10 5AD Tel: 01252 711 3389 — MB BS 1959 Lond.; FRCOG 1981, M 1967. (St. Thos.) Cons. (O & G) Farnham Hosp. & Frimley Pk. Hosp. Prev: Sen. Regist. (O & G) St. Thos. Hosp. Lond.; Res. Med. Off. Qu. Charlotte's Matern. Hosp. Lond.; Res. Surg. Off. Chelsea Hosp Wom.

INMAN, Stephen Roderick Princess Medical Centre, Princess Street, Woodlands, Doncaster DN6 7LX Tel: 01302 723406 Fax: 01302 723433 — MB ChB 1978 Leeds.

INMAN, Susan Michele Meadow End, Station Road, Claverdon, Warwick — MB ChB 1977 Birm.; DO RCS Eng. 1982.

INMAN, Professor William Howard Wallace (retired) Southcroft House, Winchester Road, Botley, Southampton SO32 2BX Tel: 02380 695181 Email: bill-inman@supanet.com — MB BChir 1957 Camb.; MA Camb. 1952; FRCP Lond. 1981, M 1970. Vice-Pres. Rehabil. Engin. Movement Advis. Panels. Prev: Prof. Pharmacoepidemiol. Univ. Soton. & Director Drug Safety Research Unit.

INMAN-MERON, Daniel 4 Fowlers Road, Salisbury SP1 2QU — BM 1998 Soton.; BM Soton 1998.

INMONGER, John Highfield Surgery, Garton Avenue, Southshore, Blackpool FY4 2LD Tel: 01253 345328 Fax: 01253 403038 — MB ChB 1978 Liverp.

INNES, Mr Alan Ronald Wansbeck General Hospital, Ashington NE63 9JJ Tel: 01670 529307 Fax: 01670 529656 Email: alan.innes@northcumbria-healthcare.nhs.uk — MB ChB 1974 Aberd.; FRCS Ed. Orthop. 1987; FRCS Ed. 1979. Cons. Orthop. Wansbeck Gen. Hosp.; Head of Serv., Traumat Orthopaedic Surg. N.umbria Healthcare NHS Trust; Chairm., Specialty Train. Comm., Traumat Aothopaedic Surg., N.ern Deanery. Prev: Sen. Regist. (Orthop.) Dundee Roy. Infirm.; Lect. Univ. Edin.; Squadron Ldr. RAF Med. Br.

INNES, Alastair Cameron Health Centre, 14 Market Place, Carluke ML8 4AZ Tel: 01555 752150 Fax: 01555 751703; 11 Belstane Park, Carluke ML8 4BY — MB ChB 1980 Glas. Clin. Asst. Rd.meeting Hosp. Carluke.

INNES, Alexander Henry 71 Argyll Place, Aberdeen AB25 2HU Tel: 01224 638653 — MB ChB 1952 Aberd. Cons. Forens. Psychiat. & Med. Admin. Roy. Cornhill Hosp. Aberd.; Sen. Clin. Lect. (Ment. Health) Univ. Aberd.

INNES, Mr Alexander James (retired) 6 Albert Place, Stirling FK8 2QL Tel: 01786 474732 — MB Chb (Hons.) Ed. 1934; FRCS Eng. 1939. Prev: Orthop. Regist. Gen. Infirm. Leeds.

INNES, Andrew Crosshouse Hospital, Kilmarnock KA2 0BE; 40 Castlehill Drive, Newton Mearns, Glasgow G77 5LB — MB ChB 1979 Aberd.; MD Aberd. 1990; FRCP Glas. 1995; MRCP (UK) 1983; FRCP Ed. 1998. (Aberdeen) Cons. Phys. (Gen. Med. & Nephrol.) CrossHo. Hosp. Kilmarnock. Prev: Sen. Regist. (Renal & Gen. Med.) City Hosp. Nottm.; Clin. Research Fell. Centre De Rein Artificiel Tassin, France; Regist. (Gen. Med.) Aberd. Teach. Hosps.

INNES, Andrew Duncan Church View Surgery, 5 Market Hill, Hedon, Hull HU12 8JE Tel: 01482 899348; Meadow Cottage, Ivy Meadow, Burton Pidsea, Hull TR27 6HA — MB ChB 1986 Leic.; MRCGP 1990; DRCOG 1990.

INNES, Mr Anthony Joseph Hill House Consulting Rooms, BUPA Hospital, Old Watton Road, Norwich NR4 7TD Tel: 01603 456181; 441 Unthank Road, Norwich NR4 7QN Tel: 01603 504622 Fax: 01603 504622 Email: ainnes441@aol.com — MB BS 1972 Lond.; FRCS (Otol.) Eng. 1977. (St. Thos.) Cons. ENT Surg. Norf. & Norwich Healthcare NHS Trust. Socs: Roy. Soc. Med. (Laryngol. & Otol. Sect.); Brit. Assn. Otol. Head & Neck Surg.; Brit. Assn. Paediat. Otol. Prev: Sen. Regist. Roy. Nat Throat Nose & Ear Hosp. Lond. & Hosp. for Sick Childr. Lond.

INNES, Audrey Caroline The Health Centre, Wharf Road, Ash Vale, Aldershot GU12 5BA; Bromstone, Beech Avenue, Camberley GU15 2JT Tel: 01276 65628 — MB BS 1981 Lond.; MRCP (Paediat.) (UK) 1985; MRCGP 1988; DRCOG 1987; Cert. Family Plann. JCC 1987; DCH RCP Lond. 1985. Prev: Clin. Med. Off. (Child Health) Richmond, Twickenham & Roehampton HA.

INNES, Caroline Gilchrist Deincourt Resource Centre, London Road, Newark NG24 1TG Tel: 01636 685985 Fax: 01636 685966 — MB ChB 1982 Aberd.; MRCPsych 1987. Cons. Psychiat. Centr. Notts. Healthcare Trust. Prev: Sen. Regist. (Psychiat.) Roy. S. Hants. Hosp.; Regist. & SHO (Psychiat.) Mapperley Hosp. Nottm.

INNES, Charles Alexander 12A Thurloe Street, London SW7 2ST Tel: 020 7589 6414 Fax: 020 7589 6424; Flat 1, 64 Church Road, Richmond TW10 6LN Tel: 020 8332 9265 — MB BS 1985 Lond.; MFHOM RCP Lond. 1992. (Homeopathic Phys.) Private Pract. Socs: Fac. Homoeop. Prev: (Homeopathic Phys.) Roy. Lond. Homeopathic Hosp.

INNES, Charles Forbes The Village Surgery, Elbow Lane, Liverpool L37 4AW Tel: 01704 878661 Fax: 01704 832488 — MB ChB 1970 Ed.; BSc (Med. Sci.) Ed. 1967; DObst RCOG 1972. (Ed.) Chair Professional Exec. Comm., S.prot and Formby PCT. Prev: SHO (Obst.) Simpson Memor. Matern. Pavilion Edin.; Ho. Phys. Edin. Roy. Infirm.; Ho. Surg. E.. Gen. Hosp. Edin.

INNES, Colin Young The Charleston Surgery, 5 South Campbell Street, Paisley PA2 6LR Tel: 0141 889 4373 Fax: 0141 848 0648; 14 Neilston Road, Paisley PA2 6LN — MB ChB 1980 Glas.; MRCGP 1984; DRCOG 1983.

INNES, Deborah Taylor Monklands District General Hospital, Monkscourt Avenue, Airdrie ML6 0JS Tel: 01236 748748 Fax: 01236 760015; Flat 0/2, 158 Garthland Drive, Dennistoun, Glasgow G31 2SG — MB ChB 1987 Ed.; MRCGP 1992. Staff Grade (Psychiat.) Monklands Hosp. Airdrie.

INNES, Elizabeth Marion 26 Frogston Road W., Edinburgh EH10 7AR Tel: 0131 445 2042 — MB ChB 1943 Ed.; FRCP Ed. 1966, M 1946. Prev: Cons. Haematol. Roy. Hosp. Sick Childr. Edin.; Sen. Lect. Dept. Child. Life & Health Univ. Edin.; Research Fell. in Med. Wash. Univ. Med. Sch. St. Louis.

INNES, Eurwen Harries (retired) 22 The Mead, Bexhill-on-Sea TN39 3TP Tel: 01424 843470 — MB ChB 1958 Aberd.; FRCP Ed. 1983, M 1968; DPhysMed Eng. 1971; DCH Eng. 1960; DObst RCOG 1961. Prev: Cons. Phys. Rheum. Hasting & Rother NHS Trust.

INNES, George (retired) 45 Kingshill Avenue, Aberdeen AB15 5HD Tel: 01224 314907 — MB ChB Aberd. 1950; MD Aberd. 1959; MRCPsych 1971; FFCM 1978, M 1974; DPH Aberd. 1957. Dir. Health Servs. Informat. Unit. Prev: Dir. Grampian Health Servs. Informat. Unit.

INNES, George David Duncan Deveron Medical Group, Banff Health Centre, Clunie Street, Banff AB45 1HY Tel: 01261 812027 Fax: 01261 818455; Funkieston House, Banff AB45 3LL — MB ChB 1981 Aberd.; DRCOG 1985.

INNES, Hannah Elizabeth Yare Valley Medical Practice, 202 Thorpe Road, Norwich NR1 1TJ Tel: 01603 437559 Fax: 01603 701773 — MB BS 1990 Lond.; BSc (Chem.) Lond. 1984, MB BS 1990. SHO (A & E) King Geo. Hosp. Ilford.

INNES, Helen Elizabeth Evergreen, Minffordd Road, Llanddulas, Abergele LL22 8EW — BM BCh 1994 Oxf.

INNES, Iain 19 Dunnyfell Road, Muchalls, Stonehaven AB39 3RP — MB ChB 1998 Aberd.; MB ChB Aberd 1998.

INNES, James 26 Frogston Road W., Edinburgh EH10 7AR Tel: 0131 445 2042 — MD (High Commend.) Ed. 1946, MB ChB (Hnrs.) 1937; FRCP Ed. 1943, M 1939. (Ed.) Chief Med. Off. Guardian Assur. Gp. Edin. Socs: Assn. Phys. Gt. Brit. Prev: Phys. Roy. Infirm. Edin. Sen. Lect. Dept. Med. Univ. Edin. Temp. Maj.; RAMC.

INNES, James Alastair Respiratory Unit, Western General Hospital, Crewe Road, Edinburgh EH4 2XU Tel: 0131 537 1783 Fax: 0131 343 3989 Email: a.innes@ed.ac.uk — MB ChB 1980 Edinburgh; MB ChB Ed. 1980; PhD Lond. 1987; BSc Med. Sci. (Hons.) Ed. 1977; FRCP Ed. 1996; MRCP (UK) 1983. Cons. Phys. & Sen. Lect. (Respirat. Med. & Cystic Fibrosis) W.. Gen. Hosp. Edin. Socs: Physiol. Soc.; Brit. Thorac. Soc. Prev: Sen. Regist. (Gen. Med. & Respirat. Med.) & Hon. Lect. (Med.) Char. Cross Hosp. Lond.; MRC Train. Fell. Char. Cross Hosp. Lond.; MRC Trav. Fell. Torrance Calif., USA.

INNES, Mr James Robertson Mistral, 3 Greenways, North Ferriby HU14 3JN Email: james@innes.org.uk — MB ChB 1976 Glas.; FRCS Glas. (Ophth.) 1981; FRCOphth. 1989. Cons. Ophth. Hull Roy. Infirm.

INNES, John Andrew Widney Cottage, Widney Manor Road, Knowle, Solihull B93 9AA — MB ChB 1970 Ed.; BSc (Path.) Ed. 1968, MB ChB (Hons.) 1970; FRCP Ed. 1981; MRCP (U.K.) 1972; FRCP (Lond.) 1988. Cons. Phys. Thoracic Med. & Communicable & Trop. Dis. E. Birm. Hosp.; Hon. Sen. Lect. Dept. Med. Univ. Birm. Med. Sch.

INNES, John Robert Faraday (retired) Old Doctor's House, Stradbroke, Eye IP21 5JG Tel: 01379 384267 Fax: 01379 384876 — MB BS 1946 Lond. Prev: Ho. Surg. St. Mary's Hosp.

INNES, John Robert Stephen (retired) 16 Hammersmith Road, Aberdeen AB10 6NB Tel: 01224 311328 — MB ChB 1940 Aberd.

INNES, John Scott (retired) 21 Shamrock Street, Dundee DD4 7AH Tel: 01382 462066 — MB ChB St. And. 1945; MRCGP 1965. Prev: GP Dundee.

INNES, Martin Ross Ravenswood Doctors Surgery, Thomson Avenue, Johnstone PA5 8SU Tel: 01505 331979 Fax: 01505 323444 — MB ChB 1983 Aberd.

INNES, Michael Anthony Stirchley Medical Practice, Sandino Road, Stirchley, Telford TF3 1FB Tel: 01952 660444 Fax: 01952 415139; Church Farm Cottage, Sheinton, Cressage, Shrewsbury SY5 6DN Tel: 01952 510878 — MB BS 1986 Lond.; MRCGP 1996; DTM & H Liverp. 1991; DRCOG 1990; DA (UK) 1989. GP Princip.; Clin. Research Fell. Dept. of Gen. Pract. Birm. Univ.

INNES, Nicholas James Chest Clinic, Ipswich Hospital, Ipswich IP4 5PD — MB BS 1990 Lond.; MRCP (UK) 1995. (St. Thos. Hosp. Lond.) Cons. Respirat. Phys., Ipswich NHS Trust, Ipswich.

INNES, Paul Alistair 47 Birmingham Road, Hagley, Stourbridge DY9 9JZ — MB ChB 1984 Birm.; FRCA 1989. Cons. Anaesth. Dudley hosp. NHS Trust. Prev: Visit.Instruct.Anaesth.Univ.michigan; Sen. Regist. (Anaesth.) Mersey RHA; Lect. (Cardiothoracic Anaesth.) Univ. Liverp.

INNES, Richard John 51 Henry Road, Gloucester GL1 3DX — MB BCh 1990 Wales.

INNES, Rosamund Bridget Bonnyrigg Health Centre, High Street, Bonnyrigg EH19 2DA Tel: 0131 663 7272 Fax: 0131 660 5636; 30 Craiglockhart Gardens, Edinburgh EH14 1LY Tel: 0131 443 1668 — MB ChB 1970 Ed.; DObst RCOG 1976; DCH RCPS Glas. 1975. (Ed.) Prev: Princip. GP Edin.; Regist. (Paediat.) Palmerston N. Hosp., N.Z.; SHO (Neonat. Paediat.) Simpson Memor. Matern. Pavil. Edin.

INNES, William George Rydal, 375 High Road, Woodford Green IG8 9QJ Tel: 020 8504 0532 Fax: 020 8559 1503 — MB ChB 1966 Aberd.; LMCC Toronto 1973.

INNS, Peter Gold Street Medical Centre, 106 Gold Street, Wellingborough NN8 4BT Tel: 01933 223429 Fax: 01933 229240; Lorne House, 58 Hatton Pk Road, Wellingborough NN8 5AQ Tel: 01933 223197 — MB BS 1980 Lond.; BSc Lond. 1977; DRCOG 1984; Cert. FPA 1984. Audit Facilitator N.ants MAAG. Prev: Trainee GP Kettering VTS; Ho. Phys. Warneford Hosp. Leamington Spa; Ho. Surg. Orpington Hosp.

INSALL, Robert Lester Kennington Road, Willesborough, Ashford TN24 0LZ Tel: 01233 616677 Fax: 01233 616019 — MB BS 1982 Lond.; PhD Lond. 1979, BSc 1976; MD Newc. 1993; FRCS Eng. 1986. (St. Thos. Lond.) Cons. Gen. & Vasc. Surg. William Harvey Hosp. Ashford, Kent. Socs: Fell. Assn. Surgs.; Vasc. Surgic. Soc. GB & Irel.; Eur. Soc. Vasc. Surg. Prev: Sen. Regist. (Surg.) Newc. HA.

INSH, Alice Margaret (retired) 5 Barriedale Avenue, Hamilton ML3 9DB Tel: 01698 424422 — MB ChB 1938 Glas.; MFCM 1974; DPH Glas. 1940. Prev: Sen. Med. Off. Lanarksh. Health Bd.

INSKIP, Mary Jessica 24 Cherrybank Gardens, Union Glen, Aberdeen AB11 6FJ — MB ChB 1972 Bristol; BSc Bristol 1969, MB ChB 1972; FRCPath 1994, M 1982; MRC Path 1982. Prev: Cons. Glas. & W. Scotl. Blood Transfus. Serv.

INSKIP, Thomas Greville Lansdowne Road Surgery, 6 Lansdowne Road, Bedford MK40 2BU Tel: 01234 270170 Fax: 01234 214033; The Manor House, Thurleigh Road, Milton Ernest, Bedford MK44 1RF Tel: 01234 824467 Fax: 01234 824468 Email: tinskip@aol.com — MB ChB 1981 Birm.; MRCGP 1985; DCH RCP Lond. 1984; DRCOG 1984. (Birm.) Prev: Trainee GP Bedford Gen. Hosp. VTS.

INSLEY, Catherine Anne 95 Sidney Grove, Newcastle upon Tyne NE4 5PE — MB BS 1988 Lond.; MRCGP 1993. Regist. (Pub. Health) Trent HA. Socs: BMA & Med. Defence Union. Prev: Trainee GP N.d.; SHO (Geriat.) Shotley Bridge Hosp. Co. Durh.; Resid. Med. Off. Gosford Hosp. NSW, Austral.

INSLEY, Jack (retired) 149 Moor Green Lane, Birmingham B13 8NT Tel: 0121 449 3354 — MB Camb. 1956, BChir 1955; FRCP Ed. 1972, M 1962; DCH Eng. 1957. Prev: Cons. Paediat. Childr. Hosp. Birm.

INSLEY, Morag Lillie (retired) 16 Ravelston Gardens, Edinburgh EH4 3LD — MD Ed. 1950, MB ChB 1946; MFCM 1980; DPH Bristol 1973. Prev: SCM (Social Servs.) Cornw. & I. of Scilly HA.

INSOLE, Jill (Surgery), 229 West Barnes Lane, New Malden KT3 6JD; Baronsmead, Pachesham Park, Leatherhead KT22 0DJ — MB BS 1982 Lond.; MRCGP 1986; DCH RCP Lond. 1986; DRCOG 1985.

INSTON, Nicholas Grant 1a Enfield Avenue, Oldham OL8 3DW — BM BS 1993 Nottm.; FRCS (Lond) 1998. (Nottingham)

INWALD, Anthony Charles Michael St Johns Way Medical Centre, 96 St. Johns Way, London N19 3RN Tel: 020 7272 1585 Fax: 020 7561 1237 — MB BS 1960 Lond.; MRCS Eng. LRCP Lond. 1960; MRCGP 1969. (Middlx.) Med. Off. Highgate Sch. Lond.; Upjohn Trav. Fell. Roy. Coll. Gen. Pract.; Mem. Islington Dist. Ethical Comm. Socs: BMA (Ex-Chairm. City Div.). Prev: GP Represen. Islington Managem. Team; Clin. Asst. Diabetic Clinic Roy. N.. Hosp. Lond.; Ho. Surg. St. Leonard's Hosp. Lond.

INWALD, David Philip Portex Unit Institute of Child Health, 30 Guildford Street, London WC1N 1EH Email: d.inwald@ich.ucl.ac.uk — MB BChir 1990 Camb.; BA Camb. 1987; MRCP (UK) 1993; DCH RCP Lond. 1994; MRCPCH 1996. Fell. Portex Unit of Anaesth. Resp. Med. Inst. Child Health Lond.

INWARD, Carol Denise Childrens Renal Unit, Southmead General Hospital, Westbury on Trym, Bristol BS10 5NB — MB BCh 1986 Wales; MRCP (UK) 1990; DCH RCP Lond. 1989; MD 1999. (Univ. Wales Coll. Med.) Sen. Regist. (Paediat.) S.mead Hosp. Socs: RCPCH; Brit. Assn. Paediat. Nephrol.

INWARD, Jean Mary The Cardinal Clinic, Bishops Lodge, Oakley Green, Windsor SL4 5UL Tel: 01753 869755 Fax: 01753 842852; Wenham, 5 Birchdale, Gerrards Cross SL9 7JA Tel: 01753 885110 Fax: 01753 885110 — MB BS 1964 Lond.; MRCS Eng. LRCP Lond. 1964; MRCPsych 1972; T(Psychiat) 1991; DPM Eng. 1971. (Guy's) Indep. Specialist (Psychiat.) Gerrards Cross & The Cardinal Clinic Windsor; Cons. Barnardos. Prev: Sen. Regist. (Child & Family Psychiat.) Oxf. Regional Hosp. Bd. & Oxf. RHA.

INWEREGBU, Kenneth Ohiri 14 Kingsway Court, Moortown, Leeds LS17 6SS — MB ChB 1993 Leeds.

INWOOD, Jane Louise 16 Beauchamp Road, Solihull B91 2BX — MB ChB 1994 Leic.

INWOOD, John Maxwell Inverleith Row Surgery, 43 Inverleith Row, Edinburgh EH3 5PY Tel: 0131 552 3369 Fax: 0131 552 5343 — MB ChB 1982 Glas.; MRCGP 1988; DRCOG 1988. (Glasgow)

INYANG, Mr Victor Asuquo 40 Nelson Road, Gorleston, Great Yarmouth NR31 6AT — MB BS 1989 Lagos; FRCS Ed. 1994.
IOANNIDES, Adonis 2 Poets Place, 378 Banbury Road, Oxford OX2 7PW — MB ChB 1992 Manch.
IOANNIDES, Charilaos 128 Bickenhall Mansions, Bickenhall St., London W1U 6BT Tel: 020 7486 4255 — MD 1989 Athens; Pytchio Iatrikes Athens 1989; PhD Nýmegen Univ. 1987; MD Athens Univ. 1989.
IOANNIDIS, Alexandros 49 Belsize Court, Wedderburn Rd, London NW3 5QP — MB BS 1997 Lond.
IOANNIDIS, Christos 79B Belsize Lane, London NW3 5AU Tel: 020 7722 9162 — MD Univ. Athens; Ptychio Iatrikes 1979 Thessalonika. Cons. Psychotherapist W. Herts. Community Health (NHS) Trust; Lect. Tavistock Clinic. Socs: Gp. Analyt. Soc; Found.Fell.Tavistock & Portman Soc.Psychother..Outcome Research; Brit.Pscho-Analyt. soc. Prev: Sen. Regist. (Adult Psychother.) Tavistock Clinic.
IOANNIDOU, Stella Savva 68 Fairholme Road, Manchester M20 4SB — MB ChB 1994 Manch.
IOANNOU, Gillian Ruth Bramcote Surgery, 2 Hanley Avenue, Bramcote, Beeston, Nottingham NG9 3HF Tel: 0115 922 4960 Fax: 0115 922 9050.
IOANNOU, John Michael Bramcote Surgery, 2 Hanley Avenue, Bramcote, Beeston, Nottingham NG9 3HF Tel: 0115 922 4960 Fax: 0115 922 9050 — MRCS Eng. LRCP Lond. 1977; PhD Birm. 1965; BA Keele 1962. (Newc.) Clin. Asst. (Family Plann.) Nottm. HA. Socs: BMA & Fac. Family Plann. & Reproduc. Healthcare, RCOG. Prev: Clin. Asst. (Orthop.) Nottm. HA.
IOANNOU, Nicholas 5 Beech Drive, London N2 9NX — MB BS 1998 Lond.; MB BS Lond 1998; BA Camb 1995 (Pembroke Coll). (UMDS of Guy's and St. Thomas')
IOANNOU, Yiannakis 169 Ashville Road, London E11 4DX Email: ioannu@dircon.co.uk — MB BS 1994 Lond.; BMedSci 1993; MRCP 1997. (Lond Hosp) Socs: RCP; MPS; BMA.
ION, Mr Lucian Eugen Charing Cross Hospital, Fulham Palace Road, London W6 8RF Email: lucian@ion.prestel.co.uk — Medic 1986 Bucharest; FRCS Eng. 1993. (University of Medicine, Bucharest) Specialist Regist. (Plastic Surg.). Socs: Assoc. Mem. Brit. Assn. Plastic Surgs.
IONESCU, Christina 357 Street Lane, Leeds LS17 6RU Tel: 0113 266 5924 — MD 1954 Bucharest; LAH Dub. 1971. (Bucharest) Clin. Asst. (Cardiol.) Gen. Infirm. Leeds. Prev: Clin. Asst. (Cardiol.) Fundeni Hosp. Postgrad. Med. Sch. Univ.; Bucharest & Dept. Med. Inst. Nat. des Sports Paris.
IONIDES, Mr Alexander Charles Weekley Moorfields Eye Hospital, City Road, London EC1V 2PD Tel: 020 7253 3411; 39A Belsize Square, London NW3 4HL Email: aionides@ad.com — MB BS 1989 Lond.; BSc (Cell Path.) Lond. 1986; FRCOphth 1994. Specialist Regist. (Ophthopaedics) N. Thames Whittington Hosp. Prev: Research Fell. Inst. Ophth.; SHO (Ophth.) Moorfields Eye Hosp. Lond. & Kingston Hosp. Lond.
IONS, Elizabeth Canton Health Centre, Wessex Street, Cardiff CF5 1XU Tel: 029 2022 6016 Fax: 029 2039 4846; Llyswen, Heol-Y-Parc, Pentyrch, Cardiff CF15 9NB Tel: 029 2089 1410 — MB BCh 1987 Wales; DCH RCP Lond. 1991; DRCOG 1990.
IONS, Mr George Keith Orthopaedic Department, Cumberland Infirmary, Newtown Road, Carlisle CA2 7HY — MB BS 1975 Newc.; FRCS Eng. 1980. Cons. Orthop. Surg. Cumbld. Infirm. Carlisle. Socs: Roy. Coll. Surg.; Fell. Orth. Assn.; Brit hip soc mem.
IONS, William Michael Arthur Street Surgery, 47 Arthur Street, Brierfield, Nelson BB9 5RZ Tel: 01282 614599; Linden Bank, 162 Todmorden Road, Burnley BB11 3EU Tel: 01282 23075 — MB ChB 1978 Manch.; BSc (Hons. Med. Biochem.) Manch. 1975; MRCGP 1986. Socs: BMA.
IORWERTH, Awen Penllyn, 30 Gwel Eryri, Llandegfan, Menai Bridge LL59 5UE — MB BCh 1994 Wales.
IP, Chei Bing 1 Norbury Close, Redditch B98 8RP — MB ChB 1988 Sheff.
IP, John Cheun Kit 12 Lindsay Drive, Glasgow G12 0HB — MB ChB 1996 Ed.
IP, Margaret 52 Heathcote Court, Heathcote Avenue, Ilford IG5 0QR — BM 1988 Soton.; MSc (Med.) Lond. 1990. SHO (Gen. Med.) St. Mary's Hosp. Portsmouth. Prev: SHO (Microbiol. & Path.) John Radcliffe Hosp. Oxf.
IP, Philip Pun Ching Flat 2/1, 22 Ashley St., Glasgow G3 6DR — MB ChB 1992 Glas. SHO (Geriat.) Ayr & Biggart Hosps. Prev: Ho. Off. (Surg.) S.. Gen. Hosp. Glas.; Ho. Off. (Med.) Stobhill Gen. Hosp.
IP MIN WAN, Davy 9/7 Sienna Gardens, Edinburgh EH9 1PQ — MB ChB 1993 Ed.
IPARRAGIRRE, Bonifacio 1 Diggory Crescent, Dorchester DT1 2SP — LMS 1994 Basque Provinces.
IQBAL, Abdul Khudoos Mohamed 21 Melbury, Red House Farm, Whitley Bay NE25 9XP — MB BS 1969 Madras.
IQBAL, Adil Flat 20 Staff Residences, Shotley Bridge General Hospital, Consett DH8 0ND — MB ChB 1988 Sheff.; MRCP (UK) 1991.
IQBAL, Amjad 27 Alderson Road, Birmingham B8 3BP — MB ChB 1992 Leeds.
IQBAL, Anjum Abernethy House, 70 Silver Street, Enfield EN1 3EP Tel: 020 8366 1314 Fax: 020 8364 4176; 20 The Orchard, Winchmore Hill, London N21 2DH Tel: 020 8360 2343 — MB BS 1986 Lond.; MRCGP 1992; DCH RCP Lond. 1991. Course Organiser Enfield & Haringey VTS.
IQBAL, Mr Azhar Department of Plastic Surgery, Wordsley Hospital, Stream Road, Stourbridge DY8 5QX — MB BS 1987 Punjab; FRCS Ed. 1993; FRCS Glas. 1993.
IQBAL, D S Halewood Health Centre, Roseheath Drive, Halewood, Liverpool L26 9UH Tel: 0151 486 5848.
IQBAL, Farrukh Flat 15, Gate Hill Court, 166 Notting Hill Gate, London W11 3QT — MB BS 1981 Punjab; MRCP (UK) 1986.
IQBAL, J Halewood Health Centre, Roseheath Drive, Halewood, Liverpool L26 9UH Tel: 0151 486 5848.
IQBAL, Mr Javaid 29 Fallows Road, Sparkbrook, Birmingham B11 1PD — MB ChB 1981 Birm.; FRCS Ed. 1987.
IQBAL, Mr Javaid 4 Maes Mawr, Bangor LL57 2LR — MB BS 1966 Newc.; FRCS Glas. 1986. Clin. Research Fell. (Craniofacial Surg. & Paediat. Neurosurg.) & Hon.Research Fell. Dept. of Neurosurg. Univ. Birm. Prev: SHO (Neurosurg.) Pinderfields Hosp. Wakefield; SHO Rotat. (Gen. Surg.) S. Tees HA; Regist. (Neurosurg.) Pinderfields Hosp. Wakefield.
IQBAL, Javed Directorate of Child Health, Burnley General Hospital, Burnley BB10 2PQ Tel: 01282 474188 Fax: 01282 474493 — MB BS 1978 Punjab; FRCPI 1994; MRCPI 1986. Cons. Paediat. Burnley Health Care NHS Trust Burnley. Socs: Internat. Paediat. Nephrol. Assn.; Brit. Paediat. Assn.; BMA. Prev: Asst. Prof. Paediat. Pakistan Inst. Med. Sci.; Sen. Regist. Manch. Childr. Hosps.; Assoc. Phys. Pakistan Inst. Med. Sci.
IQBAL, Javed Macclesfield General Hospital, Macclesfield SK10 3BL — MB BS 1985 Punjab; MRCP (UK) 1994. Socs: Brit. Soc. Echocardiogr.
IQBAL, Mangad Mohammed Brompton Medical Centre, 237 Old Brompton Road, London SW5 0EA Tel: 020 7373 4102 Fax: 020 7835 0041; 2A Cambridge Road N., Cheswick, London W4 4AA — MB BS 1967 Bangalore; AFOM RCP Lond. 1982. Princip. GP.
IQBAL, Mr Muhammad ENT Unit, Victoria Hospital, Whinney Heys Road, Blackpool FY3 8NR Tel: 01253 300000 Fax: 01253 303528 — MB BS 1982 Karachi; FRCS Glas. 1988. Regist. ENT Unit Vict. Hosp. Blackpool. Prev: Regist. ENT Unit Law Hosp. Carluke; SHO (Gen. Surg.) N. Devon Dist. Hosp. Barnstaple; SHO (Gen. Surg.) Ryhope Gen. Hosp. Sunderland.
IQBAL, Muhammad Twinwoods Specialist Medical Centre, Milton Road, Clapham, Bedford MK41 6AT Tel: 01234 310583 Email: drmiqbalmd@yahoo.com; 4 Bellamy Road, Wotton, Bedford MK43 9FA Tel: 01234 765684 — MB BS 1986 Karachi; MRCPsych Lond. Cons. Psychiat. (Psychiat. of Learning Disabil.).
IQBAL, Naeem West Barnes Surgery, 229 West Barnes Lane, New Malden KT3 6JD Tel: 020 8336 1773 Fax: 020 8395 4797 Email: ni@lineone.net — MB BS 1989 Lond.; Dip. Occupat. Med. 2001; MRCGP 1993; DRCOG 1991. (Char. Cross & Westm. Hosp.) GP W. Barnes Surg. New Malden Surrey; Occupat. Health Phys. Roy Surrey Co. Hosp. Guildf. Surrey; Occupat.Health Phys. W. Barnes Med. Serv. New Malden Surrey; Team Doctor Kingstonian Football Club. Prev: Sessional Research Phys. Glaxo Wellcome, N.wick Pk. Hosp. Middlx.
IQBAL, Pervaiz Chesterfield & North Derbyshire Royal Hospital, Calow, Chesterfield S44 5BL Tel: 01246 277271 Fax: 01246 552670; 2 Priory Close, St. John's Gardens, Walton, Chesterfield S42 7HQ — MB BS 1982 Punjab; FRCP 2001 Lond.; 2000 Dip

Mgmt (OU); FRCPI 1999; MRCP (UK) 1990; MRCPI 1990. Cons. Phys. Chesterfield & N. Derbysh. Roy. Hosp.; Mem. New cons Comm. RCP Lond; Mem. Gen/Internal Med Comm. RCP Lond. Socs: Brit. Hypertens. Soc.; Brit. Geriat. Soc.; Internat. Soc. Hypertens. Prev: Sen. Regist. (Med.) Leicester Roy. Infirm. & Leicester Gen. Hosp.; Regist. (Med.) Glenfield Hosp. Leicester & Roy. Devon & Exeter Hosp.; Regist. (Respirat. Med.) Raigmore Hosp. Inverness.

IQBAL, Perviz Khan 99 Brierley Street, Bury BL9 9HW — MB ChB 1984 Glas. SHO (Gyn.) Law Hosp. Carluke. Prev: Jun. Ho. Off. (Surg.) Law Hosp. Carluke; Jun. Ho. Off. (Gen. Med.) CrossHo. Hosp. Kilmarnock.

IQBAL, Rehana Koser 10 Waylen Street, Reading RG1 7UR — MB BS 1998 Lond.; MB BS Lond 1998.

IQBAL, Saghir 63 Parliament Road, Middlesbrough TS1 4JW — MB BS 1978 Punjab; FRCS Glas. 1987. (Nishtar Med. Coll., Multan, Pakistan) Cons. Surg. Urol. DHQ Hosp. Mirpur A.K. Pakistan. Prev: Regist. Surg./Urol. Burnley Gen. Hosp.

IQBAL, Shahid 3 Precinct Road, Hayes UB3 3AG Tel: 020 8573 6273 — MB BS 1982 Punjab; DA (UK) 1987.

IQBAL, Talat Luton & Dunstable Hospital NHS Trust, Lewsey Road, Luton LU4 0DZ — MB BS 1972 Lucknow. Staff Grade (Rehabil. Med.) Luton & Dunstable Hosp.

IQBAL, Yahiya The Surgery, 348 Bearwood Road, Smethwick, Warley B66 4ES Tel: 0121 429 1345 Fax: 0121 429 2535 — MB BS 1967 Dacca; MB BS 1967 Dacca.

IQBAL, Zafar South Staffordshire Health Authority, Mellor House, Corporation St., Stafford ST16 3SR Tel: 01785 252233 Fax: 01785 221131; 19 Maplewood, Wildwood, Stafford ST17 4SG Tel: 01785 663424 — MB BS 1985 Lond.; MFPHM RCP (UK) 1994; MRCGP 1989; DCH RCP Lond. 1988; FFPHM 2000. Cons. Pub. Health Med. S. Staffs. Health Auth.; Hon. Sen. Lect. Birm. Univ. Prev: Trainee GP Calderdale VTS.

IQBAL, Zahid 6 Spear Road, Southampton SO14 6UL — BM 1992 Soton.

IQBAL, Zubaida 2 Smallcroft, Panshanger, Welwyn Garden City AL7 2AU — MB BS 1965 Punjab; MB BS Punjab (Pakistan) 1965.

IRANI, Behman Hormasji 28 Alderwick Drive, Hounslow TW3 1SF Tel: 020 8572 0470 — MB BS 1957 Bombay; DO Eng. 1960. (Grant Med. Coll.) Med. Asst. (Ophth.) W. Roding Health Dist.

IRANI, Mr Daryush Aderbad Eye Clinic and Surgery, 31 Broad Street, Ludlow SY8 1NJ Tel: 01584 877420 Fax: 01584 877879 Email: iranida@aol.com; 41 Normandie Close, Lady Bower, Ludlow SY8 1UJ Tel: 01584 877879 — MB BS 1968 Bombay; MS (Ophth.) Bombay 1970, MB BS 1968; FCOphth. Eng. 1993; FRACS 1975; DO Eng. 1971; DOMS CPS Bombay 1969. (Grant Med. Coll.) Ophth. eye clinic & surg Ludlow Salop. Socs: Midl.s Ophth. Soc. Prev: Locum Cons. Opthalmologist Newport and Abergavenny, Wales in 1976; Locum Cons. Ophthalmologiest at the W.bourne Eye Unit, Bournemouth, in 1977.

IRANI, Godafreed Sorab Roundwood Park Medical Centre, Pound Lane Clinic, 63 Pound Lane, London NW10 2HH Tel: 020 8459 0336 Fax: 020 8451 8810 — MB BS 1968 Karachi; MRCOG 1973. (Dow Med. Coll. Karachi)

IRANI, Mehernoosh Sheriar Ashford Hospital, London Road, Ashford TW15 3AA Tel: 01784 884488 Fax: 01784 884240 Email: msirani@ashlib.demon.co.uk; 20 Devonshire Gardens, Chiswick, London W4 3TN Tel: 020 8994 0119 — MRCS Eng. LRCP Lond. 1973; MB BS Lond. 1973; BSc (Physiol.) (Hons.) Lond. 1970; FRCP Lond. 1996; MRCP (UK) 1977. (King's Coll. Hosp.) Cons. Rheum. Ashford Hosp. Middlx.; Hon. Lect. Char. Cross & W.m. Med. Schs.; Recognised. Teach. Univ. Lond. Socs: Brit. Soc. Rheum.; Internat. Assn. Olympic Med. Off.; Inst. Sports Med. Prev: Sen. Regist. (Rheum. & Gen. Med.) Char. Cross & W.m. Hosps. Lond.; Sen. Regist. & Research Fell. (Rheum.) King's Coll. Hosp. Lond.; Regist. (Rheum. & Gen. Med.) Radcliffe Infirm. Oxf.

IRANI, Mondanna Rohinton Garden Chalet, 77 Worple Rd, Staines TW18 1HJ — MB BS 1997 Lond.

IRANI, Shahbehram Irani, Dawes, Foster and Singh, The Ridgeway Surgery, 175 The Ridgeway, Sedgley, Dudley DY3 3UH Tel: 01902 884343 Fax: 01902 882101 — MB BCh 1975 Wales; BSc (Med. Sci.) St. And. 1972.

IRANI, Shirin Adi 26 Woodbourne, Augustus Road, Birmingham B15 3PH — MB BS 1985 Bombay; MRCOG 1995.

IRANI, Tehmina Namdar (retired) c/o Lloyds Bank plc, Southampton Row Branch, Victoria House, London WC1B 5HR — MB BS 1942 Bombay.

IRANZO, Jorge 26 Homewood Drive, Whitehaven CA28 8JX — LMS 1989 Saragossa.

IRBY, Miss Sarah Jane Princess Margaret Hospital, Swindon SN1 4JU Tel: 01793 536231 — MB BS 1990 Lond.; FRCS Ed. 1994. (Charing Cross & Westminster) p/t Regist. (Orthop.) P.ss Margt. Hosp. Swindon. Socs: BOA; BMA. Prev: Regist. (Orthop.) Roy. United Hosp. Bath; SHO (Orthop.) Qu. Mary's Univ. Hosp. Lond.; SHO (Plastic Surg.) Qu. Mary's Univ. Hosp. Lond.

IREDALE, John Leslie The Old School Medical Centre, Horseman Lane, Copmanthorpe, York YO23 3UA; 12 Newton Terrace, Bishophill, York YO1 6HE Email: 100622.1057@compuserve.com — MB ChB 1977 Manch.; MRCGP 1981; Dip. Ther. Newc. 1996; DRCOG 1981. (Manchester)

IREDALE, John Peter Southampton General Hospital, Tremona Road, Southampton SO16 6YD Tel: 02380 797222; 2 Dearly Croft, Hale Road, Woodgreen, Fordingbridge, Salisbury — BM 1985 Soton.; BM (Hons.) Soton. 1985; DM Soton 1995; MRCP (UK) 1988. MRC Clin. SCi. Soton. Gen. Hosp.

IREDALE, Michael John 3 Barham Close, Shirley, Solihull B90 4XY — MB BS 1983 Lond.; MRCP (UK) 1987.

IREGBULEM, Mr Lawrence Mmadu Cambridge Private Hospital, New Wimpole, Cambridge SG8 5TG Tel: 01223 208249 Fax: 01223 208251 — MB BS Lond. 1962; FRCS Eng. 1971; FRCS Ed. 1969; MRCS Eng. LRCP Lond. 1962. (St. Bart.) p/t Cons. Plastic, Reconstructure & Aesthetic Surg.: Camb. Private Hosptial, Camb.; Mem. NY Acad. Sci. Socs: Profess. Assoc. Brit. Assn. Plastic Surgs.; Eur. Acad. Cosmetic Surg.; Past (Pres.) Nigerian Soc. for Burn Injuries. Prev: Cons. Plastic Surg. Middlesbrough Gen. Hosp., S. Cleveland Hosp., Hartlepool Gen. Hosp. & S. Tees Acute Hosps. NHS Trust; Chief Cons. Plastic & Reconstruc. Surg. Nat. Orthop. Hosp. Enugu, Nigeria; Rheum. & Arthritis Foundat. Research Fell. Plastic Unit Hammersmith Hosp. & Roy. Postgrad. Med. Sch. Lond.

IRELAND, Adrian Paul The Surgery, 67 St James St., Wetherby LS22 6RS Tel: 01937 585669 Fax: 01937 522703; 67 The Square, Harewood, Leeds LS17 9LQ Tel: 0113 288 6364 Email: irelandap@aol.com — MB ChB 1988 Aberd.

IRELAND, Alan 55 New Church Road, Hove BN3 3BG Tel: 01273 720217 Fax: 01273 627050; 30 Albany Villas, Hove BN3 2RW Tel: 01273 749817 Email: ireland@pavilion.co.uk — MB ChB 1980 Ed.; FRCP Ed. 1999; FRCP Lond. 1995; DPhil Oxf. 1989; MRCP (UK) 1983; BSc (Hons.) Ed. 1977. Cons. Gastroenterol. Roy. Sussex Co. Hosp. Brighton. Socs: Christian Med. Fell.sh.; Brit. Soc. Gastroenterol.; Amer. Gastroenterol. Assn. Prev: Sen. Regist. (Med. & Gastroenterol.) John Radcliffe Hosp. Oxf.

IRELAND, Mr Alastair John Accident & Emergency Department, Royal Infirmary, Glasgow G4 0SF Tel: 0141 211 4000 Email: alastair.ireland@northglasgow.scot.nhs.uk — MB ChB 1984 Glas.; FRCS Glas. 1988; FRCS Ed. 1988; FFAEM. (Univ. Glas.) Cons. A & E Med. Roy. Infirm. Glas.; Hon. Clin. Sen. Lect. (Med.) Univ. Glas. Socs: Fell. Fac. Accid. & Emerg. Med. Prev: Sen. Regist. (A & E) Roy. Infirm. Glas.; Career Regist. (A & E Med.) W.. Infirm. Glas.; Specialist (Surg.) RAMC Brit. Milit. Hosp. (Rinteln) BFPO 29.

IRELAND, Andrew Scott (retired) 45 Craiglockhart Road N., Edinburgh EH14 1BS — MB ChB 1946 Ed.

IRELAND, Brian James Lisburn Health Centre, Linenhall Street, Lisburn BT28 1LU; Brookhill, Upper Ballinderry, Lisburn — MB BCh BAO 1965 Belf.; MRCGP 1971; DObst RCOG 1970; DA Eng. 1969. (Belf.) Authorised Med. Examr. Civil Aviat. Auth. Socs: Fell. Ulster Med. Soc. Prev: Hosp. Pract. (Anaesth.) Roy. Vict. Hosp. Belf.; Med. Ref. EHSSB.

IRELAND, David Red Bank Road Surgery, 163-165 Red Bank Road, Bispham, Blackpool FY2 9EA Tel: 01253 52780 — MB ChB 1973 Liverp.; MRCGP 1981.

IRELAND, David 23 Toller Road, Stonegate, Leicester LE2 3HP Tel: 0116 270 3977 — MD 1985 Camb.; MA Camb. 1978, MD 1985, MB 1978, BChir 1977; MRCOG 1982. Cons. Gyn. Surg. & Oncol. Leicester Roy. Infirm. Prev: 1st Asst. Univ. Dept. O & G Newc.; Research Fell. Regional Dept. Gyn. Oncol. Gateshead.

IRELAND, Elizabeth Anne 69 Holborn Hill, Aughton, Ormskirk L39 4SX — MB ChB 1986 Liverp.; DRCOG 1988. Trainee GP Ormskirk VTS.

IRELAND, Hamish Munro Radiology Department, Royal Infirmary, Edinburgh Tel: 0131 536 2901 — MB ChB 1986 Glas.; FRCR 1993; MRCP (UK) 1990. Cons. Radiologist Edin. Roy. Infirm. Socs: Roy. Coll. of Radiologists. Prev: Regist. (Med.) Roy. Alexandra Hosp. Paisley.; Cons. Radiologist & Clin. Director of Radiol. Qu. Margt. Hosp. DunfermLa. Fife.

IRELAND, Heather Cameron Balvonie, Ferry Road, Earlsferry, Leven KY9 1AJ — MB ChB 1994 Aberd.

IRELAND, Mr Ian William 29 Knox Chase, Harrogate HG1 3HZ — MB ChB 1988 Glas.; FRCS Ed. 1996. Research Fell. (Colorectal Surg.) The Gen. Infirm. Leeds.

IRELAND, Jessie Munro McMurdo, MBE 7 Madison Avenue, Cathcart, Glasgow G44 5AH — MB ChB 1950 Glas. Sen. Med. Off. Argyll & Clyde HB; Adoption Med. Advis. Renfrew Dist. Stathclyde Region.

IRELAND, John 17 King's Avenue, Woodford Green IG8 0JD; Practice, Residence & Private Secretary, 17 Kings Avenue, Woodford Green IG8 0JD Tel: 020 8505 3211 Fax: 020 8599 1161 — MB BS Lond. 1966; FRCS Eng. 1971; MRCS Eng. LRCP Lond. 1966. (Westm.) Cons. Orthop. Surg. Knee Surg. Unit Holly Hse. Hosp. Buckhurst Hill. Socs: Brit. Europ. & Internat. Knee Socs.; Founder & organiser of New Knee Golf soc. Prev: Cons. Orthop. Surg. King Geo. Hosp. Ilford; Sen. Surg. Off. Roy. Nat. Orthop. Hosp. Lond.; Ho. Surg. & Ho. Phys. W.m. Hosp.

IRELAND, Jonathan Peter Northampton Lane North Surgery, 120 Northampton Lane North, Moulton, Northampton NN3 7QP Tel: 01604 790108 Fax: 01604 670827 — MB BS 1983 Lond.; BSc (Hons.) Lond. 1980; MRCGP 1990; DRCOG 1989; DCH RCP Lond. 1988.

IRELAND, Margaret Department of Human Genetics, 19/20 Claremont Place, Newcastle upon Tyne NE2 4AA; 72 Thirlestane Road, Edinburgh EH9 1AR — MB BS 1983 Newc.; MSc Newc. 1990, MB BS 1983; MRCP (UK) 1989. MRC Clinician Sci. Fell. & Hon. Sen. Regist. (Genetics) Newc. Univ. Prev: MRC Research Fell. Newc. Univ.; Clin. Research Assoc. (Human Genetics) Univ. Newc.; Hon. Regist. (Clin. Genetics) N.. RHA.

IRELAND, Monica High Street Surgery, 145 High Street, Montrose DD10 8QN Tel: 01674 673400 Fax: 01674 672175; 23 St. Brioc Way, Ferryden, Montrose DD10 9SR Tel: 01674 673672 — MB ChB 1983 Dundee.

IRELAND, Nicholas John Acle Medical Centre, Bridewell Lane, Acle, Norwich NR13 3RA Tel: 01493 750888 Fax: 01493 751652; Lower Green Farm House, Freethorpe, Norwich NR13 3NP Tel: 01493 700320 — MB BChir 1967 Camb.; MA Camb. 1967; MRCS Eng. LRCP Lond. 1968; DObst RCOG 1969. (Camb. & St. Bart.) Specialist (Orthop. Med.) Jas. Paget Hosp. Gt. Yarmouth. Socs: Fell. Soc. Orthop. Med. Prev: Regist. Dryburn Hosp. Durh.; Ho. Surg. St. Bart. Hosp. Lond.; Ho. Phys. W. Cumbld. Hosp. Whitehaven.

IRELAND, Patrick Sidney Selly Park Surgery, 2 Reaview Drive, Pershore Road, Birmingham B29 7NT Tel: 0121 472 0187 Fax: 0121 472 0187 — MB ChB 1961 Birm.

IRELAND, Robert William Kidderminster General Hospital, Beudley Road, Kidderminster DY11 6RJ Tel: 01562 823424 — MB ChB 1985 Glas. Cons. Psychiat.kidderminster.Gen.hosp.

IRELAND, Robin Martin Department of Haematology, Greenwich Healthcare Trust, Vanburgh Hill, London SE10 9HE Tel: 020 8312 6311 Fax: 020 8312 6275 Email: ghtpath@dircon.co.uk; 79 Manor Way, Blackheath, London SE3 9XG Tel: 020 8852 8157 — MB BS 1977 Lond.; FRCP Lond. 1995; MRCP (UK) 1980; FRCPath 1997, M 1987; T(M) 1991; T(Path) 1991. (King's Coll. Lond.) Cons. Haemat. Greenwich Healthcare Trust Lond.; Hon. Sen. Lect. United Med. & Dent. Sch. Guy's & St. Thos. Lond. Socs: Brit. Soc. Haematol.; BMA. Prev: Sen. Research Fell. St. Vincent's Hosp. Sydney; Sen. Regist. & Regist. (Haemat.) King's Coll. Hosp. Lond.; Vis. Lect. (Med. & Haemat.) Univ. Malaya, Kuala Lumpur.

IRELAND, Roderick Walker 30 Maple Avenue, Mewton Mearns, Glasgow G77 5BQ Tel: 0141 639 2753 Fax: 0141 616 2403 — MB ChB 1988 Glas.; MRCGP 1992; DRCOG 1993. (Glas.) Prev: Trainee GP Paisley; SHO (ENT) Stobhill Gen. Hosp. Glas.; SHO (O & G) Ruthergelen Hosp.

IRELAND, Sharon Jane Northern General Hospital, Herries Road, Sheffield S5; 44 Aldred Road, Crookes, Sheffield S10 1PD — MB ChB 1995 Leic.; MB ChB (Hons.) Leic. 1995; BSc (Hons.) Leic. 1992. SHO (A & E) N. Gen. Hosp. Sheff. Prev: Ho. Off. Rotat. (Cardiothoracic Surg., Orthop. & Respirat. Med.) N.. Gen. Hosp. Sheff.

IRELAND, Susan Carol Kettering General Hospital, Rothwell Road, Kettering NN16 8UZ; 6 Jackson Way, Kettering NN15 7DL — MB ChB 1987 Cape Town.

IRELAND, Thomas Royal Alexandra Hospital, Paisley PA2 9PN — MB ChB 1975 Dundee; FFA RCS Eng. 1980. Cons. Anaesth. Roy. Alexandra Hosp. Paisley.

IRELAND, Vivien McKenzie Elliot Dalkeith Medical Centre, 24-26 St. Andrew Street, Dalkeith EH22 1AP Tel: 0131 663 2461 Fax: 0131 561 5555; 3 Elcho Terrace, Portobello, Edinburgh EH15 2EF Tel: 0131 669 1856 Fax: 020 8654 1179 — MB ChB 1972 Glas.; MRCGP 1978; DObst RCOG 1974. (Glas.) Socs: BMA; Med. Wom. Federat.

IRELEWUYI, Mr Oyewale Abiodun 33 Florence Street, Canning Town, London E16 4JS — MB BS 1988 Ibadan; FRCSI 1994.

IRFAN, Abid 251 Hamber House Drive, Rochdale OL11 3LS — MB ChB Leic. 1995. SHO Gen. Surg. (Urol. - Cheltenham Gen. Hosp., Cheltenham, Glos. Prev: SHO Orthop. Epsom Gen. Hosp. Feb 1998 - Aug 1998; SHO Gen. Surg. Epsom Gen. Hosp. Aug 1997 - Feb 1998; SHO Urol. Epsom Gen. Hosp. Feb 1997 - Aug 1997.

IRFAN, Feraz Ali 25 Pedmore La, Stourbridge DY9 0SY — MB ChB 1997 Manch.

IRFAN, Hassan Russells Hall Hospital, Dudley DY1 2HQ Tel: 01384 244180; 25 Pedmore Lane, Stourbridge DY9 0SY — MB BS 1958 Karachi; BSc Karachi 1953, MB BS 1958; FRCP Glas. 1976, M 1965. (Dow Med. Coll.) Cons. Phys. Russells Hall Hosp. Dudley; Clin. Dir. Dept. Med. for Elderly Dudley HA. Socs: Reg. Hosps. Cons. & Specialists Assn.; Brit. Geriat. Soc. Prev: Sen. Regist. (Med.) Withington Hosp. Manch.; Regist. (Gen. Med. & IC) W. Cumbld. Hosp. Whitehaven; Ho. Surg. Qu. Mary's Hosp. Sidcup.

IRFAN, Mohammed Coulsdon Road Surgery, 157A Coulsdon Road, Old Coulsdon, Coulsdon CR5 1EG Tel: 01737 553660 Fax: 01737 550477 — MB BS (Hons.) Punjab (Pakistan) 1966; DAB Lond. 1993; DFFP Lond. 1996. (Nishtar Med. Coll. Multan) Princip. GP Old Coulsdon. Socs: Fell. Roy. Soc. Med. Prev: SHO (ENT) Gen. Hosp. Croydon; Cas. Off. Gen. Hosp. Hexham; SHO (Gen. Surg. Orthop. & ENT) St. And. Hosp. Bow.

IRFAN, Shamim Akhtar 60 Lavender Avenue, London NW9 8HE Tel: 020 8205 4165 — MB BS 1957 Punjab; MB BS Punjab (Pakistan) 1957; DFFP 1993; DGO TC Dub. 1963. Community Med. Off. (Community Med.) Pk.side Health NHS Trust.

IRGIN, Shauna Mary 12 Peel Walk, Birmingham B17 8SR — MB ChB 1995 Birm.; ChB Birm. 1995.

IRISH, Charles James Flat 2, 28 Fellows Road, London NW3 3LH — BM BS 1983 Nottm.

IRISH, Nicholas Occupational Health Department, Hinchingbrooke Healthcare NHS Trust, Huntingdon PE29 6NT Tel: 01480 416263 Fax: 01480 416675 Email: nickirish@hbhe-tr.anglose-nhs.uk; Jasmine House, Pettitts Lane, Dry Drayton, Cambridge CB3 8BT Tel: 01954 780661 — MB BS 1967 Lond.; MRCS Eng. LRCP Lond. 1967; MFOM RCP Lond. 1992, AFOM 1989. (Guy's) Cons. Occupat Health Phys. & Cons. Communicable Dis. Control Hinchingbrooke Healthcare NHS Trust. Socs: Soc. Occupat. Med.; Assn. Local Auth. Med. Advisers; Assn. NHS Occupat. Phys. Prev: GP N. Dorset.

IRISH, William Tom The Mendip Country Practice, Anchor Road, Coleford, Bath BA3 5PG Tel: 01373 812244 Fax: 01373 813390 — MB BChir 1987 Camb.; BSc Lond. 1984; MRCGP 1991; DRCOG 1991; DCH RCP Lond. 1989. Prev: Trainee GP Melksham; SHO (Obst & Gyn.) Roy. United Hosp. Bath; SHO (Med.) Gen. Hosp. Jersey.

IRISH-TAVARES, Dianne Nadine Tel: 0118 752152 — MB BS 1988 W. Indies; MSc; MRCpath. (West indies) Locum Cons. Roy. Berks. Hosp., Dept. of Microbiol., Lond. Rd., Reading, RG1. Socs: BMA; Med. Protect. Soc; BSAC. Prev: Locum Cons. Kingston NHS Trust; Reg.Microbiol.Greenwich.Healthcare Trust; Sen. Regist. Virol.St Thomas hosp.

IRIYAGOLLE, Imiya Mudiyanselage Ranee Chandrika Isidore Crown Medical Centre, 60 Chadwick Road, London SE15 4PU Tel: 020 8592 4242; Seven Kings, Redbridge IG3 9NZ Email: sinhachan@locall.net — LRCPI & LM, LRSCI & LM 1973; 1997 MSC; 1987 JCPTGP; LRCPI & LM, LRCSI & LM 1973. (Royal College of Surgeons/ St. Georges Medical School, University of Lon.) Gen. Practitioner (EMS); Private Practitoner, Gen. med. Complimentary

Ther., Chemicel Dependency. Socs: Med. Defence Union; Brit. Med. Assn. Prev: Gen. Practitioner Princip., EMS, Self employed; Personal Med. Serv.s Liverp.; Civil. Med. Practitioner, Min. of Defence - Germany.

IRIZAR SABORIDO, Carlos 44 Broadmead, Parbold, Wigan WN8 7PB — LMS 1989 Basque Provinces.

IRLAM, Aidan Charles — MB ChB 1981 Dundee; DMJ 2001; BSc Liverp. 1976; MRCGP 1990; FFA RCS Eng. 1988; DRCOG 1990; DCH RCP Lond. 1989. (Dundee) Princip. Gen. Pract.; Dep. Police Surg. Essex. Socs: Roy. Soc. of Med.; Brit. Med. Assn.; Assn. of Police Surg.

IRLAM, Caroline Anne The Church Street Practice, David Corbet House, 2 Callows Lane, Kidderminster DY10 2JG Tel: 01562 822051 Fax: 01562 827251 — MB ChB 1982 Birm.; DCH RCP Lond. 1985; DRCOG 1985. SHO/Trainee GP Dudley VTS.

IRLAM, Pamela Anne Agnes Cross, Horsted Keynes, Haywards Heath RH17 7ED — MB BCh 1954 Wales. SCMO Mid Downs HA.

IRONMONGER, Mark Rex Howell Surgery, High Street, Brenchley, Tonbridge TN12 7NQ Tel: 01892 722007; Milestone Cottage, Brenchley Road, Horsmonden, Tonbridge TN12 8DN Tel: 01892 722778 — MRCS Eng. LRCP Lond. 1978; BSc Lond. 1975, MB BS 1978; DRCOG 1981; MSc Lond 1998. (St. Thos.) GP Brenchley.; Course Organiser Tunbridge Wells VTS; Clin. Asst. (Cardiac Rehabil.). Prev: Trainee GP Tonbridge; SHO (Paediat.) Pembury Hosp; Ho. Phys. & SHO (O & G) St. Thos. Hosp. Lond.

IRONS, Andrew Westwater (retired) Cotterwood, Main St., Ormiston, Tranent EH35 5HX Tel: 01875 610485 — MB ChB 1945 Ed.

IRONS, David John 101 Southdown Road, Bath BA2 1HL — MB ChB 1987 Sheff.

IRONS, Mr Duncan William Department Obstetrics and Gynaecology, Dryburn Hospital, Durham DH1 5TW Tel: 0191 333 2240 Fax: 0191 222 2289 — MB BS 1987 Newc.; MRCOG 1992; MD Newc. 1997. Cons. (O & G) Dryburn Hosp. Durh. Socs: Internat. Soc. Study Hypertens. in Pregn. Prev: Sen. Regist. RVI Newc.; Research Fell. RVI Newc.; Regist. N. Tyneside Dist. Hosp.

IRONS, Gregor Stewart 1 Pennyland Drive, Thurso KW14 7PA; 6 Mount Street, Aberdeen AB25 2RB — MB ChB 1992 Aberd. RGIT Med. Internat. Offshore/Remote Med. Off. Aberd.

IRONS, Richard John Graham (retired) 51 Main Street, Bishopsthorpe, York YO23 1JD Tel: 01904 778 571 Fax: 01904 778 571 Email: rjgirons@talk21.com — MB BChir 1967 Camb.; MA Camb. 1967; MRCS Eng. LRCP Lond. 1967; DObst RCOG 1970; DCH Eng. 1970. Prev: Clin. Asst. (Obst.) Rosie Matern. Hosp. Camb.

IRONS, Richard Paul 44 Stowe Avenue, Millhouses, Sheffield S7 2GP — BM BS 1990 Nottm.; MRCP (UK) 1993; DA 1996. (Nottingham) Specialist Regist. (A & E) NGH Sheff.

IRONSIDE, Fiona Claire Irish Street Surgery, 22 Irish Street, Whitehaven CA28 7BU — MB ChB 1984 Birm.; MRCGP 1992; MRCOG 1990. Clin. Asst. (Gastroenterol.) W. Cumbld. Hosp. Whitehaven. Prev: Regist. (O & G) W. Cumbld. Hosp.

IRONSIDE, Graham John Irish Street Surgery, 22 Irish Street, Whitehaven CA28 7BU; 22 Irish Street, Whitehaven CA28 7BU Tel: 01946 694457 — MB ChB 1984 Birm.; MRCGP 1988; DRCOG 1988. Sch. Doctor St. Bees Cumbria; Mem. Cumbria LMC. Socs: W Cumbria Med. Soc. Prev: SHO (Geriat.) Cumbld. Hosp. Whitehaven.

IRONSIDE, James Grant Sundal, Sandhurst Park, Tunbridge Wells TN2 3SU — MB BS 1993 Lond.

IRONSIDE, Professor James Wilson CJD Surveillance Unit, Western General Hospital, Crewe Road, Edinburgh EH4 2XU Tel: 0131 537 1980 Fax: 0131 537 3056 Email: j.w.ironside@ed.ac.uk; 1/2 Learnmonth Terrace, Edinburgh EH4 1PQ — MB ChB 1979 Dundee; FRCP Ed. 1999; FRCPath 1998; MRCPath 1986; BMSc Dund 1976. Prof of Clin. Neuropath. univ of Edin.; Hon. Cons. Neuropathol. Lothian hosps univ trust. Socs: Brit. Neuropath. Soc.; Brit. Assn. Ocular Path.; Brit. Neuro-oncol. Gp. Prev: Cons. Neuropath. W.. Gen. Hosp. Edin.; Sen. Lect. (Path.) Univ. Leeds; Sen. Regist. (Neuropath.) Roy. Hallamsh. Hosp. Sheff.

IRONSIDE, Janet Ann Dallas Edinburgh Cancer Centre, Western General Hospital, Crewe Road, Edinburgh EH4 2XU Tel: 0131 537 3045 Fax: 0131 537 3045 Email: janet.ironside@luht.scot.nhs.uk; Old Orchard House, 1 St Ninians Road, Corstorphine, Edinburgh EH12 8AP Tel: 0131 467 7874 Email: ironside@blueyonder.co.uk — MB ChB 1978 Dundee; FRCR 1981 ((1)). Cons. Clin. Oncol. W.. Gen. Hosp. Edin.; Chairm. Lothian Research Ethics Comm. For Med. + Clin. Oncol. Research. Prev: Locum Cons. (Clin. Oncol.) W.. Gen. Hosp. Edin.; Assoc. Specialist W.. Gen. Edin.; Staff Grade Clin. Oncol. W.. Gen. Hosp. Edin.

IRONSIDE, Mary Jack 9B/2 Dean Terrace, Edinburgh EH4 1ND — MB ChB 1947 Aberd. SCMO (Community Health) Child Developm. Unit Halifax. Prev: Ho. Surg. Hosp. Sick Childr. Aberd.; SHO Skin Dept. Bradford Roy. Infirm.; Asst. Sch. Med. Off. BrigHo..

IRONSIDE, Mr William McIntosh Sinclair (retired) 4 Gernhill Avenue, Fixby, Huddersfield HD2 2HR Tel: 01484 422964 Fax: 01484 422964 — MB ChB Aberd. 1945; MB ChB Aberd. 1945; FRCS Ed. 1953; FRCS Ed. 1953. Attend. Surg. Nuffield Hosp. Huddersfield & Elland Indep. Hosp. Prev: Cons. Otorhinolaryng. Roy. Halifax & Huddersfield Roy. Infirms.

IRONTON, Robert Southampton University Hospitals NHS Trust, Neonatal Unit, Princess Anne Maternity Hospital, Coxford Road, Southampton SO16 5YA Tel: 02380 794643 Fax: 02380 798522 — BM BCh 1981 Oxf.; DPhil Oxf. 1980; FRCP Lond. 1996; MRCP (UK) 1985; FRCPCH 1997. (Oxf.) Cons. Paediat. Neonat.. Univ. Soton. Gen. Hosp. Socs: Brit. Assn. Perinatal Med.; BMA.

IRSHAD, Nabila 653 Shields Road, Pollokshields, Glasgow G41 2RU — MB ChB 1998 Glas.; MB ChB Glas 1998.

IRTIZA-ALI, Ayesha Syeda 28 Park End Road, Romford RM1 4AU — MB ChB 1998 Manch.; MB ChB Manch 1998.

IRVIN, Peter James Kings Road Medical Centre, 73 Kings Road, North Ormesby, Middlesbrough TS3 6HA Tel: 01642 244766 Fax: 01642 246243; (Surgery), 73 King's Road, North Ormesby, Middlesbrough TS3 6HA — MB BS 1968 Newc. (Newc.) Prev: SHO (Obst.) Middlesbrough Matern. Hosp.; Ho. Phys. & Ho. Surg. Hemlington Hosp. Middlesbrough.

IRVIN, Mr Thomas Thoburn Royal Devon & Exeter Hospital, Barrack Road, Exeter EX2 5DN Tel: 01392 402704 Fax: 01392 402067 Email: tom-irvin80@hotmail.com; Quarry house, Harts Lane, Pinhoe, Exeter EX2 5DN Tel: 01392 468209 Fax: 01392 462898 Email: tom.irvin80@hotmail.com — MB ChB 1964 Aberd.; PhD Aberd. 1968, ChM 1974; FRCS Ed. 1969. Cons. Surg. Roy. Devon & Exeter Hosp. Socs: Assn. Surgs. GB; Brit. Assn. Surg. Oncol.; Assn. ColoProctol. GB. Prev: Reader (Surg.) Univ. Sheff.; Lect. (Surg.) Surg. Univ. Leeds; Research Surg. Univ. Calif., San Francisco.

IRVINE, Aileen Hill Medical Group, The Hill, 192 Kingsway, Dunmurry, Belfast BT17 9AL Tel: 028 9061 8211 Fax: 028 9060 3911; 5 Aberdelghy Park, Lambeg, Lisburn BT27 4QF Tel: 01846 665020 — MB BCh BAO 1972 Belf.; MRCGP 1978; DObst RCOG 1974. (Queen's University Belfast) GP Dunmurry Belf. Socs: Ulster Med. Soc.; BMA; Lagan Valley GP Assoc.

IRVINE, Alan David 75 Newtownbreda Road, Belfast BT8 7BS Email: airvine@hgmp.mrc.ac.uk — MB BCh BAO 1991 Belf.; MRCP (UK) 1994. Regist. (Dermat.) Belf. City Hosp.

IRVINE, Alan Thompson Hollywell Cottage, Rotten Row Hill, Tutts Clump, Reading RG7 6JY — MB BCh BAO 1979 Belf.; MFPM 1990. Med. Dir. Orion Clin. Servs. Ltd.

IRVINE, Alfred Kenneth (retired) 8 Drummond Park, Belfast BT9 6TL — MB BCh BAO 1952 Belf.; MRCPI 1964; DPhysMed. Eng. 1963. Cons. Phys. Physical Med. & Rheum. Roy. Vict. Hosp. Belf.

IRVINE, Alison Pauline 12 Ferndale, Clogher BT76 0AS — MB BCh BAO 1993 Belf.

IRVINE, Alison Williams Moss Lane Surgery, Madeley, Crewe CW3 9NQ Tel: 01782 750274 Fax: 01782 751835 Email: madeleypractice@hotmail.com; Breckland, Parkwood Drive, Baldwins Gate, Newcastle ST5 5EU Tel: 01782 680525 — BM BCh 1985 Oxf.; BA Oxf. 1982; MRCGP 1989; DRCOG 1988; DCH RCP Lond. 1987. (Oxford) Mem. N. Staffs. LMC; Mem. N. Staffs. HA Exec. Team & Chairm. N. Staffs. Sect. Gen. Pract.; Research Fell. Univ. Keele; GP Tutor N. Staffs. Prev: Trainee GP/SHO Macclesfield VTS.

IRVINE, Alistair John The Health Centre, Queensway, Billingham TS23 2LA Tel: 01642 360033 Fax: 01642 552892; Neasless Farm, Sedgefield, Stockton-on-Tees TS21 3HE — MB ChB 1966 Leeds; DMJ Soc. Apoth. Lond. 1979. Lect. Forens. Med. Durh. Constab. Sc. Aids Train. Sch.; Lect. Forens. Med. Cleveland Constab. Train. Sch.; Sen. Police Surg. Cleveland Constab. Socs: Fell. Roy. Soc. Med.; Assn. Police Surgs. Gt. Brit.; BMA & Brit. Acad. Foren. Sc. Prev: SHO (Gyn.) Hosp. Wom. Leeds; SHO (Obst.) Matern. Hosp. Leeds.

IRVINE, Allan Turner 77 Longdown Lane S., Epsom KT17 4JJ Tel: 01372 725136 — MB BS 1977 Lond.; MRCP (UK) 1980; FRCR 1985; DMRD Eng. 1985. (Univ. Coll. Hosp.) Cons. Radiol. Ashford & St. Peter's Hosp.s NHS Trust; Hon. Sen. Lect. UMDS St. Thos. Hosp. Lond. Socs: Fell. Roy. Coll. Radiol.; BMA; Roy. Soc. Med. Prev: Cons. Radiol. St. Thos. Hosp. Lond.; Cons. Radiol. Roy. Lond. Hosp.; Cons. Radiol. Roy. Hosp. Brisbane, Austral.

IRVINE, Anne Thérèse (retired) Castle Hill House, Middleham, Leyburn DL8 4QW Tel: 01969 623302 — MB ChB Liverp. 1958; MRCS Eng. LRCP Lond. 1958. Prev: SCMO (Community Health) N. Yorks. Health Auth.

IRVINE, Mr Brian William Hall Cremannan, Balfron, Glasgow G63 0QP — MB ChB 1974 Glas.; FRCS Glas. 1978.

IRVINE, Catriona William Harvey Hospital, Kennington Road, Willesborough, Ashford TN24 0LZ Tel: 01233 633331; Field House, Station Road, Bridge, Canterbury CT4 5AJ Tel: 01227 830896 Fax: 01227 830896 — MB BS 1974 Lond.; MRCP (UK) 1979; FRCP 1998. (St. Bart.) Cons. Dermat. William Harvey Hosp. Ashford; Hon. Cons. Dermat. Surg. St. John's Inst. Dermat. Lond. Prev: Sen. Regist. (Dermat.) SE Thames RHA; Sen. Regist. (Dermat.) Univ. Hosp. Wales Cardiff.

IRVINE, Christopher Edward William Stockwood Health Clinic, Hollway Road, Bristol BS14 8PT Tel: 01275 833103 Fax: 01275 891637 — MB ChB 1975 Dundee.

IRVINE, Cona Patricia Caroline 39 The Beeches, Hope, Wrexham LL12 9NX Tel: 01978 762589 — MB ChB 1977 Birm.; Dip.Community Paediat.1987; DFFAP.RCOG 1995. Clin. Med. Off. (Family Plann.) Clwydian Community Health Care Trust & Chester & Halton Community Care Trust.

IRVINE, Mr Craig Dick 50 Westcliffe Park Drive, Dawlish EX7 9ER; 22 Clyde Road, Frampton Cotterell, Bristol BS36 2EE Tel: 01454 775510 Email: craig_irvine@hotmail.com — BM BS 1988 Nottm.; FRCS Eng. 1992; MD 1999; FRCS Gen Surg 1999. (Univ. Nottm.) SR Vasc.Surg. Concord hosp.NSW.Aus. Socs: BMA; Assn. Surg.; Eur. Vasc. Surg. Soc. Prev: Research Regist. (Vasc. Surg.) Bristol Roy. Infirm.; Regist. Rotat. W. Yorks.; SHO Rotat. (Orthop.) Winford Orthop. Hosp. Bristol.

IRVINE, David Alexander (retired) 9 Warrender Park Crescent, Edinburgh EH9 1DX Tel: 0131 228 3239 — MB ChB 1974 Ed.; BSc Ed. 1972, MSc Community Med. 1990. Prev: Med. Off. Moray Ho. Inst. of Educat. Edin.

IRVINE, David Stewart MRC Human Reproductive Sciences Unit, Centre for Reproductive Biology, 37 Chalmers St., Edinburgh EH3 9ET Tel: 0131 229 2575 Fax: 0131 228 5571 — MB ChB 1982 Ed.; FRCOG 2001; BSc (Med. Sci.) (Hons.) Ed. 1979, MD 1988; MRCOG 1989. (Edinburgh) Cons. & Clin. Sci. MRC Human Reproductive Sci.s unit; Hon. Cons. Lothian HB, Roy. Infirm. Edin. & Simpson Memor. Matern. Pavil. Socs: Soc. Study of Fertil.; Brit. Fertil. Soc.; Brit. Andrology Soc. Prev: Lect. (O & G) Univ. Aberd. & Univ. Edin.; Lect. (O & G) Univ. Edin.; MRC Special Train. Fell. (Reproduc. Biol.) & Hon Regist. (Obst. & Gyn.) MRC Reproduc. Unit & Roy. Infirm. Edin.

IRVINE, Sir Donald Hamilton, CBE General Medical Council, 178-202 Great Portland St., London W1W 5JD Tel: 0207 915 3480 Fax: 0207 915 3640; Mole End, Fairmoor, Morpeth NE61 3JL Tel: 01670 517546 — MB BS Durh. 1958; MD Newc. 1964; FRCGP 1972, M 1965; DObst RCOG 1960. (Univ. Newc. u. Tyne) Pres. Gen. Med. Counc. Socs: Fell. BMA; Fell. Roy. Soc. Med.; Fell. RCGP. Prev: GP Ashington; Regional Adviser (Gen. Pract.) Univ. Newc.; Hon. Sec. & Chairm. Counc. RCGP.

IRVINE, Elizabeth Marjorie 137 Eastern Way, Ponteland, Newcastle upon Tyne NE20 9RH — MB ChB 1965 Aberd.

IRVINE, Fiona Flat 3L, 40 Edgehill Road, Glasgow G11 7JD — MB BS 1991 Lond.; FCOphth. Specialist Regist. Ophth., Glas. Gen. Hosp. Socs: RCOphth. Prev: SHO Ophth., Addenbrooke's Camb.

IRVINE, Mr George Barrie Mount Stuart Hospital, St Vincent's Road, Torquay TQ2 4UP Tel: 01803 321601 Fax: 01803 311498; The Old Rectory, Haccombe, Newton Abbot TQ12 4SJ — MB BS 1978 Lond.; FRCS (Orthop.) Ed. 1989; FRCS Glas. 1982. (St. Thos.) Cons. Orthop. Surg. Torbay Hosp. Torquay. Socs: Fell. BOA; Brit. Orthop. Spinal Soc. Prev: Sen. Regist. (Orthop. Surg.) St. Bart. Hosp. Lond.; Fell. (Orthop. Surg.) P.ss Margt. Rose Orthop. Hosp. Edin.; Ho. Surg. Cardiothoracic Unit St. Thos. Hosp. Lond.

IRVINE, Gerald John Gardner 36 Olde Forge Manor, Belfast BT10 0HY — MB BCh BAO 1947 Belf.; DObst RCOG 1950.

IRVINE, Mr Gerard Sutherland, CBE, Surg. Capt. RN Retd. 9 Alvara Road, Alverstoke, Gosport PO12 2HY — MB BS 1937 Lond.; FRCS Eng. 1967; MRCS Eng. LRCP Lond. 1937; DLO Eng. 1940. (Univ. Coll. Hosp.) Socs: BMA. Prev: Hon. Surg. to HM the Qu.; Cons. in Otorhinolaryngol. & Sen. Med. Off. i/c Surg. Div. RN Hosp.; Haslar.

IRVINE, Gilbert Marshall (retired) 3C Windsor Close, Malone Road, Belfast BT9 6FG Tel: 01232 280487 — MB BCh BAO 1952 Dub. Prev: Ho. Phys. Kidderminster Hosp.

IRVINE, Gillian Anne Ayrshire Central Hospital, Irvine KA12 8SS — MB ChB 1986 Ed.; MRCOG 1991; MD Ed. 1997. (Edinburgh) Cons. (O & G) Irvine. Prev: Sen. Regist. (O & G) Glas.

IRVINE, Gillian Elizabeth Aviemore Health Centre, Aviemore PH22 1SY Tel: 01479 810258 Fax: 01479 810067; Feòran, Craig-Na-Gower Avenue, Aviemore PH22 1RW Tel: 01479 810795 — MB ChB 1983 Ed.; MRCGP 1990; DCCH RCP Ed. 1991; DTM & H Liverp. 1984. (Edinburgh) Gen. Practitioner.

IRVINE, Gordon (retired) 34 Clydesdale Gardens, Richmond TW10 5EF Tel: 020 8876 1793 — MB ChB 1946 Ed. Prev: Sen. Lect. (Anat.) Univ. Coll. Cardiff.

IRVINE, Mr Gordon Henry Southmead Hospital, Westbury-on-Trym, Bristol BS10 5NB Tel: 0117 959 5177 Fax: 0117 959 5028 — MB ChB 1976 Dundee; BDS Ed. 1970; FDS RCS Ed. 1978; FRCS Ed. 1985. (Dundee) Cons. Oral & Maxillofacial Surg. S.mead Hosp. Bristol. Prev: Sen. Regist. (Maxillofacial Surg.) UCH & W.m. Hosp. Lond.; Ho. Phys. Bradford Roy. Infirm.; Ho. Surg. Ninewells Hosp. Dundee.

***IRVINE, Helene Josephine** Craigton Cottage, Fintry, Glasgow G63 0XQ — LRCP LRCS 1984 Ed.; LRCPS Glas. 1984.

IRVINE, Jean Irvine Creagandaraich, Tighnabruaich PA21 2EA Tel: 01700 811260 — MB ChB 1976 Glas.; MRCP (UK) 1980; DRCOG 1978; DCH RCPS Glas. 1978. Clin. Med. Off. Argyll & Clyde HB.

IRVINE, John James Bowman 19 Deramore Park, Malone Road, Belfast BT9 5JW Tel: 01232 668278 Fax: 01232 668278 — MB BCh BAO 1959 Belf.; LRCP LRCS Ed. LRFPS Glas. 1958; FFOM RCPI 1995; DObst RCOG 1961. Phys. Brit. Aerospace Dhahran, Saudi Arabia.

***IRVINE, Kate Louise** Flat 3/2, 83 Rosemount Viaduct, Aberdeen AB25 1NS — MB ChB 1994 Aberd.

IRVINE, Kenneth Henry Old Irvine Road Surgery, 4-6 Old Irvine Road, Kilmarnock KA1 2BD Tel: 01563 22413 — MB ChB 1987 Glas.; MRCGP 1991.

IRVINE, Kevin Gerard The Surgery, 53 Burnbank Road, Hamilton ML3 9AQ Tel: 01698 281407 — MB ChB 1977 Glas.; MRCP (UK) 1981; DRCOG 1984. GP Hamilton; Med. Off. HM Prison Barlinnie, Glas.

IRVINE, Laurie Montgomery Department of Obstetrics and Gynaecology, Watford General Hospital, Vicarage Road, Watford WD18 0HB — MB BS 1981 Lond.; MD Lond. 1993; MRCS Eng. LRCP Lond. 1981; MRCOG 1986. Cons. O & G Watford Gen. Hosp.; Cons. Obst. & Gyn. BUPA Bushey Hosp. Socs: Fell.(Counc. Mem.) Roy. Soc. Med.; Welsh Obst. & Gyn. Soc.; (Hon. Treas.) W. Herts & Watford Med. Soc. Prev: Sen. Regist. (O & G) Roy. Gwent Hosp. Newport; Regist. (O & G) Roy. Free Hosp. Lond.; SHO (Gyn.) W.minster & Char. Cross Hosps. Lond.

IRVINE, Mr Malcolm Charles Gray Department of Otolaryngology, Wexham Park Hospital, Slough SL2 4HL Tel: 01753 633090 Fax: 01753 633075; Brooklands, 7 Molly Millars Lane, Wokingham RG41 2RT Tel: 0118 979 3674 — MB BS 1984 Lond.; FRCS Glas. 1992. (St. Thos.) Staff Grade OtoLaryngol. Dept Wexham Pk. Hosp. Slough.

IRVINE, Marie-Louise 85 Stewarton Drive, Cambuslang, Glasgow G72 8DH — MB ChB 1981 Aberd.

IRVINE, Maxwell Stewart Lytham Road Surgery, 2A Lytham Road, Fulwood, Preston PR2 8JB Tel: 01772 716033 Fax: 01772 715445; Bank Hall, Broughton, Preston PR3 5JA Tel: 01772 862961 — MB ChB 1968 Ed.; MRCGP 1974; DObst RCOG 1972; DCH RCPS Glas. 1970. Med. Ref. DSS; Police Surg. (Preston Div.).

IRVINE, Nes Stewart The Sollershott Surgery, 44 Sollershott East, Letchworth SG6 3JW Tel: 01462 683637 Fax: 01462 481348 — MB ChB 1985 Manch.; BSc (Med. Sci.) St. And. 1982. Socs: BMA.

IRVINE, Norman Alexander Barham Lodge, Coddenham Road, Barham, Ipswich IP6 0PZ Tel: 01473 832091 — MB ChB 1974 Ed.; MRCP (UK) 1977. Cons. Phys. Ipswich Hosp. Prev: Internat. Research Fell. (Clin. Pharmacol.) Univ. Texas, San Antonio, USA; Lect. & Hon. Sen. Regist. Dept. Clin. Pharmacol. Ninewells Hosp. & Med. Sch. Dundee; Regist. (Cardiol.) Aberd. Roy. Infirm.

IRVINE, Robert John Macferson Medical Advisory Branch, Oldway Centre, Orchard St., Swansea SA1 1TU Tel: 01792 304416; Trewlawney, Llanmorlais, Swansea SA4 2TL Tel: 01792 850231 — MB BS 1961 Lond.; MB BS (Hnrs. Applied Pharmacol. & Therap.) Lond. 1961; MRCGP 1975. (St. Bart.) Sen. Med. Off. DVLC Swansea. Prev: GP Cockermouth; SHO St. Bart. Hosp. Lond.; SHO Brompton Hosp. Lond.

IRVINE, Mr Robert William 34 Burnside Road, High Burnside, Rutherglen, Glasgow G73 4RS Tel: 0141 634 5543 — MB ChB 1956 Glas.; FRCS Ed. 1961. (Glas.) Cons. Surg. Law Hosp. Carluke & StoneHo. Hosp. Socs: Roy. M-C Soc. Glas.; Brit. Assn. Urol. Surgs. Prev: Surg. Regist. W.. Infirm. Glas.; SHO (Surg.) W.. Infirm. Glas.; Ho. Phys. Roy. Infirm. Glas.

IRVINE, Robin Eliot, CBE (retired) Dolphin House, Le Foulon, St Peter Port, Guernsey GY1 1YY Tel: 01481 723298 Fax: 01481 714135 Email: rei@guernsey.net — MB BChir Camb. 1944; MA Camb. 1958, BA 1942, MD 1955; FRCP Lond. 1968, M 1948. Prev: Governor Les Bourgs Hospice Guernsey.

IRVINE, Mr Roderick Ewan 77 Harestone Hill, Caterham CR3 6DL — MB BS Lond. 1980; FRCS Ed. 1992; MRCOG 1996. Socs: Roy. Coll. Obst. & Gyn.

IRVINE, Ruth Robson (retired) 116 Banstead Road S., Sutton SM2 5LH Tel: 020 8770 7638 — LRCP LRCS Ed. LRFPS Glas. 1944; FFA RCS Eng. 1961; DA Eng. 1956. Prev: Cons. Anaesth. New Ealing Hosp. Lond.

IRVINE, Sarah Alice 15 Kensington Gate, Dowanhill, Glasgow G12 9LG Tel: 0141 334 7430 — MB ChB 1993 Glas.; MRCP (UK) 1996. SHO III (Rheum. & Med.) Gartnavel Hosp. Glas. Socs: BMA. Prev: SHO III (Gen. Med.) Stobhill Hosp. Glas.

IRVINE, Sarah Anne-Marie Chells Way Surgery, 265 Chells Way, Stevenage SG2 0HN Tel: 01438 313001 Fax: 01438 362322 — MB ChB 1986 Manch.; MRCGP (Distinc.) 1990; DRCOG 1988.

IRVINE, Sheena Margaret Tait 8 Nichols Green, Montpelier Road, London W5 2QU — MB BS 1977 Lond.; FFA RCS Eng. 1984.

IRVINE, Simon Timothy Freeman Hospital, Freeman Road, High Heaton, Newcastle upon Tyne NE7 7DN Tel: 0191 284 3111; 52 Percy Park, North Shields NE30 4JX — MB ChB 1988 Ed.; MRCP (UK) 1991. Regist. (Cardiol.) Freeman Hosp. Newc. u. Tyne. Prev: Regist. (Med.) S. Tyneside Dist. Hosp.; Regist. (Med.) Qu. Eliz. Hosp. Gateshead.

IRVINE, Tracey Elizabeth Orchard View, Fawkham Road, West Kingsdown, Sevenoaks TN15 6JS — MB BS 1997 Lond. (UMDS Queens College) SHO Surg. RSCH Brighton. Prev: SHO A & E Guys Lond; Ho. Off. (Med.) Greenwich; Ho. Off. (Surg.) RSCH Brighton.

IRVINE, William Student Health Service, University of Aberdeen, Block E, Taylor Buildings, Old Aberdeen, Aberdeen AB24 3UB Tel: 01224 276655 Fax: 01224 272463; 7 Rosewell Park, Aberdeen AB15 6HT Tel: 01224 326822 Fax: 01224 326824 Email: w.irvine@abdn.ac.uk — MB ChB 1965 Glas. Chief Med. Off. Stud. Health Serv. Univ. Aberd.; Hon. Phys. Aberd. Roy. Infirm. Socs: Soc. Occupat. Med.; Brit. Assn. Health Servs. in Higher Ed.; Aberd. M-C Soc. Prev: Sen. Med. Advis. Unilever S. Africa Pty Ltd.

IRVINE, William James 12 Belgrave Crescent, Edinburgh EH4 Tel: 0131 332 8764 — MB ChB 1958 Ed.; FRS Ed.; DSc Ed. 1971, BSc (Hnrs.) 1955, MB ChB 1958; FRCP Ed. 1968, M 1961; FRCPath 1978, M 1971. Cons. Phys. Roy. Infirm. Edin.; Reader Dept. Med. Univ. Edin.; Edr. Jl. Clin. & Laborat. Immunol. Socs: Soc. Endocrinol. & Brit. Soc. Immunol. Prev: Sen. Regist. Roy. Infirm. Edin.; Reader Dept. Therap. Univ. Edin.

IRVINE, William Neil St Thomas Road Health Centre, St. Thomas Road, Newquay TR7 1RU Tel: 01637 878599 — MB BCh BAO 1985 Belf.

IRVING, Antony George 183 St Andrews Road S., Lytham St Annes FY8 1YB — MRCS Eng. LRCP Lond. 1962; MSc (Community Med.) Manch. 1977. (St. Mary's) Specialist Community Med. (Plann. & Informat.) Trafford AHA. Prev: Sen. Regist. (Community Med.) N. W.. RHA; Regist. Centre Hip Surg. Wrightington Hosp. Wigan; Orthop. Regist. Stockport Infirm.

IRVING, Cameron Douglas Elmwood Health Centre, Huddersfield Road, Holmfirth, Huddersfield HD9 3TR Tel: 01484 681777 Fax: 01484 689603; The Junction House, Hade Edge, Holmfirth, Huddersfield HD9 2RT Tel: 01484 681692 Email: vh16@dial.pipex.com — MB ChB 1990 Leeds; MRCGP 1995; DFFP 1994; DCH RCP Lond. 1993.

IRVING, Colum Joseph 1 Holly Bush Lane, Hampton TW12 2QR — MB BCh BAO 1982 NUI; FRCA 1992.

IRVING, Edwin Ratcliffe (retired) Bassaguard, 86 The Grove, Marton-in-Cleveland, Middlesbrough TS7 8AP Tel: 01642 316368 — MB BS 1960 Durh. Prev: Ho. Phys. Roy. Vict. Infirm. Newc.

IRVING, Eric Watson Strathdoon, Cameron Road, Fort William PH33 6LG Tel: 01397 703390 Email: ericwirving@hotmail.com; Strathdoon, Cameron Road, Fort William PH33 6LG Email: ericwirving@hotmail.com — MB ChB 1969 St. And. p/t Locum Gen. Practitioner.

IRVING, George Anthony (retired) Greenacre, Manor Road, Tatsfield, Westerham TN16 2ND Tel: 01959 573430 — MB BChir Camb. 1957; MA Camb. 1956; MRCS Eng. LRCP Lond. 1956; DObst RCOG 1958. Prev: Ho. Surg. (Orthop.) Guy's Hosp. Lond.

IRVING, Gerald Ian (retired) 42 Sandmoor Lane, Leeds LS17 7DP Tel: 0113 268 1347 — MB ChB 1943 Leeds; DObst RCOG 1946. Prev: Resid. Obst. Off. P.ss Mary Matern. Hosp. Newc.

IRVING, Helen Mary Claypath Medical Practice, 26 Gilesgate, Durham DH1 1QW Tel: 0191 333 2830 Fax: 0191 333 2836; 47 Albert Street, Western Hill, Durham DH1 4RJ Tel: 0191 384 8504 — MB ChB 1981 Leeds; DRCOG 1983. GP. Socs: Assoc. RCGP.

IRVING, Henry Charles Dept of radiology, St James' Univ Hosp, Leeds LS8 7TF Tel: 0113 206 4330 Fax: 0113 206 5466 Email: henry.irving@gw.sjsuh.northy.nhs.uk; 24 Alwoodley Lane, Leeds LS17 7PX Tel: 0113 261 1820 Email: hcirving@compuserve.com — MB BS 1972 Lond.; FRCR 1978; DMRD Eng. 1977. (Westm.) Cons Radiologist the Leeds Teachg. Hosps NHS Trust Leeds; Sen. Clin. Lect. Leeds Univ. Socs: (Ex-Pres.) Brit. Med. Ultrasound Soc.; Brit. Soc. Interven. Radiol.; Counc. RCRadiol. Prev: Sen. Regist. (Radiol.) Yorks. RHA; Regist. (Radiol.) Hammersmith Hosp. & Roy. Postgrad. Med. Sch. Lond.; Resid. Memor. Schol. Roy. Coll. Radiol.

IRVING, Ian Joseph 60 Dinas Lane, Liverpool L36 2NR — MB ChB 1977 Liverp.

IRVING, Miss Irene Marion (retired) Sandown Lodge, 44 Blundell Road, Hightown, Liverpool L38 9EQ Tel: 0151 929 2767 — MB ChB 1952 Liverp.; MB ChB (Hons.) Liverp. 1952; BSc (Hons.) Liverp. 1949, ChM 1969; FRCS Eng. 1957. Prev: Sen. Lect. (Paediat. Surg.) Univ. Liverp. Alder Hey Childr. Hosp.

IRVING, James Duncan 170 Coleherne Court, Redcliffe Gardens, London SW5 0DX Tel: 020 7373 9939 Email: di@d-irving.demon.co.uk — MB BS 1944 Durh.; FRCR 1986; DMRD Lond 1951. Emerit. Cons. Radiol. Guys & Lewisham Hosps. Lond. Prev: Cons. Radiol. Lewisham & N. S.wark Dist.; Hon.Cons Radiol Roy Free of Hammersmith Hosps Lond; Hon Sen Lec (Radiol) Roy Postgrad Med Soc Univ Lond.

IRVING, James Michael Ross (retired) Barn Cottage, Fulbrook, Burford OX18 4BL Tel: 01993 524798 — MB BS 1957 Lond.; MRCGP 1970; DObst RCOG 1959. Prev: SHO (Obst.) Brit. Hosp. Mothers & Babies Lond.

IRVING, Joan (retired) 170 Coleherne Court, Redcliffe Gardens, London SW5 0DX Tel: 020 7373 9939 — MB BS 1941 Lond.; MRCS Eng. LRCP Lond. 1941; DMRD Eng. 1951. Prev: Cons. Radiol. Lewisham Hosp.

IRVING, John Black St Johns Hospital, Livingston EH54 6PP Tel: 01506 419666; Gardners Hall, Linlithgow EH49 7RQ Tel: 01506 842565 — MB ChB 1969 Ed.; BSc Ed. 1966, MB ChB 1969; FRCP Ed. 1983; MRCP (UK) 1972. Cons. Phys. St. John's Hosp. Livingstone; Hon. Sen. Lect. (Med.) Univ. Edin. Socs: Brit. Cardiac Soc. Prev: Sen. Regist. (Cardiol.) Roy. Infirm. Edin.; Vis. Scientist (Cardiol. Dept. Med.) Univ. Washington Seattle, USA.

IRVING, Judith Ann Park View Surgery, Haverflatts Lane, Milnthorpe LA7 7PS Tel: 015395 63327 Fax: 015395 64059; 6 The Old Woodyard, High Tenterfell, Kendal LA9 4PZ — MB BS 1990 Newc. GP.

IRVING, Margaret Anne MacDonald Child Health directorate, NHS Primary Care Trust, Nithbank, Dumfries DG1 2SD Tel: 01387 255301 Fax: 01387 244212; Bonshaw Tower, Kirtlebridge, Lockerbie DG11 3LY Tel: 01461 500256 — MB ChB 1967 Glas.

(Glas.) Cons. Paediat. (Child Health) Primary Care Trust Dumfries; Med. Adviser to Dumfies & Galloway Regional Counc. Socs: BMA; Fell. Roy. Coll. of Paediat. & Child Health; Fell Roy Inst of Pub. health. Prev: SCMO Dumfries & Galloway HB; Regist. (Bact. & Immunol.) W.. Infirm. Glas.; GP Darvel & Newmilns, Ayrsh.

IRVING, Professor Sir Miles Horsfall Chairman's Office, The Freeman Hospital, Freeman Road, Newcastle upon Tyne NE7 7DN Tel: 0191 284 26055 Fax: 0191 222 8514 Email: m.h.irving@newcastle.ac.uk; Juniper, The Old Stables, Aydon Road, Corbridge NE45 5EH Tel: 01434 634243 Fax: 01434 634249 — MB ChB Liverp. 1959; FACS (Hon) 2000; MSc Manch. 1978; MD Liverp. 1962, ChM 1967; DSc (Hon.) Salford Univ. 1996; FRCS Eng. 1964; FRCS Ed. 1964; FRCS Glas. (Ad. Eundem) 1997; FRCS Canada (Hon) 1998; FFAEM (Hon) 1995. (Liverp.) Chairm. Newc. u. Tyne Hosps. NHS Trust; Emerit. Prof. (Surg.) Univ. Manch.; Hon. Cons. Surg. Army. Socs: (Ex-Pres.) Assn. of Surgs.; Roy. Soc. Med. (Ex-Pres. Sect. Coloprotol.); (Ex-Pres.) Assn. of ColoProctol. Prev: Prof. Surg. Univ. Manch. & Hon Cons. Surg., Hope Hosp., Salford; Reader (Surg.) & Hon. Cons. Surg. St. Bart. Hosp. Lond.; Phyllis Anderson Surg. Research Fell. Sydney Univ., Austral.

IRVING, Lady Patricia Margaret (retired) Juniper, The Old Stables, Aydon Road, Corbridge NE45 5EH Tel: 01434 634243 — MB BS Durh. 1963; AFOM RCP Lond. 1981; DIH Eng. 1979; DA Eng. 1970. Prev: Phys. Occupat. Health Bolton Gen Hosp.

IRVING, Mr Richard Michael Department of Otolaryngology, University of California, San Francisco CA 94117, USA Tel: 00 1 415 4763858; 33A Carlingford Road, Hampstead, London NW3 1RY — MB BS 1985 Lond.; MD Lond. 1996; FRCS (Orl.) 1996; FRCS Eng. 1991. (King's Coll. Hosp. Sch. Med.) Clin. Instruc. (Neurotol.) UCSF San Francisco, USA. Prev: Sen. Regist. (Otolaryngol.) UCL Hosps.; Regist. (Otolaryngol.) Addenbrooke's Hosp. Camb.

IRVING, Robert John Dept. of Medical Sciences, Western General Hospital, Edinburgh EH4 2XU; Gardners Hall, Linlithgow EH49 7RQ — MB ChB 1993 Ed. Jun. Research Fell., Dept Med. Sci. W.ern Gen. Hosp. Edin.

IRVING, Sarah Anne 115 Farndale Drive, Guisborough TS14 8JX — BM BS 1995 Nottm.

IRVING, Mr Stuart Owen 56 Hague Street, Whitfield, Glossop SK13 8NS — MB ChB 1989 Manch.; FRCS Ed. 1994. SHO Rotat. (Surg.) S. Manch. Prev: Demonst. (Anat.) Univ. Bristol; SHO (Urol. & Gen. Surg.) Stepping Hill Hosp. Stockport; Ho. Off. (Surg.) Manch. Roy. Infirm.

IRVING, Professor William Lucien Department of Microbiology, University Hospital, Queens's Medical Centre, Nottingham NG7 2UH Tel: 0115 970 9163 Fax: 0115 970 9233 Email: will.irving@nottingham.ac.uk — MB BChir 1979 Camb.; PhD Lond. 1986; MA Camb. 1979; MRCP (UK) 1980; MRCPath 1987, FRCPath 1997. (Camb. & King's Coll. Hosp.) Prof. & Hon. Cons. Clin. Virol. Qu. Med. Centre. Nottm. Socs: Assn. Med. Microbiol; Soc. Gen. Microbiol.

IRWIN, Alan George Henry 46 Richmond Court, Lisburn BT27 4QU — MB BCh BAO 1973 Belf.; MRCGP 1977.

IRWIN, Alan William Finaghy Health Centre, 13-25 Finaghy Road South, Belfast BT10 0BX Tel: 028 9062 8211; 29 Malone Meadows, Malone Road, Belfast BT9 5BG — MB BCh BAO 1982 Belf.; MB BCh Belf. 1982; MRCGP 1990; MRCOG 1989; DRCOG 1984. Socs: BMA.

IRWIN, Mr Andrew Stewart Consultant Orthopaedic Surgeon, St Albans & Hemel Hempstead NHS Trust, St Albans City Hospital, Waverley Road, St Albans AL3 5PN Tel: 01727 897500 Fax: 01727 897489; Tim's Spring, Moneybury Hill, Ashridge, Berkhamsted HP4 1LX Tel: 01442 851000 Fax: 01442 851000 Email: irwin@demon.co.uk — MB BCh 1984 Witwatersrand; FRCS (Orth.) 1996; FRCS Ed. 1990. Cons. Orthop. St. Albans & Hemel Hempstead NHS Trust. Socs: Fell. BOA; BMA. Prev: Sen. Regist. (Orthop.) Robt. Jones & Agnes Hunt Dist. & Orthop. Hosp. OsW.ry; Regist. Aberd. Roy. Hosps.

IRWIN, Angela ida Mountview House, Coolreaghs Rd, Cookstown BT80 9QN — MB BS 1996 Lond.

IRWIN, Christopher Sidney Wool Surgery, Folly Lane, Wool, Wareham BH20 6DS Tel: 01929 462376 — MB ChB 1972 Bristol; Dip Occ. Med. RCP Lond. 1996; DObst RCOG 1975; DA Eng. 1974. Local med. advisor ABRO Engin., Bovington. Prev: SHO (Anaesth.) Roy. Devon & Exeter Hosp.; SHO (Obst.) MusGr. Pk. Hosp. Taunton; SHO (A & E) Roy. Devon & Exeter Hosp.

IRWIN, Clive John Robert Department of Radiotherapy, University Hospitals Coventry and Warwickshire NHS Trust, Walsgrave Hospital, Clifford Bridge Road, Coventry CV2 2DX Tel: 024 76 538905 Fax: 024 76 538900; The Elms, Moreton Paddox, Moreton Morrell, Warwick CV35 9BU — MB BS 1983 Lond.; MRCP (UK) 1987; FRCR 1991. (London) Cons. Clin. Oncol. Walsgrave Hosp. NHS Trust Coventry; Vis. Clin. Oncol. Alexandra NHS Trust Redditch. Socs: BMA; Brit. Oncol. Assn.; ESTRO. Prev: Sen. Regist. (Clin. Oncol.) Christie Hosp. Manch; Regist. (Radiother.) St. Bart. Hosp. Lond.; Regist. Roy. Lond. Hosp.

IRWIN, David George Holywood Arches Health Centre, Westminster Avenue, Belfast BT4 1NS Tel: 0289 056 3360 Fax: 0289 056 3257 — MB BCh BAO 1982 Belf.; MRCGP 1987; Dip. Sports Med. Scotl. 1992; DRCOG 1988; Cert. Family Plann. JCC 1988; DCH Dub. 1987. (Qu. Univ. Belf.) GP; Sports Med., GP Specialist, One session per week in Hosp.; Team Doctor Ulster Rugby Team (Full Time Professional Players); Private Pract., Sports Med. Socs: Brit. Assn. Sports Med. (Treas. N. Irel. Br.); Irish Sports Med. Assn.

IRWIN, David James Department of Public Health, North Essex Health Authority, Collingwood Road, Witham CM8 2TT Tel: 01376 516515 Fax: 01376 514046 Email: david.irwin@nessex-ha.nthames.nhs.uk — MB BCh BAO 1986 Belf.; MSc Pub. Health Med. Lond. 1992; MFPHM Lond. 1995. Cons. (Communicable Dis. Control) N. Essex Health Auth., Witham. Socs: Pub. Health Med. Environm. Gp.; Fac. of Pub. Health Med. Prev: Cons. (Communicable Dis. Control) Rotherham HA Hon sen lec. Pub. health med univ of Sheff.; Sen. Regist. (Pub. Health) N. Thames Regional Health Auth.; Regist. (Pub. Health) N. E. Thames Regional Health Auth.

IRWIN, David Stephen Slade Mayfield Surgery, Mayfield, Buckden St. Neots, Huntingdon PE19 5SZ; 15 Ivy Way, Spaldwick, Huntingdon PE28 0UN Tel: 01480 890066 — MB BS 1985 Lond.; MRCGP 1990; Cert. Family Plann. JCC 1987; DRCOG 1987. (St. Thomas's) Police Surg. Basic Doctor Huntingdon. Prev: SHO (Paediat. & O & G) St. Mary's Hosp. Portsmouth; Trainee GP Emsworth; Clin. Med. Off. & Child Psychiat. Portsmouth.

IRWIN, David Thompson (retired) 2 Newgate, Highgate Park, Fulwood, Preston PR2 8LR — MA Dub. 1964; MB BCh BAO 1948; FRCR 1988; FFR RCSI 1964; DMRD Eng. 1951. Sen. Cons. Radiol. Preston & Chorley Hosp. Gp.; Radiol. St. Joseph's Hosp. Preston. Prev: Radiol. Regist. David Lewis N.. Hosp. Liverp.

IRW!N, Denis Bernarr (retired) 1 Carlton Gate, 1 Balcombe Road, Branksome Park, Poole BH13 6DX Tel: 01202 761197 — MD Lond. 1948, MB BS 1940; FRCP Lond. 1973, M 1947; MRCS Eng. LRCP Lond. 1940. Hon. Cons. Phys. Geriat. E. Dorset Health Dist. Prev: Cons. Phys. Geriat. E. Dorset Health Dist.

IRWIN, Desmond Henry Clarendon House, Inmans Row, Woodford Green IG8 0NH Tel: 020 8502 9067 — MB BCh BAO 1936 Dub.; MA, MD Dub. 1948; FRCPsych 1974, M 1971; DPM RCSI 1953. (Dub.) Prev: Cons. Psychiat. Wanstead Hosp. & Claybury Hosp.; Hon. Psychiat. Tavistock Clinic.

IRWIN, Edna Margaret (retired) 112 Selly Park Road, Birmingham B29 7LH — MB BCh BAO Belf. 1954; FRCP Ed. 1973, M 1960; FRCPsych 1980, M 1971; DCH Eng. 1956, DPM 1962; DObst RCOG 1956. Prev: Cons. Adolesc. Unit Hollymoor Hosp. Birm.

IRWIN, Eileen Agnes 20 Killynure Road W., Carryduff, Belfast BT8 8EA — MB BCh BAO 1967 Belf. Med. Off. Qu.'s Univ. Belf.

IRWIN, Elizabeth Boyd Brambles London Road, Kelvedon, Colchester CO5 9AU — MB BCh BAO 1986 Belf. GP Regist. Colchester VTS. Prev: Regist. & SHO (Psychiat.) Fairmile Hosp. Wallingford & BoroCt. Hosp. Wyfold; SHO (Geriat. Med.) Battle Hosp. Reading; Ho. Off. Roy. Vict. Hosp. Belf.

IRWIN, Greg John 335 Albert Drive, Glasgow G41 5HJ — MB ChB 1992 Dundee; BMSc (Hons.) Dundee 1989. SHO Rotat. (Surg.) Tayside HB.

IRWIN, Jane Elizabeth Nutwood Surgery, Windermere Road, Grange-over-Sands LA11 6EG Tel: 015395 32108 Fax: 015395 35986; The Old Parsonage, Grange Fell Road, Grange-over-Sands LA11 6BJ Tel: 0153 95 34428 Fax: 0153 95 36288 — MB ChB 1975 Manch.; DRCOG 1978. Socs: Chairm. Local Ethics Comm.; Morecambe Bay LMC.

IRWIN, John Area 4, Ninewells Hospital, Dundee DD1 9XY Tel: 01382 633867 Email: john.irwin@tuht.scot.nhs.uk — MB ChB 1975 Manch.; MSc 1977 Manch.; MRCP (UK) 1982. (Manch.) Cons. (Audiol. Med.) Ninewells Hosp. Dundee. Prev: Sen. Regist. (Audiol. Med.) Roy. Nat. ENT Lond.; Regist. (Neurorehabil.) Pinderfields Gen. Hosp.

IRWIN, Mr John Walker Sinclair 6 Old Coach Gardens, Belfast BT9 5PQ — MB BCh BAO 1937 Belf.; MB BCh BAO (Hnrs.) Belf. 1937; FRCS Ed. 1947. (Qu. Univ. Belf.) Cons. Surg. Roy. Vict. Hosp. Belf. & Ulster Hosp. Dundonald; Tutor Dept. Surg. Qu. Univ. Belf. Fell. Roy. Soc. Med. Socs: Ulster Med. Soc. Prev: Surg. Regist. Belf. City Hosp.; Ho. Phys. & Ho. Surg. Roy. Vict. Hosp. Belf.; Demonst. Anat. Qu. Univ. Belf.

IRWIN, Joyce Margaret Anne Bomackatall, Drumquin, Omagh; 40 Moss Road, Drumbo, Lisburn BT27 5JT Tel: 01232 826833 — MB BCh BAO 1980 Belf.; MRCGP 1984; DRCOG 1983.

IRWIN, Karen Ross 31 Curragh Road, Coleraine BT51 3RY — MB ChB 1991 Dundee.

IRWIN, Kate Zabel 17 Ethelbert Road, Canterbury CT1 3ND — MB BS 1994 Lond.

IRWIN, Kristina 81 Argyle Road, Sheffield S8 9HJ — MB ChB 1990 Sheff.

IRWIN, Mr Leslie Robson Sunderland Royal Hospital, Kayll Road, Sunderland SR4 7TP Tel: 0191 565 6256 Fax: 0191 565 3973 Email: leg.irwin@chs.northy.nhs.uk; 16 Warkworth Drive, Deneside View, Chester-le-Street DH2 3JR — BM BCh 1986 Oxf.; MA Oxf. 1987, BA 1983; FRCS Ed. 1992; FRCS (Orth.) Ed. 1997. (Oxf.) Cons Orthopaedic & Hand Surg., City Hosp. Sunderland. Socs: Mem. Brit Elbow & Shoulder Soc.; Fell Brit. Orthop. Assoc.; Brit. Soc. Surg. Hand. Prev: Regist. (Orthop.) Yorks. RHA; Regist. (Gen. Surg.) Darlington Memor. Hosp.

IRWIN, Margaret Williamina (retired) Thorney Hills Farm, Newborough, Burton-on-Trent DE13 8RY — MB ChB 1953 Glas. Prev: Staff Grade (Paediat.) Premier Health SE Staffs.

IRWIN, (Mary) Aideen Mortimer (retired) 123 The High Street, Great Broughton, Middlesbrough TS9 7HB Tel: 01642 242357 — MB BS 1955 Durh.; FFR 1965; DMRD Eng. 1962. Prev: Hon. Cons. Radiol. S. Tees Health Dist.

IRWIN, Michael Henry Knox (retired) 15 Hovedene, 95 Cromwell Road, Hove BN3 3EH — MB BS Lond. 1955; MPH Columbia 1960. Prev: Med. Dir. United Nations.

IRWIN, Mr Michael Samuel Addenbrooke's Hospital, Hills Road, Cambridge CB2 2QQ — MB BS 1987 Lond.; Diplomat EBOPRAS 1998 (European Board); FRCS (Plast.) 1998 (Intercollegiate Board); FRCS Eng. 1991. Cons. Plastic Surg., Addenbrooke's Hosp., Camb. Socs: Fell. Roy. Soc. Med.; Brit. Assn. of Plastic Surg.s; Brit. MicroSurgic. Soc. Prev: Fell. in Anaesthetic Plastic Surg., The Wellington Hosp., Lond.; Specialist Regist. Plastic Surg., The Roy. Marsden Hosp., Lond.; Specialist Regist. Plastic Surg., Char. Cross Hosp., Lond.

IRWIN, Nigel Christopher Northbourne Surgery, 1368 Wimborne Road, Bournemouth BH10 7AR Tel: 01202 574100 Fax: 01202 590030 — MB BS 1972 Lond.; MRCS Eng. LRCP Lond. 1972; MRCGP 1977; DObst RCOG 1974.

IRWIN, Patricia Florence Beechcroft, Camp Road, Gerrards Cross SL9 7PG — MB BS 1987 Lond.

IRWIN, Paul Berkeley The Oaks Family Medical Centre, 48 Orritor Road, Cookstown BT80 8BH Tel: 028 7976 2249 Fax: 028 7976 6793; 7 Drumnacross Road, Cookstown BT80 9DT — MB BCh BAO 1984 Belf.; MRCGP 1989; DGM RCP Lond. 1988; DRCOG 1987.

IRWIN, Mr Paul Patrick Tel: 01270 612005 Fax: 01270 250168; 410 Hale Road, Hale Barns, Altrincham WA15 8TF — MB BCh BAO 1982 NUI; MCh 1996; FRCSI 1987; FRCS (Urol.) 1997. (Univ. Coll. Dub.) Cons. Urol. Leighton Hosp. Crewe; Med. Adviser Interstitial Cystitis Support Gp. Socs: Brit. Assn. Urol. Surgs.; Norwich Med. Soc.; Hosp. Cons.s & Specialists Assn. Prev: Lect. (Urol.) Univ. Manch.; Regist. (Urol.) Stepping Hill Hosp. Stockport; Research Fell. Emory Univ. Sch. Med. Atlanta, USA.

IRWIN, Peter Thomas John Squire and Partners, Market Place, Hadleigh, Ipswich IP7 5DN Tel: 01473 822961 Fax: 01473 824895 — MB BS 1985 Lond.; 1999 D occ. Med.; MRCGP 1989; DCH RCP Lond. 1989; Cert. Family Plann. JCC 1989. (St. Thos. Hosp. Lond.) PCG Bd. Mem.; Lead CHD. Prev: Trainee GP Aberystwyth VTS.

IRWIN, Robert Belshaw, OBE (retired) 684 Antrim Road, Belfast BT15 5GP — MB BCh BAO 1949 Belf. Prev: GP Belf.

IRWIN, Mr Samuel Terence 76 King's Road, Knock, Belfast BT5 6JN Tel: 01232 704519 — MD 1986 Belf.; MB BCh BAO 1978; FRCS Ed. 1982. Cons. Surg. Belf. City Hosp.; Postgrad. Clin. Tutor Belf. City Hosp. Socs: Ulster Med. Soc.; Assn. Surg. Gt. Brit. & Irel. Prev: Cons. Surg. Daisy Hill Hosp., Newry N. Irel.; Ho. Off. Roy. Vict. Hosp. Belf.; Clin. Lect. Surg., Univ. Aberd..

IRWIN, William David Baillie Westlawn, Killicomaine, Portadown, Craigavon BT63 5BY — MB BCh BAO 1968 Dub.; MA Dub. 1969, MB BCh BAO 1968. Prev: Med. Off. (Anaesth. & Surg.) Tembisa Hosp. Transvaal, S. Afr.; Ho. Off. (Surg.) & Ho. Off. (Med.) Lurgan & Portadown Hosp.

IRWIN, Professor William George, OBE 29 Old Coach Road, Belfast BT9 5PR Tel: 028 9060 4844 — MB BCh BAO 1948 Belf.; MD Belf. 1969; FRCGP 1972; DObst RCOG 1951. (Queens Univ of Belfast) Prof. Emerit. Qu. Univ. Belf.; Prof. Gen. Pract. Qu's Univ. Belf. 1971-90. Socs: Fell. (Ex-Pres.) Ulster Med. Soc.; BMA - mem, (ex pres E.ern Div. BMA). Prev: Cons. Roy. Vict. Hosp. & Belf. City Hosp.; Prof. Gen. Pract. Qu. Univ. Belf.; Princip. GP Belf.

IRWIN, William John, Col. late RAMC Retd. Red Cottage, Picket Twenty, Andover SP11 6LF Tel: 01264 362948 Email: billandpeggy@hotmail.com — LRCPI & LM, LRCSI & LM 1942; MFCM 1973. Prev: CO Milit. Hosp. Colchester, Brit. Milit. Hosp. Singapore & Milit. Hosp. Tidworth.

ISA, Aidah Yahaya Flat 2/1, 22 Ashley St., Glasgow G3 6DR — MB ChB 1998 Glas.; MB ChB Glas 1998.

ISAAC, Clare Frances Meltham Road Surgery, Lockwood, Huddersfield HD1 3UP Tel: 01484 432940; Hall Ing House, 132 Hall Ing, Honley, Huddersfield HD7 7QX — MB ChB 1982 Leeds; MRCGP 1986; DRCOG 1983. Lect. Univ. Huddersfield. Socs: Hudds. Med. Soc. Prev: Med. Examr. DoH; Princip. GP Ashton-under-Lyne.

ISAAC, David Henry Carisbrooke Health Centre, 22 Carisbrooke Road, Newport PO30 1NR Tel: 01983 522150 Fax: 01983 825902; Snowdrop Cottage, Snowdrop Lane, Gatcombe, Newport PO30 3EQ — MB BS 1983 Lond.; DRCOG 1990. Prev: Trainee GP/SHO (O & G) St. Mary's Hosp. I. of Wight HA VTS; Trainee GP Launceston; Regist. (Geriat. & Gen. Med.) Jersey Gen. Hosp. & Soton Gen. Hosp.

ISAAC, David Llewellyn 36 Biscay Road, Hammersmith, London W6 8JN — MB BS 1996 Lond.

ISAAC, Dawn Caroline Locking Hill Surgery, Locking Hill, Stroud GL5 1UY Tel: 01453 764222; The Old Farmhouse, Beech Lane, Sheepscombe, Gloucester GL6 7QZ Email: dawn@surgerydoor.co.uk — MB BS 1987 Lond.; DFFP Lond. 1995; MRCP Lond. 1993; DCH RCP Lond. 1990. (Charing Cross and Westminster) p/t GP Princip. Prev: Regist. (Med.) Roy. Perth Hosp., Austral.

ISAAC, Derek Herbert (retired) Ridge House, Kenny, Ashill, Ilminster TA19 9NH — MRCS Eng. LRCP Lond. 1946; MD Lond. 1951; MB BS 1946; FRCP Lond. 1972, M 1952. Prev: Cons. Phys. Som. HA.

ISAAC, Dulichand T The Surgery, 95 Tamar Drive, Chelmsley Wood, Birmingham B36 0SY Tel: 0121 749 1313 Fax: 0121 799 3420 — MB BS 1964 Sind; MB BS 1964 Sind.

ISAAC, Geoffrey Rayment (retired) East Thorpe Cottage, 13a Main St., Houghton-on-the-Hill, Leicester LE7 9GE Tel: 0116 241 5955 — MB BS 1955 Lond. Prev: Ho. Surg. Gt. Yarmouth Hosp.

ISAAC, Graham John The Health Centre, Beeches Green, Stroud GL5 4BH Tel: 01453 763980 — MB BS 1985 Lond.; DRCOG 1993; DCH RCP Lond. 1987.

ISAAC, Ian Charles Osborne High Street Surgery, 87 High Street, Abbots Langley WD5 0AJ Tel: 01923 262363 Fax: 01923 267374; Fircroft, 26A Watford Road, Kings Langley WD4 8DY Tel: 01923 266176 Fax: 01923 266176 — MB BS 1981 Lond.; MRCGP 1985; DRCOG 1984. (Univ. Coll. Lond.) Clin. Asst. Elderly Ment. Frail Unit Watford. Socs: Founder Mem. Expert Witness Inst.

ISAAC, Jennifer Parklands Flat, Parklands House, Hound House Road, Shere, Guildford GU5 9JQ — MB BS 1993 Lond.

ISAAC, John Stewart Undercross, Peters Lane, Whiteleaf, Aylesbury HP27 0LQ — MB BS 1970 Lond.; MRCS Eng. LRCP Lond. 1970.

ISAAC, Michael Terence South London & Maudsley NHS Trust, Ladywell Building, University Hospital, Lewisham, London SE13 6LH Tel: 020 8333 3030 Ext: 8490 Fax: 020 8658 2579 Email: misaac@stekel.demon.co.uk; Churchill Clinic, 80 Lambeth Road,

London SE1 Tel: 020 7928 5633 Fax: 020 8658 2579 — MB BS 1982 Lond.; MA Camb. 1982; MRCPsych 1990. Cons. & Sen. Lect. (Psychiat.) Guy's & Lewisham Hosps. UMDS Lond.; Macloghlin Schol. RCS Eng. Socs: Brit. Neuropath. Soc.; Brit. Neuropsychiat. Assn.; Acad. Experts. Prev: Sen. Regist. (Neuropsychiat.) Nat. Hosp. Nerv. Dis. Lond.; Sen. Regist. & Regist. (Psychiat.) Maudsley Hosp. Lond.; MRC Train. Fell. (Neuropath.) Univ. Glas.

ISAAC, Paul William, MBE Down House, Hussell Lane, Medstead, Alton GU34 5PF — MRCS Eng. LRCP Lond. 1939; Nat. Sc. Trip. Pt. 1, cl. II 1935 & Pt. II 1936; MA Camb. 1940, MB BChir 1939. (Camb. & St. Bart.) Surg. Lt. RNVR. Prev: Ho. Surg. St. Bart. Hosp. & Norf. & Norw. Eye Infirm.; Ho. Surg. (O & G) Norf. & Norw. Hosp.

ISAAC, Peter Morland House Surgery, 2 London Road, Wheatley, Oxford OX33 1YJ Tel: 01865 872448 Fax: 01865 874158; Brooks Cottage, Great Haseley, Oxford OX44 7LA Tel: 01844 279606 Fax: 01844 279606 — MB BS 1965 Lond.; MB BS (Hons.) Lond. 1965; MRCP (UK) 1971. (St. Mary's) Prev: Lect. Med. Unit St. Mary's Hosp. Med. Sch. Lond.; Research Fell. Univ. Calif. Med. Centre San Francisco, USA; Scientif. Staff MRC Clin. Pharmacol. Unit Radcliffe Infirm. Oxf.

ISAAC, Raymond Geoffrey 8 Hogarth Way, Hampton TW12 2EL Tel: 020 8979 2972 — MRCS Eng. LRCP Lond. 1943; MFCM 1973; DPH Eng. 1960. (St. Mary's) Med. Ref. Kingston on Thames & Mortlake Crematoria. Prev: Sen. Med. Off. Kingston & Richmond AHA; Med. Off. LCC; Supernum. Paediat. Regist. St. Mary's Hosp. Lond.

ISAAC, Stella The Surgery, 95 Tamar Drive, Chelmsley Wood, Birmingham B36 0SY Tel: 0121 749 1313 Fax: 0121 799 3420 — MB BS 1962 Punjab; MB BS 1962 Punjab.

ISAAC, Timothy Charles Dunstan Medical Centre, 284 Bury Road, Bolton BL2 6AY Tel: 01204 531557 Fax: 01204 364407; 9 Bramdean Avenue, Harwood, Bolton BL2 3HF — MB ChB 1979 Manch.; MRCGP 1984; DRCOG 1983. Socs: Co-Sec. Wigan and Bolton Local Med. Comm.

ISAACS, Anthony Donald 138 Harley Street, London W1N 1AH Tel: 020 7935 1963 Fax: 020 7724 2505 — MB BS Lond. 1954; FRCP Lond. 1980, M 1958; FRCPsych 1976, M 1971; DPM Lond. 1962. (Char. Cross) p/t Dep. Exec. Med. Dir.Florence Nightingale Hosp. Lond. Socs: Fell. Roy. Soc. Med. Prev: Cons. Psychiat. Bethlem Roy. & Maudsley Hosp.; Sub-Dean Inst. Psychiat.; Capt. RAMC.

ISAACS, Anthony John Chelsea and Westminster Hospital, London SW10 9NH; Email: Anthony.isaac@btinternet.com — BM BCh 1968 Oxf.; DFPHM Lond 1999; MA 1968 Oxf; MSc (Pub. Health Med.) Lond. 1992; BA Oxf. 1965; MRCP (UK) 1971; T(M) 1991; FRCP FRCP Lond 1997. (Westm.) p/t Cons. endocrinol Chelsea & W.minster Hosp.; Hon. Cons., Pub. Health Dept., Barnet, Enfield and Haringey Health Auth. Socs: Mem. Soc. Endocrinol.; BMA Mem. Prev: Sen. Princip. Med. Off. DoH; Princip. Med. Off. (Med.) DHSS & Med. Assessor Comm. Safety Meds.; Sen. Regist. (Med.) W.m. Hosp. Lond.

ISAACS, Austin Brett 7 Dovehouse Close, Whitefield, Manchester M45 7PE — MB BS 1992 Lond.

ISAACS, Bernard, CBE (retired) 33 Greville Drive, Birmingham B15 2UU Tel: 0121 440 3418 — MD 1957 Glas.; MD (High Commend.) Glas. 1957, MB ChB 1947; FRCP Ed. 1979, M 1973; FRCP Glas. 1964, M 1962; FRCP Lond. 1985; DObst RCOG 1951. Chas. Hayward Prof. Geriat. Med. Univ. Birm. Prev: Asst. Lect. Dept. Mat. Med. Univ. Glas.

ISAACS, Christopher John 6 Frinton Road, Sidcup DA14 4PR — MB BS 1991 Lond.

ISAACS, Geoffrey Fermoy Unit, QEH, Gayton Road, King's Lynn PE30 4GT Tel: 01553 613714 — MB BS 1980 Lond.; MRCP (UK) 1983; MRCPsych 1985. (St. Bart.) Cons. Psychiat. King's Lynn & Addenbrookes. Prev: Research Worker/Hon. Sen. Regist. (Psychiat.) Char. Cross Hosp. Lond.; Regist. (Psychiat.) Maudsley Hosp. Lond.; Regist. (Med.) N.wick Pk. Hosp. Harrow.

ISAACS, Jeremy Darryl 47 Llanvanor Road, London NW2 2AR — MB BS 1998 Lond.; MB BS Lond 1998.

ISAACS, John Alexander The Surgery, Manlake Avenue, Winterton, Scunthorpe DN15 9TA Tel: 01724 732202 Fax: 01724 734992 — MB ChB 1975 Manch.

ISAACS, John Dudley Molecular Medicine Unit, Clinical Sciences Building, St James's University Hospital, Leeds LS9 7TF Tel: 0113 2065250 Fax: 0113 244 4475 Email: rrrjdi@leeds.ac.uk — MB BS (Hons.) Lond. 1982; PhD Cantab. 1991; BSc (Hons.) Lond. 1979; MRCP (UK) 1985; FRCP (UK) 1998. (St. Geo. Hosp. Med. Sch.) p/t Reader (Rheum.), Univ. of Leeds; Cons. Rheum. Leeds Teachg. Hosps. NHS Trust. Socs: Brit. Soc. Immunol.; Brit. Soc. Rheum.; Amer. Coll. Rheum. Prev: MRC Clin. Scientist (Immunol.) Univ. Camb.; Regist. (Med.) Roy. Postgrad. Med. Sch. Hammersmith Hosp. & Ealing Hosp. Lond.; Resid. (Med.) Beth Israel Hosp. Boston Mass., USA.

ISAACS, John Lucien Department of Radiology, Torbay Hospital, Newton Road, Torquay TQ2 7AA — MB BS 1979 Lond.; MRCP (UK) 1982; FRCR 1986. Cons. Radiol. Prev: Cons.Radiol.Roy.Adelaide Hosp.Aus.

ISAACS, Peter Edward Thomas Gastroenterology Unit, Victoria Hospital, Blackpool FY3 8NR Tel: 01253 303614 Fax: 01253 306936; 6 Central Beach, Lytham St Annes FY8 5LB Tel: 01253 794236 Fax: 01253 794236 Email: 106411.465@compuserve.com — MD 1979 Manch.; MB ChB Manch. 1967; FRCP Lond. 1988; MRCP (UK) 1970. Cons. Phys. Blackpool Vict. Hosp. NHS Trust. Socs: Brit. Soc. Gastroenterol.; Manch. Med. Soc. Prev: Sen. Regist. Guy's Hosp. Lond.; Research Fell. VA Hosp., San Francisco, USA; Research Fell. Manch. Roy. Infirm.

ISAACS, Sarah Louise 17 Insole Gardens, Llandaf, Cardiff CF5 2HW — MB BS 1989 Lond.

ISAACS, Stephen Waltham Forest Child & Family Consultation, Walthamstow, London E17 3EA Tel: 020 8509 0424; 34 The Grove, London N3 1QJ Tel: 020 8346 4507 Fax: 020 8922 4668 Email: msisaacs@btinternet.com — BA (Cantab.) 1072; MB BChir 1975; MRCP (UK) 1979; MRCPsych. 1981. Cons. Child Psychiat. Waltham Forest Child & Family Consult. Serv.; Assoc. Mem. Inst. Psychoanal. Socs: Assn. for Psychoanalytic Psychother. in the NHS. Prev: Sen. Regist. Tavistock & St. Albans Clinics; Regist. Rotat. Maudsley Hosp. Lond.; SHO (Paediat.) Brook Gen. Hosp. Lond. & N.wick Pk. Hosp. Harrow.

ISAACS, Vijayan Ratnaraj Compton Health Centre, High Street, Shaw, Oldham OL2 8ST Tel: 01706 842511 Fax: 01706 847106 — MB BS 1960 Bombay. (Grant Med. Coll. Bombay) Prev: Res. Surg. Off. Oldham & Dist. Gen. Hosp.

ISAACSON, David Mark 9 Hillingdon Road, Whitefield, Manchester M45 7QQ — MB ChB 1990 Birm.

ISAACSON, Henry Percy (retired) Cascades, Kemnal Road, Chislehurst BR7 6LY Tel: 020 8467 1925 — MB BCh BAO 1949 Dub. Prev: Capt. RAMC.

ISAACSON, Jennifer Rosemary (retired) — MB BS 1966 Lond.; MRCS Eng. LRCP Lond. 1965; DObst RCOG 1968; Dip. Ven. Soc. Apoth. Lond. 1975. Cons. (Genito-Urin. Med.) Roy. Berks. Hosp. Reading. Prev: Ho. Surg. (O & G) & Ho. Phys. Lewisham Hosp. Lond.

ISAACSON, Professor Peter Gersohn Department Histopathology, University College Medical School, University St., London WC1E 6JJ Tel: 0207 679 6045 Fax: 0207 387 3674 Email: p.isaacson@ucl.ac.uk — MB ChB 1960 Cape Town; DSc. (Med.) Lond. Univ. 1991; DM Soton 1980; FRCPath 1984, M 1972. (Cape Town) Prof. Morbid Anat. Univ. Coll. Lond. Med. Sch. Prev: Reader (Path.) Univ. Soton. Med. Sch.

ISAACSON, Robert Colney Hatch Lane Surgery, 192 Colney Hatch Lane, Muswell Hill, London N10 1ET Tel: 020 8883 5877/5555 — MB BS 1978 Lond.; DRCOG 1982.

ISALSKA, Barbara Jadwiga Department of Microbiology, Wythenshawe Hospital, Southmoor Road, Manchester M23 9LT Tel: 0161 291 2885 Fax: 0161 291 2125 Email: barbara.isalska@smuht.nwest.nhs.uk; 29 Grosvenor Road, Sale M33 6NJ — MB ChB 1978 Manch.; BSc (Hons.) Manch. 1975; MRCPath 1991; FRCPath 2000. Cons. Microbiol. Wythenshawe Hosp. Manch. Socs: CPD Panel Jl. Clin. Path.; Assn. Of Clin. Path. (Counc. Mem., and Vice Chair MicroBiol. Comm.).

ISASA FINO, Irma Flat 13, St Mary's Hospital, Milton Road, Portsmouth PO3 6AD Tel: 023 92 286000 — LMS 1994 Basque Provinces. (University Basque) Regist. (Psychiat.).

ISBISTER, Andrew Richard Watercress Medical Group, Dean Surgery, Ropley, Alresford SO24 0BQ Tel: 01962 772340 Fax: 01962 772551 Email: andrew.isbister@gp-j82059.nhs.uk; The

Chimney House, 7 Alison Way, Orams Mount, Winchester SO24 0ED Tel: 01962 859868 — MB BS 1982 Lond.; DCH RCP Lond. 1986; DRCOG 1985; Cert. Family Plann. JCC 1985. (Charing Cross Hospital Medical School) Prev: Trainee GP Winchester VTS; Ho. Phys. Char. Cross. Hosp. Lond.; Ho. Surg. Worthing & S.lands Hosp. Sussex.

ISBISTER, Mr Eric Sutherland Orthopaedic Dept, Newcross Hospital, Wolverhampton WV10 0QP — MB ChB 1982 Glas.; BSc Glas. 1979, MB ChB 1982; FRCS Orth. 1993; FRCS Glas. 1986. Cons. Trauma & Orthop. Roy. Wolverhampton Hosps. NHS Trust. Socs: Brit. Orthop. Assn.

ISBISTER, Gordon Ian Reform Street Health Centre, Reform Street, Beith KA15 2AE Tel: 01505 502888 Fax: 01505 504151; 22 Glebe Road, Beith KA15 1EY — MB ChB 1980 Dundee. Clin. Asst. (Gen. Med.) CrossHo. Hosp. Kilmarnock. Prev: Regist. (Med.) Inverclyde Roy. Hosp. Greenock; SHO (Obst.) Ayrsh. Centr. Hosp. Irvine; SHO (Oncol.) Gtr. Glas. Health Bd.

ISBISTER, Mr John Foster St Clair (retired) 19 Melville Terrace, Stirling FK8 2NQ Tel: 01786 474508 Fax: 01786 445669 — MB ChB 1958 Glas.; FRCS Glas. 1968. Cons. Orthop. Surg. Stirling Roy. Infirm. Prev: Sen. Regist. (Orthop. & Accid.) Glas. Roy. Infirm.

ISENBERG, Professor David Alan Centre for Rheumatology/Bloomsbury Rheumatology Unit, Department of Medicine, Arthur Stanley House, Tottenham, The Middlesex Hospital, London W1P 9PG Tel: 020 7380 9230 Fax: 020 7380 9357 — MB BS 1973 Lond.; MD Lond. 1984; FRCP Lond. 1990; MRCP (UK) 1976; MRCS Eng. LRCP Lond. 1973. (St Barts) ARC Diamond Jubilee Prof. Rheum. Univ. Coll. Lond. Socs: Brit. Soc. Rheum.; Brit. Soc. Immunol.; Amer. Coll. Rheum. Prev: Cons. Rheum. Univ. Coll. Hosp. & Middlx. Hosp. Lond.; Sir Jules Thorne Research Fell. Univ. Coll. Hosp. Lond. & Middlx. Hosp. Lond.

ISENBERG, Harry (retired) 5 Totnes Walk, Finchley, London N2 0AD Tel: 020 8883 4439 Fax: 020 8444 8348 — MB BS 1942 Lond.; MRCS Eng. LRCP Lond. 1942; DCH Eng. 1947.

ISENBERG, Lesley Anne Baronsmere Road Surgery, 39 Baronsmere Road, East Finchley, London N2 9QD Tel: 020 8883 1458 Fax: 020 883 8854 — MB BCh 1974 Wales; MRCP (UK) 1977; MRCGP 1981.

ISERLOH, Hermann Josef 11 Audley Street, Mossley, Ashton-under-Lyne OL5 9NQ — State Exam Med 1993 Essen.

ISH-HOROWICZ, Miriam Rachel The Surgery, 117 Norwood Road, Herne Hill, London SE24 9AE Tel: 020 8674 5400 Fax: 020 8678 5405 — MB ChB 1981 Manch.; BSc (Hons. Psychol.) Manch. 197; MRCP (UK) 1990; DRCOG 1991.

ISHAG, Adam Mohamed Clacton and District Hospital, Tower Road, Clacton-on-Sea CO15 1LH — MB BS 1977 Khartoum; MRCP (UK) 1991.

ISHAK, Magdy Adib 9 West Chapleton Crescent, Bearsden, Glasgow G62 2DE; 8a Camstradden Drive E., Bearsden, Glasgow G61 4AH Email: drmishak@dircon.co.uk — MB BCh 1972 Ain Shams. Chief Exec. & Clin. Dir. Brain injury Rehal. Serv.

ISHAK, Magdy Kamel 22 Mountbatten Avenue, Sandal, Wakefield WF2 6EZ — MB BCh 1972 Assiut; MRCOG 1982; DO RCPSI 1978.

***ISHAM, Claire** Quelimane, 23 Mont-es-Croix, St Brelade, Jersey JE3 8EL — MB ChB 1996 Birm.

ISHAQ, Azmat Samina 231 Ramsay Road, Forest Gate, London E7 9ES — MB BS 1986 Lond.

ISHAQ, Mohammad The National Institute of Cardiovascular Diseases, Rafique Shaheed Road, Karachi 75510, Pakistan Tel: 00 92 21 920 1271 Fax: 00 92 21 920 1287; c/o Mrs Z. A Bati, 4 Prince Edwards Mansion, Hereford Road, London W2 Tel: 020 7229 7567 — MB BS 1973 Peshawar; BSc Peshawar 1967; FRCP Ed. 1994; FRCP Glas. 1994; MRCP (UK) 1984; FACC (Assoc.) 1993. (Khyber Med. Coll. Peshawar, Pakistan) Assoc. Prof. Cardiol. & Cons. Cardiol. Nat. Inst. Cardiovasc. Dis. Karachi, Pakistan; Sen. Lect. & Hon. Cons. Phys. & Cardiol. Aga Khan Univ. Hosp., Karachi. Socs: Pakistan Cardiac Soc. (Life Mem.); Pakistan Soc. Phys. (Life Mem.); Amer. Soc. Echo-Cardiogr. Prev: Regist. (Cardiol.) W.. Infirm. Glas.; Cons. (Cardiol.) Wharfedale Gen Hosp., Leeds.

ISHAQ, Sauid 15 Staff Residences, North Staffordshire Hospital, City General Hospital, Hilton Road, Stoke-on-Trent ST4 6SE — MB BS 1986 Bahauddin Zakariya U, Pakistan; MRCP (UK) 1992.

ISHAQUE, Joanne Sara (McCulloch) The Randolph Surgery, 235A Elgin Avenue, London W9 1NH; 6A High Gate, West Hill, London N6 6JR — MB BS 1994 Lond.; BSc Biochem. Lond. 1991; Dip Child Health (RCP) 1998; Dip. Of Roy Coll Obst & Gyn 1998; DFFP 1998. (Univ. Coll. & Middlesex Sch. Of Medzie) GP Princip. Randolph Surg. Prev: GP Regist., Kentish Town Health Care Centre.

ISHAQUE, Mohammed (retired) Padgate Medical Centre, 12 Station Road, Padgate, Warrington WA2 0RX Tel: 01925 815333 — MB BS 1954 Calcutta. Prev: Regist. (Med.) Roy. Albert Edwd. Infirm. Wigan & S.port Gen. Infirm.

ISHAQUE, Mohammed 1 Firs Park Crescent, Hall Lane, Aspull, Wigan WN2 2SJ; 112 Market Street, Hindley, Wigan WN2 3AZ Tel: 01942 55146 — MB BS 1962 Karachi; BSc Karachi 1955, MB BS 1962. (Dow Med. Coll. Karachi) Socs: BMA. Prev: SHO Alder Hey Childr. Hosp. Liverp.; Ho. Phys. Paediat. St. Stephen's Hosp. Lond.; Ho. Surg. E. Glam. Hosp. Pontypridd.

ISHAQUE, Mushtaque Ahmad 30 Clayhall Avenue, Ilford IG5 0LG Tel: 020 8550 0882 Fax: 020 8551 1447; Flat 12 Quadrangle Mews, Off Belmont Lane, Stanmore HA7 2PW Tel: 020 8954 4039 — MB BChir 1992 Camb.; MA Camb. 1996; BSc (1st cl. Hons) Lond. 1989. (Univ. Camb.) SHO Roy. Nat. Orthop. Hosp. Stanmore, Middlx. Socs: Fell. Roy. Soc. Med.; BMA. Prev: Resid. Med. Off. King Edwd. VII's. Hosp. Offs. Lond.; SHO (Gen. Surg.) Hemel Hempstead Gen. Hosp.; SHO (Neurosurg.) Nat. Hosp. Neurol. & Neurosurg. Lond.

ISHERWOOD, Charles Nicholas 27 Woodplumpton Lane, Broughton, Preston PR3 5JJ — MB ChB 1970 Liverp.; MRCP (U.K.) 1974; FFA RCS Eng. 1979; DObst RCOG 1972. Cons. Anaesth. Roy. Preston Hosp.

ISHERWOOD, David Louis 121 Thornton Road, Cambridge CB3 0NE — MB 1976 Camb.; BChir 1975.

ISHERWOOD, Dawn Murray, Kirkham and Isherwood, Surgery, Lockwood Avenue, Poulton-le-Fylde FY6 7AB Tel: 01253 886878 Fax: 01253 896670 — MB ChB 1989 Leeds; DRCOG 1993. Prev: Trainee GP/SHO (O & G) Leighton Hosp. Crewe VTS.

ISHERWOOD, Professor Ian, CBE Woodend House, Strines Road, Disley, Stockport SK6 7GY Tel: 01663 764980 Fax: 01663 766498 Email: ian.isherwood@man.ac.uk; Woodend House, Strines Rd, Disley, Stockport SK6 7GY Tel: 01663 764980 Fax: 01663 766498 Email: ian.isherwood@man.ac.uk — MB ChB 1954 Manch.; 1995 Hon. Academician Russian Acad. & Med. Sci.; FACR 1999 (Hon.) US; Hon. MD Zaragoza 1984; FRCP Lond. 1986; MRCP (UK) 1977; Hon. FFR RCSI 1981; FRCR 1975; FFR 1960; DMRD Eng. 1957. (Manch.) Emerit. Prof. of Diagnostic Radiol., Univ. of Manch.; Hon med librarian Manch. med soc; Chairm. med library comm.Univ of Manch.; Vice pres The Roy. Inst.; Chairm. Radiol. Hist. & heritage charitable trust. Socs: (Ex-Pres.) Brit. Inst. Radiol.; (Ex-Pres.) Europ. Assn. Radiol.; (Ex-Pres.)Radiol Sect. RSM. Prev: Cons. Radiol. Centr. Manch. & Derby Hosp. Gp.; Sen. Regist. (Radiol.) & Ho. Surg. & Ho. Phys. Manch. Roy. Infirm.

ISHERWOOD, James Bootham Park Hospital, Bootham, York YO30 7BY — MB ChB 1986 Leeds; MRCPsych 1991. Cons. Psychiat. (Forens. Psychiat.) Bootham Pk. Hosp. York. Prev: Sen. Regist. (Forens. Psychiat.) Knowle Hosp. Fareham; Regist. & SHO (Psychiat.) Bootham Pk. Hosp. York; SHO (Psychiat.) Clifton Hosp. York.

ISHERWOOD, Jonathan Peter The Medical Centre, Butts Road, Bakewell, Derby DE45 1ED Tel: 01629 812871; 18 Castle Mount Crescent, Bakewell, Derby DE45 1AT — MB BS 1983 Lond.; MRCGP 1987.

ISHERWOOD, Melanie Jane Flat 13, The Hollies, Oakwood Avenue, Gatley, Cheadle SK8 4NS — BM BCh 1986 Oxf.; MA Oxf. 1987.

ISHERWOOD, Sarah Camille The Bracton Centre, Bexley Hospital, Old Bexley Lane, Bexley DA5 2BW — MB BS 1992 Lond.; MRCPsych 1986. (King's Coll. Lond.)

ISIBOR, Felix Osayanuyi Flat 1 Addison House, Eastbourne District General Hospital, Kings Drive, Eastbourne BN21 2UD — MB BS 1976 Ibadan.

ISITT, Timothy Vaughan Tristram Department of Anaesthetics, Middlesex Hospital, London W1; 159 Verulam Road, St Albans AL3 4DW Tel: 01727 852289 — MB BS 1986 Lond.; MRCP (UK) 1989; FRCA 1996; DA (UK) 1994.

ISKANDER, Atef Zaki Department of Obstetrics & Gynaecology, Ipswich Hospital, Heath Road, Ipswich IP4 5PD — MB BCh 1978 Ain Shams; MRCOG 1994.

ISKANDER, Colin Marcus (retired) Whitley House Surgery, Moulsham St., Chelmsford CM2 0JJ Tel: 01245 352194 Fax: 01245 344478 — MB ChB 1960 St. And.; FRCGP 1991, M 1981; DObst RCOG 1962. Prev: GP Princip., Chelmsford.

ISKANDER, Laila Shafik Farid Cytopathology Department, Warrington Hospital, Lovely Lane, Warrington WA5 1QG — MB BCh 1973 Cairo; DTM & H 1978; DCP 1984; Phd 1989. Clin. Asst. Cytopath. Dept Warrington Hosp.

ISKANDER, Mohsen Naguib Southport District General Hospital, Town Lanse, Southport PR8 6PN Tel: 01704 577471 Fax: 01704 704636 Email: mohsen.iskander@mail.soh-tr.nwest.nhs.uk — MB BCh 1969 Cairo; FRCOG 1989; MRCOG 1976. Cons. Obst. and gyneacologist S.port & Ormskirk Hosp.; head of Obst. and gyneacologist dept S.port & Ormskirk. Socs: Internat. Continence Soc.; Internat. Urogyn. Assn.; Brit. Soc. Colpos. & Cerv. Path. Prev: Cons. O & G Kuwait Oil Co.

ISKANDER, Mr Nagy Yousef 31 Elm View, Steeton, Keighley BD20 6SZ Tel: 01535 654324 — MB BCh 1980 Ain Shams; FRCS Glas. 1993; FRCS Eng. 1992.

ISKANDER, Samir Youssef The Lomond Practice, Napier Road, Glenrothes KY6 1HL Tel: 01592 611000 Fax: 01592 611639 — MB BCh 1976 Ain Shams. (Ain Shams) GP Glenrothes, Fife.

ISKANDER-GABRA, Samira Daoud 48 St Peter's Road, Harborne, Birmingham B17 0AY — MB BCh 1961 Cairo; Dip. Med. Cairo 1964; MRCP (UK) 1977; LRCP LRCS Ed. LRCPS Glas. 1979. (Cairo Univ.) Med. Pract. (Clin. Genetics) Regional Genetics Servs. Birm. Wom. Hosp. Socs: Roy. Coll. Phys. Ed. & Lond. Prev: Clin. Asst. (Haemat.) S.. Gen. Hosp. Glas.; Regist. (Haemat.) Law Hosp.

ISLAM, Abul Kalam Md Serajul Department of Medical Microbiology, Whipps Cross Hospital, Whipps Cross Road Leytonstone, London E11 1NR Tel: 020 8539 5522 — MB BS 1956 Dacca; FRCPath 1983, M 1971; Dip. Bact. Lond 1971; DCP Punjab 1964. (Dacca Med. Coll.) Cons. (Med. Microbiol.) N.E. Thames RHA.

ISLAM, Asim Mohammad 21 Bradwell Close, Charlton, Andover SP10 4EL — MB 1987 Camb.; BChir 1986.

ISLAM, Badrul Sharrow Lane Surgery, 129 Sharrow Lane, Sheffield S11 8AN Tel: 0114 255 6600; 74 Ivy Park Road, Sheffield S10 3LD Tel: 0114 230 9881 Email: badar@thefridge.prestel.co.uk — MB BS 1971 Kanpur; MS (Orthop. Surg.) Delhi 1974. (GSVM) GP; Disabil. Analyst (Benefit Agency). Socs: BMA. Prev: GP Glas.; Regist. (Psychiat.) Hartwood Hosp. Lanarksh.; Regist. (Orthop. & Cas.) Hairmyres Hosp. E. Kilbride.

ISLAM, Carol Heather 3GR St John's Road, Gourock PA19 1PL Tel: 01475 631855 — MB ChB 1995 Manch.; BSc (Med. Sci.) St. And. 1992. SHO (O & G) Tameside Gen. Hosp. Prev: SHO (Gen. Med.) Ormskirk Dist. Gen. Hosp.

ISLAM, Chowdhury Omar Farouk 78 Dene Road, Didsbury, Manchester M20 2SU Tel: 0161 445 6617 — MB BS 1998 Lond.; MB BS Lond 1998; BA 1995. (St Marys) PRHO Med. St Marys Hosp. Paddington; SHO Med. Exeter Hosp. Prev: PRHO Surg.Qu. Alexandra hosp.portsmouth.

ISLAM, Ghazala c/o Mr Sidiqui, 8 Holcroft House, Ingrave St., London SW11 2SG — MB BS 1969 Karachi.

ISLAM, Gousul The Surgery, Lyndhurst, Church Road, Stainforth, Doncaster DN7 5PW Tel: 01302 841507 Fax: 01302 350545; 59 Station Road, Hatfield, Doncaster DN7 6QN Tel: 01302 843015 — MB BS 1967 Dacca; DA Eng. 1971. (Dhaka Med. Coll.) GP Princip. Doncaster Health Auth. Prev: Regist. (Anaesth.) Qu. Charlotte's Matern. Hosp. Lond.; Ho. Off. (Paediat. Surg.) Roy. Aberd. Childr. Hosp.; Ho. Off. (Obst.) Aberd. Matern. Hosp.

ISLAM, Mr Haroon Rafi Ul 4B Western Avenue, Perth PH1 1NY — MB BS 1981 Punjab; FRCSI 1989.

***ISLAM, Kabirul** 2 Hall Cr, Rotherham S60 3LQ Tel: 01709 379368 — BM BS 1997 Nottm.; BMedSci Nottm. 1995.

ISLAM, Md Ashraful Chartwell House, Mulberry NHS Trust, Pinfold Road, Bourne PE10 9HT Tel: 01778 422171; 11 Astor Drive, Moseley, Birmingham B13 9QR Tel: 0121 778 2829 — MB BS 1959 Dacca. (Dacca Med. Coll.) Assoc. Specialist (Ment. Handicap) Mulberry NHS Trust Bourne.

ISLAM, Md Shamsul The Surgery, Blaenavon NP4 9AG Tel: 01495 790264 — MB BS 1963 Dhaka; DObst RCPSI 1981. (Chittagong Med. Coll.) Socs: BMA. Prev: Regist. (Psychiat.) Morgannwg Hosp. Bridgend; SHO (Psychiat.) Morgannwg Hosp. Bridgend; Resid. Surg. (O & G) Dhaka Med. Coll. Hosp.

ISLAM, Md Towfique Department of Anaesthetics, St Thomas' Hospital, Lambeth Palace Road, London SE1 7EH — MB BS 1983 Dacca.

ISLAM, Mohamed Badrul 2 Hall Crescent, Rotherham S60 3LQ Tel: 01709 79368 — MB BS 1963 Dacca.

ISLAM, Mohammed Anwarul 1 Angel Court, Marton Road, Middlesbrough TS4 2EY Tel: 01642 247359 — MB BS 1968 Dacca; Dip. Ven. Liverp. 1970; DTM & H Liverp. 1970. (Dacca Med. Coll.) Regist. Med. Unit N. Ormesby Hosp. Middlesbrough.

ISLAM, Mohammed Nazrul Keldregate Surgery, 268 Keldregate, Deighton, Huddersfield HD2 1LE Tel: 01484 532399 — MB BS 1958 Dacca; DO Eng. 1969. (Dacca) Med. Asst. Ophth. N. Middlx. Hosp. Edmonton; Clin. Asst. Ophth. St. Bart. Hosp. Lond. Prev: Ophth. SHO Vict. Hosp. Blackpool.

ISLAM, Mohammed Niazul 7 Parkway, Southgate, London N14 6QU Email: nislam8@hotmail.com — MB BS 1996 Lond.; BSc (Hons.) Lond. 1993. (UMDS) SHO (Ophth.)St. Thomas'. Prev: SHO (Ophth) Roy. Lond Hosp.

ISLAM, Mohammed Shamsul Artane Medical Centre, 1 Middleton Road, Higher Crumpsall, Manchester M8 5SA Tel: 0161 740 2785 Fax: 0161 740 0399; 9 Braemore Drive, Harryfields, Broadborrom, Hyde SK14 6JX — MB BS 1965 Dacca; MRCGP 1982. (Dacca Med. Coll.) Socs: RSM & BMA. Prev: SHO (Geriat. Med.) Oldham & Dist. Gen. Hosp.; Cas. Off. A & E Dept. Roy. Halifax Infirm.; Med. Off. Pakistan Ordnance Facts. Hosp. Rawalpindi, Pakistan.

ISLAM, Muhammad Hafizul Yorkshire Street Health Centre, Yorkshire Street, Bacup OL13 9AE Tel: 01706 876644; Nirala, 50 Cowtoot Lane, Bacup OL13 8ED Tel: 01706 876628 — MB BS Dacca 1962; DA Eng. 1969. (Dacca Med. Coll.) Clin. Asst. (Anaesth.) Burnley Gen. Hosp. Socs: BMA; BDMA. Prev: Regist. (Anaesth.) Salford Gp. Hosps. & Vict. Hosp. Blackpool.

ISLAM, Muhammad Salim 9 Wenlock Road, Brooklands, Sale, Manchester M33 3TR Email: salimislam@hotmail.com — MB BS 1996 Lond. (Roy. Free Hosp. Sch. of Med.)

ISLAM, Nazrul 5 Acrefield, Blackburn BB2 7BJ Tel: 01254 672952 — MB BS Dacca 1967. Assoc. Specialist Learning Disabil. Serv. Calderstone NHS Trust Whalley Clitheroe BB7 9PE. Socs: Def. Union of Scotl.

ISLAM, Nizamul 11 Astor Drive, Birmingham B13 9QR — BM BS 1990 Nottm.

ISLAM, Saeed The Priory Hospital, Priory Lane, London SW15 5JJ; 7 Rokeby Place, Copse Hill, Wimbledon, London SW20 0HU — MB BS 1972 Sind; FRCPsych 1997, M 1979; DPM Eng. 1977. (Liaquat Med. Coll., Pakistan) Cons. Psychiat. Priory Hosp. Lond.; Vis. Cons. Psychiat. Aga Khan Med. Univ. Karachi, Pakistan & K. Edwd. VII Hosp Midhurst; Cons. Psychiat., Pk.side Hosp., Wimbledon, Lond. Socs: Fell. Roy. Soc. Med. Prev: Sen. Regist. (Psychiat.) W.m. Hosp. Lond.; Regist. (Psychiat.) Qu. Mary's Hosp. Lond.; SHO (Chest Dis.) Gr. Pk. Hosp. Lewisham.

ISLAM, Surat Flat 5, 23 Queens Road, Southport PR9 9HN Tel: 01704 533206 — MB BS 1970 Dacca; MB BS Dacca, Bangladesh 1970.

ISLAM, Tahmina 9 Braemore Drive, Marryfields, Broadbottom, Hyde SK14 6JX — MB ChB 1993 Manch.

ISLAM, Tina Mahzabin 61 Clayhall Av, Ilford IG5 0PW — MB BS 1997 Lond.

ISLAM, Vanessa 45 Abbotshall Avenue, London N14 7JU — MB BS 1996 Lond.

ISLAM, Mr Zia Ul Glebe Medical Centre, Abbeygreen, Lesmahagow, Lanark ML11 0EF Tel: 01555 892328 Fax: 01555 894094; 100 Strathaven Road, Lesmahagon, Lanark ML11 0DW — MB BS 1984 Karachi; FRCS Ed. 1992; FRCSI 1992.

ISLAMULLAH, Muhammad 14 Manor Farm Road, Alperton, Wembley HA0 1AD — MB BS 1965 Karachi; DO RCPSI 1977.

ISLES, Christopher Geoffrey Glebe House, Kirkmahoe, Dumfries DG1 1SY — MD 1988 Glas.; MB ChB 1976; MRCP (UK) 1979; FRCPS Glas. 1991. Cons. Phys. Dumfries & Galloway Roy. Infirm. Prev: Sen. Med. Off. Non Europ. Hosp. Johannesburg S. Africa.

ISLES, Flora Elizabeth (retired) Gardenhurst, Newbigging, Broughty Ferry, Dundee DD5 3RH Tel: 01382 370315 Email: flora.honeywood@btinternet.com — MB ChB Ed. 1960. Prev: SCMO Dundee Healthcare NHS Trust.

ISLES, Matthew Geraint Tyddyn, Tre-R-Ddol, Machynlleth SY20 8QD — MB BS 1997 Lond.

ISLES, Rosaleen Mary Glebe House, Kirkmahoe, Dumfries DG1 1SY — MB ChB 1975 Glas.; MRCGP 1979; DRCOG 1977. Prev: GP Soweto Health Clinics S. Africa.

ISLIP, John Christopher Emirates Clinic, PO Box 26777, Dubai, United Arab Emirates Tel: 00 971 4 391229 Fax: 00 971 4 311237 Email: josoph@emirates.net; The Red House, 4A Southway, Harrogate HG2 0EA — MB ChB 1971 St. And. Socs: Emirates Med. Soc. Dubai, UAE. Prev: GP Riyadh Milit. Hosp. Kingdom Saudi Arabia; Stud. Health Serv. Univ. Leicester; Med. Resid. Vict. Gen. Hosp. Halifax, Nova Scotia, Canada.

ISLIP, Martin Roy Tinshill Lane Surgery, 8 Tinshill Lane, Leeds LS16 7AP Tel: 0113 267 3462 Fax: 0113 230 0402; The Chase, Kenwood Mews, Outwood Lane, Horsforth, Leeds LS18 4HR Email: martin.islip@dial.pipex.com — MB ChB 1974 Leeds; BSc (Hons. Physiol.) Leeds 1971; MRCGP 1979. (Leeds) GP Tutor (Continuing Med. Educat.) Leeds.

ISMAIEL, Mr Aly Hany Mohammed Aly Prince Charles, Merthyr Tydfil Tel: 01685 721721; 3 Lodge Close, Chigwell IG7 6JL Tel: 020 8500 4632 Fax: 020 8500 4632 Email: hany@ismaiel.demon.co.uk — MB BCh Ain Shams 1980; MSc (Orth.) Ain Shams 1986; FRCS Glas. 1990.

ISMAIL, Abbas Adel 4 Chevet Lane, Sandal, Wakefield WF2 6HL — MB BS 1989 Lond.

ISMAIL, Abdul Halim Ismail Mohammed 18 Rhylstone Mount, Bradford BD7 2QB — MB BS 1982 Khartoum; MRCP (UK) 1992; MRCPI 1991.

ISMAIL, Adam Poplars Surgery, 17 Holly Lane, Erdington, Birmingham B24 9JN Tel: 0121 373 4216 Fax: 0121 382 9576; 5 Churchover Close, Wylde Green, Sutton, Sutton Coldfield B76 1WG — MB ChB 1992 Manch.

ISMAIL, Mr Adel Mahmoud 35 Ravenswood Road, Wilmslow SK9 6HL — MB BCh 1976 Ain Shams; FRCS Glas. 1985.

ISMAIL, Mr Ahmad Mobeen 1-1 Sienna Gardens, Edinburgh EH9 1PF — MB BS 1986 Peshawar; FRCS Ed. 1992.

ISMAIL, Mr Ahmed Hussain (profess.) 28A Queenscourt, Queensway, Bayswater, London W2 4QN Tel: 020 7229 7659, 077 4094 4473 Fax: 020 7727 6005, 0207 229 7659; Tel: 020 7229 7659 — MB BCh 1972 Cairo; BSc Cairo 1972; MRCOG 1980, London; FRCOG 1996 London; Cert. Family Plann. JCC 1979. (Cairo) Cons. O & G Lond.; Chairm. of Bd. of Directors; Head of Obs.& Gyn. Dept.; Head of InFertil. Dept.; Head of IVF/ICSI Dept.; Egyptian Brit. Hosp. Cairo; Hawwa Internat. Hosp. Cairo. Socs: Brit. Fertil. Soc. Prev: Cons. O & G Hereford Co. Hosp.; Egyptian/Brit. Hosp. Cairo; Hawwa Int. Hosp. Cairo.

ISMAIL, Andre Rafique 10 Clifton Avenue, London N3 1BN — MB BS 1996 Lond.

ISMAIL, Farhana 26 Clarelawn Avenue, East Sheen, London SW14 8BG — MB BS 1987 Lond.; MB BS Lond. SHO (Anaesth.) St. Geo. Hosp. Lond.

ISMAIL, Fathuma Ferina 38 Anmersh Grove, Stanmore HA7 1PA — MB BS 1998 Lond.; MB BS Lond 1998.

ISMAIL, Hana 54 Osidge Lane, London N14 5JG — BM BS 1992 Nottm.

ISMAIL, Hanan Abd Al Rasul El Ali Lower Dean House, Hexham General Hospital, Hexham NE46 1QJ — MB ChB 1981 Baghdad.

ISMAIL, Hasnaa 54 Osidge La, London N14 5JG — BM 1997 Soton.

ISMAIL, Ida Suzani House 142, 30 Kingsway Court, Scoutston, Glasgow G14 9TJ — MB ChB 1997 Glas.

ISMAIL, Mr Ismail Hamdy Mohamed 54 Osidge Lane, Southgate, London N14 5JG; (profess.), 97 Hampden Way, Southgate, London N14 5AU Tel: 020 8368 5995 — MB BCh 1958 Cairo; DS Cairo 1964, MB BCh 1958; FRCS Ed. 1972; DPMSA Lond. 1980; LicAc 1981; Dip. Genitourin Surg. Cairo 1967, Dip. Surg. 1964. (Lond.)

ISMAIL, Khalid South Lewisham Health Centre, 50 Conisborough Crescent, London SE6 2SP — MB ChB 1984 Ed.

ISMAIL, Khalida 42 Sutherland Avenue, London W9 2HQ — MB BCh 1989 Oxf.; BA (Hons.) Oxf., MB BCh 1989; MRCP (UK) 1992. SHO (Psychiat.) Maudsley Hosp. Lond. Prev: SHO (Med.) Qu. Med. Centre Univ. Hosp. Nottm.

ISMAIL, Misbah Hanoom Mohd X-Ray Department, Queen Marys Hospital, Frognal Avenue, Sidcup DA14 6LT — MB BS 1983 Malaya.

ISMAIL, Muhammad 39 Dunholme Road, Newcastle upon Tyne NE4 6XD Tel: 0151 426 4835 — MB BS 1977 Punjab.

ISMAIL, Sa'Aoah 27/7 St Mungo Place, St Mungo Avenue, Glasgow G4 0PB — MB ChB 1990 Glas.

ISMAIL, Salim Lichfield Street Surgery, 19 Lichfield Street, Walsall WS1 1UG Tel: 01922 20532 Fax: 01922 616605 — MB ChB 1988 Dundee.

ISMAIL, Salim Khodher Department of Paediatrics, Royal Aberdeen Childrens Hospital, Cornhill Road, Aberdeen AB25 2ZG — MB ChB 1976 Mosul, Iraq; MRCP (UK) 1985.

ISMAIL, Sarah Medway Hospital, NHS Trust, Windmill Road, Gullingham ME7 5NY Tel: 01634 825173 — MB BS 1985 Lond.; MRCP Lond. 1991; FRCPCH. p/t Cons. Community Paediat.; Hon. Cons. Guys & St. Thos. NHS Trust. Socs: RCP; BACCH.

ISMAIL, Sezgin Mehmet Department of Pathology, University of wales College of Medicine, Heath Park, Cardiff CF14 4XN Tel: 029 2074 2707 — MB ChB 1976 Bristol; MRCP (UK) 1980; MRCPath 1984. Sen. Lect. (Path.) & Hon. Cons. Univ. Wales Coll. Med. Cardiff.

ISMAIL, Shenaz North Staffordshire Royal Infirmary, Department A & E, Princes Road, Hartshill, Stoke-on-Trent ST4 7LN — MB BCh 1993 Witwatersrand.

ISMAIL, Mr Tariq 19 Yew Tree Road, Edgbaston, Birmingham B15 2LX Fax: 0121 627 8691 Email: tariq.ismail@universittr.wmids.nhs.uk; Tel: 01484 549609 — MB BCh 1982 Wales; FRCS (Lond.) 2001; MD (Distinc.) Wales 1992; FRCS Ed. 1986. Cons. Gen. Surg. (Surgic. Oncol.) Birm.; Hon. Snr. Lect., Univ. Birm.; Surgic. Tutor, Selly Oak Hosp. Prev: Sen. Regist. (Surg.) Qu. Eliz. Hosp. Birm.

ISMAIL, Mr Wael Waheed Mustafa Harold Wood Hospital, Romford RM3 0BE — MB BCh 1975 Ain Shams; FRCS RCPS Glas. 1988.

ISMAIL, Yasmin 4 Chevet La, Wakefield WF2 6HL — MB ChB 1997 Bristol.

ISMAILI, Jamil Anwar 51 Steeple Heights Drive, Biggin Hill, Westerham TN16 3UN — MB BS 1998 Lond.; MB BS Lond 1998.

ISMAILI, Professor Noorali, Col. late RAMC 51 Steeple Heights Drive, Biggin Hill, Westerham TN16 3UN Tel: 01959 570053 Fax: 01276 604106; Surgical Department, Frimely Park Hospital, Portsmouth Road, Frimley, Camberley GU16 7UJ — MB BS Karachi 1964; FRCS Eng. 1974; T (S) 1991; SPR (GMC). (Dow Med. Coll.) Cons. Surg. HM Forces; Cons. Surg. Frimley Pk. Hosp. Surrey; Cons. Surg. T.P.M. Hosp. RAF Akrotiri, Cyprus; Hon. Prof. In Surg.. Baqai Univ. Karachi, Pakistan. Socs: FICS 1994. Prev: Hon. Lect. St. Barts. Hosp. Lond.; Hon. Lect. Guys Hosp. Lond. Sen. Specialist (Gen. Surg.) RAMC.

ISMAILJEE, Fatima 6 Stoneyfield Gardens, Edgware HA8 9SP — MB BS 1994 Lond.

ISON, Esme Balmoral Surgery, 1 Victoria Road, Deal CT14 7AU Tel: 01304 373444 — MB ChB 1989 Witwatersrand.

ISOPESCU, Glynis Ann 84 Maes-Ty-Canol, Port Talbot SA12 8UP Tel: 01639 821161 — MB BChir 1989 Camb. SHO (Anaesth.) Pembrokesh. NHS Trust. Socs: BMA. Prev: SHO (A & E) Qu. Eliz. II Hosp. Welwyn Gdn. City; SHO (Gen. Med.) Univ. Coll. Hosp. Lond.

ISORNA, Veronica 35 Craven Pk Road, London N15 6AA — MB BS 1997 Lond.

ISPAHANI, Purvin (retired) 24 Raibank Gardens, Breckhill Road, Woodthorpe, Nottingham NG5 4HG — MB BS Dacca 1958; FRCPath 1977, M 1965; DCP Lond 1964; Dip. Bact. Manch. 1963. Prev: Cons. (Bact.) Pub. Health Laborat. Serv. Univ. Hosp. Nottm.

ISRAEL, Jaipal Vale Medical Centre, 195-197 Perry Vale, Forest Hill, London SE23 2JF Tel: 020 8291 7007 Fax: 020 8291 5111; 49 Kings Avenue, Bromley BR1 4HL — MB BS 1969 Osmania; Cert. FPA 1979.

ISRAEL, Martin Spencer (retired) 21 Soudan Road, London SW11 4HH Tel: 020 7622 5756 — MB BCh 1949 Witwatersrand; MRCP Lond. 1952; FRCPath 1975, M 1963; DCP Lond 1958. Prev: Sen. Lect. (Path.) Roy. Coll. Surg. of Eng.

ISRANI, Gurdas Kewalram Greenhill Park Medical Centre, Greenhill Park, Harlesden, London NW10 9AR Tel: 020 8965 7128 Fax: 020 8838 1303 — MB BS 1961 Agra.

ISSA, Basil George Diabetes Centre, North Manchester General Hospital, Delaunays Road, Crumpsall, Manchester M8 5RB Tel: 0161 720 2031 Fax: 0161 720 2029 Email: basil.issa@mail.nmanhc.tr.nwest.nhs.uk; 43 cecil Avenue, Sale M33 5BG Email: bissa@bissa.freeserve.co.uk — MB BCh 1986 Cairo; MRCP (UK) 1992; MD (Cardiff) 2000; MRCPI 1992. Cons. Phys., Endocrinologist, N. Manch. Healthcare NHS Trust; Hon. Cons. Endocrinologist, Christie Hosp., Manch. Socs: Collegiate Mem. RCP Lond.; Brit. Diabetes Assn.; Endocrime Soc. Prev: Sen. Regist. (Endocrinol., Diabetes & Metab.) Univ. Hosp. Wales; Clin. Research Fell. (Med.) Sect. Endocrinol., Diabetes & Metab. Univ. Hosp. Wales; Regist. Rotat. (Med.) Roy. S. Hants. & Basingstoke Dist. Hosps.

ISSAC, Joy 20 Riverdale Avenue, Stanley, Wakefield WF3 4LF — MB BS 1978 Ranchi.

ISSAC, Napolion Evan 127 Barmouth Avenue, Perivale, Greenford UB6 8JU Tel: 020 8997 9335 — MRCP (UK) 1989; MRCPI 1985.

ISSERLIN, Mr Bruno 32 The Avenue, Linthorpe, Middlesbrough TS5 6PD Tel: 01642 816307 — MB ChB 1936 Bristol; FRCS Ed. 1942. (Bristol) Hon. Cons. Orthop. Surg. Tees & N.allerton Hosp. Gps. Socs: BMA; Sen. Fell. BOA. Prev: Sen. Regist. (Orthop.) Bristol Roy. Hosp. & Hastings Gp. Hosps.; Surg. EMS Winford Orthop. Hosp.

ISSHAK, Mr Nabil Sabry 29 Mortain Road, Rotherham S60 3BY Tel: 01709 75830 — MB ChB 1966 Alexandria; FRCS Glas. 1983; DO Eng. 1974. (Alexandria) Assoc. Ophth. Specialist Trent HA. Prev: SHO & Regist. King's Mill Hosp. Sutton-in-Ashfield.

ISSITT, John Stewart Three Villages Medical Practice, Audnam Lodge, Wordsley, Stourbridge DY8 4AL Tel: 01384 395054 Fax: 01384 390969; 90 Greyhound Lane, Norton, Stourbridge DY8 3AQ — MB ChB 1976 Birm.

ISWERAN, Premala Sarva 49 Orchard Drive, Watford WD17 3DX Tel: 01923 229421 — MB BS 1974 Colombo.

ISWORTH, Mr Roy Anthony 54 Wimpole Street, London W1M 7DF; 11 Elmfield, Tenterden TN30 6RE — FRCS Eng. 1979; MBBS 1975 Lond.; MRCS Eng. LRCP Lond. 1975. (Westm.) Cons.Urol., Beneden Hosp. Socs: Mem. Brit. Assn. Urol. Surgs; Specialist Register Urol. 2000. Prev: Regist. (Surg.) Roy. Berks. Hosp. Reading; Regist. (Cardiothoracic Surg.) W.. Hosp. Soton.; Regist. Rotat. (Surg.) Roy. W. Sussex Hosp. (St. Richard's) Chichester.

ISZATT, Marie Ellen Jockey Road Surgery, 519 Jockey Road, Sutton Coldfield B73 5DF Tel: 0121 354 3050 Fax: 0121 355 1840; 34 Hermitage Drive, Sutton Coldfield B76 2XE — BM 1987 Soton.; MRCGP 1991; DRCOG 1990. (Soton.) Prev: Trainee GP Wolverhampton VTS.

ITHAYAKUMAR, Ebanezar Somasundaram Department of Radiology, North Middlesex Hospital, Sterling Way, Edmonton, London N18 1QX Tel: 020 8887 2785; 12 Benedict Way, London N2 0UR Tel: 020 8349 3930 — MB BS 1978 Sri Lanka; LRCP LRCS Ed. LRCPS Glas. 1983; DFFP 1994. (Univ. Sri Lanka) Stud. (Ultrasound Radiol.) N. Middlx. Hosp. Lond. Socs: Med. Defence Union. Prev: SHO (O & G) Vict. Hosp. Blackpool; SHO (Gyn.) Shotly Bridge Hosp. NW Durh. HA; SHO (Obst.) Scartho Rd. Hosp. Grimsby HA.

ITRAKJY, Mr Abdul Sattar Jassim Mohamed Al Cardiac Surgery Department, Queen Elizabeth Hospital, Vincent Drive, Edgbaston, Birmingham B15 2TZ Tel: 0121 472 1311 — MB ChB 1975 Mosul; FRCS Glas. 1990. Regist. (Cardiothoracic Surg.) Castle Hill Hosp. Cottingham; Staff Grade Surg. (Cardiac Surg.) Qu. Eliz. Hosp. Birm. Prev: Hon. Regist. (Cardiothoracic Surg.) Roy. Infirm. Edin.; SHO (Cardiothoracic Surg.) Univ. Hosp. Wales Cardiff.

IU, Martin The Nunhead Surgery, 58 Nunhead Grove, London SE15 3LY — MB BS 1989 Lond. GP Lond.

IU, Pui-Chuen 8 Greenfield Link, Coulsdon Woods, Coulsdon CR5 2SW — MB BS Hong Kong 1973; MRCPsych 1980.

IUEL, Benedicte Marie Whitaker and Partners, 53 Bridge Street, Brigg DN20 8NS Tel: 01652 657779 Fax: 01652 659440 — MD 1983 Copenhagen.

IVATTS, Simone Helen 33 Peter Weston Place, Chichester PO19 2PP — MB BS 1991 Lond.; MRCP (UK) 1996; MRCGP 1997; DRCOG 1994. (Roy. Free Hosp. Sch. Med.)

IVBIJARO, Gabriel Obukohwo 64 Greenlea Road, Yeadon, Leeds LS19 7RH — MB BS 1982 Benin, Nigeria; MMedSci Leeds 1994. Regist. (Psychiat.) Doncaster Roy. Infirm. Socs: Fell. W. Afr. Coll. Phys.; Brit. Neuropsychiat. Assn.; Assoc. Mem. Roy. Coll. Gen. Pract. Prev: Regist. Newton Lodge; Regist. St. Jas. Univ. Hosp. Leeds.

IVE, Francis Adrian (retired) Lindisfarne, Nevilles Cross, Durham DH1 4JP Tel: 0191 386 9697 Fax: 0191 384 0973 — MB BS 1959 Durh.; FRCP Lond. 1976, M 1964. Prev: Asst. Resid. (Internal Med.) Univ. Alta. Hosp. Canada.

IVE, Hazel (retired) Lindisfarne, Nevilles Cross, Durham DH1 4JP Tel: 0191 386 9697 — MB BS 1959 Durh. Prev: Research Asst. Dept. Photobiol. St. John's Hosp. Dis. of Skin Lond.

IVENS, Daniel Richard 93B Gaisford Street, London NW5 2EG — BM 1992 Soton.

IVER, Edith Bridget Ann Thorpe Health Centre, St Williams Way, Norwich NR7 0AJ Tel: 01603 439411 Fax: 01603 701855; 59 Cambridge Street, Norwich NR2 2BA Tel: 01603 632577 Fax: 01603 663083 Email: iver@iver.screaming.net — MB BS 1959 Lond. (Middlx.) SCMO (Audiol.) Norwich Community Health partnership.NHS Trust; Clin. Med. Off. Norf. & Norwich Hosp. Trust. Socs: BMA; BACDA; BACCH. Prev: Ho. Surg. & Ho. Phys. Ipswich & E. Suff. Hosp.; GP Vauxhall St Norwich.

IVERMEE, Stuart Peter Edberry, Main Road, Woodham Ferrers, Chelmsford CM3 8RW Tel: 01245 320308 — BM BS 1993 Nottm.; BMedSci Nottm. 1991. SHO (A & E & Intens. Care) Coffs Harbour Base Hosp. NSW, Austral. Prev: SHO (Accid & Emerg.) Katoomba, NSW, Austral.

IVERSEN, Angela Mary Tel: 01273 403591 Fax: 01273 403600 Email: aiverson@esbhhealth.cix.co.uk — MB BS 1978 Lond.; MSc Lond. 1983; FFPHM RCP (UK) 1994, M 1987; T(PHM) 1991. (St. Bart.) Cons. Communicable Dis. Control E. Sussex Brighton & Hove HA. Prev: SCM Mid-Downs HA; Sen. Regist. (Community Med.) SE Thames RHA; Regist. (Community Med.) NW Thames RHA.

IVERSEN, Simon Andrew Department Clinical Pathology, Royal Sussex County Hospital, Eastern Road, Brighton BN2 5BE Tel: 01273 696955 Ext: 4146 Fax: 01273 664792 Email: andrew.iversen@brighton-healthcare.nhs.uk; Sussex Nuffield Hospital Pathology Department, Warren Road, Woodingdean, Brighton BN2 6DX Tel: 01273 627005 Fax: 01273 627018 — MB BS 1977 Lond.; BSc Lond. 1974; FRCPath 1995, M 1984; T(Path) 1991. (St. Bart.) Cons. Chem. Path. Roy. Sussex Co. Hosp. Brighton; Vis. Lect. Univ. Brighton. Socs: Founder Mem. Brit. Hyperlipidaemia Assn.; Brighton M-C Soc.; Assn. Clin. Path. Prev: Sen. Regist. (Chem. Path.) Univ. Coll. Hosp.; Regist. (Chem. Path.) W.m. Hosp. Lond.

IVERSEN, Simon Johannes Liebmann (retired) 3 Dukes Yard, Steyning BN44 3NH Tel: 01903 879195 Fax: 01903 879195 — CAND.MED & CHIR Copenhagen 1943; DR.MED Copenhagen 1949; FRCP Glas. 1980, M 1967; MFCM 1974; FRCPath 1969; FMCP 1963. Prev: SCM Ayrsh. & Arran HB & Gtr. Glas. HB.

IVES, Andrew James 20 Medway Close, Chelmsford CM1 2LH — MB BS 1996 Lond. (Camb. & St. Mary's Hosp. Lond.)

IVES, Charlotte Louise 49 Parkstone Avenue, Bridgwater TA6 6DN — MB BS 1998 Lond.; MB BS Lond 1998.

IVES, David Ritchie Leicester Royal Infirmary, Leicester LE1 5WW; 18 Park Road, Birstall, Leicester LE4 3AU Tel: 0116 267 5118 — MB BChir 1965 Camb.; FRCP Lond. 1990; MRCP (UK) 1969. (Univ. Coll. Hosp.) Cons. Phys. (Gen. & Geriat. Med.) Leicester Roy. Infirm. Socs: Brit. Geriat. Soc.; Med. Res. Soc. Prev: Stanley Elmore Sen. Research Fell. Med. Sci.s, Sidney Sussex Coll. Camb.; Clin. Lect. & Hon. Regist. (Med.) Univ. Coll. Hosp. & Med. Sch. Lond.; MRC Trav. Fell. & Research Fell. Harvard Med. Sch. Boston, USA.

IVES, John Charles James (retired) 11 Darnaway Street, Edinburgh EH3 6DW — MB ChB 1937 Ed.; FRFPS Glas. 1960; FRCP Glas. 1964, M 1962; FRCPath 1963. Prev: Teach. Lect. Bact. Univ. Glas.

IVES, Mr Louis Arnold (retired) 10 Richmond Court, Spencer Road, New Milton BH25 6EP Tel: 01425 615446 — MB BS 1938 Lond.; MB BS (Distinc. Med.) Lond. 1938; FRCS Eng. 1941; MRCS Eng. LRCP Lond. 1938. Prev: Sen. Surg. St. Chas. Hosp. Lond.

IVES, Nicholas Kevin Neonatal Unit, Department of Paediatrics, John Radcliffe Hospital, Oxford OX3 9DU Tel: 01865 221355 Fax: 01865 221366 Email: kevin.ives@orh.nhs.uk; Abbey Cottage, 30 High St, Dorchester-on-Thames, Wallingford OX10 7HN Tel: 01865 343550 — MB BChir 1979 Camb.; MA Camb. 1980, MD 1992; MRCP (UK) (Paediat.) 1983; FRCPCH 1997; DCH RCP Lond. 1983. (Camb. & King's Coll. Hosp. Lond.) Cons. Paediat. Neonat. Med. John Radcliffe Hosp. Oxf.; Hon. Sen. Clin. Lect. (Paediat.) Univ. Oxf.

Socs: Neonat. Soc.; Brit. Assn. Perinatal Med.; Fell Roy. Coll. Paediat. & Child Health. Prev: Locum Cons. Neonat. Monash Hosp. Melbourne, Austral.; Clin. Lect. & Hon. Sen. Regist. (Paediat.) John Radcliffe Hosp. Oxf.; Action Research Train. Fell.sh. & Hon. Paediat. Regist. Univ. Coll. Hosp. Lond.

IVES, Victoria Jane Dalton Surgery, 364A Wakefield Road, Dalton, Huddersfield HD5 8DY Tel: 01484 530068 — MB ChB 1978 Leeds; MB ChB Leeds. 1978.

IVESON, James Martin Ingleby York District Hospital, Wigginton Road, York YO31 8HE Tel: 01904 453748 Fax: 01904 453459; 2 The Horseshoe, York YO24 1LX Tel: 01904 707546 — MB BS Lond. 1965; FRCP Lond. 1985; MRCP (UK) 1970; MRCS Eng. LRCP Lond. 1965. (Guy's) Cons. Rheum. York Health Dists. Socs: BMA. Prev: Sen. Regist. (Rheum. & Rehabil.) Gen. Infirm. Leeds.; Regist. (Med. & Rheum.) Oxf. Regional Rheum. Dis. Research Centre, Stoke Mandeville Hosp.

IVESON, Rachel Yates 2 The Horseshoe, Dringhouses, York YO24 1LX — MB BS 1990 Lond.; MRCPsych 1996.

IVESON, Timothy John The Wessex Medical Oncology Unit, Royal South Hampshire Hospital, Brintons Terrace, Southampton SO14 0YG Tel: 02380 825621 Fax: 02380 825441 Email: t.iveson@soton.ac.uk; Tel: 01725 513579 Fax: 01725 514812 — MB BS 1984 Lond.; MD 1996; BSc 1981 Lond.; FRCP 2000 UK. Cons. Med. Oncol. Wessex Med. Oncol. Unit Soton.; Cons. Med. Oncol. Salisbury Dist. Hosp. Prev: Sen. Regist. (Med. Oncol.) Roy. Marsden Hosp. Lond.; Sir John Stebbings Research Fell. Roy. Marsden Hosp. Lond.; Regist. (Med.) John Radcliffe Hosp. & Renal Unit Ch.ill Hosp. Oxf.

IVEY, Mr Andrew Thomas Furness General Hospital, Dalton Lane, Barrow-in-Furness LA14 4LF — MB ChB 1986 Cape Town; FRCS Ed. 1995.

IVEY, John Ross, VRD (retired) 9 Mary Twill Lane, Newton, Swansea SA3 4RB Tel: 01792 369286 — MB BS 1946 Lond.; MRCS Eng. LRCP Lond. 1943; DMR Lond 1947. Prev: Cons. Radiother. Swansea & W. Wales.

IVINSON, Mary Helen Louise Macartney House Psychotherapy Service, Beech Mount, Rochdale Road, Harpurhey, Manchester M9 5XS Tel: 0161 205 7555 Fax: 0161 203 5731 — MB ChB 1984 Dundee; MRCPsych 1988. Cons. Psychother. Manch. Ment. health Partnership. Socs: Scott. Assn. Psychoanalyt. Psychother.; Brit. Confederat. Psychother.; Inst. of PsychoAnal.: Trainee. Prev: Cons. Psychotherapist Garlands Hosp. Carlisle; Sen. Regist. (Psychother.) N.. Regional Dept. Psychother. Claremont Hse. Newc. u. Tyne.

IVINSON, Sandra Shrewsbury Road Health Centre, Shrewsbury Road, London E7 8QP Tel: 020 8586 5111 Fax: 020 8586 5046; 57 Claremont Road, Forest Gate, London E7 0QA Tel: 020 8257 7829 — MB ChB 1965 Sheff.; FRCGP 1995, M 1975. GP; Community Tutor, Roy. Lond & St Bart's Med Sch. Socs: BMA; (Ex-Chairperson & Comm. Mem.) Newham Med. Soc. Prev: Asst. Med. Off. Sheff. Co. Boro.; Ho. Phys. Sheff. Childr. Hosp.; Ho. Surg. Roy. Infirm. Sheff.

IVORY, Christine Mary Department of Radiology, York District Hospital, Wiggington Road, York YO31 8ZZ Tel: 01904 631313; Parklands, High St, Stillington, York YO61 1LG — MB BS 1970 Lond.; FRCR 1987; MRCOG 1976, DObst 1972; DA Eng. 1975. Cons. Radiol. York Dist. Hosp. Prev: Regist. (Radiol.) Freedom Fields Hosp. Plymouth; Sen. Regist. (Radiol.) Char. Cross Hosp. Lond.; Regist. (O & G Ultrasound) Ninewells Hosp. Dundee.

IVORY, Eleanor Ann Princess Margaret Hospital, Swindon SN1 4JU — MB BChir 1984 Camb.; MA Camb. 1986, BA 1981; FRCS Ed. 1994; MRCGP 1992. (St. Thos.) Specialist Regist. (A & E) P.ss Margt. Hosp. Swindon. Socs: Brit. Assn. Accid. & Emerg. Med.; Brit. Assn. Sport & Med. Prev: SHO (Obst.) John Radcliffe Hosp.; SHO (Gen. Surg.) William Harvey Hosp. Kent.

IVORY, Mr John Patrick Princess Margaret Hospital, Swindon SN1 4JU — MB BS 1984 Lond.; BA Camb. 1981, MA 1985; FRCS (Orth.) 1994; FRCS Ed. 1988; FRCS Eng. 1988; MD Leicester 1998. Cons. Orthop. Surg. P.ss Margt. Hosp. Swindon. Socs: Brit. Orthop. Assn. & Brit. Hip Soc. Prev: Sen. Regist. (Orthop.) Roy. United Hosp. Bath; Clin. Lect. (Orthop.) Univ. Leicester; Regist. (Orthop.) Nuffield Orthop. Centre Oxf.

IWANTSCHAK, Alexander Beeston Hill Health Centre, Beeston Hill, Beeston, Leeds LS11 8BS Tel: 0113 270 5131 Fax: 0113 272 0722; Brierley Court, 9A Old Hall Road, Upper Batley, Batley WF17 0AX — MB ChB 1980 Leeds.

IWASZKO, Janina Sior Vaine, 8 Street, Caplich, Kiltarlity, Beauly IV4 7HT — MB ChB 1991 Manch.

IWEGBU, Professor Chukwuedo Godwin King George Hospital, Barley Lane, Ilford IG3 8YB Tel: 020 8970 8165 Fax: 020 8970 8001; 30 Pamela Road, Birmingham B31 2QG Tel: 0121 608 9935 — Vrach 1973 Rostov; MChOrth Liverp. 1981; FRCS Ed. 1978; FRCS Glas. 1978; FICS 1985. (Med. Sch. Rostov-on-Don) Cons. Orthop. Surg.King Geo. Hosp Ilford Essex; Mem. Edit. Bd. Postgrad. Doctor; Assessor GMC. Socs: Nigerian Orthop. Assn.; BOA. Prev: Prof. & Cons. Orthop. & Trauma Surg. Ahmadu Bello Univ., Zaria; Regist. (Orthop.) Birkenhead Gen. Hosp. & Chase Farm Hosp. Enfield; Cons.Orthop.Surg,Chorley & Wrightington NHS trust lancs.

IWI, Diana Rosemary 9 Raeburn Close, London NW11 6UG — MB BS 1969 Lond.; MFOM RCP Lond. 1996. (King's Coll. Hosp.) Prev: Med. Adviser City of W.m.; Cons. Occupat.al Phys. Metroploitan Police.

IWUAGWU, Mr Chigozie Obiukwu 44 Glenfield Road, Nelson BB9 8AP — MB BS 1987 Benin, Nigeria; FRCS Ed. 1993.

IWUAGWU, Mr Fortune Chukwunonyerem St. Andrew's centre for Plastic Surgery, Broomfield, Chelmsford CM1 7HL Tel: 01245 440761 — MB BS 1986 Nigeria; FRCS (Plast.) 2000; FRCS Glas. 1993; FRCS Ed. 1993; MSC 1996. Specialist Regist. Plastic Surg; Hand Surg. Fell. Socs: RCS (Ed.); RCPS (Glas.); Brit. Assn. Plastic Surg. Prev: Specialist Regist. Plastic Surg Roy.Preston; Specialist Regist. Plastic Surg. Frenchay hosp. Bristol; research. Fell.Plastic Surg.UCL.

IYA, Mr Daniel 146 Poplar Road S., London SW19 3JY — MB BS 1977 Ahmadu Bello; FRCS Ed. 1985.

IYENGAR, Eshwar Narayan Department of Geriatric Medicine, North Manchester General Hospital, Delaunays Road, Manchester M8 5RB Tel: 0161 795 4567; 188 Manchester New Road, Alkrington, Middleton, Manchester M24 4DE — MB BS 1960 Osmania; FRCP Lond. 1994; MRCP (UK) 1973; DCH Eng. 1968. Cons. Phys. N. Manch. Gen. Hosp. Socs: Brit. Diabetic Assn.; Brit. Geriat. Soc.; BMA. Prev: Sen. Regist. (Geriat. Med.) N. Manch. Gen. Hosp.; Regist. (Med.) Vict. Hosp. Blackpool.

IYENGAR, Mandyam Osuri Narsim Rock Villa, Mount Peasant, Whittle-le-Woods, Chorley PR6 7LJ — MB BS 1953 Calcutta; DA Eng. 1958. (Calcutta)

IYENGAR, Mandyam Osuri Parthasarathy 91 King George V Avenue, King's Lynn PE30 2QE Tel: 01553 771575 — MB BS 1953 Calcutta; DCH Lond. 1957.

IYENGAR, Mythili Kenyon Lane Surgery, 152 Kenyon Lane, Moston, Manchester M40 9DF Tel: 0161 681 3383 Fax: 0161 683 4320; 188 Manchester New Road, Middleton, Manchester M24 4DE — MB BS 1967 Bangalor; MB BS Bangalore 1967; DCH RCPS Glas. 1969. Prev: GP Blackley Manch.; Regist. (Med.) Tameside Gen. Hosp. Ashton-under-Lyne; Regist. (Geriat. Med.) Withington Hosp. Manch.

IYENGAR, Narayan 91 King George V Avenue, King's Lynn PE30 2QE — MB BS 1993 Lond.; BSc Lond. 1990. (Char. Cross & Westm. Lond.)

IYENGAR, Prema Gopal Churchill Medical Centre, 191/193 Birchfield Road, Ferry Barr, Birmingham B19 1LL Tel: 0121 523 3833 — MB BS 1974 Bangalore.

IYER, Balu R Hollies Health Centre, Swan Street, Merthyr Tydfil CF47 8ET Tel: 01685 723363 Fax: 01685 350106 — MB BS 1974 Bombay. (Bombay) GP Merthyr Tydfil.

IYER, Dhanalakshmi Mill Cottage, Detling Hill, Maidstone ME14 3HS — MB BS 1963 Mysore; FFA RCS Eng. 1974; FFA RCSI 1973; DA Eng. 1969. (Mysore Med. Coll.) Cons. Anaesth. Maidstone Health Dist.

IYER, Mr Kishore Ramakrishna Surgery Unit, Inst. of Child Health & Great Ormond St. Hosps. NHS Trust, 30 Guilford St., London WC1N 1EH Tel: (20) 7242 9789 Fax: (20) 7404 6181; 1642 E56th Street, Chicago IL 60637, USA — MB BS 1986 Madras; FRCS Eng. 1990. (Stanley Med. Coll. India) Clin. Fell. Transpl. Surg. Lond. Socs: Brit. Assn. Paediat. Surg. Prev: Research Fell. RCS Glaxo; Regist. (Paediat. Surg.) Manch. Childr. Hosps.

IYER, Madhavan Ganesan The Surgery, Claudia Place, Augustus Road, Wimbledon, London SW19 Tel: 020 8788 2578 — MB BS 1973 Kerala.

IYER, Ranganathan Venkateswaran 42 Dryden Crescent, Stafford ST17 9YH — MB BS 1978 Poona; FFA RCS Eng. 1986.

IYER, Mr Subramanian Kalyan Krishnan 57 Adelaide Road, Southall UB2 5PY; 101 Parkland Apartments, Eagles St, Langford Town, Bangalore, Karnataka 560025, India Tel: 00 91 80 227 7935 Email: vikram&s@giasbga.vsnl.net.in — MB BS 1979 Bombay; MS 1982; FRCS Ed. 1983; Dip. Urol. Lond. 1987. (Grant Medical College Bombay) Socs: Amer. Urol. Assn.; Urological Soc. of India.

IYER, Swayam Jyothi 7 Highfield Drive, Sutton Coldfield B73 5HR — MB BS 1980 Madras; LMSSA Lond. 1990.

IYER, Vijay Kumar Subrahmanium Hodgson Centre Surgery, Hodgson Centre, Hodgson Avenue, Werrington, Peterborough PE4 5EG Tel: 01733 573232 Fax: 01733 328355; Tel: 01733 370222 — MB BS 1979 Calcutta; FRCS Ed. 1983; LRCP LRCS Ed. LRCPS Glas. 1983. Police Surg. Camb. Constab. P'boro.

IYNGKARAN, Thayahlan 60 Seafield Road, Dundee DD1 4NW — MB ChB 1997 Sheff.

IZARD, Ruth Kings Ransom, West View Rd, Headley Down, Bordon GU35 8JS — MB ChB 1997 Sheff.

IZATT, Louise Patricia Department of Medical & Molecular Genetics, UMDS, Guy's Hospital, St Thomas' St., London SE1 9RT Tel: 020 7955 4648 Fax: 020 7955 4646 Email: izatt@umds.ac.uk; 58 Independent Place, 1 Downs Pk Road, London E8 2HE — MB BChir 1991 Camb.; MA Camb. 1992, BA (Hons.) 1988; MRCP (UK) 1994. Specialist Regist. Clin.genetics.

IZEGBU, Victor Amechi Edozie 45 Hendon Way, London NW2 2LX Tel: 020 8201 9686 Fax: 020 8201 9027 — MB BS 1978 Benin; MB BS Benin, Nigeria 1978; FRCS Ed. 1984; FEBU 2000; FRCS (UROL) 2000. Cons. Urol. Rotherham Gen. Hosp., Rotherham; Urol. Cons. Rotherham Gen. Hosp. Socs: MDU; Brit. Assn. Urol. Surgs.; Brit. Soc. of Endocrinol. Prev: Regist. (Urol.) Char. Cross Hosp. Lond.; Regist. (Urol.) Centr. Middlx. Hosp. Lond.; Cons. Orologist (Locum) Harld Wood Hosp. Romford.

IZHAR, Mateen Department of Medical Microbiology, Frenchay Hospital, Bristol BS16 1LE — MB BS 1986 Punjab; MRCPath 1995.

IZHAR UL QAMAR, Dr Rob Royd, Hound Hill, Worsborough, Barnsley S70 6TU — MB BS 1976 Karachi; DCH 1980; MRCPI 1986. Regist. (Paediat.) King Geo. Hosp. Ilford & Barking Gen. Hosp.; Hon. Regist. (Renal Unit) Gt. Ormond St. Hosp. for Sick Childr. Lond. Prev: Regist. (Paediat.) St. Geo. Hosp. Lincoln.

IZMETH, Arshad — MB BS 1994 Lond.; BSc Lond. 1991; DRCOG 1998. (Charing Cross/Westminster)

IZMETH, Badria 20 Tudor Road, Southport PR8 2RY — Vrach 1967 1st Moscow Med. Inst.; DTM & H Liverp. 1976.

IZMETH, Mohamed Ghouse Ahmed Community Health Services (NHS) Trust, Hesketh Centre, Southport PR9 0LJ Tel: 01704 547471 Fax: 01704 578417 — MD 1967 Moscow; MD (Hons.) Moscow 1967; MPsychMed. Liverp. 1980; DPM Eng. 1977. (Friendship Univ. Moscow) Sen. Cons. Psychiat. Community Health Servs. (NHS) Trust; Cons. Psychiat. S.port & Formby DHA & S. Lancs. DHA; Med. Mem. Ment. Health Tribunal. Socs: Fell. Roy. Soc. Med.; Roy. Coll. Psychiat. Prev: Govt. Med. Off. i/c Thompson Hosp., & Centr. Hosp. Ndola, Zambia.

IZON, David Jonathon Rose Cottage, 10 Bunns Lane, Mill Hill, London NW7 2NE Tel: 07050 374966 Fax: 07970 762855 Email: doc_izon@hotmail.com — MB BCh 1990 Wales; MRCGP 1996. Clin. Asst. (Metab. Med.) Roy. Free Hosp.; Health Screening Doctor BUPA. Prev: Clin. Asst. in A & E Med., Roy. Free Hosp.

IZON, Jean Barbara 2 The Barn, Burmarsh, Sutton St Nicholas, Hereford HR1 3BW Tel: 01432 880951 — MB ChB 1969 Bristol; Dip. Palliat. Med. Wales 1997. (Bristol) Clin. Asst. (Haemat.) & (Ophth.) Hereford HA.

IZZARD, Mark Eric 107 Crowborough Road, London SW17 9QD — MB BS 1992 Lond.

IZZAT, Mr Ayham Basri 6 Pennine Close, Darlington DL3 9YA; 27 Caldwell Green, Darlington DL1 4TW Tel: 464145 — MB ChB 1970 Alexandria; FRCS Ed. 1984; DLO Eng. 1979.

IZZAT, Mr Moustafa 50 Ash Drive, Warton, Preston PR4 1DD Tel: 01772 635529 Email: izzat@msn.com — MD 1985 Damascus; FRCS Ed. 1992; FRCS (Orl.) 1997.

JAAFAR, Ainul Syahrilfazli 56 Brunswick Street, Sheffield S10 2FL — MB ChB 1997 Sheff.

JAAFAR, Feeroz 39 Harcourt Road, Sheffield S10 1DH — MB ChB 1998 Sheff.; MB ChB Sheff 1998.

JAAFAR, Hj Mohammad Isham B Flat 6, Rosebank Mews, Rosebank St., Hilltown, Dundee DD3 6PS — MB ChB 1995 Dundee.

JAAP, Alan James Crosshouse Hospital, Kilmarnock KA2 0BE Tel: 01563 577590 Fax: 01563 577973 Email: ajaap@nayrshire.scot.nhs.uk; 35 Fullarton Drive, Troon KA10 6LE — MB ChB 1988 Glas.; BSc Glas. 1985, MD 1995; MRCP (UK) 1991; FRCP (Glas) 2000; FRCP (Edin) 1999. Cons. (Gen. Med., Diabetes, Endocrinol.) CrossHo. Hosp. Kilmarnock; Hon. Sen. Lect. (Clin. Med.) Univ. of Glas. Prev: Sen. Regist. (Diabetes & Gen. Med.) Roy. Infirm. Glas.; Career Regist. (Diabetes) Roy. Infirm. Edin.; Research Fell. & Hon. Regist. (Diabetes) Univ. Exeter.

JABAR, Mohd Faisal Wordsley Hospital, Stream Road, Stourbridge DY8 5QX — BM BS 1992 Nottm.

JABARIN, Ziad Subhi The Rowans, Learning Disability Service, Whipton Hospital, Hospital Lane, Exeter EX1 3RB Tel: 01392 403677 Fax: 01392 403065 Email: ziad@jabarin.demon.co.uk; Tel: 01392 462713 — Ptychio Iatrikes 1975 Thessalonika; FRCPsych 2001; MRCPsych 1985. Cons. Psychiat. (Ment. Handicap Learning Disabilities) Exeter & Dist. Community NHS Trust; Clin. Teach. (Ment. Health) Univ. Bristol. Prev: Sen. Regist. (Psychiat. of Ment. Handicap) & Tutor (Ment. Health) Univ. Bristol; Regist. (Gen. & Psychiat.) Carlton Hayes Hosp. Leics.; SHO (Psychiat.) Carlton Hayes Hosp. Leics.

JABBAL, Satpal Singh Department of Anaesthesia, Law Hospital, Carluke ML8 5ER — MB BS 1981 Patna.

JABBAR, Abdul Harold Hill Health Centre, Gooshays Drive, Romford RM3 9SU Tel: 01708 341188 Fax: 01708 346784.

JABBAR, Mr Aijaz Ahmed 47 Kenningknowes Road, Stirling FK7 9JF — MB BS 1978 Karachi; FRCS Ed. 1985.

JABBAR, Farid 13 Poplars Road, London E17 9AT; 1 Plover Street, Preston PR1 6TT — MB ChB 1992 Dundee; DFFP 1995.

JABBAR, M A Leagrave Road Surgery, 16 Leagrave Road, Luton LU4 8HZ — MB BS 1968 Peshawar; MB BS 1968 Peshawar.

JABBAR, Nooh Khan Abdul 69 Heathrow, Bishop's Stortford CM23 5DH Tel: 01279 696366 Fax: 01279 503579 — MB BS 1960 Kerala; MRCP 1973 U.K.; FRCP Edin.; FRCP Glas. (Trivandrum Med. Coll.) Phys. Herts. & Essex Gen. Hosp. Bishop's Stortford. Socs: BMA; BGS. Prev: Regist. (Med.) Stirling Roy. Infirm.; Tutor in Med. Med. Coll. Hosp. Trivandrum, India; Med. Off. Min. of Health, Saudi Arabia.

JABCZYNSKI, Marcus Roman Almondbury Surgery, Westgate, Almondbury, Huddersfield HD5 8XJ Tel: 01484 421391 Fax: 01484 532405 — MB ChB 1986 Sheff.

JABEEN, Sabeeha 15 Hertford Fold, Leeds LS15 9ET — MB BS 1973 Mysore.

JABEEN, Z Stockbridge Lane Surgery, 45 Stockbridge Lane, Huyton, Liverpool L36 3SA Tel: 0151 489 2888.

JABEROO, Dhia Wadie Clydebank Health Centre, Kilbowie Road, Clydebank G81 2TQ Tel: 0141 531 6475 Fax: 0141 531 6478 — MB ChB 1967 Baghdad; MRCP (UK) 1977; LRCP LRCS Ed. LRCPS Glas. 1977. (Med. Coll. Baghdad) Socs: BMA. Prev: Regist. (Chest Med.) Ruchill Hosp. Glas.

JABIR, Mr Mohamad Abdulridha Ophthalmic Department, Royal Hallamshire Hospital, Sheffield S10 Tel: 0114 276 6222 Fax: 01442 3747; 7 Hallam Grange Croft, Sheffield S10 4BP — MB ChB 1980 Basrah; FRCS Ed. 1990; FRCOphth 1991. Socs: BMA; N. Eng. Ophth. Soc.

JACHACY, Christine Edith Tel: 01479 841495 Fax: 01479 810067; Tel: 01479 841495 — MB ChB 1974 Liverp.; Diploma Family Planning 1996; Vocational Training for GP 1981; DObst RCOG 1976. p/t Locum Gen. Practitioner, Highland Region and Moray Coast, Scotl. Prev: Partner, Aviemore Med. Pract., Inverness-sh.; GP Egremont, Cumbria.

JACHACY, George Bogdan Aviemore Medical Centre, Aviemore PH22 1SY Tel: 01479 810258 Fax: 01479 810067; Easter Kinakyle, Aviemore PH22 1PZ Tel: 01479 810250 — MB ChB 1974 Liverp.; DRCOG 1980. Prev: GP Egremont, Cumbria.

JACHUCK, Michael Satyajeet Jee Peterborough District Hospital, Thorpe Road, Peterborough PE3 6DA Tel: 01733 874000 Fax: 01733 874001; 9 Burwell Reach, Botolph Green, Orton Longueville, Peterborough PE2 7ZE Tel: 01733 394036 — MB BS 1996 Lond. (St. Geos. Hosp. Med. Sch.) SHO (Med.) PeterBoro. Dist. Gen. Hosp.

PeterBoro. Prev: SHO (Renal Med.) (S. Cleveland Hosp. Middlesbrough); Pre-Reg Ho. Off. Med. (Darlington Memor.).

JACHUCK, Sanjeebit Jee (retired) Chapel Park Medical Centre, Hartburn Drive, Chapel Park Estate, Newcastle upon Tyne NE5 1TD Tel: 0191 267 1416 Fax: 0191 264 8462 — MB BS Madras 1967; FRCPI 1996, M 1977; FRCGP 1991; MRCGP 1978; AFOM RCP Lond. 1983. Hon. Research Assoc. Univ. Dept. Med. Newc. u. Tyne; GP.

JACK, Alexander (retired) 6 Newcourt Road, Topsham, Exeter EX3 0BT Tel: 0139 287 3707 — MB ChB Glas. 1937. Prev: Med. Asst. Exeter.

JACK, Alexander Hunter (retired) Staveley Court, 9 Staveley Road, Eastbourne BN20 7JS — MB BS 1948 Lond.; MRCS Eng. LRCP Lond. 1937. Prev: Squadron Ldr. RAFVR Med. Br.

JACK, Andrew Smith Institute of Pathology, Algernon Firth Buildings, The General Infirmary, Leeds LS1 3EX Tel: 0113 233 3399 Fax: 0113 231 6286; 7 Southlands Drive, Leeds LS17 5NZ Tel: 0113 268 7474 — MB ChB 1980 Glas.; PhD Glas. 1986, BSc (Hons.) 1978, MB ChB 1980; MRCPath 1987. Cons. Path. United Leeds Teach. Hosps. NHS Trust. Prev: Sen. Lect. & Hon. Cons. Path. Univ. Leeds; Wellcome Lect. (Path.) Univ. Glas.

JACK, Bridget Anne Oaklands, 103 Duffield Road, Derby DE22 1AE — MB BS 1967 Lond.; MRCS Eng. LRCP Lond. 1967; MRCPsych 1980; DObst RCOG 1969; DCH Eng. 1972. Cons. Child Adolesc. Psychiat. Derby. Prev: Sen. Regist. Mapperley Hosp. Nottm.; Sen. Regist. (Child Psychiat.) St. Anns Hosp. Nottm.

JACK, Catherine Isabel Ann Care of the Elderly, Royal Liverpool & Broadgreen University Hospitals, Thomas Drive, Liverpool L14 3LB Tel: 0151 282 6463 — MB BCh BAO 1987 Belf.; MD 1994; FRCP (UK) 1990. Cons. (Geriat. Med.) Roy. Liverp. & BRd.green Univ. Hosps. Socs: Brit. Geriat. Soc.; Brit. Soc. Research on Ageing; Liverp. Med. Inst. Prev: Lect. Univ. Liverp.; Regist. Cardiothoracic Centre Liverp.; SHO (Med.) Belf. City Hosp.

JACK, Charles Morell 29 Main Street, Killinchy, Newtownards BT23 7PT — MB BChir 1978 Camb.; MA Camb. 1981, MB BChir 1978; MRCP (UK) 1982. Cons. Phys. Downe Hosp. Downpatrick. Socs: Brit. Geriat. Soc.; Europ. Assoc. Study of Diabetes. Prev: Sen. Regist. (Geriat.) Altnagelvin Hosp. Lond.derry & Belf. City Hosp.

JACK, David Alastair 33 Halesowen Road, Lydiate Ash, Bromsgrove B61 0QL Tel: 0121 453 3131; 33 Halesowen Road, Lydiate Ash, Bromsgrove B61 0QL Tel: 0121 453 3131 — MB ChB 1971 Birm.; DObst RCOG 1973. (Birmingham) Socs: Assoc. Mem. Fac. Homoeop.

JACK, David Allan (retired) 44 Overtoun Drive, Rutherglen, Glasgow G73 2QE Tel: 0141 647 5454 Fax: 0141 647 8418 Email: delmajac@cs.com — MB ChB 1947 Glas. Prev: Apptd. Fact. Doctor.

JACK, David Boag, Surg. Cdr. RN Retd. (retired) No 2 Flat, Tigh Mhor, 85 High St, North Berwick EH39 4HD Tel: 01620 894796 — MB ChB Glas. 1932.

JACK, Ernest Munro (retired) Elmfield, 8 Andrew Lane, Bolton BL1 7JQ Tel: 01204 304484 — MB ChB 1945 Aberd.; MRCGP 1962.

JACK, Fergus Robert Department Haematology, N Tyneside GH, Rake Lane, North Shields NE28 8NH Tel: 0191 259 6660 Fax: 0191293 2796 Email: f.r.jack@ncl.ac.uk; 13 Eslington Terrace, Newcastle upon Tyne NE2 2NE — MB BChir 1988 Camb.; MA Camb. 1989; MRCP (UK) 1991; MRCPath 1998. Cons. (Haemat.) N Tynesside Gen. Hosp.; Hon Lect. Univ. of Newc. Prev: Specialist Regist. (Haemat.) RVI Newc.; Regist. (Haemat.) Roy. Vict. Infirm. Newc. u. Tyne; SHO (Haemat.) Univ. Hosp. Nottm.

JACK, Heather Louise 2F3 7 Bruntsfield Avenue, Edinburgh EH10 4EZ — MB ChB 1998 Ed.; MB ChB Ed 1998.

JACK, Heather Margaret 3 Prospect Park, Portstewart BT55 7QE — MB BCh BAO 1987 Belf.

JACK, Ian Ferguson Munro Brannams Medical Centre, Brannams Square, Kiln Lane, Barnstaple EX32 8AP Tel: 01271 329004 Fax: 01271 346785; Orchard Cottage, Rumsam, Barnstaple EX32 9EW — MB ChB 1974 Dundee; BSc (Med. Sci.) St. And. 1972. Chairm. N. Devon PCG; Med. Dir. N. & E. Devon HA. Prev: SHO (Gen. Med.) N. Devon Infirm. Barnstaple; Ho. Off. (Gen. Med.) Perth Roy. Infirm.; Ho. Off. (Gen. Surg.) Ninewells Hosp. Dundee.

JACK, Ian Logan A R Newton Dunn and Partners, 61 New Street, Salisbury SP1 2PH Tel: 01722 334402 Fax: 01722 410473 — MB BS 1973 Lond.; BSc (Hons.) Lond. 1970; MRCS Eng. LRCP Lond. 1973; FRCGP 1996; DRCOG 1978; Cert. Av. Med. 1984. (St. Bart.) Treasury Med. Off.; Mem. Indep. Appeals Tribunal. Prev: Regist. (Med.) Co. Hosp. Hereford; SHO (Neurol. Surg.) & Ho. Phys. St. Bart. Hosp. Lond.

JACK, James Ford Borrowman Trades Lane Health Centre, Causewayend, Coupar Angus, Blairgowrie PH13 9DP Tel: 01828 627318 — MB ChB 1965 Glas. Prev: Ho. Phys. Roy. Alexander Infirm. Paisley; Ho. Surg. Kilmarnock Infirm.; Ho. Surg. (Obst.) Ayrsh. Centr. Hosp. Irvine.

JACK, Jennifer Anne The Surgery, Rochfield Road, Tobermory, Isle of Mull PA75 6PN Tel: 01688 302013 Fax: 01688 302092; Oakbank, Breadalbane St, Tobermory, Isle of Mull PA75 6PE Tel: 01688 302024 — MB ChB 1977 Glas.; DA (UK) 1985.

JACK, June Winifred (retired) 151 Woodrow Lane, Catshill, Bromsgrove B61 0PL Tel: 01527 874604 — MB ChB 1957 Liverp. Prev: Assoc. Specialist Moseley Hall Hosp. Birm.

JACK, Katherine Isobel (retired) 30 Brackendale Road, Queens Park, Bournemouth BH8 9JA Tel: 01202 395154 — MB ChB 1951 Glas.; BSc Glas. 1951; MRCOG 1955. Prev: Sen. Regist. (O & G) Univ. Coll. Hosp. Ibadan, Nigeria.

JACK, Margaret Elizabeth (retired) 30 Bellencroft Gardens, Merry Hill, Wolverhampton WV3 8DT — MB ChB 1955 Leeds.

JACK, Marion Etta 11 Hillcrest Road, Falkirk FK1 5NH Tel: 01324 623287 Fax: 01324 623287 — MB ChB 1961 Glas.; DObst RCOG 1963. (Glas.) Med. Off. Family Plann. Assn.

JACK, Matthew John Eric Sheaf c/o Mr S. Jack, 34 Carlton Court, Carlton Road, Harpenden AL5 4SY — BChir 1994 Camb.

JACK, Michael Ernest William Queensway Surgery, 75 Queensway, Southend-on-Sea SS1 2AB Tel: 01702 463333 Fax: 01702 603026; 54 St John's Road, Westcliff on Sea SS0 7JZ Tel: 01702 344076 — MB BS 1979 Lond.; MA (Modern Languages) Oxf. 1973; MRCP (UK) 1984. (St. Bart.) Socs: BMA. Prev: Regist. (Med.) Rochford & S.end Hosp.; SHO Renal Unit Bristol; SHO (Oncol. & Radiother.) Roy. Marsden Hosp. Lond.

JACK, Oliver Paul Catshill Village Surgery, 36 Woodrow Lane, Catshill, Bromsgrove B61 0PU Tel: 01527 872426 Fax: 01527 870507 — MB ChB 1975 Birm.; DRCOG 1977. Hosp. Pract. (Dermat.) Alexandra Hosp. Redditch. Socs: Assoc. Mem. Fac. Homoeop.

JACK, Paterson William (retired) 9 St Thomas Place, Stirling FK7 9LX — MB ChB Glas. 1942. Prev: Geriat. Base Hosp. Whangarei, NZ.

JACK, Patricia May (retired) Clydeview, Glen Road, Old Kilpatrick, Glasgow G60 5DQ Tel: 01389 873125 Fax: 01389 877662 — MB ChB 1955 Aberd.; DPH 1961. Prev: Clin. Med. Off. Gtr. Glas. HB.

JACK, Richard Alastair Fingland Catshill Village Surgery, 36 Woodrow Lane, Catshill, Bromsgrove B61 0PU Tel: 01527 877144 Fax: 01527 870507; 145 Woodrow Lane, Catshill, Bromsgrove B61 0PL Tel: 01527 880005 — MB ChB 1943 Birm.; FRCGP 1988, M 1963; FFHom 1978, M 1949. (Birm.) Socs: Fell. Brit. Soc. Med. & Dent. Hypn.

JACK, Richard Douglas Wexham Park Hospital, Wexham St., Wexham, Slough SL2 4HL Tel: 01753 633185 Fax: 020 8876 3962 Email: rjack108palewell@cs.com — MD CM 1962 McGill Univ. Canada; Lic. Newfld. Med. Bd. 1963; FFA RCS Eng. 1970. Cons. Anaesth. Wexham Pk. Hosp. Slough; Hon. Sen. Lect. Roy. Postgrad. Med. Sch. Lond.; Hon. Cons. Hammersmith Hosp. Lond. Socs: Roy. Soc. Anaesth. (Sec. Anaesth. Sect.). Prev: Examr. FFA RCS.

JACK, Stuart Angus 7 Crown Circus, Inverness IV2 3NH — MB ChB 1993 Ed.

JACK, Terence Carlson Lorenzo Lewisham Hospital, Lewisham High St., London SE13 6LH Tel: 020 8333 3000; 24 Begbie Road, Blackheath, London SE3 8DA Tel: 020 8265 6273 — MB BS 1983 Lond.; FRCA 1993; DA (UK) 1987. (St. Barts.) Cons. Anaesth. Lewisham Hosp. Socs: BMA; RCA; Assn. Paediat. Anaesth.

JACK, Timothy Michael Oxford Pain Relief Unit, Churchill Hospital, Headington, Oxford OX3 7LJ Tel: 01865 226161 Fax: 01865 226160; 46 Eaton Road, Appleton, Abingdon OX13 5JH Tel: 01865 864900 — MB BS Lond. 1970; MRCS Eng. LRCP Lond. 1970; FRCA 1977; DA Eng. 1972. (Guy's) Cons. Pain Relief & Clin. Dir. Oxf. Pain Relief Unit; Clin.Chairm.Cancer centre oxf.Radcliffe.Hosp Trust. Socs: Assn. Anaesths. & Pain Soc.; Internat. Assn. Study of Pain; BMA. Prev: Cons. Anaesth. Leeds Gen. Infirm.;

Sen. Regist. Nuffield Dept. Anaesth. Oxf.; Anaesth. Shanta Bhawan Hosp. Kathmandu, Nepal.

JACK, Victor John 18C/4 Hopetoun Road, South Queensferry EH30 9RA Tel: 0131 319 2399 — MB ChB 1993 Ed.; MRCGP 1997. (Ed.)

JACK, Wilfred (retired) The Mill House, Shotley Bridge, Consett DH8 8SE Tel: 01207 503204 — MB BS 1944 Durh. Prev: Ho. Phys. & Asst. Res. Med. Off. Roy. Vict. Infirm. Newc.

JACK, William Logan (retired) Huntington Court, Kington HR5 3PZ Tel: 01544 370657 Fax: 01544 370657 — MB BS 1929 Adelaide; MRCGP 1954. Prev: JP Heref. Supp. List.

JACK, Wilma Joy Louisa 12 Carfrae Park, Blackhall, Edinburgh EH4 3SP — MB ChB 1972 Ed.; DMRT Ed. 1976. Research Fell. (Clin. Oncol.) & Edin. BrE. Unit W.. Gen. Hosp.

JACKETT, David Michael Rowe Leicester General Hospital, Gwendolen Road, Leicester LE5 4PW Tel: 0116 258 4051; 4 Ingarsby Close, Houghton on the Hill, Leicester LE7 9JN Tel: 0116 241 7214 — MB BCh 1968 Wales; MRCP (UK) 1972; FRCP Lond. 1987. Cons. Phys., Leics Gen. Hosp. NHS Trust; Cons. Phys. Univ. Hosp. Leicester NHS Trust. Socs: Brit. Geriat. Soc. Prev: Cons. Geriat. Leics. HA; Sen. Regist. (Geriat.) & Med. Regist. Univ. Hosp. of Wales; Sen. Ho. Phys. Univ. Hosp. of Wales.

JACKLIN, Fiona Rachel 29 Elianore Road, Colchester CO3 3RY — MB BS 1991 Lond.; DA Lond. 1995. (St. Bart.)

JACKLIN, John Brian Sutton Medical Group, Allenby's Chase, Spalding PE12 9SY Tel: 01406 362081 — MB BS 1977 Lond.; DCH RCP Lond. 1988; DRCOG 1988.

JACKLIN, Molly Clemence 21 Blakehall Crescent, London E11 3RH Tel: 020 8989 2483 — MB ChB 1949 Cape Town; DA Eng. 1954. (Cape Town)

JACKLIN, Paul John The Oaks Medical Centre, 18-20 Villa Street, Beeston, Nottingham NG9 2NY Tel: 0115 925 4566 Fax: 0115 967 7470 — MB ChB 1988 Manch.; MRCP (UK) 1993; MRCGP 1993.

JACKMAN, Clive Cecil Spring House, Spring Lane, Long Burton, Sherborne DT9 5PB Tel: 01963 210240 — MRCS Eng. LRCP Lond. 1945. (St. Bart.) Prev: GP St. Albans; Anaesth. St. Albans City, Harperbury & Leavesden Hosps.; Capt. RAMC, Anaesth.

JACKMAN, Mr Jeremy Stephen Greenwood New Street Medical Centre, 130 New Street, Andover SP10 1DR Tel: 01264 335999 Fax: 01264 334331; 7 Stone Close, Andover SP10 2UG — MB BS 1976 Lond.; FRCS Eng. 1983; FRCS Ed. 1982; Cert. Family Plann. JCC 1987; DRCOG 1986; DCH Eng. 1979. (St. Bart) Clin. Asst. (Orthop.) N. Hants. Hosp.; Clin. Asst. (Orthop.) Andover & Dist. NHS Trust. Socs: Fell. Roy. Soc. Med.; BMA. Prev: Trainee GP Brecon; Regist. Rowley Bristow Orthop. Hosp. Pyrford; SHO (O & G) St. Jas. Univ. Hosp. Leeds.

JACKMAN, John Gloster 77 Ifield Road, London SW10 9AU — MB BS 1990 Lond.

JACKMAN, John Robert Langford Medical Practice, 9 Nightingale Place, Bicester OX26 6XX Tel: 01869 245665; The Villa, Main St, Charndon, Bicester OX27 0BL Tel: 01296 738676 — MB BS 1988 Lond.; MRCGP 1994; DCH RCP Lond. 1993. (St. Thos. Hosp.)

JACKMAN, Nicholas Clive Greenwood The Surgery, 36 Pagoda Avenue, Richmond TW9 2HG Tel: 020 8948 4217 Fax: 020 8332 7639; 11 Heathfield S., Twickenham TW2 7SR Tel: 020 8287 3349 — MB BS 1979 Lond.; MA Oxf. 1976; MRCP (UK) 1983; MRCGP 1986. (St. Bartholomew's) Clin Asst. (Diabetes) Qu. Mary's Univ. Hosp. Roehampton.

JACKOWSKI, Mr André Department of Spinal Surgery, Royal Orthopaedic Hospital, Northfield, Birmingham B31 2AP Tel: 0121 685 4260 Fax: 0121 685 4264; 16 Chad Road, Edgbaston, Birmingham B15 3ER — MD 1990 Lond.; BSc 1977, MB BS 1980; FRCS Eng. 1985. Sen. Lect. & Hon. Cons. Neurosurg. Univ. Dept. Neurosurg. Birm. Socs: Soc. Brit. Neurol. Surg.; Internat. Soc. Cerebral Blood Flow & Metab. Prev: Sen. Regist. (Neurosurg.) Nat. Hosp. for Nerv. Dis. Qu. Sq. & Char. Cross Hosp. Lond.; MRC Research Fell. Inst. Neurol. Qu. Sq. Lond. & Univ. Coll. Lond.

JACKS, Mr Andrew Simon, OStJ, Maj. RAMC Moorfields Eye Hospital, City Road, London EC1V 2PD Tel: 020 7253 3411 — MB BS 1988 Lond.; BSc (Hons.) Lond. 1985; FRCOphth 1996. (St. Thos. Hosp.) Specialist Regist. (Ophth.) Moorfields Eye Hosp. Lond. Prev: SHO (Ophth.) Moorfields Eye Hosp., Frimley Pk. Hosp. & Camb. Milit. Hosp.

JACKS, Margaret Elizabeth Department of Child Health, St. Leonard's Hospital, Nuttall St., London N1 5LZ Tel: 020 7301 3437 Fax: 020 7301 3270; 12B Ferme Park Road, Stroud Green, London N4 4ED — BM BS Nottm.1983; MRCGP 1988. Assoc. Specialist Off. City & Hackney Community Servs. NHS Trust Lond. Prev: SHO (Paediat.) Whittington Hosp. Lond.; Clin. Med. Off. Roy. Liverp. Childr. NHS Trust.

JACKS, Ruth Dawson Kirk and Jacks, Marus Bridge Health Centre, Highfield Grange Avenue, Wigan WN3 6SU Tel: 01942 246099 Fax: 01942 496705; 1 Vauze House Close, Blackrod, Bolton BL6 5BZ — MB ChB 1986 Manch.; MRCGP 1990. GP Wigan. Prev: Trainee GP Blackburn VTS; SHO (Obst. Paediat. & A & E) Burnley Gen. Hosp.

JACKS, Stephen Paul 140 Station Road, Pendlebury, Manchester M27 6BT — MB ChB 1980 Leeds.

JACKS, Susanna Marie Vauxhall Surgery, Vauxhall Lane, Chepstow NP16 5PZ Tel: 01291 623246 Fax: 01291 627975; Farthing House, Bishton Lane, Tidenham, Chepstow NP16 7LG — MB BS 1980 Lond.; BSc (Hons.) Lond. 1977, MB BS 1980; MRCGP 1984; DRCOG 1982; Dip. Ther. UCW 1997. (UCH)

JACKS, Thomas Alasdair Vauxhall Surgery, Vauxhall Lane, Chepstow NP16 5PZ Tel: 01291 636100 Fax: 01291 627975; Farthing House, Bishton Lane, Tidenham, Chepstow NP16 7LG Tel: 01291 623052 — MRCS Eng. LRCP Lond. 1980; BSc (Hons.) Lond. 1977, MB BS 1980; MSOM 1989; MLCOM 2001; MRCGP 1984; DRCOG 1983. (Guy's) Prev: SHO (Obst.) Highland HB; Ho. Phys. Gloucester HA; Ho. Surg. Pembury Hosp.

JACKSON, Abigail Susan Graigllwyd Fach, Darren Road, Bwlch, Brecon LD3 7RX — MB BS 1998 Lond.; MB BS Lond 1998.

JACKSON, Adrian Sylvester The Weathervane, 22A Moorend Pk Road, Leckhampton, Cheltenham GL53 0JY Tel: 01242 226918 Fax: 01242 263816 — MB ChB 1960 Ed.; LRCP LRCS Ed. LRFPS Glas. 1960; FFA RCS Eng. 1968. (Ed.) Cons. Anaesth. E. Glos. NHS Trust Cheltenham. Socs: Sen. Fell. Roy. Coll. of Anaesth.s; BMA; Assn. Anaesth. GB & N.. Irel. Prev: Sen. Regist. (Anaesth.) S. W. RHB & United Bristol Hosps.; Regist. (Anaesth.) United Leeds Hosps.; Ho. Surg. Birm. Accid. Hosp.

JACKSON, Agnes (retired) Whinhurst, Dunglass Road, Maryburgh, Dingwall IV7 8EQ — MB ChB 1945 Aberd.; MFCM 1974. Prev: Sen. Med. Off. Highland Health Bd.

JACKSON, Agnes Edith (retired) Vilamoura, The Hill, Millom LA18 5HB — LRCPI & LM, LRSCI & LM 1956; LRCPI & LM LRCSI & LM (RCPSI)1956. Prev: Ho. Surg. & Ho. Phys. N. Lonsdale Hosp. Barrow-in-Furness.

JACKSON, Professor Alan The Robert Darbishire Practice, Walmer Street, Rusholme, Manchester M14 5NP Tel: 0161 225 6699 Fax: 0161 248 4580; Department of Diagnostic Radiology, University of Manchester, Stopford Building, Oxford Road, Manchester M13 9PT Tel: 0161 275 5056 Fax: 0161 275 5594 Email: ajackson@fsl.sdr.man.ac.uk — MB ChB 1984 Manch.; PhD (Anat.) Manch. 1981; MRCP (UK) 1987; FRCR 1990. Prof. Neuroradiol. Univ. Manch.; Hon. Cons. Neuroradiol. Manch. Roy. Infirm.

JACKSON, Alan Edward 110 Elthorne Park Road, London W7 2JJ — MB BS 1992 Lond.

JACKSON, Alan Howard Ambleside Health Centre, Rydal Road, Ambleside LA22 9BP Tel: 015394 32693 Fax: 015394 32520 — MB ChB 1974 Manch.; MRCP (UK) 1978; MRCGP 1984.

JACKSON, Alan Mervyl Department of Pathology, Scarborough Hospital, Scarborough YO12 6QL Tel: 01723 342366 Fax: 01723 500097; 20 Stepney Drive, Scarborough YO12 5DH Tel: 01723 366115 — MB ChB 1971 Glas.; BSc Glas. 1969; FRCPath 1991, M 1979. Cons. Histopath. ScarBoro. Hosp.

JACKSON, Alan Peter Sheepcot Medical Centre, 80 Sheepcot Lane, Garston, Watford WD25 0EA Tel: 01923 672451 Fax: 01923 681404; Linden House, Shooters Way Lane, Berkhamsted HP4 3NW — MB BS 1979 Lond.

JACKSON, Alan Robert West Lodge, Hundred Acres Road, Wickham, Fareham PO17 6JD — MB ChB 1969 Liverp.; FRCR 1976; DMRD Liverp. 1974. Cons. (Radiol.) Portsmouth & S.E. Hants. Health Dist. Prev: Sen. Regist. (Radiol.) Soton. Univ. Hosp.; Demonst. Anat. Univ. Liverp.; Surg. Regist. Liverp. RHB.

JACKSON, Alasdair Ross (Surgery), 5 Friary Court, Inverkeithing KY11 1NU Tel: 01383 413234; Starley Bank, Burntisland KY3 0AG — MB ChB 1961 Ed.; DObst RCOG 1964; DTM & H Eng. 1963. (Ed.) Socs: BMA.

JACKSON, Alastair Randle 15 Radcliffe Drive, Kent Road, Halesowen B62 8PL — MB ChB 1992 Birm.

JACKSON, Alexander Paul Dr H J and A P Jackson, 91 Hyndland Road, Glasgow G12 9JE Tel: 0141 339 7869 Fax: 0141 334 3207; 101 Hyndland Road, Glasgow G12 9JD Tel: 0141 339 6965 — MB ChB 1982 Glas.; MRCGP 1986; DRCOG 1984.

JACKSON, Alison 9 Murton Park, Arlecdon, Frizington CA26 3UT Tel: 01946 861308 — MB BS 1996 Lond. (Roy. Free Hosp.) SHO (c/o the Elerly) Worthing Hosp. Sussex; SHO (ENT) Worthing Hosp. Sussex. Prev: Med. Ho. Off. Ilford; Surg. Ho. ff. Edmonton.

JACKSON, Alison Ashe 28 Pembroke Road, Muswell Hill, London N10 2HR — MB BS 1981 Lond.; MRCGP 1985; DRCOG 1984.

JACKSON, Allan Douglas IFL, 18 Danmure Place, Edinburgh GH3 9JJ Tel: 0131 221 1697 — MB ChB 1997 Ed. (Edinburgh) SHO Med. Paediat. Roy. Hosp. for Sick Childr. Edin.

JACKSON, Andrea Trinity Medical Centre, New George St., South Shields NE33 5DU Tel: 0191 454 7775 — MB BS 1988 Newc.; MRCGP 1992; DFFP 1994. Prev: Trainee GP Newc.

JACKSON, Andrew Colin James Shantara, 21 Carnreagh, Hillsborough BT26 6LJ — MB BCh BAO 1986 Belf.

JACKSON, Andrew James 67 Ilsham Road, Torquay TQ1 2JF Tel: 01803 211985; 137 Clifton Drive, Blackpool FY4 1RT Tel: 01253 346832 — BM BCh 1996 Oxf.; BA (Hons. Oxf.) 1993. SHO (Gen. Med.) Torbay Hosp. Prev: Princip. Ho. Off. (Surg.) Swindon; Princip. Ho. Off. (Med.) John Radcliffe Hosp. Oxf.

JACKSON, Andrew Jonathan Grassington Medical Centre, 9 Station Road, Grassington, Skipton BD23 5LS Tel: 01756 752313 Fax: 01756 753320; 3 Hardy Grange, Grassington, Skipton BD23 5AJ Tel: 01756 752595 Fax: 01756 753320 — MB ChB 1975 Birm. Med. Off. Upper Wharfedale Immediate Care Scheme. Prev: Princip. GP Trainer Pershore Health Centre Worcs.; SHO (Paediat.) & Ho. Off. (Obst.) Worcester Roy. Infirm.

JACKSON, Mr Andrew Malcolm 107 Harley Street, London W1N 1DG Tel: 020 7935 9521 Fax: 020 7935 5187; 3 Hood Avenue, East Sheen, London SW14 7LH Tel: 020 8878 6967 — MB BS 1969 Lond.; FRCS Eng. 1974; MRCS Eng. LRCP Lond. 1969. (Middlx.) Cons. Orthop. Surg. 107 Harley St.; Hon. Cons. Orthop. Surg. Roy. Nat. Orthop. Hosp. Lond. Socs: Fell. BOA (ex Mem. of Counc.); Fell. Roy. Soc. Med.; Brit. Assn. Surg. of the Knee (ex Treas., Educat.al Sec.). Prev: Cons. Orthop. Surg. Univ. Coll. Hosp. Lond. & Hosp. Sick Childr. Lond.; Cons. Orthop. Surg. Qu. Mary's Univ. Hosp. Roehampton; Sen. Regist. (Surg.) & Hon. Cons. Orthop. Surg., Roy. Nat. Orthop. Hosp. Lond.

JACKSON, Andrew Melvyn 25 Northfield Lane, Horbury, Wakefield WF4 5HZ — MB BS 1987 Lond.; MRCPath 1995. Cons. Histopath Dewsbury & Dist. Hosp. Socs: Assn. Clin. Path.; Internat. Acad. Path.; Brit. Soc. Clin. Cytol. Prev: Sen. Regist. (Histopath.) Roy. Hallamsh. Hosp. Sheff.

JACKSON, Andrew Peter 5 The Elms, Great Chesterfield, Saffron Walden CB10 1QD — MB BS 1993 Newc.

JACKSON, Andrew William 9 Seaburn Grove, Seaton Slice, Whitley Bay NE26 4HG — MB ChB 1993 Liverp.

JACKSON, Ann 30 Sunnybank Road, Bowdon, Altrincham WA14 3PW — MB ChB 1959 Manch. (Manch.) SCMO S. Manch. HA.

JACKSON, Ann Wilkie Fairykmowe View, Stonedyke Road, Carluke ML8 4BQ — MB ChB 1963 Glas.; MRCOG 1977.

JACKSON, Anne Clare Mogghill House, Abbey Road, Stratton-on-the-Fosse, Bath BA3 4QW — MB BCh 1997 Wales.

JACKSON, Anne Elizabeth Chase Farm Road, The Ridgeway, Enfield EN2 8JL Tel: 020 8366 6000; 83 Western Way, Barnet EN5 2BU — MB BS 1983 Lond.; MRCOG 1990. (Middx. Lond.) Cons. (O & G) Chase Fm. Hosp. Enfield.

JACKSON, Anne-Marie Rookery Nook, Patterdale, Penrith CA11 0NP — MB ChB 1970 Manch.; DObst RCOG 1974.

JACKSON, Anthony Derek Maurice (retired) 60 Uphill Road, Mill Hill, London NW7 4PU Tel: 020 8959 1757 Email: admj@compuserve.com — MB BS 1943 Lond.; MD Lond. 1949; FRCP Lond. 1967, M 1949; Hon. FRCPCH 1996; DCH Eng. 1947. Vice-Pres. Cystic Fibrosis Trust. Prev: Phys. Childr. Dept. Roy. Lond. Hosp.

JACKSON, Anthony Oliphant 2 Old Hall Farm Cottages, Guestwick, Dereham NR20 5QH — MB BS 1990 Lond.

JACKSON, Anthony Walter Grove Farm, The Street, Shotesham All Saints, Norwich NR15 1XH Tel: 01508 50785 — MD 1966 Manch.; MB ChB 1959; FRCR 1975; FFR 1965; DMRT Eng. 1963. (Manch.) Cons. Radiother. & Oncol. Norf. & Norwich Hosp. Socs: Brit. Inst. Radiol. Prev: Cons. Radiother. Christie Hosp. & Holt Radium Inst. Manch.

JACKSON, Arnold Peter Frank Department of Anaesthetics, Queen Elizabeth Hospital, Edgbaston, Birmingham B15 2TH; Beacon Cottage, Rednal, Birmingham B45 9XL Tel: 0121 453 2048 — MB ChB 1967 Birm.; FFA RCS Eng. 1973; DA Eng. 1972. Cons. Anaesth. Gen. Hosp. Birm. & Qu. Eliz. Hosp. Birm. Socs: BMA; Assoc. Assn. Anaesths. Prev: Instruc. Anaesth. Dept. Univ. Michigan Hosp. Ann Arbor U.S.A.

JACKSON, Arthur David Holmes Chapel Health Centre, London Road, Holmes Chapel, Crewe CW4 7BB Tel: 01477 533100 Fax: 01477 532563; Danecroft, 74 Middlewich Road, Holmes Chapel, Crewe CW4 7EB Tel: 01477 533121 Fax: 01477 532820 Email: abmtjackson@compuserve.com — MB ChB 1968 Aberd.; BSc Aberd. 1965, MB ChB 1968; MRCGP 1974; Cert. Family Plann. JCC 1977; DObst RCOG 1970; M Phil 1999. Clin. Asst. (Dermat.) Leighton Hosp. Crewe; Hon Research Fell. Dept GP Univ. Wales Coll. Med. Prev: Ho. Phys. Aberd. Roy. Infirm. & Roy. Aberd. Childr. Hosp.; Regist. (Gen. Med.) Foresterhill & Assoc. Hosps. Aberd.

JACKSON, Aubrey Robert Best (retired) Alma House, Bell Lane, Cassington, Oxford OX29 4DS Tel: 01865 881450 — MB BCh BAO 1944 Dub. Prev: Capt. RAMC.

JACKSON, Barbara Jean 91 Upwell Street, Sheffield S4 8AN Tel: 0114 261 8608; 147 Dobbin Hill, Sheffield S11 7JF — MB ChB 1981 Sheff.

JACKSON, Sir Barry Trevor The Consulting Rooms, York House, 199 Westminster Bridge Road, London SE1 7UT Tel: 020 7928 5485 Fax: 020 7928 3748; Mapledene, 7 St. Matthews Avenue, Surbiton KT6 6JJ Tel: 020 8399 3157 — MB BS 1963 Lond.; MS Lond. 1972; FRCS Eng. 1967; MRCS Eng. LRCP Lond. 1963; FRCP 1999. (Westm.) Pres. Roy. Soc. Med.; Hon. Cons. Surg. to Army; King Edwd. VI Hosp for Offs Lond. Socs: Fell. (Ex-Pres.) Assn. Surgs. GB & Irel.; Fell. Roy. Soc. Med. Pres. (Ex-Pres. Sect. Coloproctol.); Fell. RCS Eng. Ex-Pres., Ex-Edr. Anads. Prev: Surg. to HM Ho.hold; Mem. Ct. Examrs. RCS Eng.; Examr. Primary FRCS & Surg. Tutor RCS Eng.

JACKSON, Benjamin Edward Gardens Lane Health Centre, Conisbrough, Doncaster DN12 3JW Tel: 01709 860016 Fax: 01709 863543 Email: ben.jackson@gp-c86024.nhs.uk; The Cottage, Potton Road, Huntingdon PE28 9NG Email: benandceline@eircom.net — MB BS 1993 Lond.; DFFP 1998; Dip O&G (RACOG); BSc 1992 (Hons.) Lond.; MRCGP 1998; MRCP 1996. (Royal Free Hospital School of Medicine) p/t Princip. Gen. Practitioner. Socs: Roy. Coll. Gen. Practitioners; Roy. Coll. Phys.s.

JACKSON, Bridget Clare Sheffield Kidney Institute, Northern General Hospital, Herries Road, Sheffield S5 7AU Tel: 0114 243 4343 Fax: 0114 256 2514; Yew Tree Cottage, 30 Worksop Road, Thorpe Salvin, Worksop S80 3JU Tel: 01909 770367 Email: bridget.jackson@dial.pipex.com — MB BS 1966 Lond.; MSc Surrey 1974; MRCS Eng. LRCP Lond. 1966. (St Mary's, London) Assoc. Specialist Renal Unit N. Gen. Hosp. Sheff. Socs: Assn. Clin. Chemists; Brit. Diabetes UK. (Scientif. Med. & Sec.); Eur. Dialysis & Transpl. Assn. Prev: Clin. Asst. (Renal Unit) N.. Gen. Hosp.; Sen. Regist. (Clin. Chem.) Roy. Hallamsh. Hosp.; Regist. (Gen. Med.) Lodge Moor Hosp. Sheff.

JACKSON, Brinley Robert Boots Healthcare International, D6 Building, Thane Rd, Nottingham NG90 6BH Tel: 0115 968 9803 Email: brinley.jackson@bhint.com — MB BS 1993 Lond. Pharmaceutical Phys. Boots Healthcare Internat., Nottm. Prev: Demonst. (Anat.) Roy. Free Hosp. Sch. Med. Lond.; Ho. Off. (Med.) Roy. Free Hosp. Lond.; Ho. Off. (Surg.) Basildon Dist. Gen. Hosp.

JACKSON, Bryan Reginald Haslucks Green Road Surgery, 287 Haslucks Green Road, Shirley, Solihull B90 2LW Tel: 0121 744 6663 Fax: 0121 733 6895; 109 Dorridge Road, Dorridge, Solihull B93 8BP — MRCS Eng. LRCP Lond. 1964.

JACKSON, C J The New Surgery, 42 Duke Street, Formby, Liverpool L37 4AT.

JACKSON, Carole Ingersley, West Park Site, Macclesfield District General Hospital, Victoria Road, Macclesfield SK10 3BL; 12 Lakes Road, Dukinfield SK16 4TP Tel: 0161 330 2795 — MB BS 1966

Durh. (Newc.) Staff Grade E. Chesh. NHS Trust. Prev: Clin. Asst. S.mead HA.

JACKSON, Caroline Hazel Dawn 3 Lambert Avenue, Dundonald, Belfast BT16 1LE — MB BCh BAO 1987 Belf.; MRCGP 1992; DRCOG 1991; DCH Dub. 1991; DMH Belf. 1990; DGM RCP Lond. 1990. Clin. Med. Off. (Child Community Health) Lisburn. Prev: Trainee GP Newtownards; SHO (Paediat.) Ulster Hosp. Dundonald; Trainee GP/SHO Downpatrick Hosp. VTS.

JACKSON, Mr Charles Robert Sweeting (retired) 5 Kingslea Road, Houston, Johnstone PA6 7ER Tel: 01505 690989 — MA Oxf. 1942, BA 1939, DM 1970, BM BCh 1942; FRCS Ed. 1951; DOMS Eng. 1947. Prev: Ophth. Surg. Roy. Infirm. Edin.

JACKSON, Mr Charles Terry 31 Rodney Street, Liverpool L1 Tel: 0151 709 8522; Freshfield House, 95 Freshfield Road, Formby, Liverpool L37 7BJ Tel: 0170 48 79542 — MB ChB 1961 Manch.; MChOrth. Liverp. 1970; FRCS Ed. 1968. (Manch.) Cons. Orthop. Surg. Fairfield Hosp. Crank. Socs: Liverp. Med. Inst. & Low Friction Soc. Prev: Cons. Orthop. Surg. Whiston Hosp. & St. Helen's Hosp. Merseyside; Sen. Regist. United Liverp. Hosps. & Wrightington Hosp.

JACKSON, Charles William Peter Blue Dykes Surgery, Eldon Street, Clay Cross, Chesterfield S45 9NR Tel: 01246 862468; 116 Chartwell Avenue, Wingerworth, Chesterfield S42 6SP Email: cwpj@epulse.net — MB BS 1973 Lond.; BSc Lond. 1970; MRCP (UK) 1976; MRCS Eng. LRCP Lond. 1973; MRCGP 1984. (Roy. Free) Course Organiser Chesterfield VTS. Prev: Regist. (Med.) N.. Gen. Hosp. Sheff.

JACKSON, Christine Wendy Flat 2, 2 Ballbrook Avenue, Manchester M20 6AB — MB ChB 1995 Ed.

JACKSON, Claire Elizabeth, Flight Lt. RAF Med. Br. Officers Mess, RAF Laarbrugh BFPO 43; Pyethorn, Whalley Road, Wilpshire, Blackburn BB1 9LF Tel: 01254 249773 — MB ChB 1994 Liverp. (Liverp.) GP Regist. & SHO (Anaesth.) BFPO 43. Prev: Ho. Off. Arrowe Pk. Hosp. Wirral.

JACKSON, Claire Rachel 13 Holmside Place, Newcastle upon Tyne NE6 5AJ — MB BS 1997 Newc.

JACKSON, Corinne Lucy 7 Mulberry Walk, Shirley, Southampton SO15 5GA — BM 1991 Soton.; MRCP (UK) 1994. (Univ. Soton.) Regist. Rotat. (Gastroenterol.) Soton. Gen. Hosp.

JACKSON, Damian John 37 Tudor Close, Colwick, Nottingham NG4 2DR — MB ChB 1987 Leic.; MRCGP 1992.

JACKSON, David Arthur Greengates, Shoppenhangers Road, Maidenhead SL6 2QA Tel: 01628 627075 — MB ChB 1963 Manch.; FFPM RCP (UK) 1994, M 1989. (Manch.) Med. Dir. Glaxo Wellcome UK. Socs: Fell. Roy. Soc. Med.; BMA. Prev: Med. Dir. Servier Labs. Ltd Fulmer, Slough; Sen. Med. Adviser E.R. Squibb & Sons Hounslow.

JACKSON, David Atkinson Twinem (retired) c/o Barclays Bank, 220 Ealing Road, Wembley HA0 4QH Tel: 020 8659 4447 Fax: 01734 868136 — MB BS 1952 Lond.; DMJ (Clin.) Soc. Apoth. Lond. 1962. Phys. HM Customs & Excise Lond. (Heathrow) Airport; Cons. Edr. Brit. Med.; Asst. Police Surg. Thames Valley. Prev: Hon. Phys. Lond. Amateur Boxing Assn.

JACKSON, Mr David Bruce Chaucer Hospital, Nackington Road, Canterbury CT4 7AR Tel: 01227 472581; Winters Farm, Nackington Road, Canterbury CT4 7AY Tel: 01227 472636 Fax: 01227 379538 — MB BS 1969 Lond.; FRCS Ed. 1974; FRCS Eng. 1974; MRCS Eng. LRCP Lond. 1969. (St. Bart.) Cons. Surg. Kent & Canterbury Hosp. and William Harvey E. Kent Hosp.s NHS Trust; Examr. Surg. Univ. Lond.; Hon. Sen. Lect. St. Bart. Hosp. Lond. Socs: Brit. Soc. Gastroenterol.; Brit. Assn. Surg. Oncol.; A. S. G. B. I. Prev: Sen. Regist. (Surg.) St. Bart. Hosp. Lond.; Research Fell. Univ. Calif., San Diego, USA; Resid. Surg. Off. St. Mark's Hosp. Lond.

JACKSON, David George Friarage Hospital, Northallerton DL6 1JG Tel: 01609 779911; Inglenook Cottage, Hackforth, Bedale DL8 1NU Tel: 01845 811703 — MRCS Eng. LRCP Lond. 1973; FFA RCS Eng. 1979. Cons. Anaesth. N.allerton Health Auth. Prev: Sen. Regist. Yorksh. RHA; Regist. Whipps Cross Hosp. Lond.

JACKSON, Mr David Howard Tel: 01256 313333; Chalk Dell, Winchester SO21 3RT Tel: 01962 760430 — MB ChB Bristol 1967; FRCS Eng. 1973. Cons. Genitourin. Med. N. Hants. Hosps. Trust.

JACKSON, David John Windrush Surgery, 21 West Bar, Banbury OX16 9SA Tel: 01295 251491; Heathcote, 3 Glovers Lane, Middleton Cheney, Banbury OX17 2NU Tel: 01295 710302 — MB ChB 1961 Sheff. (Sheff.) Prev: Regist. (Anaesth.) United Sheff. Hosps. & Clwyd & Deeside Hosp. Gp.; SHO (Anaesth.) Sheff. RHB.

JACKSON, David Mark Department of Anaesthesia, Princess Margaret Hospital, Okus Road, Swindon SN1 4JU Tel: 01285 861244 Email: dmjackson@doctors.org.uk — BM BCh 1966 Oxf.; MA Oxf. 1969; FFA RCS Eng. 1970; DA Eng. 1968; DObst RCOG 1967. (Oxf. & Lond. Hosp.) p/t Cons. Anaesth. P.ss Margt. Hosp. Swindon Half-Time (Locum). Socs: Assn. Anaesth. & Obst. Anaesths. Assn.; BMA; Obstetric Anaesth.s Assn. Prev: Sen. Regist. (Anaesth.) Middlx. Hosp. Lond.; Lect. (Anaesth.) Mulago Hosp. Kampala, Uganda; Regist. (Anaesth.) N.ampton Gen. Hosp.

JACKSON, David Michael Anthony Department of Diagnostic Radiology, Royal Gwent Hospital, Gwent, Newport NP20 2UB Tel: 01633 234321 Email: djack1@gwent-nhs.gov.uk; 17 Berrymead Road, Cyncoed, Cardiff CF23 6QA — MB BCh 1986 Wales; BSc (Hons. Physiol.) Wales 1983; MRCP (UK) 1989; FRCR 1985. (Welsh Nat. Sch. Med.) Cons. Radiol. Roy. Gwent Hosp. Newport. Socs: Brit. Inst. Radiol. Prev: Sen. Regist. Univ. Hosp. Wales Cardiff; Regist. (Diag. Radiol.) Hammersmith Hosp. Lond.; Regist. (Med. & Endocrinol.) Char. Cross Hosp. Lond.

JACKSON, David Peter St James's University Hospital, Beckett St., Leeds LS9 7TF Tel: 0113 244 2007 Fax: 0113 242 9886; 137 Haxby Road, York YO31 8JW Tel: 01904 612069 — MB ChB 1992 Leeds; BSc (Hons.) Leeds 1989; MRCP (UK) 1995. Specialist Regist. (Med. Oncol.) St. Jas. Univ. Hosp. Leeds; Clin. Research Fell. (ICRF).

JACKSON, Mr David Stuart Drakkan, Cefnllan, Aberystwyth SY23 3TF — MB ChB 1973 Liverp.; FRCS Ed. 1980. Cons. & Tutor (Surg.) Bronglais Hosp. Aberystwyth. Socs: Welsh Surg. Soc. Prev: Cons. (Surg.) Roy. Army Med. Corps.

JACKSON, Denis James 43 Weirwood Avenue, Barrowhill, Glasgow G69 6HR — MB ChB 1980 Glas.

JACKSON, Dennis Frederick (retired) Rilla Tor, Henwood, Liskeard PL14 5BP — MB BS 1945 Lond.; MRCGP 1961.

JACKSON, Derrick 124 Shorncliffe Road, Folkestone CT20 2PQ — MD 1958 Lond.; FRCP Ed. 1982; FFPM 1989. (King's Coll. Hosp.) Cons. Clin. Pharmacol. & Therap. Socs: Brit. Pharm. Soc.; Sen. Mem. Soc. Endocrinol.; Med. Soc. Of Lond. Prev: Dir. (Clin. Pharmacol.) Beecham Pharmaceut.; Lect. (Pharmacol.) Guy's Hosp. Lond.; Hon. Clin. Research Fell. Roy. Free Hosp. Lond.

JACKSON, Dominic Kimborough Francis Hillstead 1 Downland Close, Botley, Southampton SO30 2SG — MB BS 1976 Lond.; BA (Physiol. Sci.) Oxf. 1973. Prev: Regist. (Psychiat.) N. Camden (Roy. Free) Health Dist. (T).

JACKSON, Douglas MacGilchrist (retired) 17 Milford Court, Milford on Sea, Lymington SO41 0WF Tel: 01590 645285 — MB BChir Camb. 1940; MA, MD Camb. 1951; FRCS Eng. 1943; MRCS Eng. LRCP Lond. 1940. Prev: Surg. MRC Burns Unit & Birm. Accid Hosp.

JACKSON, Duncan John c/- Anaesthetic Department, Royal Free Hospital, Pond Street, Hampstead, London NW3 2QG Tel: 020 7794 0500; Lowick, 3 Gladsmuir Road, Hadley Green, Barnet EN5 4PJ — BMedSc. Newc. 1989; DA (UK) 1994; FFARCSI 1995. Cons. (Anaesth.) Roy. Free Hosp. Lond. Socs: RSM; MRCAnaesth.

JACKSON, Edward 64 Nettleham Road, Lincoln LN2 1RH Tel: 01522 524813 Fax: 01522 524813 Email: ejackson@lineone.net — MB ChB 1960 Manch.; BSc Manch. 1957; FRCP Lond. 1975, M 1962. (Manch.) Chief Med. Off. Definitec Ltd Lincoln. Socs: Brit. Cardiac Soc. Prev: Sen. Regist. (Med.) Nottm. Gen. Hosp.; Regist. (Med.) Nat. Heart Hosp.

JACKSON, Edward Paul 65 Fonnereau Road, Ipswich IP1 3JN — MB BS 1957 Lond.; LMSSA Lond. 1956; DObst RCOG 1964. (Guy's) Prev: Med. Off. Govt. of Tanzania; Resid. Phys. Amer. Hosp. of Paris.

JACKSON, Eileen Sutcliffe An Cala, Applethwaite, Keswick CA12 4PP Tel: 017687 74487 — MB BS 1953 Lond. (Middlx.) Prev: Mem. Chartered Soc. Physiother.; Med. Off. (Occupat. Ther.) Centre High Wycombe; Clin. Asst. (Physical Med.) N.wick Pk. Hosp. Harrow.

JACKSON, Elizabeth Anne Flat 35A, Marryat Square, London SW6 6UA — MB BS 1981 Lond.; BSc (1st cl. Hons.) Lond. 1978, MB BS 1981; MRCP (UK) 1984; FFA RCS Eng. 1987. Cons. Anaesth. Gt. Ormond St. Childr. Hosp. NHS Trust Lond.

JACKSON, Elizabeth Catherine Shirley (retired) 21 Lyndhurst Road, Benton, Newcastle upon Tyne NE12 9NT Tel: 0191 266 3552

Fax: 0191 266 3552 — MB ChB 1940 MB ChB Manch; 1944 MD Manch. JP. Prev: Research Asst. Wingfield-Morris Orthop. Hosp. Oxf.

JACKSON, Elizabeth Frances 49 South View Drive, Rumney, Cardiff CF3 3LX — MB ChB 1998 Leic.; MB ChB Leic 1998.

JACKSON, Elizabeth Jane 4 Beech Road, Heswall, Wirral CH60 2SR — MB BS 1992 Lond.

JACKSON, Emma Ruth 2 Woodside, Buckhurst Hill IG9 5DR — MB ChB 1993 Manch. SHO (Med.) Leighton Hosp. Crewe. Prev: SHO (A & E Med.) Leighton Hosp. Crewe.

JACKSON, Eric Boxall (retired) 13 Peterhill Close, Chalfont St Peter, Gerrards Cross SL9 0HZ Tel: 01494 873795 — MB BS 1930 Lond.; MD Lond. 1934; FRCP Lond. 1964, M 1933; MRCS Eng. LRCP Lond. 1930. Prev: Cons. Phys. Hillingdon Hosp.

JACKSON, Eric Gordon Anthony 12 Oak Tree Close, Burpham, Guildford GU4 7JQ Tel: 01483 575236 — BSc Wales 1945, MB BCh 1948; MFCM 1972; DPH Lond. 1967; FRCA Eng. 1954; DA Eng. 1952. Prev: Cons. Pub. Health Med. Mid Surrey HA.

JACKSON, Eric Gray Milman Road Health Centre, Milman Road, Reading RG2 Tel: 01734 862285 — MRCS Eng. LRCP Lond. 1960; DObst RCOG 1963. (Univ. Coll. Hosp.) Med. Off. HM Prison Reading. Prev: Ho. Surg. Rush Green Hosp. Romford; Ho. Phys. & Ho. Surg. (O & G) OldCh. Hosp. Romford.

JACKSON, Francis Peter Widcombe Surgery, 3-4 Widcombe Parade, Bath BA2 4JT Tel: 01225 310883 Fax: 01225 421600; Wake Lodge, Dunkerton, Bath BA2 8BP — MB BS 1973 Lond.; MRCS Eng. LRCP Lond. 1973; MRCGP 1978; DCH RCPSI 1977; DObst RCOG 1975. (Guy's) Clin. Asst. (ENT) Roy. United Hosp. Bath; Dep. Div.al Police Surg. Bath.

JACKSON, Frederick Bruce (retired) Min-y-Rhiw, Llandyrnog, Denbigh LL16 4HG Tel: 01824 790336 Fax: 01824 790336 — MB ChB 1945 Manch.; FRCPath 1971, M 1963. Prev: Dir. Pub. Health Laborat. Bodelwyddan.

JACKSON, Gary Mark Dukes Priory Hospital, Stump Lane, Springfield, Chelmsford CM1 7SJ Tel: 01245 345345; 18 Walbrook, Woodford Road, London E18 2EG — MB BCh 1982 Witwatersrand; MRCPsych 1990.

JACKSON, Gaye Diana Mary Jackson, 17 Pembridge Road, London W11 3HG Tel: 020 7221 0174 Fax: 020 7229 0774 — MB BS 1977 Lond.; MRCS Eng. LRCP Lond. 1977; DRCOG 1981; Cert. Family Plann. JCC 1981. (St. Mary's) Gen. Practitioner. Prev: Trainee GP BRd.stone; SHO (O & G) Poole Gen. Hosp.; SHO (Paediat.) Poole Gen. Hosp.

JACKSON, Geoffrey Chadwick (retired) Ryebank, The Rise, Haverbreaks, Lancaster LA1 5XD Tel: 01524 66526 — MB ChB Manch. 1952. Prev: Hosp. Pract (Psychiat.) Lancaster Moor Hosp.

JACKSON, Gerald Bruce Old Forge Surgery, The Green, Upper Poppleton, York YO26 6EQ Tel: 01904 794322 Fax: 01904 788084; Doon Lodge, Longridge Lane, Upper Poppleton, York YO26 6HB Tel: 01904 795237 — MB BS 1962 Lond.; DA Eng. 1971. (St. Bart.) Socs: York Med Soc. Prev: SHO (Med. & Paediat.) Scotton Banks Hosp. KnaresBoro.; SHO Anaesth. & Ho. Off. (O & G) Essex Co. Hosp. Colchester.

JACKSON, Gillian Margaret — MB BCh BAO 1984 Belf.; MRCGP 1995; DRCOG 1988.

JACKSON, Gordon Elliott St Chads Surgery, Gullock Tyning, Midsomer Norton, Bath BA3 2UH Tel: 01761 413334 Fax: 01761 411176 — MB ChB 1970 Otago; BSc Otago 1966, MB ChB 1970; MRCGP 1982; DObst RCOG 1975. (Otago)

JACKSON, Graham Cardiac Department, Guy's & St Thomas' Hospital Trust, St Thomas Hospital, Lambeth Palace Road, London SE1 7EH Tel: 020 7928 9292 Fax: 020 7960 5680 Email: gjcardiol@btinternet.com; Petersfield, Bishops Walk, Croydon CR0 5BA Tel: 020 7407 5887 Fax: 020 7357 7408 Email: gjcardiol@talk21.com — MB BS (Hons.) Lond. 1970; FRCP Lond. 1985; MRCP (UK) 1972; MRCS Eng. LRCP Lond. 1970. (King's Coll. Hosp.) p/t Cons. Cardiol. Guy's & St. Thos. Hosp. Trust Lond.; Edr. Internat. Jl. Clin. Pract.; Trustee Peel Med. Research Trust; Trustee Peel Med. Research Trust. Socs: Fell. Europ. Soc. Cardiol.; Amer. Heart Assn.; FACC. Prev: Peel Med. Research Trust Trav. Fell. Cardiol. Div. Stanford Univ. Med. Centre, USA; Edr. Cardiol. in Pract.; Cons. Cardiol. Kings Coll. Hosp. Lond.

JACKSON, Graham Alan Leverndale Hospital, 510 Crookston Road, Glasgow G53 7TU Tel: 0141 211 6476; 29 Lynton Avenue, Giffnock, Glasgow G46 7JP — MB ChB 1978 Glas.; MRCPsych 1994; MRCGP 1982. (Glas.) Cons. Old Age Psychiat. Leverndale Hosp. Glas. Prev: GP E. Kilbride; Staff. Psychiat. (Old Age Psychiat.) Leverndale Hosp. Glas. & Udston & Hairmyres Hosps. Lanarksh.; Psychiat. Trainee, W. of Scotl. Scheme.

JACKSON, Graham Hunter Department of Haematology, Royal Victoria Infirmary, Queen Victoria Road, Newcastle upon Tyne NE1 4LP Tel: 0191 282 5042 Fax: 0191 201 0154 Email: graham.jackson@ncl.ac.uk; 14 Linden Road, Gosforth, Newcastle upon Tyne NE3 4EY Tel: 0191 285 0201 — MB BS 1983 Lond.; MA Camb. 1980; MD Newc. 1992; MRCP (UK) 1986; MRCPath 1993; FRCPath 2000 London; FRCP London 1999. (Camb./Westm. Hosp.) Cons. Haematol. Roy. Vict. Infirm. Newc. u. Tyne. Socs: Brit. Soc. Haematol.; Amer. Soc. Haemat.; MRCPath. Prev: Lect. Med. (Haematol.) Univ. Newc.; Regist. (Chest Med.) Freeman Rd. Hosp. Newc.; Research Regist., Regist. (Haemat.) & SHO (Gen. Med.) Roy. Vict. Infirm. Newc.

JACKSON, Graham John Whitehill Surgery, Whitehill Lane, Oxford Road, Aylesbury HP19 8EN Tel: 01296 424488 Fax: 01296 398774; White Lodge, Kings Road, Thame OX9 3JJ Tel: 01844 212360 Fax: 01844 217145 Email: gjjwork@aol.com — MB BS 1987 Lond.; MRCGP 1991; DFFP 1993; DRCOG 1990. (St. Bart. Hosp. Med. Sch.) Clin. Asst. (Psychiat.) Tindal Centre Aylesbury; Med. Manager Aylesbury & Dist. Doctors on Call. Prev: SHO Rotat. (Med.) Stoke Mandeville Hosp. Aylesbury Bucks.; SHO (Psychiat.) St. John's Hosp. Stone Bucks.; SHO (O & G) High Wycombe.

JACKSON, Guy Nicholas Barrie 14 Dewhurst Road, London W14 0ET — BM 1998 Soton.; BM Soton 1998.

JACKSON, Harold 25 Barcheston Road, Cheadle SK8 1LJ Tel: 0161 428 3784 — MB ChB 1945 Manch.; PhD Manch. 1938, MSc 1935, BSc (1st cl. Hons. Chem.) 1934, DSc 1964. (Manch.) Hon. Fell.sh. Med. Biophysics Univ. Manch. Prev: Dir. Unit Reproduct. Pharmacol. Univ. Manch.; Head Dept. Experim. Chemother. Christie Hosp.; Mem. Extern. Scientif. Staff Med. Research Counc.

JACKSON, Harold Gregory 40 Cannon Dale, Omagh BT78 1JU — MB BCh BAO 1994 Belf.

JACKSON, Heather Christine (retired) 64 Nettleham Road, Lincoln LN2 1RH Tel: 01522 524813 Fax: 01522 524813 Email: ejackson@lineone.net — MB ChB Manch. 1960.

JACKSON, Helen Ann Dept Of Haematology, Royal Gwent Hospital, Cardiff Rd, Newport NP20 2UB Tel: 01633 234464 Fax: 01633 222957 Email: helen.jackson@gwent.wales.nnhs.uk — MB ChB 1990 Manch.; MRCP (UK) 1993; MRCPath 1999 Haem. Cons. Haemat. Roy. Gwent Hosp. Newport.

JACKSON, Helen Jane Dr H J and A P Jackson, 91 Hyndland Road, Glasgow G12 9JE Tel: 0141 339 7869 Fax: 0141 334 3207; 25 West Chapelton Crescent, Bearsden, Glasgow G61 2DE Tel: 0141 942 2094 — MB ChB 1975 Glas.; DRCOG 1977.

JACKSON, Herbert James 2 St Stephens Villas, St Stephens Road, Bath BA1 5PN Tel: 01225 462329 — LRCP LRCS Ed. LRFPS Glas. 1960. (RCSI) p/t Med. Adviser Rotork plc Bath. Socs: BMA. Prev: Med. Off. Brit. Airways; Hon. Med. Off. Frankston Community Hosp., Australia; Ho. Surg. Adelaide Hosp. Dub.

JACKSON, Ian (retired) Souwester, The Street, Walberswick, Southwold IP18 6UE Tel: 01502 724144 — MRCS Eng. LRCP Lond. 1946; FFA RCS Eng. 1962; DA Eng. 1953. Prev: Sen. Regist. St. Bart. Hosp. Lond.

JACKSON, Ian David 10 Bewick Road, Gateshead NE8 4DP Tel: 0191 477 2296 Fax: 0191 477 2304; 10 Castle Farm Mews, Jesmond, Newcastle upon Tyne NE2 3RG Tel: 0191 284 7103 — MB BS 1988 Newc.; MRCGP 1994; DRCOG 1992. GP.

JACKSON, Ian James Blackie Sunnyside, Tollerton, York YO61 1QT — MB ChB 1981 Aberd.; FFA RCS Eng. 1986. Cons. Anaesth. York Dist. Hosp.

JACKSON, Mr Ian Macgilchrist (retired) 23 Springfield Road, London NW8 0QJ Tel: 020 7624 3580 — MRCS Eng. LRCP Lond. 1939; BA Camb. 1936, MB BChir 1939; FRCS Eng. 1940; FRCOG 1955, M 1942. Hon. Civil Cons. RAF; Examr. Midw. & Dis. Wom. Univs. Lond., Camb. & Oxf., Conj. Bd. &; Centr. Midw. Bd.; Examr. RCOG. Prev: O & G Surg. Middlx. Hosp. Lond.

JACKSON, Jacqueline Ann 2 Strathyre Gardens, Bearsden, Glasgow G61 2BD — MB ChB 1998 Glas.; MB ChB Glas 1998.

JACKSON, James Brian (retired) Woodside, 16 Moss Side, Wrekenton, Gateshead NE9 7UU — MB ChB 1959 St. And.

JACKSON, James Ellis Dept Imaging Imperial College, Hammersmith Hospital, London W12 0HS; 20 Elm Bank Gardens, Barnes DW13 0NT Tel: 020 8876 0523 — MB BS 1982 Lond.; MRCP (UK) 1985; FRCR 1989. (Roy. Free) Cons. Radiol. Imperial Coll. Hammersmith Hosp. Lond. Prev: Cook Research Fell. & Hon. Sen. Regist. (Diagnostic Radiol.) Roy. Postgrad. Med. Sch. Hammersmith Hosp. Lond.; Sen. Lect.,Iperial Coll., Hammersmith Hosp. Lond.

JACKSON, Mr James McGillivray (retired) Top Gorse, Rougham, Bury St Edmunds IP30 9NG Tel: 01359 270391 — MB BS 1954 Durh.; FRCS Eng. 1962; DLO Eng. 1960. Prev: Cons. ENT Surg. W. Suff. Hosp. Bury St. Edmunds.

JACKSON, Jane Caroline Deep Moss Farm, Scotland Lane, Birtle, Bury BL9 6UP Tel: 0161 797 4521 — MB BS 1985 Lond.; Cert. Family Plann. JCC 1989. Clin. Med. Off. Mancunian Community Health NHS Trust. Prev: Trainee GP Bolton VTS; SHO (A & E) Manch.; SHO (Psychiat.) Bury.

JACKSON, Jane Elizabeth Department of Radiology, Cumberland Infirmary, Carlisle CA2 7HY Tel: 01228 523444 — MB BS 1985 Lond.; FRCR. (Middlx.) Cons. Radiol. Cumbld. Infirm. Carlisle.

JACKSON, Jane Mary (retired) 35 Coldharbour, London E14 9NS Tel: 020 7987 1943 — MB BCh BAO Dub. 1959; MA Dub. 1960; MSc (Social Med.) Lond. 1975; MLitt (Social Anthropol.) Oxf. 1972; LAH 1959; FFPHM 1983, M 1977; DCH Eng. 1965. Prev: Dir. Pub. Health & Dir. Performance & Standards Newham HA.

JACKSON, Jeanne Marie Albion Road Health Centre, North Shields NE29 0HG Tel: 0191 219 6670 Fax: 0191 219 6650; 81 Kingston Drive, Whitley Bay NE26 1JJ Tel: 0191 252 8460 Email: jmjackson@doctors.org.uk — MB BS Newc. 1968; MSc 2000 London. (Newc.) SCMO (Community Child Health) N.umbria Health Care NHS Trust; Med. Adviser N. Tyneside Fostering & Adoption Agency; Med. Adviser St. Cuthbert's Care. Socs: BACDA; BACCH. Prev: Clin. Med. Off. (Child Health) N. Tyneside RHA; GP Tyneside; Civil. Med. Pract. BAOR.

JACKSON, Jennifer Ann 29 Meadow Way, Chigwell IG7 6LR Tel: (0181) 500 2691 Fax: (0181) 559 8727 Email: jennyrobint@hotmail.com; Erickson Medical Clinic, Box 160, Erickson MB R0J 0P0, Canada Tel: 00 1 204 6362411 Fax: 00 1 204 6362911 Email: wi14@dial.pipex.com — MB BS Lond. 1963; MRCS Eng. LRCP Lond. 1963. (Roy. Free) Prev: GP Manitoba Canada; GP Buckhurst Hill.

JACKSON, Jeremy Dawson Robertson Health Centre, High Street, Alness IV17 0UN Tel: 01349 882229 Fax: 01349 884004; Dalcraig, 1 Camden St, Evanton, Dingwall IV16 9XU Tel: 01349 830421 — MB ChB 1974 Dundee; MRCGP 1978; DRCOG 1976.

JACKSON, John (retired) 1 Lakeside Drive, Scunthorpe DN17 2AG — MB BS 1964 Lond.; MRCS Eng. LRCP Lond. 1964. Prev: GP Scunthorpe.

JACKSON, John Charles Winscombe Surgery, Hillyfields Way, Winscombe BS25 1AE Tel: 01934 842211; 21 Birch Drive, Langford, Bristol BS40 5HG — MB ChB 1987 Bristol; MRCP (UK) 1990; MRCGP 1994; DRCOG 1993; DCH RCP Lond. 1992.

JACKSON, John David Lister House Surgery, 35 The Parade, St Helier, Jersey JE2 3QQ Tel: 01534 36336 Fax: 01534 35304; Meadow Barn, Rozel Bay, Trinity, Jersey JE3 5BJ Tel: 01534 861092 — MB BS 1981 Newc.; BMedSc (1st cl. Hons.) Newc. 1978; Dip. Pract. Dermat. Wales 1993.

JACKSON, John Hubert (retired) Coniston, 11 Greyfriars Close, Roose, Barrow-in-Furness LA13 0TW Tel: 01229 812032 — LRCPI & LM, LRSCI & LM 1958; LRCPI & LM, LRCSI & LM 1958; MFOM RCPI 1980; MFOM RCP Lond. 1978; T(OM) 1991; DIH Soc. Apoth. Lond. 1974; DPH Liverp. 1969.

JACKSON, John Michael Hugh Parkway Medical Centre, 2 Frenton Close, Chapel House Estate, Newcastle upon Tyne NE5 1EH Tel: 0191 267 1313 Fax: 0191 229 0630; The Old Vicarage, 1 Hexham Road, Heddon on the Wall, Newcastle upon Tyne NE15 0BG Email: jackson@heddonvic.demon.co.uk — MA Oxf. 1979; MB BS (Hons.) 1978; MRCGP 1982 DCH Lond. 1982. GP Newburn, Tyne & Wear; GP Adviser Newc. City Health Trust.

JACKSON, John Richard High View Barn, 41 High House Lane, Tardebigge, Bromsgrove B60 3AQ Tel: 01527 873777 Fax: 01527 873888 Email: john@jacksonhocking.com — MB ChB (Hons.) Birm. 1967; MRCS Eng. LRCP Lond. 1967; FFOM RCP Lond. 1991, M 1987, A, 1981; DIH Eng. 1981; MBIOHs 1999. (Birm.) Indep. Cons. Occupat. Health & Applied Toxicology; Hon. Lect. Toxicol. Univ. Birm. Socs: Soc. Occupat. Med. & Brit. Occupat. Hyg. Soc. Prev: Dir. Med. & Health Sci. Monsanto Europe SA; Princip. Med. Off. Albright & Wilson Ltd.

JACKSON, Jonathan Simon Brindley John Tasker House Surgery, 56 New Street, Great Dunmow, Dunmow CM6 1BH Tel: 01371 872121 Fax: 01371 873793 — MB BS 1973 Lond.; MRCGP 1980; DObst RCOG 1975. Prev: Chairm. W. Essex GP Med. Advisory Comm.; Chairm. Educat. Comm. & Hon. Sec. Essex Fac. RCGP.

JACKSON, Julia Helen Dunsville Medical Centre, 128 High Street, Dunsville, Doncaster DN7 4BY Tel: 01302 890108 Fax: 01302 881425; Longcroft Close, Ancient Lane, Hatfield Woodhouse, Doncaster DN7 6PJ Tel: 01302 350568 — MB ChB 1983 Sheff.; BMedSci Sheff. 1981; MRCGP 1987. Prev: Med. Adviser Doncaster Health.

JACKSON, Juliet Mary Constance 3 Adams Road, Cambridge CB3 9AD — MB BS 1985 Lond.

JACKSON, Juliette Elouise Zoe 5 Burnside Park, Balerno EH14 7LY — MB ChB 1998 Ed.; MB ChB Ed 1998.

***JACKSON, Justyn Peter** 10 Furzefield Road, Reigate RH2 7HG — MB ChB 1994 Birm.

JACKSON, Karen Jane 81 Queensgate Drive, Birstall, Leicester LE4 3JT — MB ChB 1988 Leic. SHO (Anaesth.) Leicester Roy. Infirm.

***JACKSON, Kathryn Marie** 17 Mayfield Road, Timperley, Altrincham WA15 7TB — BM BS 1998 Nottm.; BM BS Nottm 1998; BMedSci Nottm 1996.

JACKSON, Kevin 17 Gayhurst Road, London E8 3EH — MB BS 1979 Lond.; MRCGP 1988; DRCOG 1983.

JACKSON, Kevin Alan Tinshill Lane Surgery, 8 Tinshill Lane, Leeds LS16 7AP Tel: 0113 267 3462 Fax: 0113 230 0402; Springwood, Apperley Lane, Rawdon, Leeds LS19 6BJ Tel: 0113 202 9070 — MB ChB 1986 Leeds; DRCOG 1991.

JACKSON, Kevin Andrew Chapelthorpe Surgery, Hall Lane, Chapelthorpe, Wakefield WF4 3JE Tel: 01924 255166 Fax: 01924 257653 — MB ChB 1989 Leeds.

JACKSON, Lesley Anne 14 Mylne Avenue, Dollar FK14 7HS — MB ChB 1993 Ed.

JACKSON, Lesley Stewart 30 Beauclere Street, Alva, Clackmannan Tel: 01259 62657 — MB ChB 1966 Glas.; FRCS Ed. 1973; FCOphth. 1988; DO Eng. 1969. Cons. Ophth. Forth Valley Health Bd.

JACKSON, Leslie Kinghorn Department of Diagnostic Radiology, Princess Margaret Hospital, Swindon SN1 4JU Tel: 01793 426313; Woodgate House, Bath Road, Marlborough SN8 1NN Tel: 01672 512644 — MB 1973 Camb.; BChir 1972; MRCP (UK) 1975; FRCR 1979. (Guy's) Cons. Radiol. Swindon & MarlBoro. NHS Trust. Prev: Sen. Regist. (Radiodiag.) Bristol Roy. Infirm.; SHO Renal & Transpl. Unit Guy's Hosp.; SHO Roy. Nat. Hosp. Rheum. Dis. Bath.

JACKSON, Lisa Victoria 3 Ascot Close, Eastbourne BN20 7HL — MB BS 1990 Lond.; 1998 Dip Ther.; BSc (Nutrit.) Lond. 1987; DCH RCP Lond. 1993; DFFP 1993; MRCGP 1994. (UCMSH) p/t Br. Head, Nutrit. Div., Food Standards Agency. Socs: Nutrit. Soc., Counc. Mem.

JACKSON, Lorna Elizabeth Campbell Flat 3/3, 40 Bridge St., Glasgow G5 9HU — MB ChB 1997 Glas.

***JACKSON, Louise Elaine** 24 Eddisbury Avenue, Flixton, Manchester M41 8QJ — MB ChB 1998 Birm.

JACKSON, Lyn Margaret 10 Church Road, Whitchurch, Bristol BS14 0PP — MB ChB 1973 Bristol; MRCP (UK) 1976.

JACKSON, Maldwyn Isaac (retired) Berllan, 21 Belgrave Road, Abergavenny NP7 7AH Tel: 01873 852414 — MRCS Eng. LRCP Lond. 1927.

JACKSON, Margaret Churchfield Surgery, 1 Iburndale Lane, Sleights, Whitby YO22 5DP Tel: 01947 810466 Fax: 01947 811375 — MB ChB 1988 Glas.; Diploma Therapeutics 1997; MRCGP 1993; DRCOG 1991.

JACKSON, Margaret Joan Royal Victoria Infirmary, Queen Victoria Road, Newcastle upon Tyne NE1 4LP Tel: 0191 232 4951; The Old Vicarage, Heddon on The Wall, Newcastle upon Tyne NE15 0BG Tel: 01661 853927 Email: margaret.jackson@ncl.ac.uk — MB BS 1979 Newc.; BMedSc Newc. 1976, MB BS (Hons.) 1979; FRCP (UK) 1999; MD 1996; MRCP (UK) 1981. (Newcastle) Cons. Neurol. Roy.

Vict. Infirm. Newc. Prev: Sen. Regist. (Neurol.) Roy. Vict. Infirm. Newc.; Regist. (Gen. Med.) Roy. Vict. Infirm. Newc.
JACKSON, Margaret Young (retired) 18 Stepney Road, Scarborough YO12 5BN Tel: 01723 366417 — MB ChB 1944 Glas. Prev: GP ScarBoro..
JACKSON, Marianne Elise 43 Seagry Road, London E11 2NH — MB ChB 1988 Manch.; BSc St. And. 1985; FRCS Lond. 1993. Specialist Regist. (A & E) OldCh. Hosp. Romford. Socs: Assoc. Mem. Brit. Accid. & Emerg. Med. Soc. Prev: Regist. (A & E) Newham Gen. Hosp. Lond.; SHO (Anaesth.) King Geo. Hosp.; SHO (A & E) Watford Gen. Hosp.
JACKSON, Mark 7 Riversleigh Road, Avonside, Leamington Spa CV32 6BG — MB ChB 1982 Birm.
JACKSON, Mr Mark 2 Cecil Road, Clifton, Bristol BS8 3HR — MB BS 1983 Lond.; FRCS Eng. 1988; FRCS Ed. 1988.
JACKSON, Mark Basil Dept. Chest Medicine, Brighton General Hospital, Elm Grove, Brighton BN12 3EW Tel: 01273 696955 Fax: 01273 665198; 19 Willard Way, Ashington RH20 3PQ — MB BS 1990 Lond.; MRCP (UK) 1993. (London Hospital Medical College) Cons. Phys., Respirat. Med. Brighton Health Care NHS Trust. Prev: Specialist Regist. Soton. Gen. Hosp.; Specialist Regist. Portsmouth Hosp.NHS Trust; Regist. Roy. Bournemouth Hosp.
JACKSON, Mark Bentley Oldfield Surgery, 45 Upper Oldfield Park, Bath BA2 3HT Tel: 01225 21137; Inner Meadow, Combe Hay, Bath BA2 7EE Tel: 01225 21137 — BM BCh 1980 Oxf.; DPhil. Oxf. 1989; MA Oxf. 1980, BM BCh 1980; MRCGP 1984; DRCOG 1982. Prev: Research Fell. Imperial Cancer Research Fund.
***JACKSON, Mark Peter** Bramling Oast, Lenham Road, Headcorn, Ashford TN27 9LQ — MB BS 1997 Lond.; BSc Hons 1994.
JACKSON, Martin David Mount Chambers Surgery, 92 Coggeshall Road, Braintree CM7 9BY Tel: 01376 553415 Fax: 01376 552451; 10 Tortoiseshell Way, Braintree CM7 8WG — MB BCh 1982 Wales; MRCGP 1986. Prev: Clin. Med. Off. E. Herts. HA; SHO (Geriat.) S. Glam. HA; SHO (A & E) N. E. Surrey HA.
JACKSON, Mary Gayle Chesterfield & North Derbyshire Royal Hospital NHS Trust, Calow, Chesterfield S40 3PZ Tel: 01246 277271 — MB BS 1983 Newc.; MRCPsych 1988. Cons. Psychiat. Chesterfield & N. Derbysh. Prev: Sen. Regist. (Psychiat.) Manch.; Research Fell. Manch. Univ.
JACKSON, Matthew Charles Department of Neurology, Wycombe General Hospital, Queen Alexandra Road, High Wycombe HP11 2TT — MB BS 1987 Lond.; BSc Lond. 1984, MB BS 1987; MRCP (UK) 1990. Regist. (Neurol.) Univ. Hosp. Nottm. Prev: SHO (Neurol.) Derbysh. Roy. Infirm.; SHO (Oncol.) Roy. Marsden Hosp.; SHO (Med.) Warrington Dist. Gen. Hosp.
JACKSON, Maurice Andrew York Lodge, 69 York Avenue, Finchfield, Wolverhampton WV3 9BX Tel: 01902 307999 — MD 1983 Lond.; MB BS 1972; FRCP Lond. 1990; MRCP (UK) 1976; LRCPI & LM, LRCSI & LM 1972. Cons. Phys. Wolverhampton HA. Prev: Lect. & Sen. Regist. (Gen. Med. & Internal Metab. Med.) Soton.; Univ.; Research Fell. (Nephrol.) Soton. Univ.; Regist. (Gen. Med.) Norf. & Norwich Hosp.
JACKSON, Melanie Ann Doctors Accommodation, Peterborough District Hospital, Holdich St., Peterborough PE3 6DA — MB ChB 1995 Leic.
JACKSON, Brigadier Michael Barlow Arthur, Brigadier late RAMC (retired) 124 High Street, Sandhurst GU47 8HA Tel: 01252 876284 — MB BS 1957 Lond.; MRCS Eng. LRCP Lond. 1957; FRCOG 1982, M 1968; DTM & H Eng. 1963. Cons. O & G Qu. Eliz. Milit. Hosp. Lond. Prev: Regist. (Gyn.) Roy. Berks. Hosp. Reading.
JACKSON, Michael Charles Henry, Surg. Capt. RN Retd. (retired) 10 Palmerston Way, Alverstoke, Gosport PO12 2LZ Tel: 01705 520752 Fax: 01705 520752 — MB BS Lond. 1950; LMSSA Lond. 1949; FRCOG 1979, M 1965; DObst 1961. Prev: Civil. Cons. Gyn. RN Hosp. Haslar & Cons. O & G RN.
JACKSON, Neil David 26 Greenway Close, Sale M33 4PU — MB BS 1990 Lond.
JACKSON, Neil Richard North Thames East PCG Dept, 35 Millman St., London W1N 3EE Tel: 01992 572727 Fax: 01992 574889 Email: njackson@tpnde.ac.uk; Monksway, Woodside Green, Great Hallingbury, Bishop's Stortford CM22 7UU Tel: 01279 654983 Fax: 01279 461830 Email: njack83997@aol.com — MB BS 1972 Lond.; MRCS Eng. LRCP Lond. 1972; FRCGP 1991, M 1977; DFFP 1993; DObst RCOG 1974; Cert. JCC Lond. 1974. (Lond. Hosp.) Dean of Postgrad. Gen. Pract. Educat. & Regional Dir. Postgrad. GP ED. N. Thames (E.) Region; Mem. Examrs. Panel RCGP. Prev: Course Organiser W. Essex VTS; SHO (O & G) St. Margt's. Hosp. Epping; Ho. Off. (Emerg. & Accid.) Off. Lond. Hosp.
JACKSON, Neil Warren The Surgery, 1 Crawley Lane, Pound Hill, Crawley RH10 7DX Tel: 01293 549916 Fax: 01293 615382 — BM BS 1987 Nottm.; BMedSci (Hons.) Nottm. 1985. Prev: Trainee GP Crawley VTS.
JACKSON, Neville c/o 6 Meadow Mead, Radlett WD7 8ES — MB BCh BAO 1937 Dub.; MA, MB BCh BAO Dub. 1937. (T.C. Dub.) Prev: Capt. R.A.M.C.; Res. Med. Off. Roy. Vict. Hosp. Folkestone.
JACKSON, Neville Colin Church Cottages, Shuart Lane, St Nicholas At Wade, Birchington CT7 0NG — BM BCh 1972 Oxf.; MA, BM BCh Oxf. 1972; MRCP (UK) 1977.
JACKSON, Neville Reed The Riverside Surgery, Waterside, Evesham WR11 6JP Tel: 01386 40121 Fax: 01386 442615; Trelyn, Netiheton, Elmley Castle, Pershore WR10 3JG — MB ChB 1966 Leeds; DA Eng. 1969; DObst RCOG 1968.
JACKSON, Nicholas 1 Oak Farm, Wistow, Selby YO8 3FW — MB ChB 1992 Leic.
JACKSON, Nicholas Andrew 1 Beck Grove, Shaw, Oldham OL2 8NG — BChir 1992 Camb.
JACKSON, Nicholas Raymond Jackson, Knights, Richards and Hobbis, Thorney Medical Centre, Wisbech Road, Thorney, Peterborough PE6 0SA Tel: 01733 270219 Fax: 01733 270860; Weststones, 1 St. Pega's Road, Peakirk, Peterborough PE6 7NF Tel: 01733 253483 Fax: 01733 253660 Email: nrj@nrjl.freeserve.co.uk — MB ChB 1977 Dundee.
JACKSON, Nicola Jane Bracken Hill Lodge, North Road, Leigh Woods, Bristol BS8 3PL— BM BS 1990 Nottm.
JACKSON, Nicola Mary Luton & Dunstable Hospital, Lewsey Road, Luton LU4 0DZ; Butts Farm, Stocksmoor, Huddersfield HD4 6XG Tel: 01484 664546 — MB BS 1990 Lond. Research Fell. (Cardiol.) Luton & Dunstable Hosp. Socs: BMA. Prev: SHO (Med. & Cardiol.) Luton; SHO (Med. & c/o Elderly) Edgeware Gen. Hosp.
JACKSON, Patricia Denise Community Child Health, Edinburgh Sick Childrens NHS Trust, 10 Chalmers Crescent, Edinburgh EH9 1TS Tel: 0131 536 0471 Fax: 0131 536 0570 — MB ChB 1974 Ed.; MRCP (UK) 1986; FRCPCH; DCH RCPS Glas. 1976. (Edinburgh) Cons. Paediat. Community Child Health Lothian. Socs: BACCH & SACCA; RCPCH.
JACKSON, Patricia Maria Portland Medical Centre, 184 Portland Road, London SE25 4QB — MB ChB 1988 Manch.; BA (1st cl. Hons. Chinese) Durham 1978. Prev: SHO (Med. O & G, A & E & Psychiat.) Mayday Hosp. Croydon; Ho. Off. (Surg. & Med.) Mayday Hosp.
JACKSON, Paul Anthony Peel Health Centre, Angoluleme Way, Bury BL9 0BT Tel: 0161 763 7790 Fax: 0161 761 2392 — MB BS 1986 Lond.
JACKSON, Paul Duncan St James Surgery, Gains Lane, Devizes SN10 1QU Tel: 01380 722206 Fax: 01380 721552 — MB BS 1982 Lond.; MRCGP 1988; Dip. Sports Med. 1992; DRCOG 1988. (St. Mary's) GP Sports Injury Clinic Roy. United Hosp., Ridgeway Hosp., Swindon. Socs: BASM; Amer. Coll. Sports Med. Prev: SHO (Dermat.) Ealing Hosp. S.all; SHO (O & G) Hillingdon Hosp.; SHO (Med.) Centr. Middlx. Hosp. Lond.
JACKSON, Paul Howard Woodlea House Surgery, 1 Crantock Grove, Bournemouth BH8 0HS Tel: 01202 300903 Fax: 01202 304826; 2 Erpingham Road, Branksome, Poole BH12 1EX Tel: 01202 764929 — MB BS 1974 Lond.; MRCS Eng. LRCP Lond. 1974; DRCOG 1977.
JACKSON, Paul Livesey Ash Grove, Nooklands, Fulwood, Preston PR2 8XN — MB ChB 1998 Manch.; MB ChB Manch 1998.
JACKSON, Paul Montgomery (retired) New House, The Parade, Whitchurch, Cardiff CF14 2EE Tel: 029 2069 4665 — MB BCh Wales 1957; MRCPsych 1971; DPM Eng. 1962. Prev: Cons. Child & Adolesc. Psychiat. S. Glam. AHA (T).
JACKSON, Pauline Mary 8 Cyncoed Rise, Cardiff CF23 6SF — MB BS 1947 Lond.; MRCS Eng. LRCP Lond. 1946; DCH Eng. 1948. (King's Coll. Hosp.)
JACKSON, Peter 32 Albany Terrace, Worcester WR1 3DY — MRCS Eng. LRCP Lond. 1960; FFA RCS Eng 1969.
JACKSON, Peter Shalom, 10 Furzefield Road, Reigate RH2 7HG Tel: 01737 242958 Fax: 01737 213923 Email:

p.jackson@mcmail.com — MB BS 1966 Lond.; FRCOG 1989, M 1974; DObst RCOG 1968. (Lond. Hosp.) Cons. O & G Surrey & Sussex Healthcare NHS Trust at Crawley E. Surrey & Horsham Hosps. Socs: BMA; Brit. Soc. Colpos. & Cerv. Path. Prev: Sen. Regist. (O & G) Lond. Hosp.; O & G Sudan Interior Miss. Egbe Hosp., Nigeria.

JACKSON, Peter Alexander 18 Elmside, Guildford GU2 7SH Tel: 01483 575505; Histopathology Department, Royal Surrey County Hospital, Egerton Road, Guildford GU2 7XX Tel: 01483 571122 Fax: 01483 452218 — MB BS Lond. 1981; MRCPath 1992. (Guy's) Cons. Histopath. Roy. Surrey Co. Hosp. Guildford.

JACKSON, Peter Anthony Meadway Health Centre, Meadway, Sale M33 4PS Tel: 0161 905 2850; 14 Stokesay Road, Sale M33 6GL Tel: 020 8905 2850 — MB ChB 1979 Leeds; MRCGP 1983; DRCOG 1982; DCH RCPS Glas. 1981. GP Sale. Prev: Trainee GP Macclesfield VTS; Ho. Surg. York Dist. Hosp.; Ho. Phys. St. Jas. Hosp. Leeds.

JACKSON, Mr Peter Douglas, Surg. Cdr. RN (retired) 70 Loampit Hill, Lewisham, London SE13 7SX Tel: 020 8692 5615 — MB BChir 1956 Camb.; FRCS Eng. 1968; FRCS Ed. 1961; DLO Eng. 1967. Prev: Cons. ENT Surg. S.wark & Lewisham, Greenwich & Bromley HAs.

JACKSON, Peter George Laverock Hill, 7 The Avenue, Dunstable LU6 2AA Tel: 01582 661100 — MRCS Eng. LRCP Lond. 1949. (St. Bart.) Prev: Maj. RAMC Jun. Med. Specialist; Regist. (Med.) Rossendale Gen. Hosp. Rawtenstall; SHO Luton & Dunstable Hosp.

JACKSON, Peter Gordon The Blackheath Hospital, 40-42 Lee Terrace, London SE3 9UD Tel: 020 8297 2220 Fax: 020 8852 8468 Email: gordonjackson@lew-educ.dircon.co.uk; 6 Brookway, Blackheath, London SE3 9BJ — MB 1972 Camb.; BChir 1971; FRCP Lond. 1989; MRCP (UK) 1973. Cons. Phys. Lewisham Hosp. Lond. Prev: Sen. Regist. (Gen. Med.) Guy's Hosp. Lond.; Regist. (Diabetes) & Research Fell. (Cardiol.) King's Coll. Hosp. Lond.; Chairm. Nat. Assn. Clin. Tutors 1994-1997.

JACKSON, Peter Howard The Surgery, Eyam, Hope Valley S32 5QH Tel: 01433 630836 Fax: 01433 631832; Delph House, Eyam, Hope Valley S32 5QW Tel: 01433 30851 Email: jaco@msn.com — MB ChB 1968 Bristol; 1998 Advanced Dip in Occ Med Manch.; 1996 Dip Occ Med FOM at RCP; DObst RCOG 1970. (Bristol) Occupat.al Phys., N. Derbysh. C.H.C.S., Walton Hopital, Chesterfield.

JACKSON, Peter John Charles 10 Springfield Road, Lytham St Annes FY8 1TW — MRCS Eng. LRCP Lond. 1974.

JACKSON, Peter Neil Health Centre, Kingsbridge TQ7 1HR Tel: 01548 853551 Fax: 01548 857741; Hatch Arundell, Loddiswell, Kingsbridge TQ7 4AJ Tel: 01548 550104 — MB BS Lond. 1967; MRCGP 1977.

JACKSON, Peter Robert University Department Pharmacology and Therapeutics, Royal Hallamshire Hospital, Sheffield S10 2JF Tel: 0114 271 2615; 2A Chorley Place, Sheffield S10 3RS — MB ChB 1976 Sheff.; PhD Oxf. 1988, MA 1979; FRCP Lond. 1996; MRCP (UK) 1979. (Sheff.) Sen. Lect. (Therap.) Univ. Sheff. Prev: MRC Fell. Clin. Pharmacol. Roy. Hallamsh. Hosp.

JACKSON, Peter Terence (retired) 2 Rectory Close, Eckington, Sheffield S21 4GL Tel: 01246 433334 — MRCS Eng. LRCP Lond. 1953. Prev: GP Facilitator Barnsley FPC.

JACKSON, Philip Anthony Jackson and Partners, Glastonbury Surgery, Feversham Lane, Glastonbury BA6 9LP Tel: 01458 833666 Fax: 01458 834536; Noah's Ark, Mill St, Baltonsborough, Glastonbury BA6 8RJ Tel: 01458 850594 Fax: 01458 834536 — MB BS 1969 Lond.; MFHom RCP Lond. 1987; MRCGP 1974; DObst RCOG 1973. (St. Bart.) Prev: Trainee GP Kettering VTS; SHO (Cas. Med.) St. Bart. Hosp. Lond.

JACKSON, Philip Cook High Street Surgery, 117 High Street, Clay Cross, Chesterfield S45 9DZ Tel: 01246 862237 — MB ChB 1982 Sheff.

JACKSON, Philippa Claire Eynsham Medical Centre, Conduit Lane, Eynsham, Witney OX29 9QB — BM BCh 1987 Oxf.; BA (Hons.) Camb. 1984; MRCGP 1991; DCH 1992. p/t GP Princip. Eynsham Med. Gp. Prev: GP Princip. Stoke Gifford Med. Centre Bristol 1995-2000.

JACKSON, Ralph Nevil 89 Channings, Kingsway, Hove BN3 4FU Tel: 01273 727727 — MB BS 1947 Lond.; MRCS Eng. LRCP Lond. 1947; FRCGP 1983, M 1978. (Middlx.) Socs: Sydenham Dist. Med. Soc. Prev: Clin. Asst. Paediat. Dept. Lewisham Hosp.; Cas. Med. Off. Middlx. Hosp. Lond; Ho. Surg. P.ss Alice Memor. Hosp. E.bourne.

JACKSON, Ralph Walter Freeman Hospital, Freeman Road, High Heaton, Newcastle upon Tyne NE7 7DN; 21 Keyes Gardens, High West Jesmond, Newcastle upon Tyne NE2 3RA Tel: 0191 284 7877 Email: ralphjackson@lycosmail.com — MB BS 1990 Newc.; MRCP (UK) 1993; FRCR 1998. Specialist Regist. (Diagn.Radiol) Freeman Hosp., Newc. Prev: Regist. (Diagn. Radiol.) Stopford Bldg. Univ. Manch.; Clin. Fell. (Cardiol.) S. Cleveland Hosp. Middlesbrough; SHO (Neurol.) MiddlesBoro. Gen. Hosp.

JACKSON, Raymond (retired) Landswood House, Winlaton, Blaydon-on-Tyne Tel: 0191 414 2439 — MB BS 1953 Durh. Prev: Clin. Tutor (Family Med.) Univ. Newc.

***JACKSON, Richard Anthony** 14 Whitegates Crescent, Willaston, South Wirral CH64 2UX — MB ChB 1995 Birm.

JACKSON, Richard Colin Fir Grove House, Glasshouses, Pateley Bridge, Harrogate HG2 9HQ — MB ChB 1975 Leeds; BSc Leeds 1970, MB ChB 1975.

JACKSON, Richard Douglas (retired) 3 The Stables, High Park, Oxenholme, Kendal LA9 7RE Tel: 01539 722759 — MB ChB 1958 Leeds; DObst RCOG 1963. Prev: Hosp. Pract. (O & G) W. Morland Co. Hosp. Kendal.

JACKSON, Richard Mark Huddersfield Royal Infirmary, Huddersfield; Low House Farm, Stocks Lane, Clayton House, Bradford BD13 2RW — MB ChB 1987 Leeds. Cons.

JACKSON, Robert Avonbrook, Church Road, Sherbourne, Warwick CV35 8AN Email: bob.jackson@lineone.net / robert.jackson@swest.hosp-tr.wmids.nhs.uk — 1979 MB ChB Liverp.; 1992 MD Liverp.; 1985 MRCOG; 1991 T(OG); 1999 FRCOG. Cons. O & G S. Warks. NHS Trust. Prev: Sen. Regist. NW Region; Research Fell. (O & G) Birm. Univ.

JACKSON, Robert Department of Pathology, Royal Infirmary, 84 Castle St., Glasgow G4 0SF Email: gcl127@clinmed.gla.ac.uk — MB BCh BAO 1981 NUI; MRCPI 1984; MRCPath. (Histopath.) 1992. Cons. Histopath. Vict. Infirm. Trust.; Cons. (Histopathol.) Roy. Infirm. Glas.

JACKSON, Robert Anthony Bognor Drug & Alcohol Team, 22 Sudley Road, Bognor Regis PO21 1ER Tel: 01243 869234 Fax: 01243 824023 — MB BS 1975 Newc.; MRCPsych 1980; FRCPsych 1998. (Oxf.) Cons. Psych. Alcohol & Subst. Abuse Team Sussex Weald & Downs NHS Trust Chichester. Prev: Cons. Psychiat. Graylingwell Hosp. Chichester HA.; Regist. (Psychiat.) Merton, Sutton & Wandsworth AHA (T); Regist. (Psychiat.) Newc. AHA (T).

JACKSON, Robert Hugh, OBE, MC (retired) 21 Lyndhurst Road, Benton, Newcastle upon Tyne NE12 9NT Tel: 0191 266 3552 Fax: 0191 266 3552 — BM BCh Oxf. 1942; MA Oxf. 1942; FRCP Lond. 1971, M 1955; FRCPH (Hon) 1995. Pres. Child Accid. Preven. Trust Lond. Prev: Cons. Paediat. Roy. Vict. Infirm. Newc.

JACKSON, Robert Kenneth Well Cottage, May Lane, Pilley, Lymington SO41 5QR — MB BChir Camb. 1958; MA Camb. 1958; FRCS Eng. 1964. (St. Thos.) Socs: Fell. BOA; Fell. (Pres.) Brit. Scoliosis Soc. Prev: Cons. Emerit. Orthop. Surg. Soton. Gen. Hosp.; Chief Asst. (Orthop.) St. Thos. Hosp. Lond.; Regist. P.ss Margt. Rose Orthop. Hosp. & Roy. Infirm. Edin.

JACKSON, Robert Michael — MB ChB 1990 Sheff.; MRCPath; MSc (Med. & Molecular Microbiol.) Manch. 1995. (Sheff.) Cons. (Microbiol.) Cheltenham E. Gloucestershire NHS Trust. Prev: SpR (Med. Microbiol.) PHLS Univ. Hosp. of Wales Cardiff; SHO (Med. Microbiol.) Manch. Roy. Infirm.; SHO (Orthop.) & Ho. Off. (Med.) Glan Clwyd Hosp. Bodelwyddan.

JACKSON, Robert Steven Department of Clinical Biochemistry, Box 232, Addenbrooke's Hospital, Cambridge CB2 2QQ Tel: 01223 217155 Email: rsj21@hermes.cam.ac.uk — MB ChB 1980 Sheff.; BMedSci (Hons.) Sheff. 1979, MB ChB 1980; FFA RCS Eng. 1984; MSc 1993; MRCPath 1996. (Sheffield Univ.) Sen. Regist. (Chem. Path.).

JACKSON, Robin Geoffrey, TD Rosebank Surgery, Ashton Road, Road, Lancaster LA1 4JS Tel: 01524 842284 Fax: 01524 844839; Cloudsmoor, Brettargh Drive, Haverbreaks, Lancaster LA1 5BN Email: rjackson@rjackson.demon.co — MB ChB 1977 Manch.; MRCGP 1980; DRCOG 1980; Dip. Occ. Med. 1998. Dir. Marine Med. Servs. NW Ltd.

JACKSON, Robin George 45A Marine Avenue, Whitley Bay NE26 1LZ Tel: 01770 530321 — MB ChB 1966 St. And. Socs:

BMA. Prev: Ho. Surg. Arbroath Infirm; SHO (Anaesth.) & (O & G) Co. Hosp. Hereford.

JACKSON, Robin John 5 Victoria Gardens, Watnall, Nottingham NG16 1GZ — MB ChB 1982 Liverp.; MFOM 1992. Sen. Occupat. Phys. Socs: MSOM.

JACKSON, Robin Mackay Accident & Emergency Department, Dryburn Hospital, Durham DH1 5TW Tel: 0191 333 2131; 30 Durham, Moor Crescent, Durham DH1 5AW Tel: 0191 333 2523 — MB ChB Manch. 1978. Staff Grade (A & E) Dryburn Hosp. Durh.

JACKSON, Roderick Guy Macdonald 124 Shorncliffe Road, Folkestone CT20 2PQ — MB BS 1990 Lond.

JACKSON, Roderick Neil Campbeltown Health Centre, Stewart Road, Campbeltown PA28 6AT Tel: 01586 552105 Fax: 01586 554997; Glenadale, Campbeltown PA28 6JL Tel: 01586 52197 — MB ChB 1963 Glas. (Glas.) Prev: Regist. ENT Dept. Vict. Infirm. Glas.; Jun. Ho. Off. (O & G) Robroyston Hosp. Glas; Jun. Ho. Off. (Surg.) Roy. Infirm. Glas.

JACKSON, Rodwin Albert Chase Farm Hospital, The Ridgeway, Enfield EN2 8JL Tel: 020 8366 9192 Fax: 020 8364 6936; 35 Crooked Usage, London N3 3EU Tel: 020 8346 0379 Fax: 020 8346 0379 — 1960 MB BCh Witwatersrand; 1974 MD Witwatersrand; 1965 FCP(SA); 1968 MRCP Lond.; 1998 FRCP. Cons. Phys. Chase Farm Hosp. Lond. Enfield. Socs: Brit. Diabetic Assn.; Soc. Endocrinol.; Brit. Geriat. Soc. Prev: Sen. Lect. (Med.) King's Coll. Hosp. Lond.; Regist. (Gen. Med.) Johannesburg Gen. Hosp. S. Afr.; Regist. (Clin. Endocrin.) Hammersmith Hosp. Lond.

JACKSON, Rosemary Sarah Harambee Surgery, 27 Skipton Road, Trawden, Colne BB8 8QU Tel: 01282 868482 Fax: 01282 862685 — MB ChB 1987 Leeds.

JACKSON, Roy Francis Bushmead Avenue Surgery, 21 Bushmead Avenue, Bedford MK40 3QJ Tel: 01234 349191 Fax: 01234 269649; Willow Cottage, Oldways Road, Ravensden, Bedford MK44 2RF — MB BS 1982 Lond.; DRCOG 1989. Anaesth. Bedford Hosp.

JACKSON, Ruby McLerie 68 Mill Lane, Herne Bay CT6 7DP Tel: 01227 373266 — MB ChB 1944 Glas.; LM Rotunda 1947; DGO Dub. 1947; DObst RCOG 1948. Prev: SCMO Kent CC; Obst. Ho. Surg. Canad. Red Cross Memor. Hosp. Taplow; Ho. Phys. Roy. Hosp. Sick Childr. Glas.

JACKSON, Rupert John 119 High Street, Belmont, Bolton BL7 8AX — MB ChB 1992 Manch.; FRCS Ed. 1996.

JACKSON, Ruth Abigail Sherstock Cottage, Sherstock, Shaftesbury SP7 9PS — MB BS 1998 Lond.; MB BS Lond 1998.

JACKSON, Ruth Elizabeth 5 Broun Drive, Alloway, Ayr KA7 4PD — MB ChB 1984 Glas. Regist. (Anaesth.) W.ern Infirm. Glas. Prev: Regist. (Anaesth.) Law Hosp. Carluke.

JACKSON, Sarah Mount Caire, 174 Fore St., Saltash PL12 6JS; Port View Surgery, Higher Port View, Saltash PL12 4BU — MB BS 1975 Lond.; MRCGP 1983; DRCOG 1981; DCH Eng. 1979.

JACKSON, Sarah Ann 20 Eastwoodmans Road, Giffnock, Glasgow G46 6QF Tel: 0141 638 9489 — MB ChB 1987 Ed.; FRCA 1994; DA (UK) 1991. Sen. Regist. (Anaesth.) W.. Infirm. Glas. Socs: BMA; MRCAnaesth.; Assn. Anaesth. Prev: Regist. (Anaesth.) NW RHA; Clin. Research Fell. (Anaesth.) Roy. Preston Hosp.; SHO (Anaesth.) Vict. Hosp. Blackpool.

JACKSON, Sarah Astrid Top Floor Flat, 65 Arthur Road, London SW19 7DN — MB ChB 1992 Birm.; DMCOG 1997; DFFP 1998. (Birmingham)

JACKSON, Sarah Jane Salford Royal Hospitals NHS Trsust, Hope Hospital, Slott Lane, Salford M6 8WH — BM BS 1992 Nottm.; FRCR 1999; BMedSci. Nottm. 1990; MRCP (UK) 1996. Cons. Radiologist with s/i in Musculoskeletal Radiol. Salford.

JACKSON, Shaun Francis Laburnum Cottage, 8 Main St., Milnthorpe LA7 7PN — MB ChB 1994 Leeds.

JACKSON, Mr Shaun Roy Royal Liverpool University Hospital, Prescot St., Liverpool L7 8XP Tel: 0151 706 2000; 12 Arno Road, Oxton, Wirral — MB ChB 1981 Liverp.; FRCS Ed. 1987; MRCS Eng. LRCP Lond. 1981. Cons. Otolaryngologist Head & Neck Surg. Roy. Liverp. Univ. Hosp. & Roy. Liverp. Childr.s Hosp. Alder Hey Merseyside; Hon. Clin. Lect. Univ. Liverp. Prev: Sen. Regist. (Otorhinolaryng.) Roy. Liverp. Hosp.; Oberartz Universistasspital Zurich, Switz.; Cons. Ear, Nose & Throat Whiston Hosp. Merseyside.

JACKSON, Sheila Mary Barnoldswick Medical Centre, Park Road, Barnoldswick BB18 5BG Tel: 01282 812244 — MB ChB 1984 Manch.; BMedSci St. And. 1981; DCH RCP Lond. 1989; DRCOG 1987. p/t GP Barnoldswick. Prev: SHO (O & G, Paediat, Emerg. & Gen. Med.) Tameside Gen. Hosp.; Ho. Off. (Med./Geriat.) Tameside Gen. Hosp.; Ho. Off. (Surg.) Wythenshawe Hosp.

JACKSON, Shelley Louise Hollycroft, Bryn Estyn Road, Wrexham LL13 9TY — MB ChB 1998 Sheff.; MB ChB Sheff 1998.

JACKSON, Simon Beechwood Surgery, 57 John Street, Workington CA14 3BT Tel: 01900 64866 Fax: 01900 871561 — MB BS 1973 London; MB BS Lond.1973. (London) GP Workington,Cumbria.

JACKSON, Simon Adrian Beacon Cottage, Beacon Lane, Rednal, Birmingham B45 9XL Tel: 0121 453 2048 — BM BCh 1993 Oxf.; BA (Hons.) Oxf. 1990. SHO (Paediat.) Gloucester Roy. Hosp. Prev: SHO (A & E) & Ho. Off. (Surg.) John Radcliffe Hosp.; Ho. Off. (Med.) Poole Gen. Hosp.

JACKSON, Simon Andrew Imaging Directorate, Derriford Hospital, Derriford Road, Plymouth PL6 8DH Tel: 01752 763271 Fax: 01752 763277 Email: simon.jackson@phnt.swest.nhs.uk — MB BS 1987 Lond.; FRCS Eng. 1991; FRCR 1994. (St Thomas' Hospital Medical School) Cons. Radiol. Socs: Soc. Radiol. in Train. (Ex-Pres.).

JACKSON, Simon Robert 4 Beech Road, Heswall, Wirral CH60 2SR — BM BCh 1987 Oxf.; BA Oxf. 1984, BM BCh 1987. Ho. Surg. Roy. Shrewsbury Hosp.

JACKSON, Siobhan 3 Norman Cottages, Michaelston-le-Pit, Dinas Powys CF64 4HP — MB BCh 1994 Wales.

JACKSON, Spencer (retired) 1A Bonfields Avenue, Swanage BH19 1PL Tel: 01929 423827 — MB BS 1938 Lond.; MRCS Eng. LRCP Lond. 1938; DPH Lond. 1947. Prev: Med. Off. Colon. Med. Serv.

JACKSON, Stanley Leighton Orr (retired) 26 Herbert Road, Hornchurch RM11 3LD Tel: 01708 451587 — MB BS 1947 Lond.; MD Lond. 1950; FRCP Lond. 1983, M 1949; LMSSA Lond. 1946. Prev: Cons. Geriat. Med. Barking & Havering HA.

JACKSON, Professor Stephen Hugh David Department Health Care of the Elderly, Guy's Kings and St Thomas' School of Medicine, Dulwich Hospital, London SE22 8PT Tel: 020 7346 6071 Fax: 020 7346 6370 Email: stephen.jackson@kcl.ac.uk; 106 Harpenden Road, St Albans AL3 6DA Tel: 01727 837783 Fax: 01727 837783 — MB ChB 1975 Birm.; MD Birm. 1987; FRCP Lond. 1994; MRCP (UK) 1980. (Univ. Birm.) Prof. Clin. Gerontol.Guys,St Thomas, King's Coll. Sch. Med. & Dent. Lond. Socs: Brit. Geriat. Soc. (Chairm. Drugs and Prescribing Sect.); Brit. Pharm. Soc.; Brit. Hypertens. Soc. Prev: Merck Internat. Fell. San Antonio, Texas; Lect. (Clin. Pharmacol.) St. Bart. Hosp. Med. Sch. Lond.; Research Fell. (Med.) Univ. Birm.

JACKSON, Stephen John 60 Wheatfield Road, Luton LU4 0TR Tel: 01584 601116; 37 Tring Road, Dunstable LU6 2PX Tel: 01584 605801 — MB ChB 1969 Manch.; DA Eng. 1972; DObst RCOG 1971. (Manch.)

JACKSON, Stephen Nigel Julian 91 Birchover Way, Allestree, Derby DE22 2QH Tel: 01332 559597 — MB BChir 1989 Camb.; MRCP (UK) 1993.

JACKSON, Stephen Robert Crossways, 240 Chester Road, Hartford, Northwich CW8 1LW — MB BS 1958 Lond.; DCH Eng. 1963; DObst RCOG 1969. (St. Thos.) Socs: BMA; Guild Catholic Doctors. Prev: GP N.wich.

JACKSON, Susan Elisabeth 23 Heathwell Road, Newcastle upon Tyne NE15 7UQ — MB BS 1990 Newc.

JACKSON, Susan Elizabeth 1F2 12 Morningside Drive, Edinburgh EH10 5LY — MB ChB 1998 Ed.; MB ChB Ed 1998.

JACKSON, Susan Patricia 39 Barton Hey Drive, Caldy, Wirral CH48 1PZ Tel: 0151 625 2298 — MB ChB 1971 Liverp.; MB ChB (Hons.) Liverp. 1971. Assoc. Specialist (Dermat.) Alder Hey, BRd.green & Whiston Hosp. Liverp. Socs: BMA; Brit. Assn. Dermat.; Brit. Soc. Paediat. Dermatol. Prev: Regist. (Dermat.) Clatterbridge Hosp.; Research Fell. (Dermat.) Liverp. Roy. Infirm.; Med. Off. (Dermat.) Walton Hosp. Liverp.

JACKSON, Thomas Francis McCarthy (retired) Flat 4D, Wallace House, Berryhill Road, Seafar, Cumbernauld, Glasgow G67 1LU Tel: 0141 731815 — LRCP LRCS Ed. LRFPS Glas. 1950; M Phil Glas. 1995; FFPHM 1989; MFCMI 1977; FFCM 1984, M 1974; Dip. Forens. Med. Glas. 1987; DPH Leeds 1959. Lect. Bell Coll. Hamilton; Med. Off. Lanarksh. HB. Prev: Specialist (Community Med., Infec. Dis., Environm. Health & Epidemiol. Studies) Lanarksh. HB.

JACKSON, Timothy John 2 Whittle Road, Thame OX9 3PF — MB ChB 1995 Leeds.

JACKSON, Timothy Llewelyn Sussex Eye Hospital, Eastern Road, Brighton BN2 5BF — MB ChB 1992 Otago.

JACKSON, Timothy Nevil Lower Street Health Centre, Lower Street, Tettenhall, Wolverhampton WV6 9LL Tel: 01902 444550/1; Willow House, The Highfields, Wightwick, Wolverhampton WV6 8DW Tel: 01902 762297 — MB BCh 1978 Wales; MRCGP 1982; DRCOG 1981.

JACKSON, Mr Timothy Roger Hull Royal Infirmary, Anlaby Road, Hull HU3 2JZ Tel: 01482 674058; 30 West Mill Rise, Walkington, Beverley HU17 8TP Tel: 01482 873070 — MB BS 1989 Lond.; FRCS Ed. 1994. Cons. (A & E Med.) Hull Roy. Infirm.

JACKSON, Tracy Louise 20 Ravenscar Terrace, Oakwood, Leeds LS8 4AU Tel: 0113 240 3116 — MB ChB 1988 Ed.; MRCOG 1993. Clin. Research Fell. (O & G) St. James' Univ. Hosp., Leeds. Socs: Brit. Soc. Gyn. Endoscopy; Eur. Assn. Obst. & Gyn. Prev: Specialist Regist. (O & G) Leeds, Bradford, Halifax; Trainee GP Leeds; SHO (O & G) Bradford Roy. Infirm & St. Lukes Hosp.

JACKSON, Warwick Douglas New Court Consulting Rooms, 21a Nevill St., Abergavenny NP7 Tel: 01873 856071; The Court, Glangrwyney, Crickhowell NP8 1ES Tel: 01873 811288 Fax: 01873 810317 — MB BS 1966 Lond.; MRCS Eng. LRCP Lond. 1965; FRCOG 1985, M 1972. (Lond. Hosp.) Cons. & Clin. Co-Ordinator O & G Nevill Hall Hosp. Abergavenny; Hon. Clin. Tutor (Obst & Gyn.) Welsh Nat. Sch. Med.; Mem. Gwent Local Obst. Comm.; Mem. Advis. Sub-Comm. Obst. & Gyn. to Welsh Med. Comm. Prev: Sen. Regist. (O & G) Birm. Centr. HA; Regist. Bristol Matern. Hosp. & Roy. United Hosp. Bath; SHO P.ss Margt. Hosp. Nassau, Bahamas.

JACKSON, Wendy Lesley Marie 10 Tortoiseshell Way, Braintree CM7 8WG Tel: 01376 323538 — MB BCh 1983 Wales. Prev: Clin. Med. Off. N. Herts. & S. Glam. HA; SHO (Community Paediat. & Geriat.) S. Glam. HA.

JACKSON, Wilfred (retired) St. Pirans, Perranwell Station, Truro TR3 7PY Tel: 01872 862175 Email: wilfjack@globalnet.co.uk — MB BCh BAO 1951 Dub.; BA Dub. 1951.

JACKSON, William Edward Skegoneill Health Centre, 195 Skegoneill Avenue, Belfast BT15 3LL Tel: 028 9077 2471 Fax: 028 9077 2449 Email: william.jackson@btinternet.com; 20 Waterloo Park, Belfast BT15 5HU — MB BCh BAO Belf. 1964; DObst RCOG 1967; FRCGP 1987, M 1970. (Belf.) Socs: Fell. Ulster Med. Soc.; Brit. Assn. Health Servs. in Higher Ed.; Anglo-German Med. Soc. Prev: Med. Off. Univ. of Ulster; Edr. Jl. Brit. Stud. Health Assn.

JACKSON, William Francis The Old Chapel, High St., Harwell, Didcot OX11 0EX Tel: 01235 835698 Fax: 01235 862897 Email: wfjclin@aol.com; The Old Chapel, High St., Harwell, Didcot OX11 0EX — MB BChir 1972 Camb.; FRCP 2001 Glasgow; MB BChir Camb. 1971; 1971 MA Camb.; MRCP (UK) 1973. (Camb. & Guy's) Med. Publisher & Writer Clin. Vision. Socs: Brit. Med. Assn.; Roy. Soc. of Med. Prev: Hon. Cons. Med. Guy's Hosp.; Lect. (Med.) Lond. Hosp. Med. Coll.; Edr. Update, Med. & Clin. Med.

JACKSON, William Francis Murray Meads Cottage, Rondle Wood, Milland, Liphook GU30 7LA — MB BS 1997 Lond.

JACKSON, Winston James (retired) Brook House, 71 Taunton Road, Ashton-under-Lyne OL7 9DU — MRCS Eng. LRCP Lond. 1953.

JACKSON-RICHMOND, Mr James (retired) The Gardens Cottage, Sutton Park, Guildford GU4 7QN Tel: 01483 62157 — MB BS 1933 Melbourne; FRCS Eng. 1941; FRCR 1975; FFR 1961; DMR Lond. Prev: Radiotherap. i/c Radiother. Dept. St. Geo. Hosp. Lond.

JACKSON-SMYTH, Meredith George, Col. late RAMC Retd. (retired) 42 Ashwell Avenue, Camberley GU15 2AR Tel: 01276 24393 — BA Dub. 1939, MB BCh BAO 1942.

JACKSON-VOYZEY, Ewart Neil 35 Hillingdon Road, Gravesend DA11 7LQ — BM 1994 Soton.

JACOB, Abraham Walsall Manor Hospital, Moat Road, Walsall WS2 9PS — MB BS 1980 Andhra; MB BS Andhra, India 1980; MRCP (UK) 1988; MRCPath 1993; MD. Cons. Haematologist. Prev: Sen. Regist. (Haemat.) Qu. Eliz. Hosp. Birm.

JACOB, Alexander Charles (retired) Chapel House, 2 Old Hall Courtyard Heath, Wakefield WF1 5ST — MB ChB 1946 Ed.

JACOB, Ashok Joseph Medical Unit, St John's Hospital, Howden Road W., Livingston EH54 6PP Tel: 01506 419666 Fax: 01506 417493; Annasachd, 19 Wilton Road, Newington, Edinburgh EH16 5NX — MB ChB 1985 Ed.; FRCP Ed. 1998; MD Ed. 1995; MRCP (UK) 1988; BSc (Hons.) Ed. 1983. (Ed.) Cons. Cardiol. St. John's Hosp. Livingston. Socs: Med. Res. Soc. Prev: Sen. Regist. (Cardiol.) W.. Inf. Glas.; Career Regist. (Cardiol.) Roy. Infirm. Edin.; Brit. Heart Foundat. Jun. Research Fell. (Cardiol.) Roy. Infirm. Edin.

JACOB, Badie Kamil 95 Pinewood Trail, Trumbull CT 06611, USA; 37 St Lukes Close, Dunsville, Doncaster DN7 4PA Tel: 01302 887285 Fax: 01302 887285 — MB ChB 1972 Mosul; MRCP (UK) 1982; FCCP 1985. Clin. Asst. (Gen. Med.) Doncaster Roy. Infirm.; Clin. Asst. (Gen. Med. & Asthma Clinic) Rotherham DGH. Prev: Cons. Phys. & Sen. Regist. (Resp. Med.) Kuwait; Regist. (Gen. Med., Respirat. & Gastroenterol.) Doncaster Roy. Infirm.

JACOB, Mr George 49 Newfield Crescent, Dore, Sheffield S17 3DE — MB BCh 1974 Wales; MB MCh Wales 1987, BCh 1974; FRCS Eng. 1979. Sen. Lect. (Surg.) Hon. Cons. Surg. Roy. Hallamsh. Hosp. Sheff. Prev: Lect. (Surg.) Univ. Dept. Surg. N.. Gen. Hosp. Sheff.; Wellcome Surg. Research Fell. & Hon. Sen. Regist. (Surg.) Roy. Free; Hosp. Lond.

JACOB, James Arbury Medical Centre, Cambridge Drive, Stockingford, Nuneaton CV10 8LW Tel: 024 7638 8555 Fax: 024 7635 2396; 32 Thornhill Drive, Whitestone, Nuneaton CV11 6TD Tel: 01203 327137 — MB ChB 1981 Sheff.

JACOB, John Stephen Howard 129 Hillbarton Road, Whipton, Exeter EX1 3PP — MB BS 1974 Lond.; LMSSA Lond. 1973; FRACS 1980; DObst Auckland 1976.

JACOB, Koshy Derriford Hospital, Derriford Road, Plymouth PL6 8DH Tel: 01752 777111; 30 Downham Gardens, Tamerton Foliot, Plymouth PL5 4QE Tel: 01752 786849.

JACOB, Leonard Thrybergh Medical Centre, 21 Park Lane, Thrybergh S65 4BT — MB ChB; MRCP 1979 (Part 1) UK; 1991 (F.P. Cert.) UK; 1984 (ECFMG) USA; MRCPI 1983 (Part 1) Dublin. (Mosul, Iraq) Rotherham Gen. Hosp. Moorgate, Rotherham, S60. Socs: BMA; MPS; SPA.

JACOB, Lynne Rotherham District General Hospital, Moorgate Road, Rotherham S60 2UD — MB BCh 1974 Wales. Staff Grade (Dermat.) Rotherham Dist. Gen. Hosp.

JACOB, Maurice (retired) 72 The Glen, Endcliffe Vale Road, Sheffield S10 3EW — MB ChB 1936 St. And.

JACOB, Mr Michael Peter St Peter's Road Surgery, 1 St. Peters Road, Cirencester GL7 1RF Tel: 01285 653184 Fax: 01285 655795; Kennels Lodge, Tetbury Road, Cirencester GL7 1UR — MB BCh BAO 1984 NUI; FRCS Ed. 1993. (Univ. Coll. Dub.) Hosp. Pract. (Gen. Surg.) Cirencester Hosp. E. Glos. NHS Trust. Prev: SHO (Orthop. & Trauma) P.ss Margt. Hosp. Swindon; SHO (Gen. Surg., Orthop., & Urol.) S.lands Hosp. Shoreham by Sea.

JACOB, Sabena 42 Chase Side Avenue, London SW20 8LU — MB BS 1998 Lond.; MB BS Lond 1998.

JACOB, Sanjeev John Flat K, 61 Shepherds Hill, London N6 5RE — MB ChB 1992 Sheff.

JACOB, Thampy 23 Sunningdale Close, Burtonwood, Warrington WA5 4NR Tel: 01295 290554 — MB BS 1979 Kerala; MChOrth. Liverp. 1992.

JACOB SAMUEL, Tholooparampil Queen's Hospital, Burton Hospitals NHS Trust, Burton-on-Trent DE13 0RB Tel: 01283 566333 Fax: 01283 510577; 79 Bitham Lane, Stretton, Burton-on-Trent DE13 0HP Tel: 01283 537050 Email: tjsamuel@yahoo.com — MB BS 1977 Kerala; MRCP (UK) 1993; FRCPCH 1997; DCH RCP Lond. 1990. Cons. Paediat. Qus. Hosp. Burton on Trent. Prev: Sen. Regist. (Paediat.) S. Tyneside Health NHS Trust, Newc.; Regist. (Paediat.) Colchester Gen. Hosp. & Doncaster; SHO & Regist. (Paediat.) Pontefract.

JACOBS, Adrian George South West Devon HA, The Lescaze Offices, Shinners Bridge, Dartington, Totnes TQ9 6JE Tel: 01803 861810 Fax: 01803 867679 Email: adrian.jacobs@sw-devon-ha.swest.nhs.uk; 12 Parkfield Way, Topsham, Exeter EX3 0DP Tel: 01392 8735632 — MB ChB 1972 Bristol; FRCGP; MRCGP 1989; DObst RCOG 1975; DCH Eng. 1974; FRCGP 1999; MHSM 1996. (Bristol) Director of Primary Care; Non Exec. Director, Nat. Clin. Assessm. Auth. Prev: GP Dawlish.

JACOBS, Anthony Geoffry (retired) 54 Sir Richards Drive, Birmingham B17 8SS Tel: 0121 429 4735 — MB BS Lond. 1958; FRCPath 1979, M 1967. Cons.Chem.Path.BMI priory Hosp.Birm. Prev: cons.Clin.Pathol. New Cross hosp.Wolverhampton.

JACOBS, Barbara Ruth Triangle Group Practice, 2 Morley Road, London SE13 6DQ Tel: 0208 318 7272 Fax: 0208 297 9519 — MB BS Lond. 1970; MRCP (UK) 1974; DObst RCOG 1976. (The Middlx. Hosp. Med. Sch., Univ. of Lond.) GP Princip.

JACOBS, Benjamin Northwick Park Hospital, Harrow HA1 3UJ Tel: 020 8340 0324 Fax: 020 8348 2425 Email: benjamin.jacobs@utoronto.ca — MB BS 1985 Lond.; MSc 1999 Toronto; MD Manch.; MRCP (UK) 1988; DCH RCP Lond. 1988. Cons. Paediat., N.wick Pk. and Roy. Nat. Orthopaedic Hosp. Stanmore. Prev: Lect. (Child Health) Univ. Manch.; Regist. (Paediat.) N.wick Pk. Hosp. Lond.; SHO (Metab. Unit) Hosp. Sick Childr. Gt. Ormond St. Lond.

JACOBS, Brendan Bethel (retired) 10A Redhill Road, Arnold, Nottingham NG5 8GP Tel: 0115 926 4160 — MRCS Eng. LRCP Lond. 1944; MA Camb. 1946; FRCGP 1976, M 1957; LM Rotunda 1951. Prev: Regist. (Med.) W.m. Hosp.

JACOBS, Brian Patrick 1 Clifford Road, Richmond TW10 7EB — MB ChB 1990 Cape Town.

JACOBS, Brian William 8 Maberley Road, Upper Norwood, London SE19 2JB — MB BChir 1975 Camb.; MPhil Lond. 1985; MRCP (UK) 1977; FRCPsych 1996, M 1982; DCH Eng. 1978. (Camb.) Cons. Child Psychiat. Maudsley Hosp. Lond.; Hon. Cons. St. Geo. Hosp. Lond.; Hon. Sen. Lect. St. Geo. Hosp. Med. Sch. Lond.; Hon. Sen. Lect. Inst. Psychiat. Prev: Cons. Child Psychiat. Qu. Mary's Hosp. for Childr. Carshalton; Sen. Regist. (Child Psychiat.) Maudsley Hosp. Lond.

JACOBS, Clare Isabel 15 Crick Road, Oxford OX2 6QL — MB BS 1993 Lond.

JACOBS, Daniel Stephen 1 Redbridge Lane W., London E11 2JX — MB BS 1996 Lond.

JACOBS, Denise Yvonne (retired) 80 Dragon Road, Winterbourne, Bristol BS36 1BJ Tel: 01454 772774 — MB BCh Wales 1953. Clin. Med. Off. (Paediat.) Avon AHA (T).

JACOBS, Edward David (retired) 6 Malindi Court, 161 Park Road, London N8 8JZ Tel: 020 8347 7749 Fax: 020 8347 7749 — MB ChB Cape Town 1959. Prev: Gyn. Regist. King Edwd. VII Hosp. Windsor.

JACOBS, Elmo Brian Alexander 143 Western Avenue, E. Acton, London W3 6RN Tel: 020 8992 6283 — MB BS 1951 Ceylon; MRCPsych 1973; DPM Eng. 1965. Sen. Med. Off. HM Prison Hosp. Worwood Scrubs, Lond.; Mem. Oxf. Postgrad. Fell.sh. Psychiat. Prev: Peripatetic Psychiat. Regist. Epsom Gp. Hosps.; SHO Springfield Hosp. Lond.

JACOBS, Estelle Fay 8 Lang Lane, West Kirby, Wirral CH48 5HF — MB ChB 1991 Ed.

JACOBS, Eva Mary St Andrews Medical Centre, 30 Russell Street, Eccles, Manchester M30 0NU Tel: 0161 707 5500 — MB ChB 1981 Manch.; BA (Hons.) Durham. 1960; MRCGP 1985. (Manch.) Anne Hamilton Essay Prize RCGP 1985/6. Prev: SHO/GP Trainee Hope Hosp. Salford; Ho. Off. (Surg.) Hope Hosp. Salford; Ho. Off. (Med.) N. Manch. Gen. Hosp.

JACOBS, Franklyn Kenneth Stephen Drayton Park Medical Centre, 30B Drayton Park, London N5 1PB Tel: 020 7609 2692 Fax: 020 7619 0143; 55 Ossulton Way, Hampstead Garden Suburb, London N2 0JY — MB BS 1969 W. Indies. (Univ. of the West Indies) Socs: Charter Mem. & UK Represen. Internat. Soc. Hypertens. in Blacks.; BMA. Prev: Med. Off. Remploy Ltd.

JACOBS, Gerald Joshua 148 Pershore Road, Edgbaston, Birmingham B5 7NY Tel: 0121 440 1856 — MB ChB 1945 Birm.; MRCS Eng. LRCP Lond. 1945. (Birm.) Civil Serv. Med. Off. S. Birm.

JACOBS, Mr Henry Basil (retired) 30 Cloister House, Griffiths Road, London SW19 1SS — MRCS Eng. LRCP Lond. 1943; FRCS Eng. 1951; DOMS Eng. 1950. Prev: Ophth. Surg. Surrey AHA.

JACOBS, Professor Howard Saul London Diabetes & Lipid Centre, 14 Wimpole St., London W1G 9SX Tel: 020 7636 9901 Fax: 020 7636 9902 Email: hsjacobs1@aol.com; 169 Gloucester Avenue, London NW1 8LA Tel: 020 7722 5593 Fax: 020 7722 5243 Email: hsjacobs@aol.com — MB BChir Camb. 1962; BA Camb. 1959, MD 1970; FRCP Lond. 1979, M 1965; FRCOG 1992. (Camb. & Middlx. Hosps.) Cons. Endocrinol. Regist. Lond. Diabetes and Lipid Centre; Emerit. Prof. (Reproduc. Endocrinol.) UCL Med. Sch.; Hon. Cons. (Endocrinol.) Middlx. Hosp. Lond.; Civil. Cons. (Endocrinol.) RAF. Socs: Fell. Roy. Soc. Med.; Brit. Fertil. Soc. (Pres.); Soc. Endocrinol. Prev: Reader & Hon. Cons. (Gyn. Endocrinol.) St. Mary's Hosp. Med. Sch. Lond.; Asst. Prof. Med. Univ. Calif. Los Angeles Med. Sch., USA; Leverhulme Research Fell. Middlx. Hosp. Med. Sch. Lond.

JACOBS, Professor Ian Jeffrey Department of Gynaecological Oncology, St. Bartholomew's Hospital, The Royal Hospitals Trust, London EC1A 7BE Tel: 020 7601 8261 Fax: 020 7601 7652 Email: i.j.jacobs@mds.qmw.ac.uk — MB BS 1983 Lond.; MA Camb. 1983, BA 1980; MD Lond. 1991; MRCOG 1991. (Cambridge) Cons. (Gyn. Oncol.) St. Bartholomews & Roy. Lond. Hosp.; Prof. St. Bartholomews & Roy. Lond. Med. Sch.; Hon. Cons. (Gyn. Oncol.) Roy. Marsden Hosp.; Hon. Cons. (Gyn. Oncol.) Homerton Hosp.; Hon Cons. (Gyn. Oncol) N.wilck Pk. Hosp. Socs: Pres. Brit. Gyn. Cancer Soc.; Roy. Coll. Obst. & Gyn.; Soc. Gynaeco. Oncol. Prev: CRC Fell. St. Bartholomews & Roy. Marsden; CRC Fell. Camb.; MRC Fell. Duke Univesity, NC, USA.

JACOBS, Ian Robert Morris Grovelands Medical Centre, 701 Oxford Road, Reading RG30 1HG Tel: 0118 958 2525 Fax: 0118 950 9284 — MB ChB 1973 Ed.; MRCGP 1979. (Ed.) Specialist (Family Med.) Reading; Clin. Asst. (Rheum.) Battle Hosp. Reading. Socs: Direct Mem. WONCA; Reading Path. Soc.; Newbury Med. Soc. Prev: Trainee GP Battersea VTS; SHO (Paediat.) Nottm. Childr. Hosp.; SHO (Paediat. & Psychiat.) N.wick Pk. Hosp. Harrow.

JACOBS, Isaac David Cemmaes Lodge, 9 Ty-Gwyn Road, Penylan, Cardiff CF23 5JF — MB BCh 1945 Wales.

JACOBS, Jonathan Julius 12 Aylmer Road, London N2 0BX — MB BS 1983 Lond.

JACOBS, Joseph 12 Aylmer Road, London N2 0BX Tel: 020 8340 0324 — MB ChB Liverp. 1956; PhD Lond. 1948, BSc 1946; DObst RCOG 1959. Prev: Ho. Phys. & Ho. Surg. Lond. Jewish Hosp.; Resid. Med. Off. Bearsted Memor. Hosp. Lond.

JACOBS, Laurence Gordon and Partners, 1 North Street, Peterborough PE1 2RA Tel: 01733 312731 Fax: 01733 311447 — MB ChB 1974 Ed.; BSc (Hons.) (Pharmacol.) Ed. 1971; LFHom 1999 Fac. of Homeop. Prev: SHO (Med.) N. Devon Infirm. Barnstaple; Ho. Phys. Roy. Infirm. Edin.

JACOBS, Leonard (retired) Bakker, Brown, Jacobs and Wormell, Lisson Grove Health Centre, Gateforth Street, London NW8 8EF Tel: 020 7723 2213 — MB BS 1949 Lond.; MRCGP 1973. Cons. Pub. Health Med. Kensington & Chelsea and W.m. HA. Prev: Ho. Phys. Highlands Hosp. Winchmore Hill.

JACOBS, Mr Leonardus George Hubertus 30 Pine Road, Didsbury, Manchester M20 6UZ — MB ChB 1975 Cape Town; FRCS Ed. 1986.

JACOBS, Linda Ruth 137 Coombe Lane W., Kingston upon Thames KT2 7HF — MB ChB 1976 Manch.; Clin Dip Family Ther 1999. Community Paediat., Childr.s Sleep & Behaviour Clinic, Child & Adolesc. Serv., SW Lond. & St Geoges Ment. health NHS Trust. Prev: Clin. Med. Off. Merton & Sutton HA.

JACOBS, Lynn Battlefield Road Surgery, 148 Battlefield Road, Glasgow G42 9JT Tel: 0141 632 6310 Fax: 0141 636 1180; Windyknowe, 20 Hillcrest Drive, Newton Mearns, Glasgow G77 5HH Tel: 0141 639 1682 Fax: 0141 639 8569 Email: 100564.2615@compuserve.com — MB ChB 1969 Glas. (Glas.) Prev: Ho. Surg. Glas. Vict. Infirm.; Ho. Phys. Ballochmyle Hosp.

JACOBS, Martin Clive Lister Medical Centre, Lister House, Staple Tye, Harlow CM18 7LU Tel: 01279 414882 Fax: 01279 439600 — MB ChB 1971 Sheff.; MRCOG 1976. (Sheff.) Socs: BMA.

JACOBS, Michael Andrew London Street Practice, 70 London Street, Reading RG1 4SL Tel: 0118 957 4640 Fax: 0118 959 7613; 5 Fallowfield Close, Caversham, Reading RG4 8NQ Tel: 01734 470253 — MB ChB 1973 Aberd.; DObst. RCOG 1976. Prev: SHO (O & G) Barking Hosp.; SHO (Med. & Paediat.) King Geo. Hosp. Ilford; SHO (Psychiat.) Goodmayes Hosp. Ilford.

JACOBS, Michael Graham 4 Mackeson Road, London NW3 2LT Email: m.jacobs@ic.ac.uk — MB BS 1988 Lond.; BA Oxf. 1985; MRCP (UK) 1991; DTM & H RCP Lond. 1995. Specialist Regist. Infec. Dis.s N.wick Pk. Hosp. Lond. Prev: Wellcome Research Train. Fell. (Infec. Dis.) St. Mary's Hosp. Lond.; Regist. (Respirat. & Infec. Dis.) Hammersmith Hosp. Lond.; Regist. (Gen. Med.) Ealing Hosp. Lond.

JACOBS, Michelle Faith The Hillingdon Hospital, Field Heath Road, Uxbridge UB8 3NN Tel: 01895 279314; 19 Tenterden Drive, Hendon, London NW4 1EA Tel: 020 8202 3158 — MB BCh 1993 Wales; BSc (Pharmacol.) Wales 1992; FRCS (A&E) Ed. 1998. (Univ.

Wales Coll. Med.) Specialist Regist.(A&e), The Hillingdon Hosp., Middx. Socs: Assoc. Mem. Brit. Assn. Accid. & Emerg. Med.; BMA. Prev: Staff Grade (A & E) The Lister Hosp. Stevenage; Regist. (A & E) Roy. Free Hosp.; GP Regist. N.wood Middlx.

JACOBS, Mr Nicholas Anthony 137 Coombe Lane W., Kingston upon Thames KT2 7HF Tel: 020 8942 2960 — MB ChB 1976 Manch.; FRCS Glas. 1982; FCOphth 1988. Cons. Ophth. Birch Hill Hosp. Rochdale. Socs: Internat. Perimetric Soc.; Glaucoma Soc.; Eur. Soc. Cataract & Refractive Surgs. Prev: Cons. Ophth. Kingston Roy. Eye Hosp. & Qu. Mary's Hosp. Roehampton; Sen. Regist. Char. Cross, Moorfields & W.m. Hosps.; Regist. (Clin. Research) Manch. Roy. Eye Hosp.

JACOBS, Paul Barrie (retired) Rosebank, Wyke, Gillingham SP8 4NA Tel: 01747 823310 — MB BChir 1959 Camb.; MA Camb. 1960; MRCS Eng. LRCP Lond. 1958; DCH Eng. 1961. Prev: Med. Regist. Weymouth & Dist. Hosp.

JACOBS, Mr Paul Martin Department of Ophthalmology, York District Hospital, Wiggington Road, York YO31 8HE Tel: 01904 453742 Fax: 01904 453397 — MB ChB 1978 Liverp.; MA Oxf. 1977; FRCS Glas 1984; MRCS Eng. LRCP Lond. 1978; FRCOphth 1988; T(Ophth.) 1991; DO RCS Eng. 1981; FRCS Ed. 2000. Cons. Ophth. York Dist. Hosp. Socs: Fell. Roy. Soc. Med.; The Vitreous Soc. Prev: Cons. Ophth. Borders Gen. Hosp. Melrose; Cons. Ophth. Univ. Hosp. Nottm.; Fell. Vitreoretinal Surg. Moorfields Eye Hosp. Lond.

JACOBS, Philip, TD 18 Dovehouse Court, Warwick Grange, Warwick Road, Olton, Solihull B91 1EW — MB ChB 1940 Bristol; MB ChB (Gold Medal) Bristol 1940; FRCP Lond. 1971, M 1948; MRCS Eng. LRCP Lond. 1941; FRCR 1975; FFR 1955; DMRD Eng. 1952. (Bristol & Univ. Coll. Hosp.) Cons. Warw. Orthop. Hosp. Childr. Coleshill & DHSS; Hon. Cons. Radiol. Birm. Gen. Hosp., Roy. Orthop. Hosp. Birm., Birm. Accid. Hosp.; Clin. Lect. in Radiol. Univ. Birm.; Mem. MRC Decompression Sickness Panel. Socs: Hon. Mem. Radiol. Soc. N. Amer.; Counc. Roy. Coll. Radiol. Prev: Prof. & Head Musculoskeletal Radiol. Univ. Utah, USA; Sen. Regist. Dept. Radiodiag. Lond. Hosp.; Sen. Med. Regist. Roy. Hants. Co. Hosp. Winchester.

JACOBS, Philip 212 Oldcroft Place, Aberdeen AB16 5UJ — MB ChB 1997 Aberd.

JACOBS, Phillip 3 Sandhill Crescent, Leeds LS17 8DY — MB ChB 1998 Liverp.; MB ChB Liverp 1998.

JACOBS, Robert Anthony 41 Esher Road, East Molesey KT8 0AH — MRCS Eng. LRCP Lond. 1976.

JACOBS, Ruth 15 Cyncoed Place, Cyncoed, Cardiff CF23 6SG Tel: 029 2075 2761 — MB BCh 1974 Wales; PhD Wales 1979, BSc (Hons.) 1971; MFOM RCP Lond. 1984, AFOM 1981, FFOM 1994; DIH Soc. Apoth. Lond. 1981.

JACOBS, Stanley 19 Routh Road, Wandsworth Common, London SW18 3SP Tel: 020 8870 5891 — MB ChB 1964 Glas.; BSc Glas. 1959, MB ChB 1964; DPM Ed. & Glas. 1967. Cons. Vis. Psychiat. Lambeth, S.wark & Lewisham. Socs: Exec. Counc. Brit. Holistic Med. Assn. Prev: Cons. (Psychiat.) Univ. Coll. Hosp. Lond.; Sen. Regist. (Psychiat.) Univ. Coll. Hosp. Lond.; Regist. (Psychiat.) Char. Cross Hosp. Lond. & Goodmayes Hosp. Ilford.

JACOBS, Susan Anne Flat 1, 91 Longfleet Road, Poole BH15 2HP — MB BS 1986 Sydney.

JACOBS, Susan Rosalind Hornsey Rise Health Centre, Hornsey Road, London N19 3YU Tel: 020 7263 8352; 26E Sutherland Road, London N9 7QD Tel: 020 8805 1522 — MB ChB 1978 Liverp.; MRCS Eng. LRCP Lond. 1978; MRCGP 1982; DCH RCP Lond. 1981; DRCOG 1980. Community Paediat. Islington HA; GP Pract. (A & E) Whittington Hosp. Lond. Socs: Fac. Community Health. Prev: Trainee GP Liverp. VTS.

JACOBS, Sydney Ivor (retired) Cherry Cottage, Main St., Linton, Wetherby LS22 4HT — MB ChB 1956 Leeds; MB ChB Leeds. 1956; MD Leeds 1965; FRCPath 1977, M 1965. Prev: Cons. Path. St. Jas. Hosp. Leeds.

JACOBS, Thomas Edward Hammonds, The Green, Burnham Market, King's Lynn PE31 8HE — BM BS 1997 Nottm.

JACOBS, Victoria Jane Louise 211 Queens Drive, Wavertree, Liverpool L15 6XU — MB ChB 1998 Liverp.; MB ChB Liverp 1998.

JACOBSON, Beverley Lynn 6 Belmor, Elstree, Borehamwood WD6 3JX — MB BCh 1990 Witwatersrand.

JACOBSON, Gillian Anne Longlands House, Preston, Telford TF6 6DH — MB BS 1989 Lond.

JACOBSON, Lionel David Westway Surgery, 1 Wilson Road, Ely, Cardiff CF5 4LJ Tel: 029 2059 2351 Fax: 029 2059 9956; 27 Market Road, Canton, Cardiff CF5 1QE — BM 1986 Soton. Hon. Lect., Dept. of Gen. Pract., Univ. Wales.

JACOBSON, Roberta Anne East London & The City Health Authority, 81/91 Commercial Road, London E1 1RD Tel: 020 7655 6776 Fax: 020 7655 6777 Email: bobbie@elcha.co.uk; 16 Lorne Road, London N4 3RT Tel: 020 7263 6872 Fax: 020 8292 2014 Email: bobbie@dulham.easynet.co.uk — MB BS 1982 Lond.; BSc (Hons.) Sussex 1972; MFPHM 1990; FFPHM. (Middlesex Hosp.) Head of the Pub. Health Observatory for Lond.; King's Fund Managem. Comm.; Chairm. Health of Lond.ers Prog. Prev: Dir. Pub. Health E. Lond. & The City HA; Dir. Pub. Health City & Hackney HA; Sen. Regist. (Pub. Health Med.) City & Hackney HA.

JACOBSON, Robin Richard St Georges Hospital Medical School, Department Mental Health Sciences, Jenner Wing, Cranmer Terrace, London SW17 0RE Tel: 020 8725 5509 Fax: 020 8725 3350 Email: r.jacobson@sghms.ac.uk — MB 1975 Camb.; MB BChir Camb. 1976; MA Camb. 1973, MD 1987; MRCP (UK) 1978; FRCPsych 1993, M 1981. Cons Psychiat. & Sen. Lect. (PsychoPharmacol. & Neuropsychiat.) St. Geo. Hosp. Med. Sch. Lond.; Cons. Puerperal Disorders Springfield Hosp.; Cons. Wolfson Med. Rehabil. Centre; Hon. Sen. Lect. Inst. Psychiat. Lond. Socs: Brit. Neuropsychiat. Soc.; Marcé Soc.; Brit. Assoc. Psychopharacology. Prev: Lect. Inst. Psychiat. Lond.; Sen. Regist. & Regist. Maudsley Hosp. Lond.; Regist. (Med. Ophth.) St. Thos. Hosp. Lond.

JACOBSON, Susan Kim Department of Microbiology, Royal United Hospital, Combe Park, Bath BA1 3NG Tel: 01225 825428 Fax: 01225 448262 — MB ChB 1985 Dundee; MSc 1992; MRCP 1989; MRCPath 1993. Cons. Med. Microbiol. PHL. Bath & Bristol; Hon. Sen. Lect. Microbiol. Univ. Bristol.

JACOBSON, Mr Tal Zvi 51 Stapleton Road, Headington, Oxford OX3 7LX — MB BS 1992 Lond.; MRCOG 1999; MA Camb. 1986; DFFP 1995. (Guy's Hosp. Lond.) Specialist Regist. (Ob. + Gyn.), John Radcliffe Hosp., Oxf. Socs: Brit. Fertil. Soc.; BMA. Prev: Specialist Regist. (Ob. + Gyn.), Horton Hosp., Banbury.; Clin. Research Fell. (Nuffield Dept. of O & G) John Radcliffe Hosp., Oxf.; Regist. (O & G) Wom. Hosp. Auckland, NZ.

JACOBSON, Mr Uriah (cons. rooms) 5th Floor, Wellington Hospital, Wellington Place, London NW8 9LE Tel: 020 7586 5959; (home), 25 Holne Chase, London N2 0QL Tel: 020 8455 8016 — MB ChB 1951 Glas.; FRCS Eng. 1962; MRCOG 1960. Prev: Sen. Regist. (O & G) Reading Combined Hosps.; Cas. Regist. Roy. N.. Hosp. Lond.; O & G Ho. Off. Stobhill Gen. Hosp. Glas.

JACOBY, Michael Norman Jack Whitehall Medical Practice, 11 Whitehall Road, Rugby CV21 3AQ Tel: 01788 544264 Fax: 01788 575783; 4 Birch Drive, Rugby CV22 7TQ Tel: 01788 521858 Fax: 01788 521335 Email: michael.jacoby@nationwideisp.net — MB BS 1962 Lond.; MRCS Eng. LRCP Lond. 1962; MRCGP 1972; DObst RCOG 1965. (Guy's) Socs: BMA. Prev: Med. Off. Rugby Sch.

JACOBY, Richard Keith Royal Devon & Exeter Hospital, Barrack Road, Exeter EX2 5DW Tel: 01392 411611 — MD 1975 Bristol; MB BS Lond. 1967; FRCP Lond. 1985; MRCP (UK) 1970; MRCS Eng. LRCP Lond. 1967. (Guy's) Cons. Rheum. Roy. Devon & Exeter Hosp.

JACOBY, Professor Robin John The Warneford Hospital, Oxford OX3 7JX Tel: 01865 223639 Fax: 01865 249253 Email: robin.jacoby@psychiatry.oxford.ac.uk — BM BCh Oxf. 1969; DM Oxf. 1980; FRCP Lond. 1990; MRCP (UK) 1973; FRCPsych 1987, M 1976; T(Psychiat.) 1991. Prof. (Old Age Psychiat.) Oxf. Univ.

JACOMB, Rex Gordon 75 Nether Way, Nether Poppleton, York YO26 6HW Tel: 01904 340669 — LRCP LRCS Ed. LRFPS Glas. 1949. (Roy. Colls. Ed.) Socs: Fell. Roy. Soc. Med.; (Ex-Chairm.) Assn. Med. Advisers in Pharm. Indust. Prev: Med. Dir. Upjohn Ltd.

JACOMB-HOOD, Julia Honor Lewisham Hospital, London SE13; 59A Blackheath Park, London SE3 9SQ — MB BS 1981 Lond.; MRCP (UK) 1985; FRCR 1988. Cons. Radiol. Lewisham Hosp. Lond.

JACOTT, Nicholas John Borough Road Surgery, 167a Borough Road, Middlesbrough TS4 2EL Tel: 01642 243668 Fax: 01642 222252; 125-129 Borough Road, Middlesbrough TS1 3AN — MB BS 1979 Newc.; MA Oxf. 1982; MRCGP 1983.

JACOVELLI, Joseph Bernard 1 Delahays Drive, Hale, Altrincham WA15 8DW — MB ChB Manch. 1952; DA Eng. 1956. (Lond.) Assoc. Specialist (Anaesth.) N. & Mid. Chesh. Hosp. Gp. Socs: Fell. Manch. Med. Soc. Prev: Clin. Asst. (Otorhinolaryng.) N. & Mid.-Chesh. Hosp. Gp.; Jun. Hosp. Med. Off. (Anaesth.) N. & Mid. Chesh. Hosp. Gp.

JACQUES, Adam Matthew The Towers, Castle Road, Scarborough YO11 1HY — MB BS 1997 Lond.

JACQUES, Alan Hamilton Mental Welfare Commission for Scotland, 25 Drumsheugh Gardens, Edinburgh EH3 7RB — MB BCh BAO 1970 Belf.; FRCPsych 1992, M 1974.

JACQUES, Helen Elizabeth 19 Ash Grove, Heaton Chapel, Stockport SK4 5EU Tel: 0161 432 6396 — MB ChB 1986 Manch.; MRCP (UK) 1995; DCH RCP Lond. 1991; Cert. Family Plann. JCC 1989. (Manch.) Cons. Paediat./Community Padiatrician Mancurian Community Health NHS Trus t. Prev: Part_time Sen. Regist. (Paediat.) NW RHA.

JACQUES, Mary Alison (retired) Great House, Wolvesnewton, Chepstow NP16 6NY Tel: 01291 650224 — MB BS 1953 Lond.; DA Eng. 1955; DObst RCOG 1954. Prev: Res. Anaesth. Roy. Free Hosp. Lond.

JACQUES, Paul Robert Tel: 0113 295 4040 Fax: 0113 295 4044; Tel: 01943 870215 Email: doc.prj@btinternet.com — MB ChB 1969 Leeds. p/t GP Guiseley Leeds; Medico legal Work; Occupat.al Health Advice to 2 firms Leeds/ Bradford area. Socs: Soc. of Occupat.al Med. Prev: Clin. Asst. (Psychiat.) High Royds Hosp. Menston; SHO (Med. & O & G) Preston Hosp. N. Shields.

JACQUES, Sarah Louise Claylands, Groombridge, Tunbridge Wells TN3 9PN — MB BS 1998 Lond.; MB BS Lond 1998. (St Georges Hosp Med Sch) Prev: PRHO - Med, Roy. Sussex Co. Hosp., Brighton; PRHO - Surg., St. Helier Hosp.

JACYNA, Meron Rudolph Gastroenterology Unit, Northwick Park & St Marks Hospital, Harrow HA1 3UJ Tel: 020 8869 2628 Fax: 020 8869 2626; 31 Kent Avenue, West Ealing, London W13 8BE Tel: 020 8810 7452 — MB ChB 1981 Dundee; MD Dundee 1987; FRCP Lond. 1994; MRCP (UK) 1984. Cons. Phys. & Gastroenterol. N.wick Pk. Hosp. & St Mark's Hosp. Trust; Hon. Cons. Phys. St. Mark's Hosp. Intestinal Dis.; Hon. Sen. Lect. (Med.) St Mary's Hosp. Med. Sch. Lond. Socs: Brit. Soc. Gastroenterol. Prev: Lect. & Hon. Sen. Regist. (Gen. Med.) St. Mary's Hosp. Paddington; Regist. (Med.) Ninewells Hosp. Dundee; Research Fell. Brit. Digestive Foundat.

JADALIZADEH, Nasser Hurst Green Surgery, Pollards Oak Road, Hurst Green, Oxted RH8 0JP Tel: 01883 723534; Silverly, 5 Central Way, Oxted RH8 0LS — MB BS 1973 Karachi; DRCOG 1986; DObst RCPI 1981.

JADAV, Jaideep Savji 3K Portman Mansions, Chiltern St., London W1U 5AH — MB BS 1994 Lond.

JADAV, Mark Antony Ravi Brackendene, Denton Rd, Ben Rhydding, Ilkley LS29 8QR — MB ChB 1997 Leeds.

JADEJA, Mr Ashok Kumar 105 Granville Road, London N22 5LR — MB BS 1974 Simla; FRCS Eng. 1988.

JADER, Samar Nimaan 10 Dalrymple Close, Chelmsford CM1 7RF — MB ChB 1976 Baghdad.

JADERBERG, Erik Magnus Medical Department, Pharmacia & Upjohn Ltd., Davy Avenue Knowlhill, Milton Keynes MK5 8PH Tel: 01908 603893 Fax: 01908 603095 — Lakarexamen 1982 Stockholm; FFPM RCP (UK) 1997. Med. Dir. Pharmacia & Upjohn Milton Keynes.

JADHAV, Prakash Rao The Health Centre, Bromhouse Lane, Edlington, Doncaster DN12 1PL Tel: 01709 863256; Stonehaven, 384 Melton Road, Sprotbrough, Doncaster DN5 7PA Tel: 01302 855964 Fax: 01709 867941 — MB BS Osmania 1966. (Osmania Med. Coll. Hyderabad, India) Prev: Clin. Asst. (Dermat.) Doncaster Roy. Infirm.

JADHAV, Sachin Titus 51 Stoneypath, Victoria Rd, Londonderry BT47 2AF; Flat 3/2, 993 Sauchiehall St, Kelvingrove, Glasgow G3 7TZ Tel: 0141 334 5816 Email: sachinj@compuserve.com — MB ChB 1996 Ed.; MB ChB Ed. (Hons.) 1996. (Ed.) SHO Glas. Roy. Infirm. Med. Rotat.

JADHAV, Shantaram Ningoji (Surgery) 291 Walsall Road, West Bromwich B71 3LN Tel: 0121 588 2286; 19 Athlone Road, Brookhouse Estate, Walsall WS5 3QU — MB BS 1961 Karnatak. (Kasturba Med. Coll. Mangalore) Prev: SHO (Surg.) Co. Hosp. HaverfordW. & Co. Hosp. Omagh; Regist. (Surg.) Yeovil Gen. Hosp.

JADHAV, Shivaji Devrao Bolton Road Surgery, 431-433 Bolton Road, Ewood, Blackburn BB2 4HY Tel: 01254 679781 Fax: 01254 693031 — MB BS 1972 Marathwada; MB BS 1972 Marathwada.

JADHAV, Sushrut Shankar Department of Psychiatry, University College of London, London W1N 8AA Tel: 020 7380 9292 Fax: 020 7323 1459 Email: s.jadhav@ucl.ac.uk — MB BS 1983 Bombay; MD (Psychol. Med.); MRCPsych 1991; Nat. Inst. Ment. Health and Neurosci., India 1986. (Grant Med. Sch., Bombay) Clin. Lect. (Psychiat.) Univ. Coll. Lond.; Edr. Anthropol. & Med.; Hon. Sen. Regist. Camden & Islington Community Health Trust; Course Tutor UCL; Course Organiser, MRCPscyh. Courses UCL; Vis. Lect. Nat. Inst. Advanced Studies Bangalore, India. Socs: Fell. Roy. Anthropol. Inst.; Roy. Coll. Psychiat.; World Psychiat. Assn. Prev: Sen. Regist. Maudsley Hosp.

JADRESIC, Alfredo Belmont House, Belmont Road, Hastings TN35 5NR Tel: 01424 434621 — Medico Cirujano Chile 1950; FRCP Lond. 1978. (Univ. Chile Sch. Med.) Cons. Phys. Hastings Health Dist.; Hon. Sen. Lect. & Cons. Endocrinol. Roy. Postgrad. Med. Sch. & Hammersmith Hosp. Lond. Socs: Fell. Roy. Soc. Med. (Sect. Endocrinol.). Prev: Prof. Med. Univ. Chile.

JADRESIC, Danitza Patricia Maudsley Hospital, Denmark Hill, London SE5 8AZ Tel: 020 7703 6333; 14 Cunliffe Street, Stockport SK3 9LG — MB BS 1982 Lond.; MRCPsych 1986. Sen. Regist. The Maudsley Hosp. Lond. Prev: MRC Research Fell. & Hon. Sen. Regist. Char. Cross & W.m. Med. Sch. Lond.; SHO/Regist. Rotat. (Psychiat.) Middlx & Univ. Coll. Hosp. Lond.

JADRESIC, Lyda Patricia Department of Paediatrics, Gloucestershire Royal Hospital, Great Western Road, Gloucester GL1 3NN — MB BS 1981 Lond.; MD Lond. 1994; MRCP (UK) 1985. (St. Thos. Hosp. Med. Sch. Lond.) p/t Cons. Paediat. Glos. Roy. Hosp.; Sen. Clin. Lect. Inst. Child Health, Univ. Bristol. Socs: Brit. Assn. Paediat. Nephrol.; BMA; Roy. Coll. of Paediat.s and Child Health. Prev: Sen. Regist. Gloucester & Bristol; Research Fell. (Paediat. Nephrol.) Inst. Child Health. Lond.; Regist. Hosp. for Sick Childr. Lond.

JADY, Kenneth 17 Octavia, Roman Hill, Bracknell RG12 7YZ Tel: 01344 645408 Fax: 01344 645409 Email: kjady@msm.com — MB BCh 1973 Wales; BSc Liverp. 1965; FFPM RCP (UK) 1993.

***JAENSUBHAKIJ, Lily** St Peter's Hospital, Guildford Road, Chertsey KT16 0PZ; Flat 2 Cove Villa, Bury Lane, Horsell, Woking GU21 4RP Tel: 01483 714993 — MB BS 1996 Lond.

JAFAREE, Syed Azhar Hasan 12 Arundale Court, 282 Wilbraham Road, Manchester M16 8WH — MB BS 1961 Punjab.

JAFARI, Bakhtiar 129 Fog Lane, Manchester M20 6ED — MB BS 1967 Punjab; MB BS Punjab (Pakistan) 1967; DLO Eng. 1976. (Fatimah Jinnah Med. Coll. Lahore) Regist. (ENT) Manch. RHB. Prev: SHO (ENT) Manch. Roy. Infirm., Wexham Pk. Hosp. Slough & Crawley; Hosp.

JAFFA, Anthony Jay The Pheonix Centre, IDA Darwin, Cambridge CB1 5EE Tel: 01223 884314 Fax: 01223 884313 — BM BS 1980 Nottm.; BMedSci Nottm. 1978; MRCPsych 1984; DCH RCPS Glas. 1982. Cons. Child & Adolesc. Psychiat. Camb. Prev: Cons. Child & Adolesc. Psychiat. Wandsworth HA; Sen. Regist. (Child & Adolesc. Psychiat.) Tavistock Clinic Lond.

JAFFE, Adam Respiratory Dept., Great Ormond Street Hospital, For Children NHS Trust, Great Ormond Street, London WC1N 3TH Tel: 0207 405 9200 Email: a.jaffe@ich.ucl.ac.uk — MB BS 1990 Lond.; MD 2000; (MRCPCH); BSc (Hons.) Lond. 1987; MRCP (UK) 1994. Cons. In Respirat. Research. Socs: Brit. Paediat. Respirat. Soc.

JAFFE, Ephraim (retired) 3 Oakwell Drive, Bury Old Road, Salford M7 4PY Tel: 0161 740 0379 — MB ChB 1946 Manch.

JAFFE, Gabriel Vivian (retired) A.1 Princes Gate, 55 Grove Road, Bournemouth BH1 3AW — MB BS 1946 Lond.; MRCS Eng. LRCP Lond. 1946. Prev: Cons. Wessex Clin. Trials Organisation & Sterling Winthrop Gp.

JAFFE, Louis 739 Beverley High Road, Hull HU6 7ES Tel: 01482 852212 — MB BS 1938 Durh. (Durh.) Prev: Ho. Surg. Roy. Vict. Infirm. Newc.

JAFFE, Miriam 1 The Wintons, The Rutts, Bushey Heath, Watford WD23 1LR — MB BS 1991 Lond.

JAFFE, Peter Hillingdon Hospital, Uxbridge UB8 3NN Tel: 01895 279263; 144 Harley Street, London W1 Tel: 020 7935 0023 — MB

1969 Camb.; BChir 1968; FRCP Lond. 1990; MRCP (UK) 1971. (Camb. & Univ. Coll. Hosp.) Cons. Paediat. Hillingdon Hosp. Uxbridge & Harefield Hosp. Prev: Regist. (Paediat.) N.wick Pk. Hosp. Harrow; Sen. Regist. (Paediat.) Hosp. Sick Childr. Lond.

JAFFE, Robert Jaffe and Partners, Belmont Health Centre, 516 Kenton Lane, Kenton, Harrow HA3 7LT Tel: 020 8427 1213; 7 Burnham Court, 33 Marsh Lane, Stanmore HA7 4HQ Tel: 020 8954 7267 — MB ChB 1958 Cape Town. (Cape Town)

JAFFE, Roy Flat 1, 63 Haverstock Hill, Hampstead, London NW3 4SL — MB ChB 1941 Cape Town; DOMS Eng. 1948. (Cape Town) Socs: Ophth. Soc. U.K. Prev: Capt. S. Afr. Med. Corps; Sen. Ho. Off. Soton. Eye Hosp.; Asst. Ophth. St. Thos. Hosp. & Hackney Hosp.

JAFFE, Miss Susan Margaret 82 Atwood Road, Didsbury, Manchester M20 6JN Tel: 0161 434 6770 Email: sjaffe@btinternet.com — BM 1990 Soton.; FRCS Ed. 1995. (Southampton University) Specialist Regist. (Gen. Surg.) N. Manch.

JAFFE, Victor 30 Green Walk, London NW4 2AJ — MB BChir 1979 Camb.; MA Camb. 1979.

JAFFE, Mr Wayne Windover, 23 Sheepfoot Lane, Prestwich, Manchester M25 0BN Tel: 0161 721 4567 Fax: 0161 720 9867 Email: waynejaf@plus-utd.demon.co.uk — MB ChB 1985 Manch.; BSc St. And. 1982; FRCS Ed. 1990. Sen. Regist. (Plastic Surg.) Leicester Roy. Infirm. Socs: Train. Mem. Brit. Assn. Plastic Surg.; World Assn. Disaster & Emerg. Med.; HCSA. Prev: Fell. (Anaesth. Surg.) Wellington Hosp. Lond.; Regist. Roy. Preston Hosp.; SHO (Plastic Surg.) Char. Cross & Qu. Mary's Hosps. Lond. & Qu. Vict. Hosp. E. Grinstead.

JAFFER, Kulsum St Patricks Centre for Community Health, Highgate, Birmingham B12 0YA Tel: 0121 466 1069 Fax: 0121 466 1070 — BSc 1973 Karachi Univ.; MB BS Karachi 1981; (Eng.) MFFP 1993; (England) MRCOG 1990; (Ireland) DObst RCPI 1985. (Dow Medical College, Karachi) Cons. In Reproductive & Sexual Health, Birm. Specialist Community Heath Trust, Birm. Socs: Fac. of Family Plann. & Reproductive Healthcare; W Midl. Assn. Family Plann. Doctors; Brit. Menopause Soc. Prev: Specialist Regist. (Community Gyn.) Birm. Wom. Healthcare Trust S. Birm. Community Health Trust; Regist. (O & G) Lanarksh. HB; SCMO (Family Plann.) Solihull Healthcare & N. Birm. Community Trust.

JAFFER, Nasreen 35 Braydon Road, London N16 6QL — MB BS 1998 Lond.; MB BS Lond 1998.

JAFFEY, Lawrence Hyman Royal Liverpool University Hospital, Prescot St., Liverpool L7 8XP Tel: 0151 706 2057 Fax: 0151 706 5899 — MB BS 1975 Lond.; FRCP Lond. 1995; MRCP (UK) 1981; FFAEM 1993. (Univ. Coll. Lond.) Cons. A & E Roy. Liverp. Hosp.; Clin. Lect. Univ. Liverp. Prev: Sen. Regist. (A & E) Roy. Liverp. Hosp.; Regist. (Med.) Crawley Hosp.

JAFFRAY, Bruce Department of Paediatric Surgery, Royal Victoria Infirmary, Queen Victoria Road, Newcastle upon Tyne NE1 4LP Tel: 0191 232 5131 Fax: 0191 227 5276 Email: bruce.jaffray@ncl.uc.uk — MB ChB 1986 Aberd.; ChM Aberd. 1995; BMedBiol. 1984; FRCS (Paediat.) 1996; FRCS Glas. 1990. (Aberd.) Cons. Paediat. Surg. Dept. of Paediat. Surg. Roy. Vict. Infirm. Newc. Socs: Assoc. Mem. Brit. Assn. Paediat. Surgs. Prev: Sen. Regist (Paediat. Surg.) Roy. Manch. Childr.'s Hosp.; Regist. Roy. Hosp. Sick Childr. Edin.; Regist. (Surg.) Glas. Roy. Infirm.

JAFFRAY, Mr David Charles 28 Victoria Road, Oswestry SY11 2HS Tel: 01691 654802 — MB ChB 1974 Aberd.; FRCS Ed. 1979. Cons. Orthop. Surg. & Asst. Dir. Robt. Jones & Agnes Hunt Orthop. Hosp. OsW.ry; Sen. Lect. (Orthop.) Keele Univ. Socs: Fell. Brit. Orthop. Assn. & Brit. Scoliosis Soc. Prev: Research Fell. (Orthop.) Duchess of Kent Childr. Hosp., Hong Kong; Regist. (Orthop.) Roy. Perth Hosp. Austral.; Regist. (Surg.) Aberd. Hosps.

JAFFRAY, Fiona Karen Melbury lodge, Royal Hampshire County Hospital, Romsey Road, Winchester SO22 5DG Tel: 01962 863535 — MRCPsych 1997; MB BS Lond. 1990; DRCOG 1994; MRC Psych 1997. (University College and Middlesex School of Medicine London) Specialist Regist. Psychiat. Winchester. Prev: Specialist Regist. in Old Age Psychiat.; Regist. (Psychiat.) Soton.; SHO (Psychiat.) St. Ann's Hosp. Lond. & Portsmouth.

JAFFREY, William George Anderson Ardach, Highfield Rd, Buckie AB56 1SE Tel: 01542 831555 Fax: 01542 835799; Ridgewood, Drybridge, Buckie AB56 5LB — MB ChB 1979 Aberd. GP Buckie. Prev: SHO (Obst.) & (A & E) Raigmore Hosp. Inverness.

JAFREE, Mr Afsar Jalil 16 Cambridge Avenue, Greenford UB6 0PJ — MB BS 1986 Karachi; FRCS Ed. 1993.

JAFRI, Anwar 202 Barlaston Old Road, Stoke-on-Trent ST4 8HL — MB BS 1998 Newc.; MB BS Newc 1998.

JAFRI, Mr Moazzam Sajjad Department of General Surgery, Withybush General Hospital, Haverfordwest SA61 2PZ Tel: 01437 764545 Fax: 01437 773499; The Cottage, Pensarn, Carmarthen SA31 2NG — MB BS 1975 Ranchi; FRCS Ed. 1982. Staff Grade (Gen. Surg.) Withybush Gen. Hosp. Pembrokesh. Prev: Sen. Regist. (Gen. Surg.) Centr. Hosp. Riyadh, Saudi Arabia; Regist. (Gen. Surg.) Neath Gen. Hosp. W. Glam.

JAFRI, Salman Abbas 202 Barlaston Old Road, Trentham, Stoke-on-Trent ST4 8HL — BChir 1998 Camb.; BChir Camb 1998.

JAFRI, Syed Kausar Abbas Jafri, Longton Health Centre, Drayton Road, Longton, Stoke-on-Trent ST3 1EQ Tel: 01782 312838 Fax: 01782 599018; 202 Barlaston Old Road, Trentham, Stoke-on-Trent ST4 8HL Tel: 01782 658099 Fax: 01782 599018 — MB BS 1962 Punjab; MRCGP 1974; DCH Eng. 1967. (Nishtar Med. Coll. Multan) Trainer (Gen. Pract.) Stoke-on-Trent. Socs: BMA; Overseas Doctors Assn.; GP Writers Assn. Prev: Regist. (Paediat.) Ayrsh. Centr. Hosp., E. Birm. Gp. Hosps. & Doncaster Roy. Infirm.

JAGADAMBE, Prakash Ramchandrarao 21 Berkhamstead Avenue, Wembley HA9 6DU Tel: 020 8795 1148 — MB BS 1970 Nagpur; MD (Med.) Nagpur 1976.

JAGADESHAM, Pulloori Blackburn Road Surgery, 153 Blackburn Road, Darwen BB3 1ET Tel: 01254 701961 — MB BS 1975 Osmania; MB BS 1975 Osmania.

JAGADISH, Tarikere Shanthappa Health Clinic, Gardens Lane, Conisborough, Doncaster DN12 3JW Tel: 01709 862150; 19 Sandown Road, Mexborough S64 0BL — MB BS 1970 Mysore. (Kasthurba Med. Coll. Mangalore)

JAGAJEEVANRAM, Mr Durairaj 11 Tunnel Wood Road, Watford WD17 4SN — MB BS 1974 Madras; MSc Orth. Lond. 1988; MS Madras 1980; FRCS Ed. 1983. Cons. Orthopaedic Surg., Watford Gen. Hosp. V. Carage Rd, Watford Herts. Prev: Cons. Orthop. Surg. Jubail, Saudi Arbaia.; Cons. Orthop. Surg. St. Vincent's Hosp. Pinner.

JAGANMOHAN REDDY, Garisa c/o Dr A. Theodossi, Endoscopy Unit, Mayday University Hospital, London Road, Croydon CR7 7YE — MB BS 1984 Venkateswara U, India; MRCP (UK) 1990.

JAGANNATH, Pramila (Surgery), 108 Crescent Road, Great Lever, Bolton BL3 3JR — MB BS 1962 Mysore. Socs: Fell. Roy. Soc. Health; Fell. Roy. Soc. Med.; Bolton Med. Soc. Prev: Regist. (O & G) Bolton Gen. Hosp. & New Cross Hosp. Wolverhampton; SHO (Gen. Surg.) Guy's & St. Olaves Hosps. Lond.

JAGATHESAN, Rohan Flat A, London SE4 1YP — MB BS 1992 Lond.

JAGATHESAN, Tania Flat 27, Woolcombes Court, Princes Riverside Road, London SE16 5RQ — MB BS 1996 Lond.

***JAGDEV, Daljit Singh** 9 Denbigh Road, Southall UB1 2RP Tel: 0208 843 2398 Email: dsjagdev@hotmail.com — MB ChB 1998 Dund.; MB ChB Dund 1998.

JAGDEV, Satinder Pal Kaur 15 Rutland Road, Southall UB1 2UP — MB ChB 1994 Sheff.

JAGDISH, Soundararajan, Lt.-Col. RAMC Royal Hospital Haslar, Gosport PO12 2AA Tel: 023 9258 4255 — MB BS 1981 Madras. Assoc. Specialist in Anesthesia and Resusc., RAMC. Socs: Assn. Anaesth.; The Pain Soc.; Brit. Sleep Soc. Prev: Specialist in Anaesth., RAF; Regist. (Anaesth.) Hull Roy. Infirm.

JAGGAR, Sian Isobel c/o 13 Highfield Drive, Ickenham, Uxbridge UB10 8AL — MB BS 1988 Lond.; BSc (Biochem.) Lond. 1985, MB BS 1988. Regist. (Anaesth.) P.ss Roy. Hosp. Haywards Heath. Prev: SHO (A & E) N.wick Pk. Hosp. Harrow.

JAGGER, Christopher Roy Binscombe Medical Centre, 106 Binscombe Lane, Godalming GU7 3PR Tel: 01483 415115 Fax: 01483 414925; Elmcroft, 42 Busbridge Lane, Godalming GU7 1QD — MB BS 1971 Lond.; DObst RCOG 1973. Prev: Ho. Surg. & SHO (Paediat. & O & G) St. Geo. Hosp. Lond.

JAGGER, Derek Bourne, MBE, Lt.-Col. RAMC Retd. South Lodge, 3 Highlands Close, Farnham GU9 8SP Tel: 01252 713390 — MB ChB 1938 Birm.; DOMS Eng. 1949. (Birm.) Prev: Assoc. Specialist (Ophth.) W. Surrey & NE Kents HA; SHMO Ophth. Unit. W.m. Hosp.; Sen. Specialist in Ophth. RAMC.

JAGGER, Mr Graham Mark Higgins Castle Street Surgery, 67 Castle Street, Salisbury SP1 3SP Tel: 01722 322726 Fax: 01722 410315; White Lodge, Shady Bower, Salisbury SP1 2RH Tel: 01722 334383 Fax: 01722 501600 Email: jaggerwood@castlesurg.clara.net — MB BCh 1976 Witwatersrand; FRCS Glas. 1984; MRCGP 1986. Clin. Teach. in Primary Med. Care Med. Sch. of the Univ. of Soton.; Dep. Police Surg. Amesbury. Socs: Assn. Police Surg.; Assn. Accupuncturists in Gen. Pract. & Hosp.

JAGGER, Jean Helen 13 Denby Court, Oakworth, Keighley BD22 7SF — MB ChB 1986 Sheff.; MBA Bradford 1992. SHO (O & G) Keighley.

JAGGER, Mr Jonathan David 149 Harley Street, London W1G 6DE Tel: 020 7935 4444 Fax: 020 7935 3934; 23 Loxley Road, Wandsworth, London SW18 3LL — MB BS 1974 Lond.; FRCS Eng. 1981; FRCOphth 1989; DO Eng. 1979. (St Thomas') Cons. Ophth. King Edwd. VII's Hosp. for Off.s & Roy. Free Hosp.; Surg. Oculist to HM Roy. Ho.hold; Roy. Free Hosp. Socs: Fell. Roy. Soc. Med. Prev: Sen. Regist. Moorfields Eye Hosp. & W.. Ophth. Hosp. Lond.; Sen. Resid. Moorfields Eye Hosp. Lond.

JAGGER, Philip Thornton Heathbridge House, The Old Bridge, Kenfig Hill, Bridgend CF33 6BY Tel: 01656 740359 Fax: 01656 745400; Swaledale, Derllwyn Road, Tondu, Bridgend CF32 9HD — MB ChB 1979 Manch.; BSc (Med. Sci.) St. And. 1976; MRCGP 1984; DRCOG 1982. Prev: Trainee GP Bridgend VTS; Resid. Med. Off. King Edwd. II Hosp. Bermuda.

JAGGI, Sangeeta Kaur c/o Dr G & K Chandok, 32 College Drive, Ruislip HA4 8SB — MB BS 1995 Lond.

JAGGS-FOWLER, Robert Mark, OStJ Central Surgery, King Street, Barton-upon-Humber DN18 5ER Tel: 01652 635435 Fax: 01652 636122; The Retreat, Park View, Barton-upon-Humber DN18 6AX Email: jaggs@globalnet.co.uk — MB BS 1985 Lond.; MRCGP 1990; DRCOG 1989; DCH RCP Lond. 1988; DFFP 1998. (Char. Cross Hosp. Med. Sch.) Princip. GP Barton on Humber N. Lincs.; Med. Off. 147 Port & Reclamations Company REME (V); Cdr. St. John Ambul. Humberside; Maj. 250 (Hull) Field Ambul. RAMC (V) (2nd-in-Command); Health & Safety Exec. Apptd. Doctor; Dir. Barton Med. Serv. Ltd. Socs: BMA; BASICS & LIVES. Prev: Trainee GP Hull Roy. Infirm. VTS; SHO (A & E) Lincoln Co. Hosp.; Ho. Surg. FarnBoro. Hosp. Kent.

JAGJIVAN, Bipinchandra 7 Roundhill Road, Leicester LE5 5RJ — MB ChB 1980 Leic.; FRCR 1986. Sen. Regist. (Radiol.) Roy. Hallamsh. Hosp. Sheff. Prev: Ho. Off. (Surg.) Leicester Roy. Infirm.; Ho. Phys. Groby Rd. Hosp. Leicester.

JAGO, Audrey Joan Old Cottage, Campfield Place, Leith Hill, Dorking RH5 6LX Tel: 01306 711853 — MB BS 1951 Lond.; MRCS Eng. LRCP Lond. 1951. (Roy. Free) Prev: Med. Regist. Qu. Mary Hosp. E. End; Ho. Surg. Roy. Free Hosp.; Ho. Phys. Whipps Cross Hosp.

JAGO, David George Thurstan 11 Spiers Close, Knowle, Solihull B93 9ES — MB ChB 1982 Bristol; MRCPsych 1989.

JAGO, Helen Mary 39 Northfield, Bridgwater TA6 7HA Tel: 01278 445947 — MB BCh Wales 1968; DObst RCOG 1971. (Cardiff) Cas. Off. Bridgwater Gen. Hosp.; Clin. Asst. (Genitourin. Med.) MusGr. Pk. Hosp. Taunton. Socs: Brit. Acad. Forens. Sci.; Assn. Genitourin. Med. Prev: Ho. Phys. MusGr. Pk. Hosp. Taunton; Ho. Surg. (O & G & Gen. Surg.) MusGr. Pk. Hosp. Taunton.

JAGO, John Philip Hawson X-995 Riyadh Armed Services Hospital, PO Box 7897, Riyadh 11159, Saudi Arabia; c/o 14 Mayfield Drive, Bridgwater TA6 7JQ — MB BS 1967 Lond.; MRCS Eng. LRCP Lond. 1967; MRCGP 1977; MICGP 1987; DObst RCOG 1970; DA Eng. 1970. (Guy's) Mem. Panel of Examrs. RCGP. Socs: BMA. Prev: Course Organiser (Trainers Courses) Glos., Avon & Som. SW Region.

JAGO, John Watson (retired) The Red House, Drigg, Holmrook CA19 1XS — MB ChB 1957 Sheff.

JAGO, Loveday Jane 26A Cambridge Heath Road, London E1 5QH — MB BS 1996 Lond.

JAGO, Maurice Edwin MacDowall Cape Cornwall Surgery, Market Street, St. Just-in-Penwith, Penzance TR19 7HX Tel: 01736 788306 — MRCS Eng. LRCP Lond. 1925; MD Lond. 1928, MB BS 1925. (Guy's) Prev: Sen. Ho. Surg. Blackburn Roy. Infirm.; Res. Med. Off. Miller Gen. Hosp. & Gen. Lying-in Hosp. Lambeth.

JAGO, Mr Robert Hawson (retired) 4 Little Foster's, Chaddesley Glen, Poole BH13 7PB Tel: 01202 706400 Fax: 01202 701950 — MB BChir 1962 Camb.; MA Camb. 1972; MChir Camb. 1972; FRCS Eng. 1967. Cons. Surg. Roy. Bournemouth Hosp. Prev: Regist. Rotat. (Surg.) Univ. Coll. Hosp. W. Indies Jamaica.

JAGO, Roger Hugh Elms House, The Street, Swallowfield, Reading RG7 1RE Tel: 0118 988 2115 Fax: 0118 988 2115 — MB BChir 1970 Camb.; MA Camb. 1970; FRCA 1975. (Camb. & St. Thos.) Cons. Anaesth. Roy. Berks. & Battle Hosp. NHS Trust Reading. Socs: Assn. Anaesths.; BMA; TriServ. Anaesth. Soc. Prev: Cons. Anaesth. Brit. Milit. Hosp. Hanover; Ho. Surg. (Surgic Unit) St. Thos. Hosp. Lond.; Regtl. Med. Off. 1st Bn. Duke of Wellington's Regt.

JAGO, William Boscarne House, Crows-An-Wra, St Buryan, Penzance TR19 6HU — MB BS 1976 Lond.; MRCS Eng. LRCP Lond. 1974; DA Eng. 1978. (Guy's)

JAGOE, Robert Thomas 9 Tankerville Place, Jesmond, Newcastle upon Tyne NE2 3AT — MB BChir 1989 Camb.; MRCP (UK) 1991. Specialist Regist. Respirat. Med. Roy. Vict. Infirm. Newc. Prev: Research Regist. (Respirat. Med.) Freeman Hosp. Newc. u. Tyne; Regist. Rotat. (Respirat. & Gen. Med.) N.. Region.; SHO Rotat. (Med.) City Hosp. Nottm.

JAHANGIR, Muhammad Tariq 69 Albert Road, London SE25 4JE — MB BS 1993 Lond.

JAHANGIRI, Marjan Brompton Hospital, Sydney St., London SW3 6N; 6 Pelham Court, London SW7 2NP — MB BS 1988 Lond.; FRCS Eng. 1992. (Cardiothoracic Surg.) St. Bart. Hosp., The Roy. Lond. Hosp. & Lond. Chest Hosp.; Specialist Regist. Roy. Brompton Hosp./Lond. Chest Hosp. Socs: Roy. Soc. Med.

JAHFAR, Sarah Caroline Avonvale Road, Bristol BS5 9QS Tel: 0117 955 7474 Fax: 0117 955 5402 — MB ChB 1989 Bristol; MRCP (UK) 1993. (Univ. Bristol) GP.

JAIBAJI, Mr Moneer Monked 7 Woodcock Dell Avenue, Kenton, Harrow HA3 0PW — MB ChB 1988 Al-Mustansirya Univ. Iraq; FRCS Eng. 1995.

JAIDEV, Vasudevan Changarath Department of Anaesthesia, Prince Philip Hospital, Llanelli SA14 8QF Tel: 01554 756567; 63 Sandpiper Road, Llanelli SA15 4SG Email: kam06@~dial.pipex.com — MB BS 1984 Calicut; FFA RCSI 1991; DA (UK) 1989; Dip. Amer. Bd Anaesthesiol. 1997. (Calicut Med. Coll.) Cons. Anaesth. P. Philip Hosp. LLa.lli. Socs: BMA; Assn. Anaesth.; Intens. Care Soc. Prev: Fell. (Hepatic Transpl. Anaesth.) Univ. Pittsburgh, USA; Fell. (Critical Care Med.) Univ. Virginia, USA; Regist. (Anaesth.) Hull & E. Yorks. Hosps.

JAIGIRDAR, Shamsul Huda Hartwoodhill (One Ward) Hospital, Shotts ML7 4LA Tel: 01698 245000 Fax: 01501 824583; 4 Burnbank Braes, Carluke ML8 4EW — MB BS 1966 Dhaka; FRCPsych 1995, M 1974; DPM Eng. 1972. (Chittagong Medical College) Cons. Psychiat. Hartwoodhill Hosp., Shotts, Lanarksh.; Clin. Dir. Ment. Health & Learning Disabil. Div. Lanarksh. Healthcare NHS Trust; Mem. (Ex-Chairm.) Lanarksh. Div. Psychiat. Socs: Fell.Roy. Coll. of Psychiat.s. Prev: Ex Mem., Unit Managem. Team, Community & Priority Servs. Unit, Lanarksh.; Sen. Regist. (Psychiat.) Univ. Hosp. Wales Cardiff; Regist. (Psychiat.) WhitCh. Hosp., Cardiff.

JAIKARAN, Elsie Sachie (retired) 9 Lancaster Drive, Hampstead, London NW3 4EY — MB BS Lond. 1950; MRCS Eng. LRCP Lond. 1950; MRCOG 1956; DObst 1953.

JAIN, Alok Suta 16 Lyndhurst Rise, Chigwell IG7 5BA — MB BS 1975 Delhi.

JAIN, Mr Amar Singh Department of Orthopaedics, Ninewells Hospital & Medical School, Dundee DD1 9SY Tel: 01382 660111 Fax: 01382 496201 Email: katemcf@tuht.scot.nhs.uk; 16 Grange Ave, Monfieth, Dundee DD5 4LA Tel: 01382 532843 Email: ajain@tostc.tuth.scot.nhs.uk — MB BS 1971 Rajasthan; FRCS Ed. 1977. Cons. Orthop. Surg. (Prosth.s, Orthotics, Amputat. Surg. & Foot Surg.) Ninewells Hosp. Dundee; Cons.Prosth./Orthotic Servs.; Sen. Lect. (Orthop. & Trauma Surg.) Univ. Dundee; Vis. Lect. Nat. Centre Train. Educat. (Prosth.s & Orthotics) Univ. Strathclyde Glas. Socs: Brit. Orthop. Assn.; World Orthop. Concern; Internat. Soc. Prosthesis & Orthop. (Hon. Sec. UK). Prev: Lect. (Orthop. & Traum. Surg.) Univ. Dundee.

JAIN, Anil Kumar 16 Lyndhurst Rise, Chigwell IG7 5BA — MB BS 1972 Lucknow.

JAIN, Anil Kumar Department of Radiology, Northampton General Hospital NHS Trust, Northampton NN1 5BD Tel: 01604 235875 Fax: 01604 235644; Red Gables, 19 Mears Ashby Road, Earls Barton, Northampton NN6 0HQ — MB BS 1984 Delhi; MD Delhi

1987; FRCR 1993. (Maulana Azad Med. Coll. New Delhi, India) Cons. Radiol. N.ampton Gen. Hosp. NHS Trust. Socs: BMA; Brit. Soc. Interven. Radiol.; Magnetic Resonance Radiol. Assn.

JAIN, Anoopam 7 Old Park Road, Leeds LS8 1JT Email: anoo.jain@nottinham.ac.uk — MB BS 1991 Lond.; MRCPI 1996. Lect. (Child Health) Univ. Nottm.

JAIN, Arun Kumar c/o 5 Trederwen, Ebbw Vale NP23 6WB — MB BS 1971 Calcutta; MRCPI 1982.

JAIN, Ashok Kumar Stepping Hill Hospital, Stockport SK7 2JE Tel: 0161 483 1010 Fax: 0161 419 5003; 12 Liskeard Drive, Bramhall, Stockport SK7 2JA Tel: 0161 440 9200 — MB BS 1974 Poona; MRCPsych 1981; T(Psych.) 1991; DPM Eng. 1980. (Armed Forces Med. Coll. Poona) Cons. Psychiat. Stepping Hill Hosp. Stockport. Socs: Brit. Acad. W.. Acupunc. & BMA; BMA; Overseas Doctors Assn. Prev: Sen. Regist. Rainhill & Fazakerley Hosps. Liverp. & Greaves Hall Hosp. S.port; Regist. Brookwood Hosp. Woking.

JAIN, Ashok Kumar Motilal The Kingfisher Medical Centre, 3 Kingfisher Square, London SE8 5DA Tel: 020 8692 7373 Fax: 020 8692 7373 — MB BS 1970 Poona.

JAIN, Bhupendra Kumar 5 Pellhurst Road, Ryde PO33 3BN — MB BS 1968 Indore.

JAIN, Chetna Department of Histopathology, Whipps Cross Hospital, Whipps Cross Road, Leytonstone, London E11 1NR Tel: 020 8539 5522 Email: chetna@jain.demon.co.uk — MB BS 1979 Lucknow; MRCPath 1994. (King Geo. Med. Sch., Lucknow) Cons. Histopath. Whipps Cross Hosp. Lond. Socs: Internat. Acad. Paths.; Assn. Clin. Paths. Prev: Sen. Regist. Char. Cross Hosp. Lond.

JAIN, Jagdishchandra Natvarlal 26 Woodhead Road, Read, Burnley BB12 7PH — MD 1974 Baroda; MB BS 1970; MRCPsych 1980; DPM RCPS 1979.

JAIN, Mohua 2 The Woodfines, Emerson Park, Hornchurch RM11 3HR Tel: 01708 449429 Fax: 0961 319672 Email: mjain@mcmail.com — MB BS 1992 Lond.; MRCP (UK) 1995; FRCA 1999. (United Med. & Dent. Sch. Guy's & St. Thos.) Specialist Regist. (Anaesth.) N. Thames; ALS Instruc. Resusc. Counc. (UK). Socs: Assn. Anaesth.; RCP Lond. & Edin.; MRCAnaesth. Prev: SHO (Anaesth.) St. Mary's Hosp. Lond.; SHO (Anaesth.) N.wick Pk. Hosp. Harrow.

JAIN, Narendra Kumar Highbury House, 59 Lower Edge Road, Rastrick, Brighouse HD6 3LE Tel: 01484 722229 — MB BS 1963 Lucknow; DMRD Eng. 1971. (King Geo. Med. Coll.) Cons. Radiol. Calderdale AHA. Prev: Sen. Regist. Leeds Gen. Infirm. & St. Jas. Hosp. Leeds; SHO N. Cambs. Hosp. Wisbech.

JAIN, Mr Nirmal Kumar Sanraj, 2 Bellerton Lane, Stoke-on-Trent ST6 8XP — MB BS 1971 Rajasthan; FRCS Ed. 1977.

JAIN, Pankaj 4 Whitchurch Close, Edgware HA8 6PE — MB ChB 1989 Aberd.

JAIN, Prakashchandra Roshanlal The Surgery, 2 Parklands Drive, Askam-in-Furness LA16 7JP Tel: 01229 462464 Fax: 0709 235 6823 Email: prakash@jain.net — MB BS 1975 Baroda; DRCOG 1978 Lond.; DCH 1979 Dublin. (Baroda) GP Askam in Furness, Cumbria.

JAIN, Mr Rahul 79 Christchurch Close, Edgbaston, Birmingham B15 3NE Tel: 0121 455 7430 — MB ChB 1989 Sheff.; FRCS Ed. 1996. Specialist Regist. (Trauma & Orthop. Surg.) W. Midl. Rotat.

JAIN, S K Masefield Road Surgery, Masefield Road, Lower Gornal, Dudley DY1 3BU Tel: 01922 882002 Fax: 01922 882002 — MB BS 1969 Kanpur; MB BS 1969 Kanpur.

JAIN, Mr Sandeep Rajkumar 208 Oldham Road, Royton, Oldham OL2 5AA — MB BS 1986 Bombay; MS (Gen. Surg.) Bombay 1989; FRCS Ed. 1992.

JAIN, Sanjiv Kumar Manchester Royal Infirmary, Oxford Road, Manchester M13 9WL Tel: 0161 276 1234; 17 Beechfield, Wakefield WF2 6AW Tel: 01924 255207 — MB BChir 1991 Camb.; MA Camb. 1991; MRCP (UK) 1996. (Camb.) Clin. Lect. (Gen. Med.) & Hon. Regist. Manch. Roy. Infirm. Prev: Regist. (Gen. Med. & Gastroenterol.) Warrington Hosp. NHS Trust; SHO (Nephrol.) Roy. Liverp. Univ. Hosp.; SHO (Gen. Med.) Roy. Shrewsbury Hosp.

JAIN, Stephan 14 Camden Mews, London NW1 9DA Tel: 020 7267 8729; 15 The Putterills, Harpenden AL5 4DZ Tel: 01582 497243 — MB ChB 1966 Birm.; MD Birm. 1978; FRCP Lond. 1990. Cons. Phys. Luton & Dunstable Hosp. Socs: Brit. Soc. Gastroenterol. Prev: Sen. Regist. (Med.) Selly Oak Hosp. Birm.; Regist. (Med.) Dudley Rd. Hosp. Birm.; Hon. Lect. Roy. Free Hosp. Lond.

JAIN, Subhash Chander The Health Centre, Maison Dieu Road, Dover CT16 1RH Tel: 01304 865577 Fax: 01304 865501; Nirvana, Common Lane, River, Dover CT17 0PN Tel: 01304 820590 — MB BS Delhi 1965; MRCS Eng. LRCP Lond. 1978; DA Eng. 1975; DO RCPSI 1970. GP Dover; Clin. Asst. (Anaesth.) Buckland Hosp. Dover; Med. Off. Brit. Gas. Socs: Folkestone Med. Soc. & BMA.

JAIN, Sunjay 253 Chilwell Lane, Bramcote, Nottingham NG9 3DU — MB BS 1993 Lond.

JAIN, Suresh Chand 22 Deburg Street, Cardiff CF1 8LD — MB BS 1967 Ranchi; DTM & H Liverp. 1975.

JAIN, Susan Sumita 2 The Woodfines, Hornchurch RM11 3HR — MB BS 1997 Lond.

JAIN, Swati c/o Dr A K Jain, Ward B5 Renal Unit, University Hospital of Wales, Heath Park, Cardiff CF14 4XW — MB BS 1978 Delhi; MRCOG 1996.

JAIN, Mr Vigyan Kumar Luton & Dunstable Hospital, Lewsey Road, Luton LU4 0DZ Tel: 01582 491122, 01522 575306, 01522 515364, mandy.bretman@lincs-ha.nhs.uk — MB BS 1985 Bombay; FRCS (Gen.) 1996; FRCS Ed. 1989. (Seth. G. S. Med. Coll., Bombay) Cons. Gen. Surg. Luton & Dunstable Hosp. NHS Trust. Prev: Sen. Regist. Luton & Dunstable Hosp.

JAIN, Vinod Kumar 39 Hillington Gardens, Woodford Green IG8 8QS — MB BS 1964 Agra.

JAIN, Virendra Kumar Department Psychological Medicine, Kendray Hospital, Doncaster Road, Barnsley S70 3RD Tel: 01226 730000 Ext: 4606 Fax: 01226 298422; Shantiniketan, 17 Beechfield, Sandal, Wakefield WF2 6AW Tel: 01924 255207 — MB BS Agra 1959; BSc Agra 1954; FRCPsych 1986, M 1971; T(Psych.) 1991; DPM Eng. 1965. (S.N. Med. Coll. Agra) Cons. Psychiat. Barnsley Dist. Gen. Hosp. & Med. Dir. Barnsley Community & Priority Servs. NHS Trust; Commiss.er Ment. Health Act Commiss.; Mem. Bd. Examrs. Roy. Coll. Psychiat. Socs: Brit. Assn. Med. Managers; Assn. Trust Med. Directors; Soc. Clin. Psychiat. Prev: Lect. (Psychiat.) Univ. Liverp.; Sen. Regist. (Psychiat.) United Liverp. Hosps.; Sen. Regist. Profess. Unit Rainhill Hosp. Liverp.

JAIRAJ, Maste Bhakti Cavendish Surgery, 2A Cavendish Road, Edgbaston, Birmingham B16 0HZ Tel: 0121 454 1702 Fax: 0121 455 8084; 55 Selwyn Road, Edgebaston, Birmingham B16 0SL Tel: 0121 454 1704 — MB BS 1958 Andhra. Socs: BMA. Prev: Ho. Surg. (Traum. & Orthop.) Manor Hosp. Nuneaton; Cas. Off. Coventry & Warw. Hosp.

JAIRAJ, Mr Paul Flat 31, 39/40 Queen's Gate, South Kensington, London SW7 5HR — MB ChB 1991 Birm.; FRCS Lond 1996. Specialist Regist. (Trauma & Orthop.) Imperial Coll. Sch. of Med., Trauma & Orthop. Rotat.

JAIRATH, Geeta 63 Meadow Lands, Antrim BT41 4EX — MB BS 1998 Lond.; MB BS Lond 1998.

JAISRI, Selene Sharmila Persaud 5 Braeside, Beckenham BR3 1ST — MB BS 1993 Lond. SHO (A & E) Dartford.; SHO (Paediat.) JGH; SHO (Elderly Care) JGH; SHO (Psychiat.) SHH; SHO (Obst. & Gyn.) Gravesend Hosp. Socs: MDU. Prev: Ho. Off. (Surg.) Basildon Hosp. Essex; Ho. Off. (Med.) Mayday Hosp.

JAISWAL, Ajit 39 Osborne Road, Newcastle upon Tyne NE2 2AH — MB BS 1971 Allahabad.

JAISWAL, Alak Lata The Surgery, 38 Easedale Drive, Elm Park, Hornchurch RM12 5HJ Tel: 01708 451585 Fax: 01708 459287 — MB BS 1959 Bihar; MB BS Bihar 19959.

JAISWAL, Bijay Kumar 70 Pearson Road, Ipswich IP3 8NH — MD 1980 Ranchi; MB BS 1972.

JAISWAL, Duga Prasad The Surgery, 92 Hedgemans Road, Dagenham RM9 6HT Tel: 020 8592 4242 Fax: 020 8593 2094 — MB BS 1958 Bihar; MB BS Bihar 1957; BSc Univ. Bihar 1952.

JAISWAL, Indira 23 Russell Avenue, St Albans AL3 5ES — MB BS 1964 Vikram.

JAISWAL, Mr Ramesh Chandra St. Albans City Hospital, Normandy Road, St Albans AL3 5PN Tel: 01727 66122 — MB BS 1957 Agra; MS Delhi 1969; DO Eng. 1961; MCOphth. 1989. (G.R. Med. Coll. Gwalior) Chief Clin. Asst. Moorfields Eye Hosp. Lond; Assoc. Ophth. St. Albans City Hosp. Socs: Coll. Ophth. UK; Oxf. Ophth. Congr.

JAISWAL, Ramesh Chandra Whittington Moor Surgery, Scarsdale Road, Chesterfield S41 8NA Tel: 01246 450523; 6 South Lodge

Court, Ashgate, Chesterfield S40 3QG — MB BS 1964 Jabalpur; BSc Osmania 1958; LMSSA Lond. 1976. (Jabalpur Med. Coll.) GP Chesterfield. Prev: Regist. (Orthop.) Lincoln Gp. Hosps., Raigmore Hosp. Inverness & Roy.; Infirm. Halifax.

JAISWAL, Ravindra Singh Bedford Hospital (South Wing), Mental Health Service (Weller Wing), Kempston Road, Bedford MK42 9DJ Tel: 01234 355122 Fax: 01234 792279; 10 Deep Spinney, Biddenham, Bedford MK40 4QP Tel: 01234 326882 — MB BS 1975 Allahabad; DPM Eng. 1980. (M.L.N. Med. Coll. Allahabad, India) Regist. (Psychiat.) Acad. Unit Psychiat. St. Bart. Hosp., German Hosp. & Hackney Hosp. Lond.; Assoc. Specialist (Psychogeriat.) Beds. & Luton Community NHS Trust; Affil. Mem. Roy. Coll. Psychiat. Lond. Prev: Regist. (Psychiat.) Cane Hill Hosp. Coulsdon Bromley Gr. Pk. Hosp. Lond.

JAITLY, Seema 16 Woodlands Avenue, New Malden KT3 3UN — MB BS 1992 Lond.

JAITLY, Varum Kumar 10 Hindon Square, Vicarage Road, Egbaston, Birmingham B15 3HA — MB ChB 1989 Dundee.

JAIYESIMI, Rotimi Ayodele Kayode Department of Obstetrics & Gynaecology, North Tyneside Hospital, Rake Lane, North Shields NE29 8NH Tel: 0191 259 6660 Fax: 0191 293 2594 Email: r.a.k.jaiyesimi@ncl.ac.uk, rotimi.jaiyesimi@northumbria-healthcare.nhs.uk — MB BS 1978 Ibadan; MRCOG 1988; T(OG) 1994. (Univ. Ibadan, Nigeria) Cons. O & G N. Tyneside Hosp. Tyne & Wear; FWACS W. African Postgrad. Med. Coll. 1986. Socs: Fell. W. African Coll. Surgs.; Brit. Menopause Soc.; Eur. Assn. Gyn. & Obst. Prev: Sen. Regist. Freedeom Fields & Derriford Hosps. Plymouth; Regist. Qu. Mary's Univ. Hosp. Lond.; Regist. Rotunda Hosp. Dub.

JAJA, Dagogo Millar 78B Great North Way, London NW4 1HN — MB BS 1983 Lagos; MB BS Lagos, Nigeria 1983.

JAJBHAY, Mahomed 59 Home Park Road, Wimbledon, London SW19 7HS Tel: 020 8946 1695 — MB BCh 1958 Witwatersrand.

JAJOO, Jagdish Narain 10 Arran Close, Birmingham B43 7AD — MB BS 1971 Rajasthan.

JAKEMAN, Nicola The Mount, Grange Lane, Ingham, Lincoln LN1 2YD — BM BS 1995 Nottm.

JAKEMAN, Paul The Mission Practice, 208 Cambridge Heath Road, London E2 9LS Tel: 020 8983 7300 Fax: 020 8983 6800 — MB BS 1973 Lond.; MRCS Eng. LRCP Lond. 1973; MFPHM RCP (UK) 1992; MRCGP 1980; DObst RCOG 1975. (St. Bart.) Chair., Exec. Comm., Tower Hamlets PCT. Prev: Head Eval. Unit The Leprosy Miss.; Co-ordinator for Bhutan & Nepal, The Leprosy Miss.; Dist. Med. Off. Lhuntsi, Bhutan.

JAKEMAN, Rachel Diane Flat 4, Southwood Gardens, 51 Park Road, Camberley GU15 2SP — MB BCh 1994 Wales.

JAKEWAYS, Matthew Simeon Robert 7 Wordsworth Avenue, Penistone, Sheffield S36 6EX — MB BCh 1986 Wales; BSc (Physiol.) Wales 1983, MB BCh 1986.

JAKOBSON, Richard Alexander Beech House Group Practice, Beech House, 54 Main Street, Egremont CA22 2DB Tel: 01946 820692; Woodend House, Woodend, Egremont CA22 2TA — MB BS 1981 Newc.; BMedSc Newc. 1978, MB BS 1981; MRCGP 1986; DRCOG 1985; DCCH RCGP 1986.

JAKT, Lars Magnus 22 Union Place, Truro TR1 1EP — Med. Lic Stockholm 1971. Socs: Assn. Anaesth.; Assn. Anaesth. Sweden. Prev: Cons. Mermaid Clinic, Denmark; Cons. King Khaled Nat. Guard Hosp. Jeddah, Saudi Arabia.

JAKUBOVIC, Michael Otto 219 Benfieldside Road, Shotley Bridge, Consett DH8 0QU — MB ChB 1992 Sheff.

JAKUBOWSKI, Mr Jan Royal Hallamshire Hospital, Glossop Road, Sheffield S10 2SF — MD Lødz 1969; FRCS Glas. 1974; MRCS Eng. LRCP Lond. 1973; Dip. Med. Lødz 1963. (Med. Acad. Lødz) Cons. (Neurosurg.) Roy. Hallamsh. Hosp. Sheff. Prev: Clin. Lect. (Neurosurg.) Nat. Hosp. Qu. Sq. Lond.; Sen. Regist. (Neurosurg.) Salford Roy. Hosp.; Regist. Dept. Neurosurg. Roy. Infirm. Sheff.

JAKUBOWSKI, Krzysztof Andrzej Weybridge Health Centre, Church Street, Weybridge KT13 8DW Tel: 01932 853366 Fax: 01932 859851 — MB BS 1986 Lond.; MRCGP 1991; DCH 1997. GP Princip., E. De Sousa & Partners; Police Surg. NW Surrey Div.

JAKUBSKI, Roman Jozef Antoni (retired) 49 Constantine Road, London NW3 2LN Tel: 020 7485 8652 — MD 1946 Beirut. Path. Lond. Clinic. Prev: Regist. (Path.) W. Middlx. Hosp.

JALAJAM, Mulloli Puthiyapurayil Westbury Cottages, Westbury Road, Bromley BR1 2QB — MB BS 1970 Kerala; MB BS Kerala 197o.

JALALUDDIN, Zia 56 Sheepfoot Lane, Prestwich, Manchester M25 0DN — MB BS 1993 Dundee.

JALAN, Anupama Rosy Department of Medicine, Royal Infirmary of Edinburgh, Lauriston Place, Edinburgh EH3 9YW — MB ChB 1991 Liverp.

JALAN, Rajiv Department of Medicine, Royal Infirmary of Edinburgh, Lauriston Place, Edinburgh EH3 9YW — MB BS 1988 Calcutta; MRCP (UK) 1991.

JALEEL, Khawaja Abdul (retired) 14 Greencroft Close, Darlington DL3 8HW Tel: 01325 469194 — MB BS Punjab (Pakistan) 1955; FRCP Ed. 1981, M 1964; DPhysMed Eng. 1971; DTM & H Ed. 1963. Mem. Centr. Cons. & Specialist Comm. Prev: Cons. Rheum. Darlington Memor. Hosp.

JALIHAL, Sanjeev Satyabodh Department of Haematology, Scunthorpe and Goole NHS Trust, Cliff Gardens, Scunthorpe DN15 7BH Tel: 01724 290143 Fax: 01724 865680 Email: sanjeev.jalihal@sgh-tctrent.nhs.uk — MB BS 1977 Baroda; MD (Med.) Baroda 1980; MRCPath (Haemat.) 1992; FRCPath (Haemat) 2000. (Baroda Med. Coll. MS Univ. Baroda, India) Cons. Haemat. Scunthorpe & Goole NHS Trust. Socs: Brit. Soc. Haemostasis & Thrombosis; Brit. Soc. Haematol.; Amer. Soc. of Haemat. (ASH). Prev: Clin. Research Fell. (Haemat.) Univ. Hosp. Nottm.; Regist. (Haemat). Huddersfield Roy. Infirm. & Univ. Hosp. Nottm.

JALIL, Maan Inverkeithing Medical Group, 5 Friary Court, Inverkeithing KY11 1NU Tel: 01383 413234 Fax: 01383 410098 — MB ChB 1972 Baghdad. Regist. (Orthop.) Roy. Halifax Infirm.

JALILI, Mr Ismail Kaidar Peterborough Hospitals NHS Trust, Stamford & Rutland Hospital, Thorpe Road, Peterborough PE3 6DA Tel: 01733 873057 Fax: 01733 765665 Email: ismail@aljalili.com; 68 Roman Bank, Stamford PE9 2ST Tel: 01780 755955 Fax: 01780 765655 Email: ismail@aljalili.com — MB ChB 1971 Cairo; FRCSI 1983; FRCOphth 1988; FCOphth 1989; DO RCS Eng. 1980; CHSTOph 1990. (Baghdad & Cairo) Cons. Ophth. Surg. PeterBoro. Hosp. NHS Trust. Socs: RSM; Mid. Ophth. Soc.; Pres. of Arts Arab Med. Associtaion UK & Irel. Prev: Cons. Ophth. Surg. Warrington Hosp. NHS Trust and Gwynedd Health Auth.; Sen. Reg., St John's Ophth. Hosp, Jerusalem; Sen. Reg., Guy's Hosp., Lond.

JALISI, Qazi Zafar Hasnain Queens Park Health Centre, Dart St., London W10 4LD Tel: 020 8969 1490 Fax: 020 8964 0436; 159 Anson Road, Willesden Green, London NW2 4AP — MB BS 1966 Karachi; Dip. Ther. Wales 1996; DFFP 1993; DTM & H Liverp. 1969; Cert. Av. Med. 1984. (Dow Med. Coll.) Occupat. Health Off. DSS. Socs: BMA; Assoc. Mem. RCGP; MDU.

***JALLALI, Navid** 313 Bournemouth Road, Poole BH14 9AL Tel: 01202 381455 — MB ChB 1997 Bristol; BSc (Hons) Bristol 1994; MB ChB (Hons) Bristol 1997.

JALLOH, Mr Ibrahim Sharif 6 Newcastle Avenue, Beeston, Nottingham NG9 1BT — LMSSA 1992 Lond.; MD Liberia 1980; FRCS Glas. 1989.

JALLOH, Sanusi Sheikh 69 Albert Road, London N22 7AG Tel: 020 8888 2340 — Vrach 1971 1st Leningrad Med. Inst.; Vrach First Leningrad Med. Inst. 1971; MRCPath 1982.

JALPOTA, Mr Sat Pal 21 Palmers Green, Forest Hall, Newcastle upon Tyne NE12 9HF — MB BS 1979 Himachal Pradesh, India; FRCS Ed. 1993.

JAMAL, Abdulaziz Shariff Riverside Health Centre, Wellington Street, Canton, Cardiff CF11 9SH Tel: 029 2064 5385 — MB BS 1970 Rajasthan. (S.M.S. Med. Coll. Jaipur)

JAMAL, Aneal Fara 5 Fairlands Road, Sale M33 4AX — MB ChB 1994 Manch.

JAMAL, Anita Anisa 5 St Johns Street, York YO31 7QR — MB ChB 1988 Bristol; DPhil (Biochem.) York 1985, BA (Hons.) Biol. 1980. Regist. (Clin. Biochem.) Addenbrooke's Hosp. Camb. Prev: SHO (Path.) John Radcliffe Hosp. Oxf.

JAMAL, Farouk Crosby House Surgery, 91 Stoke Poges Lane, Slough SL1 3NY Tel: 01753 520680 Fax: 01753 552780; 8 Aberdare Gardens, London NW6 3PY — MD 1969 Tours.

JAMAL, Waheed 18 Thurlston Crescent, Manchester M8 0QB — MB ChB 1994 Manch.

JAMAL, Zahra 39 Mill Road, Lisvane, Cardiff CF14 0XH — BM 1998 Soton.; BM Soton 1998.

JAMALI, Nabila Hinchingbrooke Hospital, Huntingdon PE29 6NT Tel: 01480 416416 Fax: 01480 416561; 16 Ware Lane, Wyton, Huntingdon PE28 2AJ Tel: 01480 469147 — MD 1973 Aleppo; MD Aleppo, Syria 1973; FFA RCSI 1990. (Aleppo, Syria) Cons. Anaesth. Hinchingbrooke Hosp. Huntingdon. Socs: Assn. Anaesth.; Obst. Anaesth. Assn.; Eur. Soc. Regional Anaesth.

JAMALL, Afzal 32D Shepherds Lane, Dartford DA1 2NY — MB BS 1974 Punjab.

JAMALL, Mr Omer Ahmed (retired) 17 Waldegrave Road, Bickley, Bromley BR1 2JP — MB BS 1953 Calcutta; FRCS Ed. 1962. Hon. Cons. Orthop. Surg. Newham Gen. Hosp. Lond. Prev: Cons. Surg. (Orthop.) Greenwich Dist., St. And. & Newham Gen. Hosps.

JAMALUDDIN, Mohammad 28 Jephcott Road, Birmingham B8 3ED — MB BS 1969 Patna.

JAMDAR, Raul Prabhaker 172 Castleton Road, Preston PR1 6QH — MB BS 1998 Lond.; MB BS Lond 1998.

JAMDAR, Saranaz 38 Whinhill Road, Ayr KA7 4RP — MB ChB 1998 Glas.; MB ChB Glas 1998.

JAMDAR, Saroj 27 Boarshead Avenue, Standish, Wigan WN6 0BH — MB BS 1969 Jabalpur; MD PGI Chandigarh 1973; DCH RCPS Glas. 1978.

JAMEEL, Hussein Abbass Al-Habeeb St. Mary Abbots Hospital, Marloes Road, Kensington, London W8 5LQ Tel: 020 7937 8181 — MB ChB 1972 Baghdad; MRCPsych 1985; Dip. Clin. Neurol. 1986; DPM Eng. 1983.

JAMEEL, Sabena Yasmin 9 Westlands Road, Birmingham B13 9RH — BM BS 1996 Nottm.

JAMEEL, Tahira 6 Kenwood Road, Bordesley Green, Birmingham B9 5UH — MB ChB 1992 Birm. Prev: GP Regist. Dudley Pk. Med.; SHO (Paediat.) BHH; SHO (O & G) BHH.

JAMES, Adrian John Boste Langdon Hospital, Dawlish EX7 0NR — MB BS 1985 Lond.; MSc Criminol. Cardiff 1992; MRCPsych 1988. Cons. Forens. Psychiat. Butler Clinic Dawlish.; Med. Director, Devon Partnership NHS Trust. Prev: Sen. Regist. (Forens. Psychiat.) Bristol; Regist. (Psychiat.) Guy's Hosp. Lond.; SHO (Psychiat.) Guy's Hosp. Lond.

JAMES, Alan David Greystones, The Village, Ysceifiog, Holywell CH8 8NJ; 29A Lavender Gardens, Battersea, London SW11 1DJ Tel: 020 7350 0462 — MB BS 1993 Lond.; BA (Hons.) Oxf. 1990. (Kings Coll. Hosp. Lond.) SHO (Cardiothoracic Surg.) Roy. Brompton Hosp. Prev: SHO Rotat. (Surg.) Chesterfield.

JAMES, Alan Hubert (retired) The Surgery, 54 Benhill Avenue, Sutton SM1 4EB Tel: 020 8770 0587 Fax: 020 8770 0586 — MB BCh 1973 Wales; Dip. Pharm. Ther. Wales 1998; FRCS Eng. 1980.

JAMES, Alice Margery Cheltenham General Hospital, Sandford Road, Cheltenham GL53 7AN; Bentlry Cottage, Vicarage Street, Stroud GL6 6XU — MB BS 1993 Lond.; BSc (Clin. Pharmacol.) Lond. 1990, MB BS 1993; FRC Ophth. Oct 1999. Staff Grade, Ophth. Cheltenham Gen. Hosp. Prev: SHO (Ophth.) Soton. Gen. Hosp.; SHO (Ophth.) Kingston; SHO (Ophth.) Frimley Pk.

JAMES, Alison Frances University Health Service, 2 Claremont Place, Sheffield S10 2TB Tel: 0114 222 2100 Fax: 0114 276 7223; Hillside, Back Lane, Hathersage, Hope Valley S32 1AR — MB BS 1982 Lond.; BSc Durham. 1976; MRCGP 1984; DRCOG 1985; DCH RCP Lond. 1984. (Guy's) Med. Off. Univ. Sheff. Socs: BAHSHE. Prev: GP Birm. Univ. Health Serv.; Trainee GP Swindon VTS.

JAMES, Alison Mary Glendon 2 Julian Close, Sneyd Park, Bristol BS9 1JX — MB BS 1974 Lond.; MRCP (UK) 1980. (St. Thos.) Assoc. Specialist (Community Paediat.) United Bristol Health Care Trust. Prev: Clin. Med. Off. (Child Health) United Bristol Health Care Trust; Trainee GP Manch. VTS; Regist. (Paediat.) Roy. Hosp. for Sick Childr. Edin.

JAMES, Alistair Mark Hatch Warren Surgery, Moorhams Avenue, Basingstoke RG22 4YQ Tel: 01256 330007 Fax: 01256 842692 Email: amjames@globalnet.co.uk — BM 1994 Soton.

JAMES, Allan Mitchell 10 Rannoch Avenue, Bishopbriggs, Glasgow G64 1BU — MB ChB 1991 Glas.

JAMES, Andrew John Selden 117 Hucclecote Road, Hucclecote, Gloucester GL3 3TS Tel: 01452 611363 — MB ChB 1955 Bristol. Prev: GP Gloucester; Ho. Surg. & Ho. Phys. Bristol. Roy. Infirm.; SHO N. Devon Infirm. Barnstaple.

JAMES, Mr Andrew Seaton 27 Mosshead Road, Bearsden, Glasgow G61 3HN — MB ChB 1989 Glas.; FRCS Glas. 1993; FRCS Ed. 1993. Research Fell. Univ. Dept. Surg. Glas. Roy. Infirm.

JAMES, Anne Kathryne West End Surgery, Tangmere Gardens, Northolt UB5 6LP Tel: 020 8845 6263; 151 Leybourne Road, Uxbridge UB10 9HF Tel: 01895 231632 — MB BCh BAO 1983 Belf.; MRCGP 1988; DRCOG 1986. GP Retainer Scheme Uxbridge.

JAMES, Anthony 76 Station Road, Llanishen, Cardiff CF14 5UT — MB BCh 1988 Wales.

JAMES, Anthony Christopher Digby The Highfield Family & Adolescent Unit, The Warneford Hospital, Headington, Oxford OX3 7JX Tel: 01865 226285 Fax: 01865 226381 — MB BS 1978 Lond.; MA Oxf. 1993; MRCP (UK) 1981; MRCS Eng. LRCP Lond. 1978; MRCPsych 1983; MPhil 1988. (St. Bart.) Cons. Adolesc. Psychiat. Highfield Family & Adolesc. Unit Warneford Hosp. Oxf.; Hon. Sen. Clin. Lect. Univ. Oxf. Prev: Sen. Regist. (Child & Adolesc. Psychiat.) Maudsley Hosp. Lond.

JAMES, Anthony Howard (retired) 1 West Common Close, Gerrards Cross SL9 7QR Tel: 01753 887935 Email: ahjames@cicero.netkonect.co.uk — DM Oxon. 1950, BM BCh 1944; FRCP Lond. 1964, M 1946; MD Toronto 1944. Prev: Cons. Phys. Hillingdon Hosp. Gp.

JAMES, Mr Antony Market Street Surgery, 102 Market Street, Newton-le-Willows WA12 9BP Tel: 01925 221457; 6 Grove Avenue, Lymm WA13 0HF — MB BS 1973 Lond.; FRCS Eng. 1979; MRCS Eng. LRCP Lond. 1973. (Guy's) Hosp. Pract. (Gen. Surg.) Warrington Dist. Gen. Hosp.

JAMES, Astrid The Lancet, 42 Bedford Square, London WC1B 3SL Tel: 020 7436 4981 Fax: 020 7637 3265; 8 Buckingham Street, Oxford OX1 4LH — MB BS 1986 Lond.; BSc (Hons.) Lond. 1983. (Univ. Coll. Hosp. Lond.) Sen. Edr. The Lancet Lond. Prev: Trainee GP Cardiff VTS; SHO (Paediat.) Cardiff Roy. Infirm.; SHO (O & G) St. David's Hosp. Cardiff.

JAMES, Beatrice Joan Marshlands Medical Practice, Parkside Surgery, Cliffe Woods, Rochester ME3 7DB; The Red House, St Mary Hoo, Rochester ME3 8RH — MB 1960 Camb.; BChir 1959. (Middlx.) Socs: Affil. RCPsych.

JAMES, Bernard Guy The Surgery, Northleach, Cheltenham GL54 3EQ Tel: 01451 860247 Fax: 01451 860718 Email: oursurgery@hotmail.com; Old Timbers, High St, Northleach, Cheltenham GL54 3EU Tel: 01451 860417 — MB BS 1971 Lond. (Middlx. Hosp.) Prev: SHO Cheltenham Childr. Hosp.; Ho. Off. & Ho. Surg. Cheltenham Gen. Hosp.

JAMES, Bernard Hugh Egerton 290 Marlborough Road, Swindon SN3 1NP Tel: 01793 619790 — MB ChB 1959 Liverp.; MRCGP 1972.

JAMES, Bettina Louise, Maj. RAMC 1 Royal Gurkha Rifles, Hong Kong BFPO 1 — MB ChB 1983 Sheff.; MRCGP 1987; DFFP 1993. GP HM Forces, Hong Kong. Socs: Profess. Wom. in Health Soc. HK. Prev: Med. Off. 8 Signals Regt. Catterick; Med. Off. 24 Airmoblie Field Ambld.

JAMES, Brenda (cons. rooms), 35 Kingston St., Cambridge CB1 2NU Tel: 01223 322573 Fax: 01223 357344 — MB ChB 1960 Birm. (Birm.) Indep. Psychother. Camb. Prev: Terminal Care Team Roy. Free Hosp. Lond.; Clin. Asst. Friern Hosp. Lond.; Princip. GP Lond.

JAMES, Bryan Kenneth David Armadale Group Practice, 18 North Street, Armadale, Bathgate EH48 3QD Tel: 01501 730432 — MB ChB 1974 Ed.; LF HOM 2000; MRCP (UK) 1979; MRCGP 1986; Dip. Occ. Med. RCP Lond. 1996.

JAMES, Carol 44 Alexandra Road, Hemel Hempstead HP2 5BP — MB BS 1996 Lond.; DRCOG. (London) VTS Paediat. Wexham Pk. Hosp. Slough.

JAMES, Carole Joanne 23 Anns Road, Cambridge CB5 8TN — MB BChir 1991 Camb.; MA Camb. 1991, MB BChir 1991. Trainee GP Camb. VTS.

JAMES, Catherine Elizabeth 9 Bayham Road, Chiswick, London W4 1BJ — MB ChB 1969 Manch.; FRCOG 1988, M 1975; LM Rotunda 1971; DObst RCOG 1971. Med. Secretariat Med. Defence Union. Socs: Fell. Roy. Soc. Med.; Medico-Legal Soc. Prev: Sen. Lect., Hon. Cons. & Sen. Regist. (O & G) St. Thos. Hosp. Lond.; Regist. (O & G) Pembury Hosp. & St. Thos. Hosp. Lond.

JAMES, Catherine Montague 33 Chedworth Gate, Broome Manor, Swindon SN3 1NE — MB BS 1998 Lond.; MB BS Lond 1998.

JAMES, Mr Charles Robert Hawker Torbay Hospital, Lawes Bridge, Torquay TQ2 7AA — MB BS 1975 Lond.; FRCS (Ophth.)

Eng. 1983; MRCP (UK) 1978; MRCS Eng. LRCP Lond. 1975; FRCOphth 1992. (St. Mary's) Cons. Ophth. Torbay Hosp. Torquay. Prev: Resid. Surg. Off. & Vitreoretinal Fell. Moorfields Eye Hosp. Lond.; MRC Trav. Fell. Dept. Ophth. Yale Univ. USA; SHO Ophth. Soton. Eye Hosp.

JAMES, Charles Trevor Attwood (retired) Wall House, Holbrook, Horsham RH12 4TW — MRCS Eng. LRCP Lond. 1941. Prev: Ho. Surg. St. Bart. Hosp. Lond.

JAMES, Christopher John University Health Service, University of Southampton, Building 48, Highfield, Southampton SO17 1BJ Tel: 023 8055 7531 Fax: 023 8059 3259 — MB ChB 1985 Bristol. Chairm. Centr. Soton. PCG (Commiss.ing Pilot). Socs: Brit. Performing Arts Med. Trust; Brit. Assn. Health Servs. in Higher Ed.; Brit. Assn. Sport & Med. Prev: Trainee GP S.port VTS.

JAMES, Christopher Mark Millbrook, Clarebeston Road, Haverfordwest SA62 5RG — MB BCh 1984 Wales; MRCP (UK) 1988. Cons. Gen. Med. (Dis. of Elderly) Withybush Hosp. HaverfordW.

JAMES, Christopher Michael Department of Haematology, Royal Hampshire County Hospital, Winchester SO22 5DG Tel: 01962 824453 Fax: 01962 825291 Email: chris.jones@whet.swest.nhs.uk; Email: cmjames@beech.demon.co.uk — MB BS 1980 Lond.; MBA 1994; FRCP Lond. 1995; MRCP (UK) 1985; MRCPath 1989; FRCPath 1998. (St. Thos.) Cons. Haemat. Roy. Hants. Co. Hosp. Winchester; Hon. Cons. Haemat. Soton. Univ. Hosps. Trust. Socs: BMA; ACP; BSH. Prev: Cons. Haemat. RN Hosp. Haslar Gosport.; Hon. Sen. Regist. (Haemat.) Lond. Hosp.; Hon. Clin. Asst. (Haemat.) Plymouth Gen. Hosp.

JAMES, Claire Annette The Surgery, 3 Willow Wong, Burton Joyce, Nottingham NG14 5FD Tel: 0115 931 2929 — MB ChB 1989 Birm.; MB ChB (Hons.) Birm. 1989; MRCP (UK) 1994; MRCGP 1997; MRCPCH 1997; DFFP 1997. (Birm.) GP. Prev: Regist. (Paediat.) Nottm. City Hosp.; SHO (Paediat.) Alder Hey Childr. Hosp. Liverp.; SHO (Gen. Med.) Selly Oak Hosp. Birm.

JAMES, Mr Clifford Bruce Stoke Mandeville Hospital, Mandeville Road, Aylesbury HP21 8AL Tel: 01296 315000 — BM BCh 1982 Oxf.; MA Oxf. 1985, DM 1994; FRCS Ed. 1988; FRCOphth 1989. Cons. Ophth. Stoke Mandeville Hosp. Aylesbury. Socs: Fell. Roy. Soc. Med.; Glaucoma Soc. Prev: Sen. Regist. Oxf. Eye Hosp.; Research Fell. St. Thos. Hosp. Lond.; Regist. (Ophth.) & SHO St. Thos. Hosp. Lond.

JAMES, Colin Clive The Surgery, Rambury, Marlborough SN8 2QT Tel: 01672 20366; Crabtree Cottage, Savernake, Marlborough SN8 3HP — BM BCh 1963 Oxf.; BA, BM BCh Oxf. 1963; DObst RCOG 1966. (Middlx.) Prev: Ho. Surg. Mt. Vernon Hosp. N.wood; Ho. Surg. (Obst.) St. Alfege's Hosp. Greenwich; Res. Med. Off. Childr. Hosp. Sydenham.

JAMES, David Hailwood Medical Centre, 2 Hailwood Court, Governors Hill, Douglas IM2 7EA Tel: 01624 67544 Fax: 01624 616290 — MB ChB 1981 Liverp.

JAMES, David Colin 35 Kingston Street, Cambridge CB1 2NU Tel: 01223 322573 Fax: 01223 357344 Email: james.camb@btinternet.com — MB ChB Birm. 1961; MPhil Lond. 1969; FRCP Ed. 1979, M 1965; FRCPsych 1978, M 1971. (Birm.) Private Pract. Socs: Brit. Psychoanal. Soc. & Inst. Gp. Anal. Prev: Hon. Cons. Psychother. Addenbrooke's Hosp. Camb.; Cons. Psychother. Tavistock Clinic Lond.; Cons. Psychother. Bethlem Roy. & Maudsley Hosps. Lond.

JAMES, David Cyril Owen 22 Strand-on-the-Green, Chiswick, London W4 3PH Tel: 020 8994 8938 — MB BS Lond. 1954; BPharm. Wales 1945; MSc (Immunol.) Lond. 1977, BSc (Physiol.) 1951, MD 1964; FRCPath 1976, M 1964; FIBiol. 1983, M 1982. (Univ. Coll. Hosp.) Med. Adviser Med. Diet Clinics Lond. Socs: (Vice-Pres.) Leukaemia Care Soc.; BMA; Brit. Soc. Immunol. Prev: Med. Dir. Anthony Nolan Bone Marrow Research Labs. & Internat. Unrelated Bone Marrow Donor Regist. St. Mary Abbots Hosp. Lond.; Cons. Path. Transpl. Immunol. & Blood Transfus. W.m. Hosp. Lond.; Research Asst. (Chem. Path.) & Regist. (Chem. Path.) W.m. Hosp. Med. Sch.

JAMES, David Geraint 149 Harley Street, London W1G 6BN Tel: 020 7935 4444; 41 York Terrace E., London NW1 4PT Tel: 020 7486 4560 — MB BChir 1944 Camb.; MA Camb. 1945, BA (Hons.) 1942, MD 1953; Hon. LLD Wales 1982; FRCP Lond. 1964, M 1946; MRCS Eng. LRCP Lond. 1944; FRCOphth 1994; FACP (Hon.) 1990. (Camb. & Middlx.) Vis. Prof. Med. Roy. Free Hosp. Lond.; Cons. Phys. to RN; Pres. & Lettsom Lect. & Trustee Med. Soc. Lond.; Cons. Ophth. Phys. St. Thos. Hosp. Lond.; Clin. Prof. Med. Univ. Miami, USA; Mem. Edit. Bd. Postgrad. Med. Jl., Doctor & Brit. Jl. Clin. Pract.; Co-Edr. French Thoracic Jl.; Ed.-in-Chief Jl. Sarcoidosis Biennial; Mem. Roy. Free Hosp. Sch. Med. Socs: (Pres.) World Assn. Sarcoidosis; Hon. Corr. Mem. Thoracic Socs. Italy, Portugal, France & Dominican RePub.; Harveian Soc. (Ex-Pres.). Prev: Sen. Regist. (Med.) Middlx. Hosp. Lond.; Trav. Fell. Coll. of Phys. & Surgs. Columbia Univ.; Hon. Phys. Sydney Hosp.

JAMES, David Henry (retired) Catchfrench Community, Catchfrench manor, Trerulefoot, Saltash PL12 5BY Tel: 01503 240759 — MB BCh 1968 Wales; MA Wales 1992; MRCPsych 1974; DPM Eng. 1973. Prev: Cons. Psychiat. Budock Hosp. Falmouth.

***JAMES, David Hywel** 11 Albert Square, London SW8 1BT — MB BS 1988 Lond.

JAMES, Professor David Keith University Department of Obstetrics, Queen's Medical Centre, Nottingham NG7 2UH Tel: 0115 924 9924 Ext: 43970 Fax: 0115 970 9776 Email: david.james@nottingham.ac.uk — MD 1984 Camb.; MB 1975, BChir 1974; FRCOG 1992, M 1980; DCH Eng. 1977. Prof. FetoMatern. Med. Univ. Nottm. & Dept. O & G; Hon. Cons. Univ. Hosp. Nottm. Prev: Cons. Sen. Lect. Dept. O & G Univ. Bristol; Sen. Regist. (O & G) Hope Hosp. Salford & St. Mary's Hosp. Manch.

JAMES, David Llywelyn The Darley Dale Medical Centre, Two Dales, Darley Dale, Matlock DE4 3FD Tel: 01629 733205 — MB BS 1965 Lond.; Dip. Pract. Dermat. Wales 1990; Dip. Obst. Auckland 1968. (Lond. Hosp.) Prev: Receiv. Room Off. Lond. Hosp.; SHO Auckland Hosp. Bd., N.Z.; Ho. Phys. Whipps Cross Hosp. Lond.

JAMES, David Michael South Common Farm, Lakehouse Lane, E. Brent, Highbridge TA9 4HN — MB ChB 1974 Liverp.

JAMES, David Richard 69 Hollybush Road, Cyncoed, Cardiff CF23 6SZ — MB BCh 1982 Wales.

JAMES, Mr David Rodd 57 Portland Place, London W1B 1QN Tel: 020 7436 0381 Fax: 020 7580 8837; 29a Devonshire Close, London W1G 7BD — MB BCh 1973 Wales; BDS Bristol 1960; FDS RCS Eng. 1967; FRCS Ed. 1985. (University of Wales) p/t Cons. Oral and Maxiofacial Surg., King Edwd. VII Hosp. Lond.; Med.ly Qualified Mem. of the Appeals tribund. Socs: Fell. Europ. Assn. Craniomaxillofacial Surg.; Pres. Brit. Assn. Oral & Maxillo Facial Surgs. 1998; Fell. Internat. Assn. Oral Maillofacial Surg.s. Prev: Cons. Maxillofacial Surg. Univ. Coll. Hosp. & Geat Ormond St. Hosp., Lond..; Hunt Prof. RCS Eng. 1988; Sen. Regist. Univ. Coll. Hosp. Lond. & Qu. Mary's Hosp. Roehampton.

JAMES, David Sheard (retired) — MB ChB 1962 Sheff.; Dip. Ed. 1964; FRCP Glas. 1989; FRCPsych 1987, M 1971; DPM Eng. 1967; DCH Eng. 1964. Cons. Child Psychiat. Roy. Hosp. Sick Childr. Glas.; Hon. Clin. Sen. Lect. (Child & Adolesc. Psychiat.) Univ. Glas. Prev: Sen. Regist. (Child Psychiat.) Chas. Burns Clinic Birm. & Birm. Childr. Hosp.

JAMES, David Stanley Bowen The Ashgrove Surgery, Morgan St., Pontypridd CF37 2DR Tel: 01443 404444 — MB BCh 1956 Wales; FRCGP 1984, M 1968. (Cardiff) Med. Off. Polytechnic of Wales. Socs: Rhondda Med. Soc. Prev: Sen. Ho. Off. WhitCh. Hosp. Cardiff & Cardiff Roy. Infirm.; Asst. Med. Off. Glam. CC.

JAMES, David Vaughan Bay Tree Cottage, North Green, Kirtlington, Oxford — MB BS 1982 Lond.; MA Oxf. 1982; MRCPsych 1987. (St. Bart.) Sen. Lect. Forens. Psychiat. Univ. Dept. of Psychiat. Roy. Free Hosp. Sch. Med. Lond. & Hon. Cons. Forens. Psychiat. Camlet Lodge R.S.U. Chase Farm Hosp. Campus.

JAMES, David Wynne Diana, Princess of Wales Hospital, Scartho Road, Grimsby DN33 2BA Tel: 01472 874111 Fax: 01472 875483; Orford House, Orford, Market Rasen LN8 6HW Tel: 01472 398709 Fax: 01472 399750 — MB BS 1972 Lond.; FRCP Lond. 1993; MRCP (UK) 1975. (Univ. Coll. Hosp.) Cons. Rheum. N. E. Lincs. NHS Trust. Socs: Brit. Soc. Rheum. Prev: Sen. Regist. (Rheum.) Lond. Hosp.

JAMES, Delyth Ann 48 Queen's Road, Sedgley, Dudley DY3 1HL — MB ChB 1980 Leeds; BSc Leeds 1977, MB ChB 1980; MRCPsych 1984; MMedSci Leeds 1985. Sen. Regist. (Psychiat. Rotat.) W. Midl.

JAMES, Derek Conrad (retired) 6 Holmfield Avenue, Leicester LE2 2BF — MB BS 1955 Lond.; MRCS Eng. LRCP Lond. 1950; DLO

Eng. 1954, DMRD 1956; FFR 1958. Hon. Lect. (Anat.) Univ. Leicester. Prev: Cons. Radiol. Leicester Roy. Infirm.

JAMES, Derek George Hugh 74 Yarrow Drive, Harrogate HG3 2XD — MB ChB 1991 Leeds.

JAMES, Derek Wallen (retired) Silver Birches, Sytchampton, Stourport-on-Severn DY13 9TA Tel: 01905 621248 — MB BCh Wales 1949.

JAMES, Dewi Brennig (retired) Cherry Orchard, Marlow Common, Marlow SL7 2QP Tel: 01628 483509 Email: brennigjames@msn.com — MB BS 1949 Lond. Prev: GP Marlow.

JAMES, Diana 21 Saxton Lane, Saxton, Tadcaster LS24 9QD — MB ChB 1984 Liverp.

JAMES, Diane Ashworth Hospital Authority, Parkbourn, Maghull, Liverpool L31 1HW Tel: 0151 473 0303 — MB BS 1979 Lond.; FRCPsych 1997, M 1984. Med. Dir., Cons. (Psychiat.) Ashworth Hosp. Auth.

JAMES, Domini Anne Barley Cottage, 1 Mount Pleasant, Ouseburn, York YO26 9TG; 1 Oakridge, Wetherby LS22 6GT — MB BS 1991 Lond.; BSc Lond. 1988; MRCGP (Distinc.) 1995; DRCOG 1994; DFFP 1993. (St. Mary's) GP Retainer Scheme, Gale Farm Surg., Acomb, York. Socs: RCGP; Fac. Fam. Plann. Prev: SHO (Palliat. Med.) Wheatfields Hospice Leeds; Trainee GP Haxby & Acomb, York; SHO (Psychiat.) Bootham Pk. York.

JAMES, Dyfed William Ashleigh Surgery, Napier Street, Cardigan SA43 1ED Tel: 01239 621227 — MB BCh 1980 Wales; DRCOG 1983.

***JAMES, Dylan Wyn** Dylennydd, 6 Dingle Road, Crundale, Haverfordwest SA62 4DJ; 339 Eastern Terrace, St Martins, Christchurch S. Island, New Zealand Tel: 00 64 337 5345 Email: ruth.dylan@xtra.co.nz — MB BCh 1994 Wales.

JAMES, Edmund Percival Lower Halvasso, Mabe, Penryn TR10 9BY — MRCS Eng. LRCP Lond. 1954; LMSSA Lond. 1953; MFCM 1974; MRCGP 1970; DCH Eng. 1970; DObst RCOG 1954. (Lond. Hosp.) Specialist Community Med. (Child Health) Cornw. & I. of Scilly AHA. Socs: Fell. Soc. Community Med.; BMA. Prev: Chief Outpats. USAAF Hosp. Chicksands; Sen. Med. Off. Min. of Defence.

JAMES, Edward Alexander 5 Duckett Road, London N4 1BJ — MB BS 1985 Lond.; MRCP (UK) 1991.

JAMES, Elaine Susan 14 Alma Terrace, East Morton, Keighley BD20 5UN — MB ChB 1993 Leeds.

JAMES, Elisabeth Courtenay Wright 121 North Hill, Highgate, London N6 4DP Tel: 020 8340 4021 — MB BS Lond. 1947; MRCPsych 1972; DPM Eng. 1971; DCH Eng. 1949. (Univ. Coll. Hosp.) Private Pract.; Expert Witness for Family Ct. Proc. Socs: Assn. Child Psychol. & Psychiat.; Roy. Soc. Med.; MEDACT. Prev: Cons. Child & Family Psychiat. Clinic Hemel Hempstead & W. Herts. Hosp.; Cons. Child Psychiat. Roy. Nat. Orthop. Hosp. Lond.; Sen. Regist. Tavistock Clinic.

JAMES, Elizabeth Ann 6 Grange Avenue, Milngavie, Glasgow G62 8AQ — MB ChB 1986 Glas.; FRCA 1991. Cons. (Anaesth.) Roy. Alex. Hosp. Paisley.

JAMES, Elizabeth Beatrice 3 Batchworth Lane, Northwood HA6 3AU Tel: 01923 823580 — MB BCh 1955 Wales; BSc, MB BCh Wales 1955. (Cardiff) Prev: Regist. (Med.) Llandough Hosp. Cardiff; Cas. Off. St. David's Hosp. Cardiff; SHO (Med.) Rookwood Hosp. Llandaff.

JAMES, Evan Morgan 6 Bannister Close, Iffley Road, Oxford OX4 1SH — MRCS Eng. LRCP Lond. 1945; MA, MB BChir Camb. 1946. (Camb. & St. Thos.) Prev: RN; Asst. Med. Off. Springfield Hosp. Lond.; Ho. Phys. St. Helier Hosp. Carshalton.

JAMES, Mr Evan Timothy Robert Department of Orthopaedic Surgery, Morriston Hospital, Swansea SA6 6NL — MB BCh 1973 Wales; FRCS Eng. 1979; FRCS (Orthop.) Ed. 1985. Cons. (Traum. & Orthop.) Morriston Hosp. Swansea. Prev: Sen. Regist. (Orthop.) Bristol Roy. Infirm.; Regist. (Orthop.) Robt. Jones & Agnes Hunt Orthop. Hosp. OsW.ry; Clin. Fell. in Orthop. Univ. Toronto, Canada.

JAMES, Frances Elspeth Fernleigh, Berkeley Heath, Berkeley GL13 9ES — MB ChB 1977 Bristol; DRCOG 1980. p/t GP Retainee, The Orchard Med. Centre, Cam, Dursley, GLOS.

JAMES, Francesca Ann (retired) 34 Wordsworth Avenue, Bolton-Le-Sands, Carnforth LA5 8HJ — MB BS 1972 Lond.; MRCPsych 1979; DA Eng. 1975. Prev: Psychotherapist.

JAMES, Frederick Ernest (retired) 27A Sheep Street, Cirencester GL7 1QW Tel: 01285 642649 — MD Lond. 1966, MB BS 1949; MRCS Eng. LRCP Lond. 1948; FRCPsych 1979, M 1972; DPM Eng. 1971; DCH Eng. 1953. Prev: Cons. Psychiat. (Ment. Handicap) Leeds RHA.

JAMES, Gareth John 68 Mansfield Road, London NW3 2HU — MB BS 1991 Lond.

JAMES, Geoffrey Bennett (retired) Dunglass, 284 Arbroath Road, Broughty Ferry, Dundee DD5 1QN — MB ChB St. And. 1959; FRCOG 1977, M 1964. Prev: Cons. O & G Tayside HB.

JAMES, Gillian Ruth Westway Surgery, 1 Wilson Road, Ely, Cardiff CF5 4LJ Tel: 029 2059 2351 Fax: 029 2059 9956 — BM 1991 Soton. Trainee GP/SHO (Rheum.) Derbysh. Roy. Infirm. VTS.

JAMES, Gillian Susan Elizabeth Old Timbers, High St., Northleach, Cheltenham GL54 3EU — BM BCh 1970 Oxf.; MA. Prev: Ho. Surg. & Ho. Phys. Cheltenham Gen. Hosp.

JAMES, Graham John 16 Brookfield Way, Solihull B92 7HA; 83 Hartledon Road, harborne, Birmingham B17 0AA Tel: 0121 426 6205 Fax: 0121 426 6205 Email: graham@harborne83.demon.co.uk — MB ChB 1997 Birm.; BDS Glas. 1985; FDSRCPS Glas. 1994. SHO Rotat. (Surg.) Worcester & Warks. Prev: Ho. Off. (Med.); Ho. Off. (Surg.).

JAMES, Gwladys Eira Pennant 18 Mynn Crescent, Bearsted, Maidstone ME14 4AR Tel: 01626 738047 — MB ChB 1953 Liverp.; DPH Eng. 1967. Prev: Civil. Med. Pract. MoD; Civil Serv. Local Med. Off.; Med. Off. Boots Co., GLC & ILEA.

JAMES, Hazel 23 Avondale Road, Darras Hall, Ponteland, Newcastle upon Tyne NE20 9NA — MB ChB 1962 Liverp.; DA Eng. 1969; DObst RCOG 1965.

JAMES, Heather Ann Castle Farm, Bridgwater Road, Bristol BS13 8AF — BM 1992 Soton.

JAMES, Helen Caroline 22 The Chase, Penn, High Wycombe HP10 8BA — MB BS 1998 Lond.; MB BS Lond 1998.

JAMES, Helen Margaret Ambrose Avenue Surgery, 76 Ambrose Avenue, Colchester CO3 4LN Tel: 01206 549444 Fax: 01206 369910; 23 Cambridge Road, Colchester CO3 3NS Tel: 01206 574668 Fax: 01206 369910 — MB BS 1968 Lond.; MB BS (Hons.) Lond. 1968; MRCP (U.K.) 1970; MRCS Eng. LRCP Lond. 1968. (Westm.) Prev: Clin. Asst. (Haemat. & Gen. Med.) & Med. Regist. W. Middlx. Hosp. Isleworth; Ho. Surg. & Ho. Phys. W.m. Hosp. Lond.

JAMES, Herbert Thomas Ivor 17 Vestry Mews, London SE5 8NS; Waldron Health Centre, London SE8 — MB BS 1958 Lond.; DA Eng. 1965. (King's Coll. Hosp.) Prev: Cas. Off. W. Lond. Hosp.; Capt. RAMC; Ho. Surg. Obst. Dept. St. Giles' Hosp. Lond.

JAMES, Herbert William Heinrich Anaesthetic Department, University Hospital of Wales, Heath Park, Cardiff CF14 4XW — MB BS 1974 Lond.; FFA RCS Eng. 1978.

JAMES, Hilary Joan (retired) 31 Woodville Gardens, London W5 2LL Tel: 020 8998 8138 Fax: 020 8998 8138 — MB BS Lond. 1961; MRCP Lond. 1965; MRCS Eng. LRCP Lond. 1961. Mem. Appeal Panel. Independ. Trib. Serv. Prev: GP 1968-1995.

JAMES, Howard David Plymouth Nuffield Clinic, Lipson Road, Plymouth PL4 8NQ Tel: 01752 389510 — MB BChir 1970 Camb.; MRCP (U.K.) 1973; FRCPsych 1989, M 1975; DPM Eng. 1973. Cons. Psychiat. Nuffield Clinic Plymouth. Prev: Sen. Regist. (Psychol. Med.) St. Thos. Hosp. Lond.; Sen. Regist. Fulbourn Hosp. Camb.

JAMES, Ian Gordon 22 Compton Road, Islington, London N1 2PB Tel: 020 7354 2057 — MB ChB 1974 Birm.; FFA RCS Eng. 1979. Cons. Anaesth. Hosp. Sick Childr. Gt. Ormond St. Lond. & Qu. Eliz.Hosp. Childr. Hackney. Prev: Sen. Regist. (Anaesth.) Univ. Coll. Hosp. Lond.; Fell. Intens. Care Hosp. Sick Childr. Toronto, Canada.

JAMES, Ian Gordon Vizetelly Chorley Old Road Surgery, 555 Chorley Old Road, Bolton BL1 6AF Tel: 01204 848411 Fax: 01204 849968 — MB ChB 1974 Manch.; DRCOG 1977; DCH Eng. 1976. (Manch.) Princip. (Gen. Pract.); Trainer GP Bolton. Socs: Bolton Med. Soc. Prev: Regist. (Paediat.) Roy. Alexandra Hosp. Childr. Sydney, Austral.; SHO (Paediat.) Roy. Manch. Childr. Hosp.; Ho. Surg. Manch. Roy. Infirm.

JAMES, Isabel Elizabeth (retired) The Paarl, 95 North Deeside Road, Bieldside, Aberdeen AB15 9DS Tel: 01224 867339 — MB ChB 1940 Aberd.; DPH 1957. Prev: Garden Research Fell. in Path. Pathol. Dept. Univ. Aberd.

JAMES, Jacqueline Ann 6 Dowding Close, Chipping Sodbury, Bristol BS37 6BX — BM BS 1990 Nottm.; MRCP (UK) 1994; DRCPath (Haemat.) 1997. Specialist Regist. (Haemat.) S. W. Train.

Scheme. Prev: Regist. (Haemat.) W. Midl. Train. Scheme; Regist. (Gen. Med.) Hillingdon Hosp.; Regist. (Transpl. Med.) Harefield Hosp.

JAMES, Jacqueline Anne Tyn-y-Swydd, Tregaron SY25 6LW — MB BCh 1974 Wales; MRCP (UK) 1980; DCH Eng. 1977; Dobst. RCOG 1976.

JAMES, Jacqueline Mary 10 Maple Avenue, Chorlton-cum-Hardy, Manchester M21 8BD — MB ChB 1980 Manch.; MSc Lond. 1993; MD Manch. 1992; MRCGP 1984; DRCOG 1982. Cons. Nuclear Med. Specialist Wellington, NZ. Socs: BMA; Eur. Assn. Nuclear Med.; Brit. Nuclear Med. Soc. Prev: Sen. Regist. & Clin. Asst. (Nuclear Med.) Manch. Roy. Infirm.

JAMES, Jacqueline Mary 5 Parcell Walk, Godmanchester, Huntingdon PE29 2YL — MB ChB 1980 Sheff.; MSc Health Economics & Management Sheff. 1999. (Sheffield) Asst. GP Papworth. Prev: GP Sheff.

JAMES, Janis Marie Blantyre Health Centre, 64 Victoria Street, Blantyre, Glasgow G72 0BS Tel: 01698 823260 — MB ChB 1975 Glas.; DRCOG 1977.

JAMES, Jean (retired) The Dell, 14 Windmill Lane, Avon Castle, Ringwood BH24 2DQ Tel: 01425 473222 — MB ChB Bristol 1945; MD Bristol 1974. Prev: Cons. Dermat. Mengo Hosp. Kampala, Uganda.

JAMES, Jennifer Ruth 6 St James Place, Bath BA1 2TP Tel: 01225 316679 — MB ChB 1967 Manch. Clin. Med. Off. (Blood Transfus.) Blood Servs. SW Bristol.

JAMES, Joan 3 Finedon Hall, Mackworth Drive, Finedon, Wellingborough NN9 5NL — MB BS 1966 Durh.

JAMES, John Andrew (retired) Winchelsea, 12 St Michaels Road, Llandaff, Cardiff CF5 2AP Tel: 01222 563861 — MRCS Eng. LRCP Lond. 1931; BSc Wales. Prev: Ho. Phys. Char. Cross & Bolingbroke Hosps.

JAMES, John Anthony Montpelier Health Centre, Bath Buildings, Montpelier, Bristol BS6 5PT Tel: 0117 942 6811 Fax: 0117 944 4182; 42 Frenchay Close, Bristol BS16 2QX — MB ChB 1971 Bristol; MRCGP 1987; MRCPCH 1997. Primary Care Cons. Inst. for Health Sector Developm. Lond.; Clin. Tutor (Paediat.) Inst. Child Health Bristol Roy. Hosp. Sick childr. Socs: Eur. Soc. Social Paediat.; MRCPCH. Prev: Regist. (Paediat. Haemat.) Bristol Roy. Infirm.; SHO (Paediat.) Bristol Roy. Hosp. Sick Childr.; SHO (Neonatol.) S.mead Hosp. Bristol.

JAMES, Mr John Arnallt (retired) Stone Court, Stone, Kidderminster DY10 4BD Tel: 01562 823874 — MB BS 1940 Lond.; FRCS Eng. 1953; MRCS Eng. LRCP Lond. 1939. Prev: Cons. Orthop. Surg. Kidderminster Gen. Hosp., BromsGr. Gen. Hosp.

JAMES, John Daniel 22 Southend Road, Beckenham BR3 1SD — MRCS Eng. LRCP Lond. 1967; MB BS Lond. 1967, BDS 1961; FDS RCS Eng. 1970, LDS 1961; FDS RCPS Glas. 1970. (Guy's & Cardiff) Cons. Oral Surg. E.man Dent. Hosp. Lond. & St. Mary's Hosp. Lond. Prev: Sen. Regist. Qu. Vict. Hosp. E. Grinstead & Guy's Hosp. Lond.

JAMES, John Douglas Westgate Practice, Greenhill Health Centre, Church Street, Lichfield WS13 6JL Tel: 01543 414311 Fax: 01543 256364; 4 Gorse Lane, Lichfield WS14 9HQ — MB ChB 1979 Birm.

JAMES, Mr John Nigel Leeds General Infirmary, Leeds LS2 9NS; 30 Farrar Lane, Leeds LS16 7AA — MB ChB 1983 Cape Town; FRCS Glas. 1992; MRCOphth 1991.

JAMES, Jonathan Jeffrey 20 Sunset Hill Top, Meanwood, Leeds LS6 4LP — BM BS 1992 Nottm. Specialist Regist. (Radiol.) Leeds/Bradford Train. Scheme.

JAMES, Jonathan Robert 21 Thorntree Road, Northallerton DL6 1QE — MB ChB 1977 Manch.; BSc Manch. 1974; MRCP (UK) 1982. Cons. Paediat. Friarage Hosp. N.allerton.

JAMES, Josephine Mary 30 St James Road, Edgbaston, Birmingham B15 2NX — MB BS 1975 Lond.; FFA RCS Eng. 1980. (Univ. Coll. Hosp.) Cons. Anaesth. E. Birm. Hosp.

JAMES, Judith Margaret Parkside Family Practice, Green Road Surgery, 224 Wokingham Road, Reading RG6 1JT Tel: 0118 966 3366 Fax: 0118 926 3269 — BM BCh 1994 Oxf.; DCH 1997; DRCOG 1997; MRCGP 1999. (Oxford) GP Regist. Balmore Pk. Surg. Caversham Reading.

JAMES, Mr Kallarackal Kuruvilla Head and Neck PMG, Chase Farm Hospitals NHS Trust, Enfield EN2 8JL Tel: 020 8366 6600; 9 Ridge Crest, Enfield EN2 8JU Tel: 020 8363 5846 Email: kkjames@globalnet.com — MB BS 1976 Bangalor; MB BS Bangalore 1976; FRCS Eng. 1990; DLO RCS Eng. 1983. (St Johns Medical College Bangalore, India) Staff Surg. (ENT Surg.) Chase Farm Hosps. NHS Trust Enfield. Socs: Roy. Coll. Surg. Eng.; Brit. Assn. Otol. & Head & Neck Surg. Prev: Regist. (ENT Surg.) Enfield Dist. Hosp.; SHO (ENT) Gen. Hosp. Cheltenham & Norf. & Norwich Hosps.; SHO (Orthop.) Standish Hosp. Glos.

JAMES, Keatley Elizabeth Briton Ferry Health Centre, Hunter Street, Briton Ferry, Neath SA11 2SF Tel: 01639 813272 Fax: 01639 813019; 11 Westernmoor Road, Neath SA11 1BJ Tel: 01639 644345 — MB BS 1971 Lond.; MRCS Eng. LRCP Lond. 1971; MRCGP 1978; DCH Eng. 1976; DObst RCOG 1974. (St. Mary's)

JAMES, Keith Currey Beynon Trigfan Serch, 4 High St., Kenfig Hill, Bridgend CF33 6DR Tel: 01656 746709 — MB ChB Birm. 1953; DA Eng. 1959. Anaesth. Port Talbot Gen. Hosp. Prev: Clin. Asst. in Anaesth. Roy. Gwent Hosp. Newport.

JAMES, Kenneth Seaton Department of Anaesthetics, Glasgow Royal Infirmary, Castle St., Glasgow G4 0SF — MB ChB 1986 Glas. Cons. Anaesth.

JAMES, Kenwyn Meyrick St Kervene, Higher Moresk, Truro TR1 1BW — MB BS 1996 Lond.

JAMES, Laurence Edward Flat 1 Oak Lodge, 130 Auckland Rd, London SE19 2RQ — MB BS 1997 Lond.

JAMES, Lesley Penrose Pickdick Oast, Stubb Lane, Brede, Rye TN31 6BN — MB BS 1985 Lond. Trainee GP W. Dorset HA.

JAMES, Louisa 3 Anvil Road, Claverham, Bristol BS49 4LZ — MB ChB 1997 Birm.

JAMES, Luke 27 Smalls Croft, Woodborough, Nottingham NG14 6EY — MB BS 1998 Lond.; MB BS Lond 1998.

JAMES, Lynn 7 Old Harpenden Road, St Albans AL3 6AX — MB BS 1998 Lond.; MB BS Lond 1998.

JAMES, Mrs Lynne Mary Ivry Street Medical Practice, 5 Ivry Street, Ipswich IP1 3QW Tel: 01473 254718 Fax: 01473 287790 — BM BS 1984 Nottm.; MRCGP 1995; DRCOG 1994. Prev: Trainee GP Stornoway; SHO (O & G & Med.) W.. Isles Hosp.

JAMES, Malcolm E Newbridge House, 117 Lynn Road, Snettisham, King's Lynn PE31 7QG Tel: 01485 541210 Fax: 01485 541210 — MB BS 1964 Lond.; MRCS Eng. LRCP Lond. 1964; AFOM RCP Lond. 1982; DIH 1981. (St. Geo.) Private Osteop. Pract.

JAMES, Mr Malcolm Ian Department of Plastic Surgery, Whiston Hospital, Warrington Road, Prescot L35 5DS Tel: 0151 430 1623 Fax: 0151 430 1855 — MB ChB 1980 Ed.; BSc (Med. Sci.) Ed. 1977, MD 1993; FRCS (Plast) 1992; FRCS Ed. 1985. Cons. Plastic Surg. Whiston Hosp. Prescot. Prev: Sen. Regist. (Plastic Surg.) Whiston, Merseyside; Regist. (Plastic Surg.) Chepstow.

JAMES, Margaret Eiriol Prices Mill Surgery, New Market Road, Nailsworth, Stroud GL6 0DQ Tel: 01453 832424 Fax: 01453 833833; Abbey Farm, The Vatch, Stroud GL6 7LE Tel: 01453 764986 — MB ChB 1962 Ed.; MRCGP 1979; DCH NUI 1981; DObst RCOG 1965.

JAMES, Marguerite Eleanor Mary, MBE (retired) 211 London Road, Twickenham TW1 1EJ Tel: 020 8892 1764 — MB ChB 1936 Ed.; MFCM 1972; DPH 1942. Prev: Dep. MOH Lond. Boro. Richmond-upon-Thames.

JAMES, Marianne Penelope Meadowview, Quinta Crescent, Weston Rhyn, Oswestry SY10 7RN Tel: 01691 778659 Fax: 01691 777638 — MB ChB 1976 Liverp. Clin. Asst. (Geriat. Med.), BRd.green Hosp., Liverp. Prev: Clin. Asst. Leighton Hosp. Crewe, Chesh.; Clin Research Asst. Leighton Hosp. Crewe, Chesh.

JAMES, Marjorie Lorna (retired) Heath Cliff, Marine Parade, Penarth CF64 2BE Tel: 02920 700012 — MB BCh 1948 Wales; BSc, MB BCh Wales 1948. Treasury Off. Cardiff Med. Soc. Prev: Hon. Vis. Phys. Marie Curie Foundat. Nursing Home Penarth.

JAMES, Mark Christopher Hall Floor Flat, 45 Royal York Crescent, Bristol BS8 4JS — MB ChB 1990 Liverp.; MRCOG 1995. Regist. (O & G) MusGr. Pk. Hosp. Taunton; Mem. (Chairm.) SW Regional Trainees Comm. in Obst. & Gyn.

JAMES, Mr Mark Richard Department Accid. & Emerg., Royal Preston Hospital, Fulwood, Preston PR2 9HT Tel: 01772 710303 — MB ChB 1980 Birm.; FRCS Ed. 1986; DA (UK) 1987. Cons. A & E Roy. Preston Hosp.; Clin. Dir. A & E Serv. Preston & Chorley. Prev: Sen. Regist. Rotat. (A & E) Hope Hosp. Manch. & Roy. PrestonHosp.; Regist. Rotat. (A & E) Nottm. & Lincoln.; Regist. Rotat. (Surg.) Sheff.

JAMES, Mark William 21 Ferrers Road, Oswestry SY11 2EZ — MB ChB 1991 Birm.; ChB Birm. 1991.

JAMES, Martin Anthony Royal Devon & Exeter Hospital, Barrack Road, Exeter EX2 5DW Tel: 01392 402597 Fax: 01392 402595 — BM 1986 Soton.; MD Leic. 1996; MRCP (UK) 1989. Cons. Phys. (Gen Med & med for the Elderly), Roy. Devon Exeter Hosp. and Hon. Sen. Lect., Sch. of Postgrad. Med. & Health Sci., Univ. of Exeter. Socs: Brit. Hypertens. Soc.; Brit. Geriat. Soc. Prev: Sen. Regist. (Gen. Med. & Med. for Elderly) Leicester Roy. Infirm.; Clin. Research Fell. (Med. for Elderly) Glenfield Hosp.; Regist. (Gen. Med.) Leicester Gen. Hosp. & Leicester Roy. Infirm.

JAMES, Martin Godfrey High Street Health Centre, High Street, Burton Latimer, Kettering NN15 5RH Tel: 01536 723566 Fax: 01536 420226 — MRCS Eng. LRCP Lond. 1968; DObst RCOG 1971. (Univ. Coll. Hosp.)

JAMES, Martin Philip Department of Dermatology, Royal Berkshire Hospital, Reading RG1 5AN Tel: 0118 987 7417 Fax: 0118 987 8709; Dr. Martin James, 38 Plough Lane, Wokingham RG40 1RG Tel: 0118 977 6126 Fax: 0118 987 8709 Email: mjames@arborfield.demon.co.uk — MB BS 1972 Lond.; BSc Lond. 1969; MRCP (UK) 1974. (St. andrews) Cons. Dermat. Roy. Berks. Hosp. Reading. Socs: Fell. St. Johns Hosp. Dermat. Soc.; Fell. Roy. Soc. Med. & Roy. Coll. Phys. Prev: Sen. Regist. St. Johns Hosp. Dis. Skin Lond.; Sen. Regist. (Histopath.) St. Johns Hosp. Dis. Skin Lond.; Regist. (Dermat.) St. Thos. Hosp. Lond.

JAMES, Martin Wynn 62 Johnson Road, Lenton, Nottingham NG7 2BX — BM BS 1994 Nottm.; BMedSci. 1992. (Nottingham) SHO (Gen. Med.) Qu.s Med. Centre Nottm.

JAMES, Mary Kathleen (retired) 2 The Brambles, Forest Road, Oxton, Southwell NG25 0SZ — MB BS 1953 Lond.; DA Eng. 1957; DObst RCOG 1955. Prev: Clin. Asst. (Anaesth.) Gen. Hosp. Nottm.

JAMES, Matthew Dominic 64 Cruise Road, Nether Green, Sheffield S11 7EF — MB ChB 1995 Sheff.

JAMES, Matthew Lewis (retired) Marsh Farm, Clyst Hydon, Cullompton EX15 2NF Tel: 01884 277511 Email: mlj@mlj.eurobell.co.uk — MB BS Lond. 1960; MRCS Eng. LRCP Lond. 1960; FRCA 1964. Prev: Cons. Anaesth. Roy. Devon & Exeter Hosp.

JAMES, Matthew Robert 8 Astley Cooper Place, High Green, Brooke, Norwich NR15 1JB — MB ChB 1991 Manch.

JAMES, Megan Diana Church Cottage, Park Road, Combe, Witney OX29 8NA Tel: 01993 891625 — MB ChB 1990 Bristol; MRCGP 1995. (Bristol) Asst. GP Smert St. Surg. Abingdon. Prev: Trainee GP Headington Oxf.; SHO (Psychiat.) Amersham Hosp.; SHO (Paediat.) Wycombe Gen. Hosp.

JAMES, Michael Antony Cardiology Department, Taunton & Somerset Hospital, Musgrove Park, Taunton TA1 5DA Tel: 01823 333444 — MB BS 1977 Lond.; FRCP Lond. 1998; MD Lond. 1990; MRCP (UK) 1982; MRCS Eng. LRCP Lond. 1977. (Guy's) Cons. Cardiol. Taunton & Som. Hosp. Socs: Brit. Cardiac Soc. & Brit. Hypertens. Soc.; Brit. Cardiovasc. Interven. Soc. Prev: Sen. Regist. (Cardiol.) Bristol Roy. Infirm.; Regist. (Cardiol. & Gen. Med.) Bristol Roy. Infirm.; Regist. (Gen. Med.) N.. Gen. Hosp. Sheff.

JAMES, Michael John Barnfold, Westington, Chipping Campden GL55 6EG — MRCS Eng. LRCP Lond. 1969; MSc (Occupat. Med.) Lond. 1974, BSc (Anat.) 1966; MB BS 1969; DIH Eng. 1975; LMCC 1981. (Guy's & Univ. Coll. Hosp.) Occupat. Phys. Toronto Canada. Socs: Fac. Occupat. Med.; FRES. Prev: Cons. (Occupat. Med.) Ontario Min. Labour; Airport Med. Off. Lond. Airport; Med. Dir. Petrochem. Complex No. 1 Zubair, Iraq.

JAMES, Mr Michael Jonathan Chesterfield & North Derbyshire Royal Hospital, Calow, Chesterfield S44 5BR — MB ChB 1983 Birm.; BSc (Anat. Studies) Birm. 1980, MB ChB 1983; DM Nottm. 1993; FRCS Urol. 1994; FRCS Ed. 1987; FRCS Eng. 1987. Cons. Urol. Chesterfield & N. Derbysh. Roy. Hosp. Prev: Sen. Regist. (Urol.) Nottm. & Derby.

JAMES, Nansi Eirlys (retired) 59 Caswell Road, Newton, Swansea SA3 4RH Tel: 01792 366769 — MB BCh 1936 Wales; BSc Wales 1933, MB BCh 1936; MRCP Lond. 1940. Asst. Paediat. Research Dept. Welsh Nat. Sch. Med. Cardiff. Prev: Child Psychiat. Welsh Hosp. Bd.

JAMES, Neil Martin 2 Pentwun Isaf, Energlyn, Caerphilly CF83 2NR — MB ChB 1991 Liverp.

JAMES, Nicholas David Cancer Research UK, Institute for Cancer Studies, Clinical Research Block, Queen Elizabeth Hospital, Edgbaston, Birmingham B15 2TT Tel: 0121 414 4097 Fax: 0121 414 3263 Email: n.d.james@bham.ac.uk — MB BS 1983 Lond.; PhD Lond. 1993; BSc (1st cl. Hons.) Lond. 1980; FRCR Eng. (Clin. Oncol.) 1990; MRCP (UK) 1986; FRCP Lond. 1998. (St. Bartholomew's) Reader in Clin. Oncol. Inst. Cancer Studies Qu. Eliz. Hosp. Birm. Socs: Brit. Oncol. Assn. & Brit. Assn. Cancer Research. & Amer. Soc. Clin. Oncol. Prev: Sen. Regist. (Clin. Oncol.) Roy. Marsden Hosp.; Lect. & Hon. Sen. Regist. (Clin. Oncol.) Hammermsith Hosp. Lond.; Sen. Lect. In Clin. Oncol. Qu. Eliz. Hosp. Birm.

JAMES, Mr Nicholas Kenneth Pinehill Hospital, Benson Lane, Hitchin SG4 9QZ Tel: 01402 422822; Oaklease, 5 Priory Way, Hitchin SG4 9BH Email: jamesniclk@aol.com — BM BS 1983 Nottm.; BMedSci (Hons.) 1981; FRCS (Plast Surg.) 1995; FRCS Eng. 1987. Cons. Plastic Surg. Herts NHS Trust The Lister Hosp. Stevenage. Prev: Sen. Regist. (Plastic Surg.) Stoke Mandeville Hosp.; Regist. (Plastic Surg.) Leicester Roy. Infirm.; SHO (Plastic Surg.) N.. Gen. Hosp. Sheff.

JAMES, Professor Oliver Francis Wintour School of Clinical Medical Sciences, Medical School, University of Newcastle, Newcastle upon Tyne NE2 4HH Tel: 0191 222 8266 Fax: 0191 222 0723 Email: o.f.w.james@newcastle.ac.uk; Sleightholmedale, Kirbymoorside, York YO62 7JG — BM BCh 1967 Oxf.; MA Oxf. 1967; FRCP (UK) 1981, M 1970; BA Physiology 1964 Oxf. (Oxford) Cons. Phys. Freeman Hosp. Newc.; Head Sch. of Clin. Med. Sci., Univ. of Newcatle (1994-).; Prof. Med. (Geriat.) Univ. Newc. Socs: Assn. Phys. & Irel. & Brit. Soc. Gastroenterol.(Counc.1984); (Ex Pres.) Brit. Assn. Study of Liver; Fell.Acad. of Med. Sci.s. Prev: Regist. Med. Unit. Roy. Free Hosp. Lond.; 1st Asst. Dept. Med. Roy. Vict. Infirm. Newc.

JAMES, Pamela Sylvia 136 Highbury Grove, Clapham, Bedford MK41 6DX — MB ChB 1985 Manch.

JAMES, Mr Patrick Leonard 152 Harley Street, London W1N 1HH Tel: 020 7935 2477 Fax: 01279 777894; Meesden Hall, Meesden, Buntingford SG9 0AZ Tel: 01279 777229 — MRCS Eng. LRCP Lond. 1956; FRCS Ed. 1985; FDS RCS Eng. 1959. (Lond. Hosp.) Hon. Cons. Oral & Maxillofacial Surg. Roy. Lond. Hosp. Trust & NE Thames RHA; Hon. Civil. Cons. Oral Surg. RAF; Recognised Teach. Lond. Univ. Socs: Acad. of Experts. Prev: Clin. Dir. Maxillofacial Unit W. Essex HA; Sen. Regist. Qu. Vict. Hosp. E. Grinstead; Exchange Fell. (Oral Surg.) Henry Ford Hosp. Detroit, USA.

JAMES, Paul Worsley (retired) 5 Cromer Road, Aylsham, Norwich NR11 6HE Tel: 01263 733736 — MB BS 1958 Lond.; MRCS Eng. LRCP Lond. 1958; DTM & H Eng. 1965; DObst RCOG 1960.

JAMES, Paula Rachael 15 Regents Court, 6-8 Coperscope Road, Beckenham BR3 1NB — MB BS 1991 Lond.; MRCP (UK) 1994.

JAMES, Mr Peter Ashman, MBE (retired) The Dell, 14 Windmill Lane, Avon Castle, Ringwood BH24 2DQ Tel: 01425 473222 — MB ChB 1944 MB ChB Bristol; 1951 FRCS Eng.; 1975 FRCR; 1971 FFR; 1970 DMRD Eng. Prev: Cons. Thoracic Surg. Uganda Govt. Serv.

JAMES, Peter David Histopathology Department, University Hospital, Nottingham NG7 2UH Tel: 0115 970 9175 — MB BS 1966 Lond.; MRCP (UK) 1970; MRCS Eng. LRCP Lond. 1966; FRCPath 1984, M 1972. (Middlx.) Cons. & Sen. Lect. (Histopath.) Univ. Nottm. Hosp. Socs: Brit. Div. Internat. Acad. Path. & Brit. Soc. Gastroenterol. Prev: Lect. (Path.) Bland Sutton Inst. Path. Middlx. Hosp. Lond. & Makerere Univ. Med. Sch. Kampala, Uganda.

JAMES, Peter Desmond Newnham Edge, Tylney Lane, Newnham, Basingstoke RG27 9AJ Tel: 01256 763196 — MRCS Eng. LRCP Lond. 1976; BSc (Microbiol.) Lond. 1973, MB BS 1976; FRCA 1981. (St. Mary's) Cons. Anaesth. & Intens. Care N. Hants. Hosp.; Postgrad. Clin. Tutor N. Hants. Hosp. Basingstoke. Prev: Sen. Regist. (Anaesth.) Brompton & Roy. Free Hosps.; Staff Grade & Fell. (Anaesth.) Hosp. Sick Childr. Toronto, Canada.

JAMES, Mr Peter John Nottingham City Hospital, Hucknall Road, Nottingham NG5 Tel: 0115 969 1169; 'Parklands', 191 Harrow Road, Wollaton Park, Nottingham NG8 1FL — BM BS 1985 Nottm.; BM BS (Hons.) Nottm. 1985; BMedSci Nottm. 1983; FRCS (Orth.) 1994; FRCS Eng. 1989. Cons. Orthop. Surg. Nottm. City Hosp. Prev: Cons. Orthop. Surg. Glas. Roy. Infirm.

JAMES, Peter John Collingwood Family Practice, Collingwood Drive, Great Barr, Birmingham B43 7NG Tel: 0121 480 5900 Fax: 0121 480 5902; 33 St Michaels Road, Boldmere, Sutton Coldfield B73 5TA Tel: 0121 605 2865 — MB ChB Bristol 1985; MBA Birm. 1994; MFPHM RCP Lond. 1992; MRCGP 1989; DCH RCP Lond. 1988; DRCOG 1988. Hon. Cons. (Pub. Health Med.) Walsall HA; Hon. Sen. Clin. Lect. (Pub. Health & Epidemiol.) Univ. Birm. Prev: Cons. Pub. Health Med. N. Birm. DHA & Walsall DHA; Trainee GP Banbury.

JAMES, Mr Peter Mansel Lloyd 104 Pottergate, Norwich NR2 1EQ Tel: 01603 610111 — MB BS 1963 Lond.; FRCS Eng. 1972; MRCS Eng. LRCP Lond. 1963; DO Eng. 1968. (Lond. Hosp.) Prev: Sen. Regist. St. Geo. Hosp. Lond.; Regist. Moorfields Eye Hosp. Lond.; Cons. Ophth. United Norwich Hosp.

JAMES, Peter Nicholas Ellis 6 Adel Park Close, Adel, Leeds LS16 8HR — MB BS 1976 Lond.; MRCP (UK) 1978; MRCS Eng. LRCP Lond. 1976; FRCR 1987. (Guy's Hosp.) Cons. Radiol. Dewsbury Dist. Hosp.; Radiologist to the Penine BrE. Screening Serv. Socs: Brit. Inst. Radiol. & Brit. Thoracic Soc. Prev: Sen. Regist. (Radiol.) St. Jas. Univ. Hosp. Leeds & Leeds Gen. Infirm.; Regist. (Radiol.) Guy's Hosp. Lond.; Research Regist. (Med.) Guy's Hosp. Lond.

JAMES, Philip (retired) Venners, Merstone, Newport PO30 3DE Tel: 01983 528955 — BM BCh Oxf. 1957; BA (Physiol.) Oxf. 1954; FRCA 1963; DA Eng. 1962. Prev: Cons. Anaesth. I. of Wight HA.

JAMES, Philip Bloomer 37 Newhall Gardens, Ninewells, Dundee DD2 1TW — MB ChB 1966 Liverp.; PhD Liverp. 1975, MB ChB 1966; DIH Soc. Apoth. Lond. 1972. (Liverp.) Sen. Lect. Indust. Med. Univ. Dundee. Prev: Research Fell. Dept. Surg. Univ. Liverp.; Ho. Phys. & Ho. Surg. Sefton Gen. Hosp. Liverp.

JAMES, Philip David Orchard Surgery, The Dragwell, Kegworth, Derby DE74 2EL Tel: 01509 672419; 6 The Square, Gotham, Nottingham NG11 0HX — BM BS 1980 Nottm.; MRCGP 1984; DCH RCP Lond. 1983.

JAMES, Philip Douglas (retired) 40 Bedhampton Hill, Havant PO9 3JW Tel: 023 9248 2640 — MB BS 1947 Lond.; MRCS Eng. LRCP Lond. 1942; DObst RCOG 1948. Prev: Resid. Med. Off. Brit. Hosp. Mothers & Babies, Woolwich.

JAMES, Philip Margrave The Surgery, Main Street, Northiam, Rye TN31 6ND Tel: 01797 252140/252244 Fax: 01797 252077 — MB BS 1985 Lond.; MRCGP 1989.

JAMES, Philippa Frances 6 Orchard Road E., Northenden, Manchester M22 4ER — MB ChB 1990 Manch. Socs: Roy. Coll. Gen. Pract.

JAMES, Rachel Eluned 54 Benhill Avenue, Sutton SM1 4EB Tel: 020 8642 8011 Fax: 020 8770 0856; 35 Park Hill, Carshalton SM5 3SD Tel: 020 8669 4617 — MB BCh 1974 Wales; MRCGP 1980.

JAMES, Rachel Margaret 22 Nevill Road, Bramhall, Stockport Sk7 3ET Tel: 0115 972 5243, 0161 439 4735 — BM BS 1991 Nottm.; BMedSci (Hons.) Nottm. 1989. (Nottingham) p/t GP Nottm.; Family Plann. Doctor & Clin. Asst. Paediatric Cas. Qu.s Med. Centre Nottm.

JAMES, Rajan Friarage Hospital, Northallerton DL6 1JG; 53 Boroughbridge Road, Northallerton DL7 8BG Tel: 01609 776929 Email: rajanjames@hotmail.com — MB BS 1970 Madras; MCOphth 1989; DO RCS Eng. 1976; DO 1973. (Kilpauk Med.Coll.madras) Assoc. Specialist (Ophth.) Friarage Hosp. N.allerton.

JAMES, Raymond William The Health Centre, Shoreham Health Centre, Pond Road, Shoreham-by-Sea Tel: 01273 461101 — MB BS 1958 Lond.; MRCS Eng. LRCP Lond. 1958; MRCGP 1975; DObst RCOG 1962. (King's Coll. Hosp.) Prev: Ho. Surg. King's Coll. Hosp.; Ho. Surg. Obst. Edgware Gen. Hosp.; Ho. Phys. (Paediat.) Roy. Alexandra Hosp. Brighton.

JAMES, Richard Healthcall, 1-3 The Avenue, Southampton SO17 1X Tel: 02380 717500; The Rowans, 50 Heath House Lane, Hedge end, Southampton SO30 0LE Tel: 02380 407167 — MB BS 1992 Lond. Trianed GP Dep. for Deputising Serv. Prev: SHO (Paediat.) Norf. & Norwich Hosp.

JAMES, Mr Richard (retired) Church Lane, Stoneleigh, Coventry CV8 3DN Tel: 024 7641 1617 — MB BS 1953 Lond.; 1958 FRCS Eng. 1958; 1953 MRCS Eng. LRCP Lond. 1953. Prev: Cons. Orthop. Surg. Coventry & Warks. Hosp.

JAMES, Richard David Goronwy Trevaylor Road Health Centre, Trevaylor Road, Falmouth TR11 2LH Tel: 01326 434 800 Fax: 01326 434 829; Huberts, 30 Pennance Road, Falmouth TR11 4ED — MB BS 1980 Lond.; MRCGP 1989; DRCOG 1988; FRCS 1985 Eng.; DCH 1988 RCP, Lond. (St. Thos.)

JAMES, Richard Hugh 36 Ridge Way, Oadby, Leicester LE2 5TN Tel: 0116 271 4596 — MB BS 1968 Lond.; MSc Birm. 1997; MRCS Eng. LRCP Lond. 1968; FFA RCS Eng. 1977; DA Eng. 1975; DTM & H Liverp. 1970; DObst RCOG 1969. (King's Coll. Hosp.) Cons. Anaesth. (Audit) Leicester Roy. Infirm, Univ. Hosp.s of Leicester NHS Trust; Hon. Clin. Teach. Leics. Univ. Med. Sch. Socs: Assn. Anaesths. & Sheff. & E. Midl. Soc. Anaesth.; World Anaesth. Prev: Sen. Regist. & Regist. (Anaesth.) King's Coll. Hosp. Lond.; Med. Dir. Hosp. de Matana Burundi, Afr.

JAMES, Robert Andrew — MD 1993 Newc.; MB BCh 1983; BSc (Hons.) Wales 1978; MRCP (UK) 1988; FRCP (UK) 2000. (Cardiff) Cons. Phys. Roy. Vict. Infirm. Newc.; Sen. Lect. Dept. Med. Div. Endocrinol. Socs: Brit. Endocrine Soc.; Amer. Endocrine Soc.; Amer. Thyroid Assn.

JAMES, Robert Glyn Bridge Road Surgery, 1A Bridge Road, Oufton Broad, Lowestoft NR32 3LJ Tel: 01502 565936 Fax: 01502 531539 — MRCS Eng. LRCP Lond. 1973; MB BS Lond. 1973; BSc (Hons.) (Biochem.) Lond. 1970; DCH Eng. 1977; DObst RCOG 1976. (Guy's) p/t Gen. Practitioner, DR. James & Partners, LoW.oft; Approved Med. Examr. - Civil Aviat. Auth.; Med. Off. - GT Yarmouth Race Course.

JAMES, Robert Stanley Dairy Farm, Brightwell, Ipswich IP10 0BB — BM BS 1984 Nottm.; DRCOG 1987. Prev: SHO (O & G) Derby City Hosp.; SHO (Paediat.) Derby Childr. Hosp.; SHO (O & G) Kingsmill Hosp. Mansfield.

JAMES, Roderick Alec The Park Medical Centre, Maine Drive Clinic, Maine Drive, Chaddesden, Derby DE21 6LA Tel: 01332 665522 Fax: 01332 678210; 267 Victoria Avenue, Ockbrook, Derby DE72 3RL — MB ChB 1982 Sheff.; MRCGP 1986; DRCOG 1986. Prev: Trainee GP Derby VTS.

JAMES, Roger David The Coach House, 1 Oak Road, Withington, Manchester M20 3DA — MRCS Eng. LRCP Lond. 1970; MA Camb. 1969, MB 1971, BChir 1970; MRCP (UK) 1977; FRCR 1978. Cons. Radiother. Christie Hosp. & Holt Radium Inst. Manch. Socs: Roy. Soc. Med. & Brit. Inst. Radiol. Prev: Sen. Regist. & Hon. Lect. (Radiother.) Meyerstein Inst. Middlx. Hosp. Lond.; Berkeley Fell. Mass. Gen. Hosp. Boston, USA.

JAMES, Roger David The Surgery, Denmark Street, Darlington DL3 0PD Tel: 01325 460731 Fax: 01325 362183; Hill Close House, Nunnery Lane, Darlington DL3 9QU Tel: 01325 466775 — MB ChB 1971 Ed.; BSc (Med. Sci.) Ed. 1968; FRCGP 1991, M 1975; DObst RCOG 1974. (Ed.) Prev: Trainee GP E. Cumbria VTS.

JAMES, Ronald Lester 22 Moor Croft, Rugeley WS15 3ND — MB BCh 1990 Wales.

JAMES, Rosalind Eve Skone (retired) 210 Priests Lane, Shenfield, Brentwood CM15 8LG — MB BS 1948 Lond.; MRCS Eng. LRCP Lond. 1948; FRCPsych. 1984, M 1972; DPM Eng. 1970. Cons. Psychiat. Warley Hosp.

JAMES, Sally Claire Bristol Royal Infirmary, Bristol BS2 8HW; 45 Royal York Crescent, Clifton, Bristol BS8 4JS — BM BS 1989 Nottm.; BMedSci Nottm. 1987; MRCP (UK) 1993.

JAMES, Sandra Elizabeth Chantemerle, Speen Lane, Newbury RG14 1RJ — MB BS 1980 Lond.; BSc Lond. 1969, PhD 1975, MB BS 1980.

JAMES, Sarah St Thomas Childrens Day Hospital, 35 Black Prince Road, London SE11 6JJ — MB BS 1989 Lond.

JAMES, Shagufta 76 Station Road, Llanishen, Cardiff CF14 5UT — MB BCh 1986 Wales. Ho. Off. (Gen. Surg./ENT) Univ. Hosp. Wales Cardiff.

JAMES, Sheelah Robina Norton The Woodbourne Priory Hospital, 21 Woodbourne Road, Edgbaston, Birmingham B17 8BY; 1 Woodcroft Close, Blackwell, Bromsgrove B60 1DA — MB ChB Birm. 1961; FRCPsych 1989, M 1977; DPM Eng. 1965. (Birm.) Cons. Psychiat. The Woodbourne Priory Hosp. Birm.; Second Opinion Apptd. Doctor, Ment. Health Act Commiss. Prev: Cons. Psychiat. N. Worcs. Community NHS Trust.

JAMES, Simon 3 Meadow Road, Southborough, Tunbridge Wells TN4 0HL Tel: 01892 529016 — MB BS 1994 Lond.; DRCOG 1999;

DFFP 98. (Royal Free Hospital School of Medicine) Socs: Assoc. Mem. RCGP. Prev: SHO O & G; GP Regist.; SHO Psychiat.

JAMES, Stephanie (retired) Bay Tree Cottage, North Green, Kirtlington, Kidlington OX5 3JZ Tel: 01869 350261 Email: vaughan.james@ukgateway.net — MB BS Lond. 1951; MRCS Eng. LRCP Lond. 1951. Prev: Princip. GP Jericho Health Centre Oxf.

JAMES, Stephen 25 Foxhills Crescent, Lanchester, Durham DH7 0PW Tel: 01207 520557 — MB BChir 1984 Camb.; BSc St. And. 1982; PhD CNAA 1992. Prev: Regist. (Chem. Path.) Addenbrooke's Hosp. Camb.

JAMES, Mr Stephen Eric Department of Orthopaedics, Eastbourne District General Hospital, Kings Drive, Eastbourne BN21 2UD Tel: 01323 413728 Fax: 01323 414963 — MB BS 1977 Lond.; MS Lond. 1990; FRCS Eng. 1981; MRCS Eng. LRCP Lond. 1977. (St. Geo.) Cons. Orthop. E.bourne Hosp. E. Sussex. Socs: Brit. Orthop. Assn. & Roy. Soc. Med. Prev: Sen. Regist. (Orthop.) United Hosp. Med. Sch. Lond.; Regist. Rotat. (Orthop.) St. Thos. Hosp. Lond.; Regist. (Rotat.) Middlx. Hosp. Lond.

JAMES, Stephen Piers Newton Surgery, Park Street, Newtown SY16 1EF Tel: 01686 626221/626224 Fax: 01686 622610; The Close, Milford Road, Newtown SY16 2EQ Tel: 01686 626703 Email: stevejames@barclays.net — MB ChB 1983 Birm.; DRCOG 1988. (Birmingham) Clin. Asst. Montgomery Co. Infirm. Newtown. Prev: Trainee GP Pontesbury; SHO (A & E, Geriat. Med., O & G, Paediat.) Roy. Shrewsbury Hosp.

JAMES, Mr Stuart Edward Bosworth House, 22 Westward Ho, Abbotswood, Guildford GU1 1UU Tel: 01426 180101 — MB BS 1994 Lond.; BSc Lond. 1991; FRCS Eng. 1998. (University College and Middlesex Med. School)

JAMES, Stuart Harrison 13 Woodside Avenue, Bridgend CF31 1QF Tel: 01656 657535 — BM 1998 Soton.; BM Soton 1998. Prev: Ho. Off. Med. P. Chas. Merthyr Tydal; Ho. Off. Surg. P.ss of Wales Bridgend.

JAMES, Susan Laurina Langley House, West St., Chichester PO19 1RW Tel: 01243 782266; Ark Royal, Tangmere, Chichester PO20 6HE Tel: 01243 776867 — MB BS 1966 Lond.; MSc Lond. 1992, BSc 1963; MRCP (UK) 1973; MRCS Eng. LRCP Lond. 1966; MRCGP 1975; DObst RCOG 1971; DTM & H Liverp. 1970. (St. Bart.) Hosp. Pract. (Psychiat.) Graylingwell Hosp. Chichester. Prev: Research Asst. Surg. Unit Univ. Hosp. of Wales Cardiff; Resid. Med. Off. Roy. N.. Hosp. Lond.; Med. Off. Ngora Hosp., Uganda.

JAMES, Susan Margaret Northfield Avenue Surgery, 61 Northfield Avenue, West Ealing, London W13 9QP Tel: 020 8567 1612 Fax: 020 8579 2593 — MB BS 1973 Newc.; MRCGP 1977; DCH Eng. 1976; DObst RCOG 1975.

JAMES, Susan Peta 118 Redhill Road, Rowlands Castle PO9 6DF Tel: 01705 2381 — BM 1979 Soton.; MRCGP 1983.

JAMES, Mr Teifion Emlyn The BUPA Hospital, Elland Lane, Elland HX5 9EB Tel: 01422 324000 Fax: 01422 377501 — MB BS 1983 Lond.; 1990 FRCS (Ophth.) Ed. 1990; 1988 MRCP (UK) 1988; 1991 FCOphth 1991; 1990 DO RCS Eng. 1990. (St. Mary's) Cons. Opthalmic Surg., Roy. Halifax Infirm.; Cons. Opthalmic Surg., Leeds Teachg. Hosp.s; Hon. Cons., Huddersfield Roy. Inf.; Sen. Clin. Lect., Leeds Univ.

JAMES, Thomas Morgan (retired) Hendre House, High St., Tisbury, Salisbury SP3 6PS Tel: 01747 871496 — MRCS Eng. LRCP Lond. 1954; MFCM 1972. Prev: Asst. Sec. Med. Defence Union Lond.

JAMES, Timothy Rowland 15 Bishop's Way, Andover SP10 3EH — MB BS 1968 Lond.; MRCOG 1975.

JAMES, Tracey Elizabeth Bellevue Surgery, Bellevue Terrace, Newport NP20 2WQ Tel: 01633 256337 Fax: 01633 222856 — MB BCh 1982 Wales; MRCGP 1992; DRCOG 1986. (Wales)

JAMES, Vera Ulrike Gisela 130 Limekiln Lane, Lilleshall, Newport TF10 9EU Email: dr.v.james@btinternet.com; Donnington Medical Practice, Health Centre, Wrekin Drive, Donnington, Telford TF2 8EA Tel: 01952 605252 Fax: 01952 677010 — State Exam. Med. Bonn 1984. Socs: BMA.

JAMES, Vijay Henry Christadas 1 Woodcroft Close, Blackwell, Bromsgrove B60 1DA — MB ChB 1993 Leeds. Prev: Ho. Surg. Nottm. City Hosp.; Ho. Phys. Alexandra Hosp. Redditch.

JAMES, Virge NBS Trent Centre, Longley Lane, Sheffield S5 7JN Tel: 01142 034800 Fax: 01142 034911 Email: virge.james@nbs.nhs.uk; Park Holme, Endcliffe Hall Avenue, Sheffield S10 3EL Tel: 0114 266 0880 — BM BCh Oxf. 1966; DM Oxf. 1980, MA 1966; FRCPath 1985, M 1973; MBA (CNNA) 1988. (Oxf.) Cons. Haemat. Regional Blood Transfus. Centre Sheff.; Hon. Clin. Lect. (Haemat.) Univ. Sheff. Socs: Brit. Soc. Haematol. & Brit. Blood Transfus. Soc.; Amer. Assn. Blood Banks.

JAMES, Wayne Kyneton, Southerndown Road, St Brides Major, Bridgend CF32 0SD — MB BCh 1975 Wales; FFA RCS Eng. 1979.

JAMES, Wendy Margaret 16 Parc Yr Onnen, Llwyn Meredydd, Carmarthen SA31 1ED — MB BCh 1981 Wales. SHO (O & G) W. Wales Gen. Hosp. Carmarthen. Prev: SHO Dept. Paediat. W. Wales Gen. Hosp. Carmarthen.

JAMES, William Andrew The Health Centre, Westfield Walk, Leominster HR6 8HD Tel: 01568 612084 Fax: 01568 610340 — MB BS 1974 Lond.; MRCGP 1980; DRCOG 1979; DA Eng. 1977. (St. Geo.) Prev: SHO (Anaesth.) S.mead Hosp. Bristol; Ho. Phys. Good Hope Gen. Hosp. Sutton Coldfield; Ho. Surg. St. Geo. Hosp. Lond.

JAMES, William Burbridge (retired) 113 The Manor Drive, Worcester Park KT4 7LN Tel: 020 8337 1881 — MRCS Eng. LRCP Lond. 1947. Prev: Sen. Med. Off. Community Health Merton, Sutton & Wandsworth HA.

JAMES, Professor William Philip Trehearne, CBE Rowett Research Institute, Greenburn Road, Bucksburn, Aberdeen AB21 9SB Tel: 01244 712751 Fax: 01244 715349; Wardenhill, Greenburn Road, Bucksburn, Aberdeen AB21 9SA Tel: 01244 712623 Fax: 01244 713292 — MB BS 1962 Lond.; FRSE 1986; DSc Lond. 1983, BSc 1959, MD 1968; Hon. MA Camb. 1977; FRCP Ed. 1983; FRCP Lond. 1978, M 1965. (Univ. Coll. Hosp.) Research Prof. Aberd. Univ.; Dir. Rowett Research Inst. Aberd. Prev: Asst. Dir. MRC Dunn Nutrit. Unit Camb.; Hon. Cons. Camb. AHA (T); Sen. Lect. (Nutrit.) Lond. Sch. Hyg. & Trop. Med.

JAMES, Mr William Victor (retired) 7 Castle Street, Strangford, Downpatrick BT30 7NF Tel: 028 44 881 516 Fax: 01396 881516 Email: drwilliamvjames@compuserve.com — MB BS 1951 Lond.; FRCS Ed. 1959; MRCS Eng. LRCP Lond. 1951. Hon. Fell. Orthop. & Mech. Engin. Qu. Univ. Belf.; Mem. Brit. Exec. Serv. Overseas. Prev: Cons. Orthop. Surg. Musgrave Pk. Hosp. Belf. & N. Irel. Orthop. Serv.

JAMES, Wilson Barrie 9 Quadrant Road, Glasgow G43 2QP — MB ChB 1954 Ed.; FRCP Glas. 1973, M 1971; FRCR 1975; FFR 1961; DMRD Eng. 1959. (Univ. Ed.) Cons. Radiol. S.. Gen. Hosp. Glas. Socs: Roy. M-C Soc. Glas. & Brit. Soc. Gastroenterol.

JAMES-ELLISON, Michelle Yvonne Dept. Child health, Swansea NHS Trust, Singleton Hospital, Swansea Tel: 01792 205660; Tyn yr Heol, Cilybebyll, Pontardawe, Swansea SA8 3JL — BSc (Hons.) Wales 1980, MB BCh 1985; MRCP (UK) 1990; DCH RCP Lond. 1990. Cons. Paediat. Dept Child Health Singleton Hosp. Swansea. Prev: Paediatric Nephrol. Fello, Hosp. for Sick Childr., Toronto, Canada; Specialist Regist. Univ. Hosp. Wales, Cardiff; Clin. Research Off. (Hon. Regist.) Univ. Wales Coll. Med. Cardiff.

JAMESON, Angela Isabel (retired) 29 Upper Oldfield Park, Bath BA2 3JX Tel: 01225 426334 — MB BS 1947 Lond.; MRCS Eng. LRCP Lond. 1947. Prev: Jun. Asst. Pathol. W. Lond. Hosp.

JAMESON, Benjamin Neil 6 St Johns Avenue, Clevedon BS21 7TQ — MB BS 1998 Newc.; MB BS Newc 1998.

JAMESON, Beryl (retired) 20 Napier Court, Ranelagh Gardens, London SW6 3UT Tel: 020 7731 0589 — MB ChB Sheff. 1956; FRCPath 1976, M 1964; DPath Eng. 1960; DObst RCOG 1959. Prev: Cons. Microbiol. Roy. Marsden Hosps. Lond. & Surrey.

JAMESON, Charles Francis Kingston Hospital, Galsworthy Road, Kingston upon Thames KT2 7QB — MB BCh BAO 1983 NUI; FRCPath 1999; FFPath (RCPI) 1997; MRCPath 1990. Cons. Histopath. Kingston Hosp. Surrey; Med. Acupunc. & Practitioner Traditional Chinese Med. Kingston upon Thames. Prev: Sen. Regist. (Histopath.) SW Thames RHA; Regist. (Histopath.) Merton & Sutton HA; SHO (Path.) N. Manch. HA.

JAMESON, David Michael 7 Marlborough Gate, St Albans AL1 3TX — MB BS 1988 Lond.

JAMESON, Fiona Mary (retired) 15 North Road, Grassendale Park, Liverpool L19 0LP Tel: 0151 427 7146 Fax: 0151 427 0661 — MB BS 1958 Durh. Prev: GP Liverp.

JAMESON, Jessica Kirwan Binscombe Medical Centre, 106 Binscombe, Godalming GU7 3PR Tel: 01483 415115 Fax: 01483 414925 — MB BS 1989 Lond.; MDCH, Lond. Coll. Of

Hypnotherapy, 2001; MRCGP 1995; DRCOG 1994; DCH RCP Lond. 1993. (King's Coll. Lond.) p/t GP.

JAMESON, Mr John Stuart Glenfield Hospital, Groby Road, Leicester LE3 9QP Tel: 0116 256 3445 Fax: 0116 258 3950 Email: john.jameson@uhl-tr.nhs.uk — MB BS 1984 Lond.; MA Camb. 1985; FRCS Eng. 1988; MD Lond. 1995. (Westm.) Cons. Surg. Socs: Assn. Coloproct.; Assn. Surg.; BASO. Prev: RSO St.Marks & N.wick Pk. Hosp.; SR Rotat. (Gen. Surg.) Leicester; MRC Research Fell. (Gastroenterol.) Centr. Middlx. Hosp. Lond.

JAMESON, Paul Morpeth Department of Anaesthesia, Contess of Chester Hospital, Liverpool Rd, Chester CH2 Tel: 01244 365461 — MB ChB 1986 Liverp.; FRCA 1992. Cons. Anaesth. Countess of Chester Hosp., Chester.

JAMESON, Peter Phillip Morpeth 15 North Road, Grassendale Park, Liverpool L19 0LP — MB BS 1991 Lond.

JAMESON, Robert John (retired) 29 Upper Oldfield Park, Bath BA2 3JX Tel: 01225 426334 — MRCS Eng. LRCP Lond. 1943; MRCGP 1953; DObst RCOG 1948. Prev: Clin. Asst. (Paediat.) Roy. United Hosps. Bath.

JAMESON, Mr Robin Morpeth (retired) 15 North Road, Grassendale Park, Liverpool L19 0LP Tel: 0151 427 7146 — MB BS 1957 Durh.; MB BS (Hnrs.) Durh. 1957; FRCS Eng. 1962. Prev: Cons. Urol. Regional Urol. Centre Roy. Liverp. Hosp. & Regional Paraplegic Centre Promenade Hosp. S.port.

JAMESON, Ronald James 280 Cowcliffe Hill Road, Fixby, Huddersfield HD2 2NE Tel: 01484 532429 Email: ron@rjjameson.freeserve.co.uk — MB BS 1951 Lond.; MRCGP 1972; DCH RCP Lond. 1955; DObst RCOG 1953. (King's Coll. Hosp.) JP. Prev: Cas. Off. Roy. Sussex Co. Hosp. Brighton; Clin. Asst. (Paediat.) P. of Wales Hosp. Tottenham; Ho. Phys. & Ho. Surg. (O & G) Brighton Gen. Hosp.

JAMESON, Ruth Alison Stepping Hill Hospital, Stockport SK2 7JE; 3 Marsham Road, Hazel Grove, Stockport SK7 5JB — MB ChB 1978 Manch.; MRCP (UK) 1982. Cons. Paediat. Stepping Hill Hosp. Stockport.

JAMESON, Sheila Anne 93 Beaconsfield Place, Aberdeen AB15 4AD Tel: 01224 647714 — MB ChB 1978 Ed. Prev: Clin. Med. Off. (Child Health) N. Yorks.; SHO (Paediat.) Newc. u. Tyne.

JAMESON, Thomas Henry Ogden Level F, Princess Anne Hospital, Southampton SO16 5YD; 28 Denbigh Gardens, Southampton SO16 7PH Tel: 0973 634235 Email: thoj@soton.ac.uk — MB BS 1993 Lond.; BSc Lond. (Charing Cross and Westminster) SHO O & G Soton. Prev: Clin. Research Fell. (O & G) Soton.

JAMESON, Victoria Jane Groby Road Medical Centre, 9 Groby Road, Leicester LE3 9ED Tel: 0116 253 8185 — MB ChB 1988 Leic.; MRCGP 1993.

JAMESON, Victoria Rosalind Bennetts End Surgery, Gatecroft, Hemel Hempstead HP3 9LY Tel: 01442 263511; 13 Litchfield Place, Avenue Road, St Albans AL1 3UG — BM 1993 Soton. GP Regist.

JAMESON EVANS, Mr David Charles 45 Denmark Road, Exeter EX1 1SQ Tel: 01392 256444 Fax: 01392 427872; Waterleat House, Silverton, Exeter EX5 4DS Tel: 01392 860230 — MB BS 1965 Lond.; FRCS Eng. 1970; FRCS Canada 1976. (St. Mary's) Hon. Cons. Surg. Orthop. Roy. Devon & Exeter Hosp. (Wonford) & P.ss Eliz. Orthop. Hosp. Exeter; Cons. Orthipaedic Surg., Sidmouth Vict. Hosp., Sidemouth. Socs: Brit. Orthop. Assn. Prev: Sen. Regist. (Orthop.) St. Mary's Hosp. Lond.; Sen. Resid. Hosp. Sick Childr. Toronto, Canada; Rotat. Regist. Robt. Jones & Agnes Hunt Orthop. Hosp. OsW.ry.

JAMIE, Douglas Banks, MBE (retired) 12 Sunway Grove, Styvechale, Coventry CV3 6GR Tel: 01203 415355 Email: dougal.jamie — MB ChB 1940 St. And.; BSc, MB ChB St. And. 1940. Prev: GP Coventry.

JAMIE, Gavin Millar 24 Cluny Drive, Edinburgh EH10 6DP — BM 1995 Soton. SHO (Med.) Gloucestershire Roy. Hosp. Gloucester.

JAMIESON, Alasdair Duncan Kinorth Medical Centre, 26 Abbotswell Crescent, Aberdeen AB12 5JW Tel: 01224 876000 Fax: 01224 899182; 2 Stableyard Cottages, Esslomont Estate, Ellon AB41 8PA — MB ChB 1983 Aberd.; Cert. Family Plann. JCC 1991. Prev: SHO (O & G) New Cross Hosp. Wolverhampton; SHO (Paediat.) Roy. Aberd. Childr. Hosp.

JAMIESON, Alexander Barton House Health Centre, 233 Albion Road, London N16 9JT Tel: 020 7249 5511 Fax: 020 7254 8985; 45 Sidney Street, London E1 2HH Tel: 020 7702 7050 Fax: 020 7702 7012 Email: mail@alexjamieson.com — MB ChB 1976 Glas. Assoc. Dean. Postgrad. GP. Ed. N. Thames E. 1995; Sen. Lect. Dept .GP. Primary Care St Barts & Roy. Lond. Sch. Med. Dent.

JAMIESON, Andrew Department of Medicine, Queen Margaret Hospital, Dunfermline KY12 0SU Tel: 01383 623623 — MB ChB 1989 Glas.; PhD Glas. 1995; MRCP (UK) 1992. Cons. Endocrinol., Qu. Margt. Hosp. Dunfermline. Prev: Sen. Regist. (Med. Endocrinol. & Diabetes) W.. Infirm. Glas.; MRC Research Fell. (Med. & Therap.) & Clin. Research Fell. (Cardiol.) W.. Infirm. Glas.; SHO (Med.) Hammersmith Hosp. Lond.

JAMIESON, Andrew Donald 7 Caulfield Avenue, Inverness IV2 5GA — MB ChB 1992 Ed.

JAMIESON, Mr Angus Martin Manley Hall, Erbistock, Wrexham LL13 0DH Tel: 01978 780172 Fax: 01978 781002 — MB ChB 1966 Ed.; FRCS Ed. 1971. (Ed.) Cons. Orthop. Surg. Wrexham Maelor Hosp. & Rob. Jones & Agnes Hunt Orthop. Hosp. OsW.ry. Prev: Sen. Regist. (Orthop.) St. Mary's Hosp. Lond.; Regist. (Orthop.) Robt. Jones & Agnes Hunt Orthop. Hosp. OsW.ry; Regist. (Orthop.) Leighton Hosp. Crewe.

JAMIESON, Anne Elisabeth 7 Wayside Crescent, Harrogate HG2 8NJ — MB ChB 1991 Glas. (Glas.) Flexible Trainee (Psychiat.) Harrogate. Prev: Staff Grade Doctor (Old Age Psychiat.) Gartnavel Roy. Hosp. Glas.

JAMIESON, Arthur 26 Strathclyde Court, Millig St., Helensburgh G84 9PW — MB ChB 1952 Glas.

JAMIESON, Arthur (retired) Hillcrest, Beith KA15 1EY Tel: 01505 502458 — MB ChB 1945 Glas.

JAMIESON, Colin Greyfriars Medical Centre, 33-37 Castle Street, Dumfries DG1 1DL Tel: 01387 257752 Fax: 01387 257020; 5 Devanha Gardens, Aberdeen AB11 7UU — MB ChB 1968 Aberd.

JAMIESON, Crawford Philip 12 Colnbrook Street, London SE1 6EZ — MB BS 1989 Lond.; MRCP (UK) 1992. Specialist Regist. (Gastroeneterology) Univ. Coll. Hosp. & Middlx. Hosp.

JAMIESON, Mr Crawford William (retired) The Consulting Rooms, York House, 199 Westminster Bridge Road, London SE1 7UT Tel: 020 7636 3490 Fax: 020 7636 4596 Email: c.w.jamieson@btinternet.com — MB BS 1960 Lond.; MB BS (Hons. Surg.) Lond. 1960; MS Lond. 1970; FRCS Eng. 1964; MRCS Eng. LRCP Lond. 1960. Hon. Cons. Surg. Guy's & St. Thos. Hosp. Trust Lond. Prev: Gp. Clin. Dir. (Surg. Servs.) Guy's & St. Thos. Hosp. Trust Lond.

JAMIESON, David George Blackwoods Medical Centre, 8 Station Road, Muirhead, Glasgow G69 9EE; Westbank, 1 Seven Sisters, Lenzie, Glasgow G66 3AW — MB ChB 1978 Glas.; MRCGP 1982; DRCOG 1982. Prev: Trainee GP Dumfries & Galloway VTS; Ho. Surg. Dumfries & Galloway Roy. Infirm.; Ho. Phys. Profess. Med. Unit Glas. Roy. Infirm.

JAMIESON, Donald Gavin 38 Harborne Road, Birmingham B15 3HE; (home), 81 Reddings Road, Birmingham B13 8LP — MB ChB 1958 Aberd.; FRCP Ed. 1974, M 1963; FRCP Lond. 1981, M 1965. Cons. Neurol. City Hosp. NHS Trust,Birm. Prev: Cons. Neurol. Dudley Rd. Hosp. Birm., Midl. Centre For Neurosurg. & Neurol. Smethwick & Birm. RHB.; Sen. Regist. (Neurol.) Profess. Med. Unit Dundee Roy. Infirm.; Tutor in Neurol. Univ. St. And.

JAMIESON, Douglas Ramsay Stuart Leeds General Infirmary, Great George St., Leeds LS1 3EX Tel: 0113 392 3339 Fax: 0113 392 8287 — MB ChB 1984 Birm.; MRCP 1988 UK; PhD 1994 Glas.; MA 1982 Oxf.; PhD Glas. 1994; MA Oxf. 1982; MRCP (UK) 1988. Cons. Neurol. Leeds Gen. Infirm.; Hon. Sen. Lect. Univ. Leeds. Socs: Assn. Brit. NeUrol.s; Amer. Acad. Neurol.; Brit. Assn. for the Study of Headache. Prev: Lect. (Neurol.) & Hon. Sen. Regist. Univ. Glas.; MRC Train Fell. Inst. Neurol. Glas.; Regist. (Neurol.) Inst. Neurol. Sci. Glas.

JAMIESON, Ernest Charles Jamieson, Thorpe and Burgess, Moulton Medical Centre, High St, Moulton, Spalding PE12 6QB Tel: 01406 370265 Fax: 01406 373219; Warwick House, Churchgate, Whaplode, Spalding PE12 6TA Fax: 01406 373219 — MB ChB 1967 Aberd.; DAvMed Eng. 1972. Med. Off. Welland Hosp. Spalding Lincs.; Med. Off. Holbeach Hosp. Lincs. Socs: Fell. Roy. Soc. Med. Prev: Ho. Surg. Aberd. Roy. Infirm. Foresterhill; Ho. Phys. Woodend Hosp. Aberd.; Squadron Ldr. RAF Med. Br.

JAMIESON, Gay Jane (retired) Hydegate, Long Sutton, Hook RG29 1TA Tel: 01256 862320 — MB BS Lond. 1957; DCH Eng. 1961. Prev: Sessional Med. Off. Lond. Boro. Greenwich.

JAMIESON, George Alexander (retired) Drumclair, Elmira Road, Muirhead, Chryston, Glasgow G69 9EJ Tel: 0141 779 2664 — MB ChB Glas. 1951; FRCGP 1984, M 1959; DObst RCOG 1952. Prev: Temp. Surg. Lt. RNVR.

JAMIESON, Grace Kathleen Roslyn Charles Burns Clinic, Queensbridge Road, Moseley, Birmingham B13 8LP Tel: 0121 442 4545 Fax: 0121 442 4545; 81 Reddings Road, Moseley, Birmingham B13 8LP Tel: 0121 449 0430 — MB ChB 1962 Aberd.; FRCPsych 1989, M 1974; DPM Ed. & Glas. 1967. Cons. Child & Adolesc. Psychiat. S. Birm. HA (T). Prev: Regist. Dept. Child Psychiat. Dundee Teach. Hosps.

JAMIESON, Helen Toni Broomhill Practice, 41 Broomhill Drive, Glasgow G11 7AD Tel: 0141 339 3626 Fax: 0141 334 2399; 22 Whittingehame Drive, Glasgow G12 0XX — MB ChB 1979 Dundee; MRCGP 1983.

JAMIESON, Iain Donald Mackintosh Fenwick Road Surgery, 261 Fenwick Road, Giffnock, Glasgow G46 6JX Tel: 0141 531 6993 Fax: 0141 531 6997; 22 Fleurs Avenue, Dumbreck, Glasgow G41 5AP Tel: 0141 427 6161 — MB ChB Glas. 1969. (Glas.) Sen. Partner, Drs. Jamieson, Frame & Cooper. Socs: Assoc. RCGP; BMA; Glas. S.. Med. Soc. Prev: Med. Off. Florentine Ho. Childr. Home Glas.; Ho. Surg. (O & G) S.. Gen. Hosp. Glas.; Cas. Off. Perth Roy. Infirm.

JAMIESON, Iain Seumas 11 Kelvin Gardens, Largs KA30 8SX — MB ChB 1992 Manch.

JAMIESON, Ian William (retired) Scottsdale, Hillside Road, Aldershot GU11 3LX Tel: 01252 324947 — MB ChB Glas. 1955; DObst RCOG 1960. Prev: GP Ash Vale, Aldershot.

JAMIESON, Ian William Grove Medical Practice, 49 Richford Gate, London W6 7HY Tel: 020 8846 7555 Fax: 020 8846 7538 — MB BS 1965 Lond. (King's Coll. Hosp.) Socs: Assoc. MRCGP. Prev: Ho. Phys. & Ho. Surg. Dulwich Hosp.

JAMIESON, Jean Susheila (retired) 9 Rockfield Crescent, Dundee DD2 1JE Tel: 01382 668895 — MB ChB 1956 St. And. Prev: SCMO Tayside HB.

JAMIESON, Jennifer Ruth Maelor General Hospital, Wrexham LL13 7TD Tel: 01978 353153; Manley Hall, Erbistock, Wrexham LL13 0DH — MB ChB 1969 Liverp.; FFA RCS Eng. 1973. (Liverp.) Cons. Anaesth. Wrexham Maelor Gen. Hosp. Socs: IC Soc. & Obst. Anaesth. Assn. Prev: Sen. Regist. (Anaesth.) Chester Roy. Infirm.

JAMIESON, Johanna Ann (retired) 148 Finnart Street, Greenock PA16 8HY Tel: 01475 729531 — MB ChB Glas. 1959. Prev: Sen. Med. Off. Inverclyde Health Dist.

JAMIESON, John Alexander (retired) 15 Fawcett Road, Aldeburgh IP15 5HQ Tel: 01728 452364 — MB ChB 1945 Manch.; MRCP Lond. 1951; FRCGP 1977. Prev: GP Hemel Hempstead.

JAMIESON, Katharine Anne 3 Carlingnose Park, North Queensferry, Inverkeithing KY11 1EX — MB ChB 1990 Aberd.; MB ChB (Commend.) Aberd. 1990; MRCP (UK) 1993. Regist. (Radiol.) Roy. Infirm. & W.. Gen. Hosp. Edin. Socs: Roy. Coll. Phys. Edin. Prev: SHO (A & E) Dundee Roy. Infirm.; SHO (Gen. Med.) Tayside HB; Ho. Off. (Plastic Surg., Neurosurg. & Gen. & Renal Med.) Aberd. Roy. Infirm.

JAMIESON, Keri Louise 22 Whitehall Place, Aberdeen AB25 2PA — MB ChB 1997 Aberd.

JAMIESON, Margaret Elisabeth (retired) Flat 2, Ashfield House, 8 Grove Road, Leeds LS6 2AQ Tel: 0113 278 8335 — MRCS Eng. LRCP Lond. 1943. Prev: Clin. Med. Off. (Child Health) Leeds AHA (T).

JAMIESON, Margaret Forbes (retired) Carron Villa, Viewfield St., Nairn IV12 4HW Tel: 01667 453057 — MB ChB 1951 Edin; BSc (Hons.) Ed. 1954, MD 1970, MB ChB 1951.

JAMIESON, Mary Brown (retired) 9 Inverleith Terrace, Edinburgh EH3 5NS — MB ChB 1953 Ed.; MA Ed. 1949.

JAMIESON, Morag Elizabeth 1 Lenzie Road, Stepps, Glasgow G33 6DY — MB ChB 1987 Dundee.

JAMIESON, Mr Morgan Pringle Gardner Yorkhill NHS Trust, Dalnair St., Glasgow G3 8SJ Tel: 0141 201 0605 Fax: 0141 201 0836; 25 Windsor Avenue, Newton Mearns, Glasgow G77 5NX Tel: 0141 639 2213 — MB ChB 1971 Ed.; BSc (Med. Sci.) Ed. 1968; FRCS (Cardiothor) Ed. 1982; FRCS Ed. 1976. (Univ. Ed.) Med. Dir. Yorkhill NHS Trust Glas. Socs: Soc. Cardiothoracic Surgs.; Brit. Assn. Med. Managers. Prev: Cons. Cardiac Surg. W.. Infirm. & Roy. Hosp. Sick Childr. Glas.; Sen. Regist. (Cardiothoracic Surg.) Hosp. Sick Childr. Gt. Ormond St. Lond.; Sen. Regist. (Cardiothoracic Surg.) Glas. Roy. Infirm.

JAMIESON, Neil Frazer Balvonie of Inshes, Inverness IV2 5BB — MB ChB 1992 Ed.

JAMIESON, Neil Sar Dessai 39/6 Lochrin Place, Edinburgh EH3 9RB — MB ChB 1997 Glas.

JAMIESON, Mr Neville Victor Department of Surgery, University of Cambridge, Addenbrooke's Hospital, Hills Road, Cambridge CB2 2QQ Tel: 01223 245151 Fax: 01223 247858 Email: nvj1000@cu5.cam.ac.uk; 18 School Lane, Fulbourn, Cambridge CB1 5BH — MB BS 1978 Lond.; MA Camb. 1978, MD 1991; FRCS Eng. 1983. (Univ. Coll. Hosp.) Cons. Surg. & Assoc. Lect., Univ. Camb. Socs: Coun. Mem. Brit. Transpl.ation Soc. 2000; Mem. Internat. Transpl.ation Soc.; Mem. Europ. Transpl.ation Soc. Prev: Research Assoc. Univ. Wisconsin, Madison, USA; Clin. Lect. (Surg.) Camb. Univ.

JAMIESON, Mr Paul Andrew North Cheshire Hospital Trust, Warrington Hospital, Lovely Lane, Warrington WA5 — MB ChB 1990 Liverp.; FRCS 2000 (Urol); FRCS Ed. 1996. Prev: Specialist Regist. (Urol.) Merseyside; Cons. Urolist Warrington Hosp.

JAMIESON, Robert Ross Bridgeton Health Centre, 201 Abercromby Street, Glasgow G40 2DA Tel: 0141 531 6600 Fax: 0141 531 6616; 22 Whittingehame Drive, Glasgow G12 0XX — MB ChB 1979 Dundee; FRCP Glas. 1994; MRCP (UK) 1982; MFHom RCP Lond. 1994; MRCGP 1985. (Univ. Dundee) Hon. Lect. (Physiol. & Pharmacol.) Univ. Strathclyde; Clin. Asst. Glas. Homeop. Hosp. W. Glas. Hosp. Univ. NHS Trust; GP Audit Facilitator GGHB.

JAMIESON, Rosalind 39 Quarry Road, Belfast BT4 2NP Tel: 01232 763882; 2/R 66 Novar Drive, Glasgow G12 9TZ Tel: 0141 334 1594 — MB ChB 1991 Glas.; MRCOG -RCOG 1998. SHO (Obst.) Glas. Roy. Matern. Hosp. & Specialist Regist. Obst. & Gyn, Glasg; Regist. (Obst.) Qu. Mother's Hosp. Prev: SHO (Gyn.) Roy. Infirm. & Stobhill Hosp. Glas.

JAMIESON, Susan Jane 16th Floor Hing Wai Building, 36 Queens Road Central, Central, Hong Kong Tel: 00 852 25238044 Email: drsjasso@netvigator.com; The Linn, Inshes, Inverness IV2 5BG — MB ChB 1985 Glas.; DRCOG 1988; MRCGP 1989. (Glasgow) GP Running large Holistic Med. Pract. in Centr. Hong Kong. Socs: Counc. Of Hong Kong; Fell. Hong Kong Acad. Med.; BMA. Prev: Sen. Lect. (Gen. Pract.) Chinese Univ. Hong Kong 1990-1996; SHO Ruttunjee Sanat. (med.) Hong Kong Trainee GP Stewartors; Health Centre Aysh.

JAMIESON, Virginia Luigi The Old School, 30A High St., Burwell, Cambridge CB5 0HB — MB ChB 1977 Ed.; FFA RCS Eng. 1985.

JAMIESON, Walter Crawford 9 Rockfield Crescent, Dundee DD2 1JB Tel: 01382 68895 — MB ChB 1945 Ed.; DObst RCOG 1952. (Ed.)

JAMIESON, Walter Saggar Craigmillar Medical Group, 106 Niddrie Mains Road, Edinburgh EH16 4DT Tel: 0131 536 9500 Fax: 0131 536 9545; 15 Dalkeith Street, Edinburgh EH15 2HP — MB ChB 1984 Ed.; DCCH RCP Lond. 1990; MRCGP 1989; DRCOG 1988. GP Edin.

JAMIESON-CRAIG, Thomas Kern Academic Dept Psychiatry, St Thomas' Hospital, London SE1 7EH Tel: 0207928 9292 Fax: 020 7633 0061 — MB BS 1973 West Indies; PhD 1990; FRCPsych 1991. Prof. of community Psychiat. GKYT Sch. of Med. St Thomas Hosp. Lond.

JAMIL, Ahmed Glasfryn Surgery, Glasfryn, Denbigh Rosd, Llanfairtalhaearn, Abergele LL22 8SN Tel: 01745 720253 — MB BS 1965 Dacca; LMSSA Lond. 1975; DTM & H Liverp. 1973. (Chittagong Med. Coll.) Socs: Assoc. RCGP; Med. Protec. Soc. Prev: Regist. (Dermat.) P'boro. Dist. Hosp.; SHO (Rheum. & Geriat. Med.) Nether Edge Hosp. Sheff.; Ho. Off. (Gen. Surg.) Pontefract Gen. Infirm.

***JAMIL, Fatema Waheed** 21 Deerings Dr, Pinner HA5 2NZ — MB ChB 1997 Leic.

JAMIL, Mahmud 41 Alfreton Close, London SW19 5NS — MB BS 1996 Lond.

JAMIL, Muhammad Tanvir Burnham Health Centre, Minniecroft Road, Burnham, Slough SL1 7DE Tel: 01628 605333 Fax: 01628 663743; 40 Long Drive, Burnham, Slough SL1 8AL Email: tanjamil@aol.com — BM 1986 Soton.; BSc Lond. 1981; MRCGP 1990; Cert. Family Plann. JCC 1987. (Southampton) Socs: Brit. Med. Acupunct. Soc.; MDU.

JAMIL, Muhammed Abdul Qudoos 50 Downton Avenue, London SW2 3TR Tel: 020 8671 1194; The Surgery, 64 Nelgarde Road, London SE6 4TF Tel: 020 8690 2697 Fax: 020 8690 4182 — MRCS Eng. LRCP Lond. 1966; LMSSA Lond. 1965. (Guy's) Federal Aviat. Author. Examr. Socs: Assoc. Mem. Roy. Coll. Gen. Pract. & BMA. Prev: Phys. Saudi Arabian Airline; GP Lond.; Regist. (Med.) Guy's Hosp. Med. Sch. Lond.

JAMIL, Mr Muhayman Nuri 61A The Fairway, Northolt UB5 4SN Email: muhaymanj@hotmail.com — MB ChB 1979 Baghdad. Specialist Regist. (Neurosurg.) Nat. Hosp. for Neurol. & Neurosurg. Lond.

JAMIL, Mrs Nahla Fawzi 30 Pennant Crescent, Cardiff CF23 6LN — MB ChB 1981 Baghdad; MRCP (UK) 1984; MRCPsych 1990. Cons. Psychiat. E. Glam. Gen. Hosp. Prev: Sen. Regist. (Psychiat.) WhitCh. Hosp. Cardiff.

JAMIL, Shehla The Chineham Medical Practice, Reading Rd, Chineham, Basingstoke RG24 8ND; Marl House, Nash Meadows, South Warnborough, Hook RG29 1RJ — MB BS 1987 Lond.; MRCGP 1992; Cert. Family Plann. JCC 1990; DRCOG 1990; DCH RCP Lond. 1989. p/t GP Princip. Socs: BMA. Prev: GP Winchester; SHO (ENT & Ophth.) Glas.

JAMISON, Claire Ann 50 Clare Road, Gilford, Craigavon BT63 6AG — MB BCh 1998 Belf.; MB BCh Belf 1998.

JAMISON, David George (retired) Les Fonenelles, Forest GY8 0BL Tel: 01481 63236 — BM BCh Oxf. 1949. Prev: Lect. (Anat.) Univ. Camb.

JAMISON, James Porter Glenalt, 34 Dublin Road, Omagh BT78 1HE Tel: 01662 242507 & profess. 01232 245133 — MB BCh BAO 1971 Belf.; BSc (Hons.) Belf. 1968, MD (Hons.) 1977; FRCPI 1990, M 1987. Cons. Gen. Med. Resp. Investig. Belf. City Hosp.; Lect. (Physiol.) Qu. Univ. Belf. Socs: Thoracic Soc.; Physiol. Soc.

JAMISON, Mr Michael Howard St. Tysilios Medical Centre, Llanfairpwllgwyngyll LL61 5YR Tel: 01248 384384 Email: mike.jamison@nww-tr.wales.nhs.uk; Borthwen Farm, Llandegfan, Anglesey, Menai Bridge LL59 5YD Tel: 01248 713635 Email: mjamison@compuserve.com — MB BChir 1973 Camb.; ChM Manch. 1982; FRCS Eng. 1977. Cons. Gen. Surg. (ColoProctol.) N.W. Wales NHS Trust Bangor. Socs: Assn. Coloproct. GB & Irel.; Assn. of Surg. GB & Irel. Prev: Sen. Regist. (Surg.) Roy. Preston Hosp., Stepping Hill Hosp., Stockport & Univ. Hosp. S. Manch.; Sen. Regist. (Surg.) Johannesbug Gen. Hosp. S. Africa.

JAMISON, Robert William High Street Medical Centre, 46-48 High Street, Newhall, Swadlincote DE11 0HU Tel: 01283 217092; 43 Rose Tree Lane, Newhall, Swadlincote DE11 0LN Tel: 01283 551268 — MB ChB 1984 Liverp.

JAMNICKY, Lada 77 Inverleith Row, Edinburgh EH3 5LT — MB ChB 1997 Ed.

JAMOUS, Mohamed Ali National Spinal Injuries Center, Stoke Mandeville Hospital, Aylesbury HP21 8AL Tel: 01296 315847 Fax: 01296 315868 — MD 1973 Aleppo, Syria; MSc Oxf. 1988. (Aleppo Univ. Syria) Assoc. Specialist (Spinal Injuries) Stoke Mandeville Hosp. Aylesbury. Socs: Internat. Med. Soc. Paraplegia; Soc. Brit. Neurol. Surgs.; Brit. Soc. Rehabil. Med. Prev: Regist. (Neurosurg.) Radcliffe Infirm. Oxf.

JAMPEL, Henry Herman (retired) 32 Nobelfield Heights, London N2 0NX Tel: 020 8340 2844 — MB BS 1947 Lond. Prev: Out-pat. Asst. Roy. Nat. Throat, Nose & Ear Hosp. Lond.

JAMPEL, Lilianna (retired) 32 Noblefield Heights, London N2 0NX Tel: 020 8340 2844 — MB BS 1958 Lond.; MRCS Eng. LRCP Lond. 1958. Clin. Asst. (Rheum.) St. Ann's Hosp. Lond. Prev: Ho. Surg. Roy. Free Hosp. Lond.

JAMRUTH BIBI, Akbar Basha Bournewood Resource Centre, Bournewood NHS Trust, Guildford Road, Chertsey KT16 0DA Tel: 01932 872010; 99 Staines Road E., Sunbury-on-Thames TW16 5AD Tel: 01932 765306 — MB BS 1971 Madras. Staff Grade (Psychiat.) Bournewood NHS Trust. Socs: MDU.

JAMSHIDI, Rustam Jamshid (retired) 13 Knocksilla Park, Omagh BT79 0AR Tel: 01662 245647 — MB BCh BAO Belf. 1966; FRCOG 1989, M 1976. Prev: Cons. (O & G) Tyrone Co. Hosp. Omagh & Erne Hosp. Enniskillen.

JAN, Iqbal Ahmad 64 Sheepwalk Lane, Ravenshead, Nottingham NG15 9FB — MB BS 1959 Punjab; MB BS Punjab (Pakistan) 1959; DPM Eng. 1969. (Nishtar Med. Coll. Multan)

JAN, Mr Muhammed Bilal 24 Windermere Gardens, Redbridge, Ilford IG4 5BZ — MB BS 1979 Karachi; FRCS Ed. 1993.

JAN, Sengi Mar 44 Old Trough Way, Harrogate HG1 3DE — MB BS 1968 Punjab; MB BS Punjab, Pakistan 1968; DLO RCS Eng. 1978. Sen. Staff. ENT Surg.Harrgate Health Case. N. Yorks.

JAN, Shahida Yahya 38 Canaan Lane, Morningside, Edinburgh EH10 4SU Tel: 0131 447 5558 — MB BS 1976 Peshawar; DCP Lond 1982.

JANA, Mr Kalipada Medical Centre, 4 Coronation St., South Shields NE33 1AR Tel: 0191 456 3172; 47 Harton House Road, South Shields NE34 6EE Tel: 0191 456 6693 — MB BS 1961 Calcutta; MS Calcutta 1966, MB BS 1961; FRCS Eng. 1977; FRCS Glas. 1976. (Calcutta) Approved Med. Off. Chamber of Shipping (NE); Med. Off. & Approved Offshore Med Examr. Dept. of Transport. Socs: BMA. Prev: Cons. Surg. Contai Hosp. Midnapur, W. Bengal; Reader & Assoc. Prof. Surg. Univ. Coll. Med. Sci. Univ. Maiduguri, Nigeria; Cons. Surg. (Gastroenterol.) NRS. Med. Coll. Calcutta.

JANA, Prathap Padmanabhan Napier Road Surgery, 151 Napier Road, Gillingham ME7 4HH Tel: 01634 281851 — MB BS 1974 Madras.

JANARDHAN REDDY, Sajjapalli Ramachandra 62 Christopher Road, Selly Oak, Birmingham B29 6QJ — MB BS 1967 Bangalor; MB BS Bangalore 1967; FRCP 1977; DMRD Liverp. 1971. (Bangalore) Sen. Regist. (Rotat.) Birm. AHA (T). Prev: Regist. (Radiol.) Sefton Gen. Hosp. Liverp. & BRd.green Hosp.; Liverp.; SHO (Radiol.) Clatterbridge Hosp. Bebington.

JANARDHANAN, Kalliat Chali Flat 16, Lancaster Gardens, Lancaster Road, Southport PR8 2LF — MB BS 1974 Mysore.

JANAS, Mark Antoni Caswell Clinic, Glan Rhyd Hospital, Bridgend CF31 4LN Tel: 01656 662179 — MB BCh 1988 Wales; MRCPsych 1995; LLM 1999. Prev: Sen. Regist. (Forens. Psychiat.) Caswell Clinic Bridgend; Cons. Forens. Psychiat.

JANCZAK, Josephine Jessie Victoria Hospital, Hayfield Road, Kirkcaldy KY1 1OL; 22A West Albert Road, Kirkcaldy KY1 1DL Tel: 01592 267738 — MB ChB 1979 Glas.; FFA RCS 1991; DA (UK) 1986. Assoc. Specialist (Anaesth.) Vict. Hsop. Kirkcaldy. Socs: Assn. Anaesths. Prev: Career Regist. Lothian Area Anaesth. Train. Scheme; Regist. (Anaesth.) Vict. Hosp. Kirkcaldy.

JANDA, Anita 3 Enright Cl, Leamington Spa CV32 6SQ — MB BCh 1997 Wales.

JANDIAL, Sharmila Flat 2/2, 131 Wilton St., Glasgow G20 6DQ — MB ChB 1998 Glas.; MB ChB Glas 1998.

JANDIAL, Vijay 29 Hazeldene Road, Aberdeen AB15 8LB Tel: 01224 316851 — MB BS 1964 Vikram; MS (Obst. & Gyn.) Indore 1967; FRCOG 1986, M 1972. (M.G.M. Med. Coll. Indore) Cons. O & G Aberd. Matern. Hosp. & Aberd. Roy. Infirm.; Clin. Sen. Lect. (Obst. & Gyn.) Univ. Aberd.

JANDU, Jaspal Jandu and Partners, 274 Keighley Road, Frizinghall, Bradford BD9 4LH Tel: 01274 495577 Fax: 01274 480703 — MB ChB 1982 Dundee.

***JANDU, Manjinderpal Kaur** 34 Perth Avenue, Bradford BD2 1EE — MB ChB 1998 Birm.

JANDU, Manjit Singh Briarwood Medical Centre, 514 Blackpool Road, Ashton-on-Ribble, Preston PR2 1HY Tel: 01772 726186 Fax: 01772 768823 — MB ChB 1984 Leic.; DRCOG 1987.

JANDZIOL, Andrzej Krzysztof Anaesthetic Department, Addenbrooke's Hospital, Hills Road, Cambridge CB2 2QQ Tel: 01223 245151; 111 Western Boulevard, Nottingham NG8 3NX — MB ChB 1992 Birm. Specialist Regist. (Anaesth.) Addenbrooke's Hosp. Camb.

JANE, Mr Michael John Royal Liverpool University Hospital, Prescot St., Liverpool L7 8XP Tel: 0151 706 2000 Fax: 0151 706 5806; 28 Rodney Street, Liverpool L1 2TQ Tel: 0151 709 8160 Fax: 0151 709 1655 — MB ChB 1982 Manch.; MChOrth Liverp. 1989; BSc (Med. Sci.) St. And. 1979; FRCS (Orth.) 1994; FRCS Ed. 1986. Cons. Orthop. Surg. Roy. Liverp. & BRd.green Univ. Hosps. NHS Trust. Socs: Fell. BOA; Brit. Orthop. Oncol. Soc. Prev: Sen. Regist. (Orthop. Surg.) Roy. Liverp. Univ. Hosp.; Sen. Regist. (Orthop. Oncol.) Birm. Roy. Orthop. Hosp.; Clin. Lect. (Orthop. Surg.) Roy. Liverp. Univ. Hosp.

JANES, David Peter 1 Cornfield Close, Seaford BN25 1SN — MB BS 1989 Lond.

JANES, Emma Sarah Flat 4, 364 Ormeau Road, Belfast BT7 3HW — MB BCh 1998 Belf.; MB BCh Belf 1998.

JANES, Eric Frank 48 Langbaugh Road, Hutton Rudby, Yarm TS15 0HL — MB ChB 1982 Dundee. SHO (Anaesth.) N. Gen. Hosp. Sheff. Prev: SHO (Gen. Med.) Doncaster Roy. Infirm.

JANES, Jayne Susan 3 The Lords, Crown Hill, Seaford BN25 2XJ Tel: 01323 892594 — MB BS 1969 Lond.; DA Eng. 1971. (Univ. Coll. Hosp.) Staff Grade Community Paediat. S. Downs Health Trust. Prev: Clin. Med. Off. Newc. City Health Trust; Clin. Med. Off. Norwich Health Dist & W. Essex HA; SHO (Anaesth.) & Ho. Surg. Qu. Vict. Hosp. E. Grinstead.

JANES, Joanne Louise 51 Jerome Road, Walsall WS2 9SZ — MB BCh 1991 Wales.

JANES, Jonathan Marcus Eli Lilly & Co., Erlwood Manor, Sunninghill Road, Windlesham GU20 6PH Tel: 01276 853321 Fax: 01276 853378 Email: jj@lilly.com; Gable Cottage, 49 Lockeridge, Marlborough SN8 4EL — MB BCh 1988 Wales; BSc Lond. 1983; MRCP (UK) 1992. Clin. Research Phys.

JANES, Nancy Claire (retired) The Stables, 22 White St., West Lavington, Devizes SN10 4LP Tel: 01380 813648 — MB BS 1948 Lond.; MRCS Eng. LRCP Lond. 1948. Prev: Sen. Med. Off. Borehamwood. St. Albans & Edgware Gen. Hosp. Family Plann. clinics.

JANES, Samuel McAlpine 9 Ridley Avenue, Ealing, London W13 9XW — MB BS 1992 Lond.; BSc Imperial Coll. 1991. (Char. Cross & Westm. Med. Sch.) Regist. (Respirat. Med.) Hammersmith Hosp. Socs: RCP. Prev: SHO (Med.) St. Mary's Hosp. Lond.

JANES, Sarah Lisbeth Dept. of Haematology, St Richard's Hospital, Chichester PO19 4SE; Southmere Farmhouse, 20 Langstone Rd, Havant PO9 1QX — MD 1994 Camb.; MB BChir Camb. 1983; MA Camb. 1985, MD 1994; MRCP (UK) 1985; MRCPath 1996. Cons. Haemat. St. Richard's Hosp.

JANETOS, Peter John (retired) 73 Duke Street, Grosvenor Square, London W1K 5NZ Tel: 020 7493 1427 — MD 1956 Toronto; MSc (Occupat. Med.) Lond. 1974; BA Univ. West. Ontario 1949; Lic. Nova Scotia Med. Bd. 1964; Lic. Ontario Med. Bd. 1970; DIH Eng. 1974; DPH Lond. 1966.

JANI, Bhavdeep Rameshchandra 20 St Angela Road, Heath, Cardiff CF14 4DN — MB BCh 1981 Wales; DCH RCP Lond. 1983; DRCOG 1984. SHO (Paediat.) Qu. Eliz. Hosp. Childr. Lond.

JANI, Chandravadan Maganlal 4 Holly Drive, Walton-on-The - Hill, Stafford ST17 0NH — MB BS 1951 Lond.; BSc (Hons.) Bombay 1944; DPM Eng. 1975.

JANI, Fiona Mary 33 Rope Street, Swedish Quay's, Rotherhithe, London SE16 7TE Tel: 020 7231 3347 — MB BS 1988 Lond.; MRCP (UK) 1992. Regist. (Renal) Guy's Hosp. Lond. Prev: Regist. (Gen. Med.) Greenwich Dist. Hosp. Lond.

JANI, Jagat Department of Paediatrics, University Hospital of Harplepool, Holdforth Road, Hartlepool TS24 9AH Tel: 01429 522091 Fax: 01429 522738 Email: jagect.jani@nth.northy.nhs.uk; 2 Riverston Close, Hartlepool TS26 0PY Tel: 01429 861113 Email: jagect.jani@nth.northy.nhs.uk — MB BS 1977 Gujarat; MD Gujarat 1979; MRCP (UK) 1985; DCH RCP Lond. 1982. Cons. Paediat. Univ. Hosp. of Hartlepool. Socs: Brit. Med. Assn.; Indian Med. Assn.

JANI, Janmashanker J 16 Jasper Close, Danescourt, Llandaff, Cardiff CF5 2RX — MB BS 1967 Gujarat; DMRT Eng. 1974. (B.J. Med. Coll. Ahmedabad)

JANI, Kiran Department of Anaesthesia, E&N NHS Trust, Coreys Mill Lane, Stevenage SG1 4AB Tel: 01438 781086 Fax: 01438 781302 Email: j4jani@bigfoot.com — MB BCh 1980 Wales; FRCA 1984. (Welsh Nat. Sch. Med.) Cons. Anaesth. E. & N. Herts NHS Trust, Stevenage. Socs: Soc. Intravenous Anaesth. (Counc. Mem.); Obst. Anaesth.s Assn.; Anaesthetic Research Soc. Prev: Lect. Univ. Calgary Alberta, Canada; Sen. Regist. (Anaesth.) E. Anglian Region Train. Scheme Camb. & Kings Lynn; Regist. (Anaesth.) Hammersmith Hosp. Lond.

JANI, Mr Milind Rasiklal 111 Upper Elmers End Road, Beckenham BR3 3QX Tel: 01273 735244 — MB BS 1978 Gujarat; FRCS Ed. 1983; Dip. Urol. Lond. 1986.

JANI, Mr Piyush 33 Rope Street, Swedish Quays, Rotherhithe, London SE16 7TE Tel: 020 7231 3347 — MB BS 1987 Lond.; BDS Lond. 1979; FRCS Eng. 1993. SR Roy. Marsden; Cons. ENT (Head & Neck Surg.) Addenbrooke's Camb. Prev: Regist. (ENT) Guy's Hosp. Lond.; Sen. Regist. (ENT) Roy. Nat. Throat, Nose & Ear Hosp., Hosp. for Childr. Lond. & Addenbrooke's Hosp. Camb.

JANIK, Antoni Jerzy High Street Surgery, South Milford, Leeds LS25 5AA Tel: 01977 682202 Fax: 01977 681628; 100 Main Street, Monk Fryston, Leeds LS25 5DU — MB ChB 1974 Manch.

JANIKIEWICZ, Stefan Maria Joseph Stanislaus Moreton Health Clinic, 8-10 Chadwick Street, Wirral CH46 7XA Tel: 0151 677 1207 Fax: 0151 604 0372 — MB ChB 1972 Glas.; MRCGP 1976; DObst RCOG 1974 Cert FPA 1975.

JANIKOUN, Mr Samuel Hirsch, OBE, Brigadier late RAMC Retd. 12 Roehampton Court, Queen's Ride, London SW13 0HU Tel: 020 8878 6889 — MRCS Eng. LRCP Lond. 1937; FRCS Eng. 1950. Prof. Mil. Surg. (RCS) 1967-69. Socs: Med. Soc. Lond. (Ex. Counc.lor). Prev: QHS; Cons. Surg. & Brigadier RAMC; Med. Off. (Limb Surg.) Roehampton.

JANIKOUN, Sarah Gay 143 Harley Street, London W1G 6BH Tel: 020 7935 0886 Fax: 020 7486 1956; 74 Tulse Hill, London SW2 2PT Tel: 020 8678 1520 Email: sarah.janikoun@dial.pipex.com — MB BS 1980 Lond.; MCOphth 1988; DO RCS Eng. 1985. Assoc. Specialist Guy's & St. Thos. Trust. Prev: Contact Lens Ophth. Moorfields & Chelsea & W.m. Hosps.

JANIS, Nichola Benedicte Alton Street Surgery, Alton Street, Ross-on-Wye HR9 5AB Tel: 01989 563646 Fax: 01989 769438 — MB BS 1987 Lond.

JANJUA, Fatima Costa Bedford Hospital, North Wing, 3 Kimbolton Road, Bedford MK40 2NU — Lic Med 1979 Oporto; T(M) (Paediat.) 1994.

JANKELOWITZ, Gary Sean 78 Waldren Close, Poole BH15 1XS — MB BCh 1991 Witwatersrand.

JANKOWSKA, Agnieszka Monika 2 Rogate House, Muir Road, London E5 8QR — MB BS 1991 Lond.

JANKOWSKA, Petra Jana 6 Hayward Road, Totteridge, London N20 0HA — MB BS 1996 Lond.

JANKOWSKI, Professor Janusz Antoni Zygmunt Dept of Medicine, University Hospital, Birmingham B15 2TH Tel: 0121 427 1311 Ext: 3378 Fax: 0121 627 2384 Email: j.jankowski@bham.ac.uk — FRCP Lond. 2000; MB ChB Glas. 1983; MRCP (UK) 1987; MD (Dundee) 1995; PhD (Lond.) 1996; FRCP Ed 1999. Prof. (Cons. Gasteroenterology) Univ. of B/ham. Prev: Asst. Prof. in Med., Univ. of Calif.; Clin. Scientist Univ. of Lond.

JANKOWSKI, Raymond Frank 60 Harford Drive, Watford WD17 3DG — MB ChB 1983 Glas.

JANKOWSKI, Stanislaw Kazimierz Charing Cross Hospital, Fulham Palace Road, London W6 8RF Tel: 020 8269 2444; 92 Banstead Road South, Sutton SM2 5LH — MB BS 1984 Lond.; BSc (Hons.) Lond. 1981, MB BS 1984; MRCP (UK) 1989; FCAnaesth 1991. Regist. (Anaesth.) Char. Cross Hosp. Lond.

JANKOWSKI, Stefan Leonard 47 Ascot Road, Stafford ST17 0AQ — MB ChB 1992 Leeds.

JANMOHAMED, Karim Mohamedali Ismail Vanburgh Group Practice, Vanburgh Hill Health Centre, Vanburgh Hill, Greenwich, London SE10 9HQ Tel: 020 8312 6095 Fax: 020 8293 1226; 36 Oakcroft Road, Lewisham, London SE13 7ED Tel: 020 8318 9131 Fax: 020 8244 9527 Email: grabajan@diron.co.uk — MB BS 1988 Lond.; DRCOG 1991; MRCGP 1997. (Middlx. Hosp.) Med. Dir. Grabadocc Qu. ELiz. Hosp. Lond. Socs: W Kent M-C Soc.

JANMOHAMED, Riaz Mohamedali Ismail 13 Ford End, Denham Village, Uxbridge UB9 5AL Tel: 01895 832307 Fax: 01895 832307; 52 Abbey Gardens, Fulham, London W6 8QR Tel: 020 7381 8474 — MB BS 1981 Lond.; MRCP (UK). (Middlx.) Cons. Haemat. Hillingdon Hosp. Prev: Sen. Regist. King's Coll. Hosp. Lond. & Lewisham Hosp.; Research Regist. (Haemat.) E. Birm. Hosp.

JANMOHAMED, Salim Gulamhusein Dept of Diabetes & Endocrinology, Salisbury District Hospital, Salisbury SP2 8BJ Tel: 01722 336262 Email: salimj@hotmail.com — MB BS 1988 Lond.; MB BS (Hons.) Lond. 1988; BSc (Pharmacol.) Lond. 1985; MRCP (UK) 1991. (Univ. Coll. Hosp. Lond.) Cons. Phys. Endocrinol., Diabetes, Gen. Med. Salisbury Dist. Hosp. Socs: Soc. Endocrinol.; Roy. Soc. Med.; Brit. Diabetic Assn. Prev: Lect. (Med.) Roy. Lond. NHS Trust; Research Regist. (Endocrinol.) Roy. Postgrad. Med. Sch. Lond.; Hon Sen. Regist. Roy. Lond. NHS Trust.

JANNOUN, Usamah 1 White House Farm Cottages, Brantridge Lane, Balcombe, Haywards Heath RH17 6JP — State Exam Med 1991 Dusseldorf.

JANOSI, Marianne (retired) Medical Adviser, Voluntary Services Overseas (VSO), 317 Putney Bridge Road, London SW15 2PN Tel: 020 8780 2266 — MB BS 1961 Lond.; MRCP (U.K.) 1970.

JANOSI, Marianne 17 Straffan Lodge, 1 Belsize Grove, London NW3 4XE — MB, BS Lond. 1961; MRCP 1970 UK. (St. Bart.) Socs: Brit. Med. Assn.; Soc. of Occupat.al Med.; Roy. Soc. of Trop. Med. & Hyg.

JANOSSY, George 23 Whitehall Road, Harrow HA1 3AL Tel: 020 8864 1606 — MD 1964 Budapest; PhD (Immunol.) Lond. 1975, DSc (Immunol.) 1984; FRCPath 1996, MRCPath 1979. (Med. Sch. Budapest) Prof. & Hon. Cons. Immunol. Roy. Free Hosp. Sch. Med. Lond.

JANOSSY, Katherine Monica 23 Whitehall Road, Harrow HA1 3AL — MB ChB 1998 Ed.; MB ChB Ed 1998.

JANOTA, Ivan (retired) 12 Deepdene Road, London SE5 8EG Tel: 020 7733 1024 — MB BS 1955 Lond.; MRCS Eng. LRCP Lond. 1955; FRCPath 1976, M 1964. Prev: Hon. Sen. Lect. & Cons. Neuropath. Inst. Psychiat. Maudsley & Bethlem Roy. Hosps.

***JANOUSEK, Eric Gregory** Juniper House, 5A Woodland Way, Canterbury CT2 7LS — MB BS 1996 Lond.; BSc Hons. Lond. 1993.

JANSE VAN RENSBURG, Marelna 92 Leathermarket Court, London SE1 3HT — MB ChB 1995 Stellenbosch.

JANSE VAN VUUREN, Nicholas 9 Sandstone Rise, Chatham ME5 9DH — MB ChB 1983 Pretoria.

JANSEN, Albertine 44 Dale Street, Chiswick, London W4 2BL Tel: 020 8747 3228 — Artsexamen 1991 Groningen.

JANSEN, Candace April Marie Hoyland House Surgery, Hoyland House, Gyde Road, Painswick, Stroud GL6 6RD Tel: 01452 812545 — MB BS 1978 Lond.; DRCOG 1984; DA (UK) 1982.

JANSEN, Karl Louis Rewi South london And Maudsley NHS Trust, The Chaucer Centre, 13 Ann Moss Way, London SE16 2TH Tel: 020 7231 4578 Fax: 020 7237 3526 Email: k@btinternet.com; 8 Elsworthy Terrace, Primrose Hill, London NW3 3DR Tel: 04682 181 30 — MB ChB 1985 Otago; DPhil Oxf. 1993; MMedSci Auckland 1989; MRC Psych 1995. Regist. (Psychiat.) Maudsley Hosp. Lond. Socs: Res. Fell. G. Coll. Oxf.; Fell. MRC NZ.; MRCPsych.

JANSEN, Marlies Rosalie Gabrielle St Clements Hospital, Foxhall Rd, Ipswich IP3 8LS Tel: 01473 715111; Rasa Sayang, Red House Farm Lane, Bawdsey, Woodbridge IP12 3AN Tel: 01394 410024 Email: jans@netcomuk.co.uk — Artsexamen 1987 Leiden; DA 1996. GP Regist. Suff. Socs: BMA; Med. Protec. Soc. Prev: SHO (Cas. & Anaesth.) Ipswich; SHO (Med.) N.ampton.

JANSON, William Richard Hawthorn Medical Centre, May Close, Swindon SN2 1UU Tel: 01793 536541 Fax: 01793 421049 — MB ChB 1978 Manch.; MRCGP 1982.

JANSSEN, Alfred 10 Tuckfield House, Residential Village, Bovemoors Lane, Exeter EX2 5DS — MD 1992 Louvain.

JANSSEN, John-Casimir Joseph Marie Ignatius 16 Biscay Road, London W6 8JN — MB BS 1993 Lond.

JANSSENS, Mr Mark 10 Toprgormack, Beauly IV4 7AQ — MB ChB 1979 Aberd.; FRCS Ed. 1983.

JANULEWICZ, Michael Andrew Leeds Student Medical Practice, 4 Blenheim Court Walk, Leeds LS2 9AE Tel: 0113 295 4488 — MB BS 1987 Lond.; MRCGP 1991; DRCOG 1990.

JANUS, Fred (retired) Old Stables, School Lane, Ollerton, Knutsford WA16 8SG Tel: 01565 651901 — BSc Manch. 1931, MD 1940, MB ChB 1934; MRCS Eng. LRCP Lond. 1934. Prev: Hon. Cons. Surg. Manch. Roy. Eye Hosp.

JANUSZKIEWICZ, Janek Stefan 28 St James' Court, Beckett St., Leeds LS9 7TF — MB ChB 1987 Auckland.

JANVRIN, John Patrick Pavilion, Roundhurst, Haslemere GU27 3BN Tel: 0208 967 5981 Fax: 0208 370 9043 — MRCS Eng. LRCP Lond. 1945; MRCGP 1962. (Middlx.) Med. Off. St. Dunstan's. Prev: Clin. Asst. Dept. Dermat. Roy. N.. Hosp.; ENT Ho. Surg. Middlx. Hosp.; Ho. Phys. Mt. Vernon Hosp. N.wood.

JANVRIN, Mr Simon Benest Broxmead Lodge, Broxmead Lane, Cuckfield, Haywards Heath RH17 5JH Tel: 01444 417955 — MB BS 1968 Lond.; MS Lond. 1980, MB BS 1968; FRCS Eng. 1973; MFOM RCP Lond. 1995; DAvMed FOM RCP Lond. 1991. (Guy's Hosp.) Chief Med. Off. Civil. Aviat. Auth. Prev: Sen. Med. Off. Civil Aviat. Auth.; Cons. Surg. Crawley & Horsham Hosps.; Sen. Regist. (Surg.) St. Bart. Hosp. Lond.

JAP-A-JOE, Humphrey Kenneth Countess of Chester Hospital, Liverpool Road, Chester CH2 1BQ — Artsexamen 1995 Free U Amsterdam; Artsexamen Free Univ Amsterdam 1995.

JAPPY, Mrs Mary Edgar (retired) 84 Pilrig Street, Edinburgh EH6 5AS — MB ChB 1944 Glas.; DPH Glas. 1952. Prev: Dep. M.O.H. for Co.

JAQUES, Audrey Ena 47 Childwall Priory Road, Liverpool L16 7PA — MB ChB 1955 Liverp.; Regist. Radiother. Dept. St. Geo. Hosp. Lond. Prev: Sen. Ho. Off. St. Bart. Hosp. Lond. & Walton Hosp. Liverp.; Ho. Surg. & Ho. Phys. Liverp. Roy. Infirm.

JAQUES, Mr Bryon Charles 25 Merrylee Road, Newlands, Glasgow G43 2SH Tel: 0141 633 5844 — MB ChB 1987 Glas.; FRCS Glas. 1992.

JAQUES, Roderick David Hoyland House Clinic, The Winfield Hospital, Tewkesbury Rd, Glouiester GL2 9WH Tel: 01452 331111 Fax: 01452 331200; Broughton, Moorend Rd, Cheltenham GL53 7DJ — MB BS 1984 Lond.; MRCGP 1989; Dip. Sports Med. Lond 1990; DRCOG 1988. (Middlx. Hosp.) Sports Physcian. Sports Med. English Inst. of Sport. Bath Univ.; Med. Adviser Brit. Triathlon Assn.; Mem. Internat. Triathlon Union Med. Comm.; Med. Off. Brit. Olympic Med. Centre. Socs: BMA; Brit. Assn. Sports Med. (Chairm. SW Region); (Med. Comm.) Brit. Olympic Assn. Prev: 1998 Malaysia Commonw. Games Engl. Team Doctor; 1996 Atlanta Olympics GB Team Doctor / 2000 Olympics GB Team Doctor.

***JAQUES, Wendy Anne** Barnsley District Gen Hospital, Gawber Road, Barnesly, Barnsley S75 2PS Tel: 01226 730000 — MB ChB 1997 Sheff.

JARAM, Irena Abbey Medical Centre, 63 Central Avenue, Beeston, Nottingham NG9 2QP Tel: 0115 925 0862 Fax: 0115 922 0522 — LRCP LRCS 1991 Ed.; MD Zagreb 1982; LRCP LRCS Ed. LRCPS Glas. 1991.

JARDINE, Alan George 10 Cleveden Drive, Glasgow G12 0SE Tel: 0141 357 0743; Department of Medicine and Therapeutics, Western Infirmary, Glasgow G11 6NT Tel: 0141 211 2405 Fax: 0141 211 1763 Email: a.g.jardine@clinmed.gla.ac.uk — MB ChB 1984 Glas.; BSc (Hons.) Glas. 1981, MD 1991; MB ChB (Commend.) Glas. 1984; MRCP (UK) 1987. Sen. Lect. (Med.) Cons. (Nephrol.). Prev: Lect. (Med.) W.ern Infirm. Glas.; Regist. (Renal Med.) W.. Infirm. Glas.; Clin. Scientist MRC Blood Pressure Unit Glas.

JARDINE, Andrew David Oaklands, 66 Stanton Lane, Stanton on The Wolds, Nottingham NG12 5BG — MB ChB 1971 Birm.; FFA RCS Eng. 1975.

JARDINE, Annette Hillegonda 14 Alexandra Road, Clifton, Bristol BS8 2DD Email: annettejardine@compuserve.com — MB ChB 1981 Birm.; FRCS Ed. 1993 (ENT); FRCS Ed. 1985; FRC8 ORL1998. (Birm.) Cons. Ocularyngologist, Roy. United Hosp., Bath. Prev: Fell.ship in Paediatric OtoLaryngol., The Childr.'s Hosp., W.mead, Sydney.

JARDINE, Charles Kenneth Herbert Doune Health Centre, Castlehill, Doune FK16 6DR Tel: 01786 841213 — BSc (Hons.) Dund 1982, MB ChB 1986; MRCGP 1991; DCH RCPS Glas. 1988; DRCOG 1988; FRCGP 1998. Clin. Asst. Dept Diabetes Stirling Roy. Infirm. Socs: BMA; Brit. Soc. Med. & Dent. Hypn. Prev: SHO (O & G, Paediat. & Gen. Med.) Stirling Roy. Infirm.; SHO (Psychiat.) Bellsdyke Hosp. Larbert.

JARDINE, Lady Claire Vyvien (Griffith) Rendcomb Surgery, Cirencester GL7 7EY — MB BS 1983 Lond.; MRCGP 1991; DFFP 1993; DCH RCP Lond. 1987; DRCOG 1987. (UCHMS University London) GP Retainer Rendcomb Surg., Cirencester. Socs: BMA. Prev: Clin. Asst. in Rehabil. Cirencester Hosp. Cirencester; GP Asst.

JARDINE, Donald Edgar The Lane, Cawdor, Nairn IV12 5XP Tel: 01667 404729 — MB ChB Glas. 1952.

JARDINE, George Wyllie Howie Kilmuir, 14 Etterby Scaur, Carlisle CA3 9NX Tel: 01228 521691 — MB ChB Ed. 1954; DMRT 1962; FRCR 1975; FFR 1968. Prev: Cons. (Radiother. & Oncol.) N.. RHA & Hon. Clin. Lect. (Radiother.)Univ. Newc.; Cons. Radiother. Highland HB & Hon. Sen. Clin. Lect. (Radiother.) Univ. Aberd.

JARDINE, Joanne Violet 72 Kingsthorne Park, Hunts Cross, Liverpool L25 0QS Tel: 0151 486 6864 — MB ChB 1997 Liverp. Basic Surg. Train. Rotat.; SHO. Gen. Surg. Arrowe Pk. Hosp.Wirral. Prev: SHO Orthop.Arrowe Pk..hosp.Wirral; PRHO Aintree.Hosp.Liverp.

JARDINE, Kirsty Lynda 11 Primleypark Drive, Alwoodley, Leeds LS17 7LP — MB ChB 1996 Liverp.

JARDINE, Mary Anne Whitstable Health Centre, Harbour Street, Whitstable CT5 1BZ Tel: 01277 263033 Fax: 01277 771474; 2 Dene Cottages, Adisham Road, Wingham, Canterbury CT3 1NU Tel: 01227 721967 — MB BS 1987 Lond. GP; Clin. Med. Off. Family Plann. Clinic.

JARDINE, Mary Yvonne Trinity Ward, Field Head, Ouchthorpe Lane, Wakefield WF1 3SP — MB ChB 1973 Ed.; BSc (Hons.) Ed. 1970, MB ChB 1973; MRCPsych 1977; DPM Leeds 1976. Cons. Psychiat. Pontefract Gen. Infirm.

JARDINE, Michelle Angela Ingledene, Lower Grove Common, Sellack, Ross-on-Wye HR9 6NA — BChir 1997 Camb.

JARDINE, Philip Edward Childrens Centre, Frenchay Hospital, Bristol Tel: 0117 975 3870 Email: philip.jardine@bristol.ac.uk — MB ChB 1981 Birm.; MRCP (UK) 1985; MRCGP 1989; DCH RCP Lond. 1986; MD 1997. (Birmingham) Cons. Paediat. Neurol. Bristol Roy. Hosp. for Sick Childr. & Frenchay Hosp. Bristol.

JARDINE, Sheena Law Wellwynd Surgery, Airdrie Health Centre, Airdrie ML6 0JU Tel: 01236 769333; King's Mile, Killearn, Glasgow G63 9PZ Tel: 01360 550363 — MB ChB 1968 Glas.; MFFP 1993. (Glas.) Gen. Practitioner, Wellwynd Pract., Airdrie Health Centre, Airdrie; Clin. Research Fell., Osteogym Unit, Stobhill Hosp. & W.. Infirm., Glas. Prev: Clin. Asst. in Diabetes, Monklands Hosp., Airdrie.

JARDINE-BROWN, Mr Colin Peter Yewbank House, Ibworth, Tadley RG26 5TJ Tel: 01256 850435 — MB BS 1965 Lond.; FRCS Eng. 1972; FRCS Ed. 1971; MRCS Eng. LRCP Lond. 1965; FRCOG 1986, M 1974. (Westm.) Cons. O & G N. Hants. Hosps. NHS Trust. Socs: SWOGS; BSCCP; Spencer Wells Soc. Prev: Cons. O & G Basingstoke Dist. Hosp.; Sen. Regist. (O & G) Cambs. AHA (T) & St. Mary's Hosp. Lond.; SHO Rotat. (Surg.) W.m. Hosp.

JARDINE-BROWN, Karin Paediatric Department, G Floor, Loddon Trust, North Hampshire Hospital, Basingstoke RG26 5TJ; Yew Bank House, Ibworth, Basingstoke RG26 5TJ — MB BS Lond. 1965. (Westm.) Staff Grade (Community Child Health) Loddon Trust N. Hants. Hosp. Socs: Brit. Assn. Community Drs in Audiol.; Brit. Paediat. Assn.; BMA. Prev: Clin. Med. Off. Hants. AHA; Ho. Surg. St. Stephen's Hosp. Fulham; Ho. Phys. Roy. Hants. Co. Hosp. Winchester.

JARDINE-BROWN, Timothy The Surgery, Brede Lane, Sedlescombe, Battle TN33 0PW Tel: 01424 870225; John & Mary W., Brede, Rye TN31 6EJ Tel: 01424 882573 — MB Camb. 1965, BChir 1964; Dip. Med. Acupunct. (BMAS 1997). (Camb. & Westm.) Socs: Brit. Med. Acupunct. Soc.; Osler Soc.; Anglo-French Med. Soc. Prev: Sen. Med. Off. RePub. of Kiribati.

JAREONSETTASIN, Teerakiat Department of Child & Adolescent Psychiatry, Royal Free Hospital, Pond St., London NW3 2QG — MD 1986 Chulalongkorn, Thailand; MRCPsych 1992.

JARI, Mr Sanjiv 36 Sandhurst Road, Didsbury, Manchester M20 5LR Email: sanjjari@hotmail.com — MB ChB 1990 Manch.; BSc (Hons.) Anat. Manch. 1987; FRCS Eng. 1994. (Manch. Med. Sch.) Specialist Regist. (Orthop. Surg.) Roy. Preston Hosp. Socs: Assoc. Mem. BOA; Brit. Orthop. Train. Assn.; Brit. Orthop. Sports Trauma Assn. Prev: Specialist Regist. (Orthop.) Blackburn Roy. Infirm.; Regist. (Orthop.) Burnley Gen. Hosp.; Regist. (Orthop. Surg.) Wrightington Hosp. Wigan.

JARIWALA, Sanjay Shantiniketan, 483 Winchester Road, Southampton SO16 7EH Tel: 01865 727320 Fax: 01865 727320 Email: sanj8@aol.com — BChir 1995 Camb.; MB 1995, MA 1997. (Cambridge) GP Regist. Prev: SHO (O & G) John Radcliffe Hosp. Oxf.

JARIWALLA, Asgarali 3 Eton Court, White Lodge Close, Sevenoaks TN13 3BF — MB BCh 1971 Wales; MRCP (UK) 1975. (Cardiff) Cons. Phys. Orpington, FarnBoro., Sevenoaks & Bromley Hosps.; Cons. (Phys.) Qu. Mary's Sidcup NHS Trust. Prev: Cons. Phys. (Gen. Med.) Bromley & Tun Wells Health Auth.; Sen. Regist. (Gen. & Thoracic Med.) S. Glam. (T) & Gwent AHAs; Regist. (Gen. Med.) Prof.ial Unit Manch. Roy. infirm.

JARJIS, Hilal Abdulla Badsley Moor Lane Surgery, 292 Badsley Moor Lane, Rotherham S65 2QW — MB ChB 1971 Mosul; MMedSci Sheff. 1984; DGM RCP Lond. 1985. GP Rotherham S. Yorks. Prev: Trainee GP Sheff. VTS.; Regist./SHO (Geriat. Med.) Rotherham Dist. Gen. Hosp.; Research Asst. Dept. Med. (Subdiv. Gastroenterol. & Diabetes) Univ. Sheff.

JARMAN, Arthur Sebastian (retired) Ty Bryn, Brynteg, Abersychan, Pontypool NP4 7BG Tel: 01495 772761 — MB BS 1935 Durh.; FRCGP 1975. Prev: Mem. Hon. Staff. Pontypool & Dist. Gen. Hosp.

JARMAN, Professor Sir Brian, OBE Lisson Grove Health Centre, Gateforth St, London NW8 8EG Tel: 020 7262 1366 Fax: 020 7258 1943; 62 Aberdare Gardens, London NW6 3QD Tel: 020 7624 5502 — MB BS 1969 Lond.; MA Camb. 1957; PhD Lond. 1960, MB BS (Hons. Med.) 1969; FRCP Lond. 1988; MRCP (UK) 1971; FRCGP (Distinc.) 1983, M 1978; DIC 1957. (St. Mary's) Prof. Primary Health Care St. Mary's Hosp. Lond. Socs: Director Med. Sickness Soc.; Roy. Coll. Gen. Pract.; Soc. Psychosom. Research. Prev: Ho. Phys. St. Mary's Hosp. Lond.; Resid. & Clin. Fell. Beth Israel Hosp. Harvard Univ. Boston, USA.

JARMAN, Christopher Michael Brittain Clare House, St. George's Hospital, Blackshaw Road, London SW17 0QT — MRCS Eng. LRCP Lond. 1965; MPhil (Psychiat.) Lond. 1972; MA (Hons.), BM BCh Oxf. 1965; MRCPsych 1973. (St. Thos.) Cons. Springfield Hosp. Lond.; Cons. & Hon. Sen. Lect. St. Geo. Hosp. Lond. Prev: Sen. Regist. Maudsley Hosp. Lond.; SHO St. Thos. Hosp. Lond.; Sen. Resid. Amer. Hosp. of Paris.

JARMAN, David Michael Wallingford Medical Practice, Reading Road, Wallingford OX10 9DU Tel: 01491 835577 Fax: 01491 824034; 3 Wallingford Road, Cholsey, Wallingford OX10 9LQ Tel: 01491 201623 Email: mike.jarman@virgin.net — MRCS Eng. LRCP Lond. 1971; BSc (Special Anat.) Lond. 1968, MB BS 1971; MRCS Eng. LRCP Lond. (Begley Prize) 1971; MRCGP 1977; DObst RCOG 1975. (Lond. Hosp.) Prev: Ho. Phys., Ho. Surg. & SHO (Orthop. & Accid. Dept.) Barnet Gen. Hosp.

JARMAN, Paul Richard National Hospital for Neurology & Neurosurgery, Queen Square, London WC1N 3BG Tel: 0207 837 3611 Email: paul.jarman@uclh.org — MB BS 1989 (Hons.) (Medicine, Surgery, Pharmacology, Pathology) Lond.; BA (Hons.) Oxf. 1986; MRCP (UK) 1992; PhD 1999. Cons. NeUrol., Nat. Hosp. for Neurol. & Neurosurg. Lond.; Cons. NeUrol., Homerton Hosp. and Univ. Coll. Hosps. Lond.

JARMAN, Peter Donald Charles (retired) Bratton Cottage, King Edward Road, Minehead TA24 5JB Tel: 01643 703931 Fax: 01643 703931 Email: petejarman@aol.com — MB BS 1954 Lond.; MRCS Eng. LRCP Lond. 1954; DObst RCOG 1956. Prev: Ho. Phys. & O & G Ho. Surg. Univ. Coll. Hosp.

JARMAN, Robert David 104 Stainburn Crescent, Leeds LS17 6NG — MB BS 1994 Newc.

JARMAN, Ruth Anne Bishop's Garth, 38 Main St., Bishop Wilton, York YO42 1RU — MB ChB 1992 Sheff.

JARMAN, Susan Joy Circuit Lane Surgery, 53 Circuit Lane, Reading RG30 3AN Tel: 0118 958 2537 Fax: 0118 957 6115; 3 Withy Close, Tilehurst, Reading RG31 4SQ — MB BCh 1979 Wales; MRCP (UK) 1983; MRCGP 1986; DRCOG 1986; DCH RCP Lond. 1982. Prev: Trainee GP Sunninghill VTS; Regist. (Paediat.) Heatherwood Hosp. Ascot.

JARMULOWICZ, Michael Romuald Department of Histopathology, Royal Free Hospital, Pond St., London NW3 2QG Tel: 020 7794 0500 Fax: 020 7435 3289 Email: michael.jarmulowicz@rfh.nthames.nhs.uk; 6 St. Andrews Road, Willesden Green, London NW10 2QS Tel: 020 8459 8572 Email: jarmulowicz@doctors.org.uk — MB BS 1981 Lond.; BSc Lond. 1976; FRCPath 2000. Cons. Dept. Histopath. Roy. Free Hosp. Lond.; Clin. Head of Serv. in Path. Socs: BMA; Path. Soc.; Master Guild Catholic Doctors. Prev: Path. Dept. Whittington Hosp. Lond. & RN Hosp. Haslar; Med. Off. HMS Renown (Port).

JARON, Ann Elizabeth Gieszczykiewicz Sherwood House Medical Practice, 9 Sandon Road, Edgbaston, Birmingham B67 8DP Tel: 0121 420 0100 Fax: 0121 420 0107; 272 Galton Road, Smethwick B67 5JL Tel: 0121 429 9216 — MB ChB 1983 Manch.; BSc St. And. 1980; MRCGP 1989.

JARON, Stefania Janina (retired) 54 Longrood Road, Bilton, Rugby CV22 7RE Tel: 01788 815530 — MRCS Eng. LRCP Lond. 1954. Prev: Ho. Phys. (Paediat.) St. Luke's Hosp. Bradford.

JAROSZ, Jozef Marek 73B Argyle Road, London W13 0LY — MB BChir 1986 Camb.; MA Camb. 1987, MB BChir 1986; MRCP (UK) 1989. Socs: BMA; Fell. Roy. Soc. Med.

JAROSZ, Krystyna Danuta 61 Melton Gardens, Edwalton, Nottingham NG12 4BJ — MB ChB 1987 Liverp.; BSc Liverp. 1984; MRCGP 1992; DRCOG 1990. Trainee GP Ormskirk VTS.

JARRAMS, John William Parker (retired) 73 Linden Lea, Compton, Wolverhampton WV3 8BQ — MB ChB 1954 Birm. Prev: Ho. Surg. Gen. Hosp. Birm.

JARRAMS, Richard Guy Pinfold Health Centre, Field, Bloxwich, Walsall WS3 3JP Fax: 01922 775132; 19 Highbury Road, Streetly, Sutton Coldfield B74 4TF — MRCS Eng. LRCP Lond. 1975; DRCOG 1977.

JARRATT, Christine Dewar (retired) Hillcroft, Vicarage Lane, Skirlaugh, Hull HU11 5HE Tel: 01964 562685 Fax: 01964 562685 Email: pgjarratt@talk21.com — MB ChB Manch. 1968; MFFP 1994; DCH RCPS Glas. 1971; DObst RCOG 1970. Prev: SCMO Hull & Holderness Community Health Trust.

JARRATT, David (retired) The Forum Health Centre, 1A Farren Road, Coventry CV2 5EP Tel: 01203 455402 Fax: 01203 636518 — MB ChB 1957 Leeds; DObst RCOG 1959. Prev: GP Coventry.

JARRATT, Ernest Walter (retired) 29 The Parade, Greatstone, New Romney TN28 8SU Tel: 01797 363318 — MRCS Eng. LRCP Lond. 1940; DLO Eng. 1947. Prev: Allergist ENT Dept. King's Coll. Hosp.

JARRATT, George (retired) The Garden Cottage, Hall Lane, Colston Bassett, Nottingham NG12 3FB — MB BS 1943 Lond.; MRad(T) Liverp. 1951; LMSSA Lond. 1942; DMRT Eng. 1951. Prev: Cons. Radiother. Hogarth Radiother. Centre, Gen. Hosp. Nottm.

JARRATT, Jeremy Wordsworth 40 Churchwood Road, Didsbury, Manchester M20 6TY — MB ChB 1993 Manch.

JARRATT, John Anthony Royal Hallamshire Hospital, Glossop Road, Sheffield S10 2JF Tel: 0114 271 2329 Fax: 0114 271 3769; 15 Petworth Drive, Sheffield S11 9Qu Tel: 0114 235 6927 — MB ChB 1964 Sheff.; FRCP Lond. 1981, M 1968. Cons. Clin. Neurophysiol. Sheff. Teachg. Hosps. Trust. Prev: Acad. Regist. Nat. Hosp. Lond.; Clin. Asst. Inst. Neurophysiol. Copenhagen, Denmark.; Rotating Med. Regist. Roy. Hosp. Sheff.

JARRATT, Robert Michael 519 Jockey Road, Sutton Coldfield B73 5DF Tel: 0121 354 1749; 10 Chester Road N., Sutton Coldfield B73 6SR Tel: 0121 353 2174 — MB ChB 1970 Birm. (Birm.) Socs: BMA. Prev: SHO (Obst.) Marston Green Matern Hosp. Birm.; Ho. Phys. Dudley Rd. Hosp. Birm.; Ho. Surg. Qu. Eliz. Hosp. Birm.

JARRATT, William James Rudgwick Medical Centre, Station Road, Rudgwick, Horsham RH12 3HB Tel: 01403 822103; Martins Cottage, Rudgwick, Horsham RH12 3DN Tel: 01403 822888 — MB BS 1971 Lond.; MRCS Eng. LRCP Lond. 1971; DCH Eng. 1974; DObst RCOG 1973. (King's Coll. Hosp.) Socs: BMA.

JARRETT, Alan Glyndwr Monmouth House Medical Centre, Maryport Street, Usk NP15 1AB Tel: 01291 672753 — MB BCh 1971 Wales; T(GP) 1991.

JARRETT, Arthur 1 Finchley Way, Finchley, London N3 1AG Tel: 020 8346 1474 — MB ChB Birm. 1943; DSc Lond. 1965; FRCP Ed. 1960, M 1952; FRCPath 1963; FIBiol. 1968. (Birm.) Emerit. Reader in Dermat. Histol. Univ. Lond. Socs: Fell. Roy. Soc. Med.; Brit. Assn. Dermat.; Advis. Comm. Internat. Soc. Cosmetic Dermat. Prev: Cons. SmithKline Beecham Gp.; Hon. Cons. Univ. Coll. Hosp. 1959-83; Head of Dermat. Dept. Univ. Coll. Hosp. Med. Sch. 1959-83.

JARRETT, David Richard Jonathan Queen Alexandra Hospital, Southwick Hill Road, Cosham, Portsmouth PO6 3LY Tel: 023 92 286000 Fax: 023 92 200381 — MB BS 1979 Lond.; FRCP Lond. 1995; MRCP (UK) 1982. Cons. Phys. Geriat. Med. Portsmouth Healthcare NHS Trust. Prev: Sen. Regist. (Geriat.) St. Stephen's, W.m. & St. Mary Abbot's Hosps. Lond.; Acting Head (Clin. Gerontol.) Univ. Saskatchewan, Canada; Sen. Regist. (c/o Elderly) W.m. Hosp. Lond.

JARRETT, Edward Bancroft (retired) Well Cottage, Charminster, Dorchester DT2 9QL — MB BChir 1942 Camb.; BA Camb. 1937, MA 1942, MD 1947; FRCP Lond. 1964, M 1944; MRCS Eng. LRCP Lond. 1941. Prev: Hon. Cons. Phys. Dorset Co. Hosp. Dorchester & Weymouth & Dist. Hosp.

JARRETT, Gordon Roy Richmond Medical Centre, 179 Richmond Road, Olton, Solihull B92 7SA Tel: 0121 743 7802 Fax: 0121 743 7802 — MB ChB 1966 Birm.

JARRETT, Kenneth William Malvern Health Centre, Victoria Park Road, Malvern Link, Malvern WR14 2JY Tel: 01684 612703 Fax: 01684 612779 — MB ChB 1972 Bristol; MRCGP 1979; DObst RCOG 1976.

JARRETT, Mr Llewellyn Neville Accident & Emergency Department, University Hospital, Queen Medical Centre, Nottingham NG7 2UH Tel: 0115 942 1421 Fax: 0115 970 9281 — MB BS 1971 Newc.; FRCS Eng. 1976. Cons. Surg. A & E Qu. Med. Centre Nottm.; Chief Med. Off. Donington Pk. Racing Circuit; Med. Adviser Jim Russell Racing Drivers Sch. Donington Pk.; Med. Off. Nottm. Forest Football Club; Med. Off. Long. Eaton Speedway.

JARRETT, Louise 92 Middleton Road, Hackney, London E8 4LN Tel: 020 7249 7226 — MB BS 1977 Lond.; DO RCS Eng. 1984.

JARRETT, Michael Eugene Dominic Langleys, Queens Drive, Oxshott, Leatherhead KT22 0PB Tel: 01372 842299 Fax: 01372 844257; Flat 7, 25 Marlborough Buildings, Bath BA1 2LY Tel: 01225 314635 — BM BCh 1996 Oxf.; MA Camb. 1997; BA Oxf. 1993. SHO Surg. Rotat. The Roy. United Hosp. Bath. Socs: BMA. Prev: Ho. Off. Gen. Med. Roy. Devon & Exeter Hosp.; Ho. Off. Gen. Surg. John Radcliffe Hosp. Oxf.

JARRETT, Miriam Esther (retired) 10 Ludbrook Close, Needham Market, Ipswich IP6 8EE Tel: 01449 722105 — LMS 1968 Barcelona; BSc Puerto Rico 1960. Prev: SHO (A & E) Ipswich Hosp.

JARRETT, Professor Paul Eugene Marcus Langleys, Queen Drive, Oxshott, Leatherhead KT22 0PB Fax: 01372 844257 — MB BChir 1967 Camb.; MA Camb. 1967; FRCS Eng. 1972; DObst RCOG 1968. (Camb.) Cons. Surg. Kingston Hosp.; Prof. Day Surg. & Acute Day Care (Fac. Healthcare Scis.) Kingston Univ. & St. Geo. Hosp Med Sch. Socs: BMA; (Ex-Chairm.) Brit. Assn. Day Surg.; Past Pres. Internat. Assn. Ambulatory Surg. Prev: Sen. Regist. (Surg.) St. Thos. Hosp. Lond.; Regist. (Surg.) St. Thos. Hosp. Lond. & Roy. Hosp. Wolverhampton.

JARRETT, Mr Paul Max 60 Great George Street, Glasgow G12 8RP Tel: 0141 334 2073 Email: pmjarrett@resend.ac.uk — MB ChB 1992 Glas.; FRCS Ed. 1997. (Glas. Univ.) Specialist Regist. (Orthop. Surg.) Roy. Infirm. Glas. Socs: BMA; Assoc. Brit. Orthopaedic Assoc.; Brit. Orth. Trainees Assn. Prev: Specialist Regist. (Orthop.) Stirling Roy. Infirm.; Specialist Regist. (Orthop.) W.ern Infirm. Glas.; Regist. (Orthop.) Auckland Hosp. New Zealand.

JARRETT, Peter Hugo Eltham Mental Health Team, 4-8 Pound Place, Eltham, London SE9 5DN Tel: 0208 921 3510 Fax: 0208 850 6874 Email: peter.jarrett@oxleas.nhs.uk — MRCS Eng. LRCP Lond. 1977; PhD Lond. 1992, MB BS 1978; MA Oxf. 1978; MRCPsych 1982. Cons. Psychiat. Greenwich Dist. Gen. Hosp.; Med. Dir. Oxleas NHS Trust 1996. Prev: Lect. & Hon. Sen. Regist. Guy's Hosp. Med. Sch. Lond.; Hon. Research Fell. Birkbeck Coll. Univ. Lond.; Fell. Family Ther. & Gen. Psychiat. Brown Univ. USA.

JARRETT, Richard Francis (retired) Hamfield, Edge Road, Painswick, Stroud GL6 6UP Tel: 01452 813298 — MB BChir Camb. 1935; MRCS Eng. LRCP Lond. 1935; MA, BA (Hons.) (Nat. Sc. Trip.) Camb. 1932; FRCP Lond. 1965, M 1939. Hon. Cons. Phys. Gloucester Roy. Hosp.; Mem. Minister's Advis. Panel on Drug Addic. Prev: Sen. Regist. (Med.) Brit. Postgrad. Med. Sch. Hammersmith.

JARRETT, Professor Ruth Frances LRF Virus Centre, Veterinary Pathology, Vet School, Bearsden Road, Glasgow G61 1QH Tel: 0141 330 5774/5 Fax: 0141 330 5733 Email: r.fjarrett@vet.gla.ac.uk; 4 Auchineden House, Blanefield, Glasgow G63 9AX Fax: 01360 771184 — MB ChB 1980 Glas.; 2000 FRCPath; 2001 FRCP (Glasg). Dir. LRF Virus Centre (Veterin. Path.) Veterin. Sch. Univ. Glas. Socs: Path. Soc.; Amer. Soc. of Hematology.

JARRETT, Stephen John 29 Selby Road, Leeds LS9 0EA — MB BS 1994 Lond.

JARRETT, Susan Alice Monmouth House Medical Centre, Maryport Street, Usk NP15 1AB Tel: 01291 672753 — MB BCh 1975 Wales; T(GP) 1991.

JARVIE, Andrew 48 Rosehill Road, Torrance, Glasgow G64 4HF — MB ChB 1991 Glas.

JARVIE, Anne (retired) Craggan, Victoria Terrace, Crieff PH7 4AD Tel: 01764 652067 Fax: 01764 652067 Email: ndjarvie@msn.com — MB ChB 1961 Glas. Prev: Med. Off. Crieff Hosp. & Crieff Family Plann. Clinic.

JARVIE, Fiona Elizabeth Airdrie Health Centre, Monkscourt Avenue, Airdrie ML6 0JU Tel: 01236 768181; 10 Turnberry Wynd, Bothwell, Glasgow G71 8EE Tel: 01698 853475 — MB ChB 1979 Glas.; DRCOG 1981.

JARVIE, Neil Curtis Stanmore House Surgery, Linden Avenue, Kidderminster DY10 3AA Tel: 01562 822647 Fax: 01562 827255; Gate House Cottage, Bliss Gate, Rock, Kidderminster DY14 9YE Tel: 01299 266468 — MB ChB 1976 Birm.; DRCOG 1979. Prev: Trainee GP Kidderminster VTS.

JARVIE, Norman Dobson (retired) Craggan, Victoria Terrace, Crieff PH7 4AD Tel: 01764 652067 Fax: 01764 652067 Email: ndjarvie@msn.com — MB ChB 1961 Glas.; FRCP (Glas.) 1997; FRCGP 1978, M 1973; DObst RCOG 1963. Prev: Ex-Chairm. Nat. Med. Advis. Comm.

JARVIS, Alison Mary 60 Hillside Avenue, Bromley Cross, Bolton BL7 9NJ Tel: 01204 596266 — MB ChB 1990 Manch.; BSc (Med. Sci.) St. And. 1987; DCH RCP Lond. 1994. Prev: Trainee GP/SHO Colchester VTS.

JARVIS, Mr Andrew Charles Mackechnie Goring Hall Hospital, Bodiam Avenue, Goring-by-Sea, Worthing BN12 4AT; 9 Palmer's Way, High Salvington, Worthing BN13 3DP Tel: 01903 830689 Fax: 01903 830689 Email: acjarvis1@aol.com — MB 1973 Camb.; BChir 1972; FRCS Eng. 1978. (Westminster) Cons. Orthop. Surg. Worthing & S.lands Hosps. Socs: Int. Biother. Soc. (Sec.). Prev: Sen. Regist. Guy's & St. Thos. Hosps. Orthop. Train. Scheme.

JARVIS, Anthony Fosse Medical Centre, 344 Fosse Road North, Leicester LE3 5RR Tel: 0116 253 8988 Fax: 0116 242 5178; Wyndham House, 22 Desford Road, Kirby Muxloe, Leicester LE9 2BB Tel: 0116 239 4653 Fax: 0116 242 5178 — MB ChB 1966 Aberd.; MRCGP 1974; Cert. Family Plann. JCC 1974; DObst RCOG 1973. (Aberd.) Clin. Tutor Univ. Leics. Med. Sch.; Med. Off. Leicester City Football Club. Socs: Leic. Med. Soc.; (Chairm.) Leicester Palliat. Care Gp. Prev: SHO (O & G) RAF Hosp. Wegberg, W. Germany; Squadron Ldr. RAF Med. Br.; Ho. Phys. & Ho. Surg. Leicester Roy. Infirm.

JARVIS, Anthony Patrick 60 Westerfield Road, Ipswich IP4 2XN Tel: 01473 213979 — MB BCh 1977 Wales; FFA RCS Eng. 1984. Cons. Anaesth. Ipswich Hosp.

JARVIS, Catherine Patricia 66 Langsett Avenue, Sheffield S6 4AA — MB BS 1993 Lond.

JARVIS, Christopher Anthony Neville Bottreaux Surgery, Boscastle PL35 0BG Tel: 01840 250209 Fax: 01840 250666 — MB BS Lond. 1970; MRCS Eng. LRCP Lond. 1970; LMCC 1975; DA Eng. 1972. (St. Bart.) Med. Off. Brit. Cycling Federat.; Chief Med. Off. Commonw. Games Counc. for Eng. Socs: BASM; SOM; Fell.Instit.Sports.Med.

JARVIS, Deborah Louise Department of Public Health Medicine, 5th Floor, Capital House, 42 Weston St., London SE1 3QD Tel: 020 7955 2865 Fax: 020 7955 4073; 79 Manor Way, Blackheath, London SE3 9XG — MB BS 1982 Lond.; MRCP (UK) 1986; MFPHM RCP (UK) 1994. Sen. Lect. (Pub. Health Med.) UMDS Guy's & St. Thos. Hosp. Lond. Prev: Research Regist. Roy. P. Alfred Hosp. & Univ. Sydney NSW, Austral.; Regist. (Med.) Centr. Hosp. Honiara, Soloman Is.; Regist. (Med.) King's Coll. Hosp. Lond.

JARVIS, Elizabeth Honor Butt Lane Surgery, 58 Butt Lane, Leeds LS12 5AZ; Beechwood House, Raby Park, Wetherby LS22 6SA Tel: 01937 582218 Fax: 01937 584824 — MB ChB 1972 Aberd.; MRCP (UK) 1976; MRCGP 1978. (Aberd.) Prev: Regist. (Med.) Leeds Gen. Infirm.; SHO (Paediat.) Oxon AHA (T).

JARVIS, Emma Jane Lorne Cottage, High St., Colne, Huntingdon PE28 3ND Tel: 01487 840514; 9 Coalport Way, Tilehurst, Reading RG30 6HY Tel: 0118 941 0516 — MB BS 1994 Newc.; JCVGPT; DCH 1999; DFFP; DCH 1999. (Newc.) GP Reading Univ. Health Centre. Socs: Med. Protec. Soc.; BMA. Prev: SHO (Med.) Roy. Perth Hosp. & Manly Community HA; SHO (Paediat.) Roy. Perth Hosp. & Manly Community HA; VTS Reading.

JARVIS, Ernest Trevor c/o Jonathan S. Rose Solicitors, 693 High Road, London N12 0DA — LRCPI & LM, LRSCI & LM 1964; LRCPI & LM, LRCSI & LM 1964. (RCSI) Princip. GP Derby Family Pract. Comm.

JARVIS, Mr Gerald Joseph Beechwood House, Raby Park, Wetherby LS22 6SA Tel: 01937 582218 Fax: 01937 584824 — BM BCh 1971 Oxf.; MA, BM BCh Oxf. 1971; FRCS Ed. 1976; FRCOG 1989, M 1977. Cons. O & G St. Jas. Univ. Hosp. Leeds; Hon. Clin. Sen. Lect. Univ. Leeds. Prev: Sen. Regist. Jessop Hosp. Wom. Sheff.

JARVIS, Harold (retired) 70 Crag Head, 77 Manor Road, Bournemouth BH1 3JF Tel: 01202 558528 — MRCS Eng. LRCP Lond. 1945; DA Eng. 1963. Gp. Med. Off. Electrolux Ltd. Luton; Mem. Min. Nat. Insur. Med. Bd.; Clin. Asst. Dept. Anaesth. Watford Gen. Hosp. Prev: Res. Med. Off. Mayday Hosp. Croydon.

JARVIS, Helen 93 Gerard Road, Rotherham S60 2PP — MB ChB 1991 Manch.

JARVIS, Iain Stuart London Road Medical Practice, 97 London Road, Gloucester GL1 3HH Tel: 01452 522079 Fax: 01452 387884 Email: iain.jarvis@gp-l84042.nhs.uk; Holly House, 349 Longford Lane, Longford, Gloucester GL2 9EL — MB BCh 1988 Wales. Med. Off. Gloucester's Homeless Healthcare Team. 1 Session each week.

JARVIS, Isobel Alice Duke (retired) Thrums, 15 Elcho Rd, Longniddry EH32 0LB Tel: 01875 853132 — MB ChB Ed. 1947.

JARVIS, Jeremy Ronald Windrush Health Centre, Welch Way, Witney OX28 6JS Tel: 01993 702911 Fax: 01993 700931; 2 Maidley Close, Witney OX28 1ER Tel: 01993 702601 — MB BChir 1970 Camb.; MA Camb. 1970; DCH Eng. 1972; DObst RCOG 1971. (St. Bart.)

JARVIS, Katharine Rebecca St Peter's Medical Centre, 30-36 Oxford Street, Brighton BN1 4LA Tel: 01273 606006 Fax: 01273 623896; 16 Lyndhurst Road, Hove BN3 6FA — BM BS 1989 Nottm.; MRCGP 1993; DFFP 1996; DRCOG 1992.

JARVIS, Kenneth John 98 Linden Way, Southgate, London N14 4NH Tel: 020 8882 5900 — MB BS 1966 Lond.; MB BS (Hons.) (Distinc. Obst. & Gyn.) Lond. 1966; MRCS Eng. LRCP Lond. 1966; FRCPath 1985, M 1973; DObst RCOG 1968. (St. Geo.) Cons. Histopath. N. Middlx. Hosp. Lond. Socs: Assn. Clin. Paths. Prev: Sen. Regist. (Histopath.) St. Geo. Hosp. Lond.; Sen. Regist. (Histopath.) Roy. Marsden Hosp. Lond.; Regist. (Path.) St. Geo. Hosp. Lond.

JARVIS, Lionel John, Surg. Capt. RN Royal Hospital, Haslar, Gosport PO12 2AA Tel: 02392 762508 Fax: 02392 762400 Email: lionjarv@dsca.gov.uk; Midlington Farm House, Southampton SO32 3PU Tel: 01489 877486 Email: lioneljarvis@cs.com — MB BS 1977 Lond.; MRCS Eng. LRCP Lond. 1977; FRCR 1988. (Guy's Hosp. Lond.) Cons. Radiol. Roy. Hosp. Haslar Gosport; Defence Cons. Adviser Radiol. Defence Med. Serv. Lond.; Commanding Off. Roy. Hosp. Haslar and Min. of Defence Hosp. (MDHU), Portsmouth. Socs: Chairm. Roy. Coll. of Radiologists IT Comm.; Roy. Coll. Radiol. Fac. Bd.

JARVIS, Mark Alfred Washway Road Medical Centre, 63-65 Washway Road, Sale M33 7SU Tel: 0161 962 4354 Fax: 0161 962 0046; Washway Road Medical Centre, 63-65 Washway Road, Sale M33 7SU Tel: 0161 962 4354 Fax: 0161 962 0046 — MB ChB 1988 Manch.; MRCGP 1992.

JARVIS, Martin Amadee 18 Kestrel Walk, Letchworth SG6 2TB — MB BS 1990 Lond.

JARVIS, Muriel Isobel (retired) 40 Marlborough Road, Luton LU3 1EF Tel: 01582 727548 — MRCS Eng. LRCP Lond. 1955.

JARVIS, Pamela Dianne Orchard Mead, Hob Lane, Dunham Hill, Warrington WA6 0LW Tel: 01244 300240 Fax: 01244 300240 — MB ChB 1962 Birm. (Birm.) Peripatetic Anaesth. Warrington Hosp. Trust. Socs: BASICS; Liverp. Med. Inst. Prev: Regist. (Anaesth.) Whiston Hosp. Prescot; Ho. Phys. Withington Hosp. Manch.; Ho. Surg. Dudley Rd. Hosp. Birm.

JARVIS, Paul Richard Edwin 1 Carr Hill Grove, Calverley, Pudsey LS28 5QB — MB ChB 1997 Leeds.

JARVIS, Peter Neville (retired) 42 Church Green Road, Bletchley, Milton Keynes MK3 6BL Tel: 01908 372347 Fax: 01908 372347 — MB ChB 1956 Liverp.; MRCGP 1965; DObst RCOG 1958. Med. Adviser Festiniog Railway Company Porthmadog. Prev: Med. Dir. Milton Keynes Community Hosp.

JARVIS, Ranjana Rani Genitourinary Medicine, North Manchester General Hospital, Delaunay's Road, Manchester Tel: 0161 795 4567 Email: rani@jrvs28.freeserve.co.uk; 31 Milton Road, Prestwich, Manchester M25 1PT Tel: 0161 773 8574 — MB BS 1983 Patna; MRCOG 1993; MFFP 1995. Sen. Regist. Genitourin. Med. NW Regional Rotat. Manch.; Infect. Dis. Unit N. Manch. Gen. Hosp. Socs: MSSVD; AGUM; BSSCP.

JARVIS, Richard James North Staffs Health Authority, Grove Road, Fenton, Stoke-on-Trent ST4 4LX Tel: 01782 298133 Fax: 01782 298135 Email: nchars.jarvis@nhs.uk; 129 Fairfield Road, Buxton SK17 7DU — MB BS 1991 Lond.; BSc (Hons.) Lond. 1988, MB BS 1991; MPH Birmingham 1998. (King's Coll. (Univ. Lond.)) Specialist Regist. (Pub. Health) N. Staffs. HA. Prev: GP/Regist. Buxton; Clin. Lect. (Jun. Doctor Coordinator) Trent Regional Task

Force.; SHO Rotat. (Gen. Med.) & Ho. Off. (Med. & Surg.) Hosp. Centre Stoke-on-Trent.

JARVIS, Robert James Terry Staithe Road Surgery, Staithe Road, Ludham, Great Yarmouth NR29 5AB Tel: 01692 678611 Fax: 01692 678295; Sharp Street, Catfield, Great Yarmouth NR29 5AF Tel: 01692 670617 — MB ChB (Hons.) Bristol 1965; MFFP 1995; DFFP 1993; Dip. IMC RCS Ed. 1988; DObst RCOG 1967. ((Univ. Brist.)) Hosp. Practioner (A & E) Norf. & Norwich Hosp.; Chairm. Norf. Accid. Rescue Serv.; Hon. Med. Adviser RNLI Happisburgh. Socs: Brit. Assn. Accid. & Emerg. Med.; Assoc. Roy. & Irish Coll. Gen. Pract; Fac. Pre-Hosp. Care. Prev: Med. Off. Govt. Kenya; SHO Norf. & Norwich Hosp.; Ho. Off. Bristol Roy. Infirm.

JARVIS, Miss Sara Jane Royal Berkshire Hospital, Reading RG1 5AN; Beechcroft, Bearswood End, Beaconsfield HP9 2NR — MB BS 1992 Lond.; FRCS 1998. (London) SHO (ENT) Roy. Berks. Hosp. Reading. Prev: SHO (Gen. Surg.) Good Hope Sutton Coldfield; SHO (Neurosurg.) Nat. Hosp. Neurol. & Neurosurg. Lond.; SHO (ENT) Wexham Pk. Hosp.

JARVIS, Sarah Caroline Grove Medical Practice, 49 Richford Gate, Richford Street, London W6 7HY Tel: 020 8846 7555 Fax: 020 8846 7538; 221 Hamlet Gardens, London W6 0TS Tel: 020 8563 7812 Fax: 020 8748 1631 — BM BCh 1986 Oxf.; MA Camb. 1986; MRCGP 1990; DRCOG 1989. Mem. Med. Pract Comm.; Adviser to Alcohol Concern; Edit. Bd. Doctor Magazine; Edit. Bd. Update Magazine; Mem. Career Support Forum RCGP. Prev: Trainee GP Epsom VTS; Chair Wom. Task Force RSCP.

JARVIS, Sarah Louise 2 Ocean Crescent, Maritime Quarter, Swansea SA1 1YZ — MB BS 1993 Lond.

JARVIS, Simon James Fenwick Jarvis and Partners, Westbrook Medical Centre, 301-302 Westbrook Centre, Westbrook, Warrington WA5 8UF; Brantingham, Chester Road, Higher Walton, Warrington WA4 5LP — MB BS 1985 Lond.; MRCGP 1985. (Middlx. Hosp.)

JARVIS, Professor Stephen Nicholas High Rochester, Nr. Otteburn, Newcastle upon Tyne NE19 1RB Tel: 01830 520361 — MRCS Eng. LRCP Lond. 1967; MD Lond. 1979, MB BS 1967; FRCPCH 1997; FFPHM RCP (UK) 1995, M 1990; MFCM 1984. (Westm.) Donald Ct. Prof. of Community Child Health Dept. of Child Health Univ. Newc. u. Tyne. Prev: Cons. Pub. Health Med. Gateshead HA; Sen. Lect. (Epidemiol.) Dept. Child Health Univ. Newc.; Research Fell. Wolfson Centre Inst. Child Health Lond. & Hon. Clin. Regist. Bethlem Roy. & Maudsley Hosps.

JARY, Christopher Alan Hall Road Surgery, 83-85 Hall Road, Hull HU6 8QL Tel: 01482 343390 Fax: 01482 445858; 201 Victoria Avenue, Hull HU5 3EF Tel: 01482 341352 Email: chris@jary.karoo.co.uk — MB BS 1975 Lond.; MRCGP 1979.

JARY, Marian The White House, Alton, Stoke-on-Trent ST10 4AF — MB ChB 1970 Birm.

JARY, Stephen Robert Jary, Yates and Brown, Well Street Medical Centre, Well Street, Cheadle, Stoke-on-Trent ST10 1EY Tel: 01538 753114 Fax: 01538 751485 — MB ChB 1970 Birm.; MRCP (UK) 1973.

JARZABEK, Joanna Barbara 236 Staines Road, Hounslow TW3 3LR — MB BS 1987 Lond.

JARZEMBOWSKI, Marek Kazimierz The Cannonhill Lane Medical Practice, 153 Cannon Hill Lane, Raynes Park, London SW20 9BZ Tel: 020 8542 5201 Fax: 020 8540 9049 — MRCS Eng. LRCP Lond. 1990.

JAS, Barid Baran Matching Green Surgery, Matching Green, Basildon SS14 2PB Tel: 01268 533928 Fax: 01268 289415 — MB BS 1974 Calcutta.

JASANI, Abida Faruq 3 Garden Ropyal, Kersfield Road, Putney, London SW15 3HE Tel: 020 8789 5580 Fax: 020 8789 5590 — MB BS 1984 Karachi; FRCA 1993; DA (UK) 1990.

JASANI, Bharat Department of Pathology, University of Wales College of Medicine, Cardiff CF14 4XN Tel: 029 20743523/742705 Fax: 029 20744276/742701 Email: wptbj@cf.ac.uk; 4 Upper Cliff Close, Penarth CF64 1BE — MB ChB 1976 Birm.; BSc (Hons.) Glas. 1969; PhD Birm. 1973, MB ChB 1976; MRCPath 1989; FRCPath 1997. (University of Wales College of Medicine) Hon. Cons. Immunocytochem. S. Glam.; Sen. Clin. Lect. (Path.) Univ. Wales Coll. Med. Socs: Sen. Mem. Assn. Clin. Paths.; Internat. Acad. Path.

JASANI, Iqbalhusein Abdulmalek Mohamed Spinney Brook Medical Centre, 59 High Street, Irthlingborough, Wellingborough NN9 5GA Tel: 01933 650593 Fax: 01933 653641 — LRCPI & LM, LRSCI & LM 1973. (RCS Dublin, Ireland) Trainee GP Kettering VTS. Prev: SHO (O & G) & Ho. Surg. & Ho. Phys. St. John's Chelmsford.

JASANI, Mukundrai Keshavlal (Kris) International Clinical Trials Ltd, 27 Harley St., London W1N 1DA Tel: 020 7436 8080 Fax: 020 7436 9897 Email: kjasani@ictrials.com; 21 Kenton Road, Harrow HA1 2BW Tel: 020 8422 0765 Fax: 020 8422 0765 Email: m.k.jasani@btinternet.com — MB ChB 1961 Glas.; FRCP Glas. 1976, M 1965. (Glas.) Research Phys. Osteoporsis Screening & Research Unit Guy's Hosp. Lond. Socs: Fell. Roy. Soc. Med. Lond.; Brit. Soc. Rheum.; Orthop. Research Soc. N. Amer. Prev: Assoc. Dir. Exploratory Clin. Pharmacol. CIBA-GEIGY Corp. USA; Internat. Cartilage Project Ldr. Worldwide, Ciba-Geigy Pharmaceut. Div. Horsham; Med. Dir., Internat. Clin. Trials Ltd, Lond.

JASANI, Nalini The Meanwhile Garden Medical Centre, Unit 5, 1-31 Elkstone Road, London W10 5NT Tel: 020 8960 5620 Fax: 020 8964 1964 — MB BCh BAO 1970 Dub.

JASANI, Vinay 63 Church Road, Worcester Park KT4 7RZ — MB BS 1991 Lond.

JASH, Kalyani 64 Woodland Way, London N21 3QA — MB BS 1963 Calcutta; FFA RCS Eng. 1974.

JASIM, Mr Wisam Abdul Latif 165 Wolverhampton Road, Oldbury B68 0LR Tel: 0121 422 6365 — MB ChB 1974 Baghdad; FRCS Ed. 1987.

JASINGHE, Mr Ranjith 7 Masonleys Road, Birmingham B31 5NA — MB BS 1975 Sri Lanka; FRCS Eng. 1988; MRCS Eng. LRCP Lond. 1989. Regist. (Gen. Surg.) Macclesfield Dist. Gen. Hosp.

JASKMANICKI, Boleslaw Zygmunt (retired) 486 City Way, Rochester ME1 2TN Tel: 01634 844015 — MD 1930 Lwow. Prev: Cons. Radiol. Medway & Gravesend Hosp. Gp.

JASORIA, Subhash 9 Oxburgh Close, Loughborough LE11 4TG — MB BS 1973 Patna.

JASPAL, Manjit Singh 85 Kenilworth Road, Coventry CV4 7AF — MB ChB 1993 Dundee.

JASPAN, Timothy Division of Neuroradiology, Department of Diagnostic Imaging, University Hospital, Queens Medical Centre, Nottingham NG7 2UH Tel: 0115 970 9951; 97 Selby Road, West Bridgford, Nottingham NG2 7BB — MB ChB 1978 Leeds; BSc Leeds 1975, MB ChB 1978; MRCP Ed. 1981; FRCR 1986; FRCP 1999; FRCP 1999. Cons. Neuroradiol. Univ. Hosp. Qu. Med. Centre Nottm. Socs: Brit. Soc. of NeuroRadiol.; World Federat.s of Interven.al Therapeutic Neuroradiol.; UK NeuroInterven.al Gp. Prev: Merck Fell. 1986.

JASPER, Anne Lesley 92 Stanwell Road, Penarth CF64 3LP — MB ChB 1985 Leeds; MRCPsych 1990.

JASPER, William Mark 53 Farley Road, Selsdon, South Croydon CR2 7NG Tel: 020 8651 1222 — MB BS 1983 Lond.; MRCGP 1989.

JASSAL, Baldev Singh c/o J.S. Sidhu, 73 Parkfield Road, Northolt UB5 5NW Tel: 020 8841 4710 — MB BS 1975 Rajasthan. (Sardar Patel Med. Coll.)

JASSAL, Satbir Singh Bridge Street Medical Practice, 20 Bridge Street, Loughborough LE11 1NQ Tel: 01509 263018 Fax: 01509 211427 — BM BS 1984 Nottm.; BMedSci Nottm. 1982; MRCGP 1988; DRCOG 1987. Med. Adviser Rainbows Childr. Hospice LoughBoro.

JASSEL, Govinder Singh The Surgery, 578 Stratford Road, Sparkhill, Birmingham B11 4AN Tel: 0121 772 0392; 88 Bescot Road, Walsall WS2 9DG — MB ChB 1985 Leeds; MRCGP 1989.

JASSIM, Dhafir Abdul Ameer Chesterfield & North Derbyshire Royal Hospital, Calow, Chesterfield S44 5BL — MB ChB 1973 Baghdad.

JASWAL, Joginder Singh 32 Pollards Hill W., Norbury, London SW16 4NT Tel: 020 8764 6211 — MB BS 1967 Bombay. (Grant Med. Coll.)

JASWON, Mervyn Stanley Paediatrics Department, Whittington Hospital NHS Trust, St Mary's Wing, Highgate Hill, London N19 5NF Tel: 020 7288 5315; 35A Belsize Avenue, London NW3 4BN Tel: 020 7794 2285 — MB BS 1976 Lond.; FRCP Lond. 1997; MRCP (UK) 1982. (St. Thos.) Cons. Paediat. Whittington Hosp. Lond.; Hon. Sen. Lect. (Paediat.) UCL. Socs: Neonat. Soc.; Roy. Soc. Med. (Paediat. Sect.). Prev: Clin. Lect. (Paediat. & Haemat.) Univ. Coll. Hosp. Lond.; Regist. (Paediat.) N.ampton Gen. Hosp.; SHO W.m. Childr. Hosp.

JATAU, Mr Joseph Ayunda Flat 4 Birdlip House, Gloucestershire Royal Hospital, Great Western Road, Gloucester GL1 3WW — MB BS 1983 Ahmadu Bello, Nigeria; FRCS Ed. 1992.

JATHANNA, Sushil Devaprasad 5 Hancock Court, Chapel Break, Norwich NR5 9NN Tel: 01603 747976 — MB BS 1981 Mysore; MSc Lond. 1991; MRCPI 1989; MFPHM RCP (UK) 1994; DGM RCP Lond. 1989. Cons. Pub. Health Med. N. Essex HA. Prev: Sen. Regist. (Pub. Health Med.) NW Thames RHA & N. Thames Health Agency; Regist. (Geriat. Med.) Derby Roy. Infirm. & W. Norwich Hosp.

JAUHAR, Pramod Parkhead Hospital, 81 Salamanca St., Glasgow G31 5ES Tel: 0141 211 8300, 0141211 8359 Fax: 0141 211 8431; 7 Dalziel Drive, Pollokshields, Glasgow G41 4JA Tel: 0141 427 1187 Fax: 0141 427 6661 Email: pramod.jauhar@hotmail.com — MB BS 1973 Poona; FRCPsych 1994, M 1978; DPM Eng. 1977. (Armed Forces Med. Coll. Poona) Cons. Psychiat. Pk.head Hosp. Glas.; Hon. Clin. Sen. Lect. Univ Glas.; H.M. Med. Commisioner - Ment. Welf. Commiss. for Scotl. Prev: Cons. Psychiat. St. Brendan's Hosp. Bermuda; Chief Asst. (Psychol. Med.) St. Thos. Hosp. Lond.

JAUMDALLY, Jalal-Ud-Din Rumi 94 Sutton Road, London N10 1HG — MB BS 1994 Lond.

JAUNIAUX, Eric Department of Obstetrics & Gynaecology, University College London Medical School, 86-96 Chenies News, London WC1E 6HX Tel: 020 7209 6056 Fax: 020 7383 7429 — MD 1986 Brussels; PhD Brussels 1992; T(OG) 1992. Sen. Lect. (Fetal Med.) Univ. Coll. Lond. Med. Sch.; Hon. Cons. Obst. & Gyn. Lond. Socs: Amer. Inst. Ultrasound in Med.; Eur. Soc. Human Reproduc. & Embryol.; Internat. Soc. Ultrasound in Obst. & Gyn.

JAVAID, Muhammad Kassim Dept of Rheumatology, Southampton General Hospital, Southampton SO16 6YD; 127 Whiteknights Road, Reading RG6 7BB — MB BS 1996 Lond.

JAVED, Ehsan Bari 224 Tomswood Hill, Ilford IG6 2QS Tel: 020 8500 4190 — MB BS 1961 Karachi; BSc Punjab (Pakistan) 1954; FFA RCS Eng. 1973; DA Eng. 1967. (Dow Med. Coll. Karachi) Cons. (Anaesth.) Whipps Cross & Wanstead Hosps. Lond. Socs: Assn. Anaesth. Gt. Brit. & Irel.; Fell. Roy. Soc. Med. Prev: Regist. (Anaesth.) Roy. Berks. Hosp. Reading; Sen. Regist. (Anaesth.) Brompton Chest Hosp. Lond.; Sen. Regist. (Anaesth.) Roy. Free Hosp. Lond.

JAVEED, Mazhar c/o Drive M.A. Khan, 4 Gloucester Road, Walsall WS5 3PN Tel: 01922 26658 — MB BS 1972 Bangalor; MB BS Bangalore 1972.

JAVID, Mohammad Asghar 9 Ashton Gardens, Rochdale OL11 3SG — MB ChB 1981 Leeds.

JAVID, Mr Shahab 19 Elgin Road, Ilford IG3 8LL — MB BS 1980 Karachi; FRCS Glas. 1985.

JAVIDI, Mr Mahmood 104 Milgate Lane, E. Didsbury, Manchester M20 8SD — MD 1966 Meshed; FRCSI 1984.

JAWAD, Mr Adnan Najim 142 Newcourt, Cowley, Uxbridge UB8 2LP — MB ChB 1970 Mosul, Iraq; FRCS Ed. 1985.

JAWAD, Ali Ashak Al-Jwahriy Oswaldtwistle Clinic, 119 Union Road, Oswaldtwistle, Accrington BB5 3DD Tel: 01254 233061; 18 The Paddock, Mayfield Avenue, Oswaldtwistle, Accrington BB5 3AB — MB ChB 1983 Baghdad; MRCP (UK) 1994; DCH RCP Glas. 1993; DTM & H Liverp. 1992. Staff Grade (Community Paediat.) Oswaldtwistle Clinic, Lancs. Socs: Roy. Coll. Paediat. And Child Heath. Prev: SHO (Paediat.) Lancaster Roy. Infirm.; SHO (Paediat.) Qu.s Pk. Hosp. Blackburn; SHO (Paediat.) Hosp. Sick Childr. Glas.

JAWAD, Ali Sadiq Mohammad The Royal London Hospital, Bancroft Road, Whitechapel, London E1 4DG Tel: 020 7377 7865 Fax: 020 7377 7807; 3 Oakwood Chase, Hornchurch RM11 3JT Tel: 01708 457211 Fax: 01708 477211 — MB ChB 1974 Baghdad; MSc Lond. 1986; FRCP Lond. 1995; MRCP (UK) 1981; DMedRehab RCP Lond. 1984; DCH RCP Lond. 1982; FRCP Ed. 1998. Cons. Rheum. Roy. Hosps. NHS Trust Lond.; Hon. Sen. Lect. Socs: BMA; Brit. Soc. Rheum. Prev: Cons. Rheum. & Rehabil. Chase Farm & Highlands Hosp. Middlx.; Sen. Regist. (Rheum) Lond. Hosp. & Norf. & Norwich Hosps.; Regist. (Rheum., Rehabil. & Geriat.) King's Coll. Hosp. Lond.

JAWAD, Mohammed Sami Mohammed X-Ray Department, South Clevland Hospital, Marton Road, Middlesbrough TS4 3BW — MB ChB 1976 Baghdad; FRCR 1990; T(R) (CR) 1991. Cons. Radiol. S. Tees Acute Hosps. NHS Trust. Prev: Sen. Regist. Roy. Lond. Hosp.

JAWAD, Moutaz Sadiq Mohammed 5 Woodford Close, Radyr Way, Llandaff, Cardiff CF5 2PH Tel: 029 2087 4099 Fax: 029 2087 4093 — MB ChB 1972 Baghdad; MRCP (UK) 1984; FRCP Ed. 1998. Med. Dir. Common Cold Centre Univ. Wales Coll. Cardiff; Clin. Asst. (Gen. Med.) Univ. Hosp. Wales Cardiff.

JAWAD, Naseer Hadi 22 Cefn Coed Road, Cardiff CF23 6AR — MB ChB 1984 Baghdad; MRCP (UK) 1993.

JAWAD, Sluiman Hamid 1 Merlin Close, Croydon CR0 5UQ — MB ChB 1979 Baghdad; MRCP (UK) 1985. Cons. in Rehabil. & Rheum. Socs: BSRM; BMA.

JAWAHEER, Mr Girish Department of Paediatric Surgery, Royal Hospital for Sick Children, Sciennes Road, Edinburgh EH9 1LF Tel: 0131 536 0000 Fax: 0131 536 0001 — MB ChB 1988 Manch.; FRCS Eng. 1992. Career Regist. (Paediat. Surg.) Roy. Hosp. for Sick Childr. Edin. Prev: Research Fell. (Paediat. Surg.) Roy. Liverp. Childr. Hosp.; Regist. (Paediat. Surg.) Alder Hey Hosp. Liverp.; SHO (Gen. Surg.) Countess of Chester Hosp.

JAWED, Franco Nasim 46 Bracadale Drive, Stockport SK3 8RY — MB ChB 1987 Manch.

JAWED, Shahid Kingston Hospital, Galsworthy Road, Kingston upon Thames KT2 7QB — MB BS 1989 Newc.; MRCP (UK) 1992.

JAWED, Syed Hasan Cherry Orchard House, Hospital Street, Tamworth B79 7EE Tel: 01827 308820 Fax: 01827 285598 Email: psychiatrist@totalise.co.uk — MB BS 1980 Karachi; MRCPsych 1987. (Sind Medical College, Karachi) Cons. Psychiat. S. Staffs. Healthcare NHS Trust. Prev: Cons. Psychiat. S. Warks.; Sen. Regist. (Developm. Psychiat.) W. Mid.; Regist. & SHO Prestwich Hosp. Manch.

JAWHARI, Aida Urfan Fuad Digestive Diseases Research Centre, St. Bartholomews's & The Royal London School of Med. & Dent., 2 Newark St., Whitechapel, London E1 Tel: 020 7295 7191 Fax: 020 7295 7192 Email: a.u.jawhari@mds.qmw.ac.uk; 17 Garson House, Gloucester Terrace, London W2 3DG Tel: 020 7262 4176 Email: a.jawhari@rpms.ac.uk — MB BS 1989 Lond.; MB BS (Hons.) Lond. 1989; MRCP (UK) 1992. (Med. Coll. St. Bart. Hosp.) Wellcome Research Train. Fell. (Gastroenterol.) St. Bart., Roy. Lond. Sch. Med. & Dent. Lond. Prev: Regist. (Gastroenterol.) St. Marks Hosp. Lond.; Regist. (Med.) Whipps Cross Hosp. Lond.; SHO Rotat. Addenbrooke's Hosp. Camb.

JAWORSKA-GRAJEK, Malgorzata 6 Thornwick Avenue, Willerby, Hull HU10 6LP — Lekarz 1984 Poznan.

JAWORSKI, Waclaw Feliks Birchwood Surgery, 232-240 Nevells Road, Letchworth SG6 4UB Tel: 01462 683781 — MB BS 1960 Lond.; MRCS Eng. LRCP Lond. 1959; DObst RCOG 1963. (Guy's)

JAY, Ann Lilian Meddygfa Teifi Surgery, New Road, Llandysul SA44 4QJ Tel: 01559 362221 Fax: 01559 362080; Bryn Teifi, Bangor Teifi, Llandysul SA44 5BE — MB ChB 1973 Sheff.; MRCGP 1991; DCH Eng. 1975; Dip. Palliat. Med. Wales 1995.

JAY, Professor Barrie Samuel 10 Beltane Drive, London SW19 5JR Tel: 020 8947 1771 Fax: 020 8946 0474 — MB BChir 1952 Camb.; MA Camb. 1953, MD 1965; FRCS Eng. 1962; FRCOphth 1988; Hon. FRCPCH 1996; Hon. FRCOphth 1994; DO Eng. 1959. (Univ. Coll. Hosp.) Emerit. Prof. Clin. Ophth. Univ. Lond. Prev: Hon. Sec. Acad. Med. Roy. Colls.; Hon. Sec. Specialist Train. Auth.; Master Worshipful Soc. Apoth.

JAY, Graham Edwin 14 The Spinney, Trowbridge Lodge, Trowbridge BA14 6DS Tel: 01225 769046 — MB ChB 1994 Birm.; BSc (Hons.) Sheff. 1989. (Birm.) SHO (Gen. Med. & Cardiol.) Frimley Pk. Hosp. Camberley; Med. Off. 23 Parachute Field Ambul. Socs: Med. Defence Union. Prev: Capt. Roy. Army Med. Corps.; SHO (Med. & Elderly Med.) Qu. Mary's Hosp. Sidcup; Ho. Surg. Qu. Eliz. Milit. Hosp. Lond.

JAY, Jeffrey Louis, CBE Tennent Institute of Opthalmology, Gartnavel General Hospital, Glasgow G12 0YN — MB ChB 1970 Glas.; BSc (Hons.) Glas. 1968; FRCS Eng. 1975; FRCOphth 1988. Cons. Ophth. Gartnavel Gen. Hosp., Glas..

JAY, John William Webster Sherwood, 23 Pages Lane, Bexhill-on-Sea TN39 3RD — MRCS Eng. LRCP Lond. 1939. (St. Thos.) Hon. Cons. (Radiol.) Bradford Hosps. Trust; Radiol. Bradford Hosps. Socs: Brit. Inst. Radiol. Prev: Lect. (Anat.) St. Thos. Hosp. Med. Sch.; Maj. RAMC, Specialist Radiol.; Adviser Radiol. to Army in Persia & Iraq, 1945-6.

JAY, Maureen Jane Hall 42 Kingsborough Gardens, Glasgow G12 9NL — MB ChB 1967 Glas. (Glas.)

JAY, Pamela Irene The Highway, Pipe-cum-Lyde, Hereford HR4 8AA Tel: 01432 272513 — MB ChB 1948 Bristol.

JAY, Roger Howard Department Medicine for the Elderly, South Tyneside District Hospital, Harton Lane, South Shields NE34 0PL Tel: 0191 454 8888; 18 St. George's Terrace, East Boldon NE36 0LU Tel: 0191 519 3641 Email: 113031.1755@compuserve.com — MB BS 1982 Lond.; MA Camb. 1983; MD Lond. 1993; FRCP 1998. Cons. Phys. (Geriat. & Gen. Med.) S. Tyneside Dist. Hosp. Prev: Sen. Regist. (Gen. & Geriat. Med.) Sunderland Dist. Gen. Hosp.; Assoc. Research Fell. & Hon. Lect. (Med.) Univ. Coll. & Middlx. Med. Sch.

JAY, Sheena Anne Dr B Walker and Partners, Health Centre, Gosforth Road, Seascale CA20 1PN Tel: 01946 728101; Crest House, Braystones Road, Beckermet CA21 2XX Tel: 01946 841097 — MB BS 1983 Lond.; MRCGP 1987; DRCOG 1987.

JAY, Victoria Catherine Bronislawa James Street Group Practice, James Street, Workington CA14 2DF Tel: 01900 62241 Fax: 01900 603385; Tel: 020 8352 2983 — MB BS 1984 Newc.; MRCGP 1989; DTM & H Liverp. 1992; DRCOG 1988. GP Princip. Prev: Clin. Asst. (Elderly Care & Younger Disabled) W. Cumbl .Hosp.; Volunteer Médécins Sans Frontieres, Netherlands; Princip. GP Ilkley.

JAYA-RATNAM, Mr Joseph Siripalan Williams (retired) 12 Rookwood, Chadderton, Oldham OL1 2TU — MB BS Ceylon 1967; FRCS Eng. 1980. Cons. Surg. Accid & Emerg. Med. Tameside Gen. Hosp. Ashton-under-Lyne. Prev: Sen. Regist. (A & E) Middlesbrough Gen. Hosp.

JAYABALAN, Mr Sidha Naidu Department of Orthopaedic Surgery, St. Vincent's Orthopaedic Hospital, Eastcote, Pinner HA5 2NB Tel: 020 8429 6200 Fax: 020 8866 6512; 8 Ladywood Close, Loudwater, Rickmansworth WD3 4AY Tel: 01923 896958 — MB BS 1972 Madras; MSc (Orthop.) Lond. 1987; FRCS (Orth.) Ed. 1990; FRCS Glas. 1984; T(S) 1991; FICS 1990. (Stanley Medical School) Cons. Orthop. Surg. St Vincent's Orthop. Hosp. Pinner, Sports Injury Clinic Wellington Hosp. Lond. & Sports Injury Clinic BUPA Hosp. Bushey. Socs: Fell.Brit. Orthopaedic Assoc.; Internat. Fell. Amer. Acad. Orthopaedic Surg.s. Prev: Regist. Centr. Middlx. Hosp. Lond.

JAYACHANDRA, Chickaballapur Reddiyappa The Royal Oldham Hospital, Oldham OL1 2JH Tel: 0161 624 0420; 46 Camberley Drive, Bamford, Rochdale OL11 4AZ Tel: 01706 369412 — MB BS 1956 Mysore; LMSSA Lond. 1961; FRCP Ed. 1986, M 1968; DCH Eng. 1958. Hon. Cons. Paediat. Roy. Oldham Hosp. Socs: Brit. Paediat. Assn. Prev: Regist. (Paediat.) Bradford Childr. Hosp.; Regist. (Neonat. Paediat). Walton Hosp. Liverp.; Regist. (Paediat.) Roy. Liverp. Childr. Hosp.

JAYACHANDRA REDDY, Mr Kotireddy Oldham Road Surgery, 148 Oldham Road, Manchester M4 5EE Tel: 0161 203 4511; 260 Withington Rad, Chorlton-cum-Hardy, Manchester M21 0YB — MB BS 1958 Madras; MS Andhra 1969; Do Andhra 1967. (Madras Med. Coll.) GP Manch. Prev: Asst. Prof. Ophth. Andhra Med. Coll., India; Locum Regist. Roy. Eye Hosp. Lond.; SHO (Ophth.) Oldham Roy. Infirm.

JAYADEV, Arundhathi 8 Grosmont Close, Grove Park, Blackwood NP12 1GE — MB BS 1977 Mysore.

JAYADEV, Baguriah U Hollies Health Centre, Merthyr Tydfil CF47 1UA Tel: 01685 722436 Fax: 01685 384286 — MB BS 1974 Mysore. (Mysore) GP Merthyr Tydfil.

JAYAKRISHNAN, Mr Aylliath Gosalakkal Department of Cardiothoracic Surgery, King's College Hospital, London SE5 9RS Tel: 020 7274 6222 Fax: 020 7326 3433; 47 Abbey Hill Close, Ashgate, Chesterfield S42 7JL Tel: 01246 235114 — MB BS 1975 Mysore; FRCS (Cth) 1993; FRCSI 1986. Sen. Regist. (Cardiothoracic Surg.) King's Coll. Hosp. Lond. Prev: Regist. (Cardiothoracic Surg.) Nat. Cardiac Unit Mater Misericoriae Hosp. Dub.

JAYAKUMAR, Chinnamma Sadasivan Pear Tree Surgery, South Ockendon RM15 6PR Tel: 01708 852318 Fax: 01708 853216 Email: chinnamma.jayakumar@gp-f81134.nhs.uk; 6 Green Tree Gardens, Romiley, Stockport SK6 3JL Email: amrobertson@ntlworld.com, jay_spurgate@hotmail.com — MB BS 1981 Kerala; Diploma in Internal Medicine (London Univ. 1991; T(GP) 1995; DTM & H Liverp. 1990. (Trivandrum Med. Coll.) GP. Prev: Regist. (Geriat. Med.) N.ants. Gen. Hosp.

JAYAKUMAR, Mr Copparam Srikantan (retired) 283A Turf Lane, Royton, Oldham OL2 6ET Tel: 0161 678 9944 — BSc Mysore 1949, MB BS 1955; FRCS Ed. 1965; LMSSA Lond. 1960. Prev: Assoc. Specialist (A & E & Orthop.) Oldham Roy. Infirm.

JAYAKUMAR, Mr Jay Dept. Cardiothoracic Surgery, Royal Brompton & Marefield NHS Trust, Harefield UB9 6JH Email: jayjayakumar@hotmail.com — MB BS 1992 Lond.; FRCS; BSc. (Univ. Coll. Lond.) Specialist Regist., Cardiothoracic Surg., W. Lond. (Pan-Thames) Rotat. Socs: Soc. of Cardiothoracic Surg.s (GB & Irel.); Roy. Soc. of Med.; Brit. Med. Assn. Prev: Brit. Heart Foundat. Clin. Ph.D. Fell., Acad. Dept. of Cardiothoracic Surg., Nat. Heart and Lung Inst., Imperial Coll., Lond.

JAYAKUMAR, Mr Kuderu Naganna 3 Hillfield, Oadby, Leicester LE2 4RW — MB BS 1977 Bangalor; MB BS Bangalore 1977; FRCS Eng. 1983; LRCP LRCS Ed. LRCPS Glas. 1983.

JAYAKUMAR, Latha 283A Turf Lane, Royton, Oldham OL2 6ET — MB ChB 1990 Manch.

JAYAKUMAR, Rahim Regional Medical Centre, RAF Northolt, West End Road, Ruislip HA4 6NG Tel: 020 8833 8365 Fax: 020 8833 8701; 51 Bycullah Road, Enfield EN2 8PH Tel: 020 8363 8059 Fax: 020 8367 0303 Email: jay7@btinternet.com — MB BS 1974 Madras; DFFP 1993; T(GP) 1989. (Stanley Med. Coll., Univ. Madras) Med. Pract. HM Forces MoD (UK); Sen. Lect. (Minor Surg. in Gen. Pract.) Roy. Defence Med. Coll. Gosport; Clin. Med. Off. (Family Plann. & Reproductive Health) Enfield & Haringey Community Health. Prev: Med. Pract. Brit. Forces Germany & Army Train. Regt. Pirbright.

JAYAKUMAR, Sita Northampton General Hospital, Northampton NN1 5BD Tel: 01604 544603; 30 Friars Avenue, Shenfield, Brentwood CM15 8HY Tel: 01277 213486 Email: jayakumars@ukgateway.net — MB BS 1986 Calicut, India; MRCP (UK) 1995; FRCPCH 2000. Cons.(Paediat) N.ampton Gen. Hosp., N.ampton. Socs: RCPCH; BACCH; BMA. Prev: Regist. (Paediat. Neurol. & Neonat. Intens. Care) John Radcliffe Hosp. Oxf.; Regist. (Paediat.) N.ampton Gen. Hosp. & Milton Keynes Gen. Hosp.; Sen. Regist. (Paed) N.ampton Gen. Hosp.

JAYAKUMAR, Yadiki Lings Bar Hospital, Gamston, Nottingham NG2 6GJ Tel: 0115 945 5577 Fax: 0115 952 9443; 19 Alford Road, Westbridgford, Nottingham NG2 6GJ Tel: 0115 945 2843 — MB BS Karnataka 1970. (Karnatak Medical College, Hubli South India) Assoc. Specialist (Health c/o Elderly) Lings Bar Hosp. Nottm. Socs: Brit. Geriat. Soc. & BMA; M-C. Soc. Prev: Staff Grade Phys. (Health c/o Elderly) Nottm. HA; Regist. (Geriat. Med.) & SHO (Geriat. Med., Haemat. & Path.) S. Glam. HA.

JAYAMAHA, Amarasinghe Arachchige Sepalika United Lincolnshire Hospitals Trust, Grantham and District Hospital, Manthorpe Road, Grantham NG31 8DG Tel: 01476 565232 Email: sjayamaha@ulh.nhs.uk — MB BS 1983 Colombo, Sri Lanka; FFA RCSI 1992; MBA 2000. Cons. Anasthetist Grantham & Dist. Hosp., Grantham. Socs: Brit. Med. Assn.; Assn. of Anaesth.s GB and Irel.; Age Anaesth. Assn. Prev: Cons. Anaesth. Newark Hosp.; Sen. Regist. (Anaesth.) St. Jas. Hosp., Leeds; Sen. Regist. (Anaesth.) York Dist. Hosp.

JAYAMAHA, John Egeton Lalith Nottingham City Hospital, Hucknall Road, Nottingham NG5 1PB Tel: 0115 969 1169; Spring Farm, Ferry Road, Barrow Haven, Barrow-upon-Humber DN19 7EY Tel: 01469 531981 Email: jjayamaha@aol.com — MB BS 1983 Colombo; MRCS Eng. LRCP Lond. 1986; MRCP (UK) 1988; FRCA 1992; FFA RCSI 1991; MBA Durham 1997. Cons. (Anaesth.) Nottm. City Hosp. Socs: Assoc. Fell. Fac. Accid. & Emerg. Med. Prev: Cons. (Anaesth.) Scunthorpe Gen. Hosp.; Sen. Regist. (Anaesth.) Guy's Hosp. Lond., Roy. Sussex Co. Hosp. Brighton & Manch. Roy. Infirm.

JAYAMANNE, Don Gerard Rohan 45 Glycena Road, London SW11 5TP — MB BS 1989 Newc.; FRCOphth 1993. SHO (Ophth.) Newc. Gen. Hosp.

JAYAMANNE, Indrani Lettitia Thornton Heath Health Centre, 61A Gillett Road, Thornton Heath, Croydon Tel: 020 8689 5797; 9 Speucedale Gardens, Pinecoombe, Shisley Hills, Croydon CR0 5HU Tel: 020 8776 0413 Fax: 020 8656 1220 — MB BS 1968 Ceylon; DCH Eng. 1977; DCCH Ed. 1984; DFP 1998. (Colombo) Clin. Asst. in Rheum., Mayday Hosp. Prev: Ho. Off. (Paediat. Med.) Whiston Hosp., Prescot.

JAYAPAL, Ponniah (Surgery), 72 Chadwell Heath Lane, Chadwell Heath, Romford RM6 4AF Tel: 020 8590 2800; 39 Ely Place, Woodford Green IG8 8AG — MB BS 1960 Ceylon.

JAYAPRAKASH, Vikram 13 Richmond Gardens, Highfield, Southampton SO17 1RY — BM 1998 Soton.; BM Soton 1998.

JAYARAJ, Samuel Marikili 3 Beddington Road, Ilford IG3 8PD — MB BS 1992 Lond.; FRCS (CSiG) Eng. 1996; FRCS (Otolaryngol.) Eng. 1997.

JAYARAJAH, Jayendiran Mohandas 1 Deer Park Lane, Tavistock PL19 9HB — MB BS 1987 Lond.

JAYARAJAN, Vanniasingam Royal Surrey County Hospital, Egerton Road, Guildford GU2 7XX Tel: 01483 571122 Fax: 01483 464108; 30 Roseacre Gardens, Chilworth, Guildford GU4 8RQ Email: vjayarajan@hotmail.com — MB BS 1973 Sri Lanka; MSc Lond. 1991; FRCS Ed. 1986; LMSSA Lond. 1984; DLO RCS Eng. 1983. Cons. Audiol. Phys. Roy. Surrey Co. Hosp. Guildford. Socs: Brit. Soc. Audiol.; BMA; Internat. Assn. Phys. in Audiol. Prev: Sen. Regist. (Audiol. Med.) Trent RHA.

JAYARAM, Muddaiah The Surgery, Lonfa, Glyn y Marl Road, Llandudno Junction LL31 9NS Tel: 01492 581172 Fax: 01492 593974; Tapasya, 9 Maes-y-Coed, Deganwy, Conwy LL31 9NQ Tel: 01492 583236 — MB BS 1972 Mysore; DCH Dub. 1981. (Mysore Med. Coll.) GP Princip. Llandudno. Prev: Trainee GP E.bourne VTS; SHO (Geriat. Med.) St. Luke's Hosp. Huddersfield.

JAYARAM, Neelakantapuram 27 Farndale, Widnes WA8 9JL — MB BS 1965 Bangalore.

JAYARAM, Puthukodi Kottuthodi Stantonbury Health Centre, Stantonbury, Milton Keynes MK14 6BL Tel: 01908 318989 — MD 1969 Bangalor; MD Bangalore 1969; MB BS Lucknow 1958; DTCD Wales 1975. (King Geo. Med. Coll.)

JAYARAM, Ravi 29 Upton Park, Chester CH2 1DF — MB BS 1990 Newc.

JAYARAM, Valiyezhuth Krishnankutty 29 Upton Park, Chester CH2 1DF — MB BS 1953 Madras; FRCP Lond. 1986, M 1967; DTM & H Eng. 1957; TDD Wales 1958. (Stanley Med. Coll. Madras) Cons. Phys. Geriat. Countess of Chester Hosp. Socs: BMA & Brit. Geriat. Soc. Prev: Regist. (Med.) Merthyr Gen. Hosp. Merthyr Tydfil; Regist. (Med.) Worthing Hosp.; Med. Asst. (Geriat.) St. Jas. Hosp. Leeds.

***JAYARAMAN, Neelakantan** Hollies Health Centre, Swan Street, Merthyr Tydfil CF47 8ET Tel: 01685 723363 Fax: 01685 350106; 19 Harlech Drive, Merthyr Tydfil CF48 1JU — MB BS 1974 Delhi.

JAYARAMAN, Sunderarajan 9 Mounthaven Close, Wirral CH49 6NX — MB ChB 1994 Bristol.

JAYARATNAM, Ajitha Viranjini Hermine 2 The Mount, Lexden, Colchester CO3 4JR — MB BS 1997 Lond.

JAYARATNAM, Anthony St Valentine Rabindranath 270 Chase Side, Southgate, London N14 4PR Tel: 020 8440 9301 Fax: 020 8449 9349; 56 Queen Elizabeth Drive, Southgate, London N14 6RD Tel: 020 8886 6071 Fax: 020 8449 9349 — MB BS 1965 Punjab; BSc Ceylon 1959; MB BS Punjab (Pakistan) 1965; DObst RCOG 1970. GP S.gate. Prev: Dist. Med. Off. Ceylon; SHO (Orthop. & Cas.) Corbett Hosp. Stourbridge; SHO (O & G) Warrington Gen. Hosp.

JAYARATNAM, Mariampillai Swanswell Medical Centre, Swanswell Street, Coventry CV1 5FT Tel: 02476 223250; 100A Hillmorton Road, Coventry CV2 1FW Tel: 02476 619996 — MB BS 1968 Ceylon; DFFP 1993; DRCOG 1980; DCH Ceylon 1972. (Ceylon)

JAYARATNAM, Ratnam (retired) 31 Lord Avenue, Redbridge, Ilford IG5 0HP Tel: 020 7749 7085 Fax: 020 7729 8264 — MB BS 1964 Ceylon; DPH Liverp. 1974; MFCM 1985; FFPHM RCP Lond. 1994; D Occ Med RCP 1998. Med. Advis. Benefits Agency Med. Servs. Hoxton Med. Centre. Prev: Cons. Pub. Health Med. Newham HA.

JAYARATNE, Bellanage Sunanda Sirimevan 349 Addiscombe Road, Croydon CR0 7LG Tel: 020 8654 2200 Fax: 020 8655 1358; 14 Langland Gardens, Croydon CR0 8DU Tel: 020 8776 1854 Fax: 020 8776 1854 — MB BS 1972 Colombo; MRCS Eng. LRCP Lond. 1983.

JAYARATNE, Norman Wilson General Hospital Anuradhapura, Anuradhapura (NCP), Sri Lanka Tel: 00 94 0252749 Fax: 94 332 3086; 100 Northumberland Road, Harrow HA2 7RG Tel: 0208 868 7184 Email: normanj@lanka.com.lk — MB BS 1968 Ceylon (Colombo); MB BS Ceylon 1968; MRCPI 1989. (Colombo, Ceylon) Cons. Phys. (Gen. Med.) Gen. Hosp. Anuradhapura, Sri Lanka; Vis. Cons. Phys. (Gen. Med.); Nawaloka Gen. (Private) Hosp., Colombo Sri Lanka. Socs: BMA. Prev: Regist. (Geriat. Med.) N. Middlx. & St. Ann's Hosp. Lond.; Regist. (Geriat. Med.) Vict. Hosp. Mansfield; SHO (Gen. & Geriat. Med.) N. Tyneside Gen. Hosp. & Preston Hosp.

JAYARATNE, Sunil Vijayanthi 43/96 Poorwarama Mawatha, Colombo 5, Sri Lanka Tel: 00 94 1 544 444; 100 Northumberland Road, Harrow HA2 7RG — MB BS 1975 Sri Lanka; DA (UK) 1990. (Fac. of Med. Univ. Colombo, Sri Lanka) Staff Anaesth. Nawaloka Private Hosp. Colombo, Sri Lanka. Prev: Regist. (Anaesth.) Dryburn Hosp. Durh.; SHO (Anaesth.) Shotley Bridge Gen. Hosp. Consett.; SHO (Cardiol.) Gen. Hosp. Colombo, Sri Lanka.

JAYASEKARA, Keith Saman Elm Farm House, Maldon Road, Burnham-on-Crouch CM0 8NT — MB ChB 1994 Dundee.

JAYASEKERA, Akila Indrajith department of Psychiatry, Royal Bolton Hospital, Bolton BL4 0JR — MB ChB 1990 Manch.; MRC Psych 1995; MSc 1999 Univ of Manc.

JAYASEKERA, Dushyantha Sanjeva 97 Green Lane, Horwich, Bolton BL6 7RQ — MB ChB 1991 Manch.

JAYASEKERA, Lokurallage Abhaya Gamini 11 Walmer Avenue, Bishop Auckland DL14 6NW — MB BS 1956 Ceylon; FFA RCS Eng. 1967.

JAYASEKERA, Narlaka Hillcroft, Green Lane, Chessington KT9 2DS — MB BS 1996 Lond.

JAYASENA, Kanishka 272 Chessington Road, West Ewell, Epsom KT19 9XF — MB BS 1993 Lond.

JAYASENA, Shyama Dakshina Flat B 58 Crayford Road, London N7 0ND — MB BS 1987 Lond.; BSc Immunol. & Immunopharmacol. Lond. 1984; MRCP (UK) 1992. Regist. (Renal) St. Peters Gp. Middlx. Hosp. Lond.

JAYASINGHE, Dulip Samankumara 22 Springhouse Road, Sheffield S10 1LT — MB ChB 1993 Sheff.

JAYASURIYA, Ananda Lakshman Nihal (retired) Millbrook Gardens Surgery, Millbrook Gardens, Castle Cary BA7 7EE Tel: 01963 350210 Fax: 01963 350366 — MB BS 1964 Ceylon. Prev: Regist. (Anaesth.) Metrop. Hosp. Lond.

JAYASURIYA, Hareetha 15 St Julien Close, New Duston, Northampton NN5 6QX — MB BS 1970 Ceylon.

JAYASURIYA, Nishirani Lanka Doctors Mess, St. James University Hospital, Leeds LS9 7TF Tel: 0113 206 4393 Fax: 0113 206 4393 Email: lankaj@aol.com; 6/1 Wijerama Mawatha, Colombo 7, Sri Lanka Tel: 00 94 01 691206 — MB ChB 1997 Leeds. Ho. Off. (Gen. Surg.) SJUH Leeds. Prev: Cardiol./Gen. Med. SJUH Leeds; Endocrinol./Gen. Med. SJUH Leeds; Urol. SJUH Leeds.

JAYASWAL, Mr Baidya Nath (Surgery) 171 Bawtry Road, Brinsworth, Rotherham S60 5ND; 68 Queensway, Moorgate, Rotherham S60 3EE Tel: 01709 79551 — MB BS 1963 Patna; FRCS Ed. 1971. (P. of Wales Med. Coll.) Prev: SHO (Orthop.) Norf. & Norwich Hosp.; Regist. Cumbld. Infirm. Carlisle; Regist. Sheff. RHB.

JAYASWAL, Rakesh 68 Queensway, Rotherham S60 3EE — MB ChB 1997 Manch.

JAYATILAKA, George Kingsley Elmsleigh Drive Surgery, 194 Elmsleigh Drive, Leigh-on-Sea SS9 4JQ Tel: 01702 470705 Fax: 01702 471153; 16 Wansfell Gardens, Thorpe Bay, Southend-on-Sea SS1 3SW Tel: 01702 586416 — MB BS 1970 Ceylon; MRCOG 1984; DRCOG 1979. (Univ. Ceylon, Colombo) Clin. Asst. (Dermat.) S.end Hosp.

JAYATILAKA, Mr Malwattage Nimal Deepala Priyasoma Department of Obstetrics & Gynaecology, West Cumberland Hospital, Whitehaven CA28 8JG Tel: 01960 82585101946 693181; The Leap, 5 South Lodge, Simonscales Lane Cockfrmooth, Cockermouth CA13 9DH Tel: 01900 825851 — FRCSEZ 2000; MB BS Ceylon 1968; MS (Obst. & Gyn.) Ceylon 1989; MFFP 1993; MRCOG 1987; FRCOG 1999. Cons. Obstet. & Gyn. Prev: Staff Grade (O & G) Frenchay Hosp. Bristol; Regist. (O & G) St. Mary's Hosp. Newport, I. of Wight, St. Pauls Hosp. Cheltenham & P.ss Alexandra Hosp. Harlow.

JAYATILAKE, Naomi Anne 18 Sellerdale Avenue, Wyke, Bradford BD12 9LJ — MB ChB 1997 Liverp.

JAYATILLAKE, Sarojinie Margaret Damayanthi 73 Queenborough Gardens, Gantshill, Ilford IG2 6YB Tel: 020 8550 0048 — MB BS 1976 Sri Lanka; MRCP (UK) 1984; Dip. Occ. Med. RCP Lond. 1996. (Faculty of Medicine - Colombo (Sri Lanka)) SCMO (Occupat. Health) Havering Hosp. Trust. Prev: Sen. Community Med. Off. (Adult Health) Redbridge HA Ilford.

JAYATILLAKE, Weerasinghe Arachige Henry Julius Ranjit No 26 Maidenhead Road, Windsor SL4 5EQ Tel: 01753 856303 — Vrach 1970 (per GMC); Dipl. in Therap. (Univ. Wales) 2001; Dipl. Fac. of Family Plann. and Reproductive Care 1995. Gen. Practitioner, Kensington, Chelsea & W.m. Health Auth. Socs: Med. Protec. Soc. Prev: Civil. Med. Practitioner 1993-1996; 12 RSME Regt., Chatham Barracks Sch., Kent 1993-1994; RAF Woodbridge, Suff. 1995.

JAYATUNGA, Mr Ajantha Perera Russells Hall Hospital, Dudley DY1 2HQ Tel: 01384 244243 Fax: 01384 244163; The Gables, 34 Redlake Drive, Pedmore, Stourbridge DY9 0RX Tel: 01562 886001 Fax: 01562 886001 Email: ajantha@doctors.org.uk — MB BS 1980 Colombo; MS Sri Lanka 1989; FRCS Eng. 1985; FRCS Ed. 1984. Cons. Surg. Gen. & Vasc. Russells Hall Hosp. Dudley. Socs: Vasc. Surg. Soc.; Eur. Vasc. Soc.; Assn. Surg. Prev: Sen. Regist. (Gen. Surg.) Hillingdon Hosp.; Regist. (Cardiothoracic Surg.) St. Mary's Hosp. Lond.; Regist. (Gen. Surg.) St. Chas. Hosp. Lond.

JAYATUNGA, Rasieka Paediatric Department, Sandwell District General Hospital, Lyndon, West Bromwich B71 4HJ Tel: 0121 553 1831 Fax: 0121 500 5630 Email: rasieka.jayatunga@swellhot.wmids.nhs.uk — MB BS 1979 Colombo; 2001 FSLCP; MRCS Eng. LRCP Lond. 1982; MRCP (UK) 1984; DCH RCP Lond. 1982; FRCPCH 1997. (Univ. of Colombo, Sri Lanka) Cons. Paediat. Sandwell Dist. Gen. Hosp. W. Midl.; Hon. Cons. Paediat. Twins & Multiple Births (TAMBA) Assoc.; Hon. Sen. Lect. Dept of Paed. Birm Univ. Med. Sch. Socs: Multiple Births Foundat.; RCP; RCPCH. Prev: Sen. Regist. Sandwell Dist. Gen. Hosp.; Sen. Regist. (Paediat.) N.wick Pk. Hosp. & Hosp. Sick Childr. Gt. Ormond St. Lond.; Lect. W.m. & Char. Cross Med. Sch. Lond.

JAYATUNGA, Uditha Perera — MB BS 1983 Peradeniya; MRCP (Irel.) 1996. Specialist Regist. (Rehabil. Med.) & Reg. Rehabil. Centre; Cons. in Rehabil. Med. Roy. Leamington Spa Hosp. Heathcode. NR. Warwick. Warks.. Socs: Brit. Echocardiogr. Soc. (Adult & Paediat. Accreditation); Brit. Soc. of Rehabil. Med.; Med. Defence Union. Prev: Research Regist. (Cardiac) WellHo. NHS Trust; Regist. (Med. for Elderly) Luton & Dunstable Hosp.; Regist. (Med. for Elderly) Derby Roy. Infirm.

JAYAWARDENA, Bodhini 87 Bishops Road, Trumpington, Cambridge CB2 2NR — MB BS 1980 Colombo; FFA RCSI 1985.

JAYAWARDENA, Mr Gardiya Manawaduge Upali 11 Lansdowne Close, Stanwix, Carlisle CA3 9HN Tel: 01228 39133 — MB BS 1979 Colombo; FRCS Glas. 1988; MS (Sri-Lanka) 1984; Vocational training GP Completed 1998. (Faculty of Medicine, Colombo Sri Lanka) Staff Grade A&E.

JAYAWARDENE, Satishkumar Abeythunge 42 West Park Avenue, Kew, Richmond TW9 4AL — MB BS 1996 Lond.

JAYAWARDHANA, Sunil Ranjit Department of Obstetrics & Gynaecology, Epsom General Hospital, Dorking Road, Epsom KT18 7EG Tel: 01372 735735; 89 Ashley Road, Epsom KT18 5BN Tel: 01372 723812 — MB BS 1973 Sri Lanka; MRCOG 1986. (Faculty of Medicine, Colombo, Sri.Lanka) Assoc. Specialist (O & G) Epsom Gen. Hosp. Surrey. Socs: Brit. Soc. Clin. Path.

JAYAWEERA, Raja Lakshman Arumabadu 4 Connaught Drive, London NW11 6BJ Tel: 020 8458 2548 Fax: 0208 458 7266 — MB BS 1961 Ceylon; LLB Lond. 1978, MA 1989; FFA RCS Eng. 1967; DA Eng. 1965. (Ceylon) Barrister-at-Law Middle Temple; Cons. Anaesth. Whittington Hosps. Lond. Socs: BMA. Prev: Med. Asst. Roy. N.. Hosp. Lond.; Regist. Barnet Gen. Hosp.; Ho. Off. (Anaesth.) Colombo Hosp. Gp.

JAYAWEERA, Ramanie Dimanthi 4 Connaught Drive, London NW11 6BJ — MB BS 1989 Lond. (Uniersity College) SHO Rotat. (Anaesth.) Roy. Hosps. Trust Lond. Socs: BMA; Train. Mem. Assn. AnE.h.; MRCAnaesth. Prev: SHO Rotat. (Gen. Med.) N. Middlx. Hosp. Lond.; SHO (A & E) Edgware Gen. Hosp. Lond.; Ho. Phys. Mayday Hosp. Croydon.

JAYAWICKRAMA, Nithyanand Sudrickku Caerphilly District Miners Hospital, St Martin's Road, Caerphilly CF83 2WW — MB BS 1968 Ceylon; MRCOG 1978. Cons. O & G Caerphilly Dist. Miners Hosp. Socs: FRCOG; Brit. Soc. Gyn. Endoscopy & BMA. Prev: Cons. O & G P.ss Mary's RAF Hosp. Holton & P.ss of Wales RAF Hosp. Ely.

JAYCOCK, Philip David Cheltenham General Hospital, Sandford Road, Cheltenham GL53 7AN; 26 Howey Rise, Frodsham, Warrington WA6 6DN — MB ChB 1997 Bristol; BSc (Hons.) Bristol 1994. (Bristol University) SHO Cheltenham Gen. Hosp. Socs: MDU; BMA. Prev: SHO McNash Med. Centre Melbourne Australia; Ho. Surg. Bristol Roy. Infirm.; Ho. Phys. Derriford Hosp. Plymouth.

JAYE, Peter Daniel 62 Beryl Road, London W6 8JT — MB BS 1992 Lond.

JAYESINGHE, Dinesh Christopher Rex 390 Pinner Road, North Harrow, Harrow HA2 6EF — LMSSA 1996 Lond.

JAYNE, Mr David George Professorial Surgical Unit Level 8, Clinical Sciences Building, St. James's University Hospital, Beckett St., Leeds LS9 7TF Tel: 0113 243 3144; Weir Cottage, 267 Market St, Whitworth, Rochdale OL12 8TF — MB BCh 1989 Wales; BSc Wales 1986; FRCS Eng. 1994. (Welsh National School of Medicine) Lect. in Surg. - St. Jas. Univ. Hosp., Leeds. Socs: BMA. Prev: Regist. (Gen. Surg.) Burnley Gen. Hosp.

JAYNE, David Roland Walker Box 118, Renal Unit, Addenbrookes Hospital, Cambridge CB2 2QQ Tel: 01232 217259 Fax: 01223 336846 Email: dj106@cam.ac.uk; Tel: 020 7713 7090 — MB BChir 1981 Camb.; FRCP 1999; MA Camb. 1982, MD 1995; MRCP (UK) 1985. (Univ. Camb. & St. Thos. Hosp. Lond.) Cons. Nephrol. and Vasculitis. Socs: Roy. Soc. of Med. Prev: Clin. Research Fell. Gonville & Caius Coll. Camb.; Copeman Research Fell.sh. Arthritis & Rheum. Counc.; Regist. (Med.) St. Mary's Hosp. Lond.

JAYNE, Mr William Howard Wise 10 Wolsey Close, Coombe Lane W., Kingston upon Thames KT2 7ER Tel: 020 8942 6294; 31 Queen Anne Street, London W1 Tel: 020 7580 1611 — MRCS Eng. LRCP Lond. 1940; MS Lond. 1957, MB BS 1940; FRCS Eng. 1949. (Westm.) Sen. Cons. Surg. St. Stephen's Hosp. Lond.; Cons. Surg. St. Mary Abbot's Hosp. Lond.; Sen. Surg. Tutor W.m. Hosp. Med. Sch. Socs: Fell. Roy. Soc. Med.; Assn. Surgs. Prev: Sen. Surg. Regist. W.m. Hosp.

JAYRAN NEJAD, Yadollah Anaesthetic Department, Chase Farm Hospital, Enfield EN2 8JL Tel: 020 8366 6600; 64 Ossulton Way, London N2 0LB Tel: 020 8815 0582 — MD 1979 Tehran; BA (Hons.) Tehran 1973; MRCP (UK) 1987; FCAnaesth. 1990. Cons. Anaesth. & Pain Managem. Chase Farm Hosp. Enfield. Socs: Obst. Anaesth. Assn.; Pain Soc.; Internatinal Assn. for Study of Pain. Prev: Sen. Regist. Roy. Lond. Hosp.; Regist. (Med.) Cuckfield Hosp. Haywards Heath; Supt. Tauheed Hosp. Sanandaj, Iran.

JAYSON, David William Howard Southport & Formby DGH, Town Lane, Kew, Southport PR8 6PN Tel: 01704 547471; 11 Mossgiel Avenue, Ainsdale, Southport PR8 2RE Tel: 01704 572334 — MB ChB 1981 Liverp.; FFA RCS Eng. 1986; DA Eng. 1984. Cons. Anaesth. & IC S.port & Ormskirk NHS Trust.

JAYSON, Dinah Consultant Child Psychiatrist, Child and Family Centre, Chapel Rd Clinic, Chapel Road, Manchester M33 12G Tel: 0161 969 3026 Fax: 0161 976 3224 Email: dinahjayson@yahoo.co.uk; Email: dinahjayson@yahoo.co.uk — BM BCh 1987 Oxf.; 1995 MSc (Psychiat.) Manch.; BA Oxf. 1984; MRCPsych 1993; 1998 Intermediate Level Cert. In Family Therapy. p/t Cons. (Child Psychiat.), Dept of Child Psychiat., Trafford, Manch.. Socs: Brit. RCPsych.; BMA; Manch. Med. Soc. Prev: Sen. Regist. (Child Psychiat.) Manch.; Squibb Research Fell. Univ. Oxf.; Locum Cons., Stepping Hill.

JAYSON, Gordon Charles CRC Dept Medical Oncology, Christie Hospital, Wilmslow Rd, Withington, Manchester M20 4BX Tel: 0161 446 3000 Fax: 0161 446 3299 Email: gordon.jayson@christie-tr.nwest.nhs.uk; 10 Parkfield Road South, Didsbury, Manchester M20 6DB Tel: 0161 445 3120 Email: gordonjayson@compuserve.com — BM BCh 1988 Oxf.; FRCP 2001; PhD Manch. 1996; BA (Hons.) Oxf. 1985; MRCP (UK) 1991. (Oxford) Sen. Lect. & Hon. Cons. in Med.Oncol.Christie Hosp. Manch. Socs: Assn. Cancer Phys.; Brit. Assn. Cancer Research; Eur. Soc. Med. Oncol. Prev: Sen. Regist. (Med. Oncol.) Christie Hosp. Manch.

JAYSON, Malcolm I V Rheumatic Diseases Centre, University of Manchester, Hope Hospital, Salford M6 8HD Tel: 0161 787 4369 Fax: 0161 787 4687; The Gate House, 8 Lancaster Road, Didsbury, Manchester M20 2TY Tel: 0161 445 1729 Fax: 0161 448 8195 — MB BS 1961 Lond.; MSc Manch. 1981; MD Bristol 1969; FRCP Lond. 1976, M 1964. (Middlx.) Prof. Rheum. Univ. Manch.; Hon. Cons. Phys. Salford Roy. Hosps. Trust. Socs: Pres. Internat. Soc. Study of Lumbar Spine; Assn. Phys. & Brit. Soc. Rheum. Prev: Sen.

Lect. Univ. Bristol; Cons. Bristol Roy. Infirm. & Roy. Nat. Hosp. Rheum. Dis. Bath.; Dir. Manch. & Salford Back Pain Centre.

JAYSON, Sylvia Jean Speke Health Centre, North Parade, Liverpool L24 2XP Tel: 0151 486 2694; 8 Garth Drive, Liverpool L18 6HW Tel: 0151 724 2693 Fax: 0151 724 2693 — MB BS 1955 Durh. (Newc.) Police Surg. Merseyside Police.

JAZEEL, Suvendrini Nadine (retired) 202 Ashburnham Road, Ham, Richmond TW10 7NL Tel: 020 8940 7749 Fax: 020 8940 8309 Email: star.opt@ukgateway.net — MB BS Lond. 1958; FRCPCH 1997; DCH Eng. 1962. Prev: Acting Cons. Community Paediat. Riverside HA.

JAZRAWI, Henna Habib 98 Argyle Road, London W13 8EL — MB ChB 1967 Baghdad; MRCOG 1983.

JAZRAWI, Riyadh Paulus Esa Department of Medicine II, St. George's Hospital Medical School, Cranmer Terrace, London SW17 0RE Tel: 020 8672 1255 — MB ChB 1974 Baghdad; MSc Baghdad 1978, MB ChB 1974.

JEANES, Alan Lloyd The Retreat, 4 Oldfield Road, Bickley, Bromley BR1 2LF Tel: 020 8467 1019 — MB BS 1950 Lond.; MD Lond. 1968; MRCS Eng. LRCP Lond. 1947; FRCPath 1971, M 1963. (Guy's) Emerit. Cons. Microbiol. Guy's Hosp. Lond. Socs: Fell. Roy. Soc. Trop. Med. & Hyg.; Assn. Clin. Pathols. Prev: Sen. Lect. & Hon. Cons. Microbiol. Guy's Hosp. & Med. Sch. Lond.; Sen. Regist. (Clin. Path.) Nat. Hosp. Nerv. Dis. Qu. Sq.; Regist. (Clin. Path.) Hosp. Sick Childr. Gt. Ormond St. Lond.

JEANES, Annmarie Christine Flat 3, 163 Nightingale Lane, London SW12 8NL — MB BS 1988 Lond.

JEANNON, Mr Jean Pierre 35A Devonshire Place, Jesmond, Newcastle upon Tyne NE2 2NB Tel: 0191 212 0735 — MB ChB 1991 Birm.; ChB Birm. 1991; FRCS (ENT) Eng. 1995. Specialist Regist. (Otolaryngol.) Freeman Hosp. Newc.; Clin. Research Assoc. Dept. Surg. Univ. Newc. Socs: Brit. Assn. Otol.; Brit. Assn. Head & Neck Surg.; Otorhinol. Research Soc. Prev: SHO (ENT) Qu. Eliz. Hosp.

JEANRENAUD, Paul 98 Green Lane N., Childwall, Liverpool L16 8NL — MB ChB 1998 Liverp.; MB ChB Liverp 1998.

JEANS, Alexander Francis Hugletts Farm, Hugletts Lane, Heathfield TN21 9BY — BChir 1998 Camb.; BChir Camb 1998; MB Bchir Camb 1998.

JEANS, June Evelyn (retired) Lark Rise, West Oakwood, Hexham NE46 4LB Tel: 01434 607307 — MB BS 1952 Durh.; BSc Durham. 1951, MB BS 1952, DPM 1962; MRCPsych 1972. Prev: Cons. Child Psychiat. Dept. Child & Family Psychiat. Dist. Gen. Hosp.

JEANS, Susannah Lucy Margaret Lydart House, Monmouth NP25 4RJ — MB BS 1996 Lond.

JEANS, Vanessa Constance Dartford West Health Centre, Tower Road, Dartford DA1 2HA; Pencroft, Pencroft Drive, Dartford DA1 2PB Tel: 01322 223871 — MB BS 1985 Lond.; MRCGP 1989. (St Mary's, London) Med. Off. Bridge Hse. Detox Unit StoneHo. Hosp. Dartford. Prev: SHO (Psychiat.) Joyce Green Hosp. Dartford; SHO (A & E) Brook Gen. Hosp. Lond.

JEANS, William Dampier College of Medicine, Sultan Qaboos University, PO Box 32485 Al-Khod, Muscat, Oman Tel: 00 968 515149 Fax: 00 968 513419; 3 Napier Road, Bristol BS6 6RT Tel: 01179 741036 — MB BS 1955 Lond.; MRCS Eng. LRCP Lond. 1955; FRCR 1975; FFR 1973; DMRD Eng. 1970; DObst RCOG 1958. (St. Thos.) Prof. Radiol. Sultan Qaboos Univ. Oman. Socs: BMA & Brit. Inst. Radiol. Prev: Reader in Radiodiag. Univ. Bristol; Chairm. Dept. Radiol. Bristol HA (T); Sen. Lect. (Radiodiag.) Univ. Bristol.

JEARY, Derek North House Surgery, 28 North Street, Ripon HG4 1HL Tel: 01765 690666; 10 Mallorie Park Drive, Ripon HG4 2QD Tel: 01765 605565 — MB BS 1971 Newc.; MRCGP 1975; DObst RCOG 1975. (Newc. u. Tyne) Trainer (Gen. Pract.) N.allerton VTS; Clin. Asst. (Psychiat.) Harrogate Health Care Trust; Clin. Asst. Ripon Community Hosp. Hosp.; Mem. Harrogate Health Care Trust (Drug & Therap. Comm.); Mem. N. Yorks. Area Prescribing Comm. Socs: Harrogate Med. Soc. Prev: Trainee GP Newc. VTS; Ho. Phys. & Ho. Surg. Roy. Vict. Infirm. Newc.

JEAVONS, David Anthony Netherlaw Surgery, 28 Stanhope Road, Darlington DL3 7SQ Tel: 01325 380640 Fax: 01325 350938 — MB BS 1972 Newc.; MRCGP 1980.

JEAVONS, Garth Hadley (retired) 45 Sandygate Park, Sheffield S10 5TZ Tel: 0114 230 2793 — MB ChB 1952 Birm.; MRCS Eng. LRCP Lond. 1952; FRCGP 1975, M 1966.

JEAVONS, Mary Patricia 42 Westfield Road, Edgbaston, Birmingham B15 3QG — MB ChB 1946 Birm.

JEAVONS, Paul Ecclesfield Group Practice, 96A Mill Road, Ecclesfield, Sheffield S35 9XQ Tel: 0114 246 9151; 1 Remington Avenue, Sheffield S5 9PA Tel: 0114 232 2803 Fax: 0114 285 5724 — MB ChB 1972 Sheff.; MRCGP 1977; Cert. Community Paediat. 1989; Cert. Family Plann. 1981; DObst RCOG 1975. MPS; Hosp. Pract. (Orthop.) N. Gen. Hosp. Sheff.; GP Trainer Trent RHA; Mem. Sheff. LMC. Socs: BMA; BDA. Prev: SHO (Paediat.) Sheff. AHA (T); SHO (A & E) Sheff. Roy. Infirm.; SHO (Obst.) N.. Gen. Hosp. Sheff.

JEAVONS, Sylvia Mary (retired) 45 Sandygate Park, Sheffield S10 5TZ Tel: 0114 230 2793 — MB ChB 1949 Birm.; MRCP Lond. 1953; MRCGP 1962.

JEBB, David Nicholas Richmond Road Medical Centre, 95 Richmond Road, Kingston upon Thames KT2 5BT Tel: 020 8546 1961 Fax: 020 8974 9008 — MB ChB 1975 Birm.; Cert. Family Plann. JCC 1982; Cert. Occupat. Med. 1997. Socs: Soc. Occupat. Med. Prev: SHO (Obst.) Marston Green Hosp. Birm.; SHO (Anaesth.) Qu. Eliz. Hosp. & Selly Oak Hosp. Birm.

JEBB, Gillian Aida Giggs Hill Surgery, 14 Raphael Drive, Thames Ditton KT7 0EB Tel: 020 8398 8619 Fax: 020 8398 8874; 205 Richmond Road, Kingston upon Thames KT2 5DD — MB ChB 1975 Birm.

JEDDO, Said Abdullah Tigris, 96 Okus Road, Old Town, Swindon SN1 4JP — MB ChB 1964 Baghdad; DCP Baghdad 1970; MPhil. Leic. 1977. (Univ. Baghdad) Socs: BMA; Assn. Soc. Authors. Prev: Cons. Path. Kent & Canterbury Hosp.; Cons. Path. Papworth Hosp. Camb.; Sen. Regist. (Histopath.) Roy. Devon & Exeter Hosp.

JEDDY, Mr Taleb Ali Basildon Hospital, Nether Mayne, Basildon SS16 5NL — MB BS 1982 Madras; FRCS Eng. 1988; MD 1998. Cons. Surg.

JEDRZEJCZYK, Andre 16 Bridges Road, Scunthorpe DN17 1LP — MB BS 1987 Newc.

JEDRZEJEWSKI, John Anthony White House Surgery, 1 Cheriton High Street, Folkestone CT19 4PU Tel: 01303 275434 Fax: 01303 271921 — MB BS 1979 Lond.; DRCOG 1983.

JEELANI, Ghulam Burnett Edgar Medical Centre, Central Drive, Walney Island, Barrow-in-Furness LA14 3HY Tel: 01229 474526 Fax: 01229 475282; 1 Dane Ghyll Garden, Barrow-in-Furness LA14 4RE Tel: 01229 838806 Fax: 01229 475282 — MB BS 1972 Ranchi; DMRT Aligerh 1976. (Rajendra Med. Coll. & Hosp. Ranchi Bihar, India) GP; Police Surg.; EMP for BAM.

JEELANI, Mohammad Sultan Wali Cinque Port Surgery, Cinque Port House, Cinque Port St., Rye TN31 7AN Tel: 01797 223230 Fax: 01797 227234; The Garden House, Watchbell St, Rye TN31 7HB Tel: 01797 222426 Fax: 01797 222426 Email: jeelani4@aol.com — MB BS 1966 Sind. GP; Lifeboat Med. Off.; Police Surg. Rye Sub-Div. E. Sussex. Prev: Police Surgern.

JEELANI, Noor Ul Owase 129 Beeston Road, Nottingham NG7 2JQ — BM BS 1997 Nottm.

JEELANI, Ruqia Akhtar Cinque Ports Surgery, Cinque Ports House, Cinque Ports St., Rye TN31 7AN Tel: 01797 223230 Fax: 01797 227234; The Garden House, Watchbell St, Rye TN31 7HB Tel: 01797 222426 Fax: 01797 222426 — MB BS 1966 Sind; Cert. Family Plann. JCC 1971; DA Eng. 1970. Family Plann. Off. Arthur Blackman Clinic & Buchanon Hosp. St Leonards.

JEENE, Harry Johannes Evert Health Policy Unit, London School of Hygiene & Tropical Medicine, Keppel St., London WC1E 7HT — Artsexamen 1987 Nijmegan; Artsexamen Nijmegen 1987.

JEER, Parminder Jit Singh 18 Firs Drive, Hounslow TW5 9TD — MB BS 1993 Lond.

JEET, Inder Lower Broughton Health Centre, Great Clowes Street, Salford M7 1RD Tel: 0161 839 2723 Fax: 0161 832 1210.

JEETLE, Mr Gurdev Singh 91 Wolsey Road, Northwood HA6 2ER — MB ChB 1964 Glas.; FRCS Glas. 1972. Prev: Resid. Ho. Off. (Surg.) Vict. Infirm. Glas.; Regist. (Surg.) Glas. Roy. Infirm. & Law Hosp. Carluke.

***JEETLEY, Paramjit Singh** 7 Britton Drive, Wylde Green, Sutton Coldfield B72 1EL; 53 Dewell Mews, Marlborough Road, Old Town, Swindon SN3 1QU Tel: 01793 431797 — MB ChB 1995 Bristol.

JEEVA RAJ, Manjarabad Venkataramanaswamy 30 Streetly Lane, Four Oaks, Sutton Coldfield B74 4TU Tel: 0121 308 0577 — MB BS 1962 Mysore; FRCP Lond. 1983; MRCP (UK) 1970. Cons. Phys. (Cardiol.) Good Hope Gen. Hosp. Sutton Coldfield; Hon. Sen. Lect. (Med.) Univ. Birm. Socs: Fell. Roy. Soc. Med.; W Midl. Phys. Assn.; Brit. Cardiac Soc.

JEEVAN, Mr Sivasamy Kandaswami Accident & Emergency Department, Oldchurch Hospital, Romford RM7 0BE Tel: 01708 708111 Fax: 01708 708123; 36 Ernest Road, Emerson Park, Hornchurch RM11 3JQ Tel: 01708 621005 Fax: 01708 702001 — MB BS 1974 Madras; FRCS Ed. 1981; FFAEM 1993. Cons. Surg. (A & E Med.) OlCh. Hosp. Romford. Socs: Brit. Assn. Emerg. Med.; BMA; Fell. Fac. A&E Med. Prev: Cons. Surg. Jeddah, Saudi Arabia.

JEEVARATNAM, Emil Anthony Jayawahan, Lt.-Col. RAMC Regional Clinical Director, Medical Reception Station, Hohne Garreson, B.F.P.O. 30, Ipswich Tel: 0049 5051 962218 Fax: 0049 5051 962881; c/o M.R.S. Hohne, Hohne Garrison, B.F.P.O. 30, Ipswich — MB BS 1975 Sri Lanka; DFFP (UK) 1998; T(GP) 1991; DA (UK) 1986. (Univ. Ceylon, Colombo Med. Fac.) Regional Clin. Director, Hohne Garrison, B.R.P.O. 30. Socs: Roy. Coll. Gen. Pract.; BMA; Fac. Fam. Plann. Prev: Sen. Med. Off. (Gen. Pract.) Med. Reception Station BFPO 605; Sen. Med. Off. (Gen. Pract.) Wattersham Station Med. Centre Ipswich; Sen. Med. Off. Med. Centre BFPO 106.

JEEVARATNAM, Sumathi 15 Kenley Road, Kingston upon Thames KT1 3RP — MB BS 1997 Lond.

JEEVES, Robert Simon 83 Sunfield Lane, Diggle, Oldham OL3 5PT — MB ChB 1998 Manch.; MB ChB Manch 1998.

JEEWA, Mahmood Azam Ismail 77 High Meadows, Compton, Wolverhampton WV6 8PP Tel: 01902 743532 — MB BS 1963 Rangoon; DO RCPSI 1976. (Rangoon Med. Coll.) Clin. Asst. (Ophth.) Wolverhampton & Midl. Cos. Eye Infirm.

JEFFCOATE, Catherine May 13 Grove Road, East Molesey KT8 9JS Tel: 020 8979 0609 — MB ChB 1986 Sheff.

JEFFCOATE, Stephen Lindsay 5 Elmhurst Drive, Dorking RH4 2BA Tel: 01306 884099 — MB 1964 Camb.; BChir 1963; PhD Lond. 1967; FRCPath 1984, M 1977. Freelance Indep. Cons. Surrey. Prev: Dep. Dir. Nat. Inst. Biol. Standards & Control Lond.; Prof. Biochem. Endocrinol. Chelsea Hosp. Wom. Lond.

JEFFCOATE, William James City Hospital, Hucknall Road, Nottingham NG5 1PJ Tel: 0115 962 7638 Fax: 0115 962 7959 — MB BChir 1971 Camb.; FRCP 1988; MRCP (U.K.) 1973. Cons. Phys. (Endocrinol.) City Hosp. Nottm.

JEFFERIES, Angus Edward 8 Lower Shapter Street, Topsham, Exeter EX3 0AT — MB BS 1998 Lond.; MB BS Lond 1998.

JEFFERIES, Daniel William 10 The Buntings, Covingham Park, Swindon SN3 5AS — MB BS 1989 Lond.; DRCOG 1993.

JEFFERIES, Elizabeth Myfanwy 25 Lowerbank Road, Fulwood, Preston PR2 8NS — MB ChB 1977 Sheff.

JEFFERIES, Georgina 12 Elwyn Road, Meols, Wirral CH47 7AP — MB BS 1979 Lond.; FFA RCS Eng. 1986. Cons. Anaesth. Arrowe Pk. Hosp. Wirral. Prev: Sen. Regist. (Anaesth.) Merseyside.

JEFFERIES, Gordon Douglas 6 Park Avenue, Greenock PA16 7QX — MB ChB 1976 Glas.

JEFFERIES, Nicholas John The Reptiles, 20 Inderwick Road, London N8 9LD — MB BS 1975 Lond.; FCAnaesth 1989.

JEFFERIES, Sabine CJSU, HQ BFC, EPISKOPI BFPO 53 — State Exam Berlin 1991.

JEFFERIES, Sarah Jane Royal Marsden Hospital, Downs Road, Sutton SM2 5PT Tel: 020 8642 6011; 32 Torrano Cottages, Kentish Town, London NW5 2TA Tel: 020 7267 5836 — MB BS 1989 Lond.; BSc Lond. 1986; MRCP (UK) 1993; FRCR 1997. Regist. (Radiother.) Roy. Marsden Hosp.; Clin. Lect. Roy. Marsden Hosp. (Cancer Research).

JEFFERIES, Stephen Bowcott Parade Surgery, The Parade, Liskeard PL14 6AF Tel: 01579 342667 Fax: 01579 340650; Cartuther Mill, Roseland, Menheniot, Liskeard PL14 3PQ Tel: 01579 346520 — MB ChB 1980 Liverp.

JEFFERIES, Stephen David Byron The Leith Hill Practice, The Surgery, Capel, Dorking RH5 5EN Tel: 01306 711105 Fax: 01306 712969 — MB BS 1990 Lond.; BDS Lond. 1982; DRCOG 1994; DFFP 1994; DCH RCP Lond. 1992. (Char. Cross & Westm.)

JEFFERIES, Stephen Mark Maria 8 Beechwood Drive, Cobham KT11 2DX — MB BS 1983 Lond.; DRCOG 1985.

JEFFERIES, Trevor Wynne (Surgery) 292 Munster Road, Fulham, London SW6; Coombe House, Kingston Hill, Kingston upon Thames KT2 7JR Tel: 020 8546 1976 — LRCPI & LM, LRSCI & LM 1957; LRCPI & LM, LRCSI & LM 1957. Occupat. Health Adviser Lond. Boro. Hammersmith & Hounslow.

JEFFERIES-BECKLEY, Adele Louise Orchard Medical Practice, Orchard Road, Broughton Astley, Leicester LE9 6RG Tel: 01445 282599 Fax: 01445 286772 — MB ChB 1985 Leic.; BSc (Hons.) Surrey 1980.

JEFFERIS, Mr Anthony Faulkner Heatherwood & Wexham Hospital Trust, Slough SL2 4HL Tel: 01753 633075; Cedar Lodge, Rectory Close, Farnham Royal, Slough SL2 3BG Tel: 01753 644944 Fax: 01753 648693 — MB BChir 1974 Camb.; MA Camb. 1980, BA 1970, MChir 1985; FRCS Ed. 1981; FRCS Eng. 1979; DLO Eng. 1981. (Camb. & St. Thos.) Cons. ENT Surg. E. Berks. HA; Assoc. Dir. Postgrad. Med. Educat. Oxf. Socs: Roy. Soc. Med. (Treas. Laryngol. Sect.). Prev: Sen. Regist. (ENT) St. Mary's Hosp. & Roy. Marsden Hosp. Lond.; Regist. (ENT) Roy. Free Hosp. Lond.; TWJ Foundat. Fell. (Otol.) Univ. Calif., San Francisco, USA.

JEFFERISS, Mr Christopher David Princess Elizabeth Orthopaedic Centre, Royal Devon & Exeter Hospital, Barrack Road, Exeter EX2 5DW Tel: 01392 403565 Fax: 01392 403505; Lindrick, 405 Topsham Road, Countess Wear, Exeter EX2 7AB — MB BS Lond. 1964; FRCS Eng. 1970; Specialist Accredit. (Orthop.) RCS Eng. 1975. (Middlx.) Cons. Orthop. Trauma & Hand Surg. P.ss Eliz. Orthop. Centre & Roy. Devon & Exeter Hosp. Wonford; Clin. Dir. Orthops. & Trauma & Rheum. Socs: Fell. BOA; Brit. Soc. Surg. Hand; Brit. Orthop. Foot Surg. Soc. Prev: Sen. Regist. (Orthop. & Traum. Surg.) Devon, Cornw. & I. of Scilly AHAs; Regist. (Surg.) W. Dorset Gp. Hosps.; Cas. Surg. Off. Middlx. Hosp.

JEFFERS, Lesley Margaret Danetre Medical Practice, The Health Centre, London Road, Daventry NN11 4EJ Tel: 01327 703333 Fax: 01327 311221; Middlemore House, 26 Drayton Park, Daventry NN11 5TB — MB BS 1982 Lond.

JEFFERS, Russell Francis 33 Seymour Street, Flat 2/2, Dundee DD2 1HA — MB ChB 1996 Dundee.

JEFFERSON, Mr Antony Andrew Bryn Ingli, Cardigan Road, Newport SA42 0LZ Tel: 01239 820553 — BM BCh Oxf. 1944; BSc Oxf. 1942, MA 1947; MD CM McGill 1943; FRCS Eng. 1950. Socs: Fell. Roy. Soc. Med.; Soc. Brit. Neurol. Surgs. Prev: Cons. Neurosurg. Emerit.; Cairns Lect. Adelaide S. Austral.; Pybus Lect. Newc. u Tyne.

JEFFERSON, David Linden, Potter St., Spondon, Derby DE21 7LH — MB BS 1968 Lond.; MD Lond. 1982; FRCP Lond. 1985; MRCP (UK) 1972. (St. Bart.) Cons. Neurol. Qu.s Med. Centr NHS Trust, Nottm. (T) & Derbysh. Roy. Infirm. Derby. Socs: BMA. Prev: Sen. Regist. (Clin. Neurol.) Nat. Hosp. Nerv. Dis. Qu. Sq. Lond. & King's Coll. Lond.; Ho. Phys. Med. Profess. Unit St. Bart. Hosp. Lond.

JEFFERSON, Frances Anne 1 Perthneidr Cottages, Sarnau, Llandysul SA44 6QG — MB BS 1983 Lond.

JEFFERSON, Harold Alexander Lisburn Health Centre, Linenhall Street, Lisburn BT28 1LU — MB BCh BAO 1967 Belf.; FRCGP 1992, M 1972; DObst RCOG 1969. (Qu. Univ. Belf.) Hosp. Pract. (Geriat.) Day Hosp. & Lagan Valley Hosp. Lisburn.

JEFFERSON, Ian Guy Hull Royal Infirmary, Anlaby Road, Hull HU3 2JZ Tel: 01482 328541 — MB ChB 1973 Liverp.; MD Liverp. 1987; FRCP Lond. 1994; FRCPCH 1997; DCH Eng. 1976. Cons. Paediat. Endocrinol. Hull Roy. Infirm. Prev: Cons. Paediat. Khamis Mushayt, Saudi Arabia; Sen. Regist. Oxf. RHA; Regist. Hosp. Sick Childr. Lond.

JEFFERSON, Janet Collins, MBE 78 Circular Road, Belfast BT4 2GD Tel: 01232 768206; 78 Circular Road, Belfast BT4 2GD Tel: 01232 768206 — MB ChB Glas. 1939. (Glas.) Socs: Fell. Roy. Soc. Med.; Brit. Assn. Wom. Police; BMA & Assn. Police Surgs. Gt. Brit. Prev: Accredit. Med. Off. N.. Irel. to Consul-Gen. of France; Resid. Ho. Phys. & Ho. Surg. Glas. Roy. Infirm.; Forens. Med. Off. Police Auth. N. Irel.

JEFFERSON, John Michael (retired) 3 Bishbury Close, Edgbaston, Birmingham B15 3NU — BM BCh 1942 Oxf.; BA Oxf. 1938, BSc 1940, MA, DM 1953; FRCP Lond. 1960, M 1947. Prev: Cons. Neurol. United Birm. Hosps. & Warwick Hosp.

JEFFERSON, John Michael (retired) 3 Barrymore Crescent, Comberbach, Northwich CW9 6PA — BA Oxf. 1963, BM BCh 1966; FRCP Lond. 1983; MRCP (UK) 1970. Cons. Phys. Warrington

Hosp. NHS Trust; Med. Dir. Warrington Hosp. NHs Trust 1993-1999. Prev: Sen. Med. Regist. Liverp. AHA (T).

JEFFERSON, Jonathon Ashley Level II South, Belfast City Hospital, Belfast BT9 7DB Tel: 01232 329241 Fax: 01232 263535; 1b Windsor Close, Malone, Belfast BT9 6FG — MB BCh BAO 1989 Belf.; MD Belf. 1995; MRCP (UK) 1992. Specialist Regist. (Nephrol.) Belf.

JEFFERSON, Kieran Paul Flat 6, 29 Berkeley Square, Clifton, Bristol BS8 1HP — BM BCh 1993 Oxf.; MA Camb. 1994. Demonst. (Anat.) Univ. Bristol; SHO Rotat. (Surg.) Bristol Roy. Infirm. Prev: SHO (A & E) Soton. Gen. Hosp.; Ho. Surg. John Radcliffe Hosp. Oxf.; Ho. Phys. Poole Hosp.

JEFFERSON, Margaret (retired) 3 Bishbury Close, Edgbaston, Birmingham B15 3NU — MB ChB 1942 Manch. Prev: Med. Off. Dudley Corp.

JEFFERSON, Margaret Eirlys (retired) Bryn Ingli, Cardigan Road, Newport SA42 0LZ Tel: 01239 820553 — MB BS (Hons.) Lond. 1944; MRCP Lond. 1947; MRCS Eng. LRCP Lond. 1944; DCH Eng. 1947. Prev: Carnegie Foundat. Research Asst. (Child Health) Sheff. Univ.

JEFFERSON, Melanie Jane University Hospital of Wales (UHW), Heath Park, Cardiff CF4 4YG Tel: 029 2074 3377 Fax: 029 2074 3723; 56 Herbert March Close, Danescourt, Cardiff CF5 2TD — MB BCh 1986 Wales; BSc Wales 1983; MRCP (UK) 1991; MRCGP 1990; DRCOG 1988. Cons. (Palliat. Med.) Univ. Hosp. Wales & Holme Tower. Prev: Sen. Regist. (Palliat. Med.) Velindre Hosp. Cardiff.; Regist. (Palliat. Med.) Duchess of Kent Hse. Reading; Staff Grade Phys. (Palliat. Med.) Michael Sobell Hse. Oxf.

JEFFERSON, Miles Facundo The Limes, 50 High St., Weaverham, Northwich CW8 3HB — MB ChB 1993 Manch.

JEFFERSON, Natasha Ruth Flat 6, 29 Berkeley Square, Clifton, Bristol BS8 1HP — BM BCh 1996 Oxf.; MA. (Oxf.) Med. SHO Bristol Roy. Infirm.

JEFFERSON, Paul Dominic 3 Northside, Great Whittington, Newcastle upon Tyne NE19 2HR — MB BS 1989 Newc.

JEFFERSON, Robert Drysdale Rolls-Royce Plc, Moor Lane 22, Derby DE24 8BJ Tel: 01332 248073; 9 Harboro Close, Ashbourne DE6 1JX Email: r.d.jefferson@btinternet.com — MB BS 1986 Newc.; BSc (Hons.) (Genetics) Sheff. 1981; MRCGP 1991; MFOM 1998. (Newcastle) Regional Med. Off. Rolls-Royce Plc; Hon. Lect. (EnvironMent. & Occupat. Med.). Socs: BMA; FOM; SOM. Prev: Lect. Environm. & Occupat. Med.

JEFFERSON, Rosalind Joy Dingley Child Development Centre, Battle Hospital, Oxford Road, Reading RG30 1AG; 8 Abbots Mead, Cholsey, Wallingford OX10 9RJ Tel: 01491 652603 Email: ros_jeff@hotmail.com — MB BS 1994 Lond.; PhD Univ. Lond. 1977; BSc (Hons.) Bristol 1973; DIC 1977; MRCP 1998; MRCPCH 1998. (UMDS, London) Specialist Regist. Paediat. Oxf. region, S.ern Axis Rotat. Socs: Brit. Orthop. Research Soc. Prev: SHO Paediat. S.mead Hosp. Bristol; BioEngineer (Research) Orthop. Engin. Centre Univ. Oxf.; SHO Community Paediat. Frrenchary Hosp. Bristol.

JEFFERSON, Thomas Oliver, OStJ UK Cochrane Centre, Summertown Pavilion, Middle Way, Oxford OX2 7LG Tel: 01865 516300 Fax: 01865 516311 Email: tojl@aol.com — State DMS 1979 Pisa; FFPHM 1999; T(PHM) 1991; T(GP) 1991; MFPHM RCP (UK) 1990; MSc Community Med. 1988; DTM & H RCP Lond. 1986; MRCGP 1985; DRCOG 1982. Edmund Pk.es Prof.; Vis. Prof. Univ. Pavia Italy; Sen. Hon. Lect. (Pub. Health Med.) KCH Lond.; Co-ordinator Cochrane Collaboration Vaccines Field. Socs: Internat. Health Economists' Assn.; Health Economists' Study Gp.; Cochrane Collaboration Health Economists Study Gp. Prev: Cons. Pub. Health Med. Rome; Sen. Med. Off. GI Market Testing UK Support Command, Germany; Asst. Force Med. Off. United Nations Protec. Force, Yugoslavia.

JEFFERSON, Wendy Leigh (retired) Chantry House, Vicarage Close, Cookham, Maidenhead SL6 9SE Tel: 016285 28022 — MB BS 1954 Lond.; MB BS (Hnrs., Distinc. in Obst. & Gyn.) Lond; DObst RCOG 1956. Prev: Exec. Med. Dir. Ortho-Cilag Pharmaceut. Ltd. High Wycombe.

JEFFERSON, William Wallis Ballyclare Group Practice, Ballyclare Health Centre, George Avenue, Ballyclare BT39 9HL Tel: 028 9332 2575 Fax: 028 9334 9897; 27 Rathmena Gardens, Ballyclare BT39 9HU — MB BCh BAO 1966 Belf.; DObst RCOG 1968; MRCGP 1971; DCH RCPS Glas. 1968. Socs: BMA. Prev: SHO (Med.) Ards. Hosp. Newtownards; Ho. Surg. & Ho. Phys. Roy. Vict. Hosp. Belf.; Res. Obst. Ho. Off. Ulster Hosp. Dundonald.

JEFFERSON-LOVEDAY, John William Spring Gardens Health Centre, Providence Street, Worcester WR1 2BS Tel: 01905 681681 Fax: 01905 681699 — MB 1977 Camb.; BChir 1976.

JEFFERY, Daniel Maitland Stanley Surgery, Lak Lock Road, Stanley, Wakefield WF3 4HS — MB ChB 1987 Leeds; MRCGP 1992.

JEFFERY, David Christopher (retired) 37 Parrys Close, Stoke Bishop, Bristol BS9 1AW Tel: 0117 968 3152 Email: davidjeffery@compuserve.com — MB BS Lond. 1959; MRCS Eng. LRCP Lond. 1960; DObst RCOG 1960. Prev: Ho. Phys. (Paediat.) & Ho. Phys. Skin Depts. Char. Cross Hosp. Lond.

JEFFERY, David Graham The Health Centre, Westfield Walk, Leominster HR6 8HD Tel: 01568 612084 Fax: 01568 610340; Shop Cottage, Monkland, Leominster HR6 9DB Tel: 01568 720351 — MB BS 1978 Lond.; BSc Lond. 1975; MRCGP 1985; DRCOG 1982. (Univ. Coll. Hosp.) Prev: Trainee GP Hereford VTS.

JEFFERY, David Schofield (retired) Kenmore Cottage, The Friary, Old Windsor, Windsor SL4 2NP Tel: 01753 862491 — MB BChir Camb. 1952; MA Camb. 1955; DObst RCOG 1954.

JEFFERY, Dawn Marie Good Hope General Hospital, Rectory Road, Sutton Coldfield B75 7RR Tel: 0121 378 2211; 315 Reservoir Road, Selly Oak, Birmingham B29 6TB Tel: 0121 472 3409 — MB ChB 1990 Birm.; ChB Birm. 1990. SHO Rotat. (Gen. Med.) Good Hope Hosp. Birm. Prev: Ho. Off. (Med.) Good Hope Hosp. Birm.; Ho. Off. (Surg.) Selly Oak Hosp. Birm.

JEFFERY, Debra Caroline Jane Torbay Hospital, Lawes Bridge, Torquay TQ2 7AA — MB ChB 1994 Bristol. SHO (Med.) Torbay Hosp.

JEFFERY, Mr Ian Thomas Arthur Shirral House, Church Road, Shedfield, Southampton SO32 2HY — MB BS 1970 Lond.; FRCS Eng. 1975; MRCS Eng. LRCP Lond. 1970. Cons. Orthop. Surg. Qu. Alexandra Hosp. Portsmouth; Orthop. Regional Adviser Wessex. Socs: Fell. BOA; Soc. Surg. of Hand. Prev: Regist. (Surg.) Basingstoke Dist. Hosp.; SHO (Cas.) W. Middlx. Hosp. Isleworth; Ho. Surg. & Ho. Phys. W. Lond. Hosp.

JEFFERY, Mr James Andrew Queen Elizabeth Hospital, Gayton Road, Kings Lynn PE30 4ET Tel: 01553 613613 — MB BS 1988 Lond.; FRCS Eng. 1992. Cons. Orthopaedic Surg., Qu. Eliz. Hosp., Gayton Rd., Kings Lynn, Norf. Prev: Career Regist. (Orthop.) Roy. Free Hosp. Lond.

JEFFERY, John Richard Lynton Medical Centre, 1 Lynton Avenue, Boston Spa, Wetherby LS23 6BL Tel: 01937 842115 Fax: 01937 541657; 210 High Street, Boston Spa, Wetherby LS23 — MRCS Eng. LRCP Lond. 1972; MRCGP 1978.

JEFFERY, Katherine Joanna Mary Immunology Department, Imperial College School of Medicine St Mary's, Norfolk Place, London W2 1PG Tel: 020 7402 0653 Email: k.jeffery@ic.ac.uk; 45 Stratford Street, Cross St, Oxford OX4 1SP Tel: 01865 240725 — BM BCh 1990 Oxf.; MA Camb. 1991; MRCP (UK) 1993; MRCPath 1998. Wellcome Clinc. Research Fell. (Microbiol.), Immunol. Dept., Imperial Coll. Sch. Med., Lond. Prev: Sen. Regist. & Regist. (Microbiol.) PHLS Oxf.; SHO (Gen. Med.) Centr. Oxf. Hosps.

JEFFERY, Keith Frederick Key Failsworth Health Centre, Ashton Road W., Failsworth, Manchester M35 0HN Tel: 0161 682 6297; 99 Dalston Drive, Manchester M20 5LQ Tel: 0161 448 9623 — MB ChB 1990 Manch.; BSc (Hons.) Manch. 1987; MRCGP 1995; DRCOG 1995. (Manchester)

JEFFERY, Lorraine Ann 42 Grosvenor Road, Northwood HA6 3JA — MB BS 1988 Lond.

JEFFERY, Mervyn Paul Barnhouse Surgery, Barnhouse Close, Lower St., Pulborough RH20 2HQ Tel: 0179 822815 Fax: 0179 887 2123; Lichfield, Georges Lane, Storrington, Pulborough RH20 3JH — MB BS (Hons. Med.) Lond. 1963; MRCS Eng. LRCP Lond. 1963; DObst RCOG 1965. (Guy's) Prev: Ho. Off. St. Richard's Hosp. Chichester; Ho. Surg. (Obst.) Cuckfield Hosp.

JEFFERY, Mr Patrick James Dorset County Hospital, Williams Avenue, Dorchester DT1 2JY Tel: 01305 255489 Fax: 01305 254490; The Chantry, Martinstown, Dorchester DT2 9JR Tel: 01305 889322 Fax: 01305 889919 Email: pjj@wdi.co.uk — MB BS 1967 Lond.; FRCS Eng. 1972; MRCS Eng. LRCP Lond. 1967. (St. Mary's) Cons. Gen. Surg. W. Dorset Gen. Hosps. NHS Trust. Socs: Fell. Roy. Soc. Med; Brit. Assn. Surg. Oncol.; Assoc. Colop. Of GBI. Prev:

Research Fell. (Surg.) St. Mark's Hosp. Lond.; Regist. (Surg.) Bath Gp. Hosps.; Sen. Regist. (Gen. Surg.) Roy. Free Hosp. & Roy. N.. Hosp. Lond.

JEFFERY, Rachel Caroline Susan Dept. Of Rheum., N. Middlx. Hospital, Sterling Way, Edmonton, London N18 1QX — MB BS 1994 Lond.; BA 1991 (Hons) Cantab.; MRCP (UK) 1997. (University College London) Specialist Regist. in Rheum. And Gen. Med., N. Thams Region, Lond.; Clin. Edr. for Curr. Med. Literature Rheum., UK. Socs: Mem. of Roy. Coll. of Phys.s, Lond.; Mem. of Brit. Soc. for Pheumatology; Mem. of Brit. Med. Assn. Prev: Clin. Research Fell. & Hon. Regist. (Rheum.) Paediat. Rheum. Unit Dept. of Molecular Path. Univ. Coll. Lond.; Sen. Ho. Off. (Med.) N.wick Pk. Hosp. Harrow.

JEFFERY, Riaan Department of Paediatrics, Inverclyde Royal Hospital, Larkfield Road, Greenock PA16 0XN — MB ChB 1990 Pretoria.

JEFFERY, Mr Richard McKenzie (retired) Branklet, 61 Priests Lane, Shenfield, Brentwood CM15 8HG — MB BS 1960 Lond.; FRCS Eng. 1967. Prev: Cons. Surg. Basildon & Orsett Hosps.

JEFFERY, Robert Mark Randell 37 Inglis Road, Ealing, London W5 3RL — MB BS 1993 Lond.

JEFFERY, Robert Norman Mid Sussex Health Care, The Health Centre, Trinity Road, Hurstpierpoint, Hassocks BN6 9UQ Tel: 01273 834388 Fax: 01273 834529; 3 Tott Hill, Hurstpierpoint, Hassocks BN6 9QS Tel: 01273 834388 Fax: 01273 833864 Email: jeffery@lineone.net — MB BS 1968 Lond.; MRCS Eng. LRCP Lond. 1968; FRCGP 1991, M 1974; DObst RCOG 1970; DCH Eng. 1970. (Westm.) Socs: BMA. Prev: Ho. Surg. W. Middlx. Hosp. Isleworth; Ho. Surg. (Obst.) & & SHO (Paediat.) Kingston Hosp.

JEFFERY, Mr Robert Schofield — MB BChir 1981 Camb.; MA Camb. 1981; FRCS (Orth.) 1994; FRCS Eng. 1988; FRCS Ed. 1987. (St. John's Coll. Camb. & King's Coll. Hosp.) Cons. Orthop. Surg. Derriford Hosp. Plymouth. Socs: Fell.Brit. Orthopaedic Assn.; Brit. Soc. Childr.'s Orthop. Surg.; Europ. Soc. Motion Anal. in Childr. and Adults. Prev: Sen. Regist. (Orthop.) Roy. Manch. Childr. Hosp.; Regist. (Orthop.) Portsmouth & Alton.

JEFFERY, Steven, Capt. RAMC 8 Ochil View Gardens, Crieff PH7 3EJ — MB ChB 1989 Manch.; BSc St. And. 1986.

JEFFERYS, David Barrington Medicines Control Agency, Market Towers, 1 Nine Elms Lane,, London SW8 5NQ; 17 Scotts Avenue, Shortlands, Bromley BR2 0LG — MB BS 1976 Lond.; MD Lond. 1983, BSc (Hons.) 1973; FRCP Lond. 1992; FRCP Ed. 1990; MRCP (UK) 1978; MRCS Eng. LRCP Lond. 1976; FFPM RCP (UK). (Guy's) Dir. of Licensing DoH Med. Control Agency; Vis. Prof. Univ. Newc. Prev: Princip. Med. Off. DoH; Lect. & Regist. (Med.) Guy's Hosp. Lond.; Phys. Tunbridge Wells HA.

JEFFERYS, Peter Michael Northwick Park Hospital, Watford Road, Harrow HA1 3UJ Tel: 020 8869 2309 Fax: 020 8869 3516; 49 Swains Lane, London N6 6QL Tel: 020 8340 1478 — MB Camb. 1970, BChir 1969; FRCP Lond. 1992; MRCP (UK) 1971; FRCPsych 1983, M 1974. (Univ. Coll. Hosp.) Cons. Psychiat. N.wick Pk. Hosp. Harrow; Med. Dir. Harrow & Hillingdon Healthcare NHS Trust. Prev: Sen. Regist. Maudsley Hosp. Lond.; Regist. (Gen. Med.) N.wick Pk. Hosp. Harrow; Ho. Phys. & Ho. Surg. Univ. Coll. Hosp. Lond.

JEFFORD, Fiona Margaret Highmore, Beattock, Moffat DG10 9RD — MB ChB 1998 Glas.; MB ChB Glas 1998.

JEFFORD, Helen Anne 17 Rowe Avenue, Peacehaven, Newhaven; 63 Chichester Drive W., Saltdean, Brighton BN2 8SF — MB BCh 1976 Wales; MRCP (UK) 1980; MRCGP 1987. (Welsh National School of Medicine)

JEFFREE, Jennifer Susan Department of Diagnostic Radiology, Hope Hospital, Stott Lane, Salford M6 8HD Tel: 0161 787 4935; 11A Poplar Grove, Sale M33 3AX — MB ChB 1983 Manch.; BSc St. And. 1980; FRCR 1990; T(R0 (CR) 1993. p/t Cons. Diagn. Radiol. Salford Roy. Hosps. NHS Trust.

JEFFREE, Martin Andrew Department of Neuro Imaging, Kings College Hospital, Denmark Hill, London SE5 9RS Tel: 020 7737 4000; 248 Chislehurst Road, Petts Wood, Orpington BR5 1NT — MB ChB 1973 Liverp.; MRCP (UK) 1978; FRCR 1985. Cons. Neuroradiol. Kings Coll. Hosp. Lond. Prev: Cons. Neuroradiol. Greenwich HA; Sen. Regist. (Neuroradiol.) Radcliffe Infirm. Oxf.

JEFFREY, Andrew Alexander Northampton General Hospital, Northampton NN1 5BD Tel: 01604 34700; Manor Farm House, South View, Roade, Northampton NN7 2NS — MB ChB 1980 Ed.; BSc (Hons.) Ed. 1977; FRCP Ed. 1994; FRCP London 1997. (Univeristy of Edinburgh) Cons. Phys. N.ampton Gen. Hosp.; Hon. Sen. Lect. In Respirat. and Intens. Care Med., Univ. of Oxf., Sch. of Med., Oxf. Socs: Thoracic Soc.; Europ. Respirartory Soc. Prev: Lect. (Med.) Univ. Coll. Lond. Sch. Med.; Regist. (Gen. Med. & Respirat.) City Hosp. Edin.; Regist. Rotat. (Gen. Med.) Univ. Hosp. Wales. Cardiff.

JEFFREY, Danya Rachel Dept. Clinical Radiology, Bristol Royal Infirmary, Bristol — BM BCh 1992 Oxf.; FRCR 2000; MRCP (UK) 1995. Specialist Regist. (Radiol.) Roy. Infirm. Bristol. Prev: SHO (Psychiat.) Fair Mile Hosp. Wallingford.; SHO (Gen. Med.) Qu. Med. Centre Nottm.

JEFFREY, David Ian Three Counties Cancer Centre, Department of Palliative Medicine, Cheltenham General Hospital, Cheltenham GL53 7AN Tel: 01242 273447 Fax: 01242 274182 Email: david.jeffrey@egnhst.org.uk; The Old Dairy, Noverton Lane, Prestbury, Cheltenham GL52 5DD Tel: 01242 221521 Fax: 01242 221521 — MB ChB 1972 Ed.; MA (Med. Ethics) Keele 1992; BSc Ed. 1969; FRCP Ed. 1992; MRCP (UK) 1975; MRCGP 1988; DObst RCOG 1974. (Edinburgh) Macmillan Cons. Palliat. Med. Oncol. Centre Glos.; Hon. Sen. Lect. Dept. Palliat. Med. Univ. of Bristol. Socs: Assn. Palliat. Med. Prev: GP Evesham; Course Organiser Worcester VTS; Med. Dir. Evesham Community Hosp.

JEFFREY, Douglas Edward 14 Inchcape Terrace, Broughty Ferry, Dundee DD5 2LR; 4 Dovecote Mews, Cholton-cum-Hardy, Manchester M21 9HN Tel: 0161 881 7957 Email: dougella@easynet.co.uk — MB ChB 1993 Manch. (Manchester)

JEFFREY, Helen Margaret 4/10 Kenneth Street, Tamarama 2026, Australia — BM BS 1991 Nottm.; FRCA 1997. (Nottingham) Fell. Anaesth., St. Vincent's Hosp. Sydney, Australis. Socs: Assn. Anaesth.; Fell. Roy. Coll. Anaesth.; Intens. Care Soc.

JEFFREY, Iona Jane Mary Department of Histopathology, St George's Hospital, Tooting, London SW17 0QT Tel: 020 8725 5281 Fax: 020 8767 7984 Email: iona.jeffrey@stgh-tr.sthames.nhs.uk — MB ChB 1978 Ed.; BSc (Hons.) Ed. 1976; MRCPath 1990; FRCP 1999 Path. Cons. Perinatal/Paediatric Path. St. Geo. Hosp. Lond. Prev: Sen. Regist. (Histopath.) St. Bart. Hosp. Lond.; Wellcome Trust Fell. Path. & Hon. Lect. (Path.) Manch. Univ.; Lect. (Path.) Manch. Univ.

JEFFREY, James Shiels 49 Roman Court, Bearsden, Glasgow G61 2NW — MB ChB 1941 Glas. (Univ. Glas.)

JEFFREY, John Colin Somerville, MBE (retired) 14/39 Moringg side View, Maxwell St., Edinburgh EH10 5HU — MB ChB 1949 Aberd.

JEFFREY, Mr John Cuthbertson (retired) 2 High Beach House, Claremont Road, Seaford BN25 2QA — MB ChB 1940 Glas.; FRCS Glas. 1962; MFOM RCP Lond. 1978. Prev: Med. Dir. Firestone Plantations Co., Liberia.

JEFFREY, Margaret Joan Department of Histopathology, Queen Alexandra Hospital, Cosham, Portsmouth PO6 3LY Tel: 023 92 286458 Fax: 023 92 286493; Rowland House, Bowes Hill, Rowlands Castle PO9 6BP — MB ChB 1980 Birm.; BSc (1st cl. Hons.) Birm. 1977; FRCPath 1997. Cons. Histopath. & Cytopath. Qu. Alexandra Hosp. Cosham.

JEFFREY, Maurice Rutherford (retired) 35 Spring Lane, Burn Bridge, Harrogate HG3 1NP Tel: 01423 870863 — MD 1951 Camb.; MB BChir 1942; MD Tulane Univ. 1958; FRCP Lond. 1972, M 1945. Prev: Consult. in Rheum. Roy. Bath Hosp. Harrogate & Bradford Roy. Infirm.

JEFFREY, Mr Michael Neil Queen Alexandra Hospital, Cosham, Portsmouth PO6 3LY Tel: 023 92 379451; Rowland House, Bowes Hill, Rowlands Castle PO9 6BP Tel: 023 92 413262 — MB ChB 1979 Birm.; FRCS Ed. 1986; FRCOphth 1989; DO RCS Eng. 1985. Cons. Ophth. Surg. Qu. Alexandra Hosp. Portsmouth. Prev: Cons. Adviser Ophth. RN.

JEFFREY, Pamela Mary 59 Peathill Avenue, Chryston, Glasgow G69 9NZ Tel: 0141 779 1603 Fax: 0141 779 1603 — MB ChB 1979 Glas.; MFOM RCP Lond. 1992, AFOM 1989, FFOM 1998. Sen. Employm. Med. Adviser HSE Scotl.; Sen. Med. Insp. HSE Scotl. Socs: Soc. Occupat. Med.; Dep. RSA Scotl. E. (Fom.); RSA Scotl. (FOM). Prev: Employm. Med. Adviser HSE Glas.; Regist. (Anaesth.) Gtr. Glas. HB; Occupat. Health Phys. Gtr. Glas. HB.

JEFFREY, Mr Robert Rankine Department of Cardio-thoracic Surgery, Aberdeen Royal Infirmary, Aberdeen AB25 2ZN Tel: 01224

681818; Westwood, 44 Hazledene Road, Aberdeen AB15 8LD Tel: 01224 326739 Email: rrjeffrey@abdn.ac.uk — MB ChB 1978 Ed.; BSc (Hons.) (Pharmacol.) Ed. 1975, MB ChB 1978; FRCS Ed. 1982. Cons. Cardiothoracic Surg. Aberd. Roy. Infirm. Socs: FETCS 2000.

JEFFREY, Robin Fraser Four Oaks, Otley Road, Bingley BD16 3AX — MB ChB 1982 Ed.; BSc (Hons.) Ed. 1979; MD Ed. 1989; FRCP Ed. 1997; MRCP (UK) 1985. Cons. Nephrol. & Gen. Med. Bradford Hosps. Trust. Socs: Med. Res. Soc.; Brit. Transpl. Soc.; Eur. Dialysis & Transpl. Assn. Prev: Sen. Regist. St. Jas. Univ. Hosp. Leeds; Wellcome Research Fell. Univ. Edin.; Regist. W.. Infirm. Glas.

JEFFREYS, Donovan Glyndyr Frederick Mounts Medical Centre, Campbell Street, Northampton NN1 3DS Tel: 01604 631952 Fax: 01604 634139 — MB BS 1964 Lond.; DObst RCOG 1972.

JEFFREYS, Gwyneth Eleanor Siobhain 23 Chaucer Road, London W3 6DR — MB BS 1984 Lond.; MRCPsych 1990.

JEFFREYS, Owen Michael Ernest Royal Devon & Exeter Hospital (wONFORD), Barrack Road, Exeter EX2 5DW — MB BCh 1983 Wales; BSc (Hons.) Biochem. Wales 1978; MRCP (UK) 1988. Cons. Phys. with interest in Elderly Care Roy. Devon & Exeter Hosps. Prev: Sen. Regist. (Med. & Geriat.) Guy's Hosp. St. Thos. St. Lond.; Regist. (Med.) Freemantle Hosp. W.. Austral.; Regist. Rotat. (Med.) Roy. S. Hants. Hosp. Soton & Salisbury Gen. Infirm.

JEFFREYS, Pauline Ann Tree Tops, Willow End, Totteridge, London N20 8EP Tel: 020 8446 2189 — MB BS 1966 Lond.; DA Eng. 1970. (St. Geo.) Cons. Anaesth. Manor Ho. Hosp. Prev: Regist. Anaesth. Barnet Gen Hosp.; SHO (Anaesth.) Roy. Free. Hosp. Lond.; SHO (Anaesth.) FarnBoro. Hosp.

JEFFREYS, Mr Richard Vaughan Walton Centre for Neurology & Neurosurgery, Fazakerley Hospital, Liverpool L9 7LJ Tel: 0151 529 5681 Fax: 0151 529 4772; Woodlands, 8 Blakeley Court, Wirral CH63 0ND Tel: 0151 346 1153 Fax: 0151 346 1153 — MB Camb. 1963, BChir 1962; MChir Camb. 1974; FRCS Ed. 1967. (St. Bart.) Cons. Neurosurg. NW RHA; Dir. Neurosurg. Studies & Head Dept. Neurol. Sc. Univ. Liverp. Socs: Soc. Brit. Neurol. Surg.; Brit. Med. Laser Assn. Prev: Sen. Regist. (Surg. Neurol.) Edin. Gp. Hosps.; Sen. Regist. (Neurosurg.) Lond. Hosp.; Regist. (Neurol. Surg.) Addenbrooke's Hosp. Camb.

JEFFREYS, Mr Thomas Eurig 2 Belgrave Road, Wrexham LL13 7ES Tel: 01978 290009 — MRCS Eng. LRCP Lond. 1948; FRCS Eng. 1960; FRCS Ed. 1960. (Guy's)

JEFFRIES, Christine Ann 24 Mount Charles Crescent, Alloway, Ayr KA7 4NY — MB ChB 1977 Glas.

JEFFRIES, Professor Donald James Department of Virology, St. Bartholomews Hospital, 51-53 Bartholomew Close, West Smithfield, London EC1A 7BE Tel: 020 7601 7351 Fax: 020 7726 4248 Email: d.j.jeffries@mds.qmw.ac.uk — FRCP 2001; MB BS Lond. 1966; BSc (Physiol.) Lond. 1963; FRCPath 1986, M 1974. (Roy. Free) Prof. Virol. & Head Dept. Med. MicroBiol. St. Bart. & Roy. Lond. Sch. Med. & Dent.; Head Microbiol. & Virol. Clin. Serv. & Hon. Cons. Barts and the Lond. Hosps. NHS Trust. Socs: BMA, Soc. Gen. Microbiol. & Brit. HIV Assoc. Prev: Reader and Head Dept, Sen. Lect. & Lect. (Clin. Virol.) & Hon. Cons. St. Mary's Hosp. Lond.

JEFFRIES, Douglas John The Health Centre, St. Mary's TR21 0HE Tel: 01720 422628; Email: djeffries@onetel.net.uk — BM 1982 Soton.; Dip. Primary Care Rheumatol. Bath 1999; MA Oxf. 1973; MRCGP 1987; DRCOG 1987. Prev: SHO (O & G) Odstock Hosp. Salisbury; SHO (Psychiat.) Roy. S. Hants. Hosp. Soton.; SHO (A & E) Salisbury HA.

JEFFRIES, John Dennis, Maj. RAMC Retd. Wimpole Road Surgery, 52 Wimpole Road, Colchester CO1 2DL; Tel: 01206 823485 — MB BS Lond. 1967; MRCS Eng. LRCP Lond. 1967; DObst RCOG 1971. (St. Bart.) Socs: BMA. Prev: Maj. RAMC; Ho. Surg. (Cas.) St. Bart. Hosp. Lond.; SHO (Paediat.) Essex Co. Hosp. Colchester.

JEFFRIES, Michael Godfrey Clwyd Community Care Trust, Catherine Gladstone House, Hawarden Way, Mancot, Deeside CH5 2EP Tel: 01244 538883 Fax: 01244 538884; Meddygta, Betws-y-Coed LL24 0BB Tel: 01690 710205 Fax: 01690 710051 — MB ChB 1971 Birm.; BSc (Hons.) Birm. 1968, MB ChB 1971; FRCGP 1992, M 1984; DCCH RCP Lond. 1992. Med. Dir. Clwyd Community Care Trust Deeside. Socs: Fell. Roy. Soc. Med.

JEFFRIES, Milton 313 Stand Lane, Radcliffe, Manchester M26 1JA — LRCPI & LM, LRSCI & LM 1953; LRCPI & LM, LRCSI & LM 1953. (RCSI) p/t Med. Examr., Benefits Agency. Prev: Ho. Surg. Halifax Gen. Hosp.; Ho. Phys. Qu.s Pk. Hosp. Blackburn.

JEFFRIES, Suzanne Christina 20 Bamford Road, Manchester M20 2GW — MB ChB 1991 Manch.

JEFFS, Andrew Charles 18 Jestyn Close, Tumble Hill, Culverhouse Cross, Cardiff CF5 4UR — MB BCh 1988 Wales. Trainee GP/SHO (O & G) Gwent VTS.

JEFFS, Harry George, CStJ (retired) 2 Harvest Bank Road, West Wickham BR4 9DJ — MB BS 1950 Lond.; FRCGP 1984, M 1957; DPhilMed Soc. Apoth. Lond. 1996. Fac. Mem. Worshipful Soc. Apoth. Lond. Prev: Regional Med. Off. DHSS.

JEFFS, Jill Barbara Tel: 0161 483 5155 Fax: 0161 419 9984 — MB ChB 1982 Manch.; MRCGP 1986; DRCOG 1984. GP Stockport. Prev: GP Manch.; SHO (Paediat) Booth Hall Childr. Hosp. Manch.; SHO (O & G) Wythenshawe Hosp. S. Manch.

JEFFS, Mr John Victor (retired) 7 Orchard Rise, Burford OX18 4SZ Tel: 01993 822788 — MB BS 1951 Lond.; FRCS Eng. 1959; MRCS Eng. LRCP Lond. 1951; T(S) 1991. Prev: Cons. Plastic Surg. Char. Cross Hosp. Lond.

JEFFS, Nicholas Graham 28 Ludlow Avenue, Luton LU1 3RW Tel: 01582 451504 — MB BS 1974 Lond.; FFA RCS Eng. 1978. (Middlx.) Cons. Anaesth. Luton & Dunstable Hosp. Socs: Assn. Anaesth. Prev: Sen. Regist. (Anaesth.) St. Mary's Hosp. Lond.; Lect. (Anaesth.) Lond. Hosp. Med. Sch.; Regist. (Anaesth.) Lond. Hosp.

JEFFS, Susan Ann Holmlea, 26 Victoria Road, Pontymoile, Pontypool NP4 5JU — MB BCh 1988 Wales; FRCA 1995; DA (UK) 1991. Clin. Asst. Univ. Hosp. Wales Cardiff. Socs: Assoc. of Anaesthetics; Fell.Roy. Coll. of Anaesthetics; Obst. Anaesth. Assn. Prev: SHO (Anaesth.) Roy. Gwent Hosp. Newport; SHO (Neonates & Anaesth.) Univ. Hosp. Wales Cardiff.

JEGADEVA, Ahalia Navina 56 Grafton Road, London NW5 3DY — MB BS 1987 Lond.

JEGAMOHAN, K The Surgery, 46 Southlands Road, Bromley BR2 9QP Tel: 020 8289 3981.

JEGANATHAN, Shiranee 20 The Ridgeway, Harrow HA3 0LL — MB ChB 1988 Dundee.

JEGARAJAH, Sanmugam — MB BS 1964 Ceylon; FRCP Lond. 1989; MRCP (UK) 1971; DTCD Wales 1970. (Colombo) Cons. Phys. (Gen. Med. & Respirat. Dis.) Rochdale AHA. Socs: Brit. Thorac. & Tuberc. Assn.; (Counc.) Manch. Med. Soc. Prev: Sen. Regist. Rotat. (Gen. Med. & Chest Dis.) Addenbrooke's Hosp. Camb.; Regist. Rotat. (Gen. Med.) Centr. Middlx. Hosp. Lond.; SHO (Gen. Med.) Profess. Med. Unit City Hosp. Nottm.

JEGATHEESVARAN, Malathy 110 May Bank Avenue, Wembley HA0 2TJ — MRCS Eng. LRCP Lond. 1987.

JEGEDE, Adeyemisi Adeyinka 15 South Primrose Hill, Chelmsford CM1 2RF — MB ChB 1991 Bristol.

JEHAN, R Jehan, Marus Bridge Health Centre, Highfield Grange Avenue, Wigan WN3 6SU Tel: 01942 829729 Fax: 01942 493704 — MB BS 1958 Lucknow; MB BS 1958 Lucknow.

JEHANGIR, Qazi Mohammad Nelson Health Centre, Leeds Road, Nelson BB9 9TG Tel: 01282 615577; The Health Centre, Leeds Road, Nelson BB9 9TG Tel: 01282 615577 Fax: 01282 619402 — MB BS Punjab 1963. Socs: Accred. Brit. Med. Acupunc. Soc.; Brit. Med. & Dent. Hypn. Soc.

JELENOWICZ, Elkane 10 High Sheldon, Sheldon Ave, Highgate, London N6 4NJ — MD 1938 Paris. (Paris)

JELFS, Bryan Ronald Gayton Road Health and Surgical Centre, Gayton Road, King's Lynn PE30 4DY Tel: 01553 762726 Fax: 01553 696819; 107 Gayton Road, King's Lynn PE30 4EW — MB BS 1968 Lond.; DObst RCOG 1970. (King's Coll. Hosp.) Prev: SHO (O & G) Dulwich Hosp.; Ho. Phys. & Ho. Surg. King's Coll. Hosp. Lond.

JELFS, Jonathan Philip Stoke Gifford Medical Centre, Ratcliffe Drive, Stoke Gifford, Bristol BS34 8UE Tel: 0117 979 9430 Fax: 0117 940 6999; 3 Oxbarton, Stoke Gifford, Bristol BS34 8RP Tel: 0117 975 4796 — MB ChB 1977 Bristol; BSc (Cellular Path.) Bristol 1974; MRCGP 1984; DRCOG 1981. (Bristol)

JELLEY, Anthony Paul 12 Broomhouse Dock, Carnwath Road, London SW6 3EH — MB BS 1993 Lond. (UMDS) Prev: SHO Rotat. (Psychiat.) Char. Cross Hosp.

JELLEY, Diana Mary Collingwood Surgery, Hawkeys Lane, North Shields NE29 0SF Tel: 0191 257 1779 Fax: 0191 226 9909; 5 Northumberland Terrace, Tynemouth, North Shields NE30 4BA Tel: 0191 257 5852 — BM BS 1984 Nottm.; BM BS Nottm. l984; BA

Liverp. 1975; MRCGP 1989; DCCH 1989; DRCOG 1986. Clin. Lect. (Primary Health Care) Univ. Newc. u. Tyne.

JELLEY, Rosanne Yvonne UCL Hospitals, Gower St., London WC1E 6AU; 50 Thurleigh Road, London SW12 8UD Tel: 020 8265 3350 Email: creighton.r@mc.mail.com — MB BS 1976 Lond.; MRCOG 1983; DRCOG 1978; BSc CP 1997. Clin. Asst. (Gyn.) Univ. Coll. Hosp.; Clin. Research Asst. (Gyn.) Dept. Psychol. UCL. Socs: Fell. RCOG. Prev: Research Regist. (O & G) W.m. Hosp. Lond.

JELLEY, Timothy Matthew Hillview Lodge, Royal United Hospital, Combe Park, Bath BA1 3NG Tel: 01225 825358 Fax: 01225 825327 — MB ChB 1981 Leeds; MRCPsych 1988. Cons. Psychiat. Bath Ment. Health Care Trust.

JELLICOE, Jillian Ann Shackleton Department of Anaesthetics, Southampton General Hospital, Tremona Road, Southampton SO16 6YD Tel: 02380 796135 — MRCS Eng. LRCP Lond. 1970; DObst RCOG 1973; FFA RCS Eng. 1980; DA Eng. 1973. Cons. Anaesth. Shackleton Dept. Anaesth. Soton. Gen. Hosp.; Clin. Sub-Dean Fac. Med. Univ. Soton.

JELLICOE, Paul Arthur 16 Mill Lane, Ness, South Wirral CH64 4BQ — MB ChB 1994 Manch.

JELLIFFE, Anthony Michael 152 Harley Street, London W1G 7LH Tel: 020 7935 8868 Fax: 020 7794 1395 — MB BS 1945 Lond.; MD 1947 Lond.; FRCP Lond. 1970, M 1946; FRCR 1975; FFR 1955; DMRT Eng. 1953, DCH 1946. (Middlx.) Emerit. Cons. Radiother. & Oncol. Middlx. Hosp. Lond., Edgware Gp. Hosps. & Mt. Vernon Hosp. N.wood Middlx.; Clin. Oncologist, Cromwell Hosp. Lond. Socs: Fell. Roy. Soc. Med.; Brit. Inst. Radiol.; BMA. Prev: Dir. Meyerstein Inst. Radiotherap. & Oncol. Middlx. Hosp.; Vice Pres. Roy. Coll. Radiol.; Dir. Brit. Nat. Lymphoma Investig.

JELLINEK, Mr David Andrew Department of Neurosurgery, Royal Hallamshire Hospital, Sheffield S10 2JF Fax: 0114 276 5925 Email: david.jellinek@csoh.nhs.uk; Email: david.jellinek@virgin.net — MB 1983 Camb.; BChir 1982; FRCS Eng. 1986; MD Camb. 1995. Cons. Neurosurg. Roy. Hallamshire Hosp. Sheff. Prev: Cons. Neurosurg. Roy. Melbourne Hosp. Melbourne, Australia; Sen. Regist. Neurosurg. Qu.s Med. Centre Nottm.; Clin. Lect. (Neurosurg.) Inst. Neurol. Lond.

JELLINEK, Diana Claire 54 Beech Road, Hale, Altrincham WA15 9HX Tel: 0161 929 7981 — MB BS 1984 Lond.; MSc Lond. 1991; MRCPI 1990; FRCPCH 1997; DCH RCP Lond. 1986. (Lond. Hosp. Med. Coll.) Cons. Paediat. (Community Child Health) Manch.; Hon. Clin. Lect. (Child Health) Univ. Manch. Prev: Lect. & Sen. Regist. (Community Child Health) St. Geo. Hosp. Lond.

JELLINEK, Ernest Herbert 14 Moray Place, Edinburgh EH3 6DT Tel: 0131 225 4843 Fax: 0131 225 6749; 7 Oxgangs Road, Edinburgh EH10 7BG Tel: 0131 445 2131 — BM BCh 1952 Oxf.; DM Oxf. 1961; FRCP Lond 1971, M 1955; FRCP Ed. 1969, M 1968. (Oxf.) Cons. Neurol. Edin. Prev: Cons. Neurol. Edin. N.. Hosp. Gp.

JELLIS, Trevor Sidney c/o Herts & Essex Hospital, Haymeads Lane, Bishop's Stortford CM23 5JH — MB ChB 1976 Leeds.

JELLY, James Richard Saffron Surgery, Berkley Road, Frome BA11 1EZ Tel: 01373 451256; The Tyning, Great Elm, Frome BA11 3NY — MB BS 1965 Lond.; MRCS Eng. LRCP Lond. 1965; DCH Eng. 1967. (St. Mary's) Prev: SHO (Obst.) Zachary Merton Matern. Hosp. Rustington; SHO (Paediat.) Roy. Alexandra Hosp. Brighton; Ho. Phys. Padd. Gen. Hosp.

JELLY, Louise Muriel Elizabeth 22 Courtenay Avenue, Sutton SM2 5ND — MB BCh 1988 Wales; MRCP (UK) 1992; FRCR 1998. Regist. (Diag. Radiol.) St. Bart. Hosp. Lond.

JELPKE, Matthew Francis Dawson Tudor Square Medical Practice, 1st Floor, Barclays Bank Chambers, Tudor Square, West Bridgford, Nottingham NG2 6BT Tel: 0115 914 3200 Fax: 0115 914 3201; 15 Henry Road, West Bridgford, Nottingham NG2 7NA Tel: 0115 982 0289 — BM BS 1992 Nottm.; BMedSci Nottm. 1990; DFFP 1995; DRCOG 1994; MRCGP 1997. (Nottingham) GP. Socs: BMA St Paul.

JEMAHL, Surinder 15 Elmbank Grove, Handsworth Wood, Birmingham B20 1JT — MB ChB 1988 Bristol.

JEMEC, Barbara Top Flat, 10 Hillmartin Road, Islington, London N7 9JW — MD 1991 Copenhagen.

JEMMETT, John Childs Tel: 01446 772237 Fax: 01446 775883; The Firs, Llanblethian, Cowbridge CF71 7JT Tel: 01446 774197 — MB BCh 1972 Wales; MRCGP 1978; DObst RCOG 1974.

JENA, Rajesh — BChir 1994 Camb.; MB Camb 1995; MRCP Lond 1998. (Addenbrooke's Cambridge) Macmillans Specialist Regist. (Clin. Oncol), Addenbrooke's Hosp.,Camb.

JENA, Ramakant The Island Surgery, 199 Furtherwick Road, Canvey Island SS8 7BW Tel: 01268 696800 Fax: 01268 696700 — MB BS 1969 Utkal; DPM Eng. 1980. (S.C.B. Med. Coll. Orissa) Prev: SHO (Gen. Med. & Geriat.) S. Shields Gen. Hosp.; SHO (Gen. Med.) Chester-le-St. Gen. Hosp.

JENAWAY, Alison South Building, Primrose Lane, Huntingdon PE29 1WG Tel: 01480 415130 Fax: 01480 415140 — MB BS 1987 Lond.; BSc (Hons.) Psych. Lond. 1984; MRCPsych. 1992. (Char. Cross & Westm.) Cons. Psychiat. Hinchingbrooke Hosp. Huntingdon. Prev: Sen. Regist. (Psychiat.) Addenbrooke's Hosp. Camb.

JENKIN, David Robert 10 Tremodrett Road, Roche, St Austell PL26 8JA — MB ChB 1992 Glas.; DCH RCP Lond. 1996; MRCGP 1996; DFFP RCOG 1997. (Glasgow) GP. Prev: SHO S.. Gen. Hosp. & N. Devon Dist. Hosp.; GP/Regist. N. Devon VTS.

JENKINS, Mr Alistair John Department of Neurosurgery, Newcastle General Hospital, Westgate Road, Newcastle upon Tyne NE4 6BE Tel: 0191 273 8811 Fax: 0191 272 0872 Email: ajjenkins@compuserve.com; 180 Jesmond Dene Road, Jesmond, Newcastle upon Tyne NE2 2EU — MB ChB 1980 Glas.; MD Glas. 1989; FRCS Ed. 1984. Cons. Neurosurg. & Sen. Lect. (Neurosurg.) Newc. Gen. Hosp. Univ. Newc. u. Tyne. Prev: Sen. Regist. (Neurosurg.) Mersey Regional Dept. Neurol. & Neurosurg. Walton Hosp. Liverp.; Hon. Clin. Tutor Univ. Liverp.

JENKINS, Mr Andrew McLaren Vascular Surgery Unit, Royal Infirmary, Lauriston Place, Edinburgh EH3 9YW Tel: 0131 536 1000 Fax: 0131 536 1001; Spitalhaugh House, West Linton EH46 7BH Tel: 01968 60468 — MB ChB 1962 Ed.; ChM Ed. 1973; FRCS Eng. 1966; FRCS Ed. 1965. (Ed.) Cons. Vasc. Surg. & Hon. Sen. Lect. Vasc. Surg. Unit Roy. Infirm. Edin.

JENKINS, Anita Joyce (retired) 52 Norman Avenue, Abingdon OX14 2HL — MB BS 1948 Lond.; MD Lond. 1953; MRCS Eng. LRCP Lond. 1948; FRCPCH 1997; MFCM 1974; DPH Wales 1954; DCH Eng. 1951. Prev: PMO Oxon. HA.

JENKINS, Anna-Lisa Mary 28 Campbell Road, Plymouth PL9 8UE — MB BS 1988 Lond. SHO (Med.) Roy. Naval Hosp. Plymouth.

JENKINS, Annabel Frederica Green Lanes, Church Lane, Hellingly, Hailsham BN27 4HA — MB BS 1979 Lond.; MRCS Eng. LRCP Lond. 1979; Dip Med Acupunc (Bmas 1999). (Charing Cross Hosp Med Sch) Clin. Asst. Pain Managem. Socs: Brit. Med. Acupunct. Soc.; Pain. Soc.

JENKINS, Anne Macvean (retired) The Whins, 46 Kilgraston Road, Bridge of Weir PA11 3DP Tel: 01505 612826 — MB ChB Glas. 1950; DObst RCOG 1952. Prev: SCMO (Child Health) Renfrew Health Dist.

JENKINS, Mr Anthony Ian Russell 7 Bryn Bach, Rhiwbina, Cardiff CF14 6LH — MB BCh 1973 Wales; FRCS Ed. 1980.

JENKINS, Anthony John Douglas (retired) Milberry Thatch, Stoughton, Chichester PO18 9JJ Tel: 01705 631359 — MB BS 1964 Lond.; MRCS Eng. LRCP Lond. 1964; DObst RCOG 1970. Prev: Regist. & Ho. Surg. (Surg.) Middlx. Hosp.

JENKINS, Anthony Paul Bromley Hospital, Bromley BR2 9AJ Tel: 020 8289 7164 Fax: 020 8289 7155 Email: anthony.jenkins@bromleyhospitals.nhs.uk — MB BChir 1983 Camb.; FRCP (UK) 1999; MD Camb. 1992. Cons. Phys. (Gen. Med. & Gastroenterol.) Bromley Hosp. Socs: Brit. Soc. Gastroenterol.; Internat. Mem. Amer. Gastroenterol. Assoc. Prev: Sen. Regist. (Gen. Med. & Gastroenterol.) St. Thos. Hosp. Lond.

JENKINS, Anthony William Rees (retired) 21 High Road, Epping CM16 4AY Tel: 01992 572871 — MB BCh Wales 1944; BSc Wales 1941; DMRD 1950. Prev: Cons. Radiol. W. Essex Dist.

JENKINS, Arnold James Colne Road Surgery, 34-36 Colne Road, Burnley BB10 1LQ Tel: 01282 456564 Fax: 01282 451639; 515 Colne Road, Burnley BB10 2LF — MB ChB 1972 Sheff.; DObst RCOG 1974. Prev: SHO Moorgate Hosp. Rotherham; SHO Childr. Hosp. Sheff.; SHO Jessop Hosp. Sheff.

JENKINS, Arthur Vivian (retired) 2 Grange Road, West Cross, Swansea SA3 5ES Tel: 01792 405389 — MB BS 1950 Lond.; MRCS Eng. LRCP Lond. 1949; FFA RCS Eng. 1955. Sen. Cons. Anaesth. E. Birm. Hosp.; Hon. Postgrad. Clin. Tutor (Anaesth.) Univ. Birm. Prev: Sen. Regist. United Manch. Hosps.

JENKINS, Benjamin Anthony Gwynne (retired) Ailsa Craig, 55 Treyew Road, Truro TR1 2BY Tel: 01872 77880 — MRCS Eng. LRCP Lond. 1942; MD Lond. 1951; MB BS 1947; FRCP Lond. 1971, M 1948. Prev: Sen. Phys. Cornw. & I. of Scilly AHA.

JENKINS, Bernard Stephen Department of Cardiology, St. Thomas' Hospital, London SE1 7GH Tel: 020 7261 1488 Fax: 020 7261 1488; 13 Richborne Terrace, London SW8 1AS Tel: 020 7587 1091 Fax: 020 7587 1799 — MB BChir 1964 Camb.; MA Camb. 1965; FRCP Lond. 1983, M 1967. (St. Thos.) Cons. Cardiol. Guy's & St. Thos. NHS Hosps. Trust. Socs: Brit. Cardiac Soc. Prev: Chief Exec. St. Thos. Hosp. Lond.; Chairm. Dist. Managem. Bd.; Dist. Gen. Man. W. Lambeth HA.

JENKINS, Brian James Department of Anaesthetics, University of Wales Coll. of Medicine, Heath Park, Cardiff CF14 4XW Tel: 029 2074 2096 Fax: 029 2074 7203; 46 Windsor Avenue, Radyr, Cardiff CF15 8BY — MB BS Lond. 1981; FFA RCS Eng. 1986. Sen. Lect. & Hon. Cons. Univ. Wales Coll. Med. Cardiff. Socs: Intens. Care Soc.; Soc. Computing Technol. in Anaesth.; Welsh Pain Soc. Prev: Sen. Regist. (Anaesth.) Univ. Wales Coll. Med.

JENKINS, Mr Bryan John University Hospital of Wales, Heath Park, Cardiff CF14 4XW Tel: 029 2074 3320 Fax: 029 2074 4179; 4 Cyncoed Crescent, Cyncoed, Cardiff CF23 6SW Tel: 029 2075 7357 — MB Camb. 1981, BChir 1980; MA, MChir Camb. 1991; FRCS (Urol.) 1990; FRCS Eng. 1984; FEBU 1992. (Univ. Camb. & St. Thos. Hosp. Med. Sch.) Cons. Urol. Surg. Univ. Hosp. Wales. Prev: Lect. Lond. Hosp. Med. Coll.; Sen. Regist. Lond. Hosp.

JENKINS, Caroline Beechwood, 1 Kings Acre, Crowcombe Heathfield, Taunton TA4 4BX — MB BS 1998 Lond.; MB BS Lond 1998.

JENKINS, Caroline Elizabeth Prospect House, High Street, Great Missenden HP16 0BG Tel: 01494 862325 Fax: 01494 890510; Rabbs Corner, The Lee, Great Missenden HP16 9NX — BM BCh 1974 Oxf.; MA Camb. 1974; DCH Eng. 1977. (Cambridge & Oxford)

JENKINS, Caroline Sian Dept of Anaesthetics, Worthing Hospital, Park Avenue, Worthing BN11 2DM — MB BS 1990 Lond.; FRCA 1996. Cons. (Anaesth) Worthing & S.lands Hosp. Prev: Specialist Regist. (Anaesth.) Char. Cross Hosp. Lond.

JENKINS, Cathryn 43 Queenwood, Cyncoed, Cardiff CF23 9LE Tel: 029 2047 3035; 43 Queenwood, 43 Queenwood, Cardiff CF23 9LE Tel: 029 2047 3035 — MB BCh 1994 Wales. SHO (Anaesth.), Abergavenny. Socs: BMA; MDU; Assoc. of Anaesthetrists of FB & Irel. Prev: SHO (Paeds.), Abergavenny; SHO (A&E), Abergavenny; SHO (A&E), Cardiff.

JENKINS, Christine Margaret Department of Community Child Health, East & Nth. Hertfordshire NHS Trust, Old Ambulance Head Quarters, Ascots Lane, Welwyn Garden City AL7 4HL Tel: 01707 328111 Ext: 3505 Fax: 01707 365329; 43 Lancaster Avenue, Hadley Wood, Barnet EN4 0ER Tel: 020 8364 8683 Fax: 020 8447 0545 Email: cmjenkins@hotmail.com — MB BS 1979 Lond.; BSc (Hons.) Lond. 1976; FRCP Ed. 1997; MRCP (UK) 1983; FRCPCH 1997; MRCGP 1986; DCH RCP Lond. 1987; DRCOG 1984; Cert. Family Plann. JCC 1984. (Univ. Coll. Hosp.) p/t Cons. Paediat. (Community Child Health) E. & N. Herts. NHS Trust Qu. Eliz. II Hosp., Howlands, Welwyn garden City, Herts AL7 4HQ; Cons. NeuroDevelopm. Paediat., Integrated Neurocare, Portland Hosp. Lond. 234 Gt. Portland St., Lond. W1N 5PH. Socs: Brit. Assn. Community Child Health; Fell. Roy. Coll. Paediat. & Child Health; Downs Syndrome Med. Interest Grp. Prev: SCMO (Community Child Health) E. Herts. NHS Trust; Locum Cons. Community Paediat. Barnet & E. Herts. NHS Trust; SHO (Paediat.) Univ. Coll. Hosp. Lond.

JENKINS, Christopher David Gareth 22A Islington Green, London N1 8DU — MB BS 1984 Lond.; BSc Lond. 1981, MB BS 1984; FRCS Eng. 1990; MRCP (UK) 1987; FCOphth 1990; DO RCS Eng. 1990. Cons. Maidstone Hosp. Kent. Prev: Sen. Regist. Moorfields Eye Hosp. Lond.; SHO (Med.) St. Bart. Hosp. Lond.; SHO (Ophth.) St. Thos. Hosp. Lond.

JENKINS, Christopher Ian 40 Wimmerfield Crescent, Killay, Swansea SA2 7BU Tel: 01792 201719 — MB BCh 1995 Wales. SHO (Med.) Hereford Co. Hosp. (Respirat.). Prev: SHO (Med.) Hereford Co. Hosp. (Cardiol.); SHO (Med./Age Care) Llandough Hosp. Cardiff; Ho. Off. (Med.) Margt. Hosp. New Zealand.

JENKINS, Christopher John Russell Stockwell Group Practice, 107 Stockwell Road, London SW9 9TJ Tel: 020 7274 3225 Fax: 020 7738 3005 — MB BS 1984 Lond.

JENKINS, Christopher Neil John York District Hospital, Wigginton Road, York YO31 8HE Tel: 01904 631313 — MB BChir 1987 Camb.; MA Camb. 1985; MRCP (UK) 1991; FRCR 1995. Cons. Radiol. York Dist. Hosp.

JENKINS, Clare DVLAA, DMG, 2 Sandringham Park, Swansea Vale, Swansea SA99 1DA Tel: 01792 761135 Fax: 01792 761104 Email: medadviser@dvla.dti.gov.uk; Penderyn, Pines Gardens, Llanidloes Road, Newtown SY16 1EY Tel: 01686 624765 Fax: 01686 610259 Email: cjenkin2@netcomuk.co.uk — MB BCh BAO 1970 Dub.; MA Dub. 1975; Dip. Hlth. Mgt. Keele 1995; DObst RCOG 1973. (TC Dub.) Med. Advis. DVLA. Socs: BMA; Roy. Coll. Paediat. & Child Health; MRCPCH. Prev: GP Gwent & Leeds.; SCMO Child health Powys health care trust.

JENKINS, Clare 32 Broughton Way, Rickmansworth WD3 8GW — MB BS 1996 Lond.

JENKINS, Cledwyn Watkin (retired) St. Ippolyts, 128 Christchurch Road, Winchester SO23 9QY Tel: 01962 861552 Fax: 01962 861552 — MB ChB Bristol 1957; MSc Surrey 1976; FRCGP 1981, M 1968; DCH Eng. 1960. Prev: Assoc. Adviser (Gen. Pract.) Wessex RHA.

JENKINS, Colin Department of Geriatric Medicine (Age Care), Hereford General Hospital, Nelson St., Hereford HR1 2PA Tel: 01432 355444 Fax: 01432 274039 — MB ChB 1982 Aberd.; FRCP Lond. 1999; MRCP (UK) 1990. Cons. Phys. (Geriat. Med.) Hereford Hosps. NHS Trust; Postgrad. Clin. Tutor John Ross PGMC Co. Hosp. Hereford.

JENKINS, Daniel Cecil Richmond Roose (retired) Fairhill, Roman Road, Shrewsbury SY3 9AR Tel: 01743 3375 — MRCS Eng. LRCP Lond. 1928; FFA RCS Eng. 1954; DA Eng. 1938. Prev: Cons. Anaesth. Roy. Shrewsbury Hosps.

JENKINS, David, SBStJ 78 St Martins Road, Caerphilly CF83 1EN — MB BCh 1966 Wales. Med. Servs. Manager Benefits Agency Med. Servs. DSS Cardiff. Prev: Med. Off. DHSS Cardiff; GP Caerphilliy.

JENKINS, David (retired) Academic Unit of General Practice, Trafford Centre for Medical Research, University of Sussex, Falmer, Brighton BN1 9RY Tel: 01273 877094 Fax: 01273 887075 — MB BS Lond. 1969; MSc Lond. 1988; FRCGP 1997; Cert. Family Plann. JCC 1972; DObst RCOG 1971. Prev: Ho. Surg. King's Coll. Hosp. Lond. & Ho. Phys. Cuckfield Hosp.

JENKINS, David Department of Pathology, Queens Medical Centre, Nottingham NG7 2UH Tel: 0115 970 9171 Email: david.jenkins@nottingham.ac.uk; 1 Marrison Way, Southwell NG25 0ED Tel: 01636815520 Email: dpjenkins@talk21.com — MB BChir 1970 Camb.; MA, MD Camb. 1989; FRCPath 1989, M 1977. (Camb. & Cardiff) Reader (Path.) Nottm. Univ. Socs: BMA; BSG. Prev: Cons. Histopath. Whittington Hosp. Lond.; Lect. (Surg. Path.) St. Thos. Hosp. Lond.; Demonst. (Path.) Univ. Camb.

JENKINS, David (retired) 51 Manor Way, Blackheath, London SE3 9XG Tel: 020 8852 7448 Fax: 020 8852 7448 — MRCS Eng. LRCP Lond. 1950; MRCGP 1960; AF0M RCP Lond. 1980; DMJ (Hon.) Soc. Apoth. Lond. 1992. Hon. Clin. Asst. (Forens) Lond. Hosp.; Occupat. Med. Off. Qu. Mary Coll. Lond.; Metrop. Forens. Med. Exam. City Lond. Police. Prev: Ho. Phys. St. Olave's Hosp.

JENKINS, David Diabetic Centre, Worcester Royal Infirmary, Newtown Road, Worcester WR5 1HN Tel: 01905 763333 Fax: 01905 760780 — BM BCh 1983 Oxf.; FRCP Lond. 1999; DM 1991; MRCP (UK) 1986; BA Oxf. 1980. (Oxford) Cons. Gen. Med., Diabetes & Endocrinol. Worcester Roy. Infirm. Socs: Brit. Diabetic Assn. (Med. & Scientif. Sect.); Eur. Assn. Study Diabetes; Soc. Endocrinol. Prev: Clin. Research Fell. Univ. Birm.; Regist. (Med. & Nephrol.) Leic. Gen. Hosp.; SHO (Med.) Good Hope Hosp. Sutton Coldfield.

JENKINS, David Adam Mansell Road Surgery, 73 Mansell Road, Greenford UB6 9EJ Tel: 020 8575 0083 — MB BS 1978 Lond.; BSc Lond. 1975.

JENKINS, David Andrew Stephen Queen Margaret Hospital, Whitefield Road, Dunfermline KY12 0SU; 40 Inverleith Row, Edinburgh EH3 5PY — MB BS Lond. 1978; 1971 BSc (Social Sci.) Bristol; MD Lond. 1993; FRCP Ed. 1995; MRCP (UK) 1981. (Roy. Free) Cons. Nephrol. & Gen. Med. Qu. Margt. Hosp. Dunfermline.

Prev: Lect. (Med.) Univ. Edin.; Regist. (Med.) Norf. & Norwich Hosp.; SHO (Nephrol.) Roy. Free Hosp. Lond.

JENKINS, David Geraint The Phoenix, Ashford Road, Maidstone ME17 1XH — MB ChB 1963 Sheff.; MBA Kent 1993; MD Sheff. 1973; FFR 1970; FRCR 1976; DMRT Eng. 1966. (Sheff.) Socs: Fell. RSM; Hon. Sec. Brit. Soc. Of Med. & Dent. Hypn. (Met. & Sth.). Prev: Cons. Radiother. St. Williams Hosp. Rochester; Cons. Clin. Oncol. Mid Kent Oncol. Centre Maidstone.; Hon. Cons. In Radiother. KCH.

JENKINS, David Godfrey, Lt.-Col. RAMC (retired) Little Trippetts, Rake Road, Milland, Liphook GU30 7JX Tel: 01428 741218 Fax: 01428 741660 — MB BS Lond. 1958; FRCP Lond. 1980; DPhysMed. Eng. 1968. Prev: Cons. Rheum. & Rehabil. St. Geo. Hosp. Lond.

JENKINS, David Ian Traies, Wing Cdr. RAF Med. Br. Email: ocoem@rafcam.orc.uk — MB BS 1979 Lond.; MFOM 2000 Lond.; MSc 1999 Univ. of Birm.; BSc Lond. 1976; MRCGP 1985; DAvMed FOM RCP Lond. 1991; DRCOG 1984. (St. Mary's) Off. Commanding Occupat.al and EnivironMent. Med. Wing, RAF Centre of Aviat. Med., RAF Henlow; Hon. Cons. in Occupat.al Med.; Roy. Brompton Hosp., Lond.; Regional Occupat.al Med. Cons., RAF. Socs: MRAeS; Mem. Soc. of Occupat.al Med.; Fell. Roy. Soc. of Med. Prev: Off. Commanding RAF Inst. of Health, RAF Halton; Sen. Med. Off., RAF Bruggen; Off. Commanding, RAF AMTC, RAF N. Luffenham.

JENKINS, David Martin Maesgwyn, 260 Neath Road, Briton Ferry, Neath SA11 2SL Tel: 01639 821871 — MB ChB 1975 Manch.; LLM Wales 1991. Socs: Fell. Roy. Soc. Med. Prev: Trainee Gen. Pract. Doncaster Vocational Train. Scheme; Ho. Off. (Gen. Surg./Gyn./Urol.) Salford Roy. Hosp.; Ho. Off. (Gen. Med.) Altrincham Gen. Hosp.

JENKINS, David Martyn Links Centre, 60 Newport Road, Cardiff CF24 0 Tel: 029 2045 1144; Flat 11, Anson Court, Atlantic Wharf, Cardiff CF10 4AL Tel: 029 2045 8208 — MB BS 1962 Lond.; MRCS Eng. LRCP Lond. 1962; MRCPsych 1972; DPM Eng. 1966. (St. Mary's) Phys. (Psychol. Med.) & Cons. Psychother. Univ. Hosp. Wales & WhitCh. Hosp.; Clin. Teach. (Psychol. Med.) Welsh Nat. Sch. Med. Prev: Sen. Regist. Bethlem & Maudsley Hosp. Lond.; Regist. Roy. Edin. Hosp.; Sen. Regist. (Psychiat.) Univ. Coll. Hosp. Lond.

JENKINS, David Michael Graham Mariners Surgery, Ferryside SA17 5SG Tel: 01267 267239 Fax: 01267 267482; Bristol House, Llansaint, Kidwelly Tel: 01267 267570 Fax: 01267 267482 — LMSSA 1976 Lond.; BA Camb. 1972, MA 1976, MB 1978, BChir 1977. (Camb.) Hon. Med. Adviser Swansea Flying Club & C.H.A.R.; Hon. Med. Adviser HaverfordW.. Sch. Flying; RMO Werndale Private Hosp. Socs: Brit. Soc. Med. & Dent. Hypn. & BMA. Prev: Ho. Phys. & Ho. Surg. Wycombe Gen. Hosp. High Wycombe.

JENKINS, Mr David Philip Papworth Hospitall, Papworth Everard, Cambridge CB3 8RE Tel: 01480 830541 Email: david.jenkins@papworth-tr.anglox.nhs.uk; 4 Furlong Road, Islington, London N7 8LS Tel: 020 7609 4027 Email: david_p_jenkins@compuserve.com — 2000 FRCS (CTH); 1997 Ms London; MB BS Lond. 1989; BSc Lond. 1986; FRCS Eng. 1993. (Univ. Coll. & Middlx. Hosp. Sch. Med.) Cons. Cardiothoracic Surg., Papworth Hosp. Socs: Fell. Roy. Soc. Med.; Soc. Cardiothoracic Surgs. GB & I; Mem. of the Eurpean Assn. for Cardio-thoracic Surg. Prev: Specialist Regist. (Cardiothoracic Surg.) W. Lond. Rotat.; Research Regist. (Cardiothoracic Surg.) Hatter Inst. Cardiovasc. Research & Middlx. Hosp. Lond.; SHO (Cardiothoracic Surg.) Middlx. Hosp. Lond.

JENKINS, David Richard Public Health Laboratory, Royal Sussex County Hospital, Eastern Road, Brighton BN2 5BE Tel: 01273 696955; 5 North Row, Uckfield TN22 1ES Tel: 01825 67693 — MB BS 1985 Lond.; BSc (Hons.) Med. Sci. & Pharmacol. Lond. 1982. Regist. (Med. Microbiol.) Pub. Health Laborat. Serv. Roy. Sussex Co. Hosp. Brighton. Socs: Fell. Roy. Soc. Trop. Med. & Hyg.; Brit. Soc. Parasitol. Prev: Ho. Off. Liver Unit King's Coll. Hosp. Lond.

JENKINS, David Richard Llewelyn Llanishen Court Surgery, Llanishen Court, Llanishen, Cardiff CF14 5YU Tel: 029 2075 7025 Fax: 029 2074 7931 — MB BS 1976 Lond.; MRCS Eng. LRCP Lond. 1976; DRCOG 1981. (Char. Cross) GP Cardiff. Prev: SHO (Gen. Med.) Hillingdon Hosp. Uxbridge; SHO (O & G) Univ. Hosp. Cardiff; SHO (Paediat.) Llandough Hosp. Penarth.

JENKINS, Deborah Eastern C.A.S.T., Colemal House, Brookfield Aveue, Dover CT16 2AH — MB BS 1979 Lond.; MA Camb. 1976; MRCPsych 1983. Cons. (Psychiat. for Elderly).

JENKINS, Deborah Anne St David's Foundation, Cambrian House, Newport NP19 8GR — MB BCh 1989 Wales; MRCGP 1995; DRCOG 1992. (Univ. Wales Coll. Med.) Staff Grade (Palliat. Med.) St David's Foundat. Newport. Prev: GP Salford.

JENKINS, Delyth Barton Surgery, 1 Edmunds Close, Barton Court Avenue, Barton-on-Sea, New Milton BH25 7EH Tel: 01425 620830 Fax: 01425 629812; Keir Cottage, Barnes Lane, Milford-on-Sea, Lymington SO41 0RP — MB BS 1973 Lond.; MRCGP 1977; DObst RCOG 1975. Prev: SHO (Paediat.) Qu. Eliz. Hosp. Childr. Lond.; SHO (O & G) Lond. Hosp.

JENKINS, Mr Derek Griffin (retired) 48 Cricketers Drive, Meopham, Gravesend DA13 0AX Tel: 01474 813800 — MB BS 1949 Lond.; FRCS Eng. 1956; MRCS Eng. LRCP Lond. 1949. Prev: Cons. Surg. Medway Health Dist.

JENKINS, Dominic William 315 Nechells Pk Road, Birmingham B7 5NY — MB ChB 1997 Liverp.

JENKINS, Edward Burton Nicholl Street Medical Centre, Nicholl Street, Swansea SA1 6AY Tel: 01792 653548 Fax: 01792 653411; Vivian House, 8 Myrtle Grove, Swansea SA2 0SH Tel: 01792 202345 — MB ChB 1958 Ed. (Ed.) Socs: BMA; Soc. Occupat. Med. Prev: Ho. Phys. & Ho. Surg. Swansea Gen. Hosp.

JENKINS, Eileen Joyce (retired) 44 Mayals Avenue, Blackpill, Swansea SA3 5DB — MB BCh Wales 1944. Clin. Med. Off. W. Glam. AHA. Mem. BMA. Prev: Asst. Med. Off. City of Swansea Pub. Health Dept.

JENKINS, Elaine Margaret Wheelers Lane, Smallfield, Horley RH6 9PT; Wychwood, 124 Mid St, South Nutfield, Redhill RH1 4JH — MB BS 1975 Lond.; MRCGP 1979; DRCOG 1977. (Univ. Coll. Hosp.) Prev: Trainee GP Univ. Coll. Hosp. VTS; Ho. Phys. & Ho. Surg. Whittington Hosp. Lond.

JENKINS, Elizabeth Anne Department of Rheumatology, Milton Keynes General Hospital, Standing Way, Eaglestone, Milton Keynes MK6 5LD Tel: 01908 243115 Fax: 01908 243115 — MB BS 1980 Lond.; FRCP (UK) 1999; FRCPCH 1997; MRCP (UK) 1984. Cons. Rheum. Milton Keynes Gen. Hosp. Socs: Treas. Brit. Paediatric Rheumatol. Gp. Prev: Sen. Regist. (Rheum.) Soton. Univ. Hosp. & Qu. Alexandra Hosp. Portsmouth; SHO (Rheum.) Juvenile Rheum. Unit Canad. Red Cross Hosp. Taplow.

JENKINS, Elizabeth Kathryn Brewery Cottage, Llanquian Road, Aberthin, Cowbridge CF71 7HB Tel: 01446 774779 — MB BCh 1980 Wales; DFFP 1993. Psychother. BUPA Hosp. Cardiff. Socs: BMA. Prev: GP Cardiff.

JENKINS, Mrs Elizabeth Louise 11 Southdale Road, Oxford OX2 7SE — MB ChB 1992 Liverp.; DCH 1996. SHO (Paediat.) Oxf. Prev: SHO Neonates Oxf.; SHO Paediat. Chertsey.

JENKINS, Elizabeth Mary Northlands Wood Surgery, 7 Walnut Park, Haywards Heath RH16 3TG Tel: 01444 458022 Fax: 01444 415960; Little Broomies, Holford Manor Lane, North Chailey, Lewes BN8 4DU Tel: 01444 347 1687 — MB BS 1986 Lond.; DRCOG 1991; DCH RCP Lond. 1990; DA (UK) 1989. Prev: Trainee GP Cuckfield VTS; SHO (Anaesth.) Worthing HA; Clin. Asst. (A & E) P.ss Roy. Hosp.

JENKINS, Esme Sybil (retired) 2 Grange Road W., West Cross, Swansea SA3 5ES Tel: 01792 405389 — MB BCh 1948 Wales; DObst RCOG 1952. Prev: Sessional Med. Off. Hereford & Worcester AHA.

JENKINS, Felicity Helen Department of Radiology, Alexandra Hospital, Redditch Tel: 01527 503030; 4 Balmoral Close, Fernhill Heath, Worcester WR3 7XQ Tel: 01905 454062 — MB BCh 1979 Wales; FRCR 1986; DMRD 1983. p/t Cons. Radiol. Worcs. Hosp.s Acute Trust; Cons. Radiologist Droitwich Private Hosp. Prev: Sen. Regist. & Regist. (Radiol.) Stoke-on-Trent HA; SHO (Cardio-Pulm. Med.) S. Glam. Health Auth. (T).

JENKINS, Gary Robert Parkside Clinic, 63/65 Lancaster Road, London W11 1QG; Basement Flat, 144 Shirland Road, London W9 2BT — MB BS 1991 Lond.

JENKINS, Professor George Charles 19 Bush Hill, Winchmore Hill, London N21 2DB Tel: 020 8360 1484 Fax: 020 8360 1484 — MB BS Lond. 1950; PhD Lond. 1960; FRCP Ed. 1990; MRCS Eng. LRCP Lond. 1951; FRCPath 1975, M 1964. (St. Bart.) Hon. Cons. Haematol. Roy. Lond. Hosp.; Cons. Emerit. Prof. Haemat. Univ.

Lond. Socs: (Pres.) Brit. Soc. Haematol.; (Pres.) Brit. Acad. Forens. Sci.; Fell. RSM. Prev: Prof. Haemat. Univ. Lond.; Cons. Path. (Haemat.) N. Middlx. Hosp. & Annexes; Sen. Regist. (Haemat.) Lond. Hosp.

JENKINS, Geraint 35 Hyde Park Terrace, Leeds LS6 1BJ — MB ChB 1995 Leeds.

JENKINS, Geraint Huw Regional Cardiac Centre, Morriston Hospital, Swansea SA6 6NL Tel: 01792 704111 Fax: 01792 704140 Email: geraint.jenkins@swansea-tr.wales.nhs.uk — BChir 1990 Camb.; MB 1991 Camb.; MRCP 1994 UK; BA 1988 (Hons.) Camb.; MA 1992 Camb. (Cambridge) Cons. Cardiol., Regional Cardial Centre, Morriston Hosp., Swansea, SA6 6NL. Socs: Brit. Hypertens. Research Gp.; Brit. Cardiac Soc Mem; Brit. Soc. of Echocardiography. Prev: SpR Cardiol., Hammersmith Hosps., Lond.; SpR Cardiol., QEI Hosp., Welwyn Garden City; SpR Cardiol., Harefield Hosp., Middlx.

JENKINS, Gethin Heath Lane Surgery, Earl Shilton, Leicester LE9 7PB Tel: 01455 844431 Fax: 01455 442297; 92 Heath Lane, Heath Lane, Earl Shilton, Leicester LE9 7PD Tel: 01455 848328 — MB BS 1976 Lond.; MRCS Eng. LRCP Lond. 1976; DRCOG 1979.

JENKINS, Gillian Margaret The Surgery, 1 Unity Street, Bristol BS1 5DQ Tel: 0117 929 0090 Fax: 0117 922 1293 — BM 1981 Soton.; DFFP 1994; DRCOG 1984. Flight Med. Off. Wings AeroMed. Servs. Brislington Bristol; Asst. GP.

JENKINS, Graham Watcyn Humber Road Surgery, 27 Humber Road, Chelmsford CM1 7PE Tel: 01245 268635 Fax: 01245 344552; Laceys, 22 Green Close, Springfield, Chelmsford CM1 7SL Tel: 01245 251906 — MB BS 1956 Lond.; MRCS Eng. LRCP Lond. 1956. (Guy's) Hosp. Pract. Chelmsford & Essex Hosp.; Clin. Asst. Middlx. Hosp.; Occupat. Health Adviser Mid. Essex HA. Socs: Fell. Hunt. Soc.; BMA. Prev: Ho. Surg. Roy. Surrey Co. Hosp. Guildford; Ho. Phys. E. Glam. Hosp. Pontypridd.

JENKINS, Gregory John 2/75 Longfleet Road, Poole BH15 2JB — MB BS 1988 Sydney.

JENKINS, Helen Claire Meddyfga Taf, North Road, Whitland SA34 0AT Tel: 01994 240195 Fax: 01994 241138; Cilgadan Fach, Llandyfaeldg, Kidwelly SA17 5PD — MB BCh 1987 Wales; DCH RCP Lond. 1991; DA (UK) 1990. (Cardiff) GP.

JENKINS, Mr Howard Max Lewis Tel: 01332 347314 Fax: 01332 206461 — MB BS Lond. 1971; DM Nottm. 1984; FRCOG 1990, M 1977; DObst RCOG 1973. (Middlx.) Cons. O & G Derby Hosps.; Clin. Teach. Univ. Nottm.; Med. Dir. S. Derbysh. Acute Hosps. Socs: Nuffield Vis. Soc.; Birm. & Midl. Obst. & Gyn. Soc. Prev: Lect. (O & G) Univ. Nottm.; Ho. Surg. Middlx. Hosp. Lond.

JENKINS, Huw Ritchie Department of Child Health, University Hospital of Wales, Heath Park, Cardiff CF14 4XW Tel: 029 2074 4670 — MB BChir 1978; MD Camb. 1991; FRCP Lond. 1993; MRCP (UK) 1980; FRCPCH 1997. (St. Thomas) Cons. Paediat. (Gastroenterol.) Univ. Hosp. Wales. Prev: Sen. Regist. (Paediat.) Univ. Hosp. Wales Cardiff; Regist. (Paediat.) Hosp. Sick Childr. Lond.; SHO (Gastroenterol.) Hosp. Sick Childr. Lond.

JENKINS, Ian 14 Blanchard Close, Leominster HR6 8SH — MB BS 1998 Lond.; MB BS Lond 1998.

JENKINS, Ian Alastair Department of Anaesthesia & Intensive Care, Royal Hospital for Children, Bristol BS2 8BJ Tel: 0117 928 5100 Fax: 0117 928 5114 — MB BS 1979 Newc.; MRCP (UK) 1982; FFA RCS Eng. 1985. (Newcastle upon Tyne) Cons. Paediat. Anaesth. Roy. Hosp. Sick Childr. Bristol; Director, Paediatric Intens. Care Unit, Bristol. Socs: Intens. Care Soc.; Coll. Soc. RCP Edin.; Assn. Paediat. Anaesth. Prev: Cons. Anaesth. Freeman Hosp. NHS Trust; Cons. Anaesth. Soton. & SW Hants. HA; Cons. Anaesth. Academisch Ziekenhuis, Groningen (N.L.).

JENKINS, Ian Anthony Rowland Stowmarket Health Centre, Violet Hill Road, Stowmarket IP14 1NL Tel: 01449 776000 Fax: 01449 776005 — MB BS 1976 Lond.; MRCS Eng. LRCP Lond. 1976.

JENKINS, Mr Ian Lawrence, CVO, QHS, Surg. Rear-Admiral Victory Building, Hm Naval Base, Portsmouth PO1 3LS Tel: 02392 727801 Fax: 02392 727805 — MB BCh 1968 Wales; FRCS Eng. 1973; T(S) 1991. (Cardiff) Med. Dir.Gen. Naval; Cons. Urol. RN. Socs: Fell. Roy. Soc. Med.; Assn. Surg.; Brit. Assn. Urol. Surgs. Prev: Med. Off. in Command RN Hosp. Haslar; Prof. Naval Surg. (RN & Roy. Coll. Surg. Eng.); Defence Postgrad. Med. Dean & Commandant Roy. Defence Med. Coll.

JENKINS, Ieuan Harri MRC Cyclotron Unit, Hammersmith Hospital, Du Cane Road, London W12 0NN Tel: 020 8383 2029 Fax: 020 8383 2029 Email: harri@cu.rpms.ac.uk; 34 Broughton Road, West Ealing, London W13 8QW Tel: 020 8567 1005 — MB BS 1986 Lond.; BSc (Hons.) Lond. 1983; MRCP (UK) 1990; MD Lond. 1998. (UMD (Guy's)) Sen. Lect. (Neurol) Imperial Coll. Sch. of Med.; Cons. Nerologist Hammersmith Hosp. Socs: Assoc. of Brit. NeUrol.s, Ordinary Mem. Prev: Lect. & Sen. Regist. (Neurol.) Roy. Postgrad. Med. Sch. Hammersmith Hosp. & Inst. Neurol. Qu. Sq. Lond.; Regist. (Neurol.) Char. Cross Hosp. Lond.; Clin. Research Fell. (Neurol.) MRC Cyclotron Unit Hammersmith Hosp. Lond.

JENKINS, Iris Rhianne 39 Manor Way, Risca, Newport NP11 6AA — MB BCh 1993 Wales.

JENKINS, Iwan Rhys (retired) Red Roofs, Llangunnor, Carmarthen SA31 2PA Tel: 01267 236214 — MRCS Eng. LRCP Lond. 1953; FFA RCS Eng. 1966; DA Eng. 1959. Prev: Cons. Anaesth. W. Wales Gen. Hosp. Carmarthen.

JENKINS, Janet Royal Infirmary, Lauriston Place, Edinburgh EH3 9HB Tel: 0131 536 3912 Fax: 0131 536 3912; 18 Blacket Place, Edinburgh EH9 1RL Tel: 0116 270 3260, 0131 667 2885 — MB ChB 1971 Ed.; BSc Ed. 1968; FRCA 1976. (Ed.) Cons. Anaesth. Roy. Infirm. Edin.; Pat. Servs. Director for Theatres & Anaesth. Lothian United Hosps. NHS Trust. Prev: Med. Dir. E. & Midlothian NHS Trust.

JENKINS, Janet Caroline 54 Stanley Hill Avenue, Amersham HP7 9BA Tel: 01494 431489; Chambers of K. Coonan Q.C., 6 Pump Court, Temple, London EC4Y 7AR Tel: 020 7583 6013 — MB BS Lond. 1985. (University College Hospital) Barrister Lond.; Barrister Middle Temple; Dip. Law City Univ. Lond. 1993 (called to the Bar 1994). Socs: Soc. Doctors Law. Prev: Sen. Regist., Lect. & Regist. (Microbiol.) St. Thos. Hosp. Lond.; Asst. Lect. & Regist. (Histopath.) St. Thos. Hosp. Lond.

JENKINS, Jean Elizabeth 3 Common Lane, Lach Dennis, Northwich CW9 7TB — BM BS 1983 Nottm.; BMedSci Nottm. 1983; DRCOG 1986.

JENKINS, Jennifer Rosemary 37 Newmarket Road, Norwich NR2 2HN — MB BS Lond. 1970; DObst RCOG 1972; FFA RCS Eng. 1976; DA Eng. 1972. (Westm.) Cons. Anaesth. Jas. Paget Hosp. Gt. Yarmouth.

JENKINS, Jeremy Patrick Russell Dept. of Clinical Radiology, Manchester Royal Infirmary, Oxford Rd, Manchester MI3 9WL Tel: 0161 276 4141, 0161 276 8595; 28 Pine Road, Bramhall, Stockport SK7 2JN Tel: 0161 440 7597 Fax: 0161 285 8840 Email: jeremyjenkins@jeremysmail.com — MB BCh 1975 Wales; FRCP 2000; MRCP (UK) 1978; FRCR 1981; T(R) (CR) 1991; DMRD Eng. 1980. (Welsh national School of Medicine) Cons. Radiol. Manch. Roy. Infirm.; Hon. Clin. Sen. Lect. Univ. Manch. Socs: Internat. Soc. Magnetic Resonance in Med.; Brit. Soc. Skeletal Radiol.; Brit. Soc. Neuro-Radiolog. Prev: Sen. Lect. (Diag. Radiol.) Univ. Manch.

JENKINS, Jeremy Roland Furneaux Willowbrook Medical Practice, Brook St., Sutton-in-Ashfield NG17 1ES Tel: 01623 440018 — BM BS 1984 Nottm.; MRACGP 1990; BMedSci (Hons.) Nottm. 1982; MRCGP 1990.

JENKINS, Joan Edith (retired) 11A Gloucester Terrace, Southsea PO5 4DT Tel: 01705 820368 — MRCS Eng. LRCP Lond. 1949. Prev: GP S.sea.

JENKINS, John Campbell (retired) Kinnaird, London Road, Poulton, Cirencester GL7 5JQ — MB ChB Ed. 1958; FRCPsych 1992, M 1971; DPM Eng. 1964. Med. Mem. Ment. Health Review Tribunal; Second Opinion Apptd. Dr Ment. Health Act Commiss. Prev: Med. Dir. E. Wilts. Healthcare NHS Trust.

JENKINS, Mr John Dudley (retired) Windhover, Mount Road, Dinas Powys CF64 4DG — MB 1956 Camb.; MChir Camb. 1971, MB 1956, BChir 1955; FRCS Eng. 1964; FRCS Ed. 1962. Prev: Sen. Regist. Dept. Urol. Gen. Infirm. Leeds.

JENKINS, John Emrys (retired) Chalfont, South Crescent, Llandrindod Wells LD1 5DH Tel: 01597 2000 — BM BCh 1932 Oxf.; MA Oxf. 1932, BM BCh 1932. Prev: Surg. Co. War Memor. Hosp. Llandrindod Wells.

JENKINS, John Gareth 22 Nightingale Road, Guildford GU1 1ER Tel: 01483 503720 — MB BS 1976 Lond.; FFA RCS Eng. 1981. Cons. Anaesth. Roy. Surrey Co. Hosp. Guildford. Prev: Sen. Regist. (Anaesth.) St. Geo. Hosp. & Hosp. for Sick Childr. Lond.; Asst. Prof. Clin. Anaesth. Stanford Univ. Med. Centre; Stanford, Calif..

JENKINS, John Gordon Antrim Area Hospital, 45 Bush Road, Antrim BT41 2RL Tel: 01849 424510 Fax: 01849 424156 Email: john.jenkins@uh.n-i.nhs.uk — MB BCh BAO 1974 Belf.; MD Belf. 1980; FRCP Lond. 1993; FRCP Ed. 1989; FRCPCH 1997. Cons. Paediat. United Hosp. Trust, N. Irel.

JENKINS, John Henry Community Mental Health Team, Victoria House, 405 Shooters Hill Road, Woolwich, London SE18 4LH Tel: 020 8781 4362 — MB BS 1976 Lond.; BSc Lond. 1973; MRCS Eng. LRCP Lond. 1976; MRCPsych 1982. (St. Bart. Hosp. Lond.) Cons. Psychiat. MoD Lond. Prev: Cons. Psychiat. Qu. Eliz. Milit. Hosp. Lond.; Regist. (Psychiat.) Barrow Hosp. Bristol.

JENKINS, John Lloyd The Surgery, 4 Hall Grove, Welwyn Garden City AL7 4PL Tel: 01707 323355 Fax: 01707 373139; 11 Reddings, Welwyn Garden City AL8 7LA Tel: 01707 322723 — MB ChB 1951 Birm. (Birm.) Med. Off. GP Unit Qu. Eliz. II Hosp. Welwyn Garden City; Chairm. Herts. LMC; Chairm. NW Thames LMC; Assoc. Mem. Herts. FHSA. Socs: (Pres. E. Herts. Div.) BMA. Prev: Squadron Ldr. RAF Med. Br.; Med. Off. Canad. Pacific Rly.; Ho. Surg. & Ho. Surg. (Cas.) Gen. Hosp. Birm.

JENKINS, John Rhys Westway Surgery, 1 Wilson Road, Ely, Cardiff CF5 4LJ Tel: 029 2059 2351 Fax: 029 2059 9956 — BM 1989 Soton.; MRCGP 1994; DRCOG 1993. GP Cardiff.

JENKINS, John Richard Everett (retired) Bullcroft, Michaelston-le-Pit, Dinas Powys CF64 4HE Tel: 01222 515085 Fax: 01222 515071 Email: richard.jenkins@virgin.net — MRCS Eng. LRCP Lond. 1951; MA Camb. 1947; FFA RCS Eng. 1957; DA Eng. 1954. Prev: Cons. Anaesth. S. Glam. AHA (T).

JENKINS, John Robson Roose, Group Capt. RAF Med. Br. Retd. (retired) c/o Barclays Bank, 10 Hart St., Henley-on-Thames RG9 2RX — MRCS Eng. LRCP Lond. 1934. Prev: Dir. Air Force Med., Dept. Air Canberra, Austral.

JENKINS, Professor John Sydney (retired) 40 Hampstead Way, London NW11 7JL Tel: 020 8455 7456 Email: john.jenkins6@which.net — MA Camb. 1948, MD 1954, MB BChir 1948; FRCP Lond. 1970, M 1951; MRCS Eng. LRCP Lond. 1948. Emerit. Prof. Clin. Endocrinol. St. Geo. Hosp. Med. Sch. & Cons. Phys. St. Geo. Hosp. Lond. Prev: 1st Asst. (Med.) St. Geo. Hosp. Lond.

JENKINS, John Taylor 8 Tantallon Dr, Paisley PA2 9JS — MB ChB 1997 Glas.

JENKINS, Mr John Thomas Moore Christopher Ynys Pandy, Golan, Garndolbenmaen LL51 9YU Tel: 01766 530256 — FRCS (Orl.) Eng. 1950; MRCS Eng. LRCP Lond. 1942; DLO Eng. 1949. (Guy's) Emerit. Cons. Surg. (ENT) Leics. AHA (T). Prev: Cons. Surg. (ENT) Leics. AHA (T); ENT Sen. Regist. Cardiff Roy. Infirm.; Ho. Surg. (ENT) Guy's Hosp. Lond.

JENKINS, Julia Anne Department Child Health, Kings College Hospital, Denmark Hill, London NW1 Tel: 020 7737 4000; Vine Cottage, 4 Parkgate, London SE3 9XE — BM 1994 Soton. (Southampton) SHO (Neonatology) Kings Coll. Hosp. Prev: SHO (Anaesth.) PeterBoro.; SHO (A & E) Luton & Dunstable Hosp.

JENKINS, Julian Michael St Michael's Hospital, Southwell St., Bristol BS2 8EG Tel: 0117 928 5624 Fax: 0117 928 5290 — BM 1982 Soton.; DM Soton. 1993; MRCOG 1987; FRCOL 2000. Cons. & Sen. Lect. (O & G) St. Michael's Hosp. Bristol; Clin. Director, Centre for Reproductive Med., Bristol. Prev: Lect. (O & G) Jessop Hosp. Wom. Sheff.; Clin. Research Fell. (Human Reproduc.) P.ss Anne Hosp. Soton.

JENKINS, Karen 31 Kingsmark Lane, Chepstow NP16 5LZ — MB ChB 1991 Wales; BSc (Hons.) Bristol 1988. SHO (A & E) Derriford Hosp. Plymouth.

JENKINS, Karen Ann 108 Pennard Road, South Gate, Swansea SA3 2AD — MB ChB 1997 Ed.; BSc (Med Sci) Hons. Immunol. (Edinburgh)

JENKINS, Katharine Sophie 142 Wingrove Road, Newcastle upon Tyne NE4 9BX — MB BS 1998 Newc.; MB BS Newc 1998.

JENKINS, Kathryn Lisa 3 Southend Villas, Mumbles Road, Mumbles, Swansea SA3 4EL Tel: 01792 366260 — BM BS 1990 Nottm. Specialist Regist. Rotat. (Anaesth.) Bristol.

JENKINS, Kathryn Louise 21 Birmingham Road, Hagley, Stourbridge DY9 9JZ — MB BS 1996 Lond.

JENKINS, Keith John 11A School Lane, North Hykeham, Lincoln LN6 9QS — MB BS Durh. 1963; DCH Eng. 1968; MFHOM 1997. Prev: Maj. RAMC, BAOR & FARELF; Ho. Surg. St. Jas. Hosp. Tredegar; Ho. Phys. Cumbld. Infirm. Carlisle.

JENKINS, Laura Elizabeth 19 Hampton Court, Newtownabbey BT37 0NY — MB BCh BAO 1995 Belf.

JENKINS, Leonard Richard (retired) Montrose, 2 Tygwyn Avenue, Penylan, Cardiff CF23 5JJ — LMSSA Lond. 1954. Prev: Ho. Off. (O & G & Gen. Med.) Roy. Infirm. Huddersfield.

JENKINS, Lesley Katherine Knowle House, 4 Crowthorn Road, Ashton-under-Lyne OL7 0DH Tel: 0161 330 5892 Fax: 0161 339 1438 — MB ChB 1982 Manch.; MSc Manch. 1992; MRCGP 1989; Cert. Family Plann. JCC 1989; MRCPsych 1988; DRCOG 1984. Cons. Psychiat. (Learning Disabil.) Tameside & Glossop Community & Priority Servs. NHS Trust; Cons. Psychiat. David Lewis Centre for Epilepsy Alderley Edge. Prev: Regist. (Psychiat.) Univ. Hosp. Manch.; SHO (Psychiat.) Univ. Hosp. S. Manch.; SHO (Rheum. & Rehabil., Obst. & Paediat.) Stepping Hill Hosp. Stockport.

JENKINS, Lucy Katherine Flat 9, Daws Court, High St., Iver SL0 9NQ — MB BS 1998 Lond.; MB BS Lond 1998.

JENKINS, Lyn Marshall Prospect House, High Street, Great Missenden HP16 0BG Tel: 01494 862325 Fax: 01494 890510; Rabs Corner, The Lee, Great Missenden HP16 9NX Tel: 01494 837291 Fax: 01494 837291 — BM BCh 1974 Oxf.; MA Camb. 1975; MCOphth 1989; DO Eng. 1977. (Camb. & Oxf.) Princip. in Gen. Pract.; Ophth. Laser Pract. Lond.; Hosp. Pract. (Diabetic Retinop.) Stoke Mandeville Hosp.; Clin. Dir., Prospect Eye Centre. Prev: SHO (Ophth.) Char. Cross Hosp. Lond.; Ho. Phys. Radcliffe Infirm. Oxf.; Ho. Surg. St. Mary's Gen. Hosp. Portsmouth.

JENKINS, Mair Lloyd Ailsa Craig, 55 Treyew Road, Truro TR1 2BY Tel: 01872 77880 — MB BCh 1945 Wales; BSc, MB BCh Wales 1945; MFCM 1972. (Cardiff) Sen. Med. Off. Cornw. AHA. Socs: BMA & Cornw. Clin. Soc.

JENKINS, Marged Angela 8 Chapel Fields, Charterhouse Road, Godalming GU7 2BS — MB ChB 1989 Bristol.

JENKINS, Mari Greta Chase Farm Hospital, The Ridgeway, Enfield EN2 8JL; 1A Canonbury Lane, London N1 2AS — MB BS 1989 Lond.

JENKINS, Mark Godfrey 38 Pilrig Street, Edinburgh EH6 5AN — MB ChB 1990 Glas.

JENKINS, Mary Bradford Hospitals NHS Trust, Department Histopathology, Bradford Royal Infirmary, Bradford BD9 6RJ Tel: 01274 364800 — MB BS 1987 Lond.; BSc Lond. 1984; MRCPath 1995. (St. Geo. Hosp. Med. Sch.) Cons. Histopath. & Cytopath. Bradford Hosp. NHS Trust. Prev: Regist. (Histopath.) Leeds Gen. Infirm.; Ho. Phys. (Gen. Med.) Epsom Dist. Hosp.; Ho. Surg. (Gen. Surg.) Mayday Hosp.

JENKINS, Mary Patricia Eleri Glensannox, 892 Newport Road, Rumney, Cardiff CF3 4LJ Tel: 029 2079 2764 — MB BCh 1949 Wales; BSc Wales 1946, MB BCh 1949; MFCM RCP (UK) 1983. (Cardiff) Ref. Welsh Off. Socs: Cardiff Med. Soc. & Soc. Pub. Health. Prev: Cons. Pub. Health Med. S. Glam. HA.

JENKINS, Mary Wells (private rooms), 117 Cathedral Road, Cardiff CF11 9PH Tel: 029 2022 4422 Fax: 029 2066 4113; 3 Nant Fawr Road, Cyncoed, Cardiff CF23 6JQ Tel: 029 2075 0237 — MB BCh 1944 Wales; BA (Hons.) Open 1991; BSc Wales 1941; DPH Wales 1951. (Cardiff) p/t Indep. Med. Hypn. & Acupunc. Cardiff. Socs: Hon. Fell. Amer. Med. Coll. Acupunc.; BSMDH & Mem. (Ex-Chairm.) BMAS.; BSECH. Prev: Specialist (Med.) Manpower & Plann. M. Glam. HA; Dean Fac. Life Scs. Fanshawe Coll. Lond., Ontario; Med. Off. Welsh Office Cardiff.

JENKINS, Meriel Iona Roche Cottage, Tenby — LRCP LRCS 1958 Ed.; LRCP LRCS Ed. LRFPS Glas. 1958. (Ed.) Clin. Med. Off. E. Dyfed Health Auth. Prev: Ho. Phys. & Ho. Surg. W. Wales Hosp. Carmarthen.

JENKINS, Michael Andrew Tonypandy Health Centre, Tonypandy CF40 2LE Tel: 01443 432112 Fax: 01443 432803 — MB BCh 1981 Wales; MRCGP 1988; DRCOG 1987.

JENKINS, Michael Charles Frederick Tel: 01872 255078 — MB BS 1982 Lond.; MD Bristol 1993; MRCPath. 1988. (St. Marys) Cons. Histopath.Roy. Cornw. Hosp. Truro. Prev: Cons. Histopath. Dorset Co. Hosp. Dorchester; Sen. Regist. (Histopath.) S.mead Hosp. Bristol; Ho. Phys. St. Mary's Hosp. Lond.

JENKINS, Michael David 82 Old Park Ridings, Winchmore Hill, London N21 2ES Tel: 020 8360 8170 Fax: 020 8360 8170 — MB BS 1970 Lond.; MRCP 1999 (UK); MRCS Eng. LRCP Lond. 1970;

FFHom 1976, M 1975. (Westm.) Cons. Homoeop. Phys. Roy. Lond. Homoeop. Hosp. Prev: Sen. Regist. (Research) St. Mary's Hosp. Lond.; Study Fell. Roy. Lond. Homoeop. Hosp.; Regist. (Med.) St. Mary's Hosp. Lond. (Harrow Rd. Br.).

JENKINS, Michael Eric Charles The Surgery, Torton Hill Road, Arundel BN18 9HG Tel: 01903 882517/882191 Fax: 01903 884326; 14 Arun Street, Arundel BN18 9DL Tel: 01903 884827 — MB BS 1988 Lond.; MRCGP 1995; DRCOG 1992. Socs: MDU; BMA.

JENKINS, Mr Michael Philip Ridge Cottage, Hammers Lane, Mill Hill Village, London NW7 4DY Tel: 020 8959 3284 Email: 101532.2136@compuserve.com — MB BS 1989 Lond.; BSc (Hons.) Lond. 1986; FRCS Lond. 1993. Surgic. Specialist Regist. NE Thames Rotat. Socs: Fell. Roy. Soc. Med.; ASIT; Assn. of Surg. Prev: Vasc. Research Fell. Regist. (Surg.) Middlx. Hosp. Lond.; Regist. (Surg.) Roy. Marsden Hosp. Lond.; SHO Rotat. (Surg.) Char. Cross Hosp. Lond.

JENKINS, Morfa Mairlys Department of Respiratory Medicine, Glaxo Wellcome Research & Development, Greenford Road, Greenford UB6 0HE Tel: 020 8966 3473 Fax: 020 8864 9438; 17 Fairmark Drive, North Hillingdon, Uxbridge UB10 9LP — MB BS 1978 Lond.; DA Eng. 1981. Dir. Clin. Research (Respirat. Med.) Glaxo Wellcome Research & Developm. Prev: Head Clin. Research (Respirat. Med.) Glaxo Research & Developm.; Regist. (Anaesth.) St. Bart. Hosp. Lond.

JENKINS, Neale Mark Watcyn Orchard House Surgery, St. Marys Road, Ferndown BH22 9HB Tel: 01202 897000 Fax: 01202 897888 — MB BS 1984 Lond.; DRCOG 1989.

JENKINS, Neil Edward Thatchmoor, Crowle Lane, Tibberton, Droitwich WR9 7NT — BM BCh 1996 Oxf.

JENKINS, Nicholas Howard Accident & Emergency Department, Nevill Hall Hospital, Abergavenny NP7 7EG Tel: 01873 732066 Fax: 01873 732664 Email: nick.jenkins@gwent.wales.nhs.uk; 14 Briardene, Llanfoist, Abergavenny NP7 9LJ Tel: 01873 854106 Email: nickjenkins@btinternet.com — BSc (1st cl. Hons.) Wales 1977; MCh Wales 1989; MBBCh (Wales) 1980; FRCS Eng. 1984; FFAEM 1993. (Wales) Cons. A & E Nevill Hall Hosp. Abergavenny Gwent; Gwent Healthcare NHS Trust; Lead Clin. Director; A & E Directorate. Prev: Sen. Regist. (A & E) Roy. Gwent Hosp. Newport Gwent; Regist. (A & E) Dist. Hosp. P'boro.; Lect. & Hon. Sen. Regist. (Orthop. Surg.) Univ. Wales Coll. Med. Cardiff.

JENKINS, Nicholas Paul 1 The Hedgerows, Romsley, Halesowen B62 0PS — MB ChB 1993 Manch.; MB ChB (Hons.) Manch. 1993; BSc (Experim. Immunol. & Oncol.) Manch. 1990; MRCP November 1996. Research Fell. (Cardiol.) Wythenshawe Hosp. Manch. Prev: SHO (Gastroenterol. & Gen. Med.) Wythenshawe Hosp. Manch.

JENKINS, Paul Wychwood, 124 Mid St., South Nutfield, Redhill RH1 4JH Tel: 01737 823382 — MB BS 1974 Lond.; MB BS (Hons.) Lond. 1974; FRCP Lond. 1995; MRCP (UK) 1976; MRCS Eng. LRCP Lond. 1974. (St. Geo.) Cons. Phys. (Thoracic Med.) E. Surrey Hosp. Redhill. Socs: Brit. Thorac. Soc.& BMA. Prev: Sen. Regist. (Med.) Brompton & W.m. Hosps. Lond.; Regist. (Med.) Roy. Free Hosp. Lond.; SHO (Med.) Whittington Hosp. Lond.

JENKINS, Paul Fowler Medical Assessment Unit, Norfolk and Norwich Hospital, Norwich NR1 3SR; Windetts Barn, Seething Rd, Kirstead, Norwich NR15 1EG — MB BChir 1974 Camb.; MA Camb. 1975; FRCP Lond. 1992; MRCP (UK) 1976. (Camb. & Middlx.) Cons. Phys. (Gen. & Chest Med.) & Dir. Med. Assessm. Unit United Norwich Hosp.; Regional RCP Advisor (From 01/08/2001). Prev: Sen. Regist. (Gen. & Chest Med.) Oxf. Hosps.; Regist. (Thoracic) Llandough Hosp. Cardiff; Regist. (Med.) City Hosp. Nottm.

JENKINS, Paul Jonathan Department of Endocrinology, St. Bartholomew's Hospital, London EC1A 7BE — MB BChir 1989 Camb.; MA Camb. 1989; MRCP (UK) 1991. (Lond. Hosp.) Lect. (Med.) St. Bart. Hosp. Lond. Socs: Endocrine Soc.; Roy. Soc. Med. Prev: Regist. (Med.) St. Bart. Hosp. Lond.

JENKINS, Peter (retired) Roche Cottage, 19 Lady Park, Tenby SA70 8JJ — MB BS 1954 Lond.; MRCS Eng. LRCP Lond. 1954; FFR 1970; DMRD Eng. 1968. Hon. Cons. Radiol. Dyfed AHA.

JENKINS, Peter Anthony Tadworth Medical Centre, Troy Close, Tadworth KT20 5JE Tel: 01737 362327 Fax: 01737 370954; 1 Moreplace Cottages, Wonham Lane, Betchworth RH3 7AD Tel: 01737 844249 Fax: 01737 844249 — MB BS 1971 Lond.; BSc Lond. 1968, MB BS 1971; FRCGP 1990, M 1977; DObst RCOG 1974. (St. Geo.) Assoc. Dean (Gen. Pract.) S. Thames Region (W); GP Tutor Mid-Surrey Dist.; Assoc. Lect. Univ. Surrey Guildford. Prev: Course Organiser Guildford GP VTS; Lect. (Educat. Studies) Surrey Univ. Guildford.

JENKINS, Peter David Avon Valley Practice, Fairfield, Upavon, Pewsey SN9 6DZ Tel: 01980 630221 Fax: 01980 630393 Email: Peter.Jenkins@gp-J83023.nhs.uk — MB BS 1974 Lond.; MRCS Eng. LRCP Lond. 1974; MRCGP 1980. (St. Mary's) Hon. Clin. Teach. Soton. Univ. Med. Sch.; GP Tutor Salisbury; GP; Clin. Gov. Lead. S. Wilts. PCT. Socs: BMA. Prev: Ho. Phys. St. Mary's Hosp. Lond.; Ho. Surg. Poole Gen. Hosp.

JENKINS, Peter John 35 Sunnybank Road, Oldbury, Birmingham — MB ChB 1988 Birm.

JENKINS, Peter Lionel Gethin Cardiff Consulting Rooms, 128, Newport Rd, Cardiff CF24 1DH Tel: 029 2046 4499 Fax: 029 2047 0309 Email: gethin@totalise.co.uk; St. Joseph's Hospital, Harding Avenue, Newport NP20 6EZ Tel: 029 2068 9291 Fax: 01222 689291 — MB BS 1980 Lond.; BSc Lond. 1977; MRCPsych 1985. (King's Coll. Lond.) Cons. Adult Psychiat. Gwent, NHS Trust; Fell.sh. Assn. Acad. Psychiats. USA 1986; Hon. Sen. Lect. Univ. Wales Coll. Med. 1998. Socs: Fell. Roy. Soc. Med.; Fell. Acad. Psychomatic Med. USA; Fell. Roy. Coll. Psychiat. 1996. Prev: Cons. Liaison Psychiat. Caerphilly; Lect. (Psychol. Med.) Univ. Wales Coll. Med. Cardiff; Instruc. & Fell. Forens. Psychiat. Univ. S. Carolina Sch. Med. Colombia, USA.

JENKINS, Professor Rachel WHO Collaborating Centre, Institute of Psychiatry, De Crespigny Park, Denmark Hill, London SE5 8AF Tel: 020 7740 5293 Fax: 020 7919 3669 Email: p/jenkins@iop.kcl.ac.uk — MB BChir 1974 Camb.; MA Camb. 1975, MD 1983; FRCPsych 1994, M 1978 (Camb.) Dir. (Psychiat.) WHO Collaborating Centre; Vis. Instit. Psychiat 1998; Hon. Cons. Maudesley Hosp.1997. Socs: Fell. Roy. Inst. Pub. Health & Hyg.; Internat. Federat. Psychiat. Epidemiol.; Fell. Fac. Occupat. Health. Prev: Princip. Med. Off. DOH Lond.; Sen. Lect. (Psychiat.) St. Bart. Hosp. Lond. & Inst. Psychiat. Lond.

JENKINS, Rachel Edwina Tel: 01284 712644 Fax: 01284 712644; 6 Clarkson Close, Cambridge CB3 0EJ — MB BS 1986 Lond.; BSc Lond. 1983; MRCP (UK) 1989; MD Lond. 1997. (University Colllege/ Middlesex Hsopital, London) p/t Cons. Dermatol. W. Suff. Hosps. NHS Trust Bury St Edmunds Suff. Prev: Sen. Regist. (Dermat.) St. John's Dermat. Centre, St. Thomas' Hosp. Lond.

JENKINS, Rees Curdleigh Farm, Blagdon Hill, Taunton TA3 7SJ Tel: 01823 421345 — MB BChir Camb. 1941; MRCS Eng. LRCP Lond. 1941. (Camb. & St. Thos.) Prev: Ho. Surg. St. Thos. Hosp. Lond., Roy. Vict., W. Hants. Hosp. Bournemouth & St. Helier Hosp. Carshalton.

JENKINS, Richard Christopher 1 Willow Croft, Hope Road, Bamford, Hope Valley S33 0AL Tel: 01433 650943 Email: richard@jenkinsr.demon.co.uk — MB ChB 1991 Sheff.; BMedSci (Virol.) Sheff. 1989; MRCP (UK) 1994. (Sheff.) Clin. Research Fell. & Hon. Regist. N. Gen. Hosp. Sheff. Socs: Soc. Endocrinol.; Brit. Diabetic Assn.; E. Midl. Soc. Phys. Prev: Lect. (Endocrinol. & Diabetes) & Hon. Regist. N.. Gen. Hosp. Sheff.

JENKINS, Richard Dean 14 School Street, Abercwmboi, Aberdare CF44 6AD Email: djenkins@enterprise.net — MB BCh 1990 Wales; MRCP (UK) 1997. (Univ. Wales) Specialist Regist. (Geriat. Med.) Llandough Hosp. Cardiff. Prev: Regist. (Elderly Med.) St. Woolos Hosp.); Med. Regist. Waikato Hosp. Hamilton, New Zealand.

JENKINS, Richard Geraint Portway Surgery, 1 The Portway, Porthcawl CF36 3XB Tel: 01656 304204 Fax: 01656 772605 — MB BS 1981 Lond.; MRCPsych 1988.

JENKINS, Richard Gisli 95 Erlanger Road, London SE14 5TQ — BM 1992 Soton.

JENKINS, Richard Guy 22 Farm Road, Burton-on-Trent DE13 0XQ — MB BS 1996 Lond.; BSc (Hons) UCL 1993. (Kings College Lond)

JENKINS, Richard Thomas Davies Caerwent, North Road, Whitland SA34 0AY — MB BCh 1986 Wales.

JENKINS, Robert Ian 41 Woolacott Drive, Newton, Swansea SA3 — MB BCh 1981 Wales.

JENKINS, Robert Michael Davenal House Surgery, Bromsgrove, Bromsgrove B61 0DD; Westways, Loggerheads Corner, Hanbury, Droitwich WR9 7DZ Tel: 01527 821307 — MB BCh 1976 Wales; MRCS Eng. LRCP Lond. 1975; DMed 1999; MRCP 1978 (UK); FRCGP 1996; MRCP (UK) 1978; MRCS Eng. LRCP Lond. 1975;

FRCGP 1996, M 1987. G.P. Princip.; Vocational Train.; Course Organiser; GP Trainer. Prev: Research Regist. Qu. Eliz. Med. Centre Birm.; Regist. Rotat. (Gen. Med.) Selly Oak Hosp. Birm.; Regist. (Gen. Med.) Llandough Hosp. Cardiff.

JENKINS, Robert Tudor Fulham Road Surgery, 630 Fulham Road, London SW6 5RS Tel: 020 7736 4344 Fax: 020 7736 4985 — MB BS 1977 Lond.; MRCS Eng. LRCP Lond. 1977.

JENKINS, Robin Michael Hamilton The Park Surgery, 116 Kings Road, Herne Bay CT6 5RE; The Wheel House, 40B Mill Lane, Herne Bay CT6 7EB — MB BS 1983 Lond.; DRCOG; TGP. (St Bartholomews) Socs: BMA & Med. Defence Union. Prev: GP Princip. The Pk. Surg. Herne Bay; GP Trainee Kent & Canterbury VTS; SHO (A & E) Countess of Chester Hosp.

JENKINS, Roger John 15 Cawley Street, Runcorn WA7 5PG — MB ChB 1996 Liverp.

JENKINS, Ronald Wyn (retired) Lon-Las, 288 Heol-y-Gors, Cwmgors, Ammanford SA18 1RW Tel: 01269 823156 — MRCS Eng. LRCP Lond. 1956. Prev: Jun. Hosp. Med. Off. Cefn Coed Hosp. Swansea.

JENKINS, Rosemary Penn Hospital, Penn Road, Wolverhampton WV4 5HN; The Poplars, High St, Pattingham, Wolverhampton WV6 7BB — MB ChB 1982 Leic.; MRCPsych 1989. Cons. Psychiat. of Old Age Wolverhampton Health Care Trust. Prev: Sen. Regist. (Psychogeriat.) Qu. Eliz. Psychiat. Hosp. Birm.; Regist. Rotat. (Psychiat.) Birm.

JENKINS, Sally Ann Oak Knoll, Furzefield Road, Beaconsfield HP9 1PQ — MB BS 1983 Lond.; DA Lond. 1986; DFFP 1998. (Char. Cross) p/t Locum GP; Locum Family Plann. Off., Wycombe Gen. Hosp. Prev: Trainee GP Wycombe VTS; Regist. & SHO (Anaesth.) Stoke Mandeville Hosp. Aylesbury; GP Partner, High Wycombe.

JENKINS, Sarah Beth Sheffield Kidney Institute, Northern General Hospital, Herries Rd, Sheffield S5 7A; 7 Gil Meadows, Stannington, Sheffield S6 6FP — MB BChir 1992 Camb.; MB (Hons.)BChir Camb. 1992; MA (Hons.) Camb. 1993; MRCP (UK) 1995. (Cambridge) Specialist Regist. (Nephrol. Med.) N. Gen. Hosp. Sheff. Prev: SHO Rotat. (Med.) Morriston Hosp. Swansea.

JENKINS, Sarah Christine 31 Dalnair Street, Yorkhill, Glasgow G3 8SQ — MB ChB 1991 Ed.

JENKINS, Simon Albert Philip, MBE The Minden Medical Centre, 2 Barlow St., Bury BL9 0QP Tel: 0161 764 2652 Fax: 0161 761 5967; 81 Ringley Road, Whitefield, Manchester M45 7LH — MB ChB 1960 Birm.; FRCGP 1979, M 1970. Socs: BMA (Counc., Gen. Med. Servs. Comm., Chairm. Informat. Technol. Working Party & News Review Bd.). Prev: SHO (Rheum.) Manch. Roy. Infirm.; Ho. Surg. & Ho. Phys. N. Staffs. Roy. Infirm.

JENKINS, Sioned Ann Radyr Health Centre, Park Road, Radyr, Cardiff CF15 8DF Tel: 029 2084 2767; 64 Riverglade, Gwaelod y Garth, Cardiff CF15 9SP Tel: 029 2081 0838 — MB BCh 1985 Wales; MRCGP 1989; DRCOG 1988. GP Radyr.

JENKINS, Stephanie Carol 10 Havering Street, Stepney, London E1 0LP — MB BS 1992 Lond.; BSc (Hons.) 1989; FRCS Lond. 1996. (St. Bart.) Specialist Regist. Basildon & Thurrock NHS Trust.

JENKINS, Stephanie Elizabeth Beech House Surgery, 69 Vale Street, Denbigh LL16 3AU Tel: 01745 812863; Dolhaiarn, Llanfair Talhaiarn, Abergele LL22 8SW Tel: 01745 720711 Fax: 01745 720711 — MB BS 1989 Lond.; MRCOG 2001 Lond. Gen. Practitioner, partner. Prev: Regist. (O & G) Chase Farm Hosp. Enfield & Roy. Free Hosp. Lond.; SHO (Paediat.) W. Suff. Hosp. Bury St Edmunds; SHO (O & G) Norf. & Norwich Hosp.

JENKINS, Stephen 18 Arthog Road, Hale, Altrincham WA15 0NA — MB ChB 1997 Manch.

JENKINS, Steven Huw 1A Canonbury Lane, London N1 2AS — MB BS 1990 Newc.; MRCP (UK) 1993. Clin. Research Fell. (Respirat. Med.) Lond. Chest Hosp. Socs: Med. Defence Union; BMA; Brit. Thorac. Soc.

JENKINS, Stuart Conrad 6 Wheatsheaf Drive, Cowplain, Waterlooville PO8 8PX — MB BCh 1991 Wales.

JENKINS, Stuart Poole Ty'r Felin Surgery, Cecil Road, Gorseinon, Swansea SA4 4BY Tel: 01792 898844 Fax: 01792 891752; North Croft, North Lodge Close, Penllergaer, Swansea SA4 1GP Tel: 01792 892115 — LRCP LRCS Ed. LRCPS Glas. 1963; DObst RCOG 1966. Clin. Asst. (A & E & Ment. Subn.ity) Gorseinon Hosp.; Med. Adviser Lliw Valley Boro. Counc.; Mem. EMO & DHSS. Prev: SHO (Gen. Med. & O & G), Ho. Surg. & Ho. Phys. Morriston Hosp. Swansea.

JENKINS, Susan Elisabeth Department of Psychiatry, Northwick Park Hospital, Watford Road, Harrow HA1 3UJ Tel: 020 8864 3232 — MB BS 1984 Lond.; MRCPsych 1990. (St. Bart. Med. Coll.) Clin. Asst. (Psychother.) Harrow & Hillingdon Healthcare Trust; Jun. Doctor Adviser Task Force on Jun. Doctors Hours NHS Exec. Lond. Prev: Clin. Asst. (Gen. Psychiat.) Richmond, Twickenham & Roehampton Trust; Regist. (Psychother.) Cassel Hosp. Richmond; Clin. Asst. (Psychiat.) Ealing HA.

JENKINS, Susan Jane Dow Surgery, William Street, Redditch B97 4AJ Tel: 01527 62285 Fax: 01527 596260; Westways, Loggerheads Corner, Hanbury, Droitwich WR9 7DZ Tel: 0152 784307 — MB ChB 1976 Liverp.; DFFP 2001; MRCGP 1980; Cert. Family Plann. JCC 1984; DRCOG 1980; DCH Eng. 1978. (Liverpool) Princip. in Gen. Pract. The Dow Surg. Redditch. Prev: Trainee GP S. Glam. VTS; SHO (Paediat.) Morriston Hosp. Swansea; Ho. Phys. & Ho. Surg. Singleton Hosp. Swansea.

JENKINS, Susan Lynley The Surgery, Frensham Road, Lower Bourne, Farnham GU10 3PZ Tel: 01252 793141; Oakwood, Rowhills, Farnham GU9 9AT — MB BS 1981 Lond.; DRCOG 1985. (St. Geo.) Prev: SHO (O & G & Med.) Frimley Pk. Hosp.; Ho. Phys. St. Geo. Hosp. Lond.

JENKINS, Susan Mary Bramhall Park Medical Centre, 235 Bramhall Lane South, Bramhall, Stockport SK7 3EP Tel: 0161 440 8981 — MB ChB 1978 Bristol; Dip Ther 1999 University of Wales; D Occ Med 1996; MRCGP 1983; DRCOG 1982. (Bristol University) Princip. in Gen. Med. Socs: Soc. of Occupat.al Med. Prev: Sen. Med. Off. Manch. Univ.; Princip. GP Bristol.

JENKINS, Susan Melville 59 Ockendon Road, London N1 3NL Tel: 020 7359 3452 — MB BS 1965 Lond.; FRCP Lond. 1992; MRCP (UK) 1972; MRCS Eng. LRCP Lond. 1965; DCH Eng. 1968; FRCPCH 1996. (St. Mary's) Prev: Cons. Community Paediat. City & Hackney; SCMO Paddington & N. Kensington HA; Hon. Lect. (Paediat.) Unit St. Mary's Hosp. Med. Sch.

JENKINS, Mr Terence Percy Norman 19A Abbotswood, Guildford GU1 1UX Tel: 01483 575953 — MB BS 1937 Lond.; FRCS Eng. 1943; MRCS Eng. LRCP Lond. 1936. (Univ. Coll. Hosp.) Emerit. Surg. St. Luke's Hosp. & Roy. Surrey Co. Hosp. Guildford. Socs: Fell. Roy. Soc. Med. Prev: Temp. Maj. RAMC.

JENKINS, Tessa Jane Malt Kiln House, 7 The Maltings, Wothorpe, Stamford PE9 3JE Tel: 01780 766139 — MB ChB 1982 Sheff.; MRCGP 1989; DFFP 1996; DRCOG 1985. p/t Non-Princip. Locum GP Rafwittering, P'boro., Cambs. Prev: Civil. Med. Pract. (BAOR).

JENKINS, Thomas Harold Gwynfe, 30 St Michael's Road, Llandaff, Cardiff CF5 2AP — MB BS 1938 Lond.; BSc (1st cl. Hons.) Wales 1928; MRCS Eng. LRCP Lond. 1938. (Univ. Coll. Hosp.) Med. Off. Nat. Coal Bd. S. W.. Div. Socs: BMA & S. Wales Inst. of Engin. Prev: Mem. Scientif. Staff Med. Research Counc.; H.M. Mines Med. Off. (Wales Region); Asst. Tuberc. Phys. Welsh Nat. Memor. Assn.

JENKINS, Timothy David Owen Park Road Health Centre, Park Road, Radyr, Cardiff CF15 8DF Tel: 029 2084 2767 Fax: 029 2084 2507 — MB BCh 1969 Wales; MRCPsych 1977; MRCGP 1979; DPM Eng. 1974. Socs: Cardiff Med. Soc. & Brit. Soc. Med. & Dent. Hypn. Prev: Ho. Phys. Llandough Hosp. Cardiff; SHO (Cardiothoracic Med.) Sully Hosp. Cardiff; Regist. (Psychol. Med.) Univ. Hosp. Wales, Cardiff.

JENKINS, Vanessa Margaret 63 St Georges Road West, Bickley, Bromley BR1 2NR Tel: 020 8467 6441 — MB BS (Hons. Surg.) Lond. 1961; MRCS Eng. LRCP Lond. 1961; DObst RCOG 1964. (St. Bart.) p/t Disabil. & Occupat.al Health Adviser - SEMA; Medico-Legal Adviser - Private Co. Socs: Livery Comm.; Liveryman of Worshipful Soc. Apoth.; Soc. Occupat. Health - Lond. GP. Prev: Sessional Doctor Marks & Spencer Plc. (Stores & WareHo.), BUPA Med. Centre Croydon & Chelsfield Pk. Hosp. Kent; Clin. Asst. (Rheum.) St. Thos. Hosp. Lond.; Ho. Surg. (Orthop.) & Ho. Phys. (Paediat.) St. Bart. Hosp. Lond.

JENKINS, Yvonne Claire 86 Alpha Terrace, Cambridge CB2 2HT — MB 1981 Camb.; BChir 1980; MRCPsych 1985. Indep. Psychother. Camb. Socs: Assoc. Mem. Brit. Assn. Psychother. Prev: Sen. Regist. (Psychother.) Addenbrooke's Hosp. Camb.; Sen. Regist. (Psychiat.) Lond. Hosp.; Regist. (Psychiat.) St. Geo. Hosp. Lond.

JENKINSON, Andrew David 235 Baker Street, London NW1 6XE; Top Flat, 235 Baker St, London NW1 Tel: 020 7246 7246 — BM

1990 Soton.; FRCS Ed. 1995. Specialist Regist., 235 Baker St., Lond. Prev: Hon. Research Fell. Dept. Gen. Surg. Roy. Lond. Hosp.

JENKINSON, Damian Francis Royal Bournemouth & Christchurch NHS Trust, Castle Lane E., Bournemouth BH7 7DW Tel: 01202 705387 Fax: 01202 705391 Email: damian.jenkinson@rbch.swest.nhs.uk — MB BS 1987 Lond.; PhD Lond. 1983, BSc 1978; MRCP (UK) 1990; FRCP (UK) 2000. (Charing Cross & Westminster, Lond.) Cons. Phys. (Gen. & Geriat. Med.) with Special Responsibil. for Stroke Dis. Roy. Bournemouth & ChristCh. NHS Trust; Clin. Director, ChristCh. Directorate. Socs: BMA; Brit. Geriat. Soc.; Brit. Assn. Stroke Phys. Prev: Sen. Regist. (Gen. & Geriat. Med.) Oxf. Hosps. NHS Trust; Regist. (Renal Med.) Hammersmith Hosp. Lond.

JENKINSON, Daniel Main 24 Elmbridge Drive, Shirley, Solihull B90 4YP — MB ChB 1992 Leeds.

JENKINSON, Douglas The Health Centre, Bunny Lane, Keyworth, Nottingham NG12 5JU Tel: 0115 937 3527 Fax: 0115 937 6781; The Pines, Villa Road, Keyworth, Nottingham NG12 5HD Tel: 0115 937 5470 — MB ChB 1967 Liverp.; DM Nottm. 1996; FRCGP 1985, M 1979; DCH Eng. 1972; DObst RCOG 1970. (Liverp.) Prev: Lect. (Gen. Pract.) Univ. Nottm.; Med. Off. Nchanga Consolidated Copper Mines Chingola, Zambia; SHO (Paediat. & O & G) Clatterbridge Hosp. Bebington.

JENKINSON, Frank Thomas (retired) 387 Wakefield Road, Dalton, Huddersfield HD5 8DB Tel: 01484 517253 — MRCS Eng. LRCP Lond. 1950. Prev: Ho. Phys. St. Jas. Hosp. Leeds.

JENKINSON, Helen Claire Department of Paediatric Oncology, Birmingham Children's Hospital, Steelhouse Lane, Birmingham B4 6NH Tel: 0121 333 8233 Fax: 0121 333 8241 Email: h.jenkinson@mcmail.com — BM BS 1991 Nottm. Macmillan Lect. (Paediat. Oncol.) Birm. Childr.s Hosp.

JENKINSON, Hilary Ann 23 Kings Court, Templepatrick, Ballyclare BT39 0EB Tel: 018494 32597 — MB BCh BAO 1977 Belf.; BSc (Hons.) Belf. 1974, MB BCh BAO 1977; MRCP (UK) 1980; FRCPS Glas. 1991. Cons. Dermat. Whiteabbey Hosp. Co. Antrim.

JENKINSON, Jane Louise 20 Farnham Avenue, Hassocks BN6 8NS — MB ChB 1992 Leeds. Prev: SHO (A & E) Hull Roy. Infirm.

JENKINSON, Jane Ruth Perrins and Partners, Trinity Medical Centre, New George Street, South Shields NE33 5DU Tel: 0191 454 7775 Fax: 0191 454 6787 — MB ChB 1986 Ed.; MRCGP 1991; DRCOG 1988; Cert. Family Plann. JCC 1988. (Univ. Ed.) GP; Ment. Health LEAD, S. Tynneside PCG. Prev: Bd. Mem. S. Tyneside PCG; Bd. Memb. S. Tyneside PCG.

JENKINSON, Karen Anne 9 Millyford Close, Marryat Gardens, Barton-on-Sea, New Milton BH25 7SZ Tel: 01425 629460 — BM BS 1991 Nottm.; BMedSci Nottm. 1989, BM BS 1991. GP Regist. Brockenhurst Surg. Hants.

JENKINSON, Michael David 49 Spring Lane, Sprotbrough, Doncaster DN5 7QQ Tel: 01302 859453; 48 Brampton Drive, Liverpool L8 7SU Tel: 0151 707 1237 — MB ChB 1998 Liverp.; MB ChB Liverp 1998; BSc (Hons). (Liverpool) SHO Surgic. Warrington Gen. Hosp.

JENKINSON, Michael Lloyd Queen Elizabeth, The Queen Mother Hospital, St. Peter's Road, Margate CT9 4AN Tel: 01843 225544 Fax: 01843 220048 Email: michael.jenkinson@thc-tr.sthames.nhs.uk; Chase House, Callis Court Road, Broadstairs CT10 3AH Tel: 01843 604773 Fax: 01843 604773 Email: mljenkinson@doctors.org.uk — MB ChB 1981 Otago; BSc (Hons.) Otago 1976; MRCP (UK) 1986; FRCP Lond. 1998. (Otago) Cons. Phys. i/c Elderly E. Kent Hosp. NHS Trust, Qu. Eliz., the Qu. Mother Hosp.; Hon. Cons. Phys., E. Kent Community NHS Trust. Socs: Brit. Geriat. Soc. Prev: Sen. Regist. (Geriat. & Gen. Med.) St. Thos. Hosp. Lond.; Regist. (Rheum.) Guy's Hosp. Lond.; Lect. (Geriat. & Gen. Med.) St. Bart. Hosp. Lond.

JENKINSON, Patricia Mary Anne Windy Ridge, Linkside, Hindhead GU26 6PA — MB BS 1976 Lond.; MRCS Eng. LRCP Lond. 1976; MRCGP 1980; DRCOG 1980; DCH Eng. 1978. GP Asst. Godalming. Prev: GP Hackney.

JENKINSON, Richard Burton Medical Centre, 123 Salisbury Road, Burton, Christchurch BH23 7JN Tel: 01202 474311 Fax: 01202 484412 — MB BS 1991 Lond.; BSc (Hons.) Lond. 1988; MRCGP 1995; DFFP 1995; DRCOG 1994. (Charing Cross and Westminstor)

JENKINSON, Richard Douglas Dalton Surgery, 364A Wakefield Road, Dalton, Huddersfield HD5 8DY Tel: 01484 530068 — MRCS Eng. LRCP Lond. 1979. (Sheffield) GP Huddersfield.

JENKINSON, Seth Edward The Grange Practice, Allerton Clinic, Wanstead Crescent, Allerton, Bradford BD15 7PA Tel: 01274 541696 — MB 1969 Camb.; BChir 1968; BA Camb. 1965; MPH Leeds 1994; FRCGP 1990, M 1973; DCH Eng. 1972; DObst RCOG 1971. (Camb. & King's Coll. Hosp.) GP Bradford, W. Yorks. Socs: Fell. RCGP (Yorks. Fac. Bd.); BMA. Prev: GP Bradford.

JENKINSON, Sidney, Surg. Cdr. RN Retd. Grindleford, Kilmacolm PA13 4DQ Tel: 0150 587 2471 — LMSSA 1927 Lond. (St. Bart.) Life Mem. BMA. Prev: Final Exam. Med. Off. RN, RM & WRNS Glas.; Phys. Argyll & Clyde Health Bd.; Med. Off. RN 1928-57.

JENKINSON, Simon Douglas Department of Obstetrics, Alexandra Healthcare NHS Trust, Woodrow Drive, Redditch B98 7UB Tel: 01527 503030 — MB ChB 1979 Sheff.; MRCOG 1986. Cons. O & G Alexandra Hosp. Redditch. Prev: Lect. & Hon. Sen. Regist. (O & G) Char. Cross Sch. Lond.

JENKINSON, Timothy Michael Queen Square Surgery, 2 Queen Square, Lancaster LA1 1RP Tel: 01524 843333 Fax: 01524 847550 — MRCS Eng. LRCP Lond. 1965; BA, BM BCh Oxf. 1964; DObst RCOG 1968. (Guy's) GP Princi. Qu. Sq. Surg. Lancaster. Prev: Ho. Off. Guy's Hosp. Lond.; SHO Gen. Hosp. Otley; SHO Derbysh. Childr. Hosp. Derby.

JENKINSON, William Robert 12 Castlefields, Dungannon BT71 6DZ Tel: 01868 26354 — MB BCh BAO 1981 Belf.; MRCP (UK) 1984; AFOM RCP Lond. 1989; MRCGP 1984; DRCOG 1984; DCH Dub. 1983. Area Med. Adviser Post. Office N. Irel.

JENKS, Claire Elizabeth 164 High Street, Harston, Cambridge CB2 5QD — MB BS 1994 Lond.

JENMAN, James Lowther (retired) Flat 21, The New College, Cobham by Gravesend, Gravesend DA12 3BG Tel: 01474 814331 — MRCS Eng. LRCP Lond. 1946; MRCGP 1960. Regional Med. Off. (E. Region) DHSS.

JENNER, Abigail Vashti Flat 10, 27 Sion Hill, Clifton, Bristol BS8 4AZ — MB ChB 1998 Bristol. Med. Ho. Off. W.on Gen. Hosp. W.on Super Mare. Prev: Surgic. Ho. Off. Bristol Roy. Infirm.

JENNER, Caroline Suzanna 73 Pymers Mead, London SE21 8NJ — MB BS 1997 Lond.

JENNER, Charlotte Elizabeth 112 Ashdown Road, Chandlers Ford, Eastleigh SO53 5QG — MB BS 1997 Newc.

JENNER, Christopher Stanley Elliott Hall Medical Centre, 165-167 Uxbridge Road, Hatch End, Pinner HA5 4EA Tel: 020 8428 4019; 6 Woodhall Avenue, Pinner HA5 3DX Tel: 020 8866 8585 — MB BS 1985 Lond.; BSc (Hons.) Lond. 1982; MRCP (UK) 1988; MRCGP 1989; DGM RCP Lond. 1991. (Univ. Coll. Lond.) Course Organiser N.wick Pk. Hosp. VTS; Imperial Coll. Undergrad. Teachg. Facilitator; Fac. Bd. Mem. N. W. Lond. Fac. RCGP. Prev: Trainee GP N.wick Pk. Hosp. VTS; SHO Rotat. (Gen. Med.) N.wick Pk. Hosp. Harrow; Ho. Phys. Univ. Coll. Hosp.

JENNER, David Robert College Surgery, College Road, Cullompton EX15 1TG Tel: 01884 32373 Fax: 01884 35541 — MB ChB 1982 Manch.; MRCGP 1987; DRCOG 1988.

JENNER, Professor Frederick Alexander Manor Farm, Brightholmlee Lane, Sheffield S35 0DB Tel: 0114 286 2546 Fax: 0114 286 4591 Email: f.a.jenner@sheffield.ac.uk — MB ChB Sheff. 1954; PhD Sheff. 1958; FRCP Lond. 1980, M 1969; FRCPsych 1972; DPM Eng. 1960. (Sheff.) Prof. Visitante Concepcion Chile. Socs: Fell. Roy. Soc. Med. Prev: Emerit. Prof. Psychiat. Sheff.; Prof. Psychiat. Sheff.; Hon. Dir. MRC Unit for Metabol. Studies Psychiat.

JENNER, Gillian Helen Basildon & Thurrock General Hospitals Trust Executive Offices, Basildon Hospital, Nethermayne, Basildon SS16 5NL Tel: 01268593200 Fax: 01268 593169 Email: gill.jenner@btgh-tr.nthames.nhs.uk; Loves Farm, Marden, Tonbridge TN12 9NB Tel: 01622 831279 Fax: 01622 831279 Email: gilljenner@aol.com — MB BS Lond. 1968; FRCP Lond. 1994; MRCP (UK) 1981; MRCS Eng. LRCP Lond. 1968. (Univ. of Lond.) Med Dir. & Cons. Med. for the Elderly Basildon Hosp., Basildon. Socs: Fell. Roy. Soc. Med.; Brit. Geriat. Soc.; Amer. Soc. Bone & Mineral Research. Prev: Cons. Phys. Med. for Elderly Basildon & Thurrock HA; Sen. Regist. (Internal Med. & Geriat. Med.) St. Thos. Hosp. Lond. & Canterbury HA; Regist. (Med.) Medway HA.

JENNER, Graeme James The Surgery, Tanners Meadow, Brockham, Betchworth RH3 7NJ Tel: 01737 843259 Fax: 01737

845184 — MB BS 1975 Lond.; BSc (Pharm.) Lond. 1972; MRCGP 1982. (Univ. Coll. Hosp.)

JENNER, Jennifer Anne 55 Springbrook, Eynesbury, St Neots, Huntingdon PE19 2EB — MB BS 1993 Lond.; BSc Lond. 1990. (St. Geo. Lond.) SHO (Med.) Huntingdon.

JENNER, John Richard Tel: 21223 217763 Fax: 01223 217040; 35 Luard Road, Cambridge CB2 2PJ Tel: 01223 214967 — MBBS 1971 Lond.; MA Camb. 1984; MD Lond. 1981; FRCP Lond. 1991. p/t Cons. Rheum. & Rehabil. Addenbrooke's Hosp. Camb.

JENNER, Matthew William Flat 2 Oakdene, 74 Portmore Pk Rd, Weybridge KT13 8HH — MB BS 1997 Newc.

JENNER, Michael James Rowe 10 Dry Hill Park Road, Tonbridge TN10 3BN — BChir 1989 Camb.

JENNER, Michael Robert Rowan Tree Surgery, Tunbridge Wells TN2 5PX Tel: 01892 543516 Fax: 01892 536594; 2 Hollyshaw Close, Camden Park, Tunbridge Wells TN2 5AB Tel: 01892 532241 Fax: 01892 532241 — MB BS 1965 Lond. (St. Geo.) Socs: BMA. Prev: Res. Obst. Asst. & Ho. Phys. & Ho. Surg. FarnBoro. Hosp.

JENNER, Paul Norman Little Stubbs, 41 Stubbs Wood, Chesham Bois, Amersham HP6 6EX Tel: 01494 721875 — MB BS 1975 Lond.; DRCOG 1977; Dip. Pharm. Med. 1986. (St. Mary's) Dir. & Vice Pres. Neurosci. Worldwide Strategic Product Developm. SmithKline Beecham Pharmaceut. Brentford; Mem. Fac. Pharmaceut. Med.

JENNER, Mr Richard Edward The Garden House, 7 Ivydene Terrace NN14 1NJ Tel: 01536 790536 — MB BS 1967 Lond.; MS Lond. 1981; FRCS Eng. 1972; MRCS Eng. LRCP Lond. 1967. (St. Mary's) Cons. Surg. Kettering Gen. Hosp.; Clin. Teach. (Med.) Univ. Leicester. Socs: Assn. Coloproctol.; Fell. Roy. Soc. Med.; Vasc. Surg. Soc. GB & Irel. Prev: Sen. Regist. (Surg.) King's Coll. Hosp. Lond.; Regist. (Surg.) Hillingdon Hosp. Uxbridge; Ho. Surg. & Ho. Phys. St. Mary's Hosp. Lond.

JENNETT, Professor Sheila Mary Institute of Biomedical and Life Sciences, West Medical Building, University of Glasgow, Glasgow G12 8QQ Tel: 0141 330 4483 Fax: 0141 330 4100; 83 Hughenden Lane, Glasgow G12 9XN Tel: 0141 334 5148 Fax: 0141 334 5148 Email: sjennet@compuserve.com — MRCS Eng. LRCP Lond. 1949; MB ChB Liverp. 1949; PhD Glas. 1969; MD Liverp. 1967; FRCP Glas. 1983, M 1980. (Liverp.) Sen. Hon. Research Fell. IBLS Univ. Glas. Socs: Physiol. Soc. (Ex-Mem. Comm.). Prev: Titular Prof. Physiol. Univ. Glas.

JENNETT, Professor (William) Bryan, CBE Tel: 0141 201 2023 Fax: 0141 201 2995; 83 Hughenden Lane, Glasgow G12 9XN Tel: 0141 334 5148 Fax: 0141 334 5148 — MD 1960 Liverp.; MB ChB (Hons.) 1949; DSc St. And. 1993; FRCS Glas. 1972; FRCS Eng. 1952. (Liverp.) Emerit. Prof. Neurosurg. Univ. Glas. Socs: Soc. Brit. Neurol. Surgs.; Roy. Soc. Med. (Ex-Pres. Sect. Neurol.). Prev: Lect. (Neurosurg.) Univ. Manch.; Dean Fac. Med. Glas. 1981-86; Mem. Med. Research Counc. 1979-83.

JENNEY, Meriel Evelyn Mary Llandough Hospital & Community NHS Trust, Penlan Road, Penarth CF64 2XX Tel: 02920 715229 Fax: 02920 708064 Email: meriel.jenney@uhw-tr.wales.nhs.uk; Glyn Pedr, Lisvane Road, Llanishen, Cardiff CF14 0SE Tel: 02920 753231 — MB ChB 1983 Sheff.; MD Sheff. 1994; MRCP (UK) 1987. (Sheff.) Cons. Paediat. Oncol. Llandough Hosp, Cardiff and Vale Trust. Socs: MRCPCH; Internat. Soc. Paediat. Oncol.; UK Childr. Cancer Study Gp. Prev: Cons. Paediat. Oncol. Roy. Manch. Childr. Hosp.; Lect. (Child Health) Booth Hall Childr. Hosp. Manch.

JENNINGS, Adrian Mark Gresham House, Town Lane, Castle Acre, King's Lynn PE32 2AU — MD 1990 Bristol; MB ChB 1979; MRCP (UK) 1982. Cons. Phys. Qu. Eliz. Hosp. King's Lynn. Prev: Sen. Regist. (Med.) Roy. Hallamsh. Hosp. Sheff.; Regist. (Med.) & Research Regist. Roy. Hallamsh. Hosp. Sheff.

JENNINGS, Aileen Catherine Mary Weaverham Surgery, Northwich Road, Weaverham, Northwich CW8 3EU Tel: 01606 853106 Fax: 01606 854980; 469 Chester Road, Hartford, Northwich CW8 2AG Tel: 01606 883376 — MB BCh BAO 1969 NUI; DObst RCOG 1971. Prev: Ho. Surg. & Ho. Off. (Obst.) Pk. Hosp. Davyhulme; Ho. Phys. Salford Roy. Hosp.; SHO (Anaesth.) Withington Hosp. Manch.

JENNINGS, Mr Andrew Melvin 18 High Trees Road, Reigate RH2 7EJ Tel: 01737 240847 — MB BS 1990 Lond.; FRCS Eng. 1995. (St. Bart. Hosp.)

JENNINGS, Carolyn Sarah 36 Kingsmead, Frimley Green, Camberley GU16 6LU — MB BS 1989 Lond. Clin. Med. Off. W. Berks. HA. Prev: Trainee GP Roy. Berks. Hosp. Reading VTS.

JENNINGS, Mr Christopher Richard 35 Wych Elm Road, Oadby, Leicester LE2 4EF Tel: 0116 271 0323 — MB ChB 1990 Leic.; FRCS Eng. 1994. (Leicester) Career Regist. Rotat. (Otolaryngol.) Leicester, Nottm. & Derby. Socs: BMA; Assoc. Mem. Brit. Assn. Otorhinolaryng. Head & Neck Surgs.

JENNINGS, Claire Elizabeth Castle Surgery, Kepwell Bank Top, Prudhoe NE42 5PW Tel: 01661 832209; Priory Farm, Muggleswick, Consett DH8 9DW — MB ChB 1985 Manch.; MRCGP 1989; DRCOG 1987; Cert. Family Plann. JCC 1987. (St. And., Manch.) p/t GP. Prev: GP Eaton Socan; Trainee GP Hinchingbrooke Hosp. & St. Ives VTS; SHO & Ho. Off. (Paediat., O & G, Med., & A & E) Hinchingbrooke Hosp. Huntingdon.

JENNINGS, Claire Louise 14 Widewell Road, Plymouth PL6 7DN — MB BS 1991 Lond.

JENNINGS, David Liston (retired) West Bank House, Upton-on-Severn, Worcester WR8 0SN Tel: 01684 592170 Email: davidjennings@wbhouse.freeserve.co.uk — MB Camb. 1960, BChir 1959; MRCGP 1977; DObst RCOG 1960. Prev: Ho. Phys. Middlx. Hosp. Lond.

JENNINGS, The Hon. Deanna Christine The Wall House Surgery, Yorke Road, Reigate RH2 9HG Tel: 01737 224432 Fax: 01737 244616; Barn Ridge, 18 High Trees Road, Reigate RH2 7EJ Tel: 01737 240847 Fax: 01737 226480 — MB BS 1963 Lond.; MRCS Eng. LRCP Lond. 1963; Dip. Sports Med. Lond 1990. (St. Bart.) Med. Off. Lond. Broncos Rugby League FC at Stoop Memor. Ground; Governing Body Doctor Brit. Judo Assn. Socs: Brit. Assn. Sport & Med.; BMA; Rugby League Med. Assn. Prev: Med. Off. (Sch. & Child Health) Hammersmith Lond.; Ho. Surg. St. Helier Hosp. Carshalton; Ho. Phys. Bethnal Green Hosp.

JENNINGS, Deborah Ann Fairways, Whiteleaf, Princes Risborough, Aylesbury HP27 0LX — BM BCh 1988 Oxf.

JENNINGS, Elizabeth Anne Louise Caversham Group Practice, Kentish Town Health Centre, Bartholomew Road, London NW5 2AJ — MB BS 1988 Lond.; MA Camb. 1980.

JENNINGS, Elizabeth Mary (retired) Overbecks, 6 Sutton Park, Bishop Sutton, Bristol BS39 5UQ Tel: 01275 333 414 Email: elizabeth@jenningsbs.freeserve.com — MB ChB Liverp. 1953; FRCPCH 1997; DObst RCOG 1955. Prev: SCMO Frenchay HA.

JENNINGS, Francis Oliver Royal Infirmary, Acre St., Huddersfield HD3 3EA — MB BCh BAO 1975 Dub.; FFA RCSI 1978. Cons. Anaesth. Huddersfield Roy. Infirm.

JENNINGS, Gloria Ann 32 Eaton Terrace, London SW1W 8TS Tel: 020 7730 4329 Fax: 020 7730 4329 — MB ChB 1960 Birm.; MRCS Eng. LRCP Lond. 1960. (Birm.) Socs: BMA.; FFP; Roy. Soc. Med.

JENNINGS, James Arthur Tel: 01274 541701 Fax: 01274 546533 — MB BS 1967 Lond.; MRCS Eng. LRCP Lond. 1967; DObst RCOG 1970. (St. Bart.)

JENNINGS, Jason Mark Jasmine Cottage, 18 Sun Lane, Blackheath, London SE3 8UG Email: jasminecottage@compuserve.com — MB BS 1996 Lond.; BSc (Neurosci.) 1993. (UMDS Guys & St. Thomas' Hospitals) SHO Rotat. (Basic Surg.) Greenwich Dist. Hosp. Lond.

JENNINGS, Jason Samuel Robert Cherrington, 5 Knoll Road, Abergavenny NP7 7AN — BM BS 1995 Nottm.

JENNINGS, Jonathan Peter Trelleck Surgery, Trelleck, Monmouth NP5 4PE — MB BCh BAO 1983 NUI; LRCPSI 1983.

JENNINGS, Juliet Ethna 2 Dromore Road, Lurgan, Craigavon BT66 7HN — MB BCh BAO 1997 Belf.

JENNINGS, Kate 1L, 121 Cartvale Road, Langside, Glasgow G42 9RN — BM 1995 Soton. GP Regist. 9 Cairntoul Drive Glas. Prev: SHO (Psychiat.) Gartnavel Roy. Hosp.; SHO (Geriat.) Gartnavel Gen. Hosp.; SHO (O & G) W.ern Infirm.

JENNINGS, Kathryn Lesley Bingley Health Centre, Myrtle Place, Bingley BD16 2TL Tel: 01274 362760 Fax: 01274 772345 — MB ChB 1979 Leeds; Cert. Family Plann. JCC 1983. Prev: Trainee GP Bradford; Ho. Surg. St. Lukes Hosp. Bradford; Ho. Phys. Prof.ial Med. Unit St. Jas. Hosp. Leeds.

JENNINGS, Kevin Patrick Department of Cardiology, Royal Infirmary, Foresterhill, Aberdeen AB25 2ZN Tel: 01224 681818 Fax: 01224 840692 Email: kevin.jennings.@arh.grampian.scot.nhs.uk —

MB BS 1973 Lond.; FRCP Ed. 1987; MRCP (UK) 1977; MRCS Eng. LRCP Lond. 1972; FESC 1997; FRCP Lond. 1998. (St. Bart.) Cons. Cardiol. Roy. Infirm. Aberd. Socs: (Counc.) Brit. Cardiac Soc.; Treas. Scott. Cardiac Soc. Prev: Sen. Regist. Freeman Hosp. Newc.; Regist. King's Coll. Hosp. & Lond. Chest Hosp.

JENNINGS, Lelia Beechside, 77 Downhills, Liverpool L23 8SL — MB BCh BAO 1951 NUI; DObst RCOG 1954. Prev: Ho. Phys. & Ho. Surg. Kingston Gen. Hosp. Hull; SHO (Orthop.) Walton Hosp. Liverp.; Ho. Off. (Dermat.) Newsham Gen. Hosp. Liverp.

JENNINGS, Mr Melvin Calverley Dept.of Urology, East Surrey Hospital, Canada Avenue, Redhill RH1 5RH Tel: 01737 231758 Fax: 01737 231803; Barn Ridge, 18 High Trees Road, Reigate RH2 7EJ Tel: 01737 240847 Fax: 01737 226480 — MB BS 1963 Lond.; FRCS Eng. 1969; MRCS Eng. LRCP Lond. 1963. (St. Bart.) Cons. Urol., Surrey and Sussex Healthcare NHS Trust. Socs: Fell. Roy. Soc. Med.; Brit. Assn. Urol. Surgs; BMA. Prev: SHO (Urol.),Hammersmith Hosp.; Jun. Regist. (Surg.) St. Bart. Hosp. Lond.; Sen. Regist. (Urol.) St. Mary's Hosp. Portsmouth.

JENNINGS, Michael Department of Health Care for Elderly People, Northern General Hospital, Herries Road, Sheffield S5 7AU — BM BS 1979 Nottm.; BMedSci Nottm. 1977, BM BS 1979; FRCP Lond. 1999; MRCP (UK) 1982. Sen. Lect. (Health Care for Elderly) Univ. Sheff. Prev: Lect. (Clin. Pharmacol. & Therap.) Univ. Sheff.

***JENNINGS, Michael Peter** Guy's Hospital, St Thomas St., London SE1 9RT; 74 Copleston Road, London SE15 4AG — MB BS 1988 Lond.; MRCP (UK) 1993.

JENNINGS, Natalie Karen Department of Anaesthesia, National Hospital for Neurology & Neurosurgery, Queens Square, London WC1N 3BG — MB ChB 1994 Liverp.

JENNINGS, Paul Aite Sith, Croit An Crioch, North Kessock, Inverness IV1 1XE — MB ChB 1964 Glas.

JENNINGS, Paul Edward York District Hospital, Wigginton Road, York YO31 8HE Tel: 01904 453751 Fax: 01904 453145 Email: paul.jennings@excha.yhs-tr.northy.nhs.uk; 14 Hansom Place, York YO31 8FJ Fax: 01904 624557 Email: pauljennings@excha.yhs-tr.northy.nhs.uk — BM BS 1978 Nottm.; DM Nottm. 1990; MRCP (UK) 1981; FRCP Ed 1996; FRCP 1999. (Nottm.) Cons. Phys. (Diabetes & Endocrinol.) York Dist. Hosp.; Chairm. Drugs & Therap.; Clin. Lead Drastes & Enclocrine; Hon. Sen. Lect. in Clin. Med. Univ. of Hull. Socs: Brit. Diabetic Assn.; Caledonian Endocrine Soc.; Eur. Assn. for Study Diabetes. Prev: Lect. & Sen. Regist. Dept. Med. Ninewells Hosp. Dundee.; Res. Fell. (Diabetes) E. Birm. Hosp.; Med. Regist. Leics. Roy. Infirm.

JENNINGS, Paul Edward The Ipswich Hospital, Heath Road, Ipswich IP4 5PD; The Barn, Main Road, Tuddenham, Ipswich IP6 9BZ Tel: 01473 785683 — MB BS 1981 Lond.; FRCR 1990; MRCP (UK) 1985; T(R)(CR) 1991. (St. Geo.) Cons. Radiol. Ipswich Hosp. Prev: Sen. Regist. (Diag. Radiol.) Middlx. & Univ. Coll. Hosp. Lond.; Regist. (Med.) St. Marys Hosp. Lond.; SHO (Med.) I. of Thanet Dist. Hosp.

JENNINGS, Peter George Department of Radiology, Cumberland Infirmary, Newtown Road, Carlisle CA2 7HY Tel: 01228 523444 — MB ChB 1977; BSc (Cell Path.) (Hons.) Bristol 1974; MRCP (UK) 1980; FRCR 1984; FRCP 2000. Cons. Radiol. Cumbld. Infirm.; Extern. Examr. in Cross Sect.al Imaging at Univ. of Bristol.

JENNINGS, Mr Peter John (retired) 6 Primrose Close, Chatham ME4 6HZ Tel: 01544 370657 — MB BS Lond. 1957; FRCS Eng. 1963. Hon. Cons. Surg. St. Bart. Hosp. Rochester & Medway Hosp. Gillingham. Prev: Cons. Surg. St. Bart. Hosp. Rochester & Medway Hosp. Gillingham.

JENNINGS, Philip Anthony 129 Osborne Road, Jesmond, Newcastle upon Tyne NE2 2TB — MB BS 1996 Newc.

JENNINGS, Piers Julian Francis The Surgery, Church St., Coleford, Bath BA3 5NQ Tel: 01373 812244 Fax: 01373 813390 Email: mendipep@globalnet.co.uk — MB BS 1986 Lond.; MRCGP 1991; DRCOG 1990. (Guy's Hosp. Lond.)

JENNINGS, Richard Maurice Hospital for Tropical Diseases, Mortimer Market Centre, Capper St, London WC1E 6AU Tel: 020 7387 9300 Fax: 020 7380 9761 — MB ChB 1988 Bristol; MSc (Hons.) Lond. 1995; MRCP (UK) 1992; DTM & H RCP Lond. 1994. Hon. Sen. Regist. (Trop. Med.) Hosp. for Trop. Dis. Lond. Prev: Regist. (Trop. Med.) Hosp. Trop. Dis. Lond.

JENNINGS, Robert 18 High Trees Road, Reigate RH2 7EJ — MB BS London 1995.

JENNINGS, Robert Killian Rosehall Medical Practice, 2 Mallust Road, Newtownabbey BT36 4PP — MB BCh BAO 1993 Belf.; DCH 1996; DRCOG 1996. Full time Princip. in Gen. Pract. Socs: Roy. Coll. Gen. Pract.

JENNINGS, Roderick Stanley Stone Croft, The Nook, Bitteswell, Lutterworth LE17 4RY — MB BS 1986 Lond.; MRCGP 1991.

JENNINGS, Simon 18 Hightrees Road, Reigate RH2 7EJ; 114 Upper Street, Islington, London N1 1QN Tel: 020 7354 0143 Fax: 020 7226 0116 Email: simon.jennings@virgin.net — MB BS 1992 Lond.; BSc Lond. 1991; FRCS Lond. 1997. (St. Bart. Hosp. Lond.)

JENNINGS, Stephen Francis Poolhead, Westhide, Herefordshire, Hereford HR1 3RQ — MB BS 1981 Lond.; LMSSA Lond. 1980; T(GP) 1991.

JENNINGS, Stephen James 8 Leylands Grove, Bradford BD9 5QP — MB ChB 1998 Leic.; MB ChB Leic 1998.

JENNINGS, Stuart John The Surgery, Outings Lane, Doddinghurst, Brentwood CM15 0LS Tel: 01277 821699 Fax: 01277 821226 — MB BS 1968 Lond.; MRCS Eng. LRCP Lond. 1968. (Westm.)

JENNINGS, Susan Jane 39 Bow Lane, North Finchley, London N12 0JR — MB BS 1993 Lond.; BSc (Hons.) Lond. 1979. SHO Rotat. (Psychiat.) Roy. Free Hosp. Lond.; Inceptor Roy. Coll. Psychiat.

JENNINGS, Teresa Bernadette The Surgery, 20 Low Road, Debenham, Stowmarket IP14 6QU Tel: 01728 860248 Fax: 01728 861300; The Barn, Main Road, Tuddenham, Ipswich IP6 9BZ Tel: 01473 785683 — MB BS 1981 Lond.; MRCGP 1986; DCH RCP Lond. 1985; DRCOG 1984. GP Retainer Scheme. Prev: Trainee GP Canterbury VTS.

JENNINGS, Timothy Robin Syston Health Centre, Melton Road, Syston, Leicester LE7 2EQ Tel: 0116 260 9161 Fax: 01535 698388; 12 Main Street, Hoby, Melton Mowbray LE14 3DT Tel: 01664 434219 — MB BS 1981 Lond.; MRCGP 1985; DRCOG 1985. (Guy's)

JENNINGS, Valerie Mary (retired) 56 Priestfields, Rochester ME1 3AE Tel: 01634 841905 — MB BS 1957 Lond. Prev: Clin. Med. Off. (Child Health) Medway Hosp. Gillingham.

JENNINGS, Victoria Louise 30 Parkfields, Chippenham SN15 1NX — MB ChB 1986 Bristol.

JENNISON, Kathleen Mary Department of Obstetrics & Gynaecology, Hinchingbrooke Hospital, Huntingdon PE29 6NT Tel: 01480 416416 Fax: 01480 416248; Brambles, 10A The Grove, Hartford, Huntingdon PE29 1YD Tel: 01480 450406 — MB BS Newc. 1968; FRCP Glas. 1992; MRCP (UK) 1980; FRCOG 1989, M 1975. (Newc. u. Tyne) Cons. O & G Hinchingbrooke Healthcare NHS Trust. Socs: Fell. Roy. Soc. Med.; BMA.

JENNISON, Philip Russell Elmwood Health Centre, Huddersfield Road, Holmfirth, Huddersfield HD9 3TR Tel: 01484 681777 — MB ChB 1975 Leeds; MRCGP 1979.

JENNS, Mark Andrew South Street Surgery, 83 South Street, Bishop's Stortford CM23 3AP Tel: 01279 710800 Fax: 01279 710801; Pennington, Cricketfield Lane, Bishop's Stortford CM23 2SP — MB BS 1977 Lond. (Kings London) Prev: SHO (Obst. & Paediat.) Baragwanath Hosp. S. Afr.

JENSEN, Juliet Helen (Gubbins) East Sussex Brighton & Hove HA, 36-38 Friars walk, Lewes BN7 2PB Tel: 01273 403646; St Davids Flat, Lough Rd, London N7 8RH — MB ChB 1992 Manch. Specialist Regist. (Pub. Health Med.).

JENSEN, Niels Eskild Benellen House, Benellen Road, Bournemouth BH4 9LZ Tel: 01202 764850; Benellen House, Benellen Road, Bournemouth BH4 9LZ Tel: 01202 764850 — MB BS 1961 Lond.; FRCP Lond. 1981, M 1968; MRCS Eng. LRCP Lond. 1961. (Guy's) Socs: Fell. Roy. Soc. Med.; Brit. Assn. Dermat. Prev: Cons. Dermat. Poole Hosp. Trust Roy. Bournemouth Hosp. Dorset; Sen. Regist. (Dermat.) United Sheff. Hosps. & Hon. Tutor (Dermat.) Univ. Sheff.; Regist. (Dermat. & Med.) & Cas. Off. Guy's Hosp.

JENSEN, Patricia Mary Wayside Cottage, Main St., Upton, Newark NG23 6DA Tel: 01636 813206 — MB BS 1985 Lond. GP Regist. Newark. CMO (Family Plann., Sexual Health); GP Asst. Prev: SHO (Med. & O & G) City Hosp. Nottm.; Cas. Off. Mansfield Gen. Hosp.; SHO (Anaesth.) N.ampton Gen. Hosp.

JENSEN, Peter (retired) 1 Knowsley Avenue, Blackpool FY3 9HP Tel: 01253 64104 — LMSSA 1953 Lond.; MRCGP 1961. Psychother. & Med. Hypnotist Blackpool; Clin. Asst. (Psychiat.)

Adelphi Hse. Day Hosp. Blackpool; Hon. Phys. Nujukwai Judo Club. Prev: Ho. Phys. Ashton-under-Lyne Gen. Hosp.

JENSON, Catherine Michaela Forge Close Practice, Forge Close, Hayes Tel: 020 8462 1601 Fax: 020 8462 7410; 125 Crescent Drive, Pettswood, Orpington BR5 1BA Tel: 01689 838008 Email: cathjenson@tingwork.co.uk — MB BS 1993 Lond.; MA; DCH 1997; DRCOG 1996; MRCGP 1998. (Cambridge & St. Bartholomew's) p/t GP Retainee. Socs: BMA; Med. Wom.'s Federat. Prev: SHO Pub. Health Croydon; GP Regist. Sidcup VTS; GP Partner Rinks Med. Pract., Bromley.

JENTSCH, Torsten 4 Hollyhill Road, Enniskillen BT74 6DD — State Exam Med 1992 Frankfurt.

JEPHCOTT, Anthony Edward (retired) Woodsmoke, Cadbury Camp Lane, Clapton in Gordano, Bristol BS20 7SD — MB BChir 1962 Camb.; MA Camb. 1962; MD Sheff. 1977; FRCPath 1980, M 1969; Dip. Bact. Lond 1966. Hon. Clin. Sen. Lect. Univ. Bristol; Hon. Cons. Microbiol. United Bristol Healthcare Trust, W.on Area Health Trust, & Roy United Hosp Trust (Bath). Prev: Cons. Microbiol. Pub. Health Laborat. Serv. Sheff.

JEPHCOTT, Catherine Rachel Woodsmoke, Cadbury Camp Lane, Clapton in Gordano, Bristol BS20 7SD — BM BCh 1994 Oxf.; MA Oxf. 1991; MRCP Lond. Specialist Regist. (Clin. Oncol.) Oxf. Prev: SHO (Med.) Qu. Med. Centre Nottm.

JEPHCOTT, Christopher Georg Alexander Fern Hill, Fairwarp, Uckfield TN22 3BU — MB ChB 1993 Birm.

JEPHCOTT, Christopher John Alexander 39 Eversley Crescent, Winchmore Hill, London N21 1EL Tel: 020 8360 5677 Fax: 020 8367 3354 Email: c.jephcott@fdn.co.uk — MB BChir 1960 Camb.; MA Camb. 1964; DObst RCOG 1964. (St. Bart.) Fundholding Cons. White Lodge Med. Pract. Enfield; Chairm. Community Servs. Working Gp. New River Total Care Project.

JEPHCOTT, Gwyneth Woodsmoke, Cadbury Camp Lane, Clapton in Gordano, Bristol BS20 7SD — MB ChB Sheff. 1965; BSc Sheff. 1962; FFA RCS Eng. 1969; DObst RCOG 1967. (Sheff.) Prev: Cons. Anaesth. Trent RHA; Cons. Anaesth. W.on Area Health Trust.

JEPHCOTT, Jerome Joseph The Surgery, 107 Seymour Avenue, Morden SM4 4RA Tel: 020 8337 3112 — MB BS 1971 Newc.; BSc Newc. 1968, MB BS 1971.

JEPHSON, Christopher Giles 4 Hicks Close, Wroughton, Swindon SN4 9AY — MB BS 1997 Lond.

JEPP, Katharine Summerhill, Cranbrook Road, Hawkhurst, Cranbrook TN18 4AT — MB ChB 1998 Sheff.; MB ChB Sheff 1998.

JEPPS, John Michael Allen (retired) Kimberley Corner, Reading St., Broadstairs CT10 3DZ Tel: 01843 863970 Fax: 01843 863970 — MA Camb. 1953, MB BChir 1952; MA Camb. 1953, MB BChir 1952. Prev: Med. Off. St. Lawrence Coll. Ramsgate, Wellesley Hse. Sch & Kingsgate Coll. BRd.stairs.

JEPSEN, Fiona The Chimes, 1 Westminster Drive, Wilmslow SK9 1QZ Tel: 01625 585627 — MB BCh 1995 Wales. SHO (Critical Care) Whiston Hosp. St. Helens & Knowsley Hosps. Socs: BMA (Rep. Countess of Chester Hosp.). Prev: Regist. Roy. P. Alfred Hosp., Sydney; SHO (Cas.) Countess of Chester Hosp.; SHO (Med.) Countess of Chester Hosp.

JEPSON, Alison Mary Outwood Surgery, 581A Leeds Road, Outwood, Wakefield WF1 2JL Tel: 01924 822626 Fax: 01924 870975; 11 Woolgreaves Croft, Wakefield WF2 6DU — MB ChB 1983 Manch.; MRCGP 1988; DCH 1985.

JEPSON, Mr Alistair Shaun 38 Clifton Gardens, London W9 1AU — MB ChB 1994 Birm.; FRCS (Eng) 1998. Specialist Regist. N. W. Thames Rotat. (Trauma & Orthop. srg.). Prev: SHO (Trauma & Orth) St.Peter's; SHO (Surgic. Rotat.) Guy's & St. Thomas' Hosp. Lond.

JEPSON, Anne Margaret (retired) 46 Brondesbury Park, London NW6 7AU Tel: 020 8459 5773 — MB BS Lond. 1950; MRCS Eng. LRCP Lond. 1950; FFPHM 1979, M 1972; DPH Lond. 1965; DCH Eng. 1952; FRCPCH 1977. Prev: Med. Adviser Riverside HA (T).

JEPSON, Annette Patricia Dpt. Microbiology, St Mary's Hospital, Praed St., London W2 1NY Tel: 020 7886 6666 Fax: 01865 742196 Email: annette@well.ox.ac.uk; Hamara, Whatcote Road, Oxhill, Warwick CV35 0RA — MB BS 1984 Lond.; 1997 PhD (Lond.); 1989 MSc (Clin. Microbiol.) Lond.; 1984 MB BS Lond.; 1985 MA Camb.; 1989 MRCP (UK); 1981 BA (1st cl. Hons.); 2000 MRCPath (UK). (St. George's) Cons. Microbio. St. Mary's Hosp. Trust; Hon. Sen. Lect. Imp. Coll. Med. Sch. Socs: Fell. Roy. Soc. Trop. Med. & Hyg.; Brit. Soc. Study of Infec.; Hosp. Infec. Soc. Prev: Wellcome Trust Career Developm. Fell. Wellcome Trust Centre for Human Genetics Univ. Oxf.; MRC Train. Fell. MRC Laborat., The Gambia; Lect. (Virol.) Lond. Hosp. Med. Coll.

JEPSON, Clare Mary Carlton House Surgery, 28 Tenniswood Road, Enfield EN1 3LL Tel: 020 8363 7575 Fax: 020 8366 8228 — MB BS 1980 Lond.; MRCGP 1983; DRCOG 1983. (Roy. Free) Yeoman Worshipful Soc. Apoth.

JEPSON, Deanna Suat Kiou The Cliff, Morton Lane, East Morton, Keighley BD20 5RP Tel: 01274 567535 Fax: 01274 571464 — MB ChB 1965 Sheff. Socs: BMA.; Assn. Study Obesity; Nutrit. Soc. Prev: GP Dronfield Derbysh. & Bingley Bradford; SHO (Paediat.) N.. Gen. Hosp. Sheff.

JEPSON, Ewart Martin Hospital of St John & St Elizabeth, 60 Grove End Road, London NW8 9NH Tel: 020 7286 5126; 46 Brondesbury Park, London NW6 7AU Tel: 020 8459 5773 — MD Lond. 1963, MB BS 1950; FRCP Lond. 1972, M 1955. (Westm.) Cons. Phys. St. John & St. Eliz. Hosp. Socs: Fell. Med. Soc. Lond. & Roy. Soc. Med.; Fell. Med. Soc. Lond. & Roy. Soc.; Med. & Hunt. Soc. Prev: Cons. Phys. Centr. Middlx. Hosp. & Willesden Hosp.; Sen. Med. Regist. W.m. Hosp.; Ho. Phys. Brompton Hosp. Lond.

JEPSON, Fergus Keith Flat 5, 40 Range Road, Whalley Range, Manchester M16 8FS — MB ChB 1995 Manch.

JEPSON, Mrs Gillian Jane Medwyn Surgery, Moores Road, Dorking RH4 2BG Tel: 01306 882422 Fax: 01306 742280; Clereholt, The Glade, Holmbury St. Mary, Dorking RH5 6PG Tel: 01306 730383 — MB BChir 1965 Camb.; MRCS Eng. LRCP Lond. 1964; MA (Hons.) Camb. 1965. (Camb. & Univ. Coll. Hosp.) Med. Off. Boxhill Sch. Mickleham. Prev: Med. Off. E. Surrey Health Dist.; Ho. Phys. Epsom Dist. Hosp.; Ho. Surg. Roy. Ear Hosp. Lond.

JEPSON, Mr Keith 1 Mornington Villas, Manningham Lane, Bradford BD8 7HB Tel: 01274 546861 — MB ChB Sheff. 1965; FRCS Ed. 1973. Cons. Orthop. Surg. Bradford Roy. Infirm., & St Lukes Hosp. Socs: BMA; Brit. Hip Soc.; Fell. Brit. Orthop. Assn. Prev: Sen. Regist. Rotat. (Orthop.) Bradford Roy. Infirm., Leeds Gen.; Edwd. VII Hosp. Sheff.; Regist. & Research Asst. Rotat. Roy. Infirm. Sheff.

JEPSON, Marion Elizabeth, MBE (retired) 50 Rowan Tree Dell, Totley Rise, Sheffield S17 4FN Tel: 0114 236 6605 — BSc Manch. 1941, MB ChB 1944; FFCM 1979, M 1973; DPH Leeds 1961; DCH Eng. 1946. Prev: SCM (Child Health) Sheff. AHA.

JEPSON, Simon Richard 69 Albert Road, Oswestry SY11 1NJ — MB BS 1989 Lond.

JEQUIER, Peter Winton Manor Road Surgery, 31 Manor Road, Folkestone CT20 2SE Tel: 01303 851122 Fax: 01303 220914; Enbrook Lodge, Hillside, Sandgate, Folkestone CT20 3DB Tel: 01303 252036 — MB BS 1973 Lond.; BSc Lond. 1970. (Univ. Coll. Hosp.) Hosp. Pract. (Endoscopy) William Harvey Hosp. Ashford. Socs: (Ex-Hon. Sec.) Folkestone Med. Soc. Prev: Regist. (Med.) Roy. Sussex Co. Hosp. Brighton; Regist. (Med.) Kings Coll. Hosp. Lond.; Regist. (Med.) Kent & Sussex Hosp. Tunbridge Wells.

JEREMIAH, David Spencer Meddygfa Teifi Surgery, New Road, Llandysul SA44 4QJ Tel: 01559 362221 Fax: 01559 362080; Whitegates, Llandysul SA44 — MB BCh 1971 Wales. Prev: Surg. Lt. RN; Ho. Off. & Ho. Surg. Morriston Hosp.; SHO (O & G) Prmbroke Co. War Memor. Hosp. HaverfordW..

JEREMIAH, Gareth David Rhys 78 Gabalfa Road, Sketty, Swansea SA2 8NA — MB BS 1998 Lond.; MB BS Lond 1998.

JEREMIAH, Geraint Morgan Neath General Hospital, Neath SA11 2LQ Tel: 01639 641161; 78 Gabalfa Road, Swansea SA2 8NA Tel: 01792 205322 — MB BS Lond. 1968; BSc Lond. 1965; FRCP Lond. 1985; MRCP (UK) 1972. (St. Thos.) Cons. Phys. (Gen. Med.) Neath Gen. Hosp. Socs: Fell. Roy. Soc. Med. (Mem. Endocrine Sect.); Brit. Diabetic Assn. Prev: Regist. (Endocrinol. & Metab.) St. Thos. Hosp. Lond.; Regist. (Med.) Addenbrooke's Hosp. Camb.; SHO (Cardiol.) Brompton Hosp. Lond.

JEREMIAH, Mr John David (retired) The Old Oak, Gaunts Common, Wimborne BH21 4JR Tel: 01258 841090 — MB BChir 1958 Camb.; MA Camb. 1959; FRCS Eng. 1962. Prev: Cons. Orthop. Surg. Whipps Cross & Wanstead Hosps. Lond.

JERICHOWER, Frederick Fobus (retired) 2 Tenterden Lodge, Tenterden Grove, London NW4 1SY Tel: 020 8203 8858 — MRCS Eng. LRCP Lond. 1945.

JERJIAN, Jack Christopher Marven Medical Practice, 45-50 Lupus Street, London SW1V 3EB Tel: 020 7834 1160 Fax: 020 7834 0147

— MB ChB 1982 Manch.; BSc (Med. Sci.) St. And. 1979; MRCGP Lond. 1988; DGM RCP Lond. 1986; DA (UK) 1984. (St. And. Univ. & Manch. Med. Sch.) Socs: BMA; RCGP.

JERMY, Karen Vanessa 47 Northway Road, London SE5 9AN — MB BS 1994 Lond. (King's College, London University) Research Fell. (O & G) St. Geo.'s Hosp. Lond.

JEROME, Janet Elizabeth (retired) Owlz Retreat, Lincoln Road, Welton Le Wold, Louth LN11 0QU Tel: 01507 601713 — MB BS 1973 Sydney. Prev: Med. Off./Regist. Psychiat. Callan Pk. Hosp. Rozelle NSW, Australia.

JEROME, Janet Morag Cameron The Bute Practice Health Centre, High St., Rothesay PA20 9JL Tel: 01700 502290; Taobh-An-Allt, Wade's Road, Kinlochleven PH50 4QT — MB ChB 1965 Aberd.; DA Eng. 1971; DObst RCOG 1968.

JERRAM, Kathryn Louise 23 Cwmbeth Close, Crickhowell NP8 1DX — BM 1998 Soton.; BM Soton 1998.

JERRAM, Timothy Colin St Mary's Hospital, Greenhill Rd, Leeds LS12 3QE Tel: 0113 305 5300 — MB BCh BAO 1968 Dub.; FRCPI 1995, M 1972; FRCPsych 1990, M 1976. Cons. Psychiat. Leeds Community and Ment. Health Trust. Prev: Research Fell. (Psychiat. & Biochem.) Univ. Leeds; Regist. (Psychiat.) Roy. Edin. Hosp.

JERREAT, Peter Graham Old Orchard, Wrotham Road, Meopham, Gravesend DA13 0QG Tel: 01474 813938; Stonecroft, Water Lane, Limpsfield, Oxted RH8 0SA Tel: 01883 714179 Fax: 01883 714179 — MB BS 1974 Lond.; BSc Lond. 1969, MB BS 1974; DMJ (Path.) Soc. Apoth. Lond. 1982. Sen. Forens. Med. Examr. Path. to HM Coroner for N. Kent; Home Office Path. Prev: Lect. (Forens. Med.) Lond. Hosp. Med. Coll.

JERRETT, Colin Stephen 35 Swn-y-Nant, Upper Church Village, Tonteg, Pontypridd CF38 1UE — MB ChB 1985 Birm.; ChB Birm. 1985; MRCP (UK) 1990; DRCOG 1989. Prev: Regist. (Med.) Roy. Gwent Hosp.

JERRETT, William Anthony, OBE (retired) 6 Glan yr Afon, Pontyclun CF72 9BJ Tel: 01443 225498 — MB BCh 1957 Wales; FRCGP 1981, M 1976. Prev: GP & Course Organiser.

JERROM, Samantha Clare 3 Millercourt, Newmillerdam, Wakefield WF2 6QJ — MB ChB 1997 Leeds. (Leeds) GP Regist. Dewsbury.

JERVIS, Margaret Jane Narrowcliff Surgery, Narrowcliff, Newquay TR7 2QF Tel: 01637 873363 Fax: 01637 850735; 6 Alexandra Court, Porth, Newquay TR7 3NJ — MB BS Lond. 1983; DFFP 1996; DRCOG 1988. Prev: GP Padstow, Cornw.

JERVIS, Paul Nigel 6 Fairfield Road, Oadby, Leicester LE2 4NE — MRCS Eng. LRCP Lond. 1989; BDS Manch. 1982.

JERWOOD, David Craig Morriston Hospital, Swansea SA6 6NL — MB BS 1985 Lond.; FRCA 1992. Cons. Anaesth. Morriston Hosp. Swansea. Prev: Sen. Regist. (Anaesth.) Morriston Hosp. Swansea.

JESKINS, Gareth David Queen Elizabeth Hospital, Edgbaston, Birmingham B15 2TH Tel: 0121 472 1311 Email: gareth.jeskins@university-b.mids.nhs.uk — MB ChB 1991 Sheff.; FRCA 1997. (Sheff.) Cons. Anaesth., Univ. Hosp. Birm. Prev: SHO Rotat. (Anaesth.) Sheff.; SPR Rotat (Anaesth.) Birm.

***JESPER, Elouise Catherine** 5 Waterside, The Moorings, Leamington Spa CV31 3QA — MB ChB 1998 Birm.

JESPERSEN, Erik, MBE Lorn Medical Centre, Soroba Road, Oban PA34 4HE Tel: 01631 563175 Fax: 01631 562708 Email: ejespersen@gp84581.ac-hb.scot.nhs.uk — MB ChB 1983 Glas.; MRCGP 1990; DRCOG 1989; DA (UK) 1989; DCH RCPS Glas. 1989. Clin. Director, Argyll and Bute LHCC.

JESPERSEN, Susan Bridget Wickersley Health Centre, Poplar Glade, Wickersley, Rotherham S66 2JQ Tel: 01709 549610 — MB ChB 1988 Sheff.; DRCOG 1998; MRCGP 1999. (Sheffield University) Gen. Practitioner. Socs: BMA; RCGP.

JESS, Gillian Elizabeth 4 Lownie Road, Carnoustie DD7 6DW — MB ChB 1995 Glas.

JESSEL, Caroline Rosemary Sutton Valence Surgery, South Lane, Sutton Valence, Maidstone ME17 3BD Tel: 01622 842212 Fax: 01622 844396; Wierton Cottage, Wierton Hill, Boughton Monchelsea, Maidstone ME17 4JT Tel: 01622 741647 — MB BS 1977 Lond.; MRCGP 1984; Cert. JCC Lond. 1980. Tutor (GP) & Course Organiser Maidstone VTS; Chairm. W. Kent FACE (Focus on Audit & Clin. Effectiveness).

JESSEN, Esther Christine 1 Beechfield Road, Gosforth, Newcastle upon Tyne NE3 4DR Tel: 0191 285 8362 — MB BS 1983 Newc.; MRCP (UK) 1992; DCH RCPS Glas. 1988; DRCOG 1985. Cons. Paediat. (Community Child Health) N.d. Prev: Sen. Regist. (Community Paediat.) N.'d.; Trainee Gen. Paediat. Newc. HA.

JESSIMAN, Ian McDonnell (retired) 17 Grange Drive, Chislehurst BR7 5ES Tel: 020 8467 1725 — MB BChir 1957 Camb.; MA Camb. 1958; MRCP (UK) 1971; MRCS Eng. LRCP Lond. 1957; DCH Eng. 1965; FRCP 1999. Prev: Resid. Obst. Guy's Hosp.

JESSLER, Mrs Helen (retired) 21B Hartington Road, Sherwood, Nottingham NG5 2GU Tel: 0115 9691 302 — MD 1937 Prague; PhD Prague 1931, MD 1937; DObst RCOG 1952; MRCGP 1953. Prev: Sen. Res. Obst. Surg. St. Mary's Hosp. Manch.

JESSON, Alison Jean, GM (retired) Eastwood House, Doncaster Road, Rotherham S65 2BL Tel: 01709 369596 — MB BS 1936 Lond.; DPM Eng. 1966; DObst RCOG 1946. Prev: Med. Asst. Knowle Hosp. Fareham.

JESSON, Russell Edward William (retired) Pasteur, Main St., Bishampton, Pershore WR10 2LX Tel: 01386 462394 — MRCS Eng. LRCP Lond. 1943. Prev: Surg. Lt. RNVR 1944-6.

JESSOP, Christopher Hamilton Cromwell Place Surgery, Cromwell Place, St. Ives, Huntingdon PE27 5JD Tel: 01480 462206 Fax: 01480 465313; 3 West Leys, St. Ives, Huntingdon PE27 6DS Tel: 020 8658 3296 Email: c.h.jessop@btinternet.com — MB BChir 1991 Camb.; MA Camb. 1992; MRCGP 1995; DCH RCP Lond. 1994; DRCOG 1993. (Camb.) Prev: Trainee GP Ramsey Health Centre; Ho. Off. (Surg.) Hinchingbrooke Hosp. Huntingdon; Ho. Off. (Med.) Jas. Paget Hosp. Gt. Yarmouth.

JESSOP, Edmund Griffith 171 Greenhill Road, Winchester SO22 5DR — BM BCh 1978 Oxf.; DM Oxf. 1989; FFPHM 1990. Dir. (Pub. Health) W. Surrey.

JESSOP, Elizabeth The Old Barn, Lower End, Great Milton, Oxford OX44 7NF — MB BChir 1979 Camb.; BA Camb. 1977; FFA RCSI 1985. Prev: Cons. Anaesth. Stoke Mandeville Hosp. Aylesbury; Sen. Regist. (Anaesth.) Mersey RHA; Sen. Regist. Nuffield Dept. Anaesth. John Radcliffe Hosp. Oxf.

JESSOP, Flora Ann Department of Histopathology, Box 235, Addenbrooke's Hospital, Hills Road, Cambridge CB2 2QQ Tel: 01223 217163 — MB ChB 1993 Glas.; MRCPath 2001. p/t Cons. (Histopath.) Addenbrooke's Hosp.

JESSOP, Hilda Catherine Eaton Wood Medical Centre, 1128 Tyburn Road, Erdington, Birmingham B24 0SY Tel: 0121 373 0959 Fax: 0121 350 2719 — MB BS 1990 Adelaide; MB BS 1990 Adelaide.

JESSOP, John Dermot (retired) Glamorgan House (BUPA Hospital), Croescadarn Road, Pentwyn, Cardiff CF23 8XL Tel: 01222 736011 — MA Dub. 1962, MD 1973, MB BCh BAO 1959; FRCP Lond. 1979, M 1966; FRCPI 1973, M 1962; DPhysMed Eng. 1967. Cons. Rheum. Glam. Ho. (BUPA) Cardiff. Prev: Cons. Rheum. Univ. Hosp. Wales, Cardiff.

JESSOP, Mr Julian Hywel BUPA Hospital, Heathbourne Road, Bushey Heath, Watford WD2 1RD Tel: 020 8950 8550 Fax: 01923 217859; 45 The Gardens, Watford WD17 3LN Tel: 01923 228984 Email: jj@watford.net — MB BChir 1977 Camb.; MA Camb. 1976; FRCS Glas. 1982; FRCS Eng. 1982. (Cambridge and University College Hospital) Cons. Orthop. & Traum. Surg. Mt. Vernon & Watford Hosps. NHS Trust. Socs: Fell.Brit. Orthopaedic Assoc.; BMA; Brit. Elbow & Shoulder Soc. Prev: Sen. Regist. Roy. Nat. Orthop. Hosp. Lond.; Clin. Lect. Inst. Orthop.; Regist. (Orthop.) Hammersmith Hosp. Lond.

JESSOP, Melanie Ethne 22 Elm Grove, Orpington BR6 0AB — MB ChB 1988 Manch.; MRCGP 1993; DRCOG 1991. Prev: Trainee GP Preston VTS.

JESSOP, Shirley (retired) 26 Harlow Oval, Harrogate HG2 0DS Tel: 01423 502272 — MB ChB 1950 Leeds; MFCM 1972; DPH Eng. 1961. Prev: SCM (Child Health) Calderdale AHA.

JESSUP, Eamonn Dennis Pendyffryn Medical Group, Ffordd Pendyffryn, Prestatyn LL19 9DH Tel: 01745 886444 Fax: 01745 889831; Voelnant, Gronant Road, Prestatyn LL19 9SW Tel: 01745 889814 Email: eamonn@foelnant.freeserve.co.uk — MB BS 1978 Lond.; MRCGP 1983; DCH RCP Lond. 1981; DRCOG 1980. (St. Geo.)

JESSUP, Geoffrey (retired) 27 Oakwood Lane, Bowdon, Altrincham WA14 3DL Tel: 0161 941 6024 — MB ChB 1950 Manch.; MA Manch. 1992; MRCS Eng. LRCP Lond. 1950; FRCGP

1974, M 1963. Prev: Ho. Surg. & Ho. Phys. Withington Hosp. Manch.

JESTICO, John Victor 20 St Mary's Avenue, Wanstead, London E11 2HP Tel: 020 8530 7473 Fax: 020 8530 7473 — MB BS Lond. 1969; BSc Lond. 1965, MD 1982; FRCP Lond. 1993; MRCP (UK) 1971; MRCS Eng. LRCP Lond. 1969. (Middlx.) Cons. Neurol. King Geo. Hosp. Ilford & Roy. Lond. Hosp. Socs: Assn. Brit. Neurol. Prev: Cons. Neurol. Essex Regional Neurol. Unit OldCh. Hosp. Romford; Sen. Regist. (Neurol.) Nat. Hosp. Nerv. Dis. & Guys Hosp. Lond.; Research Regist. Univ. Dept. Clin. Neurol. Nat. Hosp. Nerv. Dis. Lond.

JESUDASON, Edwin Chitran 55 Sandbach Road, Congleton CW12 4LH — MB BChir 1993 Camb.; MA Cantab. 1993; FRCS Eng. 1996. (Cambridge) Research Fell. (Paediat. Surg.). Socs: Med. Protec. Soc.

JESUDASON, G R R St. Oswalds Street, Liverpool L13 2BY.

JESUDASON, Mr Joseph Selvarajan (retired) The Quinta, 55 Sandbach Road, Congleton CW12 4LH — MB BS 1964 Ceylon; FRCS Ed. 1968; FRCS Eng. 1970; DLO Eng. 1968. Prev: Cons. Otolaryngol. Leighton Hosp. Crewe.

JESUDASON, Kiruparajan The James Paget Hospital, Lowestoft Road, Gorleston, Great Yarmouth NR31 6LA Tel: 01493 452452 Fax: 01493 453288; 1 Yallop Avenue, Gorleston on Sea, Great Yarmouth NR31 6HA Tel: 01493 652380 — MB BS 1973 Sri Lanka; FRCP (UK); LRCP Lond. 1979. Cons. Phys. Socs: Brit. Cardiac. Soc. Prev: Sen. Regist. (Geriat. & Gen. Med.) E. Anglian RHA.

JESUDASON, Peter Jebaseelan Hope Hospital, University of Manchester School of Clinical Medicine, Eccles Old Road, Salford M6 8HD — MB BChir 1989 Camb.

JESUTHASAN, Anthony Juno Barrack Lane Medical Practice, 1 Barrack Lane, Ipswich IP1 3NQ Tel: 01473 252827 Fax: 01473 250463; 43 Marlborough Road, Ipswich IP4 5AX Tel: 01473 717942 — MB BS 1984 Lond.; MRCP (UK) 1987; MRCGP 1989. Prev: SHO (O & G) Centr. Middlx. Hosp.; SHO Rotat. (Med.) Char. Cross Hosp.; Ho. Off. Char. Cross Hosp.

JESUTHASAN, Mariampillai The Croft 1B, Brackendale, London N21 3DH Tel: 020 8886 0900 Fax: 020 8351 3692 — MB BS 1976 Sri Lanka; FFA RCS Eng. 1983. (University of Ceylon, Colombo) Cons. Anaesth. The N. Middlx. Hosp. NHS Trust.

JESWANI, Tony Ashish 43 Cumbrian Gardens, London NW2 1ED — MB BS 1998 Lond.; MB BS Lond 1998.

JETHA, Helen Claire (retired) Fishponds Health Centre, Beechwood Road, Fishponds, Bristol BS16 3TD Tel: 0117 965 6281 — MB ChB 1983 Bristol; MRCGP 1988; DRCOG 1987.

JETHA, S K Pot Kiln Road Surgery, 67 Pot Kiln Road, Great Cornard, Sudbury CO10 8NP Tel: 01787 880337 Fax: 01787 373573 — MB BS 1975 Bombay; MB BS 1975 Bombay.

JETHANI, Pahlaj Rai Compton Health Centre, High Street, Shaw, Oldham OL2 8ST Tel: 01706 842511 Fax: 01706 847106 — MB BS 1961 Sind. (Liaquat Med. Coll. Hyderabad) Clin. Asst. in Geriat. Oldham & Dist. Gen. Hosp.

JETHWA, Ashok Arjan Freemen's Common Health Centre, 161 Welford Road, Leicester LE2 6BF Tel: 0116 255 4776 Fax: 0116 254 9518; 10 Rawlings Court, Leicester LE2 4UU — MB ChB 1977 Bristol; MRCGP 1985; Cert. Family Plann. JCC 1985; DCH RCP Lond. 1984; DRCOG 1983.

JETHWA, Hasmukh Albion House Surgery, 22 Heneage Road, Grimsby DN32 9ES Tel: 01472 345411 Fax: 01472 269471; Fairfield House, 16 Fairfield Road, Scartho, Grimsby DN33 3DP Tel: 01472 823524 — MB BCh 1976 Wales; MRCGP 1981; DRCOG 1981.

JETHWA, Mohan Lal Parshotam, SBStJ Northumberland House, Stourport Road, Kidderminster Tel: 01562 74571 — MB ChB 1964 Sheff.; DObst RCOG 1969. (Sheff.) Hosp. Pract. (O & G) Mid Worcs. Hosp. Gp. Prev: Ho. Phys. Roy. Hosp. Sheff.; Ho. Surg. Roy. Infirm. Sheff.; SHO Jessop Hosp. Wom. Sheff.

JETHWA, Nalini Keshav The Surgery, 42 Central Road, Morden SM4 Tel: 020 8648 9126; 5 Heath Drive, Sutton SM2 5RP Tel: 020 8642 0462 — MB BS 1966 Bombay; MRCOG 1972. (G.S. Med. Coll.) Clin. Asst. (Gyn. & Obst.) Mayday Hosp. Thornton Heath.

JETHWA, Paras Top Floor Flat, 2 Chantry Road, Bristol BS8 2QD — MB BS 1993 Lond.

JETHWA, Ratilal Nathalal Flat 20, Everglade House, Eastleigh Road, London E17 5LU — MB BS 1974 Kerala. (Calicut Med. Coll.) Trainee Gen. Pract. Wakefield Vocational Train. Scheme. Prev: SHO (Gen. Med.) Roy. Infirm. Bolton; Ho. Phys. (Gen. Med.) Qu.'s Pk. Hosp. Blackburn.

JETHWA, Sangeeta Ramnik 20 Keswick Gardens, Redbridge, Ilford IG4 5NB Email: sangeetajethwa@hotmail.com — MB BCh 1998 Wales. SHO/RMO A&E/ICU Tamworth Base Hosp. NSW Australia. Prev: Ho. Phys. Freeman Hosp. Newc.; Ho. Surg. Gronglais Hosp. Aberystwyth.

JETHWA, Satish Karabhai Malpas Medical Centre, 535 Malpas Road, Newport NP20 6NA Tel: 01633 850049; 80 Allt-yr-Yn Avenue, Newport NP20 5DE Tel: 62511 — MB BCh 1966 Wales. (Cardiff)

JETTY, Usha Harnall Lane Medical Centre, Harnall Lane East, Coventry CV1 5AE Tel: 024 7622 4640 Fax: 024 7622 3859; 94 Kenilworth Road, Coventry CV4 7AH Tel: 024 76 418310 — MB BS 1978 Osmania; LRCP LRCS Ed. LRCPS Glas. 1982.

JEWELL, Anne Patricia The Ramblers, Ash Lane, Down Hatherley, Gloucester GL2 9PS Tel: 01452 731269 — BM BCh 1983 Oxf.; BA (Hons.) Oxf. 1980; MRCGP 1991; DRCOG 1988; DCH RCP Lond. 1988.

JEWELL, Brian Reginald (retired) 37 Ben Rhydding Road, Ilkley LS29 8RL Tel: 01943 601864 — BSc Lond. 1956, PhD 1960, MB BS 1961. Chair Airedale NHS Trust. Prev: Dean Sch. of Med. Univ. Leeds.

JEWELL, Catherine 5 Yallop Avenue, Gorleston, Great Yarmouth NR31 6HA — MB ChB 1986 Bristol; DRCOG 1989. Trainee GP Loddon, Norf.

JEWELL, Professor Derek Parry Radcliffe Infirmary, Oxford OX2 6HE Tel: 01865 224829 Fax: 01865 790792 Email: derek.jewell@ndm.ox.ac.uk — BM BCh Oxf. 1966; MA, DPhil Oxf. 1972; FRCP Lond. 1979, M 1969. (Oxf.) Cons. Phys. John Radcliffe Hosp. Oxf.; Prof. Gastro Univ. Oxf. Socs: Med. Res. Soc.; Assn. Phys.; Brit. Soc. Gastroenterol. Prev: Sen. Lect. (Med.) Roy. Free Hosp. Med. Sch. Lond.; Sen. Regist. Radcliffe Infirm. Oxf.

JEWELL, Dylan Peter Arundel 20 Devonshire House, Bath Terrace, London SE1 6PT — MB BS 1998 Lond.; MB BS Lond 1998.

JEWELL, Mr Francis Michael Austen X-ray Department, Gloucestershire Royal Hospital, Great Western Road, Gloucester GL1 3NN Tel: 01452 395093 — BM BCh 1983 Oxf.; BA Oxf. 1980; MRCP (UK) 1986; FRCS Eng. 1989; FRCR 1994. Cons. Radiol. Gloucester. Prev: Sen. Regist. (Radiol.) Bristol.

JEWELL, Geoffrey John (retired) 26 Sackville Gardens, Knighton, Leicester LE2 3TH — MRCS Eng. LRCP Lond. 1956; MA, MB BChir Camb. 1957. Prev: Ho. Phys. & Ho. Surg. Hackney Gen. Hosp.

JEWELL, John Anthony Cambrigeshire Health Authority, Kingfisher House, Kingfisher Way, Hinchingbrooke Business Park, Huntingdon 01480 398609 Tel: 01480 398609; The Grove, 2 Bury Road, Stapleford, Cambridge CB2 5BP Tel: 01223 844731 Fax: 01223 502446 Email: tonyjewell8@aol.com — MB BChir 1976 Camb.; MFPHM RCP (UK) 1993; MRCGP 1984; Dip. Acupunc. Beijing 1983; DCH Eng. 1979; DRCOG 1977; FFPHM 1998. (Cambridge London) Dir. Pub. Health Cambs. HA. Prev: Dir. Pub. Health N. W. Anglia HA; Sen. Regist. E. Anglia RHA; GP City & E. Lond. FHSA.

JEWELL, Mr John Hugh Auchinleck 10 The Moorings, The Street, Lancing BN15 0PP Tel: 01903 767505 — MB BCh BAO 1936 Dub.; BA Dub. 1935; FRCSI 1940. Socs: BMA; Fell. Assn. Surgs. E. Afr.

JEWELL, Morris David Horfield Health Centre, Lockleaze Road, Horfield, Bristol BS7 9RR Tel: 0117 969 5391 — MB BChir 1975 Camb.; MRCGP 1980. (Univ. Coll. Hosp.) Edr., Brit. Jl. of Gen. Pract.; Cons. & Sen. Lect. (Primary Care) Univ. Bristol.

JEWELL, William Edward 3 Lelant Meadows, Lelant, St Ives TR26 3JS — MB BS 1987 Lond.

JEWELL, William Henry Menhenitt (retired) 4 Tal-y-Coed Court, Tal-y-Coed, Monmouth NP25 5HR — MB BS 1956 Lond.; DA (UK) 1966; DObst RCOG 1961. Prev: GP St. Ives, Cornw.

JEWES, Linda Anne 1 Old Hall Close, Kiveton Lane, Tudwick, Sheffield S31 0HL Tel: 01909 515498 — MB ChB 1982 Leic.; BSc (Hons.) Leic. 1980, MB ChB 1982; MRCP (UK) 1985; MRCPath 1989. Cons. Microbiol. Doncaster Roy. Infirm. Prev: Sen. Regist. (Microbiol.) Hallamsh. & N.. Gen. Hosp. Sheff.

JEWITT, Christopher Brian 19 Laurel Crescent, Newcastle upon Tyne NE6 4PJ — MB ChB 1995 Glas.

JEWITT, David Dennis Ernest (retired) 41 The Ridgeway, Chatham ME4 6PB Tel: 01634 845149 — MRCS Eng. LRCP Lond. 1945.

JEWITT, David Edward Cardiac Department, King's College Hospital, London SE5 9RS Tel: 020 7326 3379 Fax: 020 7326 3489; 11 Regent's Park Terrace, London NW1 7EE Tel: 020 7482 1221 — BSc (Special, Hons.) Lond. 1959, MB BS (Hons; Med., Surg. & Therap. & Univ. Medal) 1962; FRCP Lond. 1978, M 1964; MRCS Eng. LRCP Lond. 1962. (King's Coll. Hosp.) Cons. Cardiol. & Dir. Cardiac Dept. King's Coll. Hosp. Lond. Socs: Brit. Cardiac Soc.; FESC; Internat. Fell. Amer. Heart Assn. Prev: Cons. Cardiac Phys. & Lect. (Med.) MRC Cardiovasc. Unit Hammersmith Hosp. Lond.; Lect. (Med.) King's Coll. Hosp. Med. Sch. Lond.; SHO Brompton Hosp.

JEWITT, Jennie Ann Louise 36 Upper Park Road, Camberley GU15 2EF — MB BS 1985 Lond.; Dip. Pharm. Med. RCP (UK) 1989. Sen. Med. Adviser Sandoz Pharmaceut. UK. Prev: Head Med. Affairs Ipsen Internat. Lond.

JEWITT, John Anthony 7 Ripon Close, Barns Park, Cramlington NE23 7XJ — MB BS 1993 Newc.

JEWKES, Mr Alan James Good Hope Hospital, Rectory Road, Sutton Coldfield B75 7RR Tel: 0121 378 2211 Fax: 0121 311 1712; 28 Crosbie Road, Harborne, Birmingham B17 9BE Tel: 0121 426 6862 Email: aljewkes@aol.com — MB ChB 1980 Birm.; MD Birm. 1991; FRCS Eng. 1985; FRCS Ed. 1984. Cons. Gen. Surg. Good Hope NHS Trust Birm.; Hon. Sen. Clin. Lect. (Surg.) Univ. Birm. Prev: Cons. Gen. Surg. Alexandra Hosp. Worcester; Sen. Regist. & Career Regist. (Gen. Surg.) W. Midl. RHA; Hon. Research Fell. Qu. Eliz. Hosp. Birm.

JEWKES, Doreen Annie (retired) 6 Montpelier Row, Blackheath, London SE3 0RL — MB BS 1955 Lond.; MRCS Eng. LRCP Lond. 1955; FFA RCS Eng. 1965; DA Eng. 1962. Hon. Cons. Anaesth. Nat. Hosp. Neurol. & Neurosurg. Qu. Sq. Lond. Prev: Sen. Regist. (Anaesth.) Nat. Hosp. Nerv. Dis. & Roy. Free Hosp.

JEWKES, Fiona Elizabeth Mary Kruf Children's Kidney Centre, University Hospital of Wales, Heath Park, Cardiff CF14 4XW — MB ChB 1980 Birm.; MRCP (UK) 1984; FRCP 1996; FRCPCH 1997. (Birmingham) Cons. Paediat. Nephrol. S. Glam. HA.

JEWKES, Jonathan Orchard Medical Centre, Macdonald Walk, Kingswood, Bristol BS15 8NJ Tel: 0117 980 5100 Fax: 0117 980 5104; 61 Cleeve Hill, Downend, Bristol BS16 6EU — MB 1973 Camb.; BChir 1972; MRCP (UK) 1976; MRCGP 1984; T(GP) 1991; DObst RCOG 1974. (St. Mary's) Prev: Regist. (Med.) Brompton Hosp. Lond. & N.wick Pk. Hosp. Harrow; Regist. (Med.) Ahmadu Bello Univ. Hosp., Nigeria.

JEWKES, Reginald Francis (retired) 6 Montpelier Row, Blackheath, London SE3 0RL Tel: 020 8852 5988 — MB BS 1956 Lond.; MB BS (Hons.) Lond. 1956; FRCP Lond. 1979, M 1961. Hon. Cons. Nuclear Med. Char. Cross & Chelsea & W.m. Hosps. Lond. Prev: Sen. Regist. (Med.) Char. Cross Gp. Hosps. Lond.

JEWSBURY, Mr Percy (retired) 15 Oak Lane, Hingham, Norwich NR9 4JY — MB ChB 1944 Manch.; MD Minnesota 1945; BSc Manch. 1941; FRCS Eng. 1950. Prev: Cons. Cardiothoracic Surg. Vict. Hosp. Blackpool.

JEWSON, David Gerard Pinfold Medical Practice, The Health Centre, Pinfold Gate, Loughborough LE11 1DQ Tel: 01509 263753 Fax: 01509 264124; 3 Green Hill, Hathern, Loughborough LE12 5LF Tel: 01509 843213 — MB 1984 Camb.; MA Camb. 1984; BChir 1983; MRCGP 1991; DRCOG 1986. (St. Bartholomew's) GP Trainer Leics. GP VTS.

JEWSON, Taina Elina Shardeloes, Rectory Hill, West Dean, Salisbury SP5 1JL — MB ChB 1992 Leic.

JEYA-PRAKASH, Mr Annamalaikani (cons. rooms), 104 Harley St., London W1N 1AF Tel: 020 7224 1622 Fax: 020 7224 1577 Email: jeyprakash@aol.com; 1 Hillhampton House, Charters Road, Sunningdale, Ascot SL5 9TL Fax: 01334 874750 — MB BS 1975 Madurai; MS (Gen. Surg.) Madurai 1978; FRCS Ed. 1987. Specialist Plastic & Cosmetic Surg. Lond. Socs: Brit. Assn. of Cosmetic Surg.; Roy. Soc. Med.; Int. Soc. Cosmetic Laser Surg.

JEYADEVAN, Kanagasabai Saravanamuttu Leighton Hospital, MCH Trust, Crewe CW2 4QJ Tel: 01270 255141; Neptune, 52 Fuller Drive, Wistaston, Crewe CW2 6TH Tel: 01270 255141 — MB BS 1965 Ceylon; DLO Eng. 1978. (Colombo) Assoc. Specialist (ENT & Head & Neck) Leighton & Macclesfield Hosps.; Clin. Asst. (ENT) Leighton Hosp. Crewe.

JEYADEVAN, Nelesh Navendra 52 Fuller Drive, Wistaston, Crewe CW2 6TH — MB BS 1993 Lond.

JEYAGOPAL, Narayanasamy X-Ray Department, The Royal Oldham Hospital, Rochdale Road, Oldham OL1 2JH Tel: 0161 624 0420; 4 Northdene Drive, Bamford, Rochdale OL11 5NH Tel: 01706 523713 — MB BS 1981 Madras; FRCR 1989. Cons. Radiol. Roy. Oldham Hosp. Prev: Regist. (Radiol.) Frimley Pk. Hosp. Surrey; Sen. Regist. (Radiol.) Liverp.

JEYAKUMAR, Pandian Flat D, Springfield, Withybush General Hospital, Haverfordwest SA61 2PZ — MB BS 1978 Madurai Kamaraj, India.

JEYAM, Manu 6 Maple Gardens, Bradwell, Great Yarmouth NR31 8ND — MB BS 1990 Madras; MRCP (UK) 1994.

JEYANATHAN, Sangarapillai The Surgery, 27 Clifton Rise, London SE14 6ER Tel: 020 8692 1387; Lakshmi, 58 Ravensbourne Park Crescent, Catford, London SE6 4YP Tel: 020 8690 7285 — MB BS 1977 Ceylon; LRCP LRCS Ed. LRCPS Glas. 1983; MRCGP 1993; DFFP 1993; DGM RCP Lond. 1988. (Colombo)

JEYAPALAN, Inthira Leicester General Hospital, Gwendolen Road, Leicester LE5 4PW Tel: 0116 249 0490 — MB BS 1981 Colombo; LRCP LRCS Ed. LRCPS Glas. 1986; FFA RCS Eng. 1987. Cons. Anaesth. Leicester Gen. Hosp. NHS Trust.

JEYAPALAN, Kanagaratnam The Glenfield Hospital, Groby Road, Glenfield, Leicester LE3 9QP Tel: 0116 287 1471 Fax: 0116 258 3950 — LRCP LRCS 1984 Ed.; MB BS Colombo, 1981; LRCP LRCS Ed. LRCPS Glas. 1984; MRCP (UK) 1985; FRCR 1990. Cons. Radiol. Glenfield Hosp. Leicester. Prev: Sen. Regist. (Radiodiag.) W. Midl. RHA.

JEYARAJAH, Arjun Ravindran St. Bartholomew's Hospital, London EC1A 7PS — MB BS 1986 Lond.; MA; MRCOG. (King's Coll. Lond.) Consultant Gyn. Oncol. Dept. of Gyn. Oncol. St. Barth. Hosp. Lond.; Cons. Gyn. Oncol. -harold Wool / Old Ch. Hosp. & Newham Gen. Hosp. Socs: Brit. Gyn. Cancer Soc.; RCOG; BSCCP.

JEYARATNAM, Dakshika 7 Wentworth Way, Bletchley, Milton Keynes MK3 7RW — MB BS 1996 Lond.

JEYARATNAM, Premachandran Department Anaesthetics, City General Hospital, London Road, Newcastle ST5 — MB BS 1973 Madras; FFA RCSI 1978. (Christian Med. Coll. Vellore) Cons. Anaesth. N. Staffs. HA.

JEYARATNAM, Ratnam 7 Wentworth Way, Bletchley, Milton Keynes MK3 7RW — MB BS 1963 Colombo; MRCP (UK) 1971; FRCP Eng. 1986. Cons. Phys. Geriat. & Gen. Med. Milton Keynes Hosp.

JEYASEELAN, Sanjay 21 Ottershaw Gardens, Blackburn BB1 8RG — MB ChB 1997 Manch.

JEYASINGH, Nila 6 Uneeda Drive, Greenford UB6 8QB — MB BS 1997 Lond.

JEYASINGH, Sharmila 6 Uneeda Drive, Greenford UB6 8QB — MB BS 1994 Lond.

JEYASINGHAM, Mr Kumarasingham (retired) 18 Quarry Lane, Winterbourne Down, Bristol BS36 1DB Tel: 01454 773691 — MB BS Ceylon 1957; ChM Liverp. 1965; FRCS Ed. 1962; FRCS Eng. 1962. Mem. Edit. Bd. Europ. Jl. Cardiothoracic Surg.; Mem. Edit. Bd. Jl. Cardiovasc. Surg. Prev: Sen. Regist. (Cardiothoracic Surg.) Bristol Roy. Infirm.

JEYATHEVA, Daniel Nimalan Southbourne Surgery, 17 Beaufort Road, Southbourne, Bournemouth BH6 5BF Tel: 01202 427878 Fax: 01202 430730; 94 Paisley Road, Southbourne, Bournemouth BH6 5ED — MB BS 1988 Lond.; BA Johns Hopkins Univ. 1983; DRCOG 1993. Prev: SHO (Med.) Russells Hall Hosp. Dudley W. Midl.

JEYES, Kenneth Bilsland Dolphins, 15 Brudenell Avenue, Canford Cliffs, Poole BH13 7NW Tel: 01202 708427 — MRCS Eng. LRCP Lond. 1956; LDS RCS Eng. 1937. (King's Coll. Hosp.) Prev: Sen. Dent. Surg. Whittington Hosp. Lond.; Ho. Phys. W. Middlx. Hosp. Isleworth; Ho. Surg. Edware Gen. Hosp.

JEYNES, Allison Marianne Bristol Myers Squibb, 141-149 Staines Road, Hounslow TW3 3JA Tel: 020 8754 3684 Email: alisonjeynes@bms.com — MB ChB 1989 Sheff.; AFOM RCP Lond. 1995; Dip. Pharm. Med. RCP UK 1994. Med. Dir. (Oncol.) Bristol Myers Squibb Pharmaceuts. Hounslow. Socs: MDU; SubComm.

BRAPP. Prev: Med. Affairs Manager (Oncol.) Ciba Pharmaceuts. Horsham; Clin. Research Phys. Glaxo.

JEYS, Lee Marcus Royal Orthopaedic Hospital, Northfield, Birmingham B31 2AP; 27 Newton Park Road, Wirral L48 9XE — MB ChB 1995 Liverp.

JEZIERSKI, Marek Riszard Jezierski and Partners, The Health Centre, Sheen Lane, London SW14 8LP; 38 Richmond Park Road, Kingston upon Thames KT2 6AH Tel: 020 8546 2323 — MB BS 1982 Lond.; MRCGP (Distinc.) 1987. (Middlx. Hosp. Med. Sch.) Course Organiser Roehampton VTS. Prev: Trainee GP Roehampton VTS; Ho. Surg. Middlx. Hosp.; Ho. Off. (Phys.) St. Albans City Hosp.

JEZZARD, Robert Graham Dept of Health, Wellington House, 135-155 Waterloo Road, London SE1 8UG Tel: 020 7972 4335 Fax: 020 7972 4663 Email: bob.jezzard@doh.gsi.gov.uk — MB BChir 1971 Camb.; MA Camb. 1972; FRCP Lond. 1995; MRCP (UK) 1974; FRCPsych 1993, M 1977. (Camb. & Guy's) Sen. Policy Adviser DoH Wellington Ho. Lond.; Cons. Child Psychiat. S. Lond. Maudsley NHS Trust. Socs: Exec. Comm. Fac. Child Psychiat. Roy. Coll. Psychiat. Prev: Clin. Dir. Child Ment. Health Serv. Lewisham & Guy's Ment. Health NHS Trust; Sen. Regist. (Child & Adolesc. Psychiat.) Maudsley & Bethlem Roy. Hosps.; Lect. Guy's Hosp. Lond.

JHA, Mr Ajaya Nand 112 School Lane, Didsbury, Manchester M20 6JB — MB BS 1977 Poona; MS (Gen. Surg.) Delhi 1981; FRCS Ed. 1984.

JHA, Arun Kumar 1A Greenhithe Close, Sidcup DA15 8EF — MB BS 1981 India; MRCPsych 1991.

JHA, Awadh Bihari Tunbury Avenue Surgery, 16 Tunbury Avenue, Walderslade, Chatham ME5 9EH Tel: 01634 668814 Fax: 01634 311575 — MB BS 1963 Patna; FRCS (Ed.) 1972. (India) GP (WKHA); Clin. Asst. Surg./Med. & Hospice.

JHA, Binod Kumar 7 Linnet Drive, Leigh WN7 2GE — MB BS 1973 Bihar.

JHA, Ganesh Dutta Department Genitourinary Medicine, Scunthorpe General Hospital, Scunthorpe DN15 7JY — MB BS 1954 Patna; Dip. Pract. Dermat. Wales 1993. (P. of Wales Med. Coll.) Med. Asst. (Genitourin. Med.) Scunthorpe Gen. Hosp.

JHA, Jib Narayan The Surgery, 310 St Georges Road, Deepdale, Preston PR1 6NR Tel: 01772 254546 Fax: 01772 254546 — MB BS 1973 Bihar; MB BS 1973 Bihar.

JHA, K K Aintree Road Practice, 2 Aintree Road, Bootle L20 9DW Tel: 0151 922 1768.

JHA, Mr Pramod Kumar 39 Fairfield Close, Shoreham-by-Sea BN43 6BH — MB BS 1981 L. N. Mithila, India; FRCS Eng. 1990.

JHA, Mrs Reeta Rani Queen Elizabeth Hospital, Sheriff Hill, Gateshead, Newcastle upon Tyne NE9 6SX — MB BS 1982 Ranchi, India; MRCOG 1993. (Rajendra Med. Coll. Hosp.) Cons. O & G Qu. Eliz. Hosp. Gateshead. Socs: BMA. Prev: Specialist Regist. Leeds Gen. Infirm. Leeds; Specialist Regist. P.ss Roy. Hosp. Hull.

JHAGROO, Ranita Roisin Flat 23B, Fitzwilliam St., Belfast BT9 6AW — MB BCh BAO 1996 Belf.

JHALLY, S The Surgery, 315 Pickhurst Lane, West Wickham BR4 0HW Tel: 020 8460 2264.

JHANJEE, Viney Kumar The Surgery, Lodge Road, Smethwick, Warley B67 7LU Tel: 0121 558 0499 Fax: 0121 555 5348; Rattan, 77 Westfield Road, Edgbaston, Birmingham B15 3JF Tel: 0121 455 6011 — MB BS Lucknow 1967; DTCD Lucknow 1968. (G.S.V.M. Med. Coll. Kanpur) Hosp. Pract. Dudley HA. Socs: Treas. Overseas Doctor Assn.; Chairm. ASHRA Smelthwick.; Vice Chair. P.C.G. Smeth. Warley.

JHASS, Lakhbinder Singh 63 Fraser Street, Bilston WV14 7PD — BM 1991 Soton.

JHAWAR, Krishna 6 Crooks Barn Lane, Norton, Stockton-on-Tees TS20 1LW Tel: 01642 556517 — MB BS Lucknow 1967; DA Eng. 1971. (King Geo. Med. Coll. Lucknow) Clin. Med. Off. (Anaesth.) S. Tees Health Dist.

JHEETA, Amrik Singh 101 Ivor Road, Sparkhill, Birmingham B11 4NS; Montrose, 69 Parkway, Trentham, Stoke-on-Trent ST4 8AR — BSc (Hons.) Physiol. Birm. 1983, MB ChB 1986; MRCGP 1990; DCH RCP Lond. 1990; DRCOG 1989. GP Stoke-on-Trent. Prev: Trainee GP N. Staffs. VTS.

JHEETA, Bhinder Singh The Surgery, 169-171 Church Road, Sheldon, Birmingham B26 3TT Tel: 0121 743 5511 Fax: 0121 693 9797 — MB ChB 1983 Leic.; MRCGP 1987; DCCH RCP Ed. 1987; DRCOG 1986. Syntex Prize Bedford VTS 1987. Socs: BMA. Prev: Trainee GP Bedford VTS; SHO (Paediat.) Good Hope Hosp. Birm.; SHO (O & G) Dudley Rd. Hosp. Birm.

***JHEETA, Daljit Kaur** 25 Sherwood Road, Hall Green, Birmingham B28 0EX — MB ChB 1998 Birm.

JHEETA, Jouda Singh Braidcraft Medical Centre, 200 Braidcraft Road, Glasgow G53 5QD Tel: 0141 882 3396 Fax: 0141 883 3224; 200 Braidcraft, Glasgow G53 5QD Tel: 0141 882 3396 — MB ChB 1975 Glas.

JHITTAY, Mr Prem Singh The Surgery, 273 Kingsbury Road, Erdington, Birmingham B24 8RD Tel: 0121 382 7539 Fax: 0121 386 2482 — MSc Birm. 1982, MB ChB 1979; FRCS Ed. 1984; MRCGP 1986; DRCOG 1985; DCH RCP Lond. 1983.

JHOOTI, Ternjit Kaur 29 Clifton Avenue, Ashton-on-Ribble, Preston PR2 1SQ — MB ChB 1998 Manch.; MB ChB Manch 1998.

JHOOTY, Harwant Kaur 20 Orchard Avenue, Southall UB1 1LF — BM 1991 Soton.

JIAO, Long 5 Foxberry Court, Foxberry Road, Brockley, London SE4 2SQ — MRCS Eng. LRCP Lond. 1993.

JIBODU, Modupe Olajire 4 Wharfedale Close, Allestree, Derby DE22 2UQ — MB BS 1985 Ibadan.

JIBODU, Olujimi Aboaba Derby City Hospital, Uttoxeter Road, Derby DE22 3NE Tel: 01332 340131 Fax: 01332 202761 Email: jibodu@globalnet.co.uk; 4 Wharfedale Close, Allestree, Derby DE22 2UQ Tel: 01332 559169 Fax: 01332 559169 — MB BS 1984 Ibadan; MRCOG 1992. (Coll. Med. Univ. Ibadan, Nigeria) Assoc. Specialist (O & G) Derby City Hosp. NHS Trust. Socs: Derby Med. Soc.; Brit. Med. Ultrasound Soc.; Birm. & Midl. Obst. & Gyn. Soc. Prev: Regist. (O & G) N.. Gen. Hosp. Sheff. & Rotherham Dist. Gen. Hosp.

JIBRIL, Mr Jibril Ahmad 5 Gullymoss View, Westhill AB32 6PF — MB BS 1983 Ahmadu Bello U, Nigeria; FRCS Ed. 1991.

JIBRIN, Mr Umar Faruk 318 South Street, Romford RM1 2AJ — MB BS 1982 Ahmadu Bello, Nigeria; FRCSI 1989.

JIGAJINNI, Mahananda Veerappa 1 Buckstone Court, Edinburgh EH10 6UL — LRCP LRCS 1981 Ed.; LRCP LRCS Ed. LRCPS Glas. 1981.

JIGGINS, Marcus Paul The Old Rectory, Bathampton Lane, Bath BA2 6ST — BM BCh 1994 Oxf.

JILANI, Muhammad Ghaus-us-Saqlain 9 Harris Road, Parkhurst, Newport PO30 5NN — MB BS 1982 Karachi; MRCP (UK) 1987. Specialist Regist. (Rehabil. Med.) N. Staffs. Hosp. Socs: MDU; BMA.

JILANI, Muzafar Mukhtar Talygarn, County Hospital, Griffithstown, Pontypool NP4 5YA Tel: 01495 768768 Fax: 01495 765733 Email: mmjilani@gwent.nhs.gov.uk; Greenway, 38 Avenue Road, Abergavenny NP7 7DB Tel: 01873 855565 Fax: 01873 855565 — MB BS Jammu & Kashmir 1966; MRCPsych 1974; DPM Eng. 1971; FRCPsych 1998. (Govt. Med. Coll. Srinagar) Cons. Psychiat. Talygarn Co. Hosp. Griffithstown, Pontypool; Mbr. Ment. Hlth. Review Trib. Socs: Welsh Psychiat. Soc. (Ex-Sec. & Ex-Chair.). Prev: Cons. Psychiat. Maindiff Ct. Hosp. Abergavenny.

JILANI, Seema Azam 48 Marle Croft, Whitefield, Manchester M45 7NB — MB BS 1996 Lond.; BA (Hons) Physiol. Sci. Oxf. 1993. SHO (Gen. Med. & GI) St James Hosp. Leeds. Socs: MPS; BMA. Prev: SHO (Gen. Med.) Harrogate Dist. Hosp.; Jun. Ho. Off. (Gen. Surg. & Cardiothoracics) Manch. Roy. Infirm.; Jun. Ho. Off. (Gen. Med.) Wycombe Hosp.

JIMENEZ CAMARA, Victor Carlos ENT Department, City General Hospital, Fusehill Road, Carlisle CA1 2HG — LMS 1991 La Laguna.

JIMENEZ ZARATIEGUI, Luis Fernando 20 Lundy Drive, West Cross, Swansea SA3 5QL — LMS 1987 Navarre.

JINADU, Mr Fuad Olatokunbo James Paget Hospital, Lowestoft Road, Great Yarmouth NR31 6LA Tel: 01493 600611; 75 Fern Gardens, Belton, Great Yarmouth NR31 9QY — MB BS 1978 Ibadan; MB BS Ibadan, Nigeria 1978; FRCS Ed. 1994; FRCS Glas. 1985.

JINDAL, Bharat Kumar Speedwell Surgery, 1 Speedwell Street, Paddock, Huddersfield HD1 4TS Tel: 01484 531786 Fax: 01484 424249; Snowlea, 105 Lamb Hall Road, Longwood, Huddersfield HD3 3TH Tel: 01484 460577 Email: bertjindal@msncom — MB ChB 1979 Bristol; MRCGP 1989; DCH RCP Lond. 1983. (Bristol) Clin. Asst. (Oncol.) Huddersfield Roy. Infirm.; GP Trainer Huddersfield; Mem. Huddersfield GP Commiss. Gp.; Med. Ref. Brit. Sub Aqua Club; Sec. Huddersfield Div. LMC; Sec. Calderdale &

Kirklees LMC. Socs: BMA & Huddersfield Med. Soc. Prev: Trainee GP York VTS; Regist. & SHO (Paediat.) Yorks. RHA.

JINDAL, Mudit Mohan 2 Sword Gardens, Rushy Platt, Swindon SN5 8ZE — MB BS 1998 Lond.; MB BS Lond 1998.

JINDAL, Shakuntala (retired) 1 Speedwell Street, Paddock, Huddersfield HD1 3TS — MB BS 1949 Agra; MS (Gyn. & Obst.) Agra 1953, MB BS 1949. GP Kirklees. Prev: Demonst. (O & G Med.) Coll. Agra, India.

JINGREE, Madho Wrightington Hospital, Hall Lane, Appley Bridge, Wigan WN6 9ED Tel: 01257 25211; Daisy Cottage, 35 Smithy Lane, Aughton, Ormskirk L39 6SS Tel: 01695 423409 Fax: 01695 423409 Email: madho.jingree@ doctors.org .uk — MB ChB 1980 Bristol; FFA RCSI 1989. Cons. Anaesth. Wrighttinton Hosp., Lancs. Prev: Cons. Anaesth. Ormskirk, Lancs.

JIP, Harold 3 Winfrith Drive, Spital Est., Bebington, Wirral CH63 9HX — MB ChB 1968 Liverp.

JIP, James Yew Tree Farm, Regents Road, Lostock, Bolton BL6 4DG — MB ChB 1971 Liverp.; MRCPath 1979. Cons. Haemat. Bolton Gen. Hosp. Socs: Brit. Soc. Haemat.; Manch. Med. Soc. Prev: Sen. Regist.(Haemat.) Roy. Liverp. Hosp.; Regist. (Path.) Walton Hosp. Liverp.

JIVA, Mohammed Ismail 2 Caithness Drive, Ladybridge, Bolton BL3 4PG — MB ChB 1994 Liverp.; DCH 1997; DRCOG 1997; DFFP 1998. GP Regist. Prev: VTS.

JIVAN, Sharmila 72 Buckingham Dr, Loughborough LE11 4TE — MB ChB 1997 Leic.

JIVANI, Amirali Kassam New Malden Health Centre, 4 Blagdon Road, New Malden KT3 4AD Tel: 020 8942 2660 Fax: 020 8336 0378 — MB BS 1963 Lond.; MRCS Eng. LRCP Lond. 1963.

JIVANI, Nazim Amirali New Malden Health Centre, 4 Blagdon Road, New Malden KT3 4AD Tel: 020 8942 2660 Fax: 020 8336 0378; 5 Howard Road, Effingham Junction, Leatherhead KT24 5HX Email: pib.pob@virgin.net — MB ChB 1990 Liverp.; DCH Lond 1995. (Liverpool)

JIVRAJ, Shehnaaz Sadrudin 20 Headford Mews, Sheffield S3 7XL — MB ChB 1995 Sheff.

JIWA, Moyaz Bridgegate Surgery, 43 Bridgegate, Retford DN22 7UX Tel: 01777 702381/2 Fax: 01777 711880 — MB BCh BAO 1987 Dub.; MB BCh Dub. 1987; MRCGP 1993; DCH RCP Lond. 1991; T(GP) 1991. Prev: Trainee GP Dumfries; SHO (Paediat.) Dumfries & Galloway Roy. Infirm.

***JIWANY, Arif** 92 Roding Road, Homerton, London E5 0DS — MB BS 1994 Lond.; BSc Med. Sci. & Specialization in Psychol. Lond. 1991.

JOANES, Kathleen Margaret (retired) 7 Areley Court, Stourport-on-Severn DY13 0AR — MB ChB 1956 Birm.; DObst RCOG 1959. Prev: Deptm. Med. Off. Worcs. CC.

JOANES, Robert Frank (retired) 7 Areley Court, Stourport-on-Severn DY13 0AR Tel: 01299 877964 — MB BS Lond. 1949; MFCM 1974; MFPHM RCP (UK) 1989; DPH Eng. 1962. Prev: SCM Sandwell DHA.

JOANNIDES, Theophanis Radiotherapy Department, Singleton Hospital, Sketty, Swansea SA2 8QA Tel: 01792 205666 — MB BS 1975 Lond.; BSc (Hons.) Lond. 1972, MB BS 1975; FRCR (Radiother. & Oncol.) 1986. Cons. Radiother. & Oncol. Singleton Hosp. Swansea. Prev: Sen. Regist. (Radiother. & Oncol.) Guy's & St. Thos. Hosps. Lond.; Regist. (Radiother. & Oncol.) Univ. Coll. Hosp. Lond.

JOANNOU, Peter (retired) Grove Medical Centre, Windlass Place, London SE8 3QH Tel: 020 8692 1882 — MD 1953 Prague; LAH Dub. 1960. Prev: Regist. (Surg.) Postgrad. Sch. Surg. Prague.

JOASHI, Umesh Chandra 45 Carver Road, Herne Hill, London SE24 9LS Tel: 020 7274 2817 — MB BS 1988 Lond.; MRCP (UK) 1992. Research Fell. & Hon. Regist. (Paediat.) Roy. Postgrad. Med. Sch. Hammersmith Hosp. Lond.

JOASHI, Yogesh Chandra c/o Saffron House, 3 Frank Avenue, Mansfield NG18 5EL — MB BS 1990 Newc.

JOB, Maria Catharina Henriette 10 Babbacombe Road, Bromley BR1 3LW — Artsexamen 1984 Nijmegen.

JOB, Sian Angharad The Surgery, 14 Queenstown Road, Battersea, London SW8 3RX Tel: 020 7622 9295 Fax: 020 7498 5206 — MB BS 1976 Lond.; MRCS Eng. LRCP Lond. 1976; DRCOG 1979.

JOBANPUTRA, Paresh University Hospital Birmingham, Selly Oak Hospital, Raddlebarn Road, Birmingham B29 6JD Tel: 0121 627 1627 Fax: 0121 627 8480 — BM 1982 Soton.; FRCP Ed. 1999; DM Soton. 1993; MRCGP 1988. (University of Southampton) Cons. Rheum. Selly Oak Hosp. Birm.; Hon. Sen. Lect. Univ. of Birm. Socs: Brit. Soc. Rheum.; Amer. Coll. Rheum. Prev: Lect. (Med.) Univ. of Edin. W.ern Gen. Hosp.; Arthritis & Rheum. Counc. Research Fell. Guy's Hosp. Lond.; Regist. Rotat. (Gen. Med. & Rheum.) Guys & Lewisham Hosps. Lond.

JOBANPUTRA, Rajesh Southmead Health Centre, Ullswater Road, Bristol BS10 6DF Tel: 0117 950 7150 Fax: 0117 959 1110 — MB ChB 1982 Bristol; MRCGP 1988; DRCOG 1985. Socs: Med. Protec. Soc. Prev: Trainee GP Bristol VTS; SHO (Geriat. & Paediat.) Bristol.

JOBANPUTRA, Ravindra Sulochanbhai (retired) 12 Cherry Blossom Close, Littlebilling, Northampton NN3 9DN Tel: 01604 784805 — MD (Path. & Bact.) Gujarat 1967, MB BS 1963; FRCPath 1986, M 1974. Cons. Microbiol. & Dir. Pub. Health Laborat. St. John's Hosp. PeterBoro.; Hon. Cons. Microbiol. E. Anglian RHA.

JOBLING, Alison Jane 45 Broadway, Cheadle SK8 1LB — MB ChB 1991 Manch.; MRCP (Paed) 1994.

JOBLING, David Ian Stockwell Road Surgery, 21 Stockwell Road, Knaresborough HG5 0JY Tel: 01423 867433 Fax: 01423 869633 — MB ChB 1973 Sheff.; DObst RCOG 1975.

JOBLING, Mr Jonathan Craig Department of Radiology, Nottingham City Hospital NHS Trust, Hucknall Road, Nottingham NG5 1PB Tel: 0115 969 1169 Fax: 0115 962 7776; Glebe Steading, Southwell Road, Gonalston, Nottingham NG14 7JA Tel: 0115 966 5476 Fax: 0870 054 7985 — MB BChir Camb. 1982; MA Camb. 1981; FRCS Ed. 1988; FRCR 1994. (Cambridge University) Cons. Radiol. Nottm. City Hosp. NHS Trust. Prev: Sen. Regist. (Diag. Radiol.) NE Thames RHA; Regist. (Diag. Radiol.) N.. RHA; Regist. Rotat. (Gen. Surg.) NW RHA.

***JOBLING, Louise Marie** St James Hospital, Leeds — MB BS 1998 Lond.; MB BS Lond 1998; BSc.

JOBLING, Sally Anne 14 Cedar Chase, Rectory Road, Taplow, Maidenhead SL6 0EU Tel: 01628 630931 Fax: 01628 630931 — MRCS Eng. LRCP Lond. 1967; MRCGP 1978; Cert. Av Med. 1983; DObst RCOG 1969; Cert. Family Plann. JCC 1969; Dip Occ Med 1998. (Roy. Free)

JOBLING, Stuart Greystoke Surgery, Kings Avenue, Morpeth NE61 1JA Tel: 01670 511393 Fax: 01670 503282 — MB BCh 1975 Wales; MRCGP 1986; DRCOG 1977.

JOBSON, David Hunter The Surgery, Main Street, Leiston IP16 4ES Tel: 01728 830526 Fax: 01728 832029; 24 King George's Avenue, Leiston IP16 4JG Tel: 01728 831100 Email: davidjobson@compuserve.com — MB BS Lond. 1970; MRCS Eng. LRCP Lond. 1970; MRCOG 1976, DObst 1972; DCH Eng. 1977. (King's Coll. Hosp.) Socs: Fell. Hunt Soc. Prev: Cons. (O & G) Roy. Vict. Hosp. Banjul The Gambia; Regist. (O & G) S.lands Hosp. Shoreham; Med. Off. Chas. Johnson Memor. Hosp. Nqutu, Zululand.

JOBSON, Mr Patrick Hunter, TD Courtlands, 61 Kingswood Firs, Grayshott, Hindhead GU26 6ER Tel: 01428 605700 — MB BS 1938 Lond.; FRCS Eng. 1971; MRCS Eng. LRCP Lond. 1938; DLO Eng. 1946. (King's Coll. Hosp.) Founder & Trustee of the TWJ Foundat. Socs: Hon. Fell. Hunt. Soc.; Fell. Roy. Soc. Med. & Hon. Mem. Sect. Otol. Prev: Cons. Phys. (Audiol. Med.) & Cons. Otolaryngol. S.W. Surrey Health Dist. (Guildford); Regist. (ENT) King's Coll. Hosp. Lond.

JOBSON, Timothy Mark Fox Earth, Towersey, Thame OX9 3QR — BM BCh 1992 Oxf.

JOBST, Professor Kim Anthony Glasgow Nuffield Hospital, Beaconsfield Road, Glasgow G12 0PJ Tel: 0141 334 9441 Fax: 0141 339 1352 Email: kim.jobst@clinmed.gla.ac.uk; 1 Spence Street, Maryhill Park, Glasgow G20 0AW Tel: 0141 946 4372 Fax: 0141 946 4370 Email: kim.jobst@clinmed.gla.ac.uk — MB BS 1984 Lond.; 1991 MA Oxf. 1986, BA 1981; 1996 DM Oxf. 1996; 1989 MRCP (UK) 1989; 1998 LFHom 1998; 2000 MFHom; 1998 CCST Neurodegeneration & Dementia; 1984 DipAc; 1999 CCST Gen. Med. 1999. (Univ. Oxf. & St. Thos.) Cons. Phys. Roy. & Med. Homeo. Spec. in Neurodegen. & Dementia, Glas. Nuff. Hosp.; Mem. Scientif. Advis. Bd. Centre Complementary & Alternative Med. Columbia Univ. Med. Sch. New York; Chairm. Blackie Foundat. Scientif. & Ethical Research Comm.; Vis. Prof. (Healthcare &

Integrated Med.) Oxf. Brookes Univ.; Mem. Counc. Found. Integrated Med.; Hon. Cons. Phys. Roy. Lond. Homeo. Hosp.; Mem. Scientif. Adv. Bd. Pharmanex Inc. SF USA; Ed.-I.-Ch., Jl. of Hlth & Compl. Med. Socs: Fell. Roy. Soc. Med.; Assoc. Mem. Brit. Holistic Med. Assn.; Med. & Scientif. Network. Prev: Sen. Regist. (Med. & Therap.) Univ. Glas. Dept. Med. & Therap. Gardiner Inst. W.. Roy. Infirm. Glas.; Clin. Dir. Oxf. Project to Investig. Memory & Aging (OPTIMA) Neuropsychogeriat. Neurol. Disabil. & Rehabil., Pharmacol. & Psychiat. Univ. Oxf.; Sen. Regist. (Gen. Med. & Homoeopathy) Glas. Homoeop. Hosp.

JOCE, Rachel Elizabeth East Sussex, Brighton & Hove HA, 36-38 Friars Walk, Lewes BN7 2PB Tel: 01273 403597 Fax: 01273 403600 — MB BS 1979 Lond.; MSc (Community Med.) Lond. 1986; MFFP 1997; MFPHM 1989; DCH RCP Lond. 1981. (Roy. Free Hosp. Med. Sch.) Cons. Communicable Dis. Control E. Sussex, Brighton & Hove HA. Prev: Cons. Communicable Dis. Control E. & N. Herts. HA.

JODRELL, Duncan Ian Department of Oncology, Western General Hospital, Crewe Road S., Edinburgh EH4 2XU Tel: 0131 467 8447 Fax: 0131 332 8494 — BM 1982 Soton.; MRCP 1985 (UK); MSc (Biochem.) 1989 Lond.; DM 1990 Soton.; MSc (Biochem.) Lond. 1989; DM Soton. 1990; MRCP (UK) 1985. (Southampton) Reader Oncol.Univ. Edin.; Cons. Med. Oncol. W.ern Gen. Hosp. Edin.; Dep. Director, ICRF Med. Oncol. Unit, Edin. Socs: Assn. of Cancer Phys.s; Amer. Soc. of Clin. Oncol.; Brit. Assn. of Cancer Research. Prev: Sen. Regist. (Med. Oncol.) Beatson Oncol. Centre Glas.; Clin. Research Fell. Inst. Cancer Research Sutton; Regist. (Med.) St. Geo. Hosp. Lond.

JOEKES, Mavis 28 Dorothy Road, London SW11 2JP Tel: 020 7924 5131 — Artsexamen 1974 Leiden.

JOEL, Christopher Edwin Compton Health Centre, Compton, Ashbourne DE6 1DA Tel: 01335 343784 Fax: 01335 300782 — MB BS 1969 Newc.

JOEL-COHEN, Professor Sidney Joel (retired) — MB BCh 1936 Witwatersrand; FRCS Ed. 1939; FRCOG 1959, M 1947, DObst 1938. Prof. Tel Aviv Univ., Israel; Vis. Prof. KCH Lond.; Hon. Prof. Univ. Hong Kong.

JOELS, Lisa Anne 18 Westons Brake, Emersons Green, Bristol BS16 7BP Email: oglaj@ssa.bris.ac.uk — MB ChB 1985 Liverp.; MRCOG 1992. (Univ. Liverp.) Lect. & Hon. Sen. Regist. Univ. Bristol. Prev: Clin. Research Fell. Univ. Bristol; Regist. (O & G) St. Geo. Hosp. Lond., Mayday Hosp. Croydon & St. Helier Hosp. Carshalton.

JOELS, Professor Norman 49 Sheldon Avenue, Highgate, London N6 4NH Tel: 020 8348 3565 Fax: 020 8341 1514 — MB BS MB BS Lond. 1951; PhD Lond. 1960, BSc (Hons.) 1949. (Middlx.) Emerit. Prof. Physiol. Qu. Mary & W.field Coll. Lond. Socs: Fell. Roy. Soc. Med.; Physiol. Soc. Prev: Prof. Physiol. St. Bart. Hosp. Med. Coll. Lond.; Lect. (Physiol.) Middlx. Hosp. Med. Sch.; Ho. Phys. Middlx. Hosp.

JOELS, Suzanne Lea Academic Department of Psychiatry, Royal Free Hospital, Pond St., London NW3 — MB BS 1986 Lond.; MRCPsych 1993; MRCGP 1990. (Middlesex Hospital & UCL) Sen. Regist. Psychiat. Roy. Free Hosp.

JOESBURY, Helen Elizabeth Woodseats Medical Centre, 4 Cobnar Road, Woodseats, Sheffield S8 8QB Tel: 0114 274 0202 Fax: 0114 274 6835 Email: h.joesbury@sheffield.ac.uk — FRCGP 1999; MB ChB Sheff. 1969; MEd. Sheff. 1997; MRCGP 1976; DObst RCOG 1972; DCH Eng. 1972. (Sheff.) GP Advisor DOH; Sen. Clin. Lect., Inst. of Gen. Pract. (Univ. of Sheff.). Socs: BMA; (AUDGP) SAPC. Prev: SHO (Obst.) Jessop Hosp. Wom. Sheff.; Ho. Phys. Roy. Infirm. Sheff.; Ho. Surg. Childr. Hosp. Sheff.

JOFFE, Johnathan Keith Huddersfield Royal Infirmary, Lindley, Huddersfield HD3 3EA Tel: 01484 482150 Fax: 01484 482187 Email: jkjoffe@huddersfield-tr.northy.nhs.uk — MB BS 1984 Lond.; FRCP (UK) 1999; MD Lond. 1994; MRCP (UK) 1987. (Roy. Free Lond.) Macmillan Cons. in Med. Oncol. Huddersfield; Cons. Med. Oncol. St. Jas. Univ. Hosp. Leeds; Hon. Cons. Cookridge Hosp. Leeds; Hon. Lect. Univ. of Leeds. Socs: Roy. Coll. Phys. Lond.; Assn. Cancer Phys.; Brit. Assn. Cancer Research. Prev: Sen. Regist. (Med. Oncol.) St. Jas. Univ. Hosp. Leeds.; Clin. Research Fell. Inst. Cancer Research Sutton & Roy. Marsden Hosp. Sutton; Regist. (Med. & Oncol.) Roy. Free Hosp. Lond.

JOFFE, Michael Department of Epidemiology & Public Health, Imperial College School of Medicine at St Mary's, Norfolk Place, London W2 1PG Tel: 020 7594 3338 Fax: 020 7402 2150 Email: m.joffe@ic.ac.uk — MB BChir 1968 Camb.; MSc Lond. 1977; MA Camb. 1969, MD 1989; FRCP Lond. 1993; MRCP (UK) 1971; FFPHM RCP (UK) 1993; MFCM 1987. (Camb. & Middlx.) Sen. Lect. (Pub. Health) Imperial Coll. Sch. Med. Socs: Roy. Soc. Med. (Epidemiol. Sect.).

JOGARAJAH, Thevaky 9 Calverley Gardens, Harrow HA3 0PE — MB BS 1980 Colombo.

JOGEESVARAN, Sothimalar St Clement's Hospital, Foxhall Road, Ipswich IP3 8LS Tel: 01473 71511; 6 Newby Drive, Ipswich IP4 5UY Tel: 01473 273798 — MB BS Ceylon 1970; DPM RCPSI 1991. Regist. (Psychogeriat.) St. Clement's Hosp. Ipswich.

JOGIA, Piyush Laxman 34 Laburnum Grove, Hounslow TW3 3LU — MB ChB 1992 Manch.; BSc (Med. Biochem. Hons.) Manch. 1989.

JOGIYA, Aryan 6 Talbot Road, Isleworth TW7 7HH — MB BS 1998 Lond.; MB BS Lond 1998.

JOGLEKAR, Vibhakar Moreshwar 72 Holywell Avenue, Whitley Bay NE26 3AD Tel: 0191 252 1682 — MB BS 1958 Bombay; FRCP Lond. 1991; MRCP (UK) 1971; DIH Eng. 1963; DPH Lond. 1962; DTM & H Eng. 1960. (Topiwala Nat. Med. Coll.) Cons. Phys. Gen. & Geriat. Med. N. Tyneside Health Dist.

JOGLEKAR, Vijay Madhav Department of Pathology, Furness General Hospital, Dalton Lane, Barrow-in-Furness LA14 4LF Tel: 01229 870870 — MB ChB 1970 East Africa; MRCPath 1979; DCP Lond 1975. (Makerere Med. Sch. Kampala) Cons. Histopath. Furness Gen. Hosp. Barrow in Furness.

JOHAL, Baljit Singh The Surgery, 17 Rosslyn Road, Twickenham TW1 2AR Tel: 020 8892 1991 Fax: 020 8744 0533; 85 Ash Grove, Heston, Hounslow TW5 9DX Tel: 020 8892 1991 — MRCS Eng. LRCP Lond. 1984; BSc Gurunanak Dev Univ. Amritsar 1971; MB BS Gurunanak Dev Univ. Amritsar 1977; MRCGP 1990; DFFP 1993; DCH RCP Lond. 1987; DRCOG 1988.

JOHAL, Miss Balroop Department of Obstetrics and Gynaecology, Ipswich Hospital, Ipswich Tel: 01473 712233; Burnt Oak, 135 Bucklesham Road, Ipswich IP3 8UB Tel: 01473 271166/719279 Fax: 01473 271166 — MB BS 1980 Panjab; FRCOG 2000; MRCOG 1988. Cons. O & G Ipswich Trust Hosp.; Governer. Sulfolk Coll. Ipswich. Socs: Brit. Soc. of Perinatal Med.; E. Anglia Obst. & Gyn. Soc.; Brit. Merryanne Soc. Prev: Sen. Regist. (O & G) Univ. Coll., Middlx. Hosp. Lond. & Ipswich Hosp.; Research Regist. Univ. Coll. & Middlx. Hosps. Lond.

JOHAL, Jasvinder Singh Sandpipers, Packhorse Road, Gerrards Cross SL9 8JG — MB ChB 1992 Dundee.

JOHAL, Kuldhir Kaur 8 Villier Road, Southall UB1 3BP — BM 1989 Soton.

JOHAL, Navroop Singh Rose Lodge, Inkpen, Hungerford RG17 9QY — MB BCh 1998 Wales.

JOHAL, Parminder Singh 10 Christopher Lodge, Avenue Road, Highgate, London N6 5DL — MB BS 1994 Lond.

JOHAL, Shawinder Singh 19 Honeybourne Way, Willenhall WV13 1HN — MB ChB 1993 Manch.; MRCP 1995. Specialist Regist. (Gastroenterol.) Midl.

JOHAL, Mr Sukhdev Singh Tel: 01255 220010 Fax: 01255 476350; Burnt Oak, 135 Bucklesham Road, Ipswich IP3 8UB Tel: 01473 271166/719279 Fax: 01473 719279 — MB BS 1977 Panjab; FRCS Glas. 1984; T(GP) 1991. Prev: Regist. (Surg.) Rush Green & OldCh. Hosps. Romford; Regist. (Surg.) Hillingdon Hosp.

JOHAL, Sukhvinder Singh 8 Villiers Road, Southall UB1 3BP — MB BCh 1992 Wales.

JOHANNES, Stephan Gerrard Westfield Road Surgery, 11 Westfield Road, Bletchley, Milton Keynes MK2 2DJ Tel: 01908 377103 Fax: 01908 374427 — MB BS 1983 Lond.; BSc (Hons.) (Path.) Lond. 1980, MB BS 1983; DRCOG 1985; DFFP 1996. (King's Coll. Hosp.) Chief. Med. Off. Brook Advis. Family Plann. Centre; Hosp. Practitioner (Rheumatol.). Socs: Brit. Med. Acupunct. Soc.

JOHANNSEN, Kirsten 41 Deramore Park, Ballymena BT43 7ED Tel: 01266 630314 — State Exam Med 1991 Lubeck.

JOHANNSSON, Helgi Ellert 178 Maybank Road, London E18 1EL — MB BS 1996 Lond.; MRCP Part 1 1998. (St Bartholomews) SHO Med. Rotat. Homerton Hosp. Hackney Lond.

JOHANSEN, Antony Meyrick Department of Medicine, University Hospital of Wales, Heath Park, Cardiff CF14 4WZ; Brynlea Hey, St. Lythan's, Cardiff CF5 6SB Tel: 01222 591624 — MB BChir 1987

Camb.; MA Camb. 1989, MB BChir 1987; MRCP (UK) 1991; DGM RCP Lond. 1991. Cons. (Med. & Trauma Rehabil.) Univ. Hosp. Wales Cardiff. Prev: Sen. Regist. (Med. & Geriatr. Med.) Cardiff; Regist. (Rheum.) Roy. Lond. Hosp.; Regist. (Cardiol., Neurol. & Med.) Whipps Cross Hosp. Lond.

JOHANSEN, Mr Karl Antony (retired) Littlefield, Pwllmelin Road, Cardiff CF5 2NG — MB BS 1960 Lond.; MRCS Eng. LRCP Lond. 1962; FRCOG 1980, M 1967. Hon. Cons. Obst & Gyn. Llandough Hosp. Cardiff. Prev: Sen. Lect. (O & G) Univ. of Wales Coll. Of Med.

JOHANSON, Richard Brian North Staffs Hospital, Newcastle Road, Stoke-on-Trent ST4 6QG Tel: 01782 715444 Fax: 01782 713401; Ridgwardine Manor, Market Drayton TF9 3TR — MB 1983 Camb.; MD 1991; BSc, MA St. And. 1980; BChir 1982; MRCOG 1988. Prof. Obst.; Sen. Lect. Keele Univ. Prev: Sen. Regist. Rotat. (O & G) W. Midl.; Regist. (O & G) N. Staffs. Matern. Hosp. Stoke-on-Trent; Trainee GP Stoke-on-Trent VTS.

JOHANSSON, Alan Carr (retired) Trewedna, Bartestree, Hereford HR1 4BY Tel: 01432 850403 — MRCS Eng. LRCP Lond. 1954; MB Camb. 1955, BChir 1954; DObst RCOG 1961. Prev: GP Hereford.

JOHAR, Mohd Ariffin 16 Basement Flat, Cave St., Bristol BS2 8RU — MB ChB 1994 Bristol.

JOHARI, Sasha 2 Hillside Close, Bramhall, Stockport SK7 2LP — MB ChB 1997 Manch.

JOHL, Paul Patrick 1 Wentworth Lane, St. Mellons, Cardiff CF3 0LH — MB BCh 1985 Wales.

JOHL, Rita 18 St Crispins Close, Southall UB1 2UH — MB ChB 1996 Leic.

JOHL, Stevan The Surgery, Scotland Street, Llanrwst LL26 0AL Tel: 01492 640411 Fax: 01492 641402 — MB ChB 1986 Sheff.; BMedSci (Hons.) Clin. Physiol. Sheff. 1985; MRCGP 1992; DFFP 1992; DTM & H Liverp. 1989.

JOHN, Aleyamma Thams View Health Centre, Bastable Avenue, Barking IG11 0LG Tel: 020 8594 1061 Fax: 020 8594 2184 — MB BS 1973 Kerala; MB BS Keraala 1973.

JOHN, Mr Alfred Howard (retired) 19 Blueberry Downs, Coastguard Road, Budleigh Salterton EX9 6NU Tel: 01395 445403 — MB BS 1951 Lond.; FRCS Ed. 1961; MRCS Eng. LRCP Lond. 1951; FRCOG 1969, M 1958. Prev: Cons. O & G Bristol HA & Clin. Lect. Univ. Bristol.

JOHN, Mr Alun Wyn Dept. of Orthopaedic Surgery, Univ. Hospital Of Wales, Heath Park, Cardiff CF14 4 Email: alun.john@virgin.net — MB BS 1987 Lond.; FRCS Eng. 1992; FRCS T & Orth 1999. Cons. (Orthop.) Univ. of Wales. Prev: Sen. Regist. (Orthop.) Cardiff Roy. Infirm.

JOHN, Ann 1 Kingston Road, Sketty, Swansea SA2 0SS — MB BS 1993 Lond.

JOHN, Anthony Bertrand Seymour Grove Health Centre, 70 Seymour Grove, Old Trafford, Manchester M16 0LW Tel: 0161 872 5672 Fax: 0161 848 0478; 6 Longton Avenue, Withington, Manchester M20 3JN Tel: 0161 283 7785 Fax: 0161 283 7785 Email: anthony.john@cwcom.net — MB ChB 1973 Manch.; MRCP (UK) 1978; DCH RCP Lond. 1975; FRCPH (RCPCH) 1996. (Manch.) Cons. Community Paediat. Trafford Healthcare NHS Trust. Socs: Manch. Med. Soc. Prev: SCMO (Child Health) Halton HA; Clin. Med. Off. (Child Health) Centr. Manch. HA.

JOHN, Mr Anthony Christopher ENT Department, St Anthony's Hospital, London Road, Cheam, Sutton SM3 9DW Tel: 020 8337 6691; Parkside Hospital, Wimbledon, London SW19 5NX Tel: 020 8946 4202 — MB BS Lond. 1970; FRCS Eng. 1975; MRCS Eng. LRCP Lond. 1970. Cons. ENT Surg. St. Helier Hosp. Gp. & St. Geo. Hosp. Lond.; Hon. Sen. Lect. St. Geo. Hosp. Med. Sch. Lond.; Med. Assessor for Social Security Appeal Tribunals. Prev: Sen. Regist. (ENT) St. Bart. Hosp. Lond. & Roy. Nat. Throat Nose & Ear Hosp.; SHO Roy. Marsden Hosp. Lond.

JOHN, Anthony Harold (retired) Tower Hill, Selattyn, Oswestry SY10 7DX — MB BS 1953 Lond.; DObst RCOG 1955. Prev: GP OsW.ry.

JOHN, Arthur Philip Kilsha Shepshed Health Centre, Field St., Loughborough LE12 9AL Tel: 01509 601201; Brookside Cottage, 133 Tickow Lane, Shepshed, Loughborough LE12 9EY Tel: 01509 502763 Fax: 01509 502763 — BM BCh 1961 Oxf.; MA Oxf. 1961; MFFP 1993; Dip. Clin. Hypn. Sheff. 1992. (Oxf.) Socs: Accred. Mem. Brit. Soc. Med. & Dent. Hypn. Prev: SHO (ENT & Paediat.) Ashford Hosp.; Ho. Surg. Radcliffe Infirm. Oxf.; Ho. Off. (O & G) Horton Gen. Hosp. Banbury.

JOHN, Benjamin Hollins Park Hospital, Warrington WA2 8WA Tel: 01925 664000 Fax: 01925 235346 — MB BS Singapore 1968; FRCPsych 1989, M 1972; T(Psych) 1991; DPM Eng. 1971. (Singapore) Cons. Psychiat. Warrington Community Healthcare (NHS) Trust. Prev: Mem. Brit. Soc. Med. & Dent. Hypn. (Chairm. Lancs. & Chesh. Br.); Cons. Psychiat. N. Wales Hosp. Denbigh.; Lect. (Psychol. Med.) Univ. Liverp.

JOHN, Catherine Elizabeth Herbert 1 Thrifts Mead, Theydon Bois, Epping CM16 7NF — MB BS 1983 Lond.; MRCGP 1988; DFFP 1993; DRCOG 1986; Cert. Family Plann. JCC 1986. (Lond. Hosp. Med. Coll.) Clin. Med. Off. - Lond. Brook Advis. Serv. - Well Woman Centre Eliz. Garrett Anderson Hosp. - Mortimer Market Dept. of Genitourin. Med. Lond. Prev: GP Wadebridge, Cornw.

JOHN, Christopher Digby St Davids Clinic, Bellevue Terrace, Newport NP20 2LB Tel: 01633 251133 Fax: 01633 221096 Email: chris@stdavids; 10 Woodville Road, Newport NP20 4JB Tel: 01633 262015 — MB BS 1972 Lond.; MRCGP 1977; DCH Eng. 1975. (charing Cross)

JOHN, Christopher Leighton Furnace House Surgery, St. Andrews Road, Carmarthen SA31 1EX Tel: 01267 236616 Fax: 01267 222673 Email: cjohn@doctors.org.uk; Pengelli Isaf, Llangain, Carmarthen SA33 5BB — MB BS 1973 Lond.; MRCS Eng. LRCP Lond. 1973; MRCGP 1981. (Char. Cross)

JOHN, Mr Christopher Richard 17 Severnake Close, Timbre Wharf, Westferry Road, London E14 9WE — MB BS 1988 Lond.; FRCS Eng. 1992. Regist. (Vasc. Surg.) King's Coll. Hosp. Lond.

JOHN, David Durairatnam Merchiston Surgery, Highworth Road, Swindon SN3 4BF Tel: 01793 823307 Fax: 01793 820923 — BM 1992 Soton.; MRCGP 1996; DCH RCP Lond. 1995; DRCOG 1995; DFFP 1995. (Univ. Soton. Med. Sch.) GP Swindon. Socs: BMA. Prev: GP Regist./SHO P.ss Margt. Hosp. Swindon VTS.

JOHN, Mr David Gareth — MB BS 1981 Lond.; 1977 BSc (Hons.) Lond.; 1996 FRCS Ed.; 1980 MRCS Eng. LRCP Lond. (UCH Lond.) Cons. ENT Surg. Poole Hosp. NHS Trust. Prev: Sen. Regist. (Otolaryngol.) Univ. Hosp. Wales Cardiff & Singleton Hosp. Swansea; Lect. (Otolaryngol.) Chinese Univ., Hong Kong.

JOHN, David Howard Hillcrest Farm, Sandford Road, Winscombe BS25 — MB BS 1980 Lond.; MRCGP 1987; DRCOG 1985; DCH RCP Lond. 1983.

JOHN, David William St Davids Clinic, Bellevue Terrace, Newport NP20 2LB Tel: 01633 251133 Fax: 01633 221096; Stonecroft, 1 Edward VII Lane, Newport NP20 4NL Tel: 01633 253020 Fax: 01633 221096 — MB BS 1966 Lond.; DRCOG 1968.

JOHN, Mr Edward Leighton (retired) coednor, llangain, Carmarthen SA33 5AE — MB BS 1943 Lond.; FRCS Ed. 1946; MRCS Eng. LRCP Lond. 1943. Cons. Surg. Neath Gen. Hosp. & W. Glam. HA. Prev: Sen. Regist. Llandough Hosp. Cardiff.

JOHN, Emily Brenda (retired) Nargate Street, Littlebourne, Canterbury CT3 1 — MB BS 1953 Lond.; MRCS Eng. LRCP Lond. 1952; MFCM 1974; DPH Eng. 1967. Prev: Dist. Community Phys. Canterbury & Thanet Health Dist.

JOHN, Eva Gwynedd (retired) The Old Rectory, Langton Matravers, Swanage BH19 3HB — MB ChB 1926 Ed. Prev: Med. Off. Div. 8 LCC.

JOHN, George Medical Director, Godden Green Clinic, Godden Green, Sevenoaks TN15 0JR Tel: 01732 763491 Fax: 01732 673160 Email: dicgjohn@aol.com; Mangalam, St. George's Road, Bickley, Bromley BR1 2LD Tel: 020 8467 8625 Fax: 020 8402 2263 Email: docgjohn@aol — MB BS 1974 Mysore; MRCPsych 1977. (Kasturba Med. Coll.) Med. Dir. & Cons. Psychiat. Godden Green Clinic; Cons. Psychiat. ThamesGatewayNHS Trust; Hon. Research Fell. Inst. Psychiat. Socs: Fell. Linnean Soc. Lond.; Corr. Fell. Amer. Psychiat. Assn. Prev: Cons. & Chairm. Div. Psychiat. Dartford & Gravesham HA; Sen. Regist. (Psychol. Med.) St. Thos. Hosp. Lond.; Regist. Regional Addict. Unit, Mapperley Hosp. Nottm.

JOHN, Gwylfa Idloes (retired) Malthouse Farm, Hoggs Lane, Purton, Swindon SN5 4HQ Tel: 01793 770659 Email: gwylfa@lineone.net — MB BS 1958 Lond.; MRCS Eng. LRCP Lond. 1958. EMP Benefits Agency; Surg. Simon clinic Swindon Wilts. Prev: Ho. Surg. & Ho. Phys. Dulwich Hosp.

JOHN, Herbert Hugh, OBE, CStJ (retired) West Hay, 1 Sandy Lane, Petersham, Richmond TW10 7EW Tel: 020 8940 4020 — MB

BChir 1955 Camb.; MA Camb. 1956; MRCS Eng. LRCP Lond. 1955; FFPHM RCP (UK) 1989; FFCM 1973; DCH Eng. 1962; DPH Eng. 1961; DObst RCOG 1960. Prev: Med. Off. Health City & Port of Lond. & Hon. Cons. Pub. Health Med. City & Hackney HA.

JOHN, Ian Frederick Tel: 01642 471388 Fax: 01642 488701; 19 Wheatlands Park, Redcar TS10 2PD Tel: 01642 474771 — MB BS 1969 Newc.; MRCGP 1973. Diabetic GP Specialist for Langbaurgh PCG, 13 Pk. Avenue, Redcar.

JOHN, Joshy St. Albans City Hospital, Waverley Road, St Albans AL3 5PN Tel: 01727 897577 Fax: 01727 897577 — MD 1981 Sheff.; BSc Kerala 1959, MB BS 1966. (Med. Coll. Trivandrum) Cons. Phys. Genitourin. Med. St. Albans City Hosp; Hon. Cons. Chelsea & W.minter Hopsital Lond. Socs: Med. Soc. Study VD & Internat. Union against VD & Treponematoses. Prev: Cons. Phys. Genitourin. Med. St. Mary's Hosp. Luton; Cons. Venereol. Derbysh. Roy. Infirm. Derby & Chesterfield Roy. Hosp.; Hon. Lect. Acad. Div. Med. Univ. Sheff.

JOHN, Kochummen Thams View Health Centre, Bastable Avenue, Barking IG11 0LG Tel: 020 8594 1061 Fax: 020 8594 2184 — MB BS 1974 Karnatak, India; MRCS Eng. LRCP Lond. 1980.

JOHN, Lawrence Howard 47 Warlters Close, London N7 0SA — MB BS 1997 Lond.

JOHN, Mr Lindsay Clive Howard 4 Clifton Hill Studios, 95A Clifton Hill Road, London NW8 0JP — MB BS 1981 Lond.; MS Lond. 1993; BSc (Hons.) Lond. 1978; FRCS (Cth.) 1993; FRCS Eng. 1985; MRCS Eng. LRCP Lond. 1981; MD Lond. 2000. Cons. Cardiothoracic Surg. King's Coll. Hosp. Lond.

JOHN, Louise Margret 15 Nettlecombe, Agar Grove, London NW1 9SN — MB BS 1994 Lond.; BSc Lond. 1991. SHO (A & E) Watford Gen. Hosp. Prev: Ho. Off. (Surg. & Orthop.) Qu. Eliz. II Hosp. Welwyn Garden City; Ho. Off. (Med. & c/o Elderly) Hemel Hempstead Gen. Hosp. Herts.

JOHN, Margaret Emanuel (retired) Dan-y-Castell, Church St., Llantrisant, Pontyclun CF72 8EU Tel: 01443 223321 — LRCP LRCS Ed. LRFPS Glas. 1948; MRCPsych 1971; DPM Eng. 1955. Prev: Cons. Child Psychiat. E. Glam. Area.

JOHN, Martin Hugh Fairfield Surgery, 1 Park Crescent, Llanelli SA15 3AE Tel: 01554 773133 Fax: 01554 777559 — MB ChB 1963 Birm.; MRCS Eng. LRCP Lond. 1963. (Birm.) Prev: SHO (Obst.) Mt. Pleasant Hosp. Swansea; Ho. Phys. & Ho. Surg. Morriston Hosp. Swansea.

JOHN, Martin Richard Doctors Surgery, Townhead Road, Dalston, Carlisle CA5 7PZ Tel: 01228 710451 Fax: 01228 711898 — MB ChB 1984 Manchester; MB ChB Manch. 1984. (Manchester) GP Carlisle.

JOHN, Melvyn Edward The Landscape Surgery, High Street, Garstang, Preston PR3 1FA Tel: 01995 603355 Fax: 01995 601810; Maes-y-Dderwen, 4 Acorn Bank, Garstang, Preston PR3 1LP — MB ChB 1985 Liverp. (Liver.) Prev: Trainee GP Gt. Eccleston Preston VTS; SHO (Psychiat.) Blackpool, Wyre & Fylde HA.

JOHN, Mildred The Studio Cottage, Winkford Grange, Witley, Godalming GU8 5PR Tel: 01428 682121 — MRCS Eng. LRCP Lond. 1933. (Cardiff)

JOHN, Nia Elisabeth 35 St John's Crescent, Whitchurch, Cardiff CF14 7AF Tel: 029 2062 1696 Email: alun.john@virgin.net — MB BCh 1990 Wales; MRCP (UK) 1996; MRCGP 1994; DRCOG 1993. (Univ. Wales Coll. of Med.) Specialist Regist. (Paediat.) Roy. Gwent Hosp. Newport. Prev: Sen. SHO (Paediat.) Newport.

JOHN, Nicholas Griffiths 53 Meadowside Drive, Whitchurch, Bristol BS14 0NR Tel: 0117 983 6601; 5/108 Macquarie Street, St Lucia, Brisbane Qld 4067, Australia Tel: 017 371 3060 — MB ChB 1988 Bristol. Regist. (Gen. Med.) P.ss Alexandra Hosp. Woolloongabba, Qu.sland, Austral. Socs: BMA; Austral. Med. Assn. Prev: Regist. (Gen. Med.) & SHO (Gen. Surg. & Urol.) Gold Coast Hosp. Qu.sland, Austral.; SHO (Gen. Med. & Geriat.) Ronkswood Hosp. Worcester; Ho. Off. (Med.) QE II Hosp. Brisbane, Austral.

JOHN, Percy Austin (retired) 5 Towy Road, Llanishen, Cardiff CF14 0NS Tel: 01222 756555 — MB BCh 1954 Wales; MB BCh; BSc, DPH Wales 1966; MFCM 1972. Prev: Cons. Pub. Health Med. Mid. Glam. NHS Ambul. Trust.

JOHN, Peter David Lawrence (retired) 8 Oakleigh Gardens, Whetstone, London N20 9AB — MB BCh 1961 Wales; BA Wales 1951; Cert. JCC Lond. 1973; DPM Eng. 1966. Prev: Sen. Regist. (Psychiat.) Napsbury Hosp., & Qu. Charlotte's Hosp. & Chelsea Hosp. Wom. Lond.

JOHN, Philip Rowland Radiology Department, Birmingham Children's Hospital, Steelhouse Lane, Birmingham B4 6NH Tel: 0121 333972 Fax: 0121 333 9726 Email: philip.john@bhamchildrens.wmids.nhs.uk; 3 Foxhill Barns, Foxhill Lane, Alvechurch, Birmingham B48 7BY Tel: 0121 447 7583 Fax: 0121 445 2425 Email: pjohn@netcomuk.co.uk — MB ChB 1978 Liverp.; FRCR 1987; DCH RCPS Glas. 1982. (Liverp.) Cons. Paediat. Radiol. Birm. Childr. Hosp. Socs: Fell. Roy. Coll. Radio.; Brit. Soc. Interven. Radiol.; Assoc. Mem. UK Childr. Cancer Study Gp. Prev: Sen. Regist. (Paediat. Radiol.) Melbourne Childr. Hosp., Austral.; Sen Regist. & Regist. (Radiol.) Sheff. HA.

JOHN, Richard Alexander Stonecoft, 1 Edward VII Lane, Newport NP20 4NL — MB BS 1993 Lond.

JOHN, Robert Edward Broom Close Farm, Pinfold Hill, Curbar, Calver, Hope Valley S32 3YL — BM BCh 1980 Oxf.; MRCP 1985. Regist. (anaesth.) Soton. Gen. hosp.; Fell. (Anaesthesiol.) Childrs. Hosp. Denver Colorado.

JOHN, Robert Ian 87 Courtlands Avenue, London SE12 8JJ — BChir 1991 Camb.

JOHN, Roger William (retired) 11 Silverdale Road, Yealand Redmayne, Carnforth LA5 9TA Tel: 01524 781669 — MB BS 1960 Lond.; FRCP Lond. 1979, M 1965; MRCS Eng. LRCP Lond. 1959; DObst RCOG 1961; DCH Eng. 1963. Prev: Cons. Paediat. Roy. Lancaster Infirm.

JOHN, Ronald Bryn Briton Ferry Health Centre, Hunter Street, Briton Ferry, Neath SA11 2SF Tel: 01639 813272 Fax: 01639 813019 — LRCPI & LM, LRCSI & LM 1970; FRCGP 1996, M 1977; DObst RCOG 1973. (Roy. Coll. Surgs. Irel.) Socs: BMA (Chairm. Welsh Counc.); Ex Chairm. BMA Welsh Counc.; Ex Chairm. BMA WGPC. Prev: Chairm. Welsh Med. Comm.

JOHN, Tania Carolyn Berry Bank, Berry Head Road, Brixham TQ5 9AQ — BM 1995 Soton.

JOHN, Terry Martin Firs Surgery, Stephenson Road, London E17 7JT Tel: 020 8520 9286 Fax: 020 8521 1751 — MB ChB 1975 Birm. (Birmingham) GP Trainer Lond.; GP Tutor Roy. Free Hosp. & Qu. Mary W.field Med. Schs. Socs: Fell. Roy. Soc. Med.; (Vice Pres.) Afr. Caribbean Med. Soc.; GP's Comm. BMA. Prev: Chairm. Redbridge & Waltham Forest LMC.

JOHN, Thelma Marie 5 Park Drive, Littleover, Derby DE23 6FY Tel: 01332 760994 — MB BS 1968 Madras. (Jawaharlal Inst. Postgrad. Med. Pondicherry) Regist. (Psychiat.) Pastures Hosp. Mickleover.

JOHN, Mr Timothy Glyn Oak Lodge, 39 Pyotts Copse, Old Basing, Basingstoke RG24 8WE — MB BCh 1987 Wales; FRCS (Gen.) 1996; FRCS Ed. 1991. (Univ. Wales Coll. Med. Cardiff) Sen. Regist. (Surg.) Roy. Infirm. Edin.; Lect. (Surg.) Univ. Edin. Socs: Internat. Hepato Pancreato Biliary Assn.

JOHN, William Robert Brangwyn Newlands, Stockcross, Newbury RG20 8LL Tel: 0148838 680 — MRCS Eng. LRCP Lond. 1970. (Guy's) Asst. Med. Dir. Bristol-Myers Squibb. Prev: Regional Dir. Clin. Research Squibb (Europe); Surg. Lt.-Cdr. RN, PMO Commando Train. Centre Roy. Marines Lympstone; Sen. Med. Off. HMS Fife.

JOHNMAN, Lewis, CBE, TD, OStJ (retired) 2 Cullinpark Grove, Strathaven ML10 6EN Tel: 01357 523005 Fax: 01357 523005 — MB ChB (Commend.) Glas. 1956; MRCGP 1976; DObst RCOG 1961. Med. Off. Scott. Co-op. Prev: Territorial Army Adviser to Dir. Gen. Army Med. Servs.

JOHNMIAN, Catherine Janette 25 North British Road, Glasgow G71 7AG — MB ChB 1995 Glas.

JOHNPULLE, Antoninus Felician Sugitharaj Glenmanor Avenue Surgery, 69 Glenmanor Avenue, Moodiesburn, Glasgow G69 0LB Tel: 0141 787 2276; 15 Myvot Road, Condorrat, Cumbernauld, Glasgow G67 4NA — MB BS 1971 Rajasthan. (S.M.S. Med. Coll. Jaipur)

JOHNS, Mr Adam Martin The Burton Clinic, Queens Hospital Burton, Belverdere Road, Burton-on-Trent DE13 0RB Tel: 01283 566333; The White House, Lount Lane, Anslow, Burton-on-Trent DE13 9QS — MB 1969 Camb.; BChir 1968; FRCS Eng. 1973. (Oxf.) Cons. Orthop. Surg. Burton Dist. Hosp. Centre. Socs: Fell. Brit. Soc. Surg. of Hand.; Fell. BOA. Prev: Sen. Regist. (Orthop.) Cardiff Roy. Infirm.

JOHNS, Mr Andrew Norman Glengyle, 16 Bower Mount Road, Maidstone ME16 8AU Tel: 01622 692154 Fax: 01622 209480 — MB BChir 1973 Camb.; MA Camb. 1973; FRCS Eng. 1977. (Camb. & Guy's) Cons. ENT Surg. Maidstone & Tunbridge Wells NHS Trust, Kent & Sussex Hosp., Tunbridge Wells, Kent; Cons. ENT Surg. Kent Co. Ophth. & Aural Hosp., Maidstone, Kent. Prev: Sen. Regist. (ENT) St. Thos. Hosp. Lond. & Hosp. Sick Childr. Gt. Ormond St.; Regist. (ENT Surg.) Guy's Hosp. Lond.

JOHNS, Andrew Robert Professorial Unit, Broadmoor Hospital, Crowthorne RG45 7EG Tel: 01344 754119 Fax: 01344 754334; Department Forensic Psychiatry, Institute of Psychiatry, De Crespigny Park, London SE5 8AF Tel: 020 7919 3122 Fax: 020 7277 0283 — MB BS 1978 London; MB BS Lond. 1978; BSc (Hons.) Lond. 1975; MRCS Eng. LRCP Lond. 1978; FRCPsych 1996, M 1983; Dip. Forens. Psychiat. (Distinc.) Inst. Psychiat. 1997. (Univ. Lond. (Guy's)) Sen. Lect. (Forens . Psychiat.) Inst. Psychiat. Lond.; Hon. Cons. Forens. Psychiat. BRd.moor Hosp. Crowthorne; Hon. Cons. Psychiat. Roy. Bethlem Maudsley Hosp. Socs: Soc. Study of Addic.; Medico-Legal Soc. Prev: Sen. Lect. (Psychiat. Addic. Behaviour) St. Geo. Med. Sch. Lond.; Sen. Regist. & Regist. (Psychiat.) Bethlem Roy. & Maudsley Hosp. Lond.

JOHNS, Christopher Julian Charles Sketty Surgery, De la Beche Road, Sketty, Swansea SA2 9EA Tel: 01792 206862 — MB BS 1985 Lond.; DRCOG 1989.

JOHNS, Mr David Langstone Woodgate House, 43 High St., Maxey, Peterborough PE6 9EE — MB BS 1961 Lond.; FRCS Eng. 1966; MRCS Eng. LRCP Lond. 1962. (Univ. Coll. Hosp.) Cons. Orthop. Surg. PeterBoro. Dist. Hosp. Socs: Fell. Brit. Orthop. Assn. Prev: Sen. Orthop. Regist. Roy. Nat. Orthop. Hosp. Stanmore; Chief Asst. Orthop. Dept. St. Bart. Hosp. Lond.; Surg. Regist. Univ. Coll. Hsop. Lond.

JOHNS, Emily Anne Kings Healthcare NHS Trust, Kings College Hospital, Denmark Hill, London SE5 Tel: 020 7737 4000; 13 Breakspeare, 94 College Road, Dulwich, London SE21 7NB — BM BCh 1996 Oxf. SHO Gen. Med. Rotat.

JOHNS, Gwyn 83 Holywell Avenue, Whitley Bay NE26 3AG — MB BCh 1959 Wales; FFA RCS Eng. 1968. (Cardiff) Cons. Anaesth. N. Tyneside AHA. Socs: Founder Mem. I.A.S.P. Prev: Regist. in Anaesth. United Cardiff Hosps.

JOHNS, Helen Valmai Crofton Health Centre, Slack Lane, Crofton, Wakefield WF4 1HJ Tel: 01924 369413; 87 Cumbrian Way, Lupset Park, Wakefield WF2 8JS Tel: 01924 369413 — MB ChB 1987 Leeds; DRCOG 1991. (Leeds) Prev: Trainee GP Wakefield VTS.

JOHNS, Jemma Flat 4, 130 Crouch Hill, London N8 9DY — MB BS 1994 Lond. (Univ. Coll. Lond. Med. Sch.) SHO (O & G) Roy. Hosps. NHS Trust. Prev: Ho. Off. (Surg.) Whittington Hosp. Lond.

JOHNS, Jennifer 88 Nightingale Lane, London SW12 8NR Tel: 020 8673 3122 Fax: 020 8675 3859 Email: m.j.johns@dial.pipex.com — MB BS 1962 Lond.; DObst RCOG 1964. (Char. Cross) Clin. Asst. (Psychother.) Univ. Coll. Hosp. Lond. Socs: Brit. Psychoanal. Soc. Prev: Ho. Phys. & Ho. Surg. Mt. Vernon Hosp. N.wood; Ho. Surg. Kingsbury Matern. Hosp.; Ho. Phys. (Paediat.) Char. Cross Hosp. Lond.

JOHNS, Marcus Eddie David 28 Devonshire Place, London W1N 1PE Tel: 020 722 44981; 88 Nightingale Lane, London SW12 8NR Tel: 020 8673 3122 Fax: 020 8675 3859 Email: m.j.johns@dial.pipex.com — MB BS 1962 Lond.; FRCPsych 1983, M 1971; DPM Eng. 1967. (Char. Cross) Acting Director Lond. Clinic. Psychoanal. Socs: Brit. Psychoanal. Soc.; Roy. Soc. Med. Prev: Cons. Psychiat. Tavistock Clinic & Daleham Gdns. Day Unit Lond.; Cons. Psychiat. Child Guid. Train. Centre Lond.; Sen. Regist. Dept. for Childr. & Parents Tavistock Clinic Lond.

JOHNS, Michael Spring Cottage, 2 North Stroud Lane, Petersfield GU32 3PP — MB BCh 1984 Wales; MRCGP 1989; DFFP 1995; DRCOG 1988.

JOHNS, Nina Marie Flat 5, 11 Charlotte St., Bristol BS1 5PX — MB ChB 1997 Bristol.

JOHNS, Nora Maitland (retired) La Burne Millaire, Rue a L'Or, St Peter Port, Guernsey — MB BS 1926 Lond.; MRCS Eng. LRCP Lond. 1924. Prev: Asst. Sch. Med. Off. Essex CC & Asst. Med. Off. Roy. E. Cos. Hosp.

JOHNS, Norah Gertrude (retired) 11 College Gardens, Dulwich, London SE21 7BE Tel: 020 8693 2801 — MB BS 1939 Lond.; MRCS Eng. LRCP Lond. 1939. Prev: SCMO Family Plann. Servs. Merton & Sutton HA.

JOHNS, Peter Frederick Sketty Surgery, De La Beche Road, Sketty, Swansea SA2 9EA Tel: 01792 206862 Fax: 01972 280158; Acorn Lodge, 261 Gower Road, Sketty, Swansea SA2 7AA Tel: 01792 296744 — MB ChB 1954 Sheff. (Sheff.) Med. Off. G. C. B. S. Trinity Ho. Serv. & Insp.ate OIS, Unit Superheaters Min. of Transport Swansea. Prev: Regist. (Med.) Swansea Gen. Hosp.; RAMC; Ho. Phys. & Ho. Surg. Sheff. Roy. Infirm.

JOHNS, R G Avenue Medical Practice, 7 Reney Avenue, Sheffield S8 7FH Tel: 0114 237 7649.

JOHNS, Robin Howard 31/2FL India Street, Edinburgh EH3 6HE — MB ChB 1997 Ed.

JOHNS, Sandra Reid Cefn Coed Hospital, Cockett, Swansea SA2 0GH — MB BCh 1978 Wales. Cons. Psychiat. Cefn Coed Hosp. Swansea.

JOHNS, Walter Anthony Orchard Farm, St. Catherine, Bath BA1 8HA Tel: 01225 858795 & profess. Bitton 322108 — MB BS 1959 Lond.; MRCS Eng. LRCP Lond. 1959; DObst RCOG 1960. (Univ. Coll. Hosp.)

JOHNSON, Alan David c/o Queen's Road Medical Practice, Queen's Road Medical Centre, St Peter Port, Guernsey GY1 1RH — MB ChB 1984 Birm.; MRCGP 1994; DObst Otago 1989; DA (UK) 1986.

JOHNSON, Alan David Shore Alma Road Surgery, Alma Road, Romsey SO51 8ED Tel: 01794 513422 Fax: 01794 518668 — MB BS 1958 Lond.; DObst RCOG 1960. (Middlx.) Prev: Ho. Surg. Middlx. Hosp.

JOHNSON, Alan Frederick 26 Milton Avenue, Eaton Ford, St Neots, Huntingdon PE19 7LE — MB BS 1964 Lond.; MSc (Occupat. Med.) Lond. 1985; MRCS Eng. LRCP Lond. 1964; MRCGP 1977; AFOM RCP Lond. 1982; DAvMed Eng. 1979; DObst RCOG 1967. (Lond. Hosp.) Civil. Med. Pract. MoD. Socs: Soc. Occupat. Med. Prev: Med. Off. RAF.

JOHNSON, Alan George Melvin Hetton Group Practice, Hetton Medical Centre, Francis Way, Hetton-le-Hole, Houghton-le-Spring DH5 9EZ Tel: 0191 526 1177 Fax: 0191 517 3859; Carmont, Mount Pleasant, Houghton-le-Spring DH5 8AQ Tel: 0191 584 3965 — MB BS 1971 Newc.

JOHNSON, Professor Alan Godfrey University Surgical Unit, Royal Hallamshire Hospital, Glossop Road, Sheffield S10 2JF Tel: 0114 271 2025 Fax: 0114 271 3791 Email: a.g.johnson@sheffield.ac.uk; Broom Lawn, Stumperlowe Lane, Fulwood, Sheffield S10 3QQ Tel: 0114 230 5524 Fax: 0114 230 9698 — MB BChir 1963 Camb.; MChir Camb. 1972; FRCS Eng. 1967. (Univ. Coll. Hosp.) Prof. Surg. Univ. Sheff.; Hon. Cons. Surg. Roy. Hallamsh. Hosp. Sheff.; Pres. Nat. Ass. Theatre Nurses; Chairm. Standing Med. Advis. Comm. To Sec. State Health. Socs: Fell. (Ex-Pres.) Assn. Surgs. GB & Irel.; Hon. Fell. Amer. Surgic. Assn.; Brit. Soc. Gastroenterol. Prev: Reader (Surg.) Univ. Lond.; Regist. (Surg.) Redhill Gen. Hosp.; Ho. Phys. & Ho. Surg. Univ. Coll. Hosp. Lond.

JOHNSON, Alan Montague (retired) Sitcott House, St Giles-on-the-Heath, Launceston PL15 9SD — MB BS Lond. 1946; MRCS Eng. LRCP Lond. 1946; MD Lond. 1953; FRCP Lond. 1967, M 1952. Prev: Cons. Cardiol. Wessex RHA.

JOHNSON, Mr Alan Philip ENT Department, Queen Elizabeth Hospital, Edgbaston, Birmingham B15 2TH Tel: 0121 627 2294; Wordley Farm, Dunley, Stourport-on-Severn DY13 0UT Tel: 01299 896344 — MB ChB 1974 Ed.; BSc Ed. 1971; FRCS (Orl.) Eng. 1982; FRCS Ed. 1979. (Ed.) Cons. ENT Qu. Eliz. Hosp. Birm. Prev: Sen. Regist. (ENT) St. Bart. Hosp. Lond.

JOHNSON, Air Vice Marshal Alan Taylor, Air Vice-Marshal RAF Med. Br. Retd. Hoo Cottage, School Lane, Buckden, Huntingdon PE19 5TT — MB ChB Sheff. 1956; FFOM RCP Lond. 1994; MFCM 1974; DAvMed FOM RCP Lond. 1968. Cons. Occupat. Health Metrop. Police Serv. Lond. Socs: Fell. Roy. Soc. Med.; Camb. Med. Soc. - Vice Pres. Prev: Cons. Occupat. Med. & Dir. Occupat. Health Metrop. Police Lond.; Princip. Med. Off. RAF Strike Command; Asst. Surg. Gen. (Environm. Med. & Research) MoD.

JOHNSON, Alexander Thomas Market Harborough Medical Centre, 67 Coventry Road, Market Harborough LE16 9BX Tel: 01858 464242; 2 Holly Bank, Leicester Road, Market Harborough LE16 7AZ Tel: 01858 462479 — MB ChB 1966 Glas.; DObst RCOG 1972. (Glas.) Clin. Tutor (Gen. Pract.) Univ. Leic. Prev: Jun. Ho. Off.

Roy. Hosp. Sick Childr. Glas.; Med. Regist. S.. Gen. Hosp. Glas.; Sen. Ho. Surg. (Obst.) Vale of Leven Hosp. Alexandria.

JOHNSON, Alfred Thomas (retired) 34 Clarendon Park, Lymington SO41 8AX Tel: 01590 678424 — MB ChB 1945 Birm.; MRCS Eng. LRCP Lond. 1946; DA Eng. 1970; DObst RCOG 1951. Prev: GP Hall Green, Birm.

JOHNSON, Alice Helen 23 Patience Road, London SW11 2PY — MB ChB 1989 Bristol; MRCP 1993. Research Fell. in Paediat., St Geoges HMS Lond.

***JOHNSON, Alice Hilary** 4 Oakwood Rise, Roundhay, Leeds LS8 2QY — MB ChB 1994 Birm.

JOHNSON, Alison Parkfield Medical Centre, 255 Parkfield Road, Wolverhampton WV4 6EG Tel: 01902 342152 Fax: 01902 620868; 12 Foxlands Avenue, Wolverhampton WV4 5LX — MB BS 1987 Lond.; MRCGP 1993. Prev: Trainee GP Wolverhampton; SHO (Gen Med) New Cross Hosp. Wolverhampton.

JOHNSON, Alison Susan Hereford Public Health Laboratory, County Hospital, Hereford HR1 2ER Tel: 01432 277117 Fax: 01432 351396 — MB ChB 1988 Manch.; MSc 1995; MRCPath 1996. Cons. (Microbiol. & Communicable Dis. Control) Hereford Publ. Health Laborat. And Heref. Health Auth. Socs: Assn. Med. Microbiol.; Assn. Clin. Pathols.

JOHNSON, Andrea The Surgery, Much Birch, Hereford HR2 8HT Tel: 01981 540310 Fax: 01981 540748; 4 Stoney Row, Fownhope, Hereford HR1 4NJ — MB BCh 1991 Wales; MRCGP 1996; DRCOG 1994; DFFP 1994. (Univ. Wales Coll. Med. Cardiff)

JOHNSON, Andrew Beresford The Clementine Churchill Hospital, Sudbury Hill, Harrow HA1 3RX Tel: 0208 872 3899 Fax: 0208 872 3908 — MB BS 1982 Lond.; BSc Lond. 1979; MD Newc. 1994; FRCP (UK) 1985. Cons. Phys. (Diabetes & Endocrinol.) S.mead Hosp. Bristol. Socs: Diabetes UK; Europ. Assn. for the Study of Diabetes; Soc. for Endocrinol. Prev: Sen. Regist. (Diabetes & Endocrinol.) Nottm. & Derby Hosps.; Wellcome Train. Fell. (Med.) Univ. Newc. u. Tyne.

JOHNSON, Andrew Christopher 17 Peaknaze Close, Glossop SK13 6UN — MB ChB 1998 Manch.; MB ChB Manch 1998.

JOHNSON, Mr Andrew Duncan (retired) 1 Rosemary Lane, Haskayne, Ormskirk L39 7JP Tel: 01704 840707 Email: andron@globalnet.co.uk — MB ChB 1966 St. And.; FRCS Eng. 1973; FRCS Ed. 1973; DObst RCOG 1969. Chairm. S.port Ormskirk NHS Trust. Prev: Ho. Surg. & Ho. Phys. Dundee Roy. Infirm.

JOHNSON, Andrew Gordon 7 Dunmail Avenue, Blackpool FY3 9PQ — MB ChB 1992 Dundee.

JOHNSON, Andrew James Chest Clinic, Kent & Canterbury Hospital, Ethelbert Road, Canterbury CT1 3NG Tel: 01227 766877 Fax: 01227 783018 — MB BCh Wales 1969; FRCP Lond. 1991; MRCP (UK) 1973. Cons. Chest Phys. E. Kent Hosps. NHS Trust; Hon. Sen. Lect. Univ. of Kent at Canterbury 1998. Prev: Sen. Regist. (Med.) Lothian Health Bd.; Lect. Cardiothoracic Inst. Lond.; Regist. (Thoracic Med.) Brompton Hosp. Lond.

JOHNSON, Andrew John Dorset County Hospital, Princess St., Dorchester DT1 1TS Tel: 01305 263123; The Old Vicarage, Chaldon Herring, Dorchester DT2 8DN Tel: 01305 852885 — MB BS 1970 Lond.; MRCS Eng. LRCP Lond. 1970; FRCR 1978; DMRD Eng. 1976. (St. Bart.) Cons. Radiol. W. Dorset HA. Socs: Brit. Inst. Radiol.; Fell. Roy. Soc. Med. Prev: Surg. Cdr. RN.

JOHNSON, Andrew Michael The Health Centre, Station Road, Bawtry, Doncaster DN10 6RQ Email: andrewjohnson@gp-c84101.nhs.uk; Merrymeade, Martin Lane, Bawtry, Doncaster DN10 6NJ — MB BS 1975 Lond. (Lond. Hosp.) Chairm. Doctors Accid. Rescue Team S. Yorks. Socs: Doncaster Med. Soc. & BASICS. Prev: Ho. Phys. & Ho. Surg. Doncaster Roy. Infirm.

JOHNSON, Ann Elizabeth (retired) Breast Study Centre, Mount Vernon Hospital, Northwood HA6 2RN Tel: 01923 844502 Fax: 01923 844258 Email: annjohnson@doctors.org.uk — MB BS 1956 Lond.; FRCS Eng. 1960; FRCR 1975; DMRT Eng. 1965. p/t Hon. Cons. Surg. Oncol. BrE. Study Centre Mt. Vernon Hosp. N.wood.

JOHNSON, Ann Frances Northgate Surgery, Church Street, Uttoxeter ST14 8AG Tel: 01889 562010 Fax: 01889 568948 — MB BS 1986 Lond.; MRCGP 1992; DLO RCS Eng. 1990; DRCOG 1991.

JOHNSON, Anna Lindesay Mary The Old Barn, Godwell Lane, Ivybridge PL21 0LT Tel: 01752 894076 — MB ChB 1984 Manch.; FRCA 1990. Cons. Anaesth. Derriford Hosp. Plymouth. Prev: Sen. Regist. (Anaesth.) Hammersmith Hosp. Lond.; Regist. Rotat. (Anaesth.) Bloomsbury & Islington Lond.

JOHNSON, Professor Anne Mandall Department of Primary Care & Population Science, Royal Free & Univ. College Medical School, Royal Free Campus, Rowland Hill St., London NW3 2PF Tel: 020 7472 6138 Fax: 020 7794 1224 Email: a,johnson@peps.ucl.ac.uk — MB BS 1978 Newc.; F Med Sci 2001; MSc Lond. 1984; MA Camb. 1979; MD Newc. 1992; FFPHM RCP (UK) 1993; MFCM 1987; MRCGP 1982; MRCP 1999 (Hon). Prof. Epidemiol. Dept. Prim. Care Popul. Sci. Roy. Free & Univ. Coll. Med. Sch.m Lond.; Hon. Cons. (Pub. Health Med.) Camden & Islington Community NHS Trust. Prev: Reader (Epidemiol.) Dept. Genitourin. Med. Univ. Coll. Hosp. Med. Sch. Lond.; Lect. (Genitourin. Med.) Middlx. Hosp. Med. Sch.; Sen. Regist. (Community Med.) Bloomsbury HA.

JOHNSON, Annette Mary 11 Windsor Close, Stone ST15 0LD — MB ChB 1994 Liverp.

JOHNSON, Anthony Edward Staveleigh Medical Centre, King Street, Stalybridge SK15 2AE Tel: 0161 304 8009 Fax: 0161 303 7207; The Moorlands, 133 Stocks Lane, Stalybridge SK15 2NU Tel: 0161 338 2423 — BM BCh 1971 Oxf.; BA (Physiol.) Oxf. 1968, MA, BM BCh 1971. (Oxf.)

JOHNSON, Anthony Owen Carveth Chest Unit, Pontefract General Infirmary, Pontefract WF8 1PL Tel: 01977 606216 Email: owen.johnson@dial.pipex.com; Manor House, Village Green, High Ackworth, Pontefract WF7 7EJ Tel: 01977 690785 Fax: 01977 690785 — MB BCh 1982 Wales; MRCP (UK) 1988. Cons. Gen. & Chest Med. Pontefract Gen. Infirm. Socs: Brit. Thorac. Soc. Prev: Sen. Regist. (Gen. & Geriat. Med.) Leeds Gen. Infirm.; Regist. (Chest & Gen. Med.) Killingbeck Hosp. Leeds; SHO & Regist. (Med. & Anaesth.) S. Warks. Hosp.

JOHNSON, Barbara Innes Forge Cottage, 1 Sandy Lane, Taverham, Norwich NR8 6JP — MB ChB Ed. 1951; DObst RCOG 1954. Socs: Community Paediat. Staff Grade NW Anglia HA.

JOHNSON, Mrs Barbara Winifred (retired) The Old Mill House, Ewelme, Near Wallingford, Oxford OX10 6HE Tel: 01491 835608 — MRCS Eng. LRCP Lond. 1962. Prev: Assoc. Specialist (Blood Transfus. Serv.) John Radcliffe Hosp. Oxf.

JOHNSON, Benjamin Brackmuirhill Schoolhouse, Stonehaven AB39 2TT — MB ChB 1986 Aberd.

JOHNSON, Beryl Elizabeth Torridon, Ebrington, Chipping Campden GL55 6NL Tel: 01386 593362 — MB ChB 1953 Birm. (Birm.)

JOHNSON, Brenda May (retired) Orchard House, 11 Parsonage Fold, Beetham, Milnthorpe LA7 7RJ Tel: 015395 64278 — MB ChB 1950 Ed. Prev: GP Barnet.

JOHNSON, Mr Brian Frederick Hull Royal Infirmary, Anlaby Road, Hull HU3 2JZ; 36 West End, Swanland, North Ferriby HU14 3PE — MB BS 1980 Lond.; BSc (Hons.) Lond. 1976; MD Sheff. 1991; FRCS Eng. 1984; MRCS Eng. LRCP Lond. 1979. (Char. Cross) Cons. Vasc. Surg. Hull & E. Yorks. Hosps. (NHS) Trust; Intercollegiate Specialty Fell.sh. in Gen. Surg. Prev: Sen. Regist. (Gen. Surg.) Sheff. & Chesterfield Hosps.; Vasc. Fell. (Surg.) Univ. Washington Med. Sch. Seattle WA, USA; Transpl. Fell. & Lect. (Surg.) Univ. Sheff.

JOHNSON, Brian Morgan (retired) 103 Bryansford Road, Newcastle BT33 0LF Tel: 013967 22682 — MB BCh BAO 1948 Belf.

JOHNSON, Bridget Penelope Halesowen Health Centre, 14 Birmingham Street, Halesowen B63 3HL Tel: 0121 550 1010 Fax: 0121 585 0993 — MB ChB 1981 Birm.; MRCP (UK) 1984; DRCOG 1985.

JOHNSON, C David G (retired) Lynfield, Oxford Lane, Scremerston, Berwick-upon-Tweed TD15 2QQ — MRCS Eng. LRCP Lond. 1965; MFHom 1975; DObst RCOG 1967.

JOHNSON, Carole-Ann 85 Vesage Court, 8a Leather Lane, London EC1N 7RF — MB BS 1996 Lond.

JOHNSON, Caroline Ann Selden Medical Centre, 6 Selden Road, Worthing BN11 2LL Tel: 01903 234962 — MB ChB 1982 Leic.; Cert Family Plann 1984; MRCGP 1986; DRCOG 1984. GP. Prev: GP Trainee Chichester VTS; Clin. Asst. (Rheum.) Worthing Hosp.

JOHNSON, Caroline Jane 7 Bollin Court, Wilmslow SK9 2AP — MB ChB 1997 Leeds.

JOHNSON, Carolyn Mary (retired) Evergreen, 41 Chapel Lane, Hale Barns, Altrincham WA15 0AJ Tel: 0161 980 8840 — MSc

Manch. 1979; MB BS Durh. 1965. Dir. Serv. Plann. Centr. Manch. Healthcare NHS Trust. Prev: SCM (Health Care Plann.) Manch. AHA (T).

JOHNSON, Catharine Ann Glenridding Health Centre, Glenridding, Penrith CA11 0PD Tel: 01768 482383 Fax: 01768 482145 — MB ChB 1989 Liverp.; DFFP 1994; DRCOG 1995; MRCGP 1995; Dip Travel Medicine 1998. GP Princip. in Single Handed Pract. Job-Share.

JOHNSON, Charles Reginald Stockbridge Health Centre, 1 India Place, Edinburgh EH3 6EH Tel: 0131 225 9191; 1 East Fettes Avenue, Edinburgh EH4 1DN Tel: 0131 332 3910 — LRCP LRCS 1953 Ed.; LRCP LRCS Ed. LRFPS Glas. 1953. Hosp. Pract. Orthop. Dept. W.. Gen. Hosp. Edin.; Lect. Dept. Gen. Pract. Univ. Edin. Socs: BMA. Prev: Regist. Orthop. Dept. Roy. Infirm. Edin.; Ho. Surg. Roy. Infirm. Edin.; Ho. Surg. W. Gen. Hosp. Edin.

JOHNSON, Christina 28 Whitmore Road, Beckenham BR3 3NT — MB ChB 1990 Sheff.

JOHNSON, Christine White Oaks, 8 Holgate, Clifton Village, Nottingham NG11 8NH Tel: 0115 984 7829 — MB ChB 1984 Manch.; MRCGP 1988; DCH RCP Lond. 1987; DRCOG 1986. Lect. (Gen. Pract.) Nottm. Prev: Trainee GP W. Lancs. VTS; Ho. Phys. & Ho. Surg. Univ. Hosp. S. Manch.

JOHNSON, Christine Ann Rydon House, Cheddon Road, Taunton TA2 7AZ — MB ChB 1981 Leeds.

JOHNSON, Christopher James Hamilton Southmead Hospital, Westbury-on-Trym, Bristol BS10 5NB Tel: 0117 950 5050 Fax: 0117 959 5075; Hornbeam House, The Shrubbery, Frenchay Hill, Bristol BS16 1LU Tel: 0117 970 1561 Email: chrisjohnson1@compuserve.com — BM BCh 1977 Oxf.; MA Oxf. 1974; MD Aberd. 1981; FRCA Eng. 1983. (Oxf. Univ.) Cons. Anaesth. S.mead Hosp. Bristol. Prev: Med. Off. Brit. Antarctic Survey; Nuffield Dept. Anaesth. Radcliffe Infirm. Oxf.

JOHNSON, Christopher Paul Barrodger Cottage, Beith Road, Lochwinnoch PA12 4JX — MB ChB 1986 Liverp.

JOHNSON, Claire Elizabeth Mary Nightingale Surgery, Greatwall Drive, Romsey SO51 7QN — BM BCh Oxf. 1989; MA Oxf. 1989; MRCGP 1994; DCH RCP Lond. 1993; DRCOG 1992; DGM RCP Lond. 1991. (Oxf.) GP Retainer, Romsey.

JOHNSON, Clare Sian Peakes Farm Lodge, 50 Main St., Burrough on the Hill, Melton Mowbray LE14 2JQ — BM BS 1998 Nottm.; BM BS Nottm 1998.

JOHNSON, Mr Colin David University Surgical Unit, (816), Southampton General Hospital, Tremona Road, Southampton SO16 6YD Tel: 02380 796796 Fax: 02380 794020 Email: c.d.johnson@soton.ac.uk — MB BChir 1976 Camb.; MChir Camb. 1986; FRCS Eng. 1980. Reader & Hons. Cons. GI, Pancreatic & Biliary Surg. Univ. Hosp. Trust Soton. Socs: Pres. Pancreatic Assn. Gt. Britain & Irel.; Chairm. Pancreatic Sect. Brit. Soc. Gastroenterol. (ex-Sec. Pancreatic). Prev: Sen. Regist (Gen. Surg.) St. Stephen's & W.m. Hosps. Lond.; Regist. (Gen. Surg.) Frenchay Hosp. Bristol Roy. Infirm.; MRC Trav. Fell. INSERM Marseille, France.

JOHNSON, Cynthia Olusola 44B Kirkoswald Drive, Clydebank, Glasgow — MB BS 1984 Ahmadu Bello U. Nigeria.

JOHNSON, David 4 Park Way, Old Marston, Oxford OX3 0QH; Wyndways Farm, Flint Hill, Stanley DH9 9JQ — BM BCh 1992 Oxf.; MA Camb. 1989.

JOHNSON, David The Surgery, 16 Windsor Road, Chobham, Woking GU24 8NA Tel: 01276 857117 Fax: 01276 855668 — MB BS 1977 Lond.; BA York. 1969; DRCOG 1981; DCH Eng. 1980. Clin. Asst. (Gastroenterol.) St. Peter's Hosp. Chertsey. Prev: Trainee Gen. Pract. Chertsey VTS; Ho. Surg. St. Thos. Hosp. Lond.; Ho. Phys. St. Peter's Hosp. Chertsey.

JOHNSON, David Andrew Wellspring Medical Centre, Park Road, Risca, Newport NP11 6BJ Tel: 01633 612438 Fax: 01633 615958 — MB BCh 1979 Wales; MRCGP 1983; DRCOG 1982. Trainer (Gen. Pract.) Newport VTS. Prev: Trainee GP Newport VTS.

JOHNSON, David Barry Brecon Medical Group Practice, Ty Henry Vaughan, Bridge Street, Brecon LD3 8AH Tel: 01874 622121 Fax: 01874 623742; Park Mount, Cerrigcochion Lane, Brecon LD3 7NP — BSc (Hons. Physiol.) Ed. 1968, MB ChB 1971; MRCGP 1990; FRCOG 1993, M 1978; DA Eng. 1975; DObst 1974. Hosp. Pract. (Obst. & Gyn.) Brecon War Memor. Hosp. Socs: Brit. Soc. Colpos. & Cerv. Path.; Brit. Menopause Soc. Prev: Regist. (O & G) St. Mary's Hosp. Lond.; Ho. Off. (Surg.) Leith Hosp. Edin.; Ho. Off. (Med.) Roy. Infirm. Edin.

JOHNSON, MR David Paul Consultant Orttopadic Surgeon, St. Mary's Hospital, Upper Byrom Place, Clifton, Bristol BS8 1BP Tel: 0117 970 6655 Fax: 0117 970 6633 Email: sportsmed@orthopaedics.co.uk — MB ChB 1980 Manch.; MD Manch. 1990; FRCS (Orth.) Ed. 1989; FRCS Eng. 1984. (Manchester) Cons. Orthop. Surg. Chesterfield Hosp. & Bristol Orthop. Clinic. Socs: Hon. Mem. Amer. Assoc. Orthopaedic & Sports Med.; Internat. Knee Soc. & Internat. Arthroscopy Assn.; Brit. Assn. Surg. Knee. Prev: Sen. Regist. Univ. Bristol; Lect. & Research Fell. (Orthop.) Bristol Roy. Infirm.; Regist. (Orthop.) Nuffield Orthop. Centre Oxf.

JOHNSON, Mr David Sands North Manchester General Hospital, Dellaways Road, Manchester M8 5RB; 284 Worsley Road, Swinton, Manchester M27 0AG Tel: 0161 793 5354 Email: david johnson@nwota.demon.co.uk — MB ChB 1988 Manch.; BSc (Hons.) St. And. 1985; FRCS Eng. 1993. (St Andrews and Manchester) Specialist Regist. (Orthop.) N. W. Region (Manch. Deanery). Socs: Manch. Med. Soc.; Assoc. Mem. BOA; BMA. Prev: Specialist Regist. (Orthop.) Manch. Roy. Infirm., Rochdale Infirm. & Blackburn Roy. Infirm. & Tameside Gen. Hosp.;Stepping HICC Hosp.; Research Regist. Roy. Preston Hosp.; SHO Rotat. (Surg.) Univ. Hosp. S. Manch.

JOHNSON, David Thomas 50 St Vincent Crescent, Glasgow G3 8NG — MB ChB 1992 Aberd.

JOHNSON, Debra Christina Pinfold Health Centre, Field Road, Bloxwich, Walsall WS3 3JP Fax: 01922 775132; 210 Castlehill Road, Stonnall, Walsall WS9 9DB — MB ChB 1978 Manch.; MRCGP 1986. GP Bloxwich.

JOHNSON, Denise Margaret The Surgery, 60 Falcondale Road, Westbury-on-Trym, Bristol BS9 3JY Tel: 0117 962 3406 Fax: 0117 962 1404 — MB ChB Manch. 1968.

JOHNSON, Derek Anthony Norman 1 Beech Hill Road, Sheffield S10 2SA Tel: 0114 268 4242 Fax: 0114 266 3608 — MD Lond. 1976, MB BS 1966; MRCS Eng. LRCP Lond. 1966; FRCOG 1984, M 1971, DObst 1968. (Guy's) Cons. (O & G) Jessop Hosp. Wom. Sheff. Prev: Sen. Regist. (O & G) Roy. Free Hosp. Lond.; Res. Obst. Off. Camb. Matern. Hosp.; SHO (Surg.) Addenbrooke's Hosp. Camb.

JOHNSON, Derek Goddard (retired) Capeway, 8 Boswedden Terrace, St Just, Penzance TR19 7NF Tel: 01736 786388 — MB ChB 1960 Manch. Prev: GP Princip. Fleetwood, Lancs.

JOHNSON, Derek William (retired) Mesnes View Surgery, Mesnes St., Wigan WN1 1ST Tel: 01942 42350 — MRCS Eng. LRCP Lond. 1943. Exam. Med. Off. DSS Med. Bds. Prev: Med. Off. (Local) Civil Serv.

JOHNSON, Derrick Smeeton Cullentra, Sutherland Road, Longsdon, Stoke-on-Trent ST9 9QD — MB ChB 1939 Birm.

JOHNSON, Diana Sarah 10 Headingley Close, Exeter EX2 5UH — BM 1992 Soton.

JOHNSON, Donald Arthur Wheatley 14 St John Street, Manchester M3 4DZ Tel: 0161 834 2786 Fax: 01565 830544; Lyndhurst, Warrington Road, Mere, Knutsford WA16 0TE Tel: 01565 830188 Fax: 01565 830544 — LRCPI & LM, LRSCI & LM 1959; DPM 1970 Manch.; MD NUI 1980; MSc Manch. 1971; FRCPsych 1979, M 1972; DPM Eng. 1969; DObst RCOG 1964. (RCSI & Manch.) Hon. Cons. Psychiat. Univ. Hosp. S. Manch.; Hon. Lect. (Psychiat.) Univ. Manch.; JP. Socs: Fell. (Ex-Pres.) Manch. Med. Soc.; Founder Mem. Brit. Acad. Psychopharm.; Roy. Coll. Psychiat. (Ex-Chairm. & Convenor NW Div.). Prev: Regional Adviser (Psychiat.) NW HA & Health Dept.; Cons. Psychiat. N. Manch. Gen. Hosp.; Capt. RAMC.

JOHNSON, Donald Steven Brentwood, Sanquhar Road, Forres IV36 1DG — MB ChB 1998 Ed.; MB ChB Ed 1998.

JOHNSON, Douglas John Grenfell 17 Lucerne Road, Oxford OX2 7QB — MB ChB 1998 Sheff.; MB ChB Sheff 1998.

JOHNSON, Duncan Scott Flat 1, 63 Haven Lane, London W5 2HZ — MB BS 1995 Lond.

JOHNSON, Edward Stewart Ingenix International, Yorkstream House, St Ives Road, Maidenhead SL6 1QT Tel: 0162 877 8994 Fax: 01628 778430 Email: sjohnson@clinphatm.co.uk — MB BS 1966 Lond.; PhD Lond. 1964, BSc 1961; MRCS Eng. LRCP Lond. 1966. (St. Geo.) Sen.VP Med & Scientif. Affairs Ingenix Internat. Maidenhead; Emerit. Reader (Pharmacol.) Univ. Lond. Socs: Brit.

Pharm. Soc.; Physiol. Soc.; Brit. Med. Assn. Prev: Sen. Vice-Pres. Clin. R&D SmithKline Beecham Pharmaceuts.; Reader (Pharmacol.) King's Coll. Lond.; Med. Dir. Scherer DDS Swindon.

JOHNSON, Efunbowale Adeola 77 Wroughton Road, London SW11 6AS Email: efunj@aol.com — MB ChB 1986 Manch.; BSc St. And. 1983; DCH RCP Lond. 1994; MSc Community Paediat. Lond. 1997. (St Andrews Manchester) Regist. (Paediat.) St. Thos. Hosp. Lond. Socs: BMA; RSM; Assoc. Mem. RCPCH. Prev: SHO (Paediat.) Gt. Ormond St. & Qu. Eliz. Hosps. Lond.; SHO (Paediat. & Neonates) Hammersmith & Qu. Charlottes Hosp.

JOHNSON, Elaine Margaret Child Health Unit, Guardian House, Guardian St., Warrington WA5 1TP Tel: 01925 405714 Fax: 01925 405725 — MB ChB 1972 Manch.; DCH Eng. 1975; DObst RCOG 1975. Assoc. Specialist (Community Paediat.) Warrington Community NHS Trust. Socs: Foundat. Mem. Fac. Community Health.

JOHNSON, Elizabeth Ann Waterloo House Surgery, Waterloo House, 42-44 Wellington Street, Millom LA18 4DE Tel: 01229 772123 Fax: 01229 770556; Wood House, The Hill, Millom LA18 5HG Tel: 01229 770556 — MB ChB 1983 Liverp.; MRCGP 1987.

JOHNSON, Elizabeth Eirene (retired) Miles, Sea Bank Road, Chapel St Leonards, Skegness PE24 5QU Tel: 01754 72781 — MRCS Eng. LRCP Lond. 1941; DTM & H Lond 1953.

JOHNSON, Elizabeth Jane 2 Prospect Court, Thorner, Leeds LS14 3JW — MB BCh 1976 Wales; MBA Leeds 1992; MRCP (UK) 1981; FRCPath 1997, M 1988. (Welsh Nat. Sch. Med.)

JOHNSON, Elizabeth Noble Mingoed, Butteron Lane, Stroud GL5 2LX Tel: 01453 751237 Email: l.johnson@ dial.pipesc.com — MB BS 1976 Lond.; BSc Lond. 1973; MCOphth 1990; DO RCS Eng. 1980. Assoc. Specialist (Ophth.) Gloucester Roy. Hosp. Trust. Prev: Clin. Asst. (Ophth.) Cheltenham & Gloucester HAs.

JOHNSON, Emma Jane Tel: 0131 677 0739 — MB ChB 1986 Bristol; MRCP (UK) 1989; PhD Lond. 1997. (Univ. Bristol) p/t Specialist Regist. (Paediat.) S.E. Scotl. Socs: BMA; RCPCH; MDDUS. Prev: Leukaemia Research Fund Clin. Research Fell. Inst. Child Health & Gt. Ormond St. Lond.; Regist. (Paediat.) Roy. Childr. Hosp. Melbourne, Austral.; SHO (Paediat.) Hosp. for Sick Childr. Gt. Ormond St. Lond.

JOHNSON, Ena Patricia (retired) 11 Beacon Rise, Brittain's Lane, Sevenoaks TN13 2NJ Tel: 01732 453343 — MB BCh BAO 1951 Belf. Prev: Asst. Otford Med. Partnership.

JOHNSON, Ethel Barbara St Margarets Surgery, 29 Bridge Street, Bradford-on-Avon BA15 1BY Tel: 01225 863278 Fax: 01225 868648; 5 Chestnut Grove, Upper Westwood, Bradford-on-Avon BA15 2DQ Tel: 01225 865413 — MB ChB 1974 Aberd.; MRCGP 1978; DRCOG 1977. (Aberd.) Prev: Trainee GP Stirling VTS.

JOHNSON, Ethel Pattinson The Cedars, Meopham Court, Meopham, Gravesend DA13 0AA — MB BS Durh., 1934; DMRT Lond. 1951.

JOHNSON, Eunice Helen (retired) Littlecote, Oakhill Avenue, Pinner HA5 3DL Tel: 020 8868 5704 — MB BS Punjab 1944. Prev: Sen. Med. Off. Harrow Health Dist.

JOHNSON, Fiona Joan Gilbert Bain Hospital, Lerwick ZE1 0TB Tel: 01595 743000; Rafns, Upper Hillside, Gulberwick, Shetland ZE2 9JX — MB ChB 1982 Manch.; MRCP (UK) 1986. Cons. Phys. (Geriat.) Gilbert Bain Hosp. Lerwick. Socs: Brit. Geriat. Soc. Prev: Sen. Regist. & Research Regist. (Geriat.) Newc. Gen. Hosp.; Regist. (Gen. Med.) Durh., Hull & E. Yorks. HAs.

JOHNSON, Professor Francis Rea 11 Beacon Rise, Brittain's Lane, Sevenoaks TN13 2NJ Tel: 01732 453343 — MD 1949 Belf.; MB BCh BAO 1945. (Belf.) Emerit. Prof. Anat. Univ. Lond. Socs: Fell. Roy. Soc. Med.; Life Mem. Anat. Soc. Gt. Brit.; Brit. Soc. Gastroenterol. Prev: Prof. Anat. Lond. Hosp. Med. Coll.; Pre-Clin. Sub-Dean Lond. Hosp. Med. Coll.; Prof. Histol. Lond. Hosp. Med. Coll.

JOHNSON, Frank Curtis (retired) The Corner House, Leicester Road, Hinckley LE10 Tel: 01455 634683 — MB BS 1954 Lond.; MRCS Eng. LRCP Lond. 1953. Prev: GP Hinckley.

JOHNSON, Freda Mesnes View Surgery, Mesnes St., Wigan WN1 1ST Tel: 01942 45762; 113 Mesnes Road, Wigan WN1 2PJ Tel: 01942 42989 — MB BCh 1943 Wales; BSc, MB BCh Wales 1943. (Cardiff) Prev: Ho. Surg. Taunton & Som. Hosp.; Cas. Off. Roy. Gwent Hosp. Newport; Med. Off. Monsall Hosp. Manch.

JOHNSON, Gary Surgery, 75 Bank Street, Alexandria G83 0NB Tel: 01389 752626 Fax: 01389 752169; 20 Upper Glenfinlas Street, Helensburgh G84 7HD Tel: 01436 679991 Fax: 01436 679991 Email: 106312.1317@compuserve.com — MB ChB 1985 Dundee. Prev: SHO (O & G) Ninewells Hosp. Dundee.

JOHNSON, Georgina Mary Stopsley Group Practice, Wigmore Lane Health Centre, Luton LU2 8BG Tel: 01582 481294 Fax: 01582 456259 — MB BS 1979 Lond.; BSc Lond. 1976, MB BS 1979; MRCGP 1983. (Guy's) Clin. Asst. (Paediat.) Luton & Dunstable Hosp.

JOHNSON, Gillian Jean Bartongate Surgery, 115 Barton Street, Gloucester GL1 4HR Tel: 01452 422944; Glasshouse Lane, Taynton, Gloucester GL19 3HJ Tel: 01452 831205 — MB ChB Sheff. 1983; DRCOG 1988.

JOHNSON, Gillian Margaret Tel: 01892 890484/890800 Fax: 01892 891187 — MB ChB 1974 Ed.

JOHNSON, Glenys Teresa The Frith, Colchester Road, Dedham, Colchester CO7 6DL Tel: 01206 322712 — MB BS 1985 Lond.; DRCOG 1989. Asst. GP Clacton on Sea.

JOHNSON, Professor Gordon James Institute of Ophthalmology, Department of Preventive Ophthalmology, Bath St., London EC1V 9EL Tel: 020 7608 6907 Fax: 020 7250 3207; 17 Lucerne Road, Summertown, Oxford OX2 7QB Tel: 01865 556513 Fax: 01865 310941 — MD Camb. 1984, BChir 1960, MB 1961; MRCS Eng. LRCP Lond. 1960; FRCOphth 1989; FRCSC 1972. (Cambridge) Rothes Prof. Preven. Ophth. Univ. Lond.; Hon. Cons. Surg. Moorfields Eye Hosp. Socs: MRCOphth.; Sec. Internat. Soc. Geogr. Ophth. (Mem. Counc.); Roy. Soc. Med. Prev: Assoc. Prof. Ophth. Memor. Univ. Newfld., Canada; Cons. Ophth. St. Michael's & Wellesley Hosps., Toronto, Canada; Research Fell. Surg. Mass. Gen. Hosp., USA.

JOHNSON, Graham Andrew Halsted, Surg. Lt.-Cdr. RN GSMDC BFPO 52 Tel: (00 350) 55219; c/o Halford Cottage, Halford, Shipston-on-Stour CV36 5BT — MB BS Lond. 1990; BSc (Hons.) Lond. 1987; DRCOG 1998. GP Regist. GSMDC Gibraltar. Prev: SHO (Paediat.) PeterBoro.; SHO (Obst. and Gyn.) PeterBoro.; SHO (Plastic Surg.) Derriford.

JOHNSON, Graham Stewart 39 Churchill Avenue, Cottingham HU16 5NJ — BM BS 1994 Nottm.

JOHNSON, Mr Graham Stewart Accident & Emergency, St. James University Hospital, Leeds LS9 7TF Tel: 0113 268 8432 Fax: 0113 225 1478; 3 Grange Croft, Alwoodley, Leeds LS17 7TZ — MB ChB 1982 Manch.; FRCS Eng. 1986; FFAEM 1996. Cons. A & E St. Jas. Univ. Hosp. Leeds; Med. Director, W. Yorks. Metrop. Ambul. Serv., Bradford. Prev: Sen. Regist. (A & E) Derriford Hosp. Plymouth.

JOHNSON, Graham Wilfred Blackpool Victoria Hospital, Whinney Heys Road, Blackpool FY3 8NR Tel: 01253 303498 Fax: 01253 303599 Email: graham@gwj.softnet.co.uk — MB ChB 1988 Manch.; FRCA 1994. Socs: Anaesth. Assn.; Manch. Med. Soc.; Pain Soc. Prev: Sen. Regist. (Anaesth.) N. W. Region; Regist N. W. Region.

JOHNSON, Guy Andrew 380 Calder Road, Edinburgh EH11 4AU Tel: 0131 537 7030 Fax: 0131 537 7005; 24 Findhorn Place, Edinburgh EH9 2JP Tel: 0131 667 9322 — MB ChB 1983 Ed.; MA Oxf. 1981; MRCGP 1989; MFHom 1988. (Ed.) Hosp. Practitioner Glas. Homoeopathy Hosp. Socs: Brit. Holistic Med. Assn.; BMA. Prev: Asst. GP Kirkcaldy; Med. Off. Mitranketan Health Centre Kerala, India.

JOHNSON, Hazel 41B Cumberland Street, Edinburgh EH3 6RA — MB ChB 1990 Ed.

JOHNSON, Helen Claire 21 Highfield Road, Flackwell Heath, High Wycombe HP10 9AN — MB BS 1993 Lond.

JOHNSON, Helen Dorothy The Orchard Surgery, Constable Road, St Ives PE27 3ER Tel: 01480 466611 — MB ChB 1988 Sheff.; DFFP 1993; MRCGP 1994; DGM 1996; DRCOG 1995. (Sheff.) Princip. in Gen. Pract. Prev: Staff Grade Phys. (Geriat.) Addenbrookes Hosp. Camb.; SHO (O & G) W. Suff. Hosp.; Trainee GP Bury St Edmunds.

JOHNSON, Helen Margaret Tel: 01608 661755 — BM BCh 1983 Oxf.; MA Camb. 1980; MRCGP 1987; DRCOG 1986. GP Asst. Chipping Norton; Clin. Med. Off. (Family Plann.) Moreton-in-Marsh Glos.; Clin. Asst. (Palliat. Med.) Banbury. Prev: Trainee GP Oxf. VTS.

JOHNSON, Helen Margaret (retired) 22 Elmfield Road, Gosforth, Newcastle upon Tyne NE3 4BA — MB BS 1943 Lond.; MRCS Eng.

LRCP Lond. 1942; MRCOG 1950. Prev: Regist. Special Gyn. Unit. Qu. Eliz. Hosp. Gateshead.

JOHNSON, Helen Sarah St Mary's Medical Centre, Vicarage Road, Strood, Rochester ME2 4DG Tel: 01634 291299/291266 Fax: 01634 295752; The Grange, Maidstone Road, St Mary's Platt, Sevenoaks TN15 8JT Tel: 01732 886957 — MB BS 1986 Lond.; DRCOG 1989. (St. Thomas's) Prev: Trainee GP Medway VTS; Ho. Off. (Gen. Surg.) Ashford Hosp.; Ho. Off. (Gen. Med.) Medway Hosp. Gillingham.

JOHNSON, Hilary Joy Park Hospital For Children, Headington, Oxford OX3 9JW; Greenfields, 35 Barton Lane, Headington, Oxford OX3 9JW Tel: 01865 741170 — MB ChB 1989 Leic.; MRCPsych 1994. Pk. Hosp. For Childr., Headington, Oxf. Prev: Sen. Regist. (Learning Disabil.) Leicester Gen. Hosp.

JOHNSON, Ian Tel: 01305 250861 — MB BS 1989 Lond.; MRCPsych 1995. Cons. Old Age Psychiat., N. Dorset PCT. Prev: Lect. in Old Age Psychiat. (Univ. of Bristol).

JOHNSON, Ian Alexander Thomas 13 Clough Meadow, Bryants Farm, Lostock, Bolton BL1 5XB — MB ChB 1989 Aberd.

JOHNSON, Ian Andrew Sheen Lane Health Centre, 70 Sheen Lane, London SW14 8LP Tel: 020 8876 3901 Fax: 020 8878 9620; 76 East Sheen Avenue, London SW14 8AU Tel: 020 8876 6511 — MB 1974 Camb.; BChir 1973; MRCGP 1981; DRCOG 1979; DCH Eng. 1976. Tower Ho. Sch. Med. Off.; Course Organiser Roehampton VTS.

JOHNSON, Mr Ian James MacDonald 8 The Drive, Gosforth, Newcastle upon Tyne NE3 4AH — MB BS 1985 Lond.; BSc (Hons.) Lond. 1982, MB BS 1985; FRCS (Eng) Edin. 1990; FRCS (Orl) 1996; MD 1998. (London Hospital Medical College) Cons. ENT Surg. Freeman Hosp., Newc. Socs: Ortorhinlaryngol. Research Soc. (Sec.). Prev: Regist. Rotat. (Surg.) Qu. Eliz. Hosp. Birm.; Demonstr. Anat. Lond. Hosp. Med. Coll.; Ho. Surg. & Ho. Phys. Lond. Hosp.

JOHNSON, Professor Ian Richard School of Human Development, Academic Division of Obsterics & Gynaecology, D Floor East Block Queens Medical Centre, Nottingham NG7 2UH Tel: 0115 970 9240 Fax: 0115 970 9234 Email: ian.johnson@nottingham.ac.uk — MB BS 1973 Lond.; DM Nottm. 1980; BSc Lond. 1970, MB BS 1973; MRCOG 1978; FRCOG 1990. Prof. O & G Qu.s Med. Centre Nottm. Prev: Prof. O & G The City Hosp. Nottm.

JOHNSON, Ian Stirling Earl Mountbatten Hospice, Halberry Lane, Newport PO30 2ER; 33 Avondale Road, Newport PO30 1HE Tel: 01983 527918 — MB ChB 1977 Sheff.; MRCGP 1983; MFCM RCP (UK) 1987. Med. Dir. & Cons. Palliat. Med. Earl Mt.batten Hospice, I. of Wight. Prev: Cons. Palliat. Med. Leicester.

JOHNSON, Isaac Babington 124 Uxbridge Road, London W12 8AA — MRCS Eng. LRCP Lond. 1952.

JOHNSON, Isabel Doreen (retired) 22 Sandhills Road, Reigate RH2 7RJ Tel: 01737 216009 — MB BS Lond. 1952; FRCGP 1990, M 1980; DObst RCOG 1955.

JOHNSON, Isabella Sonia 46 Minton Road, Birmingham B32 2XE — BM BCh 1988 Oxf.; MSc Lond. 1990; BA Camb. 1985; MRCPsych 1993. Clin. Lect. (Community Psychiat.) Inst. Psychiat. Lond. Prev: Regist. (Psychiat.) Bethlem Roy. & Maudsley Hosp. Lond.; Ho. Phys. Glas. Roy. Infirm.; Ho. Surg. Ch.ill Hosp. Oxf.

JOHNSON, Ivan Claude Newtown House, Newtown, Newbury RG20 9AP Tel: 01635 45015 Fax: 01635 45015 — MB BS 1959 Lond.; MRCGP 1965; FFOM RCP Lond. 1994, MFOM 1983, AFOM 1980; DIH 1981; DObst RCOG 1961. (Char. Cross) p/t Covetts Corecare, Morris Singer, Direct Line Ins.; Lect. Surrey & Soton Univs. Socs: BMA & Soc. Occupat. Med.; Fell.Roy. Soc. Med. Prev: GP Harefield; Sen. Med. Off. Rank Organisation; Cons. BMI Health Serv. Hoechst Roussel, Bayer Plc.

JOHNSON, Mr James North Halton General Hospital, Hospital Way, Runcorn WA7 2DA Tel: 01928 714567 Fax: 01928 753119; Talgarth, 66 View Road, Rainhill, Prescot L35 0LS Tel: 0151 426 4306 Fax: 0151 426 6572 — MB ChB 1970 Liverp.; MD Liverp. 1980; FRCS Eng. 1977; MRCS Eng. LRCP Lond. 1970; FDSRCS 2000; FRCP Lond. 2000. (Liverp.) Cons. Surg. Halton Gen. Hosp. Runcorn; Clin. Tutor Halton Gen. Hosp.; Clin. Lect. (Surg.) Univ. Liverp. Socs: BMA (Counc.); Liverp. Med. Inst.; (Chairm.) Jt. Cons. Comm. Prev: Sen. Regist. (Surg.) Roy. Liverp. Hosp.; Research Fell. Renal Transpl. Unit & Lect. (Human Anat.) Univ. Liverp.; Vis. Fell. Univ. Texas, USA.

JOHNSON, James Wilbert Shell UK Exploration & Production, 1 Altens Farm Road, Nigg, Aberdeen AB12 3FY Tel: 01224 884489 Fax: 01224 883219; 135 Forest Avenue, Aberdeen AB15 4UJ Tel: 01224 326409 — MB ChB 1973 Aberd.; MRCGP 1978; MFOM RCP Lond. 1993; CIH Dund 1987. (Univ. Aberd.) Med. Adviser (Occupat. Health) Shell UK Exploration & Produc. Aberd. Socs: Soc. Occupat. Med. Prev: Trainee GP Grampian VTS; Ho. Phys. Arbroath Infirm.; Ho. Surg. Woodend Hosp. Aberd.

JOHNSON, Jane The Old Vicarage, Church Lane, Upton, Newark NG23 5SR — MB BS 1973 Lond.; MB BS Lond. 1073; BSc Lond. 1970; FRCPath 1992, M 1980. (St. Thos. Hosp. Lond.) Cons. Histopath. & Cytopath. City Hosp. Nottm. Socs: (Chairm.) Brit. Soc. Clin. Cytol.; Internat. Soc. Gyn. Path.

JOHNSON, Jennifer Meanwood Group Practice, 548 Meanwood Road, Leeds LS6 2AP; 16 Oakwood Lane, Leeds LS8 2JQ — MB BS 1960 Lond.; MRCS Eng. LRCP Lond. 1960. (Guy's) Sen. Clin. Med. Off. Leeds W. HA. Socs: BMA. Prev: Ho. Phys. & Jun. Resid. (Clin. Pathol.) & Ho. Surg. (Genitourin.) Guy's Hosp. Lond.; Ho. Phys. (Paediat.) Evelina Childr. Hosp. of Guy's Hosp. Lond.

JOHNSON, Jennifer Alice 11 Kirklands Road, Over Kellet, Carnforth LA6 1DP — MB ChB 1994 Glas.

JOHNSON, Jennifer Ann 18 Heol Don, Cardiff CF14 2AU — BM Soton 1988; DRCOG 1992; DCH RCP Lond. 1991. Prev: Trainee GP Basingstoke; SHO (Paediat.) Soton. Gen. Hosp.

JOHNSON, Jennifer Marianne Danes Camp Surgery, Rowtree Road, Northampton NN4 0NY Tel: 01604 709426 Fax: 01604 709427; 7 Lodge Avenue, Collingtree, Northampton NN4 0NQ Tel: 01604 769552 — MB BS 1985 Lond.; DRCOG 1990; DCH RCP Lond. 1987. Clin. Asst. (Paediat. Audiol.) N.ampton Gen. Hosp.

JOHNSON, Jennifer May (retired) The Old Stable, 3 Deevon Farm Close, Newark NG24 4RS — MB BS 1962 Lond.; MRCS Eng. LRCP Lond. 1961. Prev: Examg. Med. Pract. for Attendance & Mobility Allowance DHSS.

JOHNSON, Jeremy Richard Cecil James 38 Renfrew Drive, Wollaton, Nottingham NG8 2FX — MB ChB 1974 Birm.

JOHNSON, Joan Marchbanks Stirling (retired) Achnagaradh, Craighouse PA60 7X6 Tel: 0149 682390 — MB ChB 1948 Glas.; DCH Calcutta 1964. Prev: Med. Off. (Cytol.) S.. Gen. Hosp. Glas.

JOHNSON, Joanna Sian 4 Mevril Road, Whaley Bridge, High Peak SK23 7JS — MB ChB 1993 Manch.; MB ChB (Hons) Manch. 1993.

JOHNSON, John (retired) 7 Winchester Close, Bamford, Rochdale OL11 5NE Tel: 01706 649959 — MD 1965 Manch.; MB ChB 1953; FRCP Ed. 1970, M 1960; FRCPsych 1973; DPM Eng. 1959. Cons. Psychiat. Univ. Hosp. S. Manch.; Lect. in Psychiat. Univ. Manch. Prev: Sen. Regist. Maudsley Hosp. Lond.

JOHNSON, John Cunningham, MBE (retired) Bridge Cottage, 6 The Friary Farm, Bamburgh NE69 7AF Tel: 01668 214050 — MB ChB 1943 Ed.; MRCGP 1958; DCH Eng. 1948. Prev: RAFVR.

JOHNSON, John Damien 32 Braddyll Road, Bolton BL5 1DY — MB ChB 1997 Leic.

JOHNSON, John Kenneth (retired) 65 Rotchell Road, Dumfries DG2 7SA Tel: 01387 255932 — MB ChB 1958 Manch.; MSc Birm. 1965; FRCPath 1978, M 1966; MCB 1967; DObst RCOG 1960. Prev: Cons. Biochem. Area Laborat. Dumfries & Galloway Roy. Infirm.

JOHNSON, John William Edward The Surgery, 38 Radnor Road, Handsworth, Birmingham B20 3SR Tel: 0121 554 0070 — MB ChB 1956 Birm.

JOHNSON, Mr Jonathan Richard (cons. rooms), The Princess Grace Hospital, 42/52 Nottingham Place, London W1U 5NY Tel: 020 7935 6485 Fax: 020 79082168 Email: j.r.johnson@doctors.org.uk; 3 Bulmer Mews, London W11 3NZ Tel: 020 7727 0250 — MB BS 1971 Lond.; FRCS Eng. 1976; MRCS Eng. LRCP Lond. 1971. (St. Bart.) Cons. Orthop. Surg. St. Mary's Hosp. Lond. & Roy. Nat. Orthop. Hosp. Trust Stanmore. Socs: Fell. BOA; Internat. Soc. Study Lumbar Spine; Brit. Clin. Spine Scoiety (B.C.S.S.). Prev: Sen. Regist. Rotat. (Orthop.) Univ. Coll. Hosp. & W.m.; Regist. Rotat. (Surg.) Roy. Berks. & Battle Hosps. Reading; Ho. Surg. St. Bart. Hosp. Lond.

JOHNSON, Joseph Lionel Whitworth 6 Manor Grove, Great Broughton, Middlesbrough TS9 7EJ Tel: 01642 710287 — LRCP LRCS 1950 Ed.; LRCP LRCS Ed. LRFPS Glas. 1950. (Roy. Colls. & Univ. Ed.) SBStJ. Socs: BMA. Prev: Med. Off. Nat. Coal Bd. E. Midl.

Area; ENT Ho. Surg. Dudley Rd. Hosp. Birm.; Obst. Ho. Surg. Simpson Memor. Matern. Pavil. Roy. Infirm. Edin.

JOHNSON, Joseph William (retired) 66 Brimstage Road, Bebington, Wirral CH63 3BA — MRCS Eng. LRCP Lond. 1950.

JOHNSON, Judith 17 Fairwood Road, Llandaff, Cardiff CF5 3QF Tel: 029 2056 5525 — LMS 1982 U Autonoma Barcelona.

JOHNSON, Judith Mary The Keston House Medical Practice, 70 Brighton Road, Purley CR8 2LJ Tel: 020 8660 8292 Fax: 020 8763 2142; 32 Manor Way, Purley CR8 3BH Tel: 020 8660 4504 — MB BS 1981 Lond.; DRCOG 1984. (St. Geo.) GP Princip. Purley. Prev: SHO (O & G & Paediat.) Ashford Hosp.; SHO (Psychiat.) Latimer Ho. Day Hosp. & Middlx. Hosp. Lond.

JOHNSON, Julia Alexandra Fishergate Hill Surgery, 50 Fishergate Hill, Preston PR1 8DN Tel: 01772 254484 Fax: 01772 881835 — MB ChB 1985 Liverp.; BSc (Hons.) Liverp. 1982; Cert. Family Plann. JCC 1995; Cert. Prescribed Equiv. Exp. JCPTGP 1992; DTM & H Liverp. 1992; DCH RCP Lond. 1990.

JOHNSON, Julie 109 Wigginton Road, Tamworth B79 8RP — MB ChB 1994 Manch.; MRCP 1998; MRCPCH 1998. Specialist Regist. Paediat. Milton Keynes Gen. Hosp.

JOHNSON, Julie-Ann Department of Rheumatology, 4th Floor Hunts House, Guys Hospital, St Thomas St., London SE1 9RT; 88 High Street Mews, London SW19 5EG — MB ChB 1987 Manch.

JOHNSON, Karen Lesley Poplar Grove Surgery, Meadow Way, Aylesbury HP20 1XB Tel: 01296 482554 — MB BCh 1988 Wales; BSc Wales 1985; MRCGP 1994; DRCOG 1991. p/t GP, Aylesbury. Socs: BMA.

JOHNSON, Karl John 22 Penrith Avenue, Thornton-Cleveleys FY5 2NA — MB ChB 1990 Leic.

JOHNSON, Katharine Anne Clinical Radiology Department, Salisbury District Hospital, Salisbury SP2 Tel: 01722 336262 Fax: 01722 404005 — MB BS 1988 Lond.; FRCR 1995; BSc (Anat.) 1985; MRCP (UK) 1991. Regist. (Radiol.) Soton. Gen. Hosp.; Cons. Radiologist, Salisbury Dist. Hosp. Socs: BMA; Fell. of Roy. Coll. of Radiologists; Mem. of Roy. Coll. of Phys.s. Prev: SHO Rotat (Med.) Roy. Lond. Hosp.

JOHNSON, Kathleen (retired) 4 Mowbray Avenue, Brooklands, Sale M33 3NS Tel: 0161 973 1137 — MB ChB 1954 Manch. Prev: Clin. Med. Off. Trafford AHA.

JOHNSON, Kathryn Elizabeth Flat 5, 71 Westcombe Park Road, London SE3 7QS — MB ChB 1996 Ed.

JOHNSON, Koshy Clifton House Medical Centre, 263-265 Beverley Road, Hull HU5 2ST Tel: 01482 341423 — MB BS 1981 Mysore.

JOHNSON, Lisa Francesca The Surgery, 32 Saddleton Road, Whitstable CT5 4JQ Tel: 01227 272809 — MB BS 1988 Lond.; MRCGP 1995; DFFP 1994; DRCOG 1993. (Charing Cross & Westm.) GP Princip., Whitstable, Kent; Clin. Asst. (Rheum.), Qu. Elezabeth The Qu. Mother Hosp., Margate. Prev: GP Princip. Deal, Kent; GP Asst. Ashford, Kent; Trainee GP Bucks.

JOHNSON, Ludmila 78 Lonsdale Road, Barnes, London SW13 9JS — State Exam Med 1981 Munich; MD Munich 1981; T(GP) 1991. Socs: Roy. Coll. Gen. Pract.; Roy. Soc. Med.; BMA.

JOHNSON, Madge Elizabeth (retired) Belgrave, 2 Ladybrook Road, Bramhall, Stockport SK7 3LZ Tel: 0161 485 2671 — MB ChB 1923 Manch. Prev: Ho. Surg. Manch. N.. Hosp. Wom. & Childr.

JOHNSON, Margaret 21 Higher Knutsford Road, Warrington WA4 2JS — MB ChB 1962 Liverp.

JOHNSON, Margaret Ann National Perinatal Epidemiology Unit, Radcliffe Infirmary, Oxford OX2 6HE Tel: 01865 224876 Fax: 01865 726360 Email: ann.johnson@pevinat.ox.ac.uk; 17 Lucerne Road, Oxford OX2 7QB Tel: 01865 556513 Fax: 01865 310941 — MD Lond. 1970, MB BS 1962; FRCP Lond. 1994; MRCP Lond. 1964; MRCS Eng. LRCP Lond. 1962; FRCPCH 1997. (Kings College Medical School, Landa)

JOHNSON, Margaret Anne 27 Blomfield Road, London W9 1AA Tel: 020 7266 0105 Fax: 020 7266 2663 — MRCS Eng. LRCP Lond. 1975; MD Lond. 1987, MB BS 1975; MRCP (UK) 1978. Cons. Phys. HIV & AIDS & Hon. Sen. Lect. (Virol.) Roy. Free Hosp. Lond. Prev: Sen. Regist. (Thoracic Med.) Roy. Free & Brompton Hosps. Lond.; Regist. (Med.) St. Mary's Hosp. Lond.; Regist. Research Brompton Hosp. Lond.

JOHNSON, Margaret Anne (retired) 23 Elmhurst Court, Hamblin Road, Woodbridge IP12 1HB — MB ChB 1954 Birm.; 1954 MB ChB Birm.; 1963 FFA RCS Eng.; 1957 DA Eng. Prev: Cons. Anaesth. Nuneaton & Coventry Hosps.

JOHNSON, Margaret Elisabeth (retired) 25 Court Road, Cockington, Torquay TQ2 6SE Tel: 01803 607378 — MRCS Eng. LRCP Lond. 1948; DObst RCOG 1953. Prev: Ho. Surg. Salisbury Gen. Infirm.

JOHNSON, Margaret Hazel Longthatch, Hurstbourne Priors, Whitchurch RG28 7SE — MB BCh 1977 Wales; DA Eng. 1979. Clin. Asst. (Anaesth.) N. Hants. Hosp. (Trust).

JOHNSON, Margaret Rosemary Hinton Priory, Hinton Charterhouse, Bath BA2 7TA — MB ChB 1943 Manch.

JOHNSON, Maria Louise 1st Floor Flat, 185 Cathedral Road, Cardiff CF11 9PN — MB BCh 1992 Wales.

JOHNSON, Maria Susanna 110 Old Road, Oxford OX3 8SX — MB BS 1986 Lond.; MFFP 1995; MRCOG 1993. (St. Thos. Hosp. Med. Sch.) Clin. Asst. Colposcopy, P.ss Anne Hosp., S.ampton. Socs: BMA; BSCCP. Prev: Clin. Research Fell. ACU Leeds Gen. Infirm.; Clin. Asst. (Antenatal & Gyn.) Whittington Hosp. Lond.; SHO (Gyn.) Eliz. Garrett Anderson Hosp. & United Soho Hosp. for Wom. Lond.

JOHNSON, Mark Douglas Knockin Surgery, Knockin, Oswestry SY10 8HL Tel: 01691 682203 Fax: 01691 682700; 10 Fairburn Drive, Radbrook Green, Shrewsbury SY3 6DQ Tel: 01743 244630 — MB BS 1982 Lond.; DA (UK) 1985. Dep. Med. Dir. Shrops. & Mid-Wales Hospice. Prev: Trainee GP Shrewsbury.

JOHNSON, Mark Justin Gracelands, Elvis Rd, Exmouth EX8 2QB — BM 1997 Soton.

JOHNSON, Mark Richard Imperial College School of Medicine, Chelsea and Westminster, 369 Fulham Road, London SW10 9NH Tel: 020 8746 8932 Fax: 020 8846 7796 — MB BS 1982 Lond.; MRCP (UK) 1985; PhD London University 1995; MRCOG 1996. (St George's HMS) Sen. Lect. (Hon. Cons) Imperial Sch. of Med. in Obst., Obst. Med., & Reproductive Med. Prev: Regist. (Med. Rotat.) W.m. Lond.

JOHNSON, Mark Roy Accident & Emergency Hospital, Weston General Hospital, Uphill, Weston Super Mare BS23 — BM BS 1990 Nottm.; BMedSci Nottm. 1987. Staff Grade (A & E) W.on super Mare Hosp. Prev: Trainee GP Stornoway; SHO (Anaesth.) Stafford & SHO (Paediat.) Glos.

JOHNSON, Martin Alan Winlanton and Ryton Family Health Partnership, The Dental Clinic, Grange Road, Ryton NE40 3NH Tel: 0191 413 1399; Carmel, Lead Road, Greenside, Ryton NE40 4SJ Tel: 0191 413 4510 — MB BS 1978 Newc.; MRCGP 1984; DRCOG 1983; DA Eng. 1982. GP Ryton Tyne & Wear. Socs: BMA & Assoc. Mem. Brit. Homoeop. Assn.; Fac. Anaesths. RCS Eng. Prev: Trainee GP N.umbria VTS; SHO (Anaesth.) Newc. Gen. & Freeman Hosps.; Ho. Off. Hexham Gen. Hosp.

JOHNSON, Martin Ewart Ashville Medical Centre, 430 Doncaster Road, Barnsley S70 3RJ Tel: 01226 282280 Fax: 01226 216002 Email: mjohnson@profiad.com; Elmleigh Farm, 24 Stringer House Lane, Emley, Huddersfield HD8 9SU — MB ChB 1981 Leeds; MRCGP 1986; DCH RCP Lond. 1985; DRCOG 1984. (Leeds) Med. Adviser Koyo Bearing (Europe) Ltd; Med. Dir. Profiad Reading. Socs: Brit. Thorac. Soc. Prev: SHO (Paediat.) Middlesbrough HA.

JOHNSON, Martin Frederick Tel: 020 8680 2588 Fax: 020 8680 1415; Maddalena, 32 Manor Way, Purley CR8 3BH Tel: 020 8660 4504 — MB BS 1980 Lond.; DRCOG 1982. GP Trainer S. Croydon. Socs: Croydon Med. Soc.; Croydon Medico-Legal Soc. Prev: Trainee GP/SHO (Psychiat.) Warlingham Pk. Hosp. Surrey; Trainee GP/SHO (A & E) Mayday Hosp. Croydon.

JOHNSON, Martin Keith Department of Respiratory Medicine, Glasgow Royal Infirmary, 16 Alexandra Parade, Glasgow G31 2ER Tel: 0141 211 4948 Fax: 0141 211 4932; 12 Netherby Drive, Pollokshields, Glasgow G41 5JA Tel: 0141 427 1301 Email: johnson7@which.net — MB ChB 1993 Leeds. Specialist Regist. (Respirat. & Gen. Med.). Prev: SHO (Gen. Med.) St. James Univ. Hosp. Leeds.

JOHNSON, Martin Thomas Friarwood Surgery, Carleton Glen, Pontefract WF8 1SU Tel: 01977 703235 Fax: 01977 600527; 2 The Mount, Pontefract WF8 1ND — MB ChB 1979 Leeds; MRCGP 1984; DMJ(Clin) 1992; DGM 1988.

JOHNSON, Mary Catherine Geraldine 149 Blackpool Road, Ansdell, Lytham St Annes FY8 4AA — MB ChB 1974 Manch.; MRCP (UK) 1978.

JOHNSON, Matthew Anselm 56C Gloucester Gardens, London W2 6BN — MB ChB 1983 Bristol.

JOHNSON, Matthew Warren 43 Liberty Avenue, Merton Abbey, London SW19 2QS; The Laurels, Old Aston Hill, Ewloe, Deeside CH5 3AL — MB BS 1995 Lond.; BSc Lond. 1992; MRCP 1997. (St. Georges) SHO Rotat. (Gen. Med.) Guy's Lewisham & St. Thos. Hosps. Lond.

JOHNSON, Maura Elizabeth Barn Court, Cropwell Road, Langar, Nottingham NG13 9HD — BM BS 1980 Nottm.; MRCGP 1985. (Nottm.)

JOHNSON, Michael (retired) Birkwood, 35 Mickledale Lane, Bilsthorpe, Newark NG22 8QB Tel: 01623 870230 Fax: 01623 411407 — MB BS 1959 Lond.; MRCS Eng. LRCP Lond. 1959. Med. Adviser (Palliat. Care) Nottm. Hospice. Prev: GP Newark.

JOHNSON, Michael Alwyn (retired) Low Bank, Castleshaw, Delph, Oldham OL3 5LZ Tel: 0145 775886 — MB ChB 1968 Manch.; MRCGP 1976; DPH Manch. 1972; DObst RCOG 1970. Med. Adviser Calderdale & Kirkless HA St Lukes Ho. Prev: GP Saddleworth Med. Pract. 1974.

JOHNSON, Michael Anthony Mill Hey, Mill Hey Road, Caldy, Wirral CH48 1NH Tel: 0151 625 6548 — MB ChB 1993 Liverp.; FRCS (Eng.) 1996; BDS Liverp.; FDSRCS Ed.

JOHNSON, Michael Charles (retired) Old Orchard, Westport Road, Wareham BH20 4PR Tel: 01929 556114 Email: mjoh600419@aol.com — MB Camb. 1958, BChir 1957; MRCS Eng. LRCP Lond. 1957; DObst RCOG 1959. Prev: Hon. Off. Qu. Eliz. Hosp. Childr. Lond. & Hackney Hosp. Lond.

JOHNSON, Michael Fraser Cannington Health Centre, Mill Lane, Cannington, Bridgwater TA5 2HB Tel: 01278 652335 Fax: 01278 652453; Furzy Down, Peartwater Road, Spaxton, Bridgwater TA5 1DG — MB ChB 1974 Bristol. Prev: SHO (Psychiat.) Bristol Gen. Hosp.; SHO (Cas.) Frenchay Hosp. Bristol; Trainee Gen. Pract. Bristol Vocational Train. Scheme.

JOHNSON, Mr Michael Graham, GM Southover Lodge, Frampton, Dorchester DT2 9NQ Tel: 01300 320370 — MB BS 1961 Lond.; ChM Bristol 1974; FRCS Eng. 1966; DObst RCOG 1963. (Middlx.) Cons. Surg. W. Dorset Health Dist. Socs: Brit. Assn. Urol. Surgs. Prev: Sen. Regist. (Surg.) Bristol Roy. Infirm.; Postgrad. Fell. (Paediat. Surg.) Childr. Hosp. Cape Town S. Afr.; Research Asst. (Surg.) Unit Bristol Roy. Infirm.

JOHNSON, Michael Harvey Department of Neurology, St. James's University Hospital, Beckett St., Leeds LS9 7TF Tel: 0113 206 4454 Fax: 0113 246 5231 Email: michael.johnson@leedsth.nhs.uk — BM BCh 1974 Oxf.; DM 1985 Oxf.; MA 1974 Oxf.; FRCP Lond. 1993. (St. Bart.) Cons. Neurol. The Leeds Teachg. Hosp. NHS Trust; Sen. Clin. Lect. (Med.) Univ. Leeds. Socs: Fell. Roy. Soc. Med. Prev: Regist. (Neurol) Middlx. Hosp. Lond.; Regist. (Med.) Chelmsford Hosp.; Sen. Regist. Nat. Hosp. Nerv. Dis. & St. Mary's Hosp. Lond.

JOHNSON, Michael Henderson Flowers (retired) High Ground Cottage, Birker Moor, Eskdale, Holmrook CA19 1TJ Tel: 0193467 23364 — MB BS Lond. 1950; MA (Eng. Lit.) Oxf. 1962; BA (Hons.) Fine Art Lond. 1973; MRCS Eng. LRCP Lond. 1950. Prev: Ship Surg. Cable & Wireless Ltd.

JOHNSON, Michael James 16 Winchester Road, Carryduff, Belfast BT8 8QQ — MB BCh BAO 1990 Belf.

JOHNSON, Michael Keith, TD Pond House Farm, Hamsterly, Bishop Auckland DL13 3QF — MB ChB 1969 Leeds; FFA RCS Eng. 1977. (Leeds) Clin. Dir. (Anaesth.) Bishop Auckland Gen. Hosp. Prev: Cons. Anaesth. Sunderland City Trust.

JOHNSON, Michael Leofric Edwards and Partners, Wargrave House, 23 St. Owen Street, Hereford HR1 2JB Tel: 01432 272285 Fax: 01432 344059 — MB BCh 1991 Wales; BSc (Hons.) Bristol 1986; MRCGP 1996; DRCOG 1994; DFFP 1994. (Wales)

JOHNSON, Michael Roy The National Hospital for Neurology and Neurosurgery, Queen Square, London WC1N 3BG Tel: 020 7837 3611 Email: mjohnson@hgmp.mrc.ac.uk — MB BS 1989 Lond.; BSc (1st cl. Hons.) Sussex 1981; DPhil Oxf. 1984; MRCP (UK) 1992; FRACP 1998. Specialist Regist. (Neurol.) S. Thames Train. Progr. Socs: Assoc. Mem. Assn. Brit. Neurol.

JOHNSON, Michael Shore (retired) Seven Gables, Stockbridge SO20 6HL Tel: 0126 481336 — MB BS 1947 Lond.; MRCS Eng. LRCP Lond. 1947. Prev: Orthop. Ho. Surg. & Cas. Off. Roy. S. Hants. Hosp. Soton.

JOHNSON, Miriam Jane St. Catherine's Hospice, 137 Scalby Rd, Scarborough YO13 0HH; High Farm Lodge, 41a High Street, Scarborough YO13 0HH — MB ChB 1984 Manch.; MB ChB (Hons.) Manch. 1984; MRCP (UK) 1987; MRCGP 1988; DCH RCP Lond. 1986; MD Manc 1999. Cons. Phys., Palliat. Care, St. Catherine's Hospice, ScarBoro. Socs: Roy. Soc. of Med.; Brit. Med. Assoc. Prev: Clin. Asst. (Haemat.) S.. Gen. Hosp. Glas.; Trainee GP Lancaster VTS.

JOHNSON, Muriel Veronica Trilby Rosemead Surgery, 8A Ray Park Avenue, Maidenhead SL6 8DS Tel: 01628 622023 Fax: 01628 639495; Willow Vale, Castle End Road, Ruscombe, Reading RG10 9XG Tel: 01189 345599 — MB ChB St. And. 1966; DCH RCPS Glas. 1968. Prev: Regional Regist. Qu. Mother's Hosp. Glas.

JOHNSON, Myles Coutts 19 Lavender Sweep, London SW11 1DY — MB BS 1997 Lond.

JOHNSON, Mr Neil Arnold The Old Rectory, East Barsham, Fakenham NR21 0LH — MB BS 1976 Lond.; FRCS Ed. 1986; MRCP (UK) 1982; FRCOphth Lond. 1988; DO RCS Eng. 1985. (St. Thos.) Cons. Ophth. Surg. Qu. Eliz. Hosp. Kings Lynn Norf. Prev: Sen. Regist. Moorfields Eye Hosp. Lond.; Regist. (Ophth.) St. Thos. Hosp. Lond.; Sen. Specialist BMH Rinteln.

JOHNSON, Mr Nicholas Dept. of Gynaecology, Royal United United Hospital, Bath BA1 3NG Tel: 01425 428331 Fax: 01225 825464 Email: nicholasjohnson@msn.com — BM BS 1981 Nottm.; PhD 1996 Leeds; DM 1996 Nottm.; BMedSci (Biochem.) Nottm. 1979; FRCS Ed. 1987; MRCOG 1987; T(OG) 1991. Cons. & Sen. Lect. (O & G) Roy. United Hosp., Bath. Prev: Lect. (Obst & Gyn.) St. Jas. Leeds.; Cons. & Sen. Lect. (O & G) Leeds Gen. Infirm.

JOHNSON, Nicholas Francis Crown Yealm, Newton Ferrers, Plymouth PL8 1AW — MB BS 1983 Lond.

JOHNSON, Nicholas Grant 51 Elvaston Road, Hexham NE46 2HH — MB BS 1993 Lond.

JOHNSON, Mr Nicholas Stephen 30 Foxcroft, St Albans AL1 5SP — MB BS 1992 Lond.; FRCS Ed. 1996. Research Fell. Univ. Coll. Lond.

JOHNSON, Nicola Dale 2 Benhall Green, Saxmundham IP17 1HU — BM 1994 Soton. (Southampton)

JOHNSON, Nigel 8 Caesar Crescent, Caerleon, Newport NP18 3ER — MB ChB 1992 Leic.

JOHNSON, Norman McIntosh 88 Harley Street, London W1N 1AE Tel: 020 7224 2016 Fax: 020 7255 1904; 146 Burbage Road, London SE21 7AG — MB BS Lond. 1970; MD Lond. 1977; FRCP Lond. 1987; MRCP (UK) 1973. (St. Bart.) Cons. Phys. & Dir. of Research of Developm. Whittington Hosp., K. Edwd. VII Hosp. for O ffs. & St. Lukes Hosp. for Clergy Lond.; Hon. Sen. Lect. (Med.)Roy.Free. UCL Med. Sch. Socs: Brit. Thorac. Soc.; Amer. Thoracic Soc.; Eur. Respirat. Soc. Prev: Sen. Lect. Univ. Coll. Lond. Hosps.; Lect. (Med.) Middlx. Hosp. Lond.; Regist. (Med.) Roy. Free Hosp. Lond.

JOHNSON, Olbunmi 4 Cottesmore, Bracknell RG12 7YL — MB ChB 1998 Leeds.

JOHNSON, Pamela Valerie Institute of Obstetrics and Gynaecology, Queen Charlotte's and Chelsea Hospital, Goldhawk Road, London W6 0XG Tel: 020 8383 5311 Fax: 020 8383 3922 Email: pjohnson@rpms.ac.uk — MB BS 1978 Lond.; MD Lond. 1993; MRCOG 1989; MRCGP 1983; DRCOG 1985. Sen. Lect. & Hon. Cons. Obst. Imperial Coll. Sch. of Med. Qu. Charlotte's & Chelsea Hosp. Lond. Prev: Lect. & Hon. Sen. Regist. (O & G) St. Geo. Hosp. Med. Sch. Lond.; Research Regist. (O & G) Guys Hosp. Lond.; Regist. (O & G) St. Geo. Hosp. Lond.

JOHNSON, Patrick Alan Lower Road Surgery, 17 Lower Road, Fetcham, Leatherhead KT22 9EL Tel: 01372 378166 Fax: 01372 374734; 70 Randalls Road, Leatherhead KT22 0AD — MB ChB 1965 Bristol; DPhysMed Eng. 1970. (Bristol) Indust. Med. Off. DorinCt. Ind.; Vis. Phys. Qu. Eliz. Foundat. for Disabled Leatherhead. Socs: Fell. Roy. Soc. Med.; BMA. Prev: Ho. Phys. S.mead Hosp. Bristol; Ho. Surg. Bristol Roy. Infirm.; Clin. Asst. Lond. Hosp.

JOHNSON, Mr Patrick Allingham Johnson and Partners, Langley House, 27 West Street, Chichester PO19 1RW Tel: 01243 782266/782955 Fax: 01243 779188; Mundham Cottage, South Mundham, Chichester PO20 6LY Tel: 01243 262490 — MB BS 1964 Lond.; FRCS Eng. 1970. (King's Coll. Hosp.) Prev: Regist. (Gen. Surg.) Kings Coll. Hosp. Lond.; Res. Surg. Off. St. Richard's Hosp. Chichester; Ho. Phys. Dulwich Hosp.

JOHNSON, Mr Patrick John Elliot 81 Harborne Road, Edgbaston, Birmingham B15 3HG Tel: 0121 455 9496 Fax: 0121 455 0288 — MB ChB 1962 Birm.; FRCS Eng. 1968; FRCS Ed. 1967. (Birm.) Cons. Surg. (ENT) Univ. Hosp. S. Birm. BromsGr. & Reddith Hosps. Socs: S. W.. Otolaryngol. Assn.; Midl. Inst. Otol. Prev: Cons. Surg. S. Birm., BromsGr. & Redditch Health Dists.; Sen. Regist. (ENT) United Bristol Hosps.; Lect. (Physiol.) Univ. Birm.

JOHNSON, Paul Nuffield Department of Obstetrics, John Radcliffe Hospital, Oxford OX3 9DU — MB ChB 1963 Bristol.

JOHNSON, Mr Paul Alexander Department of Maxillofacial Surgery, Royal Surrey County Hospital, Egerton Road, Guildford GU2 7XX Tel: 01483 571122 Fax: 01483 67811; The Coach House, Sandy Lane, Guildford GU3 1HF Tel: 01483 69125 — MB BChir 1985 Camb.; BA Camb. 1982; BSc Leeds 1975, BChD 1979; FRCS Ed. 1988; FDS RCS Eng. 1986. Cons. Oral & Maxillofacial Surg. Roy. Surrey Co. Hosp. Guildford. Socs: Brit. Assn. Oral & Maxillofacial Surg. Prev: Sen. Regist. (Oral & Maxillofacial Surg.) Qu. Vict. Hosp. E. Grinstead & King. Coll. Hosp. Lond.; Regist. (Oral & Maxillofacial Surg.) N. Staffs. Roy. Infirm. Stoke-on-Trent.

JOHNSON, Paul Austell (retired) Sussex Cottage, Nutshell Lane, Farnham GU9 0HH — MB BS Lond. 1958; DObst RCOG 1960. Prev: Ho. Phys. & SHO (Surg.) Redhill Gen. Hosp.

JOHNSON, Paul Bernard St Lukes Medical Centre, 17 New Road, Brixham TQ5 8NA Tel: 01803 852731 Fax: 01803 852637 — MB BCh 1985 Wales; MRCGP 1989.

JOHNSON, Paul Charles Whitby Group Practice, Springvale Medical Centre, Whitby; High Farm Lodge, 41a High St, Scarborough YO13 0HH Tel: 01723 587 1693 — MB ChB 1983 Manch.; MRCGP 1987; DCH RCP Lond. 1986. GP Partner Whitby Gp. Pract., Whitby. Prev: Community Med. Off. Child Health Lancaster; Trainee GP Lancaster VTS; SHO (Psychiat.) Lancaster Moor Hosp.

JOHNSON, Paul Graeme — MB ChB 1983 Leic.; MRCGP 1995. GP, Coventry.

JOHNSON, Paul Kenneth 5 Oaken Lane, Claygate, Esher KT10 0RE Tel: 01372 463314 — MB BS 1986 Lond.; BSc Lond. 1983; MRCP (UK) 1990; MRCGP 1995; DCH RCP Lond. 1993. Research Fell. (Cardiol.) St. Geo. Hosp. Lond. Socs: Jun. Cardiol. Club. Prev: Regist. (Cardiol.) St. Thos. & Medway Hosps.; SHO Rotat. (Med.) N.wick Pk. Hosp.

JOHNSON, Paul Philip Ash Surgery, 1 Ashfield Road, Liverpool L17 0BY Tel: 0151 727 1155 Fax: 0151 726 0018 — MB ChB 1985 Liverp.

JOHNSON, Paul Robert Spencer (retired) The Doctor's House, Great Witley, Worcester WR6 6HR Tel: 01299 896775 — LMSSA 1959 Lond. Police Surg. W. Mercia Constab.; Med. Off. Abberley Hall Preparat. Sch. Worcester. Prev: Ho. Phys. & Obst. Ho. Surg. Ronkswood Hosp. Worcester.

JOHNSON, Mr Paul Robert Vellacott Department of Paediatric Surgery, Level 4, John Radcliffe Hospital, Headley Way, Oxford OX3 9DU Tel: 01865 741166 Fax: 01865 220323 Email: paul.johnson@nds.ox.ac.uk; Greenfields, 35 Barton Lane, Headington, Oxford OX3 9JW Tel: 01865 741170 — MB ChB 1988 Leic.; FRCS (Paed. Surg) 2000; MD 2001 (Leic.); FRCS Eng. 1993; FRCS Ed. 1993. Reader in Paediatric Surg., Univ. of Oxf. and Hon. Cons. Surg., John Radcliffe Hosp., Oxf. Socs: Brit. Transpl. Soc.; Pancreatic Soc.; Brit. Assn. Paediat. Surg. Prev: Regist. (Paediatric Surg.) Gt. Ormond St., Oxf.; Regist. (Paediatric Surg.) Melbourne, Australia; Research Regist. (Surg.) Leicester.

JOHNSON, Paula Harriet Department Respiratory Medicine, D Floor South Block, Queens Medical Centre, Nottingham NG7 2UH — MB ChB 1990 Bristol; MRCP (UK) 1993; DM Nottm 1998. Specialist Regist. Rotat. (Respirat. Med.) Nottm. Socs: Brit. Thorac. Soc. Prev: Research Regist. Univ. Hosp. Nottm.; SHO Rotat. (Gen. Med.) Gloucester Roy. Hosp.

JOHNSON, Pauline Anne Glenroyd, 1 West Park Grove, Roundhay, Leeds LS8 2HQ — MB ChB 1982 Bristol; DPD 1999; MRCGP 1986; DRCOG 1985. (Bristol) Clin. Asst. (Dermat.) Leeds Gen. Infirm. Prev: GP Retainer Scheme Leeds.

JOHNSON, Peter (retired) 182 Thunder Lane, Thorpe St Andrew, Norwich NR7 0AB — MB ChB 1957 Ed.; MRCP Ed. 1964. Prev: GP Norwich.

JOHNSON, Peter Southport General Infirmary, Scarisbrick New Road, Southport PR8 6PH; Teignmouth, 1 Briedden Way, Little Sutton, South Wirral CH66 4YN — MB ChB 1987 Liverp.

JOHNSON, Peter Anthony (retired) 58 Cleadon Lea, Cleadon, Sunderland SR6 7TQ — MB BS MB BS Durh. 1959. Prev: SHO Childr. Hosp. Sunderland.

JOHNSON, Peter David 20 Green Close, Springfield, Chelmsford CM1 7SL — MB BS 1981 Lond.

JOHNSON, Mr Peter George (retired) 88 Tilford Road, Farnham GU9 8DS Tel: 01252 713303 Fax: 01252 713303 — BM BCh 1957 Oxf.; MA Oxf. 1957; FRCS Eng. 1967. Prev: Cons. Surg. Orthop. Frimley Pk. Hosp. & Farnham Hosp.

JOHNSON, Peter George Shore, OBE (retired) Linden House, Romsey SO51 8YN Tel: 01794 512388 — MB BS Lond. 1942; MRCS Eng. LRCP Lond. 1942. Prev: Ho. Phys. & Ho. Surg. Middlx. Hosp.

JOHNSON, Peter Hegarty Liscard Group Practice, Croxteth Avenue, Liscard, Wallasey CH44 5UL Tel: 0151 638 4764 Fax: 0151637 0579 — MB ChB 1975 Dundee.

JOHNSON, Peter James 111 Butts Green Road, Hornchurch RM11 2LD — MB BS 1997 Lond.

JOHNSON, Peter Martyn Tregonce Cottage, St. Issey, Wadebridge PL27 7QJ Tel: 0120881 2066 — MB BS 1963 Lond.; MRCS Eng. LRCP Lond. 1963; MRCGP 1974; DA Eng. 1968; DTM & H Eng. 1968; DObst RCOG 1965. (Univ. Coll. Hosp.) Clin. Asst. (Anaesth.) Plymouth HA; Dep. BMA. Deputising Serv. (Health-Call. Med. Servs.) Plymouth. Prev: Med. Off. Methodist Miss. Soc. Lond.

JOHNSON, Peter Millward Woodlands, Colindale Hospital, Collindale Avenue, London NW9 5HG Tel: 020 8200 9586; 27 Bullescroft Road, Edgware HA8 8RN Tel: 020 8958 7779 — MB BS 1961 Lond. (Lond. Hosp.) Clin. Asst. Barnet Drug-Alcohol Servs. Lond. Socs: BMA. Prev: GP Lond.; Ho. Phys. Lambeth Hosp.; Mem. Inner Lond. LMC.

JOHNSON, Peter Neil Centre for Postgraduate Medical Education, Clinical Sciences Building, Leicester Royal Infirmary, Leicester LE2 7LX Tel: 01162 523121 Fax: 01162 523123 Email: mch17@le.ac.uk; Pond House, Burmington, Shipston-on-Stour CV36 5AR — BM BCh 1983 Oxf.; FRCP 2001; MD 1999 Warwick; FRCGP 1998; MSc Warwick 1993; MRCGP 1988; MRCP (UK) 1986; DRCOG 1986; MA Camb. 1980. PostGrad. Dean, Univ. of Leicester.; Research Fell. (Pub. Health & Primary Care) Oxf. Prev: Director of Post Grad. GP Educat., Oxf.; GP Shipston on Stour; SHO (Palliat. Med.) Birm.

JOHNSON, Peter Philip 8 Chive Road, Earley, Reading RG6 5XP Tel: 0118 986 0853 Email: ppjohnson@compuserve.com; University of Reading Medical Practice, University Health Centre, 9 Northcourt Avenue, Reading RG2 7HE Tel: 0118 987 4551 — MB BS Lond. 1968; DCH Eng. 1971; DObst RCOG 1970. (Middlx.) Dir. Reading Univ. Health Serv. Socs: Pres. Brit. Assn. Health Serv. Higher Educ. 1998-9. Prev: Ho. Off. Gen. Med. & Surg. Mayday Hosp. Croydon; Ho. Off. O & G Lewisham Hosp.; Ho. Off. Sydenham Childr. Hosp.

JOHNSON, Peter Richard Eckford Dept. of Haematology, Western General Hospital, Crewe Road, Edinburgh EH4 2XU Tel: 0131 537 2595 Fax: 0131 537 1172 Email: peter.johnson@luht.scot.nhs.uk; 2 Kellerstain House, Gogar Station Road, Edinburgh EH12 9BS Tel: 0131 339 0355 — MB ChB 1984 Aberd.; MD Aberd. 1993. Cons. Haemat. W.. Gen. Hosp. NHS Trust. Socs: Fell. Roy. Coll. Phys.; Fell. of Roy. Coll. of pathologists. Prev: Sen. Regist. (Haemat.) N. W.. RHA; Regist. N. W. RHA; Research Fell. Leukaemia Research Fund Manch. Roy. Infirm.

JOHNSON, Professor Peter William Montague Cancer Research UK Oncology Unit, Southampton General Hospital, Southampton SO16 6YD Tel: 02380 796186 Fax: 02380 783839 Email: johnsonp@soton.ac.uk; The Old Lodge, High St, Titchfield, Fareham PO14 4AE — MB BChir 1985 Camb.; MD Camb. 1993; MRCP (UK) 1988; FRCP 1998. (St. Thomas's Hospital) Prof. (Med. Oncol.) Soton. Univ. Hosps. Socs: Amer. Soc. Clin. Oncol.; Assn. Cancer Phys.s; Brit. Assn. Cancer Research. Prev: Sen. Lect. & Hon. Cons. Med. Oncol. St. Jas. Univ. Hosp. Leeds.; Research Fell. (Med. Oncol.) St. Bart. Hosp. Lond.

JOHNSON, Rachel 404 Roman Road, Bow, London E3 5QJ — MB BS 1996 Lond.

JOHNSON, Rachel Anne 13 Fford-y-Gollen, Tonteg, Pontypridd CF38 1TA — BM BCh 1998 Oxf.; BM BCh Oxf 1998.

JOHNSON, Rachel Elizabeth 225 Osborne Road, West Jesmond, Newcastle upon Tyne NE2 3LB — MB BS 1997 Newc.

JOHNSON, Rex Samuel 21 Malmains Drive, Frenchay, Bristol BS16 1PQ; 269 Stapleton Road, Easton, Bristol BS5 0 — MB BS 1955 Punjab; MB BS Punjab (Pakistan) 1955.

JOHNSON, Richard 14 Southmayne Road, Sunderland SR4 8QU — MB BS 1998 Newc.; MB BS Newc 1998.

JOHNSON, Richard Anthony Halesowen Health Centre, 14 Birmingham Street, Halesowen B63 3HL Tel: 0121 550 1010 Fax: 0121 585 0993 — MB ChB 1980 Birm.; DRCOG 1984; DCH RCP Lond. 1983. Clin. Asst. (Psychiat.) Barnsley Hall Hosp. BromsGr..

JOHNSON, Richard Anthony 330 Nuneaton Road, Bulkington, Nuneaton CV12 9RR — MB ChB 1981 Birm.; FFA RCS Eng. 1985. Cons. Cardiothoracic Anaesth. & Intens. Care Walsgrave Hosp. Coventry. Socs: Assn. Anaesth. Prev: Sen. Regist. (Anaesth.) Roy. Perth Hosp. W.. Austral.; Sen. Regist. (Anaesth.) Manch. Roy. Infirm. & Wythenshawe Hosp.; Regist. (Anaesth.) Birm. Matern. Hosp. & Qu. Eliz. Hosp. Birm.

JOHNSON, Richard Campbell 7 Castle Side, Sheriff Hutton, York YO60 6RF Tel: 0134 77 545 — MB BS Lond. 1970; MRCS Eng. LRCP Lond. 1970; FFA RCS Eng. 1975; DA Eng. 1972. (Char. Cross) Cons. Anaesth. York Dist. Hosp. Socs: Assn. Anaesth.; BMA. Prev: Sen. Regist. (Anaesth.) Sheff. AHA (T); Clin. Research Fell. (Anaesth.) Roy. Vict. Hosp. Montreal, Canada; Regist. (Anaesth.) Stoke Mandeville Hosp. Aylesbury.

JOHNSON, Mr Richard Charles Sunnyview, St Brides Major, Bridgend CF32 0SA Tel: 01656 881078 — MB BCh 1988 Wales; FRCS Ed. 1993; FRCS (Gen) 1998. Cons. Surg. Socs: BASO. Prev: Sen. Regist. Wrexham Maelor Hosp. UHW Cardiff.

JOHNSON, Richard Joseph Department of Diagnostic Radiology, Christie Hospital, Wilmslow Road, Withington, Manchester M20 4BX Tel: 0161 446 3885 Fax: 0161 446 3769; 6 Haywards Close, Glossop SK13 7AZ Tel: 01457 867703 — MB BS 1970 Newc.; MB BS (Hons.) Newc. 1970; BSc (Hons.) Newc. 1967; FRCP Lond. 1992; MRCP (UK) 1973; FRCR 1980. (Newc.) Dir. (Med.) Christie Hosp. & Holt Radium Inst.; Hon. Sen. Lect. (Diag. Radiol.) Univ. Manch. Prev: Sen. Lect. (Oncol. Diag. Radiol.) Univ. Manch.; Hon. Cons. Radiol. Christie Hosp. & Holt Radium Inst.

JOHNSON, Richard Kenneth 7 West Bank, West Bank Road, Macclesfield SK10 3BT Tel: 01663 745053 — MB ChB 1997 Manch.

JOHNSON, Richard Michael Chainsbridge Medical Partnership, Chainbridge House, The Precinct, Blaydon-on-Tyne NE21 5BT Tel: 0191 414 2856 Fax: 0191 499 0449; Holmcroft, Acomb Drive, Wylam NE41 8BD Tel: 01661 852200 — MB BS 1987 Newc.; MRCGP 1991.

JOHNSON, Richard Noel Market Street Surgery, 92 Market Street, Dalton-in-Furness LA15 8AB Tel: 01229 462591 Fax: 01229 468217 — MB BS 1972 Newc.; DA Eng. 1977.

JOHNSON, Richard Thomas Helsby Street Medical Centre, 2 Helsby Street, Warrington WA1 3AW Tel: 01925 637304 Fax: 01925 570430; 20 Beechways, Appleton, Warrington WA4 5ER Tel: 01925 268262 — MB ChB 1972 Manch.; MRCGP 1979; DObst RCOG 1974.

JOHNSON, Richard Verity The Calderdale Royal Hospital, Salterkebble, Halifax HX3 OPW — MB ChB 1989 Aberd.; MRCGP 1993; FRCA 1996; DA (UK) 1994; Dip. IMC RCS Ed. 1992. (Aberd.) Socs: Assn. Anaesth.; Obst. Anaesth. Assn.; Intens. Care Soc. Prev: Regist. (Anaesth.) St. Jas. Univ. Hosp. Leeds; Regist. (Anaesth.) Leeds Gen. Infirm.; SHO (Anaesth.) Airdale Gen. Hosp. Keighley & St. Jas. Univ. Hosp. Leeds.

JOHNSON, Mr Robert Sandbanks, 68 Stanley Road, Hoylake, Wirral CH47 1HZ Tel: 0151 632 5133 — MRCS Eng. LRCP Lond. 1965; MChOrth Liverp. 1974; FRCS Eng. 1973; FRCS Ed. 1972. Cons. Orthop. Surg. Arrowe Pk. Hosp.

JOHNSON, Robert Allan Andrew (retired) The Surgery, The Down, Lamberhurst, Tunbridge Wells TN3 8EX Tel: 01892 890484/890800 Fax: 01892 891187 — MB ChB 1965 Glas.; MRCGP 1978; DObst RCOG 1967.

JOHNSON, Robert Harold (retired) Orchard House, Paignton Road, Stoke Gabriel, Totnes TQ9 6SE Tel: 01803 782275 — MB BCh BAO Belf. 1952; DA Eng. 1962; DObst RCOG 1958. Prev: Ho. Surg. Roy. Vict. Hosp. Belf.

JOHNSON, Robert Ian, Surg. Lt. RN Retd. The Cottages, Millfield Terrace, Sleaford NG34 7AD; The Cottage, Millfield Terrace, Sleaford NG34 7AD — MB BS 1979 Lond. (Lond. Hosp.)

JOHNSON, Robert William Sir Humphry Davy Department of Anaesthesia, Bristol Royal Infirmary, Bristol BS2 8HW Tel: 0117 928 2163 Email: rwjbristol@aol.com — MB BS 1967 Lond.; MRCS Eng. LRCP Lond. 1967; FRCA 1972. (St. Bart.) Cons. Anaesth. & Pain Relief United Bristol Healthcare Trust; Edit. Bd. Europ. Jl. Pain. Socs: (Counc.) Pain Soc.; Internat. Herpes Managem. Forum. Bd. Mem.; VZV Research Foundat. Bd. Mem.. Prev: Vis. Asst. Prof. (Anaesth.) & Assoc. Dir. Pain Clinic Univ.; Virginia Med. Centre, Virginia, USA.

JOHNSON, Mr Robert William Greenwood Central Manchester Health Care Trust Cobbett House, Manchester Royal Infirmary, Oxford Road, Manchester M13 9WL Tel: 0161 276 4413 Fax: 0161 276 8020 Email: rwgj@bigfoot.com; 41 Chapel Lane, Evergreen, Halebarns, Altrincham WA15 0AJ Tel: 0161 980 8840 Fax: 0161 980 8840 Email: rwgj@renal.cmht.nwest.nhs.uk — MB BS Durh. 1965; MS (Distinc.) Newc. 1973; FRCS Ed. 1994; FRCS Eng. 1970. (Univ. Durh. Coll. Med.) Med.Dir. Centr.. Man.Health Care Trust; Cons. Surg. & Hon. Reader Surg. Manch. Roy. Infirm.; Pybus Lecture N Eng. Surgic. Soc.; Hon. Cons. Roy. Manch. Childr. Hosp. Socs: Assn. Surg. (Vice Pres.).; Surgic. Research Soc.; (Pres.) Brit. Transpl. Soc. Prev: Vis. Asst. Prof. Surg. Univ. Calif., USA; Sen. Regist. (Surg.) Profess. Unit Roy. Vict. Infirm. Newc.; Hunt. Prof. RCS 1981.

JOHNSON, Roderick John Haematology Department, Birmingham Heartlands Hospital, Bordesley Green E., Birmingham B9 5SS Tel: 0121 424 3698 Fax: 0121 766 7530 Email: johnson@heartsol.wmids.nhs.uk — MB ChB 1987 Ed.; MRCP (UK) 1990; MD (Edin) 1999; MRC Path (Haem) 1998. (Edinburgh University) Cons. Haemat. Birm. Heartlands Hosp. Birm. Prev: Sen. Regist. Rotat. (Haemat.) Yorks. Region.

JOHNSON, Rodney (retired) Swallows, St. Wilfrids Green, Hailsham BN27 1DR — MB BS 1961 Lond. Prev: Ho. Surg. & Ho. Phys. Whipps Cross Hosp. Lond.

JOHNSON, Roger Alexander Manchester Health Authority, Gateway House, Piccadilly S., Manchester M60 7LP Tel: 0161 237 2711 Fax: 0161 237 2813 Email: roger.johnson@mchester-ha.nwest.nhs.uk; Abbotsford Green Lane, Hyde SK14 3BD Tel: 0161 368 2535 — MB BS 1966 Lond.; AFOM RCP Lond. 1981; MRCGP RCGP 1997; DIH Eng. 1980; DAvMed Eng. 1971. (Lond. Hosp.) Med. Dir. Manch. Health Auth. Manch.; GP. Socs: BMA.

JOHNSON, Roger David Redgate Medical Centre, Weston Zoyland Road, Bridgwater TA6 5BF Tel: 01278 444411 Fax: 01278 446816 — MB ChB 1978 Birm.; MRCGP 1983; DRCOG 1982; Cert. JCC Lond. 1982; DA Eng. 1981. Prev: Trainee GP Shrops.; SHO (O & G, Paediat., Anaesth. & Psychiat.) Copthorne Hosp. Shrewsbury.

JOHNSON, Rosemary Alison Worcester Royal Infirmary, Newtown Road, Ronkswood, Worcester WR5 1HN Tel: 01905 763333 — BM Soton 1984; FRCS Ed. 1990; DCH RCP Lond. 1989; FFAEM 1996. (Southampton University) Cons. in A & E Med. Worcester Roy. Infirm.

JOHNSON, Ruby Dreweatt (retired) Llwyn Malys, Adpar, Newcastle Emlyn SA38 9NT — MRCS Eng. LRCP Lond. 1932; BA Oxf. 1928.

JOHNSON, Ruth Flat 14, Canon Frome Court, Canon Frome, Ledbury HR8 2TD Tel: 01531 670868 — MB ChB 1997 Liverp.; BSc Manch 1996. (Liverpool) SHO Basic Surgic. Train. Scheme.

JOHNSON, Ruth Heather c/o 52 Styal Road, Wilmslow SK9 4AQ — MB ChB 1995 Leeds. SHO (A & E) Dryburn. Socs: MPS; MSS. Prev: Ho. Off. (Med.) N. Tees Hosp. Stockton on Tees; Ho. Off. (Surg.) Qu. Eliz. Hosp. Gateshead.

JOHNSON, Sally Practice A, Hinckley Health Centre, 27 Hill Street, Hinckley LE10 1DS Tel: 01455 635362 Fax: 01455 619797 — MB ChB 1987 Liverp.; MRCGP 1994. (Liverp.) Prev: SHO (O & G) Geo. Eliot Hosp. Nuneaton; SHO Rotat. (Psychiat.) Mersey RHA; SHO (A & E & Orthop.) & Ho. Off. (Med. & Surg.) Walton Hosp.

JOHNSON, Sally Ann Flat 2, 6 Norwood Villas, Waterworks Road, Edgbaston, Birmingham B16 9DB — BM BS 1988 Nottm.; BMedSci 1986; MRCGP 1993; DRCOG 1991. Prev: Trainee GP/SHO (A & E) Warrington Dist. Gen. Hosp.

JOHNSON, Sally Ann 53 North Road, Harborne, Birmingham B17 9PD Tel: 0121 426 1926 — MB ChB 1996 Birm.; ChB Birm. 1996. (Birm.) SHO (Paediat.) New Cross Hosp. Wolverhampton. Socs: BMA. Prev: Ho. Off. Med.; Ho. Off. Surg.

JOHNSON, Sally Jane West Wales Dialysis Centre, Bronwydd Road, Carmarthen Tel: 01267 234344; Cwmbwri, Ferryside SA17 5TW — MB ChB 1980 Sheff.; MRCGP 1984. Clin. Asst. (Renal Med.) Morriston Hosp. Trust Swansea.

JOHNSON, Sarah Jane 3 Mount Road, Evesham WR11 6BE — MB BCh 1995 Wales.

JOHNSON, Sarah Joanne Department of Pathology, Royal Victoria Infirmary, Queen Victoria Road, Newcastle upon Tyne NE1 4LP Tel: 0191 232 5131 — MB BS 1987 Newc.; PhD Newc. 1996; MRCPath 1993. Cons. Histopath. & Cytopath. Roy. Vict. Infirm. & Assoc. Hosps. NHS Trust. Socs: BMA; Assn. Clin. Path.; Internat. Assn. Path. Prev: Lect. & Sen. Regist. (Histopath.) Univ. Newc.; Demonst. (Histopath.) & SHO (Laborat. Med.) Roy. Vict. Infirm. Newc. u Tyne; Ho. Off. Freeman Hosp. Newc. u Tyne.

JOHNSON, Sharon Lesley 13 Sandpiper Lane, Wellingborough NN8 4TW — MB ChB 1990 Dundee.

***JOHNSON, Sharon Patricia** 35 Calder Drive, Sutton Coldfield B76 1YR; 5 Brook Close, Mortonbrook, Sandown PO36 9PY — MB ChB 1994 Liverp.

JOHNSON, Sheila MacDonald Lyndhurst, Warrington Road, Mere, Knutsford WA16 0TE Tel: 01565 830188 — LRCPI & LM, LRSCI & LM 1960; LRCPI & LM, LRCSI & LM 1960. (RCSI) SCMO Community Med. Manch. AHA (T). Prev: Clin. Med. Off. Manch. AHA (T); Ho. Surg. & Ho. Phys. Ancoats Hosp. Manch.

JOHNSON, Simon Richard Division of Therapevtics, 'C' Floor, South Block, Queens Medical Centre, Nottingham NG7 2UH — MB BS 1990 Lond.; BSc (Hons.) Lond. 1980; MRCP (UK) 1993. (UCH/Middlesex) Sen. Lect., Hon. Cons., Therap. Univ. of Nottm. Prev: Regist. (Respirat. Gen. Med.) Mid Trent.; Research Fell. (Respirat. Med.) Univ. Nottm.; SHO Rotat. (Med.) N.wick Pk. Hosp. Harrow.

JOHNSON, Simon Robert Photiou and Partners, 1 Warren Road, Blundellsands, Liverpool L23 6TZ Tel: 0151 924 6464 Fax: 0151 932 0663; The Gables, 1 Lupton Drive, Crosby, Liverpool L23 9UA Tel: 0151 924 2923 — BM BCh 1984 Oxf.; MA Oxf. 1986, BM BCh 1984; MRCGP 1989; DRCOG 1988.

JOHNSON, Stafford Martin The White Cottage, 172 Grove Lane, Cheadle Hulme, Cheadle SK8 7NH — MB BS 1969 Lond.; MRCS Eng. LRCP Lond. 1968; DObst RCOG 1970. (St. Bart.) Socs: BMA. Prev: SHO (Anaesth.) Stockport & Buxton Gp. Hosps.; Cas. Ho. Phys. St. Bart. Hosp. Lond.; Ho. Off. Surg. & Obst. Cheltenham. Hosp.

JOHNSON, Stephanie Ann Great Staughton Surgery, 57 The Highway, Great Staughton, St. Neots, Huntingdon PE19 5DA Tel: 01480 860770 Fax: 01480 861514; Stileway, Pinfold Lane, Godmanchester, Huntingdon PE29 2JG — MB ChB 1985 Birm.; MRCGP 1990; DFFP 1990.

JOHNSON, Stephen Alan, Surg. Lt.-Cdr. RN Staithes Surgery, Seaton Crescent, Staithes, Saltburn-by-the-Sea TS13 5AY Tel: 01947 840480 Fax: 01947 841034 — MB BS 1984 Lond.; MRCGP 1993. Med. Off. HMS Victorious.

JOHNSON, Stephen Andrew Noel Taunton & Somerset Hospital, Musgrove Park, Taunton TA1 5DA Tel: 01823 333444 Fax: 01823 271023; 47 St. James Street, South Petherton TA13 5BN — MB BS 1972 Lond.; MRCS Eng. LRCP Lond. 1972; FRCPath 1991, M 1979; T(Path.) 1991. (Westm.) Cons. Haemat. Taunton & Som. NHS Trust; Cons. Haemat E. Som. NHS Trust. Socs: Eur. Haematol. Assn.; Amer. Soc. Clin. Oncol.; Eur. Soc. Med. Oncol. Prev: LRF Research Fell. MRC Leukaemia Unit Roy. Postgrad. Med. Sch. Lond.

JOHNSON, Stephen Karl Ronald Tel: 0208 761 4532 Fax: 0208 8766 7057; Aspen, 20 Meadow Way, Orpington BR6 8LW Tel: 01689 850882 — MB BChir 1975 Camb.; MA Camb. 1975; MRCGP 1984; DCH Eng. 1979; DRCOG 1978. (Camb. & Guy's) Socs: BMA. Prev: Resid. Obst. Guy's Hosp. Lond.; Trainee GP Tunbridge Wells VTS; Ho. Phys. Guy's Hosp. Lond.

JOHNSON, Mr Stephen Richard Department of Orthopaedics, Camarthanshire NHS Trust., West Wales General Hospital, Carmarthen SA31 2AF Tel: 01267 235151 Fax: 01267 227983; Cwmbwri, Ferryside SA17 5TW Tel: 01267 267849 Fax: 01267 267849 Email: johnson_s@email.msn.com — MB ChB 1979 Sheff.; FRCS Ed. 1984. Cons. Orthop. Surg. Carmarthenshire NHS Trust.

JOHNSON, Steven Richard The Grange, Maidstone Road, Platt, Sevenoaks TN15 8JT — MB BS 1985 Lond.; DCH RCP Lond. 1989. Prev: Trainee GP Maidstone Hosp. VTS; SHO (ENT) Kent Co. Ophth. & Aural Hosp. Maidstone; Ho. Off. (Gen. Med.) St. Jas. Hosp. Lond.

JOHNSON, Susan Station Road Health Centre, Station Road, Haydock, St Helens NA11 0JN Tel: 01744 22272; 34 Higher Lane, Rainford, St Helens WA11 8NX — MB ChB 1975 Liverp.

JOHNSON, Susan Elizabeth The Old Forge, Clunbury, Craven Arms SY7 0HG — MB BS 1991 Lond.

JOHNSON, Terence Curtis 11 Woodend Road, Bournemouth BH9 2JQ Tel: 01202 525252; 52 Glenferness Avenue, Bournemouth BH3 7ET — MB ChB 1982 Leeds; MRCGP 1988; DCH RCP Lond. 1985; DRCOG 1986. Asst. Dep. Police Surg. Poole.

JOHNSON, Thomas Ash Tree House, Church Street, Kirkham, Preston PR4 2SE Tel: 01772 686688 Fax: 01772 672054; Carrsfield Barn, Church Road, Treales, Preston PR4 3SH — MB ChB 1977 Manch.

JOHNSON, Thomas Brian William The Orchard, Village Road, Bromborough, Wirral CH62 7EU Tel: 0151 334 2084 — MB BS 1965 Lond.; MRCS Eng. LRCP Lond. 1964. (Guy's) Prev: Jun. Med. Regist. Lond. Hosp. & Brentwood Annexe; Ho. Surg. (Obst.) Lond. Hosp. (Qu. Mary's).

JOHNSON, Thomas William 52 Langham Road, Teddington TW11 9HQ — MB BS 1998 Lond.; MB BS Lond 1998.

JOHNSON, Timothy Mark Gladstone House Surgery, Gladstone Street W., Ilkeston DE7 5QS Tel: 0115 932 0248 — MB BS 1983 Lond.; MRCGP 1987; DRCOG 1986.

JOHNSON, Timothy Michael 38 St James's Park, Bath BA1 2SU — MB ChB 1990 Birm.

JOHNSON, Timothy William 67 Hale Road, Hale, Altrincham WA15 9HP — MB BS 1981 Lond.; FFA RCS Eng. 1986.

JOHNSON, Vanessa Catherine Bundaberg Base Hospital, PO Box 34, Bundaberg Qld 4670, Australia; 6 Ralston Mount, Broughty Ferry, Dundee DD5 1NN Tel: 01382 79924 — MB ChB 1993 Aberd.

JOHNSON, Victor Walker (retired) Reynard Cottage, Cannock Road, Penkridge, Stafford ST19 5DT — MB ChB 1952 Ed.; FRCP Lond. 1980, M 1964. Prev: Cons. Phys. Wolverhampton Hosp. Gp.

JOHNSON, Wendy Jane Victor Street Surgery, Victor Street, Shirley, Southampton SO15 5SY Tel: 023 8077 4781 Fax: 023 8039 0680; Summerhill, Fairfield Road, Shawford, Winchester SO21 2DA — MB BS 1968 Lond.; MRCS Eng. LRCP Lond. 1968; DObst RCOG 1970. (Guy's)

JOHNSON, William Duncan Kemble 11 Paul Street, Corsham SN13 9DG — MB BS 1994 Lond.; PhD Lond. 1992, BSc 1988, MB BS 1994.

JOHNSON, Zoe Katharina 47 Rowrah Road, Frizington CA26 3XJ — MB ChB 1990 Aberd.

JOHNSON-FERGUSON, Simon Joseph Catle Place Surgery, Tiverton EX16 7RT Tel: 01884 252333 — MB BS 1991 Lond.; DCCH RCGP 1955; DRCOG 1994; MRCGP 1996. GP Principal, Castle Pl. Surg. Prev: Trainee GP Tidworth VTS.

JOHNSON-NURSE, Mr Christopher 8 College Meadows, Lowestoft NR32 4DP — MB BCh 1975 Wales; FRCS Eng. 1980. Vis. Specialist Rockhampton Base Hosp. Qu.sland, Australia.

JOHNSON-SABINE, Eric Charles South Scarle Hall, South Scarle, Newark NG23 7JH — MB BS 1974 Lond.; MRCS Eng. LRCP Lond. 1974; FRCPsych 1997, M 1980; MRCGP 1978. (Univ. Coll. Lond.) Cons. Psychiat. St. Ann's Hosp. Lond.; Hon. Sen. Lect. Roy. Free Hosp. & Univ. Coll. Med. Sch. Lond. Prev: Trainee GP Lond. (St. Thos.) VTS; Regist. (Psychiat.) Middlx. Hosp. Lond.; Lect. Roy. Free Hosp. Lond.

JOHNSON SMITH, Edith Jeanne Parkhurst, Perrymans Lane, High Hurstwood, Uckfield TN22 4AG Tel: 01825 733202 Fax: 01825 732832 — MD 1948 Stanford Univ. USA; BA USA 1945. (Univ. Stanford)

JOHNSTON, Alan Robert West Wirral Group Practice, 530 Pensby Road, Thingwall, Wirral CH61 7UE Tel: 0151 648 1174 Fax: 0151 648 0644; 493 Pensby Road, Thingwall, Wirral CH61 7UQ — MB ChB 1977 Liverp.

JOHNSTON, Alan William (retired) Rivendell, Hillhead of Auchattie, Banchory AB31 6PT Tel: 01330 825328 — MB BChir 1951 MB BChir 1951; 1987 FRCP Glas. 1987; 1981 FRCP Ed., M 1979; 1973 FRCP Lond, M 1953; 1962 MD Camb. Cons. Phys. Aberd. Roy. Infirm.; Clin. Sen. Lect. (Med. & Genetics) Univ. Aberd. Prev: Res. Asst. Phys. & Regist. (Med.) Univ. Coll. Hosp. Lond.

JOHNSTON, Alexandra Kate 39C Parsons Green, London SW6 4UJ — MB ChB 1984 Leic.

JOHNSTON, Alison 26 Hoe Lane, North Baddesley, Southampton SO52 9NH — MB BS 1996 Lond.

JOHNSTON, Alison Julia Forestview, 83 Carnreagh, Hillsborough BT26 6LJ — MB BCh BAO 1985 Belf.

JOHNSTON, Alison Margaret Arbuthnott Lodge, Ferntower Road, Crieff PH7 3DH — MB ChB 1995 Dundee.

JOHNSTON, Andrew 64 Rubislaw Den N., Aberdeen AB15 4AN — MB ChB 1998 Aberd.; MB ChB Aberd 1998; BSc Med Sci (Hons) Aberd 1996. (Aberdeen Univ)

JOHNSTON, Andrew James The Limes, Chapel Lane, Farnsfield, Newark NG22 8JW Tel: 01623 882268 — BChir 1994 Camb.; BA Camb. 1992; MA Camb. 1996; FRCA 1997. (Cambridge) SHO (Anaesth.) Qu.s Med. Centre Nottm. Socs: BMA. Prev: SHO (Med.) Wansbeck Gen. Hosp. Ashington; SHO (Anaesth.) Wansbeck Gen. Hosp. Ashington; SHO (A & E) Leicester Roy. Infirm. Leicester.

JOHNSTON, Andrew McDonald Acute Stroke Unit, Aberdeen Royal Infirmary, Aberdeen AB25 2ZB Tel: 01224 681818; 36 Mount Street, Aberdeen AB25 2QT Tel: 01224 643778 Email: amcdj@bigfoot.com — MB ChB 1993 Dundee; MRCP (Ireland) 1998. (Cardiovasc.) Research Fell., Aberd. Roy. Infirm. Prev: SHO Aberd. Roy. Infirm.; SHO Qu. Eliz. Hosp., Gateshead; SHO, S.port & Formby DGH. S.port.

JOHNSTON, Angela Mary South Durham Health Care Trust, Health Centre, Escomb Road, Bishop Auckland DL14 6HT Tel: 01388 454000 Ext: 2776 Fax: 01388 454183; Killowen Cottage, Summerhouse, Darlington DL2 3UD Tel: 01325 374672 — MB BCh BAO 1973 Dub.; BA Dub. 1971; DCH Dub. 1975; FRCPCH 1997. (Trinity Coll. Dub.) Cons. Community Paediat. S. Durh. Health Care NHS Trust. Socs: BMA; FRCPCH; BACCH. Prev: SCMO Bishop Auckland Hosps. NHS Trust.

JOHNSTON, Ann Marie 14 Laigh Road, Newton Mearns, Glasgow G77 5EQ — MB ChB 1983 Glas.

JOHNSTON, Mr Anthony Oswald Barr 27 Cloister Crofts, Leamington Spa CV32 6QG Tel: 01926 36136 — MB BS 1966 Lond.; FRCS Eng. 1971; FRCS Ed. 1971. (St. Mary's) Cons. Gen. Surg. S. Warks. (Leamington & Warwick) Health Dist. Prev: Sen. Surg. Regist. Aberd. Roy. Infirm.; Rotat. Surg. Regist. Roy. Infirm. Sheff.

JOHNSTON, Arnold Neill Rutherglen Health Centre, 130 Stonelaw Road, Rutherglen, Glasgow G73 2PQ Tel: 0141 531 6020 Fax: 0141 531 4130; 1/2 Brownside Mews, 148B Brownside Road, Cambuslang, Glasgow G72 8AH — MB BCh BAO 1986 Belf.; DA (UK) 1989. Prev: Trainee GP Helensburgh; SHO (A & E) Inverclyde Hosp. Greenock.

JOHNSTON, Brian, Maj. RAMC Retd. Queens Road Surgery, 10B Queens Road, Blackhill, Consett DH8 0BN Tel: 01207 502071 Fax: 01207 583717; Dunadd, West Law Road, Shotley Bridge, Consett DH8 0EH Tel: 01207 501636 — MB ChB 1975 Glas.; FRCOG 1996, M 1983. GP. Prev: Cons. O & G Shotley Bridge Gen. Hosp. Co. Durh.; Cons. O & G Army Med. Servs.; SHO (Paediat.) Seafield Hosp. Ayr.

JOHNSTON, Brian Bernard Ad Astra, 127 Kinghorne Road, Lawside, Dundee DD3 6PW Tel: 01382 228146 — MB ChB 1972 St. And.; BMSc (Hons.) Dund 1969; FRCPsych 1993, M 1976; DPM Ed. & Glas. 1975. Cons. Psychiat. (Alcoholism & Drug Addic.) Roy. Dundee Liff Hosp.; Hon. Sen. Lect. (Psychiat.) Univ. Dundee. Prev: Cons. Psychiat. Stratheden Hosp. Cupar.

JOHNSTON, Brian McFarland Tarbock Road Surgery, 133 Tarbock Road, Huyton, Liverpool L36 5TE Tel: 0151 449 3020 Fax: 0151 489 9375 — MB ChB 1973 Aberd.; DMT & H Liverp. 1986. Socs: Liverp. Med. Inst.; Small Pract.s Assn. Prev: Trainee Path. Roy. Free Hosp. Lond.; Trainee GP Teesside & Liverp. VTS Liverp. Univ.; Ho. Off (Geriat. & Surg.) S. Grampian Health Dist. (Aberd.).

JOHNSTON, Brian Thomas — MB BCh BAO 1986 Belf.; FRCP 1999; MD Belf. 1992; MRCP (UK) 1989. Cons. Phys. (Gastroenterol.) Roy. Vistoria Hosp. Belf. Prev: Cons. Lagan Valley Hosp. Lisburn.

JOHNSTON, Bridget Elizabeth Lynebank Hospital, Halbeath Road, Dunfermline KY11 4UW Tel: 01383 623623; 16 Ferryhills Road, North Queensferry, Inverkeithing KY11 1HE Tel: 01383 412441 — MB BS Lond. 1970; MRCS Eng. LRCP Lond. 1970. (St Thomas's Hospital London) Clin. Asst. (Learning Disabil.) Lynebank Hosp. Dunfermline.; Staff Grade (Ment. Health) Qu. Margt. Hosp. Dunfermline. Prev: Staff Grade & Clin. Asst. (Learning Disabil.) Gogarburn Hosp. Edin.

JOHNSTON, Bryan Malcolm 4 Faraday Place, Stoke-on-Trent ST4 6RF Tel: 01782 610618 — MRCS Eng. LRCP Lond. 1982. Clin. Asst. Mid. Staffs. HA. Socs: Anglo-French Med. Soc. Prev: SHO (Orthop.) Whipps Cross Hosp. Waltham Forest; Ho. Phys. P. of Wales Hosp. Lond.; Ho. Surg. Rochford Hosp.

JOHNSTON, Bryan William The Surgery, 11 Main Street, Leuchars, St Andrews KY16 0HB Tel: 01334 839210 Fax: 01334 838770 — MB ChB 1980 Aberdeen; MB ChB Aberd. 1980; MRCGP 1986; DCCH 1987. (Aberdeen) GP Leuchars, Fife.

JOHNSTON, Carol Anne Kelso Medical Group Practice, Health Centre, Inch Road, Kelso TD5 7JP Tel: 01573 224424 Fax: 01573 226388; Goshen Bank, Edenside Road, Kelso TD5 7BS — MB ChB 1981 Ed.; DRCOG 1983.

JOHNSTON, Carole Vivienne McQueen Grampian University Hospitals Trust, Community Division HQ, Berrydeen Road, Aberdeen AB25 3HG Tel: 01224 663131; Eastside, Tillygreig, Udby, Ellon AB41 6SN Tel: 01651 842022 Email: carole.vm.johnson@talk21.com — MB BS 1985 Lond.; MRCGP 1992. (Westm.)

JOHNSTON, Caroline Mary Hawthorne Drive Surgery, 206 Hawthorne Drive, Ipswich IP2 0QQ Tel: 01473 685070; 31 Borrowdale Avenue, Ipswich IP4 2TJ — MB ChB 1980 Liverp.; MRCS Eng. LRCP Lond. 1980; MRCGP 1985; DRCOG 1985; DCCH RCP Ed. 1985. (Univ. Liverp.)

JOHNSTON, Cecilia Douglas 10 Hawthorn Park, Castlederg BT81 7BX — MB ChB 1940 Aberd.; BSc 1934, MB ChB Aberd. 1940. (Aberd.)

JOHNSTON, Charles Gardner Anaesthetic Deptartment, Derriford Hospital, Plymouth PL6 8DH Tel: 01752 777111 — MB BCh BAO 1977 Belf.; FFA RCSI 1985. Cons. Anaesth. Derriford Hosp. Plymouth.

JOHNSTON, Christine Elizabeth Flat 17, 71 St Vincent Crescent, Finnieston, Glasgow G3 8NQ — MB ChB 1998 Glas.; MB ChB Glas 1998.

JOHNSTON, Mr Christopher Alan Barr (retired) Queen Margaret Hospital, Whitefield Road, Dunfermline KY12 0SU — MB BS Lond. 1963; FRCS Ed. 1968; MRCS Eng. LRCP Lond. 1963; T(S) 1991; DObst RCOG 1965. Cons. Surg. Qu. Margt. Hosp. Dunfermline Fife. Prev: Sen. Lect. (Surg.) Makerere Univ. Med. Sch. Kampala, Uganda.

JOHNSTON, Christopher Anthony The Parklands Medical Practice, Park Road Medical Centre, Bradford BD5 0SG Tel: 01274 227575 Fax: 01274 693558 Email: cjohnston@bradford-ha.nhs.uk — MB ChB 1980 Aberd.

JOHNSTON, Colin Lindsay Wyllie Hemel Hempstead General Hospital, Hillfield Road, Hemel Hempstead HP2 4AD Tel: 01442 213141 Fax: 01442 287082; St Albans City Hospital, Normandy Road, St Albans AL3 5 Tel: 01727 866122 Ext: 4858 — MD 1985 Camb.; MA BChir 1977, MB 1978; FRCP Lond. 1994; MRCP (UK) 1979. Cons. Phys & Endocrinol. Hemel Hempstead Gen. Hosp. Prev: Sen. Regist. St. Geo. Hosp. Lond.; MRC Trav. Fell. Seattle, USA.; Research Fell. King's Coll. Hosp. Lond.

JOHNSTON, Colin Patterson 19 Old Auchans View, Dundonald, Kilmarnock KA2 9EX — MB BCh BAO 1985 Belf.

JOHNSTON, Daphne Charlton Hill Surgery, Charlton Road, Andover SP10 3JY Tel: 01264 337979 Fax: 01264 334251 — MB BS 1976 Lond.; BA (Physiol. Sci.) Oxf. 1972; MRCP (UK) 1979; MRCGP 1983; DCH RCP Lond. 1982. Prev: GP Chalfont St. Peter.

JOHNSTON, Mr David Leeds General Infirmary, Great Georges St., Leeds LS1 3EX — MB ChB 1960 Glas.; ChM Glas. 1976, MD (Hons.) 1973; MB ChB (Hons. & Brunton Prize) 1960; FRCS Ed. 1963; FRCS Glas. 1964; FRCS Eng. 1979. (Glas.) Prof. Surg. Univ. Leeds; Hon. Cons. Surg. Leeds Gen. Infirm. Socs: Surg. Research Soc. & Brit. Soc. Gastroenterol. Prev: Lect. in Surg. Univ. Dept. Surg. Sheff. Roy. Infirm.; Reader & Hon. Cons. Surg. Leeds Gen. Infirm.; Prof. Surg. Univ. Bristol & Hon. Cons. Surg. Bristol Roy. Infirm.

JOHNSTON, David Field Lane Surgery, 42 Field Lane, Kessingland, Lowestoft NR33 7QA Tel: 01502 740203; 12 Wangford Road, Reydon, Southwold IP18 6PY — MB ChB 1987 Dundee; MRCGP 1993. (Univ. Dundee)

JOHNSTON, David Alexander Wards 5 & 6, Ninewells Hospital, Dundee DD1 9SY Tel: 01382 660111; Taybank, 3 Station Crescent,

Invergowrie, Dundee DD2 5DT Tel: 01382 562445 — MB ChB 1982 Dundee; MD Dundee 1994; MRCP (UK) 1987; FRCP Ed. 1997. Cons. Phys. (Gastroenterol.) Ninewells Hosp. Dundee. Socs: Fell. Roy. Coll. Phys. Edin.; Brit. Soc. Gastroenterol. Prev: Cons. Phys. (Gastroenterol.) Vict. Hosp. Kirkcaldy; Cons. Phys. (Gastroenterol.) Baracwanath Hosp., Soweto; Cons. Phys. (Gastrointest.) Clinic Groote Schuur Hosp., Cape Town.

JOHNSTON, Mr David Frederick Hemel Hempstead General Hospital, Hillfield Road, Hemel Hempstead HP2 4AD Tel: 01442 281042; 16 Crosspaths, Harpenden AL5 3HE — MB ChB Manch. 1981; BSc (Med. Sci.) St. And. 1978; FRCS (Otol.) 1993; FRCS Ed. 1987; FRCS Eng. 1987. Cons. ENT Surg. Luton & Dunstable Hosp.; Cons. ENT Surg. St. Alban's City Hosp. & Hemel Hempstead Gen. Hosp. Prev: Sen. Regist. (ENT) Guy's Hosp. & Lewisham Hosp. Lond.; Sen. Fell. (Otolaryngol. & Head & Neck Surg.) Univ. Washington Seattle, USA.

JOHNSTON, David Henderson (retired) 2 Carisbrooke Road, Edgbaston, Birmingham B17 8NW Tel: 0121 429 1119 — MB BCh BAO Belf. 1950; MRCGP 1958. Prev: OBStJ.

JOHNSTON, David Howard 45 Ferris Bay Road, Islandmagee, Larne BT40 3RT — MB ChB 1980 Aberd.

JOHNSTON, David Iain Osborne Lodge, 121 Alexandra Parade, Dunoon PA23 8AW Tel: 01369 705079 Fax: 01369 702289 — MB ChB 1972 Glas.; MRCGP 1976; DA Eng. 1977; DObst RCOG 1975. (Univ. Glas.) Hosp. Pract. (Anaesth.) Dunoon Gen. Hosp. Prev: Regist. (Anaesth.) Vict. Infirm. Glas.; SHO (Med.), Ho. Phys. & Ho. Surg. Dumfries Roy. Infirm.; SHO Cresswell Matern. Hosp.

JOHNSTON, David John Maine Medical Practice, Old Mill Park, Main Street, Cullybackey, Ballymena BT42 1GP Tel: 028 2588 2222 Fax: 028 2588 3900; Lynwood House, Gracehill, Ballymena BT42 2NN — MB BCh BAO 1988 Belf.; MRCGP 1992; DMH Belf. 1993; DRCOG 1991; DCH RCPSI 1991; Dip. IMC RCS Ed. 1991. (Queen's University Belfast) Med. Dir. Dalriada Doctor on Call. Socs: BMA; Ulster Med. Soc. Prev: Trainee GP Ahoghill.

JOHNSTON, David William Hugh 6 Tullaghgore Road, Ballymoney BT53 6QF — MB ChB 1994 Dundee.

JOHNSTON, Derek Iain Children's Department, Queen's Medical Centre, University Hospital NHS Trust, Nottingham NG7 2UH Tel: 0115 924 9924 Fax: 0115 970 9382 Email: derek.johnston@nottingham.ac.uk; Tel: 01623 882268 — MB BChir Camb. 1967; MD Camb. 1976; FRCP Lond. 1982; MRCP (UK) 1970; DCH Eng. 1970; FRCPCH 1997. (University of Cambridge) Cons. Paediat. Univ. Hosp. Nottm. Socs: Brit. Paediat. Assn. & Europ. Soc. Paediat. Endocrinol. Prev: Lect. (Child Health) King's Coll. Hosp. Lond.; Chief Resid. & Fell. (Paediat.) Univ. Colorado Denver, USA; Ho. Phys. Hosp. Sick Childr. Gt. Ormond St.

JOHNSTON, Derek John Bonner (retired) 11 Dilke Street, Chelsea, London SW3 4JE Tel: 020 7352 0578 — MRCS Eng. LRCP Lond. 1945. Prev: Capt. RAMC.

JOHNSTON, Professor Desmond Geoffrey Endocrinology & Metabolic Medicine, Imperial College School of Medicine, St Mary's Hospital, Praed St., London W2 1NY Tel: 020 7886 1209 Fax: 020 7886 1790; 65 Albany Street, Flat C, London NW1 4BT Tel: 020 7935 5347 — MB ChB 1971 Ed.; PhD Soton 1982; FRCP Lond. 1988; FRCPath 1996. Prof. Clin. Endocrinol. Imp. Coll. Sch. Med. Lond.

JOHNSTON, Dorothy Gladys 15 Glengorm Avenue, Coleraine BT52 1TF — MB BCh BAO 1993 Belf. SHO (A & E) Coleraine Hosp. Prev: Ho. Off. (Med. & Surg.) Coleraine Hosp.

JOHNSTON, Douglas Matthew Church Farmhouse, Glapthorn, Northampton NN6 — MB ChB 1961 Liverp.; MRCP Lond. 1967; MRCP Ed. 1967; DCH Eng. 1963. Cons. Paediat. PeterBoro. Dist. Hosp. Prev: Lect. Dept. Child Health Univ. Sheff.; Sen. Med. Regist. Alder Hey Childr. Hosp. Liverp.; Fell. Dept. Neurol. Johns Hopkins Hosp. Baltimore, U.S.A.

JOHNSTON, Edward Alexander (retired) 121 Muirfield Road, Inverness IV2 4A — MB ChB 1927 Aberd.; MA, MB ChB Aberd. 1927, DPH 1931. Prev: Cons. Chest Phys. N. RHB (Scotl.).

JOHNSTON, Edward Martin Pine Lodge, 2 Old Hall Close, Mottram-in-Longdendale, Hyde SK14 6LX Tel: 0161 62960 — MB BCh BAO 1955 Belf. (Belf.) Local Treasury Med. Off.; Med. Off. Metal Box & Other Cos. Socs: Fell. Manch. Med. Soc.

JOHNSTON, Eleanora Jessie 26 Carrick Road, Ayr KA7 2RB Tel: 01292 65666 — MB ChB 1944 Glas. Clin. Med. Off. Ayrsh. & Arran Health Bd.

JOHNSTON, Elizabeth McAllister 36 Radstock Road, Reading RG1 3PS; University of Reading Medical Practice, 9 Northcourt Avenue, Reading RG2 7HE Tel: 0118 987 4551 — MB ChB 1992 Glas.; DCCH RCPG 1996; DFFP 1995; DRCOG 1995; MRCGP 1997. (Glas.) GP Princip. Univ. of Reading Med. Pract.

JOHNSTON, Fiona Alexandra Bonner The Medical Centre, 144-150 High Road, London NW10 2PT Tel: 020 8459 5550 Fax: 020 8451 7268; 7 Ebrington Road, Harrow HA3 0LP Tel: 020 8907 2541 — MB BS 1979 Lond.; MRCP (UK) 1985; MRCGP 1986; DCH Eng. 1981. (St. Mary's)

JOHNSTON, Fiona Anne Stobhill General Hospital, Balornock Road, Glasgow G21 3UN; 26 Douglas Avenue, Langbank, Port Glasgow PA14 6PE — MB ChB 1980 Glas.; FRCP Glas. 1993. Cons. Phys. Geriat. Med. Stobhill NHS Trust. Socs: Brit. Geriat. Soc.; BMA. Prev: Sen. Regist. (Geriat. & Gen. Med.) Stobhill Hosp. Glas.

JOHNSTON, Fiona Irene 1 Strude Howe, Alva FK12 5JU — MB ChB 1995 Aberd.

JOHNSTON, Mr Francis Gerard 1 Kenilworth Avenue, Stoke D'Abernon, Cobham KT11 2ST — MB BChir 1983 Camb.; MA Camb. 1984, MB BChir 1983; FRCS Eng. 1987. Cons. Neurosurg. Atkinson Morley Hosp. Lond. Prev: Sen. Regist. (Neurosurg.) Nat. Hosp. Qu. Sq. Lond.; Regist. & Lect. (Neurosurg.) Atkinson Morley Hosp. Lond.

JOHNSTON, Francis Paul Damien Dungiven Health Centre, 1 Chapel Road, Dungiven, Londonderry BT47 4RS Tel: 028 7774 1801 Fax: 028 7774 1355; 183 Glenshane Road, Cross, Londonderry BT47 3EN — MB BCh BAO 1981 Dub.

JOHNSTON, Frederick Robert Peter Hart Lodge Surgery, Jones Road, Hartlepool TS24 9BD Tel: 01429 267573 Fax: 01429 869027; 3 Hartville Road, Hartstation, Hartlepool TS24 9RG Tel: 01429 279738 — MB ChB 1980 Manch.

JOHNSTON, George (retired) 6 Westbourne Gardens, Glasgow G12 9XD Tel: 0141 339 4667 — BSc 1938, MB ChB Glas. 1941; FRCP Glas. 1973, M 1962; FRFPS Glas. 1948. Hon. Med. Adviser Commonw. Games Counc. Scotl. & Scott. Amateur Rowing Assoc. Prev: Cons. Phys. Kt.swood Hosp. & W.. Infirm. Glas.

JOHNSTON, Professor George Dennis Dept. Therapeutics and Pharmacology, Whika Medical Building, 97 Lisburn Road, Belfast BT9 7BL Tel: 02890 335770 Fax: 02890 438346 Email: g.d.johnston@qub.ac.uk; 12 Ormiston Park, Belfast BT4 3JT Tel: 02890 659957 — MB BCh BAO 1971 Belf.; PhD Belf. 1985, DSc 1996, MD 1978; FRCP Lond. 1995; FRCPI 1992, M 1990; FRCP Ed. 1985; MRCP (UK) 1974; DCH RCPSI 1975. (Qu. Univ. Belf.) Prof. Clin. Pharmacol. & Cons. Physican (Therap. & Pharmacol.) Belf. City & Roy. Vict. Hosps. & Qu.'s Univ. Belf.; Exec. Edr. Brit. Jl. Clin. Pharmacol.; Dir. Drugs & Poisons Informat. Serv. N. Irel.; Chairm. Drugs & Therap. Comms. DHSS & EHSSB N. Irel. Socs: Exec. Comm. Mem. Brit. Hypertens. Soc.; Brit. Pharmacol. Soc.; Eur. Assn. Clin. Toxicol. Prev: Merck, Sharpe & Dohme Internat. Fell. Clin. Pharmacol. 1980-81.

JOHNSTON, Professor George Weir, OBE (retired) 102 Warren Road, Donaghadee BT21 0PQ Tel: 02891 888639 — MB BCh BAO 1956 Belf.; MCh Belf. 1965; FRCS Ed. 1995; FRCSI 1977; FRCS Eng. 1962; DObst RCOG 1958; DCH Eng. 1958. Prev: Cons. Surg. Roy. Vict. Hosp. Belf.

JOHNSTON, Gordon The Surgery, Bellyeoman Road, Dunfermline KY12 0AE Tel: 01383 721266 Fax: 01383 625068 — MB ChB 1979 Ed.; MRCGP 1983. GP Dunfermline.

JOHNSTON, Graham Alexander Department of Dermatology, Leicester Royal Infirmary, Leicester LE1 5WW Tel: 0116 254 5162 Fax: 0116 258 6792 — MB ChB 1991 Manch.; MRCP (UK) 1995. Cons. Dermat. Leicester Roy. Infirm. Leic.; Cons. Dermat. Leicester Gen. Hosp. Leic.

JOHNSTON, Graham Murray 4 Springdale Park, Bieldside, Aberdeen AB15 9FB Tel: 01224 868264 — MB ChB 1982 Aberd.; FRCA. 1987. Cons. Anaesth. Aberd. Roy. Infirm. NHS Trust.

JOHNSTON, Harold Andrew Longroyde, Bollin Hill, Wilmslow SK9 4AN Tel: 01625 525904 — MB BCh BAO 1951 Belf.; DPH 1958. (Belf.)

JOHNSTON, Helen Clare 130 Roding Road, London E5 0DS — MB BS 1995 Lond.

JOHNSTON, Helen Gabrielle 20 Cairnwood Drive, Airdrie ML6 9HR — MB ChB 1988 Glas.; MRCGP 1992.

JOHNSTON, Helen Margaret Heatherlea, Kyleakin, Isle of Skye IV41 8PR Tel: 01599 4153; European Baptist Mission, Baptist Convention Sierra Leone, Kassiri, PO Box 300, Freetown, Sierra Leone — MB ChB 1985 Ed.; DCH RCPS Glas. 1991; DRCOG 1991; DTM & H Liverp. 1991.

JOHNSTON, Henry Christie The Health Centre, 19 Main St., Eglinton, Londonderry BT47 3AB Tel: 01504 811281 — MB BCh BAO 1974 Belf.

JOHNSTON, Iain Riverview Practice, Wick Medical Centre, Martha Terrace, Wick KW1 5EL Tel: 01955 602355 Fax: 01955 602434; 1 Port Dunbar, Wick KW1 4JJ Tel: 01955 603965 Email: drijohn@dircon.co.uk — MB ChB 1973 Aberd.; Dip. Med. Educat. Dund 1993. Assoc. Adviser (Gen. Pract.) Highland; Hon. Med. Asst. Wick Lifeboat; Dep. Police Surg. Caithness.

JOHNSTON, Iain George 32 Mayfair Road, Newcastle upon Tyne NE2 3DP — MB ChB 1991 Ed.; FRCA 1996. Regist. (Anaesth.) Freeman Rd. Hosp. Newc. Prev: SHO (Anaesth.) Newc. Gen. Hosp. & Roy. Vict. Hosp. Newc.

JOHNSTON, Ian Bernard 27 Narbonne Avenue, London SW4 9JR — MB BCh BAO 1983 NUI.

JOHNSTON, Ian David Alexander D Floor, Southblock, University Hospital, Nottingham NG7 2UH Tel: 0115 970 9155 Fax: 0115 942 4554 — MB BChir 1975 Camb.; MD Camb. 1985, MA 1975; FRCP Lond. 1992; MRCP (UK) 1978. (Camb. & Middlx. Hosp.) Cons. Phys. (Gen. & Respirat. Med.) Univ. Hosp. Nottm.; Med. Dir. Univ. Hosp. Nottm. Prev: Clin. Sub-Dean Nottm. Univ. Med. Sch.; Lect. & Hon. Sen. Regist. Med. Unit. Middlx. Hosp. Lond.; Clin. Research Fell. St. Geo. Hosp. Med. Sch. Lond.

JOHNSTON, Ian Ellis Old Court House Surgery, 27 Wood Street, Barnet EN5 4BB Tel: 020 8449 2388 — MB BS 1974 Lond.; MRCGP 1984.

JOHNSTON, Ian Gordon, Lt.-Col. RAMC Retd. 5 Grigor Gardens, Inverness IV2 4JU — MB ChB 1978 Dundee; FRCA 2001; FFA RCSI 1986; DA Eng. 1983. Cons. Anaesth. Raigmore Hosp. Inverness. Socs: Assn. Anaesth.; Obst. Anaesth. Assn. Prev: Cons. Anaesth. RAMC; Regist. (Anaesth.) Glas. Roy. Infirm.; SHO (Anaesth.) Aberd. Roy. Infirm.

JOHNSTON, Ian Gordon, Col. late RAMC Retd. (retired) 21 The Paddocks, Ramsbury, Marlborough SN8 2QF Tel: 01672 520602 — MSc Lond. 1963, MB BS 1950; FRCP Ed. 1971, M 1957; DO Eng. 1952. Prev: Sen. Ho. Surg. Soton. Eye Hosp.

JOHNSTON, Ian Henry Northland Surgery, 79 Cunningham's Lane, Dungannon BT71 6BX Tel: 0186 872752 — MB BCh BAO 1961 Belf. Socs: BMA. Prev: Ho. Off. Lagan Valley Hosp. Lisburn; SHO Quoile Matern. Unit Downpatrick.

JOHNSTON, Ian Stewart West Wing, Esk Medical Centre, Ladywell Way, Musselburgh EH21 6AB Tel: 0131 665 2594 Fax: 0131 665 2428; Priorsford, 42 Polwarth Terrace, Edinburgh EH11 1NJ Tel: 0131 346 7140 Fax: 0131 346 7140 — MB ChB 1976 Ed.; BSc (Med. Sci.) Ed. 1973, MB ChB 1976; MRCGP 1980. (Edinburgh) Clin. Dir. Edenhall Hosp. Musselburgh.

JOHNSTON, Professor Ivan David Alexander (retired) South Lynn House, London Road, Shipston-on-Stour CV36 4EP Tel: 01608 661771 Fax: 01608 664231 — MB BCh BAO Belf. 1953; MCh Belf. 1958; FRCS Ed. 1988; FRCS Eng. 1958; Hons. FACS 1984. Prof. Surg. Univ. Newc. u. Tyne; Surg. Roy. Vict. Infirm. Newc.; Hon. Lect. (Hist. of Med.) Univ. Newc. Prev: Lect. (Surg.) Postgrad. Med. Sch. Lond. & Cons. Surg. Hammersmith Hosp.

JOHNSTON, Ivor Norman Lennox Chawton House, St. Thomas' St., Lymington SO41 9ND Tel: 01590 672953 Fax: 01590 674137 — MA, MB Camb. 1959, BChir 1958; MRCS Eng. LRCP Lond. 1958; MRCGP 1976; DObst RCOG 1960. (Guy's) Prev: Ho. Surg. Putney Hosp.; Ho. Phys. & Ho. Surg. (Obst.) Kingston Hosp.

JOHNSTON, Jack Harley, Brigadier late RAMC Arbuthnott Lodge, Ferntower Road, Crieff PH7 3DH Email: j.h. johnston@btinternet .com — MB ChB Glas. 1967; FRCP Glas. 1988; FRCP Lond. 1986; MRCP (UK) 1973; T(M) 1991. p/t Locum Cons. Phys., Wishaw Gen. Hosp., Lanarksh. Socs: Fell. Roy. Soc. Med. Prev: Defence Cons. adviser in Med.; Cons Phy, Roy Hosp Haslar; Cons Phys, Brit. Milit. Hosp.s.

JOHNSTON, James Southfield House, 40 Clarendon Road, Leeds LS2 9PJ Tel: 0113 295 5430, 0113 295 5431 — MB ChB 1986 Sheff.; MRCPsych. 1992; MSc (Psychother.) Leeds 1998. (Sheffield) Cons. Psychiat. (Psychother.) Leeds; Hon. Sen. Lect. Leeds Univ. Socs: BMA. Prev: Cons. Psychother. Leeds; Sen. Regist. (Psychother.) Leeds; Regist. & SHO (Psychiat.) Sheff.

JOHNSTON, James Andrew (retired) 9 Drumclay Park N., Enniskillen BT74 6ND — MB ChB 1953 Glas.; FRCOG 1982, M 1962; DRCOG 1955. Assoc. Specialist (O & G) Erne Hosp. Enniskillen. Prev: Asst. (O & G) Erne Hosp. Enniskillen.

JOHNSTON, James Gerald McCavery (retired) 37 Woodcroft Park, Holywood BT18 0PS Tel: 02890 3769 — BSc (Hins. Physiol.) Belf. 1956, MB BCh BAO 1959; DPH Belf. 1970. Med. Off. Med. Ref. Serv. Prev: Sen. Med. Off. DHSS N. Irel. Med. Ref.; Serv.

JOHNSTON, Mr James Herbert (retired) 72 Wicks Lane, Formby, Liverpool L37 1PX — MB BCh BAO 1943 Belf.; FRCS Eng. 1950; FRCSI 1949; FACS 1976; Hon. FAAP 1983. Prev: Surg. (Urol.) Alder Hey Childr. Hosp. Liverp.

JOHNSTON, Jane Nicola 4 Springdale Park, Bieldside, Aberdeen AB15 9FB — MB ChB 1986 Aberd.; MRCGP 1990. Asst. GP Vict. St. Med. Gp. Aberd.; Clin. Med. Off. Menopause Clinic Aberd. Roy. Infirm.

JOHNSTON, Jennifer Mary Highfield, Cauldfield Road S., Inshes, Inverness IV2 5BQ — MB ChB 1974 Aberd.

***JOHNSTON, Jeremy James Ernest** 7 Breda Park, Drumahoe, Londonderry BT47 3SL — MB BCh BAO 1997 Belf.

JOHNSTON, Jillian Mary 26 Bristow Park, Belfast BT9 6TH — MB ChB 1998 Manch.; MB ChB Manch 1998.

JOHNSTON, Joan Minty (retired) 9 Drumclay Park N., Enniskillen BT74 6ND Tel: 01365 322574 — MB ChB 1954 Ed.; DCH RFPS Glas. 1957. SCMO Co. Fermanagh W.. Health & Social Servs. Bd.; Mem. Fac. Community Health.

JOHNSTON, John (retired) Stonehoue, Kings Pyon, Hereford HR4 8PZ Tel: 0143 271373 — MB ChB 1924 Glas.

JOHNSTON, John Drysdale Department of Biochemistry and Haematology, Queen Elizabeth Hospital, Woolwich, London SE18 4QH Tel: 020 8836 5645 Email: jdjohnston@doctors.org.uk — MB ChB 1982 Ed.; PhD Camb. 1990; MSc Lond. 1991; BSc (1st cl. Hons.) Ed. 1979; MRCPI 1996; MRCPath 1993; FRCPath 2001. (Ed.) Cons (Clin. Biochem.) Qu. Eliz. Hosp., Woolwich, Lond..; Hon. Cons. Clin. Biochem. at Qu. Mary's Hosp., Sidcup, Kent. Socs: Hon. Life Mem. Roy. Med. Soc. Edin.; Fell. Roy. Soc. Health; BMA. Prev: Lect. & Hon. Sen. Regist. (Endocrinolology & Chem. Path.) St. Thomas' Hosp. Lond.; Cons. (Chem. Path.) Greenwich Dist. Hosp. Lond.

JOHNSTON, John Edward Ballymoney Health Centre, Robinson Memorial Hospital, 21 Newal Road, Ballymoney BT53 6HB Tel: 028 2766 0300 Fax: 028 2766 0321; 6 Tullaghgore Road, Ballymoney BT53 6QF Tel: 012656 63512 — MB BCh BAO 1967 Belf.; DObst RCOG 1970; Dip. Palliat. Med. Cardiff 1997. (Queen's University Belfast) GP. Socs: Ulster Med. Soc. Prev: SHO (Med. & Obst.) Mid-Ulster Hosp. Magherafelt; Ho. Off. Roy. Vict. Hosp. Belf.

JOHNSTON, John Graham Bron Derw Surgery, Bangor LL57 2RS Tel: 01248 370900 Fax: 01248 370652; 21 Pant Lodge, Llanfairpwllgwyngyll LL61 5YW Tel: 01248 716444 — MB ChB 1979 Birm.; DRCOG 1983. Prev: Trainee GP Gwynedd HA VTS.

JOHNSTON, John Sydney (retired) 3 Heather Court, Elcho Road, Bowden, Altrincham WA14 2TJ Tel: 0161 941 2979 — MB BCh BAO 1933 Belf.; FRCGP 1978.

JOHNSTON, Judith Rosemary Currie Road Health Centre, Currie Road, Galashiels TD1 2UA Tel: 01896 752419 Fax: 01896 753876 — MB ChB 1972 Leeds; DCH Eng. 1976.

JOHNSTON, Julian Rowland Regional ICU, Royal Victoria Hospital, Belfast BT12 6BA; 1 Glenmachen Grove, Belfast BT4 2RF Email: jrjohnston@dial.pipex.com — MD 1982 Belf.; 2001 FRCA; MB BCh BAO 1975; FFA RCSI 1979. (Queens University Belfast) Cons. Anaesth. Regional ICU Roy. Vict. Hosp. Belf. Prev: Dir. of IC Servs.

JOHNSTON, Katharine Nancy — BM BS 1997 Nottm.; DRCOG 2001; BMedSci Nottm 1995. GP Trainee Oxf.

JOHNSTON, Keith James Alexander 6 Meadowfield Terrace, Stocksfield NE43 7LJ — MB ChB 1998 Dund.; MB ChB Dund 1998.

JOHNSTON, Kevin Robert 28 Heol Isaf, Radyr, Cardiff CF15 8AL Tel: 029 2084 2406 — MB BCh 1980 Wales; FFA RCS Eng. 1985. Lect. Dept. Anaesth., Univ. Wales Coll. Med. Sch., Cardiff; Hon. Sen. Regist. S. Glam. HA. Socs: BMA & Assn. Anaesth. Gt. Brit. &

Irel. Prev: Research Fell. Univ. Wales Coll. Med. Sch.; Regist. Dept. Anaesth. S. Glam. HA; SHO (Anaesth.) N.wick Pk. Hosp. Harrow.

JOHNSTON, Linda Brown Endocrine Department, St. Bartholomews Hospital, West Smithfield, London EC1A 7BE Tel: 020 7601 7444 Fax: 020 7601 8468 Email: l.b.johnston@mds.qmw.ac.uk; 2 Arundel Court, 43-47 Arundel Gardens, London W11 2LP — MB BChir 1992 Camb.; MA, MB BChir Camb. 1992; MRCP (UK) 1995. (Univ. Camb.) Research Regist. (Paediat. Endocrinol.) St Bart. Hosp. Lond. Prev: Regist. & SHO (Paediat.) Guy's Hosp. Lond.; SHO (Paediat.) Roy. Alexandra Hosp. Brighton.

JOHNSTON, Lorraine Elizabeth Royal Maternity Hospital, Grosvenor Road, Belfast BT12 6BB; 24 Lambert Rise, Dundonald, Belfast BT16 1LQ — MB BS 1986 Lond.; MRCOG. (St Bartholomews Hospital London) Specialist Regist. (O & G) Roy. Matern. Hosp. Belf.

JOHNSTON, Louisa Frances Elizabeth 173 Church Street, Dumfries DG2 7AZ Tel: 01387 266814; 17 Broomhill Road, Penicuik EH26 9EE Tel: 01968 674321 — MB ChB 1990 Aberd.; MRCGP 1994. (Aberd.) Prev: Regist. (Paediat.); SHO (Paediat.).

JOHNSTON, Lynn Christie 22 Clanbrassil Road, Cultra, Holywood BT18 0AR — MB BCh BAO 1972 Belf.; FFR RCSI 1983; FRCR 1977; DMRD Eng. 1976.

JOHNSTON, Malcolm Edward (retired) 262 Thorpe Road, Longthorpe, Peterborough PE3 6LP Tel: 01733 265040 — MRCS Eng. LRCP Lond. 1949. Prev: Asst. ENT Surg. P'boro. Hosp. Gp.

JOHNSTON, Mr Malcolm Nicholas 11 Oaklands Avenue, Tattenhall, Chester CH3 9QU — MB ChB 1987 Manch.; BSc Manch. 1984, MB ChB 1987; FRCS Eng. 1991. Regist. (Gen. Surg.) N. Manch. Gen. Hosp. Prev: SHO Rotat. (Surg.) Hope Hosp. Manch.; Demonst. (Anat.) Manch. Univ.

JOHNSTON, Margaret Anne (retired) Dunmore House, Marle Green, Horam, Heathfield TN21 9EB — MB ChB 1949 Ed. Med. Asst. (Psychiat.) Hellingly Hosp. Hailsham.

JOHNSTON, Margery Elizabeth 15A Widney Manor Road, Solihull B91 3JG Tel: 0121 705 5602 — MB BS 1967 Lond.; MRCS Eng. LRCP Lond. 1966. (Roy. Free) Prev: GP Solihull & Sheldon, Birm.; Ho. Surg. Roy. Free Hosp. Lond.; Ho. Phys. New End Hosp. Lond.

JOHNSTON, Marilynn Jean 1 Fairfield Way, Coulsdon CR5 2EP — BM BS 1985 Nottm.; DTM & H Liverp. 1994. (Nottm.) Field Med. Co-ordinator Medair Kabul, Afghanistan. Prev: Med. Off. (for Christian Outreach) Shagarab Refugee Camp Khashm Al Girba, Sudan.

JOHNSTON, Marion Ann 173 Stenhouse Street, Cowdenbeath KY4 9DH — MB ChB 1986 Ed.; MRCGP 1990; Cert. Family Plann. JCC 1990.

JOHNSTON, Mark Nicholas 182 Rutland Road, West Bridgford, Nottingham NG2 5DZ — MB ChB 1990 Birm.; BSc Birm. 1989, MB ChB Birm. 1990; FRCS (ENT) Ed. 1996. Specialist Regist. Otolargyngol. S. Trent Region.

JOHNSTON, Maureen Isobel Rowan Centre, Maryhill, Elgin; Brae Cottage, Keithhall, Inverurie AB51 0LD Tel: 01467 623399 — MB ChB 1980 Aberd.; MRCPsych 1993. Cons. in Child & Family Psychiat. Rowan Centre, Maryhill, Elgin, Moray.

JOHNSTON, Mr Michael Anthony 8 Norwood, Newport-on-Tay DD6 8DW — MB ChB 1983 Aberd.; FRCS Glas. 1989; DA (UK) 1985. (Univ. Aberd.) Cons. A & E Dundee Teach. Hosps. NHS Trust. Prev: Sen. Regist. (A & E) Vict. Infirm. Glas.; Regist. Rotat. (Surg.) Stobhill Hosp. Glas.; Regist. (A & E) Vict. Infirm. Glas.

JOHNSTON, Miles Brereton Old Crown Cottage, Hesket Newmarket, Wigton CA7 8JG — MB BS 1996 Lond.

JOHNSTON, Natalie Margaret (retired) 3 Finings Court, The Maltings, Leamington Spa CV32 5FG Tel: 01926 313642 — LRCP LRCS 1951 Ed.; LRCP LRCS Ed. LRFPS Glas. 1951; FFPHM 1989, M 1974; DPH Ed. 1954. Prev: Cons. Pub. Health Med. W. Birm. HA.

JOHNSTON, Neil Roderick (retired) 14 Chalmers Crescent, Edinburgh EH9 1TS Tel: 0131 667 1675 — MB ChB 1960 Aberd.; MRCGP 1969; DObst RCOG 1962. Clin. Asst. (A & E) Edin. Roy. Infirm. Prev: Cas. Off. Aberd. Roy. Infirm.

JOHNSTON, Nicola Jayne 23 Bar Hall Road, Portaferry, Newtownards BT22 1RQ — MB BCh 1998 Belf.; MB BCh Belf 1998.

JOHNSTON, Nigel Frederick Alexander 14 Winchester Drive, Exmouth EX8 5QA — MB BCh BAO 1980 Belf.

JOHNSTON, Nigel McLaughlan Penicuik Health Centre, 37 Imrie Place, Penicuik EH26 8LF Tel: 01968 672612 Fax: 01968 671543 — MB ChB 1970 Aberd.

JOHNSTON, Norman Macdonald Rothes Medical Centre, 28A High St., Rothes, Aberlour AB38 7AU Tel: 01340 831435 Fax: 01340 831875 Email: admin@rothes.grampian.scot.nhs.uk; Roundwood, Conrock, Rothes, Aberlour AB38 7AW Tel: 01340 831735 — MB ChB 1977 Glas.; DRCOG 1987.

JOHNSTON, Pamela Oakley 18 Craigmount Terrace, Edinburgh EH12 8BW — MB ChB 1987 Ed.; MRCGP 1991; T(GP) 1991.

JOHNSTON, Patrick (retired) 17 Stoney Wood, Londonderry BT47 2AE — MB BCh BAO 1973 NUI; DObst RCPI 1977. Prev: Gen. Practioner, Dungiven Healthcentre.

JOHNSTON, Mr Patrick Beaumont Ulster Clinic, Strawmillis Road, Belfast BT9 6TH Tel: 028 666826 — MB BCh BAO 1971 Belf.; BSc (Physiol., Hons.) Belf. 1968, MB BCh BAO 1971; FRCS Ed. (Ophth.) 1976; FCOphth. 1989. (Belf.) Cons., Opthacological Dept, Roy. Vict. Hosp. Belf..; Clin. Director Opthalmology, Roy. Vict. Hosp. Belf. Prev: Sen. Lect. & Cons. (Ophth.) Qu. Univ. & Roy. Vict. Hosp. Belf.; Fell. (Ophth.) Univ. Chicago, U.S.A.; Regist. (Ophth.) Roy. Vict. Hosp. Belf.

JOHNSTON, Patrick Gerard Department of Oncology, Queens University of Belfast, University Floor, Belfast City Hospital, Lisburn Road, Belfast BT9 7AB — MB BCh BAO 1982 NUI; MRCPI 1985.

JOHNSTON, Patrick Leslie Apple Acre, Rectory Lane, Etton, Peterborough PE6 7DB — MB BS 1979 Lond.; MRCS Eng. LRCP Lond. 1978; FFA RCS Eng. 1985. (St. Mary's) Cons. Anaesth. P'boro. Dist. & Edith Cavell Hosps. Prev: Sen. Regist. (Anaesth.) Leicester Roy. Infirm.

JOHNSTON, Paul Dryden House, 45 Cremorne Road, Four Oaks, Sutton Coldfield B75 5AQ — MB ChB 1981 Birm.; FFA RCS Eng. 1987. Cons. Anaesth. Good Hope Hosp. NHS Trust Sutton Coldfield. Socs: Assn. Anaesth. Intens. Care Soc. Prev: Sen. Regist. (Anaesth.) W. Midl. Train. Scheme.

JOHNSTON, Paul Andrew Renal Unit, Treliske Hospital, Truro TR1 3LJ Tel: 01872 74242 — MB ChB 1985 Ed.; MRCP (UK) 1989. Cons. Phys. (Nephrol.) Treliske Hosp. Truro.

JOHNSTON, Paul Weir Wards 5/6, Royal Victoria Hospital, Grosvenor Road, Belfast Tel: 01232 240503 Fax: 01232 312907 — MB BCh BAO 1988 Belf.; MD Belf. 1996; MRCP (UK) 1991. Cosultant Cardiol., Roy. Vict.n Hosp., Belf. Prev: Cons. Cardiol., Antrim Area Hosp., Antrim; Interven.al Fell., Sonnybrook Health Sci. Centre, Toronto.

JOHNSTON, Paul William Ferrier Latham House Medical Practice, Sage Cross St., Melton Mowbray LE13 1NX Tel: 01664 60101 Fax: 01664 501825; 68 Dalby Road, Melton Mowbray LE13 0BH Tel: 01664 62368 — MB ChB 1962 Glas.; DObst RCOG 1965. (Glas.) Clin. Asst. Pre Convalesc. Unit War Memor. Hosp. Melton Mowbray. Socs: BMA. Prev: SHO (Anaesth.) & Ho. Surg. W. Infirm. Glas.; Ho. Off. (O & G) Stobhill Gen. Hosp. Glas.

JOHNSTON, Peter George Bernard (retired) 7 Mithras Close, Dorchester DT1 2RF Tel: 01305 265203 Fax: 01305 265203 Email: petergbj@aol.com — MB BS 1967 Lond.; FRCP Lond. 1985; MRCP (UK) 1971; FRCPCH 1997. Hon. Cons. Paediat. W. Dorset Hosp. Dorchester; Med. Dir. Hope Now Ltd.

JOHNSTON, Peter Martin 20 Cairnwood Drive, Airdrie ML6 9HR — MB ChB 1988 Glas.

JOHNSTON, Peter Wilson Department of Pathology, Medical Buildings, Foresterhill, Aberdeen AB25 2ZD Tel: 01224 681818 Fax: 01224 663002 Email: peter.johnson@abdn.ac.uk; 68 Fountainhall Road, Aberdeen AB15 4EH Tel: 01224 639248 — MB ChB 1982 Aberd.; MB ChB (Commend.) Aberd. 1982; PhD Aberd. 1992; BMedBiol (Hons.) Aberd. 1979; FRCPath 1997, M 1988. (Aberdeen) Hon. Cons. Path. (Histopath.) Aberd. Roy. Hosps. NHS Trust; Sen. Lect. (Biomed. Sci.) Univ. Aberd. Socs: BMA (Scott. Counc.); Med. Acad. Staff Comm. Exec.; Interim Chairm. Scott. Med. Acad. Staff Comm. Prev: Lect. & Hon. Sen. Regist. (Path.) Univ. Aberd.

JOHNSTON, Phillip Wilbees Farm, Arlington, Polegate BN26 6RU Tel: 01323 484820 — BChir 1995 Camb.; MB Camb. 1996, MA 1997. (Camb.) SHO (Gen. Surg.) Chase Farm Hosp. Enfield Lond. Prev: Anat. Demonst. Camb. Univ.; SHO (A & E) Guy's Hosp. Lond.; Ho. Off. (Surg.) Addenbrooke's Hosp.

JOHNSTON, Piers Mehlem 47 The Garstons, Bookham, Leatherhead KT23 3DT — MB BS 1997 Lond.

JOHNSTON, Raymond Vincent Medical Division, Civil Aviation Authority, Aviation House, South Area, Gatwick Airport, Gatwick RH6 0YR Tel: 01293 573664 Fax: 01293 573995; 33 Foxenden Road, Guildford GU1 4DL — MB ChB 1973 Glas.; MBA 1999 Univ. of Surrey; FFOM RCP Lond. 1999; MFOM FOM, RCP Lond. 1995; DAvMed FOM RCP Lond. 1992; FRCPS Glas. 1991; MRCP (UK) 1975. (Univ. Glas.) Head Occupat. Health & AeroMed. Tutor. Centre Civil Aviat. Auth. Gatwick W.Sussex R16 OYR. Socs: Soc. Occupat. Med. Prev: Sen. Regist. (Med.) Glas. Roy. Infirm.; Regist. (Med.) Vict. Infirm. Glas.

JOHNSTON, Richard Highfield, Caulfield Road S., Inshes, Inverness IV1 2BQ — MB ChB 1974 Aberd.; BMedBiol 1971; FFA RCS Eng. 1978. Cons. Anaesth. Raigmore Hosp. Inverness.

JOHNSTON, Richard Patrick, Surg. Cdr. RN Medical Centre, RNAS Culdrose, Helston TR12 7RH Tel: 01326 552256 Email: pmo.culdrose@gtnet.gov.uk — MB BS 1983 Lond.; MRCP (UK) 1995; AFOM RCP Lond. 1996; DAvMed FOM RCP Lond. 1989; MFOM RCP Lond. 1999. (Guy's) Princip. Med. Off., RNAS Culdrose, Helston; Cons. in Occupat.al Med. Socs: Mem. Soc. of Occupat.al Med.

JOHNSTON, Robert Davis (retired) Occupational Health Department, Rhone Poulenc Rorer, Rainham Road S., Dagenham RM10 7XS Tel: 020 8984 3509 Fax: 020 8592 3509 — MB BS 1954 Lond.; MFOM RCP Lond. 1979; DIH Soc. Apoth. Lond. 1975. Cons. Occupat. Phys. Rhone Poulenc Rorer Dagenham; Authorised Med. Examr. Civil Aviat. Auth. Prev: Chief Occupat. Phys. Rhone Poulenc Ltd.

JOHNSTON, Robert John 6 Tullaghgore Road, Ballymoney BT53 6QF — MB ChB 1996 Glas.

JOHNSTON, Robert Lockhart Currie Road Health Centre, Currie Road, Galashiels TD1 2UA Tel: 01896 752419 Fax: 01896 753876 — MB ChB 1972 Glas.; MRCGP 1984; DCH Eng. 1976; DObst. RCOG 1976. Princip. GP Galashiels Health Centre.

JOHNSTON, Robert Lockhart 81 Claremont Road, London N6 5BZ Email: robertljohnston@msn.com — MB ChB 1989 Bristol; FRCOphth 1994. Specialist Regist. (Ophth.) Moorfield Eye Hosp. Prev: SHO (Ophth.) St. Thos. Hosp. Lond.; SHO (Ophth.) Cheltenham Gen. Hosp.

JOHNSTON, Robert Neilson (retired) 50 Albany Road, West Ferry, Dundee DD5 1NW Tel: 01382 778538 — MB ChB 1943 Aberd.; MB ChB (Hons.) 1943; MD Aberd. 1953; FRCP Lond. 1972, M 1949; FRCP Ed. 1963. Cons. Chest Phys. Dundee & Arbroath; Hon. Sen. Lect. Respirat. Dis. Univ. Dundee. Prev: Asst. Phys. Chest Clinic, Hammersmith Hosp. Lond.

JOHNSTON, Robert Stanley 30 Loan Road, Cullybackey, Ballymena BT42 1ES — MB ChB 1997 Glas.

JOHNSTON, Robert Trevor Department of Cardiology, Royal Cornwall Hospital, Truro TR1 3LJ; Fortunes, 75 Trefusis Road, Flushing, Falmouth TR11 5TY — MB ChB 1983 Dundee; FRCP Lond. 1998; T(M) 1993. Cons. Cardiol. Roy. Cornw. Hosp. Truro. Prev: Lect. & Hon. Sen. Regist. (Cardiovasc. Med.) Univ. Hosp. Nottm.; Regist. (Cardiol.) Groby Rd. Hosp. Leicester.

JOHNSTON, Mr Robin Alexander Dept. of Neurosurgery, Southern Gower Hospital, Gowan Rd, Glasgow G51 4TF Tel: 0141 201 2021 Fax: 01412012560 — MD 1983 Belf.; BSc (Anat.) Belf. 1971, MB BCh BAO 1974; FRCS Ed. 1979. Cons. Neurosurg. Inst. Neurol. Sci. Glas. & Qu. Eliz. Nat. Spinal Injury Unit, Glas. Socs: Soc. Brit. Neurol. Surgs. & Brit. Cervical Spine Soc.; Eur. Spine Soc. Prev: Hagar Clin. Resid. Fell. (Neurosurg.) Univ. Texas.

JOHNSTON, Rosaleen Oakwood House, Gorsey Lane, Altrincham WA14 4BN Tel: 0161 929 8112 — MB ChB 1982 Manch.; BSc (Med. Sci.) St. And. 1979; DCCH RCP Ed. 1987. Prev: Lect. (Clin. Sci.) Internat. Med. Coll., Kuala Lumpur; Clin. Med. Off. S. & N. Manch. HA's; Clin. Med. Off. Thameside H.A.

JOHNSTON, Rosalind Helen 12 Ramsholt Close, North Waltham, Basingstoke RG25 2DG — MB ChB 1994 Bristol.

JOHNSTON, Rosalynd Elizabeth 30 Loan Road, Cullybackey, Ballymena BT42 1ES — MB BS 1994 Newc.

JOHNSTON, Sally Chawton House Surgery, St. Thomas Street, Lymington SO41 9ND Tel: 01590 672953 Fax: 01590 674137 — MB BS 1982 Lond.; MRCGP 1988; DRCOG 1988; DCH RCP Lond. 1984. (Guys)

JOHNSTON, Mr Samuel Robinson 3 Green Park, Belsize Road, Lisburn BT27 4DW — MB BCh BAO 1971 Belf.; FRCS Ed. 1976. Cons. Urol. Roy. Vict. & Belf. City Hosps.

JOHNSTON, Sandra Mary Argyll Street Surgery, 246 Argyll Street, Dunoon PA23 7HW Tel: 01369 703252 Fax: 01369 706880; Osborne Lodge, East Bay, Dunoon PA23 8AW Tel: 01369 705909 Fax: 01369 702289 — MB ChB Aberd. 1976; MRCGP 1980.

JOHNSTON, Sarah Louise 28 St Johns Road, Burnham-on-Sea TA8 2AX — MB ChB 1994 Bristol. SHO (Med.) S.mead Hosp. Bristol.

JOHNSTON, Professor Sebastian Lennox University of Medicine, Level D, Centre Block, Southampton General Hospital, Southampton SO16 6YD Tel: 02380 796960 Fax: 02380 701771 — MB BS 1982 Lond.; MRCP (UK) 1985; FRCP (UK) 1999. (Guy's Hospital) Prof. of Respirat. Med., Imp. Col., Lond. Prev: Sen. Reg. (Med.) Univ. Soton.

JOHNSTON, Sharon Ann 3 Kippford Place, Rowantree Gardens, Chapelhall, Airdrie ML6 8LL Tel: 0777 182 4667 Email: shazjohnston@hotmail.com — MB ChB 1995 Glas. SHO (Med.) Gold Coast Hosp. S.port Qu.sland, Austral. Prev: Ho. Off. (Surg.) Vict. Infirm. Glas.; Ho. Off. (Med.) Dumfries & Galloway Roy. Infirm.

JOHNSTON, Sheila Elizabeth Arbour Hill, 109 Blaris Road, Lisburn BT27 5RA Tel: 0184 62 662553 — MB BCh BAO 1975 Belf.

JOHNSTON, Sheila Margaret Eileen Orchard House Day Hospital, Union St., Stirling FK8 1 Tel: 01786 474161 Fax: 01786 448210; 15 Leny Feus, Callender FK17 8AS Tel: 01877 330536 Fax: 01877 331641 — MB ChB 1979 Dundee; DGM RCPS Glas. 1995; DRCOG 1981. Clin. Asst. Orchard Hse. Geriat. Day Hosp. Stirling.

JOHNSTON, Mrs Shirley Jean Rivendell, Hillhead of Auchattie, Banchory AB31 6PT — MB BS 1959 Lond.; FRCS Eng. 1964.

JOHNSTON, Simon Douglas Department of Gastroenterology (level 6), Belfast City Hospital, Lisburn Rd, Belfast BT9 7AB Tel: 02890 329241 (ext 3474) Fax: 02890 263973 Email: simon.johnston@bch.n-I.nhs.uk; 5 Ravensdale, Manse Road, Newtownabbey BT36 6FA Tel: 02890 833896 Fax: 02890 263973 Email: sdjohnston@utvinternet.com — MB BCh BAO 1990 Belf.; MD Belf. 1996; MRCP (UK) 1993. (Qu. Univ. Belf.) Cons. Gastroentrologist (Gastroenterol.), Belf. City Hosp. Trust, Belf.

JOHNSTON, Stephen Robert David Department of Medicine, Royal Marsden Hospital, Fulham Road, London SW3 6JJ Tel: 020 7352 8171 Fax: 020 7351 3785; 18 Heathfield Gardens, London W4 4JY — MB BS 1986 Newc.; PhD 1997; MA Camb. 1987; MRCP (UK) 1990. Sen. Lect. & Hon. Cons. (Med. Onc.) Roy. Marsden Hosp. Lond. Socs: Assn. Cancer Phys.; Amer. Assn. Cancer Research; Brit. Assn. Cancer Research. Prev: Sen. Regist. (Med. Oncol.) Roy. Marsden Hosp. Lond.; Regist. Rotat. (Med.) Hammersmith Hosp. Lond.; SHO Rotat. (Med.) St. Barts. Lond.

JOHNSTON, Stuart Edwin 86 Doonfoot Road, Ayr KA7 4DP — MB ChB 1988 Ed.; PhD Lond. 1984; BSc (Hons.) Ed. 1979; MRCP (UK) 1994; MRCGP 1993; T(GP) 1993.

JOHNSTON, Susan Elizabeth 72 Killymeal Road, Dungannon BT71 6LG — MB BCh BAO 1993 Belf.

JOHNSTON, Susan Jane RamptonHospital, Retford DN22 0PD Tel: 01777 247263 Fax: 01777 247221 Email: susan.johnston@rampton-hosp.treut.nhs.uk — MB ChB 1980 Aberd.; MRCPsych 1987; FRCPsych 1999. Sen. Lect. Sch. of Hlth. & Related Research Sheff.; Cons. Psych. Rampton Hosp. Retford. Socs: Fell. Roy. Soc. Med. Prev: Cons. Psychiat. (Learning Disabil.) Lincoln Dist. Healthcare NHS Trust.; Cons. Psychiat. (Ment. Handicap) Farleigh Hosp. Bristol & W.on HA; Lect. (Ment. Handicap) Univ. Bristol.

JOHNSTON, Tanya Penelope Spence Bridge End Surgery, Chester-le-Street DH3 3SL Tel: 0191 388 3236 Fax: 0191 389 0989; 4 Browning Mill, Coxhoe, Durham DH6 4HB — MB BS 1987 Lond.; MRCGP 1991; DCCH RCGP 1993. (Royal Free Hospital, London)

JOHNSTON, Terry Christopher Cookstown Health Centre, 52 Orritor Road, Cookstown BT80 8BM Tel: 028 7976 2995 Fax: 028 7976 1383; 30 Molesworth Road, Cookstown BT80 8NR — MB BCh BAO 1987 Belf.; BSc Belf. 1985; MRCGP 1991; DCH RCP Lond. 1990; DRCOG 1989. Socs: BMA; Ulster Med. Soc.

JOHNSTON, Thomas Odwyn, DFC (retired) 28 Old Vicarage Road, Horwich, Bolton BL6 6QT — MB BCh BAO 1948 Belf.

JOHNSTON, Timothy Graeme Downshire Hospital, Ardylass Rd, Dowhpatrick, Belfast BT; Tel: 028 4187 0226 — MB ChB 1992 Leeds; MRCPsych 1996 Lond. Cons. (Adult Gen. Psychiat.) Doun Lisbum Trust, Dounpatrick; Specialist Regist. (Gen. & Community Psychiat.) Belf. City Hosp. Socs: RCPsych; BMA. Prev: SpR (Psychiat.) Belf. City Hosp. Trust, Belf.; SpR(Psychiat) Down Lisbun Trust, Dounpatrich.; SpR (Psychiat.) Craigeion & Bonbridge Community Trust, Craigeion.

JOHNSTON, Tracey Ann St Mary's Hospital for Women & Children, Whitworth Park, Manchester M13 0JH Tel: 0161 276 6116 Fax: 0161 276 6143; 3 Lea Road, Heaton Moor, Stockport SK4 4JT — MB ChB 1985 Dundee; MRCOG 1996. (University of Dundee) Cons. in Fetal Matern. Med. St Mary's Hosp. Manch.

JOHNSTON, Victor William Inverurie Medical Group, Health Centre, 1 Constitution Street, Inverurie AB51 4SU Tel: 01467 621345 Fax: 01467 625374 — MB ChB 1972 Aberd.

JOHNSTON, Victoria Jane The Hurlet, Cranshaws Drive, Redding, Falkirk FK2 9UY — BChir 1996 Camb.; MB 1996; BA (Hons.) 1994. SHO (Gen. Med.) Glas. Roy. Infirm.

JOHNSTON, Mr William George (retired) Lynfield, Thurso Road, Wick KW1 5LE — MB ChB Aberd. 1958; FRCS Ed. 1967; DTM & H Eng. 1961. Prev: Cons. Surg. Caithness Gen. Hosp.

JOHNSTON, William Rankin, MBE (retired) 31 Tobermore Road, Magherafelt BT45 5HB Tel: 01648 32437 — MB BCh BAO Belf. 1938; MFCM 1972; DPH 1946.

JOHNSTONE, Alexander Tel: 01236 727816 Fax: 01236 726306; 87 Drymen Road, Bearsden, Glasgow G61 3RP Tel: 0141 942 1515 Fax: 01236 726306 — MB ChB 1971 Glas.; MRCGP 1981. (Glasgow) Prev: SHO (Obst.) & Ho. Phys. Stirling Roy. Infirm.; Ho. Surg. Vict. Infirm. Glas.

JOHNSTONE, Alexander Adam (retired) 10 The Factory, Castle Eden, Hartlepool TS27 4SR Tel: 01429 836867 — MB ChB 1951 Glas. Prev: Ho. Off. Surg. Dumfries & Galloway Roy. Infirm.

JOHNSTONE, Alexander Fordyce (retired) Raliadh, 10 Crown Circus, Inverness IV2 3NQ — MB ChB Aberd. 1947; MRCPsych 1971; DPM Eng. 1954. Prev: Cons. Psychiat. Craig Dunain Hosp. Inverness.

JOHNSTONE, Alison Department of Anasthetics, Frimley Park Hospital, Portmouth Road, Frimley Tel: 01276 604604; Email: ali.j72@hotmail.com — MB ChB 1996 Sheffield; MB ChB 1996 Sheffield. (Sheffield University) SHO Anaesth., Frimley Pk. Hosp. Prev: SHO Paediat., Frimley Pk. Hosp.; GP Regist., Hohne, Germany.

JOHNSTONE, Anne Veronica The Health Centre, Currie Road, Galashiels TD1; 3 Berryhill Cottages, Kelso TD5 7SX — MB ChB 1984 Aberd. GP Doctors Retainer Scheme Galashiels; Community Med. Off. (Family Plann.) Duns. Prev: Trainee GP Annan; SHO (Orhop. & A & E) Borders Gen. Hosp. Melrose; SHO (O & G) Gen. Hosp. Bishop Auckland.

JOHNSTONE, Anthony Harvey Brookfield Surgery, Whitbarrow Road, Lymm WA13 9DB Tel: 01925 756969 Fax: 01925 756173 — MB ChB 1984 Liverp.; DRCOG 1988.

JOHNSTONE, Catriona 19 Crawford Road, Milngavie, Glasgow G62 7LE — MB ChB 1978 Glas.; MRCGP 1982. Med. Off. (Cas.) Grand Cayman. Prev: GP Glas.

JOHNSTONE, Charles Alexander Patrick 12 Shobrooke Village, Crediton EX17 1AU — MB BS 1994 Lond.

JOHNSTONE, Mr Charles Ian Priory Gate, Boxgrove, Chichester PO18 0EE Tel: 01243 789630 — MB BS 1966 Lond.; FRCS Eng. 1973; MRCS Eng. LRCP Lond. 1966. (Lond. Hosp.) Cons. ENT Surg. St. Richard's Hosp. Chichester, St. Mary's Hosp.; Portsmouth & Qu. Alexandra Hosp. Cosham. Prev: Sen. Regist. ENT Dept. St. Thos. Hosp. Lond.

JOHNSTONE, Charles Mark Elgar House Surgery, Church Road, Redditch B97 4AB Tel: 01527 69261 Fax: 01527 596856; Seven Hills, Dagtail Lane, Astwood Bank, Redditch B97 5QT Tel: 0152 789 2475 — MB BS 1973 Lond. Prev: SHO (O & G) St. Mary's Hosp. Portsmouth; Ho. Surg. (Surg. Unit) St. Thos. Hosp. Lond.; SHO (Med.) Stoke-on-Trent Hosp. Gp.

JOHNSTONE, Christopher Glencairn The Robert Smith Unit, 12 Mortimer Road, Clifton, Bristol BS8 4EX Tel: 0117 973 5004 Fax: 0117 973 7787; 24A Balmoral Road, St. Andrews, Bristol BS7 9AZ Email: dulcidelic@compuserve.com — MB BS 1986 Lond.; MB BS (Hons.) 1986; BSc Lond. 1983; MRCGP 1992. Clin. Asst. (Psychiat.) Robt. Smith Unit Bristol; Tutor, Bristol Univ. Counselling unit 1998-Curr. Socs: Brit. Holistic Med. Assn.; Med. Coun. Alcoholism. Prev: Trainee GP Bristol; Trainee GP/SHO Rotat. Univ. Coll. & Middlx. Hosps. Lond.; SHO (Community Psychiat.) Wells, Som.

JOHNSTONE, Christopher John Maxwell Glasgow Road Surgery, Glasgow Road, Paisley PA1 3PA Tel: 0141 889 3732 Fax: 0141 889 7502; 21 Potterhill Avenue, Paisley PA2 8BA Tel: 0141 884 2364 Fax: 0141 884 4072 — MB ChB 1982 Dundee; FRCGP 1996, M 1988; DCH RCPS Glas. 1985. (Dundee) Undergrad. Tutor Glas. Univ.; Lead Audit Facilitator Argyll & Clyde HB; Edr. Hoolet.

JOHNSTONE, Christopher Paul Hunterslee, 9 North Crescent Road, Ardrossan KA22 8LY — MB ChB 1994 Glas.

JOHNSTONE, Daniel Derrick Ness House, Stromness, Orkney KW16 3PG Tel: 01856 851100 — MB ChB Ed. 1951; DObst RCOG 1953; DCH RFPS Glas. 1959; DA Eng. 1963.

JOHNSTONE, David James 30 Wrayfield Road, Sutton SM3 9TH — MB BS 1985 Lond.

JOHNSTONE, David Noel, Group Capt. RAF Med. Br. Retd. (retired) 16 The Pitchens, Wroughton, Swindon SN4 0RU Tel: 01793 812209 — MB BCh BAO 1954 Dub.; BA Dub. 1954; MRCPsych 1971; DPM Eng. 1966. Prev: Clin. Asst. Bethlem Roy. Hosp.

JOHNSTONE, Edward David 1 Coton Road, Ravensthorpe, Northampton NN6 8EG — MB ChB 1994 Leeds.

JOHNSTONE, Professor Eve Cordelia University Department of Psychiatry, The Kennedy Tower, Royal Edinburgh Hospital, Morningside Park, Edinburgh EH10 5HD Tel: 0131 537 6000 Fax: 0131 447 6860; 9 Hallhead Road, Edinburgh EH16 5QJ — MB ChB 1967 Glas.; MD Glas. 1976; FRCP Ed. 1992; FRCP Glas. 1985; MRCP (UK) 1971; FRCPsych 1985, M 1972; DPM Ed. & Glas. 1970. (Glas.) Prof. & Psychiat. Univ. Edin. Prev: Sen. Clin. Scientist & Hon. Cons. Psychiat. Div. Clin. Research Centre Harrow; Lect. (Psychol. Med.) Univ. Glas.; SHO & Regist. (Psychiat.) S. Gen. Hosp. Glas.

JOHNSTONE, Fiona Margaret Alloa Health Centre, Alloa FK10 1AQ Tel: 01259 723817; Juniper Ridge, Leckie Road, Gargunnock, Stirling FK8 3BJ — MB ChB 1983 Manch.; BSc St. And. 1980; MRCGP 1987. Prev: SHO (O & G) Stirling Roy. Infirm.; SHO (A & E) Stirling Roy. Infirm.; SHO (Paediat.) Falkirk Dist. Roy. Infirm.

JOHNSTONE, Frank Dennis Department of Obstetrics and Gynaecology, 37 Chalmers St., Edinburgh EH3 9EW Tel: 0131 229 2575 Fax: 0131 229 2408 Email: fdj@srv1.med.ed.ac.uk — MD Aberd. 1978, MB ChB 1967; FRCOG 1987, M 1973. Sen. Lect. (O & G) Univ. Edin.; Cons. Obst. & Gyn. Edin. Roy. Infirm. & Simpson Memor. Matern. Pavil. Edin. Prev: SHO Chelsea Hosp. Wom. Lond.; Regist. (O & G) Aberd. Matern. Hosp.; Sen. Lect. (O & G) Kenyatta Nat. Hosp. Nairobi Kenya.

JOHNSTONE, Frederick Charles, SBStJ (retired) Knightsfield, Ifield Green, Crawley RH11 0ND Tel: 01293 522992 — BM BCh 1958 Oxf.; MA Oxf. 1958. Prev: Phys. (Occupat. Health) Crawley & Horsham Hosps.

JOHNSTONE, Frederick Laidlaw South Warren, Golf Lane, Aldeburgh IP15 5PY — MA 1955, MB BChir Camb. 1954; DObst RCOG 1957. (Camb. & Middlx.)

JOHNSTONE, George Murray, Col. late RAMC (retired) Ashbank, New Galloway, Castle Douglas DG7 3RL — MB ChB 1952 Glas.; FRCOG 1977, M 1961, DObst 1953. Cons. (Gyn.) Duchess of Kent's Milit. Hosp. Catterick Garrison. Prev: Jun. Ho. Off. Vict. Infirm. Glas. & Stobhill Hosp. Glas.

JOHNSTONE, Gillian Eileen Pershore Health Centre, Priest Lane, Pershore WR10 1RD Tel: 01386 502030 Fax: 01386 502058; 39 Pensham, Pershore WR10 3HB Tel: 01386 552563 — MB ChB Sheff. 1986; DRCOG 1988.

JOHNSTONE, Helen Christine 6 Windmill Way, Allery Banks, Morpeth NE61 1XQ — MB BS 1991 Newc.; BMedSci 1990.

JOHNSTONE, Hilary Margaret Gail 16 Crollshillock Place, Newtonhill, Stonehaven AB39 3RF — MB ChB 1972 Glas.; MRCGP 1976.

JOHNSTONE, Iain Campbell 34 Newton Street, Ulverston LA12 7JG — MB ChB 1996 Liverp.

JOHNSTONE, Ian Mackenzie (retired) Noon Howe, Melkinthorpe, Penrith CA10 2DR Tel: 01931 712464 Fax: 01931 712464 Email: johnstone@balnouran.prestel.co.uk — MB ChB 1949 Ed.; DObst RCOG 1954. Prev: GP Penrith.

JOHNSTONE, James Alan 115 Kirkton Avenue, Flat 7/5, Glasgow G72 0HS — MB ChB 1970 Glas.; FRCR 1976; DMRD Eng. 1973.

JOHNSTONE, Jean Rosemary Hopehaven, Maydensole, Dover CT15 5HP Tel: 01304 820748 — MB BS 1972 Lond.; MRCS Eng. LRCP Lond. 1972; MRCGP 1977. Prev: GP Sandwich; Trainee GP Banbury VTS.

JOHNSTONE, Mr John Michael Stewart Leicester Royal Infirmary NHS Trust, Leicester LE1 5WW Tel: 0116 258 5290 Fax: 0116 258 6083; 20 Westminster Road, Leicester LE2 2EG Tel: 0116 270 5202 — MB ChB 1963 Ed.; FRCS Ed. 1967. (Ed.) Cons. Gen. Surg. Leicester Roy. Infirm. Prev: Surg. Tutor & Hon. Cons. Nuffield Dept. Surg. Radcliffe Infirm. Oxf.

JOHNSTONE, Julie Carol 45 Fonthill Road, Bristol BS10 5SR — MB ChB 1993 Bristol.

JOHNSTONE, Kenneth Ironside (retired) 3 Bateman Mews, Cambridge CB2 1NN Tel: 01223 328439 — MB ChB 1934 Leeds; BSc (1st cl. Hons. Bact.) Leeds 1931, PhD (Bact.) 1938. Prev: Reader in Pub. Health Bact. Univ. Leeds.

JOHNSTONE, Marjorie Doris South Warren, Golf Lane, Aldeburgh IP15 5PY — MB BS Lond. 1954. (Roy. Free) Prev: Ho. Surg. Roy. Free Hosp. Lond.; Ho. Phys. St. Luke's Hosp. Guildford & Childr. Hosp. Birm.

JOHNSTONE, Mary MacNaughtan 1 Dalkeith Street, Joppa, Edinburgh EH15 2HP — MB ChB 1943 Glas.; BSc Glas. 1939, MB ChB 1943. (Glas.)

JOHNSTONE, Matthew 6 Boathouse Avenue, Largs KA30 8PW — MB ChB 1960 Glas.; MRCGP 1969. Prev: Med. Supt. E. Pk. Home, Largs; Ho. Phys. Larkfield Hosp. Greenock; Ho. Surg. Glas. Roy. Infirm. & Robroyston Hosp. Glas.

JOHNSTONE, Michael James Windrush, 27 Warren Road, Blundellsands, Liverpool L23 6UA Tel: 0151 924 9909 — MB ChB 1972 Manch.; FRCOG 1991.

JOHNSTONE, Michael William (retired) 36 Spinney Crescent, Blundell Sands, Liverpool L23 8TZ Tel: 0151 932 1715 — MD (Commend.) Belf. 1948, MB BCh BAO 1941; FFA RCS Eng. 1953; DA RCPSI 1945. Cons. Anaesth. Manch. AHA (T). Prev: Cons. Anaesth. Bolton & Dist. Hosps.

JOHNSTONE, Natalie Ann 11 Mallard Walk, Boroughbridge, York YO51 9LQ — MB ChB 1997 Birm.

JOHNSTONE, Nichola Catherine 9 Queens Close, Old Windsor, Windsor SL4 2PP — MB BS 1993 Lond.

JOHNSTONE, Nicholas Alan Queen Square Surgery, 2 Queen Square, Lancaster LA1 1RP Tel: 01524 843333 Fax: 01524 847550 — MB ChB 1986 Dundee; BSc (Hons.) 1982; MRCGP 1994. Prev: Regist. (Psychiat.) Auckland, NZ; Med. Off. Brit. Antarctic Survey Signy Base; SHO (O & G) Dewsbury.

JOHNSTONE, Paul Adair 3 Weaver Cr, Airdrie ML6 9HL — MB ChB 1997 Manch.

JOHNSTONE, Paul Stewart 26 Sackville Road, Sheffield S10 1GT — MB ChB 1998 Sheff.; MB ChB Sheff 1998.

JOHNSTONE, Professor Paul William Tees Health Authority, Poole House, Stokesley Road, Nunthorpe, Middlesbrough TS7 0NJ Tel: 01642 320000 Fax: 01642 304170; The Beeches, 71 High St., Great Ayton TS9 6NF — BM 1983 Soton.; 2001 FFPHM; MSc Lond. 1993; MFPHM RCP (UK) 1996; MRCGP 1990; DTM & H Liverp. 1986; DCH RCPS Glas. 1985. Director of Pub. Health; Vis. Prof., Univ. of Teesside. Socs: Med. Protec. Soc.; BMA. Prev: Sen. Regist. UK Cochrane Centre; Med. Off. Oda Montserrat, W. Indies; SHO (Paediat.) E. Dorset HA.

JOHNSTONE, Reginald Douglas 'Brooklands', Bliss Gate Road, Rock, Kidderminster DY14 9XT Tel: 01299 266401 — MB ChB 1971 Liverp.; MRCS Eng. LRCP Lond. 1971; FFA RCS Eng. 1976; DObst RCOG 1973. Cons. (Anaesth.) W. Midl. HA. Prev: Lect. (Anaesth.) Welsh Nat. Sch. Med. Cardiff.

JOHNSTONE, Robert Douglas (retired) 15 Meadow Lane, Over, Cambridge CB4 5NF Tel: 01954 232991 — MB ChB Ed. 1947; FRCOG 1972, M 1958; DObst RCOG 1949. Prev: Cons. O & G W. Suff. Hosp. Gp.

JOHNSTONE, Robert George 21 Rigby Drive, Greasby, Wirral CH49 1RD Tel: 0151 652 7371 — MB ChB 1989 Liverp. Trainee SHO/GP Wirral VTS. Prev: SHO (A & E & Paediat.) Arrowe Pk. Hosp. Wirral; Ho. Off. (Surg.) Arrowe Pk. Hosp. Wirral.

JOHNSTONE, Robert Stevenson (retired) 8 Lister Avenue, Hitchin SG4 9ES Tel: 01462 453735 — MB ChB 1952 Sheff.; DObst RCOG 1954.

JOHNSTONE, Sarah Ann Windrush, 27 Warren Road, Blundellsands, Liverpool L23 6UA — MB ChB 1973 Manch.; MB ChB (Hons.) Manch. 1973; DRCOG 1976; DCH Eng. 1975.

JOHNSTONE, Timothy Flat 25 Oaklands Court, Somerstown, Chichester PO19 4AF — MB BS 1964 Lond.; MRCS Eng. LRCP Lond. 1964; DPH Leeds 1973.

JOHNSTONE, William Alan (retired) 67 Station Lane, Birkenshaw, Bradford BD11 2JE Tel: 01274 682991 — MD 1977 Manch.; MB ChB 1951; DObst. RCOG 1955. Prev: SHO Ashton u Lyne Gen. Hosp.

JOHNSTONE, William Austin Springfield Medical Practice, 9 Springfield Road, Bishopbriggs, Glasgow G64 1PJ Tel: 0141 772 4744 Fax: 0141 772 3035 — MB ChB 1982 Glas.

JOHRI, Mr Ranjit Blyth Health Centre, Thoroton Street, Blyth NE24 1DX Tel: 01670 396560 Fax: 01670 396579; Capel Curig, 4 Preston Park, North Shields NE29 9JL Tel: 0191 258 5367 — MB BS 1969 Agra; MS Agra 1973, MB BS 1969; FRCS Eng. 1979; FRCS Glas. 1978. (Sarojini Naidu Med. Coll. Agra) Hosp. Pract. (Gastroenterol. & Gen. Surg.) N. Tyneside Health Care N. Shields. Prev: Cons. Accid.& Emerg. Sunderland Dist. Gen. Hosp.; Trainee GP N.d. VTS.

JOHRI, Suman Capel Curig, 4 Preston Park, North Shields NE29 9JL Tel: 0191 258 5367 — MB BS 1969 Agra; DCP 1973; MRCPath 1981. Cons. Histopath. N. Tyneside Dist. Hosp. N. Shields.

JOINER, Charles Louis Suite 302, Emblem House, 27 Tooley St., London SE1 2PR Tel: 020 7407 3100; Ashton, Mead Road, Chislehurst BR7 6AD Tel: 020 8467 4060 — MB BS 1946 Lond.; MD Lond. 1950; FRCP Lond. 1965, M 1949. (Guy's) Emerit. Sen. Phys. Guy's Hosp. Lond.; Emerit. Chief Cons. Phys. Sun Alliance Lond. Assur. Company; Emerit. Cons. Phys. Beckenham Hosp.; Emerit. Sen. Examr. Med. Lond. Univ.; Emerit. Clin. Examr. DIH Eng.; Emerit. Sen. Hon. Cons. Phys. to the Army. Socs: Fell. Roy. Soc. Med.; Assn. Phys. Prev: Fell. (Med.) Pennsylvania Hosp. Philadelphia; Vis. Prof. Univ. Baghdad Iraq, Cornell Univ. Med. Sch. New York & Univ. Malta.

JOINER, Christine Emma 20 Crealock Grove, Woodford Green IG8 9QZ — BM BS 1998 Nottm.; BM BS Nottm 1998.

JOINER, Ian Moir Isis, 126 Weybourne Road, Farnham GU9 9HD Tel: 01252 316976 Fax: 01252 350242 Email: 101567.3146@compuserve.com — MB ChB Bristol 1956; MRCOG 1971; DTM & H Eng. 1966; FRCOG 1998. (Bristol) Exec. Dir. Sick Doctors Trust, Farnham, Surrey.

JOINER, Peter Arthur Althorpe Street Medical Centre, Althorpe Street, Lybster KW3 6AE Tel: 01593 721216 Fax: 01593 721344; Glen Suie, Lybster KW3 6BS Tel: 01593 721254 Fax: 01593 721344 — MRCS Eng. LRCP Lond. 1977; MB BS Lond. 1977, BPharm 1972; DRCOG 1983; Dip. IMC RCS Ed. 1991. (St. Mary's) Socs: Treas. Inducement Practitioners Assn.

JOJO, Mr Karthikapalli Antony Joseph Eye Department, The Royal Oldham Hospital, Oldham OL1 2JH Tel: 0161 627 8192 Email: joseph.jojo@virgin.net; 62 Lismore Drive, Paisley PA2 8HX — MB BS 1987 Madras; FRCS Ed. 1992.

JOKELSON, Denis Ronald 52 The Fairway, Brunton Park, Gosforth, Newcastle upon Tyne NE3 5AQ — MB BS 1942 Durh.

JOKHI, Roobin Parvez 11 Harefield Road, Sheffield S11 8NU — MB ChB 1998 Sheff.; MB ChB Sheff 1998.

JOLAOSO, Adeboye Samson 200 Wanstead Lane, Redbridge, Ilford IG1 3SP — MB BS 1986 Ibadan; MRCOG 1996. (Univ. Ibadan, Nigeria) Specialist Regist. (O & G) S. E. Thames Region William Harvey Hosp. Ashford Kent. Socs: BMA. Prev: Specialist Regist. (O & G) Lewisham Hosp.; SHO (O & G) Rushgreen Hosp., Harold Wood Hosp. Romford & Qu. Eliz. Hosp. King's Lynn; SHO (A & E) Bassetlaw Hosp. Worksop.

JOLIC, Goran 12 Sentinel House, Sentinel Square, Brent St., London NW4 2EN — LMSSA 1996 Lond.

JOLLES, Michael Adam Pennine Drive Surgery, 6-8 Pennine Drive, London NW2 1PA Tel: 020 8455 9977 — MB BS 1974 Lond.; MRCS Eng. LRCP Lond. 1974; MRCGP 1979; Cert. FPA 1979; DRCOG 1978. (Univ. Coll. Hosp.) Socs: Fell. Med. Soc. Lond.; BMA. Prev: Trainee GP Watford VTS; SHO (Gen. Med.) Broomfield Hosp. Chelmsford; Ho. Phys. Stoke Mandeville Hosp. Aylesbury.

JOLLES, Stephen Roderick Alan 17 Elm Grove Road, Exeter EX3 0EQ — MB ChB 1990 Manch.; MB ChB (Hons.) Manch. 1990; MSc (Hons.) Lond. 1996; BSc (Hons.) Experim. Immunol. & Oncol.

Manch. 1987; MRCP (UK) 1993; DRC Path (UK) 1998. (Manch.) MRC Clin. Fell., NIMR MillHill Lond. Socs: Brit. Soc. Immunol.; Assn. Clin. Pathol. Prev: Sen. Regist. & Clin. Lect. (Immunol. & Clin. Immunol.) Roy. Free Hosp. & Med. Sch. Lond.; Sen. Reg. Immunol. Sydney Australia; Regist. (Respirat. Med.) GreenLa. Hosp. Auckland, NZ.

JOLLEY, Alexander William 322 Malden Road, North Cheam, Sutton SM3 8EP Tel: 020 8644 0224 — MB BS Lond. 1985.

JOLLEY, Caroline Judith 4 Sea View, Inglewhite Road, Goosnargh, Preston PR3 2EB — MB BS 1998 Lond.; MB BS Lond 1998.

JOLLEY, Professor David James Penn Hospital, Penn Road, Wolverhampton WV4 5HN Tel: 01902 444131 Fax: 01902 444127 Email: dessjol@doctors.org.uk; Haigh, 29 Oldfield Road, Altrincham WA14 4EQ Tel: 0161 928 1023 Email: dessjol@doctors.org.uk — MB BS 1969 Lond.; MSc Manch. 1996; BSc Lond. 1966; MRCS Eng. LRCP Lond. 1969; FRCPsych 1981, M 1973; DPM Eng. 1972; DPM Manch. 1973. (Guy's) Cons. Psychiat. Wolverhampton Health Care; Hon. Prof. Old Age Psychiat. & Community Health Servs. Univ. Wolverhampton; Director: Dementiaplus.wm - the W. Midl.s Learning, Educat. and Developm. Centre for Ment. Health of Older People. Based in Wolverhampton. Socs: Brit. Geriat. Soc.; Manch. Med. Soc. Prev: Cons. Old Age Psychiat. S. Manch.; Ho. Phys. St. Mary's Hosp. Newport, I. of Wight; Ho. Surg. Gen. Hosp. St. Helier Jersey.

JOLLEY, Iain Edward Charles 29 Jubilee Lane, Wrecclesham, Farnham GU10 4TA Tel: 01252 792451 — BM BS 1998 Nottm.; BM BS Nottm 1998; BMedSci Nottm 1996. (Nottingham) PRHO Gen. Surg., Lincoln Co. Hosp. Socs: BMA; MPS. Prev: PRHO Med. Huddersfield Roy. Infirm.

JOLLEY, Susan Penelope Haigh, 29 Oldfield Road, Altrincham WA14 4EQ — MB ChB 1975 Manch.; MRCPsych 1979. Prev: Cons. Psychogeriat. S. Manch. HA.

JOLLEYS, Jacqueline Victoria Country House, Stoney Lane, Coleorton, Coalville LE67 8JJ Tel: 01530 814353 Fax: 01530 811893 — MB ChB 1974 Bristol; BA Open 1985; MD Leics. 1993; MBA Nottm. 1992; MRCGP 1986. Indep. Healthcare Cons. Leics.; Hon. Lect. (Gen. Pract.) Univ. Nottm. Socs: (Chairm.) Assn. Primary Care Med. Advisers; RCGP Vale of Trent Fac. Bd. Prev: GP Leics.; Med. Dir. Notts. FHSA; Lect. (Gen. Pract.) Univs. Nottm. & Leic.

JOLLEYS, John Charles William Manor House Medical Centre, Manor House, Mill Lane, Belton, Loughborough LE12 9UJ Tel: 01530 222368 Fax: 01530 224 2273; Country House, Stoney Lane, Coleorton, Coalville, Leicester LE7 9DA Tel: 01530 814353 Fax: 01530 811893 — BM BCh 1974 Oxf.; DRCOG 1976. Hosp. Pract. (Hyperlipidaemia) Glenfield Gen. Hosp. Leicester.

JOLLIE, Ian Andrew Dickson (retired) 22 Main Street, Seathwhite House, North Frodingham, Driffield YO25 8LA Tel: 01262 488412 — MB ChB 1962 Leeds; DObst RCOG 1967. Prev: Hosp. Pract. (Obst.) Castle Hill Hosp. Hull.

JOLLIFFE, David Shrimpton, QHP, Maj.-Gen. Ministry of Defence, Army Medical Directorate, Former Army Staff College, Slim Road, Camberley GU15 4NP Tel: 01276 412700 Fax: 01276 412939 Email: red@pennswood.demon.co.uk — MB BS 1969 Lond.; FRCP Lond. 1987; MRCP (UK) 1976; MRCS Eng. LRCP Lond. 1969; T(M) 1991. (King's Coll. Hosp.) Dir. Gen. Army. Med. Serv. Socs: Fell. Roy. Soc. Med. (Mem. Dermat. Sect.). Also United Serv. Sect.; Brit. Assn. Dermat.; St John's Hosp. Dermatol. Soc. Prev: Comd. Med. HQ Land Comd. MoD; Commanding Off., Camb. Milit. Hosp., Aldershot; Cons. Adviser in Dermat. of the Army.

JOLLIFFE, David Willmot Ladywell Medical Centre, Ladywell Road, Edinburgh EH12 7TB Tel: 0131 334 5000 — MB BCh 1975 Wales; MRCGP 1983.

JOLLIFFE, Diana Margaret Department of Anaesthesia, Leicester Royal Infirmary, Leicester LE1 5WW — MB BS 1983 Lond.; BSc Lond. 1980, MB BS 1983; MRCP (UK) 1988; FRCA 1992. Cons. Anaesth. Leicester.

JOLLIFFE, Geoffrey Charles Risedale Surgery, 2-4 Gloucester Street, Barrow-in-Furness LA13 9RX Tel: 01229 822332 Fax: 01229 433636 Email: drjollife@doctors.org.uk — MB ChB 1981 Liverp.; DRCOG 1984. (Liverpool) GP Princip., Risedale Surg., Barrow in Furness; Med. Off., The Hospice of St. Mary in Furness, Ulverston, Cumbria. Socs: Roy. Coll. Gen. Pract. Prev: Prescribing Adviser LHG Bd., Barrow in Furness.

JOLLIFFE, Martin Vivian Westfield, 24 Cromer Road, Holt NR25 6DX Tel: 01263 3226 — MB BS 1968 Lond.; DObst RCOG 1970. (Univ. Coll. Hosp.) Prev: Regist. (Path.) Univ. Coll. Hosp. Lond.; SHO (Obst.) Hull Matern. Hosp.; SHO (Paediat.) Bedford Gen. Hosp.

JOLLIFFE, Peter Hugh George Devon Local Medical Committees, Secretariat Office, Ambassador House, Ambassador Dr., Exeter Business Park, Exeter EX1 3QN Tel: 01392 201654 Fax: 01392 201653; The Barton, Shobrooke, Crediton EX17 1AP Tel: 01363 772521 Fax: 01363 772521 — MB BS 1983 Lond. (Guy's Hospital) Chief Off. Devon LMCs. Prev: Med. Dir. Essex FHSA; Med. Dir.

JOLLIFFE, Robert James 45 The Knowle, Cock Lane, Hoddesdon EN11 8LD — MB BS 1991 Lond.

JOLLIFFE, Victoria Mary Lawton 61 Theberton Street, London N1 0QY Tel: 020 7226 7170 — MB BChir 1989 Camb.; MA Camb. 1989; FRCS Ed. 1993; MRCP (UK) 1991; MRCGP 1995. Prev: Ho. Off. Rotat. St. Mary's Hosp. Lond.

JOLLY, Catherine Belinda Wessex Institute for Health Research & Development, Level B, South Acadamic Block, Southampton General Hosptial, Southampton SO16 6YD Tel: 02380 798932 Fax: 02380 796529; 1 Cranhill Road, Bath BA1 2YF — MB ChB 1986 Bristol; MSc (Pub. Health Med.) Lond. 1992; MRCGP 1990; DRCOG 1990. Lect. (Pub. Health Med.) Wessex Inst. for Health Research & Developm. Univ. Soton. Socs: BMA. Prev: Trainee GP Plymouth VTS; Regist. (Pub. Health Med.) NW Thames RHA; SHO (Psychiat.) Wonford Hse. Exeter HA.

JOLLY, Christine Dorothy (retired) 12 Canterbury Close, Bamford, Rochdale OL11 5LZ Tel: 01706 648637 Fax: 01706 645194 — MB ChB Manch. 1964; DObst RCOG 1967. SCMO (Adult Health) Salford. Prev: Ho. Phys. W. Norwich Hosp.

JOLLY, Clive Rennison (retired) Wychwood, Clopton, Woodbridge IP13 6QN Tel: 01473 737294 — MB BS Lond. 1948; MRCS Eng. LRCP Lond. 1948; FRCA 1956; DA Eng. 1954. Prev: Cons. Anaesth. Ipswich Hosp. Gp.

JOLLY, David Allan Hawthorn Surgery, Scotton Road, Scotter, Gainsborough DN21 3SB Tel: 01724 764641 Fax: 01724 764265 — MB ChB 1987 Manch.; BSc (Hons.) Manch. 1985, MB ChB 1987; MRCGP 1991.

JOLLY, George Morrison (retired) 69 Millcroft, Carlisle CA3 0HT Tel: 01228 24811 — MB ChB Ed. 1938. Prev: GP Carlisle.

JOLLY, Gunita 58 Harvey, Grays RM16 2TX — MB BS 1988 Lond.; MRCGP 1992; DRCOG 1991. SHO (O & G) Greenwich Dist. Hosp. Socs: MDU & M. Sickness Soc. Prev: SHO (Psychiat. & Paediat.) Greenwich Dist. Hosp.; Trainee GP Charlton & Thamesmead; SHO (A & E) Brook Gen. Hosp. Blackheath.

JOLLY, Gursharan Kaur Windward Group Practice, 68 Worsley Road, Worsley, Manchester M28 2SN Tel: 0161 794 1603 Fax: 0161 794 2371 — MB BS 1979 Bhopal; DA (UK) 1983. GP Manch. Prev: Trainee GP Worsley Manch.; SHO (A & E) Whittington & Wythenshawe Hosp. Manch.; SHO (Anaesth.) Pk. Hosp. Manch.

JOLLY, Ian Michael Church Street Practice, 8 Church Street, Southport PR9 0QT Tel: 01704 533666 Fax: 01704 539239 — MB ChB 1988 Liverp.; MRCGP 1992; DRCOG 1991. (Liverp.) Prev: SHO (Psychiat.) Fazakerley Hosp. Liverp.; Trainee GP Ormskirk & Dist. Gen. Hosp. VTS; Ho. Off. Ormskirk & Dist. Gen. Hosp.

JOLLY, John Francis Tel: 01387 251232 — MB ChB 1988 Birm.; Mmed 1998 Keele; MRCOG 1994. Specialist Regist. (O & G). Socs: MRCOG; ASME.

JOLLY, Man Mohan Singh (retired) 4 Beech Close, Sunbury-on-Thames TW16 5PY Tel: 01932 881146 Fax: 01932 881146 — MB BS Rangoon 1957; DCH Eng. 1959.

JOLLY, Margaret Marion Phin (retired) 40 East Barnton Avenue, Edinburgh EH4 6AQ — MB ChB 1938 St. And.; DCH Eng. 1943.

JOLLY, Mary Soutar (retired) Springwood, Crossways, West Chiltington, Pulborough RH20 2QY — MB ChB 1938 St. And.; BSc 1934, MB ChB St. And. 1938; MRCOG 1948.

JOLLY, Neal Colin Lepton Surgery, Highgate Lane, Lepton, Huddersfield HD8 0HH Tel: 01484 606161; 19 Rowley Lane, Lepton, Huddersfield HD8 0JN — MB ChB 1983 Sheff.; MRCGP 1987. Socs: Hudds. Med. Soc.

JOLLY, Pran Nath Oxford Road Surgery, 101 Oxford Road, Reading RG1 7UD Tel: 0118 957 4687; 24 Hazel Road, Purley, Reading RG8 8BB — MB BS 1963 Lucknow. (King Geo. Med. Coll. Lucknow)

JOLLY, Richard Tadeusz, OBE, Surg. Capt. RN Retd. 11 Carew Close, Crafthole, Torpoint PL11 3EB Email: rickj@sama82.org.uk — MB BS Lond. 1969; MRCS Eng. LRCP Lond. 1969; DAvMed FOM RCP Lond. 1983; DMCC 1998. (St. Bart.) p/t Milit. Med. Research & Teachg. Opoth.; Author and Publisher; Exam. Dipl. Med. c/o Catastrophes/ Apoth. Soc. Prev: SMO Roy Marines; MOD Research Fell.sh. 1989-1990; Off. Commanding Ajax Bay Field Hosp. Falkland Is. 1982.

JOLLY, Ronda Verina The Surgery, 143A Uxbridge Road, London W12 9RD Tel: 020 8743 1511 Fax: 020 8740 0310; 22 Belsize Avenue, London NW3 4AU Tel: 020 7794 3625 — MB ChB 1979 Otago; MRCGP 1986. (Otago University)

JOLLY, Surinder Singh Crescent Road Surgery, 72 Crescent Road, Crumpsall, Manchester M8 9NT Tel: 0161 740 9864 Fax: 0161 740 0524; 13 Standmoor Road, Whitefield, Manchester M45 7PJ Tel: 0161 796 5505 — MB BS 1978 Ranchi. GP Manch.

JOLLY, William Shotton Lane Surgery, 38 Shotton Lane, Shotton, Deeside CH5 1QW Tel: 01244 812094; Brookside, 3 Park Avenue, Hawarden, Deeside CH5 3HY Tel: 01244 520713 — MB ChB 1962 Birm.

JOLLYMAN, Timothy Michael 19 Oak View, Wellingborough NN9 5YU — MB ChB 1993 Birm.

JOLOBE, Oscar M P Tameside General Hospital, Ashton-under-Lyne OL6 9RW Tel: 0161 331 5151; 3A Raynham Avenue, Didsbury, Manchester M20 6BW — MB ChB 1963 Natal; DPhil Oxf. 1981; FRCP Lond. 1995; MRCP (UK) 1974; FCP(SA) 1967. (Natal) Cons. Geriat. Tameside Gen. Hosp. Ashton-under-Lyne. Socs: Manch. Med. Soc. Prev: Sen. Regist. (Gen. Med.) Dudley Rd. Hosp. Birm.; Sen. Regist. (Geriat. Med.) Dudley Rd. & Selly Oak Hosps. Birm.

JOLOWICZ, Kate St Johns Way Medical Centre, 96 St. Johns Way, London N19 3RN Tel: 020 7272 1585 Fax: 020 7561 1237; 24 Anson Road, London N7 0RD Tel: 020 7607 1713 — MB BS 1984 Lond.; BSc Lond. 1981; MRCGP 1990; DRCOG 1987; DCH RCP Lond. 1986. (UCLH)

JONAS, David Robert Carter High Street Surgery, High Street, Hindon, Salisbury SP3 6DJ Tel: 01747 820222 Fax: 01747 820736 — MB BS 1974 Lond.

JONAS, Mr Ernest George Gustav (retired) Plough Farm, Lower Cadsden, Princess Risborough, Aylesbury HP27 0NB — MB BS 1947 Lond.; FRCS Eng. 1955; FRCOG 1971, M 1957; LMCC 1948. Cons. Obstetr. & Gynaecol. Hillingdon Dist. Prev: Ho. Surg. Middlx. Hosp.

JONAS, Marion 94 Mouslsham Street, Chelmsford CM2 0JF — MB ChB 1992 Sheff.

JONAS, Mark Maximillian The White House, 50 High St., Fareham PO16 7BQ Email: maxjonas@boo-bear.demon.co.uk — MB BS 1984 Lond.; FRCA. 1991. Cons. Anaesth. Soton. Univ. Hosps. Trust; Hanovay Snr Research Fell., St Thos. Hosp. Lond. Socs: Exec Comm. Resus Counc.; Assoc. of Anaesth.; Linkman Intens. Care Soc. Prev: Sen. Clin. research fell. & Hon Cons.; Sen.Reg. Anaesth. Oxf.; Clin.Fell. Anaesth. Papworth Hosp. Camb.

JONAS, Moira Patricia 192 Brookland Road, Sale M33 3PB Tel: 0161 969 9810 — MB ChB 1956 Manch.; DPM 1962; FRCPsych. 1986, M 1971. (Manch.) Cons. Child & Adolesc. Psychiat. Urderly Hall Schs. Prev: Cons. Child & Adolesc. Psychiat. Bolton Dist. Hosp.; Sen. Regist. (Child Psychiat.) Booth Hall Hosp. Manch.; Sen. Regist. (Psychiat.) Bolton Dist. Gen. Hosp. Farnworth.

JONASON, Elizabeth Rochfort (retired) White House, East Harling, Norwich NR16 2NB Tel: 01953 717602 — MB BS 1943 Lond.; MRCGP 1952. Prev: Ho. Surg. Roy. N.. Hosp.

JONASON, Paul Henry Augustus (retired) White House, East Harling, Norwich NR16 2NB Tel: 01953 717602 — MB BS 1946 Lond.; MRCS Eng. LRCP Lond. 1945. Div. Surg. St. John Ambul. Brig. Prev: Local Treasury Med. Off.

JONATHAN, Mr David Arthur Frimley Park Hospital, Frimley, Camberley GU16 7UJ; Lane House, Whitmead Lane, Tilford, Farnham GU10 2BP — MB BS 1979 Lond.; MRCS Eng. LRCP Lond. 1979; FRCS Eng. 1985. Cons. ENT Surg. Frimley Pk. Hosp. Prev: Sen. Regist. (ENT) St. Geo. & Roy. Nat. Throat Nose & Ear Hosps. Lond.; Regist. (ENT) Roy. Nat. Throat Nose & Ear Hosp. Lond.

JONATHAN, Mr Owen Morris (retired) Isallt, Portmadoc Road, Criccieth LL52 0HP — MB BS 1947 Lond.; FRCS Eng. 1950; MRCS Eng. LRCP Lond. 1942. Prev: Cons. Surg. Clwyd HA.

JONES, Mr Adam 18 Wood Street, Wallingford OX10 0AX Tel: 01491 838815 — MB BS 1991 Lond.; FRCS (Urol.) 2001; MD Lond. 2000; BSc (Hons.) Lond. 1988; FRCS Eng. 1995.

JONES, Adrian Charles Department of Radiotherapy, The Churchill Hospital, Oxford OX3 7LJ Tel: 01865 225671 Fax: 01865 225672; 57 Newland Mill, Witney OX28 3SZ — MB BS 1972 Lond.; BSc (Hons.) Lond. 1969; FRCR 1979; FRCP 1996. (Univ. Coll. Lond. & Westm.) Cons. Oxf. Radcliffe NHS Trust & P.ss Margt. Hosp. Swindon. Prev: Sen. Regist. Roy. Marsden Hosp. Lond. & Surrey; Lect. & Hon. Sen. Regist. Inst. Cancer Research & Roy. Marsden Hosp. Lond.; Regist. (Radiother.) St. Bart. Hosp. Lond.

JONES, Adrian Charles Rheumatology Unit, City Hospital, Hucknall Road, Nottingham NG5 1PB Tel: 0115 969 1169 Fax: 0115 962 7709 Email: ajones@ncht.org.uk — MB BS 1985 Lond.; FRCP (UK) 1999; MRCP (UK) 1988; DM Nottm. 1985; BSc Lond. 1982. (King's Coll.) Cons. Rheum. & Gen. Phys. City Hosp. Nottm. Socs: Brit. Soc. Rheum.; Midl. Rheum. Soc. Prev: Sen. Regist. (Rheum. & Gen. Med.) Leicester Roy. Infirm. & Nottm. City Hosp.; ARC Jun. Clin. Research Fell. Nottm.; Regist. (Gen. Med. & HCFE) City Hosp. Nottm.

JONES, Adrian Clive Nicholas Anne Prendergast Health Centre, Ashton Gardens, Chadwell Health, Romford RM6 6RT Tel: 020 8590 1401; 1 Park Cottages, North Road, Havering-Atte-Bower, Romford RM4 1PS — MB ChB 1983 Leeds; MRCGP 1987; DRCOG 1986. (Leeds) Clin. Asst. (Rheum.) Romford. Prev: Trainee GP Bradford VTS.

JONES, Adrian Robert 25 Chargot Road, LLandaff, Cardiff CF5 1EW Tel: 01222 564289; 5/26 Simpsons Road, Bardon, Brisbane Qld 4065, Australia Tel: 00 61 7 32175864 Email: agejones@ozemail.com.au — MB ChB 1990 Manch.; BSc St. And. 1987; MRCGP 1995; DRCOG 1995.

JONES, Agnes Valerie 82 The Slade, Headington, Oxford OX3 7DX — MB BCh 1962 Wales; DObst RCOG 1964.

JONES, Alan Princess Street Surgery, Gorseinon, Swansea SA4 4US Tel: 01792 895681; Hillsgreen Cottage, Reynoldston, Gower, Swansea SA3 1AE Tel: 01792 390689 — MD 1992 Wales; MB BCh 1970; FRCGP 1988. Sen. Lect. (Gen. Pract.) Univ. Wales Coll. Med. Swansea. Socs: Roy. Soc. Med. & Brit. Soc. Allergy and Clin. Immunol. Prev: Assoc. Adviser (Gen. Pract.) Univ. Wales Coll. Med.; Course Organiser Swansea VTS.

JONES, Alan Francis Birmingham Heartlands Hospital, Bordesley Green, Birmingham B9 5SS Tel: 0121 766 6611 Fax: 0121 766 8693 Email: a.f.jones@bham.ac.uk; 51 Moor Green Lane, Moseley, Birmingham B13 8NE — MB 1982 Camb.; MA Camb. 1977, MB 1982, BChir 1981; DPhil Oxf. 1977; MRCP (UK) 1984; MRCPath. (Cambridge) Cons. Chem. Path. Birm. Heartlands Hosp.; Cons. Phys. Birm. Heartlands Hosp.; Cons. Clin. Toxicol. City Hosp., Dudley Rd. Prev: Birm.

JONES, Alan George Accident and Emergency unit, Queen Elizabeth The Queen Mother Hospital, Margate CT9 4AN Tel: 01843 225544 Fax: 01843 234445; The Elms, High St, Minster, Ramsgate CT12 4BT Tel: 01843 822752 Fax: 01843 822752 Email: alanjones@talk21.com — MB ChB 1969 St. And.; FRCS Ed. 1975; FFAEM 1993. (St. And.) Cons. A & E Qu. Eliz. the Qu. Mother Hosp. Margate. Socs: Brit. Assn. Accid. & Emerg. Med.; Fac. A & E Med.; Hosp. Cons. & Spec. Assn. Prev: Cons. A & E Ipswich Hosp. Trust; Sen. Regist. (A & E) Guy's Hosp. & Kent & Canterbury Hosp.; Clin. Fell. Sen. Regist. (Cardiac Surg.) Bristol Roy. Infirm.

JONES, Alan Glynn High Street Surgery, 26 High Street, Erdington, Birmingham B23 6RN Tel: 0121 373 0086 Fax: 0121 373 2041; 164 Orphanage Road, Erdington, Birmingham B24 0AA Tel: 0121 373 4780 — LRCPI & LM, LRSCI & LM 1968; LRCPI & LM, LRCSI & LM 1968. (RCSI) Prev: SHO (Cardiol. & Gen. Med.) Jervis St. Hosp. Dub.; SHO (Paediat. Cardiol. & Gen. Paediat.) Roy. Liverp. Childr. Hosp.; Ho. Surg. (O & G) Dudley Rd. Hosp. Birm.

JONES, Alan Guy Houlbrooke Mersey Regional Health Authority, 24 Pall Mall, Liverpool L3 6AL — MB ChB 1983 Birm.; MA Camb. 1984; MSc Manch. 1990. Sen. Regist. (Pub. Health Med.) Mersey RHA. Prev: Regist. (Med. Microbiol.) N. W.. RHA; SHO (Path.) E. Birm. Hosp.

JONES, Mr Alan Hugh ENT Department, East Glamorgan Hospital, Church Village, Pontypridd CF38 1AB Tel: 01443 218218; 1 Clos-y-Bryn, Rhwbina, Cardiff CF4 6TR — MB BCh 1978 Wales; FRCS Ed.

1984. Cons. ENT Surg. E. Glam. Hosp. Pontypridd. Prev: Regist. (ENT) New Cross Hosp. Wolverhampton.

JONES, Alan Ivor Houghton Health Centre, Church Street, Houghton-le-Spring DH4 4DN Tel: 0191 584 2154; 11 Ashleigh Villas, East Boldon NE36 0LA Tel: 0191 519 2699 Email: aijones@globalnet.co.uk — MB BS 1984 Newc.; MRCGP 1988; DA (UK) 1990; DRCOG 1987; Dip. Ther. 1997 Newc. (Newcastle) GP; Police Surg.

JONES, Alan Wyn Three Crosses Surgery, 2 Cilonnen Road, Three Crosses, Swansea SA4 3PH Tel: 01792 875284 — MB BCh 1975 Wales.

JONES, Albert Bryan (retired) 27 Harborough Road, Dingley, Market Harborough LE16 8PQ — MB BCh 1957 Wales. Prev: Cons. A & E Dept. Gen. Hosp. Kettering.

JONES, Aled Wyn (retired) 12 Manor Drive, Chorlton-cum-Hardy, Manchester M21 7GQ Tel: 0161 445 6935 — MD Liverp. 1972, MB ChB 1958; FRCPath 1981, M 1969; DPath Eng. 1966. Prev: Cons. Histopath. Hope Hosp. Salford.

JONES, Aleen Margaret Craigavon Area Hospital And S. Tyrone Hospital, Dungannon BT71 6LN — MB BCh BAO 1976 Belf.; FRCP Glas. 1994; MRCP (UK) 1981; Dip. Palliat. Med. Wales 1994. (Queens University) Cons. Phys. (Elderly) Craigavon Area Hosp. & S. Tyrone Hosp.

JONES, Alex 14 Clausentum Road, Southampton SO14 6RZ — BM 1997 Soton.

JONES, Alexander Fraser Cedar House, Send, Woking GU23 7JN — MB BS 1997 Lond.

JONES, Alice Mair Ffynnon-Las, Ffos-y-Ffin, Aberaeron SA46 0HB — MB ChB 1971 Liverp.; FRCR 1976; DMRD Liverp. 1975. Cons. (Radiodiag.) Bronglais Hosp. Aberystwyth.

JONES, Alice Maria Lynne 16 St Anthony Road, Heath, Cardiff CF14 4DH Tel: 029 2052 2550 — MB BCh 1995 Wales; DRCOG 2000; MRCGP 2001; DFFP 1999.

JONES, Alison New Surgery, Victoria Street, Pontycymer, Bridgend CF32 8NW Tel: 01656 870237 Fax: 01656 870354; 19 Celtic View, Litchard, Bridgend CF31 1YG Tel: 01656 645839 — MB BCh 1986 Wales; MRCGP 1990.

JONES, Alison Clare 31 Sunningdale Drive, Prestwick, Manchester M25 1JX — BChir 1989 Camb.

JONES, Alison Linda National Poisons Information Service, Guys & St Thomas NHS Trust, Avonley Road, London SE14 5ER Tel: 020 7771 5302 Fax: 020 7771 5306 Email: alison.jones@gstt.sthames.nhs.uk; 7 Keats Avenue, Royal Victoria Dock, London E16 1TW Tel: 020 7473 4707 — MB ChB 1989 Ed.; MRCP (UK) 1992; FRCPE 1999; FIBiol 2000. (Edinburgh) Cons. Phys. & Med. Toxicologist Guy's St Thomas NHS Trust Lond.; Regional Adviser for Lond. to the Roy. Coll. of Phys.s of Edin.; Head of Med. / Dep. Clin. Dir., Guy's & St. Thomas's NHS Trust. Socs: Eur. Assn. Poisons Control Centres & Clin. Toxicol.; Brit. Toxicol. Soc.; Sec. Human Sect. of Brit. Toxicol. Soc. Prev: Sen. Regist. (Clin. Toxicol., Gastroenterol. & Gen. Med.) Roy. Infirm Edin.; Clin. Research Fell. (Hepatol.) Univ. Edin.; SHO (Coronary Care), Ho. Phys. & Ho. Surg. Roy. Infirm. Edin.

JONES, Alison Louise Department of Clinical Oncology, Royal Free Hospital, Pond Street, London NW3 2QG — MB ChB 1980 Bristol. Cons. Med. Oncologist & Hon. Sen. Lect., Roy. Free Hosp., Lond.; Chairm. Specialist Train. Comm., Med. Oncol., Lond. Socs: Educat. Adviser Jt. Counc. Oncol.; Regional Speciality Adviser (RCP) Oncol. Prev: Sen. Regist., Roy. Marsden Hosp.; Clin. Research Fell., Roy. Marsden Hosp.

JONES, Alison Margaret Dykebar Hospital, Grahamston Road, Paisley PA2 7DE Tel: 0141 884 5122; 25 Quadrant Road, Glasgow G43 2QP Tel: 0141 637 5659 — MB BS 1975 Newc.; MRCPsych 1991; DRCOG 1977. Cons. Psychiat. Gen. Adult Psychiat. & Psychiat. of Learning Disabil. Renfrewsh. Healthcare NHS Trust; Hon. Sen. Lect. Univ. Glas. Prev: Sen. Regist. (Gen. & Ment. Handicap) Dundee Tayside HB; Regist. (Psychiat.) Dundee Tayside HB.

JONES, Alison Margaret Morris Cedar Ford, Withycombe, Minehead TA24 6QE — MB BCh 1975 Wales; MRCGP 1979.

JONES, Alison Mary Department of Immunology, Great Ormond Street Hospital for Children, Great Ormond St., London WC1N 3JH Tel: 020 829 8834 Fax: 020 7813 8552 Email: alison.jones@gosh-tr.nthames.nhs.uk; 13 Thorncliffe Road, Oxford OX2 7BA Tel: 01865 426653 Email: alisonjones@doctors.org.uk — MB BChir 1978 Camb.; PhD Lond. 1992; MRCS Eng. LRCP Lond. 1978; MRCP (UK) 1982; DRCOG 1982. (Cambridge) Cons. Paediat. Immunol. Gt. Ormond St. Hosp. for Childr. NHS Trust; Hon. Sen. Lect. Inst. Child Health Lond. Socs: Fell. Roy. Coll. Paediat. and Child Health.

JONES, Allan Meddygfa Llwyncelyn Practice, Park Road, Whitchurch, Cardiff CF14 7EZ Tel: 029 2035 7602 Fax: 029 2062 3839; Clwyd y Gurnos, Watford, Caerphilly CF83 1NF Tel: 029 2062 3286 — MB BCh 1977 Wales; MRCGP 1982.

JONES, Allan Desmond Diss Health Centre, Mount St., Diss Tel: 01379 642021; The Poplars, Brewers Green, Roydon, Diss IP22 5SD Tel: 01379 652491 — MB 1975 Camb.; MA; BChir 1974.

JONES, Allan Karl 5 Craven Lea, Cravenwood L12 0NF — MB ChB 1978 Liverp.; FRCA 1991 London. Locum GP; Clin. Asst. A & E.

JONES, Allen Spencer 38 Rhyd-y-Nant, Pontyclun CF72 9HE — MB BCh 1946 Wales. (Cardiff)

JONES, Alun Henry Tal-y-Bont Surgery, Station Road, Pontardulais, Swansea SA4 1TL Tel: 01792 882368; 19 Castle Street, Loughor, Swansea SA4 6TU Tel: 01792 898211 — MB BCh 1968 Wales; MRCGP 1976. (Cardiff)

JONES, Alun Howard, OStJ Ty Gwyn, Dixton Road, Monmouth NP25 3PL Tel: 01600 714550 Fax: 01600 714550 Email: alunhow@waitrose.com — MA Camb. 1961, MB BChir 1948; FFOM RCP Lond. 1982, M 1978; DIH Soc. Apoth. Lond. 1975. (Univ. Coll. Hosp.) Socs: Soc. Occupat. Med.Mem. Soc. Occupat. Med. Prev: Cons. S. Wales Electricity; Sen. Emplym. Med. Adviser EMAS.

JONES, Alun Parry, OBE (retired) Dipford Farm, Trull, Taunton TA3 7NS Tel: 01823 333269 — MB BCh Wales 1951; FFCM RCP (UK) 1974; DPH 1956. Prev: Chief Med. Off. Hawkes Bay Area HB, NZ.

JONES, Alun Stuart 45 Cuddington Avenue, Worcester Park KT4 7DB — MB BS 1993 Lond.

JONES, Alyson Susan The Surgery, 2A Latymer Road, Edmonton, London N9 9RZ; 28 Lunedale Avenue, Tollesby, Middlesbrough TS5 7LA — BM BS 1980 Nottm.

JONES, Miss Amanda Susan Department Obstetrics and Gunaecology, North Manchester General Hospital, Delaineys Road, Manchester M8 5RB Tel: 0161 720 2130 Fax: 0161 720 2141; 11 Langley Avenue, Grotton, Oldham OL4 5RA Fax: 0161 626 8440 Email: amanda.jones@man.ac.uk — MB ChB 1978 Manch.; BSc (Med. Sci.) St. And. 1975; FRCS Ed. 1986; MRCOG 1985. Cons. O & G N. Manch. Gen. Hosp. Prev: Sen. Regist. (O & G) N. Manch. Gen. Hosp.

JONES, Amanda Suzanne Yewtree Farmhouse, Otley Road, Cretingham, Woodbridge IP13 7DP Tel: 01473 323323 — MB ChB 1981 Sheff.; FFPHM, 2001; MRCGP 1986; MFPHM RCP (UK) 1993; DRCOG 1983. p/t Cons. Pub. Health Med.Suff. HA. Prev: GP Swindon.

JONES, Andrea Bronwen Netherlaw Surgery, 28 Stanhope Road, Darlington DL3 7SQ Tel: 01325 380640 Fax: 01325 350938; Raby House, 3 Chapel Row, Sadberge, Darlington DL2 1SH — MB BS 1986 Newc.; MRCGP 1990. Clin. Asst. Rheum. S. Cleveland Hosp. Middlesbrough. Prev: Trainee GP/SHO (O & G) Cleveland VTS.

JONES, Andrea Helen 38 Crollshillock Place, Newtonhill, Stonehaven AB39 3RF — MB ChB 1998 Aberd.; MB ChB Aberd 1998.

JONES, Andrew Charles 40 Venn Grove, Hartley, Plymouth PL3 5PH — MB BS 1997 Lond.

JONES, Andrew Christopher Flat 4, 25 Egmont Road, Sutton SM2 5JR — MB BCh 1989 Wales; DCH RCP Lond. 1992.

JONES, Andrew Grahame Belmont Medical Centre, Eastholme Avenue, Hereford HR2 7XT Tel: 01432 354366 — MB ChB 1994 Birm.; Dip. In Therapeutics 1999; DRCOG 1996; DFFP 1998. GP Princip., Belmont Med. Centre, Hereford. Prev: Staff Grade Practitioner, St. Michael's Hospice, Hereford.

JONES, Andrew Guy Department of Anaesthesia, Royal Liverpool University Hospital, Prescot St., Liverpool L7 8XP Tel: 0151 706 3190 Fax: 0151 706 5823; 74 Bertram Drive, Meols, Wirral CH47 0LJ Tel: 0151 632 6760 Email: jonesag@argonet.co.uk — MB BS 1983 Lond.; BSc (Hons.) Lond. 1979; LMSSA Lond. 1982; FRCA 1991; DGM RCP Lond. 1986. (St Bartholomews) Cons. Anaesth. Roy. Liverp. Univ. Hosp.; Clin. Dir. (Theatres, Anaesth. & Sterile Servs.). Socs: Liverp. Med. Inst.; Age Anaesth. Assn.

JONES, Andrew Ian A&E Dept, North Tyneside General Hospital, North Shields NE29 8NH — MB ChB 1986 Dundee; MRCP (UK) 1991; DA (UK) 1989; FFAEM 1997. Cons. A&E N. Tyneside Gen. Hosp. Socs: Assoc. Mem. Brit. Assn. Accid. & Emerg. Med. Prev: Sen. Regist. A & E Manch.; Regist. A&E Liverp.

JONES, Andrew Mark Bradbury Cystic Fibrosis Unit, Wythenshawe Hospital, Southmoor Road, Manchester M23 9LT Tel: 0161 291 2154 Fax: 0161 291 2080 Email: andmarkj@hotmail.com; 52 Hawthorn Road, Hale, Altrincham WA15 9RG Email: andmarkj@hotmail.com — MB ChB 1992 Manch.; BSc (1st. cl. Hons.) Manch. 1990; MRCP (UK) 1995. (Manchester) Clin. Fell., Bradbury Cystic Fibrosis Unit, Wythenshawe Hosp. Manch. Socs: Brit. Thoracic Soc. Prev: Specialist Regist. (Respirat. Med.) N. W. Lung Centre, Wythenshawe Hosp.Manch.; Specialist Regist. (Med.) N.. Mem. Gen. Hosp.; Specialist Regist. (Respirat. Med.) N. W. Lung Centre, Wythenshawe Manch.

JONES, Andrew Mark Holroyd Preston, Yealmpton, Plymouth PL8 2HY — MB BS 1998 Lond.; MB BS Lond 1998.

JONES, Andrew Peter Barncroft, Dovenby, Cockermouth CA13 0PN — MB ChB 1985 Leeds.

JONES, Andrew Philip 1 Wishart Green, Old Farm Park, Milton Keynes MK7 8QB — BM BS 1986 Nottm.; BMedSci Nottm. 1984; AFPM RCP Lond. 1995; MRCGP 1991; DRCOG 1989. Med Affairs Dir. Elan Pharma Ltd. Letchworth. Prev: Med. Affairs Manager Lundbeck Ltd. Milton Keynes; Sen. Med. Adviser Hoechst Marrion Roussel Ltd. Denham Middlx.

JONES, Professor Andrew Simpson Department of Otorhinolaryngology, University of Liverpool, PO Box 147, Liverpool L69 3BX Tel: 0151 706 4051; Brook Cottage, Beeston Castle, Tarporley CW6 9TS — MB ChB 1975 Wales; MD Wales (Distinc.) 1983; FRCS Ed. 1981. Prof. Otolaryngol. & Head & Neck Surg. Univ. Liverp.; Hon. Cons. Roy. Liverp. Univ. Hosp. & Walton Hosp. Liverp.; Mem. Collegium ORLAS. Socs: Brit. Assn. Cancer Research; Brit. Assn. Head & Neck Oncol. Prev: Sen. Lect. (ENT Surg.) Univ. Liverp.; Sen. Regist. (ENT) Roy. Hallamsh. Hosp. Sheff.; Research Fell. (Physiol.) Univ. Coll. Cardiff.

JONES, Andrew Thomas 69 Kenyon Street, London SW6 6LA — MB BS 1989 Lond.; MRCP (UK) 1993. Research Fell. Unit Critical Care Nat. Heart & Lung Inst. Prev: Regist. (Respirat.) Roy. Brompton Hosp.; Regist. Rotat. (Med.) St. Geo. Hosp. Lond.

JONES, Aneuryn Morgan (retired) 20 Caerphilly Road, Cardiff CF14 4AF Tel: 0222 628645 — MB BCh 1928 Wales; BSc Wales 1925; MRCS Eng. LRCP Lond. 1927.

JONES, Angela Christine Invicta Community Care NHS Trust, Community Child Health Department, Homeopathic Hospital, Church Road, Tunbridge Wells TN1 1JU Tel: 01892 539144 Fax: 01892 532585 Email: acj@doctorss.org.uk — MB ChB 1971 Liverp.; MRCP (UK) 1975; MRCPCH 1997. (Liverpool) Cons. Community Paediat. Tunbridge Wells.

JONES, Angela Jane University Department of Clinical Radiology, Bristol Royal Infirmary, Marlborough St., Bristol BS2 8HW Tel: 0117 923 0000 Fax: 0117 928 2319 Email: angela.jones@ubht.swest.nhs.uk — BM 1979 Soton.; MRCP (UK) 1983; FRCR 1986. (Soton.) Cons. Radiodiag. Bristol Roy. Infirm. Prev: Cons. Sen Lect. Bristol Roy. Infirm.; Sen.Regist. (Radiodaig.) Bristol Roy. Infirm.

JONES, Angela Maria The Surgery, Victoria Gardens, Neath SA11 3AY Tel: 01639 643786 Fax: 01639 644609; Lletty Mawr, Tonna, Neath SA11 3QB — BM BCh 1983 Oxf.; BA (Med Sci.) Camb. 1980; MRCGP 1988; MFHom 1994; DRCOG 1987; DCH RCP Lond. 1987; DFFP 1997. (Oxf.) Mem. Fac. Homoeop. Lond. (Counc. Represen., Treas. Wales); Trustee Homeop. Trust. Socs: Fell. Roy. Soc. Med.; Brit. Med. Acupunct. Soc.

JONES, Angela Maria Clare The Surgery, 57 Plains Road, Mapperley, Nottingham NG3 5LB Tel: 0115 962 1717 Fax: 0115 962 5824; 45 Eaton Road, Handbridge, Chester CH4 7EW — BM BS 1992 Nottm.; BMedSci (Hons.) Nottm. 1990; MRCGP 1996; DRCOG 1995; DFFP 1994. (Nottm.) GP Nottm. Socs: NW Soc. Family Plann. & Sexual Med.

JONES, Angela Susan 1 Holly Grove, Huyton, Liverpool L36 4JA — MB BS 1998 Newc.; MB BS Newc 1998.

JONES, Angus Damian Nicholas 7 Thorngrove Hill, Wilmslow SK9 1DF — MB ChB 1996 Birm.; ChB Birm. 1996; DRCOG 1998.

JONES, Ann Marie Top Flat, 13 Osborne Road, Clifton, Bristol BS8 2HB — MB ChB 1997 Leeds.

JONES, Ann Mary Monica Radiology Department, Princess Margaret Hospital, Okus Road, Swindon SN1 4JU; The Cottage, Coln St Aldwyns, Cirencester GL7 5AD — MB BS 1983 Lond.; BSc Lond. 1980; FRCP 2000; FRCR 1992. Cons. Radiol. P.ss Margt. Hosp. Swindon. Prev: Sen. Regist. (Diag. Radiol.) Bristol Roy. Infirm.; Regist. (Med.) N. Staffs. Hosp. Centre.

JONES, Ann Myra 9 Redwood Drive, Wing, Leighton Buzzard LU7 0TA Tel: 01296 688451; 46 Stenkley Road, Wing, Leighton Buzzard LU7 0NE Tel: 01296 688575 — MB BS 1977 Newc.; MRCGP 1981.

JONES, Anna Clare 14 Castlefield Mews, Stone St., Manchester M3 4NE — MB BS 1991 Lond. Prev: SHO (Geriat.) Withington Hosp. Manch.; SHO (A & E) N. Manch. Gen. Hosp.; Ho. Off. (Cardiol.) St. Bart. Hosp. Lond.

JONES, Anna Elizabeth (retired) 17 Valley Road, Cheadle SK8 1HY Tel: 0161 428 9240 — MB BCh BAO Belf. 1941; FFCM 1980, M 1974; DPH Wales 1958; DGO Dub. 1944; LM Rotunda 1944. Prev: Med. Off. Environm. Health N., Centr. & S. Manch. HA.

JONES, Annabel Julia Boughton Medical Group, Boughton Health Centre, Hoole Lane, Chester CH2 3DP Tel: 01244 325421; 49 Earlsway, Chester CH4 8AY — MB BChir 1992 Camb.; MA Camb.; MRCGP 1995; DRCOG 1994. (Char. Cross & Westm.) Part. Gen. Pract. Boughton Health Centre Chester. Prev: GP Regist. Locum Gen. Pract.

JONES, Anne Eira Crud-Yr-Awel, 20 Damson Close, Thrapston, Kettering NN14 4RG Tel: 01832 731428 — MB BCh 1958 Wales.

JONES, Anne Elizabeth (retired) Still Waters, Lisvane Road, Llanishen, Cardiff CF14 0SD Tel: 01222 753329 — MB BCh Wales 1959. Prev: Med. Off. WBS.

JONES, Anne Hughes Tir Nan Og, 21A Melbost, Isle of Lewis HS2 0BG Tel: 01851 705587 Email: vm11@did.pipex.com — MB ChB 1990 Liverp.; MRCGP.

JONES, Annette 5 Raymond Avenue, Stoke-on-Trent ST1 6DN — MB BS 1990 Lond.; MRCP (UK) 1994.

JONES, Anthony Radiology Service Centre, University Hospital of Wales, Heath Park, Cardiff CF14 4XW Tel: 029 2074 3954 Fax: 029 2074 3029 — MB BCh Wales 1968; FRCR 1976. Cons. Radiol. Univ. Hosp. Wales Cardiff. Socs: BMA & BMUS.& ISUOG. Prev: Cons. Radiol. Roy. Gwent Hosp. Newport; Sen. Radiol. Brunei Med. Serv. Brunei, S.E. Asia.

JONES, Anthony Fortune 584 Mather Avenue, Liverpool L19 4UG Tel: 0151 427 6239 — MB ChB 1959 Liverp.; DObst RCOG 1965. Prev: SHO Alder Hey Childr. Hosp. Liverp.; Ho. Surg. (Obst.) & Ho. Phys. Sefton Gen. Hosp. Liverp.

JONES, Anthony James 8 Cliffe Park, Seaburn, Sunderland SR6 9NS — MB BCh 1969 Wales; FRCOG 1987, M 1974. Cons. O & G S. Tyneside HA.

JONES, Anthony Kenneth (retired) Rodmell House, Rodmell Road, Tunbridge Wells TN2 5SP — MB BS 1942 Lond.; MRCS Eng. LRCP Lond. 1939.

JONES, Anthony Kenneth Peter Rheumatic Diseases Centre, Clinical Sciences Building, Hope Hospital, Salford M6 8HD Tel: 0161 787 4266 Fax: 0161 787 4687 Email: ajones1@fs1.ho.man.ac.uk; 4 Fulshaw Avenue, Wilmslow SK9 5JA — MB BS 1978 Lond.; BA Oxf. 1975; MD Lond. 1992; FRCP Lond. 1995; MRCP (UK) 1983. Sen. Lect. & Hon. Cons. (Rheum.) Manch. Univ. Socs: BSR & IASP. Prev: MRC Sen. Lect. & Hon. Cons. MRC Cyclotron Unit & Dept. Rheum. Hammersmith Hosp.

JONES, Anthony Leigh Salisbury District Hospital, Salisbury SP2 7SX Tel: 01722 336262 Fax: 01722 429247 Email: dr.a.jones@shc-tr.swest.nhs.uk; Popes Bottom, West Grimstead, Salisbury SP5 3RL Tel: 01722 710547 Fax: 01722 710547 Email: dralj.pb@virgin.net — MB BS 1978 MB BS Lond.; BSc Lond. 1975; 1995 FRCP Lond.; 1981 MRCP (UK). (St. Thos. Hosp.) Cons. Phys. (Gen. & Cardiovasc. Med.) Salisbury Dist. Hosp. Socs: Brit. Cardiac Soc.

JONES, Anthony Mason The Vine Medical Centre, 166 Tonbridge Road, Maidstone ME16 8SS Tel: 01622 754898 Fax: 01622 751611; The Vine Medical Centre, 166 Tonbridge Road, Maidstone ME16 8SS Tel: 01622 754898 Fax: 01622 751611 — MB BCh 1983 Wales; BSc Birm. 1978; MRCGP 1987. (Univ. Hosp. Wales) Course Organiser Maidstone VTS.

JONES, Antonieta Karen 27 Stocton Road, Guildford GU1 1HH Tel: 01483 505913 — MB BS 1984 Lond.; MRCGP 1996; DRCOG 1988; Cert Family Plann. LJCC 1988. (Guy's Hosp.) GP Guildford Retainer Scheme. Prev: Trainee GP SW Surrey HA VTS.

JONES, Antony Pryce Toad Hall, Cruckton, Shrewsbury SY5 8PW Tel: 01743 860936; 109 Aldersley Road, Tettenhall, Wolverhampton WV6 9NE — MB BChir Camb. 1986; MA Camb. 1987, BA 1982; DRCOG 1991; DCH RCP Lond. 1990; DA (UK) 1989. (Roy. Free Hosp.) Trainee GP Shrops. & Powys FPC. Socs: Fac. Family Plann. Prev: SHO (Psychiat. A & E Geriat. Med. & Anaesth.) Roy. Shrewsbury Hosp.

JONES, Arthur Llwyndomen, Craig-Cefn-Parc, Swansea SA6 5RS Tel: 01792 3504 — MB BS 1949 Lond.; MRCS Eng. LRCP Lond. 1944. (St. Bart.) Med. Off. Areas 1 & 9 S.W. Div. Nat. Coal Bd. Prev: Surg. Off. Neath Gen. Hosp.; Clin. Asst. Out-pat. Dept. St. Bart. Hosp.; Ship's Surg. Roy. Mail Lines.

JONES, Arthur Cyril Vernon, MC 116 Walsall Road, Stone Cross, West Bromwich B71 3HN Tel: 0121 588 2784 — MRCS Eng. LRCP Lond. 1941.

JONES, Arthur Emlyn (retired) Crofta, Sunnycroft, Baglan, Port Talbot SA12 8ES — MB BCh 1943 Wales; BSc Wales 1943, MB BCh 1943. Prev: Med. Off. i/c Gen. Hosp. Port Talbot.

JONES, Arthur Morgan (retired) Hafod, 43 Heol-y-Plas, Fforest, Pontardulais, Swansea SA4 1TZ — MB BCh 1943 Wales; BSc Wales 1940; DMRD Eng. 1946. Prev: Cons. Radiol. Morriston Hosp.

JONES, Mrs Audrey Joan St. Thomas' Hospital (Lydia, GUM), Lambeth Palace Road, London SE1 7EH; 1 Minshull Place, Pk Road, Beckenham BR3 1QF Tel: 020 8658 6185 — MB ChB Sheff. 1950; FFPHM 1985, M 1973. (Sheff.) Psychosexual Med. Lond. Socs: (Hon. Treas.) Inst. Psychosexual Med. Prev: SCM Bromley DHA.

JONES, Avis Marguerite Blundell The Round House, Stoke Cannon, Exeter EX5 4EE Tel: 0139 284269 — MB BS 1938 Lond.; MRCS Eng. LRCP Lond. 1938. (Univ. Coll. Hosp.) Socs: Fell. BMA. Prev: Ho. Phys. Childr. Dept. & Ho. Phys. Univ. Coll. Hosp. Lond.

JONES, Azita 18 Grilse Close, Salmon's Brook Estate, Brookfield Road, London N9 0TT — MB BS 1990 Lond.

JONES, Barbara (retired) 3 Nansen Road, Gatley, Cheadle SK8 4JL Tel: 0161 428 2050 — MB ChB 1947 Birm.; MFCM 1972. Sen. Med. Off. (Clin.) Macclesfield Health Auth.

JONES, Barbara Mary 69 Dartnell Park Road, West Byfleet, Weybridge — MB BS 1979 Lond.; DRCOG 1982; DFP 1981. Prev: SHO (Paediat.) Frimley Pk. Hosp. Frimley; SHO (O & G) St. Luke's Hosp. Guildford; Ho. Off. (Surg.) Roy. E. Sussex Hosp. Hastings.

JONES, Mr Barrie Russell, CBE Buttles Steps Cottage, Froghole Lane, Crockham Hill, Edenbridge TN8 6TD Tel: 01732 866239 Fax: 01732 867467 — MB ChB 1947 New Zealand; BSc New Zealand 1942, MB ChB 1947; FRCP Lond. 1977, M 1974; FRCS Eng. 1955; DO Eng. 1953; Hon. FRACS 1972; Hon. FRACO 1984. Hon. Dir. Onchocerciasis Research Gp. Internat. Centre Eye Health Inst. Ophth. Lond. & Ahmadu Bello Univ. Kaduna, Nigeria. Socs: Fell. Roy. Soc. Med.; Fell. Roy. Coll. Ophth. Prev: Prof. Clin. Ophth. & Prof. Preven. Ophth. Univ. Lond.; Regist. (Ophth. & Neurosurg.) Dunedin Hosp.; Sen. Resid. Off. Moorfields Eye Hosp.

JONES, Barry Minster Practice, Greenhill Health Centre, Church Street, Lichfield WS13 6JL Tel: 01543 414311 Fax: 01543 418668; Broadlands, 45 Borrowcop Lane, Lichfield WS14 9DG Tel: 01543419924& profess. 0543 414311 — MB BS 1968 Newc.; FRCGP 1987, M 1973. (Newc.) Prev: Sec staffs.LMC; Non Exec S. Staffs HA.

JONES, Barry John 12 Headwell Road, Dunfermline KY12 0PW — MB ChB 1998 Ed.; MB ChB Ed 1998.

JONES, Barry John Michael Department of Gatroenterology, Russells Hall Hospital, Dudley DY1 2HQ Tel: 01384 244074 Fax: 01384 244112 Email: b.j.m.j@btinternet.com — MB BS 1973 Lond.; 1970 BSc (1st cl. Hons.) Lond.; 1992 FRCP Lond.; 1976 MRCP (UK); 1973 MRCS Eng. LRCP Lond.; 1998 European Diploma Gastrolenterology. (Guy's) p/t Cons. Phys. & Gastroenterol. Wordsley Hosp. Stourbridge & Russell's Hall Hosp. Dudley. Socs: Brit. Soc. Gastroenterol.; Eur. Soc. Ent. Paren. Nutrit.; Brit. Assn. Paren. Ent. Nutrit. Prev: Sen. Regist. (Gastroenterol. & Gen. Med.) Lond. Hosp. Whitechapel; Research Fell. (Gastroenterol.) Centr. Middlx. Hosp. Lond.; Clin. Regist. King's Coll. Liver Unit Lond.

JONES, Mr Barry Malcolm 14A Upper Wimpole Street, London W1G 6LR Tel: 020 7935 1938 Fax: 020 7935 6607 — MB BS Lond. 1974; MS Lond. 1982; FRCS Eng. 1978; MRCS Eng. LRCP Lond. 1974. (Char. Cross) Cons. Plastic & Reconstruc. Surg. & Dir. of Craniofacial Surg. Hosp. for Sick Childr. Gt. Ormond. St. Lond.; Hon. Sen. Lect. Inst. Child Health Univ. Lond.; Hon. Cons. Plastic Surg. Nat. Hosp. Neurol. & Neurosurg. Qu. Sq. Lond.; Vis. Prof. Atlanta Cleft Lip & Palate Symp. Socs: Brit. Assn. Plastic Surg.; (Pres.) Brit. Assn. Aesthetic Plastics Surgs.; Internat. Soc. Aesthetic Plastic Surg. Prev: Cons. Plastic & Reconstruc. Surg. Univ. Coll. Hosp. Lond. & Roy. Nat. Orthop. Hosp. Stanmore; Fell. (Craniofacial & Aesthetic Surg.) Hôpital des Enfant Malades, Paris; Sen. Regist. (Plastic Surg.) Mt. Vernon Hosp. N.wood & W. Middlx. Univ. Hosp. Lond.

JONES, Beri (retired) 12 Kingshill Drive, Kings Norton, Birmingham B38 8SA Tel: 0121 433 4946 — MB BS 1974 Lond.; FRCPath. 1981. Prev: Cons. Path. Selly Oak Hosp. Birm.

JONES, Bernard George Glenkens Medical Practice, The Surgery, High Street, New Galloway, Castle Douglas DG7 3RN — MB ChB 1992 Liverp. Princip. Gen. Med. Practitioner.

JONES, Bethan Alison The Surgery, 1 Kimberworth Road, Rotherham S61 1AH Tel: 01709 561442/562319 Fax: 01709 740690; 36 Parkers Road, Sheffield S10 1BN Tel: 0114 267 8436 — MB ChB 1974 Liverp.; Cert. Family Plann. JCC 1981.

JONES, Bethan Eleri 11 Bainbridge Road, Loughborough LE11 2LE — MB BCh 1992 Wales; DRCOG 1997. (University of Wales Cardiff) VTS Scheme Nottm.; VTS Scheme Nottm.. Prev: SHO (A & E) Morriston Hosp. Swansea; SHO (Med.) Cantebury Health New Zealand; SHO (A & E) Morriston Hosp. Swansea.

JONES, Bethan Gwenllian 10 Waun Sterw, Rhydyfro, Pontardawe, Swansea SA8 4NF — MB BCh 1995 Wales.

JONES, Bethan Sian 4 The Meadows, Penllyn, Cowbridge CF71 7RQ — MB ChB 1992 Ed.

JONES, Beverley Rose — MB ChB 1994 Birm.; MRCGP 1999 (Dist.). Gen. Practitioner. Socs: Med. Defence Union; BMA; MDU. Prev: SHO Birm. Wom. Hosp.; GP Locum (Birm.); GP Regist. (Kingsnorton).

JONES, Bleddyn Imperial College School Medicine, Hammersmith Hospital, Du Cane Road, London W12 0NN — MB BChir 1977 Camb.; MSc Lond. 1981; MA Camb. 1978; FRCP Lond. 1997; FRCR 1986; MD Camb. 1998. (Camb. & Guy's) Reader Oncol.Imperial Coll. Sch. Med. Lond. Socs: Brit. Inst. Radiol.; Eur. Soc. Therap. Radiol.; Roy. Soc. Med. Prev: Cons. (Radiother. & Oncol.) Clatterbridge Centre Oncol.; MRC Train. Fell. (Radiother. & Oncol.) St. Thos. Hosp. Lond.; SHO (Gen. Med.) & Ho. Phys. Guy's Hosp. Lond.

JONES, Branwen Gwenllian Llwyn Ial, Llanbedrog, Pwllheli LL53 7TG — MB BCh 1992 Wales.

JONES, Brian Collum (retired) The Old Vicarage, North Nibley, Dursley GL11 6DJ Tel: 01453 547743 — MRCS Eng. LRCP Lond. 1962; MB BS Lond 1963; DObst RCOG 1964. Prev: Ho. Surg. & Ho. Phys. Pontypool & Dist. Hosp.

JONES, Brian Lakelin Department of Bacteriology, Glasgow Royal Infirmary University NHS Trust, 84 Castle St., Glasgow G40 — MB ChB 1984 Glas.; BSc (Hons.) Glas. 1981; MRCPath 1995. Cons. Med. (MicroBiol.) Glas. Roy. Infirm. Socs: Brit. Soc. Antimicrob. Chemother. Hosp. Infect. Soc.; Amer. Soc. Microbiol. Prev: Sen. Regist. (Microbiol.) Clin. Microbiol. & Pub. Health Laborat. Addenbrooke's Hosp. Camb.; Regist. (Med. Microbiol.) Dept. Bact. W.. Infirm. Glas.

JONES, Brian Martin The Surgery, Brook End, Potton, Sandy SG19 2QS Tel: 01767 260260; 22 West Road, Gamlingay, Sandy SG19 3JT — MB BS 1961 Lond.; MRCS Eng. LRCP Lond. 1961; FRCGP 1991, M 1971; DObst RCOG 1966. (St. Mary's) Prev: Med. Off. Overseas Civil Serv. (Gibraltar); Ho. Phys. & Ho. Surg. Padd. Gen. Hosp.

JONES, Brian Philip (retired) 21 Sefton Drive, Worsley, Manchester M28 2NG Tel: 0161 794 1855 — MB ChB Manch. 1950.

JONES, Brian Read Tel: 01284 753008 Fax: 01284 724744; Church Cottage, Hessett, Bury St Edmunds IP30 9AX Tel: 01359 270421 — MB BS Lond. 1967; MRCP (UK) 1971; MRCS Eng. LRCP Lond. 1967; FRCGP 1997, M 1976. (St. Thos.) Hosp. Pract. (Dermat.) Bury St. Edmunds. Prev: Regist. (Dermat.) Addenbrooke's Hosp. Camb.

JONES, Bridget Elizabeth 45 Fitzjohn Road, Lewes BN7 1PR — MB ChB 1994 Bristol.

JONES, Mr Bruce Victor, Surg. Capt. RN Retd. (retired) 3 Haywards Close, Wantage, Wantage OX12 7AT — MB BS 1944 Lond.; FRCS Eng. 1949; MRCS Eng. LRCP Lond. 1943. Prev: Adviser In Orthop. to Med. Dir.-Gen. (Navy).

JONES, Bryan, CStJ (retired) 58 Jacksons Lane, Norbury Moor Est., Hazel Grove, Stockport SK7 5JY Tel: 0161 483 7121 — MB BCh Wales 1952; BSc Wales 1949; FFOM RCP Lond. 1991, MFOM 1978; MFOM RCPI 1980. Prev: Chief Med. Off. N. W. Gas.

JONES, Bryn Compton (retired) Green Acres, 21 Ashen Grove Road, Knatts Valley, Sevenoaks TN15 6YE — MB BS 1960 Lond.; MRCS Eng. LRCP Lond. 1959; FFA RCS Eng. 1967; DA Eng. 1963. Cons. Anaesth. S.E. Staffs. (Burton-on-Trent) Health Dist. Prev: Sen. Regist. (Anaesth.) United Birm. Hosps. & Coventry Gp. Hosps.

JONES, Bryn Gavin 34 Duckmill Crescent, Bedford MK42 0AF; 2/R 8 Mingarry Street, Glasgow G20 8NT — MB ChB 1992 Glas.; FRCS Ed. 1996. Specialist Regist. (Orthop.) Glas. Socs: FRCS.

***JONES, Bryony Anne Spencer** Flat 6, 40 Clifton Gardens, Little Venice, London W9 1AU Tel: 020 7266 5568 — MB BS 1997 Lond.; BCS (Hons.) Lond. 1994.

JONES, Carol Ann Royal Liverpool Childrens NHS Trust, Alder Hey Hospital, Eaton Road, Liverpool L12 2AP Tel: 0151 252 5223 Fax: 0151 252 5460; 14 Norlands Lane, Rainhill, Prescot L35 6NR — MB ChB 1979 Liverp.; FFA RCS Eng. 1985. Cons. Paediat. Anaesth. Alder Hey Hosp. Liverp. Prev: Sen. Regist. (Anaesth.) W. Midl. RHA.

JONES, Carol Elizabeth Branson Creffield Road Surgery, 19 Creffield Road, Colchester CO3 3HZ Tel: 01206 570371 Fax: 01206 369908 — MB ChB 1982 Leeds; DRCOG 1988. GP Princip.

JONES, Miss Carole Anne Somerfield Hospital, London Road, Maidstone ME16 0DU Tel: 01622 672837 — MB BCh 1977 Wales; FRCS Eng. (Ophth.) 1982. p/t Cons. Ophth. Kent Co. Ophth. & Aural Hosp. Maidstone. Socs: Fell. Roy. Soc. Med.; Eur. Soc. Ophth. Plastic Surgs. Prev: Jt. Sen. Regist. (Ophth.) St. Geo.'s Hosp. & Moorfields Eye Hosp. Lond.; Fell. (Ophth. Plastic Surg.) Moorfields Eye Hosp.; Regist. (Ophth.) Univ. Witwatersrand Johannesburg, S. Africa.

JONES, Caroline Ann Royal Liverpool Children's Hospital, Paediatric Medicine, Eaton Road, Liverpool L12 2AP; 9 Highfield Road, Bramhall, Stockport SK7 3BE — MB ChB 1987 Manch.; MD 2001 Liverp.; MRCP (UK) 1991; DCH RCP Glas. 1989. Cons. in Gen. Paediat. and Paediatric Nephrol., Roy. Liverp. Childr.'s Hosp., NHS Trust, Liverp.. Socs: RCPCH; BAPN; IPNA. Prev: Sen. Regist. NWRHA; Clin. Research Fell. Inst. Child Health Alder Hey Childr. Hosp. Liverp.; Regist. (Paediat.) Mersey RHA.

JONES, Caroline Ingrid 82 Wesmorland Road, Urmston, Manchester M31 1HN — MB BS 1991 Lond.

JONES, Caroline Louise 18 Savernake Road, London NW3 2JP — MB BS 1980 Lond.; MB BS (Hons. Distinc. Clin. Pharm. & Therap.) Lond. 1980. (St. Mary's) Clin. Research Asst. (Palliat. Med.) Edenhall Marie Curie Centre Lond. Socs: Assn. Palliat. Med. Prev: Clin. Research Asst. (Experim. Path.) St. Mary's Hosp. Med. Sch. Lond.; Regist. (Histopath.) St. Mary's Hosp. Lond. W2; Ho. Phys. & Ho. Surg. Edgware Gen. Hosp.

JONES, Caroline Margaret Parkfield Health Centre, Sefton Road, New Ferry, Wirral CH62 5HS Tel: 0151 644 0055 Fax: 0151 643 1679 — MB ChB 1976 Glas.; Diploma in Medical Jurisprudence, London 2000; MRCGP 1981; DCH RCPS Glas. 1978; DRCOG 1978; Dip. Psychosexual Health Care Manch. 1996. Princip. Gen. Pract., Newferry, Wirral; Sen. Clin. Med. Off.; Psychosexual Med. Clatterbridge Hosp., Wirral,; Forens. Med. Examr., Merseyside Police,. Socs: Roy. Coll. Gen. Pract.; Brit. Assn. Sexual & Marital Ther.; Assn. Police Surg.Subscription). Prev: Dep. Forens. Examr. & Clin. Asst. (Psychosexual Med.) Merseyside.

JONES, Caroline Mary The Surgery, 18 Fouracre Road, Bristol BS16 6PG Tel: 0117 970 2033; 98 Berkeley Road, Bishopston, Bristol BS7 8HG Tel: 0117 942 2644 — MB BS 1986 Lond.; MRCGP 1992; DRCOG 1991. (Middlx. Hosp. Med. Sch.) Prev: GP Lond.; Trainee GP Lond. VTS.

JONES, Caroline Rebecca Tyddyn Cynar, Llansilin, Oswestry SY10 7JW — MB BS 1987 Lond. GP Chesh. Retainer Scheme. Socs: BMA; Soc. Study VD. Prev: Trainee GP Oxf.; Clin. Asst. (Genitourin. Med.) Oxf.

JONES, Carolyn Ann Bay View Cottage, Liskey Hill, Perranporth TR6 0BB — MB ChB 1993 Birm.

JONES, Carolyn Elizabeth Mary Padarn Surgery, 26 North Parade, Aberystwyth SY23 2NF Tel: 01970 624545; Glan-yr-Afon, Pont-y-Geifr, Talybont SY24 5HL — MB ChB 1967 Leeds; MRCP (U.K.) 1970; DCH Eng. 1973; DObst RCOG 1969. (Leeds) p/t GP Aberystwyth. Prev: Sen. Regist. (Paediat.) Soton. & S.W. Hants. HA; Regist. (Paediat.) Whittington Hosp. Lond.; SHO (Neonat. Paediat.) Univ. Coll. Hosp. Lond.

JONES, Carolyn Margaret City General Hospital, Newcastle Road, Stoke-on-Trent ST4 6QG Tel: 01782 715444 Fax: 01782 718001 — MB ChB 1989 Birm.; MRCP (UK) 1993; FRCR 1997. Regist. (Diag. Ragiol.) N. Staffs. Hosps. Trust.

JONES, Carwyn Furnace House Surgery, St. Andrews Road, Carmarthen SA31 1EX Tel: 01267 236616 Fax: 01267 222673; Pentrehydd, College Road, Carmarthen SA31 3QS Email: carwyn@pentrehyod.demon.co.uk — MB BS 1981 Lond.; MRCGP 1988; DRCOG 1983. (St. Bartholomew's) CME Tutor Carmarthen.

JONES, Catherine Ann 8 The Mallows, Uxbridge UB10 8BX — MB BChir 1991 Camb. Trainee GP/SHO (O & G) Lincs.

JONES, Catherine Anne Meredith St Peters Surgery, St. Peters Street, Carmarthen SA31 1LN Tel: 01267 236241 Fax: 01267 236241 — MB BCh 1984 Wales.

JONES, Catrin Alice Clwyd 3 Fron Deg, Benllech, Tyn-y-Gongl LL74 8TD — MB BS 1990 Lond.; BSc (Hons.) Biochem. Lond. 1987; MRCGP 1995; DRCOG 1993; DGM RCP Lond. 1992. Socs: BMA.

JONES, Cecil John Macdonald Thomas (retired) Berkeley, The Links, Pembrey, Burry Port SA16 0HU Tel: 01554 833342 — MRCS Eng. LRCP Lond. 1945. Prev: Ho. Surg. Lond. Hosp.

JONES, Cenydd Richards, CBE (retired) 12 Thanet Court, Queens Drive, London W3 0HW Tel: 020 8992 0170 — MB ChB 1944 Wales; Dip. Med. Admin. Lond. 1958; DTM & H Lond. 1950. Prev: Epidemiologist World Health Organization.

JONES, Charles Hilton, TD (retired) Trigfa, 36 Calthorpe Drive, Woodland Park, Prestatyn LL19 9RF Tel: 01745 852081 — MB ChB 1948 Liverp.; MD Liverp. 1955; MRCS Eng. LRCP Lond. 1949; FRCPath 1974, M 1963. Prev: Cons. Path. Clwyd HA.

JONES, Charles Kenyon (retired) Little Lamerton, Idless, Truro TR4 9QS — MB BCh 1960 Wales; FCOphth. 1988; DO Eng. 1963. Cons. Ophth. Roy. Cornw. Hosp. Trust. Prev: Med. Asst. (Ophth.) Dyfed AHA.

JONES, Charlotte Dixton Surgery, Dixton Road, Monmouth NP25 3PL Tel: 01600 712152 Fax: 01600 772634; Ty Gwyn, Dixton Road, Monmouth NP25 3PL Tel: 01600 714550 — MB BS 1952 Lond.; MRCS Eng. LRCP Lond. 1951; DObst RCOG 1954. (Roy. Free) GP Gwent. Socs: Inst. Psychosexual Med. 1968. Prev: SCMO (Family Plann.) Glos. HA; Regist. Thorpe Coombe Matern. Hosp.; Cas. Off. Roy. Free Hosp.

JONES, Cheryl Kerry House, Comey Trowe Lane, Taunton TA1 5JB — MB BS 1980 Lond.; DCH RCP Lond. 1984.

JONES, Christine Elizabeth James Street Grove Practice, James Street, Workington CA14 2DF Tel: 01900 62241 Fax: 01900 603385; The Rookery, Main Road, Great Clifton, Workington CA14 1TR Tel: 01900 67445 — MB ChB 1975 Liverp.; DRCOG 1979.

JONES, Christine Mary Ravenswood Doctors Surgery, Thomson Avenue, Johnstone PA5 8SU Tel: 01505 331979 Fax: 01505 323444; 18 Carruth Road, Bridge of Weir PA11 3HQ Tel: 01505 614498 — MB ChB 1985 Glas.; Cert. Family Plann. JCC 1993.

JONES, Christopher 25 Trehearn Road, Derwent Surgery, Norton Road, Norton, Malton YO17 9RF — MB ChB 1984 Leeds; MRCP (UK) 1987; MRCGP 1988; Cert. Family Plann. JCC 1988; DRCOG 1988.

JONES, Christopher Plas-Coch, Waen, Rhuddlan, Rhyl LL18 5RT — MB BCh 1989 Wales.

JONES, Christopher 47 Eastfield Avenue, Fareham PO14 1EQ — MB BS 1998 Newc.; MB BS Newc 1998.

JONES, Christopher David Vaughan Taff Vale Surgery, Duffryn Road, Rhydyfelin, Pontypridd CF37 5RW Tel: 01443 400940 Fax: 01443 492900 — MB BCh 1979 Wales.

JONES, Christopher Gwyn (retired) — BM BCh 1960 Oxf.; MA Oxf. 1960; DObst RCOG 1963. Clin. Asst. Maidstone Chest Clinic. Prev: Ho. Surg. St. Mary's Hosp. Lond.

JONES, Christopher John The Aldergate Medical Practice, The Mount, Salters Lane, Tamworth B79 8BH Tel: 01827 54775 Fax: 01827 62835 — MB BCh 1986 Wales; MRCGP 1990; DCH RCP Lond. 1989; DGM RCP Lond. 1989.

JONES, Christopher John Southside Road Surgery, 43 Southside Road, Inverness IV2 4XA Tel: 01463 710222 Fax: 01463 714072; Hillside, The Old Curling Pond, Fortrose IV10 8SG Tel: 01381 621044 — MRCS Eng. LRCP Lond. 1976; DFFP 1997; DRCOG 1979. Prev: Trainee GP Inverness VTS; Ho. Phys. Raigmore Hosp. Inverness; Ho. Surg. Ophth. & ENT Depts. W.m. Hosp. Lond.

JONES, Christopher John De Parys Medical Centre, 23 De Parys Avenue, Bedford MK40 2TX Tel: 01234 350022 Fax: 01234 213402; 9 Riverside View, Milton Ernest, Bedford MK44 1SG Tel: 01234 824814 — MB BS 1977 Lond.; DA Eng. 1980.

JONES, Christopher John Hugh Princess of Wales Hospital, Coity Road, Bridgend CF31 1RQ; Bryncelyn, Castle Hill, Llanblethian, Cowbridge CF71 7JB Tel: 01446 772840 Fax: 01446 771268 — MB BS 1981 Lond.; MRCP (UK) 1984; FESC 1997; FRCP 1998. Cons. Phys. & Cardiol. Bridgend Dist. NHS Trust; Sen. Lect. Cardiol. Univ. Wales Coll. Med. Prev: Vis. Asst. Prof. Med. Phys. Texas A & M Univ., USA; Lect. & Hon. Sen. Regist. (Cardiol.) Univ. Wales Coll. Med. Cardiff; BHF Research Fell. Unit Imperial Coll. Lond.

JONES, Christopher Mark Graylingwell Hospital, 9 College Lane, Chichester PO19 4FX Tel: 01329 832271 — MB BS 1985 Lond.; BA Oxf. 1982; MRCPsych 1991. Cons. (Rehabil. & Continuing Care Psychiat.). Prev: Sen. Regist. (Psychiat.) Wessex RHA; SHO (Psychiat.) Soton. HA; SHO (O & G) Cuckfield Hosp. Haywards Heath.

JONES, Christopher Mark Longfleet House Surgery, 56 Longfleetroad, Poole 3H15 2TD Tel: 01202 666677 Fax: 01202 660319; 8 The topiary, Parkstone Heights, Poole BH14 0QU Tel: 01202 776605 — MB BS 1986 Lond.; MRCGP 1994; DCH RCP Lond. 1992; DRCOG 1990; Dip. IMC RCS Ed. 1989. GP Princip.

JONES, Christopher Nicholas Consultant Foensic Psychiatrist, Norvic Clinic, St Andrew's Business Park, Thorpe St Andrew, Norwich NR7 0HT Tel: 01603 421025 Email: christopher.jones@norfmhc-tr.anglox.nhs.uk — BM BS 1983 Nottm.; LLB Nottm. 1995; BMedSci Nottm. 1981; MRCPsych 1988; Dip. Forens. Psychother. Lond. 1996. (Nottingham) Cons. Forens. Psychiat. Norf. Ment. Health Care Trust. Prev: Sen. Regist. (Forens. Psychiat.) Mersey Region & Ashworth Hosp. Liverp.; Regist. (Psychiat.) Leicester HA.; Cons. Forens. Psychiat. N. Wales Forens. Serv.

JONES, Mr Christopher Richard St. Helier Hospital, Wrythe Lane, Carshalton SM5 1AA Tel: 020 8296 2262 Fax: 020 8296 2809; Email: c.r.jones@blueyonder.co.uk — MRCS Eng. LRCP Lond. 1974; BSc, MB BS Lond. 1974; FRCS Eng. 1979. (St. Mary's) Cons. Urol. Epsom & St. Helier NHS Trust; Hon. Sen. Lect. St. Geo. Hosp. Lond. Socs: B.A.U.S.; R.S.M. Prev: Sen. Regist. (Urol.) St. Mary's Hosp. Lond.; Lect. (Urol.) Roy. Marsden Hosp. Lond.; Lect. (Transpl. & Urol.) Char. Cross Hosp. Lond.

JONES, Christopher Scott Cockill and Partners, Group Surgery, Church St, Ossett WF5 9DE Tel: 01924 273118 Fax: 01924 261321 — MB ChB 1986 Leeds; MRCGP 1990; DRCOG 1990.

JONES, Claire Elizabeth 300 Mumbles Road, West Cross, Swansea SA3 5AB — MB BS 1993 Lond.

JONES, Claire Philippa 46 Park Avenue, Worcester WR3 7AH — MB BS 1991 Lond.; MRCGP 1995; DRCOG 1994. (St. Geo.)

JONES, Claire Susanne 7 Parkstone Cl, New Marske, Redcar TS11 8JH — MB ChB 1997 Sheff.

JONES, Clare Carolyn Union Street Surgery, 12 Union Street, Kirkintilloch, Glasgow G71 7AP Tel: 0141 776 2468 Fax: 0141 775 3341 — MB ChB 1992 Glas.

JONES, Clare Louise 18 Stanhope Street, Whitecross, Hereford HR4 0HB Tel: 01432 277246; 11 Glanbrydan Avenue, Uplands, Swansea SA2 0HR Tel: 01792 458455 — MB ChB 1990 Birm.; ChB Birm. 1990; DRCOG 1994. Socs: BMA.

JONES, Clare Nicola Overton Newtons Surgery, The Health Centre, Haywards Heath RH16 3BB Tel: 01444 412280; 2 William Allen Lane, Lindfield, Haywards Heath RH16 2SH Tel: 01444 483542 — MB BS 1987 Lond.; MRCGP 2001; DRCOG 1999; MRCP (UK) 1991. p/t GP Princip. Haywards Heath. Prev: Regist. (Med.) John Radcliffe Hosp. Oxf.; Research Fell. (Endocrinol.) Stanford Hosp. Calif., USA; Regis.Med.John.Radcliffe.Hosp.Oxf.

JONES, Claudia Ann Berinsfield Health Centre, Fane Drive, Berinsfield, Wallingford OX10 7NE Tel: 01865 340558 Fax: 01865 341973; 52 Aston Street, Oxford OX4 1EP — MB BS 1982 Lond.; MRCGP 1987; DRCOG 1985.

JONES, Cleanth (retired) — MB BCh 1972 Wales; MRCP (UK) 1975; T(M) 1991; FRCP 1998. Cons. Genitourin Med. Gwynedd Acute Hosps. NHS Trust; Hon. Clin. Teach. Univ. Wales Coll. Med. Cardiff. Prev: Sen. Regist. (Genitourin. Med.) Manch. Roy. Infirm.

JONES, Mr Cledwyn Barrie Royal United Hospital Trust, Combe Park, Bath BA1 3NG — MB ChB 1975 Leeds; FRCS Eng. 1980. Cons. Orthop. Surg. Roy. United Hosp. Bath. Socs: Brit. Orthop. Assn.; Fell.of the Roy. Coll. of Surg.s; Mem. of the Roy. Soc. of Med.. Prev: Sen. Regist. W.m. & Univ. Coll. Hosps. Lond.; Regional Rotat. Regist. Leeds AHA (T); Research Fell. Univ. Maryland Baltimore USA.

JONES, Clement Alun The Clinic, 87 Farnham Lane, Farnham Royal, Slough SL2 2AT Tel: 01753 553552 Fax: 01753 822273; 24 Larchmoor, Gerrards Cross Rd, Stoke Poges SL2 4EY Tel: 0118 984 3568, 01753 663614 — MB BS 1966 Lond.; MRCS Eng. LRCP Lond. 1966. (St. Mary's) Med. Off. W.. Geophysical; Med. Off. Bovis Construction Ltd. & Morgan Crucible Company plc. Socs: Brit. Aeromed. Pract. Assn.; Indep. Med. Forum.; Windsor Med. Soc. Prev: Clin. Asst. (ENT) St. Mary's Hosp. Lond.; SHO Obst. Unit. St. Mary's Hosp.; Ho. Surg. (ENT & Plastic) St. Mary's Hosp.

JONES, Colin Britannic House, 1 Finsbury Circus, London EC2M 7EB Tel: 020 7496 4684 Fax: 020 7496 4707 — MB BS 1963 Lond.; MRCS Eng. LRCP Lond. 1963; MFOM 1981. (Char. Cross) Gen. Manager Health, Safety, Environm. Quality & Security BP Exploration; Asst. Gen. Manager. (NNS) BP Aberd.

JONES, Colin Charles Medical Centre, High Street, Ruabon, Wrexham LL14 6NH Tel: 01978 823717 Fax: 01978 824142 — MB ChB 1973 Manch.

JONES, Colin David 29 Hantone Hill, Bathampton, Bath BA2 6XD — MB ChB 1987 Birm.; FCOphth 1992.

JONES, Colin Malcolm Ardselma House, 2 Chestnut Walk, Hooton Levitt, Rotherham S66 8QA Tel: 01709 812297 — MB ChB 1967 Birm.; MFOM (1982); DIH Eng. 1975; DObst RCOG 1970. Sen. Med. Off. B. S. Engin. Steel Rotherham. Prev: Med. Off. NCCM Chingola, Zambia.

JONES, Colin Michael 1 The Bridle Road, Purley CR8 3JB — MB BS 1981 Lond.

JONES, Colin Richard 94 St Anne's Road, Middlewich CW10 9BZ — BM 1988 Soton.; Dip. IMC RCS Ed. 1993. Socs: Brit. Assn. Sport & Med.

JONES, Colin Timothy Angus 2 North Jesmond Avenue, Jesmond, Newcastle upon Tyne NE2 3JX Tel: 0191 281 0486 — MB ChB 1965 Manch.; MSc Manch. 1971, MB ChB 1965; FRCP Lond. 1983, M 1969. (Manch.) Cons. Phys. Qu. Eliz. Hosp. Gateshead. Prev: Ho. Phys. & Sen. Regist. (Profess. Med. Unit) Manch. Roy. Infirm.; Lect. (Med.) Univ. Manch.

JONES, Colin William 57 Houndenhall Road, Edinburgh EH16 6PL Tel: 0131 664 2377 — MB ChB 1989 Glas.; DRCOG 1994; MRCGP 1996. (Glas.) GP Princip. Prev: Locum Gen. Practitioner.

JONES, Colin Woodley Chester Road East Surgery, 17-21 Chester Road East, Shotton, Deeside CH5 1QA Tel: 01244 831698 Fax: 01244 812847 — MB BCh 1970 Wales; MRCP (UK) 1976. Hosp. Pract. (Dermat.) Clwyd HA.

JONES, Coral Elizabeth 75 Mount Pleasant Lane, London E5 9EW — MB BS 1980 Melbourne; MRCGP 1989.

JONES, Cyril William Lewis, KStJ (retired) Alltwen, Galltegfa, Ruthin LL15 2AR Tel: 01824 703208 — MB BS 1946 Lond.; MRCS Eng. LRCP Lond. 1946. Prev: SHO (Orthop. & Accid.) & Ho. Phys. Lond. Hosp.

JONES, Daniel Lewis 121 Cardiff Road, Taffs Well, Cardiff CF15 7PP — MB BS 1997 Lond.

JONES, Daniel Michael Howard (retired) Skirmish Field, Waverley Road, Melrose TD6 9AA Tel: 0189 682 2727 — MB BS 1955 Durh.; FRCPsych 1984, M 1972; DPM Eng. 1961. Prev: Cons. Psychiat. Dingleton Hosp. Melrose.

JONES, Danny George 28 Langlodge Road, Whitmore Park, Coventry CV6 4EG — MB BS 1991 Lond.

JONES, David 9 Benbrook Way, Gawsworth, Macclesfield SK11 9RT — MB BS 1997 Lond.

JONES, David Alun Rhianta, Talwrn, Ynys Mon, Conwy LL777 TB Tel: 01248 723164 Fax: 01248 750765 Email: dajones@dafydd.co.uk — MD 1962 Liverp.; MB ChB 1957; BSc (Hons.) Wales 1951; FRCPsych 1971; DPM Eng. 1964. Cons. Psychiat. Ty Gwyn Ex-Serv. Unit, Llandudno, Conwy, Wales; Chariman, CAIS, Tyldesley Hse. Llandudno, Conwy, Wales. Socs: Roy. Soc. of Med.; Y Gymdeithas Feddygol; Welsh Psychiatric Soc. Prev: Cons. Psych. Nth. Wales Hosp., Denbeigh; Sen. Psychiat. Regist. Anglesey Ment. Health Survey.

JONES, David Alwyn Samuel 26B Eastgate, Cowbridge CF71 7DG — MB BCh 1993 Wales.

JONES, Mr David Andrew Beardwood Hospital, Preston New Road, Blackburn BB2 7BG Tel: 01254 57666 — MB ChB Manch. 1979; MD Manch. 1987; FRCS Eng. 1983. Cons. Urol. Surg. Blackburn, Hyndburn & Ribble Valley NHS Health Care Trust.

JONES, David Andrew 16 Trefonwys, Bangor LL57 2HU — MB BCh 1988 Wales.

JONES, David Andrew Regional Transfusion Centre, Longley Lane, Sheffield S5 7JN Tel: 0114 203 4800 Fax: 0114 203 4910 Email: bing.jones@nbs.nhs.uk; 14 Whiteley Wood Road, Whiteley Wood, Sheffield S11 7FE Tel: 0114 230 1003 — MB ChB 1975 Bristol. Assoc. Specialist (Blood Transfus.) Sheff. Prev: SCMO (Blood Transfus.) Sheff.

JONES, David Andrew Demontfort Medical Centre, Burford Road, Bengeworth, Evesham WR11 5AG Tel: 01386 443333 Fax: 01386 422884; Manor Farm House, The Cross, Bretforton, Evesham WR11 5JD Tel: 01386 833606 — MB ChB 1986 Birm.; Cert. Family Plann. JCC 1989.

JONES, Mr David Anthony Anthony Jones Orthopaedic, 11 St James Gardens, Swansea SA1 6DY Tel: 01792 459899 Fax: 01792 459899; Gurrey Manor, Llandeilo SA19 6AJ — MB BCh Wales 1968; BSc (Hons. Anat.) Wales 1965, MCh 1991; FRCS Eng. 1973; FRCS Ed. 1972. (Univ. Wales, Sch. Med.) Cons. Orthop. Surg. Swansea; Hon. Clin. Teach. Univ. Wales Sch. Med. Socs: Fell. BOA; Acad. Experts. Prev: Cons. Orthop. Surg. Morriston Hosp. Swansea; Sen. Regist. (Orthop.) Bristol Roy. Infirm.; Mem. Welsh Bd. RCS Eng. 1989-94.

JONES, David Anthony 41 Malthouse Lane, Kenilworth CV8 1AD Tel: 01926 853403 — MB BS 1973 Lond.; BSc (Hons.) (Physiol.) Lond. 1970, MB BS 1973; MRCP (UK) 1976; FRCR 1983. Cons. Radiother. & Oncol. Coventry & S. Warks. HA. Prev: Research Asst. Marie Curie Research Wing Mt. Vernon Hosp. N.wood; Sen. Regist. (Radiother. & Oncol.) The Christie Hosp. Manch.; Regist. (Radiother.) Bristol Radiother. Centre.

JONES, David Anthony Llewellyn 5 Kilmorey Park, Chester CH2 3QS — MB ChB 1946 Ed.; DObst RCOG 1950. (Ed.)

JONES, David Arthur The Old Rectory, Church Lane, Utterby, Louth LN11 0TH — MB BS Lond. 1970; FRCP Lond. 1994; MRCS Eng. LRCP Lond. 1970. (Guy's) Cons. Phys. Gen. & Respirat. Med. Grimsby Dist. Gen. Hosp. Prev: Sen. Regist. Groby Rd. Hosp. Leicester; Research Fell. Brompton Hosp. Lond.; Regist. Guy's Hosp. Lond.

JONES, David Aubrey 46 The Butts, Brentford TW8 8BL Tel: 020 8568 9600; 546A Reading Road, Winnersh, Wokingham RG41 5HA Tel: 0118 978 8214 — MB BS Lond. 1960; MFOM RCP Lond. 1979; DIH Eng. 1966; DPH Lond. 1964. (Univ. Coll. Hosp.) Occupat. Health Phys. Prev: Ho. Surg. Univ. Coll. Hosp. Lond.; Ho. Phys. Addenbrooke's Hosp. Camb.; Med. Regist. Bridgend Gen. Hosp.

JONES, David Barry Darley 133 Reigate Avenue, Sutton SM1 3JR — LMSSA 1961 Lond. (St. Geo.) GP Sutton. Socs: BMA. Prev: Anaesth. Resid. Elmhurst City Hosp. New York U.S.A.; SHO Anaesth. Ashford Hosp.

JONES, David Bowen Department of Medicine, Western General Hospital, Edinburgh — MD 1986 Wales; MB BCh 1977; MRCP (UK) 1980. Lect. Med. Univ. Edin. Prev: Research Regist. Diabetes Research Laborat. Radcliffe Infirm. Oxf.; Regist. Med. Unit Univ. Hosp. of Wales Cardiff.

JONES, Mr David Carl Regional Maxillofacial Unit, University Hospital Aintree, Liverpool L9 9AL Tel: 0151 529 5280 Fax: 0151 5295 2888 Email: carl.jones@doctors.org.uk; Bank Cottage, Parkgate Road CH64 6PG Tel: 0151 336 8478 Email: carl.jones@oral-maxfac.co.uk — MB ChB 1992 Liverp.; FRCS (OMFS) 1998; BChD Leeds 1983; FRCS Eng. 1995; FDS RCS Ed. 1987. (Liverp.) Cons. Maxillofacial Surg., Univ. Hosp., Aintree; Cons. Maxillofacial Surg., Arrowe Pk. Hosp.; Hon. Lect. Oral & Maxillofacial Surg., Univ. of Liverp. Socs: Brit. Assn. Oral & Maxillofacial Surg.; BMA; Brit. Assn. Head & Neck Oncol.

JONES, David Douglas 6 The Point, Groomsport, Bangor BT19 6JN — MB BCh BAO 1976 Belf.

JONES, Mr David Edgar Peter Royal United Hospital, Coombe Park, Bath BA1 3NG — BM BCh 1952 Oxf.; MA Oxf. 1959, BM BCh 1952; FRCS Eng. 1963; FCOphth 1988; DO Eng. 1958. (Oxf. & Westm.) Cons. Ophth. Bath Clin. Area. Socs: Fell. Roy. Soc. Med. Prev: Sen. Res. Off. Moorfields Eye Hosp. Lond.; Sen. Regist. St. Thos. Hosp. Lond.; Res. Surg. Off. Oxf. Eye Hosp.

JONES, David Emlyn The Surgery, 174 Lower Glen Road, St Leonards-on-Sea TN37 7AR Tel: 01424 721616/852270 Fax: 01424 854812; 212 Harley Shute Road, St Leonards-on-Sea TN38 9JH — MB BS 1978 Lond.; MRCGP 1984; DObst. RCOG 1980. (Guy's)

JONES, David Emrys Jeffreys 1 Eslington Terrace, Jesmond, Newcastle upon Tyne NE2 4RJ — BM BCh 1988 Oxf.

JONES, David Gareth, SBStJ London Road Surgery, 31 London Road, Sittingbourne ME10 1NQ Tel: 01795 422269 Fax: 01795 429992; Barnpool, Primrose Lane, Bredgar, Sittingbourne ME9 8EH Tel: 01622 884441 — MB BCh 1963 Wales; DObst RCOG 1966. (Cardiff) Prev: Regist. (Paediat.) E. Glam. Hosp. Pontypridd.

JONES, David Gerallt Gruffydd (retired) Rhiwfelen, Aberporth, Cardigan SA43 1DY Tel: 01239 811138 — MB BS 1942 Lond.; MRCS Eng. LRCP Lond. 1940; DPH Lond. 1947. Co. MOH Carms.; Area Med. Off. Dyfed HA. Prev: RAFVR.

JONES, David Gethin Hopcyn Elm Tree Cottage, Pencroesoped, Llanover, Abergavenny NP7 9EW Tel: 01873 880207 — MB BS 1972 Lond.; MRCS Eng. LRCP Lond. 1972; DObst RCOG 1975. (Roy. Free) Prev: SHO (Paediat. & Obst.) Leicester Gen. Hosp.; Hon. Sec. & Treas. Gwent Med. Soc.

JONES, David Glyn 8 Charles Court, Limekilns, Dunfermline KY11 3LG Tel: 01383 872074 — MB ChB 1979 Manch.; MSc Lond. 1985; MFOM RCP Lond. 1987.

JONES, Mr David Glyn (retired) 8 Beechmount Road, Lenzie, Glasgow G66 5AD Tel: 0141 776 1604 — MB BCh 1945 Wales; FRFPS Glas. 1960; FRCS Glas. 1962; DLO Eng. 1949. Prev: Cons. ENT Surg. Gartnavel Gen. Hosp. Glas. & Vale of Leven Hosp. Alexandria.

JONES, David Graham Eveswell Surgery, 254 Chepstow Road, Newport NP19 8NL Tel: 01633 277494 Fax: 01633 290709 — MB BCh 1962 Wales.

JONES, David Gwyn Vale Street Surgery, 24 Vale Street, Denbigh LL16 3BL Tel: 01754 812689 Fax: 01754 812221 — MB ChB 1974 Liverp.; MRCGP 1980.

JONES, David Gwyn Borras Park Surgery, Borras Park Road, Wrexham LL12 7TH Tel: 01978 352341 Fax: 01978 310294 — MB ChB 1983 Liverp.; MRCGP 1987; DRCOG 1986.

JONES, David Harold (retired) 21Thatcher Stanfords Close, Melbourn, Royston SG8 6DT Tel: 01763 262654 — MA Camb. 1956, BA, MB BChir 1954; MRCS Eng. LRCP Lond. 1954; FRCOG 1975, M 1961, DObst 1956; FICS 1977. Lect. & Examr. Centr. Midw. Bd. Prev: Sen. Cons. O & G Hartlepool Health Dist.

JONES, David Hugh Royal Hampshire County Hospital, Winchester SO22 5DG — MD 1987 Lond.; 1971 BSc (Hons.) Lond. 1971; 1993 FRCP Ed. 1993; 1979 MRCP (UK) 1979; 1997 FRCP (Lond.) 1997; 1974 MBBS 1974. (St. Bart.) Cons. Dermatol., Roy. Hants. Co. Hosp., Winchester. Prev: Sen Reg. (Dermat.) Gen. Infirm. Leeds; Regist. (Med.) Norf. & Norwich Hosp.; Cons. Dermatol., Raigmore Hosp. Inverness.

JONES, Rev. David Huw Oncology Centre, Box 193, Addenbrooke's Hospital, Cambridge CB2 2QQ Tel: 01223 216524 Fax: 01223 216589 Email: david.jones@msexc.addenbrookes.anglox.nhs.uk; 17 Barrow Road, Cambridge CB2 2AP Tel: 01223 358458 Fax: 01223 358458 — MB BCh 1972 Wales; MB BCh (Hons.) Wales 1972; MA Camb. 1987; MSc Lond. 1978; MD Wales 1979; FRCP Lond. 1996; MRCP (UK) 1974; FRCR 1983. (Welsh Nat. Sch. Med.) Cons. Oncol. & Radiotherap. Addenbrooke's Hosp. Camb. Prev: Clin. Scientist & Sen. Regist. (Clin. Oncol. & Radiother.) Addenbrooke's Hosp. Camb.; Research Fell. (Clin. Pharmacol.) Roy. Postgrad. Med. Sch.

JONES, David Huw Portsmouth Area Hospice, Purbrook Heath Road, Purbrook, Waterlooville PO7 5RU Tel: 01705 250001 Fax: 01705 225775; Orchard View, Hillpound, Swanmore, Southampton

SO32 2UN Tel: 01489 891402 Email: jones@orchardv.freeserve.co.uk — MB BS 1981 Lond.; BSc Lond. 1978; MRCP (UK) 1985. Cons. Phys. (Palliat. Med.) Portsmouth Healthcare NHS Trust. Socs: Assn. Cancer Phys.; Assn. Palliat. Care. Prev: Macmillan Sen. Regist. (Palliat. Med.) Moorgreen Hosp. Soton.

JONES, David Hywel The Medical Centre, Well St., Biddulph, Stoke-on-Trent ST8 6HD Tel: 01782 512822; 21 Ayrshire Way, Congleton CW12 3TN — MB ChB 1983 Sheff.

JONES, David Hywel Pensby Road Surgery, 349 Pensby Road, Pensby, Wirral CH61 9NL Tel: 0151 648 1193 Fax: 0151 648 2934 — MB ChB 1987 Liverp.; MRCGP 1993; DRCOG 1990.

JONES, David Ian The Mount, City, Llansannor, Cowbridge CF71 1RW — MB ChB 1973 Manch.; MSc Cardiff 1995; FRCA 1978. Cons. Anaesth. Roy. Gwent Hosp. Newport. Socs: (Treas.) SCATA.

JONES, David Ian 62 Grove Hill Road, Tunbridge Wells TN1 1SP — MB BS 1992 Lond.

JONES, David Ieuan Crynga, Cogd-Blow, Narberth SA67 8RL — MB BCh 1954 Wales.

JONES, David Ivor Rees Croft Cottage, Nether End, Baslow, Bakewell DE45 1SR Tel: 01246 583328 — MB BCh 1963 Sheff.; MD Sheff. 1979; MRCGP 1976; Cert. Community Paediat. Sheff. 1990; Cert. Family Plann. JCC 1977. Prev: Sen. Lect. (Gen. Pract.) Sheff.; Head Clin. Research Reckitt & Coleman Hull.

JONES, David John Ty Nant, 10 Wesley Road, Little Haven, Haverfordwest SA62 3UJ Tel: 01437 781490 Fax: 01437 781490 — MB BCh 1961 Wales; FRCP Lond. 1983, M 1964. Cons. Phys. Withybush Hosp. HaverfordW.. Prev: Sen. Regist. (Thoracic Med.) Sully Hosp. Penarth; Regist. St. Thos. Hosp. Lond.; Regist. (Thoracic Med.) Sully Hosp. Penarth.

JONES, Mr David John, Wing Cdr. RAF Med. Br. Retd. Gloucestershire Royal Hospital, Great Western Road, Gloucester GL1 3NN Tel: 01452 394671; Greycote, Green Lane, Little Witcombe, Gloucester GL3 4TY Tel: 01452 864858 Fax: 01452 863977 — MB BS 1973 Lond.; FRCS Eng. 1979; MRCS Eng. LRCP Lond. 1973; DObst RCOG 1975. (Guy's) p/t Cons. Urol. Glos. Roy. Hosp. Socs: Fell. Roy. Soc. Med.; Brit. Assn. Urol. Surgs.; Internat. Continence Soc. Prev: Cons. Urol. RAF Med. Br.; Sen. Regist. (Urol.) Inst. Urol. & St. Peters Hosp. Lond.; Ho. Phys. & Ho. Surg. Guy's Hosp. Lond.

JONES, Mr David John South Manchester University Hospitals NHS Trust, Department of Surgery, Wythenshawe Hospital, Southmoor Road, Manchester M23 9LT Tel: 0161 291 6651 Fax: 0161 291 6613 Email: david.jones@gw.smuht.nwest.nhs.uk — MB ChB 1979 Liverp.; 1988 MD Liverp.; 1983 FRCS Ed.; 1983 FRCS Eng. Cons. Gen. Surg. Wythenshawe Hosp. Manch.; Hon. Lect. Univ. Manch.; Cons. In Gen. And Colorect. Surg. Wythenshawe Hosp. Manch. Socs: Fell. Assn. Coloproctol. GB & Irel.; Fell. Assn. Surgs.; Fell. Assn. Endoscopic Surgs. GB & Irel. Prev: Lect. (Surg.) Univ. Manch.; Research Regist. Christie Hosp. Manch.; Ancien Attaché Hôspital St-Antoine, Paris.

JONES, David Keith Llewellyn Jackson and Partners, Glastonbury Surgery, Feversham Lane, Glastonbury BA6 9LP; 6 South Meadow, South Horrington, Wells BA5 3DJ Email: davidklj@hotmail.com — MB BS 1980 Lond.; MRCGP 1985; DRCOG 1983; DCH RCP Lond. 1983.

JONES, David Kevin Royal Bolton Hospital, Minerva Road, Farnworth, Bolton BL4 0JR Tel: 01204 390550 Fax: 01204 390879 — MB ChB 1977 Liverpool; FRCP; MD 1989 Liverp.; MRCP (UK) 1980. Cons. Phys. Gen. & Chest Med. Roy. Bolton Hosp. Prev: Cons. Phys. Gen. & Chest Med. Bury Gen. Hosp.; Sen. Regist. (Chest & Gen. Med.) St. Bart. & Whipps Cross Hosps. Lond.

JONES, David Lewis Monkstone House, 10 Park View, Llanddew, Brecon LD3 9RL — MB BS 1979 Lond.; MRCP Ed. 1983.

JONES, David Lewis Birchfield Health Centre, Birchfield, 4 Church Road, Whitchurch, Cardiff CF14 2DZ Tel: 029 2052 2455/2355 Fax: 029 2052 2686 — MB BCh 1990 Wales.

JONES, Mr David Llewellyn 15 St John Street, Manchester M3 4DG Tel: 0161 834 7373; Willowbrook House, Spath Lane E., Cheadle Hulme, Cheadle SK8 7NL Tel: 0161 439 7176 — MB ChB 1961 Manch.; FRCS Eng. 1967; Specialist Accredit. (Urol.) RCS Eng. 1976; DObst RCOG 1962. (Manch.) Cons. Urol. Surg. Trafford AHA (Manch.). Socs: Brit. Assn. Urol. Surgs. Prev: Sen. Regist. (Urol.) Manch. Teach. Hosps.; Research Regist. (Urol.) Manch. Roy. Infirm.; Regist. (Surg.) Leicester Roy. Infirm.

JONES, David Mark The Surgery, The Corn Stores, 12 Nargate Street, Littlebourne, Canterbury CT3 1UH Tel: 01227 721515; Woodlands Cottage, Woodlands Road, Adisham, Canterbury CT3 3LG — MB BS 1981 Lond.; MRCGP 1987.

JONES, David Martin P.O. Box 35, Nantwich CW5 8FE Tel: 01270 780954 Fax: 01270 780954 Email: david.jones@soundcare.co.uk; Tel: 01270 780954 Fax: 01270 780954 — MB ChB 1968 Liverp.; FFOM RCP Lond. 1993; MFOM RCP Lond. 1978; DObst RCOG 1971; DIH Eng. 1974. (Liverp.) Cons. Occupat. Phys. Chesh. Socs: Soc. Occupat. Med. & Brit. Occupat. Hyg. Soc.; Mem. Amer. Coll. Occupat. & Envionm. Med. Prev: Chief Med. Adviser Pilkington PLC St. Helens; SHO (Cas.) St. Helens Hosp.; SHO (Obst & Gyn.) W.wood Hosp. Beverley.

JONES, David Martin 127 Borough Road, Loughor, Swansea SA4 6RY — MB BCh 1997 Wales.

JONES, David Maurice Hafod, Llanfairpwll, Anglesey, Llanfairpwllgwyngyll LL61 5YX — MB BChir 1983 Camb.; MA MB BChir Camb. 1983.

JONES, David Michael Newbold Verdon Medical Practice, 14 Arnolds Crescent, Newbold Verdon, Leicester LE9 9PZ Tel: 01445 822171 Fax: 01445 824968; Seven Oaks, Main St, Carlton, Nuneaton CV13 0BZ Tel: 01455 290455 Email: mikej@carltonuk71.freeserve.co.uk — MB BS 1971 Lond.; MRCGP 1975; DObst RCOG 1974. (St. Geo. Hosp. Med. Sch. Lond.)

JONES, David Newton Beaumont Villa Surgery, 23 Beaumont Road, Plymouth PL4 9BL Tel: 01752 663776 Fax: 01752 261520; 24 Abbotts Park, Cornwood, Ivybridge PL21 9PP Tel: 01752 837686 Fax: 01752 837787 — MB ChB 1982 Bristol; MRCGP 1988; DRCOG 1989.

JONES, David Norman X-Ray Department, Dumfries & Galloway Royal Infirmary, Dumfries DG1 4AP Tel: 01387 246246; 30 Rotchell Park, Dumfries DG2 7RH — MB BS 1962 Lond.; MRCS Eng. LRCP Lond. 1962; FRCR 1975; FFR 1973; DMRD Eng. 1971. (Roy. Free) Cons. Radiol. Dumfries & Galloway Acute & Matern. Hosps. NHS Trust. Prev: Sen. Regist. (X-Ray) Hosp. Sick Childr. Lond.; Regist. (X-Ray) Roy. Free Hosp. Lond.; Squadron Ldr. RAF Med. Br.

JONES, David Orville (retired) 1 Brunel Avenue, High Cross, Newport NP10 0DN Tel: 01633 894338 — MB ChB 1954 Sheff.; FFA RCS Eng. 1969. Prev: Cons. Anaesth. S. Gwent Health Dist.

JONES, David Paul Ap Huw Bron Derw Surgery, Bron Derw, Garth Road, Bangor LL57 2RT Tel: 01248 370900 Fax: 01248 370652; Bryn Gwynt, 89 Penrhos Road, Bangor LL57 2BQ Tel: 01248 372392 Email: daibangor@btinternet.com — MB ChB 1980 Wales; DRCOG 1983. (Welsh Nat. Sch. Med.) Prev: GP Trainee Gwynedd HA VTS; Ho. Off. (Med. & Surg.) Roy. Gwent Hosp. Newport.

JONES, David Peter Howard Park Hospital for Children, Old Road, Oxford OX3 7LQ Tel: 01865 226274 Fax: 01865 226355 — MB ChB 1969 Birm.; FRCPsych 1991, M 1980; DCH Eng. 1978; DObst RCOG 1974. Cons. Child & Adolesc. Psychiat. Oxf. HA; Sen. Clin. Lect. (Child Psychiat.) Univ. Oxf. Socs: BMA; Assn. Child Psychol. & Psychiat.; Internat. Soc. Preven. Child Abuse & Neglect. Prev: Assoc. Prof. Child Psychiat. C. Henry Kempe Nat. Centre Univ. Colorado Health Scs. Centre Denver, USA; Sen. Regist. (Child & Adolesc. Psychiat.) Pk. Hosp. Childr. Oxf.; Regist. (Psychiat.) Roy. S. Hants. Hosp. Soton.

JONES, David Protheroe McNaughton Dolfriog Farm Cottage, Llanfrothen, Penrhyndeudraeth LL48 6SN Tel: 01766 890501 Fax: 01766 890501 — MB BCh Wales 1956; MD Wales 1974; MRCGP 1967. Exam. Med. Pract. Benefits Agency Med. Servs. Bangor, Gwynedd. Prev: Occupat. Phys. Exxon Co. Internat.

JONES, David Randolph Marcus (retired) Willows Cottage, Maidenhead Road, Windsor SL4 5TR — MB BS 1940 Lond.; MRCS Eng. LRCP Lond. 1938. Prev: Clin. Out-pats. Med. & Surgic. Depts. Lond. Hosp.

JONES, David Richard Dartford West Health Centre, Tower Road, Dartford DA1 2HA Tel: 01322 223600 Fax: 01322 292282 — MB BS 1979 Lond.; MA Camb. 1979; DRCOG 1982. Clin. Asst. Rheum. Gravesend Hosp. Kent. Prev: Med. Off. Kwazulu.; GP Tutor Joyce Green Hosp. Dartford.; Coll. Tutor RCGP.

JONES, Mr David Richard 20 Hardwicke Court, Cardiff CF5 2LB — MRCS Eng. LRCP Lond. 1976; MS Lond. 1990, MB BS 1976;

FRCS (Urol.) Ed. 1992; FRCS Ed. 1981. Cons. Urol. Surg. E. Glam. Hosp. & Caerphilly Dist. Miners Hosp. Socs: RCS Edin.; Brit. Assn. Urol. Surg. Prev: Sen. Regist. Char. Cross, St Helier & Roy. Marsden Hosps.

JONES, David Richard Huw Essex House Medical Centre, 59 Fore Street, Chard TA20 1QB Tel: 01460 63071 Fax: 01460 66560 — MB BS Lond. 1970; DA Eng. 1973; DObst RCOG 1972. (Lond. Hosp.)

JONES, David Robert Handley (retired) Velosent, Pingry Lane, Clearwell, Coleford GL16 8LD Tel: 01594 834657 — MB ChB 1970 Bristol; DA Eng. 1972. Prev: SHO (Anaesth.) W.on-super-Mare Gen. Hosp.

JONES, Mr David Roderic Bowen Glanonney, Llangattock, Crickhowell NP8 1HU Tel: 01873 810246 Fax: 01873 812204; St. Josephs Nursing Home, Harding Avenue, Malpas, Newport NP20 6ZE Tel: 01633 858203 — MB BCh 1966 Wales; MCh Wales 1980, MB BCh 1966; FRCS Eng. 1972. (Cardiff) Cons. Surg. Nevill Hall Hosp. Abergavenny. Prev: Sen. Regist. (Surg.) Univ. Hosp. Wales Hosp. & Gwent AHA; Regist. Gastro Intestinal Unit W.. Gen. Hosp. Edin.; Regist. (Surg.) Soton. Univ. Hosp.

JONES, David Roger 1 Clos Caewal, Pentyrch, Cardiff CF15 9QT Tel: 029 2089 0141 — MB ChB 1968 Liverp.

JONES, David Ross 123 Himley Crescent, Wolverhampton WV4 5BY — MB BCh 1978 Wales.

JONES, David Rowland (retired) The Surgery, 74 Castelnau, London SW13 9EX — MB BS Lond. 1950; DObst RCOG 1954. Prev: Ho. Surg. (Obst.) St. Jas. Hosp. Balham.

JONES, David Stephen Dartnell ExxonMobil Internaitonal Ltd., St. Catherine's House, 2 Kingsway, PO Box 397, London WC2B 6WJ Tel: 020 7412 2559 Fax: 020 7412 2935 Email: stephen.jones@exxonmobil.com; 1 Stonedene Close, Headley Down, Bordon GU35 8HW Tel: 01428 714327 — MB BCh 1979 Wales; MRCGP 1983; MFOM RCP Lond. 1991, AFOM 1987; FFOM 1997. (Welsh Nat. Sch. Med.) Regional Occupat. Health Manager, ExxonMobil Internat. Ltd. Lond. Socs: Soc. Occupat. Med. Prev: Occupat. Phys. ICI Fibres Glos.; Med. & Safety Manager Pasminco Europe Smelting Div.; Med. & Safety Adviser Gen. Foods.

JONES, David Stuart Sandy Lane Surgery, Sandy Lane, Leyland, Preston PR25 2EB Tel: 01772 909915 Fax: 01772 909911; Town Bridge Farm House, The Hillocks, Croston, Preston PR26 9RE — MB ChB 1984 Manch.; MRCGP 1988; Dip. Sports Med. Scotl. 1996; DRCOG 1987.

JONES, David Thomas Meddygfa Teifi Surgery, New Road, Llandysul SA44 4QJ Tel: 01559 362221 Fax: 01559 362080 — MB ChB 1978 Liverp.; DRCOG 1982. (Liverp.)

JONES, David Thomas (retired) 12 The Wigdale, Hawarden, Deeside CH5 3LL Tel: 01244 520321 Fax: 01244 520321 Email: tanjo@doctors.org.uk — MB ChB 1957 Leeds; FRCGP 1987, M 1966; FFCM RCP (UK) 1979, M 1977; DObst RCOG 1963. Hon. Prof. Univ. Wales; Director, Disabity Resources Centre, N.Wales. Prev: Chairm. Welsh Counc. for Postgrad. Med. & Dent. Educat.

JONES, David Trevor (Surgery), 107 Clare Road, Grangetown, Cardiff CF11 6QQ; 10 Heol Iestyn, Whitchurch, Cardiff CF14 1QE — MB BCh 1963 Wales; MRCGP 1974; DObst RCOG 1965. (Cardiff) Socs: Cardiff Med. Soc.

JONES, David Vernon Harnser House, Wensum Meadows, Off Hospital Lane, Norwich NR6 5NB Tel: 01603 421421 — MB BS 1965 Lond.; FRCPsych 1994, M 1974; DObst RCOG 1968; DPM Eng. 1972. (St. Bart.) p/t Locum Cons. Gen. Adult Psych. Norf. Ment. Health Care NHS Trust, Norwich. Prev: Cons. Psychiat. Rockingham Forest NHS Trust; Med. Dir. & Cons. Psychiat. Rockingham Forest NHS Trust Kettering; Cons. Psychiat. Redcliffe Centre for Community Psychiat. WellingBoro.

JONES, David William Throckley Surgery, Back Victoria Terrace, Throckley, Newcastle upon Tyne NE15 9AA Tel: 0191 267 4005 Fax: 0191 229 0646 — MB BS 1991 Newc.

JONES, David William Martin 14 Capel Evan Road, Carmarthen SA31 1HW — MB BS 1992 Lond.

JONES, David Wynford, Group Capt. RAF Med. Br. DSMRC Headley Court, Epsom Tel: 01372 378271 Fax: 01372 386739; Larchwood, 9 The Mount, Fetcham, Leatherhead KT22 9EB Tel: 01372 372172 — MRCS Eng. LRCP Lond. 1973; DDAM 2001; MRCP (UK) 1978; FISM 1997; FRCP 1998. (Charing Cross Hospital) Cons. Rheum. & Rehabil. DSMRC Headley Ct. Epsom; Hon. Cons. Rheum. St. Thos. Hosp. Lond.; Hon. Cons. Rheum. Peterboro. Hlth. Trust. Socs: BSR; BSRM. Prev: Cons. Rheum. P.ss Mary's RAF Hosp. Halton.

JONES, Dawn Mereryd Health Centre, Wynne Road, Blaenau Ffestiniog, Wrexham LL14 1TG — MB BCh 1994 Wales; DFFP 1996. (Univ. Wales Coll. Med.) GP, Blaenau Ffestiniog. Prev: SHO A & E; GP/Regist. Chirk Health Cen.; SHO Paediat.

JONES, Deborah Anne The Olde Forge, Withybrook, Coventry CV7 9LW Tel: 01455 221071 — MB ChB 1977 Birm.

JONES, Debra Shirley Harefield Day Hospital, Moorgreen Hospital, Botley Road, West End, Southampton SO30 3JB Tel: 02380 477255 Fax: 02380 475189 — BA Oxf. 1982; MB BS Lond. 1985. Med. Off. Harefield Day Hosp. Soton. Prev: Ho. Surg. & Ho. Phys. Cuckfield Hosp. Haywards Heath.

JONES, Della Cemaes Hafod Las, 10 Parklands, Corntown, Bridgend CF35 5BE — MB BCh 1984 Wales; BSc (Hons.) Wales 1981, MB BCh 1984; MSc Nott 1997. Clin. Med. Off. (Child Health) W. Glam. HA. Prev: Trainee Clin. Med. Off. (Child Health) Clwyd HA; SHO (A & E) Morriston Hosp.; Trainee GP E. Glam. Gen. Hosp. VTS.

***JONES, Delyth Angharad** Craig-Wen, Hendre, Pencoed, Bridgend CF35 6PU — MB ChB 1995 Birm.

JONES, Delyth Wyn NHS Executive Northern & Yorkshire, John Snow House, Durham University Science Park, Durham DH1 3YG Tel: 0191 301 1300 Fax: 0191 301 1413 Email: harran@compuser.com; Orchard House, Gate Helmsley, York YO41 1JT — MB ChB Liverp. 1970; MPH Leeds 1993; DObst RCOG 1973; DCH Eng. 1972; MFPHM Lond. 1998C. Cons. Pub. Health Med. NHS Exec. N.ern & Yorks. Socs: (Ex-Comm.) York. Med. Soc.; MRCPCH; Chair York BMA. Prev: Sen. Regist. PHM Durh. HA; SCMO York HA; Clin. Med. Off. Trafford HA & Leics. HA (T).

JONES, Dennis Mackay, OBE 1 Croft Cottage, Moor Lane, Woodford, Stockport SK7 1PP Tel: 0161 439 7857 — MD 1962 Manch.; MB ChB 1954; FRCPath 1977, M 1965; Dip. Bact. Lond 1959. (Manch.) Hon. Emerit. Cons. Microbiol. PHLS; Hon. Cons. Microbiol. S. Manch.

JONES, Dennis McKay 15 Oldbury Place, London W1M 3AL Tel: 020 7935 2787; Marden Mill, Marden, Devizes SN10 3RJ Tel: 01380 840619 Fax: 01380 840945 — MB BS Lond. 1954. (St. Geo.) Coroner, Saskatchewan, Canada; Assoc. Fac. Homoeop. Socs: Roy. Soc. Med.

JONES, Denys John (retired) 27 Headland Road, Bishopston, Swansea SA3 3HD — MB BCh 1951 Wales; BSc Wales 1948. Prev: Sen. Med. Off. Pneumoconiosis DHSS Med. Panel Cardiff.

JONES, Denzil Stockton (retired) Blue Bridge, Saundersfoot SA69 9AH Tel: 01834 813220 — MB BCh 1953 Wales; BSc Wales 1950; DObst RCOG 1958. Prev: Ho. Surg. & Ho. Phys. St. David's Hosp. Cardiff.

JONES, Derek Sidney Tonypandy Health Centre, Tonypandy CF40 2LE Tel: 01443 432112 Fax: 01443 432803; Maes Y Coed, Vicarage Road, Penygraig, Tonypandy CF40 1 — MB BCh 1974 Wales.

JONES, Derwyn Francis The Mount Surgery, George Street, Pontypool NP4 6YL Tel: 01495 763141 Fax: 01495 767895 — MB BCh 1970 Wales. (Cardiff)

JONES, Dewi 9 Arkwood Close, Bromborough, Wirral CH62 2AU Tel: 0151 334 3344 — MB ChB 1958 Liverp.; FRCPsych 1987, M 1971; FRCPCH 1997, M 1996; DPM Eng. 1964. (Liverp.) Emerit. Cons. Roy. Liverp. Childr. Hosp. NHS Trust. Socs: Liverp. Med. Inst. Prev: Cons. Child Psychiat. Roy. Liverp. Childr. Hosp.; Clin. Lect. (Paediat. Psychiat.) Univ. Liverp.

JONES, Dilwyn Morgan 49 Bethania Street, Maesteg CF34 9ET — MB BCh 1975 Wales.

JONES, Dilys Mair High Security Psychiatric Services, Commissioning Board, Room 038, 40 Eastbourne Terrace, Paddington, London W2 3QR Tel: 020 7725 5510 Fax: 020 7725 5514; Health Services Directorate, NHS Executive, Department of Health, Wellington House, 133-155 Waterloo Road, London SE1 8UG Tel: 020 7972 4238 — BM 1979 Soton.; MBA 1993; MRCPysch 1985; DRCOG 1981. Clin. Strategy Dir. HSPSCB Lond.; Adviser (Forens. Ment. Health) NHS Exec. DoH; Hon. Lect. (Forens. Psychiat.) Inst. Psychiat. Lond. Prev: Med. Dir. SHSA; Sen. Med. Off. DoH; Cons. Forens. Psychiat. BRd.moor Hosp.

JONES, Donald Francis Kings Head Cottage, Hungate, Brompton-by-Sawdon, Scarborough YO13 9DW Tel: 01724 859437 — MB BS 1972 Lond.; BSc Lond. 1967; MRCS Eng. LRCP Lond. 1972; FFA RCS Eng. 1976; DObst RCOG 1975; DA Eng. 1974. (Roy. Free) Cons. Anaesth. ScarBoro. Gen. Hosp. Socs: Pain Soc. & Brit. Med. Acupunc. Soc. Prev: Asst. Prof. Anaesth. Univ. Calif., USA; Sen. Regist. (Anaesth.) Bristol Health Dist. (T).

JONES, Donald Sidney (retired) Tegfynydd, Little Reynoldston, Swansea SA3 1AQ Tel: 01792 391088 Fax: 01792 541391 Email: gowergas@hotmail.com — LMSSA Lond. 1943; FFA RCS Eng. 1953; DA Eng. 1946; FRCA. Cons. Anaesth. W. Glam. & E. Dyfed HAs. Prev: Cons. Anaesth. W. Glam. & E. Dyfed Has.

JONES, Dorothy (retired) The Georgian House, St Margaret's Lane, Titchfield, Fareham PO14 4BQ Tel: 01329 842395 — MRCS Eng. LRCP Lond. 1936; BA Camb. 1948.

JONES, Dorothy Dulcie (retired) c/o National Westminster Bank, Huddersfield Road, Mirfield WF14 8AN Tel: 01924 493188 — MB ChB Leeds 1945; MD Leeds 1948; DPH Lond. 1953; DCH Eng. 1946. Prev: Lord Kemsley Trav. Fell. 1948-9.

JONES, Douglas Plas Y Bryn, Chapel St., Wrexham LL13 7DE Tel: 01978 351308; Lansdowne, 49 Ffordd Glyn, Coed Y Glynn, Erddig, Wrexham LL13 7QW Tel: 01978 290948 — MB ChB Manch. 1965; DObst RCOG 1968. Lect. (Obst.) Centr. Midw. Bd.; Hosp. Pract. (Obst. & Gyn.) Maelor Hosp. Wrexham; Lect. Dip. Med. Ultra Sound Roy. Coll. Radiol. Socs: Pres. Wrexham & Dist. Clin. Soc.; Brit. Med. Ultrasound Soc. Prev: Hon. Phys. Wrexham Assn. Football Club; Ho. Off. (O & G) Maelor Gen. Hosp.; Ho. Surg. Surgic. Profess.; Unit & Ho. Surg. & Ho. Phys. Manch. Roy. Infirm.

JONES, Douglas Maurice Martyn (retired) Barbary Kwoll, Worth Matravers, Swanage BH19 3LF Tel: 01929 291 — MB ChB Brist. 1944, DPH 1948; MRCS Eng. LRCP Lond. 1944; MPS 1934. Prev: Dir. Health Studies & Univ. Health Serv. Univ. Surrey.

JONES, Duncan Roderick Edwards 40 Parkgate Road, Wallington SM6 0AH — MB BS 1991 Lond.; BDS Lond. 1980.

JONES, Mr Dylan West Wales General Hospital, Glangwilli, Carmarthen SA31 2PP; Bwlch y Gaer, Broad Oak, Carmarthen SA32 8QJ — MB BS 1979 Lond.; FRCS Ed. 1984; FRCOphth 1990; DO RCS Eng. 1984. Cons. Ophth. W. Wales Gen. Hosp. Carmarthen. Prev: Sen. Regist. (Ophth.) Univ. Wales Hosp. Cardiff.

JONES, Dylan Frank Cumberland Infirmary, Newtown Road, Carlisle CA2 7HY Tel: 01228 23444 — MB ChB 1974 Aberd.; FFA RCS Eng. 1980. Cons. Anaesth. Cumbld. Infirm.

JONES, Edith Verrier 9 Avondale Court, Goodeve Road, Bristol BS9 1NU — MB BS 1951 Lond.; MRCS Eng. LRCP Lond. 1951; MRCP (UK) 1954; FRCPC 1981. Prev: Assoc. Prof. Med. Dalhousie Univ. Halifax, Nova Scotia, Canada.

JONES, Edmund Walkden Lloyd Clydach Health Centre, Sybil St., Clydach, Swansea SA6 5EU Tel: 01792 843831; Sudbury, 749 Clydach Road, Ynystawe, Swansea SA6 5BA Tel: 01792 842593 — MB 1962 Camb.; BChir 1961.

JONES, Edward Gareth Manor Barn, Lyndon Road, Manton, Oakham LE15 8SR — MB ChB 1977 Ed.

JONES, Edward Gwyn 244 Derwen Fawr Road, Swansea SA2 8EJ — MB BCh 1995 Wales; DRCOG 1999.

JONES, Edward John Straker Bramble Cottage, Chapel Lane, Newton Sound, Nantwich CW5 8BG Tel: 01270 780854 — MB BS 1998 Newc.; MB BS Newc 1998. PRHO Med. Hexham Gen. Hosp.

JONES, Professor Edward Lynn Department of Pathology, Medical School, University of Birmingham, Birmingham B15 2TT Tel: 0121 414 4014 Fax: 0121 414 4019 Email: e.l.jones@bham.ac.uk; 10 Woodchester, West Hagley, Stourbridge DY9 0NF Tel: 01562 885697 — MB ChB 1963 Birm.; MD Birm 1969; MRCS Eng. LRCP Lond. 1963; FRCPath 1982, M 1970. (Birm.) Robt. Leith Prof. Head Dept. Path. Univ. Birm.; Hon. Cons. Path. Univ. Hosp. Birm. NHS Trust. Socs: Path. Soc. & Assn. Clin. Path.; Brit. Lymphoma Path. GP. Prev: Sen. Lect. & Reader (Path.) Univ. Birm.; Carlson-Mead Clin. Research Fell. Path.; Ho. Surg. & Ho. Phys. Profess. Units Qu. Eliz. Hosp. Birm.

JONES, Edwin Roy King's Family Practice, 30-34 Magpie Hall Road, Chatham ME4 5JY Tel: 01634 404632; 35 Farnham Close, Gillingham ME8 8NR — MB ChB 1974 Sheff.; DGM Lond. 1992; FRCS Ed. 1983; DO Lond. 1981. (Sheff.) GP Princip. King's Family Pract. Prev: Trainee GP/SHO Rotat. Perranporth, Treliske; Med. Off. Ochadamu Med. Centre, Idah, Nigeria; Regist. (Ophth.) Manch. Roy. Eye Hosp.

JONES, Edwin William 18 Wood Lane Close, Iver Heath, Iver SL0 0LJ Tel: 01753 651163 — MB BS 1958 Lond.; MFCM 1974; Assoc. Fac. Occupat. Med. RCP Lond. 1980; DIH Eng. 1965, DPH 1966; DTM & H Liverp. 1968; Cert. Av. Med. 1986. (St. Mary's) Airport Med. Off. Heathrow Airport; Med. Off. Civil Aviat. Auth. W. Drayton; Div. Surg. St. John Ambul. Brig. Prev: SCM (EnviroMent. Health) Hillingdon HA.

JONES, Egryn Meirion (retired) 45 Kennerley Road, Davenport, Stockport SK2 6EU — MB BCh Wales 1962; MFFP 1994; MRCGP 1980. Prev: Princip. in Gen. Pract., Heald Green Health Centre.

JONES, Eilir Gilmour Clarence House, 14 Russell Road, Rhyl LL18 3BY Tel: 01745 350680 Fax: 01745 353293 — MB BCh 1988 Wales; MRCGP 1993.

JONES, Eiry Lynway, Dillwyn Avenue, Hengoed CF82 7WQ Tel: 01443 3253 — MB BCh 1944 Wales; BSc, MB BCh Wales 1944. (Cardiff) SCMO Mid. Glam. AHA. Prev: Ho. Phys. WhitCh. EMS Hosp. Cardiff.

JONES, Eleanor Margaret (retired) 22 Daimler Avenue, Herne Bay CT6 8AE — MRCS Eng. LRCP Lond. 1939.

JONES, Eleanor Mirian (retired) 15 Denewood Road, London N6 4AQ — MB BS 1950 Lond.; FRCP Lond. 1982, M 1964; MRCS Eng. LRCP Lond. 1950; MFOM RCP Lond. 1982; DIH Eng. 1981. Sen. Med. Off. Med. Advis. Serv. (Civil Serv. Dept.). Prev: Phys. Health Centre Univ. Coll. Lond.

JONES, Eleri Lloyd Brynderw, Llanerfyl, Welshpool SY21 0EU — MB ChB 1997 Liverp.

JONES, Eleri Mair Jones 22 Little Halt, Portishead, Bristol BS20 8JQ — MB BCh 1989 Wales. Sen. Regist. (Microbiol.) S.mead Health Servs. NHS Trust. Prev: Regist. (Microbiol.) Bristol Roy. Infirm.

JONES, Elizabeth 130 Bradbury Road, Solihull B92 8AL — BM 1993 Soton.

JONES, Elizabeth Coach and Horses Surgery, The Car Park, St. Clears, Carmarthen SA33 4AA Tel: 01994 230379 Fax: 01994 231449; Llandre, Llangyndeyrn, Kidwelly SA17 5BW — MB BCh 1982 Wales; DCH RCP Lond. 1992. Prev: Trainee GP/SHO Bronglais Hosp. Aberystwyth VTS.; Community Med. Off. (Child Health) Bryntirion Hosp. LLa.lli.

***JONES, Elizabeth** 123 Roker Lane, Pudsey LS28 9NB — MB BS 1997 Lond.; BSc Lond. 1994.

JONES, Elizabeth Alison 102 Grosvenor Road, Jesmond, Newcastle upon Tyne NE2 2RQ — BChir 1994 Camb.; MA Camb 1996; MB Camb 1995.

JONES, Elizabeth Ann Hughes and Partners, 15 Dereham Road, Mattishall, Dereham NR20 3QA Tel: 01326 850227 Fax: 01362 858466 Email: mattsurg@globalnet.co.uk; Email: liz@chasing_rainbows.com — MB BS 1984 Lond.; MRCGP 1990; T(GP) 1991; DRCOG 1988. p/t Asst., Gen. Pract., Mattishall Surg., Mattishall. Prev: Trainee GP W. Suff. VTS; Ho. Surg. Chase Farm Hosp. Enfield; Ho. Phys. Wanstead Hosp. Lond.

JONES, Elizabeth Anne 37 Arnold Road, London E3 4NU — BM BCh 1965 Oxf.

JONES, Elizabeth Anne Doorie Cottage, 91 Grant St., Burghead, Elgin IV30 5TZ — MB BS 1990 Lond.

JONES, Elizabeth Catherine Lakeside Mental Health Unit, West Middlesex, Twickenham Road, Isleworth TW7 6AF — MB BS 1993 Lond.

JONES, Elizabeth Clare 36 Kelston Road, Whitchurch, Cardiff CF14 2AJ — MB BS 1994 Lond.

JONES, Elizabeth Jane Kionlough Cottage, Bride, Ramsey IM7 4AG Tel: 01624 880571 — MB ChB 1981 Liverp.

JONES, Elizabeth Jenny Glandwr, Trefeinon, Talgarth, Brecon LD3 0PT — BM BS 1995 Nottm.; BMedSci. 1993. (Nottingham Medical School) GP Trainee Scheme, N. Gwent. Prev: SHO (Gen. Surg.) Crawley; SHO (Urol.) St. Geo.'s Lond.; SHO (Orthop.) Epsom Gen. Hosp.

JONES, Elizabeth Mary Ellenor Foundation, Douglas Centre, Queen Mary's Hospital, Sidcup DA14 6LT Tel: 020 8308 3014 Fax: 020 8308 3168 — MB BCh 1982 Wales. (University of Wales College of Medicine) Cons. in Palliat. Med.; Ellenor Foundat., Bexley. Prev: Cons. in Palliat. Med.Croydon Community Trust St

Christopher's Hospice; Clin. Asst. St Christopher's Hospice; Med. Dir. St. Luke's Hospice; Basildon.

JONES, Ellen Frances Accident & Emergency Department, Birmingham Heartlands Hospital, Birmingham B9 5SS Tel: 0121 766 6611; 69 Clarence Road, Kings Heath, Birmingham B13 9UH — MB ChB 1987 Birm.; MRCP (UK) 1990. Cons. (A & E Med.) Birm. Heartlands Hosp. Prev: Sen. Regist. (A & E Med.) W. Midl. Rotat.; Regist. (A & E Med.) King's Coll. Hosp. Lond.; SHO (Med.) New Cross Hosp. Wolverhampton.

JONES, Ellis Wyn Lloyd (retired) Hafod-y-Coed, Berwyn, Llangollen LL20 8AL — MB ChB 1958 Liverp.; BSc (Hons. Anat.) Liverp. 1955. Benefits Agency Med. Off.

JONES, Elwyn Thomas John (retired) 'Woodside', 1 Holly Walks, Penymaes Avenue, Wrexham LL12 7AJ Tel: 01978 353413 — MRCS Eng. LRCP Lond. 1950. Prev: Capt. RAMC.

JONES, Elwyn Tudor (retired) Berwyn, Llwyn Brith, Criccieth LL52 0TA Tel: 01766 522837 — MB BCh 1955 Wales; BSc, MB BCh Wales 1955. Indep. Med. Adviser Gwynedd Family Health Servs. Auth. Prev: GP Criccieth.

JONES, Elwynne (retired) Plas Ceiri, Gwalchmai, Holyhead LL65 4SP Tel: 01407 720214 — MB BS 1947 Lond.; MRCS Eng. LRCP Lond. 1947. Prev: Ho. Surg. Caern. & Anglesey Infirm. Bangor.

JONES, Emma Christien Angharad 6 Bristol Mews, London W9 2JF — MB BS 1998 Lond.; MB BS Lond 1998.

JONES, Emyr Wyn Taliesin Surgery, Taliesin, Lampeter SA48 7AA Tel: 01570 422665 Fax: 01570 423810 — MB BCh 1980 Wales; MRCPsych 1985. Prev: Regist. WhitCh. Hosp. Cardiff; SHO Cefn Coed Hosp. Swansea.

JONES, Emyr Wyn Felin Newydd Farm, Porthyrhyd, Carmarthen SA32 8PT Tel: 01267 275364 Email: emyr wyn jones@porthyrhyd.demon.co.uk — MB BS 1963 Lond.; MRCS Eng. LRCP Lond. 1963; FRCR 1975; FFR 1972; DMRD Eng. 1970. (St. Thos.) Cons. Neuroradiol. Morriston NHS Trust. Socs: Brit. Inst. Radiol.; Assoc. Brit. Soc. Neuroradiol. Prev: Sen. Regist. (Radiol.) Radcliffe Infirm. Oxf.; Radiol. Johns Hopkins Univ. & Hosp. Baltimore, U.S.A.; Sen. Resid. (Internal Med.) New Eng. Deaconess Hosp. Boston.

JONES, Emyr Wyn Diabetes Day Centre, Doncaster Royal Infirmary, Armthorpe Road, Doncaster DN2 5LT Tel: 01302 366666; Winder House, 16 St. Erics Road, Bessacarr, Doncaster DN4 6NG Tel: 01302 531059 Email: emyr@emyr.u-net.com — MB ChB 1973 Liverp.; DM Nottm. 1987; FRCP Lond. 1993; MRCP (UK) 1978. Cons. Phys. Doncaster Roy. Imfirmary & Med. Dir. Doncaster Roy. & Montagu Hosp. NHS Trust. Socs: BMA & Brit. Diabetic Assn. Prev: Clin. Research Fell. & Hon. Sen. Regist. Univ. Hosp. Nottm.; Regist. (Gen. Med.) Roy. Liverp. Hosp.; SHO (Med. Neurol.) Regional Dept. Med. & Surg. Neurol. Walton Hosp. Liverp.

JONES, Enid Pendle Springs, Kineton Road, Gaydon, Warwick CV35 0HB — MB ChB 1984 Bristol.

JONES, Eric Llewelyn (retired) Castle Court, Beaumaris LL58 8AL Tel: 0248 810148 — MB BS 1950 Lond.; MRCS Eng. LRCP Lond. 1950; DObst RCOG 1955.

JONES, Mr Eric Reginald Lloyd (retired) Broadmead, 1 Cherry Garden Avenue, Folkestone CT19 5LB Tel: 01303 275907 — MB BS 1962 Lond.; FRCS Eng. 1967; MRCS Eng. LRCP Lond. 1962. Med. Off. Kent CCC. Prev: Cons. Orthop. & Accid. Surg. SE Kent, Canterbury & Thanet Dist.

JONES, Eric Sherwood (retired) 29 Knowsley Park Lane, Prescot L34 3NA Tel: 0151 426 5945 — MB ChB Liverp. 1944; PhD Liverp. 1953; FRCP Lond. 1969, M 1946; DTM & H Liverp. 1953. Prev: Cons. Phys. Whiston & St. Helens Hosps.

JONES, Evan Frederick 11 Chesterfield Road, Chiswick, London W4 3HG Tel: 020 8994 1879 — MB BS 1948 Lond.; LMSSA Lond. 1948. (St. Geo.) Prev: Regist. (Med.) Neurosurg. Unit, Atkinson Morley Hosp. Wimbledon; Ho. Phys. St. Geo. Hosp.; Capt. RAMC.

JONES, Eve Boardman House, 93 Mellor Lane, Mellor, Blackburn BB2 7EN Tel: 0125 481 2210 — MB ChB 1968 Leeds; BSc (Hons. Physiol.) Leeds 1965; MRCPsych 1990; DCH Eng. 1970. (Univ. Leeds.) Assoc. Specialist (Psychiat.) Roy. Manch. Childr. Hosp. & Adolesc. Forens. Unit Ment. Health Servs. Salford NHS Trust. Prev: Clin. Asst. (Paediat. Oncol.) Leeds & Manch.; Regist. Rotat. (Psychiat.) S. Manch.

JONES, Miss Fiona Catherine Waverley House, 5 Waverley Crescent, Penn, Wolverhampton WV2 4QA — BM BS 1988 Nottm.

JONES, Mrs Frances Elizabeth 15 Graham Park Road, Gosforth, Newcastle upon Tyne NE3 4BH Tel: 0191 284 8105 — MB BS 1971 Lond.; MRCS Eng. LRCP Lond. 1971; MRCP (UK) 1973; DCH RCP Lond. 1974. (Guy's) Staff Grade (Community Child Health) Newc. u. Tyne. Socs: Brit. Assn. Community Child Health. Prev: Clin. Med. Off. Newc. HA; Clin. Asst. (Paediat. Oncol.) Leeds; Tutor (Paediat.) Univ. Leeds.

JONES, Frances Prenna 62 Meriden Court, Chelsea Manor St., London SW3 3TT — MB BCh 1993 Lond.

JONES, Francis George Charles Department of Haematology, Royal Victoria Hospital, Belfast BT12 6BA — MB BCh BAO 1972 Belf.; FRCP Ed. 1995; FRCPS Glas. 1992; MRCP (UK) 1976; FRCPath 1993, M 1981. Cons. Haemat. Roy. Vict. Hosp. Belf. Prev: Cons. Haemat. Ulster & Ards Hosps.

JONES, Frank William 206 Oakham Road, Oldbury B69 1PY Tel: 01384 56648 — MB BS 1976 Lond.; BSc Lond. 1973, MB BS 1976; MRCGP 1980. (Univ. Coll. Hosp.) GP Cradley Heath. Prev: SHO (Med.) Good Hope Hosp. Sutton Coldfield.

JONES, Gail Melanie Badger Lodge, Moorside, Cononley, Keighley BD20 8PD — BM BS 1986 Nottm.; MRCP (UK) 1989; MRCGP 1991.

JONES, Gareth David 2 Dorian Drive, Ascot SL5 7QL — MB BS 1991 Lond.

JONES, Mr Gareth Everett 72 Tanzieknowe Road, Cambuslang, Glasgow G72 8RE — MB ChB 1990 Glas.; FRCS Glas. 1995.

JONES, Gareth Hugh Llewelyn Suite, Whitchurch Hospital, Cardiff CF4 7XB Tel: 029 2069 3191 Fax: 029 2061 4799 — MB 1972 Camb.; MPhil Lond. 1977; BChir 1971; MRCP (UK) 1973; FRCPsych 1993, M 1975. Cons. Psychiat. S. Glam. HA (T). Prev: Sen. Lect. (Psychol. Med.) Univ. Wales Coll. Med. Cardiff; Sen. Regist. Morgannwg Hosp. Bridgend & WhitCh. Hosp. Cardiff; Regist. Bethlem Roy. & Maudsley Hosps.

JONES, Gareth John Dolau, 6 Newtown Close, Penybanc, Ammanford SA18 3TX — MB BCh 1986 Wales.

JONES, Gareth Lewes Victoria Place Surgery, 11 Victoria Place, Bethesda, Bangor LL57 3AG Tel: 01248 600212 Fax: 01248 602790; Felinhen Uchaf, Tregarth, Bangor LL57 4BB Tel: 01248 601319 — MB ChB 1981 Liverp.

JONES, Gareth Lloyd Shelford, Headley Road, Leatherhead KT22 8PT — MB BS 1993 Lond.; MRCP (UK) 1996.

JONES, Gareth Lloyd Camarthen Road Health Centre, Carmarthen Road, Cross Hands, Llanelli SA14 6SU Tel: 01269 831091; Maesawelon, Llanddarog, Carmarthen SA32 8NS Fax: 01267 275294 — MB BCh 1976 Wales; MRCP (UK) 1984; MRCGP 1986. (Welsh Nat. Sch. Med. Cardiff) GP Tumble & Cross Hands, Dyfed; Clin. Asst. (Cardiol.) P. Phillip Hosp. LLa.lli; Sports Med. Clinic Bancyfelin, Carmarthen (Private Pract.). Prev: Clin. Asst. (Gen. Med.) & Regist. (Med.) P. Chas. Gen. Hosp. Merthyr Tydfil; SHO (Cardiol.) Liverp. HA.

JONES, Gareth Owen Brunswick Health Centre, 139-140 St. Helens Road, Swansea SA1 4DE Tel: 01792 643001 / 643611; Bosco's Knoll, 73 Pennard Road, Southgate, Swansea SA3 2AJ — MB BCh Wales 1982; MRCGP 1986; DCH RCP Lond. 1985; DRCOG 1984. Prev: SHO (Psychiat.) Cefn Coed Hosp. Swansea; Trainee GP Cwmbwrla Health Centre, Swansea.

JONES, Gareth Richard Melville 31 Clover Park, Uzmaston Road, Haverfordwest SA61 1UE — MB BCh 1968 Wales; MRCPath 1978; DObst. RCOG 1970. (Cardiff) Cons. Pathol. Withybush Gen. Hosp. HaverfordW. Socs: BMA. Prev: Sen. Regist. (Pathol.) Univ. Hosp. Wales Hosp. Gp. Cardiff.

JONES, Gareth Wynne Anaesthetic Department, Leicester Royal Infirmary, Leicester LE1 5WW Tel: 0116 258 6474; 17 Oakmeadow Way, Groby, Leicester LE6 0YN — MB BS 1979 Lond.; BSc (Hons.) Lond. 1976, MB BS 1979; MRCP (UK) 1983; FFA RCS Eng. 1985. Cons. Anaesth. & IC Leicester Roy. Infirm. Prev: Sen. Regist. (Anaesth.) Leics. Train. Scheme.

JONES, Garth Dalmain (retired) The Cottage, Washfield, Tiverton EX16 9RA Tel: 01884 252333 — MB BCh Wales 1957; DObst RCOG 1961. Prev: Med. Adviser Whitbread W. Country, Tiverton.

JONES, Gary Anthony Orchard House, 22A The Glebe, Hildersley, Ross-on-Wye HR9 5BL — MB BCh 1998 Wales.

JONES, Mr Geoffrey Blundell The Round House, Stoke Cannon, Exeter EX5 4EG Tel: 0139 284269 — MB BS 1938 Lond.; FRCS Eng. 1943; FRCS Ed. 1942; MRCS Eng. LRCP Lond. 1938. (Univ. Coll. Hosp.) Socs: Fell. Brit. Orthop. Assn. Prev: Maj. RAMC, Orthop. Specialist; Cons. Orthop. Surg. P.ss Eliz. Orthop. Hosp. Exeter, Exeter Clin.; Area & Dame Hannah Rogers Sch. for Spastics Ivybridge.

JONES, Geoffrey Liddell New Dover Road Surgery, 10 New Dover Road, Canterbury CT1 3AP Tel: 01227 462197 Fax: 01227 786041 — MB BS 1978 Lond.

JONES, Mr Geoffrey Michael Department of Oral & Maxillofacial Surgery, Derriford Hospital, Plymouth PL6 8DH Tel: 01752 777111 Fax: 01752 763212 Email: geof.jones@phnt.swest.nhs.uk — MB BS 1983 Lond.; BDS 1971; FRCS Ed. 1987; FDS RCPS Glas. 1985. (University College Hospital Medical School) Cons. Oral & Maxillofacial Surg. Derriford Hosp. Plymouth. Prev: Sen. Regist. (Oral & Maxillofacial Surg.) Frenchay Hosp. & Bristol Roy. Infirm.; Ho. Surg. Univ. Coll. Hosp. Lond.; Ho. Phys. Chase Farm Hosp. Enfield.

JONES, Geoffrey Nicholas 29 Welcomes Road, Kenley CR8 5HA — MB ChB 1989 Manch.

JONES, Geraint Lloyd Health Care Centre, 19 Cambridge Road, Bristol BS7 8PS Tel: 0117 980 8123 — MB ChB 1984 Dundee. Med. Off. Health Care Centre Bristol.

JONES, Geraint Rhys Blackburn Royal Infirmary, Bolton Rd, Blackburn BB2 3LR Tel: 01254 687227 Fax: 01254 294557; Endmoor House, 9 Elswick Lodge, Mellor, Blackburn BB2 7RX Tel: 01254 812975 — MB BCh 1972 Wales; FRCP Lond. 1994; MRCP (UK) 1978. Cons. Phys. Blackburn, Hyndburn & Ribble Valley HA. Socs: BMA; Diabetes UK; EASD. Prev: Sen. Regist. (Gen. Med., Diabetes & Endocrinol.) Leicester; Research Fell. (Med.) Univ. Hosp. of Wales Cardiff; Regist. (Med.) Llandough Hosp. Penarth.

JONES, Gerald 58 Palace Road, London N8 8QP — BM BCh Oxf. 1965; PhD Lond. 1972, MSc 1991; BA Oxf. 1962; FRCP Lond. 1985, M 1967; FFPM RCP (UK) 1989. (Oxf. & Lond. Hosp.) Prev: Sen. Princip. Med. Off. DoH Lond.

JONES, Gerald Colman O'Brien (retired) 12 Lindsay House, 30 New Compton St., London WC2H 8DA — MB BCh BAO 1954 NUI.

JONES, Gerald Eric Shirley (retired) 1 Florence Avenue, Droitwich WR9 8NJ — BM BCh Oxon. 1948. Prev: Med. Off. Colon. Med. Serv.

JONES, Gerald Vaughan 612 Green Lanes, London N8 0RY — MB BS 1958 Lond.; DA Eng. 1962.

JONES, Gillian Mary 15 Northlands Park, Bishopston, Swansea SA3 3JW Tel: 01792 233633 — MB BCh 1992 Wales; MRCGP 1996; DCH 1995.

JONES, Glanville Hughes The Mumbles Medical Practice, 10 West Cross Avenue, Norton, Mumbles, Swansea SA3 5UA Tel: 01792 403010 Fax: 01792 401934; 3 Slade Gardens, West Cross, Swansea SA3 5QP Tel: 01792 404128 — MRCS Eng. LRCP Lond. 1962.

JONES, Glyn 24 Centre Street, South Elmsall, Pontefract WF9 2RU Tel: 01977 647050 — MB ChB 1994 Leeds; MRCP (UK) 1997. (Leeds) Specialist Regist. (Paediat.) Newc. Socs: RCP Ed.; Med. Defence Union; RCPCH.

JONES, Mr Glyn X-Ray Department, Torbay Hospital, Torquay — MB BCh 1954 Wales; FRCS Eng. 1961; FRCR 1975; FFR 1967; DMRD Eng. 1963. Cons. Radiol. Torbay Hosp. Gp. Prev: Sen. Regist. (Diag. Radiol.) United Bristol Hosps.; Cons. Radiol. New Mulago Hosp. Kampala, Uganda.

JONES, Glyn David Risca Surgery, St. Mary Street, Risca, Newport NP11 6YS Tel: 01633 612666; 79 Ruskin Avenue, The Links, Rogerstone, Newport NP10 0AD Tel: 01633 896231 — MB BCh 1980 Wales; MRCGP 1984; DCH RCP Lond. 1988; DRCOG 1983. Socs: Assoc. Mem. Brit. Med. Acupunc. Soc.; Soc. Occupat. Med. Prev: Trainee GP Newport VTS.

JONES, Glynis Louise Worcester Royal Infirmary, Newtown Road, Worcester WR5 1JG Tel: 01905 763333; 80 Kingsholm Road, Gloucester GL1 3BB Tel: 01452 331573 — MB BS 1984 Lond.; MRACOG 1994. (Middlx. Hosp. Med. Sch.) Staff Grade (O & G) Worcester Roy. Infirm.

JONES, Glynne Rhys Baylis, OBE, TD, QHP Healthcall DTI MAP, Healthcall House, 23 Windmill Hill, Enfield EN2 7AB; Never More, Little Birch, Hereford HR2 8BB Tel: 0141 637 2587, 01981 540442 — MB BCh 1964 Wales; MRCS Eng. LRCP Lond. 1964; FRCP Ed. 1983, M 1968. (Welsh Nat. Sch. of Med., Univ. of Wales) Cons. Phys. (Respirat. Dis.) and Dep. Med. Director, Healthcall Dept of Trade & Industry, Miners Assessm. process; Cons. Phys. (Col.) CVHQ AMS TA, HQ Med. Gp., York. Socs: BMA & Brit. Thoracic Soc.; Scott. Thoracic Soc.; Thoracis Soc. of Wales. Prev: Cons. Phys. (Resp. Dis.) GrossHo. Hosp., Kilmarnock; Sen. Regist. (Med.) Univ. Hosp. Wales Cardiff; Regist. (Respirat. Dis.) City Hosp. Edin.

JONES, Gordon Ian Health Centre, St. John Street, Mansfield NG18 1RH Tel: 01623 622541 Fax: 01623 423821 — MB ChB 1989 Sheff.; BMedSci (Hons.) Sheff. 1988; T(GP) 1993.

JONES, Gordon Spenceley 87 Witherford Way, Selly Oak, Birmingham B29 4AN — MB ChB 1976 Birm.; FRCR 1983; DMRD Eng. 1981. Cons. (Radiol.) E. Birm. Hosp. Bordesley Green.

JONES, Goronwy Rhys Camarthen Road Health Centre, Carmarthen Road, Cross Hands, Llanelli SA14 6SU Tel: 01269 831091; Mindi Rardi, Llanddarog, Carmarthen SA32 8BJ Tel: 01267 275693 — MB BCh 1976 Wales; MRCGP 1988; DRCOG 1982. Socs: Welsh Med. Soc. (Comm. Mem.).

JONES, Graeme Richard Sadlers Mead, Church St., Purton, Swindon SN5 4DS — MB BS 1985 Newc.

JONES, Graham Norman Department of Anaesthesia, Royal Preston Hospital, Sharoe Green Lane, Preston PR2 9HT Tel: 01772 710555 Fax: 01772 710992 Email: graham.jones@patr.nhs.uk — MB ChB 1983 Manch.; FFA RCS Eng. 1988; DA (UK) 1985. Cons. Anaesth. Roy. Preston Hosp. Socs: Fell. Manch. Med. Soc. Prev: Regist. (Anaesth.) Manch. Roy. Infirm.;Wythenshawe Hosp. Manch.; Sen. Regist. (Anaesth.) NW RHA; Clin. Instruc. (Anaesthesiol.) Univ. Calif., Irvine, USA.

JONES, Gregory Charles 1st Floor Right, 23 Havelock Street, Dowanhill, Glasgow G11 5JF — MB ChB 1991 Dundee; MRCP (UK) 1995. Specialist Regist (Diabetes & Endocrinol.); Wellcome Research Fell.

JONES, Griffith Williams (retired) Bryn Helig, 7 Holyrood Avenue, Old Colwyn, Colwyn Bay LL29 8BA Tel: 01492 56407 — MB ChB 1958 Liverp.; MRCS Eng. LRCP Lond. 1958; DObst RCOG 1963. Prev: GP Colwyn Bay.

JONES, Gruffydd Owen Pendre Surgery, Coleshill Street, Holywell CH8 7RS Tel: 01352 712029 Fax: 01352 712751; Cilan, Gorsedd, Holywell CH8 8QY Tel: Jones & Partners — MB ChB 1965 Liverp.; DObst RCOG 1968.

JONES, Guy Alwyne Horwood Village Farm, Great Salkeld, Penrith CA11 9LW — MB ChB 1951 Birm.; MRCS Eng. LRCP Lond. 1951; DObst RCOG 1952. (Birm.) Prev: Ho. Phys. Guest. Hosp. Dudley; Ho. Surg. (Obst.) Matern. Hosp. Marston Green Birm.

JONES, Gwen Fox 24 Yr Allt, Llangewech, Llanelli SA14 8YU — MB BCh 1987 Wales; T(GP) 1992.

JONES, Gwenan Meirion Bodowen Surgery, Halkyn Road, Holywell CH8 7GA Tel: 01352 710529 Fax: 01352 710784 — MB ChB 1966 Liverp.

JONES, Gweneth Haf Bryn Rodyn, Tan-Y-Bryn Road, Rhos on Sea, Colwyn Bay LL28 4TU — MB BCh 1979 Wales.

JONES, Gwenllian Sian Albany Road Medical Centre, 24 Albany Road, Roath, Cardiff CF24 3YY Tel: 029 2048 6561 Fax: 029 2045 1403; Whiteacre, 6 The Avenue, Llandaff, Cardiff CF5 2LQ — MB BCh 1974 Wales; MRCGP 1979; DCH Eng. 1978; DObst RCOG 1976.

JONES, Gwilym Alun (retired) 6 Conway Square, Scunthorpe DN15 8JN — MB ChB 1954 Birm. Prev: Assoc. Specialist Anaesth. Scunthorpe Gen. Hosp.

JONES, Gwyn David Treherne 78 Gordon Road, Carshalton SM5 3RE — MB BS 1965 Queensland; DObst RCOG 1972. (Queensld.) Prev: Regist. (O & G) N.wick Pk. Hosp.; Regist. (O & G) St. Helier Hosp. Carshalton.

JONES, Gwyn Morris (retired) 244 Derwenfawr Road, Swansea SA2 8EJ Tel: 01792 204588 — MB ChB 1960 Birm.; DObst RCOG 1963.

JONES, Gwynedd Innisfallen, Llanrhaeadr Yn Mochnant, Oswestry Tel: 0169 189202 — MB ChB 1950 Liverp.

JONES, Hannah David (retired) 11 Lougher Gardens, Porthcawl CF36 3BJ Tel: 01656 784071 — MB BCh 1959 Wales; BA (Hons.) Open 1988.

JONES, Harri Gwyn 6 Bryn Newydd E., Prestatyn LL19 8BU — MB BCh 1993 Wales.

JONES, Haydn Hugh Griffiths, OBE (retired) Wearside, 51 Highwalls Avenue, Dinas Powys CF64 4AQ Tel: 029 2051 3315 — MB BCh Wales 1960; MRCS Eng. LRCP Lond. 1960; DObst RCOG 1961; LLM Wales 1990. Prev: Gen. Practitioner.

JONES, Heather Elizabeth 32 High Street, Gosforth, Newcastle upon Tyne NE3 1LX Tel: 0191 284 8864 — MB ChB 1975 Sheff.; MSc (Community Child Health) Newc. 1994; DCH RCP Lond. 1989; DRCOG 1979. (Sheff.) Staff Grade (Community Child Health) Gateshead Health Care.

JONES, Hector Owen Lynway, Dillwyn Avenue, Hengoed CF82 7WQ Tel: 01443 3248 — MB BCh 1944 Wales; BSc, MB BCh Wales 1944. (Cardiff) Prev: Ho. Phys. Mid-Glam. Co. Hosp. Bridgend; Obst. Regist. St. David's Hosp. Cardiff.

JONES, Hedydd Parry Meddygfa Emlyn, Lloyds Terrace, Newcastle Emlyn SA38 9NS Tel: 01239 710479 Fax: 01239 711683 — MB ChB 1979 Liverp.

JONES, Hefin Pontcae Surgery, Dynevor Street, Georgetown, Merthyr Tydfil CF48 1YE Tel: 01685 723931 Fax: 01685 377048 — MB ChB 1970 Birm.

JONES, Heledd Llinor Maesyffynnon, 2 Heol Ty'n-y-coed, Pentyrch, Cardiff CF15 9NP — MB BCh 1997 Wales.

***JONES, Heledd Wyn** 1 Rookwood Close, Llandaf, Cardiff CF5 2NR — MB ChB 1995 Birm.

JONES, Helen Elizabeth 39 Meadow Rise, Bewdley DY12 1JP — MB ChB 1991 Birm. Regist. (Med. Microbiol.) Birm. Childr. Hosp. Prev: Trainee GP/SHO Kidderminster Gen. Hosp. VTS.

JONES, Helen Elizabeth 2 Thatcher's View, Cues Lane, Bishopstone, Swindon SN6 8PL Tel: 01793 791427 — MB BS 1983 Lond.; FFA RCS Eng. 1988. (St. Bart.) Cons. Anaesth. P.ss Margt. Hosp. Swindon. Prev: Sen, Regist. (Anaesth.) Guy's Hosp. Lond.; Regist. (Anaesth.) Roy. Sussex Co. Hosp. Brighton; Regist. (Anaesth.) Guy's Hosp. Lond.

JONES, Helen Isobel 10 Annesley Road, Blackheath, London SE3 0JX — MB ChB 1991 Liverp.

***JONES, Helen Louise** 30 Rotchell Park, Dumfries DG2 7RH — MB BS 1998 Lond.; MB BS Lond 1998; BA (Hons) Clare College, Camb 1993.

JONES, Helen Miriam Pool Health Centre, Station Road, Pool, Redruth TR15 3DU Tel: 01209 717471 Fax: 01209 612160 — MB BS 1981 Lond.; DCH RCP Lond. 1984.

JONES, Helen Wyn Williams, Roberts & Jones, Liverpool House Surgery, Waunfawr, Caernarfon LL55 4YY Tel: 01286 650223; Maes y Coed, Caeathro, Caernarfon LL55 2TD Tel: 01286 677814 — MB BCh 1966 Wales; DCH Eng. 1969. GP Princip. Prev: GP Princip., Penarth Health Centre, S. Glam.; Regist. (Paediat.) Plymouth Gen. Hosp.; Sen. Ho. Off. (O & G) S.mead Gen. Hosp. Bristol.

JONES, Helen Wynne Eynon Berwyn, Llwyn Brith, Criccieth LL52 0TA Tel: 0176 671 2837 — MB BCh 1957 Wales. (Cardiff) Clin. Asst. (Geriat.) & Asst. Sch. Med. Off. Gwynedd AHA. Prev: Sen. Ho. Off. Caernarvon & Anglesey Gen. Hosp. Bangor.

JONES, Henry Howel 279 Gooch Street, Birmingham B5 7JE Tel: 0121 440 1561 — MB ChB 1960 Birm. (Birm.)

JONES, Herbert Arnold (retired) 25 Barr's Road, Cradley Health, Cradley Heath B64 7HG Tel: 01384 569337 — MB ChB Ed. 1947. Prev: Ho. Surg. Profess. Unit. Edin. Roy. Infirm.

***JONES, Miss Holly Bethan** Old Stonelynk Edge, 63 Battery Hill, Fairlight, Hastings TN35 4AP Tel: 01424 812570 — MB ChB 1997 Bristol; DR COG.

JONES, Howard Wynford Leighton Hospital, Crewe CW1 4QJ Tel: 01270 255141; 41 Audlem Road, Nantwich CW5 7DT Tel: 01270 629811 — MB ChB 1971 Liverp.; BA Open 1995; FRCP Lond. 1993; MRCP (UK) 1976; FRCP Edin. 1999. Cons. Phys. Leighton Hosp. Crewe.; UnderGrad. Med. Tutor Manch. & Liverp. Universities; Hon. Clin. Lect Med. Univ. Manch.. Socs: Brit. Geriat. Soc.; Liverp. Med. Inst.; Brit. Assoc. Stroke Phys.s. Prev: Sen. Regist. (Med.) Radcliffe Infirm. Oxf.; Regist. (Neurol.) Walton Hosp. Liverp.

JONES, Howel Buckland (retired) Keepers Cottage, Chase End St., Bromesberrow, Ledbury HR8 1SE Tel: 01531 650419 — MB BS 1955 Lond. Prev: Ho. Phys. (Med.) Ho. Surg. Univ. Coll. Hosp. Lond.

JONES, Howell Pritchard (retired) 79 Ffordd Glyn, Coed y Glyn, Wrexham LL13 7QW Tel: 01978 361614 — 1942 MB BS Lond. 1942; 1949 FRCS Eng. 1949; 1941 MRCS Eng. LRCP Lond. 1941; 1969 DPhysMed. Eng. 1969. Prev: Med. Off. Artific. Limb & Appliance Servs. Welsh Office Cardiff.

JONES, Hugh Priory Lane Surgery, Priory Lane, Prestatyn LL19 9NL Tel: 01745 854496; 17 Bryntirion Drive, Prestatyn LL19 9NT — MB BS 1981 Lond.; DRCOG 1984; Cert. Family Plann. JCC 1984. Socs: Assn. Police Surg. (Counc. Mem. Wales). Prev: Trainee GP VTS N. Clwyd.

JONES, Hugh 3 Harriet Place, Greenbank, Falmouth TR11 2SU Tel: 01326 211604 — MB ChB 1985 Bristol; BSc (Path.) Bristol 1980; MRCPath 1993. Cons. Histocytopath. Treliske Hosp. Truro. Socs: Internat. Acad. Path.; Assn. Clin. Path.; Brit. Soc. Clin. Cytol.

JONES, Hugh Alan 27 Thames Court, Victoria Avenue, West Molesey KT8 1TP Tel: 020 8979 0660 Fax: 020 8979 0660 Email: hughjones@onetel.net.uk — MB ChB 1944 Liverp. p/t Med. Adviser Medico-Legal, Market Form Ltd., Lond. EC3M. Socs: BMA; Austral. Med. Assn. Prev: Capt. RAMC; Ho. Surg. Liverp. Matern. Hosp. & Wom. Hosp. Liverp.

JONES, Hugh Davies (retired) 30 Moor Hall Drive, Sutton Coldfield B75 6LR Tel: 0121 308 0172 — MB BS Lond. 1952; FFA RCS Eng. 1963. Cons. Anaesth. Goodhope Gen. Hosp. Sutton Coldfield. Prev: Jun. Res. Anaesth. St. Bart. Hosp. Lond.

JONES, Hugh Dennis 27 Towers Close, Kenilworth CV8 1FG — MB BS 1954 Lond.; MRCS Eng. LRCP Lond. 1954; FFOM RCP Lond. 1988, M 1978; DIH Soc. Apoth. Lond. 1962. (St. Bart.) Dep. Chief Med. Off. Centr. Med. Dept. Ct.aulds Ltd. Coventry. Prev: Cas. Off. St. Bart. Hosp. Lond.; Paediat. Ho. Phys. & O & G Ho. Surg. Salisbury Gen. Hosp.

JONES, Hugh Idris Coed y Glyn Surgery, Coed y Glyn, Church Street, Llangefni LL77 7DU Tel: 01248 722229; Maes Yr Haf, Penmynydd Road, Llangefni LL77 7HS Tel: 01248 723334 — MB ChB 1977 Manch.; PhD 1972 (Chem.) Manch.; MA Camb. 1972; MRCP (UK) 1981; MRCGP 1983; DCH Eng. 1979.

JONES, Hugh Morley 1FR, 39 Woodland Gardens, London N10 3UE — MB BS 1993 Lond.

JONES, Mr Hugh Owen (retired) 8 Cyncoed Rise, Cardiff CF23 6SF Tel: 029 2075 1128 — MRCS Eng. LRCP Lond. 1941; MS Lond. 1949; MB BS (Hons.) 1941; FRCS Eng. 1947. Prev: Cons. Gen. Surg. Cardiff United Hosps.

JONES, Hugh Richard Health Services Centre, Wynne Road, Blaenau Ffestiniog LL41 3DW Tel: 01766 830205 Fax: 01766 831121; Hafod Uchaf, Rhyd, Penrhyndeudraeth LL48 6DX — MB ChB 1978 Liverp.; DRCOG 1981.

JONES, Hugh Williams 12 Milton Road, Wimbledon, London SW19 8SE Email: drhughjones@msn.com — MB ChB 1987 Liverp.; MRCP 1991. (Liverpool) Cons. Phys. & Rheum. Kingston Hosp. NHS Trust Qu. Mary's Hosp.

JONES, Huw Glyn Breydon, 291 Greys Road, Henley-on-Thames RG9 1QT — BM 1983 Soton.; MSc (Sports Medicine) 1998 Notts.

JONES, Huw Lloyd Eryri, Wern Road, Llangollen LL20 8DU — MB ChB 1991 Birm.; ChB Birm. 1991.

JONES, Huw Richard Health Centre, Llanfairpwllgwyngyll LL61 5YZ Tel: 01248 714388 Fax: 01248 715826 — MB ChB 1963 Liverp.; MRCGP 1974; DA Eng. 1970; DObst RCOG 1968. (Liverp.)

JONES, Huw St John 92 Vicars Moor Lane, London N21 1BN — MB ChB 1986 Sheff.

JONES, Hywel Morgan 1 Llanfair Gardens, Mumbles, Swansea SA3 5TR Email: hywel.jones@nortan1.demon.co.uk — MB BCh 1977 Wales; FRCA 1981 Lond. (University of Wales College of Medicine) Cons. Anaesth. Roy. Gwent Hosp. Newport Gwent.

JONES, Hywel Wyn Hughes and Partners, 15 Dereham Road, Mattishall, Dereham NR20 3QA Tel: 01362 850227 Fax: 01362 858466 Email: mattsurg@globalnet.co.uk; Email: hywel@chasing-rainbows.com — MB BS 1985 Lond.; MRCGP 1991; T(GP) 1991; DRCOG 1989. Princip., Gen. Pract., Mattishall Surg., Mattishall. Prev: Trainee GP Bury St. Edmunds VTS; Ho. Phys. W. Suff. Hosp. Bury St. Edmunds; Ho. Surg. St. Bart. Hosp. Lond.

JONES, Hywel Wyn Health Centre, New Street, Beaumaris LL58 8EL Tel: 01248 810818 Fax: 01248 811589; Ty Gwyn, Denmon, Beaumaris LL58 8RT — MB BCh 1988 Wales; DFFP 1993. Prev: SHO Gwynedd HA VTS; SHO (Surg.) Notts. Hosps.

JONES, Hywel Wyn Scridain, Forest Crescent, Ashtead KT21 1JU Tel: 01372 278265 — MB BS 1989 Lond.; FRCA 1994; DA (UK) 1991. (St. Thos. Hosp. Med. Sch.) Locum Cons. St Geo.s Hosp.

Lond. Socs: Roy. Soc. Med.; Eur. Assn. Cardiothoracic Anaesth.; Intens. Care Soc. Prev: Clin. Fell. (Cardiothoracic Anaesth.) Roy. Brompton NHS Trust & Lond. Chest Hosp.; Regist. St. Geo.s Hosp.; SHO (Special Care Baby Unit & Anaesth.) St. Thos. Hosp. Lond.

JONES, Ian Andrew 34 Gillespie Crescent, Edinburgh EH10 4HX — MB ChB 1984 Ed.

JONES, Ian George Scottish Centre for Infection and Environmental Health, Clifton House, Clifton Place, Glasgow G3 7LN Tel: 0141 300 1102 Fax: 0141 300 1170 Email: ijones@scieh.tcom.co.uk — MB ChB Ed. 1969; BSc Ed. 1966, MD 1979; MRCP (UK) 1975; MFCM RCP (UK) 1979; DCM Ed. 1976. (Ed.) Dir. Scott. Centre for Infec. & Environm. Health; Hon. Sen. Lect. Univ. Edin. Prev: Med. Dir., Centre for Health & Social Research; Chief Admin. Med. Off. & Dir. Pub. Health Fife HB; Community Med. Specialist Fife HB.

JONES, Ian Howard Tel: 01257 268955 Fax: 01257 241870 — MB ChB 1984 Birm. GP.

JONES, Mr Ian Howard 18 Rosamond Drive, Trinity Gardens, Salford M3 6BN — MB BCh 1988 Wales; BSc (Hons.) Wales 1985; FRCS Ed. 1994; Dip. IMC RCS Ed. 1995; FFAEM 1997. (Univ. Wales Coll. Med.) Cons. (A & E) Roy. Bolton Hosp. Socs: BMA. Prev: Specialist Regist. (A & E) Manch. Roy. Infirm.; Specialist Regist. (A & E) S. Manch. Univ. Hosp. Trust; Regist. (A & E) Roy. Bolton Hosp.

JONES, Ian James c/o RAMC, 45 Millbank, London SW1P 4RJ — MB ChB 1991 Leeds.

JONES, Ian Nicholas 376 St Helens Road, Bolton BL3 3RR; 639 Chorley New Road, Lostock, Bolton BL6 4AA — MB BS 1970 Lond.; MSc Lond. 1993, MB BS 1970; MRCGP 1974; DObst RCOG 1972.

JONES, Ian Philip St Marys Health Centre, Cop Lane, Penwortham, Preston PR1 0SR Tel: 01772 744404 Fax: 01772 752967 — MB ChB 1985 Liverp.; MRCGP 1992; DRCOG 1988. (Liverp.) Prev: Community Med. Off. (Community Paediat.) Blackburn; Trainee GP Stoke-on-Trent VTS.

JONES, Ian Philip Uppingham Road Medical Centre, 190 Uppingham Road, Leicester LE5 0QG Tel: 0116 276 6605; 87 Station Lane, Scraptoft, Leicester LE7 9UG Tel: 0116 241 5867 — MB ChB 1977 Sheff.; MRCGP 1983; DRCOG 1982; DCH Eng. 1980. Prev: GP Trainee Leicester VTS.

JONES, Ian Richard 46 Park Avenue, Worcester WR3 7AH — MB BS 1991 Lond.; BSc Lond. 1988; MRCPsych 1995. Research Hon. Sen. Regist. (Psychiat.) Heath Hosp. Cardiff. Prev: SHO (Psychiat.) Abergavenny.

JONES, Ian Richard Arrowe Park Hospital, Upton, Wirral L49 1PE; Graylands, 27 Croft Drive E., Caldy, Wirral CH48 1LU — MD 1986 Wales; MB BCh 1977; MRCP (UK) 1980. Cons. Phys. Gen. Med., Diabetes & Endocrinol. Arrowe Pk. Hosp.

JONES, Ieuan Wynne, CStJ, TD Rhandirmwyn, Bryn Dymchwel, Bangor LL57 4LD Tel: 01248 364594 — MB BS 1959 Lond.; MRCS Eng. LRCP Lond. 1959; FFAEM 1995. (Guy's) Cons. A & E Med. Gwynedd Hosp. Bangor. Prev: Assoc. Specialist (Traum. & Orthop. Surg.) Gwynedd Hosp. Bangor; Area Med. Off. Nat. Coal Bd. E. Mid. Div.

JONES, Ifan Crawford (retired) 48 Acacia Road, London NW8 6AP — MRCS Eng. LRCP Lond. 1946. Mem. Gray's Inn. Prev: Dir., Med. Dept. Brit. Counc.

JONES, Ingrid Susan 15 Furze Road, Maidenhead SL6 7RY — MB ChB 1992 Bristol.

JONES, Ioan Tudur Hafod y Coed, 17 Clayton Road, Pontardulais, Swansea SA4 1US — MB BCh 1994 Wales.

JONES, Irene Emma Maindiff Court Hospital, Ross Road, Abergavenny NP7 8NF Tel: 01873 735508; Maes Y Coed, Vicarage Road, Penygraig, Tonypandy CF40 1HR — MB ChB 1976 Dundee; MRCPsych 1988; MRCGP 1980. (Dundee) Cons. Psychiat. (Gen. Adult & Liaison Psychiat.) Maindiff Ct. Hosp. Ross Rd. Abergavenny Mon. Prev: Dept. Psychol Med. Univ. Hosp. of Wales Heath Pk. Cardiff.

JONES, Isaac Wyn Wrighton, Wigan and Leigh NHS Trust, Royal Albert Edward Infirmary, Wigan Lane, Wigan WN1 2NN Tel: 01942 822086 Fax: 01942 822089 Email: Issac.Jones@wiganRhs-tr.nwest.nhs.uk; 59 Springfield Lane, Eccleston, St Helens WA10 5HB, iwynjones@freeuk.com — MB ChB 1973 Liverp.; BA Open 1996; FFA RCS Eng. 1977; DObst RCOG 1975. Cons. Anaesth. Wrighton Wigan of Leigh NHS Trust. Socs: Liverp. Med. Inst.; Liverp. Soc. Anaesth.; Assn. Anaesth. Prev: Sen. Regist. Mersey RHA.

JONES, Isabel Ethel Health Centre, Heath Road, Haywards Heath RH16 3BB Tel: 01444 414767; 21 Fairford Close, Haywards Heath RH16 3EF Tel: 01444 452209 — MB BS Lond. 1962; MRCS Eng. LRCP Lond. 1962. (Roy. Free) GP. Prev: Clin. Asst. Cas. Dept. Cuckfield Hosp. Haywards Heath; Anaesth. & Orthop. Ho. Surg. Altnagelvin Hosp. Lond.derry; Ho. Phys. Roy. Cornw. Infirm. Truro.

JONES, Isabel Teresa Nuria Elisa Blond Mcindoe centre, Queen Victoria Hospital, East Grinstead RH19 3DZ Tel: 01342 313088 Fax: 01342 301701 Email: mcindoe@dial.didex.com; 58 Blenheim Cresent, Notting Hill, London W11 1WY Tel: 020 7221 9443 Email: is-jones@hotmail.com — MB BS 1993 Newc.; FRCS Lond 1998. Research Fell.

JONES, Ivor Gareth Pen-Y-Bont Farmhouse, Church Road, Silwern, Abergavenny NP7 — MB BS 1978 Newc. SHO (Med.) N. Tees Gen. Hosp. Stockton.

JONES, Jacqueline 22 Pant Yr Odyn, Tycoch, Swansea SA2 9GR — MB BS 1991 Lond.; MRCGP 1995. Clin. Asst. (Pychogeriats.) Swansea; Locum GP.

JONES, Jacqueline Ann Family Consultation Centre, Newtown Centre, Nursery Road, Huntingdon PE29 3RJ Tel: 01480 415300; 34 Loompits Way, Saffron Walden CB11 4BZ — MB BS 1969 Lond.; MRCS Eng. LRCP Lond. 1969; MRCPsych 1974. Cons. Child & Adolesc. Psychiat. Family Consult. Centre Huntingdon.

JONES, James Brian (retired) 37 Westmorland Way, Newton Aycliffe DL5 4NN Tel: 01325 312906 Fax: 01325 312906 — MB BS Durh. 1956. Prev: RAMC.

JONES, James Devaney (retired) 49 Beryl Road, Noctorum, Prenton CH43 9RS Tel: 0151 677 2524 — MB ChB 1955 Liverp.; MRCGP 1968; DObst RCOG 1958. Prev: Ho. Off. N.. Hosp. Liverp., Matern. Hosp. Liverp. & St. Catherine's Hosp. Birkenhead.

JONES, James Howard (retired) The Paddocks, Mill Lane, Goostrey, Crewe CW4 8PN Tel: 01477 537810 — BSc Wales 1945, MD 1957. MB BCh 1948; MRCS Eng. LRCP Lond. 1948; FRCPath 1973, M 1964. Prev: Cons. Path. (Haemat.) Gwent AHA.

JONES, Janet Elin Midway Surgery, 93 Watford Road, St Albans AL2 3JX — MB ChB 1992 Birm.; DCH; DRCOG; MRCGP 1998. p/t GP Princip., St Albans.

JONES, Janet Elizabeth Southport & Ormskirk NHS Trust District General Hospital, Town Lane, Kew, Southport PR8 6PN Tel: 01704 547471 Fax: 01704 548229; Rosedale, 5 Tailors Lane, Maghull, Liverpool L31 3HD — MB ChB 1978 Liverp.; FFA RCS Eng. 1982. Cons. Anaesth. S.port & Formby NHS Trust.

JONES, Janet Louise 24 Alexandra Road, Leicester LE2 2BB — MB ChB 1987 Leic.

JONES, Jason Robert Wayside, Swanhill Road, Colyford, Colyton EX24 6QJ Tel: 01297 552278 — MB ChB 1993 Leeds.

JONES, Jean Cynthia (retired) Glen Gorse, Heaton, Rushton Spencer, Macclesfield SK11 0SH Tel: 01260 226366 — MB ChB Liverp. 1960; DA Eng. 1963; DObst RCOG 1962. Prev: SCMO Warrington Community NHS Health Care Trust.

JONES, Jennifer Ann 60 King Henry's Road, London NW3 3RR Tel: 020 7722 1947 — MB BS 1962 Lond.; BSc (Hons.) Lond. 1959, MB BS (Hons.) 1962; FRCP Lond. 1987, M 1969; FFA RCS Eng. 1968. (Char. Cross) Cons. Anaesth. St. Mary's Hosp. Lond.

JONES, Jennifer Judith Spring Bank Group Practice, 168 Spring Bank, Hull HU3 1QW Tel: 01482 328581 Fax: 01482 221970; Keldgate House, 51 Keldgate, Beverley HU17 8HU — MB ChB 1971 St. And.; DObst. RCOG 1973.

JONES, Jennifer Mary 100 Eton Place, Eton College Road, London NW3 2DT Tel: 020 7586 4638 Fax: 020 7586 4638 — MB BS 1991 Lond.; BSc Lond. 1989. (Roy. Free Hosp. Sch. Med. Lond.)

JONES, Jennifer Palmer London Road Medical Centre, 2 London Road, Uppingham, Oakham LE15 9TJ Tel: 01572 823531; Manor Barn, Lyndon Road, Manton, Oakham LE15 8SR Tel: 01572 737670 — MB ChB 1977 Ed.; MRCGP 1981.

JONES, Jennifer Provost (retired) 2 Church Hill Close, Llanblethian, Cowbridge CF71 7JH Tel: 01446 774945 — MB ChB 1950 Ed.; Dip. Ven. Soc. Apoth. Lond. 1974. Prev: Cons. Venereol. Aylesbury & Milton Keynes Health Dist.

JONES, Jill 1 The Gardens, Sadler St., Wells BA5 2SF — MB ChB 1982 Leic.; MRCGP 1987.

JONES, Jill Elizabeth The Surgery, 292 Derby Road, Lenton, Nottingham NG7 1QG Tel: 0115 947 4002 Fax: 0115 924 0783 — MB ChB 1986 Leic.; MRCGP 1993; DRCOG 1991; DGM RCP Lond. 1990; Cert. Family Plann. JCC 1990. Prev: Regist. (Cas.) Redcliffe Hosp. Qu.sland, Austral.; SHO (Paediat.) Derby Childr. Hosp.; SHO (Health Care Elderly & O & G) Qu. Med. Centre Nottm.

JONES, Joan Mary Barkerend Health Centre, Barkerend Road, Bradford BD3 8QH; Fairstowe House, Queens Drive, Ilkley LS29 9QW Tel: 01943 607051 — MB BS 1960 Lond. SCMO Bradford HA.

JONES, Joan Meredyth Emily (retired) Abberton Manor Nursing Home, Abberton, Colchester CO5 7NL — MRCS Eng. LRCP Lond. 1939; MA (Nat. Sc. Trip.) 1935, MB BChir. Camb; DPM Eng. 1962. Prev: Regist. (Med.) Hampstead Gen. Hosp.

JONES, Joan Rhoda Keith Ty Isaf, Ffestiniog, Blaenau Ffestiniog LL41 4LS Tel: 0176 676 2739 — MB BS 1945 Lond.; MRCS Eng. LRCP Lond. 1945.

JONES, Joanna Mary Ryder New Cottage, Bridge Lane, Ladbroke, Leamington Spa CV47 2DE Tel: 01926 815706 Email: adamandjo-elliott@barclays.net; Glyn Orig, Cemmaes, Machynlleth SY20 9PR Tel: 01650 511632 — MB BS 1992 Lond.; BSc (Hons. Anat.) Lond. 1989; MRCP (UK) 1996. (Univ. Coll. Middlx. Sch. Med.) Spec. Reg. (Paediat.) Walsgrave Hosp., Coventry (Gen. Paeds). Prev: SHO (Paediat.) St. Geo. Hosp. Lond.; SHO (Paediat. Oncol. & Endocrinol.) Middlx. Hosp. Lond.; Specialist Regist. (Paed) Worc. Roy. Infirm.

JONES, John Hafannedd, Dwyran, Llanfairpwllgwyngyll LL61 6BJ Tel: 01248 430743 — MB ChB 1974 Manch.; FRCR 1982; DMRD Eng. 1979. Cons. Radiol. Ysbyty Gwynedd Bangor. Prev: Sen. Regist. & Regist. (Radiol.) Manch. Teach. Hosps.

JONES, John, Group Capt. RAF Med. Br. Department of Pathology, The Royal Hospital, Haslar, Gosport PO12 2AA Tel: 01705 762369 Fax: 01705 762549 Email: johnjone@dsca.gov.uk; 6 Penrith Way, Aylesbury HP21 7JZ Tel: 01296 425634 — MB BCh 1971 Wales; MSc (Med. Immunol.) Lond. 1988; FRCPath 1991, M 1979; DObst RCOG 1973. (Welsh National School Medicine) Cons. Haemat. (Head Path.) Roy. Hosp. Haslar; RCPath Regional Adviser Armed Forces; Defence Cons. Adviser Path. Socs: Brit. Soc. Haematol.; Brit. Soc. Immunol.; Assn. Clin. Paths.

JONES, John Alwyn Meddygfa'r Llan, Church Surgery, Portland Street, Aberystwyth SY23 2DX Tel: 01970 624855 Fax: 01970 625824; 2 Cae Argoed, Aberdyfi, Aberdovey LL35 0DY Tel: 01654 767833 — MB BS 1981 Lond.; MRCS Eng. LRCP Lond. 1981; MRCP (UK) 1986; DRCOG 1993.

JONES, Mr John Bernard (retired) Blackmore Park Farm, Malvern WR14 3LF Tel: 01684 565430 — MB BS 1963 Lond.; FRCS Eng. 1969; MRCS Eng. LRCP Lond. 1963; FRCOG 1986, M 1974. Prev: Cons. O & G Worcester Health Dist.

JONES, Mr John Booth (retired) The Mead, Torkington Road, Wilmslow SK9 2AE Tel: 01625 525487 — MB ChB Manch. 1953; ChM Manch. 1964; FRCS Ed. 1962; FRCOG 1973, M 1960. Prev: Cons. O & G Withington Hosp. Manch.

JONES, John Cedric (retired) Winstone, Alverstone Road, Apse Heath, Sandown PO36 0LE — MRCS Eng. LRCP Lond. 1940.

JONES, John Christopher Berwyn House Surgery, 13 Shrubbery Avenue, Worcester WR1 1QW Tel: 01905 22888 Fax: 01905 617352 — MB BS 1980 Lond.; MRCGP 1984; DRCOG 1983. Police Surg. Worcs.

JONES, Professor John Gareth Cambridge University Department of Anaesthesia, Addenbrooke's Hospital, Hills Road, Cambridge CB2 2QQ; Woodlands, Rufforth, York YO23 3QF Tel: 01904738804 Email: gareth@garjons.demon.co.uk — MB BCh Wales 1960; MD Birm. 1967; FRCP Lond. 1983, M 1963; FANZCA Australia/NZ 1992; FRCA 1970. (Cardiff) Prof. Anaesth., Univ. of Camb. Socs: Roy. Soc. Med. Prev: Prof. Anaesth. & Intens. Care Univ. Leeds; Mem. Scientif. Staff MRC Clin. Research Centre Harrow Middlx.; Asst. Prof. (Med.) Cardiovasc. Research Inst. Univ. Calif. San Francisco, USA.

JONES, John Gerard Seaford Health Centre, Dane Road, Seaford BN25 1DH Tel: 01323 490022 Fax: 01323 492156 — BM BCh 1973 Oxf.; DObst RCOG 1976.

JONES, John Goddard (retired) 14 Crugan Avenue, Kinmel Bay, Rhyl LL18 5DG Tel: 01745 344328 — MB BS Lond. 1935; MRCS Eng. LRCP Lond. 1934; DTM Antwerp 1937. Prev: GP Rhyl (Kinmel Bay).

JONES, John Graham Wickham Market Medical Centre, Chapel Lane, Wickham Market, Woodbridge IP13 0SB Tel: 01728 747101 Fax: 01728 747580; Tallow Wood, Lower Road, Ufford, Woodbridge IP13 6DL Tel: 01394 460784 Fax: 01394 460784 — MB ChB 1975 Sheff.; BSc (Hons.) Pharmacol. Lond. 1970; MRCGP 1981; DRCOG 1982; DCH RCP Lond. 1982.

JONES, John Graham (retired) 30 Park Road, Twickenham TW1 2PX Tel: 0208 892 8389 — MRCS Eng. LRCP Lond. 1940; FFOM RCP Lond. 1981; MFCM 1974; DIH Soc. Apoth. Lond. 1948. Cons. Occupat. Health Twickenham. Prev: Hon. Lect. (Occupat. Health) Welsh Nat. Sch. Med. Cardiff.

JONES, John Harold (retired) Scrabo, 54 Roberts Close, Cirencester GL7 2RP Tel: 01285 644318 — MB BCh BAO 1953 Belf.; MSc Manch. 1974; MD Belf. 1959; FFD RCSI 1977; LDS RCS Eng. 1962; FRCPath 1974, M 1963. Prev: Prof. Oral Med. Univ. Manch.

JONES, John Henry (retired) 77 Cyncoed Road, Cardiff CF23 5SB Tel: 012920 484549 — MD (Distinc.) Wales 1964, MB BCh (Hons.) 1954; FRCP Lond. 1972, M 1961. Prev: Cons. Phys. Univ. Hosp. of Wales, Cardiff.

JONES, John Howard Arthur 59 Merriefield Avenue, Broadstone BH18 8DB Tel: 01202 696896 — MB BS 1981 Newc.; DRCOG 1984. (Newcastle upon Tyne)

JONES, John Howel (retired) 6 Staverton Leys, Rugby CV22 5RD Tel: 01788 812632 — MB BChir 1952 Camb.; MD Camb. 1964; FRCP Lond. 1973; MRCP (UK) 1958. Prev: Cons. Phys. Walsgrave Hosp. Coventry & Hosp. of St. Cross Rugby.

JONES, John Hywel (retired) Eden House, The Bryn, Sketty Green, Swansea SA2 8DD Tel: 01792 206204 — MB BS Lond. 1961; BSc (1st cl. Hons. Anat.) Lond. 1958, MD 1974; FRCP Lond. 1978, M 1964; MRCS Eng. LRCP Lond. 1961. Prev: Cons. Phys. Singleton Hosp. Swansea.

JONES, John Ifan Lloyd 81 Newfoundland Road, Cardiff CF14 3LB — MB BCh 1991 Wales.

JONES, John Ivor Wynn 12 Curzon Park N., Chester CH4 8AR — BM BCh 1993 Oxf.; MA Camb. 1994; MRCP (UK) 1996. (Oxf.) Regist. (Gastroenterol.) Nottm. Prev: SHO (Gastroenterol.) Oxf. Radcliffe Hosp.; SHO (Gen. Med.) N. Staffs. Hosp. Stoke-on-Trent; Ho. Off. Nuffield Dept. Surg. John Radcliffe Hosp. Oxf.

JONES, John James, TD (retired) Nibley House, Badminton Road, Nibley, Bristol BS37 5JE — MB ChB 1963 Bristol. Prev: Regist. (Surg.) Luton & Dunstable Hosp.

JONES, John Kenneth 10 Maescelyn, Brecon LD3 7NL Tel: 01874 624999 — LMSSA 1948 Lond.; MFCM 1972; DPH Wales 1958; FRSH. (Univ. Coll. Hosp.) Civil Med. Pract. Jt. Servs. Careers Off. Cardiff. Prev: Med. Off. NTW Dering Lines Brecon; Sen. Med. Off. Powys AHA; MOH Combined Dists. Breconsh.

JONES, Mr John Maurice BUPA Hospital, Gartree Road, Oadby, Leicester LE2 2FF Tel: 0116 265 3043 Fax: 0116 265 3688 — MB BS Lond. 1966; FRCS Ed. 1972; MRCS Eng. LRCP Lond. 1966. (Middlx.) Cons. Orthop. BUPA Hosp. Oadby; Examr. RCS of Edin. Socs: Fell. BOA; Brit. Soc. Surg. Hand; BMA. Prev: Con. Orthopaedic Leciester Gen. Hosp. NHS Trust; Sen. Regist. (Orthop.) S. Glam. (Cardiff) AHA (T); Regist. (Orthop.) St. Geo. Hosp. Lond.

JONES, John Meirion, Wing Cdr. RAF Med. Br. Rose Lea Cottage, Tholthorpe, York YO61 1SN — MB BCh 1972 Wales; AFOM RCP Lond. 1981; DAVMed. Eng. 1981.

JONES, John Michael Llewellyn (retired) 4 Maesyfelin Crescent, Pontyclun CF72 9BQ Tel: 01443 237070 — MB BChir 1959 Camb.; MRCS Eng. LRCP Lond. 1958; DObst RCOG 1962. Prev: SHO Anaesth. E. Glam. Hosp. Pontypridd.

JONES, John Milton Brynglas, Llanfair Caereinion, Welshpool SY21 0BS Tel: 01938 810338 — LMSSA 1946 Lond.

JONES, John Morris Dolwenith, 13-15 Snowdon St., Penygroes, Caernarfon LL54 6NG Tel: 01286 880202 — MB BCh 1983 Wales; BSc (Hons.) Cardiff 1980; MRCGP 1994; DRCOG 1987; DA (UK) 1985; Dip. Ther. Wales 1997. (Cardiff)

JONES, John Morris (retired) Foxhayes, 6 Foxholes Hill, Exmouth EX8 2DF Tel: 01395 265211 — BM BCh 1953 Oxf.; MA, BM BCh Oxf. 1953; DObst RCOG 1956. Prev: Gp Exmouth.

JONES, John Phillip St James Surgery, 8-9 Northampton Buildings, Bath BA1 2SR Tel: 01225 422911 Fax: 01225 428398; 4 St.

Catherine's Close, Bath BA2 6BS — MB BS 1975 Lond.; MRCGP 1979.

JONES, John Richard Langford Medical Practice, 9 Nightingale Place, Bicester OX26 6XX Tel: 01869 245665; Saxon House, Little Paddock, Fringford, Bicester OX27 8EJ Tel: 01869 277929 Fax: 01869 322025 Email: richardjones@pgec-horton.demon.co.uk — MB BCh 1980 Wales; MRCGP 1986; DFFP 1993; DAvMed 1989; DRCOG 1985; MRAeS 1989. (Welsh Nat. Sch. Med.) Mem. Panel Examrs. RCGP; JAR Approved Aviat. Med. Examr. Prev: Sen. Med. Off. RAF Bruggen; Sen. Med. Off. RAF Coltishall & RAF Brawdy; Aeromed. Evac. Co-Ord. Off. RAF Belize.

JONES, John Richard The Surgery, Lambourn, Newbury RG16 7PS Tel: 01488 71715 Fax: 01488 73569; 36 Baydon Road, Lambourn, Newbury RG17 8NT Tel: 01488 72385 — MB BS 1984 Lond.; DRCOG 1988; Cert. Family Plann. JCC 1987.

JONES, John Robert The Surgery, 67 Vineyard Hill Road, London SW19 7JL Tel: 020 8947 2579; 47 Erridge Road, Wimbledon, London SW19 3JD — MB BS 1978 Lond.; MRCGP 1988. (Charing Cross Hospital)

JONES, John Spencer (retired) 8 Lower Blackhouse Hill, Hythe CT21 5LS Tel: 01303 267724 — MB BS Lond. 1948. Prev: Cons. Chest Phys. Canterbury, I. of Thanet & SE Kent Hosp. Gps.

JONES, John Stuart 3 Robert Terrace, Coedpoeth, Wrexham LL11 3TE — MB BS 1994 Lond.

JONES, John Stuart (retired) 17 Drake Road, Skegness PE25 3BH Tel: 01754 764658 — MB ChB 1951 Liverp.; DObst RCOG 1954. Hon. Phys. Grace Swan Hosp. Spilsby; Med. Off. Nat. Deposit Friendly Soc. Skegness & Min. of Educat.; Local Treasury Med. Off. Prev: Ho. Phys. City Hosp. Chester.

JONES, John Thomas Wimble Weather, Hammer Vale, Haslemere GU27 1QG Tel: 01428 51704 — MB BCh 1953 Wales; BSc Wales 1951, MB BCh 1953, DPH 1958; MFCM 1972. (Cardiff) Sen. Med. Off. Dept. Health & Social Security. Socs: Fell. Soc. MOH; MRSH. Prev: Dep. MOH Lond. Boro. Havering; Sen. Med. Off. (Admin.) Newc. Upon Tyne; Dep. MOH Lincoln Co. Boro.

JONES, John Trevor Craig y Nos Castle, Brecon Road, Penycae, Swansea SA9 1GL — MB BCh 1961 Wales.

JONES, Professor John Vann Cardiology Department, Royal Infirmary, Bristol BS2 8HW Tel: 01179 282645 Fax: 01179 282666 — PhD Glas. 1972, MB ChB 1968; FRCP Lond. 1987. (Glas.) Cons. Cardiol. Roy. Infirm. Bristol. Socs: Brit. Cardiac Soc.; (Treas.) Brit. Hypertens. Soc. Prev: Reader (Cardiovasc. Med.) Univ. Oxf.; Lect. (Med. Cardiol.) Univ. Glas.; MRC Trav. Research Fell. Univ. Gothenburg, Sweden.

JONES, John Verdun (retired) 100 Lake Road E., Cardiff CF23 5NP Tel: 01222 752011 — MB BCh 1940 Wales; BSc Wales 1937. Prev: on Staff St. David's Hosp. Cardiff & Rhymney Cottage Hosp.

JONES, John Verrier (retired) 9 Avondale Court, Goodeve Road, Bristol BS9 1NU — BM BCh 1955 Oxf.; FRCP Lond. 1973; MRCP (UK) 1958; FRCPC 1981. Prev: Prof. & Head Div. Rheum. Dalhousie Univ. Halifax, Canada.

JONES, John Wynne Tel: 01443 228922 Fax: 01443 228319; 5 Highgrove, Sandy Lane, Ystradowen, Cowbridge CF71 7TE Tel: 01446 775884 Email: wynne@ystradowen.demon.co.uk — MB BCh 1978 Wales; Dip. Med. 1995; MSc (Med. Educat.) Wales 1995; MRCGP 1983; DRCOG 1984; Cert. Family Plann. JCC 1981. (Univ. Wales Coll. Med. Cardiff) Trainer GP Talbot Green M. Glam; Clin. Asst. (Dermatol. Minor Surg.) Bridgend Gen. Hosp.; C.P.D. Co-ordinator (Rhoudda, Cyron, Taff & Mertteyr). Socs: Brit. Inst. Musculoskel. Med.; Brit. Med. Acupunct. Soc.; Rhondda Med. Soc. Prev: Chairm., Treas. & Sec. Local Young Princip.s Gp.

JONES, Johnathon Neil 9 Bulford Close, Johnston, Haverfordwest SA62 3EX — MB BCh 1993 Wales.

JONES, Jonathan Alun Griffiths Dinas Powys Health Centre, 75 Cardiff Road, Dinas Powys CF64 4JT Tel: 029 2051 2293 Fax: 029 2051 5318; The Old Mill Farm House, Lettons Way, Dinas Powys CF64 4BY — BM 1982 Soton.; MRCP (UK) 1985; MRCGP 1990. Prev: Hon. Clin. Asst. (Rheum.) Llandough Hosp. Cardiff; Trainee GP Milford-on-Sea; SHO Rotat. (Med.) Leics. HA.

JONES, Jonathan David Department of Radiology, Bristol Royal Infirmary, Marlborough St., Bristol BS2 8HW — MB BS 1991 Lond.

JONES, Jonathan Mark 4 Ashfield House, 8 Grove Road, Headingley, Leeds LS6 2AQ — MB ChB 1994 Leeds; BSc (Hons) Leeds 1992. (Leeds)

JONES, Jonathan Owain Diagnostic Imaging, Royal Hospital NHS Trust Royal London Hosp., Whitechapel, London E1 2BB Tel: 020 7377 7000; 50 Fuller Close, Bethnal Green, London E2 6DX Tel: 020 7729 6059 Email: jonathan.jones@btinternet.com — MB BS 1994 Lond. Specialist Regist. Diagnostic Imaging Roy. Hosps. Trust Lond.

JONES, Jonathan Richard 66 Henshaw Street, London SE17 1PD Tel: 020 7252 6509 Email: hzjjones7@aol.com — BM 1993 Soton.; MRCP 1997. (Southampton) Research Regist. Soton. Gen. Hosp. Soton.

JONES, Jonathan Richard 933 Blackburn Road, Bolton BL1 7LR; Ngaurahoe, 1 Jumbles Beck, Turton, Bolton BL7 0EY Tel: 01204 853869 — MB ChB 1982 Manch.; DCH RCP Lond. 1986; DRCOG 1986. (Manchester) GP. Socs: Fac. Homoeop.

JONES, Mr Jonathan Robert 9 Beaumont Road, Windsor SL4 1HY Tel: 01753 854659 Fax: 01753 850128; Mintaro, Stewarts Drive, Farnham Common, Slough SL2 3LB Tel: 01753 644400 — MB BS 1977 Lond.; BSc Lond. 1974; FRCS Eng. 1981. (Univ. Coll. Hosp.) Cons. Orthop. Surg. Heatherwood & Wexham Pk. Hosps. Trust. Socs: Fell. BOA; BMA; Brit. Hip Soc. Prev: Sen. Regist. (Orthop.) St. Mary's Hosp. & Char. Cross Hosp. Lond.; Clin. Fell. (Orthop.) Adelaide Childr. Hosp., S. Austral.

JONES, Jonathan Stafford 3 Maes-y-Deri Close, Pencoed, Bridgend CF35 6YY — MB BCh 1995 Wales.

JONES, Jonathan Stuart Llys Meddyg, Llys Meddyg, Victoria Road, Penygroes, Caernarfon LL54 6HD Tel: 01286 880207 Fax: 01286 880859 — MB BS 1979 Lond.; DRCOG 1983.

JONES, Joseph Hedley (retired) 30 Kings Road, Sale M33 6GB — MB ChB 1959 Manch.; DObst RCOG 1961.

JONES, Joseph Orduma Emmanuel 13 Queensland House, Rymill St., London E16 2LG — MB BS 1996 Lond.

JONES, Joseph Philip Pencoed and Llanharan Medical Centres, Heol-yr-Onnen, Pencoed, Bridgend CF35 5PF Tel: 01656 860270 Fax: 01656 861228; Craigwen, Hendre Road, Pencoed, Bridgend CF35 — MB BCh 1969 Wales.

JONES, Josephine Anne Department of Learning Disabilities, Highbury Hospital, Bulwell, Nottingham NG6 9DR Tel: 0115 977 0000 — MB ChB 1980 Sheff.; BMedSci Sheff. 1977; MRCPsych 1986. Cons. Psychiat. Learning Disabil. Nottm.shire Healthcare NHS Trust, Nottm.; Assoc. PostGrad. Dean, Nottm. Deanery. Prev: Sen. Regist. (Ment. Handicap) Qu. Med. Centre Nottm.; Regist. (Psychiat.) Nottm. HA; SHO (Paediat.) Sheff. Childr. Hosp.

JONES, Judith Ann North Nottinghamshire Health Authority, Ransom Hall, Southwell Road West, Rainworth, Mansfield NG21 0ER — MB ChB 1987 Leic.; MSc Manch. 1994; MRCGP 1991; MFPHM RCP (UK) 1994; DFFP 1991. Cons. Pub. Health Med. & Sen. Lect. (Gen. Pract.) N. Notts. HA. Prev: Clin. Lect. (Pub. Health Med.) Univ. Manch.; Regist. (Pub. Health Med.) N. W.. RHA.

JONES, Judith Ann Penarth Health Centre, Stanwell Road, Penarth CF64 3XE Tel: 029 2070 0911 — MB BCh 1988 Wales; MRCGP 1992.

JONES, Judith Elizabeth Malago Surgery, 40 St. Johns Road, Bedminster, Bristol BS3 4JE; 16 Camden Terrace, Clifton, Bristol BS8 4PU — MB ChB 1980 Bristol; MRCGP 1987; DRCOG 1986. (Bristol) Socs: (Sec.) Bristol Medico Legal Soc.; (Comm.) Bristol M-C Soc.; Pres. of the BMA (Bristol Div.). Prev: Regist. (Gen. Med.) Bristol Roy. Infirm.; Clin. Asst. (Diabetes & Endocrinol.) Bristol Roy. Infirm.

JONES, Judith Frances Mary Undercliffe Surgery, 273 Healey Lane, Batley WF17 8DQ Tel: 01924 403406 Fax: 01924 412890 — MB ChB 1986 Leeds; DRCOG 1990.

JONES, Julia Anne The Surgery, Chestnut Walk, Stratford-upon-Avon CV37 6HQ Tel: 01789 292895 Fax: 01789 414721; Elmwood Lodge, Wimpstone, Stratford-upon-Avon CV37 8NS Tel: 01789 450950 — MB ChB 1982 Liverp.; MRCGP 1986; DRCOG 1985; Cert. Family Plann. JCC 1984. Clin. Asst. (Dermat.) Stratford upon Avon Hosp.

JONES, Julie Glan Clywd DGH, Bodelwyddan, Denbigh LL18 SUJ Tel: 01745 583910; 6 Brondyffryn, St Asaph LL17 0YA — MB ChB 1990 Manch. Staff Grade in Haemat. &Oncol.(p/t).

JONES, Julie Ruth Childrens Services, Rockingham Forest NHS Trust, Floor 3, Derbyshire House, Lower St., Kettering NN16 8BG Tel: 01536 410099; Arden House, 27 Great Bowden Road, Market Harborough LE16 7DE — MB BS 1981 Lond.; MRCGP 1985; DCH RCP Lond. 1994; DRCOG 1983. Clin. Med. Off. Kettering HA. Prev: GP Corby.

JONES, Karen Ann The Ashgrove Surgery, Morgan Street, Pontypridd CF37 2DR Tel: 01443 404444 Fax: 01443 480917; 28 Windsor Avenue, Radyr, Cardiff CF15 8BY — MB BCh 1988 Wales; MRCGP 1992; DCH RCP Lond. 1991. Prev: Trainee GP Cardiff VTS.

JONES, Karen Lynn The Grange Medical Centre, 39 Leicester Road, Nuneaton CV11 6AB Tel: 024 7632 2810 Fax: 024 7632 2820 — MB ChB 1987 Leic.; MRCGP 1993; DRCOG 1991. (Leicester)

JONES, Kate Justina Department of Anaesthesia, St. George's Hospital, Blackshaw Road, Tooting, London SW17 0QT Tel: 0208 672 1255 — MB ChB 1989 Leeds; MRCP (UK) 1993; FRCA 1995. Cons. (Anaesth.) St Geo.'s Hosp. Lond. Prev: Regist. (Anaesth.) St. Mary's Hosp. Lond.

JONES, Katharine Alison 24 Abbotts Park, Cornwood, Ivybridge PL21 9PP — MB BS 1980 Lond.; BSc Lond. 1977, MB BS 1980; DRCOG 1983. (Middlx.) Clin. Asst. (c/o the Elderly) Mt. Gould Hosp. Plymouth. Prev: Trainee GP Cornw. & I. of Scilly VTS.

JONES, Katharine Rounsfell (retired) Twthill Cottage, West Twthill, Caernarfon LL55 1PE — MB ChB 1926 Glas.; DPH Ed. & Glas. 1933.

JONES, Katherine Emma Flat 1, 13 Ladybarn Road, Manchester M14 6WN — MB ChB 1997 Manch.

***JONES, Katherine Louise** 22 Roman Way, Egdbaston, Birmingham B15 2SJ — MB ChB 1998 Birm.; ChB Birm. 1998.

JONES, Kathleen Mary (retired) 19 Grove Road, Totley Rise, Sheffield S17 4DJ Tel: 0114 236 6516 — MB BChir 1955 Camb.; LLD (Hon.) 1994; DCH Eng. 1957; MA Camb. 1961. Prev: Community Med. Off. Sheff. HA.

JONES, Kathryn Nottingham Healthcare NHS Trust, Duncan Macmillan House, Porchester Road, Nottingham NG3 6AA Tel: 0115 969 1300; 2 Conway Road, Carlton, Nottingham NG4 2PX — MB ChB 1993 Manch. SHO (Psychiat.) Nottm. Healthcare NHS Trust.

JONES, Kathryn Anne 21 Wychford Drive, Sawbridgeworth CM21 0HA — MB ChB 1982 Bristol.

JONES, Kathryn Mary Wickham Market Medical Centre, Chapel Lane, Wickham Market, Woodbridge IP13 0SB Tel: 01728 747101 Fax: 01728 747580; Tallow Wood, Lower Road, Ufford, Woodbridge IP13 6DL Tel: 01394 460784 Fax: 01394 460784 — MB ChB 1974 Bristol; MRCGP 1987; MRCOG 1979.

JONES, Katrin Elisabeth 57 Ashleigh Grove, West Jesmond, Newcastle upon Tyne NE2 3DJ — MB BS 1996 Newc. SHO (Med.) Newc. u. Tyne.

JONES, Keith 20 Oaklands Court, Aldcliffe, Lancaster LA1 5AT Tel: 01524 64833 — MB BS Lond. 1965; FRCOG 1985, M 1971. Cons. O & G Roy. Lancaster Infirm. & W.morland Co. Hosp. Kendal.

JONES, Mr Keith The Orchard, Slade Lane, Wilson, Melbourne, Derby DE73 1AG Tel: 01332 864647 Fax: 01332 864647 — MB BCh 1983 Wales; FRCS Ed. 1988; FDSRCS Eng. 1979; BDS Wales 1975. Cons. Oral & Maxillofacial Surg. Trent RHA. Prev: Sen. Regist. (Oral & Maxillofacial Surg.) NRHA; Regist. (Oral & Maxillofacial Surg.) S. Glam. HA.

JONES, Keith Ernest 408 Crewe Road, Wistaston, Crewe CW2 6QR — MB BChir 1972 Camb.; MA, MB Camb. 1972, BChir 1971; LMSSA Lond. 1971; FFA RCS Eng. 1976.

JONES, Keith Gordon 7 Blackthorns Close, Haywards Heath RH16 2UA — MB BS 1992 Lond.; BSc Physiol. Lond. 1989. SHO (Surg.) Epsom Gen. Hosp. Prev: SHO (Surg.) E. Surrey Hosp. Redhill; SHO (Neurosurg.) Radcliffe Hosp. Oxf.; SHO (Orthop. & A & E) Roy. Berks. Hosp. Reading.

JONES, Keith Howard, CB Shelford, Headley Road, Leatherhead KT22 8PT Tel: 01372 376747 — MD Wales 1966, MB BCh 1960; FRCP Lond. 1993; FRCP Ed. 1990; FFPM RCP (UK) 1991. Chief Exec. Med. Control Agency Lond.; Vis. Prof. Pharmacol. Sch. of Pharmacy Univ. Lond.; Chairm. Scientif. Comm. Med. Products & Med. Devices, EC, Brussels; Mem. Scientif. Steering Comm. EC, Brussels. Socs: Med. Res. Soc. & Brit. Pharmacol. Soc. Prev: Exec. Dir. (Med. Affairs) Merck Sharp & Dohme Rahway, USA; Adjunct Prof. Med. Thos. Jefferson Med. Sch. Philadelpha USA; Head Toxicol. Drug Metab. & Clin. Pharmacol. Beecham Research Laborat.

JONES, Keith Joseph Medical Centre, Derby Road, Peel IM5 1HP Tel: 01624 843636 Fax: 01624 844543 — BM BS 1976 Nottm.; BMedSci Nottm. 1974; MRCGP 1982; DRCOG 1980. (Nottingham) GP I. of Man. Socs: Matern. Liaison Comm.; Ment. Health Tribunal; I. of Man Med. Soc. Prev: Trainee GP Leicester VTS.

JONES, Keneth Robert Newmill Cottage, Truro TR4 9EU — MRCS Eng. LRCP Lond. 1973; MRCOG 1982.

JONES, Kenneth (retired) Spicers Hall, Claverley, Wolverhampton WV5 7DA Tel: 01746 710432 Email: kebjones@doctors.org.uk — MB ChB 1956 Liverp.; MRCGP 1974; DObst RCOG 1959. Prev: Ho. Off. (Med., Paediat., Surg. & Obst.) Whiston Hosp. Prescot.

JONES, Kenneth Dickson, Maj. RAMC Retd. Downfield Medical Practice, 325 Strathmartine Road, Dundee DD3 8NE Tel: 01382 812111 Fax: 01382 858315; 5 Rankine Court, Wormit, Newport-on-Tay DD6 8TA Tel: 01382 542923 — MB ChB 1979 Dundee; MRCGP 1986; Dip. Ther. Wales 1996. (Dundee) Prev: RAMC Med. Off. 1981-89; GP Elgin.

JONES, Kenneth Elwyn (retired) Field House, Sudbrooke, Lincoln LN2 2QU Tel: 01522 751557 — MB ChB 1958 Liverp.; MFFP 1993; FFPHM RCP (UK) 1988, M 1974; DPH Liverp. 1966. Prev: Dir. Pub. Health & Dist. Med. Off. N. Lincs. HA.

JONES, Kenneth Simpson (retired) 13 The Mount, Dinas Powys CF64 4DP Tel: 01222 512791 — MB BS Lond. 1946; FRCPsych 1971; DPM Lond. 1951. Prev: Cons. Psychiat. Morgannwg Hosp. Bridgend.

JONES, Mr Kevin David St. Peters Hosp, Chertsey Tel: 01483 303053; Tel: 01483 503143 Email: kjones@rschguildford.freeserve.co.uk — MB BCh BAO 1990 NUI; BSc (Hons.) St. And. 1984; MRCOG 1995; MSc Birm. 1985. Sen. Regist. in Obst. & Gyn., St. Peter's Hosp Chertsey; Specialist Regist. Obst/Gyn SW Thames Rotat. Socs: Brit.Soc. Gynae & Endoscopy Mem.; Brit. Fert. Soc. Mem; Europ. Soc Gynae Endoscopy mem. Prev: Clin. Fell. In Gynae Endoscopy Guildford; SR O & G & RF Gyn. ultrasound St Geo.s HMS; Clin. Fell. in Reproductive Med. Univ. of Bristol.

JONES, Kevin Eamonn Ty-Elli Group Practice, Ty Elli, Llanelli SA15 3BD Tel: 01554 772678 / 773747 Fax: 01554 774476; 42 Corporation Avenue, Llanelli SA15 3NG Tel: 01554 775498 — MB BCh 1978 Wales; DRCOG Lond. 1982.

JONES, Kevin Peter Oxford Terrace Medical Group, 1 Oxford Terrace, Gateshead NE8 1RQ Tel: 0191 477 2169 Fax: 0191 477 5633; Department of Primary Health Care, School of Health Sciences, The Medical School, Framlington Place, Newcastle upon Tyne NE2 4HH Tel: 0191 222 8897 Fax: 0191 222 7892 Email: k.p.jones@ncl.ac.uk — MB BS 1979 Lond.; MA Camb. 1980; DM Soton. 1992; MRCS Eng. LRCP Lond. 1979; MRCGP (Distinc.) 1987. (Char. Cross) Sen. Lect. (Primary Health Care) Univ. Newc. Socs: AUDGP; BTS. Prev: Sen. Lect. (Primary Med. Care) Univ. Soton.; Specialist (Med.) Qu. Eliz. Milit. Hosp. Woolwich.

JONES, Miss Kirsten Elaine Accident and Emergency Department, Frenchay Hospital, Bristol BS16 1LE Tel: 01179 186544 Fax: 01179 572335; Mulberry House, 125 Slad Road, Stroud GL5 1QZ Tel: 01453 764621 — MB BS Lond. 1988; DA; FRCS (A&E) Ed. (CXWMS London) A & E Cons. Frenchay Hosp. Bristol. Socs: Fell. Fac. Accid. & Emerg. Med.; Brit. Assn. Accid. & Emerg. Med.

JONES, Laura Brigid Kennedy Roberton 4 Bilsmoor Avenue, High Heaton, Newcastle upon Tyne NE7 7BJ — MB BS 1991 Newc. SHO (A & E) S. Tees Acute NHS Hosp. Trust Middlesbrough.

JONES, Laura Margaret 21 Tudor Avenue, Prestatyn LL19 9HN — MB ChB 1989 Manch.

JONES, Leslie Russell House Surgery, Russell House, Bakers Way, Codsall, Wolverhampton WV8 1HD Tel: 01902 842488 Fax: 01902 846170 — MB BCh 1980 Wales.

JONES, Lewis Owen 45 Baldslow Road, Hastings TN34 2EY — MB ChB 1995 Bristol.

JONES, Lilian Jean Blyton Shelford, Headley Road, Leatherhead KT22 8PT Tel: 01372 376747 — MB BCh Wales 1962; MFPM RCP Lond. 1994, A 1992. Research Phys. (Drug Surveillance) Glaxo Wellcome Greenford. Socs: Fell. Roy. Soc. Med.

JONES, Linda Ann Kennington Health Centre, 200 Kennington Road, Kennington, Oxford OX1 5PY Tel: 01865 730911 Fax: 01865

327759 — MB BCh 1987 Wales; MRCGP 1992; DCH RCP Lond. 1991; DRCOG 1991. Prev: SHO (Anaesth.) W. Glam. HA.

JONES, Linda Carol (retired) 13 Peverells Wood Avenue, Eastleigh SO53 2AX — MB BS 1970 Lond.; FRCP Lond. 1988; MRCP (UK) 1975; MRCS Eng. LRCP Lond. 1970. Prev: Cons. Phys. Geriat. Med. Portsmouth & SE Hants. HA.

JONES, Linda Mary 10 Browning Street, Stafford ST16 3AT Tel: 01785 258249 Fax: 01785 253119; Desford House, Hyde Lea, Stafford ST18 9BG Tel: 01785 251682 — MB ChB 1976 Leeds; DRCOG 1982; DCH Eng. 1980. (Leeds)

JONES, Mr Lionel Evan (retired) The Beeches, Wolston, Coventry CV8 3HH Tel: 01203 542226 — MS Lond. 1940, MB BS (Hnrs. in Med.) 1934; FRCS Eng. 1935; MRCS Eng. LRCP Lond. 1934. Prev: Surg. Specialist R.A.F.V.R.

JONES, Llewelyn Bunner Pugh Penymaaes, Llanfyllin SY22 5LA — LRCP LRCS 1945 Ed.; LRCP LRCS Ed. LRFPS Glas. 1945. (Roy. Colls. Ed.)

JONES, Llion Wyn Clarence House, 14 Russell Road, Rhyl LL18 3BY Tel: 01745 350680 Fax: 01745 353293 — MB ChB 1966 Liverp.

JONES, Louis Ian Claremont House, 2 Woodcote Valley Road, Purley CR8 3AG Tel: 020 8668 0801 Fax: 020 8763 9872; 4 Sandhurst Way, Sanderstead, South Croydon CR2 0AH Tel: 020 8657 8466 Fax: 020 8657 8466 Email: drlouisjones@supanet.com — MB BS 1957 Durh.; MRCGP 1973; Cert. Family Plann. JCC 1974. (Durh.) p/t Hosp. Pract. Diabetic Clinic Mayday Hosp. Croydon; Private Orthop. Phys. Claremont Ho. Purley Surrey. Socs: BMA; Croydon Med. Soc., past Pres. Prev: Regist. (Med.) St. Stephen's Hosp. Lond.; SHO (Neurol.) SE Metrop. Region Neurol. Centre Brook Gen. Hosp. Lond.; Ho. Phys. (Paediat.) Newc. Gen. Hosp.

JONES, Louise Margaret Tel: 01704 876363 Fax: 01704 833808 — MB ChB 1981 Liverp.; DRCOG 1983. Prev: SHO (Paediat.) St. Helens Hosp.; SHO (Gyn.) Roy. Liverp. Hosp.; SHO (Obst.) Mill Rd. Matern. Hosp. Liverp.

JONES, Lucille Ellaline 10 Llandaff Close, Great Sutton, South Wirral CH66 2HS — MB ChB 1992 Liverp.

JONES, Lucy Ann The Coach House, Ellerton Grange, Newport TF10 8DS Tel: 01952 550339 — MB BCh 1993 Wales; DCH 1995. Retainer GP, Eccleshall Surg. Prev: salaried GP Gnosall Surg.

JONES, Lydia Epsom General Hospital, Dorking Road, Epsom KT18 7EG Tel: 01372 735144 Fax: 01372 748802 — MB BS (Hons.) Lond. 1980; BSc (Hons.) Physiol. Lond. 1977; FRCP Lond. 1996; FRCPath 1997, M 1988. (St. Bart.) Cons. Haemat. Epsom Gen. Hosp. Socs: Brit. Soc. Haematol.; Eur. Haematol. Assn.; Brit. Blood Transfus. Soc. Prev: Sen. Regist. (Haemat.) Lond. Hosp.; Research Fell. Bone Marrow Transpl. Unit Dept. Haemat. Roy Postgrad. Med. Sch. Hammersmith Hosp. Lond.; SHO (Oncol.) Roy. Marsden Hosp. Lond.

JONES, Lydia Richmond Clinic, 172 Caerleon Road, Newport NP19 7FY Tel: 01633 259970 Fax: 01633 221210; Easedale, 16 Court Crescent, Bassaleg, Newport NP10 8NH — MB BCh 1976 Wales; DRCOG 1983. (Wales) Socs: BMA. Prev: Trainee GP Gwent VTS; Regist. (Gen. Med.) & SHO (Cas.) Roy. Gwent Hosp.

JONES, Mr Lyndon Stewart Withnell Health Centre, Railway Road, Withnell, Chorley PR6 8UA Tel: 01254 830311 Fax: 01254 832337 — MB ChB 1987 Dundee; FRCS Ed. 1992.

JONES, Lynn Elias Lloyd East Kent Community, Drug Service, 171 Beaver Road, Ashford CT14 8AA Tel: 01233 640046; Undercliffe, 28 Wellington parade, Walmer, Deal CT14 8AA Tel: 01304 239329 — MB BCh 1972 Wales; MRCGP 1976; MRCPsych 1991; DObst RCOG 1975. (Cardiff Medical School) Clin. Dir. E. Kent Drug Misuse Serv. E. Kent Health Auth. Socs: Brit. Doctors & Dent. Gp.; BMA; MDU. Prev: Princip. GP Burry Port, BromsGr. & Porthmadog.

JONES, Lynne Myfanwy, OBE Centre for Family Research, Cambridge University, Freeschool Lane, Cambridge CB2 3RF Tel: 01223 330574 Email: lmj21@cam.ac.uk; 22 Manor Court, Grange Road, Pinehurst, Cambridge CB3 9BE Tel: 01223 301993 — MB ChB 1979 Bristol; PhD Bath 1995; MA Oxf. 1978; MRCPsych. 1989; Cert. Family Plann. JCC 1985. Research Assoc. Centre for Family Research, Camb. Univ.; Med. Director, Achild Psychiat. project in Kosovo. Child advocacy InternnNat.. Socs: BMA; MDU. Prev: Sen. Regist. Rotat. (Child Psychiat.) Camb.; Regist. Rotat. (Psychiat.) Oxf.; SHO Rotat. (Psychiat.) Warneford Hosp. Oxf.

JONES, Mair Pantyfedwen, 40A Fairwood Road, Dunvant, Swansea SA2 7UL Tel: 01792 204142 — MB BCh 1963 Wales; MFOM RCP Lond. 1979; DIH Soc. Apoth. Lond. 1975. Cons. Occupat.al Health Phys., Visteon, Swanses; Med. Adviser, Hyder plc. Brit. Healthcare Ltd., Wales Gas.. Prev: Employm. Med. Adviser EMAS.

JONES, Mr Malcolm Anthony Sandwell General Hospital, Lyndon, West Bromwich B71 4HJ Fax: 0121 607 3545; 26 Osmaston Road, Norton, Stourbridge DY8 2AL Tel: 01384 370927 Email: majonesosmaston@hotmail.com — MB BS 1970 Lond.; LRCP 1970 Lond.; FRCS 1975 Eng.; MS 1981 Lond.; MRCS 1970 Eng.; MB BS Lond. 1970; MS Lond. 1981; FRCS Eng. 1975; MRCS Eng. LRCP Lond. 1970. (Westm.) Cons. Urol. Sandwell Gen. Hosp. W. Bromwich; Hon. Clin. Lect. Univ. Birm.; Hon. Cons. Urol. City Hosp. NHS Trust Birm. Socs: Brit. Assn. Urol. Surgs. & BMA. Prev: Lect. (Urol.) & Hon Sen. Regist. Char. Cross Hosp. Lond.; Lect. (Urol.) Inst. Cancer Research Lond.; Hon. Sen. Regist. Roy. Marsden Hosp. Lond.

JONES, Malcolm Edward Kew Cottage, Dorrington, Lincoln LN4 3PX Tel: 01526 832204 — MB ChB 1961 St. And.; DObst RCOG 1963. Prev: Ho. Surg. Stratford-upon-Avon Hosp.; Ho. Phys. Ipswich & E. Suff. Hosp.; Ho. Off. O & G PeterBoro. Memor. Hosp.

JONES, Malcolm Howard Cross Keys Practice, High Street, Princes Risborough HP27 0AX Tel: 01844 344488 Fax: 01844 274714; Chestnut Farm, Chestnut Way, Longwick, Princes Risborough HP27 9SD Tel: 01844 343942 — MB ChB 1973 Manch.; BSc (1st cl. Hons.) (Anat.) Manch. 1973; DRCOG 1978; MRCGP 1980. (Manch.) Med. Off. BOC Thame & Molins Ltd Saunderton. Prev: SHO (Obst. & Paediat.) Bolton Gen. Hosp.; Ho. Surg. Manch. Roy. Infirm.

JONES, Mr Malcolm Hugh 39 Broad Meadows, Newcastle upon Tyne NE3 4PZ Tel: 0191 284 1877 — MB BS 1991 Newc.; BMedSc (Hons.) Newc. 1990; FRCS Eng. 1996; FRCS Glas. 1996. (Univ. Newc. u. Tyne) Specialist Regist. Rotat. (A & E) N. Region. Prev: SHO (A & E) Newc. Gen. Hosp.; SHO (Gen. Surg.) Sunderlands Dist. Gen. Hosp.; Demonst. (Anat.) Univ. Newc.

JONES, Malcolm Nigel Roger 63 Newry Road, Armagh BT60 1ES — BChir 1996 Camb.

JONES, Malcolm Rosser Bonnar and Partners, Sunnyside Surgery, Hawkins Road, Penzance TR18 4LT Tel: 01736 63340 Fax: 01736 332116 — MB ChB 1982 Bristol.

JONES, Margaret (retired) Blue Bridge, Saundersfoot SA69 9AH — MB BCh 1957 Wales; DObst RCOG 1958. Prev: SCMO (Family Plann.) Pembrokesh. HA.

JONES, Margaret Berwyn Wyndomen, Cfaig-Cefn-Parc, Swansea SA6 5RS Tel: 01792 3504 — MB BS 1953 Lond.; DA Eng. 1961. (St. Bart.) Med. Asst. (Anaesth.) Singleton Hosp. Swansea; Med. Off. Nat. Blood Transfus. Serv. Prev: Ho. Surg. Morriston Hosp.; Ho. Phys. City Gen. Hosp. Gloucester.

JONES, Margaret Carol Penkridge Medical Practice, St. Michael's Road, Penkridge, Stafford ST19 5AJ Tel: 01785 712300 Fax: 01785 713696; The Farm House, 171 Chaseley Road, Rugeley WS15 2LQ Tel: 01889 582044 — MB ChB 1974 Manch.; MB ChB (Hons.) Manch. 1974; BSc (Hons. Physiol.) Manch. 1971; MRCP (UK) 1976; Dip. Hlth. Mgt. Keele 1996. (Univ. Manch.)

JONES, Margaret Ceredwen Patrick and Partners, Rise Park Surgery, Revelstoke Way, Nottingham NG5 5EB Tel: 0115 927 2525 Fax: 0115 979 7056; 27 Pateley Road, Woodthorpe, Nottingham NG3 5QF Tel: 0115 926 0280 Email: margaret_c_jones@compuserve.com — MB BS 1979 Lond.; MRCGP 1983; DRCOG 1981. (London Hospital Medical College) GP; Clin. Asst. (c/o the Elderly) Highbury Hosp. Nottm.; GP Tutor; Assessor GMC. Socs: BMA; Roy. Coll. Gen. Pract. (Sub. Fac.).

JONES, Margaret Elizabeth Plascoch, Dolanog, Welshpool SY21 0LA — MB BCh 1980 Wales; MRCGP 1985; DRCOG 1983; Cert. Family Plann. JCC 1983. GP Newtown.

JONES, Margaret Hedydd Ridgeway, Green Hill Close, Carmarthen SA31 1DR — MB BS 1979 Lond.

JONES, Margaret Iris Catherine Sunnycroft, Whitburn Road E., Cleadon, Sunderland SR6 7UP Tel: 0191 536 7650 — MB BS 1956 Durh.; DA Eng. 1973. Assoc. Specialist (Anaesth.) Sunderland Dist. Gen. Hosp. Prev: SHO (O & G), Ho. Surg. & Ho. Phys. Roy. Vict. Infirm. Newc.

JONES, Margaret Monica Coughlan 229 Mereside Way, Olton, Solihull B92 7AY — MB BCh BAO 1942 NUI.

JONES, Margaret Rosaleen Boileau Road Surgery, 104 Boileau Road, London W5 3AJ Tel: 020 8997 6604; 23 Kings Avenue, Eailing, London W5 2SJ Tel: 020 8997 1418 — MB BS 1966 Lond.; MRCS Eng. LRCP Lond. 1966; MRCOG 1971, DObst 1968. (Middlx.)

JONES, Margaret Rose 7 Windsor Avenue, Radyr, Cardiff CF15 8BW — MB BCh 1964 Wales; FRCR 1975; FFR 1971; DMRD Eng. 1968. (Cardiff) Cons. Radiol. Univ. Hosp. Wales Cardiff. Socs: Brit. Inst. Radiol. & Brit. Med. Ultrasound Soc. Prev: Lect. Radiol. Univ. Hosp. Wales Cardiff; Sen. Regist. (Radiol.) United Cardiff Hosps.; SHO (Med.) Llandough Hosp.

JONES, Margaret Seymour 7 Henleaze Park Drive, Henleaze, Bristol BS9 4LH — MB ChB 1967 Bristol.

JONES, Mari Owen Pentre Cwm, Cwm, Dyserth, Rhyl LL18 5SD — MB BCh 1995 Wales.

JONES, Mari Rhiannon Abbey Fields, 12 Bewley Lane, Lacock, Chippenham SN15 2PG — MB BS 1991 Lond.

JONES, Marian Morris Villa Medical Centre, Roman Road, Prenton CH43 3DB Tel: 0151 608 4702 Fax: 0151 609 0067 — MB ChB 1973 Liverp.; DCH Eng. 1977; DObst RCOG 1975.

JONES, Marie Nanteos, Tynybedw Terr, Treorchy, Cardiff CF42 6RL Tel: 01443 773785 — MB BCh 1968 Wales. (Cardiff)

***JONES, Marie Christine** Homelands, Lugg Bridge Road, Hereford HR1 3ND — MB ChB 1998 Birm.

JONES, Marilyn Valda (retired) 1A Common Road, York YO19 5NG Tel: 01904 488433 — MB BS 1964 Sydney. Forens. Med. Examr. Humberside Police. Prev: Indust. Med. Off. BP Ltd. Aden & BBC Lond.

JONES, Mark Royal Victoria Hospital, Belfast BT12 6BA Tel: 01232 240503; 23 Greenacres, Carnmoney, Newtownabbey BT36 6NL Tel: 01232 842060 — MB BCh BAO 1990 Belf.; MRCP (UK) 1993. SHO (Rehabil. Med.) Roy. Vict. Hosp. Belf. Socs: Roy. Coll. Phys. Edin.

JONES, Mark Bryan The Maudsley Hospital, Denmark Hill, London SE5 8AZ Tel: 020 7703 6333; 8 Bunning Way, Frederica St, London N7 9UN — MB BS 1987 Lond.; MRCPsych 1984. Regist. Rotat. (Psychiat.) Maudsley Hosp. Lond. Prev: Regist. Rotat. (Psychiat.) St. Bart. Hosp. & Affil. Teach. Hosps. Lond.; Ho. Surg. St And. Newham Gen. Hosp. Lond.; Ho. Phys. Lond. Hosp. (Mile End) Lond.

JONES, Mark Ian 50 Tyelands, Billericay CM12 9PB — MB BS 1996 Lond.

JONES, Mark Lawrence 143 Bradley Street, Crookes, Sheffield S10 1PA — MB ChB 1998 Sheff.; MB ChB Sheff 1998.

JONES, Mr Mark Trevor Lynngarth, 6 Howard Drive, Hale, Altrincham WA15 0LT Email: mark.jones@gw.smuht.nwest.nhs.uk — MB ChB 1977 Manch.; FRCS Eng. 1981. Cons. (Cardiothoracic Surg.) Wythenshawe Hosp. Manch.; Sen. Regist. (Cardiothoracic Surg.) Wythenshawe Hosp. Manch. Socs: Fell. Manch. Med. Soc.; Soc. Cardiothoracic Surgs. Gt. Brit. & Irel. Prev: Research Fell. (Thoracic Surg.) Toronto Gen. Hosp. Canada; Research Fell. (Cardiac Surg.) Univ. Hosp. Lond. Ontario, Canada; Regist. (Gen. Surg.) Univ. Hosp. S. Manch.

JONES, Martin Anthony Princess Royal Hospital, Haywards Heath RH16 4EX Tel: 01444 441881; Tel: 01444 416052 — MB ChB 1986 Bristol; BSc Bristol 1983; MD Bristol 1997; MRCP (UK) 1990. Cons. Phys. P.ss Roy. Hosp. Prev: Sen. Regist. Rotat. (Med. & c/o Elderly) Oxf.; Trafford Research Fell. (Renal Med.) Roy. Sussex Co. Hosp. Brighton; Regist. (Renal Med.) St. Mary's Hosp. Lond.

JONES, Martin Arthur Church Lane Surgery, Boroughbridge, York YO51 9BD; Aldborough Court, Front Street, Aldborough, Boroughbridge, York YO51 9ES — MB BS 1987 Lond.; BSc Lond. 1984, MB BS 1987; MRCGP 1998; DRCOG 1992.

JONES, Mr Martin Barry Watercress Cottage, Oulton Mill Lane, Cotebrook, Tarporley CW6 9DT Tel: 01829 760564 — MB ChB 1967 Liverp.; FRCS Ed. 1973.

JONES, Martin Christopher Hesketh 30 Norfolk Road, Tunbridge Wells TN1 1TD Tel: 018492 519858 — MB ChB 1994 Bristol; DCH 1997; MRCGP 1998. GP.

JONES, Martin David Ivy Grove Surgery, 1 Ivy Grove, Ripley DE5 3HN Tel: 01773 742286 Fax: 01773 749812; Meadow Rise, Smalley Mill Road, Horsley, Derby DE21 5BL Tel: 01332 882929 — MB ChB 1973 Liverp.

JONES, Mr Martin Edward 34 Southfield Gardens, Strawberry Hill, Twickenham TW1 4SZ Tel: 020 8891 40 60 — MB BS 1993 Lond.; BSc Hons (Anatomy& Neuroscience) 1990; FRCS 1998.

JONES, Martin Glynne Bewick Crescent Surgery, 27 Bewick Crescent, Newton Aycliffe DL5 5LH Tel: 01325 313289 Fax: 01325 301428; 16 East Green, Heighington, Newton Aycliffe DL5 6PP — MB BS 1984 Newc.; MRCGP 1988; DRCOG 1987.

JONES, Martin Keston 19 Rhyd y Defaid Drive, Sketty, Swansea SA2 8AH Tel: 01792 208855 — MD 1982 Wales; MB BCh 1972; MRCP (UK) 1975. (Univ. Wales Coll. Med.) Cons. Phys. Singleton Hosp. Swansea. Socs: Med. Res. Soc.; Endocrine Soc. Roy. Soc. Med. Prev: Research Fell. (Med.) King's Coll. Hosp. Med. Sch. Lond.; Regist. (Med.) Middlx. Hosp. Lond.; Sen. Regist. (Med.) Univ. Hosp. Wales, Cardiff.

JONES, Martin Leslie Grange Road Surgery, Bishopsworth, Bristol BS13 8LD; Viaduct House, Culvry Lane, Pensford, Bristol BS39 4AG — MB BS 1985 Lond. GP Bristol. Prev: Trainee GP Whittington Hosp. VTS Lond.

JONES, Martin Michael Swanswell Medical Centre, 370 Gospel Lane, Acocks Green, Birmingham B27 7AL; 319 Warwick Road, Solihull B92 7AA Tel: 0121 682 4506 — BM 1978 Soton.; DRCOG 1983.

JONES, Martin Stewart 45 Broadway W., Gosforth, Newcastle upon Tyne NE3 2HY — MB ChB 1988 Ed.; FRCA 1996; MRCGP 1992; DRCOG 1992; DA (UK) 1994. Specialist Regist. (Anaesth.) N. Sch. of Anaesth. Prev: SHO (Anaesth.) Freeman Hosp. Newc. & Cumbld. Infirm. Carlisle.

JONES, Martyn Gregory 83 Station Road, Ackworth, Pontefract WF7 7HG — MB BCh 1981 Wales.

JONES, Martyn Ray 11 Cow Lane, Edlesborough, Dunstable LU6 2HT; Westleigh House, 42 High St, Edlesborough, Dunstable LU6 2HS — MB BS 1973 Lond.; MB BS (Hons. Obst. & Gyn.) Lond. 1973; DRCOG 1982. (Lond. Hosp.) GP EdlesBoro..

JONES, Mary Allan Craig 9 Gladstone Road, Sheffield S10 3GT Tel: 0114 230 1747 — MB ChB 1948 Birm.; FRCS Eng. 1959. Cons. Ophth. Roy. Hallamsh. Hosp. Sheff.

JONES, Mary Elizabeth Kings Head Cottage, Hungate, Brompton-by-Sawdon, Scarborough YO13 9DW Tel: 01723 859437 Fax: 01723 859437 — MB BS 1972 Lond.; MRCS Eng. LRCP Lond. 1972; DCCH RCP Ed. RCGP & FCM 1984; DObst RCOG 1975; MMedSci Leeds 1997. SCMO ScarBoro. Healthcare Trust; Mem. Roy. Coll. Paediat. & Child Health. Socs: Brit. Assn. Community Child Health; Brit. Assn. Community Drs in Audiol.

JONES, Mary Esyllt Beynon (retired) 19 Castle Street, Loughor, Swansea SA4 6TU Tel: 01792 898211 — MB BCh 1968 Wales.

JONES, Mary Helen 3 Ridgeway, Wilmslow SK9 2BP — MB ChB 1979 Manch.; FFA RCS Eng. 1985; DA Eng. 1981. Clin. Asst. (Anaesth.) Withenshawe Hosp. Manch. Prev: Regist. (Anaesth.) N. Manch. Gen. Hosp.

JONES, Mary Mason Far Causeway House, Long Causeway, Leeds LS16 8DU Tel: 0113 267 8556 — MB BS Lond. 1953; DPM (Distinc.) Leeds 1958. (Lond. Hosp.) Chairm. Leeds Gp. Nat. Osteoporosis Soc. Prev: Clin. Asst. Menopause & PMS Clinic Dept. Gyn. Clarendon Wing Leeds Gen. Infirm.; Clin. Asst. MRC Mineral Metab. Unit Leeds Gen. Infirm.; Psychiat. Nat. Childr. Home Bramhope & Harrogate Brs.

JONES, Matthew Edward Paul The Spinney, Chapel Hill, Eythorne, Dover CT15 4AY — MB BS 1993 Lond.

JONES, Mr Matthew Oliver 66 BRoadfields Avenue, Winchmore Hill, London N21 1AH; 20 Gressingham Road, Allerton, Liverpool L18 6JT — MD 1994 Liverp.; MB BS Lond. 1985; FRCS Eng. 1989. Sen. Regist. (Paediat. Surg.) Hosp. Childr. Gt. Ormond St. Lond. Prev: Sen. Regist. (Paediat. Surg.) Gt. Ormond St. Hosp. for Childr. Lond.; Regist. (Paediat. Surg.) Liverp.; Regist. (Gen. Surg.) Norwich HA.

JONES, Maureen Margaret (retired) Horeb, 26 College Close, Rowlands Castle PO9 6AJ Tel: 01705 412070 — MB BS Lond. 1960. Prev: GP Abbots Langley.

JONES, Maurice John Dept of Anaesthesia, Royal preston Hospital, Sharoe Green Lane North, Fulwood, Preston PR2 9HT Tel: 01772 710555 — MB ChB 1986 Manch.; MRCP (UK) 1991; FRCA 1992; DA (UK) 1990. Cons. Anaesth. Preston Acute Hosps. NHS Trust. Socs: BMA & Assn. Anaesth. Prev: Sen. Regist. & Regist. (Anaesth.) NW Region.

***JONES, Megan Eleri** 27 Dalderby Crescent, Nettleham, Lincoln LN2 2QB — MB ChB 1996 Birm.

JONES, Meirion Wyn 7 Stad Eryri, Bethel, Caernarfon LL55 1BX — MB BS 1990 Lond.

JONES, Melanie Jane Tinnion Department Anaesthetics, Princess of Wales Hospital, Coity Road, Bridgend CF31 1RQ Tel: 01656 752752 — MB BCh 1978 Wales; FFA RCS Eng. 1984. Cons. Anaesth. P.ss of Wales Hosp. Prev: Sen. Regist. (Anaesth.) S. Glam. & Gwent HA.

JONES, Mr Melfyn Wyn Ysbyty Gwnedd, Penrhosgarnedd, Bangor LL57 2PW; Parc House, Druid Road, Menai Bridge, Anglesey LL59 5BY Tel: 01248 716991 Fax: 01248 715144 Email: meljones@btinternet.com — MB ChB 1982 Liverp.; MChOrth Liverp. 1991; FRCS (Orth.) 1992; FRCS Eng. 1986; FRCS Ed. 1986; MRCS Eng. LRCP Lond. 1982; LLM Cardiff 1999. Cons. Orthop. Surg. Ysbyty Gwynedd Bangor. Socs: Fell. BOA; Liverp. Med. Inst.; Fell.of the Roy. Soc. of Med. Prev: Lect. & Hon. Sen. Regist. (Orthop. Surg.) Univ. Leic.; Regist. (Orthop.) Mersey RHA; Regist. Rotat. (Surg.) Singleton & Morriston Hosp. Swansea.

JONES, Melvyn Mark Department of Primary Care & Population Sciences, Royal Free Hospital School of Medicine, London NW3 2PF Fax: 020 7794 1224 Email: m.jones@pcps.ucl.ac.uk — MB BS 1987 Lond.; MRCGP 1992; T(GP) 1993; DRCOG 1992; MSc 1997; DFFP 1998. (Royal Free) Lect. (Gen. Pract.) Roy. Free Hosp. Sch. Med. & UCLMS. Socs: Roy. Soc. Med. (Bd. Mem. Sect. Gen. Pract.). Prev: Lect. St. Bart. Med. Sch.; Trainee GP Summertown Health Centre Oxf.; Trainee GP Barnet Gen. Hosp. VTS.

JONES, Mercia Madonna (retired) 53 St Michael's Road, Llandaff, Cardiff CF5 2AN Tel: 02920 564234 — MB BCh Wales 1957. Prev: Ho. Surg. Cardiff Roy. Infirm.

JONES, Michael Chave Renal Unit, Ninewells Hospital & Medical School, Ninewlls, Dundee DD1 9SY Tel: 01382 660111 Fax: 01382 632327; Stewart Hall, Main St, Longforgan, Dundee DD2 5EU — MB ChB 1981 Dundee; BSc (Hons.) Sheff. 1977; MD (Hons.) Aberd. 1990; FRCP Glas. 1995; FRCP Ed. 1994; MRCP (UK) 1984. Cons. Phys. (Nephrol.) Ninewells Hosp. Dundee Teach. Hosps. NHS Trust; Hon. Sen. Lect. Univ. Dundee. Prev: Lect. (Med.) Aberd. Univ.; Regist. Gtr. Glas. HB.

JONES, Michael Edward 13 Heron Avenue, Sandy Water Park, Llanelli SA15 4SL — MRCS Eng. LRCP Lond. 1975.

JONES, Michael Emlyn Ephinstone International Health Centre, Elphinstone Wing, Carberry, Musselburgh EH21 8PW Tel: 0131 653 6767 Fax: 0131 653 3646 Email: mejones@eihc.org; 255 Carnathie Street, Rosewell EH24 9DR Tel: 0131 440 2602 Email: micheal&jones@doctors.org.uk — MB ChB 1972 Aberd.; FRCP Ed. 1995; MRCP (UK) 1975. (Aberdeen) p/t Dir. Phys. Elphinstone Internat. Health Centre; Assoc. Specialist Regional Infec. Dis. Unit W..Gen.Hosp. Edin.; Edr. Trop. Doctor. Socs: Fell. Roy. Soc. Trop. Med. & Hyg.; Fell. Roy. Coll. Phys. Edin.; Roy. Coll. Phys. Lond. Prev: Specialist (Med.) Kilimanjaro Christian Med. Centre Moshi, Tanzania; Regist. & SHO (Gen. Med.) Foresterhill & Assoc. Hosps. Aberd.

JONES, Michael Howard Minster Health, 35 Monkgate, York YO31 7WE Tel: 01904 626234; 34 Main Street, Bishopthorpe, York YO23 2RB Tel: 01904 702958 Email: mike@minsterhealth.co.uk — MRCS Eng. LRCP Lond. 1978; BSc Lond. 1975, MB BS 1978; MRCGP 1983; DRCOG 1980.

JONES, Mr Michael Hugh Dept. of Obstetrics & Gynaecology, Darent Valley Hospital, Darenthwood Road, Dartford DA2 8DA Tel: 01322 428768 Fax: 01322 428448 Email: mike.jones@dag-tr.sthames.nhs.uk; Cabbage Cottage, 14 Blackheath Rise, Blackheath, London SE13 7PN Tel: 020 8852 4044 Fax: 01474 746106 Email: mhjones007@hotmail.com — MB BS 1980 Lond.; 1994 MD Lond. 1994; 1983 MRCS Eng. LRCP Lond.; 1987 MRCOG. (Char. Cross Hosp.) Cons. O & G Darent Valley Hosp. Dartford; Cons. O & G Fawkham Manor Hosp., Fawkham; Cons. O & G The Blackheath Hosp., Lond. Socs: Brit. Soc. Colpos. & Cerv. Path. Prev: Sir Jules Thorn Research Fell. (Colposcopy) Roy. N.. Hosp. Lond.; Sen. Regist. St. Geo. Hosp. Lond.; Ho. Off. (Med., Surg. & O & G) Char. Cross Hosp. Lond.

JONES, Michael John Chapel House, Church Lane, East Norton, Leicester LE7 9XA — MB ChB 1978 Manch.; BSc (Hons.) (Anat.) Manch. 1976, MB ChB 1978; MRCP (UK) 1982; FFA RCS Eng. 1986. Cons. Anaesth. & Intens. Care Glenfield Gen. Hosp. Socs: Intens. Care Soc. & Assn. Anaesth. Prev: Lect. (Anaesth.) Leic. Univ.; Regist. Anaesth. Edin.

JONES, Michael Maysmor 50 Church Street, Marple, Stockport SK6 6BW.

JONES, Michael Robert Creswell Martins Farm House, Langham, Colchester CO4 5PY — MB BS 1990 Lond.; MRCGP 1994; DRCOG 1992.

JONES, Michael Robin Ryan (retired) 4 Buckeridge Road, Teignmouth TQ14 8NU Tel: 01626 775806 — MRCS Eng. LRCP Lond. 1968; DPM Eng. 1975. Clin. Asst. (Learning Disabilities & Ment. Health) S. Devon Healthcare Trust. Prev: Sen. Regist. (Ment. Handicap.) Lea Castle Hosp. Kidderminster, Chelmsley Hosp. Marston Green & Monyhull Hosp. Kings Norton.

JONES, Michael Victor 1 Court Barn Close, Lee-on-the-Solent PO13 9PD — MB ChB 1983 Leic.

JONES, Michael William Kew Cottage, Dorrington, Lincoln LN4 3PX — MB ChB 1992 Manch.

JONES, Modest Clarence (retired) 307 Bromford Road, Birmingham B36 8EU Tel: 0121 783 2012 — MB BS 1953 Bombay; BSc (Hons.) Bombay 1946, MB BS 1953; DObst RCOG 1961. Prev: Res. Surg. Off. W.mld. Co. Hosp. Kendal.

JONES, Morgan Brian Stuart (retired) 10 Tivoli Road, Cheltenham GL50 2TG — MB 1963 Camb.; BA Camb. 1959, MB 1963, BChir 1962; FRCP Lond. 1981, M 1967. Cons. Phys. Gloucester Roy. Hosp. Mem. Brit. Cardiac Soc. Prev: Sen. Med. Regist. & Wellcome Research Fell. St. Mary's Hosp. Lond.

JONES, Muriel Louise (retired) 17 Bell Court, The Maltings, Lillington Avenue, Leamington Spa CV32 5FH — MB BS 1954 Lond.; PhD Lond. 1965; FRCPsych 1978, M 1972; DPM Eng. 1968. Mem. Ment. Health Review Tribunal. Prev: Cons. Psychiat. Walsgrave Hosp. Coventry, Hosp. St. Cross Rugby & Centr. Hosp. Warwick.

JONES, Natalia Victorovna Flat 6/45 James Square, Caledonian Crescent, Edinburgh EH11 2AQ — LMSSA 1997 Lond.; LRCP (Lond) 1997; LRCS (Eng) 1997. SHO Psychiat. Stirling Roy. Infirm. Prev: SHO Med. King's Cross Hosp. Dundee; Jun. Ho. Off. Surg. Perth Roy. Infirm.

JONES, Natasha Sophie Claire 44 Church Street, Hampton Lucy, Warwick CV35 8BE — MB BS 1992 Lond.

JONES, Neil David 23 Ffordd Walwen, Lixwm, Holywell CH8 8LW — MB BS 1989 Lond.

JONES, Neil David North Berwick Health Centre, 54 St. Baldreds Road, North Berwick EH39 4PU Tel: 01620 892169 Fax: 01620 897005; Lynrock, Dirleton, North Berwick EH39 5EA Tel: 01620 85698 — MB ChB 1986 Aberd.; MRCGP 1991; DCH RCPS Glas. 1990.

JONES, Mr Neil Ford Hill View, Dean Lane, Hazel Grove, Stockport SK7 6DJ — BM BCh 1975 Oxf.; MA Oxf. 1975; FRCS Eng. 1980. (Oxf.) Prof. Plastic & Reconstruc. Surg. & Orthop. Surg. & Dir. Hand Surg. Microsurg. UCLA Sch. of Med. Los Angeles, USA. Prev: Assoc. Prof. Plastic & Reconstruct. Surg./Dir. Hand Surg. & Microsurg. Univ. Pittsburgh, USA; Fell. (Hand Surg. & Microsurg.) Harvard Med. Sch. & Mass. Gen. Hosp. Boston, USA; Regist. (Plastic Surg.) Lond. Hosp. & NE Thames Regional Centre St. And. Hosp. Billericay.

JONES, Neill Kenneth South Tyneside Area Health Authority, The Health Centre, Marsden Road, South Shields NE34 6RE Tel: 0191 454 0457 Fax: 0191 427 1793 — MB BS 1981 Newcastle; MB BS Newc. 1981. (Newcastle) GP S. Shields, Tyne & Wear.

***JONES, Nicholas Adrian** Pitchfork Cottage, Lasham, Alton GU34 5SG Tel: 01256 381785 — MB BS 1994 Lond.; BDS Lond. 1986.

JONES, Nicholas Cadwaladr Rutter St Chads Surgery, Gullock Tyning, Midsomer Norton, Bath BA3 2UH Tel: 01761 413334 Fax: 01761 411176; 29 Bloomfield Park, Bath BA2 2BX Tel: 01225 484694 — MB BS 1990 Lond.; DCH RCP Lond. 1993; MRCGP 1995; DRCOG 1995; Dip Occ Health 1999.

JONES, Nicholas Cann Anaesthetic Department, Bromley Hospital, Cromwell Avenue, Bromley BR2 9AJ Tel: 020 8289 7120; 22 Pinewood Road, Bromley BR2 9AD — MB BS 1984 Lond.; FRCA 1993; MRCGP 1990; DCH RCP Lond. 1990; DRCOG 1987. (King's Coll. Hosp.) Cons. Anaesth. Bromley Hosp. NHS Trust. Prev: Sen Regist. (Anaesth.) St. Geo. & St. Heliers NHS Trust; Regist. (Anaesth.) Brook Gen. Hosp. Lond.; SHO (Paediat.) St. Richard's Hosp. Chichester.

JONES, Nicholas David Humphreys 16 Rodborough Avenue, Stroud GL5 3RS — MB BS 1973 Lond. (St. Mary's) GP StoneHo.. Prev: Asst. Med. Off. Old Perlican, Newfld., Canada; SHO (Cas.) & Ho. Phys. Edgware Gen. Hosp.

JONES, Nicholas Joseph Philip Ellwood 37 Piercefield Avenue, Chepstow NP16 5JB — MB BCh 1992 Wales.

JONES, Nicholas King (Surgery), 37 Galbalfa Avenue, Cardiff CF4 2SG Tel: 029 2052 2811 Fax: 029 2052 0201; 172 Lake Road E., Roath Park, Cardiff CF23 5NR Tel: 029 2075 6390 — MB BS 1970 Lond.; MRCS Eng. LRCP Lond. 1970; Dip. Palliat. Med. Wales 1992; DObst RCOG 1973; DA Eng. 1972. (Lond. Hosp.) Prev: SHO (Anaesth.) Bath. Hosp. Gp.; Resid. Off. (Rotat.) Lond. Hosp.; Ho. Phys. St. Martin's Hosp. Bath.

JONES, Nicholas Michael The Broadshires Health Centre, Broadshires Way, Carterton OX18 1JA Tel: 01993 844567 Fax: 01993 841551 Email: nmjones@doctors.org.uk; The Mill House, Alvescot, Bampton OX18 2RX Tel: 01993 841196 — MB BS 1988 Lond.; BDS (Hons.) 1983; LDS RCS Eng. 1984; MRCGP 1991; Section 12 Approved under NHS 1983. (University College London) GP Carterton; Police Surg. Thames Valley Police. Socs: BMA; RCGP. Prev: Trainee GP Burford.; SHO (Paediat. & Psychiat.) P.ss Margt. Hosp. Swindon; SHO (O & G) St. Peters Hosp. Chertsey.

JONES, Mr Nicholas Philip Manchester Royal Eye Hospital, Oxford Road, Manchester M13 9WH Tel: 0161 276 5582; 3 Ridgeway, Wilmslow SK9 2BP — MB ChB 1981 Manch.; BSc St. And. 1978; FRCS Ed. 1986; FRCOphth 1989; DO RCS Eng. 1984. Cons. Surg. Manch. Roy. Eye Hosp. Socs: Fell. Roy. Soc. Med. Prev: Sen. Lect. (Ophth.) Univ. Manch.; Sen. Regist. & Regist. (Ophth.) Manch. Roy. Eye Hosp.; SHO (Ophth.) Soton. Eye Hosp.

JONES, Professor Nicholas Spencer Queens Medical Centre, University of Nottingham, Nottingham NG7 2UH Tel: 0115 924 9924 Email: nick.jones@nottingham.ac.uk — MB BS 1982 Lond.; BDS 1975; FRCS (Orl.) Eng. 1987; FRCS Eng. 1986; FRCS Ed. 1986; T (S) 1991; MD Lond. 1997. (Guy's Hospital) Cons. Rhinologist Univ. of Nott.; Prof. Univ. of Nottm. Socs: Eur. Acad. Facial Surg. Prev: Fell.ship Univ. of Washington.

JONES, Nicola Brocklebank Health Centre, 249 Garratt Lane, London SW18 4UE Tel: 020 8870 1341/871 4448 — MB ChB 1990 Sheff.; MBA 1999; MRCGP 1995. Prev: Trainee GP/SHO Chesterfield Roy. Infirm. VTS.

JONES, Nicola 37 Hawkswell Gardens, Oxford OX2 7EX — MB BS 1991 Lond.; MRCP (UK) 1994.

JONES, Nicola Claire 1 Springfield Lodge, Lasswade EH18 1DX — MB ChB 1994 Aberd.

JONES, Nigel 9 Waters Lane, Westbury on Trym, Bristol BS9 4AA — MB ChB 1984 Bristol; MRCP (UK) 1990. Sen. Regist. (Gen. Med. & c/o Elderly) Derriford Hosp. Plymouth. Prev: Regist. (Med.) MusGr. Pk. Hosp. Taunton; SHO (Med.) Gloucester Roy. Hosp. & S.mead Hosp.

JONES, Mr Nigel Andrew Gordon 15 Graham Park Road, Gosforth, Newcastle upon Tyne NE3 4BH Tel: 0191 284 8105 — MRCS Eng. LRCP Lond. 1971; MS Lond. 1981, MB BS 1971; FRCS Eng. 1976. (Guys Hospital Medical School) Cons. Gen. & Vasc. Surg. Freeman Hosp. Socs: Christ. Med. Fell.sh.; Fell. of Assoc. of Surgs. of GB & Irel.; Vasc. Surg. Soc. GB & Irel. Prev: Sen. Regist. (Surg.) Leeds & Bradford HAs; MRC Research Fell. Thrombosis Research Unit King's Coll. Hosp. Lond.; Regist. Rotat. (Surg.) St. Thos. Hosp. Lond.

JONES, Nigel Edward Brian The Orrell Park Surgery, 46 Moss Lane, Orrell Park, Liverpool L9 8AL Tel: 0151 525 2736 Fax: 0151 524 1037 — MB ChB 1990 Liverp.; Dip Sports Med 2000 Bath. Federal; Pract. Princip., Liverp.; Assoc. Specialist Orthop. Univ. Hosp. Aintree; Sports Injury Phys., Renacres Hall Hosp. Ormskirk.

JONES, Nigel Huw The Arwystili Medical Practice, Mount Lane, Llanidloes SY18 6EZ Tel: 01686 412228 / 412322 Fax: 01686 413536; The Friary, Penygreen Road, Llanidloes SY18 Tel: 01686 412281 — MB BS 1979 Lond.; BSc Lond. 1976; MRCGP 1983; DRCOG 1982. (Guy's) Prev: Trainee GP Gt. Yarmouth VTS; Ho. Phys. & Ho. Surg. Guy's Hosp. Lond.

JONES, Nitu 51 Holdenhurst Avenue, London N12 0JA — BM 1994 Soton.

JONES, Nkoyo Anthony Emmanuel 199 Coldharbour Lane, London SE5 9PA — MB BS 1994 Lond.

JONES, Noel Owen Groves Head Cottage, Worcester WR6 5AQ Tel: 01885 490243 — MB BS 1961 London; FRCA 1968; MB BS 1961 London. (St Bartholomew's)

JONES, Non Lloyd 57 The Barns, Bostock Hall, Bostock Road, Bostock, Middlewich CW10 9JN — MB BChir 1987 Camb.; MRCP (UK) 1993.

JONES, Norman Fielding The Old Coach House, Forest Park Road, Brockenhurst SO42 7SW — MB BChir 1956 Camb.; MA Camb. 1957, MD 1966; FRCP Lond. 1970, M 1958. (St. Thos.) Emerit. Cons. Phys. St. Thos. Hosp. Lond. Socs: Med. Res. Soc. & Assn. Phys. Prev: Treas. & Sen. Censor Roy. Coll. Phys.; MRC (Rockefeller) Trav. Fell. 1963-4; Sen. Regist. (Med.) St. Thos. Hosp. Lond.

JONES, Norman Joseph The Loxwood Surgery, Farm Close, Loxwood, Billingshurst RH14 0SU Tel: 01403 752246 Fax: 01403 752916 — MRCS Eng. LRCP Lond. 1969; DObst RCOG 1972.

JONES, Olive Christine (retired) 5 Lon Draenen, Sketty, Swansea SA2 9EW Tel: 01792 204367 — MB BCh 1951 Wales; BSc Wales 1948; DA Eng. 1958. Prev: Assoc. Specialist Anaesth. Bridgend Gen. Hosp.

JONES, Olive Marjorie Gordon (retired) 8 Benson Place, Norham Road, Oxford OX2 6QH Tel: 01865 55336 — MRCS Eng., LRCP. Lond. 1928; FFA RCS Eng. 1953; DA Eng. 1946. Prev: Cons. Anaesth. United Oxf. Hosps. Anaesth. Neurosurgic. Dept. Lond.

JONES, Oliver Gordon (retired) Aldborough Court, Front Street, Aldborough, Boroughbridge YO51 9ES Tel: 01423 324710 — MD 1947 Leeds; MB ChB 1945; FRCP Ed. 1969, M 1952. Prev: Cons. Chest Phys. Hull Roy. Infirm.

JONES, Oriel Bronwen Christina 67 Manor Way, London SE3 9XG — MB BS 1998 Lond.; MB BS Lond 1998.

JONES, Osmond Wynstan 97 Harley Street, London W1G 6AG Tel: 0207 935 3298 Fax: 0207 9535 3495; Cedar House, Vicarage Lane, Send, Woking GU23 7JN Tel: 01483 223019 — MRCS Eng. LRCP Lond. 1968; DObst RCOG 1970; DFFP 1998. (Roy. Free) GP Lond. (Private). Socs: BMA; Fell. Roy. Soc. Med.; Fell. Med. Soc. of Lond. Prev: Ho. Surg. Qu. Vict. Hosp. E. Grinstead; Surg. Lt. RN at RN Hosp. Haslar.; Ho. Surg. Obst. St Mary's Hosp. Ports.

JONES, Owen Bowden 4 Covert Close, Oadby, Leicester LE2 4HB — MB ChB 1992 Birm.

JONES, Owen Pearson Plas Tirion, Llanrug, Caernarfon LL55 4PY — MRCS Eng. LRCP Lond. 1958; DTM & H Eng. 1964. (Liverp.) Lt.-Col. RAMC RARO. Prev: Res. Obst. Off. Maelor Gen. Hosp. Wrexham; Cas. Off. Roy. Liverp. Childr. Hosp.; Lt.-Col. RAMC ADMS HQ Wales.

JONES, Owen Spencer 6 Lamb La, Crickhowell NP8 1AS — MB BS 1997 Lond.

JONES, Pamela (retired) The Surgery, High St., Llanberis, Caernarfon LL55 4SU Tel: 01286 870634 Fax: 01286 871722 — MB ChB 1962 Liverp. Prev: Ho. Surg. & Ho. Phys. BRd.green Hosp. Liverp.

JONES, Pamela Ann Primrose Unit, Level 7, Derriford Hospital, Plymouth PL6 8DH; 16 Whitehall Drive, Elburton, Plymouth PL9 8NN — MRCS Eng. LRCP Lond. 1966; MRCP (UK) 1971; FRCR 1975; DMRD Eng. 1972. (Roy. Free) Cons. Radiol. Plymouth Hosps. NHS Trust. Prev: Sen. Regist. (Radiol.) Birm. AHA (T).

JONES, Pamela Wayne (retired) The Old Manse, 46 Westgate, Cowbridge CF71 7AR Tel: 01446 773322 — MB BCh 1962 Wales; DPH Wales 1966; DObst RCOG 1964. Prev: SCMO (Genetics) M. Glam. AHA.

JONES, Patricia Bryson Street Surgery, 115 Newtownards Road, Belfast BT4 1AB Tel: 028 9045 8722 Fax: 028 9046 6766; 3 Notting Hill, Malone Road BT9 5NS — MB BCh BAO 1984 Belf.; DRCOG 1988.

JONES, Patricia Ann Downfield Surgery, 325 Strathmartine Road, Dundee DD3 Tel: 01382 812111 — MB ChB 1985 Ed.; MRCGP 1993. Prev: Trainee GP Forfar; Trainee GP/SHO Borders Gen. Hosp. VTS; Regist. (Histopath.) Ninewells Hosp & Med. Sch. Dundee.

JONES, Patricia Anne Beechwood Day Hospital, Evinpton Centre, Leicester General Hospital, Coleman Road, Leicester LE5 Tel: 0116 225 6141 — MB BS 1974 Newc.; MRCPsych 1980. Cons. Psychiat. (Old Age Psychiat.) Leics. & Rutland Health Servs. Trust. Prev: Sen. Regist. (Psychiat.) Leics. AHA (T); Regist. (Psychiat.) Leics. AHA (T).

JONES, Patricia Anne (retired) The Orchard, Horsecombe Vale, Combe Down, Bath BA2 5QR Tel: 01225 832643 — MB BS 1964

Lond.; MRCS Eng. LRCP Lond. 1964. Prev: Assoc. Specialist in Chest Dis. Roy. United Hosp. Bath & Bath Health Dist.

JONES, Patricia Heather Morris (retired) 10 St Mary's Grove, London N1 2NT Tel: 020 7226 0927 — MB BS Lond. 1957; FRCP Lond. 1978, M 1968; MRCS Eng. LRCP Lond. 1957; DCH Eng. 1960. Hon. Cons. Paediat. Oncol. Salford HA. Prev: Reader (Paediat. Oncol.) Univ. Manch. & Roy. Manch. Childr. Hosp.

JONES, Patricia Manel (retired) 24 Lakeview Court, Wimbledon Park Road, London SW19 6PP — MB BS Ceylon 1952; MRCP Lond. 1967; DCH Eng. 1955. Cons. Genitourin. Med. Greenwich Dist. & Guy's Hosps. Lond.

JONES, Paul Anthony 23 Fields Road, Newport NP20 4PJ — BM 1994 Soton.

JONES, Paul Nicholas Cottingham Road Surgery, 138 Cottingham Road, Hull HU6 7RY Tel: 01482 441333 Fax: 01482 493886; 10 Cedarwood Drive, Springhead Grange, Hull HU5 5YA — MB ChB 1987 Leeds.

JONES, Professor Paul Wyatt St. George's Hospital Medical School, Department of Medicine, Cranmer Terrace, London SW17 0RE Tel: 020 8725 5371 Fax: 020 8725 5955 Email: pjones@sghms.ac.uk — MB BS 1973 Lond.; PhD Lond. 1980, MB BS 1973; BSc Soton 1968; FRCP (UK) 1992; MRCP (UK) 1975. Prof. Respirat. Med. St. Geo. Hosp. Med. Sch. Lond. Socs: Physiol. Soc.; Brit. Thorac. Soc.; Eur. Respirat. Soc. Prev: MRC Trav. Fell. 1979-80; Lect. & Sen. Regist. Middlx. Hosp. Lond.; Wellcome Sen. Research Fell. (Clin. Sci.) Middlx. Hosp. Lond.

JONES, Paula 86 Ranby Road, Sheffield S11 7AL — MB ChB 1992 Sheff.

JONES, Pauline Anne Jackson and Partners, Glastonbury Surgery, Feversham Lane, Glastonbury BA6 9LP Tel: 01458 833666 Fax: 01458 834536; Sunnycroft, 43 Milton Lane, Wells BA5 2QS Tel: 01749 673232 — MB BS 1971 Lond.; MRCS Eng. LRCP Lond. 1971. (London Hospital Medical School) Med. Off. Millfield Sch. Som. Prev: Ho. Phys. Roy. S. Hants. Hosp. Soton.; Ho. Surg. FarnBoro. Hosp. Kent.

JONES, Percy Owen Steyn House, Mill Hey Road, Caldy, Wirral Tel: 0151 625967 — MRCS Eng. LRCP Lond. 1953; MSc Wales 1958, BSc (Hnrs. Chem.) 1944; MA, MB BChir Camb. 1953; FRCPath 1974, M 1962. (Camb. & Westm.) JP; CChem; Cons. Chem. Path. Roy. Liverp. Hosp., Sefton Gen. Hosp., Liverp.; Matern. Hosp., Wom. Hosp. & St. Paul's Eye Hosp. Liverp. Socs: FRSC; Assn. Clin. Biochems. & Liverp. Med. Inst. Prev: Asst. Chem. Pathol. St. Bart. Hosp.; Lect. Chem. Path. Univ. Lond. & Sen. Regist. Nat. Hosp. Nerv. Dis. Qu. Sq.; Med. Adviser Wellcome; Foundat. & Hon. Sen. Clin. Asst. Dept. Med. Univ. Coll. Hosp. Lond.

JONES, Peter Alan Winterbottom and Partners, The Health Centre, 97 Derby Road, Stapleford, Nottingham NG9 7AT Tel: 0115 939 2444 Fax: 0115 949 1751; 26 Wollaton Hall Drive, Wollaton Park, Nottingham NG8 1AF Tel: 0115 978 6981 — BM BCh 1970 Oxf.; DCH Eng. 1973.

JONES, Mr Peter Alan The Maidstone Hospital, Maidstone ME16 9 Tel: 01622 720702 Fax: 01622 723045; Old Timbers, Dairy Lane, Marden, Tonbridge TN12 9ST Tel: 01622 820840 Fax: 01622 820837 — MB BS 1972 Lond.; MS Lond. 1983; FRCS Eng. 1976; MRCS Eng. LRCP Lond. 1972. (Westm.) Cons. Gen. Surg. Maidstone Hosp. Socs: Brit. Assn. Surgic. Oncol. (Nat. Comm. Mem.); Pancreatic Soc.; Fell. Assn. Surgs. GB & N. Irel. Prev: Sen. Regist. (Surg.) W.m. Hosp. Lond.; Lect. (Surg.) St. Geo. Hosp. Med. Sch. Lond.; Regist. (Surg.) St. Jas. Hosp. Balham.

JONES, Peter Benjamin Turnley Pool Health Centre, Station Road, Pool, Redruth TR15 3DU Tel: 01209 717471 Fax: 01209 612160 — MB BS 1980 Lond.; MRCGP 1985; DRCOG 1984; DA Eng. 1982.

JONES, Professor Peter Brian Department of Psychiatry, University of Cambridge, Addenbrookes Hospital (Box 189), Hills Road, Cambridge CB2 2QQ Tel: 01223 336960 Fax: 01223 336968 Email: pbj21@cam.ac.uk — MB BS 1984 Lond.; MSc (Distinc.) Epidemiol. Lond. 1992, BSc 1981, PhD 1997; MRCP (UK) 1987; MRCPsych 1990. (Westm.) Prof. Psychiat. & Community Ment. Health Univ. Nottm.; Hon. Cons. Psychiat. Addenbrookes NHS Trust. Prev: Prof. Of Psychiat. & Community Ment. Health, Univ. of Nottm.; Sen. Lect. (Psychol. Med.) Inst. Psychiat. Lond.; Regist. & Hon. Sen. Regist. (Psychiat.) Bethlem Roy., Maudsley & King's Coll. Hosps.

JONES, Peter Brian Barrie 5 Lord Street, Glossop SK13 7DN — MB ChB 1985 Sheff.; PhD Sheff. 1982, BMedSci 1979; MRCP (UK) 1989. Sen. Regist. (Rheum.) NW Regional HA Manch. Roy. Infirm. Socs: Brit. Soc. Rheum. Prev: SHO & Regist. (Gen. Med.) Kings Coll. Hosp. Lond.; Regist. (Gen. Med., Diabetes & Endocrinol.) Hope Hosp. Salford; Tutor (Rheum.) Univ. Manch. & Univ. Hosp. S. Manch.

JONES, Peter David Fairfield Medical Centre, Julian Terrace, Port Talbot SA12 6UQ Tel: 01639 890916; Sandrose, Ton Kenfig, Pyle, Bridgend CF33 4PT Tel: 01656 740787 — MB BCh 1965 Wales. (Cardiff) Prev: Anaesth. SHO E. Glam. Hosp. Pontypridd; Ho. Phys. Llandough Hosp.; Ho. Surg. Accid. Unit. Cardiff Roy. Infirm.

JONES, Peter David The Surgeries, Lombard Street, Newark NG24 1XG Tel: 01636 702363 Fax: 01636 613037 — MB BS 1971 Lond.; MRCS Eng. LRCP Lond. 1971; FRCGP 1995, M 1977; DObst RCOG 1974. (North Nottinghamshire) Clin. Asst. (Oncol.) City Hosp. Nottm. Socs: BMA. Prev: SHO (Accid. & Orthop.) Poole Gen. Hosp.; SHO (Paediat.) Geo. Eliot Hosp. Nuneaton; SHO (Psychiat.) Basingstoke Dist. Hosp.

JONES, Peter Edmund 103 Allt-yr-yn Avenue, Newport NP20 5DE Tel: 01633 252757 — MB BCh 1959 Wales; DObst RCOG 1962. (Cardiff.)

JONES, Peter Edward St George's Medical Centre, 7 Sunningfields Road, London NW4 4QR — MB BS 1977 Lond.; BSc (Hons.) Lond. 1974, MB BS 1977; MRCGP 1981.

JONES, Peter Eugene Yorkshire Street Surgery, 190 Yorkshire Street, Rochdale OL16 2DN Tel: 01706 644973/5; 34 Woodcock Close, Bamford, Rochdale OL11 5QA — MB ChB 1984 Manch.; MRCGP 1988; DRCOG 1986. Prev: Trainee GP Birch Hill Hosp. Rochdale VTS.

JONES, Mr Peter Ferry 7 Park Road, Cults, Aberdeen AB15 9HR Tel: 01224 867702 — MB BChir 1943 Camb.; BA Camb. 1940, MA, MChir 1956; FRCS Eng. 1948; FRCS Ed. 1962. (St. Bart.) Emerit. Clin. Prof. Surg. Univ. Aberd.; Cons. Surg. Aberd. Gen. Hosp. & Roy. Aberd. Hosp. Sick Childr. Socs: Hon. Mem. Brit. Assn. Paediat. Surgs. Prev: Sen. Regist. (Surg.) Centr. Middlx. Hosp.; Ho. Surg. St. Bart. Hosp. Lond.

JONES, Peter Guy The Health Centre, Manor Road, Beverley HU17 7BZ Tel: 01482 862733 Fax: 01482 864958 — MB ChB 1973 Dundee; DObst RCOG 1975.

JONES, Peter Huxley Graigwen, Llanfair Discoed, Chepstow NP16 6LX Tel: 01633 543 — MB BCh 1967 Wales; DObst RCOG 1969.

JONES, Peter Lloyd Peel Croft Surgery, Lichfield St., Burton-on-Trent DE14 3RH Tel: 01283 511546 Fax: 01283 515761 — MB ChB 1986 Manch.; MBA OU 1996; BSc St. And. 1983; MRCGP 1990; DCH RCP Lond. 1992; DRCOG 1990; MBA 1997. (Manch.) Mem. Burton Fundholding Consortium Steering Gp.; Med. Manager BURDOC Out of Hours Co-op.

JONES, Peter Lloyd 7 Windsor Avenue, Radyr, Cardiff CF15 8BW Tel: 029 2084 2712 — MB BCh 1964 Wales; FFA RCS Eng. 1967. (Cardiff) Cons. Anaesth. Univ. Hosp. Wales (Cardiff) Gp. Hosps. Socs: Assn. Anaesths. Prev: Lect. Anaesth. Welsh Nat. Sch. Med.; Regist. (Anaesth.) & Sen. Regist. (Anaesth.) United Cardiff Hosps.; Research Fell. Dept. Anaesth. Cardiff Roy. Infirm.

JONES, Peter Mercer Millfield House, 1 Millfield Court, Whickham, Newcastle upon Tyne NE16 4RX Tel: 0191 488 3834 — MD 1968 Newc.; MB BS Durh. 1962; FRCP Lond. 1979; MRCP (U.K.) 1970; DCH RCPS Glas. 1964. Cons. Paediat. Newc. Univ. Gp. Hosps.; Clin. Lect. in Child Health Univ. Newc.; Dir. Newc. Haemophilia Centre. Prev: 1st Asst. (Child Health) Univ. Newc.; Sen. Regist. (Haemat.) W.. Gen. Hosp. & Roy. Infirm. Edin.; Regist. (Paediat. & Adult Med.) Roy. Vict. Infirm. Newc.

JONES, Peter Morgan Bishop Auckland General Hospital, Bishop Auckland DL14 6AD Tel: 01388 454000 Fax: 01388 454127; 11 Station Road, Witton-Le-Wear, Bishop Auckland DL14 0AN Tel: 01388 488415 Fax: 01388 488415 Email: pmjwitton@aol.com — LRCP LRCS Ed. LRCPS Glas. 1976; MB ChB (Hons.) Rhodesia 1976; FRCP Lond. 1995; FRCP Ed. 1993; MRCP (UK) 1981; FRCPCH 1997; DCH S Afr 1979. (Univ. Rhodesia) Cons. Paediat. (Community Child Health) Bishop Auckland Gen. Hosp.; Clin. Directtor Child Health, S. Durh. Health Care NHS Trust.

JONES, Peter Neville The Surgery, Spicers Close, Claverley, Wolverhampton WV5 7BY Tel: 01746 710223/424 Fax: 01764 710744 — MB ChB 1987 Birm. (Birmingham)

JONES, Peter Nicholas Graham Llanfyllin Medical Centre, High Street, Llanfyllin SY22 5DG Tel: 01691 648054 Fax: 01691 648165 — MB BS 1974 Lond. Prev: Sen. Med. Off. Solomon Is.s.

JONES, Peter Richard 30 Poplar Walk, London SE24 0BU — MB BChir 1993 Camb.; BSc (Immunol.) Lond. 1990.

JONES, Peter Robert Mason Harbinson House Surgery, Front Street, Sedgefield, Stockton-on-Tees TS21 3BN Tel: 01740 620300 Fax: 01740 622075; 25 Rectory Row, Sedgefield, Stockton-on-Tees TS21 2AE Tel: 01740 630193 — MB BS 1978 Newc.; MRCGP 1982. GP Trainer Stockton-on-Tees; Clin. Asst. (PsychoGeriat.) Winterton Hosp. Sedgefield.; Lect. Gen. Pract. Univ. Newc. Prev: SHO (Paediat. & O & G) S. Shields Gen. Hosp.; SHO (A & E) Roy. Vict. Infirm. Newc.

JONES, Peter Roscoe The Surgery, Back Lane, Stillington, York YO61 1LL Tel: 01347 810332; Dale End House, Brandsby, York YO61 4RP Tel: 01347 888110 — MB ChB 1979 Birm.; MA Oxf. 1976; MRCGP 1983; DRCOG 1983; Cert. Family Plann. RCOG & RCGP 1983. (Oxford and Birmingham) GP Princip. Stillington, New York. Socs: York Med. Soc. Prev: GP KnaresBoro.; Trainee GP York VTS.

JONES, Peter Vaughan 25 Harrow Way, Weavering, Maidstone ME14 5TU — MB ChB 1994 Liverp. (Liverpool) Regist. (Psychiat.) Centr. Sydney Area Health Serv., Sydney, Australia.

JONES, Peter William Brayton, Creigiau, Cardiff CF15 9NN Tel: 029 2089 0216 — MB BCh 1961 Wales. (Cardiff) Liason Off. for out of hours Bro TAH. H.A. Socs: Assn. Child Psychol. & Psychiat. & Rhondda Med. Soc. Prev: GP Cardiff; Regist. St. Jas. Hosp. Portsmouth & Dept. Psychol. Med. Hosp. Sick Childr. Gt. Ormond St. Lond.; SHO WhitCh. Hosp. Cardiff.

JONES, Petre Timothy Cedric Wordsworth Health Centre, 19 Wordsworth Avenue, Manor Park, London E12 6SU Tel: 020 8548 5960 Fax: 020 8548 5983 — MB ChB 1985 Sheff.; MRCGP 1989; DGM RCP Lond. 1987.

JONES, Mr Philip, Surg. Cdr. RN 2 Vollards Lane, Hatt, Saltash PL12 6PT Tel: 01752 843335; Room 822, First Ave. House, High Holborn, London WC1V 6HE Tel: 020 7430 6455 — MB ChB 1969 Birm.; FRCS Eng. 1978. Cons. Orthop. RN. Prev: Cons. Orthop. RN Hosp. Plymouth.

JONES, Philip 2 Colville Terrace, Thorpe, Wakefield WF3 3DZ; 24 St Martins Street, Wakefield WF1 3PN — MB ChB 1982 Leeds; MRCP (UK) 1986; DA (UK) 1993. Regist. Regional Burns Unit Pinderfields Hosp. Wakefield.

JONES, Philip Albert (retired) 7 Pinetree Close, Burry Port SA16 0TF Tel: 01554 832880 — MB BS 1960 Lond.; MRCS Eng. LRCP Lond. 1960; DObst RCOG 1962. Prev: Med. Adviser Dept. Transport.

JONES, Philip Andrew Hamer Royal Hull Hospitals NHS Trust, Hull Royal Infirmary, Anlaby Road, Hull HU3 2JZ — MB ChB 1988 Leeds; MRCP (UK) 1991; FRCR 1995; DMRD Liverp. 1994. Cons. Radiol. Prev: Sen. Regist. Rotat. (Radiol.) Mersey RHA.

JONES, Philip Ashley Emlyn Department of Haematology, Nottingham City Hospital, Hucknall Road, Nottingham NG5 1PB Tel: 0115 962 7708 Fax: 0115 962 7742 Email: pjones@ncht.org.uk; 62 Parkside, Wollaton, Nottingham NG8 2NN Tel: 0115 925 7910 — MB BCh Wales 1968; BSc (Hons.) Wales 1965; FRCP Lond. 1991; MRCP (UK) 1972; FRCPath 1988, M 1976. Cons. Haemat. Nottm. City Hosp.; Clin. Teach. Univ. Nottm.; Regional Adviser Roy. Coll. Path.; Clin. Dir. Haemat. Nottm. City Hosp. Prev: Lect. (Haemat.) Middlx. Hosp. Med. Sch.; Research Fell. Univ. Hosp. Wales Cardiff.

JONES, Philip David Bronglais General Hospital, Aberystwyth — MB BCh 1987 Wales; MRCP (UK) 1990; FRCP (Con) 2000. Cons. Phys. (c/o Elderly & Neurol. & Rehabil.) Bronglais Gen. Hosp. Aberystwyth. Socs: Brit. Geriat. Soc. Prev: Sen. Regist. (Gen. & Geriat. Med.) Bridgend & Cardiff; Regist. (Gen. Med. & Neurol.) Hurstwood Pk. Neurosci. Centre.

JONES, Philip Edward 41 The Downs, Altrincham WA14 2QG Tel: 0161 998 7070 Fax: 0161 927 9175; 31 Pine Road, Didsbury, Manchester M20 6UZ — MB ChB 1968 Lond; MB ChB Lond. 1968; MSc Lond. 1976; MD Birm. 1982; FRCP Lond. 1989; MRCP (UK) 1972. (Birmingham) Cons. Phys. Wythenshawe Hosp. Manch.; Assoc. Lect. (Med.) Univ. Manch. Sch. Med; Med. Dir. S. Manch. Univ. Hosp. Trust 1996. Socs: Brit. Soc. Gastroenterol.; Manch. Med. Soc. Prev: Sen. Regist. (Med.) Univ. Dept. Gastroenterol. Manch. Roy. Infirm. & Manch. Gen. Hosp.; Research Fell. Roy. Postgrad. Med. Sch. & Hon. Sen. Regist. (Med.) Hammersmith Hosp. Lond.

JONES, Philip Godfrey Redlands Surgery, 86 St. Johns Road, Stansted CM24 8JS Tel: 01279 813200 Fax: 01279 812426 — MB BS 1972 Lond.

JONES, Philip Harold Public Health Laboratory, Ipswich Hospital, Heath Road, Ipswich IP4 5PD — MB BS 1972 Lond.; MSc (Med. Microbiol.) Lond. 1976; MRCPath 1982. Cons. Microbiol. Dir. Pub. Health Laborat. Ipswich Hosp.

JONES, Mr Philip Hodgson The Croft, 161 Brooklands Road, Sale M33 3PD Tel: 0161 976 5355 Fax: 0161 969 3547 Email: pjonesent@aol.com; 4 Melrose Crescent, Hale, Altrincham WA15 8NN Tel: 0161 973 2563 — MB BChir 1973 Camb.; MB BChir Camb. 1974; MA Camb. 1974; FRCS Eng. 1980. (St. Thos.) Cons. Surg. ENT S. Manch. Univ. Hosps. NHS Trust. Prev: Sen. Regist. (ENT) Manch. HA & W.m. Hosp.; Regist. (ENT) St. Bart. Hosp.

JONES, Philip Howard 148 Stapleton Hall Road, London N4 4QJ — MB BS 1979 Lond.

JONES, Philip Howlett 1 CRF Medical Oncology Unit, Churchill Hospital, Oxford OX3 7LJ Tel: 01865 741841; 7 Peacock Road, Headington, Oxford OX3 0DQ — BM BCh 1986 Oxf.; MRCP (UK) 1989; PhD Lond. 1995. Specialist Regist. CRF Med.Oncol.Unit, Oxf.; ICRF Clinician Scientist, Inst. Molecular Med., John Radcliffe Hosp., Oxf. Prev: Sen. Clin. Research Fell. Imperial Cancer Research Fund Lond.

JONES, Philip Ioan Ellis Tel: 01342 410210 ex. 256 — MB BS 1969 Lond.; MRCS Eng. LRCP Lond. 1969; FFA RCS Eng. 1978; FFA RCSI 1977; DA Eng. 1972; DObst RCOG 1971. (Lond. Hosp.) Cons. Anaesth. Qu. Vict. Hosp. W. Sussex. Socs: Fell. Roy. Soc. Med.; Obst. Anaesth. Assn.; Assn. Plastic Surgs., Burns & Anaesth. Prev: Cons. Anaesth. King's Coll. Hosp. Lond.; Sen. Regist. (Anaesth.) King's Coll. Hosp. Lond.; Fell. (Anaesth.) Hosp. Sick Childr. Toronto, Canada.

JONES, Philip Leslie Stockbridge Village Health Centre, Leachcroft, Waterpark Drive, Stockbridge Village, Liverpool L28 1ST Tel: 0151 489 9924 — MB ChB 1982 Manch.

JONES, Philip Stuart 54 Victoria Park Road, London E9 7NB — MB BS 1994 Lond.; MA Camb. 1995, BA 1991; MRCP (UK) 1997; Primary FRCA 1999. (Lond. Hosp. Med. Coll.) SHO (Anaesth.) St Bartholomews Roy. Lond. & Homerton Hosps. Socs: Assn. Anaesths.; MRCA; Intens. Care Soc. Mem. Prev: SHO (Cardiol.) Lond. Chest Hosp. Lond.; Regist. (Gen. Med., Gastroenterol. & Endocrinol.) Frimley Pk. Hosp. Camberley.

JONES, Phyllis Ann The Leeds Road Practice, 49/51 Leeds Road, Harrogate HG2 8AY Tel: 01423 566636; Llwyncelyn, 50 Cornwall Road, Harrogate HG1 2PP Tel: 01423 507149 — MB BS 1964 Lond.; MRCS Eng. LRCP Lond. 1964; DObst RCOG 1966; Cert. Family Plann. JCC 1965. (King's Coll. Hosp.) Gen. Practitioner, The Leeds Rd Pract., Harrogate. Socs: MFFP; BMA & Harrogate Med. Soc. Prev: Ho. Phys. St. Olave's Hosp. Lond.; Ho. Surg. & Ho. Surg. (O & G) Dulwich Hosp. Lond.; Med. Off. Harrogate Family Plann. Clinic.

JONES, Rachel Bronwen 72 Wheathampstead Road, Harpenden AL5 1JA — MB BS 1998 Lond.; MB BS Lond 1998.

JONES, Rachel Caenwen Forest Edge, Culford, Bury St Edmunds IP28 6DW — MB BS 1993 Lond.

JONES, Rachel Elizabeth 42 Harwood Rise, Woolton Hill, Newbury RG20 9XW — MB ChB 1990 Sheff.

JONES, Rachel Mary NICU, Chelsea & Westminster Hospital, Fulham Road, London; 86 Devonshire Road, Chiswick, London W4 2HS — MB BChir 1992 Camb.; MA Camb. 1992; MRCP (UK) 1994. (Camb. Univ.) p/t Flexible Trainee (Neonates.) Chelsea & W.minster Hosp. (Yr. 3 Calman). Socs: MRCPCH. Prev: Regist. (Paediat.) Qu. Eliz. Hosp. Childr. Lond.; SHO Gt. Ormond St. Hosp. for Childr. Lond.; Retsitrar (Paediat.) Ealing Hosp. Lond.

JONES, Rachel Mary 11 Ilwyn Passat, Penarth Haven, Penarth CF64 1SE — MB BS 1997 Lond.

JONES, Rachel Mary 5 Kilvelgy Park, Kilgetty SA68 0TZ — MB BS 1996 Lond.

JONES, Rachel Nasmyth The Dower House, Penhow, Newport NP26 3AD — MB ChB 1992 Sheff.; BSc (Hons.) Lond. 1986. Regist. (Virol.) Univ. Hosp. Wales Cardiff.

JONES, Radcliffe Dougan (retired) Whiteliggate, The Stell, Kirkcudbright DG6 4TH — MB ChB 1952 Ed.; DPH Glas. 1963. Prev: GP Kilmarnock.

JONES, Raymond Charnwood, Upper Way, Upper Longdon, Rugeley WS15 1QD Tel: 01543 490567 — MB ChB 1961 Birm.; DObst RCOG 1963. Private Pract. Prev: Ho. Surg. & Ho. Phys. Worcester Roy. Infirm.; O & G Ho. Surg. Hillingdon Hosp.; GP Princip.

JONES, Raymond George Gordon 25 Reading Drive, Sale M33 5DJ Tel: 0161 962 3286 — MB BS 1945 Lond.; LMSSA Lond. 1945; FFA RCS Eng. 1954; DA Eng. 1946. (Guy's) Hon. Med. Off. St. Anns Hospice Manch.; Hon. Lect. (Anaesth.) Univ. Manch. Socs: Fell. Manch. Med. Soc. (Pres. Sect. Anaesth.). Prev: Cons. Anaesth. S. Manch. Health Dist. (T); Cons. Anaesth. Univ. Hosp. of S. Manch.; Sen. Regist. (Anaesth.) Manch. Roy. Infirm.

JONES, Raymond Henry Risca Surgery, St. Mary Street, Risca, Newport NP11 6YS Tel: 01633 612666 — MB BS 1974 Lond.; MRCS Eng. LRCP Lond. 1974; DRCOG 1978. (St. Mary's) Prev: Cas. Med. Off. Middlx. Hosp. Lond.; Ho. Phys. St. Mary's Hosp. Lond.

JONES, Raymond Neil Bradford Road Medical Centre, 60 Bradford Road, Trowbridge BA14 9AR Tel: 01225 754255 Fax: 01225 774391; Larkfield, Main St, Keevil, Trowbridge BA14 — MB BS 1968 Lond.; MRCS Eng. LRCP Lond. 1968; DObst RCOG 1970. (Guy's) Prev: SHO (O & G) Roy. United Hosp. Bath; Ho. Surg. Lewisham Hosp. Lond.; Ho. Phys. Roy. United Hosp. Bath.

JONES, Rebecca Ann 32 Laneside Road, New Mills, High Peak SK22 4LX — MB ChB 1994 Liverp.; DRCOG 1996; DCH 1998. SHO (Paediat.), Sunderland Roy. Hosp., Sunderland. Prev: SHO (Neonatology) S. Cleveland Hosp. MiddlesBoro.; Trainee GP N.d. VTS; Ho. Off. (Med. & Surg.) Arrowe Pk. Hosp. Merseyside.

JONES, Rebecca Louise Flat 4, 47 Clarence Square, Cheltenham GL50 4JR — MB BS 1991 Lond.; BA Oxon. 1988; MRCP Lond. 1994.

JONES, Rebecca Louise Swn-y-Gwynt, Mochdre, Newtown SY16 4JX — MB BCh 1995 Wales; DRCOG 1999. (Univ. Wales Coll. Med.) SHO GP VTS Train. Scheme Swansea. Prev: SHO (Gen. Med.) P.ss of Wales Hosp. Bridgend; Ho. Off. (Gen. Med.) P.ss of Wales Hosp. Bridgend; Ho. Off. (Gen. Surg.) P. Chas. Hosp. Merthyr Tydfil.

JONES, Rhian 11 Warminster Road, St Werburgh's, Bristol BS2 9UH — MB ChB 1988 Liverp.; MRCP (UK) 1992; DRCOG 1996.

JONES, Rhian Elisabeth 105 Paramount Court, University St., London WC1E 6JW — MB BS 1995 Lond.; DFFP 1998; DRCOG 1998; DCH 1999. (University College London Medical School)

JONES, Rhodri Huw Morris Bera Bach, 15 Cae Bach Aur, Bodffordd, Llangefni LL77 7DX Tel: 01248 724937 — MB BS 1984 Lond.

JONES, Rhodri Wyn Winch Lane Surgery, Winch Lane, Haverfordwest SA61 1RN Tel: 01437 762333 Fax: 01437 766912; 9 New Road, Haverfordwest SA61 1TU Tel: 01437 765359 — MB ChB 1982 Liverp.; MRCGP 1988; DRCOG 1986.

JONES, Rhys Mansel Anaesthetic Department, University Hospital of Wales, Cardiff CF14 4XW Tel: 029 2074 4348 — MB BS 1987 Lond.; FRCA 1992; DA (UK) 1990. Cons. Paediat. Anaesth. Univ. Hosp. Wales Cardiff. Prev: Sen. Regist. Univ. Hosp. Wales Cardiff; Regist. (Anaesth.) Hosp. Sick Childr. Gt. Ormond St. Lond.

JONES, Richard Anthony Portsmouth Cardiology, St. Mary's Hospital, Portsmouth PO3 6AD Tel: 023 92 866012 Fax: 023 92 866067 — MB BS 1988 Lond.; MRCP (UK) 1991. Cons. Cardiol.; Research Fell. (Cardiol.) Univ. Hosp. Wales Cardiff. Prev: Regist. (Med.) St. Mary's Hosp. Portsmouth; Specialist Regist. Cardiol. Soton. Gen.; Regist. (Med.) Jersey Gen. Hosp. CI.

JONES, Richard Arnold Department of Pathology, Middlesborough General Hospital, Ayrsome Green Lane, Middlesbrough TS5 — MRCS Eng. LRCP Lond. 1968; BSc (1st cl. Hons.) Lond. 1965, MB BS (Hons.) 1968; MRCPath 1974. (Univ. Coll. Hosp.) Cons. Histopath. S. Tees Health Dist. Prev: Lect. Dept. Path. Univ. Nottm.; Lect. Sch. Pathol. Middlx. Hosp. Med. Sch. Lond.

JONES, Richard Barry Children's Department, Moorfields Eye Hospital, London EC1 Tel: 020 7253 3411 — BM BCh 1962 Oxf.; MA Oxf. 1962; FRCP Lond. 1980, M 1969; FRCOphth 1989; DPhil Med Soc. Apoth. Lond. 1990; DCH Eng. 1965; DObst RCOG 1964. (Oxf. & Guy's) Cons. Paediat. Moorfield Eye Hosp. Lond. Socs: Brit. Paediat. Assn. Prev: Cons. Paediat. Qu. Eliz. Hosp. for Childr. Lond.; Research Fell. (Developm. Paediat.) Wolfson Centre Inst. Child Health; Hon. Sen. Regist. Hosp. Sick Childr. Gt. Ormond St. Lond.

JONES, Richard Barry 7 Sanderson Road, Newcastle upon Tyne NE2 2DR — MB ChB 1997 Leeds.

JONES, Richard David South Lodge, Townfield Lane, Mollington, Chester CH1 6NJ — MB ChB 1952 Liverp.; MRCS Eng. LRCP Lond. 1952. (Liverp.) Prev: RAMC.

JONES, Richard David Old Hall Grounds Health Centre, Old Hall Grounds, Cowbridge CF7 7AH Tel: 01446 772383 Fax: 01446 774022; 62 The Verlands, Cowbridge CF71 7BY Tel: 01446 774442 — MB BCh 1975 Wales; BSc Wales 1971, MB BCh 1975.

JONES, Richard David 5 The Oaks, Killearn, Glasgow G63 9SF — MB BChir 1979 Camb.; MB BChir Camb. 1980; MA Camb. 1980; MRCP (UK) 1982; FRCR 1985. Cons. Clin. Oncol. Beatson Oncol. Centre Glas.

JONES, Richard David 62 Sherbuttgate Road, Pocklington, York YO42 2ER — MB BS 1989 Lond.

JONES, Richard Dennis 42 Eaton Road, Norwich NR4 6PZ — MB 1956 Camb.; MA Camb. 1958, BA 1952, MB 1956, BChir 1955; FRCP Lond. 1985; FRCP Ed. 1979, M 1965; DCH Eng. 1962. (Camb. & St. Mary's) Cons. Paediat. Norwich Health Dist. Socs: BMA; Brit. Paediat. Assn. Prev: SHO (Neurol.) United Camb. Hosps.; Regist. (Paediatr.) United Newc. Hosps.; Sen. Regist. (Paediatr.) Newc. Gen. Hosp.

JONES, Richard Edward Department of Neurology, Sunderland Royal Hospital, Kayll Road, Sunderland SR4 7TP; 17 Elgy Road, Gosforth, Newcastle upon Tyne NE3 4UU Tel: 0191 285 2407 — MB ChB 1975 Sheff.; FRCP Lond. 1995. Cons. Neurol. Sunderland Roy. Hosp. & Regional Neurosci. Centre Newc. u. Tyne; Hon. Lect. (Neurol.) Univ. Newc.

JONES, Richard Eryl Isfryn Surgery, Isfryn, Ffordd Dewi Sant, Nefyn, Pwllheli LL53 6EA Tel: 01758 720202 Fax: 01758 720083; Bryn Eithin, 5 Holborn Court, Nefyn, Pwllheli LL53 6HB Tel: 01758 720730 Fax: 01758 721615 — MD 1971 Wales; MB BCh 1965. (Cardiff) Socs: BMA. Prev: Tenovus Clin. Research Asst. Cardiff Roy. Infirm.; Lect. (Physiol.) King's Coll. Lond.; Ho. Surg. Profess. Surg. Unit Cardiff Roy. Infirm.

JONES, Richard Glyn Learning Disability Directorate, Bromorgannwg, NHS Trust, Treseder Way, Cardiff CF5 5WF — MB BCh 1984 Wales; MSc Wales 1995; MRCPsych 1993; MRCGP 1989. (Welsh Nat. Sch. Med.) Cons. Psychiat. Bro Morgannwg NHS Trust, Cardiff. Prev: Trainee Psychiat. Mid/S. Glam. VTS; Trainee GP Bridgend VTS.

JONES, Richard Gwent 13 Cumberland Road, Leeds LS6 2EF — BM BCh 1978 Oxf.; MA Oxf. 1978, DM 1988, BM BCh 1978; MRCP (UK) 1980. Hon. Tutor Univ. Leeds; Sen. Regist. (Chem. Path.) Yorks. RHA. Socs: BDA & Biochem. Soc. Prev: Tutor (Med.) Univ. Leeds; MRC Train. Fell.sh.

JONES, Richard Harries Town Gate Practice, Chepstow Community Hospital, Tempest Way, Chepstow NP16 5XP Tel: 01291 636444 Fax: 01291 636465; Silverpill Lodge, 3 St. Ann St, Chepstow NP16 5HE Tel: 01291 625005 — MRCS Eng. LRCP Lond. 1973. (Guy's) Civil Serv. Local Med. Off.

JONES, Richard Hefin Trefor Princess of Wales Hospital, Bridgend CF31 1JP — MB ChB 1958 Liverp.; FRCP Lond. 1994; FRCP Canada 1966; DCH Eng. 1964. (Liverp.) Cons. Paediatr. P.ss Wales Hosp. Bridgend. Socs: Brit. Paediat. Assn. & Welsh Paediat. Soc. Prev: Paediat. Regist. St. David's Hosp. Bangor; Research Fell. in Paediat. Dept. Child Health Univ. Liverp.; Assoc. Prof. Paediat. Univ. Sask., Canada.

JONES, Mr Richard Henry Vaughan Ward 14, Stafford General Hospital, Stafford ST16 3SA; Scotts Cottage, Stowe, Stafford ST18 0LF — MB BS 1983 Lond.; BSc Biochem. Lond. 1980; FRCS Ed. 1987; FRCS Eng. 1989; FRCS (Orl.) 1995. (Charing Cross) Cons. Worcester Roy. Infirm., Worcester; Mid./Sth. Staffs. Deaf Childr.'s Soc. Pres. Socs: BMA; Brit. Assn. Otol.; Scott. Otolaryngol. Soc. Prev: Sen. Regist. (ENT) N. Riding Infirm. Middlesbrough Cleveland;

Sen. Regist. Ninewells Hosp. Med. Sch. Dundee; Cons. Stafford Dist. Gen. Hosp. & Cannock.

JONES, Richard Hugh 7 Rhodfa Sian Dyserth, Denbigh LL16 6BJ — MB ChB 1996 Ed.

JONES, Richard Huw St Philips Health Centre, London School of Economics & Political Science, Houghton St., London WC2A 2AE Tel: 020 7955 7016; Maple House, Maypole Road, Chelsfield Village, Orpington BR6 7RB — MB BS 1977 Lond.; BSc (Hons.) Lond. 1974, MB BS 1977; LMSSA Lond. 1977. (Guy's) Prev: GP Kent.

JONES, Richard John 611 Bolton Road, Aspull, Wigan WN2 1PZ — MB ChB 1997 Manch.

JONES, Richard Joseph Basil Heritage (retired) Tynllwyn, Llanafan Fawr, Builth Wells LD2 3LU Tel: 01591 620695 — MB BS Lond. 1950; MRCS Eng. LRCP Lond. 1950; DObst RCOG 1957. Prev: Cas. Surg. St. Mary's Hosp. Lond.

JONES, Richard Matthew 29 Ffrwd Vale, Neath SA10 7BA — MB BCh 1998 Wales.

JONES, Richard Meredith Welsh Blood Service, Ely Valley Road, Talbot Green, Pontyclun CF72 9WB Tel: 01443 622027 Fax: 01443 622028 Email: richard.jones@web.waks.nhs.uk — MB BS 1971 Lond.; MSc (Immunol.) Lond. 1985; FRCP Ed. 1995; MRCP (UK) 1978; FRCPath 1993; DObst RCOG 1974. (Lond. Hosp.)

JONES, Mr Richard Spencer The Robert Jones and Agnes Hunt, Orthopaedic Hospital NHS Trust, Oswestry Tel: 01691 404429 Fax: 01691 404052 Email: rsj-knee@email.msn.com; Pheasant's Keep, Castle Court, Shrawardine, Shrewsbury SY4 1AH Fax: 01743 850263 — MB BS 1985 Lond.; FRCS (Orth.) 1995; FRCS Eng. 1990. (St Thomas' Hosp. Med Sch.) Cons. (Orthop.) Robt. Jones & Agnes Hunt Orthop. Hosp. OsW.ry.; Roy. Shrewsbury Hosp. Socs: Assoc. Mem. BOA; Brit. Assn. for Surg. of Knee. Prev: Regist. (Orthop.) Merseyside RHA; SHO (Neurosurg.) Walton Hosp. Liverp.; Sen. Reg RJAH & N.Staffs. Roy. Infirm.

JONES, Richard Wynn, MC (retired) 26 Marlborough Road, Buxton SK17 6RD — MB ChB 1937 Ed.

JONES, Robert 18 Morrison Street, Blackwood NP12 1QG — MB BCh 1978 Wales.

JONES, Robert 15 Amos Way, Sibsey, Boston PE22 0SD — MB ChB 1979 Leeds.

JONES, Robert Market Street Practice, Ton-y-Felin Surgery, Bedwas Road, Caerphilly CF83 1XP Tel: 02920 887831 Fax: 02920 869037 — MB BS 1977 Lond.; MRCS Eng. LRCP Lond. 1977; MRCGP 1983. (St. Mary's Hosp. Med. Sch.) GP.

JONES, Robert Allen Maes-y-Gof, Nercwys, Mold CH7 4EW — MB BCh 1969 Wales; FFA RCS Eng. 1975. Cons. Anaesth. Maelor Gen. Hosp. Wrexham.

JONES, Mr Robert Anthony Charles (retired) 21 Hartley Road, Altrincham WA14 4AZ Tel: 0161 928 5904 — MB BCh 1956 Wales; FRCS Eng. 1962. Hon. Cons. Neurosurg. Hope Hosp. Salford & Roy. Manch. Childr. Hosp. Pendlebury. Prev: Sen. Regist. (Neurosurg.) Frenchay Hosp. Bristol.

JONES, Robert David Allesley Park Medical Centre, Whitaker Road No.2, Coventry CV5 9JE Tel: 024 7667 4123 Fax: 024 7667 2196; 28 Priory Road, Kenilworth CV8 1LL Tel: 01926 50886 — MB BS 1986 Lond.; MRCGP 1991; DRCOG 1989. (St. Bart. Hosp.) Prev: Trainee GP Coventry VTS; SHO (Geriat.) Whitley Hosp. Coventry; SHO (Med., Paediat. & O & G) Walsgrave Hosp. Coventry.

JONES, Robert David Wentloog Road Health Centre, 98 Wentloog Road, Rumney, Cardiff CF3 8EA Tel: 029 2079 7746 Fax: 029 2079 0231; Edgebaston House, 86 Lascelles Drive, Pontrenway, Cardiff CF23 8NQ Tel: 029 2054 0851 — MB BCh Wales 1969. (Cardiff) Prev: Rotating Intern Cook Co. Hosp. Chicago, USA; Cas. Off. Roy. Gwent Hosp. Newport; Ho. Surg. (O & G) St. David's Hosp. Cardiff.

JONES, Robert David 5 Wilton Court, Crossways, Park Lane, Beaconsfield HP9 2HX — MSc Lond. 1971; MRCS Eng. LRCP Lond. 1967; FFOM RCP Lond. 1986; DA Eng. 1973; DIH Eng. 1971; DObst RCOG 1970; DCH Eng. 1970; FRCP 1997. (St. Mary's) Med. Dir. Corporate Health Ltd. Prev: Dep. Dir. Med. Serv. Health & Safety Exec.; Ho. Surg. Qu. Eliz. II Hosp. Welwyn Gdn. City; Ho. Phys. Roy. S. Hants. Hosp. Soton.

JONES, Robert Frank Neville (retired) 21 Ravensbourne Road, Twickenham TW1 2DG Tel: 020 8892 3525 — MB BS Lond. 1953. Prev: Ho. Phys. & Ho. Surg. (O & G) St. Helier Hosp. Carshalton.

JONES, Robert Geraint Brinsley Avenue Surgery, 11 Brinsley Avenue, Trentham, Stoke-on-Trent ST4 8LT Tel: 01782 657199 — MB BS 1980 Lond.; MRCS Eng. LRCP Lond. 1980; MRCGP 1987. (Guy's) Prev: SHO Surg. Roy. Naval Hosp. Haslar; Ho. Surg. Guy's Hosp. Lond.; Ho. Phys. Pembury Hosp. Tunbridge Wells.

JONES, Robert Glyn Carrington Way Health Centre, 9 Carrington Way, Wincanton BA9 9JY Tel: 01963 32000 Fax: 01963 32146; Combe Meade, Horsington, Templecombe BA8 0DJ Tel: 01963 370562 — MB BS 1966 Lond.; MRCS Eng. LRCP Lond. 1966; DObst RCOG 1971; DCH Eng. 1971. (St. Geo.) Clin. Asst. (Geriat. Med.) E. Som. NHS Trust. Socs: BMA. Prev: Ho. Surg. St Peter's Hosp. Chertsey; SHO (Paediat.) Makerere Med. Sch. Kampala, Uganda; SHO (Anaesth.) Cuckfield Hosp.

JONES, Robert Gregg 51 Greenfield, Newbridge, Newport NP11 4QY — MB ChB 1997 Leic.

JONES, Robert Howard Northlands Wood Surgery, 7 Walnut Park, Haywards Heath RH16 3TG; 31 Meadow Drive, Lindfield RH16 2RS — MB BS 1981 Lond.; MRCGP 1985; DRCOG 1985; DCH RCP Lond. 1984. (Kings Coll. Hosp.)

JONES, Robert Hugh The Broadway Surgery, 3 Broadway Gardens, Monkhams Avenue, Woodford Green IG8 0HF Tel: 020 8491 3344 Fax: 020 8491 0116 — MB BS 1974 Lond. (St. Bart.) Company Med. Off. Wiggins Teape.

JONES, Robert John 10 Woodlands Road, Witney OX28 2DN Tel: 01993 702296; Beatson Institute for Cancer Research, Garscube Estate, Switchback Road, Bearsden, Glasgow G61 1BD Tel: 0141 330 3953 Email: ojjiq@udct.gla.ac.uk — MB ChB 1993 Ed.; BA Oxf. 1990; MB ChB (Hons.) Ed. 1993; MA Oxf. 1996; MRCP (UK) 1996. Clin. Research Fell. Cancer Research Campaign; Hon. Regist. Beatson Oncol. Centre Glas. Prev: SHO (Med.) Perth Roy. Infirm.; SHO (Med.) W.ern Glas. Universities NHS Trust.

JONES, Robert Logan Dickson, Lt.-Col. RAMC Retd. The Medical Centre, 2 Frances St., Doncaster DN1 1JS Tel: 01302 349431; Tighnreoch, Carr Lane, Wadworth, Doncaster DN11 9AR Tel: 01302 850374 — MB ChB 1977 Manch.; BSc (Med. Sci.) St. And. 1974; MRCGP 1984; DRCOG 1982. Prev: Command. Off. NTGP, Hong Kong.

JONES, Mr Robert Norman 4 Park Road, Gorleston, Great Yarmouth NR31 6EJ Tel: 01493 601770 Fax: 01493 452066; Stubbs Cottage, Stubbs Green, Loddon, Norwich NR14 6EA Tel: 01508 528800 — MB BS Lond. 1970; FRCS Eng. 1976; MRCS Eng. LRCP Lond. 1970. (St. Thos.) Cons. Orthop. Surg. Jas. Paget Hosp. Gt. Yarmouth. Socs: Fell. BOA; BMA. Prev: Sen. Regist. (Orthop.) P.ss Eliz. Orthop. Hosp. Exeter; Regist. (Orthop.) Robt. Jones & Agnes Hunt Orthop. Hosp. OsW.ry; SHO (Orthop.) Rowley Bristow Orthop. Hosp. Pyrford.

JONES, Robert Peter Alexandra Healthcare NHS Trust, Woodrow Drive, Redditch B98 7UB Tel: 01527 503030 Fax: 01527 512024 Email: robert.jones@worcsacute.wmids.nhs.uk — MB ChB 1982 Birm.; DA (UK) 1985. Staff (Anaesth.) Alexandra Hosp. Redditch.

JONES, Mr Robert Pierce 93 Mellor Lane, Mellor, Blackburn BB2 7EN — MB ChB 1968 Leeds; BSc (Hons. Physiol.) Leeds 1965, MB ChB 1968; FRCS Eng. 1976. (Leeds) Cons. Plastic Surg. Roy. Preston Hosp. Preston. Prev: Sen. Regist. & Regist. (Plastic Surg. & Burns Unit) Withington Hosp.; Manch.; Regist. (Gen. Surg.) York Dist. Gen. Hosp.

JONES, Robert Russell Brunswick Health Centre, 139-140 St. Helens Road, Swansea SA1 4DE Tel: 01792 643001 / 643611; 91 Gower Road, Sketty, Swansea SA2 9BH Tel: 01792 201362 — MB BS 1969 Lond.; MRCS Eng. LRCP Lond. 1969. (Lond. Hosp.) GP; Med. Off. HMP Swansea.

JONES, Robert Stewart 8 Cundall Way, Harrogate HG2 0DY — MB ChB 1971 Leeds; BSc (Hons. Anat.) Leeds 1968, MB ChB (Hons.) 1971; DObst RCOG 1973.

JONES, Robert Vernon Holmes (retired) Foxenholes, Seaton EX12 2JH — MB BChir 1953 Camb.; MA Camb. 1954, MB BChir 1953; FRCGP 1978, M 1964. Prev: Milroy Lect. RCP Lond. 1981.

JONES, Robert Watkin Caerwen, Old Ruthin Road, Denbigh LL16 4RA — MB ChB 1980 Liverp.; MRCGP 1985; DRCOG 1984.

JONES, Robert William Alexander Hillfarrance House, Hillfarrance, Taunton TA4 1AW — BM BS 1994 Nottm.

JONES, Robert William Arthur 12th Floor, Derriford Hospital, Derriford Road, Plymouth PL6 8DH Tel: 01752 763452 Fax: 01752 763467 — MB BS 1970 Lond.; FRCP Lond. 1993; MRCP (UK)

1974; DCH Eng. 1973. (St. Geo.) Cons. Paediat. Plymouth Gp. Hosps. Socs: Brit. Paediat. Assn. & Neonat. Soc.; Brit. Assn. Paediat. Nephrol. Prev: Sen. Regist. (Paediat.) & Brit Kidney Pat. Assn. Lect. (Paediat. Nephrol.) Guy's Hosp. Lond.; Cons. Paediat. Cwm Hosp. Suva, Fiji & Sen. Clin. Tutor Univ. S. Pacific, Fiji.

JONES, Robert Wyn ENT Department, Royal Alexandria Hospital Trust, Paisley PA2 9PN Tel: 0141 887 9111; 90 Preston Field, Milngavie, Glasgow G62 7PZ Tel: 0141 956 1725 — MB ChB 1962 Glas. Assoc. Specialist (ENT Surg.) Roy. Alexander Hosp. Trust Paisley. Socs: Scott. Otol. Soc. Prev: Regist. ENT Hosp. Glas.

JONES, Robin Blair Yorkley Health Centre, Bailey Hill, Yorkley, Lydney GL15 4RS Tel: 01594 562437; The Old Vicarage, St Briavels, Lydney GL15 6RG — MB BCh 1980 Wales; DRCOG 1983.

JONES, Robin Gregory 4 Lyndon Drive, Liverpool L18 6HP — MB ChB 1992 Liverp.

JONES, Robin Lewis Llwynmeredydd, Myddfai, Llandovery SA20 0JE — MB BS 1996 Lond.

JONES, Robin Trevor Eaton Lodge, 10 Station Road, East Leake, Loughborough LE12 6LQ — MB BS 1997 Lond.

JONES, Rodney Marshall Silloth Group Medical Practice, Lanewn Terrace, Silloth, Carlisle CA7 4AH Tel: 016973 31309 Fax: 016973 32834; Hima House, 270 Skinburness Road, Silloth, Carlisle CA7 4QU Tel: 016973 31747 Fax: 016973 31525 Email: rjones8356@aol.com — MB ChB 1972 Manch.; FRCGP 1995, M 1977. (Manch.) Assoc. Dir. Postgrad. Educat. (Gen. Pract.). Prev: Trainer (Gen. Pract.) & Scheme Organiser E. Cumbria VTS.

JONES, Mr Roger Barritt 8 St James View, Ravenfield, Rotherham S65 4NL Tel: 01709 852368 Fax: 01709 304545 — MB ChB 1968 Manch.; BSc Manch. 1965; FRCS Eng. 1974. Cons. Surg. & Clin. Dir. (Surg. & Urol.) Rotherham Gen. Hosp. NHS Trust. Prev: Sen. Regist. (Gen. Surg.) Roy. Hallamsh. Hosp. Sheff.; Regist. (Surg.) Univ. Hosp. S. Manch.; Asst. Lect. (Anat.) Manch. Univ.

JONES, Professor Roger Hugh Lambeth Walk Group Practice, 5 Lambeth Walk, London SE11 6SP Tel: 020 7735 4412 Fax: 020 7820 1888; 56 Scotts Sufferanc Wharf., Mill St, London SE1 2DE Tel: 020 7394 9586 — BM BCh 1973 Oxf.; DM Soton. 1990; MA Oxf. 1973; FRCP Ed. 1993; MRCP (UK) 1976; MFPHM RCP (UK) 1997; FRCGP 1990, M 1981; F MED SCI 1998. (Oxf. & St. Thos.) Prof. Gen. Pract. Univ. Lond. Socs: Assn. Univ. Depts. Gen. Pract.; Brit. Soc. Gastroenterol.; (Chairm.) Primary Care Soc. for Gastroenterol. Prev: Prof. Primary Health Care Univ. Newc.; Sen. Lect. (Primary Med. Care) Univ. Soton.; Regist. (Renal) King's Coll. Hosp. Lond.

JONES, Roger Youdell Swn y Wylan, Rating Row, Beaumaris LL58 8AF — MB ChB 1972 Liverp.; BEng. (Hons.) Liverp. 1966, MB ChB 1972; FRCR 1979; DMRD Liverp. 1977. (Liverp.)

JONES, Roland Morgan Penbelan, Llanfair Caereinion, Welshpool SY21 0DD — MB ChB 1997 Liverp.

JONES, Ronald Herbert, TD, KStJ (retired) Drinkwater Cottage, Thornton Hough, Wirral CH63 4JT Tel: 0151 336 2082 — MB ChB Liverp. 1949; MRCGP 1963. Prev: Col. RAMC (RARO).

JONES, Professor Ronald Mervyn Department of Anaesthetics, St. Mary's Hospital, Paddington, London W2 1NY Tel: 020 7725 1681 Fax: 020 7725 6425; Wychwood, Pine Way, Southampton SO16 7HF — MB ChB 1971 Liverp.; MD Liverp. 1990; FFA RCS Eng. 1978. Prof. Anaesth. Imperial Coll. Sci. & Technol. Med. St. Mary's Hosp. Med. Sch.; CME Dir. Roy. Coll. Anaest.; Hon. Cons. Anaesth. St. Mary's Hosp. & N.wick Pk. Hosp.; Mem. Advis. Comm. NHS Drugs. Socs: Hon. Life Mem. Austral. Soc. Anaesth.; Acad.ian Europ. Acad. Anaesth; (Chairm.) Assn. Profs. Anaesth. Prev: Sen. Lect. (Anaesth.) Guy's Hosp. Med. Sch.; Instruc. (Anaesth.) Univ. Michigan Med. Center Ann Arbor, USA.

JONES, Mr Ronald Osborne (retired) Oakham Farm, Aylesbury Road, Winslow, Buckingham MK18 3LF — MB ChB 1961 Liverp.; BSc Liverp. 1958, MD 1965; FRCS Eng. 1967.

JONES, Ronald Vaughan (retired) Stangate, Malthouse Lane, Fox Corner, Guildford GU3 3PS Tel: 01483 233474 — MB BChir 1953 Camb.; MA Camb. 1963, BA (Hons.) 1950; FRCP Lond. 1979, M 1956; FRCPath 1993, M 1963. Prev: Cons. Haemat. St. Peters Hosp. Chertsey.

JONES, Rosalind Anne Longfield Medical Centre, Princes Road, Maldon CM9 5DF; 54 Stable Croft, Springfield, Chelmsford CM1 6YX — MB BS 1990 Lond.

JONES, Rosamond Anne Kay Department of Paediatrics, Wexham Park Hospital, Wexham, Slough SL2 4HL Tel: 01753 633000 Fax: 01753 634599; 15 Fairfield Lane, Farnham Royal, Slough SL2 3BX Tel: 01753 643991 — MB BS 1971 Lond.; MB BS (Hons.) Lond. 1971; MD Lond. 1982; FRCP Lond. 1993; MRCP (UK) 1974; DObst RCOG 1973. (Lond. Hosp.) Cons. Paediat. Heatherwood & Wexham Pk. Hosp. Trust. Socs: Brit. Paediat. Assn.; Neonat. Soc. Prev: Cons. Paediat. Ealing Hosp. & Hon. Sen. Lect. Roy. Postgrad. Med. Sch. Hammersmith Hosp.; Sen. Regist. (Paediat.) E. Anglian RHA; Research Fell. (Paediat.) Hammersmith Hosp. Lond.

JONES, Rosamund Ground Floor Flat, 21 King Charles Road, Surbiton KT5 8NY — MB BChir 1990 Camb.

JONES, Rosemarie 25 Northfield Lane, Horbury, Wakefield WF4 5HZ — MB BS 1987 Lond.; MSc Lond. 1991; DRCPath 1992. SHO (O & G) N. Gen. Hosp. Sheff. Prev: Sen. Regist. (Chem. Path.) Univ. Coll. Lond. Hosps.; SHO (A & E) Sheff. Childr. Hosp.

JONES, Rosemary Dept of Community Child Health, Bath NHS House, Newbridge Mill, Bath BA1 3QE Tel: 01225 313640; South Leigh, Belgrave Road, Bath BA1 6LU Tel: 01225338488 Email: cledjones@aol.com — MB ChB 1977 Leeds; MB ChB (Hons.) Leeds 1977; MRCP (UK) 1980; MRCGP 1984; DCH Eng. 1980. (Univ. Leeds) Cons. Paediat. - Community Child Health Bath & W. NHS Trust, Bath.

JONES, Rosemary Cheshire Community Health Care Trust, Barony Head Quarters, Barony Road, Nantwich CW5 5QU Tel: 01270 415384 Fax: 01270 627469 Email: rosemary.jones@cheschc-tr.nwest.nhs.uk — MB ChB Liverp. 1968; DFFP 1993; FRCPCH 1997. (Liverp.) Cons. Community Paediat. Chesh. Community Healthcare Trust. Socs: Fac. Comm. Health; Foundat. Fell. Roy. Coll. Paediat. & Child. Health; Nat. Assn. Family Plann. Doctors. Prev: Sen. Med. Off. Warrington HA; Departm. Med. Off. E. Riding CC; Ho. Phys. & Ho. Surg. St. Helens Hosp.

JONES, Rosemary Ann (retired) Hales Mead, Pitchcombe, Stroud GL6 6LU Tel: 01452 813103 Email: rosemary@halesmead.co.uk — MB BS 1959 Lond.; MFFP 1993; DObst RCOG 1962; DCH Eng. 1961. Sen. Clin. Med. Off. (Family Plann.) Severn NHS Trust. Prev: GP Stroud.

JONES, Rosemary Claire The Downings, Barker Lane, Mellor, Blackburn BB2 7EE Tel: 01254 813595 — MB ChB 1981 Ed.

JONES, Rosemary Diana Graham Royal Infirmary, Lauriston Place, Edinburgh EH3 9HB; Southview, Dolphinton, West Linton EH46 7HH — MB BS 1983 Lond.; BSc Lond. 1978; MRCP (UK) 1988; MRC Path 1998. (Univ. Coll. Hosp. Lond.) Staff Grade (Haemat.) Roy. Infirm. Edin. Prev: Sen. Regist. (Haemat.) Roy. Infirm Edin.

JONES, Rosemary Isobel Ann 12 West Catherine Place, Edinburgh EH12 5HZ — MB BCh BAO 1989 Belf.

JONES, Rosslyn Margaret Anyho, Tregarth, Bangor LL57 4NF — MB BCh 1979 Wales.

JONES, Rowena Mari 25 Wrde Hill, Highworth, Swindon SN6 7BX — MB ChB 1992 Ed.

JONES, Roy William Research Institute for the Care of the Elderly, St. Martin's Hospital, Bath BA2 5RP Tel: 01225 835866 Fax: 01225 840395 Email: r.w.jones@bath.ac.uk; Agra, Cleevedale Road, Bath BA2 5QS — MB BS 1972 Lond.; BSc (1st cl. Hons.) Lond. 1969; FRCP Lond. 1994; MRCP (UK) 1975; FFPM RCP (UK) 1995, MFPM 1989; Dip Pharm Med RCP (UK) 1980. (Roy. Free) Dir. Research Inst. for c/o Elderly St. Martins Hosp. Bath; Hon. Sen. Lect. Univ. Bath; Hon. Cons. Phys. Bath. Socs: Brit. Geriat. Soc.; Brit. Pharm. Soc. Prev: Head Clin. Pharmacol. Roussel Laborats. Ltd.; Regist. (Med.) St. Thos. Hosp. Lond.; Ho. Phys. (Med.) Roy. Free Hosp. Lond.

JONES, Rupert Charles Marshall Roborough Surgery, 1 Eastcote Close, Southway, Plymouth PL6 6PH Tel: 01752 701659 Fax: 01752 773181 — MB BS 1979 Lond.; BSc Lond. 1976; MRCGP 1984; DRCOG 1982; DCH RCPSI 1982; D.Occ.Med. Lond. 1996. Prev: Trainee GP N.ampton VTS; Med. Off. Holy Cross Hosp. Transkei, S. Afr.

JONES, Russell Lloyd City Hospital, Dudley Road, Birmingham B18 7Q Tel: 0121 554 3801; 9 Cambridge Road, Moseley, Birmingham B13 9UE Tel: 0121 443 2852 — MB ChB 1988 Birm.; ChB Birm. 1988; MRCP 1992; FRCR 1996. Cons. Radiol. City Hosp.

Dudley Rd. B/ham. Socs: BMA; RCR. Prev: Sen. Regist. Rotat. (Radiol.) W. Midl.

JONES, Russell Melvyn 28 Graylands, Theydon Bois, Epping CM16 7LB — MB BS 1993 Lond.

JONES, Russell Wynn Chorleywood Health Centre, 7 Lower Road, Chorleywood, Rickmansworth WD3 5EA Tel: 01923 287100 Fax: 01923 287120 — MB BCh 1972 Wales; MRCGP 1986. (Wales) Assoc. Reader (Elect. Engin. & Electronics) Brunel Univ. Uxbridge.

JONES, Ruth Alison 4 Millbank Court, Frodsham, Warrington WA6 7AW Tel: 01928 739802 — MB ChB 1985 Liverp.; MRCGP 1988; DRCOG 1987.

JONES, Ruth Margaret Department of Anaesthesia, Addenbrooke's Hospital, Cambridge CB2 2QQ Tel: 01223 217434; Whitefriars, Carmel St, Great Chesterford, Saffron Walden CB10 1PH — MA Camb. 1982; MB ChB Manch. 1966; FRCA 1972; DA Eng. 1970; DObst RCOG 1969. (Victoria University of Manchester) Cons. Anaesth. Addenbrooke's Hosp. Camb.; Assoc. Lect. Univ. Camb. Socs: Roy. Soc. Med.; Assn. Anaesth.; Brit. Assoc. of Orthopaedic Anaesth.s. Prev: Sen. Regist. (Anaesth.) Addenbrooke's Hosp. Camb.; Regist. (Anaesth.) P.ss Alexandra Hosp. Harlow; Ho. Phys. & Ho. Surg. Univ. Hosp. S. Manch.

JONES, Sadie Jane 28 Manadon Close, Crownhill, Plymouth PL5 3DQ — MB BCh 1986 Wales; MRCGP 1990. Trainee GP Plympton Health Centre Plymouth VTS. Prev: Trainee GP Plymouth VTS.

JONES, Sally Ann 15 Woodlands, Cefnllys Lane, Llandrindod Wells LD1 5DE — MB BCh 1993 Wales.

JONES, Sally Ann 51 Thornhill Way, Rogerstone, Newport NP10 9FS; Flat 3, Havelock House, Lucknow Road, Mapperley Park, Nottingham NG3 5AY Tel: 0115 924 5153 — MB ChB 1989 Aberd.; MRCP (UK) 1993. Regist. (A & E) Derbysh. Roy. Infirm.

JONES, Sally Elizabeth 11 Pretoria Road, Halstead CO9 2EG Tel: 01787 475706 — MB BS 1992 Lond.; MRCGP 1996; DFFP 1996; DRCOG 1995. (Univ. Lond. & King's Coll.) Prev: GP/Regist. Weymouth; SHO (Elderly Care) Dorset Co. Hosp. Dorchester; SHO (O & G& Paediat.) W. Dorset Hosp. Dorchester.

JONES, Sally Marie Fields Corner, Middleton, Oswestry SY11 4LP — MB ChB 1998 Liverp.; MB ChB Liverp 1998.

JONES, Samantha Anne Vaughan — MB BS 1988 Lond.; MD Lond. 1997; MRCP (UK) 1992; MD 1998. (St. Thomas's) Cons. (Dermat.) St. Peter's Hosp. Chertsey Surrey. Socs: Roy. Soc. Med. & BMA; Brit. Assn. Dermat. Prev: Specialist Regist. (Dermat.) St. John's Inst. Dermatol.; Regist. (Gastroenterol. & Cardiol.) St. Peters Hosp. Chertsey; SHO (Gen. Med.) Kingston Hosp.

JONES, Sandra 70 Dan-y-Bryn Avenue, Radyr, Cardiff CF15 8DD Tel: 029 2084 2864 — MB BCh 1965 Wales. (Cardiff) Coll. Med. Off. Univ. Coll. Cardiff; Clin. MOH S. Glam. Prev: Ho. Phys. & Ho. Surg. Roy. Gwent Hosp. Newport; Asst. MOH Newport Co. Boro.

JONES, Sandra 50 Tyelands, Billericay CM12 9PB — MB BS 1998 Lond.; MB BS Lond 1998.

JONES, Sandra Catherine 44 College Avenue, Maidenhead SL6 6AX — MB BCh 1990 Wales.

JONES, Sara Louise 67 Park Street, Tonna, Neath SA11 3JQ — MB BCh 1995 Wales.

JONES, Sarah Catherine Furnace House Surgery, St. Andrews Road, Carmarthen SA31 1EX Tel: 01267 236616 Fax: 01267 222673; Pentrehydd, College Road, Carmarthen SA31 3QS — MB BS 1981 Lond.; DRCOG 1984. Prev: GP Llandysul & Cwmbran.

JONES, Sarah Elisabeth Whipps Cross Hospital, Whipps Cross Road, Leytonstone, London E11 1NR — MB BS 1989 Lond.; BSc (Hons.) Lond. 1986; MRCP (UK) 1992. (UMDS Guy's Hosp. Lond.) Sen. Regist. (Elderly Med.) Whipps Cross Hosp. Lond. Socs: Chair Trainee Gp. Brit. Geriat. Soc.

JONES, Sarah Jane 98 Commonside, Sheffield S10 1GG — MB ChB 1994 Sheff.

JONES, Sarah Joan Shellsborough, The Esplanade, Woolacombe EX34 7DJ — MB BS 1992 Lond.; BSc Lond. 1989; MRCP London 1998. Specialist Regist. Anaesth. Soton. Gen. Hosp.

JONES, Sarah Joanne Grange View, Station Road, Bretforton, Evesham WR11 5HX; 12 Kings Acre, Fields Pk Road, Newport NP20 5BR Tel: 01633 212635 — MB ChB 1995 Leic. SHO (O & G); SHO (Obst. & Gyn.) RGH Newport. Prev: SHO (A & E) Abergavenny; SHO (O & G) Abergavenny.

JONES, Sarah Lynne 14 William Jessop Court, Piccadilly Village, Manchester M1 2NL — MB ChB 1992 Manch.

JONES, Seiriol Wyn 32 Windermere Road, Wrexham LL12 8AN — MB ChB 1964 Liverp.; DObst RCOG 1967. (Liverp.)

JONES, Seth 27 Brynamman Road, Lower Brynamman, Ammanford SA18 1TR Tel: 01269 3370 — LMSSA 1954 Lond. (Char. Cross) Prev: Ho. Surg. High Wycombe War Memor. Hosp.; Ho. Phys. Roy. Alexander Hosp. Rhyl; Obst. Ho. Surg. St. Jas. Hosp. Tredegar.

JONES, Sharon Lynn City Hospital NHS Trust, Dudley Road, Birmingham B18 7QH Tel: 0121 507 4104 Fax: 0121 507 4988 — BM BCh 1982 Oxf.; MA Oxf. 1983, DM 1991. Cons. Phys. & Hon. Clin. Sen. Lect. Univ. Birm. Med. Sch. Socs: Brit. Diabetic Assn.; Fell. RCP; Eur. Assn. Study Dis. Prev: Sen. Regist. (Gen. Med, Diabetes & Endocrinol.) Guy's Hosp. Lond.; Lect. (Endocrinol.) St. Bart. Hosp. Lond.; Regist. (Gen. & Metab. Med.) Guys Hosp. Lond.

JONES, Sheena Dunthwaite, Waverbridge, Wigton Tel: 0169 73 42513 — MB ChB 1951 Birm. (Birm.) Prev: Paediat. Ho. Off. Monkmoor Hosp. Shrewsbury.

JONES, Shirley Patricia (retired) 83 Montalt Road, Woodford Green IG8 9TB Tel: 020 8504 8548 — MB BS 1959 Lond.; MRCP Lond. 1963; MRCS Eng. LRCP Lond. 1959; DPhysMed Eng. 1965. Prev: Clin. Asst. (Rheum. & Rehabil.) Chingford, Whipps Cross, N. Middlx. Hosps. Lond. & King Geo. Hosp. Goodmayes Essex.

JONES, Sian Esther The Yorkshire Clinic, Bradford Road, Bingley BD16 1TW Tel: 01274 560311; 2 The Bullfield, Wilsden Road, Harden, Bingley BD16 1HN Tel: 01274 364618 Fax: 01274 366690 — MB BCh 1977 Wales; FRCOG 1995, M 1982. (Welsh Nat. Sch. Med.) Cons. O & G Bradford Roy. Infirm.

JONES, Sian Lesley The Old Dairy, Home Farm Court, Shillinglee, Chiddingfold, Godalming GU8 4SY — MB BS 1985 Lond.; DRCOG 1989; DCH RCP Lond. 1988. Staff Grade (Community Paediat.) N. Downs Trust Guildford.

JONES, Sian Tudor Nant y Mor, Bull Bay Road, Amlwch LL68 9ED — MB BCh 1998 Wales.

JONES, Simon Barry 17 Glamis Crescent, Rowlands Gill, Newcastle upon Tyne NE99 1AT — MB ChB 1992 Bristol.

JONES, Simon Burkitt The Lodge, 51a High St, Wallingford OX10 0DB Tel: 01491 825199 Fax: 01491 825199 — MB BS 1969 Lond.; MRCPsych 1975; FRCP 1999. (St. Bart.) Indep. Psychiaric Cons., Wallingford, Oxon.; InDepend. Psychiatric Cons.. Prev: Cons. Psychiat.. W. Berks. P.C. NHS Trust; Sen. Regist. (Psychiat.) Univ. Hosp. S. Manch.; Regist. (Psychiat.) Warneford & Littlemore Hosps. Oxf.

***JONES, Simon Edward** Greenways, Kings Lane, Stansted, Stansted CM7 8AQ Tel: 01376 348884 — MB BS 1996 Lond.

JONES, Simon George William Northgate Surgery, Church Street, Uttoxeter ST14 8AG Tel: 01889 562010 Fax: 01889 568948; Tel: 01538 755658 — MB ChB 1989 Birm.; MRCP (UK) 1992; MRCGP 1998; DRCOG 1997. (Birmingham) P Uttoxeter Staffs. Prev: Regist. (Gen. Med. & Gastroenterol.) Univ. Hosp. S. Manch. & Roy. Hallamsh. Hosp.; SHO (Med.) The N. Staffs. Hosp.

JONES, Simon Hedley Dept of Paediatrics, G Floor, North Hants. Hospital, Aldermaston Rd, Basingstoke RG24 9NA — MB BCh 1988 Wales; MRCPCH; MRCP (UK) 1994. Cons. Paediat., N. Hants. Hosp., Basingstoke.

JONES, Mr Simon Michael Gwynn Wansbeck General Hospital, Woodhorn Lane, Ashington NE63 9JJ Tel: 01670 529306 Fax: 01670 529656 Email: simon.jones@northumbria-healthcare.nhs.uk — MB BCh 1983 Wales; FRCS (Orth.) 1996; FRCS Glas. 1989. (Univ. Wales Coll. Med.) Cons. Orthop. & Trauma Surg. Wansbeck Gen. Hosp. Ashington. Prev: Sen. Regist. (Orthop.) N.. RHA; Regist. (Orthop.) Newc.

JONES, Simon Nicholas Western Avenue, Branksome Park, Poole BH13 7AL Tel: 01202 708719 Fax: 01202 701051 Email: cxrdoc@aol.com — MB BS 1979 Lond.; FRCP (UK) 1982; FRCR 1987. (Middlx.) Cons. Radiol. Poole & Roy. Bournemouth NHS Trusts Dorset. Prev: Sen. Regist. Middlx. Hosp. Lond.; Regist. (Radiol.) St. Geo. Hosp. Lond.; Regist. (Med.) St. Thos. Hosp. Lond.

JONES, Simon Robert Auckland Medical Group, 54 Cockton Hill Road, Bishop Auckland DL14 6BB Tel: 01388 602728; New Broomielaw Cottage, Marwood, Barnard Castle Tel: 01833 695067 — MB ChB 1988 Ed.; MRCGP 1995. Princip. GP. Socs: Brit. Assn. Sport & Med.

JONES, Sonia Enid X-Ray Department, Gloucestershire Royal Hospital, Great Western Road, Gloucester GL1 3NL Tel: 01452 395559; Millside, 30 Bond End Road, Upton St Leonards, Gloucester GL4 8DY — MB BS 1965 Lond.; MRCS Eng. LRCP Lond. 1965; Prime Higher Diploma 1975 FRCR; FFR 1974; DMRD Eng. 1971. (Roy. Free) Prev: Sen. Regist. (Radiol.) Radcliffe Infirm. Oxf.; Ho. Surg. (Gyn.) Roy. Free Hosp.; Ho. Phys. (Paediat.) S.mead Hosp.

JONES, Miss Sophia Megan Queen Victoria Hospital, Holtye Road, East Grinstead RH19 3DZ Tel: 01342 410210; Stubbs Cottage, Stubbs Green, Loddon, Norwich NR14 6EA Tel: 01508 528800 — MB BS 1997 Lond.; MRCS (Eng) 2000; BA (Hons.) Oxf. 1994. (St Thos. Guys) Clin. Research Fell. (Plastic Surg.) Qu. Vict. Hosp. Socs: BMA; MPS. Prev: PRHO (Surg.) St Peters Hosp. Chertsey; SHO (Plastic Surg.) Norf. & Norwich Hosp.; sHO (Paed. Surg.) Norf. & Norwich Hosp.

JONES, Stanley Edward Owen (retired) 92A Bradford Road, Atworth, Melksham SN12 8HY — MB ChB 1958 Birm.; DObst RCOG 1967. Prev: Exam. Med. Off. Benefits Agency.

JONES, Stella Mary (retired) Kaia, Dog Kennel Lane, Lyminge, Folkestone CT18 8ER — MB ChB 1950 Sheff.

JONES, Stephen 30 Rotchell Park, Dumfries DG2 7RH Tel: 01387 263574 Fax: 01387 263574 — MB BS 1994 Lond.; BSc Lond. 1993. (Roy. Free Hosp. Sch. Med. Lond.) SHO Rotat. (Surg. & Orthop.) Whittington Hosp. Lond.

JONES, Stephen Austen 18 Hillcrest Road, Keyworth, Nottingham NG12 5JH — MB BS 1990 Lond.

JONES, Mr Stephen Austin Plot 12, Dol-y-Llan, Miskin, Pontyclun CF72 8RY Tel: 01443 225281 — MB BCh 1995 Wales; BSc 1992; MRCS 1998. (Univ.Wales) Specialist Regist. Trauma Orthop. Socs: MRCS; Assoc.Brit.Orthop.Soc. Prev: Basic. Surg. Trainee S. Wales Rotat.

JONES, Stephen Brian 23 Bolton Road, Salford M6 2HL Tel: 0161 736 1616; 15 Pear Tree Grove, Tyldesley, Manchester M29 8PD — MB BS 1984 Lond.; MRCGP 1989.

JONES, Stephen Charles Ward 23 Office, Royal Victoria Infirmary, Newcastle upon Tyne NE1 4LP Tel: 0191 232 5131 Fax: 0191 201 0155 Email: chobaa@hotmail.com — MB BS 1990 Newc.; BMedSc (Hons.) Newc. 1987; MRCP (UK) 1993. (Univ. Newc.) Sen. Regist. Diabetes, Endocrinol. & Gen. Internal Med. Roy. Vict. Infirm.; Freeman Hosp. Newc. Socs: Brit. Endocrine Soc.; Brit. Diabetic Assn.; Collegiate Mem. Roy. Coll. Phys.s Lond. Prev: research fell., Roy. N.share Hosp. Sydney; Sen. Regist. Qu. Eliz. Hosp. Gateshead; Sen. Regist. Freeman Hosp. Newc.

JONES, Stephen David High Street Family Practice, 37-39 High Street, Barry CF62 7EB Tel: 01446 733355 Fax: 01446 733489; Glenthorne, 35 Romilly Park, Barry — MB BCh 1977 Wales; MB BCh Wales (January) 1977; MRCGP 1980.

JONES, Stephen David Victoria Surgery, Victoria Road, Rhymney NP2 5NW Tel: 01685 840614 — MB BCh 1977 Wales; Dip. Ther. Wales 1995; Dip. Palliat. Med. Wales 1991.

JONES, Stephen Edward Morgan 193 Cemetery Road, Ipswich IP4 2HL — MB BS 1993 Lond. SHO (ENT) Addenbrooke's Hosp. Camb. Socs: BMA.

JONES, Stephen Ernest East Barnwell Health Centre, Ditton Lane, Cambridge CB5 8SP Tel: 01223 728900 Fax: 01223 728901 Email: steve.jones@doctors.org.uk — MB BS 1987 Lond.; MA Camb. 1988; MRCGP 1992; DCH RCP Lond. 1991; DRCOG 1990. (Cambridge and St. Bartholomew's) p/t GP Princip. Camb.; Club Doctor Camb. United Football Club; Bd. Mem. Camb. City PCG. Prev: Clin. Lect. (Gen. Pract.) Camb. Univ.; Trainee GP/SHO Addenbrooke's Hosp. Camb. VTS; Ho. Surg. St. Bart. Hosp. Lond.

JONES, Stephen Gareth 11 Y Wern, Llanfairpwllgwyngyll LL61 5AQ; 3 Springhill Cottages, Springhill, Colston Bassett, Nottingham NG12 3FR — MB BCh 1992 Wales.

JONES, Stephen Gwyn 7 St Georges Court, Shrewsbury SY3 8BG — MB BCh 1986 Wales.

JONES, Stephen Howlett Red Roofs, 31 Coton Road, Nuneaton CV11 5TW Tel: 024 7635 7100 Fax: 024 7664 2036; 15 Arden Road, Whitestone, Nuneaton CV11 6PT Tel: 01203 325607 — MB ChB 1988 Leic.; BSc Leic. 1985; MRCGP 1994; DCH RCP Lond. 1992. (Univ. Leic.) GP Tutor N. Warks.

JONES, Stephen Kenneth Department of Dermatology, Clatterbridge Hospital, Bebbington, Wirral CH63 4JY Tel: 0151 334 4000 Fax: 0151 604 7413; Redcroft, 37 Gayton Road, Lower Village, Wirral CH60 8QE Tel: 0151 342 9082 — BM BS 1978 Nottm.; MD Bristol 1991; MRCP (UK) 1981; FRCP 1996. Cons. Dermat. Clatterbridge Hosp. Wirral. Prev: Sen. Regist. (Dermat.) Bristol Roy. Infirm.

JONES, Stephen Mark Bethel Child & Family Centre, Mary Chapman House, Hotblack Road, Norwich NR2 4HN Tel: 01603 421950 Fax: 01603 421990 — MB BS 1986 Lond.; Specialist Register, Child & Adolescent Psychiatry 1997; 1982 BSc Anat. Lond.; 1994 MRCPsych; 1990 MRCGP. (United Med. & Dent. Sch. St. Thos. Hosp. Lond.) Cons. Child & Adolesc. Psychiat. Norf. Ment. Health Care NHS Trust Norwich. Prev: Sen. Regist. (Child & Adolesc. Psychiat.) Camb. Higher Train. Scheme.

JONES, Mr Stephen Michael Monks Walk, Ash Prior, Taunton TA4 3ND Tel: 01823 432231 Fax: 01823 433369 Email: steve.jones@tauntonsom-tv.swest.nhs.uk — MB ChB 1966 Birm.; FRCS Eng. 1971. (Birm.) Cons. Surg. Taunton & Som. Hosp.; Clin.Effectiveness.Comm.RCS Eng; Chairm. SW LMWAG. Socs: Vasc. Surg. Soc. GB & Irel. (Audit Working Party). Prev: Sen. Regist. (Surg.) Bristol Roy. Infirm.; Regist. Frenchay Hosp. Bristol; Regist. P.ss Margt. Hosp. Swindon.

JONES, Stephen Paul 115 Sapley Road, Hartford, Huntingdon PE29 1YU — MB BS 1997 Lond.

JONES, Stephen Rhydian Brynhyfryd Surgery, Llangyfelach Road, Brynhyfryd, Swansea SA5 9DS Tel: 01792 655083; Bay Tree Cottage, Chapel Lane, Murton, Swansea SA3 3AX — MB BS 1989 Lond.; BSc (Physiol.) Lond. 1986; MRCGP 1993. (St. Bart. Hosp.) Socs: Brit. Med. Acupunc. Soc. Prev: Trainee GP Swansea VTS; Ho. Off. (Surg.) St. Bart. Hosp. Lond.; Ho. Off. (Med.) N. Middlx. Hosp. Lond.

JONES, Stephen Robert 6 Linksview, Wallasey CH45 0NQ Email: stevie.jones@bigfoot.com — MB ChB 1994 Manch. Res. Fell. (Emerg. Dept.) Manch. Roy. Infirm. Prev: SHO (Anaesth.) Roy. Liverp. Univ. Hosp.

JONES, Stephen Robert Putnoe Medical Practice, 93 Queens Drive, Bedford MK41 9JE Tel: 01234 360482 Fax: 01234 219361 — MB BS 1987 Lond.; DRCOG 1990. Clin. Asst. Dermat. Dept., Bedford Hosp., Bedford. Prev: Trainee GP/SHO FarnBoro. & Bromley Hosp. VTS; SHO (Geriat.) Orpington Hosp.; Ho. Off. (Gen. Med.) Orpington & FarnBoro. Hosps.

JONES, Stephen Ronald East Tilbury Surgery, Princess Margaret Road, East Tilbury, Grays RM18 8YS Tel: 01375 843217 Fax: 01375 840423 — MRCS Eng. LRCP Lond. 1982.

JONES, Stephen Timothy Morris 3 Wadsworth Close, Handforth, Wilmslow SK9 3AY Tel: 01625 532946 Email: scs.jones@virgin.net — MB ChB 1982 Manch.; BSc (Hons.) Manch. 1979; MRCP (UK) 1987. (Manchester) Cons. Rheum. Vict. Hosp. Blackpool. Socs: Brit. Soc. Rheum.; BMA. Prev: Sen. Regist. (Rheum.) Manch. Roy. Infirm.; Research Fell. (Rheum.) Univ. Manch.

JONES, Stephen Tyler Pinderfields General Hospital, Aberford Road, Wakefield WF1 4DG Tel: 01924 201688 — MB BS 1979 Lond.; FRCP Lond.1995; MRCP (UK) 1982. (Char. Cross) Cons. Paediat. Pinderfields Hosp. Wakefield. Prev: Sen. Regist. (Paediat.) W.m. Hosp. Lond.

JONES, Stephen Wynne Royal United Hospital, Coombe Park, Bath BA2 8AZ Tel: 01225 428331; The Beeches, Nimlet, Cold Ashton, Chippenham SN14 8JX — MB BS 1988 Lond.; FRCPCH 1997; BSc (1st. cl. Hons.) Lond. 1985; MRCP (UK) 1991. (St. Mary's Hosp.) Cons. Paediat. Roy. United Hosp. Bath. Prev: Sen. Regist. (Paediat.) Univ. Hosp. Wales Cardiff; Neonat.. Fell. Hosp. Sick Childr. Toronto, Canada; Regist. (Paediat.) Soton. Gen. Hosp.

JONES, Steven Pendre Surgery, Coleshill Street, Holywell CH8 7RS Tel: 01352 712029 Fax: 01352 712751 — MB ChB 1982 Ed.; MRCGP 1988; DRCOG 1985.

JONES, Steven Roy Hartley Corner Surgery, 51 Frogmore Road, Blackwater, Camberley GU17 0DB Tel: 01252 872791 Fax: 01252 878910 — MB BS 1976 Lond.; MRCS Eng. LRCP Lond. 1976; MRCGP 1980; DCH Eng. 1980; DRCOG 1979.

JONES, Stewart David Flat 4, 1 Stoneygate Avenue, Leicester LE2 3HE; 4 Walton Walk, Chesterfield S40 2QQ — MB ChB 1989 Leic.

JONES, Stuart Robert 121 Old Station Road, Bromsgrove B60 2AS — MB ChB 1989 Sheff.; BMedSci (Hons.) Sheff. 1989; MRCGP 1994; T(GP) 1994; DRCOG 1993. (Univ. Sheff.)

JONES, Susan 15 Weaver Avenue, Crookfur, Newton Mearns, Glasgow G77 6AS Tel: 0141 616 0353; 1 Otterwood Bank, Wetherby LS22 7XT Tel: 01937 588135 — MB ChB 1988 Glas. GP Retainer.

JONES, Susan Barbara Normanby Road Surgery, 502-508 Normanby Road, Normanby, Middlesbrough TS6 9BZ Tel: 01642 452727/440501 Fax: 01642 466723; Ravenscar, Hill Road, Kirby-in-Cleveland, Middlesbrough TS9 7AN — MB BS 1985 Newc.; MRCGP 1989; DRCOG 1990.

JONES, Susan Carol Huddersfield Royal Infirmary, Lindley, Huddersfield HD5 3EA — MB ChB 1985 Leeds; MD (Commend.) Leeds 1995; MRCP (UK) 1988. p/t Cons. in Gen.Med. & Gasteroenterology Huddersfield Roy. Infirm. Prev: Sen. Regist. (Med. & Gastroenterol.) St. Jas. Hosp. Leeds.

JONES, Susan Elizabeth 138 Bewick Park, Rainhill, Wallsend NE28 9RY Email: susan.jones@ncl.ac.uk — MB ChB 1991 Birm.; MRCP (UK) 1994. (Birmingham) Regist. (Med., Diabetes & Endocrinol.) N. & Yorks. RHA; Clin. Res. Assoc. The Med. Sch. Newc. u. Tyne. Prev: SHO (Med.) S. Birm. HA.

JONES, Mrs Susan Elizabeth The Maidstone Hospital, Mid Kent Health Care Trust, Hermitage Lane, Barming, Maidstone ME16 9QQ Tel: 01622 224111 Fax: 01622 224714; Old Timbers, Reed Place, Dairy Lane, Chainhurest, Marden, Tonbridge TN12 9ST Tel: 01622 820840 Fax: 01622 820837 Email: old.tim@net.comuk.co.uk — MB BS 1976 Lond.; FRCS Eng. 1980; Cert. Family Plann. JCC 1986. (St. Geo.) Assoc. Specialist (Gen. Surg.) Maidstone Hosp. Prev: Regist. (Gen. Surg.) Mayday Hosp. Croydon; Regist. (Gen. Surg.) St. Jas. Hosp. Lond. & Kingston Hosp.

JONES, Susan Elizabeth Frances 7 Bishbury Close, Edgbaston, Birmingham B15 3NU Tel: 0121 454 8013 — MB BS 1966 Durh.; FFA RCS Eng. 1971; FRCA 2000. Cons. Anaesth. Birm. Childr. Hosp.

JONES, Susan Karen Medical Protection Society, Granary Wharf House, Leeds LS11 5PY; Flat C Regal Flats, 6 Clarence Drive, Harrogate HG1 2PN — MB BS 1990 Lond.; LLB Liverp. 1985; MRCGP 1994; DRCOG 1993; MA 1998. Medico Legal Adviser Med. Protec. Soc. Leeds. Prev: Med. Off. Lond. LightHo.; Trainee GP Medway HA.

JONES, Susan Lesley Wilson — BM 1987 Soton.; MRCPsych 1999; Dip. Psychiat.; DRCOG. Old age Psychatry, Shrewsbury.

JONES, Suzanne Patricia 10 The Green, Amington, Tamworth B77 4AD Tel: 01827 60661 Email: 106343.3200@compuserve.com — BM BS 1985 Nottm.; BMedSci Nottm. 1983; MPH Birm. 1997; DRCOG 1991; DTM & H Liverp. 1989; DCH RCP Lond. 1987. (Nottingham) Regist. (Pub. Health Med.) W. Midl.; Hon. Clin. Lect.

JONES, Sybil Angela Margaret (retired) Bleak House, Horsted Keynes, Haywards Heath RH17 7ED — MB BS 1965 Lond.; MRCS Eng. LRCP Lond. 1965; FFPHM RCP (UK) 1985, M 1980; AKC 1965. Prev: Cons. Pub. Health Med. N. Thames RHA.

JONES, Tanya Louise 6 Penrith Way, Aylesbury HP21 7JZ; 30 Myddelton Street, Islington, London EC1R 1UA — MB ChB 1997 Manch. Gen. Med. Rotat. Whittington Hosp. Lond.

JONES, Tara Naomi 147 Florence Road, London SW19 8TL — MB BS 1994 Lond.

JONES, Tecwyn Health Centre, Meddygfa, Canolfan Iechyd, Bala LL23 7BA Tel: 01678 520308 Fax: 01678 520883 — MB BCh 1971 Wales.

JONES, Terence Livingstone 27 Swanwick Road, Leabrooks, Derby Tel: 01773 602746 — MB BS 1980 Lond.

JONES, Terence Morgan 95 Deansfield, Cricklade, Swindon SN6 6BW — MB BS 1993 Lond.

JONES, Theodore Inslee (retired) Fishermans Cottage, Ulva Ferry, Isle of Mull PA73 6NA Tel: 0168 85 207 — LMSSA 1975 Lond.; MD Cornell 1952; Dip. Amer. Bd. Surg. 1959. Prev: Clin. Assoc. Prof. Surg. Univ. Rochester Med. Sch., U.S.A.

JONES, Thomas Alan Cairnsmore Medical Practice, Creebridge, Newton Stewart DG8 6NR Tel: 01671 403609 Fax: 01671 404008; Meikle Eldrig, Newton Stewart DG8 6QP Tel: 01671 402013 Fax: 01671 404092 — MB ChB 1981 Birm.; DRCOG 1986. (Birmingham)

JONES, Mr Thomas Alun The Croft, Shackerstone Walk, Carlton, Nuneaton CV13 0BY — MB BS 1980 Lond.; FRCS Eng. 1987; FRCS Ed. 1985.

JONES, Thomas Dyfrig (retired) Porters Lodge, Knapton, North Walsham NR28 0AD Tel: 01263 720523 — MB BCh 1949 Wales; BSc Wales 1945, MB BCh 1949; DObst RCOG 1974; DTM & H Eng. 1967. Prev: Lt. Col. (Retd.) RAMC.

JONES, Thomas Evan Griffith Arosfa, Pen-y-Berth, Llanfairpwllgwyngyll LL61 5YT Tel: 01248 714404 Email: tejones@ypiag-asthma.org — MB BCh 1974 Wales.

JONES, Thomas Gareth (retired) 9 Poolfield Drive, Solihull B91 1SH Tel: 0121 705 6599 — MB BS Lond. 1946; DObst RCOG 1951. Prev: Ho. Surg. (Obst.) Coventry & Warw. Hosp.

JONES, Thomas Glyn (retired) — MB BChir Camb. 1962; MA Camb. 1962; FRCGP 1985, M 1969; DObst RCOG 1963; MFPH (RCP) 2000. Prev: Regional Med. Off. (Oxf. & Berks.) E. Midl. Div.

JONES, Thomas Hugh Centre for Diabetes and Endocrinology, Barnsley District General Hospital, Gawber Road, Barnsley S75 2EP Tel: 01226 777947 Fax: 01226 777947 Email: hugh.jones@bdgh-tr.trent.nhs.uk — MD 1990 Sheff.; BSc (Hons.) Sheff. 1975, MB ChB 1980; MRCP (UK) 1984, MD 1990. (University of Sheffield) Cons. Phys. & Endocrinol. Barnsley Dist. Gen. Hosp. Barnsley; Hon. Sen. Lect., Endocrine and Cardiovasc. Research Gp., Univ. of Sheff. Socs: Soc. for Endocrinol.; Internat. Pituitary Pathologist Club; Endocrine Soc., USA. Prev: Lect. & Hon. Sen. Regist. Univ. Dept. Med. N.. Gen. Hosp. Sheff.; Clin. Research Fell. Dept. Human Metab. & Clin. Biochem Univ. Sheff. Med. Sch.; Regist. (Med.) Roy. Hallamsh. Hosp. Sheff.

JONES, Thomas John (retired) Gaywood, Llandysul SA44 4AE Tel: 01559 362209 — MB BS Lond. 1945. Prev: Ho. Off. Guy's Hosp. Lond. & Hillingdon Hosp.

JONES, Thomas Llewelyn (retired) 12 King Edward Road, Minehead TA24 5EA — MB BCh 1944 Wales; BSc Wales 1940, MB BCh 1944. Prev: Cons. Anaesth. S. Som. Clin. Area.

JONES, Thomas McNevin 24 Erlington Avenue, Manchester M16 0FW — MB ChB 1992 Manch.

JONES, Thomas Michael Bramwell (retired) Banc-Yr-Eos, Llanddarog, Carmarthen SA32 8NU Tel: 01267 275238 — MB BS 1960 Lond.; MRCS Eng. LRCP Lond. 1961; DObst RCOG 1962. Prev: GP LLa.lli, Dyfed.

JONES, Thomas Peter John 118 Newland Park, Hull HU5 2DU Tel: 01482 492707 Fax: 01482 492707 Email: tpjjones@globalnet.co.uk; 118 Newlands Park, Hull HU5 2DU Tel: 01482 492707 Fax: 01482 492707 Email: tpjjones@globalnet.co.uk — MB BS 1962 Lond.; MRCS Eng. LRCP Lond. 1962; DObst RCOG 1964. (St. Mary's) Works Med. Off. B.P. Chem.s Ltd. Socs: Hull Med. Soc.; Soc. Occupat. Med. Prev: Ho. Surg. St. Mary's Hosp.; Ho. Phys. Harold Wood Hosp.; Ho. Surg. (Obst.) Paddington Gen. Hosp. Lond.

JONES, Thomas Roy (retired) Heulwen, St. George Road, Abergele LL22 7HB — MRCS Eng. LRCP Lond. 1938; MRCS Eng., LRCP Lond. 1938.

JONES, Thomas Ryland 2 Ynyswen, Penycae, Swansea SA9 1YS — MB BCh 1985 Wales.

JONES, Thomas Terry 4 Church Road, Hazelbeach, Llanstadwell, Milford Haven SA73 1EE — MB BCh 1960 Wales.

JONES, Timothy David Flat A, Northwood, Clumber Road E., Nottingham NG7 1BD — MB ChB 1992 Cape Town.

JONES, Timothy David 99 St Michaels Road, Crosby, Liverpool L23 7UL — MB ChB 1998 Liverp.; MB ChB Liverp 1998.

JONES, Timothy George Southampton General Hospital, Tremona Road, Southampton SO16 6YD — MB BS 1989 Lond.

JONES, Mr Timothy James Julian 47 Wynds Point, Bournville Copse, Bournville, Birmingham B31 2EF Email: timjones5@compuserve.com — MB BS 1992 Lond.; FRCS Eng. 1996.

JONES, Timothy John Henry 21 Marshcourt, Lychpit, Basingstoke RG24 8UY — BM 1988 Soton.

JONES, Timothy Martin 17 Marriotts Close, Felmersham, Bedford MK43 7HD — MB ChB 1995 Leeds.

JONES, Timothy Martin Watkin Doctors Surgery, Pierce Street, Queensferry, Deeside CH5 1SY Tel: 01244 813340 Fax: 01244 822882 — MB ChB 1976 Manch.; Dip. Psychosexual Healthcare Manch. 1996. (Univ. Manch.)

JONES, Timothy Robert Rubislaw Place Medical Group, 7 Rubislaw Place, Aberdeen AB10 1QB Tel: 01224 641968; 39

Woodburn Avenue, Aberdeen AB15 8JQ — MB ChB 1978 Dundee; MRCGP 1984; DA Eng. 1981.

JONES, Tom Morgan Lloyd Taliesin Surgery, Taliesin, Lampeter SA48 7AA Tel: 01570 422665 Fax: 01570 423810; Penrhos, Cwmann, Lampeter SA48 8DT — MB BCh 1969 Wales.

JONES, Tracy Anne The Mumbles Medical Practice, 10 West Cross Avenue, Norton, Mumbles, Swansea SA3 5UA Tel: 01792 403010 Fax: 01792 401934 — MB BCh 1984 Wales; T(GP) 1992. Prev: SHO (Gen. & Geriat. Med. & Haemat.) Arrowe Pk. Hosp. Wirral; SHO (Paediat.) Ysbyty Glan Clwyd; Regist. (Geriat.) Ysbyty Glan Clwyd.

JONES, Trevor John, Capt. RAMC 9 Erleigh Dene, Newbury RG14 6JG — MB BCh 1983 Wales; BSc Wales 1978. Med. Off. Dhekelia Garrison.

JONES, Trevor John Duncan St Johns House Surgery, 28 Bromyard Road, St. Johns, Worcester WR2 5BU Tel: 01905 423612 Fax: 01905 740003 — MB ChB 1979 Manch.; BSc St. And. 1976; MRCGP 1988; DFFP 1995; DRCOG 1983. Socs: Medico-Legal Soc. Worcs.; Assur. Med. Soc.

JONES, Valerie Anne 71 St James Road, Sutton SM1 2TG — MB BS 1988 Lond.; MRCP (UK) 1992. Cons. Phys. with an interest in Stroke & Elderly Care Mayday Univ. Hosp. Thornton Heath Surrey. Socs: Brit. Geriat. Soc. Prev: Sen. Regist. Rotat. (Geriat. Med.) St. Geo. Hosp. Lond.; Trainee GP Chichester VTS; SHO Rotat. (Med.) Battle Hosp. Reading.

JONES, Valerie Pierce The Cedars, Marsh Lane, Nantwich CW5 5HP Tel: 01270 63464 — MB ChB 1964 Manch.; DObst RCOG 1966. Med. Asst. (Ultrasonics) St. Mary's Hosp. Manch.

JONES, Vaughan Wyn 2 The Knowl, Churton, Chester CH3 6NE — MB ChB 1974 Liverp.; FRCR 1982; DMRD Liverp. 1979.

JONES, Vera 115A Heol Isaf, Radyr, Cardiff CF14 6RJ — B.Sc. 1935, M.B., B.Ch. Wales 1941. (Cardiff) Clin. Asst. (Radiother.) Velindre Hosp. & United Cardiff Hosps. Socs: BMA. Prev: Jun. Asst., Med. Unit & Ho. Surg. Cardiff Roy. Infirm.

JONES, Vernon Llewelyn (retired) 271 Clasemont Road, Morriston, Swansea SA6 6BT — MB BCh 1957 Wales.

JONES, Vicki Lee Doctors Residence, North Manchester General Hospital, Central Drive, Manchester M8 5RB — MB ChB 1989 Otago.

JONES, Victoria Elise 27 Hook Hill, Sanderstead, Purley CR2 0LB — MB ChB 1998 Sheff.; MB ChB Sheff 1998.

JONES, Vivien Jane Ione Marlowe House Partnership, Marlowe Close, Popley 1, Basingstoke RG24 9DD Tel: 01256 328860/323796 Fax: 01256 351911 Email: jane.jones@gp-j82096.nhs.uk — MB BS 1970 Lond.; MRCS Eng. LRCP Lond. 1970; DObst RCOG 1972. (St. Mary's) Gen. Practitioner. Prev: Clin. Med. Off. Cornw. & Isles of Scilly AHA; Ho. Phys. & Ho. Surg. Bedford Gen. Hosp.

JONES, Vyvyan David (retired) Springs House, Union St., Ramsbury, Marlborough SN8 2PR — MB BS 1955 Lond.; FRCOG 1977, M 1963, DObst 1960. Hon. Tutor St. Mary's Hosp. Med. Sch. Lond. Prev: Cons. O & G P.ss Margt. Hosp. Swindon.

JONES, Vyvyan Hugh, VRD (retired) Garden House, Solva, Haverfordwest SA62 6TR — MRCS Eng. LRCP Lond. 1944; DCH Eng. 1948. Prev: Supernum. Regist. Childr. Unit, Roy. Infirm. Cardiff.

JONES, Walter Williamson (Surgery) 525 New Chester Road, Rock Ferry, Birkenhead CH42 2AG Tel: 0151 645 3464; 10 Prospect Road, Prenton, Birkenhead CH42 8LF Tel: 0151 608 1820 — MB ChB 1948 Liverp.; DCH Eng. 1952. (Liverp.) Prev: Paediat. Regist. Mill Rd. Matern. Hosp. Liverp.; Sen. Ho. Off. Paediat. Clatterbridge Hosp.; Med. Off. RAF Rehabil. Unit, Collaton Cross.

JONES, Wilfrid Llewelyn (cons. rooms) Convent Hospital, Mansfield Road, Woodthorpe, Nottingham NG5 3FZ Tel: 0115 920 4166; 26 Oak Tree Drive, Gedling, Nottingham NG4 4DA Tel: 0115 952 3111 — MB BS 1938 Durh.; FRCPsych 1971; DPM Bristol 1948; Dip. Hist. Med. Soc. Apoth. Lond. 1986. (Newc.) Cons. Psychiat. Emerit. Mapperley Hosp. Nottm. Prev: Cons. Psychiat. Mapperley Hosp. Nottm., Nottm. Gen. Hosp. & City Hosp. Nottm.; Maj. RAMC Specialist Psychiat.

JONES, William Alan Ysgubor Fawr, Clynnogfawr, Caernarfon LL54 5DW; 82 Statham Road, Bidston, Birkenhead CH43 7XS — MB ChB 1993 Dundee; MBChB Liverp. 1993; MRCP (UK) 1998. (Liverpool) SHO (Med. (Gastroenterol.) Arrowe Pk. Hospita Wirral. Socs: MDU; BMA; Roy. Coll. Phys. Lond. Prev: SHO (Respirat. Med.); SHO (Haemat.); SHO (Diabetes & Endocrinol.).

JONES, Mr William Anthony 28 Rodney Street, Liverpool L1 2TQ Tel: 0151 709 8160 — MB ChB 1976 Liverp.; MChOrth. Liverp. 1983, MB ChB 1976; FRCS Eng. 1981; FRCS Ed. 1981. (Liverpool) Cons. Orthop. Surg. Roy. Liverp. & BRd.green Univ. Hosp. Trust. Socs: Fell. BOA; Fell.Brit. Soc. Surg. of the Hand. Prev: Sen. Regist. (Orthop.) Mersey RHA; Fell. Hand Surg. Louisville Hand Surg. Kentucky, USA.

JONES, William Arthur Kenneth The Whittington Medical Centre, High Street, Old Whittington, Chesterfield S41 9JZ Tel: 01246 455440 Fax: 01246 261851; Oakedge House, Oakedge Lane, Tansley, Matlock DE4 5FQ — MB ChB 1977 Sheff.; BSc (Hons.) Wales 1969; PhD Sheff. 1977; MRCGP 1982; DRCOG 1981.

JONES, William George The Leeds Teaching Hospitals NHS Trust, Yorkshire Centre for Clinical Oncology, Cookridge Hospital, Hospital Lane, Leeds LS16 6QB Tel: 0113 392 4276 Fax: 0113 392 4441 Email: bill.jones@leedsth.nhs.uk; 32 Adel Towers Court, Adel, Leeds LS16 8ER Tel: 0113 261 0330 Fax: 0113 261 0330 Email: billjonesleeds@compuserve.com — MB ChB Birm. 1969; FRCR 1975; FFR 1974; DMRT Eng. 1972. (Birm.) Cons. Radiother, & Clin. Oncol. Leeds Teachg. Hosps. NHS Trust Cookridge Hosp.; Sen. Clin. Lect. Univ. Leeds. Socs: Fell. Roy. Soc. Med.; Rad. Soc.; BMA. Prev: Sen. Lect. (Radiother.) Univ. Leeds at Cookridge Hosp.; Cons. Radiother. & Oncol. Singleton Hosp. Swansea; Sen. Regist. (Radiother.) Birm. Centr. Health Dist. (T).

JONES, William Hugh Lewis 69 Walter Road, Swansea SA1 4QA Tel: 01792 643000; Killan Fach Farm, Killan Road, Dunvant, Swansea SA2 7US Tel: 01792 290682 — MB BCh 1967 Wales; MRCP (UK) 1973. Prev: Regist. Selly Oak Hosp. Birm.; Regist. Groote Schur Hosp., Capetown; SHO United Cardiff Hosps.

JONES, Mr William Ian, OBE (retired) Trem-y-Don, 4 Beaufort Avenue, Langland, Swansea SA3 4NU Tel: 01792 368214 — MB BCh 1956 Wales; FRCS Eng. 1964. Med. Off. (Complaints) Welsh Office. Prev: Cons. ENT Surg. Singleton Hosp. Swansea.

JONES, William Kenneth Harnall Lane Medical Centre, Harnall Lane East, Coventry CV1 5AE Tel: 024 7622 4640 Fax: 024 7622 3859; Harnall Lane Medical Centre, Coventry CV1 5ER Tel: 024 76 224640 — MB ChB 1964 Glas.; DObst RCOG 1966. Socs: Brit. Soc. Med. & Dent. Hypn. Prev: Ho. Phys. (Gen. Med. & Tuberc.) Hairmyres Hosp. E. Kilbride; Ho. Surg. Swansea Gen. Hosp.; Ho. Off. (O & G) Cardiff Roy. Infirm.

JONES, William Kenneth (retired) Apple Cross, Macclesfield Road, Alderley Edge SK9 7BN Tel: 01625 582171 — MRCS Eng. LRCP Lond. 1943; FFA RCS Eng. 1954; DA Eng. 1948. Prev: Cons. Anaesth. United Manch. Hosps. & Christie Hosp. Manch.

JONES, William Norman, KStJ (retired) 'Beechmount', 149 Galgorm Road, Ballymena BT42 1DE Tel: 01266 656642 — MB BCh BAO 1941 Belf.; MRCGP 1953.

JONES, William Rees Stuart Doctors Surgery, Pierce Street, Queensferry, Deeside CH5 1SY Tel: 01244 813340 Fax: 01244 822882; Llys Gwyn, Village Road, Nercwys, Mold CH7 4EL — MB ChB 1976 Manch.; DRCOG 1984.

JONES, Winifred Mary (retired) Queen Elizabeth Court, Craig-Y-Don, Llandudno LL30 1TR — MB ChB 1944 Birm.; FRCPath 1975, M 1964. Prev: Clin. Asst. Path. Dept. Leeds Matern. Hosp.

JONES, Mr Wyn Morris (retired) The Royal Hallamshire Hospital, Glossop Road, Sheffield S10 2JF Tel: 0114 276 6222 — MD 1992 Leic.; MCh Wales 1969, MB BCh 1959; FRCS Eng. 1967; FRCS Ed. 1966; FRCS Glas. 1964; MRCS Eng. LRCP Lond. 1959. Cons. Vasc. & Gen. Surg. Roy. Hallamsh. Hosp. Sheff.; Lect. (Surg.) Univ. Sheff. Prev: Sen. Regist. Roy. Infirm. Sheff. & Leicester.

JONES, Wynford Jenkyn (retired) 14 Lyceum Close, Crewe CW1 3YB — MB BS 1952 Lond.; MB BS (Hons. Surg.) Lond. 1952; DTM & H Eng. 1966. Prev: Sen. Med. Off. Shell Internat. Petroleum Co.

JONES-DAVIES, Gwyneth Anne East Dyfed Health Authority, Starling Park House, Johnstown, Carmarthen SA31 3HL Tel: 01267 234501; Principal's Residence, Trinity College, Carmarthen SA31 3EP Tel: 01267 236234 — MB BCh 1965 Wales; MSc (Social Med.) Lond. 1981; MFCM 1986. (Cardiff) Specialist Community Med. E. Dyfed HA. Socs: BMA. Prev: SCMO E. Dyfed HA.; Sen. Regist. (Community Med.) S.W. Thames AHA; Regist. (Community Med.) Lond. Sch. Hyg. & Trop. Med.

JONES-EDWARDS, Gwen Uned Iechyd Meddyliol Dwyfor, Cilan, Stryd Penlan, Pwllheli LL53 5DH Tel: 01758 614647 Fax: 01758 614648 — MB BCh 1981 Wales; MRCPsych 1988. Cons. Psychiat.

JONES-EVANS, Dafydd Huw Frondeg, Heol Ffrydan, Bala LL23 7RT Email: huwje@tesco.net — MB BS 1993 Lond.

JONES-EVANS, Robat Alun Frondeg, Heol Ffrydan, Bala LL23 7RT — MB BS 1993 Lond.

JONES-KEY, Wendy Patricia Bossiney Lodge, Bossiney, Tintagel PL34 0AY — LRCPI & LM, LRSCI & LM 1969; LRCPI & LM, LRCSI & LM 1969.

JONES-UNWIN, Christine Agnes St Anthony's Medical Group, Thomas Gaughan House, Pottery Bank, Newcastle upon Tyne NE6 3SW Tel: 0191 265 5689; 49 Amherst Road, Withington, Manchester M20 4WS Tel: 0161 434 7850 — MB BS 1983 W. Indies; MRCGP 1989; DRCOG 1989.

JONES WILLIAMS, William (retired) 143 Lake Road W., Roath Park, Cardiff CF23 5PJ — MRCS Eng. LRCP Lond. 1948; MD Lond. 1953, MB BS 1948; FRCP Lond. 1982, M 1977; FRCPath 1971, M 1964. Prev: Cons. Path. Llandough Hosp. Penarth.

JONG, Michelle 1 Malone Manor, Belfast BT9 6SR — MB BCh BAO 1993 Belf.

JONSSON, Kerry Elizabeth 1 Hampstead Walk, Parnell Road, London E3 2JN — MB BS 1998 Lond.; MB BS Lond 1998.

JOOTUN, Neerunjun 179 Inderwick Road, Hornsey Vale, London N8 9JR — BM BS 1989 Nottm.

JOPSON, Caetlin Jill 78 Weir Road, London SW12 0NB Tel: 020 8675 2080 — MB BS 1990 Sydney.

JORASZ, Barbara Maria Heaton Moor Medical Centre, 32 Heaton Moor Road, Stockport SK4 4NX Tel: 0161 432 0671 — MB ChB 1975 Manch.

JORDACHE, Susan Mary 36 The Park, St Albans AL1 4RY — MB BS 1991 Lond.

JORDAN, Alan James Torrington Park Health Centre, 16 Torrington Park, North Finchley, London N12 9SS Tel: 020 8445 7622; 43 Oakleigh Avenue, Whetstone, London N20 9JE Tel: 020 8445 4463 — MB BS 1956 Lond.; MRCS Eng. LRCP Lond. 1956; DObst RCOG 1960. (St. Geo.) Socs: BMA. Prev: SHO (Obst.) Bearsted Memor. Hosp.; Cas. Off. & Ho. Phys. St. Geo. Hosp. Lond.

JORDAN, Alexander Reid, SBStJ (retired) Long Combe Lodge, Manor Road, Minehead TA24 6EJ Tel: 01643 703714 — MB BS 1953 Lond.; DObst RCOG 1955. Prev: GP Minehead.

JORDAN, Alison Claire 4 Churchwood Close, Rough Common, Canterbury CT2 9BT — MB ChB 1991 Bristol; MRCP (UK) 1994. Asst. Rheum. Kent & Canterbury Hosp. Prev: SHO (Gen. Med.) Thanet Dist. Hosp.

JORDAN, Alison Faith South Street Surgery, 83 South Street, Bishop's Stortford CM23 3AP Tel: 01279 710800 Fax: 01279 710801; 1 Grange Road, Bishop's Stortford CM23 5NG Tel: 01279 653183 — MB BS 1985 Lond.; MRCGP 1989; DCH RCP (UK) 1990; DRCOG 1987.

JORDAN, Andrew David Alrewas Surgey, Exchange Road, Alrewas, Burton-on-Trent DE13 7AS Tel: 01283 790316 Fax: 01283 791863 Email: andrew.jordan@ndirect.co.uk; 69 A Berryhedge Lane, Winshill, Burton-on-Trent DE15 0DP Tel: 01283 533868 — MB ChB 1996 Birm.; DRCOG 1998. (Birm.) SHO (O & G) Qu. Hosp. Burton-on-Trent. Socs: Med. Defence Union; BMA; MSS. Prev: SHO (O & G) Qu. Hosp. Burton-on-Trent; SHO (A&E) Watford Gen. Hosp.; SHO (Paediat.) Burton on Trent.

JORDAN, Angela Lyn 44 Cripps Post Graduate Centre, Northampton General Hospital, Northampton; 17 Glenshesk Park, Bangor BT20 4US — BM BS 1995 Nottm. SHO (Gen. Med.) N.ampton Gen. Hosp.

JORDAN, Arthur Frederick (retired) Stapleton House, Truemans Way, Hawarden, Deeside CH5 3LS Tel: 01244 535271 — MB ChB 1952 Bristol; MRCS Eng. LRCP Lond. 1952.

JORDAN, Barbara Louise Fareham Health Centre, Osborn Road, Fareham PO16 7ER Tel: 01329 822111 Fax: 01329 286636; Nelson Villa, Trampers Lane, North Boarhunt, Fareham PO17 6BT Tel: 01329 833691 — MB ChB 1976 Sheff.; DCH Eng. 1979.

JORDAN, Christopher 23 Drake Avenue, Minster on Sea, Sheerness ME12 3SA — MB BS 1990 Lond.

JORDAN, Christopher Anthony 20 Links Way, Wallasey L44 6UP — MB ChB 1987 Leeds.

JORDAN, Christopher Noel Duke medical Centre, 28 Talbot Road, Sheffield S2 2TD Tel: 0114 272 0689; Dyson Holmes House, Dyson Holmes Lane, Wharncliffe Side, Sheffield S35 0DJ Tel: 0114 286 2800 — MB ChB 1982 Ed.; MRCGP 1987. (Edinburgh) Socs: BMA. Prev: Trainee GP Aberfeldy VTS; GP Princip. Dunvegan Isle of Skye 1988-1998; SHO (Paediat.) Seafield Childr. Hosp. Ayr.

JORDAN, Gareth John 16 Clos yr Alarch, Cardiff CF14 9JD — MB BCh 1995 Wales. GPV. T. S. Rotat.

JORDAN, Geraldine Banchory Group Practice, The Surgery, Bellfield, Banchory AB31 5XS Tel: 01330 822121 Fax: 01330 825265; Tomdarra, Annesley, Torphins, Banchory AB31 4HL — MB ChB 1991 Aberd.; MRCGP 1995.

JORDAN, Guy Matthew 74 Gilbey Road, London SW17 0QG — MB BS 1996 Lond.

JORDAN, Hector William (retired) 9 Parkside, Alexandra Road, Heathfield TN21 8EB Tel: 01435 865684 Fax: 01435 865684 — MB BS 1931 Lond.; MRCS Eng. LRCP Lond. 1929. Prev: Ho. Surg. Roy. Ear Hosp.

JORDAN, John Warren Carl Royd, Cleevethorpe Grove, Sandal, Wakefield WF2 7NA Tel: 01924 255315 — MB BS 1946 Lond.; MD Lond. 1948; FRCP Lond. 1975, M 1948; MRCS Eng. LRCP Lond. 1946. (St. Bart.) Prev: Cons. Phys. (Chest Dis.) Pontefract & Killingbeck Hosps. Leeds; Regist. Med. Dept. Whittington Hosp. (St. Mary's Wing); Ho. Phys. Lister EMS Hosp. Hitchin.

JORDAN, Joseph Allan Birmingham Women's Hospital NHS Trust, Edgbaston, Birmingham B15 2TG Tel: 0121 472 1377 Fax: 0121 627 2667; 20 Church Road, Edgbaston, Birmingham B15 3TA Tel: 0121 454 2345 Fax: 0121 454 5129 — MB BS Durh. 1960; MD Birm. 1972; FRCOG 1981, M 1966; DObst RCOG 1962. (Durh.) Cons. Gyn. & Med. Dir. Birm. Wom. Hosp. NHS Trust; Hon. Sen. Lect. Univ. Birm. Socs: Brit. Soc. Colpos. & Cerv. Path.; Brit. Gyn. Cancer Soc.; Birm. & Midl. Obst. & Gyn. Soc. Prev: Pres. Internat. Fed. Cervical Path. & Colposcopy; Pres. Brit. Soc. Colposcopy & Cervical Path.; Pres.Europ. Federat. of coloroscopy.

JORDAN, Josephine Mary Jepson House Day Hospital, 8 Manor Court Avenue, Nuneaton CV11 5HY Tel: 01203 326111; 20 Sidmouth Close, Horeston Grange, Nuneaton CV11 6FA Tel: 01203 370916 — MB ChB 1956 St. And.; DPM RCPSI 1988. Clin. Asst. (Psychiat.) Jespon Hse. Day Hosp. Nuneaton. Prev: Regist. & SHO (Psychiat.) Roundway Hosp. Devizes; Regist. (Psychiat.) Hill End Hosp. St. Albans.

JORDAN, Kelsey Maria Tel: 01947 604017 Fax: 01947 604017; Florence Cottage, 17 Dover St, Southampton SO14 6GG Tel: 023 8063 0374 Email: kelseyjordan@doctors.org.uk — MB ChB 1993 Leeds; MRCP (UK) 1998. SPR in Rheum.&Gen. Medecine.

JORDAN, Mr Kerry, Wing Cdr. RAF Med. Br. Retd. Oxford Cottage, Edes Paddock, Great Barton, Bury St Edmunds IP31 2TY Tel: 01284 788224 Fax: 01284 788238 Email: kerry.jordan@virgin.net — MB BS 1971 Lond.; FRCS Ed. 1978; FCOphth 1989; DO Eng. 1975. (King's Coll. Hosp.) Cons. Ophth. Surg. W. Suff. Hosp. Bury St. Edmunds. Prev: Cons. Ophth. Surg. RAF; Hon. Cons. Ophth. Surg. Addenbrooke's Hosp. Camb.; Ho. Surg. (Ophth.) King's Coll. Hosp. Lond.

***JORDAN, Lee Baines** 1A Clarence Street, Stockbridge, Edinburgh EH3 5AE Tel: 0131 556 6064 Email: lbj@bouj.freeserve.co.uk — MB ChB 1997 Ed.; BSc (1st cl. Hons.) Genetics Ed. 1996.

JORDAN, Lesley Christine 32 Alma Road, Eton Wick, Windsor SL4 6LA — MB ChB 1987 Leic.

JORDAN, Lesley Margaret Northville Family Practice, 521 Filton Avenue, Horfield, Bristol BS7 0LS Tel: 0117 969 2164 Fax: 0117 931 5743; 19 School Road, Frampton, Cotterell, Bristol BS36 2DB Tel: 01454 776808 — MB ChB 1981 Bristol; MRCGP 1985; DRCOG 1983.

JORDAN, Lizbeth Jean Scottish Office, St. Andrew's House, Edinburgh EH1 3DG; 55 Partickhill Road, Glasgow G11 5AB Tel: 0141 334 2834 Email: lizj@freeserve.co.uk — MB ChB 1982 Ed.; MPH Glas. 1988; MRCGP 1986; DRCOG 1985. (Edinburgh) Sen. Med. Adviser Scott. Off. Edin. Prev: GP Glas.; Regist. (Community Med.) Glas. Health Bd.

JORDAN, Louise Kathleen Alderman Mowbray Croft, Moorlands Lane, Froggatt, Calver, Hope Valley S32 3ZF — BM BS 1985 Nottm.; BMedSci Nottm. 1983; Cert. Family Plann. JCC 1988; DRCOG 1988. (Nottingham) GP Hope Valley Derbysh.; Clin. Asst. Ashgate Hospice Chesterfield. Prev: GP Corbridge; SHO (O & G)

Nether Edge Hosp. Sheff.; SHO (A & E) Roy. Hallamshire Hosp. Sheff.

JORDAN, Louise Mabel 4 Chesterfield House, Pond Square, Highgate, London N6 6BE Tel: 020 8340 1462 — LRCPI & LM, LRSCI & LM 1950; LRCPI & LM, LRCSI & LM 1950. (RCSI) Med. Examr. DSS. Prev: GP Lond.

JORDAN, Martin Neil 89 Stanhope Drive, Hosforth, Leeds LS18 4EU — MB ChB 1980 Leic.

JORDAN, Mary Teresa 73 Busby Road, Clarkston, Glasgow G76 7BW — MB ChB 1972 Glas.

JORDAN, Matthew Burra Tel: 01754 766766 Fax: 01754 760632 — MB BS 1981 Newc.; FRCS Ed. 1987; MRCGP 1990. (Newcastle upon Tyne) GP Skegness. Prev: Regist. (ENT) Freeman Hosp. Newc.; SHO (Gen. Surg.) Bishop Auckland Gen. Hosp.; SHO (ENT Surg.) Roy. Vict. Infirm. Newc.

JORDAN, Michael John North Down, 2 Fort Road, Guildford GU1 3TB Tel: 01483 567510 Fax: 01483 563044 Email: mike_jordan@email.msn.com — MB BChir 1975 Camb.; MA Camb. 1975; FFA RCS Eng. 1978. Cons. Anaesth. St. Peter's Hosp. Chertsey, Surrey. Socs: Anaesth. Res. Soc.; Soc. Computing & Technol. In Anaesth. Prev: Cons. Anaesth. St. Bart. Hosp. Lond.; Sen. Regist. (Anaesth.) St. Thos. Hosp. Lond.; Vis. Asst. Prof. Anaesth. Univ. Texas, Dallas.

JORDAN, Niall Patrick David 3 Maxwell Road, Bangor BT20 3RA — MB BS 1996 Newc.

JORDAN, Nigel Royal Hallamshire Hospital, Glossop Road, Sheffield S10 2JF; Mowbray Croft, Moorlands Lane, Froggatt, Calver, Hope Valley, Sheffield S32 3ZF — BM BS 1983 Nottm.; DM Nottm. 1994, BMedSci 1991; MRCP (UK) 1986; FRCP (UK) 1997. (Nottingham) Cons. (Neurol.) Roy. Hallamshire Hosp. Sheff. Prev: Sen. Lect. Huntersmoor; Hon. Cons. Roy. Vict. Infirm. Newc.; Sen. Regist. (Neurol.) Roy. Vict. Infirm. Newc. u. Tyne.

JORDAN, Patricia Carl Royd, Cleevethorpe Grove, Sandal, Wakefield WF2 7NA Tel: 01924 255315 — MB BS 1949 Lond.; MRCS Eng. LRCP Lond. 1949; DPM Eng. 1971; DObst RCOG 1952. (Roy. Free) Socs: Affil. RCPsych. Prev: Assoc. Specialist & Regist. (Psychiat.) Stanley Royd Hosp. Wakefield; Ho. Phys. & Ho. Surg. (Obst.) Whittington Hosp. Lond.

***JORDAN, Paul Damian** 27 Lower Northcroft, South Elmsall, Pontefract WF9 2TB Email: jordan@global.netco.uk — MB ChB 1996 Ed.; BSc (Hons.) Ed. 1994; DGM Lond. 1998.

JORDAN, Paul John Good Hope Hospital Trust, Rectory rd, Sutton Coldfield, Birmingham B75 7RR Tel: 0121 378 2211 — MB ChB 1985 Birm.; MRCP (UK) 1989. Lect. & Sen. Regist. (Cons. Cardiol.) Qu. Eliz. Hosp. Birm. Prev: Research Fell. (Cardiovasc. Med.) Qu. Eliz. Hosp. Birm.; Regist. (Cardiol.) Selly Oak Hosp. Birm.; SHO (Med.) Dudley Rd. Hosp. Birm.

JORDAN, Peter, CMG (retired) Faraday, 71 Dunmore St., Balfron, Glasgow G63 0PZ Tel: 01360 440283 — MB BS Lond. 1946; MD Lond. 1959; FRCP Lond. 1978, M 1972; MRCS Eng. LRCP Lond. 1946; FFCM 1988, M 1974. Mem. WHO Expert Advis. Panel on Parasitic Dis. (Schistosomiasis). Prev: Dir. Research & Control Dept. St. Lucia, W. Indies.

JORDAN, Mr Peter Robert Consultant Plastic/ Cosmetic Surgeon, Parkhill Hospital, Thorne Road, Doncaster DN2 5TH Tel: 01302 730300; Laundon Hall, Threekingham, Sleaford NG34 0AX Tel: 01529 241060 Fax: 01529 240951 Email: laundonhall@btinternet.com — MB BS 1969 Lond.; FRCS Eng. 1973; MRCS Eng. LRCP Lond. 1969. (St. Bart.) Socs: BMA. Prev: Chief Cons. Plastic & Maxillofacial Surg. Internat. Hosp. Bahrain; Chief Cons. Plastic & Maxillofacial Surg. Al Hada Hosp. & Rehabil. Centre Taif, Saudi Arabia; 1st Asst. Dept. Plastic Surg. St. Geo. Hosp. Lond.

JORDAN, Rene Philip (retired) 10 Viceroy Close, Edgbaston, Birmingham B5 7UR Tel: 0121 440 4599 — MB ChB 1956 Birm.; MRCS Eng. LRCP Lond. 1955. Prev: Ho. Surg. (O & G) German Hosp. Lond.

JORDAN, Robert Andrew Water Meadow Surgery, Red Lion Street, Chesham HP5 1ET Tel: 01494 782241; Harley House, 180 White Hill, Chesham HP5 1AZ Tel: 01494 786966 Email: meldrum@epulse.net — MB BS 1973 Lond.; MRCGP 1982; Dip. Pract. Dermat. Wales 1995; DRCOG 1980. (Univ. Coll. Hosp.) Hosp. Pract. (Dermat.) Amersham Gen. Hosp.; Mem. Med. Staff Comm. Chesham Hosp. Socs: BMA & Assur. Med. Soc.; Primary Care Dermat. Soc. Prev: Regist. (Med.) Wycombe Gen. Hosp. High Wycombe; SHO (Neurol.) Walton Hosp. Liverp.; SHO (Med.) N.wick Pk. Hosp. Harrow.

JORDAN, Roisin Helen Anne Lordswood House, 54 Lordswood Road, Harborne, Birmingham B17 9DB Tel: 0121 426 2030 Fax: 0121 428 2658 — MB ChB 1985 Birm.; MRCP (UK) 1988; MRCGP 1993. Prev: Regist. (Med.) Qu. Eliz. Hosp. Birm. VTS; SHO (O & G) Solihull Hosp.; SHO (Chest Med.) Torbay Hosp. Torquay.

JORDAN, Sarah Catherine Anne Flat 4, 15 Newcastle Drive, The Park, Nottingham NG7 1AA — MB BS 1989 Lond.

JORDAN, Simon James 20 Church Road, Edgbaston, Birmingham B15 3TA — MB BCh 1992 Wales; FRCS. Specialist Regist. Brompton Hosp. Lond.

JORDAN, Stephen Christopher (retired) 3 Chatford House, The Promenade, Clifton, Bristol BS8 3NG Tel: 0117 973 6589 Fax: 0117 973 6589 Email: sc.jordan@virgin.net.uk — MB ChB Bristol 1957; MD Bristol 1967; FRCP Lond. 1975, M 1962. Prev: Cons. Cardiol. Bristol Roy. Hosp & Bristol Hosp. Sick Childr.

JORDAN, Suzanne Elizabeth The Royal Gwent Hospital, Cardiff Road, Newport NP20 2UB Tel: 01633 234234 — MB BCh 1995 Wales. (UWCM) S. Gwent VTS; Newport VTS.

JORDAN, Sylvia Joyce Brook House Workshop, Royal Earlswood Hospital, Brighton Road, Redhill RH1 6JL Tel: 01737 763591; Middle Fell, Rockshaw Road, Merstham, Redhill RH1 3BZ Tel: 01737 643313 — MB BS 1953 Lond. (King's Coll. Hosp.) Assoc. Specialist (Rheum. & Rehabil.) E. Surrey & Roy. Earlswood Hosps.; Med. Dir. Brook Hse. Workshop Roy. Earlswood Hosp. Prev: Ho. Phys. & Cas. Off. Lambeth Hosp.; Ho. Surg. (O & G) St. Jas. Hosp. Balham.

JORDAN, Mr Timothy Leonard Southampton Eye Unit, Southampton General Hospital, Tremona Road, Southampton SO16 6YD Tel: 02380 794401 Email: tjordan@hgmp.mrc.ac.uk; 100 Upper Shirley Avenue, Southampton SO15 5NN Tel: 02380 785910 — MB ChB 1981 Sheff.; PhD Open 1993; FRCS Eng. 1988; FRCOphth 1989. (Sheff.) Clin. Research Fell. (Ophth. & Genetics) Soton. Socs: Brit. Soc. Human Genetics; Assn. Research in Vision & Ophth.; Genet. Soc.

JORDAN, Trevor Eric (retired) Eardley House, 14 Windmill Close, Ashby-de-la-Zouch LE65 1EQ Tel: 01530 413828 Fax: 01530 560817 Email: tjordan@tesco.net — MB BS 1968 Lond.; MRCS Eng. LRCP Lond. 1967; MA Univ Notts.1999. Prev: GP Coalville.

JORDINSON, Harry (retired) 10 Bachelor Lane, Horsforth, Leeds LS18 5NA Tel: 0113 258 9256 — MB ChB 1958 Leeds; DObst RCOG 1964.

JORDON, Margaret (retired) Old Moor Farmhouse, Longhirst, Morpeth NE61 6PR Tel: 01670 812116 — MB BS 1951 Durh. Prev: SCMO N.ld. AHA.

JORGE, Elizabeth Ayoub Portsmouth & South East Hampshire Health Authority, Finchdean House, Milton Road, Portsmouth PO3 6DP Tel: 023 92 835091 Fax: 023 92 733292 — MB BS 1972 Maranhao, Brazil; MSc (Cardiol.) Univ. Catolica do Rio de Janeiro 1974; FFPHM RCP (UK) 1993, M 1990; MFCM RCP (UK) 1983. (Foundat. Univ. Maranhao, Brazil) Dir. Pub. Health Portsmouth & SE Hants. HA. Prev: Dir. Pub. Health E. Surrey HA; Dist. Med. Off. & Community Unit Gen. Manager Brent HA; Dist. Community Phys. N. Surrey Health Dist.

JORGENSEN, Marianne Elisabeth 12 Trinity College, Lynedoch Place, Glasgow G3 6AB — MB BS 1986 New South Wales.

JORGENSEN, Svend Erik Buhl (retired) Little Headfoldswood, Plaistow Road, Loxwood, Billingshurst RH14 0TR Tel: 01403 752259 Fax: 01403 752497 Email: svebuhljo@btinternet.com — MD 1963 Copenhagen.

JORGENSEN, Thomas Axel 39 Herbert Street, Cambridge CB4 1AG Tel: 01223 563536 — MD 1963 Copenhagen; MB BS 1954.

JORNA, Frederick Hal Marfleet Group Practice, 350 Preston Road, Hull HU9 5HH Tel: 01482 701834 — MB ChB 1977 Manch.; MRCGP 1981; DRCOG 1980.

JORRO, Bridget Sinikka Christine Frithwood Surgery, 45 Tanglewood Way, Bussage, Stroud GL6 8DE Tel: 01453 884646 Fax: 01453 731302; 1 York Villas, Springfield Road, Uplands, Stroud GL5 1TP Tel: 01453 756100 — MB BS 1989 Lond.; BSc Cardiff 1982. Trainee GP/SHO Glos. VTS.

JORRO, Mary Teresa Catherine Ann The Surgery, Oakfield St., Ystrad Mynach, Hengoed CF82 7WX Tel: 01443 813248 Fax: 01443 862283; Birchwood, Park Lane, Ystrad Mynach, Hengoed CF82 7BX Tel: 01443 813237 — MB ChB 1955 Bristol; DObst RCOG 1965. Prev: Ho. Off. Bristol Roy. Infirm. & Childr. Hosp.; Ho. Off. Ham Green Hosp. Pill; Ho. Off. Brit. Hosp Mothers & Babies Woolwich.

JORY, David William The London Centre for Refractive Surgery, 21B Devonshire Place, London W1G 6HZ Tel: 020 7935 7723 Fax: 020 7487 5639 Email: jory@lcrs.co.uk; 48 Golders Gardens, Golders Green, London NW11 9BU — MB BS 1990 Lond.; FRCOphth 1997. (St. Barts Hosp. Med. Coll. Lond. Univ.) Cons. The Lond. Centre for Refractive Surg. Socs: Roy. Soc. Med.; Eur. Soc. Cataract & Refractive Surgs.; Amer. Soc. Cataract & Refractive Surgs. Prev: SHO (Ophth.) St. Thos. Hosp. Lond.; Prosector Univ. Oxf.; SHO (Ophth.) Roy. Lond. & Moorfields Hosps. Lond.

JORY, Harold Ian, TD (retired) The Old Rectory, Tewin, Welwyn AL6 0JN Tel: 0143 871 7220 — BM BCh 1949 Oxf.; MA Oxf. 1951, BM BCh 1949; FRCGP 1982, M 1961; DMRD Eng. 1959. Prev: Cons. Radiol. Qu. Eliz. II Hosp. Welwyn G.C. & Hertford Co. Hosp.

JORY, William John 21B Devonshire Place, London W1G 6HZ Tel: 020 7487 4176 Fax: 020 7487 5639 Email: jory@lcrs.co.uk; The Old House, Michelmersh, Romsey SO51 0NQ Tel: 01794 368262 — MA Camb. 1963, MB BChir 1962; MRCS Eng. LRCP Lond. 1961; FRCSC 1971; FRCOphth. 1988; DO RCS Eng. 1967. (St. Bart. Hosp. Lond.) Cons. Ophth. Lond. Centre Refractive Surg.; Cons. Ophth. Wellington Hosp. Lond.; Cons. Ophth. The Lond. Clinic. Socs: Fell. Roy. Soc. Med.; Soc. Med. Witnesses; Internat. Soc. Refractive Keratoplasty. Prev: Presid. Brit. Columbia Med. Assn. 1976-77 & 1982-83; Mem. Gen. Counc. Canad. Med. Assn. 1974-84; Mem. Bd. Dir.s Canad. Med. Assn. 1977-78.

JOSCELYNE, Joanna Charlotte 14 Beechwood Drive, Shrewsbury SY1 2RF; Flat 1, 425 Wilmslow Road, Withington, Manchester M20 — MB ChB 1994 Manch. SHO (Paediat.) St. Mary's Hosp. Manch. Prev: Ho. Off. (Gen. Med. & Gen. Surg.) Roy. Albert Edw. Infirm. Wigan.

JOSE, Kochuthresia Department of Obstetrics & Gynaecology, West Wales Hospital, Carmarthen SA31 2AF Tel: 01267 235151; 13 Mill Wood, Lisvane, Cardiff CF14 0TL — MB BS 1977 Kerala; MD (Obst. & Gyn.) India 1981; MRCOG 1991. Regist. (O & G) W. Wales Hosp. E. Dyfed HA. Prev: SHO (O & G) Aberdare Gen. Hosp. M. Glam.

JOSE THAMPI, Chemparathimootil Mathew 3 Coolsara Park, Lisburn BT28 3BG Tel: 01846 679066 — MB BS 1964 Calcutta; MRCOG 1984; DObst RCPI 1975. (Nat. Med. Coll. Calcutta) Cons. O & G S. Tyrone Hosp. Dungannon. Socs: BMA & Ulster Obst. & Gyn. Soc. Prev: Sen. Regist. (O & G) SHSSB Craigavon Area Hosp.

JOSEPH, Aleyamma 5 Lowton Road, Sale M33 4LD Tel: 0161 969 9772 — MB BS 1971 Madras; MRCPath 1980. (Christian Med. Coll. Vellore) Cons. (Haemat.) Tameside Gen. Hosp. Ashton-under-Lyne. Socs: Manch. Med. Soc. & Brit. Soc. Haemat. Prev: Sen. Regist. (Haemat.) Manch. AHA (T).

JOSEPH, Ann Elizabeth Parkfield House, Parkfield Road S., Didsbury, Manchester M20 0DB — MB ChB 1983 Leeds. SHO (Geriat. Med.) Manch. Roy. Infirm. Prev: SHO (A & E) Pk. Hosp. Manch.

JOSEPH, Ann Elizabeth Palathingal 1 Highfields, South Cave, Brough HU15 2AJ — MB ChB 1994 Liverp.

JOSEPH, Anthony Peter (Surgery), 110 Norman Road, Smethwick, Smethwick B67 5PU Tel: 0121 429 1373 Fax: 0121 434 4549; Victoria Health Centre, 5 Suffrage St., Smethwick B66 3PZ Tel: 0121 558 0216 Fax: 0121 558 4732 — MB BChir Camb. 1962; MRCS Eng. LRCP Lond. 1961; MRCGP 1968; DObst RCOG 1964. (Camb. & St. Bart.) Socs: Birm. Med. Inst.; BMA. Prev: Ho. Phys. & Ho. Surg. (ENT) St. Bart. Hosp. Lond.; Resid. Med. Off. Wom. Hosp. Sydney, NSW.

JOSEPH, Anton Emmanuel Arulraj Oldfields, 76 Park Hill Road, Wallington SM6 0RQ Tel: 020 8647 4995; Department of Radiology, St Georges Hospital, Blackshaw Road, London SW17 0QT Tel: 020 8725 1468 Fax: 020 8725 1468 Email: anton.joseph@ccmail.st.gh_tr.sthames.nhs.uk — MSc Lond. 1972; MB BS Ceylon 1962; FRCR 1976. (Ceylon) Cons. Radiol. (Nuclear Med. & Ultrasound) St. Geo. Hosp. Lond.; Hon. Sen. Lect. St. Geo. Hosp. Med. Sch. Lond. Prev: Cons. Radiol. Soton. Gen. Hosp.; Sen. Regist. (Nuclear Med. & Ultrasound) Roy. Marsden Hosp. Lond.

JOSEPH, Mr Cappil Philip The Park Medical Centre, Ball Haye Road, Leek Tel: 01538 399302 — MB BS 1959 Sydney; FRCS Ed. 1966. Prev: Surg. Regist. St. And. Hosp. Lond.

JOSEPH, Cheryl Therese Dilrukshi Flat 1, 298 Burton Road, Didsbury, Manchester M20 2NB — MB ChB 1989 Manch.

JOSEPH, Claire Frances (retired) 8 Victor Street, Pelsall, Walsall WS3 4BU Tel: 01922 685914 — MB BS 1964 Lond. Prev: Clin. Med. Off. Walsall HA.

JOSEPH, Emily 9 CLifton Terrace, Portscatho, Truro TR2 5HR; 10 Spring Dale, Wallingford OX10 0HQ — MB BCh 1992 Wales; MRCP. Specialist Regist. (Paediat.) Stoke Mandeville Hosp. Socs: MDU.

JOSEPH, Fady Georges 49 Seaview Drive, Ogmore-by-Sea, Bridgend CF32 0PB — MB BCh 1994 Wales; MRCP (UK) 1999. (University Hospital of Wales) Socs: RCP (Lond.).

JOSEPH, Mr Henry Theodore 35 Wimpole Street, London W1G 8GY Tel: 020 7486 9500 Fax: 020 7224 4162 — MB BS 1981 Lond.; FRCS Eng. (Orl.) 1988; FRCS Eng. 1985. (Middlx.) Cons. Otolaryngologist Roy. Nat. Throat, Nose & Ear Hosp. & Whittington Hosp. Lond.; Hon. Cons. Otolaryngol. UCL Hosps. Socs: Brit. Assn. Otorhinol. Head & Neck Surg.; Fell. Roy. Soc. Med. (Former Vice Pres. Sect. of Laryngol. & Rhinol.). Prev: Sen. Regist. & Regist. (Otolaryngol.) Radcliffe Infirm. Oxf; Clin. Fell. (Otolaryngol.) Hosp. Sick Childr. Univ. Toronto; Demonst., Anat., Middlx. Hosp. Med. Sch.

JOSEPH, Mr Jeremy Paul Central Eye Service, Central Middlesex Hospital, Acton Lane, Park Royal, London NW10 7NS Tel: 020 8453 2436 Fax: 020 8453 2404 — MB BS 1982 Lond.; MD Lond. 1990; FRCS Glas. 1989; FRCOphth 1989; DO RCS Eng. 1985. Cons. Ophth. Centr. Middlx. Hosp. Socs: Roy. Coll. Of Opthalmologists; Internat. Glaucoma Assn. Prev: Sen. Regist. Roy. Free Hosp. & Moorfields Eye Hosp. Lond.; Regist. (Ophth.) St. Thos. Hosp. Lond.; Research Regist. Inst. Ophth. Lond.

JOSEPH, Joanna Victoria 17 Lorn Road, London SW9 0AB Tel: 020 72740666 Email: joanna_joseph@hotmail.com — MB ChB 1993 Ed.; MRCGP 1997. (Univ. Ed.) Locum GP.Wellington New Zealand. Socs: BMA. Prev: GP/Regist. Edin.; SHO (O & G & Psychiat.) Roy. Edin. Hosp.; SHO (A & E) Roy. Infirm. Edin.

JOSEPH, Mr Jos Velokaren Surical Directorate., University Hospital, Aintree Long moor Lane, Liverpool L9 7AL — MB BS 1981 Bangalor; FRCS Ed. 1987; MB BS Bangalore 1981. Cons. Surg.

JOSEPH, Joseph 48 Wimpole Street, London W1 — LRCP LRCS 1948 Ed.; LRCP LRCS Ed. LRFPS Glas. 1948. Socs: BMA. Prev: Ho. Surg. Lond. Jewish Hosp. & W.m. Childr. Hosp.; Ho. Phys. Hackney Hosp.

JOSEPH, Joseph 5 Arlington Road, Ashford TW15 2LS Tel: 017842 56117 Email: coedwig@cyberstop.net — MB BCh 1992 Wales; MRCP (UK) 1996. SHO (Med.) Morriston Hosp. Swansea. Prev: Ho. Off. (Med.) Llandough Hosp. Cardiff; Ho. Off. (Surg.) P.ss of Wales Hosp. Bridgend.

JOSEPH, Leela Anna Department of Microbiology, Salford Royal Hospitals NHS Trust, Hope Hospital, Stott Lane, Salford M6 8HD Tel: 0161 787 5024 Fax: 0161 787 1675; 8 Preston Avenue, Eccles, Manchester M30 0DZ Tel: 0161 707 4141 — MB BS (Distinc.) Madras 1962; PhD Ed. 1966; T(GP) 1991; T(Path) 1991; Dip. Bact. Manch. 1974. (Christian Med. Coll. Vellore India) Cons. Microbiol. Hope Hosp. Salford & Hon. Clin. Lect. Manch. Med. Sch. Socs: Assn. Clin. Path.; Brit. Soc. Study of Infec.; Brit. Soc. Antimicro. Chemo. Prev: Sen. Lect. & Hon. Cons. Manch. Med. Sch.; Sen. Regist. (Microbiol.) Manch. RHB; Lect. (Bact.) Univ. Edin.

JOSEPH, Linda Rosalind Woodsome, 25 Beech Hill Avenue, Hadley Wood, Barnet EN4 0LN — MB BS 1979 Lond.

JOSEPH, Marie Shantidevi 17 Ontario Gardens, Worthing BN13 2RZ — MB BS 1981 Sri Lanka; MRCP (UK) 1985. (Fac. Med. Colombo, Univ. Sri Lanka) Clin. Asst. (Gen. Med. & Gastroenterol.) Colchester Gen. Hosp. Prev: Clin. Asst. St. Helena Hospice Colchester; Regist. (Med.) The Battle Hosp. Reading.

JOSEPH, Mary Jasmine Geraldine 62 Penberth Road, Catford, London SE6 1ES — MB BS 1985 Lond.

JOSEPH, Michael Christopher 9 Ham Street, Ham, Richmond TW10 7HR Tel: 020 8948 2464 — MB BChir 1945 Camb.; MD

Camb. 1957, BA 1945; FRCP Lond., Hon. FRCPCH 1970, M 1950; MRCS Eng. LRCP Lond. 1945; DCH Eng. 1950. (St. Mary's) Emerit. Cons. Paediat. Cardiol. Guy's & Brompton Hosps. Lond.; Voluntary work with Evelina Children's Hosp. Appeal Lond. Prev: Cons. Paediat. & Paediat Cardiol. Guy's & Brompton Hosps. Lond.; Dir. (Paediat.) Cardiothoracic Inst. Lond. Univ.; Fellsh. Paediat. Cardiol. Childr. Med. Center Boston. Mass., USA.

JOSEPH, Minnie Department of Psychiatry, Highcroft Hospital, Highcroft Road, Erdington, Birmingham B23 6AX — LMSSA 1984 Lond.

JOSEPH, Neil Minden Medical Centre, 2 Barlow Street, Bury BL9 0QP Tel: 0161 764 2651 Fax: 0161 761 5967; 8 Park Road, Higher Crumpsall, Manchester M8 4HU Tel: 0161 795 7894 — MB BChir 1974 Camb.; MA Camb. 1975, MB BChir 1974; MRCGP 1982. (Camb. & Westm.)

JOSEPH, Paramundayil Kuruvilla Dill Hall Lane Surgery, 158 Dill Hall Lane, Church, Accrington BB5 4DS Tel: 01254 398350 — DGM 1995; FRIPHH 1991; MB BS 1975 Kerala; MB BS 1975 Kerala. (Kottayam, Kerala, India) Socs: BMA; Med. Protec. Soc.; Local Med. Comm.

JOSEPH, Peter Felix Eastcote Health Centre, Abbotsbury Gardens, Eastcote, Pinner, Ruislip HA5 1TG Tel: 020 8866 0121 Fax: 020 8866 8382; 32 Love Lane, Pinner HA5 3EX — MB BS Lond. 1984; BSc Lond. 1981; MRCGP 1991; DRCOG 1988.

JOSEPH, Philip Lewis Alan Paterson Centre, St. Mary's Hospital, Praed St., London W2 1NY Tel: 020 7886 1638 Fax: 020 7886 1637 — MB BS 1979 Lond.; FRCPsych 2001; BSc Lond. 1976, MD 1992; MRCPsych 1983; T(Psych) 1991; Dip. Law. City Univ. 1986; Barrister at Law Lond. 1987. (Univ. Coll. Hosp. Lond.) Cons. Forens. Psychiat. Paterson Centre St. Mary's Hosp. Lond. Prev: Sen. Lect. (Forens. Psychiat.) & Hon. Cons. St. Mary's Hosp. Med. Sch. Lond.; Sen. Regist. Fell. (Forens. Psychiat.) Inst. Psychiat. Lond.; Sen. Regist. Rotat. (Forens. Psychiat.) Maudsley Hosp. Lond.

JOSEPH, Rajan 5 Heaton Drive, Sutton Coldfield B74 2QZ — MB BS 1979 Mysore; LMSSA Lond. 1988.

JOSEPH, Rowland Huw Laren, Bondend, Upton St., St Leonards, Gloucester GL1 4 — MB ChB 1972 Birm.

JOSEPH, Sarah Nurani 45 Hertford Street, Mill Hill, Blackburn BB2 4EX — MB BS 1950 Madras; MMSA Lond. 1963; MFCM 1974; DObst RCOG 1952; DPH Manch. 1964. Socs: BMA.

JOSEPH, Shumita 79 Kenworthy Road, London E9 5RB — MB BS 1998 Lond.; MB BS Lond 1998.

JOSEPH, Simon Gordon Flat 20, Ravenswood, Spath Road, Manchester M20 2GA Tel: 0161 224 5540 — MB ChB 1991 Manch.; MRCGP 1995; DRCOG 1994. Socs: BMA. Prev: SHO (Psychiat.) Stepping Hill Hosp. Stockport.

JOSEPH, Simon Philip Mayday Cardiology, Mayday University Hospital, London Road, Thornton Heath, Croydon CR7 7YE Tel: 020 8401 3040 Fax: 020 8665 0842 — BM BCh 1965 Oxf.; MA Oxf. 1965; FRCP Lond. 1986; MRCP (UK) 1971; FESC 1992. (Oxf. & Westm.) Cons. Cardiol. Mayday Univ. Hosp. Croydon; Assoc. Clin. Teach. Kings Coll. Med. Sch. Univ. Lond. Socs: Fell. Europ. Soc. Cardiol.; Brit. Cardiac Soc. & Brit. Pacing & Electrophys. Gp. Prev: Sen. Regist. (Cardiol.) Middlx. Hosp. Lond.; Regist. (Cardiol.) Nat. Heart Hosp. & Hosp. for Sick Childr. Gt. Ormond St. Lond.; Ho.Phys.W.minster.Hosp.

JOSEPH, Sonia 1 Birkwood Place, Newton Mearns, Glasgow G77 5FW — MB ChB 1996 Aberd.

JOSEPH, Stephen Royce 55 Ivy Road, Macclesfield SK11 8QN — MB BS 1974 West Indies.

JOSEPH, Stonny Emmanuel Osarenren Department of Medicine, King's College School of Medicine and Dentistry, Bessemer Road, Denmark Hill, London SE5 9PJ Tel: 020 7737 4000 Fax: 020 7346 3313 Email: stonnyjoseph@msn.com; 35 Shrubbery Close, Sutton Coldfield B76 1WE Tel: 0121 373 6734 Fax: 0121 373 6734 — MB BS 1985 Lagos; MRCP (UK) 1991. Research Fell. (Specialist Regist.) (Diabetes) Dept. Med. King's Coll. Sch. Med. & Dent. Lond. Prev: Regist. Rotat. (Diabetes, Endocrinol. & Gen. Med.) Birm.; Regist. (Cardiol. & Neurol.) City Hosp. Birm.; SHO Rotat. (Cardiol. & Gastroenterol.) Birm. City Hosp.

JOSEPH, Suresh Anthony Hadrian Clinic, Newcastle General Hospital, Newcastle City Health Trust, Westgate Road, Newcastle upon Tyne NE4 6BE Tel: 0191 273 6666 Fax: 0191 256 3027 — MB BS 1979 Poona; MRCPsych 1983; MMedSc Leeds 1985; FRCPsych 1996. (Armed Forces Med. Coll. Poona India) Cons. Psychiat. Newc. Gen. Hosp. Newc.; Dir. of Med. Educat. Newc. City Health Trust; Hon. Clin. Lect. (Psychiat.) Univ. of Newc. Socs: BMA. Prev: Lead Cons., Ment. Health Div. Newc.City Health Trust.; Progr. Dir. Psychiat. Train. Scheme, PostGrad. Inst. for Med. & Dent. Univ. Newc. upon Tyne.

JOSEPH, Theresa Annet Suchilla (Surgery), 53 Lansdown Gardens, London SW8 2EL Tel: 020 7622 2877; Oldfields, 76 Park Hill Road, Wallington SM6 0RQ Tel: 020 8647 4995 — MB BS 1962 Ceylon. (Ceylon)

JOSEPH, Vettukattil John 3 Hookwater Road, Chandlers Ford, Eastleigh SO53 5PQ — MB BS 1988 Bangalore.

JOSEPHIDOU, Marios Deva Crossways, Abergavenny Road, Gilwern, Abergavenny NP7 0AB — MB BCh 1989 Wales.

JOSEPHS, Cyril (retired) 16 Keswick Road, New Milton BH25 5JA Tel: 01425 615837 Email: cyril@josephs.greatxscape.net — MB BS 1943 Durh.; MD Durh. 1950; FRCGP 1977, M 1960; DCH Eng. 1946. Prev: Sen. Med. Off. Nightingale Hse. Lond.

JOSEPHS, Ilan 12 Totnes Walk, London N2 0AD — MB BS 1997 Lond.

JOSEPHS, Jane 20 Pemberley Avenue, Bedford MK40 2LQ Tel: 01234 267004 — BSc Birm. 1961, MB ChB 1963. SCMO N. Beds. HA. Prev: Clin. Med. Off. Beds. AHA; Ho. Phys. Warneford Hosp. Leamington Spa; Ho. Surg. Dudley Rd. Hosp. Birm.

JOSEPHS, Jessel (retired) Sentosa, Aydon Road, Corbridge NE45 5EJ Tel: 01434 632757 — MB BS 1947 Durh.; MRCGP 1953. Prev: Ho. Surg. (O & G) S. Shields Gen. Hosp.

JOSEPHS, Lynn Karen Burton Medical Centre, 123 Salisbury Road, Burton, Christchurch BH23 7JN Tel: 01202 474311 Fax: 01202 484412; Cedars, 111 Burley Road, Bransgore, Christchurch BH23 8AY Tel: 01425 672611 — MB BS 1977 Lond.; DM Soton. 1992; MRCP UK 1980; MRCGP 1984; DRCOG 1985. (London) Prev: Research Fell. (Respirat. Med.) Univ. Soton. & Soton. Gen. Hosp.

JOSEPHSON, Jenny-Margrethe 26 Hartfield Road, Forest Row RH18 5DY Tel: 01342 824422; The Coach House, Chapel Lane, Forest Row RH18 5BD Tel: 01342 823183 — MB BS 1976 Lond. Indep. Practioner; Sch. Doctor, S. W. Lond. Waldorf Sch., Greenwich Rudolf Steiner Sch.

JOSHI, Amar Rameshchandra 2 Clumber Avenue, Edwinstowe, Mansfield NG21 9PE — MB ChB 1996 Liverp.

JOSHI, Anil Austen 47 Broadway, Walsall WS1 3EZ — MB ChB 1992 Manch.

JOSHI, Anil Kumar c/o 25 Tybenham Road, London SW19 3LB — MB ChB 1982 Bristol.

JOSHI, Ashish Ashok Charnwood Surgery, 5 Burton Road, Derby DE1 1TH Tel: 01332 737737 Fax: 01332 737738; 1 Park Close, Ashby-De-La-Zouch, Leicester LE9 — MB ChB 1990 Leeds; MRCGP 1994; DCH RCP Lond. 1992. (Leeds) Prev: Trainee GP Derby; SHO (Med.) Derby City Gen. Hosp.; SHO (A & E) Derbysh. Roy. Infirm.

JOSHI, Bakul Vishnuprasad Ruislip Road Surgery, 337 Ruislip Road, Northolt UB5 6AS Tel: 020 8578 1537 — MB BS 1973 Saurashtra.

JOSHI, Bharat Prabhashanker The Surgery, 36 The Avenue, Watford WD17 4NT — MB BS 1975 Lond.; MRCS Eng. LRCP Lond. 1976; DRCOG 1979. (St. Bartholomew's) Prev: Med. Off. (Squadron Ldr.) RAF.

JOSHI, Mr Chandra Shekhar 63 Bunning Way, Islington, London N7 9UP Tel: 020 7700 1601 — MB BS 1980 Madras; FRCS Glas. 1988.

JOSHI, Changulanda Medappa Flat 9, Block 1, Royal Shrewsbury Hospital (North), Mytton Oak Road, Shrewsbury SY3 9XQ — MB BS 1985 Madras; MRCGP 1993.

JOSHI, Mr Dilip Ambalal 4 Stockton Gardens, Mill Hill, London NW7 3AB Tel: 020 8959 4197 — MB BS 1960 Bombay; FRCS Glas. 1970. (T.N. Coll.) Regist. (Gen. Surg.) Downe Hosp. Downpatrick. Prev: SHO Accid. Unit N. Staff. Roy. Infirm. Stoke-on-Trent; Regist. (Gen. Surg.) Lagan Valley Hosp. Lisburn & Ards Hosp.; Newtownards.

JOSHI, Girish Chander 15 Rutland Road, Maidenhead SL6 4HZ — BM 1984 Soton.; MRCGP 1989; DRCOG 1989.

JOSHI, Gopal Das 53 Marlborough Road, Flixton, Urmston, Manchester M41 5QP — MB BS 1969 Calcutta; DCH RCPSI 1979. (R.G. Kar Med. Coll.) SHO (Paediat. Med.) OldCh. Hosp. Romford.

JOSHI, Harish 18 Littlecote Gardens, Appleton, Warrington WA4 5DL — MD 1976 Rajasthan; MD (Paediat.) Rajasthan 1976, MB BS 1972.

JOSHI, Hasmukh Prataprai Old Road Surgery, Old Road, Abersychan, Pontypool NP4 7BH Tel: 01495 772239 Fax: 01495 773786; 4 Uskvale Court, Usk Road, Pontypool NP4 8AS Tel: 01495 752453 — MB BS 1970 Gujarat; FRCGP 1977, M 1995; DGM RCP Lond. 1986. (B. J. Med. Coll. Ahmedabad, India) Course Organiser N. Gwent VTS; Examr. RCGP. Prev: Med. Educator Family Med. Progr. S. Austral.

JOSHI, Mr Jayantilal Balashankar 3 Woodcocks Crescent, Castledean, Bournemouth BH7 7JW Tel: 01202 425062 — MB BS 1975 Gujarat; FRCS Ed. 1984. (B.J. Med. Ahmedabad) Prev: Regist. & Sen. Regist. (ENT) Poole Gen. Hosp.

JOSHI, Jayendrakumar Premshanker 26 Newdene Avenue, Northolt UB5 5JE — MB BS 1972 Baroda.

JOSHI, Kalpana Castle Practice, 2 Hawthorne Road, Castle Bromwich, Birmingham B36 0HH Tel: 0121 747 2422; 22 Beaudesert Road, Handsworth, Birmingham B20 3TG Tel: 0121 554 0462 — MB ChB 1977 Liverp.; MRCGP 1984; DTM & H Liverp. 1980.

JOSHI, Kaushik Madhavji The Millfield Surgery, 10 Serjeant Street, Peterborough PE1 2LR Tel: 01733 563051 Fax: 01733 563051 — MB BS 1972 Bombay.

JOSHI, Manhar Fakenham Medical Practice, The Fakenham Medical Centre, Greenway Lane, Fakenham NR21 8ET Tel: 01328 851321 Fax: 01328 851412 — MB BChir 1989 Camb.; BA Oxf. 1987; MRCGP 1993.

JOSHI, Mukund Diwakar 61 Tillyard Croft, Selly Oak, Birmingham B29 5AH Tel: 0121 472 2561 — MB BS 1958 Poona; FRCR 1976; DMRD Eng. 1970. (B.J. Med. Coll.) Cons. Radiol. Dudley Rd. Hosp. Birm.; Hon. Sen. Lect. Radiol. Univ. Birm. Prev: Regist. (Radiol.) Glas. Roy. Infirm.; Sen. Regist. (Radiol.) Midl. Centre Neurosurg. & Neurol. Smethwick; Cons. Radiol. Min. of Health Bahrain.

JOSHI, Mr Narayan Ram South Grange Medical Centre, Trunk Road, Eston, Middlesbrough TS6 9QG Tel: 01642 467001 Fax: 01642 463334; 30 Egton Avenue, Nunthorpe, Middlesbrough TS7 0QY Tel: 01642 313766 — MB BS 1964 Delhi; FRCS Ed. 1974. (M.A. Med. Coll.) Socs: (Ex-Chairm.) Nepalese Doctors Assn. UK.

JOSHI, Narendra Dhwaj The Sands, 113 Millway, London NW7 3JL; The Sands, Teen Bato, Kalimati, Kathmandu, Nepal Tel: 00 977 12 71161 — MB BS 1952 Calcutta. Vis. Prof. BPKLcos, Trighuvan Univ. Teachg. Hosp. Kathmandu, Nepal; Sen. Cons. Ophtalmol. CFC Hosps. Kathmandu Nepal. Socs: FRCOphth. Prev: Sen. Specialist (Ophth.) Negara Brunei, Darassalam.

JOSHI, Mr Naresh Dept.of Ophthalmology, Chelsea & wEst. NHS Trust, 369 Fulham Rd, London SW10 9NH — MB BS 1986 Lond.; FRCOphth. 1990, M 1989; DO RCS Eng. 1989. Cons. Ophth. Plastic Surg. Chelsea & W.minster Hosp. Lond. Prev: Sen. Regist. (Ophth.) Chelsea & W.m., Char. Cross & Moorfields Eye Hosps. Lond.; Cecelia Vaughan Fell. In Anterior Segment Proctor Foundat. UCSF, Calif., USA; Oculoplastic Fell. Oculoplastic Serv. Moorfields Hosp. Lond.

JOSHI, Navajeevan Achyutrao Silksworth Health Centre, Silksworth, Sunderland SR3 2AN Tel: 0191 521 2282 Fax: 0191 523 5827 — MB BS 1972 Marathwada. (Marathwada) GP Sunderland.

JOSHI, Naveen 80 Lansdowne Road, Ilford IG3 8NG Email: naveenjoshi@oxford.epulse.net — MB BS 1994 Lond.; BSc (Hons.) Pharmacol. with Basic Med. Scis. Lond. 1991; DRCOG 1997; DCH 1998; DFFD 1998. (Lond. Hosp. Med. Coll.) Oxf. VTS John Radcliffe Hosp. Socs: BMA; Med. Protec. Soc. Prev: SHO (Dermat.) Ch.ill Hosp. Oxf.; SHO (O & G) Wom. Centre Oxf.; SHO (Paediat.) John Radcliffe Hosp. Oxf.

JOSHI, Mr Nayan Dhoj 113 Millway, Mill Way, London NW7 3JL — MB BS 1978 Karnatak; DO RCS Eng. 1983; FRCS Ed. 1986.

JOSHI, Nitin Harilal Clyde Street Medical Centre, 1A Clyde Street, Leicester LE1 2BG Tel: 0116 262 8368 — MB ChB 1987 Manch.; MRCGP 1991; DRCOG 1990. Socs: BMA.

JOSHI, Pradip Frimley Park Hospital, Portsmouth Road, Frimley, Camberley GU16 7UJ Tel: 01276 692777 — MB BS 1982 Lond.; FRCA 1987; FFA RCSI 1987. Cons. Anaesth. & Intens. Care Frimley Pk. Hosp. Prev: Sen. Regist. St. Geo. Hosp.; Attend. Duke Univ. Med. Centre USA 1992-93.

JOSHI, Rahul 175 Chamberlayne Road, London NW10 3NU — MB BS 1998 Lond.; MB BS Lond 1998.

JOSHI, Ramesh Chandra 47 Broadway, Walsall WS1 3EZ Tel: 01922 629570 Fax: 01922 629570 — MD 1963 Punjab (India); MB BS 1958; MB BS 1958; FRCP Lond. 1981; MRCP (UK) 1971. (Christian Med. Coll. Ludhiana) Cons. Phys. (Chest Dis.) Walsall Gp. Hosps. Socs: Med. Research Soc. & Thoracic Soc. Prev: Research Assoc. Johns Hopkins Univ., USA; Commonw. Fell. Qu. Eliz. Hosp. Birm.

JOSHI, Ravi Kumar 28 Whitfdord Drive, Shirley, Solihull B90 4YG — MB BS 1973 Rajasthan.

JOSHI, Ravindra c/o Dr Popat, 4 Southcroft, Old Marston, Oxford OX3 0PF — MB BS 1976 Bombay; FFA RCSI 1993. Sen. Regist. (Anaesth.) John Radcliffe Hosp. Oxf. Socs: Life Mem. Indian Soc. Anaesth.; Train. Mem. Assn. AnE.h.; Med. Protec. Soc. Prev: Regist. Roy. Berks. Hosp. Reading; Specialist Roy. Hosp. Muscat, Oman; Asst. Specialist King Fahd Univ. Hosp. Alkhobar, Saudi Arabia.

JOSHI, Reema 10 Leopold Road, Leicester LE2 1YB — MB ChB 1997 Leic.

JOSHI, Rupa 14 Sevington Road, London NW4 3SB — MB BS 1997 Lond.

JOSHI, Shailaja A Block, Medway Hospital, Windmill Road, Gillingham ME7 5NY Tel: 01634 830000 Ext. 3829; 32 Valley View Road, Rochester ME1 3NY — MB BS 1975 Poona; LMSSA Lond. 1983. Clin. Asst. (Psychiat.) Medway Hosp. Gillingham. Prev: SHO & Acting Regist. (Psychiat.) Medway Hosp. Gillingham; SHO (Psychiat.) StoneHo. Hosp. Gravesend; Trainee GP Gravesend Hosp. & Gillingham Kent.

JOSHI, Shama Uday Health Centre, Marmaduke Street, Hessle Road, Hull HU3 3BH Tel: 01482 327708 Fax: 01482 210250; 14 Croft Park, Woodgates Lane, North Ferriby HU14 3JY Tel: 01482 633336 — MB BS 1973 Bombay. (Topiwala, Bombay) GP; Staff Grade (Community Paediat.); Clin. Asst. (Family Plann.). Socs: MDG. Prev: Clin. Asst. (Med. for Elderly) Glas.

JOSHI, Sharada M Joshi and Reddy, Aston Health Centre, 175 Trinity Road, Aston, Birmingham B6 6JA Tel: 0121 327 0144 Fax: 0121 326 9784 — MB BS 1962 Calcutta; MB BS 1962 Calcutta.

JOSHI, Shridhar Vinayak Mount Pleasant, Blackburn BB1 5BJ — MB BS 1955 Bombay; MB BS 1955 Bombay.

JOSHI, Uday Yadaorao Department of Genitourinary Medicine, Castle Hill Hospital, Castle Road, Cottingham HU16 5JQ Tel: 01482 623287 Fax: 01482 624027; 14 Croft Park, Woodgates Lane, North Ferriby HU14 3JY Tel: 01482 633336 Fax: 01482 633343 Email: sujoshi@thefree.net — MB BS 1975 Nagpur; FRCP 1998; Dip. Ven. Soc. Apoth. Lond. 1982; MRCP (UK) 1989. (Nagpur, India) Cons. Phys. Genitourin. Med. Castle Hill Hosp. Cottingham; Hon. Cons. Hull Roy. Infirm. Socs: Med. Soc. Study VD; Assn. Genitourin. Med. Prev: Sen. Regist. (Genitourin. Med.) Glas. Roy. Infirm.; Hon. Clin. Lect. (Genitourin. Med.) Glas. Univ.

JOSHI, Vijaya Balkrishna Chapel Medical Centre, Liverpool Road, Irlam, Manchester M44 6FE Tel: 0161 775 7373 Fax: 0161 775 5603 Email: joshivijaya@hotmail.com — MBBS 1973 Poona; Dipl. In Anaesth. (Univ. Bombay, India). (BJ Medical College Univ. Of Poona)

JOSHI, Vinod Shashank 30 New Heath Close, New Cross Hospital, Wednesfield, Wolverhampton WV11 1XX — MB BS 1986 Bombay.

JOSHI, Virat 1 Alstone Close, Stafford ST16 1UH — MB ChB 1994 Birm.

JOSHI, Vishnuprasad Premshanker Old Station Road Surgery, 157 Old Station Road, Hayes UB3 4NA Tel: 020 8573 2037 Fax: 020 8813 7552 — MB BS Baroda 1970.

JOSHI GODREZ, Dorabji Minocher (retired) 37 Old Road, Mottram-in-Longdendale, Hyde SK14 6LW Tel: 01457 62232 Email: godrez@dralstart.net — BSc Sind. 1948; MB BS Karachi 1954; FRFPS Glas. 1959; FRCP Glas. 1979, M 1962; FRCP Ed. 1977, M 1961; LRCP LRCS Ed. LRFPS Glas. 1959; DTM & H Eng. 1955. Cons. Phys. (Geriat.) Oldham & Dist. Hosp. Gp. Prev: Cons. Phys. (Geriat.) Ashton, Hyde & Glossop Hosp. Gp.

JOSHUA, John Mathic But-Kim, Les Grupieaux, St Peter, Jersey JE3 7ED — MRCS Eng. LRCP Lond. 1940; MB ChB Bristol 1940, DPH 1961; FRCPC 1974; FFCM 1977, M 1974. (Bristol) Prev: Sen.

Med. Cons. Communicable Dis. Control Min. Health Ont. Canada; Assoc. Prof. Dept. Preven. Med. & Biometrics Univ. Toronto, Canada.

JOSHUA-AMADI, Mabel Ihihemegbulam 17 Dawpool Road, Neasden, London NW2 7LD Tel: 020 8450 0522 — MB BS 1981 Lond.; DTM & H RCP Lond. 1988. (Roy. Free Med. Sch.) Prev: RMO Freedman Hosp. Aba, Abia Stare; SHO Warri Gen. Hosp. Bendel Stare; Ho. Phys. St. Anne's Hosp. Tottenham.

JOSLIN, Professor Charles Albert Frederick Innisfree, 109 Pannal Ash Road, Harrogate HG2 9AL Tel: 01423 566197 Email: cjoslin@talk21.com — MB BS Lond. 1958; FRCR 1975; FFR 1966; DMRT Eng. 1962. (Char. Cross) Emerit. Prof. Socs: (Ex-Chairm.) Brit. Gyn. Cancer Soc.; (Hon. Pres.) Europ. Gyn. Cancer Soc.; (Ex-Pres.) Brit. Inst. Radiol. Prev: Prof. Radiother. Univ. Leeds; Cons. Radiother. Univ. Hosp. Wales & Welsh Hosp. Bd.; Sen. Regist. (Radiother.) Char. Cross Hosp. Lond. & Hammersmith Hosp.

JOSLIN, Christopher Charles Thistlefield House, Ringwould, Deal CT14 8HW Tel: 01304 363344 — MB ChB 1995 Bristol. Clin. Demonst. Leicester Univ.

JOSLIN, Jennifer May 18 Dersingham Road, London NW2 1SL — LMSSA 1960 Lond.

JOSLIN, Joanna Elizabeth Mary Thistlefield House, Hangman's Lane, Ringwould, Deal CT14 8HW; 21a Romilly Crescent, Canton, Cardiff CF11 9NP — MB BS 1992 Lond.; DRCOG. (London Hospital) GP Locum S. Wales; SHO (Gen. Med. & Dermat.) Roy. Gwent Hosp. Socs: BMA & Med. Defence Union. Prev: Trainee GP Newport Gwent; SHO (Ophth. & ENT) St Woolos Hosp. Newport; SHO (A & E) Norf. & Norwich Hosp.

JOSLIN, Matthew Edward The 3 Horseshoes, Lower Hardes, Canterbury CT5 4NZ — MB BS 1997 Lond. (Royal London Hosp. Med. Sch.)

JOSS, Dorothy Vanda Milton Keynes General Hospital, Standing Way, Eaglestone, Milton Keynes MK6 5LD Tel: 01908 660033 Fax: 01908 243108 Email: vanda.joss@mkg-tr.anglox.nhs.uk — MB BS 1970 Lond.; FRCP Lond. 1994; MRCP (UK) 1974; MRCS Eng. LRCP Lond. 1970. (Roy. Free Hosp. Lond.) Cons. Paediat. Milton Keynes Dist. Gen. Hosp.; Clin. Dir. Paediat. Socs: BMA (Ex-Chairm. Milton Keynes Div.); (Ex-Chairm.) Milton Keynes Med. Soc. Prev: Sen. Regist. (Paediat.) W.m. Childr. Hosp. Lond. & Ahmadu Bello Univ. Hosp. Kaduna, Nigeria.

JOSS, Mr George Smith (retired) BUPA Hospital Cons. Rooms, Colney, Norwich NR4 7TD Tel: 01603 456181 Fax: 01603 250968 — MB ChB Aberd. 1950; FRCS Ed. 1960; LMCC 1953 McGill. Cons. Plastic Surg. BUPA Hosp. Norwich & ChristCh. Pk. Hosp. Ipswich. Prev: Cons. Surg. E. Anglian Plastic Surg. Unit W. Norwich Hosp.

JOSS, Nicola Margaret Larchwood, Fyvie, Turriff AB53 8PB — MB ChB 1994 Glas. SHO (Med.) Glas. Roy. Infirm.

JOSSE, Jeannette Denise Cambridge Consultation Centre, 2 Grange Road, Cambridge CB3 9DU Tel: 01223 460122 Fax: 01223 329597 Email: josse@grangerd.u-net.com — MB BS 1968 Lond; MB BS Lond. 1968; MRCPsych 1978; FRCPsych 1999. (Middlx.) Psychother. & Family Therapist Camb. Consult. Centre; Sessional Cons. & Psychotherapist NWA Healthcare NHS Trust; Psychiat. Cons. USAF; Guest Lect. Camb. Bd. of Continuing Educat. Socs: Tavistock Soc. Psychother.; Fam. Mediators Assn.; Indep. Doct. Forum. Prev: Research Assoc. (Paediat.) Univ. Camb.; Course Tutor Tavistock Clinic Lond.; Sen. Regist. (Psychother.) Addenbrooke's Hosp. Camb.

JOSSE, Silvain Edouard, OBE 2 Shirehall Gardens, Hendon, London NW4 2QS Tel: 020 8202 7740 Fax: 020 8203 9891 — MB BS 1956 Lond.; MB BS (Hons. Obst. & Gyn.) Lond. 1956; MA (Higher & Further Educat.) Lond. 1989; MRCS Eng. LRCP Lond. 1956; DMJ(Clin) Soc. Apoth. Lond. 1970; FRCGP 1977, M 1966. (Middlx.) Trust Respirat. Phys. Chest Clinic, N. Middlx. Hosp. Lond.; Princip. Forens. Med. Examnr. Metrop. Police; Cons. Clin. Forens. Med. Socs: Fell. Roy. Soc. Med. (Counc. Mem. RSM & Sect. Gen. Pract.); (Pres.) Assn. Police Surgs.; Brit. Acad. Forens. Sci. Prev: Regional Adviser (Gen. Pract.) & Assoc. Dean Postgrad. Med. N. Thames Region; Ex-Chairm. Conf. Postgrad. Advis. in Gen. Pract. & Ex-Sec. Gen. UEMO; Ex-Chairm. & Hon. Jt. Sec. Jt. Comm. Postgrad. Train. in Gen. Pract.

JOSTY, Mr Ian Christopher 226 Christchurch Road, Newport NP19 8BJ Tel: 01633 278047; 70 Lon Enfys, Llansamlet, Swansea SA7 9XQ Tel: 01792 772204 — MB BS 1992 Lond.; BSc Lond. 1989; FRCS Eng. 1996. (St. Geo. Hosp. Med. Sch.) Specialist Regist. (Burns & Plastic Surg.) Morriston Hosp. Swansea. Socs: Christian Med. Fell.sh.; Brit. Burns Assoc. Mem. Prev: Specialist Regist. (Burns & Plastics) Countess of Chester Hosp.; SHO (Burns & Plastics) Stoke Mandeville Hosp. Aylesbury; SHO (Gen. Surg., A & E & Orthop.) Stoke Mandeville Hosp. Aylesbury.

JOTANGIA, Tribhovan Premjibhai The Surgery, Monkswood Crescent, Coventry CV2 1BP Tel: 024 76 616803 Fax: 024 76 617420 — MB BS 1973 Saurashtra. Clin. Asst. (Dermat.) Coventry.

JOTHILINGAM, Sabalingam Department of Anaesthesia, Lister Hospital, Coreys Mill Lane, Stevenage SG1 4AB Tel: 01438 781086; Kurinji, Millfield Lane, Hitchin SG4 7NH — MB BS 1972 Ceylon; FFA RCSI 1979; DA Eng. 1977. (Peradeniya) Cons. Anaesth. & Pain Relief Lister Hosp. Stevenage. Prev: Sen. Regist. (Anaesth.) Lond. Hosp.; Lect. (Anaesth.) Lond. Hosp. Med. Coll.; Regist. (Anaesth.) Kings Coll. Hosp. Med. Sch.

JOUGHIN, Brigid Margot Throckley Surgery, Back Victoria Terrace, Throckley, Newcastle upon Tyne NE15 9AA Tel: 0191 267 4005 Fax: 0191 229 0646; 5 Brentwood Gardens, Jesmond, Newcastle upon Tyne NE2 3LP — MB ChB 1987 Ed.; MRCGP 1991; DRCOG 1991.

JOUGHIN, Neil Alan Priory Hospital Marchwood, Hythe Road, Marchwood, Southampton SO40 4WU Tel: 02380 877525 Fax: 02380 207554 — MB BChir 1979 Camb.; MPhil (Psychiat.) 1990; MA Camb. 1980; MRCPsych 1985; T(Psych) 1991. (St. Geo.) Cons. Psychiat. Priory Hosp. Marchwood, Soton. Prev: Lect & Hon. Sen. Regist. St. Geo. Hosp. Lond.

JOURDAN, Iain Campbell 55 Shirlock Road, London NW3 2HR — MB BChir 1993 Camb.

JOURDAN, Martin Henry 55 Shirlock Road, Hampstead, London NW3 2HR Tel: 020 7267 1582 — MRCS Eng. LRCP Lond. 1966; PhD Lond. 1970, BSc (Physiol.) 1962, MS 1982, MB; BS 1966; FRCS Eng. 1975. (Guy's) Reader (Surg.) & Cons. Surg. Guy's Hosp. Lond.; Mem. Ct. Examrs. RCS Eng.; Mem. Ct. Asst. Soc. Apoth. Lond. Socs: Surg. Research Soc. & Nutrit. Soc.; Brit. Soc. Gastroenterol.; Fell. Roy. Soc. Med. Prev: Lect. (Surg.) Guy's Hosp. Lond. & Wellcome Surg. Research Fell.; Regist. (Surg.) Norf. & Norwich Gp. Hosps.; MRC Trav. Fell. (Nutrit. Scs.) Berkeley, USA.

JOURNEAUX, Mr Simon Francis Department of Orthopaedics, Royal Liverpool University Hospital, Prescot St., Liverpool L7 8XP Tel: 0151 706 3443 Fax: 0151 706 5839 Email: simonjourneaux@25riversdale.freeserve.co.uk; 25 Riversdale Road, West Kirby, Wirral CH48 4EY Tel: 0151 625 1678 Fax: 0151 625 2984 Email: simonjourneaux@25riversdale.freeserve.co.uk — MB BS 1986 Lond.; BSc (Hons.) Lond. 1983; FRCS (Orth.) 1995; FRCS Eng. 1990. (Char. Cross and Westm.) Cons. Trauma & Orthop. Roy. Liverp. Univ. Hosp.; Surg. Lt Coln., Roy. Naval Reserve. Socs: BMA & Med. Defence Union; Brit. Orthop. Train. Assn. Prev: Sen. Regist. (Orthop.) Leeds Gen. Infirm. & St. Jas. Univ. Hosp. Hull Roy. Inf.

JOUSSEF, Magdy Max Abdel-Malek Rosebank, 13 Bathurst Drive, Alloway, Ayr KA7 4QN Tel: 01292 441671 Email: m.joussef@virgin.net — MB BCh 1972 Cairo. Staff Psychiat. Ailsa Hosp. Ayr. Socs: BMA; Affil. MRC Psych. Prev: Clin. Asst. (Psychiat.) Ailsa Hosp. Ayr; Regist. & SHO Woodilee Hosp. Glas.

JOVASEVIC, Branislav Rock Villa, Tutshill, Chepstow NP16 7DL — LRCP LRCS 1965 Ed.; LRCP LRCS Ed. LRCPS Glas. 1965.

JOWETT, Mr Albert Edwin, OBE Hoyells, Ford, Wiveliscombe, Taunton TA4 2RL Tel: 01984 23244 — MB ChB 1935 Bristol; FRCS Ed. 1938; MRCS Eng. LRCP Lond. 1935. (Bristol) Socs: Sen. Fell. Brit. Orthop. Assn. Prev: Cons. (Opthop) Surg. S. Som.; Vis. Surg. War Pensioners Unit, MusGr. Pk. Hosp. Taunton; Res. Surg. Off. P.ss Eliz. Orthop. Hosp. Exeter.

***JOWETT, Andrew James Lund** Sandecotes Lodge, 34 Sandecotes Road, Parkstone, Poole BH14 8NZ Tel: 0973 629656 Fax: 01202 740696 Email: billj@sportdoc.demon.co.uk — MB BS 1996 Lond.; BSc (Hons) Lond. 1993.

JOWETT, Anthony Moir Medical Centre, Regent St., Long Eaton, Nottingham NG10 1JX Tel: 0115 973 5820 Fax: 0115 946 0197 — MB ChB 1972 Leeds; DObst RCOG 1975. (Leeds) Socs: Leeds Med. Soc. Prev: SHO (Paediat.) Barnsley Gp. Hosps.; SHO (Accid., Emerg. & Obst.) Wakefield Gp. Hosps.

JOWETT, Christopher Stephen Kendrick, Marsh Lane, Taplow, Maidenhead SL6 0DE — MRCS Eng. LRCP Lond. 1978; BSc Lond. 1973, MB BS 1977. (St. Bart.)

JOWETT, Fiona Sarah 3 Allan Park, Stirling FK8 2QG — MB ChB 1991 Aberd.

JOWETT, John Henry Gordon 15 The Priory, Monks Close, Redbourn, St Albans AL3 7NR Tel: 01582 793711 — MRCS Eng. LRCP Lond. 1949. (St. Bart.) Prev: RAF Med. Br.; Asst. Pathol. Lond. Clinic; Sen. Ho. Phys. Metrop. Hosp.

JOWETT, Lincoln John 15 Heathfield Close, Bingley BD16 4EQ — MB BS 1993 Newc.

JOWETT, Nigel Ian Withybush General Hospital, Haverfordwest SA61 2PZ Tel: 01437 773258 Fax: 01437 773449 Email: nigel.jowett@pdj-tr.wales.nhs.uk; The Coach House, Treffgarne, Haverfordwest SA62 5PJ Tel: 01437 741266 Fax: 01437 741718 Email: jabba@jowettn.freeserve.co.uk — MB BS 1976 Lond.; MD Lond. 1984; FRCP Lond. 1997; MRCP (UK) 1980; MRCS Eng. LRCP Lond. 1976. (St. Bart.) Cons. Phys. & Dir. Clin. Med. Pembrokesh. & Derwen NHS Health Trust; Clin. Dist. Tutor RCP. Socs: Brit. Cardiac Soc.; Eur. Soc. Study Diabetes; Brit. Soc. Echocardiogr. Prev: Research Fell. Lipid Laborat. St. Bart. Med. Coll. Lond.; Hon. Sen. Regist. Profess. Med. Unit. St. Bart. Hosp. Lond.; Clin. Asst. Moorfields Eye Hosp. & Inst. Ophth. Lond.

JOWETT, Mr Richard Lund (retired) Bournemouth Nuffield Hospital, 67 Lansdowne Road, Bournemouth BH1 1RW Tel: 01202 291866 — BM BCh Oxf. 1963; MA Oxf. 1973; FRCS Eng. 1968. Private Consg. for Personal Accid. Medicological Reporting at The Bournemouth Nuffield Hosp. Prev: Sen. Regist. Roy. Nat. Orthop. Hosp. Stanmore.

JOWETT, Roger Endless Street Surgery, 72 Endless Street, Salisbury SP1 3UH Tel: 01722 336441 Fax: 01722 410319; Bake Farm, Coombe Bissett, Salisbury SP5 4DU — MB BS 1962 Lond.; MRCS Eng. LRCP Lond. 1962. Prev: Ho. Surg. & Ho. Phys. Pembury Hosp.; Resid. Obst. Taunton & Som. Hosp.

JOWETT, Sally Ann The Health Centre, 2A Forest Road, Edmonton, London N9 8RZ Tel: 020 8804 0121 — MB BS 1983 Lond.; DRCOG 1986; DCH 1987. (UCH London)

JOWETT, Sarah Louise 177 Heath Road, Runcorn WA7 4XG Tel: 019285 72126 — MB BS 1992 Newc.; MRCP (UK) 1995.

JOWETT, Victoria Charlotte 47 Kentish Lane, Brookmans Park, Hatfield AL9 6NG — MB BS 1998 Lond.; MB BS Lond 1998.

JOWITT, John Dymoke, MBE (retired) Little Acre, Upton Manor Road, Brixham TQ5 9QZ Tel: 01803 853563 Email: dymoke@lineone.net — MB BS Lond. 1957; MRCS Eng. LRCP Lond. 1957; FRCGP 1987, M 1966; DObst RCOG 1963; DCH Eng. 1960. Provost. Tamar Fac. RCGP. Prev: Ho. Off. (Paediat.) Soton. Hosp. Gp.

JOWITT, Malcolm David 65 Gainsborough Road, Blackpool FY1 4DZ Tel: 01253 626187 — MRCS Eng. LRCP Lond. 1975; DA (UK) 1985.

JOWITT, Simon Noel 12 Craven Terrace, Sale M33 3GA — MB BS 1984 Lond.; MD Lond. 1997; MRCP (UK) 1987; MRCPath 1994. Cons. Haemat. Stepping Hill Hosp. Stockport.

JOY, Alison 29 Cadogan Place, London SW1X 9RX Tel: 020 7235 5850 Fax: 020 7235 9171 — MB 1985 Camb.; BChir 1984; MRCP (UK) 1992; MRCGP 1991; DRCOG 1991; DCH RCP Lond. 1988.

JOY, David (retired) Greenbanks, Horn St., Nunney, Frome BA11 4NP Tel: 01373 836410 — MRCS Eng. LRCP Lond. 1935. Prev: Res. Med. Off. Gen. Infirm. Salisbury.

JOY, Graham John Aston Cornwall Gardens Surgery, 77 Cornwall Gardens, Cliftonville, Margate CT9 2JF Tel: 01843 291833 Fax: 01843 293126 — MB BS 1978 Lond.; DCH RCP Lond. 1982.

JOY, Harriet Mary House 1, Block 1, Royal Bournemouth Hospital, Castle Lane E., Bournemouth BH7 7DW Tel: 01202 704298 — MB BS 1992 Lond.; BSc Lond. 1989; MRCP (UK) 1996. (King's Coll. Sch. Med. & Dent.)

JOY, Howard Allan Department of Surgery, New Cross Hospital, Wolverhampton Road, Heath Town, Wolverhampton WV10 0QP — MB BS 1993 Lond. SHO (Gen. & Orthop. Surg.) Orsett Hosp.

JOY, Kanakkattuseril Raghavan Roper Street Surgery, 11 Roper Street, Workington CA14 3BY Tel: 01900 602997 Fax: 01900 870142 — MB BS 1967 Kerala.

JOY, Professor Michael David St Peter's Hospital (Trust), Chertsey KT16 0PZ Tel: 01932 810230 Fax: 01932 872011; Cedar House, Longcross Road, Longcross, Chertsey KT16 0DR Tel: 01932 873309 Fax: 01932 874905 Email: mj@aviationcardiology.com — MB BS 1966 Lond.; FESC 1991; MD Lond. 1973; FRCP Lond. 1980, M 1968; MRCS Eng. LRCP Lond. 1966; FACC 1989. (St. Thos.) Cons. Phys. & Cardiol. St. Peter's Hosp. Chertsey; Trav. Prof. Internat. Civil Aviat. Organisation; Cons. Cardiol. (Mem. Med. Advis. Panel) Civil Aviat. Auth.; Adviser in Cardiol. to Internat. Civil Aviat. Organisation & Europ; Civil Aviat. Conf.; Mem. Sec. State's Hon. Med. Advis. Comm. Fitness to Drive; Visting Prof. of Clin. Cardiol., Univ. of Surrey. Socs: FRAeS; Fell. Europ. Soc. Cardiol. & Amer. Coll. Cardiol.; Brit. Cardiac Soc. Prev: Sen. Regist. (Med.) Lond. Hosp.; Lect. (Med.) St. Thos. Hosp. Lond.; Regist. (Med.) Nat. Heart Hosp. Lond.

JOY, Paul William Caeherbert Lane Surgery, Caeherbert Lane, Rhayader LD6 5ED Tel: 01597 810231 Fax: 01597 811080; The Old School, Gaufron, Rhayader LD6 5PB Tel: 01597 811657 — MB ChB 1984 Leeds; Diploma Primary Care Rheumatology, Bath, 2000; MRCGP 1988; DFFP 1993; DCH RCP Lond. 1988; DRCOG 1988. Clin. Asst. (Geriat. & Rheum.) Llandrindod Wells Hosp. Powys.

JOY, Peter John 51 Burkes Road, Beaconsfield HP9 1PW — MB BS 1962 Lond.; DA Eng. 1965.

JOY, Robin Wrington Vale Medical Group, Station Road, Wrington, Bristol BS40 5NG Tel: 01934 862532 Fax: 01934 863568; The Surgery, Ladymead Lane, Churchill, Bristol BS25 5NH Tel: 01934 852362 — MB ChB 1966 Bristol; DObst RCOG 1968; DA Eng. 1968.

JOY, Roger Mark Wellington Medical Practice, Chapel Lane, Wellington, Telford TF1 1PZ Tel: 01952 226000 — MB BChir 1982 Camb.; MA Camb. 1983; MRCGP 1986; DGM RCP Lond. 1987; DRCOG 1985. Prev: GP Hokitika W.land NZ; Trainee GP Derby VTS; SHO Nottm. City Hosp.

JOY, Trudy Kathlyn The Limes Surgery, 172 High Street, Lye, Stourbridge DY9 8LL Tel: 01384 422234 — MB BCh BAO 1989 NUI; LRCPSI 1989.

JOY, Mrs Vyvyan Jennifer North Hill House, Cooks Bridle Path, Backwell, Bristol BS48 3DJ Tel: 01275 472247 — MB ChB 1967 Bristol. (Bristol) Clin. Asst. (O & G) Bristol Health Dist. (T); Clin. Asst. GUM, W. Area NHS Trust. Socs: BMA.

JOYCE, Mr Adrian Derrek Department of Urology, St. James University Hospital, Leeds LS9 7TF Tel: 0113 206 6993 Fax: 0113 292 6490; 35 Main Street, Thorner, Leeds LS14 3DX — MB BS 1978 Lond.; MS Lond. 1990; FRCS (Urol.) Eng. 1991; FRCS Eng. 1983; FRCS Ed. 1982. (Westm. Hosp.) Cons. Urol. St. Jas. Univ. Hosp. Leeds. Prev: Sen. Regist. (Urol.) King's Coll. Hosp. Lond.; Research Fell. Harvard Med. Sch. Boston, USA.

JOYCE, Mr Alan PO Box 3032, London W4 5RG Email: kfg@globalnet.co.uk — MB BS Bombay 1957; FRCS Ed. 1967.

JOYCE, Benita 117A Harley Street, London W1N 1DH Tel: 020 7350 1716 — MB BS 1984 Lond.; MRCGP 1989; Cert. Family Plann. JCC 1988; MRCGP 1989. (Royal Free Hospital, London) GP Vocational Train. Rotat., Roy. United Hosps., Bath; Private Pract. Harley St. Prev: Princip., Highgate Gp. Pract.

JOYCE, Caroline Ann 53 Skripka Drive, Billingham TS22 5JD — MB BS 1996 Lond. (Roy. Free Hosp. Sch. Med.) GP Regist. Cleveland.

JOYCE, Caroline Mary Margaret 135 Weavers Way, Elm Village, London NW1 0XG — MB BS 1993 Lond.; DRCOG 1996; MRCGP 1997. (Univ. Coll. Med. Sch.) GP Clin. Asst. Paxton Green Health Centre Lond.

JOYCE, Christina Clare Lean Govanhill Health Centre, 233 Calder St., Glasgow G42 7DR Tel: 0141 531 8370; 23 Torridon Avenue, Dumbeck, Glasgow G41 5AT Tel: 0141 427 4146 Email: tinajoyce@oloyede23.freeserve.co.uk — MB BS 1988 Lond.; MRCGP 1993; DFFP 1993; Dip. GU Med. Soc. Apoth. Lond. 1992; DRCOG 1991. (UMDS (Guy's)) Clin. Asst. Genitourin. Med. Inverclyde Roy. Infirm. Greenock. Prev: Regist. (Genitourin. & HIV Med.) Chelsea & W.m. Hosp. Lond.; Trainee GP Lewisham Hosp. VTS; SHO (Genitourin & HIV Med.) John Hunter Clinic St. Stephens.

JOYCE, Ciaran Claremont Clinic, 459-463 Romford Road, Forest Gate, London E7 8AR Tel: 020 8522 0222 Fax: 020 8522 0444 — MB ChB 1987 Bristol; MRCGP 1993; DCH RCP Lond. 1992.

JOYCE, David Norman (retired) Stone Mill, Woodford, Berkeley GL13 9JU Tel: 01454 260542 profess. 0272 731323 — BM BCh 1964 Oxf.; DM Oxf. 1974, MA, BM BCh 1964; FRCOG 1982, M 1970. Prev: Cons. Sen. Lect. (O & G) S.mead Hosp. Bristol.

JOYCE, Eileen Maria Dept. Psychiatry, Imperial College School of Medicine, Charing Cross Campus St Dunstans Road, London

W6 8PN Tel: 020 8846 7390 Fax: 020 8846 7372 Email: ejoyce@ic.ac.uk — MB BChir 1982 Camb.; PhD Camb. 1980, BA 1975; MRCP (UK) 1985; MRCPsych 1986. (Camb.) Reader (Psychiat.) Imperial Coll. Sch. Med. Lond.; Hon. Cons. Psychiat. Ealing Hammersmith & Fulham, Ment. Health NHS Trust. Socs: Brit. Assn. Psychopharmacol. (Sec.); Brit. Neuropsychiat. Assn.; Soc. Neurosci. Prev: Wellcome Trust Lect. Ment. Health Inst. Psychiat. Lond.; Hon. Sen. Regist. Maudsley Hosp. Lond.; Regist. Bethlem Roy. & Maudsley Hosps. Lond.

JOYCE, Elizabeth Ann Liversedge and Joyce, Egerton & Dunscar Health Centr, Darwen Road, Bromley Cross, Bolton BL7 9RG Tel: 01204 309525 Fax: 01204 596562 — MB ChB 1986 Manch.; DCH RCP Lond. 1988; DRCOG 1988; Cert. Family Plann. JCC 1990.

JOYCE, Elizabeth Louise Cleland House, Page St., London SW19 4LN Tel: 020 7217 6895 Fax: 020 7217 6412; 14 Wilbury Gardens, Hove BN3 6HY Tel: 01273 725293 — MB BS 1983 Lond.; MSc Lond. 1987; MFPHM RCP (UK) 1989. Head of Pub. Health Plann. & Profess. Developm. Directorate of Health Care HM Prison Serv. Lond. Prev: Dir. Pub. Health Chichester HA.

JOYCE, John Joseph 45 Lyndon Avenue, Sidcup DA15 8RL — MB BCh 1983 Wales; DTM & H Liverp. 1993; DCH RCP Lond. 1989. (Welsh Nat. Sch. Med.) Regist. (Pub. Health Med.) E. Kent HA. Prev: Community Doctor Tibetan Refugee Settlem. Pokhora, Nepal; Med. Off. HALO Demining Trust, Afghanistan; Clin. Doctor Med. Foundat. for Victims of Torture Lond.

JOYCE, Joseph Patrick Northgate Hospital, Morpeth NE61 3BP — MB BCh BAO 1981 NUI; MRCPsych 1988; DPM RCPSI 1988. Cons. Psychiat. (Learning Disabil.) N.gate Hosp. Morpeth.

JOYCE, Kathleen Joan 4 Ryelands Grove, Bradford BD9 6HJ — MB BCh BAO 1947 Belf.

JOYCE, Kay Alison Stennack Surgery, The Old Stennack School, St Ives TR26 1RU Tel: 01736 793333 Fax: 01736 793746; Lower Trenowin Farm, Ludgvan, Penzance TR20 8BL Tel: 01736 740995 — MB BS 1988 Lond.; BSc Lond. 1985; MRCP (UK) 1991; MRCGP 1995; DRCOG 1994. (Char. Cross & Westm. Lond.)

JOYCE, Mr Martin Oakley, The Park, Cheltenham GL50 2SA — MB ChB St. And. 1962; FRCS Eng. 1968; DO Eng. 1965. (St. And.) Cons. Ophth. Winfield Hosp. Tewesbury Rd., Sloucester GL13NN. Prev: Sen. Regist. Birm. & Midl. Eye Hosp., & United Birm. Hosps.

JOYCE, Mary Elizabeth Re-hab Unit, Springfield Hospital, 61 Glenburnie Road, London SW17 7DJ — MB BCh BAO 1988 NUI.

JOYCE, Mr Michael Richard Langford Leigham Cottage, Cedar Walk, Kenley CR8 5JL Tel: 020 8660 8758 — MB BS 1966 Lond.; FRCS Eng. 1971; MRCS Eng. LRCP Lond. 1966. (Guy's) Surg., Dept. Urol. Guy's Hosp. Lond.; Urol. FarnBoro. Hosp. Kent.

JOYCE, Pamela Ruth Churchgate Surgery, 119 Manchester Road, Denton, Manchester M34 3RA Tel: 0161 336 2114 Fax: 0161 320 7045; 6 Moss Lane, Broadbottom, Hyde SK14 6BD — MB ChB 1981 Manch.; DRCOG 1986. Socs: Brit. Menopause Soc.

JOYCE, Mr Patrick Weston Rennie Eye Clinic, St. Helens Hospital, St Helens WA9 3DA Tel: 01744 458327; Rushmere, 35 Freshfield Road, Formby, Liverpool L37 3JA Tel: 01704 831621 — MB BCh BAO 1976 NUI; MSc Manch. 1988; FRCS Ed. 1984; DO RCPSI 1980; FRCOphth. (Univ. Coll. Dub.) Cons. Ophth. Surg. St. Helens & Knowsley Hosps. Socs: Roy. Coll. Ophth.; Eur. Soc. Cataract & Refrective Surgs.; BMA.

JOYCE, Peter King Montserrat, Little Saughall, Chester CH1 6AE — MB BCh BAO 1943 NUI. (Galway)

JOYCE, Siobhan 7 St James Street, London W6 9RW — MB BS 1989 Lond.; DRCOG 1994; MRCGP 1995; DCH 1994.

JOYCE, Thomas (retired) 36 South Beach, Troon KA10 6EF — MB ChB 1945 Ed.; FRCP Ed. 1994; MRCP Ed. 1949; MRCGP 1954. Prev: Regist. Edin. N.. Hosp. Gp.

JOYNER, Miles Victor The Old Rectory, Huxham, Exeter EX5 4EJ — MB BS 1969 Lond.; MRCS Eng. LRCP Lond. 1969; FRCPath 1988, M 1976. (King's Coll. Hosp.) Cons. Haemat. Roy. Devon & Exeter Hosp. Prev: Lect. (Haemat.) King's Coll. Hosp. Med. Sch. Lond.; Chef de Clin. Univ. de Nice.

JOYNER, Nicholas Albion Surgery, Pincott Road, Bexleyheath DA6 7LP Tel: 020 8304 8334 Fax: 020 8298 0408 — MB BS 1979 Lond.; BSc (Hons.) Lond. 1976; MRCGP 1984; DRCOG 1983. (Guy's) Co-Course Organiser Qu. Mary's Hosp. Sidcup VTS. Prev: Trainee GP/SHO Qu. Mary's Hosp. Sidcup VTS; Ho. Surg. Guy's Hosp. Lond.; Ho. Phys. Joyce Green Hosp. Dartford.

JOYNER, Saskia Elizabeth The Old Rectory, Huxham, Exeter EX5 4EJ — MB BS 1996 Lond.

JOYNER, Steven Robert 90 Kings Road, Harrogate HG1 5JX — MB ChB 1993 Leic.

JOYNSON, Claire Philippa Woodstock, Oldfield Drive, Heswall, Wirral CH60 6SS — BM BS 1997 Nottm.

JOYNSON, David Huw Malcolm Public Health Laboratory, Singleton Hospital, Sgeti, Swansea SA2 8QA Tel: 01792 205666 Fax: 01792 202320 — MB BCh Wales 1967; FRCP Lond. 1993; MRCP (UK) 1971; FRCPath 1996; FIBiol 1991, M 1980; Dip. Bact. Lond 1973. (Cardiff) Cons. Microbiologist. & Dir. Pub. Health Laborat. & Head Plths Toxoplasma and crytosporidium Ref. Unit Singleton Hosp. Swansea. Socs: Assn. Clin. Path.; Welsh Microbiol. Assn.; Europ. Soc. of Emerging Infec.s (Chairm. Exec. Bd.). Prev: Sen. Regist. Regional Pub. Health Laborat. Univ. Hosp. Wales.

JOYPAUL, Mr Baboo Vickram South Tyneside District Hospital, Harton Lane, South Shields NE34 0PL Tel: 0191 202 2165 Fax: 0191 202 2164 Email: vickram.joypaul@eem.sthct.northy.nhs.uk; Newlands, The Drive, Low Fell, Gateshead NE9 5BL Tel: 0191 491 5456 — MB ChB 1984 Dundee; MD 1997 Dundee; FRCS Glas. 1990; FRCS Ed. 1990; FRCS (Gen) 1998. (Ninewells Hosp. and Med. Sch.) Cons. GI Surg., S. Tyneside Dist. Hosp., S. Shields. Prev: Sen. Regist., Ninewells Hosp. Dundee; Career Regist., Ninewells Hosp. Dundee; Research Fell. (Surg.), Ninewells Hosp.,Dundee.

JOYSTON-BECHAL, Montague Philip 10 Harley Street, London W1G 9PF Tel: 020 7467 8340 Fax: 020 7467 8312 Email: bechal@ftech.co.uk — BM BCh 1954 Oxf.; BA Oxf. 1951; FRCP Lond. 1986, M 1960; FRCPsych. 1981, M 1971; Acad. DPM Univ. Lond. 1964. (Westm.) Hon. Cons. Psychiat. Centr. Middlx. Hosp. & Edgware Gen. Hosp. Socs: Fell. Roy. Soc. Med. Prev: Sen. Regist. Lond. Hosp.; Regist. Maudsley Hosp. Lond.; Ho. Phys. Brompton Hosp. Lond.

JOYSTON-BECHAL, Simon 10 Waterside Place, London NW1 8JT — MB BChir 1988 Camb. Prev: Ho. Phys. Roy. Free Hosp.; Ho. Off. (Surg.) Edgware Gen. Hosp.

JUBB, Alexandrea Samantha 48 Churchfields, Rotherham S61 1PU — MB ChB 1998 Sheff.; MB ChB Sheff 1998.

JUBB, Lawrence Gordon (retired) 10 Pilmuir Avenue, Glasgow G44 3HX Tel: 0141 637 4001 — MB ChB 1939 Glas.; BSc Glas. 1936, MB ChB 1939; MRCGP 1953. Prev: Clin. Asst. (Anaesth.) Vict. Infirm. & Hairmyres Hosp. Glas.

JUBB, Ronald William Department of Rheumatology, University Hospital Birmingham NHS Trust, Selly Oak Hospital, Birmingham B29 6JD Tel: 0121 627 1627 Fax: 0121 627 8480 — MB ChB 1972 Glas.; BSc Glas. 1968, MB ChB 1972; MD (Hons.) 1981; FRCP Lond. 1994; MRCP (UK) 1974. Cons. Rheum. Univ. Hosp. Birm. NHS Trust; Sen. Clin. Lect. Univ. Birm. Socs: Brit. Soc. Rheum. Prev: Mem. Sci. Staff Strangeways Research Laborat. Camb.; Hon. Cons. Rheum. Newmarket Gen. Hosp.; Sen. Regist. (Rheum.) W.m. Hosp. Lond.

JUBY, Bernard Arthur 18 Russel Terrace, 4 Clifton Lodge, Leamington Spa CV31 1EZ Tel: 01926 450241 Fax: 01926 450241 Email: bjuby@fshdial.co.uk — MRCS Eng. LRCP Lond. 1962; MRCGP 1969. (Birm.) Indep. Pract. (Physical Med.) Birm.; Phys. BUPA Med. Screen. Birm. Prev: Ho. Phys. (Radiother.) Qu. Eliz. Hosp. Birm.; Ho. Surg. Marston Green Matern. Hosp.

JUBY, Mr Herbert Bernard (retired) 1 The Limes, Rushmere St Andrew, Ipswich IP5 1EA Tel: 01473 712586 — MB BS 1947 Lond.; FRCS Eng. 1954; MRCS Eng. LRCP Lond. 1947; DLO Eng. 1952. Prev: Cons. ENT Surg. Ipswich Hosp.

JUBY, Linda Diane Whitecroft, 20 Talbot Avenue, Edgerton, Huddersfield HD3 3BG — MB ChB 1980 Leeds; MRCP (UK) 1983. Cons. Gastroenterol. Bradford Roy. Infirm.

JUCHNIEWICZ, Henryk Jerzy The Surgery, 1 Troy Close, Tadworth Farm, Tadworth KT20 5JE Tel: 01737 362327 Fax: 01737 373469; 2 Upper Pines, Banstead SM7 3PZ — MB BS 1990 Lond. Socs: Roy. Coll. Gen. Pract.

JUCKES, Thomas Richard Brodie Barn Close Surgery, 38-40 High Street, Broadway WR12 7DT Tel: 01386 853651 Fax: 01386 853982 — MB BS 1973 Lond.; MRCS Eng. LRCP Lond. 1973; MRCGP 1980; DRCOG 1979. (St. Bart.)

JUCKES, William Renwick (retired) Renwick Lodge, Springfield Lane, Broadway WR12 7BT Tel: 01386 852212 Email:

mick.juckes@virginnet.c.uk — MB BChir 1950 Camb.; MRCS Eng. LRCP Lond. 1945. Prev: Ho. Surg. St. Bart. Hosp.

JUDAH, Jacob David Department Physiology, University College London, Rockefeller Building, University St., London WC1E 6JJ — BM BCh 1945 Oxf.; MRCP Lond. 1946. (Oxf. & Univ. Coll. Hosp.) Emerit. Prof. Physiol. Univ. Coll. Lond.; Hon. Research Assoc. (Physiol.) UCL. Prev: Wellcome Prof. Experim. Path Univ. Coll. Lond.; Prof. Metab. Research Chicago Med. Sch. USA; Assoc. Mem. Wistar Inst. Philadelphia, USA.

JUDAH, Matthew John 7 Oak Street, Littleborough OL15 0HH — MB ChB 1987 Manch.

JUDD, Brian Anthony Royal Liverpool Childrens Hospital, Eaton Road, West Derby, Liverpool L12 2AT Tel: 0151 228 4811; Clay Lane Farm, Clay Lane, Eccleston, St Helens WA10 5PX Tel: 01744 451922 — MB BS 1975 Lond.; FRCP Lond. 1995; MRCP (UK) 1980; MRCS Eng. LRCP Lond. 1975; DCH Eng. 1979. (Westm. Med. Coll.) Cons. Paediat. & Paediat. Nephrol. Roy. Liverp. Childr. Hosp.

JUDD, Delyth Riversdale Surgery, Riversdale House, Merthyrmawr Road, Bridgend CF31 3NL Tel: 01656 766866 Fax: 01656 668659; 27 Preswylfa Court, Merthyr Mawr Road, Bridgend CF31 3NX Tel: 01656 656640 — MB BCh 1982 Wales; MRCGP (Distinc.) 1987; DRCOG 1987. Course Organiser Bridgend GP VTS. Prev: Trainee GP Bridgend VTS; SHO (Research Gastroenterol.) Univ. Hosp. Wales; SHO (Gen. Med.) Neath.

JUDD, Margaret Belinda 121 Wilbury Road, Letchworth SG6 4JG Tel: 01462 674694 — MB BCh Wales 1965; FFPHM RCP (UK) 1998; T(PHM) 1991; DCH Eng. 1968; DObst RCOG 1967; FRCPCH 1997. (Welsh Nat. Sch. Med.) Prev: Dir. (Pub. Health) E. & N. Herts. HA; Cons. Community Med. N. Herts. DHA; Sen. Regist. (Community Med.) NW Thames RHA.

JUDD, Melissa Jane Martin Townhill Surgery, Townhill District Centre, Southampton SO18 3RA Tel: 023 8047 2232 Fax: 023 8046 5107; Webb's Land Cottage, Titchfield Lane, Wickham, Fareham PO17 5QA Tel: 01329 835319 — BM 1978 Soton. Socs: Primary Care Rheum. Soc.

JUDD, Owen Franklin 42 Spring Terrace Road, Burton-on-Trent DE15 9DU — BM BS 1998 Nottm.; BM BS Nottm 1998.

JUDD, Philip Albert 13 Borrowdale Avenue, Ipswich IP4 2TN — MD 1978 Birm.; BSc Birm. 1963, MD 1978, MB ChB 1966; FRCPath 1984, M 1972. Cons. Histopath. Ipswich Hosp.

JUDELSOHN, Felicity Ann Coventry Healthcare NHS Trust, Clifford Bridge Road, Coventry CV2 2TE — MB ChB 1963 Cape Town; FRCPsych 1992, M 1972; T(Psych) 1991; DPM Eng. 1968. p/t Cons. Psychiat.Coventry. Health Care NHS Trust.

JUDGE, Ann Patricia Great Sutton Medical Centre, Old Chester Road, Great Sutton, South Wirral L66 3PE Tel: 0151 339 3126 Fax: 0151 339 9225; Thendara, 9 Uplands Road, Bromborough, Wirral CH62 2BY — MB ChB 1985 Liverp. Clin. Asst. (Dermat.) S. Wirral.

JUDGE, Barry Paul Judge, McElroy and Thompson, 15 Sefton Road, Litherland, Liverpool L21 9AH Tel: 0151 928 4820 — MB ChB 1959 Sheff.

JUDGE, Brendan Patrick Pearse Ilsham Leigh, 36 Ilsham Road, Torquay TQ1 2JD Tel: 01803 294249 — MB BCh BAO 1951 Dub.; MA Dub. 1956, MB BCh BAO 1951; LAH Dub. 1962. (TC Dub.) Med. Off. Newman Teachs. Train. Coll. Birm. Socs: Brit. Stud. Health Assn. Prev: Ho. Phys. W. Cornw. Hosp. Penzance; Ho. Surg. WillesBoro. Hosp. Ashford (Kent); Ho. Surg. (Obst.) Camborne-Redruth Miners & Gen. Hosp. Cornw..

JUDGE, Colin Barrington Homedene, High St., Chewton Mendip, Bath BA3 4LL — MB BCh 1979 Wales; MA Camb. 1979; MRCGP 1984; DRCOG 1983.

JUDGE, Deborah Jane St Mary's Department of Child and Adolescent Psychiatry, 17 Paddington Green, London W2 1LG Tel: 020 7723 1081 Fax: 020 7723 1926; Windigo, Chiltern Road, Ballinger Common, Great Missenden HP16 9LH Tel: 01494 837322 Fax: 01494 836902 — MB BS 1989 Newc.; BMedSci. 1988; MRCPsych 1993. Sen. Regist. (Child & Adolesc. Psychiat.) St. Mary's Hosp. Lond. Prev: Sen. Regist. (Child Psychiat.) Edgware Gen. Hosp.

JUDGE, Grace Johann 18 Victoria Avenue, Crosby, Liverpool L23 8UH — MB ChB 1982 Liverp.; DRCOG 1985.

JUDGE, Gurdip Singh Copsewood Medical Centre, 95 Momus Boulevard, Coventry CV2 5NB Tel: 024 7645 7497 Fax: 024 7663 6395 — MB BS 1977 Karnatak; LRCP LRCS Ed. LRCPS Glas. 1979; DRCOG 1982. (M.R. Med. Coll. Gulbarga) Socs: Overseas Doctors Assn. (Pres. Coventry & Warks. Div.).

JUDGE, James Francis (retired) Orchard Close, 20 Upton Park, Chester CH2 1DF — MRCS Eng. LRCP Lond. 1962; DObst RCOG 1964. Prev: Ho. Off. Med., Surg. & Obst. Clatterbridge Gen. Hosp. Bebington.

JUDGE, Jean Windgather, Nicholas Road, Blundellsands, Liverpool L23 6TS — MB ChB 1961 Sheff. (Sheff.)

JUDGE, Jennifer Ellen 117 Smallwood Road, London SW17 0TU — MB BS 1996 Newc.; BMedSci (Hons.) 1995. Psychiat. SHO Maudsley & Bethlem NHS Trust Maudsley Hosp. Lond.

JUDGE, Mary R 130 Salisbury Road, Queens Park, London NW6 6PB — MB BCh BAO 1979 NUI; MRCP (UK) 1982; MRCPI 1981. Lect. Haemat. Univ. Hosp. Wales Cardiff.

JUDGE, Rajinder Flat 11, 33 Rutland Gate, London SW7 1PD — MB ChB 1984 Birm.; MRCPsych 1991. (Birm.) Dir. Neurosci. Research Indianapolis, USA. Socs: Roy. Soc. Med.; Brit. Assn. Psychopharmacol.; ECNP. Prev: Med. Strategy Head, Psychiat. Glaxo-Wellcome N. Carolina, USA; Assoc. Med. Dir. Neurosci. SmithKline Beecham; Sen. Regist. & Regist. Rotat. Char. Cross Hosp. Lond.

JUDGE, Sangita 21 Glamis Close, Walderslade, Chatham ME5 7QQ — MB BS 1996 Lond. SHO (Ophth.).

JUDKINS, Keith Charles Medical Director, Pinderfield & Pontefract, Hospitals NHS Trust, Rowan House, Wakefield WF1 4EE Tel: 01924 212240 Fax: 01924 212032 Email: keith.judkins@panp_tr.northy.nhs.uk; The Old Vicarage, 3 Church Lane, E. Ardsley, Wakefield WF3 2LJ Tel: 01924 826802 Email: kcjudkins@aol.com — MB ChB 1973 Bristol; FRCA 1977. (Bristol) Trust Med. Dir.; Cons. (Anaesth./Intens. Care) Pinderfields Hosp. Wakefield; Hon. Sen. Clin. Lect. Univ. Leeds Sch. Med.; Dep. Edr. Today's Anaesth. Socs: Assn. Anaesth.; (ex-Chairm.) Brit. Burn Assn.; Hon. Sec. Internat. Soc. Burn Injury. Prev: Clin. Dir. Pinderfields Burn Centre; Cons. Anaesth. Qu. Vict. Hosp. E. Grinstead; Sen. Regist. (Anaesth.) S. Glam. & Gwent HA's.

JUDODIHARDJO, Harryono Heath Park, Department Dermatology, Cardiff CF14 4XN Tel: 029 2074 2904 Email: wdmhj@cardiff.ac.uk; 32 Southminster Road, Penylan, Cardiff CF23 5AT Tel: 029 2048 1184 Fax: 01222 481184 Email: harryono@msn.com — MB BCh BAO 1992 Belf.; MSc Dermatol. Wales 1997; DCH RCP Lond. 1996; Dip. Dermat. (Sci.) Wales 1996; Dip. GU Med. Soc. Apoth. Lond. 1996. (Qu. Univ. Belf.) Clin. Lec. (Dermat.) Univ. Wales Coll. Med. Socs: Med. Protec. Soc.; Internat. Dermatol. Soc.; Roy. Soc. Med. Prev: SHO (Med.) Belf. City Hosp., Ulster Hosp. Dundonald & Roy. Vict. Hosp. Belf.

JUDSON, David Henry (retired) Salter's Cottage, Dingestow, Monmouth NP25 4DY — MB BS Lond. 1948; FRCGP 1970.

JUDSON, Ian Robert Cancer Research UK, Centre for Cancer Therapeutics, Block E, The Institute of Cancer Research, 15 Cotswold Road, Belmont, Sutton SM2 5NG Tel: 020 8722 4302 Fax: 020 8642 7979 — MB BChir 1977 Camb.; BA (Nat. Sc.) Camb. 1972, MD 1989; FRCP Lond. 1994. (King's College Hospital Medical School) Readerof Cancer Pharmacol. Inst. Cancer Research; Hon. Cons. Med. Oncol. Roy. Marsden Hosp. Lond. Socs: Mem. Amer. Soc. of Clin. Oncol.; Mem. Amer. Assn. for Cancer Research; Ex. Com. Mem. Assn. of Cancer Phys.s. Prev: Lect. & Sen. Regist. Inst. Cancer Research & Roy. Marsden Hosp.; Research Fell. Inst. Cancer Research Sutton; Regist. (Med. Oncol.) Roy. Marsden Hosp. Lond.

JUDSON, Martin Lawrence The Surgery, Cross Road, Sacriston, Durham DH7 6LJ Tel: 0191 371 0232; 209 Gilesgate, Durham DH1 1QN Tel: 0191 384 3591 Fax: 0191 384 3591 — MB BS 1977 Newc. Clin. Asst. Young Disabled Unit.

JUEL-JENSEN, Bent Einer Monckton Cottage, 56 Old High St, Old Headington, Oxford OX3 9HW Tel: 01865 762848 — BM BCh 1953 Oxf.; MA Oxf. 1955, DM 1972; Cand. Med. Univ. Copenhagen 1949; FRCP Lond. 1978, M 1975; MRCGP 1962. (Oxf. & Copenhagen) Hon. Cons. Phys. Infec. Dis. & Trop. Med. Nuffield Dept. Med. Oxf.; Clin. Lect. (Med.) Univ. Oxf.; Emerit. Fell. St. Cross Coll. Oxf. Socs: Fell. Roy. Soc. Trop. Med. & Hyg.; Hon. Fell. Liverp. Sch. Trop. Med.; Hon. Fell. (Ex-Med. Adviser) RGS. Prev: Emerit. Med. Off. Univ. Oxf.; Regist. (Med.) Regius Prof. Med. Univ. Oxf.; SHO (Gen. Med.) Nuffield Med. Unit & Regist. (Med.) Radcliffe Infirm. Oxf.

JUER, Linda Dorothy Fraser Greenacres, 35 Homefield Road, Worthing BN11 2HY; 2 Adversane Road, Worthing BN14 7QH — BM 1987 Soton.

JUERGENS, Maike West Cumberland Hospital, Whitehaven CA28 8JG — State Exam Med 1991 Berlin.

JUGESSUR, Dharmamitra Westcotes Family Practice, 2 Westcotes Drive, Leicester LE3 0QR Tel: 0116 255 8588 — LRCPI & LM, LRSCI & LM 1969; LRCPI & LM, LRCSI & LM 1969. GP Leicester. Prev: Sen. Regist. (Genitourin. Med.) Leicester Roy. Infirm.

JUHASZ, Andras Gyula Blackburn Royal Infirmary, Norwood House, 11 Infirmary Road, Blackburn BB2 3LR; 22 Farnborough Road, Sharples, Bolton BL1 7HJ — Artsexamen Leiden 1989. SHO Rotat. (Psychiat.) Crumpsall Hosp. Manch. Prev: SHO (Gen. Surg.) Blackburn Roy. Infirm.; SHO (Trauma) Torbay Hosp.

JUHASZ, Peter Laszlo Woodhead, 51 Kilmardinny Ave, Bearsden, Glasgow G61 3NL Tel: 0141 942 1921 Fax: 0141 942 1921 Email: peter@hung.demon.co.uk — MB ChB 1988 Ed.; DLO RCS Eng. 1992; MRCGP 1995. (Ed.) GP Hartlepool, Cleveland. Prev: SHO (Psychiat.) ScarBoro.; SHO (ENT) Roy. Infirm & City Hosp. Edin.; SHO (Paediat.) Roy. Hosp. Sick Childr. Glas.

JUHASZ, Yvonne Catherine Camberwell Green Surgery, 17 Camberwell Green, London SE5 7AF Tel: 020 7703 3788 — BChir 1991 Camb.; MA; MRCGP 1996; DFFP 1995. (Camb.) GP Princip. The Gp. Pract. Camberwell Green Lond. Socs: RCGP; BMA.

JUKES, Anthony Martin 34 Kingsley Road, Northampton NN2 7BL; 34 Kingsley Road, Northampton NN2 7BL Fax: 01604 720470 — MB ChB Birm. 1962; MRCPsych 1973; Dip Pharm Med RCP (UK) 1978; DPM Eng. 1967; DA RCPSI 1970. (Birmingham) p/t Vis. Cons. (Psych.) St. Andrews Gp. of Companies, Isham Ho., N.ampton; Regional Cons. (Psych.) War Pens. Agency. Prev: Cons. Psychiat. St. And. Hosp. N.ampton.

JUKES, David Stephen 7 Gloucester Way, Birmingham B37 5PA — MB ChB 1995 Manch.

JUKES, Marjory Matheson Russell 27 Lidyard Road, London N19 5NR Tel: 020 7263 6538 — MA MB Camb. 1959, BChir 1958; MRCS Eng. LRCP Lond. 1958; DA Eng. 1960. (Camb. & St. Mary's) Med. Dir. Complete Health Care. Prev: Clin. Asst. (Anaesth.) Edgware Gen. Hosp.; Regist. (Anaesth.) Barnet Gen. Hosp.; Regist. (Anaesth.) Roy. N.. Hosp. Lond.

JUKES, Rachel Alison Mary 59 College Drive, Manchester M16 0AD — MB ChB 1987 Leic.

JUKES, Sophie Elizabeth 16 Biscay Road, London W6 8JN — MB BS 1993 Lond.

JUKES, Stephen John 13 Sheppard's Field, Wimborne BH21 1PX — MB ChB 1993 Dundee. (Dundee) Specialist Regist. Anaesth. Wessex Rotat.

JUKKA, Cecilia Marie 23 Mersey Avenue, Aigburth, Liverpool L19 3QU — MB ChB 1985 Leeds. Regist. (Med. Microbiol.) Liverp.

JULI, Christoph Ferdinand 26 Ashburnham Drive, Coldean, Brighton BN1 9AX — State Exam Med 1993 Frankfurt.

JULIAN, Celia Georgina Department of Dermatology, Treliske Hospital, Truro TR1 3LJ Tel: 01872 253253 Fax: 01872 252657; Glendale Farm, Wheal Butson, St Agnes TR5 0PU Tel: 01872 552772 Email: celiajulian@btinternet.com — BM BCh 1970 Oxf.; DObst RCOG 1975. (Univ. Oxf. & Guy's Hosp. Lond.) Assoc. Specialist, (Dermat.) Treliske Hosp. Truro. Socs: Brit. Assn. Dermat.; Brit. Soc. Dermat. Surg.; Internat. Soc. Dermat. Surg. Prev: Research Regist. (Dermat.) Treliske Hosp. Truro; Clin. Asst. (Dermat.) Cornw. & I. of Scilly AHA; SHO (Obst.) Birm. Matern. Hosp.

JULIAN, John Trevor Pengarth Road Surgery, Pengarth Road, St Agnes TR5 0TN Tel: 01872 553881 Fax: 01872 553885; Glendale Farm, Wheal Butson, St Agnes TR5 0PU Email: john.julian@bt.internet.co — MB ChB 1971 Birm.; MSc Birm. 1975, MB ChB 1971; DObst RCOG 1976. (Birmingham)

JULIAN, Paul Anthony Collyer The Surgery, 52B Well Street, London E9 7PX Tel: 020 8985 2050 Fax: 020 8985 5780; 19 Groombridge Road, London E9 7DP Tel: 020 8986 0288 — MB BS 1967 Lond.; MRCP (UK) 1972; FRCGP 1992. (Lond. Hosp.) Sen. Lect. Acad. Dept. Gen. Pract. St. Bart. & Lond. Hosps. Med. Colls. Socs: Balint Soc. Prev: SHO Lond. Chest Hosp.; Ho. Phys. & Ho. Surg. Lond. Hosp.

JULIAN, Sophia Lorraine 141 Sheridan Street, Leicester LE2 7NH — MB ChB 1998 Leic.; MB ChB Leic 1998.

JULIAN, Trevor Richard Holgate Road Surgery, 167 Holgate Road, York YO24 4DF Tel: 01904 791915 — MB BCh BAO Dub. 1976; BA Dub. 1976; MRCGP 1982; DRCOG 1982. (TC Dub.) GP York.

JULIEN, David Robert 181 Shuttle Street, Tyldesley, Manchester M29 8BG — MB BS 1994 Newc.

JULIER, David Lawrence (retired) 20 Abberbury Road, Iffley, Oxford OX4 4ES Tel: 01865 777013 — MA Oxf. 1954; MD Lond. 1974, MB BS 1960; FRCP Lond. 1982, M 1964; FRCPsych 1977, M 1972; DPM Lond. 1967; DObst RCOG 1962. Prev: Cons. Psychiat. Littlemore Hosp. Oxf.

JULIER, Marcus 20 Abberbury Road, Oxford OX4 4ES — MB ChB 1994 Manch.

JULKA, Surinder Kumar Grove Medical Centre, 175 Steel House Lane, Wolverhampton WV2 2AU Tel: 01902 455771 Fax: 01902 457594; Homestead, 67 Wrottesley Road, Tettenhall, Wolverhampton WV6 8SG — MB BS 1966 Panjab; MB BS Panjab (India) 1966. (Glancy Med. Coll.)

JUMA, Najafali Moh'dhusein Hassanali The Surgery, 145 Elliott Street, Tyldesley, Manchester M29 8FL Tel: 01942 892727 Fax: 01942 888847 — MB BS 1971 Poona. (B.J. Med. Coll.) Princip. GP. Prev: Regist. (Anaesth.) Wigan AHA.

JUMAILY, Amad Gani The Surgery, 38 Stroudley Walk, London E3 3EW Tel: 020 8983 0991 Fax: 020 8981 9165 — MB ChB 1975 Baghdad; MSc (Substance Misuse) Lond. 1998; MRCPI 1986; LRCP LRCS Ed. LRCPS Glas. 1979. (Baghdad Univ. Med. Sch.) Trainer GP Whitechapel; Clin. Asst. (Obst.) Mile End Hosp. Lond. Socs: BMA Med. Defence Union. Prev: GP Trainee Whitechapel; Regist. (Med.) Greenwich Dist. & Dreadnought Seaman's Hosps.; SHO (Med.) Tameside Gen. Hosp.

JUMANI, Almas Najma 9 Dolphin Court, High Road, Chigwell IG7 6PH — MB BS 1972 Pakistan.

JUMP, Allison Elizabeth Dapdune House Surgery, Wharf Road, Guildford GU1 4RP Tel: 01483 573336 Fax: 01483 306602 — MB ChB 1982 Leeds; MRCP (UK) 1986. GP Guildford; Clin. Asst. (Dermat.) Roy. Surrey Co. Hosp. Guildford. Prev: Regist. (Med.) Epsom Dist. Hosp.

JUNAID, Mr Islam Department of Urology, The Royal Hospital NHS Trust, Whitechapel, London E1 1BB; 213 Shepherds Lane, Dartford DA1 2PT — MB BS 1981 Karachi; FRCS Ed. 1986. Specialist Regist. (Urol.) St. Bart. & Roy. Lond. Hosp. Lond.; Hon. Lect. Roy. Lond. Hosp. Whitechapel Lond. Prev: Lect. in Transpl. Surg. Roy. Lond. Hosp. Whitechapel Lond.; Res. Fell. Surgic. Unit Roy. Lond. Hosp. Whitechapel Lond.

JUNAID, Kubra Nahead The Surgery, 563 Valence Avenue, Dagenham RM8 3RH Tel: 020 8592 9111 Fax: 020 8593 6524 — MB BS 1960 Osmania; MB BS 1960 Osmania.

JUNAID, Olatunji St. Francis Unit, Nottingham City Hospital, Hucknall Road, Nottingham NG5 1PB Tel: 0115 962 8010 Fax: 0115 962 8071 Email: ola.junaid@nottingham.ac.uk — MB BS 1983 Lagos; MB BS Lagos, Nigeria 1983; MBA Keele 1994; MRCPsych 1990. Cons. Old Age Psychiat. Nottm.. Healthcare NHS Trust, Nottm.

JUNAID, Olawale Hakeen Four Acre Health Centre, Burnage Avenue, Clock Face, St Helens WA9 4QB Tel: 01744 819884 Fax: 01744 850382; 99 Barbondale Close, Whittle Hall, Great Sankey, Warrington WA5 3GY Tel: 01925 710980 — MB BS 1986 Lagos.

JUNAID, Rafiq Ahmed (Surgery), 563 Valance Avenue, Dagenham RM8 3RH Tel: 020 8592 9111 — MB BS 1962 Karachi.

JUNEJO, Shahid Department of Cardiology, Sunderland Royal Hospital, Kayll Road, Sunderland SR4 7TP Tel: 01915 656256 Fax: 01915 699126 — MBBS 1986 Sind; MBBS 1986 Sind; MRCPI 1993 RCPI; MSc 1997 Trinity Coll., Dub. (Liaquat Med. Coll., Pakistan) Cons. Cardiol. Sunderland Roy. Hosp.; Cons. Cardiol., Sunderland Roy. Hosp.; Hon. Cons. Cardiol., Freeman Hosp., Newc. upon Tyne; Hon. Cons. Caridiologist, Freeman Hosp., Newc. Upon Tyne. Socs: Mem. of Brit. Cardiac Interven. Soc.; Mem. of Brit. Cardiac Interven. Soc.; Mem. of Brit. Soc. for Echocardiography.

JUNG, Kai-Dieter Feldstrasse 21, St Wendel 66606, Germany; 50 St Vincent Crescent, Finnieston, Glasgow G3 8NG Tel: 0141 248 3624 — State Exam Med. Giessen 1991.

JUNG, Professor Roland Tadeusz Diabetes Centre, Ninewells Hospital, Dundee — MB BChir 1972 Camb.; MA Camb. 1973, MD Camb. 1980; FRCP Lond. 1989; FRCP Ed. 1985; MRCP (UK) 1974;

MRCS Eng. LRCP Lond. 1972. (St. Thos.) Cons. Phys. (Endocrinol. & Diabetic) & Hon. Prof. (Med.) Ninewells Hosp. & Med. Sch. Dundee. Socs: Scott. Soc. Phys.; Assn. Phys. Prev: Dir. R&D NHS Consortium Tayside; Clin. Dir. (Med.) Ninewells Hosp. Dundee; Clin. Scientif. Staff MRC Camb.

JUNGALWALLA, Hoshang Nowshir 30B Thames Road, Chiswick, London W4 3RJ — MRCS Eng. LRCP Lond. 1976; MRCPsych 1983. (Lond. Hosp.) Cons. Elderly Ment. Illness Ealing HA. Prev: Sen. Regist. Rotat. (Psychiat.) Char. Cross Hosp.; Regist. (Psychiat.) W.m. Rotat.; SHO (Gen. Med.) Bevendean Hosp. Brighton.

JUNGELS, Alexandra Louise 9 Chelsea Square, London SW3 6LF — MB ChB 1998 Bristol.

***JUNGER, Doron** Nuffield Department of Surgery, John Radcliffe Hospital, Oxford OX3 9DU Tel: 01865 741166; 37 Hamilton Gardens, London NW8 9PX Tel: 020 7266 1903 — BM BCh 1994 Oxf.; BA Oxf. 1991, BM BCh 1994.

JUNIPER, Colin Pudan Shoulders, Hundred Acre Lane, Streat, Hassocks BN6 8SH Tel: 01273 890417 — LMSSA 1959 Lond.; MD Lond. 1979, MB BS 1960; FFOM RCPI 1983, MFOM 1977; FFOM RCP Lond. 1981, MFOM 1978. (St. Bart.) Sen. Med. Adviser UK Unilever plc. Socs: Fell. Roy. Soc. Med.; BMA & Indust. Injuries Advis. Counc. Prev: Cas. Off. St. Bart. Hosp.; Med. Adviser Unilever Research Laborats. Colworth & Welwyn; Med. Adviser Lever Brothers Ltd. Port Sunlight.

JUNIPER, Mark Colin Princess Margaret Hospital, Okus Raod, Swindon SN1 4JU Tel: 01793 425040, 01793 437117 — MB BS 1989 Lond.; MRCP (UK) 1993. (St Barts Hosp.) Cons., Respirat. Med. and Intens. Care, P.ss Margt. Hosp., Swindon. Socs: Brit. Thoracic Soc.; Intens. Care Soc. Prev: Sen. Regist. Osler Chest Unit, Oxf..; Research Fell. (Intens. Care) John Radcliffe Hosp. Oxf.; Regist. Nuffield Dept. Med. Oxf.

JUNIPER, Susan Elizabeth Jane Mill Race Cottage, Adel Mill, Eccup Lane, Leeds LS16 8AH Tel: 0113 230 1800 — MB BS 1985 Lond.

JUNOR, Brian James Ross The Barn, Ballagan, Strathblane, Glasgow G63 9AE — MD 1979 Dundee; MB ChB St. And. 1970; FRCP Glas. 1982; FRCP Ed. 1988; MRCP (UK) 1973. Cons. Nephrol., W.. Infirm. Glas.; Hon. Clin. Lect. Univ. Glas.

JUNOR, Elizabeth Jean The Barn, Ballagan, Strathblane, Glasgow G63 9AE — MD 1993 Aberd.; MB ChB 1976; FRCP Glas. 1994; MRCP (UK) 1978; FRCR 1988. Cons. Clin. Oncol. Beatson Oncol. Centre Glas.; Hon. Sen. Lect. Univ. Glas. Prev: Sen. Regist. Beatson Oncol. Centre Glas.

JUPP, Caroline Monica Louise Bay Horse Farm, Maulds Meaburn, Penrith CA10 3HN — MB BS 1983 Lond.

JUPP, Elizabeth Julia St Clement's Hospital, Foxhall Road, Ipswich IP3 8NJ Tel: 01473 715111 — MB BS 1980 Lond.; LMSSA Lond. 1980; DRCOG 1986. Assoc. Specialist in Rehabil. Psychiat., Local Health Partnership, Ipswich.

JUPP, Graeme Frederick Woodside Health Centre, 3 Enmore Road, London SE25 5NT Tel: 020 8655 1223 Fax: 020 8656 7984; The Hurst, 5 Woodbury Close, Croydon CR0 5PR Tel: 020 8654 6249 Fax: 020 8656 7984 — MB BS 1968 Lond. (Lond. Hosp.) Socs: BMA. Prev: Ho. Surg. E. Ham. Memor. Hosp.; Ho. Phys. Brook Hosp. Shooters Hill.; Ho. Surg. (Obst.) Mile End Hosp. Lond.

JUPP, Kathryn Queensway Surgery, 75 Queensway, Southend-on-Sea SS1 2AB Tel: 01702 463333 Fax: 01702 603026; The Myrtles, 215 Hockley Road, Rayleigh SS6 8BH Tel: 01268 777872 Fax: 01268 779333 — MB BS 1974 Lond.; DCH Eng. 1977. (UCHMS)

JUPP, Sarah Marion 300 Durnsford Road, Wimbledon Park, London SW19 8DU Tel: 020 8286 2945 — MB ChB 1992 Bristol.

JURADO, Raul 10 Riverside Drive, Chertsey Lane, Staines TW18 3JN Tel: 01784 453795 — Medico Cirujano San Andres 1966. Clin. Asst. (A & E) Scunthorpe Gen. Hosp. Prev: Sen. Med. Off. (Gen. Surg.) Baragwanath Hosp. Johannesburg S. Afr.; Regist. (Orthop. & Traum. Surg.) Hillingdon Hosp. Uxbridge; Regist. (Orthop.) Scunthorpe Gen. Hosp.

JURANGPATHY, M Ferhad The Surgery, 391 High Road, Wood Green, London N22 8JB Tel: 020 8889 1115 Fax: 020 8881 4372 — MB BS 1972 Sri Lanka; MRCS Eng. LRCP; MB BS 1972 Sri Lanka. Med. Off. Walk in Clinic N. Middlx. Hosp. Edmonton N18. Socs: Brit. Med. Assn. Mem.; Roy. Soc. of Med. Mem.; Soc. of Occupat.al Med. Mem.

JUREK, Paul Maciej Peter Finsbury Health Centre, Pine Street, London EC1R 0JH Tel: 020 7713 5256 — MRCS Eng. LRCP Lond. 1977. Prev: Trainee GP/SHO Whipps Cross Hosp. VTS; SHO (Paediat., O & G, A & E & Med.) Whipps Cross Hosp.

JURGES, Eman Salim 17 Colwyn Avenue, Greenford UB6 8JY — MB ChB 1979 Basrah; MRCP UK 1986. Regist. (Paediat.) Bone Marrow Transpl. Unit W.m. Childr. Hosp. Lond. Prev: Regist. (Paediat.) Lewisham Hosp. Lond.

JURKOVIC, Davor Department of Obstetrics & Gynaecology, King's College Hospital, Denmark Hill, London SE5 8RX Tel: 020 7346 3168 Fax: 020 7346 3471 Email: davor.jurkovic@kcl.ac.uk — MD 1981 Zagreb; PhD Zagreb 1989; MRCOG 1993. Cons.(Obstet. & Gyn), Kings Coll. Hosp., Lond. Socs: Internat. Soc. Ultrasound in Obst. & Gyn.; Comm. Mem. Europ. Soc. Endosonography in Gyn. & Obst.; BMA. Prev: Regist. (O & G) King's Coll. Hosp.; Research Fell. Ultrasonic Inst. Zabgreb, Croatia.; Lect. Hon.Sen. Regist. Kings Coll. Hosp.

JURY, Catherine Sarah Flat 2, 43 Kersland St., Glasgow G12 8BS — MB ChB 1994 Glas. Specialist Regist. W.ern Infirm. Glas.

JUSTE, Rodney Norman 36 Claremont Drive, Ormskirk L39 4SP — MB ChB 1988 Manch.; FRCA 1994. Specialist Regist. in Anaesth. Hammersmith Hosp., Lond. Prev: Lect. (Anaesth.) Char. Cross & W.m. Med. Sch. & Chelsea & W.m. Hosp. Lond.

JUSTICE, Agnes Wood (retired) 1 High House Close, Morpeth NE61 2BL Tel: 01670 512905 — MB ChB 1945 Glas.; FRCPsych 1986, M 1973; DPM Eng. 1960. Prev: Cons. Psychiat. Gateshead HA.

JUSTICE, Andrew Alexander Colne Medical Centre, 40 Station Road, Brightlingsea, Colchester CO7 0DT Tel: 01206 302522 Fax: 01206 305131; 16 Cherrywoods, Great Bentley, Colchester CO7 8QF Tel: 01206 251474 — MB BS 1986 Lond.; MRCGP 1992; DRCOG 1990. (Lond.)

JUSTICE, James Michael (retired) Park House, Badby, Daventry NN11 3AF Tel: 01327 702691 — MB BS 1959 Lond.; DObst RCOG 1965. Prev: GP Daventry.

JUSTICE, John Macarthur Simpson House Medical Centre, 255 Eastcote Lane, South Harrow, Harrow HA2 8RS Tel: 020 8864 3466 Fax: 020 8864 1002; 2 Shenley Hill, Radlett WD7 7BA Tel: 01923 852653 — BM BCh 1974 Oxf.; MRCGP 1981; DRCOG 1977.

JUSTICE, Richard James West Winds, The Street, Sedlescombe, Battle TN33 0QJ — MB BS 1991 Lond.

JUSTINS, Douglas Malcolm Department Anaesthetics, St. Thomas Hospital, London SE1 7EH Tel: 020 7928 9292 Fax: 020 7922 8318 — MB BS 1970 Queensland; FRCA 1979. Cons. Pain Managem. & Anaesth. St. Thos. Hosp. Lond. Socs: Pain Soc.; Internat. Assn. Study of Pain; (Counc. Mem.) Roy. Coll. Anaesth.

JUTLLA, Gurmeet Singh Luton & Dunstable Hospital Radiology Department, Lewey Road, Luton LU4 0DZ; 8 Chruchill Road, Marston Moreteyne, Bedford MK43 0QB — MB ChB 1975 Leeds; FRCR 1983; MRCP 1979 (UK); BSc 1972 Leeds; BSc Leeds 1972; MRCP (UK) 1979; FRCR 1983. Cons. Radiol. Luton & Dunstable Hosp. Luton. Prev: Cons. Radiol. Pontefract Gen. Infirm.; Sen. Regist. (Radiol.) Leeds Gen. Infirm. & St. Jas. Hosp. Leeds; Regist. (Gen. Med.) Bradford Roy. Infirm.

JUTTING, Ian George Caton Dunorlan Medical Group, 64 Pembury Road, Tonbridge TN9 2JG Tel: 01732 352907 Fax: 01732 367408; Cage Farm Lodge, 68 The Ridgeway, Tonbridge TN10 4NN — MB BS 1980 Lond.; MRCGP 1989; DFFP 1993; DRCOG 1986; St. Mary's). Med. Staff Mem. Tonbridge Cottage Hosps. Prev: Trainee GP Tunbridge Wells VTS; SHO (Gen. Med. & Paediat.) Pembury Hosp. Tunbridge Wells HA; SHO (Psychiat.) Maidstone Hosp.

JWAD, Anees Ishak Hartlepool General Hospital, Hartlepool TS24 9AH Tel: 01429 266654 Fax: 01429 868830 Email: drjwad@x.hed-tr.northy.nhs.uk; 46 Ashwood Close, Woodstock Park, Hartlepool TS27 3QX Tel: 01429 231758 — MB ChB 1973 Basrah; FRCR 1985; DMRD 1982; DMRD Baghdad 1978. Cons. Radiol. Hartlepool Gen. Hosp. Socs: Scott. Radiol. Soc.; Roy. Coll. Radiol. Prev: Sen. Regist. (Diag. Radiol.) Altnagelvin Hosp. Lond.derry; Regist. (Diag. Radiol.) Altnagelvin Hosp. Lond.derry, Blackburn Roy. Infirm & Ch.ill Hosp. Oxf.; Regist. (Radiol.) Char. Cross Hosp. Lond.

KAAR, John Daniel William Lindeem Medical Practice, 1 Cabourne Court, Cabourne Avenue, Lincoln LN2 2JP Tel: 01522

569033 Fax: 01522 576713; Westfield Farm, Hawthorn Road, Reepham, Lincoln LN3 4JU Tel: 01522 753344 Email: drjdwk@aol.com — MB BCh BAO 1975 NUI. (Cork)

KAAWACH, Wael Fayez 15 Baker Street, Aberdeen AB25 1UQ — MB ChB 1992 Aberd.

KABA, Riyaz Amirali 17 Kempshott Road, London SW16 5LG — MB ChB 1994 Dundee.

KABALA, Julian Eamon Department of Clinical Radiology, Bristol Royal Infirmary, Marlborough St., Bristol BS2 8HW Tel: 0117 928 2729 Fax: 0117 928 3267 — MB ChB 1980 Bristol; MRCP (UK) 1983; FRCR 1988. Cons. Radiol. Bristol Roy. Infirm. Prev: Sen. Regist. & Regist. (Radiol.) Bristol Roy. Infirm.; SHO (Med.) Exeter.

KABBANI, Maher 4 Dunster Close, Stafford ST17 9QA — MD 1985 Aleppo.

KABEER, Abdul Wahid Adil 2 Glan Rhyd, Coed Eva, Cwmbran NP44 6TY — MB BCh 1986 Wales.

KABEER, Atika Amtul Kalim 2 Glanrhyd Coedeva, Cwmbran NP4 6TY; Flat 14, 54 Russell Road, Mosely, Birmingham B13 8RF Tel: 0121 449 3972 — MB BCh 1990 Wales; FRCA 1995. (Univ. Hosp. Cardiff Heath) Specialist Regist. (Anaesth.) Qu. Eliz. Hosp. Birm. Socs: BMA; Assn. Anaesth. Prev: SHO (Anaesth.) Gloucester Roy. Hosp.; SHO (Med. & Anaesth.) Abergavenny Neville Hall Hosp.

KABELI, Sabieli 8 St Andrews Road, London NW11 0PJ — MB BS 1991 Lond.

KABIL, Mr Yahia Abd El-Moneim Frimley Park Hospital, Portsmouth Road, Frimley, Camberley GU16 7UJ Tel: 01276 692777 — MB BCh 1969 Cairo; FRCS Ed. 1991; DLO RCS Eng. 1984.

KABIR, Alamgir Mahmud Nasimul 2 Manor Park, London SE13 5RN — MB BS 1996 Lond.

KABIR, Jahangir Mahmud Moinul 2 Manor Park, London SE13 5RN — MB BS 1993 Lond.

KABLER, Jonathan Joseph Chipping Surgery, 1 Symn Lane, Wotton-under-Edge GL12 7BD Tel: 01453 842214 — MB BS 1987 Lond.; MRCGP 1991.

KABUKOBA, Josaphat Joseph Department of Obstetrics & Gynaecology, Sandwell Hospital, Lyndon, West Bromwich B71 4HJ Tel: 0121 607 3475 Fax: 0121 607 3374 Email: kabukoba@onestopclinic.co.uk; 345 Monmouth Drive, Sutton Coldfield B73 6JX Tel: 0121 321 3340 Fax: 0121 355 4644 Email: kabukoba@onestopclinic.co.uk — MD 1978 Dar-es-Salaam, Tanzania; MRCOG 1988; Dip Med Educat 2001 Dundee. Cons. O & G Sandwell Healthcare NHS Trust. Socs: Roy. Soc. Med.; Brit. Soc. Gyn. Endoscopy.

KABUUBI, Joseph Balidde Lwanga, Lt.-Col. RAMC Ministry of Defence Hospial Unit, Friarage NHS Trust, Northallerton DL6 1JG Tel: 01609 763109 Fax: 01609 763453; 69 Wanstead Park Avenue, London E12 5EE Tel: 020 8989 9511 — MB BS Lond. 1969; FRCP Lond. 1994; MRCP (UK) 1974; MRCS Eng. LRCP Lond. 1969; Acad. Dip. Biochem. Univ. Lond. 1966. (Guy's) Cons. Phys. (Med.) RAMC, MOD Hosp. Unit, Friarage NHS Trust, N.allerton, N. Yorks. Socs: BMA; Brit. Soc. Study of Infec.; Roy. Soc. Trop. Med. & Hyg. Prev: Sen. Regist. (Med. & Infec. Dis.) N.wick Pk., St. Ann's & St. Bart. Hosps. Lond.; Regist. (Med.) Hither Green & Lewisham Hosps.; SHO (Med.) Gravesend Hosp.

KACHCHUMARIKKAR, Mathar Sahib X-Ray Department, Hylton Block, Distict & General Hospital, Sunderland SR4 7TP — Vrach 1968 Peoples' Friendship Moscow; DMRD Eng. 1976. (Peoples' Friendship Univ.) Cons. (Radiol.) Sunderland AHA.

KACHHIA, Bhavinchandra Govindlal The Surgery, Riversley Road, Nuneaton CV11 5QT Tel: 024 7638 2239/7664 2409 Fax: 024 7632 5623; 366A Higham Lane, Nuneaton CV11 6AP Tel: 01203 386602 — MB BS 1972 Gujarat. (B.J. Med. Coll. Ahmedabad) Clin. Asst. (Fract. Orthop.) Coventry & Warwick Hosp.; Clin. Asst. (Dermat.) Geo. Eliot Hosp. Nuneaton.

KACHROO, Maharaj Krishen 635 Western Boulevard, Nottingham NG8 5GS Tel: 0115 976557 — MB BS 1969 Jammu & Kashmir. (Srinagar Med. Coll.)

KACKER, Prem Prakash Highgate Surgery, Highgate, Tinsley, Sheffield S9 1WN Tel: 0114 244 2256 — MB BS 1960 Lucknow; BSc, MB BS Lucknow 1960. (King Geo. Med. Coll.)

KACKER, Satya Highgate Surgery, Highgate, Tinsley, Sheffield S9 1WN Tel: 0114 244 2256 — MB BS 1961 Agra; MS Lucknow 1965; DObst 1966. (S.N. Med. Coll. Agra)

KACKER, Sujata 67 Slayleigh Lane, Sheffield S10 3RG — MB BS 1998 Lond.; MB BS Lond 1998.

KACZMARSKI, Edward Boguslaw Public Health Laboratory, Withington Hospital, Manchester M20 2LR Tel: 0161 291 3603 Fax: 0161 446 2180 Email: ed@manphl.demon.co.uk — MB BS 1978 Lond.; MRCPath. 1989; Dip. Bact. Manch. 1987; FRCPath 1997. Cons. Med. Microbiol. Manch. Pub. Health Laborat. & Withington Hosp. Manch.

KACZMARSKI, Richard Stanislaw 36 Second Avenue, London SW14 8QE — MB BS 1984 Lond.; MRCP (UK) 1987.

KADAM, Umesh Thakorbhai 23 Glamis Drive, Stone ST15 8SP — MB ChB 1989 Birm.

KADAMBARI, Syamala Rao St Georges Hospital Medical School, Jenner Wing, Cranmer Terrace, Tooting, London SW17 0RE; 4 Ashmere Avenue, Beckenham BR3 6PQ Tel: 020 8658 5627 — MB BS 1974 Andhra; MPhil Lond. 1990; MRCPsych 1981; T(Psychiat.) 1991; DPM Eng. 1978. Cons. Psychiat. & Hon. Sen. Lect. St. Geo. Hosp. Med. Sch. Lond. Prev: Sen. Regist. Guy's Hosp. Lond.; Regist. Mersey RHA.

KADAS, Thomas The Newton Medical Centre, 14-18 Newton Road, London W2 5LT Tel: 020 7229 4578 Fax: 020 7229 7315 — LAH Dub. 1964.

KADDOURA, Samer Department of Cardiology, Chelsa and Westminster Hospital, 369 Fulham Road, London SW10 9NH Tel: 020 8746 5681 Fax: 020 8746 8040; Department of Cardiology, Royal Brompton Hospital, Sydney St, London SW3 6NP — BM BCh 1987 Oxf.; FRCP 2001; FESC 1999; DIC 1998; PhD Lond. 1998; MRCP (UK) 1990; BSc (1st cl Hons.) Lond. 1984. (Oxford) Cons. Cardiol. Chelsea & W.m. & Roy. Brompton Hosps., Lond.; Hon. Sen. Lect. Nat. Heart & Lung Inst. Imperial Coll. Lond.; Assoc. Edr., Europ. Heart Jl. Socs: BMA, Brit. Cardiac Soc. & Amer. Heart Assn. (Clin. Cardiol. Counc.); Fell.Europ. Soc. of Cardiol. Prev: MRC Clin. Train. Fell. & Hon. Sen. Regist. NHLI & Roy. Brompton Hosp.; Regist. (Cardiol.) Roy. Brompton Hosp.; Regist. (Gen. Med. & Cardiol.) St Mary's Hosp. Lond & Hillingdon Hosp.

KADE, Chauke The Gainsborough Practice, 1 County Lane, Warfield, Bracknell RG42 3JP Tel: 01344 428742 — 1978 Medico-Cirujano. (University of Zulia, Venezuela) G. P. Princip. Socs: GMC; M.D.U.; Roy. Coll. of Gen. Practitioners.

KADEMANI, Yeshwant Laughton Forest Nursing Home, Scotter, Gainsborough DN21 3JF; Fir Tree Cottage, Gainsborough Road, Scotter Common, Gainsborough DN21 3JF — MB BS 1970 Mysore.

KADER, Hosam Eddin Hamed Hamed Abdel 4 Peterborough Way, Sleaford NG34 8TW — MB BCh 1975 Ain Shams; MRCP (UK) 1982; FRCR 1989; T(R) (CO) 1991. Sen. Regist. (Radiother & Oncol.) Leicester Roy. Infirm.; Clin. Teach. Fac. of Med. Univ. Leicester. Prev: Regist. (Radiother. & Oncol.) W.on Pk. Hosp. Sheff.

KADER, Leonard, CStJ — LMSSA 1949 Lond.; MRCS Eng. LRCP Lond. 1952; MFOM RCP Lond. 1979; MRCGP 1956; FRSH T(OM) 1997. (King's Coll. Hosp.) p/t Indep. Occupat. Health Phys. Socs: Fell. Inst. Occupat. Safety & Health; Soc. Occupat. Med. Prev: Dir. Med. Serv. The Plessey Company.

KADHIM, Rashid Yahya The Avicenna Health Centre, 2 Verney Way, London SE16 3HA Tel: 020 7237 1685 Fax: 020 7394 7200 — MRCS Eng. LRCP Lond. 1977.

KADIANI, Mohammed Rajab 16 Wellwood Close, Bicton Heath, Shrewsbury SY3 5BP — MB BS 1986 Karnatak.

KADIM, Mohammed Yahya Moorfields Eye Hospital, City Road, London EC1V 2PD Tel: 020 7566 2387 — MB ChB 1977 Baghdad; FRCA 1990; FFA RCSI 1986; DA (UK) 1984. Cons. Anaesth. Moorfields Eye Hosp. Lond. Prev: Sen. Regist. (Anaesth.) Hammersmith Hosp. Lond.

KADIR, Nurul 28 Lord Avenue, Clayhall Road, Ilford IG5 0HP — MB BS 1963 Calcutta; MRCP (UK) 1973; DTM & H Calcutta 1966. (Calcutta Med. Coll.) Cons. Rheum. Manor Hse. Hosp. Lond. Prev: Sen. Regist. (Rheum.) Roy. Free Hosp. Lond.; Regist. (Gen. Med.) Qu. Mary's Hosp. Kent.

KADIRGAMAR, Ajit Gordon Vimalendran Presnor, Windsor Lane, Little Kingshill, Great Missenden HP16 0DZ — BSc Lond. 1985, MB BS 1988; DRCOG 1992; DCH RCP Lond. 1991. Prev: Trainee GP High Wycombe.

KADIRKAMANTHAN, Mr Sritharan Sangarapillai Academic Department of Surgery, Royal London Hospital, Whitechapel, London E1 1BB Tel: 020 7377 7000 Ext: 3151; Tel: 01763 248826 — MB

BS 1983 Colombo; PhD 2000 Lond.; FRCS Ed. 1988; FRCS (Gen) 1998. Sen. Lect./ Hon. Cons. (Gen Surg), Roy. Hosps. NHS Trust & Homerton Hosps. NHS Trust, Lond. Socs: Assoc. Mem. Brit. Soc. Gastroenterol. (Clin. Measurem. Gp.); BMA. Prev: Specialist Regist. (Gen. Surg.) Roy. Hosps. NHS Trust Lond.; Specialist Regist. (Gen. Surg.) Colchester Gen. Hosp.

KADOM, Mr Abdul Hadi Mohammed 5 Hartfield Close, Kents Hill, Milton Keynes MK7 6HN — MB ChB 1972 Baghdad; FRCS Ed. 1982; FCOphth 1988; DO RCPSI 1980. Assoc. Specialist (Ophth.) Oxf. RHA. Prev: Clin. Asst. (Ophth.) Milton Keynes HA; Regist. (Ophth.) Tennent Inst. Glas. & S.. Gen. Hosp. Glas.

KADOUS, Helmy Abd El Mohsen 14 The Avenue, Whitley Bay NE26 3PH Tel: 0191 252 8943 — MB BCh Ain Shams 1964; Dip. Gen. Med. Ain Shams 1968; Dip. Cardiol. Alexandria 1971. (Ain Shams) Locum GP Private Phys. Socs: MPS; Roy. Soc. Med.; BMA July 2001. Prev: Regist. (Med.) Preston Hosp. & Roy. Infirm. Falkirk; SHO (Cardiol.) Vict. Hosp. Blackpool.; Indep. Med. Off. Disabil. Appeal Tribunal & S.S. Appeal Tyne & Wear 1991-99.

KADOW, Mr Krzysztof Wladyslaw Solihull Hospital, Hope Lane, Solihull B91 2JL; Hardacres, 81 Chessetts Wood Road, Lapworth, Solihull B94 6EL — MB BCh 1974 Wales; BSc Wales 1971, MB BCh 1974; FRCS Eng. 1979. Cons. Urol. Solihull & E. Birm. Hosps. Prev: Sen. Regist. (Urol.) Kings Coll. Hosp. Lond.; Research Regist. (Urol.) Ham Green Hosp. Bristol; Regist. (Surg./Urol.) St. Thos. Hosp. Lond.

KADR, Honer Hossein Department of Cardiology, Queen Mary Block, Old Church Hospital, Romford RM7 0BE Tel: 01708 727046 Fax: 01708 732085; 128 Mashiters Walk, Marshalls Park, Romford RM1 4BS Tel: 01708 768971 — MB ChB 1974 Baghdad; MSc Glas. 1987; MRCP (UK) 1988; FRCP Glas. 1998. (Baghdad, Iraq) Sen. Research Fell. Cardiol. Old Ch. Hosp. Romford; Collegiate Mem. Lond. & Glas. RCP. Socs: Brit. EchoCardiol. Soc.; Eur. Writing Gp. on Echocardiol.; Brit. Heart Failure Soc. Prev: Hon. Regist. & Research Fell. (Cardiol.) Glas. Roy. Infirm.; Regist. (Gen. & Elderly Med.) York Dist. Hosp.; Regist. (Gen. Med. & Clin. Pharmacol.) Glas. Roy. Infirm.

KADRI, Amyn Zahur St Peters Surgery, 49-55 Portsmouth Road, Woolston, Southampton SO19 9RL Tel: 023 8043 4355 Fax: 023 8043 4195 — BM BCh 1984 Oxf.; DFFP 1996; MRCGP 1990; MA 2000 (Oxon); MRCP 1987 (UK); DCH RCP 1988 Lond.; BA (Physiol.) 1981 Oxf.; DRCOG 1989; BA (Physiol.) Oxf. 1981; MRCP (UK) 1987; MRCGP 1990; DFFP 1996; DRCOG 1989; DCH RCP Lond. 1988. Clin. Governance head, Soton. City PCT.

KADRI, Ayodeji Olayinka 301 Saltash House, 3 Seaton Close, Penwith Manor Estate, Kennington, London SE11 4HD; 13 Sancroft House, Sancroft St, Vauxhall Gardens, London SE11 5PP Email: aok@global.net.co.uk — MB BS Lagos 1987; MRCP (UK) 1993; MRCPCH 1997. Specialist Regist. (Paediat.) Paediat. Accid & Emerg. Dept. Chelsea & W.m. Hosp. Lond.; Qu. Charlotte's Hosp. Gold Hawk Rd. Lond. Socs: Med. Def. Union; RCPCH. Prev: Regist. (Paediat.) Watford Gen. Hosp.; SHO (Hepatol.) Birm. Childr. Hosp.; SHO (Community Paediat.) S. Birm. HA.

KADURUWANE, Eustace Nanda Queen Street Surgery, 13A Queen Street, Deal CT14 6ET Tel: 01304 363181 Fax: 01304 381996 — MB BS 1958 Ceylon; DCH Eng. 1965. (Ceylon)

KADVA, Miss Aban Bhicaji 166 Temple Avenue, Dagenham RM8 1NB Email: a.kadva@mds.qmw.ac.uk — MB BS 1978 Mysore; MRCS Eng. LRCP Lond. 1979; MRCOG 1990. (Kasturba) Sen. Regist. Roy. Hosps. NHS Trust Lond.; Clin. Research Fell. (Obst. & Gyn.) Lond. Hosp. Med. Coll. & Newham Gen. Hosp. Prev: Regist. (O & G) Crawley Hosp.; Specialist Regist. P.ss Alexandra Hosp. Harlow.

KADZOMBE, Mr Edward Andrews Maonga Fazakerley Hospital, Longmoor Lane, Liverpool L9 7AL — MB ChB 1975 Manch.; FRCS Ed. 1980; FRCS Eng. 1980; DCH 1991; FFAEM 1993. (Manch.) Surg. Regist. N. Manch. Gen. Hosp. & Cons. (A & E) Fazekeley Hosp., Aintree Hosps. NHS Trust Liverp.; Private Pract. Liverp. Prev: Ho. Phys. & SHO (Surg.) Manch. Roy. Infirm.; Regist. (Surg.) S. Lothian (Edin.) Health Bd.; Sen. Regist. Aintree Hosp. NHS Trust & Roy. Liverp. Childr.s Hosp. Alder Hey.

KAESER, Anthony Carl (retired) 3 Woodland Close, Ingatestone CM4 9SR — MB BS 1957 Lond.; FRCP Lond. 1992, M 1961; MRCS Eng. LRCP Lond. 1957; FRCPsych 1978, M 1971; DPM Lond. 1964. Prev: Cons. Psychiat. Basildon & Runwell Hosps.

KAFETZ, Kalman Meir Connaught Day Hospital, Whipps Cross Hospital, London E11 1NR Tel: 020 8535 6525 Fax: 020 8535 6970 Email: kalman.kafetz@whippsx.nhs.uk; 22 Offham Slope, London N12 7BZ Tel: 020 8922 5642 — MB BS 1973 Lond.; BSc (Biochem.) Lond. 1970; FRCP Lond. 1994; MRCP (UK) 1976. (St. Thos.) Cons. Phys. Med. for Elderly Whipps Cross & Chingford Hosps.; Hon. Sen. Lect. Med. Coll. Roy. Lond. & St. Bart. Hosp. Lond.; Recognised Teach. Univ. Lond. Socs: (Ex-Mem. Counc. & Policy Comm. & Chairm. Liaison Comm. with RCPsych) Brit. Geriat. Soc.; Old Etonian Med. Soc.; Lond. Jewish Med. Soc. Prev: Sen. Regist. (Med. & Geriat.) Hammersmith Hosp. Lond.; Regist. (Cardiol., Renal & Med.) Lond. Hosp.; Ho. Phys. (Med. & Metab. Dis.) St. Thos. Hosp. Lond.

KAFETZAKIS, Emanuel Hickley Cottage, Sully Road, Penarth CF64 2TQ.

KAFTAN, Safa Mohammed Hamza 21 Clay Butts, Birkby, Huddersfield HD2 2FW Tel: 01484 422191 Fax: 01484 422191 — MB ChB 1981 Baghdad; MSc (Path.) Lond. 1986. Clin. Asst. (Histopath.) Yorks.

KAGALWALA, Anil Ramanlal Queen Mary's Sidcup NHS Trust, Queen Mary's Hospital, Sidcup DA14 6LT Tel: 020 8302 2678; 128 Old Church Lane, Stanmore HA7 2RR Tel: 020 8954 6610 — MB BS 1959 Bombay; DDerm Lond 1970; Dip. Ven. Liverp. 1969; MFFP 1993; MICGP 1987; MRCGP 1977; DHMSA Lond. 1974; Dip. Phil. Med. Soc. Apoth. Lond. 1981; Cert Contracep. & Family Plann. RCOG, RCGP & Family Plann. Assn. 1975; Dip. Ven. Soc. Apoth. Lond. 1974. (Grant Med. Coll.) Hon. Cons. Dermat. Qu. Mary's Sidcup NHS Trust. Socs: Fell. Roy. Soc. Med. & Fac. Hist. & Philosophy of Med. & Pharm.; Roy. Soc. Med. (Dermat. Sect.); Brit. Assn. Dermat. Prev: Cons. Dermat. & Venereol. Shehar Hosp. Tarif, Saudi Arabia; Cons. Dermat. Bromley HA; Sen. Regist. (Genitourin. Med.) Roy. Free Hosp. Lond. & Roy. N.. Hosp. Lond.

KAGAN, Richard Stanley (retired) Rounday, White Post Lane, Round Street, Cobham, Gravesend DA13 9AX Tel: 01474 814473 Email: richardkagan@supanet.com — MRCS Eng. LRCP Lond. 1946; MRCGP 1962. Prev: on Med. Staff Livingstone Hosp. Dartford.

KAHAN, Alexander (retired) Flat 1, 24 Sussex Square, Brighton BN2 5AB Tel: 01273 687689 — MD Lond. 1935, MB BS 1931; FRCP Ed. 1969, M 1951; MRCS Eng. LRCP Lond. 1931; DCH Eng. 1945. Prev: Cons. Phys. & Phys. i/c Diabetic Clinic St. Jas. Hosp. Balham.

KAHAN, Gloria Kachorn Staddon Castle Surgery, 1 Prince of Wales Drive, Neath SA11 3EW Tel: 01639 641444 Fax: 01639 636288; 40 Wenallt Road, Tonna, Neath SA11 3HZ — MB BCh 1978 Wales.

KAHAN, Robert Owen 2 Chestnut Close, Rhyddings, Neath SA10 7AU — MRCS Eng. LRCP Lond. 1967; MB Camb. 1968, BChir 1967; MRCP (U.K.) 1974. Cons. Phys. W. Glam. AHA.

KAHANE, Richard Martin Giffords Surgery, 28 Lowbourne, Melksham SN12 7EA Tel: 01225 703370; The Grove, 407 The Spa, Melksham SN12 6QL Tel: 01225 706545 — MB BS 1971 Lond.; MRCS Eng. LRCP Lond. 1971; MRCGP 1979; DObst RCOG 1974. (St. Bart.) Med. Off. Melksham Hosp. Prev: Ho. Surg. St. Bart. Hosp. Lond.; Ho. Phys. & SHO (Obst.) Rochford Gen. Hosp.

KAHLENBERG, Hans George Grove Cottage, The Green, Chiddingfold, Godalming GU8 4TU Tel: 01428 682071 — MRCS Eng. LRCP Lond. 1938; DA Eng. 1942. (St. Mary's) Anaesth. Haslemere Hosp., Midhurst Cott. Hosp., Pk. Prewett Hosp.; Basingstoke & Holy Cross Hosp. Haslemere. Socs: Fac. Anaesth. RCS Eng. & Internat. Anaesth. Research Soc. Prev: Ho. Surg. Salisbury Gen. Infirm.; Res. Anaesth. Roy. Hosp. Wolverhampton; Hon. Asst. Anaesth. Roy. Surrey Co. Hosp. Guildford.

KAHLON, Karnail Singh Westbury Cottage, Westbury Road, Bromley BR1 2QB — MB BS 1970 Panjab.

KAHN, Ashraf Addictive Behaviours Centre, North Birmingham Mental Health NHS Trust, 71 Fentham Road, Erdington, Birmingham B23 6AL Tel: 0121 623 5500 Fax: 0121 685 6230; Woodbourne Priory Hospital, 21 Woodbourne Road, Edgbaston, Birmingham B17 8BZ Tel: 0121 434 4343 Email: ash.kahn@blueyonder.co.uk — MB ChB 1972 Birm.; MRCPsych 1978. (Birm.) Cons. Psychiat. Addictive Behaviour Centre N. Birm. Ment. Health NHS Trust; Hon. Sen. Clin. Lect. (Psychiat.) Univ. Birm.; Med.Dir. Woodbourne Priory Hosp. Prev: Sen. Regist. (Psychiat.) All St.s Hosp. Birm.; Regist. (Psychiat.) Centr. Birm. Health Dist.; Ho. Off. United Birm. Hosps.

KAHTAN, Nadji Three Bridges RSU, Uxbridge Rd, Southall UB1 3EU Tel: 020 8354 8049 — MB BS 1986 Lond.; BSc 1982; MRCPsych 1994. (King's College Hospital) Cons. (Forens. Psych.) Three Bridges Regional Secure Unit, Ealing. Prev: Sen. Regist. in Forens. Psychiat., Camlet Lodge Regional Secure Unit/John Howard Centre, Hackney; Research Fell. in Forens. Psychiat., St Bartholomews Hosp. Med. Coll.

KAHTAN, Susannah Rose 166 Hendon Way, London NW2 2NE Tel: 020 8455 4140 — MRCS Eng. LRCP Lond. 1992; MA (Hons.) Oxf. 1988. Indep. Medico-Legal Arbitrator Lond.; Mem. Med. Ethics Gp. Socs: Fell. Roy. Soc. Med. Prev: Train. (Psychiat.) Bethlem & Maudsley Hosps. Lond.

KAI, Joseph Peter Department of Primary Care and General Practice, Medical School, Edgbaston, Birmingham B15 2TT Email: j.p.kai:bham.ac.uk — MB BS 1987 Newc.; MRCGP (Distinc.) 1991. Clin. Sen. Lect. Univ. of Birm.; GP Dir. Midl. Research Pract. Consortium. Prev: Lect. (Primary Health Care) Univ. Newc.; Trainee GP N.umbria VTS; Ho. Phys. & Ho. Surg. Freeman Hosp. Newc. upon Tyne.

KAI, Maria Alison Flat 8, Connaught House, Queen Alexandra Hospital, Southwick Hill Road, Cosham, Portsmouth PO6 3LY; 6 Chilworth Old Village, Chilworth, Southampton SO16 7JP — BM 1989 Soton.; BM Soton 1989.

KAI, Peter 11 Lower Grinsty Lane, Redditch B97 5PJ; 15 Barley Court, The Maltings, Leamington Spa CV32 5FQ — MB ChB 1962 Cape Town; FRCA Eng. 1968. Cons. Anaesth. Univ. Hosp. Coventry & Warks., NHS Trust. Prev: Cons. Anaesth. King Faisal Specialist Hosp. & Armed Forces Hosp. Riyadh S. Arabia; Cons. Anaesth. Lancs. AHA; Sen. Regist. Liverp. Region Hosps.

KAIKINI, Deepak Wasant Wallace (Surgery), 19 Harvard Road, Isleworth TW7 4PA Tel: 020 8560 4841; 109 The Grove, Isleworth TW7 4JE Tel: 020 8560 4841 — MRCS Eng. LRCP Lond. 1974; Dip. Med. Freie Univ. W. Berlin 1970. Prev: Ho. Off. (Gen. Med. & Chest Dis.) Centr. Middlx. Hosp. Lond.; Ho. Surg. (Obst.) W. Middlx. Hosp. Isleworth.

KAIKINI, Dinkar Ramrao 109 The Grove, Isleworth TW7 4JE Tel: 020 8560 4841 — MB BS 1939 Bombay; DTM Calcutta 1941, DPH 1945. (Seth G.S. Med. Coll. Bombay) Prev: Asst. Surg. B.B. & C.I. Rly. Bombay, India; Demonst., Dept. Anat. G.S.M. Coll. Bombay.

***KAILEY, Jasraj Singh** 8 Burnside, Coventry CV3 2RS — MB ChB 1994 Birm.

KAILEY, Lakhbir Kaur 37 Woolacombe Road, Blackheath, London SE3 8QJ — BM 1984 Soton.; Cert. Family Plann. JCC 1991; DRCOG 1990; DCH RCP Lond. 1989.

KAILEY, Surjit Singh Northumberland Heath Medical Centre, Hind Crescent, Northumberland Heath, Erith DA8 3DB Tel: 01322 336556 Fax: 01322 351475 — MB BS 1985 Lond.; DCH RCP Lond. 1990; DA (UK) 1988.

KAIN, Kirti Chapeltown Road Surgery, 178 Chapeltown Road, Leeds LS7 4HR Tel: 0113 262 1239 Fax: 0113 262 1239 — MB BS 1978 Panjab; MB BS 1978 Panjab; LRCP Edin LRCS Edin LRCPS Glasg 1984. (Panjab) GP Leeds.

KAINTH, Manjit Singh 36 Talbot Road, Blakenhall, Wolverhampton WV2 3EW — BM BS 1998 Nottm.; BM BS Nottm 1998.

KAIPER-HOLMES, Cornelius Darley House, Hazel Old Lane, Hensall, Goole DN14 0QA Tel: 01977 661582 — MRCS Eng. LRCP Lond. 1968. (Leeds) Gp. Med. Dir. Healthcall Gp. plc Milton Keynes. Prev: GP Knottingley W. Yorks.; SHO Cas. Dept. Leeds Gen. Infirm.; SHO (Obst.) St. Mary's Hosp. Leeds.

KAIQOBAD, Mr Raja Muhammad 43 Woodlands Avenue, Law, Carluke ML8 5JL — MB BS 1982 Punjab; FRCS Ed. 1988.

KAISARY, Mr Amir Victor 70 Harley Street, London W1N 1AE Tel: 020 7436 4944 Fax: 020 7323 9493 Email: amir.kaisary@btinternet.com; Totteridge View, Hedgerow Lane, Arkley, Barnet EN5 3DT — MB BCh 1967 Cairo; ChM Bristol 1987; MA Oxf. 1984; FRCS Eng. 1975. Cons. Urol. Surg. Roy. Free Hosp. Lond.; Vis. Prof. Dept. Urol. Downstate Med. Centre State Univ. N. York, USA; Hon. Sen. Lect. Roy. Free & Univ. Coll. Med. Sch. Lond. Prev: Lect. (Urol. & Renal Transpl.) Univ. Oxf.; Tutor & Research Fell. Urol. Univ. Bristol; Regist. (Urol.) Char. Cross. Hosp. Lond.

KAISER, Anthony Michael St. Thomas' Hospital, Lambeth Palace Road, London SE1 7EH Tel: 020 7928 9292 — MB BS 1979 Lond.; BSc Lond. 1975; FRCP Lond. 1995; MRCP Lond. 1982; MRCS Eng. LRCP Lond. 1978; FRCPCH 1997; MD 1998. (St. Mary's, Lond.) Cons. Neonat. Guy's & St. Thos. Hosp. Lond.; Hon. Sen. Lect. Kings Coll. Sch. of Med. Socs: Paediat. Research Soc.; Neonat. Soc.; Brit. Assn. Perinatal Med. Prev: Research Fell. Roy. Postgrad. Med. Sch. Hammersmith Hosp. Lond.; Sen. Regist. (Neonat..) Univ. Coll. Hosp. Lond.; Sen. Regist. Respirat. Unit. Hosp. for Sick Child. Gt. Ormond St. Lond. & Lond. Hosp.

KAISER, Fawad North Lodge, Lodge Road, Caerleon, Newport NP18 3QQ — MB BS 1984 Punjab.

KAISER, Gert Martin 3 Sandringham House, 19 Newport Road, Cowes PO31 7PA — MD 1991 Wurzburg; State Exam Med 1990.

***KAISER, John Paul** 42 Severn Drive, Guisborough TS14 8AT — BChir 1996 Camb.; MB Camb. 1998; MA Camb. 1998.

KAISER, Rizwan Ali 134 Wellington Road S., Hounslow TW4 5JH — MB BS 1998 Lond.; MB BS Lond 1998.

KAISER, Thomas 18 Parkgate Road, Reigate RH2 7JD — State Exam. Med. Erlangen 1990.

KAITIFF, Nina Charlotte 285 Beacon Road, Loughborough LE11 2RA — MB ChB 1995 Birm.; ChB Birm. 1995.

KAKAD, Jitendra Chhotalal Harold Hill Centre, Gooshays Drive, Romford RM3 9JP Tel: 01708 343815 Fax: 01708 379790 — MB BS 1974 Bombay. (Topiwala Nat. Med. Coll.)

KAKAD, Kantilal Liladhar Stoney Stanton Medical Centre, 475 Stoney Stanton Road, Coventry CV6 5EA Tel: 024 7688 8484 Fax: 024 7658 1247 — MB BS 1973 Bombay. (Grant Med. Coll.) Prev: Ho. Off. (Med.) Gulson Hosp. Coventry.

KAKADE, Mohan 72 Broadhill Road, Stalybridge SK15 1HW — MB BS 1979 Bangalor; MB BS Bangalore 1979; MRCS Eng. LRCP Lond. 1988; DRCOG 1990. Trainee GP Ashton-under-Lyne Lancs. VTS. Prev: SHO (O & G) Tameside Gen. Hosp. Ashton-under-Lyne; SHO (Paediat.) Birch Hill Hosp. Rochdale; SHO (Psychiat.) Oldham Dist. Gen. Hosp.

KAKALETRIS, Dimitrios 1 Groveside Crescent, Nottingham NG11 8NT — Ptychio Iatrikes 1991 Athens.

KAKANI, Sanjeeva Rao Staff Grade A/E, Hinchingbrooke Hospital, Huntingdon PE29 6NT Tel: 01480 459788; 2 Brecon Way, Hinchingbrooke Park, Huntingdon PE29 6XZ Tel: 01480 459788 — MB BS 1963 Andhra; Dch Univ Madras 1969. (Andhra Medical College, India & Christian Medical College, Vellore) Staff Grade, A & E, Hinchingbrooke Health Care. Prev: SHO A & E, Orthop. Surg., Grantham Dist. Hosp.

KAKAR, Sanjeev 71 Keats Way, Greenford UB6 9HE — MB BS 1998 Lond.; MB BS Lond 1998.

KAKAS, Mr Michael Andrew 2 Llangenny Lane, Crickhowell NP8 1AN — MB BS 1984 Lond.; FRCS Eng. 1988.

KAKATI, Benudhar 40 Swanpool Lane, Aughton, Ormskirk L39 5AZ — MB BS 1968 Gauhati; MRCPI 1980.

KAKKAR, Ajay Kumar 43 Pickwick Road, London SE21 7JN — MB BS 1988 Lond.; BSc Lond. 1985, MB BS 1988. SHO (Surg.) Roy. Postgrad. Med. Sch. Hammersmith Hosp. Lond. Socs: Fell. Roy. Soc. Med. Prev: Demonst. (Anat.) Univ. Camb.; SHO (A & E) St. Mary's Hosp. Lond.

KAKKAR, Aparajit 58 Wheatlands Park, Redcar TS10 2PF — MB ChB 1996 Dundee.

KAKKAR, Sanjay Kumar 51 King's Court S., Chelsea Manor Gardens, London SW3 5EG — MB BS 1991 Lond.

KAKKAR, Savitri Hambles Edge, Brook Avenue, Warsash, Southampton SO31 9HN Tel: 01489 570850 Fax: 01489 570805 — MB BS 1960 Vikram; DA (UK) 1962. Research (Anaesth.) Lond.

KAKKAR, Professor Vijay Vir Hamble's Edge, Brook Avenue, Warsash, Southampton SO31 9HN Tel: 01489 570850 Fax: 01489 570805; 51 King's Court S., Chelsea Manor Gardens, Chelsea, London SW3 6LR Tel: 020 7351 4776 — MB BS 1960 Vikram; FRCS Ed. 1964; FRCS Eng. 1964; LMSSA Lond. 1967. (Gandhi Med. Coll. Bhopal) Prof. Surgic. Sci. & Hon. Cons. Surg. Roy. Brompton Hosp. & King's Coll. Hosp. Med. Sch. Lond. Socs: Fell. Internat. Soc. Cardiovasc. Surg.; Surg. Research Soc. Prev: Sen. Lect. (Surg.) & Hon. Cons. Surg. King's Coll. Hosp. Med. Sch. Lond.; Sen. Lect. (Surg.), Hon. Sen. Regist. & Pfizer Research Fell. King's Coll. Hosp. Lond.

KAKLAMANIS, Loukas Nuffield Department of Pathology, Level 4 Academic Book, John Radcliffe Hospital, Oxford OX3 9DU Tel: 01865 751359 — Ptychio Iatrikes 1983 Patras. Hon. Sen. Regist.

(Path.) John Radcliffe Hosp. Oxf. Prev: Research Teach. Fell. (Hist. & Anat.) Univ. Patras Greece.

KAKLUGIN, Vassily Ivanov 33 Marina Drive, Marple, Stockport SK6 6JL — LMSSA 1970 Lond.; MD Sofia 1955. Socs: BMA.

KAKOTY, Prakash Chandra The Surgery, 170 Sheffield Road, Barnsley S70 4NW Tel: 01226 204404 Fax: 01226 779669 — MB BS 1967 Dibrugarh; DTM & H Liverp. 1971; DCH RCPSI 1971. (Assam Med. Coll.) Prev: Ho. Off. (Paediat. Surg.) Roy. Hosp. Sick Childr. Glas.; Ho. Off. (Gen. Med.) Hairmyres Hosp. E. Kilbride; SHO (Paediat. Med.) Barnsley Dist. Gen. Hosp.

KAKOULLIS, Thekli Maria 24 Cameo Way, Stafford ST16 1SR — MB ChB 1996 Birm.; BSc 1993. (Birm.) SHO (Med.) New Cross Hosp Wolverhampton. Socs: BMA; MDU; MSS. Prev: SHO S. Birm. HA; MHO City Hosp. Birm.

KAKROO, Saleema 6 Chevet Croft, Sandal, Wakefield WF2 6QR — MB BS 1973 Jammu.

KAKUMANI, Vijayasri Epsom General Hospital, Dorking Road, Epsom KT18 7EG Tel: 01372 735735 — MB BS 1975 Sri Venkateswara; MRCOG 1983. Cons. O & G Epsom Gen. Hosp. Prev: Cons. O & G King Fahd Armed Forces Hosp. Jeddah, Saudi Arabia; Sen. Regist. (O & G) Guy's Hosp. Lond.

KALAHER, Martin Edward The Glebe Surgery, Monastery Lane, Storrington, Pulborough RH20 4LR Tel: 01903 742942 Fax: 01903 740700; Cherry House, Kithurst Lane, Storrington, Pulborough RH20 4LP Tel: 01903 740047 — MB BS 1975 Lond.; MRCGP 1983; DRCOG 1982; DCH Eng. 1979.

KALAIRAJAH, Muthupalaniappan 6 Hatcliffe Close, London SE3 9UE — MB BS 1991 Lond.

KALAIRAJAH, Mr Yegappan 62 The Hall, Foxes Dale, London SE3 9BG — BChir 1995 Camb.; MRCS (Eng) 1998. (Cambridge University)

KALAIYA, Pravinchandra Bhagwanlal The Surgery, 23 Wingletye Lane, Hornchurch RM11 3SU Tel: 01708 471573 Fax: 01708 459287 — MB BS 1969 Gujarat; Dip. Paediat. Saurashtra 1970. (M.P. Shah Med. Coll. Jamnagar)

KALAN, Ali Mohammed Hussain Southend Hospital, Prittlewell Chase, Westcliff on Sea SS0 0RY — MB BS 1986 Poona.

KALAP, Mr Gennadi 4 Oakwood Rise, Oakwood, Leeds LS8 2QY — BM BS 1991 Nottm.; FRCS Eng. 1996. (Nottingham) SHO (Orthop.) Yorks. Orthop. Higher Surgic. Train. Scheme, Leeds Teachg. Hosps. Socs: BOA. Prev: SHO (Orthop.) Glenfield Gen. Hosp. Leicester.

KALBAG, Mr Ramanand Mangesh (retired) 3 Towers Avenue, Jesmond, Newcastle upon Tyne NE2 3QE Tel: 0191 281 4724 Fax: 0191 281 4724 Email: ram.kalbag@quista.net — MB BS Bombay 1951; FRCS Eng. 1963. Cons. Neurosurg. Newc. Gen. Hosp. Prev: Sen. Regist. United Birm. Hosps. & Birm. RHB.

KALBASI, Mr Heshmatollah c/o National West. Bank, 1 Grosvenor Gardens, London SW1W 0BD — MD 1965 Istanbul; FRCS Eng. 1974.

KALCEV, Boris (retired) 1 Tyrone Drive, Bamford, Rochdale OL11 4BE Tel: 01706 360773 Fax: 01706 360773 — MD 1949 Vienna; LRCP LRCS Ed. LRFPS Glas. 1960; DPH Eng. 1961.

KALE, Mita 2 Priory Gardens, Clothorn Road, Didsbury, Manchester M20 6BG — MB BCh 1990 Wales; MRCP (UK) 1994.

KALE, Nadine Jane Holywell House Surgery, Holywell Street, Chesterfield S41 7SD Tel: 01246 273075 Fax: 01246 555711; Northwood Cottage, Sydnope Hill, Two Dales, Matlock DE4 5LN Tel: 01629 734079 — BM BS 1985 Nottm.; BSc (Hons.) Nottm. 1983; DRCOG 1989. (Nottm.) Three-Quarter Time Gen. Pract. Princip. Chesterfield.

KALE, Mr Vidyadhar Ramkrishna 322 Norton Lane, Earlswood, Solihull B94 5LP — MB BS 1967 Vikram; FRCS Ed. 1971; MRCS Eng. LRCP Lond. 1974; FRCR 1978; DMRD Eng. 1977. Cons. Radiol. Selly Oak Hosp. Birm. Socs: Roy. Coll. Radiol.; BMA. Prev: Hon. Sen. Clin. Lect. Univ. Birm.; Sen. Regist. (Radiodiag.) Birm Centr. Health Dist. (T) & W. Midl. RHA; Regist. (Surg.) Geo. Eliot Hosp. Nuneaton.

KALE, Vidyawati 322 Norton Lane, Earlswood, Solihull B94 5LP — MB BS 1967 Vikram; DObst 1969; FFA RCS Eng. 1980; DA Eng. 1976. Regist. (Anaesth.) Selly Oak Hosp. Birm. Prev: Regist. (O & G & Anaesth.) Geo. Eliot Hosp. Nuneaton.

KALEBA, Jozef (retired) 2 Marywood Square, Flat 1/1, Glasgow G41 2BH Tel: 0141 423 5023 — Med. Dipl. 1937 Cracow.

KALEBIC, Branko 321 The Drive, Ilford IG1 3PW Tel: 020 8554 4211; 9 Meriden Close, Hainault, Ilford IG6 2HX — State Exam Padua 1975.

KALEEL, Mohamed Fahmy 20 Conway Road, Southgate, London N14 7BA — MRCS Eng. LRCP Lond. 1962. (St. Mary's)

KALEEL, Mohamed Faizal Hassan 20 Conway Road, London N14 7BA — MB BS 1998 Lond.; MB BS Lond 1998.

KALEEM, Naila Marlybone Health Centre, The Crypt, 17 Marlybone, London NW1 5LT Tel: 020 7935 6328; 124b Green Street, Northwood HA6 1AW Tel: 01923 826399 Fax: 01923 826399 Email: naila_kaleem@hotmail.com — MB ChB 1992 Manch.; BSc. St. And 1989. GP.

KALEEM, Tariq The Surgery, 1 Uxendon Crescent, Wembley HA9 9TW Tel: 020 8904 3883 Fax: 020 8904 3899; 111 Uxbridge Road, Rickmansworth WD3 7DN — MB ChB 1990 Manch.; BSc (Med. Sci.) St. And. 1987; DFFP 1993.

KALER, Sarbjit Singh Florence Road Surgery, 26 Florence Road, Ealing, London W5 3TX Tel: 020 8567 2111 — MB BS 1988 Lond.; MRCGP 1993. GP. Prev: SHO (Paediat.) Luton & Dunstable Gen. Hosp.; SHO (A & E) Bedford Gen. Hosp.

KALFAYAN, Paul Yealand The Family Practice, Western College, Cotham Road, Bristol BS6 6DF Tel: 0117 946 6455 Fax: 0117 946 6410 — MB BChir 1981 Camb.; BA Camb. 1977, MB BChir 1981; MRCGP 1988; DRCOG 1986.

KALGUTKAR, Sadanand Kalyan (retired) 76 Avondale Road, Bromley BR1 4EZ Tel: 020 8460 8712 — MRCS Eng. LRCP Lond. 1944.

KALHA, Ishaan Singh 8 Brackendale Close, Hounslow TW3 4AZ Tel: 020 8737 7872 — MB BS 1996 Lond. (St Batholomew's Hospital Medical School) Med. SHO Frimley Pk. Hosp. Camberley Surrey. Prev: Sug. Ho. Off. Whipps Cross Hosp. Lond.; Med. Ho. Off. St Bart. & Roy. Lond. Hosps.

KALHORO, S The Surgery, 487 Barking Road, Plaistow, London E13 8PS Tel: 020 8471 7160 Fax: 020 8652 0794 — MB BS 1971 Sind; MB BS 1971 Sind.

KALIA, Praveen 28 St James's Court, St James's University Hospital, Beckett St., Leeds LS9 7TF — MB BS 1979 Delhi.

KALIA, Rajeev Stoke Mandeville Hospital, Mandevillle Road, Aylesbury HP21 8AL Tel: 01296 315000; 27 Shenfield Gardens Rise Park, Nottingham NG5 5BH Tel: 01159 270934 — MB BS 1998 Lond.; MB BS Lond 1998; B.Sc. Od 1995, Royal Free Hospital.

KALICIAK, Alish Ilana c/o Doctors Mess, North Devon District Hospital, Raleigh Park, Barnstaple EX31 4JB — MB ChB 1997 Bristol.

KALIDINDI, Sridevi 98 Headcorn Drive, Canterbury CT2 7TR — MB BS 1996 Lond.; BSc 1995. (St. Mary's Hospital) SHO (Psych.) Maudsley Hosp., Denmark hill, Lond.

KALIDINDI, Usha Royal Gwent Hospital, Newport NP20 2UB Tel: 01633 234234; 98 Headcorn Drive, Canterbury CT2 7TR — MB BS 1994 Lond.; BSc (Hons.) Lond. 1992, MB BS 1994. (Roy. Lond. Hosp. Med. Coll.) Ho. Phys. (SHO Med. & Chest Med.) Roy. Lond. Hosp.

KALILANI, Margaret Joseph Martin The Surgery, Station Road, Knebworth SG3 6AP — MB ChB 1979 Manchester. Socs: Med. Protec. Soc.

KALIM, Kanwal 10 Cashmoor Walk, Manchester M12 4LS — MB ChB 1997 Manch.

KALINA, Montague Arnold 109 Ebury Street, London SW1W 9QU Tel: 020 7730 4805 Fax: 020 7730 7845 — MB BS Lond. 1950; MRCS Eng. LRCP Lond. 1948; MRCGP 1966; DObst RCOG 1956. (Univ. Coll. Hosp.) Socs: Founder Mem. Balint Soc. Prev: Flight Lt. RAF Med. Br.; Ho. Phys. Highlands Hosp. Winchmore Hill; Ho. Surg. (Obst.) W. Middlx. Hosp. Isleworth.

KALINIECKI, Jerzy Pawel Julian Sedlescombe House, 8 Sedlescombe Road South, St Leonards-on-Sea TN38 0TA Tel: 01424 720574/435004 Fax: 01424 440199 — MB BS 1979 Lond.; MRCGP 1983; DFFP 1993; Cert. Family Plann. JCC 1982; DRCOG 1982; DCH RCP Lond. 1982. (Guy's Hospital, London)

KALINKIEWICZ, Mary Christine 3 Tithe Meadows, Virginia Water GU25 4EU — MB BS 1979 Lond. Staff Grade (OtoLaryngol.) Qu. Alexandra Hosp. Portsmouth Hants.

KALINSKY, Sidney 13 Dunsdon Road, Woolton, Liverpool L25 6JF Tel: 0151 722 6444 — MB ChB 1947 Liverp. (Liverp.)

KALISZER, Olga Elizabeth 34 York Road, York YO24 4LZ — MB ChB 1977 Bristol.

KALKAT, Gurkirit Singh 5 Richmond Park, Loughton IG10 4PQ — MB ChB 1989 Liverp.; MRCGP 1993.

KALLA, Mr Vijay Kumar 246 Woodlands Road, Batley WF17 0QJ Tel: 01924 479337 — MB BS 1974 Rajasthan; FRCS Ed. 1990.

KALLAN, Bavna House 15, The Princess Royal Hospital NHS Trust, Apley Castle, Grainger Drive, Telford TF1 6TF — MB BCh 1996 Witwatersrand.

KALLBERG, Marie Henriette 12d Belsize Crescent, London NW3 5QU Tel: 020 7794 5367 — MB BS 1952 Lond. (Roy. Free) Prev: Med. Regist. Colindale Hosp. Lond.; Sen. Ho. Off. Geriat. Whittington Hosp. Lond.; Ho. Surg. & Cas. Off. Eliz. G. Anderson Hosp.

KALLI, Manorama Department of Anaesthesia, Dewsbury & District Hospital, Healds Road, Dewsbury WF13 4HS — MB BS 1970 Bangalor; MB BS Bangalore 1970.

KALLIS, Mr Panny 88 Harley Street, London W1G 7HR Tel: 020 7225 1895 Fax: 020 7255 1897 Email: kallis@88harleystreet.fsnet.co.uk — BSc Lond. 1981; (HONS) MB BS Lond. 1984; FRCS Eng. 1988; MS Lond. 1996. (University College Hospital Medical School) Cons. Cardiothoracic Surg. Univ. Coll. Lond. Hosp. The Heart Hosp.; Cons. Cardiothoracic Surg. The Harley St. Clinic, The Wellington Hosp., The Heart Hosp., St Anthony's Hosp. Socs: BMA; MPS; Soc. Cardiothoracic Surg. Prev: Sen. Regist. Cardiothoracic Surg. St Geo.'s Hosp., Middlx. Hosp., Harefield Hosp.

KALLIS, Paul Frederick Sorrel Group Practice, 23 Bolton Rd, Salford M6 7HL Tel: 0161 736 1021; 5 Twyford Close, Didsbury, Manchester M20 2YR — MB ChB 1968 Manch.; MRCGP 1974; DObst RCOG 1971. Socs: Fell. Manch. Med. Soc.

KALLOOR, Mr George John Hillsfield Health Centre, 1 Howard Street, Coventry CV1 4GH Tel: 024 7622 3446 Fax: 024 7622 5846 — MB BS 1963 Punjab; FRCS Eng. 1970.

KALMAN, Christopher John 6 Dampark, Dunlop, Kilmarnock KA3 4BZ — MB ChB 1976 Manch.; MSc Lond. 1984; FRCP (Glas.) 2000; MRCP (UK) 1981; FFOM RCP Lond. 1990, A 1999; DIH Lond. 1987. Cons. Occupat.al Phys. Lanarksh. Acute NHS Trust and Salus Occupat.al Health Soc.; Hon. Sen. Lect. Pub. Health Med. Univ. of Glas. Socs: Soc. of Occup. Med.; Assn. of Radiat. Research; Internat. Assn. for Radiat. Pathol. Prev: Chief Med. Off. BNFL Fuel Business Unit; Chief Med. Off. Scott. Nuclear Ltd.; Dep. Chairm. Naval Nuclear Technical Safety Panel.

KALMANOVITCH, Deborah Victoria Anne University Hospital Of Hartlepool, Hartlepool; Hurworth Burn House, Hurworth Burn, Wingate TS28 5NS — MB ChB 1976 Dundee; FFARCS Eng. 1982. Cons (Anaesth.) Univ. Hosp. Hartlepool; Cons. (Anaest) Community Dent. Serv., Teeside. Socs: Assn. Of Anaesth. Gt. Brit.; Assn. Dent. Anaesth. Prev: Sen. Regist. (Anaesth.) Roy. Free Hosp. Lond.

KALMUS, Eva Janet 40 Devonshire Road, Sutton SM2 5HH Tel: 020 8642 1847 — MB BS 1985 Lond.; MA Camb. 1982; MRCGP 1990; DGM RCP Lond. 1989. Socs: Med. Wom. Federat. Prev: Trainee GP Lond.

KALODIKI, Evi 6 Leinster Square, London W2 4PL Tel: 020 7886 1741 Fax: 020 7886 1012; 2A Diakou Street, Holargos, Athens 15562, Greece Tel: 652 2356 — Ptychio Iatrikes 1979 Athens; MD (Hons.) Athens 1983; Surgeon Athens 1983; PhD Lond. 1996; Dip. Imperial College 1997. Sen. Research Fell (Vasc.) Acad. Surg. Unit St. Mary's Hosp. Med. Sch.Lond. Socs: Surg. Research Soc. & Europ. Soc. Vasc. Surg.; Internat. Union of Angiology; Pres. Hellinic Soc. of Professional People and Scientists in GB. Prev: Acad. Surg. Unit St. Mary's Hosp. Lond.; 1st Surg. Unit Univ. Athens.

KALOO, Philip David 93 Thornton Road, Girton, Cambridge CB3 0NR — MB BS 1993 Lond.; BSc (Hons.) Lond. 1990, MB BS 1993.

KALOUGIN, Anna Sullivan Way Surgery, Sullivan Way, Scholes, Wigan WN1 3TB Tel: 01942 243649 — MB BS 1983 Lond.; MA Camb. 1987, BA 1980; MRCGP 1988; DRCOG 1986.

KALRA, Deepak Surendra New Cross Hospital, Wolverhampton WV10 0QP Tel: 01902 307999 Fax: 01902 643051 — MB ChB 1976 Manch.; FRCP Lond. 1995; FRCPCH 1997; DCH Eng. 1978. (Univ. Manch.) Cons. Paediat. Wolverhampton Hosps. Prev: Sen. Regist. Kingston Hosp. Surrey.

KALRA, Dipak (retired) Centre for Health Informatics and, Multiprofessional Education (CHIME), Archway Campus, Highgate Hill, London N19 3UA Email: d.kalra@chime.ucl.ac.uk — MB BS 1982 Lond.; FRCGP 1994, M 1986; DRCOG 1986. Clin. Sen. Lect. (Health Informatics) Univ. Coll. Lond. Prev: GP Lond.

KALRA, Professor Lalit Department of Medicine, Guy's, King's and St Thomas' School of Medicine, Bessemer Road, London SE5 9PJ Tel: 020 7346 3487 Fax: 020 7346 3195 — MB BS 1980 All Indian Inst. Med. Scs.; MB BS All India Inst. Med. Scs. 1980; PhD Lond. 1992; MD Lond. 1994; MD All India Inst. Med. Scs. 1983; FRCP Lond. 1994; MRCP (UK) 1984. Prof. Stroke Med., Guy's, King's & St.Thomas' Sch. of Med., King's Coll., Lond.; Hon Cons. King's Health Care Trust. Prev: Prof. Clin. Health Serv. Studies King's Coll. Sch. Med. & Dent. Lond.; Hon. Cons. Bromley Hosps. NHS Trust.

KALRA, Leela Anne Trevor Old Mill, Bryn Howel Lane, Llangollen LL20 7UD — MB ChB 1981 Bristol. SHO (Paediat.) Maelor Gen. Hosp. Wrexham. Prev: SHO (Cas.) W. Chesh. Hosp. Chester; Ho. Off. (Gen. Surg.) Maelor Gen. Hosp. Wrexham; Ho. Off. (Gen. Med.) W.on-Super-Mare Gen. Hosp.

KALRA, Narain Dass 18 High Street, Hampton-in-Arden, Solihull B92 0AA — MB ChB 1944 Birm.

KALRA, Paul Raj 24 Elizabeth Way, Bishop's Waltham, Southampton SO32 1SQ Tel: 01489 891390 — MB BChir 1993 Camb.; MRCP (UK) 1995. Research Fell. Nat. Heart & Lung Inst., DoveHo. St, Lond. Socs: Treas. Brit. Jun. Cardiac Assn. Prev: Specialist Regist. (Cardiol.), Soton. Univ. NHS Trust; Regist. (Cardiol.) Portsmouth NHS Trust; Regist. (Cardiol.) St. Richards Hosp. Chichester.

KALRA, Philip Anil Department of Renal Medicine, Hope Hospital, Salford M6 8HD — MB BChir 1982 Camb.; MA, MB Camb. 1982, BChir (Distinc.) 1982; MRCP (UK) 1985; MD 1995 Cambridge; FRCP 1999 UK. (Cambridge University /St. Thomas' Hospital) Cons. Nephrologist, Salford Roy. Hosp.s Trust. Socs: UK Renel Assn.; EDTA (Europ. Dialysis Transpl. Assoc.); ASN (Amer. Soc. of Nephology). Prev: Sen. Regist. (Nephrol. & Gen. Med.) Preston, Hope & Manch. Roy. Infirm.; Tutor (Med.) & Regist. (Renal) Univ. Manch. & Hope Hosp.; Regist. (Renal Med.) Leeds Gen. Infirm.

KALRA, Pritam Lal (retired) Shanti-niketan, 243 Eccleshall Road, Stafford ST16 1PE Tel: 01785 56111 — MB ChB 1951 Birm.; BSc Punjab 1944; MRCPsych 1971; DPM Eng. 1958. Hon. Cons. Psychiat. Wolverhampton & Mid Staffs HA Trusts. Prev: Hon. Cons. Psychiat. & Chairm. Med. Staff Comm. Psychiat. Unit New Cross Hosp. Wolverhamton.

KALRA, Rajendra Singh Doctor R Kalra, 61 Naseby Road, Dagenham RM10 7JS Tel: 020 8592 1841 Fax: 020 8593 2879; 128 Hainault Road, Chigwell IG7 5DL — MB BS 1967 Ranchi; DA Eng. 1971. (Ranchi)

KALRA, Shakuntala Surendranath 45 Highgrove, Wood Road, Tettenhall, Wolverhampton WV6 8LQ Tel: 01902 757203 — MB BS 1950 Delhi. (Lady Hardinge Med. Coll.) Socs: Emerit. Mem. Internat. Acad. Cytol. Prev: Assoc. Specialist (Cytopath.) Univ. Coll. Med. Sch. Lond.; Locum cons.

KALRA, Surinder Kumar 52 Chevington Drive, Heaton, Mersey, Stockport SK4 3RG — MB BS 1970 Punjab.

KALRA, Tej Kamal Kaur Crawley Road Medical Centre, 479 High Road, Leyton, London E10 5EL Tel: 020 8539 1880 Fax: 020 8556 1318; The Slades, 128 Hainault Road, Chigwell IG7 5DL Tel: 020 8559 8931 — MB BS 1976 Ranchi; MRCS Eng. LRCP Lond. 1981. (Ranchi, India) GP Leyton. Socs: Indian Med. Assn. & Overseas Doctors Assn.

KALSHEKER, Noor Ahmed Department of Clinical Chemistry, Queen's Medical Centre, Nottingham NG7 2UH Tel: 0115 970 9166 Fax: 0115 970 9167 Email: noor.kalsheker@nottingham.ac.uk — MB ChB 1974 Birm.; MSc Birm. 1978, MD 1983; FRCPath 1993, M 1981. Prof. Chem. Path. Univ. Hosp. Qu. Med. Centre Nottm.; Head of Div. of Clin. Chem., Univ. Hosp, Nottg. Socs: Brit. Soc. Human Genetics; Assn. Clin. Biochem.; Biochem. Soc. Prev: Sen. Lect. & Hon. Cons. Med. Biochem. Univ. Wales Coll. of Med.; Sen. Regist. (Clin. Biochem.) Addenbrooke's Hosp. Camb.; Head of Sch. of Clin. Laborat. Sci.s, Univ. Hosp. Qu.s Med. Centre, Nottg, 1997-2001.

KALSI, Baljit Singh Queens Medical Centre, 6/7 Queen Street, Barnstaple EX32 8HY Tel: 01271 372672 Fax: 01271 341902 — MB ChB 1988 Ed.; BSc (Hons.) Bact. Ed. 1985; MRCGP 1992.

(Edin. Univ.) Prev: SHO (Gyn. & Paediat. & Cas.) N. Devon Dist. Hosp.

KALSI, Basant Singh 2 Grafon Road, Worcester Park KT4 7QP Tel: 020 8337 5533 Fax: 020 8330 7229; Balhar, 5A Longdown Rd, Epsom KT17 3PT — MB BS 1963 Lond.; MRCS Eng. LRCP Lond. 1963; DObst RCOG 1970. (Guy's) Socs: BMA. Prev: Dist. Med. Off. Govt. of Tanzania; Clin. Asst. (Anaesth.) Horton Hosp.

KALSI, Gurmukh Singh 2 St Michael's Court, Crocketts Lane, Smethwick, Warley B66 3BX — MB BS 1990 Lond.

KALSI, Jasjit Singh 68 Broad Walk, Heston, Hounslow TW5 9AB — MB BS 1997 Lond.

KALSI, Manvinder Singh 167 Surbiton Hill Park, Surbiton KT5 8EJ — MB BS 1998 Lond.; MB BS Lond 1998.

KALTSAS, Dimitris Stilianos King George Hospital, Barley Lane, Ilford IG3 8YB — Ptychio Iatrikes 1973 Thessalonika; MD 1976; Orthop. Spec 1992; CCST 1995. Cons. Orthopaedic Surg. Socs: Fell. Brit. Orthopaedic Assoc.; Fell. Amer. Assoc. Orthopaedic Surg.; Fell. Brit. Assoc. of the Surg. in the knee. Prev: Mem Euro soc sports & knee arthroscopy; Fell Internat. soc traumas; Assoc. Orthop. Surg. Medway Hosp. Gillingham.

KALU, Gregory Ugboaja 8 Gill Avenue, Guildford GU2 7WW — MB BS 1986 Nigeria; MB BS Univ. Nigeria 1986; MRCOG 1993.

***KALU, Peter Ugboaja** The General Infirmary at Leeds, Great George St., Leeds LS1 3EX Tel: 0113 292 6599 Fax: 0113 292 6347; 4 Rowdon Avenue, London NW10 2AL Tel: 020 8459 5010 — MB BS 1997 Lond.; BSc (Neuroscis.) Lond. 1994.

KALUBA, Joseph Banja Lameck UCL Medical School, Department of Histopathology, Rockerfeller Building, University St., London WC1E 6JJ — MB ChB 1988 Univ. Zambia.

KALUSKAR, Mr Shashikant Keshavrao 31 Knockgreenan Avenue, Omagh BT79 0EB Tel: 01662 243566 — MB BS 1967 Gujarat; MS (ENT) Gujarat 1971, MB BS 1967; FRCSI 1979; DLO Eng. 1974; DLO Gujarat 1970. (M.P. Shah Med. Coll.) Cons. ENT Surg. Tyrone Co. Hosp. Omagh & Erne Hosp. Enniskillen. Socs: Europ. Acad. Facial Plastic Surg.; Amer. Acad. of Otolaryngol. & Head-Neck Surg.; Amer. Rhinology Soc.

KAM, Hubert Kung Van 75 Woodcroft Avenue, Aberdeen AB22 8WY — MB ChB 1992 Aberd.

KAM, Kee Yuen Edward 10 Charles Street, Croydon CR0 1TR — MB BCh BAO 1992 Belf.; DRCOG Glas. 1996; DGM RCPS Glas. 1995; DMH Belf. 1994; FRCS (A&E) Ed. 1997.

KAMAL, Mr Abul Khayer Mustofa Royal Lancaster Infirmary, Ashton Road, Lancaster LA1 4RP; 6 Trent Close, Grosvenor Park, Morecambe LA3 3SR — MB BS 1968 Dacca; FRCS Glas. 1984. Assoc. Specialist Roy. Lancaster Infirm.

KAMAL, Deborah Soraya Moorfields Eye Hospital, City Road, London EC1V 2PD Email: deborah.kamal@compuserve.com — MB BS 1991 Lond.; BSc Psychol. Lond. 1987; FRCOphth. Lond. 1995. Moorfields Eye Hosp. Lond. Prev: Research Fell. (Ophth.) Moorfields Eye Hosp. Lond.

KAMAL, Livleen 45 Birch Lane, Oldbury, Oldbury B68 0NZ — MB BS 1993 Lond.

KAMAL, Lutfe Rabbi Mustafa The Grange, Highfield Road, Hemsworth, Pontefract WF9 4DP Tel: 01977 610009 Fax: 01977 617182; Harepark Farm, Harepark Lane, Crofton, Wakefield WF4 1HT Tel: 01924 865200 Fax: 01977 617182 — MB BS 1962 Dacca; Cert. Family Plann. JCC 1991; Cert. Developm. Paediat. Leeds 1980. (Dacca) Clin. Asst. (A & E) Gen. Infirm. Pontefract; Clin. Med. Off. (Family Plann.) Wakefield; Vice-Chairm. Local Med. Comm. Socs: Fell. Roy. Soc. Med. & Roy. Inst. Pub. Health & Hyg.; (Ex-Chairm.) BMA & Mem. Local Med. Comm. Prev: Clin. Med. Off. (Child Health) Barnsley HA; Regist. (A & E) Roy. S. Hants. Hosp. Soton.; Clin. Asst. (Psychiat.) Stanley Royd Hosp. Wakefield.

KAMAL, Mujahid 205 Station Road, Kings Heath, Birmingham B14 7TB Tel: 0121 444 5051 — MB BS 1983 Peshawar; MRCP (UK) 1990.

KAMAL NOR, Norzalin 7 Park View Gardens, White Hart Lane, London N22 5SH — MB BS 1998 Lond.; MB BS Lond 1998.

KAMALA, Kamma St Johns Hospital, Wood St., Chelmsford CM2 9BG Tel: 01245 491149; 90 Patching Hall Lane, Chelmsford CM1 4DB Tel: 01245 354085 — MB BS 1966 Andhra; FRCOG 1994, M 1978. (Andhra Med. Coll. Visakhapatnam) Clin. Asst. (O & G) St. John's Hosp. Chelmsford.

KAMALAGHARAN, Sugina Christine (Surgery), 166 Tonbridge Road, Maidstone ME16 8SS Tel: 01622 678500; The Vicarage, 55 Pattens Lane, Chatham ME4 6JR — MB BS 1988 Lond.; MRCGP 1992; DRCOG 1991; DCH RCP Lond. 1990. (King's Coll. Lond.) GP Maidstone Retainer Scheme. Prev: Trainee GP Streatham.

KAMALANATHAN, Fatima Anandasoundari Sloane Hospital, 125 Albermarle Rd, Beckenham BR3 2HS; 8 St Peter's Close, Chislehurst BR7 6PD Tel: 020 8467 5763 — MB BS 1972 Ceylon; MRCP (UK) 1980; MRCS Eng. LRCP Lond. 1984; 2000 D. Oec. Med. Health Screening Phys.; Sloane Hosp., 125 Albermarle Rd, Beckenham, Kent, BR3 2HS. Socs: Fac. of Occupat.al Health.

KAMALANATHAN, Mr Vairamuthu 5 The Crescent, Dane Ghyll Park, Barrow-in-Furness LA14 4RA — MB BS 1981 Colombo; MB BS Colombo, Sri Lanka 1981; MRCS Eng., LRCP Lond. 1987; FRCS Ed. 1988.

KAMALARAJAH, Brinda 68 Devonshire Road, Northfields, London W5 4TP — MB ChB 1993 Manch.

KAMALARAJAH, Srikandan 68 Devonshire Road, London W5 4TP; 14 Upper Malone Crescent, Belfast BT9 6PR Tel: 01232 616278 Email: sri17@aol.com — MB ChB 1991 Dundee; FRCOphth 1997. Specialist Regist. (Ophth.). Socs: Med. Protec. Soc.

KAMALUDDIN, Nizamuddin Ahmed 156 Swakeleys Road, Ickenham, Uxbridge UB10 8AZ Tel: 01895 633191 — MB BS 1973 Poona. GP Hayes; Mem. Hillingdon FPC. Prev: Trainee GP Ipswich VTS; Regist. & SHO St. Clements Hosp. Ipswich.

KAMALUDDIN, Shaikh Mohammed Haire Mai, 61 The Avenue, Woodland Park, Prestatyn LL19 9RE — MB BS 1952 Calcutta; DO Eng. 1959; DOMS Calcutta 1956. (Calcutta Med. Coll.) Asst. Ophth. Clwyd N. Health Dist.

KAMALVAND, Keyvan William Harvey Hospital, Kennington Park Road, Willesborough, Ashford TN2 0LZ; 17 Edenvale Road, Mitcham CR4 2DP — MB BS 1987 Lond.; BSc Hons. 1984; MRCP 1991. (St. Georges Hospital) Cons. (Cardiol. and Phys.) William Harvey Hosp. Ashford; St Thomas' Hosp. Lond.; Buckland Hosp. Dover; Roy. Vict. Hosp. Kilkestone. Socs: Brit. Cardiac Soc.; Brit. Pacing & Electrophysiol. Gp.; Roy. Coll. Phys.s. Prev: SPR Roy. Sussex Co. Hosp. Brighton; SPR E.bourne Dist. Hosp.; Regist. Guy's Hosp. Lond.

KAMALY-ASL, Mr Ian Daryoush Department of Neurosurgery, Hope Hospital, Stott Lane, Salford, Manchester M6 8HD Tel: 0161 789 7373 — MB ChB 1993 Manch.; FRCS (Eng.) 1998. (Manchester University) Specialist Regist. (Neurosurg.) Hope Hosp., Manch. Prev: SHO Rotat. (Gen. Surg.) Hope Hosp. Manch.; Temp. Lect. (Anat.) Manch. Univ.; Ho. Off. (Med. & Surg.) Manch. Roy. Infirm.

KAMALY-ASL, Yadoullah 1 Fieldside, Hawarden, Deeside CH5 3JB — MD Tabriz 1961; LMSSA Lond. 1971; DLO Eng. 1969. (Tabriz) Hosp. Pract. (ENT) Deeside. Socs: Roy. Soc. Med.; BMA. Prev: Regist. (ENT) Kent & Canterbury Hosp.; Regist. (ENT) Salisbury Gen. Hosp.

KAMAR, Simon Hanna 92 Victory Avenue, Gretna DG16 5DR — LMS 1974 Barcelona; T(GP) 1992.

KAMAR, Ziya 9 Pexwood, Chadderton, Oldham OL1 2TS — MB ChB 1996 Leeds.

***KAMARA, Monera Nini Bonkapru** 45 Mall Chambers, Kensington Mall, London W8 4DZ — MB BS 1994 Lond.; MRCP (uk) 1999.

KAMARYLZAMAN, Shahryl Bahyah 35A Shirley Road, Cardiff CF23 5HL — MB BCh 1997 Wales.

KAMAT, Mr Narayan Dattatray 102 Douglas Park Crescent, Bearsden, Glasgow G61 3DW Tel: 0141 942 2428 — MD 1953 Bombay; MB BS 1945; FRCS Eng. 1951. (Grant Med. Coll.) Asst. Surg. Gtr. Glas. Health Bd.

KAMATH, Belady Sumanth Kumar Department of Anaesthesia, Barnet General Hospital, Barnet EN5 3DJ Tel: 020 8216 4000 — MB BS Mysore 1968; FFA RCS Eng. 1975; DA Eng. 1972. Cons. Anaesth. Barnet Hosp.; Cons. Anaesth. Harefield Hosp.

KAMATH, Mangalore Bhasker Anaesthetic Department, Hull Royal Infirmary, Anlaby Road, Hull HU3 2JZ Tel: 01482 328541 — MB BS 1974 Bangalore; FRCA 1982. (St. John's Bangalore Univ.) Cons. Anaesth. Hull & E. Yorks. HAs. Prev: Sen. Regist. Rotat. (Anaesth.) Nottm. & E. Midl. Hosps.; Sen. Regist. St. Bart. Hosp. Lond.; Regist. Char. Cross Hosp. Lond.

KAMATH, Mohandas Krishna Rotherham District General Hospital, Moorgate Road, Rotherham S60 2UD; 37 Haworth Crescent, Rotherham S60 3BW — MB BS 1963 Karnatak.

KAMATH, Sitaram Keshav Roathwell Surgery, 116 Newport Road, Roath, Cardiff CF24 1YT Tel: 029 2049 4537 Fax: 029 2049 8086; 42 Llandennis Avenue, Cyncoed, Cardiff CF23 6JH — MB BS 1968 Mysore. (Kasturba Med. Coll.)

KAMATH, Mr Subash Ravalnath Shashvath, 10/1 Barnaby Road, Kilpauk, Madras 600010, India; 44 Middleton Avenue, Fenham, Newcastle upon Tyne NE4 9NB Tel: 0191 273 6916 — MB BS 1983 Madras; MChOrth Liverp. 1990; FRCS Glas. 1988. Regist. (Orthop.) Train. Progr. N.. Region.

KAMATH, Umesh Manjunath c/o Dr U.B.N. Rau, Anand, Craythorne Road, Stretton, Burton-on-Trent DE13 0AZ — MB BS 1968 Mysore; FFA RCS Eng. 1983.

KAMATH, Vadan Ferguson Surgery, 153 Monks Road, Lincoln LN2 5JJ Tel: 01522 523995 Fax: 01522 567170.

KAMBITSIS, Nicholas The Health Centre, Somerford Grove, London N16 7TX; 50B Offord Road, London N1 1EB — MB BChir 1985 Camb.; DRCOG 1989.

KAMBOJ, Avtar Singh Capelfield Surgery, Elm Road, Claygate, Esher KT10 0EH Tel: 01372 462501 Fax: 01372 470258 — MB BS 1991 Lond.; DRCOG 1995.

KAMDAR, Mr Batookrai Anopchand (cons. rooms), Fawkham Manor Hospital, Fawkham, Longfield DA3 8ND Tel: 01474 879900 Fax: 01474 875630; 7 Liskeard Close, Chislehurst BR7 6RT Tel: 020 8467 9851 Fax: 020 8295 0592 — MB BS 1965 Gujarat; FRCS Ed. 1970; FRCS England (ad eundum) 1998. (M.P. Shah Med. Coll. Jamnagar) Cons. Surg. Orthop. Darent Valley Hosp. Dartford. Socs: Fell. Brit. Orthop. Assn. & Roy. Soc. Med. Prev: Sen. Regist. Rotat. (Orthop.) Roy. Free Hosp. Lond. & Windsor Gp. Hosps.; Regist. Rotat. (Orthop. Surg.) Hammersmith Hosp. & Heatherwood Hosp.

KAMDAR, Beni Batookrai 7 Liskeard Close, Chislehurst BR7 6RT Tel: 020 8467 9851 — MB BS 1964 Gujarat. (M.P. Shah Med. Coll. Jamnagar) Clin. Med. Off. Dartford & Gravesham HA. Prev: SHO (Anaesth.) Halifax Roy. Infirm., Rochdale Infirm. & Greenwich; Dist. Hosp. Lond.

KAMEEN, Alison Fiona Salters Medical Practice, The Health Centre, Ombersley Street, Droitwich WR9 8RD Tel: 01905 773535 Fax: 01905 794098; Well Cottage, Mere Green, Hanbury, Droitwich WR9 7EB — MB ChB 1982 Birm.; MRCGP 1986; DRCOG 1985.

KAMEL, Hassan Mohamed Hassan Pathology Department Hairmyres Hospital, Eaglesham Road, East Kilbride, Glasgow G75 8RG Tel: 0141 572563 Fax: 0141 234064; Berwyn, 93 Lanark Road, Crossford, Carluke ML8 5RA Tel: 01555 860626 Fax: 01555 860626 Email: hkamel121@msn.com — MB ChB 1976 Cairo; PhD Path. Glas. 1986; MSc (Path.) Zagazig 1981; MRCPath 1991. (Univ. Cairo, Univ. Zagazig & Univ. Glas.) Cons. Path. Hairmyers Hosp. E. Kilbride. Socs: Assn. Clin. Paths. Prev: Lect. (Path.) Qu. Univ. Belf.; Regist. (Path.) Roy. Vict. Hosp. Belf.

KAMEL, Kamel Mehanny Chapel Hill Surgery, 4 Chapel Hill, Tilehurst, Reading RG31 5DG Tel: 0118 942 7177 — MB BCh 1962 Cairo.

KAMILL, Paul Geoffrey Omar Rooley Lane Medical Centre, Rooley Lane, Bradford BD4 7SS Tel: 01274 770777 — MB BS 1971 Lond.; MRCGP 1983. (St. Mary's) Sen. Med. Off. Univ. Bradford. Prev: 1st Sec. Brit. Embassy Moscow.; Clin. Asst. (Sexually Transm. Dis.) Middlx. & St. Stephen's Hosps. Lond; Resid. Phys. Winnipeg Gen. Hosp. Canada.

KAMINENI, Mr Srinath 40 Calverton Road, Stony Stratford, Milton Keynes MK11 1HL — MB BCh 1990 Wales; FRCS Ed. 1994.

KAMINOPETROS, Petros Ioannis 14 Parkmont, Park Avenue, Roundhay, Leeds LS8 2JJ — Ptychio Iatrikes 1984 Athens.

KAMINSKI, David John Hollyhedge Road Surgery, 283 Hollyhedge Road, Wythenshawe, Manchester M22 4QR Tel: 0161 428 9411 Fax: 0161 428 9116 — MB ChB 1980 Manch.

KAMINSKI, Eduardo Roman Derriford Combined Laboratory, Level 07, Derriford Hospital, Plymouth PL6 8DH Tel: 01752 792406 Fax: 01752 792400 — Lekarz 1982 Warsaw; PhD Lond. 1990; MRCPath 1994; T(Path.) 1994; Dip. Immunol. Lond. 1987. Cons. Clin. Immunol. Derriford Hosp. Plymouth; Hon. Sen. Lect. Univ. Plymouth. Socs: Brit. Soc. Allergy & Clin. Immunol.; Europ. Soc. Immunodeficiencies; Brit. Soc. Immunol. Prev: Cons. & Sen. Lect. (Transfus. Med.) Univ. Aberd. & Aberd. Roy. Infirm.; Sen. Regist. (Immunol.) St. Helier Hosp. Surrey; Wellcome Europ. Trav. Fell. Univ. Hosp. Leiden, The Netherlands.

KAMLANA, Sikander Hayat Univ. Hospital North Tees, Hardwick, Stockton-on-Tees TS19 8PE Tel: 01642 617617; Balcraig, 33 Stainburn Road, Workington CA14 1SW — MB BS 1970 Punjab; 2001 England; FRCPsych 1994; 1998 England; MRCPsych 1977; Dip. Psychother. Sheff. 1982; DPM Eng. 1975. (Nishtar Med. Coll.) Cons. Psychiat./Psychotherapist, Univ. Hosp. N. Tees, Stockton-on-Tees; Clin. Assessor at Indep. Review Stage for new NHS complaints procedure January 1996; Specialist Adviser to Assessm. Referral Comm. and Comm. onProfessional Performance with Gen. Med. Counc. 1998; Second Opinion Apptd. Doctor for purposes of Part IV of Ment. Health Act 1983. Socs: Apptd. POWAR (Pl. of Work Accredit. Represen.) and Mem. of the Exec. Comm. with BMA 1999; Elected Chairm. For Governing Body Counc., Constituency of Cleveland and Durh. SHCA (Sen. Hosp.Cons. Assoc.) 1998. Prev: Home Office-Apptd. as a Med. Ref. for Appeal under the Firemen's Pension Scheme 1992; Mem. of SIGP working Gp. for appraisal of Newer Atypical Antipsychotics 2001 NICE.

KAMLIN, Camille Omar Farouk 34 Treve Avenue, Harrow HA1 4AJ — MB BS 1993 Lond.; BSc (Biochem.) Lond. 1990, MB BS 1993; MRCP (UK) 1996. (Charing Cross & Westminster) Specialist Regist. (Paediat.) P.ss Margt. Hosp. Swindon.

KAMLOW, Fawzi Joseph The Burnham Surgery, Foundry Lane, Burnham-on-Crouch CM0 8SJ Tel: 01621 782054 Fax: 01621 785592 — MB ChB 1974 Basrah; MRCP (UK) 1985. Hosp. Practitioner in Cardiol. Broomfield Hosp., Chelmsford, Essex. Prev: Trainee GP Ashford VTS; Regist. (Cardiol.) Brook Gen. Hosp. Lond.

KAMM, Professor Michael Albert St Mark's Hospital, Northwick Park, Watford Road, Harrow HA1 3UJ Tel: 020 8235 4160 Fax: 020 8235 4162 — MB BS 1978 Melbourne; MD Melbourne 1989; FRCP Lond. 1994; MRCP (UK) 1981; FRACP 1985. Cons. Gastroenterol. St. Mark's Hosp. Lond.; Dir. Med. Physiol. Unit St. Marks Hosp. Lond.; Chairm. Dept. of Med. St. Mark's Hosp. Lond.; Prof. of Gastroenterol., Imperial Coll. Sch. Med. Univ. Lond. Prev: Research Fell. St. Mark's Hosp. Lond.; Sen. Regist. (Gastroenterol.) St. Vincents Hosp. Melbourne, Austral.

KAMMERLING, Robert Max NHS Executive South East, 40 Eastbourne Terrace, London W2 3QR Tel: 020 7725 2828 Email: max.kammerling@doh.gsi.gov.uk; Somerfield House, Slade Lane, Lympsham, Weston Super Mare BS24 0DP Tel: 01934 750372 — BM 1978 Soton.; MFPHM RCP (UK) 1988; MRCGP 1983; DRCOG 1982; FFPHM 1997. (Southampton) Cons. in Pub. Health Med., S. E. Regional Office, Lond. Prev: Director of Pub. Health, Som. Health Auth., Taunton.

KAMMING, Damon 3 Lorraine Gardens, Glasgow G12 9NY — MB ChB 1995 Glas.

KAMPERS, Wayne Trevor South Kensington and Chelsea Mental Health Centre, 1 Nightingdale Place, London SW10 9NG Tel: 0411 035160 Fax: 020 8846 6060; Flat 3, 176 Bedford Hill, Balham, London SW12 9HL Tel: 020 8673 6089 Fax: 020 8673 6089 Email: kampers@btinternet.com — MBChB Cape Town 1988; LMCC Canada 1993; MRCPsych 1998. (University of Cape Town)

KAMPFNER, Fred Bedrich Evzen 21 Oak house, Westfield, 15 Kidderpore Avenue, London NW3 7SF Tel: 020 7435 5321 Fax: 020 7431 3170 — BM BCh 1950 Oxf.; MA Oxf. 1950. (Oxf. & Univ. Coll. Hosp.) Hon. Phys. Brit. Performing Arts Med. Trust. Socs: BMA & Roy. Coll. GPs; Roy. Soc. Med. Prev: Staff Surg. GHQ FARELF Singapore; Med. Off. Malaysian, Singapore & Antigua High Commiss. & Indonesian Embassy; Clin. Asst. (VD) Univ. Coll. Hosp. Lond.

KAMPMANN, Beate Department of Paediatrics, St. Mary's Hospital, Praed St., London W2 1NY Tel: 020 7725 6377 Email: b.kampmann@ic.ac.uk — State Exam Med 1988 Cologne; MD Cologne 1990; MRCP (Paediat.) Lond. 1992; DTM & H RCP Lond. 1995.

KAMUGISHA, Chris Kashangoha 10 Heather Close, Langney, Eastbourne BN23 8DF Tel: 01323 768792 — MB ChB 1975 Makerere, Uganda; MSc Univ. Lond. 1985.

KAMYA, Dorothy 20 Hartsbourne Avenue, Bushey Heath, Watford WD23 1JL — MB BS 1996 Lond.

KAMYAB, Roshanak Flat 3, Linfield Gardens, Hampstead, London NW3 6PU — MB ChB Bristol 1987; FRCS Ed. 1992.

KAN, Siu Man 26 Princes Court, 6 Croxteth Road, Liverpool L8 3UJ Tel: 0151 727 6959 Fax: 0151 708 7756; Block 303, Jurong East St., 32 600303, Singapore Tel: 00 65 5648203 — MB ChB 1991 Liverp.; BSc (Hons.) Liverp. 1988. SHO (Med. for Elderly) Halton Gen. Hosp. Runcorn. Prev: Hon. Research Assoc. (Scientif. Servs.) Inst. Sci. & Forens. Med., Singapore.

KAN, Yuk-Man 65 Rudgwick Drive, Bury BL8 1YE — MB ChB 1993 Manch.

KANAAN, Richard Antony Alexander 108A Regents Park Road, London NW1 8UG — MB BS 1998 Lond.; MB BS Lond 1998.

KANABAR, Dipak Jayantilal Department of Paediatrics, Guy's Hospital, 10th Floor, Guy's Tower, London SE1 9RT Tel: 020 7955 5000 Fax: 020 7955 4405 — MB BS Lond. 1988; MRCP (UK) 1992; FRCPCH 1997. (St. Thomas') Cons. Paediat. Guy's Hosp. Lond.; Lect. (Paediat.) St. Bart. Hosp. Lond. Prev: Regist. (Paediat.) Roy. Berks. Hosp. Reading; SHO (Paediat.) All St.s Hosp. Chatham & St. Thos. Hosp. Lond.

KANABAR, Rajnikant Chhaganlal 1 Barley Close, Glenfield, Leicester LE3 8SB — MB BS 1970 Gujarat.

KANABAR, Sudhin Dhiraj 148 Mount Pleasant, Barnet EN4 9HG — MB BS 1990 Lond.

KANAGALINGAM, Jeevendra Flat 11 Poplar, Woodland Crescent, Surrey Quays, London SE16 1YN Tel: 020 7232 2484 Email: jeeve.estee@virgin .net — BM BCh 1996 Oxf.; MA (Camb.) 1997; MRCS (Eng) 1999 Royal College of surgeons of England. SHO (ENT Surg.) Char. Cross Hosp.). Prev: SHO (Neurosurg.) Char. Cross Hosp.; SHO (A & E) Roy. Lond. Hosp.; Ho. Surg. John Radcliffe Hosp. Oxf..

KANAGARAJAH, Dhayanthi 35 Kenrick Square, Bletchingley, Redhill RH1 4PU — MB ChB 1981 Zambia. Regist. (Psychiat.) Luton & Dunstable Hosp. Luton. Prev: Regist. (Psychiat.) Kingsway Hosp. Derby.

KANAGARATNAM, Christina Nirupa 15 Travellers Way, Bath Road, Hounslow TW4 7QB — MB BS 1996 Lond.

KANAGARATNAM, Prapakaran 146 Streetly Lane, Sutton Coldfield B74 4TD — BChir 1994 Camb.; MB BChir Camb. 1994; MA Camb. 1994; MRCP (UK) 1997.

KANAGARATNAM, Mr Thilliyar 32 Box Lane, Wrexham LL12 7RB Tel: 01978 354165 Email: premratram@aol.com; Orthopaedic Department, Maelor Hospital Trust, Wrexham Tel: 01978 291100 Fax: 01978 725391 — MB BS 1973 Sri Lanka; FRCS Glas. 1987; LRCP LRCS Ed. LRCPS Glas. 1985. Assoc. Specialist (Orthop.). Socs: Brit. Orthop. Assn.

KANAGASABAI, Kajan 37 Stradbroke Grove, Clayhall, Ilford IG5 0DN — MB BS 1998 Lond.; MB BS Lond 1998.

KANAGASABAY, Robin Rabindranath 21 Old Sun Wharf, 40 Narrow St., London E14 8DG Tel: 020 7780 9145 Email: rkanaga@sghms.ac.uk; Trinity House, Pk Road, Abingdon OX14 1DB — MB BS 1990 Lond.; BSc Lond. 1987; FRCS Eng. 1995; MRCP 1995. (Char. Cross and Westminster) Specialist Regist.(Cardiothoracic Surg.) Harefield Hosp. Middlx. Socs: Fell. Roy. Soc. Med. Prev: Specialist Regist. Lond.; Specialist Regist. St. Geo.'s Hosp. Lond.

KANAGASABAY, Sivananthan Civil Serv. Occupat. Health Service, RARDE (Chertsey), Chobham Lane, Chertsey KT16 0EE Tel: 01344 635429; Trinity House, Pk Road, Abingdon OX14 1DB — MB BS 1953 Ceylon; MD Ceylon 1983; MSc Lond. 1970; FFOM RCP Lond. 1990, M 1979; MFCM 1973. Lady Cade Medal RCS Eng.; Sen. Med. Off. Civil Serv. Occupat. Health Serv. Cabinet Office. Socs: Fell. Roy. Soc. Med. Prev: Sen. Med. Off. Research & Developm. Directorate of Civil. Med.; Servs. MoD (PE); Wing Cdr. RAF; Dep. Dir. Community Med. RAF.

KANAGASABAY, Thirumalar Rivermead Rehabilitation Centre, Abingdon Road, Oxford OX1 4XD Tel: 01865 240321; Trinity House, Pk Road, Abingdon OX14 1DB — MB BS 1954 Ceylon; Dip. Rehabil. Studies Lond. 1977. Research Phys. Non-stipendary Rivermead Rehabil. Centre Oxf. Prev: Assoc. Specialist (Rehabil. & Neurol. Disabilities) Rivermead Rehabil. Centre Oxf.

KANAGASEGAR, Sivalingham c/o Mr P. Thevarajah, 22 Cresswell Grove, West Didsbury, Manchester M20 2NH — MB BS 1985 Peradeniya, Sri Lanka; MB BS Peradeniya Sri Lanka 1985.

KANAGASINGAM, Rajasingam (retired) 3 The Willows, Whitecroft, St Albans AL1 1UL Tel: 01727 865649 Fax: 01727 865649 — MB BS 1955 Ceylon; DPM Eng. 1979; DTM & H Ed. 1968. Prev: Assoc. Specialist in Psychiat. Napsbury Hosp. St. Albans.

KANAGASOORIAM, Gunalakshman Mohan Hensman Whitstable Health Centre, Harbour Street, Whitstable CT5 1BZ Tel: 01277 263033 Fax: 01277 771474; Pinners Farm, Pinners Hill, Nonington, Dover CT15 4LL — MB BS 1980 Lond.; MRCS Eng. LRCP Lond. 1980; MRCGP 1986. Med. Off. Promis Recovery Centre; Clin. Asst. (Psychogeriat.) St. Martin's Hosp. Canterbury; BASICS Doctor E. Kent, Canterbury & Dover Dist.; EMP Benefits Agency; PCCT, Ment. Health Gp.

KANAGASUNDARAM, Mohan 1 Haling Park Gardens, South Croydon CR2 6NP — MB BS 1996 Lond.

KANAGASUNDARAM, Nigel Suren 54 Moorside S., Newcastle upon Tyne NE4 9BB — MB ChB 1992 Manch.

KANAGASUNDREM, Aynkaran Oak Tree Medical Centre, 273-275 Green Lane, Seven Kings, Ilford IG3 9TJ Tel: 020 8599 3474 Fax: 020 8590 8277 — MB BS 1981 Colombo; LRCP LRCS Ed. LRCPS Glas. 1983; DRCOG 1987.

KANAGAVEL, Natarajan The District General Hospital, Lovely Lane, Warrington WA5 1QG — MB BS 1988 Madurai Kamaraj; MB BS Madurai Kamaraj, India 1988.

KANAKARATNAM, Gunaseelan Greenways', Nevells Green, Letchworth SG6 4UA Tel: 01462 678586 — MB BS 1959 Ceylon; FRCPsych 1983, M 1971; DPM Eng. 1967. (Ceylon) Socs: BMA. Prev: Cons. Psychiat. Fairfield Hosp. Stotfold & Bedford Gen. Hosp.; Regist. Fairfield Hosp. Stotfold; Ho. Off. Gen. Hosp. Jaffna & Govt. Hosp. Watupitiwela Ceylon.

KANAL, Lilo Weycot House, 89 Surrenden Road, Brighton BN1 6PQ — MB BS 1952 Lucknow.

KANAMIA, Tasneem The Loughton Health Centre, The Drive, Loughton IG10 1HW Tel: 0208 508 8117 — MB ChB 1994 Univ. of Natal, Republic of S. Africaa; 1995 DCH (S.A.) Coll. of Paediat. of S. Africa; 1998 DRCOG Lond.; 1997 DFFP Lond. p/t Gen. Practitioner.

KANANI, Mazyar 17 Serlby Court, Addison Rd, London W14 8EF — MB BS 1997 Lond.

KANANI, Ramniklal Raghavjibhai Kanani, The Surgery, 1 Highfield Road, Hemsworth, Pontefract WF9 4DP Tel: 01977 610926 Fax: 01977 616717 — MB BS 1967 Calcutta. (Calcutta Nat. Med. Inst.)

KANANI, Saifu-Allah Haverfield Surgery, 34 High Street, Kings Langley WD4 9HT Tel: 01923 262514 — LRCPSI 1973; LRCPSI.

KANANI, Sanjay Family Doctor Unit Surgery, 92 Bath Road, Hounslow TW3 3LN Tel: 020 8577 9555 Fax: 020 8570 2266 — MB ChB 1985 Manch.; BSc St. And. 1982; MRCGP 1989. Prev: GP VTS Burnley; Trainee GP Cheadle, Stockport, Chesh.

KANANI, Shantilal Raghavji 52 Heath Gardens, Twickenham TW1 4LZ — MB BS 1963 Lond.

KANAPATHIPPILLAI, Sithamparapillai New Health Centre, Third Avenue, Canvey Island SS8 9SU; 2 Cleveland Road, Canvey Island SS8 9AU Tel: 01268 514625 — MB BS Ceylon 1965; DCH RCPSI 1973. (Colombo)

KANAPATHIPPILLIA, Rishikeswaran 16 Cross Road, London SW19 1PF — MB BS 1996 Lond.

KANAPATHY RAJA, Mariapillai Sellamuthupillai Department of Anaesthetics, West Wales General Hospital, Dolgwili Road, Carmarthen SA31 2AF — MB BS 1977 Madurai Kamaraj U, India.

KANAS, Robert Paul Lincomb House, Lincomb, Stourport-on-Severn DY13 9RB — BM BS 1976 Nottm.; MRCP (UK) 1981; MFOM RCP Lond. 1985.

KANCHAN, Bodh Sagar 59 Vicarage Farm Road, Hounslow TW3 4NH Tel: 020 8570 5098 — MB BS 1961 Agra; BSc. Agra 1956; DA Eng. 1968; Cert FPA. 1970. (N. Med. Coll., Agra) GP Hounslow; Med. Off. Family Plann.

KANCHAN, Sarita 59 Vicarage Farm Road, Hounslow TW3 4NH — MB BS 1993 Lond.

KANDASAMY, Katharine Elizabeth Lower Letton Farm, Lower Letton, Bucknell SY7 0DS — MB ChB 1991 Glas.

KANDASAMY, Krishnamuhunthan North Devon District Hospital, Barnstaple EX32 4JB Tel: 01271 22577; Myrtle Cottage, 4 Station Hill, Swimbridge, Barnstaple EX32 0QR Tel: 01271 830508 — MB ChB 1991 Glas.; BSc (Biochem.) Glas. 1991. Anaesth. N. Devon

Dist. Hosp. Barnstaple. Prev: Ho. Off. (Surg.) N. Devon Dist. Hosp.; Ho. Off. (Med.) Glas. Roy. Infirm.

KANDASAMY, Ramanathan Flat C-3, 52 Grainger Park Road, Newcastle upon Tyne NE4 8RQ — MB BS 1988 Madras; FRCA 1994.

KANDASAMY, Ranjan Bradworthy Surgery, The Square, Bradworthy, Holsworthy EX22 7SY Tel: 01409 241215 Fax: 01409 241086; Gables, First Raleigh, Bideford EX39 3NJ — MRCS Eng. LRCP Lond. 1977; MRCGP 1988; FFA RCS Eng. 1983.

KANDASWAMY, Sangarappillai 25 Unicorn Avenue, Eastern Green, Coventry CV5 7GJ — MB BS 1970 Ceylon; MRCP (UK) 1983. (Ceylon)

KANDAVEL, Rajaluximi Thanikai, 4 Howards Crest Close, Beckenham BR3 6NW — MB BS 1971 Ceylon; DPM Eng. 1982. (Colombo) Clin. Asst. (Psychiat.) Canehill Hosp. Coulsdon.

KANDAVEL, Ratnam The Surgery, 27 Clifton Rise, London SE14 6ER Tel: 020 8692 1387; Thanikai, 4B Howards Crest Close, Beckenham BR3 6NW — MB BS 1971 Ceylon; MRCOG 1980. (Peradeniya) GP Newcross, Lond.; Clin. Asst. Dulwich Hosp. Lond.

KANDELA, Peter Feltham Hill Road Surgery, 107 Feltham Hill Road, Ashford TW15 1HH Tel: 01784 252027 Fax: 01784 469145; 29 Greenlands Road, Staines TW18 4LR Tel: 01784 461999 Fax: 01784 469145 — MB BS 1972 Dibrugarh; MRCGP 1993. GP Trainer Ashford; Managing Dir., Pacemaker Med. Publishing Ltd.; Edr. Clin. Dialogue; Foreign Corresp. The Lancet; Edit. Cons. Health & Human Right Harvard Univ.; Correspondent Jl. of the Amer. Med. Assoc.; Pres. Phys. Human Rights UK; Mem. Roy. Inst. Internat. Affairs Lond. Socs: Fell. Roy. Soc. Med.; Med. Jl.ists Assn. Prev: Med. Examr. Amnesty Internat.

KANDER, Mr Peter Leslie Holly House, 17A Birches Lane, Kenilworth CV8 2AB Tel: 01926 855019 Fax: 01926 855019 — MB BS Lond. 1966; FRCS Eng. 1972; MRCS Eng. LRCP Lond. 1966. (St. Mary's) Cons. ENT Surg. Univ. Hosps. Coventry + Warks. Hosps. NHS Trust. Socs: Fell. Roy. Soc. Med. Prev: Sen. Regist. Univ. Hosp. Wales Cardiff; Regist. Roy. Nat. Throat Nose & Ear Hosp. Lond.

KANDIAH, Ayakannu Sparcells Surgery, Midwinter Close, Peatmoor, Swindon SN5 5AN Tel: 01793 881928 Fax: 01793 879264 — MRCS Eng. LRCP Lond. 1979; MB BS Colombo, Sri Lanka 1979. (Colombo, Sri Lanka)

KANDIAH, Bernard Jayanesan General Hospital, Bishop Auckland DL14 6AD Tel: 01388 604040 — MB BS 1975 Sri Lanka; MRCS Eng. LRCP Lond. 1991.

KANDIAH, Dhevendran (Surgery), 483 Downham Way, Bromley BR1 5HU Tel: 020 8698 4774; 25 St. James's Avenue, Beckenham BR3 4HF — MB BS 1963 Ceylon. (Ceylon)

KANDIAH, Nadeswary 15 Plover Way, Surrey Quays, London SE16 7TS — MB BS 1968 Ceylon.

KANDLER, Rosalind Helen Royal Hallamshire Hospital, Glossop Road, Sheffield S10 2JF; 39 Whiteley Wood Road, Sheffield S11 7FF — MB BS 1982 Lond.; BSc Lond. 1979; MD Sheff. 1989; FRCP Lond. 1995; MRCP (UK) 1985. Cons. Clin. Neurophys. Roy. Hallamsh. Hosp. Sheff. Socs: EEG Soc. & Assn. Brit. Neurol.; Assn. Brit. Clin. Neurophysiol. Prev: Sen. Regist. (Clin. Neurophys.) Roy. Hallamsh. Hosp. Sheff.; SHO (Neurol.) Nat. Hosp. Nerv. Dis. Lond.; Ho. Phys. (Med.) Lond. Hosp.

KANDOLA, Linda Hermesh Kaur Gamston Medical Centre, Beckside, Gamston, Nottingham NG2 6PS Tel: 0115 945 5946 Fax: 0115 969 6217 — BM BS 1987 Nottm.; BMedSci Nottm. 1985; MRCGP 1991; DRCOG 1991; DCH RCP Lond. 1990. (Nottm.)

KANDULA, Dhanamjaya Rao 15 Rowlands Road, Yardley, Birmingham B26 1AT Tel: 0121 706 6623 Fax: 0121 706 9888; 4 Greyfriars Close, Solihull B92 7DR Tel: 0121 708 0368 — MB BS 1970 Andhra; DA (UK) 1976. Hosp. Pract. (Anaesth.) Birm. Heartlands Hosp.

KANDULA, Prasanti 4 Greyfriars Close, Solihull B92 7DR — MB BS 1998 Lond.; MB BS Lond 1998.

KANDULA, Vasundhara The Surgery, 15 Rowlands Road, Yardley, Birmingham B26 1AT Tel: 0121 706 6623 Fax: 0121 706 9888 — MB BS 1969 Sri Venkateswara; MB BS 1969 Sri Venkateswara.

KANE, Eileen Patricia 26 Rockport Park, Londonderry BT47 6JJ Tel: 01504 44560 — MB BCh BAO 1946 Belf.; FRCPI 1978, M 1965; MRCPsych 1972; DPM Eng. 1960, DCH 1951. Cons. Psychiat. Gransha Hosp. Lond.derry. Socs: Ulster Neuro-psychiat. Soc. Prev: Res. Med. Off. Mater Infirm. Hosp. Belf.; Sen. Regist. Psychiat. Purdysburn Hosp. Belf. & Holywell Hosp.; Antrim.

KANE, Henry Emmanuel 1 Helmsdale House, Carlton Vale, London NW6 5EN Tel: 020 7624 5064; 7 Crespigny Road, London NW4 3DT — MB BS 1948 Lond.; MRCS Eng. LRCP Lond. 1948. (Lond. Hosp.) Prev: Med. Off. RAF; Ho. Phys. Radiother. Dept. & Ho. Surg. Gyn. Dept. Lond. Hosp.

KANE, Iain McEwan Ayr Road Surgery, 69 Ayr Road, Douglas, Lanark ML11 0PX Tel: 01555 851226 — MB ChB 1968 Glas.; MRCGP 1977. Socs: BMA; Disp. Doctors Assn. Prev: SHO (Paediat.) Stobhill Gen. Hosp. Glas.; SHO (Paediat.) Falkirk Roy. Infirm.; Ho. Off. (O & G) S.. Gen. Hosp. Glas.

KANE, Ingrid Alice Invercannich House, Cannich, Beauly IV4 7LS — MB BS 1996 Lond. (Char. Cross & Westm.) Med. SHO (Gen. Med.) St. Richards Hosp. Chichester.

KANE, Mr James Francis Countess of Chester Hospital, Liverpool Road, Chester CH1 3ST Tel: 01244 365000 Fax: 01244 365252; 11 Westminster Avenue, Chester CH4 8JB Tel: 01244 680130 — MB ChB 1958 Liverp.; ChM Liverp. 1966; FRCS Ed. 1990; FRCS Eng. 1964; FRCS Eng. (ad eund.) 1992; MRCS Eng. LRCP Lond. 1958. Cons. Surg. Chester Roy. Infirm. & Countess Chester Hosp.; Med. Dir. Countess of Chester Hosp.; Clin. Lect. (Surg.) Univ. Liverp. Socs: Assoc. Mem. BAUS. Prev: Lect. (Surg.) Univ. Liverp.; Sen. Regist. Liverp. Roy. Infirm.; Regist. (Urol.) Sefton Gen Hosp.

KANE, James Lennox Womens Services, Hemel Hempstead Hospital, West Herts. NHS Trust, Hill Field Rd, Hemel Hempstead HP2 4AD Tel: 01442 287793; Skeets Farm, Flanchford, Reigate RH2 8RD — MB BCh BAO 1970 Dub.; BA Dub. 1968, MD 1982; FRCOG 1992, M 1975. (Trinity Coll. Univ. Dub.) p/t Cons. O & G St. Albans & Hemel Hempstead Hosp.s, W. Herts. NHS Trust. Prev: Sen. Regist. Hammersmith Hosp.

KANE, James Robert Boyd Brook Street Surgery, 9 Brook Street, Holywood BT18 9DA Tel: 028 9042 6984 Fax: 028 9042 6656; 15 Lynwood Park, Holywood BT18 9EU — MB BCh BAO 1968 Belf.

KANE, Judith Anne Canbury Medical Centre, 1 Elm Road, Kingston upon Thames KT2 6HR Tel: 020 8549 8818 Fax: 020 8547 0058; Wych Hill, George Road, Kingston upon Thames KT2 7PF Tel: 020 8949 1149 — MB BS 1968 Lond. (St. Geo.)

KANE, Katherine Fiona Department of Medicine, University Hospital Birmingham NHS Trust, Selly Oak Hospital, Raddlebarn Road, Birmingham B29 Tel: 0121 627 1627 Fax: 0121 627 8245 Email: kate.kane@university-b.wmids.nhs.uk — MB ChB 1988 Birm.; MRCP (UK) 1991; MD Birm. 1997. (Birm.) Cons. (Gastroenterol. & Gen. Phys.) Univ. Hosp. Birm. NHS Trust. Socs: Brit. Soc. Gastroenterol.; Amer. Gastroenterol. Assn.; Roy. Coll. Phys. Prev: MRC Research Fell. & Sheldon Research Fell.; Hon. Regist. (Med. & Gastroenterol.) Qu. Eliz. Hosp. Birm.; Lect. (Med. & Gastroenterol.) Univ. Dept. Med. Qu. Eliz. Hosp. Birm.

KANE, Kathleen 47 Newlands Road, Crumpsall, Manchester M8 — MB ChB 1979 Manch.

KANE, Louise Ann Contraception and Sexual Health Service, Central Health Clinic, Tower Hall, Bristol BS2 0JD Tel: 0117 927 6781; Pigeon Ogo, 10 Wesley Lane, Bristol BS30 8BU Tel: 0117 960 3387 — MB ChB 1988 Liverp.; MRCGP 1995; MFFP 1995; DRCOG 1994. SCMO Family Plann. Prev: Trainee GP Brierley Hill VTS; Ho. Phys. & Ho. Surg. Russells Hall Hosp. Dudley.

KANE, Meridith Lindsay Children's Hospital, Leicester Royal Infirmary, Leicester LE1 5WW Tel: 0116 254 1414; 7 Old Field Lane, Rothley, Leicester LE7 7QD — BM BS 1993 Nottm.; BMedSci 1991 Nottm.; MRCP 1996 (UK). Specialist Regist., Padiatrics, Leicester Roy. Infirm. Socs: MRCP; MRCPCH.

KANE, Nicholas Mark Grey Walter Department Clinical, Neurophysiology, Frenchay Hospital, Bristol BS16 1LE Tel: 01179 701212 Email: nick.kane@north-bristol.swest.nhs.uk; Tel: 0117 960 3387 — MB ChB 1986 Birm.; MSc Birm. 1990; MD (Hons.) Birm. 1996; FRCS Eng. 1991. (Birmingham) Cons. Clin. Neurophysiol. Frenchay Hosp. Socs: Assn. Brit. Neurol; Brit. Soc. of Clin. NeuroPhysiol. Prev: Sen. Regist. (Clin. Neurophysiol.) Nat. Hosp. Neurol. & Neurosurg. Lond.; Sen. Regist. (Clin. Neurophysiol.) Gt. Ormond St. Hosp. Lond.; Research Fell. (Neurosci.) Burden Neurol. Inst. Bristol.

KANE, Mr Philip John Dept. of Neurosurgery, Middlesbrough General Hospital, Ayresome Green Lane, Middlesbrough TS5 5AZ Tel: 01642 854435 Fax: 01642 854118 — MB BS 1983 Newc.;

MD Newc. 1995; BMedSci (Hons.) Newc. 1980; FRCS (SN) 1996; FRCS Eng. 1988. Cons. Neurosurg. Middlesbrough Gen. Hosp. Prev: Sen. Regist. (Neurosurg.) Nat. Hosp. Neurol. & Neurosurg., Hosp. Childr. Gt. Ormond St. & Char. Cross Hosp. Lond.

KANE, Rosemary Whiteabbey Health Centre, 95 Doagh Road, Newtownabbey BT37 9QW Tel: 028 9086 4341 Fax: 028 9086 0443; 1 Hedgelea Lane, Newtownabbey BT37 0WJ — MB BCh BAO 1992 Belf.; MRCGP 1996; DRCOG 1995. Socs: BMA & Med. Protec. Soc. Prev: GP Regist. Albert St. Health Centre Belf.; Trainee GP/SHO Rotat. Lagan Valley Hosp. Lisburn VTS; Ho. Off. (Med. & Surg.) Lagan Valley Hosp. Lisburn.

KANE, Sharon c/o Lloyds Bank, University of Manchester, 324 Oxford Road, Manchester M13 9NG; 36 Cranbourne Road, Old Trafford, Manchester M16 9PZ Tel: 0161 872 7292 — MB ChB 1991 Manch.; BSc Hons. (2) Immunol & Oncol Manch. 1988; Dip. of Child Health (RCP) 1996; DFFP (RCOG) 1997. Locum GP. Prev: GP Regist., Oswald Med Pract. Manch.; SHO (Obst.) N. Manch. Gen. Hosp.; SHO (Paediat.) Trafford Gen. Hosp.

KANE, Stephen Paul West Middlesex University Hospital, Isleworth TW7 6AF Tel: 020 8565 5353 Fax: 020 8565 5152; Wych Hill, George Road, Kingston upon Thames KT2 7PF Tel: 020 8949 1149 — BM BCh 1967 Oxf.; BA Oxf. 1964 (1st cl. Hons) MA 1967; FRCP Lond. 1985; MRCP (UK) 1971. (Oxf. & St. Geo.) Cons. Phys. & Gastroenterol. W. Middlx. Hosp. Isleworth. Socs: BMA; Brit. Soc. Gastroenterol. Prev: Sen. Regist. (Med.) Char. Cross Hosp. Lond.; Regist. (Med.) Hammersmith Hosp. Lond.; Ho. Surg. St. Geo. Hosp. Lond.

KANE, Thomas Peter c/o X-Ray Department, Victoria Hospital, Whinney Heys Road, Blackpool FY3 8NR — MB ChB 1978 Liverp.; FRCR 1984; DMRD Liverp. 1982. Cons. Radiol. Vict. Hosp. Blackpool.; Hon. Vis. Fell. Dept. of Health Studies Univ. of Salford. Socs: Brit. Nuclear Med. Soc.; Brit. Nuclear Cardiol. Soc.; Brit. Soc. of Paediatric Radiol. Prev: Sen. Regist. (Radiol.) Mersey RHA; Regist. Rotat. (Radiodiag.) Liverp. AHA (T); SHO (Surg.) Preston Health Dist.

KANE, Timothy Peter Christian Invercannich, Cannich, Beauly IV4 7LS — MB BS 1996 Lond.

KANEGAONKAR, V G Orgarswick Avenue Surgery, 9 Orgarswick Avenue, Dymchurch, Romney Marsh TN29 0NX Tel: 01303 872245 Fax: 01303 872610 — MB BS 1969 Poona; MB BS 1969 Poona.

KANEKAL, Keshavrao Venkatrao Department of Geriatric Medicine, Dudley Road Hospital, Birmingham B18 7QH Tel: 0121 554 3801; 74 Birch Grove, Hempstead, Gillingham ME7 3RB — MB BS 1980 Karnatak; LMSSA Lond. 1988.

KANESAN, Krishnaveni 126C Maltby House, South Cleveland Hospital, Marton Road, Middlesbrough TS4 3TH — MB BS 1981 Mysore.

KANESIAH, Sinnadurai 101 Old Road E., Gravesend DA12 1PB Email: kanesiah@cwcom.net — MB BS 1956 Ceylon; DCH RCPS Glas. 1968. GP Gravesend.

KANFER, Edward Joseph Hammersmith Hospital, Du Cane Road, London W12 0NN — MB BS 1979 Lond.; FRCP Lond. 1997; MRCP (UK) 1983; MRCPath 1989; FRCPath 1998. (St. Geo.) Sen. Lect. (Haemat.) Imperial Coll. Sch. of Med. Lond.; Cons. Haemat. Hammersmith Hosps. NHS Trust. Prev: Sen. Lect. (Haemat.) Char. Cross & W.m. Med. Sch. Lond.; Research Fell. (Haemat.) Roy. Postgrad Med. Sch. Lond.; Lect. (Haemat.) Char. Cross & W.m. Med. Sch. Lond.

KANG, Chai Har 6 Campden Hill Gardens, London W8 7AY — MB BS 1989 Singapore.

KANG, Lakhbinder Singh Victoria Superstore, 80-84 Cape Hill, Smethwick, Smethwick B66 4PB — MB ChB 1995 Leeds.

***KANG, Nishpal Kaur** 29 Delves Road, Walsall WS1 3JX — MB ChB 1998 Birm.

KANG, Surinder 199 Ecclesall Road S., Sheffield S11 9PN — BChir 1981 Camb.

KANG-BUDIALAM, Mr Norbert Venantius Doctor's Residence, Mount Vernon Hospital, Rickmansworth Road, Northwood HA6 2RN — MB BS 1989 Lond.; FRCS Eng. 1994.

KANGA, Mr Suresh Babu 74 Whielden Street, Amersham HP7 0JB Tel: 01494 721033 — MB BS 1974 Himachal Pradesh; FRCS Ed. 1988.

KANGATHARAN, Alagaratnam Flat 2, Hill Crest, Upper Green Road, St Helens, Ryde PO33 1UG — MB BS 1986 Jaffna; MSc (Clin. Microbiol.) Lond. 1992; MB BS Jaffna Sri Lanka 1986; LRCP LRCS Ed. LRCPS Glas. 1993.

KANGESAN, Mr Kanapathipillai Sydenham Surgery, 2 Sydenham Road, London SE26 5QW Tel: 020 8778 8552 — MRCS Eng. LRCP Lond. 1986; MB BS Colombo Sri Lanka 1976; FRCS Eng. 1990; T(GP) 1991. (Univ. Colombo Fac. Med. Ceylon)

KANGESU, Eragupillai 30 St Martins Drive, Walton-on-Thames KT12 3BW Tel: 01932 224565 — MB BS 1957 Ceylon; FRCPCH 1997; FFPHM 1994; MFPHM 1989; MFCM 1974; DCH Eng. 1973; DPH Lond. 1967. (Ceylon) Locum Cons. Socs: Brit. Med. Assn.; Roy. Soc. of Med. Prev: Princip. Med. Off. (Community Health) King's Coll. Hosp. Lond.; Sen. Regist. (Community Med.) St. Geo. Hosp. Lond.; Hon. Lect. (Community Med.) King's Coll. Hosp. Med. Sch. Lond.

KANGESU, Mr Thirloshan 17 Beaumont Place, Isleworth TW7 7LB — MB BS 1986 Lond.; BSc Lond. 1983, MB BS 1986; FRCS Eng. 1990. Research Fell. (Plastic Surg.) Clin. Research Centre N.wick Pk. Hosp. Harrow. Prev: SHO (Plastic Surg.) Billericay.

KANI, Wajiha Coldharbour House, Kingsley Common, Kingsley, Bordon GU35 9LP — MB BS 1986 Lond.; MA Oxf. 1985, BA 1982; MSc Lond. 1990, MB BS 1986; MFPHM 1992. Sen. Regist. (Pub. Health Med.) NE Thames RHA. Socs: Soc. Social Med.

KANIS, Professor John Anthony WHO Collabotrating Centre for Metabolic Bone Diseases, Medical School, Beech Hill Road, Sheffield S10 2RX Tel: 0114 273 9176 Fax: 0114 272 6938 — MD 1985 Sheff.; BSc (Hons.) Ed. 1967, MB ChB 1970; FRCP Ed. 1986; FRCP Lond. 1984; MRCP (UK) 1973; MRCPath 1982. (Edin) Prof. (Human Metab. & Clin. Biochem.) Univ. Sheff.; Dir. WHO Collaborating Centre Metab. Bone Dis.; Edr. Bone. Socs: Med. Res. Soc. & Assn. Phys.; Trustee Internat.Osteoporosis Found; Dir.Internat.Bone & Mineral.Soc. Prev: Pres. Europ. Foundat. for Osteoporosis & Bone Dis.; Wellcome Sen. Clin. Res. Fell. (Clin. Sci.) Univ. Oxf.; MRC Clin. Res. Fell. Univ. Oxf.

KANJARIA, Nilesh Jayantilal Sandhurst Group Practice, 72 Yorktown Road, Sandhurst GU47 9BT Tel: 01252 872455 Fax: 01252 872456; 63 Harewood Road, Isleworth TW7 5HN Tel: 020 8560 6778 Fax: 020 8560 6778 Email: nilesh@kanjaria.freeserve.co.uk — MB ChB 1994 Dundee; BMSc (Hons.) Dund 1991; DFFP 1998. (Dundee University) GP. Prev: GP/Regist. & SHO E. Berks. VTS; Ho. Off. Stoke Mandeville Hosp. Aylesbury; Ho. Off. Dundee Teachg. Hosps. NHS Trust.

KANJI, Amyn Abdulmalik Alibhai The Chequers Surgery, 3 Chequers Drive, Prestwood HP16 9DU Tel: 01494 863899/862858 Fax: 01494 865202 — MB BS 1983 Lond.; MA Oxf. 1984; DCH RCP Lond. 1987; DRCOG 1986. (Oxford & King's London)

KANJI, Hemali Khatau 25 Molesworth Avenue, Stoke Aldermoor, Coventry CV3 1BU — MB ChB 1991 Leeds.

KANJILAL, Gopal Chandra (retired) The Hollies, Northwich Road, Cranage, Knutsford WA16 9LE Tel: 01477 533355 — MB BS 1950 Patna; FRCPsych 1979, M 1971; DTM Calcutta 1950; DPM NUI 1954. Locum Sen. Clin. Med. Off. Child Health and Plann. Rotherham Priority Health NHS Trust. Prev: Regist. Severalls Hosp. Colchester.

KANJILAL, Jiten Milton Road East Surgery, 45-47 Milton Road East, Lowestoft NR32 1NU Tel: 01502 572938 Fax: 01502 539132 — MB BS 1960 calcutta; MB BS 1960 Calcutta.

KANKA, David Cambridgeshire Health Authority, Kingfisher House, Kingfisher Way, Hinchinbrook Business Park, Huntingdon PE29 6FH Tel: 01480 398613 Fax: 01480 398501 Email: david.kanka@cambs-ha.nhs.uk; 10 Eleanor Place, Great Barton, Bury St Edmunds IP31 2TQ Tel: 01284 787140 — MB BS 1980 Lond.; 2002 FFPHM RCP (UK); MRCGP 1984; DPH Camb. 1992; DObst 1982. (St. Thos.) Cons. Pub. Health Med. Cambs HA. Prev: GP Crickhowell, Powys.

KANN, Peter Eric Ernest (retired) 16 Brookmans Avenue, Brookmans Park, Hatfield AL9 7QL Tel: 01707 659969 — LMSSA 1950 Lond.; MRCS Eng. LRCP Lond. 1950. Prev: Indep. GP Hatfield.

KANNAN, Angela Jane 53 The Green, Shustoke, Birmingham B46 2AT Tel: 01675 481349 Email: kannan@globalnet.co.uk; Leicester General Hospital, Leicester LE5 4NZ — MB ChB 1992 Birm.; MRCP (UK) 1995. Regist. Rotat. (Med.) Leicester Gen. Hosp. Socs: Brit. Geriat. Soc. Prev: SHO Rotat. (Med.) E. Birm. Heartlands Hosp.

KANODIA, Sushil Kumar c/o Drive S. K. Kanchan, 2 Turnham Grove, Hunters Ridge, Perton, Wolverhampton WV6 7TA — MB BS 1973 Rajasthan; DLO Eng. 1978. (S.M.S. Med. Coll. Jaipur)

KANORIA, Mr Sanjeev 78 Apsley House, Finchley Road, St John's Wood, London NW8 0NZ Tel: 020 7586 0935 Fax: 020 7722 8559 Email: 101457.2537@compuserve.com — MB BS 1988 Calcutta; FRCS Eng. 1992; FRCS Glas. 1992.

KANSAGRA, Bhupatlal Ambalal Sankalp, 1 Pine Shaw, Pound Hill, Crawley RH10 7TN Tel: 01293 884976; Sankalp, 1 Pine Shaw, Pound Hill, Crawley RH10 7TN Tel: 01293 884976 — MB BS Bombay 1969; FCPS Bombay (Ophth.) 1972; DO Eng. 1975; DOMS CPS Bombay 1971. (Grant Med. Coll.) Indep. Eye Surg. Crawley; Ophth. Med. Practioner.

KANSAGRA, Deepak Maganlal The Surgery, Flat 1, 10 Compayne Gardens, London NW6 3DH; 74 Priory Park Road, London NW6 7UN Tel: 020 7328 5520 Email: dkansagra@thefreeinternet.co.uk — MB ChB 1992 Liverp.; DRCOG 2000 Roy. Coll. of Obst. & Gynaec.; DCH 1997 RCP Lond. GP Caompayne Garden Surg.; GP. Socs: BMA; MDU. Prev: SHO (Psychiat.) N.wick Pk. Hosp.; SHO (O & G) Barnet Gen. Hosp.; SHO Paediatric (WellHo. Trust).

KANSAGRA, Indumati Bhupatlal Sankalp, 1 Pine Shaw, Pound Hill, Crawley RH10 7TN — MB BS 1970 Gujarat; DRCOG 1978; DObst Dub. 1978. (B.J. Med. Coll. Ahmedabad) Clin. Med. Off. (Community Health) Crawley W. Sussex; Mem. GMC. Prev: Regist. (O & G) W. Sussex; GP India.

KANSAGRA, Ketan Bhupatlal Sankalp, 1 Pine Shaw, Crawley RH10 7TN — MB BS 1998 Lond.; MB BS Lond 1998.

KANSAGRA, Mokshad Harilaz 3 Bellis Grove, Woughyon on the Green, Milton Keynes MK6 3EZ — MB BCh 1982 Wales; MRCGP 1987.

KANSE, Prakash Tatyaba 15 Queens Road, Enfield EN1 1NE — MB BS 1977 Bombay.

KANSKI, Mr Jacek Jerzy (cons. rooms), Thames Valley Nuffield Hospital, Wexham St., Slough SL3 6NH Tel: 01753 662241 Fax: 01753 662129; Bay Lodge, 15 Woodhill Avenue, Gerrards Cross SL9 8DP Tel: 01753 884467 Fax: 01753 884467 — MB BS Lond. 1963; MS Lond. 1989, MD 1985; FRCS Eng. 1967; FRCOphth 1990. (Royal London Hospital) Hon. Cons. Ophth. Surg. King Edwd. VII Hosp. Windsor. Prev: Resid. Surg. Off. Moorfields Eye Hosp. Lond.; Regist. W.m. Hosp. Lond.; Ho. Surg. & Ho. Phys. Roy. Lond. Hosp.

KANT, Madhu 7 Clos Cefn Bychan, Pentyrch, Cardiff CF15 9PF — MB BS 1963 Rangoon; DA Eng. 1970. Regist. (Anaesth.) Univ. Hosp. of Wales Cardiff. Prev: SHO (Anaesth.) Roy. Devon & Exeter Hosp.; Med. Off. (Med. & Surg.) Govt. of Burma; SHO (Orthop. & Trauma) Barnet Gen. Hosp.

KANT, Subodh Rambhai 91 Potter Street, Northwood HA6 1QH — MB BS 1986 Lond.; MRCGP 1991; DCH RCP Lond. 1990; DRCOG 1990; DGM RCP Lond. 1989.

KANTA, Krishna 60 Regent House, Newbold Terrace, Leamington Spa CV32 4HD — MB BS 1951 Lucknow; DObst Madras 1956. (King Geo. Med. Coll. Lucknow) Socs: BMA. Prev: SHO (O & G) G.M. Hosp. Lucknow; SHO (O & G) Postgrad. Inst. O & G Wom. & Childr. Hosp. Madras.

KANTHAN, Kangaratnam Kathirgama The Surgery, 6 Well Court, 740 London Road, North Cheam, Sutton SM3 9BX Tel: 020 8644 8400 — MB BS 1979 Mysore; DObst RCPI 1984.

KANTHAN, Padma Rekha Station Road Surgery, 259 Station Road, Hayes UB3 4JE Tel: 020 8573 9787 Fax: 020 8561 5152 — MB BS 1973 Bangalor; MB BS Bangalore 1973; DGO Agra 1975.

KANTOR, Robin Jonathan Radiology Department, The Hillingdon Hospital, Uxbridge UB8 3NN Tel: 01895 238282 Fax: 01895 279865; 8 Sandy Lodge Way, Northwood HA6 2AJ Email: robinkantor@hotmail.com — MB ChB 1977 Univ. Cape Town; FRCR 1984; DMRD Lond. 1982. (Univ. Cape Town) Cons. Radiol. Hillingdon Hosp. Uxbridge. Socs: Fell. Roy. Coll. Radiol.; BMA; Roy. Soc. Med.

KANU, Francis Cornelius Suba 10 Newby Place, Beacon Lough, Gateshead NE9 6YJ — Vrach 1975 Rostov Med Inst.

KANUMILLI, Naresh 22 Brodley Close, Hipperholme, Halifax HX3 8LS — MB BS 1989 Madras.

KANUNGO, Subhash Motilalji 46 Clapham Road, Bedford MK41 7PW — MB BS 1974 Nagpur; DCH Nagpur 1975. (Govt. Med. Coll. Naqpur) SHO (A & E & Orthop.) Stoke Mandeville Hosp. Aylesbury.

KANWAR, Mr Sunjay Flat 1 F2, 101 East Claremont Square, Edinburgh EH7 4JA — MB ChB 1989 Liverp.; FRCS Ed. 1993.

KANYIKE, Frederick Buule Ministry of Health, Kuwait, Amiri Hospital, Clinical Laboratories, PO Box 4077, Safat 13041, Kuwait Tel: 00 09 65 2463799 Fax: 00 09 65 2463790; 4 Hemlock Street, Anniesland, Glasgow G13 1AB Tel: 0141 579 5502 Fax: 0141 579 5502 — MB ChB 1974 Kampala; MMed Kampala 1978; MRCPath 1987; FRCPath 1997. (Makerere University Kampala) Cons. Haemat. Kuwait MoH; Clin. Tutor (Haemat.) Kuwait Med. Fac. Socs: Brit. Soc. Haematol.; Kuwait Med. Assn.; Uganda Med. Assn. Prev: Sen. Regist. (Haemat.) MoH, Kuwait; Regist. (Haemat.) W.. Infirm. Glas.; Specialist Haemat. MoH Uganda, Kampala.

KAO, Richard Nan Pin New Park Medical Practice, 163 Robertson Road, Dunfermline KY12 0BL Tel: 01383 629200 Fax: 01383 629203 — MB BS 1971 Calcutta; MB BS Calcutta 1979; LRCP Edin.; LRCS Edin.; LRPCS Glas. 1981. (Calcutta) GP Dunfermline, Fife.

KAPACEE, Dipak Rasiklal Chandulal 55 Upcroft Avenue, Edgware HA8 9RA — MB BS 1983 Lond.

KAPADIA, Angela The Westerham Practice, Winterton Surgery, Market Square, Westerham TN16 1DR Tel: 01959 564949 — MB ChB 1988 Dundee; MRCGP 1992; DGM RCPS Glas. 1992. (Dundee) GP W.erham, Kent.

KAPADIA, Armaity Pervez Parkwood, Lodge Road, Sunridge Park, Bromley BR1 3ND — MB BS 1956 Lond.; MRCS Eng. LRCP Lond. 1956. (Roy. Free) Med. Dir. Ayerst Laborat. Ltd. FarnBoro., Hants. Prev: Ho. Phys. St. Mary's Hosp. Plaistow; Ho. Phys. (Paediat.) St. Geo. Hosp. Bombay.

KAPADIA, Bai (retired) 24 Consort Road, Peckham, London SE15 2PU — MB BS 1946 Bombay.

KAPADIA, Kantilal Khemchand (retired) 237 Burnt Oak Khemchand, Edgware HA8 5EG — MB BS 1945 Bombay; DTM & H Eng. 1975.

KAPADIA, Mr Kayomars Barjor 10 Courtfarm Road, Northolt UB5 5HQ — MB BS 1986 Bombay; FRCS Eng. 1993.

KAPADIA, Laila Homi Marks & Spencer plc, 47 Baker St., London W1A 1DN Tel: 020 7268 8202 Fax: 020 7268 3107; Bennett House, Coombe Park, Kingston upon Thames KT2 7JB Tel: 020 8546 5983 Fax: 020 8547 3603 — MB ChB Sheff. 1969; MRCS Eng. LRCP Lond. 1969; AFOM RCP Lond. 1991; FRCOG 1991, M 1975; DObst RCOG 1971. (Sheffield University) Med. Off. (Occupat. Health) Marks & Spencer plc; Med. Off. (Family Plann. & Menopause) Char. Cross Hosp. Lond. Socs: RCOG; (Med. Comm.) Wom. Nationwide Cancer Control Campaign; Roy. Soc. Med. Prev: Regist. (O & G & Family Plann.) Char. Cross Hosp. Lond.; SHO (Obst.) N.wick Pk. Hosp.; SHO (Path.) Roy. Free Hosp. Lond.

KAPADIA, Mustafa Karimbhai 39 Hunstanton Avenue, Harborne, Birmingham B17 8SX — MB ChB 1976 Birm.

KAPADIA, Mustak 187 Watling Street Road, Fulwood, Preston PR2 8AE — MB ChB 1993 Manch. SHO (ENT) Roy. Lancaster Infirm.

KAPADIA, Mr Rumy Dhunjishaw (retired) BUPA Hospital, Ambrose Lane, Harpenden AL5 4BP Tel: 01582 763191 Fax: 01582 712312 — MS (ENT) Bombay 1966, MB BS 1963; FRCS Eng. 1969; DLO Eng. 1967; Dip. Otorhinolaryng. Bombay 1964. Prev: Cons. ENT Surg. Lister Hosp. Stevenage & Qu. Eliz. II Hosp. Welwyn Gdn. City.

KAPADIA, Sanim Banu W.S.C.R., St Bartholmews Hospital, Smithfield, London EC1A 7BE; 10B Chepstow Road, London W2 5BD — MB BS 1994 Lond.

KAPADIA, Suneil Arvind New Cross Hospital, Wolverhampton WV10 0QP Tel: 01902 643182 — MB ChB 1983 Sheff.; MD Sheff. 1994; MRCP (UK) 1989. Cons. Phys. (Gastroenterol. & Gen. Med.) New Cross Hosp. Wolverhampton. Socs: Fell. of The Roy. Coll. of Phys.s; Mem. of the Brit. Soc. of Gastroenterol. Prev: Sen. Regist. Selly Oak Hosp. & Liver Unit Qu. Eliz. Hosp. Birm.

KAPADIA, Yasmin Katy 17 Marshbarns, Bishop's Stortford CM23 2QN — MB BS 1994 Lond.

KAPAS, Kamala Charan Melbourne House, High Street, Rhosllanerchrugog, Wrexham LL14 1AW Tel: 01978 840784 Fax: 01978 844077 — MB BS 1960 Calcutta; BSc, MB BS Calcutta 1960. (Nilratan Sircar Med. Coll.)

KAPASI, Faiyaz Mohomedhusein Princess Alexandra Hospital, Harlow CM20 1QT Tel: 01279 444455 Email: fmkapasi@yahoo.co.uk; 7 Cutlers Close, St Michaels Mead, Bishop's Stortford CM23 4FW Tel: 01279 757445 — MB BS 1985 Saurashtra; Dip. Urol. Lond 1993; CRCS Eng. 1992; FICS (Urol) 1993; FAIS (Urol.) 1993; MS 1987; FEBU 1997; MSC (Urol) Lond. 2000. (MP Shah Med. Coll., India) Staff Urol. P.ss Alexandra NHS Trust Harlow Essex. Socs: FAIS (Urol.).; Amer. Urol. Assn.; FICS (Urol). Prev: Locum Cons. Urol. Hinchingbrooke Hosp. Huntingdon Cambs.; Staff Urol. Medway Hosp., Gillingham, Kent; Post Fell.sh. Regist. (Urol. & Gen. Surg.) Glan Clwyd Hosp. Wales.

KAPASI, Mustafa Abdulkarim The Health Centre, 20 Duncan Street, Greenock PA15 4LY Tel: 01475 724477 Fax: 01475 723450 — MB BS 1968 Poona.

KAPEMBWA, Moses Silungwe 141 Pinner Hill Road, Pinner HA5 3SQ — MB ChB 1976 Zambia; BSc Zambia 1972; MSc Lond. 1980; MRCP (UK) 1984; FRCP Lond. 1996; FRCP Ed. 1996; PhD Lond. 1994. Clin. Research Fell. MRC & Hon. Sen. Regist. St. Geo. Med. Sch. Dept. Communicable Dis. Lond.; Cons. Phys. (GU & HIV Med.) N.wick Pk. & Marks Hosps. NHS Trust. Socs: MSSVD; Assoc. GU Phys.s. Prev: Regist. (Gastroenterol. & Gen. Med.) Raigmore Hosp. Inverness; Lect. (Med. & Therap.) Aberd. Univ. Med. Sch.

KAPENDA, Alec Yolomoni Abbey Street Surgery, 60 Abbey Street, Accrington BB5 1EE Tel: 01254 382224 — MB ChB 1975 Zambia; MB ChB 1975 Zambia.

KAPFF, Peter David Fordie House, 82 Sloane St., London SW1X 9PA Tel: 020 7235 8298 Fax: 020 7235 3721; 32 Newburgh Road, London W3 6DQ Tel: 020 7993 0467 Fax: 020 7993 0467 Email: peter.kapff@virgin.net — MB BS 1982 Lond.; BSc (Hons.) Lond. 1979; DRCOG 1990. (Guy's) Socs: Worshipful Soc. of Apoth. Prev: GP Croft Hall Med. Pract. Torquay Devon; SHO (Paediat. & O & G) N. Devon Dist. Hosp.; SHO (Gen. Surg.) Roy. Devon & Exeter Hosp.

KAPIL, Gyan Prakash The Surgery, 291 Ashby Road, Scunthorpe DN16 2AB Tel: 01724 864426/7/8 Fax: 01724 282570 — MB BS 1961 Lucknow.

KAPILA, Atul Department of Anaesthetics, Royal Berkshire Hospital, London Road, Reading RG1 5AN Tel: 0118 987 7068 Fax: 0118 987 7067 — MB BS 1984 Lond.; BSc (Hons) Lond. 1981; FRCA 1991. (Middlesex) Cons. Anaesth. Roy. Berks. Hosp. Reading. Socs: MRCAnaesth.; Assn. Anaesths.; Intens. Care Soc.

KAPILA, Helen Edith Cavell Hospital, Bretton Gate, Peterborough PE3 9GZ Tel: 01733 874000 Fax: 01733 875719; 3 Burnt House Sidings, Turves, Peterborough PE7 2HS Tel: 01733 840793 Fax: 01733 840684 — MB ChB 1975 Leeds; FRCP (Lond) 1996, M (UK) 1979. p/t Cons. Phys. (Geriat.) P'boro Dist. Hosp. Socs: Brit. Geriat. Soc.; Brit. Stroke Research Gp. Prev: Sen. Regist. (Geriat.) Addenbrooke's Hosp. Camb.

KAPILA, Indeewar 18 Attlebridge Close, Derby DE21 4SP — MB ChB 1990 Glas.

KAPILA, Miss Leela, OBE University Hospital, Queen's Medical Centre, Nottingham NG7 2UH Tel: 0115 924 9924 Fax: 0115 970 9006; 56 Main Street, Willoughby on the Wolds, Loughborough LE12 6SZ Tel: 01509 880035 Fax: 01509 880035 — MB BS Madras 1962; FRCS Eng. 1966. (Christian Med. Coll. Hosp. Vellore) Cons. Paediat. Surg. Univ. Hosp. Nottm. Socs: (Counc.) Roy. Coll. Surg. Eng.; Brit. Assn. Paediat. Surg.; Pres. Brit. Assn. Paed. Surg. Prev: Resid. Asst. Surg. Hosp. Sick Childr. Gt. Ormond St. Lond.; Mem. Ct. Examrs. Roy. Coll. Surg. Eng.; SHO (Surg.) Rush Green Hosp. Romford.

KAPILA, Mukesh Department for International Development, 1 Palace Street, London SW1E 5HE Tel: 020 7023 0778 Fax: 020 7023 0502 Email: m-kapila@dfid.gov.uk; 3 Burnt House Sidings, Turves, Peterborough PE7 2HS Tel: 01733 840793 Fax: 01733 840684 Email: mkapila@aol.com — BM BCh 1980 Oxf.; MSc Lond. 1985; MA Oxf. 1981, BA (Hons.) 1977; MRCGP 1984; MFCM 1988; DRCOG 1982; FFPHM 1997. Head Conflict. & Humanitarian Affairs Dept., Dept. for Internat. Developm. Socs: Roy. Soc. Trop. Med. & Hyg. Prev: Sen. Humanitarian Adviser Dept. of Internat. Developm.; Sen. Regist. (Community Med.) Camb. HA; Cons. Pub. Health Med. & Dep. Dir. (AIDS) Health Educat. Auth. Lond.

KAPILA, Piyusha Institute of Child Health, 30 Guilford St., London WC1N 1EH — MB ChB 1989 Manch.; MRCP 1993. Clin. Research Fell.

KAPILA, Rakesh 178 Dunraven Drive, Derriford, Plymouth PL6 6AZ — MB BS 1993 Lond.; BSc (Hons.) Anat. Lond. 1990, MB BS 1993. Demonst. (Anat.) Univ. Camb.

***KAPILA, Rakesh** 4Bowsdale Close, Spring Mews, Garnston, Nottingham NG2 6QZ — MB ChB 1998 Birm.

KAPLAN, Brian 140 Harley Street, London W1N 1AH Tel: 020 7487 3416 Fax: 020 7372 1615 Email: bkaplan@dircon.co.uk; Flat 7, Windsor House, 102 Greencroft Gardens, London NW6 3PH Tel: 020 7328 9476 — MB BCh 1980 Witwatersrand; MB BCh Witwatersand 1980; MFHom 1983. Lect. (Homoeop.) Roy. Lond. Homoeop. Hosp.; Lect. (Homoeop.) Homoeop. Phys. Train. Gp. Oxf.

KAPLAN, Carole Ann Fleming Nuffield Unit for Children & Young People, Burdon Terrace, Jesmond, Newcastle upon Tyne NE2 3AE Tel: 0191 219 6424 Fax: 0191 219 6434 — MB ChB 1976 Cape Town; FRCPCH; FRCPsych 1986. (Cape Town, South Africa) Sen. Lect. & Cons. Child & Adolesc. Psychiat. Fleming Nuffield Unit for Childr. & Young People Newc. u Tyne.; Mem. Lord Chancellor's Advis. Bd. on Family Law; Non-Exec. Dir. NHS Litigation Auth. Socs: Fell.Roy. Coll. Psychiat.s; Fell.Roy. Coll. Paediat. & Child Health. Prev: Mem. Counc. on Tribunals 1993.

KAPLAN, Professor Colin (retired) 5 Warwick Road, Reading RG2 7AX Tel: 0118 987 1717 Fax: 0118 962 1647 Email: colin.kaplan@cwcom.net — MB ChB Cape Town 1947; MSc Cape Town 1944; FRCPath 1970, M 1966; Dip. Bact. Lond 1951. Prev: Prof. Microbiol. Univ. Reading.

KAPLAN, Jonathan 37 Highbury Park, London N5 1TH Tel: 020 7226 3220 — MB ChB 1977 Cape Town; FRCS (Ed.) 1983; FRCS (Eng.) 1984; MS Boston 1989. (Cape Town)

KAPLAN, Mark Jon Chiswick Health Centre, Fishers Lane, London W4 1RX Tel: 020 8321 3518/9 Fax: 020 8321 3568 — MB BS 1977 Lond.; MRCGP 1982; DFFP 1993; Dip. Practical Dermat. Wales 1998. (St Mary's)

KAPLAN, Nasser Mousa Faleh Microbiology Department, Sandwell General Hospital, Lyndon, West Bromwich B71 4HJ — MB BCh 1982 Cairo.

KAPLAN, Selwyn Anthony Service for Adolescents and Families in Enfield, Rownhams, 24 Dryden Road, Bush Hill Park, Enfield EN1 2PP Tel: 020 8360 7391 Fax: 020 8360 5483 Email: xgt12@dial.pipex.com — MB ChB 1977 Cape Town; MRCPsych 1983; Dip. Clin. Hypn. UCL 1997; Cert. Adv Training Family Ther 1988. Cons. Child & Adolesc. Psychiat. Enfield; Vis. Lect. Tavistock Clinic, Child & Family Dept. Hampstead; Vis. Cons. Gr.lands Priory Hosp. S.gate; Hon. Sen. Lect. (Child & Adolesc. Psychiat.) Roy. Free Hosp. Med. Sch. Lond. & UCL Middlx. Hosp. Med. Sch.; Hon. Cons. Traum. Stress Clinic (Camden & Islington Community Trust) Lond. Prev: Cons. (Child & Adolesc. Psychiat.) Enfield Child Guid. Serv.

KAPLAN, Mr Vahan 30 Pembroke Road, Ruislip HA4 8NE — Tip Doktoru 1971 Istanbul; FRCS Ed. 1982. (Istanbul) Assoc. Specialist (Gen. Surg.) Mt. Vernon & Hillingdon Hosps.; Police Surg. Prev: Staff Surg. Mt. Vernon & Hillingdon Hosps.; Sen. Regist. (Gen. Surg.) Hillingdon Hosp. Uxbridge; Regist. (A & E) N.wick Pk. Hosp. Harrow.

KAPLAN, Yehuda Shemariah (retired) 25 Woodfoot Road, Rotherham S60 3DZ Tel: 01709 370342 — MB ChB 1954 Cape Town; DIH Eng. 1978; DTCD Wales 1968. Locum Sen. Clin. Med. Off. Child Health & Plann. Rotherham Priority Health NHS Trust. Prev: SCMO Community Child Health Roth. Priority Health Trust.

KAPMA, Jan Auke Aries 6 Alderminster Grove, Hatton, Warwick CV35 7TB — Artsexamen 1992 Nijmegen.

KAPOOR, Anita Law Medical Group Practice, 9 Wrottesley Road, London NW10 5UY Tel: 020 8965 8011 Fax: 020 8961 6239 — MB BS 1991 Lond.

KAPOOR, Asha Lata Deneside Medical Centre, The Avenue, Deneside, Seaham SR7 8LF Tel: 0191 513 0884 Fax: 0191 581 1855 — MB BS 1972 Kanpur; MRCOG 1982.

KAPOOR, Ashish Glenlyn Medical Centre, 115 Molesey Park Road, East Molesey KT8 0JX Tel: 020 8979 3253 Fax: 020 8941 7914; 4 Hillside, Portsmouth Road, Esher KT10 9LJ — BM 1991 Soton.; MRCGP 1996; DCCH 1996; DCH RCP Lond. 1995; DGM RCP Lond. 1995; DRCOG 1995; DFFP 1995. (Soton. Univ. Med. Sch.) GP Principle, Gleslyn Med. Cnetre, Surrey; GP Trainer, The Postgrad. Deasery for Kent, E. Surrey and Sussex, Dept. of Postgrad. Gen. Pract. Educat. Prev: Trainee GP/SHO Ealing VTS; Ho. Off. Med. Soton. Gen. Hosp.; Ho. Off. (Surg.) Roy. S. Hants. Hosp. Soton.

KAPOOR, Mr Balbir Lal 10 Auchnacloich Road, Rothesay PA20 0EB Tel: 01700 2223 — MB BS 1955 Punjab, MB BS Punjab (India) 1955; FRCS Ed. 1964. Assoc. Specialist (Gen. Surg.) Vict. Hosp. Rothesay. Prev: Surg. Regist. Inverness Hosps., Ashford Hosp. Kent & Gen. Hosp.; Dewsbury.

KAPOOR, Dinesh Grange Park Medical Centre, 24 Grange Park Road, Leyton, London E10 5EP Tel: 020 8539 2962 Fax: 020 8539 7940 Email: dinesh.kapoor@gp_f86074.nhs.uk; 36 The Drive, South Woodford, London E18 2BL Tel: 020 8989 7280 Email: dineshkapoor@aol.com — MB BS 1969 Indore; DA Eng. 1980. (M.G.M Med. Coll. Indore) Prev: Resid. Regist. (Anaesth.) Jersey Gp. Hosps. & Hartlepool HA; Resid. SHO (Anaest.) HA.

KAPOOR, Gurnam Kaur (retired) St. Edwards Hospital, Cheddleton, Leek ST13 7EB — MB BS 1961 Agra; DPM Eng. 1969. Assoc. Specialist St. Edwd. Hosp. Cheddleton. Prev: SHO St. Matthew's Hosp. Burntwood.

KAPOOR, Jagdish Chandra Wern Surgery, Bon y Wern, Bagillt, Flint CH6 6BT Tel: 01352 761907 Fax: 01352 730265 — MB BS 1974 Delhi.

KAPOOR, Kavita 10 Quantock Court, Greenford Rd, Greenford UB6 0DR — MB BS 1996 Lond.

KAPOOR, Kulbhushan Rai Deneside Medical Centre, The Avenue, Deneside, Seaham SR7 8LF Tel: 0191 513 0884 Fax: 0191 581 1855 — MB BS 1964 Agra. (Agra) GP Seaham, Co. Durh.

KAPOOR, Mr Praveshkumar Desraj 1 Delfhaven Court, Standish, Wigan WN6 0EZ — MB BS Bombay 1973; FRCS Ed. 1987.

KAPOOR, Prem Datt 147 Hornchurch Road, Hornchurch RM12 4SZ Tel: 0140 24 42626; 36 Nelmes Way, Hornchurch RM11 2QZ Tel: 0140 24 40225 — MB BS 1950 Patna. (P. of Wales Med. Coll. Patna) Socs: BMA; Indep. Med. Assn. U.K. (Mem. Exec. Comm.). Prev: Clin. Asst. (Ophth.) W. Hill Hosp. Dartford; Ho. Surg. P. of Wales Med. Coll. Hosp. Patna; SHO Manch. Roy. Eye Hosp.

KAPOOR, Raju National Hospital for Neurology & Neurosurgery, Queen Square, London WC1N 3BG Tel: 020 7837 3611 — BM BCh 1981 Oxf.; DM 1990 Oxf.; MA Oxf.; MRCP (UK) 1984; FRCP 1998. Cons. Neurol. Nat. Hosp. for Neurol. & Neurosurg. & N. W. Lond. Hosps. NHS Trust; Honarary Sen. Lect., Inst. of Neurol.; Hon. Sen. Lect., GKT Sch. of Med. Prev: Sen. Regist. & Scarfe Lect. Inst. Neurol. & Middlx. Univ. Coll. Hosps. Lond.; ICI Jun. Research Fell. Pembroke Coll. Oxf.

KAPOOR, Ram Gopal North Park Health Centre, 290 Knowsley Road, Bootle L20 5DQ Tel: 0151 922 3841 Fax: 0151 933 7335; Shangri-La, Burbo-Bank Road, Blundellsands, Liverpool L23 6TQ Tel: 0151 931 1549 Fax: 0151 933 7335 — MB BS 1963 Panjab; MB BS Panjab (India) 1963; DTM & H Liverp. 1968. (Christian Med. Coll. Ludhiana)

KAPOOR, Ranjana Grange Park Medical Centre, 24 Grange Park Road, Leyton, London E10 5EP Tel: 020 8539 2962 Fax: 020 8539 7940; 36 The Drive, South Woodford, London E18 2BL — MB BS 1969 Indore; MS (Obst. & Gyn.) Indore 1977. Prev: Clin. Asst. (Psychiat.) Goodmayes Hosp. Ilford; Resid. SHO (Psychiat.) Jersey Gp. Hosps.

KAPOOR, Satish Chander Department of Anaesthesia, Oldchurch Hospital, Romford RM7 0BE Tel: 01708 46090; 118 Shenfield Place, Shenfield, Brentwood CM15 9AG Tel: 01277 219524 — MB BS 1971 Jammu & Kashmir; DA Eng. 1978; FFA RCS Eng. 1981. (Med. Coll. Srinagar) Cons. Anaesth. OldCh. Hosp. & Rushgreen Hosp. Romford. Prev: Sen. Regist. (Anaesth.) Nat. Hosp. Nerv. Dis. & Univ. Coll. Hosp. Lond.; Regist. (Anaesth.) N.wick Pk. Hosp. Harrow; Sen. Med. Off. (Anaesth.) Grantham Hosp. Aberd.

KAPOOR, Seema 99 Tewkesbury Road, Longford, Gloucester GL2 9BG — MB ChB 1995 Bristol.

KAPOOR, Vikas Shangri-La, Burbo Bank Road, Liverpool L23 6TQ — MB ChB 1990 Liverp.

***KAPOOR, Vikas** 54 Chairborough Road, High Wycombe HP12 3HJ — MB ChB 1998 Birm.

KAPP, Elinor Margaret (retired) 46 Cathedral Road, Cardiff CF11 9LL Tel: 01222 397850 — MB BS Lond. 1963; FRCPsych 1992, M 1972; DPM Eng. 1970. Prev: Cons. Child & Adolesc. Psychiat. Gwent Community Trusts & Dir. of Serv.

KAPRE, Mr Madan Laxmanrao c/o Drive Sudhir Marathe, 152 Holyoake Road, Wollaston, Wellingborough NN9 7RZ — MB BS 1974 Nagpur; FRCS Ed. 1981; DLO Eng. 1977. (Govt. Med. Coll. Nagpur) Cons. ENT Surg. NEETI Clinics, Nagpur, India; Hon. Surg. RST Cancer Research Centre, Nagpur, India. Prev: Overseas Sen. (ENT) Regist. Trent RHA; SHO Dept. ENT Roy. Hosp. Wolverhampton.

KAPRIELIAN, Raffi Robert Royal Brompton Hospital, Sydney St., London SW3 6NP Tel: 020 7352 8121 Fax: 020 7351 8476 Email: r.kaprielian@ic.ac.uk; 72 Hatfield Road, London W4 1AF — MB BS 1989 Lond.; BA (Hons.) Oxf. 1986; MRCP (UK) 1992. (Guy's Hosp. (United Med. Dent. Schs.)) Specialist Regist. (Cardiol.) Roy. Brompton Hosp. Lond. Prev: Brit. Heart Foundat. Research Fell. (Cardiol.) Roy. Brompton Hosp. Lond.; Regist. (Cardiol.) Hammersmith Hosp. Lond.

KAPSE, Anamika Anil 30 Melrose Gardens, Edgware HA8 5LN — MB BS 1997 Lond.

KAPSE, Nikhil Anil 30 Melrose Gardens, Edgware HA8 5LN — BM BCh 1997 Oxf.

KAPUR, Ajit Kumar Sandy Health Centre Medical Practice, Northcroft, Sandy SG19 1JQ Tel: 01767 682525 Fax: 01767 681600; Church Farm, Church Road, Sutton, Sandy SG19 2ND Tel: 01767 260126 Fax: 01767 260126 Email: ajit@kapur.demon.co.uk — MB BChir 1978 Camb.; MA (Hons.) Camb. 1978; MRCGP 1982; DRCOG 1981. (Jesus Coll. Camb.) Gen. Med. Practitioner; Dep. Police Surg. Beds.; Trainer (Gen. Pract.) Beds.; Facilitator BAEG; Mem. Beds. LMC; Mem. Ethics Comm.; Mem. Anglia & Oxf. Gen. Pract. Educat. Comm.; Chairm. N. Beds. Protocol/Guidelines Gp.

KAPUR, Akhil 387 St John's Steet, London EC1V 4LD; Dept. of Cardiology, 2nd Floof B block, Hammersmith Hospital, London W12 0HS Tel: 01737 789139 Email: simonstern10@hotmail.com — MB ChB 1990 Sheff.; BMedSci Sheff. 1988; MRCP (UK) 1994. Specialist Regist. (Cardio), Hammersmith Hosp., Lond. Prev: Research Regist. (Cardiol.) Roy. Brompton Hosp. Lond.; Regist. (Cardiol.) Glenfield Hosp. Leicester; SHO Qu. Med. Centre Nottm.

KAPUR, Birbal The Health Centre, Braithwell Road, Maltby, Rotherham S66 8JE Tel: 01709 812615; 9 Hill Top Close, Maltby, Rotherham S66 8QF Tel: 01709 813208 — MB BS 1960 Punjab. (Med. Coll. Amritsar)

KAPUR, Mr Davinder Kumar Oriel Surgery, 31 Oriel Road, Antrim BT41 4HR Tel: 028 9446 4936 Fax: 028 9446 1316; 10 Rathblane, Antrim BT41 1JT Tel: 0184 94 63032 — MB BCh BAO 1968 Belf.; FRCS Ed. 1976; MRCGP 1985.

KAPUR, Hira Lal Heysgan Health Centre, Middleton Way, Heysham, Morecambe LA3 2LL Tel: 01524 853851 Fax: 01524 855688; 25 Middleton Road, Heysham, Morecambe LA3 2QE Tel: 01524 852071 Fax: 01524 855388 — MB BS 1968 Rajasthan. (S.M.S Med. Coll.) Med. Off. Family Plann. Clinic Qu. Vict. Hosp. Morecambe; Med. Off. Marine Med. Servs. (NW) Ltd. Prev: SHO (O & G) & Ho. Off. (Med.) Sharoe Green Hosp. Preston.

KAPUR, Jagjit Kumar Werneth Hall Road Surgery, 94 Werneth Hall Road, Oldham OL8 4BD Tel: 0161 624 9856 Fax: 0161 633 4663; 32 Oulder Hill Drive, Rochdale OL11 5LB Tel: 01706 50016 — MB ChB 1980 Sheff.; DRCOG 1983. GP Oldham.

KAPUR, Kapil Chandnarain 16 High Bank Way, Leeds LS15 9HA — MB BS 1988 Bombay; MRCP Lond. 1992.

KAPUR, Mr Karam Vir The Surgery, 83 Clifden Road, Clapton, London E5 0LJ Tel: 020 8985 4554 Fax: 020 8986 0667; 10 The Drive, South Woodford, London E18 2BL Tel: 020 8985 4554 — MB BS 1962 Panjab; MB BS Panjab (India) 1962; FRCS Ed. 1968; FRCS Eng. 1967. (Med. Coll. Amritsar) Clin. Med. Off. City & E. Lond. AHA (T). Socs: BMA. Prev: Resid. Surg. Off. Brompton Hosp. Lond.; Regist. Broomfield Hosp. Chelmsford & Hackney Hosp. Lond.

KAPUR, Karan 18 Portrush Road, Coleraine BT52 1RD — MB BCh BAO 1977 Belf.

KAPUR, Natasha Middlesex Hospital, Mortimer St., London W1T 3AA Tel: 020 7836 8333; 37A Arkwright Road, Hampstead, London NW3 6BJ Tel: 020 7431 7889 — MB BS 1992 Lond.; BSc Lond. 1989; MRCP 1997. (Charing Cross & Westminster Medical School, University Lond.) SHO Dermat. Roy. Free Hosp. Lond. NHS; SHO (Dermat.) St John's Inst. of Dermat. St Thomas' Hosp.; SHO (Cardiol.) Roy. Brompton Hosp. Lond.; Specialist Regist. (N. Thames) Middlx./UCH Hammersmith/Ealing. Socs: Brit. Assn. Dermatol.; Roy. Soc. Med. Prev: SHO Med. St. Marys Hosp. Praest. Lond.; SHO (A & E) W. Middlx. Univ. Hosp.; Ho. Surg. Hemel Hempstead Gen. Hosp.

KAPUR, Navneet 20 Gladstone Avenue, London E12 6NS — MB ChB 1992 Leeds; MMedSc Leeds 1997; MRCPsych Lond. 1996. Lect. (Psychiat.) Univ. of Manch.

KAPUR, Pierina 212 Rosemary Hill Road, Sutton Coldfield B74 4HS — MB BS 1991 Lond.

KAPUR, Pran Kishan 319 Westdale Lane, Mapperley, Nottingham NG3 6EW Tel: 0115 962 5211 — MB BS 1945 Punjab; BSc Punjab 1940, MB BS 1945; DTD Delhi 1952. (King Edwd. Med. Coll.) Prev: Regist. Gen. Med. Roy. Infirm. Huddersfield.

KAPUR, Rajan Kishan 3 Leicester Close, Kettering NN16 8EZ — MB ChB 1989 Leic.

KAPUR, Ran Vir 47 Englestede Close, Birmingham B20 1BJ — MB BS 1965 Punjabi.

KAPUR, Rohen Neer Cottage, 9 Hilltop Close, Maltby, Rotherham S66 8QF — MB ChB 1994 Dundee.

KAPUR, Sandeep Kumar 54 Elmbourne Drive, Belvedere DA17 6JF — MB BS 1996 Lond.; BSc (Hons.) Lond. 1993. Ho. Off. (Gen. Med.) Kingston Hosp. Kingston u. Thames; Ho. Off. (Urol.) Guy's Hosp. Lond.

KAPUR, Mr Satya Bhushan 23 Farnham Close, Whetstone, London N20 9PU — MB BS Punjab 1946; FRCS Eng. 1959; FRCS Ed. 1956; FCOphth 1989; DO RCS Eng. 1952. (Rangoon & King Edwd. Med. Coll. Lahore) Ophth. Med. Pract. Lond., Middlx. & Herts. Socs: Fell. Roy. Soc. Med.; BMA; (Counc.) Med. Eye Centres Assn. Prev: Cons. Ophth. Surg. W & S Middlx. Hosps. Isleworth, St. Albans City Hosp. & Qu. Eliz. II Hosp.; Research Regist. & Sen. Res. Off. Moorfields Eye Hosp. Lond.; Regist. (Ophth.) Guy's Hosp. Lond.

KAPUR, Satya Ketu 12 Dorchester Close, Berry Hill, Mansfield NG18 4QW Tel: 01623 649523 — MB BS 1954 Nagpur; DTM & H Liverp. 1958. (Nagpur Med. Coll.) Med. Assessor for Long-Term Disabil. Incapacity Benefit for DHSS. Socs: Mansfield Med. Soc.; Small Pract.s Assn. Prev: GP Mansfield (Retd.); Regist. (Chest Dis. & Cardiol.) Papworth Hosp. Camb.; Regist. (Gen. Med.) Larkfield Hosp. Greenvoe.

KAPUR, Sudarshan (Surgery), 244 Barking Road, East Ham, London E6 3BB Tel: 020 8552 2959; 10 The Drive, South Woodford, London E18 2BL Tel: 020 8530 4644 — MB BS 1962 Punjab; MB BS Punjab (India) 1962; MRCOG 1970, DObst 1969. (Christian Med. Coll. Ludhiana) Clin. Med. Off. Barking & Havering AHA. Socs: Indian Med. Assn. Prev: Ho. Surg. City Lond. Matern. Hosp., Bristol Matern. Hosp. & Harefield; Hosp.

KAPUR, Mr Tilak Raj (retired) 21 Sutherland Drive, Westlands, Newcastle ST5 3ND Tel: 01782 618 — MB BS 1953 Osmania; FRCS Eng. 1958; DLO Eng. 1966. Cons. ENT Surg. in Private Pract. Prev: Cons. ENT Surg. N. Staffs. Roy. Infirm. Stoke-on-Trent.

KAPUR, Yogeshwar Parshad Pennant Surgery, County Offices, Coleshill St., Holywell CH8 7TR Tel: 01352 716766 Fax: 01352 716859; Meadow House, Wrexham Road, Chester CH4 7QQ Tel: 01244 671572 — MB BS 1975 Delhi; MS Delhi 1997. (Maulana Azad Medical College) Gen. Med. Pract. Socs: Diplomate Family Plann.

KAPWEPWE, Sampa 258 Hewitt Avenue, Coventry CV6 1NP Tel: 024 76 601208 — LRCPI & LM, LRSCI & LM 1976; LRCPI & LM, LRCSI & LM 1976; Dip. GU Med. Soc. Apoth. Lond. 1988. Clin. Med. Off. (Pub. Health) City & Hackney HA. Socs: BMA & MFFP. Prev: Regist. (Gernito-urin. Med.) Coventry; SHO (Geriat. Med.) St. Albans.

KAR, Mr Asit Kumar Scunthorpe General Hospital, Cliff Gardens, Scunthorpe DN15 7BH Tel: 01724 282282; BF-166, Sector 1, Calcutta 700064, India Tel: 333 376417 — MB BS 1968 Calcutta; FRCS Ed. 1976; FRCS Glas. 1976; FRCS Eng. 1974. Cons. Surg. Scunthorpe Gen. Hosp. Socs: Fell. Internat. Biograpic Assn. Camb.; Vasc. Soc. GB & Irel. & Assn. Endoscopic Surg. of Gt. Brit. & Irel. (AESGBI); Eur. Vasc. Soc. Prev: Resid. Surg. Off. Bolton Dist. Gen. Hosp.; Regist. (Surg.) P'boro Dist. Gen. Hosp.; Cons. Surg. & Asst. Chief Med. Off. Mufulira div ZCCM Ltd., Zambia.

KAR, Girish Shamkant 38B Charteris Road, London N4 3AB Tel: 020 7263 1553; 3 Mannamead, Epsom KT18 6HU — MB BS 1991 Lond.; BSc Lond. 1990, MB BS 1991. SHO (ITU) Nat. Hosp. Neurol. & Neurosurg. Lond. Prev: SHO (Anaesth.) Worthing Gen. Hosp. & UCLH Lond.; Ho. Phys. King Edwd. VII Hosp. Midhurst W. Sussex; Ho. Surg. Colchester Gen. Hosp.

KAR, Shamkant Vinayak (retired) Health Centre, Robin Hood Lane, Sutton SM1 2RJ Tel: 020 8642 3848 Fax: 020 8286 1010 — MB BS 1958 Poona; DLO Eng. 1969. Prev: Ho. Surg. (Gen. Surg. & ENT) Sassoon Hosps. Poona, India.

KAR, Sharmila Shamkant 24 Shirley Avenue, Cheam, Sutton SM2 7QR; 29 Garibaldi Road, Redhill RH1 6PB — MB BS 1993 Lond.; FRCOPhth 1998. (Charing Cross & Westminister) GP Regist., Tadworth Surrey. Prev: SHO Ophth.

KAR, Shyam Chandra (retired) Flat 3, Grace Court, 12 Hampton Road, Twickenham TW2 5QD Tel: 020 8898 7297 — MB BS Calcutta 1956.

KAR-PURKAYASTHA, Sujit Kar Bassetlan General Hospital, Kilton Hill, Worksop S81 0BD Tel: 01909 500990; 39 Torrington Road, Greenford UB6 7EP — MB BS 1985 Dibrugarh, India; MRCP (UK) 1985; FRCP Glas. 1998. Cons. Phys. Bassatlan Gen. Hosp. Notts. Socs: BMA; Brit. Soc. Of Gastro.; Indian Soc. Gastroenterol.

KARABATSAS, Konstadinos University of Bristol, Department of Ophthalmology, Bristol Eye Hospital, Bristol BS1 2LX Tel: 0117 928 4827 Fax: 0117 925 1421 Email: costas.h.karab@bristol.ac.uk; A Papagou 1, Larissa GR 41222, Greece Tel: 00 30 041 623685 — Ptychio Iatrikes 1987 Thessalonika; MRCOphth 1994; Europ. Bd. Ophth. Dip. 1996; MD Bristol 1997. (Univ. Aristotlean Thessaloniki, Greece) Lect. (Ophth.) Univ. Bristol Eye Hosp. Socs: Internat. Soc. Refractive Surg.; UK & Irel. Soc. Cataract & Refractive Surg.; Panhellenic Ophth. Soc. Prev: Corneal Fell. & Hon. Regist. Univ. Bristol; SHO (Ophth.) Bristol Eye Hosp. & OldCh. Hosp. Romford; SHO (Neurosurg.) Walsgrave Hosp. Coventry.

KARADIA, Sundeep (retired) 84 Whaddon Road, Cheltenham GL52 5NF Tel: 01242 242881 — MB BS 1990 Lond.; BSc (Hons.) Lond. 1987; FRCA 1995; DCH RCP Lond. 1995. Regist. (Anaesth.) Soton Gen. Hosp.; Regist. (Anaesth.) N. Hants. Hosp. Prev: SHO (Paediat.) Glos. Roy. Hosp.

KARAGEVREKIS, Charalampos 72 Bilbury Close, Redditch B97 5XW — Ptychio Iatrikes 1988 Thessalonika.

KARAGOUNIS, Apostolos Norwood Cottage, Tentelow Lane, Norwood Green, Southall UB2 4LG Tel: 020 8893 5047 — Ptychio Iatrikes Athens 1987; FRCS Glas. 1995; MPhil Keele 1996. (Athens Medical School Greece) Sen. Regist. Cardiothoracic Surg. Mater Misericordiac Hosp. Dub., Irel.

KARAJEH, Mohammed Abdel-Rahim 20 Bolton Avenue, Manchester M19 1RP — MB ChB 1993 Dundee.

KARAKUSEVIC, Caroline Anne Channel View Surgery, Seacroft Court, 3 Courtenay Place, Teignmouth TQ14 8AY Tel: 01626 774656 Fax: 01626 779266 — MB BS 1988 Lond.; MRCGP 1992; T(GP) 1992; DRCOG 1991. (Guy's Hosp. Lond.)

KARALLIEDDE, Janaka Lakshman 58 Alleyn Park, London SE21 8SF — MB BS 1998 Lond.; MB BS Lond 1998.

KARALLIEDDE, Lakshman Delgoda Department of Anaesthetics, UMDS, Guys Hospital, London SE1 9RT Tel: 020 7955 4047; 58 Alleyn Park, London SE21 8SF — MB BS 1965 Ceylon; FFA RCS Eng. 1971; DA (UK) 1970. Sen. Lect. & Hon. Cons. United Med. Sch. Guys & St. Thos. Lond. Socs: Fell. Roy. Coll. Anaesth.; Roy. Soc. Med.; Assn. Anaesth. UK. Prev: Head Dept. of Anaesthesiol. Fac. Med. Peradeniya, Sri Lanka; Cons. Anaesth. Qu. Eliz. Milit. Hosp. Lond.

KARALLIEDDE, Srikanthi Community Health South London NHS Trust, Elizabeth Blackwell House, Avonley Road, London SE14 5ER; 58 Alleyn Park, London SE21 8SF Tel: 020 8670 1517 Fax: 020 8766 7317 Email: dkarallied@aol.com — MB BS 1970 Ceylon; MD Sri Lanka 1981; MSc (Community Paed.) Lond. 1996. (University of Faculty of Medicine, Peradeniya, Sri Lanka) Cons. Comm. Paediat. Comm. Health S. Lond. NHS Trust. Socs: MRCPCH; Brit. Assn. Study & Preven. Child Abuse & Neglect; BMA.

KARAM, Khalid (retired) Hillsgarth, Baltasound, Unst, Shetland ZE2 9DY Tel: 01957 711550 — MB BCh 1965 Wales; Cert. Prescribed Equiv. Exp. JCPTGP 1981. Prev: GP Shetland HB.

KARAMADOUKIS, Lazarus 27 Waterman Way, London E1W 2QN — MB BS 1998 Lond.; MB BS Lond 1998.

KARAMDAD, D R The Surgery, 5-7 Little Oaks Road, Aston, Birmingham B6 6JY Tel: 0121 328 1977 Fax: 0121 327 3755 — MB BS 1968 Rajshahi; MB BS 1968 Rajahahi; LMSSA 1980 London.

KARAMÉ, Muhieddine Marwan Abdallah The Surgery, Brook End, Potton, Sandy SG19 2QS — MB BS 1965 Lond.

KARAMICHALIS, Ioannis Michael Magdalen College, Oxford OX1 4AU — BM BCh 1993 Oxf.

KARAMURA, Lydia Nyanzi Lancaster Acute Hospitals NHS Trust, Royal Lancaster Infirmary, Ashton Road, Lancaster LA1 4RP — LMSSA 1997; LMSSA Lond. LRCS Eng 1997.

KARANDIKAR, Nikitin 49 Ambleside Avenue, South Shields NE34 0DY — MB ChB 1987 Leeds.

KARANDIKAR, Ram Vishnu New Street Surgery, New Street, Hill Top, West Bromwich B70 0HN Tel: 0121 556 0190 Fax: 0121 505 3705 — MB BS 1973 Bombay.

KARANI, John Barr 47 Hayes Lane, Kenley, Purley CR8 5LF — MRCS Eng. LRCP Lond. 1976; BSc Lond. 1973, MB BS 1977; FRCR 1983. (Guy's) Cons. Radiol. Kings Coll. Hosp. Lond.

KARANJAVALA, Mr Jehangir Dara Royal United Hospital, Dept. of Urology, Combe Park, Bath BA1 3NG Tel: 01225 824575 Fax: 01225 824192; Falt 2 Parkfield, Park Gardens, Bath BA1 2XP Tel: 01225 422985 — MB BS 1984 Bombay; FRCS Glas. 1992; MS Bromley 1989. Staff Grade Urol., Roy. United Hosp., Bath. Socs: Assoc. Mem. BAUS; BMA; RSM.

KARANJIA, Caroline Rosemary Dapdune House Surgery, Wharf Road, Guildford GU1 4RP Tel: 01483 573336 Fax: 01483 306602; Croft House, 226 Epsom Road, Guildford GU4 7AA Tel: 01483 533767 Email: rustdel@aol.com — MB BS 1983 Lond.; MRCGP 1987; DCH RCP Lond. 1987; DRCOG 1986. (Guy's) Partner GP Dapdune Ho., Guildford; GP Trainer. Prev: Clin. Asst. (Genitourin. Med.) Farnham Rd. Hosp. Guildford; Trainee GP. Haselmere; Trainee GP/SHO St. Richards Hosp. Chichester VTS.

KARANJIA, Mr Nariman Dady Royal Surrey County Hospital, Guildford GU2 7XX Tel: 01483 571122 Ext: 4552 Fax: 01483 575029 Email: nkaranjia@liver.co.uk; Croft House, 226 Epsom Road, Guildford GU4 7AA Tel: 01483 575029 Fax: 01483 569936 — MB BS 1983 Lond.; MS Lond. 1990; FRCS (Gen.) 1994; FRCS Eng. 1987; FRCS Ed. 1987. (Guy's) Cons. Surg. (Gastrointestinal Surg.) Roy. Surrey Co. Hosp. Guildford. Socs: Roy. Soc. Med. (Surg. & Coloproctol. Sect.); Brit. Soc. Gastroenterol.; Brit. Pancreatic Soc. Prev: Sen. Regist. Rotat. (Gen. Surg.) SW Thames; Research Fell. Univ. Calif., Los Angeles & St. Geo. Hosp. Lond.; Regist. (Gen. Surg.) Basingstoke Dist. Hosp.

KARANOUH, Dia Darwiche Appt. 12A, 85 New Cavenish St., London W1M 7RA — MB BS 1991 Lond.

KARAT, Mr Dayalan 37 Woodbine Road, Newcastle upon Tyne NE3 1DD — MB BS 1987 Newc.; FRCS Ed. 1992.

KARAT, Mrs Sakuntala (retired) 11 Sherwater, Whitburn, Sunderland SR6 7SF Tel: 0191 529 3177 — MB BS 1957 Madras; MChOrth Liverp. 1974; FRCS Ed. 1964; FACS 1973. Prev: Cons. Orthop. Surg. S. Tyneside Dist. Hosp.

KARCHER, Anne Marie Department of Microbiology, Homerton Hospital, London E9 6SR Tel: 020 8510 7180 Fax: 020 8510 7183 — MB ChB 1987 Glas.; MRC Path 2000. (Univ. Glas.) p/t Cons. Microbiologist, MicroBiol., Homerton Hosp., Lond.

***KARDER, Marden Ahmed** 17 Jim Bradley Close, London SE18 6QA — LMSSA 1995 Lond.

KARET, Brian John Leylands Medical Centre, 81 Leylands Lane, Bradford BD9 5PZ Tel: 01274 770771 Fax: 01274 771088; 15 The Grove, Shipley BD18 4LD Tel: 587060 Email: brian@legend.co.uk — MB ChB 1975 Leeds; MRCP (UK) 1981; MRCGP 1982; DRCOG 1981. (Leeds) Prev: Regist. (Haemat.) Leeds AHA; SHO (Gen. Med.) N. Manch. Gen. Hosp.; SHO (Paediat.) Duchess of York Hosp. Manch.

KARET, Fiona Eve Cambridge Institute For Medical Research, Addenbrookes Hospital, Cambridge CB2 2XY Tel: 01223 762 617 Fax: 01223 331 206 Email: fek1000@cam.ac.uk — MB BS 1986 Lond.; FRCP 2001; PhD Camb. 1995; BSc (Hons.) Lond. 1983; MRCP (UK) 1989. (Univ. Coll. Lond. Med. Sch.)

KARI, Jameela Abdul Aziz 5 Salcombe Park, Loughton IG10 4QT Tel: 020 8532 1039; Great Ormond Street NHS Trust ospital, Great Ormond St, London WC1N 1EH Tel: 020 7405 9200 Email: j.kari@ich.ucl.ac.uk — MB ChB 1986 King Saud U, Saudi Arabia; MB ChB King Abdulaziz University Saudi Arabia 1986; MRCP (UK) 1989. Flexible Trainee Sen. Regist. (Paediat. Nephrol. & Gen. Surg.). Socs: MRCPCH; Internat. Paediat. Nephrol. Assn. Prev: Flexible Trainee Sen. Regist. Roy. Free Hosp. Lond.; Regist. Roy. Free Hosp. Lond.

KARIA, Arvindchandra Velji Water Eaton Health Centre, Fern Grove, Bletchley, Milton Keynes MK2 3HN Tel: 01908 371318 Fax: 01908 643843; 5 Wentworth Way, Bletchley, Milton Keynes MK3 7RW Tel: 01908 373448 Email: arvind@karia.powernet.co.uk — MB BS 1971 Baroda. (Baroda) Forens. Med. Examr. Thames Valley Police.

KARIA, Deepak Jayant Anaesthetic Department, Derby City General Hospital, Uttoxeter New Road, Derby DE22 3NE Tel: 01332 340131; 55 Cadgwith Drive, Darley Abbey, Derby DE22 2AF Tel: 01332 558279 — MB BS 1979 Bombay; DA (UK) 1987. Staff Anaesth. S.. Derby City Gen. Hosp. NHS Trust. Prev: Regist. (Anaesth.) Qu. Eliz. King's Lynn & Blackburn Roy. Infirm.; SHO (Anaesth.) Blackburn Roy. Infirm.

KARIA, Kantilal Ranchhodbhai Diagnostic Imaging, Ipswich Hospital NHS Trust, Heathroad, Ipswich IP4 5PD Tel: 01473 703363 Fax: 01473 270655; The Pines, 210 rushmere Road, Ipswich IP4 3LT — MB BCh 1973 Wales; FRCR 1980; DMRD Eng. 1978. Cons. Radiol. Ipswich hosp NHS Trust Ipswich. Prev: Sen. Regist. (Radiol.) Manch. AHA (T).

KARIA, Kaushikkumar 27 Carew Road, Northwood HA6 3NJ Tel: 019274 22302 — MB BCh BAO 1979 NUI; L LM RCP Irel. L LM RCS Irel. 1979; DRCOG 1988. Regist. (O & G) Centr. Middlx. Hosp. Lond.

KARIA, Niral 7 Welbeck Villas, Highfield Road, London N21 3HN — MB BS 1992 Lond.; BSc Lond. 1989.

KARIA, Mr Sushilkumar Jagjivandas c/o Drive J. K. Vyas, 165 Waldegrave, Vange, Basildon SS16 5EJ — MB BS 1973 Saurashtra; MS (Gen. Surg.) Saurashtra 1976, MB BS 1973; FRCS Ed. 1980; FRCS Eng. 1980; FRCS Glas. 1980. (M.P. Sha Med. Coll., Jamnagar) SHO (Urol.) S.mead Gen. Hosp. Bristol; Regist. (Surg.) & Tutor (Surg.) M.P. Sham Med. Coll. Jamnagar India.

KARIA, Upma 47 Harrow Road, Wembley HA9 6DG — MB ChB 1993 Leic. (Leicester)

KARIM, Abdul Sattar Abdul (retired) Cobblestones, Widworthy Hayes, Hutton Mount, Brentwood CM13 2LN — MB ChB 1958 Baghdad; FRCR 1979; DMRD Eng. Lond. 1963. Prev: Cons. Radiol. NE Thames RHA.

KARIM, Abul Hazeque Mohammad Husnul Tilehurst Surgery, Tylers Place, Pottery Road, Tilehurst, Reading RG30 6BW Tel: 0118 942 7528 Fax: 0118 945 2405; Thornton, 117 Cockney Hill, Reading RG30 4EY Tel: 01734 599357 — MB BS 1967 Dacca; MRCP (UK) 1975; DCH Eng. 1971; DCTD Dacca 1969. (Dacca Med. Coll.) Prev: Ho. Phys. (Paediat.) Morriston Hosp.; Regist. (Med.) Singleton Hosp. Swansea & St. And. Hosp. Bow.

KARIM, Amin 56 Grove Way, Esher KT10 8HN — MB BS 1996 Lond.

KARIM, Amina Ladygate Lane Surgery, 22 Ladygate Lane, Ruislip HA4 7QU Tel: 01895 632741 Fax: 01895 637343 — MB BS 1964 Osmania.

KARIM, Amynah 34D Colney Hatch Lane, London N10 1DU — MB BS 1992 Lond.

KARIM, Hajera 20 Warrenside Close, Wilpshire, Blackburn BB1 9PF Tel: 01254 246235 — LRCP 1989 Ed.; MB BS Dacca 1982; LRCP Ed. LRCS Ed. LRCPS Glas. 1989. Prev: Ho. Off. (Gen. Surg.) Burnley Gen. Hosp.

KARIM, Jahrun 13 Glasshouse Fields, London E1W 3HY — LRCP LRCS Ed. LRCPS Glas. 1997.

KARIM, Khalid Abdul 56 Lytton Road, Leicester LE2 1WJ — MB ChB 1994 Leic.; BSc (Hons.) Leic. 1992. SHO (Paediat.) Leicester Roy. Infirm.

KARIM, Mahzuz 144 Edwin Road, Gillingham ME8 0AG Tel: 01634 374473 — MB BChir 1993 Camb.; MA BM (Oxford) 2000; MA 1994, BA Camb. 1990; MRCP (UK) 1996. (Univ. Camb.) Regist. (Nephrol. & Gen. Med.) Ch.ill & John Radcliffe Hosps. Oxf.; Research Fell., Nuffield Dept. of Surg., Univ. of Oxf. Socs: Renal Assn.; Brit. Transpl.ation Soc.; Brit. Soc. for Immunol. Prev: Specialist Regist. (Nephrol. & Gen. Med.) Roy. Berks. Hosp., Reading; SHO (Cardiol.) Papworth Hosp. Camb.; SHO (Nephrol., Oncol. & Radiother.) Addenbrooke's Hosp. Camb.

KARIM, Mohamed Rezaul Brookhouse Medical Centre, Blackburn BB1 6EA Tel: 01254 677944 — LAH Dub. 1971. GP Blackburn.

KARIM, Mohammad Bazlay Mabarak Health Centre, 8-12 Cannon Hill Road, Balsall Heath, Birmingham B12 9NN Tel: 0121 440 4666 Fax: 0121 446 5986 — MB BS 1956 Karachi. (Dow Med. Coll.)

KARIM, Mr Mohammad Mahbubul King George Road Surgery, 52A King George Road, Walderslade, Chatham ME5 0TU Tel:

01634 863305 Fax: 01634 671194 — MB BS 1962 Dacca; FRCS Eng. 1969; FRCS Ed. 1968. (Dacca Med. Coll.) Socs: BMA. Prev: Regist. (Surg.) Medway & Gravesend Gp. Hosps.; SHO Radcliffe Infirm. Oxf.; Ho. Surg. Ch.ill Hosp. Oxf.

KARIM, Mr Mohammad Sarkawt Sheffield Kidney Institute, Northern General Hospital, Sheffield S5 7AU Tel: 0114 243 4343; 40 Glebe Street, London W4 2BG — MB ChB 1967 Baghdad; FRCS Eng. 1976; MRCS Eng. LRCP Lond. 1976 (Coll. Med. Baghdad). Cons. Surg. N. Gen. Hosp. Sheff. Socs: BMA. Prev: Regist. (Surg.) Hammersmith Hosp. Lond.

KARIM, Mr Mohammed Rezaul 1 Sherwood Avenue, London E18 1PB — MB BS 1964 Dacca; FRCS Glas. 1980. (Dacca Med. Coll.) Sen. Regist. (Gen. Surg.) BRd.green & Roy. Liverp. Hosps. Liverp. Socs: Fell. Roy. Soc. Health. Prev: Regist. (Gen. Surg.) P. Chas. Hosp. Merthyr Tydfil & Pontypool & Dist.; Hosp.; Regist. (Cardiovasc. Surg.) Glas. Roy. Infirm.

KARIM, Mohammed Yousuf 14 Arden Mhor, Pinner HA5 2HR Email: ykarim89@hotmail.com — MB BChir 1993 Camb.; MA Camb. 1994; MRCP (UK) 1996; MSc 1998. (University of Cambridge, Guys' and St. Thomas' Hospitals) Clin. Lect./Hon. specialist Regist. (Immunol.), Guy's & St. Thomas' Hosps. Socs: Roy. Coll. Phys. Prev: Regist. (Renology) Char. Cross Hosp.

KARIM, Naila Woodside, 144 Edwin Road, Rainham, Gillingham ME8 0AG — MB BS 1987 Lond.; MRCGP 1992; DRCOG 1991. (Lond. Hosp. Med. Coll.) Staff Grade Phys. (Palliat. Med.) St. Francis Hospice. Prev: SHO (Palliat. Med.) St. Francis Hospice.

KARIM, Navin Richmond Medical Centre, Brown Street, Accrington BB5 0RS Tel: 01254 232832 Fax: 01254 393325 — MB BS 1969 Vikram; MB BS 1969 Vikram.

KARIM, Niaz Bin Friends Road Surgery, 49 Friends Road, Croydon CR0 1ED Tel: 020 8688 0532 Fax: 020 8688 2165 — MB BS 1983 Lond.

KARIM, Quazi Najma 1 Birkdale Road, Ealing, London W5 1JZ Tel: 020 7886 1074 Email: q.karim@ic.ac.uk; Department of Microbiology, St. Mary's Hospital (Campus) of Imperial College School of, Medicine, Science & Technology, London W2 1PG Tel: 020 7886 1074 — MB BS Dacca 1969; FRCPath 1989, M 1977. Sen. Lect. (Med. Microbiol.) & Hon. Cons. St. Mary's Hosp. Lond. Socs: Hosp. Infec. Soc. & Brit. Soc. Study Infec.; Pathol.Soc. Prev: Sen. Regist. & Regist. Liverp. Roy. Infirm.; Lect. Garyounis Univ. Benghazi Libya.

KARIM, Raja Safiy Limetree Surgery, 1 Limetree Avenue, Cinderhill, Nottingham NG8 6AB Tel: 0115 979 1281 Fax: 0115 979 2864 — MB ChB 1981 Manch.; MBA Keele 1993; MRCGP 1985. (Manch.) CME Course Organiser Nottm. Socs: Nottm. M-C Soc. Prev: GP Nottm.; Adjudicating Examr. Med. Bds. DHSS; Med. Adviser Trent RHA.

KARIM, Rubina Limetree Surgery, 1 Limetree Avenue, Cinderhill, Nottingham NG8 6AB Tel: 0115 979 1281 Fax: 0115 979 2864 — BM BS 1981 Nottm.; BMedSci (Hons.) Nottm. 1979. Socs: M-C Soc. Prev: Ho. Off. (Med.) City Hosp. Nottm.; Ho. Off. (Surg.) Hallamsh. Hosp. Sheff.; Trainee GP Nottm. VTS.

KARIM, Shaikh Serajul 9 Wyndham Road, New Waltham, Grimsby DN36 4WA — MB BS 1964 Dacca. (Dacca) Socs: BMA; Assoc. RCGP. Prev: SHO Roy. Hosp. Richmond; Regist. Tooting Bec Hosp. Lond.

KARIM, Shakir Zamil Forth Park Hospital, 30 Bennochy Road, Kirkcaldy KY2 5RA; 4 Wedderburn Road, Newliston, Kirkcaldy KY2 6UY — MB ChB 1975 Baghdad; FRCPath 1996, M 1986; DRCPath 1995. Cons. Path. Kirkcaldy Acute Hosp. Socs: Assn. Clin. Path.; FIAC 1994; Internat. Acad. Cytol.

KARIM, Syed Inamul Richmond Medical Centre, Brown Street, Accrington BB5 0RS Tel: 01254 232832 Fax: 01254 393325 — MB BS 1967 Vikram; MB BS 1967 Vikram.

KARIM, Syed Irfan-Ul Richmond Medical Centre, Brown Street, Accrington BB5 0RS Tel: 01254 232832 Fax: 01254 393325 — MB BS 1964 Vikram; MB BS 1964 Vikram.

KARIM, Tarannum Tan Hey, Tan House La, Great Harwood, Blackburn BB6 7UL — MB ChB 1997 Glas.

KARIM, Usame Hakki Abdul The Stables, Wilne Farm, Wilne Lane, Shardlow, Derby DE72 2HF Tel: 01332 799545 — Tip Doktoru Istanbul 1957; DLO RCS Eng. 1964. Asst. Surg. ENT Manor Hosp. Walsall. Prev: Cons. ENT Surg. Baghdad.

KARIM, Yasine The Surgery, St. Barnabas House, Duncan Road, Gillingham ME7 4LD Tel: 01634 850067 — MB BS 1965 Punjab.

KARIMJEE, Shabnam Flat 8, 24 Palace Court, London W2 4HU — MB BS 1977 Lond.; MA Oxf. 1974; MSc Lond. 1988; FRCR 1985. (St. Bart.)

KARIYAWASAM, Harsha Hemantha 150 Fleeming Road, London E17 5EU — MB BS 1994 Lond.

KARIYAWASAM, Ranasinghe Arachchige Ayomi Priyanwada Surrey & Sussex Healthcare NHS Trust, Canada Avenue, Redhill RH1 5RH Tel: 01737 768511; 64 Hartley Down, Purley CR8 4EB Tel: 020 8660 9519 — MB BS 1978 Sri Lanka; MSc (Community Paediat.) Lond. 1993; MRCP (UK) 1986. Cons. Paediat. Surrey & Sussex Healthcare NHS Trust. Prev: Sen. Regist. (Paediat.) N.wick Pk. Hosp. Trust Harrow.

KARKANEVATOS, Apostolos 12 Shaw Street, Culcheth, Warrington WA3 5EX — Ptychio Iatrikes 1988 Thessalonika.

KARKEE, Mr Nrip Dhoj 62 Cranbourne Road, Portsmouth PO6 2BQ — MB BS 1973 Punjab; MB BS Punjabi 1973; FRCS Glas. 1986.

KARKERA, Mr Raviraj The Cottage, The Stores, Nomansland, Salisbury SP5 2BP; 98 The Drive, Feltham TW14 0AL Tel: 020 8890 4772 — MB ChB 1986 Manch.; FRCS Ed. 1991. Regist. (Gen. Surg.) Wessex RHA.

KARKI, Bhadra Dhoj 32 Egerton Gardens, Seven Kings, Ilford IG3 9HP — MB BS 1963 Nagpur.

KARKI, Chuda Bahadur Bridge Hospital, Hatfield Road, Witham CM8 1EQ Tel: 01376 308039 Fax: 01376 308075; 21 Sandford Mill Road, Chelmer Village, Chelmsford CM2 6NS Tel: 01245 494690 Fax: 01245 494690 Email: cbkarki@aol.com — MB BS 1973 Allahbad; MRCPsych 1984. (MLN Med. Coll. Allahabad, UP, India) Med. Dir. & Cons. Psychiat. New Possibilities NHS Trust Essex; Chair Research and Developm. Culver Lead Caldicott Guardiar. Socs: Fell.Roy. Coll. of Psychiat.s. Prev: Regist. (Psychiat.) Chiltern Wing Sutton Hosp.; Sen. Regist. Stoke Pk. Gp. Hosp. Bristol.

KARLMAN, Inger Margareta Optimum Health Services, EBH, Wardalls Grove, Avonley Road, London SE14 5ER Tel: 020 7635 5555; 17 Rances Lane, Wokingham RG40 2LG Tel: 01734 782033 — Med Lic 1972 Uppsala; MPH Philippine Union Coll. 1992. (Univ. Uppsala, Sweden) Staff Grade Pract. (Community Paediat.) Optimum Health Servs. Lewisham; Specialist (Paediat.) Stockholm 1981. Prev: Regist. (Paediat.) NDC Sweden; Lect. & Asst. Prof. Pub. Health Philippines.

KARLOWSKI, Teresa Anne St. Luke's Vicarage, 2 Birchwood Road, Parkstone, Poole BH14 9NP Tel: 01202 741030 — MB BS 1979 Lond.; FRCS Ed. 1984. (St. Thos.) Assoc. Specialist (Gen. Surg.) Poole Hosp. Trust. Prev: Sen. Regist. (Gen. Surg.) Benenden Hosp.; Regist. (Gen. Surg.) Pembury Hosp.; Regist. (Gen. & Cardiothoracic Surg.) Leic. Roy. Infirm.

KARMAKAR, Manoj Kumar Department of Anaesthesia, Alder Hey Childrens Hospital, Eaton Road, Liverpool L12 2AP — MB BS 1986 Madras; FRCA 1994.

KARMALI, Jan Waddesdon Surgery, Goss Avenue, Waddesdon, Aylesbury HP18 0LY Tel: 01296 658585 Fax: 01296 658467; 1 Popes Acre, Haddenham, Aylesbury HP17 8AQ Tel: 01844 290922 Email: jan.karmali@which.net — BM BS 1986 Nottm.; MA Oxf. 1972; BMedSci Nottm. 1984; MRCGP 1990. (Nottm.) GP Princip. Waddesdon Surg. Socs: BMA. Prev: Trainee GP Aylesbury VTS; Bd. Mem. Aylesbury PCG; Clin. Exec. Comm. Mem.,.

KARMANI, Mohammed Shuaib 2 Dafforne Road, London SW17 8TZ — MB BS 1997 Lond.

KARMI, Ghada North Thames Regional Health Authority, 40 Eastbourne Terrace, London W2 3QR; 51 Hodford Road, London NW11 8NL — MB ChB 1964 Bristol; PhD Lond. 1978; MFPHM RCP (UK) 1988; MRCP Lond. 1967. Cons. Pub. Health N. Thames RHA; Head Regional Health & Ethnicity Unit. Prev: GP Lond.; Research Fell. Hist. of Arabic Med. Wellcome Inst. for Hist. Med. Lond.; Med. Historian, Inst. Hist. Arabic Sc. Aleppo Univ. Syria.

KARN, Kaushlendra Prasad c/o Dr Ramji Gautam, 16 Alpine Way, Hambledon Hill, Sunderland SR3 1TN — MUDr 1985 Charles Univ. Prague; MUDr Charles U Prague Czechoslovakia 1986.

KARNEY, Ganga Ram 18 Llwyn-y-Broden, Parc Gwernfadog, Morriston, Swansea SA6 8TG — MB BS 1975 Osmania. (Gandhi Med. Coll.) SHO (Orthop.) Barnsley Dist. Gen. Hosp.

KARNEY, Patrick Lawrence 20 Mowbray Avenue, Byfleet, West Byfleet KT14 7PG Tel: 01932 346386 — MB BS 1938 Madras; MFCM 1973; DPH Eng. 1949. Prev: Dist. Community Phys. W. Surrey & NE Hants. Dist.; MOH Woking UD; Sen. Med. Off. Hants. CC.

KARNEY, Victoria Mary McNulty and Partners, Torkard Hill Medical Centre, Farleys Lane, Hucknall, Nottingham NG15 6DY Tel: 0115 963 3676 Fax: 0115 968 1957 Email: victoria.karney@gp-84053.uk.nhs.uk; Fax: 0115 968 1957 — MB BS 1979 Lond.; MA Camb. 1980; MRCGP 1984; MFHom 1987; DCH RCP Lond. 1983. Prev: GP Nottm. VTS; SHO Co. Hosp. Louth; SHO Ch. S. India Hosp. Chickballapur.

KARNICKI, Jadwiga (retired) 22 Dartmouth Row, London SE10 8AW Tel: 020 8692 3951 — MB ChB St. And. 1942; MB ChB Polish Sch. of Med. 1941; FRCOG 1959, M 1945. Cons. Gyn. & Obst. Lewisham Hosp.; Hon. Tutor Guy's Hosp. Med. Sch. Lond. Prev: Resid. Med. Off. Chelsea Hosp. Wom. & Qu. Charlotte's Hosp.

KARNICKI, Marta Teresa 38 Queen's Park Rise, Brighton BN2 2ZF Tel: 01273 603499 — MB BS 1975 Lond.; DRCOG 1977. Hosp. practitioner, Roy. Sussex Co. Hosp, Brighton.

KAROLYI, Barbara Maria Gabrielle (retired) 42 Drayton Gardens, London SW10 9SA Tel: 020 7373 2255 Fax: 020 7370 5297 — MB BCh BAO Dub. 1956.

KAROO, Richard Odin Subhash Rakefoot House, Burnley Rd, Rossendale BB4 8LZ — MB ChB 1997 Leic.

KARP, Kjell Helmer Department of Nuclear Medicine, Southampton General Hospital, Southampton SO16 6YD — Lakarexamen 1978 Umea.

KARP, Stephen Julian Clinical Oncology Centre, North Middlesex Hospital, Sterling Way, London N18 1QX Tel: 020 8887 2784 Fax: 020 8887 2799 Email: coin@rcr.ac.uk; 1 Hamlyn Close, Pipers Green Lane, Edgware HA8 8DB — MB BS 1979 Lond.; MB BS (Hons.) (Distinc. Surg.) Lond. 1979; BSc (1st cl. Hons.) (Pharmacol.) Lond. 1976; FRCP Lond. 1997; MRCS Eng. LRCP Lond. 1979; MRCP (UK) 1982; FRCR 1988. (King's Coll. Lond. & Westm.) Cons. Clin. Oncol. N. Middlx. Hosp. & Chase Farm Hosp. Enfield. Socs: Fell. Roy. Soc. Med. (Counc. Mem. Sect. Radiol.); BMA; ASCO. Prev: Sen. Regist. & Regist. (Radiother. & Oncol.) Middlx Hosp. Lond. & Mt. Vernon Hosp. N.wood; Regist. (Gen. Med. & Gastroenterol.) N.wick Pk. Hosp. Harrow; SHO (Neurol.) Nat. Hosp. Nerv. Dis. Qu. Sq. Lond.

KARPHA, Sanatkumar Hollies Health, Swan St., Merthyr Tydfil CF47 8ET — MB BS 1972 Calcutta.

KARRACH, Rev. Herbert Adolf (retired) Narnia, 5 Docking Road, Fring, King's Lynn PE31 6SQ Tel: 01485 518346 — MB BCh BAO 1948 Dub.; DTM & H Eng. 1955. Prev: Obst. Ho. Surg. Harrogate Gen. Hosp.

KARRAN, Mr Stephen John Level F, Centre Block, Southampton General Hospital, Tremona Road, Southampton SO16 6YD — MB BChir 1964 Camb.; MA, MB Camb. 1964, MChir 1982, BChir 1963; FRCS Eng. 1967; FRCS Ed. 1967; MRCS Eng. LRCP Lond. 1963. (Camb. & St. Mary's) Reader Surg. Univ. Soton.; Hon. Cons. Roy. S. Hants. Hosp. Soton.; Mem. Bd. Examrs. Univ. Lond., Welsh Nat. Sch. Med. & RCS Ed.; Regional Adviser Wessex Region RCS Ed.; Chairm. Subcomm. Surgic. Train. Wessex Region. Prev: Sen. Lect. Univ. Soton.; Lect. Surg. Welsh Nat. Sch. Med. & Hon. Sen. Regist. Univ. Hosp. Wales; Cardiff; Research Fell. Boston Univ. Med. Centre USA.

KARRAR, Ali Ahmed Ali The Statles, Whickham Park, Whickham, Newcastle upon Tyne NE16 4EQ — MB BS 1980 Khartoum; MRCP (UK) 1990.

KARRAS, Kyriakos 44 Curie Court E11, Queens Medical Centre, Nottingham NG7 2UH — Ptychio Iatrikes 1984 Athens.

KARRI, Bhavam 117 Frenchwood Avenue, Preston PR1 4NE — MB ChB 1996 Liverp.

KARSERAS, Mr Alec George 16 Church Road, Whitchurch, Cardiff CF14 2DZ — MB BS 1961 Lond.; FRCS Eng. 1969; MRCP Ed. 1967; MRCS Eng. LRCP Lond. 1961; DO Eng. 1966. (St. Geo.) Cons. Ophth. Surg. St. Woolos Hosp. Newport. Socs: BMA. Prev: Sen. Regist. Moorfields Eye Hosp.; Research Fell. Hosp. Sick Childr. Lond.; Sen. Lect. Ophth. Welsh Nat. Sch. Med. & Hon. Cons. Ophth. Univ.

KARTHIKESALINGAM, Mary Philomena 18 Castlebar Park, Ealing, London W5 1BX — MB BS 1975 Sri Lanka.

KARTHIKESALINGAM, Sinnappoo 18 Castlebar Park, Ealing, London W5 1BX — MB BS 1975 Sri Lanka; MRCS Eng. LRCP Lond. 1982; MRCOG 1987.

KARUNADASA, Abesinghemudiyanselage Thushithangi R K 86 Ramsgate Road, Broadstairs CT10 2DF — MB BS 1990 Colombo, Sri Lanka.

KARUNAHARAN, Paranjothy 18 Norlands Lane, Rainhill, Prescot L35 6NR — MB ChB 1993 Manch.

KARUNAKARA, Marikinti Department of Obstetrics & Gynaecology, Bradford Royal Infirmary, Duckworth Lane, Bradford BD9 6RJ — MB BS 1985 Sri Venkateswara; MRCOG 1994.

KARUNAKARAN, Kanapathipillai 7 Blaen Wern, Myddleton Park, Denbigh LL16 4AW — MB BS 1975 Sri Lanka; MRCS Eng. LRCP Lond. 1989.

KARUNAKARAN, Shirine 73 St Nicholas Road, Wallingford OX10 8HX Tel: 01491 833779 Fax: 01491 832701 Email: shirineb@aol.com; Department of Diabetes & Endocrinology, Royal Berkshire & Battle Hospital NHS Trust, London Road, Reading RG1 5AN Tel: 0118 987 5111 — MB BS 1988 Malaya; MRCP (UK) 1992. Sen. Regist. (Diabetes & Endocrinol.) Roy. Berks. Hosp. Reading. Socs: BMA & BDA. Prev: Sen. Regist. Radcliffe Infirm. Oxf.; Regist. (Med.) Nottm. City Hosp.; SHO (Med.) Leicester Roy. Infirm.

KARUNAKARAN, Mr Varadappan Department of Otolaryngology, Prince Charles Hospital, Merthyr Tydfil CF47 9DT Tel: 01685 721721 — MB BS 1968 Madras; FRCS RCPS Glas. 1979.

KARUNAKARAN, Veluppillai 49 Marlborough Park Avenue, Sidcup DA15 9DL — MB BS 1965 Ceylon.

KARUNANAYAKE, Malavi Gamage Sugathadasa Barking, Havering & Brentwood Community Health Care Trust, Highwood Hospital, Geary Drive, Brentwood CM15 9DY Tel: 01708 465000 Fax: 01277 212416 — MB BS Ceylon 1965; FRCP Ed. 1988; MRCP (UK) 1974. (University of Ceylon, Colombo, Sri Lanka) Staff Phys. (c/o the Elderly) Highwood Hosp. Brentwood & St. Geo. Hosp. HornCh.; Mem. (Counc.) Sri Lanka Coll. Paths. Socs: (Ex-Hon. Treas., Sec. & Vice-Pres.) Sri Lanka Med. Assn.; Expert Advis. Panel of WHO on Human Blood Products & Related Subst.s; (Ex-Hon. Sec.) Ceylon Coll. Phys. Prev: Cons. Haemat. Centr. Blood Bank Gen. Hosp., Colombo; Supt. Nat. Blood Transfus. Centre, Sri Lanka; Regist. (Gen. Med.) Old Ch. Hosp. Romford.

KARUNAPALA, Loku Gan Hewage 3 Halsey Park, London Colney, St Albans AL2 1BH — MB BS 1965 Ceylon; MRCPsych 1993.

KARUNARATNE, Dayantha Christopher Premalal Grosvenor Road Surgery, 23 Grosvenor Road, Muswell Hill, London N10 2DR Tel: 020 8883 5600 Fax: 020 8883 3324 Email: dayantha.karunaratne@gp-f85658.nhs.uk — MB BS 1973 Colombo; FRCS Eng. 1981. Surg. (Community Health) Enfield & Haringey HA.

KARUNARATNE, Weeraman Maithra St John's Surgery, Main Road, Terrington St. John, Wisbech PE14 7RR Tel: 01945 880471 Fax: 01945 880677 — MB BS 1978 Sri Lanka; MRCP (UK) 1987. (University of Sri Lanka, Colombo)

KARUNARATNE, Weeraman Upekha Castle Hill Hospital, Castle Road, Cottingham HU16 5JQ Tel: 01482 875875; 206 Northgate, Cottingham HU16 5QW — MB BS 1978 Sri Lanka; FRCA 1989. (Peradeniya) Assoc. Specialist (Anaesth.) Cardiothoracic Unit Castle Hill Hosp. Cottingham.

KARUNASEKARA, Hettiarachchige Sumitra 143 Horseshoe Lane, Garston, Watford WD25 7HT — MB BS 1966 Ceylon; DPH Eng. 1979. (Ceylon) Regist. (Psychiat.) Leavesden Hosp. Socs: BMA.

KARUNASEKARA, Nishan Rohana 143 Horseshoe Lane, Watford WD25 7HT — MB ChB 1994 Dundee.

KARUNASEKERA, Indunil Kelum 63 West Drive, South Cheam, Sutton SM2 7NB — MB BS 1991 Lond.; MRCP (UK) 1995. (St. Geo. Hosp. Med. Sch.) Regist. (Radiol.) Roy. Hallamsh. & N. Gen. Hosps. Sheff. Prev: SHO (Med.) Castle Hill Hosp. Cottingham St. Helier Hosp. Carshalton; SHO (A & E) Ashford Hosp. Middlx.

KARVOUNIS, Spyros-Spyridon Mental Health Unit, Chase Farm Hospital, The Ridgeway, Enfield EN2 8SL Tel: 020 8266 6600 — Ptychio Iatrikes 1983 Athens; MRCPsych 1995. Cons. (Adult Psych.) Enfield Community Care NHS Trust. Socs: BMA. Prev: Specialist Regist. (Gen. Psychiat.) Oxleas NHS Trust.

KARWA, Ravindra Kumar 39 Arklow Road, Doncaster DN2 5LB — MB BS 1987 Calcutta; MRCP (UK) 1995. (NRS Medical College,

Calcutta, India) Staff Grade (Gen. Med. & Gastroenterol.). Prev: SHO Med. Rotat., Roy. & Montague Hosps. NHS Trust.

KARWAL, Naveen Nelson Road Surgery, 156 Nelson Road, Gillingham ME7 4LU Tel: 01634 850943 — MB BS 1975 Delhi.

KARWATOWSKI, Stefan Peter 25 Doneraile Street, Fulham, London SW6 6EL — MD 1993 Lond.; MB BS 1983; MRCP (UK) 1987.

KARWATOWSKI, Mr Wojciech Stefan Stanislaw Department of Ophthalmology, Leicester Royal Infirmary, Leicester LE1 5WW Tel: 0116 258 6478 Fax: 0116 258 5927 Email: wkarwatowski@uhl.trent.nhs.uk — MB ChB 1983 Sheff.; BSc (Biochem.) Sheff. 1978; MD Brist. 1997; FRCS Glas. 1988; FCOphth. 1989; DO 1987. Cons. Ophth. Surg. Leicester. Prev: Sen. Regist. (Ophth.) Bristol Eye Hosp.; Fell. Glaucoma UCSD Shirley Eye Centre, San Diego, Calif., USA.

KARWOWSKI, Irena Stanislawa Peel Health Centre, Angouleme Way, Bury BL9 0BT Tel: 0161 764 0311 Fax: 0161 761 7548 — Lekarz 1971 Stettin, Poland; Lekarz Stettin Poland 1971.

KARYAMPUDI, Padmavathi Bellfield, Noctorum Lane, Birkenhead CH43 7PL — MB ChB 1993 Dundee.

KARYAMPUDI, Raja Sekhar Kanchana, Noctorum Lane, Birkenhead CH43 7PL — MB ChB 1994 Dundee.

KARZOUN, Farouk Khamis 26 Oakwood Road, Sparkhill, Birmingham B11 4HA Tel: 0121 777 3082 Fax: 0121 777 0956 Email: faroukkarzoun@pc.birminghamha.wmids.nhs.uk — MB ChB; DGO; MRCOG. (Alexandria, Egypt) Generap Practitioner, Birm.

KASAKA, Nulu 43 Redpost Hill, London SE24 9JJ — MB BS 1995 Lond.

KASARANENI, Mr Ramesh 136 Abbots Way, North Shields NE29 8LY — MB BS 1977 Andhra; FRCS Glas. 1992.

KASASIAN, Anthony Halton (retired) 9 Tan House Lane, Parbold, Wigan WN8 7HG Tel: 0125 762511 — MRCS Eng. LRCP Lond. 1947; FFA RCS Eng. 1955; FFA RCSI 1960; DA RCPSI 1951. Prev: Cons. Anaesth. Wigan & Leigh Hosp. Gp.

KASBARIAN, Arshalouis Briar Cottage, Horringer, Bury St Edmunds IP29 5PL Tel: 01284 735388 — MB BS 1959 Lond.; MRCS Eng. LRCP Lond. 1959; MRCOG 1964. (Roy. Free) Prev: Indep. O & G United Arab Emirates; Cons. O & G Itegue Mennen Hosp. Asmara, Ethiopia; Regist. (O & G) Roy. Free Hosp. Lond.

KASEM, Hasan c/o Drive Kasem, Hartwood Hospital, Hartwood, Shotts ML7 4LA — MB ChB 1991 Ed.

KASEM, Kerry Fiona 1/R, 49 Park Road, Glasgow G4 9JD — MB ChB 1991 Glas.; MRCP (UK) 1997. SHO III (Med. Paediat. & Neonates) Yorkhill NHS Trust Glas.; ECMO Fell. Socs: MRCPCH 1997.

KASHI, Isaac Kingsley Way Surgery, 55 Kingsley Way, Hampstead Garden Suburb, London N2 0EJ Tel: 020 8458 5275 Fax: 020 7636 3863 — MB ChB 1961 Sheff.; MRCS Eng. LRCP Lond. 1961; DObst RCOG 1964; DCH Eng. 1963. (Sheff.)

KASHI, Mr Seyed Habib Department of Surgery, Walsgrave Hospital, Clifford Bridge Road, Coventry CV2 2DX Tel: 02476602020 Fax: 02476 604431 Email: shkashi@btinternet.com — MB ChB 1984 Sheff.; ChM Sheff. 1993; FRCS Ed. 1989. (Sheffield) Cons. Gen. Surg. & Transpl. Walsgrave Hosp. Coventry. Socs: Brit. Transpl. Soc.; Assn. Coloproctol.; Assn. Surg. Prev: Lect. & Tutor (Surg.) Univ. Leeds; Regist. (Transpl. Surg.) St. Jas. Hosp. Leeds; Regist. (Gen. Surg.) York Dist. Hosp.

KASHIF AL-GHITA, Fadhil Abbas Ahmed Mayday University Hospital, London Road, Thornton Heath, Croydon CR7 7YE Tel: 020 8401 3192 Fax: 020 8401 3100; 150 Somerset Road, London SW19 5HP Tel: 020 8944 5931 — MB ChB 1976 Cairo. (Cairo Univ. Med. Sch.) Dir. Dept. Trauma & Orthop. Mayday Univ. Hosp. Socs: Brit. Orthop. Assn.; BMA; Roy. Soc. Med.

KASHIN, Munes Abdul Hameed Clayhall Clinic, 14 Clayhall Avenue, Ilford IG5 0LG Tel: 020 8550 5050 Fax: 020 8551 6393; 102 Coopersale Common, Coopersale, Epping CM16 7QU Tel: 01992 560127 — MB ChB 1972 Baghdad; FRCS Ed. 1984. GP Epping. Socs: BMA.

KASI, Abdul Ghafoor 8 Chestnut Close, Sudbrooke, Lincoln LN2 2RD; 8 Chestnut Close, Sudbrooke, Lincoln LN2 2 RD Email: a.kasi@melworld.com — MB BS 1976 Karachi; LRCP LRCS Ed. LRCPS Glas. 1983; DA 1986 (UK). (Dow Medical College) Locum Cons. (Anaesth.) Kings Mill Hosp. Sulton in Ashfield Notts.; Locum Cons. Anaesth.; Rotherham NHS Trust - Rotherham; Lincoln NHS Trust - Lincoln; City Hosp. NHS Trust - Birm. Socs: Mem.: Doctors in Law Soc.; Mem.: Lincoln INN. Prev: Regist. (Anaesth.) St. Jas. Hosp. Dub. & Merlin Pk. Hosp. Galway; Ho. Off. Daisy Hill Hosp. Newry.

KASINSKI, Kajetan Ludwik Jan The Tavistock Clinic, 120 Belsize Lane, London NW3 5BA — MB BS 1980 Lond.; BA Oxf. 1975; MRCPsych 1986. Cons. N.gate Jun. Addesc. Unit Lond.; Vis. Teach. Tavistock Clinic. Prev: Sen. Regist. Tavistock Clinic; Regist. Maudsley & Bethlem Hosps.

KASIRI, Firuz 30 Sandhurst Road, Palm Bay Estate, Cliftonville, Margate CT9 3JQ Tel: 01843 223265 — MB BS 1974 Karachi. Assoc. Specialist (Orthop.) Thanet Dist. Hosp. Margate.

KASPEROWICZ, Regina Ewa The Bridge Sexual Health Clinic, Baillic St Health Centre, Penn St, Rochdale; 17 Highfield Drive, Monton, Eccles, Manchester M30 9PZ Tel: 0161 707 6157 Email: mfinnegan@bigwig.net — MB ChB 1983 Leeds; DFFP 2000. p/t Clin. Asst. Genito-Urin. Med., Rochdale; Clin. Med. Off. Rochdale.; Clin. Asst. Cardiol., Burt. Socs: N. W. Soc. Family Plann. & Reproductive Health. Prev: GP Bradford.

KASS, Thomas Lewis Chester House, 17 The Avenue, Newmarket CB8 9AA — MB BChir 1983 Camb.; MA Camb. 1985; PhD Cornell 1975. Socs: Fell.of the Roy. Soc. of Med.

KASSAB, Ahmed Sami Mohawad West Dorset General Hospital, Dorchester DT1 2JY; Flat 1, 85 Longfleet Road, Poole BH15 2HP — MB BCh 1988 Cairo; MRCOG 1995.

KASSAB, Mr Riadh Daniel The Wyatts, Wyatts Green Road, Wyatts Green, Brentwood CM15 0QB — MB ChB 1957 Baghdad; FRCS Eng. 1969. (Baghdad) Cons. Traum. & Orthop. Surg. Barking & Havering AHA.

KASSAB, Susan Catherine 8 Lon-y-Meillion, Bangor LL57 2LE — MB BS 1984 Lond.

KASSAM, Malik Laki East Calder Medical Practice, 147 Main St., East Calder, Livingston EH53 0EW Tel: 01506 882882; Silverwells, 9 Old Mill Road, Bothwell, Glasgow G71 8AY Tel: 01698 854017 — MB ChB 1979 Manch.; BSc St. And. 1976; MRCGP 1984; DRCOG 1983. (St. And. Manch.)

KASSAM, Nooralla Noormohamed Mocha Parade Surgery, 4-5 Mocha Parade, Salford M7 1QE Tel: 0161 839 2721 Fax: 0161 819 1191.

KASSAM, S G Yeading Medical Centre, 18 Hughenden Gardens, Northolt UB5 6LD Tel: 020 8845 3434 Fax: 020 8841 6402 — MB BS 1973 All-India Institute; MB BS 1973 All-India Institute.

KASSIANOS, George Birch Hill Medical Centre, Leppington, Bracknell RG12 7WW Fax: 01344 450312; Keeper's Lodge, 61 Plough Lane, Wokingham RG40 1RQ Tel: 0118 978 4572 — LRCP LRCS Ed. LRCPS Glas. 1977; LRCPS 1977 Glas.; LRCP LRCS 1977 Ed.; MRCGP 1979; DRCOG 1977; Dip. Med. (Hons.) Lodz 1974; FRCGP 1999. (Med. Acad. Lodz 1974) Bracknell PCG Chairm.; Hon. Sec. Brit. Travel Health Assn. Socs: Coun. Brit. Travel Health Assoc.; BMA; Coun. Primary Care Virol. Gp. Prev: SHO (O & G, Med. & Cas.) Hammersmith Hosp. Lond.; SHO (Paediat.) Paddington Green Childr. Hosp.; Ho. Phys. & Ho. Surg. Worthing Health Dist.

KASSIM, Zena 11a Pennhouse Avenue, Penn, Wolverhampton WV4 4BG — BM BS 1998 Nottm.; BM BS Nottm 1998.

KASSIMOS, Dimitrios Doctor's Residence, Huddersfield Royal Infirmary, Acre St., Huddersfield HD3 3EA; 79 Woodland Road, Clifton, Bristol BS8 1US — Ptychio Iatrikes 1986 Thessalonika.

KASTELIK, Jack Andrew Dept. of Academic Medicine, Respiratory Med., Castle Hill Hospital, Castle Road, Cottingham HU16 5JQ Tel: 01482 624067 Fax: 01954 91482624068 Email: j.a.kastelik@medschool.hull.ac.uk; 11 The Copse, Scarborough YO12 5HG Tel: 01723 376075 — MB ChB 1994 Manch.; BSc (Med.) St. And. 1991; MRCP (uk) 1998. Ho. Off. (Surg.) Hull Roy. Infirm.; Clin. Research Fell. of Acad. Med., Respirat. Med. Castle Hill Hosp., Cottingham. Prev: Ho. Off. (Med.) ScarBoro. Gen. Hosp.

KASTHALA, Rajeswara Prasad Royal Infirmary, Stirling FK8 2AU Tel: 01786 434000; 18 Snowdon Place, Stirling FK8 2JN Tel: 01786 464617 — MB BS 1972 Andhra. Staff Grade (Anaesth.) Roy. Infirm. Stirling.

KASTHURI, Nithya Histopathology Department, Burton Hospitals, Belvedere Road, Burton-on-Trent DE13 0RB Tel: 01283 566333 — MD 1979 Nagpur; MD (Path.) Nagpur 1979, MB BS 1975; MRCPath 1986. Cons. Histopath. Burton Gen. Hosp.

KASTNER-COLE, Dagmar 26 Queen Street, Perth PH2 0EH — State Exam Med. Cologne 1991.

KASTURI, Siripurapu Family Planning Clinic, Creggan Day Centre, Londonderry BT48 Tel: 01504 269082; 4 Dunhugh Park, Londonderry BT47 2NL Tel: 01504 48994 — MB BS 1966 Andhra; MS (Gyn. & Obst.) Banaras Hindu 1974; MFFP 1993; MRCOG 1978. (Andhra Med. Coll. Visakhapatnam) Med. Off. (Family Plann.) Gt. Jas. St. Health Centre; Clin. Med. Off. (Family Plann.) Creggan Day Centre, Stantallow Health Centre & Waterdside Health Centre.

KASZUBOWSKI, Henry Albert Taverham Surgery, Sandy Lane, Taverham, Norwich NR8 6JR Tel: 01603 867481 Fax: 01603 740670; 23 Beechcroft, New Costessey, Norwich NR5 0RS Tel: 01603 746409 — MB BS 1983 Lond.

KAT, Haw Shi 133 Vicarage Road, Watford WD18 0HA — MB BS 1986 Singapore.

KATAI, Freddy Masimba 41 Chevington Drive, Stockport SK4 3RF — MB BCh 1986 Wales; MRCP (UK) 1989. SHO (Gen. Med.) Russells Hall Hosp. Dudley W. Midl.

KATAMANENI, Raveendra Kumar Flat 4, Arrowhouse, The Alexandra Hospital, Woodrow Drive, Redditch B98 7UB — MB BS 1989 Kakatiya.

KATARIA, Bhavesh 300 Lonsdale Drive, Oakwood, Enfield EN2 7LE — MB ChB 1995 Birm.; ChB Birm. 1995; BSc (Hons) Birm 1992. (Univ of Birmingham)

KATARIA, Mohan S 5 Star & Garter Mansions, Lower Richmond Road, Putney, London SW15 1JW — MRCS Eng. LRCP Lond. 1948; DIH Eng. 1950; DPH Lond. 1949. (Robertson Med. Sch. Nagpur & Guy's) Hon. Cons. King's Coll. Hosp. Lond.; Emerit. Lect. (Geriat. Med.) Kings Coll. Hosp. Med. Sch. Lond. Socs: Brit. Geriat. Soc. & BMA; Assoc. Mem. Med. Jl.ists Assn. Prev: Capt. IAMC 1940-6 (Mentioned in Despatches).

KATAY, Elizabeth Ildiko Fairhill Medical Practice, 81 Kingston Hill, Kingston upon Thames KT2 7PX Tel: 020 8546 1407 Fax: 020 8547 0075; 24 Avenue Elmers, Surbiton KT6 4SE Tel: 020 8399 1372 — LMSSA 1989 Lond.; MD Hungary 1985; MRCGP 1993.

KATCHBURIAN, Marcos Viggiani 55 Church Lane, Great Sutton, Wirral — MB BS 1987 Lond.

KATEB, Heskel Joseph Tufnell Park Road Surgery, 244 Tufnell Park Roa, London N19 5EW Tel: 020 7272 9105 Fax: 020 7272 8996; 5 Church Way, London N20 0JN — MB BS 1978 Lond.; BSc Lond. 1975; MRCP (UK) 1982; MRCGP 1988. (St. Geo. Hosp. Med. Sch.) Clin. Asst. (Chest Med.) Middlx. Hosp.; Clin. Asst. (Diabetes) Whittington Hosp. Lond. Prev: Regist. (Med. & Gastroenterol.) Enfield & Haringey AHA; SHO (Dermat.) St. John's Hosp. Dis. Skin.

KATECK, Victor Henry The White House, 12 Movers Lane, Barking IGU 7UN Tel: 0208 594 4042/2838/2943 Fax: 0208 507 1390; Charnwood, 11 New Forest Lane, Chigwell IG7 5QN Tel: 020 8506 1655 Email: drvik@newforestlane.freeserve.co.uk — MB BS Lond. 1970; MRCS Eng. LRCP Lond. 1970; DObst RCOG 1973. (Lond.Hosp.Med.Coll) Hosp. Pract. (Med.) OldCh. Hosp. Romford; Phys. E. Anglian Metals Co. & Smiths Plastics Ltd.; Med. Examr. Sun Life, Scott. Life, Sun Alliance & Lond. Assur. Co., Refuge Life Assur. Co. & Others. Socs: Assur. Med. Soc. Prev: SHO (Gen. Med. & Toxicol.) Gen. Med. & Regional Toxicol. Unit; SHO (O & G) Harold Wood Hosp.; Ho. Phys. & Ho. Surg. OldCh. Hosp. Romford.

KATES, Wendy Elsa 2 Willifield Way, London NW11 7XT Tel: 020 8455 1153 Fax: 020 8455 1153 — MB BS 1949 Lond.; MRCS Eng. LRCP Lond. 1949; Dip. Med. Law, Ethics 1986; DObst RCOG 1950. (Univ. Coll. Hosp.) Fell. Leo Baeck Coll.

KATESMARK, Mr Michael Epsom Hospital Trust, Epsom Hospital, Dorking Road, Epsom KT18 7EG; 78 Aylmer Road, Stamford Brook, London W12 9LQ — MB BChir 1984 Camb.; MA Camb. 1985, MB BChir 1984; FRCS Ed. 1989; MRCOG 1992. (Cambridge and Charing Cross Hospital) Cons. Gyn. Epsom Hosp. Trust. Prev: Sen. Regist. Kings Coll. Hosp. Lond.

KATHANE, Rajkumar Hiralal Family Consultation Clinic, 24 Grove Place, Bedford MK40 3JJ Tel: 01234 310800 Fax: 01234 310801 — MB BS 1972 Nagpur; FRCPsych 2001; MRCPysch 1983. Cons. Psychiat. Beds. & Luton Community NHS Trust. Socs: Pres Brit. Assn. of Phys.s of Indian Origin; Psychiat. Tutor RCPsych. Prev: Sen. Regist. (Child & Adolesc. Psychiat.) Camb. & P'boro.; Regist. (Psychiat.) Ipswich.

KATHEL, Mr Babu Lal The Gables, Londonthorpe, Grantham NG31 9RU — MB BS 1955 Lucknow; ChM Liverp. 1972; FRCS Eng. 1970; FRCS Ed. 1964; DCH RCPS Glas. 1960. (Lucknow) Cons. Gen. Surg. Grantham Gen. Hosp.

KATHIRGAMAKANTHAN, Sukirthalojini The Surgery, 6 Well Court, 740 London Road, North Cheam, Sutton SM3 9BX Tel: 020 8644 8400 — MB BS 1977 Colombo.

KATHIRGAMAKARTHIGEYAN, Mr Thurairatnam Department of Ophthalmology, Sandwell District General Hospital, Lyndon, West Bromwich Tel: 0121 553 1831; 54 Park Hall Road, Walsall WS5 3HL Tel: 01922 20193 — MB BS 1972 Ceylon; FRCS Glas. 1989; FCOphth 1989; DO Dub. 1984. (Dub.) Assoc. Specialist Sandwell & Dudley NHS Trusts. Prev: Staff Grade Ophth. Sandwell & Dudley HAs.; Regist. & SHO (Ophth.) Roy. Preston Hosp.; SHO (Ophth.) Coventry & Warks. Hosp.

***KATHIRGAMANATHAN, Aravindan** 309 Moorside Road, Flixton, Manchester M41 5RX Tel: 0161 748 6119 — BChir 1996 Camb.

KATHIRKAMASEKARAN, Shanmugasuntharam 47 Hawthorn Rise, Haverfordwest SA61 2BD — MB BS 1983 Colombo.

KATHURIA, Barinder Singh 53 Springwood Hall Gardens, Huddersfield HD1 4HA — MB ChB 1995 Manch.

KATHURIA, Renee Lata The Surgery, High Street, Lowestoft NR32 1JE Tel: 01502 589151 Fax: 01502 566719; Highfield, The St, Barnby, Beccles NR34 7QB — MB BS 1980 Newc.; MRCGP 1984; DRCOG 1983. Prev: GP Chiswick.

KATHURIA, Umesh Chandra City Health Centre, 449 City Road, Edgbaston, Birmingham B17 8LG Tel: 0121 420 2384 Fax: 0121 434 3931; 58 Kelmscott Road, Harborne, Birmingham B17 8QN Tel: 0121 426 1622 — MB BS 1970 Rajasthan; DA RCPSI 1976. (Sardar Patel Med. Coll. Bikaner) GP. Prev: Regist. (Anaesth.) Hackney Hosp. Lond. & P.ss Margt. Hosp. Swindon; SHO Essex Co. Hosp. Colchester.

KATHURIA, Vinod 36 Oakenshaw Road, Greenlands, Redditch B98 7PJ — MB BS 1980 Poona; MChOrth Liverp. 1991.

KATIB, Janan 19 Whitby Avenue, Guisborough TS14 7AP — MB ChB 1997 Liverp.

KATIC, Barbara Mary (retired) Highview, 60 Lower Hill Drive, Heath Charnock, Chorley PR6 9JP Tel: 01257 483176 Fax: 01257 475028 — MB BCh BAO Dub. 1953.

KATIFI, Haider Aziz Abdullah Wessex Neurological Centre, Southampton General Hospital, Shirley, Southampton SO16 6YD Tel: 02380 777222 Fax: 02380 794148; 12 Crofton Close, Highfield, Southampton SO17 1XB — MB ChB 1979 Bagdad; PhD Soton. 1988; MRCP (UK) 1989; FRCP 1998. Cons. Neurol. Wessex Neurol. Centre Soton. Gen. Hosp.; Cons. NeUrol., Salisbury Dist. Hosp. Socs: Fell. Roy. Soc. Med.; Assn. Brit. Neurol.; Peripheral Nerve Soc. Prev: Hon. Cons. Neurol. Wessex Neurol. Centre Soton. Gen. Hosp.; Sen. Lect. (Neurol.) Soton. Univ.; Sen. Regist. (Neurol.) Roy. Lond. Hosp.

KATIYAR, Ashok Kumar The Surgery, Cox Lane Centre, Cox Lane, West Ewell, Epsom KT19 9PS; 55 Ruxley Lane, Ewell, Epsom KT19 0JF Tel: 020 8394 1141 — MB BS 1973 Allahabad; DLO Agra 1976. (M.L.N. Med. Coll. Allahabad) SHO (Geriat.) Rotherham Dist. Gen. Hosp.; SHO (ENT) St. Peters Hosp. Chertsey, N.ampton Gen. Hosp. & Roy. Hants. Co. Hosp. Winchester.

KATONA, Professor Cornelius Louis Emanuel Department Psychiatry, University College London, Wolfson Building, Middlesex Hospital, London W1N 8AA Tel: 020 7380 9475 Fax: 020 7323 1459; 27 Cassland Road, London E9 7AL Tel: 020 8986 7714 — MB BChir 1979 Camb.; MB BChir. Camb. 1979; MA Camb. 1979, MD 1990; MRCPsych. 1983; FRCPsych 1994; MD Cantab. 1990. (Camb. & Lond. Hosp.) Prof. Psychiat. of Elderly Univ. Coll. Lond. & Hon. Cons. Psychiat. Wessex HA.; Dean Roy. Coll. Psych.; Edr. in Chief, Jl. Affective Disorders. Prev: Sen. Lect. (Psychiat.) Univ. Coll. Lond.; Research Fell. & Lect. (Psychiat.) St. Geo. Hosp. Med. Sch.

KATONA, Stephen John Derriford Hospital, Plymouth PL6 8DH Email: skatona@hotmail.com; 815 Wilmslow Road, Didsbury, Manchester M20 2SN — MB ChB 1994 Bristol; MRCP 1997. (Bristol) Specialist Regist. (Immunol.) Derriford Hosp. Plymouth. Socs: BMA; MDU. Prev: SHO (Renal) Ch.ill Hosp. Oxf.; SHO (Clin. Oncol./Endocrinol.) Christie Hosp. Manch.; SHO (Gen. Med.) N. Devon Dist. Hosp.

KATOPI, Despina 5 Oak Hill House, Oak Hill Park, London NW3 7LP — Ptychio Iatrikes 1993 Thessalonika.

KATORY, Mark 12 Hepple Way, Newcastle upon Tyne NE3 3HS — MB ChB 1995 Sheff.

KATRAGADDA, Usha 32 Redbourn Road, Bloxwich, Walsall WS3 3XT Tel: 01922 408332; Manor Hospital, Moat Road, Walsall

WS2 9PS Tel: 01922 721172 — MB BS 1974 Andhra. (Guntur Med. Coll.) Clin. Asst. (Anaesth.) Manor Hosp. Walsall. Prev: Regist. (Anaesth.) Burton Gen. Hosp.

KATRAK, Pesi Minoo Clements Surgery, Haverhill CB9 8LU Tel: 01440 702462; Brickfields, Withersfield, Haverhill CB9 7RR Tel: 01440 702462 — MRCS Eng. LRCP Lond. 1958; DObst RCOG 1964. (Leeds) Apptd. Doctor (Fact. Act.) Health & Safety Exec. Socs: BMA. Prev: Ho. Phys. & Ho. Surg. Co. Hosp. York; Ho. Surg. (Obst.) Stepping Hill Hosp. Stockport; Resid. Med. Off. Childr. Hosp. Sydenham.

KATSARMA, Eyfrossini Department of Plastic Surgery, Royal Free Hospital, Pond St., London NW3 2QG Tel: 020 7794 0500; 28 Devonshire Place Mews, London W1G 6DA Tel: 020 7486 3623 — Ptychio Iatrikes 1985 Athens; Ptychio Iatrikes (Dentistry) Athens 1985; Ptychio Iatrikes (Medicine) Thessalonika 1989; Nat. Exam Plas. Surg. (Greek Ministry of Health) 1997. (Thessalonika) Clin. Fell. Specialist (Plastic Surg.) The Roy. Free Hosp. Socs: Athens Med. Assn.; BMA; Greek Assn. Plast. Surg. Prev: Regist. (Plastic Surg.) St. Thomas's Hosp. Lond.; SHO (Plastic Surg.) St. Andrews Hosp. Billericay, N.ern Gen. Hosp. Sheff. & Mt. Vernon Hosp. N.wood.

KATSIMIHAS, Michael 12 Harris Street, Stoke-on-Trent ST4 7EZ — MB ChB 1996 Liverp.

KATTAN, George Victor Keats Surgery, 290A Church Street, Edmonton, London N9 9HJ; 24 Conway Road, Southgate, London N14 7BA — MB BS 1965 Amer. U Beirut, Lebanon. Prev: Regist. (Gen. Surg. & Orthop.) Highlands Gen. Hosp. Lond.; SHO (Gen. Surg. & Orthop.) Hosp. Sick Childr. Gt. Ormond St. Lond.

KATTAN, Jessica Claire Chainsbridge Medical Partnership, Chainbridge House, The Precinct, Blaydon-on-Tyne NE21 5BT Tel: 0191 414 2856 Fax: 0191 499 0449 — MB BS 1987 Newc. Prev: GP Partner, Falcon Ho., Heaton Rd., Newc. upon Tyne; GP Partner, Saville Med. Gp., Saville Pl., Newc. upon Tyne.

KATTAN, Mohammad Momtaz 67 Gander Green Lane, Sutton SM1 2EP Tel: 01582 497358 — MD 1981 Damascus; MRCP (UK) 1989.

KATTASH, Mr Maan Mohammad Ismail Plastic Surgery Department, Leazes Wing, Royal Victoria Infirmary, Newcastle upon Tyne NE1 4LP — MB ChB 1983 Mosul; MB ChB Mosul Iraq 1983; FRCS Ed. 1990.

KATTI, Shyam Sunder Windmill Road Health and Family, 85 Windmill Road, Coventry CV6 7AT Tel: 024 7663 7636 Fax: 024 7658 1412 — MB BS 1971 Osmania; T(GP) 1991.

KATTI, Siddalingaprabhu Mallikarjun 8 Sri Giri, Perivale Close, Radbrook Green, Shrewsbury SY3 6DH Tel: 01743 352234 — MB BS 1978 Karnatak; MB BS Karnatak India 1978; DA (UK) 1991.

***KATUGAMPOLA, Ruwani Priyanka** c/o Dr G katugampola, F9 Residences, Princess of Wales Hospital, Coity Road, Bridgend CF31 1RQ; No 6 Turberville Crescent, Bridgend CF31 1QT Tel: 01656 654284 — BM 1998 Soton.; BM Soton 1998.

KATUGAMPOLA, Sudharma Lilamani Princess of Wales Hospital, F9 Residences, Coity Road, Bridgend CF31 1RQ — MB BS 1970 Ceylon.

KATUGAMPOLA, Sujatha Manil 129 Burbage Road, Dulwich, London SE21 7AF — MB BS 1967 Ceylon; MRCP (UK) 1975; DCH Eng. 1973. (Colombo) Cons. Paediat. Epsom Gen. Hosp. Prev: Regist. (Paediat.) N. Middlx Hosp. Edmonton.

KATUMBA-LUNYENYA, Jasper Ndugga Milton Keynes NHS, Dept of Paediatrcians, Eaglespar, Milton Keynes MK6 5LD Tel: 01908 660033 Fax: 01908 243108 Email: jasper.katumba@mkg-tr.anglax.nhs.uk; Mukono, 2 Marjot Close, Newport Ragnell MK16 9PP Tel: 01908 612597/612597 Email: kate@sheri31.freeserve.co.uk — MB ChB 1976 Makerere; MRCPCH 1996; DCH RCP Lond. 1988. Assoc. Specialist (Paediat.) Neonatology Milton Keynes Hosp. Socs: BMA. Prev: Staff Grade (Paediat.) Milton Keynes Hosp.; Regist. (Paediat.) Luton & Dunstable Hosp. & Milton Keynes Hosp.

KATZ, Anthony Wolfe MHCOP, St. Pancras Hospital, St Pancras Way, London NW1 0PE Tel: 020 7387 4411 — MB ChB 1980 Cape Town; 2000 MAE; MRCPsych 1987. (University of Cape Town Medical School) Cons. Psychiat. Old Age. St. Pancras Hosp. Lond.; Hon. Sen. Lect. UCL Med. Sch. Prev: Sen. Regist. (Psychiat.) St. Geo. Hosp. Lond.; Regist. (Psychiat.) Roy. Free Hosp.

KATZ, David Errol Northwick Park Hospital & Clinical Research Centre, Watford Road, Harrow HA1 3UJ Tel: 020 8864 5311 — MB BCh 1972 Witwatersrand; BSc Witwatersrand 1967, MB BCh 1972; FRCR 1979.

KATZ, David Meredith Glan Rhyd Surgery, Riverside, Beaufort, Ebbw Vale NP23 5NT Tel: 01495 301210 Fax: 01633 350684 — MB BS 1975 Lond.; PhD Lond. 1976, BSc 1968; MRCGP 1979; DRCOG 1978. (Univ. Coll. Hosp.)

KATZ, Professor David Rael Dept of Immunology, University College London Medical School, Windeyer Institute, 46 Cleveland St., London W1T 4JF Tel: 020 7504 9397 Fax: 020 7636 5481 Email: d.katz@ucl.ac.uk; 6 Lawn Road, London NW3 2XS — MB ChB Cape Town 1969; PhD Lond. 1980; FRCPath 1990, M 1977. Prof. Immunopath. & Hon. Cons. Path. Univ. Coll. Lond. Sch. Med. Prev: Reader (Experim. Path.) & Hon. Cons. Histopath. Univ. Coll. Lond. Sch. Med.; Research Fell. (Experim. Path.) ICRF Tumour Immunol. Unit. Dept. Zool. Univ. Coll. Lond.; Lect. (Histopath.) St. Bart. Hosp. Med. Coll. Lond.

KATZ, Felicity 6 Oakhill Avenue, London NW3 7RE — MB ChB 1995 Manch.

KATZ, Gary The Garden Hospital, 46 50 Sunnygardens Road, London NW4 1RA Tel: 020 8201 8270 Fax: 020 8201 8270; 6 Oakhill Avenue, Hampstead, London NW3 7RE Tel: 020 7794 3582 Fax: 020 8201 8270 — MB BCh 1960 Witwatersrand; MD Witwatersrand 1971; FRCP Lond. 1979, M 1965; FRCPCH 1997; DCH Eng. 1964. Cons. Paediat. Barnet & Chase Farm Hosp. NHS Trust; Hon. Sen. Lect. (Paediat.) UCL Roy. Free Med. Sch. Socs: Neonat. Soc.; Roy. Soc. Med. Prev: Sen. Regist. (Paediat.) Univ. Coll. Hosp. & Whittington Hosp. Lond.; Lect. (Neonat. Research Unit) Lond. Hosp. Med. Coll.; Regist. (Paediat.) Lond. Hosp.

KATZ, Jonathan The Penryn Surgery, Saracen Way, Penryn TR10 8HX Tel: 01326 372502 Fax: 01326 378126 — MB ChB 1991 Bristol; BSc (1st cl. Hons.) Applied Biol. Sci. CNAA 1986; MRCGP 1996; DFFP 1995; DRCOG 1995; DCH RCP Lond. 1994. (Bristol) Socs: BMA; MDU.

KATZ, Jonathan Richard 6 Oakhill Avenue, London NW3 7RE — MB BChir 1991 Camb.; MRCP (UK) 1994.

KATZ, Maurice 148 Harley Street, London W1N 1AH Tel: 020 7935 1207 Fax: 020 7224 1528; Department of Obstetrics & Gynaecology, Royal Free and University College Medical School, 86-96 Chenies Mews, London WC1E 6HX Tel: 020 7679 6055 Fax: 020 7383 7429 Email: m.katz@ucl.ac.uk — MB ChB 1963 Cape Town; FRCP Lond. 1988, M 1969; FCP(SA) 1968. Cons. Endocrinol. & Sen. Lect. Roy. Free & Univ. Coll. Med. Sch. & Univ. Coll. Lond. Hosp. NHS Trust. Socs: Soc. Endocrinol.; Brit. Fertil. Soc.; Brit. Androl, Soc. Prev: Regist. (Endocrinol.) New End Hosp. Lond.; Research Fell. Sheba Med. Center, Tel-Hashomer Israel; Sen. Specialist & Sen. Lect. Groote Schuur Hosp. Cape Town.

KATZ, Ruth Elaine 19 Myddelton Park, Whetstone, London N20 0HT Tel: 020 8445 7128 Fax: 020 8445 7128 — MB BS 1975 Lond.; BSc (Biochem.) Lond. 1972; MSc (Occupat. Med.) Lond. 1982, MB BS 1975; MRCS Eng. LRCP Lond. 1975. (Roy. Free) Occupat. Health Phys. Socs: Assoc. Fac. Occupat. Med.; Soc. Occupat. Med. Prev: Regional Med. Adviser United Biscuits UK Ltd. Lond.; Med. Off. GLC & ILEA.

KAUFFMANN, Edgar Alexander Hospital of St John & St Elizabeth, Grove End Road, London NW8 9NH Tel: 020 7286 5126 Fax: 020 7266 2316; Bush House, Oakleigh Pk Avenue, Chislehurst BR7 5PB Tel: 020 8467 6999 Fax: 020 8467 2404 — MA Camb. 1950, MB BChir 1948; FRCP Ed. 1971, M 1958; DPhysMed Eng. 1960. (Middlx.) Emerit. Cons. (Rheum. & Rehabil.) Orpington & Sevenoaks Hosps. & Qu. Mary's Hosp. Sidcup. Socs: Fell. Roy. Soc. Med.; Brit. Soc. Rheum. Prev: Sen. Asst. Arthur Stanley Inst. Rheum. Middlx. Hosp.; Regist. Dept. Physical Med. & Rheum. Roy. Free Hosp. Lond.; Med. Regist. Rheum. Unit, St. Stephen's Hosp. Lond.

KAUFFMANN, Lisa Angelica Dare Longsight Health Centre, 526/8 Stockport Road, Manchester M13 0RR Tel: 0161 248 1203 Fax: 0161 248 1238; 2 Ollerbarrow Road, Hale, Altrincham WA15 9PW Tel: 0161 941 5032 — MB BS 1982 Lond.; MSc Lond. 1994; MRCP (UK) 1987. (Middlx. Hosp. Med. Sch.) Cons. Paediat. (Community Child Health) Mancunian Community NHS Trust.

KAUFMAN, Anthony Lawrence Western Avenue Medical Centre, Gordon Road, Blacon, Chester CH1 5PA Tel: 01244 390755 Fax: 01244 383955; 4 Upon Park, Upton, Chester — MB ChB 1978 Sheff.; BMedSci (Hons.) Sheff. 1975, MB ChB 1978; DRCOG 1982.

KAUFMAN, Dina The Ravenscroft Surgery, 166-168 Goldens Green Road, London NW11 8BB Tel: 020 8455 2477; 3 Basing Hill, London NW11 8TE Tel: 020 8458 0998 Fax: 020 8201 9142 — MB BS 1981 Lond.; MRCGP 1985; DRCOG 1984; DCH RCP Lond. 1983. (Univ. Coll. Hosp.) GP Retainer (p/t). Prev: Trainee GP N.wick Pk. Hosp. VTS.

KAUFMAN, Mr Harvey David 2 Fern Chase, Scarcroft, Leeds LS14 3JL Tel: 0113 289 3330 Fax: 0113 289 3893 — MB ChB 1960 Liverp.; MRCS Eng. LRCP Lond. 1960; ChM Liverp. 1966; FRCS Eng. 1964; FRCS Ed. 1964. Prev: Cons. Surg. Selly Oak Hosp.; Sen. Clin. Lect. (Surg.) Univ. Birm.; Sen. Regist. (Surg.) Roy. S.. Hosp. Liverp.

KAUFMAN, Leon 7 North End Rd, London NW11 7RJ Tel: 0208 455 9368 Fax: 0208 455 9368 Email: licaufman@lineone.net; 941 Finchley Road, London NW11 7PE Tel: 020 8458 1228 — MB ChB 1949 Ed.; MD 1962 Ed.; FFA RCS Eng. 1956. (Ed.) Cons. Anaesth. Univ. Coll. Hosp. Lond. & St. Marks Hosp. Lond. Socs: Fell. Roy. Soc. Med. (Mem. Sects. Anaesth., Neurol. & Experim. Med.); Brit. Acad. Experts; Mem. Assn. of Anaesth. Prev: Examr. Final FDS; Examr. Physiol. RCS Ed.; Examr. (Pharmacol.) & Final FFA RCS Eng.

KAUFMAN, Professor Matthew Howard Anatomy Department, University Edinburgh, Edinburgh EH8 9AG Tel: 0131 650 3113 Fax: 0131 650 6545 — MB ChB 1967 Ed.; PhD Camb. 1973, MA 1975; ScD Camb. 1993; DSc Ed. 1984; FRCP Ed. 1996. (Ed.) Prof. (Anat.) Univ. Edin. Socs: Brit. Soc. Developm. Biol.; Anat. Soc. Prev: Lect. (Anat.) Univ. Camb.; Fell. King's Coll. Camb.

KAUFMAN, Roger Brian Scott Road Medical Centre, Scott Road, Selby YO8 4BL Tel: 01757 700231 Fax: 01757 213647 — MB BS 1978 Lond.; BSc (Hons.) Lond. 1970, MB BS 1978; DRCOG 1983.

KAUFMANN, Peter 99 Harley Street, London W1G 6AQ Tel: 020 7935 5944 Fax: 01494 483424 Email: pkaufmann@doctors.org.uk — MB BS Lond. 1969; MRCP (UK) 1974; MRCS Eng. LRCP Lond. 1969; FRCP (Lond.) 1998. (St. Geo.) Hon. Cons. Neurol. Chalfont Centre for Epilepsy Chalfont St. Peter. Socs: Assn. Brit. Neurol. Prev: Sen. Resid. Nat. Hosp. Nerv. Dis. Qu. Sq. Lond.; Research Asst. Inst. Neurol. Lond.; Regist. (Neurol.) Bristol Roy. Infirm.

KAUFMANN, Sarah Jane 43 Primley Park Cresc, Leeds LS17 7HY — MB ChB 1986 Leeds.

KAUL, Adarsh 2 Deanery Crescent, Leicester LE4 2WD — MB BS 1981 Kerala; MRCPsych 1986.

KAUL, Mr Ashutosh 61 Colin Crescent, London NW9 6EU — MB BS 1988 Meerut; FRCS Ed. 1993.

KAUL, Harjinder Kumar Occupational Health Service, Leicester Royal Infirmary, Leicester LE1 5WW Tel: 0116 258 7683 — MB BS 1991 Lond.; MFOM 2000; BSc (Hons.) Lond. 1988; MRCGP 1995; AFOM 1998. (Charing Cross & Westminster) Cons. (Occupat.al Med.) Univ. Hosp. Leicester - Occupat.al Health Serv. Leicester. Prev: Sen. Regist. (Occupat. Med.) Univ. Hosp. Nottm.

KAUL, Oma Castletown Medical Centre, 6 The Broadway, Castletown, Sunderland SR5 3EX Tel: 0191 549 5113 — MB BS 1968 Jammu and Kashmir. (Jammu and Kashmir) GP Sunderland.

KAUL, Pyre Lal Broadstone Avenue Surgery, 59-61 Broadstone Avenue, Leamore, Walsall WS3 1ER Tel: 01922 476277 Fax: 01922 403208 — MB BS 1969 Jammu and Kashmir.

KAUL, Sapna Plaisance, Tamworth Road, Bassetts Pole, Sutton Coldfield B75 5RX — MB ChB 1994 Birm.; ChB Birm. 1994.

KAUL, Sundeep Plaisance, Tamworth Road, Bassetts Pole, Sutton Coldfield B75 5RX — MB ChB 1995 Birm.; ChB Birm. 1995.

KAUL, Veena Shehjar, Number One Norwood, Carleton, Pontefract WF8 3SD — MB BS 1973 Jammu & Kashmir; MB BS Lond.; MD Lond.; DRCOG Lond.; MRCOG Lond. Assoc. Gyn. Pontefract & Pinderfields NHS Trust. Socs: RCOG; Eur. Assn. Colposcopy Obstet. & Gyn.; Brit. Soc. Colpos. & Cerv. Cytol.

KAULA, Charles Vivian Woodlands, High St., Bembridge PO35 — MB ChB 1944 Birm.

KAULU, Kenneth Katwamba 84 Burnside Road, Dagenham RM8 1YD — LMSSA 1987 Lond.; MB ChB U Zambia 1976.

KAUNTZE, Ralph, MBE Arran House, La Rue de la Forge, St Martin, Jersey JE3 6BD — MB BChir 1937 Camb.; MD Camb. 1946, MA, MB BChir 1937; FRCP Lond. 1950; MRCS Eng. LRCP Lond. 1935. (Camb. & St. Geo.) Cons. Phys. Emerit. Guy's Hosp. Lond. Prev: Phys. i/c Cardiac Dept. Guy's Hosp. Lond.; Ho. Vis. Phys. Johns Hopkins Hosp. Baltimore, USA; Temp. Lt.-Col. RAMC, Off. i/c Med. Div.

KAUR, Balvinder 144 Haunch Lane, Birmingham B13 0PY — MB ChB 1988 Birm.; BSc (Hons.) Birm. 1985, MB ChB 1988.

KAUR, Hardamanjit Rosie 135 Henwood Road, Wolverhampton WV6 8PJ — MB ChB 1992 Liverp.

KAUR, Inderjeet 72 Freelands Road, Bromley BR1 3HY — MB BS 1960 Lucknow.

KAUR, Kamlash Radford Health Centre, 1 Ilkeston Road, Radford, Nottingham NG7 3GW; 84 Elterwater Drive, Gamston, Nottingham NG2 6PX — MB ChB 1976 Sheff.; MRCGP 1982; DRCOG 1981.

KAUR, Malveen King's Mill Hospital, Mansfield Tel: 01623 22515; 11 Stanley Close, Ravenshead, Nottingham NG15 9GE Tel: 01623 796435 — BM 1993 Soton. SHO (Gen. Surg.) King's Mill Hosp. Mansfield. Prev: SHO (O & G) Addenbrooke's Hosp. Camb.

KAUR, Narinder 594 Great West Road, Hounslow TW5 0TH — MB BS 1963 Panjab; MB BS Panjab (India) 1963; FRCPsych 1994, M 1974; DPM Eng. 1970. (Christian Med. Coll. Ludhiana) Prev: Sen. Regist. Napsbury Hosp.; Lect. Psychiat. Maulana Azad Med. Coll. New Delhi, India; Cons. Psychiat. W. Surrey & NE Hants. HA.

KAUR, Rupinder 16 Macauley Road, Manchester M16 0FA — MB ChB 1994 Sheff.

KAUR, Satnam Gorse Hill Medical Centre, 879 Chester Road, Stretford, Manchester M32 0RN Tel: 0161 864 3037 Fax: 0161 864 3066 — MB BS 1969 Lucknow; MB BS 1969 Lucknow.

KAUR, Satpal 30 Chomeley Road, Reading R61 3 NQ Tel: 01189 666696 Fax: 01189 263230; 3 Souring Meadows, Souring -on-Thames, Reading RQ4 6XB Tel: 01189 696578 — MBBS 1975. (Varanasi, Institute of Medical Sciences, India) GP; Clin. Asst. in Rehab. In Pychiat. Fairmile Hosp. Wallingford.

KAUR, Sharon 9 Perryn House, Bromyard Avenue, London W3 7JD — MB BS 1966 Delhi.

KAUR, Simran 24 Beardwood Park, Beardwood, Blackburn BB2 7BW — MB BS 1977 Bihar; MS (Obst & Gyn.) Patna 1982.

KAUR, Sukhvender (retired) 10 Charlbert Street, London NW8 7BP — MB BS 1961 Punjab; MRCP (UK) 1972. Prev: Sen. Cons. Phys. Manor Ho. Hosp. N. End Rd. Lond.

KAUR, Surjit 726 Melton Road, Thurmaston, Leicester LE4 8BD Tel: 0116 269 5252 Fax: 0116 269 5252; 14 Brightside Road, Leicester LE5 5LD Tel: 0116 273 7647 — MB BS 1965 Delhi. Socs: Med. Defence Union (MDU); Brit. Med. Assn. (BMA); Gen. Med. Counc. (GMC).

KAUR, Surrinder Warley Road Surgery, 118 Warley Road, Oldbury B68 9SZ Tel: 0121 544 5681 Fax: 0121 544 0155 — MB BS 1971 Panjab; MB BS Panjab (India) 1971; DPM Eng. 1983. (Amritsar Med. Coll.)

KAURA, Anjum The Surgery, 1 Rawling Road, Benshaw, Gateshead NE8 4QS Tel: 0191 477 2180; 31 Baronswood, Gosforth, Newcastle upon Tyne NE3 3UB — MB BS 1988 Lond. Prev: Trainee GP/SHO N.d. VTS.

KAURA, Dipak Wallington Medical Centre, 52 Mollison Drive, Wallington SM6 9BY Tel: 020 8647 0811/8659 2272; 70 Lenham Road, Sutton SM1 4BG Tel: 020 8642 9534 — MB BS 1971 Banaras Hindu. (Banaras Hindu)

KAURA, Varun Chandar The Croft Surgery, Wrekenton, Gateshead NE9 7BJ Tel: 0191 487 6129 Fax: 0191 487 3136 — BM BS 1986 Nottm.; BMedSci Nottm. 1984, BM BS 1986; MRCGP 1991; DRCOG 1988. Prev: SHO/Trainee GP N.umbria VTS.

KAURA, Vikas 3 The Drey, Ponteland, Newcastle upon Tyne NE20 9NS — MB ChB 1997 Ed.

KAUSAR, Mahmood 14 Courtenay Av, Harrow HA3 5JJ Tel: 01523 121050 Email: medic@doctor.com — MB ChB 1997 Dundee. SHO Plastic Surg., St. Andrews Centre Broomfield. Prev: Anat. Demonst., St. Geo.'s Hosp., Lond.; SHO Urol. and Gen. Surg., Kingston Hosp, Kingston; SHO Orthopaedic Surg., Ealing Hosp. Ealing.

KAUSAR, Muhammad Shafi Kausar, 26 Bank Street, Glasgow G12 8ND Tel: 0141 339 5513 Fax: 0141 357 5554; 10 Upper Bour Tree Drive, Glasgow G73 4EH Tel: 0141 637 9776 — MB BS 1965 Punjab; MB BS Punjab (Pakistan) 1965; ECFMG Cert 1974; MRCGP 1977; Dip. Pract. Dermat. 1991; Dip. Ven. Liverp. 1969. (Nishtar Med. Coll. Multan) Gen. Sec. Pakistani Doctors (Overseas) Assn.

KAUSAR, Sana 10 Upper Bourtree Drive, Rutherglen, Glasgow G73 4EH — MB ChB 1998 Glas.; MB ChB Glas 1998.

KAUSE, Juliane Barbara 3 Purbrook Cottage, High St., Hamble, Southampton SO31 4JF — MB BS 1994 Lond.; BSc (Hons.) Lond. 1989; AKC 1989.

KAUSER, Ayyaz 50 Allen Road, Peterborough PE1 3BT — MB BS 1992 Lond.; MRCGP 1997. (UCMSM, Uni. Lond.)

KAUSHAL, Chander Shekhar 6 Oldnall Road, Kidderminster DY10 3HW Tel: 01562 751755 — MB BS 1973 Ranchi. Staff Psychiat. Lea Castle Hosp. Kidderminster.

KAUSHAL, Kalpana 24 Hardy Grove, Swinton, Manchester M27 0DA Tel: 0161 794 3701 — MB ChB 1992 Manch.; MRCP 1995. (Manchester) Clin. Research Fell. In Diabetes & Endacrinology Hope Hosp. Salford. Prev: SPR Stepping Hill Hosp. Stockport; SPR Hope Hosp. Salford; SPR Bvrnley Gen. Hosp.

KAUSHAL, Mr Krishan (retired) 16 Norford Way, Bamford, Rochdale OL11 5QS Tel: 01706 868056 — MB BS 1958 Punjab; FRCS Ed. 1968; FRCOphth 1989; DO Eng. 1965. Cons. Ophth. Birch Hill Hosp. Rochdale & Bury Gen. Hosp. Prev: Sen. Regist. St. Paul's Eye Hosp. Liverp.

KAUSHAL, Nazia Anwar 31 Kensington Avenue, Manchester M14 5PG — MB BS 1994 Lond.

KAUSHAL, Pushpa 6 Oldnall Road, Kidderminster DY10 3HW Tel: 01562 751755 — MB BS 1978 Ranchi. Staff Psychiat. Worcs.

KAUSHAL, Sanjay Crowborough House, Cherry Tree Road, Farnham Royal, Slough SL2 3EF — MB ChB 1991 Glas. Ho. Off. (Surg. & Med.) Stobhill Gen. Hosp. Glas.

KAUSHAL, Tejendra Singh (retired) Higher Broughton Health Centre, Bevendon Square Centre, Salford M7 0UF Tel: 0161 792 2582 — MB BS 1956 Punjab; BSc Punjab 1950; MRCP (UK) 1971; MRCGP 1976. Prev: Regist. (Med. & Chest Dis.) Hope Hosp. & Ladywell Hosp. Salford.

KAUSHAL, Vijay L Porth Farm Surgery, Porth Street, Porth CF39 9RR Tel: 01443 682579 Fax: 01443 683667.

KAUSHIK, Vishal Yogendra Namavi, 4 Oakwood, South Hetton, Durham DH6 2SE — MB BS 1990 Baroda; MRCP (UK) 1993.

KAUSHIK, Vivek 24 Bankside Road, East Didsbury, Manchester M20 5GD — MB ChB 1997 Manch.

KAVADIA, Vasiliki 61 East Dulwich Road, London SE22 9AP — Ptychio Iatrikes 1992 Patras.

KAVALIER, Frederick Charles 7:th Floor New Guy's House, Guy's Hospital, St Thomas Street, London SE1 9RT Tel: 020 7955 4648 Fax: 020 7955 2550 Email: fred.kavalier@gstt.sthames.nhs.uk; 10 Archibald Road, London N7 0AL Tel: 020 7607 7718 Fax: 020 7700 1042 Email: kavalier@btinternet.com — MB BS 1981 Lond.; BA Pennsylvania 1970; MRCP (UK) 1984; MRCPCH 1997. (Roy. Free) Primary Care Geneticist, Guy's Hosp. Lond. Prev: Princip. James Wigg Pract.; SHO (Paediat.) St. Thos. & Whipps Cross Hosp. Lond.; Ho. Phys. Hosp. Sick Childr. Lond.

KAVAN, Rama Groom Cottage, The Drive, Church Lane, Oakley, Bedford MK43 7ST Tel: 012302 4157 — MB BS 1965 Calcutta; MRCS Eng. LRCP Lond. 1982; FFA RCS Eng. 1972; DA Eng. 1969; DObst RCOG 1968. Cons. Anaesth. Bedford Gen. Hosp. Socs: Assn. Anaesth. & BMA. Prev: Sen. Regist. (Anaesth.) N.ampton Gen. Hosp.; SHO O & G Hemel Hempstead Gen. Hosp.; Ho. Off. Obst. Eliz. G. Anderson Hosp.

KAVANAGH, David 77 Ayr Road, Newton Mearns, Glasgow G77 6QU — MB ChB 1998 Glas.; MB ChB Glas 1998.

KAVANAGH, Jayne Flat 9, Tufnell House, 14 Pleasant Place, London N1 2BY — MB ChB 1990 Liverp.

KAVANAGH, Joseph Upholme, Blackamoor Crescent, Dore, Sheffield S17 3GL Tel: 0114 236 0339 — MB ChB 1978 Sheff.

KAVANAGH, Mary Jeanne Patricia Quayside Medical Practice, Chapel Street, Newhaven BN9 9PW Tel: 01273 615000 Fax: 01273 611527 — MB BCh BAO 1980 NUI; LRCPI & LM, LRCSI & LM 1980. (Royal College of Surgeons in Dublin) Principle Gen. Practitioner 3/4 Time. Prev: Trainee GP Mid Sussex VTS; Ho. Off. (Surg.) Redhill Gen. Hosp.; Ho. Off. (Phys.) Cuckfield Hosp.

KAVANAGH, Melanie Jane 14 Waterside Mill, Denholme Road, Oxenhope, Keighley BD22 9NP Tel: 01535 644552 Fax: 01535 640900 — MB ChB 1994 Leeds. SHO Med. Harrogate.

KAVANAGH, Michael 4 Overton Drive, Wanstead, London E11 2NJ Tel: 020 8989 1729 — MB BCh BAO NUI 1950; MLCOM 1981 Lond. (Univ. Coll. Dub.) Socs: Brit. Osteop. Assn. Prev: Ho. Surg. Mater Miser. Hosp. Dub.; Ho. Phys. War Memor. Hosp. Scunthorpe; O & G Ho. Surg. Orsett Lodge Hosp. Grays.

KAVANAGH, Richard James 69 Shortlands Road, Kingston upon Thames KT2 6HF — MB BS 1991 Lond.

KAVANAGH, Rose Julia Cottage, Stalling Down, Cowbridge CF71 7DT Tel: 0144 632866 — MB BCh BAO 1986 Dub.; DCH RCP Lond. 1989. SHO (Psychiat.) WhitCh. Hosp. Cardiff.

KAVANAGH, Sean James Gerrard 42 George Street, Sedgley Park, Prestwich, Manchester M25 9WS — MB ChB 1992 Manch.; BSc (Med. Biochem.) Manch. 1989, MB ChB 1992; MRCP 1996. (Manch.) Specialist Regist. & Hon. Clin. Lect. (Elderly Med.) N.W. Deanery. Socs: Brit. Geriat. Soc. Prev: SHO (Gen. Med.) N. Manch. Gen. Hosp.

KAVANAGH, Mr Thomas Gerald St Helier Hospital, Wrythe Lane, Carshalton SM5 1AA Tel: 020 8644 4343 Fax: 020 8641 4546; St. Anthony's Hospital, London Road, North Cheam, Sutton SM3 9DW Tel: 020 8337 6691 Fax: 020 894 6477 — MB BS 1972 Lond.; MRCS Eng. LRCP Lond. 1972; BSC Hons Physiology; FRCS Eng. 1978. (St Bartholomews Hospital) Cons. Orthop. Surg. St. Helier Hosp. Socs: Brit. Orthop. Assn.; BMA; Fell. Roy. Soc. Med.

KAVI, Jayendra Department of Medical Microbiology, Level 6, Ninewells Hospital & Medical School, Dundee DD1 9SY Tel: 01382 660111 — MB ChB 1984 Glas.; BSc (Hons. Immunol.) Glas. 1981; MRCPath 1991. Cons. & Hon. Sen. Lect. (Med. Microbiol.) Ninewells Hosp. & Med. Sch. Dundee. Socs: Assn. Clin. Path.; Assn. Med. Microbiol.; Coun. Mem. Scot. MicroBiol. Assn. Prev: Sen. Regist. (Med. Microbiol.) Pub. Health Laborat. E. Birm. Hosp.

KAVI, Lesley Anne Church Road Surgery, 169 Church Road, Sheldon, Birmingham B26 3TT Tel: 0121 743 3409 — MB ChB 1983 Glas.; DRCOG 1988.

KAVI, Supriy Pagoda Community Mental Health Centre, Hemitage Lane, Maidstone ME16 9PD Tel: 01622 724200 Fax: 01622 724201 — MB ChB 1989 Liverp.; MRCPsych 1994; MBA (Lond) 1999. Cons.Adukt Psychiat., Invicta Community Care NHS Trust, Maidstone. Prev: Sen. Regist., Roy. Lond. Hosp.

KAVIA, Sanjay 2 Hiron Croft, Coventry CV3 6HU — MB BS 1998 Lond.; MB BS Lond 1998.

KAVURI, Seshu Babu Albert Street Surgery, 63 Albert Street, Rugby CV21 2SN Tel: 01788 573366 Fax: 01788 573473; 37 Long Furlong, Rugby CV22 5QT Tel: 01788 334496 Fax: 01788 334497 — MB BS 1972 Andhra. (Rangaraya (Andhra)) Med. Practitioner Benefits Agency. Socs: Rugby & Dist. Med. Soc. Prev: Regist. (Anaesth.) Walsgrave Hosp. Coventry & E. Birm. Hosp.; Clin. Asst. (Anaesth.) Coventry Health Trust.

KAWA, Z I Addison House Surgery, Hamstel Road, Harlow CM20 1DS Tel: 01279 692780 Fax: 01279 692781 — MB BCh 1970 Cairo; MB BCh 1970 Cairo.

KAWAFI, Khalil Rajab 17 Ellesmere Road S., Chorlton, Manchester M21 0TE — MB ChB 1990 Manch.; MRCP 1996.

KAWAR, Prakash Mal St James Health Centre, 47 St. James's Street, Walthamstow, London E17 7NH Tel: 020 8521 6138 Fax: 020 8521 4931 — MB BS 1973 Rajasthan.

KAWECKI, Jacek Zygmunt Turnie, Hixton, Stafford ST18 0PU — MB ChB 1975 Leeds.

KAWIK, Leslaw Kazimierz 15 Foxhunt Grove, Fords Farm, Calcot, Reading RG31 7PE Tel: 01734 412980 — MD 1955 Warsaw; LMSSA Lond. 1971; Specialist Anaesth. Warsaw 1965. Assoc. Specialist (Anaesth.) Roy. Berks. Hosp. Reading. Socs: Reading Path. Soc.; Assn. Anaesths. Prev: Chairm. Anaesth. Dept. Hosp. Childr. Traum. Surg. Warsaw.

KAWONGA, Raphael Mlinda Peter c/o MSRC, Manchester Medical School, Oxford Road, Manchester M13 9PT — MB ChB 1978 Manch.

KAWOOYA, Benedict The Surgery, 21 Shawbrooke Road, Eltham, London SE9 6AE Tel: 020 8850 1613 Fax: 020 8859 5199 — MB ChB 1975 Manchester; MB ChB 1975 Manchester.

KAWSAR, Mrs Mohanarathi 33 Melrose Gardens, Edgware HA8 5LN — MRCS Eng. LRCP Lond. 1992.

KAY, Mr Alan Robert 23 Chepstow Park, Downend, Bristol BS16 6SQ Tel: 0117 957 0717 — MB BS 1986 Lond.; FRCS Eng. 1990; FRCS (Plast) 1997. (Westm.) Specialist Regist. (Plastic, Reconstruc. & Burns Surg.) Frenchay Hosp. Bristol. Socs: Assoc. Mem. Brit. Assn. Plastic Surgs.; Internat. Soc. Burn Injury; Assoc. Mem. Brit. Soc. Surg. Hand. Prev: Fell. Hand Surg. NW Region; Regist. (Plastic, Reconstruc. & Burns Surg.) Countess of Chester

Hosp.; SHO (Plastic & Reconstruc. Surg.) Qu. Mary's Univ. Hosp. Lond.

KAY, Alison Jane The Flat, 224 Psalter Lane, Sheffield S11 8UT — MB ChB 1977 Sheff.

KAY, Alison Jane Fraser Central Health Centre, North Carbrain Rd, Cumbernauld, Glasgow G67 1BJ Tel: 01236 731771; 13 Smithycroft, Hamilton ML3 7UL — MB ChB 1978 Aberd.; MFFP 1993; DCCH RCP Ed. 1985; DRCOG 1981. Assoc. Specialist (Community Paediat.) N. Lanarksh.; Clin. Med. Off. (Family Plann.) Lanarksh.; Assessor Lanarksh. Area Family Plann. Prev: Assoc. Specialist (Child Health) Cumbernauld & Kilsyth; Clin. Med. Off. Cumbernauld, Kilsyth & Bellshill; GP Hamilton.

KAY, Alison Laura 11 Staveley Avenue, Bolton BL1 7HD — MB ChB 1995 Manch.

KAY, Andrew Duncan Birmingham University, Department of Intensive Care, Queen Elizabeth Medical Centre, Edgbaston, Birmingham B15 2TH — MB BS 1991 Lond.

KAY, Andrew John 1 Sycamore Tree Close, Radyr, Cardiff CF15 8RT — BM BS 1996 Nottm.

KAY, Professor Anthony Barrington Allergy and Clinical Immunology, Imperial College School of Medicine at the, National Heart & Lung Inst., Dovehouse St., London SW3 6LY Tel: 020 7351 8181 Fax: 020 7376 3138 Email: a.b.kay@ic.ac.uk; Stamford Brook House, 12 Stamford Brook Avenue, London W6 0YD — MB ChB 1963 Ed.; FRSE 1993; PhD Camb. 1970, MA 1965; DSc Ed. 1979, MB ChB 1963; FRCP Lond. 1980, M 1967; FRCP Ed. 1975, M 1974; FRCPath 1989, M 1977; F Med Sci 1999. (Ed.) Prof. & Head Allergy & Clin. Immunol. Imperial Coll. Sch. Med. Nat. Heart & Lung Inst. Lond.; Jt. Edr. Clin. Exp. Allergy; Hon. Cons. Roy. Brompton Hosp. Lond. Socs: Fell. Amer. Acad.; (Ex-Pres.) Europ. Acad. Allergol. & Clin. Immunol.; (Ex-Pres.) Br. Soc. Allergy & Clin. Immunol. Prev: Reader & Sen. Lect. (Experim. Path.) Univ. Edin. Med. Sch.; Dep. Dir. & Cons. Immunol. Div. SE Scotl. Regional Blood Serv.

KAY, Anthony John Noblet Ponteland Medical Group, Thornhill Road, Ponteland, Newcastle upon Tyne NE20 9PZ Tel: 01661 825513 Fax: 01661 860755; Dissington Old Farm, Ponteland, Newcastle upon Tyne NE18 0DE Tel: 01661 23240 — BM BCh 1971 Oxf.; MA Oxf. 1976, BM BCh 1971; MRCGP 1980; DObst RCOG 1973.

KAY, Bernard 'Ridgeway', 55 Priory Lane, Kents Bank, Grange-over-Sands LA11 7BJ — LMSSA 1950 Lond.

KAY, Clifford Ralph, CBE (retired) 12 Dene Park, Didsbury, Manchester M20 2GF Tel: 0161 445 9686 Fax: 0161 434 2040 Email: cliffordkay@compuserve.com — MB ChB Liverp. 1950; PhD Manch. 1975; MD Liverp. 1960; FRCGP 1971; FFFP (Hon.) 1994. Prev: GP Barlow Med. Centre Manch.

KAY, Clive Laurence 37 Park Lane, Whitefield, Manchester M45 7PU — MB ChB 1987 Manch.; BSc (Hons.) Manch. 1984, MB ChB 1987; MRCP (UK) 1990. Regist. (Diag. Radiol.) Univ. Manch. Prev: SHO (Neurol.) Roy. Hallamsh. Hosp. Sheff.; SHO (Med.) Hammersmith Hosp. Lond. & N.. Gen. Hosp. Sheff.

KAY, Daniel Paterson The Surgery, Northfield Road, Blaby, Leicester LE8 4GU Tel: 0116 277 1705; 10 West Street, Blaby, Leicester LE8 4GY — MB ChB 1961 Ed.; Cert. JCC Lond. 1976; DObst RCOG 1965. Socs: BMA & Leicester Med. Soc. Prev: Ho. Surg. & Ho. Phys. (Obst.) Buckland Hosp. Dover; Ho. Surg. Dunfermline & W. Fife Hosp.

KAY, David Hunter 2 Maclachlan Avenue, Denny FK6 5HF — MB ChB 1997 Glas.

KAY, David Louis (retired) (cons. rooms), The End House, 56 Hendon Avenue, Finchley, London N3 1UH Tel: 020 8346 3320 Email: davidlkay@talk21.com — MB ChB 1961 Manch. Train. Analyst (BCP UK CP) Soc. Analyt. Psychol. Lond.; Train. Therapist Brit. Assn. Psychotherapists Lond. Prev: GP Watford & Manch.

KAY, David Nicholas 15 The Avenue, Chichester PO19 4PX Tel: 01243 779901 — MB BS 1968 Lond.; FRCR 1977; DMRD Eng. 1973. (Char. Cross) Cons. Radiol. St. Richard's Hosp. Chichester. Prev: Sen. Regist. St. Geo. Hosp. Lond.; Ho. Phys. Brompton Hosp. Lond.; Research Fell. Roy. Marsden Hosp. Lond.

KAY, David Samuel George Department Of Psychiatry, Victoria Hospital, Blackpool FY3 8NR — MB ChB 1975 Dundee; MRCPsych. 1980. Cons. Psychiat. Vict. Hosp. Blackpool. Prev: Cons. Psychiat. Cheadle Roy. Hosp.; Lect. Univ. Dundee; Sen. Regist. Tayside Health Bd.

KAY, David Whittle (retired) 102 Overstone Road, Sywell, Northampton NN6 0AW Tel: 01604 645001 — MB BS 1959 Lond.; BSc (Anat.) Lond. 1956; MFOM RCP Lond. 1983; DIH 1982. Prev: Med. Off. STC plc. New S.gate Lond.

KAY, Professor David William Kilbourne MRC Neurochemical Pathology Unit, Newcastle General Hospital, Westgate Road, Newcastle upon Tyne NE4 6BE Tel: 0191 273 5251 Fax: 0191 272 5291 Email: d.w.kay@ncl.ac.uk; 8 Grosvenor Place, Newcastle upon Tyne NE2 2RE Tel: 0191 281 0249 — BM BCh 1943 Oxf.; DM Oxf. 1960; FRCP Lond. 1972, M 1964; FRCPsych 1971; MRANZCP 1976. Prof. Emerit. Prev: Vis. Prof. Dept. of Pschiat. Univ. of Newc.; Cons. Psychiat. Roy. Vict. Infirm. Newc.; Prof. Psychiat. Univ. Tasmania.

KAY, Diana Muriel Cheam Family Practice, The Knoll, Parkside, Cheam, Sutton SM3 8BS Tel: 020 8770 2014 Fax: 020 8770 1864; 41 Bradstock Road, Stoneleigh, Epsom KT17 2LD Tel: 020 8393 8928 — MB BS 1982 Lond.; Cert. Family Plann. JCC 1986; DCH RCP Lond. 1985. (St. Geo.) Prev: SHO (O & G) St. Geo. Hosp. Lond.; Clin. Med. Off. (Community Child Health) Camberwell HA; SHO (Paediat.) William Harvey Hosp. Ashford.

KAY, Douglas Michael Insch Health Centre 2, Rannes Street, Insch AB52 6JJ Tel: 01464 820673 Fax: 01464 820395; Candlehill Lodge, Premnay, Insch AB52 6PX Tel: 01464 820727 Fax: 01464 820727 — MB ChB 1979 Aberd.; MRCGP 1991. Socs: Garloch Med. Soc.

KAY, Douglas Telfer (retired) 30 Manor Place, Cults, Aberdeen AB15 9QN Tel: 01224 867768 — MB ChB 1944 Ed.; FRCP Ed. 1998, MRCP Ed. 1952. JP.; Hon. Chest Phys. Grampian HB. Prev: Chest Phys. & Clin. Lect. Univ. Aberd.

KAY, Elizabeth Marguerite Downlands House, Southdown Road, Shawford, Winchester SO21 2BY Tel: 01962 712915; The Brownhill Surgery, 2 Brownhill Road, Chandlers Ford, Eastleigh SO53 2ZB — MB ChB Birm. 1976; MRCGP 1981; DRCOG 1978.

KAY, Gillian Elizabeth Readesmoor Medical Group Practice, 29-29A West Street, Congleton CW12 1JP Tel: 01260 276161 Fax: 01260 297340 — MD 1974 Toronto; BA Toronto 1970; Lic. Nova Scotia Med. Bd. 1977; Lic. Coll. Phys. & Surg. Ontario 1975; CCFP 1976. (Univ. Toronto Med. Sch.) Congleton Represen. Matern. Serv. Comm. Macclesfield Dist. Gen. Hosp. Socs: BMA. Prev: LMC Represen. Congleton & Macclesfield.

KAY, Herbert (retired) 14 Cortland Road, Nunthorpe, Middlesbrough TS7 0JX Tel: 01642 313186 Fax: 01642 313186 Email: h.kay@nteworld.com — MB ChB 1952 Glas.; FRCGP 1979, M 1966. Prev: Ho. Phys. Univ. Med. Unit Stobhill Hosp. Glas.

KAY, James Sherwood House Medical Practice, 9 Sandon Road, Edgbaston, Birmingham B67 8DP Tel: 0121 420 0100 Fax: 0121 420 0107; 1 Hampshire Drive, Edgbaston, Birmingham B15 3NY Email: jandrkay@argonet.co.uk — MB ChB 1977 Sheff.; MRCGP 1981; DRCOG 1982. Prev: Trainee GP Rotherham VTS; Ho. Off. (Surg.) Moorgate Gen. Hosp. Rotherham; Ho. Off. (Med.) Dist. Gen. Hosp. Rotherham.

KAY, James Thomas Melville Lodge Surgery, Lodge Road, Chippenham SN15 3SY Tel: 01249 660667 Fax: 01249 447350; Field House, East Tytherton, Chippenham SN15 4LT Tel: 01249 74268 — MB BS 1984 Lond.; MA Camb. 1990; MRCGP 1990.

KAY, Janet Spalding (retired) Underfell, Lancaster LA1 5EE Tel: 01524 2643 — M.B., Ch.B. Glas. 1924.

KAY, Jean Margaret (retired) 12 Queens Place, Shoreham-by-Sea BN43 5AA Tel: 01273 453252 — MB BS Lond. 1969; MRCS Eng. LRCP Lond. 1969; DObst RCOG 1971. Prev: Cons. Adviser Palliat. Med. St. Peter & St. Jas. Home & Hospice Lewes.

KAY, Jennifer Zelda Sheringham Avenue Surgery, 1 Sheringham Avenue, Southgate, London N14 4UB Tel: 020 8360 9044; 10 Woodgrange Avenue, London N12 0PS Tel: 020 8445 2498 — MRCS Eng. LRCP Lond. 1976; BSc (Hons.) Lond. 1973, MB BS 1976; MRCP (UK) 1979. (Roy. Free)

KAY, Jonathan Daniel Simon Stonecross House, Southend, Garsington, Oxford OX44 9DD — MB BS 1977 Lond.; MSc Oxf. 1977, BA 1973; MRCS Eng. LRCP Lond. 1977; MRCPath 1985. (Oxf. & St. Bart.) Cons. Chem. Pathol. & Lect. Nuffield Dept. Clin. Biochem. John Radcliffe Hosp. Oxf.; Dist. Tutor Roy. Coll. Path.; Chairm. Scientif. Developm. Subcomm. of Assn. Clin. Biochem. Prev:

Clin. Lect. & Sen. Regist. Nuffield Dept. Clin. Biochem. Oxf.; Clin. Lect. (Clin. Biochem.) Inst. Child Health Lond.; Hon. Sen. Regist. Hosp. Sick Childr. Gt. Ormond St. Lond.

KAY, Joseph Fraser (retired) 25 Braidwood Road, Braidwood, Carluke ML8 5PD — MB ChB Glas. 1948. Prev: Gen. Practitioner, Hamilton.

KAY, Lesley Anne HCA Princess Grace Hospital, 42 Nottingham Place, London W1M 3FD Tel: 020 7486 1234 Fax: 020 7486 5412 — MB BS 1974 Newc.; FRCP (UK) 1990; MRCP (UK) 1977; FRCPath 1994 M 1982. Cons. Haemat. & Clin. HCA Internat. Laboratories. Socs: Brit. Blood Transfus. Soc.; Brit. Soc. Haematol.; (Sec.) Autologous Transfus. Gp. Prev: Cons. Haemat. Sunderland HA.

KAY, Lesley Jane Department of Rheumatology, Freeman Hospital, Newcastle upon Tyne NE7 7DN — BM BCh 1990 Oxf.; MA Oxf. 1993; MRCP (UK) 1993; MSc (Pub. Health) Newc. 1997. (Oxford University Medical School) Cons. Rheum. Freeman Hosp. Newc. u. Tyne; Hon. Assoc. Specialist in Rheumatol., Freeman Hosp., Newc. Socs: Brit. Soc. Rheum.; Assn. Med. Educ. in Europe. Prev: ARC Clin. Lect. in Rheum., Univ. of Newc.; Specialist Regist. (Rheum.) Freeman Hosp. Newc.; Specialist Regist. (Rheum.) Freeman Hosp. Newc. u. Tyne.

KAY, Lucille Church End Medical Centre, 66 Mayo Road, Church End Estate, Willesden, London NW10 9HP Tel: 020 8930 6262 Fax: 020 8930 6260 Email: lucille.kay@gp-e84013.nhs.uk — MB BCh 1970 Witwatersrand; MFFP 1993. (Witwatersrand) Sen. Clin. Med. Off. (Family Plann.) Barnet HA. Socs: Menopause.Soc; Brit.Med.Acupunc..Soc.

KAY, Margaret Family Consultancy, The Health Centre, Vicarage St., Barnstaple EX32 7BH Tel: 01271 371761; Haldon House, 2 Park Lane, Barnstaple EX32 9AJ Tel: 01271 373814 Email: mkayatbarum@aol.com — MB BS 1971 Lond.; MRCPsych 1975; Dip. Psychother. Leeds 1985. (Middlx. Hosp.) Cons. Child. & Adolesc. Psychiat. Devon Partnership Trust. Socs: Inst. of Gp. Anal.; Gp. Analytic Soc., new Assn. of Child Psychologists & Psychiat.s. Prev: Cons. Child & Adolesc. Psychiat. Wakefield & Pontefract Community Health NHS Trust.

KAY, Mark Sidley (retired) 7 Keevil Avenue, Calne SN11 0JN Tel: 01249 813553 — BM BCh 1947 Oxf.; MA Oxf. 1951, BM BCh 1947; MRCGP 1955; DObst RCOG 1951. Prev: Estab. Med. Off. Min. Defence ChristCh.

KAY, Matthew Red c/o MSO, Macclesfield District General Hospital, Victoria Road, Macclesfield SK10 3BL — MB ChB 1998 Manch.; MB ChB Manch 1998.

KAY, Michael Jeremy Richard Pheasant House, Booths Hall Road, Boothsdown, Worsley, Manchester M28 1LB — MB ChB 1974 Dundee.

KAY, Mr Neville Rupert Mason, TD 362 South Road, Walkley, Sheffield S6 3TF Tel: 0114 231 3555 Fax: 0114 231 4646 — FRCS Eng. 1969; MRCS Eng. LRCP Lond. 1959. (Sheff.) Socs: (Ex-Pres.) S. Yorks. Medico-Legal Soc.; Brit. Orthop. Assn.; Brit. Soc. Surg. Hand. Prev: Regist. Rotat. (Surg.) Roy. Infirm. Sheff.; Resid. Surg. Off. Robt. Jones & Agnes Hunt Orthop. Hosp. OsW.ry; Sen. Clin. Fell. (Orthop. & Hand Surg.) Univ. Colorado Denver.

KAY, Mr Nicholas Joseph 15 Lancaster Road, Didsbury, Manchester M20 2QU — MB ChB 1975 Liverp.; FRCS Eng. 1981. Cons. ENT Surg. Stepping Hill Hosp. & Buxton Cottage Hosp. Socs: Fell. Roy. Soc. Med.; N. Eng. Otolaryng. Soc.; Brit. Assn. Otol. Prev: Cons. ENT Surg. Oldham & Dist. Gen. Hosp.; Sen. Regist. Leeds & Bradford Hosps.; Regist. Liverp. HA.

KAY, Nigel Howerd Department of Anaesthetics, Northampton General Hospital, Cliftonville, Northampton NN1 5BD Tel: 01604 34700 — MB BS 1977 Lond.; BSc Lond. 1974, MB BS 1977; FFA RCS Eng. 1982. (Middlx.) Cons. Anaesth. N.ampton Gen. Hosp.; Tutor Coll. Anaesth. Prev: Clin. Lect. Nuffield Dept. Anaesth. Univ. Oxf.; Hon. Sen. Regist. John Radcliffe Hosp. Oxf.; Regist. Nuffield Dept. Anaesth. Oxf.

KAY, Peter Alexander 2 Maclachlan Avenue, Denny FK6 5HF — MB ChB 1998 Glas.; MB ChB Glas 1998.

KAY, Peter George Belbroughton House, Hailey, Witney OX29 9UB Tel: 01993 702236 Fax: 01993 702236; Belbroughton House, Hailey, Witney OX29 9UB Tel: 01993 702236 — MB BS 1961 Lond.; MRCS Eng. LRCP Lond. 1961; FRCGP 1983, M 1968; DCH Eng. 1964; DObst RCOG 1963. (Middlx. Hosp.) Socs: (Ex-Pres.) Oxf. Med. Soc. Prev: SHO (Paediat.) Shrodells Hosp. Watford; Ho. Surg. & Ho. Phys. Chase Farm Hosp. Enfield; Ho. Off. (Obst.) St. Paul's Hosp. Hemel Hempstead.

KAY, Peter Hammond Larkby Young People's Unit, Victoria Park Road, Exeter EX4 2NU; Easthocme Farm, Newton St Cyres, Exeter EX5 5BS — MB BS 1980 Newc.; FRCPsych 2001; MRCP (UK) 1983; MRCPsych 1985. 1990 to date: Cons. Child and Adolesc. Psychiat., N. and E. Devon Partnership (NHS) Trust. Lead Counsultant in Adolscent Psychiat., Larkby Young People's Club, Exeter. Socs: Assn. Child Psychols. & Psychiats.

KAY, Mr Peter Richard Department Orthopaedic Surgery, North Manchester General Hospital, Crumpsall, Manchester M8 6RL Tel: 0161 720 2307 Fax: 0161 839 4202 Email: peter@kayr.demon.co.uk; 12 Davyhulme Road, Urmston, Manchester M41 7DS Tel: 0161 720 2307 Fax: 0161 839 4202 — MB ChB 1981 Manch.; BA (Maths) Open 1988; FRCS Glas. 1985. (Manch.) Sen. Lect. (Orthop. Surg.) Univ. Manch.; Hon. Cons. Orthop. & Trauma Surg. N. Manch. NHS Healthcare Trust. Socs: Brit. Orthop. Assn.; BMA; Brit. Orthop. Research Soc. Prev: Sen. Regist. N.W. Region. Orthop.; Regional Research Fell. (Orthop.) NW RHA; Regist. Rotat. (Orthop.) N. Manch. & Trafford HAs.

KAY, Peter Teik Soon Somerford Grove Practice, Somerford Grove Health Centre, Somerford Grove, London N16 7UA Tel: 020 7249 2078 Fax: 020 7275 7198 — MB BS 1979 Lond.; MRCS Eng. LRCP Lond. 1979. (St. Bart.)

KAY, Mr Philip Haworth Department of Cardiothoracic Surgery, Leeds General Infirmary, Great George St., Leeds LS1 3EX Tel: 0113 392 3368 Fax: 0113 392 8092 — BM BCh 1974 Oxf.; MA Oxf. 1974; DM Oxf. 1986; FRCS Eng. 1979. (Univ. Oxf.) Cons. Cardiac Surg. Gen. Infirm. Leeds; Hon. Sen. Lect. Univ. Leeds. Socs: Soc. Cardiothoracic Surgs. GB & Irel.; Europ. Soc. Cardiothoracic Surgs. Prev: Sen. Regist. (Surg.) Nat. Heart & Chest Hosps. Lond.; Internat. Fell. Cardiac Surg. Oregon Health Sci. Univ. Portland, Oregon; Regist. (Cardiothoracic Surg.) Brompton Hosp. Lond.

KAY, Philip Martin c/o Anaesthetic Office, Airedale General Hospital, Skipton Road, Steeton, Keighley BD20 6TD Tel: 01535 652511 — MB BS 1979 Lond.; BSc Lond. 1976, MB BS 1979; FFA RCS Eng. 1984. (Kings Coll. Hosp.) Cons. Anaesth. Airedale Gen. Hosp. Keighley. Prev: Sen. Regist. (Anaesth.) S. Tees & Newc. Health Dists.; Regist. (Anaesth.) Univ. & City Hosps. Nottm.; Regist. & SHO (Anaesth.) Norf. & Norwich Hosp.

KAY, Phyllis Irene (retired) 24 Cassiobury Drive, Watford WD17 3AB Tel: 01923 223409 — MB BCh 1924 Manch.; FRCS Ed. 1932; MB Bch (Hnrs.) Manch. 1924. Prev: Asst. Med. Off. St. Chas.' Hosp.

KAY, Richard Andrew 16 Rippingham Road, Withington, Manchester M20 3EX — MB ChB 1980 Manch.

KAY, Ronald William 13 Grange Loan, Edinburgh EH9 2NP — MB ChB 1980 Ed.

KAY, Sheelagh Waterloo Surgery, 617 Wakefield Road, Waterloo, Huddersfield HD5 9XP Tel: 01484 531461; One Acre, 97 Linfit Fold, Linfit Lane, Kirkburton, Huddersfield HD8 0UA Tel: 01484 604849 — MB ChB 1984 Leeds; BSc (Hons.) Leeds 1981. (Univ. Leeds)

KAY, Sidney 83 Northway, London NW11 6PD Tel: 020 8458 6727 — MB BCh BAO Belf. 1945; MD Belf. 1951. (Belf.) Socs: Fell. Roy. Soc. Med.; Roy. Coll. Gen. Pract. Prev: Med. Adviser Mobil Oil Company Ltd.; Clin. Asst. Brompton Hosp. & W.m. Hosp. Chest Clinic Lond.; Sen. Regist. Windsor Chest Clinic & Harefield Hosp.

KAY, Mr Simon Peter Jabir Department of Plastic Surgery, University Hospital of St James, Leeds LS9 7TF Tel: 0113 206 5719 Fax: 0113 243 8162; Roundhay Hall, Jackson Avenue, Leeds LS8 1NT Tel: 0113 268 8788 Fax: 0113 268 1340 Email: simon.kay@dial.pipex.com — BM BCh 1976 Oxf.; BA Oxf., BM BCh 1976; FRCS (Plast Surg.) Eng. 1988; FRCS Eng. 1979. Cons. Plastic Surg. St. Jas. Univ. Hosp. Leeds; Hon. Clin. Lect. Leeds Univ. Socs: Brit. Assn. Plastic Surg.; Brit. Soc. Surg. Hand. Prev: Sen. Regist. (Plastic Surg.) N.W. Region.

KAY, Simon Robert Haldon House Surgery, 37-39 Imperial Road, Exmouth EX8 1DH Tel: 01395 222777/222888 Fax: 01395 269769 — MB BS 1981 Lond.; MRCGP 1985; DRCOG 1984; Dip. Sport Med. (Ed.) 1997. (St. Bart.)

KAY, Stephen Michael Elmwood Medical Centre, 7 Burlington Road, Buxton SK17 9AY Tel: 01298 23019; Hawk How, Level Lane,

Burbage, Buxton SK17 6TU — MB BCh 1970 Wales; MRCGP 1976; DObst RCOG 1973. Prev: Squadron Ldr. RAF Med. Br.

KAY, Stewart Aylesbury Partnership, Aylesbury Medical Centre, Taplow House, Thurlow Street, London SE17 2XE Tel: 020 7703 2205; 3 Ferguson Close, Scotts Lane, Bromley BR2 0LY — MRCS Eng. LRCP Lond. 1976; BSc (Hons.) Lond. 1973, MB BS 1976. (Westm.) GP Lond. Prev: Trainee GP Brighton Vocat. Train. Scheme; Ho. Surg. (Orthop.) W.m. Hosp. Lond. Ho. Phys. St. Helen's Hosp.; Hastings.

KAY, Tracey Anne Autumn Rise, Burnt House Lane, Bransgore, Christchurch BH23 8AL — BM BS 1996 Nottm.

KAY, Valerie Jean Department of Radiology, Northampton General Hospital, Billing Road, Northampton NN1 5BD — MB BS 1977 Lond.; FRCR 1985. (Middlx.) Cons. Radiol. N.ampton Gen. Hosp. Prev: Regist. (Radiol.) John Radcliffe Hosp. Oxf.

KAY, Vanessa Juliet 18 Telny Place, Aberdour, Burntisland KY3 0TG — MB ChB 1987 Dundee; MD Dundee 1994; MRCOG 1995. Lect. (O & G) Univ. Edin.; Hon. Sen. Regist. (Obst. & Gyn.) Roy. Infirm. Edin.

KAY, William David Doctors Surgery, Southwood Medical Centre, Links Way, Farnborough GU14 0NA Tel: 01252 371715 Fax: 01252 524344 — MB ChB 1978 Glas.; BSc Glas. 1975, MB ChB 1978. Prev: Med. Off., RAF Med. Br.

KAYA, Banu 7 Park View Gardens, White Hart Lane, London N22 5SH — MB BS 1998 Lond.; MB BS Lond 1998.

KAYA, Ebru 7 Park View Gardens, White Hart Lane, London N22 5SH — MB BS 1998 Lond.; MB BS Lond 1998.

KAYAN, Altan 52A Park Road, Nottingham NG7 1JG — Tip Doktoru 1962 Aegean Univ. Turkey.

KAYANI, Javid Akhter Accident & Emergency Department, University Hospital Birmingham NHS Trust, Selly Oak Hospital, Raddlebarn Road, Birmingham B29 6JD Tel: 0121 627 8873 Fax: 0121 627 8294 — MRCS Eng. LRCP Lond. 1985; MB BS Lahore 1983; BMedSci Nottm. 1979; FRCS Glas. 1993; FRCS Ed. 1992. Cons. A & E Univ. Hosp. Birm.; Hon. Sen. Lect. Birm. Prev: Sen. Regist. W. Midl. A & E Train. Scheme.

KAYANI, Junaid Tony 100 Rolls Ct, Inks Green, London E4 9EJ — MB BS 1997 Lond.

KAYANI, Riaz Mustapha 90 Tanfield Av, London NW2 7RT — MB BS 1997 Lond.

KAYARKAR, Mr Vishwas Vasant Meltwood, 141A Bawtry Road, Bessacarr, Doncaster DN4 7AH; Doncaster Royal Infirmary, Thorne Road, Doncaster DN2 5LT Tel: 01302 366666 — MB BS Bombay 1975, MS 1978; FRCSI 1981; FRCOphth 1989. Cons. Ophth. Doncaster Roy. Infirm. Doncaster. Socs: Fell. Roy. Coll. of Ophth.s; BMA.

KAYE, Andrew 47 Combe Park, Weston, Bath BA1 3NS — MB BS 1992 Lond.

KAYE, Angela Mary Elm House Surgery, 29 Beckenham Road, Beckenham BR3 4PR Tel: 020 8650 0173 Fax: 020 8663 3911 — MB BS Lond. 1980; MRCGP 1984; LicAc 1992; MFFP 1994; DRCOG 1983; DCH RCP Lond. 1982. (King's Coll. Hosp. Med. Sch.) Prev: Co-ordinator Servs. for Wom. E. Surrey Hosp. & Community Healthcare NHS Trust.

KAYE, Anna Catherine Benhill &Belmont GP Centre, Istation Approach, Belmount, Sutton; 44 Burdon Lane, Bearsden, Cheam, Sutton SM2 7PT — MB BS 1975 Lond.; DCH Eng. 1977. p/t Princip. GP Sutton; GP Tutor St Geo.'s Hosp. Redral Sch. Grad. entry Progr.

KAYE, Anthony Howard Canterbury Road Surgery, 186 Canterbury Road, Davyhulme, Manchester M41 0GR Tel: 0161 748 5559 Fax: 0161 747 1997; 27 Delamere Road, Gatley, Cheadle SK8 4PH Tel: 0161 491 6789 Fax: 0161 282 1556 — MB BS 1979 Lond. (Royal Free Hospital)

KAYE, Brenda Xray Department, Royal Victoria Infirmary, Queen Victoria Road, Newcastle upon Tyne NE1 4LP Tel: 0191 282 0220; Old Prior Manor, Stagshaw Road, Corbridge NE45 5HR Tel: 01434 632185 — MB ChB (Hons.) Manch. 1978; FRCR 1984; DMRD Eng. 1982. Cons. Radiol. Roy. Vict. Infirm. Prev: Sen. Regist. (Radiol.) Sheff. HA; Regist. (Radiol.) Brist. HA.

KAYE, Georges Sabry 2 Pennant Mews, London W8 5JN Tel: 020 7460 2000 Fax: 020 7370 4633 Email: georges.kaye@sbil.co.uk — MB BS 1975 Lond.; BSc Lond. 1972. Europ. Med. Dir. Gen. Electric; Phys. i/c Occupat. Health Dept. Cromwell Hosp. Lond.; Company Phys. Air France, Salomon Bros. Internat. & Hill Samuel Financial Servs. Socs: Soc. Occupat. Health; Internat. Commiss. Occupat. Health. Prev: Regist. (Med.) Char. Cross Hosp. Lond.; Ho. Surg. Cardiothoracic Unit W.minster Hosp. Lond.

KAYE, Georgina Susan Box 730, Bristol BS99 5GP — MB ChB 1998 Bristol.

KAYE, Gerald Cyril Department of Cardiology, Castle Hill Acute Unit, Cottingham HU16 7JN Tel: 01482 875875 Fax: 01482 623223; 55 West Ella Road, Kirk Ella, Hull HU10 7QL — MB ChB 1978 Manch.; MD Manch. 1988; FRCP 1997. Cons. Cardiol. Cottingham. Socs: Brit. Cardiac Soc.; Brit. Cardiac Interven. Soc.; Brit. Pacing & Electrophysiol. Gp. Prev: Lect. (Cardiol.) Univ. Leeds; Research Regist. (Cardiol.) St. Bart. Hosp. Lond.; Regist. (Med.) Hackney Hosp. Lond.

KAYE, Hayley Jillian 51 Chepstow Road, Leicester LE2 1PB — MB ChB 1997 Leic.

KAYE, Henry Hope Northway Clinic, Northway, Scarborough YO12 7AF; Hawthorn House, Sawdon, Scarborough YO13 9DX — MB BS 1966 Lond.; FRCP Ed. 1989; MRCP (UK) 1972; MRCS Eng. LRCP Lond. 1966; FRCPCH 1997; DCH Eng. 1969. (St. Thos.) Cons. Community Child Health ScarBoro. Health Dist. Prev: Sen. Regist. Roy. Aberd. Childr. Hosp.; Sen. Research Assoc. (Child Health) Univ. Newc.; Regist. (Child Health) United Newc. Hosps.

KAYE, Miss Jacqueline Isabel 18 Lancashire Road, Bishopston, Bristol BS7 9DL — MB ChB 1988 Birm.; DRCOG 1991. Prev: SHO (A & E) Bristol Roy. Infirm.; SHO (O & G) St. Michael's Hosp. Bristol; SHO (Paediat.) S.mead Hosp. Bristol.

KAYE, Mr Jeremy Charles Arrowe Park Hospital, Wirral CH49 5PE Tel: 0151 678 5111; Puddington Hall, Puddington, South Wirral CH64 5ST Fax: 0151 353 1673 — MB BS 1977 Lond.; FRCS Eng. 1982. (St. Bart. Hosp. Lond.) Cons. Orthop. Surg. Arrowe Pk. Hosp. Liverp. Prev: Cons. Orthop. Surg. Roy. Liverp. Univ. Hosp.; Sen. Regist. (Orthop.) Robt. Jones & Agnes Hunt Orthop. Hosp., & N. Staffs. Roy. Infirm. Stoke-on-Trent; Research Fell. Cape Town Univ., S. Afr.

KAYE, Jonathan Edward Kingsway Surgery, 655 Kingsway, Burnage, Manchester M19 1RD Tel: 0161 432 2725 Fax: 0161 947 9192 — MB ChB 1987 Manch.

KAYE, Kenneth (retired) Berndene, Cadeby, Doncaster DN5 7SS Tel: 01709863727 — MB ChB Sheff. 1957. Prev: Ho. Surg. (O & G) & Ho. Phys. Kilton Hosp. Worksop.

KAYE, Lesley Carole 38 Westhaven Crescent, Aughton, Ormskirk L39 5BW — MB ChB 1983 Dundee.

KAYE, Martin George 56 Monkgate, York YO31 7PF Tel: 01904 59291 — LMSSA 1948 Lond. (Guy's)

KAYE, Myra Sylvia (retired) 31 Churchburn Drive, Morpeth NE61 2BZ Tel: 01670 513923 — MB ChB 1951 Ed. Prev: Assoc. Specialist St. Geo. Hosp. Morpeth.

KAYE, Nicholas Mark The Health Centre, Commercial Road, Skelmanthorpe, Huddersfield HD8 9DA Tel: 01484 862239 Fax: 01484 863120 — MB ChB 1992 Leeds; MRCGP 1997. (Univ. Leeds)

KAYE, Norman 6 St Davids Crescent, Leicester LE2 2RL Tel: 0116 270 8910 — MB BS 1951 Lond.; MRCS Eng. LRCP Lond. 1950; FRCPsych 1980, M 1971; DPM Eng. 1959. (Lond. Hosp.) Emerit. Cons. Psychiat. Leics. Ment. Health Serv.; Hon. Fell. Dept. Psychiat. Univ. Leicester. Socs: Fell. Roy. Soc. Med.; Fell. RCPsych (Ex-Chairm. Midl. Div).; Life Mem. Leicester Med. Soc. Prev: Hon. Fell. Dept. Psychiat. Univ. Leicester; Sen. Regist. (Psychiat.) Graylingwell Hosp. Chichester; Regist. (Neurol.) Gen. Infirm. Leeds.

KAYE, Patrick John P.J. Kaye and Partners, Northwick Surgery, 36 Northwick Park Road, Harrow HA1 2NU Tel: 020 8427 1661 Fax: 020 8864 2737 — MRCS Eng. LRCP Lond. 1970; MRCGP 1975; DObst RCOG 1971. (Char. Cross)

KAYE, Patrick Matthew Overlands, Byford, Hereford HR4 7LD — MB ChB 1998 Dund.; MB ChB Dund 1998.

KAYE, Paul Donald Cochrane Manor House Farm, Brearton, Harrogate HG3 3BX — MB ChB 1969 Birm.; MMedSci Leeds 1984.

KAYE, Peter Martin 41 Park Avenue N., Northampton NN3 2HT — MB 1978 Camb.; BChir 1977; FRCP Lond. 1994; MRCP (UK) 1980; MRCGP 1983; DRCOG 1982. Cons. Phys. Med. Dir. Cynthia Spencer Hse. N.ampton.

KAYE, Philip David 12 Denbigh Street, Cardiff CF11 9JQ — MB BCh 1990 Wales.

KAYE, Sharon Marie Palmers Farmhouse, Palmers, Wantage OX12 7HA — MB ChB 1994 Bristol.

KAYE, Simon Andrew 1 Hawkfield Cottages, Little Urswick, Ulverston LA12 0PU — MB ChB 1984 Birm.; DRCOG 1986. SHO (Paediat.) Furness Gen. Hosp. Barrow. Prev: SHO (O & G) Furness Gen. Hosp. Barrow; Trainee GP S. Cumbria VTS; Ho. Off. (Surg.) Qu. Eliz. Hosp. Birm.

KAYE, Professor Stanley Bernard Royal Marsden Hospital, CRC Department of Medical Oncology, Downs Road, Sutton SM2 5PT Tel: 020 8661 3538 Fax: 020 8661 3541 Email: stan.kaye@rmh.nthames.nhs.uk; 11 Milverton Avenue, Bearsden, Glasgow G61 4BE Tel: 0141 942 4920 — MB BS 1972 Lond.; MD Lond. 1980, BSc 1969; FRCP Lond. 1989; MRCP (UK) 1975; FRCR 1992; FRCPS Glas. 1991. (Char. Cross Hosp.) Socs: Fell. Roy. Soc. Med. Prev: Prof. Med. Oncol. Univ. Glas. & Honary Cons. in Med.Oncol.W.ern Infirm.; Non Exec. Dir. N. Glas. Hosps. Univ. NHS Trust; Sen. Lect. (Oncol.) Univ. Glas.

KAYE, Stanley Laurie 24 Eaton Place, Brighton BN2 1EH Tel: 01273 686863; 2 Bishops Road, Hove BN3 6PQ Tel: 01273 553525 — MRCS Eng. LRCP Lond. 1942; MD (Gold Medal) Lond. 1947, MB BS 1942; MRCP Lond. 1948; MRCGP 1953. (Char. Cross) Socs: Counc. Brighton M-C Soc.; Med. Assur. Soc. Prev: Dep. Chief Med. Off. (Life) Legal & Gen. Assur. Soc.; Phys. (SHMO) Roy. Sussex Co. Hosp. Brighton; Clin. Asst. (Neurol.) Radcliffe Infirm. Oxf.

KAYE, Stephanie Ann Department of Rheumatology, Chelsea & Westminster Hospital, 369 Fulham Road, London SW10 9NH Tel: 020 8746 8348 Fax: 020 7370 4398 Email: s.kaye@cxwms.ac.uk; 20 Campden Hill Square, Kensington, London W8 7JY — MB ChB 1983 Liverp.; MD Liverp. 1999; MRCP (UK) 1987. Cons. Phys. & Rheum. Chelsea & W.m. Hosp. Lond. Socs: Brit. Soc. Rheum. Prev: Sen. Regist. (Rheum.) St. Mary's Hosp. & Char. Cross Hosp. Lond.; ARC Jun. Clin. Research Fell. Roy. Free Hosp. Lond.; Regist. (Cardiol. & Gen. Med.) Centr. Middlx. Hosp. Lond.

KAYE, Stephen Nicholas Boughton Medical Group, Boughton Health Centre, Hoole Lane, Chester CH2 3DP Tel: 01244 325421 — MB ChB 1987 Bristol; MRCGP 1992; DCH RCP Lond. 1992.

KAYENTE, Martin Luther 8 Rolling Mill Close, Edgbaston, Birmingham B5 7QD Tel: 0121 440 0515 Email: benua@btinternet.com — MD Szeged 1970; FFR Budapest 1980. Socs: Fell. Roy. Soc. Med.

KAYES, Mohammad Imrul 22 Camsey House, St Matthews Road, London SW2 1SX — LMSSA 1997 Lond.

KAYLAN, Ajitpal Singh 4 Reeves Road, Kings Heath, Birmingham B14 6SQ — MB ChB 1996 Liverp.

KAYLL, Jeremy Norman (retired) Greenway, 19 St John's Road, Cove, Farnborough GU14 9RL — MB BS Lond. 1962; MRCS Eng. LRCP Lond. 1962; DObst RCOG 1964. Prev: Ho. Surg. W.m. Childr. Hosp. Lond. & Poole Gen. Hosp.

KAYTAR, Jane 145 Galgorm Road, Ballymena BT42 1DE — MB BS 1991 Lond.

KAYTAR, Tibor (retired) 23 The Paddock, Old Park Road, Ballymena BT42 1RN Tel: 01266 658718 — MB BS 1961 Lond.; MRCS Eng. LRCP Lond. 1961; FRCOG 1981, M 1968. Prev: Cons. O & G Waveney Hosp. Ballymena.

KAYTON, Daphne Masuda Elnalene (retired) 71 Harrington Gardens, South Kensington, London SW7 4JZ Tel: 020 7373 6576 — LRCP LRCS Ed. LRFPS Glas. 1943; FRCOG 1969, M 1952. Prev: Cons. O & G Whipps Cross Hosp. Lond. & Wanstead Hosp. Lond.

KAYZAKIAN, Armine Mannya 14 Dunkeld House, Abbott Road, London E14 0LS Tel: 020 7515 4621; 4 Leonards Close, Welwyn AL6 0QJ — MB BS 1991 Lond. SHO (A & E) P.ss Alexandra Hosp. Harlow.

***KAZ-KAZ, Hanadi** 47A Pembridge Villas, London W11 3EP — LRCP LRCS Ed. LRCPS Glas. 1996.

KAZA, Madhu 11 Kent Bank, Harrogate HG1 2NQ — MB BS 1969 Andhra India.

KAZA, Ramagopal 11 Kent Bank, Harrogate HG1 2NQ — MB BS 1971 Andhra India.

KAZANTZIS, Professor George Environmental Geochemistry Research, Imperial College of Science, Technology & Medicine, Prince Consort Road, London SW7 2BW Tel: 020 7594 6409 Fax: 020 7594 6408 Email: g.kazantzis@ic.ac.uk; 35 Mount Park Crescent, Ealing, London W5 2RR Tel: 020 8997 3287 — MB BS Lond. 1949; PhD Lond. 1956; FRCP 1979, M 1962; MRCS Eng. LRCP Lond. 1949; FRCS Eng. 1957; FFCM RCP Lond. 1979, M 1972; FFOM RCP Lond. 1979. (St. Bart.) Emerit. Prof. Occupat. Med. Environm. Geochem. Research Imperial Coll. Sci., Technol. & Med. Lond.; Vis. Prof. Imperial Coll. 1992; Hon. Cons. Med. Profess. Unit Middlx. Hosp. 1989; Mem. Perm. Internat. Commiss on Occupat. Health; Mem. WHO Expert Advis. Panel on Food Additives. Socs: Fell. Roy. Soc. Med.; Soc. Occupat. Med. (Ex-Chairm. Research Panel). Prev: Prof. Occupat. Med. Lond. Sch. Hyg. & Trop. Med.; on Scientif. Staff, MRC Indust. Med. & Air Pollution Research Units; Sen. Lect. (Community Med.) Middlx. Hosp. Med. Sch. Lond.

KAZEM, Rahnuma Nurture, Floor B East Block, Queen's Med Centre, Nottingham NG7 2UH Tel: 0115 924 9924; 125 Woodthorpe, Mapperley, Nottingham NG3 5JL Tel: 0115 962 3511 — MB BS 1985 Calcutta; MD Aberd. 1995; MRCOG 1990. Cons in reproductive med nurture Univ of Nottm. Qu.'s Med Centre Notts; Hon Cons OBS & Gynae Qu.'s med centre Notts. Socs: Brit. Fertil. Soc.; Amer soc of reproductive med. Prev: Clin. Research Fell. Univ. Aberd.; Regist. (O & G) S.mead Hosp. Bristol; Sen. Regist. (Reproduc. Med.) Roy. Infirm. Edin.

KAZEMI, Mr Ali-Reza 8 Wentworth Avenue, London N3 1YB — LMSSA 1988 Lond.; FRCS Glas. 1994; FRCS Ed. 1993; MRCS Eng. LRCP Lond. 1989. SHO (Cardiothoracic Surg.) Guy's Hosp. Prev: SHO (A & E) Guys Hosp., Lewisham & N. S.wark HA; SHO (Orthop.) Greenwich Dist. Hosp.; Ho. Surg. Guys Hosp. Lond.

KAZEMI-JOVESTANI, Arash 1 Talbot Avenue, Edgerton, Huddersfield HD3 3BQ — MB BS 1996 Lond.

KAZEMI-JOVESTANI, Mehdi 1 Talbot Avenue, Edgerton, Huddersfield HD3 3BQ Tel: 01484 515630 — MD 1969 Tehran. Clin. Asst. (Gen. Surg.) Huddersfield Roy. Infirm.

KAZER, Michael Wycombe Hospital, Queen Alexandra Road, High Wycombe HP11 2TT; 30A Northcourt Avenue, Reading RG2 7HA — MB ChB 1982 Leeds. Staff Phys. (A&E) Wycombe Hosp., High Wycmbe.

KAZI, Abdul Rashid 35 Bayswater Road, Perry Barr, Birmingham B20 3AJ Tel: 0121 356 1116 Fax: 0121 356 1116 — MB BS 1971 Poona; DTM & H Lond. 1980; Dip. Ven. Liverp.1976. (B.J. Medical College, Poona) Cons., Genito Urin. Med., James Pagent Hosp., Garleston, Gt. Yarmouth; Forens. Med. Examr., Police Surg. Prev: Cons., Genito Urin. Med., Laura Mitchell Health Centre, Halifax.

KAZI, Arif Marzook Maqbul Ahmed 18 Rothwell Road, Halifax HX1 2HA — MB ChB 1989 Aberd.

KAZI, Azizullahkhan B 17 Pembridge Road, Notting Hill Gate, London W11 3HG Tel: 020 7221 0174; 79 Thirlmere Gardens, Wembley HA9 8RD — MB BS 1953 Bombay. (Grant Med. Coll.) Socs: BMA & BHMA.

KAZI, Bilal Mohamed 57 Regent Street, Gloucester GL1 4XG — MB BS 1980 Karnatak.

KAZI, Gulam Akber (retired) BUPA Fylde Coast Hospital, St Walburghs Road, Blackpool FY3 8BP Tel: 01253 394188 — MB BS 1963 Karachi; Dip Med Acu 1997 BMAS, Eng.; BSc 1957 Karachi; FFA RCS Eng. 1972; DA Eng. 1967. Prev: Regist. Vict. Hosp. Blackpool & Roy. Infirm. Glas.

KAZI, Nazir Mohammad 2 Sorrento Road, Sutton SM1 1QU — MB BS 1962 Karachi; FACS 1975; FRCS Eng. 1965; FRCS Ed. 1964. (Dow Med. Coll. Karachi) Sen. Surg. & Head of Dept. Surg. Centr. Hosp. Abu Dhabi.

KAZI, Thofim 90D Clifton Hill, London NW8 0JT — MB BS 1993 Lond.

KAZIM, Mr Houriya Ahmed Abdalla 58A Redcliffe Gardens, London SW10 9HD — LRCPSI 1988; LRCSPI 1988; FRCSI 1993.

KAZMI, Farhat Ali 4 Naseby Close, Mickleover, Derby DE3 5QU — MB BS 1996 Lond.

KAZMI, Majid Ali 4 Naseby Close, Mickleover, Derby DE3 5QU — MB ChB 1991 Aberd.; MRCP (UK) 1994; MRC Path (UK) Aberdeen. Clin. Research Fell.

KAZMI, Mr Muhammad Shabbar 8 Brambleacres Close, Sutton SM2 6NJ — MB BS 1986 Punjab; FRCS Ed. 1994.

KAZMI, Sayed Mansoor Akbar The Medical Centre, Beaver Road, Ashford TN23 7PS Tel: 01233 625527 Fax: 01233 661227 Email: drmkazmi@aol.com; Cotswold, Malvern Road, Ashford TN24 8JA Tel: 01233 624971.

KAZMI, Mr Syed Abul-Hasan Department of Surgery, Ward 8, Ninewells Hospital, Dundee DD1 9SY Tel: 01382 660111 Email: s.a.kazmi@dundee.ac.uk; 1 Strathaird Place, Dundee DD2 4TN Tel:

01382 646078 — MB BS 1977 Punjab; FRCS Ed. 1989. (Nishtar Med. Coll., Multan, Pakistan) Staff Surg. Ninewells Teach. Hosp. Dundee.; Hon. Research Fell. Dundee Univ.

KAZMI, Mr Syed Muhammad Nasir Abbas Fleet House, Beckenham Place Park, Beckenham BR3 5BS — MB BS 1982 Karachi; FRCS Ed. 1991.

KAZMIE, M Cliftonville Surgery, 5 Cliftonville Avenue, Margate CT9 2AL Tel: 01843 292873 — MB BS 1967 Pakistan. (Fatima Jinnah Med. Coll. Lahore) Clin. Asst. (Paediat., Geriat. & Psychiat.) I. of Thanet Dist. Hosp. Margate. Socs: Brit. Med. Acupunct. Soc. Prev: SHO (Cas.) St. Mary's Hosp. Lond.

KAZZAZ, Haytham Jarjees Salih Al 40 Beardsley Way, London W3 7YQ — MB ChB 1971 Mosul; FRCR 1988; DMRD Eng. 1986.

KEABLE-ELLIOTT, David Antony Flat G1, Lloyds Wharf, Mill St., London SE1 2BA — MB BChir 1978 Camb.; MA, MB BChir Camb. 1978. Prev: GP Lond.

KEABLE-ELLIOTT, Robert Anthony, OBE (retired) Peels, Grays Lane, Ibstone, High Wycombe HP14 3XX Tel: 0149 163 8385 Email: tony@keable-elliot.fsnet.co.uk — MB BS Lond. 1948; FRCGP 1975. Prev: Treas. BMA.

KEAL, Edwin Ernest Frederick (retired) 55 Church Street, Orford, Woodbridge IP12 2NT Tel: 01394 450515 — MB BS 1952 Lond.; MD Lond. 1971; FRCP Lond. 1973, M 1957; MRCS Eng. LRCP Lond. 1952; DCH Eng. 1954. Hon. Cons. Phys. St. Mary's, Roy. Brompton & Nat. Heart Hosps. Lond. Prev: Cons. Phys. St. Chas. Hosp. Lond., Kensington Chest Clinic, St. Mary's, Roy. Broompton & Nat. Heart Hosp.

KEAL, Richard Paul 4 Freer Close, Houghton-on-the-Hill, Leicester LE7 9HU Tel: 0116 241 8380 — MB BS 1976 Lond.; FRCR 1987; DMRD Aberd. 1986. (Middlx.) Cons. Radiol. Glenfield Hosp. & Leicester Roy. Infirm. Prev: Sen. Regist. (Radiol.) Leicester Teach. Hosps.; Regist. (Radiol.) Aberd. Roy. Infirm.; Regist. (Med.) Good Hope Gen. Hosp. Sutton Coldfield.

KEALEY, George Terence Evelyn 19 Cope Place, London W8 6AA — MB BS 1975 Lond.

KEALEY, Lesley Elizabeth Wonford Green Surgery, Burnthouse Lane, Exeter EX2 6NF Tel: 01392 250135 Fax: 01392 498572 — MB ChB 1979 Leeds; Cert. Family Plann. JCC 1984.

KEALEY, Mr William David Cameron 15 Grangewood Heights, Ballyregan Road, Dundonald, Belfast BT16 1GG — MB BCh BAO 1990 Belf.; FRCS Ed. 1994.

KEALL, Gaynor Mary Apples, Widford Road, Much Hadham SG10 6AT Tel: 01279 842256 — MB BCh 1966 Wales; DObst RCOG 1968.

KEALY, Mark Raymond Wallaford Farm, Buckfastleigh TQ11 0HG — MB ChB 1982 Birm.; MA Camb. 1983. SHO (Med.) Russells Hall Hosp. Dudley.

KEAN, David McCrone Department of Neuroradiology, Southern General Hosptial, Govan Road, Glasgow G51 4TF Tel: 0141 201 2040; Bracadale, 29 Station Road, Killearn, Glasgow G63 9NZ Email: gauss2@netcomuk.co.uk — MB ChB 1975 Glas.; FRCR 1983; DMRD Eng. 1983. Cons. Neuroradiol. S.ern Gen. Hosp. Glas. Socs: Roy. Coll. Radiol.; Brit. Soc. Neuroradiol.; BMA. Prev: Cons. Neuroradiol. Roy. Hallamsh. Hosp. Sheff.; Sen. Lect. & Hon. Cons. Edin. Univ.; Research Fell. & Hon. Sen. Regist. Nottm. Univ.

KEAN, Lucy Harriet 11 Brook Vale, Bewdley DY12 1BQ — BM BCh 1987 Oxf.

KEANE, Anne Bernadette (retired) Chatsworth, 17 The Heronry, Walton-on-Thames KT12 5AT — MB BCh BAO 1960 NUI; DA (UK) 1967.

KEANE, Brigid (retired) 7 Dalefield, Roebuck Lane, Buckhurst Hill IG9 5QT Tel: 020 8505 1158 — MB BS 1953 Lond.; DMRD Eng. 1957.

KEANE, Claire Catherine Engleton House, 1A Engleton Road, Coventry CV6 1JF Tel: 024 7659 2012 Fax: 024 7660 1913 — MB ChB 1989 Manch.; MRCGP (Distinc.) 1993.

KEANE, Claire Judith 18 Fountain Road, London SW17 0HQ — MB BS 1997 Lond.

KEANE, Declan Patrick 100B St Michael's Hill, Bristol BS2 8BQ — MB BCh BAO 1985 NUI.

KEANE, Denis Vincent Tel: 01626 770297 Fax: 01626 777331 Email: denis.keane@9p-183022.nhs.uk; Rowden House, Lindridge Road, Bishopsteignton, Teignmouth TQ14 9TA — MB BCh BAO 1963 NUI; DCH NUI 1965; DObst Univ. Coll. Cork 1965. (Cork) Gen. Practitioner, Teignmouth Med. Pract., 2 Den Cresc., Teignmouth. Socs: Torquay & Dist. Med. Soc.; Roy. Devon & Exeter Med. Soc. Prev: Regist. (Med.) Dulwich Hosp. Lond.; Regist. (Diabetic) King's Coll. Hosp. Lond.; Regist. (Med.) Co. Hosp. Sligo.

KEANE, Frances Emer Anne Department GU Medicine, Royal Cornwall Hospital, Truro TR1 3LJ Tel: 01872 255044 — MB BCh BAO 1987 Belf.; MD Belf. 1999; BSc (Hons.) Med. Microbiol. Belf. 1985; MRCP (UK) 1991. Cons. Genitourin. Med. Roy. Cornw. Hosp. Prev: Clin. Research Fell. (Genitourin. Med.) St. Mary's Hosp. Lond.; Regist. (Genitourin. Med.) Leicester Roy. Infirm.; SHO (Dermat. & Genitourin. Med.) Roy. Vict. Hosp. Belf.

KEANE, Francis (retired) 1 Pretty John House, Gunners Row, Southsea PO4 9XG Tel: 01705 825170 — MB BCh BAO 1936 Dub.; DPH (1st Hons.) 1938. Prev: Med. Off. Remploy Ltd. Portsmouth.

KEANE, Friedericke 40A King's Gardens, West End Lane, London NW6 4PX — State Exam Med 1989 Munich.

KEANE, Helen Mary Ita 34 Adelaide Park, Malone Road, Belfast BT9 6FY Tel: 01232 382875 — MB BCh BAO 1979 NUI. Clin. Med. Off. Genitourin. Med. Socs: Irish Coll. Gen. Pract.; Fac. Reproduc. Med. & Family Plann.

KEANE, Julia Anthony 6 Quadrant Road, Glasgow G43 2QJ Tel: 0141 632 3295 — MB ChB 1956 Glas.; FRFPS Glas. 1960; MRCP Glas. 1962. Prev: Med. Regist. S.. Gen. Hosp. Glas.

KEANE, Kathleen (retired) 1A Abbots Way, Finchfield, Wolverhampton WV3 9LR Tel: 01902 422757 — MB BCh BAO 1946 NUI; MRCPsych 1971; DPM Leeds 1963; DObst RCOG 1949; DPH Manch. 1956; DCH Eng. 1958. Prev: Cons. Child Psychiat. Wolverhampton & St. Geo. Hosp. Gps.

KEANE, Mary Teresa North Parade Surgery, 6 North Parade, Belfast BT7 2GG — MB BCh BAO 1980 NUI; MRCGP 1986; DRCOG 1985. Prev: Trainee GP Belf. VTS.

KEANE, Michael Andrew Robert 53 Lynette Avenue, Clapham, London SW4 9HF Tel: 0208 675 6787 Email: markeane@aol.com — MB ChB 1985 Birm.; MRCP (UK) 1989; FRCR 1993. Cons. Radiol. St. Helier Hosp. Carshalton; Cons. Radiol. St Anthony's Hosp. Cheam.

KEANE, Michael Anthony Paris House, 133 The Rocks Road, East Malling, West Malling ME19 6AU — MB ChB 1980 Manch.; MSc (Dist.) Lond. 1986; BSc (Hons.) Manch. 1977, MB ChB 1980. Dir. Clin. Operat. Europe & Austral. Pfizer Centr. Research Sandwich. Socs: Fac. Pharmaceut. Med. Prev: Europ. Med. Research Dir. Schering Plough Corp. Rickmansworth.; Ho. Surg. (Neurosurg.) Manch. Roy. Infirm; Ho. Phys. (Gen. Med.) Hope Hosp. Salford.

KEANE, Michael Francis 79 Glenister Park Road, London SW16 5DS Tel: 020 8764 4646 — MB BCh BAO 1941 NUI; LM Coombe 1946. (Univ. Coll. Dub.)

KEANE, Mr Patrick Francis Level 3, City Hospital, Lisburn Road, Belfast BT9 7AB — MB BCh BAO 1978 NUI; MCh NUI 1984, MB BCh BAO 1978; FRCSI (Urol.) 1982. Cons. Urol. City Hosp. Belf. Socs: Brit. Assn. Urol. Surgs.

KEANE, Patrick Martin The Mountfield Surgery, 55 Mountfield Road, Finchley, London N3 3NR Tel: 020 8346 4271 Fax: 020 8371 0187; 10 Holmwood Gardens, Finchley, London N3 3NS Tel: 020 8343 0716 — MB BCh BAO 1978 NUI; DRCOG 1981. (University of Galway) Cas. Off. Finchley Memor. Hosp.; Dep. Forens. Med. Examr. Adviser Metrop. Police.

KEANE, Ronald 51 Canford Cliffs Road, Poole BH13 7AQ Tel: 01202 707004 — MRCS Eng. LRCP Lond. 1946. (King's Coll. & St. Geo.) Socs: Bournemouth Med. Soc. & Assn. Manip. Med. Prev: Phys. CharterHo. Rheum. Clinic; Ho. Phys. St. Geo. Hosp.; Surg. B.I.S.N. Co.

KEANE, Thomas Kieran Dryburn Hospital, Durham DH1 5TW — MB BCh BAO 1983 NUI; MB BCh BAO NUI I983.

KEANE, Thomas Raphael 3 Blyth Close, Symonds Green, Stevenage SG1 2NQ Tel: 01438 314245 — MB BCh BAO 1985 NUI; LRCPSI 1985.

KEANE, William Giles (retired) Dunseverick, 20 Crossparks, Dartmouth TQ6 9HP Tel: 01803 832478 — MB BCh BAO 1944 Dub.; MD Dub. 1954; MRCPI 1949; FRCGP 1978, M 1953. Prev: Ho. Phys. Lond. Chest Hosp. Vict. Pk.

KEANEY, Aideen Anne Mary Impala, Belcoo East, Belcoo, Enniskillen BT93 5FN — MB BCh BAO 1993 Belf.

KEANEY, Francis Patrick Sylvester The London Institute, 10 Warwick Road, Earl's Court Square, London SW5 9UG Tel: 020 7373 0901 Fax: 020 7244 0900 — MB BCh BAO 1978 NUI; MRCPsych 1997; MICGP 1989; DObst RCPI 1980. (Univ. Coll. Galway) Specialist Regist. (Psychiat.) Maudsley Hosp. Denmark Hill.

KEANEY, Maeve Geraldine Louise 5 Duke's Wharf, Worsley, Manchester M28 2GS — MB BCh BAO 1974 NUI; MRCPath. 1980. (Univ. Coll. Dub.) Cons. Med. Microbiol. Hope Hosp. Salford. Prev: Asst. Lect. Sch. Path. Middlx. Hosp. Lond.; Med. Intern & Surg. Intern St. Jas. Hosp. Dub.; Sen. Regist. (Med. Microbiol.) Roy. Free Hosp. Lond.

KEANEY, Niall Patrick Sunderland Royal Hospital, Kayll Road, Sunderland SR4 7TP Tel: 0191 565 6256 Fax: 0191 569 9292; Fyndoune Mews, Hartside, Durham DH1 5RJ Tel: 0191 371 1344 Email: zucchini@mcmail.com — MB BCh BAO 1967 NUI; PhD Leeds 1978; BSc NUI 1969; FRCP Lond. 1989; FRCP Ed. 1988; MRCP (UK) 1974. (Univ. Coll. Dub.) Cons. Phys. (Respirat. Med.) Sunderland Roy. Hosp.; Head of Med. Educat. & Research. Socs: Brit. Thorac. Soc. & Brit. Pharmacol. Soc.; Brit. Pharm. Soc.; Eur. Respirat. Soc. Prev: Lect. (Mat. Med. Pharmacol. & Therap.) Univ. Manch.; Lect. (Med.) St. Jas. Univ. Hosp. Leeds; Research Asst. (Anaesth.) Univ. Leeds.

***KEANY, Christina Irene** 8 East Drive, Kettering NN15 7AF — BM BS 1998 Nottm.; BM BS Nottm 1998.

KEANY, Mary 13 St Johns Road, Southall UB2 5AN — MB ChB 1991 Leic.; BSc Leic. 1988, MB ChB 1991; DRCOG 1993. SHO (Integrated Med.) Glenfield Gen. Hosp. Leicester.

KEAPPOCK, Catherine Gemma Anne Keappock, 9 Streatham Vale, London SW16 5SE Tel: 020 8764 9406 — MB BCh BAO 1966 NUI. (Univ. Coll. Dub.) Princip. Gen. Pract. Lond. Prev: Ho. Surg. & Ho. Phys. & SHO (Geriat.) Orpington Hosp.

KEAR, Christopher St John Wath Health Centre, Church Street, Wath-On-Dearne, Rotherham S63 7RF Tel: 01709 877886 — MB ChB 1983 Leeds.

KEARLEY, Karen Elizabeth Williamson and Partners, Jericho Health Centre, Walton Street, Oxford OX2 6NW Tel: 01865 429993 Fax: 01865 458410 — MB ChB 1983 Liverp.; DRCOG 1989. Prev: Trainee GP Liverp.

KEARNEY, Angela Bernadette 40 Chapel Road, Killeavy, Newry BT35 8JY Email: a.j.kearney@btinternet.com — MB BCh BAO 1989 Belf.; MRCPsych Lond. 1994.

KEARNEY, Catherine Elizabeth 6 Chequers Cottages, Gaddesden Row, Hemel Hempstead HP2 6HH — MB ChB 1990 Leic.; MRCPH 1995; MSc 1998.

KEARNEY, Clare Elizabeth 51 Ferriby Road, Hessle, Hull HU13 OHS Tel: 0115 985 6553 — MB ChB 1990 Glas.; MRCOG 1996. SpR Yorks. Deanery.

KEARNEY, Garrett Donagh Anthony 10 Warwick Court, Manchester M16 0JG — MD 1977 Dub.; MA 1961, BA 1954, MB BCh BAO 1957; MRCPsych 1972; DPM Eng. 1964.

KEARNEY, James Michael (retired) 15 Walton Road, Milton Keynes Village, Milton Keynes MK10 9AQ Tel: 01908 665601 — MB BCh BAO Belf. 1953; FFOM RCP Lond. 1995, MFOM 1979; DIH Eng. 1966; DIH RCPS Glas. 1965. Cons. Occupat. Health Milton Keynes Hosp. Gen. Trust; Apptd. Doctor, Health and Safety Exec. Prev: Phys. Occupat. Health N. Beds. DHA.

KEARNEY, Joseph William Barnet Health Authority, Hyde House, The Hyde, Edgware Rd, London NW9 6QQ Tel: 020 8201 4839 Fax: 020 8201 4716 Email: joe.kearneybarnet-ha.nthames.nhs.uk; The Thrushes, Vicarage Road, Potten End, Berkhamsted HP4 2QZ Email: joe@kearneyfamily.freeserve.co.uk — MB BS 1975 Lond.; MSc 1997; FRCP (UK) 1997, M 1978; FRCPath 1993, M 1981; MFPHM 1998. (St. Mary's) Cons. (Pub. Health) Barnet Health Auth. Socs: Brit. Soc. Haematol.; Soc. Soc. Med. Prev: Regist. (Pub. Health) Kensington, Chelsea & W.minister HA.; Cons. Haemat. Hemel Hempstead Dist. Gen. Hosp. & St. Albans City Hosp.; Lect. & Hon. Sen. Regist. (Haemat.) Lond. Hosp.

KEARNEY, Mark Thomas 32 Haddon Place, Leeds LS4 2JU — MB ChB 1989 Leeds.

KEARNEY, Mary Patricia United Hospital Group Trust, Antrim Hospital, 45 Bush Road, Antrim BT41 2RL Fax: 028 94 424143 Email: paddy.kearney@uh.n-i.nhs.uk; Fax: 028 7938 6350 — MB BCh BAO 1977 NUI; MSc NUI 1971, MB BCh BAO 1977; BSc Belf. 1969; MRCPath 1985. Cons. Microbiol. Cons. Microbiolologist, United Hosp. Gp. Trust, Antrim Hosp., 45 Bush Rd. Antrim, N. Irel..

KEARNEY, Matthew John Castlefields Health Centre, Chester Close, Runcorn WA7 2HY Tel: 01928 566671 Fax: 01928 581631 Email: matthew.kearney@liv.ac.uk; Tel: 01743 366999 Fax: 01743 366555 — MB ChB 1982 Birm.; MRCP (UK) 1986; Cert. Family Plann. JCC 1990. p/t GP, Castlefields Health Centre Runcorn; Univ. Community Clin. Teach., Univ. Liverp. Prev: Regist. Rotat. (Haemat.) W. Midl.; Leukaemia Research Fund Research Fell. Univ. Birm.; SHO (O & G) Selly Oak Hosp.

KEARNEY, Norma Mary Perpetua 59 Kents Road, Haywards Heath RH16 4HQ — MB BCh BAO 1986 Dub. Prev: Trainee GP/SHO (Geriat.) Vict. Hosp. Mansfield.

KEARNEY, Peter Patrick Department of Cardiology, Western General Hospital, Crewe Rd, Edinburgh EH4 2XU — MB BCh BAO 1987 NUI.

KEARNEY, Raymond Thomas (retired) 208 Greenmount Lane, Bolton BL1 5HZ Tel: 01204 841704 — LRCPI & LM, LRSCI & LM 1946; LRCPI & LM, LRCSI & LM 1946. Med. Off. Leigh's Paints Bolton; Med. Off. Leigh's Paints Bolton. Prev: Resid. Surg. Off. Townley's Hosp. Bolton.

KEARNEY, Susan Elizabeth 126 Lime Walk, Headington, Oxford OX3 7AF — MB ChB 1987 Liverp.

KEARNEY, Suzanne Elizabeth Wood End House, Wood End Lane, Fillongley, Coventry CV7 8DF — MB ChB 1995 Birm.; ChB Birm. 1995.

KEARNEY, Tara Maria Edgware General Hospital, Edgware HA8 Tel: 020 8952 2381; 5 Rustic Place, Wembley HA0 3BJ — MB BS 1992 Lond.; BSc (Hons.) Lond. 1989, MB BS 1992. SHO (Cardiol.) Edgware Gen. Hosp. Prev: SHO (Endocrinol.) Edgware Gen. Hosp.; SHO (Transpl. Med.) Harefield Hosp.; Ho. Phys. (Gastroenterol. & c/o Elderly) Edgware Gen. Hosp.

KEARNS, Anthony Hadley Lodge, Chase Farm Hospital, The Ridgeway, Enfield EN2 8JL Tel: 020 8366 9140 — MB BCh BAO 1978 NUI; FRCPsych 1998; MRCPsych 1983. Cons Forens. Psychiat., N Lond. Forens. serv Chase farm hosp Enfield; Sen. Lect. Acad. Dept. Psychiat. Roy. Free. Hosp. Lond. Socs: BMA.; Assn. of Univ. Teach.s in Psychiat.; Penrose Soc. Prev: Clin. Dir. Hosp.ler Brothers of St. John of God Dunleer, Irel.

KEARNS, Christopher Francis Nuffield Department of Anaesthetics, The Radcliffe Infirmary, Woodstock Road, Oxford OX2 6HE Tel: 01865 311188; The Old Brew House, 31 High St, Eynsham, Oxford OX29 4HE Tel: 01865 464034 — MB BS 1984 Lond.; BSc Lond. 1981; FRCA 1992. (Charing Cross Hospital London) Cons. Anaesth. Nuffield Dept. of Anaesth. Radcliffe Infirm. Oxf.

KEARNS, Deborah Margaret Central Surgery, Bell Street, Sawbridgeworth CM21 9AQ Tel: 01279 723172; 62 Warwick Road, Bishop's Stortford CM23 5NW — MB ChB 1985 Sheff.; DCH RCP Lond. 1987.

KEARNS, Janet Reynell 8 Mount Pleasant Close, Hatfield AL9 5BZ Tel: 01707 264539 — MB BS 1976 Lond. Regist. (Psychiat.) St. Brigid's Hosp. Ardlee.

KEARNS, Joseph Louis (retired) 80 Haven Green Court, London W5 2UY Tel: 020 8991 0926 Fax: 020 8991 0926 Email: joekear99@hotmail.com — MB BCh BAO 1956 NUI; MRCGP 1965; DIH Soc. Apoth. Lond. 1965; FFOM RCPI 1977; MSc (Occupat. Med.) Lond. 1971; FFOM RCP Eng. 1983, M 1978. Prev: Head Health & Safety J. Lyons Gp. Companies.

KEARNS, Norman Patricia 12 Falkland Mount, Leeds LS17 6JG — MB BCh BAO 1975 Belf.; MB BCh Belf. 1975.

KEARNS, Pamela Renate Department of Child Health, Sir James Pence. Inst., RVI, Newcastle upon Tyne NE1 4LP Tel: 0191 202 3053 Email: pamela.kearns@ncl.ac.uk; 11 Houxty Road, South Wellfield, Whitley Bay, Newcastle upon Tyne NE25 9QN — MB ChB 1988 Aberd.; MRCP (Paediat.) (UK) 1993. 1st Asst. In Child Health RVI Newc. Prev: Clin. Research Fell. (Paediat. Oncol.) Univ. Newc.; Regist. (Paediat. Oncol.) Roy. Vict. Infirm. Newc. u. Tyne.

KEARNS, Patrick James Manchester Road Medical Centre, 27 Manchester Road, Knutsford WA16 0LZ Fax: 01565 750135; The White House, Tabley Rd, Knutsford WA16 0NG — MB ChB 1990 Manch.

KEARNS, Mr Patrick Paul Woodburn, 36 Kirkliston Road, South Queensferry EH30 9NY — MB ChB 1985 Ed.; FRCS Ed. 1990;

FRCOphth 1990. Cons. Ophth. Qu. Margt. Hosp. Dunfermline & P.ss Alexandra Eye Pavil., Roy. Infirm. Edin. Prev: Sen. Regist. (Ophth.) P.ss Alexandra Eye Pavil. Roy. Infirm. Edin.

KEARNS, William Edward 5 Midholm, Wembley HA9 9LJ Tel: 020 8908 1511 Fax: 020 8904 3884 Email: williamkearns@compuserve.com — MB ChB 1958 Liverp.; MSc Lond. 1972; MRCS Eng. LRCP Lond. 1958; FFCM RCP (UK) 1980, M 1974. Cons. Health Policy & Pub. Health Middlx. Socs: Fell. Roy. Soc. Med. Prev: Regional Med. Off. NE Thames RHA; Dist. Community Phys. Paddington & N. Kensington HA; Regional Admin. Scientif. Off. NW Metrop. RHB.

KEARSEY, Susan Yvonne Littleton Surgery, Buckland House, Esher Park Avenue, Esher KT10 9NY Tel: 01372 462235 Fax: 01372 470622; 8 Arnold Drive, Chessington KT9 2GD Tel: 020 8397 4567 Fax: 020 8397 4567 — MRCS Eng. LRCP Lond. 1981; BSc Lond. 1978, MB BS 1982; DRCOG 1984. (Char. Cross) Chairm. E. Elmbridge PCG. Prev: SHO (Geriat. & Paediat.) W. Middlx. Univ. Hosp. Isleworth; Ho. Off. (Obst.) W. Middlx. Univ. Hosp. Isleworth.

KEARSLEY, Nicholas John Richmond Medical Centre, 462 Richmond Road, Sheffield S13 8NA Tel: 0114 239 9291 Fax: 0114 253 0737; 13 Ranmoor Park Road, Sheffield S10 3GX — MB ChB 1979 Sheff.; MRCGP 1984.

KEAST-BUTLER, Mr John Riverside House, Clayithe Road, Horningsea, Cambridge CB5 9JB Tel: 01223 861534 Fax: 01223 863666 Email: john.keast-butler@virgin.net — MB Camb. 1965, BChir 1964; MA Camb. 1965; FRCS Eng. 1973; FRCOphth 1989; DO Eng. 1971. (Univ. Coll. Hosp.) Cons. Ophth. Surg. Addenbrooke's NHS Trust, Camb. Univ. Teach. Hosps. Trust & Saffron Walden Community Hosp.; Assoc. Lect. (Med.) Univ. Camb; Dir. Studies (Clin. Med.) Trinity Coll. Camb.; Attachment director in Ophth., Univ. of Camb. Sch. of Clin. Med. Socs: Roy. Soc. Med.; & Hon. Sec. Camb. Grad.'s Med. Club; BMA (Chairm. Ophth. Gp. Comm.). Prev: Sen. Regist. (Ophth.) St. Thos. Hosp. & Nat. Hosp. Nerv. Dis. Lond.; Sen. Resid. Off. Moorfields Eye Hosp. (City Rd. Br.) Lond.; Regist. (Ophth.) Addenbrooke's Hosp. Camb.

KEAT, Andrew Charles Department of Rheumatology, Northwick Park Hospital, Watford Road, Harrow HA1 3UJ Tel: 020 8869 2656 Fax: 020 8869 2657; Coombe End, 4 Beaumont Road, Southfields, London SW19 6LY Tel: 020 8788 5864 Fax: 020 8780 9607 — MB BS 1972 Lond.; MD Lond. 1980; FRCP Lond. 1989; MRCP (UK) 1975. (Char. Cross) Cons. Phys. (Rheum. & Gen. Med.) N.wick Pk. Hosp. Harrow; Hon. Cons. Phys. Rheum. Char. Cross Hosp. Lond. Socs: Fell. (Ex-Pres.) Med. Soc. Lond.; Fell. Roy. Soc. Med.; Brit. Soc. Rheum. Prev: Reader (Clin. Rheum.) Char. Cross & W.m. Med. Sch. Lond.; Sen. Regist. (Med.) W.m. Hosp. Lond.; Clin. Scientist Clin. Research Centre Harrow.

KEAT, Euan Charles Beverley Scott, MC (retired) Halletts, Ditchling Common, Hassocks BN6 Tel: 0179 182235 — MRCS Eng. LRCP Lond. 1943; MD Lond. 1949, MB BS 1944; FRCP Lond. 1968, M 1948. Prev: Hon. Clin. Asst. & Sen. Regist. (Med.) Char. Cross Hosp. Lond.

KEATES, Michael Donald 30 Bakewell Street, Penkhull, Stoke-on-Trent ST4 5HJ — MRCS Eng. LRCP Lond. 1944.

KEATING, Alanna Ruth 145 Stonehouse Street, Clapham, London SW4 6BQ — MB BS 1991 Lond.

KEATING, Desmond Andrew Elm Lane Surgery, 104 Elm Lane, Sheffield S5 7TW Tel: 0114 245 6994 Fax: 0114 257 1260; Stockwell House, 81 Tom Lane, Sheffield S10 3PA Tel: 0114 230 2033 Email: dakeating@compuserve.com — MB ChB Sheff. 1978; MRCGP 1989.

KEATING, Donncadha Caoimhgin (retired) 53 Willoughby Drive, Empingham, Oakham LE15 8PY Tel: 01780 460677 — MB BCh BAO 1946 NUI.

KEATING, Edmund Francis 29 Fernhill Road, Shipley BD18 4SL — LM 1941 Rotunda; MA Dub. 1989; BA, MB BCh BAO Dub. 1939. (T.C. Dub.) Prev: Ho. Surg. Richmond Hosp. Dub.; Res. Extern. Matern. Asst. Rotunda Hosp. Dub.; Sen. Res. Med. Off. City Gen. Hosp. Gloucester.

KEATING, Elaine Jenny Brighton General Hospital, Elm Grove, Brighton BN2 3EW; 60 Tumulus Road, Saltdean, Brighton BN2 8FS — MB BS 1995 Lond.; BSc (Hons.) Lond. 1991. (Royal Free Hospital Hampstead London) SHO (Psychiat.) Brighton Gen. Hosp.

KEATING, Elizabeth Mary 22 Rupert Road, Sheffield S7 1RP — MB ChB 1995 Sheff. SHO (Gen. Med.) N. Gen. Hosp. Sheff.

KEATING, Felicity Ann 9 Sciennes Gardens, Edinburgh EH9 1NR Email: jfak@aol.com; 3 Douglas Drive, Smith's Parish HS01, Bermuda Tel: 00 01 441 2931876 — MB ChB 1994 Ed.; BSc Biol. 1st cl. Canada 1988. (Ed.) GP. Socs: BMA.

KEATING, Fergus Stephen Jonathon 8 Tregarvon Road, London SW11 5QE — MB BS 1992 Lond.; BSc (Hons.) Lond. 1989, MB BS 1992.

KEATING, Gerald William 5 Mary Church Road, Bucknall, Stoke-on-Trent ST2 9BJ Tel: 01782 212700; Ivy House Farm, Standon, Stafford ST21 6RN — MB BCh BAO 1948 Dub.; BA, MB BCh BAO Dub. 1948. (T.C. Dub.)

KEATING, Mr John Francis 9 Sciennes Gardens, Edinburgh EH9 1NR — MB BCh BAO 1983 Dub.; FRCS Ed. 1987; FRCSI 1987. (Trinity, Dublin) Cons. (Orthop Surg.), Roy. Infirm. Edin. & P.ss Margt. Rose Orthop. Hosp. Prev: Sen. Regist. (Orthop.) Roy. Infirm. Edin.

KEATING, John Joseph Furness General Hospital, Dalton Lane, Barrow-in-Furness LA14 Tel: 01229 870870; Croftlands House, Rake Lane, Ulverston LA12 9NG Tel: 01229 870870 — MD 1989 NUI; MB BCh BAO 1979; MRCP (UK) 1983; MRCPI 1982; FRCP 1999. Cons. Gastroenterol. Furness Gen. Hosp. (and Lancaster Roy. Infirm.). Socs: Brit. Soc. Gastroenterol. Prev: Sen. Fell. Chelsea & W.m. Lond.; Sen. Regist. (Gastroenterol. & Gen. Med.) Trinity Coll. Dub.; Research Fell. Liver Unit King's Coll. Hosp. Lond.

KEATING, Patrick Gerard Dudley Southbury Surgery, 73 Southbury Road, Enfield EN1 1PJ Tel: 020 8363 0305 Fax: 020 8364 4288; Tel: 020 8360 5992 Fax: 020 8360 5992 — MB BCh BAO 1977 NUI; MICGP 1987; DObst RCPI 1981; DCH UCD 1979. Socs: Soc. of Occupat.al Med. Prev: Club Doctor Tottenham Hotspur FC; Med. Off. Telstar Leisure Ltd. Enfield & Severnside Paper Edmonton; Occupat. Phys. W. Lond. Occupat. Health Servs.

KEATING, Peter James Somerville Abbotswood Medical Centre, Defford Road, Pershore WR10 1HZ Tel: 01386 552424 — MB BS 1968 Lond.; MRCS Eng. LRCP Lond. 1968. (Lond. Hosp.)

KEATING, Richard Joseph (retired) Heathcroft, Greenfield Lane, Heswall, Wirral CH60 9HG Tel: 0151 342 1943 — MB ChB 1938 Liverp.; DMRE 1940; FRCR 1975; FFR 1952. Prev: Cons. Radiol. Wirral Hosps. ICI & BNF Ltd.

KEATING, Victor James, Lt.-Col. RAMC Retd. Grove Lodge, Watledge, Nailsworth, Stroud GL6 0AP Tel: 0145 383 3679 — MB BCh BAO NUI 1937; FFA RCS Eng. 1953; DA Eng. 1938. (Univ. Coll. Dub.) Hon. Cons. Anaesth. St. Chas. Hosp. Lond., Italian Hosp. Lond. & Qu. Charlotte's Matern Hosp Lond. Socs: Fell. Roy. Soc. Med. Prev: Rockefeller Fell. 1957; Lect. (Anaesth.) Univ. Coll. of W. Indies, Jamaica; Lt.-Col. RAMC.

KEATING, William Joseph (retired) 4 Grange Road, Saltwood, Hythe CT21 4QS Tel: 01303 264399 — MB BCh BAO 1944 NUI. Prev: Med. Off. Gen. Counc. Brit. Ship.

KEATINGE, Joanna Mary 3 Alexandra Road, Lymington SO41 9HB Tel: 01590 672426 — MB ChB 1992 Bristol; DRCOG 1995; MRCGP 1997; DTM & H Liverp. 1997. (Bristol) GP Regist. Lymington. Prev: SHO (Paediat.) Plymouth; SHO (O & G) N. Devon.

KEATINGE, Professor William Richard Medical Sciences Building, Queen Mary & Westfield College, Mile End Road, London E1 4NS Tel: 020 78826365 Fax: 020 8983 0466 Email: w.r.Keatinge@qmul.ac.uk — MB BChir 1956 Camb.; PhD Camb. 1960; FRCP Lond. 1991; MRCP (UK) 1985. (St. Thos.) Emerit. Prof. Physiol. Qu. Mary & W.field Coll. Lond. Socs: Fell. Roy. Soc. Med.; Physiol. Soc. Prev: Prof. Physiol. Lond. Hosp. Med. Coll.; Fell. & Tutor (Physiol.) Pembroke Coll. Oxf.; MRC Appt. Dept. Regius Prof. Med. Oxf.

KEATINGS, Brian Thomas, Wing Cdr. RAF Med. Br. Regional Occupational Medical Centre, RAF Lyneham, Chippenham SN15 4PZ Tel: 01249 890381 Ext: 7386 Fax: 01249 890381 ext 6872 Email: keatings_bt@stones.com; 36 Mallard Avenue, Lyneham, Chippenham SN15 4QD Tel: 01249 891609 Email: keatings_bt@msn.com — MB ChB 1977 Glas.; MMedSc (Occupat. Health) Birm. 1995; MFOM RCP Lond. 1997; DAvMed FOM RCP Lond. 1988. (Glas.) Cons. in Occupat. Med. Socs: Fac. Occupat. Med.; Soc. of Occup. Med. Prev: Sen. Med. Off. RAF Lyneham.

KEATINGS, Hugh Seymour (retired) Higher Treedown House, Chittlehampton, Umberleigh EX37 9QS — MB BCh BAO 1951 Belf.; MRCGP 1968. Prev: Res. Med. Off. Roy. Vict. Hosp. Belf.

KEATINGS, John (retired) Woodcroft, Marsden Road, Cleadon, Sunderland SR6 7RA Tel: 0191 519 3113 — MB ChB 1956 Glas. Prev: GP Boldon Colliery.

KEATINGS, Veronica Mary 101 Radbourne Road, London SW12 0EE — MB BCh BAO 1987 NUI; MRCP (UK) 1990.

KEATLEY, John Desmond 19 Tobermore Road, Magherafelt BT45 5HB Tel: 01648 32327 — MB BCh BAO 1948 Dub.

KEAVNEY, Bernard David Freeman Hospital, High Heaton NE7 7DN Tel: 0191 2843111 — BM BCh 1988 Oxf.; 2000 DM, Oxf; BSc St. And. 1985; MRCP (UK) 1991. (Oxford) Cons. Cardiol., Newc. upon Tyne Hosp. Trust; Sen. Lect. in Cardiol., Univ. Newc.

KEAVNEY, Michael James Bridge House Surgery, Alderbrough St John, Richmond DL11 7SY Tel: 01325 374332; 1 The Green, Middleton Tyas, Richmond DL10 6QY — MB ChB 1990 Glas.; MRCGP 1996; DFFP 1996; DRCOG 1993. (Glasgow) Socs: MRCGP.

KEAVNEY, Patrick Joseph The Health Centre, Bailey Street, Old Basford, Nottingham NG6 0HD Tel: 0115 978 1231 Fax: 0115 979 0419 Email: paddykeavney@btinternet.com; Flat 4 Mapperley Hall, Lucknew Avenue, Mapperley Park, Nottingham NG3 5AZ Tel: 0115 962 0179 Fax: 0115 924 5130 — LRCPI & LM, LRSCI & LM 1971; MRCGP 1998. (Roy. Coll. Surg. Irel.) Managing Med. Off. HM Prison Nottm.; Exam. Med. Off. DSS. Prev: Div. Police Surg. (Nottm. Constab.).

KEAY, Alexander John (retired) 4 Craiglockhart Park, Edinburgh EH14 1ER Tel: 0131 443 3511 — MB ChB 1951 Ed.; FRCP Glas. 1977; FRCP Ed. 1963, M 1954; DCH Eng. 1953; FRCPCH 1998; FRCPS 1990; DCCH 1985. Prev: Cons. Paediatr. W. Gen. Hosp. Edin.

KEAY, Debra Amanda 15 Ringley Avenue, Horley RH6 7EZ — MB BS 1998 Lond.; MB BS Lond 1998.

KEAY, Kenneth Robert (retired) 7 Broomieknowe, 126 Irvine Road, Largs KA30 8EY Tel: 01475 674998 — MD 1951 St. And.; MD (Commend.) St. And. 1951, MB ChB (Commend.) 1945; FRCP Ed. 1994; DCH Eng. 1950. Prev: Cons. Paediat. W. Wales Hosp. Gp.

KEAY, Stephen David Springfield, Comeytrowe Road, Trull, Taunton TA3 7NE — MB ChB 1987 Ed.

KEAYS, Richard Timothy 16 Donaldson Road, London NW6 6NB — MB BS 1983 Lond.

KEBA, Simon 62 Burnedge Fold Road, Grasscroft, Oldham OL4 4EE — MB ChB 1980 Manch.

KEBBIE, Margaret Miatta 23 Edbrook Walk, Longsight, Manchester M13 0DA — MB ChB 1981 Manch.

KEBLE-WILLIAMS, Gwilym (retired) Lodore, 17 Porth-y-Castell, Barry CF62 6QA Tel: 01446 733095 — MB BCh 1951 Wales; BSc Wales 1948, MB BCh 1951; MRCGP 1959; DObst RCOG 1953. Prev: Ho. Off. (Gen. Med. & O & G) Roy. Infirm. Cardiff.

KECZKES, Kalman The Department of Dermatology, The Princess Royal Hospital, Saltshouse Road, Hull HU8 9HE Tel: 01482 676798; The Blue Danube, 47 Redland Drive, Kirkella, Hull HU10 7UX Tel: 01482 656498 — MB ChB 1959 Glas.; FRCP Ed. 1978, M 1962. Cons. Dermat. Humberside AHA. Socs: Fell. Roy. Soc. Med. (Mem. Sect. Dermat.); BMA & N. Eng. Dermat. Soc. Prev: Sen. Regist. Dundee Roy. Infirm.; Regist. Glas. Roy. Infirm.; Ho. Phys. S.. Gen. Hosp. Glas.

KEDDIE, Frank Stuart 11 Penlee Gardens, Stoke, Plymouth PL3 4AN Tel: 01752 562298 — BM BCh 1951 Oxf.; MA, BM BCh Oxf. 1951; FFA RCS Eng. 1958. (Middlx.) Socs: (Ex-Pres.) Plymouth Med. Soc. Prev: Sen. Anaesth. Plymouth Dist. Gen. Hosp.; Sen. Regist. (Anaesth.) Roy. Infirm. Edin.; Regist. (Anaesth.) Whittington Hosp. Lond.

KEDDIE, James 91 Kirkintilloch Road, Bishopbriggs, Glasgow G64 2AA Tel: 0141 772 2241/2 Fax: 0141 762 3482; 7 Balfleurs Street, Milngavie, Glasgow G62 8HW Tel: 0141 956 4898 — MB ChB 1974 Glas.; MRCGP 1978.

KEDDIE, Kenneth Malcolm Grant (retired) Dunira, Inverkeilor, Arbroath DD11 5RT Tel: 01241 830229 — MB ChB 1956 Ed.; FRCPsych 1986, M 1972; DPM Eng. 1962. Prev: Cons. Psychiat. Sunnyside Roy. Hosp. Montrose.

KEDDIE, Mr Nigel Chalmers (retired) Rosemary Cottage, Lonsties, Keswick CA12 4TD Tel: 017687 71330 — BM BCh 1959 Oxf.; MA Oxf. 1959; FRCS Ed. 1982; FRCS Eng. 1962. Prev: Cons. Surg. W. Cumbld. Hosp. Whitehaven.

KEDDILTY, James Thomas Hutcheson 1A Freeland Road, London W5 3HR — MB ChB 1985 Manch.; BSc (Med.) St. And. 1982.

KEDIA, Kapil 47 Kings Road, London Colney, St Albans AL2 1ES — MB BS 1996 Lond.

KEDIA, Mrs Pushpa Kings Road Surgery, 45 Kings Road, London Colney, St Albans AL2 1ES Tel: 01727 822138 — MB BS 1968 Rajasthan; BSc 1962 Rajasthan; DA Eng. 1970. (S.M.S. Med. Coll. Jaipur) Prev: Res. Anaesth. FarnBoro. Hosp. Kent; Res. Anaesth. St. James Hosp. Balham.

KEDWARD, John Francis London Road Practice, 84-86 London Road, Bedford MK42 0NT Tel: 01234 266851 Fax: 01234 363998 — MB BChir 1987 Camb.; MSc Lond. 1998; MRCGP 1992; DCH RCP Lond. 1992; DRCOG 1991; MA Camb. 1989. (Cambridge) Partner Lond. Rd. Health Centre Bedford; GP Researcher S. Beds. Practitioners Gp.; Clin. Governance Lead Bedford PCG.

KEE, Frank 4 Finchley Gardens, Old Holywood Road, Belfast BT4 2JH — MB BCh BAO 1983 Belf.; MRCP (UK) 1986.

KEE, John Crennell (retired) St. Olave's Old Vicarage, Ramsey IM8 3PF Tel: 01624 814031 — MB ChB 1938 Liverp.; DMRE 1940. Prev: Cons. Radiol. Liverp. AHA (T) & DHSS.

KEE, Maria Agnes Ann 20 Sharman Park, Belfast BT9 5HJ — MB ChB 1980 Belf.; MRCPsych 1984.

KEEBLE, Brian Robert 53 Graham Road, Ipswich IP1 3QF — MB BS 1975 Lond.; BSc (Hons.) Lond. 1972; MRCS Eng. LRCP Lond. 1975; MFPHM RCP (UK) 1990; MRCGP 1980; T(PHM) 1992. (St. Mary's) Ho. Phys. Edgware Gen. Hosp. Prev: Ho. Surg. St. Mary's Hosp. Lond.

KEEBLE, Margaret Mary Droitwich Health Centre, Ombersley Street E., Droitwich WR9 8RD Tel: 01905 773535; 18 St George's Walk, Worcester WR1 1QY — MB BS 1988 Lond.; BSc (Hons.) Lond. 1985; MRCGP 1993; DRCOG 1992. Clin. Asst. (Gen. Pract.) Droitwich Health Centre.

KEEBLE, Michael 5 Mill Farm Road, Harborne, Birmingham B17 0QX — MB ChB 1985 Birm.

KEEBLE, Richard James 14 Cliffside Gardens, Woodhouse, Leeds LS6 2HA — MB ChB 1998 Leeds.

KEEBLE, Tanya 1 Cholmeley Crescent, London N6 5EZ — MB BS 1998 Lond.; MB BS Lond 1998.

KEEBLE, William Flat 2/2, 289 Kenmure St., Glasgow G41 2QX — BM BS 1993 Nottm.

KEECH, James Peter BP Amoco Exploration, Farburn Industrial Estate, Dyce, Aberdeen AB21 7PB Tel: 01224 834110 Fax: 01224 834448 Email: keechjj@bp.com — MB BS 1978 Lond.; MSc (Occupat. Med.) Lond. 1990; MRCS Eng. LRCP Lond. 1978; AFOM RCP Lond. 1990; DRCOG 1982; DTM & H Liverp. 1980. Manager Health Servs. Prev: Sen. Med. Off. BP Exploration Uxbridge.

KEECH, Timothy Peter Andrew House Surgery, 2 South Terrace, Camborne TR14 8ST Tel: 01209 714876 — MB BS 1985 Lond.; DFFP 1993; DRCOG 1988; Cert. Family Plann. JCC 1988. (Lond. Hosp. Med. Coll.) GP Cornw. Socs: BMA.

KEEDWELL, Paul Anthony Dept. of Neuroscience and Emotion, Psychological Medicine Division, Institute of Psychiatry, Decrespigny Park, Camberwell, London SE5; Email: pkeedwell@aol.com — MB ChB 1991 Leeds; MRCPsych (Lond.) 1998; BSc (Hons.) Psychology in relation to Medicine Leeds 1989. p/t Clin. Research Fell., Mood Disorders, Dept. of Neurosci. and Emotion, Inst. of Psychiat., Decrespigny Pk., Camberwell, Lond. SE5. Socs: Roy. Coll. of Psychiat.; Med. Protec. Soc. Prev: Specialist Regist., Community Psychiat., Maudsley Hosp., Lond.; Addic. Sci., Nat. Alcohol Unit, Maudsley Hosp., Lond.

KEEFE, John Victor 34 Mawney Road, Romford RM7 7HD Tel: 01708 743627 Fax: 01709 738244; 28 Rural Close, Hornchurch RM11 1FH — MB BS 1955 Lond. (Lond. Hosp.) Socs: Fell. Roy. Soc. Med.; Brit. Soc. Study of Infec. Prev: Ho. Surg. (Ophth. & Plastic) & Receiv. Room Off. Lond. Hosp.; Ho. Phys. Buckland Hosp. Dover.

KEEFE, Martin Royal South Hampshire Hospital, Brinton Terrace, Off St Mary's Road, Southampton SO14 0YG Tel: 02380 825458 Fax: 02380 825353 — MB ChB 1979 Liverp.; DM Soton. 1994; FRCP 1998. (Liverpool) Cons. Dermat. Roy. S. Hants. Hosp. S.ampton. Prev: Sen. Regist. (Dermat.) Roy. S. Hants. Hosp.; Regist. (Dermat.) Stobhill Gen. Hosp. Glas.

KEEFE, Oonagh Rose (retired) 65 High Street, Bellfield RM11 3SZ CO Tel: 01206 304480 — MB BS 1956 Lond. Prev: Ho. Surg. O & G Unit. & Ho Phys. Rush Green Hosp. Romford.

KEEFE, Wendy Joy 18 Mavis Avenue, Cookridge, Leeds LS16 7LJ — MB ChB 1978 Leeds; BSc (Hons.) Pharmacol. Leeds 1975, MB ChB 1978; MRCGP 1982; DRCOG 1980. (Leeds)

KEEGAN, Aileen Agatha May (retired) 107 Bunbury Road, Birmingham B31 2ND Tel: 0121 475 2400 — LRCPI & LM, LRSCI & LM 1945; LRCPI & LM, LRCSI & LM 1945.

KEEGAN, Donal Arthur John, OBE Altnagelvin Hospital, Londonderry BT47 6SB; Auskaird, 5 Greenwood, Londonderry BT48 8NP Tel: 01504 351292 — MB BCh BAO 1964 Belf.; BSc (Hons.) Belf. 1961; FRCP Lond. 1990; FRCP Ed. 1989; FRCPI 1973, M 1968; DPhysMed Eng. 1970. (Qu. Univ. Belf.) Cons. Phys. Altnagelvin Hosp. Lond.derry; DL. Socs: Brit. Soc. for Rheum.; Irish Soc. for Rheum. Prev: Cons. Rehabil. & Physical Med. Highland HB; Sen. Regist. (Physical Med.) Roy. Vict. Hosp. Belf.

KEEGAN, Nigel John 5 Elm Close, Newark NG24 1SG — MB BS 1985 Lond.

KEEGAN, Mr Philip Edward Dept. of Urology, The James Cook University Hospital, Marton Road, Middlesbrough TS4 3BW Tel: 01642 854506 Fax: 01642 854708 Email: p.e.keegan@newcastle.ac.uk; 14 Holly Avenue, Jesmond, Newcastle upon Tyne NE2 2PY — MB BS 1992 Newc.; BMedSc (Hons.) Newc. 1989, MB BS 1992; FRCS Eng. 1997. (Newc.) Specialist Regist. in Urol., Dept. of Urol., James cook Univ. Hosp. Socs: EAU - Junoir Mem.; BAUS - Junoir Mem. Prev: Research Regist. (Urol.) Dept. of Surg. Newc. Univ. Med. Sch.; Urol. Regist., Dept. of Urol., Cumbld. Infirm.

KEEGAN, Simon 83 Pickmere Road, Sheffield S10 1GZ — MB ChB 1992 Sheff.

KEEGANS, Pauline 48 Firpark Street, Motherwell ML1 2PR — MB ChB 1987 Glas.; MRCGP 1993; T(GP) 1993. SHO (A & E) Glas. Roy. Infirm. Prev: Ho. Off (Med.) Vict. Infirm. Glas.; Ho. Off. (Surg.) Stobhill Hosp. Glas.

KEEL, Aileen Margaret Scottish Executive Health Department, St Andrews House, Edinburgh EH1 3DG Tel: 0131 244 2799 Fax: 0131 244 3185; 23 Danube Street, Edinburgh EH4 1NN Tel: 0131 332 5332 — MB ChB 1976 Glas.; FRCPath 1996; MRCP 1979 (UK); FRCP 1992 Glas.; M 1986; FRCP Glas. 1992; MRCP (UK) 1979; FRCPath 1996, M 1986. Dep. Chief Med. Off., Scott. Exec. Health Dept.; Hon. Cons. Haemat. Edin. Roy. Infirm. Prev: Dir. (Path.) Cromwell Hosp. Lond.; Regist. (Haemat.) Roy. Infirm. Glas.; Leukaemia Research Fund Fell. Roy. Hosp. Sick Childr. Glas.

KEEL, John Christopher Tel: 01482 667108 Fax: 01482 665090 — MB ChB 1970 Leeds; MRCGP 1978; DCH Eng. 1977; DObst RCOG 1976; DA Eng. 1972.

KEEL, Jonathan David Woodhouse Medical Centre, 5 Skelton Lane, Woodhouse, Sheffield S13 7LY Tel: 0114 269 2049 Fax: 0114 269 6539 — MB ChB 1989 Sheff.

KEEL, Melaine Jayne Gosford Hospital, Anaesthetic Division, Holden St., Gosford NSW 2250, Australia Tel: 00 61 2 4320 3800 Fax: 00 61 2 4320 3713; 25 Victoria Gardens, Hounslow TW5 9DD Tel: 020 8737 2609 — MB ChB 1992 Leeds; DA (UK) 1995. (Univ. Leeds) Regist. (Anaesthetics and ITU) Gosford. Socs: MRCAnaesth. Prev: Staff Grade (Anaesthetics) York Dist. Hosp.; SHO (Anaesthetics) Harrogate; SHO (Anaesthetics) York.

KEELE, Gerard Priscilla Bazon Lodge, Colman Hospital, Unthanil Road, Norwich NR2 2PJ Tel: 01603 288938 Fax: 01603 288988 Email: gk@sys.uea.ac.uk — MD 1982 Camb.; MB 1968, BChir 1967; FRCGP 1989, M 1972. (Camb. & Middlx.) Clin. Asst. Palliat. Med. Prev: Research Off. (Gen. Pract.) Manch. Univ.; GP.

KEELER, John Francis 470 Haworth Road, Allerton, Bradford BD15 9LL — MB BS 1982 Lond.; FFA RCS Eng. 1987. Cons. Anaesth. Bradford Roy. Infirm. Prev: Sen. Regist. (Anaesth.) Gen. Infirm. Leeds; Regist. (Anaesth.) Bradford Roy. Infirm.; SHO (Anaesth.) Hull Roy. Infirm. SHO (Anaesth.) Kent & Canterbury Hosp.

KEELEY, Duncan James Thame Health Centre, East Street, Thame OX9 3JZ Tel: 01844 261066; 25 Croft Road, Thame OX9 3JF — MB BS 1979 Lond.; BA Camb. 1976; MRCP (UK) 1982; MRCGP 1989; DRCOG 1983.

KEELEY, Russell (retired) 317 Health Road, Leighton Buzzard LU7 8AX Tel: 01525 377133 — MB BChir 1952 Camb.; MRCS Eng. LRCP Lond. 1951; DObst RCOG 1958.

KEELEY, Vaughan Laurence Nightingale Macmillan Unit, Derbyshire Royal Infirmary NHS Trust, 117A London Road, Derby DE1 2QS Tel: 01332 254900 Fax: 01332 254984 — MB BS 1977 Lond.; PhD Camb. 1985; MRCGP 1986. Cons. Palliat. Med. Nightingale Macmillan Unit Derby.

KEELING, Anne Louise Long Furlong Medical Centre, 45 Loyd Close, Abingdon OX14 1XR Tel: 01235 522379; 49 Littleworth, Oxford OX33 1TR Tel: 01865 875501 — MB BS 1982 Lond.; MRCGP 1987; DFFP 1994; DCH RCP Lond. 1986; DRCOG 1984. GP Partner.

KEELING, Carolyn Jean Vicarage Road Medical Centre, Vicarage Road, Mickleover, Derby DE3 5EB Tel: 01332 513283 Fax: 01332 518569; 12 Lowther Drive, Garforth, Leeds LS25 1EW — MB BS 1981 Newc.; MRCGP 1988; DRCOG 1985. GP Mickleover. Prev: SHO (O & G) Pk. Hosp. Manch.; SHO (Med.) Dunedin Pub. Hosp. New Zealand; SHO (Psychiat.) St. Nicholas Hosp. Newc.

KEELING, David Harry (retired) Torlands, Westella Road, Yelverton PL20 6AS Tel: 01822 852305 — MB BChir 1960 Camb.; MSc Lond. 1971; MA Camb. 1960; FRCR 1983. Prev: Cons. Phys. (Nuclear Med.) Derriford Hosp. Plymouth & Treliske Hosp. Cornw.

KEELING, David Michael Oxford Haemophilia Centre and Thrombosis Unit, The Churchill Hospital, Oxford OX3 7LJ Tel: 01865 225318 Fax: 01865 225608 Email: david.keeling@ndm.ox.ac.uk; 49 Littleworth, Oxford OX33 1TR Tel: 01865 875501 — MB BS (Distinc. Path.) Lond. 1982; BSc (1st cl. Hons. Physiol.) Lond. 1979, MD 1996; MRCP (UK) 1986; FRCPath 2002. (St. Bart.) Cons. Haemat. Oxf. Radcliffe NHS Trust; Hon. Sen. Clin. Lect. Univ. Oxf. Prev: Sen. Regist. (Haemat.) Addenbrooke's Hosp. Camb.

KEELING, Jean Winifred Department of Paediatric Pathology Lothian Univ Hosp NHS Trust, Royal Hospital for Sick Children, 2 Rillbank Crescent, Edinburgh EH9 1LF Tel: 0131 536 0440 Fax: 0131 536 0455 — MB BS 1964 Lond.; FRCP Ed. 1993; MRCS Eng. LRCP Lond. 1964; FRCPath 1983, M 1971; FRCPCH 1997. (Roy. Free) Cons. Paediat. Path. Roy. Hosp. Sick Childr. Edin. Socs: Path. Soc.; (Past Pres.) Paediat. Path. Soc.; Pres. elect Internat. Paed. Path. Assn. Prev: Cons. Paediat. Path. John Radcliffe Hosp. Oxf.; Lect. (Morbid Anat.) Inst. Child Health & Hosp. Sick Childr. Gt. Ormond St. Lond.

KEELING, John David Gallwey House, Gallwey Road, Aldershot GU11 2DD — MB BS 1983 Lond.; MRCGP 1988; DFFP 1993; DRCOG 1990.

KEELING, Martin The Park Medical Centre, Maine Drive Clinic, Maine Drive, Chaddesden, Derby DE21 6LA Tel: 01332 665522 Fax: 01332 678210; The Park Medical Centre, Maine Drive, Chaddesden, Derby DE21 6LA Tel: 01332 665522 — BM BS 1982 Nottm.; BMedSci Nottm. 1980, BSc 1977, BM BS 1982; FRCGP 1996, M 1987; DCH RCP Lond. 1986; DObst 1984. Fell.sh. by Assesm. Working GP, RCGP. Socs: RCGP (Fac. Bd. Vale of Trent).

KEELING, Mr Neil John West Suffolk Hospital, Hardwick Lane, Bury St Edmunds IP33 2QZ Tel: 01284 713000; The Croft Farmhouse, Gent's Lane, Shimpling, Bury St Edmunds IP29 4HR — MB BS 1988 Lond.; FRCS Eng. 1992; MS Lond. 1997; FRCS (Gen. Surg.) 1998. (Univ. Coll. & Middlx. Hosp.) Socs: Roy. Soc. Med.; SRS; BASO. Prev: Specialist Regist. & Sen. Regist. (Gen. Surg.) Whipps Cross Hosp. Lond.; Specialist Regist. & Sen. Regist. (Gen. Surg.) Univ. Coll. & Middlx. Hosps. Lond.; Sen. Regist. Colchester Gen. Hosp.

KEELING, Peter Alastair Tel: 01620 893263 Fax: 01620 897005 — MB ChB 1974 Dundee; BSc (Med. Sci.) St. And. 1971; MRCGP 1980; Cert. Family Plann. JCC 1981. (Dundee)

KEELING, Philip John Torbay Hospital, Devon TQ2 7AA; 4 Seymour Villas, Bridgetown, Totnes TQ9 5QR — MB BS 1985 Lond.; BSc Lond. 1982, MD 1995; FRCP 2001; BSc 1982 Lond. (St. Bart. Lond.) Prev: Sen. Regist. (Cardiol.) St. Geo. Hosp. Lond.; Regist. (Cardiol.) St. Thos. Hosp. Lond.; Hon. Regist. (Cardiol. Sci.) St. Geo. Hosp. Med. Sch. Lond.

KEELING, Trevor John Easthampstead Practice, Easthampstead Surgery, 23 Rectory Lane, Bracknell RG12 7BB Tel: 01344 457535 Fax: 01344 301862 Email: trevor.keeling@gp-k81087.nhs.uk; The Odd House, Nevelle Close, Binfield, Bracknell RG42 4AZ Tel: 01344 411200 Email: keeofodd@globalnet.co.uk — MB ChB 1980 Bristol;

MRCGP 1986; DCH RCP Lond. 1986. Trainer (Gen. Pract.) Oxf. VTS. Socs: Windsor Med. Soc. Prev: Trainee GP E.bourne VTS.

KEELING-ROBERTS, Christopher Stuart Dept.of Radiology, Stepping Hill Hospital, Stockport SK2 7JE Tel: 0161 419 5976 — MB BS 1975 Lond.; BA Oxf. 1972; MRCP (UK) 1979; MRCS Eng. LRCP Lond. 1975; FRCR 1984; DMRD Eng. 1982. (Westm.) Cons. Radiol. Stepping Hill Hosp.Stockport.; Hon. Clin. Lect. in Radiol., Univ. of Manch.. Prev: Sen. Regist. (Diag. Radiol.) N.W. RHA.

KEELING-ROBERTS, John (retired) 61 The Crescent, Wem, Shrewsbury SY4 5AE Tel: 01939 234777 — MRCS Eng. LRCP Lond. 1943. Prev: Surg. Brit. Red Cross Soc. & St. John Ambul. Brig.

KEELY, Geraldine Mary Jude Old Station Surgery, 39 Brecon Road, Abergavenny NP7 5UH Tel: 01873 859000 Fax: 01873 850163; Tel: 01873 850158 — MB BCh BAO 1987 NUI; 1999 (Masters) Medical Education; Dip. Med. Educat. 1998; Dip. Palliat. Med. Wales 1995; DFFP 1994; Cert. Family Plann. JCC 1993; MRCGP 1991; DGM RCP Lond. 1991; DCH RCP Lond. 1989; DObst RCOG 1989. GP Trainer Abergavenny; Course Organiser Gwent BTS (GP Train.). Prev: GP Cardiff.

KEELY, Vernon Harris (retired) 19 The Warren, Gravesend DA12 4DA — MB BCh BAO 1961 Dub.; BA Dub. 1961; DObst RCOG 1963.

KEEN, Alison Laura Flat 4, Sycamore Court, Sycamore Grove, New Malden KT3 3DG — BM 1998 Soton.; BM Soton 1998.

KEEN, Charles Edward Department of Pathology, Royal Devon and Exeter Healthcare NHS Trust, Church Lane, Heavitree, Exeter EX2 5AD Tel: 01392 402963 Fax: 01392 402964 Email: charlie.keen@rdehc-tr.swest.nhs.uk — MB ChB 1979 Cape Town; MRCP (UK) 1985; MRCPath 1989; DO RCS Eng. 1983; FRCPath 1997. Cons. Histopath. & Cytopath. Roy. Devon & Exeter Healthcare NHS Trust. Prev: Cons. (Histopath. & Cytopath.) Univ. Hosp. Lewisham; Sen. Regist. (Histopath.) Kings Coll. Hosp. Lond. & Kingston Hosp. Surrey; Regist. (Histopath.) Char. Cross Hosp. Lond.

KEEN, Christina McMillan Haematology Department, Western Infirmary, Glasgow G12; 2 Clathic Avenue, Bearsden, Glasgow G61 2HF — MB ChB 1969 Glas.; MRCP (UK) 1977; MRCPath. 1981. Assoc. Specialist (Haemat.) W.. Infirm. Glas. Socs: Brit. Soc. Haemat.; RCPS Glas. (Collegiate Mem.).

KEEN, Colin William (retired) Mid Kent Oncology Centre, Maidstone Hospital, Maidstone ME16 9QQ Tel: 01622 729000 Fax: 01622 721303 — MB BS Lond. 1958; MA Wales 1991; FRCPC 1973; FRCR 1989; MRACR 1967; DMRT Eng. 1966. Prev: Cons. Radiother. & Oncol. S. Glam.

KEEN, Daphne Vivien Rm221 2nd Floor Clare House, St Georges Healthcare, Blackshaw Road, London SW17 0QT Tel: 0208 725 3380 Fax: 0208 725 0598 — MRCS Eng. LRCP Lond. 1978; BA (Architect Stud) Liverp. 1971; FRCP Lond. 1996; MRCP (UK) 1983. (Univ. Sheff.) Cons. Neuro Develop. Paediat. St Geo.s Healthcare NHS Trust; Hon. Sen. Lect. Prev: Sen. Regist. (Paediat.) Trent RHA; Cons. Community Paediat. & Clin. Advisor Childr. Serv. Doncaster Roy. Infirm. & Montagu NHS Trust.

KEEN, Mr Gerald 8 Glenavon Park, Bristol BS9 1RN Tel: 0117 968 5385 Fax: 0117 968 1461 Email: gkeen@amserve.net — MS Lond. 1959, MB BS 1950; FRCS Eng. 1954; MRCS Eng. LRCP Lond. 1949. (Westm.) Cons. Cardiothoracic. Surg. Bristol & Frenchay HA; Clin. Lect. (Surg.) Univ. Bristol; Examr. Cardiothoracic Surg. RCS Edin. Socs: Soc. Thoracic Surgs.; Brit. Cardiac Soc. Prev: Sen. Regist. (Thoracic Surg.) W.m. Hosp. Lond.; Fell. (Cardiac Surg.) Stanford Univ. Calif.; Capt. RAMC.

KEEN, Professor Harry, CBE Unit for Metabolic Medicine, 5th Floor Thomas Guy House, Guy's Hospital Campus, King's College London, London SE1 9RT Tel: 020 7955 4136 Fax: 020 7955 2985 Email: harrykeen@compuserve.com; 58 Kingsfield Road, Oxhey WD19 4TR Tel: 01923 231753 Fax: 01923 231753 Email: harrykeen@compuserve.com — MB BS Lond. 1948; MD Lond. 1971; FRCP Lond. 1970, M 1957. (St. Mary's) Emerit. Prof. of Human Metab.& Cons Phys Guy's Hosp Campus, King's Coll. Lond.; Mem Rank Prize Funds Nutrit. Avd. Comm. Lond; Mem Med Advisory Panel ITC; Co-director WHO Collaborating Centre for Long-term Complications of Diabetes. Socs: (Vice-Pres.) Diabetes UK; Hon. Mem. Europ. Assn. for Study of Diabetes; (Hon. Pres.) Internat. Diabetes Federat. Prev: Dir. Unit for Metab. Med. & Phys. Guy's Hosp. Gp.; Direct. Clin. Servs. (Med.) Guy's Hosp. Lond.; Research Fell. (Med.) & Clin. Asst. Med. Unit St. Mary's Hosp. Lond.

KEEN, Jenny Amanda Institute of General Practice, Community Sciences Centre, Northern General Hospital, Herries Road, Sheffield S5 7AU Tel: 0114 271 5925 Email: j.keen@sheffield.ac.uk; 66 Southgrove Road, Sheffield S10 2NQ Tel: 0114 271 5925 Fax: 0114 242 2136 — MB BS 1989 Lond.; MSc Lond. 1982; BA (Hons.) Oxf. 1980; DRCOG 1992; Cert. Family Plann. JCC 1992; MRCGP 1995. (Guy's) GP Research Fell. Inst. of Gen. Pract. Sheff..; Primary Care Specialist Drug Abuse. Socs: Med. Pract. Union. Prev: GP The Crookes Pract. Sheff..

KEEN, Jeremy Charles Broxwood Park, Sandbank, Dunoon PA23 8PD — MB ChB 1987 Ed.; BSc Ed. 1985; MRCP (UK) 1991.

KEEN, John Harwood (retired) Boundary lodge, 40 Chester Road, Middlewich CW10 9EU Tel: 01606 737103 Email: keenmiddlewich@netline.com — MB BS 1954 Lond.; FRCP Lond. 1977, M 1965; DObst RCOG 1963; DCH Eng. 1959. Prev: Cons. Paediat. Booth Hall Childr. Hosp. Manch.

KEEN, John William Bedford Park Surgery, 55 South Parade, Chiswick, London W4 5LH Tel: 020 8994 3333 Fax: 020 8742 1246 — BM 1983 Soton.; MRCGP 1987; DRCOG 1986; Cert. Family Plann. JCC 1986. (Southampton) Med. Adviser Lond. Boro.s of Hammersmith & Fulham & Ealing; Assoc. Mem. KCW Health Auth; Med. Adviser Fullers Brewery Lond.; Mem. Research Ethics Comm., St Mary's Hosp. Lond.

KEEN, Julia Jane 7 Carlton Road, Derby DE23 6HB — MB BS 1989 Newc.; DCH RCP Lond. 1994. Trainee GP Derby VTS.

KEEN, Michael Jonathan Cassio Surgery, 62-68 Merton Road, Watford WD18 0WL Tel: 01923 226011 Fax: 01923 817342 — MB BS 1977 Lond.; MRCS Eng. LRCP Lond. 1977; LMCC 1983. (St. Mary's) GP Tutor St. Mary's Hosp. Med. Sch.; Div. Police Surg. Herts. Constab.; Gp. 4 Med. Off. Prev: Sen. Med. Resid. Family Med. Progr. McMaster Univ. Med. Centre Canada; Med. Resid. & Emerg. Resid. KEMH, Bermuda.

KEEN, Morfydd Rozella, OBE 128 Newport Road, Cardiff CF24 1DH Tel: 029 2046 4499; 34 Heol-y-Coed, Rhiwbina, Cardiff CF14 6HT Tel: 0292 065 8229 — MB BCh Wales 1959; MRCPsych 1991; DPM Eng. 1973. (Welsh National School of Medicine) Cons. & Psychiat. Private Pract. Cardiff; Staff Cons., Psychiat., Priory Hosp., Bristol. Socs: BMA; Welsh Psychiat. Soc.; Cardiff Med. Soc. Prev: Cons. Psychiat. (Subst. Abuse) Cardiff Community Health Care.

KEEN, Richard William Metabolic Bone Disease Unit, Royal National Orthopaedic Hosp, Brokeley Hill, Stanmore HA7 4LP Tel: 020 8909 5314 Fax: 0208420 7487 Email: richard.keen@ucl.ac.uk — MB BS 1988 Lond.; BSc Lond. 1985; MRCP UK) 1992. (St. Mary's Hosp. Lond.) Sen Lec Univ coll Lond.; Hon cons Rheum, Roy. Nat Ortho Hosp Stanmare; Hon Cons Rheum Midd Lond. Socs: Fell. Roy. Soc. Med.; Brit. Soc. Rheum.; Amer. Soc. Bone & Mineral Research. Prev: Research Fell. & Sen. Regist. (Rheum.) St. Thos. Hosp. Lond.; Regist. (Rheum.) N.wick Pk. Hosp.; Regist. (Gen. Med.) Centr. Middlx. Hosp.

KEEN, Ronald Ivan (retired) 8 Bramway, Bramhall, Stockport SK7 2AP Tel: 0161 439 6842 — MB ChB Sheff. 1951; BA Open 1996; MRCS Eng. LRCP Lond. 1951; FFA RCS Eng. 1956; DA Eng. 1954. Prev: Cons. Anaesth. Centr. Manch. HA.

KEENAN, Caroline White House Surgery, Horsefair, Chipping Norton OX7 5AL Tel: 01608 642742 Fax: 01608 642794 — BM BS 1985 Nottm.

KEENAN, Caroline Eldred Sarah Clinical Biochemistry, Ashford Hospital, Ashford TW15 3AA Tel: 01784 884499 Fax: 01784 884099; Millstream House, Stadhampton, Oxford OX44 7TP Tel: 01865 890228 — MB BS Lond. 1966; FRCPath 1988, M 1975; Dip. Gen. Biochem. Lond. 1974. (Middlx.) Cons. Chem. Path. Ashford Hosp. Middlx. Prev: Lect. (Chem. Path.) Ct.auld Inst. Middlx. Hosp. Lond.

KEENAN, Mr Daniel Joseph Marquess Department of Cardiothoracic Surgery, Manchester Heart Centre, Manchester Royal Infirmary, Oxford Road, Manchester M13 9WL Tel: 0161 276 8521 Fax: 0161 276 8522 Email: djmk.cabgxall@man.ac.uk; The Beeches, Mill Lane, Cheadle SK8 2PY Tel: 0161 428 0288 Fax: 0161 428 1692 — MB BCh BAO 1975 Belf.; MB BS BAO Belf. 1975; BSc (Hons.) Belf. 1972; FRCS Ed. 1979. (Queen's University Belfast) Cons. Cardiothoracic Surg. Manch. Roy. Infirm. Socs: Soc. Thoracic & Cardiovasc. Surgs. of GB & Irel.; Brit. Thorac. Soc.; Brit. Cardiac Soc.

KEENAN, Fiona Margaret Hurbuck Farmhouse, Lanchester, Durham DH7 0RT — MB ChB 1982 Glas.; MRCP (UK) 1985; MRCPath 1991. Prev: Sen. Regist. (Haemat.) Roy. Hallamsh. Hosp. Sheff.; Regist. (Haemat.) W.. Infirm. Glas.; Regist. (Med.) Inverclyde Roy. Hosp. Greenock.

KEENAN, Mr Gary Fitzgerald 10 Knoxhill Avenue, Prehen Park, Londonderry BT47 2PN — MB ChB 1988 Aberd.; FRCS Glas. 1992.

KEENAN, Jacqueline Motherwell Health Centre, 138-144 Windmill Street, Motherwell ML1 1TB Tel: 01698 264164; 22 Glen Eagles, East Kilbride, Glasgow G74 2JN Tel: 013552 46561 — MB ChB 1987 Glas.; MRCGP 1991; DRCOG 1990. (Univ. Glas.) Trainee GP Monklands Dist. Gen. Hosp. VTS; Trainee GP Newarthill. Socs: BMA.

KEENAN, Janet The alexandra Hospital, Mill Lane, Cheadle SK8 2PX Tel: 0161428 3656; 32, Porchfield Square, St John's Gardens, Manchester M3 4FG Tel: 0161 832 7761 — MB ChB 1963 Lond.; MB ChB (Hnrs.) Lond. 1963; FRCP Lond. 1990, M 1965; MRCS Eng. LRCP Lond. 1963. (St. Geo.) Cons. Rheum and Rehabil. NemoPhysiol., Alexandra Hosp. Cheadle. Prev: Cons Rheum & Rehab Manch.. Roy. Infirm.

KEENAN, John Department of Clinical Biochemistry, Level 4, John Radcliffe Hospital, Headington, Oxford OX3 9DU Tel: 01865 220473 Fax: 01865 220348 — MB BChir 1962 Camb.; MA, MB BChir Camb. 1962; FRCPath. 1981, M 1969; Dip. Biochem. Lond 1967. (Middlx.) Chem. Path. Oxf. Radcliffe Trust. Socs: Fell. Roy. Soc. Med.; Assn. Clin. Path.; Assn. Biochem. Prev: Chem. Path. King' s Coll. Hosp. & Roy. Free Hosp. Lond.; Asst. Path. Middlx. Hosp. Med. Sch. Lond.

KEENAN, John (retired) Froyle House, Tamworth Road, Keresley End, Coventry CV7 8JJ Tel: 01203 337158 — MB ChB Ed. 1948. Med. Off. Roy. Agricultural Soc. Eng. Prev: Ho. Phys. W.. Gen. Hosp. Edin.

KEENAN, Mr Jonathan The Old Estate House, South Town, Kenton, Exeter EX6 8JE — MB ChB 1989 Liverp.; FRCS Ed. 2001; FRCS Ed. 1994. Specialist Regist. (Orthop. & Trauma) Devon.

KEENAN, Mr Joseph Mary 8 Waterden Road, Guildford GU1 2AP Tel: 01483 575760 Fax: 01483 575701 — MB BCh BAO 1981 NUI; FRC Ophth. 1990; FRCS Ed. 1987. p/t Cons. Opthalmic Surg., Roy. Surrey Co. Hosp., Guildford.

KEENAN, Marie Catherine 54 Woodhead Green, Hamilton ML3 8TN — MB ChB 1982 Glas.

KEENAN, Mary Frances White House Surgery, Horsefair, Chipping Norton OX7 5AL Tel: 01608 642742 Fax: 01608 642794 — MB ChB 1982 Liverp.; MRCGP 1988; DRCOG 1989. Med. Dir. Oxon. Community Health NHS Trust. Prev: GP Adviser Changing Childbirth Implementations Team NHSE Camb.

KEENAN, Monica 3/2, 49 Bellshaugh Gardens, Kelvinside, Glasgow G12 0SA Tel: 0141 339 8405 — MB ChB 1991 Glas. SHO (Psychiat.) Glas. Comm. & Ment. Health Trust Gartnavel Roy. Hosp. 1055 Gt. W.. Rd. Glas.

KEENAN, Mr Ronald Albert 55 Springfield Gardens, Aberdeen AB15 7RX Tel: 01224 314314 — MB ChB 1971 Aberd.; ChM Aberd. 1983, MB ChB 1971; FRCS Ed. 1978. Cons. Surg. Grampian Health Bd.

KEENAN, Russell David 61 Stoneleigh Road, Solihull B91 1DQ — MB ChB 1990 Birm.; ChB Birm. 1990; MRCP (UK) 1993; MRCPath 1997. (Birmingham) Career Regist. (Haemat.) W. Midl. RHA; Research Regist. (Haemat.) Birm. Univ. Socs: Brit. Soc. of Haematologists. Prev: SHO (Med.) Warwick Hosp.

KEENAN, Mr William Nigel Wilson Orthopaedic Department, Royal Children's Hospital, Flemington Rd, Parkville, Melbourne 3052, Australia Tel: 61 3 9345 5354 Fax: 61 3 9345 5447 Email: keenann@cryptic.rch.unimelb.edu.au; Woodlands, 21 Millisle Road, Donaghadee BT21 0HY Tel: 028 9188 2261 — MB BCh BAO 1984 Belf.; Dip. Epid. Biostat. Univ. of Melbourne 2001; FRCS Ed. 1988. (Queens Univ. Belf.) PhD Fell. (Paediat. &Orthop.) Roy. Childr.'s Hosp. Melbourne, Austral.; Hon. Research Fell. Murdock Childr.'s Research Inst. Roy. Childr.'s Hosp., Melbourne. Socs: BMA; Brit. Orthop. Assn.; Brit. Skeletal Dysplasia Soc. Prev: Clin. Fell. Hosp. Sick Childr. Toronto Canada; Iliorpov Fell. Maryland Center Limb Lengthening & Resconstruc., USA; Fell. (Orthop.) New Childr.'s Hosp. Sydney Austral.

KEENE, Anthony David Somerford Grove Practice, Somerford Grove Health Centre, Somerford Grove, London N16 7TX Tel: 020 7241 9700 Fax: 020 7275 7198 — MB ChB 1976 Leeds; MRCS Eng. LRCP Lond. 1976; MFFP 1993, MRCGP 1982. (Univ. Leeds) Prev: Ho. Phys. Enfield Dist. Hosp. (Highlands Wing); Ho. Surg. Black Notley Hosp. Braintree.

KEENE, Mr Graham Stanley 6 Trafalgar Road, Cambridge CB4 1EU — MB BS 1987 Lond.; FRCS Eng. 1990; FRCS (Orth.) Eng. 1995. (St. Thos. Hosp. Univ. Lond.) Cons. (Trauma & Orthop. Surg.) Addenbrooke's NHS Trust.

***KEENE, Louise Clare** 73 North Road, Harborne, Birmingham B17 9PD — MB ChB 1996 Birm.

KEENE, Mr Malcolm Howard 35 Wimpole Street, London W1M 7AE Tel: 020 7224 6249 Fax: 020 7224 4162; 41 Arden Road, London N3 3AD — MB BS 1970 Lond.; FRCS Eng. 1976. (Lond. Hosp.) Cons. ENT Surg. St. Bart. Hosp. Lond. & Homerton Hosp.; Hon. Cons. ENT Surg. Hosp. of St. John & St. Eliz. Lond.; Hon. Otolaryngol. Guildhall Sch. Music & Drama. Socs: Fell. Roy. Soc. Med.; Brit. Assn. Otol. Prev: Sen. Regist. (ENT) Middlx. Hosp.; TWJ Research Fell. Univ. Toronto; Regist. Roy. Ear Hosp. Lond.

KEENLESIDE, Claire Lindsay Beech House Surgery, 1 Ash Tree Road, Knaresborough HG5 0UB Tel: 01423 542564; 2 Red Cottages, Nidd, Harrogate HG3 3BW — MB ChB 1989 Leeds; MRCGP 1994; DCH RCP Lond. 1992; DRCOG 1991.

KEENLEYSIDE, Georgina Helen 5 Withypool Dr, Stockport SK2 6DT — BM 1997 Soton.

KEENLYSIDE, Ronald Michael Holmside Medical Group, 142 Armstrong Road, Benwell, Newcastle upon Tyne NE4 8QB Tel: 0191 273 4009 Fax: 0191 273 2745; North East Mason Farm, Seaton Burn, Newcastle upon Tyne NE13 6DN — MB BS 1962 Durh.

KEENOR, Celina Borough Green Medical Practice, Quarry Hill Road, Borough Green, Sevenoaks TN15 8BE Tel: 01732 883161 Fax: 01732 886319 — MB ChB 1991 Ed.; DRCOG 1997. (Ed.) GP Princip. W. Kent HA.

KEEP, Jeffrey William 31C Lansdowne Place, Hove BN3 1HF — MB BS 1994 Lond.

KEEP, Matthew James 128 Beechwood Mount, Leeds LS4 2NQ — MB ChB 1994 Leeds.

KEEP, Neville Kenneth Creywell Surgery, Creywell, Wark, Hexham NE48 3LQ Tel: 01434 230654 Fax: 01434 230059 — MB BS 1978 Lond.

KEEP, Philip James 7 Bluebell Crescent, Eaton, Norwich NR4 7LE Tel: 01603 58668 — MB BS 1966 Lond.; MRCS Eng. LRCP Lond. 1966; FFA RCS Eng. 1972; DA Eng. 1970; DObst RCOG 1969. (Univ. Coll. Hosp.) Cons. Anaesth. Norwich Health Dist. Prev: Sen. Regist. (Anaesth.) United Bristol Hosps. & SW RHB; Regist. (Anaesth.) St. Geo. Hosp. Lond.

KEEPING, Iain Michael Countess of Chester NHS Trust, Liverpool Road, Chester CH2 1UL Tel: 01244 366292 Email: iain.keeping@coch-fr.nwest.nhs.uk; Flacca Lodge, Burwardsley Road, Tattenhall, Chester CH3 9QF Tel: 01829 770935 Email: iain.keeping.@ukonline.co.uk — MB BChir 1974 Camb.; BA Camb. 1970, MD 1982; FRCP Lond. 1991; MRCP (UK) 1976. (Camb. Univ. & St. Thos. Hosp.) Cons. Phys. Chester Hosps. Prev: Lect. (Med.) Soton. Univ. Hosps.; Regist. (Med.) Soton. Univ. Hosps. & Salisbury Gen. Hosp.

KEERTHI KUMAR, Shavenabelgula 162 Empire Road, Greenford UB6 7EF — MB BS 1970 Mysore; DA Eng. 1974. (Med. Coll. Mysore)

KEET, John Peter Dominic Croydon Health Authority, Mayday Hospital, Mayday Road, Thornton Heath CR7 7YE; 9 Upper Wimpole Street, London W1 7TD Tel: 020 7486 9259/2729 — MB BS 1969 Western Australia; MRCP (UK) 1971. Cons. Phys. (c/o Elderly) Croydon HA. Socs: Brit. Geriat. Soc. & BMA (Hon. Sec. Croydon Div.). Prev: Sen. Regist. Whittington Hosp. Lond. & Acad. Dept. Geriat. Med. St.; Pancras Hosp. Lond.; Lect. (Geriat. Med.) Univ. Coll. Hosp. Med. Sch. Lond.

KEETARUT, Mr Sureshchandr The Wirral Limb Centre, Clatterbridge Hospital, Wirral CH63 4JY Tel: 0151 334 4000 Fax: 0151 334 7860 Email: keetarut@aol.com; 50 Blakeley Road, Raby Mere, Wirral CH63 0NA Tel: 0151 334 7860 — MD Jerusalem Hebrew Univ. 1970; FRCS Eng. 1976; MRCS Eng. LRCP Lond. 1975. (Hadassah Med. Sch.) Cons. Rehabil. Med. Wirral Hosp. NHS Trust. Socs: BMA & Internat. Soc. Prosth. & Orthotics. Prev: Med. Off. Disablem. Serv. Centre Birm.; Hon. Sen. Regist. (Rehabil. Med.) Birm. Health Dists.; Regist. (Orthop.) Chelmsford Health Dist.

KEETON, Barry Roger Soton. Univ. Hosps. NHS Trust, Wessex Cardiothoracic Centre, Southampton General Hospital, Southampton SO16 6YD — MB BS 1968 Lond.; MRCS Eng. LRCP Lond. 1968; FRCPCH 1997; FRCP Lond. 1985; MRCP (UK) 1973; DCH Eng. 1971; DObst RCOG 1970. (Char. Cross) Cons. Paediat. Cardiol. Wessex Cardiothoracic Centre Soton. Gen. Hosp.; Clin. Teach. Univ. Soton. Socs: Fell. Roy. Soc. Med.; Assn. Europ. Paediat. Cardiol.; Brit. Cardiac Soc. Prev: Clin. Research Fell. (Paediat. Cardiol.) Mayo Clin. Rochester, USA; Sen. Regist. (Paediat. Cardiol.) Brompton Hosp. Lond.; Regist. (Paediat.) Hammersmith Hosp. & Inst. Child Health Lond.

KEFFORD, Penelope June Gould Farm Oast, Mill Lane, Frittenden, Cranbrook TN17 2DT — MB BS 1974 Lond.; DCH Eng. 1978; DObst RCOG 1976. (Lond. Hosp.)

KEFFORD, Richard Hugh Gould Farm Oast, Mill Lane, Frittenden, Cranbrook TN17 2DT — MB BS 1969 Lond.; MRCS Eng. LRCP Lond. 1969; FRCOG 1988, M 1975, DObst 1971. (Lond. Hosp.) Cons. (O & G) Maidstone Dist. Gen. Hosp. Prev: Sen. Regist. (O & G) Lond. Hosp.

KEFFORD, Sharon Jane Elizabeth 55 Rowan Close, Guildford GU1 1PW — MB BCh 1997 Wales.

KEGG, Stephen John 26 Borth Avenue, Stockport SK2 6AL; 446 Harborne Park Road, Harborne, Birmingham B17 0LN Tel: 0121 428 3590 — MB ChB 1993 Birm. SHO (Med. Oncol.) Univ. Hosps. Birm. NHS Trust. Prev: Ho. Phys. Good Hope Hosp. Sutton Coldfield; Ho. Surg. Univ. Hosp. Birm. NHS Trust.

KEH, Christopher Hang Liang 21 Richards Street, Cardiff CF24 4DA — MB BCh 1991 Wales.

KEHELY, Anne Mary — MB BCh BAO 1983 Dub.; FRCPath 1999; FRCPI 1998; MRCPath 1991; MRCPI 1986. Sen. Pharmacovigilance Phys., Eli Lilly & Co Ltd. Prev: Cons. Chem. Path. Ealing Hosp.

KEHINDE, Mr Oladunni Elijah University Department of Surgery, Leicester General Hospital, Leicester LE5 4PW Tel: 0116 249 0490; 48 Hospital Close, Leicester LE5 4WQ Tel: 0116 249 0490 Fax: 0116 273 6179 — MB BS 1979 Ibadan; FRCS Eng. 1990; Dip. Urol. Lond 1987. Regist. (Urol. & Renal Transpl. Surg.) Leics. HA. Socs: Med. Protec. Soc.; BMA. Prev: Regist. (Urol.) Edith Cavell Hosp. P'boro.; Regist. St. Peters Hosp. Lond.; Sen. Regist. (Urol.) UCH Ibadan, Nigeria.

KEHLER, Lisa Martine 112 Stafford Road, Bloxwich, Walsall WS3 3PA — MB ChB 1998 Sheff.; MB ChB Sheff 1998.

KEHOE, Anthony Avila, 282 Woolton Road, Childwall, Liverpool L16 0JA — MB ChB 1994 Ed.

KEHOE, Christine Patricia 6 Bridge Street, Ambleside LA22 9DU — MB ChB 1992 Liverp.; MRCGP 1996. Assoc. (GP) Old Forge Surg. Hawkeshead.

KEHOE, Jane Elizabeth 4 Coastguard Cottages, Ramehead, Torpoint PL10 1LH; 4 Coastguard Cottages, Ramehead, Torpoint PL10 1LH Tel: 01752 822784 — MB BS 1983 Lond.; FRCA; CCST 1998. (Charing Cross Hospital) Assoc. Specialist in Anaesth. Derriford Hosp., Plymouth.

KEHOE, Mary Josephine 7 Stafford Close, Kilburn, London NW6 5TW Tel: 020 7624 8766 — MB ChB 1984 Aberd.; MRCGP 1989.

KEHOE, Robert Francis Airedale General Hospital, Skipton Road, Steeton, Keighley BD20 6TD Tel: 01535 651260 Fax: 01535 651262 — MB ChB 1985 Leeds; BSc Psychol. Leeds 1983; MPhil Ed. 1993; MRCPsych 1990. Cons. Psychiat. Airedale Gen. Hosp.; Assoc. Med. Director, Airedale NHS Trust. Prev: Sen. Regist. (Psychiat.) Roy. Edin. Hosp.; Regist. (Psychiat.) Roy. Edin. Hosp.; SHO (A & E) St. Jas. Univ. Hosp. Leeds.

KEHR, Michael Joseph (retired) 10 Maybush Road, Hornchurch RM11 3LB Tel: 01708 442161 — MB BCh Witwatersrand 1951.

KEIDAN, Alison Jane Department of Haematology, The Queen Elizabeth Hospital, Gayton Road, King's Lynn PE30 4ET Tel: 01553 613613; Rectory Farm, Dereham Road, Gressenhall, Dereham NR19 2QG — BM BCh 1978 Oxf.; MA Oxf. 1980, DM 1990; FRCP Lond. 1996; MRCP (UK) 1981; MRCPath 1990; FRCPath 1998. (Oxf.) p/t Cons. Haemat. King's Lynn & Wisbech Hosps. Trust.

KEIDAN, Isaiah Jacob 9 Chessington Lodge, Regents Park Road, Finchley, London N3 3AA — MB ChB 1930 Leeds. (Leeds) Socs: BMA. Prev: Sen. Receiv. Room Off. & Ho. Surg. Leeds Infirm.; Hon. Demonst. Anat. Leeds Med. Sch.

KEIDAN, Mimi (retired) 22 Bower Road, Liverpool L25 4RQ Tel: 0151 428 3412 — MB ChB Liverp. 1950. Prev: Ho. Phys. & Ho. Surg. Bootle Gen. Hosp.

KEIGHLEY, Brian Douglas Buchanan Street, 41-47 Buchanan Street, Balfron, Glasgow G63 0TS Tel: 01360 440515 Fax: 01360 440831; Hector Cottage, Banker's Brae, Balfron, Glasgow G63 0PY Tel: 01360 440520 Fax: 01360 440829 — MB ChB 1972 Glas.; FRCGP 1990, M 1977; Dip. Forens. Med. Glas 1988. Police Surg. Centr. Scotl. Police; Med. Off. Ballikinrain Sch. Balfron; Bd. Mem. Scotl. Counc. For Postgrad. Med. & Dent. Educat. Socs: Fell. Roy. Soc. Med.; (Ex-Chairm.) Forth Valley LMC; Chairm. Scott. GMSC. Prev: SHO (O & G) Robroyston Hosp. Glas.; SHO (Paediat.) Falkirk Roy. Infirm.

KEIGHLEY, Dorothy Margaret Cofton Medical Centre, 2 Robinsfield Drive, Off Longbridge Lane, West Heath, Birmingham B31 4TU Tel: 0121 693 4414; Whalebone Cottage, Vicarage Hill, Tanworth-in-Arden, Solihull B94 5AN Tel: 01564 742903 Fax: 01564 742705 — MB ChB 1969 Leeds; DObst RCOG 1971.

KEIGHLEY, Jane Milnrow Village Practice, 44-48 Newhey Road, Milnrow, Rochdale OL16 4EG; Carr Cottage, Ripponden, Sowerby Bridge HX6 4NP Tel: 01422 823601 — MB ChB 1988 Manch.; MRCGP 1993; DFFP 1994. GP Princip. Drs Thakor, Gunn & Keighley Milnrow Village Pract. Milnrow Rochdale.

KEIGHLEY, Judith Elizabeth Royal Hospital for Sick Children, Edinburgh EH9 1LF Tel: 0131 536 0000; Gruinard, 9 Burngrange Road, West Calder EH55 5HA — MB ChB 1990 Ed.; MRCGP 1995. (Ed.) SHO (A & E) Hosp. Sick Childr. Edin.

KEIGHLEY, Professor Michael Robert Burch Barling Professor & Head Department Surgery, University of Birmingham, Birmingham B15 2TH Tel: 0121 627 2276 Fax: 0121 472 1230 Email: l.e.hopwood@bham.ac.uk; Whalebone Cottage, Tanworth in Arden, Solihull B94 5AN Fax: 0156 4742705 Email: keighleycolo@uk-consultants.co.uk — MS Lond. 1976, MB BS 1967; FRCS Eng. 1972; FRCS Ed. 1971; MRCS Eng. LRCP Lond. 1967. (St. Bart.) Barling Prof. Head of Dept. of Surg. & Hon. Cons. Gen. Surg. Coloproctol. Qu. Eliz. Hosp. Univ. Birm.; Hon. Fell. Brazilian Coll. Surgs.; Chairm.; UEGL Pub. Affairs Comm., (Europ. GasthoreUrol.). Socs: Brit. Soc. Gastroenterol. & Surg. Research Soc.; BMA; Ass. Of Coloproetology GB & I. Prev: Res. Surg. Off. St. Jas. Hosp. Leeds; Ho. Phys. & Ho. Surg. Redhill Gen. Hosp.; Sen. Lect. (Surg.) Univ. Birm.

KEIGHTLEY, Alison Mary Radiology Department, Frimley Park Hospital, Frimley, Camberley GU16 5UJ Tel: 01276 604141 Fax: 01276 604891 Email: alison.keightley@fph-tr.nhs.uk — MB BChir 1978 Camb.; MA Camb. 1979; MRCP (UK) 1980; FRCR 1983. (King's Coll. Hosp.) Cons. Radiol. Frimley Pk. Hosp. Surrey. Prev: Cons. Radiol. Lewisham & Guy's Hosps. Lond.; Sen. Regist. (Radiol.) St. Thos. Hosp. Lond.; Fell. (Radiol.) Univ. Calif. San Diego, USA.

KEIGHTLEY, Margaret Ann Alma Road Surgery, Alma Road, Romsey SO51 8ED Tel: 01794 513422 Fax: 01794 518668; The Old Parsonage, Steepleton Hill, Stockbridge SO20 6JE Tel: 01264 810125 Fax: 01264 810237 — MB BS 1977 Lond.; BSc (Hons.) Lond. 1974, MB BS 1977; MRCGP 1981; DRCOG 1981.

KEIGHTLEY, Simon John North Hampshire Hospital, Aldermaston Road, Basingstoke RG24 9NA Tel: 01256 313261; The Old Parsonage, Steepleton Hill, Stockbridge SO20 6JE Tel: 01264 810237 Fax: 01264 810237 Email: s.keightley@virgin.net — MB BS 1978 Lond.; BSc (Hons.) Lond. 1974, MB BS 1978; FRCS (Ophth.) Eng. 1984; FRCOphth 1988; DO RCS Eng. 1983. (Univ. Coll. Hosp.) Cons. Ophth. N. Hants. Hosp.; Regional Adviser (Ophth.) Wessex; Sen. Examr. Pt. R. MRCOphth/Optics Refraction Module Roy. Coll. Ophth. Socs: (Chairm.) Visual Standards Sub Comm. Roy. Coll. Ophth. Prev: Cons. Ophth. Basingstoke Dist. Hosp.; Lect. (Ophth.) Univ. Soton., Soton Eye Hosp.

KEILLER, Nigel Patrick The Orchard, Church Road, Cookham Dean, Maidenhead SL6 9PD Tel: 0162 842572 — MB BS 1971 Lond.; FFA RCS Eng. 1976. Cons. (Anaesth.) Char. Cross Hosp. Lond. Prev: Sen. Regist. (Anaesth.) Univ. Coll. Hosp. Lond.; Regist. (Clin. Measurem.) W.m. Hosp. Lond.; Regist. (Anaesth.) St. Thos. Hosp. Lond.

KEILLER, Peter William Lochmaddy Surgery, Lochmaddy HS6 5AE Tel: 01876 500333 Fax: 01876 500877; Aird Nam Madadh, Lochmaddy HS6 5AE Tel: 01876 500222 Fax: 01876 500474 Email: peter@keiller.u-net.com — MB ChB 1981 Ed.; MRCGP 1989; Dip.

Obst. Otago 1988. (Edinburgh) Prev: Regist. (Psychiat.) Roy. Edin. Hosp.

KEILLOH, Derek Andrew 11 Baillieswells Terrace, Bieldside, Aberdeen AB15 9AR — MB ChB 1998 Aberd.; MB ChB Aberd 1998.

KEILTY, Samuel Robinson White Gables, 182 Finaghy Road S., Belfast BT10 0DH Tel: 01232 621228 — MB BCh BAO Belf. 1962; FFA RCSI 1972; FFA RCS Eng. 1966. (Qu. Univ. Belf.) Cons. Anaesth. Roy. Belf. Hosp. Sick Childr. & Roy. Matern. Hosp. Belf. Socs: Assn. Anaesths. Gt. Brit. & Irel. & Assn. Paediat. Anaesth. Gt. Britain & Irel. Prev: Sen. Regist. & Sen Tutor Dept. Anaesth. Qu.'s Univ. Belf.

KEINI, Mr Karkala Shrivas 11 Avon Close, Higham, Barnsley S75 1PD — MB BS 1976 Mysore; FRCS Ed. 1988; LMSSA Lond. 1990. Assoc. Specialist Gen. Surg./Regist. (Gen. Surg.) Qu. Eliz. Hosp. King's Lynn.

KEIR, Jennifer Reid — MB ChB 1994 Aberd.; DRCOG 1997; MRCGP 1998. GP Princip. Prev: GP Locum.

KEIR, Michael Ian Stenhouse The London Independent Hospital, 1 Beaumont Square, Stepney Green, London E1 4NL Tel: 020 7790 0990 — BM BCh 1959 Oxf.; MA Oxf. 1959; FRCP Ed. 1977, M 1965. (Oxf. & Guy's) Hon. Cons. Dermat. Roy. Lond. Hosp. Socs: Fell. Roy. Soc. Med. (Mem. Dermat. Sect.); Fell. Roy. Soc. Trop. Med. & Hyg.; Brit. Assn. Dermat. Prev: Cons. Dermat. Whipps Cross Hosp. Lond.; Cons. Dermat. Kent & Canterbury Hosp.; Hon. Lect. St. Bart. Hosp. Med. Coll. Lond.

KEIR, Peter Murray BUPA Hospital Harpenden, Ambrose Lane, Harpenden AL5 4BP Tel: 0800 585112 Fax: 01582 761358; Highlands House, 17 Battlefield Road, St Albans AL1 4DA Tel: 01727 840480 Fax: 01727 840480 — MB BChir 1966 Camb.; MA Camb. 1967; FRCP Lond. 1989; MRCP (UK) 1971. (Camb. & Royal Lond. Hosp.) Cons. Phys. & Cardiol. E. & N. Herts. NHS Trust & Harefield Hosp.; Cons. Med. Adviser Roche Products Ltd. Welwyn Gdn. City. Socs: Fell. Roy. Soc. Med.; Assoc. FACC 1993; Brit. Cardiac Soc. Prev: Sen. Regist. (Med.) Roy. United Hosp. Bath & Bristol Roy. Infirm.; Regist. (Cardiol.) Nat. Heart Hosp. Lond.; Regist. Roy. Free Hosp. Lond.

KEIR, Robert David Leven Health Centre, Victoria Road, Leven KY8 4ET; Bourtree Brae House, Crescent Road, Lundin Links, Leven KY8 6AE Tel: 01333 320383 Fax: 01333 422249 — MB ChB 1970 St. And.; MRCGP 1975; DObst RCOG 1972. Med. Assessor Indep. Appeal Tribunals. Prev: Ho. Off. (Gen. Surg. & Med.) & SHO (Cas. & Obst.) Vict. Hosp. Kirkcaldy.

KEIR, Sarah Louise 24 Whiteclosegate, Carlisle CA3 0JD — BChir 1991 Camb.

KEIRBY, Donald Perry Lancastria, 67 Blackpool Old Road, Poulton-le-Fylde FY6 7DL — MB ChB 1947 Manch. (Manch.) Prev: on Staff Preston Roy. Infirm.; RAMC.

KEITCH, Ian Allan Philip Rampton Hospital, Retford DN22 0PD Tel: 01777 248321 Email: Ian.Keitch@rampton-hos.trent.nhs.uk — MB ChB 1976 Birm.; MRCPsych 1981. (Birmingham) Cons. Forens. Psychiat. Rampton Hosp. Prev: Dir. of Med. Serv. Rampton Hosp.; Sen. Regist. Profess. Unit Mapperley Hosp. Nottm.; Regist. (Psychiat.) Knowle Fareham.

KEITH, Alan James The Surgery, 1 Kimberworth Road, Rotherham S61 1AH Tel: 01709 561442/562319 Fax: 01709 740690; Loch Sloy, Green Lane, Moorgate, Rotherham S60 3AT Email: dkeith@lineone.net — MB ChB 1977 Leeds; MRCGP 1982; DRCOG 1979. (Leeds) Socs: Internat Dermat. Soc.; Cardiol. Soc.

KEITH, Colin Bennett (retired) 1 Rhoda Villas, Taroveor Road, Penzance TR18 2DA Tel: 01736 364933 — MB BS Lond. 1963; MB BS Lond. 1963; MRCS Eng. LRCP Lond. 1963; MRCS Eng. LRCP Lond. 1963; DObst. RCOG 1965; DObst. RCOG 1965.

KEITH, Diane Christine 12 Lakeside Drive, Esher KT10 9EZ — MB BS 1975 Lond. Clin. Research Phys.

KEITH, Dorothea Bird (retired) 1 Coolmoyne Park, Belfast BT15 5HG — MB BCh BAO 1946 Belf.; DPH Belf. 1949. Prev: Sen. Med. Off. (Child Health) Fast. Area Health & Social Servs. Bd.

KEITH, Evadney Yvonne — BM Fin. '95 (accelerated) Grad. '96; BSc (Hons.) Canada. (Southampton) O & G, SHO (GP Trainee). Socs: Med. Protec. Soc.; BMA.

KEITH, Hazel Irene Salisbury Gardens, Wimbledon, London SW9 — MB ChB 1960 Manch.; MRCP Lond. 1966. (Manch.) Prev: SHO (Med.) Manch. Roy. Infirm.; Ho. Phys. Lond. Chest Hosp.

KEITH, Ian Alistair Alma Road Surgery, Alma Road, Romsey SO51 8ED Tel: 01794 513422 Fax: 01794 518668; Yew Tree Cottage, Dunbridge Lane, Awbridge, Romsey SO51 0GQ — MB BS 1986 Lond.; MRCGP 1992; DRCOG 1991; DCH RCP Lond. 1989.

KEITH, J Richard Pinhoe Surgery, Exeter EX1 3SY Tel: 01392 469666 Fax: 01392 464178 — MB BS 1962 Lond.; MRCS Eng. LRCP Lond. 1962; MRCGP 1976; DA Eng. 1968; DObst RCOG 1966. (Roy. Lond. Hosp.) Socs: BMA & Devon & Exeter Med. Soc.

KEITH, Mrs Margaret Sian (retired) H.M. Prison, New North Road, Exeter EX4 4EX Tel: 01392 78321 — MB BS 1966 Lond.; DPM Eng. 1975. Sen. Med. Off. Home Office HM Prison Exeter. Prev: Clin. Asst. (Psychiat.) Exe Vale Hosp. Exeter.

KEITH, Marion Anne Bonnyrigg Health Centre, High Street, Bonnyrigg EH19 2DA; 30 Alva Street, Edinburgh EH2 4PY — MB ChB 1984 Aberd.

KEITH, Pauline Resmay 5 Oldridge Close, Holme Hall, Chesterfield S40 4UF Tel: 01246 297443 — MB ChB Liverp. 1949; MFCM 1974; DObst RCOG 1951. Emerit. Community Phys. Leics. HA. Socs: I. of Wight Med. Soc. Prev: Cons. Pub. Health Med. I. of Wight; Specialist (Community Med. & Environm. Health) Leics. HA; Asst. Med. Off. King Geo. V Hosp. Malta.

KEITH, Peter Paul, SBStJ (retired) 35 Hampsell Grange, Hampsell Road, Grange-over-Sands LA11 6AZ Email: peterkeith@lineone.net — MB ChB Liverp. 1952; MSc Occupat. Med. Lond. 1983; MFOM RCP Lond. 1984, AFOM 1981; MRCGP 1974; T(OM) 1991; DIH 1982; DMRD 1959. Prev: Specialist (Occupat. Health) I. of Wight HA.

KEITH-DE WITTE-SCOTT-SPENCER, Sonia Fay 5 West Drive, Reading RG4 6GE — MB ChB 1969 Ed.; MRCPsych 1975. Clin. Asst. (Psychiat.) Connaught Ho. Winchester. Prev: Cons. Psychiat. GGZ Venlo, Holland; Sen. Regist. Playfield Ho. Cupar; Resid. Med. Coll. Virginia USA.

KEKWICK, Christopher Alan Lower Burrow Coombe, Cheriton Fitzpaine, Crediton EX17 4JS — MB BS 1969 Lond.; MRCS Eng. LRCP Lond. 1969. Assoc. Specialist Cardiol. Roy. Devon & Exeter Hosp. Prev: Regist. (Cardiol.) Roy. Devon & Exeter Hosp.; Ho. Surg. & Ho. Phys. Roy. Sussex Co. Hosp. Brighton.

KELHAM, Ian The Old Tannery Medical Centre, The Old Tannery, High Street, Porlock, Minehead TA24 8PS Tel: 01643 862575 — MB ChB 1979 Leeds; MRCGP 1984; Cert Family Plann. JCC 1983; DRCOG 1982. Course Organiser Taunton Som. Prev: Trainee GP W. Middlx. Univ. Hosp. VTS; Course Organiser & Trainer (Gen. Pract.) Aylesbury.

KELION, Andrew David 89 Gibson Close, Abingdon OX14 1XS — BM BCh 1991 Oxf.; MRCP (UK) 1994. Regist. (Cardiol.) John Radcliffe Hosp. Oxf. Prev: Regist. (Med.) Battle Hosp. Reading; SHO (Med.) Guy's Hosp. Lond.

KELL, Brian The Health Centre, 11 Hull Road, Hessle HU13 9LZ; Wayside, Kemp Road, Swanland, North Ferriby HU14 3LZ Tel: 01482 645295 — MB BS 1960 Lond. (Char. Cross) Clin. Asst. (Path.) W.wood Hosp. Beverley. Prev: Regist. (Path.), Cas. Off. & Ho. Phys. & Ho. Surg. Char. Cross Hosp. Lond.

KELL, Christine Belgrave Medical Centre, 22 Asline Road, Sheffield S2 4UJ Tel: 0114 255 1184; 46 Springfield Avenue, Sheffield S7 2GA — MB BS 1979 Newc.; MRCGP 1985; DRCOG 1985. (Newc. u. Tyne)

KELL, Geoffrey Parkside Family Practice, Eastleigh Health Centre, Newtown Road, Eastleigh SO50 9AG Tel: 023 8061 2032 Fax: 023 8062 9623; 12 Western Road, Chandlers Ford, Eastleigh SO53 5DA — BM 1988 Soton.; MRCGP 1992; DCH RCP Lond. 1992; DRCOG 1991. (Soton.) GP Pk.side Family Practi., E.leigh, Hants.

KELL, Malcolm Robin Little Greenlaw, Crookfur Road, Newton Mearns, Glasgow G77 6NE — MB ChB 1993 Glas.

KELL, Philip David 44 Grosvenor Road, London N10 2DS — MB BS 1980 Sydney; MRCOG 1989.

KELL, Mr Robert Anthony Little Greenlaw, Crookfur Road, Newton Mearns, Glasgow G77 6NE Tel: 0141 639 2759 — MB ChB 1963 St. And.; FRCS Glas. 1993; FRCS Eng. 1969; FRCS Ed. 1968. Cons. ENT Surg. Vict. Infirm. Glas.; Vis. Cons. ENT Surg. S.. Gen. Hosp. Glas. & Roy. Infirm. Paisley. Prev: Sen. Regist. ENT Enfirm. Liverp.; SHO Dundee Roy. Infirm.; Demonst. Anat. Qu.'s Coll. Dundee.

KELL, Sarah Ann 3 Pritchard Drive, Stapleford, Nottingham NG9 7GW Tel: 01159 390916 — BM BS 1994 Nottm.; BMedSci

Nottm. 1992. SHO (A & E) QMC, Nottm. Prev: SHO (Paediat.) Derry Childr. Hosp.; GP Regist. Arnold Health Centre Nottm.; SHO (Psychiat.) Wells Rd. Centre, Nottm.

KELL, Stephen Wallace The Health Centre, Station Rd, Bawtry, Doncaster DN10 6RQ Email: keus@talk21.com — BM BS 1994 Nottm.; DCH 1997. (Nottingham) GP. Prev: Nottm. VTS.

KELL, William Jonathan Department of Haematology, University Hospital of Wales, Cardiff CF14 4XN Tel: 029 2074 7747 Fax: 029 2074 4655 Email: kellwj@cf.ac.uk — MB BChir 1980 Camb.; MB BChir Camb. 1990; MA Camb. 1991; DRCPath 1996; MRCPI 1994. (Camb.) Regist. (Haemat.) Univ. Hosp. Wales Cardiff. Socs: Brit. Soc. of Haemat. Prev: SHO (Gen. Med.) P.ss of Wales Hosp. Bridgend; SHO (Gen. Med.) Morriston Hosp. Swansea; Ho. Phys. Ipswich Gen. Hosp.

KELL, Winifred 12 Denewell Avenue, Gateshead NE9 5HD Tel: 0191 487 7209 — MB ChB 1950 Liverp.; MFCM RCP (UK) 1971; DPH Newc. 1964. (Liverp.) Community Med. Specialist (Child Health) Gateshead HA. Prev: Dep. MOH Co. Boro. Gateshead.

KELLAM, Alexander Murray Plenderleith 50 Palace Road, Llandaff, Cardiff CF5 2AH Tel: 029 2056 3355 Fax: 029 2021 2630 — MB BS Lond. 1962; MD Lond. 1971; MRCS Eng. LRCP Lond. 1962; FRCPsych 1983, M 1972; DPM Eng. 1966. (St. Geo.) Cons. Forens. Psychiat., Cardiff and Vale NHS Trust; Clin. Teach. (Psychiat.) Univ. Wales Coll. Med. Socs: Welsh Psychiat. Soc.; (Treas.) Assn. Univ. Teachs. Psychiat. Prev: Sen. Regist. (Psychiat.) WhitCh. Hosp., Dept. Psychol. Med. Cardiff & Morgannwg Hosp. Bridgend; Sen. Resid. Med. Off. Lusaka Centr. Hosp., Zambia.

KELLAND, Nicholas Francis 143 Burgess Road, Southampton SO16 7AA — BM BCh 1998 Oxf.; BM BCh Oxf 1998.

KELLAND, Paul Chase Farm Hospital, The Ridgeway, Enfield EN2 8JL Tel: 020 8366 6600 — MB BS 1994 Lond.

KELLAND, Sandra Anne Bradley Stoke Surgery, Brook Way, Bradley Stoke North, Bristol BS32 9DS Tel: 01454 616262 Fax: 01454 619161 — MB ChB 1988 Bristol. Princip., Bradley Stoke Surg., Brook Way, Bradley Stoke BS32 9DS.

KELLAS, Alan Roger Penrose Phoenix NHS Trust, Milward House, 1 Bristol Road, Keynsham, Bristol BS31 2BA Email: a.kellas@bristol.ac.uk; The Moorings, 5 Watch House Road, Pill, Bristol BS20 0EN Email: 106145.175@compuserve.com — BA Oxf. 1978; MB BS Lond. 1981; DGM RCP Lond. 1991; MRCPsych 1994. Cons. Psychiat. in Learning Disabilities. Prev: Lect. Psychiat. of Learning Disabilities; Specialist Regist. Learning Disabilities Bristol; Specialist Regist. Learning Disabilities Stoke Pk. Hosp. Bristol.

KELLAWAY, Thomas Donald (retired) Flat 2 Southleigh House, Lemon St., Truro TR1 2PE Tel: 01872 260477 — MB BS 1951 Lond.; MA Camb. 1959; MRCS Eng. LRCP Lond. 1951; FRCPath 1975, M 1963. Prev: Lect. (Path.) Univ. Camb.

KELLEHER, Andrea Anne 27 Ferndene Road, London SE24 0AQ — MB BS 1988 Lond.

KELLEHER, Bernard Joseph 38 Peakdean Lane, East Dean, Eastbourne BN20 0JE Tel: 0132 153016 — MRCS Eng. LRCP Lond. 1942.

KELLEHER, Mr Cornelius John Guy's & St Thomas' HospitalNHS Trust, c/o 8 Devonshire Place, London W1N 1PB Tel: 020 7487 5909 Fax: 020 7224 2797 Email: no8devplace@aol.com — MB BS 1988 Lond.; BSc 1985 (Hons.) Lond.; MRCOG 1995. (Kings College London) Cons. (O & G) Guy's & St Thomas' NHS Trust Lond. Socs: RSM (Sect. of Obst. & Gyn. Coun.); BMA; ICS.

KELLEHER, Denis (retired) 55 Church Way, Sanderstead, South Croydon CR2 0JU Tel: 020 8657 7747 — MB BS 1951 Lond.; DObst RCOG 1954. Prev: Ho. Surg. (Gyn.) & Ho. Phys. (Obst.) St. Mary's Hosp.

KELLEHER, Dermot Ian Francis The Surgery, 100 Beaconsfield Villas, Brighton BN1 6HE Tel: 01273 555999/557908 Fax: 01273 540990 — MB BS 1972 Lond.; MRCS Eng. LRCP Lond. 1972. GP Brighton; Course Organiser Brighton VTS.

KELLEHER, Florence Joseph (retired) 5 Luscombe Road, Parkstone, Poole BH14 8ST Tel: 01202 734560 — MB BCh BAO NUI 1941; MRCPsych 1971; DPM Eng. 1949. Prev: Cons. Psychiat. Grimsby & Dist.

KELLEHER, Harry Christopher High Street Surgery, Wombourne, Wolverhampton WV5 9DP Tel: 01902 892209; 12 Wedgwood Close, Wombourne, Wolverhampton WV5 8EL — MB BCh BAO 1987 NUI; MRCGP (Distinc.) 1992; DRCOG 1991; DCH RCP Lond. 1990; DGM RCP Lond. 1989. Socs: BMA & MDU. Prev: Trainee GP Wolverhampton.

KELLEHER, Mr John Justin Raymond ENT Department, Victoria Hospital, Kirkcaldy KY2 5AH Tel: 01592 643355 Fax: 01592 648155; 1 Blinkbonny Road, Edinburgh EH4 3HY — MB BCh BAO 1979 NUI; MBA Ed. 1991; FRCS Ed. 1986; FRCSI 1983. Cons. Otolaryngol. Fife Acute Hosp.s and Tayside Univ. Hosp.s NHS Trusts; Resource Managem. Project Doctor Vict. Hosp. Kirkcaldy. Socs: BMA; Brit. Assn. Med. Managers; Health & Economics Gp. in Scotl. Prev: Cons. Otolaryngol. Fife HB; Lect. (Otolaryngol.) Edin. Univ. & Roy. Infirm. Edin.; Regist. (Otolaryngol.) City Hosp. Edin.

KELLEHER, Mr John Patrick Wycombe General Hospital, Queen Alexandra Road, High Wycombe HP11 2TT Tel: 01484 526161; Mulberry House, Highfield Park, Marlow SL7 2LE Tel: 01628 477021 Fax: 01628 477021 — MB BS 1980 Lond.; MS Lond. 1992; FRCS (Urol.) 1993; FRCS Eng. 1985; FRCS Ed. 1985. Cons. Urol. S. Bucks NHS Trust. Socs: Roy. Soc. Med. & Brit. Assn. Urol. Surgs. Prev: Sen. Regist. (Urol.) Roy. Marsden Hosp. & St. Mary's Hosp. Lond.; Sen. Regist. (Paediat. Urol.) Gt. Ormond St. Hosp. Childr.

KELLEHER, Kevin Gerard 44 The Mead, Beckenham BR3 5PF — MB BCh BAO 1982 NUI; MRCPI 1992; MICGP 1990; DGM RCP Lond. 1989; DCH Dub. 1986; DObst RCPI 1985. Cons. Phys. (Gen. Internal Med. & Geriat. Med.) Qu. Mary's Hosp. Sidcup. Socs: Brit. Geriat. Soc.; Irish Gerontol. Soc.; Amer. Geriat. Soc. Prev: Sen. Regist. (Gen. Med. & Geriat.) Centr. Middlx. Hosp. Lond.

KELLEHER, Mortimer Francis Howlett, OBE, MC, Brigadier late RAMC Retd. (retired) 2 Ravenswood House, Lower Hale, Farnham GU9 9RP — MB BCh BAO NUI 1933; FRCP Ed. 1963, M 1958. Prev: Phys. i/c Diag. Unit The Lond. Clinic.

KELLEHER, Patrick Columba Runnymede, Belvoir Road, Lower Walton, Warrington WA4 6PE; 164 Longford Street, Warrington WA2 7PX — MB BCh BAO 1950 NUI; LAH Dub. 1950. (Univ. Coll. Dub.) Dep. Med. Off. Admiralty Depot, Risley, & Padgate Train. Coll.

KELLER, Elizabeth Miriam 27 Mayfield Road, Newcastle upon Tyne NE3 4HE — MB BS 1997 Newc.

KELLER, Peter Hans Bell Street, Sawbridgeworth CM21 9AQ — State Exam Med 1972 Lond.

KELLERMAN, Mr Anthony James Regional Centre for Neurosurgery & Neurology, Oldchurch Hospital, Romford RM7 0BE Tel: 01708 746090 Fax: 01708 732184; Proverbs Green, High Roding, Dunmow CM6 1NQ Tel: 01245 231636 — MB BS 1974 Lond.; BSc Lond. 1971; FRCS Eng. 1979. Cons. Neurosurg. OldCh. Hosp. Romford. Socs: Soc. Brit. Neurologic. Surgs. Prev: Sen. Regist. (Neurosurg.) Guy's, Maudsley & King's Coll. Hosps.; Sen. Regist. (Neurosurg.) SE Thames Regional Neurosurg. Unit.

KELLET, Sarah Helen 7 Glenalmond, Norwich NR4 6AG — MB ChB 1990 Manch.

KELLETT, Brendan Charles Halkett Place Surgery, 84 Halkett Place, St Helier, Jersey JE1 4XL Tel: 01534 36301 Fax: 01534 887793; La Genestiere, Faldouet, St Martin, Jersey JE3 6UE Tel: 01534 856775 Email: kellbj@localdial.co.uk — MB BS 1991 Lond.; BSc Lond. 1988; MRCGP 1995. (St Thomas' London)

KELLETT, Diane (retired) — MB ChB 1981 Dundee. Staff Grade Anaesth. York Dist. Hosp. Prev: Regist. (Anaesth.) Dundee & York HAs.

KELLETT, Frank Richard Stanford (retired) 5 Park Way, Weston Favell, Northampton NN3 3BS Tel: 01604 405967 — MB 1940 Calcutta; DPH Lond. 1953. Prev: Med. Off. (Sen. Regional Malaria Adviser) World Health Organizat.

KELLETT, Herbert Spencer (retired) 32 Coniston Grove, Bradford BD9 5HN Tel: 01274 541597 — MB BChir 1938 Camb.; MA (1st cl. Hons. Biochem.) Camb. 1937, MD 1947; DCP Lond. 1943; FRCPath 1964. Prev: Cons. Pathol. Roy. Infirm. Bradford.

KELLETT, John Keith 12 Norfolk Road, Lytham St Annes FY8 4JG — MB BS 1973 Lond.; FRCP Lond. 1993; MRCP (UK) 1979. Cons. Dermat. Blackpool, Wyre & Fylde HA. Prev: Sen. Regist. (Dermat.) Manch. Skin Hosp.

KELLETT, John Montchal (retired) The Chalet, Mount Gardens, London SE26 4NG Tel: 020 8699 9910 Fax: 0208 748 1977 — MA Camb. 1962, MB 1963, BChir 1962; DPM Eng. 1965; FRCP Lond. 1987, M 1968; FRCPsych. 1981, M 1972. Prev: Sen. Lect. & Cons. in Psychiat. St. Geo. Hosp. Lond.

KELLETT, Michael James 136 Harley Street, London W1N 1AH Tel: 020 7580 1772 Fax: 020 7436 7059; 2 Stormont Road, London N6 4NL Tel: 020 8340 6307 — MB BChir 1969 Camb.; MB Camb. 1969, BChir 1968; MA Camb. 1969; FFR 1974; DMRD Eng. 1972. (Camb. & St. Bart.) Radiol. & Dir. Dept. X-Ray Diagn. St. Peters Hosps. & Inst. Urol. Lond. Prev: Sen. Regist. (Diagn. Radiol.) St. Bart. Hosp. & Hosp. Sick Childr. Lond.; Clin. Instruc. (Diagn. Radiol.) Univ. Calif. San Francisco.

KELLETT, Patrick Stephen Friary Surgery, Dobbin Lane, Armagh BT61 7QG Tel: 028 3752 3165 Fax: 028 3752 1514; 4 St. Marks Place, The Mall, Armagh BT61 9BH Tel: 01861 523624 — MB BCh BAO 1969 Dub.; MA Dub., 1992, BA 1967, MB BCh BAO 1969; FRCGP 1990, M 1973. (TC Dub.) Represen. S.. (N. Irel.) LMC. Socs: BMA (Sec. S.. N. Irel. Div.).

KELLETT, Richard James 11 Lansdown Road, Abergavenny NP7 6AN Tel: 01873 857903 — LLM Wales 1990; MB BS Lond. 1964; MRCS Eng. LRCP Lond. 1964; FRCPath 1984, M 1972,D 1970; DMJ Soc. Apoth. Lond. 1985. (Lond. Hosp.) Cons. (Histopath.) Nevill Hall Hosp. Abergavenny. Prev: Ho. Surg. (Thoracic Surg.) Lond. Hosp.; Regist. (Path.) Hammersmith Hosp. Lond.; Sen. Regist. (Histopath.) Welsh Nat. Sch. Med.

KELLETT, Roger John Ward 22, Royal Infirmary, Edinburgh EH3 9YW Tel: 0131 536 2554 Fax: 0131 536 1922 Email: roger.kellett@ed.ac.uk; 5 Burgess Terrace, Edinburgh EH9 2BD Tel: 0131 667 0300 — MB BChir Camb. 1965; MA Camb. 1965; FRCP Lond. 1983, M 1968; FRCP Ed. 1982, M 1980; MRCS Eng. LRCP Lond. 1964. (Camb. & Lond. Hosp.) Cons. Phys. Roy. Infirm. Edin. & Roodlands Hosp. Haddington; Hon. Sen. Lect. Prev: Cons. Phys. E. Gen. Hosp. Edin.; Lect. (Med.) W.. Infirm. Glas.; Regist. (Med.) Chelmsford Hosps.

KELLEY, Simon Paul 3 Damy Green, Corsham SN13 9TN — MB ChB 1997 Birm.

KELLEY, Stephen Thomas 24 Broadwater Road, Worthing BN14 8AB — MB ChB 1976 Sheff.; MA Oxf. 1977; MRCGP 1980; DCH Eng. 1980; DRCOG 1978.

KELLGREN, Professor Jonas Henrik (retired) Beckside Cottage, Rusland, Ulverston LA12 8JY Tel: 01229 860244 — MB BS 1934 Lond.; MSc Manch. 1957; FRCP Lond. 1951, M 1935; FRCS Eng. 1936. Prev: Prof. Rheum. & Dir. Rheum. Research Centre, Univ. Manch.

KELLIHER, Teremiah Joseph Prospect House Medical Group, Prospect House, Prospect Place, Newcastle upon Tyne NE4 6QD Tel: 0191 273 4201 Fax: 0191 273 0129 — MB BCh BAO 1980 NUI. GP Newc.

KELLINGS, Martina Luton & Dunstable Hospital, Anaesthetic Department, Lewsey Road, Luton LU4 0DZ — State Exam Med 1991 Marburg. SHO (Anaesth.) Luton & Dunstable Hosp.

KELLNER, Thomas 294 Pleck Road, Walsall WS2 9EU — State Exam Med 1992 Hamburg.

KELLOCK, David Jonathan Sherwood Forest Hospital (NHS) Trust, King's Mill Hospital, Mansfield Road, Sutton-in-Ashfield NG17 4JL Tel: 01623 672379 Fax: 01623 672364 — MB ChB 1990 Liverp.; MRCP (UK) 1994; DFFP 1995; Dip. Ven. Liverp. 1995. (Liverpool University) Cons. (Genitourin. Med.) King's Mill Hosp. Sutton-in-Ashfield. Socs: Med. Soc. Study VD; Assn. Genitourin Med.; Diplomat Fac. Fam. Plann. & Reproduc. Health. Prev: Sen. Regist. (Genitourin. Med.) Roy. Hallamsh. Hosp. Sheff.; Regist. (Genitourin. Med.) Chester Roy. Infirm. & Arrowe Pk. Hosp. Merseyside; SHO Rotat. (Med.) Aintree Hosps. NHS Trust & Liverp. Univ. Hosp. NHS Trust.

KELLOCK, James Campbell (retired) Treetops, 9 Greenhaugh Way, Dunblane FK15 9PT Tel: 01786 880389 — MB ChB 1958 Glas.; DObst RCOG 1962; MRCGP 1968.

KELLOCK, Sara Louise School Health, Saltergate Health Centre, Saltergate, Chesterfield S40 1SX; 101 Folds Lane, Sheffield S8 0ET — MB ChB 1990 Sheff.; MRCGP 1996; DFFP 1996; DRCOG 1995. Staff Grade (Community Paediat.) Chestefield. Prev: Trainee GP Chesterfield VTS; SHO (O & G & Paediat.) Chesterfield Roy. Hosp.

KELLOCK, Mr William de Montmorency (retired) The Glen, Broomhills Chase, Little Burstead, Billericay CM12 9TG Tel: 01277 651093 — MRCS Eng. LRCP Lond. 1945; FRCS Eng. 1955. Prev: Cons. Orthop. Surg. Tilbury & S.E. Essex Hosp. Gp. & S. Ockendon.

KELLOW, Nigel Huw Vine Cottage, 71 High St., Linton, Cambridge CB1 6HS — MB BS 1985 Lond.; FCAnaesth 1990. (Roy. Free) Prev: Regist. (Anaesth.) Nuffield Dept. Anaesth. Oxf.; Med. Adviser Paris, France.

KELLS, Gordon Henry George 100 Harley Street, London W1N 1AF Tel: 020 7935 8251 — MB BS 1966 Lond.; MRCS Eng. LRCP Lond. 1966. Med. Dir. RavensCt. Laborat.; Phys. Various Life Assur. Cos. Socs: Fell. Roy. Soc. Med.; Assur. Med. Soc. (Mem. Counc.). Prev: Phys. BUPA & Inst. Dir.s Med. Centre; Pres. Helping Hands Assn. for Handicap. & Disabled; Med. Off. Brit. Airways.

KELLY, Adele Margaret 16 Grosvenor Road, Wrexham LL11 1BU Tel: 01978 356551 Fax: 01978 290950; 2 Stonehouse Drive, West Felton, Oswestry SY11 4HZ Tel: 01691 610301 — MB ChB Liverp. 1967. Cons. Paediat. Community Child Health Clwyd. Socs: Fell. Roy. Coll. Paediat. & Child Health.

KELLY, Alan Robert Mitchell Burcott House, Blunsdon St Andrew, Swindon SN25 2DY — MB ChB 1978 Dundee.

KELLY, Alison 104A Constantine Road, London NW3 2LS — MB BS 1997 Lond.

KELLY, Alison Mary Psychiatry in Action Ltd, The Globe Centre, St James Square, Accrington BB5 0RE Tel: 01254 300100 Fax: 01254 300101 Email: alison@expert-witness.co.uk — MB ChB 1985 Manch.; MSc Manch. 1993, MB ChB 1985; MRCPsych 1990. (Manchester) Psychiat. Socs: Brit. Assn. Psychopharmacol.; Brit. Assn. Forens. Sci.s; Manch. Medicolegal Soc. Prev: Cons. Psychiat. Amersham S. Bucks.; Cons. Psychiat. Ment. Health Serv.s of Salford.

KELLY, Aloysius Dominick (retired) 3 Radford Lane, Lower Penn, Wolverhampton WV3 8JT — LRCPI & LM, LRCSI & LM 1950; DCH RCPSI 1960; DPH NUI 1956. Prev: Ho. Surg. Meath Hosp. Dub.

KELLY, Mr Andrew John Musgrave Park Hosp, Taunton TA1 5DA Tel: 01823 342963 Email: ajkelly@doctors.net; Mansell House, Fore Street, Milverton, West Malling TA4 5DA Tel: 01823 401321 Email: andrewkelly@compuserve.com — BM BCh 1988 Oxf.; MA Camb. 1989; FRCS Eng. 1992; FRCS Ed. 1992; FRCS (Orth.) 1997. (Oxford) Cons orthopaedic surg musGr. Pk. hosp Taunton. Socs: Assoc. Mem. BOA; Brit. Orthop. Train. Assn.; Brit. Orthop. Foot Surg. Soc. Prev: Arthroscopy Fell. Flinders Med. Centre, Asdelaide, S. Australia; Arthroscopy Fell. Sportsmed SA Stepney, Australia.; Regist. Rotat. (Orthop. Surg.) SW Region.

KELLY, Andrew Niall 17 Hyde Lane, Kinver, Stourbridge DY7 6AE — MB ChB 1998 Leic.; MB ChB Leic 1998.

KELLY, Andrew Stephen Box Cottage, Aish, South Brent TQ10 9JH Tel: 01364 73777; Lutterbum Cottage, 6 Lutterbum St, Ugborough, Plymouth PL21 0NG Tel: 01752 895565 — MB BS 1991 Lond.; BDS Liverp. 1983; FRCS Ed 1996; DRCOG 1994. (St. Georges) Staff Grade (A&E) Derriford Hosp. Plymouth. Socs: Assoc. Mem. Brit. Assn. Accid. & Emerg. Med.

KELLY, Angela Therese Brigid 89 Lower Camden, Chislehurst BR7 5JD — MB BCh BAO 1987 NUI; T(GP) 1993.

KELLY, Ann Marie Dept of Paediactrics, York District Hosp, York YO31 8HE Tel: 01904 453746 — MB BS 1986 Lond.; MRCP (UK) 1990; DCH RCP Lond. 1989. (Royal Free Hospital) Cons. Paediat., Childr.'s Centre, York. Prev: Sen. Regist. (Community Paediat.) Leeds Roy. Infirm.

KELLY, Anthony James 26 Champion Grove, London SE5 8BW — MB BS 1992 Lond.

KELLY, Anthony John Spa Medical Practice, Ombersley Street, Droitwich WR9 8RD Tel: 01905 772389 Fax: 01905 797386; Cadbury Cottage, Post Office Lane, Fernhill Heath, Worcester WR3 8RB Tel: 01905 452372 — MB ChB 1973 Birm.; MRCGP 1977; Dip. Community Paediat. Warwick 1989; DCH Eng. 1976; DObst RCOG 1976. (Birm)

KELLY, Anthony Joseph Parr House, Walker Lane, Fulwood, Preston PR2 7AP — MB ChB 1973 Liverp.; MRCP (UK) 1978; FRCR 1983.

KELLY, Anthony Thomas The Health Centre, Gotham Lane, East Leake, Loughborough LE12 6JG Tel: 01509 852181 Fax: 01509 852099; Ryber House, 4 Castle Hill, East Leake, Loughborough LE12 6LX Tel: 01509 852181 — MB ChB 1978 Leeds; BSc (Hons.) Biochem. Leeds 1975; MRCGP 1985; DRCOG 1983. (Leeds)

KELLY, Arthur William (retired) The Old Surgery, Bay View Road, Port St Mary IM9 5AB Tel: 01624 833282 — MB BS 1947 Lond.; MRCS Eng. LRCP Lond. 1942; DObst RCOG 1948. Prev: Vice-Pres. I. of Man Med. Soc.

KELLY, Babette Mary Josephine The Surgery, West Kilbride KA23 9AR Tel: 01294 823607; 10 Caldwell Road, West Kilbride KA23 9LE Tel: 01294 822667 — MB ChB 1957 Manch. (Manch.)

KELLY, Barbara Kathleen Smugglers Lane Surgery, Smugglers Lane, Reepham, Norwich NR10 4QT Tel: 01603 870271 Fax: 01603 872995; Shimna, Norwich Road, Reepham, Norwich NR10 4NH — MB BCh BAO 1979 Belf.; DRCOG 1984. Socs: Ulster Med. Soc.

KELLY, Barbara Therese 114 Harvist Road, London NW6 6HJ — MB BS 1991 Adelaide.

KELLY, Barry Eoin Department of Radiology, Royal Victoria Hospital, Grosvenor Road, Belfast BT12 6BA Tel: 01232 894960 Fax: 01232 310920 — MB BCh BAO 1984 Belf.; FRCS Ed. 1985; FFR RCSI 1993; FRCR 1993; MD 1998. (Queens University Belfast) Cons. Radiol. Roy. Vict. Hosp. Belf.

KELLY, Barry John Farmhouse Surgery, Christchurch Medical Centre, 1 Purewell Cross Road, Purewell, Christchurch BH23 3AF Tel: 01202 488487 Fax: 01202 486724; Peverel House, Hill Lane, Bransgore, Christchurch BH23 8BL — MB ChB 1973 Ed.; BSc (Med. Sci.) Ed. 1970, MB ChB 1973; MRCGP 1980; DRCOG 1978. (Edin.) Prev: Resid. Emerg. Dept. King Edwd. VII Memor. Hosp. Bermuda; SHO (Orthop. Surg.) P.ss Margt. Rose Orthop. Hosp. Edin.; Resid. Phys. Amer. Hosp. of Paris, France.

KELLY, Bernard Joseph 124 King Street, Dukinfield SK16 4LG — MB BCh BAO 1951 NUI; DPH Liverp. 1956; DCH NUI 1954.

KELLY, Blathnaid Ann High Street Surgery, 100 High Street, Dover CT16 1EQ Tel: 01304 206463 Fax: 01304 216066; 1 The Mews, Waldershare Park, Eythorne, Dover CT15 5LS Tel: 01304 827460 — MB BCh BAO 1979 NUI; MRCGP 1983; DRCOG 1982.

KELLY, Brenda Ann IFL, 13 Spottiswoode Rd, Edinburgh EH9 1BH — MB ChB 1996 Ed.

KELLY, Brendan Peter Health Centre, Omagh BT79 7BA Tel: 01662 3521 — MB BCh BAO 1946 NUI. (Univ. Coll. Dub.) Prev: Ho. Phys. & Ho. Surg. St. Vincent's Hosp. Dub.

KELLY, Brendan Valentine Dowlais Practice, Ivor St Dowlais, Merthyr Tydfil CF48 3LU Tel: 01685 721400; Grovesend, 34 West Grove, Merthyr Tydfil CF47 8HJ Tel: 01685 723701 — MB BCh BAO 1952 NUI; LM Coombe 1952. (Galw.)

KELLY, Brian James 28 Beechwood Avenue, Richmond TW9 4DE Tel: 020 8876 6813 — MB ChB 1979 Glas. Managing Dir. Sudler & Hennessey Lond.; Managing Dir. Intra Med Lond. Prev: Med. Adviser Merck Sharpe & Dohme Hoddesdon; SHO Rotat. (Gen. Med.) Soton. Gen Hosp.

KELLY, Brian Paul 2/2 45 Craigmillar Road, Glasgow G42 9HS — MB ChB 1991 Glas.

KELLY, Carmel Ann Sonny-Meed Surgery, 15-17 Heathside Road, Woking GU22 7EY Tel: 01483 772760 Fax: 01483 730354 — MS NUI 1971, MB BCh BAO 1986; MRCPath 1979; DCH NUI 1989; DObst RCPI 1989.

KELLY, Catherine Anne Bruce Medical Centre, 388 Main Street, Bellshill ML4 1AX Tel: 01698 747666 Fax: 01698 740363; 33 Sheepburn Road, Uddingston, Glasgow G71 7DT — MB ChB 1984 Glas.; MRCGP 1988; DRCOG 1988.

KELLY, Catherine Anne Royal Infirmary, Lauriston Place, Edinburgh EH3 9YW Tel: 0131 536 1000 Fax: 0131 536 2555; 71/3, Carnbee Avenue, Edinburgh EH16 6GA Tel: 0131 664 1648 Fax: 0131 664 1964 Email: cathy.kelly@luht.scot.nhs.uk — MB ChB 1987 Ed.; MRCP (UK) 1991; FFAEM 1998. Cons. in Acute Med. Edin. Roy. Infirm. Socs: BMA; Roy. Coll. of Phys.s of Edin.; Fac. of A&E Med. Prev: Research Fell., Sleep Centre, Roy. Infirm. of Edin.; Helicopter Emerg. Med. Serv. Doctor; Sen. Regist. (A&E) Edin. Roy. Infirm.

KELLY, Catherine Monique 29 Kendalls Close, High Wycombe HP13 7NN Tel: 01494 529954 — MB ChB 1992 Bristol; BSc Biochemistry Bristol 1989; DRCOG Bristol 1996; FRACGP 1998. (Bristol)

KELLY, Charles Gerald Northern Centre for Cancer Treatment, Newcastle General Hospital, Westgate Road, Newcastle upon Tyne NE4 6BE Tel: 0191 219 4244 Fax: 0191 272 4236 Email: c.g.kelly@ncl.ac.uk; 3 Birch Close, Highford Park, Hexham NE46 2RG — MB ChB 1980 Glas.; FRCP 2001 Lond.; MRCP (UK) 1987; FRCR 1991; DMRT Ed. 1989. Cons. Clin. Oncol. N. Centre for Cancer Treatm. Newc. Gen. Hosp. Socs: Counc mem Brit Assoc of Head & Neck Oncologists. Prev: Sen. Regist. (Clin. Oncol.) W.. Gen. Hosp. & Roy. Infirm. Edin.

KELLY, Christopher Brendan 58 Portglenone Road, Randalstown, Antrim BT41 3EG — MB BCh BAO 1982 Belf.; MD Belf. 1994; MRCPsych 1986. Cons. Psychiat. Holywell Hosp. Co. Antrim. Prev: Sen. Tutor & Sen. Regist. (Ment. Health) Qu. Univ. Belf.

KELLY, Christopher John Gerard 111 Hyndland Road, Flat 3/2, Hyndland, Glasgow G12 9JB Tel: 0141 334 3376 Email: ck32r@clinmed.gla.ac.uk — MB ChB 1991 Glas.; MRCP (UK) 1994. (Glasgow)

KELLY, Christopher Leslie 4 The Wells, North Anston, Sheffield S25 4ED Tel: 01909 566201 Email: syker@msn.com — MB ChB 1980 Glas.; MRCPsych 1984. Cons. Psychiat. Doncaster Roy. Infirm. Prev: Sen. Regist. (Psychiat.) WhitCh. Hosp. Cardiff; Regist. (Psychiat.) Sheff. HA; Ho. Phys. Burnley Gen. Hosp.

KELLY, Ciaran Peter 42 Grovelands Close, Camberwell Grove, London SE5 8JN — MB BS 1987 Lond.

KELLY, Clive Anthony Rheumatology Department, Queen Elizabeth Hospital, Sheriff Hill, Gateshead NE8 4SX Tel: 0191 487 8989; Greencroft, 31 Grange Road, Ryton NE40 3LU Tel: 0191 413 8692 — MD 1989 Newc.; MB BS 1980; MRCP Ed. 1983; FRCP 1997. (Newcastle upon Tyne) Cons. Phys. Rheum. Gateshead. Socs: Brit. Soc. Rheum. & Brit. Thoracic Soc. & Brit. Med. Soc. Prev: Sen. Regist. (Rheum.) Freeman Hosp. Newc.; Sen. Regist. (Med.) Roy. Vict. Infirm. Newc.; Research Regist. Gen. Hosp. Newc.

KELLY, Mr Conor Accident and Emergency Department, Coventry and Warwickshire Hospital, Stoney Stanton Road, Coventry CV1 4FH Tel: 024 7622 4055 Fax: 024 7684 4197; 43 Moss Drive, Sutton Coldfield B72 1JQ Tel: 0121 554380 Fax: 0121 507 5583 — MB BCh BAO 1982 Dub.; FRCS Eng. 1991; FFAEM 1997. Cons. A & E Coventy.

KELLY, Mr Cormac Patrick Oulton, 10 Bowbrook Grange, Shrewsbury SY3 8XT Tel: 01743 231897; c/o 21 Kincora Drive, Clontarf, Dublin 3, Republic of Ireland — MB BCh BAO 1980 Dub.; FRCS (Orth.) Ed. 1990; FRCSI 1985. Cons. Orthop. Roy. Shresbury & Robt. Jones & Agnes Hunt Hosp. OsW.ry. Socs: BOA; BSSH; BESS. Prev: Orthop. Train. Progr. Stoke & OsW.ry.

KELLY, Cornelius Anthony Old Age Psychiatry, Homerton Hospital, Homerton Row, London E9 6SR Tel: 020 8510 8889 Fax: 020 8510 8404; 5 Colville Terr, London W11 2BE Fax: 020 8510 8404 — MB BCh BAO 1984 NUI; MPhil Lond. 1994; MRCPsych 1988. Cons. (Psychiat. Old Age) Lond.; E. Lond. and the City Ment. Health NHS Trust. Prev: Hon. Sen. Lect. (Psychiat. Old Age) Lond.

KELLY, Craig Swineshead Medical Group, The Surgery, Church Lane, Swineshead, Boston PE20 3JA Tel: 01205 820204 Fax: 01205 821034; The Beeches, Mill Road, Bicker, Boston PE20 3AD Tel: 01775 820929 Fax: 01775 820929 Email: 113002.564@compuserve.com — MB BS 1986 Lond.; BSc (Hons.) Lond. 1983; MRCGP 1990; DGM RCP Lond. 1989; DCH RCP Lond. 1988; DRCOG 1988. (Univ. Coll. & Lond. Univ.) Mem. LMC; Examr. RCGP; Course Organiser, Boston VTS. Socs: (Treas.) Vale of Trent Fac. RCGP & FBA RCGP.

KELLY, Damian Rex Lyndhurst, Main Road, Cadoxton, Neath SA10 8AP — MB BS 1993 Lond.

KELLY, Daniel Reeves Laytus Hall Farm, Inskip, Preston PR4 0TT — MB ChB 1977 Glas.; FFA RCS Eng. 1982. Cons. Cardiothoracic Anaesth. Vict. Hosp. Blackpool.

KELLY, David 4 Summerdale, Dewsbury Rd, Gomersal, Cleckheaton BD19 4LD — MB ChB 1985 Leeds; DRCOG 1989.

KELLY, David Arthur White House Farm, Boreham Road, Little Waltham, Chelmsford CM3 3NF — MB BS 1978 Lond.; FFA RCS Eng. 1985. Cons. Anaesth. Broomfield Hosp. Chelmsford. Prev: Cons. Anaesth. Colchester Gen. Hosp.; Cons. Anaesth. Burns Unit St. And. Hosp. Billericay; Sen. Regist. (Anaesth.) St. Bart. Hosp. Lond.

KELLY, Deborah Jane 21 Yon Street, Kingskerswell, Newton Abbot TQ12 5EA — BM BS 1991 Nottm.

KELLY, Deirdre Anne Marie The Liver Unit, The Childrens Hospital, Steelhouse Lane, Birmingham B4 6NH Tel: 0121 333 8256 Fax: 0121 333 8251; 34 Frederick Road, Edgbaston, Birmingham B15 1JN — MB BCh BAO 1973 Dub.; FRCPCH 1997; FRCP Lond. 1995; FRCPI 1990; MD Dub. 1979. (Dublin) Cons. & Reader Paediat. Hepatol. Childr. Hosp. Birm. Prev: Asst. Prof. Univ. Nebraska; Lect. (Child Health) Lond. Hosp.; Hon. Lect. & Wellcome Research Fell. Roy. Free Hosp. Lond.

KELLY, Deirdre Mary Bewicke Health Centre, 51 Tynemouth Road, Wallsend NE28 0AD Tel: 0191 262 3036 Fax: 0191 295 1663; 10 Chester Crescent, Newcastle upon Tyne NE2 1DH — BM 1978 Soton.

KELLY, Derek Joseph 38 Ormlie Crescent, Thurso KW14 7DW — MB ChB 1997 Ed.

KELLY, Desmond Hamilton Wilson Roehampton Priory Hospital, Priory Lane, Roehampton, London SW15 5JJ Tel: 020 8876 8261 Fax: 020 8392 4223 Email: desmond.kelly@ukgateway.net; 152 Harley Street, London W1H 1HH Tel: 020 7935 2477 Fax: 020 7224 2574 — MB BS 1958 Lond.; MD Lond. 1965; FRCP Lond. 1977, M 1963; FRCPsych 1975, M 1971; DPM Eng. 1961. (St. Thos.) Vis. Cons. Roehampton. Priory. Hosp. Lond; Vis. Prof. Psychiat. UCL; Hon. Cons. Psychiat. St. Geo. Hosp. Lond. Socs: Fell. Roy. Soc. Med.; (Pres.) Internat. Stress Managem. Assn. Prev: Chief Asst. (Psychol. Med.) St. Thos. Hosp. Lond.; Nuffield Foundat. Med. Fell. Johns Hopkin's Hosp. Baltimore, USA; Med.Dir.Roehampton priory.Hosp.

KELLY, Diane Rutherford Kenwood Park, High St., Auchterarder PH3 1DF — MB ChB 1984 Glas.; MD Glas. 1995; MRCGP 1988; DRCOG 1987. Research Fell. (Postgrad. Med. Educat.) Glas.

KELLY, Dominic Francis No 1 Cottage, Parkside Hospital, Macclesfield SK10 3JE — MB BChir 1994 Camb.

KELLY, Dorothy (Surgery), 65 London Wall, London EC2M 5TU Tel: 020 7638 2999 Fax: 020 7638 9580; Notleys, 15 Spareleaze Hill, Loughton IG10 1BS Tel: 020 8508 5298 Fax: 020 8502 5328 — MB ChB 1965 St. And. (Dundee) Socs: Assur. Med. Soc.; Brit. Med. & Dent. Hypn. Soc.; Soc. Occupat. Med. Prev: Pres. Harlow Marriage Guid. Counc.; GP Harlow.

KELLY, Dympna Mary Catherine Department of Surgery, Kings College Hospital, London SE5 9RS; 6 Cotman Court, 61 Farquhar Road, London SE19 1SN — MB BCh BAO 1983 NUI.

KELLY, Elizabeth Rosalie 18 Harberton Park, Balmoral, Belfast BT9 6TS — MB BCh BAO 1987 Belf. Clin. Asst. Ophth. Belf. Socs: MRCOphth.

KELLY, Eric John Academic Unit of Paediatrics, CSB, St James Hospital, Beckett St., Leeds LS9 7TF Email: mrpejk@leeds.ac.uk — MB ChB 1996 Leeds; MB ChB (Hons.) Leeds 1996; BSc (Hons) Leeds 1991; MRCP (UK) 1998; MRCPCH 1998. (Leeds) MRC Clin. Train. Fell. (Developm. Gastroenterol.); Hon. Lect. (Paediat.). Prev: Res. Fell. (Pediatric Gastroenterol.) Harvard Med. Sch., Boston, Mass.

KELLY, Eric Peter Henley House, Chelsham Road, Warlingham CR6 9PA — MB BS 1974 Lond.; FFA RCS Eng 1980. Cons. Anaesth. Joyce Green Hosp. Dartford. Prev: Sen. Regist. St. Mary's Hosp. Lond.

KELLY, Eunice 22 Gortnasaor, Dungannon BT71 6DA — MB BCh BAO 1994 Belf.

***KELLY, Fiona Elizabeth** 4 Ambrose Lane, Harpenden AL5 4AX Tel: 01582 762106; 18A Barnsdale Road, Maida Vale, London W9 3LL Tel: 020 8960 7507 — MB BS 1994 Lond.; MA Lond. 1994.

KELLY, Frances Denburn Health Centre, Rosemount Viaduct, Aberdeen AB25 1QB; 46 Prospect Terrace, Aberdeen AB11 7TD — MB ChB 1967 Aberd.; MA Ed. 1959; DA Eng. 1974. Prev: Ho. Surg. Woodend Gen. Hosp. Aberd.; Ho. Phys. Bridge of Earn Hosp.

KELLY, Francis Peter Larkfield Road, Greenock PA16 0 — MB BCh BAO 1977 NUI.

KELLY, Gavin Edward St Marys Medical Centre, Wharf Road, Stamford PE9 2DH Tel: 01780 64121 Fax: 01780 756515; The Old Vicarage, Main Road, Tinwell, Stamford PE9 3UD — MB BS 1974 Lond.; BSc Liverp. 1969; MRCGP 1979; DRCOG 1978. (St. Geo.)

KELLY, Geraldine Mary Woodside Health Centre, Barr Street, Glasgow G20 7LR Tel: 0141 531 9521 Fax: 0141 531 9545; 182 Bardowie Street, Glasgow G22 Tel: 0141 336 8011 — MB ChB 1984 Glas.; MRCGP 1989; Dip. Forens. Med. Glas 1992; DRCOG 1988.

***KELLY, Gillian Denise** 31 Rookery Road, Selly Oak, Birmingham B29 7DG; 11Sandgate Road, Hall Green, Birmingham B28 0UN — MB ChB 1994 Birm.

KELLY, Mr Glenn Anthony 8 Gerrards Fold, Abbey Village, Withnell, Chorley PR6 8DL — MB BS 1980 Lond.; FRCS Eng. 1985; FRCS Ed. 1985; FRCR 1990.

KELLY, Grant Stuart-Black 8 Lavant Road, Chichester PO19 4RH Tel: 01243 527264 Fax: 01243 530607; Keynor House, Cow Lane, Sidlesham, Chichester PO20 7LN Tel: 01243 641746 Fax: 01243 641745 Email: gkelly@enterprise.net — MB BS 1974 Lond. (Lond. Hosp.) Socs: GP Comm.; Chair Informat. Managem. and Technol. Sub-Comm. OPC. Prev: Regist. (Med.) Poole Gen. Hosp.

KELLY, Helen Bronwen PO Box 50, Clitheroe BB7 4GH Tel: 01200 440622 Fax: 01200 440622 — MB BCh Wales 1959; MRCPsych 1972; DPM Eng. 1972. Hon. Cons. Forens. Psychiat. Darwen. Prev: Cons. Forens. Psychiat. Prestwich Hosp.

KELLY, Henry Hugh Derek (retired) 4 High Street, Great Horwood, Milton Keynes MK17 0QL Tel: 01296 712228 — MB BCh BAO 1945 NUI. Prev: Regist. (Med.) Bury Gen. Hosp. & Stockport Infirm.

KELLY, Herbert Brian, CB, LVO, Air Vice-Marshal RAF Med. Br. Retd. (retired) 32 Chiswick Quay, Hartington Road, London W4 3UR Tel: 020 8995 5042 Email: b-kelly@dircon.co.uk — MB BS Lond. 1943; MD Lond. 1948; FRCP Lond. 1968, M 1945; MRCS Eng. LRCP Lond. 1943; MFOM RCP Lond. 1983; DCH Eng. 1966. Prev: Cons. Civil Aviat. Auth.

KELLY, Mr Herbert Derek Brown (retired) Little Barn, Oddington, Moreton-in-Marsh GL56 0XG — MB BCh 1931 Camb.; MA, MD Camb. 1944, MB BCh 1931; DLO Eng. 1933; FRFPS Glas. 1937; FRCS Glas. 1962. Prev: Surg. i/c Dept. Otolaryn. Vict. Infirm. Glas.

KELLY, Mr Ian George Orthopaedic Directorate, Royal Infirmary, Glasgow G4 0SF Tel: 0141 211 5186 Fax: 0141 211 5929; 33 Blackwood Road, Milngavie, Glasgow G62 7LB Tel: 0141 956 3350 Fax: 0141 955 0040 Email: igkel@aol.com — MB ChB 1972 Ed.; MD Ed. 1984, BSc (Med. Sci.) 1969; FRCS Glas. 1991; FRCS Ed. 1977. Cons. Orthop. Surg. Roy. Infirm. Glas.; Hon. Clin. Sen. Lect. Univ. of Glas.; Hon. Lect. Bioeng. Unit Univ. of Strathclyde. Socs: Fell. BOA; (Pres.) Brit. Elbow & Shoulder Soc.; (Bd. of Directors) Europ. Soc. Surg. of Shoulder & Elbow. Prev: Sen. Lect. (Orthop. Surg.) Univ. of Glas.; Lect. (Orthop. Surg.) Univ. of Glas.; Regist. Rotat. (Surg.) Liverp. HA.

KELLY, James (retired) Myrton, High St., Dalbeattie DG5 4QX Tel: 01556 610642 — MB ChB Glas. 1960.

KELLY, James Anthony 32 Fairmile Lane, Cobham KT11 2DQ — MB BS 1991 Lond.

KELLY, James Conleth 29 Winchelsea House, Swan Road, London SE16 4LH — MB BS 1992 Lond.; DCCH RCGP 1996; DFFP 1995; DRCOG 1995. (Roy. Free Hosp. Sch. Med.)

KELLY, James Francis 16 Upper Celtic Park, Enniskillen BT74 6JA — MD 1988 NUI; MB BCh BAO 1981; MRCP (UK) 1984; FRCP Ed 1997; FRCP Lond. 1997. Cons. Phys. Geriat. Med. Erne Hosp. Enniskillen.

KELLY, James Joseph Rushden Medical Centre, Adnitt Road, Rushden NN10 9TU Tel: 01933 412444 Fax: 01933 317666; 70 Gypsy Lane, Kettering NN16 8UA Tel: 01536 415384 — MB BCh BAO 1990 NUI; MRCGP 1995; DRCOG 1994; DCH RCP Lond. 1993. (Univ. Coll. Dub.) GP Rushden.

KELLY, Jane Elizabeth 9 Sandilands Grove, Hightown, Liverpool L38 9EZ — MB BS 1993 Lond.

KELLY, Jean Diana (retired) 7 Woodland Road, Weston Super Mare BS23 4HE Tel: 01934 621571 — MB ChB 1954 Bristol. Prev: Clin. Asst. (Ophth.) W.on-super-Mare Hosp. Trust.

KELLY, Jessie Elizabeth 194 Upper Malone Road, Dunmurry, Belfast BT17 9JZ; 194 Upper Malone Road, Dunmurry, Belfast BT17 9JZ — MB BCh BAO 1977 Belf.; MRCGP 1981, DCH 1980. (Queen's University, Belfast) p/t Examing Med. Practitioner Med. Support Servs. & Med. Off. in Dept. Of Social Dev. Belf. Socs: Med. Wom.'s Federat.

KELLY, Joan Mary (retired) 5 St Andrews Road, Blundellsands, Liverpool L23 7UP — MB BCh BAO 1954 NUI; FFA RCS Eng. 1959; DA Eng. 1957. Prev: Cons. Anaesth. Roy. Liverp. Univ. Hosp.

KELLY, Joanne Emily Mary Bryson Street Surgery, 115 Newtownards Road, Belfast BT4 1AB Tel: 028 9045 8722 Fax: 028 9046 6766; 76 Marlborough Park N., Malone Road, Belfast BT9 6HJ — MB BCh BAO 1987 Belf.; MRCGP 1991.

KELLY, John Cleeve Lodge, 9a Southborough Road, Surbiton KT6 6JN — MB BChir 1976 Camb.; MA, MB Camb. 1977, BChir 1976.

KELLY, Mr John 18 Hintlesham Avenue, Birmingham B15 2PH Tel: 0121 454 3156 — MB ChB 1956 Glas.; FRCOG 1973, M 1961;

FRCS Ed. 1964. Sen. Lect. Dept. O & G Univ. Birm.; Cons. Obstetr. & Gynaecol. United Birm. Hosps. Socs: Fell. Roy. Soc. Med.; Blair-Bell Research Soc. Prev: Sen. Regist. Dept. O & G Lond. Hosp.; Research Fell. in Neonat. Physiol. Lond. Hosp. Med. Coll.

KELLY, Mr John, OStJ (retired) 3 Little London Mews, Chichester PO19 1YA — MB BCh BAO 1940 NUI; MCh TC Dub. 1956; MB BCh BAO (Hons.) NUI 1940; MRCGP 1953. Hon. Capt. RAMC. Prev: Res. Surg. Off. Bury Infirm.

KELLY, John Riddings Road Surgery, 34 Riddings Road, Timperley, Altrincham WA15 6BP Tel: 0161 962 9662; 50 Westwood Avenue, Timperley, Altrincham WA15 6QF — MB ChB 1982 Manch.; MRCGP 1986. Prev: Trainee GP N. Trafford VTS.

KELLY, John Brien MacMillan Services, King Edward VII Hospital, Midhurst GU29 0BL Tel: 01730 812341; Alma, West Meon, Petersfield GU32 1LU Tel: 01730 829237 — MB BS 1959 Lond.; MRCS Eng. LRCP Lond. 1959; DA Eng. 1969; DObst RCOG 1968; DTM & H Eng. 1961. (Guy's) Dep. Dir. W. Sussex MacMillan Serv. Midhurst. Prev: GP Chichester.

KELLY, Mr John Christopher Edgefield Avenue Surgery, 2 Edgefield Avenue, Lawford, Manningtree CO11 2HD Tel: 01206 392617 Fax: 01206 391148; 50 High Street, Manningtree CO11 1AJ Tel: 01206 395461 — MB BS 1966 Lond.; BSc Lond. 1963, MB BS (Hons. Obst.) 1966; FRCS Eng. 1972; MRCOG 1974. (St. Thos.)

KELLY, John Clark Carruthers (retired) Auchenheath House, Auchenheath, Lanark ML11 9UX Tel: 01555 89234 — MB ChB 1943 Glas.; MB ChB (Commend.) Glas. 1943; FRFPS Glas. 1950; FRCP Glas. 1982, M 1962.

***KELLY, John Daniel Gerard** 22 Cranmore Gardens, Belfast BT9 6JL — MB BCh BAO 1988 Belf.; MB BCh Belf. 1988.

KELLY, Mr John Desmond Charles Thoresby Lodge, North Thoresby, Grimsby DN36 5PL Tel: 01472 840337 Fax: 01472 840983; Thoresby Lodge, North Thoresby, Grimsby DN36 5PL — BM BCh Oxf. 1956; MA Oxf. 1956; FRCS Glas. 1967; MRCS Eng. LRCP Lond. 1954; T(S) 1991. (Oxf. & Westm.) Cons. Gen. Surg. & Urol. Grimsby Trust.; Med. Director Grimsby Trust. Prev: Wing. Cdr. RAF Med. Br. Cons. Surg.; Ho. Surg. (Thoracic Surg.) Ch.ill Hosp. Oxf.

KELLY, John Edmund West View Cottage, Compton St., Compton, Winchester SO21 2AT — MB BS 1980 Lond.

KELLY, John Lanagan 16 Laggan Road, Glasgow G43 2SY — MB ChB 1945 Glas. (Glas.)

KELLY, Mr John Malcolm Fairlight, Brook Avenue, Warsash, Southampton SO31 9HR Tel: 01489 573187 — MS Lond. 1973, MB BS 1962; FRCS Eng. 1967; MRCS Eng. LRCP Lond. 1962; DObst RCOG 1966. (St. Mary's) Cons. Surg. Qu. Alexandra Hosp. Cosham. Socs: Brit. Soc. Gastroenterol.; Assn. Surg. Prev: Research Fell. & Sen. Regist. (Surg.) Roy. Vict. Hosp. Belf.; Ho. Surg. St. Mary's Hosp. Paddington.

KELLY, John Michael Ingleside, 8 The Sycamores, Sunderland SR2 7UW Tel: 0191 567 3358 — MB BCh BAO 1945 NUI. (Univ. Coll. Dub.)

KELLY, John Stephen Ebenezar House, 15 Chapel Row, Broad Lane, Burnedge, Rochdale OL16 4QQ — MB ChB 1978 Manch.; BSc (Med. Sci.) St. And. 1975.

***KELLY, Julia Claire** Woody Bay, Kingswood Road, Penn, High Wycombe HP10 8JL Tel: 01494 812656 — BM BCh 1998 Oxf.; BM BCh Oxf 1998.

KELLY, Mr Justin Francis (retired) Bank House, Priest Hutton, Carnforth LA6 1JL Tel: 01524 781042 Email: jkellyfish@aol.com — MB BChir 1962 Camb.; FRCS Eng. 1967; DObst RCOG 1964. Hon. Cons. Gen. Surg. Roy. Lancaster Infirm. Prev: Sen. Regist. (Surg.) St. Mary's Hosp. Lond.

KELLY, Katherine Jane 3 The Crescent, Rhos-on-Sea, Colwyn Bay LL28 4LH — MB BCh 1990 Wales.

KELLY, Keith Patrick 27 Wardie Road, Edinburgh EH5 3LH — MB ChB 1986 Ed.; MRCP (UK) 1990; FRCA. 1992; DA (UK) 1991.

KELLY, Kevin (retired) 22 Clerks Croft, Church Lane, Bletchingley, Redhill RH1 4LH Tel: 01883 743519 Fax: 01883 742216 — MB BS 1953 Lond.; MRCS Eng. LRCP Lond. 1953; FRCGP 1989, M 1980; DObst RCOG 1955. Prev: Med. Dir. St. Jude Hosp. St. Lucia W. Indies.

KELLY, Kristina Brigid Edenbridge Medical Practice, West View, Station Road, Edenbridge TN8 5ND Tel: 01732 864442 Fax: 01732 862376; 28 Hazelwood Heights, Oxted RH8 0QQ Tel: 01883 716287 Fax: 01883 716287 — MB ChB 1984 Leic. GP Edenbridge. Prev: Princip. Gen. Pract. Gostone Surrey; SHO (Med. & Endocrinol.) Luton & Dunstable Hosp.; Ho. Surg. Leicester Gen. Hosp.

KELLY, Laura Catherine 130 Mull, East Kilbride, Glasgow G74 2DY — MB ChB 1994 Aberd.; MRCP (UK) 1999.

KELLY, Linda Samantha Grovesnor Road Surgery, 216 Grovesnor Road, Belfast BT12 5LT Tel: 01232 320777 — MB BCh BAO 1993 Belf.; DCH Dub. 1995; DRCOG 1996; DMH QUB 1997; MRCGP 1998. (QUB) GP Princip. Socs: BMA & Med. Sickness Soc. Prev: SHO Rotat. (Gen. Pract.) Belf.

KELLY, Lisa Francesca Norwest House, Redwood Lane, Medstead, Alton GU34 5PE; 7 Northcote, Rickmansworth Road, Pinner HA5 3TW — MB BS 1993 Lond.; BSc (Hons.) Lond. 1991. Prev: SHO (Cardiol.) Roy. Brompton Hosp. Lond.; SHO (Med.) Hammersmith Hosp. Lond.

KELLY, Louise Michelle 39 Bond Street, Stirchley, Birmingham B30 2LB — MB ChB 1997 Birm.

KELLY, Maire Cailin 46 Tongdean Avenue, Hove BN3 6TN — MB ChB 1989 Leeds; MRCOG 1996. Prev: Regist. (O & G) Pindersfield Hosp. Wakefield; Regist. (O & G) St. Jas. Univ. Hosp. Leeds.

KELLY, Margaret Glebelands, Rostrevor Road, Warrenpoint, Newry BT34 3RT Tel: 01693 773691 — MB BCh BAO 1944 NUI; LM 1946. (Univ. Coll. Dub.)

KELLY, Margaret Mary Theresa 19 Cambourne Park, Belfast BT9 6RL Tel: 01232 665553 — MB BCh BAO 1964 Belf. (Belf.)

KELLY, Mark Ian 13 Struell Road, Downpatrick BT30 6JR — MB BCh BAO 1996 Belf.

KELLY, Martin Gerard Dept. of Respiratory Medicine, Lecel 11, Belfast City Hospital, Lisburn rd, Belfast BT9 7AB Tel: 01232 329241 Ext: 3119 Fax: 01232 263879 Email: m.g.kelly@qub.ac.uk; 9 Hollybrook Avenue, Hightown Rd, Glengormley, Newtownabbey BT36 4ZL Tel: 01232 839888 Email: mgkelly@btinternet.com — MB BCh BAO 1993 Belf.; MRCP (UK) 1997. (Qu. Univ. Belf.) Clin. research Fell. (Respirat. Med. & Clin. Biochem.ry) Qu.s Univ. Belf. Socs: BMA; Brit. Thorac. Soc.; Roy. Coll. Phys. Edin.

KELLY, Mary Bernadette (retired) The Old Vicarage, School Lane, Husborne Crawley, Bedford MK43 0UY Tel: 01908 583425 — MB BS 1958 Lond.; MRCS Eng. LRCP Lond. 1958. Prev: GP Bletchley.

KELLY, Mary Catherine Joan Audiology Clinic, Lance Bury, Churchill Way, Salford M6 Tel: 0161 368 7868; 9 West Park, Gee Cross, Hyde SK14 5EW — MB BCh BAO 1954 NUI; LM TC Dub. 1955. SCMO Audiol. Salford HA. Socs: Brit. Soc. Audiol., Soc. Community Med. & BMA. Prev: SCMO Community Child Health Salford HA; Clin. Asst. (Paediat.) Stockport; Sen. Paediat. Res. Mercy Hosp. & Univ. Hosp. Baltimore, USA.

KELLY, Mary-Catherine Margaret Vauxhall House, Monmouth NP25 3AX — BM BCh 1975 Oxf.; DO 1980. (St. Mary's) Clin. Asst. (Ophth.) Vict. Eye Hosp. Hereford.

KELLY, Mary Clare 43 South Parade, Belfast BT7 2GL — MB BCh BAO 1988 Belf.; FFA RCSI 1992; FRCA 1992; MD Belf. 1997. Cons. Anaesth. Belf. City Hosp.

KELLY, Maurice Paul Department of Adult & Paediatric Gastroenterology, Barts & The London, Queen Mary's School of Medicine & Dentistry, Turner St, London E1 2AD Tel: 020 7882 7191 Fax: 020 7882 7192 Email: m.p.kelly@qmul.ac.uk — MB BS 1986 Lond.; FRCP 2001; BA Oxf. 1983; MRCP (UK) 1989; MD 1997. (Brasenose Coll., Oxf. - The Lond. Hosp. Med. Coll.) Wellcome Trust Sen. Lect.; Hon. Sen. Lect., Lond. Sch. of Hyg. & Trop. Medicince, Keppel St., Lond. WC1N 7HT. Socs: Brit. Soc. of Gastroenterol.; Amer. Gastroenterol. Assn.; Roy. Soc. of Trop. Med. & Hyg. Prev: Specialist Regist. Whipps Cross Hosp.; Specialist Regist. Roy. Lond. Hosp.; Regist. (Med.) Whittington Hosp. Lond.

KELLY, Michael Daniel 23 Nethervale Avenue, Netherlee, Glasgow G44 3XP Tel: 0141 637 3201; 23 Nethervale Avenue, Netherlee, Glasgow G73 2PQ Tel: 0141 531 6020 Fax: 0141 531 6070 — MB ChB 1990 Glas.; DRCOG 1992; BSc 1987. (Glasgow) Benefits Agency Med. Assessor with NBA in Glas.; Med. Adviser St Margt.s Adoption Soc. Socs: BMA; MDDUS. Prev: GP Princip., Rutherglen Health Centre, Glas.

KELLY, Mr Michael John The Leicester Nuffield Hospital, Scraptoft Lane, Leicester LE5 1HY Tel: 0116 276 9401 Fax: 0116 246 1076; Stone House, 57 Main St, Woodhouse Eaves, Loughborough LE12 8RY Tel: 01509 890173 Fax: 01509 891431 Email:

mlchaeljkelly@compuserve.com — MB BChir 1970 Camb.; MA Camb. 1972, BA (Nat. Sc. Trip. Pt. II 1st cl. Hons.) 1967; MChir Camb. 1978; FRCS Eng. 1974; MRCP (UK) 1973. (Camb. & St. Geo.) Cons. Surg. (Colorectal) Leic. & LoughBoro. Gen. Hosps.; Exam. (Surg.) Univ. Camb. (1988-92) & Leic.; RCS Tutor Leic.; HCSA Co. Chairm. Leic.; RCS Ct. of Examrs. 2000; Elected Tutors's Represen. on Resid.s' Train. Bd.; Lead Clinician in Colorectal Cancer, Univ. Hosp. of Leicester; Nat. Lead Clinician for Colorectal Cancer, Cancer Serv.s Collaborative Project. Socs: Fell. Roy. Soc. Med. (Mem. Counc. Coloproctol. Sect. 2000-03); Assn. Coloproctol. (UK); Anglo-French Med. Soc. Prev: Sen. Regist. (Surg.) Bristol Roy. Infirm.; Sen. Regist. St. Mark's Hosp. for Rectal Dis. Lond.; Regist. (Surg.) Addenbrooke's Hosp. Camb.

KELLY, Mr Michael Patrick 17 Bemershed Avenue, Manswood, Glasgow G43 1DA — MB ChB 1986 Glas.; FRCS Glas. 1993.

KELLY, Michaeline Mary 41 Landgarve Manor, Crumlin BT29 4SE — MB BCh BAO 1991 Belf.

KELLY, Michelle Melanie 17 Binley Close, Shirley, Solihull B90 2RB; Newtown Health Centre, 171 Melbourne Avenue, Newtown, Birmingham B19 2JA Tel: 0121 554 7541 Fax: 0121 515 4447 — MB ChB 1989 Sheff.; MRCGP 1994; DFFP 1993; DRCOG 1992. (Sheff.)

KELLY, Moira Bernadette 1 Marston Lane, Eaton, Norwich NR4 6LZ Tel: 01603 456495 Fax: 01603 456495 — MB BS 1959 Lond.; MRCS Eng. LRCP Lond. 1959; MRCOG 1970, DObst 1961; FRCOG. (Roy. Free) Assoc. Specialist O & G Norf. & Norwich Hosp. Prev: Sen. Regist, (O & G) Norf. & Norwich Hosp.

KELLY, Moya Helen Williamwood Medical Centre, 85 Seres Road, Clarkston, Glasgow G76 7NW Tel: 0141 638 7984 Fax: 0141 638 8827; 48A Seres Road, Clarkston, Glasgow G76 7QF Tel: 0141 638 7984 Fax: 0141 638 8827 — MB ChB 1979 Glas.; PhD Glas. 1994; FRCGP 1994, M 1984. Asst. & Assoc. Adviser Univ. Glas.; Asst. Dir. Postgrad. Med. Educat. (Hosp. Posts & Accreditation) Univ. Glas. Prev: Assoc. Adviser, Univ. Glas.; Lect. (Gen. Pract.) Woodside Health Centre Glas.

KELLY, Neil Grant Greencroft Medical Centre (North), Greencroft Wynd, Annan DG12 6BG; Nursery House, Dornock, Annan DG12 6SU Tel: 01461 40298 — MB ChB 1986 Aberd.; MRCGP 1990; DRCOG 1989.

KELLY, Nial Joseph (retired) Higher Court, Five Bells, Watchet TA23 — MB BCh BAO 1957 NUI; MRCPsych 1972; DPM Eng. 1962. Hon. Cons. Psychiat. Som. HA. Prev: Cons. Psychol. Med. Tone Vale Hosp. Taunton.

KELLY, Patricia Ann (retired) 58 Esplanade Road, Scarborough YO11 2AU — MB BCh BAO 1963 NUI.

KELLY, Patrick (retired) 97 Longdale Lane, Ravenshead, Nottingham NG15 9AG — LRCPI & LM, LRSCI & LM 1939; LRCPI & LM, LRCSI & LM 1939; LM Rotunda 1945; CPH NUI 1947. Prev: Res. Med. Off. & Ho. Surg. St. Catherine's Co. Hosp. Tralee.

KELLY, Patrick Declan Weaver Vale Surgery, The Health Centre, High St., Winsford CW7 2AS Tel: 01606 556111 Fax: 01606 556551 — MB BCh BAO 1983 NUI; MRCGP 1988; DCH Dub. 1987; DObst. RCPI 1986. (University College Calway)

KELLY, Paul TFL 11 Luton Place, Edinburgh EH8 9PD — MB ChB 1996 Ed.; BSc (Hons.) (Immunol.) 1994.

KELLY, Paul Antony Southend Hospital, Prittlewell Chase, Westcliff on Sea SS0 0RY Tel: 01702 221222 Fax: 01702 221984; 239 Vicarage Hill, Benfleet SS7 1PG Tel: 01268 799064 Fax: 01268 799064 — MB ChB 1986 Ed.; FRCP 2001; BSc Ed. 1984; MD Ed. 1995; MRCP (UK) 1989. Cons. Cardiol. S.end Hosp. & Lond. Chest Hosp. Socs: Brit. Cardiovasc. Interven. Soc. Prev: Sen. Regist. (Cardiol.) Roy. Brompton Hosp. Lond.; Regist. (Cardiol.) Roy. Brompton Nat. Heart & Lung Hosp.; Research Regist. (Cardiol.) Leeds Gen. Infirm.

KELLY, Paul David Highfield Surgery, Garton Avenue, Southshore, Blackpool FY4 2LD Tel: 01253 345328 Fax: 01253 407801 — MB ChB 1979 Manch.; FRCGP 1996, M 1983; DRCOG 1982. Prev: SHO/GP Trainee Preston VTS; Trainee GP Gt. Eccleston.

KELLY, Mr Peter David The White House, Graveley, Hitchin SG4 7LA — MB BS 1968 Lond.; FRCS Eng. 1977; FRCS Ed. 1976; FFAEM 1994. Cons. Surg. A & E Herts.

KELLY, Peter Gordon, MBE The Health Centre, Beeches Green, Stroud GL5 4BH Tel: 01453 763980 — MB BS Lond. 1963; MRCS Eng. LRCP Lond. 1962; DObst RCOG 1966. (Guy's)

***KELLY, Philip Anthony** 9 West Park, Gee Cross, Hyde SK14 5EW Tel: 0161 368 7868 — MB BS 1996 Lond.; MRCP 1999.

KELLY, Phillip Stuart Plas y Bryn Surgery, Chapel Street, Wrexham LL13 7DE Tel: 01978 351308 Fax: 01978 312324; 9 Old Hall Close, Rhostyllen, Wrexham LL14 4DJ Tel: 01978 351308 — MB BCh 1979 Wales; BSc (Med. Sci.) St. And. 1976.

KELLY, Richard John 2 Stonehouse Dr, West Felton, Oswestry SY11 4HZ Tel: 01691 610301 — MB ChB 1997 Manch.; BSc Hons. St. And. 1994.

KELLY, Robin Nigel Rushall Medical Centre, 107 Lichfield Road, Rushall, Walsall WS4 1HB — MB ChB 1982 Birm.; MRCGP 1987. (Birm.) Prev: Clin. Asst. (ENT) Wolverhampton.

KELLY, Ronan Philip Francis 22 Divinity Road, Oxford OX4 1LJ — BM BCh 1992 Oxf.

KELLY, Rosaleen Ciara Cecilia Dept. Of Psycological Medicine, Gartnavel Royal Hospital, 1055 Gt Heston Rd, Glasgow G12 0XH Email: r.c.kelly@clinmed.gla.ac.uk; 24 Station Road, Bearsden, Glasgow G61 4AL — MB ChB 1989 Ed.; MRCPsych 1994. Cons. Psych. Gartnavel Roy. Hosp. Glas. Prev: Lect. In Dept. Of Psych. Med., Univ. Of Glas. 1995-2001.

KELLY, Rosemary Elizabeth 36 Royal Lodge Avenue, Belfast BT8 7YR — MB BCh BAO 1985 NUI.

KELLY, Rosemary Warren Fairlight, Brook Avenue, Warsash, Southampton SO31 9HR — MB BS 1965 Lond.; MRCS Eng. LRCP Lond. 1965; DO Eng. 1973. (St. Mary's) Clin. Asst. Soton. Eye Hosp.

KELLY, Ruth Alison White House Farm, Boreham Road, Little Waltham, Chelmsford CM3 3NF — MB BChir 1979 Camb.; MA Oxf. 1978; MRCGP 1984. GP Lond.

KELLY, Sara Katharine 8 Lavant Road, Chichester PO19 4RH Tel: 01243 527264 Fax: 01243 530607; Keynor House, Cow Lane, Sidlesham, Chichester PO20 7LN Tel: 01243 56746 Fax: 01243 56746 Email: gkelly@enterprise.net — BM 1978 Soton.; MRCP (UK) 1981; MRCGP 1983. GP Trainer.

KELLY, Sarah Elizabeth Jane Community Child Health, Musgrove Park Hospital, Taunton TA1 5DA Tel: 01823 342696; 37 Dobree Park, Rockwell Green, Wellington TA21 9RX — MB BS 1978 Lond.; MSc (Community Paediat.) Lond. 1996; DCH RCP Lond. 1982; MRCPCH 1997. SCMO (Child Health) Som. HA. Socs: Brit. Assn. Community Child Health. Prev: Clin. Med. Off. (Child Health) Tower Hamlets; Regist. (Audiol. Med.) Nuffield Hearing & Speech Centre Lond.

KELLY, Mr Seamus Benedict Department of Surgery, North Tyneside General Hospital, Rake Lane, North Shields NE29 8NH — MB BCh BAO 1980 Belf.; MD Belf. 1989; FRCSI 1984. (Queen's University Belfast) Sen. Lect. & Hon. Cons. (Surg.) Univ. Newc. u. Tyne & N.ubria Health Care NHS Trust; Mem of the Newc. & N Tyneside Jt. ethics Comm. Socs: Hon Treas N Eng Surg. Soc.; Fell. Assn. Surgs. & Assn. ColoProctol. GB & Irel.; Soc. of Acad. & Research Surg. Prev: Sen. Regist. (Gen. Surg.) Belf.; Vis. Lect. (Surg.) P. of Wales Hosp., Chinese Univ., Hong Kong; Research Fell. (Surg.) Univ. Bristol & Bristol Roy. Infirm.

KELLY, Mr Sean Martin Raigmore Hospital, Inverness IV2 3UJ Tel: 01463 70400 Email: sean.kelly@raigmore.scot.nhs.uk — MB ChB 1988 Manch.; BSc (Med. Sci.) St. And. 1985; FRCS Ed. 1993; FRCS Orth 1997. (St. And. Manch.) Cons. Orthop. Surg. Socs: BMA; MDU; BUA. Prev: Sen. Regist. Orthop. W. Scotl.

KELLY, Sean Michael 6 Drakes Close, Huntington, York YO32 9GN — MB ChB 1984 Liverp.; MD Liverp. 1994; MRCP (UK) 1987. Cons. Phys. & Gastroenterol. York Dist. Hosp.

KELLY, Sheila Anne Department of Pathology, Whiston Hospital, Warrington Road, Prescot L35 5DS — MB BS 1983 Lond.; BSc (Hons.) Lond. 1980; MRCP (UK) 1986; MRCPath 1993. Cons. Histopath. St Helens & Knowsley NHS Trust. Prev: Sen. Regist. (Histopath.) Mersey RHA.

KELLY, Sheila Anne Teresa Marcella Belfast Marie Curie Centre, Kensington Road, Belfast BT5 6NF Tel: 028 9079 4200 Fax: 028 9040 1962; 82 Seahill Road, Craigavad, Holywood BT18 0DS Tel: 02890 426114 — MB BCh BAO 1971 NUI; FRCSI 1981; DTM & H RCP Lond. 1975. (University College Dublin) Cons. Palliat. Med. Marie Curie Centre & Belf. City Hosp.; Hon. Clin. Lect. In Oncol. QUB. Socs: BMA; APM; EAPC. Prev: Cons. Palliat. Med. St.

Gemma's Hospice Leeds; Sen. Lect. Leeds Univ.; Sen. Regist. (Palliat. Med.) Our Lady's Hospice Dub.

KELLY, Mr Simon Peadar Dub Dara Bolton Hospitals NHS Trust, Minerva Road, Farnworth, Bolton BL4 0JR Tel: 01204 390694 Fax: 01204 390554; Tel: 0161 962 9199 — MB BCh BAO 1980 NUI; FRCS Ed. 1984; FCOphth. 1989; DO RCPSI 1982. Cons. Ophth. Surg. Bolton Hosp. Trust. Socs: Bolton Med. Inst.; Manch. Med. Soc.; Coun. Mem. Roy. Coll. of Ophth.s. Prev: Sen. Regist. Manch. Roy. Eye Hosp.; Regist. Leic. Roy. Infim.

KELLY, Stephanie Elizabeth Richmond House, Dunnington, Driffield YO25 8EG — MB ChB 1988 Leeds.

KELLY, Stephen Arthur Plymouth Oncology Centre, Derriford Hospital, Plymouth PL6 8DH Tel: 01752 763994 — MB ChB 1980 Leeds; PhD Lond. 1991; FRCR 1986. Cons. (Clin. Oncol.). Prev: Sen. Regist. Hammersmith Hosp. Lond.; Clin. Research Fell. (Biol. Ther.) Imperial Cancer Research Fund.

KELLY, Stephen Daniel Edward Worcester Street Surgery, 24 Worcester Street, Stourbridge DY8 1AW Tel: 01384 371616; Ingelby House, Hyde Lane, Kinver, Stourbridge DY7 6AE Tel: 01384 371616 — MB ChB 1970 Birm.; MRCP (U.K.) 1974; MRCGP 1988; DObst RCOG 1972; DCH Eng. 1973. (Birm.) Prev: Ho. Surg. & Ho. Phys. Dudley Rd. Hosp. Birm.; SHO (Paediat.) Worcester Roy. Infirm.

KELLY, Stephen Gerard 2 Beechfield Court, Coleraine BT52 2HY — MB ChB 1998 Ed.; MB ChB Ed 1998.

***KELLY, Stephen John** Lincoln County Hospital, Greetwell Road, Lincoln LN2 5QY — MB ChB 1987 Bristol; MRCP Lond. 1990.

KELLY, Stephen John Hill Head Cottage, Hollowgate, Bradwell, Hope Valley S33 9JA Tel: 01433 621543 Email: skelly1@compuserve.com — BM BCh 1992 Oxf.; MA 1992. (Oxf.) Specialist Regist. (Respirat. Med.) Sheff. Rotat. Socs: Brit. Thorac. Soc.

KELLY, Stephen John 10 Exeter Close, Stevenage SG1 4PN — MB BCh 1993 Wales.

KELLY, Mr Stephen Richard 5 Comfrey Close, Romsey SO51 7RE — MB BChir 1992 Camb.; FRCS Lond. 1995. (Univ. Camb.) Specialist Regist. (Gen. Surg.) Salisbury Dist. Hosp.

KELLY, Susan Elizabeth The Royal Shrewsbury Hospital, Shrewsbury SY3 8DN; The Green Dragon, Alberbury, Shrewsbury SY5 9AH — MD 1989 Glas.; MB ChB 1980; FRCP 1998; MRCP (UK) 1984. Cons. Dermat. P.ss Roy. Hosp. Telford & Roy. Shrewsbury Hosp. Prev: MRC Train. Fell. (Dermat.) Univ. Edin.; Sen. Regist. (Dermat.) Lothian Regional HB; Regist. (Dermat.) Roy. Berks. Hosp. & St. Thos. Hosp. Lond.

KELLY, Susan Jane Wycombe General Hospital, High Wycombe HP11 2TT Tel: 01494 26161, 01494 526161 Email: susan.kelly@hotmail.com; 101 High Street, Kidlington, Oxford OX5 2DS Tel: 01865 847681 Email: susanjkelly@hotmail.com — BM BCh 1978 Oxf.; DPhil Oxf. 1976; FRCP Lond. 1995; MRCP (UK) 1981; FRCPath 1997, M 1987. (Oxf.) Cons. Haemat. Wycombe Gen. Hosp.

KELLY, Suzette Elizabeth South Staffordshire Health Authority, Mellor House, Corporation St., Stafford ST16 3SR — MB ChB 1991 Birm.; MPH 1996. Regist. (Pub. Health Med.) Dorset Health Commiss.,. Socs: Fell. Soc. Social Med.

KELLY, Teresa Hope Hospital, Stott Lane, Salford M6 8HD Tel: 0161 789 7373 — MB ChB 1988 Glas.; MRCOG 1993. Cons. (O & G) Hope Hosp. Salford. Prev: Specialist Regist. (O & G) Glas. Roy. Matern. Hosp.

KELLY, Timothy William Joseph (retired) 3 The Oaks, Wimbledon Hill Road, London SW19 7PB — LRCPSI 1973; LRCP & SI 1973; MSc Surrey 1981; FRCPath 1994, M 1982. Prev: Cons. Clin. Microbiol. Mayday Univ. Hosp. Thornton Heath.

KELLY, Trixie Baronsmere Road Surgery, 39 Baronsmere Road, East Finchley, London N2 9QD Tel: 020 8883 1458 Fax: 020 883 8854; 54 Vivian Way, London N2 0HZ Tel: 020 8883 7601 — MB BS 1959 Calcutta; DObst RCOG 1960. (Calcutta Med. Coll.) Prev: Med. Off. Kodak Ltd. Harrow.

KELLY, William Francis Tel: 01642 850850 Fax: 01642 854327; Gill House, Greta St, Saltburn-by-the-Sea TS12 1LS — MB BS 1972 Lond.; BSc (Hons.) Lond. 1969, MD 1984; FRCP Lond. 1989; MRCP (UK) 1975; MRCS Eng. LRCP Lond. 1972; FRCP Ed 1996. (St. Mary's) Cons. Phys. (Diabetes & Endocrinol.) Middlesbrough Gen. Hosp. Cleveland; Hon. Clin. Sen. Lect. (Med.) Univ. Newc.; Vis. Fell. Computing & Mathematics Univ. Teesside. Socs: Diabetes UK; Soc. for Endocrinol.; Assn. of Phys.s. Prev: Sen. Regist. Manch. Roy. Infirm.; Research Fell., Hon. Sen. Regist. & Regist. Hammersmith Hosp. Lond.

KELMAN, Colin George Shay Lane Medical Centre, Shay Lane, Hale, Altrincham WA15 8NZ Tel: 0161 980 3835 Fax: 0161 980 9215 Email: colin.kelman@gp-p91008.nhs.uk — MB ChB 1978 Manch.; BSc (Med. Sci.) St. And. 1975; DRCOG 1981; Cert. Family Plann. JCC 1980. Princip. in Gen. Pract., Doctors Rich, Kelman, Cranston; Professional Mem. of Exec. Comm., Trafford S. Primary Care Trust.

KELMAN, Jeannie Robertson 89 Buckstone Road, Fairmilehead, Edinburgh EH10 6UX Tel: 0131 445 4868 — MB ChB 1973 Aberd.; DMRD Ed. 1977. Clin. Asst. Peripheral Vasc. Clinic Roy. Infirm. Edin. Prev: Sen. Regist. (Radiol.) Roy. Infirm. Edin.; SHO (Med.) Edenhall Hosp. Musselburgh; Ho. Off. (Neurosurg.) Aberd. Roy. Infirm.

KELMAN, Lucy Royal Infirmary Of Edinburgh, 1 Lawriston Place, Edinburgh EH3 9YN Tel: 0131 536 3163; The Grange, Inverarity, Forfar DD8 2JN Tel: 01307 820333 — MB ChB 1998 Aberd.; MB ChB Aberd 1998. SHO (Sen. Ho. Off.) A & E Roy. Infirm. Of Edin. Prev: Pre-Regist. Ho. Off. Gen. Surg.

KELMAN, Margaret Barron Amber Cottage, Smithymoor, Stretton, Alfreton DE55 6FE — MB ChB 1989 Sheff.; MRCGP 1994.

KELNAR, Christopher John Harvey Royal Hospital for Sick Children, Sciennes Road, Edinburgh EH9 1LF Tel: 0131 5260611 Fax: 0131 536 0821 Email: chriskelnar@hotmail.com; 9 Easter Belmont Road, Edinburgh EH12 6EX Email: chris@kelnar.com — MB BChir 1973 Camb.; MA Camb. 1973, MD 1985; FRCP Ed. 1985; MRCP (UK) 1976; FRCPCH 1997; DCH Eng. 1975. (St. Bartholomews) Cons. (Paediat.) Roy. Hosp. Sick Childr. Edin.; Reader (Reproductive and Developm.al Sci.s) Univ. Edin. Socs: Eur. Soc. Paediat. Endocrinol.; Brit. Soc. Paediatric Endocrinol. & Diabetes; Endocrine Soc. (US). Prev: Sen. Regist. (Paediat.) Hosp. Sick Childr. Lond.; Research Fell. & Regist. (Paediat.) The Middlx. Hosp. Lond.; SHO (Neonat. Paediat.) Qu. Charlotte's Matern. Hosp. Lond.

KELPIE, Anthony George Cheviot Road Surgery, 1 Cheviot Road, Millbrook, Southampton SO16 4AH Tel: 01703 774040 Fax: 01703 702748 — MB BChir 1980 Camb.; BA Camb. 1976, MA 1980, BChir 1979; MRCGP 1984; DRCOG 1982; DCH (Eng.) 1981. (King's Coll.) Chairm. Out of Hours CoOperat. Prev: SHO (Psychiat.) Shelton Hosp. Shrewsbury; SHO/Trainee GP Shrewsbury VTS.

KELSALL, Anthony Wilfred Ross Neonatal Intensive Care Unit, Rosie Maternity Hospital, Box 226, Robinson Way, Cambridge CB2 2SW Tel: 01223 245853 Fax: 01223 217064 Email: wilf.kelsall@addenbrookes.nhs.uk; 26 Rathmore Road, Cambridge CB1 7AD — MB BChir 1986 Camb.; BSc (Hons.) Zool. St. And. 1981; FRCP 2001; Dip. Med. Sci. St. And. 1981; MRCP (UK) 1991; FRCPCH 1997. Cons. Paediat. Neonat. Rosie Matern. Hosp. Camb.; Hon. Cons. Paediatric Cardiol. Hosp. for Sick Childr., Gt. Ormond St., Lond. Socs: Program Director Paediatric Specialist Regist. Train. Anglian Deanery. Prev: Research Fell. (Neonat.) Rosie Matern. Hosp. Camb.; Regist. (Paediat.) Addenbrookes's Hosp. Camb.; SHO (Neonat.) Rosie Matern. Hosp. Camb.

KELSALL, David John (retired) 4 Avenue Road, St Albans AL1 3QQ Tel: 01727 850139 Email: d.kelsall@doctors.org.uk — MB BS 1955 Lond. Prev: GP St. Albans.

KELSALL, Janet Elderton Paediatric Department, Poole General Hospital NHS Trust, Longfleet Road, Poole BH15 2JB Tel: 01202 665511; Linden House, Dullar Lane, Sturminster Marshall, Wimborne BH21 4AD — MB ChB 1979 Bristol; MSc 2001 Warwick; MRCGP 1983; DCH RCP Lond. 1987. (Bristol) Cons. Community Paediat. Poole Gen. Hosp. NHS Trust. Socs: Fell. Roy. Coll. Paediat. and Child Health. Prev: SCMO (Community Paediat.) Poole Gen. Hosp. NHS Trust; Trainee GP Portishead Health Centre Bristol; Regist. (Community Paediat.) Child Health Unit Memor. Hse. Nottm.

KELSALL, Mary Elizabeth Department of Child Psychiatry, Royal Manchester Children's Hospital, Hospital Road, Pendlebury, Manchester M27 4HA Tel: 0161 794 4696 — MB ChB 1986 Sheff.; MRCPsych. 1990. Cons. Child Psychiat. Roy. Manch. Childr. Hosp. Prev: Sen. Regist. Rotat. (Child & Adolesc. Psychiat.) Manch.

KELSALL, Olivia Margaret 7 Mardale Crescent, Lymm WA13 9PA — MB ChB 1997 Manch.

KELSALL, Mr Richard Alan Marys Bridge Health Centre, Highfield Grange Avenue, Wigan WN1; 8 Elkwood Crescent, Beechwood, Whitley, Wigan WN1 2PD — MB ChB 1985 Liverp.; FRCS Eng. 1990.

KELSEY, Andrew Sean Charles Ramsey Group Practice Centre, Grove Mount South, Ramsey IM8 3EY Tel: 01624 813881 Fax: 01624 811921 — MB ChB 1975 Manch.; MRCGP 1984; DA (UK) 1982. (Manch.) GP I. of Man; Assoc. Specialist Anaesth. Ramsey Cottage Hosp. Prev: Regist. (Anaesth.) Raigmore Hosp. Inverness; SHO (Orthop. Surg.) Stockport Infirm.; SHO (Gen. Surg.) Stepping Hill Hosp. Stockport.

KELSEY, Anthea Mabel The Cottage, 7 Deer Park Lane, Tavistock PL19 9HB Tel: 01822 616171 — MB BS 1963 Lond.; MRCS Eng. LRCP Lond. 1963; MRCGP 1975. (Middlx.) BrE. Clinician Derriford Hosp. Plymouth. Prev: Regtl. Med. Off. Jun. Soldiers Bn.; Civil. Med. Pract. RAOC Depot Blackdown; Cas. Clin. Asst. Qu. Eliz. II Hosp. Welwyn Garden City.

KELSEY, Christopher Richard Rheumatology Unit, Oldchurch Hosptial, Romford RM7 0BE Tel: 01708 708367; 4 Wells Cottage, Cookham Dean Bottom, Cookham Dean, Maidenhead SL6 9AP — MB BS 1975 Lond.; BSc Med. Sci. St. And. 1972; MSc Lond. 1984; MRCP (UK) 1978; FRCP (UK) 1998. (Guy's Hospital & St. Andrews University) Cons. Rheum. OldCh. Hosp. & Harold Wood Hosp. Essex. Socs: Brit. Soc. Rheum. & Bone & Tooth Soc. Prev: Sen. Regist. Oxf. RHA.

KELSEY, Francis Derek (retired) White Cottage, Church Lane, Cley next the Sea, Holt NR25 7UD — BM BCh 1948 Oxf.; DPM Eng. 1955. Prev: Cons. Psychiat. Claybury Hosp.

KELSEY, Helen Clare Kettering General Hospital, Rothwell Road, Kettering NN16 8UZ Tel: 01536 492699 Email: helen.kelsey@kgh.nhs.uk — MB BS 1985 Lond.; BSc Lond. 1982; MRCP (UK) 1988; MRCPath 1995. p/t Cons. Haematologist, Kettering Gen. Hosp. Prev: Sen. Regist. (Haemat.) NW Thames RHA.

KELSEY, Ian Grant Bartongate Surgery, 115 Barton St., Gloucester GL1 4HR Tel: 01452 422944 — MB BS 1963 Lond.

KELSEY, Jocelyn Campbell (retired) c/o Daniel & Edwards, 44/46 Queen St., Ramsgate CT11 9EF — MD 1960 Camb.; MB BChir 1951; Dip. Bact. Lond 1955; FRCPath 1969, M 1963. Prev: Dep. Dir. Pub. Health Laborat. Serv.

KELSEY, Mr John Hugh (retired) 5 Northumberland Road, Barnet EN5 1EF Tel: 020 8449 0435 — MB BChir Camb. 1956; MA Camb. 1958; FRCS Eng. 1963; FRCOphth 1988; DO Eng. 1960. Prev: Cons. Ophth. Surg. Bloomsbury HA.

KELSEY, Michael Charles Department of Microbiology, Whittington Hospital, Highgate Hill, London N19 5NF Tel: 020 7288 5082 Fax: 020 7288 5009 Email: m.kelsey@whittington.thenhs.com — MB BS 1972 Lond.; FRCP Glas. 1995; MRCP (UK) 1975; MRCS Eng. LRCP Lond. 1972; FRCPath 1991, M 1979. Cons. Microbiol. Whittington Hosp. Lond.; Hon. Sen. Lect. Dept. Microbiol. UCL. Socs: Pres. Elect. Assn. Med.Microbiol. Prev: Cons. (Microbiol.) Barnet Gen. Hosp.; Sen. Regist. (Microbiol.) Univ. Coll. Hosp. Lond. & Whittington Hosp. Lond.

KELSEY, Paul Robert Department of Pathology, Victoria Hospital, Blackpool FY3 8NR Tel: 01253 306934 Fax: 01253 303675 — MB BS 1977 Lond.; MRCP (UK) 1979; MRCPath 1985. Cons. Haemat. Vict. Hosp. Blackpool.

KELSEY, Rachel Elizabeth Southern Debyshire Acute Hospitals NHS Trust, Derbyshire Royal Infirmary, London Road, Derby DE1 2QY Tel: 01332 347141 — MB ChB 1998 Leic.; MB ChB Leic 1998. SHO. Med. Rotat. Derby. NHS. Trust; Ho. Gen. Surg. Glenfield NHS Trust Leics. Socs: MPS; BMA; MSS. Prev: HO.Gen.Med.Leics.Gen.Hosp; Ho.Gen.med.Leics.Roy.Infirm.

KELSEY, Roger William 123 Westbrook Avenue, Westbrook, Margate CT9 5HE — MB BS 1972 Lond.; MRCGP 1976; DObst RCOG 1976. (Middlx.)

KELSEY, Russell James 24 Greenhill Avenue, Kidderminster DY10 2QU — MB BS 1984 Lond. Med. Adviser Social Security Med. Worcs. Prev: Med. Quality Manager Benefits Agency Med. Serv. Birm.; GP Auckland, NZ.

KELSEY, Sandra Julia Elizabeth Community Child Health Department, Royal Northern Infirmary, Inverness — MB ChB 1969 Sheff.

KELSEY, Stephen Michael Department of Haematology, St Bartholomews Hospital, 42-44 Little Britain, London EC1A 7BE Tel: 020 7601 8214 Fax: 020 7601 8215 Email: s.m.kelsey@mds.qmw.ac.uk; The Old House, Carmel St, Great Chesterfield, Saffron Walden CB10 1PH — MB ChB 1984 Birm.; MB ChB Birm. 1994; FRCP 1998; BSc (Hons.) (Pharmacol.) Birm. 1981, MD 1995; MRCPath 1993. Cons. & Sen. Lect. (Haemat.) St Bartholomews & the Roy. Lond. Sch. of Med. & Dent. Socs: BMA; Brit. Soc. Haematol.; Amer. Soc. Hematology. Prev: Sen. Regist. Roy. Lond. Hosp.; Hon. Lect. Lond. Hosp. Med. Coll.; SHO (Med.) Selly Oak Hosp. Birm.

KELSEY, Wendy Ann 301 Kingsbury Road, London NW9 9PE — MB BS 1966 Lond.; MRCS Eng. LRCP Lond. 1966. (Roy. Free Hosp. Sch. Med.) Prev: Asst. Resid. & Intern Mt. Auburn Hosp. Camb., Mass.

KELSHIKER, Amol Sharad Pinn Medical Centre, 8 Eastcote Road, Pinner HA5 1HF Tel: 020 8866 5766 Fax: 020 8429 0251 — MB ChB 1986 Sheff.

KELSHIKER, Ashok Ramesh c/o 223 Charlton Road, Kenton, Harrow HA3 9HT Tel: 0208 204 2686 Fax: 0208 204 5005 — MB ChB 1993 Manch.; DGM 1996; DCH 1996. GP, non Princip.; Clin. Asst. Dermat., N.wick Pk. Hosp. Harrow; Harrow E. & Kingsbury PCG Bd. Mem. Prev: GP Regist. Hillingdon Hosp. VTS; Trainee GP/SHO (c/o Elderly) Hillingdon Hosp. VTS.

KELSHIKER, Ramesh Yeshwant Charlton Medical Centre, 223 Charlton Road, Kenton, Harrow HA3 9HT Tel: 020 8294 2686; 212 Streatfield Road, Kenton, Harrow HA3 9BX Tel: 020 8204 2686 — LRCPI & LM, LRSCI & LM 1966; LRCPI & LM, LRCSI & LM 1966. (RCSI) Socs: BMA. Prev: SHO (Geriat. Med.) Barnes & Tolworth Hosps.; SHO (Accid., Emerg. & Orthop.) Whittington Hosp. Lond.

KELSHIKER, Sharad Yeshwant 177 Streatfield Road, Kenton, Harrow HA3 9B Tel: 020 8204 5561 — MB BS 1956 Lucknow; BSc, MB BS Lucknow 1956. (King Geo. Med. Coll.) Prev: Med. Off. King Geo. VI Hosp. Nairobi; Med. Off. i/c The Agakhan Health Servs. Iringa, Tanzania.

KELSO, Andrew Robert Christie 23/1 Dalgety Road, Edinburgh EH7 5UH Tel: 0131 652 1408 — MB ChB 1998 Ed.; MB ChB Ed 1998. (Edinburgh) SHO Gen. Med., Roy. Vict. Infirm., Newc. Prev: PRHO (Gen. Surg.) St. John's at Howden, Livingston; PRHO (Gen. Med.) Monklands D.G. Hosp., Aidrie.

KELSO, Ian James St. Quinton Health Centre, St. Quinton Avenue, London W10 6NY Tel: 020 8960 5677 Fax: 020 8968 5933 — MB ChB; MSc (Univ. Of Lond.). (Otago University, Dunedin, New Zealand) Gen. Pract.

KELSO, John Whittaker Leesbrook Surgery, Mellor Street, Lees, Oldham OL4 3DG Tel: 0161 621 4800 Fax: 0161 628 6717; Parkhill, 24 Burnedge Lane, Grasscroft, Oldham OL4 4EA — MB ChB 1970 Liverp.; DObst. RCOG 1972.

KELSO, Robin David Tel: 01327 359953 Fax: 01327 358929; Stone House, 15 Gayton Road, Eastcote, Towcester NN12 8NG Tel: 01327 830315 — MB BS 1969 Lond.; MRCS Eng. LRCP Lond. 1969; MRCGP 1974; DObst RCOG 1971. (St. Mary's) Sen. Med. Off. Towcester Racecourse; Med. Off. Marconi Towcester. Socs: BMA. Prev: Regist. (Med.) & SHO (Paediat. & O & G) Gen. Hosp. N.ampton.

KELSO, William (retired) 1 Badbury Court, Rushford Warren, Mudeford, Christchurch BH23 3NX Tel: 01202 473311 — MB ChB 1951 St. And.; FRCOG 1973, M 1960. Cons. (O & G) Stockport Health Dist. Prev: Sen. Regist. (O & G) United Manch. Hosps.

KELT, Christine Hilda Community Child Health Department, Stirling Royal Infirmary, Stirling FK8 2AU; 10 Cleuch Road, Stirling FK9 5EX — MB ChB 1970 Ed.; MRCGP 1986; MFFP 1993; DCCH RCP Ed. 1981; DObst RCOG 1972. Clin. Co-ordinator (Family Plann.) Forth Valley HB.

KELT, John David St Phillips Health Centre, Houghton Street, London WC2A 2AE Tel: 020 7955 7016 Fax: 020 7955 6818 — MB ChB 1971 Ed.; MPhil Glas. 1996; BSc Ed. 1968; MRCGP 1981; Dip. Forens. Med. Glas. 1990. (Ed.) Partner Health Serv. Lond. Sch. Economics. Socs: Brit. Assn. Sport & Med. Prev: GP Stirling; Med. Off. (Haemat.) Roy. Hosp. Sick Childr. Glas.

KELTY, Clive Johnston 3 Edgehill Road, Aberdeen AB15 5JG — MB ChB 1994 Glas.

KELVIN, Graeme Mount Farm Surgery, Lawson Place, Bury St Edmunds IP32 7EW Tel: 01284 769643 Fax: 01284 700833; Glencorse, 11 Birkdale Court, Fornham St. Martin, Bury St Edmunds IP28 6XF Tel: 01284 724474 Email: exuo@aol.com — MB BS 1978

Lond.; BSc (Hons.) Lond. 1975; MRCGP 1983; DRCOG 1983. (King's Coll. Hosp.) Health & Safety Exec. Approved Doctor for Asbestosis at Work & Ionising Radiat. Regulats.; Chairm. Suff. Doctors on Call GP Co-op. Prev: Clin. Asst. (Rheum.) W. Suff. Hosp. Bury St. Edmunds.

KELVIN, Martin (retired) 6 Crossways, Ladybrook Road, Bramhall, Stockport SK7 3NZ — MB ChB Glas. 1958; DObst RCOG 1960. Prev: Ho. Phys. Roy. Alexandra Infirm. Paisley.

KELVIN, Neil Brendan 142 Howard Road, Clarendon Park, Leicester LE2 1XJ — MB ChB 1998 Leic.; MB ChB Leic 1998.

KELVIN, Raphael George Brookside Family Consultation Clinic, 18d Trumpington Road, Cambridge CB2 2AH Tel: 01223 746001 Fax: 01223 746002; Tel: 01638 507632 — MB BCh 1984 Wales; MRCPsych 1992; DCH RCP Lond. 1988; DRCOG 1988. (Welsh National School of Medicine) Cons. Child & Adolesc. Psychiat. Prev: Clin. Lect. & Hon. Sen. Regist. (Child & Adolesc. Psychiat.) Univ. of Camb.; Welcome Trust Research Fell. (Child & Adolesc. Psychiat.); SHO & Regististrar (Psychiat.) Cambs. Train. Scheme.

KELWAY, Sally Pryor Fir Tree Cottage, White Chimney Row, Emsworth PO10 8RS — MB BS 1981 Lond.

KELYNACK, John Bradley The Hildenborough Medical Group, Tonbridge Road, Hildenborough, Tonbridge TN11 9HL Tel: 01732 838777 Fax: 01732 838297; The Old Cottage, Commor Road, Ightham, Sevenoaks TN15 9EB Tel: 01732 886935 Fax: 01732 882803 — MB BS 1969 Lond.; MRCS Eng. LRCP Lond. 1969; DCH Eng. 1972; DObst RCOG 1971. (Guy's) Prev: SHO (Paediat.) Roy. Alexandra Hosp. Sick Childr. Brighton; Resid. Obst., Ho. Surg. & Ho. Phys. Guy's Hosp. Lond.

KEMBALL, Gavin Andrew 15 Waterden Road, Guildford GU1 2AN — MB BS 1991 Lond.

KEMBALL, Heather Jane Rutherford House, Langley Park, Durham DH7 9XD Tel: 0191 373 1386 Fax: 0191 373 4288 — MB ChB 1988 Manch.; BSc (Med. Sci.) St. And. 1986; MRCGP 1993; DRCOG 1992. Prev: Trainee GP/SHO Rotat. Trafford Gen. Hosp. Manch.; Ho. Off. (Med.) Blackburn Roy. Infirm.; Trainee GP Horwich.

KEMBER, Malcolm John Barnet Enfield Haringey, Mental Health NHS Trust, Mental Health Unit, Chase Farm Hospital Site, The Ridgeway, Enfield EN2 8JL Tel: 0208 366 6600; 54 Firs Lane, London N21 3HX Tel: 020 8360 6950 — MB BS 1966 Lond.; MRCS Eng. LRCP Lond. 1966; FRCPsych 1996, M 1972; DPM Eng. 1970. (Univ. Coll. Hosp.) p/t Cons. Psychiat. Chase Farm Hosp. Enfield. Prev: Regist. Claybury Hosp. Woodford Bridge; 1st Asst. Roy. Free Hosp. Lond.; Med. Dir. Enfield Community Care NHS Trust.

KEMBER, Peter Gordon Radiology Department Torbay Hospital, Lawes Bridge, Torquay TQ2 7AA Tel: 01803 655620 Fax: 01803 655638 Email: peter.kember@sdevonhc-tr.swest.nhs.uk; Bartons, Stoop Cellar, Broadhempston, Totnes TQ9 6AX Tel: 01803 814029 — MB ChB 1988 Sheff.; MRCP (UK) 1992; FRCR 1995. Cons. Radiol. Torbay Hosp. Prev: Sen. Regist. & Hon. Clin. Tutor (Radiol.) Centr. Sheff. Hosps. & N.. Gen. Hosp. Trusts Sheff.; Fell.sh. (Musculoskeletal Radiol.) Leeds Gen. Infirm.

KEMBER, Selina May 32 Priory Road, Hampton TW12 2PD — MB BS 1986 Lond.; MRCGP 1991; DRCOG 1990; DCH RCP Lond. 1989.

KEMBLE, Harry Royston 8 The Paddock, Cowbridge CF71 7EJ Tel: 01446 773566 — MB BCh 1954 Wales; BSc Wales 1951; FFOM RCP Lond. 1990, MFOM 1978; DIH Eng. 1969. (Cardiff) Accredit. Specialist Occupat. Med. Socs: Soc. Occupat. Med.; Cardiff Med. Soc. Prev: Sen. Med. Off. Ford Motor Company S. Wales; Ho. Phys. & Ho. Surg. Morriston Hosp. Swansea.

KEMBLE, James Victor Harvey 27 Tor Bryan, Ingatestone CM4 9JZ — MA, MB Camb. 1963, BChir 1962; FRCS Eng. 1967; MRCS Eng. LRCP Lond. 1962. (Camb. & Guy's) Socs: Brit. Soc. Surg. Hand; Brit. Assn. Plastic Surg. Prev: Cons. Plastic Surg. Regional Plastic Surg. Centre St. And. Hosp. Billericay, Harold Wood Hosp. & OldCh. Hosp. Romford; Cons. Plastic Surg. St. Bart. Hosp. Lond.; Sen. Regist. Odstock Hosp. Salisbury & Hammersmith Hosp. Lond.

KEMENY, Mr Andras Department Neurosurgery, Royal Hallamshire Hospital, Glossop Road, Sheffield S10 2JF Tel: 0114 276 6222 Fax: 0114 276 5925 Email: a.kemeny@shef.ac.uk; Storm End, 1 Belgrave Road, Ranmoor, Sheffield S10 3LL Tel: 0114 230 2089 — MD 1977 Semmelweis; MD Sheff. 1991; FRCS Glas. 1987. Director, Nat. Centre for Stereotactic RadioSurg., Sheff.; Hon. Sen. Lect. Univ. Sheff. Socs: Soc. Brit. Neurol. Surgs. Prev: Cons. Neurosurg. Roy. Hallamsh. Hosp. Sheff.; Regist. (Neurosurg.) Roy. Hallamsh. Hosp. Sheff.; Sen. Regist. (Neurosurg.) St. Bart. Hosp. Lond. & OldCh. Hosp. Romford.

KEMM, Ian St John The Surgery, High Street, Ninfield, Battle TN33 9JP Tel: 01424 892569 Fax: 01424 893233 — MB ChB 1977 Sheff.

KEMM, John Robert Dept. Public Health, NHS Executive W. Mids Reg. Office, 142 Hagley Road, Birmingham B16 9PA Tel: 0121 224 4773 Fax: 0121 224 4680 Email: john.kemm@doh.gsi.gov.uk — MB Camb. 1969, BChir 1968; MD Camb. 1976; FRCP Lond. 1992; MRCP (UK) 1973; FFCM 1988, M 1982. (St. Thos. & Camb.) Cons. NHS Exec. W. Mids Reg. Office, Birm. Prev: Dir. Pub. Health, Health Promotion Wales; Sen. Lect. (Pub. Health Med.) Birm. Univ.; Cons. Pub. Health Med. S. Birm. HA.

KEMMERLING, Regina (retired) 23 Birchwood Drive, Leigh-on-Sea SS9 3LD — LRCP LRCS Ed. LRFPS Glas. 1943.

KEMP, Adrian Roy Siam Surgery, Sudbury CO10 1JH Tel: 01787 370444 Fax: 01787 880322; 7 Siam Place, Sudbury CO10 1JH Tel: 70444 — MB ChB 1982 Leic.

KEMP, Alice Mary (retired) 18 High Street, Kenton, Exeter EX6 8ND Tel: 01626 891079 — MRCS Eng. LRCP Lond. 1946. Prev: Assoc. specialist Ment. handicap Roy. W.on Counties Hosp. Stancross Devon.

KEMP, Alison Mary Department of Child Health, Academic Unit, Llandough Hospital, Penarth CF64 2XX Tel: 01222 716933 Fax: 01222 350140; 34 Western Road, Abergavenny NP7 7AD Tel: 01873 853831 — MB BCh 1981 Wales; MRCP (UK) 1989; DCH RCP Lond. 1987; FRCPCH 1997. Sen. Lect. (Child Health Community Paediat.) Univ. Wales Sch. Med. Prev: Sen. Regist. (Community Paediat.) Lansdowne Hosp. Cardiff.

KEMP, Anna Ruth (retired) Arden Cottage, Pomtantwn, Kidwelly SA17 5NA Tel: 01269 860382 — MB BS 1943 Lond.; MRCS Eng. LRCP Lond. 1942; DPM Eng. 1962; MRCOG 1956. Prev: Med. Asst. St. David's Hosp. Carmarthen.

KEMP, Anne Helen Bullock Fair Close Surgery, Bullock Fair Close, Harleston IP20 9AT Tel: 01379 853217 Fax: 01379 854082 — MB BS 1970 Lond.; MRCS Eng. LRCP Lond. 1970.

KEMP, Catherine Elizabeth 124 Walton Road, Chesterfield S40 3BU Tel: 01246 200907 — MB BChir 1987 Camb. p/t GP Derbysh. Prev: Trainee GP Chesterfield VTS.; SHO (Psychiat.) Chesterfield & N. Derbysh. Roy. Hosp.

KEMP, Catriona Ann Daisy Villa, South Ronaldsay, Orkney KW17 2SN; The Old Schoolhouse, Grimness, South Ronaldsay, Orkney KW17 2 TH — MB ChB 1990 Aberd.; DRCOG 1997; MRCGP 1996. Gen. Practitioner, S. Ronaldsay and Burray, Orkney Is.s.

KEMP, David Stuart The Surgery, 32 Clifton, York YO30 6AE Tel: 01904 653834 Fax: 01904 651442 Email: postmaster@gp-b82048.nhs.uk — MB BS 1973 Lond.; MRCGP 1981; DRCOG 1977. (St. Bart.) Clin. Asst. Chest Clinic York Dist. Hosp.; Med. Off. St. Peters Sch., York. Socs: Yorks. Med. Soc. & LMC. Prev: Regist. (Med.) N. Middlx. Hosp. Lond.

KEMP, Deborah Michele Gade Surgery, Gade House, 99b Uxbridge Road, Rickmansworth WD3 2DJ Tel: 01923 775291 Fax: 01923 711790; 101 Raglan Gardens, Oxhey, Watford WD19 4LJ — MB BS 1988 Lond.; MRCGP 1995; DFFP 1996; T(GP) 1995. (St. Mary's Hosp. Med. Sch.) GP Gade Surg. Rickmansworth; Clin. Asst. (Radiother. & Oncol.) Watford Gen. Hosp.; Co-Dir. Watford Doctors on Call (GP Co-op). Prev: Trainee GP Watford; SHO (O & G & Paediat.) Watford Gen. Hosp.; SHO (Radiother. & Oncol.) Mt. Vernon Hosp.

***KEMP, Emma Marie** 19 Shrubbery Road, Drakes Broughton, Pershore WR10 2AX — MB ChB 1997 Dundee.

KEMP, Evelyn Frances Dept. Occupational Health, John Radcliffe Hospital, Headington, Oxford OX3 9DU Tel: 01865 220799 Fax: 01865 220949 — MB BS 1985 Lond.; AFOM RCP Lond. 1996; Msc. Manch. 1998. (Univ. Coll. Hosp.) p/t Flexible Specialist Regist. (Occupat. Med.) John Radcliffe Hosp., Oxf. Socs: Soc. Occupat. Med. Prev: Sen. Regist. (Occupat. Med.) N. Manch. Gen. Hosp. & Stepping Hill Hosp. Stockport.

KEMP, Mr Ewan Graham (cons. rooms) 12 Barns Street, Ayr KA7 1XA Tel: 01292 260024 Fax: 01292 610522 Email:

ekemp@wghut nhs.org.uk; Creag Mhor, Auchendoon, Hollybush, Ayr KA6 7EB Email: egkemp@aol.com — MB ChB 1976 Glas.; FRCS Ed. 1982; FRCOphth 1988; DO Eng. 1980. (Glasgow) Cons. Ophth. Surg. Gartnavel Gen. Hosp. Glas.; Hon. Sen. Lect. (Ophth.) Univ. Glas. Socs: Eur. Soc. Ophthal. Plastic & Reconstruc. Surg.; BMA; EORTC Ophthal. Oncol. Gp. Prev: Cons. Ophth. Ayr Hosp.; Sen. Regist. Ninewells Hosp. Dundee; Fell. Moorfields Eye Hosp. Lond.

KEMP, Fiona Gay Royal Surrey County Hospital, Guildford GU2 7XX Tel: 01483 571122; Jarvis Breast Screening Centre, Stoughton, Guildford — MB BS 1989 Lond. SCMO & Clin. Asst. Roy. Surrey Co. Hosp. Prev: Trainee GP/SHO Roy. Surrey Co. Hosp. Guildford VTS.

KEMP, Graham John Department of Musculoskeletal, Royal Liverpool University Hospital, Liverpool L69 3GA Tel: 0151 706 4124 Fax: 0151 706 5815 Email: gkemp@liv.ac.uk — MB BCh 1980 Oxf.; MA Oxf. 1981, DM 1995; MRCPath 1996. Sen. Lect. & Hon. Cons. Clin. Chem. Roy. Liverp. Univ. Hosp. Socs: Assn. Clin. Biochem.; Biochem. Soc.; Soc. Magnetic Resonance. Prev: Clin. Lect. MRC Biochem. Clin. Magnetic Resonance Unit, John Radcliffe Hosp. Oxf.; Research Regist. (Human Metab. & Clin. Biochem.) Sheff.; Regist. (Chem. Path.) N.. Gen. Hosp. Sheff.

KEMP, Helen Quoybanks, St. Margarets Hope, Orkney KW17 2RH — MB ChB 1992 Ed.

KEMP, Helena Jane Department of Chemical Pathology, Southmead Hospital, Westbury on Trym, Bristol BS10 5NB Tel: 0117 950 5050 Fax: 0117 959 1792 — MB ChB 1990 Bristol; BSc Biochem. Bristol 1994; DRCPath 1995; MRCP 2000 Path. (Univ. Bristol) Sen. Regist. (Chem. Path.) S.mead Hosp. Bristol. Prev: Regist. (Chem. Path.) Bristol Roy. Infirm.; SHO (Gen. Path.) S.mead Hosp. Bristol.

KEMP, Mr Hubert (Hugh) Bond Stafford Private Consulting Rooms, Royal National Orthopaedic Hospital Trust, 45-51 Bolsover St., London W1W 5AQ Tel: 020 7383 5256 Fax: 020 7383 5107; Red Lodge, 55 Loom Lane, Radlett WD7 8NX Tel: 01923 854265 — MB BS 1949 Lond.; MS Lond. 1969; FRCS Eng. (ad eund.) 1976; FRCS Ed. 1960; MRCS Eng. LRCP Lond. 1947. (St. Thos.) Hon. Cons. Orthop. Surg. Nat. Orthop. Hosp. Lond. & Stanmore & Middlx. Hosp. Socs: Fell. BOA (Robt. Jones Gold Medal & Assn. Prize 1969); Brit. Orthop. Research Soc.; Emerit. Mem. Europ. Med. Surgic. Oncol. Soc. Prev: Cons. Orthop. Surg. Roy. Nat. Orthop. Hosp. Lond. & Stanmore & Middlx. Hosp.; Univ. Teach. Orthop. Roy. Nat. Orthop. Hosp. Lond.; Hon. Sen. Lect. (Orthop.) Inst. Orthop. Lond.

KEMP, Ian Charles Dr D J McNie and Partners, 4 St. Barnabas Road, Caversham, Reading RG4 8RA Tel: 0118 478123; 66 Northcourt Avenue, Reading RG2 7HQ Tel: 01189 751399 Email: docick@hotmail.com — MB BS 1974 Lond.; MRCP (UK) 1979; MRCGP 1979; DCH Eng. 1977; DRCOG 1976. (St. Geo.) GP Princip.; Hosp. Pract. (Gastroenterol.) Reading.; Bd. Mem. PCG. Prev: SHO (Med.) Roy. Berks. Hosp. Reading; SHO (O & G & Paediat.) Roy. Berks. Hosp. Reading.

KEMP, Ian Wilson 8 Frogston Terrace, Edinburgh EH10 7AD Tel: 0131 445 1194 — MD 1973 Ed.; MB ChB 1956; FFCM 1985, M 1979; DObst RCOG 1959; DSM Ed. 1968. Hon. Research Fell. (Cancer Registration & Cancer Epidemiol.) Scott. Home & Health Dept. Prev: SCM Informat. Servs. Div. Common Servs. Agency Edin.

KEMP, Judith Rosemary 47 Burney Street, Greenwich, London SE10 8EX — MB BS 1969 Lond.; MRCS Eng. LRCP Lond. 1969; MRCPath 1978. (Guy's Hosp.) Cons. Haemat. S. Lond. Blood Transfus. Serv. Prev: Cons. Haemat. Lewisham Hosp. Lond.; Sen. Regist. (Haemat.) King's Coll. Hosp. Lond.; Ho. Phys. (Paediat.) & Ho. Surg. (Orthop.) Guy's Hosp. Lond.

KEMP, Katherine Susan Anne Margarete Centre, Primary Care Unit, St James's House, 108 Hampstead Row, London NW1 2LS Tel: 020 7530 3233 Fax: 020 7530 3087; 168C Albion Road, Stoke Newington, London N16 9JS Tel: 020 7254 2255 — MB BS 1982 Lond.; MRCGP 1990; DRCOG 1990; DCH RCP Lond. 1990.

KEMP, Lindsey Isabel Priority House, Hermitage Lane, Barming, Maidstone ME16 9PH Tel: 01622 725000 Fax: 01622 723000; Tel: 01622 728370 Fax: 01622 721276 — MB ChB Dundee 1981; MRCPsych 1993; Cert. Family Plann. JCC 1984. (Dundee) Cons. Psychiat. Invicta Community Care NHS Trust. Prev: Sen. Regist. (Psychiat.) UMDS Higher Train. Scheme Guy's Hosp. Lond.; Regist. & SHO Rotat. (Psychiat.) Mid Kent; SHO (A & E) Maidstone Hosp. Kent.

KEMP, Marion Murchie — MB ChB 1978 Glas.; MRCPsych 1983. Cons. Garthavel Roy. Hosp., Glas.; Honarary Clin. Lect. Socs: Fell. of Roy. Soc. of Med. 2001. Prev: Sen. Regist. (Psychiat.) Gtr. Glas. HB.

KEMP, Michael Thomas Andrew Omagh Health Centre, Mountjoy Road, Omagh BT79 7BA Tel: 028 8224 3521 — MB BCh BAO 1975 Belf.

KEMP, Moyra Strachan Mortimer (retired) 17 Kepplestone Avenue, Aberdeen AB15 7XF Tel: 01224 317003 — MB ChB 1947 Aberd.; DPM Lond. 1952. Prev: Lect. Anat. Univ. Aberd.

KEMP, Naomi Melicent — MB BS 1985 Lond.; MA Camb. 1988, BA 1982; MRCGP 1990; DRCOG 1989. Prev: Trainee GP N. Lond.; SHO (O & G) Newham Gen. Hosp. Lond.; SHO (Paediat. & c/o the Elderly) Whipps Cross Hosp. Lond.

KEMP, Nigel Harvey Saul's Farm, Wembworthy, Chulmleigh EX18 7RW — MB BS 1955 Lond.; MB BS (Hons.) Lond. 1955; MRCP (UK) 1986; MRCS Eng. LRCP Lond. 1955. (Univ. Coll. Hosp.) Gibb Fell., Cancer Research Campaign; Dir., Sci. Dept. Cancer Research Campaign. Socs: Brit. Soc. Cell Biol.; Brit. Assn. Cancer Research. Prev: Sir Henry Wellcome Fell. Nat. Insts. Health Bethesda, U.S.A.; Regist. Blood Transfus. & Haematol. Dept. W.m. Hosp.; Sen. Research Fell. St. Geo. Hosp. Med. Sch. Lond.

KEMP, Paul Michael, MBE, Surg. Lt.-Cdr. RN Retd. Department Nuclear Medicine, Southampton General Hospital, Trenoma Road, Shirley, Southampton Tel: 02380 796200 Fax: 02380 796927 Email: p.kemp@suht.swest.nhs.uk; The Folly, North Weirs, Brockenhurst SO42 7QA — MB BS 1984 Newc.; MSc (Nuclear Med.) Lond. 1990; BSc Open 1993; DM Soton. 1994; BMedSc (Hons.) Newc. 1981. Cons. Nuclear Med. Soton. Gen. Hosp.; Hon. Sen. Lect. Soton. Univ. Socs: Brit. Nuclear Med. Soc.; Roy. Soc. Statisticians. Prev: Cons. Nuclear Med. Addenbrooke's Camb.; Cons. Nuclear Med. RNH Haslar; Hon. Lect. Camb. Univ.

KEMP, Peter Scott 38 Allen Road, Rainham RM13 9JX — MB BS 1994 Lond.

KEMP, Peter Wyndham Bullock Fair Close Surgery, Bullock Fair Close, Harleston IP20 9AT Tel: 01379 853217 Fax: 01379 854082 — MB BS 1970 Lond.; MRCS Eng. LRCP Lond. 1970; DObst RCOG 1976. (Char. Cross) Socs: BMA. Prev: Ho. Off. Char. Cross Hosp. Lond.

KEMP, Rachel Catherine 9 Rosa Road, Sheffield S10 1LZ — MB ChB 1998 Sheff.; MB ChB Sheff 1998.

KEMP, Mr Richard Ernest (retired) Red Lodge, 28 Circular Road, Newtownabbey BT37 0RF Tel: 01232 862828 — MB BCh BAO 1954 Belf.; FRCS Eng. 1958. Prev: Cons. Surg. NHSSB.

KEMP, Richard Timothy Burncross Surgery, 1 Bevan Way, Chapeltown, Sheffield S35 1RN Tel: 0114 246 6052 Fax: 0114 245 0276 — BM BS Nottm. 1987, BMedSci 1985; MRCGP 1991; DRCOG 1991; DCH RCP Lond. 1990.

KEMP, Roger John Pardons, East End Lane, Ditchling, Hassocks BN6 8UR Tel: 01273 844161 Fax: 01273 846961 Email: rogerkemp@dial.pipex.com — MB BS Lond. 1969. (Univ. Lond. & Middlx. Hosp. Lond.) Cons. Pharmaceut. Med. Hassocks. Socs: FFPM; Roy. Soc. Med.

KEMP, Rose Anne 147 Half Moon Lane, London SE24 9JY — MB BCh BAO 1985 NUI.

KEMP, Sarah Hannah Hamelin Cottage, Horn Hill Road, Adderbury, Banbury OX17 3EU — MB BS 1998 Lond.; MB BS Lond 1998.

KEMP, Simon Daisy Villa, South Ronaldsay, Orkney KW17 2SN; The Old School House, Grimness, South Ronaldsay, Orkney KW17 2TH — MB ChB 1990 Aberd.; MRCGP 1994; AFOM 1996. (Aberdeen University) Occupat. Phys.; Gen. Practitioner. Socs: Assoc. Mem. Fac. Occupat. Med.; Soc. Of Occupat.al Med.

KEMP, Simon Patrick Thomas Rugby Football Union, Rugby House, Rugby Road, Twickenham TW1 1DS Tel: 020 8892 6578 Fax: 020 8831 6721; 61 Southway, London NW11 6SB Tel: 020 8455 8777, 020 8946 4516 — MB BS 1986 Lond.; MA Camb. 1985; MRCGP 1993; Dip. Sports Med. 1992. Head of Sports Med. to Rugby Football Union; Sports Phys., Pk.side Hosp., Lond., SW19 5NX. Socs: Brit. Assn. Sport & Med.; Amer. Coll. Sports Med. Prev: Sports Phys. Fulham Football Club Lond.; Clin. Asst. Crystal Palace

Sports Injuries Clinic Nat. Sports Centre; Lect. (Sports Med.) Nottm. Univ.

KEMP, Stanley Wilson Yeovil District Hospital, Higher Kingston, Yeovil BA21 4AT — MRCS Eng. LRCP Lond. 1951; FFA RCS Eng. 1958; DA Eng. 1956; Cons. Anaesth. Yeovil Gen. Hosp.

KEMP, Thomas Michael Dewsbury District Hospital, Halifax Road, Dewsbury WF13 4HS; Carden, Wheelwright Drive, Dewsbury WF13 4JB — BM BCh Oxf. 1968; MRCP (UK) 1971; FRCP Lond. 1990. (St. Mary's) Cons. Phys. Dewsbury Dist. Hosp. Prev: Sen. Clin. Tutor (Med.) Fiji Sch. Med.; Sen. Regist. (Med.) St. Mary's Hosp. Lond.; Regist. (Med.) Radcliffe Infirm. Oxf.

KEMP, Trudi Jane Croydon Health Authority, Knollys House, 17 Addiscombe Road, Croydon CR0 6SR Tel: 020 8401 3789 Fax: 020 8401 3769 Email: trudi.kemp@croydon-ha.sthames.nhs.uk — MB ChB 1986 Leic.; MA (Med. Law & Ethics) Lond. 1991, MSc (Pub. Health) 1994; MFPHM 1997 London. Cons. Pub. Health Med. Croydon Health Auth. Socs: Soc. Social Med. Prev: Lect. Pub. Health Med. Univ. of Nottm.; Sen. Regist. (Pub. Health Med.) S. Thames RHA; Research Fell. Wellington Sch. of Med., New Zealand.

KEMPLE, Terence John Horfield Health Centre, Lockleaze Road, Horfield, Bristol BS7 9RR Tel: 0117 969 5391; Failand House, Ox House Lane, Lower Failand, Bristol BS8 3SL Tel: 01275 375690 Email: tk@elpmek.demon.co.uk — MB ChB 1975 Bristol; MRCP (UK) 1980; FRCGP 1993, M 1981; DCH Eng. 1978.

KEMPLEN, Anthony Michel Northern Avenue Surgery, 141 Northern Avenue, Sheffield S2 2EJ Tel: 0114 239 8686 Fax: 0114 253 1929; Cloonmore, 29 Meadowhead, Sheffield S8 7UA — MB ChB 1982 Sheff.; BA (Hons.) Sheff. 1995. Prev: Trainee GP Worksop VTS; Ho. Surg. N.. Gen. Hosp. Sheff.; Ho. Phys. Kilton Hosp. Worksop.

KEMPLEY, Stephen Terence Neonatal Unit, The Royal London Hospital, Whitechapel, London E1 1BB Tel: 020 7377 7000 Fax: 020 7377 7712 — MB BChir 1981 Camb.; MA Camb. 1983, MB BChir 1981; MRCP (UK) 1987; FRCP; FRCPCH. Cons. Neonat. Paediat. The Roy. Lond. Hosp. Socs: Neonat. Soc.; Brit. Assn. Perinatal Med.

KEMPSEY, Mr Eric Peter (retired) Wavecrest, 7 St Aidans, Seahouses NE68 7SR Tel: 01665 720605 — MB BS Lond. 1940; FRCS Eng. 1949; MRCS Eng. LRCP Lond. 1940. Prev: Cons. Gen. Surg. Ryhope Gen. Hosp. & Roy. Infirm. Sunderland.

KEMPSILL, Gillian Rachel Joan Flat 1/3, 69 Ashley St., Glasgow G3 6HW — MB ChB 1993 Glas.

KEMPSON, David Anthony Gloucestershire Royal Hospital, Great Western Road, Gloucester GL1 3NN — MB ChB 1988 Bristol. SHO (Anaesth.) Cheltenham Gen. Hosp.

KEMPSTER, Adam 11 Weavers End, Hanslope, Milton Keynes MK19 7PA — MB ChB 1998 Leeds.

***KEMPSTER, Stuart John,** Lt.-Col. RAMC Medical Reception Station, Ypres Road, Colchester CO2 7NL Tel: 01206 782947; Princely Cottage, 36 Blue Road, Tiptree, Colchester CO5 0TX — MB ChB 1976 Bristol.

KEMPSTON, Andrew Thomas 140 Antrim Road, Ballymena BT42 2JY — MB BCh BAO 1993 Belf.; DCH Dublin 1998. (Queens University Belfast)

KEMPTON, Barry Nigel Charles (retired) St. Alphage, Newbury Road, Lambourn, Hungerford RG17 7LL Tel: 01488 71401 Email: barry@kempton36.fsnet.co.uk — MB BS 1959 Lond.; MRCS Eng. LRCP Lond. 1959; DObst RCOG 1964. Prev: Ho. Surg. (ENT) Guy's Hosp Lond.

KEMSLEY, Susan Bilbrook Medical Centre, Brookfield Road, Bilbrook, Wolverhampton WV8 1DX Tel: 01902 847313 Fax: 01902 842322 — MB ChB 1993 Liverp.

KENCHINGTON, Noel Scott, OStJ (retired) Catesby, 10 North Road, Bromsgrove B60 2NP Tel: 01527 872219 — MRCS Eng. LRCP Lond. 1940. Prev: Capt. RAMC.

KENDAL, Ridley Yarrow Denton Park Health Centre, West Denton Way, West Denton, Newcastle upon Tyne NE5 2QZ Tel: 0191 267 2751 Fax: 0191 264 1588; 12 Highfield Road, Westerhope, Newcastle upon Tyne NE5 5HS Tel: 0191 271 1824 — MB BS 1967 Newc.

KENDALL, Anna Maria 15 Victoria Road, Teddington TW11 0BB — Artsexamen 1976 Utrecht; MRCGP 1987.

KENDALL, Anne Heather 54 Cross Deep Gardens, Twickenham TW1 4QU — BM BS 1996 Nottm.

KENDALL, Mr Brian Ernest High House, Hornbeam Lane, Sewardstonebury, London E4 7QT Tel: 020 7837 7660 — MB BCh BAO 1953 Dub.; FRCP Lond. 1974, M 1957; FRCS Lond. 1991; FFR RCSI (Hon.) 1990; FFR 1961; DMRD Eng. 1959. (TC Dub.) Cons. Radiol. Hosp. for Sick Childr., Middlx. Hosp. & Nat. Hosp. Neurol. & Neurosurg. Lond. Socs: Fell. Roy. Soc. Med.(Pres. Sect. Neurol.); (Pres.) Brit. Soc. Neuroradiol.; Brit. Inst. Radiol.

KENDALL, Brian Ross Department of Neurology, Leicester Royal Infirmary, Leicester LE1 5WW Tel: 0116 258 6630 — MB BS 1977 Lond.; MRCP (UK) 1980; MRCS Eng. LRCP Lond. 1977; MRCGP 1983; DRCOG 1981. (St. Bart.) Assoc. Specialist (Neurol.) Leicester Roy. Infirm. Prev: Research Asst. (Neurol) Leicester Roy. Infirm.; SHO (Neurol) Derbysh. Roy. Infirm; Ho. Off. St. Bart. Hosp. Lond.

KENDALL, Charles Henry Department of Pathology, Leicester Royal Infirmary, Leicester LE1 5WW — MB ChB 1975 Birm.; MRCPath 1987. Cons. Histopath. Leics. Roy. Infirm.

KENDALL, Christopher Neil Claremont Bank Surgery, Shrewsbury SY1 1RL — MB ChB 1980 Liverp.; MRCS Eng. LRCP Lond. 1980; MRCGP 1984; DRCOG 1983.

KENDALL, Clare Elizabeth 16 Sorrel Close, Thornbury, Bristol BS35 1UH Tel: 01454 419767 Fax: 01454 419767 Email: jason.kendall@cableinet.co.uk — MB ChB 1988 Birm.; ChB Birm. 1988; MRCGP 1992; DRCOG 1992; DCH RCP Lond. 1990. (Birmingham) Clin. Asst. (Palliat. Care) Cossham Hosp. Bristol.

KENDALL, David John The Health Centre, Whyteman's Brae, Kirkcaldy KY1 2NA Tel: 01592 641203 — MB ChB 1968 Ed. Prev: Ho. Off. Leith & E. Gen. Hosps. Edin. & Forth Pk. Matern. Hosp., Kirkcaldy; Surg. Lt. RN.

KENDALL, David John 1 Redmile Road, Nottingham NG8 5LH — BM BS 1995 Nottm.

KENDALL, Edith Patricia The Old Barn, Holystone, Sharperton, Morpeth NE65 7AJ — MB BS 1952 Durh.; DPH Newc. 1969. (Newc.)

KENDALL, Garry Peter Nigel Torbay Hospital, Lawes Bridge, Torquay TQ2 7AA Fax: 01803 655593 — MD 1987 Lond.; MB BS 1978; FRCP 1995; MRCP (UK) 1980. (Middlx. Hosp. Med. Sch.) Cons. Phys. Torbay Hosp. Torquay. Socs: Brit. Geriat. Soc.; Movement Disorders Soc.

KENDALL, Giles 2 Highfield Road, Bromley BR1 2JW — MB BS 1997 Lond.

KENDALL, Hilda Mary (retired) 1 The Hawthorns, Lutterworth LE17 4UL Tel: 01455 557620 — MB ChB Birm. 1945. Prev: Ho. Surg. Qu. Eliz. Hosp. Birm. & Birm. Matern. Hosp.

KENDALL, Mr Ian Geoffrey Accident & Emergency Department, Princess Margaret Hospital, Okus Road, Swindon SN1 4JU Tel: 01793 426574 Fax: 01793 426636 — BM 1981 Soton.; FRCS Ed. 1990; FRCS Eng. 1986; FFAEM 1993. Cons. A & E Swindon & MarlBoro. Hosps. Prev: Sen. Regist. (A & E) Leicester Roy. Infirm.; Regist. (A & E) Basingstoke Dist. Hosp.; Demonst. (Anat.) Univ. Soton.

KENDALL, Mr James Gordon Trewinnard, Whittington Road, Gobowen, Oswestry SY11 3ND — MB ChB 1944 Birm.; MRCS Eng. LRCP Lond. 1944; FRCS Eng. 1953. (Birm.) Med. Dir. Derwent Coll. for the Disabled, OsW.ry. Prev: Cons. Orthop. Surg. Cornw. Clin. Area; Sen. Regist P. of Wales Orthop. Hosp.; Maj. RAMC, Orthop. Specialist.

KENDALL, Jason Marc Accident and Emergency Department, Frenchay Hospital, Frenchay Park Road, Bristol BS16 1LE Tel: 0117 918 6544 Fax: 0117 918 6595 Email: frenchayed@cableinet.co.uk; The Old Forge, Redhill Lane, Elberton, Bristol BS35 4AE Tel: 01454 413334 Fax: 01454 413334 Email: jason.kendall@cableinet.co.uk — MB ChB 1988 Birm.; MD 1998; FFAEM 1998; Dip IMC RCS Ed. 1993; MRCP (UK) 1991. (Birm.) Cons. A & E Med. Frenchay Hosp. Bristol. Socs: BMA; BAEM; FAEM. Prev: Sen. Regist. (A & E Med.) Bristol Roy. Infirm.

KENDALL, John Crisp Chater (retired) 6 Park Crescent, Abingdon OX14 1DF Tel: 01235 520539 — MB BS 1951 Lond.; MRCS Eng. LRCP Lond. 1951. Prev: Med. Off. Abingdon Sch.

***KENDALL, Jonathan Barry** 14 Highland Road, Mansfield NG18 4PT — MB ChB 1994 Birm.

KENDALL, Julia Sarah Manel (retired) 6 Currie Hill Close, Wimbledon, London SW19 7DX Tel: 020 8944 8784 Fax: 020 8946 9038 — MB BS 1984 Lond.

KENDALL, Katriona Mary 5 Victoria Road, Sheffield S10 2DJ — MB ChB 1981 Sheff.; MRCPsych 1986. Lect. (Psychiat.) Univ. Sheff.

KENDALL, Keith Stanley Maylands Healthcare, 300 Upper Rainham Road, Hornchurch RM12 4EQ Tel: 01708 476411 Fax: 01708 620039 — MB BS 1984 Lond.

KENDALL, Marian Lucy (retired) 55 Pikemere Road, Alsager, Stoke-on-Trent ST7 2SN Tel: 01270 875212 — MB ChB Birm. 1938.

KENDALL, Professor Martin John Department of Medicine, Queen Elizabeth Hospital, Birmingham B15 2TH Tel: 0121 414 6874 Fax: 0121 414 1355 Email: m.j.kendall@bham.ac.uk; 12 Middle Park Close, Selly Oak, Birmingham B29 4BT Tel: 0121 475 6345 — MB ChB 1965 Birm.; MD Birm. 1971; FRCP Lond. 1982, M 1968; MRCS Eng. LRCP Lond. 1965. (Birm.) Prof (Clin. Pharmacol.) Qu. Eliz. Hosp. Birm.; Assoc. Dean Acad. Affairs Birm. Univ. Med. Sch; Mem. Comm. Safety Med; Chairm. Subcomm. Pharmacovigilance. CSM. Socs: Brit. Hypertens. Soc.; Brit. Pharm. Soc. Prev: Sen. Regist. (Med.) & Ho. Phys. Qu. Eliz. Hosp. Birm.; Regist. (Med.) N. Staffs. Hosp. Centre.

KENDALL, Nicholas — MB BS 1983; MFPHM 2001; BSc Lond. 1980; MSc (Med. Informatics) City Univ. 1992; MRCGP 1991; DRCOG 1990; DCH RCP Lond. 1990. Regist. (Pub. Health) S.E. Thames RHA.

KENDALL, Nigel David The Health Centre, Beach Avenue, Rhos, Wrexham LL14 1AA Tel: 01978 845955 — MB ChB 1988 Sheff.; MRCGP 1993. Prev: Trainee GP Doncaster VTS; Ho. Off. (Gen. Surg.) Doncaster Roy. Infirm. & Rotherham Dist. Gen. Hosp.; Ho. Off. (Gen. Med.) Doncaster Roy. Infirm.

KENDALL, Sandra The Middlesex Hospital, Department of Ortopaedic Surgery, Mortimer St., London W1T 3AA Tel: 020 7380 9037 Fax: 020 7380 9081; 30 Rowlands Road, South Yardley, Birmingham B26 1AS Tel: 0121 706 5324 Fax: 020 7380 9081 — MB BCh 1963 Wales. (Cardiff) Clin. Asst. Middlx. Hosp. Lond. Prev: Clin. Asst. Qu. Eliz. Hosp. Childr. Lond.

KENDALL, Mr Simon William Henry 5 High Green, Great Ayton, Middlesbrough TS9 6BJ Tel: 01642 854892 Fax: 01642 854613 — MB BS 1984 Lond.; MB BS Lond. 1986; MS Lond. 1995, BSc (Hons) 1981; FRCS (Cth) 1993; FRCS Ed. 1989. Cons. Cardiothoracic Surg. S. Cleveland Hosp. Prev: Sen. Regist. Papworth Hosp.; Research Fell. Duke Univ.; Sen. Regist. John Radcliffe Oxf.

KENDALL, Miss Susan Jane Holland — MB BS 1987 Lond.; PhD Lond. 1992; FRCS Eng. 1994. Regist. Rotat. (Orthop.) NW Thames. Prev: SHO (Gen. Surg. & Orthop.) Roy. Surrey Co. Hosp. Guildford.; Research Asst. (Surg.) Guy's Hosp. Lond.

KENDALL, Timothy James Greaves Community Health Sheffield, Lightwood House, Lightwood Lane, Sheffield S8 8BG Tel: 0114 271 8740 Fax: 0114 271 6695 Email: tim2.kendall@virgin.net; The Old School House, 5 Victoria Road, Sheffield S10 2DJ — MB ChB 1983 Sheff.; BMedSci 1980; MRCPsych 1988. (University of Sheffield) Cons. Psychiat. Community Health Sheff.; Co-Director, Nat. Collaborating Centre for Ment. Health; Assoc. Med. Director, Community Health Sheff. NHS Trust; Dep. Dir., Roy. Coll. Psychiat. Research Unit, Lond. Socs: Roy. Coll. Psychiat.; UKCP. Prev: Dir. & Hon. Cons. Psychiat. Centre for Psychother. Studies Univ. Sheff.; Lect. (Psychiat.) Univ. Sheff.

KENDALL, William Nigel Greaves (retired) The Garden House, Myddylton Place, Saffron Walden CB10 1BB Tel: 01799 26425 — MRCS Eng. LRCP Lond. 1951. Prev: Regional Med. Off. Min. Health & Sen Med. Off. Carver Barracks.

KENDELL, Judith North Reed Cottage Seaside, Errol, Perth PH2 7TA — MB BS 1991 Lond.

KENDELL, Neil Philip The Portmill Surgery, 114 Queen Street, Hitchin SG4 9TH Tel: 01462 434246 — MB ChB 1984 Leic.; DRCOG 1988. (Leicester)

KENDELL, Robert Evan, CBE The Royal College of Psychiatrists, 17 Belgrave Square, London SW1X 8PG Tel: 020 7235 2351 Fax: 020 7245 1231; 3 West Castle Road, Edinburgh EH10 5AT Tel: 0131 229 4966 — MB BChir Camb. 1960; MD Camb. 1967; FRCP Ed. 1977; FRCP Lond. 1974, M 1962; Hon. FRCS Ed. 1995; Hon. FRCPS Glas. 1995; LMSSA Lond. 1959; FRCPsych 1979, M 1971; DPM (Distinc.) Lond. 1965. Pres. Roy. Coll. Psychiat.; Mem. WHO Expert Advis. Panel on Ment. Health. Socs: Fell. Roy. Soc. Edin.; Fell. Acad. Med. Sci. Prev: Chief Med. Off. Scott. Off. DoH; Reader (Psychiat.) Inst. Psychiat. Lond.; Prof. Psychiat. Univ. Edin.

KENDERDINE, Arthur Richard (retired) 16 Southville Gardens, Kingsbridge TQ7 1LE Tel: 01548 857275 — MB ChB Birm. 1943; MRCS Eng. LRCP Lond. 1943. Prev: GP Coventry.

KENDLE, Gloria 9 Dalesman Close, Kingswinford DY6 9DF — MB BCh BAO 1973 Belf.

KENDRA, James Royston Department of Pathology, Burnley General Hospital, Burnley BB10 2PQ Tel: 01282 474314; 43 Reedley Drive, Reedley, Burnley BB10 2QZ — MB 1975 Camb.; BChir 1974; FRCP Lond. 1994; MRCP (UK) 1977; FRCPath 1993, M (Haemat.) 1981. Cons. Haemat. Burnley Gen. Hosp.

KENDREW, Allan, Squadron Ldr. RAF Med. Br. 15 Halstead Road, Harrogate HG2 8BP — MB ChB 1970 Liverp.; MRCS Eng. LRCP Lond. 1970; MRCOG 1976, DObst 1972. Specialist O & G P.ss Mary's Hosp. Halton; Hon. Regist. (Obst. & Gyn.) Roy. Bucks. Hosp. & Stoke Mandeville Hosp.

KENDREW, Jonathan Mark Satis House, Upper Stroke, Rochester ME3 9TB — MB BS 1996 Lond. (University College London Medical School) SHO (Orthop. Surg.), PeterBoro. Dist. Hosp.

KENDREW, Mary Elizabeth (retired) c/o 14 Conesford Drive, Bracondale, Norwich NR1 2BB Tel: 01603 492674 — MB BChir 1950 Camb. Prev: GP Seaford.

KENDRICK, Professor Anthony Robert Primary Medical Care, University of Southampton, Aldermoor Health Centre, Southampton SO16 5ST Tel: 02380 241050 Fax: 02380 701125 Email: ark1@soton.ac.uk — MB BS 1981 Lond.; FRCPsych 2001; 2000 M; BSc Med. Sci. & Psychol. Lond. 1978, MD 1996; FRCGP 1997, M 1985; DCH RCP Lond. 1984; DRCOG 1983. (St. Geo.) Prof. (Primary Med. Care) - Director, Div. of Community Clin. Sci.; GP Soton. Socs: Soc. for Acad. Primary Care; Internat. Soc. for Affective Disorders; Sec., Heads of Dept.s Gp. Prev: Sen. Lect. St. Geo.'s Lond.; GP Weybridge; Reader Univ. of Lond.

KENDRICK, Claire Helen The Health Centre, Station Approach, Bradford-on-Avon BA15 1DQ Tel: 01225 866611; 7 Frankley Terrace, Bath BA1 6DP Tel: 01225 447026 — MB BS 1989 Newc.; MRCP Glas. 1992; DRCOG 1995.

KENDRICK, Denise Newthorpe Medical Practice, Eastwood Clinic, Nottingham Road, Eastwood, Nottingham NG16 3GL Tel: 01773 760202 Fax: 01773 710951 — BM 1984 Soton.; BM Soton 1984; MFPHM RCP (UK) 1992; MRCGP 1988; DRCOG 1987; DCH RCP Lond. 1986. Lect. (Pub. Health Med. & Epidemiol.) Univ. Nottm.

KENDRICK, Richard George Mason The Old Rectory, Scaldwell, Northampton NN6 9JS — MB BS 1976 Lond.; MRCS Eng. LRCP Lond. 1974; DMRD Eng. 1979; FRCR 1981. (Roy. Free) Cons. Radiol. N.ampton Gen. Hosp. Prev: Sen. Regist. (Radiol.) W.m. & Brompton Hosps.; Regist. (Radiol.) Plymouth Gen. Hosp.; Ho. Surg. Roy. Free Hosp. Lond.

KENDRICK, Richard William 42 Greystown Park, Belfast BT9 6UP — MB BCh BAO 1977 Belf.; FDS RCPS Glas. 1980; FFD RCSI 1980. Cons. Oral Surg. N.I. Plastic & Maxillo Facial Serv. Ulster Hosp. N.I. & Roy. Vict. Hosp. Belf.

KENEALY, Mr John Myles Department of Plastic Surgery, Frenchay Hospital, Bristol Road, Bristol BS16 1LE Tel: 0117 970 1212 Fax: 0117 956 9171; BUPA Hospital Bristol, The Glen, Redland Hill, Durdham Down, Bristol BS6 6UT Tel: 0117 973 2562 — MB ChB 1982 Otago; FRACS (Plast & Reconstr. Surg.) 1990. Cons. Plastic Surg. Frenchay Hosp. Bristol. Socs: BMA; Brit. Assn. Plastic Surg.; Brit. Assn of Aesthetic Plastic Surg.s.

KENEFICK, Mr John Stanislaus (retired) The Dutch Cottage, 125 Totteridge Lane, London N20 8NS — MB BCh BAO 1960 NUI; MCh NUI 1965; FRCS Eng. 1965; FRCS Ed. 1964. Cons. Surg. Barnet Gen. Hosp. Prev: Sen. Regist. Roy. Free Hosp. Lond.

KENI, Manjusha 99 Whitchurch Lane, Edgware HA8 6NZ — MB ChB 1993 Birm.

KENI, Niyati 99 Whitchurch Lane, Edgware HA8 6NZ — MB BS 1992 Lond.

KENICER, Karol James Anthony Department of Dermatology, Ninewells Hospital and Medical School, Dundee — MB ChB 1970 Glas.; MRCP (UK) 1976. Cons. Dermat. Tayside Health B.

KENICER, Margaret Brown 14 St Fort Road, Wormit, Newport-on-Tay DD6 8LA — MB ChB 1970 Glas.; MFPHM 1989. Cons. Pub. Health Med. Tayside HB.

KENIG, Maurice 6 Bentinck Mansions, Bentinck St., London W1M 5RJ Tel: (20) 7935 3888 — LRCP LRCS 1936 Ed.; MD Montpelier 1933; LRCP LRCS Ed. LRFPS Glas. 1936. (Montpelier &

Lond. Hosp.) Socs: BMA. Prev: Phys. French Hosp. Lond. & French Consulate-gen. Lond.; Med. Off. Air France; Sen. Regist. Civil Hosp. Toulon.

KENN, Christopher William South West London & St George's NHS mental health trust, Kew Foot Road, Richmond TW9 2TE Tel: 020 8940 3331 — MB ChB 1977 Birm.; MMedSc Leeds 1985; MRCPsych 1984; DRCOG 1980; FRCPsych 1996. Cons. Psychiat. Roy. Hosp. Richmond. Prev: Cons. Psychiat. Lynfield Mt. Hosp. Bradford.

KENNA, Anthony Philip (retired) 36 Towers Avenue, Newcastle upon Tyne NE2 3QE — MB ChB Liverp. 1961; FRCP Lond. 1978, M 1965; DCH Eng. 1963; FRCPCH 1997. Clin. Lect. Dept. Child Health Univ. Newc. upon Tyne. Prev: Cons.Paediat.New.Gen.Hosp.

KENNA, Josephine (retired) 36 Towers Avenue, Newcastle upon Tyne NE2 3QE — MB ChB Liverp. 1961. Clin. Med. Off. N.d. AHA. Prev: Cas. Regist. Roy. Liverp. Childr. Hosp.

KENNAIR, Philomena Walnut Place Surgery, 1 Walnut Place, Montagu Estate, Newcastle upon Tyne NE3 4QS Tel: 0191 285 3816; Ashville, 18 Station Road, Benton, Newcastle upon Tyne NE12 9NQ Tel: 0191 270 0497 — MB BS 1966 Durh.; MRCGP 1978. (Newc.)

KENNAIRD, David Lambert Woodlands, Lustleigh, Newton Abbot TQ13 9TE Tel: 01647 277250 — PhD Lond. 1971; MB ChB Sheff. 1962; FRCP Lond. 1983; MRCP Lond. 1967; DCH Eng. 1966; FRCPCH 1997. (Sheff.) Cons. Paediat. Exeter & Torbay Health Dists. Socs: Neonat. Soc. & Brit. Paediat. Assn. Prev: Sen. Regist. Guy's Hosp. Lond.; Ho. Phys. & Ho. Surg. Roy. Infirm. Sheff.; Lect. (Paediat.) Lond. Hosp. Med. Coll.

KENNAIRD, Luba Woodlands, Lustleigh, Newton Abbot TQ13 9TE — MB ChB Sheff. 1963. (Sheff.) Med. Off. Exeter Health Dist. Socs: BMA. Prev: Med. Off. Lond. Boro. Lewisham.

KENNAN, Eamonn The Health Centre, Prince Consort Road, Gateshead NE8 1NB Tel: 0151 733 7172 — MB BCh BAO 1981 NUI; MRCGP 1986.

KENNAN, Nuala Maire 24 New Walk, Beverley HU17 7DJ — MB BCh BAO 1982 NUI.

KENNARD, Professor Christopher Division of Neuroscience and Psychological Medicine, Imperial College School of Medicine, Charing CrossCampus, London W6 8RF Tel: 020 8846 7598 Fax: 020 8846 7715 Email: c.kennard@icac.uk — MB BS 1970 Lond.; PhD Lond. 1979, BSc (Anat.) 1967; FRCP Lond. 1988; MRCP (UK) 1972; MRCS Eng. LRCP Lond. 1970. (Char. Cross) Prof. Clin. Neurol. Imperial Coll. Sch. Med. Lond.; Chairm. & Head, Div. Neurosci. & Psychol. Med., ICSM; Clin. Dir. (Neurosci.) Hammersmith Hosps. NHS Trust; Hon. Cons. Neurol. Char. Cross Hosp.; Chairm. RCP Comm. Neurol.; Edr. Jl. Neurol., Neurosurg. & Psychiat. Socs: Fell. Roy. Soc. Med.; (Counc.) Europ. Neurol. Soc.; (Counc.) Assn. Brit. Neurol. Prev: Cons. Neurol. Lond. Hosp. & Newham HA; MRC Jun. Research Fell. Nat. Inst. Med. Research Mill Hill; Sen. Regist. (Neurol.) Lond. Hosp.

KENNARD, Donald Arthur (retired) Hill Crest, The Park, Thurgarton, Nottingham NG14 7HA Tel: 01636 830699 Email: donald@dkennard.fsnet.co.uk — MB BS 1955 Lond.; MRCS Eng. LRCP Lond. 1955. Prev: Receiv. Room Off. Lond. Hosp.

KENNAUGH, Alec James Fairhill Medical Practice, 81 Kingston Hill, Kingston upon Thames KT2 7PX Tel: 020 8546 1407 Fax: 020 8547 0075 — MB BS 1975 Lond.; MRCGP 1980; DA Eng. 1978.

KENNAWAY, Christina Veronica Combe Down House Surgery, Combe Down House, The Avenue, Combe Down, Bath BA2 5EG Tel: 01225 832226 Fax: 01225 840757; Devonshire Cottage, 70 Wellsway, Bath BA2 4SB Tel: 01225 424441 Fax: 01225 424441 — MB ChB Cape Town 1958; MRCGP 1980. GP. Socs: BMA; RCGP.

KENNEA, Nigel Leonard 1 Monteagle, Summerhouse Road, Godalming GU7 1QA Email: n.ykennea@btinternet.com — BChir 1992 Camb.; BA (Hons) Cantab 1990; MB BChir Camb 1992. (Cambridge) Specialist Regist. Paediat., Neonatology, St. Geo.'s Hosp., Lond. Socs: MRCP; MRCPCH.

KENNEDY, Adele 15 Junction Road, Randalstown, Antrim BT41 4NP — MB BCh BAO 1992 Belf.; MB BCh Belf. 1992.

KENNEDY, Aldon 50 Gibson Street, Glasgow G12 8NW; 631 Alexandra Parade, Glasgow G31 3BX Tel: 0141 554 3103 — MB ChB 1994 Glas. (Glas.) SHO (Anaesth.) Monklands Dist. Gen. Hosp. Airdrie. Socs: Assn. Anaesth.; Scott. Soc. of Anaesth.; W Scotl. Anaesth. Soc. Prev: SHO (A & E) Roy. Infirm. Glas.; Ho. Off. (Gen. Med.) Vict. Infirm. Glas.; Ho. Off. (Gen. Surg.) W.. Infirm. Glas.

KENNEDY, Alexander (retired) 16 Brincliffe Gardens, Sheffield S11 9BG Tel: 0114 255 7920 — MB ChB 1956 Liverp.; MD Liverp. 1964; FRCPath 1984, M 1966. Prev: Cons. Histopath. N.. Gen. Hosp. NHS Trust Sheff.

KENNEDY, Alexander Shearer Lovat (retired) Murrayfield, 34 James St., Pittenween, Anstruther KY10 2QN Tel: 01333 310194 — MB ChB Glas. 1949; DPH Glas. 1958; DObst RCOG 1955. Prev: Ho. Phys. & Sen. Res. W.. Infirm. Glas.

KENNEDY, Andrew Gerard Croft Medical Centre, Calder Walk, Leamington Spa CV31 1SA Tel: 01926 421153 — MB ChB 1977 Birm.

KENNEDY, Angus Michael David Department of Neurology, Chelsea & Westminster Hospital, 369 Fulham Road, London SW10 9NH Tel: 020 8746 8320 Fax: 020 8846 7872; The Camp Farm, Cayn Ham, Ludlow SY8 3BN — MD 1994; MB BS Lond. 1985; MRCP 1988. Cons. Neurol. Char. Cross, Chelsea & W.m. Hosp. Lond.

KENNEDY, Ann-Maree Bonny View, Lower Auchenwreath, Speybay, Fochabers IV32 7PS — MB ChB 1998 Aberd.; MB ChB Aberd 1998.

KENNEDY, Anne Julie Campbell Racecourse Road Surgery, 3 Racecourse Road, Ayr KA7 2DF Tel: 01292 886622 Fax: 01292 614303; Clova Lodge, 54 Midton Road, Ayr KA7 2SQ Tel: 01292 610458 — MB ChB 1980 Glas.; DRCOG 1982.

KENNEDY, Arthur Colville, CBE (retired) 16 Boclair Crescent, Bearsden, Glasgow G61 2AG Tel: 0141 942 5326 — FRSE 1984; Hon. FACP 1988; MD Glas. 1956, MB ChB 1945; FRCPI 1988; FRCP Lond. 1977, M 1972; FRCP Glas. 1964, M 1962; FRCP Ed. 1960, M 1951; FRFPS Glas. 1949; Hon. FRACP 1988; Hon. FACP 1987. Prev: Muirhead Prof. Med. Roy. Infirm. Glas.

KENNEDY, Brian William 18 Blairforkie Drive, Bridge of Allan, Stirling FK9 4PH — MB ChB 1983 Ed.; FFA RCSI Dub. 1989; DA Eng. 1991. Cons. Anaesth. Roy. Infirm. Stirling. Prev: Sen. Regist. (Anaesth.) W.. Infirm. Glas.

KENNEDY, Bryan Ross, TD Upper BalBlair, Midmar, Sauchen, Inverurie AB51 7NA Tel: 013303 487 — MB ChB 1960 Aberd.; FFA RCS Eng. 1964. (Aberd.) Cons. Anaesth. Aberd. Roy. Infirm.; Maj. RAMC T & AVR. Socs: Assn. Anaesths. Prev: Lect. in Anaesth. Welsh Nat. Sch. Med.; Sen. Regist. Anaesth. United Cardiff Hosps.; Lect. in Anat. Univ. Aberd.

KENNEDY, Caitriona Mary Marsh, Kennedy, Phipps, Chapman and Wilde, Netherfield Medical Practice, 2A Forester Street, Netherfield, Nottingham NG4 2NJ Tel: 0115 940 3775 Fax: 0115 961 4069 — MB BCh BAO 1986 Belf.

KENNEDY, Cameron Thomas Campbell Bristol Royal Infirmary, Marlborough St., Bristol BS2 8HW Tel: 0117 928 2520 Fax: 0117 928 2845; 16 Sion Hill, Clifton, Bristol BS8 4AZ Tel: 0117 974 1935 Fax: 0117 928 2845 Email: cameron.kennedys@btinternet.com — MB BChir 1971 Camb.; MA Camb. 1972; FRCP Lond. 1986; MRCP (UK) 1973. (Cambridge and University College Hospitals London) Cons. Dermatol. Bristol Roy. Infirm., Bristol Childr.'s Hosps. & S.mead Hosp. W.bury-on-Trym. Socs: Fell. Roy. Soc. Med. (Mem. Dermat. Sect.).; Brit. Soc. Paediat. Dermat.; Brit. Assn. Dermat. Prev: Sen. Regist. (Dermat.) St. Geo.'s Hosp. Lond.; Regist. (Dermat.) Lond. Hosp.; SHO (Med. & Chest Dis.) Whittington Hosp. Lond.

KENNEDY, Carol 107 Walkley Crescent Road, Walkley, Sheffield S6 5BA — MB ChB 1988 Sheff.

KENNEDY, Charles Cotton (retired) The Garden House, Netherbury, Bridport DT6 5NB — MRCS Eng. LRCP Lond. 1944; MA Oxf. 1946, DM 1954, BM BCh 1947; LMCC 1948; FRCPath 1966, M 1964. Prev: Cons. Clin. Path. Belf. City Hosp.

KENNEDY, Charles Oliver (retired) 49 Stokes Court, Diploma Avenue, East Finchley, London N2 8NX — MB ChB Glas. 1944; BSc Glas. 1941; FFHom 1966. Prev: Lect. Fac. Homoeop. Lond.

KENNEDY, Charles Richard 21 The Arboretum, Gibbet Hill, Coventry CV4 7HX Tel: 024 76 418889 Email: 100105.1135@compuserve.com — MB ChB 1976 Dundee; MRCOG 1982; T(OG) 1991. Dir. of Research & Developm. Walsgrave Hosps. NHS Trust.

KENNEDY, Colin George, Wing Cdr. RAF Med. Br. Retd. (retired) The New Surgery, 106 High Street, Tring HP23 4AF Tel: 01442

890661 — MB BS 1977 Newc.; MSc Lond. 1995; MRCGP 1983; DAvMed FOM RCP Lond. 1987; DRCOG 1983; FRCGP 1997. Prev: Adviser Gen. Pract. (RAF).

KENNEDY, Mr Colin Leslie The Grange Farmhouse, Tustock Road, Beyton, Bury St Edmunds IP30 9AG — MB BS 1971 Lond.; FRCS Eng. 1976; MRCS Eng. LRCP Lond. 1971. (Lond. Hosp.) Cons. Urol. W. Suff. HA. Socs: Brit. Assn. Urol. Surg. Prev: Sen. Regist. (Urol.) St. Mary's Hosp. & Roy. Marsden Hosp. Lond.; Sen. Regist. (Surg.) Roy. Free Hosp. Lond.; Regist. Hammersmith Hosp. & Roy. Postgrad. Med. Sch. Lond.

KENNEDY, Cornelius Patrick Islington House, 3 Islington Square, Liverpool L3 8DD — MB BCh BAO 1953 Belf.

KENNEDY, Daniel Benjamin James 2 Raygill Cottages, Lothersdale, Keighley BD20 8HH — MB ChB 1988 Leic.

KENNEDY, Daniel David Mary 299 Manor Road, London E15 3AW — MB BCh BAO 1990 NUI; FRCA 1996. Specialist Regist. (Anaesth.) Roy. Hosps. NHS Trust. Socs: BMA; Assn. Anaesth.

KENNEDY, David (retired) 9 Brougham Hall Gardens, Brougham, Penrith CA10 2DB — MB ChB 1955 Glas.; MRCPsych 1971; DPM Ed. & Glas. 1964; DPH Glas. 1960. Prev: Cons. Psychiat. Crichton Roy. Hosp. Dumfries.

KENNEDY, David Duncan (retired) 1 Utterby Drive, Grimsby DN34 4UA — MB ChB 1961 Bristol; FRCPath 1980, M 1968. Prev: Cons. Chem. Path. NE Lincs., Scunthorpe & Lincoln Louth NHS Trusts.

KENNEDY, David John Grant Peterhead Group Practice, The Health Centre, Peterhead AB42 2XA Tel: 01774 474841 Fax: 01774 474848; 6 New Block, Harbour St, Cruden Bay, Peterhead AB42 7NB Tel: 01779 812479 — MB ChB 1986 Glas.; MRCGP 1991; DRCOG 1992. Mem. LMC (GP Sub Comm.).

KENNEDY, David McMaster 30 Grange Avenue, Ballymena BT42 2DX Tel: 01266 6167 — MB BCh BAO 1942 Belf. (Belf.) Prev: Ho. Surg. & Ho. Phys. Merthyr Gen. Hosp.; Ho. Surg. Roy. Infirm. Bristol; Regtl. Med. Off. RAMC.

KENNEDY, Deborah Michelle 5 Straws Hadely Court, Lower End, Wingrave, Aylesbury HP22 4PG — MB ChB 1992 Sheff.

KENNEDY, Denise Jane Department of Anaesthesia, Addenbrooke's NHS Trust', Cambridge CB2 2QQ Tel: 01223 217434 Fax: 01223 217223; 30 High Street, Orwell, Royston SG8 5QN Tel: 01223 207808 Fax: 01223 207167 — MB ChB 1975 Leeds; FFA RCS Eng. 1983. Cons. Anaesth. Addenbrooke's Hosp. Camb. Socs: Assn. Anaesth. Prev: Sen. Regist. & Regist. (Anaesth.) Addenbrookes Hosp. Camb.; SHO (Gen. Med.) P.ss Margt. Hosp. Nassau Bahamas.

KENNEDY, Dermot Hugh Michael Infection,Tropical Medicine & Counselling Service, Gartnavel General Hospital, Gt Western Road, Glasgow G12 0YN Tel: 0141 211 0294 Fax: 0141 211 1097; 81 Randolph Road, Glasgow G11 7DU Tel: 0141 357 1100 — MB ChB 1968 Glas.; FRCP Glas. 1987; MRCP (UK) 1975; DObst RCOG 1970. (Glas.) Cons. Phys. (Infec. Dis.) Gartnavel Gen. Hosp.; Hon. Clin. Lect. Univ. Glas.; Hon. Sen. Clin. Lect. Univ. Glas. Socs: Brit. Soc. Infec. Prev: Lect. (Epidemiol. Infec. Dis.) & Hon. Sen. Regist. Univ. Glas.; Lect. (Infec. Dis.) & Hon. Regist. Univ. Glas.; Post Doctoral Fell. Yale Univ. Comm.

KENNEDY, Dolores Colette Mary Department of Radiology, Lewisham Hospital NHS Trust, Lewisham High St., London SE13 6LH Tel: 020 8333 3000 — MB BCh BAO 1981 NUI; MRCPI 1985; LRCPSI 1981; FRCR 1989. (Royal College of Surgeons in Ireland) Cons. Radiol. Lewisham Univ. Hosp. NHS Trust Lond. Prev: Sen. Regist. (Radiol.) Middlx. Hosp. Lond.; Regist. (Radiol.) Middlx. Hosp. Lond.; SHO (Chest Med.) Lond. Chest Hosp.

KENNEDY, Dorothy Joan (retired) 5 Dame School Court, Pook Lane, East Lavant, Chichester PO18 0SA Tel: 01243527621 — MRCS Eng. LRCP Lond. 1938; MRCS Eng., LRCP Lond. 1938. Prev: Res. Biochem. & Diabetic Ho. Phys. King's Coll. Hosp.

KENNEDY, Douglas Hay 3 Fen Road, Heighington, Lincoln LN4 1JL — MB ChB 1979 Aberd.

KENNEDY, Douglas Samuel Toberargan Surgery, 27 Toberargan Road, Pitlochry PH16 5HG Tel: 01796 472558 Fax: 01796 473775 — MB ChB 1982 Glas.; MRCGP 1986.

KENNEDY, Douglas William Flat 1, 8 Taits Lane, Dundee DD2 1EB — MB ChB 1996 Dundee.

KENNEDY, Elizabeth Morag Macdonald 68 Clarence Gardens, Glasgow G11 7JW — MB BCh BAO 1993 NUI.

KENNEDY, Fiona Deirdre Northern Health & Social Services Board, 182 Galgorm Road, Ballymena BT42 1QB; 11 Tobermore Road, Magherafelt BT45 5HB — MB BCh BAO 1979 Belf.; MB BCh BAO (Commend. Obst. & Gyn.) Belf. 1979; MFPHM RCP (UK) 1991; MRCGP (Distinc.) 1983; DCH RCP Lond. 1984; DCCH RCP Ed. 1984; Cert. Family Plann. JCC 1983; DRCOG 1982. Cons. Pub. Health & Social Serv. Bd. Co. Antrim. Socs: BMA.

KENNEDY, Fiona Louise Deanswood, Bishopstone, Hereford HR4 7HX — MB BCh 1994 Witwatersrand.

KENNEDY, Fraser Macdonald 64 Heathcroft, Hampstead Way, London NW11 7HJ Tel: 020 8458 0560, 020 8458 9357 Email: fraser.kennedy@btinternet.com — MB ChB 1979 Aberd.; MD Aberd. 1995; MFOM RCP Lond. 1993, AFOM 1987; MRCGP 1983; DRCOG 1983; CIH Dundee 1987. Cons. Occupat.al Phys. (InDepend. Practitioner); Examr. Fac. Occupat. Med. Socs: Fac. Occupat. Med.; BMA; Soc. Occupat. Med. (Former Sec., SOM Scotl. Region). Prev: Sen. Med. Adviser (Environm. Chem.) DoH Lond.; Med. Adviser Health & Safety Exec. Edin.; Dir. Occ. Health, BMI Health Serv.s / Gen. Health Care.

KENNEDY, Gary 50 Station Road, Carluke ML8 5AD — MB ChB 1987 Aberd.

KENNEDY, Geoffrey Launcelot (retired) Petercroft, 59 North Brink, Wisbech PE13 1JX Tel: 01945 584826 — MB BCh BAO 1945 Dub.; BA Dub. 1943; FRCGP 1978, M 1960; DObst RCOG 1948; LM Rotunda 1946; MA Dub 2000. Prev: GP Wisbech.

KENNEDY, Gerard Philip Ty Morlais, Berry Square, Merthyr Tydfil CF48 3AL Tel: 01685 722782 Fax: 01685 722951 — MB BS 1986 Lond.; BSc (Hons.) Lond. 1983; MRCGP 1990.

KENNEDY, Gilbert (retired) Duncraig, bridge St., Tranent EH33 1AL Tel: 01875 610099 — MB ChB 1948 Ed. Prev: GP Tranent E. Lothian.

KENNEDY, Gillian Fraser Accident & Emergency Department, Perth Royal Infirmary, Perth PH1 1NX Tel: 01738 623311 Fax: 01738 473536; 25 Haston Crescent, Kinnoull, Perth PH2 7XD Tel: 01738 637153 Email: drgkennedy@25naston.freeserve.co.uk — MB ChB 1980 Ed.; BMedSci Ed. 1977; Dip. IMC RCS Ed. 1996. Assoc. Specialist in A & E Perth Roy. Infirm. Socs: Brit. Assn. for Accid. & Emerg. Med.; Fac. Pre Hosp Care; Brit. Assn. for Immed. Care. Prev: Princip. in Gen. Pract.

KENNEDY, Gordon David Church Street Surgery, 1 Church Street, Newtownards BT23 4FH Tel: 028 9181 6333 Fax: 028 9181 8805; 42 Bangor Road, Conlig, Newtownards BT23 7PX — MB BCh BAO 1984 Belf.; MRCGP 1988; DRCOG 1987; DCH Dub. 1986. GP Vocational Train. Course Organiser.

KENNEDY, Gordon Eckford Bogs Corner, Ayr KA6 6HQ Tel: 01292 570271 — MB ChB 1955 Glas.; DCH Eng. 1957.

KENNEDY, Heather Ruth Highlands Surgery, 1643 London Road, Leigh-on-Sea SS9 2SQ Tel: 01702 710131 Fax: 01702 471154; 15 Cliff Road, Leigh-on-Sea SS9 1HJ Tel: 01702 713504 — MB BS 1985 Lond.; MRCGP 1995; DFFP 1995; Cert. Prescribed Equiv. Exp. JCPTGP 1994; DCH RCP Lond. 1990. (Lond. Hosp. Med. Coll) GP Highlands Surg. Leigh-on-Sea Essex. Prev: GP Croydon; Trainee GP Ct. Ave. Surg. Old Coulsdon; Cas. Off. Qu. Mary's Hosp. Sidcup.

KENNEDY, Helen Cecilia Bulstrode, Oxford Road, Gerrards Cross SL9 8SZ — MB ChB 1950 Aberd. (Aberd.) Prev: Clin. Med. Off. Hillingdon AHA.

KENNEDY, Helen Mary 5 Castlefields, Dungannon BT71 6DZ — MB BCh BAO 1980 Belf. (Queens University Belfast) CMD Family Plann., Duneannon,.

KENNEDY, Helen Stewart (retired) — MB ChB 1950 Glas.; DCH RCPS Glas. 1968; MRCGP 1975; BA Open 1985. Prev: GP, Glas.

KENNEDY, Henry Gerard Camlet Lodge Secure Unit, Chase Farm Hospital, The Ridgeway, Enfield EN2 8JL Tel: 020 8364 4690 Fax: 020 8342 0806 Email: hgkennedy@compuserve.com; Royal Free Hospital, Pond St, Hampstead, London NW3 Tel: 020 7794 0500 — MB BCh BAO 1980 NUI; BSc NUI 1977, MD 1996; MRCP (UK) 1983; MRCPI 1982; MRCPsych 1988. (Univ. Coll. Dub.) Cons. Forens. Psychiat. N. Lond. Medium Secure Unit, Chase Farm Hosp. Enfield & Roy. Free Hosp.; Hon. Sen. Lect. UCH & Roy. Free Hosp. Lond. Socs: Fell. Roy. Soc. Med. Prev: Sen. Regist. & Regist. (Forens. Psychiat.) Maudsley & BRd.moor Hosps.; Regist. Hammersmith Hosp. Lond.; Ho. Off. Mater Miser. Hosp. Dub.

KENNEDY, Howard William Blair and Kennedy, The Surgery, 4 South Liddle Street, Newcastleton TD9 0RN Tel: 013873 75202 Fax: 013873 75817; Camperdown, Newcastleton TD9 0TA Tel: 013873 75849 — MB ChB 1990 Dundee; BSc (Hons.) Pharmacol. Dund 1985. Prev: Trainee GP Tayside VTS; SHO (Cas.) Dundee Roy. Infirm.; SHO (Psychiat.) Roy. Dundee Liff Hosp.

KENNEDY, Mr Hugh Bryce (retired) 52 Durward Avenue, Shawlands, Glasgow G41 3UE Tel: 0141 632 0883 Email: hugokenn@aol.com — MB ChB 1950 Glas.; FRCS Glas. 1982; FRCS Ed. 1967; FCOphth 1989; DO Eng. 1965; DTM & H Liverp. 1952. Prev: Cons. Ophth. S.. Gen. Hosp. & Vict. Infirm. Glas.

KENNEDY, Hugh Cameron (retired) 733 Shields Road, Glasgow G41 4PL Tel: 0141 423 0098 — MB ChB Glas. 1937; FRCGP 1981, M 1956. Prev: Sen. Resid. Ho. Surg. & Ho. Phys. Vict. Infirm. Glas.

KENNEDY, Hugh John Norfolk & Norwich University Hospital NHS Trust, Norfolk & Norwich University Hospital, Conney Lane, Norwich NR4 7UY Tel: 01603 288367; Hackford Hall, Reepham, Norwich NR10 4RL Tel: 01603 872576 — MB BS 1973 Lond.; BSc Lond. 1970, MD 1982; FRCP Lond. 1993; MRCS Eng. LRCP Lond. 1973. Cons. Phys. Norf. & Norwich Health Care Trust.

KENNEDY, Iain 40 Rangemore Road, Inverness IV3 5EA — MB ChB 1993 Ed.; DRCOG 1995; DFFP 1996; MRCGP 1997. Higher Professional Train. Fell., Gen. Pract., Scotl. Socs: NANP; BMA. Prev: Non-Princip. (Locum); SHO (A&E); SHO (ENT).

KENNEDY, Iain Martin Glenmill Medical Centre, 1191 Royston Road, Glasgow G33 1EY Tel: 0141 770 4052 Fax: 0141 770 4255; 19 Kelvinside Gardens E., Glasgow G20 6BE — MB ChB 1984 Glas.

KENNEDY, James 8 Reservoir Retreat, Birmingham B16 9EH — MB ChB 1994 Birm.; ChB Birm. 1994.

KENNEDY, Mr James Andrew 18 Harberton Park, Belfast BT9 6TS — MB BCh BAO 1987 Belf.; FRCS 1992; FRCSI 1991.

KENNEDY, Mr James Edward 40 Bartlemas Road, Oxford OX4 1XX — MRCS 2000 (Eng.); MA 1998 (Hons) Camb.; MA (Hons.) Camb. 1998. (Magdalene College Cambridge and St. Mary's Hospital London) p/t SHO (Gen. Surg.) Roy. Hants. Hosp. Winchester - Research Regist. (Urol.), Ch.ill Hosp., Oxf.). Prev: Ho. Off. (Gen. Surg.) St. Mary's Hosp. Lond.; Ho. Off. (Gen. Med.) Hemel Hempstead Gen. Hosp.; SHO (Gen. Surg.), Roy. Hants. Co. Hosp., Winchester.

KENNEDY, James Gerard 42 Heaton Road, Heaton, Newcastle upon Tyne NE6 1SE; Wolfson Unit of Clinical Pharmacology, Newcastle University, Newcastle upon Tyne NE2 4DH Tel: 0191 230 3193 Fax: 0191 261 5733 — MB BCh BAO 1986 NUI; MRCGP 1990; DRCOG 1990. Lect. (Primary Care & Therap.) Wolfson Unit Clin. Pharmacol. Newc. u.Tyne. Socs: BMA. Prev: SHO (Paediat.) Newc. Gen. Hosp.; SHO (A & E) Sunderland Gen. Hosp.

KENNEDY, James Henry Gynaecology Department, Glasgow Royal Infirmary University NHS Trust, 84 Castle St., Glasgow G4 0SF — MB ChB 1973 Glas.; FRCPS Glas. 1991; FRCOG 1990, M 1978. Cons. Gynaecologist, Glas. Roy. Infirm., Dept. Of Gyn. Oncol., Stobhill Hosp., Glas.

KENNEDY, Janet Elizabeth Grange Medical Centre, Seacroft Crescent, Leeds LS14 6NX Tel: 0113 295 1801 Fax: 0113 295 1799; Ave. House, Aberford, Leeds LS25 3DP — MB ChB 1974 Leeds; DRCOG 1976. Prev: SHO (A & E & O & G) St. Jas. Hosp. Leeds; SHO (Geriat. Med.) Hull Roy. Infirm.

KENNEDY, Janet Farquhar (retired) Oakview, Bartholomew Close, Hythe CT21 4BS Tel: 01303 267288 — MB BS 1943 Lond.; MRCS Eng. LRCP Lond. 1943; DObst. RCOG 1947. Prev: Ho. Phys. Roy. Devon & Exeter Hosp.

KENNEDY, Jean Margaret (retired) Little Croft, 3 Maple Avenue, Pershore WR10 1NL Tel: 01386 552203 — MB ChB 1949 Birm.

KENNEDY, Jennifer Pauline Ballymena Health Centre, Cushendall Road, Ballymena BT43 6HQ Tel: 01266 42181; 55 Shelling Hill Road, Cullybackey, Ballymena BT42 1NR — MB BCh BAO 1976 Belf.; MRCGP 1983; DRCOG 1978. SCMO N. HSSB Antrim & Ballymena. Socs: Fac. Comm. Health. Prev: Trainee GP Ballymena; Regist. (O & G) Route Hosp. Ballymoney & Ulster Hosp. Dundonald.

KENNEDY, Joanne Louise Child and Family Mental Health, The Mill, Lodge Lane, Derby DE1 3HB Tel: 01332 291794 — MB BS 1987 Newc.; MRCPsych 1992. (Newcastle upon Tyne) Cons. (Child & Adolesc. Psychiat. Paediat. Liaison) S.ern Derbysh. Ment. Health Trust Derby. Socs: BMA; Roy. Coll. Psychiat. Prev: Sen. Regist. (Child & Adolesc. Psychiat.) Nottm. Derby.

KENNEDY, John — MB ChB 1990 Aberd.; MRCGP 1995; DCH RCP Lond. 1994; DRCOG 1993. (Aberdeen) GP Princip. NHS Inverness. Socs: Educat. Convenor Fac. of RCGP (N.). Prev: SHO (Psychiat.) Vale of Leven, Lomond; Trainee GP Tunbridge Wells VTS; SHO (Anaes.) Stobhill Hosp, Glas.

KENNEDY, John 493 Kettering Road, Northampton NN3 6QW — MB BCh BAO 1954 NUI.

KENNEDY, John Alan Greyfriars Medical Centre, 33-37 Castle Street, Dumfries DG1 1DL Tel: 01387 257752 Fax: 01387 257020; Ferguslea, 29 Dalbeattie Road, Dumfries DG2 7PJ Tel: 01387 262672 — MB ChB 1979 Aberd.; MRCGP 1983; DRCOG 1981.

KENNEDY, John Alexander (retired) 9 Grange Crescent, Hooton, South Wirral CH66 5NA Tel: 0151 327 2260 — MB BCh BAO NUI 1956. Prev: Ho. Off. Vict. Centr. Hosp. Wallasey & Newsham Gen. Hosp. Liverp.

KENNEDY, John Alexander (retired) 16 St Mary's Road, Leatherhead KT22 8EY — MB BS 1939 Lond.; MRCS Eng. LRCP Lond. 1939; DMR Lond 1947; DMRD Eng. 1948. Prev: Sen. Radiol. St. Helier Hosp. Carshalton.

KENNEDY, John Andrew 66 Newlands Road, Glasgow G43 2JH Tel: 0141 632 8540 — MB ChB 1959 Glas.; FRCP Glas, 1972, M 1962; FRCP Ed. 1979, M 1962; FRCP Lond. 1979, M 1966. Ross Hal Hosp., Glas.; Glas. Nuffield Hosp., Glas. Prev: Sen. Regist. (Med.) & (Cardiol.) & Ho. Off. (Med.) Roy. Infirm. Glas.; Cons. Cardiol. W.. Infirm. Glas.

KENNEDY, John Charles Baird Shaw Nether Rigg, Closeburn, Thornhill DG3 5JU — MB ChB 1977 Ed.

KENNEDY, Rev. John Hunter East Belmont Orchard, Overtown, Wishaw ML2 0RU Tel: 01698 376084 & 72865 — LRCP LRCS 1949 Ed.; LRCP LRCS Ed. LRFPS Glas. 1949. (Anderson Coll. & Univ. Glas.) Clin. Asst. Psychiat. E. Dist. Hosp. Glas. Prev: Clin. Asst. (Geriat.) Cowglen Hosp. Glas.; Mem. Glas. Local Med. Comm.

KENNEDY, John Julian Alister Accident Department, Royal Bournemouth Hospital, Castel Lane E., Bournemouth BH7 7DW Tel: 01202 704176; 133 Beaufort Road, Southbourne, Bournemouth BH6 5AX Tel: 01202 463922 — MB ChB 1976 Ed. Staff Grade Roy. Bournemouth Hosp. Prev: SHO (A & E) Ayr Hosp. & Hairmyres Hosp. E. Kilbride; SHO (Paediat. & A & E) S.. Gen. Hosp. Glas.

KENNEDY, John McKenzie (retired) 18 Luctons Avenue, Buckhurst Hill IG9 5SG Tel: 020 8540 6367 — MB BS Lond. 1956; MRCS Eng. LRCP Lond. 1956. Prev: Apptd. Fact. Doctor.

KENNEDY, John Myles Gallions Reach Health Centre, Thamesmead, London SE28 8BE Tel: 020 8311 1010 — MB BCh BAO 1975 NUI; MRCGP 1979.

KENNEDY, John Richard 2a Bromley Road, Bingley BD16 4BU — MB BCh 1976 Wales.

KENNEDY, Mr Joseph Aloysius (retired) Summer Hill, Mount Pleasant, Belfast BT9 5DS Tel: 01232 668686 — MCh Belf. 1962, MB BCh BAO 1955; FRCS Ed. 1959. Cons. Urol. S. Belf. & Belf. Gps. Hosps. Fell. Roy. Soc. Med. Prev: Sen. Lect. Inst. Urol. Lond.

KENNEDY, Juliette Mary Bootham Park Hospital, York YO30 7BY — MB BS 1991 Newc. Regist. (Tutor Psychiat.) Leeds Community Ment. Health Trust.

KENNEDY, Karen Elaine Harewood Downs House, Amersham Road, Chalfont St Giles HP8 4RS — MB BCh 1983 Witwatersrand.

KENNEDY, Kathleen (retired) Culzean, Main St., South Scarle, Newark NG23 7JH Tel: 01636 892698 — MB BS 1960 Lond.; MRCS Eng. LRCP Lond. 1959; DCH Eng. 1963. Prev: SCMO (Child Health) W. Surrey & N.E. Hants. HA.

KENNEDY, Kenneth William 30 Harley Street, London W1G 9PN Tel: 020 7631 1771 Fax: 020 7631 1771; 5 Edgecoombe Close, Warren Road, Kingston upon Thames KT2 7HP — MB BCh BAO 1965 Belf.; DPhysMed Eng. 1975; DObst RCOG 1968. (Qu. Univ. Belf.) Med. Dir. (Rehabil.) Roy. Star & Garter Hosp. Richmond. Socs: Fell. Med. Soc. Lond.; Brit. Assn. Rheum. & Rehabil. Prev: Regist. (Med.) St. Stephen's & St. Mary Abbots Hosps.; Resid. Med. Off. Guy's Hosp. Lond.

KENNEDY, Margaret Mary The Annexe, Springfield, Larkins Lane, Headington, Oxford OX3 9DW — MB BCh BAO 1987 NUI.

KENNEDY, Marguerite Mary 1 Craigton Crescent, Newton Mearns, Glasgow G77 6DN — MB ChB 1998 Glas.; MB ChB Glas 1998.

KENNEDY, Marie Teresa 7 Ormiston Gardens, Belfast BT5 6JD Tel: 01232 656359 — MD Belf. 1973, MB BCh BAO 1957; DPM RCPSI 1960; DCH RCPS Glas. 1964. (Belf.) Socs: BMA & Roy. Med. Psychiat. Assn. Prev: Sen. Regist. & Sen. Tutor (Ment. Health) City Hosp. Belf.; Regist. Craig Dunain Hosp. Inverness & Dept. Child Psychiat. Yorkhill Hosp. Sick Childr. Glas.

KENNEDY, Maurice Neil c/o 2 Ard Na Ree, Groomsport, Bangor BT19 6JL — MB ChB 1990 Manch.; BSc (Hons.) Manch. 1987; MRCP (UK) 1993; DTM & H (Distinct.) Liverp. 1996. Med. Miss. Embangweni, Malawi. Prev: Regist. Booth Hall Childr. Hosp. & Qu. Pk. Hosp. Blackburn.

KENNEDY, Michael (retired) 241 Kirkintilloch Road, Bishopbriggs, Glasgow G64 2JB Tel: 0141 777 3188 — MB ChB Glas. 1957; DObst RCOG 1959.

KENNEDY, Michael Campbell Surgery, 10 Quarry Road, Dungannon BT70 1QR Tel: 028 8772 2751; 5 Castlefields, Dungannon BT71 6DZ Tel: 018687 25100 — MB BCh BAO 1978 Belf.; MRCGP 1982; DRCOG 1980. (Belfast)

KENNEDY, Michael John 234 Mauldeth Road, Manchester M19 1AU — MB BS 1989 Lond.

KENNEDY, Michael Richard Group Practice Centre, Old Chester Road, Great Sutton, South Wirral CH66 3PB Tel: 0151 339 3126; The Outlook, Parkgate Road, Neston, South Wirral CH64 6QE Tel: 0151 336 6522 — MB ChB 1968 Liverp.; AFOM 1988; MRCGP 1983. Med. Off. Vauxhall Motors Ellesmere Port, Brit. Nuclear Fuels Capenhurst & SGS Redwood Ltd. Prev: Regist. (Med.) Birkenhead Gen. Hosp.; SHO (Gen. Med.) Sefton Gen. Hosp. Liverp.

KENNEDY, Moira Steele Wallacetown Health Centre, Lyon Street, Dundee DD4 6RB Tel: 01382 457629 Fax: 01382 450365; 39 Park Road, Dundee DD3 8LB — MB ChB 1983 Dundee; MRCGP 1988; DRCOG 1986. (Dundee) GP Princip. Red Wing & Fintry Mill Med. Centre; GP Trainer. Prev: SHO (Psychiat.) Roy. Dundee Liff Hosp.; SHO (O & G) Falkirk & Dist. Roy. Infirm.; SHO (Med. & Cas.) Arbroath Infirm.

KENNEDY, Neil Stewart Brimmond Medical Group, 106 Inverurie Road, Bucksburn, Aberdeen AB21 9AT Tel: 01224 713869 Fax: 01224 716317; Deverson, North Deeside Road, Pitfolds, Cults, Aberdeen AB15 9PL Tel: 01261 861215 Fax: 01261 818455 — MB ChB 1981 Glas.; MRCGP 1992; DRCOG 1984; Dip Occ Med 1997. GP Banff. Prev: Trainee GP Dumfries & Galloway VTS.

KENNEDY, Nicholas Area Infectious Diseases Unit, Monklands Hospital, Monkscourt Avenue, Airdrie ML6 0JS Tel: 01236 748748 Fax: 01236 712449 Email: nicholas.kennedy@laht.scot.nhs.uk — MB ChB 1988 Bristol; MD Bristol 1995; MRCP (UK) 1991; DTM & H RCP Lond. 1993; FRCP (Edin) 1999. (Bristol) Cons. Phys. and Hon. Sen. Lect. in Infec. Dis.s and Gen. Med., Area Infec. Dis.s Unit, Monklands Hosp., Airdrie. Prev: Sen. Regist. (Infec. Dis & Trop.Med.), Fazakerley Hosp. Liverp.; Regist. Rotat. (Infec. Dis.) Roy. Hallamsh. Hosp. Sheff.; Regist. (Med.) Barnsley Dist. Gen. Hosp.

KENNEDY, Nicholas Michael Jonathan 32 Gaza Close, Coventry CV4 9EF — MB ChB 1985 Birm.; ChB Birm. 1985.

KENNEDY, Nigel Damien Whitehill Surgery, Whitehill Lane, Oxford Road, Aylesbury HP19 8EN Tel: 01296 424488 Fax: 01296 398774; The Hollies, 27 Leighton Road, Wingrave, Aylesbury HP22 4PA Tel: 01296 681627 — MB BS 1971 Lond.; MRCP (UK) 1976; MRCS Eng. LRCP Lond. 1971; DCH Eng. 1974; DObst RCOG 1973; FRCP 1997; FRCPCH 1997. (Char. Cross) Hosp. Pract. (Paediat.) Stoke Mandeville Hosp. Prev: Clin. Asst. (Paediat.) Stoke Mandeville Hosp.; Regist. (Paediat.) Roy. Devon & Exeter Hosp.; Med. Specialist RAF Med. Br..

KENNEDY, Paula 49 Tillysburn Park, Holywood Road, Belfast BT4 2PD Tel: 01232 468818; 49 Tillysburn Park, Holywood Road, Belfast BT4 2PD Tel: 01232 768818 — MB ChB 1997 Dundee; DRCOG 1999. SHO (Paediat.) GP Rotat., Ulster Hosp., Dundonald. Prev: SHO (O & G.) The Ulster Hosp. Dundonald; Hse. Off. The Ulster Hosp. Dundonald; Hse. Off. The Ulster Hosp. Dundonald.

KENNEDY, Penelope Anne Nendrum, Martin End Lane, Great Missenden HP16 9HR — MB BCh BAO 1979 Belf.; DO Dub. 1984.

KENNEDY, Peter Francis 10A St George's Place, York YO24 1DR Tel: 01904 621636 — MD 1971 Leeds; MB ChB 1964; FRCPsych 1983, M 1972; DPM Leeds 1968. (Leeds) Chief Exec. York Health Servs. Trust. Prev: Sen. Lect. (Psychiat.) Univ. Edin.; Hon. Cons. Roy. Edin. Hosp.

KENNEDY, Professor Peter Graham Edward Department of Neurology, University of Glasgow, Institute of Neurological Sciences, Southern General Hospital NHS Trust, Glasgow G51 4TF Tel: 0141 201 2474 Fax: 0141 201 2993 Email: p.g.kennedy@clinmed.gla.ac.uk; 23 Hamilton Avenue, Pollokshields, Glasgow G41 4JG — MB BS 1974 Lond.; F Med Sci 1998; PhD Lond. 1980, DSc 1991, MD 1983; M.Litt Glas. 1995; MPhil Glas. 1993; FRSE 1992; FRCP Glas. 1989; FRCP Lond. 1988; MRCP (UK) 1976; FRCPath 1997, M 1988. (Univ. Coll. Hosp.) Burton Prof. Neurol. Univ. Glas.; Cons. Neurol Inst. Neurol. Sci. S. Gen. Hosp. Glas. Socs: Assn. Brit. Neurols.; Assn. Phys.; Amer. Neurol. Assn. Prev: Sen. Lect. (Neurol. & Virol.) Univ. Glas.; Asst. Prof. (Neurol.) Johns Hopkins Univ. Sch. Med. Baltimore, USA; Fleming Lect. RCPS Glas. 1990.

KENNEDY, Mr Peter Terence Department of Radiology, Royal Victoria Hospital, Grosvenor Road, Belfast BT12 6BA Tel: 01232 894711; 39 Malone Heights, Upper Malone Road, Belfast BT9 5PG Email: 101606.2677@compuserve.com — BM BCh 1989 Oxf.; FRCSI 1994. Regist. (Radiol.) Roy. Vict. Hosp. Belf. Prev: SHO (Surg.) John Radcliffe Hosp. Oxf. & Roy. Vict. Hosp. Belf.

KENNEDY, Philip Wessex Neurological Centre, Southampton General Hospital, Tremona Road, Southampton SO16 6YD Tel: 02380 796783 Fax: 02380 798793 Email: philip.kennedy@btinternet.com — MB BCh BAO (1st cl. Hons.) Belf. 1967; FRCP Lond. 1983; MRCP (UK) 1970. (Qu. Univ. Belf.) Cons. Neurol. Soton. Univ. Hosps. NHS Trust. Prev: Cons. Neurol. Soton. & SW Hants. Health Dist. (T); Sen. Regist. St. Mary's Hosp. & Nat. Hosp. Lond.; Regist. Nat. Hosp. Lond.

KENNEDY, Rachel Mary 34 Bramwith Road, Nether Green, Sheffield S11 7EZ — MB ChB 1994 Manch.

KENNEDY, Raymond Gerald 4 Willow Drive, Countesthorpe, Leicester LE8 5TN — MB BS 1986 Lond.

KENNEDY, Richard Darrah Millhouse, 3 Main St., Millisle, Newtownards BT22 2BL — MB BCh BAO 1995 Belf.

KENNEDY, Richard Johnston Castlehill Health Centre, Castlehill, Forres IV36 1QF Tel: 01309 672233 Fax: 01309 673445 — MB BCh BAO 1986 Belf.; MRCP (UK) 1991; MRCGP 1994; DRCOG 1992.

KENNEDY, Professor Richard Lee Dept. of Medicine, Sunderland Royal Hospital, Sunderland SR4 7TP — MB ChB 1980 Ed.; BSc (Hons.) Ed. 1978, MB ChB 1980; MRCP (UK) 1983. Clin. Lect. (Med.) Univ. Camb. Prev: Research Fell. (Endocrine/Immunol. Unit) Roy. Infirm. Edin.

KENNEDY, Robert Cameron Parkbury House Surgery, St. Peters Street, St Albans AL1 3HD Tel: 01727 851589; The Knoll, 14 Harpenden Road, St Albans AL3 5AD — MB BS 1960 Lond.; DObst RCOG 1962; DCH Eng. 1963. (St. Bart.) Prev: Ho. Phys. Essex Co. Hosp. Colchester; Ho. Surg. St. Albans City Hosp.; SHO (Paediat.) Shrodells Hosp. Watford.

KENNEDY, Robert Ian (retired) 1A Church Hill, Edinburgh EH10 4BG Tel: 0131 447 1518 — MRCS Eng. LRCP Lond. 1963; MA Camb. 1964, MB 1964, BChir 1963; FRCP Ed. 1977; MRCP (U.K.) 1970; FRCPsych 1985, M 1972; DPM Ed. 1968. Prev: Cons. Roy. Edin. Hosp.

KENNEDY, Mr Robert James 2 Highgate Close, Newtownabbey BT36 4WE — MB ChB 1992 Dundee; Diploma in Occupational Medicine MD Queen's University of Belfast 2000; FRCS 1996. Specialist Regist. (Gen. Surg.).

KENNEDY, Robert Kirk Inches (retired) The Garden Flat, 118 Hamilton Terrace, London NW8 9UT Tel: 020 7625 6598 — MRCS Eng. LRCP Lond. 1940; MA, MB BChir Camb. 1941; MRCGP 1962. Prev: Temp. Surg. Lt.-Cdr. RNVR.

KENNEDY, Mr Robin Harold Yeovil District Hospital, Yeovil BA21 4AT Tel: 01935 707244 Fax: 01935 410752 Email: milll@msmail.esomerset-tr.swest.nhs.uk — MB BS 1976 Lond.; MS Lond. 1987; FRCS Eng. 1981. Cons. Gen. Surg. with s/i in Gastrointestinal Surg. Yeovil Dist. Hosp. Socs: Brit. Soc. Gastroenterol.; Assn. Surg.; Assn. Endoscopic Surgs. Prev: Sen. Regist. SW Region.

KENNEDY, Roger Ian Laurence Cassel Hospital, 1 Ham Common, Richmond TW11 7JF — MB BS 1973 Lond.; BSc Lond. 1970; FRCPsych 1996, M 1978. (Univ. Coll. Hosp.) p/t Cons. Psychother. Cassel Hosp. Richmond; Hon. Sen. Lect. (Psychiat.) Imperial Coll., Lond. Socs: Brit. Psychoanal. Soc.; Mem. Train.

Analyst. Prev: Sen. Regist. (Child & Adolesc. Psychiat.) Guy's Hosp. Lond.; Regist. (Child Psychiat.) Child Guid. Train. Centre, Lond.; SHO (Psychiat.) Roy. Free Hosp.

KENNEDY, Rosalind Penelope Nailsea Health Centre, Somerset Square, Nailsea, Bristol BS48 1RR Tel: 01275 856611 Fax: 01275 857074; 16 Sion Hill, Clifton, Bristol BS8 4AZ Tel: 0117 974 1935 — MB BS 1973 Lond.; MRCP (U.K.) 1975; MRCGP 1979; DCH Eng. 1977. Socs: Bristol Medico-Legal Soc. & Med. Clin. Soc. Prev: Princip. GP Lond. & Ho. Off. (O & G) N. Middlx. Hosp. Lond.; Ho. Off. (Paediat.) Whipps Cross Hosp. Lond.

KENNEDY, Ruth Whitehouse Surgery, 189 Prince of Wales Road, Sheffield S2 1FA Tel: 0114 239 7229 Fax: 0114 253 1650; Courtyard House, Newfield Lane, Sheffield S17 3DB Tel: 0114 235 1884 — MB ChB 1980 Liverp.; MRCGP 1985; DRCOG 1984.

KENNEDY, Shireen Riverside Medical Centre, Victoria Road, Walton-le-Dale, Preston PR5 4AY Tel: 01772 556703; 27 Windsor Road, Walton Le Dale, Preston PR5 4GE Tel: 01772 321085 — MB ChB 1990 Leeds; MRCGP 1994.

KENNEDY, Shona Mairi Park Avenue Medical Centre, 9 Park Avenue, Stirling FK8 2QR Tel: 01786 473529 — MB ChB 1988 Glas.; MRCGP 1993; DRCOG 1993.

KENNEDY, Simon Anaesthetic Department, Cumberland Infirmary, Newtown Road, Carlisle CA2 7HY Tel: 01382 644868 — MB ChB 1987 Dundee; FRCA 1993. Anaesthetic Dept, Cumbld. Infirm. Neutown Rd. Carlisle. Prev: SHO (Anaesth.) Tayside RHA.

KENNEDY, Stephen Howard 37 Oakthorpe Road, Oxford OX2 7BD Tel: 01865 556131 Fax: 01865 769141 Email: skennedy@worf.molbiol.ox.ac.uk — MB BS 1984 Lond.; MA Oxf. 1993, BA 1978; MD Lond. 1992; MRCOG 1991. (Guy's) Clin. Reader & Hon. Cons. Nuffield Dept. O & G John Radcliffe Hosp. Oxf.; Eden Trav. Fell. Roy. Coll. Obst. & Gyn. Vis. Asst. Prof. Dept. Reproduc. Med. Univ. Texas, USA. Prev: Sen. Fell. (Reproduc. Med. & Fertil.) & Hon. Cons. Nuffield Dept. O & G John Radcliffe Hosp. Oxf.; Clin. Lect. & Sen. Regist. (O & G) John Radcliffe Hosp. Oxf.; SHO (O & G) Qu. Charlotte's & Chelsea Hosp. Lond.

KENNEDY, Susan 66 Chippendale Rise, Bradford BD8 0NB — MB BCh 1967 Wales; DObst RCOG 1969. (Cardiff) Chemother. Regist. Bradford Roy. Infirm. Socs: BMA. Prev: SHO Dept. Dermat. Roy. Vict. Infirm. Newc.; Ho. Off. Depts. Paediat. & Obst. Welsh Nat. Sch. Med. Cardiff; Ho. Surg. Llandough Hosp. Cardiff.

KENNEDY, Susan Dorothy Salen Surgery, Pier Road, Aros, Isle of Mull PA72 6JL Tel: 01680 300327; Wanaka, Beadoun, Tobermory, Isle of Mull PA75 6QA — BM 1989 Soton. p/t Assoc. GP.

KENNEDY, Thomas Duncan Wirral Hospital Trust, Arrowe Park Road, Upton, Wirral CH49 5PE Tel: 0151 678 5111 Fax: 0151 604 7214 Email: tomdken@aol.com; The Malt House, Mill Lane, Willaston, South Wirral CH64 1RQ Tel: 0151 327 4162 Email: tomdken@aol.com — MB BS 1977 Lond.; FRCP Lond. 1995; MRCP (UK) 1980; MRCS Eng. LRCP Lond. 1977. Cons. Phys. & Rheum. Mersey RHA. Prev: Sen. Regist. Riverside HA.

KENNEDY, Thomas Graeme 44 University Road, Belfast BT7 1NJ — MB BCh BAO 1968 Belf.

KENNEDY, Thomas McNay (retired) Four Winds, 7 Hillside Crescent, Langholm DG13 0EE Tel: 013873 80450 Fax: 013873 80450 Email: tklangholm@aol.com — MB ChB Ed. 1960; FRCGP 1980, M 1971; DObst RCOG 1968. Prev: GP Langholm.

KENNEDY, Vivien Rosemary Greer 73 Carnreagh, Hillsborough BT26 6LJ — MB BCh BAO 1946 Belf. (Belf.)

KENNEDY, Walter Peter Ualrig (retired) 49 The Avenue, Wivenhoe, Colchester CO7 9PP Tel: 01206 827852 — MB ChB Ed. 1960; FRCP Ed. 1975, M 1964. Prev: Cons. Phys. (Gen. & Thoracic Med.) Colchester Gen. Hosp.

KENNEDY, William Walter (retired) Craigewan, Glen Road, Dunblane FK15 0DJ Tel: 01786 823541 Email: billken@easicom.com — MB ChB 1955 Glas. Authorised Med. Examr. Bd. of Trade Civil Aviat.

KENNEDY-COOKE, Caroline Jane Bosmere Medical Practice, PO Box 41, Civic Centre Road, Havant PO9 2AJ Tel: 023 9245 1300 Fax: 023 9249 2624 Email: bosmeremedical@cs.com; Mays Coppice Farm House, Havant PO9 5NE — MB ChB 1980 Bristol; MRCGP 1984; DRCOG 1984.

KENNEDY SCOTT, John Peter (retired) Groton House, Groton, Sudbury CO10 5EH Tel: 01787 210319 — MRCS Eng. LRCP Lond. 1967; DObst RCOG 1969. Prev: GP Ipswich.

KENNEDY YOUNG, Alistair Grange (retired) Fairways, 29 Ladythorn Crescent, Bramhall, Stockport SK7 2HB Tel: 0161 439 2312 Fax: 0161 439 2312 — MB ChB 1961 Glas.; MA Camb. 1960; Cert. Av. Med. 1992. Clin. Asst. (Neurol.) Univ. Hosp. S. Manch.; Sen. Clin. Med. Off. David Lewis Centre, Warford, Chesh. Prev: GP Chesh.

KENNERLEY, Peter Charles Springfield Surgery, Springfield Way, Brackley NN13 6JJ Tel: 01280 703431 Fax: 01280 703241; Toad Hall, Church Road, Brackley NN13 7BU Tel: 01280 703236 — MB ChB 1969 Aberd.; DCH Eng. 1972; DA Eng. 1975; DObst RCOG 1972. Clin. Asst. (Paediat.) N.ampton Gen. Hosp. Prev: SHO (Paediat./Anaesth.) Middlx. Hosp. Lond.; SHO (Paediat.) N.. Gen. Hosp. Sheff.; SHO (Obst.) Addenbrooke's Hosp. Camb.

KENNERLEY, Peter Mark 4 The Old School, Church St., Shillington, Hitchin SG5 3LJ — MB ChB 1982 Manch.; DA (UK) I986; MFPM 1991. Med. Dir. Europ. Mdical Advisery Servs. Ltd. Socs: BMA; RSM; Fac. Pharmaceut. Med. Prev: Head Med. Affairs Astra UK; Med. Dir. Schwarz Pharma UK; Head Cardiovasc. R&D Unit izsens Internat.

KENNETT, Katherine The Poplars, Summrsdale Rd, Chichester PO19 4PN — MB BS 1996 Lond. (St Georges Hospital Medical School) Socs: Med. Protec. Soc.; BMA.

KENNETT, Robin Peter Radcliffe Infirmary, Woodstock Road, Oxford OX2 6HE Tel: 01865 224839 Fax: 01865 224303; Ryvoan, Church Lane, Horton cum Studley, Oxford OX33 1AW — MB BS 1979 Lond.; BSc (1st cl. Hons.) Lond. 1976, MD 1988; FRCP Lond. 1996; MRCP (UK) 1983. Cons. Clin. Neurophysiol. Radcliffe Infirm. NHS Trust Oxf.

KENNEY, Mr Anthony 17 Wimpole Street, London W1G 8GB Tel: 020 8942 0440 Fax: 020 8949 9100; 92 Coombe Lane W., Kingston upon Thames KT2 7DB — MB BChir 1966 Camb.; MA Camb. 1967; FRCS Eng. 1970; FRCOG 1987, M 1972. (Camb. & Lond. Hosp.) Cons. O & G St. Thos. Hosp. Lond.; Examr. Univ. Lond. & Roy. Coll. Obst. & Gyn. Socs: Fell. Roy. Soc. Med.; Fell. Med. Soc. Lond. (Counc.). Prev: Examr. Univ. Camb. & Liverp.; Sen. Regist. (O & G) W.m. Hosp. Lond; Ho. Surg. Chelsea Hosp. Wom. Lond.

KENNEY, Barbara Anne Katherine Southmead Health Centre, Ullswater Road, Bristol BS10 6DF Tel: 0117 950 7100 Fax: 0117 959 1110; 6 Trelawney Road, Cotham, Bristol BS6 6EA — MB ChB 1982 Bristol; MRCGP 1987. Princip. Gen. Pract. (p/t).

KENNEY, Christine Gail Hills Road Surgery, Beechwood Practice, 41 Hills Road, Cambridge CB2 1NT Tel: 01223 315541 Fax: 01223 301422; 4 Sedley Taylor Road, Cambridge CB2 2PW Tel: 01223 211547 Fax: 01223 211547 — MB ChB 1964 Ed. (Ed.)

KENNEY, Ian Joseph X-Ray Department, Royal Alexandra Hospital for Sick Children, Dyke Road, Brighton BN1 3JN Email: i.kenney@bspr.org.uk; Fax: 01273 736685 — MB ChB 1978 Ed.; BSc Med. Sc. Ed. 1975; FRCR 1983; DRMD 1982. (Ed.) Cons. Radiol. (Gen. & Paediat.) Roy. Alexandra Hosp. for Sick Childr. Brighton. Socs: Assoc. Mem. BPA; Eur. Soc. Paediat. Radiol. Prev: Regist. & Sen. Regist. (Diag. Radiol.) Roy. Infirm. Edin.

KENNEY, Jack Ginesi (retired) Greenlands, 46 Wellesley Park, Wellington TA21 8PZ Tel: 0182 622695 — MB BS Lond. 1951; BSc (Hons. Physiol.) Lond. 1948; MRCS Eng. LRCP Lond. 1951; DMRD Eng. 1959. Hon. Cons. Radiol. W. Som. Clin. Area. Prev: Regist. (X-Ray Diag.) & Ho. Phys. King's Coll. Hosp.

KENNEY, Nicholas Charles 92 Coombe Lane W., Kingston upon Thames KT2 7DB — MB BS 1994 Lond.; BSc Lond. 1991. (St. Thos.) SHO Roy. Marsden Hosp. Lond. Prev: SHO (O & G) Brighton & King's Coll. Hosp. Lond.

KENNEY, Patricia Mary (retired) Greenlands, 46 Wellesley Park, Wellington TA21 8PZ Tel: 01823 662695 — MB BS Lond. 1952; MRCS Eng. LRCP Lond. 1952; DCH Eng. 1956. Prev: Asst. Med. Off. Surrey CC (SE Div.).

KENNEY-HERBERT, Jeremy Patrick Reaside Clinic, Birmingham Great Park, Rubery, Birmingham B45 9BE Tel: 0121 678 3000 Fax: 0121 678 3014 — MB BS 1987 Sydney; FRANZCP 1995. Cons. Forens. Psychiat. Reaside Clinic; Hon. Sen. Clin. Lect., Univ. of Birm. Prev: Hon. Sen. Regist. (Forens. Psychiat.) Reaside Clinic Bristol; Regist. (Psychiat.) E.. Sydney Area Health Serv., Austral.

KENNIE, Agnes Thomson, MBE (retired) 7 Mead Close, Paignton TQ3 2PS Tel: 01803 554960 — MB ChB Glas. 1932; MD Glas.

1937; FRCP Glas. 1990; FRFPS Glas. 1937; MRCP (UK) 1962; FRCGP 1969, M 1953. Prev: GP Paignton.

KENNIE, David Campbell 1 Birkhill Road, Stirling FK7 9LT Tel: 01786 471245 Email: davidkennie@hotmail.com — MB ChB 1969 Glas.; FRCP Glas. 1987; FRCP Ed. 1987; MRCP (U.K.) 1973; DCH RCPS Glas. 1972; DObst RCOG 1971. Cons. Phys. Geriat. Med. Roy. Infirm. Stirling; Hon. Sen. Lect. (Geriat. Med.) Univ. Edin. Prev: Cons. Geriat. S. Gen. Hosp. Glas.; Vis. Assoc. Prof. Community & Family Med. Duke Univ. N.C., USA.

KENNING, Mr Brian Richard 30 Holme Lacey Road, London SE12 0HR Tel: 020 8851 4675 — MB BS 1971 Lond.; FRCS Eng. 1975; MRCS Eng. LRCP Lond. 1970.

***KENNINGHAM, James Alexander** Countess of Chester Hospital, Chester CH2 1UL Tel: 01244 365000; Hallas Cote Farm, Cullingworth, Bradford BD13 5BW Tel: 01535 274430 — MB BCh 1994 Wales.

KENNISH, Nicola Patricia 119 Bradenham Beeches, Walters Ash, High Wycombe HP14 4XN Email: brucekennish@compuserve.com — MB BCh 1990 Wales; DFFP 1999; Dip. Clin. & Analyt Hypnother. & Psychother. 1999; MRCGP 1997. (Wales) GP (p/t); Clin. Asst. Family Plann. & GU Med. Wycombe Gen. Hosp. (p/t). Socs: MDU.

KENNON, Brian 15 Kensington Gate, Dowanhill, Glasgow G12 9LG Tel: 0141 334 7430 Email: bk8h@clinmed.gla.ac.uk — MB ChB 1993 Glas.; MRCP (UK) 1996. (Univ. Glas.) Research Fell. (Diabetes & Endocrinol.) W.. Infirm. Glas. Socs: BMA; Brit. Diabetic Assn.; Brit. Hypertens. Research Gp. Prev: SHO III (Diabetes & Endocrinol.) W.. Infirm. Glas.; SHO III (Med.) CrossHo. Hosp.; SHO (A & E) CrossHo. Hosp. Kilmarnock.

KENNON, Robert Warton (retired) The Surgery, Church Lane, Mobberley, Knutsford WA16 7QY Tel: 01565 872195 — MB ChB 1945 Liverp.; FRCGP 1976, M 1953; DObst RCOG 1947. Prev: Mem. Ment. Health Act 1983 Commiss.

KENNY, Beverley Jane Park Road Surgery, 93 Park Road, Wallsend NE28 7LP Tel: 0191 262 5680 Fax: 0191 262 3646; 50 The Grove, Gosforth, Newcastle upon Tyne NE3 1NJ — MB BS 1983 Newc. Prev: Trainee GP N.umbria VTS.

KENNY, Brian Douglas The Area Laboratory, Antrim Hospital, 45 Bush Road, Antrim BT41 2QB — MB BCh BAO 1982 Belf.; MRCPath 1989. Cons. Path. Histopath. & Cytopath. Antrim Hosp. N. Health & Social Servs. Bd. Prev: Sen. Regist. (Histopath.) Roy. Vict. Hosp. Belf.

KENNY, Carol Jane Portmill Surgery, 114 Queen, Hitchin SG4 9TH Tel: 01462 434246 — MB ChB 1977 Manch. Partner GP Herts.; BrE. Clinician Lister Hosp. Stevenage. Socs: Fac. Fam. Plann. & Reproduc. Health Care; Assn. BrE. Clinicians. Prev: GP Leeds, Manch. & Chesh.

KENNY, Christina Stony Stratford Surgery, Market Square, Stony Stratford, Milton Keynes MK11 1YA Tel: 01908 565555 — MB ChB 1981 Glas.; Dip Hlt Mgt 2001 (Kneele); MRCGP 1986; DCH RCP Glas. 1986; DRCOG 1985; DFFP 1996. Director of Clin. Governance,Milton Keynes. Prev: Clin. Med. Off. (Community Paediat.) Milton Keynes HA.; Trainee GP Milton Keynes VTS; Regist. (Dermat.) Vict. Infirm. Glas.

KENNY, Christopher Department of Public Health, NHS Executive Trent, Fulwood House, Sheffield S10 3TH Tel: 0114 282 0335 Fax: 0114 282 0397 Email: christopher.kenny@doh.gsi.gov.uk; 7 Highbury Close, Nuthall, Nottingham NG16 IQN Tel: 0115 9795 927 — BM BS 1983 Nottm.; BMedSci Nottm. 1981; MFPHM RCP (UK) 1991; FFPHM RCP (UK) 1999. (Nottm.) Cons. Pub. Health Med. NHS Exec. Trent. Prev: Sen. Regist. (Pub. Health Med.) Nottm. HA; Regist. (Community Med.) S.. Derbysh. HA.; Cons in Pub. Health Med. S.. Derbysh. HA.

KENNY, Clare 10 The Rowans, Gateshead NE9 7BN — MB ChB 1998 Sheff.; MB ChB Sheff 1998.

KENNY, Colin Jordan Gallows Street Surgery, 50 Gallows Street, Dromore BT25 1BD Tel: 028 9269 2758 — MB BCh BAO 1979 Belf.; FRCGP 1996; DRCOG 1983; DCH Dub. 1983; DGM RCP Lond. 1985; Dip Med. Educat. Dund. 1996. GP Dromore; Course Organiser. Prev: GP Tutor S.. HSSB.

KENNY, Damian The Westgate Surgery, 40 Parsonage Street, Dursley GL11 4AA Tel: 01453 545981; 18 High Furlong, Cam, Dursley GL11 5UZ Tel: 01453 544171 — MB ChB 1981 Bristol; MRCGP 1986; DRCOG 1985. (Bristol) Asst. Tutor Gen. Pract. Gloucestershire. Socs: Med. Action Global Security. Prev: Dist. Health Off. Rumphi, Malawi; Trainee GP N. Devon VTS.

KENNY, Dermot Alexander Court Yard Surgery, John Evans House, 28 Court Yard, London SE9 5QA Tel: 020 8850 1300 Fax: 020 8294 2378; 23 Hawes Road, Bromley BR1 3JS — MB BS 1982 Lond.; BSc (Hons.) Lond. 1979, MB BS 1982; DRCOG 1987. (King's Coll. Hosp.)

KENNY, Professor Gavin Nicolson Cleghorn Beneffrey, 124 Spring Kell Avenue, Pollokshields, Glasgow G41 4EU Tel: 0141 427 2425 Fax: 0141 951 5603 — MB ChB 1972 Glas.; BSc (Hons., Physiol.) Glas. 1970, MD 1982; FFA RCS Eng. 1976; FANZCA 197. Prof. Univ. Dept. Glas. Roy. Infirm. Prev: Sen. Lect. (Anaesth.) Univ. Dept. Glas. Roy. Infirm.; Lect., Regist. & SHO (Anaesth.) Glas. Roy. Infirm.; Ho. Off. (Med. & Surg.) Stirling Roy. Infirm.

KENNY, Helen Marie 132 Fulford Road, York YO10 4BE — BM BS 1991 Nottm.; BMedSci (1st cl. Hons.) Nottm. 1989; DRCOG 1995; MRCGP 1996.

KENNY, John Bernard Radiology Department, Whiston Hospital, Prescot L35 5DR Tel: 0151 430 1309; 17 Grange Drive, Eccleston Hill, St Helens WA10 3BG Tel: 01744 27661 — MB ChB 1982 Liverp.; FRCR 1987; DMRD Liverp. 1986. Cons. Radiol. Whiston & St. Helens Hosps. Mersey Regional HA; Clin. Lect. Dept. Radiodiag. & Magnetic Resonance Research Centre Univ. Liverp.

KENNY, John Robert 5 Baker's Buildings, Wrington, Bristol BS40 5LQ — MB BS 1981 Lond.; MRCGP 1995; MRCPsych 1993.

KENNY, Laura Monica 4 Alexandra Gardens, Belfast BT15 3LJ — MB BCh BAO 1995 Belf.

KENNY, Louise City Hospital, Hucknall Road, Nottingham NG5 1PJ Tel: 0115 969 1169 Email: louise.kenny@nottingham.ac.uk; Cavendish Cottage, 25C Cavendish Road E., The Park, Nottingham NG7 1BB — MB ChB 1993 Liverp. Clin. Research Fell. (O & G) City Hosp. Nottm.

KENNY, M. Antoinette Department of Cardiology, Freeman Hospital, High Heaton, Newcastle upon Tyne NE7 7DN Tel: 0191 284 3111 Fax: 0191 223 1175 Email: antoinette.kenny@ncl.ac.uk; 16 Lily Avenue, Jesmond, Newcastle upon Tyne NE2 2SQ Tel: 0191 281 1807 Fax: 0191 281 4675 — MB BCh BAO 1983 NUI; FRCPI 1999; FRCP 1998; MD NUI 1994; MRCP (UK) 1987; MRCPI 1986. (Dublin) Cons. Cardiol. Freeman Hosp. Newc. u. Tyne. Socs: Brit. Cardiac Soc. (Mem. Technicians Comm.); Brit. Soc. Echocardiogr. (Counc. Mem. and Chairm. Scientif. & Research Comm.); Eur. Working Gp. Echocardiog. Prev: Reseach Assoc. (Echocardiography) Oregon Health Sci.s Univ., Portland, Oregan, USA; Cardiol. Regist. & Research Fell. (Cardiol.) Papworth Hopsital Camb.

KENNY, Martin Thomas Gayton Road Health and Surgical Centre, Gayton Road, King's Lynn PE30 4DY Tel: 01553 762726 Fax: 01553 696819; The Old Barn, Lynn Road, Hillington, King's Lynn PE31 6BJ Tel: 01485 600994 Email: kenny@doctors.org.uk — MRCS Eng. LRCP Lond. 1974; DA Eng. 1978.

KENNY, Martin Whitthorn Haematology Department, Royal Sussex County Hospital, Brighton BN2 5BE — MB ChB 1970 Birm.; MRCP (U.K.) 1974; MRCPath 1977. Cons. Haemat. Brighton HA.

KENNY, Mary Katherine Gayton Road Health and Surgical Centre, Gayton Road, King's Lynn PE30 4DY Tel: 01553 762726 Fax: 01553 696819; The Old Barn, Warren Farm, Hillington, King's Lynn PE31 6BJ Tel: 01485 600994 Fax: 01485 600995 — MB BCh 1973 Wales.

KENNY, Niav Mary Health Centre, Bank Street, Cupar KY15 4JN Tel: 01334 653478 Fax: 01334 657305 — MB BCh BAO 1983 NUI.

KENNY, Mr Nicholas William c/o Fracture Clinic, Manchester Royal Infirmary, Oxford Road, Manchester M13 9WL Fax: 0161 276 8006 — MB ChB 1983 Manch.; FRCS (Orth.) 1994; FRCS Eng. 1987. Cons. Orthop. Surg. Manch. Roy. Infirm. Socs: BMA & Brit. Orthop. Assn. Prev: Sen. Regist. (Orthop. Surg.) Univ. Hosp. S. Manch.; Regist. (Surg.) Stockport Infirm.; Fell. (Knee Surg.) Hope Hosp.

KENNY, Pamela The Surgery, The Green, Haddenham, Ely CB6 3TA Tel: 01353 740205 Fax: 01353 741364; Church End, Church Lane, Haddenham, Ely CB6 3TB Tel: 01353 740662 — MB BS Lond. 1969; MRCS Eng. LRCP Lond. 1969; Dip. IMC RCS Ed. 1991. (Middlx.) Chairm. Mid Anglia Gen. Pract. Accid. Serv. Prev: SHO (Med.) Papworth Hosp. Papworth Everard; SHO Edgware Gen. Hosp.; Ho. Surg. Chelmsford & Essex Hosp.

KENNY, Patricia Anne Lewisham University Hospital, London SE13 6LH Tel: 020 8333 3000; 45 Hillgate Place, London W8 7SS Tel: 020 7229 3700 — MB BS Lond. 1972; FRCP Lond. 1993; MRCP (UK) 1977; DCH Eng. 1976; DObst RCOG 1974; FFAEM 1996; FRCPCH 1997. Cons. Paediat. A & E Lewisham Univ. Hosp. Prev: Cons. Paediat. Qu. Eliz. Hosp. Childr. Lond.; Sen. Regist. Hosp. Sick Childr. Lond. & St. Bart. Hosp. Lond.

KENNY, Robert Park Road New Surgery, Park Road, Barnoldswick, Colne BB18 5BG Tel: 01282 812244 Fax: 01282 850220; 11 Bancroft Fold, Barnoldswick, Colne BB18 5QS — MB ChB 1979 Manch.

KENNY, Robert James Portglenone Road Surgery, 23 Portglenone Road, Ahoghill, Ballymena BT42 1LE Tel: 028 2587 1200 Fax: 028 2587 8628; 52 Lisnafillan Road, Gracehill, Ballymena BT42 1JA — MB BCh BAO 1975 Belf.; MRCGP 1979; DRCOG 1978. Clin. Asst. (Hypertens.) N.. Health & Social Servs. Bd.

KENNY, Rosaleen Ann Marie Cardiovascular Investigative Unit, Royal Victoria Hospital, Queen Victoria Road, Newcastle upon Tyne NE1 4LP — MB BCh BAO 1977 NUI.

KENNY, Ruth Hannah Westlands, Susworth, Scunthorpe DN17 3AN — BM BS 1985 Nottm.

KENNY, Sheila 5 Frobisher Close, Goring-on-Sea, Worthing BN12 6EY Tel: 01903 45468 — MB BCh BAO 1939 Dub.; MA, MD Dub. 1941, MB BCh BAO 1939; DMRD Eng. 1950. (Univ. Dub.) Socs: Fell. Fac. Radiol. RCSI; Roy. Coll. Radiol. Prev: Cons. Radiol. Armagh City Hosp. & S. Down Hosp. Gp.; Asst. Path. Chester Roy. Infirm.; Sen. Resid. Phys. WhitCh. E.M.S. Hosp. Cardiff.

KENNY, Mr Simon Edward 14 Alexandra Road, West Kirby, Wirral CH48 0RT Tel: 0151 625 3437 Fax: 0151 625 3437 Email: simon.kenny@liv.ac.uk — MB ChB 1990 Birm.; ChB (Hons.) Birm. 1990; BSc (Hons.) Birm. 1987; FRCS Eng. 1995. Lect. (Paediat. Surg.) & Hon. Specialist Regist. (Paediat. Surg.) Inst. Child Health Alder Hey Liverp. Prev: SHO (Surg.) Mersey RHA.; Research Fell. (Paediat. Surg.) &Hon. Regist. (Paediat. Surg.) Inst. Child Health Alder Hey, Liverp.

KENNY, Susan Jane 18 Upper Tooting Park, London SW17 7SR — MB BS 1976 Lond.; MRCPath 1987; DRCOG 1978.

KENNY, Terence Edward 47 Hillcrest Rise, Leeds LS16 7DJ — MB ChB 1975 Leeds.

KENNY, Teresa Mary Measham Medical Unit, High Street, Measham, Swadlincote DE12 7HR Tel: 01530 270667 Fax: 01530 271433; 3 St. James Court, Main St, Barton under Needwood, Burton-on-Trent DE13 8HN — MB BCh BAO 1984 NUI; MRCGP 1991; DRCOG 1991; DCH NUI 1987. GP Measham Med. Unit. Measham.

KENNY, Thomas David Warren Farm, Hilligton, King's Lynn PE31 6BJ — BM 1998 Soton.; BM Soton 1998.

KENNY, Timothy 2 Manor Walk, Benton, Newcastle upon Tyne NE7 7XX Tel: 0191 266 5246; 50 The Grove, Gosforth, Newcastle upon Tyne NE3 1NJ Tel: 0191 285 1874 — MB BS 1983 Newc.; BMedSc (Hons.) Newc. 1980; MRCGP 1989; DCH RCP Lond. 1991. Prev: Trainee GP N.umbria VTS.

KENNY, Timothy James Wolfenden China Cottage, Tarrant Grunville, Blandford Forum DT11 8JR; Flat 2, 10 Oakhill Road, Putney, London SW15 — MB BS 1984 Lond.; MRCGP 1990; DCH RCP Lond. 1988.

KENRICK, Dawn Alexandra 662A Stockport Road, Longsight, Manchester M12 4GA — MB ChB 1996 Dundee; BSc (Hons.) Pharmacy - Strathclyde 1988.

KENRICK, Jeremy Martin Tyrrell The Branden Unit, Leicester General Hospital, Leicester LE5 4PW Tel: 0116 249 0490 — MB BS 1971 Lond.; MRCPsych 1980. (Middlx.) Cons. Psychiat. LoughBoro. Community Team, Leics. Prev: Lect. (Psychiat.) Univ. Leic.; Regist. (Psychiat.) St. Crispin Hosp. N.ampton; Ho. Surg. Middlx. Hosp. Lond.

KENRICK, John Edward Arthur, OBE (retired) Bronnydd, Abergele Road, Llanrwst LL26 0NG Tel: 01492 640560 Fax: 01492 640605 — MB BCh Wales 1958. Prev: Chairm. N. Wales HA.

KENRICK, Rhian Mair Bronnydd, Abergele Road, Llanrwst LL26 0NG Tel: 01492 640560 — MB BS 1985 Lond.; BSc (Hons.) Lond. 1982; MRCGP 1989; DGM RCP Lond. 1989; DRCOG 1987; Cert. Family Plann. JCC 1987. (St. Geo. Med. Sch. Lond.) GP Darwin, Austral. Prev: Sen. Med. Off. (Community) Torres Straits Qu.sland, Austral.; Med. Off. RFDS Broken Hill, NSW, Austral.; Trainee GP/SHO Mayday Hosp. Croydon VTS.

KENSHOLE, Diana Helen Clift Surgery, Minchens Lane, Bramley, Tadley RG26 5BH — BM 1989 Soton.; MA Camb. 1985; MRCGP; DRCOG; DCH. (Southampton) Prev: SHO (Paediat.) Frimley Pk. Hosp. Surrey; SHO (A & E & O & G) Ealing Gen. Hosp.; SHO (O & G) Heatherwood Hosp. Ascot.

KENSIT, John Geoffrey 18 Wood Ride, Orpington BR5 1PX — MB BS 1969 Lond.; MRCS Eng. LRCP Lond. 1969; MRCPath 1976. (Kings Coll. Hosp.) Cons. Microbiol. Qu. Mary's Hosp. Sidcup. Prev: Sen. Regist. (Clin. Bacteriol. & Virol.) Guy's Hosp. Lond.; Lect. (Med. Microbiol.) Lond. Hosp. Med. Coll.; Intern Hamilton Civic Hosps. Ontario, Canada.

KENT, Andrew Frank Tel: 01325 462762 — BM BCh 1981 Oxf.; BSc (Hons.) St. And. 1978; MRCGP 1987.

KENT, Andrew John Department of General Psychiatry, St. George's Hospital and Medical School, Cranmer Terrace, London SW17 0RE Tel: 020 8725 2548 Fax: 020 8725 3538 Email: a.kent@sghms.ac.uk — MB BS 1984 Lond.; MRCPsych 1989; MD Lond.1999. Sen. Lect. (Community Psychiat.) St. Geo. Hosp. Med. Sch. Lond.; Hon. Cons. Psychiat. S. W. Lond. St Geo. Ment. Health NHS Trust.

KENT, Andrew Stephen Harding 21 Mill Pond Estate, West Lane, Rotherithe, London SE16 4NA — MB BS 1987 Lond.; BSc Lond. 1984, MB BS 1987.

KENT, Mr Andrew William, Maj. RAMC Royal Army Medical College, Millbank, London SW1 — MB ChB 1987 Ed.; FRCS Ed. 1994. Regist. (Orthop. Surg.) P.ss Alexandra's RAF Hosp. Wroughton. Prev: SHO (Surg.) Qu. Eliz. Milit. Hosp.

KENT, Barbara Broxburn Health Centre, Holmes Road, Broxburn EH52 5LZ Tel: 01506 852016; 22 Lidgate, Shot, Ratho, Newbridge EH28 8TY Tel: 0131 335 3583 — MB ChB 1982 Aberd.; MRCGP 1987; T (GP) 1991; DRCOG 1986; DFFP. (Aberdeen) GP Princip. Broxburn. Socs: Scott. Family Plann. Soc. Prev: Med. Off. (Family Plann.) Lothian HB.

KENT, Charles Philip St Martins, Western Road, Crediton EX17 3NF Tel: 01647 24298 — BM BCh 1978 Oxf.; MA Oxon.

KENT, Christopher Jan Green End Surgery, 58 Green End, Comberton, Cambridge CB3 7DY Tel: 01223 262500 Fax: 01223 264401; Grove Cottage, 47 High St, Bourn, Cambridge CB3 7TR Tel: 01954 719232 — MB BS 1987 Lond.; MRCGP 1993; DRCOG 1990; DGM RCP Lond. 1988. Prev: Trainee GP P.ss Alexandra Hosp. Harlow VTS; Ho. Phys. James Paget Hosp. Gt. Yarmouth; Ho. Surg. Qu. Eliz. Hosp. Kings Lynn.

KENT, David Gregory Flat 823 William Goodenough House, Mecklenburgh Square, London WC1 2AN — MB ChB 1986 Auckland; FRACO 1993.

KENT, David Laurence Unit of Ophthala, Univ. of Liverpool, Duncan Building, Daulbx Street, Liverpool L69 3GA Tel: 0151 706 3969; Melvin, Enniscorthy, Republic of Ireland Email: dkent@liv.ac.uk — MB BCh BAO 1990 NUI; FRCOphth 1995. (University College Hospital, Galway, Ireland) Specialist Regist. St. Pauls' Eye Unit, Liverp.; Hon. Staff Mem., Univ. of Liverp. Socs: Assn. Research Vision & Ophth.; Fell. Roy. Coll. Ophth.; Irish Coll. Ophth. Prev: SPR/SHO (Ophth.) Roy. Liverp. Univ. Hosp. & Walton Hosp. Liverp.; Res. Fell. Ophthalm. Univ. Liverp.; SHO (Ophth.) St. Paul's Eye Unit Liverp.

KENT, David Robert Danebridge Medical Centre, London Road, Northwich CW9 5HR Tel: 01606 49317 Fax: 01606 331977; 93 Mornant Avenue, Hartford, Northwich CW8 2FG — MB ChB 1986 Leic.; DRCOG 1991.

KENT, Elspeth Marie Atwill Ward, RDE Heavitree, Exeter; 4 Hawthorn Drive, Sidmouth EX10 9XW — MD 1948 Manitoba. (Manitoba) Clin. Asst. Exe Vale Hosp. (Exminster Br.); Clin. Asst. Roy. Devon & Exeter Hosp. (Exeter Br.).

KENT, Fiona Janet 22 Balvie Road, Milngavie, Glasgow G62 7AG — MB ChB 1968 Glas.

KENT, James Timothy Barr House, 51 Farm Lane S., New Milton BH25 7BW — BM BS 1988 Nottm.; MRCP (UK) 1991.

KENT, Jane Audrey 18 Hartington Place, Edinburgh EH10 4LE Tel: 0131 229 1155 — MB ChB Sheff. 1968; MPH Glas. 1985.

KENT, Jennifer The Coach House, Norman Cross, Peterborough PE7 3TB — MB BS 1973 Lond.; FFA RCS Eng. 1982. (St. Mary's) Assoc. Specialist (Anaesth.) PeterBoro. Hosp. Prev: Regist.

(Anaesth.) PeterBoro. Dist. Hosp.; SHO (Anaesth.) City Hosp. Nottm.; Ho. Surg. St. Mary's Hosp. Lond.

KENT, Jill Elizabeth The Surgery, 30 Old Road West, Gravesend DA11 0LL Tel: 01474 352075/567799 Fax: 01474 333952 — MB BS 1983 Lond.; BSc (Hons. Pharmacol.) Lond. 1979, MB BS 1983, LMSSA 1982; MRCGP 1986; DRCOG 1985. Prev: Trainee GP Dartford VTS.

KENT, John Henry Charles (retired) 8 Burnside, Highcliffe, Christchurch BH23 4QZ Tel: 01425 276880 — MB BS Lond. 1958. Prev: GP Soton.

KENT, John Howard c/o Newton Lodge Regional Secure Unit, Ouchthorpe Lane, Wakefield WF1 3SP — MB BS 1981 Newc.; MRCPsych 1986; MMedSci (Clin. Psychiat.) Leeds 1987. Cons. Forens. Psychiat. Newton Lodge Regional Secure Unit Wakefield. Prev: Sen. Regist. (Forens. Psychiat.) Newton Lodge Regional Secure Unit Wakefield; Sen. Regist. (Gen. Psychiat.) Trent RHA.

KENT, Leslie Neil 12 Bolton Road, Farnworth, Bolton BL4 7JW Tel: 012004 571178; 16 Kinloch Drive, Bolton BL1 4LZ Tel: 01204 849787 — MB ChB 1975 Manch. SHO (Anaesth.) N. Manch. Gen. Hosp. Prev: Trainee GP Bolton; SHO (O & G) Oldham & Dist. Gen. Hosp.; SHO (Cas.) N. Manch. Gen. Hosp.

KENT, Lilian Joan (retired) 15 Brimhay, Dartington, Totnes TQ9 6HX — MRCS Eng. LRCP Lond. 1927. Prev: Ho. Phys. Bermondsey Med. Miss. Hosp. Wom. & Childr.

KENT, Martin Barry 93 North Street, Great Wakering, Southend-on-Sea SS3 0HT — MB BS 1982 Lond.; MRCP (UK) 1985; MRCGP 1989. Prev: Trainee GP Timperley; Regist. (Radiol.) Manch. Univ.

KENT, Michael Alan Kenland House Surgery, 37 Station Road, Milngavie, Glasgow G62 8BT Tel: 0141 956 1005 Fax: 0141 955 0342 — MB ChB 1968 Glas. (Glas.)

KENT, Michael John Halifax Crescent Surgery, 4 Halifax Crescent, Thornton, Liverpool L23 1TH Tel: 0151 924 3532 Fax: 0151 924 3171 — MB ChB 1977 Liverp.; DRCOG 1980.

KENT, Nicholas Julian The Surgery, Heywood, Lodway Gdns, Pill, Bristol BS20 0DN Tel: 01275 372105 Fax: 01275 373879 — BM 1980 Soton.; MRCP (UK) 1985; MRCGP 1991; DRCOG 1990. Prev: Regist. (Neurol.) Frenchay Hosp. Bristol; Regist. Rotat. (Gen. Med.) (Rotat.) Stoke Mandeville Hosp. Aylesbury.

KENT, Richard John Ipswich Public Health Laboratory, Ipswich Hospital, Heath Road, Ipswich IP4 5PD Tel: 01473 703741 — MB BS 1985 Lond.; MSc Lond. 1990, BSc 1982; MRCP (UK) 1988; MRCPath 1992; MD Lond. 1997. (Westminster)

KENT, Richard Vincent The Surgery, 83 South St., Bishop's Stortford CM23 3AL Tel: 01279 653225; Kingswood, 34 Walnut Drive, Bishop's Stortford CM23 4JT Tel: 01279 656544 — MB BS 1969 Lond. (Middlx.) Prev: Regist. (Anaesth.) Johannesburg Gen. Hosp., S. Afr.; Ho. Phys. Kingston Hosp. Surrey; Ho. Off. (Surg.) Middlx. Hosp. Lond.

KENT, Mrs Rosalind Stella Mary (retired) 34 Back Lane, Eynsham, Witney OX29 4QW — BM BS 1976 Nottm. Prev: Princip. in Gen. Pract. Riverside Pract. Winchester.

KENT, Ruth Margaret Hunters Moor Regional Rehabilitation Centre, Hunters Road, Newcastle upon Tyne NE2 4NR; 53 Princes Meadow, Gosforth, Newcastle upon Tyne NE3 4RZ — MB BS 1991 Newc.; BMedSc Newc. 1988; MRCP (UK) 1994. Sen. Regist. Rotat. (Neurol. Rehabil.) Hunters Moor Regional Rehabil. Centre. Socs: Brit. Soc. Rehabil. Med.; Soc. Research in Rehabil. Prev: Clin. Research Assoc. & Hon. Regist. (Neurol. Rehabil.) Univ. Newc. u.Tyne; SHO Rotat. (Med.) Newc.

KENT, Sidney George (retired) Long Reach, Higher Contour Road, Kingswear, Dartmouth TQ6 0DE — MRCS Eng. LRCP Lond. 1952. Prev: JHMO Farnham Hosp.

KENT, Mr Stephen Edward Eyton House, Baschurch, Shrewsbury SY4 2JJ — MB ChB 1977 Birm.; FRCS Eng. 1983; T(S) 1991.

KENT, Mr Stuart John Stanley North House, Casewick, Stamford PE9 4RX Tel: 01778 560244 — MRCS Eng. LRCP Lond. 1966; MS Lond. 1976, MB BS 1966; FRCS Eng. 1971. (St. Thos.) Cons. Surg. P'boro. Hosps. NHS Trust. Prev: Sen. Surg. Regist. St. Thos. Hosp. Lond.

KENT, Valerie Jane Leiper, 102 Mayfield Road, Edinburgh EH9 3AG — MB ChB 1997 Aberd.

KENT-JOHNSTON, Caroline Anne Dayshs Farm, Hospital Road, Shirrell Heath, Southampton SO32 2JR Tel: 01329 832346 Fax: 01329 832346 Email: kj@fribb.stargate.co.uk — MB ChB 1977 Auckland; DRCOG 1981. Police Surg. Portsmouth Area Hants. Constab. Prev: GP Portsmouth; GP Retainer Scheme Lee-on-Solent.

KENTISH, Lesley Elizabeth 45 Ramsay Road, Banchory AB31 5TS Fax: 01330 824752 — MB ChB 1987 Aberd. Supervisory SHO (Neonatol.) Neonat. Unit Roy. Aberd. Matern. Hosp. Prev: Supervisory SHO (Med. Paediat.) Roy. Aberd. Childr. Hosp.; SHO (A & E) Roy. Aberd. Childr. Hosp.; SHO (Med. Paediat.) Roy. Aberd. Childr. Hosp.

KENTON, Anthony Robert Dept. of Neurology, Queen Elizabeth Hospital, Edgbaston, Birmingham B15 2 TH Tel: 0121 472 1311; 911 Bristol Road, Selly Oak, Birmingham B29 6ND Tel: 0121 415 5721 — MB ChB 1990 Leic.; MD 1998; MRCP (UK) 1993. (Leicester University) SpR (Neurol.) QE. Hosp. B'ham. Socs: Assn. Brit. NeUrol.s. Prev: SpR. (Neurol.) Leicester Roy. Infirm.; Research Fell. (Neurol.) Leicester Roy. Infirm.

KENTON-SMITH, Jesse Garden Flat, 42 Ainger Road, London NW3 3AT — MB BS 1990 Lond.

KENWARD, David Howard (retired) Herdholt, Little Ayton Lane, Great Ayton, Middlesbrough TS9 6HD Tel: 01642 722521 — MB ChB 1960 Leeds; FRCP Ed. 1980, M 1967. Prev: Cons. Nephrol. S. Tees. HA.

KENWARD, Shelagh Elaine 3 Winton Grove, Lostock, Bolton BL6 4JQ — MB BS 1983 Lond.; MRCGP 1992; DRCOG 1987. Clin. Asst. Wigan Hospice. Socs: Assn. Palliat. Med. & BMA.

KENWOOD, Claire Frances Department of Psychiatry, Royal South Hampshire Hospital, Graham Road, Southampton SO14 0YG — MB ChB 1988 Birm.; ChB Birm. 1988. Cons. (Psychiat.) Roy.S.Hants. Hosp. Solon. Prev: Sen. Regist. (Psychiat.) Roy. S. Hants. Hosp. Soton.; SHO (Psychiat.) Burton Rd. Hosp. Dudley.

KENWORTHY, Jonathan Ward 95 Delph Lane, Delph, Oldham OL3 5UP — MB ChB 1991 Ed.

KENWORTHY, Richard John 10 Ryles Crescent, Macclesfield SK11 8DD — BM BS 1991 Nottm.

KENWORTHY-BROWNE, James Michael Jericho Health Centre, Walton Street, Oxford OX2 6NW Tel: 01865 311234 Fax: 01865 311087; (cons. rooms & home), Windflower House, Horton-cum-Studley, Oxford OX33 1AY Tel: 01865 358112 Fax: 01865 358112 Email: micheal.kenworthy-b@oriel.ox.ac.uk — BM BCh 1964 Oxf.; MA, BM BCh Oxf. 1964; FRCP Lond. 1997; MRCP (UK) 1975; FRCGP 1982, M 1976. (Oxf.) Socs: Fell. Roy. Soc. Med.; BMA & Brit. Assn. Med. Dent. Hypn.; (Ex-Pres.) Oxf. Med. Soc. Prev: Med. Represen. Oxf. City & Co. Community Unit Exec.; Course Organiser (Gen. Pract.) Oxf. VTS; RCGP Tutor (Oxf. Dist.) Thames Valley Fac.

KENWRIGHT, Professor John (retired) Nuffield Orthopaedic Centre, Headington, Oxford OX3 7LD Tel: 01865 227377 Fax: 01865 227354 — BM BCh 1960 Oxf.; MA Oxf. 1965; MD Stockholm 1973; FRCS Eng. 1966. Nuffield Prof. Orthop. Surg. Oxf. Univ. & Cons. in Orthop. Surg. & Traumatol. Nuffield Orthop. Centre & John Radcliffe Hosp. Oxf. Prev: Resid. Surg. Off. Roy. Marsden Hosp. Lond.

KENWRIGHT, Katie Anne Well Cottage, Mapleton Road, Westerham TN16 1PS — BM BS 1998 Nottm.; BM BS Nottm 1998.

KENWRIGHT, Paula 4 Chepstow Park, Downend, Bristol BS16 6SQ — MB ChB 1989 Manch.; MRCGP 1994; DRCOG 1993; DCH RCP Lond. 1992.

KENYON, Andrew Charles William Salters Medical Practice, The Health Centre, Ombersley Street, Droitwich WR9 8RD Tel: 01905 773535 Fax: 01905 794098; Four Winds, Himbleton, Droitwich WR9 7LG Tel: 01905 391200 — MB BS 1979 Lond.; BSc (Path.) Lond. 1976; MRCS Eng. LRCP Lond. 1979; MRCGP 1984; LicAc 1993. (Guy's)

KENYON, Anna Patricia 54 Trajan Gate, Stevenage SG2 7QG Tel: 01438 359114 — MB ChB 1995 Birm.; ChB Birm. 1995. Socs: Med. Protec. Soc.; BMA.

KENYON, Anthony John (retired) 274 Havant Road, Drayton, Portsmouth PO6 1PA Tel: 023 92 370422 — MB ChB 1963 St. And. Prev: Ho Phys. Perth Roy. Infirm.

KENYON, Barrie The Surgery, 26 Rough Road, Kingstanding, Birmingham B44 0UY Tel: 0121 354 4560; 12 Cedarwood Croft, Birmingham B42 1HS — MB ChB 1969 Birm.

KENYON, Beatrix Kate Margot 46 Norbiton Avenue, Kingston upon Thames KT1 3QR Tel: 020 8546 3091 — MB BS 1986 Lond. Instruc. Doctor (Family Plann. & Well Wom.) Richmond, Twickenham

& Roehampton, Merton, Chem & Kingston HAs; Clin. Asst. (Genitourin. Med.) Roehampton Clinic.

KENYON, Christopher Mark Beaumont Street Surgery, 19 Beaumont Street, Oxford OX1 2NA Tel: 01865 240501 Fax: 01865 240503 Email: chris.kenyon@gp-k84018.nhs.uk — MB ChB 1983 Liverp.; MRCP (UK) 1987; MRCGP 1989; DRCOG 1988. Prev: SHO (Paediat.) Roy. United Hosp. Bath; Regist. (Med.) Clatterbridge Hosp. Wirral; SHO (Cardiothor.) BRd.green Hosp. Liverp.

KENYON, Colin Michael Villa Medical Centre, Roman Road, Prenton CH43 3DB Tel: 0151 608 4702 Fax: 0151 609 0067; 28 Rathmore Road, Oxton, Prenton CH43 2HF Tel: 0151 0652 0882 — MB ChB 1972 Liverp. (Liverp.) Prev: Regist. (Med.) Birkenhead Gen. Hosp.; SHO (Cardiol.) & Ho. Off. Sefton Gen. Hosp. Liverp.

KENYON, Mr Guy Stuart Whipps Cross Hospital, Leyton Stone, London E11 1NB Tel: 020 8539 5522 Fax: 020 8535 6834 Email: guykenyon@compuserve.com; Pentlands, East Common, Harpenden AL5 1DG Tel: 01582 767593 Fax: 01582 767751 — MB ChB 1974 Ed.; MD 1990 Edin.; FRCS 1980 Edin.; FRCS 1983 Eng.; BSc 1971 (Hons); MBA 1995 Surrey. (Edinburgh) p/t Cons. Otolaryngol.Whipps Cross; Hon. Cons. Otolaryngol. Roy. Hosp. Trust; Edr. Laryngol. & Otol. Socs: Fell. Roy. Soc. Med.; Med. Soc. Lond. & BMA. Prev: Cons. Otolaryngol. Qu. Eliz. Hosp. Childr. Lond.; Sen. Regist. (Otolaryngol.) Roy. Free Hosp. Lond. & Roy. Surrey Co. Hosp. Guildford; Regist. (Otolaryngol.) Lond. Hosp. Whitechapel.

KENYON, John Barrington The Surgery, 356 Southborough Lane, Bromley BR2 8AA Tel: 020 8468 7081 — MB BS 1982 Lond.

KENYON, Mr John Richard (Ian) (retired) The Rye Peck, Chertsey Road, Shepperton TW17 9NU Tel: 01932 563366 — MB ChB 1942 Glas.; BSc Glas. 1939, ChM 1960, MB ChB 1942; FRCS Ed. 1948; FRCS Eng. 1953. Hon. Cons. Surg. St. Mary's Hosp. Lond. W2. Prev: Asst. Dir. Surgic. Unit, St. Mary's Hosp. Lond.

KENYON, Joseph Bernard Chalefont, Stockbridge Road, Kimbridge, Romsey SO51 0LE — MB ChB 1952 Liverp.; MRCS Eng. LRCP Lond. 1952. (Liverp.) Prev: Ho. Phys. Sefton Gen. Hosp. Liverp.; Ho. Surg. O & G Chester City Hosp.

KENYON, Katherine Lucy 59 Braemar Avenue, Wimbledon Park, London SW19 8AY Tel: 020 8947 0650; Rectory Farm House, Broadwell, Moreton-in-Marsh GL56 0TL — MB BS 1987 Lond.; MRCGP 1994; T(GP) 1994; DFFP 1994; DRCOG 1994; DCH RCP Lond. 1992. (St. Thos. Hosp.) Acad. Asst. (Gen. Pract.) St. Geo. Hosp. Lond. Prev: Trainee GP Lond.; Med. Off. (Community Paediat.) St. Geo. Hosp. Lond.; SHO (Geriat.) Gloucester Roy. Hosp.

KENYON, Nicola Jane 8 Thorn Drive, Bearsden, Glasgow G61 4NB — MB ChB 1978 Sheff.; MRCOG 1985.

KENYON, Nuala 3 East Drive, Hawk Green, Marple, Stockport SK6 7JJ Tel: 0161 427 1064 — MB BCh BAO 1944 NUI. (Univ. Coll. Dub.) Prev: Asst. Div. Med. Off. Ashton-under-Lyne & Mossley, Lancs. CC; Receiv. Room Off. N. Middlx. Hosp.; Res. Med. Off. Meath Co. Hosp.

KENYON, Peter Sylvanus Brandon Road Surgery, 108 Brandon Road, Binley, Coventry CV3 2JF Tel: 024 7645 3634 Fax: 024 7663 6886; Ave. House, Stretton-on-Dunsmore, Rugby — MRCS Eng. LRCP Lond. 1971.

KENYON, Rachael Margaret Flat 15, Brompton Court, 2A Brompton Avenue, Sefton Park, Liverpool L17 3BU — MB ChB 1997 Liverp.

KENYON, Robert Christopher The Thickett, Gare Hill, Frome BA11 5EY Tel: 01985 844319 — MB BS 1972 Lond.; MRCGP 1984; DCH RCP Lond. 1986.

KENYON, Sally Elisabeth HM Prison Service, HMP Holme House, Stockton-on-Tees Tel: 01642 673759; West End, The Byre, Borrowby, Thirsk YO7 4QG Tel: 01845 537028 — MB BS 1985 Lond.; MRCGP 1995; DRCOG 1994; DAB 1998. (Westm.) Med. Off. HMP Holme Hse. Stockton-upon-Tees. Prev: Maj. RAMC; SHO (Acute Med. & Geriat.) W.morland Gen. Hosp. Kendal; SHO (Psychiat.) Darlington Memor. Hosp.

KENYON, Stella Teresa Burnley Wood Medical Centre, 50 Parliament St., Burnley BB11 3HR Tel: 01282 425521 — MB ChB 1986 Birm; Cert. Family Plann. JCC 1992; T(GP) 1991. Prev: Trainee GP Stafford VTS.

KENYON, Susan Jane Chadderton (Town) Health Centre, Middleton Road, Chadderton, Oldham OL9 0LH Tel: 0161 628 4543 Fax: 0161 284 1658; 45A Oldham Road, Grasscroft, Oldham OL4 4JD — MB ChB 1982 Manch.; DRCOG 1986.

KENYON, Victor Gordon 7 Buckler's Yard, Gatehouse Lane, Water Tower, Bedworth, Nuneaton CV12 8WE; 7 Buckler's Yard, Gatehouse Lane, Water Tower, Bedworth, Nuneaton CV12 8WE Tel: 01203 733448 — MB ChB 1965 Ed.; FRCOG 1983, M 1970. (Univ. Ed.) Cons. O & G Geo. Eliot Hosp. NHS Trust Nuneaton. Socs: Nuffield Vis. Soc.; Birm. & Midl. Obst. & Gyn. Soc.

KENYON, William Edward Department of Pathology, Countess of Chester Hospital, Liverpool Road, Chester CH2 1UL Tel: 01244 365642 Fax: 01244 365386 Email: we.kenyon@coch-tr.nwest.nhs.uk; Hillside House, Glenrose Road, Woolton, Liverpool L25 5JT Tel: 0151 428 2742 — MB ChB 1972 Liverp.; MA Camb. 1973; MB BChir Camb. 1973; FRCPath 1990, M 1978. (Camb. & Liverp. Univ.) Cons. Histopath. Countess of Chester Hosp. NHS Trust; Regional Adviser RCPath Mersey Deanery; Med. Dir. Countess of Chester Hosp. NHS Trust. Socs: Assn. Clin. Path.; Internat. Acad. Path. (Brit. Div.); Liverp. Med. Inst. Prev: Clin. Dir. Path. Countess of Chester Hosp. NHS Trust; Clin. Lect. (Path.) Univ. Liverp.; Cons. Histopath. BRd.green Hosp. Liverp.

KENYON, William Islay (retired) Thameside District Hospital, Fountain Street, Ashton-under-Lyne OL6 9RW — MB ChB 1945 Glas.; FRCP Lond. 1976, M 1956. Cons. Phys. Tameside Dist. Hosp. Ashton-under-Lyne. Prev: Sen. Med. Regist. W. Lond. Hosp.

KENYON, Zoe Ebbor House, Barrack Hill, Hythe CT21 4BY Tel: 01303 267884 Email: zoekenyon@msn.com — MB ChB Liverp. 1956; MA (Social Anthropol.) Univ. Kent 1995; FRCGP 1988, M 1977. Course Organiser W. Kent Vocationally Trained Acad. Assoc. Socs: Balint Soc. Prev: Med. Adviser Kirklees FHSA; Assoc. Adviser (Gen. Pract.) SE Thames RHA.

KEOGH, Ann Katherine 16 Ranelagh Drive, Ecclesall, Sheffield S11 9HE — MB BS 1979 Lond. (Char. Cross) Prev: SHO (Paediat.) Hammersmith Hosp. & John Radcliffe Hosp. Oxf.

KEOGH, Anthony Joseph Beech House Surgery, 1 Ash Tree Road, Knaresborough HG5 0UB Tel: 01423 542580 Fax: 01423 864450 — MB ChB 1981 Leeds.

KEOGH, Belinda Patricia Hillview Medical Centre, 60 Bromsgrove Road, Redditch B97 4RN Tel: 01527 66511; The Moat House, Radford Road, Alvechurch, Birmingham B48 7ST Tel: 0121 445 1773 — MB ChB 1976 Leeds.

KEOGH, Brian Francis Department of Anaesthesia, Royal Brompton Hospital, London SW3 6NP Tel: 020 7351 8526 Fax: 020 7351 8524 Email: b.keogh@rbh.nthames.nhs.uk — MB BS 1978 Sydney; MB BS (Hons.) Sydney 1978; FFA RCS Eng. 1986; T(Anaesth.) 1991. Cons. Anaesth. & IC Roy. Brompton Hosp. Lond. Prev: Doverdale Fell (IC) Roy. Brompton Hosp.; Regist. (Anaesth.) Roy. Free Hosp. Lond.; Regist. (Anaesth.) Roy. P. Alfred Hosp. Sydney, Australia.

KEOGH, Mr Bruce Edward Queen Elizabeth Hospital, Edgbaston, Birmingham B15 2TH Tel: 0121 627 2533 Fax: 0121 627 2533; Claremont House, 68 Oakfield Road, Selly Park, Birmingham B29 7EG Tel: 0121 472 7419 — MB BS 1980 Lond.; BSc (Hons) Lond. 1977, MD 1989; FRCS Ed. 1985; MRCS Eng. LRCP Lond. 1980. (Char. Cross) Cons. Cardiothoracic Surg. Qu. Eliz. Hosp. & Birm. Univ. Hosp. NHS Trust. Socs: Fell. Roy. Soc. Med. (Sec. Cardiothoracic Sect.); Fell. Europ. Soc. Cardiol.; Brit. Assn. Clin. Anat. Prev: Brit. Heart Foundat. Sen. Lect. & Cons. Cardiothoracic Surg. Roy. Postgrad. Med. Sch. Hammersmith & Char. Cross Hosps. Lond.; Sen. Regist. Rotat. (Cardiothoracic Surg.) Hammersmith, Harefield, Middlx. Hosps. & St. Geo. Hosp.; Regist. (Cardiothoracic Surg.) Roy. Postgrad. Med. Sch. Hammersmith Hosp. Lond.

KEOGH, James Robert The Falt, Willow Grange, Yaffle Rd, Weybridge KT13 0QF — MB ChB 1978 Birm.

KEOGH, Joanna Mary Elizabeth Torr Farmhouse, Torr Lane, Yealmpton, Plymouth PL8 2HW — MB BS 1998 Lond.; MB BS Lond 1998.

KEOGH, Mr Sean Paul 4 Meadfoot Drive, Kingswinford DY6 9DB — MB BS 1987 Lond.; MRCP (UK) 1992; FRCS Ed. 1994; DTM & H RCP Lond. 1992. Regist. (Helicopter Emerg. Med. Servs.) Roy. Lond. Hosp. Prev: SHO (Neurosurg.) Nat. Hosp. Neurol. & Neurosurg. Lond.; SHO (Transpl. Surg.) Addenbrooke's Hosp. Camb.; Regist. (Trauma Surg.) Baragwanath Hosp. Soweto, SA.

KEOGHANE, Mr Stephen Richard Dept. of Urology, Churchill Hospital, Headington, Oxford OX3 7LJ — MB BS 1989 Lond.; FRCS 2001 (Urol.); MS Lond. 1997; FRCS Eng. 1993. Specialist Regist. (Urol.), Ch.ill Hosp., Oxf. Prev: Research Regist. (Urol.) Ch.ill Hosp.

Oxf. & Health Servs. Research Unit Univ. Oxf.; SHO (Urol.) Cheltenham Gen. Hosp.; Regist. (Urol.) Glos. Roy. Hosp.; N.ampton Gen. Hosp.; Battle Hosp., Reading.

KEOHANE, Katharine Mary Sutton Hill Medical Practice, Maythorne Close, Sutton Hill, Telford TF7 4DH Tel: 01952 586471 Fax: 01952 588029; 2c Wesley Road, Iron Bridge, Telford TF8 7PE Tel: 01952 453565 — MB ChB 1978 Birm.; MRCGP 1985; DA Eng. 1983; DObst Auckland 1982.

KEOHANE, Patrick Peter European Research Centre, Sunninghill Road, Windlesham GU20 6PH Tel: 01276 853000 Fax: 01276 853378 — MB BS 1976 Lond.; MRCP (UK) 1979. Europ. Med. Dir. Lily Research Lab.

KEOHANE, Stephen Gerard 3 Thetford Road, New Malden KT3 5DN — MB BS 1990 Lond.; BSc (Hons.) Lond. 1986; MRCP (UK) 1993. Lect. & Hon. Sen. Regist. (Dermat.) Univ. Sheff. Roy. Hallamsh. Hosp. Sheff. Prev: Regist. (Dermat.) Roy. Infirm. Oxf.

KEOUGH, Alexander Daniel Hillrise, Lovedon Lane, King's Worthy, Winchester SO23 7NL — MB BS 1992 Lond.

KEOWN, Adrienne Patricia 29 Rowley Meadows, Newcastle BT33 0RW — MB BCh BAO 1991 Belf.

KEOWN, Christine Elizabeth Peaslake Lane, Peaslake, Guildford GU5 9RL Tel: 01306 730875 Fax: 01306 731509 — MB ChB 1975 Manch.; MRCGP 1984; DObst RCPI 1983; DCH Dub. 1981. Prev: Trainee GP Farnham VTS; Paediat. Resid. Ottawa, Canada; SHO (Paediat.) Manch.

KEOWN, Mr Denis Willow House, 2 Bodenham Road, Folkestone CT20 2NU Tel: 01303 56399 — MB ChB 1952 Glas.; FRCS Eng. 1962. Cons. Gen. Surg. S.E. Kent Hosps.

KEOWN, Patrick John 11 Peterborough Road, London SW6 3BT — MB BS 1994 Lond.

KEPPIE, Wilma 1 Townhead, Kettlewell, Skipton BD23 5RL; (Surgery) 46 Grey Road, Liverpool L9 1DB Tel: 0151 525 3533 — LRCP LRCS 1950 Ed.; LRCP LRCS Ed. LRFPS Glas. 1950. (Roy. Colls. Ed.) Prev: Ho. Phys. Roy. Infirm. Edin. & Rush Green Hosp. Romford.

KER, David Andrew James Oakham Medical Practice, Cold Overton Road, Oakham LE15 6NT Tel: 01572 722621/2 — MB BS 1983 Lond.; MRCGP 1987. (Westm. Med. Sch. Lond.)

KER, David Brownhill Health Centre, West Byfleet KT14 6DH Tel: 01932 336880 Fax: 01932 355681; Ferniehurst, Hockering Gardens, Woking GU22 7DA — MB BS 1953 Lond. (St. Thos.) Prev: Cas. Off. & Ho. Phys. St. Thos. Hosp.

KER, Denis Stuart Scott (retired) 2 Birch Close, Wickham Market, Woodbridge IP13 0QR — MB ChB 1950 Ed. Prev: Surg. Lt. RNVR.

KER, Gordon John Surgery, Gorbals Health Centre, 45 Pine Place, Glasgow G5 0BQ Tel: 0141 429 6291; 69 Langside Drive, Newlands, Glasgow G43 2QX Tel: 0141 637 0018 — MB ChB 1945 Glas.; MRCGP 1963. Socs: Fell. BMA; Fell. Brit. Soc. Med. & Dent. Hypn. Prev: Ho. Surg. Vict. Infirm. Glas. & Roy. Matern. Hosp. Glas.

KER, Jean Scott 1 Dove Court, 16 Albert Terrace, Churchill, Edinburgh — MB ChB 1982 Manch.

KER, John Wellwood (retired) Ciddy Hall, Liss GU33 7HE Tel: 01730 893993 — MB BChir 1946 Camb.; BA, MB BChir Camb. 1946. Prev: Med. Off. Pain Managem. Centre King Edwd. VII Hosp. Midhurst.

KER, Mr Nicholas Brett Maldon Wycke, Wycke Hill, Maldon CM9 6SQ — MB BS 1975 Lond.; FRCS Ed. 1981. Cons. Orthop. Surg. Basildon & Thurrock HA. Prev: Sen. Regist. Whittington, W.m & Univ. Coll. Hosps. Lond.

KER, Norman Downie (Surgery) Gorbals Health Centre, 45 Pine Place, Glasgow G5 Tel: 0141 429 6291; 355 Carmunnock Road, Glasgow G44 Tel: 0141 634 0431 — LRCP LRCS 1948 Ed.; LRCP LRCS Ed. LRFPS Glas. 1948. Prev: Ho. Phys. Vict. Infirm. Glas.

KER, William Alison (retired) 164 Eccleshall Road, Stafford ST16 1JA — MRCS Eng. LRCP Lond. 1951; MRCPsych 1971; DPM Eng. 1954. Hon. Cons. Psychiat. Wolverhampton HA. Prev: Sen. Regist. Univ. Dept. Psychol. Med. S.. Gen. Hosp. Glas.

***KERAC, Marko** 3 Kingsridge, London SW19 6LG Email: mkerac@hotmail.com — MB BS 1998 Lond.; MB BS Lond 1998; BSc Lond. 1994.

KERAWALA, Cyrus Jimmy Department of Oral & Maxillofacial Surgery, Middlesbrough General Hospital, Ayresome Green Lane, Middlesbrough TS5 5AZ Tel: 01642 854257 — MB BS 1992 Lond.; BDS Lond. 1985; FDS RCS Eng. 1990; FRCS Ed. 1995. (St. Geo. Hosp.) Higher Surgic. Trainee (Oral & Maxillofacial Surg.)MiddlesBoro. Gen. Hosp. Socs: Brit. Assn. Oral & Maxillofacial Surg.; Eur. Assn. Cranio-Maxillo. Surg.; Brit. Assn. Head & Neck Oncol. Prev: Higher Surgic. Trainee (Oral & Maxillofacial Surg.) Sunderland Dist. Gen. Hosp.

KERAWALA, Firoze Manek Cameron-Mowat and Partners, Manford Way Health Centre, 40 Foremark Close, Hainault, Ilford IG6 3HS Tel: 020 8500 9938 Fax: 020 8559 9319; The Edge, Ongar Road, Abridge, Romford RM4 1UB — MB BS 1983 Lond. (Royal London Hospital) Prev: Clin. Med. Off. (Child Health) Tower Hamlets HA.

KERAWALA, Jimmy Jal 3 Glendonnell Lodge, 59 Albemarle Road, Beckenham BR3 5HL — MB BS 1945 Bombay; BSc Bombay 1945. (Grant Med. Coll.)

KERBEL, David Gary Saffron Group Practice, 509 Saffron Lane, Leicester LE2 6UL Tel: 0116 244 0888 Fax: 01162 831405 — MB ChB 1989 Cape Town. Trainee GP Leicester VTS. Socs: BMA.

KERBY, Catherine Cardiff and Vale NHS Trust, Lansdowne Hospital, Canton, Cardiff CF11 8PL Tel: 029 2037 2451; Ruperra Park Lodge, Rudry, Caerphilly CF83 3DD — MB BS Durham 1963. Cons. Family Plann. & Reproductive Health Care Cardiff and Vale NHS Trust. Socs: Inst. Biol.; Founder Mem. Soc. Community Health; Fac. Family Plann. & Reproduc. Healthcare. Prev: Community Med. Off. (Child Health & Family Plann.) S. Glam. HA & Community Health Servs.

KERBY, Catherine Bradgate Mental Health Unit, Glenfield Hospital, Croby Rd, Leicester LE3 9EJ — MB BS 1988 Lond. Staff Grade (Adult Psych.) Bradgate Metal Health Unit, Leicester. Socs: Affil. Roy. Coll. of Psychiat.s. Prev: Regist. (Psychiat.) Leicester Gen. Hosp.; SHO (Psychiat.) Leicester Gen. Hosp.; SHO (Anaesth.) Leicester Roy. Hosp. & Qu. Eliz. Hosp. King's Lynn.

KERBY, Ian John Velindre Hospital, Whitchurch, Cardiff CF14 2TL Tel: 029 2061 5888; Ruperra Park Lodge, Rudry, Caerphilly CF83 3DD Tel: 01633 441054 — MB BS 1963 Durh.; FRCR 1975; FFR 1970; DMRT Eng. 1968. Cons. Radiother. & Oncol. Velindre Hosp. Cardiff. Prev: Cons. Radiother. S. Grampian (Aberd.) Health Bd.; Cons. Radiother. Christie Hosp. Manch.; Clin. Sen. Lect. Univ. Aberd.

KERECUK, Larissa Flat 11 Spencer Court, Hartington Close, Farnborough, Orpington BR6 7TP Tel: 01689 859568 Fax: 01689 859568 — MB BS 1998 Lond.; MB BS Lond 1998; BSc (Hons) 1995. (Guy's and St. Thomas' Hospitals) SHO (Paediat.). Prev: Ho. Off. (Med) St. Thomas'; Ho. Off. (Surg), Lewisham Hosp.

KERFOOT, Jacqueline Ann 11 Aberconway Road, Prestatyn LL19 9HH — MB BCh 1996 Wales.

KERFOOT, Neil Edward Kingswood Health Centre, Alma Road, Kingswood, Bristol BS15 4EJ Tel: 0117 961 1774 Fax: 0117 947 8969; 33 Oakleigh Gardens, Oldland Common, Bristol BS30 6RJ — MB ChB 1991 Manch.; MRCGP 1996; DRCOG 1993. (Manch.) GP Avon. Prev: GP Clwyd; SHO (Paediat.) S.mead Hosp. Bristol.

KERIGAN, Paul Anthony Kerigan and Partners, The Surgery, 4 Captain French Lane, Kendal LA9 4HR Tel: 01539 720241 Fax: 01539 725048 — MB ChB 1969 Manch. (Manchester) Hosp. Pract. (Geriat.) Kendal Green Hosp.; Co. Med. Off. Furmanite.

KERIN, Mr Michael Joseph 54 Westwood Road, Beverley HU17 8EJ — MB BCh BAO 1984 NUI; FRCS Ed. 1988; FRCSI 1988.

KERIN, Patricia Judith Mary Uxbridge Health Centre, George St., Uxbridge UB8 1UB Tel: 01895 231925 Fax: 01895 813190; 2 Cherrywood Close, Seer Green, Beaconsfield HP9 2XY Tel: 01494 676502 Email: trishfearn@aol.com — MB BS 1967 Lond.; DA Eng. 1972; DObst RCOG 1969. (Lond. Hosp.) Founder Trustee Thames Valley Hospice Windsor.

KERKAR, Nanda Rajendra 4 Clos Darran Las, Cardiff Road, Creigau, Cardiff CF15 9SL — MB BS 1988 Calcutta; MRCP (UK) 1994.

KERKAR, Rajendra Achyut 78 Pymers Mead, Croxted Road, West Dulwich, London SE21 8NJ — MB BS 1985 Bombay; MRCOG 1995.

KERKHOFF, Ross Vaughan 4 Cedar Walk, 45 Romsey Road, Winchester SO22 5EU — MB ChB 1991 Stellenbosch.

KERKIN, Edward Hibell (retired) 23 Gresham Avenue, Margate CT9 5EH — MB ChB 1952 N.Z.; DPhysMed. Eng. 1967.

KERMEEN, Ronald Stanley 20 Dean Street, Aberdare CF44 7BN Tel: 01685 872146 — MB BCh 1977 Wales.

KERMODE, Allan Graham Moorside, Higher Hud Hey, Haslingden, Rossendale BB4 5BW — MB BS 1985 Western Australia; MRCP (UK) 1987; FRACP 1992. Research Fell. NMR Research Nat. Hosp. Lond.

KERMODE, Audrey Edwina, MBE (retired) 5 Sutton Place, Brockenhurst SO42 7TX Tel: 01590 623343 Fax: 01590 623343 Email: aekermode@aol.com — MB BChir 1958 Camb.; MA Camb. 1982. Chair S.ampton SW Hants. Jt. local research ethics Comm.

KERNAHAN, Jennifer (retired) 23 Station Road, Heddon-on-the-Wall, Newcastle upon Tyne NE15 0DY Tel: 0166 14 853403 — MB BS 1961 Durh.; FRCP Ed. 1982; DCH Eng. 1964. Cons. Paediat. Roy. Vict. Infirm. Newc. Prev: Sen. Regist. (Paediat.) Newc. Gen. Hosp.

KERNER, Adrian Mark Copthall Green House, Upshire, Waltham Abbey EN9 3SZ Tel: 01992 711273 Email: kerner@btinternet.com, upshirepearson@yahoo.co.uk — MB ChB 1988 Sheff.; FFAEM 2000; FRCS 1996 Ed. (Sheffield) Cons. (A+E Med.), Dewsbury. Prev: Specialist Regist. (A & E Med.) Yorks. Deanery Leeds.

KERNICK, David Penrose St Thomas Health Centre, Cowick Street, St. Thomas, Exeter EX4 1HJ Tel: 01392 676677 Fax: 01392 676677 — MB BCh 1976 Wales; BSc (Engin.) Exeter 1970; MRCGP 1995; DA Eng. 1982; DRCOG 1979; DCH RCPS Glas. 1978; MD Wales 1998. GP; Research Fell. Postgrad. Med. Sch. Univ. of Exeter.

KERNOFF, Peter Bernard Allan (retired) Haemophilia Centre & Haemostasis Unit, Academic Dept of Haematology, Royal Free Hospital, Pond St., London NW3 2QG Tel: 020 7794 0500 — MD 1974 Lond.; MB BS 1967; FRCP Lond. 1987; MRCP (UK) 1975; MRCPath 1984. Cons. (Haemat.) Roy. Free Hosp. Lond. Prev: Asst. Prof. (Med.) Columbia Presbyt. Med. Centre New York.

KERNOHAN, Elizabeth Eleanor Marguerite New Mill, Victoria Road, Saltaire, Shipley BD18 3LD Tel: 01274 366020 Fax: 01274 366060; Woodbourne Cottage, 16 North Hill Road, Leeds LS6 2EN Tel: 0113 275 9605 Fax: 0113 275 1200 — MB BCh BAO 1976 Belf.; FFPHM 1989; MFCM RCP (UK) 1984; MPH Leeds 1980. Cons. in Pub. health Med./Director of Clin. Epidemiol. Research Unit, Bradford; Dir. of Clin. Epidemiol. Research Unit. Bradford Managem. Centre Univ. Bradford. Socs: Fell. Fac. Pub. Health Med. (Bd. Mem.); (Comm. Mem.) Soc. Social Med.; BMA. Prev: Dep. Dir. of Pub. Health & Dir. of Clin. Epidemiol. Research Unit Bradford W. Yorks.; Dir. of Pub. Health Bradford HA; Head of Developm. Servs. & Dist. Med. Off. Bradford HA.

KERNOHAN, George Andrew (retired) 4 The Point, Groomsport, Bangor BT19 6JN Tel: 01247 464246 — MB BCh BAO Belf. 1948; DPM RCPSI 1956; DPH Belf. 1952; FRCPI 1974, M 1960; MRCPsych 1971. Prev: Cons. Psychiat. Downshire Hosp. Downpatrick.

KERNOHAN, Mr James Geddis 2 Clarendon Road, Westbourne, Bournemouth BH4 8AH Tel: 01202 760313 Fax: 01202 751038; Westray, 4 de Mauley Road, Canford Cliffs, Poole BH13 7HE Tel: 01202 707614 Fax: 01202 707614 — MB BCh BAO 1972 Belf.; FRCS Eng. 1980; FRCS Ed. 1977. p/t Cons. Orthop. Surg. Roy. Bournemouth & ChristCh. NHS Hosps. Trust. Socs: BOA; RSM; BMA. Prev: Sen. Surgic. Off. Roy. Nat. Orthop. Hosp. Lond.; Regist. (Orthop.) Char. Cross Hosp. Lond.; Regist. (Gen. Surg.) Mater Infirmorum Hosp. Belf.

KERNOHAN, Jessica Anne — MB BCh BAO 1995 Belf.; MRCGP (2000) Ed.; DGM (Dip Geriatric Med) 1997 Glasgow; DCH Dublin 1998; DRCOG Ed 1999. (Queens University Belfast) Med. Off., Newry Hospice, Co. Down. Socs: BMA. Prev: SHO (Paediat.) Altragelvin Hosp., Lond.derry; SHO (Med. & Geriat.) Coleraine Hosp.; SHO (Obst. & Gyn.) S. Tyrone Hosp., Coleraine.

KERNOHAN, Muriel Margaret (retired) 37 Deramore Park, Belfast BT9 5JX Tel: 01232 666273 — MB BCh BAO 1936 Belf. Prev: Med. Off. Ely Disp. Derrygonnelly.

KERNOHAN, Neil Mackenzie Department of Pathology, University Medical Buildings, Foresterhill, Aberdeen AB25 2ZD Tel: 01224 681818 — MB ChB 1985 Aberd.; PhD Aberd. 1992; MRCPath 1993. Sen. Clin. Research Fell. (Biochem. & Histopath.) Univ. Dundee.; Hon. Lect. (Path.) Univ. Aberd. Prev: Research Fell. (Cruden Schol.sh.) Path. Univ. Aberd.

KERNOHAN, Peter Godfrey (retired) Red Bank Health Centre, Unsworth St., Radcliffe, Manchester M26 3GH Tel: 0161 764 2153 — MB BCh BAO 1959 Dub.; BA Dub. 1957. Local Treasury Med. Off.

KERNOHAN, Mr Robert Millar 7 Muckleramer Road, Randalstown, Antrim BT41 3EZ — MB BCh BAO 1977 Belf.; FRCS Ed. 1981. Cons. Urol. & Transpl. Surg. Belf. City Hosp.

KERNOHAN, Sheila Mary 22 Brookfield Lane, Ormskirk L39 6SP — MB ChB 1986 Aberd.; MRCP (Paediat.) Ed. 1993; MRCGP 1991; DRCOG 1990; DCH RCP Glas. 1989. CMO (Paediat.) S.port. Prev: Research Asst. (Med. for Elderly) Woodend Hosp. Aberd.; Trainee GP Aberd.; SHO (O & G & Paediat.) Grampian HB.

KERNS, William, OBE 8 Cleabarrow Drive, Boothstown, Manchester M28 1UL Tel: 0161 703 7799 Fax: 0161 703 7799 — MB ChB Manch. 1950; MSc Manch. 1973; FFOM RCP Lond. 1985, MFOM 1979; DIH Soc. Apoth. Lond. 1964. Indep. Cons. Occupat. Health Manch.; Approved Med. Examr. (Merchant Shipping-Diving Operats.) Dept. Trade & (Off-shore & Submarine Pipe-Lines-Diving Operats.) Dept. Energy; Authorised Med. Examr. Norwegian Maritime Directorate; Approved Med. Examr. of Divers. Socs: Soc. Occupat. Med.; Fell. Fac. Occupat. Med.; Fell. Roy. Soc. Med. Prev: Sen. Area Med. & Safety Adviser Post Office; Clin. Asst. Nat. Blood Transfus. Serv. & Bolton Roy. Infirm.; Squadron Ldr. RAF Med. Br.

KERR, Mr Alan Grainger, OBE 6 Cranmore Gardens, Belfast BT9 6JL Tel: 02890 669181 Fax: 02890 663731 Email: agkerr@unite.net — MB BCh BAO Belf. 1958; FRCS Ed. 1987; FRCS Eng. 1964; DObst RCOG 1961. p/t Cons. Otolaryngol. Roy. Vict. Hosp. Belf. & Belf. City Hosp. Socs: Fell. Roy. Soc. Med. (Ex-Pres. Sect. Otol.).; (Ex-Pres.) Otorhinolaryngol. Res. Soc.; (Ex-Pres.) Brit. Assn. Otorhinolaryngol. Head & Neck Surgs. Prev: Prof. Otorhinolaryng. Qu. Univ. Belf.; Vis. Prof. Univ. Washington, USA; Clin. & Research Fell. (Otol.) Harvard Med. Sch.

KERR, Alastair Douglas 4 Lochend, Tweedbank, Galashiels TD1 3RY Tel: 01896 753485; 3rd Floor Flat, 14 Widcombe Crescnet, Widcombe Hill, Bath BA2 6AH — MB ChB 1994 Birm.; ChB Birm. 1994. (Univ. Birm.) SHO Rotat. (Med.) Roy. United Hosp. Bath. Prev: SHO (Med. Reliever) Auckland Pub. Hosp. Auckland, NZ; SHO (Gen. Med.) Sandwell Dist. Gen. Hosp. W. Bromwich; SHO & Cas. Off. (A & E) Birm. Heartlands Hosp.

KERR, Mr Alastair Ian Grant 5 Buckstane Park, Braids, Edinburgh EH10 6PA — MB ChB 1969 Glas.; FRCS Ed. 1975; FRCS Glas. 1973. Cons. (Otolaryngol.) Edin. Roy. Infirm.; Hon. Sen. Lect. Univ. Edin. Prev: Sen. Regist. (Otolaryngol.) City Hosp. Edin.; Regist. (Otolaryngol.) W.. Infirm. Glas.

KERR, Alastair Magnus Weavers Lane Surgery, 1 Weavers Lane, Whitburn, Bathgate EH47 0SD Tel: 01501 740297 Fax: 01501 744302; 54 Kirkfield W., Livingston Village, Livingston EH54 7BE Tel: 01506 411116 Email: a.m.kerr@doctors.net.uk — MB ChB 1978 Dundee. Prev: Ho. Surg. Law Carluke; Ho. Phys. Middlesbrough Gen. Hosp.

KERR, Alison Jo Willow Cottage, 25 The Village, Bebington, Wirral CH63 7PJ — MB ChB 1990 Bristol.

KERR, Alison Margaret Monitoring Unit, Academic Centre, Department Psychological Medicine, Gartnaval Royal Hospital, 1055 Great Western Road, Glasgow G12 0XH Tel: 0141 211 0281 Fax: 0141 357 4899; Homebank, 29 Fountain Road, Bridge of Allan, Stirling FK9 4AT Tel: 01786 833608 Fax: 01786 833608 — MB ChB 1963 Ed.; MRCP (UK) 1978; FRCPCH 1997; DCH RCPS Glas. 1965. (Ed.) Sen. Lect. (Paediat. Chronic Impairment) Glas. Univ.; Hon. Cons. (Community Child Health Paediat.) Roy. Hosp. Sick Childr. Glas; Hons. Cons. (Learning Disabil.) Lennox Castle Hosp. Socs: Brit. Paediat. Neurol. Assn.; Soc. Study of Behavioural Phenotypes; RCP Edin. Prev: Sen. Regist. (Paediat.) Roy. Hosp. Sick Childr. Glas.; Regist. (Paediat.) Roy. Hosp. Sick Childr. Glas.; Regist. (Paediat.) Stirling Roy. Infirm. & Falkirk Dist. Roy. Infirm.

KERR, Alison Margaret The Surgery, 139 Valley Road, London SW16 2XT Tel: 020 8769 2566 Fax: 020 8769 5301 — MB ChB 1987 Liverp.; MRCGP 1992; DCH RCP Lond. 1991.

KERR, Alison Margaret Elmwood, Milliken Park Road, Kilbarchan, Johnstone PA10 2DB — MB ChB 1993 Glas.

KERR, Alistair Thomas Glebe Medical Centre, Abbeygreen, Lesmahagow, Lanark ML11 0EF Tel: 01555 892328 Fax: 01555 894094 — MB ChB 1991 Glas.

KERR, Allan Robertson (retired) 9 Ganton Way, Fixby Park, Huddersfield HD2 2ND Tel: 01484 424741 — MB ChB 1945 Glas.; DA Eng. 1954. Prev: Cons. Anaesth. Huddersfield Hosp. Gp.

KERR, Andrea Ruth 24 Rye Grove, Liverpool L12 9NF — MB BS 1989 West Indies; MB BS (Hons.) West Indies 1989; FRCS Ed. 1994. Prev: SHO P.ss Alexandra Eye Pavil. Edin.

KERR, Mr Andrew Newell 69 Green Park Avenue, Newtownbreda, Belfast BT8 7YF Tel: 01232 643952 — MB BCh BAO 1990 Belf.; FRCSI 1994.

KERR, Andrew William Sharp (retired) 28 Hailes Gardens, Colinton, Edinburgh EH13 0JL — MB ChB 1948 Ed. Prev: Sen. Lect. (Anat.) Univ. Edin.

KERR, Anne Linklater 153 Ochiltree, Dunblane FK15 0PA Tel: 01786 821083 — MB ChB 1977 Glas. Clin. Asst. (Pychogeriats.) Orchard Ho. Day Hosp. Stirling.

KERR, Arthur (retired) 8 Old Coach Avenue, Belfast BT9 5PY Tel: 01232 667460 — MB BCh BAO 1954 Belf.; FRCPI 1972, M 1965; FRCPsych. 1980, M 1972; DPM RCPSI 1960. Cons. Psychiat. Alexander Gdns. Day Hosp., Purdysburn Hosp. & Albertbridge Rd. Day Hosp. Belf.; Clin. Lect. & Examr. Qu. Univ. Belf.; Examr. MRCPsych Lond. Prev: Sen. Regist. Purdysburn Ment. Hosp. Belf.

KERR, Arthur Henry Halothane, Mount Sandal Road, Coleraine BT52 1 — LAH Dub. 1963; DA RCPSI 1966. Asst. Specialist Anaesth. Coleraine & Portrush Gp. Hosps.

KERR, Arthur Ian Keith Garvagh, Coleraine BT51 5 — MB BCh BAO 1942 Belf.

KERR, Aubrey Robert Fawcett Wayland House, Scoulton, Norwich NR9 4PH Tel: 01953 851531 Fax: 01953 851558 Email: jane@waylandhouse.swimanet.co.uk — MB BCh BAO 1967 Belf. Private Gen. Med.Pract.; Dep. Police Surg. Norf. Constab. Socs: BMA; Fell. Roy. Soc. Med.; Assn. Police Surg. Prev: Specialist (Path.) RAMC; Hosp. Pract. (Cytol.) Severalls Hosp. Colchester.

KERR, Barbara Anne (retired) 41 Westwick Gardens, London W14 0BS — MRCS Eng. LRCP Lond. 1930; BSc Lond. 1930. Prev: Asst. Edr. Butterworth's Brit. Encyc. Med. Pract.

KERR, Brian Andrew Greenock Health Centre, 20 Duncan Street, Greenock PA15 4LY — MB ChB 1988 Glas.; DRCOG 1992; MRCGP 1992. GP Greenock, Renfrewsh.

KERR, Carol Margaret Hawthorn House, 28-30 Heaton Rd, Newcastle upon Tyne NE6 1SD Tel: 0191 265 5543; 19 Wilson Gardens, Newcastle upon Tyne NE3 4JA Tel: 0191 285 3215 — MB ChB 1964 Leeds; DObst RCOG 1967. Prev: Ho. Phys. Dept. Neurol. & Ho. Surg. Gen. Infirm. Leeds; SHO Dept. O & G Roy. Vict. Infirm. Newc.

KERR, Catherine Anne Mere Park Medical Centre, 38 Crewe Road, Alsager, Stoke-on-Trent ST7 2ET Tel: 01270 882004; Abraham's House, The Square, Main Road, Betley, Crewe CW3 9AA Tel: 01270 820185 — MB BS 1987 Lond.

KERR, Christine Alexandra South House, Old Mill, High St., Ormiston, Tranent EH35 5LN; 5 Carnham Close, Gosforth, Newcastle upon Tyne NE3 5DX Tel: 0191 284 8306 — MB ChB 1992 Ed. Specialist Regist. (Anaes), Newc. Gen. Hosp. Prev: Specialist Regist. (Anaes), RVI, Newc.; Specialist Regist. (Anaesth), NGH, Newc.; Specialist Regist. (Anaes), Sunderland Roy. Infirm.

KERR, Colin William (retired) The Health Centre, 20 Duncan Street, Greenock PA15 4LY Tel: 01475 724477 Fax: 01475 727140 — MB ChB 1957 Glas.; AFOM RCP Lond. 1982; DObst. RCOG 1959. Med. Off. IBM (UK) Ltd. Greenock. Prev: Ho. Surg. S.. Gen. Hosp. Glas.

KERR, Daniel MacDonald 17 Green Close, Stannington, Morpeth NE61 6PE — MB ChB 1979 Aberd.

KERR, David Royal Bournemouth Hospital, Castle Lane E., Bournemouth BH7 7DW Tel: 01202 704603 Fax: 01202 704759 Email: david.kerr@rbch-tr.swest.nhs.uk; The Gables, 71 Bure Lane, Friars Cliff, Christchurch BH23 4DL — MB ChB 1981 Aberd.; DM Nottm. 1989; FRCP Ed. 1995; FRCP Lond. 1998. Cons. Phys. Roy. Bournemouth Hosp.; Hon. Sen. Lect. Univ. Soton. Socs: Amer. Diabetes Assn.; Diabetes UK. Prev: Research Assoc. (Endocrinol.) Yale Univ., USA; Lect. Soton. Univ.; Research Fell. Univ. Hosp. Nottm.

KERR, David Bingham (retired) — MB BCh BAO 1947 Belf. Prev: Ho. Surg. & Ho. Phys. Roy. Vict. Hosp. Belf.

KERR, Professor David James CRC Institute for Cancer Studies, Clinical Research Block, University of Birmingham, Edgbaston, Birmingham B15 2TT Tel: 0121 414 3802 Fax: 0121 414 3263 Email: d.j.kerrr@bham.ac.uk — MB ChB 1980 Glas.; PhD Glas. 1990, MSc 1985, BSc (Hons.) 1977, MD 1987, DSc 1997; FRCP Lond. 1996; FRCP Glas. 1995; MRCP (UK) 1983. Prof. Clin. Oncol. Univ. Birm.; Eortic Pharmacol. & Metab. Gp. Brit. Assoc. for Cancer Research. Socs: Eur. Soc. Med. Oncol. (Chairm. Scientif. Comm.); Amer. Soc. Clin. Oncol.; Amer. Assn. Cancer Research. Prev: Sen. Regist. (Med. Oncol.) W.. Infirm. Glas.

KERR, David Leigh (retired) 19 Calder Avenue, Brookmans Park, Hatfield AL9 7AH Tel: 01707 653954 Fax: 01707 660346 Email: david.kerr@hertscc.gov.uk — MB BS 1946 Lond.; MRCS Eng. LRCP Lond. 1946; MRCGP 1953. Prev: Chief Exec. Manor Ho. Hosp.

KERR, Professor David Nicol Sharp, CBE National Kidney Research Fund, Kings Chambers, Priestgate, Peterborough PE1 1FG Tel: 01733 704678 Fax: 01773 704699 Email: davidkerr@nkrf.org.uik; 22 Carbery Avenue, Acton, London W3 9AL Tel: 020 8992 3231 Fax: 020 8992 3231 Email: dnskerr@aol.com — MB ChB Ed. 1951; MS Wisconsin 1953; FRCP Lond. 1967, M 1956; FRCP Ed. 1966, M 1956. Emerit. Prof. Renal Med. Imperial Coll. Socs: Assn. Phys.; Hon. Mem. Renal Assn.; Hon. Mem. Europ. Renal Assn. Prev: Postgrad. Med. Adviser N. Thames RHA; Dean Roy. Postgrad. Med. Sch. Hammersmith Hosp. Lond.; Prof. Med. Univ. Newc.

KERR, David Sinclair (retired) Tehidy House, Farnsfield, Newark NG22 8EF Tel: 01623 882377 — MRCS Eng. LRCP Lond. 1949; MA, MB BChir Camb. 1949; MFOM RCP Lond. 1979. Prev: Area Med. Off. Nat. Coal Bd.

KERR, Deborah Jean (retired) Knockmanoul, Ballinamallard, Enniskillen BT94 2HF Tel: 01365 388285 Email: andrewshughes@msn.co.uk — MB ChB 1991 Ed.; BSc (Hons.) Med. Sci. Ed. 1989; DFFP 1996; DRCOG 1996; MRCGP 1997. Civil. Med. Practitioner Jt. Support Unit N.wood; Occupat. Health Phys. Marks & Spencer. Prev: DPMO HMS Warrior N.wood.

KERR, Deirdre Nicole 50 Belvedere Park, Belfast BT9 5GT Tel: 01232 683728 — MB BCh BAO 1991 Belf.; MRCGP 1995. Prev: SHO (Psychiat.) Purdysburn Hosp. Belf.; SHO (Obst.) Roy. Matern. Hosp. Belf.; SHO (Paediat.) Roy. Belf. Hosp. Sick Childr.

KERR, Dolores New Farm, Mill Lane, Blakenhall, Nantwich CW5 7NP Tel: 01270 820063 — MB ChB 1961 Liverp.; MRCS Eng. LRCP Lond. 1961. (Liverp.)

KERR, Donald Ferguson Chapel House, Priest Lane, Mottram St Andrew, Macclesfield SK10 4QL Tel: 01625 583188; 135 Palatine Road, West Didsbury, Manchester M20 3YA Tel: 0161 445 1187 — MB ChB Ed. 1951; LRCP LRCS Ed. LRFPS Glas. 1951. (Ed.)

KERR, Donald Gilray (retired) Woodwinds, 6 Wynlass Park, Windermere LA23 1ET Tel: 0153 944 7012 Email: dgkerr@globalnet.co.uk — MB ChB Ed. 1961; MRCGP 1976. Prev: GP W. Calder.

KERR, Douglas Castlehill Health Centre, Castlehill, Forres IV36 1QF Tel: 01309 672233 Fax: 01309 673445; 2 Chapelton Place, Forres IV36 2NL Tel: 01309 73295 Email: kerrs@globalnet.co.uk — MB ChB Glas. 1969; DObst RCOG 1971; MRCGP 1973. (Glas.) Prev: SHO (O & G), SHO (Med.) & SHO (Paediat.) S. Gen. Hosp.; Glas.

KERR, Duncan Campbell (retired) (Surgery), 6 Woodlands Road, Middlesbrough TS1 3BE Tel: 01642 247982 Fax: 01642 241636 — MB ChB 1963 Ed.; DObst RCOG 1966. Prev: Ho. Phys. Sedgefield Gen. Hosp.

KERR, Eamonn Gerard Riverside Practice, Upper Main Street, Strabane BT82 8AS Tel: 028 7138 4100 Fax: 028 7138 4115 — MB BCh BAO 1980 Belf. Socs: BMA & Med. Protec. Soc. Prev: Chief (A & E) Tawam Hosp., United Arab Emirates; Chief (A & E) King Khaled Milit. City Hosp. Hafir-Al-Batin, Kingdom of Saudi Arabia.

KERR, Eileen (retired) 6 Albert Road, Eccles, Manchester M30 9QJ — LRCS 1928 Ed.; L.R.C.P., L.R.C.S. Ed., L.R.F.P.S. Glas. 1928; L.M. Rot. 1928.

KERR, Eileen Curran Motherwell Health Centre, 138-144 Windmill Street, Motherwell ML1 1TB Tel: 01698 264164; 7 St. Andrew's Avenue, Bothwell, Glasgow G71 8DN Tel: 01698 853589 — MB ChB 1968 Glas.; DObst RCOG 1970.

KERR, Eleanor Elizabeth Aman, 120 Finnart St, Greenock PA16 8HU Tel: 01475 794783 Email: dr.eleanor.kerr@ntlworld.com — MB ChB 1979 Dundee; MRCPsych 1992. (Dundee) Cons. Child and Adolesc. Psychiat., Ayrsh. and Arran Primary Care NHS Trust, The Adolesc. Team, 70 New St., Stevenston; Hon. Research Fell. Acad. Dept. Child & Adolesc. Psychiat. Univ. Glas. Prev: Sen.

Regist., W. of Scotl. Higher Train. Scheme in Child and Adolesc. Psychiat.; Regist. (Psychiat.) Ravenscraig Hosp. Greenock; Doctors Retainer Scheme Gtr. Glas. HB.

KERR, Elizabeth Angela 10 Fleurs Avenue, Glasgow G41 5AP — MB BS 1973 Newc.; MRC Psych. 1979. Cons. Psychiat. Woodilee Hosp. Lenzie.

KERR, Eric David, MC (retired) 60 The Cloisters, Pegasus Grange, White House Road, Oxford OX1 4QQ Tel: 01865 721910 — BA Dub. 1940, MD 1951, MB BCh BAO 1941.

KERR, Finlay, Deputy Lt. Raigmore Hospital, Inverness IV2 3VJ Tel: 01463 704000 Fax: 01463 705460 Email: finlay.kerr@raigmore.scot.nhs.uk; The Birks, 2 Drummond Place, Inverness IV2 4JT Tel: 01463 234779 — MB ChB 1965 Glas.; FRCP Glas. 1984; FRCP Ed. 1978; MRCP (U.K.) 1971; DObst RCOG 1967. (Glas.) Cons. Phys. Raigmore Hosp. Inverness; Hon. Sen. Lect. Univ. Aberd. Socs: Brit. Cardiac Soc.; Scott. Cardiac Soc.; Scott. Soc. of Phys.s. Prev: Sen. Regist. (Med.) Edin. Teach. Hosps.; Lect. in Med. Roy. Infirm. Edin.; Resid. Univ. S. Calif. Los Angeles Co. Med. Centre.

KERR, Fiona Margaret 139 Restenneth Dr, Forfar DD8 2DD — MB ChB 1997 Dundee.

KERR, Frances Felicity (retired) 32 Downs Road, Epsom KT18 5JD — MB BS 1950 Lond.; MRCS Eng. LRCP Lond. 1949. Prev: Clin. Asst. Manor Hosp. Epsom.

KERR, Frances Naomi (retired) Maryport Group Practice, 12A Selby Terrace, Maryport CA15 6NF Tel: 01900 815544 Fax: 01900 816626 — MB ChB 1961 Bristol; MRCGP 1984.

KERR, Geoffrey Alan, SJM Cleeve Priors, 11 Westmeston Avenue, Rottingdean, Brighton BN2 8AL Tel: 01273 304759 — MRCS Eng. LRCP Lond. 1952; LDS RCS Eng. 1947, DOrth 1957. (Guy's) Prev: Cons. Dent. Surg. Emerit. St. Mary's Hosp. Paddington; Cons. Orthodont. Emerit. Roy. N. & Highlands Hosps. Lond.; Sen. Regist. Dent. Dept. Childr., Asst. To Vis. Dent. Surgs. & Orthodont. Asst. Guy's Hosp.

KERR, Mr George Douglas, TD Lane House, Denmans Lane, Lindfield, Haywards Heath RH16 2JR Tel: 01444 459944 Fax: 01444 459944; Lane House, Denmans Lane, Lindfield, Haywards Heath RH16 2JR Tel: 01444 459944 Fax: 01444 459944 — MB ChB 1961 Ed.; FRCS Ed. 1967; FRCOG 1982, M 1969; DObst 1963. (Ed.) Cons. O & G Mid Downs Health Dist.; Cons. Gyn. Ashdown Hosp.; Cons. Gyn. Gatwick Pk. Hosp.; Lt.-Col. RAMC/TA, Cons Surg. AMS. Socs: Fell. Roy. Med. Soc. Edin.; Hosp. Cons. & Spec. Assn.; BMA. Prev: Sen. Lect. (O & G) St. Thos. Hosp. Med. Sch.; SHO (Surg.) Roy. Infirm. Edin.; SHO Simpson Memor. Matern. Pavil. Edin.

KERR, Gillian Dickson 2 Garteows Place, Falkirk FK1 5PL — MB ChB 1996 Dundee.

KERR, Mr Gregor Robert Northampton General Hospital, Northampton NN1 5BD Tel: 01604 634700 — MB BS 1981 Lond.; FRCS Eng. 1986; FRCS Ed. 1986. (Middlx.) Cons. Trauma & Orthop. N.ampton Gen. Hosp. Socs: Brit. Orthop. Assn.; Brit. Soc. Surg. Hand. Prev: Sen. Regist. Rotat. (Orthop.) Oxf.; Regist. Rotat. (Surg.) Univ. Coll. Hosp. Lond. & Bloomsbury HA; Lect. (Anat.) Roy. Free Hosp. Sch. Med. Univ. Lond.

KERR, Hazel 69 Green Park Avenue, Belfast BT8 7YF — MB BCh BAO 1992 Belf.; MB BCh Belf. 1992.

KERR, Heidi 9 Station View, Bangor BT19 1EU — MB ChB 1997 Birm.

KERR, Iain Crawford Williamwood Medical Centre, 85 Seres Road, Clarkston, Glasgow G76 7NW Tel: 0141 638 7984 Fax: 0141 638 8827; 20 Fruin Avenue, Newton Mearns, Glasgow G77 6HA Tel: 0141 639 6020 — MB ChB Ed. 1969.

KERR, Ian Balfour 60 Fergus Drive, Glasgow G20 6AW — MB ChB 1977 Ed.

KERR, Ian Durie (retired) Clare House Practice, Clare House Surgery, Newport Street, Tiverton EX16 6NJ Tel: 01884 252337 Fax: 01884 254401 — MA, MB Camb. BChir 1964; FRCGP 1990, M 1973; DA Eng. 1968; DObst RCOG 1967. Prev: Ret. Partner Clare Ho. Tiverton Devon.

KERR, Ian Fitzalan Wishart (retired) Penny Meadow Clinic, Glebe St., Ashton-under-Lyne OL6 6HD Tel: 0161 330 6635 — MB ChB 1961 Sheff.; MRCGP 1971; DObst RCOG 1963. Prev: SHO (O & G) Ashton-under-Lyne Gen. Hosp.

KERR, Mr Ian Forrester 24 Langside Drive, Newlands, Glasgow G43 2QA Tel: 0141 632 1240 — MB ChB 1956 Glas.; FRCS Glas. 1966; FRCS Ed. 1959. Cons. Surg. Stobhill Hosp. Glas. Prev: Sen. Regist. W.. Infirm. Glas.

KERR, Ian Hamilton (retired) Eldene, Golf Course Road, Grantown-on-Spey PH26 3HY Tel: 01479 870020 — MB BChir Camb. 1952; FRCP Lond. 1972, M 1956; MRCS Eng. LRCP Lond. 1951; FRCR 1975; FFR 1962; DMRD Eng. 1959. Prev: Cons. Diag. Radiol. King Edwd. VII Hosp. Midhurst, Brompton Hosp. & St. Geo. Hosp. Lond.

KERR, Ian James Pentland Medical Centre, 44 Pentland View, Currie EH14 5QB Tel: 0131 449 2142 Fax: 0131 451 5855; 1 Cherrytree Crescent, Edinburgh EH14 5AX — MB ChB 1983 Aberd.; MRCGP 1988; DA (UK) 1988.

KERR, Ian Peter Carcroft Health Centre, Chestnut Avenue, Carcroft, Doncaster DN6 8AG Tel: 01302 723510; 7 Church View, Campsall, Doncaster DN6 9RA Tel: 01302 702430 — MB ChB 1978 Ed.; MRCGP 1982; DRCOG 1981; DCH Dub. 1981. GP Carcroft. Prev: Dewsbury VTS Gen. Pract.

KERR, Isabella Mary Westpark, Brightons, Polmont, Falkirk FK2 0JJ Tel: 01324 2327 — MB ChB 1939 Glas.; BSc Glas. 1936, MB ChB 1939. (Glas.) Socs: BMA. Prev: Regist. (Med.) Hairmyres Hosp. E. Kilbride; Med. Off. Windsor Hosp. Falkirk.

KERR, Isobel Evelyn Flat 3, Hickleton, Camden St., London NW1 0HB — MB ChB 1996 Ed.

KERR, Jacques George David 14 Pomarium, Perth PH2 2JF — MB BS 1992 Newc.

KERR, James Wright (retired) 34 North Grange, Bearsden, Glasgow G61 3AF Tel: 0141 942 2402 Fax: 0141 942 2402 — MB ChB 1947 Glas.; MD Glas. 1968; FRCP Lond. 1974, M 1954; FRCP Glas. 1968, M 1962; FRFPS Glas. 1951. Hon. Lect. (Respirat. Dis.) Glas. Univ. Prev: Cons. Phys. Respirat. Dis. W.. Infirm. Glas. & Kt.swood Hosp. Glas.

KERR, Jan Marjorie Princess Alexandra Eye Pavilion, Chalmers St., Edinburgh EH3 9HA Tel: 0131 536 4056 Email: jankerr@ed.ac.uk — MB ChB 1990 Ed.; FRCOphth 1995. (Ed.) Specialist Regist. (Opthalmology) P.ss Alexandra Eye Pavilion, Edin. Prev: Research Regist. (Ophth.) P.ss Alexandra Eye Pavil. Edin.

KERR, Janet Isobel 89 Novar Drive, Glasgow G12 9SS — MB ChB 1972 Glas.

KERR, Jean Mary (retired) 35 Ravenscourt, Thorntonhall, Glasgow G74 5AZ Tel: 0141 644 3745 Fax: 0141 644 3745 — MB ChB Glas. 1951; DObst RCOG 1953.

KERR, Jeffrey Stewart Greencroft Medical Centre (North), Greencroft Wynd, Annan DG12 6BG — MB ChB 1972 Glas.

KERR, Joan De L'Angle House, Chartham, Canterbury CT4 7JW Tel: 01227 448 — MB BCh BAO 1948 Belf. (Belf.) Med. Asst. St. Augustine's Hosp. Chartham. Prev: SHO St. Augustine's Hosp. Chartham; Ho. Phys. & Ho. Surg. W. Kent Gen. Hosp. Maidstone.

KERR, John Deanpark, Bothwell, Glasgow G66 1DP Tel: 0141 852561 — MB ChB 1960 Glas. Specialist ENT Surg. Vict. Hosp. Gp. & S.. Gen. Hosp. Glas. Prev: Regist. ENT Vict. Hosp. Gp. & S.. Gen. Hosp. Glas.; Sen. Ho. Off. (ENT) & Ho. Off. Vict. Infirm. Glas.

KERR, John Alexander Auchtermuchty Health Centre, 12 Carswell Wynd, Auchtermuchty, Cupar KY14 7AW Tel: 01337 828262 Fax: 01337 828986 — MB ChB 1968 Ed.; MRCP (U.K.) 1974; MRCGP 1977; DObst RCOG 1972. Prev: Med. Regist. Broken Hill Hosp. N.S.W., Austral.; SHO Respirat. Dis. Unit N.. Gen. Hosp. Edin.

KERR, John Bernard Keith Garvagh Health Centre, 110 Main Street, Garvagh, Coleraine BT51 5AE Tel: 028 2955 8210 Fax: 028 2955 7089; Ballygawley House, 2 Brone Road, Garvagh, Coleraine BT51 4EQ Tel: 01265 868205 — MB BCh BAO 1975 Belf.; DRCOG 1977.

KERR, John David 14 Rectory Road, Wokingham RG40 1DH Tel: 01889 784566; Gwynant, 21 St Margaret's Road, Hereford HR1 1TS Tel: 01432 269130 — MB BS 1972 Lond.; DRCOG 1974; DCH Eng. 1975. (Middlx.) Princip. GP Wokingham. Socs: Reading Path. Soc. & Windsor Med. Soc. Prev: Ho. Surg. Middlx. Hosp.; Resid. Med. Off. King Edwd. VII Hosp. for Offs.; GP Kitimat B.C. Canada.

KERR, John Duncan Scott (retired) 3 Whitehall Road, Sittingbourne ME10 4HB Tel: 01795 425167 Email: jdskerr@freeserve.co.uk — MB BCh BAO 1964 Belf.; DObst RCOG 1967. Prev: GP Sittingbourne.

KERR, John Hall (retired) 57 Staunton Road, Headington, Oxford OX3 7TJ Tel: 01865 761249 Fax: 01865 433744 Email: john.kerr@green.ox.ac.uk — BM BCh 1963 Oxf.; DM Oxf. 1971, BM BCh 1963; FFA RCS Eng. 1967. Prev: Vis. Asst. Clin. Prof. Univ. Calif. San Diego, U.S.A.
KERR, John Stevenson St Peters Hill Surgery, 15 St. Peters Hill, Grantham NG31 6QA Tel: 01476 590009 Fax: 01476 570898 — MB ChB 1972 Ed.; BSc (Med. Sci.) Ed. 1969, MB ChB 1972. (Ed.)
***KERR, Jonathan Paul** 19 Calder Avenue, Brookman's Park, Hatfield AL9 7AH — MB ChB 1995 Birm.
KERR, Judith Sarah Old Manor Hospital, Wilton Road, Salisbury SP2 7EP Tel: 01722 336262 — MB BChir 1987 Camb.; BSc (Hons.) St. And. 1984; MRCPsych 1993; DRCOG 1990. (Cambridge) Cons. Old Age Psychiat. Old Manor Hosp. Salisbury.
KERR, Karen 88 Island View, Ardrossan KA22 7PJ — MB ChB 1993 Aberd. SHO (Anaesth.) Harrogate & York. Prev: SHO (A & E Surg. & Anaesth.) Caboolture Hosp. Qu.sland, Austral.
KERR, Karen Anne Margaret Flat 1, 20 Ruthven St., Hillhead, Glasgow G12 9BT — MB ChB 1998 Glas.; MB ChB Glas 1998.
KERR, Karen Marie Alexandra Hospital, Woodrow Drive, Redditch B98 7UB Tel: 01527 503030 — MB ChB 1986 Bristol; DA (UK) 1989; FRCA 1996. (Bristol) Cons. Anaethetist, Alexandra Hopital, Redditch. Socs: Assn. of Anaesth. GB & Irel.; Obst. Anaesth. Assn.; Europ. Soc. of Regional Anaesth. Prev: Specialist Regist. (Anaesth.) Coventry Sch. of Anaesth.; SHO (Anaesth.) P.ss Margt. Hosp. Swindon.
KERR, Katharin Isobel (retired) 3C South Lodge Court, Racecourse Road, Ayr KA7 2TA Tel: 01292 41991 — MB ChB 1945 Glas.; DPH 1949; MFCM 1972; DCH Eng. 1948. Prev: Sen. Med. Off. (Community Med.) Ayrsh. & Arran Health Bd.
KERR, Katherine Mary 2 Drumkeen Court, Upper Gallwally, Belfast BT8 7TU — MB BCh BAO 1984 Belf.; FFA RCSI 1993; FRCS Ed. 1989.
KERR, Keith Minto Department Pathology, Aberdeen Royal Infirmary, Foresterhill, Aberdeen AB25 2ZD Tel: 01224 681818; East Loanhead, Auchnagatt, Ellon AB41 8YH — MB ChB 1981 Ed.; BSc (1st cl. Hons.) Ed. 1978; MRCPath 1988; FRCPath 1997. Cons. Histopath. Grampian Univ. Hosp.s NHS Trust; Hon. Clin. Sen. Lect. Univ. Aberd. Socs: Path. Soc.; Brit. Thorac. Soc.; Internat. Assn. for the study of lung cancer. Prev: Hon. Sen. Regist. (Path.) Lothian HB; Lect. (Path.) Univ. Edin.; Regist. (Path.) Lothian HB.
KERR, Kenneth Francis 169 Malone Road, Belfast BT9 6TA Tel: 01232 662942 — MB BCh BAO 1963 Belf.; FFHom 1996; MFHOM 1978. (Belf.) Prev: Assoc. Specialist (Geriat. Med.) Roy. Vict. Hosp. Belf.; Ho. Phys. & Ho. Surg. Roy. Vict. Hosp. Belf; Sen. Ho. Phys. Ards Hosp. Newtownards.
KERR, Kenneth James 5 Highcroft Avenue, Glasgow G44 5RP — MB ChB 1997 Aberd.
KERR, Kevin Gerard Department of Microbiology, University of Leeds, Leeds LS2 9JT Tel: 0113 233 5617 Fax: 0113 233 5649 Email: mickgk@leeds.ac.uk; 2 Ewood Coach House, Midgely Road, Mytholmroyd, Hebden Bridge HX7 5QY — MB ChB 1983 Manch.; MRCPath 1991; MD (Manch.) 1994. Sen. Lect. in Microbiol. Univ. Leeds; Hon. Cons. Microbiol. United Leeds Teachg. Hosps. Trust. Prev: Ho. Surg. & Ho. Phys. Univ. Hosp. S. Manch.
KERR, Lindsay McMillan 3A Tay Square, Dundee DD1 1PB — MB ChB 1997 Dundee.
KERR, Lorna Isobel Norfolk and Norwich Hospital, Brunswick Road, Norwich NR1 3SR Tel: 01603 286286 — MB BS 1982 Lond.; MBA Lond. 1993; FFA RCS Eng. 1987. Cons. Anaesth. Norf. & Norwich Hosp. Prev: Sen. Regist. St. Geo. Hosp. Lond.; SHO (Anaesth.) Papworth Hosp. Huntingdon; Regist. (Anaesth.) Guy's Hosp. Lond.
KERR, Malcolm Macfarlane Brodick Medical Practice, Brodick Health Centre, Shore Road, Brodick KA27 8AJ Tel: 01770 302175 Fax: 01770 302040; Tuathair, Shore Road, Brodick KA27 8AJ Tel: 01170 302651 — MB ChB 1977 Ed.; BSc Ed. 1974; MRCP (UK) 1981; MRCGP 1983; DRCOG 1979. (Ed.) Med. Off. (Med. & A&E.) Arran War Memor. Hosp.; Chairm. Arran LHCC. Prev: Research Fell. Belf. Monica Project; Regist. (Med.) Ulster Hosp. Belf.; Ho. Off. Lagan Valley Hosp. Lisburn.
KERR, Margaret Anne Guardian Street Medical Centre, Guardian Street, Warrington WA5 1UD Tel: 01925 650226 Fax: 01925 240633 — MB ChB 1987 Manch.
KERR, Margaret Heather 94 Longmuirhead Road, Auchinloch, Glasgow G66 5DU — MB ChB 1987 Dundee. Hon. Research Fell. Roy. Hosp. Sick Childr. Glas. Prev: SHO (Anaesth.) Glas. Roy. Infirm.
KERR, Margaret Mary (retired) 110 Southbrae Drive, Glasgow G13 1UB Tel: 0141 959 3115 — MD Glas. 1957, MB ChB 1948; FRCP Glas. 1972, M 1969; DCH Eng. 1952. Prev: Cons. Paediat. Qu. Mother's Hosp. & Roy. Hosp. Sick Childr. Glas.
KERR, Margaret Scott Douglas Weir View, Wargrave Road, Henley-on-Thames RG9 3HX Tel: 01491 576314, 02476 715716 Fax: 01491 573683 — MB ChB 1982 Bristol; BSc Bristol 1978; MRCPsych 1987. Socs: Roy. Coll. Psychiatr. Prev: Sen Regist (Psychother.) W. Midl.s RHA; Sen Regist (Psychiat.) W. Midl.s RHA; Regist (Psychiat.) Coventry HA.
KERR, Marilyn Elizabeth Sevenways Surgery, 152-154 Derbyshire Lane, Stretford, Manchester M32 8DU Tel: 0161 865 2880 Fax: 0161 865 4990 — MB ChB 1976 Manch.; BSc (Hons.) Pharm. Manch. 1973.
KERR, Mary Ross (retired) 35 Navarre Street, Barnhill, Dundee DD5 2TW Tel: 01382 779219 — MB ChB (Distinc.) St. And. 1950; FRCP Ed. 1968, M 1959. Hon. Univ. Fell. Univ. Dundee. Prev: Cons. Phys. (Gen. Med., Communicable Dis. & Infec. Dis.) King's Cross Hosp. Dundee.
KERR, Michael Andrew 10 Curzon Terrace, Southbank, York YO23 1HA — MB ChB 1996 Leeds.
KERR, Michael Patrick 14 Windsor Road, Abergavenny NP7 7BB — MB ChB 1985 Bristol; MRCGP 1989. SHO (Psychiat.) WhitCh. Hosp. Cardiff.
KERR, Naomi Gordon Drummond 11 Braid Road, Edinburgh EH10 6AE — MB ChB 1985 Dundee.
KERR, Patrick David The Wall House Surgery, Yorke Road, Reigate RH2 9HG Tel: 01737 224432 Fax: 01737 244616; 9 The Chase, Reigate RH2 7DJ Tel: 01737 765228 — MB ChB 1980 Leeds; MRCPI 1986; MRCGP 1988; DCH RCP Lond. 1986.
KERR, Paul Frew Terrace Surgery, 9 Frew Terrace, Irvine KA12 9DZ Tel: 01294 272326 Fax: 01294 314614 — MB ChB 1983 Glas.; MRCGP 1987; Dip. Therap. (Wales) 1998. Prev: Princip. GP Tokyo, Japan.
KERR, Mr Paul Patrick 71 Galwally Avenue, Belfast BT8 7AJ — MB BCh BAO 1987 Belf.; MRCP (UK) 1992; FRCS Ed. 1994.
KERR, Peter Murray, DSC (retired) Belgrove House, Lamerton, Tavistock PL19 8SA — MB ChB 1941 Ed.; MRCGP 1963; DObst RCOG 1947. Prev: Ho. Surg. Roy. United Hosp. Bath & Leicester Roy. Infirm.
KERR, Mr Philip Simon Scott Department of Orthopaedic Surgery, Lister Hospital, Corey's Mill Lane, Stevenage SG1 4AB Tel: 01438 314333; Ley Green House, Ley Green, Kings Walden, Hitchin SG4 8LJ Tel: 01462 768667 — MB ChB 1985 Bristol; FRCS Eng. 1989. Cons. Orthop. Surg. Lister Hosp. Stevenage. Prev: Sen. Regist. (Orthop.) Bristol & Plymouth; Regist. (Orthop.) Cheltenham Gen. Hosp. & Bristol Roy. Infirm.; SHO (Surg.) Frenchay & S.mead Hosps. Bristol.
KERR, Rebecca Elizabeth Irvine 24 Langside Drive, Glasgow G43 2QA — MB ChB 1964 Glas.; FRCP Glas. 1981; MRCP (UK) 1971. (Glas.) Cons. (Dermat.) Stobhill Hosp. Glas. Prev: Lect. (Dermat.) Univ. Glas.
KERR, Mr Richard Sidney Campbell 82 Gidley Way, Horspath, Oxford OX33 1TG — MB BS 1979 Lond.; BSc Lond. 1976, MS 1990; FRCS Eng. 1984. Cons. Neurosurg. Radcliffe Infirm Oxf.; Hunt. Prof. RCS. Prev: Regist. (Gen. Surg.) N.ampton Gen. Hosp.; Sen. Regist. & Regist. (Neurosurg.) Radcliffe Infirm.; Clin. Reader Nuffield Dept. Surg.
KERR, Robert The Health Centre, North Road, Stokesley, Middlesbrough TS9 5DY Tel: 01642 710748 — MB ChB 1960 Ed. (Ed.) Prev: SHO Middlesbrough Matern. Hosp.; Ho. Phys. & Ho. Surg. Sedgefield Gen. Hosp.
KERR, Robert John Noel Thorny Cottage, Thorny Road, Douglas IM2 5EA — MB BCh BAO 1956 Dub.
KERR, Robert Vincent Charles (retired) 65 Church Road, Newtownbreda, Belfast BT8 7AN Tel: 01232 642602 — MB BCh BAO 1945 Belf.
KERR, Sandra 11 Greenshields Court, Lesmahagow, Lanark ML11 0PP — MB ChB 1991 Glas.
KERR, Sean Anthony 35 The Drive, Bognor Regis PO21 4DT — MB BS 1992 Lond.

KERR, Shanks Paterson Jack (Surgery), 9 Alloway Place, Ayr KA7 2AQ Tel: 01292 611835; 12 Doonholm Road, Alloway, Ayr KA7 4QQ Tel: 01292 442303 — MB ChB 1962 Glas.; DPH Newc. 1968. (Glas.) Prev: Asst. MOH & Sch. Med. Off. Carlisle Co. Boro.

KERR, Simon John Coleridge Medical Centre, Canaan Way, Ottery St Mary EX11 1EQ Tel: 01404 814447 — MB BS 1988 Lond.; BSc Lond. 1985; MRCGP 1994; DFFP 1994; DRCOG 1993; DGM RCP Lond. 1992. (Univ. Coll. & Middlx. Hosp. Med. Sch. Lond.)

KERR, Stephen John 8 Logton Avenue, Manchester M20 3JN — MB BS 1974 New South Wales; FRACP 1984.

KERR, Susan Jean England The Health Centre, Sea Road, Milford on Sea SO41 0LG Tel: 01590 643022; 23 Downton Lane, Downton, Lymington SO41 0LG — MB ChB 1973 Birm.; MRCGP 1978; DCH Eng. 1978; DRCOG 1977. Socs: BMA; RCGP; RCGP. Prev: SHO (Paediat. & O & G) St. Mary's Hosp. Portsmouth; SHO (Gen. Med. & A & E) Roy. Hosp. Portsmouth.

KERR, Thomas Alan — MD 1974 Leeds; MB ChB 1961, DPM 1965; FRCPsych 1979, M 1971; DObst RCOG 1963. (Leeds) Cons. Psychiat. Newc. Univ. Hosp. Gp. Socs: BMA. Prev: Cons. Psychiat. Newc. Univ. Hosp. Gp.; Regist. (Psychol. Med.) Newc. Gen. Hosp.; Ho. Surg. (O & G) St. Jas. Hosp. Leeds.

KERR, Mr Thomas Stewart Abbey Kings Park Hospital, Polmaise Road, Stirling FK7 9PU Tel: 01786 451669 Fax: 01786 465296 Email: tkerr82684@aol.com; 29 Fountain Road, Bridge of Allan, Stirling FK9 4AT Tel: 01786 833608 Fax: 01786 833608 Email: tkerr82684@aol.com — MB ChB 1963 Ed; MB ChB Ed. 1963; FRCS Ed. 1968. (Ed.) Prev: Cons. Orthop. Surg. Stirling Roy. Infirm.; Sen. Regist. Addenbrooke's Hosp. Camb.; Regist. Aberd. Roy. Infirm.

KERR, Wendy Jane Woodrising, 47 Colquhoun St., Helensburgh G84 9LQ — MB ChB 1988 Manch.

KERR, William (retired) Gordon House, 45 High St., Billinghay, Lincoln LN4 4AU Tel: 01526 860588 — MB ChB 1955 St. And. Prev: GP Billinghay, Lincoln.

KERR, William Dalton (retired) 15 Garthlands, Heighington Village, Newton Aycliffe DL5 6RE Tel: 01325 312971 — MB BS Durh. 1949. Prev: Clin. Asst. Aycliffe Hosp.

KERR, Mr William Findlay (retired) 2 Softley Drive, Cringleford, Norwich NR4 7SE Tel: 01603 453799 — MB ChB 1944 Witwatersrand; FRCS Ed. 1956. Prev: Cons. Cardiothoracic Surg. E. Anglian RHA.

KERR, William Jack 10 Fleurs Avenue, Glasgow G41 5AP — MB ChB 1973 Ed.; FFA RCS Eng. 1979. Cons. Anaesth. S.. Gen. Hosp. Glas.

KERR, William Samuel (retired) Haigh End, Alne, York YO61 1SD Tel: 01347 838312 — MB BCh BAO 1953 Belf.; MRCPsych 1971; DPM RCPSI 1963. Prev: Cons. Psychiat. Clifton Hosp. York.

KERR, Yvonne Lucille 11 The Cannogate, St Andrews — MB ChB 1961 St. And.

KERR- MUIR, Mr Malcolm Gallaway 98 Harley Street, London W1g 7HR Tel: 020 79352552 Email: kerr-muir@dial.pipex.com — FRCOphth 1988; MB BS Lond. 1970; FRCS Ed. 1980; MRCP (UK) 1974; MRCS Eng. LRCP Lond. 1970; DO Eng. 1977; DTM & H Liverp. 1976; FRCP 1998. (St. Thomas' London) Cons. Ophth. Addenbrooke's Hosp. Camb.; Hon. Lect. Sch. of Trop. Med. Liverp. Prev: Cons. Ophth. St. Thos. Hosp. Lond.

KERR-WILSON, Mr Richard Henry James St Paul's Wing, Cheltenham General Hospital, Sandford Road, Cheltenham GL53 7AN Tel: 01242 222222 Fax: 01242 272403 Email: richard.ker-wilson@egnhst.org.uk; Pear Tree House, 26 Moorend Road, Leckhampton, Cheltenham GL53 0HD Tel: 01242 578575 Fax: 01242 578575 Email: rkerrwilson@aol.com — MB BChir 1974 Camb.; MA Camb. 1974; FRCS Ed. 1978; FRCOG 1990, M 1978. (St. Thos.) Cons. O & G E. Glos. NHS Trust. Cheltenham. Socs: Brit. Soc. Colpos. & Cerv. Path.; Brit. Gyn. Cancer Soc.; Internat. Gyn. Cancer Soc. Prev: Vis. Asst. Prof. Birm., Alabama; Sen. Regist. Roy. Infirm. Edin.; Regist. St. Geo. Hosp. Lond.

KERRANE, Jerome 45 Grosvenor Road, Swinton, Manchester M27 5EG Tel: 0161 794 4526; 15 Buckingham Way, Carleton, Poulton-le-Fylde FY6 7UT — BM BS 1996 Nottm. SHO (A & E) Leicester Roy. Infirm. Prev: SHO (A & E) Lincoln Co. Hosp.

KERRIDGE, Fiona Jayne Colne Health Centre, Market Street, Colne BB8 0LJ Tel: 01282 862451 Fax: 01282 871698 — MB ChB 1987 Leeds; MRCGP 1992.

KERRIDGE, Susan Catherine Elizabeth 20 Bentinck Street, Greenock PA16 7RN — MB ChB 1984 Glas.

KERRIGAN, Aidan Joseph Marie Xavier c/o Barclays Bank, 9 Russell Square, London WC1 — MB BCh BAO 1949 NUI; MD NUI 1954, MB BCh BAO 1949; MRCPI 1971 DPH Eng. 1959; DCH RCPSI 1955; LM Rotunda 1951.

KERRIGAN, Brid Mairead 44 Orpen Park, Finaghy, Belfast BT10 0BN — MB BCh BAO 1989 NUI.

KERRIGAN, Mr David Daniel Department Surgery, University Hospital, Aintree, Longmoor Lane, Fazakerley, Liverpool L9 1AE Tel: 0151 529 2405 Email: david.kerrigan@aht.nwest.nhs.uk — MB ChB 1982 Liverp.; MD (Distinc.) Sheff. 1992; FRCS Eng. 1986; FRCS Ed. 1986. (Liverpool) Cons. Gen. Surg. Aintree Hosps. NHS Trust Liverp. Prev: Lect. & Sen. Regist. (Surg.) Univ. Manch.; Lect. (Surg.) Univ. Sheff.; Research Regist. (Surg.) Univ. Dept. Surg. Sheff.

KERRIGAN, Gervase Niall William West Suffolk Hospital, Bury St Edmunds IP33 2QZ Tel: 01284 713481 Fax: 01284 713481; The Old Manor, Dalham, Newmarket CB8 8TF Tel: 01638 500395 — MB BChir Camb. 1967; MA Camb. 1964; MRCS Eng. LRCP Lond. 1966; FRCP Lond. 1982, M 1969. (Camb. & St. Bart.) Cons. Phys. & Gastroenterol. W. Suff. Hosp. Bury St. Edmunds; Regional Adviser (Med.) RCP; Assoc. Lect. & Examr. (Med.) Univ. Camb. Socs: Fell. Roy. Soc. Med.; Brit. Soc. Gastroenterol. Prev: Sen. Regist. (Med.) St. Bart. Hosp. Lond.; Research Fell. (Med. Oncol.) Imperial Cancer Research Fund; Ho. Phys. St. Bart. Hosp. Lond.

KERRIGAN, Patrick Joseph Charles Laindon Health Centre, Basildon SS15 5TR Tel: 01268 546411 Fax: 01268 493804 — MRCS Eng. LRCP Lond. 1969; MRCGP 1977; DRCOG 1984. (Sheff.) Med. Edr. Practitioner; Med. Edr. Pulse. Prev: SHO (O & G) Nether Edge Hosp. Sheff.; Ho. Surg. Roy. Hosp. Sheff.; Ho. Phys. Roy. Hosp. Annexe Fulwood.

KERRIN, Diarmuid Patrick c/o 10 Trafford Grove, Stretford, Manchester M32 8LW — BM Soton. 1988; MRCP (Paediat.) (UK) 1993; DCH RCP Lond. 1990.

KERRUISH, Timothy Benedict William Kilkenny Lodge, The Cooil, Braddan, Douglas — MB ChB 1989 Liverp.

KERRY, Alan Peter Ackworth, 8 High Road, Hockley SS5 4SX — MB BS 1988 Lond.; MRCGP 1993.

KERRY, Anthony Leom 8 Aubrey Road, Manchester M14 6SE — MB ChB 1996 Liverp.

KERRY, Clare Michelle 68 Ivypark Road, Sheffield S10 3LD Tel: 0114 230 4802 Fax: 0114 230 4802 Email: cmkerry@doctors.org.uk — MB ChB 1993 Sheff. (Sheffield) p/t GP Trainee; SHO (Gyn.).

KERRY, David Brian Bennetts End Surgery, Gatecroft, Hemel Hempstead HP3 9LY Tel: 01442 63511 Fax: 01442 235419; 46 Wrensfield, Hemel Hempstead HP1 1RP — MB BS 1983 Lond.; BSc Lond. 1980; DRCOG 1987.

KERRY, Frederick Michael Retna Beach Road Surgery, 15 Beach Road, Lowestoft NR32 1EA Tel: 01502 572000 Fax: 01502 508892; Oulton Village Medical Centre, Meadow Road, Oulton Village, Lowestoft NR32 3AZ Tel: 01502 501535 Fax: 01502 531117 — MRCS Eng. LRCP Lond. 1976; DRCOG 1980. (Roy. Free) Prev: Trainee GP/SHO Lister Hosp. Stevenage VTS; SHO (Obst.) N. Herts. Hosp. Hitchin; SHO (Paediat.) Lister Hosp. Stevenage.

KERRY, Mr Neil Andrew (retired) 2 Betts Avenue, Newcastle upon Tyne NE15 8TQ — MB BS 1985 Newc.; FRCS Eng. 1990; MRCGP 1992; Cert. Family Plann. JCC 1991; DRCOG 1991. Princip. GP; Occupat. Health Phys. S. Tyneside Counc.; Cas. Clin. Asst. Newc. Gen. Hosp. Prev: Regist. Rotat. (Gen. Surg.) Newc.

KERRY, Raphael James 21 Whitworth Road, Ranmoor, Sheffield S10 3HD Tel: 0114 230 5255 — MRCS Eng. LRCP Lond. 1951; FRCPsych 1974, M 1972; DPM Eng. 1959. (Sheff.) Lord Chancellor's Visitor. Socs: Sheff. M-C Soc. & Brit. Assn. Psychopharmacol. Prev: Cons. Psychiat. Sheff. HA (T); Regist. Mapperley Hosp. Nottm.; Sen. Regist. Dept. Psychiat. United Sheff. Hosps.

KERRY, Mr Robert Michael Northern General Hospital, Herries Road, Sheffield S5 7AU Tel: 0114 226 6259 Fax: 0114 226 6371; 68 Ivy Park Road, Sheffield S10 3LD — MB BS 1987 Lond.; FRCS (Orth.) 1996; FRCS Eng. 1991. (Middlesex Hospital) Cons. Orthop. Surg. N.ern Gen. Hosp. Sheff. Prev: Career Regist. & SHO (Orthop.) Sheff.; Sen. Regist. (Orthop.) Sheff.; Clin. Fell. Vancouver, Canada.

KERSEY, Howard John Gordon (retired) Wykeham, 12 Coombe Rise, Shenfield, Brentwood CM15 8JJ — MA, BM BCh Oxf. 1959;

FRCOG 1982, M 1966. DObst 1962. Cons. O & G Orsett & Basildon Hosps.; Clin. Teach. Univ. Coll. & Middlx. Hosp. Med. Sch. Prev: Sen. Regist. Univ, Coll. Hosp. & Whittington Hosp. Lond.

KERSEY, James Peter Westlake Littlecourt, Down Road, Tavistock PL19 9AQ Email: jameskersey@compuserve.com — MB BS 1997 Lond.; BA (Hons) 1994; MA (Hons) 1998. (Royal London Hospital School of Medicine and Dentistry) SHO (Neurol.), Roy. Free Lond. Hosp. Prev: PRHO, OldCh., Romford; PRHO, S.end Dist. Gen. Hosp., Essex; SHO (A&E), S.end-on-Sea, Essex.

KERSEY, Peter John Westlake Department Dermatology, Derriford Hospital, Derriford Road, Plymouth PL6 8DH Tel: 01752 763057 Email: peter.kersey@phnt.swest.nhs.uk; Littlecourt, Down Road, Tavistock PL19 9AQ Tel: 01822 616449 — MB BS 1969 Lond.; FRCP Lond. 1993; MRCP (UK) 1973; MRCS Eng. LRCP Lond. 1969. (Roy. Free) Cons. Dermat. Derriford Hosp. Plymouth. Socs: (Treas.) Brit. Soc. Dermat. Surg. (Founder Mem. & Ex-Chairm.); Brit. Assn. Dermat.; Founder Mem. Europ. Soc. Dermatologic Surg. Prev: Regist. & Sen. Regist. (Dermat.) Roy. Vict. Infirm. Newc.

KERSH, Lloyd Gary Narrowcliff Surgery, Narrowcliff, Newquay TR7 2QF Tel: 01637 873363 Fax: 01637 850735; 30 Trebarwith Crescent, Newquay TR7 1DX Tel: 01637 873489 — MB ChB 1982 Dundee; MRCGP 1987.

***KERSH, Rodney Stephen** 4 Orchard Court, Orchard Park Avenue, Giffnock, Glasgow G46 7BL — MB ChB 1997 Dundee; BMSc 1994.

KERSHAW, Mr Christopher John 7 Stoneygate Avenue, Stoneygate, Leicester LE2 3HE — MB ChB 1979 Sheff.; FRCS Eng. 1984; FRCS Ed. 1983. Cons. Orthop. Surg. Univ. Hosps. of Leicester Roy. NHS. Trust. Socs: Assoc. Mem. BOA; Brit. Soc. Childr. Orthop. Surg. Prev: Sen. Regist. (Orthop.) Leicester Roy. Infirm.; Regist. (Orthop.) Nuffield Orthop. Centre Oxf.; Ho. Surg. & Phys. Roy. Hallamshire Hosp. Sheff.

KERSHAW, Christopher Robert, Surg. Cdr. RN Paediatric Department, Royal Hospital Haslar, Gosport PO12 2AA Tel: 01705 762424 Fax: 01705 762188 Email: paediatrics@haslib.demon.co.uk; Glencliff, Pk Avenue, Ventnor PO38 1LF Tel: 01983 852409 Email: c.kershaw@virgin.net — MB BChir 1972 Camb.; MB Camb. 1972, BChir 1971; FRCP Lond. 1989, M 1974; MRCS Eng. LRCP Lond. 1971; FRCPCH 1997; DCH Eng. 1974. (St. Geo. Hosp. Lond.) Cons. Paediat. Roy. Hosp. Haslar; Defence Cons. Adviser (Paediat.) to Surg. Gen. 1996. Prev: Research Fell. (Hon. Regist.) Inst. Child Health Hammersmith Hosp. Lond.; Regist. (Paediat.) Bristol Childr. Hosp.; SHO Hosp. for Sick Childr. Gt. Ormond St. Lond.

KERSHAW, David Alan Department of Anaesthesia, Barnsley District Hospital, Pogmoor Road, Barnsley S75 2EP Tel: 01226 730000 — MB ChB 1981 Manch.; BSc (Med. Sci.) St. And. 1978. Staff Grade Anaesth. Barnsley Dist. Gen. Hosp. NHS Trust.

KERSHAW, David Michael Lawrence Southmead Health Centre, Ullswater Road, Bristol BS10 6DF Tel: 0117 950 7150; 4 Alexandra Road, Clifton, Bristol BS8 2DD Tel: 0117 973 3187 — MB ChB 1975 Bristol; MRCGP 1981.

KERSHAW, Denyse Kings Lane Surgery, 100 Kings Lane, Wirral CH63 5LY Tel: 0151 608 4347 Fax: 0151 608 9095; 22 Ford Road, Upton, Wirral CH49 0TF — MB ChB 1982 Liverp.; MRCGP 1987.

KERSHAW, Edward John Speedwell, Seale Road, Elstead, Godalming GU8 6LF — MB BS 1971 Lond.; MRCS Eng. LRCP Lond. 1971; FFA RCS Eng. 1975. (King's Coll. Hosp.) Cons. (Anaesth.) Roy. Surrey Co. Hosp. Guildford. Prev: Sen. Regist. (Anaesth. Dept.) King's Coll. Hosp. Lond.

KERSHAW, Geoffrey Ross, VRD (retired) Flat 12C Bedford Towers, Cavendish Place, King's Road, Brighton BN1 2JG Tel: 01273 324964 — MRCS Eng. LRCP Lond. 1941; MA Camb. 1942; DPH Lond. 1948. Pastmaster Framework Knitters Co.; Trustee Bilton Grange Developm. Trust. Prev: Med. Off. Rolls-Royce Ltd. Coventry.

KERSHAW, Helen Carolyn Bristol Royal Hospital for Sick Children, St Michaels Hill, Bristol BS2 8BJ Tel: 0117 928 5520 Fax: 0117 928 5682; 4 Alexandra Road, Clifton, Bristol BS8 2DD Tel: 0117 973 3187 — MB ChB 1974 Bristol; MRCP (UK) 1977. Staff Grade. (Paediat. Oncol. & Haemat.) Bristol Roy. Hosp. for Sick Childr. Socs: RCPCH; Assoc. Mem. UKCCSG.

KERSHAW, Irene Flora Mary 7 Stoneygate Avenue, Stoneygate, Leicester LE2 3HE — MB ChB 1979 Ed.; BSc Ed. 1976. Staff Grade (Child Health)Leics. & Rutland Healthcare NHS Trust Leicester.

KERSHAW, Jill Anne (Cave) Woodlands Medical Centre, Woodland Road, Didcot OX11 0BB Tel: 01235 511355 Fax: 01235 512808; 43 Bishops Orchard, East Hagbourne, Didcot OX11 9JS Tel: 01235 511080 — MB BS 1974 Lond.; BSc (Biochem.) Lond. 1971, MB BS 1974; MRCP (UK) 1977; MRCGP 1983. (Univ. Coll. Hosp.) Prev: Regist. (Geriat. & Gen. Med.) Oxon AHA (T); SHO (Gen. Med.) Oxon. AHA (T); Ho. Surg. Whittington Hosp. Lond.

KERSHAW, John Barry Department of Histopathology, North East Lincolnshire NHS Trust, Scartho Road, Grimsby DN33 2BA Tel: 01472 875478 Fax: 01472 875333; The Manor, North Elkington, Louth LN11 0SE Fax: 01507 600408 Email: john.kershaw@virgin.net — MB ChB 1972 St. And.; MRCPath 1984; FRCPath 1996. (St Andrews) Cons. Cellular Path. N. E. Lincs. NHS Trust; Med. Dir. N. E. Lincs. NHS Trust. Socs: Brit. Div. Internat. Acad. Path. & Assn. Clin. Path. Prev: Cons. Histopath. Grimsby & Louth Co. Hosps.; Cons. Path. RAF Med. Br.

KERSHAW, Juliet Diane 99 Freedom Road, Sheffield S6 2XA — MB ChB 1995 Sheff.

KERSHAW, Lawrence Colin Ward (retired) 14 Snaithing Lane, Sheffield S10 3LG — MB ChB 1949 Sheff.; FRCGP 1976, M 1969. Prev: Capt. RAMC.

KERSHAW, Melanie Joy Rosina 2 Packwood Cottages, Grange Road, Dorridge, Solihull B93 8QA — MB ChB 1995 Birm.; ChB Birm. 1995; MB Birm. 1995; BSc Birm. 1994. (University of Birmingham)

KERSHAW, Michael John 24 Park Court, Park Road, New Malden KT3 5AE — MB BS 1973 Lond.; BA Camb. 1967; MRCPath 1981.

KERSHAW, Peter Samuel Petrene, 18 Wood Lane, Elm Park, Hornchurch RM12 5JD Tel: 01708 450777 Fax: 01708 450903 Email: p.s.k@btinternet.com — MRCS Eng. LRCP Lond. 1951; Barrister Inner Temple 1980. (Lond. Hosp.) Assoc. Med. Dir. St. Francis Hospice Havering. Socs: Internat. Assn. Study of Pain, USA; Assn. Palliat. Care & Hospice Doctors UK. Prev: Ho. Surg. King Geo. Hosp. Ilford; Jun. Specialist Dermat. RAMC.

KERSHAW, Peter Whaley 2 Carseview Drive, Bearsden, Glasgow G61 3NJ Tel: 0141 942 8525 — MD 1973 Ed.; MB ChB 1959; FRCP Ed. 1975, M 1963; FRCPsych 1981, M 1972; DPM Ed. & Glas. 1965; DObst RCOG 1961. (Ed.) Sen. Lect. (Psychol. Med.) Univ. Hosp. Glas. Prev: Phys. Supt. & Cons. Psychiat. Gartnavel Roy. Hosp. Glas.

KERSHAW, Philip Ann Street, Denton, Manchester M34 2AJ — MB ChB 1986 Manch.; CIPCD 2001 Warick Uni.; MRCGP 1990. Prev: Clin. Asst. (Diabetes) Manch. Diabetes Centre; SHO (Paediat.) Qu. Pk. Hosp. Blackburn; SHO (O & G) Roy. Oldham Hosp.

KERSHAW, Robert (retired) 22 Clee Avenue, Fareham PO14 1RR Tel: 01329 231555 — MRCS Eng. LRCP Lond. 1939.

KERSHAW, Stephen William 59 Hague Street, Glossop SK13 8NS — MB ChB 1975 Sheff.; MRCGP 1980; DA (W. Indies) 1978; DRCOG 1979; Cert. FPA 1980. Prev: Anaesth. Qu. Eliz. Hosp. Barbados; Gen. Surg. Torquay; Sen. Med. Rotherham.

KERSHAW, Mr Steven Andrew 6 Lane Drive, Grotton, Oldham OL4 5QZ Tel: 0161 624 5590 — MB ChB 1993 Manch.; FRCS Eng. 1998. (Manchester) SHO (Trauma & Orthop.) Stepping Hill Hosp. Stockport. Socs: BMA; MDU. Prev: SHO (Gen. Surg.) Roy. Oldham Hosp.; SHO (Gen. Surg.) Rotat. Manch. Roy. Infirm.

KERSHAW, Sylvia (retired) 22 Clee Avenue, Fareham PO14 1RR — MB BS 1949 Lond.; MRCS Eng. LRCP Lond. 1949; DObst RCOG 1950; MRCGP 1971.

KERSHAW, Mr Will Wear (retired) Angorfa, Coed y Garth, Furnace, Machynlleth SY20 8PG Tel: 01654 781317 Email: willkker@supanet.com — MB ChB 1956 Leeds; FRCS Eng. 1963. Prev: Cons. Surg. Bronglais Gen. Hosp. Aberystwyth.

KERSLAKE, David McKie, OBE (retired) Lime Tree Cottage, Chandlers Lane, Yateley GU46 7SP Tel: 01252 872240 Email: david.kerslake@tinyworld.co.uk — MB BS Lond. 1946; PhD Lond 1950; DSc Lond. 1962,. Prev: Physiol. RAF Inst. Aviat. Med.

KERSLAKE, John Charles Oakwood Medical Centre, Oakwood Lane, Barnton, Northwich CW8 4HE Tel: 01606 74718 Fax: 01606 784529 — MB ChB 1969 Liverp.

KERSLAKE, Robert William Imaging Centre, University Hospital, Nottingham NG7 2UH Tel: 0115 924 9924 Fax: 0115 849 3311 Email: robert.kerslake@nott.ac.uk — MB BS 1980 Lond.; MRCP (UK) 1984; FRCR 1988. Cons. Radiol. Univ. Hosps. NHS Trust Nottm.

KERSLAKE, Miss Siân Department of Obstetrics & Gynaecology, Central Middlesex Hospital NHS Trust, Acton Lane, Park Royal, London NW10 7NS Tel: 020 8965 5733 Fax: 020 8453 2105 — MB BCh 1978 Wales; FRCS Ed. 1985; MRCOG 1984. (UHW Cardiff) Cons. O & G Centr. Middlx. Hosp. NHS Trust Lond. Socs: Fell. Roy. Soc. Med.; Christ. Med. Fell.sh. (Hosp. Represent.). Prev: Sen. Regist. (O & G) FarnBoro. Hosp. Kent & St. Thos. Hosp. Lond.; Regist. St Bart. Hosp. Lond.; SHO (Obst.) Qu. Charlotte's Matern. Hosp.

KERSLEY, Henry Jonathan 143 Harley Street, London W1G 6BH Tel: 020 7935 0886 Fax: 020 7486 1956; 8 York Mansions, Earl's Court Road, London SW5 9AF — MB BChir Camb. 1967; MA Camb. 1965; MRCS Eng. LRCP Lond. 1965; MRCOphth 1988; DO Eng. 1968. (Camb. & St. Bart.) Indep. Ophth. Lond.; Europ. Edr. Jl. Contact Lens Assn. Ophth. (USA). Socs: Hon. Life. Mem. Med. Contact Lens & Ocular Surface Assn.; Hon. Pres. Europ. Contact Lens Soc. of Ophth. 1999; Pres. Internat. Contact Lens Soc. Ophth. 1996. Prev: Pres. Europ. Contact Lens Soc. of Ophth.; Pres. Med. Contact Lens Assn.; Pres. Brit. Contact. Lens Assn.

KERSLEY, Mr Jonathan Bernard 41 Moor Green Lane, Moseley, Birmingham B13 8NE Tel: 0121 449 1707 Fax: 0121 442 4987 Email: kersley@fdn.co.uk; 41 Moor Green La, Moseley, Birmingham B13 8NE Tel: 0121 449 1707 Fax: 0121 442 4987 Email: kersley@fdn.co.uk — MB BS Lond. 1966; FRCS Eng. 1974; MRCS Eng. LRCP Lond. 1971; DObst RCOG 1971. (St. Bart.) Cons. Surg. (Orthop.) Roy. Orthop. Hosp. Birm. & Nuffield Orthop. Serv. Socs: Fell. BOA; Soc. Internat. de Chirurgie Orthopedique et de Traumatol.; Brit. Assn. Surg. Knee. Prev: Cons. (Orthop.) Birm. Heartlands Hosp.; Sen. Regist. (Orthop.) Addenbrooke's Hosp. Camb.; Regist. (Surg.) Portsmouth Gp. Hosps.

KERSS, Alistair Scott Medical Centre, Cambridge Avenue, Bottesford, Scunthorpe DN16 3LG Tel: 01724 842415 Fax: 01724 271437 — MB BS 1973 Newc.; MRCGP 1978.

KERSS, Ian Montgomery Scott St Pauls Medical Centre, St. Pauls Square, Carlisle CA1 1DG Tel: 01228 524354 Fax: 01228 616660; 12 Portland Square, Carlisle CA1 1PY Tel: 01228 24354 — MB BS 1971 Newc.; MRCGP 1977.

KERTON, Ian Lindsay Salters Medical Practice, The Health Centre, Ombersley Street, Droitwich WR9 8RD; Treetops, 133 The Holloway, Droitwich WR9 7AJ Tel: 01905 774006 — MB ChB 1972 Birm. (Birm.) Prev: Mem. (Sec.) Worcs. LMC; SHO (Paediat.) E. Birm. Hosp.; SHO (O & G) Dudley Rd. Hosp. Birm.

KERTON, James Joseph 18 Comer Avenue, Worcester WR2 5HZ — MB BS 1992 Lond.

KERTON, John Edwin (retired) 81 St Bernard's Road, Olton, Solihull B92 7DF Tel: 0121 706 1896 — MB ChB 1942 Birm.; MRCS Eng. LRCP Lond. 1942; DObst RCOG 1947. Prev: Ho. Phys., Ho. Surg. & Obst. Ho. Surg. Selly Oak Hosp. Birm.

KERVICK, Mr Gerard Nicholas Ophthalmic Department, Mater Hospital, Cromlin Road, Belfast BT14 6AB Tel: 028 9080 3106 Ext: 3106 Fax: 01232 742903; 51 Malone Park, Belfast BT9 6NN Tel: 028 9066 4880 Fax: 01232 665134 Email: gkervick@aol.com — MB BCh BAO 1981 NUI; FRCS Ed. 1985. Cons. Ophth. Surg. Mater Hosp. Belf.

KERWICK, Shaun William Department of General Practice, UMDS, Guy's & St Thomas Hospitals, 5 Lambeth Walk, London SE11 6SP — MB BS 1988 Lond.; MRCP(UK) 1992; MRCGP 1994.

KERWIN, Professor Robert William Department Psychological Medicine, Section of Clin. Neuropharmacology, Institute of Psychiatry,, De Crespigny Park, Denmark Hill, London SE5 8AF Tel: 020 7848 0727 Fax: 020 7848 0059 Email: r.kerwin@iop.kcl.ac.uk; 35 Gorst Road, London SW11 6JB Tel: 020 7738 1694 Fax: 020 7738 1694 — MB BChir 1984 Camb.; DSc Lond. 1996; PhD (Pharmacol.) Bristol 1980; MA Camb. 1980; FRCPsych 1996, M 1988. (Camb.) Prof. of Clin. Neuropharmacol. & Cons. Psych. Inst. of Psychiat. Socs: Brit. Pharm. Soc. (Clin. Treas.); Brit. Assn. for Psychopharm. (Treas.). Prev: Reader in Clin. Neuropharmacol.; Sen. Lect. (Neurosci.) & Hon. Cons. Psychiat. Inst. Psychiat. Lond.

KESARI, Veernarayan Selston Surgery, 139 Nottingham Road, Selston, Nottingham NG16 6BT Tel: 01773 810226 Fax: 01773 863957 — MB BS 1959 Osmania. (Osmania Med. Coll. Hyderabad) Socs: BMA.

KESAVA REDDY, Mannur 50 Meakin Avenue, Newcastle ST5 4EY — MB BS 1977 Sri Venkateswara; FRCPS Glas. 1988; LRCP LRCS Ed. LRCPS Glas. 1982.

KESAVAN, Sandeep 8 East Causeway Crescent, Adel, Leeds LS16 8LW — MB ChB 1991 Leeds; MRCP (UK) 1994. Specialist Regist. (Geriat. Med./Gen. Med.) Yorks. Region.

KESHAV, Satish Chandra Dept. of Medicine, Rowland Hill Street, Royal & Free Universtity College Medical School, London NW3 2PF — MB BCh 1985 Witwatersrand; DPhil Oxf. 1990; BSc (Hons.) Witwatersrand 1984; MRCP (UK) 1995. (Univ. Witwatersrand, Johannesburg) Sen Lect.& Cons Phys. Med. Roy. Free Hosp. Sch. Med. Lond. Socs: Brit. Soc. Cell Biol. & Brit. Soc. For Immunol.; BMA; Brit. Soc. for Gastroenterol. Prev: Doctoral Stud. Sir William Dunn Sch. Path. Oxf.; Staines Research Fell. Exeter Coll. Oxf.; Med. Lect., Roy. Free Hosp., Lond.

KESHAVARZ-KERMANI, Hossein c/o Midland Bank, 83 High St., Sidcup — MD 1960 Tehran; LAH Dub. 1967. (Tehran) SHO (Gen. Surg.) Roy. Cornw. Hosp. Truro. Prev: SHO (Gen. Surg.) IC Unit Derbysh. Roy. Infirm.; SHO (Plastic Surg.) Plymouth Dist. Hosp.; SHO (Gen. Surg. & Orthop.) Portland Hosp.

KESHRI, Ramchandra The Surgery, 36 Bucklands End Lane, Castle Bromwich, Birmingham B34 6BP Tel: 0121 747 2160 Fax: 0121 747 3425 — MB BS 1967 Bihar; MB BS 1967 Bihar.

KESHTGAR, Mr Mohammad Reza Safaei 83 Balmoral Road, Harrow HA2 8TE — MB BS 1987 Punjab; FRCSI 1991.

KESSAR, Preminda 37 Hasock Road, London SW17 7QW Tel: 020 8673 0694 — MRCS Eng. LRCP Lond. 1986; PhD Lond. 1980, BSc 1976; MRCP (UK) 1991; FRCR 1992. Cons. Radiol. Roy. Marsden Hosp. Lond. Prev: Sen. Regist. (Radiol.) St. Bart. Hosp. Lond.; Regist. (Radiol.) Roy. Lond. Hosp.; Regist. (Diabetes, Endocrinol. & Med.) King's Coll. Hosp. Lond.

KESSEL, Anthony Stephen 11 Downage, London NW4 1AS — MB BS 1989 Lond.

KESSEL, Belinda Louise Bromley Hospital, 17 Cromwell Ave, Bromley BR2 9AJ Tel: 01689 815000 (Orpington Appt), 0208 289 7000 Email: belkessel@doctors.org.uk; Flat 1, 100 Cavendish Road, Clapham S., London SW12 0DF Tel: 020 8673 9256 — MB BS 1987 Lond.; MSc 2000 King's College, Lond.; MRCP Glas. 1994. (St Mary's Hosp. Lond. Univ.) Cons. Gen. & Geriat. Med., Bromley Hosp., Bromley; Orpington Hosp., Sevenoaks Rd, Orpington, Kent, BR6 9JU. Socs: BGS; BMA. Prev: Specialist Regist. (Geriat. Med.) St Thomas' Hosp. Lond.; Specialist Regist. (Geriat.s & Gen. Med.) Qu. Mary's Hosp., Sidcup; Research Regist. (Geriat.) King's Coll. Hosp. Lond.

KESSEL, David Oliver The Moorings, 8 Water Row, Cawood, Selby YO8 3SW — MB BS 1986 Lond.; MA Camb. 1986; MRCP (UK) 1989; FRCR 1993. Sen. Regist. Dept. of Imaging Middlx. Hosp. Lond.

KESSEL, Michael Samuel 188 Golders Green Road, London NW11 9AY Tel: 020 8455 1907 — MB BS 1957 Lond.; MRCS Eng. LRCP Lond. 1957. (King's Coll. Hosp.)

KESSEL, Professor William Ivor Neil 24 Lees Road, Bramhall, Stockport SK7 1BT Tel: 0161 439 5121 — MB BChir 1949 Camb.; MSc Manch. 1969; MA Camb. 1962, BA (Hons.) 1945, MD 1963; FRCP Ed. 1968, M 1965; FRCP Lond. 1967, M 1955; FRCPsych 1972; T(Psych) 1991; DPM (Distinc.) Lond. 1958. (Camb. & Univ. Coll. Hosp.) Emerit. Prof. Psychiat. Univ. Manch. Socs: Past Pres. Manch. Med. Soc. Prev: Prof. Psychiat. Univ. Manch.; Dean & Postgrad. Dean Med. Sch. Univ. Manch.; Asst. Dir. MRC Unit Research on Epidemiol. of Psychiat. Illness.

KESSELER, Gale Doncaster Royal Infirmary, Armthorpe Road, Doncaster DN2 5LT Tel: 01302 366666; The Beeches, Doncaster Road, Thrybergh, Rotherham S65 4NU Tel: 01709 850307 — MB ChB 1972 Liverp.; MB ChB (Hons.) Liverp. 1972; FFA RCS Eng. 1976. (Liverp.) Cons. Anaesth. Doncaster Roy. Infirm. Socs: Roy. Soc. Med. Prev: Sen. Regist. (Anaesth.) Soton. & Liverp. Hosps.

KESSELER, Michael Edward Department of Dermatology, Rotherham General Hospital, Moorgate Road, Rotherham S60 2UD Tel: 01709 304161 Fax: 01709 304481 Email: michael.kessler@rgh-tr.trent.nhs.uk; The Beeches, Doncaster Road, Thrybergh, Rotherham S65 4NU Tel: 01709 850307 — MB ChB Birm. 1970; MRCP (UK) 1977; FRCP Lond. 1989. Cons. Dermat. & Dep Clin. Dir. Rotherham Gen. Hosps. NHS Trust; Hon. Clin. Lect. (Dermat.) Univ. Sheff. Socs: Fell. Roy. Soc. Med.; Fell. St. John's

Hosp. Dermat. Soc. Prev: Sen. Regist. (Dermat.) Roy. S. Hants. Hosp. Soton.; Regist. (Dermat.) Liverp. Roy. Infirm.

KESSELL, Gareth Dept. of Anaesthesia, South Tees Acute Hospitals Trust, Marton Rd, Middlesbrough TS4 3BW; 58 High Street, Swainby, Northallerton DL6 3EG — MB ChB 1986 Bristol; MRCP (UK) 1991; FRCA 1994. Cons. (Anaesth.) S. Tees Acute Hosps. Trust, Middlesbrough. Socs: Assn. Anaesth.; Difficult Airway Soc.; Brit. Ophth. Anaesth. Soc. Prev: Regist. (Anaesth.) Centr. Sheff. Univ. Hosp.

KESSELL, Maurice 3/10 Queens Gardens, London W2 3BA — MB BS 1950 Adelaide; MRCP (UK) 1954.

KESSLER, David Samuel The Surgery, Gaywood House, North St, Bedminster, Bristol BS3 3AZ Tel: 0117 966 1412 Fax: 0117 953 1250 — MB BS 1984 Lond.; BA (Hons.) Oxf. 1977; MRCPsych 1989; MRCGP 1991.

KESSLING, Professor Anna Maria Academic Unit of Medical Community Genetics, (Imperial Coll. School Med.) Kennedy Galton Centre, Level 8V, Northwick Park & St Mark's NHS Trust, Watford Road, Harrow HA1 3UJ Tel: 020 8869 3163 Fax: 020 8869 3167 Email: a.kessling@ic.ac.uk; 110 Highfield Way, Rickmansworth WD3 7PH — MB ChB 1978 Dundee; MB ChB Lond. 1978; PhD Lond. 1986; BMSc (Hons.) Dund 1975. Prof. Community Genetics. Imperial Coll. Sch. Med. Lond. Socs: Clin. Genetics Soc., Amer. Soc. Human Genetics; FRIPHH. Prev: Sen. Lect. (Biochem.) St. Mary's Hosp. Med. Sch. Lond.; Clin. Research Fell. (Molecular Genetics) Lipid Research Laborat. Montreal, Canada; Clin. Research Asst. (Molecular Genetics) Char. Cross Sunley Research Centre Lond.

KESSLING, Juliusz Maria (retired) 13 Malwood Road, London SW12 8EN Tel: 0208 675 9967 Fax: 020 8675 9967 Email: jkessling@onetel.uk.com — MB ChB 1965 St. And.

KESSLING, Waclaw (retired) 82 Ryecroft Road, London SW16 3EH — Med. Dipl. Warsaw 1933.

KESSON, Anna Jackson 76 Kelvin Court, Glasgow G12 0AQ Tel: 0141 357 3055 — MB ChB 1938 Glas.; DOMS Eng. 1950. (Glas.)

KESSON, Colin Mackay Medical Division, Victoria Infirmary, Glasgow G42 9TY Tel: 0141 201 5329 Fax: 0141 201 5090; 14 Easter Drumlins, 47 Patrickhill Road, Glasgow G11 5AB Tel: 0141 339 5590 Email: colinkesson@hotmail.com — MB ChB 1970 Glas.; FRCP Glas. 1986; MRCP (UK) 1973. Cons. Phys. Vict. Infirm. Glas. Socs: Diabetes UK; ABCD.

KESSON, Roderick Alexander Faversham Health Centre, Bank Street, Faversham ME13 8QR Tel: 01795 562000; Preston Lodge, The Mall, Faversham ME13 8JL — MB BS 1976 Lond.; DRCOG 1979; DCH Eng. 1978. Hon. Med. Off. Faversham Cott. Hosp. Socs: BMA. Prev: SHO (Paediat.) St. Mary's Hosp. Portsmouth; Ho. Phys. Renal Unit St. Thos. Hosp. Lond.; Ho. Surg. St. Mary's Hosp. Portsmouth.

KESTER, Professor Ralph Charles 39 The Avenue, Roundhay, Leeds LS8 1JG Tel: 0113 293 3371 — MD 1973 Cape Town; FRCS Eng. 1966. (Cape Town) Cons. Vasc. Surg. St. Jas. & Seacroft Hosps. Leeds; Prof. Vasc. Surg. Univ. Leeds. Socs: Roy. Soc. Med.; Europ. Soc. Cardiovasc. Surg. & Internat. Union Angiol.; Vasc. Surg. Soc. Gt. Brit. & Surg. Research Soc. Prev: Sen. Surg. Lect. Univ. Leeds; Sen. Fulbright Trav. Schol. & Research Fell. in Surg. Univ. Calif.; San Diego, U.S.A.; Sen. Surg. Regist. Dundee (T) Hosps.

KESTIN, Ian Geoffrey Department of Anaesthesia, Western Infirmary, Glasgow G11 6NT Tel: 0141 211 1806 Email: ian.kestin@altavista.net — MB BS 1981 Lond.; FFA RCS Eng. 1985. Cons. Anaesth. W.ern Infirm. Glas.

KESTIN, Kathryn Johnson Long Stratton Health Centre, Flowerpot Lane, Long Stratton, Norwich NR15 2TS Tel: 01508 530781 Fax: 01508 533030; Tawny Lodge, The Green, Wacton, Norwich NR15 2UN Tel: 01508 532358 Fax: 01508 530848 — MB BS 1980 Lond.; MRCGP 1988; DA Eng. 1983. (Univ. Coll. Hosp. Med. Sch.) Princip. Gen. Pract. Socs: Coll. Anaesth. Prev: Mem. LMC.

KESTON, Robert Bruce The Surgery, Queens Ferry Road, Rosyth, Dunfermline KY11 2LR Tel: 01383 414874 — MB ChB 1968 Glas. Socs: BMA & Diving Doctors Assn. Prev: Surg. Lt. Cdr. RNR; Ho. Off. (Surg.) Vict. Infirm. Glas.; Ho. Off. (Med.) Roy. Alexandra Hosp. Paisley.

KETCHELL, Robert Ian 34 Hunter House Road, Sheffield S11 8TW Tel: 0114 266 0470 — MB ChB 1991 Sheff.; BSc (Biochem.) Sheff. 1986; MRCP (UK) 1994. Regist. (Med.) N. Gen. Hosp. Sheff. Prev: SHO (Gen. Med.) N.. Gen. Hosp. Sheff.

KETCHIN, Alexander (retired) Redcot, 9A Lakes Road, Dukinfield SK16 4TP Tel: 0161 330 1327 — MB ChB 1938 Ed.

KETCHIN, Gordon Stuart Sandringham Practice, Sandringham Road Health Centre, Sandringham Road, Intake, Doncaster DN2 5JH Tel: 01302 321521 Fax: 01302 761792; 126 Stoops Lane, Bessacarr, Doncaster DN4 7RR Tel: 01302 370916 — MB BS 1985 Newc.; BMedSci (Hons.) 1982; MRCGP 1990; Dip. Palliat. Med. Wales 1997; Cert. Family Plann. JCC 1990. (Univ. Newc.) Clin. Asst. St. Johns' Hospice Doncaster.

KETHARTHAS, Rasiah 'Glendale', 193 Derby Road, Ilkeston DE7 5FF Tel: 0115 320826 — MB BS 1964 Colombo.

KETHARTHAS, Sivananthavalli 'Glendale', 193 Derby Road, Ilkeston DE7 5FF Tel: 0115 320826 — MB BS 1963 Colombo; FFA RCS Eng. 1971.

KETKAR, Vinay Hemant The University Medical Practice, Elms Road, Edgbaston, Birmingham B15 2SE Tel: 0121 414 5111 — MB ChB 1990 Birm.; DRCOG 1995; MRCGP 1995. (Birmingham)

KETLEY, Andrea Mary Doreen South Vernigore, Welham, Castle Cary BA7 7NF Tel: 01963 350159 — MB BChir 1959 Camb.; MB Camb. 1959, BChir 1958; MRCS Eng. LRCP Lond. 1958; DObst RCOG 1959. (Camb. & Univ. Coll. Hosp.) Clin. Asst. Coldharbour Hosp. Sherborne W. Dorset Ment. Health Trust. Prev: Asst. GP Qu. Camel Health Centre Yeovil.

KETLEY, Jacqueline Brenda Chrisp Street Health Centre, 100 Chrisp Street, London E14 6PG Tel: 020 7515 4860 Fax: 020 7515 3055 — MB BS 1987 Lond.; MA Camb. 1988; MRCGP 1991; DRCOG 1991. (Lond. Hosp. Med. Coll.) GP. Prev: Trainee GP Lond. Hosp. VTS; Ho. Phys. Broomfield Hosp. Chelmsford; Ho. Surg. N. Middlx. Hosp.

KETLEY, Nicolas James Dr Nic Ketley, Consultant Haematologist, Queen Elizabeth Hospital, Woolwich SE18 4QH Tel: 020 8312 6312 Fax: 020 8312 6025 — MB BS 1987 Lond.; MA Camb. 1988; MRCP (UK) 1991; DRCPath 1993; MRCPath 1998. Cons. Haematologist,Qu. Eliz. Hosp. NHS Trust. Prev: Sen. Regist. (Haemat.) Univ. Coll. Lond. Hosps.; Sen. Regist. (Haemat.) Watford Gen. Hosp.; Regist. (Haemat.) Roy. Lond. Hosp.

KETT, David William Wake Green Surgery, 7 Wake Green Road, Moseley, Birmingham B13 9HD Tel: 0121 449 0300 — MB ChB 1967 Birm.; DMJ (Clin.) Soc. Apoth 1985 Lond.; Dobst RCOG 1970; MRCGP 1984; MRCGP 1984; DMJ (Clin.) Soc. Apoth Lond. 1985; DObst RCOG 1970. (Birmingham)

KETT-WHITE, Mr Charles Edmund Rupert University Department of Neurosurgery, Box 166, Addenbroke's Hospital, Cambridge CB2 2QQ; Iford Park, Hinton Charterhouse, Bath BA2 7TG — MB BS 1991 Lond.; BSc (Hons.) Lond. 1988; FRCS. Specialist Regist. (Neurosurg.) E. Anglia.

KETTELEY, Sara Jane Keeway, Ferry Road, Burnham-on-Crouch CM0 8PL — BM 1993 Soton.

KETTELL, Jonathan Alexander Tunnel Road Surgery, 24 Tunnel Road, Beaminster DT8 3AB Tel: 01308 862225; 6A Station Road, Burton Joyce, Nottingham NG14 5AN Tel: 0115 931 3110 — BM 1992 Soton.; DRCOG RCOG Lond. 1995; DFFP RCOG Lond. 1995; DCH RCP Lond. 1994; Dip. P.T. C.S.P. 1980. GP Princip. Beaminster. Socs: Chartered Soc. Physiother. Prev: SHO (A & E) Qu. Alexander Hosp. Portsmouth; SHO (Paediat.) Qu. Alexandra Hosp. Portsmouth; SHO (O & G) St. Marys Portsmouth.

KETTING, Kees Paul 135 Prince Rupert Drive, Tockwith, York YO26 7PT — Artsexamen 1985 Utrecht.

KETTLE, Austin Braybrooke (retired) Flat 35, Clarence House, 17 Clarence Road N., Weston Super Mare BS23 4AS Tel: 01934 625237 — MRCS Eng. LRCP Lond. 1927; MD Lond. 1931, MB BS 1928; FRCP Lond. 1968, M 1931; DPH Eng. 1931. Prev: Phys. W.on-super-Mare Hosp. Gp.

KETTLE, Margaret Anne 11 Redgate Road, Girton, Cambridge CB3 0PP — MB BS 1973 Newc.; MRCGP 1978; DObst RCOG 1975.

KETTLE, Paul Jonathan 2 Baronscourt Gardens, Carryduff, Belfast BT8 8EW — MB BCh BAO 1978 Belf.; MRCPath 1987; MRCPI.

KETTLE, Paul Raymond Hoy and Walls Health Centre, Lowthope, Orkney KW15 3PA Tel: 01856 701209 Fax: 01856 701309; Bayview, Lowthope, Orkney KW16 3PQ Tel: 01856 201422 Email: prkettle@yfi.co.uk — MB BChir 1975 Camb.; MA, MB Camb. 1975, BChir 1974; MRCGP 1979; DGM RCP Lond. 1988; DRCOG 1977.

KETTLE, Sarah Jane Alma 20 Daws Lea, High Wycombe HP11 1QF — MB ChB 1995 Sheff.

KETTLEWELL, Gordon (retired) 10 Birchwood Drive, Wilmslow SK9 2RL Tel: 0161 248 6644 — MB ChB Manch. 1949; MRCGP 1968; DObst RCOG 1951. Prev: Ho. Off. (Gyn.) St. Mary's Hosp. Manch.

KETTLEWELL, Mr Michael George Wildman (retired) Old School House, Over Norton, Chipping Norton OX7 5PU Tel: 01608 644693 — MB 1966 Camb.; MA Camb. 1974, MChir 1975, BChir 1965; FRCS Eng. 1971. Cons. Surg. Oxf. AHA (T). Prev: Clin. Reader in Surg. Univ. Oxf.

KETTLEWELL, Stephen 110 Burnbank Road, Ayr KA7 3QJ — MB ChB 1993 Bristol.

KEVELIGHAN, Mr Euan Department of Obstetrics & Gynaecology, Singleton Hospital, Sketty, Swansea SA2 8QA Tel: 01792 285686 Fax: 01792 285874 Email: euan.kevellghan@swansea-tr.wales.nhs.uk; Fax: 01792 207844 Mobile: 0793 0531053 Email: euankevelighan@hotmail.com — MRCOG London RCOG 1993; MB ChB BAO 1987 N U Ireland. Cons. Obstetrition & Gynaecologist Singleton Hosp. Swansea; Lead Clinician for Med. Educat. in Obst. & Gyn.; Sen. Clin. Tutor for Obst. & Gyn.Swansea Clin. Sch.; RCOG Tutor in O&G for Singleton Hosp. Swansea. Prev: Specialist Regist. Obst. & Gyn. St Jas. Hosp. Leeds; Clin. Research Regist. Leeds.

KEVERN, Andrew Brian 7 Wren Street, Netherton, Dudley DY2 0NP — BM 1987 Soton.; MRCP (Peads) Glasgow 1993; DTM & H Liverp 1993.

KEW, Fiona Margaret 21 Beresford Park, Thornhill, Sunderland SR2 7JU — MB ChB 1993 Liverp. Specialist Regist. (O & G) Sunderland.

KEW, Jonathan Martin David 43 Keepers La, Codsall, Wolverhampton WV8 2DP — MB BS 1997 Lond.

KEW, Lowri Diana 11 Smardon Avenue, Brixham TQ5 8JN — MB ChB 1994 Bristol; DRCOG 1996. GP Regist. Aylesbury VTS. Socs: BMA.

***KEWIN, Peter James** Top Left, 605 Great Western Road, Glasgow G12 8HX Tel: 0141 357 5826; The Viking, Station Road, Castletown IM9 1EF Tel: 01624 823656 — MB ChB 1998 Glas.; MB ChB Glas 1998; BSc Glas 1995.

KEWLEY, Geoffrey Douglas Learning Assessment Centre, 48-50 Springfield Road, Horsham RH12 2PD Tel: 01403 240002 Fax: 01403 260900 Email: info@l-a-p-c.com — FRCP Lond. 1996; FRACP 1983; DCH . Lond. 1971; FCPCH 1997. (Sydney University) Cons. Paediat. Learning Assessm. Centre. Socs: BMA; Austral Coll. Paediat.; Brit assoc of community child health. Prev: Cons. Paediat. Crawley Horsham Health Trust; Cons. Paediat. Gosford Dist. Hosp. NSW, Austral.; Hon. Assoc. Phys. Roy. Alexandra Hosp. for Childr. Camperdown NSW, Austral.

KEWLEY, Iain Scott Railway Road Surgery, 11 Railway Road, Ormskirk L39 2DN Tel: 01695 572096 — MB ChB 1982 Liverp.

KEWLEY, Malcolm Lathom Road Clinic, Huyton, Liverpool L36 9XZ Tel: 0151 489 2516 Fax: 0151 489 7577; 1 Harthill Road, Liverpool L18 6HU — MB ChB 1959 Liverp.; MRCGP 1976; DObst RCOG 1962. Prev: SHO (Obst.) New Cross Hosp. Wolverhampton; SHO (Gyn.) Farnham Hosp. Surrey; Ho. Off. Clatterbridge Hosp. & Roy. Liverp. Childr. Hosp.

KEWLEY, Michael Arthur Scotland Road Surgery, 77-79 Scotland Road, Carlisle CA3 9HL Tel: 01228 25768 Fax: 01228 592965 — MB ChB 1982 Manch.; PhD Manch. 1977, MB ChB 1982; BSc (Hons.) Liverp. 1974. Clin. Asst. Dept. of Genitourin. Med. Cumbld. Infirm. Carlisle. Socs: BMA. Prev: SHO (Med. & Paediat.) Cumbld. Infirm. Carlisle; SHO (O & G) City Matern. Hosp. Carlisle.

KEWN, David Lewisham Medical Centre, 158 Utting Avenue East, Liverpool L11 1DL — MB ChB 1970 Liverp.; DObst RCOG 1972. (Liverp.) Princip. Gen. Pract. Socs: Liverp. Med. Inst. Prev: Med. Off. (Occupat. Health) Fazakerley & Walton Hosp. Liverp.

KEY, Adrienne Jane 2 Kingfisher Lodge, Strawberry Vale, Twickenham TW1 4SL — MB ChB 1989 Sheff. SHO Rotat. (Psychiat.) St. Geo. Hosp. Lond.

KEY, Barbara 36 Dalkeith Road, Dundee DD4 7JJ — MB ChB 1998 Aberd.; MB ChB Aberd 1998.

KEY, Cheryl 113 Park Road, Conisborough, Doncaster DN12 2EY — MB BS 1991 Lond.

KEY, Howard Royal Devon & Exeter Hospital (Wonford), Barrack Road, Exeter EX2 5DW — MB ChB 1994 Bristol.

KEY, Ian Alexander (retired) Shaston Beeches, Shaftesbury Drove, Salisbury SP2 8QH Tel: 01722 339429 — MB BS 1954 Lond. Prev: Ho. Surg. Weymouth & Dist. Hosp.

KEY, Paul Reginald 19A Halford Road, Fulham, London SW6 1JS — MB BS 1978 Lond.; MRCP (UK) 1980. (Char. Cross) Sen. Regist. (Genito-Urin. Med.) Char. Cross Hosp. Lond. Socs: Med. Soc. Study VD.

KEY, Penelope Joan, OBE Department for International Development, Victoria Street, London SW1; Hestia, 14 Crokers Meadow, Bovey Tracey, Newton Abbot TQ13 9HL Tel: 01626 833331 Fax: 01926 836888 — MB BS 1961 Lond.; MSc Lond. 1986; MRCS Eng. LRCP Lond. 1961; DObst RCOG 1970; DTM & H Sydney 1965. (Guy's) Pub. Health Cons. to W.H.O and DFID; Princip. Health & Populat. Adviser African Div. Overseas Developm. Admin. Foreign & Commomwealth Off. Lond. Socs: Fell. Roy. Soc. Trop. Med. & Hyg. Prev: WHO Sen. Pub. Health Advisor MoH Phnom Penh; Med. Supt. Dept. Pub. Health Kundiawa, Papua New Guinea; Rpincipal Health and Populat. Adviser, Dept. for Internat. Developm., UK.

KEY, Steven John 7 Westville Road, Cardiff CF23 5DE — MB BCh 1997 Wales.

KEYANI, Javid Ahmed The Surgery, 13 Westway, London W12 0PT; 9 Wynlie Gardens, Pinner HA5 3TN — MB BS 1963. (Bihar Med. Coll., Laheria Sarai, India) Prev: GP at E. Acton, Lond., W12 0PT.

KEYES-EVANS, Owen David 21 Hartley Hill, Purley CR8 4EP — MB BS 1986 Lond.; MA Camb. 1986, BA 1982; MFPHM 1999. (St. Mary's) Prev: Cons. (Pub. Health Med.), Kensington & Chelsea and W.minster Health Auth.

KEYES-EVANS, Mrs Philippa Fleur (retired) Giles Quay, 46a Strand St, Sandwich CT13 9EX Tel: 01304 614128 — MB BS 1955 Lond.; FFA RCS Eng. 1970; DA Eng. 1957. Prev: Cons. Anaesth. Canterbury & Thanet HA.

KEYMER, Mary Rae, MBE 16A Greyfriars Gardens, St Andrews KY16 9HG Tel: 01334 472424 — MB ChB 1939 Glas.

KEYNES, Gregory Robert Edward Boundary Medical Practice, 63 Booth Street West, Hulme, Manchester M15 6PR Tel: 0161 227 9785 Fax: 0161 226 0471 — MB ChB 1982 Birm.; MRCGP 1990; DRCOG 1985. Prev: GP Manch.; Trainee GP Asst. Moss-Side Manch.; Med. Off. Makunduchi Hosp. Zanzibar, Tanzania.

KEYNES, Roger John 70 Grantchester Meadows, Cambridge CB3 9JL — MB 1976 Camb.; BChir 1975; MRCP (UK) 1978.

KEYNES, Mr William Milo (retired) 3 Brunswick Walk, Cambridge CB5 8DH Tel: 01223 353886 — MD 1954 Camb.; DM Oxf. 1964; MChir Camb. 1961; MA, MB BChir Camb. 1948; FRCS Eng. 1955. Prev: Clin. Anat. Dept. Anat. Univ. Camb.

KEYS, Carol Margaret 13 St Ellens, Belfast BT8 8JN — MB BCh BAO 1995 Belf.

KEYS, Derek William 46 Kingswood Court, West End Lane, West Hampstead, London NW6 3SX — MB BS Lond. 1957; MRCS Eng. LRCP Lond. 1957; DObst RCOG 1959. (Westm.) Sen. Forens. Phys. Metrop. Police; Med. Off. Polygram Records & Britvic Corona Ltd.; Examr. Med. Off. Civil Aviat. Auth. Socs: BMA; Brit. Med. Pilots Assn.; Roy. Soc. Med. Prev: Hosp. Pract. (Obst.) Lond. Hosp. (Mile End); Cas. Off. & Sen. Ho. Phys. P. of Wales Gen. Hosp. Lond.; Ho. Surg. (Gyn. & Obst.) Cuckfield Hosp.

KEYS, Jennifer Alison 20/5 Balfour Place, Edinburgh EH6 5DW — MB ChB 1991 Dundee; MB ChB (Hons.) Dundee 1991; MRCP (UK) 1994. SHO (Infec. Dis.) City Hosp. Edin.

KEYS, Leila 63 Pont Street, London SW1X 0BD Tel: 020 7589 2716 Fax: 020 7589 2716 — MB BS Madras 1950; MRCPsych 1972; DPM Eng. 1970. Vis. Cons. Psychiat. The Priory Hosp. Roehampton. Prev: Cons. Psychiat. Bowden Ho. Clinic, Harrow on the Hill; Cons. Psychiat. St. Bernard's Hosp. S.all, Heatherwood Hosp. Ascot & King Edwd. VII Hosp. Windsor.

KEYS, Paul Frederick The Old Cottage, Church Road, Bloxham, Banbury OX15 4ET — MB ChB 1990 Otago.

KEYS, Robert Fleming (retired) 52 Ballougry Road, Londonderry BT48 9XL — MB BCh BAO 1945 Belf.

KEYS, Sydney Scott Stephen 8 Chapel Lane, Barrow-in-Trent, Derby DE73 1TJ Tel: 01332 704234 — MB ChB 1953 Ed. Med. Off. DHSS. Prev: Med. Off. Rolls-Royce Ltd. Derby; Regist. (Surg.) Hereford Hosp. Gp.; Sen. Ho. Off. (Surg & Orthop.) Co. Hosp. Doddington.

KEYSER, Andreas Tobias 16 Viola Street, Bootle, Liverpool L20 7DR — State Exam Med 1992 Cologne.

KEYVAN-FOULADI, Massoud 73A Gaisford Street, London NW5 2EE — MB ChB 1990 Bristol.

KEYWOOD, Charlotte Gwenfron Annette 4 Albany Reach, Queen's Road, Thames Ditton KT7 0QH Email: c.keywood@vanguardmedica.com — MB BS 1986 Lond.; MRCP (UK) 1989; AFPM RCP Lond. 1995. Clin. Research Phys. Vanguard Medica Ltd; Clin. Asst. (Cardiol.) St. Mary's Hosp. Lond.

KEYWORTH, Madeleine Jane 11 Bridgers Close, Rownhams, Southampton SO16 8DU — MB ChB 1974 Bristol; DA Eng. 1976.

KHA, Oak Soe The Surgery, The Limes, Hawley Street, Margate CT9 1PU Tel: 01843 227567 Fax: 01843 230167; Yamana, North Foreland Avenue, Broadstairs CT10 3QR Tel: 01843 866805 — MB BS 1972 Rangoon; MB BS Med. Inst. (I) Rangoon 1972; MFFP 1993; DCCH RCP Ed. 1984. Sen. Prod. Princip. Socs: MFCH 1989; Fac. Comm. Health; Fac. Fam. Plann. & Reprod. Health Care, Roy. Coll. Obst. & Gyn.

KHABAZA, Elizabeth 12A Miles Road, Bristol BS8 2JN — MB ChB 1986 Bristol.

KHADER, Mohamed Ali Bin Abdul Department of Nuclear Medicine, Guy's Hospital, St Thomas St., London SE1 9RT — MB BS 1983 Malaya.

KHADILKAR, Anjali Shrirani 2 Westburn Cottages, Royal Aberdeen Childrens Hospital, Westburn Drive, Aberdeen AB10 9ZA — MB BS 1988 Shivaji U, India; MRCOG 1993.

KHADJEH-NOURI, Mr Dara Flat 20, Rupert House, Nevern Square, London SW5 9PL — MB BS 1962 Lond.; FRCS Eng. 1970; FRCS Ed. 1967; MRCS Eng. LRCP Lond. 1962; DCH RCP Lond. 1964. Cons. Surg. (A & E) Edgware Gen. Hosp. Socs: Fell. Roy. Soc. Med.; Assn. Surgs. Gt. Brit. & N. Irel. Prev: Cons. Surg. Univ. Tehran Cancer Inst.; Regist. Papworth Hosp. Camb.; SHO St. Bart. Hosp. Lond.

KHADRA, Abbas 71 Ullswater Crescent, London SW15 3RE — MB BCh 1994 Wales.

KHADRA, Khaldou Abdalla 38 Moyne Place, London NW10 7EN — LMS 1992 Saragosa.

KHAFAGY, Reda Sayed 30 Woodlands Road, Handforth, Wilmslow SK9 3AU — MB BCh 1964 Cairo.

KHAFAGY, Richard Tarrick 30 Woodlands Road, Handforth, Wilmslow SK9 3AU — MB ChB 1998 Manch.; MB ChB Manch 1998.

KHAGHANI, Mr Asghar Harefield Hospital, Harefield, Uxbridge UB9 6JH Tel: 01895 828799 Fax: 01895 828932; 13 Deep Acres, Amersham HP6 5NX Tel: 01494 722351 Fax: 01494 722351 Email: akhaghani@classic — Tip Doktoru 1972 Istanbul; FRCS Ed. 1983. (Istanbul Med. Fac. Univ. Istanbul) Hon. Cons. Cardiac Surg. & Transpl. Roy. Brompton & Harefield NHS Trust; Sen. Lect. Nat. Heart & Lung Inst. Imperial Coll. Lond. Socs: BMA; Brit. Cardiac Soc.; Internat. Soc. Heart & Lung Transpl. Prev: Sen. Regist. (Cardiac Surg. & Transpl.ation) Harefield Hosp.

KHAIR, Anuradha Satish 15 Alnwick House, Marton Road, Middlesbrough TS4 3SP — MB BS 1978 Poona; DGO Bombay 1980.

KHAIR, Omer Abdel Ghayoum Babiker Mohmad City Hospitals NHS Trust, Dudley Road, Birmingham B18 7QH Tel: 0121 554 3801 Fax: 0121 507 5581 Email: o.khair@cityhospbham.wmids-nhs.uk — MB BS 1983 Khartoum, Sudan; MSc Lond. 1992; MRCP (UK) 1990; PhD 1998. (Khartoum, Sudan) Cons. Phys., City Hosp., Birm.; Hon. Sen. Lect. Birm. Univ. Socs: Amer. Thoracic Soc.; Brit. Thoracic Soc.; W Midl.s Thoracic Soc. Prev: Clin. Research Fell. & Sen. Regist. (Respirat. Med.) St. Bart. Hosp. Lond.; Sen. Regist. Birm. Heartlands Hosp. Birm.

KHAIR, S S Queens Court Surgery, 7 Harris Street, Middlesbrough TS1 5EF Tel: 01642 253234 Fax: 01634 246737 — MB BS 1974 Bombay; MB BS 1974 Bombay.

KHAIRA, Gurpreet Kaur 26 Midgley Drive, Sutton Coldfield B74 2TW — BM BCh 1992 Oxf.

KHAIRA, Harmeet Singh 26 Midgley Drive, Fouroaks, Sutton Coldfield B74 2TW — BM BCh 1988 Oxf.

KHAIRA, Jattinder Singh 916 Bristol Road, Selly Oak, Birmingham B29 6NB — BM BCh 1994 Oxf.

KHAJA, Ghiasuddin The Surgery, 196 Pinner Road, Harrow HA1 4JT Tel: 020 8427 0130 Fax: 020 8424 2509; Fairwinds, 20 Drakes Drive, Northwood HA6 2SL Tel: 01923 824774 — MB BS 1969 Osmania. (Osmania) GP Brent & Harrow Family Plann. Centre; Gen. Med. Pract. Assoc. N.wick Pk. Hosp. Harrow. Socs: BMA; FRSM. Prev: Regist. (Chest Dis. & Gen. Med.) Shrewsbury Gp. Hosps.; SHO (Med.) Herts. & Essex Gen. Hosp. Bishops Stortford; SHO (Med.) Colindale Hosp. Lond.

KHAKHAR, Anjli 62 Tudor Road, Leigh-on-Sea SS9 5AU — MB BS 1997 Lond.

KHAKHAR, Mitesh Bhalchandra 19 Parkfield Close, Crawley RH11 8RS — MB BS 1998 Lond.; MB BS Lond 1998; BSc (Hons) Lond. 1997. (Royal Free Hospital School of Medicine)

KHAKOO, Akhtarbanu Abdulrasul Thameslink Health Care Services NHS Trust, Livingstone Hospital, East Hill, Dartford DA1 1SA Tel: 01322 622222; 44 Claylands Road, London SW8 1NZ — MB BS 1983 Lond.; MSc (Community Med.) Lond. 1991; BSc (Hons.) Biochem. Lond. 1978; DCH RCP Lond. 1988; DRCOG 1987; Cert. Family Plann. JCC 1986. (Univ. Coll. Hosp., Lond.) Staff Grade (Community Paediat.) Thameslink Healthcare Servs. NHS Trust. Dartford. Socs: Fac. Pub. Health Med.; BMA; Brit. Paediat. Assn. Prev: Regist. (Pub. Health Med.) NW Thames Regional Pub. Health Directorate; SHO (Paediat.) Alder Hey Childr. Hosp. Liverp.; SHO (Community Med. & Paediat.) Dept. Community Med. Centr. Birm. HA.

KHAKOO, Gulamabbas Abdulrasul Hillingdon Hospital, Uxbridge UB8 3NN Tel: 01895 279263 Fax: 01895 279388 — BM BCh 1987 Oxf.; FRCPCH (UK) 1994. Cons. (Paediat. & Neonat.) Hillingdon Hosp. Uxbridge; Hon. Cons. (Paediat. Allergy) St. Mary's Hosp. Paddington. Prev: Sen. Regist. (Paediat.) N.wick Pk. Harrow & St. Mary's Hosp. Paddington; Regist. (Paediat.) Roy. Brompton Nat. & Lung Hosp. Lond.; Regist. (Paediat.) Hillingdon Hosp. Uxbridge.

KHAKOO, Salim Iqbal 6 Warwick Street, South Park, Sevenoaks TN13 1EQ — MB BS 1988 Lond.; BSc (Hons.) Lond. 1986, MB BS 1988; MRCP (UK) 1991; MD July 1997. Post Doctoral Research Fell. Stanford Univ. Calif., USA. Prev: Research Regist. Roy. Free Hosp. Lond.; Regist. (Gen. Med.) Glos. Roy. Hosp.

KHAKSAR, Sara Jane 4 The Burlings, Ascot SL5 8BY — MB BCh 1993 Wales.

KHALAF, Mohammad Saeed Chingford Health Centre, 109 York Road, Chingford, London E4 8LF Tel: 020 8529 1541 Fax: 020 8559 4091 — MB BCh 1969 Baghdad.

KHALAFPOUR, Taraneh 14 Ashurst Close, Horsham RH12 4JN — MB BS 1988 Lond.; MRCGP 1991. Trainee GP Woodford Green. Socs: MDU.

KHALED, Mohammed Abu Kennoway Health Centre, Jordan Lane, Kennoway, Leven KY8 5JZ Tel: 01333 350241 Fax: 01333 352884 — MB BS 1962 Dacca. (Dacca) GP Leven, Fife.

KHALED, Mohd Abbas Residences, Hope Hospital, Stott Lane, Salford M6 8 — LMSSA 1990 Lond.; MB BS Sudan 1982; MRCOG 1992.

KHALEELI, Ali Aga Halton Trust Hospital, Hospital Way, Nr Shopping City, Runcorn WA7 2DA Tel: 01928 714567; Gai Logis, Chester Road Mere, Knutsford WA16 6LQ Tel: 01565 830240 Fax: 01565 830240 — MB BS 1969 Lond.; MD Lond. 1984; MRCP (UK) 1973; FRCP Lond. 1990. (Lond. Hosp.) Cons. Phys. Dept. Med. & Endocrinol. Halton Gen. Hosp. Trust Runcorn. Socs: (Comm. Mem.) NW Endocrine Soc.; (Comm. Mem.) Mersey Diabetes Gp.; Diabetes (UK). Prev: Lect. & Hon. Sen. Regist. (Human Metabol.) Univ. Coll. Hosp. Lond.; Asst. Prof. Dept. Med. Endocrinol. Shiraz Univ.; Regist. Char. Cross Hosp. Lond.

KHALID, Mr Abdur Rahman 16 Cambridge Road, St Albans AL1 5LQ — MB BS 1957 Punjab, Pakistan; FRCS Eng. 1972.

KHALID, Abul Faiz Ahmed 148 Palmerston Road, Walthamstow, London E17 6PY — MB BS 1963 Dacca; MRCPI 1976. (Dacca Med. Coll.)

KHALID, Arshad Mahmood Orchard Medical Practice, Orchard Road, Broughton Astley, Leicester LE9 6RG Tel: 01445 282599 Fax: 01445 286772 — MB ChB 1988 Leeds.

KHALID, Asma 27 Mackenzie Road, Birmingham B11 4EP — MB BS 1993 Lond.

KHALID, Linda Jayne 106 Grassington Road, Nottingham NG8 3PE; 167 Queens Drive, Enderby, Leicester LE9 5LL — MB ChB 1994 Leic.; BSc Lond. 1989; DFFP 1998; DRCOG 1998. (University College and Leicester University) GP Regist. Limes Med. Centre NarBoro. Prev: SHO (c/o Elderly) Leicester Gen. Hosp.; SHO

(O & G) Leicester Gen. Hosp.; SHO (Palliat. Care) Staunton Harold Hall Ashby.

KHALID, Mohammed Asadullah Al 10 Greenhithe Close, Sidcup DA15 8EF — MB BS 1972 Dacca; DA Eng. 1976.

KHALID, Muhammad Idrees Al Hada Military Hospital, PO Box 1347 (HHRC 1399), Taif, Saudi Arabia Tel: 00 966 2 7542051; 18 Middleton Avenue, Fenham, Newcastle upon Tyne NE4 9NB Tel: 0191 273 3107 — MB BS 1979 Karachi; MSc (Cardiol.) Glas. 1991; MRCP (UK) 1991. Cons. Cardiol. Al Hada Armed Forces Hosp. Taif, Saudi Arabia. Prev: Staff Grade (Cardiol.) Freeman Hosp. Newc. u. Tyne; Research Fell. (Cardiol.) Glas. Roy. Infirm.; Regist. (Med.) CrossHo. Hosp. Kilmarnock.

KHALID, Nadeem Plot 1, Springfield Avenue, Lye, Stourbridge DY9 8XT — MB ChB 1996 Dundee.

KHALID, Shareefa The Surgery, 234 Stoney Lane, Sparkhill, Birmingham B12 8AW Tel: 0121 449 9685; 27 Mackenzie Road, Moseley, Birmingham B11 4EP Tel: 0121 449 1515 — MB BS 1962 Punjab; MB BS Punjab (Pakistan) 1962; DObst RCOG 1974. (Nishtar Med. Coll. Multan)

KHALID, Shehzana Irlam Medical Centre, Macdonald Road, Irlam, Manchester M44 5LH Tel: 0161 775 5421 Fax: 0161 775 2568; Flat 1, 5 Talford Grove, West Didsbury, Manchester M20 2HL Tel: 0161 434 5777 — MB ChB 1987 Leics.; MRCGP 1993; DRCOG 1991.

KHALID, Mr Tamton 58 Main Street, Walton-on-Trent, Swadlincote DE12 8LZ — MB BS 1956 Andhra; FRCS Eng. 1963; FRCR 1975; FFR 1974; DMRD Eng. 1972. (Andhra) Cons. Radiol. Burton-on-Trent Hosps.; Postgrad. Clin. Tutor Burton Grad. Med. Centre. Prev: SHO (Trauma & Orthop.) Gen. Hosp. Kettering; Regist. (Gen. Surg.) Geo. Eliot Hosp. Nuneaton; Regist. (Radiodiag.) Qu. Eliz. Hosp. Birm.

KHALID, Unnisa Khamar 3 Hayfield Road, Moseley, Birmingham B13 9LG Tel: 0121 449 6665 — MB BS Madras 1953. (Madras) Prev: GP Staffs & Birm. FHSA's; Regist. (Anaesth.) Coventry Gp. Hosps.; Clin. Asst. (Anaesth.) Nuneaton Gp. Hosps.

KHALIFA, Babiker El Bashir 87 Comiston Road, Morningside, Edinburgh EH10 6AG — MB BS 1985 Khartoum.

KHALIFA, Wael 18 Ennismore Avenue, London W4 1SF — MD 1986 Louvain.

KHALIFA, Yasser 11 Warmwell Close, Coventry CV2 2JT — MB BS 1984 Jordan; MRCOG 1993.

KHALIFE-RAHME, Rashid 144 Harley Street, London W1N 1AH Tel: 020 7935 0023 Fax: 020 7435 1757; Flat 7B, Langland Mansions, 228 Finchley Road, London NW3 6QA — MB BS 1982 Lond.; BSc (Arts & Sci.) Lond. 1976. Indep. Specialist A & E. Socs: Fell. Roy. Soc. Med. (Accid. & Emerg. Sect.); Vice-Pres. Middle E. Sect. Doctors Without Frontiers. Prev: Sen. Regist. (A & E) Hotel Dieu De France, Lebanon; Sen. Regist. (A & E) St. Mary's Hosp. Lond.

KHALIFEH, Hind 21 Southdale Road, Oxford OX2 7SE — BM BCh 1998 Oxf.; BM BCh Oxf 1998.

KHALIL, Amal Lamey Winwick Hospital, Winwick Road, Winwick, Warrington WA2 8RR Tel: 01925 55221; 80 Warwick Road, Alkrington, Middleton, Manchester M24 1HX Tel: 0161 643 0293 — MB ChB 1973 Alexandria. Staff Grade Psychiat. Winwick Hosp. Warrington. Prev: Regist. (Psychiat.) Winwick Hosp. Warrington; SHO (Geriat.) Warrington Gen. Hosp.

KHALIL, Amir Alfy Glan Clwyd Hospital, Bodelwyddan, Rhyl LL18 5UJ Tel: 01745 583910 — MB BCh 1971 Cairo; DA Eng. 1977. (Cairo) Assoc. Specialist (Anaesth.) Clwyd HA; Regist. (Anaesth.) BRd.green Hosp. Liverp. Socs: Soc. Anaesth. Prev: SHO (A & E) Roy. N.. Hosp. Lond.; Regist. (Anaesth.) Clwyd AHA; Regist. (Anaesth.) Roy. Alexandra Hosp. Rhyl.

KHALIL, Donna Sabah 13 Priory Cl, Pontypridd CF37 2ER — MB BCh 1997 Wales.

KHALIL, Hany Roshdy The Heys, Caldy Road, Caldy, Wirral CH62 8EZ — MB BCh 1971 Cairo; FACP 1980. Cons. Gen. Intern. Med./Med. Oncol. Caldy.

KHALIL, Khalil Ibrahim Buckingham, 39 Marine Drive, Rhyl LL18 3AY Tel: 01745 332275 — MB BCh 1952 Cairo; FFA RCS Eng. 1976; DA Ain Shams 1958. (Kasr-el-Einy Fac. Med. Cairo) Cons. Anaesth. Medway Health Dist. Prev: Fac. Tutor in Anaesth. Medway HA.; Sen. Regist. Univ. Hosp. Wales Cardiff & Cardiff Roy. Infirm.; Regist. (Anaesth.) W. Middlx. Hosp. Isleworth.

KHALIL, Nabil George Southern Derbyshire Health Authority, Community Health Services, Sintin Health Centre, Derby DE24 3DS — LRCP LRCS 1979 Ed.; LRCP LRCS Ed. LRCPS Glas. 1979. SCMO S.. Derbysh. HA.

KHALIL, Nofal Mohammed West London Neurosciences Centre, Charing Cross Hospital, London W6 8RF Tel: 020 8846 1655 Fax: 020 8846 1300 Email: m.khalil@ic.ac.uk; 23 Gibbon Road, E. Acton, London W3 7AF Tel: 020 8749 4893 — MB ChB 1977 Mosul; MB ChB Mosul Iraq 1977; MD Mosul Univ 1981; PhD Lond. 1991. Cons. Clin. Neurophysiol. W. Lond. Neurosci.s Centre, Char. Cross Hosp. Socs: Brit. Soc. Clin. Neurophysiol.; Amer. Assn. Electrodiagn. Med. Prev: Clin. & Research Fell. (Neurol.) Mass. Gen. Hosp. Boston, USA.

KHALIL MARZOUK, Mr Youssef Fahmy East Heartlands Hospital, Bordesley Green E., Birmingham B9 5ST Tel: 0121 766 6611 Fax: 0121 766 5823 — MB BCh 1977 Ain Shams; MCh Ain Shams 1981, MB BCh 1977; FRCS (C Th) Eng. 1989; FRCS Ed. 1983. Cons. Cardiothoracic Surg. E. Birm. Hosp. NHS Trust. Socs: Soc. of Cardiothoracic Surg. Of GB & Irel.; Roy. Soc. Med.; Eur. Assn. Cardiothoracic Surg. Prev: i/c Cardiothoracic Surg. Al-Hada Armed Forces Hosp. Taif, KSA; Sen. Regist. (Cardiothoracic Surg.) Middlx. Hosp. Lond.

KHALILI-NAYER, Nadereh The Health Centre, Pond Road, Shoreham-by-Sea BN43 5US Tel: 01273 440550 Fax: 01273 462109 — MD 1965 Tehran; DRCOG 1983; DGO 1974. Socs: BMA; BMAS. Prev: Cons. Gyn. Madaen Hosp. Tehran, Iran; Hon. Regist. (O & G) St. Thos. Hosp. Lond.

KHALIQ, Kessar Wards Medical Practice, 25 Dundonald Road, Kilmarnock KA1 1RU Tel: 01563 526514 Fax: 01563 573558 — MB ChB 1993 Manch.; DRCOG 1998.

KHALIQ, Salem Abdul c/o Midland Bank, 43 Queensway, London W2 4QL — MB ChB 1958 St. And.; MRCPsych 1972; DPM Eng. 1965. (St. And.) Sen. Med. Off. Home Off.

KHALIQ MASOOD, Abdul Department Anaesthesia, Dewsbury District Hospital, Healds Road, Dewsbury WF13 4HS Tel: 01924 465105; 5 Christchurch Gardens, Christchurch Mount, Epsom KT19 8RU Tel: 01372 720449 — BSc Punjab 1961, MB BS 1967; DA Eng. 1970; DA RCPSI 1970. (King Edward Medical College, Lahore Pakistan) Assoc. Specialist Anaesth. Dewsbury & Dist. Hosp. Dewsbury W. Yorks.; Assoc. Specialist (Anaesth.) Dewsbury Dist. Hosp. Prev: Regist. (Anaesth.) Dewsbury Dist. Hosp.; Regist. (Anaesth.) Barnsley Dist. Gen. Hosp.

KHALIQUE, Abraze Bilborough Medical Centre, Bracebridge Drive, Bilborough, Nottingham NG8 4PH Tel: 0115 929 2354 Fax: 0115 929 1656; 244 Melton Road, Edwalton, Nottingham NG12 4AG — BM BS 1984 Nottm.; MRCGP 1988; DCH RCP Lond. 1988; DRCOG 1987; DGM RCP Lond. 1986. Socs: Soc. Occupat. Med.

KHALIQUE, Parvaze The Surgery, 492 Nottingham Road, Giltbrook, Nottingham NG16 2GE Tel: 0115 938 3191 Fax: 0115 945 9556 — MB ChB 1980 Manch.; BSc (Med. Sci.) St. And. 1977; MRCGP 1984; DRCOG 1984; DCH RCP Lond. 1983. Clin. Tutor (Gen. Pract.) Univ. Nottm.; Hon. (Obst.) City Hosp. Nottm. & Qu. Med. Centre Nottm.

KHALIQUE, Sophia 69 Cranbrook Road, Chiswick, London W4 2LJ — MB ChB 1991 Leic. GP Asst.

KHALLAF, Ahmed Amin The Surgery, Station Road, Treorchy, Cardiff CF42 Tel: 01443 2595 — MB BCh 1955 Ein-Shams Univ. Cairo; LMSSA Lond. 1965; DTM & H Eng. 1960. (Ein-Shams Univ.) Local Treasury Med. Off.; Admiralty Surg. & Agent. Socs: BMA; Fell. Roy. Soc. Med. Prev: Med. Regist. & Clin. Demonst. Ein-Shams Univ. Hosps.; Research Asst. Lond. Hosp. Med. Coll.

KHALPEY, Zain Ismail Room 303 Nockolds House, Lewisham University Hospital, Lewisham, London SE13 6LH — MB BS 1998 Lond.; MB BS Lond 1998.

KHAMASHTA, Munther Andrawes Lupus Research Unit, The Rayne Institute, St Thomas Hospital, London SE1 7EH Tel: 020 7928 9292 Fax: 020 7620 2658 — LMS 1983 Barcelona; PhD Autonoma Madrid 1991. Sen. Lect. & Cons. Phys. Lupus Unit St. Thos. Hosp. Lond. Socs: Internat. Soc. Internal Med.; Ilustre Colegio de Medicos de Madrid; Brit. Soc. Rheum.

KHAMBATA, Mr Ardeshir Shiavax (retired) 152 Harley Street, London W1N 1HH Tel: 020 7935 8868 — MB BS Bombay 1959; FRCS Eng. 1965. Cons. (Otolaryngol.); Cons. Laryngol. Roy. Coll.

Music, Roy. Opera Hse & English Nat. Opera Lond. Prev: Cons. ENT Fawkham Manor Hosp. Kent.

KHAMBATTA, Roeinton Burjor (retired) c/o 160 Rivermead Court, Ranelagh Gardens, London SW6 3SF Tel: 020 7731 5290 Fax: 020 7731 5290 — MB BS 1946 Bombay; FRCP Lond. 1970, M 1951; FRCP Ed. 1961, M 1951; DTM & H Eng. 1951. Prev: Cons. Phys. Roy. Masonic Hosp. Lond.

KHAMIS, Mr Khamis Abdullatif Tanzania Student Office, 43 Hereford St., London W1; 4 Parkwood Rise, Barnby Dun, Doncaster DN3 1LY — MB ChB 1971 Leeds; FRCS Ed. 1977. Staff Grade (Gen. Surg.) Lond.

KHAMMAR, George Souhel 35 Iverna Court, Wrights Lane, London W8 6TR — MB BS 1987 Lond.; MRCP (UK) 1991.

***KHAMZINA, Elena Ildarovna** 11 Bridgeford House, Cassio Road, Watford WD18 0QR Tel: 01923 239530 Fax: 01923 218564 — LMSSA 1997; Dip. Med. (Urals) 1994; LMSSA Lond. 1997.

KHAN, A T M Mutahar Hussain Aylsby Crescent, Knutsford WA16 8AE — MB BS 1964 Dacca; Dip. Ven. Liverp. 1971. (Dacca Med. Coll.) Cons. Genitourin. Med. Mersey RHA. Socs: Fell. WHO.

KHAN, Aamer Bournville Surgery, 41B Sycamore Road, Bournville, Birmingham B30 2AA Tel: 0121 472 7231; 95 Harborne Road, Edgbaston, Birmingham B15 3HG — MB ChB 1986 Birm.; ChB Birm. 1986. GP Clin. Asst. (Psychiat.) Health Screening Nuffield Hosp. Birm. Prev: Ho. Off. (Surg.) Selly Oak Hosp. Birm.; Ho. Off. (Med.) Gen. Hosp. Birm.

KHAN, Aamer 5 The Boundary, Bradford BD8 0BQ — MB ChB 1996 Leeds.

KHAN, Abdul Ghani 224 Stockwell Road, London SW9 9SU Tel: 020 7733 3411 — MB BS 1940 Lucknow. (King Geo. Med. Coll.)

KHAN, Abdul Hameed Amison Street Surgery, Shopping Centre, Amison Street, Longton, Stoke-on-Trent ST3 1LD Tel: 01782 335795 Fax: 01782 593903; Oaklea, 168 Stallington Road, Blythe Bridge, Stoke-on-Trent ST11 9PA Tel: 01782 393415 — MB BS 1967 Ranchi; DA Eng. 1970.

KHAN, Abdul Khaliq 11 Sandringham Drive, Stockport SK4 2DE — MB BS 1968 Punjab.

KHAN, Mr Abdul Latif 15 Callum Crescent, Kings Wels, Aberdeen AB10 8XQ — MB BS 1979 Peshawar; FRCS Ed. 1988.

KHAN, Abdul Majeed 81 Ajax Drive, Unsworth, Bury BL9 8EF Tel: 0161 766 4853 — MB BS 1958 Karachi; DTM & H Eng. 1962. (Dow Med. Coll.) Prev: Med. Asst. (Geriat.) Crumpsall Hosp. Manch.; Med. Regist. & Regist. (Geriat.) FarnBoro. Hosp., Kent.

KHAN, Abdul Majid Prince of Wales Road Medical Centre, 671 Prince of Wales Road, Sheffield S9 4ES Tel: 0114 244 1384 — MB BS 1969 Dacca, Bangladesh.

KHAN, Abdul Mobin South Warwick Hospital NHS Trust, Lakin Road, Warwick CV34 5BW; 1 Knight Cote Drive, Leamington Spa CV32 5FA Tel: 01926 426576 — MB BS 1972 Lucknow; MRCPCH 1996; DCH RCPS Glas. 1996. Cons. Paediat. Warwick. Prev: Staff Grade (Paediat.) Stafford & Wakefield; Regist. (Paediat.) Dumfries & Galloway Roy. Infirm. Dumfries.

KHAN, Abdul Quddus Akram 342 Uttoxeter New Road, Derby DE22 3HS — MB ChB 1984 Manch.

KHAN, Abdul Rashid Whitworth Road Surgery, 9 Whitworth Road, South Norwood, London SE25 6XN Tel: 020 8653 1414 Fax: 020 8771 3038; 66 Mayfield Road, Sanderstead, South Croydon CR2 0BF Tel: 020 8657 3919 — MB BS Sind 1963; DCH RCPS Glas. 1976.

KHAN, Abdul Rauf The Coppice, 39 Station Road, Alresford, Colchester CO7 8BU Tel: 01206 823377 — MB BCh BAO 1978 Belf.; DPM Eng. 1982. (Qu. Univ. Belf.) Cons. Acute Adult Psychiat. (Long Term Locum), N. E. Essex Ment. Health NHS Trust, Clacton Hosp., Essex. Prev: Cons. Forens. Psychiat. (long term locum) BRd.moor Hosp.; Head Med. Servs. HMP Whitemoor Cambs.

KHAN, Abdul Waheed 26 Taylor's Green, London W3 7PF — MB BS 1985 Peshawar.

KHAN, Abdur Rahim Chartwell House, Pinfold Road, Bourne PE10 9HT Tel: 01778 422171 Fax: 01778 422171 — MB BS 1967 Dacca; DPM RCPSI 1973. (Chittagong Med. Coll.) Cons. Psychiat. Learning Disabil. (Ment. Handicap) Lincs. Healthcare NHS Trust. Prev: Sen. Regist. (Ment. Handicap & Developm. Paediat.) Hants. AHA.

KHAN, Abdur Rashid (retired) 23 Radbrook Road, Shrewsbury SY3 9BD Tel: 01743 232853 — MB BS 1956 Karachi; FRCP Lond. 1992; FRCP Glas. 1979, M 1966; DTM & H Liverp. 1959. Cons. Phys. (Geriat. Med.) Telford Gen. Hosp. Prev: Cons. Phys. (Geriat. Med.)Roy. Shrewsbury Hosp.

KHAN, Abdurrahman Mohammed Shammas-Aldheim, Butlers Dene Road, Woldingham, Caterham CR3 7HH Tel: 01883 3088 — MB BS 1945 Bombay; MRCP Ed. 1954 FRFPS Glas. 1954; MRCP Glas. 1962; DTM & H Eng. 1950. (Grant Med. Coll.) Prev: Ho. Phys. Sir J.J. Hosp. Bombay; Res. Med. Off. Stapleton Hosp. Bristol; Cons. Phys. Civil Hosp. Hyderabad (Sind).

KHAN, Abid Ali The Foundation NHS Trust, Corporation St., Stafford ST16 3AG Tel: 01785 257888 Fax: 01785 258969 — MB BS 1982 Punjab; MRCPsych 1989. Cons. Psychiat. St. Geo. Hosp. Stafford.

KHAN, Abida Shah Noor Thorpe Road Surgery, 8 Thorpe Road, Middleton, Leeds LS10 4BA Tel: 0113 270 5221 Fax: 0113 249 0261 — MB BS 1966 Osmania. (Osmania) GP Leeds.

KHAN, Abul Khair Mohamed Shajahan Carreg Wen Surgery, Blaenavon Health Centre, Blaenavon NP4 9XS Tel: 01495 790264 Fax: 01495 790334; 10 The Park, Blaenavon NP4 9AG — MB BS 1958 Dacca; DTM & H Eng. 1964. (Dacca Med. Coll.) GP Trainer, Blaenavon; Hon. Tutor Gen. Pract. Univ. Wales Med. Sch.

KHAN, Adil Yousaf 28 The Avenue, Sale M33 4PD — BM BCh 1996 Oxf.

KHAN, Aftah Ahmed 46 Meadow Way, Wembley HA9 7LG — MB BS 1984 Punjab; MRCPI 1992.

KHAN, Ahmed Fateh Mohammed 55 Mansewood Road, Glasgow G43 1TL — MB ChB 1988 Glas.

KHAN, Aijaz Ali Thorncroft, Morton Lane, East Morton, Keighley BD20 5RP — MB ChB 1991 Manch.

KHAN, Akhtar 40 Alwen Avenue, Huddersfield HD2 2SJ — MB ChB 1991 Manc.

KHAN, Akram 48 Crossflatts Avenue, Leeds LS11 7BG — MB ChB 1989 Sheff.

KHAN, Miss Alam Ara Grizebeck Close Surgery, 1 Grizebeck Close, Gorton, Manchester M18 8AY Tel: 0161 223 0017 Fax: 0161 223 9421 — MB BS 1962 Karachi; FRCOG 1989; FFA RCS Eng. 1977; FRCS Ed. 1972; MRCOG 1968, DObst 1965. (Dow Medical College) Cons. Anaesth.; Hon. Clin. Lect. Anaesth. Vict. Univ. Manch. Socs: Elected Mem. Gen. Med. Counc. 1989 to date; Dep. Chairm. Performance Comm.; Sec. of State's Nominee to Centr. Counc. for Nurses & Midw. Prev: Regist. (Obst & Gyn.) Hope Hosp. Salford.

KHAN, Ali Nawaz Department of Radiology, North Manchester General Hospital, Crumpsall, Manchester M8 5RB — MB BS 1965 Peshawar; FRCP Ed. 1994; MRCP (UK) 1974; MRCS Eng. LRCP Lond. 1974; FRCR 1978; DMRD Eng. 1976. (Khyber Med. Coll.) Cons. Radiol. Manch. Health Dist.; Lect. Univ. Manch. Prev: Sen. Regist. (Radiol.) Sheff. AHA (T); Regist. Roy. Hosp. Sheff. & Mansfield & Dist. Hosp.

KHAN, Almas Latif Newcastle General Hospital, Westgate Road, Newcastle upon Tyne NE4 6BE — MB BS 1997 Newc.

KHAN, Amanullah 6 Hubert Road, Slough SL3 7SF — MB BS 1972 Peshawar; MRCPI 1987.

KHAN, Amanullah Northstead, Doncaster Road, Bawtry, Doncaster DN10 6NE; 71 Eton Rise, Eton College Road, London NW3 2DA — MB BS 1991 Lond.; MRCGP 1995; DGM RCP Lond. 1994. Prev: Trainee GP Doncaster VTS.

KHAN, Mr Ameenuddin Stafford District General Hospital NHS Trust, Stafford ST16 3SA Tel: 01785 257731 Fax: 01785 245211; Ashiana, 9 Claremont Grove, Western Downs, Stafford ST17 9UQ Tel: 01785 227887 Fax: 01785 227887 — MB BS 1973 Bangalore; MSc (Orth.) Lond. 1985; FRCS Glas. 1983; Mmed Sci Keele 1998. Staff Grade Orthop. Surg. Stafford Dist. Gen. Hosp. NHS Trust; Mediated Entry Specialist Regist. N. Staffs. Roy. Infirm. Socs: Brit. Orthop. Assn.; Internat. Med. Soc. of Paraplegia; Assoc. Mem. BASK. Prev: Regist. (Orthop.) & Fell. Spinal Injuries & Spinal Disorders Robt. Jones & Agnes Hunt Orthop. Hosp. OsW.ry; Cons. Orthop. Surg. King Abdul Aziz Naval Base Hosp. Jubail, Saudi Arabia.

KHAN, Amer 24 Wycombe House, Grendon St., London NW8 8SN — MB BS 1994 Lond.

KHAN, Amiduzzaman Abedur Rahman 1 Ridge View Close, Barnet EN5 2QB — MB BS 1988 Dacca; MRCP (UK) 1994.

KHAN, Amjad Hussain Kingsley, 17 Oaken Lanes, Codsall, Wolverhampton WV8 2AH — MB ChB 1986 Dundee.

KHAN, Amjid Mahmood 73 Park Road, Bolton BL1 4RQ — MB BS 1994 Lond.; BSc (Hons.) Lond. 1991. (UMDS Guy's & St. Thos. Hosps. Lond.) SHO (Med.) Brighton. Prev: SHO (A & E) Norf. & Norwich Hosp.; Ho. Surg. Lewisham Hosp. Lond.; Ho. Phys. Roy. Sussex Co. Hosp. Brighton.

KHAN, Mr Ans Balal 4 Hyndland Avenue, Glasgow G11 5BW — MB ChB 1985 Glas.; FRCS Glas. 1989.

KHAN, Anwar Ali Loughton Health Centre, The Drive, Loughton IG10 1HW Tel: 020 8508 8117 Fax: 020 8508 7895 — MB BS 1982 Lond.; BSc (Intercalated) Lond. 1979; MRCGP 1986; DRCOG 1984; DCH RCP Lond. 1987; DCCH RCP Ed. 1987. (Westm.) Assoc. Course Organiser Whipps Cross Hosp. VTS. Prev: SCMO (Med. Genetics) St. Mary's Hosp. Manch.; CMO Child Health Dartford; Trainee GP Neath Rotat. VTS.

KHAN, Anwar Ali East Tilbury Health Centre, 85 Coronation Avenue, East Tilbury, Grays RM18 8SW Tel: 01375 846232 Fax: 01375 840440; 11 Dunstable Road, Stanford-le-Hope SS17 8QT Tel: 01375 675629 Fax: 01375 840440 — MB BS 1969 Jammu & Kashmir.

KHAN, Arfa Southend Healthcare NHS Trust, Southend General Hospital, Prittlewell Chase, Westcliff on Sea SS0 0RY Tel: 01702 435555 Fax: 01702 221252; 96 Burges Road, Thorpe Bay, Southend-on-Sea SS1 3JJ Tel: 01702 587273 — LRCP LRCS Ed. LRCPS Glas. 1978; MRCP (UK) 1983; DCH RCP Lond. 1980. Cons. Paediat. & Neonatol. S.end Health Care NHS Trust. Prev: Cons. Paediat. & Neonatol. Matern. & Childr. Hosp. Jeddah, Kingdom Saudi Arabia.

KHAN, Arshid Amir 118 Park Road, Low Moor, Bradford BD12 0DJ — MB ChB 1994 Leeds.

KHAN, Ashraf 40 Donaldson Road, Shooters Hill, London SE18 3JY Tel: 020 8319 1706 — MD 1983 Aligarh; MB BS 1980; MRCPath 1991. Sen. Regist. (Histopath.) Guy's Hosp. Lond. Prev: Regist. (Histopath.) Lewisham Hosp. Lond.; Lect. (Path.) J.N. Med. Coll. Aligarh Muslim Univ. Aligarh, India.

KHAN, Ashraf Mohammad Mental Health Unit, Walsgrave Hospital, Coventry Tel: 024 76 602020; 15 Lamont Avenue, Harborne, Birmingham B32 3XF Tel: 0121 427 2899 — MB BCh 1982 Wales; MRCGP 1986; DCH RCP Lond. 1984; DRCOG 1984.

KHAN, Asma 5 The Boundary, Bradford BD8 0BQ — BM BCh 1996 Oxf.

KHAN, Asmat Ullah The Clinic, Church Road, Denaby Main, Doncaster DN12 4AB Tel: 01709 863302; 1 Backside Lane, Warmsworth, Doncaster DN4 9NB Tel: 01302 851440 — MB BS 1965 Karachi; BSc Karachi 1958, MB BS 1965. (Dow Med. Coll.)

KHAN, Atifa 250 Kingsway, Rochdale OL16 4AW — MB ChB 1997 Liverp.

KHAN, Aurangzeb 16 Steeplestone Close, London N18 1JH — MB BS 1998 Lond.; MB BS Lond 1998.

KHAN, Ayla Sabrina 18 Chestnut Drive, Pinner HA5 1LY Tel: 020 8866 0290 — MB ChB 1996 Birm.; ChB Birm. 1996. (University of Birmingham) SHO (Psychiat.), St. Anne's Hosp., Tottenham, Lond. Socs: BMA; MDU. Prev: SHO (Psychiat.) Meadowbrook Unit Ment. Health Servs. of Salford; SHO (A & E) Bury Gen. Hosp.; Ho. Off. (Med.) Heartlands Hosp. Bordesley Green Birm.

KHAN, Azim D'Mello and Partners, The Health Centre, Curtis Street, Hucknall, Nottingham NG15 7JE Tel: 0115 963 2535 Fax: 0115 963 2885 — MB ChB 1994 Liverp.

KHAN, Birjees James Street Medical Centre, James Street, Markham, Blackwood NP12 0QN Tel: 01495 224134 Fax: 01495 221449 — MB BS 1968 Vikram; MB BS 1968 Vikram.

KHAN, Cliff Fazal Stockley Field House, 4 Stockley Lane, Oakenshaw, Crook DL15 0TQ — MB BS 1987 Newc.

KHAN, Daud Basharat Akbar The Surgery, 87 Northcote Road, London SW11 6PL Tel: 020 7223 2417 Fax: 020 7924 6722 — BSc Karachi 1961, MB BS 1965; MFHom Lond. 1969. (Dow Med. Coll.) Clin. Med. Off. Wandsworth HA; Clin. Asst. & GP St. Geo. Hosp. Lond. Prev: SHO (ENT) Radcliffe Infirm. Oxf.; SHO (Gen. Med.) Roy. Lond. Homoeop.. Hosp. Lond.; Clin. Asst. Tooting Bec Hosp.

KHAN, David Saleem Ahmed 115 Cleveleys Avenue, Scale Hall, Lancaster LA1 5HN — MB ChB 1985 Manch.

KHAN, Emran Ghaffar Diabetes Centre, Noble's Isle of Man Hospital, Westmoreland Road, Douglas IM1 4RA Tel: 01624 642728 Fax: 01624 642389 Email: emran.khan@nobles.dhss.gov.im — MB BS 1986 Peshawar; MRCP (UK) 1991. (Khyber Med. College) Cons. Diabetologist & Endocrinologist, Nobles Hosp..; Roy. Coll. of Phys.s Clin. Tutor. Prev: Cons., Nottm. City Hosp.; Cons., Nothern Gen. Hosp., Sheff.; Sen. Regist., Riyad Armed Forces Hosp., Saudi Arabia.

KHAN, Faheem A Victoria Health Centre, 5 Suffrage Street, Smethwick, Warley B66 3PZ Tel: 0121 558 0216 Fax: 0121 558 4732 — MB BS 1964 Osmania; MB BS 1964 Osmania.

KHAN, Mr Fahim Carnarvon Road Surgery, 7 Carnarvon Road, Southend-on-Sea SS2 6LR Tel: 01702 466340 Fax: 01702 603179 — MB BS 1972 Aligarh, Muslim; LRCP LRCS Ed. LRCPS Glas. 1980; FRCS Ed. 1979.

KHAN, Fakhruzzaman Sunny Croft, 106 Pleckgate Road, Blackburn BB1 8PN Tel: 01254 677271 — MB BS 1971 Calcutta; DO RCPSI 1977.

KHAN, Mr Farid, Lt.-Col. RAMC (V) (retired) Queen Elizabeth Hospital, Stadium Road, Woolwich SE18 4QH Tel: 0208 836 5453, 0208 836 5458 — MRCS Eng. LRCP Lond. 1978; FRCSI 1984. Cons. Orthop.Qu. Eliz. Hosp., Woolwich; Cons. Orthopaedic Surg. BMI Blackheath,Lond. Prev: Cons. Orthop. MDHU Frimley Pk. Surrey.

KHAN, Farida Fife Healthcare NHS Trust, Lochgelly Health Centre, David Street, Lochgelly KY5 9QZ Tel: 01592 780358; 20 Station Road, Lochgelly KY5 9QW — MB BS 1967 Dhaka; DObst RCOG 1971. GP Lochgelly.

KHAN, Farooq Ali 48 Balmoral Drive, Hayes UB4 0BX — MB BS 1996 Lond.; BSc (Hons) 1993. (University College London Medical School) SHO (Surg.) Addenbroke's Hosp. Camb.

KHAN, Farzana Naz Beckfield House, 143 Bradford Road, Shipley BD18 3TH — MB ChB 1996 Dundee.

KHAN, Fauzia 11 Woodmansterne Road, Carshalton SM5 4JJ — MB ChB 1992 Leeds.

KHAN, Feroz 10 Beaconsfield Road, Knowle, Bristol BS4 2JF — MB ChB 1992 Dundee.

KHAN, Geofrey 35 Wentworth Park Avenue, Birmingham B17 9QU — MB BS 1988 Lond.; BSc Lond. 1985, MB BS 1988. SHO (Med.) OldCh. Hosp. Romford.

KHAN, Georgina Margaret Tresaith, Plas Bennion, Rhos, Wrexham LL14 1TP — MB ChB 1969 Leeds; BSc (Pharmacol.) Leeds 1967, MB ChB (Hons.) 1969. (Leeds) Med. Off. Clwyd AHA.

KHAN, Ghulam Mustafa c/o 130 The Stroud Green Road, London N4 3RZ — LAH BAO 1960 Dub. Dir. Islamic Health Clinic Ankpa, Nigeria. Socs: Islamic Med. Assn. UK & Irel. (Founder Pres. Princip. Adviser).

KHAN, Golam Morshed Abdul Ahad 2 Third Avenue, Dagenham RM10 9BA — MB BS 1963 Dacca; DA Eng. 1971; DTM & H Liverp. 1965. (Dacca Med. Coll.) Regist. (Anaesth.) Barking Hosp.

KHAN, Gul Muhammad Alfeshan Medical Centre, 3 Shirley Road, Cheetham, Manchester M8 0WB Tel: 0161 795 0200 Fax: 0161 795 4908; 29 Boar Green Close, Manchester M40 3AW Tel: 0161 795 0200 — MB BS 1971 Punjab; DTM & H Liverp. 1985.

KHAN, Gulzar Hussain Galtee More Surgery, Galtee More, 2 Doncaster Road, Barnsley S70 1UD Tel: 01226 282555 — MB BS 1970 Punjab, Pakistan; MB BS Punjab 1970. Socs: BMA.

KHAN, Hamed Noor 18 Langley Drive, London E11 2LL — MB BS 1996 Lond.

KHAN, Hameed Ullah Loughton Health Centre, The Drive, Loughton IG10 1HW Tel: 020 8508 8117 Fax: 020 8508 7895; 12 Beresford Drive, Woodford Green IG8 0JH Tel: 020 8508 7895 — MB BS 1972 Jammu & Kashmir. (Govt. Med. Coll. Srinagar) GP Loughton. Prev: GP Trainee Reading; SHO (Med.) Ramsgate Hosp.; SHO (Med.) Mansfield & Dist. Gen. Hosp.

KHAN, Hamid Ali Gordon Street Surgery, 72 Gordon Street, Burton-on-Trent DE14 2JB Tel: 01283 563175 Fax: 01283 500638; 46A Rolleston Road, Burton-on-Trent DE13 0JZ Tel: 01283 63175 — MB BS 1963 Karachi.

KHAN, Hamid Kamal The Hillingdon Hospital, Dept of Clinical Radiology, Pield Heath Road, Uxbridge UB8 3NN Tel: 01895 217 9327; 85 Northwood Way, Northwood HA6 1RT Tel: 01923 784 0637 — State Exam Med 1971 Gottingen; MD Facharzt Radiologie 1978; DMRD Eng. 1985. (Göttingen) Cons. Radiol. (Diagnostic).

KHAN, Hamidul Hoque 35 Greenhill Close, Winchester SO22 5DZ — MB BS 1985 Lond.; LMSSA Lond. 1985.

KHAN, Hamidullah Liversedge Health Centre, Valley Road, Liversedge WF15 6DF Tel: 01924 407771 Fax: 01924 411727; Shaftsbury House, 5 York Road, Upper Batley, Batley WF17 0LG Tel: 01924 479251 — MB BS Peshawar 1966. (Khyber Med. Coll.)

KHAN, Hannah Rosemary 43 Mount Street, Aberdeen AB25 2QX — MB ChB 1990 Aberd.

KHAN, Hassan Flat 14, Bernhard Baron House, 71 Henriques St., London E1 1LZ — MB BS 1994 Lond.

KHAN, Husain Ali (retired) Clyst Haven, 8 Cross Park, Crafthole, Torpoint PL11 3BH Tel: 01503 230349 — MB BS Punjab (Pakistan) 1953; DTM & H Eng. 1959. Prev: GP Cornw. & I. of Scillies FHSA.

KHAN, Mr Iftikhar Ahmed 259 Clifton Drive S., St. Annes Sea, Lytham St Annes FY8 1HW Tel: 01253 723301 — MB BS 1957 Punjab; MB BS Punjab (Pakistan) 1957; FRCS Eng. 1968; FRCS Ed. 1964. (King Edwd. Med. Coll. Lahore) Cons. Surg. (ENT) Blackpool Health Dist. Socs: Fell. Manch. Med Soc. Prev: Lect. (Otolaryng.) Univ. Manch.; Sen. Regist. (ENT) Manch. Roy. Infirm.

KHAN, Ilam Dad 67 Seven Star Road, Solihull B91 2BZ — MB BS 1981 Peshawar; MRCPI 1988.

KHAN, Mr Imdad Hussain Inverclyde Royal Hospital, Greenock PA16 0X — MB BS 1954 Calcutta; FRCS Eng. 1961. (Calcutta) Assoc. Specialist (Surg.) Inverclyde Roy. Hosp.

KHAN, Imteyaz Ahmed 4 St Helen Grove, Sandal, Wakefield WF2 Tel: 01924 72361 — MB BS 1966 Ranchi; FFA RCSI 1977. (Rajendra Med. Coll.) Cons. Anaesth. Pontefract Gen. Infirm. Prev: Sen. Regist. (Anaesth.) Nottm. Teach. Hosps.; Regist. (Anaesth.) PeterBoro. Dist. Hosp.; Regist. (Anaesth.) S.end Gen. Hosp. S.end-on-Sea.

KHAN, Imtiaz 39 Swanage Road, Birmingham B10 9ER — MB BS 1997 Lond.

KHAN, Imtiaz Ahmad The Surgery, Welbeck Street, Creswell, Worksop S80 4HA Tel: 01909 721206 — MB BS 1961 Punjab; MB BS Punjab (Pakistan) 1961. (Nishtar Med. Coll. Multan) Socs: BMA.

KHAN, Imtiaz Ali Rooley Lane MC, Bradford BD4 7SS — MB ChB 1992 Liverp.

KHAN, Inayat Hasan 248 Salthoue Road, Hull Tel: 01482 78298 — MRCS Eng. LRCP Lond. 1960.

KHAN, Inayat Ul Haq 2 Dolphin Court, Woodlands, London NW11 9QY Tel: 020 8455 2442 — MB BS 1949 Punjab, Pakistan; DLO Eng. 1960. (King Edwd. Med. Coll. Lahore) Socs: Mem. Pakistan Med. Soc. Prev: Clin. Asst. (Otolaryng.) W.m. Gp. Hosps.; Med. Off. i/c ENT Out-pats. Dept. Mayo Hosp. Lahore & Nishtar Hosp.; Multan, Pakistan; Clin. Asst. (Otolaryng.) N. Middlx. Hosp. Lond.

KHAN, Itrat Hazur Lattimore Surgery, 1 Upton Avenue, St Albans AL3 5ER Tel: 01727 855160 Fax: 01727 839617 — MB BS 1982 Lond.; DRCOG 1984. Trainee GP St. Albans City Hosp. VTS.

KHAN, Izharul Haq 101 South Anderson Drive, Aberdeen AB10 7PL Tel: 01224 319348 Fax: 01224 699884 — MB BS 1985 Karachi; MD Aberd. 1996; FRCP Ed. 1997; MRCP (UK) 1989. Cons. Phys. (Nephrol.) Aberd. Roy. Hosp. NHS Trust. Socs: BMA; SSP; SRA. Prev: Lect. (Med.) Univ. Aberd.; Regist. (Renal Med.) Ninewells Hosp. Dundee; Regist. (Gen. Med.) Inverness.

KHAN, Jabeen Akhtar 8 Portland Street, Normanton, Derby DE23 8PZ — BM BS 1989 Nottm.

KHAN, Jahanara Begum 5 Exeter Gardens, Stamford PE9 2RN Tel: 01780 56704 — MB BS 1972 Rajshahi. (Rajshahi Medical School) Socs: Med. Protec. Soc.

KHAN, Jahangir Afzal First Floor (2nd Right), 90 Dunholm Road, Dundee DD2 4RU — MB ChB 1995 Dundee.

KHAN, Jamil Ahmad Brighton Road Surgery, 66 Brighton Road, Coulsdon CR5 2BB Tel: 020 8660 2700 Fax: 020 763 2706 — MB BS 1976 Lond.; MRCS Eng. LRCP Lond. 1976.

KHAN, Javaid Ahmad 74 Norton Crescent, Birmingham B9 5TD — MB BS 1981 Karachi; MRCP (UK) 1986.

KHAN, Javed 3 Melvin Way, Histon, Cambridge CB4 9HY — MB 1987 Camb.; MA Camb. 1989, MB 1987, BChir 1986; MRCP (UK) 1990. Clin. Lect. (Paediat.) Univ. Camb. Prev: Leukaemia Research Fell.

KHAN, Jawad Mustafa 16 Jasmine Road, Dudley DY2 7NN — MB BS 1996 Lond.; BSc (Hons.) Lond. 1993. (St. Geos. Hosp. Med. Sch.) SHO (A & E) Sandwell Hosp. W. Bromwich Birm. Prev: Ho. Off. (Med.) Walsall Manor Hosp. Walsall; Ho. Off. (Surg.) City Hosp. NHS Trust Dudley Rd. Birm.

KHAN, Jawad Sajid 56 Rother Street, Stratford-upon-Avon CV37 6LT — MB BS 1975 Lond.; FRCS Eng. 1981; FRCS Ed. 1980. (Roy. Lond. Hosp. Med. Coll.) Prof. Cardiothoracic & Vasc. Surg. King Edwd. Med. Coll. Lahore, Pakistan. Socs: Fell. Roy. Soc. Med.; Fell. Cardiothoracic Soc. Brit.; Cardiac Soc. Pakistan.

KHAN, Jawaid Akhtar 29 Copsewood Avenue, Nuneaton CV11 4TQ Tel: 01203 326111 — MB BS 1975 Karachi; Dip. Psychiat. Keele 1995. Clin. Asst. (Acute Adult Psychiat.) Ave. Clinic Nuneaton.

KHAN, Jawaid Akthar Flat 1, 94 Princes Rd, Liverpool L8 8AD — MB ChB 1996 Liverp.

KHAN, Jennifer Flat 4, 18 Frithwood Avenue, Northwood HA6 3LX — MB BS 1994 Lond.

KHAN, Kamaluddin Tel: 0151 428 8899 Email: dr_kamal_khan@hotmail.com — MB BS 1960 Lucknow; PhD Liverp. 1987; BSc Agra 1955; FRCPsych 1988, M 1974; T(Psych) 1991; DPM Eng. 1974; DPM Newc. 1973. (King Geo. Med. Coll. Lucknow) Med. Adviser Brit. Mem. Counc. of World Veteran's Federat.; Lord Chancellor's Med. Visitor.; Med. Mem. Ment. Health Review Tribunal. Socs: Liverp. Psychiat. Soc. Prev: Cons. Psychiat. Clatterbridge Hosp. Bebington; Sen. Regist. (Psychiat.) Liverp. AHA (T); Regist. (Psychiat.) Darlington Memor. Hosp.

KHAN, Kamran 43 Cemetery Road, Heckmondwike WF16 9DZ — MB ChB 1998 Leic.; MB ChB Leic 1998.

KHAN, Kamran Ahmed Lower Addiscombe Road Surgery, 188 Lower Addiscombe Road, Croydon CR0 6AH Tel: 020 8654 1427 Fax: 020 8662 1272; 19 Maycross Avenue, Morden SM4 4DD — BM BS 1981 Nottm.; BMedSci. Nottm. 1979; MRCGP 1985; DRCOG 1983. Clin. Asst. (Dermat.) Croydon Community Health. Prev: Trainee GP Croydon VTS; Clin. Asst. (Cardiol.) Croydon Gen. Hosp.

KHAN, Kamran Noel 1st Battalion Welsh Guards, Medical Centre, Wellington Barracks, London SW1E Tel: 020 7414 3369 Fax: 020 7414 3244 Email: kamkhan@compuserve.com; 57 Granville Road, London SW1E 6HQ — MB ChB 1996 Leeds. Regtl. Med. Off.

KHAN, Kanwar Abdul Manan (retired) — MB BS 1964 Punjab; BSc Punjab (Pakistan) 1958; DA Eng. 1970. Prev: Regist. Accid. and Emerg.

KHAN, Karim Manor Court Surgery, 5 Manor Court Avenue, Nuneaton CV11 5HX Tel: 024 7638 1999 Fax: 024 7632 0515 — MB ChB 1988 Birm.

KHAN, Karim Michael Desborough Surgery, 35 High Street, Desborough, Kettering NN14 2NB Tel: 01536 760345 Fax: 01536 418373 — MB ChB 1985 Leic.; MRCGP 1991; DRCOG 1990. (Leicester) Partner; Police Surg. N.ants Police. Socs: RCGP; Assn. Police Surg. Prev: Sen. Med. Off. BMH, Hong Kong.

KHAN, Mr Khalid 25 Glendhu Manor, Garnerville Road, Belfast BT4 2RJ — MB BS 1984 Peshawar; FRCSI 1990.

KHAN, Khalid Aziz Gosbury Hill Health Centre, Orchard Gardens, Chessington KT9 1AG — MB BS 1992 Lond.; BSc (Pharm.) Hons. 1985. Socs: Roy. Pharmaceut. Soc. GB.

KHAN, Khalid Jawaid Bentley House, Skutterskelfe, Yarm TS15 0JR — MB BS 1981 Karachi; FFA RCS Eng. 1991; DA (UK) 1985. Regist. (Anaesth.) S. Birm. HA. Prev: Regist. (Anaesth.) N.ampton HA; SHO (Anaesth.) Leicester Gp. Hosps. & Mid-Staffs. HA.

KHAN, Mr Khalid Mahmood 6 Torcote Crescent, Huddersfield HD2 2JU — MB BS 1982 Newc.; FRCS Glas. 1987; FRCOphth 1989; DO RCS Eng. 1987. Cons. Ophth. Birch Hill Hosp. Rochdale. Prev: Regist. (Ophth.) Roy. Hallamsh. Hosp. Sheff.; SHO (Ophth.) Roy. Vict. Hosp. Bournemouth; SHO (Neurosurg.) Pinderfields Gen. Hosp. Wakefield.

KHAN, Khalid Mahmood 80 Southend Road, Grays RM17 5NW Tel: 01375 350565 — MB ChB 1987 Leic.; MRCP (UK) 1992; DCH RCP Lond. 1993. Sen. Regist. (Paediat.) St. Geo. Hosp. Lond. Prev: Sen. Regist. (Paediat. & Neonat.) Mayday Hosp. Croydon; Regist. (Gen. Paediat. & Neonat.) Basildon Hosp.

KHAN, Khalid Masood 1 Greenfield View, Billinge, Wigan WN5 7UE Tel: 0956 875167 Email: kmkhan@hotmail.com — MB BChir 1994 Camb.; MA (Hons.) Camb. 1994; BA (Hons.) Camb. 1991; MRCPI 1995; MRCP (Pt. II) 1997. Specialist Regist. (Cardiol.)

Roy. Liverp. Hosp. Prev: BHF Research Fell. Univ. of Leicester; SHO (Gen. Med.) Leicester.

KHAN, Khalid Ullah X-Ray Department, District General Hospital, Scartho Road, Grimsby DN33 2BA Tel: 01472 874111 — MB BS 1973 Punjab; MSc Lond. 1991; FFR RCSI 1981; DMRD (Eng.) 1980. Cons. Radiol. Grimsby Dist. Gen. Hosp.

KHAN, Khan Shah-E-Zaman 87 Nutbush Drive, Birmingham B31 5SG — MB BS 1979 Karachi; MRCP (UK) 1987; MRCS Eng. LRCP Lond. 1988.

KHAN, Laeeq Ur Rahman 51 Fairfield Drive, Burnley BB10 2PU — MB BS 1996 Lond.

KHAN, Lillian Nasreen 59 St Olaves Est, Druid St., London SE1 2EX — MB BS 1991 Lond.

KHAN, Luqman Ahmed 37 Hamble Belgrave, Tamworth B77 2JE — MB ChB 1991 Manch.

KHAN, Mr Mahir Abdul Majid Law Hospital, Carluke ML8 5ER Tel: 01698 351100 — MB BS 1958 Kerala; FRCS Ed. 1972. (Trivandrum Med. Coll.) Assoc. Specialist (Surg.) S. Lanark. Hosp. Gp. Prev: Tutor in Surg. Med. Coll. Hosp. Trivandrum, India; Surg. i/c Burao Dist. Hosp., Somalia.

KHAN, Mahmood Crosses Farm, Catford Road, Catforth nr Preston, Preston PR4 0HH — MB ChB 1989 Liverp.; BSc (Hons.) Liverp. 1986, MB ChB 1989; MRC Psych. Specialist Regist. (Psych.) Leeds Gen. Infirm. Prev: SHO (A & E) Blackpool Vict. Hosp.

KHAN, Mr Manawar 30 Runnymede Road, Hall Green, Birmingham B11 3BW — MB BCh BAO 1989 Belf.; FRCSI 1993. Cas. Off. E. Birm. Hosp. Bordesley Green. Prev: Ho. Surg. & Phys. Roy. Vict. Hosp. Belf.

KHAN, Mr Mansoor Shahid 11 Dunstable Road, Stanford-le-Hope SS17 8QT Tel: 01375 675104 Email: mskhan@idzero.co.uk — MB ChB Aberd. 1995; MRCS 1999. (Univ. Aberd.) Socs: Med. Protec. Soc.; BMA.

KHAN, Masood Ahmed 18 Langley Drive, London E11 2LL — MB BChir 1994 Camb.

KHAN, Masood Ali (retired) Barton, 63 Green St., Brockworth, Gloucester GL3 4LX Tel: 01452 862366 — MB BS 1956 Karachi; BSc (Microbiol.) Sind 1949. Prev: Assoc. Specialist (Accid. Unit) Gloucester Roy. Hosp.

KHAN, Mazullah Peel Health Centre, Angouleme Way, Bury BL9 0BT Tel: 0161 764 9940 Fax: 0161 763 6148 — MB BS 1967 Karachi. (Dow Med. Coll.) SHO (Orthop.) Gt. Yarmouth & Gorleston Gen. Hosp. Prev: SHO (Gen. Med.) & SHO (Gen. Surg.) J.P.M.C. Karachi, Pakistan; SHO (Cas., Orthop. & Gen. Surg.) W.mld. Co. Hosp. Kendal.

KHAN, Md Abdul Latif Parc Derw, 16 West Cross Lane, West Cross, Swansea SA3 5LS — MB BS 1969 Dacca; DO RCS Eng. 1977.

KHAN, Mr Md Mahmudar Rahman Louth County Hospital, Louth LN11 0EU — MB BS 1968 Rajshahi; FRCS Glas. 1985.

KHAN, Mendhy Hussain Bilton Medical Centre, 120 City Road, Bradford BD8 8JT Tel: 01274 782080 — MB ChB 1992 Leeds.

KHAN, Mhd Asif Hameed 47 Leighton Road, Old Trafford, Manchester M16 9WU — MB ChB 1991 Manch.

KHAN, Michael Mohammed Tarik 154 Ifield Road, Chelsea, London SW10 9AF Tel: 020 7370 3458 — MB BS 1985 Lond.; BSc (Hons.) Lond. 1982, MB BS 1985; MRCP (UK) 1988. (King's) MRC Train. Fell. Developm. Neurobiol. Univ. Coll. Lond. Prev: SHO (Neurol.) Maudsley Hosp.; SHO (Med. Ophth. & Thoracic Med.) St. Thos. Hosp.

KHAN, Mir Bashiruddin Ali 61 Daryington Drive, Greenford UB6 8BH Tel: 020 8578 5844 — MB BS 1965 Osmania; MRCGP 1981; DPM Eng. 1973. (Osmania Med. Coll. Hyderabad) Clin. Asst. (Alcohol & Drug Abuse) Pk. Prewitt Hosp. Basingstoke.

***KHAN, Mohamad Wajahat Ali** The Oaks Medical Centre, 1 Paisley Road, Barrhead, Glasgow G78 1HG; 263 Fenwick Road, Giffnock, Glasgow G46 6JX — MB BS 1988 Lond.

KHAN, Mohamed Adiluzzaman New Road Surgery, 24 New Road, Chatham ME4 4QR Tel: 01634 811463/4; 231 Cliffe Road, Strood, Rochester ME2 3NJ — MB BS 1976 Lond.; LMSSA Lond. 1976; DTM & H Ed. 1969.

KHAN, Mohamed Cassim 24 Manor Road, Hartlepool TS26 0EH Tel: 01429 267687; 15 bullfinch Court, Lee-on-the-Solent PO13 8LQ Tel: 023 9255 6391 Fax: 023 9255 6391 Email: 114342.2261@compuserve.com — MB ChB Glas. 1966; FRCPsych 1986, M 1972; DPM Eng. 1969. Civil Cons. Psychiat. RNH Haslar Gosport. Socs: BMA; Roy. Coll. Psychiat. Prev: Cons. Psychiat. Winterton Hosp. & Hon. Cons. Hartlepool Gen. Hosp.; Regist. (Psychiat.) Gartnavel Roy. Hosp. Glas.

KHAN, Mr Mohammad Abdul Raheem Castledene, 59 Headroomgate Road, Annes-on-Sea, Lytham St Annes FY8 3BD — MB BS 1958 Karachi; FRCS Ed. 1969; FICA 1988. (Dow Med. Coll. Karachi) Cons. Cardio Thoracic Surg. Vict. Hosp. Blackpool. Socs: Fell. Internat. Coll. Angiol.; BMA & Soc. Thoracic & Cardiovasc. Surgs. Gt. Brit. & Irel. Prev: Sen. Regist. Dept. Cardio-Thoracic Surg. Manch. Roy. Infirm.; Regist. (Thoracic Surg.) Childr. Hosp. Birm.; Regist. (Cardio-Thoracic Surg.) Vict. Hosp. Blackpool.

KHAN, Mohammad Abdus Jaheed 5 Exeter Gardens, Stamford PE9 2RN — MB BS 1997 Lond.

KHAN, Mohammad Ayub The Health Centre, Rose Tree Avenue, Cudworth, Barnsley S72 8UA Tel: 01226 710326 Fax: 01226 780627 — MB BS 1970 Punjab. (Punjab) GP Barnsley, S. Yorks.

KHAN, Mohammad Azhar 2 Kestrel Drive, Sandal, Wakefield WF2 6SA — MB BS 1961 Punjab; MRCPath 1979.

KHAN, Mohammad Irshad Low Hill Medical Centre, 191 First Avenue, Low Hill, Wolverhampton WV10 9SX Tel: 01902 731319 — MB ChB 1988 Glas.; MRCGP 1993.

KHAN, Mr Mohammad Rafiq 6 The Crescent, Ebbw Vale NP23 6EG Tel: 01495 303331 — MRCS Eng. LRCP Lond. 1974; MB BS Panjab 1959, BDS 1953; FRCS Ed. 1968.

KHAN, Mr Mohammad Shahid Hossain 149 Wallwood Road, London E11 1AQ — MB BS 1969 Dacca; FRCS Eng. 1979; FRCS Glas. 1978. Cons. Gen. Surg. N.W. Armed Forces Hosp. Tabuk, Kingdom of Saudi Arabia; Locum Cons. Surg., Barnsley Dist. Gen. Hosp. Socs: BMA; Med. Protec. Soc. Prev: Staff Surg. Qu. Eliz. Hosp. King's Lynn; Cons. Surg. Riyadh Centr. Hosp., Kingdom Saudi Arabia; Assoc. Prof. Surg. Bangladesh Med. Coll. Dhaka, Bangladesh.

KHAN, Mohammad Tajamal 22 Bay Tree Avenue, Chadderton, Oldham OL9 0NH — MB BS 1978 Punjab; LMSSA Lond. 1989; DTCD Wales 1988.

KHAN, Mohammed Ali 24 Carnoustie Drive, Heald Green, Stockport SK8 3EW Email: samar@umf.net — MB ChB 1993 Manch.; MRCP (UK) 1996. (Manchester) Specialist Regist. (Radiol.) Manch. Roy. Infirm. Prev: SHO (Med.) Manch. Roy. Infirm.; SHO (A&E); SHO (Paediat.).

KHAN, Mohammed Amjed 164 Seymour Grove, Old Trafford, Manchester M16 9GR Tel: 0161 881 2163 — MB ChB 1987 Dundee; MRCP (UK) 1992. (Dundee) Clin. Lect. & Hon. Specialist Regist. (Cardiol. & Med.) Manch. Roy. Infirm. Socs: Brit. Soc. Echocardiogr. Prev: Research Regist. (Cardiol.) Wythenshawe Hosp. Manch.; Career Regist. (Cardiol.) Liverp. Mersey RHA; SHO Rotat. (Med.) Leicester.

KHAN, Mohammed Ashfaq Alam Evergreen, 32 Shaw Crescent, Sanderstead, South Croydon CR2 9JA Tel: 020 8657 6878 — MB BS 1952 Punjab; BSc Punjab (Pakistan) 1946, MB BS 1952; FRCP Ed. 1967 M 1960; DCH Eng. 1963; DTM & H Liverp. 1956 CPH Eng. 1956. (King Edwd. Med. Coll. Lahore) Represen. Regional Adviser MCH WHO Geneva Alexandria. Prev: Prof. & Head, Dept. Paediat. & Child Health Univ. Zambia Teach. Hosp. Lusaka, Zambia; Head, Dept. Paediat. & Child Health Kenyatta Nat. Hosp. Nairobi, Kenya; Dir. of Child Health MoH, Kenya.

KHAN, Mohammed Aurangzeb The Mount Group Practice, 54 Thorne Road, Doncaster DN1 2JP — MB BS 1984 Lond.; MRCGP 1988; DRCOG 1988; Cert. Family Plann. JCC 1987; DGM RCP Lond. 1986. Socs: Brit. Med. Acupunct. Soc.

KHAN, Mohammed Dalilur Rahman 21 Boclair Road, Bearsden, Glasgow G61 2AF Tel: 0141 531 6660 Fax: 0141 531 6668 Email: mohammed.khan@gp46409.glasgow-hb.scot.nhs.uk — BSc Dacca 1955, MB BS 1962; DCH RCPS Glas. 1970; DTM & H Liverp. 1966. (Chittagong Med. Coll.) GP Glas. Prev: SHO Nether Edge Hosp. Sheff.; Regist. Leverndale Hosp. Glas.

KHAN, Mohammed Faizuddin 5 Upfields, Burntwood, Lichfield — MB ChB 1992 Manch.

KHAN, Mr Mohammed Idris Haddington, 21 The Grove, Merthyr Tydfil CF47 8YR Tel: 01685 4406 Fax: 01685 350022 — MB BS 1958 Punjab; MB BS Punjab (Pakistan) 1958; FRCS Ed. 1966; FICS 1967; FACS 1970. (King Edwd. Med. Coll. Lahore) Cons. Surg. P.

Chas. Hosp. Merthyr Tydfil; Clin. Tutor Univ. Hosp. Wales Cardiff; Tutor (Surg.) RCS Eng. Socs: Fell. Assn. Surgs. Prev: Sen. Surg. Regist. St. Helier Hosp. Carshalton; Surg. Resid. Mt. Sinai Hosp. New York; Surg. Regist. Roy. Vict. Hosp. Bournemouth.

KHAN, Mohammed Iqbal 42 Main Street, Birmingham B11 1RU — MB ChB 1997 Sheff.; BSc (Hons) 1990; PhD 1994. (Sheffield) SHO (Med.), Birm. Heartlands Hosp.

KHAN, Mr Mohammed Rafiqul Hassan 66 Northumberland Road, Harrow HA2 7RE Tel: 020 8723 6626 Fax: 020 8723 6626 Email: skhan3@compuserve.com; PO Box 641, College of Medicine, King Khaled University, Abha, Saudi Arabia Tel: 00 966 72245039 Fax: 00 966 72247570 — MB BS 1972 Dacca; MPhil (Orth.) Ed. 1985; FRCS Ed. 1984. (Dacca Med. Coll.) Regist. (Orthop.) Vict. Hosp. Kirkcaldy; Assoc. Prof. Orthop. Surg. Coll. Med. King Khaled Univ. Abha, Saudi Arabia. Prev: Lect. (Orthop.) Univ. Edin.; Research Fell. Roy. Postgrad. Med. Sch. Lond.

KHAN, Mohammed Rizwan 13 Glenwood Avenue, Westcliff on Sea SS0 9DJ — MB BS 1997 Lond.

KHAN, Mohammed Samin Jan 68 Carnarvon Road, London E15 4JW — MB BS 1994 Lond.

KHAN, Mohammed Sanaullah 39 Bagnell Road, Birmingham B13 0SJ — LRCP LRCS 1983 Ed.; LRCP LRCS Ed. LRCPS Glas. 1983.

KHAN, Mohammed Shuja Brookhouse Medical Centre, Whalley Range, Blackburn BB1 6EA — MB BS 1960 Karachi; DTM & H Eng. 1962. (Dow Med. Coll.) Prev: SHO (Gen. Med.) N. Lonsdale Hosp. Barrow-in-Furness & Jersey Gen. Hosp.

KHAN, Mohammed Yahya 213 Chestergate, Stockport Tel: 0161 480 3372 — MB BS 1960 Karachi. (Dow Med. Coll. Karachi) Socs: BMA. Prev: Paediat. Regist. Birch Hill Hosp. Rochdale; Paediat. Regist. St. Catherine's Hosp. Birkenhead; Res. Pathol. Oldham & Dist. Gen. Hosp.

KHAN, Mr Muhammad Absar Uddin The Health Centre, Forum Way, Cramlington NE23 6QN Tel: 01670 713911 Fax: 01670 735958; 16 Beaumont Drive, Whitley Bay NE25 9UT — MB BS 1963 Karachi; FRCS Ed. 1969. (Dow Med. Coll.) Prev: Regist. (Gen. Surg.) NE N.d. Hosp. Gp.; SHO (Gen. Surg.) Friarage Hosp. N.allerton; SHO (Urol.) Roy. Infirm. Sunderland.

KHAN, Muhammad Amanullah 32 Matlock Crt., Kensington Park Road, London W11 3BS — MB BS 1949 Punjab; MB BS Punjab (Pakistan) 1949; DO Eng. 1959, MPH Johns Hopkins Univ. 1953. Prev: Regist. (Ophth.) Derbysh. Roy. Infirm. Derby; Regist. (Ophth.) Selly Oak & Little Bromwich Gp.; Regist. (Ophth.) Roy. Bucks. Hosp. Aylesbury & Amersham Gp. Hosps.

KHAN, Muhammad Arif Yoxall Health Centre, Savey Lane, Yoxall, Burton-on-Trent DE13 8PD Tel: 01543 472202 Fax: 01543 472362 — MB BS 1966 Karachi. (Dow Med. Coll.) Prev: SHO (Paediat. Surg. & Paediat. Med.) Roy. Manch. Childr. Hosp.; SHO (Neonat. Paediat.) Dept. Child Health St. Mary's Hosp. Manch.

KHAN, Muhammad Aslam, Wing Cdr. RAF Med. Br. 14 Delacourt Road, Fallowfield, Manchester M14 6BX Tel: 0161 286 0584 — MB BS 1977 Punjab; MRCP (UK) 1984; FRCP Lond. 1998; DTM & H RCP Lond. (King Edward Medical College Pakistan) Cons. Phys. (Gen. Med. & Aviat. Cardiol.) Manch.

KHAN, Mr Muhammad Ayub 30 Naples Drive, Newcastle ST5 2QD — MB BS 1986 Karachi; FRCS Glas. 1992.

KHAN, Muhammad Azizur Rahman Fife Healthcare NHS Trust, Lochgelly Health Centre, David Street, Lochgelly KY5 9QZ Tel: 01592 780358; 20 Station Road, Lochgelly KY5 9QW — MB BS 1963 Dhaka. GP Lochgelly.

KHAN, Mr Muhammad Haroon Zafarullah 3 Allington Drive, Eccles, Manchester M30 9EG Tel: 0161 789 6270 — MB BS 1975 Karachi; FRCS Glas. 1991; DLO RCS Eng. 1986. Socs: Coll. Phys. & Surgs. Pakistan 1978; BMA; Brit. Assn. Otol. Head & Neck Surg. Prev: Regist. Rotat. Mersey Region; Regist. Salford HA.

KHAN, Muhammad Sayeed Akhtar St Johns House Surgery, St Johns House, Cross Church Street, Cleckheaton BD19 3RQ Tel: 01274 851188 Fax: 01274 851042; 31 Headlands Road, Liversedge WF15 7NT Tel: 01924 403027 — MB BS 1961 Sind; DA Eng. 1964. (Liaquat Med. Coll. Hyderabad) Hosp. Pract. (Anaesth.) Kirklees HA.

KHAN, Mr Muhammad Shamim 268 Perry Road, Nottingham NG5 1GP Tel: 0115 962 2887 — MB BS 1979 Karachi; FRCS Ed. 1987.

KHAN, Mr Muhammad Umar The Paddocks, High St., Grainthorpe, Louth LN11 7HS — MB BS 1979 Punjab; FRCS Ed. 1992; FRCS Glas. 1992.

KHAN, Muhammad Younus Marsh Farm Health Centre, Purley Centre, The Moakes, Luton LU3 3SR Tel: 01582 502336 Fax: 01582 494541; 326 Old Bedford Road, Luton LU2 7EJ Tel: 01582 429705 Fax: 01582 494541 — MB BS 1964 Karachi. (Dow Med. Coll.)

KHAN, Muhammad Yunus Department of Anaesthesia, King George Hospital, Barley Lane, Ilford IG3 8YB Tel: 020 8983 8000 Email: aalia@aaliakhan.freeserve.co.uk; 68 St Barnabas Road, Woodford Green IG8 7DB Tel: 020 8559 0868 — MB ChB 1970 Manch.; FFA RCS Eng. 1975. p/t Cons. Anaesth. s/i in Pain BHR Health Care NHS Trust Ilford. Socs: Assn. Anaesth.; Pain Soc. Prev: Cons. Anaesth. Armed Forces Hosp. Riyadh, Saudi Arabia; Sen. Regist. (Anaesth.) Roy. Lond. Hosp.; Regist. (Anaesth.) Dudley Rd. Hosp. Birm.

KHAN, Muhammad Zakariya Goolam Mahomed 4 Litchurch Street, Derby DE1 2RG Tel: 01332 47141 — MB ChB 1985 Natal; FCS(SA) 1992.

KHAN, Muhammed Tajuddin 4 Friary Road, Lichfield WS13 6QL Tel: 01543 263486 Email: mokhan@compuserve. com; Trent Valley Road, St. Michaels Hospital, Lichfield WS13 6EF Tel: 01543 414555 Fax: 01543 416715 — MB BS 1967 Andhra Med. Coll.; MB BS (Andhra) India 1967; DPM Eng; RCPSI 1975. (Andhra Med. Coll. Viskhapatnan, India) Cons. Psychogeriat. Premier Health Trust, St. Michael's Hosp. Lichfield. Socs: Roy. Soc. Med.; I. of Man Med. Soc. Prev: Assoc. Specialist (Psychiat.) Ballamona Hosp. Braddan, I. of Man.

KHAN, Mujeeb Ahmed The Surgery, 93 Crompton Road, Handsworth, Birmingham B20 3QP Tel: 0121 523 0427 — MB BS 1973 Mysore; MB BS 1973 Mysore.

KHAN, Mujib-ul Haq The Surgery, 78 Granville Road, London SW18 5SG Tel: 020 8874 2471; 102 Girdwood Road, Southfields, London SW18 5QT — MB BS 1968 Punjab; BSc Punjab 1970, MB BS 1968. (King Edwd. Med. Coll. Lahore) Prev: Vis. Med. Off. Ashmead Old Peoples' Home Lond.; Cas. Off. Putney Hosp. Lond.

KHAN, Mr Mulbagal Afzal Ali 29 Carlton Avenue W., North Wembley, Wembley HA0 3RA Tel: 020 8908 5025 — MB BS 1976 Sri Venkateswara; BSc Sri Venkateswara 1968, MB BS 1976; FRCS Glas. 1983.

KHAN, Muneir Mohammad Hill Top Medical Centre, 15 Hill Top Road, Oldbury, Oldbury B68 9DU Tel: 0121 422 2146 Fax: 0121 421 5967; Cheshunt, 15 Hermitage Road, Edgbaston, Birmingham B15 3UP Tel: 0121 242 1891 — MB ChB Birm. 1964; DObst RCOG 1967. (Birm.) Benefits Agency Med. Adviser; Med. Dir. Exec. Screening Servs. Birm.; Med. Off. Bevan Simpson Foundry Ltd., CLC Ltd; Med. Off. Dayco Eurpa Ltd.; GP. Socs: Med. Assur. Soc. Prev: Med. Off. Herefore-Worcester Army Cadet Force; Med. Dir. Med. Health Ltd.

KHAN, Munera Iqbal 1 Tower Cottages, Middleton Road, Morecambe LA3 2RD — MB BS 1982 Khartoum, Sudan.

KHAN, Munir Ahmed The Surgery, 161 Lumb Lane, Bradford BD8 7SW Tel: 01274 734994 Fax: 01274 723174 — MB BS 1962 Lucknow; BSc India 1957.

KHAN, Murad Moosa Thameslink Healthcare Service NHS Trust, Stone House Hospital, Cotton Lane, Dartford DA2 6AU — MB BS 1977 Karachi; MRCPsych 1986.

KHAN, Murtuza Asif 8 Thornbury Avenue, Isleworth TW7 4NQ — MB ChB 1985 Dundee; BMSc Dund 1983; MRCP 1991; MRCPCH 1997. (University of Dundee) Cons. (Paediat.) St. Thomas' Hosp. Lond. Socs: BMA; RCPCH; BPRS. Prev: Specialist Regist. (Paediat. Respirat. Med.) The Hosp. for Sick Childr. Gt. Ormond St.; Specialist Regist. Kings Coll. Hosp. Lond.; Hon. Sen. Regist., St Thomas' Hosp., Lond.

KHAN, Mr Mushtaq Ali Flat 3, 2 Hill Place, Edinburgh EH8 9DS — MB BS 1981 Peshawar; FRCS Ed. 1992.

KHAN, Nadir Zafar 17 Canada Road, Acton, London W3 0NP — MB BS 1985 Karachi; MRCP (UK) 1994.

KHAN, Naeem Ahmed Sultani 2 Amherst Road, Plymouth PL3 4HH — MB BS 1981 Karachi; MRCP (UK) 1993.

KHAN, Naeem Shahzada 20 Kitchener Road, Leicester LE5 4AS — MB BS 1993 Lond.

KHAN, Naheed Lubna Institute of Neurology &Neurogenetics, Queen's Square, London WC1N 3BG — BChir 1994 Camb.; MA Camb. 1995; MRCP 1997. (Camb.) Clin. Research Fell. (Neurogenetics) Inst. of Neurol., Nat. Hosp. of Neurol. & Neurosurg. Prev: Clin. Research Fell. (Neurol.) Nat. Hosp. Neurol. & Neurosurg.

KHAN, Nargis 5 Cedar Court, 267 Hainault Road, London E11 1ET — MB BS 1970 Karachi; DCH Eng. 1975. (Dow Med. Coll.) Prev: Regist. (Paediat.) S.end Hosp.

KHAN, Nasar Barkerend Health Centre, Bradford BD3 8QH Tel: 01274 663553 — MB ChB 1996 Sheff.

KHAN, Naseer Ahmad The Surgery, 17B Warmdene Road, Brighton BN1 8NL Tel: 01273 508811 Fax: 01273 559860; 109 Valley Drive, Withdean, Brighton BN1 5LG — MB BS 1982 Lond.; DRCOG 1985. Prev: Trainee GP Brighton VTS; Ho. Phys. Med. Unit Roy. Free Hosp. Lond.; Ho. Surg. Roy. E. Sussex Hosp. Hastings.

KHAN, Nasir 56 Broadmark Road, Slough SL2 5PR — MB BS 1993 Lond.; MRCP (UK) 1997. (Univ. Coll. & Middlx. Sch. Med.) SHO (HIV Med.) Roy. Lond. Hosp. Prev: SHO (Nephrol.) Roy. Lond. Hosp.

KHAN, Nasir Ahmed Balnaguard, Halifax Road, Briercliffe, Burnley BB10 3QS Tel: 01282 50411; 24-26 Ightenhill Park Lane, Burnley BB12 0LE Tel: 01282 24464 — MB BS 1962 Punjab; MB BS Punjab (Pakistan) 1962. (Nishtar Med. Coll. Multan) Clin. Asst. Orthop. Dept. Burnley Health Dist.; GP Burnley.

KHAN, Nasser Qamar Flat 2C Howitt Road, London NW3 4LL — MB BS 1997 Lond.

KHAN, Nazura Hyder Zaman Dilnasheen, Pyle Hill, Woking GU22 0SR — MB BS 1995 Lond.

KHAN, Neelam Ara 14 Jellicoe Gardens, Roath Park, Cardiff CF23 5QW Tel: 029 2075 5797 — MB BCh 1985 Wales.

***KHAN, Nighat** 27 Lela Avenue, Hounslow TW4 7RU; 38 Taunton Avenue, Hounslow TW3 4AF Tel: 020 8570 2816 — MB ChB 1998 Leeds.

KHAN, Nisar Ahmad 19 Bridge Road, Uxbridge UB8 2QW — MB BS 1980 Peshawar; MRCP (UK) 1988; MRCPI 1987.

KHAN, Noreen Sajid 48A Rochdale Road, Middleton, Manchester M24 2PU Tel: 0161 643 9131 — MB BS 1974 Lucknow; MRCOG 1981; Dip. Gyn & Obst. Lucknow 1977. (Lucknow)

KHAN, Omar The Kingfisher Medical Centre, 3 Kingfisher Square, London SE8 5DA Tel: 020 8692 7373 Fax: 020 8692 7373 — MB BS 1977 Newc.; PhD Lond. 1970, MSc 1982, BSc 1968.

KHAN, Omar Medway NHS Trust, Medway Hospital, Windmill Road, Gillingham ME7 5NY Tel: 01634 833985; 30 Maidstone Road, Rochester ME1 1RJ — MB BS Karachi 1968; MS Lond. 1990; FRCS Ed. 1976. (Dow Med. Coll.) Cons. Gen. Surg. Medway NHS Trust. Socs: Fell. Roy. Soc. Med.; BMA; Assn. Surg. Prev: Lect. King's Coll. Hosp. Med. Sch. (Dulwich Hosp.) Lond.; MRC Clin. Research Fell. & Hon. Sen. Regist. (Surg. & Urol.) Roy. Postgrad. Hosp. Lond.; Regist. (Surg.) Hosp. Sick Childr. Gt. Ormond St. Lond.

KHAN, Mr Omer Daraz 55 Newton Garth, Leeds LS7 4HG Tel: 0113 262 4191; 35 Oakwell Mount, Leeds LS8 4AD Tel: 01132 932912 — MB BS 1978 Karachi; FRCS Eng. 1993. Pontefract VTS, Pontefract, Yorks.

KHAN, Parvez Saeed Attenborough Surgery, Bushey Health Centre, London Road, Bushey, Watford WD23 2NN Tel: 01923 231633 — MB BS 1986 Lond.; MRCP (UK) 1990; MRCGP 1992; DCH RCP Lond. 1991.

KHAN, Pipir 77 Ashleigh Street, Keighley BD21 3BL — MB ChB 1996 Liverp.

KHAN, Qamar Ara Herschel Medical Centre, 45 Osborne Street, Slough SL1 1TT Tel: 01753 520643 Fax: 01753 554964 — BM 1986 Soton.

KHAN, Quamer Ahmed The Surgery, 885 Chester Road, Stretford, Manchester M32 0RN Tel: 0161 865 3807 Fax: 0161 865 4964 — MB BS 1968 Calcutta; MB BS 1968 Calcutta.

KHAN, Qurrat-ul-Aen Ashvale Medical Centre, 4 Ashvale Road, London SW17 8PW Tel: 020 8672 2085; The Surgery, 4 Ashvale Road, London SW17 8PW Tel: 020 8672 2085 — MB BS 1965 Pakistan; BSc Panjab 1967; MB BS Panjab Univ. (Pakistan) 1965. (Nishtar Med. Coll. Multan)

KHAN, R Salim Hayat Drake House, Greave Park, Uppermill, Oldham OL3 6LB Tel: 01457 873135 — MB BS 1959 Punjab; MB BS Punjab (Pakistan) 1959; DMRD Eng. 1968. (King Edwd. Med. Coll. Lahore) Cons. Radiol. Gen. Hosp. Ashton-under-Lyne. Socs: Brit. Inst. Radiol. Prev: Sen. Regist. (Radiol.) Manch. Roy. Infirm.

KHAN, Mr Rabnawaz, Squadron Ldr. RAF Med. Br. 2 Tong Street, Walsall WS1 2DX Tel: 01922 611672 Email: rkh01@hotmail.com; 16 Alvercliffe Drive, Alverstoke, Gosport PO12 2NB Tel: 01705 352310 Fax: 01705 352310 — MB BS 1991 Lond.; BSc Lond. 1988; FRCS Eng. 1996. (Roy. Free Med. Sch. Univ. Lond.) SHO Plastic & Reconstruc. Surg., Salsbury Dist. Hosp. Prev: Sen. Specialist Surg. P.ss Mary's Hosp. RAF Akrotiri, Cyprus; SHO (Plastics & Burns) Stoke Mandeville Hosp. Aylesbury; SHO (A & E) P.ss Margt. Hosp. Swindon.

KHAN, Rashed Manzur 20 Aylward Road, London SW20 9AF — MB BS 1994 Lond.

KHAN, Riaz Jan Kjell Rumsey, Old Bath Road, Reading RG4 6TA — MB BS 1993 Lond.

KHAN, Rizvia 101 Esme Road, Birmingham B11 4NJ — MB ChB 1997 Manch.

KHAN, Roohi Shahid East Tilbury Medical Centre, 85 Coronation Avenue, East Tilbury, Grays RM18 8SN Tel: 01375 846232 Fax: 01375 840440; 11 Dunstable Road, Stanford-le-Hope SS17 8QT Tel: 01375 675629 Fax: 01375 840440 — MB BS 1967 Punjab, Pakistan. (Fathma Jinnha (Lahore)) Socs: Med. Protec. Soc.; BMA.

KHAN, Sadaf 3 Marlow Crescent, Twickenham TW1 1DD — BChir 1994 Camb.

KHAN, Sadia Naseem 48 Arnison Av, High Wycombe HP13 6DB — BM BCh 1997 Oxf.

KHAN, SAFI Doyle Close Surgery, 3 Doyle Close, Sholver, Oldham OL1 4RG Tel: 0161 652 0302 Fax: 0161 633 6547 — MB BS 1966 Peshawar; MB BS 1966 Peshawar.

KHAN, Sahib Khan and Partners, Medical Centre, Church Road, Seven Sisters, Neath SA10 9DT Tel: 01639 700203 Fax: 01639 700010; Hunza House, Church Road, Seven Sisters, Neath SA10 9DT — MB BS 1965 Peshawar. (Khyber Med. Coll.)

KHAN, Mr Saifuddin The Pavillion, The Wickets, Ashford TW15 2RR — MB BS 1983 Karachi; FRCS Glas. 1990.

KHAN, Saifullah The Clinic, McConnel Crescent, Rossington, Doncaster DN11 0PN Tel: 01302 868421; Northstead, 13 Doncaster Road, Bawtry, Doncaster DN10 6NE Tel: 01302 710216 Fax: 01302 710216 — MB BS 1958 Karachi. Health & Safety Med. Off. G. B. Glass Ltd. Harworth, Doncaster.

KHAN, Sajid Barmet General Hospital, Wellhouse Lane, Barnet EN5 3DJ Tel: 0208 2165465; 32 Hamilton Road, Barnet EN4 9HE Tel: 0208 4498949 — MB BS 1981 Punjab; MB BS Punjab 1981; MRCP (UK) 1990. (King Edward Medical College Lahore, Pakistan) Cons. Respirat./ Gneral Med. Socs: MDU; BMA. Prev: Lect. (Med.) Imperial Coll. of Sci. Technol. & Med. Lond.; Specialist Regist., N. W. Thames Respirat./Gen. Med.

KHAN, Sajid Hussain 41 Hathaway Road, Croydon CR0 2TQ — MB BS 1994 Lond.

KHAN, Sajid Saeed Rochdale Road Surgery, 48A Rochdale Road, Middleton, Manchester M24 2PU Tel: 0161 643 9131 — MB BS 1974 Kashmir. (Govt. Med. Coll. Srinagar)

KHAN, Sajid Sohrab Boland House, Guys Hospital, London SE1 9RT — MB BS 1996 Lond.

KHAN, Salahuddin Camberley Medical Centre, 11b Camberley Drive, Halewood, Liverpool L25 9PS Tel: 0151 486 1178 — MB ChB 1988 Liverp. GP Facilitator (Primary Care Health Servs.) St. Helens & Knowsley FHSA.

KHAN, Salahuddin Tel: 01536 265311/400600 Fax: 01536 403263; 9 Drayton Close, Coldermeadow Avenue, Corby NN18 9AD Tel: 01536 745737 Fax: 01536 403263 — MB BS 1968 Delhi; DA (UK) 1976. (Maulana Azad Med. Coll., New Dehli India) Prev: Clin. Asst. (A & E) Kettering Gen. Hosp.; Regist. (Anaesth.) & SHO (ENT) Kettering & Dist. Gen. Hosp.; SHO (Anaesth.) Derbysh. Roy. Infirm.

KHAN, Mr Saleem 60 Colwood Gardens, Colliers Wood, London SW19 2DT — MB BS 1983 Karachi; FRCS Ed. 1995.

KHAN, Sameer 78 Shenstone Avenue, Rugby CV22 5BL — MB BS 1996 Lond.

KHAN, Mr Samin Ahmed c/o Drive N.H. Bangash, 414 Alum Rock Road, Birmingham B8 3HT — MB BS 1968 Peshawar; FRCS Ed. 1979. (Khyber) Regist. (Orthop.) Cumbld. Infirm. Carlisle.

***KHAN, Samina** 3 Shay Lane, Bradford BD9 6SL Tel: 01274 406641 — MB ChB 1994 Leeds.

KHAN, Sarfraz Royal Preston Hospital, Sharoe Green Lane, Fulwood, Preston PR2 9HT Tel: 01772 710334 Fax: 01772 710944; 9 Wykeham Mews, Bolton BL1 5JG Tel: 01204 492548 Email: 106754.3677@compuserve.com — MB BS 1972 Peshawar; MRCS Eng. LRCP Lond. 1987; FRCP Irel. 1996; MRCPI 1988; T(M) 1995; FCPS 1978. (Khyber Med. Coll., Peshawar) Cons. Phys. (Cardiol.) Roy. Preston Hosp. Socs: Fell. Roy. Soc. Health; Brit. Soc. Echocardiogr.; Brit. Cardiac Soc. Prev: Cons. Phys. Nigeria & Pakistan; Cons. Cardiol. ScarBoro.

KHAN, Sayeed Occupational Health Department, Rolls-Royce plc (Bristol), PO Box 3, Filton, Bristol BS34 7QE Tel: 0117 979 5862 Fax: 0117 979 5906; The Firs, Northwick Road, Northwick, Bristol BS35 4HE Tel: 01454 632459 Email: sayeed.khan@rolls-royce.com — BM BS 1985 Nottm.; BMedSci (Hons.) Nottm. 1983; MRCGP 1990; MFOM RCP Lond. 1996; DGM RCP Lond. 1987. (Nottm. Univ. Med. Sch.) Head Occupat. Health Rolls Royce Defence (Europe) & Energy Business; Hon. Clin. Lect. Inst. Occupat. Health Univ. Birm.; Informatics Off. Fac. Occupat. Med. Lond. Socs: Soc. Occupat. Med.; Inst. Occupat. Safety & Health. Prev: GP Nottm.; Trainee GP/SHO Nottm. VTS.

KHAN, Seemab Nasar 8 North Dene, London NW7 3AT — MB BS 1997 Lond.

KHAN, Shafqat Hayat 66 Gilnow Road, Bolton BL1 4LJ — MB ChB 1998 Liverp.; MB ChB Liverp 1998.

KHAN, Shah Noor Thorpe Road Surgery, 8 Thorpe Road, Middleton, Leeds LS10 4BA Tel: 0113 270 5221 Fax: 0113 249 0261. GP Leeds.

KHAN, Shahed Latif 36 Fairfield Street, Leicester LE5 5BF — MB ChB 1992 Leeds.

KHAN, Shaheen Begum 32 Coney Burrows, Chingford, London E4 6EB — MB BCh 1977 Wales.

KHAN, Shahid Anis Strathmore Wing, Lister Hospital, Stevenage SG1 4AB — MB BS 1983 Punjab; BSc Punjab 1983; MRCP (UK) 1989; FRCP 2000 UK. Cons. Phys. (Elderly Care & Gen. Med.) Lister Hosp. Stevenage. Socs: BMA; Brit. Geriat. Soc.; Brit. Soc. Echocardiogr. Prev: Sen. Regist., Char. Cross Hosp.

KHAN, Shahid Aziz 146 Bristol Road, Forest Gate, London E7 8QF Tel: 020 8472 5821 — MB BS 1994 Lond.; BSc (Hons.) Lond. 1992; MRCP (UK) Lond. 1998. (Guy's Hospital, London) Specialist Regist. (Gastroenterol., Hepat. & Gen. Internal Med.) S.-W. Thames Region, Lond. Socs: BMA; Med. Protec. Soc. Prev: SHO (Renal Med.), Char. Cross Hosp. Lond.; SHO (Gen. Med.) W. Middlx. Univ. Hosp., Glenarth; SHO (Oncol.), Char. Cross. Hosp., Lond.

KHAN, Shahid Nadeem 35 Waverley Road, Bristol BS6 6ES — BM BCh 1994 Oxf.; MA Camb. 1995. Head Demonst. (Anat.) Camb. Univ. Prev: Ho. Surg. John Radcliffe Hosp. Oxf.

KHAN, Shahid Saeed Department of Radiology, Queen Elizabeth II Hospital, Welwyn Garden City AL7 4HQ Tel: 01707 328111 — MB BS 1982 Lond.; MRCP (UK) 1987; FRCR 1990. Cons. Radiol. Qu. Eliz. Hosp. Herts. Prev: Sen. Regist. Kings Coll. Hosp. Lond.

KHAN, Shahinul Islam 32 Percival Street, Bradford BD3 9JU — MB ChB 1998 Dund.; MB ChB Dund 1998.

KHAN, Shams 20 Station Road, Lochgelly KY5 9QW — MB ChB 1997 Ed.

KHAN, Sharmina Rony 2 Allingham Court, Haverstock Hill, London NW3 2AH — MB BS 1998 Lond.; MB BS Lond 1998.

KHAN, Mr Shaukat Nawaz c/o K. R. Makhdoomi, 156 Ivanhoe Road, Greenfaulds, Cumbernauld, Glasgow G67 4BB — MB BS 1987 Karachi; FRCS Ed. 1992.

KHAN, Sher Ali Jonathan 280 North Woodside Road, Glasgow G20 6LX — MB ChB 1998 Glas.; MB ChB Glas 1998.

KHAN, Shoib 52 Brent Way, London N3 1AP — MB BS 1992 Lond.

KHAN, Mr Showkat Hayat 16 Westfield Road, Bishop Auckland DL14 6AE — MB BS 1977 Andhra; FRCS Ed. 1993. Prev: SHO (Gen. Surg.) Gen. Hosp. Bishop Auckland; SHO (Gen. Surg.) Gilbert Bain Hosp. Lerwick; SHO (Gen. Surg.) Pinderfields Gen. Hosp. Wakefield.

KHAN, Sophia Yasmin 25 Northumberland Road, Leamington Spa CV32 6HE — MB ChB 1998 Bristol.

KHAN, Mr Suheal Ali 27 Kings Road, Cheadle Hulme, Cheadle SK8 5NE; 72 Northern Grove, Didbsury, Manchester M20 2NN — MB ChB 1987 Sheff.; FRCS Ed. 1991. (Sheff.) Career Regist. Rotat. (Orthop.) NW. Socs: BORS. Prev: Research Fell. & Hon. Regist. (Orthop.) Metab. Unit Roy. Hallamsh. Sheff.; Peri-Fell.sh. Rotat. Leeds Gen. Infirm.; Demonst. (Anat.) Univ. Liverp.

KHAN, Sultana 3 Allington Drive, Eccles, Manchester M30 9EG — MB BS 1977 Karachi; MRCPI 1994.

KHAN, Syyed Ahmed Ashvale Medical Centre, 4 Ashvale Road, London SW17 8PW Tel: 020 8672 2085 — MB BS Punjab (Pakistan) 1965. (Nishtar Med. Coll. Multan)

KHAN, Tabrez 104 Kings Road, Cardiff CF11 9DD — MB BCh 1994 Wales. (Univ. Wales Coll. of Med.) SHO (ENT) Whittington Hosp. Lond. Socs: BMA. Prev: Surg. SHO Rotat. Roy. Gwent Hosp. Newport.

KHAN, Tahir Iqbal 47 Woodfield Road, Cranford, Hounslow TW4 6LL — BM 1993 Soton.

KHAN, Talat Queens Road Surgery, 8 Queens Road, Portsmouth PO2 7NX; Talat Villa, Upper Northam Drive, Hedge End, Southampton SO30 4BG Tel: 01703 462908 — MB BS 1968 Lucknow; DA Eng. 1973.

KHAN, Mr Talat Bashir 34 Conway Road, Southgate, London N14 7BA Tel: 020 8886 4746 — MB BS 1982 Punjab; FRCSI 1990.

KHAN, Ummey Zohra Northumberland Community Health Centre, Civic Precinct, Forum Way, Cramlington NE23 6QN Tel: 01670 713911 Fax: 01670 735958 — MB BS 1962 Punjab; MB BS Punjab (Pakistan) 1962; MRCOG 1971. (Fatima Jinnah Med. Coll. Lahore) GP Cramlington, N.d.

KHAN, Umraz 37 Whatman Road, London SE23 1EY — MB BS 1991 Lond.

KHAN, Yasmin Chailey Heritage Clinical Services,, Beggars Wood Road, North Chailey, Lewes BN8 4JN Tel: 01825 722112 Fax: 01825 721063 Email: yasmin.khan@southdowns.nhs.uk; 10 Semley Road, Hassoaks BN6 8PE Tel: 01273 843583 — MB BCh BAO 1980 NUI; MD NUI 1996; FRCPCH 1997; DCH RCPI 1983. (University College Cork) Cons. Paediat. (Neurodisabil.) Chailey Heritage Sussex; Hon.Sen. Lect., Neurosci.s Unit, Inst. of Child Health, Lond.; Cons. Paediat. (Neurodisabil.) Guy's & Sir Thomas NHS Trust Lond. Socs: Brit. Paediat. Assn.; BMA; Brit. Sleep Soc. Prev: Regist. (Paediat.) St. Helier Hosp. Carshalton; Regist. (Paediat.) Our Lady's Hosp. Dub.

KHAN, Yasmin Zohra Ayesha 80 Ash Road, Headingley, Leeds LS6 3EZ — MB ChB 1993 Leeds.

KHAN, Zaafran 43 Langton Road, London NW2 6QF Tel: 020 8208 3207 — MB BS 1979 Peshawar; MRCP (UK) 1991; MRCPI 1990; DTM & H RCP Lond. 1992.

KHAN, Zafar Hashmat 1 Stonefield Street, Dewsbury WF13 2BW Tel: 01924 468991 — MB BS 1963 Karachi. (Dow Med. Coll.)

KHAN, Zafar Iqbal 47 Woodfield Road, Cranford, Hounslow TW4 6LL — MB ChB 1993 Leeds.

KHAN, Zafar Ullah Royal Infirmary, Bolton Road, Blackburn BB2 3LR Tel: 01254 55222 — MB BS 1966 Peshawar; DA Eng. 1976. (Khyber Med. Coll.) Med. Asst. (Anaesth.) Blackburn Roy. Infirm.

KHAN, Zahid Parvez Flat 3, 21 Brondesbury Villas, Kilburn, London NW6 6AH — MB BS 1987 Lond.; FRCA 1994.

KHAN, Zahida 47 Highville Road, Liverpool L16 9JE — MB ChB 1983 Liverp. SHO Warrington Gen. Hosp.

KHAN, Zahoor Khan, Mary Potter Health Centre, Gregory Boulevard, Hyson Green, Nottingham NG7 5HY Tel: 0115 942 3216 Fax: 0115 970 4640; 41 Arleston Drive, Nottingham NG8 2FR — MB ChB 1982 Manch.

KHAN, Mr Zahoor Ahmad 21 Malam Gardens, London E14 0TR — MB BS 1978 Peshawar; FRCSI 1985. Regist. (Cardiothoracic Surg.) Roy. Vict. Hosp. Belf.

KHAN, Zarrar Aqueel Blackburn Street Health Centre, Blackburn Street, Radcliffe, Manchester M26 1WS; Health Centre, Blackburn St, Radcliffe, Manchester — MB BS 1965 Punjab; MB BS Punjab (Pakistan) 1965. (King Edwd. Med. Coll. Lahore)

KHAN, Zia ur Rehman (retired) 24 Monkfrith Way, Southgate, London N14 5NA Tel: 020 8361 7082 — MB BS 1957 Punjab. Prev: GP Kent FHSA.

KHAN, Zulfikar Ali Queens Medical Centre, Muglet Lane, Maltby, Rotherham S66 7NA Tel: 01709 817755 Fax: 01709 817409; Faircroft, Sledgate Drive, Wickersley, Rotherham S66 1AW — MB

BS 1981 Lond. (University College London) GP Rotherham FPC.; Director Qu.s Nursing Home Millard La. Maltby S66 7LZ. Socs: MPS.

KHAN-GILBERT, Homaa 128 Sinclair Road, London W14 0NL Tel: 020 8668 3701 Fax: 020 8668 3701 — MB BS 1994 Lond.; BDS (Lond.) 1983; LDS RCS ENG 1984. (Lond.) Oral & Maxillofacial Surg. Prev: SHO Oral Surg. Char. Cross W.minster; Ho. Off. Med. & Rheum.; Ho. Off. Gen. Surg.

KHAN-LIM, Doreen Hasneen 35 Greenhill Close, Westhill Park, Winchester SO22 5DZ — MB BS 1991 Lond.

KHAN-LODHI, Naheed 59 Harptree Drive, Chatham ME5 0TH Tel: 01634 669859 — MB BS 1989 Lond.; MRCGP 1994; DCH RCP Lond. 1993. Prev: Trainee GP/SHO Maidstone VTS.

KHAN MADNI, Mishrzal (Bhavani) Mohammad c/o Dr I. K. Hebbar, 32 Firth Drive, Beeston, Nottingham NG9 6NL Email: drmohammadin@hotmail.com; Email: drmohammadin@hoymail.com — MB BS 1973 Andhra; FRCS Ed. 1982. (Andhra Med. Coll.) Resid. Surg. Off. (Paediat. Surg.) W.m. Childr. Lond.; Cons. Paediat. Surg. Kinmg Khalid Hosp., Saudi Arabia. Socs: Roy. Coll. Surg. Edin. Prev: Sen. Regist. (Paediat. Surg.) Q. Mary's Hosp. Carshalton; Regist. (Paediat. Surg.) Bristol Childr. Hosp; SHO (Paediat. Surg.) Nottm. City Hosp.

KHAN-SINGH, Jasmin Tresguthan Farm, Lower Machen, Newport NP10 8GB — BM 1985 Soton.; DCH 1995; MFFP 1993.

KHANAM, Aklakun Nesa Eltham Park Surgery, 46 Westmount Road, London SE9 1JE Tel: 020 8850 1030 Fax: 020 8859 2036 — MB BS 1965 Dacca; MB BS 1965 Dacca.

KHANAM, Surraya 37 Geneva Drive, Westlands, Newcastle ST5 2QQ; 205A High Lane, Burslem, Stoke-on-Trent ST6 7BS Tel: 01782 819925 — MB BS 1962 Punjab. (Fatima Jinnah Med. Coll. Lahore)

KHANAM, Tanvir (retired) 17 Northcliffe Drive, Totteridge, London N20 8JX Tel: 020 8445 5292 Fax: 020 8445 5292 — MB BS 1962 Karachi; FFA RCS Eng. 1968; DA Eng. 1965. Cons. Anaesth. Roy. Free Hosp. Lond. Prev: Sen. Regist. Brompton Hosp. & Roy. Free Hosp. Lond.

KHANBHAI, Abitalib Tayabali Bedford Road Surgery, 273 Bedford Road, Kempston, Bedford MK42 8QD Tel: 01234 852222 Fax: 01234 843558; 163 Putnoe Lane, Bedford MK41 8LX — MRCS Eng. LRCP Lond. 1973. (Lond. Hosp.) GP Kempston. Prev: Trainee GP Bedford VTS; Ho. Surg. Lond. Hosp.; Ho. Phys. Connaught Hosp. Lond.

KHANCHANDANI, Hargundas Ladharam (retired) 8 Ringwood Road, Luton LU2 7BG Tel: 01582 593232 — MB BS 1951 Bombay. Prev: Hosp. Pract. Bedford & Luton Chest Clinics.

KHANCHANDANI, Raj Biscot Road Surgery, 21 Biscot Road, Luton LU3 1AH Tel: 01582 732697 Fax: 01582 402554 — MB BS 1976 Lond.; MRCP (UK) 1979. Course Organiser, Luton & Dunstable Hosp. VTS; Trainer (Gen. Pract.) Luton.; Clin. Governor Leeds Luton PCG. Prev: Chairm. Beds. Audit & Educat. Gp.

KHAND, Aleem 12 Walton Avenue, Newton Mearns, Glasgow G77 6ET — MB ChB 1992 Glas.

KHAND, Reheela 288 Renfrew Street, Glasgow G3 6TT — MB ChB 1995 Glas.

KHANDERIA, Ajita Vinod 44 Beverley Gardens, Stanmore HA7 2AR — MRCS Eng. LRCP Lond. 1981.

KHANDHADIA, Samir Dwijendra 61 Narborough Road S., Leicester LE3 2HD — MB BS 1997 Lond.

KHANDHERIA, Sharda Harishchandra (retired) — MD (Obst. & Gyn.) Gujarat 1956, MB BS 1952; DObst RCOG 1967. Prev: SCMO Sandwell AHA.

KHANDURI, Sheena 26 Victoria Road, Acocks Green, Birmingham B27 7YA — BChir 1996 Camb.

KHANDWALA, Sheila 14 The Gables, Sylvan Hill, London SE19 2QE — MB BS 1982 Lond.; DCH RCP Lond. 1986.

KHANEM, Noor Mariam 16 Merridale, Carston Close, London SE12 8TG — MB BCh 1990 Wales.

KHANKASHI, Hilary Ann Cranborne Practice, Lake Road, Verwood Tel: 01753 842265 — MB BS 1994 Lond.; DFFP 1999; BSc (Psychol.) Lond. 1990; DCH 1998; DRCOG 1999. (Charing Cross and Westminster Medical School) p/t GP Retainer, Lake Rd Surg., Verwood. Prev: SHO (O & G) Poole Gen. Hosp.

KHANNA, Asha Tunley Holme, Clayton Brook, Bamber Bridge, Preston PR5 8JS — MB BS 1971 Delhi.

KHANNA, Mr Atul Dept. of Plastic Surgery, Sandwell Healthcare NHS Trust, Lyndon, West Bromwich B71 4HJ Tel: 0121 607 3355 — MB BS 1983 Hyderabad; FRCS 1997 (Plast); FRCS Glas. 1990; MBA 1994; FRCS 1997; 1998 Dip Eur B (plast.). (Osmania Medical college) Cons. in Plastic Surg., Sandwell Healthcare NHS Trust; Cons. In Plastic Surg. Manor Hosp. Walsall. Socs: Brit. Burns Assn.; Soc. Of Expert Witnesses; BMA. Prev: Specialist Regist. Plastic Surg.; Fell. in Hand Surg., Derbysh. Roy. Infirm.; Regist. (Burns. & Plastic Surg.) Leicester Roy. Infirm.

KHANNA, Daya Saran Ewing Street Surgery, 26 Ewing Street, Kilbarchan, Johnstone PA10 2JA Tel: 01505 702410; Satsang, 10 Fulton Gardens, Houston, Johnstone PA6 7NU Tel: 01505 321023 — MB BS 1964 Calcutta; MD All India Inst. 1969. (Calcutta) GP Princip. Johnstone. Prev: Regist. (Anaesth.) Argyll & Clyde HB.

KHANNA, Kathryn Ann The Surgery, 14 Leach Green Lane, Rubery, Birmingham B45 9BL Tel: 0121 453 3516; 109 Bristol Road, Edgbaston, Birmingham B5 7TX — MB ChB 1981 Birm.; BSc (Hons.) Birm. 1978; FRCS Eng. 1990. Princip. GP; Hosp. Practitioner.

KHANNA, Manju Monton Medical Centre, Canal Side, Monton Green, Eccles, Manchester M30 8AR.

KHANNA, Monica 31 Tangmere Gardens, Northolt UB5 6LS — MB BS 1998 Lond.; MB BS Lond 1998.

KHANNA, Pradeep-Balbir Nevill Hall Hospital, Breacon Road, Abergavenny NP7 7EG Tel: 01873 732162 Fax: 01873 732157 Email: pradeep.khanna@gwent.wales.nhs.uk — MB BS 1976 Pune; FRCP 1996 Ireland; FRCP 1998 London; MRCP 1984 Ireland. (Armed Forces Medical College, Pune) Cons. Phys. Nevill Hall Hosp. Abergavenny; Hon. Sen. Lect. Univ. of Wales, Coll. of Med., Cardiff; Lead Clinician, Stroke Care, Nevill Hall Hosp.; Med. Superintendent, Co. Hosp., Pontypool. Socs: Chairm., Brit. Geriat. Soc. (Wales); Brit. Med. Assn.; Med. Defense Counc.

KHANNA, Rachel Mary Eva 24C Blackall Road, Exeter EX4 4HE — BM BS 1995 Nottm.

KHANNA, Rajesh Mill Farm House, Path Head, Blaydon-on-Tyne NE21 4SP — MB BS 1994 Newc.

KHANNA, Mr Rakesh 289 Birmingham Road, Sutton Coldfield B72 1ED Tel: 0121 350 4327 — MB BS 1983 Osmania; FFAEM 2000; FRCS Ed. 1988. Cons. (A&E) New Cross hosp. Wolverhampton. Prev: Specialist Regist. (A & E) Staffs. Hosp.; Fell. (Cardio-Pulm. Transpl.ation) Freeman Hosp. Newc.; Sen. Regist. (Cardio-Thoracic Surg.), Waikato Hosp., Hamilton, New Zealand.

KHANNA, Rishi Flat 2/2, 8 Dunearn St., Glasgow G4 9EF — MB ChB 1998 Glas.; MB ChB Glas 1998.

KHANNA, Satish Chirag House Doctors Surgery, 1 Fir Tree Close, Langley Green, Crawley RH11 7LS Tel: 01293 611399 — MB BS 1969 Kanpur.

KHANNA, Shobhna Ballymena Health Centre, Cushendall Road, Ballymena BT43 6HQ Tel: 028 2564 2181 Fax: 028 2565 8919 — MB BCh BAO 1991 Belf.

KHANNA, Vinod Kumar Clayton Brook Surgery, Tunley House, Clayton Brook, Chorley PR5 8ES Tel: 01772 313950 Fax: 01772 620467 — MB BS 1969 Panjab.

KHANNA, Virendra Kumar Ashmeadows, 21 Norfolk Road, Lytham St Annes FY8 4JG Tel: 01253 733080 — MB BS 1968 Delhi; FFA RCS Eng. 1975. (Maulana Azad Med. Coll. New Delhi) Cons. Anaesth. Blackpool DHA. Socs: Assn. Anaesth. Gt. Brit. & Irel.; Obst. Anaesth. Assn. Prev: Sen. Regist. Manch. Roy. Infirm. Wythenshawe Hosp.; Regist. Dudley Rd. Hosp. Birm.; Regist. United Liverp. Hosps.

KHANU, David Dura Dept. Anaesthesia, Luton-Dunstable Hospital NHS Trust, Lewsey Rd, Luton LU4 0DZ Tel: 01582 491122 Fax: 01582 497230; 36 Halford Close, Edgware HA8 5QF Tel: 020 8952 1006 Fax: 020 8952 7944 — MB BCh BAO 1982 NUI; BSc Amer. Univ. Beirut 1974; LRCPI & LM, LRCSI & LM 1982. (Royal Coll. Surg. Of Ireland) Staff Garde Doctor in Naaesthesia, Luton & Dunstable Hosp. NHS Trust, Luton. Socs: BMA & Med. Protec. Soc.; Assn. Anaesth.; Assn. Obstetric Anaesth. Prev: Regist. (Anaesth.), N. Tees Gen Hosp., Stockton on tees; Rehgist. (Anaesth.) Hartlepool Gen Hosp.; Ho. Off. St. Lawrence's Hosp. Dub.

KHANUM, Khalida 72 Derwentdale Gardens, High Heaton, Newcastle upon Tyne NE7 7QN Tel: 0191 270 0571 — MB BS 1973 Punjab; MRCOG 1979.

KHANZADA, Atta Mohammad 301 New Road, Porthcawl CF36 5BE — MB BS 1964 Karachi; FCOphth 1991.
KHARA, Bhajan Singh Mansfield Medical Centre, 56 Binley Road, Coventry CV3 1JB Tel: 024 7645 7551 Fax: 024 7644 2250; 33 Asthill Grove, Coventry CV3 6HN — MB BS 1979 Lond.; MRCS Eng. LRCP Lond. 1979; MRCGP 1984; DRCOG 1982. Trainer Gen. Pract. Coventry.
KHARA, Bhupat Ray Barkerend Health Centre, Bradford BD3 8QH Tel: 01274 663553 — MB BS 1960 Calcutta; DMRT Eng. 1965. Prev: Jun. Ho. Surg. & Jun. Ho. Phys. St. Luke's Hosp. Bradford; Regist. Radium Inst. Bradford.
KHARA, Milan Adelaide Medical Centre, 111 Adelaide Road, London NW3 3RY Tel: 020 7722 4135 Fax: 020 7586 7558; 1 Gainsborough Gardens, London NW11 9BJ — MB ChB 1989 Leic.; DRCOG 1993.
KHARADE, Meena Anne 10 Mayfield Road, Bromley BR1 2HD — MB BCh 1988 Wales.
KHARAUD, Baljinder Singh 10 Joinings Bank, Oldbury, Oldbury B68 8QJ — MB ChB 1992 Aberd.
KHARBANDA, Rajesh Kumar Cardiology Department, Middlesex & University College Hospitals, Mortimer St., London W1N 8AA Tel: 020 7636 8333 — MB ChB 1991 Ed.; BSc Ed. 1989; MRCP (UK) 1994. (Ed.) Regist. (Cardiol.) Univ. Coll. Hosp. NHS Trust. Prev: Regist. (Cardiol.) Whittington NHS Trust.
KHARBANDA, Yatinder c/o Dr S. Sonanis, 22 Styveton Way, Steeton, Keighley BD20 6TP — MB BS 1985 Bombay.
KHARE, Kailash Chandra Hampton Practice, 57 Hampton Road, London E4 8NH Tel: 020 8529 8588 Fax: 020 8523 7054 — MB BS 1962 Vikram; FRSH. (Gandhi Med. Coll. Bhopal) Socs: Assoc. Mem. RCGP. Prev: Res. Ho. Surg. (Gen. Surg.) Gandhi Med. Coll. & Hosps. Bhopal, India; SHO (Cas. & Orthop.) Harrogate Gen. Hosp.; SHO (Psychol. Med.) Moorhaven Hosp. Ivybridge.
***KHARIM, Shalim Rajaul** 21 Wordsworth Close, Lichfield WS14 9BY — MB ChB 1998 Birm.; ChB Birm. 1998.
KHARKONGOR, Sormanick Khadsingh Newark General Hospital, London Road, Newark NG24 1TG; 5 The Platts, Newark NG24 4PY — MB BS 1970 Gauhati. (Gauhati) Staff. Grade (A & E) Newark Gen. Hosp.; GP (PMS) Balderton Surg. Bulpit Rd. balderton Newark Notts NG24 3PT. Prev: Regist. Orthopaedic Rotherham; Princip. GP Redditch; Staff Grade (A & E) Newark.
KHASGIWALE, Ashok Kumar Brierley Hill Health Centre, Albion Street, Brierley Hill DY5 3EE Tel: 01384 77382 Fax: 01384 483931; Bromton Lodge, Quarry Pk Road, Pedmore, Stourbridge DY8 2RE — MB BS 1971 Indore. (MGM Med. Coll. Indore, India) GP.
KHASHABA, Ahmed Mohamed Hosny 39 Essex Road, London W3 9JA — MB BS 1994 Lond.
KHASTGIR, Gautam 12 Lewis Road, Mitcham CR4 3DE Tel: 020 8646 1895 Email: gkhastgir@cablenet.co.uk — MB BS 1985 Calcutta; MRCOG 1991; FRCS 1992. (Calcutta Medical College) Subspeciality Sen. Regist. in Reproductive Med. & Surg., Chelsea & W.minster Hosp., Lond.; Hon. Lect. (Obs. & Gyn.). Socs: Brit. Fertil. Soc.; Brit. Menopause Soc.; Brit. Soc. of Gyn. Endoscopy. Prev: Wellbeing research fell. in O & G, Chelsea & W.minster Hosp., Lond.
KHATER, Mr Mohamed Salah El Din 90 Cornwall Gardens, London SW7 4AX Tel: 020 7584 8431 — LAH Dub. 1953; FRCS Eng. 1964. Sen. Cas. Off. Edgware Gen. Hosp. Socs: BMA. Prev: Surg. Regist. Burnley Gen. Hosp.; SHO Orthop. Vict. Hosp. Burnley; Ho. Surg. Maidenhead Hosp.
KHATIB, Mr Humayun Athar Whitley Batch, 65 Cardiff Road, Cardiff CF5 2AA — MB BS 1971 Nagpur; FRCS Ed. 1980; FRCOphth 1989.
KHATIB, Mrs Mutaher Jehan 65 Cardiff Road, Llandaff, Cardiff CF5 2AA Tel: 029 2056 0011; Royal Gwent Hospital, Newport NP20 2UB — MB BS 1978 Osmania; MRCOG 1983; Dobst. RCPI 1982. Staff Grade Specialist (O & G) RGH Newport. Socs: WOGS; BSCEP. Prev: Sen. Regist. KKNGH, KFAFH Jeddah Saudi Arabia; Sen. Regist. RKH Riyadh Saudi Arabia.
KHATIB, Shujauddin Najmuddin Branch Surgery, 181 Burton Road, Lincoln LN1 3LT Tel: 01522 544222 Fax: 01522 560665; 181 Burton Road, Lincoln LN1 3LT Tel: 01522 544222 Fax: 01522 560665 — MB BS Mysore 1966. (Kasturba Med. Coll. Mangalore)
KHATOON, Amina 68 Thornbury Drive, Bradford BD3 8JE — MB BS 1987 Punjab; MRCPI 1992. Cons. Rehab Med. Willesden Hosp. Lond. Socs: Brit. Rehabil. Soc.; Brit. Rheum. Soc. Prev: Staff Grade Rheumatol. Wexham Pk. Hosp. Slough.
KHATRI, Ashok Kumar Sorsby Health Centre, 3 Mandeville Street, London E5 0DH Tel: 020 8986 5613 Fax: 020 8986 8108 — MB BS 1974 Karachi; LRCP LRCS Ed. LRCPS Glas. 1984. (Karachi, Pakistan) Socs: St Pauls. Prev: Resid. Med. Off. A.S. Hosp. Karachi, Pakistan; SHO (Orthop. & Trauma) Memor. Hosp. Darlington; SHO (Psychiat.) Sedgefield Hosp.
KHATRI, Gordhandas Narandas Central Middlesex Hospital, Acton Lane, London NW10 7NS — MB BS 1957 Poona; MRCGP 1968; DA Eng. 1976. (B.J. Med. Coll.) Socs: BMA & Indian Med. Assn. Prev: Rotating Res. Intern Wanless Hosp. Miraj, India; Res. Intern Christian Med. Coll. Hosp. Vellore, India; Ho. Off. Jehangir Nurs. Home Poona, India.
KHATRI, Hussein Issak Grove Hill Medical Centre, Kilbride Court, Hemel Hempstead HP2 6AD Tel: 01442 212038; 14 Basildon Square, Grove Hill, Hemel Hempstead HP2 6AS — MB ChB 1972 Makerere; DFFP 1992. (Makerere Med. Sch. Kampala) Clin. Asst. (Elderly Care) Hemel Hempstead Gen. Hosp. Prev: Trainee GP I. of Wight VTS; Ho. Off. Mutimbili Hosp. Dar es Salaam, Tanzania; Ho. Surg. Stracathro Hosp. Brechin.
KHATTAB, Mr Ahmed Abd El Nasser Hassan 1 Warwick Court, Newcastle upon Tyne NE3 2YS Tel: 0191 214 6070 Fax: 0191 214 6070 Email: a.khattab@netscape.net — MB BCh 1979 Ain Shams; MS 1983; FRCS Ed. 1988. (Ain Shams, Egypt) Locum Cons. Surg. N.ern Region. Socs: BMA; PMS; MIS. Prev: Cons. Surg. King Fahd Hosp. Qassim & Al-Ras, Saudi Arabia; Pos Fell.sh. Surg. Regist. Rotat. N.ern Region HA; Clin. Research Fell. King's Coll. Lond.
KHATTAB, Bashir Lord Street Surgery, 2 Lord Street, Ince, Wigan WN2 2AJ Tel: 01942 242403 Fax: 01942 242403 — LAH Dub. 1971.
***KHATTAB, Hassan Peter** 49 Glenside, Appley Bridge, Wigan WN6 9EG Tel: 01257 254696 — MB ChB 1997 Bristol; BSc Bristol 1994.
KHATTAK, Abdul Samad 31 Maes-y-Castell, Llanrhos, Llandudno LL30 1NG Tel: 01492 83610 — MB BS 1964 Karachi. (Dow Med. Coll.) Regist. (Med.) Llandudno Gen. Hosp.
KHATTAK, Fazi-i-Hakim 4 Tebbutt Close, Rothwell, Kettering NN14 6TR Tel: 01536 418805 — MB BS 1983 Peshawar; MRCP (UK) 1990.
KHATTAK, Mir Alam Khan Woodhall Health Centre, Valley Green, Off Shenley Road, Hemel Hempstead HP2 7RJ Tel: 01442 61805 Fax: 01442 261750.
KHATTAK, Mohammad Salim Khan 9 Bole Hill Road, Walkley, Sheffield S6 5DD — MB ChB 1980 Sheff.; MRCP (UK) 1988.
KHATTAK, Saima Sajjad The Surgery, 58 Benton Road, Sparkbrook, Birmingham B11 1TX Tel: 0121 773 4822; 13A Wake Green Road, Moseley, Birmingham B13 9HB Tel: 0121 449 7449 — MB BS 1970 Punjab; MRCOG 1995; DFFP 1995; DRCOG 1993. Socs: Menopause Soc.
KHATTAK, Sajjad Hussain The Surgery, 58 Benton Road, Sparkbrook, Birmingham B11 1TX Tel: 0121 773 4822; 13A Wake Green Road, Moseley, Birmingham B13 9HB Tel: 0121 449 7449 Fax: 0121 771 2218 — MB BS 1968 Peshawar; BSc Peshawar 1963, MB BS 1968; DTM & H Liverp. 1976. (Khyber Med. Coll.)
KHATTAK, Taj Mohammad Lower Farm Health Centre, 109 Buxton Road, Bloxwich, Walsall WS3 3RT Tel: 01922 476640 Fax: 01922 491836; 46 Sneyd Lane, Essington, Willenhall — MB BS 1968 Punjab; MB BS Punjab (Pakistan) 1968. (King Edwd. Med. Coll. Lahore)
KHATTAR, Rajdeep Singh 17 Worton Gardens, Isleworth TW7 4BD — BM 1986 Soton.; MRCP (UK) 1991.
KHATU, Bharat Vishnu Orthopaedic Department, Burnley Green Hospital, Casterton Avenue, Burnley BB10 2PQ Tel: 01282 425071 — MB BS 1974 Poona; MB BS Poona 1970; MS Bombay 1976. Assoc. Specialist Burnley Gen. Hosp. Prev: Regist. (Orthop.) Falkirk & Dist. Roy. Infirm.; Regist. (Orthop.) Bridge of Earn Hosp. & Raigmore Hosp. Inverness.
KHAUND, Rathindra Ram (retired) 4 Collieston Drive, Bridge of Don, Aberdeen AB22 8SN Tel: 01224 702340 — MB BS 1959 Gauhati; FRCPath 1983, M 1971; DCP Lond 1964. Prev: Demonst. (Path.) Assam Med. Coll. Dibrugarh, India.
KHAW, Fu Meng 40 The Chare, Burnopfield, Newcastle upon Tyne NE1 4DD — MB BS 1990 Newc.

[illegible] **[illegible]y-Tee** 32 Wilberforce Road, Cambridge CB3 0EQ — MB [illegible]/6 Camb.; MSc (Epidemiol.) Lond. 1980; MA, MB Camb. [illegible], BChir 1975; MRCP (UK) 1977; DCH Eng. 1978. Prof. Clin. [illegible]erontol. Univ. Camb. Sch. Clin. Med. Socs: Fell. Counc. Epidemiol. Amer. Heart Assn. Prev: Sen. Regist. (Community Med.) Addenbrooke's Hosp. Camb.; Asst. Adj. Prof. Univ. Calif., San Diego; Wellcome Research Fell. St. Mary's Hosp. Lond. & Univ. Calif., San Diego.

KHAW, Kim Sun 31 Townsend Way, Northwood HA6 1TG — MB BS 1988 Lond.; FRCA 1993. Regist. (Anaesth.) Char. Cross Hosp. Lond. Socs: Assn. Anaesth. & BMA. Prev: Regist. (Anaesth.) Roy. Surrey Co. Hosp.; SHO (Intens. Care) Nat. Hosp. Lond.; SHO (Anaesth.) Middlx. Hosp. Lond.

KHAW, Kok-Tee Radiology Department, St. George's Hospital, Blackshaw Road, Tooting, London SW17 0QT Tel: 020 8672 1255; 2 Woodstock Road, London W4 1UE — MB BChir 1979 Camb.; MA, MB Camb. 1980, BChir 1979; MRCP Lond. 1982; FRCR 1987. Cons. Radiol. St. Geo. Hosp. Lond.

KHAW, Professor Peng-Tee Institute of Ophthalmology, Moorfields Eye Hospital, 11-43 Bath St., London EC1V 9EL Tel: 020 7566 2334 Fax: 020 7566 2334 — BM 1980 Soton.; FRCP 1999; FRCS (Eng.) 1997; PhD Lond. 1995; FRCOphth. 1989; DO RCS Eng. 1985; FRCS Glas. 1985; MRCP (UK) 1983; FIBiol 2000. Prof. of Glaucoma and Wound Healing, Univ. Coll. Lond. & Moorfields Eye Hosp. Prev: Cons. Ophth. Surg. Moorfields Eye Hosp. Lond.; Wellcome Vision Research Fell. Inst. Ophth. Lond.; Sen. Regist. Moorfields Eye Hosp. Lond.

KHAWAJA, Afshan Naseem 4 Highgrove Road, Cheadle, Stockport SK8 1NR Tel: 0161 374 5350 — MB ChB 1994 Leeds; MRCPsych 1999. (Leeds) Regist. (Psychiat.) Prestwich Hosp. Manch. Roy. Infirm. Socs: Inceptor Roy. Coll. Psych. Prev: Regist. (Psychiat.) Withington Hosp. Manch.

KHAWAJA, Mr Hamid Queen Mary's Hospital, Frognal Avenue, Sidcup DA14 6LT Tel: 020 8302 2678 — MD 1975 Beirut; MS Soton. 1987; FRCS Eng. 1981; FRCS Ed. 1981. Cons. Surg. Qu. Mary's Hosp. Sidcup. Socs: Fell. Roy. Soc. Med.; Assn. Surg.& Med. Research Soc.; Brit. Soc. Gastroenterol. & Minimally Invasive Ther.. Prev: Sen. Regist. King's Coll. Hosp. Lond.; Trav. Lect., USA 1988; Research Fell. Soton. Univ. & Portsmouth Hosps.

KHAWAJA, Shakil Salam 105 Windsor Road, Leyton, London E10 5LP — MB ChB 1987 Liverp. SHO (O & G) Liverp. Matern. Hosp.

KHAWAJA, Usman Latif 32 Whinney Heys Road, Blackpool FY3 8NP — MB BS 1985 Punjab; MRCPI 1993.

KHAWAJA, Yasmeen Rana 73 Charlotte Street, London W1P 1LB Tel: 020 7530 3629 Fax: 020 7436 8717 — MB BS 1962 Punjab; MFFP 1993. (Fatima Jinnah Med. Coll. Lahore) SCMO Camden & Islington Community NHS Trust; NE Thames Region Co-ordinator Fac. Family Plann. & Reproduc. Health. Socs: Fac. Family Plann. & Reproduc. Health c/o Roy. Coll. Obst. & Gyn.

KHAWAR, Farooq Raza 45 Sandringham Road, Gosforth, Newcastle upon Tyne NE3 1QB Tel: 0191 284 7315 Email: f.r.khawar@newcastle.ac.uk; 101 Framlingham Road, Sale M33 3RL — MB ChB 1994 Manch. SHO (Anaesth.) Wansbeck Gen. Hosp. Ashington N.umberland.

KHAWERI, Farhang Azizullah 15 Moray Park Terrace, Culloden, Inverness IV2 7RQ Tel: 01463 792230 — MB BS 1972 Karachi; MCh (Orth) 1998. Assoc. Specialist (Orthop. Surg.) Raigmore Hosp. Inverness.

KHAZNE CHARIMO, Zouhair The Surgery, 6 Rushton Street, London N1 5DR Tel: 020 7739 5164 Fax: 020 7739 5166 — LMS 1992 Saragossa.

KHEHAR, Sheila 4 Sandall Close, London W5 1JE — MB ChB 1988 Leic.; MRCGP 1992; DRCOG 1991; DGM RCP Lond. 1990. Prev: SHO (A & E) Medway HA.

KHEMANI, Mr Chander Dayaram Tel: 01843 863353 — MB BS 1968 Rajasthan; MS (Ophth.) Gujarat 1973; MRCOphth 1989; DO RCS Eng. 1977. GP & Hosp. Pract. (Ophth.) Kent.

KHEMANI, Shakuntala Tel: 01843 863353 — MB BS Gujarat 1971; TDD Gujarat 1974. Clin. Med. Off. Thanet Child Health Serv.

KHER, Kewal Krishan 295 Lowestoft Road, Gorleston, Great Yarmouth NR31 6JW — MB BS 1957 Bombay. (Grant Med. Coll. Bombay) Orthop. Surg. (Orthop. & Trauma) James Paget Hosp. Gorleston. Socs: Fell. Brit. Orthop. Assn.; BMA. Prev: SHO Urol. Lewisham Hosp. Lond.; SHO Thoracic Surg. Brook Gen. Hosp. Lond.; SHO Orthop. Roy. E. Sussex Hosp. Hastings.

KHERA, Goldie 209 Pitville Avenue, Mossley Hill, Liverpool L18 7JH — MB ChB 1998 Liverp.; MB ChB Liverp 1998.

KHERAJ, Sadrudin 15 Keldane Gardens, Fenham, Newcastle upon Tyne NE4 9PS — MB BS 1984 Lond.

KHETANI, Bharatkumar Narshidas Jagjivan Main Road Surgery, Main Road, Parson Drove, Wisbech PE13 4LF Tel: 01945 700223 Fax: 01945 700915 — MB BS 1979 Lond. (St. Mary's) Prev: Clin. Asst. Diabetic Retinopathy Clinic (Ophth.) P'boro. Dist. Hosp.

KHETANI, Mukund Jamnadas The Surgery, 30 Hagley Road, Hayley Green, Halesowen B63 1DH — LRCPI & LM, LRCSI & LM 1967; DFFP 1996; Cert. Family Plann. JCC 1973. (Roy. Coll. Surgs. Dub.) Clin. Med. Off. (Child Health) Halesowen. Socs: BMA; MDU. Prev: Sen. Med. Off. (Cas.) Greenwich Dist. Hosp. Lond.; SHO Our Lady's Hosp. Sick Childr. Crumlin; GP Staffs. FPC.

KHETARPAL, Bal Krishan 2 Les Bois, Layer de la Haye, Colchester CO2 0EX — MB BS 1957 Madras; MRCPsych 1973.

KHETERPAL, Mr Sundeep King Edward vii Hosp, Windsor SL4 3DS Tel: 01753 860441 Email: ukeyes@ukeyes.com; 30 Keble road, Maidenhead SL6 6BA Email: ukeyes@ukeyes.com — BM BCh 1989 Oxf.; FRCS Ed. 1994; MA Cambridge 1986. Cons P. Chas. eye hosp king Edwd. vii windsor. Socs: MRCOphth.; Amer. Acad. Ophth.; Amer soc of cataract & refractive surg. Prev: Univ. Prosector (Human Anat.) Oxf.; Specialist reg Birm & Midl. eye centre; Fell. Ocular Oncol. Wills Eye Hosp. Philadelphia.

KHIANI, Mrs Chandra (retired) 105 Wentworth Drive, Bedford MK41 8QE — MB BS 1968 Poona; DA Eng. 1970. Prev: Police Surg. Bedford.

KHIANI, Mohan Lal (retired) The Medical Centre, 76-78 Shakespeare Road, Bedford MK40 2DN Tel: 01234 327337 Fax: 01234 270969 — MB BS 1965 Agra; FRCS Ed. 1973. Prev: Regist. (Cardiothoracic Surg.) N. Staffs. Roy. Infirm. Stoke-on-Trent.

KHILKOFF-CHOUBERSKY, Alexandra 52 West Hill, East Grinstead RH19 4EP Tel: 01342 312708 — BM BCh 1973 Oxf.; Cert. Family Plann. JCC 1981. (Oxf. & St. Thos.) Clin. Asst. (Genitourin. Med.) Kent & Sussex Hosp. Tunbridge Wells; Clin. Med. Off. (Family Plann.) E. Surrey & Mid Downs HAs. Socs: Brit. Soc. Nutrit. Med.; Brit. Soc. Clin. Ecology; Fac. Fam. Plann. & Reproduc. Health Care. Prev: Ho. Surg. St. Thos. Hosp. Lond.; Ho. Phys. Hereford Co. Hosp.; Asst. Med. Off. Harbour Breton Hosp., Canada.

KHIMJI, Hassanali Mohamedali Rajabali Addison House Surgery, Hamstel Road, Harlow CM20 1DS Tel: 01279 692780 Fax: 01279 692781; 51 Theydon Grove, Epping CM16 4PX — MB BS 1976 Lond. Clin. Asst. (Neurol.) St. Margt's. Hosp. Epping.

KHIN-MAUNG-ZAW, Dr Department of Child Psychiatry, Birmingham Childrens Hospital, Steelhouse Lane, Birmingham B4 6NH Tel: 0121 333 9182 Fax: 0121 333 9181 Email: frank.zaw@bhamchildrens.wmids.nhs.uk — MB BS Rangoon 1970; FRCPsych 1996, M 1982. Head Dept., Cons. Psychiat. & Hon. Sen. Lect. Birm. Childr. Hosp. NHS Trust. Prev: Cons. Psychiat. & Clin. Tutor Glos. Postgrad. Psychiat. Rotat. Scheme.; Clin. Teach., Dept of Psychiat., Univ. of Bristol.

KHIN, Mar Htwe St. Mary's Hospital, Milton Road, Portsmouth PO3 6AD; 53 Oyster Quay, Port Solent, Portsmouth PO6 4TE — MB BS 1977 Rangoon; MB BS Rangoon 1978; DGM RCP Lond. 1991. Staff Grade Phys. (Med. for Elderly) St. Mary's Hosp. Portsmouth. Prev: Staff Grade Phys. (Med. for Elderly) Walsall Hosps. NHS Trust.

KHIN KHIN NWE, Dr Department of Accident & Emergency, Pilgrim Hospital, Sibsey Road, Boston PE21 9QS — MB BS 1973 Rangoon.

KHIN MAR MAR, Dr c/o Dr M. Nyunt, Hexham General Hospital, Hexham NE46 1QJ — MB BS 1965 Med. Inst. (I) Rangoon.

KHIN MAUNG NYUNT, Mr Department of Ophthalmology, Worthington Hospital, Lyndhurst Rd, Worthing BN11 2DH Tel: 01903 205111 — MB BS 1982 Rangoon; FRCS Ed. 1993; MRCOphth 1991; M.Med.Sci. Keele 1999. Staff Grade (Ophth.) Worthing Hosp. Socs: BMA; MDU. Prev: Staff Grade Ophth. Worcester Roy. Infirm.; SHO (Ophth.) Bridgend Gen. Hosp., Burton-on-Trent & Wolverhampton.

KHIN MAY SEIN, Dr (retired) Mayville, Bridge of Weir Road, Kilmacolm PA13 4AP Tel: 01505 872112 — MB BS 1960 Rangoon; DTM & H Lond 1963. Assoc. Specialist. (Geriat. Med.)

Inverclyde Health Dist. Prev: Regist. (Chest, Geriat. & Young Disabled) Bridge of Weir Hosp.

KHIN PYONE YI, Dr Plot 35, Byeways Est., Muxton, Telford — MB BS 1971 Rangoon; MB BS Med Inst (I) Rangoon 1971.

KHIN THET MAW, Dr (Surgery), 42 Abbots Road, Southall UB1 1HT Tel: 020 8574 7746 — MB BS 1973 Med. Inst. (I) Rangoon.

KHIN THIDA, Dr 3 Kingfisher Close, Whitstable CT5 4DU Tel: 01227 262588 — MB BS 1976 Rangoon. SCMO Canterbury & Thanet HA.

KHINE, Thwe Thwe 44 Horsted House, Whitelands, Franklynn Road, Haywards Heath RH16 4HR Tel: 01444 441758 Fax: 01444 441758 Email: pkhine@aol.com — MB BS 1978 Med. Inst. (I) Rangoon; LMSSA Lond. 1992; MRCOG 1997. Staff Grade (O & G) Epsom Gen. Hosp. Socs: Protec. Soc. Prev: Regist. (O & G) P.ss Roy. Hosp. Haywards Health.

KHINE-SMITH, Mae Chit Knine Folkestone Surgeries Group, 65-69 Guildhall Street, Folkestone CT20 1EJ Tel: 01303 851411 Fax: 01303 220443; 85 The St, Hawkinge, Folkestone CT18 7DE Tel: 01303 2026 — MB BS 1968 Med.; MB BS Med. Inst. (II) Mingaladon 1968.

KHIR, Amir Sharifuddin Mohd 7 Willowgrove Gardens, Kinellar, Aberdeen AB21 0XW; 3 Jalan Teruntong, Damansara Heights, Kuala Lumpur 504940, Malaysia Tel: 00 60 3 2542380 — MB ChB 1973 Ed.; FRCP Ed. 1990; MRCP (UK) 1977. Prof. Dept. Med. Univ. Malaya Kuala Lumpur; Sen. Cons. Internal Med. & Endocrinol. Univ. Hosp. Kuala Lumpur, Malaysia. Socs: Malaysia Endocrine & Metab. Soc.; (Vice-Pres.) Malaysian Diabetes Assn. Prev: Assoc. Prof. & Lect. (Med. & Therap.) Univ. Aberd.

KHIROYA, Divya Vinod Bicknoller, 59 Bells Hill, Barnet EN5 2SG Tel: 020 8449 3514 Fax: 020 8440 8067; 34 Lambert Road, Finchley, London N12 9ES Tel: 020 8445 2076 — MB BS 1968 Bombay; DCH Eng. 1970; DObst RCOG 1969. (Grant Med. Coll.)

KHIROYA, Raj 183 Coalshaw Green Road, Chadderton, Oldham OL9 8JS — MB ChB 1990 Manch.

KHIROYA, Ranjana Chhotalal Chase Farm Hospital, The Ridgeway, Enfield EN2 8JL Tel: 020 8366 6600; 1 Aragon Close, The Ridgway, Enfield EN2 8LW — MB BS 1971 Bombay; FFA RCS Eng. 1978; DObst RCOG 1974. (Topiwala Nat. Med. Coll.) Cons. Anaesth. NE Thames RHA & Chase Farm Hosps. NHS Trust.

KHIROYA, Vinodrai Parmanand Bicknoller, 59 Bells Hill, Barnet EN5 2SG Tel: 020 8449 3514 Fax: 020 8440 8067; 34 Lambert Road, Finchley, London N12 9ES Tel: 020 8445 2076 — MB BS 1968 Bombay; DObst RCOG 1968. (Grant Med. Coll.) Prev: SHO (O & G) W. Herts. Hosp. Hemel Hempstead; SHO (Obst.) Bearsted Memor. Hosp. Lond.; Ho. Off. (Obst.) Thorpe Coombe Hosp. Lond.

KHIRWADKAR, Pramod Mangesh Whitwick Road Surgery, Whitwick Road, Coalville LE67 3FA Tel: 01530 836507; 88 Blackwood, Coalville LE67 4RF Tel: 01530 834379 — MB BS 1968 Indore. Clin. Asst. & Med. Off. Coalville Community Hosp. Socs: Overseas Doctors Assn.; GP's in Asthma Gp.; Primary Soc. Gastroenterol.

KHO, Boon Chong 7 Hamilton Close, Nelson Reach, London SE16 6QJ — MB ChB 1985 Aberd.

KHOGALI, Mr Kamal Ahmed HCI (Scotland) Ltd., Beardmore St., Clydebank G81 4HX Tel: 0141 951 5747 Fax: 0141 951 5652 Email: doctor.kamal.khogali@hci.co.uk; 22 Rutherford Avenue, Bearsden, Glasgow G61 4SE Tel: 0141 942 3044 Email: kkhogali@aol.com — MB BS 1979 Khartoum; FRCSI 1991. Cardiac Surg. HCI Scotl.

KHOGALI, Saib Salem 140A London Road, Worcester WR5 2EB — MB ChB 1989 Birm.; MRCP (UK) 1993.

KHOKHAR, Azhar Altaf The Royal Alexandra Hospital, Corsebar Road, Paisley PA2 9PN — MB BS 1982 Punjab; MRCP (UK) 1987.

KHOKHER, Tariq Hussain Carlisle Road Surgery, 233 Carlisle Road, Queens Park, Bedford MK40 4HT Tel: 01234 351661 Fax: 01234 364884; Tel: 01234 857065 — MB BS 1988 Lond.; BSc Biochem. (Hons.) Lond. 1985; MRCGP 1995; DGM RCP Lond. 1991; DCH RCP Lond. 1992. (The Royal London Hospital) GP Qu.s Pk. Health Centre Bedford. Prev: SHO Grimsby GP VTS.

KHOLEIF, Mr Yasser Abdel Kader KKNGH Medical City, Block 13, Apartment 12, PO Box 9515, Jeddah, Saudi Arabia Tel: 00 966 2 6653400; 100 Elderslie Street, Charing Cross, Glasgow G3 7AR Tel: 0141 204 1232 — MB BCh 1981 Assiut; FRCS Glas. 1990. Assoc. Cons. KKNGH Jeddah, Saudi Arabia.

KHONDAKER, Ehsan Hadi 5 Pinders Grove, Wakefield WF1 4AH — MB ChB 1998 Dund.; MB ChB Dund 1998.

KHONDKER MOSLEHUDDIN, Dr South Grange Medical Center, Trunk Road, Middlesbrough TS6 9QG; 40 Grey Towers Drive, Nunthorpe, Middlesbrough TS7 0LT Tel: 01642 312514 Fax: 01642 312514 — MB BS Dacca 1965; FRCPsych 1987, M 1973; DPM Eng. 1972. (Dacca) S. Grange Med. Trunk Rd. Center Middlesbrough.

KHONG, Chee Hoong Flat 1, 38 Caledonia Place, Clifton, Bristol BS8 4DN — BM BS 1992 Nottm.; BMedSci Nottm. 1990.

KHONG, Chee Keen Lutterworth Health Centre, Gilmorton Road, Lutterworth LE17 4EB Tel: 01455 553531 — MB ChB 1988 Leic.; DObst RCPI 1992; Dip. Ther. Wales 1997; Cert. Community Paediat. Warwick 1992. (Leic.) GP Lutterworth, Leics. Prev: SHO Rotat. (Med.) Leicester; SHO Rotat. (A & E) Nuneaton.

KHONG, Su-Yen 12A Top Flat Cotham Road, Bristol BS6 6DR — MB ChB 1997 Bristol.

KHONG, Tech Kean Top Left, 23 Blackness Avenue, Dundee DD2 1EW Tel: 01382 68575 — MB ChB 1992 Dundee; MRCP (UK) 1995. SHO (Gen. Med.) Dundee. Socs: BMA & Med. Defence Union.

KHONG, Teck Keong Pasley Road Health Centre, Pasley Road, Eyres Monsell, Leicester LE2 9BU Tel: 0116 278 6112 — MB ChB 1976 Sheff.; LLM Cardiff 1999. GP Leicester; Police Surg. Leics. Prev: SHO & Regist. Leeds AHA (E.).; Res. Regist. (Rheum.) Glas.; Ho. Phys. Prof. Med. Unit Roy. Hosp. Sheff..

KHONG YANG-SUI, Michael The Surgery, 121 Wrythe Lane, Carshalton SM5 2RT Tel: 020 8644 2727 Fax: 020 8641 7994; 18 Barrow Avenue, Carshalton Beeches, Carshalton SM5 4NY Tel: 020 8643 5714 Fax: 020 8643 5714 — MB BS 1988 Lond.; BSc (Basic Med. Scis. & Biochem.) Lond. 1984. (Char. Cross & Westm.) Prev: SHO (Paediat.) Ashford Hosp. Middlx.; SHO (O & G & Paediat.) Milton Keynes Hosp.; SHO (A & E) Hillingdon Hosp. Middlx.

KHONJI, Acacia Alaleh 31 Sevington Road, London NW4 3RY — BM BS 1997 Nottm.

KHONJI, Nader Ismail 26 Corelli Street, Newport NP19 7AR — MB ChB 1994 Bristol.

KHONSARI, Mehrdad Rotherham District General Hospital, Moorgate Road, Oakwood, Rotherham S60 2UD Tel: 01709 820000; 9 Rostherne Way, Sandbach CW11 1WS — MB ChB 1992 Sheff. SHO (Gen. Med.) Rotherham Dist. Hosp. Prev: Ho. Off. (Med.) N.. Gen. Hosp.

KHOO, Brian Chung Hoe 19 The Crescent, Belfast BT10 0GJ — MB BCh 1998 Belf.; MB BCh Belf 1998.

KHOO, Mr Christopher Teik-Kooi Bakers Barn, Touchen End, Maidenhead SL6 3LD Tel: 01628 671319 Email: ctkkhoo@bakersbarn.clara.net — MB BChir 1972 Camb.; MB BChir Camb. 1973; MA Camb. 1973; FRCS Eng. 1977. Cons. Plastic Surg. Wexham Pk. Hosp. Slough & St. Marks Hosp. Maidenhead; Cons. Plastic & Hand Surg. Heatherwood Hosp. Ascot. Socs: Brit. Assn. Plastic Surg. & Brit. Soc. Surg. Hand.; Brit. Assn. Aesthetic Plastic Surg.s. Prev: Cons. Plastic Surg. & Dir. Burns Unit Stoke Mandeville Hosp. Aylesbury.

KHOO, Chun Kheng Queen Marys Hospital, Frognal Avenue, Sidcup DA14 6LT — MB BS 1996 Melbourne.

KHOO, Mr David Eugene Seow Aun Oldchurch Hospital, Waterloo Road, Romford RM7 0BE Tel: 01708 708191 — MB BS 1983 Lond.; MS Lond. 1991; FRCS Eng. 1987. (Guy's Hosp.) Cons. Gen. Surg. OldCh. Hosp. Romford. Socs: Assn. Surg.; BMA; BSG.

KHOO, Eric Yin Hao 8 Pendlebury Drive, Leicester LE2 6GY — MB ChB 1998 Leic.; MB ChB Leic 1998.

KHOO, Khui Teong 46 Dan-y-Coed, Aberystwyth SY23 2HD — MB BS 1975 Lond.; MRCS Eng. LRCP Lond. 1974.

KHOO, Poh Choo 50A Frognal, London NW3 6AG — MB ChB 1990 Leic.

KHOO, Saye Hock Department of Infectious Diseases, North Manchester General Hospital, Delauneys Road, Manchester M8 6RL Tel: 0161 795 4567 Fax: 0161 720 2562 Email: khoo@liverpool.ac.uk — MB BS 1985 Lond.; MD Lond. 1997; MRCP (UK) 1988; DTM & H RCP Lond. 1989. Sen. Regist. (Infec. Dis.) Monsall Unit N. Manch. Gen. Hosp. Prev: Lect. Univ. Liverp.; Regist. (Infec. Dis.) Monsall Hosp. Manch. & N.wick Pk. Hosp. Lond.; SHO (Infec. Dis.) E. Birm. Hosp.

Meng Doctors' Residence, Birch Hill Hospital, Union ...ndale OL12 9QB — MB BS 1995 Melbourne.

..., Sharon Mei-Ling 40 Lisburn Av., Belfast BT9 7FX — MB ... BAO 1991 Belf.

KHOOBARRY, Kamal Capoor Birmingham Heartlands Hospital, 45 Bordesley Green E., Birmingham B9 5ST — MB BS 1992 Lucknow; MRCP (UK) 1995.

KHOOSAL, Deenesh Ishver Leicester General Hospital, Psychiatric Department, Gwendolen Road, Leicester LE5 4PW Tel: 0116 249 0490 Fax: 0116 258 4745 — MB BCh BAO 1978 NUI; LRCPI & LM, LRCSI & LM 1978; FRCPsych 1994, M 1983; T(Psych) 1991. Cons. Psychiat. Leics. Ment. Health Servs. NHS Trust. Socs: Roy. Coll. Psychiat. (Transcultural Gp.). Prev: Cons. Psychiat. Carlton Hayes Hosp. Leicester; Cons. Psychiat. Worcester Roy. Infirm.; Sen. Regist. Rotat. (Psychiat.) Leeds & Yorks.

KHOPKAR, Deepak Dinkar Flat G, 2/8 Birmingham Road, Cowes PO31 7BH — MB BS 1974 Bombay.

KHOR, Louis Jen Hee Gloucestershire Royal Hospital, Great Western Road, Gloucester GL1 3NN Tel: 01452 528555 Email: louis.khor@glover-tr.swert.nhs.uk; Georg-Cantor Strasse 29, Halle D-06108, Germany Tel: 01684 299017 Email: ukor@bigfoot.com — MB ChB 1991 Bristol. Cons. Anaesth., Gloucestershire Roy. Hosp. Prev: Specialist Reg. (Anasth.) Birm.

KHOR, Mr Timothy Tong Guan 119 Fort Road, London SE1 5PU; 2/3 Arbor Grove, Leeming, Perth, Australia — MB BCh 1987 Wales; FRCSI 1994. Regist. (Urol.) Roy. Shrewsbury Hosp. Prev: Regist. (Cardiothoracic Surg. & Urol.) Perth, W. Austral.

KHORASANI, Mohamed Hamid Flat 5, 5 Talbot Square, Sussex Gardens, London W5 1TR — MB BCh 1970 Cairo; MRCP (UK) 1978.

KHORSANDI, Shirin Elizabeth 10 Shaftsbury House, Vauxhall Walk, London SE11 5EW — MB BS 1993 Lond.

KHOSA, Naranjan Singh Khan and Partners, Medical Centre, Church Road, Seven Sisters, Neath SA10 9DT Tel: 01639 700203 Fax: 01639 700010; Pant-y-Celyn, 39 Neath Road, Crynant, Neath SA10 8SE — MB BS 1975 Punjab; MB BS Punjabi 1975; Dip. Pract. Dermat. Wales 1990; DRCOG 1983; DA Eng. 1979. (Govt. Med. Coll. Patiala) Clin. Asst. (EMI) Ystradgynlais Community Hosp. S. Wales. Prev: Regist. (Anaesth.) Hexham Gen. Hosp. N.ld.

KHOSLA, Sandeep Charnwood Surgery, 5 Burton Road, Derby DE1 1TH Tel: 01332 737737 Fax: 01332 737738 — MB ChB 1993 Manch.

KHOSRAVI-NEZHAD, Beman The Health Centre, 139/141 Ormneau Road, Belfast BT7 1DA; 8 Kingsway Park, Cerry Valley, Belfast BT5 7EU — MB BCh BAO 1966 Belf. (Belf.)

KHOSRAVIANI, Mr Kourosh Methodist College, 1 Malone Road, Belfast BT9 6BY; 23 Ogles Grove, Hillsborough BT26 6RS — MB BCh BAO 1989 Belf.; FRCS Ed. 1993; FRCSI 1993.

KHOT, Alexander Sharen Suresh The Surgery, 27-29 Links Road, Portslade, Brighton BN41 1XH Tel: 01273 412585 Fax: 01273 885800; 76 St. Leonards Road, Hove BN3 4QS Tel: 01273 276013 — MB BChir 1977 Camb.; DCH Eng. 1980.

***KHOUBEHI, Bijan** 7 March Court, Warwick Drive, London SW15 6LE; 11 Warwick House, Windsor Way, 46 Brook Green, London W14 0UQ — MB BS 1994 Lond.

KHOURY, Fawaz St Nicholas Surgery, Queen Street, Withernsea HU19 2PZ Tel: 01964 613221 Fax: 01964 613960; The Elms, 4 Church View, Patrington, Hull HU12 0SQ Tel: 01964 30796 — MD 1973 Damascus. (Damascus) Socs: Yorks. Thoracic Soc. & Hull Med. Soc. Prev: Regist. (Chest Med.) Castle Hill Hosp. & Hull Roy. Infirm.; SHO (Gen. Med.) Salford Gp. Hosps. (T). & Manch Univ. Dept. Med.; SHO (Gen. Med.) Leicester Gen. Hosp.

KHOURY, Mr George Alexander Conquest Hospital, The Ridge, St Leonards-on-Sea TN37 7RD — MB BS 1973 Lond.; MS Lond. 1984; FRCS Eng. 1979. (St. Geo.) Cons. Surg. Conquest Hosp. St. Leonards-on-Sea. Socs: Brit. Soc. Gastroenterol.; Assn. Coloproctol.; Brit. Assn. Surg. Oncol. Prev: Sen. Regist. Roy. Free Hosp. Lond.; Regist. (Surg.) Roy. Free & St. Mary's Hosps. Lond.; SHO (Surg.) St. Geo. Hosp. Lond.

KHOURY, Ghassan George Samaan St. Mary's Hospital, Milton Road, Portsmouth PO3 6AD Tel: 023 92 822331 Fax: 023 92 866313 — MB BS 1978 Lond.; MRCP (UK) 1981; FRCR 1985; FRCP 1998. Cons. Radiother. & Oncol. St. Mary's Hosp. Portsmouth, K. Edwd. VII Hosp. Midhurst & St. Richard's Hosp. Chichester W. Sussex. Socs: Radiother. Co-operat. Gp. Europ. Org. for Research; Brit. Gyn. Cancer Soc. Prev: Lect. & Hon. Sen. Regist. (Radiother.) Cookridge Hosp. Leeds; Regist. (Radiother. & Oncol.) Velindre Hosp. Cardiff; SHO (Radiother. & Oncol.) Roy. Marsden Hosp. Sutton Surrey.

KHOURY, Ghassan Wadie 35 Iverna Court, Wrights Lane, High Street Kensington, London W8 — MD 1979 Amer. Univ. Beirut.

KHOW, Goay Meng Claudy Health Centre, Irwin Crescent, Claudy, Londonderry BT47 4AB Tel: 028 7133 8371 — MB BCh BAO 1978 Dub.; MB BCh Dub. 1978. Gen. Pract.; Med. Off. (Family Plann.).

KHRAISHI, Mr Dirar Mustafa Muhammad Said 79 Aragon Drive, Hainault, Ilford IG6 2TJ Tel: 01708 891658 — MB BS 1984 Punjab; FRCS Ed. 1989.

KHUDADOS, Etedal Suliaman Said Flat 5, Lakeview, London Road, Ascot SL5 8DH — MB BCh BAO 1983 NUI; LRCPI & LM, LRCSI & LM BAO 1983; FRCS Eng. 1987; MD thesis Manch. 1997.

KHULLAR, Puja Flat 15 J, Stuart Tower, 105 Maida Vale, London W9 1UL — MB BS 1993 Lond.

KHULLAR, Sanjiv Kumar Derby City Hospital, Uttoxeter New Road, Derby DE22 3NE Tel: 01332 40131; 2 Lister Close, Uttozxeter New Road, Derby DE22 3NA — MB BS 1981 Delhi; MRCP (UK) 1987.

KHULLAR, Vikram Dept. of Obstetrics & Gynaecology, Mint Wing, St Mary's Hospital, Norfolk Place, London W2 2YP Tel: 020 7886 1061 Fax: 020 7886 6054 Email: vik.khullar@ic.ac.uk — MB BS 1988 Lond.; MD 2000; BSc 1985 Lond.; MRCOG 1996; AKC 1985. (King's Coll. Hosp.) Cons. Gynaecologist, St. Mary's Hosp., Lond. Socs: (Counc.) Roy. Soc. Med.; Blair Bell Res. Soc.; Internat. Continence Soc. (Advisery Bd. Mem.). Prev: Subspecialty Trainee (Urogyn.) King's Coll. Hosp. Lond.; Regist. Edgware Hosp. Middlx.; Regist. Whittington Hosp. & Roy. Free Hosp. Lond.

KHULUSI, Samim 32 Ashbury Road, Battersea, London SW11 5UJ — MB ChB 1987 Bristol; BSc (Hons.) Bristol 1984; MRCP (UK) 1990. Regist. (Med.) St. Geo. Hosp. Lond. Prev: SHO N.wick Pk. Hosp. Harrow. Middlx.

KHUMRI, Aymen 3 Goring Road, London N11 2BU — MB BS 1996 Lond.

KHUNGER, Abnash Chander Somerset Surgery, Somerset Road, Stoke-on-Trent ST1 2BH Tel: 01782 212192 — MB BS 1968 Panjab.

KHUNTI, Kamlesh Winstanley Drive Surgery, 138 Winstanley Drive, Leicester LE3 1PB Tel: 0116 285 8435 Fax: 0116 275 5416 — MB BCh 1984 Dundee; MD 2000 Leicester; FRCGP 1995, M 1989; DRCOG 1988; DCH RCP Lond. 1987. Lect. (Gen. Pract.) Leicester; Sen. Lect. (Gen. Pract.) Leicester. Prev: Trainee GP Lancaster VTS; Ho. Off. (Med. & Surg.) Profess. Unit Ninewells Hosp. Dundee.

KHUNTI, Pratima Freemen's Common Health Centre, 161 Welford Road, Leicester LE2 6BF Tel: 0116 255 4776 Fax: 0116 254 9518; Gresham House, 156 Evington Lane, Leicester LE5 6DG — MB ChB 1985 Dundee; MRCGP 1989; DRCOG 1988. Prev: Trainee GP Lancaster VTS.

KHURAIJAM, Gourashyam Singh Noble's Hospital, Douglas IM1 4QA Tel: 01624 642126 Fax: 01624 642498; 12 Cronk Drean, Douglas IM2 6AY Tel: 01624626155 Fax: 01624 642498 Email: samema.khuraijam@virgin.net — MB BS Delhi 1966; BSc (Hons.) Gauhati 1961; MD Delhi 1973; FRCP Lond. 1996; FRCP Ed. 1994; FRCP Glas. 1992; MRCP (UK) 1981. Cons. Phys. Noble's Hosp. Douglas Isle of Man. Socs: Fell. Internat. Coll. Angiol, New York. Prev: Regist. (Med. & Geriat.) Noble's Hosp. Douglas; Asst. Prof. Med. Regional Med. Coll. Imphal, India.

KHURANA, Anand St Thomas Street South Surgery, 2 St. Thomas Street South, Oldham OL8 1SG Tel: 0161 665 3488 Fax: 0161 620 5510; 10 Pexwood, Chadderton, Oldham OL1 2TS — MB BS 1963 Delhi. (Lady Hardinge Med. Coll.) Clin. Asst. (Psychiat.) Prestwich Hosp. Manch.

KHURANA, Chander Small Burnside, Polmont, Falkirk FK2 0YD — MB BS 1963 All India Inst. Med. Scs. Prev: Gen. Duties Med. Off. Kota, India; Asst. Med. Off. Centr. Hosp. New Delhi; Regist. (Cas.) Roy. Alexandra Infirm. Paisley.

KHURANA, Mr Ish Kumar Small Burnside Cottage, Polmont, Falkirk FK2 0YD Tel: 01324 715711 — MB BS 1960 Lucknow; MS (Surg.) Lucknow 1963, MB BS 1960. Socs: BMA; Brit. Med. Acupunc. Soc. Prev: Ho. Surg. & Demonst. Surg. Med. Coll. Kanpur; Asst. Med. Off. Centr. Hosp. New Delhi.

KHURANA, Jagdish Chander St Thomas Street South Surgery, 2 St. Thomas Street South, Oldham OL8 1SG Tel: 0161 665 3488 Fax: 0161 620 5510; (Surgery) 2 St. Thomas St. Sth., Oldham OL8 1SG Tel: 0161 665 3488 — MB BS 1961 Vikram; Dip. Dermat. Delhi 1969. (Gandhi Med. Coll. Bhopal) Clin. Asst. (Dermat.) Oldham & Dist. Gen. Hosp.

KHURANA, Krishan Mohan Clinic Centre, Central Road, Partington, Urmston, Manchester M31 4FL Tel: 0161 775 7033 Fax: 0161 775 8411; 8 Wychwood Bowdon, Altrincham WA14 3DP Tel: 0161 929 0383 — MB BS 1956 Lucknow; DMRD Eng. 1962; DMRE Bombay 1958. (King Geo. Med. Coll. Lucknow) Prev: Cons. Radiol. Colonial War Memor. Hosp. Suva, Fiji; Cons. Radiol. Lusaka & Ndula Hosps., Zambia; Regist. (Radiol.) Norf. & Norwich Hosp.

KHURANA, Madhuri Brooks Bar Medical Centre, 162-164 Chorlton Road, Old Trafford, Manchester M16 7WW Tel: 0161 226 7777 Fax: 0161 232 9963 — MB BS 1971 Delhi; MRCOG 1980.

KHURANA, Prabha Stantonbury Health Centre, Purbeck, Stantonbury, Milton Keynes MK14 6BL Tel: 01908 316262; 51 Wentworth Way, Bletchley, Milton Keynes MK3 7RW Tel: 01908 374444 — MB BS Bombay 1963; DGO CPS Bombay 1965. (Grant Med. Coll.) Prev: Hosp. Practitioner in Gyn.

KHURANA, Rohit 10 Pexwood, Chadderton, Oldham OL1 2TS — MB BCh 1996 Oxf.; MB BCh Oxf 1996.

KHURANA, Vineet 1 Green Wood, Kinross KY13 8FG — MB ChB 1988 Ed.; LLB 1995; MRCGP 1992; DCCH RCP Ed. 1993; DRCOG 1991.

KHURJEKAR, Sachin 118 Brampton Grove, Harrow HA3 8LF Tel: 020 8930 4750 Fax: 020 8930 4750 Email: skhurj@dircon.co.uk — MB BS 1993 Lond. (UCH/Middlx.) SHO (Otolaryng.) Chase Farm NHS Trust. Socs: BMA. Prev: SHO (Orthop. Surg.) Chase Farm NHS Trust; SHO (Cardiothoracic Surg.) Harefield Hosp.

KHURSHID, Mian Nasim 6 Ascot Parade, Clapham Park Road, London SW4 7EY Tel: 020 8674 3013 — MB BS 1969 Lond.; LMSSA Lond. 1954. (St. Bart.) Prev: Ho. Surg. Whipps Cross Hosp. Lond.; Ho. Phys. Poole Hosp. Nunthorpe; Med. Off. I.C.I. Pakistan.

KHWAJA, Asim 31 Derwent Road, Harpenden AL5 3PA — MD 1994 Lond.; MB BS Lond. 1984; MRCP (UK) 1987; MRCPath 1994. (Guy's) Lect. & Hon. Sen. Regist. (Haemat.) Univ. Coll. Lond. Med. Sch. Prev: Regist. (Haemat.) Middlx. & Whittington Hosps. Lond.; SHO (Gen. Med.) Lewisham Hosp. Lond.

KHWAJA, Ferhat Anwer 10 Slaithwaite Road, London SE13 6DJ — MB ChB 1988 Birm.; ChB Birm. 1988.

***KHWAJA, Haris** 22 Beechcroft Court, Beechcroft Av, Golders Green, London NW11 8BP Tel: 020 8455 7094 — MB BS 1997 Lond.; BSc (Hons.) 1994; MBBS (Hons) 1997; MRCS (Part I) 1999.

KHWAJA, Masum Gulnawaz West End Community Mental Health Team, Soho Centre for Health & Care, 3rd Floor, 1 Frith Street, London W1D 3HZ Tel: 0207 534 6685 Fax: 0207 534 6643 — MB BS 1989 Lond.; MRCPsych 1996. (Charing Cross and Westminster) Cons. Psychiat., Gen. Adult Psychiat., Brent, Kensington, Chelsea and W.m. Ment. Health NHS Trust. Prev: Specialist Regist. (Spychiatry of Subst. Misuse) Chelsea & W.minster Hosp. Lond.

KHWAJA, Mr Mohammed Saleem 10 Whins Crest, Lostock, Bolton BL6 4NH Tel: 01204 45912 — MB BS 1963 Sind; FRCS Ed. 1966; FACS 1988.

KHWAJA, Nadeem 3 Pexwood, Chadderton, Oldham OL1 2TS — MB ChB 1995 Manch.

KHWAJA, Salim Arif Imam 19 Ferndale Grove, Bradford BD9 4LE — MB BS 1992 Lond.

KIAN, Kaveh Flat 1, 8 John Maurice Close, London SE17 1PY Email: kaveh23@yahoo.com — MB BS 1996 Lond.

KIANA, Soultana 15 Stevenstone Close, Leicester LE2 4TF — Ptychio Iatrikes 1980 Thessalonika; MSc Manch. 1995; MRCPsych 1990. Cons. Child & Adolesc. Psychiat. N.ampton NHS Trust. Socs: Assn. Child Psychiat. & Psychols. Prev: Sen. Regist. (Child & Adolesc. Psychiat.) Leicester Univ. & Trent RHA; Regist. & SHO Rotat. (Psychiat.) Manch.; Cons. (Child & Adolesc. Psychiat.) Solihull NHS Trust.

KIANI, Sujad Haider 127 Drewry Lane, Derby DE22 3QS; 46 Osmaston Road, Leicester LE5 5JF Tel: 0116 273 8027 — MB ChB 1990 Leic.; FRCA 1996. (Leicester) Specialist Regist. (Anaesth.) Leicester Gp. Hosps.

KIBBLER, Christopher Charles Royal Free Hospital, Pond St., London NW3 2QG Tel: 020 7794 0500 — MB BS 1979 Camb.; FRCP 1997; FRCPath 1997; MA Camb. 1980; MRCP (UK) 1982; MRCPath 1989. Cons. Med. Microbiol. Roy. Free Hosp. Lond.

KIBBLER, Malcolm Arthur Robert Ranworth, Pier Avenue, Clacton-on-Sea CO15 Tel: 01255 422587 — MB BS 1958 Lond. (Char.Cross) Mem. Med. Staff & Asst. Orthop. & Accid. Dept. Clacton & Dist. Hosp.; Mem. Med. Staff Clacton Matern. Hosp. Prev: Ho. Phys. Ho. Surg. & Obst. Off. St. Helier Hosp. Carshalton.

KIBBLEWHITE, Derek George (retired) Hendford Wing, Henford Lodge, 74 Henford, Yeovil Tel: 01935 4353 — MB BS 1951 Lond.; MRCS Eng. LRCP Lond. 1950; DPM Eng. 1974.

KIBERU, Samuel William 187 Surbiton Road, Stockton-on-Tees TS19 7SH Tel: 01642 670831; 187 Surbiton Road, Stockton-on-Tees TS19 7SH Tel: 01642 570831 — MD 1975 Dar-Es-Salaam; FRCPath 1999; PhD 1999; MRCPath 1991. (Dareslam Tanzania) Cons. Path. P. Chas. Hosp. Merthr Tydfil Wales. Socs: Fell.Roy. Coll. of Pathologists. Prev: Cons. Histopath. Saad Med. Center Alghabar, Saudi Arabia; Research Fell. Leicester Roy. Infirm.

KIBIRIGE, Janice Irene 3 Braeside, Kirklevington, Yarm TS15 9NB — MB BS 1981 Newc.

KIBRIA, Mr Shah MD Golam 24 Birkdale Drive, Leeds LS17 7SZ — MB BS 1984 Dacca; FRCS Ed. 1995; FRCS Glas. 1995. Specialist Regist. (Gen. Surg.) York Dist. Hosp.

KICHLU, Jai Kishen (retired) 76 Wood Vale, London N10 3DN Tel: 020 8883 1400 — MB BS 1931 Lucknow.

KIDAMBI, Ananta Venkatachary General Hospital, Hartlepool TS24 9AH Tel: 01429 266654 Fax: 01429 868830; 15 Hardwick Court, Hartlepool TS26 0AZ Tel: 01429 234610 — BSc Nagpur 1963, MB BS 1969; FFR RCSI 1984; FRCR 1976; DMRD Eng. 1976; DMRD Nagpur 1970. (Govt. Med. Coll. Nagpur) Cons. Radiol. Gen. Hosp. Hartlepool. Socs: Fell. Roy. Coll. of Radiiologist; BMA; Fell. Fac.Radiologists. Prev: Cons. Radiol. Altnagelvin Hosp., Lond.derry, N. Irel.

KIDD, Alexa Mary Josephine Dept. Medical Genetics, Aberdeen Royal Infirmary, Aberdeen; 70 Cameron Street, Stonehaven AB39 2HE Email: jon.campbell@zetnet.co.uk — MB BS 1982 Lond.; BSc Lond. 1979; MSc (Med. Genetics) Glas. 1991; MRCP (UK) 1989; MRCGP 1988; DObst NZ 1986; DCH RCP Lond. 1985. Sen. Regist. (Med. Genetics) Aberd. Roy. Infirm. Socs: Clin. Genetics Soc.; Roy. Coll. Phys.s, Edin. Prev: Regist. (Paediat.) Invercargill NZ; Trainee GP Halesworth Suff. VTS; Trainee GP Oban Argyll VTS.

KIDD, Alison Mary Ballygomartin Group Practice, 17 Ballygomartin Road, Belfast BT13 3BW; 10 Lynda Gardens, Newtownabbey BT37 0NP Tel: 01232 861243 — MB ChB 1991 Ed.; DMH Belf. 1994; DGM RCP Lond. 1993. Trainee GP Belf.

KIDD, Amelia Lucy 23 Cowley Road, London SW14 8QD — MB BS 1993 Lond.

KIDD, Antony John Middlestown Health Centre, Ramsey Crescent, Middlestown, Wakefield WF4 4QQ Tel: 01924 272121 — MB BS 1983 Newc.

KIDD, Barbara Caroline 110 Liverpool Road, Crosby, Liverpool L23 5TG — MB ChB 1983 Liverp.; DA (UK) 1989. Staff Anaesth. Halton Trust.

KIDD, Betty (retired) 10 Whitehouse Road, Stockton-on-Tees TS22 5ES Tel: 01642 554373 — MB Camb. 1954, BChir 1953; MRCS Eng. LRCP Lond. 1954. Prev: SCMO Family Plann. N. Tees HA.

KIDD, Bruce Lindsay Bone and Joint Unit, St. Bartholomew's and Royal London Hospital School Medicine, Turner St., London E1 2AD Tel: 020 7377 7764 Fax: 020 7377 7763 Email: b.l.kidd@mds.qmw.ac.uk; Department of Rheumatology, Royal London Hospital (Mile End), Bancroft Road, London E1 4DG Tel: 020 7377 7859 — MB ChB 1976 Auckland; DM Soton. 1990; FRCP Lond. 1996; FRACP 1986. Reader St Bartholomews & Roy. Lond. Hosp. Sch. Med.; Cons. Rheum. Roy. Lond. Hosp. Prev: Sen. Regist. & Lect. (Rheum.) Lond. Hosp. Med. Coll.; Sen. Regist. Auckland Hosp., NZ.

KIDD, Caroline Anne Lochgelly Health Centre, David Street, Lochgelly KY5 9QZ Tel: 01592 780277 Fax: 01592 784044; 79 Scotland Drive, Dunfermline KY12 7TW Tel: 01383 737786 — MB ChB 1987 Ed.

KIDD, Catherine Mary Theresa Wirral and West Cheshire Community NHS Trust, St. Catherine's Hospital, Church Road, Birkenhead CH42 0LQ Tel: 0151 604 7290 Fax: 0151 670 1223 — MB BCh BAO 1973 Dub.; BA Dub. 1973; MBA (Health Exec.) Keele

Univ. 1996; MFFP 1993. (Trinity Coll. Dub.) Cons. Family Plann. Wirral & W. Chesh. NHS Trust; Dep. Ref. for Cremat.s, Wirral Boro. Counc.. Socs: Fac. Family Plann.; Comm. Mem., N. W.. Soc. Sexual Med. & Family Plann.; Chairm., Mersey Region Gp. for Family Plann. Train. Prev: SCMO Wom. Serv. Wirral HA; Clin. Med. Off. Chester HA; Ho. Phys. & Ho. Surg. Sir P. Dun's Hosp. Dub.

KIDD, Charlotte Elizabeth Cumberland Infirmary, Carlisle CA2 7HY Tel: 01228 523444; 213 Brampton Road], Carlisle CA3 9AX — MB BS 1992 Newc.; MRCP (UK) 1995. Cons. Rhematologist Cumbld. Infimary, Carlisle. Socs: BMA; Brit. Soc. of Rheum.; Brit. Paediatric Rheum. Gp. Prev: Specialist Regist. (Rheum.) Freeman Hosp. Newc. upon Tyne; Specialist Regist. (Rheum.) Dryburn Hosp. Durh.; Specialist Regist. (Rheum. and Gen. Med.) S. Cleveland Hosp. Middlesbrough.

KIDD, Charlotte Mary Student Health Centre, Manchester Metropolitan University, Lower Chatham St., Manchester M15 6HA Tel: 0161 247 3522 — MB BS 1988 Lond.; DRCOG 1994. (St. George's) Socs: Diplomate Fac. Fam. Plann. & Reproduc. Health Care. Prev: SHO (Anaesth.) Ashford Hosp. Middlx.; SHO (Paediat.) Alder Hey Childr. Hosp. Liverp.; SHO (O & G) Sharoe Green Hosp. Preston.

KIDD, David Walter (retired) 58 Edzell Drive, Newton Mearns, Glasgow G77 5QY — LRCP LRCS Ed. LRFPS Glas. 1951. Prev: Ho. Surg. (Plastic Unit) Ballochmyle Hosp.

KIDD, Desmond Patrick Campbell Cecil The Royal Free Hospital, London NW3 Tel: 020 7794 0500 Fax: 020 7431 1577 Email: d.kidd@rfc.ucl.co.uk — MB BCh BAO 1986 Belf.; MD Belf. 1995; MRCP (UK) 1989. Cons. Neurol. Roy. Free Hosp. Lond. Socs: Assn. Brit. Neurol.; Eur. Neurol. Soc.; Roy. Soc. Med. Prev: Regist. (Neurol.) Nat. Hosp. Neurol. & Neurosurg. Lond.; Regist. (Neurol.) St. Thos. Hosp. Lond.; Clin. Asst. (Neurol.) Nat. Hosp. Lond.

KIDD, George Mervyn 7 Bertram Drive, Meols, Wirral CH47 0LG — MB BCh BAO 1971 Dub.; FRCOG 1994, M 1977; MFFP 1993. Cons. O & G Liverp. Wom. Hosp. Prev: Sen. Regist. (O & G) Mersey RHA; Asst. Master Coombe Lying in Hosp. Dub.; Ho. Phys. Sir Patrick Dun's Hosp. Dub.

KIDD, Graham Terence Barton 119 Elsenham Street, Southfields, London SW18 5NY — MB BS 1970 Lond.; MRCPsych. 1981. Cons. Psychiat. St. Peter's Hosp. Chertsey.

KIDD, Hugh McPherson (retired) 1 Lismore Grove, Buxton SK17 9AW Tel: 01298 23316 — MB ChB 1952 Sheff.; BA Open. Univ. 1989; MRCS Eng. LRCP Lond. 1953; MRCGP 1960. Prev: Med. Ref. Brit. Sub-Aqua Club.

KIDD, Jane Logan c/o Roupsend, Kilmory Road, Lochgilphead PA31 8SZ Tel: 01546 603923 — MB ChB 1977 Glas.; DRCOG 1981. Prev: Med. Dir. Luther St. Med. Centre (Health Centre for the Homeless) Oxf.

KIDD, Jane Louise 3 Beechwood Drive, Skipton BD23 1TY — MB BS 1998 Newc.; MB BS Newc 1998.

KIDD, John Dennys (retired) Flat 1, Beech House, 48 Station Road, Marlow SL7 1NN Tel: 01628 478416 — MB BChir Camb. 1940; FRCP Lond. 1965, M 1947. Prev: Phys. Reading & High Wycombe Hosp. Gps.

KIDD, Juliet Theresa The Old Vicarage, Southburn, Driffield YO25 9ED — MB ChB 1993 Leeds.

KIDD, Kenneth Roland 6 Partridge Walk, Lilliput, Poole BH14 8HL — MB ChB 1951 Bristol; MRCGP 1980; DRCOG 1955. Prev: Chief of Primary Care & Emerg. Serv. K. Faisal Milit. Hosp. Jeddah; Clin. Tutor (Primary Care) Riyadh Milit. Hosp.

KIDD, Lorna Christine 8 Daleside Road, Harrogate HG2 9JE — MB ChB 1976 Dundee; FRCOG 1996, M 1981. Cons. O & G Harrogate Healthcare NHS Trust.

KIDD, Mr Martin Norman Kent County Ophthalmic Hospital, Church St., Maidstone ME14 1DT Tel: 01622 673444 — MB BCh BAO 1978 Belf.; FRCS Ed. 1983; FRCOphth. 1989. Cons. Ophth., Kent Co. Hosp., Maidstone.

KIDD, Mary Lytle (retired) 1 Lismore Grove, Buxton SK17 9AW Tel: 01298 23316 — MB ChB 1952 Sheff.; MRCS Eng. LRCP Lond. 1952; MRCGP 1960. Prev: Cas. Off. & ENT Ho. Surg. Roy. Infirm. Sheff.

KIDD, Michael Department of Anatomy, St George's Hospital Medical School, Cranmer Terrace, London SW17 0RE Tel: 020 8729 5224 Fax: 020 8725 3326 Email: mkidd@sghms.ac.uk — BSc (Anat.) Lond. 1953, MB BS 1956. (Univ. Coll. Hosp.) Hon Research Fell. St Geo.'s Hosp. Med. Sch. Socs: Anat. Soc.; Neuropath. Soc.; Fell. Roy. Soc. Med. Prev: LSen. Lect. in Human Morphol. Univ. Nottm.; Asst. Lect. in Anat. Univ. Coll. Lond.; Research Asst. & Hon. Lect. Inst. Neurol. Lond.

KIDD, Michelle 38 Hollocombe Road, Liverpool L12 0RW — MB ChB 1997 Liverp.

KIDD, Paul Henderson 8 Sydenham Road, Glasgow G12 9NP — MB ChB 1981 Glas.

KIDD, Rory John Gareth The Medical Centre, Market St., Whitworth, Rochdale OL12 8QS — MB BS 1993 Lond.

KIDD, Sarah Judith 37 Victoria Street, Englefield Green, Egham TW20 0QX — MB BS 1997 Lond.

KIDD, Sheila Blanche Buckelands, 9 Station Road, Fulbourn, Cambridge CB1 5ER Tel: 01223 880738 — MB BCh 1956 Wales. (Cardiff) Prev: Cons. (Ment. Handicap) Cambs. AHA (T); Asst Psychiat. Ida Darwin Hosp. Fulbourn; Regist. (Psychiat.) Hensol Castle Ment. Defic. Inst.

KIDD, Susan Alison 34 Somerville Close, Bromborough, Wirral CH63 0PH — MB ChB 1987 Liverp.

KIDD, Susan Louise 16/1 Merchiston Gardens, Edinburgh EH10 5DD — MB ChB 1991 Ed.; MRCP Ed. 1995; DTM & H Liverp. 1992. (University of Edinburgh) SHO (Paediat.) Simpson Memor. Matern. Pavil. Edin. Prev: Clin. Research Fell. (Paediat.) Univ. of Edin.; SHO (A & E) Roy. Hosp. for Sick Childr.; SHO (Paediat.) Roy. Hosp. for Sick Childr. Glas.

KIDD, Valerie Elaine Maryhill Road Surgery, 96 Napiershall Street, Maryhill, Glasgow G20 Tel: 0141 211 9597 Fax: 0141 331 0071 — MB ChB 1980 Ed.; MRCGP 1989.

KIDDIE, James Mitchell 1/1 Arboretum Court, 249 Garrioch Road, Glasgow G20 8QZ — MB ChB 1993 Glas.

KIDDLE, Michael William Childrens Services, Rockingham Forest NHS Trust, St Mary's Hospital London Road, Kettering Tel: 01536494708 Fax: 01536 494706 Email: kiddlem@rockhm-tr.anglox.nhs.uk; Churchview, 29 Main Street, Sudborough, Kettering NN14 3BX Tel: 01832 732947 Email: mike.kiddle@btopenworld.com — MB BS Lond. 1966; FRCPCH 1997. (St. Mary's) Clin. Dir. & Cons. Community Paediat. Childr. Serv. N.amptonshire Heartslands PCT; Profess. Adviser (Comm. Child Health) NSPCC. Socs: Assn. Research Child Developm. Prev: Princip. Phys. Child Health Kettering DHA & Alexandra Hse. Child Developm. Centre, P.ss Marina Hosp. N.ampton.

KIDDLE, Veronika Jennetta Poole Hospital NHS Trust, Longfleeb Road, Poole BH15 2JB Tel: 0116 274 5003 Email: veronicakiddle@yahoo.co.uk — MB ChB 1998 Leic.

KIDGER, Timothy Isham House, St. Andrew's Hospital, Billing Road, Northampton NN1 5DG Tel: 01604 616100 — MB BS 1972 Lond.; FRCPsych 1995, M 1977. (Guy's) Cons. Psychiat. Isham Ho., N.ampton. Prev: Sen. Regist. (Psychiat.) York Clinic, Guy's Hosp. Lond.; Sen. Regist. (Psychiat.) St. Olave's Hosp. Lond.; Research Asst. Guy's Hosp. Med. Sch.

KIDMAN, Lucy Victoria New Manor Farmhouse, Forty Acre La, Whiteparish, Salisbury SP5 2QU — BM 1997 Soton.

KIDMAN, Penelope Ann 7 St Edmunds Road, Bebington, Wirral CH63 2QU — MB ChB 1984 Liverp.

KIDMAN, Stephen Paul St Albans Medical Centre, 26-28 St. Albans Crescent, Bournemouth BH8 9EW Tel: 01202 517333 Fax: 01202 517336 — BM 1986 Soton.; MRCGP 1991; Dip Occ. Med. RCP Lond. 1996; DRCOG 1990. (Southampton) Occupat. Med. Adviser Dorset Healthcare Trust Bournemouth. Socs: Assur. Med. Soc.; Soc. Occupat. Med. Prev: Trainee GP E. Dorset VTS; Ho. Phys. Norf. & Norwich Hosp.; Ho. Surg. Roy. United Hosp. Bath.

KIDNER, Sally Buchanan Foreign & Commonwealth Office (Sofia), King Charles St., London SW1A 2AH — MB BS 1992 Lond.; DRCOG 1996; DCH RCP Lond. 1995. Post Doctor Brit. Embassy Sofia, Bulgaria.

KIDNEY, Elizabeth Mary 5 Pontings Close, Blunsdon, Swindon SN26 7AH — MB ChB 1995 Leeds.

KIDSLEY, Sally Gay 8 Pipers Close, Bromsgrove B61 7HG — MB BCh 1994 Wales.

KIDSON, Christopher John 31 Woodrow Park, Grimsby DN33 2EF — MB BS 1993 Newc.

KIDSON, Mr Iain Gordon 25 Richmond Road, New Barnet, Barnet EN5 1SA Tel: 020 8441 3960 Fax: 020 8441 3960 Email: kidson@compuserve.com; 25 Richmond Road, New Barnet, Barnet

EN5 1SA Tel: 020 8441 3960 — MB BChir 1971 Camb.; MA Camb. 1972, MChir 1980; FRCS Eng. 1975; MRCS Eng. LRCP Lond. 1971. (Camb. & St. Geo.) Managem. & Medico-Legal Cons. Prev: Chief Exec. The Whittington Hosp. NHS Trust; Cons. Surg. Whittington & Roy. N.. Hosps.; Hon. Sen. Lect. (Surg.) Univ. Coll. & Middlx. Hosp. Med. Sch. Lond.

KIDWAI, Bakhtiar Jalil Cardiology Directorate, Royal Victoria Hospital, Grosvenor Road, Belfast BT12 6BA — MB BS 1985 Karachi; MRCPI 1990.

KIEHLMANN, Peter Alexander Danestone Medical Centre, Fairview Street, Danestone, Aberdeen AB22 8ZP Tel: 01224 822866 Fax: 01224 707532 — MB ChB 1981 Dundee; MRCGP 1985; DCCH RCP Ed. 1986; DRCOG 1986. Prev: GP Reading; Mem. Hants, Berks. & Surrey Immediate Care Scheme; Med. Off. Kapsowar Hosp. Kenya.

KIEHLMANN, Tricia Ann Danestone Medical Centre, Fairview Street, Danestone, Aberdeen AB22 8ZP Tel: 01224 822866 Fax: 01224 707532 — MB ChB 1981 Dundee.

KIEHN, Barry Cedar Court, 65 Victoria Park, Colwyn Bay LL29 6AL Tel: 01492 532458 Fax: 01492 535030 Email: b.kiehn@talk21.com; 58 Cherry Tree Lane, Colwyn Bay LL28 5YH — MB BS 1972 Lond.; MSc Manch. 1981; MRCPsych 1977. (King's Coll. Univ. Lond.) Cons. Child & Adolesc. Psychiat. N. Wales Adolesc. Serv. Colwyn Bay. Prev: Sen. Regist. (Adolesc. Psychiat.) Young People's Unit Macclesfield; Sen. Regist. (Child & Adolesc. Psychiat.) Booth Hall Hosp. Manch.; Regist. (Psychiat.) Univ. Hosp. S. Manch.

KIEL, Andrew William 5 Higher Downs, Altrincham WA14 2QL — BM BS 1991 Nottm.

KIEL, Azing Leendert Martinus Hundon Hall, Hall Road, Hundon, Sudbury CO10 8EY — Artsexamen 1988 Free U Amsterdam; Artsexamen Free Univ Amsterdam 1988.

KIEL, James Edward 5 Higher Downs, Altrincham WA14 2QL — MB BS 1992 Lond.

KIELTY, Peter Francis 18 Salisbury Avenue, Harpenden AL5 2QG Tel: 01582 713925 — MRCS Eng. LRCP Lond. 1962; MRCGP (Hon) 1994. (King's Coll. Hosp.) Socs: Trustee BMA Foundat. for AIDS; Past Mem. BMA Counc. & Finance Comm.; Past Jt Dep. Chairm. GMSC. Prev: GMP Hardpenden; Med. Adviser Herts. Area Health Auth.

KIELTY, Robert Andrew Globetown Surgery, 82-86 Roman Road, Bethnal Green, London E2 0PG Email: globetown@aol.com — MB ChB 1991 Manch.

KIELTY, Vincent John 38 Hendon Hall Court, Parson St., London NW4 1QY — MB BS 1977 Lond.; MRCS Eng. LRCP Lond. 1977. (Guy's) SHO (A & E Dept.) Lewisham Hosp. Lond. Prev: Ho. Surg. Lewisham Hosp. Lond; Ho. Phys. New Cross Hosp. Lond.

KIELY, David Gerard 28 Dalbeattie Road, Dumfries DG2 7PL — MB ChB 1991 Ed.

KIELY, Mr Edward Matthew St Gerard Hospital for Sick Children, Great Ormond St., London WC1N 3JH Tel: 020 7405 9200 Fax: 020 7813 8428 Email: edwardkiely@yahoo.co.uk; 19 Chartfield Avenue, Putney, London SW15 6DX Tel: 020 8788 5061 — MB BCh BAO 1968 NUI; FRCS Eng. 1975; FRCSI 1974. (Cork) Cons. Paediat. Surg. Hosp. Sick Childr. Gt. Ormond St. Lond. Prev: Sen. Regist. (Paediat. Surg.) Hosp for Sick Childr. Gt. Ormond St. Lond.; Sen. Surg. (Paediat.Surg.) Johannesburg Hosp.; Surg. Regist. Childr. Hosp. Birm.

KIELY, Gerard Patrick 63 Birdhall Road, Cheadle Hulme, Cheadle SK8 5QE — MB ChB 1991 Manch.

KIELY, Mary Therese Huddersfield Roy. Infirm., Acre Street, Lindley, Huddersfield HD3 3EA Tel: 0114 230 1646, 01484 342965 Fax: 01484 347068 Email: jemoody@dial.pipex.com — MB BCh BAO 1988 Belf.; MRCGP 1992; DRCOG 1991; Dip. Ethics Keele 1997. (Queens Uni. Belfast) Cons In Palliat. Care Team, Huddersfield Roy. Infirm. Prev: Specialist Regist. (Palliat. Med.) Yorks. Region.

KIELY, Nigel Terence 11 Durell Gardens, Dagenham RM9 5XX — BM BS 1991 Nottm.

KIELY, Nuala Mary 25B Carlingford Road, London NW3 1RY — MB BS 1990 Lond.

KIELY, Patrick David Wolfenden Department of Rheumatology, St George's Healthcare, Blackshaw Road, London SW17 0QT Tel: 020 8725 2109 Fax: 020 8725 3297 — MB BS 1988 Lond.; PhD (Camb.) 1997; BSc (1st cl. Hons.) Lond. 1985; MRCP (UK) 1991. (Middlx. Hosp.) Cons. (Rheum. & Gen. Med.) St. Geo.'s Healthcare NHS Trust Lond. Socs: Brit. Soc. Rheum.; Brit. Soc. Immunol. Prev: Sen. Regist. (Rheum. & Gen. Med.) St. Geo.'s Healthcare NHS Trust Lond.; Sen. Regist. (Gen. Med. & Rheum.) St. Helier NHS Trust Carshalton; MRC Train. Fell. (Med.) Univ. Camb.

KIERAN, Diarmuid Niall Brian Cottingham Medical Centre, 17-19 South Street, Cottingham HU16 4AJ Tel: 01482 845078 Fax: 01482 845078; 49 Redland Drive, Kirk Ella, Hull HU10 7UX Tel: 01482 658991 — MB BCh BAO 1979 NUI; Cert. Family Plann. JCC 1983; DRCOG 1983. (Univ. Coll. Dub.) Med. Off. Humberside Fire Brig.

KIERAN, John Desmond Murphy (retired) Tara, 6 Grange Close, Lowton, Warrington WA3 1JS — LRCPI & LM, LRSCI & LM 1936; LRCPI & LM, LRCSI & LM 1936. Prev: Med. Off. Cott. Hosp. Newton le Willows.

KIERAN, William John Gerard Greencroft Medical Centre (South), Greencroft Wynd, Annan DG12 6GS Tel: 01461 202244 Fax: 01461 205401 — MB BCh BAO 1980 NUI; LRCPI & LM, LRCSI & LM BAO 1980; MRCGP 1985.

KIERNAN, Emma Jane Aylesbury Partnership, Aylesbury Medical Centre, Taplow House, Thurlow Street, London SE17 2XE Tel: 020 7703 2205 — MB BCh BAO 1989 NUI; LRCPI 1989.

KIERNAN, John Alan c/o Department of Anatomy, Medical Sciences Building, University of Western Ontario, London ON N6A 5C1, Canada Tel: 00 1 519 6612111 Fax: 00 1 519 6613936 Email: kiernan@uwo.ca; 231 Western Road, Crookes, Sheffield S10 1LE Tel: 0114 266 6696 — MB ChB 1966 Birm.; PhD Birm. 1969, BSc 1963, DSc 1979; MA Camb. 1969; MRCS Eng. LRCP Lond. 1966. (Birm.) Prof. Anat. Univ. W.. Ontario Lond., Canada; Trustee Biological Stain Commiss. USA 1995-. Socs: Fell. Roy. Microscopical Soc.; Camb. Philosophical Soc.; Neurosci. Assn. Prev: Sen. Research Fell. Sidney Sussex Coll. Camb.; MRC Research Fell. (Anat.) Birm. Med. Sch.; Ho. Surg. (Accid. & Emerg.) E. Birm. Hosp.

KIERNAN, Patrick Joseph Scarsdale Place Medical Centre, 2 Scarsdale Place, London W8 5SX Tel: 020 7938 1887 Fax: 020 8376 2784 — MB ChB 1976 Liverp.; MRCGP 1996. (Liverp.) Course Organiser St. Mary's Lond. GP VTS; Exec. Mem. of PCG.

KIERNAN, Susan Jaqueline Rachel Fountayne Road Health Centre, 1A Fountayne Road, London N16 7EA Tel: 020 8806 3311 Fax: 020 8806 9197; 36 Park Avenue S., London N8 8LT Tel: 020 8340 4712 — MB ChB 1980 Glas.; DRCOG 1988; DA (UK) 1985.

KIERNAN, Thomas Francis Rathmore Clinic, Cliff Road, Belleek, Enniskillen BT93 3FY Tel: 028 6865 8382 Fax: 028 6865 8124 — MB BCh BAO 1977 NUI; MRCGP 1982; DCH RCPSI 1980; DObst RCPI 1979.

KIERNAN, Wolfgang Edward Sergei (retired) 39 Donovan Avenue, London N10 2JU — MB BCh BAO 1955 Belf.; FRCP Ed. 1971, M 1959; FRCP Glas. 1983, M 1981; FRCPsych 1975, M 1971; Dip Psych Ed. 1960. Hon. Clin. Lect. (Psychol. Med.) Univ. Glas.; Mem. WHO Expert Comm. on Ment. Health. Prev: Phys. Supt. & Cons. Psychiat. Gartnavel Roy. Hosp. Glas.

KIFF, Mr Edward Smalley 135 Palatine Road, Didsbury, Manchester M20 3YA Tel: 0161 445 0127 Fax: 0161 232 2441; 33 Pine Road, Didsbury, Manchester M20 6UZ — MD 1985 Manch.; MB ChB 1974; FRCS Eng. 1978. (Manch.) Cons. Gen. Surg. S. Manch. Univ. Hosp. Trust. Prev: Sen. Regist. (Gen. Surg.) Manch. Roy. Infirm.; Research Fell. St. Marks Hosp. Lond.; Ho. Surg. & Ho. Phys. Manch. Roy. Infirm.

KIFF, Kevin Mark 1 Aldeburgh Way, Chelmsford CM1 7PB Tel: 01245 350464 Email: 100660.744@compuserve.com — MB BS 1986 Lond.; MRCP (UK) 1989; FRCA 1993. Cons. Anaesth. & Intens. Care Broomfield Hosp. Chelmsford. Socs: ICS; ESICM.

KIFF, Martin Laurence Wylcwm Street Surgery, 3 Wylcwm Street, Knighton LD7 1AD Tel: 01547 528523 Fax: 01547 529347 — MB BS 1981 Lond.; BSc Lond. 1978, MB BS 1981; MRCGP 1985; DGM RCP Lond. 1988; DRCOG 1983. (St. Thos.)

KIFF, Peter Stuart 109 Sheerstock, Haddenham, Aylesbury HP17 8EY Tel: 01844 290920 — BM BCh 1977 Oxf.; MA, BM BCh Oxf. 1977; MRCP (UK) 1979. (St. Thos.)

KIFF, Mr Robert Smalley Spring Vale, Moorside Lane, Parkgate, Neston, South Wirral CH64 6QP Tel: 0151 426 1600 Email: rob@svale.demon.co.uk — MB ChB 1977 Manch.; ChM Manch.

1991; FRCS Ed. 1982; FRCS (Gen.) 1997. Cons. (Gen. Surg.) Whiston Hospita. Prev: Sen. Regist. Messey Region; Regist. Stepping Hill Hosp. Stockport; SHO (Surg.) Manch. Roy. Infirm.

KILARU, Naga Panender Prasad Hawthorn Medical Centre, May Close, Swindon SN2 1UU Tel: 01793 536541 Fax: 01793 421049 — MB BS 1973 Osmania; DGM RCP Lond. 1986.

KILBANE, Mary Paula Jane King Eastern Health & Social Services Board, Champion House, 12-22 Linenhall St., Belfast BT2 8BS Tel: 01232 321313 Fax: 01232 321520 Email: pkilbane@ehssb.n-i.nhs.uk; Quiet Waters, 47 Warrenpoint Road, Rostrevor, Newry BT34 3EB — MB BCh BAO 1973 Belf.; MSc (Soc. Med.) Lond. 1978; FFPHM RCP (UK) 1988, M 1979. Chief Exec. E. HSSB. Prev: Chief Exec. & Dir. (Pub. Health) S.. HSSB.

KILBEY, John Howard 18 The Rise, Sevenoaks TN13 1RQ — MB BS 1979 Lond.; BSc Lond. 1976, MB BS 1979; MRCP (UK) 1984; FRCR 1993.

KILBEY, Richard Stanley Department of Cardiology, Musgrove Park Hospital, Taunton TA1 5DA — MB ChB 1980 Sheff.; BMedSci Sheff. 1979, MB ChB 1980; MRCP (UK) 1984; MRCGP 1986. Assoc. Specialist (Cardiol.) MusGr. Pk. Hosp. Taunton. Prev: Regist. (Med.) Waikato Hosp., NZ.; Trainee GP/SHO Sheff. HA; Regist. (Med.) Hallamsh. Hosp. Sheff.

***KILBORN, Hannah Joyce** The Old Rectory, Old Quay Lane, St Germans, Saltash PL12 5LH — MB ChB 1997 Bristol.

KILBORN, John Robert 27 Harley Street, London W1N 1DA Tel: 020 7255 1818 Fax: 020 7255 1817 Email: jkilborn@uk.watrail.com; 2 Moreton End Lane, Harpenden AL5 2EX Tel: 01582 712500 Fax: 01582 760072 — MB BS 1969 Newc.; PhD Newc. 1966, BSc 1961, MB BS 1969; FFPM RCP (UK) 1989. (Newc.) Vice-Pres. Europ. Operat.s, Worldwide Clin. Trials Ltd, Pharmaceut. Research.

KILBURN, Julian Richard 31 Hazelwood Avenue, West Jesmond, Newcastle upon Tyne NE2 3HU — MB BS 1992 Newc.

KILBURN, Mr Peter (retired) Langdale, Clifford Avenue, Middleton, Ilkley LS29 0AS Tel: 01943 609405 — MB ChB 1948 Liverp.; MChOrth 1955; FRCS Ed. 1953; FICS 1977. Cons. Orthop. Surg. Airedale Gen. Hosp., Skipton Gen. Hosp., Ilkley Coronation Hosp. & Woodlands Orthop. Hosp. Rawdon; Cons. Orthop. Surg. Leeds & W. Riding CC & Sch. Health Serv.; Lect. (Orthop. Path.) Univ. Liverp.; Examr. in Surg. Assn. Occupat. Theraps.; Examr. Part 1 FRCSEd. (Path.); Maj. RAMC/AER. Prev: Sen. Orthop. Regist. Liverp. Roy. Infirm. & Roy. Liverp. Childr.

KILBY, Anne Margaret University College Hospital, Paediatric Department, Gower St., London WC1E 6AU Tel: 020 7387 9300; 114 Middleton Road, London E8 4LP Tel: 020 7249 2998 — MB BChir 1969 Camb.; MA, MB Camb. 1969, BChir 1969; FRCP 1990; MRCP (UK) 1973. (Camb. & Univ. Coll. Hosp.) Cons. (Paediat.) Middlx. Hosp. & Univ. Coll. Hosp. Lond. Prev: Sen. Clin. Lect. (p/t) (Paediat.) Whittington Hosp. Lond.; Research Sen. Regist. (Paediat.) Univ. Coll. Hosp. Lond.

KILBY, Mr David 90 Beach Road, North Shields NE30 2QP — MB ChB 1963 Sheff.; MB ChB (Hons.) Sheff. 1963; FRCS Eng. 1969. (Sheff.) Cons. Otolaryngol. Newc. upon Tyne Univ. Hosps. Prev: Research Fell. in Otol. Dept. Otolaryngol. Wayne State Univ. Michigan,USA; SHO (Otolaryngol.) Roy. Hosp. Sheff. Ho. Surg. & Ho. Phys. Sheff.

KILBY, Fiona Kathryn Middlewich Road Surgery, 163-165 Middlewich Road, Northwich CW9 7DB Tel: 01606 43850; 12 Parker Avenue, Hartford, Northwich CW8 3AH Tel: 01606 74215 — MB ChB 1988 Manch.; MRCGP 1992; DRCOG 1991. (Manchester) GP Princip. Socs: BMA; Med. Protec. Soc. Prev: Trainee GP Fulwood Preston; SHO (O & G) Sharoe Green Hosp. Preston; SHO (Med. & Paediat.) Roy. Preston Hosp.

KILBY, Mr John Oliver Greenaway, Lower Washwell Lane, Stroud GL6 6XW Tel: 01452 812114 — MB BS 1958 Lond.; MS Lond. 1971; FRCS Eng. 1962; MRCS Eng. LRCP Lond. 1958. (Char. Cross) Socs: Fell. Roy. Soc. Med. Prev: Sen. Regist. (Surg.) United Bristol Hosps.; Sen. Fell. (Surg.) Univ. Washington, USA; Regist. (Surg.) S.mead Hosp. Bristol.

KILBY, Mark David Department of Fetal Medicine, Academic Department of Obstetrics & Gynaecology, Edgbaston, Birmingham B15 2TG Tel: 0121 627 2778 Fax: 0121 415 4837; 201 Moor Green Lane, Moseley, Birmingham B13 8NT Tel: 0121 449 0559 Email: m.d.kilby@bham.ac.uk — MD 1990 Nottm.; MB BS Lond. 1984; MRCOG 1991. (Guy's Hosp. Univ. Lond.) Hon. Cons. & Sen. Lect. (Fetal Med.) Birm. Wom. Hosp.; MRC Research Fell. Univ. Toronto. Socs: Soc. Perinatal Obsts.; Internat. Soc. Study Hypertens. in Pregn. Prev: Sen. Regist. Rotat. (O & G) & Lect. W. Midl. & Birm.; Regist. (O & G) Birm. Matern. & Hosp. for Wom. Birm.; Research Regist. Univ. Hosp. Nottm.

KILCOYNE, Marie Therese Ayot House, Neville Park, Tunbridge Wells TN4 8NW — LRCPI & LM, LRSCI & LM 1957; LRCPI & LM, LRCSI & LM 1957; DA Eng. 1966. Regist. & Assoc. Specialist (Anaesth.) Kent & Sussex Hosp. Tunbridge Wells. Prev: SHO & Regist. (Anaesth.) Cuckfield Hosp. Haywards Heath; SHO Glas. Eye Infirm.

***KILDAY, John-Paul** 1 Melville Terrace, Dalkeith EH22 3AR — MB ChB 1998 Glas.; MB ChB Glas 1998.

KILDING, Jackie-Anne Department Community Health, Bedford House, Havelock Place, Shelton, Stoke-on-Trent ST1 4PR Tel: 01782 270688; 27 Longdown Road, Congleton CW12 4QH Tel: 01260 275609 — MB ChB 1986 Sheff.; MB ChB (Hons.) Sheff. 1986; DRCOG 1990. Staff Grade (Community Paediat.) Stoke-on-Trent; CMO (Family Plann.) Stoke-on-Trent. Prev: Trainee GP Stoke-on-Trent VTS.

KILDING, Rachael Fiona 37 Toyne Street, Crookes, Sheffield S10 1HH — MB ChB 1995 Sheff.

KILDUFF, Katherine Monica Psychiatric Unit, Craigavon Area Hospital, Lurgan Road, Portadown, Craigavon BT63 5QQ — MB BCh BAO 1987 NUI.

KILDUFF, Roderick Ciaran 7C Westleigh Avenue, Putney, London SW15 6RF — MB BCh BAO 1987 NUI; MRCP (UK) 1991; MRCGP 1995; DRCOG 1995; Dip. Pract. Dermat. Wales 1997. Regist. Rotat. (Med.) St. Thos. Hosp. Lond.; SHO (Paediat.) St. Peter's Hosp. Chertsey; SHO (Psychiat.) Roy. Lond. Hosp. Whitechapel; SHO (Obst.) St. Geo. Hosp. Tooting. Prev: SHO Rotat. (Med.) P.ss Roy. Hosp. Telford; SHO (Med.) Dudley Rd. Hosp. Birm.

KILGALLEN, Cecil James 55 Westwood Park Road, Peterborough PE3 6JL — MB BCh BAO 1955 NUI.

KILGALLON, Brian Muirhead Medical Centre, Muirhead, Dundee DD2 5NH Tel: 01382 580264 Fax: 01382 581199; 342 Blackness Road, Dundee DD2 1SD Tel: 01382 667305 — MB ChB 1978 Dundee; PhD Dundee 1975; MRCGP 1982. (Dund.) Clin. Asst. (Diabetes) Dundee Teachg. Hosp. Trust.

KILGORE, Heather Jean 62 Church Road, Dundonald, Belfast BT16 2LW — MB BCh BAO 1966 Belf.; DObst RCOG 1968. (Qu. Univ. Belf.) Sen. Med. Off. DHSS N. Irel. Socs: Fell. Ulster Med. Soc.; BMA. Prev: Princip. GP Belf.; Gen. Med. Off. E.. Health & Social Servs. Bd.; SHO Ards Hosp. Newtownards.

KILGOUR, Alastair John Worden Medical Centre, West Paddock, Leyland, Preston PR5 5HA Tel: 01772 423555 Fax: 01772 623878 — MB ChB 1987 Ed.; MRCGP 1995; Dip. IMC RCS Ed. 1991. Clin. Asst. (Endoscopy) Chorley Dist. Gen. Hosp.

***KILGOUR, David** Church Street, 7 Church Street, Coatbridge ML5 3EE Tel: 01236 422678; Ravenswood, 3 Belmont Avenue, Uddingston, Glasgow G71 7AX — MB ChB 1987 Glas.; MRCGP 1991.

KILGOUR, Mr David Ronald (retired) Harmony, Rhinefield Road, Brockenhurst SO42 7QE Tel: 01590 622044 — MB ChB 1936 Ed.; FRCS Ed. 1948; FRCOG 1965, M 1940. Prev: O & G Soton. Univ. Hosp. Gp.

KILGOUR, Hamish Andrew The Health Centre, Whitley Road, Whitley Bay NE26 2ND Tel: 0191 253 1113 — MB BS 1975 Newc.; MRCGP 1979; DRCOG 1978.

KILGOUR, Hugh Kershaw Inglewood, 332 Eastfield Road, Peterborough PE1 4RA Tel: 01733 312900 Fax: 01733 762599 Email: skipsych@skipsych.demon.co.uk — MB BS Lond. 1970; MRCPsych 1977. Cons. Adult Psychiat. Kneesworth Ho. Psychiat. Hosp.; Hon. Cons. Adult Psychiat. St. Lukes Hosp. for the Clergy. Socs: Mem. BMA; MRCPsych. Prev: Cons. Adult Psychiat. NW Anglia Healthcare Trust; Cons. Adult Psychiat. Mendip Hosp. Wells; Sen. Regist. (Psychiat.) Middlx. Hosp. Lond.

KILGOUR, John Lowell, CB, Lt.-Col. RAMC Retd. Stoke House, 22 Amersham Road, Chesham Bois, Amersham HP6 5PE Tel: 01494 726100 Fax: 01494 726100 — MB ChB Aberd. 1947; FFCM 1976, M 1973; MRCGP 1961. p/t Occupat. Health Screening Amersham. Socs: WHO Cons. Panel Communicable Dis. & AIDS Special Progr. Prev: Dir. of Prison Med. Servs. Home Office; Dir. of Coordination

(D2) WHO; Chief Med. Adviser & Under-Sec. Min. Overseas Developm.

KILGOUR, Simon Walter Lowell Scotia Pharmaceuticals (Holdings plc), Castle Business Park, Stirling FK9 4TZ Tel: 01786 895165 Fax: 01786 895450 Email: skilgour@scotia-holdings.com; 6 Carsaig Court, Bridge of Allan, Stirling FK9 4DL Tel: 01786 831134 Fax: 01494 726100 Email: 113147.462@compuserve.com — MB BS 1981 Lond.; PhD (Washington International University) in Strategic Management 1998; MBA WBS 1995. Assoc. Med. Dir. Scotia Holdings plc. Prev: Lect. (Anat.) St. Barts. Med. Coll.; Cas. Off. Guy's Hosp. Lond.; Ho. Phys. Char. Cross Hosp.

KILGOUR, Teresa Catherine Children's Centre, Durham Road, Sunderland SR3 4AF Tel: 0191 565 6256; 201 Parkside, Darlington DL1 5TD — MB ChB 1978 Manch.; BSc (Med. Sci.) St. And. 1975. Staff Grade (Community Child Health) City Hosps. Sunderland.

KILI, Sven Armin Grosvenor Cottage, 25 Culross St., London W1K 7HF — MB ChB 1996 Stellenbosch.

KILKENNY, Lesley Ann 5 Bayley Hall Mews, Queens Rd, Hertford SG14 1XH — BM 1995 Soton.; DRCOG 1997. Manager of UK Drug Surveillance, Roche Products Ltd. Welwyn Gdn City. Prev: GP Vocational Taining Scheme, Chase Farm Hosp., Enfield.

KILLALA, Neal John Patrick (retired) — MB BChir 1971 Camb.; MA Camb 1970; MRCS Eng. LRCP Lond. 1971; FRCPsych 1997, M 1978; DPM Eng. 1976; DObst RCOG 1974; DCH Eng. 1973. Prev: Med. Dir. S.end Drug & Alcohol Advis. & Treatm. Serv.

KILLALEA, Daniel Robert 5 Ibis Close, Kidderminster DY10 4RX — MB BS 1984 Lond.

KILLALEA, Suzanne Elizabeth 1 Hampton Grove, Kinver, Stourbridge DY7 6LP — MB BS 1984 Lond.; DCH 1991.

KILLASPY, Helen Therese University Dept. Psychiatry, Royal Free & Univ. College Medical School, Royal Free Campus, Rowland, Hill Street, London NW3 2PF Tel: 0207 794 0500 Ext: 3709 — MB BS 1991 Lond.; PhD 2001; MRCPsych 1997. (St. Mary's Hosp.) Specialist Regist. (Psychiat.) Roy. Free Hosp. Lond. Train. Scheme.

KILLCROSS, Andrew 68 Church Road, Smithills, Bolton BL1 6HH — MB ChB 1998 Manch.; MB ChB Manch 1998.

KILLEEN, Anne-Marie 50 Manor Heath Road, Halifax HX3 0BE — MB ChB 1986 Leic.

KILLEEN, Deborah Meriel Wirral Hospital, Arrowe Park, Arrowe Park Road, Wirral CH49 5PE Tel: 0151 678 5111 — MB ChB 1984 Sheff.; MB ChB Sheff. l984; MRCP (UK) 1987; FRCR 1990; DMRD Liverp. 1989. Cons. Radiol. Wirral Hosp. Trust.

KILLEEN, Deirdre Mary 4 Jane's Court, Packet Quays, Falmouth TR11 2BZ — MB BCh BAO 1989 NUI; MRCGP 1993; DCH Dub. 1992; DObst RCPI 1992. (Univ. Coll. Galway) GP Cornw.; Clin. Asst. (Palliat. Med.) St. Julias Hospice St. Michaels Hosp. Hayle, Cornw.

KILLEEN, Ian Philip Hastings House, Kineton Road, Wellesbourne, Warwick CV35 9NF Tel: 01789 840245 Fax: 01789 470993; Salters Lane House, Fulready, Ettington, Stratford-upon-Avon CV37 7PE — MB ChB 1978 Birm.; MRCP (UK) 1981; MRCGP 1984; DRCOG 1984. Gen. Practitioner.

KILLEEN, Michael Anthony 47 Glebe Street, London W4 2BE — MB BCh BAO 1992 Dub.

KILLEEN, Michael Philip (retired) 12 Albany Reach, Queens Road, Thames Ditton KT7 0QH Tel: 020 8224 8233 — MB BCh BAO NUI 1947; CPH 1951; LM Coombe 1947.

KILLEEN, Nora Christine 1 Torrens Drive, Lakeside, Cardiff CF23 6DQ Tel: 029 2075 6491 — MB BCh 1946 Wales; BSc, MB BCh Wales 1946; DObst RCOG 1948. (Cardiff) Clin. Med. Off. S. Glam. Health Auth. (T).

KILLEEN, Nora Christine Joan Old Station Surgery, 39 Brecon Road, Abergavenny NP7 5UH Tel: 01873 859000 Fax: 01873 850163 — MB ChB 1978 Bristol; MRCGP 1987; DCH RCP Lond. 1984.

KILLEEN, Philip Damian Laurel House Surgery, 12 Albert Road, Tamworth B79 7JN Tel: 01827 69283 Fax: 01827 318029; The Gables, 32 Comberford Road, Tamworth B79 8PD Tel: 01827 61550 — MB BS 1977 Lond.; MRCS Eng. LRCP Lond. 1977; MRCGP 1982. (Char. Cross) GP Tamworth. Prev: Trainee Gen. Pract. Nottm. VTS; SHO (Cas.) Derby Roy. Infirm.; Ho. Surg. (Orthop.) & Ho. Phys. (Radiother. & Gen. Med.) Char. Cross.

KILLEN, Bruce Ussher (retired) 3 Ferndale Grove, East Boldon NE36 0TG Tel: 0191 536 7462 — MB BCh BAO 1946 Belf.; DO Eng. 1950. Prev: Sen. Regist. Birm. & Midl. Eye Hosp.

KILLEN, Jeremy William Wallace Department of Medicine, Queen Elizabeth Hospital, Gateshead NE9 6SX Tel: 0191 482 0000 — MB BChir 1990 Camb.; MRCP (UK) 1994. (Univ. Camb.) Cons. in Respirat. and Gen. Med. Socs: Brit. Thorac. Soc.

KILLEY, Stuart Howie The Laurels, Cote Lane, Thurgoland, Sheffield S35 7AE — MB BS 1964 Lond. (St. Geo.) Regist. (Community Med.) King's Coll. Hosp. Lond. Prev: Regist. (Geriat. & Med.) Roy. Devon & Exeter Hosp. Exeter; Clin. Asst. (Psychogeriat.) Exe Vale Hosp.

KILLICK, Caroline Jane Paediactric Intensive Care, St Mary's Hospital, Praed Street, London W2 1NY Tel: 0207 886 6666; 56 Kidmore End Road, Emmer Green, Reading RG4 8SE Tel: 0118 948 2842 — MB BS 1990 Lond.; BSc Phys. Lond. 1987; MRCP (UK) 1993. Clin fell Paediactric Intens. care St mary's Hosp. Lond. Prev: Sen. Regist. (Neonat.) John Radcliffe Hosp. Oxf.; Sen. Regist. (Paediat.) Roy. Berks. Hosp. Reading; Regist. (Paediat.) St. Geo. Hosp. Lond. & St. Peter's Hosp. Chertsey.

KILLICK, Frances Mary Tel: 01793 536515 Fax: 01793 491161; School House, Braydon, Swindon SN5 0AB Tel: 01793 771662 — MB BS 1986 Lond.; DFFP 1994; MRCGP 1991; DRCOG 1992; DTM & H Liverp. 1990. p/t Sen. Partner. Prev: Trainee GP Reading VTS; SHO (O & G) Glos. Roy. Hosp.; SHO (Gen. Med.) Glos. Roy. Hosp.

KILLICK, Sally Belinda Dept Haematology, Royal Bournemouth Hospital, Castle Lane east, Bournemouth BH7 7Dw — MB BS 1990 Lond.; MRCPath 2000 (UK); MD 2000 (London); MRCP (UK) 1994. (St Thomas' Hospital Medical School) Cons. Haematologist, Roy. Bournemouth Hosp.

KILLICK, Professor Stephen Robert Department of Obstetrics & Gynaecology, Princess Royal Hospital, Saltshouse Road, Hull HU8 9HE Tel: 01482 676647 Fax: 01482 676646 Email: s.r.killick@hull.ac.uk; 4 St. Barnabas Drive, Swanland, North Ferriby HU14 3RL Tel: 01482 632108 — MB BS 1976 Lond.; BSc (Anat., Hons.) Lond. 1973, MD 1988; MRCS Eng. LRCP Lond. 1976; FRCOG 1995, M 1982. (Guy's) Prof. Reproduc. Med. & Surg. Univ. Hull; Head (Obst. & Gyn.) P.ss Roy. Hosp. Hull; Dir. of Hull IVF Unit. Prev: Sen. Lect. (O & G) Univ. Manch.

KILLICK, Victoria 7 Oakhill Road, Reigate RH2 7HA — MB ChB 1991 Bristol. SHO (Anaesth.) S. Devon Healthcare Trust Torquay. Prev: Ho. Off. (Med.) Bristol Roy. Infirm.; Ho. Off. (Surg.) Torbay Hosp.

KILLIN, William Peter Pedmore Road Surgery, 22 Pedmore Road, Lye, Stourbridge DY9 8DJ Tel: 01384 422591 — MB ChB 1973 Ed.

KILLINER, William Scott 15 Maxwell Park, Bangor BT20 3SH — MB BCh BAO 1995 Belf.

KILLINGLEY, Benjamin Michael Lindon House, Royal Liverpool University Hospital, Prescot St., Liverpool L7 8XP — MB ChB 1998 Liverp.; MB ChB Liverp 1998.

KILLOCH, Michael Morris Abbotsbury Road Surgery, 24 Abbotsbury Road, Weymouth DT4 0AE Tel: 01305 786257 — MB BS 1968 Lond.; MRCS Eng. LRCP Lond. 1968; DObst RCOG 1971.

KILLOUGH, Elizabeth Angela 45 Quay Road, Ballycastle BT54 6BH — MB BCh 1998 Belf.; MB BCh Belf 1998.

KILLOUGHERY, Maura Patricia 93 St James Drive, London SW17 7RP — MB BS 1986 Lond.

KILMARTIN, Edward John Dial House Medical Centre, 131 Mile End Lane, Offerton, Stockport SK2 6BZ Tel: 0161 456 9905 Fax: 0161 456 7127 — MB BCh BAO 1962 NUI. (NUI) Socs: Brit. Soc. Med. & Dent. Hypn.

KILMURRAY, Edward Joseph Dale Cottage, Sandy Brae, Kennoway, Leven KY8 5JW — MB ChB 1961 Ed.

KILN, Matthew Robert Rosendale Surgery, 103A Rosendale Road, West Dulwich, London SE21 8EZ Tel: 020 8670 3292 Fax: 020 8761 7310; 12 Elm Road, Beckenham BR3 4JB Tel: 020 8650 0802 — MB BS 1980 Lond.; DRCOG 1984. (Guy's) Med. Off. Dulwich Coll. & Alleyn's Sch.; GP Co-ordinator Educat. Nat. Sports Centre Crystal Palace; Dir. Sports Med. Clinic Sloane Hosp. Lond.; Co-Chairm. Insulin Depend. Diabetes Trust.; Dir. Educat. Diabetes Primary Care Gp. Prev: Med. Adviser World Runners Assn.; Mem. Brit. Assn. Sport & Med.

KILN, Philip Andrew Riverside Medical Practice, Ballifeary Lane, Inverness IV3 5PW Tel: 01463 715999 Fax: 01463 718763 — MB

BS 1991 Lond.; BSc (Hons.) Lond. 1988, MB BS 1991; DRCOG 1993, MRCGP 1995. (Lond. Hosp. Med. Coll.) GP Princip. Inverness. Prev: Med. Off. Kempsey; Trainee GP Inverness; Ho. Off. Roy. Lond. Hosp.

KILNER, Andrew John Department of Anaesthesia, Freeman Hospital, High Heaton, Newcastle upon Tyne NE7 7DN Tel: 0191 284 3111 Fax: 0191 223 1401 Email: andrew.kilner@nuth.northy.nhs.uk — BM BS 1988 Nottm.; BMedSci (Hons.) Nottm. 1986; FRCA 1995. (Nottingham) Cons. Anaesth. Freeman Hosp. Newc. Prev: Regist. (Anaesth.) N.. RHA; SHO (Anaesth.) Newc. Centr. Teach. Hosps.; SHO (Anaesth.) Macclesfield Dist. Gen. Hosp.

KILNER, Gillian Frances St Brannocks Road Medical Centre, St. Brannocks Road, Ilfracombe EX34 8EG Tel: 01271 863840 — MB ChB 1985 Bristol.

KILNER, Peter Brian Angel Hill Surgery, 1 Angel Hill, Bury St Edmunds IP33 1LU Tel: 01284 753008 Fax: 01284 724744 — MB BS 1977 Lond.; MRCGP 1981.

KILNER, Philip John Cardiovascular Magnetic Resonance Unit, Royal Brompton Hospital, Sydney St., London SW3 6NP Tel: 020 7351 8808 Fax: 020 7351 8816 Email: p.kilner@rbh.nthames.nhs.uk — PhD 1999 London; MB BS Lond. 1973; MD Lond. 1994. Cons. in Cardiovasc. magnetic resonance, Roy. Brompton Hosp. Lond. Prev: Clin. Lect. (Paediat. Cardiol.) Inst. of Child Health Lond.; Brit. Heart Foundat. Intermediate research Fell., CMR unit, Roy. Brompton Hosp. Lond.

KILOH, Malcolm Penalverne Surgery, Penalverne Drive, Penzance TR18 2RE Tel: 01736 63361 Fax: 01736 67485 — MB BS 1957 Lond.; LMSSA Lond. 1957. (St. Geo.) Socs: S. W.. Soc. Anaesth.; Ex-Pres. W. Penwith Med. Soc. Prev: Regist. (Anaesth.) Roy. Surrey Co. Hosp. Guildford.

KILPATRICK, Alexander (retired) The Firs, 10 Hillmount Avenue, Morecambe LA3 2DQ Tel: 01524 852234 — LRCP LRCS Ed. LRFPS Glas. 1948; BA (Hons.) Open 1978; FRCA Eng. 1981; DObst RCOG 1952; DA Eng. 1954. Cons. Anaesth. Roy. Lancaster Infirm. Prev: Regist. (Anaesth.) Vict. Infirm. Glas.

KILPATRICK, Alison Wilma Allan Glasgow Royal Infirmary University NHS Trust, 84 Castle St., Glasgow G4 0SF Tel: 0141 211 4000; 58 Glencairn Drive, Glasgow G41 4PR — MB ChB 1982 Birm.; FFA RCS Eng. 1988. Cons. Anaesth.

KILPATRICK, Andrew Douglas Tayview Medical Practice, 16 Victoria Street, Newport-on-Tay DD6 8DJ Tel: 01382 543251 Fax: 01382 542052 — MB ChB 1984 Manch.; BSc St. And. 1981; MRCGP 1988; DCH RCPS Glas. 1989; DRCOG 1987. Prev: Community Paediat. Aberd.; Trainee GP Bodelwyddan VTS.

KILPATRICK, Ann Wilhelmina (retired) Cranleigh, 107 Havant Road, Emsworth PO10 7LF Tel: 01243 372250 — MB BCh BAO Belf. 1947, DPH 1952; MFCM 1974; DCH Eng. 1951. Prev: SCMO Portsmouth & SE Hants. Health Dist.

KILPATRICK, Anne The Health Centre, 2 Kirkland Road, Kilbirnie KA25 6HP Tel: 01505 683333 — MB ChB 1989 Glas.; DRCOG 1992. Prev: SHO (Paediat. & Dermat.) CrossHo. Hosp. Kilmarnock VTS; Trainee GP Kilbirnie.

KILPATRICK, Eric Stephen Department of Clinical Biochemistry, Hull Royal Infirmary, Hull HU3 2JZ — MB ChB 1988 Glas.; MD Glas. 1996; MRCPath 1997. Cons. (Clin. Biochem.) Hull Roy. Infirm. Socs: Assn. Clin. Biochem.; Brit. Diabetic Assn.; BMA. Prev: Sen. Regist. (Chem. Path.) Withington Hosp. Manch.; Career Regist. (Path. Biochem.) W.. Infirm. Glas.; Ho. Off. (Med.) S.. Gen. Hosp. Glas.

KILPATRICK, Mr Francis Rankin Hookwood, Tripp Hill, Fittleworth, Pulborough RH20 1ER Tel: 01798 865415 — MRCS Eng. LRCP Lond. 1933; MS Lond. 1939, MB BS 1934; FRCS Eng. 1936. (Guy's) Emerit. Surg. (Genitourin.) Guy's Hosp.; Emerit. Surg. St. Peter's Hosp. for Stone.

KILPATRICK, George Stewart, OBE (retired) 14 Millfield, Millbrook Road, Dinas Powys CF64 4DA Tel: 029 2051 3149 — MB ChB Ed. 1947; MD Ed. 1954; FRCP Lond. 1975; FRCP Ed. 1966; MRCP (UK) 1971; MRCP Ed. 1952. Prev: Vice Provost & David Davies Prof. of Tuberc. & Chest Dis. Univ. of Wales Coll. of Med. Cardiff.

KILPATRICK, Herbert Kenneth Ross (retired) Malthouse Barn, Queen's St., Bloxham, Banbury OX15 4QQ Tel: 01295 721524 — BM BCh Oxf. 1944; MA 1945.

KILPATRICK, James Wolfe MacConnell Salisbury House, Lake St., Leighton Buzzard LU7 1RS Tel: 01525 373288; Chapel Cottage, Pound Hill, Great Brickhill, Milton Keynes MK17 9AS — MB BCh BAO 1964 Belf.

KILPATRICK, John Ranald Burt The Old School Surgery, 2A Station Street, Kibworth, Leicester LE8 0LN Tel: 0116 241 3801 — MB ChB 1982 Birm.

KILPATRICK, Mary Malthouse Barn, Queen's St., Bloxham, Banbury OX15 4QQ Tel: 01295 721524 — MB BCh BAO NUI 1946. (Univ. Coll. Dub.) Community Med. Banbury, Oxf. AHA. Prev: Ho. Surg. Mater Miser. Hosp. Dub.; Capt. RAMC.

KILPATRICK, Norman Drean (retired) Winnards Perch, Sunnyside, Ridge, Wareham BH20 5BQ — MB BChir 1956 Camb.; MRCS Eng. LRCP Lond. 1956; FRCOG 1977. Prev: Cons (O&G) I of Man Dept Health.

KILPATRICK, Lord Robert, CBE 12 Wester Coates Gardens, Edinburgh EH12 5LT Tel: 0131 337 7304 — MB ChB (Hons.) Ed. 1949; FRCP Lond. 1975, M 1969; FRCP Ed. 1964, M 1953; Hon FRCP Ed. 1996; Hon. FRCP Dub. 1995; Hon. FRCS Eng. 1995; FRSE 1998; MD (High Commend.) Ed. 1961; Dr Lc Ed. 1987; Hon. DSc Hull 1994; Hon. DSc Dundee 1994; Hon. DSc Leics. 1994; Hon. LLD Sheff. 1995; Hon. LLD Dundee 1992; FRCP Glas. 1991; Hon. FRCS ED 1996. Chair Scot. Hosp. Research Endow. Trust. Socs: Assn. Phys. & Physiol. Soc. Prev: Pres. Gen. Med. Counc.; Dean Med. & Prof. Med. Univ. Leic.; Pres. BMA.

KILPATRICK, Robert James The Surgery, Lochgoilhead, Cairndow PA24 8AQ Tel: 01301 703258 Fax: 01301 703258; Craig-an-Righ, Lochgoilhead, Cairndow PA24 8AH Tel: 013013 258 — MB ChB 1980 Glas. Prev: Trainee GP Mid Yell, Shetland; SHO Rotat. (Med.) & Ho. Off. (Med.) S.. Gen. Hosp. Glas.

KILPATRICK, Stewart Matheson Whitelands, Long Sutton, Hook RG29 1SP — MB 1971 Camb.; BChir 1970; FFA RCS Eng. 1974; DA Eng. 1973. Cons. Anaesth. Frimley Pk. Hosp. Surrey. Prev: Clin. Instruc. (Anaesth.) Memor. Univ. Newfld. Canada; Regist. (Anaesth.) Alder Hey Childr. Hosp. Liverp.; Ho. Surg. Roy. Sussex Co. Hosp. Brighton.

KILPATRICK, Trevor John London House, Mecklenburgh Square, London WC1N 2AB — MB BS 1982 Melbourne; FRACP 1990.

KILPATRICK, William Gillespie, Brigadier late RAMC (retired) Springfield House, Potterne Road, Devizes SN10 5DD — MB ChB 1952 Glas.; FRCGP 1978, M 1971; T(GP) 1991; DCH Eng. 1969; DObst RCOG 1956. Prev: Dir. of Army Gen. Pract.

KILROY, Ian Mark 2 Brookside Close, Haydock, St Helens WA11 0UQ — MB BS 1998 Lond.; MB BS Lond 1998.

KILSBY, Anna Bethan 8 Westfield Road, Newport NP20 4ND — MB ChB 1998 Sheff.; MB ChB Sheff 1998.

KILSBY, Evelyn Bernice (retired) Orange Cottage, Brookley Road, Brockenhurst SO42 7RA — MRCS Eng. LRCP Lond. 1955; BA Camb. 1950; BSc Lond. 1945. Prev: GP Billingshurst.

KILSHAW, Ian Michael The Grange Surgery, 41 York Road, Southport PR8 2AD Tel: 01704 560506 Fax: 01704 563108 — MB ChB 1981 Liverp.; MRCGP 1988; DRCOG 1985.

KILSHAW, Lesley Anne 157 Clovelly Road, Coventry CV2 3GW — MB ChB 1986 Sheff.

***KILSHAW, Lucy Elizabeth** Whales Farm, Southlands Lane, West Chiltington, Pulborough RH20 2JU — MB ChB 1996 Birm.

KILTIE, Anne Elizabeth Cookridge Hospital, Hospital Lane, Leeds LS16 6QB Tel: 0113 267 3411 Fax: 0113 392 4214 — BM BCh 1988 Oxf.; MA Camb. 1989; MRCP (UK) 1992; FRCR 1995; DM Oxf. 1999. (Univ. Camb. & Univ. Oxf.) Specialist Regist. Cookridge Hosp. Leeds. Prev: Clin. Research Fell. (Experim. Radiat. Oncol.) Paterson Inst. Cancer Research Christie Hosp. NHS Trust Manch.; Regist. (Radiother. & Clin. Oncol.) Christie Hosp. NHS Trust Manch.

KILTY, Bridget 58 Carisbrooke Road, Leicester LE2 3PB — MB ChB 1998 Dund.; MB ChB Dund 1998.

KILVERT, Jennifer Anne Diabetes Centre, Northampton General Hospital, Cliftonville, Northampton Tel: 01604 545576 Fax: 01604 544716; 65 Bawnmore Road, Rugby CV22 6JN — MB BS Lond. 1974; FRCP 1999; MD Lond. 1988, BSc (Human Genetics) 1971; MRCP (UK) 1976. (Univ. Coll. Hosp.) Cons. Diabetes N.ampton Gen. Hosp. Prev: Sen. Regist. (Med.) Diabetic Clinic Gen. Hosp. Birm.; Regist. (Med.) N.ampton Gen. Hosp.; Res. Regist. (Diabetes) Gen. Hosp. Birm.

KILVERT, Peter John Whitehall Medical Practice, Morton Gardens, Rugby CV21 3AQ Tel: 01788 544264 Fax: 01788 575783; 65 Bawnmore Road, Rugby CV22 6JN Tel: 01788 334316 — MB BS 1973 Lond.; BSc (Genetics) Lond. 1970; DCH Eng. 1977; DObst RCOG 1975. (Univ. Coll. Hosp.) Med. Off. Rugby Sch.; Med. Off. Rugby United. Socs: (Counc.) Med. Off. Schs. Assn.; Brit. Assn. of Sport Med.; Diabetes UK. Prev: Clin. Asst. (Genitourin. Med.) Hosp. St Cross Rugby; Clin. Asst. (Diabetic Clin.) Coventry & Warwicksh. Hosp.; Med. Advis. Coventry Sports Injury Clinic.

KILVINGTON, Jane Mary (retired) 122 Marshalswick Lane, St Albans AL1 4XD Tel: 01727 53156 — MB BS 1951 Lond. Prev: Med. Off. Marital & Sex Ther. Clin. B.U.P.A. Med. Centre Lond.

KILVINGTON, Kenneth Anthony The Burns Practice, 4 Albion Place, Bennetthorpe, Doncaster DN1 2EQ Tel: 01302 810888 Fax: 01302 812150; 2 Whin Hill Road, Bessacarr, Doncaster DN4 7AE Tel: 01302 531637 — MB ChB 1972 Sheff.; DObst RCOG 1974. (Sheff.) Med. Assessor Disabil. Benefits Doncaster; Clin. Asst. (Learning Disabil.) Doncaster Health Care Trust. Prev: Med. Off. Marks & Spencer Doncaster; SHO (O & G, Orthop. & Cas.) N.. Gen. Hosp. Sheff.; Clin. Asst. (O & G & Orthop.) Doncaster Roy. Infirm.

KIM, Jong Bin 84 Framingham Road, Sale M33 3RJ — MB ChB 1997 Ed.

KIM LIN LIM, Dr Parkhead Hospital, 81 Salamanca St., Glasgow G31 5ES Tel: 0141 211 8300 — MB ChB 1996 Glas. SHO (Psychiat.) Pk.head Hosp., Glas.

KIMBELL, Joanne Sarah Mawsley House, Loddington, Kettering NN14 1LA — MB BS 1998 Lond.; MB BS Lond 1998.

KIMBER, Jeffery Robert Eric 8 Salesian View, Park Road, Farnborough GU14 6JQ — MB BS 1989 Lond.; BSc (Hons.) Lond. 1986; MRCP (UK) 1993. Lect. (Neurovasc. Med.) St. Mary's Hosp. Med. Sch. Lond. & Inst. Neurol. Lond.

KIMBER, Keren Ann Court Mead, Bramley Road, Silchester, Reading RG7 2LJ — MB BS 1968 Lond.; MRCS Eng. LRCP Lond. 1968; MRCPath 1983; Dip. Biochem. Lond. 1965. (Roy. Free) Med. Off. DHSS Lond. Prev: Sen. Regist. (Chem. Path.) Roy. Berks. Hosp. Reading; Sen. Regist. Nuffield Dept. Clin. Biochem. Radcliffe Infirm. Oxf.; SHO (Wom. Doctors' Retainer Scheme) Basingstoke & N. Hants. HA.

KIMBER, Rachel Mary Leicester General Hospital, Gwendolen Road, Leicester LE5 4PW Tel: 0116 249 0490 Fax: 0116 258 4666; Flat 8A, Landseer Road, Leicester LE2 3EG Tel: 0116 270 9244 — BM BS 1996 Nottm.; BMedSci Nottm. 1994. (Nottingham) Surg. Rotat.

KIMBER, Timothy John The Park Surgery, St. Flora's Road, Littlehampton BN17 6BF Tel: 01903 717154 Fax: 01903 732908; 66 Golden Avenue, East Preston, Littlehampton BN16 1QU Tel: 01903 850130 — MB ChB 1983 Manch.; MRCGP 1987; DCH RCP Lond. 1986. Trainer in Gen. Pract. Prev: Trainee GP Worthing.; SHO Worthing & S.lands Hosp.

KIMBER, Victor Robert Mansion House Surgery, Abbey Street, Stone ST15 8YE Tel: 01785 815555 Fax: 01785 815541; Rowan House, Beech Court, Stone ST15 8QG Tel: 01785 817642 — MB ChB 1969 Aberd.; DObst RCOG 1973.

KIMBERLEY, Adam Peter Salt Department of Anaesthesia, Queen Mary's University Hospital, Roehampton Lane, London SW15 5PN Tel: 020 8789 6611; 6 Dulwich Wood Park, London SE19 1XQ — MB BS 1977 Lond.; FFA RCS (Eng.) 1981. (Univ. Coll. Hosp.) Cons. Anaesth. & Dir. Intens. Care Unit Qu. Mary's Univ. Hosp. Lond. Socs: Roy. Inst. GB. Prev: Sen Regist. (Anaesth.) W.m. & Brompton Hosps. Lond.

KIMBLE, Francis Wallace Flat A, St. Lawrence Hospital, Chepstow NP6 5YX Tel: 01291 2334 — MB ChB 1984 Zimbabwe; MB ChB (Hons.) Zimbabwe 1984; LRCP LRCS Ed. LRCPS Glas. 1986.

KIME, Robert The Surgery, 6 Lambley Lane, Burton Joyce, Nottingham NG14 5BG Tel: 0115 931 2500 Fax: 0115 931 2118.

KIMERLING, Julius John 14 Hornton Street, Kensington, London W8 4NR Tel: 020 7937 9520 Fax: 020 7937 9520; 36 Hartington Road, London W4 3UB — MB BS 1962 Lond.; MRCP Lond. 1966; MRCS Eng. LRCP Lond. 1961. Prev: Clin. Asst. (Med. & Rheum.) Char. Cross Hosp. Lond.

KIMMANCE, Keir John The Maltings, Cowesfield Green, Whiteparish, Salisbury SP5 2QS — MB BS 1962 Lond.; FFCM 1987, M 1974; FFPHM RCP (UK) 1989; DPH Bristol 1969; DObst. RCOG 1964.

KIMMANCE, Simon Nicholas The Maltings, Cowesfield Green, Whiteparish, Salisbury SP5 2QS — MB ChB 1991 Liverp.

KIMMINS, Bernard Arthur Gerard Medical Centre, Barrow Hill, Chesterfield S42 5ND Tel: 01246 474683; 7 Wateringbury Grove, Staveley, Chesterfield S43 3TS Tel: 01246 472309 — MB ChB 1957 Liverp.; DPH Liverp. 1962. (Liverp.) Dent. Anaesth. Derbysh. CC; Civil. Med. Pract. TAVR. Socs: BMA. Prev: JHMO Waterloo Hosp. Liverp.; SHO (Chest Dis.) Newsham Gen. Hosp. Liverp.; SHO (Anaesth.) N. Liverp. Hosps.

KIMMITT, John Blyth Health Centre, Thoroton Street, Blyth NE24 1DX Tel: 01670 396560 Fax: 01670 396579; 19 Green Close, Stannington, Morpeth NE61 6PE — MB BS 1976 Newc.; MRCGP 1981.

KIMULI, Michael 39 Bootham Park Court, York YO31 8JT — MB ChB 1996 Sheff.

KINAHAN, Kathleen Blanche, MBE (retired) 53 Broadacres, Templepatrick, Ballyclare BT39 0AY Tel: 01849 432379 — MB BS 1940 Lond.; MRCS Eng. LRCP Lond. 1940; DCH RCP Lond. 1943. JP. Prev: Med. Off. i/c Childr. Dept. Gen. Hosp. Malacca.

KINAHAN, Mr Patrick Joseph Ophthamlmology Department, Ysbyty Gwynedd, Bangor LL57 2PW — MB BCh BAO 1982 Dub.; FRCSI 1988; FRCOphth 1989.

KINANE, Catherine Francis De Sales The Dene, Gatehouse Lane, Goddards Green, Hassocks BN6 9LE — MB BCh BAO 1987 NUI; DObst Ireland; DCH Ireland; MICGP 1991; MRCGP 1991; MRCPsych 1994; MSc 1996 University of London. (University College Cork) Cons Forens. Psychiat. Hume Office Suite Springfield Hosp. Socs: MRC Psych; MRC GP.

KINCAID, Alexander John James (retired) 262 Castlewellan Road, Banbridge BT32 3SF Tel: 0182 06 23247 — MB BCh BAO 1957 Dub. Assoc. Specialist (Gen. Med.) Craigavon Area & Banbridge Dist. Hosps. Prev: Ho. Off. (Med.) Lurgan & Portadown Hosp.

KINCAID, Robin James 73 Earlbank Avenue, Scotstown, Glasgow G14 9DU; Flat 0/2, 4 Dudley Drive, Hyndland, Glasgow G12 9SD — MB ChB 1991 Ed.; FRCS Ed. (Tr. & Orth.) 2001; FRCS Ed. 1996; FRCS Glas. 1996. (Edin.) Specialist Regist. (Opthop.) W. Scotl.

KINCAID, Williamina Clements The Lochans, Strathblane, Glasgow G63 9EX — MB ChB 1984 Glas.; MB ChB Glas. l984; FRCR 1990. Cons. Diag. Radiol. W.. Infirm. Glas.

KINCH, Andrew Philip Joseph 36A Ramshill Road, Scarborough YO11 2QG — MB ChB 1986 Leeds.

KINCH, Denise Northfield Health Centre, 15 St. Heliers Road, Northfield, Birmingham B31 1QT Tel: 0121 478 1850 Fax: 0121 476 0931; 41 Hightree Close, Bartley Green, Birmingham B32 3QP — MB ChB 1978 Birm.; MSc Warwick 1993; MRCGP 1986; DCCH RCP Ed. 1985; DCP Warwick 1985; DRCOG 1981. Gen. Practitioner.

KINCH, Henry William Antti The Surgery, 24 Albert Road, Bexhill-on-Sea TN40 1DG Tel: 01424 730456/734430 Fax: 01424 225615; Glenthorn, 20 Collington Rise, Bexhill-on-Sea TN39 3RT — MB BChir 1984 Camb.; BMSc (1st cl. Hons.) Gen. Path. Dund 1982; MRCGP 1989; DRCOG 1989; Cert. Family Plann. JCC 1989. GP Bexhill-on-Sea. Prev: Trainee GP Cambs. VTS.

KINCHIN, Christopher Geoffrey John Chaddlewood Surgery, 128 Bellingham Crescent, Plympton, Plymouth PL7 2QP Tel: 01752 345317 Fax: 01752 347216 — MB BS 1976 Lond.; BSc Lond. 1973; MRCS Eng. LRCP Lond. 1976; MRCGP 1986. (Guy's) GP Princip. Prev: Trainer (Gen. Pract.) Plymouth; Princip. Police Surg. 'E' Div. Devon & Cornw. Constab.

KINDELL, Christopher Whitehill Surgery, Whitehill Lane, Oxford Road, Aylesbury HP19 8EN Tel: 01296 424488 Fax: 01296 398774; 20 Amersham Road, High Wycombe HP13 6QU Tel: 01494 438219 — MB BS 1981 Lond.; MRCP (UK) 1989. Prev: SHO (Med.) St. Bart. Hosp. Lond.; Regist. (Med.) Epsom Dist. Hosp.; Trainee GP Wellington Hse. Surg. P.s RisBoro..

KINDER, Alison Jane 27 Roman Way, Sandbach CW11 3EW Tel: 01270 765686 Email: alisonkinder@hotmail.com — BM BS 1995 Nottm. SHO (Med.) Glenfield Hosp., Leicester.

KINDER, Concepcion Narrowcliff Surgery, Narrowcliff, Newquay TR7 2QF Tel: 01637 873363 Fax: 01637 850735; Tel: 01209 715169 — MB BS 1985 Lond.; BSc Basic Med. Scs. & Psychol. Lond. 1982; MRCGP 1990; DRCOG 1988. (Univ. Coll. Lond. Sch.

Med.) Socs: BMA. Prev: Trainee GP Newquay Cornw. & Lewisham Hosp. VTS; SHO (A & E) Rugby.

KINDER, Mr Cyril Hugh (retired) Woodfen House, School Road, South Walsham, Norwich NR13 6DZ Tel: 01603 270202 — MB BChir 1945 Camb.; MA Camb. 1942, MChir 1957; FRCS Eng. 1950. Prev: Cons. Surg. Urol. Guy's Hosp. Lond. & Beckenham Hosp. Kent.

KINDER, Joan District General Hospital, Kings Drive, Eastbourne BN21 2UD Tel: 01323 413708; 4 Old Mansion Close, Ratton Manor, Eastbourne BN20 9DP Tel: 01323 505839 — MB BChir 1978 Cantab.; MA Cantab. 1978; MRCP (UK) 1983; FRCPCH. (Univ. Camb. & Lond. Hosp.) Cons. in Child Health E.bourne Hosps. NHS Trust. Socs: BMA; Fell.Roy. Coll. of Paediat. and Child Health; Brit. Soc. of Allergy, Environm. and Nutrit.al Med. Prev: Sen. Regist. NE Thames HA.

KINDER, Joanna Jane 17 Sid Lane, Sidmouth EX10 9AN — MB BS 1985 Lond.; MRCGP 1989; DRCOG 1987. (St. Thos.) Prev: Trainee GP Cuckfield Hosp. Winchester; Ho. Phys. St. Helier Hosp. Carshalton; Ho. Surg. Cuckfield Hosp.

KINDER, Judith Ann Linden Medical Centre, 9A Linden Avenue, Maidenhead SL6 6HD Tel: 01628 20846 Fax: 01628 789318; Long Grove House, Longbottom Lane, Seer Green, Beaconsfield HP9 2UL — MB BS 1979 Lond.; MRCGP 1985.

KINDER, Mr Richard Brian The Cheltenham & Gloucester Nuffield Hospital, Hatherley Lane, Cheltenham GL51 6SY Tel: 01242 246527; Adderstone House, Cleeve Hill, Cheltenham GL52 3PY Tel: 01242 672005 Email: rblinder@doctors.org.uk — MB BS 1973 Lond.; FRCS Eng. 1977; MRCS Eng. LRCP Lond. 1973. (Guy's) Cons. Urol. Surg. Cheltenham Gen. Hosp. Socs: BMA; Brit. Assn. Urol. Surgs.; Internat. Continence Soc. Prev: Sen. Regist. (Urol.) Leics. Gen. Hosp.; Sen. Regist. (Surg.) Guy's Hosp.; Regist. (Gen. Surg. & Urol.) Guy's Hosp. Lond.

KINDER, Susan Margaret McRae Adderstone House, Cleeve Hill, Cheltenham GL52 3PY Tel: 01242 672005 — MB ChB 1972 St. And.; MSc Warwick 1996; MRCGP 1977; DCH Eng. 1975. Assoc. Specialist (Paediat.) Cheltenham Gen. Hosp.

KINDLEY, Angus David Raeden Centre, Mid Stocket Road, Aberdeen AB15 5PD Tel: 01224 321381 Fax: 01224 311109 — MB ChB 1972 Leeds; FRCP Ed. 1995; FRCP Lond. 1991; MRCP (UK) 1976; FRCPCH 1997; DCH Eng. 1974. (Leeds) Cons. Paediat. Raeden Centre & Aberd. Roy. Infirm.; Clin. Dir. Raeden Centre; Hon. Clin. Sen. Lect. Aberd. Socs: Brit. Paediat. Neurol. Assn. Prev: Cons. Paediat. Fairfield Gen. Hosp. Bury, Lancs.; Sen. Regist. (Paediat. Neurol.) Alder Hey & Walton Hosp. Liverp.; Sen. Regist. (Paediat.) Alder Hey Childr. Hosp. Liverp.

KINDLEYSIDES, Angela Community Directorate, Wendover, 170 Downend Road, Bristol BS16 5EB Tel: 0117 957 3206; 10 Eggshill Lane, Yate, Bristol BS37 4BL Tel: 01454 887433 — MB ChB 1984 Manch.; BSc St. And. 1981; Dip. Community Paediat. Warwick 1991. (St. And. & Manch.) SCMO (Community Paediat.) Frenchay Trust Bristol. Socs: BACCH; MRCPCH; SW Paediat. Club.

KINDNESS, Hugh Michael John Thames Medical, 157 Waterloo Road, London SE1 8US Tel: 020 7902 9000 Fax: 020 7928 0927 Email: interhealth@compuserve.com; Waratah, Paddocks Way, Ashtead KT21 2QY Tel: 01372 274833 — MB ChB Ed. 1961. Dir. IH Ltd. & Med. Adviser Salvage Assn. & Kingfisher; Examr. Friends Provident & other companies; Med. Adviser & Vis. Phys. Interhealth Lond.; Clin. Asst. Stapleford Centre Lond. Socs: Fell. Roy. Med. Soc.; Harv. Soc.; Assur. Med. Soc. Prev: SHO (Neurosurg.) Roy. Infirm. Edin.; Demonst. (Anat.) Univ. Edin.; Examr. Bupa Med. Centre.

KINDY, George Robert PO Box 5, Monmouth NP25 4XJ — MB BS 1973 Lond.; MRCS Eng. LRCP Lond. 1973. (Westm.)

KING, Abigail Louise Withybush Hospital, Fishguard Road, Haverfordwest SA61 2PZ Tel: 01437 773612 — MB BCh 1997 Wales. (University of Wales College of Medicine)

KING, Adrian Howard Glannrafon Surgery, Glannrafon, Amlwch LL68 9AG Tel: 01407 830878 Fax: 01407 832512; Bwlch, Llanfechell, Amlwch LL68 0UF — MB ChB 1981 Liverp.; MRCGP 1986.

KING, Aileen English Portland Park Medical Centre, 51 Portland Park, Hamilton ML3 7JY Tel: 01698 284353; 3 Ardenclutha Avenue, Hamilton ML3 9BW Tel: 01698 285657 — MB ChB 1981 Dundee. Prev: Clin. Med. Off. Hamilton & E. Kilbride Unit Lanarksh. HB.

KING, Alan Laurie Psychiatric Department, Leicester General Hospital, Gwendolen Road, Leicester LE5 4PW Tel: 0116 490490 — MB ChB 1973 Birm.; BSc Birm. 1970, MB ChB 1973; MRCPsych 1977. Cons. Psychiat. Leics. Gen. Hosp.

KING, Alan Philip Unna Stakes Lodge Surgery, 3A Lavender Road, Waterlooville PO7 8NS Tel: 023 9225 4581 Fax: 023 9235 8867 Email: alan.king@gp-j82093.nhs.uk — MB BS 1987 Lond.; MRCGP 1993; DRCOG 1991; Cert. Family Plann. JCC 1991; DGM RCP Lond. 1990. (St. Thos.) GP Princip. Stakes Lodge Surg. Waterlooville.

KING, Alan William 21 Stoney Lane, Winchester SO22 6DP Tel: 01962 884437 — MB ChB 1977 Manch.; DRCOG 1981.

KING, Alison Louise The School House, Midgeholme, Lambley, Carlisle CA8 7LT — MB BS 1998 Newc.; MB BS Newc 1998.

KING, Alistair (retired) Fairfax, 23 Main St., Newstead, Melrose TD6 9DX Tel: 01896 822785 — MB ChB Ed. 1953; MRCOphth 1988; DO RCS Eng. 1964. Prev: Med. Pract. (Ophth.) Galashiels.

KING, Alistair Lawrence Brighton Health Care NHS Trust, Eastern Road, Brighton BN2 5BE Tel: 01273 696955; 86 Mansfield Road, Hampstead, London NW3 2HX — MB BS 1991 Lond.; BSc (1st cl. Hons.) Lond. 1988; MRCP (UK) 1995. SpR (Gastroenterol.), Brighton Hosps .NHS Trust. Prev: Regist. (Hepat., Gastoenterol. & Gen. Med.) King's Coll. Hosp. Lond.

KING, Amanda Jane Friendsward, BOX 309, Fulbourn Hospital, Cambridge Tel: 01223 218618 — MB BCh 1991 Wales; MRCPsych 1996. (Univ. Wales Coll. Med.) p/t Specialist Regist. (Psych.) Fulbourn Hosp. Camb. Socs: BMA; RCPsych. Prev: Specialist Regist. Barrow Hosp., Barrow Gurney; Specialist Regist. (Psychiat.) W.on Gen. Hosp. W.on-Supermare; Regist. (Psychiat.) Blackberry Hill Hosp. Bristol.

KING, Andrew James Fairmont Park Road, Bingley — MB ChB 1967 Ed.; BSc (Physiol., Hons.) Ed. 1964, MB ChB 1967; FRCP Ed. 1984. Cons. Phys. St. Lukes Hosp. Bradford. Prev: Lect. Dept. Med. Univ. Edin.; Hon. Regist. Edin. Roy. Infirm.

KING, Andrew Peter Dept of Neuropathology, Oldchurch Hospital, Waterloo Road, Romford RM7 8E — MB ChB 1989 Manch.; BSc (Hons.) Pharmacol. Manch. 1986; MRCPath 1997, D 1994. (Manch.) Cons Neuropathologist, Barking-Havering and Redbridge Hosps NHS Trust; Hon. Cons., King's Coll. Hosp., Lond.; Hon. Sen. Lect. Inst. of Psychiat., Lond. Socs: Brit med Assoc; Internat. Acad. of Pathol.; Brit. NeuroPath. Soc. Prev: Sen. Regist. (Neuropath.) King's Neurosci. Centre Lond.; Lect. (Path.) Liverp. Univ.; SHO (Path.) Roy. Liverp. Hosp.

KING, Mr Andrew Thomas 14 Ashfield Road, Altrincham WA15 9QJ Email: aking14ash@aol.com — MB BS 1988 Lond.; FRCS (SN) 1997; FRCS Eng. 1992. (Lond. Hosp. Med. Coll.) Sen. Regist. (Neurosurg.) Hope Hosp. Salford & Manch. Roy. Infirm. Socs: Fell. Roy. Soc. Med.; Assoc. Mem. Brit. Soc. Neurol. Surg. Prev: Regist. (Neurosurg.) Brook Hosp. & Maudsley Hosp. Lond.

KING, Andrew Timothy 30 Branksome Avenue, Southampton SO15 5NY — BChir 1994 Camb.

KING, Ann Dorothy 112 Gayton Road, King's Lynn PE30 4ER — MB ChB 1984 Sheff.; MRCP (UK) 1987.

KING, Ann Morris Harrogate District Hospital, Lancaster Park Road, Harrogate HG2 7SX Tel: 0113 268 4598; The Vicarage, Church View, Thorner, Leeds LS14 3ED Tel: 0113 289 2437 — MB BS 1969 Lond.; MRCS Eng. LRCP Lond. 1969; MRCOphth 1989; DO Eng. 1974. (St. Bart.) Staff Ophth. Harrogate Dist. Hosp. Socs: RCOphth. Prev: Clin. Asst. (Ophth.) Leeds Gen. Infirm. & St. Jas. Hosp. Leeds.

KING, Anna Maria 57 Arden Road, Acocks Green, Birmingham B27 6AH — MB BS 1993 Lond.

KING, Anna-Maria 2 Arnos Grove, Southgate, London N14 7AS Tel: 020 8886 0178 — LMSSA 1973 Lond.

KING, Anna Maria Minsmere House, Ipswich Hospital NHS Trust, Heath Road, Ipswich IP4 5PD Tel: 01473 704227 — MB BS 1984 Lond. Clin. Med. Off. E. Suff. HA. Prev: Psychiat. Rotat. & SHO (Orthop. & A & E) W. Suff. Hosp. Bury St. Edmunds; Ho. Phys. Heatherwood Hosp. Ascot; Ho. Surg. Roy. Lancaster Infirm.

KING, Anne 190 Goodman Park, Slough SL2 5NL — MB ChB 1988 Liverp.; MSc Clin. Biochem. Lond. 1991, BSc (Hons.) Physiol. 1985. Regist. (Chem. Path.) Roy. Postgrad. Med. Sch. Hammersmith Hosp. Lond. Prev: SHO (Chem. Path.) St. Mary's Hosp. Med. Sch. Lond.; Ho. Off. Walton Hosp. Liverp.

KING, Archibald George (retired) 5 Wilson Avenue, Troon KA10 7AF Tel: 01292 316264 — MB ChB Glas. 1951.

KING, Ashley King's College, Cambridge CB2 1ST Tel: 01223 33727 Email: ashley.king@kings.cam.ac.uk — MB 1974 Camb.; BChir 1973; MD 1990; MRCPath 1984; MRCP (UK) 1975. (Cambridge) Med. Fell. King's Coll. Camb.; Assoc. Lect. (Path.) Univ. of Camb. Prev: Research Assoc. Wellcome Trust.

KING, Barbara Anne Wolverton Health Centre, Gloucester Road, Wolverton, Milton Keynes MK12 5DF Tel: 01908 316633 Fax: 01908 225397; Southview, London Road, Broughton Village, Milton Keynes MK10 9AA — MB ChB 1972 Bristol.

KING, Barbara Anne 265 Blossomfield Road, Solihull B91 1TA — MB BS 1976 Lond.; MRCP (UK) 1980; MRCGP 1983; DCH RCP Lond. 1981; DRCOG 1982. (Univ. Coll. Hosp.) Prev: Med. Regist. Walsgrave Hosp. Coventry; SHO (Paediat.) Lond. Hosp.; Ho. Surg., Univ. Coll. Hosp. Lond.

KING, Barbara Caroline 34 Baillieswells Drive, Bieldside, Aberdeen AB15 9AX — M.B., Ch.B. Glas. 1936. (Univ. Glas.) Socs: B.M.A. Prev: Res. Ho. Surg. & Sen. Res. Ho. Phys. Sick Childr. Hosp. Yorkhill.

KING, Barbara Caroline Anne Carteknowle and Dore Medical Practice, 1 Carterknowle Road, Sheffield S7 2DW Tel: 0114 255 1218 Fax: 0114 258 4418; 137 Dore Road, Dore, Sheffield S17 3NF Tel: 01724 350933 — MB ChB 1978 Sheff.; BSc (Hons.) Sheff. 1973, MB ChB 1978.

KING, Barbara Mary The Castle Practice, Elm House Surgery, St Georges Road, Tidworth SP9 7EW; Lapwings, Aughton, Collingbourne Kingston, Marlborough SN8 3SA Tel: 01264 850247 — MB ChB 1985 Dundee; DCH 1994; DRCOG 1993; DFFP 1998; DCH RCP Lond. 1994; DRCOG 1992. (Dundee) GP Princip. Prev: GP HM Forces Germany.

KING, Barbara Ruth Northfield Health Centre, 15 St. Heliers Road, Northfield, Birmingham B31 1QT Tel: 0121 478 1850 Fax: 0121 476 0931 — MB ChB 1991 Birm.; ChB Birm. 1991.

KING, Barry John The Lilacs, Old Hall Lane, Fornham St Martin, Bury St Edmunds IP31 1SS Tel: 01284 754472 — MB BS 1967 Lond.; MRCP (UK) 1976; AKC. (King's Coll. Hosp.) Regist. (Gen. Med.) W.. Suff. Hosp. Prev: Ho. Surg. (O & G) King's Coll. Hosp. Lond.; Ho. Phys. (Paediat.) King's Coll. Hosp. Gp.; Asst. Sen. Med. Off. S.W. Thames RHA.

KING, Beverley Ann School Health Department, Cheshire Community Healthcare Trust, Barony Hospital, Nantwich Tel: 01270 415373; 25 Sandbach Road S., Alsager, Stoke-on-Trent ST7 2LW Tel: 01270 877681 — MB ChB 1979 Manch. Staff Grade Community Paediat. Barony Hosp. Chesh. Prev: Trainee GP Lancaster VTS; Asst. GP Stoke-on-Trent.

KING, Brenda Grace (retired) 27 Guardian Court, Moorend Road, Charlton Kings, Cheltenham GL53 9DP Tel: 01242 513668 — MB BS Lond. 1935; MRCS Eng. LRCP Lond. 1935.

KING, Brian KR Occupational Health Services, Moss Farm, Off blackwood Road, Rossendale OL13 0PS Tel: 01706 876407 Fax: 01706 876407 Email: bkingkrohs@aol.com; Moss Farm, Off Blackwood Road, Rossendale OL13 0PS Tel: 01706 872132 — MB ChB 1981 Manch.; MFOM RCP Lond. 1995, AFOM 1986. (Manchester) Occupat. Phys. KR Occupat. Health Serv. Socs: Soc. Occupat. Med. Prev: Occupat. Phys. Ct.aulds Textiles; Regional Occupat. Phys. AMARC (TES) Ltd. Hebburn; Research Regist. Respirat. & Exercise Physiol. Laborat. (Occupat. Health & Hyg.) Univ. Newc.

KING, Brian Robert Harwood Elmhurst Surgery, Elmhurst Road, Aylesbury HP20 2AH Tel: 01296 484054 Fax: 01296 397016; Watbridge Farm House, Ashendon, Aylesbury HP18 0HA Tel: 01296 651140 Email: brianrhking@compuserve.co.uk — MB BChir 1971 Camb.; MRCGP 1978. (St. Thos.) Prev: Regist. (Med.) MusGr. Pk. Hosp. Taunton; Supt. & Med. Off. St. Jas. Miss. Hosp. Mantsonyane, Lesotho; Med. Regist. MusGr. Pk. Hosp. Taunton.

KING, Bruce Blakistin Renal Unit, Western Infirmary, Dumbarton Road, Glasgow G11 6NT — MB ChB 1986 Auckland; FRACP 1992.

KING, Caroline Fiona The St Thomas Health Centre, Cowick St., Exeter EX4 1HJ Tel: 01392 78031; 61 St. Leonards Road, Exeter EX2 4LS — MB BS 1985 Lond.; BSc Lond. 1982, MB BS 1985; MRCGP 1989; DRCOG 1991; DGM RCP Lond. 1988. Socs: BMA. Prev: Trainee GP Exeter VTS.

KING, Catriona Mary 33 Fruithill Park, Belfast BT11 8GD — MB BCh BAO 1982 Belf.

KING, Charles Anthony James 7 Lorne Road, Walthamstow, London E17 7PX Tel: 020 8520 1583 — MB ChB 1988 Cape Town.

KING, Christina Paula Maria Kahnters Farm, Gay St., Pulborough RH20 2HJ — MB BS 1995 Lond.

KING, Christopher John 14 Crespin Way, Brighton BN1 7FG — MB BS 1985 Lond.

KING, Christopher John Barnhouse Surgery, Barnhouse Close, Lower Street, Pulborough RH20 2HQ Tel: 01798 872815 Fax: 01798 872123; The Oaks, Monkmead Lane, West Chiltington, Pulborough RH20 2NH Tel: 01798 812600 Fax: 01798 813577 — MB BS 1973 Lond.; MRCS Eng. LRCP Lond. 1973. CAA Aviat. Med. Examr.

KING, Christopher Michael Philip Redwood, 63 Benslow Lane, Hitchin SG4 9QZ — MB BS 1984 Lond.; BSc (Hons.) Lond. 1981; MRCP (UK) 1987; FRCR 1991. Cons. Diagn. Radiol. Lister Hosp. Stevenage. Socs: Brit. Inst. Radiol.; Brit. Soc. Interven. Radiol.; Magnetic Resonance Radiol. Assn. Prev: Regist. & Sen. Regist. (Diag. Radiol.) St. Bart. Hosp. Lond.

KING, David 21 Beaconsfield Road, Hastings TN34 3TW Tel: 01424 422389; Mapledurham, Friars Hill, Guestling, Hastings TN35 4EP Tel: 01424 813704 — MB BS 1960 Lond.; MRCS Eng. LRCP Lond. 1960; DObst RCOG 1962. (Westm.) Socs: BMA. Prev: Med. Supt. Lilongwe Gen. Hosp., Malawi.

KING, Mr David Gordon York District Hospital, Radiology Department, Wiggington Road, York YO31 8HE; 130 Fulford Road, Fishergate, York YO10 4BE — MB ChB 1985 Liverp.; FRCS Eng. 1990; FRCR 1994. Cons. Radiol. York Dist. Hosp. Prev: Sen. Regist. Rotat. Sheff.; Regist. (Diag. Radiol.) Hull Roy. Infirm.

KING, David Harold Royal Shrewsbury Hospital, Mytton Oak road, Shrewsbury SY3 8XQ Tel: 01743 261196; Cantlop Mill, Berrington, Shrewsbury S75 6HQ Tel: 01743 761623 — MB BS 1976 Lond.; MRCS Eng. LRCP Lond. 1976; FRCA Eng. 1981; MFPM RCP (UK) 1993. (St. Bart.) Cons. Anaesth. Roy. Shrewsbury Hosp. Prev: Hon. Cons. (Anaesth.) St. Mary's Hosp. Lond.; Internat. Med. Dir. Wellcome Foundat. Ltd.; Clin. Fell. (Anaesth.) Harvard Med. Sch. & Beth Israel Hosp. Boston, Mass., USA.

KING, David James 18 Middleton Road, Rickmansworth WD3 8JE — MB ChB 1992 Dundee.

KING, Professor David John Queen's University Belfast, Department of Therapeutics & Pharmacology, The Whitla Medical Building, 97 Lisburn Road, Belfast BT9 7BL Tel: 028 90335771 Fax: 028 90438346 Email: d.king@qub.ac.uk — MB BCh BAO Belf. 1964; MD Belf. 1971; FRCPI 1997; FRCPsych 1983, M 1972; DPM Eng. 1967. (Qu. Univ. Belf.) Prof. Clin. Psychopharmacol. Dept. Therap. & Pharmacol. Qu. Univ. Belf.; Asst. Head Sch. Med Research QUB; Cons. Psychiat. Holywell Hosp. Antrim. Socs: Brit. Assn. Psychopharmacol.; Europ. Coll. Neuropsychopharmacol.; Collegium Internat. Neuropsychopharmacol. Prev: Asst. Prof. Psychiat. Dalhousie Univ. Halifax, Canada; Andy Darlington Memor. Fell. Ment. Health Research Fund.

KING, David Robert The Surgery, The Street, Holbrook, Ipswich IP9 2PZ Tel: 01473 328263 Fax: 01473 327185 — MB BS 1984 Lond.; DRCOG 1987. GP Holbrook.

KING, Deborah Kay Lifespan Healthcare NHS Trust, Community Child Health, Ida Darwin, Fulbourn, Cambridge CB1 5EE Tel: 01223 884160 Fax: 01223 884161; 80 Downlands, Baldock Road, Royston SG8 5BY — MB 1973 Camb.; BA (Hons.) Cantab., MA; BChir 1972. (Middlx. Hosp.) Staff Grade Pract. (Community Child Health) Lifespan Healthcare NHS Trust Camb. Prev: Clin. Med. Off. N. Herts Dist. HA Hitchin.

KING, Deborah Samantha 11 Someries Road, Hemel Hempstead HP1 3PJ Tel: 01442 268879 — MB ChB 1995 Leic. SHO (Paediat.) Hemel Hempstead. Socs: MDU; MSS. Prev: SHO (Elderly Care) Welwyn Garden City; SHO (O & G) Warwick; SHO (Ear, Nose & Throat) Warwick.

KING, Debra 14 Melksham Drive, Irby, Wirral CH61 4YE Tel: 0151 648 7796; Arrowe Park Hospital, Wirral CH49 5PE Tel: 0151 604 7218 — MB ChB 1983 Leeds; MRCP (UK) 1987; FRCP 1997. Cons. Phys. (Gen. Med.) Wirral Hosp.; Hon. Clin. Lect. Univ. Liverp. Socs: BMA; Brit. Geriat. Soc. Prev: Sen. Regist. (Geriat. Med.) Roy. Liverp.

Univ. Hosp.; Regist. (Geriat.) Roy. Liverp. Hosp.; Regist. (Gen. Med.) Arrowe Pk. Hosp. Wirral.

KING, Denis Walter (retired) 25 Windmill Rise, Kingston upon Thames KT2 7TU Tel: 020 8549 3807 — MB BS 1952 Lond.; MRCS Eng. LRCP Lond. 1952; DA Eng. 1954. Hon. Anaesth. New Vict. Hosp. Kingston. Prev: Clin. Asst. (Anaesth.) Kingston Hosp. Gp.

KING, Derek John 17 Rosebery Street, Aberdeen AB15 5LN Tel: 01224 648925 — MB ChB 1976 Aberd.; FRCP (Ed.) 1993; MRCP (UK) 1979; FRCPath 1995, MR 1985. Cons. Haemat. Roy. Aberd. Childr. Hosp. & Aberd. Teach. Hosp. Prev: Ho. Off. Aberd. Roy. Infirm.; Resid. (Haemat.) McMaster Univ. Canada; Lect. (Med.) Univ. Aberd.

KING, Donald Stuart (retired) Butts Farm, Eves Corner, Danbury, Chelmsford CM3 4QF Tel: 01245 222017 — MB 1963 Camb.; MB Camb. 1964, BChir 1963; MRCS Eng. LRCP Lond. 1963; DObst RCOG 1968. Prev: GP Danbury Essex.

KING, Doreen Maxwell (retired) 5 Churchill Gate, Woodstock OX20 1QW Tel: 01993 813115 — MRCS Eng. LRCP Lond. 1944; MFFP 1993; DCH Eng. 1947. Hon. Clin. Asst. (Venereol.) W. Lond. Hosp.; Instruc. Med. Off., Vasectomy Counsellor Family Plann. Assn. Prev: Cons. Wom.'s Servs. Univ. Brunel.

KING, Dorothy Anne 64 Panton Road, Hoole, Chester CH2 3HN Tel: 01244 350706 — MB BS 1982 Lond.; BSc Lond. 1979, MB BS 1982; MRCGP 1986; DRCOG 1985; DCH RCP Lond. 1985. Clin. Asst. (Endoscopy), Countess of Chester Hosp. Prev: Clin. Asst. (Oncol.), P.ss Roy. Hosp., Haywards Heath; Trust Practitioner (Endoscopy) P.ss Roy. Hosp. Haywards Heath; Trainee GP Cuckfield Hosp. VTS Mid Downs HA.

KING, Douglas Baird Mackenzie The Clinic, 4 Firs Entry, Bannockburn, Stirling FK7 0HW Tel: 01786 813435 Fax: 01786 817545; 9 Albert Place, Stirling FK8 2QL Tel: 01786 72425 — MB ChB 1980 Dundee; DRCOG 1982.

KING, Douglas Michael Harwood House, Lodge Hill Road, Lower Bourne, Farnham GU10 3RD Email: mike.king@ic.ac.uk — MB BS 1971 Lond.; MRCS Eng. LRCP Lond. 1971; FRCR 1977; DMRD Eng. 1976. Cons. Radiol. Chelsea & W.m. & Roy. Marsden Hosps. Lond. Socs: RCR (Examr.). Prev: Edr. Brit. Jl. Radiol.; Sen. Regist. (Radiol.) & SHO (Chest Med.) W.m. Hosp.

KING, Edward James Highdown, 40 Dyke Road Ave., Brighton BN1 5LE Tel: 01273 503023; 20 Sackville Road, Hove BN3 3FF Tel: 01273 778585 Fax: 01273 724648 — MB BS 1963 Lond.; MRCS Eng. LRCP Lond. 1963; DTM & H Eng. 1965; DObst RCOG 1966. (Westm.) Mem. E. Sussex Local Med. Comm.; Bd. Mem. Brighton & Hove Primary Care Gp. Socs: Brighton & Sussex M-C Soc.; Innominate Soc. Prev: SHO (Obst.) BMH Rinteln, Germany; Ho. Phys. & Cas. Off. W.m. Hosp. Lond.

KING, Eric Tharratt, Wing Cdr. RAF Med. Br. Retd. (retired) 24 Bushfield Road, Albrighton, Wolverhampton WV7 3PD — LMSSA 1949 Lond.; DPH Bristol 1965; MFCM 1974. Prev: Med. Off. Shrops. HA.

KING, Ernest 57 Dowsett Road, London N17 9DL — LRCP LRCS 1940 Ed.; LRCP LRCS Ed. LRFPS Glas. 1940. (Ed.) Prev: Maj. RAMC; Res. Med. Off. Waterloo Hosp. & Beckenham Hosp.

KING, Frances Mary Anaesthetic Department, Portsmouth Hospitals NHS Trust, Queen Alexandra Hospital, Cosham, Portsmouth PO6 3LY Tel: 023 92 379451; Mayhill, Mayhill Lane, Swanmore, Southampton SO32 2QW Tel: 01489 878519 — MB BS 1984 Lond.; FCAnaesth 1989. (Univ. Coll. Hosp. Sch. Med.) Cons. Anaesth. Portsmouth Hosps. NHS Trust. Prev: Sen. Regist. (Anaesth.) Middlx. Hosp. Lond.; Regist. (Anaesth.) Univ. Coll. Hosp.; SHO (ITU & Chest Med.) Stoke Mandeville Hosp.

KING, Geoffrey Denis 9 Bryniau Road, Llandudno LL30 2BL — MB ChB 1973 Liverp.; DRCOG 1981; DCH Eng. 1979.

KING, Geoffrey Richard Gold Street Medical Centre, 106 Gold Street, Wellingborough NN8 4BT Tel: 01933 223429 Fax: 01933 229240; 1 Lea Way, Wellingborough NN8 3LX Tel: 01933 443364 — MB ChB 1986 Leic.; BSc Med. Sci. Leic. 1983; MRCGP 1990.

KING, George Michael (retired) Hillcrest, Thornhill, Bamford, Hope Valley, Sheffield S33 0BR Tel: 01433 651414 — MB ChB Sheff. 1945; BSc (Hons.) Sheff. 1944, MD 1951; FRCR 1975; FFR 1954; DMRT Eng. 1948. Prev: Hon. Cons. Radiother. & Oncol. W.on Pk. Hosp. Sheff.

KING, Gregor Conrad T/L 48 Thornwood Terrace, Glasgow G11 7QZ — MB ChB 1992 Glas.

KING, Hannah Bedfont House, Prospect Place, Hythe, Southampton SO45 6AT — MB ChB 1994 Leic.

KING, Harold Anthony Patrick Clonmel, 114 Crabtree Lane, Lancing BN15 9PW Tel: 01903 754876 — MB BS 1955 Lond.; DObst RCOG 1958. (St. Bart.) Prev: Ho. Surg. (O & G) St. Bart. Hosp.; Ho. Phys. & Cas. Off. St. Helier Hosp. Carshalton.

KING, Heather Alexandra 17 Mill Lane, St Ippolyts, Hitchin SG4 7NN — MB BS 1998 Lond.; MB BS Lond 1998.

KING, Helen Central Health Clinic, 1 Mulberry St., Sheffield S1 2PJ Tel: 0114 271 6790 Fax: 0114 271 6791 Email: helenk@chsheff-tr.trent.nhs.uk; 81 Dransfield Road, Sheffield S10 5RP Tel: 0114 230 1810 Email: kingsheffield@tesco.net — MB ChB 1972 Sheff.; DObst RCOG 1974; MFFP 1993. Cons. Family Plann. & Reproduc. Health Care, Community Health Sheff. NHS Trust. Socs: Fac. Fam. Plann. & Reproduc. Health Care; Brit. Menopause Soc.; Soc. Pub. Health. Prev: SCMO (Family Plann. & Wom.'s Health) Community Health Sheff. NHS Trust; Sen. Clin. Asst. Sheff. Fertil. Centre; Clin. Asst. Univ. Research Clinic Jessop Hosp. Wom. Sheff.

***KING, Helen Mary** 1 Swanns Meadow, Bookham, Leatherhead KT23 4JX — MB ChB 1997 Bristol.

KING, Helen Roasalind Roslea, 51 Station Road, Bamber bridge PR5 6PE Tel: 01772 335128 Fax: 01772 492248 — MB ChB 1979 Manchester Univ.; MRCGP 1984. p/t GP, 3/4 time Princip.

KING, Hilary Lucina Emperor's Gate Centre for Health, First Floor, 49 Emperors Gate, London SW7 4HJ Tel: 020 8237 5333 Fax: 020 8237 5344; 70 Chaucer Road, London W3 6DP Tel: 020 8993 1235 — MB BS 1982 Lond.; MRCGP 1989. (Charing Cross)

KING, Ian 15 Menteith View, Dunblane FK15 0PD — MB ChB 1977 Glas.

KING, Ian David Hall Heene and Goring Practice, 145 Heene Road, Worthing BN12 4PY Tel: 01903 235344 Fax: 01903 247099; 15 Pevensey Road, Worthing BN11 5NP Tel: 01903 501159 — BSc Lond. 1981, MB BS 1984; MRCGP 1988; DRCOG 1986; DCH RCP Lond. 1986. (Westm.) GP Worthing. Prev: Trainee GP Huntingdon VTS.; Ho. Off. Watford Gen. Hosp. & W.m. Hosp. Lond.

KING, Isabel Jean Crossbrook Surgery, 126 Crossbrook Street, Cheshunt, Waltham Cross EN8 8JY Tel: 01992 622908 Fax: 01992 624756; 45 Moorhurst Avenue, Goffs Oak, Waltham Cross EN7 5LD Tel: 01707 873102 — MB BS 1973 Lond.; MRCS Eng. LRCP Lond. 1973; DRCOG 1979. (Roy. Free) GP Herts. FHSA. Socs: BMA; Assoc. RCGP. Prev: Sen. Med. Off. Nixon Memor Hosp. Sierra Leone; Ho. Off. (O & G) N. Middlx. Hosp. Lond.; Ho. Phys. Roy. Free Hosp. Lond.

KING, Jacqueline Elizabeth Delapre Medical Centre, Gloucester Avenue, Northampton NN4 8QF Tel: 01604 765408 — MB ChB 1986 Sheff.; MRCGP 1990; DRCOG 1990. GP partner.

KING, James Adam Tillicoultry Health Centre, Park Street, Tillicoultry FK13 6AG Tel: 01259 750531 Fax: 01259 752818; Tel: 01259 742521 — MB ChB 1986 Ed.; MRCGP 1990; T(GP) 1991; DCCH RCP Ed. 1991; DRCOG 1990. Socs: Forth Valley LMC - Vice Chairm.; Forth Valley AMC; N. Forth Valley LHCC - Clin. Bd. Mem. Prev: Trainee GP Borders HB VTS.

KING, James Ian (retired) Brookbarn, Stonebridge, Durham DH1 3RX Tel: 0191 386 1990 Email: oanking14@hotmail.com — MB BS 1957 Durh.; DObst RCOG 1959. Prev: Ho. Surg. & Ho. Phys. Roy. Vict. Infirm. Newc.

KING, Jamie Patrick Top Left, 213 Wilton St., Glasgow G20 6DE — MB ChB 1996 Dundee.

KING, Janet Margaret Princess Margaret Hospital, Okus Road, Swindon SN1 4JH Tel: 01793 536231 Fax: 01793 426774 Email: janetking@smnhst.swest.uk — MB ChB 1976 Manch.; FRCP; MRCP (UK) 1979; FRCPCH. (Manch.) Cons. Paediat. P.ss Margt. Hosp. Swindon. Prev: Lect. Dept. Paediat. Univ. Sheff.; Tutor Child Health Dept. Child Health Univ. Manch.

KING, Jayne Victoria Howgrave-Graham and Partners, The Surgery, Moot Lane, Downton, Salisbury SP5 3JP Tel: 01725 510296 Fax: 01725 513119 — MB BS 1986 Lond.; MRCGP 1991; DCH RCP Lond. 1990; DRCOG 1989. (Char. Cross & Westm.) Clin. Med. Off. (Family Plann.) Salisbury. Prev: Trainee GP Som. & Roy. Free Hosp. Lond. VTS; SHO (Paediat.) Taunton & Som. Hosp.

KING, Jeannette Anne Coach House Surgery, 12 Park Avenue, Watford WD18 7LX Tel: 01923 223178 Fax: 01923 816464; 37 Elstree Road, Bushey Heath WD2 3EE Email: drjennyking@aol.com — MB BS 1989 Lond.; BSc Lond. 1986; MRCGP 1993. (Charing

Cross & Westminster) GP Princip. Coach Ho. Surg. Watford; Hospice Pract. Peace Hospice Watford; Cancer Lead Watford & 3 Rivers Pot. Socs: RCGP.

KING, Jennifer Ann University Health Service, 2 Claremont Place, Sheffield S10 2TB Tel: 0114 222 2100 Fax: 0114 276 7223 — MB ChB 1975 Sheff.; DRCOG 1977.

KING, Mr John Beverley Well Cottage, Chislehurst Road, Bromley BR1 2NW Tel: 020 8467 6095 — MB BS 1967 Lond.; FRCS Eng. 1973; MRCS Eng. LRCP Lond. 1967. (Lond. Hosp.) Sen. Lect. Lond. Hosp. Med. Coll.; Hon. Cons. (Orthop. & Trauma Surg.) Lond. Hosp.; Dir. Acad. Dept. Sports Med. Lond. Hosp. Med. Coll. Socs: ISAKOS; Chairm. Brit. Assn. Sport & Med. Prev: Cons. Orthop. Surg. Newham Health Dist.

KING, John David 100 Harley Street, London W1G 7JA Tel: 020 7935 3084 Fax: 020 7935 3084; 126 Ferndene Road, London SE24 0AA Tel: 020 7274 3171 Fax: 020 7733 9142 — MB BS Lond. 1966; MRCS Eng. LRCP Lond. 1965; Assoc. Fac. Occupat. Med. RCP Lond. 1979. (King's Coll. Hosp.) Med. Dir. Lond. Hyperbaric Med. Serv.; Mem. Compressed Air Working Gp.; Hse Med. Examr. of Divers. Socs: E.U.B.S. Prev: Sen. Research Assoc. (Surg.) Newc. Med. Adviser Balfour Beatty Construc. Ltd.; Regist. (A & E) King's Coll. Hosp. Lond.

KING, Mr John Gordon, Group Capt. RAF Med. Br. Retd. 9 Purbeck Close, Uploders, Bridport DT6 4PR Tel: 01308 485282 — FRCS Glas. 1974; MRCS Eng. LRCP Lond. 1955. (Leeds) Prev: Cons. Surg. RAF.

KING, John Lee Clark Avenue Surgery, Clark Avenue, Pontnewydd, Cwmbran NP44 1RY Tel: 01633 482733 Fax: 01633 867758; Lattice Cottage, Bettws Newydd, Usk NP15 1JP Tel: 01873 881080 — MRCS Eng. LRCP Lond. 1979; MA Camb. 1980. (Guy's)

KING, John Magnus 10 Longmeade Gardens, Wilmslow SK9 1DA — MB ChB 1987 Liverp.

KING, John Magoveny (retired) 11 Kings Avenue, Morpeth NE61 1HX Tel: 01670 512707 — MB ChB 1940 Glas.; FRCOG 1965, M 1949. Hon. Cons. O & G Ashington Hosp. & Newc. HA (T). Prev: Examr. RCOG Univ. Newc. & Centr. Midw. Bd.

KING, John Matthew Well Street Medical Centre, Well Street, Biddulph, Stoke-on-Trent ST8 6HD Tel: 01782 513939 Fax: 01782 523085 — MB ChB 1984 Manch.

KING, John Richard Hill Crest, Quinneys Lane, Redditch B98 7WG Tel: 01527 500575 — MB ChB Leeds 1970; BSc (Hons.) (Chem. Physiol.) Leeds 1970; MRCPsych 1979. Cons. Psychiat. Worcs Community Trust; Hon. Sen. Clin. Lect. (Psychiat.) Univ. Birm.; Assoc. Fell. (Pschology) Univ. Warwick. Socs: Assoc. Fell. (Psychol.) Univ. Warwick. Prev: Sen. Regist. & Hon. Lect. (Psychol. Med.) Middlx. Hosp. Lond.; Research Fell. (Biochem. & Psychiat.) Univ. Leeds; Regist. N.wick Pk. Hosp. Clin. Research Centre Harrow.

KING, Jonathan Peter 3 Top Row, Newall with Clifton, Otley LS21 2HF — MB BS 1988 Lond.

KING, Joseph Andrew 15 Warwick Drive, Washington NE37 2NQ — MB BS 1992 Lond.

KING, Judith Christine Drs. Wharton and King, Burntwood Health Centre, Hudson Drive, Burntwood WS7 0EW — MB BChir 1980 Camb.; BA 1978 Camb.; MA 1983 Camb.; MRCGP 1986; DRCOG 1985. (Cambridge) Gen. Practitioner.

KING, Judith Maybrey Bassett Road Surgery, 29 Bassett Road, Leighton Buzzard LU7 1AR Tel: 01525 373111 Fax: 01525 853767; Sycamore House, Cane End Farm, Hulcott, Aylesbury HP22 5AX Tel: 01296 393837 Fax: 01296 395859 — MB BS 1974 Lond.; MRCGP 1978; DRCOG 1976. (St. Geo.) GP Leighton Buzzard; OHP Marks & Spencer plc. Prev: Trainee GP Aylesbury VTS; Ho. Phys. & Ho. Surg. Stoke Mandeville Hosp. Aylesbury.

KING, Juliet Elizabeth Flat 52, Viceroy Court, Wilmslow Road, Manchester M20 2RH — BM 1990 Soton.; FRCS Eng. 1996. (Soton.)

KING, Katharine Jane Rother House Medical Centre, Alcester Road, Stratford-upon-Avon CV37 6PP Tel: 01789 269386 Fax: 01789 298742; Whitestones, Haselor, Alcester B49 6LU Tel: 01789 488013 — MB BS 1988 Lond.; MRCGP 1993; DRCOG 1993; DCH RCP Lond. 1992. (Roy. Free Hosp. Sch. Med.) Med. Lect. Asthma Train. Center; Asst. GP Tutor Warwick. Socs: BMA. Prev: SHO (Paediat.) Qu. Eliz. Hosp. Childr.; SHO (O & G) St. Thos. Hosp. Lond.; SHO Rotat. (Med.) Whipps Cross & Wanstead Hosps.

KING, Katherine Ievers (retired) Ashcombe House, Fosse Way, Stow on the Wold, Cheltenham GL54 1DW Tel: 01451 830408 — MB ChB Ed. 1941.

KING, Kathleen Marion 251 Chesterfield Road, Sheffield S8 0RT Tel: 0114 551164 — MB BCh BAO 1945 Belf. (Belf.) Prev: RAMC.

KING, Kathleen Rosemary 23 Harberton Drive, Belfast BT9 6PF — MB BCh BAO 1956 Dub.

KING, Kathryn Ann East Suffolk Health Authority, PO Box 55, Ipswich IP3 8NN Tel: 01473 712272; Mitford House, Station Road, Elmswell, Bury St Edmunds IP30 9HD Tel: 01359 242789 — BM 1982 Soton. Cons. Pub. Health Med. Suff. HA. Prev: Sen. Regist. (Pub. Health Med.) E. Anglian RHA.

KING, Lamin Aggrey 23 Denmark House, Maryon Road, Charlton, London SE7 8DE — MB BS 1996 Lond.

KING, Lawrence Hatton Stenfors The Almshouse Surgery, Trinity Medical Centre, Thornhill Street, Wakefield WF1 1PG Tel: 01924 327150 Fax: 01924 327165 — MB ChB 1984 Leic.; MA (Hons.) (Physiol. Sci.) Oxf. 1985; DRCOG 1988. Prev: Trainee GP Airedale VTS.

KING, Leonard John Department of Clinical Radiology, Royal Hospital Haslar, Haslar Road, Gosport PO12 2AA Tel: 02392 762930 Fax: 02392 762400 Email: leonking@dsca.gov.uk; 1 West Road, Barton Stacey, Winchester SO21 3SB Tel: 01962 761287 Fax: 01962 761485 — MB ChB 1989 Dundee; MRCP (UK) 1993; FRCR 1996. (Univ. Dundee) Cons. Radiologist, Roy. Hosp. Haslar, Gosport. Prev: Regist. (Diagn. Radiol.) St. Bart. Hosp. Lond.; MRI Fell. Chelsea & W.m. Hosp. Lond.

KING, Lesley-Gaye Carolyn Royal Hospital for Sick Children, Yorkhill, Glasgow G3 8SJ; 17 Mossneuk Drive, Paisley PA2 8PG — MB BS 1992 West Indies; MRCP (UK) 1997. SHO (Paediat.) Roy. Hosp. Sick Childr. Glas.

KING, Linda Elizabeth Broxham Manor, Four Elms, Edenbridge TN8 6LS — MB BS 1979 Lond.; DRCOG 1982. (Kings)

KING, Linda Jayne Erne Health Centre, Enniskillen BT74 6AY Tel: 02866 322707 Fax: 02866 324690; Tiermacspird, Lack, Enniskillen BT93 0FA Tel: 02868 632022 — MB BCh BAO 1993 Belf.; MRCGP 1998; DRCOG 1996; DME RCPI 1995; DCH RCPSI 1997. (Queens University Belfast) p/t GP Princip., Erne Health Centre, Enniskillen. Prev: GP Regist. Castlederg, Co. Tyrone.

KING, Louise 36 Newlands Road, Halifax HX2 7RE — MB ChB 1997 Leeds.

KING, Malgorzata 43 Blakeney Road, Sheffield S10 1FD — MB ChB 1994 Sheff.

KING, Margaret Naomi Rivers 31 Myrtle Avenue, Ruislip HA4 8SA — MB BS 1961 Lond.; MRCS Eng. LRCP Lond. 1961.

KING, Marie Woodlea, 37 Ernespie Road, Castle Douglas DG7 1LD — MB ChB 1998 Manch.; MB ChB Manch 1998.

KING, Marie Martina 5 Avondale Court, 85 Brighton Road, Sutton SM2 5TR — MB BCh BAO 1992 Dub.

KING, Martin Howard Teignmouth Medical Practice, 2 Den Crescent, Teignmouth TQ14 8BG Tel: 01626 770297 Email: martin.king@gp-183022.nhs.uk — BM 1986 Soton.; MRCGP 1991; Dip. Pract. Dermat. Wales 1991; T(GP) 1991; Cert. Family Plann. JCC 1990. (Soton.) Clin. Med. Off. (Psychiat.) Tiverton & Mid Devon; Med. Off. S. Devon Railway; Sect. 12 approved practitioner under terms of the 1983 Ment. Health Act. Socs: Fell. Roy. Soc. Health; BMA. Prev: Trainee GP N. Devon & Exeter; SHO (Psychiat.) Wonford Hse. Hosp. Exeter; SHO (Ophth.) N. Devon Dist. Hosp.

KING, Martin James South Birmingham Trauma Unit, Selly Oak Hospital, Raddlebarn Lane, Birmingham B29 6JD Tel: 0121 426 6400 Fax: 0121 426 6400 Email: martin.king@lineone.net; 52 Oakham Road, Harborne, Birmingham B17 9DG Tel: 0121 426 6400 — MB BS 1980 Lond.; FFA RCS Eng. 1985. Cons. S. Birm. Trauma Unit. Prev: Regist. (Anaesth.) Univ. Coll. Hosp., Roy. Nat. Orthop. Hosps. & Brompton Hosp. Lond.; Staff Anaesth. Roy. Wom. Hosp. Melbourne Austral.; Regist. (Anaesth.) St. Bart. Hosp. Lond.

***KING, Martyn Ian** 17 Keble Road, Knighton Fields, Leicester LE2 6AF — MB ChB 1998 Leic.; MB ChB Leic 1998.

KING, Mary (retired) Ppiers Pool, Shoreham Lane, Halstead, Sevenoaks TN14 7DD — MRCS Eng. LRCP Lond. 1927; DPH 1929. Prev: Ho. Surg. St. Mary's Hosp. Lond.

KING, Matthew Owen 7 Ivor Close, Aldersey Road, Guildford GU1 2ET; Fernhurst, Willey Broom Lane, Caterham CR3 5BD — MB

BS 1984 Lond.; BSc Lond. 1981, MB BS 1984; MRCGP 1988; DRCOG 1987. (Char. Cross)

KING, Matthew Raymond Coleridge Medical Centre, Canaan Way, Ottery St Mary EX11 1EQ Tel: 01404 814447 — MB BS 1988 Lond.; MRCGP 1992; DGM RCP Lond. 1994. (St. Thos. Hosp. Med. Sch. Lond.) GP; Clin. Asst. Reablement; Examr. Dipl. of Gen. Med. RCP. Prev: Trainee GP Exeter; Staff Grade (Geriat. Med.) Exeter.

KING, Matthew Roderick Gerardus 10 (4F2) St Peters Buildings, Gilmore Place, Edinburgh EH3 9PG Tel: 0131 229 8594 Email: matt@edintolx.demon.uk — MB ChB 1994 Ed.; BSc (Med. Sci.) Ed. 1991; MRCP (UK) 1997. (Edinburgh) SHO (Renal) Roy. Infirm. Edin. Socs: BMA; Med. & Defence Union of Scotl. Prev: SHO (Geriat.s) Roy. Infirm. Edin.; SHO (Med.) Falkirk & Dist. Roy. Infirm.; SHO (Rheumatics) W.ern Gen. Hosp. Edin.

KING, Melanie Rhena Golden Grove, Estavarney Lane, Monkswood, Usk NP15 1QE — MB ChB 1993 Manch.; DRCOG 1996; DFFP 1996; DGM RCP Lond. 1995. Trainee GP/SHO (O & G) Glos. VTS.

KING, Professor Michael Bruce Department of Psychiatry & Behavioural Sciences, Royal Free & university Colleege, Medical Schee, Royal Free Campus, London NW3 2PF Tel: 020 7830 2397 Fax: 020 7830 2808 Email: mike@rfhsm.ac.uk — MB ChB 1987 Auckland; MB ChB Auckland 1976; PhD Lond. 1989; BSc Canterbury 1971; BSc (Human Biol.) Auckland 1973, MD 1987; FRCP Lond. 1996; MRCP (UK) 1979; MRCPsych 1984; FRCGP 1991, M 1981. Prof. & Hon. Cons. Roy. Free Hosp. Lond.; Hon. Sen. Lect. Inst. Psychiat. Lond. Socs: Fell. Roy. Soc. Med. (Pres. Counc. Psychiat.). Prev: Sen. Lect. (Gen. Pract.) Research Unit. Inst. Psychiat. Lond.

KING, Michael Dudley (retired) Ashcombe House, Fosse Way, Stow-on-the-Wold, Cheltenham GL54 1DW Tel: 01451 830408 — MB BChir 1946 Camb.; MRCS Eng. LRCP Lond. 1941. Prev: Ho. Phys. N. Middlx. Co. Hosp.

KING, Mr Michael Stanton, OBE 34 Redfern Close, Cambridge CB4 2DU Tel: 01223 328557 — MB BChir Camb. 1962; MA Camb. 1963; FRCS Eng. 1966. Vis. Surg. Nkhata Bay Hosp., Malawi. Socs: Fell. Assn. Surgs. E. Afr. Prev: Chief Surg. Qu. Eliz. Hosp. Blantyre, Malawi.

KING, Michaela Jane 176 Queen Alexandra Mansions, Judd St., London WC1H 9DJ — MB ChB 1987 Manch.; DRCOG 1992; Dip. GU Med. Soc. Apoth. Lond. 1990.

KING, Monique Maria Kristina Straight Bit Surgery, 17 Straight Bit, Flackwell Heath, High Wycombe HP10 9LS Tel: 01628 522838 Fax: 01628 529255 — BM BCh 1986 Oxf.; MA Oxf. 1991; MRCGP 1996; DFFP 1994; Cert. Managem. (OU) 1997. (Oxford) GP. Prev: Assoc. Lect. Open Univ.

KING, Nicholas Anthony 29 Stock Lane, Wybunbury, Nantwich CW5 5ED — MB ChB 1983 Manch.; MRCGP 1987.

KING, Nicholas Clive Health Care Group, St. Martins Health Centre, Grand Rue, St Martin's, Guernsey Tel: 01481 37757 Fax: 01481 39591; Les Pelerins, La Rue De La Planque, St Martin, Guernsey GY4 6TH Tel: 01481 37168 — MB BS 1979 Lond.; MRCS Eng. LRCP Lond. 1978. (Char. Cross) GP St. Peter Port; Med. Off. Andrew Mitchell Hse. Les Bourgs Hospice St. And. Guernsey; States Venereologist St. Peter Port Guernsey. Socs: Assn. Palliat. Med. Prev: SHO (Paediat.) St. Richard's Hosp. Chichester; SHO (Gen. Surg. & Urol.) & SHO (Neurotrauma & Orthop.) Addenbrooke's Hosp. Camb.

KING, Nicholas John Sedgeford House, 27 Underdale Road, Shrewsbury SY2 5DW — MB ChB 1976 Sheff.; MRCGP 1980; DCH 1981; DRCOG 1979. Prev: SHO (Paediat., O & G) Roy. Shrewsbury Hosp.; Ho. Surg. Norf. & Norwich Hosp.

KING, Nigel Henry Thomas Keeling Street Doctors Surgery, Keeling Street, North Somercotes, Louth LN11 7QU Tel: 01507 358623 Fax: 01507 358746; 203 East Gate, Louth LN11 8DB Tel: 01507 601995 — MB BS 1976 Lond.; MRCS Eng. LRCP Lond. 1976; MRCGP 1984; DRCOG 1982. (St. Mary's) Clin. Asst. (Gastroenterol. Endoscopy). Prev: SHO (O & G) Harold Wood Hosp. Essex; Cas. Off. Hereford Gen. Hosp. & St. Mary's Hosp. Lond.

KING, Norma Elizabeth Links Medical Centre, Restalrig Park Medical Centre, 40 Alemoor Crescent, Edinburgh EH7 6UJ Tel: 0131 554 2141 Fax: 0131 554 5363; 32 Drumsheugh Gardens, Edinburgh EH3 7RN — MB ChB 1983 Ed.; MRCGP 1987; DRCOG 1986.

KING, Norman Wilfred Department of Anaesthetics, Leicester General Hospital, Gwendolt Road, Leicester LE5 4PW Tel: 0116 249 0490 Ext: 4661/4659 — MB BS 1963 Lond.; BSc (Physiol.) Lond. 1960; MRCS Eng. LRCP Lond. 1963; FRCA 1971. (King's Coll. Lond. & King's Coll. Hosp.) Cons. Anaesth. Leicester Gen. Hosp. Socs: Assn. Anaesth.; Anaesth. Res. Soc. Prev: Research Asst. Research (Anaesth.) RCS; Sen. Regist. S. W.. RHB; Regist. Soton. Gen. Hosp.

KING, Paromita Derbyshire Royal Infirmass, Londond Road DE1 2NQ Tel: 01332 347141 — MB BS 1988 Newc.; BMedSci (1st cl. Hons.) 1985; MRCP (UK) 1992; DM Nottm 1998 Newcastle Upon Tyne. Cons. Phys. with a Interest in Diabetes & Endocnnology. Prev: Sen. Regist. (Gen. Med., Diabetes & Endocrinol.) Nottm. Derby Rotat.; Regist. Rotat. (Gen. Med., Diabetes & Endocrinol.) Mid. Trent.; Research Regist. (Diabetes) Univ. Hosp. Nottm.

KING, Paul Anthony Oakleigh, Bailey Lane End, Ross-on-Wye HR9 5TR — MB ChB 1988 Bristol; MRCGP 1993; DRCOG 1992; DCH RCP Lond. 1991.

KING, Paul Herbert Mark Eden Medical Group, Port Road, Carlisle CA2 7AJ Tel: 01228 24477; Eden Vale, Grinsdale, Carlisle CA5 6DS — BM BS 1987 Nottm.; BMedSci Nottm. 1985; DCH 1996; DRCOG 1995; MRCGP 1996. (Nottm.) GP Partner. Socs: BMA. Prev: Regist. Histopath. Roy. Vict. Infirm. Newc.; SHO (Histopath.) Leicester Roy. Infirm.; SHO (A & E & Orthop.) W. Cumbld. Hosp. Whitehaven.

KING, Penelope Anne 10 Farrar Drive, Marlborough SN8 1TP Tel: 01672 511871 — MB ChB 1978 Ed.; MRCOG 1986; Dip. Human & Clin. Genetics Lond. 1987. Med. Off. Internat. Organisation for Migration. Prev: Med. Off. Internat. Organisation for Migration; Lect. (O & G) Univ. Hong Kong; Regist. (O & G) St. Mary's Hosp. Lond.

KING, Peter (retired) Prescott Lodge, Baschurch, Shrewsbury SY4 2DS — MB ChB 1954 Liverp.; MRCGP 1964. Prev: GP BasCh.

KING, Peter Barrett Department of Anaesthesia, Bromley Hospital, Cromwell Avenue, Bromley BR2 9AJ Tel: 020 8289 7120; 103 Hamilton Road, West Norwood, London SE27 9SE Tel: 020 8670 6291 — MB BChir 1980 Camb.; BA Camb. 1976; MRCS Eng. LRCP Lond. 1979; FRCA 1991; FFA RCSI 1990. (Camb. & King's Coll. Hosp.) Cons. Anaesth. & Dir. (Intens. Care) Bromley Hosps. Trust. Socs: Assn. Anaesth.; Brit. Assn. Day Surg. Prev: Sen. Regist. King's Coll. Hosp. Lond.; Regist. (Anaesth.) St. Bart. Hosp. Lond.

KING, Mr Peter Francis, CB, OBE, CStJ, Air Vice-Marshal RAF Med. Br. Retd. (retired) 5 Churchill Gate, Oxford Road, Woodstock OX20 1QW Tel: 01993 813115 — MRCS Eng. LRCP Lond. 1945; FRCS Ed. 1947; MFOM RCP Lond. 1982; DLO Eng. 1947. Cons. Otol. King Edwd. VII Hosp. Midhurst; Cons. Otol. Civil Aviat. Auth.; Vice-Pres. Roy. Nat. Inst. for Deaf; Hunt. Prof. RCS Eng.; Whittingham Prof. Aviat. Med. RCP. Prev: Hon. Surg. to HM the Qu.

KING, Peter John (retired) 36 Kings Wall, Malmesbury SN16 9DB Tel: 01666 824508 — MB BS Lond. 1952; MRCGP 1965; DCH Eng. 1957; DObst RCOG 1957.

KING, Peter John Far Lane Medical Centre, 1 Far Lane, Sheffield S6 4FA Tel: 0114 234 3229 — MB ChB 1974 Sheff.; MRCGP 1980; DRCOG 1977.

KING, Mr Peter Mackenzie Ward 49, Aberdeen Royal Infirmary, Foresterhill, Aberdeen AB25 2ZN Tel: 01224 554571 Email: p.m.king@ark.grampian.scot.nhs.uk; 6 St Ronan's Circle, Peterculter AB14 0NE — MD 1987 Ed.; MB ChB 1978; FRCS Ed. 1983. (Edinburgh) Cons. Surg. Aberd. Roy. Infirm.; Hon. Sen. Lect. Univ. Aberd. Prev: Fell. (Trauma & Gen. Surg.) Toronto, Canada; Sen. Regist. (Gen. Surg.) Lothian Hosps.

KING, Peter Michael 7A Clarendon Gardens, London W9 1AY Tel: 020 7286 2971 Fax: 020 7286 2512; Glaxo Welcome UK Limited, Bio Stockley Park W., Uxbridge UB11 1BT Tel: 020 8990 2567 Fax: 020 8990 4357 Email: pmk2711@glaxowellcome.co.uk — MB BS 1979 Lond.; BSc Lond. 1976; MFPM RCP (UK) 1992; Dip. Pharm. Med. RCP (UK) 1991. (Barts.) Assoc. Med. Dir. Glaxo Welcome UK Ltd. Socs: Soc. Pharm. Med.; BMA. Prev: Sen. Med. Advisor Roche, UK; Int. Med. Manager Roche, Basel; Sen. Clin. Research Phys. Syntex.

KING, Peter Thomas (retired) 137 Station Street, Rippingale, Bourne PE10 0TA Tel: 01778 440387 — MB BS Lond. 1963; FRCR 1975; DMRD Eng. 1970. Prev: Cons. Radiol. Pilgrim Hosp. Boston.

KING, Philip Austin (retired) 14 Berkeley Road, Barnes, London SW13 9LZ Tel: 020 8748 2288 Fax: 020 8748 2288 Email:

phil@pagrk.demon.co.uk — MB ChB 1948 Sheff.; FRCS Eng. 1953. Hon. Cons. Surg. Hosp. St. John & St. Eliz. Prev: Cons. Surg. St. Stephen Hosp. Chelsea.

KING, Polly Megan Well Cottage, Chislehurst Road, Bickley, Bromley BR1 2NW — MB BS 1997 Lond.

KING, Quentin Gilbert Alan 29 Byron Hill Road, Harrow HA2 0JD — MB BS 1988 Tasmania.

KING, Richard Brookfield House, Spoutwell Lane, Corbridge NE45 5LF — MB BS 1991 Newc.

KING, Richard Alan 1 Wilkes Row, Orcop Hill, Hereford HR2 8EP — MB ChB 1989 Birm.

KING, Richard Granville Pearson (retired) Oxford Farm, Keysoe, Bedford MK44 2JD Tel: 01234 376402 — MB BChir 1951 Camb.; MA, MB BChir Camb. 1951; DObst RCOG 1958. Prev: Clin. Asst. (ENT) Clayton Hosp. Wakefield.

KING, Richard Herbert (retired) 15 Durnsford Way, Cranleigh GU6 7LN Tel: 01483 271607 — MRCS Eng. LRCP Lond. 1951. Prev: Ho. Surg. & Ho. Phys. Epsom Dist. Hosp.

KING, Mr Richard Jonathan Oldchurch Hospital, Romford RM7 0BE Tel: 01708 708460; 3 Campden House Terrace, Kesington, Church St, London W8 4BQ Tel: 020 7727 2625 — MB BS 1969 Lond.; FRCS Eng. 1974. Cons. Orthop. Surg. OldCh. Hosp. Socs: Fell. Roy. Soc. Med. Prev: Sen. Regist. (Orthop.) St. Mary's Hosp. Lond; Clin. Lect. Roy. Nat. Orthop. Hosp. Lond.; Regist. (Orthop.) Roy. Free & Windsor Gp. Hosps.

KING, Robert Brook Cottage, 53 Cameron Park, Old Galgorm Road, Ballymena BT42 1OJ Tel: 02825 653273 — FFA RCSI 1971; FFA RCS 1957 Eng.; MB BCh BAO 1951 Dub.; DA 1954 Eng.; MB BCh BAO Dub. 1951; FFA RCSI 1971; FFA RCS Eng. 1957; DA Eng. 1954. (Dub.) Cons. Anaesth. Craigavon Area Hosps.; Examr. FFA RCSI. Socs: Fell. Assn. Anaesth. GB & Irel. Prev: Sen. Tutor (Anaesth.) Qu. Univ. Belf.; Sen. Regist. Roy. Vict. Hosp. Belf.; Regist. Belf. City Hosp.

KING, Robert Charles 36 Harvey Road, Mandeville Est., Aylesbury HP21 9PJ; 60 Huntingdon Way, Tycoch, Swansea SA2 9HN — MB BS 1991 Lond.; BSc Lond. 1991, MB BS 1991.

KING, Robert Cowley (retired) Fulford House, Hawes DL8 3NN Tel: 01969 667851 — LMSSA 1965 Lond. Prev: Ho. Surg. (Gen. Surg. & Urol.) Bradford Roy. Infirm.

KING, Robert Ian 4 Curzon Road, Southport PR8 6PL — MB ChB 1987 Liverp.; MRCGP 1992; DRCOG 1991.

KING, Roberta Ann Gervis Road Surgery, 14 Gervis Road, Bournemouth BH1 3EG Tel: 01202 293418 Fax: 01202 317866 — MB BS 1987 Lond.; DCH RCP Lond. 1990. p/t GP Bournemouth.; Clin. Asst. Dermat. Poole Hosp. Prev: GP Regist. Hythe, Kent; SHO (O & G) Char. Cross Hosp.; SHO (Paediat.) Char. Cross Hosp.

KING, Ronald Charles (retired) Owl's Hollow, Cound Moor, Shrewsbury SY5 6BA Tel: 01694 731669 — MB BS Lond. 1947; MD Lond. 1951; FRCP Lond. 1970, M 1949; MRCS Eng. LRCP Lond. 1947. Prev: Hon. Cons. Phys. Tunbridge Wells HA.

KING, Ronald Hugh Tel: 01227 728900 — MB 1972 Camb.; BChir 1971; MRCP (UK) 1974; FRCGP 1993, M 1977. Prev: Med. Off. Chas. Johnson Memor. Hosp. Zululand, S. Afr.

KING, Rosalind Ann Old Manor Hospital, Wilton Road, Salisbury SP2 7EP Tel: 01722 336262 — MB BS Lond. 1969, Acad. Dip. Biochem. 1966; MRCS Eng. LRCP Lond. 1969; MRCPsych 1974; DPM Eng. 1973. (Roy. Free) Cons. (Psychiat. Learning Disabil.) Salisbury Healthcare NHS Trust; Pract. Cognitive Analytic Ther. Salisbury Healthcare. Socs: Roy. Coll. Psychiats. Prev: Clin. Asst. Alcoholic Unit & Drug Addic. Clinic Bournemouth.; Sen. Regist. (Psychiat.) Old Manor Hosp. Salisbury; Regist. (Psychiat.) St. Ann's Hosp. Canford Cliffs.

KING, Rosalind Leonie Black and Partners, Sherwood Health Centre, Elmswood Gardens, Sherwood, Nottingham NG5 4AD Tel: 0115 960 7127 Fax: 0115 985 7899 — BM BS 1989 Nottm.; MRCGP 1994.

KING, Rosamond Houlgate Way Surgery, Houlgate Way, Axbridge BS26 2BJ Tel: 01934 732464 Fax: 01934 733488 — MB BS 1973 Newc.; DObst RCOG 1976; Cert FPA 1975. Prev: Ho. Surg. Cumbld. Infirm. Carlisle; Ho. Phys. Battle Hosp. Reading; SHO (O & G) Roy. Berks. Hosp. Reading.

KING, Rosemary Lynne St Lawrence Medical Centre, 4 Bocking End, Braintree CM7 9AA Tel: 01376 552474 Fax: 01376 552417 — MB ChB 1979 Sheff.

KING, Ruth Elizabeth Red Ley, Letton, Hereford HR3 6DT — MB ChB 1990 Bristol.

KING, Sandra Margaret Water Meadow Surgery, Red Lion Street, Chesham HP5 1ET Tel: 01494 782241; 63 Bois Lane, Amersham HP6 6BZ Tel: 01494 727733 — MB BS 1967 Lond.; DCH Eng. 1970. (St. Mary's) Prev: Ho. Surg. St. Mary's Hosp. Harrow Rd.; Ho. Phys. (Paediat.) St. Mary's Hosp. Paddington; Ho. Phys. Edgware Gen. Hosp.

KING, Sarah Jane The Abingdon Surgery, 65 Stert St., Abingdon OX14 3LB; 16 Ferny Close, Radley, Abingdon OX14 3AN — MB ChB 1986 Bristol; MRCGP 1991; DRCOG 1989; DCH RCP Lond. 1989. Clin. Asst. (Gen. Pract.) Oxon. Prev: Trainee GP Reading VTS.

KING, Sarah Jennie 144 Upper Chobham Road, Camberley GU15 1ET — BM 1997 Soton.

KING, Sarah Kate Frederica 141 New Road, Croxley Green, Rickmansworth WD3 3EN — MB BS 1987 Lond.

KING, Sarah Louise 14 Ashfield Road, Altrincham WA15 9QJ — MB BS 1991 Lond.; MRCGP 1996; DCH RCP Lond. 1995; DFFP 1995; DRCOG 1994. (St. Geo. Hosp. Med. Sch.) GP Chesh.

KING, Sean Frederick Elmwood Medical Centre, 7 Burlington Road, Buxton SK17 9AY Tel: 01298 23019 — MB ChB 1981 Manch.

KING, Shelagh Ann Glasgow Royal Maternity Hospital, Rotten Row, Glasgow G4 0NA Tel: 0141 211 5337; 45 Trinley Road, Glasgow G13 2HZ — MB ChB 1979 Dundee; MRCOG 1986. Staff Grade Obst. Glas. Roy. Matern. Hosp.

KING, Sine Morag Cromwell Place Surgery, Cromwell Place, St. Ives, Huntingdon PE27 5JD Tel: 01480 462206 Fax: 01480 465313; Grove House, Tenterleas, St Ives PE27 5QP Tel: 01480 468775 Fax: 01480 468775 Email: rs.k@virgin.net — MB ChB 1976 Ed.; FRCGP 1996, M 1983; DRCOG 1978.

KING, Siobhan Margaret 4 Glencregagh Court, Belfast BT6 0PA — MB BCh BAO 1990 Belf.

KING, Stephen Cameron Crahamel Medical Practice, Crahamel House, 2 Duhamel Place, St Helier, Jersey JE2 4TP Tel: 01534 735742 Fax: 01534 735011 — MB ChB 1988 Glas.; DRCOG 1990. (Univ. Glas.)

KING, Stephen Edward Cedars Medical Centre, 12 Sandbach Road S., Alsager, Stoke-on-Trent ST6 2DS Tel: 01270 882179 Fax: 01270 872564; 25 Sandbach Road S., Alsager, Stoke-on-Trent ST7 2LW Email: s-e-king@hotmail.com — MB ChB 1979 Manch.; MRCGP 1983. (Manchester) Prev: Trainee GP Lancaster VTS.

KING, Stephen Geoffrey Rao and Partners, 90 Darnley Road, Gravesend DA11 0SW Tel: 01474 355331 Fax: 01474 324407 — MB BS 1972 Lond.; MRCOG 1981.

KING, Stephen John Lascelles (retired) Bramley, 67 Goldsel Road, Swanley BR8 8HA Tel: 01322 662233 Fax: 01322 614867 — MRCS Eng. LRCP Lond. 1962. Prev: SHO Geriat.s Orpington Hosp. Kent 1964.

KING, Steven Richmond Surgery, Richmond Close, Fleet GU52 7US Tel: 01252 811466 Fax: 01252 815031 — MB BS 1987 Lond.; DRCOG 1989.

KING, Stuart Geoffrey St Johns House Surgery, 28 Bromyard Road, St. Johns, Worcester WR2 5BU Tel: 01905 423612 Fax: 01905 740003 — MB ChB 1965 Birm.; MRCP Lond. 1969. Socs: BMA. Prev: Ho. Phys. Qu. Eliz. Hosp.; Ho. Surg. Gen. Hosp. Birm.

KING, Susan Idle Medical Centre, 440 Highfield ROAd, Idle, Bradford BD10 8RU Tel: 01274 771999 Fax: 01274 772001 — MB BCh 1967 Wales. (Wales) GP Bradford, W. Yorks.

KING, Susan Jennifer Department of Diagnostic Radiology, Royal Liverpool Children's NHS Trust, Eaton Road, Liverpool L12 2AP — MB ChB 1983 Leic.; MRCP (UK) 1986; FRCR 1990; T(R) (CR) 1992. Cons. Radiol. Roy. Liverp. Childr. NHS Trust. Socs: BMA. Prev: Sen. Regist. (Radiol.) King's Coll. Hosp. Lond.; Regist. (Paediat.) Lond. Hosp.

KING, Susan Lesley 102 Kingfisher Way, Upton, Wirral CH49 4PS — MB ChB 1982 Liverp. (Liverp.) Socs: Fam. Plann. Assn.; BMA. Prev: Clin. Med. Off. (Community Health) Wirral HA; Trainee GP Liverp. FPC; SHO (Geriat.) Liverp. HA.

KING, Susan Linda Littlefort Health Centre, Granby St., Littleport, Ely CB4 1NE Tel: 01353 860223; Tel: 01353 666851 — MB ChB 1992 Aberd.; MRCGP 1996; DRCOG 1995. Job-sharing Partner in Gen. Pract. Prev: SHO (O & G & A & E) Aberd. Roy. Infirm.; SHO (Psychiat.) Kingseat Hosp. Aberd.sh.; Trainee GP Aberd.

KING, Suzanne Jennifer Aaröe The Ounsted Clinic for Children, Churchill Hospital, Old Road, Oxford OX3 7L Tel: 01865 225617 Fax: 01865 225618; 26 Leckford Road, Oxford OX2 6HX — MB BS 1974 Lond.; MRCS Eng. LRCP Lond. 1974; DCH Eng. 1976. (Char. Cross) SCMO (Community Paediat.) Oxf. Radcliffe Trust. Socs: Fac. Community Health; Fac. Family Plann.; Roy. Coll. Paediat. & Child Health. Prev: SCMO (Family Plann.) & Clin. Med. Off. (Community Paediat.) Oxf. HA; Regist. (Paediat.) Oxf. HA; SHO (Paediat. & Ophth.) Char. Cross Hosp. Lond.

KING, Suzanne Marie Grange Cottage, Dale End Road, Hilton, Derby DE65 5FW — MB BS 1988 Lond.; BSc Lond. 1985; MRCP (UK) 1994. (University College, London) SHO (Neonates) Leicester Roy. Infirm. Prev: SHO (Paediat.) Roy. Hosp. Sick Childr. Edin.; SHO (Obst.) Qu. Mary's Hosp. Glas.

KING, Thomas Clement Flood Springfield Medical Practice, 463 Springfield Road, Belfast BT12 7DN Tel: 028 9032 7126 Fax: 028 9032 5976 — MB BCh BAO 1984 Belf.

KING, Thomas James 15 Basil Mansions, Basil St., Knightsbridge, London SW3 1AP Tel: 020 7584 6718 Fax: 020 7581 0244 — MB BS 1956 Lond.; MRCP Lond. 1964; DObst RCOG 1958. (St. Mary's) Chief Med. Adviser Barclays Bank plc; Med. Adviser BAT Industries plc & BASF UK Ltd; Cons. Med. Off. Legal & Gen. Gp. plc; Med. Examr. World Bank; Exam. Phys. United Nat. Organisation; Designated Med. Examr. Canad. & Austral. Immigr. Auth. Socs: Fell. Roy. Soc. Med.; Assur. Med. Soc. & Soc. Occupat. Med.; Nat. Assn. Family Plann. Doctors. Prev: Regist. (Med. & Paediat.) Barnet Gen. Hosp.; Hon. Clin. Asst. Brompton Hosp. Lond.; Surg. Lt. RN.

KING, Mr Thomas Tyrrell 144 Harley Street, London W1N 1AH Tel: 020 7935 0023 Fax: 020 7935 5972; Ridgemount, Heronway, Hutton Mount, Brentwood CM13 2LX Tel: 01277 225511 Fax: 01277 232020 — MB BS Melbourne 1953; FRCS Eng. 1957. Socs: Fell. Roy. Soc. Med. (Ex-Pres. Sect. Neurol.); Soc. Brit. Neurol. Surgs.; Corr. Mem. Neurosurgic. Soc. Austral. Prev: Cons. Neurosurg. Roy. Lond. Hosp.; Asst. Neurosurg. St. Vincent's Hosp. Melbourne; 1st Asst. Neurosurgic. Dept. Lond. Hosp.

KING, Timothy Shon 178 Saint Bernards Road, Solihull B92 7BJ — MB BChir 1991 Camb.

KING, Trevor Aubrey Department of Anaesthetics, District General Hospital, King's Drive, Eastbourne BN21 2UD Tel: 01323 417400 — MB ChB 1979 Zimbabwe; LRCP LRCS Ed. LRCPS Glas. 1979; T(Anaesth.) 1991; FFA RCS Eng. 1986. Cons. Anaesth. E.bourne Hosps. NHS Trust. Prev: Sen. Regist. (Anaesth.) Guy's Hosp. Lond.

KING, Trevor John Sprays Surgery, 9 Sprays, Burbage, Marlborough SN8 3TA Tel: 01672 810566 Fax: 01672 811329; Little Thatch, Shalbourne, Marlborough SN8 3QH Tel: 01672 870060 — MB BS 1978 Lond.

KING, Wendy Diana Malting Farm, Little Bentley, Colchester CO7 8SJ — MB BS 1998 Lond.; MB BS Lond 1998.

KING, William Charles Family Doctor Unit Surgery, 92 Bath Road, Hounslow TW3 3LN Tel: 020 8570 6271 Fax: 020 8570 3243; 12 Kingswood Creek, Wraysbury, Staines TW19 5EN Tel: 01784 483228 — MB BS 1969 Lond.; MRCS Eng. LRCP Lond. 1969. (Char. Cross) Socs: BMA; Assoc. Mem. Occupat. Med. Prev: Regist. (Surg.) Roy. Masonic Hosp. Lond.; SHO (Orthop.) St. Mary Abbots Hosp. Lond.

KING, William John Health Centre, Bank Street, Cupar KY15 4JN Tel: 01334 653478 Fax: 01334 657305; 6 Dewars Mill, St Andrews KY16 9TY Tel: 01334 470490 — MB ChB 1984 Ed.; DCCH RCP Ed. 1988; DRCOG 1987.

KING, Wilmert Fiona Irwin (retired) 5 Rosemary Park, Belfast BT9 6RF — MD 1951 Belf.; MB BCh BAO 1947. Prev: Med. Off. Cytol. Clinic EHSSB.

KING-DAVIES, Audrey Anne (retired) Stoven Old Vicarage, Beccles NR34 8ER Tel: 01502 575636 — MB BS 1957 Lond.

KING-DAVIES, David Humphrey (retired) Stoven Old Vicarage, Beccles NR34 8ER Tel: 01502 79636 — MB BS Lond. 1956; MRCS Eng. LRCP Lond. 1956; DA Eng. 1958.

KING-EVANS, Victoria Margaret MRS Osnabruck BFPO 36 — MB ChB 1974 Birm. Civil. Med. Pract. HM Forces Osnabrück, W. Germany.

KING-HOLFORD, Christopher Geoffrey (retired) The Copse, Barrow Lane, Pilton, Shepton Mallet BA4 4BH — MB BS 1963 Lond.

KING-LEWIS, Peter William 6 Sloane Square, London SW1W 8EE Tel: 020 7730 6611 Fax: 020 7730 0505 Email: doctor@large.co.uk; 1 Walton Place, London SW3 1RH Tel: 020 7589 6474 — MB BS Lond. 1990; BSc (Hons.) Lond. 1980. (St Bart. Hosp. Lond.) Socs: Fell Roy. Soc. Med.; Med. Soc. Lond.; Internat. Travel. Med. Prev: Regist. (Psychiat.) The Priory Roehampton; SHO (Paediat.) Chelsea & W.m. Hosp.; SHO (O & G) St. Thos. Hosp. Lond.

KINGAN, James Gordon, Group Capt. RAF Med. Br. Retd. 15 Elms Road, Hook, Basingstoke RG27 9DX Tel: 01256 762769 — MB ChB 1948 Liverp.; MFCM 1973; Assoc. Fac. Occupat. Med. RCP Lond. 1979; DPH Liverp. 1960. (Liverp.) Prev: CO P.ss Mary's RAF Hosp. Halton; CO Jt. Servs. Med. Rehabil. Unit.

KINGDOM, Mr Leonard Grantley Stoneygate Top Park, Gerrards Cross SL9 7PW Tel: 01753 883615 Fax: 01753 883615 — MB BChir 1943 Camb.; FRCS Eng. 1950; MRCS Eng. LRCP Lond. 1942. (St. Bart.) Cons. ENT Surg. Univ. Coll. Hosp. Lond.; Hon. Cons. ENT Surg. St. Luke's Hosp. Lond. & Hosp. SS John & Eliz. Lond.; Lect. ENT Univ. Lond. Socs: Fell. Roy. Soc. Med.; Brit. Assn. Otol. Prev: Chief Asst. (ENT) St. Bart. Hosp. Lond.; Demonst. (Anat.) Univ. Camb.; Capt. RAMC (Graded Surg.).

KINGDON, Alan John 6 Harley Street, London W1G 9PD Tel: 020 7631 5494; 6 Chiswick Staithe, Hartington Road, Chiswick, London W4 3TP Tel: 020 8994 6104 — MB BS 1968 Lond.; MRCS Eng. LRCP Lond. 1967. (Guy's) Med. Dir. Harley Med. Gp. Lond. Socs: BMA & Roy. Soc. Med. Prev: Med. Off. RN; Ho. Surg. & Ho. Phys. Torbay Hosp. Torquay.

KINGDON, Camilla Clare Flat 8, 58 Longley Road, London SW17 9LL Tel: 020 8672 8161 Fax: 020 8672 8161 Email: 106157.470@compuserve.com — MB ChB 1989 Cape Town; MRCP (UK) 1994. (Univ. Cape Town, SA) Lect. (Child Health) St. Geo. Hosp. Med. Sch. Lond. Prev: Regist. Rotat. (Paediat.) SW Thames Region; SHO (Haemat. & Oncol.) Hosp. Childr. Gt. Ormond St. Lond.; SHO (Paediat. Infec. Dis.) St. Mary's Hosp. Lond.

KINGDON, Professor David Graham School of Medicine, University of Southampton, Royal South Hants Hospital, Brintons Terrace, Southampton SO14 0YG Tel: 02380 825191 Fax: 02380 234243 Email: dgk@soton.ac.uk — MB ChB 1978 Bristol; MD Sheff. 1996; MRCPsych. 1983. Prof. of Ment. Health Care Delivery. Prev: Med. Dir. Nottm. Healthcare Trust; Sen. Med. Off., Ment. Health Div. DoH; Cons. Psychiat. & Dir. Ment. Health Servs. Bassetlaw Dist. Gen. Hosp. Worksop.

KINGDON, Edward James Royal Free Hospital School of Medicine, Pond St., London NW3 2QG Tel: 020 7794 0500 Fax: 020 7830 2125; 56 Charteris Road, London NW6 7EX — MB BS 1990 Lond.; BSc 1987; MRCP (UK) 1994. Socs: Renal Assn.; Internal. Soc. Nophrol. Prev: Regist. (Nephrol.) Middlx. Hosp. Lond.; Regist. (Med.) Basildon Hosp.

KINGDON, Susan Joan St Lukes, Radford HC, Radford, Nottingham NG7 3GW Tel: 0115 978 4374 Fax: 0115 970 1478 Email: stlukes.surgery@gp-c84136.nhs.uk; Tel: 0115 960 2798 — MB ChB 1977 Sheff.; MRCGP 1982; DRCOG 1981. Gen. Practitioner.

KINGETT, Robert William James Corbridge Health Centre, Manor Court, Corbridge NE45 5JW Tel: 01434 632011 Fax: 01434 633878; Beechcroft, Aydon Road, Corbridge NE45 5EG Tel: 01434 712011 — BM BS 1977 Nottm.; DRCOG 1981; MRCGP 1981.

KINGHAM, Dorcas Bristol Priory Hospital, Heath House Lane, Bristol BS16 1EQ Tel: 0117 952 5255 Fax: 0117 952 5552 — MB ChB 1974 Bristol; MRCS Eng. LRCP Lond. 1973; MRCPI 1989; MRCPsych 1978. (Univ. Bristol) Cons. Psychiat. (Gen. Adult Psychiat.) & Med. Dir.Bristol Priory Hosp. Bristol. Socs: Brit. Neuropsychiat. Assn.; Roy. Soc. of Med. Prev: Cons. Psychiat. (Gen. Adult Psychiat.) Barrow Hosp. Bristol; Sen. Regist. (Psychiat.) St. Thos. Hosp. Lond.; Teach. Asst. St. Michael's Hosp. Toronto, Canada.

KINGHAM, Jeremy Giles Carlton Ashgrove, Lunnon, Parkmill, Swansea SA3 2EJ Tel: 01792 371285 — MB BS 1970 Lond.; MD Lond. 1976; FRCP Lond. 1990; MRCP (UK) 1973. (Westm.) Cons. Phys. Singleton Hosp. Swansea. Socs: Brit. Soc. Gastroenterol.; Brit. Assn. Study Liver. Prev: Cons. Phys. Morriston Hosp. Swansea; Sen. Regist. (Gastroenterol.) St. Bart. Hosp. Lond.; Research Fell. Profess. Med. Unit Soton. Gen. Hosp.

KINGHAM, Michael William Bridge Cottage, Ketteringham Lane, Ketteringham, Wymondham NR18 9RZ Tel: 01603 810052 — MB

BS 1993 Lond. Prev: SHO (Med.) Jas. Paget Hosp. Norf.; SHO (A & E) N.wick Pk. Hosp. Harrow.

KINGHORN, George Robert Department Genitourinary Medicine, Royal Hallamshire Hospital, Glossop Road, Sheffield S10 2JF Tel: 0114 271 3524 Fax: 0114 271 3408 Email: g.r.kinghorn@sheffield.ac.uk; Kerala, 3 Serlby Drive, Harthill, Sheffield S26 7UJ Email: george.kinghorn3@virgin.net — MB ChB 1972 Sheff.; MB ChB Sheff. 1985; MD Sheff. 1985; FRCP Lond. 1988; MRCP (UK) 1976. Cons. Genitourin. Med. & Clin. Dir. Communicable Dis. Centr. Sheff. Univ. Hosp. Trust; Hon. Sen. Clin. Lect. i/c Sub.-Dept. Genitourin. Med. Univ. Sheff.; Edit. Bd. Mem. Genitourin. Med., Internat. Jl. STD & AIDS. Socs: Assn. Genitourin. Med.; Exec. Mem. Nat. Assn. of Providers of HIV Treatm. and CARE; Brit. HIV Assn. Exec. Prev: Cons. Genitourin. Phys. Leeds HA; Chairm. SAC Genitourin Med. & RCP Genitourin. Med. Comm.; WHO & EEC Short-Term Cons.

KINGHORN, Sheila Anne Health Centre, Gosber Road, Eckington, Sheffield S21 4BD Tel: 01246 432131; Kerala, 3 Serlby Drive, Harthill, Sheffield S26 7UJ — MB ChB 1972 Sheff.; MRCGP 1986.

KINGHORN, Susan Hall 5 Woodburne, Park Avenue, Leeds LS8 2JW — MB BS 1967 Newc.

KINGMAN, Charlotte Elizabeth Cromwell 42 Ashley Gardens, Ambrosden Avenue, London SW1P 1QE — MB BS 1996 Lond.

KINGMAN, Hannah Mary 81 Middleton Hall Road, Birmingham B30 1AG — MB ChB 1994 Bristol.

KINGS, Gillian Ann 7 Woodland Way, Failand, Bristol BS8 3UJ — MB ChB 1967 Birm.; FFA RCS Eng. 1974.

KINGS, Mr Graham Leonard Morgan Hull Royal Infirmary, Anlaby Road, Hull HU3 2JZ Tel: 01482 328541 Fax: 01432 674121; BUPA Hospital, Hull & East Riding, Lowfield Road, Anlaby Rd., Hull HU10 7AZ Tel: 01482 659471 Fax: 01482 652822 Email: gkings@compuserve.com — MB ChB Sheff. 1967; MSc Bradford 1977; FRCS Eng. 1974; DObst RCOG 1969. Cons. Surg. (Orthop.) Hull Roy. Infirm. Socs: Brit. Orthop. Assn.; Brit. Soc. Surg. Hand; Hull Med. Soc. Prev: Sen. Regist. (Orthop.) Leeds AHA; Regist. (Orthop. & Traum. Surg.) Woodlands Orthop. Hosp. & Bradford Roy. Infirm.

KINGSBURY, Alan William (retired) Little Avenings, Church Road, Angmering, Littlehampton BN16 4JP — MB BS Lond. 1962; DObst RCOG 1965. Prev: Med. Dir. St. Barnabas Hospice Worthing.

KINGSBURY, Quentin David 11 South Road, Amersham HP6 5LX Tel: 01494 433746 — MB BS 1987 Lond.; BSc Lond. 1983; FRCA 1994. Specialist Regist. (Anaesth.) Coventry Sch. Anaesth. Warks. Prev: Postgrad. Fell. (Anaesth.) Roy. Perth Hosp., W. Austral.

KINGSBURY, Stephen John Queen Elizabeth II Hospital, Welwyn Garden City AL7 4HQ Tel: 01707 328111 — MB BS 1983 Lond.; MRCPsych 1987. Cons. Child & Adolesc. Psychiat. Qu. Eliz. II Hosp. Welwyn Gdn. City.

KINGSBURY, Sylvia Lillian 11 South Road, Amersham HP6 5LX Tel: 01494 432776 — MB BS 1952 Lond.; MRCS Eng. LRCP Lond. 1952. (St. Mary's) SCMO Wycombe Dist.

KINGSBURY, Winifred Nora, CStJ (retired) Inkberrow, West Quantoxhead, Taunton TA4 4EA Tel: 01984 32376 — MB ChB 1949 Birm.

KINGSCOTE, Andrew David 43 Walton Park, Pannal, Harrogate HG3 1EJ — MB ChB 1974 Birm.; MRCPsych. 1980.

KINGSCOTE, Jane Mary 43 Walton Park, Pannal, Harrogate HG3 1EJ — MB ChB 1974 Birm.; DRCOG 1976.

KINGSHOTT, Brigit Mari-Margaret 16 Chapel Hill, St Erth, Hayle TR27 6HL Tel: 01736 753352 — MB ChB 1988 Ed.

KINGSLAND, Charles Richard Liverpool Women's Hospital, Crown St., Liverpool L8 7SS Tel: 0151 702 4215 Fax: 0151 702 4042; 27 Farr Hall Drive, Heswall, Wirral CH60 4SH Tel: 0151 342 2242 — MB ChB 1982 Liverp.; MD Liverp. 1993; MRCOG 1987; DRCOG 1984. Cons. O & G Wom. Hosp. Liverp.; Hon. Lect. Univ. Liverp. & John Moores Univ. Liverp. Socs: (Comm. Mem.) Brit. Fertil. Soc.; Amer. Fertil. Soc.; N. Eng. Obst. & Gyn. Soc. Prev: Lect. (O & G) Roy. Liverp. Hosp.; Regist. (O & G) Woms. Hosp. Liverp.; Research Fell. Middlx. Hosp. Lond.

KINGSLAND, James Patrick St Hilary Brow Group Practice, 204 Wallasey Road, Wallasey L44 2AG; 7 Holm Hill, Wirral CH48 7JA Tel: 0151 625 5556 Email: james.p.kingsland@btinternet.com — MB ChB 1984 Liverp.; DFFP 1998; DRCOG 1988. (Liverp.) Trainer (Gen. Pract.) & Undergrad. Tutor Univ. Liverp.; Mem. Wirral LMC; GP Advisor D.O.H. Socs: Liverp. Med. Inst.; Liverp. Med. Inst. Prev: SHO (A & E) BRd.green Hosp. Liverp.; SHO (ENT) Roy. Liverp. Hosp.; SHO (O & G) Arrowe Pk. Hosp. Wirral.

KINGSLEY, David Michael North Sefton and West Lancashire Community NHS Trust, Ormskirk District General Hospital, Wigan Road, Ormskirk L3 — MB ChB 1993 Liverp. Basic Specialist Trainee in Psychiat. at N. Sefton & W. Lancahsire Community NHS Trust. Socs: Guild of Catholic Doctors Co-ordinator of LIFE Doctors. Prev: SHO (Community Paediat.) S.port & Formby NHS Trust.

KINGSLEY, Mr Derek Peter Englefield 10 Bryanston Mews E., London W1H 2DB — MB BS 1960 Lond.; FRCS Eng. 1967; FRCR 1975; DMRD Eng. 1974. (St. Bart.) Sen. Lect. Inst. Neurol. Socs: Fell. Roy. Soc. Med. Prev: Cons. Neuradiologist, The Cromwell Hosp. Lond. W5 0TU; Cons. Neuroradiol. St. Bart. Hosp. Lond., Lond. Hosp. & Moorfields Eye Hosp. Lond.; Sen. Regist. (Diag. Radiol.) Hammersmith Hosp.

KINGSLEY, Gabrielle Helen Rheumatology Unit, Lewisham Hospital, Lewisham High St., London SE13 6LH Tel: 020 8333 3000; Rheumatology Unit, 4th Floor, Hunts House, Guy's Hospital, London SE1 9RT Tel: 020 7955 4394 Fax: 020 7955 2472 — MB ChB 1979 Bristol; MB ChB (Hons.) Bristol 1979; BSc (Hons.) Bristol 1976; FRCP Lond. 1994; MRCP (UK) 1982; T(M) 1991. (Bristol) Cons. & Sen. Lect. (Rheum.) Lewisham NHS Hosp. Trust. Prev: Lect. (Rheum.) UMDS Guy's Hosp. Lond.; Regist. (Med.) Guy's Hosp.; SHO (Gen. Med.) Plymouth Gen. Hosp.

KINGSLEY, Martin (retired) 17 Elizabeth Court, Hempstead Road, Watford WD17 4LR Tel: 01923 227282 Fax: 01923 231719 — MB ChB St. And. 1950; MRCGP 1965. Prev: Capt. RAMC.

KINGSLEY, Maurice East Penthouse, St. Anthonys, West Cliff Road, Bournemouth BH4 8BD — MRCS Eng. LRCP Lond. 1931.

KINGSLEY, Nadia Alys 55 Highsett Hills Road, Cambridge CB2 1NZ — MB BS 1989 Lond.; MRCGP 1993.

KINGSLEY, Patrick John 72 Main Street, Osgathorpe, Loughborough LE12 9TA Tel: 01530 223622 Fax: 01530 223622 — MB BS 1973 Lond.; MRCS Eng. LRCP Lond. 1965; DA Eng. 1968; DObst RCOG 1968. (St. Bart.) Indep. Pract. Nutrit. & Environm. Med. LoughBoro. Socs: Fell. Soc. Clin. Ecol.; Fell. Amer. Acad. Environm. Med. Prev: Clin. Pharmacol. Fisons Pharm. Ltd.; SHO (O & G) St. Mary's Hosp. Kettering; Ho. Phys. & Ho. Surg. Qu. Eliz. Hosp. Bridgetown, Barbados.

KINGSLEY, Sidney Malcolm 1 Ashurst Court, Ashurst Close, Northwood HA6 1EL Tel: 01923 828801 — MB BS 1944 Lond.; MRCS Eng. LRCP Lond. 1943. (Middlx.) Clin. Asst. Obst. Unit, Edgware Gen. Hosp.; Hon. Med. Off. Harrow Hosp. & Lond. Amateur Boxing Assn.; GP Assoc. N.wick Pk. Hosp. Harrow; Anaesth. Middlx. CC Sch. Dent. Serv. Socs: BMA; Fell. Roy. Soc. Med. Prev: Ho. Phys. Middlx. Hosp.; Ho. Surg. Miller Gen. Hosp.; Capt. RAMC.

KINGSLEY-JONES, Joyce Springfield Way, Westcott, Dorking Tel: 01306 885789 — MRCS Eng. LRCP Lond. 1946; DCH Eng. 1971.

KINGSLEY PILLERS, Elizabeth Mary (retired) 244 Hills Road, Cambridge CB2 2QE Tel: 01223 247419 — MB BChir 1944 Camb.; MA Camb. 1945, MD 1955; MRCS Eng. LRCP Lond. 1944; FRCR 1978; DMRT Eng. 1956, DCH 1946. Life Fell. Girton Coll. Camb. Prev: Dir. Cancer Registration Bureau Camb.

KINGSMILL, Joanna Clare Grand Drive Surgery, 132 Grand Drive, London SW20 9EA Tel: 020 8542 5555 Fax: 020 8542 6969; 194 Coombe Lane, West Wimbledon, London SW20 0QT Tel: 020 8946 5360 — MB BS 1983 Lond.; MRCGP 1987; DRCOG 1987. GP Trainer. Prev: GP Maidenhead.

KINGSMILL MOORE, Mr John Miles (retired) Jacaranda, Queens Hillrise, Ascot SL5 7DP Tel: 01344 623100 — MB BCh BAO Dub. 1953; FRCS Eng. 1961; FRCSI 1965. Cons. Orthop. & Traum. Surg. Ashford Hosp. Middlx. Prev: Sen. Regist. (Orthop.) St. Geo. Hosp. Lond. & Rowley Bristow Orthop. Hosp. Pyrford.

KINGSMORE, David Brian 3FR, 42 Polwarth Street, Glasgow G12 9TJ — MB ChB 1992 Aberd.

KINGSNORTH, Professor Andrew Norman University of Plymouth, Postgraduate Medical School, Level 7, Derriford Hospital, Plymouth PL6 8DH Tel: 01752 763017 Fax: 01752 763007 Email: andrew.kingsnorth@phnt.swest.nhs.uk; Somerville, 43 Thorn Park, Mannamead, Plymouth PL3 4TF Tel: 01752 664208 Fax: 01752 672085 Email: kingsnort@hotmail.com — MB BS 1973 Lond.; BSc (Hons.) Lond. 1970, MS 1983; FRCS Eng. 1978. (Roy. Free Hosp.

Sch. Med.) Hon. Cons. & Prof. Surg. Univ. Plymouth. Socs: (Comm.) Surgic. Research Soc.; Pancreatic Soc.; Assn. Surg. Prev: Reader (Surg.) Univ. Liverp.; Lect. (Surg.) Univ. Edin.; Research Fell. Harvard Med. Sch.

KINGSNORTH, Jane Mary Collings Park Medical Centre, 57 Eggbuckland Road, Hartley, Plymouth PL3 5JR Tel: 01752 771500; 43 Thorn Park, Mannamead, Plymouth PL3 4TF — MB BS 1973 Lond.; BSc Lond. 1970; DCH RCP Lond. 1976. (Royal Free Hospital School of Medicine) Prev: SHO (Dermat.) Slade & John Radcliffe Hosps. Oxf.; SHO (Cardiol.) Lond. Chest Hosp.; SHO (Paediat.) Hillingdon Hosp.

KINGSTON, Andrea Helen Hilltops Medical Centre, Kensington Drive, Great Holm, Milton Keynes MK8 9HN Tel: 01908 568446; 9 Castlethorpe Road, Hanslope, Milton Keynes MK19 7HQ Tel: 01908 510330 Email: andrea@hanslope.powernet.co.uk — MB ChB 1978 Manch.; MRCGP 1983; DCH RCP Lond. 1986; DRCOG 1982. (Manch.)

KINGSTON, Catherine Ann 36 Burlington Avenue, Kew Gardens, Richmond TW9 4DQ — MB BS 1991 Lond.; BSc (Hist. of Med.) Lond. 1988; MRCP (UK) 1994. (Univ. Coll. & Middlx. Sch. Med.) Regist. (Radiol.) Univ. Coll. & Middlx. Hosps. Lond. Prev: SHO Rotat. (Gen. Med.) OldCh. Hosp. Romford.

KINGSTON, Daniel Stephen Rhodes 4 Chester Close, Garstang, Preston, Preston PR3 1LH — MB BS 1997 Newc.

KINGSTON, Fiona Rosemary Alice Health Centre, Wharf Road, Ash Vale, Aldershot GU12 5BA Tel: 01252 317551; The Rough, Hurtmore Road, Godalming GU7 2RB — MB ChB 1972 Birm.; MRCGP 1984; MRCOG 1977.

KINGSTON, Frank Edward (retired) 8 Moreton Place, London SW1V 2NP — MB BS 1927 Lond.; MRCS Eng. LRCP Lond. 1926; MRCPsych 1971; DPM Leeds 1932. Prev: Cons. Psychiat. & Dep. Phys. Supt. Knowle Hosp. Fareham.

KINGSTON, Helen Margaret Regional Genetics Service, St. Mary's Hospital, Hathersage Road, Manchester M13 0JH Tel: 0161 276 6285 Fax: 0161 276 6145 Email: helenk@central.cmht.nwest.nhs.uk — MB ChB 1975 Manch.; MD Manch. 1983; FRCP Lond. 1992; MRCP (UK) 1978; DCH Eng. 1977. (Manchester) Cons. Clin. Geneticist Regional Genetics Centre St. Mary's Hosp. Manch. Socs: Brit. Soc. Human Genetics; World Muscle Soc. Prev: Research Fell. Div. Med. Genetics Harbor/UCLA Med. Centre, Torrance, Calif., USA; Sen. Regist. (Med. Genetics & Paediat.) Univ. Hosp. Wales Cardiff; Regist. (Paediat.) Roy. Manch. Childr. Hosp.

KINGSTON, Helen Mary Frome Medical Practice, Health Centre, Park Road, Frome BA11 1EZ Tel: 01373 301300 Fax: 01373 301313 Email: helen.kingston@fromemedicalpractice.nhs.uk; Linden Mead, Frome BA11 3JX — BM BCh 1990 Oxf. Gen. Practitioner.

KINGSTON, John Mervin Coronation Road, Downend, Bristol BS16 5DH; 15 Westons Brake, Emersons Green, Bristol BS16 7BQ Tel: 0117 956 6137 — MB ChB 1961 Liverp.; DObst RCOG 1964. (Liverp.) Prev: Ho. Surg. Walton Hosp. Liverp.; Sen. Ho. Surg. (O & G) Yeovil Gen. Hosp.; Ho. Surg. (Obst.) BromsGr. Gen. Hosp.

KINGSTON, Jonathan Mark Barnard Medical Practice, 43 Granville Road, Sidcup DA14 4TA Tel: 020 8302 7721 Fax: 020 8309 6579 — BM BCh 1991 Oxf.; BA Oxf. 1988; DRCOG 1995; DFFP 1994; DCH RCP Lond. 1994; MRCGP 1996. GP Princip.

KINGSTON, Judith Eve Department of Paedicatric Oncology, St. Bartholomews Hospital, West Smithfield, London EC1A 7BE Tel: 020 7601 8004 Fax: 020 7601 8194 Email: j.e.kingston@mds.qmw.ac.uk — MB ChB 1973 Bristol; BSc Bristol 1970, MB ChB 1973; FRCP Lond. 1991; MRCP (UK) 1977; FRCPCH 1997; DCH Eng. 1976. Sen. Lect. & Cons. Paediat. Oncol. St. Bart. Hosp. Lond. Prev: Clin. Research Fell. (Paediat. Oncol.) Univ. Oxf.; Regist. (Paediat.) Addenbrooke's Hosp. Camb.

KINGSTON, Margaret Alice 1 Boulton Drive, Old Cartley Village, Doncaster DN3 3QX — BM BS 1996 Nottm.

KINGSTON, Michael Robert Mechie and Partners, 67 Owen Road, Lancaster LA1 2LG Tel: 01524 846999 Fax: 01524 845174; Holly Cottage, Beaumont Hall, Green Lane, Slyne, Lancaster LA1 2ES — MB ChB 1984 Manch.; MRCGP 1989; DRCOG 1988. Prev: UMO RAF Laarbruch; Cas. Off. & SHO (Med. & O & G) RAF Hosp. Ely.

KINGSTON, Paul Bath Natural Medical Centre, 7 Laura Place, Bath BA2 4BJ Tel: 01225 466271; Old rectory stables, Wellow, Bath BA2 8QS Tel: 01225 840286 Email: todrpk@aol.com — MB BCh BAO 1971 NUI; MRCP (U.K.) 1975. Indep. Practitioner Integrative Med. Bath Natural Med. Centre Bath. Prev: Sen. Regist. (Gen. & Geriat. Med.) Ch.ill & John Radcliffe Hosps. Oxf.; Cons. Phys. (Geriat. Med.) Gloucester Roy. Hosp.

KINGSTON, Paul Andrew University of Manchester, Department of Medicine, Molecular Medicine Unit, Room 1.302, Stupford Building, Oxford Road, Manchester M13 9WL Tel: 0161 275 5669 Email: paul.a.kingston@man.ac.uk; 8 Field View Walk, Whalley Range, Manchester M16 8GU Tel: 0161 226 5387 — MB ChB 1989 Manch.; BSc (Hons.) Manch. 1985, MB ChB (Hons.) 1989; MRCP (UK) 1992. (University of Manchester) BMS Cardiovasc. Research Fell. Univ. of Manch. Dept. of Med. Prev: Clin. Lect. (Vasc. Biol.) Univ. of Manch.; Clin. Research Fell. (Cardiol.) Manch. Roy. Infirm.; Regist. (Cardiol.) N. Manch. Gen. Hosp.

KINGSTON, Peter Mark Giffords Surgery, 28 Lowbourne, Melksham SN12 7EA Tel: 01225 703370; 5 Grosvenor Place, Bath BA1 6AX Tel: 01380 870277 Email: ark.kingston@steepleashton.demon.co.uk — MB BChir 1980 Camb.; MA, MB Camb. 1980, BChir 1979; MBA Open 1999; MRCGP 1985; DRCOG 1984. (St. Bart.) Assoc. Med. Dir. Wilts. Healthcare NHS Trust Trowbridge; Chairm. (Progr. Commiss. Strategic Change) Wilts. HA. Prev: Trainee GP W. Norf. & Wisbech VTS; SHO (Med.) Poole Gen. Hosp.; Ho. Phys. Poole Gen. Hosp.

KINGSTON, Philip John (retired) The Croft, Nympsfield Road, Nailsworth, Stroud GL6 0EA Tel: 01453 832023 — BSc Lond. 1962, MB BS 1965; MRCS Eng. LRCP Lond. 1965; FRCPath 1986, M 1974. Prev: Cons. (Haemat.) Glos. Roy. Hosp. Gloucester.

KINGSTON, Mr Reginald David 91 Stretford Road, Urmston, Manchester M41 9LG Tel: 0161 748 4022 — MB ChB 1964 Liverp.; FRCS Eng. 1971; FRCS Ed. 1970; FICS 1990. (Liverp.) Cons. Gen. Surg. Trafford Gen. Hosp. Manch.; Sec. N.W. BrE. Cancer Study Gp.; Head Dept. Clin. Studies Trafford Gen. Hosp. Socs: (Vice-Pres.) Brit. Assn. Surg. Oncol. Prev: Sen. Regist. (Surg.) W. Midl. RHA; Resid. Surg. Off. United Birm. Hosps.; Regist. (Surg.) N. Staffs. Hosp. Centre.

KINGSTON, Richard William Cowley The Rafters, Warden Road, Totland Bay PO39 0AD — MB BS 1996 Lond.

KINGSTON, Mr Robert Ewen Liverpool Women's Hospital, Crown St., Liverpool L8 7SS Tel: 0151 702 4021 Fax: 0151 702 4137; 1 Fairways Close, Woolton, Liverpool L25 7AB — MB ChB 1975 Leeds; FRCS Eng. 1980; FRCOG 1993, M 1980. Cons. Gyn. Surg. & Oncol. Liverp.; Hon. Cons. Gyn. Clattebridge Centre for Oncol. Prev: Lect. (O & G) Univ. Leeds; Clin. Fell. (Gyn. Oncol.) Jackson Memor. Med. Center Miami, USA.

KINGSTON, Susan Pamela 28 Lawns Avenue, Raby Mere, Wirral CH63 0NF — MB ChB 1981 Liverp.

KINGSTON, Timothy Patrick Fernleigh, 77 Alderley Road, Wilmslow SK9 1PA Tel: 01625 539360 Fax: 01625 548348; 2 Planetree Road, Hale, Altrincham WA15 9JJ Tel: 0161 904 0980 — MB ChB 1975 Lond.; MB ChB 1975; BSc (Hons. Physiol.) Manch. 1972, MD 1985; FRCP Lond. 1994; MRCP (UK) 1980; DRCOG 1980; DCH RCP Lond. 1979. (Manch.) p/t Cons. Dermat. Macclesfield Dist. Gen. Hosp. Socs: Non-Resid. Fell. Amer. Acad. Dermat.; Brit. Assn. Dermat.; Sec. N. Eng. Dermatol. Soc. Prev: Adjunct Instruct. Dept. Dermat. UCLA Med. Centre Los Angeles, Calif.; Regist. (Dermat.) Univ. Hosp. Wales Cardiff; Ho. Phys. Manch. Roy. Infirm.

KINGSTON, Wendy Elaine York Street Medical Centre, 20-21 York Street, Stourport-on-Severn DY13 9EH Tel: 01299 827171 Fax: 01299 827910; Brant Farm House, Shrawley, Worcester WR6 6TD — MB ChB 1985 Birm.; MRCGP 1989; DRCOG 1988.

KINGSTON-SHRUBB, Josephine Mary, Wing Cdr. RAF Med. Br. (Hague) 4 Warwick Road, Swindon SN1 3JL Tel: 01793 481682 Fax: 01793 481682 Email: busheyjo@cs.com — MB BS Lond. 1966; MRCS Eng. LRCP Lond. 1966; DAvMed FOM RCP Lond. 1995. (St. Thos. Hosp. Med. Sch. Lond.)

KINGSWELL, Robin Stephen Rowanhurst, Northbrook Avenue, Winchester SO23 0JW — MB BS 1978 Lond.; BSc Lond. 1975, MB BS 1978; FFPM RCP (UK) 1994, M 1991. Regional Med. Dir. Warner Lambert (UK) Ltd. Socs: Fell. Roy. Soc. Med.

KINGSWOOD, John Christopher Renal Unit, Royal Sussex County Hospital, Eastern Road, Brighton BN2 5BE Tel: 01273 696955 Fax: 01273 679788 — MB BS 1977 Lond.; FRCP Lond. 1994; MRCP

(UK) 1981; MRCS Eng. LRCP Lond. 1977. (Guy's) Cons. Phys. Brighton HA. Socs: Renal Assn.; Med. Res. Soc.; Internat. Soc. Nephrol. Prev: Sen. Regist. (Nephrol.) St. Phillips Hosp. Lond.; Lect. St. Peters Gp. of Hosps.

KINI, Kulai Narayana City Walls Medical Centre, St. Martin's Way, Chester CH1 2NR Tel: 01244 357800; Downton, 13 Ormonde Road, Chester CH2 2AH Tel: 01244 380425 Fax: 01244 380425 Email: vish.kini@dial.pipex.com — MB ChB 1976 Liverp.; FRCGP 1995; MRCGP 1984. (Liverp.) GP & Assoc. Regional Dir. Liverp. Univ.

KINI, Kundadka Kalpana Newstreet Health Centre, Upper New St., Barnsley S70 1LP — MB BS 1977 Mysore; DCH RCPS Glas. 1987.

KINI, Mr Mangalore Damodar Amberley Grange, Lewes Road, Haywards Heath Rh17 7SX Tel: 01294 222255, 01444 440950 Fax: 01444 440950 Email: deekini@yahoo.co.uk; 5 Langmuir Avenue, Perceton, Irvine KA11 2DR Tel: 01294 222255, 01444 440950 Fax: 01444 440950 Email: deekini@yahoo.co.uk — MB BS Univ. Of Mysore, India; FRCOG 1987; MRCOG 1974. (Bangalore Med. Coll.) Cons. In Infertil. & IVF Harley St. Fertil. Centre, Harley St. Lond.; Harley St. Fertil. Centre, 122 Harley St, Lond, W1G 7JP, Tel: 020 7935 2234, Fax: 020 7935 7401. Socs: Roy. Soc. of Med.; Europ. Soc. of Reproduc. & Embrology; Amer. Soc. of Reproductive Med. Prev: Dir. Of Infertil. & IVF, Dammay Saudi Arabia; Cons. In Gyn. Endocrinol., Dammay Saudi Arabia.

KINI, Mr Ullal Subhash Wimat Medicentre, Health Park, Cardiff CF4 4UJ Tel: 029 2068 2131 Fax: 029 2068 2132; 11 King George V Drive W., Cardiff CF14 4ED Tel: 029 2076 3264 — MB BS 1986 Madras; FRCS Eng. 1992; FRCS Ed. 1992; FRCS Glas. 1992. Clin. Research Fell. Welsh Inst. Minimal Access Ther. Socs: Assn. Coloproctol. Prev: Regist. (Gen. Surg.) Univ. Hosp. Wales Cardiff, Morriston Hosp. Swansea & Neath Gen. Hosp.

KINIRONS, Brian Mary Peter Flat 7, York House, Queen Alexandra Hospital, Cosham, Portsmouth PO6 3LY — MB BCh BAO 1986 NUI; LRCPSI 1986.

KINIRONS, Mark Thomas Mary Department of Ageing and Health, ECU, 9th Floor, North Wing, St Thomas' Hospital, London SE1 7EH Tel: 020 7928 9292 Ext: 3820 Fax: 020 7928 2339 Email: mark.kinirons@gstt.sthames.nhs.uk — MB BCh BAO 1984 NUI; BSc NUI 1986; MRCP (UK) 1989; MRCPI 1987; LRCPSI 1984; MD (NUI) 1996; FRCPI 1999; FRCP (Lond) 2000. (Roy. Coll. Surgs. Irel.) Cons. Phys.Guys' & St. Thomas Hosp. Lond; Hon. Sen. Lect. GRT Sch. of Med. Socs: Brit. Geriat. Soc.; Amer. Geriat. Soc. Prev: Lect. & Hon. Sen. Regist. (Health c/o Elderly) King's Coll. Sch. Med. & Dent. Lond.; Regist. (Gen. Med.) Univ. Coll., Middlx. & Whittington Hosps. Lond.; Research Fell. In Clin. Pharmacol., Vanderbig Univ. USA.

KINLEN, Leo Joseph 46 Bartlemas Road, Oxford OX4 1XX Tel: 01865 241762 — MB BS 1959 Durh.; FRCP Lond. 1981, M 1965.

KINLEY, Mr James Garner (retired) 25 Bayhead Road, Portballintrae, Bushmills BT57 8RZ Tel: 028 2073 1861 — MB BCh BAO 1956 Belf.; FRCS Ed. 1962; FRCSI 1985. Prev: Cons. Surg. Waveney Hosp. Ballymena & Masserene Hosp. Antrim.

KINLOCH, David Rodney The Surgery, 49 Essenden Road, St Leonards-on-Sea TN38 0NN Tel: 01424 720866 Fax: 01424 445580 — MB ChB 1983 Cape Town. (Cape Town) GP St. Leonards-on-Sea, E. Sussex.

KINLOCH, John Donald (retired) 30 Claremont Road, Hadley Wood, Barnet EN4 0HP Tel: 020 8449 2387 — MB ChB 1953 Glas.; FRFPS Glas. 1959; FRCP RCPS Glas. 1987, M 1962; FRCP Ed. 1981, M 1962; FRCP Lond. 1977, M 1969. Prev: Cons. Phys. Chase Farm Hosp. Enfield.

KINLOCH, Lorna Creighton (retired) 145 Quarry Street, Liverpool L25 6HD Tel: 0151 428 2661 — MB ChB Glas. 1951. JP. Prev: GP Halewood Liverp.

KINLOCH, Peter McCallum (retired) 145 Quarry Street, Liverpool L25 6HD — MB ChB 1948 Glas.; DObst RCOG 1953. Div. Med. Off. DHSS. Prev: GP Halewood Liverp.

KINLOCH, Thomas Scott The Health Centre Surgery, 60 Roseheath Drive, Halewood, Liverpool L26 9UH Tel: 0151 486 3780; 19 Sinclair Drive, Liverpool L18 0HN Email: ea59@rapid.co.uk — MB ChB 1981 Liverp.; MRCGP 1985; DRCOG 1984.

KINMOND, Sheena Special Care Baby Unit, Ayrshire Central Hospital, Kilwinning Road, Irvine KA12 8SS Tel: 01294 274191 Fax: 01294 323162 Email: skinmond@nayrshire.scot.nhs.uk; 109 Bank Street, Irvine KA12 0PT Tel: 01294 312022 — MB ChB 1980 Aberd.; MRCP (UK) 1986; MRCGP 1984; DCH RCPS Glas. 1983; DRCOG 1982; FRCPCH. Cons. Paediat. Neonatology Ayrsh. Acute Hosps. NHS Trust. Prev: Sen. Regist. (Med. Paediat.) Roy. Hosp. Sick Childr. Glas.

KINMONT, Mr John Christian The Lent House, Clevedon Road, Flax Bourton, Bristol BS48 1NQ — MB BS 1989 Lond.; FRCS Eng. 1994. Specialist Regist. (Orthop.) SW Thames Train. Progr.

KINMONT, Patrick David Clifford, MBE, TD Park Leaze House, Ewen, Cirencester GL7 6PZ Tel: 01285 770460 — MRCS Eng. LRCP Lond. 1939; MB BS Lond. 1939; MD Lond. 1946; FRCP Lond. 1965, M 1946. (King's Coll. Hosp.) Socs: Hon. Mem. (Ex-Pres.) Brit. Assn. Dermat.; Internat. Hon. Mem. Amer. Dermat. Assn.; Hon. Mem. Irish Assn. Dermat. Prev: Emerit. Dermat. Univ. Hosp., Gen. Hosp. & City Hosp. Nottm.; Dermat. Derby Roy. Infirm.; Regist. (Med. & Dermat.) King's Coll. Hosp.

KINMONTH, Professor Ann-Louise General Practice and Primary Care Research Group, IPH Forvie Side, Robinson Way, Cambridge CB2 2SR Tel: 01223 330329 Fax: 01223 330330 Email: alk25@medschl.cam.ac.uk; 1 Cambridge Road, Great Shelford, Cambridge CB2 5JE Tel: 01223 843314 — MB BChir 1976 Lond.; MSc (Epidemiol.) Lond. 1989, BA 1972, MA 1979; MD Camb. 1984; FRCP Lond. 1994; MRCP (UK) 1978; FRCPCH 1997; FRCGP 1992, M 1982; F Med Sci 1998. (St. Thos.) Prof. Gen. Pract. Univ. of Camb. Socs: Scientif. Sect. Brit. Diabetic Assn.; N. Amer. Primary Care Research Gp.; Fell. Brit. Acad. Med. Sci. Prev: Prof. Primary Med. Care, Soton.; Reader (Primary Med. Care) Univ. Soton.; Research Fell. (Paediat.) Oxf.

KINMONTH, Mr Maurice Henry (retired) Home Farm House, E. Langton, Market Harborough LE16 7TW Tel: 01858 277 — MB BS 1940 Lond.; FRCS Eng. 1947; MRCS Eng. LRCP Lond. 1939. Co. Med. Off. Leics. Br. Brit. Red Cross Soc. Prev: Cons. Plastic Surg. Leicester Area & Lincs.

KINMONTH, Ralph John 24 Atherton Street, London SW11 2JE — MRCS Eng. LRCP Lond. 1978.

KINN, Deborah Ruth 11 Mayville Road, Liverpool L18 0HG — MB ChB 1985 Liverp.

KINNAIRD, Timothy David 90 Trem Twyn, Two Locks, Cwmbran NP44 7HP — MB BCh 1992 Wales; MRCP (UK) 1995. Regist. (Cardiol.) Lond. Chest Hosp. Bonnet Rd. Lond. E29JX. Prev: Regist. (Cardiol.) Broomfield Hosp. Chelmsford; Regist. (Cardiol.) King Geo. Hosp. Ilford; SHO (Med.) P.ss of Wales Hosp. Bridgend.

***KINNAIRD, Timothy Philip** 2 Paxton Place, Norwich NR2 2JE — MB ChB 1995 Birm.

KINNEAR, Edward (retired) Christmas Tree Cottage, Monks Eleigh, Ipswich IP7 7AU Tel: 01449 740790 — MB ChB Birm. 1952; DPH Bristol 1959.

KINNEAR, Fiona Catherine King Edward VII Hospital, Windsor SL4 3DP — MB ChB 1979 Sheff.; FRCS Ed. 1986. Clin. Asst. P. Chas. Eye Unit King Edwd. VII Hosp. Windsor; Clin. Asst. Roy. Berks. Hosp. Reading.

KINNEAR, Frances Barley Laboratory 105, Pathology Department, Western Infirmary, Glasgow G11 6NT Tel: 0141 211 2052 Fax: 0141 337 2494; Oathlaw Pottery, Oathlaw, Forfar DD8 3PQ Tel: 01307 850272 — MB ChB 1992 Glas.; BSc (Hons.) Immunol. Glas. 1989. Research SHO (Ophth.) W.. Infirm. Glas.

KINNEAR, John Alexander Flat 3, Ingledene Court, Horace Road, Southend-on-Sea SS1 2DN — MB BCh 1985 Witwatersrand; FRCA (UK). Cons. Anaesth., S.end Hosp., Essex.

KINNEAR, Jonathan Clive 30 Heol Drindod, Johnstown, Carmarthen SA31 3NU Tel: 01267 234707 — MB BCh 1991 Wales. Trainee GP St. Clears Dyfed.

KINNEAR, Paul Ernest 62 Wimpole Street, London W1G 8AJ Tel: 020 7935 5416 Fax: 020 7460 5943; 20 Gerard Road, Barnes, London SW13 9RG Tel: 020 8748 1053 Email: pkinnear@globalnet.co.uk — MB BS 1974 Lond.; FRCS Eng. 1982; FRCOphth. 1988. (Westm.) Cons. Ophth. Char. Cross Hosp. Lond.; Cons optha Chelsea & W.minster Hosp Lond. Socs: Fell. Roy. Soc. Med.; Amer. Acad. Ophth. Prev: Resid. Surg. Off. Moorfields Eye Hosp. Lond.; Sen. Regist. Moorfields Eye Hosp. & Char. Cross Hosp. Lond.; Fell. Proctor Foundat. Univ. Calif., San Francisco.

KINNEAR, William John Morrison 161 Harrow Road, Nottingham NG8 1FL — MB BS 1979 Lond.; MRCP (UK) 1982.

KINNELL, Herbert Gladstone 18 Cross Street, Reading RG1 1SN — MB ChB 1968 Aberd.; MRCP (U.K.) 1974; MRCPsych 1976; DPM Ed. 1976.

KINNELL, John Dunford (retired) The Meads, Tollerton, York YO61 1QB Tel: 01347 838793 Fax: 01347 838793 — MB ChB Aberd. 1954; FFA RCS Eng. 1960; DA Eng. 1957. Prev: Cons. Anaesth. York Hosps.

KINNERSLEY, Ann Formby Clinic, Phillips Lane, Formby, Liverpool L37 4AY; 35A Victoria Road, Formby, Liverpool L37 7DH — MB ChB 1964 Liverp.; DObst RCOG 1966. SCMO S.port & Formby Community Health Servs. NHS Trust. Socs: S.port Med. Soc. Prev: Clin. Med. Off. S.port HA; GP Formby.

KINNERSLEY, Dale Steven The Old School Surgery, Bolts Hill, Chartham, Canterbury CT4 7JX Tel: 01227 738282; The Surgery, Branch Road, Chilham, Canterbury CT4 8DR Tel: 01227 730210 — BSc (Hons.) Lond. 1981, MB BS 1984; MRCGP 1988; DGM RCP Lond. 1987; Cert. Family Plann. JCC 1986; DRCOG 1986; DCH RCP Lond. 1986; AKC 1984. (King's Coll. Hosp.) Trainee GP Windsor VTS. Prev: Ho. Off. King's Coll. Hosp. Lond.

KINNERSLEY, Paul Llanedeyrn Health Centre, Maelfa, Llanedeyrn, Cardiff CF23 9PN Tel: 029 2073 1671 Fax: 029 2054 0129 — MB ChB 1981 Bristol. GP Cardiff; Sen. Lect. (Gen. Pract.) Univ. Wales Coll. Med.

KINNEY, Anne Michele 87 Fortwilliam Park, Belfast BT15 4AS; Robespierre House, 8 Scott's Place, Claughton, Birkenhead L41 0ED — MB BCh BAO 1988 Belf.; MB BCh Belf. 1988; MRCGP 1993; DRCOG 1992; DGM RCP Lond. 1991. Socs: BMA.

KINNIBURGH, Alisdair John 11 Glencora Drive, Dykebar, Paisley PA2 7QE — MB ChB 1987 Glas.

KINNIBURGH, David 12 Trull Green Drive, Trull, Taunton TA3 7JL — BM BS 1994 Nottm.

KINNIBURGH, Diane Elizabeth Union Street Surgery, 75 Union Street, Larkhall ML9 1DZ Tel: 01698 882105 Fax: 01698 886332; 12 Vicars Road, Stonehouse, Larkhall ML9 3EB Tel: 01698 792333 — MB ChB 1988 Dundee; MRCGP 1992; DRCOG 1991.

KINNIBURGH, Norman Andrew The Surgery, 10 Bolton Road, Eastbourne BN21 3JY Tel: 01323 730537 Fax: 01323 412759 — MB BS 1973 Lond.; DCH Eng. 1975. (King's Coll. Hosp.) Socs: E.bourne Med. Soc.

KINNING, Esther 17 Old Warwick Road, Solihull B92 7JQ — MB ChB 1997 Leic.

KINNINMONTH, Mr Andrew William George 7 Mill Road, Bothwell, Glasgow G71 8DQ — MB ChB 1977 Ed.; FRCS (Orthop.) Ed. 1989; FRCS Ed. 1981.

KINNIS, Terry Darrell (retired) Stoneydelph Health Centre, Ellerbeck, Stoneydelph, Tamworth B77 4JA Tel: 01827 892809 Fax: 01827 331167 — MB BS 1966 Newc. GP Hosp. Pract. S.E. Staffs. Health Dist. Prev: Regist. (Anaesth.) Dundee Health Dist.

KINNISH, Ian Keith Grassington Medical Centre, 9 Station Road, Grassington, Skipton BD23 5LS Tel: 01756 752313 Fax: 01756 753320; Gregory Cottage, 10 Chamber End Fold, Grassington, Skipton BD23 5BA Tel: 01756 752313 — MB ChB 1973 Liverp.; Dip. IMC RCS Ed. 1990; MRCGP 1996. Med. Off. Upper Wharfedale Immediate Care Scheme. Socs: BMA; Assoc. RCS Edin.

KINNISON, Robert Norman 2 Seacroft Drive, Skegness PE25 3AH — MB ChB 1927 St. And. Prev: Flight Lt. RAF Med. Br.

KINNON, John Fraser Crimond Medical Centre, Crimond, Fraserburgh AB43 8QJ Tel: 01346 532215 Fax: 01346 531808; Makira, Crimond, Fraserburgh AB43 8SQ Tel: 01346 532753 Fax: 01346 532839 — MB ChB 1971 Aberd.; DObst RCOG 1974. (Aberd.) Hosp. Pract. (Psychogeriat.) Ugie Hosp. Peterhead. Prev: Sen. Med. Off. Solomon Is.s Govt.; Trainee GP Aberd. VTS; Ho. Off. Woodend Gen. Hosp. Aberd.

KINOULTY, Mary 1 Park House, Church Road, Snitterfield, Stratford-upon-Avon CV37 0LE — MB BS 1981 Lond.; MSc Occupat. Health Med. Lond. 1989; MFOM RCP Lond. 1992; MRCGP 1985. Head (Occupat. Health) Rover Gp. Longbridge. Prev: Princip. Med. Off. Zeneca AgroChem.s; Occ. Phys. Lucas Industries.

KINROSS, Ivone Le Jardinet, Rue Belin, St Martin's, Guernsey GY4 6 Tel: 01534 854583 — MA, MB BChir Camb. 1951. (St. Thos.)

KINSELLA, Brendan William Winstanley Drive Surgery, 138 Winstanley Drive, Leicester LE3 1PB Tel: 0116 285 8435 Fax: 0116 275 5416; Pine Garth, 6 Enderby Road, Blaby, Leicester LE8 4GD — MB ChB 1980 Leic.; MRCGP 1986; DRCOG 1984; Cert. Family Plann. JCC 1984.

KINSELLA, Catherine Mary 29 Lyndale Road, Redhill RH1 2HA — MB BCh BAO 1988 Dub.; MB BCh Dub. 1988.

KINSELLA, Denis Charles c/o Department of Radiology, Royal Devon & Exeter Hospital (Wonford), Barrack Road, Exeter EX2 5DW Tel: 0117 929 8895 — MB BS 1982 Lond.; MA Camb. 1979; MRCP (UK) 1985; FRCR 1989. Cons. Radiol. Roy. Devon & Exeter Healthcare Trust.

KINSELLA, Heather Patricia Green Lane Surgery, Belper, Derby DE56 1BZ Tel: 01773 823521; Bent Farm, Nether Heage, Derby DE56 2AP Tel: 01773 857021 — BA Dub. 1979, MB BCh BAO 1979; MRCGP 1984; DRCOG 1984; DCH Dub. 1982.

KINSELLA, John 12 Douglas Muir Drive, Milngavie, Glasgow G62 7RJ — MB BS 1980 Newc.; FFA RCS Eng. 1986. Cons. Anaesth. & Intens. Care Glas. Roy. Infirm. Prev: Sen. Regist. (Intens. Care & Anaesth.) Glas.; Regist. (Anaesth.) Glas. Roy. Infirm.

KINSELLA, Lawrence Michael Joseph The Northern Medical Centre, 580 Holloway Road, London N7 6LB Tel: 020 7445 8100/8101 Fax: 020 7445 8114; Tel: 020 7445 8100/8101 Fax: 020 7445 8114 Email: lmjk01@aol.com — LRCPI & LM, LRSCI & LM 1975; MICGP 1987; DRCOG 1982. (Dublin) GP; Med. Tutor UCL & Roy. Free Med. Sch. Prev: Regist. & SHO (Med.) Mayday Hosp. Croydon; SHO (O & G) Greenwich Dist. Hosp. Lond.; SHO (Child Health) St. Bart. Hosp. Lond.

KINSELLA, Stephen Michael Department of Anaesthesia, St. Michael's Hospital, Southwell St., Bristol BS2 8EG — MB BS 1980 Lond.; FFA RCSI 1990. Cons. Anaesth. St. Michael's Hosp. Bristol.

KINSELLA, Timothy John Oaklands, 68 Crofts Bank Road, Urmston, Manchester M41 0UH Tel: 0161 755 3567 — MB ChB 1976 Manch.; FFA RCS Eng. 1980. Cons. Anaesth. Pk. Hosp. Manch.

KINSEY, Matthew Alan 10 Littlebrook Cl, Hadfield, Hyde SK13 2AW — MB ChB 1997 Manch.

KINSEY, Melvyn Moir Medical Centre, Regent St., Long Eaton, Nottingham; 22 Katherine Drive, Toton, Nottingham NG9 6JB Tel: 0115 973 3079 — MB ChB 1967 Liverp.; MRCS Eng. LRCP Lond. 1968. Socs: M-C. Soc.

KINSEY, Robert Moseley (retired) Townhead Farm, Townhead Road, Dore, Sheffield S17 3GE Tel: 0114 236 6429 — MB ChB 1957 Liverp.; MRCS Eng. LRCP Lond. 1957; MFOM RCP Lond. 1981; MRCGP 1968; DIH Eng. 1975. Med. Adviser Univ. Sheff.; Med. Adviser Hepworth Refractones Ltd. & T.C. Harrison Gp. Ltd. Prev: Dir. Health Serv. Univ. Sheff.

KINSEY, Sally Elizabeth Paediatric Haematology Department, St. James University Hospital, Beckett St., Leeds LS9 7TF Tel: 0113 206 4985 Fax: 0113 247 0248 Email: sally.kinsey@gw.sjsuh.northy.nhs.uk — MB ChB 1982 Liverp.; MRCP (UK) 1985; MRCPath 1990; MD Liverp. 1992; FRCPCH 1997; FRCPath 1998; FRCP 1998. (Liverp.) Cons. Paediat. Haematologist St Jas. Univ. Hosp. Leeds.; Sen. Clin. Lect. Leeds Univ. Socs: Brit. Soc. Haematol.; Amer. Soc. Haemat.; Eur. Blood & Marrow Transpl. Prev: Sen. Regist. (Haemat.) Univ. Coll. Hosp. & Gt. Ormond Stre+et Hosp. Lond.; Asst. Lect. (Haemat.) Middlx. Hosp.; Sen. Ho. Off. Liverp. Hosp. & Centr. Birm. Hosps.

KINSEY, Vanessa Elizabeth Plot A Mill Lane, Whilborough, Newton Abbot TQ12 5LW — MB ChB 1981 Leeds.

KINSEY, Wayne Leonard Peveril, Mill Way, Barnby, Beccles NR34 7PS — MB ChB 1985 Birm. Sen. Regist. (Histopath.) Kettering Gen. Hosp. Prev: Regist. (Histopath.) Leicester Hosp.

KINSHUCK, Mr David Joseph 19 Spring Road, Edgbaston, Birmingham B15 2HG — MB BS 1978 Newc.; FRCS Ophth. Glas. 1983; FRCOphth 1989; DO RCS Eng. 1983; MBA Univ. Birm. (Public Sector) 1996. Assoc. Specialist Good Hope Hosp. Socs: Midl. Ophth. Soc. Prev: Regist. Wolverhampton & Midl. Counties Eye Infirm.; Research Fell. Diabetic Retinopathy Unit Hammersmith Hosp. Lond.

KINSLER, Hilary Jane The Royal London Hospital Trust, Whitechapel, London E1 — MB BS 1988 Lond.; MRCPsych 1993.

KINSLER, Rachel Ann 14 Dunkeld House, Abbott Road, London E14 0LS — MB BS 1992 Lond.

KINSLER, Veronica Anne 40 Park Road, Abingdon OX14 1DS — MB BChir 1995 Camb.; MA (Hons.) Camb. 1996, BA (Hons.) 1992; MRCP Lond. (Addenbrooke's Hospital Cambridge) Regist. (Paediat.)

Gt. Ormond St. Hosp. Lond. Socs: BMA. Prev: Regist. (Paediatrican) Ealing Hosp., Lond.; SHO (Paediat.) Gt. Ormond St. Lond.; SHO (Neonat.) John Radcliffe Hosp. Oxf.

KINSMAN, Francis Michael, CBE, Surg. Rear-Admiral Pound House, Meonstoke, Southampton SO32 3NP — MRCS Eng. LRCP Lond. 1950; MFCM 1973; DA Eng. 1956. (St. Bart.) Prev: Ho. Surg. & SHO (Anaesth.) Luton & Dunstable Hosp.

KINSMAN, Richard Inigo Spa Medical Practice, Ombersley Street, Droitwich WR9 8RD Tel: 01905 772389 Fax: 01905 797386; The Spa House, 131 Worcester Road, Droitwich Spa, Droitwich WR9 8AR Tel: 01905 778167 — MB ChB 1985 Sheff.; BMedSci Sheff. 1984; MRCGP 1991. Prev: GP King's Norton Birm.; Trainee GP/SHO Rotat. Good Hope Hosp. Sutton Coldfield; SHO Rotat. (Med.) New Cross Hosp. Wolverhampton.

KINSTON, Martin Adrian 2 Eldon grove, London NW3 5PS — MB BS 1970 Sydney; MRCPsych 1975. (Sydney) Cons. Psychotherap. Chelsea & W.m. Hosp. Lond. Socs: Brit. Psychoanalyt. Soc.

KINSTON, Paul 35A Albert Court, Prince Consort Road, London SW7 2BG Tel: 020 7581 1141 — MD 1935 Bologna; LDS RCS Eng. 1954.

KINSTON, Warren John 29 Netherhall Gardens, London NW3 5RL Tel: 020 7435 5941 — MB BS 1970 Sydney; BSc (Hons.) Sydney 1966, MB BS (Hons.) 1970; MRCPsych 1974.

KINTON, Lucy Department of Clinical Neurology, Institute of Neurology, Queen Square, London WC1N 3BG Tel: 020 7837 3611 Ext: 4305 Fax: 020 7278 5616 Email: l.kinton@ion.ucl.ac.uk — MB BChir 1994 Camb.; MRCP 1997. Clin. Research Fell. (Neurol.), Lond.

KIPGEN, David 12 Worcester Road, Hatfield AL10 0DX — MB BS 1998 Lond.; MB BS Lond 1998.

KIPLING, David Hart Lodge Surgery, Jones Road, Hartlepool TS24 9BD Tel: 01429 267573 Fax: 01429 869027; East Batter Law Farm, Hawthorn, Seaham SR7 8RP Tel: 0191 527 2293 — MB 1978 Camb.; BChir 1977; MRCGP 1981; DRCOG 1980. Hon. Med. Advisor Hartlepool Lifeboat Station; Dep. Area Med. Off. Brit. Boxing Bd. Control. Prev: Founding Chairm. NG Br. of BASM.

KIPLING, Maria Lisa 20 Drift Road, Pagham, Bognor Regis PO21 3NS — MB BS 1994 Lond.; DCH RCPCH 1999. (St. Mary's HMS) SHO (Paediat.) Roy. Alexandra Hosp., Brighton.

KIPLING, Paul Thomas The Quakers Lane Surgery, Quakers Lane, Richmond DL10 4BB Tel: 01748 850440 Fax: 01748 850802; 10 Oliver Road, Richmond DL10 5AQ — MB BS 1984 Lond.; DRCOG 1989.

KIPLING, Roger Maitland Department Anaesthesia, Yeovil District Hospital, Yeovil BA21 4AT Tel: 01935 475122; Lyles House, Hummer, Trent, Sherborne DT9 4SH Tel: 01935 850926 — MB BS 1973 Lond.; FFA RCS Eng. 1979. (Barts.) Cons. Anaesth. Yeovil Dist. Hosp. Socs: Assn. Anaesth. Gt. Brit. & Irel.; Intens. Care Soc. Prev: Sen. Regist. (Anaesth.) Addenbrooke's Hosp. Camb.; Staff Mem. (Anaesth.) Univ. Hosp. Leiden, Netherlands; Regist. (Anaesth.) Magill Dept. Anaesth. W.m. Hosp. Lond.

KIPPAX, Andrew Gordon Burscough Health Centre, Latham House Surgery, 31 Lord Street, Burscough, Ormskirk L40 4BZ Tel: 01704 895566 Fax: 01704 897510 — MB ChB 1987 Liverp.; MRCGP 1994; Cert. Family Plann. JCC 1992; DRCOG 1991; DCH RCP Lond. 1990. Prev: SHO (Psychiat.) Greaves Hall Hosp. S.port.

KIPPAX, Nicholas John Westall (retired) Ladies Walk, Butleigh, Glastonbury BA6 8SJ Tel: 01458 850314 — MB BS 1961 Lond.; MRCGP 1972; DObst RCOG 1964. Locum work. Prev: Ho. Phys. Middlx. Hosp. Lond.

KIPPAX, Thomas Paul Ladies Walk, Butleigh, Glastonbury BA6 8SJ — MB BS 1991 Lond.

KIPPEN, Douglas John 24 Ladysneuk Road, Stirling FK9 5NF — MB ChB 1995 Glas.

KIPPING, Mr Rupert Arthur (retired) Belvedere, 56 Bloxham Road, Banbury OX16 9JR Tel: 01295 262809 — MB BChir 1958 Camb.; MA Camb. 1959; FRCS Eng. 1966. Prev: Cons. Gen. Surg. Horton Gen. Hosp. Banbury.

KIRBY, Adam Jonathan Willis House, Cumber Lane, Whiston, Prescot L35 2YZ Tel: 0151 426 5885 — MB ChB 1986 Birm.; MRCPsych 1992. Cons. Ment. Handicap St Helens & Knowsley Community NHS Trust. Prev: Sen. Regist. (Psychiat.) Merseyside.; SHO (Psychiat.) Doncaster Roy. Infirm.

KIRBY, Aisling Mary Main Street Surgery, 75 Main Street, Derrylin, Enniskillen BT92 9LB Tel: 028677 48250 Fax: 028677 48999 Email: akirby@derrylin.pcwestni.nhs.uk; Knockninny, Derrylin, Enniskillen BT92 9JU Tel: 028677 48775 — MB BCh BAO 1981 NUI; DCH Dub. 1984; DObst RCPI 1985. Princip. - Derrylin. Prev: GP Derrybeg; Trainee GP Hay-on-Wye VTS.

KIRBY, Alan 6 Hodge Road, Worsley, Manchester M28 3AT Tel: 0161 790 3615 Fax: 0161 703 7638; 6 The Warke, Worsley, Manchester M28 2WX Tel: 0161 790 5354 — MB ChB 1956 Liverp.; BSc Liverp. 1953, MB ChB 1956; DObst RCOG 1961. (Liverp.) GP Manch. Prev: Fact. Med. Off. Roy. Ordnance Fact. Patricroft.; Ho. Surg. (Obst.) BRd.green Hosp. Liverp.

KIRBY, Amanda Caroline 4 The Coppice, Walters Ash, High Wycombe HP14 4TX — MB ChB 1987 Sheff.

KIRBY, Amanda Hilda Four Elms Medical Centre, 103 Newport Road, Cardiff CF24 0AF Tel: 029 2048 5526 — MB BCh 1984 Wales; MRCGP 1991.

KIRBY, Andrew Park 11 North Drive, Inskip, Preston PR4 0US — MB ChB 1991 Liverp. SHO (Psychiat.) Whittingham Hosp. Preston.

KIRBY, Angela Kristel Romney House Surgery, 39-41 Long Street, Tetbury GL8 8AA Tel: 01666 502303 Fax: 01666 504549; Brownshill House, Brownshill, Stroud GL6 8AS — MB 1973 Camb; MB 1973 Camb.; ATLS 2001; ATLS 2001; BChir 1972 Camb; BChir Camb. 1972; MRCP (UK) 1976; DCH RCP Lond. 1979; DObst RCOG 1974. (St. Bart.)

KIRBY, Professor Brian John, OBE 3 Pennsylvania Crescent, Exeter EX4 4SF Tel: 01392 669346 Email: b.j.kirby@ex.ac.uk — MB ChB 1960 Leeds; FRCP Ed. 1996; FRCP Lond. 1979, M 1967. (Leeds) Prof.Med Sch. of Postgrad. Med. & Health Sci.s; Chairm. Advis. Bd. on Registration of Homoeop. Products; Exec.Nat.Heart.Forum; Mem. Expert Gp. on Vit.s & Minerals(Food Safety Agency); Gen. Med. Counc. Fitness to Practise Comm. 2002. Socs: Brit. Cardiac Soc.; Assn. Phys.; Eur. Soc. Cardiol. Prev: Lect. (Med.) Univ. Edin.; Regist (Clin. Cardiol.) Roy. Postgrad. Med. Sch.; Instruc. (Med.) Med. Coll. Virginia, USA.

KIRBY, Caitriona Mary 12 Westbroke Gardens, Fishlake Meadows, Romsey SO51 7RQ Tel: 01703 840044 — MB BCh BAO 1980 NUI; LRCPI & LM LRCSI & LM 1980.

KIRBY, Christine (retired) 42 St Botolph's Road, Worthing BN11 4JS — MB BS Lond. 1940; MRCS Eng. LRCP Lond. 1940; DObst RCOG 1946; DCH Eng. 1957, DPH 1958. Prev: Asst. to PMO I.C.I Ltd. Head Office Lond.

KIRBY, Christopher Pomfret St Stephens Surgery, Adelaide Street, Redditch B97 4AL Tel: 01527 65444 Fax: 01527 69218; Meadowbank, Rowney Green, Alvechurch, Birmingham B48 7QP Tel: 0121 445 1815 — MB Camb. 1963, BChir 1962; DObst RCOG 1965. (Lond. Hosp.) Med. Adviser Worcs. HA. Prev: SHO (Cas.) Roy. Gwent Hosp. Newport; Ho. Surg. St. And. Hosp. Bow; Ho. Off. O & G Lond. Hosp.

KIRBY, David Anthony Gill Street Health Centre, 11 Gill Street, London E14 8HQ Tel: 020 7515 2211 — MB BChir 1976 Camb.; MA Camb. 1977, MB BChir 1976; MRCP (UK) 1979; DRCOG 1981; MRCGP 1981. GP City & E. Lond. Family Pract. Comm.

KIRBY, David Philip James 34 Swinton Crescent, Unsworth, Bury BL9 8PB — BM BS 1996 Nottm.

KIRBY, Gemma Victoria Victoria House, 66 Victoria Road, Earby, Colne BB18 6UR — MB ChB 1997 Liverp.

KIRBY, Graham 9 Chaucer Gardens, Tonbridge TN9 2QA — MB BS 1986 Lond.; MRCP (UK) 1990.

KIRBY, Helen 40 Kings Road, Melton Mowbray LE13 1QF; 28 Wheatcroft Road, Allerton, Liverpool L18 9UE Tel: 0151 280 9119 — MB ChB 1998 Liverp.; MB ChB Liverp 1998.

KIRBY, Ivor John 6 Ryder Close, Aughton, Ormskirk L39 5HJ — MB ChB 1979 Manch.; FFARCS Eng. 1984. Cons. Anaesth. S.port & Formby NHS Trust Hosp. Socs: Assn. Anaesth. & Liverp. Med. Inst. Prev: Assoc. Prof. Anaesth. Texas Tech Univ. Health Scis. Centre, El Paso, Texas, USA; Regist. (Anaesth.) Univ. Hosp. S. Manch. & Roy. Infirm.; SHO (Gen. Med.) Roy. Preston Hosp.

KIRBY, Jane Michelle 80 Stirling Court, Briercliffe, Burnley BB10 3QT — MB ChB 1997 Manch.

KIRBY, John Ramsland Cottage, Ford, Holbeton, Plymouth PL8 1LJ — MB ChB 1968 Manch.; MRCS Eng. LRCP Lond. 1968.

KIRBY, John Angus Lamont Bradshaw Brow, 30 Bradshaw Brow, Bradshaw, Bolton BL2 3DH Tel: 01204 302212 Fax: 01204

543264; 1 Riding Gate Mews, Harwood, Bolton BL2 4DS Tel: 01204 594915 Fax: 01204 593264 — MB BS 1981 Newc.; MRCGP 1986; DRCOG 1984; FRCGP 1997.

KIRBY, John Martin 6 Fortfield, Dromore BT25 1DD — MB BCh BAO 1993 NUI.

KIRBY, John Mary Main Street Surgery, 75 Main Street, Derrylin, Enniskillen BT92 9LB Tel: 028677 48250 Fax: 028677 48999 Email: jkirby@derrylin.pcwestni.nhs.uk; Knockninny, Derrylin, Enniskillen BT92 9JU Tel: 028677 48775 — MB BCh BAO 1981 NUI; MRCGP 1987; DRCOG 1985. Gen. Pract. Principle. Prev: Trainee GP Crickhowell VTS; GP Rotat. Erne Hosp. Enniskillen N. Irel.

KIRBY, Kathleen Mairi (retired) 164 Grange Road, Hartlepool TS26 8LX Tel: 01429 267478 — MB ChB 1951 Ed.; DCH Eng. 1958. Prev: SCMO Darlington HA.

KIRBY, Michael Geoffrey The Surgery, Nevells Road, Letchworth SG6 4TS Tel: 01462 683051 Fax: 01462 485650; 30 Wedon Way, Bygrave, Baldock SG7 5DX Tel: 01462 892234 Fax: 01462 6771 Email: kirbym@globalnet.co.uk — FRCP 2000; MRCS Eng. LRCP Lond. 1969; MB BS Lond. 1970; MRCP (UK) 1973. (St. Mary's) GP; Hosp. Pract. (Med. Unit) Qu. Eliz. II Hosp. Welwyn Gdn. City; Dir. HertNet (Herts. Primary Care Research Network) 1998. Socs: Fell. Roy.Coll. Of Phys.s; Assoc. Mem. of BAUS; Mem. Primary Care Cardiovasc. Soc. Prev: Regist. (Med.) Qu. Eliz. II Hosp. Welwyn Gdn. City; Ho. Phys. St. Mary's Hosp. Lond.; Ho. Surg. Hillingdon Hosp.

KIRBY, Norman George, OBE, Maj.-Gen. late RAMC Guy's Nuffield House, Newcomon St., London SE1 1YR Tel: 020 7955 4752 Fax: 020 7955 4754; 12 Woodsyre, Sydenham Hill, Dulwich, London SE26 6SS Tel: 020 8670 5327 — MB ChB Birm. 1949; FRCS Ed. 1980; FRCS Eng. 1964; MRCS Eng. LRCP Lond. 1949; FFAEM 1993; FICS 1980; DMCC Soc. Apoth. Lond. 1997. (Birm.) Cons. A & E Surg. Guy's Nuffield Hse. Lond.; Examr. (Anat. A & E) RCS Edin.; Hon. Cons. Surg. W.m. Hosp. Lond.; Emerit. Cons. (A & E Surg.) Guy's Hosp. Lond.; Invited Mem. Counc. RCS Eng.; Mem. Ct. Examr. RCS Eng. Socs: Sen. Fell. BOA; (Hon. Librarian) Roy. Soc. Med.; (Ex-Pres.) Brit. Assn. Accid. & Emerg. Med. Prev: Dir. Army Surg. MoD & Cons. Surg. to Army; Hon. Surg. to HM the Qu.; Cons. Surg. Qu. Eliz. Milit. Hosp. Lond.

KIRBY, Patrick John Kirby and Partners, Charlton Group Medical Practice, Charlton Street, Oakengates, Telford TF2 6DA Tel: 01952 620138 Fax: 01952 615282 — MB BS 1969 Lond.; MRCGP 1975. (Univ. Coll. Hosp.) Prev: Ho. Phys. & Ho. Surg. Edgware Gen. Hosp.

KIRBY, Mr Robert Mark The Old Vicarage, Maer, Newcastle ST5 5EF Tel: 01782 680725 — MB ChB 1977 Birm.; MD Birm. 1988; FRCS Eng. 1981. Cons. Surg. N. Staffs. Roy. Infirm. & City Gen. Hosp. Stoke-on-Trent; Hon. Sen. Clin. Lect. Univ. Keele. Socs: Fell. Assn. Surgs.; Brit. Assn. Surg. Oncol.; BMA. Prev: Sen. Regist. (Gen. Surg.) W. Midl. Surg. Train. Scheme; Research Fell. (Liver Transpl.) Qu. Eliz. Hosp. Birm.; Regist. Rotat. (Surg.) Roy. Surrey Co. Hosp. & St. Geo. Hosp. Lond.

KIRBY, Robin Nicholas The Surgery, 2 Manor Road, West Wickham BR4 9PS Tel: 020 8777 1293 Fax: 020 8776 1977 — MB BS 1966 Lond.; MRCS Eng. LRCP Lond. 1966. (Guy's)

KIRBY, Mr Roger General Hospital, Hartlepool TS24 9AH Tel: 01429 266654; 13 Elm Grove, Hartlepool TS26 8LZ Tel: 01429 267272 — MB BS 1962 Durh.; MS Newc. 1974; FRCS Eng. 1969; DObst RCOG 1964. (Durh.) Cons. Surg. N. Tees. Hartlepool NHS Trust. Socs: BMA; N. Eng. Surg. Soc. Prev: Sen. Regist. (Surg.) RVI Newc.; Resid (Surg.) Univ. Penna, Philadelphia USA.

KIRBY, Professor Roger Sinclair 145 Harley Street, London W1G 6BJ Tel: 020 7935 9720 Fax: 020 7224 5706; 71 Church Road, Wimbledon, London SW19 5AL Tel: 020 8946 8445 Fax: 020 8879 1272 — MB BChir 1976 Camb.; MB BChir (Distinc.) Camb. 1976; MD Camb. 1986; FRCS (Urol.) 1986; FRCS Eng. 1979. (Camb. & Middlx.) p/t Cons. Urol. St. Geo. Hosp. Lond.; Cons. Urol., The Lond. Clinic, Lond. Socs: (Hon. Sec.) Brit. Assn. Urol. Surgs.; Roy. Soc. Med. (Vice-Pres. Urol. Sect.); Eur. Assn. Urol. (Mem. Scientif. Comm.). Prev: Cons. Urol. St. Bart. Hosp. Lond.; Sen. Regist. (Urol.) Middlx. Hosp. Lond.; Regist. (Surg.) St. Thos. Hosp. Lond.

KIRBY, Susan Anne Hammersmith Hosptial, Ducane Road, London W12 0HS Tel: 020 8743 2030; 32 Downage, Hendon, London NW4 1AH — MB BS 1981 Newc.; FFA RCSI 1993. Cons. Anaesth. Qu. Charlotte's & Hammersmith Hosp. Lond. Prev: Sen. Regist. (Anaesth.) Roy. Brampton Hosp.; Sen. Regist. (Anaesth.) Chelsea & W.minster Hosp.; Regist. (Anaesth.) Bristol.

KIRBY, Suzanne St John's Group Practice, 1 Greenfield Lane, Balby, Doncaster DN4 0TH Tel: 01302 854521 Fax: 01302 310823 — MB ChB 1986 Leic. Socs: RCGP.

KIRCHIN, Miss Vivienne Sally Freeman Hospital, High Heaton, Newcastle-Upon-Tyne NE7 7DN Tel: 0191 284 3111 — MB BS 1992 Lond.

KIRCHNER, Vincent 18 Rhondda Grove, London E3 5AP — MB ChB 1987 Cape Town.

KIRIAKAKIS, Vassilios Department of Neurology, The National Hospital, Queen Square, London WC1N 3BG — Ptychio Iatrikes 1988 Athens.

KIRK, Adam 32 Warwick Road, New Barnet, Barnet EN5 5EH — MB BS 1996 Lond.

KIRK, Mr Alan John Ballantyne Department of Cardiothoracic Surgery, Western Infirmary, Dumbarton Road, Glasgow G11 6NT Tel: 0141 211 2190 Fax: 0141 211 1751 Email: alanjbkirk@hotmail.com; 8 Thomson Drive, Bearsden, Glasgow G61 3NU — MB ChB 1979 Glas.; FRCS Glas. 1983. (Glas.) Cons. (Cardiothoracic Surg.) W. Infirm. Glas. Socs: Scot. Thoracic Soc. Prev: Sen. Regist. (Cardiothoracic Surg.) Roy. Infirm. & Frenchay Hosp. Bristol; Research Fell. (CardioPulm. Transpl.) Freeman Hosp. Newc. u. Tyne.

KIRK, Alexander Ernest Morrison Hounslow Health Centre, 92 Bath Road, Hounslow TW3 3EL Tel: 020 8570 6271 — MB BS 1954 Lond. (Middlx.) Socs: BMA.

KIRK, Andrew Weir The Moorings, Shore Road, Garelochhead, Helensburgh G84 0AS — MB ChB 1977 Glas.

KIRK, Anne Maria The Surgery, Laggan, Newtonmore Tel: 01843 842787 — MB BCh BAO 1985 NUI. Prev: SHO (Cas.) Kent & Canterbury Hosp.; Trainee GP Forres Scotl.

KIRK, Charles Richard Congenital Heart Disease Centre, Healthcare NHS Trust, Heath Park, Cardiff CF14 4XW Tel: 029 2074 4743 Fax: 029 2074 4744 — MB BChir 1980 Camb.; MA Camb. 1980; FRCP Lond. 1994; MRCP (UK) 1983; MRCS Eng. LRCP Lond. 1979; DRCOG 1982. Cons. Paediat. Cardiol. Univ. Hosp. Wales. Socs: Brit. Cardiac Soc.; Brit. Paediat. Cardiac Assn. Prev: Hon. Cons. Paediat. Cardiol. Roy. Childr. Hosp. Cardiff.

KIRK, Christine Anne Bootham Park Hospital, Bootham, York YO30 7BY Tel: 01904 454071 Fax: 01904 453794; Golson's Cottage, Oulston, York YO61 3RA Tel: 01347 868274 Fax: 01347 868156 — MB BChir 1973 Camb.; MA Camb. 1974; FRCPsych 1992. Cons. Psychiat. for the Elderly Bootham Pk. Hosp. York.; Clin. Dir. (Ment. Health). Prev: Cons. Psychogeriat. St. Luke's Hosp. Middlesbrough, Cleveland.

KIRK, Christine Margaret 4 Kylepark Avenue, Uddingston, Glasgow G71 7DF — MB ChB 1985 Glas.

KIRK, Czarina Dawn 16 Ford Road, Dundonald, Belfast BT16 1XR — MB BCh BAO 1995 Belf. SHO (Psychiat.) Knockbracken Healthcare Pk. Belf.; SHO (Psychiat.) Ards Hosp., Newtownards, Co. Down. Prev: SHO (Neurol.) Roy. Gp. Hosps. Belf.

KIRK, Professor David Urology Department, Gartnavel General Hospital, Glasgow G12 0YN Tel: 0141 211 0047 Fax: 0141 357 1679 Email: david.kirk.wg@northglasgow.scot.nhs.uk; Woodend Prospect Road, Dullatur, Glasgow G68 0AN Tel: 01236 720778 Email: dkirk70683@aol.com — BM BCh Oxf. 1968; MA Oxf. 1968, DM 1979; FRCS Ed. 1997; FRCS Glas. 1989; FRCS Eng. 1973. (Oxf.) Cons. Urol. W.. Glas. Hosps. Univ. NHS Trust; Hon. Prof. Glas. Univ. Socs: Fell. Roy. Soc. Med. (Ex-Counc. Mem. Sect. Urol.); (Ex Counc.) Brit. Assn. Urol. Surgs.; Internat. Soc. Urol. Prev: Sen. Regist. (Gen. Surg. & Urol.) Avon AHA (T); Research Asst. (Surg.) Univ. Sheff.; Regist. Rotat. (Surg.) Roy. Infirm. & Childr. Hosp. Sheff.

KIRK, David Arthur 17 Allendale, Ilkeston DE7 4LE — MB ChB 1987 Liverp.

KIRK, David Patterson Alloa Health Centre, Marshill, Alloa FK10 1AQ Tel: 01259 212088 Fax: 01259 724788 — MB ChB 1972 Ed.; DObst RCOG 1974.

KIRK, Gareth Richard 43 Ferndene Gardens, Dundonald, Belfast BT16 2EP — MB BCh BAO 1995 Belf.

KIRK, Gillian Elizabeth East Ardsley Health Centre, Bradford Rd, Wakefield WF3 2DN — MB ChB 1990 Sheff.; M Med Sci 2000; MRCPsych 1998. Specialist Regist. (Gen. Adult Psychiat.), Yorks. Socs: Roy. Coll. Psychiat.; Leeds & W. Riding Medico-Legal Soc.; S.

Yorks. Medico-Legal Soc. Prev: SHO Rotat. (Psychiat.) Leeds; Clin. Asst. (A & E) Pinderfields Hosp. Wakefield; Resid. Med. Off. Claremont Hosp. Sheff.

KIRK, Heather Jane 1FR, 209 Rosemount Place, Aberdeen AB25 2XS — MB ChB 1997 Aberd.

KIRK, Hector Howard (retired) The Pine, 1 Marguerite Park, Bryansford Road, Newcastle BT33 0PE Tel: 0139 67 22986 — LRCP LRCS 1940 Ed.; LRCP LRCS Ed. LRFPS Glas. 1940; FRCOG 1967, M 1953, DObst 1948. Prev: Cons. O & G N.W. Hosp. Gp. N. Irel. Regist. Jubilee Matern.

KIRK, Helen Louise c/o 111 Wilmot Way, Banstead SM7 2QA — BM 1990 Soton.

KIRK, Jacqueline Mary Elizabeth Department of Diagnostic Radiology, Dartford and Gravesham NHS Trust, Darent Valley Hospital, Darenth Wood Road, Dartford DA2 8DA Tel: 01322 428100; 142 Court Lane, London SE21 7EB Tel: 020 8693 3173 — MB BChir 1976 Camb.; MD Camb. 1986, MA 1976; MRCP (UK) 1978; T(CR) 1992; FRCR 1990. Cons. Radiol. Dartford & Gravesham Healthcare Trust. Prev: Sen. Regist. (Radiol.) St. Geo. Hosp. Lond.; Resid. Fell. Cardiothoracic Inst. Brompton Hosp. Lond.; Regist. & SHO (Med.) N. Staffs. Hosp. Centre Stoke-on-Trent.

KIRK, James Fulton (retired) 19 Averill Crescent, Dumfries DG2 6RY — MB ChB Glas. 1956; FRCP Glas. 1972, M 1970; FFCM 1972, M 1972. Chief Admin. Med. Off. Dumfries & Galloway HB. Prev: Asst. Sen. Admin. Med. Off. S. E. RHB (Scotl.).

KIRK, Jane Sheila Goodacre and Partners, Swadlincote Surgery, Darklands Road, Swadlincote DE11 0PP Tel: 01283 551717 Fax: 01283 211905; 2 Highfields Close, Ashby-de-la-Zouch LE65 2FN — BM 1977 Soton.; MFFP 1993; MRCGP 1983. (Southampton)

KIRK, Jeremy Mark Wakelin Birmingham Childrens Hospital, Steelhouse Lane, Birmingham B4 6NH Tel: 0121 333 9999 Fax: 0121 333 8191 Email: jeremy.kirk@bhamchildrens.wmids.nhs.uk; 47 Pereira Road, Harborne, Birmingham B17 9JB Tel: 0121 247 1407 — MB BS 1980 Lond.; MD Lond. 1994; MRCP (UK) 1983; MRCS Eng. LRCP Lond. 1980; DCH RCP Lond. 1987; FRCPCH 1997. (Char. Cross) Cons. Paediat. Endocrinol. Birm. Childr. Hosp.; Hon. Sen. Lect. Univ. Birm. Prev: Sen. Regist. Hosp. Sick Childr. Lond. & King's Coll. Hosp.; Regist. (Paediat.) Middlx. Hosp.; Research Fell. (Paediat. Endocrinol.) St. Bart. Hosp. Lond.

KIRK, Mr John Oronsay, 1 Bonhard Road, New Scone, Perth PH2 6QL — MB BS 1945 Lond.; FRCS Ed. 1973; FRCS Eng. 1954. (Middlx.) Socs: Brit. Assn. Plastic Surgs. Prev: Cons. Plastic Surg. Tayside Health Bd.; Sen. Regist. in Plastic Surg. Bangour Hosp. Broxburn & Roy. Hosp.; Sick Childr. Edin.; Surg. Lt. RNVR.

KIRK, John Michael Dacre Cottage, Dacre, Penrith CA11 0HL Tel: 017684 86224 Fax: 017684 86224 — MB 1958 Camb.; BA Camb. 1953, MB 1958, BChir 1957; MRCGP 1986; DObst RCOG 1962; DCH Eng. 1963. (Camb. & Leeds) Prev: Med. Off. Overseas Civil Serv. (Basutoland).

KIRK, Jonathan Edward James 26 Wallace Hill Road, Downpatrick BT30 9BU — MB BCh 1997 Belf.

KIRK, Juliet Anne Dalrymple Melville Street Surgery, 17 Melville Street, Ryde PO33 2AF Tel: 01983 811431 Fax: 01983 817215 — BM BCh 1986 Oxf.; BA Oxf. 1983; Cert. Family Plann. JCC 1989. (Oxf.) Clin. Asst. (Elderly Ment. Health) Ryde, I. of Wight.

KIRK, Katherine Siobhan 69 Glendarragh, Belfast BT4 2WB — MB ChB 1993 Birm.

KIRK, Kirsty Talitha Kum 7 Prospect Road, Ballygowan, Newtownards BT23 6LS; 2 Rowallane Close, Saintfield, Ballynahinch BT24 7PA — MB BCh BAO 1995 Belf.

***KIRK, Louise Amanda** 40 Stevenson Gardens, Cosby, Leicester LE9 1SN — MB ChB 1995 Birm.; ChB Birm. 1995.

KIRK, Margaret Audiology Unit, St. Ann's Hospital, St Ann's Road, Tottenham, London N15 3TH; 10 Southwood Lane, Highgate, London N6 5EE Tel: 020 8340 8575 — MB BS 1952 Lond.; DCH Eng. 1955. (Char. Cross) Sen. Med. Off. & Dir. Audiol. Serv. Haringey Health Care Trust. Socs: Med. Soc. Lond.; BMA; Brit. Soc. Audiol. Prev: Med. Off. Marks & Spencer Ltd. Lond.; Ho. Phys. & Cas. Off. Vict. Hosp. Childr. Lond.; Ho. Phys. & Ho. Surg. Char. Cross Hosp.

KIRK, Michael Lower Barns House, Lower Barnes Road, Ludford, Ludlow SY8 4DS — MRCS Eng. LRCP Lond. 1964.

KIRK, Nicola Radford Ashford Hospital, Ashford TW15 3AA Tel: 01784 884512 Fax: 01784 884099 — MB BS 1976 Lond.; FRCPath 1997. Cons. (Microbiol.) Ashford & St. Peters Hosps. NHS Trust.

KIRK, Paul Robert 27 Blackburn Gardens, West Didsbury, Manchester M20 3YH — MB ChB 1989 Sheff.

KIRK, Mr Raymond Maurice Royal Free Hospital, Pond Street, London NW3 2QG Tel: 020 7794 0500 Fax: 020 7431 4528 Email: kirk@rfhsm.ac.uk; 10 Southwood Lane, Highgate Village, London N6 5EE Tel: 020 8340 8575 — MB BS 1952 Lond.; MS Lond. 1962; FRCS Eng. 1956; MRCS Eng. LRCP Lond. 1952. (Char. Cross) Hon. Cons. Surg. Roy. Free Hosp. Lond.; Lect. (Anat.) (Recognised Teach.) Roy. Free Hosp. Sch. Med.; Dir. Overseas Doctors Train. Scheme in Gen. Surg. RCS Eng. Socs: Surg. Research Soc.; Brit. Soc. Gastroenterol.; Roy. Soc. Med. (Ex-Pres. Surg. Sect.). Prev: Cons. Surg. Roy. Free Hosp. Lond.; Edr. Annals RCS Eng.; Sen. Regist. (Surg.) Roy. Free Hosp. & Char. Cross Hosp. Lond.

KIRK, Robert Stewart 9 Brigham Place, Felpham, Bognor Regis PO22 7NW Tel: 01243 582636 — MB ChB 1930 Ed.

KIRK, Robert Stewart Kirk and Jacks, Marus Bridge Health Centre, Highfield Grange Avenue, Wigan WN3 6SU Tel: 01942 246099 Fax: 01942 496705; 17 Amber Grove, Westhoughton, Bolton BL5 3LE Tel: 01942 818009 Fax: 01942 841015 — MB ChB 1984 Manch.; MB ChB Manch. l984; MRCGP 1989. GP Princip.; Assoc. Dir. Postgrad. Gen. Pract. Educat. N. W. E. Deanery.

KIRK, Sarah Jane Broadway Medical Centre, 65-67 Broadway, Fleetwood FY7 7DG Tel: 01253 874222 Fax: 01253 874448; 3 Woburn Way, Catterall, Preston PR3 0QF Tel: 01995 600568 — MB ChB 1986 Leic.; DRCOG 1990.

KIRK, Shona Elizabeth 10 Hill Crescent, Wormit, Newport-on-Tay DD6 8PQ Tel: 01382 541214 — MB ChB 1994 Dundee.

KIRK, Simon Brynn Whickham Health Centre, Whickham, Newcastle upon Tyne NE16 4PD — BM BS 1988 Nottm.; BMedSci (Hons.) 1986; MRCGP 1993. Prev: SHO Nottm. VTS; SHO (Cas.) P'boro Dist. Hosp.

KIRK, Stephen Francis Health Centre, Rectory Lane, Whickham, Newcastle upon Tyne NE16 4PD — MB ChB 1989 Birm.; MRCGP 1993; DRCOG 1992.

KIRK, Mr Stephen James 3 Avondale, Circular Road, Belfast BT4 2WA — MB BCh BAO 1982 Belf.; MD Belf. 1991; FRCS Glas. 1987; FRCSI 1987. (Qu. Univ. Belf.) Cons. Surg. Ulster Hosp. Dundonald.

KIRK, Susan Rachel 54 Reading Drive, Sale M33 5DL — MB BS 1997 Newc.

KIRK, Thomas Hobson (retired) Oakfield, Stocksfield Tel: 01661 3336 — MD 1932 Durh.; MB BS 1920. Prev: Gen. Practitioner, Barton-on-Humber.

KIRK - BAYLEY, Justin 16 Bamborough Close, Southwater, Horsham RH13 7XF Tel: 0140 373 1174 Fax: 0797 053375354 Email: jkb@orange.net — MB BS; MRCP 2000 U.K.; BSc (Hons) 1992. SHO (Anaesth.) Crawley Hosp. Prev: SHO,Gen. Med., ST.RICHARDS Hosp.,CHICHESTER,1997-1999.

KIRK-SMITH, Paul Robert John Fen Farm, Swineshead Road, Frampton Fen, Boston PE20 1SF — MRCS Eng. LRCP Lond. 1970; DObst RCOG 1972.

KIRKBRIDE, Ann Veronica 1 Kew Gardens Road, Kew, Richmond TW9 3HN Tel: 020 8940 1048 Fax: 020 8332 7644; 18 Pensford Avenue, Kew, Richmond TW9 4HP Tel: 020 8876 2312 — MB ChB 1957 Leeds.

KIRKBRIDE, Anne Fishers Brook House, Calne SN11 9HB — MB BS 1953 Lond.; LMSSA Lond. 1953. (Guy's) SCMO Swindon DHA (p/t). Prev: Med. Off. Stone & Webster Construc. Co. Ltd. Abadan; Ho. Surg. St. Olave's Hosp. Lond.; Obst. Ho. Surg. S. Lond. Hosp. Wom.

KIRKBRIDE, David Andrew 67 Furnace Lane, Nether Heyford, Northampton NN7 3JS — BM BS 1994 Nottm.

KIRKBRIDE, Hilary Ann CDSC, PHIS, 61 Colindale Avenue, London NW9 5E9 Tel: 0208 200 6868; Tel: 01534 728777 Fax: 01534 788977 Email: ivyhouse@itl.net — MB ChB 1988 Bristol; MRCP (UK) 1992; MRCGP 1995. (Bristol) p/t Specialist Regist. (Pub. Health) Communicame Dis. Suweillance Centre (CDSC). Prev: SHO (Med.) Qu. Mary's Hosp. Lond.; SHO (O & G) Ealing Hosp. Lond.; Trainee GP Richmond, Surrey.

KIRKBRIDE, Ian Richard Queens Park Medical Centre, Farrer Street, Stockton-on-Tees TS18 2AW Tel: 01642 679681 Fax: 01642 677124 — MB BS 1978 Lond.; MRCGP 1982.

KIRKBRIDE, Peter Department of Radiation Oncology, Princess Margaret Hospital, 500 Sherbourne St., Toronto Ontario, Canada; 60 Woodcote Avenue, Kenilworth CV8 1BG — MB BS 1980 Lond.; MRCP (UK) 1984; FRCR 1989. Staff (Radiat. Oncol.) P.ss Margt. Hosp. Toronto; Sen. Lect. Univ. Toronto, Canada. Prev: Regist. (Radiother. & Oncol.) St. Barts. Hosp. Lond.; Regist. (Radiother. & Oncol.) St. Thos. Hosp. Lond.

KIRKBRIDE, Vincent c/o Neonatal Medical Secretaries, Jessop Hospital for Women, Leavygreave Road, Sheffield S3 7RE Tel: 0114 226 8214 Fax: 0114 226 8299 Email: v.kirkbride@shef.ac.uk — MB BS 1988 Lond.; MRCP (UK) 1991; MRCPCH 1997. Cons. Neonat. Paediat. Jessop Hosp. Sheff. Prev: Sen. Fell. MECB Australia; Perinatal Fell. Hosp. Sick Childr. Toronto, Canada; MRC Clin. Lect. Univ. Coll. Lond.

KIRKBRIDE-JAMU, Kam — MB ChB 1990 Aberd. Trainee GP Beds. VTS.

KIRKBRIGHT, Alan 14 Leeds Road, St. Johns, Wakefield WF1 3JU — MRCS Eng. LRCP Lond. 1954; DO Eng. 1966.

KIRKBY, Mr Graham Reginald 7 Chad Road, Edgbaston, Birmingham B15 3EN Tel: 0121 454 2991 Fax: 0121 454 8945; 36 Carpenter Road, Edgbaston, Birmingham B15 2JJ Tel: 0121 440 1059 — MB BS 1975 Newc.; FRCS Eng. 1980; FRCOphth 1988; T(Ophth.) 1991; DO Eng. 1977. (Newc. u. Tyne) Cons. Ophth. Surg. Birm. & Midl. Eye Centre, Selly Oak Hosp. Birm.; Hon. Sen. Clin. Lect. Univ. of Birm. Socs: Roy. Soc. Med. (Ophth. Sect.); (Ex-Hon. Sec.) Midl. Ophth. Soc. Prev: Sen. Regist. (Ophth.) Leeds Gen. Infirm.; Regist. (Ophth.) St. Thos. Hosp. Lond.

KIRKBY, John Arundel Portway Surgery, 1 The Portway, Porthcawl CF36 3XB Tel: 01656 304204 Fax: 01656 772605 — LRCPI & LM, LRSCI & LM 1967; LRCPI & LM, LRCSI & LM 1967; DObst RCOG 1969. (RCSI)

KIRKBY-BOTT, James 12 Haynes Road, Worthing BN14 7JY — MB BS 1998 Lond.; MB BS Lond 1998.

KIRKE, Christopher Nelson 9 Lowry Hill Road, Carlisle CA3 0DW — MB ChB 1995 Leeds.

KIRKE, Elizabeth Margaret 9 Parkhill Drive, Dalry KA24 5DA Tel: 0129 483 2459 — MB ChB 1976 Glas.

KIRKER, Jessica Mary Department of Psychotherapy, Gordon Hospital, Bloomburg St., London SW1V 2RH Tel: 020 8746 8740 Fax: 020 8746 5501; Flat 1, 25A Christchurch Avenue, Brondesbury, London NW6 7QP Tel: 020 8459 7130 — MB ChB 1972 Otago; FRANZCP 1983; Dip. Psychiat. Auckland l980. Cons Psychiat. in Psychother. BKCW Ment. health trust; Cons Psychiat. in Psychother. EHF Ment. health Trust Lond. Socs: Assoc. Mem. Brit. Psycho-Analytic Soc.; Fell.Roy. Austral. and New Zealand Coll. of Psychiat.; Assn. Psycho-Analytic Psychother. NHS chair. Prev: Cons. Psychiat. Auckland Hosp. Bd.; Lect. Auckland Univ. Med. Sch.; Sen. Regist. (Func. Nerv. Disorders) Cassel Hosp. Richmond.

KIRKER, Stephen Gilbert Bamford Lewin Rehabilitation Unit, Box 34, Addenbrooke's Hospital, Hills Road, Cambridge CB2 2QQ Tel: 01223 217870 Fax: 01223 242038 Email: stephen.kirker@addenbrookes.nhs.uk — MB BCh BAO 1985 Dub.; MA Dub. 1989, MD DVB 1998; MRCPI 1988; FRCPI 1998. (Trinity Coll. Dub. Univ.) Cons. Rehabil. Addenbrooke's Hosp. Camb. Prev: Sen. Regist. (Rehabil.) Addenbrooke's Hosp. Camb. & Colman Hosp. Norwich; Lect. (Neurol.) Univ. Edin.; Research Regist. Dept. Neurol. Inst. Psychiat. & Kings Coll. Hosp. Lond.

KIRKHAM, Alexander Paul Squire 45 Queens Gate Mews, London SW7 5QN — BM BCh 1994 Oxf.

KIRKHAM, Christopher John Woodlands Surgery, 24 Woodlands, Meeting House Lane, Balsall Common, Coventry CV7 7FX Tel: 01676 532587 Fax: 01676 535154; Woodside, Kelsey Lane, Balsall Common, Coventry CV7 7GL Tel: 01676 534066 — MB ChB 1973 Birm.; DObst RCOG 1975. Prev: Trainee GP E. Birm. VTS.

KIRKHAM, Mr Colin Sydney (retired) Upper Ballayack, Earystane, Colby, Castletown IM9 4HN Tel: 01624 834982 — MB BChir 1947 Camb; MRCS Eng. LRCP Lond. 1947; FRCS Eng. 1953; MA Camb. 1960; MChir 1963. Prev: Cons. Surg. Roy. Berks. Hosp. Reading & Newbury Dist. Hosp.

KIRKHAM, Fenella Jane The Wolfson Centre, Mecklenburgh Square, London WC1N 2AP Tel: 020 7837 7618 Fax: 020 7833 9469 Email: fkirkham@ich.ac.uk; 15 Ashchurch Park Villas, London W12 9SP — MB BChir 1979 Camb.; MA Camb. 1979; FRCP Lond. 1994. Sen. Lect. (Paediat. Neurol.) Inst. Child Health Lond. Prev: Sen. Regist. (Paediat.) Guy's Hosp. Lond.; SHO (Neurol.) Nat. Hosp. for Nerv. Dis.

KIRKHAM, Ian Charles The Surgery, Lockwood Avenue, Blackpool; 39 Tudor Close, Carleton, Poulton-le-Fylde FY6 7TD — MB ChB 1981 Dundee; MRCGP 1986.

KIRKHAM, John Abbey Medical Centre, Norman Street, Leeds LS5 3JN Tel: 0113 295 1844 Fax: 0113 295 1845 — MB ChB 1977 Leeds; MRCGP 1983; DRCOG 1982.

KIRKHAM, Mr John Squire 149 Harley Street, London W1N 2DH Tel: 020 7935 4444 Fax: 020 7935 3690; 56 Sterndale Road, London W14 0HU Tel: 020 7603 0495 — MB BChir 1961 Camb.; MB 1961; MA Camb. 1961; FRCS Eng. 1965; FRCS Ed. 1965. (Westm.) Hon. Sen. Lect. St. Geo. Hosp. Med. Sch.; Examr. (Surg.) Univ. Khartoum Sudan, Univ. Basrah Iraq & Univ. Lond.; Examr. (Anat.) RCS Ed. Socs: Fell. Roy. Soc. Med. (Vice-Pres. Clin. Sect. & Surg. Sect.); Fell. Brit. Assn. Clin. Anat.; Fell. Assn. Surgs. Prev: Cons. Gastroenterol. Surg. & Clin. Dir. Qu. Mary's Univ. Hosp. Lond.; Cons. Surg. & Endoscopist Norman Tanner Unit St. Geo. Hosp. & St. Jas. Hosp. Lond.; Regist. (Surg.) Aberd. Roy. Infirm.

KIRKHAM, Jonathan Andrew Tel: 01767 316410 Fax: 01767 312568; Mulberry House, 12 Church Lane, Everton, Sandy SG19 2JS Tel: 01767 692776 Fax: 01767 312568 Email: drjak@waitrose.com — MB BS 1980 Newc.; Cert. Family Plann. JCC 1986; DRCOG 1983. (Newc. u. Tyne) GP Princip., Dr Kirkham & Partners, Biggleswade. Socs: BMA; St. Paul; Beds & Herts LMC. Prev: Trainee GP Redbridge & Waltham Forest HAs VTS; SHO & Demonst. (Cas. & Anat.) Univ. Leic. & Leic. Roy. Infirm.; Ho. Surg. Qu. Eliz. Hosp. Birm.

KIRKHAM, Karen Valerie Frederick Place Surgery, 11 Frederick Place, Weymouth DT4 8HQ Tel: 01305 774411 Fax: 01305 760417; 35 Bincleaves Road, Rodwell, Weymouth DT4 8RS Tel: 01305 784280 — MB BS 1988 Lond. (Middlx. & Univ. Coll. Hosp. Med. Sch.)

KIRKHAM, Melissa Jane 6 St Johns Drive, Plymouth PL9 9SD — MB ChB 1997 Bristol.

KIRKHAM, Nigel Histopathology Department, Royal Sussex County Hospital, Brighton BN2 5BE Tel: 01273 664501 Fax: 01273 479589 Email: nigelk@pavilion.co.uk; Shepherd's Rest, Ashcombe Lane, Kingston, Lewes BN7 3JZ Tel: 01273 479589 Fax: 01273 481012 Email: nigelk@pavilion.co.uk — MB ChB 1974 Liverp.; MD Liverp. 1995; FRCPath 1994, M 1982. Cons. Histopath. & Cytopath. Brighton Healthcare NHS Trust; Vis. Fell. Univ. Sussex. Prev: Lect. (Path.) Univ. Soton.; Sen. Regist. (Morbid Anat.) Whiston Hosp. Prescot; Vis. Fell. Univ. Sussex.

KIRKHAM, Peter William 7 Esmond Close, Emsworth PO10 7HX Email: petekirkham@msn.com — MB BS 1990 Newc.; MRCP (UK) 1994. GP VTS Chichester W. Sussex. Prev: SHO Rotat. (Med.) N. Durh.; Regist. (Dermat.) Roy. Vict. Infirm. Newc.

KIRKHAM, Sian Elizabeth 32 Christchurch Drive, Daventry NN11 4RW — MB BS 1996 Lond.

KIRKHAM, Stephen Kenneth Tottington Health Centre, 16 Market Street, Tottington, Bury BL8 4AD Tel: 01204 885106 Fax: 01204 887717; 45 Bye Road, Shuttleworth, Ramsbottom, Bury BL0 0HH — MB ChB 1983 Manch.; DRCOG 1987.

KIRKHAM, Stephen Richard Poole Hospital NHS Trust, Longfleet Road, Poole BH15 2JB Tel: 01202 448118 Fax: 01202 660472; 57 Dorchester Road, Lytchett Minster, Poole BH16 6JE Tel: 01202 631932 — MB BChir 1976 Camb.; MA Camb. 1977; FRCP Lond. 1996; MRCP (UK) 1978. (Camb. & Guy's) Cons. Palliat. Med. Poole Hosp. NHS Trust; Edr. Palliat. Med. Socs: BMA; Assn. Palliat. Med. Prev: Clin. Research Fell. St. Christopher's Hospice Lond.; Med. Dir. Pilgrims' Hospice Canterbury; Hon. Cons. Palliat. Med. Canterbury & Thanet HA.

KIRKLAND, Alison Ann Louise Balmuir Gardens, London SW15 6NG; 14 Larpent Avenue, Putney, London SW15 6UP Tel: 020 8789 6564 Fax: 020 8780 1737 — MB ChB 1977 Bristol; MRCGP 1986; DRCOG 1979. (Bristol) Prev: Regist. (Med.) Roy. Berks. Hosp. & Battle Hosp. Reading; SHO (Accid. Serv.) Radcliffe Infirm Oxf.; Ho. Phys. Profess. Unit. Bristol Roy. Infirm.

KIRKLAND, Brian Portslade County Clinic, Old Shoreham Road, Portslade, Brighton BN41 1XR Tel: 01273 411229 Fax: 01273 412078; 13 The Daisycroft, Henfield BN5 9LH Tel: 01273 494875 Fax: 01273 494875 — MB ChB Leeds 1966; MRCGP 1972. Course

Organiser Brighton VTS. Prev: Ho. Phys. & Ho. Surg. St. Jas. Hosp. Leeds.

KIRKLAND, Graham Peter (retired) Westgate Medical Centre, Westgate, Otley LS21 3HD Tel: 01943 465406 — MB ChB 1959 Leeds; DObst RCOG 1961. Chairm. Leeds LMC. Prev: Ho. Surg. Leeds Gen. Infirm. & Leeds Matern. Hosp.

KIRKLAND, Mr Ian Brown 83 Hyndland Road, Glasgow G12 9JE — MB ChB 1956 Glas.; FRCS Ed. 1967; FRCS Glas. 1966; SHO Orthop. West. Infirm. Glas. Prev: Ho. Surg. & Ho. Phys. W.. Infirm. Glas.

KIRKLAND, Joan Alice (retired) Westholme, Westgate, Otley LS21 3AT Tel: 01943 467271 Email: jaon@otley.co.uk — MB ChB 1960 Leeds. Prev: Ho. Phys. & Ho. Surg. City Gen. Hosp. Stoke-on-Trent.

KIRKLAND, Nicolas Barrie (retired) 10 Barkfield Avenue, Formby, Liverpool L37 3JH — MB ChB 1958 Liverp.; MRCP Lond. 1967; DCH Eng. 1963; DObst RCOG 1960. Prev: Cons. Paediat. Sefton AHA.

KIRKLAND, Mr Paul Mart St.George's Hospital, Blackshaw Road, London SW17 0QT Tel: 0208 672 1255 Fax: 0208 672 5304; Email: pk.nik@virgin.net — MB BS 1989 Lond.; FRCS Eng. 1993; FRCS (Oto.) Eng. 1997. (St. Thos. Hosp. Lond.) Specialist Regist. (OtoLaryngol. - Head & Neck Surg.) S. W. Thames Region.

KIRKLIN, Deborah Lee 11 Ingram Avenue, London NW11 6TG — BM BCh 1986 Oxf.

KIRKMAN, Daphne Mary (retired) 22 Windfield, Epson Road, Leatherhead KT22 8UG — MRCS Eng. LRCP Lond. 1952; MB BS Lond. 1952, DPH 1966; DCH Eng. 1955. Prev: Sen. Med. Off. E. Sussex AHA.

KIRKMAN, Jillian Louise 17 Newbold Grove, Liverpool L12 0NS — MB ChB 1997 Liverp.

KIRKNESS, Professor Colin Mainland Tennent Institute, Upper Ground Floor, University of Glasgow, Gartnaval General Hospital, Glasgow G12 0YN Tel: 0141 211 2640 Fax: 0141 339 7485 Email: ehs1n@clinmed.gla.ac.uk; 9A Great Western Terrace, Glasgow G12 0UP Tel: 0141 334 9092 — MB ChB 1974 Aberd.; BMedBiol Aberd. 1971; FRCS Ed. 1982; FRCOphth 1989; FRCS Glas. 1991. (Aberdeen) Tennent Prof. Ophth. Univ. Glas.; Hon. Cons. Opthalmologist, W. Glas. Hosp.s, Glas. Socs: Fell. (Vice-Pres.) Roy. Coll. Ophth. 1996-2000; Pres. Europ. Bd. Ophth. 1998-2000; Eur. Prof. Ophth. Prev: Dir. Pocklington Eye Transpl. Unit Inst. Ophth. Moorfields Eye Hosp. Lond.; Sen. Lect. Inst. Ophth. Lond.; Resid. Surg. Off. Moorfields Eye Hosp. Lond.

KIRKPATRICK, Aidan Peter 4 Windsor Street, Dundee DD2 1BP — MB ChB 1995 Dundee. (Dundee)

KIRKPATRICK, Alastair Elliot SE Scotland Division, Ardmillan House, 42 Ardmillan Terrace, Edinburgh EH11 2JL Tel: 0131 537 7401 Fax: 0131 537 7420; 1 Ballencrieff Cottages, Longniddry EH32 0PJ Tel: 01875 870294 — MB ChB 1964 Ed.; FRCS Ed. 1985; FRCR 1975; FFR 1971; DMRD Ed. 1968. (Ed.) Dir. SE Scotl. Div. Scott. BrE. Screening Progr.; Knox Memor. Lect. Roy. Coll. Radiol.; Cons. Radiol. Roy. Infirm. Edin.; Chairm. RCR BrE. Gp. Socs: Brit. BrE. Gp.; Scott. Radiol. Soc.; Roy. Coll. Radiologists BrE. Gp. Prev: Staff Radiol. Toronto Gen. Hosp., Canada; SHO (Surg.) Dunfermline & W. Fife Hosp.; Vis. Prof. Radiol. Stanford Univ. Med. Centre.

KIRKPATRICK, Alexander (retired) 1 Cavehill Drive, Belfast BT15 5GU — MB BCh BAO Belf. 1945.

KIRKPATRICK, Alison Jacqueline Jean 10 High Street, Clifton, Bristol BS8 2YF — MB BS 1994 Lond. (St. Bart.) SHO (O & G) S.mead Hosp. Bristol. Prev: RMO (Neonatol.) Roy. Wom. Hosp. Melbourne, Austral.; SHO (A & E) Salisbury Dist. Hosp.; SHO (O & G) Roy. Hants. Co. Hosp.

KIRKPATRICK, Anahita Houshangi 15 Hampton Court, King & Queen Wharf, 189 Rotherhithe St., London SE16 5SU Tel: 020 7237 9145 Email: 100743.1210@compuserve.com — MB BS 1992 Lond.; BSc Lond. 1990.

KIRKPATRICK, Barbara Louise Frenchay Hosptial, Bristol BS16 1; The White House, St. Martins, Long Ashton, Bristol BS41 9HP — MB ChB 1981 Bristol; MRCPath 1993. Sen. Regist. (Med. Microbiol.) Frenchay Hosp. Bristol.

KIRKPATRICK, Brian Dugald HMS Raleigh, Torpoint PL11 2PD Tel: 01752 553740 ext. 349; Yet An Lor, Antony, Torpoint PL11 3AB Tel: 01752 812300 — MB BS 1965 Lond.; MRCS Eng. LRCP Lond. 1965; MRCGP 1975. (St. Geo.) Civil. Med. Off. (MOD Civil Serv.) HMS Raleigh Torpoint. Prev: Med. Off. Sultan of Omans Landforces; Med. Off. Nat. Guard Kingdom of Saudi Arabia; Med. Off. MOD RN.

KIRKPATRICK, Carol Gillian Eveline Woodside, Broadoaic, Odiham, Hook RG29 1AQ — MB BS 1965 Lond.; BSc Lond. 1962; MRCS Eng. LRCP Lond. 1964; FRCR 1985; DMRD Eng. 1980. (Guy's) p/t Cons. X-Ray Dept. Roy. Surrey Co. Hosp. Guildford. Prev: Sen. Regist. (Radiol.) Frimley Pk. Hosp.; SHO St. Peter's Hosp. Chertsey; Ho. Off. Guy's Hosp. Lond.

KIRKPATRICK, Catherine Mary Rose (retired) Pear Tree Cottage, Chalk Road, Walpole St Peter, Wisbech PE14 7PG Tel: 01945 780313 — MB BS 1946 Lond.; MRCS Eng. LRCP Lond. 1945; DCH Eng. 1949. Prev: Clin. Med. Off. W. Norf. & Wisbech HA.

KIRKPATRICK, Christopher Thomas Roche products Ltd, 40 Broadwater Road, Welwyn Garden City AL7 3AY Tel: 01707 366480 Fax: 01707 390590 Email: christopher.kirkpatrick@roche.com — MB BCh BAO 1969 Belf.; BSc (1st cl. Hons. Physiol.) Belf. 1966, MD (Hons.) 1973, MB BCh BAO 1969; MFPM 1995; FFPM 1999. (Belf.) Head of Clin. Pharm. Unit. Socs: Fell. Roy. Acad. Med. Irel. (Biol. Sc. Sect.); Physiol. Soc. & Brit. Pharmacol. Soc. Prev: Med. Dir. Pfizer Clin. Research Unit Kent & Canterbury Hosp.; Clin. Research Dir. BIOS (Consult. & Contract Research) Ltd. Bagshot; Med. Off. (Research) Inst. Aviat. Med. FarnBoro.

KIRKPATRICK, Dianne Helen 13 Windsor Park, Belfast BT9 6FQ — MB BCh BAO 1985 Belf.; FFR RCSI 1991.

KIRKPATRICK, Hamish Williamson Moorside, York Lane, Langho, Blackburn BB6 8DP Tel: 01254 248530 — MB BChir 1955 Camb.; MRCS Eng. LRCP Lond. 1955; FRCOG 1975, M 1961. (Univ. Oxf. Med. Sch.) Socs: Obst. & Gyn. Soc. N. Engl. Prev: Cons. O & G Blackburn Roy. Infirm. & Qu.'s Pk. Hosp. Blackburn; Sen. Regist. (O & G) Hammersmith Hosp. & St. Helier Hosp.; Asst. Nuffield Dept. O & G Radcliffe Infirm. Oxf.

KIRKPATRICK, Mr James John Rafferty Department of Plastic Surgery, Canniesburn Hospital, Switchback Road, Glasgow G61 Tel: 0141 211 5600 Fax: 0141 211 5652 Email: j.j.r.kirkpatrick@bradford.ac.uk; Flat Top Left, 12 Glencairn Drive, Glasgow G41 4QN — BM BCh 1987 Oxf.; MA Oxf. 1989, BA 1984; FRCS Ed. 1992; FRCS Eng. 1992. (Oxf.) Specialist Regist. (Plastic Surg.) Canniesburn Hosp. Glas.; Hon. Research Fell. (Plastic Surg.) Plastic Surg. & Burns Research Unit, Bradford Univ. Prev: Clin. Fell. (Plastic Surg.) Glas. Roy. Infirm. Univ. NHS Trust; Research Fell. (Plastic Surg.) Bradford Univ.; SHO (Plastic Surg.) Frenchay Hosp. Bristol.

KIRKPATRICK, Mr James Nigel Pollock Cheltenham General Hospital, Sandford Road, Cheltenham GL53 7AN Tel: 01242 274192 Fax: 01242 253816 — MB ChB 1986 Bristol; BSC pharm Bristol 1983; MD 1997; FRCOphth 1991. (Bristol 1986) Cons. Ophthamologist, Cheltenham Gen. Hosp. Socs: Brit. & Eire Assoc. & VitreoRetinal Surg.s. Prev: Sen. Regist., Aberd. Roy. Hosp.s, Retinal Fell. Roy. Perth Hosp.s, Australia.

KIRKPATRICK, John Reid (retired) Woodlands Family Medical Centre, 106 Yarm Lane, Stockton-on-Tees TS18 1YE Tel: 01642 607398 Fax: 01642 677846 — MB BS 1959 Durh. Clin. Asst. (ENT) N. Riding Infirm. Middlesbrough. Prev: SHO (Matern.) & Ho. Phys. (Paediat.) Gen. Hosp. Middlesbrough.

KIRKPATRICK, Katharine Louise Lister Hospital, Coreys Mill Lane, Stevenage SG1 4; 58 Oster Street, St Albans AL3 5JL — MB BS 1994 Lond.; BSc Lond. 1991. (Roy. Free Hosp.) SHO (Surg.) Lister Hosp. Stevenage.

KIRKPATRICK, Lucy Teresa Moorside, York Lane, Langho, Blackburn BB6 8DP Tel: 01254 248530 — MB BCh BAO 1952 NUI; DA Eng. 1954. Prev: Regist. (Anaesth.) Norf. & Norwich Hosp.

KIRKPATRICK, Martin Roger Department of Paediatrics, Ninewells Hospital & Medical School, Dundee DD1 9SY Tel: 01382 660111 Fax: 01382 633849 Email: martink@dth.scot.nhs.uk; Gallowbank House, Emma Terrace, Blairgowrie PH10 6JA — MB BS 1981 Lond.; MRCP (UK) 1986; DCH RCP Lond. 1984; FRCPCH 1996; FRCP Ed. 1998. Cons. Paediat. Neurol. Dundee Teach. Hosps. NHS Trust. Socs: Brit. Paediat. Neurol. Assn.; Fell. Roy. Coll. Paediat. and Child Health. Prev: Cons. Paediat. Community Child Health Forth Health Care Trust Stirling; Lect. (Child Health) & Hon.

Sen. Regist. Univ. Aberd.; Project Co-ordinator & Med. Off. Save the Childr. Fund, Nepal.

KIRKPATRICK, Mary Helen Elizabeth Orrfield, 19 Trench Road, Hillsborough BT26 6JL — MB BCh BAO 1962 Belf.

KIRKPATRICK, Pansy Elizabeth (retired) Windridge, Snitterfield, Stratford-upon-Avon CV37 0PH — MB ChB 1949 Ed.

KIRKPATRICK, Mr Peter John University Department of Neurosurgery, Box 167, Addenbrooke's Hospital, Cambridge CB2 2QQ Tel: 01223 245151 Fax: 01223 216926 Email: pjk21@medschl.cam.ac.uk; Rectory Farm, New Road, Guilden Marden, Royston SG8 0JN Tel: 01763 852240 Fax: 01763 852011 — MB ChB 1984 Bristol; FRCS Eng. (Ad initio) 1999; FRCS (SN) 1994; FRCS (Ed.) 1989; MMSc Dundee 1987; BSc (Anat.) Bristol 1981. Cons. Neurosurg. & Hon. Lect. (Neurosurg.) Univ. of Camb. Socs: Brit. Soc. of Neurosurg.; Vasc. Soc. Prev: Lect. & Sen. Regist. (Neurosurg.) Addenbrooke's Hosp. Camb.; Regist. (Neurosurg.) Maudsley Hosp. Lond.; SHO (Gen. Surg.) Frenchay Gen. Hosp. Bristol.

KIRKPATRICK, Richard Brian James, Wing Cdr. RAF Med. Br. 32 Barnby Road, RAF Coltishall, Norwich NR10 5JN — MB BS 1985 Lond.; DAvMed 1994. (St. Thos. Hosp. Lond.) RAF GDMO. Socs: Med. Protec. Soc.

KIRKPATRICK, Robert Arthur Central Surgery, 23 Boston Avenue, Southend-on-Sea SS2 6JH Tel: 01702 342589 Fax: 01702 437015 — MRCS Eng. LRCP Lond. 1979; DRCOG 1983; Cert. Family Plann. JCC 1983. (Sheffield Univ. Med. Sch.) Socs: Assoc. Mem. Roy. Coll. Gen. Pract. Prev: SHO (Paediat.) Sydenham Childr. Hosp.; SHO (O & G) Lewisham Hosp.; SHO (Path.) Roy. Gwent Hosp. Newport.

KIRKPATRICK, Ronald (retired) Vaila, Perth Road, Dunblane FK15 0BU — MB ChB 1964 Glas.; Dip. Soc. Med. Ed. 1971.

KIRKPATRICK, Stuart Ross Longfield, Horsham Lane, Ewhurst, Cranleigh GU6 7SW — MB ChB 1989 Leic.

KIRKPATRICK, Terence 5 Barncliffe Road, Sheffield S10 4DF — MB ChB 1979 Bristol.

KIRKPATRICK, Ms Ursula Jean 24 Limedale Road, Liverpool L18 5JF — MB ChB 1990 Liverp.; FRCS Ed. 1994.

KIRKPATRICK, William Arthur, Col. late RAMC Retd. (retired) Green Pastures, Soper's Field, Chard TA20 2HT Tel: 01460 63161 — MB BCh BAO 1951 Belf.; FRCOG 1977, M 1961, DObst 1953. Prev: Cons. Gyn. Qu. Eliz. Milit. Hosp. Lond.

KIRKPATRICK, Mr William Niall Alexander 15 Hampton Court, King & Queen Wharf, 189 Rotherhithe St., London SE16 5SU Tel: 020 7237 9145 Email: 100743.1210@compuserve.com — MB BS 1990 Lond.; MD Lond. 1996; BDS Lond. 1984; FRCS Eng. 1996. (Guy's Hosp.)

KIRKUP, Brian Latham House Medical Practice, Sage Cross Street, Melton Mowbray LE13 1NX Tel: 01664 854949 Fax: 01664 501825 — MB BS 1974 Newc.; BSc (Physiol.) Newc. 1971, MB BS 1974. Clin. Asst. (Orthop.) Melton & Dist. War Memor. Hosp. Melton Mowbray. Prev: Demonst. (Anat.) Univ. Newc.; SHO (Orthop.) Sanderson Orthop. Hosp. Gosforth; Ho. Off. (Gen. Surg.) Roy. Vict. Infirm. Newc.

KIRKUP, John Raymond Summerside Medical Centre, 29B Summerside Place, Edinburgh EH6 4NY Tel: 0131 554 3533 Fax: 0131 554 9722; 54 Inverleith Row, Edinburgh EH3 5PX — MB ChB 1987 Ed.; MRCGP 1991; DRCOG 1991; DCH RCPS Glas. 1990. Prev: Trainee GP Lothian VTS.

KIRKUP, Mr John Robson Weston Hill, 1 Weston Park E., Bath BA1 2XA Tel: 01225 423060 Fax: 01225 423060 Email: john.kirkup@btinternet.com — MD Camb. 1994, MB BChir 1952; FRCS Eng. 1960; MRCS Eng. LRCP Lond. 1952; DHM Soc. Apoth. 1979. (Camb. & St. Mary's) Emerit. Cons. Orthop. Surg. Bath Clin. Area; Curator Historical Inst. Collection RCS Eng. Socs: Fell. (Ex-Pres.) Hist. of Med. Sec. Roy. Soc. Med.; Fell. & Archiv. BOA.; (Ex-Pres.) Brit. Soc. Hist. of Med. Prev: Vicary Lect. RCS Eng.; Hunt. Soc. Orator; Sydenham Lect., Soc. of Apoth.

KIRKUP, Margaret Eileen Mary Department of Dermatology, Bristol Royal Infirmary, Marlborough St., Bristol BS2 8HW Tel: 0117 928 4458 Fax: 0117 928 2845 — MB ChB 1977 Glas.; MRCP (UK) 1982. p/t Specialist Regist. (Dermat.) Bristol Roy. Infirm. Bristol. Socs: BMA; BAD; Dowling Club. Prev: Clin. Asst. (Dermat.) Frenchay Hosp. Bristol; Regist. (Med.) Duchess of Kent's Milit. Hosp.; Sen. Specialist (Med.) Qu. Eliz. Hosp. Woolwich.

KIRKUP, William John Snow House, Durham University Science Park, Durham DH1 3YG Tel: 0191 301 1345 Fax: 0191 301 1405 Email: bkirkup@aol.com — BM BCh 1974 Oxf.; MA Oxf. 1974; FRCOG 1993, M 1979; FFPHM RCP (UK) 1994, M 1986. Reg.Dir. Pub.Health.Dir.Healthcare NHS ec.N.ern & Yorks; Reg. Dir Publ. Health, N. E. Prev: Dir. NHS Trusts Div. NHS Exec. N.. & Yorks.; Dir. (Pub. Health) N. Tyneside HA; Specialist (Community Med.) Newc. HA.

KIRKWOOD, Catherine Joan Burley Park Medical Centre, 273 Burly Road, Leeds LS4 2EL; Tel: 0113 269 6158 Email: kate@kate66.fsnet.co.uk — MB ChB 1993 Glas.; DFFP 1997; MRCGP 1998. (Glasgow) p/t GP Leeds. Prev: GP Locum, Edin.; GP Locum, Nottm.; GP Regist., Nottm.

KIRKWOOD, David Watson The Surgery, Main Street, Bridge of Earn, Perth PH2 9PW Tel: 01738 812000 Fax: 01738 812333 — MB ChB 1971 Glas.; DObst RCOG 1973.

KIRKWOOD, Dennis Murray (retired) Larkfield, 23 Southside Road, Inverness IV2 3BG Tel: 01463 233455 — MB ChB 1952 Glas.; DObst RCOG 1954.

KIRKWOOD, Evelyne Mary — MB ChB 1969 Glas.; FRCP 1984 (Glasgow); BSc Glas. 1965; MRCP (U.K.) 1974. (Glas.) p/t Sen. Lect. (Hon. Cons.) Dept. Bacteriol. & Immunol. W.ern Infirm. Glas. Socs: BMA. Prev: Rotating Regist. (Med.) Stobhill Hosp. Glas.

KIRKWOOD, Gillian Anne 2 Mid Street, Clachnaharry, Inverness IV3 8RD — MB ChB 1985 Glas.

KIRKWOOD, Helen Lightbody (retired) Hillview, Dalrymple St., Girvan KA26 9BG — LRCP LRCS Ed. LRFPS Glas. 1948; DCH RCPS Glas. 1974. Prev: SCMO Ayrsh. & Arran HB.

KIRKWOOD, Helen Lightbody Steven Murrayfield Medical Practice, 35 Saughton Crescent, Edinburgh EH12 5SS Tel: 0131 337 2166 — MB ChB 1983 Glas.; MRCGP 1987; DRCOG 1985. GP Edin. Retainer Scheme.

KIRKWOOD, Isobel (retired) 1B Newton Court, Newton Grove, Newton Mearns, Glasgow G77 5QL Tel: 0141 639 4678 Fax: 0141 639 4678 — MB ChB 1953 Glas.; FFA RCS Eng. 1960; DA Eng. 1956; FRCA Eng. Prev: Cons. Anaesth. Roy. Infirm. Glas. & Roy. Matern. Hosp. Glas.

KIRKWOOD, Jenny Lynne Selly Oak Health Centre, Katie Road, Birmingham B29 6JG Tel: 0121 472 0016; 96 Prince Thorpe Road, Weoley Castle, Birmingham B29 5QA — BM 1987 Soton.; MRCGP 1995; DRCOG 1991; DCH RCP Lond. 1991; DTM & H Liverp. 1991. Prev: SHO (Psychiat.) All St.s Hosp. Birm.; SHO (Paediat. & O & G) Dudley Rd. Hosp. Birm.; SHO (A & E) Russells Hall Hosp. Dudley.

KIRKWOOD, John Mitchell (retired) Balla Wray, Wray, Ambleside LA22 0JQ — MB ChB 1932 Glas. Prev: Ho. Surg. & Ho. Phys. Glas. Roy. Infirm.

KIRKWOOD, Julie Ann 12 Sequoia Park, Lambeg Road, Lisburn BT27 4SJ Tel: 01846 667048 — MB BCh BAO 1993 Belf.; DGM; DRCOG. (Qu's. Univ. Belf.) GP Regist. Lisburn Health Centre. Socs: BMA.

KIRKWOOD, Wendy Susan The Surgery, 15 King Street, Paisley, Glasgow Pa1 2PS Tel: 0141 889 3144 — MB ChB 1991 Glas.; DRCOG 1994 UK; MRCGP 1995 UK; MB ChB (Commend.) Glas. 1991. GP Princip., King St. Surg., Paisley, PA1 2PS; Police Surg. Dep., K Div., Strachclyde Police Force. Prev: Trainee GP/SHO Rotat. Vict. Infirm. Glas. VTS.

KIRMANI, Mrs Syeda Sabera 84 George V Avenue, Pinner HA5 5SW — MB BS 1967 Osmania.

KIRMANI, Mr Tajuddin Hasan 17 Toley Avenue, Wembley HA9 9TD Tel: 020 8537 0282 Fax: 020 8537 0282 Email: tajkirmani@aol.com; 14 East Street, Bexleyheath DA7 4HP Tel: 020 8303 7986 — MB BS Panjab 1954; FRCS Ed. 1962; FCPS Pakistan 1979; DO RCS Eng. 1957. (King Edward Medical College, Lehore, Pakistan) Ophth. Med. Practitioner Optical Express Bexleyheath; Prof. Ophth. Jinnah PostGrad. Med. Centre Karachi, Pakistan. Socs: Pakistan Med. Assn. Karachi; Chairm. Pakistan Eye Found.; Pres. SAARC Found. Prev: Sen. Regist. (Ophth.) The Roy. Infirm. Edin.

KIRN, Gerd Ulrich Yeovil District Hospital, Higher Kingston, Yeovil BA21 4AT — State Exam Med 1993 Essen.

KIRN, Tabea Eva-Maria Yeovil District Hospital, Higher Kingston, Yeovil BA21 4AT — State Exam Med 1993 Essen.

KIROLLOS, Camelia Tut Jeffrey Kelson, Diabetic Centre, Central Middlesex Hospital, Acton Lane, London NW10 7NS Tel: 020 8453 2415; 515 Kenton Road, Kenton, Harrow HA3 0UL Tel: 020 8930

7656 — MRCS Eng. LRCP Lond. 1989; MB BS Khartoum 1979; PhD Univ. herts. 1995; MSc Clin. Trop. Med. Lond. 1986; Dip. Internal Med. Lond. 1990; DTM & H Lond. 1986. Assoc. Specialist (Diabetes) Centr. Middlx. Hosp. Trust Lond. Socs: BMA; BDA. Prev: Clin. Asst. Diabeticare Hllingdon Hosp. Uxbridge; Clin. Asst. (Diabetic Retinopathy) Hammersmith Hosp. Lond.; SHO (Geriat. Med.) N.wick Pk. Hosp. Harrow.

KIROLLOS, Ramez Wadie Mikhael Department of Neurosurgery, Addenbrooke's Hospital, Hills Road, Cambridge DB2 2QQ Tel: 01223 245151; 3 Edenvale Close, Hills Avenue, Cambridge CB1 7XD Tel: 01223 249773, 01932 713399 Email: ramez@kirollos.freeserve.co.uk — MB ChB 1984 Alexandria; 2000 Europ. Certficate of Neurosurg.; MD 2000 Leeds; FRCS 1998 (SN); FRCS Eng. 1991; FRCS Ed. 1990. (Alexandria Univ. Egypt) Cons. Neurosurg., Addenbrooke's Hosp. Camb. Prev: Sen. Regist. (Neurosurg.) Walton Centre for Neurol. & Neurosurg. Liverp.

KIROV, Georgi Kirilov Department of Psychological Medicine, University of Wales College of Medicine, Heath Park, Cardiff CF14 4XN Tel: 029 2074 2434 Fax: 029 2074 6554 Email: kirov@cardiff.ac.uk — State Exam Med 1986 Sofia Bulgaria; State Exam Med Sofia, Bulgaria 1986; MRCPsych 1992. (Acad. of Med.) Wellcome Advanced Fell. Univ. of Wales Coll. of Med. Prev: Wellcome Train. Fell. Univ. of Wales Coll. of Med.; Research Fell. (Psychiat.) Inst. Psychiat. Lond.; Trainee GP/SHO Rotat. Warlingham Pk. Hosp. VTS.

KIRPALANI, Geena 35 Buckingham Road, Edgware HA8 6LY — MB BS 1997 Lond.

KIRRAGE, David Christopher Downside Farm, Bromyard HR7 4NU — MB ChB 1983 Bristol; MFPHM RCP (UK) 1995; MRCGP 1987; DA (UK) 1990. Cons. Pub. Health Med. Prev: GP VTS Exeter.

KIRRESH, Mr Zuhair Othman Issa ENT Department, Northampton General Hospital, Cliftonville, Northampton NN1 5BD — MB ChB 1980 Alexandria; FRCS (ENT) 1991.

KIRSOP, Bridget Anne Llynfi Surgery, Llynfi Road, Maesteg CF34 9DT Tel: 01656 732115 Fax: 01656 864451; Craig Wen, Station St, Maesteg CF34 9AL — MB BS 1982 Lond.; BSc (Physiol.) Lond. 1977; DRCOG 1984. (Univ. Coll. Hosp. Lond.) GP Princip. Llynfi Surg. Maesteg.

KIRTCHUK, Gabriel Hector 54 Barrowgate, London W4 4QU — Medico Cirujano Nat. U. Cordoba Argentina 1972.

KIRTHISINGHA, Viveca Anjali By-the-Wey, Tannery Lane, Send, Woking GU23 7EF — BM BCh 1994 Oxf.; BSc (Hons.) Physiol. St. And. 1988; MRCP (Lond.). (Oxford) Specialist Regist. Oxf. Radcliffe Hosp. Trust.

KIRTLEY, Paul Richard Compton Health Centre, Compton, Ashbourne DE6 1GN Tel: 01335 300588; 43 St. John Street, Ashbourne, Derby DE6 1GP Tel: 01335 343688 Fax: 01335 343688 — MRCS Eng. LRCP Lond. 1974; DRCOG 1979. (Guy) Prev: SHO (Paediat.) Freedom Fields Hosp. Plymouth; SHO (Obst. & Gyn & Gen. Med.) Gloucester Roy. Hosp.

KIRTON, Christine Bernadette 86 Forres Road, Sheffield S10 1WE — BM BS 1984 Nottm.; BMedSci Nottm. 1982; FCAnaesth. 1991; DCH RCP Lond. 1987; DA (UK) 1986. cons. Paediat. Anaesth. Sheff. Childr. Hosp.

KIRTON, Janet Louise Queensbridge Group Practice, 24 Holly Street, London E8 3XP Tel: 0208 254 1101; Spen House, 241 Spen Lane, Leeds LS16 5EL Tel: 0208 254 1101 — MBBS 1983 London; MRCGP 1987; DRCOG 1986. (St Barts. Med. College, Univ. London) GP Princip., Hackney, Lond.; Course Organiser, Hackney GPVTS (Gen. Pract. Vocational Scheme).

KIRTON, Veronica The Chiltern Hospital, London Road, Great Missenden HP16 0EN Tel: 01494 890890 Fax: 01494 890250; Highlands, Gravel Path, Berkhamsted HP4 2PQ Tel: 01442 876300 Fax: 01442 871200 — MB BS 1961 Lond.; BA Lond. 1993. (St. Mary's) Assoc. Specialist (Dermat. & Allergy) Amersham & High Wycombe Hosp. Socs: Brit. Assn. Dermat. & Brit. Assn. Allergy & Clin. Immunol.

KIRUBAHARAN, Kalyani Freuchen Medical Centre, 190 High Street, Harlesden, London NW10 4ST Tel: 020 8965 5174 Fax: 020 8838 0255 — MB BS 1975 Sri Lanka; MB BS 1975 Sri Lanka; LRCP LRCS Ed. LRCPS Glas. 1989 Edinburgh & Glasgow.

KIRUBAKARAN, Padmavathi 456 Old Bedford Road, Luton LU2 7BN — MB BS 1970 Madras; MRCOG 1978, DObst 1972. (Madras Med. Coll.) SHO (Chest Med. & Geriat.) St. Mary's Hosp. Luton.

KIRUBAKARAN, Senthil 146 Putnoe Lane, Bedford MK41 8LT — MB ChB 1998 Manch.; MB ChB Manch 1998.

KIRUPANANTHAM, Pathmarani Plot 70, 140 Lowry Crescent, Mitcham CR4 3QU — MB BS 1978 Sri Lanka; MRCS Eng. LRCP Lond. 1988.

KIRUPANANTHAN, Mr Subramaniam c/o Drive R. Rajakumar MRCP, 83 Derwent Avenue, Allestree, Derby DE22 2DP — MB BS 1967 Ceylon; FRCS Ed. 1982; FCOphth 1989.

KIRWAN, Miss Cliona Clare 5 Foxford Close, Northampton NN4 9UH Tel: 01604 700540 — MB BS 1994 Lond.; BSc Lond. 1991, MB BS 1994; FRCS (Eng.) 1998. (CXWMS) SHO (Gen. Surg.) Frenchay Bristol. Prev: SHO (GE, Surg.) Bristol Roy. Infirm.; Sho (Paediat. Surg.) Bristol Childr.'s Hosp.; SHO (Orthop.) Poole Hosp. Dorset.

KIRWAN, Elisabeth Valerie 18 Greenhill Gardens, Edinburgh EH10 4BW — MB BS 1959 Durh. Prev: Ho. Phys. Brook Gen. Hosp. Lond. & Roy. Cornw. Infirm. Truro; Ho. Surg. Newc. Gen. Hosp.; Clin. Asst. (Psychol. Med.) Univ. Coll. Hosp. Lond.

KIRWAN, Ellen Patricia (retired) 3 Birch Lea, Three Bridges, Crawley RH10 8AR Tel: 01293 535906 — LRCPI & LM, LRSCI & LM 1950; LRCPI & LM, LRCSI & LM 1950. Prev: Ho. Surg. Wexford Hosp.

KIRWAN, Mr Ernest O'Gorman Private Consulting Rooms, Royal National Orthopaedic Hospital, 45 Bolsover St., London W1W 5AQ Tel: 020 7935 8412 Fax: 020 7383 5107; 17 Lansdowne Road, Tunbridge Wells TN1 2NG Tel: 01892 619979 Fax: 01892 619969 — MA, MB BChir Camb. 1953; FRCS Eng. 1960; FRCS Ed. 1960. (Middlx.) Civil Cons. (Orthop.) RN; Civil Cons. (Spinal Surg.) RAF. Socs: Fell. Brit. Orthop. Assn. Prev: Cons. Orthop. Surg. Univ. Coll. Hosp. Lond., Roy. Nat. Orthop.; Cons. Orthop. Surg. Chelmsford & St. Helena Hosp. Gps.; Sen. Regist. Roy. Nat. Orthop. Hosp.

KIRWAN, James Francis 121B Bedford Hill, Balham, London SW12 9HE Tel: 020 8675 3956 Email: jfk@netmatters.co.uk — MB BS 1990 Lond.; FRCOphth 1994.

KIRWAN, John Martin James 5 Padstow Drive, Bramhall, Stockport SK7 2HU — MB ChB 1988 Liverp.

KIRWAN, John Richard Rheumatology Unit, University Department of Medicine, Bristol Royal Infirmary, Bristol BS2 8HW Tel: 0117 928 2902 Fax: 0117 928 3841 Email: john.kirwan@bristol.ac.uk; 19 Wellington Park, Clifton, Bristol BS8 2UR Tel: 0117 973 4994 — MB BS 1974 Lond.; BSc (Hons.) Lond. 1971, MD 1983; FRCP Lond. 1994; MRCP (UK) 1978. (Middlx.) Cons. & Reader (Rheum.) Bristol Univ. Socs: Amer. Coll. Rheum.; Brit. Soc. Rheum.; Soc. Judgement & Decision Making. Prev: Lect. & Sen. Regist. (Rheum.) Lond. Hosp.; Regist. (Gen. Med.) Harefield Hosp.; SHO (Med.) N.wick Pk. Hosp. & Clin. Research Centre Harrow.

KIRWAN, Maeve Moira The Surgery, 57 Plains Road, Mapperley, Nottingham NG3 5LB — MB BS 1991 Lond.

KIRWAN, Marie Christine 17 Lansdowne Road, Tunbridge Wells TN1 2NG Tel: 01892 619979 — MB BS Lond. 1957; DA Eng. 1960. (St. Bart.)

KIRWAN, Maurice (retired) 209 South Mossley Hill Road, Liverpool L19 9BB Tel: 0151 427 1828 — MB ChB 1945 Liverp.; MRCS Eng. LRCP Lond. 1945; DMJ (Clin.) Soc. Apoth. Lond. 1970; MRCGP 1965. Prev: Sen. Cas. Off. Roy. S.. Hosp. Liverp.

KIRWAN, Michael Abington Health Complex, Doctors Surgery, 51A Beech Avenue, Northampton NN3 2JG Tel: 01604 791999 Fax: 01604 450155 — LRCPI & LM, LRSCI & LM 1967; LRCPI & LM, LRCSI & LM 1967; MRCGP 1974; DObst RCOG 1972.

KIRWAN, Philip Henry 8 Ashfield Road, Stoneygate, Leicester LE2 1LA — MD 1986 Leic.; MB BCh BAO NUI 1973; MRCOG 1980; DO RCPSI 1978; DCH RCPSI 1978.

KIRWAN, Sarah Elizabeth Mary Kent and Sussex Hospital, Mount Ephraim, Tunbridge Wells TN4 8AT — MB BS 1989 Lond.; MRCP (UK) 1992; FRCR 1997. Cons., Radiol., Kent and SussexHosp., Tunbridge Wells, Kent. Prev: Sen. Regist. (Radiol.) King's Coll. Hosp. Lond.

KIRWAN, Trottie 191 East Surrey Grove, London SE15 — MB BChir 1973 Camb.; FFA RCS Eng. 1979.

KIRWIN, Patrick Alan Health Management Group, 3 Cricklade Court, Crickdale St., Swindon SN1 3EY Tel: 01793 614636 Fax:

01793 490001; Rats Castle, Harnhill, Cirencester GL7 5PU Tel: 01285 861770 — MRCS Eng. LRCP Lond. 1968; DA Eng. 1972. (St. Geo.) Prev: Princip. Med. Off. Qu. Eliz. 2; Surg. Lt. RN.

KISEMBO-LULE, Estella 2 Ruxbury Court, Cumberland Road, Ashford TW15 3DL — LMSSA 1984 Lond.

KISHAN, Mr Billa c/o Mr Prasad Palimar, 38 Pasture Lane, Longbarn, Warrington WA2 0PZ — MB BS 1967 Osmania; FRCSI 1981.

KISHAN RAO, V Upper Parliament Street Surgery, 334 Upper Parliament Street, Liverpool L8 3LD Tel: 0151 709 1263.

KISHORE, Archana c/o Drive P.K. Verma, 17 Trent Close, Oadby, Leicester LE2 4GP; 30 Cliftonville Court, Cliftonville Road, Northampton NN1 5BY — MRCS Eng. LRCP Lond. 1987; MB BS Patna, India 1983.

KISHORE, Keshav 17 Trent Close, Oadby, Leicester LE2 4GP — MB BS 1980 Patna.

KISHORE KUMAR, Rajagopal Whiston Hospital, Prescot L35 5DR Tel: 0151 426 1600 — MB BS 1987 Gulbarga, India; MRCPI 1993.

KISHORI, Arcot A and N Medical Centre, 172 Ansty Road, Coventry CV2 3EX Tel: 024 7645 8151 Fax: 024 7644 7697 — MB BS 1962 Andhra; MB BS 1962 Andhra.

KISKU, William 44 Granby Road, Nuneaton CV10 8EL — MB BS 1983 Madras.

KISLER, Jonathan Daniel 49 Cavendish Avenue, Eastbourne BN22 8EP — MB ChB 1998 Leeds.

KISNAH, Vidia Prakash Occupational Health Department, PowerGen, Westwood Business Park, Coventry CV4 8LG Tel: 024 76 424681 Fax: 024 76 425181 — MB ChB 1978 Aberd.; AFOM RCP Lond. 1990. Socs: Assoc. Fac. Occupat. Med. Prev: Chief Med. Off., Powergen plc; Regist. (Surg.) Aberd. Teach. Hosps. Grampian HB; SHO (Surg.) N. Staffs. Roy. Infirm. Stoke-on-Trent.

KISS, Anton c/o K Tolladay, 10 Woodcutters, Scaynes Hill, Haywards Heath RH17 7NL — State Exam Med. Tubingen 1992.

KISS, Ida Shakuntala 13 Highfield Court, Avenue Road, Southgate, London N14 4DX — MB BS 1951 Madras; DCH Eng. 1954. (Madras) Indep. Cons. Path. (Toxicol.) Lond.; Free-Lance Med. & Scientif. Edr. Prev: Cons. Pathol. Dept. Med. Biochem. Birm. Univ.; Cons. Pathol. Brit. Indust. Biol. Research Assn. Carshalton; Cons. Pathol. Life Sc. Research, Stock Essex.

KISSACK, Christopher Mark 30 High View Road, Douglas IM2 5BH — MB ChB 1994 Liverp.

KISSEN, George David Niman Sevenways Surgery, 152-154 Derbyshire Lane, Stretford, Manchester M32 8DU Tel: 0161 865 2880 Fax: 0161 865 4990; The Coppice, 9 Brookwood Avenue, Sale M33 5BZ Email: home@kiss.nwnet.co.uk — MB ChB 1978 Manch.; BSc St. And. 1975; DCH RCP Lond. 1981. (St. And. & Manch.) Hosp. Pract. (Paediat. & Oncol.) Roy. Manch. Childr. Hosp. Prev: SHO Roy. Manch. Childr. Hosp. Pendlebury; SHO Pk. Hosp. Davyhulme; Ho. Phys. Manch. Roy. Infirm.

KISSEN, Lois Hoad Histopathology Department, Royal Bournemouth Hospital, Castle Lane East, Bournemouth BH7 7DW Tel: 01202 704832 Fax: 01202 704833; Home Mead, 84 Southampton Road, Lymington SO41 9GZ Tel: 01590 672528 — MB ChB 1971 Glas.; FRCPath 1989, M 1977. p/t Cons. Histopath., Roy. Bournemouth Hosp., Bournemouth. Prev: Cons. (Cytopath.) Portsmouth Hosps. NHS Trust; Cons. Path. Ayrsh. Area Laborat.

KISSIN, Caroline Mary Jarvis Screening Centre, Stoughton Road, Guildford GU1 1LJ Tel: 01483 782000 Fax: 01483 783299; Morningside, Trodds Lane, Guildford GU1 2XY Tel: 01483 574741 — MB ChB 1979 Bristol; MRCP (UK) 1982; FRCR 1985. (Univ. Bristol) Cons. Radiol. Jarvis BrE. Screening Centre Guildford. Prev: Sen. Regist. (Radiol.) St. Geo. Hosp. Lond.

KISSIN, Mr Mark William 8 Waterden Road, Guildford GU1 2AW Tel: 01483 568286; Morningside, 31 Trodds Lane, Merrow, Guildford GU1 2XY Tel: 01483 574741 Fax: 01483 440063 — MB 1976 Camb.; MB BChir Camb. 1975; MA Camb. 1976, MChir 1986; FRCS Eng. 1980. Cons. BrE. & Melanoma Surg. Roy. Surrey Co. Hosp., St Lukes Cancer Centre & Jarvis BrE. Screening Centre Guildford; St Lukes Cancer Centre Guildford & Jarvis BrE. Screening Centre Guildford; Sir Alexander MacCormack Trav. Fell.sh. St. Vincent Hosp. Melbourne, Austral.; Quality Assur. (BrE. Surg.) S. Thames. Socs: Surg. Reseach Soc.; Nat. Comm. Brit. Assn. Surg. Oncol.; Nat. Exec. BASO BrE. Specialty Gp. Prev: Sen. Regist. Bristol, Exeter & Melbourne, Austral.; Regist. Rotat. (Gen. Surg.) St. Geo. Hosp.; Surgic. Research Fell. & Hon. Sen. Regist. Roy. Marsden Hosp. & Inst. Cancer Research.

KISSUN, Dean 72 Wychbury Road, Wolverhampton WV3 8DN — MB ChB 1997 Birm.; BDS 1989; FDS (Eng) 1996. (Birmingham) SHO (Surgic.) Rotat., City Hosp., Birm.

KIST, Paulus Constant Mattheus Department of Geriatrics, St. George's Hospital, Tooting, London SW17; 26 Wood Lane, Fleet GU51 3EA Tel: 01252 616077 — Artsexamen 1978 Leiden; MRCP (UK) 1993. Sen. Regist. (Geriat. Med.) St. Geo. Hosp. Lond. Socs: Brit. Geriat. Soc. Prev: Regist. (Gen. & Geriat. Med.) New Cross Hosp. Wolverhampton & St. Johns Hosp. Livingston; Project Co-ordinator Leprosy Control Polihara, W. Nepal.

KITARA-OKOT, Pellegrini 29 Jerusalem Street, Belfast BT7 1QN — MB ChB 1974 Makerere; MRCPath 1985; T(Path) 1991.

KITCHEN, Carol Ann Highfield Surgery, Holtdale Approach, Leeds LS16 7ST Tel: 0113 230 0108 Fax: 0113 230 1309 — MB ChB 1979 Sheff.; 1996 Dip Ther Newcastle; MRCGP 1985.

KITCHEN, Catherine Vera 72 Maisemore Gardens, Emsworth PO10 7JX — MB ChB 1991 Ed.

KITCHEN, George (retired) The Old Smithy, 13 Sambrook, Newport TF10 8AP — MRCS Eng. LRCP Lond. 1962; FRCR 1975; FFR 1968; DMRT Eng. 1965. Prev: Dir. Radiother. & Oncol. Servs. Shrops. HA.

KITCHEN, Hugo John Stratford Orthopaedic Clinic, 6 Mansell St., Stratford-upon-Avon CV37 6NR Tel: 01789 414289 Fax: 01789 299003 — MB ChB 1983 Birm.; MB ChB Birm. 1982. Dir. Fightback (UK) Orthop. Centre for Assessm. & Rehabil. of Disorders of Lumbar Spine; Stratford DermaTher. Clinic.

KITCHEN, Jennifer Vivien 2 Lion Cottages, Brewery Lane, Nailsworth, Stroud GL6 0JQ Tel: 01453 834146 — BM 1979 Soton.; FRCP Lond. 1996; MRCP (UK) 1983; T(M) 1992. Prev: Cons. Palliat. Med. St. Christopher's Hospice Sydenham; Med. Dir. Hospice at Home Tunbridge Wells; Hon. Cons. Palliat. Med. Tunbridge Wells HA.

KITCHEN, Mr Neil David Private Consulting Rooms, 23 Queen Square, London WC1N 3BG Tel: 020 7829 8732 Fax: 020 7833 8658 Email: neil.kitchen@uclh.org; 31 Noel Road, London N1 8HQ — MB BChir Camb. 1986; BSc Lond. 1983; MD Camb. 1996; FRCS (SN) 1995; FRCS Eng. 1989. (Univ. Camb.) Cons. Neurosurg. Nat. Hosp. Neurol. & Neurosurg. Qu. Sq. Lond. Socs: Assoc. Mem. Soc. Brit. Neurol. Surgs.; Brit. Neuro-oncol. Gp. Prev: Sen. Regist. Atkinson Morley's Hosp. Lond.; Research Fell. Inst. Neurol.; Regist. (Neurosurg.) Roy. Free Hosp. Lond.

KITCHEN, Mr Paul Essex Rivers Healthcare NHS Trust, Colchester General Hospital, Turner Road, Colchester CO4 5JL Tel: 01206 742645; Owlstree House, Church Lane, Stanway, Colchester CO3 5LP Email: paul.kitchen@erhc-tr.nthames.nhs.uk — MB BS 1967 Lond.; FRCS Eng. 1973; FRCS Ed. 1972; MRCS Eng. LRCP Lond. 1967. (King's Coll. Hosp.) Cons. ENT Surg. & Med. Director Essex Rivers healthcare NHS Trust Colchester Gen Hosp. Socs: Brit Assn. Otolaryngologists & head & neck surg; RSM; BMA. Prev: Sen. Regist. ENT Dept. St. Bart. Hosp. Lond.

KITCHEN, Paul Anthony 18 Middle Road, Harrow HA2 0HL — MB BS 1991 Lond.

KITCHEN, Stephen Paul War Pensions Agency, Norcross, Thornton-Cleveleys FY5 3WP; 5 Carr Drive, Wesham, Preston PR4 3DS — MB ChB 1975 Glas.; MRCGP 1980; DRCOG 1977. (Glasgow) Med. Dir. War Pens. Agency Blackpool.

KITCHEN, Valerie Susan 23 Elnathan Mews, London W9 2JE Tel: 020 7286 7529 Email: v.kitchen@ic.ac.uk — MB ChB 1981 Leic.; FRCP Lond. 1996; MRCP (UK) 1985. (Univ. Leicester Med. Sch.) Clin. Sen. Lect. (Genitourin. Med. & Communicable Dis.) St. Mary's Hosp. Lond. Prev: Sen. Regist. (Gen. Med.) St. Mary's Hosp. Lond.; Regist. (Clin. Immunol.) Roy. Perth Hosp. W. Austral.

KITCHENER, Alan David Grange Medical Centre, West Cliff Road, Ramsgate CT11 9LJ Tel: 01843 595051 Fax: 01843 591999 — MB BChir 1980 Camb.; MA Camb. 1980.

KITCHENER, Professor Henry Charles Academic Unit of Obstetrics & Gynaecology & Reproductive Health, Research Floor, St Mary's Hospital, Whitworth Park, Manchester M13 0JH Tel: 0161 276 6461 Fax: 0161 276 6134 Email: hkitchener@central.cmht.nwest.nhs.uk; Southlands, Bridge End Drive, Prestbury, Macclesfield SK10 4DL — MB ChB 1975 Glas.; MD Glas. 1983; FRCS Glas. 1988; FRCOG 1994, M 1980. Prof.

Gyn. Oncol. & Head of Univ. Dept. Manch.; Hon. Cons. St. Mary's Hosp. & Christie Hosp. Socs: Brit. Gyn. Cancer Soc.; Brit. Soc. Colpos. & Cerv. Path.

KITCHENER, Paul Alvin 5 The Mead, Clevelands, London W13 8AZ Tel: 020 8998 7466 — MB 1965 Camb.; MSc Lond. 1972; MA Camb. 1964, BA 1961, MB 1965, BChir 1964; MRCP Lond. 1969; FFPHM 1990; MFCM 1980. (Camb. & Guy's) Dir. Pub. Health N. Beds. HA. Socs: Soc. Social Med.; Internat. Epidemiol. Assn. Prev: Ho. Surg. Guy's Hosp.; Med. Off. Save Childr. Fund Nigeria; Post-doctoral Fell. Johns Hopkins Sch. Hyg. & Pub. Health Baltimore.

KITCHENER, Peter Geoffrey Diagnostic X-Ray Department, Norfolk & Norwich Hospital, St Stephen's Road, Norwich NR1 3SR — MB BS 1969 Lond.; MRCP (U.K.) 1973; FRCR 1980; DCH Eng. 1971. (St. Bart.) Cons. Radiol. Norf. & Norwich Hosp. Prev: Sen. Regist. (Radiol.) Addenbrooke's Hosp. Camb.; SHO (Paediat.) & Regist. (Gen. Med.) United Norwich Hosps.

KITCHIN, Alfred Philip (retired) Efail Feurig, Bryn Crug, Tywyn LL36 9RW — M.B., B.Chir. Camb. 1938; F.R.C.S. Ed. 1948. Prev: Sen. Surg. Regist. W.Herts. Hosp. Gp.

KITCHIN, Arthur Henderson (retired) 4A Kinnear Road, Edinburgh EH3 5PE Tel: 0131 552 3580 — PhD Lond. 1955; MB ChB Ed. 1947; FRCP Lond. 1971, M 1956; FRCP Ed. 1965, M 1956. Hon. Fell. Fac. Med Univ. Edin. Prev: Cons. Phys. & Sen. Lect. Univ. Edin. Dept. Med. W.. Gen. Hosp. Edin.

KITCHIN, John Cecil Grey Willows, Horton Road, Ashley Heath, Ringwood BH24 2EN Tel: 0142 543088 — MB ChB 1938 Liverp.; MRCS Eng. LRCP Lond. 1938. (Liverp.)

KITCHIN, Nicholas Randolph Everard Pasteur Merieux MSD, Clivemont House, Clivemont Road, Maidenhead SL6 7BU Tel: 01628 785291; 9 Martingale Road, Burbage, Marlborough SN8 3TY Tel: 01672 810278 Fax: 01672 810278 Email: nickkitchin@globalnet.co.uk — MB BS 1991 Lond.; BSc Lond. 1988; DA (UK) 1993. Phys. (Pharmaceut.) Pasteur Merieux MSD.

KITCHIN, Steven Edward 30 Queens Road E., Beeston, Nottingham NG9 2GS Tel: 01159 922 5681 Email: serhchin@booyakcackew.freeserve.co.uk; 50 Fairway, Whitestone, Nuneaton CV11 6NP — MB ChB 1996 Sheff. SHO (A & E) Roy. Chesterfield Hosp.; Bar Vocational Course, Nottm. Law Sch., Chaucer St. Nottm. (Full Time Stud.) Locum Sho - A & E Qu. Med. Centre. Socs: BMA; Brit. Med. Acupunct. Soc.; Med. Protec. Soc. Prev: Ho. Surg. Geo. Eliot Hosp.; Ho. Phys. Doncaster Roy.

KITCHING, Andrew John 20 Kelsey Avenue, Finchampstead, Wokingham RG40 4TZ — MB ChB 1986 Manch.; DA (UK) 1989; DCH RCP Lond. 1989. Regist. (Anaesth.) N.ampton & Oxf. Hosps. Socs: Reading Path. Soc.; Intens. Care Soc. Prev: Cons. (Anaes), Roy. Berks. Hosp. NHS Trust, Reading; Ho. Phys. Roy. Lancaster Infirm.; Ho. Surg. Withington Hosp. S. Manch.

KITCHING, Catherine South King Street Medical Centre, 25 South King Street, Blackpool FY1 4NF Tel: 01253 26637; 13 Arnold Avenue, Blackpool FY4 2EP Tel: 01253 46590 — MB ChB 1966 Manch.; DA Eng. 1970; DObst RCOG 1969. (Manch.) Clin. Asst. Trinity Hospice Lancs.

KITCHING, Claire Madeleine (retired) 11 Spring View Road, Crookes, Sheffield S10 1LS Tel: 0114 268 0993 — MB ChB 1988 Sheff. Trainee GP Sheff. GP VTS.

KITCHING, David Franklin 51 School Road, Frampton Cotterell, Bristol BS36 2BU — MB ChB 1962 Bristol.

KITCHING, Gary Terence 237 Cop Lane, Penwortham, Preston PR1 9AB — MB ChB 1990 Manch.

KITCHING, Mark David 9 Stonefold Close, Windsor Gardens, Kenton, Newcastle upon Tyne NE5 4BQ Tel: 0191 271 5255 — MB BS 1994 Newc. SHO Qu. Eliz. Hosp. Gateshead.

KITCHING, Michael Richard The Loddon Vale Practice, Hurricane Way, Woodley, Reading RG5 4UX Tel: 0118 969 0160 Fax: 0118 969 9103 — MB BS Lond. 1992; BSc Lond. 1988; MRCGP 1997; DRCOG 1996; DFFP 1996.

KITCHING, Paul Andrew Department of Cellular Pathology, Royal United Hospital, Combe Park, Bath BA1 3NG Tel: 01225 825677 Fax: 01225 824503 Email: paul.kitching@ruh-bath.swest.nhs.uk — MB BCh 1987 Wales; BSc Wales 1984, MB BCh 1987; MRCP (UK) 1990; DRCPath 1994; MRCPath 1996. Cons. Histopath., Roy. United Hosp. Bath. Socs: Assn. Clin. Path. & BMA; BMA; BSCC. Prev: Lect. & Hon. Sen. Regist. (Histopath.) Roy. Free Hosp. Lond.; Regist. (Histopath.) Univ. Hosp. Wales Cardiff; SHO (Histopath. & Med.) Univ. Hosp. Wales. Cardiff.

KITCHING, Sarah Jane Westover House, 18 Earlsfield Road, London SW18 Tel: 0208 877 1877 — MB BS 1987 Lond.; MA (Hons.) Camb. 1984. Prev: Regist. (Psychiat.) Priory Hosp. Roehampton; SHO (O & G) Guy's Hosp. Lond.; SHO (Cas.) St. Stephen's Hosp. Chelsea.

KITCHING, Wendy Jane Avenue Medical Centre, 51-53 Victoria Avenue, Blackley, Manchester M9 6BA Tel: 0161 720 8282 Fax: 0161 740 7991 — MB ChB 1991 Manch.; MRCGP 1995. (Manchester)

KITE, Julie Elizabeth 67 Canada Road, Heath, Cardiff CF14 3BX — BM 1992 Soton.; MRCGP 1997; DRCOG 1995; DFFP 1995. Asst. GP Barry. Prev: GP/Regist. Cardiff.

KITE, Stephen Andrew The Surgery, Station Road, Knebworth SG3 6AP Tel: 01438 812494 Fax: 01438 816497; Tower Lodges, Hitchin Road, Codicote, Hitchin SG4 8TQ — MB BS 1982 Lond.; DRCOG 1987. Princip. GP Partner.

KITE, Suzanne Margaret Leeds General Infirmary, Great George Street, Leeds LS1 3EX — MB ChB 1990 Sheff.; BMedSci Sheff. 1990; MRCP (UK) 1994; MA Medical Ethics Keele 2000. Sen. Clin. Lect. in Palliat. Med., Leeds Gen. Infirm., Leeds Teachg. Hosp.s Trust, Leeds.

KITELEY, Neil Andrew Kingswinford Health Centre, Standhills Road, Kingswinford DY6 8DN Tel: 01384 271241 Fax: 01384 297530 — BM BS 1985 Nottm.; MRCGP 1989; DRCOG 1989. Prev: Trainee GP Nottm. VTS; SHO (Geriat. Med.) Nottm. HA; Ho. Off. (Med.) N.ampton Gen. Hosp.

KITHULEGODA, Lalith Mohan 48 St Leonards Way, Hornchurch RM11 1FR Tel: 01708 438777; Benefits Agency Medical Services, Olympic House, Olympic Way, Wembley HA9 0DL Tel: 020 8795 8759 Fax: 020 8795 8992 — MB BCh BAO 1982 NUI; LRCPI & LM, LRCSI & LM 1982. (Royal College of Surgeons in Ireland) Med. Adviser Benefit Agency Med. Serv. Wembley. Prev: GP Romford; Trainee GP Romford; SHO (O & G) Rush Green Hosp. Romford.

KITIYAKARA, Chagriya Flat 4, Sutherland House, Marloes Road, London W8 5LG — MB BS 1990 Lond.; MRCP Lond. 1993. SHO (Renal Med.) Dulwich Hosp. Lond. Prev: Ho. Off. (Med. & Surg.) Lewisham & Guy's NHS Trust.

***KITIYAKARA, Taya** Flat 4, Sutherland House, Marloes Road, London W8 5LG Tel: 020 7376 1535 — MB BS 1996 Lond.; MA Camb. 1997.

KITLOWSKI, Andrew Jerzy Walkley House Medical Centre, 23 Greenhow Street, Sheffield S6 3TN Tel: 0114 234 3716; 296 Ecclesall Road S., Sheffield S11 9PT Tel: 0114 235 1771 — MB ChB 1984 Sheff.

KITLOWSKI, Julie Anne St Ann's Medical Centre, Effingham Street, Rotherham S65 1BL Tel: 01709 379283/364437; 296 Ecclesall Road S., Sheffield S11 9PT Tel: 0114 235 1771 Fax: 0114 262 0256 Email: a.j.kitlowski@btinternet.com — MB ChB 1984 Sheff.; DRCOG 1988. (Sheffield) Police Surg. Sheff. Socs: Assn. Police Surg.

KITSBERG, Anthony Adrian 26 Broadfields Avenue, Edgware HA8 8PG — MB ChB 1992 Manch.; DA (UK) 1995.

KITSON, Geoffrey Edwin 2 Wren Close, Woosehill, Wokingham RG41 3YT Tel: 01734 792456 — BM BS 1982 Nottm.; BM BS Nottm. 19782; BMedSci Nottm. 1980; Dip. Pharm. Med. RCP (UK) 1990. Assoc. Inst. Dir. Syntex Research & Developm. (Europ.) Maidenhead. Prev: Regist. (Anaesth.) Sheff. HA.

KITSON, Jeffrey Sycamore House, Main Road, Exeter EX6 8BU Tel: 01392 833651 — MB BS 1993 Lond. Specialist Regist. (Orthop.) SW Sch. Socs: MDU.

KITSON, Jennifer 9 Cuillin Heights, Larne BT40 2DJ — MB ChB 1998 Ed.; MB ChB Ed 1998.

KITSON, Mr Jonathan Lane Department of Orthopaedic Surgery, Queen Elizabeth II Hospital, Welwyn Garden City AL7 4HQ Tel: 01707 365079 Fax: 01707 390894; 5 Roundabout Lane, Welwyn AL6 0TH Tel: 01438 718998 Fax: 01438 718998 — MB BS 1984 Lond.; FRCS (Orth) 1995; FRCS Ed. 1989; FRCS Eng. 1989. Cons. (Ortho. Surg.) Qu. Eliz. II Hosp. Welwyn Garden City. Socs: Fell. BOA. Prev: Spinal Surg. Fell. Sydney, Australia; Sen. Regist. (Orthop.) Hammersmith Hosp.

KITSON, Martin Moore Helston Medical Centre, Trelawnt Road, Helston TR13 8AU — MB BS 1991 Lond.; BSc Lond. 1989; DRCOG 1995; DCCH RCP Ed. 1996; MRCGP 1998. (King's College London)
KITSON, Meriel Perpetua The Mannamead Surgery, 22 Eggbuckland Road, Plymouth PL3 5HE Tel: 01752 223652 Fax: 01752 253875; The Old Vicarage, Morval, Looe PL13 1PN — MA Oxf. 1975, BM BCh 1976; DCH RCP Lond. 1981. (Middlx.) Socs: Pres. Plymouth Med. Soc. Prev: Clin. Asst. (Paediat. Out Pats.) Freedom Fields Hosp. Plymouth; SHO (Paediat.) Taunton & Som. Hosp. (MusGr. Pk. Br.).
KITSON, Michael Charles Hellesdon Hospital, Drayton High Road, Hellesdon, Norwich NR6 5BE — MB BS 1972 Lond.; MRCPsych 1978; DPM Eng. 1978; FRCPsych. (Char. Cross) Cons. Psychiat. Waveney Clin. Hellesdon Hosp. Norwich. Prev: Sen. Regist. (Psychiat.) Fulbourn Hosp. Camb.; Sen. Regist. (Psychiat.) Yare Clinic W. Norwich Hosp.
KITSON, Nicholas Ian Alexandra House, Alexandra Road, St Austell PL25 Tel: 01762 296302 Email: nick.kitson@cht.swest.nhs.uk — MB BS 1975 Lond.; FRCPsych 1996, M 1980; UKCP registered Psychoanalytic& Psychotherapist. (St Bartholomews) Cons. Psychait.S. Restormel, Cornw. health care NHS trust. Socs: (Hon. Vice Pres.) Europ. Soc. Ment. Health & Deafness; Lond. Centre Psychother.; Hon.life Mem. of Counc. Brit. Soc. Ment. Health & Deafness. Prev: Clin. Dir. & Cons. Psychiat. Nat. Deaf Servs. S. W. Lond. & St. Geo.'s Ment. Health Servs. NHS Trust Springfield Hosp. Lond.; Hon. Cons. Psychiat. St. Geo. Healthcare NHS Trust; Med. Dir. Pathfinder Ment. Health Servs. NHS Trust.
KITSON, Ross Matthew 33 Harewood Gardens, Longthorpe, Peterborough PE3 9NF — MB ChB 1995 Leeds. SHO (A & E) PeterBoro. Dist. Hosp.
KITSON, Stephen Richard 10 Rosslyn Road, Weston, Bath BA1 3LH — MB 1981 Camb.; MA MB Camb. 1981, BChir 1980; MRCGP 1984; DRCOG 1983.
KITT, Mrs Renata Cor Unum, 17 Scholl Crescent, Godshill, Ventnor PO38 3JL Tel: 01983 840427 — Lekarz 1971 Stettin Poland; DA (UK) 1987. Staff Grade Anaesth. Qu. Eliz. Hosp. King's Lynn Norf. Prev: Regist. (Anaesth.) Sandwell Dist. Hosp.; Regist. (Anaesth.) Qu. Alexandra Hosp. Portsmouth.
KITTERINGHAM, Lara Jane 2 Misbowne Close, Gerrards Cross SL9 0PT; Touchwood, 2 Misbourne Close, Chalfont-st.-Peter, Gerrards Cross SL9 0PT — MB ChB 1992 Leic. Demonst. (Anat.) Leicester Univ. Prev: Ho. Off. (Surg. & O & G) Leicester Roy. Infirm.; Ho. (Gen. Med. & Rheum.) Leicester Gen. Hosp.
KITTLE, Denyer John Ash Surgery, Chilton Place, Ash, Canterbury CT3 2HD — MB BS 1986 Lond. Clin. Asst. (Endoscopy) Kent & Canterbury Hosp.
KITTLE, Geoffrey Peter Church View Surgery, Burley House, 15 High Street, Rayleigh SS6 7DY Tel: 01268 774477 Fax: 01268 771293 Email: geoffrey.kittle@gp-f81125.nhs.uk; Dingle Dell, 4A Daws Heath Road, Rayleigh SS6 7QH Tel: 01268 781576 Email: geoff.kittle@bigfoot.com — MB ChB 1972 Sheff.; DFFP 1996; T(GP) 1991; Pre Hosp. Emerg. Care Cert. RCS (Edin.) 1994; Mem. Pre Hosp. Care Fac. RCS (Edin.) 1996. (Sheff.) GP Princip. Ch. View Surg. Rayleigh; CMO. St. John Ambul. Brig. Essex; Med. Off. Brit. Automobile Racing Club. Socs: BMA (Ex-Mem. Counc., Ex-Chairm. Jun. Mems. Forum, Ex-Chairm.Trainees Sub Comm. GMSC, Ex-Mem. GMSC); (Past Chairm.) S. Essex LMC; BASICS. Prev: Regist. (Med.) & SHO (O & G & Paediat.) St. Luke's Hosp. Guildford; Ho. Off. Derby City Hosp.; Mem. Dist. Managem. Team S.end HA.
KITTLER, Zelpha Katherine 70 Well Street, London E9 7JA Tel: 020 8985 3806 Fax: 020 8525 5891 Email: bajuu@aol.com — MB BCh BAO 1988 Dub.; MRCPsych Lond. 1995. (Trinity Coll. Dub.) Specialist Regist. Bethlem Roy. Hosp. Beckenham Kent.
KITTO, Wasif Daood 13 Whiston Grove, Moorgate Road, Rotherham S60 2TX Tel: 01709 364596 — MB ChB 1970 Baghdad.
KIU, Chek Ing 8A Howard Street, Newcastle upon Tyne NE1 2AZ — MB BS 1992 Newc.
KIVLICHAN, Anne-Marie McKay (retired) 24 Kinmount Avenue, Glasgow G44 4RR Tel: 0141 632 8909 — MB ChB 1943 Glas.
KIWANUKA, Mr Abubakar Ibrahim 181 Stamford Road, Audenshaw, Manchester M34 5NP Tel: 0161 331 6646 Fax: 0161 331 6074 — MB ChB 1974 Manch.; FRCS Ed. 1979; MRCOG 1983. (Manchester UK) Cons. O & G Tameside Gen. Hosp. Ashton u. Lyne. Socs: N. Eng. Soc. Obsts. & Gyns.; Fell. Manch. Med. Soc. Prev: Sen. Regist. (O & G) N. W.. RHA; Regist. Rotat. (Surg.) Manch. Roy. Infirm.; Ho. Surg. Manch. Roy. Infirm.
KIYANI, Tahir Maqsood Langthorne Health Centre, 13 Langthorne Road, Leytonstone, London E11 4HX; 101 Coventry Road, Ilford IG1 4QT — MB BS 1984 Lond.; MRCGP 1997; DFFP 1997; Dip. Ther. Wales 1997. (St Bartholomew's) GP Princip. Prev: Trainee GP Lond. VTS.
KLAASSEN, Mr Barry Accident & Emergency Department, Perth Royal Infirmary, Perth PH1 1NX Tel: 01728 473842; Carse View, The Old Orchard, Wester Ballindean, By Inchture, Perth PH14 9QS Tel: 01828 686711 — MB ChB 1983 Dundee; MB ChB Dundee 1987; BSc (Hons.) Med. Microbiol. Dund 1983; FRCS Ed. 1994; FAEM 1998. (Dundee) Cons. (A & E) Perth Roy. Infirm. Socs: BMA; BAEM; Fell. Fac. A&E Med. Prev: Sen. Regist. & Lect. (Emerg. Med.) Aberd. Roy. Infirm.; Regist. (A & E) Aberd. Roy. Infirm.; Regist. Rotat. (Surg.) Dundee.
KLABER, Mary Clare Venables Cuckoos Farm, Little Baddow, Chelmsford CM3 4BN Tel: 01245 224539 Fax: 01245 222910 — MB BS 1971 Lond.; MA Med. Law & Ethics Lond. 1994; LLB Anglia 1993; MRCS Eng. LRCP Lond. 1971; DCH Eng. 1974; DObst RCOG 1973. (Roy. Free) Princip. Basildon, Essex. Socs: Medico-Legal Soc. Prev: GP Danbury.
KLABER, Michael Robert 152 Harley Street, London W1G 7LH Tel: 020 7935 8868 Fax: 020 7224 2574; Cuckoos Farm, Little Baddow, Chelmsford CM3 4BN Tel: 01245 222910 Fax: 01245 222910 — MB BChir 1964 Camb.; MA, MB Camb. 1965, BChir 1964; FRCP Lond. 1987; MRCP (UK) 1973; AMQ 1966. (Camb. & St. Bart.) Cons. Dermat. Mid Essex Hosps.; Hon. Cons. Dermat. Lond. Hosp. Whitechapel; Hon. Sen. Lect., St Barthlolomews and Roy. Lond. Sch. of Med. Socs: Fell. Roy. Soc. Med. (Mem. Sect. Dermat.); Brit. Assn. Dermat. Prev: Sen. Regist. (Dermat.) Lond. Hosp.; Regist. (Dermat.) St. Bart. Hosp. Lond.; Med. Regist. W. Norf. & King's Lynn Gen. Hosp.
KLAFKOWSKI, Gillian 44 Meadow Lane, Willaston, South Wirral CH64 2TZ — MB ChB 1994 Sheff.
KLAIR, Palwinder Singh 7 Parkview Crescent, Walsall WS2 8TY — MB ChB 1995 Manch.
KLAKUS, Mr Jerzy Antoni 31 Riverview Avenue, North Ferriby HU14 3DY Tel: 01482 633274 — MB ChB 1975 Leeds; FRCS Eng. 1980. Staff Grade Off. (A & E) Hull Roy. Infirm. Socs: Assoc. Mem. Brit. Assn. Plastic Surgs.; Assoc. Mem. Brit. Assn. Accid. & Emerg. Med. Prev: Clin. Asst. (A & E) Hull Roy. Infirm.; Regist. (A & E) Morriston Hosp. Swansea.
KLAR, Hans-Martin Bootham Park Hospital, York YO30 7BY Tel: 01904 454013 Fax: 01904 453794 — Medico Sao Paulo 1968; DrMed Rupert Karl Univ. 1971; MRCPsych 1972; DPM Ed. & Glas. 1972. (Univ. Sao Paulo Brazil) Cons. Psychiat. Bootham Pk. Hosp. York. Prev: Sen. Regist. Roy. Edin. Hosp.; Postgrad. Schol. German Acad. Exchange Serv. Heidelberg.
KLASEN, Henrika The Maudsley Hospital, Denmark Hill, London SE5 Tel: 020 7703 6333 Email: spjuhtk@iop.kcl.ac.uk; 39 Venetian Road, London SE5 9RR — State Exam Med 1990 Kiel; MSc (Anthropol.) Lond. 1993; MD Kiel 1990. Specialist Regist., St. Geo.s Hosp., Lond. Socs: MRCPsych. Prev: Regist. (Psychiat.) Maudsley Hosp. Lond.
KLASS, Howard Julian 15 Gorse Bank Road, Halebarns, Altrincham WA15 0BE; North Manchester Healthcare Trust, Delaunays Road, Crumpsall, Manchester M8 5RB — MB BChir 1971 Camb.; MA, MB Camb. 1972, BChir 1971; MRCP (UK) 1974. (Caius College, Cambridge and Guys London) Cons. Phys. & Gastroenterol. N. Manch. Gen. Hosp. Prev: Sen. Regist. (Med.) Manch. Roy. Infirm.; Regist. (Gastroenterol.) Hammersmith Hosp. Lond.; Ho. Phys. & Ho. Surg. Guy's Hosp. Lond.
KLASSNIK, Benjamin (retired) 39 Inderwick Road, Crouch End, London N8 9LB — MB BCh 1947 Witwatersrand; MRCPsych 1971; DPM Eng. 1966. Prev: Cons. Psychiat. Claybury Hosp. Whipps Cross & Thorpe Coombe Hosps.
KLAYE, Mr Thomas Okine 21 Roydon Close, Battersea, London SW11 5BE Tel: 020 7350 2879 — MB ChB 1975 Ghana; FRCS Ed. 1983.
KLEANTHOUS, Mr Kleanthis Loucas 10 Montserrat Road, Putney, London SW15 2LA — MB BS 1982 Lond.; FRCS Eng. 1988;

FCOphth 1989. Cons. Ophth. Qu. Eliz. II Hosp. Welwyn Gdn. City. Prev: Regist. (Ophth.) St. Geo. Hosp. Lond.; SHO (Ophth.) King's Coll. Hosp. Lond. & The Lond. Hosp.

KLEEBERG, Birgit Kristin 87 Windus Road, London N16 6UR — MB ChB 1984 Cape Town.

KLEEBERG, Claudia Susan 19C Chardmore Road, London N16 6JA — MB ChB 1989 Cape Town.

KLEIMANIS-TAYLOR, Nicolette Shelley 22 Imperial Road, Beeston, Nottingham NG9 1ET Tel: 0115 925 6475; 14 Mill Paddock, Letcombe Regis, Wantage OX12 9JE Tel: 012357 3035 — BM BS 1987 Nottm.

KLEIN, Andrew Alexander 2 The Garth, Holden Road, Woodside Park, London N12 7DL — MB BS 1993 Lond.

KLEIN, Dorothy (retired) Prospect Cottage, 16 Wharf Hill, Winchester SO23 9NQ Tel: 01962 851092 — MB ChB 1947 Ed.; Dip. Audiol. Manch. 1960. Prev: Cons. Audiol. Cromwell Hosp. & St. Geo. Hosp. Lond.

KLEIN, Graeme Stour Surgery, 49 Barrack Road, Christchurch BH23 1PA Tel: 01202 464500 Fax: 01202 464529 — BM 1986 Soton.; MRCGP 1991; DRCOG 1992; DCH RCP Lond. 1990. GP ChristCh.. Prev: Trainee GP/SHO (O & G) Wessex VTS.

KLEIN, Hans 11 The Whins, Beverly Parklands, Beverley HU17 0RZ — State Exam Med. Frankfurt 1989.

KLEIN, Hyam Sydney (retired) 3 Langford Close, London NW8 0LN Tel: 0207 328 6632 — MB ChB Leeds 1942; MD (Distinc.) Leeds 1948; FRCPsych 1972; DPM Eng. 1947. Psychoanalyst Lond.; Chairm. Child Psychoanal. Comm. & Mem. Train. Comm. Brit. Psychoanal. Soc.; Phys. i/c (Child Dept.) Lond. Clinic Psychoanal. Prev: Cons. Child Psychiat. King's Coll. Hosp. & Belgrave Childr. Hosp.

KLEIN, Jason Simpson Daniel 12A Cavell Close, Edith Cavell Hospital, Bretton Gate, Bretton, Peterborough PE3 9GZ — MB ChB 1995 Leeds.

KLEIN, John Lawrence 71 The Glade, Fetcham, Leatherhead KT22 9TF — MB BChir 1990 Camb.; MSc 1999 Lond.; Dip. RCPath. 1999; BA Camb. 1985; MRCP (UK) 1994; DTM & H Liverp. 1996. (Univ. Coll. & Middx. Sch. Med.) Lect. (Clin. MicroBiol.) Guy's, King's & St. Thomas' Med. & Dent. Schs., Lond. Socs: Brit. Soc. Study of Infec.; Roy. Soc. Trop. Med. & Hyg. Prev: Regist. HIV Med. Infect. Dis. St. Mary's Hosp. Lond.

KLEIN, Juergen Ralph 4 Burgh Hall Cottages, Park End, Swaffham Bulbeck, Cambridge CB5 0NA Tel: 01223 811978 Email: drjvergen.klein@tesco.net — State Exam Med 1988 Saarland; Dip. IMC RCS Ed. 1993; DA (UK) 1993. Specialist Regist. (Anaesth. & Intens. Care) Leicester Gp. Teachg. Hosps.; Program Dir. UK, InterNat. 1st Responder; Mem. Pre-Hosp. Trauma Life Support Internat. PHTLS Fac. Socs: ICS; AABGI; BASICS. Prev: Mem. Mid Anglia Gen. Pract. Accid. Serv. (Hon. Sec. & Train. Off.).

KLEIN, Kathryn Amy Langton 44 Fairfield Approach, Wraysbury, Staines TW19 5DS Tel: 01784 482239 Fax: 01784 482239 Email: kklein@doctors.org.uk — MB BS 1977 Lond.; MRCP (UK) 1981; MRCPsych 1990. (Middlx.) Private Pract. only. Prev: Lect. (Child Adolesc. Psychiat.) United Med. & Dent. Schs. Guy's & St. Thos. Hosps. Lond.; Cons. (Child Psych.) NeuroDevelopm. team, Hammersmith & Fulham Hosp.

KLEIN, Leslie Ellis The Beeches, 1A Wainwright Road, Altrincham WA14 4BS — MB ChB 1975 Manch.; MSc Manch. 1983, MB ChB 1975; MFCM RCP (UK) 1986. Direct Pub. Health Med. Macclesfield HA. Prev: Dist. Med. Off. S. Sefton HA.

KLEIN, Nigel Jonathan Department of Immunology & Infectious Diseases, Hospital for Sick Children, Great Ormond St., London WC1N 1EH Tel: 020 7405 9200 Fax: 020 7831 4366 Email: nklein@ich.ucl.ac.uk; 32 Northcote Road, Twickenham TW1 1PA — MB BS 1984 Lond.; PhD Lond. 1996; BSc Lond. 1981; MRCP (UK) 1987. (Univ. Coll. Hosp. Lond.) Sen. Lect. (Immunol. & Infec. Dis.) Inst. Child Health Lond. & Gt. Ormond St. Hosp. for Childr. NHS Trust. Prev: Lect. Inst. Child Health Lond. & St. Mary's Hosp. Lond.

KLEIN, Richard (retired) Marston Surgery, 9 Cherwell Drive, Oxford OX3 0NB — LRCPI & LM, LRSCI & LM 1969; LRCPI & LM, LRCSI & LM 1969. Prev: Ho. Phys. Mercer's Hosp. Dub.

KLEIN, Stephanie Corner Surgery, 99 Coldharbour Lane, London SE5 9NS (Stactetaven, Berlin 1989)

KLEIN, Valerie Helen 67 Corve Street, Ludlow SY8 1DU Tel: 01584 872669 — MB BS Lond. 1967. (U.C.H.M.S.)

KLEINBERG, Judith Eveline Flat 20 Eagles Nest, Butterstile Lane, Prestwick, Manchester M25 9PP Tel: 0161 773 9441 — MB ChB 1965 Manch. (Manch.) SCMO Salford AHA (T).

KLEINBERG, Karl 38 Roseneath Road, London SW11 6AQ Tel: 020 7223 2417 — MB ChB 1934 Ed. (Ed.) Prev: Clin. Asst. St. Thos. Hosp. Lond.; Clin. Asst. Edin. Roy. Infirm.; Mem. Recruiting Med. Bds. Liverp.

KLEINBERG, Sharon Ruth 21 High Mount, Station Rd, London NW4 3SS Email: shazbaz@hernia.org — MB BS 1996 Lond. (Lond.)

KLEINGLASS, Albert Harold 17 Arnside Avenue, Giffnock, Glasgow G46 7QQ — MB ChB 1956 Glas. (Glas.)

KLEINMAN, Ronald Louis Bickersteth House, 31 Grove Place, London NW3 1JS Tel: 020 7435 5313 — MB ChB Cape Town 1949; DObst RCOG 1953. (Cape Town) Socs: Med. Jl.ists' Assn. Prev: Med. Edr. for Internat. Planned Parenthood Federat.; Med. Edr. Med. Digest; Asst. Edr. S. Afr. Med. Jl.

KLEMPERER, Frances Jane Speedwell Clinic, 62 Speedwell St., London SE8 4AT Tel: 020 8691 4535 Fax: 020 8691 4537 Email: 100576.311@compuserve.com; Email: frances.klemperer@virgin.net — MB BS 1984 Lond.; MA Camb. 1984; MRCPsych 1989. Cons. Psychiat. in Gen. Adult Psychiat., Brent Kew Ment. Health, Lond.

KLENERMAN, Professor Leslie (retired) Pentre Garth, Llwynmawr, Pontfadog, Llangollen LL20 7BG Tel: 01691 718326 Fax: 01691 718326 Email: klenerman@btinternet.com — MB BCh Witwatersrand 1951; ChM Witwatersrand 1973; FRCS Ed. 1957; FRCS Eng. 1957. Assoc. Edr. Brit. Jl. Bone & Jt. Surg. Prev: Prof. Orthop. Surg. Univ. Liverp.

KLENERMAN, Paul 3 Rivercourt, 1 Trinity St., Oxford OX1 1TQ; Nuffield Department of Medicine, John Radcliffe Hospital, Oxford OX3 9DU Tel: 01865 221348 Fax: 01865 220993 Email: paul.klenerman@ndm.ox.ac.uk — BM BCh 1988 Oxf.; DPhil Oxf. 1995; BA Camb. 1985; MRCP (UK) 1991. Research Fell. Nuffield Dept. of Med. John Radcliffe Hosp. Oxf.; Research Fell. (Experim. Immunol.) Univ. Hosp. Zurich. Prev: Regist. (Infec. Dis.) Ch.ill Hosp. Oxf.

KLENKA, Helena Marketa Child Development Centre, St. Catherine's Hospital, Church Road, Birkenhead CH42 0LQ Tel: 0151 678 5111 Fax: 0151 604 7311; 19 Long Meadow, Heswall, Wirral CH60 8QQ Tel: 0151 342 3066 Fax: 0151 604 7310 Email: klenka@dial.pipex.com — MUDr Prague 1968; FRCP Lond. 1995; FRCPCH Lond. 1997; DCH RCP Lond. 1977. (Charles University Prague) Cons. Paediat. (Child Health) St. Catherine's Hosp. Birkenhead.

KLENKA, Lucie Helena 19 Long Meadow, Wirral CH60 8QQ Tel: 0151 342 3066 — MB ChB 1993 Birm.; MRCPsych. 1998. (Birmingham) Adult Gen. Psych.

KLENKA, Zdenek Richard 19 Long Meadow, Heswall, Wirral CH60 8QQ Tel: 0151 342 3066 — MUDr 1968 Charles Univ. Prague; MUDr Charles Univ. 1968; FRCR 1977; DMRD Liverp. 1973. (Charles Univ. Prague) Cons. Radiol. Mersey RHA.

KLENTZERIS, Loukas Dimitrios Cardiff Assisted Reproduction Unit, University Hospital of Wales, Heath Park, Cardiff CF5 2LP Tel: 02920743047; Akropolis, 9 The Avenue, Llandaff, Cardiff CF5 2LP Tel: 029 2055 3657 — Ptychio Iatrikes 1981 Athens; MD Sheff. 1992; MRCOG 1988; T(OG) 1994; FRCOG 2000. (Athens) Cons. Gyn./ Dir. of Cardiff Assisted Reproduc. Unit Univ. Hosp. Wales. Socs: Brit. Fertil. Soc.; Blair Bell Research Soc.; ESHRE. Prev: Sen. Lect. & Cons. O & G Univ. Warwick - Walsgrave Hosp. Coventry; Lect. & Sen. Regist. (O & G) Qu. Med. Centre Nottm.; Research Fell. (Reproductive Med.) Univ. Sheff. - Jessop. Hosp.

KLEYN, Christine Elizabeth C/O Medacs Professional Recruitment, The Old Surgery, 49 Otley St., Skipton BD23 1ET — MB ChB 1996 Cape Town.

KLIDJIAN, Mr Alan Michael Taunton and Somerset NHS Trust, Musgrove Park Hospital, Taunton TA1 5DA; 5 Cedar Falls, Bishops Lydeard, Taunton TA4 3HR — MB BS 1972 Lond.; MS Lond. 1983; FRCS Eng. 1977; MRCS Eng. LRCP Lond. 1972. (St. Bart.) Cons. Surg. & Gen. Paediat. Surg. Taunton & Som. NHS Trust. Socs: Brit. Assn. Surg. Oncol.; Brit. Assn. Paediat. Surg. Prev: Cons. Surg. Solihull Hosp.; Sen. Regist. (Surg.) Leics. Gen. Hosp.; Regist. (Surg.) & Resid. Fell. Soton. Gen. Hosp.

KLIDJIAN, Mr Arsene (retired) 2 The Orchard, Broome Manor, Swindon SN3 1NG — MB BS 1942 Lond.; FRCS Eng. 1946; MRCS

Eng. LRCP Lond. 1941. Prev: Surg. Regist. Roy. Waterloo Hosp. Wom. & Childr.

KLIJNSMA, Marinus Peter 41 St James Drive, London SW17 7RN — Artsexamen 1986 Groningen; MRCPsych 1992.

KLIM, Edward Andrew The Surgery, Sydenham House, Mill Court, Ashford TN24 8DN Tel: 01233 645851 Fax: 01233 638281; Yew Tree House, 150 Faversham Road, Kennington, Ashford TN24 9DE — MB BS 1991 Lond.; BSc (Hons.) Lond. 1987; MRCGP 1995. (Univ. Coll.)

KLIMACH, Mr Otto Erwin Fron Deg, Marian, Trelawnyd, Rhyl LL18 6EB Tel: 01745 570173 — MB BS 1975 Newc.; MD 1982; FRCS Eng. 1980. Cons. Surg. Glan Clwyd Hosp. Bodelwyddan.

KLIMACH, Valerie Jean Colwyn Bay Hospital, Hesketh Road, Colwyn Bay LL29 8AY Tel: 01492 807503 Fax: 01492 518103 Email: val.klimach@cd-tr.wales.nhs.uk; Fron Deg, Marian, Treldwnyd, Flintshire, Rhyl LL18 6EB Tel: 01745 570173 Email: oandv.klimach/pop.virgin.net — MB ChB 1979 Manch.; MB ChB 1979 (Hons) Manch.; BSc (Hons.) Manch. 1976. MD 1987; FRCP Lond. 1995; MRCP (UK) 1982; FRCPCH 1997. (Manchester) p/t Cons. Paediat. (Community Child Health) Colwyn Bay Hosp. (p/t). Prev: Cons. Paediat. (Community Child Health) S. Manch.; Sen. Regist. (Paediat.) NW RHA & Clwyd HA.

KLIMEK, Jan Vaclav 94 Iliffe Street, London SE17 3LL — MB ChB 1988 Cape Town.

KLIMIUK, Peter Stanley The Royal Oldham Hospital, Rochdale Road, Oldham OL1 2JH Tel: 0161 627 8490 Fax: 0161 627 8474 — MB ChB 1973 Bristol; FRCP Lond. 1994; MRCP (UK) 1976. Cons. Phys. Roy. Oldham Hosp. Socs: Fell. Manch. Med. Soc.; Brit. Soc. Rheum. Prev: Sen. Regist. Rheum. Dis. Centre. Hope Hosp. Salford; Lect., Regist. & SHO Univ. Dept. Med. Manch. Roy. Infirm.

KLINCK, John Rutherford Department of Anaesthesia, Box 93, Addenbrooke's Hospital, Hills Road, Cambridge CB2 2QQ Tel: 01223 217434 — MDCM McGill Univ. Canada 1976; FRCPC 1984; FRCA 1982. Cons. Anaesth. Addenbrooke's Hosp. Camb.

KLOCKE, Rainer Department of Rheumatology, Walsgrove Hospital, Coventry CV2 2DX; 55 Mickleton Road, Earlsdon, Coventry CV5 6PP — State Exam Med 1991 Hanover; State Exam Hanover 1991; MRCP (UK) 1996. Regist. (Gen. Med.) Walsgrave Hosp. Coventry.

KLOER, Joan Underwood Surgery, 139 St. Georges Road, Cheltenham GL50 3EQ Tel: 01242 580644 Fax: 01242 253519; 78 Painswick Road, Cheltenham GL50 2EU Tel: 01242 584339 — MB ChB 1965 Manch.; DObst RCOG 1967. GP Cheltenham. Prev: Clin. Med. Off. (Child Health) Glos. AHA; SHO (O & G) Walton Hosp. Liverp.; Ho. Phys. Walton Hosp. Liverp.

KLOER, Mary Joanne 78 Painswick Road, Cheltenham GL50 2EU — MB BS 1995 Lond.

KLOER, Philip John 78 Painswick Road, Cheltenham GL50 2EU — MB BCh 1995 Wales. (Univ. Wales Coll. Med.) SHO Rotat. (Med.) Morriston Hosp. Swansea. Socs: Med. Defence Union; BMA.

KLONIN, Hilary 53 Balfour Road, Lenton, Nottingham NG7 1NY — MB BS 1982 Nottm.; MRCP (UK) 1986; DA (UK) 1987.

KLOPPER, Anthea Donay Highview, 20 Southgate Road, Potters Bar EN6 5DZ Tel: 01707 53866; 40 The Fairway, Southgate, London N14 4NY Tel: 020 8441 6236 — MB ChB 1983 Cape Town; MRCGP 1989; DA (UK) 1988; DCH RCP Lond. 1987. Med. Off. Qu.swood Sch.

KLOPPER, Arnoldus Ilardus Department of Obstetrics & Gynaecology, Royal Infirmary, Aberdeen AB39 3TP Tel: 01569 730213; Sea Cottage, Newtonhill, Stonehaven AB3 2PU — MD 1965 Witwatersrand; PhD Ed. 1957; BSc Witwatersrand 1943, MD 1965, MB BCh 1946; FRCOG 1964, M 1952. (Witwatersrand) Emerit. Prof. of Reproduc. Endocrinol. Univ. Aberd.; Hon. Cons. Gyn. & Obstetr. Aberd. Roy. Infirm. Socs: Soc. Endocrinol. & Scott. Soc. Experim. Med. Prev: on Permanent Scientif. Staff Med. Research Counc.; Jun Regist. Roy. Postgrad. Med. Sch. Lond.; Clin. Research Fell. Med. Research Counc.

KLOS, Anna Maria 66 Blenheim Gardens, Wallington SM6 9PS — MB BS 1984 Lond.

KLOSOK, Mr Jan Kazimierz 61 Perrymead Street, Fulham, London SW6 3SN — MB BS 1973 Lond.; FRCS Eng. 1983; MRCS Eng. LRCP Lond. 1972. Cons. Orthop. Surg. Newham HA, Lond. Indep. Hosp. & Lister Hosp. Lond. Socs: Fell. Brit. Orthop. Assn.; Brit. Orthop. Research Soc. Prev: Sen. Regist. (Orthop.) Hammersmith Hosp. Lond.; Regist. (Orthop.) Roy. Nat. Orthop. Hosp. & Qu. Eliz. II Hosp. Welwyn Garden City.

KLOUDA, Anthony Thomas 32 Countess Road, London NW5 2XJ Tel: 020 7267 5625 Fax: 020 7267 5625 Email: anthonyk@aklouda.demon.co.uk — BM BCh 1974 Oxf.; MA Oxf. 1974. (Oxf.) Regional Health Adviser - Africa - CAREInternat. Prev: Manager Sexual Health Project Internat. Planned Parenthood Federat. Lond.; PHC Co-ordinator, Private Hosp. Assn., Malawai; Med. Adviser Oxfam, Tanzania.

KLUENDER, Olaf Stafford District General Hospital, Weston Road, Stafford ST16 3SA — State Exam Med 1993 Essen.

KLUENKER, Christiane Erna Margrid Department of Ophthalmology, West Norwich Hospital, Bowthorpe Road, Norwich NR2 3TU Tel: 01603 286286 Fax: 01603 288261 — State Exam Med 1990 Hannover; State Exam Med. Hannover 1990; MRCOphth 1994. (Hannover) Clin. Ophth. Norf. & Norwich Health Care Trust.

KLUGE, Georg Heinrich c/o Dr J. Baines, 37 Forrestburn Court, Monkscourt Avenue, Airdrie ML6 0JS — State Exam Med. Wurzburg 1991.

KLUGMAN, Mr David Julian Oakbank, 2 Tanners Hill, Hythe CT21 5UE — MB BCh 1961 Witwatersrand; FRCS Eng. 1970. (Witwatersrand) Cons. Orthop. Surg. Canterbury & Thanet, & E. Kent Health Dist. Prev: Sen. Orthop. Regist. King's Coll. Hosp. Lond.; on Staff BrE. Clinic Guy's Hosp. Lond.

KLUKOWSKI, Andrzej Krzysztof 12 Leopold Street, Derby DE1 2HE Tel: 01332 364361 — Lekarz 1965 Warsaw.

KLUTH, David Charles 18 Argyll Place, Aberdeen AB25 2EL — MB BS 1989 Lond.; MRCP (UK) 1992. Regist. (Med.) Ashford Hosp. Middlx.

KLYNMAN, Nicole Luise Flat 3, 16 Craven Terrace, London W2 3QD — MB BS 1993 Lond.

KMIOT, Mr Witold Andrew Directorate of surg, 1st Floor, North Wing, St Thomas' Hosp, Lambeth Palace Road, London SE1 7EH Tel: 0207 928 9292 Ext: 2997 — MB BS 1983 Lond.; MS Lond. 1991; FRCS 1993; FRCS Eng. 1987. (Westminster med sch London) Cons surg Guy's & St Thomas' Hosp trust Lond. Socs: Assn. Coloproctol. (GB & Irel.); Assn. Surg.(GB & Irel.). Prev: Cons sen. Lec. Surg. Hammersmith hosp Lond.; Cons surg. Centr. Middlx. hosp Lond.

KNAGGS, Geoffrey Stewart (retired) 222 Hyde End Road, Spencers Wood, Reading RG7 1DG Tel: 0118 988 5783 — MB BS 1980 Lond.; BSc Sheff. 1961; PhD Reading 1966.

KNAGGS, Terence William Liley (retired) 18 Tremaine Close, Hartside, Hartlepool TS27 3LE Tel: 01429 276071 — MB BS 1954 Durh.; DPH Newc. 1958. Prev: GP Durh.

KNAPMAN, Anthony Charles The Surgery, 148 Forton Road, Gosport PO12 3HH Tel: 023 9258 3333 Fax: 023 9260 1107 — MB ChB Bristol 1966; DObst RCOG 1968. (Bristol) Socs: BMA. Prev: Ho. Surg. Bristol Roy. Infirm.; Ho. Phys. S.mead Gen. Hosp. Bristol; Ho. Phys. Brighton Childr. Hosp.

KNAPMAN, Fiona Marilyn Mary 46 Woodway, Great Notley Garden Village, Braintree CM7 8JS — MB BS 1990 Lond.

KNAPMAN, John Humphrey Kiltearn Medical Centre, 33 Hospital Street, Nantwich CW5 5RN Tel: 01270 610200 Fax: 01270 610637 — MB BS 1979 Lond.; MRCGP 1983; DRCOG (Middlx.) 1981.

KNAPMAN, Paul Anthony Westminster Coroners Court, 65 Horseferry Road, London SW1P 2ED Tel: 020 7834 6515 — MB BS 1968 Lond.; MRCS Eng. LRCP Lond. 1968; DMJ Soc. Apoth. Lond. 1975. (St. Geo.) HM Coroner Inner W. Lond.; Barrister-at-Law Gray's Inn 1972; Hon. Lect. Med. Jurisprudence to four Lond. Hosp. Med. Schs.; Occasional Charm. Med. Appeal Tribunal & Pres. Ment.; Health Rev. Tribunal. Socs: Med.-Leg. Soc. & Brit. Acad. Foren. Scs. Prev: Vis. Phys. BUPA Med. Centre Lond.; HM Dep. Coroner Inner W. Lond.; SHO St. Geo. Hosp. Lond.

KNAPP, Donald Robert (retired) 23 Cavendish Road E., The Park, Nottingham NG7 1BB — MB ChB 1953 Birm.; FFR 1962; DMRD Eng. 1959. Cons. Radiol. City Hosp. Nottm. Prev: Sen. Regist. (Diag. Radiol.) United Sheff. Hosps.

KNAPP, John Andrew 15 Dutch Barn Close, Chorley PR7 1PR — MB ChB 1986 Manch.; MRCPsych 1992. Cons. Psychiat. for the Elderly Chorley & S. Ribble NHS Trust.

KNAPP, Patricia (retired) 30 River View, Mundella Court, The Embankment, Nottingham NG2 2GF Tel: 0115 986 2838 — MB ChB 1959 Bristol.

KNAPPER, David Orme Morecambe Health Centre, Hanover Street, Morecambe LA4 5LY Tel: 01524 418418 Fax: 01524 832584; 1 Pembroke Avenue, Bare, Morecambe LA4 6EJ Tel: 01524 412295 — MB ChB 1981 Manch.; MRCGP 1985; DRCOG 1983; FRCGP 1997. Clin. Asst. Dept. of Med. for Elderly. Prev: GP Tutor Lancaster.

KNAPPER, Steven 157 Werburgh Drive, Trentham, Stoke-on-Trent ST4 8LF — BM BCh 1996 Oxf.

KNAPPETT, Peter Alister Glenthorne, Lode Pit Lane, Eldwick, Bingley BD16 3AN — MB ChB 1972 Leeds; MBA Bradford 1992; FFA RCS Eng. 1979; DA Eng. 1975; DObst RCOG 1974. Cons. Anaesth. Roy. Infirm. Bradford. Socs: BMA & Assn. Anaesth. Prev: Sen. Regist. (Anaesth.) St. Mary's Hosp. Lond.; SHO (Clin. Measurem.) W.m. Hosp. Lond.

KNAPTON, Alexander Hilltop, Idmiston Road, Porton, Salisbury SP4 0LB — MB BS 1984 Lond.; MA Oxf. 1984, BA Oxf. 1981.

KNAPTON, John Riversdale Surgery, 51 Woodcroft Road, Wylam NE41 8DH Tel: 01661 852208 Fax: 01661 853779; Greenhaugh, West Road, Ovingham, Prudhoe NE42 6BN Tel: 01661 832614 — MB BS 1983 Newcastle; AFOM 2000; DFFP 1990; Dip. Obst. Otago New Zealand 1988. (Newcastle) GP Wylam, N.d.; Med. Off. Boots Co plc; Med. Adviser SCA Hyg. Produtcs Ltd. Socs: Soc. of Occupat.al Med.; Assoc. of Fac. of Occupat.al Med.

KNAPTON, Paul Michael 94 Shelford Road, Trumpington, Cambridge CB2 2NF Tel: 01223 844517 Fax: 01223 844517 Email: pmknapton@bigfoot.com — MB BChir 1982 Camb.; MA 1984 Camb.; FRCGP 2001; DRCOG 1985. (Camb.) GP Tutor Addenbrooke's Hosp. Postgrad Centre.; VTS Course Organiser Camb.; Clin. Asst. (Cardiol.) Addenbrooke's Hosp.; Chairm. Camb. City PCT.

KNAUSENBERGER, Hans-Peter 12 Hemyock Road, Selly Oak, Birmingham B29 4DG — State Exam Med 1993 Tubingen.

KNEAFSEY, Reginald William 261 Harlestone Road, Northampton NN5 6DD Tel: 01604 52049 — LRCPI & LM, LRSCI & LM 1957; LRCPI & LM, LRCSI & LM 1957.

KNEALE, Barbara Nicola PSA Peugeot Citroen, Ryton Plant, London Rd, Ryton CV8 3DZ — MB ChB 1988 Liverp.; MFOM 2000; MRCGP 1994; DRCOG 1992. Manager Occupat.al Health & Safety.

KNEALE, Barry James St. Thomas' Hospital, London SE1 7EH — MB BS 1988 Lond.; BA (Hons.) Oxf. 1985; MRCP (UK) 1991. Regist. (Cardiol.) St. Thos. Hosp. Lond. Prev: Regist. (Cardiol.) Poole Hosp. NHS Trust.

KNEALE, Eleanor Mary (retired) 13 Kirkton Crescent, Milton of Campsie, Glasgow G66 8DP — LRCP LRCS 1953 Ed.; LRCP LRCS Ed. LRFPS Glas. 1953. Prev: Asst. Med. Off. Blood Transfus. Serv. W. Scotl. Region.

KNEATH, Anthony Carlyle Tel: 01843 593252 Fax: 01483 850817; Villa Cap Martin, 7 Callis Court Road, Broadstairs CT10 3AE Tel: 01843 865736 — MB BS 1969 Lond.; MRCS Eng. LRCP Lond. 1969. (Lond. Hosp.)

KNECHTLI, Christopher John Cranstoun Department of Haematology, Royal Units Hospital, Combe Park, Bath BA1 3NG Tel: 01225 428331 Fax: 01225 461044 Email: christopher.knechtli@ruh-bath.somerset.nhs.uk — MB ChB 1988 Bristol; MRCP (UK) 1991; MRCPath 1999; PhD 2000 Bristol. Cons. Hematologist, Roy. United Hosp., Bath. Socs: Brit. Soc. Haematol. Prev: Specialist Regist. Rotat. (Haemat.) Bristol & Bath Haemat.; Research Fell. (Paediat. Haemat.) Bristol Childr.'s Hosp.; SHO (Med.) Medway & Swindon HA's.

KNEE, Graham Department of Histopathology, Kingston NHS Trust, Galsworthy Road, Kingston upon Thames KT2 7QB Tel: 020 8934 2239 Fax: 020 8934 3288 — MB BS 1986 Lond.; MRCPath. 1994. (St Georges Hospital Medical School) Cons. Histopath. & Cytopath. Kingston NHS Trust. Prev: Sen. Regist. (Histopath.) St. Geo. Hosp. Med. Sch. Lond.; Regist. (Histopath.) Qu. Mary's Univ. Hosp. Roehampton Lond. & Roy. Marsden Hosp. Sutton.

KNEEBONE, Carol Ann Dean Street Surgery, 8 Dean Street, Liskeard PL14 4AQ Tel: 01579 343133 Fax: 01579 344933 — MB ChB 1989 Leic.; BSc (Hons.) Lond. 1983; MRCGP 1995.

KNEEBONE, John Michael (retired) 9 Belgrave Road, Luton LU4 9AR Tel: 01582 573655 — MB BS 1954 Lond.

KNEEBONE, Mr Roger Lister Lovemead Group Practice, Roundstone Surgery, Polebarn Circus, Trowbridge BA14 7EH Tel: 01225 752752 Fax: 01225 776388; 36 Hilperton Road, Trowbridge BA14 7JG Tel: 01225 768787 — MB ChB 1977 Manch.; FRCS Eng. 1986; FRCS Ed. 1985; MRCGP 1987; DRCOG 1981. Prev: Trainee GP Lichfield; Regist. (Surgic.) Groote Schuur Hosp., Cape Town & Baragwanath Hosp. Johannesburg; SHO (O & G) Nottm. HA.

KNEEN, Jacqueline Ann 37 Croft Road, Poulner, Ringwood BH24 1TG — MB ChB 1978 Liverp.; DRCOG 1980.

KNEEN, Lesley Celia 41 Innage Lane, Bridgnorth WV16 4HS — MB BS 1982 Lond.; BSc Ed. 1977; MRCGP 1986; DRCOG 1985. p/t Sen. Community Med. Off., Community Paediat., Shrops.; Clin. Asst., Ophth. Dept., Roy. Shrewsbury Hosp., Shrewsbury. Socs: MRCPCH; MRCGP.

KNEEN, Margaret 15 Higher Brook Park, Ivybridge PL21 9UA Tel: 01752 690013 — MB BS 1954 Lond.; MRCS Eng. LRCP Lond. 1954. (King's Coll. Hosp.)

KNEEN, Rachel Wellcome Trust Clinical Research Unit, Centre for Tropical Diseases, Cho Quân Hospital, Hoo Chi Minh City, Vietnam; 12 Albany Road, Peel — BM BS 1991 Nottm.; MRCP (UK) 1994; DCH RCP Lond. 1994. Wellcome Trust Clin. Research Regist. (Paediat. Infec. Dis.) Centre for Trop. Dis. Cho Quân Hosp. Vietnam.

KNEEN, Robert Christopher Beresford Saltash Health Centre, Callington Road, Saltash PL12 6DL Tel: 01752 842281 Fax: 01752 844651; 29 Essa Road, Saltash PL12 4EE — MB BS 1979 Lond.; MRCGP 1987; DRCOG 1982.

KNEESHAW, John David Department of Anaesthesia, Papworth Hospital, Papworth Everard, Cambridge CB3 8RE Tel: 01480 830541 — MB ChB 1976 Bristol; FRCA 1981. Cons. Anaesth. Papworth Hosp. Camb. Prev: Sen. Regist. (Anaesth.) E. Anglia RHA.

KNELL, Alan John 13 Northumberland Road, Leamington Spa CV32 6HE Tel: 01926 424705 Email: ajk@mastigo4.demon.co.uk — MB BChir Camb. 1965; PhD Warwick 1971, MSc 1968; MD Camb. 1983, BA 1961; FRCP Lond. 1980; MRCP (UK) 1970. (Camb. & Guy's) Socs: Brit. Soc. Gastroenterol.; Roy. Soc. Trop. Med. & Hyg. Prev: Sen. Cons. Sultan Qaboos Univ. Hosp. Muscat, Sultanate of Oman; Asst. to Dir. Wellcome Trop. Inst. Lond.; Cons. Phys. S. Warks. Gp. Hosps.

KNELL, Jean Elizabeth Rait (retired) 13 Northumberland Road, Leamington Spa CV32 6HE Tel: 01926 24705 — BA, MB BChir Camb. 1964. Prev: Sen. Regist. (Histopath.) W. Midl. RHA.

KNELL, Patrick John Warren (retired) 173 Moor Lane, Woodford, Stockport SK7 1PF — MB BS 1953 Lond.; FFA RCS Eng. 1960; DA Eng. 1958. Prev: Sen. Regist. United Manch. Hosps.

KNIBB, Aston Andrew Adolphus Department of Anaesthesia, Mayday University Hospital, London Road, Croydon CR7 7YE Tel: 020 8670 6292 Email: aston@webstar.co.uk; 36 Thornlaw Road, West Norwood, London SE27 0SA Tel: 020 8670 6292 Fax: 020 8401 3424 — MB BS 1980 Lond.; FRCA 1987. (Univ. Coll. Hosp.) Cons. Anaesth. Mayday Univ. Hosp. Lond. Socs: Assn. Anaesth. & Pain Soc.; Afr. & Caribbean Med. Soc. Prev: Cons. Anaesth. S.end Hosp.; Sen. Regist. (Anaesth.) Kings Coll. Hosp. Lond.; Regist. (Anaesth.) Guy's Hosp. Lond.

KNICKENBERG, Christel Joan Haymills, Kenilworth Road, Hampton-in-Arden, Solihull B92 0LW — MB ChB 1973 Manch.; FFA RCS Eng. 1980; DA Eng. 1975. (Manchester) Socs: Vasc. Anaesth. Soc.; Birm. Med. Research & Expeditionary Soc. Prev: Cons. Walsgrave Univ. Hosps. Trust; Sen. Regist. Birm. Rotat.; Cons. Anaesth. Coventry HA.

KNIFTON-SMITH, Howard c/o Milton House, The Square, Wensley, Matlock DE4 2LJ — MB ChB 1990 Sheff.

KNIGHT, Alexandra Marian Bulling Lane Surgery, Bulling Lane, Crich, Matlock DE4 5DX Tel: 01773 852966 Fax: 01773 853919; South View, The Common, Crich, Matlock DE4 5BJ Tel: 01773 857236 — MB ChB 1979 Leeds. (Leeds) p/t Gen. Pract.

KNIGHT, Amanda Jane 80 Gwendoline Drive, Countesthorpe, Leicester LE8 5SF — MB ChB 1993 Leic.

KNIGHT, Andrew Charles Child & Family Service, Lawnside, Olinda St., Rhyl LL18 3EP Tel: 01745 330881 — MB BCh 1971 Wales; MRCPsych 1977. Cons. Child & Family Serv. Rhyl. Prev: Cons. Regional Young Peoples Centre Chester.

KNIGHT, Andrew Leslie Marches Surgery, Westfield Walk, Leominster HR6 8HD Tel: 01568 614141 Fax: 01568 610293 — MB BS 1987 Lond.; MRCGP 1993; DFFP 1994; DCH RCP Lond. 1992.

KNIGHT, Anna Clare Holly Ct, Summerlands, 56 Preston Road, Yeovil BA20 2BN Tel: 01935 428420 — MB BChir 1978 Camb.; MA 1979 Camb.; MRCPsych. 1984. (Cambridge) Cons. Psychiat. Avalon Trust Yeovil. Prev: Sen. Regist. (Gen. Psychiat.) Som.

KNIGHT, Anthony Harrington Stoke Mandeville Hospital NHS Trust, mandeville Road, Aylesbury HP21 8AL Tel: 01296 315533 Fax: 01296 315538; The Old Vicarage, 101 Aylesbury Road, Bierton, Aylesbury HP22 5BT — MB BS Lond. 1963; FRCP Lond. 1980, M 1968; MRCS Eng. LRCP Lond. 1963. (St. Bart.) Cons. Phys. Stoke Mandeville Hosp. Bucks. Socs: Diabetes UK (Ex-Chairm. Educat. & Profess. Care Sect.). Prev: Sen. Regist. (Med.) Roy. Hosp. Sheff.; Regist. (Med.) Roy. Free Hosp. Lond.; Ho. Surg. St. Bart. Hosp. Lond.

KNIGHT, Anthony Overbeck Cureton Shirley Avenue Surgery, 1 Shirley Avenue, Shirley, Southampton SO15 5RP Tel: 023 8077 3258/1356 Fax: 023 8070 3078 — MB BS 1973 Lond.; MRCP (UK) 1978; DCH Eng. 1977.

KNIGHT, Arthur Grice Glamorgan House, BUPA Hospital, Cardiff CF23 8XL Tel: 029 2048 3948; 38 Llanedeyrn Road, Cardiff CF23 9DY Tel: 029 2048 3948 — MD 1973 Sheff.; MB ChB 1964; FRCP Lond. 1986; FRCP Ed. 1984, M 1967. (Sheff.) Cons. Dermat. Univ. Hosp. Wales Cardiff. Prev: Sen. Regist. & Tutor in Path. St. John's Hosp. Dis. of Skin Lond.; Research Fell. Dept. Dermat. Scripps Clinic La Jolla, U.S.A.

KNIGHT, Professor Bernard Henry, CBE Wales Institute of Forensic Medicine, University of Wales College of Medicine, Royal Infirmary, Cardiff CF2 1SZ Tel: 029 2048 4358 Fax: 029 2048 4358; 26 Millwood, Cardiff CF14 0TL — MD 1966 Wales; MB BCh 1954; FRCPath 1976, M 1964; MRCP (UK) 1984; DMJ Soc. Apoth. Lond. 1967. Prof. Forens. Path. Univ. of Wales Coll. of Med. Cardiff; Hon. Cons. Path. S. Glam. HA; Home Office Path.; Mem. Home Off. Policy Advis. Bd. Forens. Path. Socs: Hon. Fell. Roy. Soc. Med.; Vice-Pres. Internat. Acad. Legal Med. Pres. Forens. Sci. Soc.; Pres. Brit. Assn. Forens. Med. Prev: Sen. Lect. (Forens. Path.) Univ. Newc.; Lect. (Forens. Med.) Welsh Nat. Sch. Med. Cardiff & Lond. Hosp. Med. Coll.

KNIGHT, Carol Mary 15 Beechwood Grove, Belfast BT8 7UR — MB BCh BAO 1982 Dub.; DO RCPSI 1987.

KNIGHT, Caroline Elizabeth Fordingbridge Surgery, Bartons Road, Fordingbridge SP6 1RS Tel: 01425 652123 Fax: 01425 654393; High Hazeley, Frogham Hill, Fordingbridge SP6 2HP — MB BS 1984 Lond.; MRCGP 1990; DRCOG 1989. Prev: Trainee GP Salisbury VTS; Clin. Med. Off. (Child Health) Hants.; SHO (A & E) Winchester.

KNIGHT, Carolyn Jane Marches Surgery, Westfield Walk, Leominster HR6 8HD Tel: 01568 614141 Fax: 01568 610293 — MB BS 1985 New South Wales; MRCP (UK) 1991; MRCGP (Distinc.) 1995; DFFP 1995; DRCOG 1993.

KNIGHT, Catherine (retired) High House, Staunton, Coleford GL16 8NX — MB ChB Liverp. 1967; DObst RCOG 1970.

KNIGHT, Charles James King George's Hospital, Barley Lane, Ilford IG3 8YB Tel: 020 8983 8000 — BM BCh 1988 Oxf.; MA (Camb) 1985; MRCP (Lond) 1991. (Oxford) Cons. Cardiol. King Geo.'s Hosp., Ilford; Cons. Cardiol., Lond. Chest Hosp., Lond. Prev: Sen. Regist., St. Geo.s Hosp., Lond.; Regist., Roy. Brompton Hosp., Lond.

KNIGHT, Charlotte Ann Shere Surgery and Dispensary, Gomshall Lane, Shere, Guildford GU5 9DR Tel: 01486 202066 Fax: 01486 202761; Winter Fold End, Houndhouse Road, Shere, Guildford GU5 9JJ Tel: 01483 203491 — MB BS 1984 Lond.; BSc Lond. 1981; MRCGP 1988; DRCOG 1987.

KNIGHT, Christopher James Bristol Royal Hospital for Sick Children, St. Micheal's Hill, Bristol BS2 8BJ; 59 Springfield Avenue, Horfield, Bristol BS7 9QS Email: 106427.2453@compuserve.com — MB ChB 1990 Birm.; MRCP UK 1996. Specialist Regist. Rotat. (Paediat.) S.-W. Socs: BMA. Prev: SHO Rotat. Bristol; SHO (Paediat.) Jersey & (Paediat. Cardiol.) Soton.; SHO (O & G) Portsmouth.

KNIGHT, Christopher Lloyd Department of Anaesthesia, City General Hsopital, Newcastle Road, Stoke-on-Trent ST4 6QG; 42 Sutherland Drive, Newcastle ST5 3NZ Tel: 01782 632624 — MB BS 1971 Lond.; BSc (Hons.) Lond. 1968, MB BS 1971; FFA RCS Eng. 1976. (St. Thos.) Cons. Anaesth. Pain Managem. N. Staffs. Hosps. Socs: Pain Soc.; IASP. Prev: Sen. Regist. (Anaesth.) Addenbrooke's Hosp. Camb.; Regist. (Anaesth.) W.m. Hosp. Lond. & Nat. Heart Hosp. Lond.

KNIGHT, Mr David Gerard St Anne's, Monorgan, Longforgan, Dundee DD2 5HT — MB ChB 1975 Glas.; FRCS Glas. 1979.

KNIGHT, David Graham Barnabas Medical Centre, Girton Road, Northolt UB5 4SQ; 32A Eastcote Lane, Harrow HA2 8BS Tel: 020 8864 6549 — MB BS 1981 Lond.; DRCOG 1986.

KNIGHT, Mr David James Department Orthopaedics, Woodend Hospital, Aberdeen AB15 6ZQ Tel: 01224 681818 Fax: 01224 556376; 47 Braemar Place, Aberdeen AB10 6EN Tel: 01224 574120 Email: d.j.knight@abdn.ac.uk — MB ChB 1978 Aberd.; FRCS Ed. (Orth.) 1988; FRCS Glas. 1982. (University of Aberdeen) Cons. Orthop. Surg. Aberd. Teach. Hosps.; Hon. Clin. Lect. Univ. Aberd. Socs: Fell. BOA; Comm. Christian Med. Fell.sh. Prev: Sen. Regist. (Orthop.) Aberd. Hosps.; Regist. (Orthop.) Glas. Roy. Infirm.

KNIGHT, David John William 137 Swallow Lane, Golcar, Huddersfield HD7 4NB — MB ChB 1994 Leeds.

KNIGHT, David Kenneth Sawyer Church Grange Health Centre, Bramblys Drive, Basingstoke RG21 8QN Tel: 01256 329021 Fax: 01256 817466; 5 Monk Sherborne Road, Ramsaell, Tadley RG26 5RA Tel: 01256 889292 Email: dajeberu@compucie.com — MB BS 1982 Lond.; BSc (Hons.) 1979; MRCP (UK) 1985; MRCGP 1990; DCH 1988. Prev: SHO (Paediat.) Qu. Mary's Hosp. Sidcup; Regist. (Haemat.) Kings Coll. Hosp. Lond.; SHO (Med.) Rotat. Roy. Free Hosp. Lond.

KNIGHT, David Paul (retired) Rosebank Surgery, 153B Stroud Road, Gloucester GL1 5JQ Tel: 01452 522767 — MB ChB 1979 Bristol; BSc (Hons.) Bacteriol. Birm. 1973; DRCOG 1982. GP Gloucester. Prev: SHO (O & G, Paediat. & Med.) Gloucester Roy. Hosp.

KNIGHT, Diana Rosemary (retired) Northbank House, 12 Manor Road, Spratton, Northampton NN6 8HN — MB BS 1958 Lond.; FRCPsych 1991, M 1972; DPM Eng. 1968; DA Eng. 1960. Med. Adviser Nursing Home Insp.ate N.amptonshire HA. Prev: Cons. Neuropsychiat. N.ants. Gen. Hosp.

KNIGHT, Dominique Marietta Andrea 42 Frankfield Rise, Tunbridge Wells TN2 5LF — MB BS 1997 Lond.

KNIGHT, Donald Nalderswood Cottage, Dean Oak Lane, Leigh, Reigate RH2 8PZ Tel: 01293 862251 — MB BCh 1961 Wales. Cons. (A & E) E. Surrey Hosp. Redhill. Socs: Mem. Brit. Assoc. of A & E Med.; Fell. Of Fac. of A & E Med.; Fell. RSM. Prev: Asst. Orthop. Surg. Redhill Gen. Hosp.; Ho. Surg. Roy. Gwent Hosp. Newport; Ho. Phys. & Cas. Off. St. Jas. Hosp. Tredegar.

KNIGHT, Edward James 38 Parkside Drive, Watford WD17 3AX — MB ChB 1960 Birm.; FRCP Lond. 1983, M 1967. Cons. Gen. Phys. & Cardiol. Watford Gen. Hosp.; Cons. Cardiol. Harefield Hosp.; Hon. Clin. Tutor Char. Cross & W.m. Hosps. Socs: Brit. Cardiac Soc. Prev: Regist. Univ. Coll. Hosp. Lond.; Sen. Med. Regist. Roy. Free & Harefield Hosps.

KNIGHT, Elizabeth 1 Canon Drive, Barnack, Stamford PE9 3EG Tel: 01780 740347 — MB BS 1962 Lond.; MRCS Eng. LRCP Lond. 1962; DCH Eng. 1965. (St. Bart.) Prev: Asst. Med. Off. Lond. Boro. Barnet; SHO (Paediat. & Med.) Bedford Gen. Hosp.; Ho. Phys. (Paediat.) Childr. Annexe Luton & Dunstable Hosp.

KNIGHT, Ellen Dunn Rosebank, Newry Road, Banbridge BT32 3HP Tel: 028 4062 2227 — MB BCh BAO 1952 Belf. Dept. Med. Off. S.. Health & Social Servs. Bd. Banbridge. Socs: Fell. Ulster Med. Soc.; Assoc. RCGP. Prev: GP Broughshane Co. Antrim; Resid. Med. Off. Roy. Vict. Hosp. Belf. & Roy. Matern. Hosp. Belf.

KNIGHT, Emma 173 Cornhill Dr, Aberdeen AB16 5HN — MB ChB 1997 Aberd.

KNIGHT, Esther Rachel Apartment 4, 1486 Commonwealth Avenue, Brighton MA 02135, USA; c/o 12 Marquis Court, Anglesea Road, Kingston upon Thames KT1 2EN — MB BS 1990 Lond. Boston Univ. Psychiat. Resid. Program.

KNIGHT, Fiona Jean, MBE Locks Hill Surgery, 95 Locks Hill, Frome BA11 1NG Tel: 01373 454446 Fax: 01373 454447; Fernleigh House, High St, Nunney, Frome BA11 4LZ Tel: 01373 836487 — MB BCh 1980 Wales; MRCGP 1985; DAvMed 1993; DFFP 1994; DRCOG 1986. GP Princip. Prev: RAF Med. Off.

KNIGHT, Francis Robert Stanley Little Causey, Ewhurst Road, Cranleigh GU6 7EA Tel: 01483 274580 — MB BS 1948 Lond.; LMSSA Lond. 1944. (Guy's) Prev: Ho. Phys. Guy's Hosp.

KNIGHT, Frederick Donald Wills (retired) The Orchard, Higher Lane, Egloshayle, Wadebridge PL27 6HW Tel: 01208 815 8879 — MRCS Eng. LRCP Lond. 1937. Prev: Cas. Off. & Resid. Anaesth. Metrop. Hosp. Lond.

KNIGHT, Glenys Bideford Medical Centre, Abbotsham Road, Bideford EX39 3AF Tel: 01237 476363 Fax: 01237 423351; Furlong Farm House, Littleham, Bideford EX39 5HL — MB ChB 1985 Glas.; MRCGP 1989.

KNIGHT, Graham 45 Turves Green, Birmingham B31 4AH — MB ChB 1976 Birm.

KNIGHT, Gwendoline Dorothy (retired) 10 Greyfriars Avenue, Hereford HR4 0BE Tel: 01432 265223 — MRCS Eng. LRCP Lond. 1933; MRCPsych 1973; DPM Leeds 1937. Prev: Cons. Psychiat. Child Guid. Clinic, Newport, I. of Wight.

KNIGHT, Hans-Peter Frederick Department of Anaesthetics, West Dorset Hospital Trust, Dorchester DT1 2JY Tel: 01305 251150; 40 Saxon Leas, Winterslow, Salisbury SP5 1RW Tel: 01980 862837 — MB BS 1978 Lond. Staff Anaesth. W. Dorset Hosps. Trust. Prev: Sen. Regist. King Edwd. VIII Hosp. Durban, Natal.

KNIGHT, Heather Christine (retired) Burgh House, Burgh Hill, Hurst Green, Etchingham TN19 7PE Tel: 01580 860210 Fax: 01580 860210 — MB BS Lond. 1961; BSc Lond. 1956; MRCS Eng. LRCP Lond. 1961; DCH Eng. 1966; DObst RCOG 1966. Apptd. Med. Pract. Benefits Agency Med. Serv. Prev: GP Cranbrook.

KNIGHT, Heather Mary Louise 21 Fordington Avenue, Winchester SO22 5AN Fax: 01962 627541 — MB BChir 1994 Camb. Specialist Regist. (Anaesth.) Wessex.

KNIGHT, Ian Jason Ash Park Farm, Burgh Hill Road, Whitesmith, Lewes BN8 6JF — MB BS 1996 Lond. Basic Surg. Rotat. Medway Hosp. Kent. Socs: BMA; MDU.

KNIGHT, Jacqueline 67 St James Street, Wetherby LS22 6RS Tel: 01937 585669 — MB BS 1980 Newc.; DRCOG 1983.

KNIGHT, James William Dept. of Anaesthesia, Southampton Gen Hospital, Southampton; Little Morton, Tile Barn Lane, Brockenhurst SO42 7UE — MB BS 1993 Lond. Sen. Regist. (Anaesth.) Wessex Rotat.

KNIGHT, Jane Cree Department of Public Health, University of Aberdeen, Medical School, Polcoarth Building, Foresterhill, Aberdeen AB25 2ZD Tel: 01224 553802 — MB ChB 1976 Manch.; MFPHM 2000; MPH Dundee 1996; BSc St. And. 1973. Sen. Clin. Epidemiologist, Aberd. Univ. & Med. Adviser to Scott. Food Standards Agency Aberd.; Hon. Research Fell. Univ. Dundee. Prev: Sen. Regist. (Pub. Health Med.) Tayside HB.

KNIGHT, Janet Elizabeth Lynmore Cottage, 23 Norwich Road, Lingwood, Norwich NR13 4BH Tel: 01603 715657 — MB ChB 1987 Manch.; BSc (Med. Sci) St. And. 1984; FRCOphth 1995. Clin. Ophth. W. Norwich Hosp. Prev: SHO (A & E) Bolton Roy. Infirm.; SHO Rotat. (Surg.) Roy. Preston Hosp.; SHO (Orthop.) Bolton Roy. Infirm.

KNIGHT, Janet Rachel Tel: 01978 860625 Fax: 01978 860174 — MB BCh 1989 Wales; MRCGP 1993; DRCOG 1992. Prev: Trainee GP Wrexham VTS.

KNIGHT, Mr Jeffrey Robert Mayday Healthcare Trust, London Road, Thornton Heath, Croydon CR7 7YE Tel: 020 8401 3327 Fax: 020 8401 3339 — MB ChB 1975 Sheff.; FRCS Eng. 1981. Cons. ENT Surg. & Neuro-Otologist Mayday Healthcare Trust Croydon & St. Geo. Healthcare NHS Trust. Prev: Sen. Regist. (ENT Surg.) Char. Cross & St. Mary Abbots Hosps. Lond.; Sen. Regist. Roy. Nat. Throat Nose & Ear Hosp. Lond.; Regist. (Neurosurg.) Sheff. Roy. Infirm.

KNIGHT, Jennifer Wendy Helen The Rose Cottage, Church Road, Whimple, Exeter EX5 2SU — MB BCh 1988 Witwatersrand.

KNIGHT, Jenny 17 School Terrace, Reading RG1 3LS — MRCS Eng. LRCP Lond. 1981; Dip. GU Med. Soc. Apoth. Lond. 1991. Prev: Clin. Asst. Roy. Berks. Hosp. Reading.

KNIGHT, John David Spurin (retired) 1 West Close, Hoddesdon EN11 9DA Tel: 01992 462806 — MD 1959 Camb.; MA Camb. 1947, BA 1943, MD 1959, MB BChir 1945; MRCP Lond. 1949.

KNIGHT, John Sebastian 35 Lancer Way, Billericay CM12 0XA — MB BS 1996 Lond. (St, Bartholomews Hospital Medical College)

KNIGHT, Jonathan Clive 19 Beaconsfield Road, Woodbridge IP12 1EQ — MB BS 1990 Lond.; MRCGP 1994; DCH RCP Lond. 1993; DRCOG 1993. (Univ. Coll. & Middlx. Hosp. Med. Sch.) Prev: Trainee GP Watford VTS; SHO Rotat. (Paediat.) Watford Gen. Hosp.; Ho. Off. (Med. & Surg.) Chase Farm. Hosp. Enfield.

KNIGHT, Julian Charles Department of Paediatrics, Institute of Molecular Medicine, John Radcliffe Hospital, Oxford OX3 9DU; Riverbank Cottage, Collice St, Islip, Kidlington OX5 2TB — MB ChB 1992 Ed.; BA (Hons.) Camb. 1989; MRCP (UK) 1995. Clin. Train. Fell. Univ. Oxf.

KNIGHT, Karen Michelle 2 St Mary's Park, Langport TA10 9HD — MB ChB 1992 Bristol.

KNIGHT, Karyn Elizabeth 23 Stein Road, Emsworth PO10 8LB — MB BS 1984 Lond.; MRCGP 1991; DRCOG 1990; Cert. Family Plann. JCC 1990.

***KNIGHT, Kathryn Joanna** Burgh House, Burgh Hill, Etchingham TN19 7PE — MB BChir 1994 Camb.; BA Camb. 1994.

KNIGHT, Mr Lindsey Charles Department of Otolaryngology, Leeds General Infirmary, Leeds LS9 7TF Tel: 0113 392 8040 — MB BCh 1985 Wales; MPhil Wales 1991; FRCS ORL 1994; FRCS Eng. 1990; FRCS Ed. 1989. (Univ. Wales Coll. Med.) Cons. ENT Leeds Gen. Infirm. & St James Univ. Hosp. Leeds; Hon. Sen. Lect. Univ. Leeds; Lead Clinician. Socs: Brit. Assn. Otol. Head & Neck Surg.; Roy. Soc. Med.; Brit. Assn. Paediat. Otolaryngol. Prev: Sen. Regist. Univ. Hosp. Wales Cardiff; TWJ Research Fell. San Francisco.

KNIGHT, Louise Elizabeth 2 The Mews, High St., Pembury, Tunbridge Wells TN2 4NU — MB ChB 1997 Bristol.

KNIGHT, Margaret Beryl Bethany House Surgery, 85 Battle Road, Hailsham BN27 1UA Tel: 01323 848485 — MB ChB 1993 Sheff.; MRCGP 1998; DRCOG 1997. Asst. Gen. Pract. Prev: Trainee GP/SHO Rotat. Sheff.; SHO (Paediat. & O & G) Chesterfield Roy. Hosp.

KNIGHT, Marian Nuffield Department of Obstetrics & Gynaecology, John Radcliffe Hospital, Oxford OX3 9DU Tel: 01865 221017 Fax: 01865 69141 Email: marian.knight@obs-gyn.ox.ac.uk; Riverbank Cottage, Collice St, Islip, Kidlington OX5 2TB — MB ChB 1992 Ed.; MA Camb. 1993, BA (Hons.) 1989. Clin. Research Fell. (O & G) John Radcliffe Hosp. Oxf. Prev: SHO (Neonat.) Roy. Vict. Infirm. Newc.; SHO (O & G) Roy. Infirm. Edin.

KNIGHT, Martin Geoffrey Standford Boundary House Surgery, Boundary House, Mount Lane, Bracknell RG12 9PG Tel: 01344 483900 Fax: 01344 862203; 14 Sylverns Court, Warfield, Bracknell RG42 3SL Tel: 01344 301903 Fax: 01344 301903 Email: drknight@gping_asthma.org — MB BS Lond. 1981; MB BS Lond. 1981; MRCGP 1985; MRCGP 1985; DRCOG 1984; DRCOG 1984. (Roy. Free) Prev: Trainee GP/SHO W. Middlx. Hosp., Isleworth VTS; Ho. Surg. Lister Hosp., Stevenage; Ho. Phys. Roy. Free Hosp. Lond.

KNIGHT, Mr Martin Tonbridge Norton Spinal Foundation, Arbury Consulting Centre, Manchester Road, Rochdale OL11 4LZ Tel: 01706 358229 Fax: 01706 711209 Email: mknight@spinal-foundation.org; The Sycamores, Greenfield, Oldham OL3 7PB Tel: 01457 870682 Fax: 01457 820857 — MB BS 1969 Lond.; FRCS Eng. 1975. (St. Bart.) p/t Cons. Spinal Surg. & Dir. Spinal Foundat. Arbury Consg. Centre Rochdale; Hon. Sen. Lect. Univ. Centr. Lancs.; Hon research Fell.. Uni. Manc. Socs: Founder Mem. Internat. Musculoskeletal Laser Soc. (Pres.); Brit. Orthop. Assn.; Internat. Intradiscal Soc. Prev: Sen. Regist. (Orthop. Train. Prog.) St. Thos. Hosp. Lond. & RN Hosp. Haslar; Hon. Research Fell. Roy. Postgrad. Med. Sch. Lond.

KNIGHT, Mary Felicity (retired) 1B Sandforth Court, Queens Drive, Liverpool L13 0DQ — MB ChB Birm. 1953; MFPHM 1972; DCH Eng. 1955; FRCPCH 1996 (Founder/Snr Fell). Hon chief med off Liverp. archdiocesan Lourdes pilgrimage assoc. Prev: Cons. Pub. Health Med. & Community Paediat. St. Helens & Knowsley Community Health (NHS) Trust.

KNIGHT, Michael Alan Penvern, Nacton, Ipswich IP10 0EW Tel: 01473 659532 Fax: 01473 659014 Email: knight@nacton.demon.co.uk — DOce Med. Re. Phys. 2000; LLM Cardiff 1994; MB BS Lond. 1970; MRCS Eng. LRCP Lond. 1970; MRCGP 1978; DMJ Soc. Apoth. Lond. 1978; DA Eng. 1972. (Guy's) Princip. Policy Surg. & Force Med. Advisor Suff. Constab.; Med. Adviser; Med. Regist. Socs: (Hon. Sec.) Assn. Police Surg.

KNIGHT, Mr Michael James 135 Harley Street, London W1N 1DJ Tel: 020 7487 3501 Fax: 020 7935 3148; 1 St. Aubyn's Avenue, Wimbledon, London SW19 7BL Tel: 020 8947 2888 — MB BS 1963 Lond.; MS Lond. 1975; FRCS Eng. 1967; MRCS Eng. LRCP Lond. 1963. (St. Geo.) Cons. Surg. St. Geo. Hosp. Lond.; Cons.

Surg. Roy. Masonic Hosp. Lond.; Hon. Sen. Lect. St. Geo. Hosp. Med. Sch. Lond.; Mem. Ct. of Examrs. RCS; Examr. Surg. Univ. Lond.; Extern. Examr. (United Exam. Bd.) RCS Irel., Edin. & Colombo, Sri Lanka. Socs: (Ex-Pres.) Pancreatic Soc.; Roy. Soc. Med.; Eur. Soc. Surg. Research. Prev: Cons. Surg. St. Jas. Hosp. Balham; Research Fell. (Surg.) & Sen. Regist. (Gen. Surg.) St. Geo. Hosp. Lond.; Research Fell. (Surg.) Washington Univ. St. Louis, USA.

KNIGHT, Mr Nicholas Francis Knight, Todd, Jackson and Gilliland, Hawthorn House Medical Centre, 28-30 Heaton Road, Newcastle upon Tyne NE6 1SD Tel: 0191 265 5543/6246 Fax: 0191 276 2985 — MB BS 1972 Lond.; BSc Cape Town 1967; FRCS Ed. 1979.

KNIGHT, Paul Richard Flat 1, 6 Park Mount, Kirkstall, Leeds LS5 3HE — MB ChB 1991 Birm.

KNIGHT, Paul Vincent Strathmore, Lochwinnoch Road, Kilmacolm PA13 4DZ Tel: 01505 873875 — MB ChB 1979 Glas.; FRCP Ed. 1990; MRCP (UK) 1983; FRCPS Glas. 1992. Cons. Phys. Geriat. Med. Roy. Infirm. Glas.; Hon. Clin. Sen. Lect. (Geriat. Med.) Univ. Glas.; Adjunct Assoc. Prof. Internal Med. N. E.. Ohio Univ. Coll. of Med. Prev: Lect. (Geriat. Med.) S.. Gen. Hosp. Glas.

KNIGHT, Peter Frederick (retired) Mulberry House, Taynton, Burford OX18 4UH Tel: 01993 823262 — MB BS Lond. 1954; FFA RCS Eng. 1959; DA Eng. 1958. Prev: Sen. Cons. (Anaesth.) St. Mary's Hosp. Lond.

KNIGHT, Peter Frederick (retired) 2 The Mews, Barkhill Road, Liverpool L17 6BQ Tel: 0151 427 2090 — LMSSA 1952 Lond. Prev: RAMC.

KNIGHT, Peter Norman (retired) 31 Lethbridge Road, Old Town, Swindon SN1 4BY Tel: 01793 496496 — MB BS 1954 Lond.; DPhysMed. Eng. 1960; DObst RCOG 1955. Prev: Cons. Rheum. & Rehabil. P.ss Margt. Hosp. Swindon.

KNIGHT, Peter Timothy Home Farm, Kenwick, Louth LN11 8NP Tel: 01507 608772 — BM 1995 Soton. (Soton.) SHO (Paediat.) Gloucester Roy. Hosp. Gloucester. Prev: SHO (Paeds.) Chesterfields Roy. Hosp.; SHO (Gen. Med.) Chesterfield Roy. Hosp. Chesterfield; SHO (A & E) Roy. Hants. Co. Hosp. Winchester.

KNIGHT, Priscilla Ruth c/o 32 Old Mold Road, Gwersyllt, Wrexham LL11 4SB — MB ChB 1988 Ed.

KNIGHT, Richard 34 Beacon Road, Ditchling, Hassocks BN6 8UL — MB 1963 Camb.; PhD Lond. 1977; BChir 1962; FRCP Lond. 1979, M 1965; MRCS Eng. LRCP Lond. 1962; DTM & H Eng. 1965. (St. Mary's) Assoc. Specialist Gen. Med. Brighton Health Care NHS Trust. Socs: Fell. Roy. Soc. Trop. Med. & Hyg.; Internat. Epidemiol. Assn. Prev: Sen. Lect. Dept. Trop. Med. Liverp. Sch. Trop. Med. and; Hon. Cons. Phys. Liverp. AHA (T).; Lect. Dept. Med. Makerere Coll. Uganda.

KNIGHT, Richard Andrew Union Brae Surgery, Union Brae, Tweedmouth, Berwick-upon-Tweed TD15 2HB Tel: 01289 330333 Fax: 01289 331075 — MB BS 1978 Newc.; MRCGP 1983; DA Eng. 1982. GP Berwick upon Tweed.

KNIGHT, Richard John Pyle Street Health Centre, 27 Pyle Street, Newport PO30 1JW Tel: 01243 670707 Fax: 01243 672808; The Dower House, 27 Pyle St, Newport PO30 1JW — MB BS 1975 Lond.; MRCS Eng. LRCP Lond. 1973; MRCGP 1981; DA Eng. 1980; DRCOG 1979. (Guy's)

KNIGHT, Richard Sydney Godfrey Ballencrieff Garden Cottage, By Drem, Longniddry EH32 0PJ Tel: 0131 343 1404 — BM BCh 1977 Oxf.; FRCP Ed. 1993; MRCP (UK) 1980. Cons. Clin. Nat. CJD Surveillance Unit, W.. Gen. Hosp. Crewe Rd. Edin.; Hon. Sen. Lect. (Neurol.) Edin. Univ. Prev: Cons. Neurol. Aberd. R. I.

KNIGHT, Robert Karl Pharmi Kom Inc., 926 Brittney Terrace, Downingtown PA 19335, USA Tel: 610 873 6346 Fax: 610 873 0183 Email: kknight@bellatlantic.net; 42 Llwyn-y-Môr, Caswell Bay, Swansea SA3 4RD Tel: 01792 361779 Email: rhicert@juno.com — MB BCh 1974 Wales; MRCP (UK) 1978; MFPM 1990; FFPM 1997. (Welsh Nat. Sch. Med.) Pres., Pharmikom Inc. of PA. Socs: Brit. Soc. Rheum.; BMA; BRAPP. Prev: Vice-Pres. Med. & Scientif. Affairs; SmithKline Beecham Pharmaceut., Coll.ville, PA.

KNIGHT, Robert Kingston Tel: 020 7589 5315; 1 Rutland Gate Mews, London SW7 1PH Tel: 020 7589 5315 — MB BS 1955 Lond.; FRCP Lond. 1972, M 1960. (Guy's) Cons. Phys. Emerit., Guy's Hosp. Lond.; Director, Med. Sickness Soc..; Director, Wesleyan Assur. Soc.; Chief Med. Off., Hannover RE. (UK). Socs: Fell. Assur. Med. Soc.; Thoracic Soc. Prev: Cons. Phys. Lond. Chest Hosp.; Sub-Dean Postgrad. Studies Guy's Hosp. Med. Sch.; Fell. Med. Johns Hopkins Hosp. Baltimore, USA.

KNIGHT, Roger Andrew (retired) Rookwood Cottage, Rushmere Lane, Denmead, Waterlooville PO7 6HA Tel: 02392 632137 Email: raknight@cwcom.net — MB BChir Camb. 1962; MA Camb. 1961; DObst RCOG 1964. Prev: GP, Portsmouth.

KNIGHT, Ronald Kelvin Frimley Park Hospital, Portsmouth Road, Camberley GU16 7UJ Tel: 01276 604122; Brambley Wood, Snowdenham Links Road, Bramley, Guildford GU5 0BX — MB BChir 1970 Camb.; BA (1st cl.) Camb. 1967; FRCP Lond. 1991; MRCP (UK) 1972. (Cambridge University/St Bartholomew's Hospital Med. School) Cons. Phys. Brompton Hosp. & Frimley Pk. Hosp. Camberley. Prev: Director of Frimley Pk. cystic fibrosis unit; Sen. Regist. (Thoracic Med.) W.m. & Brompton Hosps. Lond.; Brackenbury Schol. Med. St. Bart. Hosp. Med. Coll. Lond.

KNIGHT, Ross John 117 Mortlake Road, Kew Gardens, Richmond TW9 4AW — MB BS 1993 Lond.

KNIGHT, Sarah Ellen — MB BS 1992 Lond.; MB BS (Hons.) Lond. 1992; BSc (Hons.) Lond. 1987; MRCPsych 1997. Specialist Regist. Rotat. (Gen./Old Age Psychiat.) St. Geo. Hosp. Lond. Prev: Regist. Rotat. (Psychiat.) St. Geo. Hosp. Lond.; SHO Rotat. (Psychiat.) St. Geo. Hosp. Lond.; Trainee GP E. Surrey VTS.

KNIGHT, Sheryl Anne The Surgery, 124 New Church Road, Hove BN3 4JB Tel: 01273 729194 Fax: 01273 881992; 18 Leyton Lea, Haywards Heath RH17 5AT — BM 1983 Soton.; MRCGP 1987; DRCOG 1987.

KNIGHT, Simon Joseph 61 Park Drive, Grimsby DN32 0EQ — MB ChB 1998 Liverp.; MB ChB Liverp 1998.

KNIGHT, Mr Simon Langdon Department of Plastic Surgery, St. James's University Hospital, Leeds LS9 7TF — MB BS 1978 Newc.; FRCS Eng. 1983; T(S) 1991. Cons. Plastic Surg. St. Jas. Univ. Hosp. Leeds. Socs: (Counc.) Brit. Soc. Surg. of Hand; Brit. Assn. Plastic Surg.; Brit. Assn. Aesthetic Plastic Surgs. Prev: Cons. Plastic & Hand Surg. Canniesburn Hosp. Glas.; Sen. Regist. (Plastic Surg.) Withington Hosp. Manch.

KNIGHT, Simon Nicholas Kirkus Ashleigh Surgery, Napier Street, Cardigan SA43 1ED Tel: 01239 621227 — MB BCh 1980 Wales; DRCOG 1982.

KNIGHT, Mr Stephen Edward Fairholme, Hawkes Hill, Hedsor, Bourne End SL8 5JQ Tel: 0162 85 23006 — MB BS 1968 Lond.; FRCS Eng. 1974; MRCS Eng. LRCP Lond. 1968. (Char. Cross) Cons. (Gen. Surg.) Wexham Pk. Hosp. & King Edwd. VII Hosp. Windsor. Prev: Lect. in Surg. St. Mary's Hosp. Lond.; Regional Research Fell. (Gen. Surg.) St. Mary's Hosp. Lond.; Regist. (Gen. Surg.) N.wick Pk. Hosp. & Clin. Research Centre.

KNIGHT, Stephen John 78 Fairview Way, Stafford ST17 0AX — BM BS 1997 Nottm.

KNIGHT, Steven Robert 21 Nook Lane, Fearnhead, Warrington WA2 0RT — MB ChB 1995 Manch.

KNIGHT, Susan Margaret 10 Browning Street, Stafford ST16 8AT Tel: 01785 258249 Fax: 01785 257911; 6 High Park, Stafford ST16 1BL Tel: 01785 606947 Email: knightsofhighpark@supanet.com — BM 1987 Soton.; DFFP 1993; DRCOG 1992; DCH RCP Lond. 1990. (Soton.) p/t Princip. in Gen. Pract. Prev: Regist. (Geriat.) Melbourne, Austral.; SHO (Paediat.) Poole Gen. Hosp.; SHO (O & G) Walsall Hosp.

KNIGHT, Susan Mary 41 St Cuthbert Avenue, Wells BA5 2JS — MB ChB 1984 Birm.; MA Oxf. 1983, BA 1977. SHO (Med.) Som. HA.

KNIGHT, Thomas Hobson Court Leys, Toot Baldon, Oxford OX44 9NF — MB BS 1997 Lond.

KNIGHT, Timothy John 2 Gaveston Road, Leamington Spa CV32 6EU Tel: 01926 311807 — MB BChir 1989 Camb.; MRCGP 1994. Socs: BMA.

***KNIGHT, Timothy John** 143 Heavy Gate Road, Crookes, Sheffield S10 1PG Tel: 0114 268 2630 Email: tandmknight@compuserve.com — MB ChB 1994 Sheff.

KNIGHT, Wayne Robert Dorchester Road Surgery, 179 Dorchester Rd, Weymouth DT3 7LE Tel: 01305 766472 Fax: 01305 766499 — MB ChB 1990 Bristol; DCH 1993; MRCGP 1994; DRCOG 1997. (Bristol) Gen. Pract. (Principle); Med. Off., Elderly Care, Weymouth Community Hosp. Prev: Locum GP.

KNIGHT, William Arthur The Cumberland Centre, Cumberland Centre, Damerel Close, Devonport, Plymouth PL1 4JZ Tel: 01752

562802/561054 Fax: 01752 500514; Oaklands, Elfordleigh, Plympton, Plymouth PL7 5EB Tel: 01752 338438 — MB ChB 1961 Bristol; MRCS Eng. LRCP Lond. 1961; DA Eng. 1969; DObst RCOG 1970. (Bristol) Socs: BMA & Advis. Mem. Med. Protec. Soc. Prev: SHO (Orthop.) Bath & Wessex Orthop. Hosp.; SHO (Dermat.) Walker-Gate Hosp. Newc.; SHO (O & G) Roy. Devon & Exeter Hosp.

KNIGHT-JONES, Mr David The Old Vicarage, Maplebeck, Newark NG22 0BS — MB 1961 Camb.; BChir 1960; FRCS Eng. 1968; MRCP Glas. 1964. Cons. Ophth. Surg. Univ. Hosp. Nottm. Socs: Ophth. Soc. U.K. Prev: Res. Surg. Off. Moorfields Eye Hosp.; Med. Regist. St. Anne's & P. of. Wales Hosps. Tottenham.

KNIGHT-JONES, Eveline Child Development Centre, City Hospital, Nottingham Tel: 01636 636259; Old Vicarage, Maplebeck, Newark NG22 0BS Tel: 0163 686259 — MB BS Lond. 1960; MRCP Lond. 1965; MRCS Eng. LRCP Lond. 1960; DCH Eng. 1963; DObst RCOG 1963; FRCP. (Univ. Coll. Hosp) Cons. Developm. Paediat. & Childh. Disabil. Nottm. Socs: Brit. Paediactric Neurol. assoc; Euro Acad. of Childh. Disabil.

KNIGHT-NANAN, Donna Marie Department of Ophthalmology, Leicester Royal Infirmary, Leicester LE1 5WW Tel: 0116 254 1414; 29 Burnet Close, Hamilton, Leicester LE5 1TQ — MB BS 1984 West Indies; FRCS Ed. 1993. Vis. Regist. (Ophth.) Leicester Roy. Infirm. Prev: SHO (Ophth.) Russells Hall Hosp. Dudley.

KNIGHTLEY, Martin John The New Surgery, 5 Station Road, Chinnor OX9 4PX Tel: 01844 351230 Fax: 01844 354328 Email: mknightly@doctors.org.uk; Chiltern Cottage, Askett, Princes Risborough, Aylesbury HP27 9LT Tel: 01844 343855 Email: martin@knightlie.powernet.co.uk — MB BChir 1972 Camb.; MA, MB Camb. 1973, BChir 1972; FRCGP 1991, M 1978; DObst RCOG 1976. (Oxf.) Tutor Roy. Coll. Gen. Practs.; Tutor Aylesbury Vale HA. Prev: SHO (Accid.) Radcliffe Infirm. Oxf.; Ho. Off. (Obst.) John Radcliffe Hosp. Oxf.; Ho. Off. (Paediat.) Radcliffe Infirm. & Ch.ill Hosp. Oxf.

KNIGHTON, John David 11 Queens Park South Drive, Bournemouth BH8 9BQ — MB BS 1988 Lond.; MRCP (UK) 1992; FRCA 1995. Specialist Regist. 4 (Anaesth. & IC) Soton. Gen. Hosp. Prev: Regist. (Anaesth.) Poole, Bournemouth & Soton.; Vist. Instruc. (Anaesth.) Ann Arbor Hosp. Univ. Michigan, USA.

KNIGHTON, Katy Helen 11 Queens Park South Drive, Bournemouth BH8 9BQ — BM 1988 Soton.; BM Soton 1988; MRCGP 1993; DCH RCP Lond. 1992.

KNIGHTON, Marion Emma 38 The Avenue, Potters Bar EN6 1ED Tel: 01707 655909 — MB BS Lond. 1959; MRCS Eng. LRCP Lond. 1959. (Roy Free)

KNIGHTS, Andrew John Jackson, Knights, Richards and Hobbis, Thorney Medical Centre, Wisbech Road, Thorney, Peterborough PE6 0SA Tel: 01733 270219 Fax: 01733 270860; 57 Wisbech Road, Thorney, Peterborough PE6 0SA Tel: 01733 270691 Email: aknights@netcomuk.co.uk — MB BS 1981 Lond.; MRCGP 1985; DRCOG 1984. (Westm.) Socs: BMA. Prev: Trainee GP PeterBoro. VTS; Ho. Phys. Weymouth & Dist. Hosp.; Ho. Surg. Poole Gen. Hosp.

KNIGHTS, Angela Clayton 21 Blackthorn Close, Lutterworth LE17 4UX — MB ChB 1969 Bristol; FRCPsych 1995, M 1975. (Bristol) Cons. Psychiat. Bradgate Unit Glenfield Gen. Hosp. Leicester. Prev: Lect. (Psychiat.) Char. Cross Hosp. Med. Sch.; Research Regist. DHSS Project Qu. Mary's Hosp. Roehampton; Regist. W.m. Hosp. Med. Sch. Dept. Psychiat. Qu. Mary's Hosp.

KNIGHTS, Anna Louise 6 Welwyn Mews, Up Hatherley, Cheltenham GL51 3YB — MB BS 1996 Lond.

KNIGHTS, David Lennox Marlborough Street Surgery, 1 Marlborough Street, Devonport, Plymouth PL1 4AE Tel: 01752 568864 Fax: 01752 606974; 18 Culme Road, Plymouth PL3 5BJ Tel: 01752 660750 — MRCS Eng. LRCP Lond. 1963; MB Camb. 1964, BChir 1963; DA Eng. 1968; DObst RCOG 1968. (Westm.) Prev: Med. Off. Methodist Miss. Hosp. Meru, Kenya; Ho. Surg. Eye & ENT Depts. W.m. Hosp. Lond.; SHO Anaesth. Ipswich & E. Suff. Hosp.

KNIGHTS, David Thomas The Hedges, 4 Landmere Lane, Ruddington, Nottingham NG11 6ND — BM BS 1984 Nottm.; FRCA 1991. (Univ. Nottm.) Cons. Anaesth. (Burns) Nottm. City Hosp.

KNIGHTS, Henry Daniel Hillview Medical Centre, 3 Heathside Road, Woking GU22 7QP Tel: 01483 766333 — MB BS 1988 Lond.; DRCOG 1992.

KNIGHTS, Karina Victoria Hampton Hill Medical Centre, 23, Wellington Rd, Hampton Email: fionachadwick@hotmail.com — MB BS 1992 Lond.; MRCGP; DRCOG; DFFP. (St. Thomas' Hospital, London) GP Partner.

KNIGHTS, Martin John Guy Hilary Cottage Surgery, Keble Lawns, Fairford GL7 4BQ; Jenners Cottage, Poulton, Cirencester GL7 5JE Tel: 01285 851421 — MB BS 1978 Lond.; MRCGP 1982; DA (UK) 1983. GP Princip.; Hosp. Pract. (Anaesth.) Cirencester Hosps.; Med. Off. Race Course Cheltenham. Socs: Community Hosp. Assn.; BASICS. Prev: SHO (Anaesth.) Cheltenham Gen. Hosp.; Ho. Surg. St. Mary's Hosp. Lond.; Ho. Phys. King Edwd. VII Hosp. Windsor.

KNIGHTS, Peter Davison Oak Street Medical Practice, 1 Oak Street, Norwich NR3 3DL Tel: 01603 613431 Fax: 01603 767209; 8 Albemarle Road, Norwich NR2 2DF Tel: 01603 53954 — MB BS 1964 Lond.; DObst RCOG 1966. (Middlx.) Clin. Asst. Norf. & Norwich Hosp.; Local Treasury Med. Off.; ADMO to HMSO. Prev: Ho. Surg. Hertford Co. Hosp. & Lewisham Hosp.; Ho. Phys. Middlx. Hosp.

KNIGHTS, Richard Charles 43 Newton Street, Newton St Faith, Norwich NR10 3AD — MB ChB 1997 Dundee.

KNIGHTS, Sally Elizabeth Department of Rheumatology, Bristol Royal Infirmary, Marlborough St., Bristol B52 8HW — MB BS 1990 Lond.; MRCP (UK) 1993. Prev: Regist. (Rheum.) St Thos. Hosp. Lond.; Specialist Regist. (Rheum.) Bristol Roy. Infirm. MalBoro. St, Bristol B52 8HW.

KNIGHTS, Steve Gerard Windmill Practice, The Health Centre, Beaumont Street, Sneinton, Nottingham NG2 4PJ Tel: 0115 950 5426 — BM BS 1988 Nottm.

KNILL, Robert Penketh Health Centre, Honiton Way, Penketh, Warrington WA5 2EY Tel: 01925 725644 Fax: 01925 791017; 23 Higher Ashton, Balmoral Park, Widnes WA8 9GN — MB ChB 1981 Liverp.; MRCGP 1986; DRCOG 1984; DCH RCP Lond. 1983.

KNILL-JONES, Jennifer Gillian (retired) 8 Whittingehame Drive, Glasgow G12 0XX Tel: 0141 334 9752 — MB BS Lond. 1964; MRCS Eng. LRCP Lond. 1964; MRCPsych 1979. Prev: Cons. Psychiat. Pk.head Hosp. Glas.

KNILL-JONES, Robin Peter Department Public Health, University of Glasgow, 2 Lilybank Gardens, Glasgow G12 8RZ Tel: 0141 330 5010 Fax: 0141 330 5018 Email: rpkj1n@udcf.gla.ac.uk — MSc (Computer Sc.) Lond. 1970; MA Camb. 1967, MB 1965, BChir 1964; FRCP Lond. 1984, M 1967; FFPHM 1991, M 1983; DPH Glas. 1979; Dip. Sports Med. Scott. Roy. Colls. 1997. (St. Bart.) Sen. Lect. (Clin. Epidemiol.) Univ. Glas. Clin.; Hon. Community Med. Specialist Gtr. Glas. Health Bd.; Med. Mem., Criminal Injuries Appeals Panel. Socs: Fell. Roy. Soc. Med.; Brit. Soc. Gastroenterol.; Fell Roy.Stat.Soc. Prev: W. Scotl. Dir. Managem. Educat.; Research Fell. & Hon. Lect. (Med.) King's Coll. Hosp. Lond.; Ho. Phys. Hammersmith Hosp. & St. Bart. Hosp. Lond.

KNIPE, Charles Waring Daniels Armagh Health Centre, Dobbin Lane, Armagh BT61 7QG Tel: 028 3752 3165 Fax: 028 3752 2319; Maghery, 85 Monaghan Road, Armagh BT60 4DR — MB ChB 1976 Ed.; MRCGP 1981; DCH Eng. 1979; DRCOG 1978.

KNOCK, Martin Alastair Rodgie 37 Linton Crescent, Leeds LS17 9PZ — MB ChB 1974 Ed. Surg. Regist. Leeds AHA (T). Prev: SHO (Paediat. Surg.) W.. Gen. Hosp. Edin.; Demonst. Anat. Edin. Univ.; Ho. Surg. (Orthop.) Vict. Hosp. Kirkcaldy.

KNOPS, Michelle Jane 16 Jesmond Vale Terrace, Newcastle upon Tyne NE6 5JT — MB BS 1991 Newc.

KNOTT, David Swanage Health Centre, Railway Station Approach, Station Road, Swanage BH19 1HB Tel: 01929 422231 Fax: 01929 426037 Email: dknott@swanagemedical.org.ujk — MB BS 1979 Lond.; MRCGP 1983; DRCOG 1982; FSOM. (St. Bart.) Socs: Fell. Soc. Orthop. Med., BMA.

KNOTT, Debbie Kirstie 23 Shelley Avenue, Nottingham NG11 8GS — MB BS 1994 Lond.; BSc Lond. 1992; DTM & H RCP Lond. 1996. SHO (Gen. Med.) Derbysh. Roy. Infirm. Prev: Med. Off. Manguzi Hosp. Kwazulu-Natal, S. Afr.; SHO (A & E) Roy. Lond. Hosp.; Ho. Phys. Roy. Lond. Hosp.

KNOTT, Felicity Anne Riverview Road, Pangbourne, Reading RG8 7AU — MB BCh 1994 Wales.

KNOTT, Laurence John Freezywater Primary Care Centre, 2B Aylands Road, Enfield EN3 6NS Tel: 01992 763794 Fax: 01992 764570; 17 Brookside S., E. Barnet, Barnet EN4 8TT — MB BS 1973 Lond.; BSc Lond. 1970, MB BS 1973. (Univ. Coll. Hosp.) Prev:

SHO (Anaesth.) Enfield Dist. Hosp.; Ho. Off. (Human Metab.) Univ. Coll. Hosp.; Ho. Surg. Edgware Gen. Hosp.

KNOTT, Martin Henry The Surgery, 31 St James Avenue, Brighton BN2 1QD Tel: 01273 675252 Fax: 01273 682405; 46 Longhill Road, Ovingdean, Brighton BN2 7BE Tel: 01273 302561 — MB BChir 1970 Camb.; MA, BChir 1969; MRCS Eng. LRCP Lond. 1969. (Camb.) Police Surg. Brighton & Hove. Prev: Ho. Phys. Hosp of St. John & St. Eliz. Lond.; Ho. Surg. St. Bart. Hosp. Lond.; Ho. Surg. (O & G) Centr. Middlx. Hosp. Lond.

KNOTT, Mr Peter David Directorate of Women's Health Services, University Hospital Lewisham, Lewisham High St., London SE13 6LH Tel: 020 8333 3067 Fax: 020 8690 1963 Email: peter.knott@uhl.nhs.uk; Tel: 020 8660 5277 Fax: 020 8763 2047 Email: knott@23kenley.freeserve.co.uk — MB BS 1979 Lond.; MD Lond. 1990; MRCOG 1984; FRCOG 1997. (Kings College Hospital Medical School, London) Cons. O & G Lewisham Hosp.; Hon. Sen. Lect. (Obst. & Gyn.) Kings Coll.

KNOTT, Samuel Robert George Chapel Road Surgery, Chapel Road, Boughton, King's Lynn PE33 9AG Tel: 01366 500331 Fax: 01366 501375; Tower Lodge, Foresters Avenue, Hilgay, Downham Market PE38 0JU — MB BCh 1990 Wales; MRCGP 1995. SHO (O & G) E. Glam. Gen. Hosp. Prev: SHO (ENT) Roy. Gwent Hosp.; Ho. Off. (Med.) Llandough Hosp. Cardiff; Ho. Off. (Surg.) Nevill Hall Abergavenny.

KNOTT, Sarah Department Pathology, Wharfedale General Hospital, Newall Car Road, Otley LS21 2LY — MB ChB 1965 Liverp.; MRCPath 1979.

KNOTT-CRAIG, Janice Lynn c/o Furness General Hospital, Department of Orthopaedics, Barrow-in-Furness LA14 4LF Tel: 01229 870870 — MB ChB 1988 Cape Town.

KNOTTENBELT, Christine Marie 1 Oakleigh Grange, Mount Park Road, Harrow HA1 3JU Email: jknotten@dircon.co.uk; M.R.C. Epidemiology & Medical Care Unit, Medical Care Unit, Northwick Park Hospital, Harrow HA1 3UJ Tel: 020 8869 3557 Fax: 020 8422 1421 — MB ChB Birm. 1968. Clin. Asst. Med.

KNOTTENBELT, Mr John Duncan Accident & Emergency Department, Northwick Park & St Mark's NHS Trust, Watford Road, Harrow HA1 3UJ Tel: 020 8869 3071 Fax: 020 8869 3089 — MB ChB 1988 Birm.; MB ChB Birm. 1968; BSc (Comp. Sci.) Cape Town 1984; FRCS Eng. 1977; FRCS Ed. 1977; MRCP (UK) 1977; FFAEM 1995; FRCP (Lon) 2000. Cons. Accid & Emerg. N.wick Pk. Hosp. Harrow Middlx. Prev: Head of Trauma Unit Groote Schuur Hosp. Cape Town.

KNOTTENBELT, Richard George 1 Oakley Grange, Harrow HA1 3JU — MB ChB 1993 Cape Town.

KNOWELDEN, David John Claremont Surgery, 56-60 Castle Road, Scarborough YO11 1XE Tel: 01723 375050 Fax: 01723 378241 — BM BCh 1975 Oxf.; MRCGP 1980; DRCOG 1981; DCH Eng. 1979.

KNOWLDEN, Michael John 3 Broughton Gardens, London N6 5RS — MB BS 1995 Lond.

KNOWLDEN, Peter Richard 3 Broughton Gardens, London N6 5RS — MB BS 1990 Lond.

KNOWLDEN, Mr Richard Paul 144 Harley Street, London W1G 7LD Tel: 020 7580 3499 Fax: 0207 244 6616; 246 Munster Road, London SW6 6BA — MB BS Lond. 1964; MRCS Eng. LRCP Lond. 1964; FRCS Eng. 1972; FRCOphth 1988; DO Eng. 1970. (Middlx.) p/t Cons. Ophth. Chelsea & W.m. Hosp.; Cons. Shell (UK) & Brit. Telecom. Socs: Roy. Soc. Med. Prev: Chief Asst. Retinal Diag. Dept. Moorfields Eye Hosp. Lond.; Sen. Regist. (Ophth.) W.m. Hosp. Lond.; Sen. Resid. Off. Moorfields Eye Hosp. Lond.

KNOWLES, Alan Keith (retired) 21 Bawburgh Lane, Costessey, Norwich NR5 0TR Tel: 01603 743402 — MRCS Eng. LRCP Lond. 1951; MA Camb. 1951, BA (Nat. Sc. Trip.) MB BChir 1950; DObst RCOG 1956. Fact. Med. Off. Remploy Ltd. Norwich. Prev: Ho. Surg. (Orthop.) Middlx. Hosp.

KNOWLES, Andrew Christopher 40 Colenso Road, Blackburn BB1 8DR — MB ChB 1990 Manch.

KNOWLES, Charles Henry Flat 3, 49 Cavell St., London E1 2BP — MB BChir 1993 Camb.

KNOWLES, Clare Old Bells, Bramley, Tadley RG26 5DD — MB BS 1989 Lond.; MRCPI 1993. Regist. (Genitourin. Med.) St. Thos. Hosp. Lond.

KNOWLES, David 17 Oxford Drive, Woodley, Stockport SK6 1HU — MB BChir 1993 Camb.

KNOWLES, Mr Edward Wilshire (cons. rooms), 30 Upper Dicconson St., Wigan WN1 2AG Tel: 01942 42366; Palmyra, Higher Lane, Dalton, Wigan WN8 7TW Tel: 0125 763262 — MRCS Eng. LRCP Lond. 1935; MChOrth Liverp. 1938, MB ChB 1935; FRCS Ed. 1942. (Liverp.) Socs: BMA; Fell. Brit. Orthop. Assn. Prev: Surg. i/c Orthop. Dept. Roy. Albert Edwd. Infirm. Wigan; Sen. Orthop. Surg. Middlesbrough, Stockton & N.allerton Gp. Hosps.; Lt.-Col. RAMC, Orthop. Specialist & O.C. Surg. Div.

KNOWLES, Erin Thérèse Health Centre, Great James St., Londonderry BT48 7DF Tel: 01504 365177; 144 Main Street, Dungiven, Londonderry BT47 4LG Tel: 01504 741221 — MB BCh BAO 1978 Belf.; BSc (Hons.) (Path.) 1976; MPhil Belf. 1993; DCCH RCP Ed. 1983; MRCPCH 1987. SCMO WHSSB. Socs: Fac. Comm. Health.

KNOWLES, Geoffrey Kenneth Kingston Hospital, Galsworthy Road, Kingston upon Thames KT2 7QB Tel: 020 8546 7711 Fax: 020 8934 3244 — MB BChir Camb. 1970; MA Camb. 1970; MD Camb. 1986; FRCP Lond. 1990; MRCP (UK) 1973; T(M) 1991. (Camb. & Univ. Coll. Hosp.) Cons. Phys. Gen. & Respirat. Med. Kingston Hosp. Surrey; Hon. Cons. Roy. Marsden Hosp. Sutton; Hon. Sen. Lect. Nat. Heart & Lung Inst. Lond.; Registered Special. Advis. Repiratory. Med. RCP; chrm speciality train Comm. resp med S W Thames. Socs: Brit. Thorac. Soc. (Regional Represen. SW Thames); Brit. Soc. Allergy & Clin. Immunol.; Fell. Roy. Soc. Med. Prev: Sen. Regist. St. Bart. Hosp. Lond.; Lect. Cardiothoracic Inst. Lond.; Ho. Phys. Univ. Coll. Hosp. Lond.

KNOWLES, Geraldine Mary Stobb House Farm, Dipton, Stanley DH9 9AX — MB ChB 1977 Manch.

KNOWLES, Ian 79 Larkhill Lane, Formby, Liverpool L37 1LU — MB ChB 1995 Dundee.

KNOWLES, James Alan (retired) Martinhoe, 5 Wold View Road S., Driffield YO25 6RR Tel: 01377 253357 — MRCS Eng. LRCP Lond. 1942. Prev: Surg. Regist. Warwick Hosp.

KNOWLES, Mr James Edward Arthur (retired) 21 College Street, Bury St Edmunds IP33 1NL Tel: 01284 753452 Fax: 01284 755164 Email: jknowles@waitrose.com — MB BChir 1962 Camb.; MB Camb. 1962, BChir 1961; FRCS Ed. 1969; MRCS Eng. LRCP Lond. 1961; DLO Eng. 1968. Prev: Cons. ENT Surg. Pilgrim Hosp. Boston.

KNOWLES, Jean Mary Geirhilda Surgery, Geirhilda, Back Road, Port Ellen PA42 7DR Tel: 01496 302103 Fax: 01496 302112 — MB BS 1981 Newc.; MRCGP 1987. GP Port Ellen I of Islay.

KNOWLES, John Kirkwood c/o The Old Cottage, Upper Swainswick, Bath BA1 8BU — MB ChB 1974 Glas.

KNOWLES, John Orrell (retired) Brick Kiln Farm, Hingham Road, Great Ellingham, Attleborough NR17 1JE Tel: 01953 452257 — MRCS Eng. LRCP Lond. 1957. Prev: Ho. Surg. & Ho. Phys. Lister Hosp. Hitchin.

KNOWLES, Keith Anthony Brian Lavender Cottage, 2 Hayle Road, Fraddam, Hayle TR27 6EH Tel: 01736 850782 — MB BS 1993 Lond.

KNOWLES, Kim 2 Ben Nevis Drive, Little Sutton, South Wirral CH66 4YZ — MB ChB 1994 Liverp.; DRCOG 1997; DFFP 1998. (Liverpool) GP Retainee Liverp. Prev: GP Regist. Liverp.; Sho (Psych.) Liverp.; SHO (O & G) Liverp.

KNOWLES, Lesley Jane Winterbourne House, 53-55 Argyle Rd, Reading RG8 7BH; 7 Albert Road, Reading RG4 7AN Tel: 01226 777739 — MB BS 1974 Lond.; FRCPsych 1998. (St. Bart.) p/t Cons. Psychother. Berks. Healthcare NHS Trust; Mem. Of the Gp. Analytic Pract. 88 Montagu Mans. Lond. W1U 6LF. Prev: Sen. Regist. (Psychother.) Nottm. HA; Regist. (Psychiat.) Soton HA; Ho. Off. (Vasc. Surg. & Med.) Roy. S. Hants. Hosp. Soton.

KNOWLES, Macpherson (retired) 252 Hylton Road, Worcester WR2 5LA Tel: 01905 429691 — MB BS 1943 Lond.; MRCS Eng. LRCP Lond. 1943; MRCGP 1953. Prev: GP Worcester.

KNOWLES, Margaret Anne Public Health Laboratory, Cumberland Infirmary, Carlisle CA2 7HY Tel: 01228 23654 Fax: 01228 512229 — MB ChB 1973 Aberd.; FRCPath 1993, M 1981. Dir. Area Pub. Health Laborat. Carlisle; Hon. Cons. Med. Microbiol. E. Cumbria HA. Prev: Cons. Med. Microbiol. St. Helens & Knowsley HA; Asst. Med. Microbiol. Regional Pub. Health Laborat. Liverp.

KNOWLES, Mary Leigh's Cottage, 174-180 Station Road, Downholland, Ormskirk L39 7JW — MB ChB 1979 Liverp.

KNOWLES, Mary (retired) Clift Surgery, Minchens Lane, Bramley, Tadley RG26 5BH Tel: 01256 881228 — MB BCh BAO NUI 1955;

LAH Dub. 1954; FFA RCSI 1965; DA RCPSI 1957. Prev: Regist. (Anaesth.) BRd.green Hosp. Liverp. & Altnagelvin Hosp. Lond.derry.

KNOWLES, Mary Louise Clifton Lodge Surgery, Clifton Lane, Meltham, Huddersfield HD9 4AH Tel: 01484 852073; 4 Field Hurst, Barkisland, Halifax HX4 0JE — MB ChB 1985 Manch.; MRCP (UK) 1989; MRCGP 1991.

KNOWLES, Michael Gareth Queen elizabeth Hospital, Edgbaston, Birmingham B15 2TH Tel: 0121 627 2395 — MB ChB 1984 Bristol; MRCP (UK) 1989; FCAnaesth 1991; DA (UK) 1987. (Univ. Bristol) Cons. Anaesth. Qu. Eliz. Hosp. & Univ. Hosp. Birm. NHS Trust. Prev: Cons. Neuroanaesth. Addenbrooke's NHS Trust Camb.

KNOWLES, Pamela Mary Gillies and Overbridge Medical Partnership, Brighton Hill, Sullivan Road, Basingstoke RG22 4EH Tel: 01256 479747; The Glen, Axford Road, Ellisfield, Basingstoke RG25 2QG Tel: 01256 381117 — MB BS 1987 Lond.; BSc Lond. 1984; DFFP 1991. (Univ. Coll. Lond.)

KNOWLES, Patrick Raymond c/o Anaesthetic Department, Northern General Hospital, Hernes Road, Sheffield S5 7AU Tel: 0114 271 4818; Woodview, 2 Middlewood hall, Mowson Lane, Worral, Sheffield S35 0AY Tel: 0114 229 9594 — MB ChB 1987 Manch.; FRCA 1993; DA (UK) 1990. Cons cardiothoracic anaes N.ern Gen. Hosp Sheff. Socs: Assn. Anaesth. & BMA. Prev: Vis. Instruc. Anaes Ann Arbor USA; Sen. Regis Anaes NW Regional regis scheme; Clin Fell Anaes Papworth Hosp.

KNOWLES, Mr Paul Andrew 2 Ben Nevis Drive, Little Sutton, South Wirral CH66 4YZ Email: paul.knowles@virgin.net — MB ChB 1994 Liverp.; MB ChB (Hons.) Liverp. 1994; FRCS Ed. (Liverpool) Specialist Regist. (A&E) Mersey Region. Prev: SHO (Paediat.) Whiston Hosp.; SHO (Orthop.) Roy. Liverp. Hosp.; SHO (Critical Care) Whiston Hosp. Merseyside.

KNOWLES, Philip Arthur The Faversham Health Centre, Bank Street, Faversham ME13 8QR Tel: 01795 532186 — MB 1973 Camb.; MA Camb. 1970, MB 1973, BChir 1972. (King's Coll. Hosp.) Clin. Asst. (Rheum.) William Harvey Hosp. Ashford, Kent. Socs: Vice Chairm. & Fell. Soc. Orthop. Med.

KNOWLES, Phillipa Joy Lilac Cottage, 20 Lickey Square, Lickey, Rednal, Birmingham B45 8HA Tel: 0121 445 1955 — MB BChir 1984 Camb.; BB BChir Camb. 1984; MA Camb. 1984, BA 1980; FRCS Eng. 1989; DO RCS Eng. 1988. Staff Grade (Ophth.) Birm. Heartlands Hosp. Prev: Regist. (Ophth.) Sussex Eye Hosp. Brighton; SHO (Ophth.) Norwich HA; SHO (Neurol. & Neurosurg.) Addenbrooke's Hosp. Camb.

KNOWLES, Rachel Louise Enfield and Haringay Health Authority, Churchwood House, Cockfosters Road, Enfield EN4 0DR Tel: 020 8272 5500 Fax: 020 8272 5800 — MB ChB 1991 Ed.; MRCGP 1995; DFFP 1995; DCCH RCP Ed. 1994; MSc 1998. (Ed.) Specialist Regist. in Pub. Health Med., N. Thames. Prev: CMO Community Child Health.

KNOWLES, Simon Renfred Frazer Gethin, Davies and Knowles, Harris Memorial Surgery, Robartes Terrace, Illogan, Redruth TR16 4RX Tel: 01209 842515 Fax: 01209 842380; Breeze Cottage, 194 Bodmin Road, Truro TR1 1RB Tel: 01872 272520 — MB ChB 1989 Birm. (Birmingham) Socs: BMA; MDU.

KNOWLES, Stephen Paul Eli Lilly & Co, Dertra Court, Chapel Hill, Basingstoke RG21 5SY — MB BS 1984 Newc.; MRCP (UK) 1987; MRCGP 1995. (Newc. u. Tyne) Prev: Trainee GP Soton. VTS; Regist. (Radiother.) Glas. HA & Middlx. Hosp.; Gen. Practitiner.

KNOWLES, Susan Margaret National Blood Service, North London, Colindale Avenue, London NW9 5BG Tel: 020 8200 7777 Fax: 020 8381 1214; Kingsmede, Fairfield Park, Cobham KT11 2PR Tel: 01932 868424 — MB BS 1972 Lond.; MB BS (Hons.) Lond. 1972; BSc Lond. 1969; FRCP Lond. 1996; MRCP (UK) 1975; MRCS Eng. LRCP Lond. 1972; FRCPath 1992, M 1980. (Roy. Free Hosp. Sch. Med.) Clin. Dir. Nat. Blood Serv. Lond. & SE Zone. Socs: Brit. Blood Transfus. Soc.; Internat. Soc. Blood Transfus.; AABB. Prev: Clin. Dir. S. Thames Blood Transfus. Serv.; Cons. N. Lond. & NE Thames Blood Transfus Serv.; Cons. Roy. Free Hosp. Lond.

KNOWLES, Timothy Keith Chesterfield Road Medical Centre, Chesterfield Road, North Wingfield, Chesterfield S42 5ND Tel: 01246 851035 Fax: 01246 856139; Station House, Smithymoor, Stretton, Alfreton DE55 6FE — MB BS 1988 Newc.; DFFP 1993. GP.

KNOWLES, Virginia Margaret 6 Close Bank, Cornmill Lane, Tutbury, Burton-on-Trent DE13 9HD — MB BS 1990 Lond.

KNOWLES, Wendy Patricia Chadderton Health Centre, Chadderton, Oldham; 7 Upton Close, Alkrington, Middleton, Manchester M24 1PG — MB ChB 1966 Sheff.; DObst RCOG 1969.

KNOWLSON, George Timothy Gilby 22 Norris Road, Sale M33 3QR — MB ChB 1968 Manch.; MRCGP 1988; MRCPath 1976. (Manch.) Prev: Sen. Regist. Birm. Childr. Hosp.; Lect. (Path.) Manch. Univ.; Ho. Surg. & Ho. Phys. Manch. Roy. Infirm.

KNOWLSON, Hilary Akenhead 133 Shepherds Hill, Harold Wood, Romford RM3 0NR Tel: 0140 23 42646 — MB BS 1963 Lond. (Char. Cross) Prev: Asst. Co. Med. Off. Essex CC.

KNOWLSON, Patrick Akenhead Milley Farm, Milley Road, Waltham St Lawrence, Reading RG10 0JR Tel: 01189 343574 — MB BS 1959 Lond.; FFPM RCP (UK) 1989; Dip. Pharm. Med. RCP (UK) 1976. (Lond. Hosp.) Chair Boehringer Ingelheim Ltd. Bracknell. Socs: Fell. Roy. Soc. Med.; Fell. Overseas Doctors Assn.; Brit. Assn. Pharmaceut. Phys. Prev: Regist. (Med.) German Hosp. Lond.; Ho. Surg. (ENT & Ophth.) & Regist. Receiv. Room Lond. Hosp.

KNOX, Professor Alan John Respiratory Medicine Unit, City Hospital, Nottingham NG5 1PB — MB ChB 1981 Ed.; DM Nottm. 1989; FRCP Lond. 1996; FRCP Ed. 1996; MRCP (UK) 1984. Prof. & Hon. Cons. Phys. Respirat. Med. Unit City Hosp. Nottm.; Edr. Thorax, Edr.ial Bd. Clin. Sci., Amer. Jl. of Physiol. Prev: Research Regist. Respirat. Med. Unit. City Hosp. Nottm.; MRC Train. Fell. San Francisco, Calif.

KNOX, Alexander Mavor (retired) Forest Lodge, 23 Forestfield, Kelso TD5 7BX Tel: 01573 224475 — MB ChB 1945 Aberd.

KNOX, Mr Andrew John Stuart 1 The Quadrant, Wonford Road, Exeter EX2 4LE Tel: 01392 256774 Fax: 01392 421662 Email: ajk@quadrant1.u-net.com; Dandyland, Dunsford, Exeter EX6 7BH — MRCS Eng. LRCP Lond. 1964; MS Lond. 1978, MB BS 1964; FRCS Eng. 1969. (St. Bart.) Cons. Gen. Surg. Roy. Devon & Exeter Hosp. Wonford. Socs: BMA; Assn. Surgs. Prev: Sen. Surg. Regist. United Bristol Hosps.; Wellesley Research Fell. Toronto, Canada; Ho. Surg. St. Bart. Hosp. Lond.

KNOX, Anne Drummond The Surgery, 3 Glasgow Road, Paisley PA1 3QS Tel: 0141 889 2604 Fax: 0141 887 9039; 3 Glasgow Road, Paisley PA1 3QS Tel: 0141 889 2604 — MB ChB 1981 Glas.; MRCGP 1986; DRCOG 1986.

KNOX, Anne Patricia The Health Centre, Marmaduke St., Hull HU3 3BH Tel: 01482 327708 Fax: 01482 210250; Rivendell, 12 Aston Hall Drive, North Ferriby HU14 3EB Tel: 01482 633116 — MB BS 1965 Durh.; DMJ (Clin.) Soc. Apoth. Lond. 1992; DA (UK) 1968. p/t Clin. Asst. Health Centre Hull; Forens. Med. Examr. Humberside Police. Socs: Hull Med. Soc.; BMA; Assn. Police Surg. (Past Mem. Counc.). Prev: GP Hull; Regist. (Anaesth.) Dumfries & Galloway Roy. Infirm.

KNOX, Caroline Jane 12 Aston Hall Drive, North Ferriby HU14 3EB Tel: 01482 633116 — MB BS 1993 Newc. SHO (Anaesth.) N. Tyneside Dist. Gen. Newc.

KNOX, Catherine Susan Juliet Royal Devon & Exeter Hospital, Heavitree, Gladstone Road, Exeter Tel: 01392 405105; Dandyland, Dunsford, Exeter EX6 7BH Tel: 01392 811468 — MB BS 1964 Lond.; MRCS Eng. LRCP Lond. 1964. (St. Bart.) Assoc. Specialist (Obst. Ultrasound) Roy. Devon & Exeter Hosp.

KNOX, David Darragh (retired) Hartington Street Medical Practice, 36-38 Hartington Street, Barrow-in-Furness LA14 5SL Tel: 01229 820250 Fax: 01229 813718 — MB BCh BAO 1973 Belf.; BSc Ed. 1964; MRCGP 1977; DRCOG 1976. Prev: SHO (Psychiat.) & Ho. Off. Belf. City Hosp.

KNOX, Douglas Alexander (retired) 3 Hustler Road, Bridlington YO16 6QZ Tel: 01262 602245 — MB ChB 1949 Glas.

KNOX, Edward Wilson (retired) 1 Cherryvalley Park W., Belfast BT5 6PU Tel: 01232 795090 — MD 1961 Belf.; MD (Commend.) Belf. 1961, MB BCh BAO 1947; FRCPI 1969, M 1955. Hon. Cons. Phys. (Geriat. Med.) Ulster & N. Down Hosp. Gps. Prev: Sen. Regist. (Gen. Med.) Belf. City Hosp.

***KNOX, Ellen Mary** 41 Butlers Court Road, Beaconsfield HP9 1SQ — MB ChB 1995 Birm.; ChB Birm. 1995.

KNOX, Professor Ernest George (retired) Mill Cottage, Great Comberton, Pershore WR10 3DU Tel: 01386 710524 — MB BS Durh. 1949; MD Durh. 1955; FRCP Lond. 1973, M 1956; FFPHM RCP (UK) 1989; FFOM RCP Lond. 1985; FFCM 1972. Prof. Pub. Health & Epidemiol. Univ. Birm. Prev: Sen. Lect. (Paediat.) Univ. Newc.

KNOX, Fiona Mary Department of Anaesthetics, Aberdeen Royal Infirmary, Foresterhill, Aberdeen AB25 2ZN Tel: 01224 681818 Fax: 01224 685307; 27 Thomson Street, Aberdeen AB25 2QN — MB ChB 1975 Aberd.; MD Aberd. 1990; FFA RCS Eng. 1980. Cons. Anaesth. Aberd. Roy. Infirm. Prev: Research Fell. Assn. Anaesth. GB & Irel.; Ho. Off. (Gen. Med.) Raigmore Hosp. & Roy. N.. Infirm. Inverness; Ho. Off. (Neurosurg.) Unit Aberd. Roy. Infirm.

KNOX, Geoffrey Malcolm 14 Queensway, Heald Green, Cheadle SK8 3JE — MB ChB 1994 Manch.

KNOX, George Watson (retired) Crooks Cottage, Burnham Overy Town, King's Lynn PE31 8HU Tel: 01328 738731 — MB BChir 1958 Camb.; MB Camb. 1958, BChir 1957; MRCS Eng. LRCP Lond. 1957; FRCGP 1983, M 1976; DCH Eng. 1959; DObst RCOG 1959. Prev: Course Organiser & Clin. Asst. (Psychiat.) Dewsbury VTS.

KNOX, James David Edgar University Department of General Practice, Westgate Health Centre, Charleston Drive, Dundee DD2 4AD Tel: 01382 644425 — MD 1967 Ed.; MB ChB 1949; FRCP Ed. 1969, M 1958; FRCGP 1970. (Ed.) Prof. Gen. Pract. Univ. Dundee; Sreenivasan Orator Coll. Gen. Pract., Singapore. Socs: Medico-Legal Soc.

KNOX, James William Stewart 3 Jesmond Avenue, Linthorpe, Middlesbrough TS5 5JY — MB ChB 1953 Glas. Prev: Ho. Phys. S.. Gen. Hosp. Glas.; Ho. Surg. Stirling Roy. Infirm. & Middlesbrough Matern. Hosp.

KNOX, Jean Margaret 209 Woodstock Road, Oxford OX2 7AB — MB BS 1971 Lond.; MRCPsych 1977. (Guy's Hosp.) Prev: Psychother. HM Prison Grendon; Research Psychiat. Oxf. Univ. Dept. Psychiat.; Regist. (Psychiat.) Oxon AHA (T).

KNOX, John Castle Hill Hospital, Cottingham HU16 5JQ — MB BS 1963 Durh.; FRCP Ed. 1983, M 1968; DObst RCOG 1965. Cons. Dep. Med. for Elderly Hull.

KNOX, John Charles 17 Manorway, Tynemouth, North Shields NE30 4ND — MB BS 1950 Durh.; BSc Durham 1933, MB BS 1950. (Durh.)

KNOX, Karen Louise Top Floor Flat, 27 Mattock Lane, London W5 5BH — MB ChB 1992 Cape Town.

KNOX, Kathleen Dorothy Tigh An Rudha, Plockton IV52 8TL — MB BS 1944 Durh.

KNOX, Kenneth William 72 Polwarth Gardens, Edinburgh EH11 1LL Tel: 0131 221 9897, 0131 229 5914 — MB ChB 1989 Ed.; MRCGP 1995; DRCOG 1993.

KNOX, Kyle Alexander Department of Microbiology, Level 7, John Radcliffe Hospital, Headley Way, Oxford OX3 Tel: 01865 741166; 6 Minster Road, Oxford OX4 1LX — MB ChB 1989 Glas.; BSc (Hons.) Glas. 1987; MRCP (UK) 1992; DTM & H Liverp. 1993. Career Regist. (Med. Microbiol.) John Radcliffe Hosp. Oxf. Socs: BMA. Prev: SHO Yorkhill Hosp. & Ruchill Hosp. Glas.; SHO (Med.) Vict. Infirm. Glas.

KNOX, Linda Marion Crumlin Road Surgery, 130-132 Crumlin Road, Belfast BT14 6AR — MB BCh BAO 1983 Belf.

KNOX, Muriel Inez Ruth Flat 34, 60 Bingham Drive, Edinburgh EH15 3JS Tel: 0131 669 9679 — MB ChB 1938 Manch.; MD Manch. 1953; FFR RCSI 1962; DMR Ed. 1940.

KNOX, Mr Robert Andrew 68 Rossett Green Lane, Rossett Green, Harrogate HG2 9LJ — MB ChB 1973 Sheff.; FRCS Eng. 1977. Cons. Surg. Harrogate Dist. Hosp. Socs: Vasc. Soc.

KNOX, Stafford Joseph (retired) Larne BT40 1PW — MD (Hnrs.) Belf. 1962. MB BCh BAO 1954; FRCPsych 1974, M 1971; DPM RCPSI 1958. Prev: Med. Supt. & Cons. Psychiat. Purdysburn Hosp. Belf.

KNOX, Stephen Gordon The Wilson Practice, Lisburn Health Centre, Linenhall St., Lisburn BT28 1LU; 15 Laurel Grove, Lisburn BT28 3EW — MB BCh BAO 1988 Belf.; DRCOG; DCH; MRCGP. (Queens University Belfast) GP Princip.; Primary Care Practitioner Matern. Hosp. Belf. Socs: BMA.

KNOX, Vivien Elizabeth Winterton Surgery, Westerham TN16 1RB Tel: 01959 564949 Fax: 01959 565722; 173 Main Road, Sundridge, Sevenoaks TN14 6EH Tel: 01959 562531 — MB BCh 1977 Wales; MRCP (UK) 1980. (Welsh Nat. Sch. Med.) Socs: Med. Defence Union; BMA.

KNOX, Winifred Annie (retired) Forest Lodge, 23 Forestfield, Kelso TD5 7BX Tel: 01573 224475 — MB ChB 1948 Glas.; MA Glas. 1945, MB ChB 1948.

KNOX, Winifred Fiona Department of Histopathology, Withington Hospital, Nell Lane, Manchester M20 2LR Tel: 0161 291 3602; 10 Evesham Close, Alkrington, Middleton, Manchester M24 1PU Tel: 0161 643 6735 — MB ChB 1975 Aberd.; FRCPath 1994, M 1982. Cons. (Histopath.) Withington Hosp., Manch.; Hon. Cons. (Path.) Withington Hosp. Manch.

KNOYLE, Paul Anthony Woodlands Surgery, 1 Greenfarm Road, Ely, Cardiff CF5 4RG Tel: 029 2059 1444 Fax: 029 2059 9204; Cherry Trees, 6 Ger Y Llan, St. Nicholas, Cardiff CF5 6SY — MB BCh 1967 Wales; FRCGP 1984, M 1972; DObst RCOG 1970; DCH Eng. 1970. (Cardiff) Clin. Teach. (Gen. Pract.) Univ. Wales Coll. Med. Socs: Cardiff Med. Soc.; Hist. Med. Soc. Wales. Prev: SHO (Med. & Neurol.) United Cardiff Hosps.; Ho. Off. (Paediat. & Obst.) St. David's Hosp. Cardiff.

KNUDSEN, Anthony (retired) St. Gall, 36 Windsor Road, Gerrards Close SL9 7NE Tel: 01753 883069 Email: anthony.knudsen@virgin.net — MB BS 1947 London; MRCP 1949 London; MD 1950 Lond.; FRCP Lond. 1975; FRCPath 1963. Prev: Sen. Cons. Pathol. W. Middlx. Univ. Hosp. Isleworth.

KNUDSEN, Eric Theodore Brelades, 37 Knowle Park, Cobham KT11 3AA Tel: 01932 863551; Wastwater Cottage, Barrock Park, Low Heskett, Southwaite, Carlisle Tel: 016974 73737 — MB BS 1952 Lond.; MRCS Eng. LRCP Lond. 1949; FRCPath 1966; MRCGP 1962. (Middlx.) Socs: Fell. Roy. Soc. Med. Prev: Med. Dir. Beecham Pharmaceut. Div.; Sen. Lect. (Chem. Path.) S.A. Ct.auld Inst. of Biochem. Middlx. Hosp.; Asst. Path. & Jun. Lect. (Path.) Bland-Sutton Inst. Path. Middlx. Hosp.

KO, Aaron Hoi Nam Ko, 244 Tufnell Park Road, London N19 5EW Tel: 020 7272 8747 Fax: 020 7272 2030 — MB BS 1975 Newc.; MRCGP 1980.

KO, Man Leung Ben Lister Ward, Plaistow Hospital, Samson St., Plaistow, London E13 9EH Tel: 020 8586 6417 Fax: 020 8586 6420 Email: ben.ko@newhampct.nhs.uk — MB ChB 1984 Ed.; MRCP (UK) 1987; FRCPCH 1997. (Ed.) Cons. Paediat. Community Child Health Newham Lond.; Med.ly Qualified Panel Mem., Appeal Serv., Lord Chancellor's Dept. Socs: BAACH; Fell., RCPCA & BMA. Prev: Sen. Regist. (Paediat.) Qu. Eliz. Hosp. for Childr. Hackney; Regist. (Paediat.) N.wick Pk. Hosp.; SHO (Paediat.) Brompton Hosp. Lond. & Roy. Hosp. Sick Childr. Edin.

KO, Seng Huat 689 Welford Road, Leicester LE2 6FQ — MB ChB 1997 Leic.

KOAK, Mr Yashwant Pal Singh 25 Sherborne Avenue, Norwood Green, Southall UB2 4HX Tel: 020 8574 6058 Fax: 020 8574 6058 Email: yashwant.koak@virgin.net — MB ChB 1990 Glas.; FRCS Eng. 1997. (Univ. Glas.) Research Fell. Roy. Free Hosp. Med. Sch. Socs: RSM; ASGBIT; BMA. Prev: SHO (Surg. Rotat.) Chelsea & W.minster Hosp. Lond.; SHO (Surg. Rotat.) Roy. Surrey Co. Hosp.; SHO (ENT) Qu. Eliz. Hosp. Birm.

KOAY, Cheng Boon 1 Westwood Court, Westwood Park, London SE23 3RU Tel: 020 8699 9238 — MB BS 1988 Lond.

KOBBEKADUWE, Mr Asoka Eugene Rajaguru Heights Farm, Thurston Clough Road, Dobcross, Saddleworth, Oldham OL3 5RE — MB BS 1968 Ceylon; FRCS Ed. 1978. (Sri Lanka) Cons. ENT Surg. Tameside Gen. Hosp. Ashton-under-Lyne. Socs: Brit. Assn. Otolaryngs. Prev: Sen. Regist. (ENT Surg.) Newc. Gp. Hosps.; Regist. (ENT Surg.) Leeds Gp. Hosps.

KOBER, Peter Howard The Surgery, Tanners Meadow, Brockham, Betchworth RH3 7NJ Tel: 01737 843259 Fax: 01737 845184; Newlands, Deepdene Wood, Dorking RH5 4BE — MB ChB 1975 Dundee; DRCOG 1980.

KOBER, Susan Jane New House Surgery, 142A South Street, Dorking RH4 2QR Tel: 01306 881313 Fax: 01306 877305; Newlands, Deepdene Wood, Dorking RH5 4BE — MB ChB 1975 Dundee; BSc St. And 1972; DRCOG 1977.

KOBZA BLACK, Aniko St. John's Institute of Dermatology, St. Thomas's Hospital, London SE1 7EH Tel: 020 7928 9292 Fax: 020 7620 0369; 21 Deansway, East Finchley, London N2 0NF — MB BS 1963 Queensland; MD Lond. 1985; FRCP Lond. 1991; MRCP (UK) 1974. Cons. Dermat. & Hon. Sen. Lect. Inst. Dermat. United Med. & Dent. Sch. St. Thos. Hosp. Lond. (p/t). Socs: Brit. Assn. Dermat. & Amer. Acad. Dermat.

KOCAN, Michajlo Karl c/o Department of Anaesthetics, Nevill Hall Hospital, Brecon Road, Abergavenny NP7 7EG — MB BCh 1976 Wales; FFA RCS Eng. 1981. Cons. Anaesth. Nevill Hall Hosp.

Abergavenny. Prev: Cons. Anaesth. Qu. Eliz. Hosp. Gateshead Tyne & Wear; Cons. Anaesth. 23 (Parachute) Field Ambul. RAMC.

KOCEN, Jane Lisa 23 Ferndale Road, Hove BN3 6EU — MB BS 1988 Lond.; BSc Lond. 1985, MB BS 1988; MRCGP 1993; DRCOG 1992; DCH RCP Lond. 1990. (Middlx. Hosp. Med. Sch.) Retainer in Gen. Pract. E. Sussex HA. Prev: GP Princip. Lond.; Trainee GP Lond.

KOCEN, Roman Stefan, TD Tel: 020 7837 3611 Fax: 020 7833 8658; 127 Willifield Way, London NW11 6XY Tel: 020 8455 9000 Fax: 020 8201 8486 — MB ChB (Hons.) Leeds 1956; FRCP Lond. 1974, M 1958. (Leeds) Hons. Cons. Phys. Nat. Hosp. Neurol. & Neurosurg. Qu. Sq. Lond.; Hon. Civil Cons. Neurol. RAF. Socs: Assn. Brit. Neurols. Prev: Civil Cons. Neurol. RAF; Resid. Med. Off. Nat. Hosp. Nerv. Dis. Qu. Sq. Lond.; Sub-Dean Inst. Neurol. Lond. Univ.

KOCH, Bridget Kymsland, Blowing House, Bodmin PL30 5AX — MB BS 1985 Lond.

KOCH, Janet Ena 71 Bailie Drive, Bearsden, Glasgow G61 3AH — MB ChB 1991 Manch.

KOCH, Stephan North Hampshire Hospital, Aldermaston Road, Basingstoke RG24 9NA — State Exam Med 1991 Kiel.

KOCHAN, Michael Dennis 9 Hills Mews, Florence Road, Ealing, London W5 3RG Tel: 020 8579 9104 — MB BS 1949 Lond.; MPhil Cranfield 1988; MRCS Eng. LRCP Lond. 1949; Dip. Ven. Soc. Apoth. Lond. 1977; DObst RCOG 1951. (Univ. Coll. Hosp.) Assoc. Specialist (Genitourin. Med.) Char. Cross & Hillingdon Hosps. Prev: Ho. Surg. (Obst.) Univ. Coll. Hosp.; Clin. Asst. P. of Wales Hosp. Tottenham; Clin. Asst. Postgrad. Med. Sch. Hammersmith.

KOCHANOWSKI, Stanislaw Jerzy 92 Cherry Garden Road, Eastbourne BN20 8HF — MB BS 1968 Lond.; MRCP (U.K.) 1973.

KOCHAR, Arvind 29 Menteith Avenue, Bishopbriggs, Glasgow G64 1HP Tel: 0141 762 3562 — MB ChB 1992 Glas. GP Regist. Newarthill Health Centre Motherwell. Socs: BMA.

KOCHETA, Mr Alexis Andre John Trem-y-Bryn, Carreghofa Lane, Llanymynech SY22 6LA — MB BS 1993 Lond.; FRCS 1997. Specialist Regist. Mr OsW.ry Stoke Orthop. Rotat.

KOCHHAR, Arun 259 Goodman Park, Slough SL2 5NP — MB ChB 1992 Aberd.; BMedBiol Aberd. 1989, MB ChB 1992.

KOCHHAR, Mohanjit Singh 213 Priest Lane, Shenfield, Brentwood CM15 8LE — MB BS 1996 Lond.

KOCHHAR, Neeraj 20 Wentworth Avenue, London N3 1YL — MB BS 1994 Lond.

KOCHHAR, Pavan Kumar 86 Brighton Road, Worthing BN11 2EN Tel: 01903 820893 — MB ChB 1996 Ed. (Ed.) SHO (Gen Med), Manch. Roy. Infirm. Socs: BMA; MDDUS; MDU. Prev: SHO A & E Glas. Roy. Infirm.; Ho. Off. Roy. Infirm. of Edin.; Ho. Off. St.John's Hosp. Livingston.

KOCHHAR, Rupa — MB BS Saurashtra 1974; MD Gujarat 1977; Dip. Psychiat. Lond. 1987. Regist. (Psychiat.) SW Durh. HA; Staff Grade (Psychiat. for Elderly) Kidderminster Hosp. Prev: Regist. (Paediat.) & Ho. Phys. (Med.) Civil Hosp. Ahmedabad, India; Cons. Paediat. Rajkot, India.

KOCIALKOWSKI, Andrzej 4 Greenway Close, Sale M33 4PU — Lekarz 1982 Poznan, Poland; FRCS (outh) 1998. Specialist Regist. Orthop. Prev: Lect. in Orthop.

KOCJAN, Gabriela Department of Histopathology, Cytology Laboratory, University College London, University St., London W1E 6JJ Tel: 020 7380 9392 Email: g.kocjan@ucl.ac.uk — Lijecnik Zagreb 1975; Special Clin. Cytol. Zagreb 1980; MRCPath. 1988; FRCPath 1996. Sen. Lect. Hon. Cons. Cytopath. Dept. Histopath. Middlx. & Univ. Coll. Sch. Med. Lond. Socs: Roy. Soc. Med. Lond.; Roy. Coll. Path. Lond.; Brit. Soc. Clin. Cytol. Prev: Sen. Regist. Char. Cross Hosp. Lond.

KOCKELBERGH, Mr Roger Clive Department of Urology, Leicester General Hospital, Gwendolen Road, Leicester LE5 4PW Tel: 01162 490490 Fax: 01162 730639; The Poplars, 30 Main Street, Houghton on the Hill, Leicester LE7 9GD Tel: 0116 212 7115 Fax: 0116 212 7116 Email: rogerk@doctors.org.uk — MB ChB 1983 Birm.; DM Nottm. 1994; FRCS (Urol.) 1995; FRCS Ed. 1988. (Birm.) Cons. Urol. Leicester Gen. Hosp. Socs: Brit. Assn. Urol. Surgs.; BMA. Prev: Sen. Regist. (Urol.) Leicester Gen. Hosp.; Regist. (Urol.) Norf. & Norwich Hosp.; Lect. (Surg.) Univ. Melbourne, Austral.

KOCZAN, Phillip James Churchill Medical Centre, 1 Churchill Terrace, Chingford, London E4 8DA Tel: 020 8524 1777 Fax: 020 8559 4142; Meryweathers, 34 Blackacre Road, Theydon Boib, Epping CM16 7LU Tel: 01992 815629 — MB BS 1988 Lond.; MRCGP 1994; Dip. IMC RCS Ed. 1992; DRCOG 1991. GP. Prev: Trainee GP Chelmsford VTS.

KODATI, Mr Shyam Mohan Rao Mount Vernon & Watford NHS Trust, Vicarage Road, Watford WD18 0HB Tel: 01923 217543; Nirvana, 121 Ducks Hill Road, Northwood HA6 2SQ Tel: 01923 842132 Fax: 01923 842132 Email: shyamkodati@compuserve.com — MB BS 1977 Osmania; LMSSA Lond. 1985; FRCS Ed. 1989; FCOphth 1989. (Osmania Med. Coll. Hyderabad, India) Cons. Ophth. Mt. Vernon Hosp. & Watford Gen. Hosp. Middlx. Socs: Fell. Roy. Soc. Med.; W Herts. Med. Soc.; BMA. Prev: Fell. (Ocular Oncol.) P.ss Margt. Hosp. Toronto, Canada; Sen. Regist. (Ophth.) King's Coll. Hosp. Lond.

KODICEK, Jindriska Hradecka (retired) 4 Croft Gate, Fulbrooke Road, Cambridge CB3 9EG Tel: 012231 357321 — MD Prague 1932; DOMS Prague 1938.

KODIKARA, Malthi 4 Mayfair Close, Surbiton KT6 6RR — MB BS 1998 Lond.; MB BS Lond 1998.

KODILINYE, Herbert Chukuwetalu 45 St Thomas Drive, Hatch End, Pinner HA5 4SX Tel: 020 8428 4756 — MB ChB 1935 Glas.; DO Oxf. 1943; DOMS Eng. 1945. (Glas.) Vice-Chancellor & Prof. Ophth. Univ. Nigeria. Socs: Fac. Ophthalmols. & Ophth. Soc. U. K.; FRCOphth. Prev: Dir. Nat. Inst. Ophth., Nigeria; Dean Fac. Med. & Prof. Ophth. Univ. Nigeria; Cons. Ophth. Surg. No. 1 Clin. Area Manch. RHB.

KOEFMAN, Robert James The Binfield Practice, Binfield Health Centre, Terrace Road North, Binfield, Bracknell RG42 5JG Tel: 01344 425434 Fax: 01344 301843; Little Constantia, 25 Camellia Way, Wokingham RG41 3NB Tel: 01189 797221 Email: robert@koefman.freeserve.co.uk — MB ChB 1986 Stellenbosch.

KOEHLI, Nicholas The Haven, 14 Mariners Drive, Bristol BS9 1QQ Tel: 0117 909 2136 — MB BChir 1980 Camb.; MA Camb. 1982; FFA RCS Eng. 1986. Cons. Anaesth. S.mead Hosp. Bristol.

KOELLER, Anna Wanda (retired) Langeline, Manor Road, Sole St., Cobham, Gravesend DA13 Tel: 01474 814440 — MRCS Eng. LRCP Lond. 1957; FFA RCS Eng. 1964; DA Eng. 1960. Prev: Cons. Anaesth. Dartford & Gravesham Health Dist.

KOEZE, Thomas Henry Neurosurgical Unit, The Royal London Hospital, Whitechapel, London E1 1BB Tel: 020 7377 7000 — MD 1958 George Washington Univ. USA; DPhil Oxf. 1968. Locum Cons., NeUrol., Barts and Roy. Lond. NHS Trust; Sen. Lect. Neuro Surgic. Unit, Qu. Mary Univ. of Lond. Med. Sch.

KOFFMAN, Dorothea 30 The Broadway, Oadby, Leicester LE2 2HE Tel: 0116 270 3304 — MD 1949 Berne; FFPHM 1982, M 1974; DPH Eng. 1953; FRCPCH 1997. (Univ of Berne Switzerland) Emerit. Specialist Community Med. (Child Health) Leics. AHA (T). Socs: BMA &RCPCH; Fell. of RCPCH (Roy. Coll. of Paediat. and Child Health); Fell. of Fac. of Pub. Health Med. Prev: SCM (Child Health) Leics. AHA (T); PMO (Child Health) Leics. CC; Sen. Med. Off. Lond. Boro. Brent.

KOFOKOTSIOS, Alexandros Flat 1, 19 Clifton Terrace, Wigan WN1 2LB Tel: 01972 244000 — Ptychio Iatrikes 1993 Thessalonika. SHO (Gen. Med.) Roy. Albert Edwd. Infirm. Prev: Ho. Off. (Med.) Hinchingbrooke Hosp. Huntingdon & Pinderfields Hosp. Wakefield.

KOH, Boon Chai 4A Emmanuel Road, London SW12 0PE; Royal Free Hospital, Pond St, London NW3 2PQ Tel: 020 7830 2092 Email: mickey@rfhsm.ac.uk — MB BS 1989 Singapore; MRCP (UK) 1993. Specialist Regist. (Haemat.); Hon. Lect. 1999-2000 Roy. Free Hosp. Lond.

KOH, Chen Siang Vincent c/o Lloyds Bank PLC, Charlotte Row, Great Charlotte St., Liverpool L1 1QY — MB ChB 1993 Liverp.

KOH, Jeffrey Chin Hoe North Ormesby Health Centre, Elizabeth Terrace, Westbourne Gr., North Ormesby, Middlesbrough TS3 6EN — MB ChB 1986 Glas.

KOH, Sock Huang Hall Floor Flat, 124A Redland Road, Bristol BS6 6XY — MB ChB 1995 Bristol. SHO (Anaesth.), Frenchay Hosp., Bristol. Socs: Assoc of Anaes- Train. Mem. Prev: SHO (Anaesth.) Cheltenham Gen. Hosp. Cheltenham.

KOH, Mr Tat Ngee Flat 15, Northways, College Crescent, London NW3 5DR — MB BCh BAO 1987 NUI; FRCS Ed. 1994; FRCSI 1991; LRCPSI 1987.

KOH, Tat Woon Flat 15, Northways, College Crescent, London NW3 5DR — MB BS 1989 Lond.; BSc (Hons.) Lond. 1986; MRCP (UK) 1992.

KOHEN, Dora Devora Leigh Infirmary, The Avenue, Leigh WN7 Tel: 01942 264562; 31 Derwent Avenue, London NW7 3DY Tel: 020 8959 3468 Fax: 020 8931 9194 Email: dokohen@doctors.org.uk — MD 1972 Istanbul; MD Istanbul 1978; Tip Doktoru Istanbul 1972; MRCPsych 1988. Sen. Lect. & Hon. Cons. Char. Cross. & W.m. Med. Sch. Lond. Socs: RC Psych; Brit. Neuro Clinic Assn.; Brit. Assn. Psychophomecology.

KOHI, Mr Yadon Mtarima c/o McLeish Carswell, 29 St Vincent Place, Glasgow G1 2DT — MD 1989 Glas.; MB ChB Makerere 1975; FRCS RCPS Glas. 1981; FRCSI 1980.

KOHLER, Hamish MacGregor (cons. rooms), Infirmary Drive, Alnwick NE66 2NR Tel: 01665 602388 — MB ChB 1957 Ed.; BA Open Univ. 1990; MRCGP 1981; DObst RCOG 1961.

KOHLER, Hans Gerhart (retired) 60 Foxhill Court, Weetwood, Leeds LS16 5PN Tel: 0113 267 9114 — MD 1938 Prague; FRCPath 1966. Prev: Cons. Path. Leeds Matern. Hosp.

KOHLER, Janice Ann Department of Child health, Southampton General Hospital, Tremona Road, Southampton SO16 6YD — MB ChB 1975 Bristol; FRCP Lond. 1994; MRCP (UK) 1977. Cons. & Sen. Lect. Paediat. Oncol. Soton Gen. Hosp.

KOHLHAGEN, Nalini Cottage 40, Residential Complex, Inverclyde Royal Hospital, Larkfield Road, Greenock PA16 0XN — MB BS 1995 Melbourne.

KOHLI, Bhupinder Market Street Health Group, 52 Market Street, East Ham, London E6 2RA Tel: 020 8548 2200 Fax: 020 8548 2288 — MB BS 1984 Newc.

KOHLI, Brij Lal 150 Finchley Lane, Hendon, London NW4 1DB Tel: 020 8203 5380 — MB BS 1965 Delhi.

KOHLI, Harpreet Singh Lanarkshire Health Board, 14 Beckford St., Hamilton ML3 0TA Tel: 01698 206331 Fax: 01698 424316 Email: harpreet.kohli@lanarkshirehb.scot.nhs.uk; 13 Selborne Road, Glasgow G13 1QG Tel: 0141 576 7740 Email: h.s.kohli@clinmed.gla.ac.uk — MB ChB 1981; MB ChB Ed. 1981; BSc Ed. 1978; FFPHM RCP (UK) 1996, M 1989; MFCM 1988; MPH Glas. 1986; MRCGP 1985; DRCOG 1984. (Ed.) Cons. Pub. Health Med. Lanarksh. HB; Lect. (Pub. Health Med.) Univ. Glas. Socs: Soc. Social Med. Prev: Sen. Regist. (Pub. Health Med.) Gtr. Glas. HB; Clin. Teach. (Pub. Health Med.) Univ. Glas.

KOHLI, Rakesh Royton Medical Centre, Rochdale Road, Royton, Oldham OL2 5QB Tel: 0161 624 4857 Fax: 0161 628 5010 — MB BS 1974 Calcutta; MB BS 1974 Calcutta.

KOHLI, Sanjay Kumar 150 Finchley Lane, London NW4 1DB — BM 1994 Soton.

KOHLI, Subhash Chandra 15 Redhouse Close, Lower Earley, Reading RG6 4XB — MB BS 1964 Lond.; MRCS Eng. LRCP Lond. 1964; MRCOG 1969.

KOHLI, Vinod Kumar 73 Balfour Road, Southall UB2 5BX — MB BS 1972 All India Inst. Med. Sci.; FFA RCSI 1978.

KOHLL, Simone Josee Marie 26 Highview Gardens, Edgware HA8 9UE — MB BS 1988 Lond.; BSc (Physiol.) Lond. 1985, MB BS Lond. 1988. GP Middlx.

KOHN, Alan Daniel Ealing Independent Family Practice, 38C Mount Avenue, Ealing, London W5 2QJ Tel: 020 8810 7977 Fax: 020 8997 5525 — MB ChB 1976 Birm. Med. Dir. Ealing Indep. Family Pract.; Med. Dir. Indep. Med. Loss Adjusting Serv.; Med. Adviser Braitrim, Roland Internat. (UK), Thorn EMI, Plasser Railway Machinery & Newline Bldg. Co., Lindt Chocolates, Carnavon Hotel, Trans-World Publishers, CCG Catering, Scan Press, Crystal Video, Katsouris Fresh Foods & Transradio; Apptd. Med. Panel Migration Dept. Austral. Consulate. Socs: BMA; Indep. Doctors Forum. Prev: Princip. Beachside Med. Pract. Hobart; Trainee GP N. Birm. VTS; Area Train. Co-ordinator S.. Tasmania (Family Med. Program Hobart).

KOHN, Michelle Rachel 50 West Heath Road, London NW3 7UR — MB BS 1990 Lond.; MB BS (Hons.) Lond. 1990; MRCP Lond. 1998.

KOHNER, Professor Eva Maria, OBE 32 Monckton Court, Strangways Terrace, London W14 8NF Tel: 020 7602 3064 Fax: 020 7602 3064 Email: e.kohner@kcl.ac.uk — MRCS Eng. LRCP Lond. 1959; BSc Lond. 1956, MD 1970, MB BS 1959; FRCP Lond. 1977, M 1963; FCOphth 1991; FRCOphth 1999. (Roy. Free.) Emerit. Prof.Dept Med . St. Thomas Hosp. Lond. Socs: Med. Res. Soc., Brit. Diabetic Assn. & Amer. Diabetic; Assn.; Assn. Research In Vision & Ophth. Prev: Regist. (Med.) & Research Fell. Hammersmith Hosp.; Asst. Lect. (Med.) Hammersmith Hosp. Roy. Postgrad. Med. Sch.; SHO Middlx. Hosp.

***KOJODJOJO, Pipin** Flat 4, 22 Lancaster Gate, London W2 3LH Email: pipinko@hotmail.com — MB BS 1998 Lond.; MB BS Lond 1998.

KOK, D'Almero Wolfson College, Cambridge CB3 9BB Tel: 01223 335900; 36 Barrow Road, Cambridge CB2 2AS Tel: 01223 351515 — MB BS 1942 Lond.; BSc Witwatersrand 1938; MD Lond. 1950, MB BS 1942; FRCP Lond. 1977, M 1949; Hon. MA Camb. 1955. (Witwatersrand & St. Bart.) Emerit. & Hon. Cons. Phys. Addenbrooke's Hosp. Camb.; Emerit. Fell. Wolfson Coll. Camb. Prev: Lect. (Med.) Univ. Camb.; Chief Asst. St. Bart. Hosp.; Graded Pathol. RAMC.

KOK, Keng Weng 1 Whittell Gardens, London SE26 4LN; Tivoli Villas 2-6-10 Jalan Medang, Tanbuk Bukit Bandaraya, Kuala Lumpar 59100, Malaysia — MB BS 1984 Malaya; MRCP (UK) 1989. Cons. Phys. Haemat. Kuala Lumpar Gen. Hosp., Malaysia; Hon. Clin. Asst. (Haemat.) KCH Lond. Socs: Malaysian Med. Assn. Prev: Phys. Pekan Dist. Hosp., Malaysia; Personal Phys. to HRH Sultan of Pakang, Malaysia.

KOK, Mr Ronald Huck Chye Belgrave Surgery, 16-18 Falsgrave Road, Scarborough YO12 5AT Tel: 01723 361279 Fax: 01723 501589 — MB BS 1960 Malaya; FRCS Eng. 1966; MRCS Eng. LRCP Lond. 1971. Prev: SHO Roy. Nat. Orthop. Hosp. Lond.; Regist. Roy. Orthop. Hosp. Birm.; Lect. Dept Orthop. Surg. Univ. Malaya.

KOK SHUN, Jean Laval Chung Seng Department of Clinical Haematology, Manchester Royal Infirmary, Oxford Road, Manchester M13 9WL Tel: 0161 276 1234 — MB ChB 1979 Leeds; MRCP (UK) 1983. Staff Grade (Haemat.) Manch. Roy. Infirm.

KOK SHUN, Marie Ginette Woodbrook Medical Centre, 28 Bridge St., Loughborough LE11 1NH Tel: 01509 239166 — MB ChB 1982 Leeds.

KOKIET, Stefan John Bedford House Medical Centre, Glebe Street, Ashton-under-Lyne OL6 6HD Tel: 0161 330 9880 Fax: 0161 330 9393; 2 Lyme Road, Disley, Stockport SK6 5BE — MB ChB 1978 Manch.; MRCGP 1983; DRCOG 1982.

KOKO, Isoken 43 Ravenswood Drive S., Solihull B91 3LP — MB BS 1985 Benn, Nigeria; MRCP (UK) 1994.

KOKRI, Mr Manmohan Singh 71 Low Lane, Brookfield, Middlesbrough TS5 8EG — MB BS 1969 Newc.; FRCS Eng. 1975; FFA RCS Eng. 1982. Cons. Anaesth. S. Cleveland Hosp. Middlesbrough.

KOLACKI, Barbara Margaret Teresa 7a St Martins Road, Finham, Coventry CV3 6ET — MB BS 1996 Lond.

KOLAR, Mr Kadappa Mallappa Basset Law Hospital, Worksop S81 0BD Tel: 01909 500990 Email: hkkolal@yahoo.com; 4 Boscombe Road, Worksop S81 7SB Tel: 01909 480064 Fax: 01909 502598 — MB BS 1974 Karnatak; FRCSI 1982; FRCS Ed. 1981. (Karnatak Med. Coll. Hubli, India) Cons. Surg. (Gen. Surg.) & BrE. Surg. Basset Law Hosp. Worksop. Socs: BMA; SMIT; Assn. Surg. Prev: Cons. Surg. Qatif Centr. Hosp. & King Fahads Hosp., Saudi Arabia; Cons. Surg. (Gen. Surg.) S. Tyrone Hosp. Dungannon N. I.

KOLB, Mr Charles Stanley Ingleby, 35 Dales Lane, Whitefield, Manchester M45 7WU Tel: 0161 766 4825 Fax: 0161 796 5491 Email: ckolb@virgin.net; Ingleby, 35 Dales Lane, Whitefield, Manchester M45 7WU Tel: 0161 766 4825 Fax: 0161 796 5491 Email: c.s.kolb@virgin.net — MA Camb. 1968, MB BChir 1967; FRCS Eng. 1974. (Camb. & St. Thos.) Cons. Orthop. Surg. Roy. Oldham Hosp. & Highfield Hosp. Rochdale. Prev: SHO Roy. Nat. Orthop. Hosp. Stanmore; Regist. (Orthop.) Norf. & Norwich Hosp.; Lect. (Orthop. Surg.) Sheff. Univ.

KOLENDO, Janusz Grand Drive Surgery, 132 Grand Drive, London SW20 9EA Tel: 020 8542 5555 Fax: 020 8542 6969; 17 Delta Road, Worcester Park KT4 7HP — MB BS 1972 Lond.; DRCOG 1978.

KOLHATKAR, Lilita Madhav c/o 47 Holyrood Gardens, Edgware HA8 5LS — MB BS 1973 Bombay.

KOLHATKAR, Mr Rajaneekant Krishnarao c/o Revd. Ian Q. Coltart BD, Kirk Road, Wishaw ML2 — MB BS 1957 Poona; MRCS Eng LRCP Lond. 1967; FRCS Ed. 1967.

KOLIND, Annette Langhoff Winterfold House, Cranleigh GU6 7NH — MD 1971 Copenhagen. (Univ. Copenhagen) Specialist Child & Adolesc. Psychiat. Nat. Bd. Health Denmark.

KOLINSKY, Baldur Ivan Danesbard, 9 Valley Road, West Bridgford, Nottingham NG2 6HG Tel: 0115 923 1320 — MB ChB 1939 Ed.; MRCGP 1953. (Ed.) Socs: BMA. Prev: Ship Surg.

KOLKIEWICZ, Lucja Anna St James University Hospital, Beckett St., Leeds LS9 7TF; 14 Dockroyd, Oakworth, Keighley BD22 7RH — MB BS 1985 Lond.; MRCPsych 1990. SHO/Regist. Rotat. (Psychiat.) Leeds.

KOLLI, Mr Lajipathi Rai Royal Infirmary, Doncaster DN2 5LT Tel: 01302 66666 — MB BS 1971 Andhra; FRCS Ed. (Ophth.) 1976; DO Andhra 1972. (Guntur Med. Coll.) Cons. Ophth. Doncaster Roy. Infirm. Prev: Sen. Regist. (Ophth.) Hallamshire Hosp. Sheff.; Ho. Off. (Ophth.) Regional Hosp. Galway; Regist. (Ophth.) Glas. Eye Infirm. & Nottm. Eye Hosp.

KOLLI, Sathish 44 Butterys, Southend-on-Sea SS1 3DU — MB BS 1994 Lond.

KOLLI, Subbarao Venkata 19 Clover Way, Hedge End, Southampton SO30 4RN Tel: 01489 790366 — MB BS 1957 Madras; BSc Madras 1948; DPhysMed 1972. Prev: Med. Off. DSC Middlesbrough Gen. Hosp., St. Mary's Hsop. Portsmouth & Harold Wood Hosp. Essex.

KOLLIMADA, Mr Achaya Rajiv 86 The Ladysmith, Ashton-under-Lyne OL6 9AR Tel: 0161 343 1893 — MB BS 1978 Bangalore; FRCSI 1988. Staff Grade (A & E) Tameside Gen. (Acute) NHS Trust Hosp. Ashton-under-Lyne. Prev: SHO (Gen. Surg., Vasc. Surg. & Urol.) Tameside Gen. Hosp. Ashton-under-Lyne.

KOLLIPARA, Premila King George Hospital, Barley Lane, Goodmayes, Ilford IG3 8YB Tel: 020 8970 5701; 36 Ernest Road, Hornchurch RM11 3JQ Tel: 020 8970 8060 Fax: 01708 702001 — MD 1976 Madras; FRCOG 1996, M 1983; MFFP 1995; DRCOG 1980. Cons. O & G King. Geo. Hosp. Goodmayes, Essex. Socs: Brit. Soc. Gyn. Endoscopy; Internat. Soc. Gyn. Endoscopy; Brit. Menopause Soc.

KOLMAN, Mrs Pia Cornelia Kolman and Partners, Rochdale Surgery, Broomfield Avenue, Palmers Green, London N13 4JJ Tel: 020 8886 3631 — MRCS Eng. LRCP Lond. 1974; DA (UK) 1975. GP Enfield.

KOLOCASSIDES, Mr Kyriacos Georgiou 215 Sydney Road, Muswell Hill, London N10 2NL — MB BS 1985 Lond.; FRCS Eng. 1989. Regist. (Cardiothoracic Surg.) Middlx. Hosp. Lond. Prev: Regist. (Cardiothoracic Surg.) St Mary's Hosp. Lond.

KOLOKITHAS, Dimitrios 24 Lowfield Road, Acton, London W3 0AY — MSc Med. Microbiol. Lond. 1984; Ptychio Iatrikis Athens 1968; Dip. Clin. Path. Lond 1983. Socs: BMA; Assoc. RCPath. Prev: Regist. (Med. Microbiol.) St. Stephen's Hosp. Lond.; SHO/Regist. (Path.) King Edwd. Memor. Hosp. Lond.; SHO (Path.) Brook Gen. Hosp. Lond.

KOLOMAINEN, Desiree Fleur Department of Obstetrics, Hammersmith House, Hammersmith Hospital, Du Cane Road, London W12 0HS — MB BS 1996 Lond.; BSc Lond. 1993. (King's Coll. Sch. Med. and Dent.)

KOLOSINSKA, Zofia Stanislawa 22 Redbridge Lane W., London E11 — LRCPI & LM, LRSCI & LM 1961; LRCPI & LM, LRCSI & LM 1961; DA Eng. 1966.

KOLOWSKI, Stefan Jan 54 Watson Avenue, Nottingham NG3 7BL — MB ChB 1989 Bristol.

KOLPANOWICZ, Edyta Matylda Flat 9, 36 Morris Lane, Kirstall, Leeds LS5 3JD Tel: 0113 275 6168; c/o Mr M. Solarz, Flat 10, Makepeace Walk, Manchester M8 4HL Tel: 0161 721 4807 — MB ChB 1990 Leeds. SHO (Anaesth.) St. Jas. Univ. Hosp. Leeds. Prev: SHO (Anaesth.) Alexandra Hosp. Redditch; SHO (Paediat.) Leeds Gen. Infirm.; SHO (O & G) Bradford.

KOLVEKAR, Mr Shyamsunder Krishna Cardiac Services Directorate, The Middx Hospital, Mortimer St., London W1N 8AA Tel: 020 7386 9297 Fax: 020 7436 1755 Email: skolvekar@compuserve.com — MB BS 1983 Bombay; MS (Gen. Surg.) Bombay 1984, MB BS 1983; FRCS (Cth) 1994; FRCS Glas. 1992. (Grant Med. Coll. Bombay) Cons. (Cardiothoracic Surg.) The Middx Hosp. Lond. Socs: Cardiothoracic Surg. Soc.; Cardiovasc. & Thoracic Surg. Soc. India.; BMA. Prev: Sen. Clin. Fell. (Cardiothoracic Surg.) Soton. Gen. Hosp.; Sen. Regist. (Cardiothoracic Surg.) St. Geo.'s Hosp. Lond.; Sen. Regist. (Cardiothoracic Surg.) Glenfield Hosp. Leicester.

KOLVIN, Professor Israel Tavistock Clinic, 120 Belsize Lane (Main Office), London NW3 Tel: 020 4473 8111 Email: isro.kolvin@virgin.net; 86 Heathcroft, Hampstead Way, London NW11 7HL Fax: 020 7447 3733 — MD 1966 Witwatersrand; BA S. Afr. 1952; FRCPsych 1972; Dip. Psych. Ed. 1961; MFPHM 1993; FCPCH 1997 (Hon. 2001). Emerit. Prof. Child. & Family Ment. Health Roy. Free Hosp. & Univ. Coll. Lond. & Tavistock Clinic Lond.; Hon. Cons. Tavistock Clinic Lond. Socs: Fell. Roy. Soc. Med. (Ex-Pres. Counc. Psychiat. Sec.); Fell. Roy. Coll. Psychiat. (Ex-Vice-Pres., Ex-Chairm. Child & Adolesc.; Fell. Roy. Coll. Paed. Child Health. Prev: Sen. Regist. Warneford Hosp. & Pk. Hosp. Oxf.; Regist. (Psychol.) Med. Roy. Hosp. Sick Childr. Edin.; Prof. Child Psychiat. & Dir. Human Developm. Unit Univ. Newc.

KOMOCKI, Edward Charles Department of Old Age Psychiatry, Mapleton Day Hospital, Derby City General Hospital, Uttoxeter Road, Derby DE22 3NE Tel: 01332 625843 — BM 1985 Soton.; MSc (Clin. Psychother.) Lond. 1993; MRCPsych 1991; T(Psych) 1994. (Southampton) Cons. Old Age Psychiat. S.. Derbysh. Ment. Health NHS Trust. Prev: Sen. Regist. (Psychiat.) Roy. S. Hants. Hosp. Soton.

KON, Chee Hing Moorfields Eye Hospital, City Road, London EC1V 2PD; Flat 5, Providence Tower, Bermondsey Wall W., London SE16 4US Tel: 020 7237 6157 Email: chee@private.nethead.co.uk — MB BS 1985 Lond.; MSc Lond. 1987, MD 1997; FCOphth 1991; DIC 1987. Specialist Regist. Moorfields Eye Hosp. Lond. Prev: Regist. (Ophth.) St. Geo. Hosp. Lond.; SHO (Ophth.) Roy. Vict. Hosp. W.bourne & Sussex Eye Hosp. Brighton.

KON, Mr Mark Wei Syn Dept. Radiology, Northwick Park Hospital, Watford Road, Harrow HA1 3UJ Email: m.kon@xrays.demon.co.uk; 33 Greeenham Road, Muswell Hill, London N10 1LN — MB BS 1990 Lond. Specialist Regist. Radiol. Socs: Fell. Roy. Coll. Surgs. Eng.

KON, Onn Min Chest and Allergy Clinic, St. Mary's Hospital, Praed St., London W2 1NY Tel: 020 7886 1344 Fax: 020 7886 1613 Email: onn.kon@st-marys.nhs.uk — MB BS 1988 Lond.; MRCP (UK) 1992; MD Lond. 2000. (Middlx & Univ. Coll.) Cons. Respirat. Phys., St. Mary's Hosp., Lond.; Hon. Sen. Lect., Imperial Coll. Sch. Of Med. Lond. Socs: BMA & BTS; BSACI. Prev: Specialist Regist. (Respirat. Med.) Char. Cross Hosp. Lond.; Specialist Regist. (Respirat. Med.) Roy. Brompton Hosp. Lond.; Research Fell. Nat. Heart & Lung Inst. Lond.

KON, Peke Yan Northpoint, 2 Cambridge Road, Middlesbrough TS5 5NA Tel: 01642 855441; 4 Copeland Court, Durham DH1 4LF — MB BS 1984 Lond.; MRCPsych 1989. Cons. Psychiat. (Learning Disabil.)Tees & N. E. Yorks. NHS trust. Prev: Sen. Regist. (Psychiat. of Learning Disabil.) N.. RHA.

KON, Pimprapa Abbott Laboratories Ltd., Abbott House, Norden Road, Maidenhead SL6 4XE Tel: 01628 644193; 44A Courtfield Gardens, London SW5 0LZ — MB BS 1985 Lond.; MRCP (UK) 1991; Dip. Pharm. Med. RCP (UK) 1996. Sen. Med. Adviser Abbott Laborat. Ltd. Maidenhead. Prev: SHO Roy. Sussex Co. Hosp. Brighton; SHO Poole Gen. Hosp.

KON, Sui Phin Renal Unit, King's College Hospital, East Dulwich Grove, London SE22 8PT; 36 Western Avenue, Golders Green, London NW11 9HJ — MB BS 1983 Lond.; MD Lond. 1994; MRCP (UK) 1987. Cons. (Nephrol.) King's Coll. Hosp. Lond. Prev: Sen. Regist. (Gen. Med. & Nephrol.) Roy. Lond. Hosp.; Lect. (Nephrol.) Roy. Lond. Hosp.; Research Regist. (Nephrol.) Manch. Roy. Infirm.

KONARZEWSKI, William Henry Maltings Farm, Lexden, Colchester CO3 4AS — MB BS 1973 Lond.; MRCS Eng. LRCP Lond. 1973; FFA RCS Eng. 1978. (Guy's) Cons. (Anaesth. & Intens. Care) Colchester Gen. Hosp. Prev: Sen. Regist. (Anaesth.) Hammersmith Hosp. Lond.

KONDOL, Antoni Joseph East Donnington Street Clinic, East Donnington Street, Darvel KA17 0JR Tel: 01560 320205 Fax: 01560 321643 — MB ChB 1977 Aberd.

KONDRACKI, Sara Gawad 20 Marchmont Crescent, Edinburgh EH9 1HL — MB ChB 1990 Ed.; MSc Lond. 1982; BSc Ed. 1980. (Edinburgh University) p/t Negist. (Psychiat.) Edin. Lothian Train. Scheme; Specialist Regist.

KONDRATOWICZ, Ewa Anna 287 Haslucks Green Road, Shirley, Solihull B90 2LW Tel: 0121 744 6663 — MB ChB 1983 Manch.

KONDRATOWICZ, George Mark Department of Pathology, Kidderminster General Hospital, Kidderminster DY11 6RY — MB ChB 1981 Manch.; MRCPath 1988. Cons. Path. Kidderminster Gen. Hosp. & Alexandra Hosp. Redditch. Prev: Lect. (Path.) Univ. Birm.

KONDRATOWICZ, Tadeusz Trafford General Hospital, Davyhulme, Manchester M41 5SL — MB ChB 1970 Manch.; FRCP Lond. 1988; DObst RCOG 1973. Cons. Phys. Pk. Hosp. Manch.

KONERU, Usha Sundari c/o Drive Rani, 51 Belvedere Road, Blackburn BB1 9NS — MB BS 1974 Osmania; FRCOG 1996. Prev: Cons. O & G Armed Forces Hosp. Tabuk, Saudi Arabia; Regist. (O & G) Qu. Pk. Hosp. Blackburn.

KONG, Andrew Seun 17 Warrington Road, Ipswich IP1 3QU — MB BS 1981 Lond.; FFA RCS Eng. 1988. Cons. Ipswich Hosp. Prev: Sen. Regist. (Anaesth.) Addenbrooke's Hosp. Camb.; Lect. Chinese Univ., Hong Kong; Regist. Rotat. Bristol.

KONG, Etheldreda Kee Ching Church End Medical Centre, 66 Mayo Road, Church End Estate, Willesden, London NW10 9HP Tel: 020 8930 6262 Fax: 020 8930 6260; Church End Medical Centre, 66 Mayo Road, London NW10 9HP Tel: 020 8930 6262 Fax: 020 8930 6260 — MB BS 1984 Lond.; MRCGP 1996; DFFP 1993. (Univ. Coll. Hosp. Lond.) GP Lond.; Exec. Mem. of the Brent Commiss.ing Gp. Socs: Brit. Med. Acupunct. Soc.; BMA.

KONG, Hee Anthony Room 1, 3 Hollymead Close, Colchester CO4 5JU — MB BS 1997 Lond.

KONG, Mr James Han Boon 15 Langdon Park Road, Highgate, London N6 5PS Tel: 020 8341 4688; Apartment 16a, Kwun King Mansions, Lie King Wan, Hong Kong — MB BS 1979 Lond.; FRCS Ed. 1986; MRCS Eng. LRCP Lond. 1978. (St. Bart.) Lect. Chinese Univ. Fac. Med. P. Wales Hosp. Hong Kong. Prev: Regist. (Surg.) The Lond. Hosp. Whitechapel.

KONG, Kam Fung 49 Willet Way, Orpington BR5 1QE — MB BS 1982 Lond.; MRCOG 1990; DRCOG 1985. Regist. (In Vitro Fertilisation) St. Bart. & Portland Hosps. Lond. Prev: Regist. (O & G) P.ss Alexandra Hosp. Harlow; Regist. (O & G) Barnet & Edgware Hosp.

KONG, Mr Kin Chong Homerton Hospital, Homerton Row, London E9 6SR — MB BS 1980 Malaya; FRCS Glas. 1984. Cons. Orthop. Surg. Homerton Hosp. Lond. Prev: Research Regist. (Orthop.) Mayday Hosp.; Sen. Regist. (Orthop.) Greenwich Dist. & Brook Hosp.; Sen. Regist. (Orthop.) Luton & Dunstable Hosp.

KONG, Kin Leong Department of Anaesthesia, City Hospital NHS Trust, Dudley Road, Birmingham B18 7QH Tel: 0121 554 3801; 25 Hampshire Drive, Birmingham B15 3NY — MB BS 1981 Malaya; MD Bristol 1991; FFA RCS Eng. 1986; FFA RCSI 1985. City Hosp. NHS Trust Birm. Prev: Lect. (Anaesth.) Univ. Birm.; Research Fell. Sir Humphry Davy Dept. Anaesth. Univ. Brist.; Regist. Rotat. (Anaesth.) Bristol.

KONG, Ngai Department of Diabetes, Selly Oak Hospital, University Hospital NHS Trust, Raddlebarn Road, Birmingham B29 6JD Tel: 0121 627 1627 — MB ChB 1989 Dundee; MRCP (UK) 1994. Specialist Regist. (Diabetes & Endocrinol.) Selly Oak Hosp. Birm. Prev: Regist. Rotat. (Gen. Med.) Morriston Hosp. Swansea; SHO Rotat. (Gen. Med.) York Dist. Hosp. & Hull Roy. Infirm.; SHO (A & E) N. Tees Gen. Hosp. Stockton on Tees.

KONG, Robert See-Kun University College London Hospitals, Mortimer St., London W1 Tel: 020 7636 8333; 25 White Street, Brighton BN2 2JH — MB BS 1985 Lond.; FRCA 1992. Sen. Regist. (Anaesth.) Univ. Coll. Hosp. Lond. Prev: Clin. Research Fell. (Intens. Care) Hôpital Lariboisiére Paris, France; Regist. (Anaesth.) Qu. Eliz. Hosp. Birm.; SHO (Anaesth.) Roy. Sussex Co. Hosp. Brighton.

KONG, San Choon 120 Wingrove Road, Fenham, Newcastle upon Tyne NE4 9BT — MB BS 1993 Newc.

KONG, Suet-Kei Flat 12, 46 Lowndes Square, London SW1X 9JU Tel: 020 7235 4697 — MB BS 1992 Lond. SHO (Anaesth.) E. Surrey Hosp. Redhill. Socs: BMA & Med. Defence Union. Prev: SHO (Anaesth.) Mt. Vernon Hosp. & Watford Gen. Hosp.; SHO (A & E) Barnet Gen. Hosp.

KONG, Suet-Man 5 Rogerson's Green, Church Road, Halewood, Liverpool L26 — MB ChB 1990 Liverp.

KONG, Wing Ming 18 Westray Close, Beeston, Nottingham NG9 3GP — BM BS 1991 Nottm.

KONG YAO FAH, Sew-Chine Marie-France Dept. of Diabetes/ Endocrinology, Nottingham City Hospital, Hacknell Rd, Nottingham NG5 1BG Tel: 0115 969 1169 Email: mfkong@hotmail.com; 47 Camelot Avenue, Sherwood, Nottingham NG5 1DW — MB ChB 1989 Aberd.; MRCP (UK) 1992. Specialist Regist. Nottm. City Hosp. Prev: Specialist Regist. King's Mill Hosp. Sutton-in-Ashford; Research Fell., Roy. Adelaide Hosp., Australia; Research Regist. Univ. Hosp. Qu. Med. Centre Nottm.

KONG YAO FAH, Sew Kiow Unit of Metabolic Medicine, St. Mary's Hospital, Praed St., London W2 1HY; Flat 6, Amos Residence, St. Charles Hospital, Exmoor St, London W10 6DZ — MB ChB 1989 Leeds; MRCP (UK) 1993. (Univ. Leeds) Clin. Research Fell. (Diabetes & Encocrinol.) St. Mary's Hosp. Lond. Socs: Med. Protec. Soc.; BMA & Brit. Diabetic Assn. Prev: Regist. Rotat. (Diabetes & Endocrinol.) St. Mary's Hosp. Lond.; SHO Rotat. (Med.) Wolverhampton New Cross Hosp.; Ho. Phys. Chapel Allerton Hosp. Leeds.

KONGAR, Nirmalendu Cranleigh Drive Surgery, 33 Cranleigh Drive, Leigh-on-Sea SS9 1SX Tel: 01702 75485 Fax: 01702 471365 — MB BS 1962 Calcutta.

KONIECZKO, Krystyna Malgorzata 143 Park Road, Chiswick, London W4 3EX — MB BS 1976 Lond.; FFA RCS Eng. 1980. (Univ. Coll. Hosp.) Cons. Anaesth. & ICM N.wick Pk. Hosp. Harrow Middx. Prev: Sen. Regist. Roy. Free Hosp., E.man Dent. Hosp. N. Middlx. Hosp., N.wick Pk. Hosp. & Clin. Research Centre.; Regist. (Anaesth.) Univ. Coll. Hosp., Gt. Ormond St. Hosp. Lond. & Brompton Hosp.

KONIG, Philip Carl Winfried Christoph 11 The Wiend, Wirral CH63 7RG — State Exam Med 1992 Cologne.

KONIG, Silvia Regent, Holly Tree Lodge, 42A The Ridgeway, Enfield EN2 8QT — MD 1988 Munich; State Exam Med 1986.

KONJE, Justin Chi Leicester Royal Infirmary, Clinical Services Building, Leicester LE2 7LX Tel: 0116 254 1414 Fax: 0116 252 3154 — MB BS 1982 Ibadan; MD (Leicester) 1997; FWACS 1991; FMCOG (Nigeria) 1990; MFFP 1993; MRCOG 1990; LLB 1999; MBA 1998. Sen. Lect./ Cons., Univ. of Leicester. Socs: BMA & Brit. Fertil. Soc.; BMUS, IASOG; Eur. Soc. Perinatal Med. Prev: Lect. & Sen. Regist. Univ. Leicester; Clin. Research Fell. Univ. Leicester; Lect. & Regist. Bristol Matern. Hosp.

KONOTEY-AHULU, Felix Israel Domeno 10 Harley Street, London W1N 1AA Tel: 020 7467 8300 Fax: 020 7467 8312 Email: felix@konotey-ahulu.com; Cromwell Hospital, 17 Southsea Avenue, Watford, Herts. WD1 7NJ, London SW5 0TU Tel: 020 7460 2000 Fax: 020 7244 6678/460 5555 Mobile: 07876 682345 Email: konotey-ahulu@cromwell-hospital.co.uk — MB BS 1959 Lond.; MD Lond. 1972; FRCP Lond. 1975, M 1965; FRCP Glas. 1971, M 1964; MRCS Eng. LRCP Lond. 1959; DTM & H Liverp. 1962. (Univ. Coll. Lond. & Westm.) Vis. Cons. Phys. Cromwell Hosp. Lond.; Dr Kwegyir Aggrey dist prof of Human Genetics, Univ of Cape Coast Ghana. Socs: Fell. Roy. Soc. Med.; Fell. Roy. Soc. Trop. Med. & Hyg.; Fell. Ghana Med. Assn. Prev: Dir. Ghana Inst. Clin. Genetics & Phys. Korle Bu Teachg. Hosp., Accra; Phys. Specialist Ridge Hosp. Accra; Research Fell. Dept. Med. Roy. Free Hosp. Lond.

KONSTAM, Sheila Thompson Thule, Kirkwall KW15 1SU Tel: 01856 872821 — MB ChB 1943 Aberd. (Aberd.) Prev: Med. Off. W.. Region Tuberc. Serv., Nigeria; Ho. Surg. Aberd. Matern. Hosp. & Roy. Aberd. Hosp. Sick Childr.

KONSTANTINIDOU, Maria 10C Ashington Road, Rochford SS4 1NJ — Ptychio Iatrikes 1985 Thessalonika.

KONTOGIANNI, Ionna B7 Sloane Avenue Mansions, Sloane Avenue, London SW3 3JG — Ptychio Iatrikes 1992 Thessalonika.

KONTOS, Katina 27 Howard Gardens, Cardiff CF24 0EF — MB BCh 1991 Wales.

KONU, Godwin Kwaku 8 Ermington Road, Park Hall Est., Wolverhampton WV4 5DZ Tel: 01902 331525 — Lekarz 1971 Krakow. Staff Grade Pract. (A & E) Derbysh. Roy. Infirm. Prev: Regist. (A & E) Hosp. of St. Cross Rugby; SHO (Orthop.) N. Lonsdale Hosp. Barrow-in-Furness; SHO (A & E & Orthop. Surg.) Vict. Hosp. Blackpool.

KONZON, Nigel Ian Iveagh House Surgery, Iveagh House, Loughborough Road, London SW9 7SE Tel: 020 7274 8850 Fax: 020 7733 2102 — MB BS 1982 Lond.

KOO, Chi Kai Radiology Department, Darent Valley Hospital, Darenth Wood Rd, Dartford DA2 8DA Tel: 01322 428100 — MB ChB 1988 Liverp.; FRCR 1999; MRCP (UK) 1993. Cons. Radiologist, Dartford & Gravesham NHS Trust, Darent Valley Hosp., Dartford. Prev: SHO (Oncol.) Qu. Eliz. Hosp. Birm.; SHO Rotat. (Gen. Med.) Wrexham Maelor Hosp. & S. Cleveland Hosp. Middlesbrough; Ho. Off. Whiston & St. Helens Hosps.

KOOIMAN, Diane Elizabeth 52 Waverley Road, Oxshott, Leatherhead KT22 0RZ Tel: 01372 801592 — MB BS Lond. 1993;

BSc 1990; MRCP 1996; DRCOG 1998; DFFP 1998. (U.M.D.S.) GP Regist. Kingston-on-Thames.

KOOIMAN, Edith Dorothea Hedwig Residence 6, Medway Hospital, Windmill Road, Gillingham ME7 6NY — MB ChB 1993 Stellenbosch.

KOOIMAN, Gordon Gys 52 Waverley Road, Oxshott, Leatherhead KT22 0RZ — MB BS 1993 Lond.

KOONAR, Kalwant Singh Lawn Medical Centre, 31 Dudley Street, Healing, Grimsby DN31 2AW Tel: 01472 251444; 13 Brooklands Avenue, Cleethorpes DN35 8QP — BM 1982 Soton.

KOONER, Harinder Singh c/o Doctors' Mess, Mayday Hospital, Thornton Heath, Croydon CR9 2RH — MB BS 1985 Lond.

KOONER, Harpreet Singh 42 Burwell Avenue, Greenford UB6 0NU — BM 1985 Soton.

KOONER, Jaspal Singh 7 Alexandra Gardens, Hounslow TW3 4HT — MRCS Eng. LRCP Lond. 1981; MD Lond. 1990, MB BS 1981; MRCP (UK) 1985. Sen. Lect. & Hon. Cons. Cardiovasc. Med. Roy. Postgrad. Med. Sch. Hammersmith Hosp. Lond. Prev: Lect. & Sen. Regist. St. Mary's Hosp. Lond.

KOONER, Mandeep 34 Highlands Heath, London SW15 3TR — MB BS 1988 Lond.; DRCOG 1992. Trainee GP Crawley Hosp. VTS.

KOONER, Paul 64 Wynchgate, London N14 6RL — MB BS 1996 Lond.

KOONER, Ravinder Kaur 7 Alexandra Gardens, Hounslow TW3 4HT; 224 London Road, Twickenham TW1 1EU Tel: 020 8892 1858 — MB BS 1981 Lond.; MRCP (UK) 1986; MRCGP 1986; DRCOG 1984; DCH RCP Lond. 1983; Cert. Family Plann. JCC 1984.

KOONER, Tehal Singh 1 Collington Close, Gravesend DA11 9JX — MB BS 1994 Lond.

KOOY, Sander Adrianus 4 Tideway Court, 238 Rotherhithe St., London SE16 5QS — Artsexamen 1989 Amsterdam.

KOPCKE, David Howard Francis Ash Trees Surgery, Market Street, Carnforth LA5 9JU Tel: 01524 720000 Fax: 01524 720110 — MB ChB 1980 Manch.

KOPELMAN, Harry (retired) Llanfoist, 5 Kendal Avenue, Epping CM16 4PN Tel: 01992 72056 — MRCS Eng. LRCP Lond. 1939; MD Lond. 1943, MB BS 1939; FRCP Lond. 1964, M 1941; DA Eng. 1940. Hon. Cons. Phys. St. Margt. Hosp. Epping & P.ss Alexandra Hosp. Harlow; Asst. Dir. Brit. Postgrad. Med. Federat.; Postgrad. Dean NE Thames RHA. Prev: Hon. Lect. in Med. Lond. Hosp. Med. Coll.

KOPELMAN, Professor Michael David Division of Psychiatry & Psychology, UMDS, St. Thomas's Hospital, Lambeth Palace Road, London SE1 7EH Tel: 020 7928 9292 Fax: 020 7633 0061 Email: m.kopelman@umds.ac.uk — MB BS Lond. 1978; PhD Lond. 1988; BA (Hons.) Psychol. & Economics Keele 1972; FRCPsych 1993, M 1983. (Glasgow) Reader (Neuropsychiat.) & Hon. Cons. Psychiat. St. Thos. Hosp. W. Lambeth Community Care Trust & UMDS Lond. Socs: Fell. Brit. Psychol. Soc.; Memory Disorders Research Soc. Prev: Wellcome Trust Lect. Inst. Psychiat. Lond.

KOPELMAN, Professor Peter Graham Medical Unit, The Royal London Hospital, London E1 1BB Tel: 020 7377 7696 Fax: 020 7377 7636 Email: p.g.kopelman@mds.qmw.ac.uk — MB BS 1974 Lond.; MD Lond. 1982; FRCP Lond. 1992; MRCP (UK) 1976. (St. Geo.) Prof. (Clin. Med.) & Asst. Warden (Educat.) St. Bart. & Roy. Lond. Sch. Med. & Qu. Mary's W.field Coll. Lond.; Hon. Cons. Phys. Roy. Hosps. Trust. Prev: Cons. Phys. Newham HA; Lect. (Gen. Med., Metab. & Endocrinol.) Lond. Hosp. Med. Coll.; Regist. (Gen. Med.) St. Geo. Hosp. Lond.

KOPELOWITZ, Lionel 10 Cumberland House, Clifton Gardens, London W9 1DX Tel: 020 7289 6375; Kunz Cottage, 7 Sea Lane, Middleton-on-Sea, Bognor Regis PO22 7RU Tel: 01243 582167 — MRCS Eng. LRCP Lond. 1951; MA Camb. 1951; MRCGP 1964. (Camb. & Univ. Coll. Hosp.) Indep. GP Lond.; Chairm. Centr. Advis. Comm. BMA Dep. Servs.; JP.; Pres. Bd. Deputies of Brit. Jews. Socs: Fell. BMA (Counc. & Mem. Armed Forces Comm.); Gen. Optical Counc.; (Counc.) Roy. Coll. Gen. Practs. Prev: Chairm. Newc. Family Pract. Comm.; Mem. (Pres. 1978-1979) Soc. Family Pract. Comms.; Chairm. Newc. LMC.

KOPER, Margaretha c/o Department of Anaesthesia, Fazakerley Hospital, Longmoor Lane, Liverpool L9 7AL — Artsexamen 1985 Amsterdam.

KOPERSKI, Marek Tadeusz James Wigg Group Practice, Kentish Town Health Centre, 2 Bartholomew Road, London NW5 2AJ Tel: 020 7530 4747 Fax: 020 7530 4750 — MB BS 1976 Lond.; MSc Lond. 1990; MRCGP 1981; DTM & H RCP Lond. 1978. (University College London) Hon. Sen. Lect. Dept. Care & Populat. Sci.s UCL/Roy. Free Hosps.

KOPPADA, Veerabhadra Rao Department of Anaesthetics, Wrightington Hospital NHS Trust, Hall Lane, Appley Bridge, Wigan WN6 9EP Tel: 01257 256244 Fax: 01257 256340; 12 Church Walk, Euxton, Chorley PR7 6HL — MB BS 1973 Andhra; FFA RCSI 1985. (Andhra Med. Coll.Andhra Med. Coll.) Cons. Anaesth. WrightingtonHosp. NHS Trust. Socs: Assn. Anaesth.; Assn. SW Soc. Anaesth.

KOPPEL, Mr David Andrew Department of Oral & Maxillofacial Surgery, Canniesburn Hospital, Switchback Road, Bearsden, Glasgow G61 1QL Tel: 0141 211 5600 Fax: 0141 943 1385 — MB BS 1991 Lond.; BDS Lond. 1984; FRCS Eng. 1994; FRCS Glas. 1994; FDS RCS Eng. 1992; FRCS 1997. Cons. (Craniofacial/Oral & Maxillofacial Surg.), Canniesburn Hosp., Galsgow; Hon. Clin. Lect. Univ. Glas.; Hon. Cons. to the Roy. Navy. Socs: Fell.Roy. Soc. of Med.; Fell.Brit. Assn. of Oral and Maxillofacial Surg.s. Prev: Sen. Regist. (Oral & Maxillofacial Surg.) Canniesburn Hosp. Glas.; Cas. Off. (Surg.) St. Thos. Hosp. Lond.

KOPPEL, Jozef Ivan Grove Medical Practice, 49 Richford Gate, Richford Street, London W6 7HY Tel: 020 8846 7555 Fax: 020 8846 7538; 11 Prebend Gardens, London W4 1TN Tel: 020 8994 6287 Fax: 020 8994 7463 Email: ivan@ikop.demon.co.uk — MB BS 1972 Lond.; MMed Ed. 1992; MRCP (UK) 1975; FRCGP 1992, M 1977. (St. Mary's) Princip. Lect. Centre for Community Care & Primary Health Univ. W.m. Socs: RSM. Prev: Trainee GP Hammersmith VTS; Ho. Surg. (Orthop. & O & G) St. Mary's Hosp. Lond.; Ho. Phys. Edgware Gen. Hosp.

KOPPEL, Sian Melanie Caswell Clinic, Glanrhyd Hospital, Bridgend CF31 4LN Tel: 01656 662179 — MB BCh 1983 Wales; 1977 PGCE; MSc (Psychiat.) Wales 1996; BSc (Hons. Zool.) Lond. 1976; MRCPsych 1996. (Welsh Nat. Sch. Med., Cardiff) Specialist Regist. (Forens. Psych.) Mid. Glam. Prev: Specialist Regist. (Psychiat.) S. Glam.

KOPPIKAR, Mr Mohan Gopalrao General Surgery Department, West Middlesex University Hospital, Isleworth TW7 6AF; 25 Hayling Avenue, Feltham TW13 7JN — MB BS 1975 Bombay; FRCS Ed. 1989.

KOR, Hung Song 3 Honister Avenue, Newcastle upon Tyne NE2 3PA — MB BS 1988 Newc.; T(GP) 1993.

KORAB-KARPINSKI, Mr Marek Romuald Castle Hill Hospital, Cottingham HU16 Tel: 01482 623022; The Consulting Rooms, 10 Packman Lane, Kirk Ella, Hull HU10 7TL Tel: 01482 659048 Fax: 01482 659048 Email: mrkkarpinski@orthopaedic.org.uk — BM BS 1977 Nottm.; BMedSci (Hons.) Nottm. 1975; MChOrth Liverp. 1985; FRCS (Orth.) 1985; FRCS Eng. 1981; FRCS Ed. 1981; Dip. Soc. Radiogr. 1971; FRSM 1997. Cons. Spinal & Orthop. Surg. Castle Hill Hosp. Cottingham; Hon. Prof. Orthop. Surg. Poznan Acad. Orthop. Socs: Fell. BOA; Hon. Fell. Univ. Hull Med. Soc.; Brit. Cervical Spine Soc. Prev: Pre-Fell.sh. Regist. Scheme Centr. Birm. Hosps.; Post-Fell.sh. Regist. (Orthop.) Roy. Orthop. Hosp. Birm.; Sen. Regist. Derbysh. Roy. Infirm. & Harlow Wood Hosp. Notts.

KORAM, Kwadwo Okwaning Flat 2, 7 Curzon Road, Southport PR8 6PL — MB ChB 1979 Ghana.

KORDAN, Mark Alexander Dudley Park Medical Centre, 28 Dudley Park Road, Acocks Green, Birmingham B27 6QR Tel: 0121 706 0072 Fax: 0121 707 0418 — MB ChB 1983 Bristol; MRCGP 1989.

KORDAY, Mr Sujit Nandkumar 3 Litchurch Street, Derby DE1 2RG — MB BS 1988 Bombay; FRCS Ed. 1994.

KORENDOWYCH, Eleanor 13 Larkhall Terrace, Larkhall, Bath BA1 6RZ — BM BCh 1993 Oxf.; MRCP (uk) 1996. Specialist Regist. (Rheum.), Soutmead Hosp., Bristol.

KORGAONKAR, Subhash Vasudeo Kalmar, Icknield Way E., Baldock SG7 5DE Tel: 01462 893096 — MB BS 1958 Bombay; MRCPsych 1972; DPM Eng. 1963. (G.S. Med. Coll.) Cons. Psychiat. Bedford Gen. & Fairfield Hosps.

KORIA, Ashok Parshottam Whitehall Medical Practice, Morton Gardens, Lower Hillmorton Road, Rugby CV21 3AQ Tel: 01788 544264 Fax: 01788 575783 Email: ashokoria@hotmail.com; Tel: 07550 462978 Email: ashkoria@hotmail.com — MB ChB 1991 Leeds. (Leeds University) Gen. Pract. Princip.; GP Clin. Asst. for the

Rugby Community Drugs Team, Orchard centre, Lower Hillmorton Rd., Rugby.

KORIA, Kaushiklal MacDonald Road Medical Centre, MacDonald Road, Irlam, Manchester M44 5LH Tel: 0161 775 5421 Fax: 0161 775 2568; 39 Priestnall Road, Heaton Mersey, Stockport SK4 3HW Tel: 0161 442 8929 — MB ChB 1983 Manch.; MRCGP 1988; DRCOG 1990. (University of Manchester) Princip. Gen. Pract. Irlam Med. Centre Manch. Prev: Trainee GP Pendlebury, Manch.; SHO (Psychiat.) Fairfield Gen. Hosp. Bury; SHO (O & G) Bedford Gen. Hosp.

KORIA, Rakesh Flat 70, Broomfield, Kennington Road, Ashford TN24 0LY — MB BS 1989 Lond.

KORKODILOS, Marilena 24 Huxley Gardens, London NW10 7DX — MB BS 1994 Lond.

KORLIPARA, Krishnar Rao Pike View Medical Centre, 2-10 Albert Street, Horwich, Bolton BL6 7AS Tel: 01204 699311 Fax: 01204 668387 — MB BS 1964 Karnatak. (Kasturba Med. Coll. Mangalore) Chairm. Bolton Dist. Med. Servs.; Pres. Nat. Assn. GP Co-operats. Socs: Bolton Med. Soc. & BMA. Prev: Regist. & SHO (Gen. Med.) Bolton Dist. Hosp.; SHO (Gen. Med.) Mansfield & Dist. Gen. Hosp.

KORN, Henry Ernest Thomas Haematology Department, Gwynedd Hospital, Bangor LL57 2PW — MB BS 1964 Lond.; FRCPath 1984, M 1972. (Middlx.)

KORNER, Jacqueline 19 Elder Avenue, London N8 9TE — MB BS 1977 Lond.; MRCGP 1981; DRCOG 1981.

KORNFELD, Alexander (Surgery), 58B Billet Lane, Hornchurch RM11 1XA Tel: 01708 440187 Fax: 01708 457919; 6 The Witherings, Hornchurch RM11 2RA Tel: 01708 443435 — MB BS 1970 Sydney. (Sydney)

KORPAL, Kamlesh K S Medical Centre, 33 Dormers Wells Lane, Southall UB1 3HY Tel: 020 8574 3986/8571 7632 Fax: 020 8893 6188; 35 Dormers Wells Lane, Southall UB1 3HX Tel: 020 8571 7632 — MB BS 1972 Delhi. (Lady Hardinge Med. Coll.) Regist. (Path.) St. Luke's Hosp. Guildford.; GP. Prev: SHO Orthop. & Traum. Unit Roy. Surrey Co. Hosp. Guildford; SHO (Path.) St. Luke's Hosp. Guildford.

KORSAH, Philip Kwesi Gyandoh Department of Anaesthesia, Glasgow Royal Infirmary University NHS Trust, 84 Castle St., Glasgow G4 0SF Tel: 0141 211 4620; 12 Dunskey Road, Southcraigs Meadow, Kilmarnock KA3 6FJ Tel: 01563 550623 Fax: 01563 550840 Email: philip.korsah@virgin.net — MB ChB 1989 Glas.; DA (UK) 1994; FFARCS Irel. 1997. (Univ. Glas.) Specialist Regist. (Anaesth.) Glas. Roy. Infirm. Glas. Socs: Train. Mem. Assn. AnE.h.; Intens. Care Soc.; Scot. Soc. Anaesth. Prev: Intens. Care Fell. & Mem. Clin. Shock Study Gp. W.ern Infirm. Glas.

KORSZUN, Anna-Krystyna Department of Psychiatry, 1500 E. Medical Center Drive, Ann Arbor MI 48109, USA; 2 Witley Road, London N19 5SQ — MB BS 1987 Lond.; PhD Lond. 1982, MSc 1976, BDS (Hons.) 1974; MSc Brunel 1980. Assoc. Prof. & Lect. Dept. Psychiat. & Sch. Dent. Univ. Michigan Ann Arbor Michigan, USA. Prev: Assoc. Prof. Dept. Psychiat. Univ. Texas Houston, USA; Assoc. Prof. Dows Inst. Dent. Research Univ. Iowa, USA; Ho. Surg. (Urol., Gen. Surg., Cardiol. & Gen. Med.) N.wick Pk. Hosp. Harrow.

KORUTH, Mr Nathramannil Mathai Aberdeen Royal Infirmary, Foresterhill, Aberdeen AB25 2ZL — MB BS 1969 Kerala; MS (Gen. Surg.) Calicut 1973; ChM Aberd. 1986; FRCS Ed. 1976. (Calicut Med. Coll.) Cons. Surg. i/c Hepato-Biliary & Pancreatic Surg. Aberd. Roy. Infirm.; Hon. Sen. Lect. Univ. Aberd.

KORUTHU, Annamma 45 Woodstock Road, Aberdeen AB15 5EX Tel: 01224 314838 Fax: 01224 314838 — MB BS Madras 1969; DMRD Aberd. 1982; DA (UK) 1976. (Christian Med. Coll. Vellore, India)

KOS, Katarina Nuffield House, QE Medical Centre, Edgbaston, Birmingham B15 2TH — State Exam Med 1993 Munich.

KOSCIESZA, Elzbieta 97 Dudley Gardens, London W13 9LU — LMSSA 1994 Lond.

KOSHY, Elizabeth Susan 7 Sandhurst Way, Sanderstead, Purley CR2 0AH — MB BS 1998 Lond.; MB BS Lond 1998.

KOSHY, Mathew 31 Southpark Avenue, Mansfield NG18 4PJ — MB BS 1978 Kerala; MRCP (UK) 1991.

KOSKY, Nicholas Matthew Department of Psychiatry, St. Georges Hospital, Tooting, London SW17; 32 Effra Road, Wimbledon, London SW19 8PP — MB BS 1986 Lond.; MRCPsych. 1992. Research Fell. Psychiat. St. Geo. Hosp. Lond.

KOSLOWSKY, Nicholas Shaftesbury Medical Centre, 480 Harehills Lane, Leeds LS9 6DE Tel: 0113 248 5631 Fax: 0113 235 0658 — MB ChB 1982 Manch.

KOSO-THOMAS, Olajumoke Masire Ground Floor Flat, 67 Haverstock Hill, London NW3 4SL — MB ChB 1987 Leeds; MRCOG 1992.

KOSO-THOMAS, Olayinka Aina 28 Beechwood Avenue, London N3 3AX — LRCP LRCS 1963 Ed.; LRCP LRCS Ed. LRCPS Glas. 1963.

KOSOWSKI, Klaudiusz Flat 59, Blcok G, Kennington Road, Willesborough, Ashford TN24 0LZ — Lekarz 1983 Poland.

KOST, Emanuel (retired) 69 Bickenhall Mansions, Bickenhall St., London W1U 6BS — MD Berlin 1932; MD Naples 1934; DCH Eng. 1944. Prev: on Staff Neukoelln Krankenhaus Berlin.

KOSTELNIK, Jane Rea 15 Church Street, Westbury BA13 3BY — MB BS 1998 Lond.; MB BS Lond 1998.

KOSTICK, Anthony Robert Bedwell Medical Centre, Sinfield Close, Bedwell Crescent, Stevenage SG1 1LQ Tel: 01438 355551 Fax: 01438 749704 — MB BS 1984 Lond.

KOSTYN, Max 267 Ealing Road, Wembley HA0 1EZ Tel: 020 8997 3486; 228 Watford Road, Harrow HA1 3TY Tel: 020 8904 6404 — MB ChB 1957 St. And. Med. Off. Johnson Matthey (Metals) Ltd. Wembley; Med. Adviser Bell & Howell Ltd. A-V Consumer Div.

KOTAK, Anita S. Kensington and Chelsea Ment. Health Centre, 1 Nightingale Place, London SW7 9NG; 4 Marloes Road, London W8 5LJ — MB BS 1988 Lond.; FRANZCP 2001; MRCPsych 1994; DCH RCP Lond. 1991; DRCOG 1990. Cons. in Old Age Psychiat., S. Kensington and Chelsea Ment. Health Centre, Lond. Prev: Regist. Rotat. (Psychiat.) St. Mary's & St. Chas. Hosp. Lond.; SHO (Psychiat.) St. Mary's & St. Chas. Hosp. Lond.

***KOTAK, Deepak Chandulal** 5 Denbigh Close, Chislehurst BR7 5EB — MB BS 1991 Lond.; BA Oxf. 1988; FRCA 1995 (Lond.); MRCP 1997 (UK).

KOTAK, Pravin Kumar Department of Anaesthesia, Fairfield General Hospital, Rochdale Old Road, Bury BL9 7TD — MB BS 1971 Osmania; FFA RCSI 1977.

KOTECHA, Mr Bhikhalal Meadowsweet, 29 Wykeham Avenue, Hornchurch RM11 2LA Tel: 01708 509594 — MB BCh 1984 Wales; MPhil Sussex 1994; FRCS (Orl.) 1994; FRCS Eng. (Orl.) 1990; FRCS Ed. (Orl.) 1989; DLO RCS Eng. 1988. Cons. Otolaryngol. Roy. Nat. Throat, Nose & Ear Hosp. Lond. & Harold Wood Hosp.; Hon. Regist. & Hon. Fell. (Otolaryngol.) Univ. Sussex & Roy. Sussex Co. Hosp. Brighton. Prev: Sen. Regist. (Otolayngol.) Roy. Nat. Throat, Nose & Ear Hosp. Lond. & Roy. Sussex Co. Hosp. Brighton; Regist. (ENT) Hope Hosp. & Univ. Manch. Sch. Med.; Demonst. (Anat.) Univ. Liverp.

KOTECHA, Krishna 60 Brownfield Street, London E14 6NE — MB BS 1998 Lond.; MB BS Lond 1998.

KOTECHA, Krishnakumar Morarji 22 Crespigny Road, Hendon, London NW4 3DY — MB ChB 1968 East Africa.

KOTECHA, Mr Mahendra Bhagwanji 45 Belmont Avenue, Alperton, Wembley HA0 4HL — MB ChB 1975 Glas.; FRCS Glas. 1981. Sen. Regist. (A & E) Addenbrooke's Hosp. Camb.

KOTECHA, Mansukh Gordhandas Ash Tree Surgery, 33 Fobbing Road, Corringham, Stanford-le-Hope SS17 9BG Tel: 01375 643000 Fax: 01375 677150; 36 Hill Crest View, Basildon SS16 4QU — MB BS 1970 Baroda. (Med. Coll. Baroda)

KOTECHA, Nimeetta Queens Park Health Centre, 23 Carlisle Road, Bedford MK40 4HR — MB BS 1984 Mysore; LMSSA Lond. 1989.

KOTECHA, Sailesh Hiralal Department of Child Health, University of Leicester, Leicester Royal Infirmary, Clinical Sciences Building, PO Box 65, Leicester LE2 7LX — MB BS 1984 Lond.; PhD Lond. 1995; MA Camb. 1985, BA (Hons.) 1981; MRCP (UK) 1989; DCH RCP Lond. 1988. Sen. Lect. & Hon. Cons. Univ. of Leicester, Leicester Roy. Infirm. Prev: Lect. & Hon. Sen. Regist. Univ. Leicester; MRC Research Fell. & Hon. Sen. Regist. Roy. Postgrad. Med. Sch. Hammersmith Hosp. Lond.

KOTECHA, Shilpa 218A Abbots Road, Abbots Langley WD5 0BP — MB BS 1993 Lond.

KOTECHA, Sunil Babulal Grove Road Surgery, 3 Grove Road, Solihull B91 2AG Tel: 0121 705 1105 Fax: 0121 711 4098; 90B Alderbrook Road, Solihull B91 1NR — MB ChB 1982 Sheff.; MRCGP 1987. (Sheffield) Prev: Hon. Treas. RCGP Midl. Fac.

KOTECHA, Yatish Jamnadas 17 Bloomfield Road, Bath BA2 2AD — BM 1980 Soton.

KOTEGAONKAR, Kumar Shamrao Spring Lane Surgery, 17 Spring Lane, Radcliffe, Manchester M26 2TQ Tel: 0161 724 6938 Fax: 0161 724 0172 — MB BS 1972 Marathwada; MRCGP 1996; Cert. Family Plann. JCC 1980; DCH RCPS Glas. 1976. (Govt. Med. Coll. Aurangabad) Tutor (Gen. Pract.) Bury. Socs: (Chairm.) Nat. Assn. GP Tutors UK; (Hon. Treas.) Small Practs. Assn. Prev: Regist. (Paediat.) Bury Gen. Hosp.

KOTEGAONKAR, Manju Kumar Spring Lane Surgery, 17 Spring Lane, Radcliffe, Manchester M26 2TQ Tel: 0161 724 6938 Fax: 0161 724 0172 — MB BS 1971 Marathwada; Cert. Family Plann. JCC 1985; DObst RCPI 1976. (Aurangabad Med. Coll. India) Prev: Regist. (Obst.) Fairfield Gen. Hosp. Bury.

KOTESWARA RAO, Maddineni 30 Royal Drive, Hamilton ML3 7DJ — MB BS 1971 Andhra.

KOTHARI, Ashitkumar Kantilal 7 Nursery Gardens, Earl Shilton, Leicester LE9 7JE — MB ChB 1983 Leic.; MRCGP 1987; DCH RCP Lond. 1988; DRCOG 1987. GP Earl Shilton; Clin. Med. Off. (Community Child Health) Leicester; Clin. Asst. (Genito-urin. Med.) Leicester Roy. Infirm.

KOTHARI, Dau Dayal (retired) Hutton Unit, St Luke's Hospital, Middlesbrough TS4 3AF Tel: 01642 283338 Fax: 01642 283345 — MB BS Rajasthan 1967; MRCPsych 1975; DPM Eng. 1974. Cons. Forens. Psychiat. Tees & N. E. Yorks. NHS Trust; Hon. Assoc. Clin. Lect. (Psychiat.) Univ. Newc. Prev: Cons. Forens. Psychiat. Tees & N. E. Yorks. NHS Trust.

KOTHARI, Hitesh Pranlal Abbeystead Road Surgery, 4 Abbeystead Road, Liverpool L15 7JF Tel: 0151 722 1080 — MB BS 1980 Delhi; LRCP LRCS Ed. LRCPS Glas. 1983.

KOTHARI, Jyoti Jaysukhlal 74 Sandy Lane, Cheam, Sutton SM2 7EP Tel: 020 8642 9653 — MB BS 1971 Bombay; FFA RCS Eng. 1975. (Grant Med. Coll.) Cons. (Anaesth.) Roy. Marsden Hosp. Lond. & Surrey. Prev: Sen. Regist. (Anaesth.) Guy's Hosp. Lond., Brook Gen. Hosp. Lond. & Greenwich Dist. Hosp.

KOTHARI, Manorama Pradipkumar 15 Bell Close, Meldreth, Royston SG8 6LE Tel: 01763 996 61573 — MB BS 1974 Bombay. (Grant Med. Coll.)

KOTHARI, Prasad 12A West Court, Wembley HA0 3QH — MB BS 1998 Lond.; MB BS Lond 1998; BDS Bombay 1986; MDS Bombay 1988; FDSRCS Ed 1991. (St Bartholomew's & London Hospitals) Socs: Assoc. Mem. Brit Assoc. of Oral & Maxillofacial Surg.s; Fell. Roy. coll of Surg.s of Edin.

KOTHARI, Sudhir Himatlal Heem Kanta, 23 Pemberton Valley, Alloway, Ayr KA7 4UH Tel: 01292 443731 — MB BS 1966 Bombay; DA Eng. 1972. (Grant Med. Coll.) Assoc. Specialist (Anaesth.) Ayr Hosp. Socs: Assn. Anaesth. Prev: Med. Asst. Kilmarnock Infirm.

KOTIAN, Padmanabh Dasu Hounslow Road Surgery, 158 Hounslow Road, Feltham TW13 6AA Tel: 020 8890 9376 Fax: 020 8890 9376 — MB BS 1966 Bombay. (Topiwala Nat. Med. Coll.) Clin. Asst. Char. Cross Hosp. Lond.

KOTIDIS, Konstantinos 12 Town Street, Rodley, Leeds LS13 1HP — Ptychio Iatrikes 1990 Thessalonika. (Aristotle Univ. Med. Sch. Thessalonika) SHO Rotat. (A & E, Orthop. & Gen. Surg.) Qu. Eliz. Hosp. King's Lynn; SHO (Cardiothracic Surg.). Socs: Panhellenic Med. Assn.; BMA. Prev: SHO (A & E) Solihull Hosp.

KOTOWSKI, Konrad Edmund 148 Harley Street, London W1N 1AH Tel: 020 7935 5814 Fax: 020 7224 4157; 25B Westbourne Park Road, London W2 5PX — MB BChir 1972 Camb.; MA Camb. 1972; MRCP (UK) 1976; MRCGP 1985; Specialist Accredit. Rheum. & Rehabil. JCHMT 1981. Gen. Phys. & Rheum. Lond. Prev: Sen. Regist. (Rheum. & Rehabil.) Roy. Free Hosp. Lond.

KOTSIRAKIS, Antonios Institute of Orthopaedics, Royal National Orthopaedic Hospital, Brockley Hill, Stanmore HA7 4LP — Ptychio Iatrikes 1982 Thessalonika.

KOTTA, Mr Satish Consultant Ophthalmologist, Grimsby NHS Trust, Scartho Road, Grimsby DN33 2BA Tel: 01472 875565; Moor Lodge, Station Road, North Thoresby, Grimsby DN36 5QS Tel: 01472 840998 — MB BS 1981 Andhra; MD (Ophth.) Delhi 1984; FRCS Glas. 1991; FCOphth 1991, M 1990; DO RCS Eng. 1990. Cons. Ophth. Grimsby NHS Trust.

KOTTING, Susan Caroline Keepers Cottage, Star Hill, Chevening, Sevenoaks TN14 6HA Tel: 01959 532388 — MB BS 1968 Lond.; MRCS Eng. LRCP Lond. 1968. (St. Bart.) Cons. E. Surrey Hosp. FarnBoro. & Bromley Hosp.

KOTWALL, Fiji Byramji, TD Adan House, St Andrews Road, Spennymoor DL16 6QA Tel: 01388 817777; 15 St Charles Road, Spennymoor DL16 6JY Tel: 01388 815983 — MB BS 1958 Karachi; MRCGP 1975; DO RCPSI 1968; DA RCPSI 1967; DA (UK) 1967. (Dow Med. Coll.) Dep. Police Surg. Spennymoor; Maj. RAMC T & AVR, Regtl. Med. Off. 7th Bn. Light Inf. (V) Durh.. Prev: SHO (Anaesth.) LLa.lly Gen. Hosp.; SHO (Ophth.) Burton-on-Trent Gen. Hosp.; Regist. (Anaesth.) Roy. Alexandra Hosp. Rhyl.

KOUCHOUK, A A Askern Health Centre, Spa Pool Road, Askern, Doncaster DN6 0HZ — MB ChB 1971 Mosul; MB ChB 1971 Mosul; LMSSA London.

KOUIMTSIDIS, Christos 81A St Peters Street, London N1 8JR; 81A St. Peters Street, London N1 8JR — Ptychio Iatrikes 1990 Thessalonika; MRCPsych. RCOP 1997.

KOUKOURAKIS, Michael ICRF Clinical Oncology Unit, Churchill Hospital, Old Road, Headington, Oxford OX3 7LJ — Ptychio Iatrikes 1986 Athens.

KOUL, Kishni Kumari 2 The Pickerings, Humber Road, North Ferriby HU14 3DW — MB BS 1970 Jammu & Kashmir.

KOULI, Mr Oussama Department of Neurosurgery, Leeds General Infirmary, Great George St., Leeds LS1 3EX — MD 1977 Damascus; FRCS Ed. 1983.

KOULOUMAS, Georgios Park Lodge Medical Centre, 3 Old Park Road, Palmers Green, London N13 4RG Tel: 020 8886 6866 Fax: 020 8882 8884; 60 Old Park Road, London N13 4RE Tel: 020 8886 2093 Fax: 020 8350 9178 — MB BS 1981 Lond.; BSc Lond. 1978; MRCGP 1987; DRCOG 1984. (Univ. Coll.) GP Princip.; Assoc. Tutor (Gen. Pract.) TPMDE; Sen. Lect. Roy. Free Hosp. Med. Sch. Lond.; Med. Off. Bank of Cyprus & Cyprus Popular Bank. Socs: (Pres.) Hellenic Med. Soc.; Roy. Soc. Med. Prev: Med. Adviser in Prescribing Camden & Islington FHSA; Trainee GP Edgware VTS; SHO (Med.) Worthing Hosp.

KOUPPARIS, Luke Simon 51 Danemead Grove, Northolt UB5 4NY — MB BS 1996 Lond.

KOURAH, Mr Mohamed Abd El Azim Khadre Abou Rochdale Infirmary, Whitehall Street, Rochdale OL12 0NB Tel: 01706 377777; 41 Tandle Hill Road, Royton, Oldham OL2 5UX Tel: 0161 626 7556 — MB BCh 1968 Cairo; MB BCh Cairo, Egypt 1968; FRCS Ed. 1980; FRCS RCPS Glas. 1980. Cons. Urol. Rochdale AHA. Socs: Brit. Assn. Urol. Surgs.; Amer. Urol. Assn.; Euro Urolg Assn. Prev: Cons. Urol. Armed Forces Hosp. Riyadh, Saudi Arabia.

KOURI, Agathi Woodhouse Hall, 18 Clarendon Road, Leeds LS2 9NT — Ptychio Iatrikes 1989 Ioannina.

KOURIEFS, Chryssanthos Flat B 1st Floor, 13B Thornton Avenue, Stretham, London SW2 4HL — MB ChB 1997 Manch.

KOURTIS, Michail 37B New Cavendish Street, London W1G 8JR — Ptychio Iatrikes 1977 Athens.

KOUSSA, Fares Fawzy Department of Anaesthetics, Royal Albert Edward Infirmary, Wigan Lane, Wigan WN1 2NN Tel: 01942 822088 Fax: 01942 822089 — MB ChB 1974 Alexandria; FRCA 2001; FFA RCSI 1987; DA (UK) 1983. Cons. Anaesth. Roy. Albert Edwd. Infirm. Wigan. Socs: Obst. Anaesth. Assn.; Assn. Anaesth.; PANG. Prev: Sen. Regist. (Anaesth.) Newc. Gp. of Teachg. Hosps.; Sen. Regist. (Anaesth.) Riyadh Milit. Hosp.; Regist. (Anaesth.) Nat. Welsh Sch. of Med. Cardiff.

KOUSSA, Frances Christina Rivendell, Beaumont, Carlisle CA5 6ED — MB ChB 1981 Leic. Staff Grade (Anaesth.) Cumbld. Infirm., Carlisle. Prev: SHO (Anaesth.) Univ. Hosp. Wales Cardiff.

KOUTENTIS, Christos Andreas 41 Northumbria Drive, Bristol BS9 4HL — MB ChB 1994 Aberd.

KOUTROUMANIDIS, Michael 73 Canterbury House, Royal St., London SE1 7LW — Ptychio Iatrikes 1984 Athens.

KOUVARELLIS, David Scott Flat 3, 128 Upper St., London N1 1TQ — MB BCh 1997 Witwatersrand.

KOVACS, Iren B (retired) — MD 1965 Pecs Hungary; PhD Acad. Scs. Hungary 1975; FRCPath 1989, M 1985.

KOVALIC, Alexandra Janet 37 Potier Street, London SE1 4UX — MB BS 1998 Lond.; MB BS Lond 1998.

KOVAR, Ilya Zdenek Chelsea & Westminster Hospital, London SW10 9NH Tel: 020 8846 7193 Fax: 020 8846 7998 Email: i.kovar@ic.ac.uk; 3 Adelaide Cottage, Homesfield, London NW11 6HP Tel: 020 8209 0980 Fax: 020 8209 0980 — MB BS

Sydney 1970; FRCP Lond. 1990; MRCP (UK) 1973; FRCPC 1978; FRCPCH 1997; Dip. Amer. Bd. Paediat. 1979; DObst RCOG 1974; FAAP 1979. (Sydney) Cons. Paediat. & Perinatal Med. Chelsea & W.m. Healthcare NHS Trust; Hon. Sen. Lect. (Perinatal Med.) Imperial Coll. Med. Sch. Lond. Socs: Fell. Amer. Acad. Paediat.; Eur. Soc. Paediat. Research. Prev: Sen. Lect. (Child Health) Lond.

KOWALCZYK, Adam Michael Eldene Surgery, Eldene Health Centre, Eldene Centre, Swindon SN3 3RZ Tel: 01793 522710 Fax: 01793 513217; 9 Penfold Gardens, Old Town, Swindon SN1 4EL Tel: 01793 421449 Email: adamk1@globalnet.co.uk — BM 1977 Soton. Hosp. Practitioner (Gen. Med.) P.ss Margt. Hosp. Swindon. Prev: Regist. (Radiol.) Nottm. Gp. Hosps.; Regist. (Gen. Med. & Gastroenterol.) Burnley Gen. Hosp.

KOWALSKA, Krystyna Anna 49 Kildonan Road, Grappenhall, Warrington WA4 2LJ — LRCP LRCS 1984 Ed.; LDS RCS Eng. 1976; BDS Liverp. 1976; FFD RCSI 1980; LRCP LRCS Ed. LRCPS Glas. 1984; LRCPS Glas. 1984; FRCS Ed. 1988. Lect. & Regist. (Oral & Maxillofacial Surg.) Univ. Manch.; Staff Grade (Cas.) Warrington Hosp. NHS Trust. Prev: SHO (Gen. Surg. & Cas.) Warrington Dist. Gen. Hosp.

KOWNACKI, Stephen Albany House Medical Centre, 3 Queen Street, Wellingborough NN8 4RW Tel: 01933 222309 Fax: 01933 229236; Rostherne, 18 Debdale Road, Wellingborough NN8 5AA Tel: 01933 441393 — MB BS 1973 Lond.; MRCS Eng. LRCP Lond. 1973; MRCGP 1979; DObst RCOG 1975. (Middlx.) Clin. Asst. (Dermat.) N.ampton Gen. Hosp. Prev: Trainee Gen. Pract. N.ampton Vocational Train. Scheme; Ho. Surg. Mt. Vernon Hosp. N.wood; Ho. Phys. City Gen. Hosp. Stoke-upon-Trent.

KOYA, Mahendra Ratilal Doctors Surgery, 652 Holloway Road, London N19 3NU Tel: 020 7272 2877 Fax: 020 7561 0744; 16 Chalgrove Gardens, London N3 3PN — MB BS 1956 Bombay. (Grant Med. Coll.) Prev: Ho. Phys. & Ho. Surg. J.J. Hosp. Bombay, India; Intern St. Clare's Hosp. Schenectady, U.S.A.

KOZDON, Alfred Addison House, Harlow CM20 1DS Tel: 01279 426129 — MD 1943 Czechoslovakia; DTM Paris 1958. Vis. Med. Off. Harlow Indust. Health Serv. Socs: Fell. Roy. Soc. Med. (Med. & Dent. Hypn. Sect.); Internat. Soc. Hypn. (Philadelphia). Prev: Cons. Diabetic Dept. Co. Hosp. Ostrava Czechoslovakia; Asst. Hopital De La Pitie, Paris.

KOZIELL, Anna Barbara c/o Molecular Medicine, Institute of Child health, 30 Guilford St., London WC1N Tel: 020 7242 9789 Email: a.koziell@ich.icl.ac.uk; 2 Riverview Road, London W4 3QH — MB BS 1986 Lond.; BSc (Pharmacol.) Lond. 1983; MRCP (UK) 1991. (St. Thomas Hospital) Clin. Research Fell. Inst. Child Health Lond. Prev: Regist. (Renal.) Hosp. for Childr. Gt. Ormond St. Lond.; Regist. (Paediat.) Kings Coll. Hosp. Lond.; SHO (Renal) Gt. Ormond St. Lond.

KOZIELL, Stanislaw 2 Creswick Road, London W3 9HD Tel: 020 8992 1101 — MB BCh 1954 Wales; BSc Wales 1950, MB BCh 1954. (Cardiff) SHO Acton Hosp. Lond. Prev: Ho. Surg. Lambeth Hosp. Lond.; Ho. Phys. St. Luke's Hosp. Bradford; Sen. Ho. Off. Woking Vict. Hosp.

KOZIELSKI, Yvette Michelle 46A Aboyne Drive, London SW20 0AL — MB BChir 1995 Camb.; MB BChir Camb. 1994; MA Camb. 1995. (Cambridge/UMDS)

KOZIOL, Leszek Feliks Stanislaw 214 Sirdar Road, London N22 6QX — MB BS 1991 Lond.

KOZLOWSKA, Christina Louise 14 Station Road, Hest Bank, Lancaster LA2 6HP Tel: 01524 824585, 01787 370011 — MB ChB 1978 Manch.; FRCPath 1998. p/t Cons. Haematologist, Morecombe Bay Acute Hosps. Trust. Socs: Brit. Soc. of Haemat.; Brit. Med. Assn.

KOZLOWSKA, Wanda Janina Dept. Paediatrics, Fielden House (c/o secretary to Dr Carr), Royal London Hospital, Whitechapel, London E1 1BB Tel: 020 7377 7000 Fax: 020 7377 7462 — MB BS 1994 Lond.; 1999 MRCPCH; BSc (Hons.) Lond. 1991; MRCP Lond. 1998. (St. Bart. Hosp. Med. Coll.) Specialist Regist. (Paediat.) N. Thames. Prev: Sen. SHO (Paediat.) St. John's Hosp., Chelmsford; SHO (Respirat. Paediat.) Gt. Ormond St. Hosp.; SHO (Paediat.) Qu. Eliz. Hosp. for Childr., Hackney, Lond.

KOZMAN, Ezzat Leon Louis Warrington Hospital NHS Trust, Lovely Lane, Warrington WA5 1QG Tel: 01925 635911; 34 Cartier Close, Old Hall, Warrington WA5 8TD Tel: 01925 575598 — MB BCh 1977 Cairo; MRCOG 1988. Assoc. Specialist (O & G) Warrington Hosp.

KPIASI, Mr Ebenezer Omatsola 37 Elvetham Road, Edgbaston, Birmingham B15 2LZ — MB BS 1986 Lagos; MB BS Lagos 1975; FRCSI 1986.

KRAAIJEVELD, Lauren Margot-Alice Llys Meddyg, 23 Castle St., Conwy LL32 8AY Tel: 01249 592424; Glanffrwd, Fernbrook Road, Penmaenmawr LL34 6DE — MB ChB 1985 Manch.; MRCGP 1990; DRCOG 1989.

KRAEMER, John Wolfgang Sebastian Child & Family Department, Tavistock Clinic, Tavistock & Portman NHS Trust, 120 Belsize Lane, London NW3 5BA Tel: 020 7435 7111 Fax: 020 7447 3733; 59 Brixton Water Lane, London SW2 1PH Tel: 020 7733 0752 Email: sebastian@kraemer-zurne.freeserve.co.uk — MB BS 1970 Lond.; FRCP Lond. 2001; MRCS Eng. LRCP Lond. 1970; FRCPCH 1998; MRCPCH 1997; FRCPsych 1989, M 1976; MRCP (UK) 1973; BA (Hons) Philosophy Lond. 1964. (Guy's Hosp.) p/t Cons. Child & Family Psychiat. Tavistock Clinic & Whittington Hosp. Lond.; Postgrad. Clin. Tutor Tavistock & Portman NHS Trust Lond.; Hon. Sen. Lect. Roy. Free Hosp./Univ. Coll. Lond. Socs: Inst. Family Ther. Lond. Prev: Sen. Regist. (Child Psychiat.) Tavistock Clinic Lond.; Regist. (Psychiat.) Maudsley Hosp. Lond.; SHO (Paediat.) St. Mary's Hosp. Manch.

KRAFFT, Jill Mary 5 Downside, Hove BN3 6QJ Tel: 01273 509648 — MB BS (Hons.) Lond. 1974; MRCP (UK) 1978; MRCS Eng. LRCP Lond. 1974; Cert. Family Plann. JCC 1977. (Guy's) Prev: GP Brighton.

KRAFT, Thomas 80 Harley Street, London W1G 7HL Tel: 020 7580 2692; Lakeside, 9 The Fairway, Barnet EN5 1HH Tel: 020 8440 3434 Fax: 020 8440 3434 — MB ChB 1956 Leeds; MRCPsych 1973; DPM Eng. 1965. (Leeds) Cons. Psychiat. Private Pract.; Hon. Cons. Psychiat., St Lukes Hosp. for the Clergy,Lond. Socs: Fell. Roy. Soc. Med.; BMA; Brit. Soc. Experim. & Clin. Hypn. Prev: Cons. Psychiat. Charter Nightingale Lond.; Cons. Psychiat. Edenhall Marie Curie Centre Lond.

KRAJEWSKI, Andrew Stephen 10 Braid Crescent, Edinburgh EH10 6AU — MB ChB 1975 Ed.; PhD Ed. 1985, MB ChB 1975; MRCPath 1983. Sen. Lect. Edin. Univ.; Hon. Cons. Lothian HB.

KRALL, Karin 80 Beaconsfield Road, London SE3 7LQ — State Exam Med 1985 Freiburg.

KRAMER, Agnes (retired) 57 Bramcote Drive, Beeston, Nottingham NG9 1AR Tel: 0115 925 6077 — LRCP LRCS Ed. LRFPS Glas. 1952; FRCS Ed. 1955. Prev: Asst. Surg. Childr. Hosp. Nottm.

KRAMER, Mr Hyman The Stone House, Elmley Lovett, Droitwich WR9 0PS Tel: 0129 923631 — MB BCh 1947 Witwatersrand; FRCS Eng. 1960. Cons. Surg. Dudley & Stourbridge Hosp. Gp. Socs: W Midl. Surg. Soc.; Assn. Surgs. of Eng. & Irel.; Brit. Assn. Surg. Oncol. Prev: Ho. Phys. Johannesburg Gen. Hosp.; Surg. & Orthop. Regist. Addington Hosp. Durban; Res. Surg. Off. Hosp. of St. Cross Rugby.

KRAMER, Ingrid Margaret Eva 2 High Street, Macclesfield SK11 8BX Tel: 01625 423692; 26 Moss Brow, Bollington, Macclesfield SK10 5HH — MB ChB 1991 Manch. Trainee GP/SHO Trafford Gen. Hosp. Manch. VTS. Socs: BMA. Prev: SHO (A & E & Med.) Bolton Roy. Infirm.; Ho. Off. (Gen. Med.) Wythenshawe Hosp. Manch.; Ho. Off. (Gen. Surg.) Glan Clwyd Hosp. Rhyl.

KRAMER, Jeffery John Crowmoor House, Crowmoor Lane, Tillington, Hereford HR4 8LB — MB BS 1962 Lond.; MRCS Eng. LRCP Lond. 1962; MRCPath 1969. (King's Coll. Hosp.) Cons. Haemat. Co. Hosp. Hereford. Prev: Lect. (Haemat.) Inst. Child Health & Hosp. Sick Childr. Gt. Ormond St. Lond.; Demonst. (Path.) King's Coll. Hosp. Med. Sch. Lond.

KRAMER, Padraig Bert Maria Mara Priory Medical Group, Cornlands Road, Acomb, York YO24 3WX Tel: 01904 781423 Fax: 01904 784886 — Artsexamen 1985 Leiden. Trainee GP York VTS.

KRAMER, Susan 3 De la Warr Court, De la Warr Parade, Bexhill-on-Sea TN40 1JX — MB BCh 1983 Witwatersrand.

KRAMER, Susan Linda (retired) 39 Park Rise, Harpenden AL5 3AP Tel: 01582 768427 — MB BS 1968 Lond.; MRCS Eng. LRCP Lond. 1966; MRCPsych 1980. Cons. Child & Adolesc. Psychiat. S. Beds Community Trust. Prev: Sen. Regist. (Child & Adolesc. Psychiat.) Roy. Manch. Childrs. Hosp. & Young Peoples Unit Macclesfield.

KRAMER-HERMANN, Ellen-Babette 6 Greenbank Avenue, Saltdean, Brighton BN2 8QS Tel: 01273 301832 — MB ChB 1987

Manch.; BSc Biochem. 1982. SHO (Orthop.) Roy. Sussex Co. Hosp. Brighton. Prev: SHO (BrE. & Gen. Surg.) Univ. Hosp. Manch.; SHO (Gen. Surg.) Stepping Hill Hosp. Stockport; SHO (A & E) Newport Gwent.

KRANIDIOTIS, Laki Solon Flat 215 Doctors Quarters, Sandwell District General Hospital, Lydon, West Bromwich B71 4HJ — MB BCh 1983 Witwatersrand.

KRAPEZ, John Robert Squirrels Oak, Woodland Way, Kingswood, Tadworth KT20 6NX — MB BS 1971 Lond.; MRCS Eng. LRCP Lond. 1971; FFA RCS Eng. 1975; DObst RCOG 1973. Cons. (Anaesth.) St. Bart. Hosp. Lond. Prev: Regist. (Anaesth.) St. Bart. Hosp. Lond.

KRARUP, Kim Charles Department Radiology, Leicester Royal Infirmary, Infirmary Square, Leicester LE1 5WW Tel: 0116 254 1414 Fax: 0116 258 5584 Email: kkrarup@uhl.treat.nhs.uk — MB ChB 1981 Bristol; MRCP (UK) 1985; FRCR 1989. Cons. Radiol. Leicester Roy. Infirm. Prev: Sen. Regist. & Regist. (Radiol.) Leicester Roy. Infirm.; SHO (Med.) Cheltenham Gen. Hosp.

KRASNER, Claude Donald Aberwheeler, Bodfari, Denbigh LL16 4DE — MB ChB 1955 Liverp.; FRCR 1975.

KRASNER, David Henry 35 Sherwood Road, London NW4 1AE — MRCS Eng. LRCP Lond. 1977; MSc Lond. 1972, MB BS 1977; MRCGP 1981.

KRASNER, George (retired) 43 Ashdown, Eaton Road, Hove BN3 3AQ Tel: 01273 329596 — MB ChB Glas. (Commend.) 1930; MD (Commend.) Glas. 1936; MRCGP 1953. Prev: Resid. Phys. & Surg. Glas. Municip. Hosps.

KRASNER, Professor Neville The Gastrointestinal Unit, The University Hospital Aintree, Lower Lane, Liverpool L9 7AL Tel: 0151 529 2804 Fax: 0151 529 2809 — MB ChB Glas. 1967; MD Glas. 1975; FRCP Lond. 1984; FRCP Glas. 1980; MRCP (UK) 1971. (Glas.) Cons. Phys. & Gastroenterol. Fazakerley Hosp. Liverp.; Vis. Prof. Dept. Engin. Liverp. Univ.; Clin. Director, Lasers for Life, Med. Laser Inst., Liverp. Socs: Brit. Soc. Gastroenterol.; (Immediate Past Pres.) Brit. Med. Laser Assn.; (Pres.) Europ. Laser Assn. Prev: Sen. Regist. (Med. & Gastroenterol.) S. W.. (Glas.) Health Dist.; Research Fell. (Liver Unit) King's Coll. Hosp. Lond.; Ure Research Fell. Glas. Univ. Stobhill Hosp. Glas.

KRASNER, Nicholas Ian 23 Acrefield Park, Liverpool L25 6JX — MB ChB 1992 Liverp.

KRASOPOULOS, Mr Georgios East London Rotation, Royal Brompton Hospital/, St. Marys Hospital/, St. Barthoomews Hospital/ The London Chest Hospital, London — Ptychio Iatrikes 1993 Athens; MRCS 1998; PhD 1999; MRGS. (Athens) SPR-Cardiothoraeic Surg.. E. Lond. Rotat. Socs: Brit. Med. Soc.; Soc. of Cardiotheraeic Surg.s of Gt. Britain & Irel.; Helleric Med. Soc.

KRASS, Iris Mary 53 Berkeley Gardens, Winchmore Hill, London N21 2BE Tel: 020 8360 9100 — MB BS Lond. 1952; MRCS Eng. LRCP Lond. 1952; DObst RCOG 1957. (Westm.) Med. Off. (Occupat. Health) Med. Advis. Serv. Civil Serv. Lond. SW1. Prev: GP Edmonton; Regist. (Med.) S.mead Hosp. Bristol.

KRASUCKI, Christopher George Institute of Psychiatry, De Crespigny Park, Denmark Hill, London SE5 8AF Tel: 020 7919 3546 Fax: 020 7701 0167 Email: spjucgk@iop.bpmf.ac.uk — MB BS 1989 Lond.; MSc Lond. 1996; MRCP (UK) 1992; MRCPsych 1995. Clin. Lect. (Old Age Psychiat.) Inst. Psychiat. Lond.; Hon. Sen. Regist. Maudsley Hosp. Lond. Prev: Regist. (Psychiat.) Maudsley Hosp. Lond.; SHO (Psychiat.) Bethlem Roy. Hosp. Beckenham; SHO (Gen. Med.) S.end Hosp. W.cliff on Sea.

KRASUCKI, Robert Edward 2 Gordon Road, London W5 2AD — MB BS 1993 Lond.

KRASZEWSKI, Andrew 17 St John's Road, Glasgow G41 5QP Tel: 0141 423 8466 — MB ChB 1964 Glas.; FRCOG 1985, M 1971. (Glas.) Cons. (O & G) Roy. Samarit. Hosp. Wom. Glas. & Rutherglen Matern. Hosp. Glas. Socs: BMA. Prev: Sen. Regist. (O & G) Stobhill Gen. Hosp. Glas.; Regist. in Laborat. Med. W.. Infirm. Glas.

KRATIMENOS, Marysia Lidia Krysia The Royal London Homoeopathic Hospital, Great Ormond St., London WC1N 3HR Tel: 020 7837 8833 Fax: 020 7833 7212; 38 Hilldrop Lane, London N7 0HN Tel: 0207 607 1821 — MB BS Lond. 1982; FRCS Ed. 1988; MFHom 1996. (Guy's Hosp. Med. Sch.) Regist. The Roy. Lond. Homoeop. Hosp.; Private Practise in Med. Homoepathy and Neuro-Linguistic Programming. Socs: Mem. of Fac. of Homeopaths; Assn. of Neuro-Linguistic Programing Practitioners. Prev: SHO (Orthop.) St. Hilda's Hosp. Hartlepool; SHO (A & E) Lewisham Hosp. Lond.; Ho. Surg. Lewisham Hosp. Lond.

KRATKY, Adrian Philip Baber, St. Dominick, Saltash PL12 6TE — MB BS 1972 Lond.; BSc; MRCGP (Distinc.) 1979; DRCOG 1978.

KRATTER, Frederick Edward (retired) Corfu, 82 Barker Lane, Mellor, Blackburn BB2 7EE — MB ChB 1943 Manch.; MRCPsych 1971; DPM Eng. 1955. Hon. Cons. Ment. Handicap Blackburn Roy. Infirm. Prev: Med. Dir. & Cons. Psychiat. Brockhall Hosp. Langho.

KRAUS, Peter David Tel: 020 8905 0355; Collingwood, 50 Gordon Avenue, Stanmore HA7 3QH — MB BS 1979 Lond.; MRCGP 1984. (Middlx.) GP Kingsbury.; GP Trainer N.wick Pk. Hosp. VTS. Prev: Trainee GP Edgware Gen. Hosp. VTS.

KRAUS, Sigurd Block 2, Flat 12, Nottingham City Hospital, Hucknall Road, Nottingham NG5 1PB — State Exam Med 1991 Berlin.

KRAUSE, Annemarie Angelika Department of Microbiology, Royal Infirmary, 84 Castle St., Glasgow G4 0SF — State Exam Med. Hanover 1991. SHO (Microbiol.) Glas. Roy. Infirm. Socs: BMA. Prev: SHO (Microbiol.) Qu. Eliz. Hosp. Birm.

KRAUSE, Ulrike 371A Holloway Road, London N7 0RN Tel: 020 7700 7560 Fax: 020 7700 7560 — State Exam Med 1990 Berlin; DCH RCP Lond. 1995; DFFP 1994; MRCOG 1997. Regist. (O & G) Basildon Hosp.; Specialist Regist. Roy. Lond. Hosp. Prev: SHO (Gyn.) St. Bart. Hosp. Lond.; SHO (Perinatol.) St. Mary's Hosp. Lond.; SHO (O & G) P.ss Anne Hosp. Soton.

KRAUTH, Guy Anson 19 Newmills Road, Balerno EH14 5SU — MB ChB 1995 Ed.

KRAUTHAMER, Irwin (retired) 6 St Meddan's Street, Troon KA10 6JU Tel: 01292 311877 — BSc New York 1934; LRCP LRCS Ed. LRFPS Glas. 1941.

KRAWIECKI, Jurand Aleksander (retired) Flat 13, Stonecroft Court, Parkfield Road S., Manchester M20 6DA Tel: 0161 446 2916 — MB ChB 1949 Ed.; FRCPsych 1975, M 1971; DPM Eng. 1954.

KREEGER, Anne Judith The Old Gatehouse, Green Lane, Foulsham, Dereham NR20 5PN — MB BS 1983 Lond. Regist. (Psychiat.) Hosp. Sick Childr. Gt. Ormond St. Lond.

KREEGER, Charles Geoffrey 184 Mayeswood Road, London SE12 9SB — State Exam Med 1984 Berlin; BA Warwick 1974.

KREEGER, Lionel Cyril The Group-Analytic Practice, 88 Montagu Mansions, London W1U 6LF Tel: 020 7935 3103 Fax: 020 7935 1397 Email: lk@gappractice.org.uk; 19 Platts Lane, London NW3 7NP Tel: 020 7435 5535 — MB BS Lond. 1949; FRCP Ed. 1994; MRCP Ed. 1963; FRCPsych 1978, M 1971; DPM Eng. 1959. (Guy's) Cons. Psychiat. Private Pract. Socs: Founder Mem. Inst. Gp. Anal.; Assoc. Mem. Brit. Psychoanalyt. Soc. Prev: Cons. Psychother. Tavistock Clinic Lond.; Cons. Psychiat. Halliwick Hosp.; Sen. Regist. (Psychiat.) W.m. Hosp.

KREEGER, Louisa Claire Rosalind Kingston Hosp., Community Palliative Care Team, Leak Centre, Kingston Hosp., Golsworthy Road, Kingston-upon-Thames KT2 7QB Tel: 020 8546 7711 Fax: 020 8549 7865 — MB BS 1985 Lond.; MRCP (UK) 1989. Cons. (Palliat. Med.) Kingston Hosp. & P.ss Alice Hosp., Esher. Socs: Asooc. Of Palliat. Med. Prev: Clin. Fell. (Palliat. Med.) St Vincent's Hosp. & Sacred Heart Hospice, Sydney, Australia; Macmillan Clin. Fell. (Palliat. Care) Pembridge Unit Hammersmith Hosp., Lond.; Regist. (Radiother.) Char. Cross Hosp. Lond.

KREEGER, Philip Lindsay The Whitecliff Surgery, Whitecliff Mill Street, Blanford DT11 7BH Tel: 01258 452501 Fax: 01258 455675; 6 Davis Gardens, Blandford Forum DT11 7UX Tel: 01258 52958 Email: kregger-family@compuserve.com — MB BS 1977 Lond.; DRCOG 1980. (King's Coll. Hosp.) GP Trainer W. Dorset VTS; Med. Off. Clayesmore Prep. & Sen. Sch.

KREEL, Louis 38 Park Hall Road, London N2 9PU — MD 1968 Witwatersrand; MB BCh 1948; FRCP Lond. 1972, M 1957; FRCR 1975; FFR 1962; DMRD Eng. 1958. (Witwatersrand) Dir. Radiol. Newham Dist. Gen. Hosp.; Sen. Lect. Lond. Hosp. Med. Coll.; Hon. Cons. Radiol. Roy. Free Hosp. Lond. & Leeds RHB. Socs: Fell. Roy. Soc. Med.; Brit. Inst. Radiol. Prev: Cons. Radiol. N.wick Pk. Hosp. Harrow; Head of Radiol. Clin. Research Centre N.wick Pk.; Cons. Radiol. Roy. Free Hosp. Gp.

KREINDLER, Jack Richard 10 Heathway Court, West Heath Road, London NW3 7TS — MB BS 1998 Lond.; MB BS Lond 1998.

KREITMAN, Norman Basil 24 Lauder Road, Edinburgh EH9 2JF — MRCS Eng. LRCP Lond. 1949; MD Lond. 1959, MB BS 1950;

FRCP Ed. 1979, M 1972; FRCPsych 1973, M 1972; DPM Lond. 1958. (Westm.) Prev: Dir. MRC Unit Epidemiol. Studies in Psychiat.; Hon. Cons. Roy. Edin. Hosp.; Hon. Prof. Dept. Psychiat. Edin. Univ.

KREKORIAN, Haroutyon Antranik Wartan Long Fox Unit, Weston General Hospital, Weston Super Mare BS23 4TQ — MB ChB 1976 Mosul; MRCPsych 1986; Dip. Clin. Psychiat. Lond 1985. Cons. Psychiat. Outpats. Ment. Health Servs. W.on-Super-Mare. Prev: Sen. Regist. (Psychiat.) Bristol.

KREMER, Daniel John The Surgery, 24 Albert Road, Bexhill-on-Sea TN40 1DG Tel: 01424 730456/734430 Fax: 01424 225615 — MB BS 1989 Lond.; DCH RCP Lond. 1994. Prev: Trainee GP E.bourne VTS.

KREMER, Jeanette Kathleen (retired) Manor Stable Cottage, 8 Manor Drive, Bathford, Bath BA1 7TY Tel: 01225 852313 Email: 113264.2763@compuserve — MB BS Lond. 1963; MRCS Eng. LRCP Lond. 1963; FRCR 1981; DMRT Eng. 1978. Prev: Cons. Clin. Oncol. Roy. Berks. Hosp.

KREMER, Lionel Maurice (retired) 8 High Laws, South Gosforth, Newcastle upon Tyne NE3 1RQ Tel: 0191 284 7421 Fax: 0191 284 7421 Email: lion_elk@compuserve.com — MB BS Durh. 1960; FRCPsych 1984, M 1971; DPM Newc. 1965. Prev: Cons. Psychiat. Cherry Knowle Hosp. Ryhope.

KREMER, Malcolm Geoffrey (retired) Low Ickenthwaite Barn, Rusland, Ulverston LA12 8LD Tel: 01229 860221 Email: geoffkrem@aol.com — MB BS 1963 Lond.; MA Oxf. 1957; MRCS Eng. LRCP Lond. 1963; DCH RCPS Glas. 1968. Prev: GP Bracknell.

KRENTZ, Andrew John Southampton General Hospital, Tremona Road, Southampton SO16 6YD Tel: 02380 794716 Fax: 02380 798624 Email: a.j.krentz@soton.ac.uk — MB ChB 1980 Birm.; MD Birm. 1992; MRCP (UK) 1983. Hon. Sen. Lect. (Med.) Univ. Soton. Socs: Diabetes UK; Amer. Diabetic Assoc.; Eur. Gp. Study of Insulin Resistance. Prev: Regist. (Gen. Med. & Diabetes) & Research Regist. Gen. Hosp. Birm.; Research Fell. Univ. New Mexico Sch. Med. Albuquerque, USA; Sen. Regist. Gen. Hosp. Birm.

KREPPEL, Maria (retired) Flat 1, 34 Elm Park Gardens, London SW10 9NZ Tel: 020 7352 9354 — MB ChB 1945 Polish Sch. of Med. Prev: Sen. Med. Off. Lothian Health Bd. Community Health Serv.

KREPPEL, Peter Richard Mesnes View Surgery, Mesnes Street, Wigan WN1 1ST Tel: 01942 242350 Fax: 01942 826431 — MB ChB 1979 Manch.; BSc (Med. Sci.) St. And. 1976; MRCGP 1988.

KRESTIN, Marie 6 Rundell Crescent, London NW4 3BP — MRCS Eng. LRCP 1928 Lond.; MRCS. Eng. LRCP Lond. 1928. (Char. Cross) Prev: Clin. Asst. Nat. Temperance Hosp., Hosp. Sick Childr. Gt. Ormond St. &Paediat. Dept. W.m. Hosp.

KREUTZER, Bernhard Rudolf Ludger Department of Ophthalmology, University of Aberdeen, Foresterhill, Aberdeen AB25 2ZD — State Exam Med 1988 Freiburg.

KRICHELL, Alan John 19 Alburgh Road, Hempnall, Norwich NR15 2NS — MB ChB 1993 Aberd.

KRICK, Robert Charles Berrisford The Glebeland Surgery, The Glebe, Belbroughton, Stourbridge DY9 9TH Tel: 01562 730303 Fax: 01562 731220 — MB ChB 1989 Birm.

KRIJGSMAN, Mr Brandon University Department of Surgery, The Royal Free Hospital, Pond St., London NW3 2QG Tel: 020 7794 0500 Ext: 3938 Email: beekay@hunter.netkonect.co.uk; 64 Chobham Road, Stratford, London E15 1LZ — MB BS 1985 Lond.; FRCS Eng. 1991. (St. Geo. Hosp. Med. Sch.)

KRIKLER, Dennis Michael 55 Wimpole Street, London W1G 8YL Tel: 020 7935 2098 Fax: 020 7486 1542 Email: dennis.krikler@btinternet.com; 2 Garden Court, Grove End Road, London NW8 9PP Tel: 020 7286 1440 — MB ChB (Hons.) 1951; MD Cape Town 1973; FRCP Lond. 1973, M 1956; FRCP Ed. 1970, M 1956; FACC 1971. (Cape Town) Socs: Fell. Europ. Soc. Cardiol.; Brit. Cardiac Soc.; Corr. Mem. Soc. Française de Cardiol. Prev: Cons. Phys. P. of Wales's & St. Ann's Gen. Hosps. Lond.; Fell. (Med.) Lahey Clinic Boston, USA; Sen. Regist. (Med.) Groote Schuur Hosp. Cape Town.

KRIKLER, Mr Stephen Jeremy Coventry & Warwickshire Hospital, Coventry CV1 4FH Tel: 024 76 844157 Fax: 024 76 221655; Southcot, Crackley Crescent, Kenilworth CV8 2FF Tel: 01926 852508 — MB BS 1980 Lond.; PhD Aberd. 1985; BSc Lond. 1977; FRCS (Orth.) 1995; FRCS Ed. 1988. (Middlx.) Cons. Orthop. Surg. Coventry & Warks. Hosp. Prev: Sen. Regist. (Orthop.) Birm.; Clin. Fell. Sunnybrook Hosp., Toronto, Canada; Med. Off. Brit. Antarctic Survey (1982-1985).

KRIMHOLTZ, Alene 34 The Crescent, Barnes, London SW13 0NN — MB BS 1993 Lond.; MRCP uk 1996. (St. Bart.) Prev: SHO (Gen. Med.) St. Helier Hosp. Carshalton.

KRIMHOLTZ, Michael John 7 Tideway Wharf, 153 Mortlake High St., London SW14 8SW Tel: 020 8392 1102 Email: alene.k@virgin.net — MB BS 1991 Lond.; MRCP (UK) 1996. (Char. Cross & Westm. Med. Sch.) Regist. Rotat. (Gen. Med. & Endocrinol.) Guy's, St. Thos. & Lewisham Hosps. Lond. Prev: Regist. (Med.) Lewisham Hosp. Lond.; SHO (Med.) St. Helier Hosp. Carshalton; SHO Rotat. (ITU) Univ. Coll. Lond. Hosps.

KRIMMER, Monika Helga Department of Anaesthesia, University Hospital of Wales, Heath Park, Cardiff CF14 4XW — State Exam Med 1990 Berlin; FRCA 1994. Regist. (Anaesth.) Univ. Hosp. Wales.

KRIPAL, Kaur Guys Cliffe House, Clana Drive, Calverley, Pudsey LS28 5QP Tel: 01274 616314 — MB BS 1973 Rajasthan.

KRISCHER, Jasmin Maria Top Floor Flat, 44 Sommerville Road, St Andrews, Bristol BS7 9AB — MB ChB 1988 Bristol.

KRISHAN, Kewal Singh Cromwell Road Surgery, 60 Cromwell Road, Bushbury, Wolverhampton WV10 8UT Tel: 01902 784784 — MB ChB 1978 Manch.; MFFP 1993.

KRISHNA, Mr Ganapathy Mill View Surgery, 1a Godsmith St., Mansfield NG18 5PF Tel: 01623 649528 Fax: 01623 624595; 6 Waterson Oaks, Mansfield NG18 4LL — MB BS Rangoon 1960; FRCS Ed. 1967. (Rangoon Med. Coll.) Socs: Mansfield Med. Soc.; BMA. Prev: Demonst. (Anat.) Rangoon Med. Coll.; SHO (Gen. Surg.) Mansfield Gen. Hosp.; Ho. Off. (O & G) Stepping Hill Hosp. Stockport.

KRISHNA, Mr Manoj Orthopaedic Unit, North Tees Hospital, Hardwick, Stockton-on-Tees TS19 8PE — MB BS 1986 Poona; MChOrth Liverp. 1991; FRCS Eng. 1998. (Poona, (India)) Cons. Othop. Surg. N. Tees Hosp. Stockton-on-Tees. Socs: N.Amer. Spine Soc.; Med. Protec. Soc.

KRISHNA, Professor Sanjeev Tel: 020 8725 5827 Fax: 020 8725 3487 Email: s.krishna@sghms.ac.uk; Tel: 020 8942 6967 Fax: 020 8942 6989 — BM BCh 1982 Oxf.; BA Camb. 1979; DPhil Oxf. 1990; FRCP 1998. (Cambridge and Oxford) Hon. Sen. Lect. & Cons. Phys. St. Geo. Hosp. Med. Sch. Lond. - Prof. of Molecular Parasitology and Med. Socs: Fell. Roy. Soc. Trop. Med. & Hyg.; Am. Soc. Trop. Med. & Hyg. Prev: Hon. Clin. Lect. John Radcliffe Hosp. Oxf.; SHO Nat. Hosp. Nerv. Dis. Lond.; SHO (Cardiol.) Lond. Chest Hosp.

KRISHNA KUMAR, Mr Palepu Chesterfield and, North Derbyshire Royal Hospital NHS Trust, Calow, Chesterfield S44 5BL Tel: 01246 277271 — MB BS 1981 Madras; MS Madras 1986, MB BS 1981; FRCS Ed. 1990; FRCS Ed. (Gen.) 1997. Cons. Surg. Prev: Specialist Regist. Yorks. Deanery; Regist. Rotat. (Surg.) Gen. Infirm. Leeds & Pontefract Gen. Infirm.

KRISHNA KUMAR, Venketachalam Department of Anaesthetics, North Tees General Hospital, Hardwick Road, Stockton-on-Tees TS19 8PE — MB BS 1973 Kerala; MB BS Kerala, India 1973.

KRISHNA MURTI, Lammata Lemoors Retirement Home, 285-289 Whalley Road, Clayton le Moors, Accrington BB5 5QU — MB BS 1968 Andhra.

KRISHNA RAO, Chekka Rillwood Medical Centre, Tonmead Road, Lumbertubs, Northampton NN3 8HZ Tel: 01604 405006 Fax: 01604 410826; Rillwood Medical Centre, Tonmead Road, Northampton NN3 8HZ Tel: 01604 405006 Fax: 01604 410826 Email: 72132.2322@compuserv.com — MB BS 1973 Andhra. (Andhra Med. Coll. Visakhapatnam) GP & Police Surg. N.ampton. Socs: BMA; Assn. Police Surg. Prev: SHO (Orthop.) Manfield Hosp. N.ampton; Ho. Surg. St. And. Hosp. Bow.

KRISHNA REDDY, Palnati Goodmayes Hospital, 157 Barley Lane, Goodmayes, Ilford IG3 8XJ Tel: 020 8983 8000 — MB BS 1984 Madras; MRCPsych 1991; DPM RCSO 1992.

KRISHNA REDDY, Mr Thipireddy Venkata Warrington Hospital NHS Trust, Warrington WA5 1QG Tel: 01925 662034 Fax: 01925 662042; BUPA North Cheshire Hospital, Warrington WA4 4LU Tel: 01925 215041 Fax: 01925 604469 — MB BS 1978 Sri Venkateswara; FRCS Eng. 1990; FRCS Glas. 1985. Cons. Ent Surg. Warrington Hosp. NHS Trust. Socs: BMA; M.P.S.; RSM.

KRISHNAMOORTHY, Latha c/o 198 Caulfield Road, London E6 2DQ — MB ChB 1991 Glas.; FRCS Ed. 1996. (Univ. Glas.) SHO (Plastic Surg.) Leicester Roy. Infirm.

KRISHNAMURTHY, Arun Kumar 14 Witherington Road, Highbury, London N5 1PP Tel: 020 7607 2524 — MB BS 1991 Lond.; FRCA 1996. Regist. Rotat. (Anaesth.) UCL Hosps. Prev: Regist. Rotat. (Anaesth.) Harefield Hosp. Roy. Nat. Orthop. Hosp., Stanmore & Roy. Nat. Throat, Nose & Ear Hosp.

KRISHNAMURTHY, Kalpana Witham Health Centre, 4 Mayland Road, Witham CM8 2UX Tel: 01376 302747 Fax: 01376 502411 — MBBS 1970 Madras, India; DA 1972 Madras, India. (Christian Medical College, Vellore, India) Princip. GP, N. Essex Health Auth., Witham; Family Plann. Off., Family Plann. Dept. Chelmsford. Prev: SHO Anaesth., St. Andrews Hosp. Billericay.

KRISHNAMURTHY, Magadi Ramaswarmy Witham Health Centre, 4 Mayland Road, Witham CH8 2UX Tel: 01376 302747 Fax: 01376 502411 — MBBS 1970 Madras, India; FRCS 1977 Edinburgh; MS 1972 Madras, India; GENL. Surgery. (Christian Medical College, Vellore, India) Princip. GP, HE Essex Health Auth., Witham; Private Cosmetic Surg., Witham & Lond. Socs: Brit. Assoc. of Plastic Surg. Allied Assoc. Prev: Clin. Assist. Plastic Surg., Billericay; Clin. Assist. Orthapaedics, Basildon; Cons. Plastic Surg., QE Hosp. Woolich.

KRISHNAMURTHY, Prema Flat 1, Redlands Court, Maud Road, Dorchester DT1 2ND — MB BS 1984 Madras.

KRISHNAMURTHY, Ramanthapur S S Rhos House Surgery, 55 Oxford Street, Mountain Ash CF45 3HD Tel: 01443 473214 Fax: 01443 473289.

KRISHNAMURTI, Devarajan, OBE 23 Pine Tree Close, Radyr, Cardiff CF15 8RQ Tel: 029 2084 3454 — MB BS 1962 Madras; FRCPsych 1992, M 1976; DPM Eng. 1976. (Stanley Med. Coll.) Prev: Cons. Psychiat. Ely Hosp.

KRISHNAN, Anantini Tatparanandam 23 Beech Hill Road, Sheffield S10 2SA — MB ChB 1993 Sheff.

KRISHNAN, Mr Hari Brooksby House, Brooksby Drive, Oadby, Leicester LE2 5AA — MB BS 1979 Bombay; FRCS Ed. 1987; FRCS (Gen.) 1997; M.Ch. Cardiff 1996. Specialist Regist. (Gen. Surg.) Newc.

KRISHNAN, Prassana 23 Colonsay Drive, Newton Mearns, Glasgow G77 6TY — MB ChB 1995 Glas.

KRISHNAN, Ramachandra Ibstock House, 132 High St., Ibstock, Leicester LE9 7LQ Tel: 0116 226 0216; 6 Mill Lane, Heather, Leicester LE9 5NW — MB BS 1966 Mysore; DCH Delhi 1969. (Kasturba Med. Coll. Mangalore)

KRISHNAN, Ramamirtham 1 Cranage Close, Middlesbrough TS5 5HN — MB BS 1950 Madras; BSc Madras 1944, MB BS 1950. (Madras) Asst. Orthop. Surg. Dept. Accid. & Orthop. Surg. Gen. Hosp. & Hemlington Hosp. Middlesbrough. Socs: BMA & Cas. Surgs. Assn. Prev: Regist. (Orthop. & Accid Surg.) Middlesbrough Gen. Hosp.; Regist. (Orthop. & Cas.) Sedgefield Gen. Hosp. & Hartlepools Hosp.; Regist. (Surg.) Gen. Hosp. Malacca Maylaya.

KRISHNAPILLAI, Mr Ravi Directorate of Neurosciences, Frenchay Hospital, Frenchay Park Road, Bristol BS16 1LE — MB BS 1989 Malaya; FRCS Ed. 1993.

KRISHNASWAMY, Mr Bangarpet Ramarao North Glen Medical Practice, 1 Huntsmans Court, Glenrothes KY7 6SX Tel: 01592 620062 Fax: 01592 620465; 1 Alburne Crescent, Glenrothes KY7 5RE — MB BS 1969 Bangalore; MS BS Bangalore 1969. (Bangalore) Clin. Asst. (Rheum.) Glenrothes.

KRISHNASWAMY, Chelliah Konar The Surgery, 35 Barnsley Road, Goldthorpe, Barnsley S63 9LT Tel: 01709 880977 Fax: 01709 891457 — MB BS 1971 Madras.

KRISHNASWAMY, Dhanalakshmi Shanthi, Wester Balgedie, Kinross KY13 9HE — MB BS 1971 Madras; DA Eng. 1973. (Stanley Med. Coll.)

KRISHNASWAMY, Sharmila Andaman Surgery, 303 Long Road, Lowestoft NR33 9DF Tel: 01502 517346 Fax: 01502 531450; 115 Elm Tree Road, Lowestoft NR33 9ES — MD (Gen. Med.) Madras 1970, MB BS 1966. (Madras Med. Coll.) GP LoW.oft.; Clin. Asst. GU Med. Bure Clinic James Paget Hosp.; Dep. Police Surg. Suff. Constab. Socs: BMA; ODA; Assn. of Police Surg.

KRISHNASWAMY, Urmila 115 Elm Tree Road, Lowestoft NR33 9ES Tel: 01502 562296 — MD 1980 Madras; DA (UK) 1990.

KRISHNATHASAN, Mylvaganam (retired) 67 Melton Mill Lane, High Melton, Doncaster DN5 7TE — MB BS 1964 Ceylon.

KRISNAMURTHY, Meena Heron Practice, John Scott Health Centre, Green Lanes, London N4 2NU Tel: 020 8800 0111; 65 Falkland Road, London NW5 2XB — MB BS Lond. 1982; BSc Lond. 1979; MRCGP 1986; DCH RCP Lond. 1986; DRCOG 1985. (Univ. Coll. Hosp. Med. Sch.)

KRISTELEIT, Rebecca Sophie 21 Gloucester Square, London E2 8RS — MB ChB 1995 Manch.

KROESE, Mark James David Cairnmill Cottage, Penpont, Thornhill DG3 4LX — MB ChB 1992 Ed.

KROHN, Peter Leslie Coburg House, New St John's Road, St Helier, Jersey JE2 3LD Tel: 01534 874870 — BM BCh 1940 Oxf.; FRS; BA (1st cl. Hons. Sch. Animal Physiol.) Oxf. 1940. (Middlx.) Socs: Physiol. Soc. & Soc. Endocrinol. Prev: Prof. Endocrinol. Univ. Birm.; Nuffield Sen. Gerontol. Research Fell.

KROIJENGA, Jacob 11 Wellingtonpark, Montrose DD10 8QG — Artsexamen 1988 Groningen.

KROKER, Peter Bernhard 29 Brecon Road, London W6 8PY — State Exam Med 1986 Saarland.

KROL, Janet Evelyn Stuartfield, Godolphin Road, Weybridge KT13 0PT — MB ChB 1980 Auckland; MRCGP 1984.

KROLL, Professor John Simon Imperial College of Science, Technology & Medicine, St. Mary's Hospital, Norfolk Place, London W2 1PG Tel: 020 7886 6220 Fax: 020 7886 6284 Email: s.kroll@ic.ac.uk — BM BCh 1980 Oxf.; FRCPCH 1997; FRCP Lond. 1995; MRCP (UK) 1983. Prof. Paediat. & Molecular Infec. Dis. St. Mary's Hosp. Imperial Coll. Sch. of Med. Lond. Socs: (Ex-Research Fell.) Lister Inst. Preven. Med. Prev: Lect. (Paediat.) Univ. Oxf.

KROLL, Leanda Abigail Dept of Clinical Pharmacology, St Georges Hospital Medical School, Cranmer Terrace, London SW17 Tel: 020 8725 0966 Email: lkroll@sghms.ac.uk; 18 Pilgrim's Lane, London NW3 1SN — MB BS 1984 Lond.; MRCPsych 1989. (University College Hospital, London) Chadburn Lect. in Med. Educat., St Geo.s Hosp.Med. Sch. Prev: Sen. Regist. (Child & Adolesc. Psychiat.) Tavistock Clinic Lond.; Regist. (Psychol. Med.) Hosp. Sick Childr. Gt. Ormond St. Lond.

KROLL, Leopold 96 Summerseat Lane, Ramsbottom, Bury BL0 9TP — MB BS 1983 Lond.; MRCP (UK) 1986; MRCPsych 1991. Cons. (Child Psych.) Roy. Manch. Childr.'s Hosp Salford. Prev: Cons child Psychiat. Stockport; Sen. Regist. (Child Psychiat.) NW Region.; Regist. (Psychiat.) St. Geo. Hosp. Lond.

KROLL, Una Margaret Patricia (retired) St Mary's Lodge, Priory St, Monmouth NP25 3BR Tel: 01600 713465 Email: unakroll@aol.com — MB BChir 1951 Camb.; MRCGP 1962. Prev: SCMO Hastings HA.

KRONE, Susanne Cornelia 11 Victoria House, Hinchingbrook Hospital, Huntingdon PE18 8NT Tel: 01480 416416 — MD 1992 Munster; State Exam Med. Munster 1991; DA (UK) 1994.

KROON, Stuart Maxwell William Goodenough House, Mecklenburgh Square, London WC1N 2AN Tel: 020 7278 9765 — MB ChB 1984 Cape Town.

KROPACH, Koloman, Lt.-Col. RAMC (retired) 108 Quadrangle Tower, Cambridge Square, London W2 2PL Tel: 020 7723 2535 Fax: 020 7723 2535 — MD Vienna 1937. Prev: Regist. (Med.) Padd. Hosp. Lond.

KROSNAR, Alena 3 Polmont Park, Polmont, Falkirk FK2 0XT — LRCP LRCS 1976 Ed.; LRCP LRCS Ed. LRCPS Glas. 1976.

KROSNAR, Suzanne Claire 3 Polmont Park, Polmont, Falkirk FK2 0XT; 86 Bonaly Road, Colinton, Edinburgh EH13 0PE — MB ChB 1994 Ed.; FRCA Lond. 1999. (Ed.) SHO (Anaesth.) Roy. Infirm. Edin. Prev: SHO 3 (Anaesth.) SE Scotl. Rotat.; SHO (Anaesth.) SE Scotl. Rotat.; SHO (A & E) Addenbrooke's NHS Trust Camb.

KROTOSKY, Laurence Ashley Stanley Corner Medical Centre, 1-3 Stanley Avenue, Wembley HA0 4JF Tel: 020 8902 3887; 43 Mowbray Road, Edgware HA8 8JG — MB BS 1981 Lond.; MRCGP 1985. Socs: BMA. Prev: Trainee GP/SHO Barnet Gen. Hosp. VTS; Ho. Phys. OldCh. Hosp. Romford; Ho. Surg. King Geo. Hosp. Ilford.

KRUCHEK, Donald George Ludovic Langley Lodge, Jackmans Lane, Woking GU21 1RL — MB ChB 1978 Ed.

KRUEGER, Joachim Klaus Willi Accident & Emergency Department, North Tyneside General Hospital, Rake Lane, North Shields NE29 8NH — State Exam Med 1992 Frankfurt.

KRUGER, Marelise Royal Gwent Hospital, Department of Anaesthesia, Cardiff Road, Newport NP20 2UB Tel: 01633 234234; 31 Westland Close, Cardiff CF24 2PJ — MB ChB 1992 Pretoria.

KRUKOWSKI, Professor Zygmunt Henderson Aberdeen Royal Infirmary, Foresterhill, Aberdeen AB25 2ZN; Tel: 01224 742866 — MB ChB 1972 Aberd.; PhD Aberd. 1979; FRCS Ed. 1976; FRCS Glas 2000. Cons. Surg. Grampian Univ. Hosp.s Trust; Prof. of Clin. Surg., Univ. Aberd. Prev: Sen. Lect. (Surg.) Univ. Aberd.

KRUSZEWSKA, Jadwiga Waleria Mary Oliver Street Surgery, 57 Oliver Street, Ampthill, Bedford MK45 2SB Tel: 01525 402641 Fax: 01525 840764; The Stables, College Farm, Barton Road, Pulloxhill, Bedford MK45 5HP — MB ChB 1990 Manch.; MRCGP 1994.

KRYSA, Jolanta 78 Kettering Court, 4 Brigstock Road, Thornton Heath, Croydon CR7 8SR — MB BS 1997 Lond.

KRYSIAK, Mr Piotr 6 Fountain Avenue, Hale, Altrincham WA15 8LY Tel: 0161 980 1842 Fax: 0161 980 1842 Email: pkrysiak@aol.com; High Point, Elmsway, Halebarns, Altrincham WA15 0DZ — Lekarz 1981 Warsaw; FRCS Ed. 1994. (RCS of Ed.) Sen. Transpl. Fell. (Cardiothoracic Surg.) Wythenshawe Hosp. Manch. Socs: Brit. Transpl. Soc.; Internat. Soc. Heart & Lung Transpl.

KRYSZTOPIK, Mr Richard Joseph 27 Promenade Street, Heywood OL10 4EH Email: rkry@msn.com — MB ChB 1988 Manch.; FRCS Eng. 1992. Higher Surgic Trainee Roy. United Hosp. Bath. Prev: Research Fell. Univ. Louisville Kentucky, USA; Regist. (Gen. Surg.) Hope Hosp. Salford.

KRYWAWYCH, Mia Natalya Flat 1, 73 Anson Road, London N7 0AT — MB BS 1998 Lond.; MB BS Lond 1998.

KSHETRY, Mr Lakshman Das 43 Beulah Road, Rhiwbina, Cardiff CF14 6LU — MB BS 1953 Agra; FRCS Eng. 1966.

KUAN, Bing Hua 74a Guisborough House, South Cleveland Hospital, Marton Road, Middlesbrough TS4 3SY — MB ChB 1994 Manch.

KUAN, Ying Ching 87 Greystown Avenue, Upper Malone Road, Belfast BT9 6UH — MB BCh BAO 1993 Belf.

KUBBA, Mr Adam Kadir 1/R, 32 Falkland St., Glasgow G12 9QX — MB ChB 1990 Glas.; MD Glas. 1996; FRCS Ed. 1994. Specialist Regist. hepatobiliary unit Qu.'s med centre. Nottm. Socs: Caledonian Soc. Gastroenterol.; Surgic. Research Soc.; Scott. Soc. for Hist. of Med. Prev: Specialist Regist., Gt.er Manch. Higher Surgic. Train. Scheme; Specialist Regist., Mid Trent Higher Surgic. Train. Scheme; Research Fell., Univ. of Edin. & W.ern Gen. Hosp.

KUBBA, Ali Abdullah Gainsborough Clinic, 80 Lambeth Road, London SE1 7PW Tel: 020 7411 5728 Fax: 020 7411 5733 — MB ChB 1973 Baghdad; FRCOG 1995, M 1981; MFFP 1993. (Baghdad) Cons. Community Gyn. Community Health S. Lond. Trust; Hon. Sen. Lect. GKT Sch. of Med.; Hon. Cons. Guy's and St Thomas's Hosp. Lond. Socs: Brit. Soc. Colpos. & Cerv. Path.; Brit. Menopause Soc.; Eur. Soc. Contracep. Prev: Dep. Dir. Med. Margt. Pyke Centre Lond.; SHO (O & G) St. Mary's Hosp. Manch.; Resid. Surg. Off. (Gyn.) Hosp. for Wom. Soho Sq. Lond.

KUBER, Anil, TD, SBStJ Group Practice, St Andrew's Road, Tidworth SP9 7EP Tel: 01980 602620 Fax: 01980 602780 — MB BS 1973 Madras. (Madras Med. Coll.) Civil. Med. Pract. MoD; Approved Doctor Sect. 12 Ment. Health Act S. & W. RHA; Apptd. Doctor Ionising Radiat. Regulats. Health & Safety Exec; Regional Casework Med. Adviser (Army); Civil. Occupat. Health; Examr. Wilts. St. John Ambul. Serv.; Bd. Mem. S. Wilts. PCG; Mem. Civil Serv. Med. Off. Gp. Socs: Fell. Roy. Soc. Health; GP Clin. Tutor Salisbury Plain Med. Soc.; BMA. Prev: Approved Doctor Diving Operats. Work Health & Safety Exec.; Med. Off. Sch. Electronic Engin. P.ss Marina Coll. Reading; Regional Tutor Postgrad. Educat. Foundat.

KUBER, Uma Anil Staff Grade in Psychiatry, Green Lane Hospital, Devizes SN10 5DS — MB BS 1974 Bombay; DA Eng. 1978. (G.S. Med. Coll.) Staff Grade (Psychiat.) Green La. Hosp. Devizes Wilts.; Approved Doctor Sect. 12 Ment. Health Act. Wessex RHA. Socs: Affil. Roy. Coll. Psychiat.; BMA. Prev: Clin. Asst. (Psychiat.) Savernake Hosp. MarlBoro.; Clin. Asst. (Psychiat.) Old Manor Hosp. Salisbury & Roundway Hosp. Devizes; SHO (Psychiat.) Frimley Pk. Hosp. Camberley & Salisbury Gen. Hosp.

KUBIAK, Elizabeth Mary Microbiology Department, Royal Gwent Hospital, Cardiff Road, Newport NP20 2UB — MB BS 1984 Lond.; BSc Lond. 1981, MB BS 1984; MRCPath 1993. (King's Coll. Hosp.) Cons. Med. Microbiol. Roy. Gwent Hosp. Newport; Hon. Lect. (Med. Microbiol.) Univ. Birm. Prev: Sen. Regist. Rotat. (Med. Microbiol.) W. Midl. RHA; Regist. (Med. Microbiol.) Qu. Eliz. Hosp. Birm. & St. Geo. Hosp. Lond.; SHO (Path.) Bristol Roy. Infirm.

KUBIANGHA, Mr Bassey Okon The Surgery, 31 Falkland Road, London NW5 2PU Tel: 020 7485 4602 Fax: 020 7485 3635; 7 Queen Annes Grove, Enfield EN1 2JP — MB BS 1974 Ibaddan; FRCS Ed. 1987.

KUBIE, Alena Department Haematology, Hillingdon Hospital, Uxbridge UB8 3NN Tel: 01895 238282 Fax: 01895 279931 — MB ChB 1973 Birm. Assoc. Specialist (Haemat.) Hillingdon Hosp. Uxbridge. Socs: BMA; Assn. Clin. Path.; Brit. Soc. Haematol. Prev: Sen. Regist. (Haemat.) St. Thos. Hosp. Lond.; SHO (Neurol.) Roy. Surrey Hosp. Guildford.

KUBIK, Mirko Michael Green Gables, Cross Bank, Bewdley DY12 2XB Tel: 01299 266705 — MD 1945 Prague; FRCP Ed. 1971, M 1957; MRCS Eng. LRCP Lond. 1951. (Prague & Lond.) Emerit. Cons. Phys. Burton Rd. Hosp. Dudley. Socs: Internat. Soc. Internal Med. & Brit. Cardiac Soc. Prev: Asst. Phys. & Nuffield Research Fell. Gen. Hosp. Sunderland.

KUBIK, Natalie Anne Loft 106, Sherbourne wharf, Grosvenor St., Birmingham B16 8DE — BM BS 1998 Nottm.; BM BS Nottm 1998.

KUBIS, Veronica Maria Stowmarket Health Centre, Violet Hill Road, Stowmarket IP14 1NL Tel: 01449 776000 Fax: 01449 776005 — MB BS 1986 Lond.; MRCGP 1991. Prev: Trainee GP/SHO (Paediat.) W. Suff. Hosp. VTS; Ho. Surg. Char. Cross Hosp. Lond.; Ho. Phys. St Richard's Hosp. Chichester.

KUC, Wladyslaw Wlodzimierz (retired) 8 Sibthorpe Drive, Sudbrooke, Lincoln LN2 2RQ Tel: 01522 750074 — Med. Dipl. 1953 Stettin; LMSSA Lond. 1976; Dip. Dermat. & Venereol. Warsaw Inst. 1957. Prev: GP Lincoln.

***KUCHAI, Romana** North Middlesex Hospital, Sterlingway, Edmonton, London N18; 47 Selwood Road, Brentwood CM14 4QA — MB BS 1996 Lond.

KUCHARCZYK, Wojciech Andrzej Jerzy Rockley House, High Flatts, Huddersfield HD8 8XU — MRCS Eng. LRCP Lond. 1977. Socs: W Yorks. Medico Legal Soc.; T/A Dutton-Mason Med. (Medico Legal Reporting Serv.).

KUCHEMANN, Nancy Katherine 119 St James' Drive, London SW17 7RP Tel: 020 8767 4319 Fax: 020 8767 4319 — MB ChB 1995 Bristol; BSc (Hons.) Psychol. Bristol 1992; DCH RCP 1998. (University of Bristol) Prev: SHO (A & E) Ealing Hosp.; Ho. Off. (Med.) Derriford Hosp. Plymouth; Ho. Off. (Surg.) N. Devon Dist. Hosp.

KUCHERIA, Mr Rakesh 38 Western Avenue, London NW11 9HJ — MB BS 1990 Delhi; FRCS Eng. 1994.

KUCHHAI, Nazir Ahmad Harold Hill Health Centre, Gooshays Drive, Harold Hill, Romford RM3 9SU Tel: 01708 343991 Fax: 01708 346795; 47 Selwood Road, Brentwood CM14 4QA Tel: 01277 264606 — MB BS Jammu & Kashmir 1967. (Govt. Med. Coll. Srinagar) Prev: SHO St. Edmund's Hosp. N.ampton; SHO Harrogate Dist. Hosp.; SHO Scotton Banks Hosp. KnaresBoro..

KUCK, Marjorie Amy Clara (retired) Anderida, Dene Lane W., Lower Bourne, Farnham GU10 3PS Tel: 01252 793205 — MB BS Lond. 1946; MRCS Eng. LRCP Lond. 1946; FRCOG 1968, M 1954; MFCM 1972. Prev: Sen. Regist. (O & G) Roy. Free Hosp.

KUCYJ, Michael Dennis 16 Upper Long Leys Road, Lincoln LN1 3NH — MB ChB 1980 Bristol; MMedSci (Clin. Psychiat.) 1988; MRCPsych 1985.

KUCZYNSKA, Anna-Maria Elzbieta Janina 28 Queen Ediths Way, Cambridge CB1 7PN — MB BCh 1997 Wales.

KUCZYNSKA, Maria Jozefa 28 Queen Edith Way, Cambridge CB1 7PN — MB BS 1965 Lond.; MRCS Eng. LRCP Lond. 1965.

KUCZYNSKI, Aleksander Cornford House Surgery, 364 Cherry Hinton Road, Cambridge CB1 8BA Tel: 01223 247505 Fax: 01223 568187 — MB BS 1965 Lond.; MRCS Eng. LRCP Lond. 1965.

KUDESIA, Goura Public Health Laboratory, Northern General Hospital, Herries Road, Sheffield S5 7AU Tel: 0114 243 7749 Fax: 0114 242 1385; 74 Ivy Park Road, Ranmoor, Sheffield S10 3LD Tel: 0114 230 9881 — MB BS 1975 Delhi; MRCPath 1986; Dip. Health Mgt. Keele 1997; FRCPath 1996. Cons. Virol Pub. Health Laborat. Serv. Sheff.; Hon. Lect. Univ. Sheff.; Examr., Roy. Coll. of Pathol. Socs: Assn. Clin. Path.; Soc. Study of Infec.; Soc. Gen. Microbiol. Prev: Sen. Regist. Regional Virus Laborat. Ruchill Hosp. Glas.

KUDLAC, Hana May 16A West Cliff, Southgate, Swansea SA3 2AN — MB BS 1975 Lond.; DRCOG 1984.

KUDRATI, Munir Esmail 209 Willesden Lane, London NW6 7YR — MB 1978 Camb.; BA Camb. 1974; BChir 1977; DO RCS Eng. 1987.

KUENSSBERG, Bernard Von Crewe Medical Centre, 135 Boswall Parkway, Edinburgh EH5 2LY Tel: 0131 552 5544 Fax: 0131 551 5364; 16 Inverleith Avenue S., Edinburgh EH3 5QA Tel: 0131 552 3534 — MB ChB 1973 Bristol; CIH Dund 1982; AFOM RCP Lond. 1996; Cert. Av Med. 1984; Dip. Pract. Dermat. Wales 1992. (Univ. Bristol) Med. Adviser GEC-Marconi Avionics Scotl., Univ. Edin. & Blakes Ltd. Socs: Soc. Occupat. Med.; Brit. Med. Acupunct. Soc.; Primary Care Dermat. Soc. Prev: Regist. (Anaesth.) Roy. Infirm. Edin.; GP Toowoomba, Austral.; SHO (O & G) Barragwanath Hosp., Johannesburg.

KUGAN, Geetha 200 Maltings Lane, Witham CM8 1JN — MB BS 1979 Madras; MRCS Eng. LRCP Lond. 1986.

KUGAN, Gnanamurthy 200 Maltings Lane, Witham CM8 1JN — MB BS 1978 Madras; MRCS Eng. LRCP Lond. 1988.

KUGAPALA, Girija 35 Maplestead Road, Dagenham RM9 4XH — MB BS 1981 Peradeniya; MB BS 1981 Peradeniya.

KUGATHASAN, Thilagawathy 38A Tapton Crescent Road, Sheffield S10 5DA — MB BS 1967 Ceylon.

KUHAN, Velautham Lincluden Surgery, 53 Bellshill Road, Uddington, Glasgow G71 7PA Tel: 01698 813873; 12 Keppock Place, Falkirk FK1 5UQ Tel: 01324 636286 — MB ChB 1991 Glas.; DRCOG 1994; MRCGP 1995; DCCH 1997. Prev: Trainee GP Falkirk.

KUHN, Katherine Ann Kingswood Surgery, Hollis Road, Totteridge, High Wycombe HP13 7UN Tel: 01494 474783 Fax: 01494 438424 — MB BS 1988 Lond.

KUIPERS, Adrian John The Robert Jones & Agnes Hunt Orthopaedic Hospital, Oswestry SY10 7AG Tel: 01691 404000; Tel: 01743 741295 Fax: 01743 741605 Email: a.j.k@btinternet.com — MRCS Eng. LRCP Lond. 1971; FFA RCS Eng. 1976. Cons. Anaesth. Socs: Midl. Soc. Anaesth.; Hickman Anaesth. Soc.

KUITERT, Lieske Meta Elizabeth Department of Respiratory Medicine, Clock Attic, The Royal London Hospital, London E1 1BB — MB ChB 1983 Auckland; FRACP 1991. Cons., Repiratory Med., The Roy. Lond. Hosp..; Research Fell. Nat. Heart & Lung Insitute Lond.. Socs: Brit. Thorac. Soc.; Thoracic Soc. of Austral. & NZ. Prev: Research Fell. Lond. Chest Hosp.

KUJAWA, Miss Magda Lucia Stepping Hill Hospital, Poplar Grove, Stockport SK2 7JE Tel: 0161 483 1010 — MB ChB 1994 Manch.; MB ChB (Hons.) Manch. 1994; BSc St. And. 1991; FRCS (Eng) 1999. (St. Andrew's, Manchester) Specialist Regist. (Urol.), Manch. Roy. Infirm. Socs: Manch. Med. Soc.; BMA. Prev: SHO (Urol), Stepping Hill; SHO (Surg), Stepping Hill; SHO (Ortho), Withington Hosp.

KUKATHASAN, Mr Ganesharatnam The Medical Centre, 2a Southfield Way, Great Wyrley, Walsall WS6 6JZ Tel: 01922 415151 Fax: 01922 415152; 3 Walton Lodge, Walton on the Hill, Stafford ST17 0LR Tel: 01785 665122 — MB BS 1972 Ceylon; FRCS Glas. 1981.

KUKATHASAN, Ponnuthuray 31 Stonechat Road, Billericay CM11 2NZ Tel: 01277 632740 — MB BS 1976 Kerala; DMH Belf. 1990.

KUKENDRARAJAH, Kalichelui Bedford General Hospital (South Wing), Kempston Road, Bedford MK42 9DJ; 26 Bickley Street, Tooting Broadway, London SW17 9NE Tel: 020 8682 3122 — MRCS Eng. LRCP 1988 Lond.; MRCS Eng LRCP Lond. 1988.

KUKREJA, Amarjit Singh Westwood Medical Centre, 298 Tile Hill Lane, Coventry CV4 9DR Tel: 024 7646 6106 Fax: 024 7642 2475 — MB BS 1964 Panjab; DLO RCS Eng. 1968. Hosp. Pract. (ENT) Coventry.

KUKREJA, Neil 49 Cleveland Terrace, Darlington DL3 8HN — MB BS 1998 Lond.; MB BS Lond 1998.

KUKREJA, Neville 47 Kenilworth Road, Coventry CV4 7AF — MB BS 1996 Lond.; MA Cambridge 1996; MRCP UK 1999. (Cambridge)

KUKREJA, Ravinder Kaur Westwood Medical Centre, 298 Tile Hill Lane, Coventry CV4 9DR Tel: 024 7646 6106 Fax: 024 7642 2475; 47 Kenilworth Road, Coventry CV4 7AF Tel: 024 76 413746 — MB BS 1964 Delhi; DA Eng. 1970.

KUKULA, Marek Stanislaw 131 Clegg's Lane, Little Hulton, Manchester M38 9RS — MB ChB Manch. 1963; MRCGP 1973; DObst RCOG 1965.

KULANAYAGAM, Peter Chelliah (retired) 200 Bridle Road, Shirley, Croydon CR0 8HL Tel: 020 8777 7182 — MB BS Ceylon 1950; DTCD Wales 1960. Prev: Prison Med. Serv. 1969-1990.

KULANTHAIVELU, Angela Rajeswari Selvakumari 3 Meadow Garth, Outwood, Wakefield WF1 3TE; 3 Meadow Garth, Outwood, Wakefield WF1 3TE — MB BS 1975 Sri Lanka; LMSSA Lond. 1988.

KULANTHAIVELU, Markkandu Warrengate and Batley Road Surgery, Upper Warrengate, Wakefield WF1 4PR Tel: 01924 371011 — MB BS 1973 Sri Lanka; DCH RCP Lond. 1992; DObst RCPI 1984.

KULARATNE, H Tel: 020 8660 0193 Fax: 020 8763 8952 — MB BS 1970 Ceylon; MB BS 1970 Ceylon.

KULASEGARAM, Ranjababu Department of Genitourinary Medicine, St. Thomas' Hospital, Guy's & St Thomas' Hospital Trust, Lambeth Palace Road, London SE1 7EH Tel: 020 7928 9292 Fax: 020 7922 8291; Saisthan, 61 Lord Avenue, Clayhall, Ilford IG5 0HN Tel: 020 8551 2183 — MRCS Eng. LRCP Lond. 1990; MRCP (UK) 1994. Cons. Socs: BMA; Med. Protec. Soc.; Med. Soc. Study VD. Prev: SHO Rotat. (A & E) Bromley Hosp.; Ho. Off. St. Bart. Hosp. Lond.; Locum Cons. Phys., Specialist Regist.

KULASEGARAM, Yalini 37 Bunting Bridge Road, Ilford IG2 7LR — LMSSA 1993 Lond.; MRCP 1995. Specialist Regist. Bolton Hosp. Prev: Specialist Regist. Bromley Hosp.; Specialist Regist. Bedford Hosp.; Specialist Regist. S.end Hosp.

KULASEKERAM, Veluppillai 77 Cambridge Road, Harrow HA2 7LB — MB BS 1964 Ceylon.

KULATILAKE, Mr Ariyasinghe Edmund Cromwell Hospital, Cromwell Road, London SW5 0TU Tel: 020 7470 2000 Fax: 020 7460 5700 — MB BS 1957 Ceylon; FRCS Eng. 1961; FRCS Ed. 1961. (Univ. Ceylon) Prof. & Head Dept. Nephrourol. Sai Sathya Sai Inst. Higher Med., India; Cons. Urol. Cromwell Hosp.; Affil. Cleveland Clinic Foundat. Cleveland Ohio 44106 USA. Socs: Fell. Roy. Soc. Med.; Amer. Urol. Assn.; Amer. Acad. Paediat. Prev: Cons. Urol. Nottm. Teachg. Hosps.; Sen. Regist. (Urol.) Hammersmith Hosp. Lond.; Cons. Urol. Surg. Birm. E. Hosp.

KULENDRAN, Selvaratnam 127 Herent Drive, Ilford IG5 0HQ — MRCS Eng. LRCP Lond. 1989.

KULHALLI, Vasudev 35 Byron Avenue, London E18 2HH — MB BS 1981 Jabalpur, India; MRCP (UK) 1990.

KULIGOWSKI, Mark 5B Moss Grove, Kingswinford, Dudley DY1 9JQ Tel: 01384 277377 — MB BS 1982 Lond.; DRCOG 1988. GP Kingswinford Dudley.

KULKARNI, Aravind Swamirao Group Practice Centre, Rosemary St., Mansfield NG19 6AB Tel: 01623 23600 — MB BS 1964 Karnatak; MRCGP 1975; DCH Eng. 1970. Prev: Clin. Asst. (Haemat.) Kings Mill Hosp. Sutton in Ashfield; SHO (Paediat.) St. Helen's Hosp. Hastings; Regist. (Med.) G.T. Hosp. Bombay.

KULKARNI, Aruna Kalidas 23 Gubyon Avenue, London SE24 0DU — MB BS 1980 Nagpur.

KULKARNI, Mr Bhalchandra Narayanrao 7 Jerbourg Close, Newcastle ST5 3LR — MB BS 1975 Indore; FRCS Ed. 1981.

KULKARNI, Devidas Jaya Stanhope Parade Health Centre, Gordon Street, South Shields NE33 4HX Tel: 0191 456 4611 Fax: 0191 451 6101 — MB BS 1975 Indore. (Indore) GP S. Shields, Tyne & Wear.

KULKARNI, Devidas Rabindranath The Galleries Health Centre, Town Centre, Washington NE38 Tel: 0191 416 6084 — MB BS 1971 Bombay. (Bombay) GP Washington, Tyne & Wear.

KULKARNI, Gopal Raghavendrarao (retired) 128 High Street, Bentley, Doncaster DN5 0AT Tel: 01302 874551 Fax: 01302 820820 — MB BS 1955 Gujarat; MD Gujarat 1959.

KULKARNI, Jayant Ramchandra Manchester DSC, Withington Hospital, Manchester M20 1LB Tel: 0161 613 7259; 10 Redbrook Way, Adlington, Macclesfield SK10 4NF — MB BS 1979 Bombay; MS (Orthop.) Bombay 1982; FRCSI 1986; LMSSA Lond. 1986; FRCP Lond. 1998. Cons. Rehabil. Withington Hosp.; Hon. Lect. Univ. Manch.; Hon. Lect. Univ. Salford. Socs: BMA; BSRM; ISPO. Prev: Hon. Sen. Regist. Univ. Leeds.

KULKARNI, Krishna Anantrao The Surgery, 1 New Cross Road, London SE14 5DS Tel: 020 7639 1631 — MB BS 1959 Bombay. (Grant Med. Coll.) Prev: Regist. (ENT) Plymouth Gen. Hosp.

(Greenbank Br.); SHO (Anaesth.) Essex Co. Hosp. Colchester; Regist. (Anaesth.) Birch Hill Hosp. Rochdale.

KULKARNI, Prabhakar 83 London Road, Rayleigh SS6 9HR Tel: 01268 784003 — MB BS 1955 Poona. (B.J. Med. Coll. Poona)

KULKARNI, Pradeep Ravindra Department of Anaesthesia, Northwick Park & St Mark's NHS Trust, Watford Road, Harrow HA1 3UJ Tel: 020 8869 3974 Fax: 020 8869 3975; 12 Brookdene Drive, Northwood HA6 3NS Tel: 020 8204 5934 Email: prkulkarni@msn.com — MB BS 1985 Bombay; MD (Anaesth.) Bombay 1988; FCAnaesth 1991; DA (UK) 1990. Cons. Anaesth. N.wick Pk. & St. Mark's NHS Trust Harrow. Prev: Clin. Fell. Montreal Childr. Hosp. & McGill Univ.; Sen. Regist. Roy. Free Hosp. Lond. & Roy. Brompton Hosp.

KULKARNI, Mr Ravindra Pandurang Ashford and St Peter's Hospital, London Road, Ashford TW15 3AA Tel: 01784 884059 Fax: 01784 884393 Email: ravikulkarni1@hotmail.com; Touchwood, 41 Langley Road, Slough SL3 7AH — MB BS 1977 Poona; MS Poona 1980; FRCS Glas. 1986. Cons. Urol. Ashford & St Peter's Hosp. Socs: BAUS; BAU. Prev: Sen. Regist. (Surg.) W. Middlx. Univ. Hosp. & Char. Cross Hosp. Lond.; Regist. (Surg.) Wexham Pk. Hosp. Slough; Reader (Surg.) BJ Med. Coll. Poona, India.

KULKARNI, Mr Rohit Flat 8, Cheverton Tower, Yeovil District Hospital, Yeovil BA21 4AT — MB BS 1986 Mysore; FRCS Ed. 1993.

KULKARNI, Sadhana Sanjay 517 Watford Road, St Albans AL2 3DU Tel: 01727 836838 — MB BS 1987 Lond. (St. Geo. Hosp.) Asst. GP Cricklewood, Lond. & St. Albans. Prev: Clin. Med. Off. (Paediat.) E. Herts.; SHO (O & G) N.wick Pk. Hosp.; SHO (Cas. & Geriat.) Edgware Hosp. Lond.

KULKARNI, Shobhana Pradeep 27 Claremont Avenue, Harrow HA3 0UH — MB BS 1986 Lond. Regist. (Microbiol.) PHLS Lond. Prev: Research Regist. (Microbiol.) Univ. Coll. Hosp. Lond.; SHO (A & E) Chase Farm Hosp. Enfield; SHO (Microbiol.) N.wick Pk. Hosp. Harrow.

KULKARNI, Mr Shrikant Khanderao Knee Fellow, Department of Orthopaedics, Southampton General Hospital NHS Trust, Tremona Road, Southampton SO16 6YD; c/o Secretary to Mr. D. A. Jones, Department of Orthopaedics, Morriston Hospital, Swansea SA6 6NL Tel: 01792 703090 — MB BS 1986 Bombay; MCh (Orth.) Liverp. 1994; MS (Orth.) Bombay 1988. Knee Fell. Dept. of Orthop. Soton. Gen. Hosp. Soton. Socs: Assoc. Mem. BASK; MDU. Prev: Clin. Asst. (Orthop.) Warrington Hosp. NHS Trust; Regist. (Orthop.) Warrington Hosp., Morriston Hosp. Swansea & W. Wales Hosp.

KULKARNI, Shriniwas Raghunath 13 London Street, Mountain Ash CF45 4BN — MB BS 1958 Baroda.

KULKARNI, Sunita Bhalchandra 7 Jerbourg Close, Newcastle ST5 3LR — MB BS 1976 Nagpur.

KULKARNI, Vivek Anand 15 Highfield Avenue, Scunthorpe DN15 7DZ — MB BS 1978 Bangalore; PhD Aberd. 1995; MSc (Informat. Tech. Med. Physics) Aberd. 1988; FFA RCS Eng. 1982; FFA RCSI 1982. (St. John's Med. Coll. Bangalore, India) Sen. Lect. (Anaesth. & Intesn. Care) Univ. Aberd.; Hon. Cons. Anaesth. & IC Aberd. Roy. Hosps.; Hon. Sen. Research Fell. (Biomed. Physics & Biol.) Univ. Aberd. Socs: Soc. Critical Care Med.; Intens. Care Soc.; Roy. Soc. Med. Prev: Critical Care Fell. Johns Hopkins Hosp. Baltimore, USA; Med. Off. Halley Brit. Antarctic Territory Camb.; Cons. Anaesth. Bollnas Hosp., Sweden.

KULLAR, Hardeep Singh 8 Almorah Road, Hounslow TW5 9AD — MB ChB 1994 Leeds.

KULLAR, Narinderjit Singh 49 Sackville Gardens, Ilford IG1 3LJ — MB BS 1997 Lond.

KULLMANN, Professor Dimitri Michael Institute of Neurology, National Hospital for Neurology & Neurosurgery, Queen Square, London WC1N 3BG — MB BS (Hons. Univ. Medal) Lond. 1986; FRCP; DPhil, MA Oxf. 1984. Socs: FRCP; F Med Sci. Prev: Nuffield Med. Research Fell. New Coll. Oxf.

KULSHRESTHA, Manoj Kumar 36 Over Mill Drive, Birmingham B29 7JL — MB ChB 1992 Birm.

KULSHRESTHA, Rajendra Prakash Aberdeen Medical Centre, Aberdeen Street, Winson Green, Birmingham B18 7DL Tel: 0121 554 7311; 36 Over Mill Drive, Selly Park, Birmingham B29 7JL — MB BS 1966 Agra; BSc Agra 1961; MS (Ophth.) Kanpur 1970; DO Eng. 1977. (Med. Coll. Agra) GP Birm.; Ophth. Med. Pract.; Mem. Birm. LMC. Socs: BMA & Assoc. Mem. Coll. Ophth.; ODA (Exec. Mem. Birm. Div.). Prev: Trainee GP Stone Staffs. VTS.; SHO (Ophth.) N. Staffs. Roy. Infirm. Stoke-on-Trent; Resid. Surg. Off. (Ophth.) Med. Coll. Kanpur India.

***KULSHRESTHA, Randeep Kumar** 36 Over Mill Drive, Birmingham B29 7JL — MB BS 1997 Lond.

KUMAR, A Bousfield Health Centre, Westminster Road, Liverpool L4 4PP Tel: 0151 207 1468 Fax: 0151 284 6864.

KUMAR, Aditi Singh 7 Dingle Close, Aughton, Ormskirk L39 5AL; 22 High Ashton, Kingston Hill, Kingston upon Thames KT2 7QL Tel: 020 8546 8673 — LRCP LRCS LRCPS 1998 Ed., Glas.; MBBS. (St. George's Hospital Medical School, London) Ho. Off., pre-registration, (Gen. Med.) Epsom Gen. Hosp., Surrey. Prev: HO, pre-reg., (Gen.Surg.) S.end Gen. Hosp.

KUMAR, Ajay 3 Wike Ridge Avenue, Leeds LS17 9NL — MB ChB 1984 Leic.; MRCP (UK) 1992.

KUMAR, Amarpal Singh Bobby 10 Orchard Close, Wembley HA0 1TZ — MB BS 1998 Lond.; MB BS Lond 1998.

KUMAR, Anil Calderstones Hospital, Whalley, Blackburn BB7 9PE Tel: 01254 822121 Fax: 01254 823023; 3 The Woodlands, Old Langho, Blackburn BB6 8BH Tel: 01254 248685 — MB BS 1972 Lucknow; MRCPsych 1986; MSc 2000. Cons. Psychiat. Learning Disabilities, Calderstones, Whalley. Prev: Sen. Regist. (Ment. Handicap) ColdE. Hosp. Soton.

KUMAR, Anil The Surgery, Second St., Bensham, Gateshead NE8 2UR Tel: 0191 477 2430 Fax: 0191 477 2430; 22 Foxhills Covert, Whickham, Newcastle upon Tyne NE16 5TN Tel: 0191 488 1164 — MD 1979 Patna; MB BS 1974.

KUMAR, Anil 106 Blenheim Road, Harrow HA2 7AF; 106 Blenheim Road, Harrow HA2 7AF Tel: 020 8863 5859 — MB BS 1960 Bombay; DCP Lond 1967. (Topiwala Nat. Med. Coll.) Prev: Regist. Path. Dept. Harefield Hosp. & Soton. Gen. Hosp.; SHO Path. Dept. Roy. Devon & Exeter Hosp.

KUMAR, Anju Sheffield Fertility Centre, Glen Road, Nether Edge, Sheffield S7 Tel: 0114 258 9716; Infertility Research Trust, Jessop Hospital for Women, Leavygreave Road, Sheffield S3 7RE Tel: 0114 276 6333 — MB BS 1977 Lucknow; DGO 1980; MRCOG 1987. Sen. Clin. Asst. Sheff. Fertil. Centre (Centr. for In Vitro Fertilisation). Socs: Brit. Fertil. Soc. Prev: Regist. & Clin. Asst. (O & G) Rotherham Dist. Gen. Hosp.

KUMAR, Anupma 7 Dingle Cl, Aughton, Ormskirk L39 5AL — MB ChB 1997 Manch.

KUMAR, Mr Appajappa Vasanth (retired) 191 Eccleshall Road, Stafford ST16 1PD Tel: 01785 253686 — MB BS Mysore 1959; FRCS Eng. 1971; MRCS Eng. LRCP Lond. 1972; FFAEM 1993. Cons. A & E Staffs. Gen. Hosp. Prev: Resid. Surg. Off. Staffs. Gen. Infirm. Stafford.

KUMAR, Arun 13 Field Close, South Croydon CR2 9BH — MB BS 1981 Jabalpur India; MRCP (UK) 1992.

KUMAR, Mr Ashok 2 Beech Court, North Tyneside General Hospital, Rake Lane, North Shields NE29 8NH — MB BS 1985 Karachi; FRCS Glas. 1990.

KUMAR, Mr Ashok c/o Dr L. B. Mandal, Telscombe Surgery, 365 South Coast Road, Telscombe Cliff, Peacehaven BN10 7HA; 7 Stockdale Place, Edgbaston, Birmingham B15 3XH Tel: 0121 452 1471 Fax: 0121 689 8750 — MB BS 1978 India; FRCSI 1986; FRCS Glas. 1987. Staff Surg. Derbysh. Roy. Infirm. Prev: Regist. Rotat. (Surg.) Qu. Med. Centre.

KUMAR, Asis FD 177, Sector III, Salt Lake, Calcutta 700091, India Tel: 00 91 33 349636; 79 St. Thomas's Road, London N4 2QJ Tel: 020 7359 0204 — MB BS 1979 Calcutta; FRCP 1997; MRCP (UK) 1988; MRCPI 1987; FCCP 1995; DTM & H Calcutta 1981. Cons. Phys. Calcutta Med. Research Inst.; Hon. Cons. Cardiol. B.M. Birla Heart Research Centre & Anandalok Hosp. Socs: Assn. Phys. India; Indian Soc. Gastroenterol.; Collegiate Mem. RCP Lond. & Glas. Prev: Regist. (Gen. Med.) Heathfield Hosp. Ayr; Regist. (Geriat. & Gen. Med.) Barnsley Dist. Gen. Hosp.

KUMAR, Asokananda Manor Road Surgery, 65 Manor Road, Dagenham RM10 8BD Tel: 020 8592 0868 — MB BS 1964 Calcutta; MB BS 1964 Calcutta.

KUMAR, Mr Balmiki The Health Centre, Bartholomew Avenue, Goole DN14 6AW Tel: 01405 767711 — MB BS 1965 Patna; MS Patna 1971, MB BS 1965.

KUMAR, Benjamin Park House W., Eccles Road, Whaley Bridge, High Peak SK23 7EL — MB ChB 1998 Sheff.; MB ChB Sheff 1998.

KUMAR, Chandra Hope Hospital, Eccles Old Road, Salford M6 8HD — MB BS 1975 Delhi; MSc Newc. 1986; MS Delhi l977, MB BS 1975. (Maulana Azad Med. Coll. New Delhi) Sen. Regist. (Neurosurg.) N.W. RHA. Socs: Manch. Med. Soc.; Assoc. Mem. Soc. Brit. Neurol. Surgs. Prev: Regist. (Neurosurg.) Newc. HA (T).

KUMAR, Chandrakant 107 Heavygate Road, Sheffield S10 1PE — MB ChB 1991 Sheff.

KUMAR, Mr Davendra Little Lever Health Centre, Mytham Road, Little Lever, Bolton BL3 1JF Tel: 01204 701834 Fax: 01204 862051; 17 Kinloch Drive, Bolton BL1 4LZ — MB BS 1961 Lucknow; MS Lucknow 1964; FRCS Ed. 1968. Socs: Med. Defence Union; BMA.

KUMAR, Devinder Claireforth, Waterhouse Lane, Kingswood, Tadworth KT20 6HU — MB BS 1975 Delhi.

KUMAR, Dhavendra Clinical Genetics Unit, Sheffield Children's Hospital, Western Bank, Sheffield S10 2TH Tel: 0114 271 7035 Fax: 0114 273 7467; 654 Manchester Road, Crosspool, Sheffield S10 5PU Tel: 0114 230 5227 Email: dhavekumar@yahoo.com — MB BS 1973 Lucknow; MD (Paediat.) Lucknow 1978; MMedSci Sheff. 1987; FRCPI 1992, M 1990; Dip. Amer. Bd. Med. Genetics 1990; DCH RCPSI 1979; MRCPCH 1996. (King George's Medical College Lucknow, India) Assoc. Specialist (Med. Genetics) Centre for Human Genetics Childr. Hosp. Sheff.; Hon. Clin. Tutor (Med. Genetics) Sheff. Univ. Socs: BMA; Ord. Mem. Brit. Soc. Human Genetics; Ord. Mem. Amer. Soc. Human Genetics. Prev: Clin. Asst. (Med. Genetics) Centre for Human Genetics Childr. Hosp. Sheff.

KUMAR, Easwar Bhaskar Cons. Cardiol., Queen Elizabeth Hospital, Gayton Road, King's Lynn PE30 4ET Tel: 01553 613613; 1 Beech Cres., West Winch, King's Lynn PE33 0PZ Tel: 01553 842654 — MB ChB 1970 Glas.; MRCP (UK) 1974; FRCP Glas. 1987. (Glas.) Cons. (Cardiol.) Qu. Eliz. Hosp. King's Lynn. Socs: Brit. Cardiac Soc. Prev: Staff Cardiol. Bradford Roy. Infirm.

KUMAR, Girish 2 Waggon Road, Barnet EN4 0HL — MB BS 1974 Patna.

KUMAR, Harsh Grasmere Avenue Surgery, 59 Grasmere Avenue, Slough SL2 5JE Tel: 01753 579803 Fax: 01753 553745 — MB BS 1974 Delhi.

KUMAR, John Sampath 24 Totnes Avenue, Bramhall, Stockport SK7 3PH — MB BS 1971 Madras.

KUMAR, Kamlesh 3 Melrose Gardens, Edgware HA8 5LN Tel: 020 8905 0222 Fax: 020 8905 0123 — MB BS 1965 Delhi; DTM & H Liverp. 1969.

KUMAR, Kathryn Alison Claireforth, Waterhouse Lane, Kingswood, Tadworth KT20 6HU — MB BS 1977 Lond.; FRCS Lond. 1982. Research Fell. Guy's Hosp. Lond.

KUMAR, Mr Kranti Milton Keynes General Hospital, Standing Way, Milton Keynes MK6 5LD Tel: 01908 660033 Fax: 01908 243931 Email: kranti.kumar@mkg-tr.anglox.nhs.uk; 6 Northleigh, Furzton, Milton Keynes MK4 1ED Tel: 01908 501115 — MB BS 1972 Aligarh; MChOrth Liverp. 1979; FRCS Eng. 1977; FFAEM 1995; D.Occ.Med. FOM Lond. 1997. (JN Med. Coll.) Cons. A & E Milton Keynes; Med. Director, Two Shires Ambul. Trust. Socs: Roy. Soc of Med Fac. of A & E Med. Prev: Sen. Regist. Walton Hosp. & Alder Hey Childr. Hosp. Liverp.; Sen. Cons. Secondment Sultanate of Oman.

KUMAR, Krishna Vijay 18 Wood End Close, Halifax HX3 0JU — MB BS 1982 Osmania, India; MRCPI 1992.

KUMAR, Mahesh 31 Ainsdale Crescent, Pinner HA5 5SF — MB BS 1998 Lond.; MB BS Lond 1998.

KUMAR, Malcolm Albin (retired) 30 Astra House, Kings Road, Brighton BN1 2HJ Tel: 01273 207186 — M.R.C.S. Eng., L.R.C.P. Lond. 1942. Prev: Ho. Surg. Taunton & Som. Hosp.

KUMAR, Manorma (Surgery) 434 Lodge Avenue, Dagenham RM9 4QT Tel: 020 8592 5251; 97 Parkstone Avenue, Emerson Park, Hornchurch RM11 3LP Tel: 01708 475147 — MB BS 1969 Rajasthan.

KUMAR, Namita Freeman Hospital, High Heaton, Newcastle-upon-Tyne NE7 7DN — MB ChB 1993 Liverp.; Mmed 2001 Dundee; MRCP (UK) 1997. (Liverpool) Specialist Regist. Rheum. N.ern Region. Socs: BMA; BSR; RCP. Prev: SHO (Med.) S. Cleveland Hosp. Middlesbrough; SHO (Med.) Qu. Eliz. Hosp. Gateshead.

KUMAR, Navin 64 Brackenberry Crescent, Roseberry Park, Redcar TS10 2PP — LRCP LRCS 1983 Ed.; LRCP LRCS Ed. LRCPS Glas. 1983.

KUMAR, Nisha — BM 1988 Soton.; MSc Lond. 1984, BSc 1983; FRCA 1994. Cons. In Anaesth., Uni. Hosp. Of Leicester NHS Trust. Prev: Lect. in Anaesth., Uni. Of Leicester; Regist. (Anaesth.) St. Geo. Hosp. Lond.; Sen. Regist. (Anaesth.) Roy. Brompton Hosp. Lond.

KUMAR, Mr Pankaj 7 Dingle Close, Aughton, Ormskirk L39 5AL Tel: 01695 423819; 22 High Ashton, Kingston Hill, Kingston upon Thames KT2 7QL Tel: 020 8546 8673 — BM BCh 1993 Oxf.; MA Camb. 1994; FRCS Eng. 1997; FRCS Ed. 1997. (University of Cambridge and University of Oxford) Specialist Regist. (Cardiothoracic Surg.) Roy. Brompton & Harefield Hosp. Lond. Prev: SHO (A & E) St. Mary's Hosp. Lond.; SHO (Cardiothoracic Surg.) Roy. Brompton Hosp.; SHO Rotat. (Surg.) St. Geo. Hosp. Lond.

KUMAR, Parameswaran Nair Hari c/o Fracture Clinic, Doncaster Royal Infirmary, Doncaster DN2 5JY — Vrach 1978 Moscow; Vrach People's Friendship Univ. Moscow 1978.

KUMAR, Mr Pradeep 8 Middlefield Road, Hardwick, Stockton-on-Tees TS19 8PF — MB BS 1983 Soton.; MB BS Univ. Soton. 1983; FRCS Ed. 1991.

KUMAR, Prakash The Tilehurst Medical Centre, 5-7 Norcot Road, Tilehurst, Reading RG30 6BP Tel: 0118 942 8484 Fax: 0118 942 5301 — MB BS 1974 Calcutta; MB BS 1974 Calcutta.

KUMAR, Pramod 73 Waverley Drive, Chertsey KT16 9PF; 73 Waverley Drive, Chertsey KT16 9PF — MB BS 1970 Allahabad; DLO Lond. (RCS) 1977; MS ENT Allahabad 1974. (MLN Medical College Allahabad India) Staff Surg. ENT Dept. St. Peter's Hosp. Chertsey Surrey.

KUMAR, Prarabdha 2 Plasnewydd Place, Roath, Cardiff CF24 3HD — MB BS 1995 Lond.

KUMAR, Prasun St Michael's Surgery, St. Michael's Square, Gloucester GL1 1HX — MB BS 1983 Poona; MRCS Eng. LRCP Lond. 1988.

KUMAR, Pratapnarain Vishnudatt Kings Edge Medical Centre, 132 Stag Lane, Kingsbury, London NW9 0QS Tel: 020 8204 0151; 3 Melrose Gardens, Edgware HA8 5LN Tel: 020 8905 0222 Fax: 020 8732 2545 — MB BS Jabalpur 1964; MSc Lond. 1982; DHMSA Lond. 1981; DTCD Wales 1980. (Govt. Med. Coll. Jabalpur) Socs: Fell. & Diplomate of Amer. Bd. Trop. Med.

KUMAR, Mr Prem 12 Woodwise Lane, Manchester M23 9QY Tel: 0161 945 9817 — MB BS 1973 Patna; MS (Gen. Surg.) Patna 1976; FRCS Glas. 1980. Clin. Fell. (Plastic Surg.) Univ. Hosp. Manch. Prev: Sen. Regist. (Plastic Surg.) King Khalid Univ. Hosp. Riyadh, Saudi Arabia; Regist. (Plastic Surg.) Manch.

KUMAR, Priya Darshini 20 Monmouth Drive, Merthyr Tydfil CF48 1JA — MB ChB 1998 Liverp.; MB ChB Liverp 1998.

KUMAR, Priyadarshi 8 Toftwood Av, Rainhill, Prescot L35 0PU — MB BS 1997 Lond.

KUMAR, Mr Rajendra Frimley Park Hospital NHS Trust, Portsmouth Road, Frimley, Camberley GU16 7UJ Tel: 01276 604015 Fax: 01276 604856; Tudor Grange, 5 Tekels Park, Camberley GU15 2LE Tel: 01276 66215 Fax: 01276 66215 — MS (ENT) Lucknow 1969; MB BS Agra 1964; FRCS (Orl.) Ed. 1972. (S.N. Med. Coll. Agra) Cons. Surg. (ENT) Frimley Pk. Hosp. Socs: Fell.Roy. Soc. of Med.; Brit. Assn. of Otolaryngologists. Prev: Sen. Regist. Roy. Infirm. Sheff. & Roy. Infirm. Leics.

KUMAR, Rajesh 119 Ashfield Street, London E1 3EX — MB BS 1997 Lond.

KUMAR, Rajeshwar 367 St. Nicholas Drive, Grimsby DN37 9RD — (Cert. In Aviation Medicine) Farnborough, UK; MBBS 1971 India; F.P. Cert.; FRSM; F.M.E. (Senior Cambridge, India & Prince of Wales Medical Coll. India) p/t Clin. Asst. Oncol., Diana P.ss of Wales Hosp. Grimsby; Forens. Med. Examr. with Humberside Police. Socs: RSM; BMA; Assoc. of Police Surg.s.

KUMAR, Rajinder 51B & 51C Robertson Street, Hastings TN34 1HL — MB ChB 1986 Dundee.

KUMAR, Mr Rajiv Department of Urology, Princess Margaret Hospital, Okus Road, Swindon SN1 4JU — MB BS 1981 Delhi; FRCS Ed. 1987.

KUMAR, Ram 33 Bentley Mount, Sowerby Bridge HX6 2SQ — BChir 1994 Camb.

KUMAR, Rani 3 Gloucester Way, Bewdley DY12 1QF — MB BS 1974 Patna.

KUMAR, Ravi Bhushan The Surgery, London Road, Teynham, Sittingbourne ME9 9QR Tel: 01795 521205 Fax: 01795 522795 —

MB BS 1970 Punjab; MB BS Punjabi 1970. (Govt. Med. Coll. Patiala)

KUMAR, Ravindra 272 Wanstead Park Road, Ilford IG1 3TT — MB BS 1957 Lucknow.

***KUMAR, Reena** 14 Kendal Drive, Beeston, Nottingham NG9 3AW — MB ChB 1996 Birm.

KUMAR, S Townsend Lane Surgery, 263 Townsend Lane, Clubmoor, Liverpool L13 9DG Tel: 0151 226 1358.

KUMAR, Samarendra Kumar The Surgery, 58 Cumberland Drive, Bexleyheath DA7 5LB Tel: 020 8310 5764 Fax: 020 8310 5377 — MB BS 1967 Calcutta; MB BS 1967 Calcutta.

KUMAR, Sanjay Kumar and Mehta, 12 Queens Road, London SE15 2PT Tel: 020 7639 1133 — MB ChB 1992 Leeds.

KUMAR, Sanjay 12 Marlowe Close, Billericay CM12 0YF — MB BS 1996 Lond.

KUMAR, Santosh Kumar and Kumar, Upton Medical Centre, Bechers, Hough Green, Widnes WA8 4TE Tel: 0151 424 9518 Fax: 0151 420 4979; 11 Churchfields, Widnes WA8 9RP — MB BS 1969 Delhi; DObst RCOG 1972. (Lady Hardinge Med. Coll.) GP Widnes.

KUMAR, Sarvadamanjeet 31 Onslow Gardens, London E18 1ND — MB BS 1978 Panjab.

KUMAR, Satinder Dept of General Practice, University of Southampton, Southampton SO16 5ST — MB ChB 1987 Liverp. Sen. Research Fell., Dept. of Gen. Pract., Univ. S.ampton.

KUMAR, Shanta Ajit Storresdale Medical Centre, 1 Storresdale Road, Liverpool L18 7JY Tel: 0151 724 2396 — MB BS 1971 Bombay.

KUMAR, Sharyu Prashanti, 9 Mizen Way, Cobham KT11 2RG Tel: 01932 862301 — MB BS 1967 Osmania; DFFP 1993; DA Eng. 1970. (Osmania) SCMO (Community Med.) Kingston & Esher HA. Socs: Fac. Community Health.

KUMAR, Shashi Surjit Larkshall Medical Centre, 1 Larkshall Road, Chingford, London E4 7HS Tel: 020 8524 6355 Fax: 020 8524 0605 — MB BS 1963 Rajasthan; MB BS 1963 Rajasthan.

KUMAR, Sheo Kumar, 434 Lodge Avenue, Dagenham RM9 4QS Tel: 020 8592 5251 Fax: 020 8592 1183; 97 Parkstone Avenue, Emerson Park, Hornchurch RM11 3LP Tel: 01708 475147 — MB BS 1958 Nagpur. Prev: Clin. Asst. (Orthop. & Cas.) W. Hill Hosp. Dartford.

KUMAR, Shiv Rochdale Road Surgery, 48A Rochdale Road, Middleton, Manchester M24 2PU Tel: 0161 643 9131; 102 Manchester Road, Heywood OL10 2PN Tel: 01706 621285 — MB BS 1960 Osmania; DTM & H Liverp. 1968; DCH Osmania 1963. (Osmania Med. Coll. Hyderabad)

***KUMAR, Sonia** 239 Fleetside, West Molesey KT8 2NL Tel: 020 8941 0744 Fax: 020 8941 7446 — MB BS 1997 Lond.; BSc (Hons) 1994.

KUMAR, Sudesh Manor Park Medical Centre, 2 Lerwick Drive, Off Granville Avenue, Slough SL1 3XU Tel: 01753 526625 Fax: 01753 552962 — MB BS 1967 Panjab.

KUMAR, Sudhesh Undergraduate Centre, Birmingham Heartlands Hospital, Bordesley Green E., Birmingham B9 5SS Tel: 0121 766 6611 Fax: 0121 685 5536 Email: s.kumar.med@bham.ac.uk; 61 Elmbridge Drive, Shirley, Solihull B90 4YP — MB BS 1986 Madras; FRCP 1999; MD Manch. 1994; MRCP (UK) 1990. Cons. Phys. (Gen. Med., Diabetes & Endocrinol.) Birm. Heartlands Hosp.; Sen. Lect. Univ. Birm. Socs: Brit. Diabetic Assn.; Eur. Assn. Study Diabetes. Prev: Lect. (Med.) Univ. Birm.; Research Fell. & Hon. Regist. Manch. Roy. Infirm.; SHO Rotat. (Med.) Manch. Roy. Infirm.

KUMAR, Mr Sudhir Dunfermline & West Fife Hospital, Reid St., Dunfermline KY11 7EZ Tel: 01383 737777; 34 Grange Terrace, Edinburgh EH9 2LE — MSc (Med. Sci.) Surg Glas. 1988; FRCS Ed. 1988.

KUMAR, Mr Sunil Barking, Havering & Redbridge NHS Trust, Oldchurch Hospital, Romford Tel: 01708 708227, 01708 708492 Fax: 01708 708227 — MB BS 1989 Lond.; Dip Sports Med 1998 RCS Ed.; FRCS 1998 Eng.; MB BS (Hons.) Lond. 1989; FRCS Eng. 1994; FRCSI 1993. Cons. Orthopaedic Surgeion OldCh. & Harold Wood Hosps.

KUMAR, Surendra, SBStJ Kumar and Kumar, Upton Medical Centre, Bechers, Hough Green, Widnes WA8 4TE Tel: 0151 424 9518 Fax: 0151 420 4979; 11 Churchfields, Widnes WA8 9RP — MB BS 1968 Delhi; DIH Eng. 1981; DCH NUI 1970; DCH RCPSI 1970; DPMC 1994; MRCGP 1995. (Maulana Azad Med. Coll.) GP Widnes. Prev: SHO (Chest Dis. & Geriat.) Newport & E. Mon. Gp. Hosps.; SHO (Acute Geriat.) Exeter & Mid Devon Gp. Hosps.

KUMAR, Surinder 4 Flowerdale Close, The Larchway, Coseley, Bilston WV14 9QT — MB ChB 1985 Manch.

KUMAR, Mr Surinder 7 Avenue Lourdes, Scunthorpe DN15 8EP — MB BS 1971 Punjab; FRCS Ed. 1979.

KUMAR, Surrinder Manor Park Medical Centre, 2 Lerwick Drive, Off Granville Avenue, Slough SL1 3XU Tel: 01753 526625 Fax: 01753 552962 — MB BS 1965 Delhi.

KUMAR, Vasant Nampally Wharton's Cottage, Gorsuch Lane, Scarisbrick, Ormskirk L40 9RP Tel: 01704 841612 Fax: 01704 841612 — MB BS 1962 Osmania; BSc Osmania 1956; MFFP 1993; DObst RCOG 1965. Gyn. Surg. Brit. Pregn. Advisery Serv. Liverp., Merseyside; Cons., Vasectomy Surg. S.port & Formby NHS Trust, S.port, Merseyside. Socs: Fac. Fam. Plann. & Reproduc. Health Care; NW Soc. Family Plann. & Psycho-Sexual Med. Prev: SCMO (Family Plann.) St Helens & Knowsley Community NHS Trust; Regist. (O & G) Liverp. Matern. & Wom. Hosps.; Regist. (O & G) Ormskirk Gen. Hosp. & S.port Infirm.

KUMAR, Mr Vijay Shiv Prasad 34A Ash Grove, Leeds LS6 1AY — MB BS 1974 Poona; FRCS Ed. 1982.

KUMAR, Vinod 18/19 St John Street, Mansfield NG18 1QJ Tel: 01623 650721; 130 Nottingham Road, Ravenshead, Nottingham NG15 9HL — MB BS 1974 Punjab; MRCPsych 1983. Cons. (Child Psychiat.) Notts. NHS Trust.

KUMAR, Vinod Vauxhall Health Centre, Limekiln Lane, Liverpool L5 8XR Tel: 0151 207 2274 Fax: 0151 207 1272; Flat 20, Waterloo Docks,, Waterloo Road, Liverpool L3 0BE Tel: 0151 236 4967 — MB BS Med. Inst. (III) Mandalay 1966; DCH RCPSI 1978; DRCOG 1978. Princip. GP.

KUMAR, Vinod 7 Dingle Close, Ormskirk L39 5AL — MB ChB 1993 Manch.

KUMAR, Vinod X Ray Department, James Paget Healthcare NHS Trust, Gorleston, Great Yarmouth NR31 6LA Tel: 01493 452403 — MB BS 1973 Punjab; FRCR 1981; DMRD (Delhi-India) Gold Medal 1975; DMRD Lond. 1979. Cons. Radiologist.

KUMAR GUPTA, Anil Queen Elizabeth Hospital for Children, Hackney Road, London E2 8PS — MB BS 1986 Delhi; MRCP (UK) 1994.

KUMAR-LEAVER, Professor Parveen June, CBE Tel: 020 7882 7191 Fax: 020 7882 7192 Email: p.j.kumar@mds.qmw.ac.uk; 4 Ridgeway, Epsom KT19 8LB — MB BS 1966 Lond.; BSc. Lond 1963; MRCS Eng. LRCP Lond 1966; MRCP (UK 1970; FRCP Lond 1987; FRCP Ed. 1995. (St. Bart.) Prof. of Clin. Med. Educat. (Univ. of Lond.); Director of Continuing Professional Developm., Roy. Coll. of Phys.s; Non-Exec. Director Nat. Ins. For Clin. Excellence (NICE) and Barts and the Lond. NHS Trust.; Med.s Commiss. (Vice-Chairm.); Cons. Phys. And Gastronenterologist, Homerton Hosp.; Hon. Cons. Phys. And Gastronenterologist, Barts and the Lond. NHS Trust. Socs: Brit. Soc. Gastroenterol.; Brit. Soc. Immunol. Prev: Sub-Dean (Undergrad.) St. Bart & Roy. Lond. Sch Med And Dent.; Postgrad. Sub-Dean Med. Coll. St. Bart. Hosp. Lond.; Dir. PGMDE Roy. Hosps. Trust.

KUMAR SINGH, Prabha Kumar 51 Kingsdale Avenue, Burnley BB10 2PY — LRCP LRCS 1986 Ed.; LRCP LRCS Ed. LRCPS Glas. 1986.

KUMAR SURENDRAN, Mr Sailesh Centre for Fetal Care, Queen Charlottes Hospital, Du Cane Road, London W12 0HS Tel: 020 8383 3998 Email: sailesh.kumar@ic.ac.uk — MB BS 1990 Singapore; FRCS Ed. 1994; M.Med (O & G) Singapore 1995; MRCOG 1994; FRACOG 1997; DPhil (Oxon) 2000. (Singapore) Cons. in Feta and Matern. Med., Qu. Charlotte's & Chelsae Hosp., Lond.; Hon. Sen. Lect., Imperial Coll. Sch. of Med., Lond. Socs: Blair Bell Res. Soc.; Brit. Matern. & Fetal Med. Soc. Prev: Sen. Regist. (O & G) King Edwd. Memor. Hosp., Perth, Australia; Regist. (O & G) St Richard's Hosp., Chichester; Fotheringham Research Fell./Hon. Sen. Regist. (O & G), John Radcliffe Hosp.,Oxf.

KUMARAJEEWA, Donald Ignatius Sri Chandra Tatchbury Mount Hospital, Calmore, Southampton SO40 2RZ — MB BS 1968 Ceylon; MRCPsych 1982; DPM Eng. 1980. (Peradeniya) Assoc. Specialist (Psychiat. of Ment. Handicap.) Tatchbury Mt. Hosp. Prev: Regist. (Psychiat.) Barnsley Hall Hosp. BromsGr. & Herrison Hosp.; Dorchester; SHO (Psychiat.) Burton Rd. Hosp. Dudley.

KUMARAKULASINGHAM, Ranjitharany 7 Brantwood Gardens, Ilford IG4 5LG — MB BS 1973 Sri Lanka; DA (UK) 1986.

KUMARAN, Jeyagowry 24 Sixth Cross Road, Twickenham TW2 5PB — MB BS 1981 Sri Lanka; MRCS Eng. LRCP Lond. 1989.

KUMARAN, Thuraisamy Ooyirilangkumaran Consultant Haematologist, North Middlesex Hospital, London N18 1QX Tel: 020 8887 2000 Fax: 020 8807 9644; 20 Littleton Crescent, Harrow HA1 3SX Tel: 020 8422 2358 — MB BS 1965 Ceylon; PhD Lond. 1972; FRCP Lond. 1996; FRCPath 1990,M 1975. (Colombo) Cons. Haemat. N. Middlx. Hosp. Lond. Prev: Lect. Dept. Physiol. Univ. Ceylon Colombo; Sen. Regist. & Regist. Dept. Haemat. Hammersmith Hosp. Lond.

KUMARAN, Vallipuran Eliyathamby 24 Sixth Cross Road, Twickenham TW2 5PB — MB BS 1977 Sri Lanka; MRCS Eng. LRCP Lond. 1987.

KUMARARATNE, Buvenekaba Neonatal Unit, Newcross Hospital, Wednesfield Road, Wolverhampton WV10 0QP Tel: 01902 307999 Fax: 01902 642861 — MB BS 1983 Colombo; MD (Paediat.) Sri Lanka 1990; MRCP (UK) 1992; MRCPCH 1997. Cons. Neonat. Newcross Hosp. Wolverhampton. Socs: BMA; RCPCH.

KUMARARATNE, Dinakantha Suramya Department of Clinical Immunology, Box 109, Addenbrooke's Hospital, Cambridge CB2 2QQ Tel: 01223217166 Fax: 01223217166 Email: dsk22@cam.ac.uk — MB BS 1972 Sri Lanka; DPhil Oxf. 1980; MRCPath 1984; FRC Path 1991. Cons. Immunol., Dept. of Clin. Biochem.ry and Immunol., Addenbrooke's Hosp., Camb. Prev: Cons. Immunol. & Dir. Regional Immunol. Dept. Birm. Heartlands Hosp.; Hon. Reader Clin. Immunol. Univ. of Birm.; Cons. Immunol. City Hosp. Birm.

KUMARASENA, Mr Halamba Aratchige Don, Lt.-Col. RAMC Retd. 14 Old Mill View, Dewsbury WF12 9QJ — MB BS Ceylon 1962; FRCS Eng. 1973. (Colombo) Socs: Assoc. Mem. BAUS. Prev: Cons. Surg. Duchess of Kent Milit. Hosp. Catterick N. Yorks.; Cons. Surg. Brit. Milit Hosp. Iserlohn, BAOR; Sen. Specialist (Urol.) Qu. Eliz. Milit. Hosp. Woolwich & (Surg.) RAMC Lond.

KUMARASWAMY, Sri Pathmajothy The Bold Street Medical Centre, 25-29 Bold Street, Warrington WA1 1HH Tel: 01925 244655 Fax: 01925 241855 — MB BS 1970 Ceylon. (Colombo)

KUMARENDRAN, Mylvaganam Depts. Obstetrics & Gynaecology/Medical Molecular Biology, University of Newcastle upon Tyne, Newcastle upon Tyne NE2 4HH Tel: 0191 222 6000; 12 Southside, Shadforth, Durham DH6 1LL Tel: 01385 372 0756 — MB BS 1982 Colombo; MRCOG 1991. Sen. Regist. (O & G) & Hon. Research Fell. (Med. Molecular Biol.) Univ. Newc. u. Tyne. Prev: Clin. Research Assoc. (O & G & Med. Molecular Biol.) Univ. Newc.; Regist. Rotat. (O & G) N.. Regional Train Scheme; Regist. (O & G) Newc. Gen. Hosp.

KUMBLE, Jaiker Rao Stockland Green Health Centre, 192 Reservoir Road, Erdington, Birmingham B23 6DJ Tel: 0121 384 8244 Fax: 0121 377 6199 — MB BS 1968 Mysore; Dip. Pract. Dermat. Wales 1993. (Govt. Med. Coll. Mysore) Hosp. Pract. (Anaesth.) Highcroft Hosp. Birm. Socs: BMA; Brit. Soc. Med. & Dent. Hypn.; Brit. Acupunc. Soc.

KUMI, Geoffrey Otempong Buckland Hospital, Coombe Valley Road, Dover CT17 0HD; 19 Old Mead, Folkestone CT19 5UR — MB ChB 1975 Ghana; MB ChB U Ghana 1975; MRCOG 1983.

KUNA, Koteswarawma Seymour Grove Health Centre, 70 Seymour Grove, Old Trafford, Manchester M16 0LW Tel: 0161 877 9230 — MBBS; DFFP; DObst; Dip. in Acupuncture. (Karnatak University, India) Gen. Med. Practitioner; Family Plann. Med. Off.

KUNA, Parameswarappa Timperley Health Centre, Grove Lane, Timperley WA15 6PH Tel: 0116 980 8041 — MB BS 1971 Karnatak; MSc (Audiol. Med.) Manch. 1987; FRIPHH 1988; DCCH RCP Ed. 1985; DPM Eng. 1982; DPM RCPSI 1981; DCH RCPSI 1976. Cons. Community Paediat. (Audiol. Med.) Trafford Health Care NHS Trust; Clin. Director, Child Health. Socs: Fac. Community Health. Prev: Clin. Med. Off. Chester HA; Regist. (Psychiat.) Wirral HA; SHO (Paediat.) Derby & Birm. HAs.

KUNAPULI, Venkata Saraswati 6 Pasture Road, Wembley HA0 3JD — MB BS 1994 Lond. SHO (Anaesth.) Kettering Gen. Hosp. Prev: SHO Neurosurg. Roy. Lond. Hosp.; SHO Accid. & Emerg. Centr. Middlx. Hosp.

KUNASINGAM, Velupillai 183 City Way, Rochester ME1 2BG — MB BS 1971 Ceylon.

KUNCEWICZ, Izabela Greenhill Health Centre, Church St., Lichfield WS13 6JL Tel: 01543 414311; 11 Gable Croft, Lichfield WS14 9RY Tel: 01543 257631 — MB ChB 1983 Birm.; MRCGP 1988; DRCOG 1987. Prev: Trainee GP Selly Oak Hosp. & Dudley Rd. Hosp. Birm. VTS.; Trainee GP Wyldegreen Hawthorns Surg. Birm.

KUNDE, Dattakumar Pandharinath 35 Fobbing Farm Close, Basildon SS16 5NP — MB BS 1988 Bombay; MRCOG 1994.

***KUNDRA, Vinit** 26 Rowan Close, Sutton Coldfield B76 2PB — MB ChB 1994 Birm.; ChB Birm. 1994.

KUNDU, Mr Biswa Nath Shreea, Tan House Lane, Great Harwood, Blackburn BB6 7UL — MB BS 1964 Calcutta; FRCS Eng. 1976. GP Blackburn. Prev: Regist. (Dept. Gen. Surg.) Blackburn Roy. Infirm.

KUNDU, Chitta Ranjan (retired) Himaloy, 155A Soothill Lane, Batley WF17 6HW Tel: 01924 47123 — MB BS 1957 Calcutta; BSc Calcutta 1950, MB BS 1957; MRCP (U.K.) 1970. Cons. Phys. Dewsbury HA. Prev: Cons. Phys. St. Columb's Hosp. Lond.derry.

KUNDU, Dilip Kumar The Surgery, 18 St Johns Road, Tottenham, London N15 6QP Tel: 020 8442 8220 Fax: 020 8802 8539; 18 St. John's Road, London N15 Tel: 020 8800 6404 — LMSSA 1979 Lond.; MB BS 1969. Socs: The Med. Professional Soc.

KUNDU, Pabitra Mohan 221 Cottingham Road, Hull HU5 4AU Tel: 01482 42911 — MB BS 1961 Calcutta; DA Eng. 1972. (R.G. Kar Med. Coll.)

KUNDU, Sara Elizabeth — MB BChir 1990 Camb.; MA Camb. 1991; MRCPsych 1994. (Selwyn Coll. Camb. & Lond. Hosp. Med. Coll.) Prev: Sen. Regist. (Child & Adolesc. Psychiat.) Roy. Lond. Hosp. Train. Scheme; Hon. Clin. Research Fell. (Psychiat.) Roy. Lond. Hosp. (St. Clements); Regist. & SHO (Psychiat.) Roy. Lond. Hosp. Train. Scheme.

KUNDU, Sujan Kumar The Surgery, 79-81 Lichfield Road, Walsall Wood, Walsall WS9 9PE Tel: 01543 377285 Fax: 01543 454004 — MB BS 1961 Calcutta.

KUNDU, Miss Sujata Shreea, Tan House Lane, Great Harwood, Blackburn BB6 7UL — MB BS 1994 Newc.; FRCS 1998; FRCS 1999.

KUNDU, Suman 94 Newmount Road, Fenton, Stoke-on-Trent ST4 3HU — MB ChB 1998 Manch.; MB ChB Manch 1998.

KUNDU, Timirbaran 353 Upper Rainham Road, Hornchurch RM12 4DB Tel: 0142 24 70029 — MB BS 1964 Calcutta; DObst RCOG 1973; DGO Calcutta 1966. (R.G. Kar Med. Coll.)

KUNJU, Mohamed Pallath Kunjumoideen Medical Centre, 1 Rawling Road, Gateshead NE8 4QS Tel: 0191 477 2180 Fax: 0191 477 6979; Norton House, 22 Cornmoor Road, Whickham, Newcastle upon Tyne NE16 4PU — MB BS 1972 Mysore; BSc Kerala 1964; MRCP (UK) 1977; MRCGP 1988. Clin. Asst. Gateshead.

KUNKLER, Ian Hubert Western General Hospital, Crewe Road, Edinburgh EH4 2XU Tel: 0131 537 2214 Fax: 0131 537 1029; 47 Dick Place, Edinburgh EH9 2JA Tel: 0131 667 3454 Fax: 0131 667 3454 — MB BChir 1979 Camb.; FRCP Ed. 1995; MRCP (UK) 1981; FRCR 1985; DMRT Ed. 1983. Cons. Radiother. & Oncol. W.. Gen. Hosp. Edin.; Hon. Sen. Lect. Univ. Edin. Socs: Fell. Roy. Soc. Med.; BMA; Pres. Elect Brit. Oncol. Assn. Prev: EEC Cancer Research Fell. Inst. Gustave Roussy, Paris; Sen. Regist. & Regist. (Radiat. Oncol.) W.. Gen. Hosp. Edin.; SHO (Gen. Med.) Nottm. City Hosp.

KUNKLER, Mr Roger Bertrand Department of Surgery, Northampton General Hospital, Cliftonville, Northampton NN1 5BD Tel: 01604 634700; Field House, 17 Mears Ashby Road, Earls Barton, Northampton NN6 0HQ — MB BS Lond. 1987; BSc Lond. 1980; FRCS Ed. 1992; FRCS Eng. 1991; DM (Nottm) 1997; FRCS (Urol.) 1997. (Charing Cross and Westminster Medical School) Cons. Urol. N.ampton Gen. Hosp. Prev: Sen. Regist. (Urol.) Leicester Gen. Hosp.; Research Fell. (Urol.) Nottm. Cancer Research Campaign; Sen. Regist. (Urol.) Derby city Hosp.

KUNWAR, Alfarah Mohammad 34 Swayfield Avenue, Manchester M13 0NQ — MB ChB 1994 Manch.

KUNZEMANN, Martin 12 Hibaldstow Close, Lincoln LN6 3PY — State Exam Med 1990 Hanover.

KUNZRU, Mr Krishna Mohan Nath 33 Monkhams Drive, Woodford Green IG8 0LG Tel: 0208 8504 9616; 33 Monkhams Drive, Woodford Green IG8 0LG Tel: 020 8504 5098 — MS Agra 1964, MB BS 1961; FRCS Eng. 1967. (SN Med. Coll. Agra) Cons. Orthop. Surg. Holly Ho. Hosp. Essex & BUPA Roding Hosp. Essex;

Hon. Cons. Orthop. Surg. Whipps Cross Hosp. Lond. Socs: (Pres.) Brit. Orthop. Foot Surg. Soc.; Brit. Soc. Surg. Hand; (Ex-Pres.) Hunt. Soc. Lond. Prev: Sen. Regist. (Orthop.) Roy. Free Hosp. & Windsor Hosp. Gp.; Resid. Surg. Off. SN Hosp. Agra; Regist. (Orthop.) W.m. Hosp. & Qu. Mary's Hosp. Roehampton.

KUO, Mr James Hang Ung South West Cardiothoracic Centre, Derriford Hospital, Derriford, Plymouth PL6 8DH Tel: 01752 763831 Fax: 01752 763830; Poundhanger, Crapstone, Yelverton PL20 7PW Tel: 01822 855515 — MB BS 1984 Newc.; FRCS Eng. 1988; FRCS (CTh) 1996; MD 1997. (University of Newcastle-upon-Tyne) Cons. Cardiothoracic Surg. S. W. Cardiothoracic Centre Derriford Hosp. Plymouth. Prev: Clin. Fell. (Cardiovasc. Surg.) The Toronto Hosp.; Sen. Regist. (Cardiothoracic Surg.) Univ. Hosp. of Wales; Regist. (Cardiothoracic Surg.) The Roy. Lond. Hosp.

KUO, Mr Michael Jeo-Ming University of Birmingham, Birmingham B15 2TT Tel: 0121 472 1311 Email: m.j.kuo@bham.ac.uk; 5 Belgrove Close, Birmingham B15 3RQ Email: 100766.2352@compuserve.com — MB ChB 1989 Birm.; FRCS Eng. 1993. (Univ. Birm.) Regist. Rotat. (ENT) W. Midl.; Fell. Otolaryngol. (MRC/RCS Eng. Jt. Special Train.). Prev: Regist. (Surg.) Univ. Hong Kong.

KUOK, Samantha Su Wen 6 The Beeches, 43 Queens Road, Leicester LE2 1WQ — MB ChB 1998 Leic.; MB ChB Leic 1998.

KUPELIAN, Mr Sarkis Manoug 17 Royal Court, Carleton Rise, Pontefract WF8 4RX — MB BCh 1970 Cairo; MChir Cairo 1972, MB BCh 1970.

KUPER, Martin Brian 77 Maldon Road, Brighton BN1 5BD — BM BCh 1993 Oxf.

KUPFER, Richard Mark University Hospital, Nottingham NG7 2UH — MB BChir 1975 Camb.; MA Camb. 1976, MB BChir 1975; FRCP Lond. 1993. Cons. Phys. Geriat. Med. Univ. Hosp. Nottm. Socs: Fell. Roy. Coll. Phys.; Brit. Geriat. Soc. & Brit. Soc. Gastroenterol. Prev: 1st Asst. (Med. & Geriat.) Newc. Gen. Hosp.

KÜPPER, Anita-Luise 16 Mecklenburgh Square, London WC1N 2AD Tel: 020 7833 4110 — MB ChB 1988 Cape Town.

KUPPUSAMI, Timakkondu Narasimman Royal Marsden Hospital, Downs Road, Sutton SM2 5PT — MB BS 1963 Madras.

KURAR, Anish Kumar 31 Northumberland Avenue, Isleworth TW7 5HZ — MB BS 1975 Panjab.

KURBAAN, Arvinder Singh 147 Barker Drive, London NW1 0JZ — MB BS 1990 Lond.

KURDY, Mr Nasser Mohammed Orthopaedic Department, Wythenshawe Hospital, Southmoor Road, Wythenshawe, Manchester M23 9LT Tel: 0161291 2399; 24 Squires Court, Canterbury Gardens, Eccles New Road, Salford M5 2AD Tel: 0161 707 2654 — MB ChB 1983 Dundee; BMedSci 1980; FRCS Ed. 1987; FRCS Glas. 1988; FRCSG (Orth.) 1997; MD Manch. 1998. (Dundee) Cons. Orthop. Surg. Prev: Clin. Fell. Brit. Columbia Childr.'s Hosp.; Sen. Regist. (Orthop. Surg.) S. Manch. Hosp. NHS Trust; Sen. Regist. (Orthop. Surg.) Stockport Hosps. NHS Trust.

KURER, Mr Michael Hugh Jeremy PO Box 14961, London NW11 6ZS Tel: 01923 442739 Email: michael@kurer.co.uk — MB BS 1982 Lond.; BSc Lond. 1979; FRCS (Orthop.) Eng. 1992; FRCS Eng. 1986. Cons. (Orthop. Surg.) N. Middlx. Hosp. Lond. Socs: Brit Orthopae Assoc. Prev: Sen. Regist. Roy. Nat. Orthop. Hosp. Stanmore; Shoulder Research Fell. Roy. Nat. Orthop. Hosp. Stanmore.

KUREYA, Peter (Surgery) 146 Halfway Street, Sidcup DA15 8DF; 27 Birkhall Road, Catford, London SE6 1TF Tel: 020 8695 1125 — MB BS 1987 Lond.; BA Camb. 1984; MA Camb. 1987; MRCP (UK) 1991. Prev: Trainee GP Luton & Dustable Hosp. VTS; Regist. (Gen. Med.) Dudley Rd. Hosp. Birm.; SHO (Med.) W. Middlx. Univ. Hosp.

KURIACOSE, Joseph Kaiparambat Moneymore Medical Centre, Fairhill, Moneymore BT45 7QX Tel: 028 8674 8350 — MB BS 1976 Madras; MRCP (UK) 1980. (Madras) Locum Cons. Phys., Mid Ulster Hosp. Magherafelt.

KURIAN, George Verghese Glanfa, Orme Road, Bangor LL57 1AY Tel: 01248 362055 Fax: 01248 372771 — MB BS 1974 Bombay; MSc (Med. Educat.) Wales 1997; MRCS Eng. LRCP Lond. 1976; DFFP 1994; DRCOG 1980. (Grant Med. Coll.) GP Trainer Bangor; Med. Adviser Diocese of Bangor; Hosp. Pract. (Gen. Med.) Ysbyty Gwynedd Bangor; Med. Assessor & Mem. for Indep. Tribunal Serv. Prev: Trainee GP Bangor VTS; SHO (Gen. Med.) Caerns. & Anglesey Gen. Hosp. Bangor & Llandudno Gen. Hosp.

KURIAN, Kathreena Mary 25 Longcrofte Road, Edgware HA8 6RR Tel: 020 8952 9301 — MB BS 1994 Lond.; BSc (Experim. Path.) Lond. 1991. Specialist Regist. (Histopath.) Poy. Infirm. Edin.; Edin. Univ. Med. Fac. Fell. Prev: SHO (Histopath.) Roy. Infirm. Edin.; Ho. Off. St. Helier Hosp. & St. Thos. Hosp. Lond.

KURIAN, Oommen Kandathil 6 Garvock Drive, Greenock PA15 4BZ Tel: 01475 724558 — MB BS 1974 Kerala; MRCP (UK) 1991; DCH RCPSI 1987. (Trivandrum Med. Coll., Kerala) Cons. Paediat. Inverclyde Roy. Hosp. Socs: RCPS Glas.; Brit. Paediat. Assn.; BMA.

KURIEN, George Department of Pathology, The Doncaster Royal & Montagu Hospital, Armthorpe Road, Doncaster DN2 5LT Tel: 01302 553130 Fax: 01724 865680 Email: george.kurien@dbh.nhs.uk; 8 Silica Crescent, Silica Lodge, Scunthorpe DN17 2XA Tel: 01724 338032 — MB BS 1973 Osmania; FRCPath 1992, M 1981. (Osmania Med. Coll., Hyderabad, India) Cons. Pathologist, Doncaster & Montagu Hosp.s, Doncaster. Socs: Internat. Acad. Path.; Assn. Clin. Path.; BMA. Prev: Cons. Pathologist, Scunthorpe Gen. Hosp., Scunthorpe & Goole Hosps. Trust; Lect. & Sen. Regist. (Path.) Univ. of Nottm..

KURIEN, Jacob Pickering Lodge, Barnet General Hospital, Wellhouse Lane, Barnet EN5 3DJ — MB BS 1975 Madras.

KURL, Daven Kumar 13 Ormond Crescent, Hampton TW12 2TJ — MB BS 1988 Lond.

KURL, Mrs Leela Sunningdale, 13 Ormond Crescent, Hampton TW12 2TJ Tel: 020 8979 1834; The White House, 4 Cambridge Road, Teddington TW11 8DR Tel: 020 8977 2409 — MB BS 1952 Agra; MS (Obst. & Gyn.) Agra 1955, MB BS 1952. (Agra) Socs: Mem. BMA.

KURLBAUM, Phillip Flat 4, 11 Pittville Lawn, Cheltenham GL52 2BE — State Exam Med 1991 Hanover.

KURMA RAO, Bondada King's Lynn & Wisbech Hospitals NHS Trust, Chatterton House, Queen Elizabeth Hospital, King's Lynn PE30 4ET Tel: 01553 613613 Fax: 01553 613703; 1 Horton Road, Springwood Estate, King's Lynn PE30 4XU Tel: 01553 692205 — MB BS 1978 Andhra; DPM RCPSI 1984. Hon. Cons. Old Age Psychiat. Chatterton Hse. Qu. Eliz. Hosp. Socs: BMA; MDU. Prev: Assoc. Specialist (Psychiat.) Qu. Eliz. Hosp.; Regist. (Psychiat.) Fermoy Unit Qu. Eliz. Hosp. King's Lynn; Regist. St. Cadoc's Hosp. Newport, Gwent & Hellesdon Hosp. Norwich.

KUROWSKA, Anna Christina Edenhall Marie Curie Centre, 11 Lyndhurst Gardens, London NW3 5NS Tel: 020 7853 3400 Fax: 020 7853 3438 — MB BS 1981 Lond.; BA Lond. 1991, BSc 1976; FRCP Lond. 1994; MRCP (UK) 1984. (Univ. Coll. Lond.) Dep. Med. Dir. Edenhall Marie Curie Centre Hampstead; Cons. Palliat. Med. (Oncol. & Palliat. Care Unit) Whittington Hosp. Lond. Prev: Regist. (Radiother. & Oncol.) Mt. Vernon & Middlx Hosps. Lond.; SHO (Med. Oncol.) St. Bart. & Hackney Hosps. Lond.; SHO Rotat. (Med.) Centr. Oxf. Hosps.

KURPIEL, Andrzej Jan Whitefields Surgery, Hunsbury Hill Road, Camp Hill, Northampton NN4 9UW Tel: 01604 760171 Fax: 01604 708528; 21 Collegiate Crescent, Sheffield S10 2BA Tel: 0114 267 1072 Fax: 0114 267 1736 — MB ChB 1986 Sheff.

KURREIN, Felix (retired) Flat 3, Chacewater, Chacewater Avenue, Worcester WR3 7AW Tel: 01905 24136 — MB BS Lond. 1945, DCP 1950; DPath Eng. 1957; FRCPath 1971, M 1964.

KURRI, Pakeera Reddi (retired) Department of Psychiatry, Pilgrim Hospital, Sibsey Road, Boston PE21 9QS Tel: 01205 364801 — MB BS 1973 Sri Venkateswara; BSc Andhra 1966; MRCPsych 1983. Prev: Cons. Psychiat. of Old Age S. Lincs. Community & Ment. Health Servs. NHS Trust.

KURSTJENS, Sef Paul Barnfield, 26 The Street, Kingston, Canterbury CT4 6JB — MB BCh 1988 Witwatersrand.

KURT-ELLI, Sarah Louise 49 Assembly Street, Edinburgh EH6 7BQ — MB ChB 1998 Ed.; MB ChB Ed 1998.

KURTIS, Richard Edward Dr Hewish, Dangare and Partners, The Health Centre, Bartholomew Avenue, Goole DN14 6AW Tel: 01405 767711 Fax: 01405 768212 — MB BS 1987 Lond.; MRCGP 1991; DRCOG 1991.

KURTZ, Antony Bellair The Middlesex Hospital, Mortimer St., London W1T 3AA Tel: 020 7631 0178 Fax: 020 7436 1536 — MB BChir 1965 Camb.; PhD Camb. 1970, MA 1965; FRCP Lond. 1981, M 1966. (Middlx.) Emerit. Cons. Middlx. Hosp. Lond. Prev: Cons. Phys. Diabetes Middlx. Hosp. Lond.

KURTZ, John Bellair (retired) National Blood Service, Vincent Drive, Birmingham B15 2SG Tel: 0121 253 4000 Fax: 0121 253 4032 — MB BChir 1967 Camb.; MA Camb. 1967; MRCP (UK) 1970; FRCPath 1987, M 1975. Prev: Cons.Virol.Nat.Blood.Serv.Birm./Oxf.

KURTZ, Zarrina 12 Blithfield Street, London W8 6RH — MB BS 1962 Lond.; MSc Lond. 1976; FRCP Lond. 1994; FFPHM RCP (UK) 1990; FRCPCH (UK) 1996. Indep. Cons. Pub. Health, Health Policy & Research Lond. Prev: Cons. Pub. Health Med. S. Thames RHA Lond.; Hon. Sen. Lect. St. Geo. Hosp. Med. Sch. Lond.; Sen. Lect. (Paediat. Epidemiol.) Inst. Child Health Lond.

KURUKCHI, Emile Francis 8 Iron Bridge Crescent, Park Gate, Southampton SO31 7FX — BM 1998 Soton.; BM Soton 1998.

KURUKULAARATCHY, Ramesh Jagath 134 Olivers Battery Road South., Winchester SO22 4HB — BM 1994 Soton.; MRCP (Lond.) 1997. Clin. Research Fell., The David Hide Asthma & Allergy Research Centre, St. Mary's Hosp., Newport, Isle of Wight; Hon. Vis Regist., Dept. of Univ. Med., Soton. Gen. Hosp.

KURUVATTI, Chandrashekhar Chanabasappa The Surgery, 108 Victoria Road, Pinxton, Nottingham NG16 6NH Tel: 01773 810207 — MB BS 1970 Karnatak; DRCOG 1978. (Karnatak Med. Coll. Hubli)

KURUVILLA, George Taylor, Parsons, Donnelly, Kuruvilla and Mulrine, Woolton House Medical Centre, 4/6 Woolton Street, Woolton, Liverpool L25 5JA Tel: 0151 428 4184 Fax: 0151 428 4598 — MB BS 1979 Kashmir; MRCGP 1992.

KURUVILLA ZACHARIAH, Mr Kampakalunkal 28 Southfields, Dudley, Cramlington NE23 7HU — MB BS 1978 Madras; FRCS Ed. 1988.

KURWA, Aziz Rajabali St. Anthony's Hospital, London Road, North Cheam, Sutton SM3 9DW Tel: 020 8337 6691 Fax: 020 8335 3325; 1 Alder Lodge, 73 Stevenage Road, Fulham, London SW6 6NP Tel: 020 7385 2482 Fax: 020 7385 2482 — MB BS 1958 Bombay; FRCP Lond. 1996; FRCP Ed. 1978, M 1965. (Seth G.S. Med. Coll.) p/t Cons. Dermat. Shirley Oaks Hosp. Shirley Oaks Village Shirley Croydon; Cons. Dermat. St Anthony's Hosp. N. Cheam Surrey; Cons. Dermat. The Stamford Hosp., RavensCt. Pk., Lond. W6 0TN; Cons. Dermat. Lasercare Clinics, Sutton Hosp., Cotswald Rd., Sutton S2 5NF. Socs: Fell. Roy. Soc. Med.; Brit. Assn. Dermatol.; St. John's Hosp. Dermat. Soc. Prev: Cons. Dermat. Univ. Coll. Lond. Hosp. (Retd.); Cons. Dermat. St. Helier Trust Sutton Gen. & Qu. Mary's Hosps. (Retd.); Cons. Dermat. Mayday Univ. Hosp. Croydon.

KURWA, Badrudin Rajabali 19 Addington Road, South Croydon CR2 8RF — MB ChB 1975 Birm.

KURWA, Habib Aziz Dept of Dermatology, Churchill Hosp, Old Road, Headington, Oxford OX3 7LJ Tel: 01865 228265 Fax: 01865 28260 Email: kurwa@cf.ac.uk — MB BCh 1988 Wales; MRCP (UK) 1993. (Univ of Wales Coll of med) Cons, Dermat. dept, Ch.ill Hosp, Oxf. Radcliffe NHS Trust Oxf.; Clin fell Amer coll of Micrographic surg and cutaneous Oncol. fell Univ of Calif. San Francisco USA. Socs: BMA; Dowling Club; Train. Mem. Brit. Assn. Dermat. Prev: Sen regis (dernat) St Johns' Inst. of Derm St Thomas' hosp Lond.; Regist. (Dermat.) Roy. Lond. Univ. Hosp. Lond.; Clin. Research Fell. Univ. Wales Coll. Med. Cardiff.

KURZEJA, John Andrew Four Acre Health Centre, Burnage Avenue, Clock Face, St Helens WA9 4QB Tel: 01744 819884 Fax: 01744 850382 — MB ChB 1981 Liverp.; MRCS Eng. LRCP Lond. 1981. (Liverpool) Mem. St. Helens & Knowsley LMC. Prev: Trainee GP Whiston Hosp. VTS; SHO (Phys.) Bodelwyddan Hosp.; Ho. Off St. Helen's & Whiston Hosps.

KURZER, Anthony Jeffrey The Harrow Health Care Centre, 84-88 Pinner Road, Harrow HA1 4HZ Tel: 020 8861 1221 — MB BS 1984 Lond.; MRCGP 1989. GP Lond. Socs: Brit. Med. Acupunct. Soc. Prev: Clin. Asst. (Diabetes) Edgware Gen. Hosp.

KURZER, Leonard 12 Antrim Grove, London NW3 4XR Tel: 020 7722 1767 — MD 1938 Genoa. Socs: BMA. Prev: Obst. Ho. Surg. P.ss Beatrice Hosp.

KURZER, Mr Martin Norman 100 Harley Street, London W1N 1AF Tel: 020 8922 8481 Fax: 020 8202 6590 Email: martin@kurzer.demon.co.uk — MB BS Lond. 1975; FRCS Eng. 1980. (Univ. Coll. Hosp.) Socs: Brit. Assn. Cosmetic Surg. Prev: Surg. Resid. & Research Fell. Univ. Hosp. Syracuse NY, USA; Regist. & Sen. Regist. Rotat. (Surg.) Univ. Coll. Hosp. & Roy. Free Hosp. Lond.

KUSHALAPPA, Chembanda Kariappa 28 Greystoke Gardens, Hangers Lane, London W1 1EP — MB BS 1968 Madras. (Madras) Med. Asst. (Psychiat.) Herrison Hosp. Dorchester. Prev: Regist. All St.s Hosp., Uffculme Clinic & Chas. Burns Clinic; Birm.

KUSHLICK, Anna Child and Family Consultation Service Springhill, Tameside General Hospital, Fountain St., Ashton-under-Lyne OL6 9RW Tel: 0161 331 5268 Fax: 0161 331 5270 — MB BCh 1984 Wales; MRCPsych 1988. Cons., Child Psychiat. Tameside & Glossop NHS Trust. Prev: Sen. Regist. (Child Psychiat.) Roy. Manch. Childr. Hosp.

KUSHWAHA, Alakshendra Pal Singh Broadway Medical Centre, 213 Broadway, Walsall WS1 3HD Tel: 01922 22064 Fax: 01922 613544; Highgate House, 6 Highgate, Sutton Coldfield B74 3HW — MB BS Lucknow 1967. (G.S.V.M Med. Coll. Kanpur) Clin. Asst. Diabetic Clinic Manor Hosp. Walsall; Sen. Clin. Med. Off. Dudley, Sandwell & Walsall AHAs.

KUSHWAHA, Rajeev Singh Flat 4, 15 Sussex Square, Brighton BN2 5AA Tel: 01273 676614; Highgae House, 6 Highgate, Steetly, Sutton Coldfield B74 3HW Tel: 0121 352 1600 — BChir 1995 Camb.; MA (Cantab.) 1996. (Guy's & St. Thomas' Hosps. UMDS) Surg. Rotat. Roy. Sussex Co. Hosp. Brighton. Prev: SHO (A & E) Roy. Sussex Co. Hosp. Brighton; SHO (Med.) Roy. Sussex Co. Hosp. Brighton.

KUSHWAHA, Sudhir Singh Cardiovascular Institute,Division of Cardiology, MAYO CLINIC, 200 First Street SW, Rochester MN 55905, USA Tel: 5072844072 Fax: 507284 4200 Email: kushwaha.sudhir@mayo.edu; 14 Sunnydale Gardens, Mill Hill, London NW7 3PG — MB BS 1981 Lond.; MRCP (UK) 1986; MD Lond. 1992. (Univ. Lond.) Cons in Cardiol. Mayo clinic minnesota 55905. Socs: Amer. Heart Foundat.; Amer Coll. of Cardiol. Prev: Fell. (Cardiol.) Mass. Gen. Hosp. Boston, USA; Research Fell. Harefield Hosp. Middlx.; Regist. (Med.) Centr. Middlx. Hosp. Lond.

KUSTOW, Bernard 55 Brondesbury Park, London NW6 7AY Tel: 020 8459 6446 Fax: 020 8451 2235 — MB BS Lond. 1947; MRCS Eng. LRCP Lond. 1942. (Guy's) Socs: BMA. Prev: Ho. Phys. Guy's Hosp. & Kent & Canterbury Hosp.; Maj. RAMC.

KUTAR, Shirin Sohrab (retired) 117 King Harolds Way, Bexleyheath DA7 5RB Tel: 020 8311 4295 — MB BS 1939 Bombay; MD, MS (Homoeop.) Bombay 1942, MB BS 1939. Med. Off. Family Plann. Assn. Prev: Med. Off. i/c Matern. & Child Welf. Clinic Dadar.

KUTARSKI, Andrew Anthony Chronic pain management service, Robey suite, Lincoln LN2 5QY Tel: 01522 512512 — MB BS 1976 Lond.; FRCA 1982. (St. Mary's Hosp. Med. Sch.) Cons. In chronic pain Managem. Socs: Scott. Soc. Anaesth.; N. Brit. Pain Assn.; Pain Soc. Prev: Sen. Regist. (Anaesth.) Roy. Infirm. Glas.; Regist. (Anaesth.) Roy. Infirm. Edin.; SHO (Anaesth./ITU) Roy. Cornw. Hosps. Truro.

KUTARSKI, Mr Paul Witold Wirral Hospital, Arrowe Park, Arrowe Park Road, Wirral CH49 5PE Tel: 0151 678 5111 Fax: 0151 604 7143 — MB BS 1978 Lond.; FRCS (Urol) 1994; FRCS Ed. 1984. (Middlx. Hosp.) Cons. Urol. Wirral Hosp. Socs: Brit. Assn. Urol. Surg.; Brit soc of endoUrol.; Brit. Erectile Disorder Soc.

KUTEESA, William Mark Anthony 5 Denbigh House, Portobello Court, London W11 2DJ — MB BS 1994 Lond.

KUTIYANAWALA, Mr Mustafa 172 Lyon Park Avenue, Wembley HA0 4HG — MB BS 1988 Bombay; FRCS Ed. 1991.

KUTSCHBACH, Julia Marcella Browne 87 Highview Avenue, Edgware HA8 9TY Tel: 0191 958 6598 — MB BCh BAO 1917 NUI; DPH RCSI 1920. (Univ. Coll. Cork) Socs: BMA. Prev: MOH Metrop. Boro. Stepney; Edr. Proc. Roy. Soc. Med.

KUTT, Elisabeth Avon Breast Screening, Tower Hill, Bristol BS2 0JD Tel: 0117 925 2867; 5 Cotham Grove, Cotham, Bristol BS6 6AL Tel: 0117 942 0591 — MB ChB 1980 Bristol; MRCP (UK) 1983; FRCR 1987. Cons. Radiol. W.on Gen. Hosp. & Avon BrE. Screening. Prev: Sen. Regist. (Radiodiag.) Bristol & W.on HA.

KUTTE, K J Beverley Road Surgery, 415 Beverley Road, Hull HU5 1LX Tel: 01482 342808 Fax: 01482 342011 — MB BS 1961 Karnatak; MB BS 1961 Karnatak.

KUTTLER, Anja Daniela Sabine Long Acre, Blissford, Fordingbridge SP6 2JG — State Exam Med 1992 Bonn.

KUUR, Carol Rosemary Pembroke House Surgery, 1 Fortescue Road, Paignton TQ3 2DA Tel: 01803 553558 Fax: 01803 663180; Dormer House, Westerland, Paignton TQ3 1RR — MB BS 1965 Lond.; MRCS Eng. LRCP Lond. 1965. (St. Bartholomews)

KUVELKER, Ghanasham Waman 113 Hall Drive, Acklam Hall Est., Acklam, Middlesbrough TS5 7HU Tel: 01642 84849 — MB BS 1964 Bombay; MCPS Bombay 1964; FFA RCSI 1972; DA Eng. 1968; DA RCPSI 1968. (G.S. Med. Coll.) Cons. Anaesth. N. & S. Tees Health Dists.

KUWANI, Thungo Anaesthetic Department, Hammersmith Hospital, Du Cane Road, London W12 0NN; 79 Firs Avenue, London N11 3NF — MB ChB 1993 Leic. (Leic.) SHO (Anaesth.) Hammersmith Hosp. Lond. Prev: SHO (Anaesth.) Luton & Dunstable Hosp.; SHO (Anaesth.) Kettering Gen. Hosp.

KUYYAMUDI, Chitralekha Ullasa c/o Department of Obstetrics and Gynaecology, Maternity Unit, Torbay Hospital, Lawes Bridge, Torquay TQ2 7AA — MB BS 1988 Bombay; MRCOG 1994.

KUZEL, Julie Janina 29 Barthropp Street, Newport NP19 0JQ — MB ChB 1985 Bristol; MRCGP 1990; DCH RCP Lond. 1992. GP Newport.

KUZMIN, Paul John Southview Surgery, Guildford Road, Woking GU22 7RR Tel: 01483 763186 Fax: 01483 821526 — MB BS 1984 Lond.; MRCGP 1988; DCH 1988. (Charing Cross Hospital)

KVALSVIG, Amanda Jane Crossways Cottages, Abbots Leigh Road, Abbots Leigh, Bristol BS8 3QG — MB ChB 1991 Cape Town.

KWAN, Douglas Kee Yat The Rectory, Rectory Road, Little Burstead, Billericay CM12 9TP — MB BS 1986 Lond.; LLB (Hons) Nottm. 1997; MRCGP 1990; DRCOG 1990; DGM RCP Lond. 1989. Socs: Soc. Occupat. Med. Lond.; Brit. Med. Acupunct. Soc.

KWAN, James Wei Yung 131A Queens Court, London NW5 4EG — MB BS 1996 Lond.

KWAN, Jonathan T. C. S. W. Thames Renal Unit, St. Helier Hospital, Wrythe Lane, Carshalton SM5 1AA Tel: 020 8296 2384 Fax: 020 8296 2941 Email: jkwan@sthelier.sghms.ac.uk — MB BS 1981 Lond.; MSc Lond. 1989, MD 1992; MRCP (UK) 1986; FRCPI 1995, M 1986; FRCP 1998; FRCPE 1998; MBA 1998. (King's Coll. Hosp. Med. Sch.) Cons. Phys. & Nephrol.; Sen. Lect. (Med.) St. Geo. Hosp. Med. Sch. Lond. Socs: Renal Assn.; Internat. Soc. Nephrol; Internat. Soc. of Periotoneal Dialysis. Prev: Sen. Regist. (Nephrol.) Roy. Lond. Hosp.; SHO & Regist. Rotat. (Med.) King's Coll. Hosp. Lond.; Clin. Research Fell. SW Thames Regional Renal Unit St. Helier Hosp. Surrey.

KWAN, Joseph Shiu Kwong Apartment 88 Mews House, 50 Kensington Gardens Square, London W2 4BA Tel: 020 7243 8730 — MB ChB 1994 Bristol. SHO Rotat. (Med.) City Hosp. NHS Trust Birm. Socs: Fell. Roy. Soc. Med. Prev: SHO (c/o Elderly) Poole Hosp.; SHO (A & E) Qu. Alexandra Hosp. Portsmouth.

KWAN, Mark Chi-Han 2A Barrie House, Lancaster Gate, London W2 3QJ — MB BCh 1994 Wales.

KWAN, Shiu Lun Anthony Institute of Opthalmology, Bath St., London EC1V 9EL; 12 More Close, St. Paul's Court, London W14 9BN — MB ChB 1992 Liverp.; FRC Lond. 1997. Research Fell. Inst. of Ophth. Lond. Prev: SHO (Ophth.) Arrowe Pk. Hosp. Liverp. & Lancaster; Demonst. (Anat.) Liverp. Univ.; SHO (Ophth.) Moorfield Eye Hosp. Lond.

KWAN, Swee Cheong The Conquest Hospital, The Ridge, St Leonards-on-Sea TN37 7RD — MB BS 1989 Malaya; MRCP (UK) 1994.

KWAN, William Joe Yau Princess of Wales Hospital, Coity Road, Bridgend CF31 1RQ — MB BCh 1982 Wales.

KWAN, Winnie Kwun Chee 16 Cleeve Park Gardens, Sidcup DA14 4JL — MB BS 1985 Lond.; MRCGP 1989; DCH RCP Lond. 1989. GP Bexleyheath.

KWANTES, Willem (retired) Tavistock House, 76 Parc Wern Road, Sketty, Swansea SA2 0SF Tel: 01792 204967 — MB BChir 1944 Camb.; MA, MB BChir Camb. 1944; FRCPath 1963; Dip. Bact. Lond 1947. Prev: Dir. Pub. Health Laborat. Swansea.

KWAPONG, Akosua Oseiwa 19 Highfield Avenue, London NW11 9EU— MB BS 1984 Lond.

KWARKO, Harriet Akosua 3 Westmede, Chigwell IG7 5LR — MB ChB 1986 Univ. Ghana; MRCP (UK) 1992.

KWARKO, Kwasi Assoku 5 Maplebeck Drive, Sheffield S9 1WH — MB ChB 1986 Ghana; MRCOG 1993.

KWARTZ, Mr Jeffrey 23 Highclere Road, Higher Crumpsall, Manchester M8 4FE Tel: 0161 740 8537 — MB ChB 1986 Birm.; FRCS Eng. 1990; FRCOphth 1990; DO RCS Eng. 1989. Cons. Ophth. Bolton Hosp. NHS Trust; Cornea Fell. Univ. Toronto. Socs: Manch. Med. Soc.; BMA. Prev: Sen. Regist., Regist. & SHO (Ophth. Surg.) Manch. Roy. Eye Hosp.; SHO (Ophth. Surg.) St. Jas. Univ. Hosp. Leeds.

KWEH, Mei Wei c/o J G Khor, Queen's Building, De Montfort University, The Gateway, Leicester LE1 9BH — MB ChB 1998 Leic.; MB ChB Leic 1998.

KWEKA, Edward Lawrence Max Department of Radiology, Diana Princess of Wales Hospital, Scartho Road, Grimsby DN33 2BA Tel: 01472 875202 Fax: 01472 875450; 139 Scartho Road, Grimsby DN33 2AN Tel: 01472 875658 — MD 1977 Dar Es Salaam, Tanzania; FRCR 1985; DMRD 1983. (Dar-Es-Salaam) Cons. Radiol. Diana P.ss of Wales Hosp. N. E. Lincs. NHS Trust. Socs: Roy. Coll. Radiol.; BMA. Prev: Cons. Radiol. orecambe Bay Hosps. NHS Trust; Asst. Prof. Radiol. Univ. Kuwait; Regist. (Radiol.) Bristol Roy. Infirm.

KWELLA, Jozef Peter (retired) 67 Hightrees House, Nightingale Lane, London SW12 8AH — Med. Dipl. Warsaw 1938. Prev: Cons. Anaesth. Mansfield Hosp. Gp.

KWIATKOWSKI, Professor Dominic Peter Department of Paediatrics, John Radcliffe Hospital, Oxford OX3 9DU Tel: 01865 221071 Fax: 01865 220479 — MB BS 1979 Lond.; FMed Sci. 1999; MA Oxf. 1997; FRCP Lond. 1996; FRCPCH (UK) 1997. MRC Clin. Research Prof. Oxf. Univ.; Hon. Cons. Paediat. Oxf. Radcliffe Trust; Prof. (Trop. Paediat.) Oxf. Univ. Prev: MRC Sen. Clin. Fell. Univ. Oxf.; MRC Special Train Fell. MRC Laborats. Gambia; Regist. (Paediat.) Guy's Hosp. Lond.

KWOK, Jonathan Gemini Consulting Ltd., One Knightsbridge, London SW1X 7LX Tel: 020 7340 3284 Fax: 020 7340 3400 Email: jonathan.k@lineone.net; 7 Iris Close, Tamworth B79 8TZ Tel: 01827 53500 — MB BChir 1994 Camb.; BSc (Hons.) St. And. 1992. Cons. Strategy Consg. Gemini Consg. Ltd. Lond. Socs: BMA & Med. Protec. Soc. Prev: Ho. Phys. (Gen. Med.) Addenbrooke's Hosp. Camb.; Ho. Surg. (Surg. Oncol.) Christie Hosp. NHS Trust Manch.; Ho. Off. (Gen. Surg.) S. Manch. Univ. Hosps. Trust.

KWOK, Ken Doh 57 Harley Street, London W1N 1DD Tel: 020 7637 2161 — MB BS 1964 Sydney; MRCP (U.K.) 1970. (Sydney) Socs: BMA. Prev: Ho. Phys. Roy. Newc.Hosp., Australia; Regist. Lond. Chest Hosp. & St. Mary's Hosp. Lond.

KWOK, Mr Leung Sun Route Hospital, Coleraine Road, Ballymoney BT53 6BU — MB BCh BAO 1986 NUI; FRCSI 1991; LRCPI 1986.

KWOK, Michelle Camillla Cookridge Hospital, Hospital Lane, Leeds LS16 6QB; 8 Barkers Well Fold, New Farnsley, Leeds LS12 5TR — MB ChB 1994 Leeds; BSc (Hons.) Leeds 1992; MRCP RCOP 1999. Specialist Regist. (Clin. Oncol.) Cookridge Hosp. Leeds. Socs: BMA; MPS. Prev: SHO Rotat. (Gen. Med.) Leeds Gen. Infirm.

KWOK, Quintin Siu Kay 15 Castleview Close, London N4 2DJ Tel: 020 8800 4059 — MB ChB 1995 Sheff.; BMedSci Sheff. 1992. (Univ. Sheff.) SHO Rotat. (Med.) City Hosp. NHS Trust Birm. Prev: SHO (Oncol.) Mt. Vernon Hosp N.wood, Middlx.

KWOK, See Barlow Medical Centre, 8 Barlow Moor Road, Didsbury, Manchester M20 6TR Tel: 0161 445 2101 Fax: 0161 445 9560 — MB ChB 1978 Leeds; MRCGP 1983; DRCOG 1982.

KWOK CHAI SUM, Apollinaris 11 Claret Close, Liverpool L17 5DF — MB ChB 1991 Liverp.

KWONG, Ava 4 Dunstan Road, London NW11 8AA Tel: 020 8455 8943 Fax: 020 8455 8943 Email: avak@lycosmails.com — MB BS 1997 Lond.; BSc St. And. 1993. (St. Mary's Hospital (Imperial College) University of London) SHO (Gen. Surgency) Kwong Wah Hosp., Hong Kong. Prev: Med. Ho. Job. Edgware & Barnet Gen. Hosp. Surgic.; Surg. Ho. Job Qu. Eliz. II Hosp. Welwyn Garden City.

KWONG, Ho Tak 5 Tarrington Close, Manchester M12 4TB — MB ChB 1997 Manch.

KWONG, Louis Junior 9 Ashbourne House, Oxford Place, Manchester M14 5SF Tel: 0161 224 7945 Fax: 0161 224 7945 Email: lkwongjr@dial.pipex.com — MB ChB 1993 Manch. (Manch.) Prev: SHO (Gen. Surg.) Bury Gen. Infirm.; SHO (A & E) Manch. Roy. Infirm.; SHO (Orthop.) Manch. Roy. Infirm.

KYAW, Tint 50 Percival Street, Peterborough PE3 6AU — MB BS 1982 Med. Inst. (I) Rangoon.

KYAW HTIN, Maung c/o Rev. G. Rowland, 3 Amber Court, Longford Avenue, Southall UB1 3QR — MB BS 1988 Med. Inst. (I) Rangoon.

KYAW HTUN, Dr Coggeshall Road Surgery, 9 Coggeshall Road, Braintree CM7 9DD Tel: 01376 552508 Fax: 01376 552690 — MB BS 1975 Rangoon.

KYAW KHIN SAW, Dr Department of Anaesthetics, Ayr Hospital, Dalmellington Road, Ayr KA6 6DX — MB BS 1977 Med. Inst. (II) Rangoon; DTM & H Liverp. 1987; DA Eng. 1985.

KYAW WIN, Dr 9 Mordaunt Avenue, Scartho, Grimsby DN33 3EJ — MB BS 1970 Rangoon; MB BS Med. Inst. (11) Rangoon 1970.

KYD, Karen Leslie 7 Boulter Lane, Southwick, Fareham PO17 6HH; 20 Gateways, Guildford GU1 2LF Tel: 01483 69269 — MB BChir 1992 Camb.; MA (Hons.) Camb. 1989. SHO (Gen. Med.) Roy. Surrey Co. Hosp. Guildford. Prev: SHO (Cardiol. & ICU) Roy. Brompton Nat. Heart & Lung Hosp. Lond.; Ho. Surg. (Gen. & Vasc. Surg.) W. Suff. Hosp. Bury St. Edmunds; Ho. Phys. (Med.) Addenbrooke's Hosp. Camb.

KYDD, James Lowdon (retired) Wilton Lodge, Craven Arms SY7 9QS Tel: 01588672536 — MB ChB Glas. 1960.

KYDD, Marjorie Violet Half Acre, Coach Road, Ivy Hatch, Sevenoaks TN15 0PF Tel: 01732 810433 — MB ChB 1947 Ed. (Ed.)

KYEI-MENSAH, Amma Adwibi Anima Jenner Building, Whittington Hospital, Highgate Hill, London N19 5NF Tel: 020 7288 5117 Fax: 020 7288 5066 — MB BS 1986 Lond.; MA Camb. 1983; MRCP (UK) 1990; MRCOG 1992. (Queens Coll. & St. Bartholomews Hosp. Med. Sch.) Cons. Obst. & Gynaecologist, Whittington Hosp. NHS Trust, Lond. Socs: Fell. of Roy. Soc. of Med.; Brit. Materno-Fetal Med. Soc.; Brit. Fertil. Soc.

KYEI-MENSAH, Kwamena (cons. rooms) Suite 2, Lister House, 11/12 Wimpole St., London W1; 5 Buckingham Avenue, Whetstone, London N20 9BU — MRCS Eng. LRCP Lond. 1960; BSc (Hons.) Lond. 1957, MB BS 1960; MRCP (U.K.) 1969; FFA RCS Eng. 1967; DA Eng. 1972. Cons. Anaesth. & Phys. Nigerian Defence & High Commiss. Lond. Prev: Cons. Anaesth. Tottenham Gp. Hosps. & Pontefract Gp. Hosps.

KYEREMATENG, Samuel Paul Kofi 4 Falkland Place, Kingoodie, Invergowrie, Dundee DD2 5DY — MB ChB 1998 Aberd.; MB ChB Aberd 1998.

KYFFIN, Douglas Neil Ribblesdale House Medical Centre, Market Street, Bury BL9 0BU Tel: 0161 764 7241 Fax: 0161 763 3557; Ribblesdale House Medical Centre, Market St, Bury BL9 0BU Tel: 0161 764 7241 Fax: 0161 763 3557 — MB ChB 1987 Manch.; BSc Manch. 1984; MRCGP 1992; DRCOG 1991. (Manchester)

KYI, Tin Tin 49 Ashford Drive, Ravenshead, Nottingham NG15 9DE — MB BS 1982 Rangoon; MRCP (UK) 1991.

KYI KYI TIN-MYINT, Dr 20 Atherton Way, Yarm TS15 9TB — MB BS 1968 Med. Inst. (I) Rangoon.

KYLE, Andrew (retired) 12 Winchester Court, 93 Cleveden Road, Glasgow G12 0JN Tel: 0141 334 3083 — MB ChB 1949 Glas.

KYLE, Andrew Watson Pittenweem Surgery, 2 Routine Row, Pittenweem, Anstruther KY10 2LG Tel: 01333 311307 Fax: 01333 312520; Rydal, Balmonth Farm, Carnbee, Anstruther KY10 2RU — MB ChB 1984 Glas.; DRCOG 1987.

KYLE, Christopher James Rosehall Surgery, 2 Mallusk Road, Newtownabbey BT36 4PP Tel: 028 9083 2188 Fax: 028 9083 8820 — MB BCh BAO 1980 Belf.; MRCGP 1984.

KYLE, David William Ridgeway House, Hartlip, Sittingbourne ME9 7TL Tel: 01795 842595 — MB BCh BAO 1949 Dub.; BDentSc 1953. (T.C. Dub.)

KYLE, Elizabeth Anne 5 Shrewsbury Gardens, Belfast BT9 6PJ — MB BCh BAO 1977 Belf.; BSc Belf. 1972; MRCP Ed. 1982; MRCPath (Haemat.) 1989. Cons. Haemat. United Hosps. Trust Antrim Hosp. Socs: Brit. Soc. Haematol. Prev: Cons. Haemat. GreenPk. Healthcare Trust Belf.; Sen. Regist. (Haemat.) Belf. City Hosp.

KYLE, Mr Graham Miller (cons. rooms), 86 Rodney St., Liverpool L1 9AR Tel: 0151 709 7509 Fax: 0151 709 7509; Glascoed Cottage, Ffrith, Wrexham LL11 5LT — MB ChB 1973 Glas.; MSc 1998; LLM 1995; FRCOphth 1987; FRCS Ed. 1982. Cons. Ophth. Surg., Univ. Hosp., Aintree, Liverp.

KYLE, James, CBE (retired) Grianan, Fasaich, Gairloch IV21 2DB Tel: 01445 712398 Fax: 01445 712398 — MB BCh BAO Belf. 1947; DSc Belf. 1973, MCh (Gold Medal) 1956; FRCS Ed. 1964; FRCS Eng. 1954; FRCSI 1954. Hon. Cons. Surg. Aberd. Roy. Infirm.; Hon. Sen. Lect. (Surg.) Univ. Aberd.; Mem. (Ex-Chairm.) Scott. Jt. Cons. Comm. Prev: Chairm. BMA Represen. Body.

KYLE, John Martin Causeway Surgery, 2 Causeway Place, Newcastle BT33 0DN Tel: 028 4372 3438 Fax: 028 4372 6731; 31 Ardaluin Heights, Newcastle BT33 0RA Tel: 0139 67 24913 — MB BCh BAO 1965 Belf. Socs: BMA. Prev: Dir. Evangelical Med. Center Nyankunde Zaire.

KYLE, Mr Kenneth Francis 13 Campsie View Drive, Strathblane, Glasgow G63 9JE Tel: 0141 70522 — MD 1967 Belf.; MCh (Hons.) 1964, MB BCh BAO 1957; FRCSI 1963; FRCS Ed. 1961. (Belf.) Cons. Urol. W.. Infirm. Glas. Socs: Brit. Assn. Urol. Surgs. & BMA. Prev: Surg. Tutor Qu. Univ. Belf.; Sen. Regist. (Surg.) Roy. Vict. Hosp. Belf.; Fell. in Surg. Cleveland Clinic, U.S.A.

KYLE, Margaret Valerie North Bristol NHS Trust, Frenchay Hospital, Bristol BS16 1LE Tel: 0117 918 6512 Fax: 0117 957 3075 Email: sandra.charlton@north-bristol.swest.nhs.uk; Bluegates, Clapton, Berkeley GL13 9QU Tel: 01453 511171 — MB ChB 1977 Glas.; MD Glas. 1988; FRCP Lond. 1995; FRCP Glas. 1990; MRCP (UK) 1980. p/t Cons. Rheum. Frenchay Dist. Bristol. Prev: Clin. Lect. & Hon. Sen. Regist. (Rheum. & Gen. Med.) Addenbrooke's Hosp. Camb.

KYLE, Peter David Newbury Street Practice, Newbury Street, Wantage OX12 7AY Tel: 01235 763451; Bablakes, Letcombe Regis, Wantage OX12 9JD Tel: 01235 765810 Fax: 01235 771829 — MB BS 1971 Lond.; MRCS Eng. LRCP Lond. 1971; DObst RCOG 1973. Prev: SHO (Obst.) W. Middlx. & Kingston Hosp. Surrey; Ho. Phys. Essex Co. Hosp.; Ho. Surg. St. Mary's Hosp. Lond.

KYLE, Mr Peter McLeod Gustafsberg, 36 Sutherland Avenue, Pollokshields, Glasgow G41 4ES Tel: 0141 427 4400 — MB ChB 1974 Glas.; FRCS Ed. 1979. Cons. Ophth. S.. Gen. Hosp. & Vict. Infirm. Glas.; Hon. Clin. Lect. Univ. Glas. Prev: Lect. (Ophth.) Univ. Glas.; Lect. (Anat.) Dept. Univ. Glas.; Regist. (Ophth. Train. Scheme) W.. Infirm. Glas.

KYLE, Phillipa Marie Fetal Medicine Unit, St Michaels Hospital, Bristol BS2 8EG Fax: 0117 928 5180 Email: p.m.kyle@bristol.ac.uk; 33 Anglesea Place, Clifton, Bristol BS8 2UN — MB ChB Auckland 1984; MD Auckland 1994; MRCOG 1990. (Univ. Auckland, NZ) Cons. Fetal Med. United Bristol Healthcare Trust. Prev: Sen. Regist. (Fetal Med.) Qu. Charlotte's & Chelsea Hosp. Lond.

KYLE, Samuel George William Irvinestown, Enniskillen BT94 1DY — MB BCh BAO 1958 Belf. Clin. Asst. ENT Erne Hosp. Enniskillen.

KYLE, Samuel John Holywood Arches Health Centre, Westminster Avenue, Belfast BT4 1NS Tel: 028 9056 3354 Fax: 028 9065 3846 — MB BCh BAO 1976 Belf.; MRCGP 1980; DCH RCPSI 1979.

KYLE, Stuart David Bablakes, Letcombe Regis, Wantage OX12 9JD — MB ChB 1998 Bristol.

KYLES, Alison Elizabeth 15A Leatham Avenue, New Plymouth, New Zealand Tel: 00 64 06 7574403; 28 Victoria Place, Stirling FK8 2QT Tel: 01786 473581 — MB ChB 1989 Aberd.; MRCGP 1995; Dip. Obst. Auckland 1991. GP New Plymouth, NZ. Prev: Trainee GP Stirling; Ho. Surg. Taranaki Base Hosp. New Plymouth, NZ; Ho. Phys. Woodend Hosp. Aberd.

KYLES, Gordon (retired) 11 Balmyle Grove, Dunblane FK15 0QB Email: isabel.kyles@virgin.net — MB ChB 1963 St. And. Prev: Princip. Gen. Pract.

KYLES, Iain McAlpine Kirkland, Main St., Dunlop, Kilmarnock KA3 4AG Tel: 01560 484752 — MB ChB 1958 Glas.; DObst. RCOG 1960. (Univ. Glas.) Assoc. Specialist Scott. Nat. Blood Transfus. Serv. Prev: Ho. Surg. W.. Infirm. Glas.; Ho. Phys. Stobhill Gen. Hosp. Glas.; Surg. Lt. RN.

KYLES, Isabel Manson Gilchrist (retired) 11 Balmyle Grove, Dunblane FK15 0QB Tel: 01786 821804 Email: isabel.kyles@virgin.net — MB ChB Ed. 1962; DA (UK) 1975. Prev: Regist. (Anaesth.) Stirling Roy. Infirm.

KYNASTON, James Humfrey Fairfax Glover Street Medical Centre, 133 Glover Street, Perth PH2 0JB Tel: 01738 621844 Fax: 01738 636070; 1 Tullylumb Terrace, Perth PH1 1BA — MB ChB 1976 Dundee; MRCGP 1981; DRCOG 1980. Med. Off. MacMillan Ho. Day Centre for Terminally Ill Perth.

KYNOCH, Rosslyn Margaret (retired) Newton of Drumduan, Dess, Aboyne AB34 5BD Tel: 0133 988 4341 — MB ChB 1970 Glas.

KYRIACOU, Ekaterini 3 South Villas, Camden Square, Camden, London NW1 9BS — MB BS 1982 Lond.; MRCPI 1988. (St. Mary's Hosp. Med. Sch.) Socs: Roy. Soc. Med.; St. Mary's Hosp. Med. Sch. Assn. Prev: Lect. (Med.) Univ. Edin.; Regist. (Gastroenterol.) Chase Farm Hosp. Enfield; Regist. (Radiol.) Middlx. Hosp.

KYRIAKIDES, Constantinos Andreas 86 Arnfield Road, Withington, Manchester M20 4AR — MB ChB 1991 Manch.

KYRIAKIDES, Janet Penelope 37 Stocks Road, Kimberley, Nottingham NG16 2QF — MB ChB 1985 Bristol.

KYRIAKIDES, Kyriacos 37 Stocks Road, Kimberley, Nottingham NG16 2QF — MB ChB 1985 Bristol.

KYRIAKIDES, Theodore 8 Chesterfield Road, St. Andrews, Bristol BS6 5DL — MB ChB 1983 Bristol; BSc (Hons.) Bristol 1980, MB ChB 1983; MRCP (UK) 1986. Cons. Neurol. Cyprus Inst. Neurol. & Genetics.

KYRIAKOU, Kyriakos Pantelis 263 Popes Lane, Ealing, London W5 4NH Tel: 020 8567 6059 — MB ChB 1962 Birm.; FFA RCS Eng. 1973.

KYRIAZIS, Marios 14 The Avenue, Cliftonville, Northampton NN1 5BT Tel: 01604 630779 — Laurea 1982 Rome; Laurea in Medicina e Chirurgia Rome 1982; MSc (Gerontol.) Lond. 1990; DGM RCP Lond. 1990. Socs: Brit. Soc. Research in Ageing; Brit. Soc. of Gerontology.

KYRIONYMOU, George 1 Westminster Road, London W7 3TU — LMSSA 1982 Lond.

KYTE, Denise Ellen The Roost, 70 Main Road, Brereton, Rugeley WS15 1DU — MB BS 1987 Lond.; MSc Keele 1992. Regist. Rotat. (Psychiat.) Keele Train Scheme N. Staffs. HA.

KYWE, Htay Paddington Surgery, 11 Praed Street, London W2 1NJ Tel: 020 7262 4123 Fax: 020 7262 4107 — MB BS 1976 Med Inst (III) Mand.

L'ANSON, Mary-Jo Low Shilford House, Low Shilford, Stocksfield NE43 7HW Tel: 01661 843656 — MB ChB 1980 Leic.

LA COSTE, Julia Jane Heathwaite House, Gaskell Avenue, Knutsford WA16 0DA Tel: 01565 750313 — MB ChB 1987 Bristol; MRCGP 1992; DRCOG 1990; DCH RCP Lond. 1989. GP Chesh.

LA FRENAIS, Walter Simon Lodge Tower House Practice, St. Pauls Health Centre, High Street, Runcorn WA7 1AB Tel: 01928 567404; Gorse Hill, 29 Weston Road, Runcorn WA7 4JX Tel: 01928 573824 Fax: 01928 590212 — MB ChB Liverp. 1964; DObst RCOG 1966. (Liverp.) Socs: Coun. & Bd. of The Med. Defence Union Ltd. Prev: Ho. Off. Whiston Hosp. Prescot.

LA PAGLIA, Jonathan Edward 59 Uverdale Road, London SW10 0SN — MB BS 1991 Adelaide.

LA PORTA, Santina Emilia 7 Eatonville Road, London SW17 7SH — MB ChB 1994 Liverp.; DRCOG 1996. (Liverp.) GP.

LA ROSA, Cristina Francesca Royal Berkshire Hospital, London Road, Reading RG1 5AN Tel: 01734 875111; 51 Bramwell House, Falmouth Road, London SE1 4JN Tel: 020 7207 9175 — State DMS 1987 Milan. SHO (O & G) Roy. Berks. Hosp. Reading. Socs: Med. Protec. Soc. Prev: SHO (O & G) St. Helier Hosp. Carshalton & Ipswich Hosp.; SHO (A & E) Newham Gen. Hosp. Lond.

LAAKKONEN, Victoria 56 Culverden Road, London SW12 9LS — MB BS 1994 Lond.; BSc Lond. 1991; DCH 1997. (St. George's Hospital Medical School)

LAB, Darielle Margaret 1 Murray Road, Northwood HA6 2YP — MB BS 1990 Lond; BSc (Hons.) Lond. 1987; DCH RCP Lond. 1994. Prev: G.P. Pract. Train. Rotat., Hillingdon Hosp., Pield Heath Rd, Uxbridge.; Ho. Off. (Med.) Hemel Hempstead Hosp.; SHO Rotat. (Psychiat.) St. Mary's Hosp. & Ealing Gen. Hosp. Lond.

LABADARIOS, Vasiliki Vicky Grace 118 Haydon Close, Gosforth, Newcastle upon Tyne NE3 2BZ Tel: 0191 284 4502 — MB ChB 1992 Stellenbosch.

LABAN, Christiana Angela 1 Southgate Grove, London N1 5BT — MB BS 1996 Lond.

LABAN, Sarah Jayne 70 Waverley Lane, Burton-on-Trent DE14 2HG — MB ChB 1998 Sheff.; MB ChB Sheff 1998.

LABAND, John Robert 102 Sandford Road, Winscombe BS25 1JJ — MB BS 1984 Lond. Ho. Phys. (Gen. Med.) Horton Gen. Hosp. Prev: Ho. Surg. (Gen. Surg.) Dorset Co. Hosp. Dorchester; Ho. Surg. (Gen. Surg.) Roy. Infirm. Lancaster; Ho. Surg. (Gen. Med.) Freedom Fields Hosp. Plymouth.

LABAND, Kathryn Mary 40 Croft Road, Ringwood BH24 1TA — MB BS 1998 Lond.; MB BS Lond 1998.

LABARRE, Steven Mark 12 Riley Close, Sale M33 4WR — MB ChB 1988 Leeds.

LABIA, Joseph Benjamin La Vergée, Mont Gras D'Eau, St Brelade, Jersey JE3 8ED Tel: 01534 45761 — MB ChB 1955 Cape Town; DPM Eng. 1969. (Cape Town) Affil. RCPsych. Socs: Fell. Roy. Soc. Med.; BMA. Prev: Clin. Asst. Bethlem Roy. Hosp.; Clin. Asst. Maudsley Hosp.

LABIB, Ashraf Samy 7 Upfields, Burntwood, Walsall — MB ChB 1983 Alexandria.

LABIB, Magdi Mounir Department of Obstertics & Gynaecology, Kidderminster General Hospital, Bewdley Road, Kidderminster DY11 6RJ — MB ChB 1975 Cairo; MRCOG 1984.

LABIB, Mourad Hafez Zaki 9 The Brambles, Pedmore, Stourbridge DY9 7JH Tel: 01384 371781 — MB ChB 1977 Alexandria; MRCPath 1986. Cons. Chem. Path. Russells Hall Hosp. Dudley W. Midl.; H reader ic chem path univ wolver. Prev: Sen. Regist. (Clin. Biochem.) St. Luke's Hosp. Guildford; Regist. & SHO (Chem. Path.) Leicester Roy. Infirm.

LABINJO, Kenneth Olatunde Fairfax, 205 Station Road, Wythall, Birmingham B47 6ET Tel: 01564 822647 — MB BCh BAO 1959 Dub.; BA Dub. 1954. (TC Dub.) Socs: BMA.

LABINJOH, Catherine Department of Cardiology, Western General Hospital, Crewe Rd, Edinburgh EH4 2XU — MB ChB 1993 Ed.; BSc (Hons)1988; MRCP (UK) 1996. (University of Edinburgh)

LABRAM, Mr Emmanuel Kingsley Department of Neurosurgery, Derriford Hospital, Derriford Road, Plymouth PL6 8DH Tel: 01752 777111; Nyamekye House, 2 Silver Birch Close, Woolwell, Plymouth PL6 7QL Tel: 01752 775643 — MB ChB 1981 Ghana; FRCS Ed. 1988; FRCS (SN) 1994. Clin. Fell. & Lect. Derriford Hosp. Plymouth. Socs: Assoc. Mem. Soc. Brit. Neurol. Surgs.

LABRUM, Anthony Stephen The Surgery, 221 Whaddon Way, Bletchley, Milton Keynes MK3 7EA Tel: 01908 373058 Fax: 01908 630076 — MB BS 1965 Lond.; DObst RCOG 1967. (St. Bart.) Prev: Hon. Hosp. Pract. (Accid. & Orthop. Surg.) Milton Keynes Gen. Hosp.; Regist. (Surg.) Worthing, S.lands & Dist. Hosp. Gp.; SHO Roy. Nat. Orthop. Hosp. Stanmore.

LACAMP, Camilla Jeanette 5 Dalton Heights, Dalton, Richmond DL11 7LA — MB BS 1996 Newc.

LACASIA PURROY, Maria Del Carmen The Royal Infirmary, Lindley, Huddersfield HD3 3ED Tel: 01484 422191 — LMS 1984 Saragossa.

LACE, Edward John (retired) Woodcote Grove House, Meadow Hill, Coulsdon CR5 2XL Tel: 020 8668 6919 — MRCS Eng. LRCP Lond. 1937; DObst RCOG 1940. Prev: Ho. Surg. Bristol Gen. Hosp.

LACEY, Anne Gregory (retired) 15 Post Office Road, Ingatestone CM4 9ES — MB ChB 1952 St. And.; DA Eng. 1968. Prev: GP Ingatestone.

LACEY, Arthur James Willowbrook Medical Practice, Brook Street, Sutton-in-Ashfield NG17 1ES Tel: 01623 440018; Cairnbaan, 2 Robin Down Lane, Mansfield NG18 4SW Tel: 01623 636779 — BM BS 1976 Nottm.; BMedSci (Hons.) 1974; MRCGP 1984; MRCOG 1982. Mem. LMC. Prev: Trainee GP Nottm. VTS; Regist. (O & G) John Radcliffe Hosp. Oxf. & City Hosp. Nottm.

LACEY, Audrey Jean (retired) Watlington House, Watlington, King's Lynn PE33 0HS Tel: 01553 810276 — MB ChB 1954 Leeds; LMSSA Lond. 1954; DPH Eng. 1957. Prev: Asst. Co. MOH Norf.

LACEY, Professor Brian Westgarth 19 St Johns Hill, Shrewsbury SY1 1JJ Tel: 01743 248834 — BSc (1st cl. Hons.) Lond. 1934, MD 1954, MB BS 1938 University of London; MRCS Eng. LRCP Lond. 1936; FRCPath 1963; FIBiol. 1963. (Middlx.) Emerit. Prof. Bacteriol. Univ. Lond. 1978; Hon. Cons. Bacteriol. W.m. Hosp. Lond. Socs: Fell. Roy. Soc. Med.; Med. Soc. Lond. Prev: Prof. Bact. W.m. Med. Sch. Lond.; Hon. Cons. Path. to The Army; Lt. Col., Asst. Dir. Path. GHQ MEF.

LACEY, Charles David (retired) 20 Moreton Road, Bosham, Chichester PO18 8LL Tel: 01243 572296 Email: doc.lacey@bosham.fsnet.co.uk — MB BChir 1951 Camb.; MRCP Lond. 1952. Prev: Med. Dir. St. Wilfrids Hospice Chichester.

LACEY, Charles John Nash GU Medicine & Communicable Diseases, Imperial College, Norfolk Place, London W2 1PG Tel: 020 7886 6604 Fax: 020 7886 6123 Email: c.lacey@ic.ac.uk — MB BS 1974 Lond.; FRCP Lond. 1991; MRCP (UK) 1977; MRCS Eng. LRCP

Lond. 1974; Dip. Ven. Soc. Apoth. Lond. 1981; DRCOG 1980. (Guy's) Hon. Cons. Phys. St. Mary's Hosp. Lond. Socs: Med. Soc. Study VD; Brit. Soc. Colpos. & Cerv. Path. Prev: Cons. Phys. Genitourin. Med. Gen. Infirm. Leeds.

LACEY, Elizabeth Mary 6 Knebwoth Road, Bexhill-on-Sea TN39 4JH — MB BS 1961 Lond.; MRCS Eng. LRCP Lond. 1961; MRCOG 1973. (University College Hospital, London) p/t GP Bexhill-on-Sea.

LACEY, Emma Jane 12 Baylands Crescent, Peterhead AB42 2YA — MB ChB 1992 Aberd.

LACEY, Helen Barbara Department Genitourinary Medicine, Baillie St. Health Centre, Rochdale OL16 1XS Tel: 01706 517655 Fax: 01706 517652 Email: helen-lacey@hotmail.com; Department of Genitourinary Medicine, North Manchester General Hospital, Crumpsall, Manchester M8 6RL Tel: 0161 720 2681 — MB ChB 1980 Manch.; MRCOG 1985. Cons. Genitourin. Med. Rochdale & N. Manch. NHS Trusts.

LACEY, Hugh Philip Watlington House, Watlington, King's Lynn PE33 Tel: 01553 810276 — MB ChB 1953 Leeds; DA Eng. 1957; FRCGP 1980, M 1968. Prev: SHO (Anaesth.) Withington Hosp. Manch. & York Hosp. Gp.

LACEY, Professor John Hubert Department of Psychiatry, St. Georges Hospital Medical School, London SW17 0RE Tel: 020 8725 5528 Fax: 020 8725 3350 Email: h.lacey@sghms.ac.uk; 5 Atherton Drive, Wimbledon, London SW19 5LB Tel: 020 8947 5976 Email: jhubertlacey@hotmail.com — MB ChB St. And. 1969; MPhil Lond. 1974, MD (Commendat.) 1988; FRCPsych 1985, M 1974; DObst RCOG 1971. Prof. & Head Psychiat. & Hon. Cons. St. Geo. Hosp. Med. Sch. Socs: Fell. CINP; Fell. Roy. Coll. Psychiat.; (Former Pres.) Internat. Coll. Psychosomatic Med. Prev: Sen. Lect. & Hon. Cons. Psychiat. Middlx. Hosp. Med. Sch. Lond.; Reader & Hon. Sen. Regist. (Psychiat.) St. Geo. Hosp. Med. Sch. Tooting.

LACEY, Michael James The Health Centre, St. Peters Crescent, Selsey, Chichester PO20 0NN Tel: 01243 604321/602261 Fax: 01243 607996; 35 Bonnar Road, Selsey, Chichester PO20 9AU Tel: 01243 606322 Fax: 01243 606322 Email: mikelacey@dilshaud.globalnet.co.uk — MB BS 1980 Lond.; MRCP (UK) 1983; MRCGP 1989; Dip. Pract. Dermat. Wales 1995; DRCOG 1986; DCH RCP Lond. 1986. (St. Mary's) Hosp. Practitioner, Dermat., St. Richards Hosp., Chichester. Prev: SHO (Paediat.) St. Richards Hosp. Chichester; SHO Rotat. (Med.) W.m. Hosp. Lond.

LACEY, Michele Lesley The Medical Centre, Cakeham Road, East Wittering, Chichester PO20 8BH Tel: 01243 673434 Fax: 01243 672563; 35 Bonnar Road, Selsey, Chichester PO20 9AU — MB ChB 1983 Birm.; DFFP 1994; DRCOG 1987. (Birm.) GP; Community Med. Off. (Family Plann.) Bognor Regis and Chichester. Prev: Trainee GP Basingstoke.

LACEY, Nicola Ann 51 Bow Field, Hook, Basingstoke RG27 9SA — BM 1991 Soton.

LACEY, Orla Josephine 44 Stoke Farthing, Broad Chalke, Salisbury SP5 5ED — MB ChB 1993 Bristol.

LACEY, Patrick John (retired) Greensward Surgery, Greensward Lane, Hockley SS5 5HQ Tel: 01702 202353 Fax: 01702 204535 — MB BS 1959 Lond.; MRCS Eng. LRCP Lond. 1959; DObst RCOG 1962; MRCGP 1970. Prev: Med. Off. Prison Commiss.

LACEY, Peter Alexander Brockhurst Medical Centre, 139-141 Brockhurst Road, Gosport PO12 3AX Tel: 023 9258 3564 Fax: 023 9251 0782; 1 Brodrick Avenue, Alverstoke, Gosport PO12 2EN Tel: 01705 526116 Fax: 01705 510782 — BM BCh 1976 Oxf.; MA Oxf. 1977; MRCGP 1980; D.Occ.Med. RCP Lond. 1995; DRCOG 1978; DFFP ROCG 1996. (Oxf. Uni.) Socs: Soc. Occupat. Med. Prev: Med. Advisor Ferguson Ltd.

LACEY, Peter Holt P & O Line, Richmond House, Terminus Terrace, Southampton SO14 3PN Tel: 02380 534200; 14 Cramond Road S., Edinburgh EH4 6AA — MB BS 1973 Lond.; MRCGP 1982; LMCC Alberta Canada 1980. (King's Coll. Hosp.) Med. Adviser Ethicon Ltd. Socs: Hunt. Soc. & Chelsea Clin. Soc. Prev: Med. Adviser Schroder Gp. of Companies; Med. Adviser Pfizer Ltd. Sandwich Kent; Trainee GP Tunbridge Wells VTS.

LACEY, Philip George Charnwood Surgery, 5 Burton Road, Derby DE1 1TH Tel: 01332 737737 Fax: 01332 737738; 13 Birkdale Close, Mickleover, Derby DE3 5YG Tel: 01332 605118 — MB ChB 1982 Birm.; MRCGP 1988; DRCOG 1987. Clin. Asst. (Endoscopy) Derby City Gen. Hosp.; Centr. Derby PCT Exec. and Precribing cold. Socs: Derby Med. Soc.; Derby Obst. Gp. Prev: Trainee GP Burton-on-Trent VTS.; SHO (Med. for The Elderly) Derby City Hosp.; SHO & Ho. Off. (Med.) Derbysh. Roy. Infirm.

LACEY, Richard Westgarth Carlton Manor, Carlton, Nr. Yeadon, Leeds LS19 7BE — MRCS Eng. LRCP Lond. 1964; PhD Bristol 1974; MA Camb. 1965, MD 1969, MB 1965, BChir 1964; MRCPath 1971; DCH Eng. 1966. (Camb. & Lond. Hosp.) Prof. Clin. Microbiol. Leeds Univ. Prev: Cons. Bacteriol. N. Cambs. Hosp. Wisbech; Cons. Bacteriol. Qu. Eliz. Hosp. Kings Lynn; Lect. & Reader Clin. Bact. Univ. Bristol.

LACEY, Stephen James Health First Medical Group, King George Surgery, 135 High Street, Stevenage SG1 3HT Tel: 01438 361111 Fax: 01438 361227 — MB BS 1974 Lond.; MRCS Eng. LRCP Lond. 1974. (Roy. Free) Prev: Trainee GP Welwyn Garden City VTS.

LACEY, Stephen Martin (retired) — MB BS 1953 Lond.; MRCS Eng. LRCP Lond. 1953. Prev: Surg. Clin. Asst. Hinckley Hosp.

LACEY, Verity Jane Hawthorn House, Regent St., Chapel Allerton, Leeds LS7 4PE — MB ChB 1974 Bristol; BSc Ed. 1970; FFA RCSI 1976. GP VTS, Dewsbury & Dist. Hosp. Prev: Clin. Ass. St Jas Hosp. Leeds.

LACH, Henry (retired) 99 Langton Way, London SE3 7JU Tel: 020 8858 0906 — MD 1939 Paris.

LACH, Somaly Lee House Surgery, Eves Corner, Danbury, Chelmsford CM3 4QA Tel: 01245 225522 Fax: 01245 222196 — MB BS 1993 Lond.; DCH RCP Lond. 1996. Trainee GP/SHO Mid Essex Hosps. Prev: SHO (A & E) Roy. Bournemouth NHS Trust; Ho. Off. (Med.) P.ss Alexandra Hosp.; Ho. Off. (Surg.) Colchester Gen. Hosp.

LACHELIN, Gillian Claire Liborel Obstetric Unit, 88-96 Chenies Mews, Huntley St., London WC1E 6HX Tel: 020 7209 6054 Fax: 020 7383 7429 Email: gillian.lachelin@ucl.ac.uk — MB BChir Camb. 1964; MA Camb. 1965; MD Lond. 1981; FRCOG 1982, M 1969; DObst RCOG 1967. (Camb. & St. Thos.) Emeritrus-Reader & Hon. Cons. O & G Univ. Coll. Lond. Hosps. Trust. Socs: Blair Bell Res. Soc.; Soc. Gyn. Investig.; Brit. Fertil. Soc. Prev: Mem. Comm. Safety of Meds.; Research Fell. (Reproduc. Med.) Univ. Calif., San Diego; Lect. (O & G) Univ. Coll. Hosp. Lond.

LACHLAN, Mr Geoffrey William Belford Hospital, Belford Road, Fort William PH33 6BS Tel: 01397 702481 Fax: 01397 702770 — MB ChB 1976 Ed.; FRCS Ed. 1981. (Edinburgh University) Cons. Gen. Surg. (Accd. & Emerg.). Socs: Lochaber Med. Soc.; Viking Surgic. Club.

LACHLAN, Margaret Stepps Cottage, Banavie, Fort William PH33 7LX — MB ChB 1976 Ed.

LACHMAN, Peter Irwin Northwick Park Hospital, Directorate of Paediatrics, Harrow HA1 2UJ Tel: 020 8864 3232 Fax: 020 8869 3477; 76 Parkhill Road, London NW3 2YT Email: peterlachman@compuserve.com — MB BCh 1979 Witwatersrand; M.Med Cape Town 1989; MD Capetown/UCT 1997; FCP (S. Afr.) 1987; FRCPCH. Cons. Paediat. Norwick Pk. Hosp. Harrow N. W. Lond. Hosp. NHS Trust. Socs: BMA. Prev: Cons. Paediat. Qu. Med. Centre Nottm.; Sen. Specialist (Paediat.) & Sen. Lect. Red Cross War Memor. Childr.s Hosp. Univ. Cape Town, S. Africa.

LACHMANN, Helen Jane 36 Conduit Head Road, Cambridge CB3 0EY — MB BChir 1993 Camb.; MA Camb. 1993; MRCP (UK) 1995.

LACHMANN, Professor Peter Julius University of Cambridge, Centre for Veterinary Science, Madingley Road, Cambridge CB3 0ES Tel: 01223 766242 Fax: 01223 766244 Email: pjl1000@cam.ac.uk; 36 Conduit Head Road, Cambridge CB3 0EY Tel: 01223 354433 Fax: 01223 354433 — MB BChir Camb. 1957; FRS 1982; PhD Camb. 1962, MA 1957, ScD 1974; FRCP Lond. 1973, M 1958; FRCPath 1981; P Med Sci 1998. (Camb. & Univ. Coll. Hosp.) Emerit. Sheila Joan Smith Prof. of Immunol. Univ. Camb.; Pres. Acad. of Med. Scis.; Hon. Cons. Immunol. Camb. HA; Fell. Christ's Coll. Camb.; Assoc. Edr. Clin. & Experimen. Immunol. Socs: Fell. Roy. Soc., Brit. Soc. Immunol. & Academia Europaea. Prev: Biological Soc. & Vice Pres. Roy. Soc. 1993-1998; Pres. Roy. Coll. Path. (1990-93); Prof. of Immunol. Roy. Postgrad. Med. Sch. Lond.

LACHMANN, Robin Henry Department Medicine, Level 5, Box 157 Addenbrooke's Hospital, Hills Road, Cambridge CB2 2QQ Email: rhl20@cam.ac.uk; 45 Rathmore Road, Cambridge CB1 7AB Tel: 01223 504724 — MB BChir 1991 Camb.; MA Camb. 1993, MB BChir 1991; MRCP (UK) 1993; PhD 1998. Clin. Research Assoc.

Metab. Med. Addenbrooke's Hosp. Camb. Prev: MRC Clin. Train. Fell. Dept. Path. Camb. Regist. (Med.) Norf. & Norwich Hosp.

LACHMANN, Sylvia Mary (retired) Rehabilitation Unit, Addenbrooke's Hospital, Hills Road, Cambridge CB2 2QQ Tel: 01223 217763 Fax: 01223 242038 — MB BChir 1962 Camb.; MA Camb. 1963; FRCP Lond. 1988, M 1964; M Phil 1998. Univ. Lect. & Hon. Cons. Rehabil. Med. Addenbrooke's Hosp. Camb. Prev: Sen. Med. Off. Camb. Disablem. Serv. Centre.

LACK, Gideon Department of Paediatrics, Salton House, St Mary's Hospital, Praed St., London W2 1NY Tel: 020 7886 6384 Fax: 020 7886 1129 Email: gideon.lack@st-marys.nhs.uk — MB BCh 1985 Oxf. Cons. Paediat. Allergy & Immnunol. St. Mary's Hosp. Lond.; Sen. Lect. at Imperial Coll. Socs: Counc. Mem. of Brit. Soc. of Allery & Clin. Immunol.; Clin. Edr. of Allergy, Curr. Med. Literature.

LACK, John Alastair Anaesthetic Department, Salisbury Hospital, Salisbury SP2 8BJ Tel: 01722 336262 Fax: 01722 414143 Email: jal@scata.org.uk; The River House, Coombe Bissett, Salisbury SP5 4LX Tel: 01722 718303 — MB BS 1965 Lond.; FRCA Eng. 1968; DIC 1971. (Univ. Coll. Hosp.) Cons. Anaesth. Salisbury HA. Socs: Counc. Roy. Coll. Anaesths. 1997; (Pres. & Ex-Chairm.) Europ. Soc. Computing & Technol. Anaesth.; Pres. Soc. Computing & Technol. Anaesth. Prev: Asst. Prof. Anesth. Stanford Med. Center, USA.

LACK, Josephine Jessica 2 Morrab Place, Penzance TR18 4DG Tel: 01736 69536 — MB BCh 1981 Wales; DA Eng. 1983; Dip. Geriat. Med. 1988. Staff Grade Barncoose Hosp. Redruth; Regist. Geriat. Barncoose Hosp. Redruth; Regist. (Med.) Plymouth Hosp.; SHO (Med.) Roy. Cornw. Hosp. Truro.

LACK, Liza Jane Yarm Medical Centre, 1 Worsall Road, Yarm TS15 9DD Tel: 01642 786422 Fax: 01642 785617 — BM BS 1989 Nottm.; BMedSci Nottm. 1987; MRCGP 1994; DFFP 1994; DCH RCP Lond. 1994; DRCOG 1993. (Nottm.)

LACK, Robin Philip (retired) The Laurels, 31 Bedford Road, Sandy SG19 1EP Tel: 01767 681309 Fax: 01767 683340 Email: docrobin@fsmail.net — MB ChB Birm. 1970.

LACK, Sarah Jane 3 Bridges secure unit Ealing Hospital, Mental West London Health NHS Trust, Uxbridge Road, Southall UB1 3EU Tel: 020 8967 5085 Fax: 020 8571 9296 — MB ChB 1983 Bristol; MRCPsych 1991. (Univ. of Bristol) Cons. (Foren. Psychiat.) Ealing Hosp. Lond. Prev: Sen. Regist. (Forens. Psychiat.) St. Geo. Hosp. Lond.; Sen. Regist. (Psychiat.) St. Mary's Hosp. Lond.; Lect. (Psychiat.) St. Mary's Hosp. Lond.

LACK, Susan Irene Manford Way Health Centre, 40 Foremark Close, Ilford IG6 3HS Tel: 020 8500 3088; The Oaks, 18 Connaught Avenue, Loughton IG10 4DS — MB BS 1978 Lond.; MRCGP 1984. (St. Bart.) Socs: Med. Wom. Federat.; BMA.

LACKEY, Shaun Andrew 29 Stonecross Gardens, Ulverston LA12 7XA — MB BS 1997 Newc.

LACY, Alison Mary 30 Beacon Drive, West Kirby, Wirral CH48 7ED Tel: 0151 625 4376 — MB ChB 1984 Leic.; MB ChB Leic. l984; MRCGP 1990. Clin. Asst. (Psychiat.) St. Helens & Knowsley Hosps. Prev: SHO (O & G) Walsgrave Hosp. Coventry; SHO (Psychiat.) Carlton Hayes Hosp. Leicester; SHO (Gen. Med.) Standish Hosp. Stroud.

LACY, David Ernest 30 Beacon Drive, West Kirby, Wirral CH48 7ED Tel: 0151 625 4376; Arrowe Park Hospital, Arrowe Pk Road, Upton, Wirral CH49 5PE Tel: 0151 678 5111 — MB ChB 1985 Leic.; MD Leic. 1996; MRCPI 1990; DTM & H RCP Lond. 1991; FRCPCH. Cons. Paediat. (Respirat. Med.) Arrowe Pk. Hosp. Wirral; Hon. Cons. Paediat. (Respirat. Med.) Alder Hey. Socs: Fell. Roy. Coll Paed. & Child Health; Brit. Paediat. Respirat. Soc.; Paediat. Research Soc. Prev: Sen. Regist. (Paediat.) Alder Hey Hosp.; Clin. Research Fell. Birm. Univ. & Hon. Regist. Birm. Childr. Hosp.; Regist. (Paediat.) E. Birm. Hosp.

LACY, Ian Robert Nettleham Medical Practice, 14 Lodge Lane, Nettleham, Lincoln LN2 2RS Tel: 01522 751717 Fax: 01522 754474; 12 Lime Grove, Cherry Willingham, Lincoln LN3 4BD Tel: 01522 752848 — MB 1976 Camb.; BChir 1975; MRCGP 1979; DTM & H Liverp. 1984. Exec. Mem., W. Lincs. Primary Care Trust; Mem. Lincs. Med. Comm. Prev: Project Direct. Kunri Christian Hosp. Kunri Pakistan.

LACY, Melanie Kate 70 Hitchin Road, Stotfold, Hitchin SG5 4HT — MB BS 1997 Lond.

LACY, Winifred Joan (retired) 22 Manesty View, Keswick CA12 4JF Tel: 017687 75297 — MB ChB Manch. 1948.

LACY-COLSON, Jon Carlo Hattersley 151 Bellhouse Way, Foxwood Lane, Acomb, York YO24 3LW — MB ChB 1998 Leeds.

LACZKO-SCHROEDER, Tina Janet Department Psychiatry, St. George's Hospital Med. School, Blackshaw Road, London SW17 0QT — MS BS Lond. 1988. Regist. (Psychiat.) St. Geo. Hosp. Lond.

LAD, Nareshkumar The Surgery, Harborough Road N., Northampton NN2 8LL Tel: 01604 845144 Fax: 01604 820241; 26 Scarborough Road, Leicester LE4 6PF — MB ChB 1987 Leic.; DFFP 1995. (Univ. Leic.)

LAD, Rajnikant Purshottam 60 Gilnow Road, Bolton BL1 4LJ — MB ChB 1983 Sheff.

LADA-GRODZICKA, Hanna Maria (retired) 32 Church Vale, East Finchley, London N2 9PA Tel: 020 8444 4297 — MRCS Eng. LRCP Lond. 1953.

LADAS, Mr George Department of Thoracic Surgery, Royal Brompton Heart & Lung Hospital, Sydney St., London SW3 6NP Tel: 020 7351 8567 Fax: 020 7351 8555 — Ptychio Iatrikes 1980 Athens; T(S) 1994; Specialty Title in Thoracic Surgery and Accreditation: October 1989 Athens. (Athens) Cons. Thoracic Surg. Roy. Brompton Hosp. Lond.; Hon. Cons. Thoracic Surg. Chelsea & W.m. Hosp. Lond.; Hon. Sen. Lect. Imperial Coll. Sch. of Med. Lond. Socs: Eur. Soc. Thoracic Surgs.; Roy. Soc. Med. (Cardiothoracic Sect.); Soc. Cardio-Thoracic Surgs. GB and Irel. (Cons. Mem.). Prev: Cons. Thoracic & Vasc. Surg. Sismanoglion Hosp., Athens; Sen. Regist. (Thoracic Surg.) Roy. Brompton Hosp. Lond.; Resid. (Cardiothoracic & Vasc. Surg.) Evangelismos Hosp., Athens.

LADBROOKE, Kathryn Jane 133 Western Way, Ponteland, Newcastle upon Tyne NE20 9LY — MB BS 1984 Lond.; MA Camb. 1985; DCH RCP Lond. 1988; DRCOG 1988.

LADBROOKE, Timothy Eric Courtfield Medical Centre, 73 Courtfield Gardens, London SW5 0NL Tel: 020 7370 2453 Fax: 020 7244 0018; 36 Doneraile Street, London SW6 6EN — MB BChir 1983 Camb.; MA Camb 1983; MRCGP 1986; DCH RCP Lond. 1986.

LADD, George Higgon Young Dysart House Surgery, 13 Ravensbourne Road, Bromley BR1 1HN Tel: 020 8464 0718; 99 Westmoreland Road, Bromley BR2 0TQ Tel: 020 8464 8040 — MB BS 1962 Lond.; Cert. Family Plann. JCC 1978. (St. Bart.) GP Trainer S. Thames Region.

LADD, Hannah Ceinwen 34 Nickleby Close, Rochester ME1 2LE — MB BS 1998 Lond.; MB BS Lond 1998.

LADD, Jonathan Ellis West Moors Group Practice, Heathlands House, 175 Station Road, West Moors, Ferndown BH22 0HX Tel: 01202 872585 Fax: 01202 892155; 1 Sherwood Avenue, Ferndown BH22 8JS — MB ChB 1973 Bristol; MRCGP 1984; DRCOG 1976. Clin. Asst. (Diabetes) Poole Gen. Hosp. Prev: Trainee GP Chichester VTS; SHO (Med.) Horton Gen. Hosp. Banbury.

LADE, Jeremy Charles The Loddon Vale Practice, Hurricane Way, Woodley, Reading RG5 4UX Tel: 0118 969 0160 Fax: 0118 969 9103; Wards Cross House, Hurst, Reading RG10 0DH Tel: 01734 345038 — MB 1970 Camb.; BChir 1969; DA Eng. 1971. Prev: Clin. Asst. Neurol. Roy. Berks. Hosp. Reading.

LADENBURG, Harriet Isabella 62 Cloncurry Street, London SW6 6DU — MB ChB 1998 Manch.; MB ChB Manch 1998.

LADER, Professor Malcolm Harold, OBE (retired) Institute of Psychiatry, de Crespigny Park, London SE5 8AF Tel: 0207 848 0372 Fax: 0207 252 5437 Email: m.lader@iop.kcl.ac.uk — MB ChB 1959 Liverp.; MB ChB (Hons.) Liverp. 1959; DSc Lond. 1976, PhD 1963; BSc (Hons.) Liverp. 1956, MD 1964; MRCS Eng. LRCP Lond. 1959; FRCPsych 1976, M 1971; DPM Lond. 1966; F.Med.Sci 1999. Prof. Clin. Psychopharmacol. Inst. Psychiat. Univ. Lond. Emerit.

LADHA, Abubaker Mohammed 9 Acres End, Amersham HP7 9DZ Tel: 01494 582636 Email: amladhaa@yahhoo.co.uk — MB BS 1979 Karachi; MRCPI 1989; Dip Nephrol & Hypertension 1989. (Dow medical college, Karachi, Pakistan) Prev: Regist. (Med.) St. Marys Hosp. E.bourne.; Cons. (Phys. & Nephrol.), King Abdul Aziz Hosp. Jeddah; Cons. (Phys. & Nephrol.), King Sand Hosp. Unayza, Saudi Arabia.

LADHA, Karim The Dovecote Surgery, 464 Hagley Road West, Oldbury, Warley B68 0DJ Tel: 0121 422 2267 Fax: 0121 422 4808 — MB BS 1988 Newc.

LADHA, Sikander Sherali The Lindens, Barrington Road, Altrincham WA14 1HZ; 7 Wellington Place, Altrincham WA14 2QH Tel: 0161 929 9309 Fax: ss149@x stream.co.uk — MB ChB 1989 Dundee; MRCGP 1994. (Dundee University) GP Princip. Prev: GP Trainee Nantwich HC; VTS N. Staffs. Hosps.

LADLOW, Miles Edward 48 Park Lane, Grove Harwood, Blackburn BB6 7RF — MB ChB 1992 Dundee.

LADUSANS, Edmund Jazeps St. Mary's Hospital, Whitworth Park, Manchester M13 0JH Tel: 0161 276 6252 — MB ChB 1980 Manch.; BSc (Hons.) Physiol. Manch. 1977, MB ChB 1980; FRCP (UK) 1993 MRCP 1983; FRCPCH 1997. Cons. Paediat. Cardiol. St. Mary's Hosp. & Roy. Manch. Childr. Hosp. Pendlebury; Hon. Lect. (Child Health) Univ. Manch. Prev: Brit. Heart Foundat. Research Fell. (Paediat. & Cardiol.) Guy's Hosp. Lond.

LADWA, Vrajlal Govind 3 Eaglewood Close, Torquay TQ2 7SS — MB BS 1975 Bombay; LRCP LRCS Ed. LRCPS Glas. 1984. Staff Grade Doctor Torbay Hosp.

LAFFAN, Michael Arthur Department of Haematology, Imperial College School of Medicine, Hammersmith Hospital, Du Cane Road, London W12 0NN Tel: 020 8383 1320 Fax: 020 8742 9335 Email: m.laffan@ic.ac.uk — BM BCh 1981 Oxf.; DM Oxf. 1993; FRCP 1996; MRCPath 1991; FRCPath 1999. Sen. Lect. ICSM; Hon Cons. Haemat. Hammersmith Hosp. Socs: Brit. Soc. Haematol.; Internat. Soc. Thrombosis & Haemostasis.; Amer. Soc. Haemat.

LAFFERTY, Evelyn Mary Bank House, Winterbourne Down, Bristol BS36 1DE Tel: 01454 2259 — LRCP LRCS 1945 Ed.; LRCP LRCS Ed. LRFPS Glas. 1945; FFA RCS Eng. 1957; DA Eng. 1950. (Univ. Ed.) Cons. Anaesth. Frenchay Hosp. Bristol. Socs: BMA & S.W. Anaesths. Assn. Prev: Regist. Anaesth. Bridge of Earn Hosp.; Res. Anaesth. Roy. Infirm. Manch. & E.. Gen. Hosp. Edin.

LAFFERTY, Mr Kevin Claydons Manor, Back Lane, East Hanningfield, Chelmsford CM3 8AJ — MB BS 1975 Lond.; MS Lond. 1985; FRCS Eng. 1979. (Middlx.) Cons. Surg. Basildon & Thurrock NHS Trust. Socs: Fell. Roy. Soc. Med.; Vasc. Surgs. Soc. Gt. Brit. & Irel. Prev: Lect. (Surg.) King's Coll. Hosp. Lond.

LAFFERTY, Maureen Elizabeth Renal Unit, Ninewells Hospital & Medical School, Dundee DD1 9SY — MB ChB 1988 Glas.; MRCP (UK) 1991.

LAFFERTY, Mr Philip Martin Sancta Maria Centre, Daiglen Drive, South Ockendon RM15 5SZ — MRCS Eng. LRCP Lond. 1980; FRCS Eng. 1986; FRCS Ed. 1985.

LAFFERTY, Thomas Gerard Parkhead Health Centre, 101 Salamanca Street, Glasgow G31 5BA Tel: 0141 531 9058 Fax: 0141 531 9026; 27 Elm Road, Rutherglen, Glasgow G73 4ET Tel: 0141 634 9788 — MB ChB 1982 Glas.; DRCOG 1986.

LAFONG, Antoine Cyril Department of Medical Microbiology, Fife Area Laboratory, Hayfield Road, Kirkcaldy KY2 5AG; 3 Colinton Court, Whinnyknowe, Glenrothes KY6 3PE — MB BCh BAO 1978 Belf.; MB BCh BAO Belfast 1978; MRCPath London 1985; FRCPath 1995. Cons. Med. MicroBiol. Fife Area Laborat. Prev: Sen. Regist. Med. MicroBiol. Belf. City Hosp.

LAFRENIERE, Lynn Margaret Princess Royal Hospital, Lewes Rd, Haywards Heath RH16 4EX Tel: 01444 441881 — MB ChB 1988 Leeds; MRCP (UK) 1991; FRCA 1994; DA (UK) 1992. Cons. Anaest., P.ss Roy. Hosp., Haywards Heath. Prev: Regist. (Anaesth.) St. Geo. Hosp. Lond.; SHO (Anaesth.) Middlx. & Univ. Coll. Hosp.; Sen. Regist. (Anaesth.) Leeds.

LAFUENTE BARAZA, Jesus 74 Leamington Avenue, Morden SM4 4DN — LMS 1992 U Autonoma Barcelona.

LAGAN, James Aidan 3 Bracken Mews, Tamlaght Road, Omagh BT78 5RU — LRCPI & LM, LRSCI & LM 1950; LRCPI & LM, LRCSI & LM 1950.

LAGAN, Kathleen 3 Bracken Mews, Tamlaght Road, Omagh BT78 5RU Tel: 01662 245275 — MB BCh BAO 1949 NUI; BDS Belf. 1959.

LAGANOWSKI, Miss Hania Carolyn Queen Elizabeth Hospital, Stadium Road, Woolwich, London SE18 4QH — MB BChir 1978 Camb.; MA Camb. 1975; FRCS Eng. 1986; FRCOphth 1989. Cons. Ophth.,Qu. Eliz. Hosp., Woolwich, Lond. Prev: Sen. Regist. (Ophth.) Moorfields Eye Hosp. Lond.; Cons. Ophth. Greenwich Dist. Hosp. Lond.

LAGATTOLLA, Mr Nicholas Raoul Francesco Benville House, Benville, Corscombe, Dorchester DT2 0NW Tel: 01935 891297 Email: n_lag@compuserve.com — BM BS 1985 Nottm.; BMedSci Nottm. 1983; FRCS Eng. 1990; FRCS (Gen) 1997. (Nottingham) Cons. (Gen. & Vasc. Surg.) Dorset Co. Hosp. Prev: Sen. Regist. Guy's Hosp. Lond.; Sen. Regist. Canterbury Hosp.; Sen. Regist. E.bourne Hosp.

LAGGAN, Michael Joseph Oliver and Partners, Millhill Surgery, 87 Woodmill Street, Dunfermline KY11 4JW Tel: 01383 621222 Fax: 01383 622862; 36 Gallowhill Road, Kinross KY13 8RA — MB ChB 1980 Ed.; BSc Ed. 1977, MB ChB 1980; MRCGP 1984. (Ed.) Prev: Ho. Off. Milesmark Hosp. Dunfermline; Ho. Off. Deaconess Hosp. Edin.

LAGNADO, Ellis Adrian 32 Sutton Crescent, Barnet EN5 2SS — MB BS 1990 Lond.

LAGNADO, Max Leon Joseph 4 Page Meadow, Page St., London NW7 2EN — MB BS 1988 Lond.

LAGRELIUS, Anders Skragge Swedish Medical Centre, 15 Harley St., London W1N 1DA — Lakarexamen 1973 Linkoping.

LAHA, Samar Nath Trafford General Hospital, Moorside Road, Davyhulme, Manchester M41 5SL Tel: 0161 748 4022; 8 Blueberry Road, Bowdon, Altrincham WA14 3LT Tel: 0161 929 0770 Email: a2snl@aol.com — MB BS Calcutta 1963; FRCPI 1990, M 1974; DTCD Wales 1973. Cons. Phys. Med. Elderly Trafford HA. Prev: Sen. Regist. (Geriat. Med.) Clwyd S. HA; Hon. Sen. Regist. (Geriat. Med.) Univ. Liverp.; Regist. (Geriat. & Gen. Med.) Dryburn Hosp. Durh.

LAHA, Shilpi 8 Blueberry Road, Bowden, Altrincham WA14 3LT — MB ChB 1997 Liverp.

LAHA, Shondipon Kumar 8 Blueberry Road, Bowdon, Altrincham WA14 3LT — BM BCh 1997 Oxf.

LAHAISE, John Edward Herbert Hayesland Farm House, Beckley, Rye TN31 6XP Tel: 01424 882524 — MB BS 1948 Lond.; DIH Soc. Apoth. Lond. 1959; DTM & H Eng. 1955. (Guy's) Socs: BMA & Soc. Occupat. Med. Prev: Chief Med. Off. Kuwait Oil Co., Kuwait; Chief Med. Adviser Iraq Petrol. Co. & Assoc. Cos., Iraq & Iranian Oil; Operat. Cos., Iran.

LAHBIB, Flora Jael 12 Elgar Row, Shop Lane, Wells-next-the-Sea NR23 1AW — MB BS 1996 Lond.

LAHER, Jason Paul Siraj 24 Hadfield Road, Heckmondwike WF16 9PW — MB ChB 1998 Manch.; MB ChB Manch 1998.

LAHIRI, Barindranath Red House Surgery, Renfrew Road, Hylton Red House, Sunderland SR5 5PS Tel: 0191 548 1269 Fax: 0191 549 8998 — MB BS 1962 Calcutta. (Sir Nilratan Sircar Med. Coll. Calcutta)

LAHIRI, Manatosh 74 Egerton Road, Liverpool L15 2HW Tel: 0151 733 5538; Shyama, 4 Mount Park Court, Woolton Park, Liverpool L25 6JP — MB BS 1955 Agra.

LAHIRI, Sujit Kumar Les Rosssignols, 36a Queens Gate, Stoke Bishop, Bristol BS9 1TZ; Les Rossingnols, 36A Queens Gate, Stoke Bishop, Bristol BS9 1TZ Tel: 0117 962 3775 — MB BS 1960 Calcutta; FFA RCS Eng. 1969; DA Eng. 1962. (N.R. Sircar Med. Coll. Calcutta) Cons. Anaesth. S.mead Hosp. Bristol. Socs: Roy. Soc. Anaesth.; BMA; S.W. Soc of Anaesth. Prev: Regist. Anaesth. Frenchay Hosp. & S.mead Hosp. Bristol & Bournemouth & E. Dorset Hosp. Gp.

LAHIRI, Sumitra 3 Nursery Close, Sunderland SR3 1PA — MB ChB 1998 Ed.; MB ChB Ed 1998.

LAHON, Khogeswar The Surgery, 243 Western Road, Southall UB2 5HS; 109 Mansell Road, Greenford UB6 9EH — MB BS 1968 Dibrugarh; MRCOG 1976. (Assam Med. Coll. Dibrugarh Assam, India) Socs: St. Paul's Med. Insur. Prev: Cons. O & G Benghazi, Libya.

LAHOUD, George Youssef George Scarborough Hospital, Woodland Drive, Scarborough YO12 6QL Tel: 01723 368111 Fax: 01723 342394 — MB BCh 1966 Ain Shams; MD Mass., USA 1991; FFA RCSI 1980. Cons. Anaesth. (Intens. Care) ScarBoro. & NE Yorks. Health Trust. Socs: Yorks. Soc. Anaesth.; Assn. Anaesth.; BMA. Prev: Chief (Anaesth.) Ludlow Hosp. Mass., USA; Clin. & Research Fell. (Anaesth.) Mass. Gen. Hosp. Boston, USA; Lect. (Anaesth.) Harvard Med. Sch. Camb., Mass., USA.

LAI, Anthony Ka Tung The Surgery, Ruckinge Road, Hamstreet, Ashford TN26 2NJ Tel: 01233 732262 Fax: 01233 733097 Email: tony.lai@hamstreetsurgery.com — MB ChB 1981 Glas.; DA (UK) 1983. (Glas.) Gen. Practioner HamSt., Romney Marsh.

LAI, Clement Wing Yan 5 Sandals Rise, Halesowen B62 8SQ — BM BCh 1992 Oxf.

LAI, Dilys 42 Newman Road, Rotherham S60 3JE — MB BS 1992 Lond.; MRCP (UK) 1996; BSc Basic Sciences Lond. 1989. (Charing Cross & Westminster) Specialist Regist. Respirat. Med. S. W. Thames Region. Socs: BMA; Brit. Thorac. Soc.

LAI, Hee Kit Musgrave & Clark House, Royal Victoria Hospital, Grosvenor Road, Belfast BT12 6BA — MB BCh 1998 Belf.; MB BCh Belf 1998.

LAI, Horn Ming 21 Tudor Gardens, West Acton, London W3 0DT — MB BS 1987 Lond.

LAI, Kamla (retired) 7 Elderfield Crescent, Chilton, Didcot OX11 0RY — MB BS 1943 Punjab; MFHom 1968.

LAI, Kelly Yee-Ching 807B Hertford Road, Enfield EN3 6UG — MB BS 1984 Newc.

LAI, Lee Min 23 Conway Street, London W1T 6BW — MB BCh 1991 Wales; FRCS Eng. 1995.

LAI, Manuelita Maria Rosaria London Hospital Medical College, 56 Ashfield St., London E1 2AJ Tel: 020 7377 7000; Cystaninga, Fox Lane, Keston BR2 6AL Tel: 01689 852313 — State Exam 1978 Cagliari; MD (Hons.) Cagliari 1978; Dip. Human & Clin. Genetics Lond. 1988. Clin. Asst. (Immunol.) Lond. Hosp. Med. Coll. Prev: Regist. 2nd. Clin. Paediat. Cagliari, Italy; Research Fell. (Genetics) Guy's Hosp. Lond.

LAI, Pauline Gorton Medical Centre, 46 Wellington Road, Gorton, Manchester M18 8LJ — MB ChB 1993 Manch.; BSc (Med. Sci.) St. And. 1990; DFFP 1996. GP Princip. Manch. Prev: Trainee GP/SHO N. Manch. Gen. Hosp. VTS.

LAI, Robert Yiu Ki Ward G2, Box 36, Addenbrookes Hospital, Hills Road, Cambridge CB2 2QQ — BChir 1995 Camb.

LAI, Susannah Hwee-Lin 171 Western Road, Billericay CM12 9JD — MB BS 1994 Lond.

LAI, Wai Kwan Department of Gastroenterology, c/o Dr Hillenbrand' Secretary, Good Hope Hospital, Rectory Road, Sutton Coldfield B75 7RR — MB ChB 1993 Sheff.

LAI CHUNG FONG, Patrick 17 Laurel Gardens, London NW7 3HA — MB BS 1981 Lond.

LAI CHUNG FONG, Peter Barnet General Hospital, Well House Lane, Barnet EN5 3DJ Tel: 020 8216 4000; 36 Aldenham Avenue, Radlett WD7 8HX Tel: 01923 852512 — MB BCh BAO 1978 NUI; LRCPI & LM, LRCSI & LM 1977; FRCR 1987. Sen. Regist. (Radiol.) N. Staffs. Roy. Infirm. Stoke-on-Trent; Cons. Radiol. Barnet Gen Hosp., N. W. Thames HA. Prev: SHO (Med.) St. Laurence's Hosp. Dub.

LAIDLAW, Allan James Winterdyne, 8 Cromwell Crescent, Worcester WR5 2JW Tel: 01905 353121 — LRCP LRCS Ed. LRCPS Glas. 1957; FRCGP 1970, M 1953; AFOM RCP Lond. 1979. (St. Mungo's, Glas. University) Police Med. Adviser W. Mercia; Fact. Med. Adviser Yamazaki Mazak; Local Med. Treas. Off. Worcs.; Med. Adviser. DVLA; Med. Off. Reality; Med. Off., Yamazaki Mazak, Worcester; Med. Off. Reality Gp. Socs: Medico-Legal Soc. Worcs.; Roy. Soc. Med.; Roy. Coll. Gen. Pract. Prev: Regist. Glas. Eye Infirm.; SHO & Regist. Glas. Roy. Infirm.; Upjohn Trav. Fell. 1958, 1966 & 1979.

LAIDLAW, Mr David Alistair Hunter St. Thomas' Hospital, Lambeth Palace Road, London SE1 7EH Email: allaidlaw@aol.com — MB BS 1985 Newc.; FRCS Glas. 1990; FRCOphth 1990; DO RCS Eng. 1987; MD Newc. 1998. (Newcastle) Cons. (Vitreo Retinal Surg.) St. Thomas' Hosp. Lond. & Kent & Co. Ophth. Hosp. Maidstone. Socs: Coll. Ophthalmol. & Oxf. Ophth. Congr. Prev: Fell. (Vitreo Retinal Surg.) Moorfields Eye Hosp. Lond.; Sen. Regist. (Ophth.) Moorfields Eye Hosp. Lond.; Lect. (Ophth.) Univ. Bristol.

LAIDLAW, Eric Fortescue (retired) 10 Glendale Close, Wootton, Ryde PO33 4RF Tel: 01983 882320 — MB BChir 1941 Camb. Prev: Cons. Phys. Chest. Med. & Geriat. I. of Wight AHA.

LAIDLAW, Evelyn Myra Edwina (retired) Wildfield House, Clenchwarton, King's Lynn PE34 4AH Tel: 01553 772332 — MB ChB Glas. 1961. Assoc. Specialist in Palliat. Care at Macmillan & Hudson Palliat. Care Centre Wisbech. Prev: Assoc. Specialist (Gen. Med.) Qu. Eliz. Hosp. King's Lynn.

LAIDLAW, Frances Christine Child Health Services, 17 Cogdeast Way, Salisbury SO31 7YJ Tel: 01202 665511 Fax: 02392 482154 — MB BS 1978 Lond.; DCH RCP Lond. 1986; MSc (Community Paediat.) Lond. 1993. Cons. Paediat. Community Child Health Portsmouth City P.C.T.

LAIDLAW, Hilda Lucy (retired) Grampian View, 132 Dundee Road, Forfar DD8 1JB Tel: 01307 63412 — MA, MB ChB Aberd. 1919; DPH Camb. 1923. Prev: Asst. Sch. Med. Off. Angus CC.

LAIDLAW, Mr Ian James Bupa Hospital Clare Park, Crondall Lane, Crondall, Farnham GU10 5XX Tel: 01252 795654 Fax: 01252 795654 — MB BS 1982 Newc.; MD Newc. 1993; FRCS Ed. 1987; FRCS 1987. (Newc. u. Tyne) Cons. Surg. Frimley Pk. Hosp. Camberley. Prev: Lect. (Surg.) Roy. Marsden Hosp. Lond.; Career Regist. (Gen. Surg.) NW RHA; Research Fell. Christie Hosp. & Paterson Inst. Manch.

LAIDLAW, James Duncan Drybrough Brownhill Centre, Swindon Road, Cheltenham GL51 9DZ Tel: 01242 275070 Fax: 01242 272421 — MB ChB 1989 Ed.; MRCPsych 1995; BSc (Hons.) Ed. 1989. (Edinburgh) Cons. Psychiat. (Gen. Adult Psychiat.) E. Gloucestershire NHS Trust Cheltenham. Prev: Sen. Regist. (Psychiat.) W. Midl.; Regist. (Psychiat.) Oxf. Regional Rotat.; SHO (Psychiat.) Coney Hill Hosp. Gloucester.

LAIDLAW, John Patrick (retired) Courtburn House, Coldingham, Eyemouth TD14 5NS Tel: 0189 07 71266 — MB ChB 1952 Ed.; FRCP Ed. 1966, M 1955. Prev: Cons. Phys. Epilepsy Centre Quarrier's Homes Bridge of Weir.

LAIDLAW, Kelvin Alexander Mair Thorneloe Lodge Surgery, 29 Barbourne Road, Worcester WR1 1RU Tel: 01905 22445 Fax: 01905 610963 — MB ChB 1980 Birm.; MRCGP 1984; DMJ(Clin) Soc. Aporth Lond. 1996; DRCOG 1983; Dip. Occ. Med. RCP Lond. 1997. Princip. (Gen. Pract.); Police Surg. W. Mercia Constab. Socs: Assn. Police Surg.; BMA; Roy. Soc. Med.

LAIDLAW, Sheonad Catherine 10 Hardgate, Haddington EH41 3JW — MB ChB 1998 Aberd.; MB ChB Aberd 1998.

LAIDLAW, Stuart Thomas 99 Kimberley Road, Penylan, Cardiff CF23 5DP — MB BS 1985 Lond.; MRCP (UK) 1989. Regist. (Haemat.) Roy. Hallamsh. Hosp. Sheff.

LAIDLAY, Nigel David Roderick (retired) 5 Bell's Road, Lerwick ZE1 0QB Tel: 01595 695147 — MB ChB 1964 St. And. Prev: Med. Off. Radaa Hosp., Yemen Arab Repub. & Shilokh Hosp. Jalalpur Jattan, Pakistan.

LAIDLER, Christine Wendy 9 Park Avenue, Gosforth, Newcastle upon Tyne NE3 2HJ; Flat 5, 2 Granville Road, Jesmond, Newcastle upon Tyne NE2 1TP Tel: 0191 209 1021 — MB BS 1998 Newc.; MB BS Newc 1998.

LAIDLER, Peter Department of Pathology, University of Wales College of Med., Cardiff CF14 4XN Tel: 029 2074 7747 Fax: 029 2074 4276 Email: wptpl@cf.ac.uk — DM Oxf. 1978, MA 1968, BM BCh 1968; FRCPath 1987; MRCPath 1975. Sen. Lect. (Path.) Univ. Wales Coll. Med. Cardiff.

LAIDLOW, Elisabeth Hannah 10 College Road, Cheltenham GL53 7HX Tel: 0124 513427; Brookland Villa, 10 College Road, Cheltenham GL53 7HX Tel: 01242 513427 Fax: 01242 572160 Email: ehannah@blueyonder.co.uk — MB BS Lond. 1969; MRCS Eng. LRCP Lond. 1969; T(GP) 1991. (Middlx.) Self employed locum GP; Medico legal report specialist. Prev: Med. Off. King Edwd. VII Hosp. Midhurst; GP Nat. Guard King Khalid Hosp. Jeddah, Saudi Arabia; GP St. Martins Guernsey.

LAIDLOW, John Michael X-Ray Department, Royal Hampshire County Hospital, Winchester SO22 5DG Tel: 01962 825001 Fax: 01962 825009 Email: dadslaid@yahoo.co.uk; 17 Wentworth Grange, Winchester SO22 4HZ Tel: 01962 825001 — MB BS 1972 Lond.; MRCP (UK) 1976; FRCR 1982; DMRD Lond. 1981. (St. Bart.) Cons. Radiol. Roy. Hants. Co. Hosp. Prev: Sen. Regist. (Radiol.) St. Bart. Hosp. Lond.; Regist. (Med.) St. Mark's Hosp. Lond.; Ho. Phys. (Med.) St. Bart. Hosp. Lond.

LAIN, Dawn Karen Blakelow Cottage, Butterton, Leek ST13 7TD — MB BChir 1992 Camb.; DCH RCP Lond. 1994.

LAINE, Christine Helen X-Ray Department, Wrexham Maelor Hospital, Wrexham LL13 7TD Tel: 01978 725707; Tel: 01244 570501 — MB ChB 1974 Dundee; MSc Wales 1995; FRCR 1983; DMRD Eng. 1980. p/t Cons. Radiol. Wrexham Maelor Hosp. Prev: Sen. Regist. (Radiol.) St. Geo. Hosp. Lond.; Regist. (Radiol.) Addenbrooke's Hosp. Camb.

LAING, Alistair Henry (retired) Sprole Cottage, 67 Barrow Road, Shippon, Abingdon OX13 6JQ Tel: 01235 520551 — MB ChB 1955 Glas.; FRCP Glas. 1971, M 1962; MRCP Ed. 1961; FRCR 1975; FFR 1962; DMRT Eng. 1958. Prev: Cons. Radiotherap. Oxf. HA.

LAING, Anne Catherine (retired) The Cottage, Fingest, Henley-on-Thames RG9 6QD — MB ChB 1947 Ed.

LAING, Arthur Gordon (retired) Ataraxia, Tree Road, Tarves, Ellon AB41 7JY Tel: 01651 851676 Fax: 01651 851562 — MB ChB Aberd. 1948; DObst RCOG 1953. Prev: Ho. Phys. Roy. Infirm. Aberd.

LAING, Dorothy Elizabeth Department of Child & Family Psychiatry, Dudhope House, 15 Dudhope Terrace, Dundee DD3 6HH — MB ChB 1986 Aberd.; MRCPsych 1991. Sen. Regist. (Child & Adolesc. Psychait.) Dudhope Hse. Dundee.

LAING, Emma Margaret Sharmini 19 Gresham Av, Margate CT9 5EH — MB BS 1991 Lond.

LAING, Gabrielle Jane City & Hackney Primary Care Trust, Child & Adolescent Services, St Leonards, London N1 5LZ Tel: 020 7301 3437 Fax: 020 7301 3270 Email: gabrielle.laing@chpct.nhs.uk; 15 Oval Road, London NW1 7EA Tel: 020 7267 8209 Email: gabrielle.laing@virgin.net — MB BS 1980 Lond.; MSc Lond. 1992; MRCP (UK) 1991; DCH RCP Lond. 1987; FRCPCH 1997; FRIPHH 1988. (Kings College London) Cons. Community Child Health City & Hackney Childr. Health Servs.; Hon. Sen. Lect. St. Bart. Roy. Lond. Sch. Med. Dent.; Hon. Sen. research Fell., Inst. of Child Health, Lond. Socs: Fell. Roy. Coll. Paediat. Child Health; Brit Assoc.comm. Child health academ. Convenor. Prev: Sen. Regist. (Community Child Health) W. Lambeth Community Care NHS Trust.

LAING, Mr Gordon Stewart (retired) 17 Langden Close, The Paddock, Culcheth, Warrington WA3 4DR Tel: 01925 767993 — MRCS Eng. LRCP Lond. 1948; FRCS Eng. 1986. Prev: Cons. A & E Hope Hosp. Salford.

LAING, Hugh Christopher Blackthorn Surgery, 73 Station Road, Netley Abbey, Southampton SO31 5AE Tel: 023 8045 3110 Fax: 023 8045 2747; Christmas House, Warsash, Southampton SO31 9HA Tel: 01489 581998 Fax: 01489 578398 — MRCS Eng. LRCP Lond. 1974; BSc (Physiol.) Lond. 1971, MB BS 1974; MRCP (UK) 1977. (St. Bart.) GP Princip. Hamble; Hosp. Pract. (Med.) Soton. Gen. Hosp.; CMO Norwich Union Healthcare. Socs: BMA; Assur. Med. Soc.; Amer. Acad. Insur. Med. Prev: SHO (Cardiol. & Thoracic Med.) Soton. W.. Hosp. SHO (Neurol.); Wessex Neurol. Centre; SHO (Gen. Med.) Soton. Gen. Hosp.

LAING, Ian Alexander Neonatal Unit, Simpson Memorial Maternity Pavilion, Lauriston Place, Edinburgh EH3 9EF Tel: 0131 229 2477 Fax: 0131 536 4297 Email: laingi@telemedicine.clh.ed.ac.uk; 36 Comely Bank, Edinburgh EH4 1AJ Tel: 0131 332 6644 — MD 1992 Ed.; MB ChB 1976; MA Camb. 1976; FRCP Ed. 1989; MRCP (UK) 1979; FRCPCH 1997. Cons. Neonat. Lothian Health Bd.; Clin. Dir. Neonat. Unit Edin. Roy. Infirm. Socs: Counc. Mem. Brit. Assn. Perinatal Med.; Eur. Soc. Paediat. Research; Paediat. Research Soc. Prev: Lect. Dept. Child Life & Health Univ. Edin.; Hon. Sen. Regist.(Paediat.) Special Care Baby Unit, Simpson Mem. Matern. Pavilion Edin.; Fell. Jt. Program in Neonat. Harvard Univ. Boston, USA.

LAING, Mr James Hamish Ellsworth Welsh Centre for Burns and Plastic Surgery, Morriston Hospital, Swansea SA6 6NL Tel: 01792 703859 Fax: 01792 703875 Email: hamish.laing@morrnhs-tr.wales.nhs.uk; The Lodge, Church Road, Cilybebyll, Pontardawe, Swansea SA8 3JQ Tel: 01792 863445 Email: hamish.laing@virgin.net — MB BS 1984 Lond.; BSc (Hons.) Lond. 1980; FRCS (Plast.) 1996; FRCS Eng. 1988. (King's Coll. Hosp.) Cons. (Plastic & Reconstruc. Surg.), Welsh Centre for Burns & Plastic Surg., Swansea; Clin. dir, Welsh centre for burns and plastic surg; Cons plastic surg Roy. Gwent Hosp, Newport and Llandouth Hosp Cardiff. Socs: Fell. Roy. Soc. Med.; Livery. Worshipful Soc. Apoth. Lond.; Brit. Assn. Plastic Surgs. Prev: Sen. Regist. (Plastic Surg.) Morriston Hosp. Swansea; Research Regist. Centre for Plastic Surg. Mt. Vernon Hosp. NHS Trust Middlx.; SHO (Plastic Surg.) Mt. Vernon Hosp. N.wood Middlx.

LAING, James Horatio William Beechwood, 9 The Balk, Pocklington, York YO42 2QJ — MB ChB 1986 Leic.

LAING, Jeremy Drake c/o 33 Manor Court, Newland, Sherborne DT9 3JX — MB ChB 1983 Dundee; MSc (Health Economics) York 1997.

LAING, Judith Ann The Village Surgery, Dudly Lane, Cramlington NE23 6US Tel: 01670 712821; 1 Moor Crescent, Gosforth, Newcastle upon Tyne NE3 4AP Tel: 0191 284 2304 — MB ChB 1985 Glas.; MRCGP 1991; DRCOG 1990. GP Princip.

LAING, Kathleen Mary (retired) 23 Magdala Road, Mapperley Park, Nottingham NG3 5DE Tel: 0115 960 7963 — BSc Lond. 1951, MB BS 1955; DCH Eng. 1958. Prev: Sen. Med. Off. Child Health Unit, Nottm.

LAING, Mr Malcolm Ronald Raigmore Hospital, Inverness IV2 3UJ Tel: 01463 704000; Kerrowaird, 48 Crown Drive, Inverness IV2 3QG Tel: 01463 230391 — MB ChB 1979 Aberd.; FRCS Glas. 1993; FRCS Ed. 1985; MRCGP 1984; DRCOG 1983. (Aberdeen) Cons. OtoLaryngol. Raigmore NHS Trust. Socs: Scott. E.N.T. Soc. (Counc. Mem.). Prev: Sen. Regist. (OtoLaryngol.) Grampian Health Bd.

LAING, Margaret Sinclair 33 North Birbiston Road, Lennoxtown, Glasgow G66 7LZ — MB ChB 1977 Ed. Clin.Asst. Path.Stobhill.Hosp.Glas.; Clin. Asst. Gyn. Stobhill. Hosp. Glas.

LAING, Margaretta Lilias (retired) 86 King's Road, Ilkley LS29 9BZ — MB ChB Aberd. 1954; MA Aberd. 1943.

LAING, Michael Begbie (retired) The Pocklington Group Practice, The Surgery, 7 Barmby Road, Pocklington, York YO4 2DN Tel: 01759 302500 Fax: 01759 305123 — MRCS Eng. LRCP Lond. 1961; DObst RCOG 1964. Prev: SHO (Paediat.) Copthorne Hosp. Shrewsbury.

LAING, Murdoch Scardroy, Muir of Ord IV6 7QQ Tel: 01997 477280 Fax: 01997 477272 — MB BS 1975 Lond.; MA Oxf. 1971; DTM & H RCP Lond. 1982.

LAING, Mr Patrick William Wrexham Maelor Hospital, Croesnewydd Road, Wrexham LL13 7TD Tel: 01978 725721 Fax: 01978 725391; Wood Farm, Threapwood, Malpas SY14 7AW — MB BS 1975 Lond.; FRCS Ed. 1982. (Univ. Coll. Hosp.) Cons. Orthop. Surg. Wrexham Maelor Hosp. & Robt. Jones & Agnes Hunt Orthop. Hosp. OsW.ry Shrops. Socs: Fell. BOA; Europ. Foot & Ankle Soc.; Brit. Orthopaedic Foot Surg. Soc. (Hon. Treas.). Prev: Lect. (Orthop.) Univ. Liverp.; Regist. (Surg.) Manly Hosp. Sydney; Resid. Med. Off. Blacktown Hosp. Sydney.

LAING, Richard Iain 58A Heath Road, Lexden, Colchester CO3 4DJ — MB ChB 1976 Glas.; DA Eng. 1979; MFHom. Lond. 1980.

LAING, Richard Thomas Robert c/o Kent & Canterbury Hospital, Ethelbert Road, Canterbury CT1 3NG — MB ChB 1991 Otago.

LAING, Robert Bruce Stirling The Infection Unit, Aberdeen Royal Infirmary, Aberdeen AB25 2ZN Fax: 01224 849154 Email: rbs.laing@arh.grampian.scot.nhs.uk; 2 Pinecrest Circle, Bielside, Aberdeen AB15 9FN — MB ChB 1986 Ed.; MRCP (UK) 1989; FRCPE 1999; MD Edin 1999. Cons. Phys. (Infec. Dis.s) Aberd. Roy. Infirm.; Hon. Sen. Clin. Lect., Univ. of Aberd. Socs: Brit. Infec. Soc.; Brit. HIV Assoc.; Scott. Soc. Phys.s. Prev: Sen. Regist. (Infec. & Trop. Med.) Aberd. Roy. Infirm.; Regist. (Infec. Dis.s) City Hosp. Edin.; Regist. (Med.) Aberd. Roy. Infirm. & Victory Hosp. Kirkcaldy.

LAING, Robert William St Lukes Cancer Centre, Royal Surrey County Hospital, Egerton Road, Guildford GU2 7XX — MB BS 1982 Lond.; MRCP (UK) 1986; T(R) (CO) 1992; FRCR 1990. Cons. Clin. Oncol. Roy. Surrey Co. Hosp. Guildford. Prev: Sen. Regist. Roy. Marsden Hosps. Fulham & Sutton; Regist. (Radiother.) Middlx. & Mt. Vernon Hosps. Lond.; Regist. (Radiother.) Char. Cross Hosp. Lond.

LAING, Mr Rodney John Charles Adddenbrooke's Hospital, Cambridge CB2 2QQ Tel: 01223 245151 Fax: 01223 216926 Email: rjcl2@medschl.cam.ac.uk; Grove House, Bury Road, Stapleford, Cambridge CB2 5BP Tel: 01223 846249 — MB BChir 1983 Camb.; MA Camb. 1984, MD 1994; FRCS (SN) 1994; FRCS Eng. 1987. (Cambridge and London) Cons. Neurosurg. Addenbrooke's Hosp. Camb. Socs: Soc. Brit. Neurol. Surgs.; Brit. Cervical Spine Soc. Prev: Sen. Regist. (Neurosurg.) Addenbrooke's Hosp. Camb.; Research Regist. & Regist. (Neurosurg.) Roy. Hallamsh. Hosp. Sheff.; SHO Frenchay & S.mead Hosps.

LAING, Stephanie Adele (retired) 2A Guthrum Road, Hadleigh, Ipswich IP7 5BQ Tel: 01473 823736 — MRCS Eng. LRCP Lond. 1945; MFCM 1974; DCH Eng. 1948, DPH 1966. Prev: Sen. Med. Off. Suff. AHA.

LAING, Stephen Rea Stuart (retired) Ivy Cottage, Iping, Midhurst GU29 0PF Tel: 01730 815317 — MB BChir 1954 Camb.; MA Camb. 1940; MRCS Eng. LRCP Lond. 1952; LMSSA Lond. 1952; DObst RCOG 1954. Prev: Med. Asst. (Genitourin. Med.) St. Mary's Hosp. Portsmouth.

LAING-MORTON, Patricia Anne, Maj. RAMC Retd. HM Inspectorate of Prisons, 50 Queen Annes Gate, London SW1H 9AT Tel: 020 7273 2144 Email: tish.laing-morton@homeoffice.gov.uk; Pyrus House, Lands Cove TQ13 7LZ Tel: 01803 762176 — MB ChB 1985 Bristol; MRCGP 1989; DRCOG 1988; Cert. Family Plann. JCC 1988; MFPHM 1996. (Brist.) Med. Insp. HM Insp.ate of Prisons, Home Office. Socs: Fell. Roy. Soc. Health.; Fell. RSM. Prev: Cons (Pub. health med.) Brent & Harrow health auth.; Sen. Regist. (Pub. Health Med.) S. E. Inst. of Pub. Health.; Cons. (Pub. Health Med.) Nhs Exec. S. E. regional office reg lead for prisons health care.

LAIRD, Mrs Alison Jane Wyke Regis Health Centre, Portland Road, Weymouth DT4 9BE Tel: 01305 782226 — BM 1988 Soton.; DGM RCP Lond. 1990. p/t GP. Prev: SHO (Cas.) E. Surrey Hosp. Redhill.

LAIRD, Alison Mary Morar, Main St., Darley, Harrogate HG3 2QF — BM BS 1993 Nottm.

LAIRD, Alistair Noble Stoney Stanton Medical Centre, 475 Stoney Stanton Road, Coventry CV6 5EA Tel: 024 7688 8484 Fax: 024 7658 1247; 36 Warwick Avenue, Coventry CV5 6DG — MB ChB 1955 Aberd. (Aberd.)

LAIRD, Barry James Anderson 65 Cromarty Road, Airdrie ML6 9RL — MB ChB 1997 Glas.

LAIRD, Catherine Jane Frances King Street Surgery, 22A King Street, Hereford HR4 9DA Tel: 01432 272181 Fax: 01432 344725 — BM 1989 Soton.

LAIRD, Christine Scapa Medical Group, Kirkwall KW15; Waterbank, Evie, Orkney KW17 2PH Tel: 01856 751351 Fax: 01856 751458 — MB BS 1982 Lond. (Roy. Free Hosp. Sch. Med.) Prev: GP Rousay Orkney; Regist. & SHO (Med.) Lewis Hosp. Stornoway.

LAIRD, Donald Balfour (retired) Broad Croft, 5 Church Close, Frampton Cotterell, Bristol BS36 2BB Tel: 01454 776064 — MB BS 1952 Lond. Prev: Ho. Surg. Enfield War Memor. Hosp. & Dept. O & G Chase Farm.

LAIRD, Euan Ronald Chesterton, 57 Hightown Road, Banbury OX16 9BE Tel: 01295 257589 Fax: 01295 256701 — MB ChB 1982 Otago; FRNZCOG 1995; MRCOG 1991. (Otago, Dunedin, NZ) Cons. O & G Horton Gen. Hosp. NHS Trust.

LAIRD, Gavin Wilson 37 Willow Brae, Greenburn, Fauldhouse, Bathgate EH47 9HE Tel: 01501 770506 — MB ChB 1982 Ed.

LAIRD, George Stephen, RD (retired) 6 Arden Close, Ashton-under-Lyne OL6 9AY Tel: 0161 330 1659 — MB ChB 1950 Aberd. JP. Prev: Surg. Lt.-Cdr. RNR.

LAIRD, Graham David Wyke Regis Health Centre, Portland Road, Weymouth DT4 9BE Tel: 01305 782226 Fax: 01305 760549 — BM 1988 Soton.; MRCGP 1995. Prev: Trainee GP W. Dorset Train. Scheme; SHO (Elderly Care) Dorset Co. Hosp.; SHO Dunedin Hosp. NZ.

LAIRD, James Colville St Margarets Health Centre, St. Margaret's Drive, Auchterarder PH3 1JH Tel: 01764 662614/662275 Fax: 01764 664178; Collyhill Lodge, Auchterarder PH3 1ED Tel: 01764 663719 — MB ChB 1978 Dundee; Dip. IMC RCS Ed. 1992; DRCOG 1984.

LAIRD, James Dunn 74 Ballyclare Road, Doagh, Ballyclare BT39 0PF Tel: 02893 41334 — MB BCh BAO 1963 Belf.; FFR 1969; DMRD Eng. 1967; DObst RCOG 1965. (Belf.) Cons. (Radiol.) Roy. Vict. Hosp. Belf. Prev: Cons. (Radiol.) Altnagelvin Hosp. Lond.derry.

LAIRD, Liliana 41 Lansdowne Crescent, Glasgow G20 6NH — LMS 1990 Navarra.

LAIRD, Malcolm James The Karis Medical Centre, Waterworks Road, Edgbaston, Birmingham B16 9AL Tel: 0121 454 0661 Fax: 0121 454 9104; 21 Knightlow Road, Harborne, Birmingham B17 8PS Tel: 0121 246 1725 Email: thelairds@aol.com — MB ChB 1982 Birm.; MRCGP 1987; DRCOG 1986.

LAIRD, Patricia (retired) Midwood, 14 Martello Road, Canford Cliffs, Poole BH13 7DH Tel: 01202 708550 Fax: 01202 701314 — MB ChB Glas. 1955. Prev: Clin. Asst. (Occupat. Health) ChristCh. Hosp. Dorset.

LAIRD, Richard Baillie Moorfield House Surgery, 35 Edgar Street, Hereford HR4 9JP Tel: 01432 272175 Fax: 01432 341942; Bryn Hafod, Hafod Road, Hereford HR1 1SG Tel: 0143 354900 — MB BS 1975 Lond.; MRCGP 1980; DRCOG 1979; Cert. Av Med. 1985; Dip. Occ. Med 1995. (Middlx.)

LAIRD, Mr Robert Marshall (retired) 6 Hawthorn Hill, The Roddens, Larne BT40 1PW Tel: 01574 273228 — MB BCh BAO 1942 Belf.; MB BCh BAO (Hons.) Belf. 1942; FRCS Eng. 1951. Prev: Cons. Surg. E. Antrim Hosp. Gp.

LAIRD, Sharon 16 Gadloch Avenue, Kirkintilloch, Glasgow G66 5NP — MB ChB 1993 Manch.

LAIRD, Mrs Shirley Ann 5 Craigiebuckler Place, Aberdeen AB15 8SW Tel: 01224 321541; Danestone Medical Centre, Fairview St, Danestone, Aberdeen AB22 8ZP Tel: 01224 822866 — MB ChB 1988 Aberd.; MRCGP 1992.

LAIRD, Susan 90 Emscote Road, Warwick CV34 5QJ Tel: 01926 494199 Fax: 01926 410338 — MB ChB 1983 Birm. (Birmingham) GP; GPCA.GU Med. Prev: Trainee GP Coventry; SHO (Med.) N. Warks. HA; Ho. Off. Coventry HA.

LAIRD, Timothy Peter Bloomfield Surgery, 95 Bloomfield Road, Bangor BT20 4XA Tel: 028 9145 2426; Shanagarry, 4 Kathleen Drive, Helens's Bay, Bangor BT19 1NE Email: tim.laird@dial_pipet.com — MB BCh BAO 1974 Belf.; MRCGP 1978; DRCOG 1977; FRCGP 1996.

LAIRD, William Herbert (retired) 58 Ballykennedy Road, Gracehill, Ballymena BT42 2NP — MB BCh BAO 1941 Belf.; FRCOG 1963, M 1949. Hon. Cons. O & G N. Bd. DHSS N. Irel. Prev: Examr. Jt. Nursing & Midw. Counc. N. Irel.

LAISHLEY, Richard Stephen Department of Anaesthesia, Ealing Hospital, Uxbridge Road, Southall UB1 3HW Tel: 020 8967 5328 (Sec.) — MRCS Eng. LRCP Lond. 1977; MD Lond. 1977; MB BS 1977; FFA RCS Eng. 1983. (St. Thos.) Cons. Anaesth. Ealing Hosp. Middlx. Socs: Fell. Roy. Soc. of Med.; Obstetric Anaesth. Assn.; Fell. Roy. Soc. of Med. Prev: Sen. Regist. (Anaesth.) St. Thos. Hosp. Lond.; Clin. Fell. (Anaesth.) Hosp. Sick Childr. Toronto, Canada; Regist. (Anaesth.) Qu. Charlotte's Matern. Hosp. Lond.

LAISHLEY, Roger Frederick 48 Dudsbury Avenue, Ferndown BH22 8DU — MB ChB 1982 Leeds; DA (UK) 1988; DRCOG 1986. Med. Off. Brunei Shell Petroleum Co.

LAITE, Peter Antony Chemical Pathology, Gloucester Royal Hospital, Great Western Road, Gloucester GL1 3NL — MB ChB Manch. 1968; MSc Lond. 1974; FRCPath 1975. (Manch.) Cons. Chem. Path. Glos. Roy. Hosp. & Cheltenham Gen. Hosp. Socs: Assn. Clin. Biochem.; BMA. Prev: Sen. Regist. (Chem. Path.) King's Coll. Hosp.; Ho. Surg. Manch. Roy. Infirm.; Ho. Phys. Stepping Hill Hosp. Stockport.

***LAITHWAITE, David Prescott** Arden House, Arden Road, Dorridge, Solihull B93 8LJ — MB ChB 1998 Birm.

LAITNER, Steven Mark West Hertfordshire Health Authority, Tonman House, 63-77 Victoria St., St Albans AL1 3ER; 35 Worley Road, St Albans AL3 5NR — MB BS 1991 Lond.; MRCGP 1997; MRCP (UK) 1994; DCH 1996. (Royal Free Hospital) Specialist Regist. (Pub. Health Med.) W. Herts. HA; GP Herts. Socs: RCGP; Sen. Mem. FPHM. Prev: GP Regist Bridge Cottage Surg. Welwyn; SHO (Paediat./Obst & Gyn.) QEII Hosp. Welwyn Gdn. City.

LAITT, Roger David 2 Laburnum Lane, Hale, Altrincham WA15 0JR Tel: 0161 941 2598 — MB ChB 1987 Manch.; BSc (Hons.) Manch. 1985; BSc (Hons.) Soton. 1979; MRCP (UK) 1990; FRCR 1994. Cons. Neuroradiol. Centr. Manch. Health Care Trust. Prev: Sen. Regist. (Neuroradiol.) Centr. Manch. Health Care Trust.

LAITUNG, Mr Jeekong Gerard Royal Preston Hospital, Sharoe Green Lane, Preston PR2 9HT Tel: 01772 716565; 11 Moor Park Avenue, Preston PR1 6AS — MB ChB 1976 Manch.; ChM Manch. 1992; FRCS Ed. 1981. Cons. Plastic Surg. Roy. Preston Hosp. Socs: BMA; Brit. Hand Soc.; Brit. Burns Assn. Prev: Sen. Regist. (Plastic Surg.) Frenchay Hosp. Bristol; Research Regist. Yorks. Regional Burns Centre; Regist. (Plastic Surg.) Leeds, Bradford & Manch.

LAKASING, Edin Chorleywood Health Centre, 7 Lower Road, Chorleywood, Rickmansworth WD3 5EA Tel: 01923 287100 Fax: 01923 287120; 2 Talman Grove, Stanmore HA7 4UQ Tel: 020 8954 8019 — MB ChB 1990 Dundee; 2001 Post Grad. Cert. For Teachers in Primary Care (Univ. of Westminister); MRCS Eng. LRCP Lond. 1991; MRCGP 1996; DFFP 1995; T(GP) 1995; DRCOG 1994; DCH RCP Lond. 1993. (Univ. Dundee) GP Princip. Chorleywood Herts.; Examr. to Medico-Legal Reporting reading Berks.; Adviser to Greenlines Healthcare Communications Lond. Socs: Fell. Roy. Soc. Med. (Gen. Pract.); Roy. Coll. (Herts. & Beds. Coll.); GP Writers Assn. Prev: Trainee GP/SHO (A & E O & G, Paediat. & Psychiat.) Watford Gen. Hosp. & Oxf. Region VTS; Ho. Surg. P.ss Margt. Hosp.

Swindon; Ho. Phys. Profess. Clin. Pharmacol. Unit Ninewells Hosp. & Med. Sch. Dundee.

LAKASING, Lorin Elizabeth Garret Anderson Hospital, 144 Euston Road, London NW1 2AP — MB ChB 1992 Dundee.

LAKE, Alfred Philip James Glan Clwyd Hospital, Bodlelwyddan, Rhyl LL18 5UJ; 21 Bishop's Walk, St Asaph LL17 0SU Tel: 01745 584505 — MB BS 1973 Lond.; BSc (Hons.) Lond. 1970; FFA RCS Eng. 1979; DObst RCOG 1976. (Middlx.) Cons. (Anaesth.) Glan Clwyd Trust. Socs: Assn. Anaesth.; Pain Soc. Prev: Sen. Regist. (Anaesth.) N. W. RHA, (Salford); Med. Adviser Smith Kline & French Labs. Ltd.; Regist. (Anaesth.) Roy. Free Hosp. Lond. & Middlx. Hosp. Lond.

LAKE, Andrew Kevin Heacham Group Practice, 45 Station Road, Heacham, King's Lynn PE31 7EX Tel: 01485 572769 Fax: 01485 750306; Barn Lodge, Sherborne Road, Ingoldisthorpe, King's Lynn PE31 6PE Email: andrew@oklake.demon.co.uk — MB ChB 1983 Sheff.; MRCGP 1988; DRCOG 1988. (Sheffield)

LAKE, Anne Christine 147 Worcester Road, Chichester PO19 4ED — MB ChB 1972 Sheff.; FFA RCS Eng. 1976; DObst RCOG 1974. (Sheff. Univ.)

LAKE, Beryl Muriel (retired) Orchard House, Higher St., Cullompton EX15 1AJ Tel: 01884 33943 — MRCS Eng. LRCP Lond. 1941. Prev: Jun. Resid. Roy. Free Hosp. Lond.

LAKE, Brian 19 The Green, Richmond DL10 4RG Tel: 01748 83262 — LRCP LRCS 1945 Ed.; LRFPS Glas. 1945; FRCPsych 1988, M 1973; DCH Eng. 1949; DPM Eng. 1961. Hon. Cons. Psychother. St. Jas. Univ. Hosp. Leeds. Prev: Ho. Phys. Edin. Roy. Infirm.; Sen. Res. Med. Off. Roy. Liverp. Childr. Hosp.; Cons. (Psychother.) St. Jas. Univ. Hosp. Leeds.

LAKE, Colin George East Tilbury Surgery, Princess Margaret Road, East Tilbury, Grays RM18 8YS Tel: 01375 843217 Fax: 01375 840423; Bali Hai, Crays Hill, Billericay CM11 2XR Tel: 01268 520903 — MRCS Eng. LRCP Lond. 1959. (Liverp. & W . Lond.) Prev: Cas. Off. St. Peter's Hosp. Chertsey; SHO Vict. Hosp. Woking; Ho. Surg. (Orthop.) Ashford Hosp. Middlx.

LAKE, Damian Brian Flat 3/1, 122 Kent Rd, Glasgow G3 7BB — MB ChB 1997 Glas.

LAKE, Mr David Nigel Wynn Y Bwthyn, Ystradgynlais, Swansea SA9 2LB Tel: 01639 844920 Fax: 01639 844920 Email: davidlake@davidlake.demon.co.uk — MB BS 1970 Lond.; FRCS Eng. 1976; MRCS Eng. LRCP Lond. 1970. Cons. Orthop. Surg. Morriston Hosp. Swansea; Chairm. W. Glam BMA. Socs: Brit. Orthop. Assn.

LAKE, Harold Fraser, TD (retired) Priestfield Cottage, Burnopfield, Newcastle upon Tyne NE16 6AF Tel: 01207 271075 — MB BS 1947 Durh.; FRCOphth 1989; DO Eng. 1957. Hon. Cons. Ophth. Sunderland Eye Infirm.; Maj. RAMC (TARO), Cons. Ophthalmol. Prev: Cons. Ophth. Sunderland & S. Shields Hosp. Gps.

LAKE, Ian Denis 159 Slad Road, Stroud GL5 1RD Email: ian.lake@btinternet.com; Regent Street Surgery, Stonehouse GL10 2AA Tel: 01453 822145 — BM 1985 Soton.; BSc (Cell Biol. & Biochem.) Liverp. 1981; MRCGP 1993; Dip. Chinese Med. Beijing 1998. (Southampton) GP Princip.; Clin. Asst. (Ophth.) Gloucestershire Roy. Hosp.

LAKE, Janet Louise Corners, Bourne Fields, Twyford, Winchester SO21 1NY Tel: 01962 713127 — MB BS 1957 Lond. (Roy. Free)

LAKE, Jonathan 15 Chequers Park, Wye, Ashford TN25 5BA — BM 1997 Soton.

LAKE, Lorna Mary Meredith (retired) 41 Erskine Hill, London NW11 6EY Tel: 020 8455 1972 — MB BS 1941 Lond.; MRCS Eng. LRCP Lond. 1940. Cons. Phys. Paddington & Kensington Chest Clinic.

LAKE, Lucy Aileen Regent Street Surgery, Stonehouse GL10 2AA; Tel: 01453 756718 — BM 1986 Soton.; Dip. Pract. Dermat. Wales 1993.

LAKE, Mary Rowans, Poughill, Bude EX23 9EN Tel: 01288 352926 — MRCS Eng. LRCP Lond. 1963. (Guy's) Prev: Ho. Surg. Ashford Hosp. Kent; Ho. Phys. WillesBoro. Hosp.

LAKE, Peter John South King Street Medical Centre, 25 South King Street, Blackpool FY1 4NF Tel: 01253 26637; 233 Highcross Road, Poulton-le-Fylde FY6 8DB — MB ChB 1979 Liverp.; Dip. Palliat. Med. Wales 1995; DA Eng. 1981.

LAKE, Philip Marcus John (retired) Belmont Surgery, Broomside Lane, Belmont, Durham DH1 2QP Tel: 0191 386 2517 — MB BS 1968 Newc.; Cert. Family Plann. JCC 1970; DObst RCOG 1970; ECFMG Soc. Apoth. Lond. 1970. Med. Off. Univ. Durh. Prev: Off. Coles Cranes Sunderland.

LAKE, Rebecca Sian Eastney Health Centre, Highland Road, Southsea PO4 9HU Tel: 01705 871999 — MB BS 1993 Lond.; BSc 1990; DRCOG 1996; Dip. Family Plann.1996. (Charing Cross/Westminster) p/t GP. Prev: SHO (Geriat. Med.) Bolingbroke Hosp. Lond.; SHO (A & E) St. Geo. Hosp. Lond.

LAKE, Ronald Hickman (retired) 5 Conifer Close, West Farley, Wimborne BH22 8PJ — MRCS Eng. LRCP Lond. 1946. Prev: Resid. Med. Off. Margate Gen. Hosp.

LAKE, Mr Stephen Philip Department of General Surgery, Worcester Royal Infirmary, Newtown Road, Worcester WR5 1HN — MD 1990 Leic.; MB ChB (Hons.) Birm. 1978; FRCS Eng. 1982. Cons. Gen. Surg. Worcester Roy. Infirm. Prev: Lect. & Sen. Regist. Leic. Roy. Infirm.; Regist. (Surg.) Roy. Free Hosp. Lond. & United Birm. Hosp.

LAKE, Mr Stewart Robert Radcliffe Infirmary, Woodstock Road, Oxford OX2 6HE Tel: 02865311888 — MB ChB 1994 (Hons) Sheff.; 1994, BMedSci 1992; FRCOphth 1998. Specialist Regist.,(Ophth.), Radcliffe Infirmery, Oxf.

LAKELAND, Dominic Anthony Ivy Cottage, Casterton, Carnforth LA6 2RX — BM BS 1998 Nottm.; BM BS Nottm 1998.

LAKEMAN, John Michael Borough Road Surgery, 167a Borough Road, Middlesbrough TS4 2EL Tel: 01642 243668 Fax: 01642 222252; 13 Rookwood Road, Nunthorpe, Middlesbrough TS7 0BN Tel: 01642 320580 — MB ChB 1976 Sheff.; MRCP (UK) 1978.

LAKEMAN, Margaret Amy (retired) 4 Lawrence Road, Heath Park, Romford RM2 5SS Tel: 0140 24 41866 — MB BS 1952 Lond.; MRCS Eng. LRCP Lond. 1946; MRCOG 1957, DObst 1950. Prev: Specialist Gyn. E. Region Nigeria.

LAKER, Martin Keith Dept. of Forensic Psychiatry, Runwell Hospital, The Chase, Wickford SS11 7XX Tel: 01268 366260 Fax: 01268 570946 Email: martin.laker@southessex_trust.nhs.uk; Tel: 01245 362744 Fax: 01245 362589 — MB BS 1979 Lond.; BA (Hons.) Oxf. 1975; MRCPsych 1991; MRCGP 1986; DCH RCP Lond. 1983. (UCHMS Lond.) Cons. Forens. Psych. Essex. Forens. Ment. Health Serv., Runwell Hosp. Wickford Essex; Chair, LNC, S. Essex Ment. Health & Community NHS Trust. Prev: Sen. Regist. (Forens. Psychiat.) Wessex Forens. Psychiat. Serv., Fareham, Hants, Ravenswood Hse. Medium Serv. Unit, Fareham, Hants; Hse. Medium Secure Unit, Fareham, Hants.

LAKER, Michael Francis Royal Victoria Infirmary, Newcastle upon Tyne NE1 4LP Tel: 0191 282 5067 Fax: 0191 282 4042 Email: mike.laker@nuth.northy.nhs.uk — MB BS Lond. 1969; MD Lond. 1979; MRCS Eng. LRCP Lond. 1969; FRCPath 1988, M 1976; Dip. Biochem. Lond 1966. (St. Thos.) Reader (Clin. Biochem.) Univ. Newc. u Tyne; Med. Dir. Newc. upon Tyne Hosps. NHS Trust. Socs: Brit. Hyperlipid. Assn.; BMA & Med. Res. Soc. Prev: Sen. Lect. (Clin. Biochem.) Roy. Vict. Infirm. Newc.; Ho. Phys. St. Thos. Hosp. Lond.; Lect. (Chem. Path.) St. Thos. Hosp. Med. Sch. Lond.

LAKEY, Pamela Janet (retired) Topknott, Pine Rise, Meopham, Gravesend DA13 0JA Tel: 01474 812551 — MB ChB 1957 Sheff. Hon. JP 1981. Prev: SCMO Medway HA.

LAKHA, Amirali Gulamhusein Nassar Sun Street Surgery, 34 Sun Street, Waltham Abbey EN9 1EE Tel: 01992 718711 Fax: 01992 788943; 10 North View, Eastcote, Pinner HA5 1PE — MB ChB 1974 Nairobi; DPM Eng. 1981. GP Waltham Abbey.

LAKHA, Shirin Hassanali Farnes, Linden Avenue, Gosforth, Newcastle upon Tyne NE3 4HD Tel: 0191 285 2786 — MB ChB 1986 Glas.; BSc (Hons.) Glas. 1981, MB ChB 1986; MRCGP 1990.

LAKHAN, Amarjit Kaur 23 King Edward Street, Slough SL1 2QT — MB BS 1990 Lond.

LAKHANI, Anil Kumar Vallabhdass Tel: 01689 814039 Fax: 01689 814233 Email: anillakhani@bromleyhospital.nhs.uk; Tel: 020 8688 1795 — MB ChB 1976 Glas.; FRCP Glas. 1994; MRCP (UK) 1979; FRCPath 1996, M 1985. Cons. Haemat. Bromley Hosps. NHS Trust. Socs: Brit. Soc. Haematol. Prev: Sen. Regist. (Haemat.) St. Geo. Hosp. Lond.; Regist. (Haemat. & Med.) Stobhill Hosp. Glas.

LAKHANI, Azim Didarali Hashim Central Health Outcomes Unit, Deptartment of Health, Wellington House, 133-155 Waterloo Road, London SE1 8UG Tel: 020 7972 4696 Fax: 020 7972 4673; 61 Clifton Court, Maida Vale, London NW8 8HU Tel: 020 7289 8034 — BM BCh 1978 Oxf.; MA Oxf. 1978; FFPHM RCP (UK) 1990, M

1985. Dir. Centr. Health Outcomes Unit DoH Lond.; Hon. Sen. Lect. UMDS Guy's & St. Thos. Hosps. Socs: Soc. Social Med. Prev: Sen. Med. Off. HCD Pub. Health Div. DoH; Dir. of Pub. Health & Hon. Sen. Lect. W. Lambeth HA; Specialist & Sen. Lect. (Community Med.) Medway HA & St. Thos. Hosp. Med. Sch. Lond.

LAKHANI, D N Abercromby Health Centre, Grove Street, Edge Hill, Liverpool L7 7HG Tel: 0151 708 9370.

LAKHANI, Dilesh Ramniklal 89 Peebles Way., Leicester LE4 7ZB — MB BCh 1995 Wales.

LAKHANI, Mark The Moir Medical Centre, Regent St., Long Eaton, Nottingham NG10 1QQ Tel: 0115 973 5820 Fax: 0115 946 0197 — BM BS 1990 Nottm.; BMedSci Nottm. 1988; MRCGP 1994; T(GP) 1994; DRCOG 1994.

LAKHANI, Mayur K Highgate Surgery, 5 Storer Close, Sileby, Loughborough LE12 7UD Tel: 01509 816364 Fax: 01509 815528; 6 Cross Hedge, Rothley, Leicester LE7 7RR Tel: 0116 230 3453 — MB ChB 1983 Dundee; MRCP (UK) 1986; MRCGP 1991; DCH RCP Lond. 1991. (Univ. Dundee) Lect. (Audit.) Eli Lilly Nat. Clin. Audit Centre Univ. Leicester. Prev: Trainee GP Camb. VTS; SHO Rotat. (Internal Med.) Tayside HB; Ho. Phys. & Ho. Surg. Ninewells Hosp. & Roy. Infirm. Dundee.

LAKHANI, Muhammad Yasin 2 Mariner Avenue, Birmingham B16 9DG — MB BS 1984 Karachi.

LAKHANI, Nitin Nanji Osidge Medical Practice, 182 Osidge Lane, London N14 5DR Tel: 020 8368 2800; Ras Leela, 13 Coombehurst Close, Hadley Wood, Barnet EN4 0JU Tel: 020 8440 4999 Fax: 020 8441 8777 — MB ChB 1979 Birm.; MRCGP 1985; DA Eng. 1981; DRCOG 1984. Lect. (Gen. Pract.) Univ. Lond. Socs: Pres. Thalassemia Soc.; Fac. Anaesth. RCS Eng.; Assur. Med. Soc. Prev: Occupat. Phys. St. Bart. & Homerton Hosps. Lond.

LAKHANI, Pravin Kumar Milton Keynes General NHS Trust Hospital, Standing Way, Eaglestone, Milton Keynes MK6 5LD Tel: 01908 243616 Fax: 01908 243108; 13 Whetstone Close, Heelands, Milton Keynes MK13 7PP Tel: 01908 321659 — MB ChB 1975 Bristol; FRCP Lond. 1995; MRCP (UK) 1979; DRCOG 1978; FRCPCH 1997. Cons. Paediat. Milton Keynes Gen. Hosp. Prev: Tutor & Hon. Sen. Regist. (Child Health) Univ. Manch.; Regist. (Paediat.) Qu.'s Med. Centre Nottm.; Research Regist. (Paediat.) N.wick Pk. Hosp. & Clin. Research Centre Harrow.

LAKHANI, Sanjaykumar Shantilal 219 Cannon Lane, Pinner HA5 1JA — MB BS 1988 Bombay; MRCS LRCP 1989; MRCP (UK) 1991. Trainee GP W. Middlx. Univ. Hosp. Lond. Prev: SHO & Regist. (Geriat.) W. Middlx. Univ. Hosp. Lond.; SHO (Geriat.) Pilgrim Hosp. Boston Lincs.

LAKHANI, Sunil Department of Histopathology UCLMS, Rockerfeller Building, University St., London WC1E 6JJ Tel: 020 7209 6019 Fax: 020 7387 3674 Email: s.lakhani@ucl.ac.uk; 38 Batchworth Lane, Northwood HA6 3DT — MB BS 1983 Lond.; MD Lond. 1996; BSc Lond. 1980; MRCPath 1991. (St. Geo. Hosp. Med. Sch.) Reader & Hon. Cons. Histopath. Univ. Coll. Lond. Med. Sch. Prev: Sen. Regist. (Histopath.) Roy. Marsden Hosp. Sutton.

LAKHANPAUL, Monica Department of Paediatrics, Queens Medical Centre, E floor, East Block, Nottingham NG5 2UH — MB ChB 1992 Manch.; MRCP MRCPCH 1995. (Manch.) Specialist Regist. (Paediat.) Qu. Med. Centre Nottm. Socs: Roy. Coll. Paediat. & Child Health; BMA; MRCPCH. Prev: Specialist Regist. Qu. Med. Centre Notts; Regist. King's Mill Hosp. Mansfield; SHO Rotat. (Paediat.) Nottm. & N.. Gen. Hosp. Sheff.

LAKHANPAUL, Roop Shila 110 Sudbury Court Drive, Harrow HA1 3TG — MB BS 1960 Panjab. SCMO (Family Plann. & Child Health) Bury HA. Socs: Soc. Pub. Health & Nat. Assn. Family Plann. Doctors; Fac. Community Health. Prev: GP Oldham; Clin. Med. Off. Bury HA; Lect. (Path.) Govt. Med. Coll. Patiala, India.

LAKHDAR, Abdulfattah Ali 4 Wester Steil, Edinburgh EH10 5XA — MB BS 1976 Garyounis; MB BS Garyounis, Libya 1976; MRCP (UK) 1981.

LAKIC, Jovo 2 Coastgard Cottage, Trevelyon Avenue, St Ives TR26 2AB Tel: 01756 795425 — MD Zagreb 1962; LRCP LRCS Ed. LRCPS Glas. 1969. (Zagreb) Prev: Orthop. Regist. Scunthorpe Gen. Hosp.; GP Princip. Centr. Surg. Barton on Humber N. Lincs.

LAKIN, Allen John The Surgery, 32 Clifton, York YO30 6AE Tel: 01904 653834 Fax: 01904 651442; 142 York Road, Haxby, York YO32 3EL Fax: 01904 768202 — MB ChB 1972 Leeds; BDS Lond. 1965; LDS RCS Eng 1965.

LAKIN, Anne Rowena North Ormesby Health Centre, Elizabeth Terrace, North Ormesby, Middlesbrough TS3 6EN Tel: 01642 277000 Fax: 01642 281000; 57 Cambridge Road, Middlesbrough TS5 5NL Tel: 01642 826715 — MB BS Lond. 1969; MRCP (UK) 1973; MRCS Eng. LRCP Lond. 1969; DRCOG 1980; Dip. Biochem. Lond 1966; Dip. Ther. 1994. (Roy. Free) GP N. Ormesby. Socs: BMA.; BMA. Prev: Clin. Asst. King Edwd. Memor. Hosp. Lond.; Ho. Surg. St. Mary Abbot's Hosp. Lond.; Ho. Phys. Roy. Free. Hosp. Lond.

LAKIN, Heather Mary 142 York Road, Haxby, York YO32 3EL Tel: 01904 768202 — MB ChB 1969 Leeds; DCH Eng. 1972; DObst RCOG 1971. (Leeds) SCMO (Community Med.) York Health Dist.

LAKIN, Judith Parkway, Sherford Road, Taunton TA1 3RA — MB BS 1981 Lond.; MSc Soton. 1974; BSc Sussex 1973. Regist. (Anaesth.) MusGr. Pk. Hosp. Taunton.

LAKIN, Kenneth Halsey Headingley, 5 The Drive, Horton, Northampton NN7 2AY — BM BCh 1985 Oxf.

LAKIN, Nigel Peter The Surgery, 232-234 Milton Road, Weston Super Mare BS22 8AG Tel: 01934 625022 Fax: 01934 612470; Springfield House, Axbridge Road, Cheddar BS27 3BZ Tel: 01934 741251 Email: nigellakin@compuserve.com — MB ChB 1984 Birm.; MRCGP 1990; DRCOG 1987. (Birmingham) Prev: Trainee GP Stratford u. Avon; Trainee GP Solihull VTS; SHO (A & E) Russells Hall Hosp. Dudley.

LAKING, Paul John Ivry House, Child Adolescent and Family Consultation Service, 23 Henley Road, Ipswich IP1 3TF Tel: 01473 214811 Fax: 01473 280809 — MB ChB 1979 Bristol; BSc (Hons.) Bristol 1976; MRCPsych 1984. Cons. Child & Adolesc. Psychiat. Loc. Health Partnshp NHS Trust. Prev: Sen. Regist. (Child & Adolesc. Psychiat.) Oxf. RHA; SHO & Regist. (Psychiat.) St. Geo. Hosp. Med. Sch. Lond.

LAKSHMAN, Jagga Chinna The Medical Centre, 4a Waltham Road, Gillingham ME8 6XQ Tel: 01634 231074 — MB BS 1967 Andhra; DObst RCOG 1976; Cert JCC Lond. 1976. (Guntur Med. Coll.) Prev: Regist. (O & G) & SHO (O & G) Cameron Hosp. Hartlepool; Regist. (Anaesth.) Gen. Hosp. S. Shields.

LAKSHMI, Vijaya Flat 10, Portland House, Park Road, Salford M6 8HJ — LRCP LRCS Ed. LRCPS Glas. 1984; MB BS Andhra 1981; MRCP (UK) 1989.

LAKSHMINARAYANA, Cheedella Learning Disability Service, Central Nottinghamshire Health Care NHS Trust, 70 Portland Street, Nottingham NG18 7AG Tel: 01623 785484 Fax: 01623 785483; 10 North Park, Mansfield NG18 4PA Tel: 01623 627945 Fax: 01623 486878 Email: clnarayana@aol.com — MB BS Andhra 1965; BSc Andhra 1960, MD 1969; MRCPsych 1979; DPM Eng. 1979. (Guntur Med. Coll., India) Cons. Psychiat. Centr. Notts. Health Care NHS Trust Mansfield; Mem. Ment. Health Review Tribunals; Vis. Cons. to HM Prison Serv.; Ment. Health Act Commiss. Apptd. Doctor for Second Opinions. Socs: BMA; Tutor Roy. Coll. of Psychiat. Prev: Asst. Prof. Med. Guntur Med. Coll. India; Tutor (Psychiat.) Guntur Med. Coll. India; Sen. Regist. Little Plumstead Hosp. Norwich.

LAKSHMINARAYANA, M West Bank Medical Centre, 2 Lower Church Street, Widnes WA8 0NG Tel: 0151 424 3113 Fax: 0151 420 2969 — MB BS 1967 Bangalore; MB BS 1967 Bangalore.

LAL, Adarsh Behari c/o Mr D. Srivastava, 59 Portsmouth Road, Camberley GU15 1JD — MB BS 1980 Osmania.

LAL, Amrit 4 Leamington Grove, Swindon SN3 1NU Tel: 01793 520664 — MB BS Patna 1958; Cert Family Plann. RCOG RCGP & Family Plann; Assn. 1976. (P. of Wales Med. Coll.) Prev: Regist. (Orthop. & Traum. Surg.) St. Martin's Hosp. Bath & Bath & Wessex Orthop. Hosp.; Regist. Beckett Hosp. Barnsley.

LAL, Annu 35 Hunters Way W., Chatham ME5 7HP — MB BS 1994 Lond.

LAL, Aroon Steven 84A Melbourne Grove, East Dulwich, London SE22 8QY — MB BS 1988 Lond.; BSc (1st cl. Hons.) Lond 1985; MRCP (UK) 1991. Specialist Regist. (Nephrol.) Roy. Lond. Hosp. Prev: Sen. Regist. & Fell. (Med.) Univ. Coll. Lond.; Regist. (Nephrol.) St. Peter's Gp. Hosps. Lond.; Regist. (Endocrinol.) Middlx. Hosp. Lond.

LAL, B K The Health Centre, Coatham Road, Redcar TS10 1SX Tel: 01642 482647 Fax: 01642 489166 — MB BS 1964 Patna; MB BS 1964 Patna.

LAL, Chaman Bradley Medical Centre, 83-84 Hallgreen Street, Bradley, Bilston WV14 8TH Tel: 01902 491323 Fax: 01902 402247;

7 Muchall Road, Penn, Wolverhampton WV4 5SE — MB ChB 1979 Birm.

LAL, Dev Paul Simon Satinder 25 Brooklands Road, Holcombe Brook, Bury BL0 9SW Tel: 01204 882525 — MB ChB 1993 Manch.; BSc (Hons.) Manch. 1990; MRCP (UK) 1996. (Manch.) Specialist Regist. (Gastroenterol.) N. W. Reg.). Prev: SHO Rotat. (Med.) Hope Hosp. Salford; SHO (Cardiothoracic Med.) Wythenshawe Hosp. Manch.

LAL, Hira Warrington General Hospital, Warrington WA5 Tel: 01925 35911; 12 Kirkcaldy Avenue, Great Sankey, Warrington WA5 3NS — MB BS 1954 Bihar; DTM & H Eng. 1957. Assoc. Specialist Warrington Dist. Gen. Hosp. Socs: BMA.

LAL, Jawahar The Surgery, 480 Footscray Road, New Eltham, London SE9 3TU Tel: 020 8850 2458 Fax: 020 8859 5763 — MB BS 1970 Agra; D Card. (Vienna) 1983. (S.N. Med. Coll.) GP New Eltham.; Clin. Asst. (Cardiol.) Qu. Eliz. Hosp., Stadium Rd, SE18.

LAL, Kumar Rohit 1 Wheatlands Park, Redcar TS10 2PD — MB BS 1994 Lond.

LAL, Madan Mohan 16 Ingleby Way, Wallington SM6 9LR — MB BS 1974 Lucknow.

LAL, Mark The Old Beer House, High St., Yoxford, Saxmundham IP17 3HP — MB BS 1991 Lond.

LAL, Mr Pyare 33 Lees Road, Uxbridge UB8 3AT — MB BS 1968 Lucknow; FRCSI 1984; FRCS Glas. 1981; FRCS Ed. 1980.

LAL, Rekha King Street Surgery, 55 King Street, Great Yarmouth NR30 2PW Tel: 01493 855589 Fax: 01493 332824 — MB BS 1975 Ranchi; MB BS 1975 Ranchi.

LAL, Satinder (retired) 25 Brooklands Road, Holcombe Brook, Bury BL0 9SW Tel: 0120 488 2525 — MB BS 1950 Punjab; FRCP Lond. 1975, M 1961; FRCP Ed. 1971, M 1957; LRCP LRCS Ed. LRFPS Glas. 1953. Cons. Phys. & Phys. i/c Chest Servs. Bury & Rossendale Gp. Hosps. Prev: Med. Off. E. Afr. Rlys. Uganda.

LAL, Sufia Anil Southlands Hospital, Shoreham-by-Sea BN43 6BJ Tel: 01273 455622; 98 Hammy Lane, Shoreham-by-Sea BN43 6BJ Tel: 01273 440358 Fax: 01273 440358 — MB BS 1973 Bangalor; MB BS Bangalore 1973; MRCOG 1990; DGO TC Dub. 1979. Regist. (O & G) S.lands Hosp. Shoreham-by-Sea. Socs: Med. Defence Union. Prev: Regist. Morriston Hosp. Swansea; Regist. (O & G) Redhill Gen. Hosp.

LAL-SARIN, Rabindra Robin Wood End Health Centre, Hillmorton Road, Coventry CV2 1SG Tel: 024 7661 2929 Fax: 024 7661 8665 — MB BS 1982 Lond.; BSc (Hons.) Lond. 1979, MB BS 1982; DRCOG 1986.

LALA, Aneesa Banu Hashim 39 Derby Road, Gloucester GL1 4AE — MB ChB 1996 Dundee.

LALANI, El-Nasir Mussa Ahmed Dept. of Histopathology, Imperial College School of Medicine, London W12 0NN; 21 Carr Manor Place, Leeds LS17 5DL Tel: 0113 684426 — MB ChB 1983 Ed. Prof. of Micro & Cellular Path.

LALE, Mr Andrew Michael Kestrels, Norlands Drive, Otterbourne, Winchester SO21 2DT Tel: 01962 713345 Email: amlale@hotmail.com — MB ChB 1990 Birm.; BSc 1st cl. Hons. (Med. Biochem.) Birm. 1987; FRCS Orl. 1997; FRCS Eng. 1996. (Birmingham) Specialist Regist. in OtoLaryngol., Oxf. Region; Regist. (Otolaryng.) Radcliffe Infirm. Oxf. Socs: Brit. Assn. of Otolaryngologists - Head & Neck Surg.s (BAO-HNS) Trainee Represen. Prev: SHO (Neurol. Surg.) Radcliffe Infirm. Oxf.; SHO (OtoLaryngol.) Addenbrooke's Hosp. Camb.

LALGEE, Claude Hamilton 15 Jersey Close, Bootle L20 4BL Tel: 0151 933 0956 — LRCP LRCS Ed. LRFPS Glas. 1952; DTM & H Liverp. 1953. (Univ. & RCS Edin.) Med. Off. DHSS.

LALIWALA, Mohsin Ahmed Husain, Squadron Ldr. RAF Med. Br. Regional Medical Centre, RAF Aldergrove BFPO 808 Tel: 01849 420419; 1 Trenchard Road, Crumlin BT29 4AY Tel: 01849 423381 — MB BS 1977 Karachi; DTM & H RCP Lond. 1979. Socs: Assoc. Mem. Brit. Med. Acupunc. Soc. Prev: GP RAF Laarbruch BFPO 43.

LALJEE, Ruth Mary Belgrave Surgery, 16-18 Falsgrave Road, Scarborough YO12 5AT Tel: 01723 361279 Fax: 01723 501589 — MB ChB 1993 Leeds.

LALJI, Mansukh Keshawji 1 Rushford Close, Willowpark Est., Leicester LE4 9UG — MB ChB 1975 Manch.

LALL, Abhimanu 133 Sea Road, Westgate-on-Sea CT8 8PZ — MB BS 1994 Lond.

LALL, Anita 133 Sea Road, Westgate-on-Sea CT8 8PZ Tel: 01843 833150 — MB BS 1968 Lucknow. (G.S.V.M. Med. Coll. Kanpur) GP Margate; Community Med. Off. (Child Health) Canterbury & Thanet HA. Prev: SHO (Geriat.) Kent & Canterbury Hosp.; SHO & Regist. (Psychiat.) Burnley Gen. Hosp.; Med. Off. Krishna Nagar Matern. Hosp. Kanpur, India.

LALL, Mr Dev Gouri 37 Little Lances Hill, Southampton SO19 4DU — MB ChB 1994 Leic.; BSc (Hons.) Physiol. St. And. 1989; ATLS 1998; FRCS (Eng) 1998. (Leicester Medical School) Hon. Research Fell. (Surg.) Roy. Free Hosp. Lond. Prev: Sen. SHO (Hepatobiliary Surg.), Roy. Surrey Co. Hosp.; SHO (Cardiothoracic Surg.), St. Bart's.

LALL, Govind Narain 133 Sea Road, Westgate-on-Sea CT8 8PZ Tel: 01843 833150 — MB BS 1968 Lucknow; BSc Agra 1962; MS (Gen. Surg.) Kanpur 1972. (G.S.V.M. Med. Coll. Kanpur) Prev: GP Margate; Police Surg. I. of Thanet.; Resid. Surgic. Off. Lalalajput Rai Hosp. Kanpur, India.

LALL, Gurdeep Singh 27 Barmouth Close, Willenhall WV12 5SH — MB ChB 1991 Birm.; ChB Birm. 1991.

LALL, Mr Kulvinder Singh 77 Hainault Road, Chigwell IG7 5DL Email: klall@atlas.co.uk — MB BS 1989 Lond.; FRCS Eng. 1993. Specialist Regist. W. of Scotl. Socs: Roy. Soc. Med. Prev: Regist. (Cardiothoracic Surg.) Lond. Chest Hosp.

LALL, Raghunath 178 Perth Road, Dundee DD1 4JS — MRCS Eng. LRCP Lond. 1991.

LALL, Ravinder Singh The Surgery, Alexandra Road, Lowestoft NR32 1PL Tel: 01502 574524 Fax: 01502 531526; Crestview Medical Centre, Crestview Drive, Lowestoft NR32 Tel: 01502 501008 — MB BS 1981 Lond.; MRCGP 1986; Cert. Family Plann. JCC 1984. Prev: Trainee GP Gt. Lumley N.umbria VTS; SHO (Psychiat.) Co. Hosp. Durh.; SHO (O & G & Paediat.) Bishop Auckland Gen. Hosp.

LALL, Rosina Patricia 4 Cheyham Way, Cheam, Sutton SM2 7HX — MB BS Lond. 1967. SCMO Merton & Sutton Community NHS Trust.

LALLA, Mr Mithu Mansing Prince Charles Hospital, Merthyr Tydfil CF47 9DT — MB BS 1952 Lucknow; BSc (Hons.) (Microbiol.) Bombay 1947; DOMS 1954; FRCS Eng. 1965. Cons. Ophth. P. Chas. Hosp. Merthyr Tydfil; Mem. Oxf. Ophth. Congr. & Internat. Corneo-Plastic Conf. Prev: Cons. Ophth. Surg. Merthyr. Gen. Hosp. Merthyr Tydfil; SHO (Ophth.) Leicester Roy. Infirm. & Eye Infirm. Wolverhampton; Regist. (Ophth.) Mid Glam. Hosp. Gp.

LALLA, Omprakash Vishindas Ashfield Road Surgery, Ashfield Road, Newbridge, Newport NP11 4RE Tel: 01633 246531 Fax: 01633 249169 — MB BS 1964 Calcutta; DA Eng. 1973; DCH Eng. 1970. (Calcutta Nat. Med. Coll.) Prev: Regist. (Anaesth.) Roy. Gwent Hosp. Newport; SHO (Paediat.) Neath Gen. Hosp.; Ho. Off. (Paediat.) St. Woolos Hosp. Newport.

LALLA, Soogan Celeste 31A Old Sneed Road, Bristol BS9 1ES — MB ChB 1992 Bristol.

LALLEMAND, Mr Roger Christopher 80 Tilford Road, Farnham GU9 8DW Tel: 01252 725240 Fax: 01252 725240 — MRCS Eng. LRCP Lond. 1961; MA, MB BChir Camb. 1962; FRCS Eng. 1967. (Guy's) Cons. Surg. Frimley Pk. Hosp. (Emerit.). Socs: Brit. Assn. Surg. Oncol.; BMA. Prev: Regist. (Surg.) Guy's Hosp. Lond.; Regist. (Surg.) Guildford Hosp. Gp.; Ho. Off. & Lect. (Physiol.) Guy's Hosp. Lond.

LALLI, Cynthia Ann Tobin, Redwood and Lalli, 25 Alms Hill, Bourn, Cambridge CB3 7SH Tel: 01954 719313 Fax: 01954 718012 — MB BChir 1987 Camb.; DRCOG 1990. Trainee GP Cambs.

LALLJEE, Mr Natzim (retired) 18 Selba Drive, Habberley, Kidderminster DY11 6HW Tel: 01562 751 9161 Email: nat.lalljee@virginnet.co.uk — MB BS Bombay 1952; FRCS Eng. 1958; FFAEM 1994; Dip. Sports Med. Scotl. 1995; MB BS 1952 Bombay. Prev: Cons. Traum. Surg. Kidderminster DHA.

LALLOO, David Griffith Liverpool School of Tropical Medicine, Pembroke Place, Liverpool L3 5QA Tel: 0151 708 9393 Fax: 0151 708 8733 — MB BS 1984 Newc.; FRCP 2001; MD Newc. 1994; MRCP (UK) 1987. Sen. Lect. & Hon. Cons. (Trop. Med.), Liverp. Sch. of Trop. Med. Prev: Sen. Regist. (Infec. Dis.) Ch.ill Hosp. Oxf.; Research Fell. Nuffield Dept. Med. Univ. Oxf.; Hon. Lect. (Med.) Univ. Papua New Guinea.

LALLOO, Drushca 16 Oakfield Avenue, Glasgow G12 8JE — MB ChB 1997 Glas.

LALLOO, Fiona Irene Dept Clinical Genetics, St Marys Hospital, Hathersage Road, Manchester M13 0JH Tel: 0161 276 6206 Fax: 0161 276 6145 Email: flalloo@control.cmht.nwest.nhs.uk — MB BS 1990 Newc.; BMedSc (Hons.) Newc. 1989; MRCP (UK) 1994; MD 1998. (Newcastle upon Tyne) Specialist Regist. Clin. Genetics. St Marys. Hosp. Manch.

LALLOO, Naomi Catherine Edgeley Medical Practice, 1 Avondale Road, Edgeley, Stockport SK3 9NX Tel: 0161 477 8230 Fax: 0161 476 1915 — MB ChB 1986 Manch.; MRCGP 1992; DRCOG 1990.

LALLOO, Ranchor Damodar 43 Newstead Road North, Shipley View, Ilkeston DE7 8UB — MB ChB Bristol 1953; MRCGP 1968; Cert Contracep. & Family Plann. RCOG, RCGP &; Cert FPA 1975. (Bristol) Socs: Derby Med. Soc.; Nottm. M-C Soc.

LALLOO, Umesh Gangaram Flat 2A Neville Street, London SW7 3AR — MB ChB 1980 Natal.

LALLY, Sukhjeet Singh 57 Hillside Road, Southall UB1 2PE — MB ChB 1994 Leeds.

LALONDE, Anna Katherine Long Barn, Church Lane, Braishfield, Romsey SO51 0QH — MB BS 1998 Lond.; MB BS Lond 1998.

LALOR, Anthony John Maolmuire The Surgery, 56 Northern Road, Portsmouth PO6 3DS Tel: 023 9237 3321; 34 Links Lane, Rowlands Castle PO9 6AE Tel: 023 92 413079 Fax: 01705 413080 Email: john@johnlalor.demon.co.uk — MB BS 1978 Lond.; MRCGP 1983; DFFP 1996; DRCOG 1981. (Guys) Med. Assessor Indep. Tribunal Serv. Hants. Prev: GP Morpeth.

LALOR, Brian Ciaran Royal Halifax Infirmary, Free School Lane, Halifax HX1 2YP Tel: 01422 357222; Hough House, The Hough, Stump Cross, Halifax HX3 7AP Tel: 01422 355743 — MD 1984 NUI; MB BCh BAO 1976; FRCPI 1985, M 1979; FRCP 1999. Cons. Phys. Calderdale HA.; Med Dir Calderdale NHS Trust. Prev: Lect. (Med.) Univ. Manch. & Manch. Roy. Infirm.; Regist. (Med.) Mater Hosp. Dub.

LALOR, Judith Margaret Anaesthetic Department, Lister Hospital, Coreys Hill Lane, Stevenage SG1 4AB Tel: 01438 781086; 7 Chancellors Road, Old Stevenage, Stevenage SG1 4AP Tel: 01438 724817 — MB BS 1977 West. Austral.; BSc West. Austral. 1974; FFA RCS Eng. 1983. (W. Austral.) Cons. Anaesth. Lister Hosp. Stevenage. Socs: Obst. Anaesth. Assn.; BMA & Assn. Anaesth. Prev: Sen. Regist. (Anaesth.) Hammersmith Hosp. Lond.; Staff Mem. (Anaesth.) Sophia Childr. Hosp. Rotterdam; Hon. Lect. & Sen. Regist. (Anaesth.) Lond. Hosp.

LALSINGH, Ian Reuben 76 Rugby Avenue, Belfast BT7 1RG — MB BCh BAO 1995 Belf.

LALSINGH, Reuben Ranjit 69 Blackfort Road, Omagh BT78 1PT — LRCPI & LM, LRSCI & LM 1966; LRCPI & LM, LRCSI & LM 1966; FFA RCSI 1975. (RCSI) Cons. Anaesth. Tyrone Co. Hosp. Omagh. Socs: Assn. Anaesth. Gt. Brit. & Irel. & Soc. Anaesth. N.. Irel. Prev: Sen. Regist. Ulster Hosp. Dundonald; Regist. Daisy Hill Hosp. Newry; SHO Belf. City Hosp.

LALSINGH, Stephen Lionel 69 Blackfort Road, Omagh BT78 1PT — MB BCh BAO 1994 Belf.

LALUDE, Mr Olatunde Akinremi 42 Carolina Close, Stratford, London E15 1JR — MB BS 1985 Lagos; FRCS Ed. 1994.

LALVANI, Ajit Nuffield Department of Clinical Medicine, University of Oxford, John Radcliffe Hospital, Oxford OX3 9DU Tel: 01865 557465 Email: ajit.lalvani@ndm.ox.ac.uk — MB BS 1989 Lond.; MA Oxon. 1986; MRCP (UK) 1992; DM Oxon 1999. (Royal Free Hosp Sch Med) Wellcome Sen. Clin. Research Fell. and Hon. Cons. Phys., Nuffield Dept. Of Clin. Med. Univ. of Oxf., John Radcliffe Hosp., Oxf.; Nuffield Dept. of Clin. Med. Univ. Oxf. John Radcliffe Hosp. Oxf.; Sherrington Lec in clin Med; Magdalen Coll Univ Oxf. Prev: Clin. Lect. in Infec. Dis.s & Gen. Med., Nuffield Dept. of Clin. Med., Univ. of Oxf.; John Redcliffe Hosp., Oxf.

LALVANI, Mira 19 Wessex Gardens, Golders Green, London NW11 9RS Tel: 020 8455 3658 — MB BS 1960 Lucknow.

LALWANI, Kirk 88 Bellamy Drive, Stanmore HA7 2DA Tel: 020 8907 6835; 19 Lister House, Restell Close, London SE3 7UL Tel: 020 8293 4725 — MB BS 1988 Bangalor; MB BS Bangalore 1988; FRCA 1993. Regist. Rotat. (Anaesth.) King's Coll. Hosp. Lond. Socs: BMA; Med. Protec. Soc.; Roy. Soc. Med. Prev: Regist. Brook Hosp. & Greenwich Hosp. Lond.

LAM, Alice Cheuk Wah 41 Hazelwood Road, Wilmslow SK9 2QA — MB ChB 1998 Manch.; MB ChB Manch 1998.

LAM, Boon Leong University of Leeds, Flat E-322 St Marks Student Flats, St Marks St., Leeds LS2 9EL — MB ChB 1997 Leeds.

LAM, Mr David Gee Kin 9 Maple Leaf Drive, Sidcup DA15 8WG Tel: 020 8309 5046 Email: david.lam@doctors.org.uk — MB BS 1993 Lond.; BSc (Hons.) Lond. 1990; FRCS Eng. 1998. (Guy's Hosp. Lond.) Specialist Regist. (Plastic Surg.), Stoke Mandeville Hosp., Aylesbury. Prev: SHO (Plastic Surg.) Salisbury Dist. Hosp.; SHO (Plastic Surg.) St. Geo. Hosp. Lond.; Registra (Plastic Surg.), The Radcliffe Infirm., Oxf.

LAM, Fang Yee Department of Anaesthetics, City General Hospital, Newcastle Road, Stoke-on-Trent ST4 6QG Tel: 01782 552884; 3 Batten Walk, Yarnfield, Stone ST15 0TA — MB BCh BAO 1982 Belf.; FFAFRCS 1991. Cons. Anaesth. City Gen. Hosp. Stoke-on-Trent. Socs: Mem. Assn. Anaesth. GB & Irel.; Mem. Assn. Cardiothoracic Anaesth. Prev: Sen. Regist. (Anaesth.) Midl. Train. Scheme; Regist. (Anaesth.) Sheff. HA.

LAM, For Tai 30 Whitefield Close, Coventry CV4 8GY — MB ChB 1978 Manc.

LAM, Francis Hin Tseuk 4 Middlefield, St Johns Wood, London NW8 6NE — MB BS 1996 Lond. (UMDS London) SHO (A & E) Guys Hosp. Lond. Prev: SHO (Cardiothoracics) St Thomas' Hosp. Lond.; Ho. Off. (Med.) Guys Hosp. Lond.; Ho. Off. (Surg.) Kingston Hosp. Lond.

LAM, Jane Yuk Chun Birchfield Practice, 23 Spencer Road, New Milton BH25 6BZ — MB ChB 1991 Glas.

LAM, Jeroo Sorab Jamshed 45 Quentin Road, Blackheath, London SE13 5DG Tel: 020 8318 2173 — MB BS Bombay 1962.

LAM, Kai-Ping The Surgery, 1 Troy Close, Tadworth Farm, Tadworth KT20 5JE Tel: 01737 362327 Fax: 01737 373469; 7 Lackford Road, Chipstead, Coulsdon CR5 3TB Tel: 01737 557722 — MB BCh BAO Dub. 1970; BA Dub. 1970; MRCGP 1981; DCH Eng. 1979; DRCOG 1977. (TC Dub.)

LAM, Kenneth Ho Fai 45 Hermitage Way, Stanmore HA7 2AX — MB BS 1993 Lond.

LAM, Pui Shan Emma 180 St Michaels Hill, Bristol BS2 8DE — MB ChB 1994 Liverp.

LAM, Ricky Wai Fat 10 Jasmine Court, Cherry Hinton Road, Cambridge CB1 8BG — MB BS 1995 Lond.

LAM, Mr Soli Jamshed 10 Harley Street, London W1N 1AA Tel: 020 7467 8300 Fax: 020 7467 8312; Cheverells, 4 Old Bartholmy Brooms, New Road, Sundridge, Sevenoaks TN14 6AR Tel: 01959 562390 Fax: 01959 562390 — MB BS Lond, 1957; FRCS Eng. 1961; FRCS Ed. 1961; MRCS Eng. LRCP Lond. 1957; FACS 1972; FICS 1969. (Guy's) Emerit. Cons. Orthop. Surg. Bromley Hosps. NHS Trust & Tunbridge Wells HA. Socs: Fell. BOA; Eur. Spine Soc.; Brit. Elbow & Shoulder Soc. Prev: Sen. Regist. (Orthop.) Guy's Hosp. Lond.; Hunt. Prof. RCS Eng. 1968/9; Fulbright Schol. 1965.

LAM, Tak Hung 25 Bevington Road, Ladbroke Grove, London W10 5TL — MB BS 1987 Lond.

LAM, Thomas Sit-Tin Lister House, Staple Tye, Harlow CM18 7JF Tel: 01279 414882; 5 Watlington Road, Harlow CM17 0DX — MB BS 1959 Sydney. (Sydney)

LAM, Wai Kuen Doctors Mess, Billinge Hospital, Upholland Road, Billinge, Wigan WN5 7ET — MB BS 1982 Hong Kong.

LAM, Wee Leon 20(1F2) Livingstone Pl, Edinburgh EH9 1PD — MB ChB 1997 Ed.

LAM, William 2 Milan Street, Leeds LS8 5JW Tel: 0113 249 0598; 355 Harrogate Road, Leeds LS17 6PZ Tel: 0113 268 0066 — BM BS 1987 Nottm.; BMedSci (Hons.) 1985; Cert. Av. Med. 1993. Prev: Trainee GP Leeds; SHO (Paediat.) Lincoln Co. Hosp.; SHO (Med. for Elderly) St. Jas. Univ. Hosp. Leeds.

LAM, William Wing-Lok 45 Sussex Gardens, Great North Road, London N6 4LY — MB ChB 1987 Bristol.

LAM, Wing Keung 5 Portinscale Close, Walshaw Park, Bury BL8 1DB — MB ChB 1988 Manch.

LAM, Yen Hoang 133B Melfort Road, Thornton Heath, Croydon CR7 7RX — MB BS 1997 Lond.

LAM KIN TENG, Leung Ting Lord Lister Health Centre, 121 Woodgrange Road, Forest Gate, London E7 0EP Tel: 020 8250 7510 Fax: 020 8250 7515; 28 Glebelands Avenue, South Woodford, London E18 2AB — MB ChB 1979 Brist.; MRCGP 1983; DRCOG 1981. Prev: Trainee GP City & E. Lond. AHA VTS; Ho. Surg. Yeovil Hosp.; Ho. Phys. Roy. Cornw. Truro.

LAM-PO-TANG, Kwet Long Michael 6 The Greenway, Uxbridge UB8 2PH — MB ChB 1988 Leic.

LAM SHANG LEEN, Clifford Regional Infectious Disease Unit, Western General Hospital, Crewe Road, Edinburgh EH4 5XU Tel: 0131 537 2852 Fax: 0131 537 2878 Email: clifford.leen@ed.ac.uk — MB ChB 1978 Ed.; MD Edin. 1987; MRCP (UK) 1982; FRCP Ed.; FRCP Lond 2000. (Univ. Ed.) Cons. Phys. & Sen. Lect. (Med.) Edin. Univ. Socs: Fell. RCP Ed.; (past Treas.) Brit. Soc. for the Study of Infec.; Brit. Soc. Immunol. Prev: Sen. Regist. (Infec. Dis.) Manch. Monsall Hosp.; Regist. (Gen. Med. & Endocrinol.) Roy. Infirm. Edin.; Research Regist. (BTS) Roy. Infirm. Edin.

LAM SHANG LEEN, Edward Doctor's Mess, Maidstone Hospital, Hermitage Lane, Maidstone ME16 9NN — MB BCh BAO 1984 NUI.

LAM SHANG LEEN, Guillaume 12 Marlborough Drive, Darlington DL1 5YA — MB ChB 1979 Aberd.; FRCR 1987.

LAMA, Ashish Kumar 25 Courtlands Close, Ruislip HA4 8AX — MB ChB 1993 Manch.

LAMA, Meera John Radcliffe Hospital, University of Oxford, Oxford OX3 9DU Tel: 01865 741166; 60 Ivy Lane Flats, Osler Road, Headington, Oxford OX3 9DT Tel: 01865 741707 — MB BS 1981 Delhi; MRCP (UK) 1987. Clin. Lect. (Paediat.) John Radcliffe Hosp. Oxf.

LAMACRAFT, Gillian Knowle House, Timberscombe, Minehead TA24 6TZ Tel: 01643 841342 Fax: 01643 841644 Email: glamacraft@aol.com — MB BS 1986 Lond.; MRCP (UK) 1991; FRCA 1994 (UK); Cert. Pain Managem. (ANZCA) 1997. (Guy's) Specialist Regist., Soton. Socs: Brit. Med. Acupunct. Soc.; Pain Soc.; Obst. Anaesth. Assn. Prev: Sen. Regist. (Anaesth. & Pain Managem.) Roy. N. Shore Hosp., Sydney; Pain Fell. New Childr. Hosp. W.mead, Sydney; Regist. Rotat. (Anaesth.) Soton., Poole & Bournemouth.

LAMAH, Mr Marc Digestive Diseases Centre, Royal Sussex County Hospital, Brighton Tel: 01244 316057; 10 Langley Road, London SW19 3NZ — MB BChir 1987 Camb.; MA Camb. 1989; FRCS Ed. 1992; MD (Doctor of Medicene) Lond. 1999. (University of Cambridge) Cons. Surg. Roy. Sussex Co. Hosp. Brighton. Socs: BMA; Assoc. of Surg.s; Assoc. of ColoProctol. of GB & I. Prev: Lect. (Surg.) St. Geo. Hosp. Lond.

LAMAS, Cristiane Da Cruz 51 Stangate, Royal St., London SE1 7EQ — Medico 1991 Federal U Rio de Janeiro; MRCP (UK) 1994.

LAMB, Adrian Justin 66 Mount Road, Stone ST15 8LJ — MB ChB 1997 Leic.

LAMB, Adrian Keith Heaton Medical Centre, 2 Lucy Street, Bolton BL1 5PU Tel: 01204 843677; 14 Somerdale Avenue, Bolton BL1 5HS Tel: 01204 492721 — MB BChir 1976 Camb.; MA (Med. Sci.) Camb 1976, BA 1973. (St. Bart.) Prev: Trainee GP Norwich VTS; Ho. Phys. P. of Wales Hosp. Lond.; Ho. Surg. Harold Wood Hosp. Essex.

LAMB, Andrew Stephen Theakston Stafford District General Hospital, Weston Road, Stafford ST16 3SA Tel: 01785 57731 — MB BS 1971 Lond.; MRCS Eng. LRCP Lond. 1971; FFA RCS Eng. 1975. (Char. Cross) Cons. (Anaesth.) Stafford Dist. Gen. Hosp. Prev: Sen. Regist. (Anaesth.) Addenbrooke's Hosp. Camb.

LAMB, Anthony Brian Browning Street Surgery, Stafford ST16 3AT — MB ChB 1993 Sheff.; MRCGP 1997; DFFP 1997; DRCOG 1996. (Sheff.) GP Stafford.

LAMB, Catriona Buchanan — MB ChB 1984 Glas.; MRCGP 1988.

LAMB, Mr Christopher Edmund Manley Princess Alexandra Hospital, Hamstel Road, Harlow CM20 1QX Tel: 01279 444455; 4 Inglewood Copse, Bromley BR1 2BB Tel: 020 8467 4063 — MB BS 1965 Lond.; FRCS (Orl.) Eng. 1971; MRCS Eng. LRCP Lond. 1965; FDS RCS Eng. 1967. (Guy's) Cons. Otolaryngol. W. Essex Health Dist. Socs: Fell. Roy. Soc. Med. (Mem. Sects. Otol. & Laryngol.); Eur. Acad. Facial Surg. Prev: Lect. (Oral Surg.) Guy's Hosp. Dent. Sch.; Cons. ENT Surg. Univ. Hosp. W. Indies Kingston, Jamaica; Sen. Regist. Roy. Nat. Throat, Nose & Ear Hosp. Lond.

LAMB, Christopher John Kent & Canterbury Hospital, Canterbury CT1 3NG — MB BS 1972 Lond.; MRCS Eng. LRCP Lond. 1972; FFA RCS Eng. 1979. (Guy's)

LAMB, Christopher Thomas Rothmans of Pall Mall (International) Ltd., Oxford Rd, Aylesbury HP21 8SZ Tel: 01296 335151 Fax: 01296 335971; Cedar Cottage, Dark Lane, Chearsley, Aylesbury HP18 0DA Tel: 01844 208436 — MB ChB 1972 Leeds; AFOM RCP Lond. 1986 MFOM 1991; MRCGP 1976. Chief Med. Off. Rothmans Aylesbury. Socs: BMA; Soc. Occupat. Med. Prev: Occupat. Health Phys. ICI Pharmaceuts. & Mobil Oil.

LAMB, Dominic Windsor Tel: 01373 462136 — MB BS 1990 Lond.; MRCP (UK) 1994. Specialist Regist. Cardiol. Hammersmith Hosp. Lond.

LAMB, Douglas Iain Henderson 46 Ferry Road, Edinburgh EH6 4AE Tel: 0131 554 0558; 11 Barnton Park Crescent, Edinburgh EH4 6ER Tel: 0131 336 2775 — MB ChB 1972 Ed.; MRCGP 1985. Assoc. Adviser (Gen. Pract.) SE Scotl. Region; Police Surg. Lothian & Borders.

LAMB, Elizabeth Francis The Surgery, School Hill House, High Street, Lewes BN7 2LU; 41 Wanderdown Road, Ovingdean, Brighton BN2 7BT Tel: 01273 386776 Fax: 01273 386781 Email: erl@aquamist.co.uk — MB BS 1983 Lond.; DRCOG 1986. Clin. Asst. Vict. Hosp. Lewes. Prev: GP Brighton VTS.

LAMB, Erich Werner Brunton Possilpark Health Centre, 85 Denmark Street, Glasgow G22 5EG Tel: 0141 531 6150 Fax: 0141 531 6152; 14 Dunlin, Stewartfield, E. Kilbride, Glasgow G74 4RU — MB ChB 1983 Glas.; MRCP (UK) 1988; MRCGP 1988.

LAMB, Fiona Jillian 32 Bargate Close, New Malden KT3 6BQ — MB BS 1988 Lond.; FRCA 1993; DA (UK) 1992. Cons. (anaesth.) NHS, Surrey & Sussex Trust Healthcare. Socs: Lond. Intens. Care GP; Assn. Anaesth.; BMA. Prev: Specialist Regist. (Anaesth.) S. Thames (W.); Research Fell (ICU) St. Geo. Hosp. Lond.; Regist. (Anaesth.) S. Thames (W.).

LAMB, Gabriel Harold Richard Burygreen, Courtenay Road, Liverpool L25 4RL — MB ChB 1969 Liverp.; FRCR 1975; DMRD Liverp. 1973. Cons. Radiol. Roy. Liverp. Hosp. Prev: Cons. Radiol. BRd.green Hosp. Liverp.; Sen. Regist. St. Thos. Hosp. Lond.

LAMB, Gabrielle Mary Department of Radiology, QEQM Building, St Mary's Hospital, Praed St., London W2 1NY Tel: 020 7725 6125 — MB BS 1986 Lond.; BA (Hons) Oxf. 1983; MRCP (UK) 1989; FRCR 1995. Sen. Regist. (Radiol.) St. Mary's Hosp. Lond. Prev: Regist. (Radiol.) St. Mary's Hosp. Lond.; Regist. (Med.) St. Geo. Hosp. Lond.

LAMB, Gavin William Andrew 2/1, 57 Clouston St., North Kelvinside, Glasgow G20 8QW — MB ChB 1998 Glas.; MB ChB Glas 1998.

LAMB, Georgina Catherine 11 Polepark Road, Dundee DD1 5QT — MB ChB 1998 Dund.; MB ChB Dund 1998.

LAMB, Graeme 24 Yoakley Road, London N16 0BA — MB BChir 1989 Camb.

LAMB, Ian 25 Swanston View, Edinburgh EH10 7DG — MB ChB 1986 Ed.

LAMB, Joan (retired) 17 Dalhousie Terrace, Morningside, Edinburgh EH10 5NE — MB BCh Wales 1959; MRCPath 1970; DObst RCOG 1961; FRCPath 1980.

LAMB, Joan Skeoch Hillbank Health Centre, Flat 1A, 1 Constitution Street, Dundee DD3 6NF Tel: 01382 221976 Fax: 01382 201980 — MB ChB 1980 Dundee.

LAMB, Joanna Kathryn Renmoor, 1 Heathside Road, Moor Park, Northwood HA6 2EE — MB BS 1982 Lond.; DRCOG 1985. Prev: GP Hayes Middlx.

LAMB, Joanna Louise Haworth (Surgery), 41 Broomwood Road, St Paul's Cray, Orpington BR5 2JP Tel: 01689 832454; 4 Inglewood Copse, Bickley, Bromley BR1 2BB — MB BS 1979 Lond.; BSc (1st cl. Hons.) Lond. 1976, MB BS 1979; MRCGP 1983; DRCOG 1982. (St. Thos.) GP St. Pauls Cray. Prev: Ho. Phys. St. Thos. Hosp. Lond.

LAMB, Joanne Mary University Hospital, Queen's Medical Centre, Nottingham NG7 2UH Tel: 0115 924 9924; 9 Leigh Close, West Bridgford, Nottingham NG2 7TN Tel: 0115 981 5537 — MB BS 1984 Lond.; FRCA 1991. Cons. Anaesth. Univ. Hosp. Nottm.

LAMB, John Richard Mill House, Offchurch, Leamington Spa CV33 9AP Tel: 01926 422489 — MB ChB 1955 Sheff.; MRCGP 1967; DObst RCOG 1957. (Sheff.) Hosp. Pract. (Orthop.) Warwick Dist. Gen. Hosp., Warks. Prev: Clin. Asst. (Orthop.) Warneford Gen. Hosp. Leamington Spa; Ho. Surg. Accid. & Orthop. Dept. & Ho. Phys. Roy. Infirm. Sheff.; SHO Univ. Unit Obst. City Gen. Hosp. Sheff.

LAMB, John Tunstall 34 Gledhow Lane, Roundhay, Leeds LS8 1SA Tel: 0113 266 8891; 34 Gledhow Lane, Roundhay, Leeds LS8 1SA Tel: 0113 266 8891 — MB ChB 1948 Ed.; FRCR 1975;

FFR 1960; DMRD Eng. 1957; DMRT Ed. 1955. Socs: (Ex-Pres.) Brit. Soc. Neuroradiol.; (Ex-Pres.) N. Eng. Neurol. Assn.; Hon. Mem. Amer. Soc. Neuroradiol. Prev: Sen. Lect. (Radiodiag.) Univ. Leeds; Cons. Radiol. Gen. Infirm., St. Jas. Univ. Hosp. Leeds & Pinderfields Hosp. Wakefield; Vis. Prof. Neuroradiol. Univ. Hosp. Pennsylvania, Philadelphia.

LAMB, Professor Joseph Fairweather (retired) Department of Biology & Preclinical Medicine, Bute Medical Buildings, St Andrews KY16 9TS Tel: 01334 463542 Fax: 01334 463537 Email: jfl@st.andrews.ac.uk — MB ChB Ed. 1955; FRSE 1985; PhD Ed. 1960, BSc (Hons. Physiol.) 1957; FRCP Ed. 1983. Med. Adviser Appeals Serv.; Governor Rowett Research Inst. Aberd. Prev: Chandos Prof. Physiol. Univ. St. And.

LAMB, Katherine 17 Dalhousie Terrace, Edinburgh EH10 5NE — MB BS 1996 Newc.

LAMB, Kenneth Siegfried Robertson 16 Winton Drive, Kelvinside, Glasgow G12 0QA — MB ChB 1981 Dundee; FFA RCS Eng. 1986. Cons. Anaesth. Stobhill Hosp. Glas. Prev: Cons. Anaesth. Groote Schuur Hosp., Cape Town, RSA; Sen. Regist. (Anaesth.) Vict. Infirm. Glas.; Regist. (Anaesth.) W.. Infirm. Glas.

LAMB, Kirsten Mary Davenport House Surgery, Bowers Way, Harpenden AL5 4HX Tel: 01582 767821 Fax: 01582 769285; 9 Lyndhurst Drive, Harpenden AL5 5QW — MB BChir 1979 Camb.; MRCGP 1983; DRCOG 1981; DCH Eng. 1980.

LAMB, Mr Martin Piers United Lincolnshire Hospitals NHS Trust, Lincoln County Hospital, Greetwell Road, Lincoln LN2 5QY Tel: 01522 573261 Fax: 01522 573640; Dunston House, Front St, Dunston, Lincoln LN4 2ES Tel: 01526 320175 Fax: 01526 323239 Email: mplamb@uk-consultants.co.uk — MB BS 1969 Lond.; MRCS Eng. LRCP Lond. 1969; FRCOG 1989, M 1976; DObst RCOG 1971. (Lond. Hosp.) Cons. O & G Co. Hosp. Lincoln; Clin. Teach. Univ. Nottm.; Lead Clin. Cancer Servs. United Linc. Hosp. NHS. Trust.

LAMB, Nicholas Charles Castle Hill Surgery, Castle Hill Gardens, Torrington EX38 8EU Tel: 01805 623222 Fax: 01805 625069; Kingscott House, Kingscott, Torrington EX38 7JW Tel: 01805 23976 — MB BS Lond. 1976; MRCGP 1981; DRCOG 1978. (Lond. Hosp.) GP Trainer Devon. Prev: Sqdn. Ldr. RAF Med. Servs.; GP Train. Scheme RAF Germany.

LAMB, Nicola Jane Uplands, Mill Lane, Framingham Pigot, Norwich NR14 7QF — MB BS 1998 Lond.; MB BS Lond 1998.

LAMB, Peter Desmond (retired) Exton House, Exton, Exeter EX3 0PZ Tel: 01392 874176 — MRCS Eng. LRCP Lond. 1952. Prev: GP Exeter.

LAMB, Peter James 17 Dalhousie Terrace, Edinburgh EH10 5NE Tel: 0131 447 5079 — MB BS 1994 Newc.; FRCS (Eng.) Lond. 1998.

LAMB, Philippa Marguerite 21 Old Sun Wharf, 40 Narrow St., Limehouse, London E14 8DG Email: rkanaga@sghms.ac.uk — MB BS 1990 Lond.; BSc Lond. 1987; MRCP (UK) 1994; FRCR 1997. (Char. Cross and Westm.) Specialist Regist. (Radiol.) Roy. Lond. Hosps.

LAMB, Mr Robert Jeremy Eye Department, West Suffolk Hospital, Hardwick Lane, Bury St Edmunds IP33 2QZ Tel: 01284 763131; St. Edmunds Hospital & Nursing Home, St. Mary's Square, Bury St Edmunds IP33 2AA Tel: 01284 701371 — MB BS 1972 Lond.; FRCS Ed. 1979; MRCS Eng. LRCP Lond. 1972; FRCOphth 1988; DO Eng. 1975. (Lond. Hosp.) Cons. Ophth. W. Suff. Hosp. Gp. & Newmarket Gen. Hosp. Prev: Sen. Specialist (Ophth.) RAF Med. Br.; Sen. Regist. (Ophth.) Leeds Gen. Infirm.

LAMB, Roy William (retired) Chapel Lane Cottage, Chapel Lane, Minchinhampton, Stroud GL6 9DL — MB BS Lond. 1956; DObst RCOG 1959; DA Eng. 1960. Prev: GP Stroud.

LAMB, Sheena Gardiner 3 Broomiknowe Park, Bonnyrigg EH19 Tel: 0131 663 8113 — MB ChB 1968 Ed. (Ed.) Med. Off. Lothian Health Bd. Prev: Paediat. Ho. Phys. Elsie Inglis Matern. Hosp. Edin.; Ho. Surg. & Ho. Phys. Bruntsfield Hosp. Edin.

LAMB, Stephanie Nicole Chapel Lane Cottage, Chapel Lane, Minchinhampton, Stroud GL6 9DL — MB BS 1990 Lond.; DRCOG 1994.

LAMB, Steven Richard 36 Herne Road, Petersfield GU31 4DP — MB ChB 1994 Auckland.

LAMB, Sydney Graham Stephen (retired) 49 Stoneydeep, Twickenham Road, Teddington TW11 8BL Tel: 020 8977 8519 — MB ChB 1951 Birm; DPH Eng. 1954. Cons. Phys. Dept. Infec. Dis. S. & W. Middlx. Hosps. Isleworth; Sen. Lect. in Communicable Dis. UCL; Sen. Lect. Infec. Dis. Char. Cross & W.m. Med. Sch. Lond.; Recognised Teach. Univ. Lond.; Cons. in Smallpox DHSS. Prev: Regist. Infec. Dis. Unit, St. Geo. Hosp. Lond.

LAMB, William Hedworth The General Hospital, Bishop Auckland DL14 6AD Tel: 01388 454000 Fax: 01388 454107 Email: w.h.lamb@ncl.ac.uk — MB BS 1976 Newc.; MD (Distinc.) Newc. 1987; FRCP Lond. 1994; FRCP Ed. 1992; FRCPCH 1997. (Newc.) Cons. Paediat. Gen. Hosp. Bishop Auckland; Hon. Lect. Paediat. Newc-u-Tyne; Cons Paediat diabetologist Roy. Vict. Infirm Newcatle Upon Tyne. Prev: Sen. Regist. (Paediat.) Newc.; Project Ldr. MRC Dunn Nutrit. Unit, Keneba The Gambia.

LAMB, William Lindsay, TD (retired) c/o Anderson Strathean, 48 Castle st, Edinburgh EH2 3LX Tel: 0131 332 2185 — MB ChB 1926 Ed.; MB ChB Ed. (2nd Cl. Hnrs.) 1926; FRCP Ed. 1932. Prev: Phys. i/c Wards Roy. Infirm. Edin.

LAMB, Mr William Robert 40 Linden Way, Boston PE21 9DS Tel: 01205 364358 — MB BCh BAO 1946 Dub.; FRCSI 1949; FFA RCS Eng. 1955. Prev: Cons. Anaesth. Boston Gp. Hosps.

LAMB, William Theodore Canterbury House, 191 Huntingdon Road, Cambridge CB3 0DL Tel: 01223 276144 Fax: 01223 276871 — MB BS 1965 Lond.; MA Camb. 1978; MRCS Eng. LRCP Lond. 1965; BDS Lond. 1961; FDS RCS Eng. 1968, LDS 1960. (Guy's) Emerit. Cons. Oral & Maxillofacial Surg. Addenbrooke's Hosp. Camb. & P'boro Dist. Hosp.; Assoc. Lect. Fac. Clin. Med. Univ. Camb. Socs: Fell. Internat. Assn. Oral & Maxillofacial Surgs.; Fell. Brit. Assn. Oral & Maxillofacial Surg.; Eur. Assn. Cranio-Maxillo. Surg. Prev: Sen. Regist. (Clin. Dent. Surg. & Oral Surg.) Guy's Hosp. Lond. & Plastic & Jaw Injuries Centre, Q.V.H., E. Grinstead; Ho. Surg. & Cas. Off. Guy's Hosp. Lond.

LAMB, Yvonne Jean SmithKline Beecham Pharmaceuticals, Welwyn Garden City AL7 1EY — MB BS 1981 Lond.; MFPM RCP (UK) 1988. Dir. Clin. Developm. SmithKline Beecham Welwyn Garden City.

LAMBA, Harpal Singh Jefferiss Wing, St Mary's Hospital, Praed St., London W2 1NY Tel: 020 7886 6666 Fax: 020 7886 6645; Flat 5, 3rd Floor, 39 Maclise Road, London W14 0PR Email: pauldoc@dircon.co.uk — MB BS 1994 Lond.; BSc (Hons.) Lond. 1991; MRCP (UK) Oct 1997; Dip. GU. Med.1998. (Lond. Hosp. Med. Coll.) Specialist Regist. (HIV & Genitourin. Med.) St. Mary's Hosp. Lond. Prev: SHO (Infec. Dis. & Trop. Med.) N.wick Pk. Hosp.; SHO (HIV Med.) Middlx. Hosp. Lond.; SHO (GUM) Mortimer Market Centre Lond.

LAMBA, K S Weston Favell Health Centre, Weston Favell Centre, Northampton NN3 8DW Tel: 01604 415157 Fax: 01604 407472 — MB BS 1958 Punjabi U; MB BS 1958 Punjabi U.

LAMBA, Mandeep Singh 3 Arrowhead Court, James Lane, London E11 1NT — MB BS 1984 Delhi.

LAMBA, Manubhai Karsanbhai Colindeep Lane Surgery, 61 Colindeep Lane, Colindale, London NW9 6DJ Tel: 020 8205 6798 Fax: 020 8200 5242 — MB BS 1976 Bombay; LRCP LRCS Ed. LRCPS Glas. 1980; DRCOG 1983.

LAMBAH, Ian Roy 11 Pennhouse Avenue, Penn, Wolverhampton WV4 4BG — LRCP LRCS 1945 Ed.; LRCP LRCS Ed. LRFPS Glas. 1945. (Roy. Colls. Ed.) Socs: BMA. Prev: Capt. RAMC Graded Specialist in Anaesth.; Ho. Phys. & Surg. S.. Gen. Hosp. Edin.; Anaesth. EMS Nuneaton.

LAMBAH, Paul North End Cottage, Whitgreave Lane, Great Bridgeford, Stafford ST18 9SJ Tel: 0178 575468 — MRCS Eng. LRCP Lond. 1942; MA Camb.; DO Eng. 1962. (Camb. & Westm.) Prev: Ho. Surg. W.m. Hosp.; Regist. Wolverhampton Eye Infirm.

LAMBAH, Paul Alexander North End Cottage, Whitgreave Lane, Great Bridgeford, Stafford ST18 9SJ — MB ChB Manch. 1993; FRCS Ed. Oct 1997. SHO Plastic Surg. Univ. Hosp. Manch.

LAMBALLE, Alan Kedward (retired) 11 Dickens Wynd, Durham DH1 3QR Tel: 0191 386 3782 — MB BS 1940 Durh.; DMRD Eng. 1947. Prev: Cons. Radiol. Middlesbrough & Newc. RHA.

LAMBALLE, Deirdre Patricia Holmeside, 64 Cambridge Road, Linthorpe, Middlesbrough TS5 5HG Tel: 01642 817248 — MB ChB 1966 Manch. (Manch.) SCMO S. Tees Community & Ment. Health NHS Trust.

LAMBALLE, John Linthorpe Road Surgery, 378 Linthorpe Road, Middlesbrough TS5 6HA Tel: 01642 817166 Fax: 01642 824094; Holmeside, 64 Cambridge Road, Middlesbrough TS5 5HG Tel:

01642 817248 — MB ChB 1965 Manch.; DObst RCOG 1968. (Manch.) Socs: BMA.

LAMBALLE, Philip Saville Medical Group, 7 Saville Place, Newcastle upon Tyne NE1 8DQ Tel: 0191 232 4274 Fax: 0191 233 1050 — MB BS 1985 Newc.; FRCP 1987; MRCGP 1992. Clin. Asst. (ENT) Freeman Hosp. Newc.u.Tyne. Socs: BATS; Med. Soc. Ball Comm.

LAMBDEN, Pamela May The Yews, Hare Lane, Ashley, New Milton BH25 5AF Tel: 01425 611868 — LRCP LRCS 1952 Ed.; FRCP Ed. 1972 M 1960; LRCP LRCS Ed. LRFPS Glas. 1952. (Ed.) Prev: Med. Asst. (Cardiol.) United Norwich Hosps.; Ho. Surg. & Ho. Phys. King Edwd. VII Hosp. Windsor; Med. Regist. ChristCh. & W. Norwich Hosps.

LAMBDEN, Paul William St Paul International Insurance Company Ltd, St Paul House, 61-63 London Road, Redhill RH1 1NA Tel: 01737 787936 Fax: 01737 786728 Email: paul_lambden@stpaul.com; 61 Tolmers Road, Cuffley, Potters Bar EN6 4JG — MRCS Eng. LRCP Lond. 1975; BSc Lond. 1972, MB BS 1975, BDS 1969; FDS RCS Eng. 1973, L 1969; DRCOG 1979. (Guy's) Prev: SHO (Gen. Med. & O & G) FarnBoro. Hosp. Kent.

LAMBE, Cheryl Jayne Totten 28 Davigdor Road, Hove BN3 1RB — MB BS 1996 Lond.

LAMBE, Dympna Elizabeth 50 Glen Road, Belfast BT11 8BG — MB BCh BAO 1989 Belf.

LAMBE, Maeve Breige Dundalk Street Surgery, 53 Dundalk Street, Newtownhamilton, Newry BT35 0PB Tel: 028 3087 8204 Fax: 028 3087 8196 Email: mmurphy761@aol.com; 172 Lower Dromore Road, Warrenpoint, Newry BT34 3LN Tel: 016937 73919 — MB BCh BAO 1986 Belf.; MRCGP 1990; DRCOG 1988. (Qu. Univ. Belf.) GP; GP Tutor, S.. Bd.

LAMBERT, Anne Margaret 59 High Street, Irthlingborough, Wellingborough NN9 5GA Tel: 01933 650593 Fax: 01933 653641; Warren Grange, Bythorn, Huntingdon PE28 0QU Tel: 01832 710178 — MB ChB 1982 Leic. GP Princip.

LAMBERT, Mr Anthony Wayne, Surg. Cdr. RN Department of Vascular Surgery, Level 4, Derriford Hospital, Plymouth Tel: 01752 517536 Fax: 01752 792537 Email: anthony.lambert@phnt.swest.co.uk; 16 Health Park Avenue, Cardiff Tel: 01752 769557, 02920 751718 — MB BS 1985 Lond.; MS 1998; FRCS Eng. 1992; Dip. Sports Med. Scotl. 1996; Intercol.Exam.Gen.Surg. 1999. (Charing Cross Hospital Medical School) Cons. Gen. and Vasc. Surg. Lead Clician Paediatric Gen. Surg., Derriford Hosp. Plymouth; Med. Off. RN. Socs: Vasc. Surgic. Soc. GB & Irel.; Brit. Assn. Sport. Med; Europ. Soc. of Vasc. & EndoVasc. Surg.s. Prev: Specialist Regist. (Surg.) Roy. United Hosp.; Regist. (Gen. Surg.) RN Hosp. Haslar; Princip. Med. Off. HMS Invincible.

LAMBERT, Barbara Anne 20 Bentfield Drive, Prestwick KA9 1TT — MB ChB 1973 Dundee.

LAMBERT, Barry Glenn 22 Shepherd Gardens, Abingdon OX14 5PR — MB BCh 1997 Wales.

LAMBERT, Brian West Road Surgery, 9 West Road, Annfield Plain, Stanley DH9 7XT Tel: 01207 214925 Fax: 01207 214926 — MB ChB 1980 Manch.; MRCGP 1987; DCH RCP Lond. 1989; Cert. Family Plann. JCC 1988; DRCOG 1988. GP Anfield Plain & Stanley. Prev: Trainee GP Caersws Powys VTS; SHO (Geriat. Med.) Manor Hosp. Walsall.; SHO (Rheumat.) W. Suff. Hosp. Bury St. Edmonds.

LAMBERT, Brian Edward, Surg. Capt. RN 12 Monckton Road, Alverstoke, Gosport PO12 2BQ Tel: 01705 503044 — MB ChB St. And. 1967; FRCOG 1989, M 1973; ECFMG Cert 1967; MBA 1994. (St. And.) Healthcall Soton. (GP Deputising Serv.). Prev: Med. Personnel Off. to Med. Dir. Gen. (RN); Cons. (O & G) RN; Ho. Surg. & Ho. Phys. (Profess. Unit) Dundee Roy. Infirm.

LAMBERT, Caroline Jane Church View Surgery, 5 Market Hill, Hedon, Hull HU12 8JE Tel: 01482 899348; 59 Souttergate, Hedon, Hull HU12 8JR — MB ChB 1976 Manch.; DRCOG 1976; DRCOG 1978.

LAMBERT, Charles Graham, Col. late RAMC Retd. Penydyffryn, Maentwrog, Blaenau Ffestiniog LL41 4HT Tel: 01766 590296 — MRCS Eng. LRCP Lond. 1952. (Liverp.)

LAMBERT, Christopher 37 Alwyne Road, London N1 2HW — MB BS 1998 Lond.; MB BS Lond 1998.

LAMBERT, Christopher Michael Rheumatic Diseases Unit, Western General Hospital, Crewe Road, Edinburgh EH4 2XU Tel: 0131 537 1805 Fax: 0131 558 7147; 18 Regent Terrace, Edinburgh EH7 5BS Tel: 0131 556 8490 Fax: 0131 558 7147 Email: michael.lambert@pipemedia.co.uk — MB BS 1983 Newc.; MRCP (UK) 1987; FRCP Ed 1997; MD Edin. 1999. Cons. Phys. Rheum. W.. Gen. Hosp. Trust Edin. & Vis. Cons. (Rheum.) Borders Gen. Hosp. Melrose; Cons. (Rheum.) Murrayfield Hosp. Edin.; Hon. Sen. Lect. Univ. Edin.; Vis. Prof. St. Geo. Med. Sch. Grenada, W. Indies. Socs: Fell. Roy. Soc. Med.; (Counc.) Roy. Coll. Phys. Edin. (Chairm. Coll. Mem. Prev: Regist. (Rheum.) Rheum. Dis. Unit Univ. Edin.; SHO Rotat. (Gen. Med.) Roy. United Hosp. Bath.

LAMBERT, Mr David Northern Vascular Centre, Freeman Hospital, Newcastle upon Tyne NE7 7DN Tel: 0191 223 1268 Fax: 0191 223 1225; Cedar Lodge, 30 Lodge Close, Hamsterley Mill, Rowlands Gill NE39 1HB Tel: 01207 542088 — MB BS 1977 Newc.; BA Camb. 1974; MD Newc. 1989; FRCS Eng. 1982. Cons. Vasc. Surg. Freeman Hosp. Newc. u. Tyne; Lect. (Surg.) Univ. Newc. u. Tyne. Socs: Surg. Research Soc. & Vasc. Surg. Soc. Prev: Cons. Surg. Roy. Vict. Infirm. Newc.; Sen. Research Assoc. (Surg.) Univ. Newc. u. Tyne; Sen. Regist. (Surg.) N.. RHA.

LAMBERT, David Hammond (retired) Riversleigh, Staithe St., Bubwith, Selby YO8 6LS Tel: 01757 288355 — MB ChB 1940 Leeds.

LAMBERT, Deryck Michael Denys, MBE (retired) 18 Ashley Rise, Ashley, Tiverton EX16 5PW Tel: 01884 243372 Fax: 01884 243372 Email: derickjill@aol.com — MB ChB Ed. 1951; FRCGP 1977, M 1971. Prev: Sen. Med. Off. DHSS.

LAMBERT, Elizabeth Jane 1 Hillside, Awbridge Hill, Awbridge, Romsey SO51 0HF — MB ChB 1986 Leeds.

LAMBERT, Elizabeth Loudon 17 Alicia Court, Bury St Edmunds IP33 2BB — MB ChB 1947 Ed.; MRCP Ed. 1959. (Ed.) Socs: E. Anglian Thoracic Soc. & Soc. Occupat. Med. Prev: Company Dr. Baxter Healthcare Ltd. Thetford.; Med. Asst. Thoracic Dept. W. Suff. Gen. Hosp. Bury St. Edmunds & Newmarket Gen. Hosp.; SHMO Norwich Chest Clinic.

LAMBERT, Frederick Roy 47 Castle Street, Portchester, Fareham PO16 9PZ Tel: 01705 377496 — MB BChir 1948 Camb. (Guy's) Socs: BMA. Prev: Regist. (O & G) Lewisham Hosp. Lond.

LAMBERT, George Leslie (retired) 53 Bassett Crescent W., Bassett, Southampton SO16 7DW — MB BS 1941 Lond.; MRCS Eng. LRCP Lond. 1938. Prev: GP Leicester & Nuneaton

LAMBERT, Godfrey Meyer 1 Birch House, Lingwood Close, Bassett, Southampton SO16 7GH — MB BS 1957 Sydney.

LAMBERT, Hannah Eva (retired) Copelands, 24 Copperkins Lane, Chesham Bois, Amersham HP6 5QF Tel: 0124 03 21007 — MB BS Lond. 1957; FRCR 1976; FRCOG 1981, M 1963, DObst 1959; DMRT Eng. 1973. Hon. Sen. Lect. Roy. Postgrad. Med. Sch. Lond.; Co-ordinator N. Thames Ovary Gp. Prev: Cons. Radiother. & Oncol. Hammersmith Hosp. Lond.

LAMBERT, Professor Harold Philip Greenfields, 69 Christchurch Road, London SW14 7AN Tel: 020 8876 1156 — MB BChir Camb. 1949; MD Camb. 1955; FRCP Lond. 1968, M 1953; FRCPCH (Hon.) 1996; FRCPath 1991; FFPHM RCP (UK) 1983, M 1976. (Camb. & Univ. Coll. Hosp.) Emerit. Prof. Microbial. Dis. Univ. Lond; Vis. Prof. Lond. Sch. Hyg. & Trop. Med. Socs: Fell. Infect. Dis. Soc. Amer.; Assn. Phys. Prev: Teale & Marc Daniels Lects Roy. Coll. Phys. Lond.; Sen. Censor Roy. Coll. Phys. Lond.; Cons. Phys. St. Geo. Hosp. Lond. & SW Thames RHA.

LAMBERT, Heather Joan Department of Paediatrics, Royal Victoria Infirmary, Queen Victoria Road, Newcastle upon Tyne NE1 4LP Tel: 0191 232 5131 — MB ChB 1981 Bristol; PhD Newc. 1993; MRCP (UK) 1985. Cons. Paediat. Nephrol. & Paediat. Roy. Vict. Infirm. Newc. u. Tyne.

LAMBERT, Ian Kenneth 11 Fourth Avenue, Blackpool FY4 2ET Tel: 01253 404089 — MRCS Eng. LRCP Lond. 1965; BSc (Physiol.) Lond. 1962, MB BS 1966. (St. Geo.) AKC; Sen. Med. Off. DHSS. Prev: Ho. Phys. Dorset Co. Hosp.; Ho. Surg. Glenroyd Hosp. Blackpool; Flight Lt. RAF Med. Br.

LAMBERT, Joan Ellen Maude (retired) 14 Holly Lodge Gardens, Highgate, London N6 6AA Tel: 020 8340 7725 — MB BS 1954 Lond.; MRCS Eng. LRCP Lond. 1943; FRCOG 1964, M 1949. Prev: Cons. O & G Barking Hosp. & King Geo. Hosp. Lond.

LAMBERT, John Ronald Caradoc House, 5 Burnham Road, Epworth, Doncaster DN9 1BU — MB ChB 1969 Birm.; MRCP (U.K.) 1973; FRCP Lond. 1987. Cons. (Rheum.) Doncaster Roy. Infirm.

Socs: Brit. Soc. Rheum. & Med. Disabil. Soc. Prev: Sen. Regist. (Rheum. & Rehabil. Med.) Yorks. RHA.

LAMBERT, Katherine Elizabet 35 Moorside S., Newcastle upon Tyne NE4 9BD — MB ChB 1998 Leeds.

LAMBERT, Kathryn Heather Queen Elizabeth Hospital, Sherrif Hill, Gateshead NE9 6SX — MB ChB 1989 Manch.; FFAEM 2001; MSc 2000; MRCP (UK) 1992. (Manchester) Regist. (A & E Med.) N. Region.

LAMBERT, Kathryn Jean 684 Chatsworth Road, Chesterfield S40 3NU Tel: 01246 567239 — MB ChB 1971 Sheff.; DObst RCOG 1974. Asst. GP Chesterfield; Clin. Med. Off. (Child Health) N. Derbysh. HA; Clin. Asst. (Diabetes) Chesterfield & N. Derbysh. Roy. Hosp. Trust.

LAMBERT, Lynn Alison Catherine Good Hope NHS Trust, Rectory Road, Sutton Coldfield B75 7RR Email: lambchopper85@hotmail.com — MB ChB 1985 Birm.; PhD Birm. 1980; MRCP (UK) 1988; DTM & H RCP Lond. 1988; FRCP 1999. (Birm.) Cons. Phys. Good Hope Hosp. Birm. Socs: Brit. Geriat. Soc. Prev: Clin. Lect. (Geriat. Med.) Univ. Birm.; Regist. (Med.) N. Staffs. Roy. Infirm. Stoke-on-Trent; Regist. (Renal Med.) Qu. Eliz. Hosp. Birm.

LAMBERT, Malcolm Timothy EHF NHS Trust, Uxbridge Road, Southall UB1 3EU — MB ChB 1979 Manch.; MRCPsych 1985. Cons. Psychiat. Ealing, Hammersmith & Fulham Heathcare NHS Trust. Prev: Lect. St. Mary's Hosp. Med. Sch. Lond. W2.; Cons. Psych. N.W. Lond. NHS Trust.

LAMBERT, Margaret Waugh 3 Kingsway, Tynemouth, North Shields NE30 2LY — MB ChB 1947 St. And.; BSc St. And. 1944, MB ChB 1947. (St. And.) Prev: Lect. Path. Univ. Durh. Med. Sch.

LAMBERT, Mr Mark Edward Lomond House, Raikes Road, Great Eccleston, Preston PR3 0ZA — MB ChB 1973 Sheff.; MD 1986; FRCS Ed. 1977. Cons. Surg. Vic. Hosp., Blackpool. Prev: Lect. (Surg.) Univ. Hosp. S. Manch.; Research Regist. (Med. Onocol.) Christie Hosp. & Holt Radium Inst., Manch.; Regist. (Surg.) Stepping Hill Hosp. Stockport & Withington Hosp.

LAMBERT, Mark Francis Gateshead and South Tyneside HA, Ingham House, Hobley Hill Road, South Shields NE33; 102 Northgate Lodge, Pontefract WF8 1LZ — MB BS 1987 Lond.; MFPHM RCP (UK) 1996; DTM & H Liverp. 1991. (Guy's Hosp.) Cons. Pub.Health.Mrd.Gateshead.S.Tyneside.HA. Prev: Regist. (Pub. Health Med.) Yorks. RHA.

LAMBERT, Mary Jane Children's Services, Leicester City West PCT, Bridge Park Plaza, Bridge Park Road, Thurmaston, Leicester LE4 8PQ Tel: 0116 2256742 — BM 1989 Soton.; MRCP (UK) 1995. (Soton. Univ.) Cons. Paediat. in Community Child Health. Socs: MRCPCH. Prev: Lect. (Paediat.) Univ. Hosp. Kuala Lumpur, Malaysia; SHO (Cardiol., Paediat., Gen. Med. & Neurol.) Soton. Gen. Hosp.; Sp. Regist. Paediat., Newc. Rotat.

LAMBERT, Mr Michael Allen Accident & Emergency Department, Norfolk & Norwich Hospital, Norwich NR1 3SR Tel: 01603 286286 Fax: 01603 286747; Model Farm, Tharston, Norwich NR15 2YR Tel: 01508 532170 Email: mikealambert@msn.com — MB BS 1981 Lond.; FRCS Eng. 1986; FFAEM 1994. (Middlx.) Cons. A & E Norf. & Norwich Health Care NHS Trust. Prev: Sen. Regist. (A & E) Char. Cross Hosp. Lond.; Regist. (A & E) Gen. Infirm. Leeds; Regist. (Surg.) Whittington Hosp. Lond.

LAMBERT, Michael Glenn Barnard Friarsgate Practice, Friarsgate Medical Centre, Friarsgate, Winchester SO23 8EF Tel: 01962 853599 Fax: 01962 849982; Rivendell, 8 Lynn Way, Kings Worthy, Winchester SO23 7TG Tel: 01962 883709 Email: lambert@worhty8.freeserve.co.uk — MB BS 1989 Lond.; MB BS London 1989; MRCGP 1994; DCH RCP Lond 1993; DRCOG 1992. (St. Thomas' Hospital Medical School) Prev: Trainee GP/SHO Roy. Hants. Co. Hosp. Winchester VTS; SHO (A & E) Kingston Hosp. Surrey; SHO (Orthop.) Waikato Hosp. Hamilton, NZ.

LAMBERT, Michelle Vanessa Blackberry Hill Hospital (Glenside Site), Manor Road, Fishponds, Bristol BS16 2EW Tel: 0117 965 6061; 22 Whitley Close, Yate, Bristol BS37 5XX — MB ChB 1987 Bristol; MRCPsych 1992. Regist. Rotat. (Psychiat.) Blackberry Hill Hosp. Bristol. Socs: Brit. Neuropsychiat. Assn.

LAMBERT, Norman Glenn (retired) 21 Thames Bank, Thames Road, Goring on Thames, Reading RG8 9AH Tel: 01993 779347 Fax: 01993 779347 — MB ChB Birm. 1959; MRCS Eng. LRCP Lond. 1959. Hosp. Pract. All St.'s Hosp. Drug Addic. Unit Birm. & Clin.; Asst. Addic. for S. Warks & Rugby. Prev: Princip. Rural Dispensing GP.

LAMBERT, Pamela Anne Brockley Chase, Cleeve, Bristol BS49 4PP Tel: 01275 462820 — MB BS 1973 Lond.; MRCS Eng. LRCP Lond. 1973; MRCGP 1979; DObst RCOG 1976. (St. Bart.) Clin. Asst. (Reproduc. Med. & Gyn. Endocrinol.) Avon AHA. St. Michaels Hosp. Bristol & Centre for Reproduc. Med.Colposcopy. Prev: SHO (Gyn.) Bristol Gen. Hosp.; SHO (Paediat. & Obst.) S.mead Hosp. Bristol.

LAMBERT, Patricia Mary 48 Broomleaf Road, Farnham GU9 8DQ Tel: 01252 722161 Email: pandalambert@compuserve.com — MB BCh Wales 1955; BSc Wales 1955; DCH Eng. 1960; DObst RCOG 1958. (Cardiff) Prev: Cons. Community Paediat. Loddon NHS Trust Basingstoke; Princip. Med. Off. (Child Health) Basingstoke & N. Hants. Health; Sen. Med. Off. Hants. CC.

LAMBERT, Peter Michael 10 Pethill Close, Earlswood, Plymouth PL6 8NL Tel: 01752 704121 — MB ChB 1955 Bristol; DPH 1961; FFCM 1979, M 1974. (Bristol) Prev: Lect. (Edipemiol.) Lond. Sch. Hyg. Trop. Med.; Sen. Med. Statistician Off. Populat. Censuses & Surveys; Cons. Pub. Health Med. Plymouth HA.

LAMBERT, Rachel Derrydown Clinic, St. Mary-Bourne, Andover SP11 6BS Tel: 01264 738368 — MB BS 1985 Lond.; MRCGP 1991; DRCOG 1989; DCH RCP Lond. 1988.

LAMBERT, Richard Anthony 2 Oaklands, Cradley, Malvern WR13 5LA — MB ChB 1991 Birm.; ChB Birm. 1991.

LAMBERT, Richard Charles Priestthorpe Medical Centre, 2 Priestthorpe Lane, Bingley BD16 4ED Tel: 01274 568383 Fax: 01274 510788 — MB ChB 1974 Leeds.

LAMBERT, Robert Bruce Hamilton Newtons, The Health Centre, Heath Road, Haywards Heath RH16 3BB Tel: 01444 412280 Fax: 01444 416943 — MB BCh 1973 Dublin; MB BCh Dub. 1973. (Dublin) GP Haywards Heath, W. Sussex.

LAMBERT, Robert George William 11 Stranmillis Park, Belfast BT9 5AU Tel: 028 682282 — MB BCh BAO 1980 Belf.; FRCR 1985. Sen. Regist. Radiol. Roy. Vict. Hosp. Belf. Prev: Ho. Off. & Regist. (Radiol.) Roy. Vict. Hosp. Belf.

LAMBERT, Robin George The Surgery, 15 West Town Road, Backwell, Bristol BS48 3HA Tel: 0117 462026 Fax: 0117 795609; Little Brock, 39 Uncombe Close, Backwell, Bristol BS48 3PU Tel: 01275 464461 — MB BS 1970 Lond.; MRCS Eng. LRCP Lond. 1970; DObst RCOG 1973. (St. Bart.) Prev: SHO (Paediat.) Bristol Roy. Hosp. Sick Childr.; SHO (Gen. Med.) St. Leonard's Hosp. Lond.; Ho. Surg. (Orthop.) St. Bart. Hosp. Lond.

LAMBERT, Roger John Brent House Surgery, 14 King Street, Bridgwater TA6 3ND Tel: 01278 458551 Fax: 01278 431116; Bramblings, Church Lane, Enmore, Bridgwater TA5 2DU — MB BS 1972 Lond.; MRCS Eng. LRCP Lond. 1971. (St. Bart.) Prev: Cas. Off. Cardiff Roy. Infirm.; Regist. (Gen. Pract.) Welsh Nat. Sch. Med. Cardiff; SHO (Paediat.) Univ. Hosp. Wales Cardiff.

***LAMBERT, Saba Maria** 265 Blackness Road, Dundee DD2 1RX Tel: 01382 642211 — MB ChB 1998 Dund.; MB ChB Dund 1998.

LAMBERT, Sara Katharine Salop Road Medical Centre, Salop Road, Welshpool SY21 7ER Tel: 01938 553118 Fax: 01938 553071; Fearnley Hey, Briggs Lane, Pant, Oswestry SY10 8LD Tel: 01691 830595 — MB BS 1987 Lond.; MRCGP 1991. Socs: BMA. Prev: GP Asst. Keswick, Cumbria.

LAMBERT, Sean Harvey 39 Knapps Close, Elburton, Plymouth PL9 8UX — MB ChB 1990 Leic.; MB ChB Leic. 1991; T(GP) 1996.

LAMBERT, Mr Simon Martin Problem Shoulder Unit, Royal National Orthopaedic Hospital, Brockley Hill, Stanmore HA7 4LP Tel: 020 8909 5727 Email: slambert@rnoh-tr.nthames.nhs.uk; Highview, Lady Meadow, Rucklers Lane, Kings Langley WD4 9NF Tel: 01923 265606 — MB BS 1984 Lond.; BSc (Hons.) Lond. 1981; FRCS (Orth.) 1993; FRCS Ed. 1989; FRCS Eng. 1989. (Char. Cross) Cons. Orthopaedic Surg., Problem Shoulder Unit, Roy. Nat. Orthopaedic Hosp., Stanmore; Cons. Orthopaedic Surg. & Hon Sen Lec., Roy. Free Hosp. Socs: Brit. Elbow & Shoulder Soc.; Brit. Trauma Soc.; Europ. Shoulder & Elbow Surg. Soc. Prev: Cons. Orthopaedic Surg., S.ampton Gen. Hosp.

LAMBERT, Susan Penelope Bentley House, Clungunford, Craven Arms SY7 0PN — MB ChB 1978 Leeds. Prev: Trainee GP Bradford VTS; Ho. Off. (Surg.) St. Luke's Hosp. Bradford; Ho. Phys. Bradford Roy. Infirm.

LAMBERT, Violet Mary Joyce 47 Castle Street, Portchester, Fareham PO16 9PZ Tel: 01705 377496 — MRCS Eng. LRCP Lond. 1947; DObst RCOG 1951. (Roy. Free)

LAMBERT, Mr William Gordon Department of Surgery, Chesterfield & North Derbyshire Royal Hospital, Chesterfield S44 5BL Tel: 01246 552314 Fax: 01246 552313; 684 Chatsworth Road, Chesterfield S40 3NU Tel: 01246 567239 — MB ChB 1971 Sheff.; FRCS Eng. 1976. Cons. Surg. & Exec. Med. Director. Prev: Sen. Regist. (Surgic.) Roy. Hallamsh. Hosp. Sheff.; Regist. (Surg. & Urol.) Roy. United & St. Martin's Hosps. Bath; Regist. (Surg.) Sheff. Roy. Infirm. & Sheff. Childr. Hosp.

LAMBERTON, Gillian Elizabeth 64 Lochside Road, Bridge of Don, Aberdeen AB23 8QW — MB ChB 1984 Glas.; MB ChB Glas. l984. Clin. Asst. (Geriat.) City Hosp. Aberd.

LAMBERTON, Margaret Hazel 100A Drumnaconagher Road, Crossgar, Downpatrick BT30 9JJ — MB BCh BAO 1984 Belf. Trainee GP St.field N. Irel.

LAMBERTON, Robert Brown Scotstown Medical Centre, Cairnfold Road, Bridge of Don, Aberdeen AB22 8LD Tel: 01224 702149 Fax: 01224 706688; 64 Lochside Road, Denmore Park, Bridge of Don, Aberdeen AB23 8QW — MB ChB 1982 Glas.; MRCGP 1986; DRCOG 1984; DCH RCPS Glas. 1985.

LAMBERTY, Mr Byrom George Harker Department Plastic Surgery, Addenbrooke's Hospital, Hills Road, Cambridge CB2 2QQ Tel: 01223 245151; The Old Vicarage, High St, Swaffham Prior, Cambridge CB5 0LD Tel: 01638 741150 Fax: 01638 743971 — MB BChir 1968 Camb.; MB BChir Camb. 1969; MA Camb 1969; FRCS Eng. 1974. Cons. Plastic Surg. Addenbrooke's Hosp. Camb.; Hon. Lect. Univ. Camb.; Civil Cons. (Plastic Surg.) RAF. Socs: Fell. Roy. Soc. Med. (Ex-Pres. Sect. Plastic Surg.); Brit. Assn. Plastics Surg.; Brit. Assn. Aesthetic Plastic Surgs. Prev: Lect. (Anat.) St. Bart. Hosp. & Univ. Lond.; Sen. Regist. (Plastic Surg.) NE Thames RHA.

LAMBERTY, Doreen Sara (retired) Croft House, Crawshawbooth, Rossendale BB4 8AJ Tel: 01706 214184 — MRCS Eng. LRCP Lond. 1940. Med. Off. Burnley Family Plann. Clinic. Prev: Regist. (ENT), Ho. Phys. & Ho. Surg. Vict. Hosp. Burnley.

LAMBERTY, Filiz The Old Vicarage, Swaffham Prior, Cambridge CB5 0LD — MD 1970 Istanbul; DA (UK) 1981. Clin. Asst. (Anaesth.) Addenbrooke's Hosp. Camb.

LAMBERTY, John Martin 2 Deanery Cottages, Malling Deanery, Lewes BN7 2JD Tel: 01273 476888 — MB BS 1976 Lond.; MRCS Eng. LRCP Lond. 1976; FFA RCS 1981. (Guy's) Cons. Anaesth. & Chronic Pain Managem. Roy. Sussex Co. Hosp. Brighton. Socs: Assn. Anaesth. Intractable Pain Soc. Prev: Sen. Regist. SW RHA; Clin. Fell. Hosp. Sick Childr. Toronto, Canada; Clin. Fell. Flinders Med. Centre Adelaide, Australia.

LAMBERTY, Norman Alister (retired) 27 Lakeside Road, Kirkcaldy KY2 5QJ Tel: 01592 203430 — MB ChB 1939 Ed.; MRCP Ed. 1951; FRCP Ed. 1998. Prev: Cons. Venereol. N. Yorks. AHA.

LAMBERTZ, Mr Matthias Manfred Rotherhams Hospital NHS Trust, Rotherham S60 24D Tel: 01226 383990, 01709 307165; Riverside Farm, Huddersfield Road, Barnsley S75 4DE — State Exam Med 1986 Aachen; MD Baden 1988; FRCS Ed. 1992. (Univ.Aachen Germany) Cons. Gen. Surg., Rotherham Hosp. NHS Trust. Socs: Assn. of Surg.s of GB & Irel.; Assn. of Upper Gastrolintestinal Surg.s.

LAMBIASE, David Pier Rayne Institute, Cardiovascular Sciences, St Thomas Hospital, London SE1 7EH — BM BCh 1992 Oxf.; BA (Physiol. Sci.) Oxf. 1989; MRCP (UK) 1995. Research.Fell. Cardiol.St Thomas.Hosp. Lond. Prev: SHO (Respirat. & Renal Med.) Hammersmith Hosp. Lond.; SHO Rotat. (Med.) St. Geo. Hosp. Lond.; Ho. Phys. (Gastroenterol.) N.wick Pk. Hosp.

LAMBIE, Aileen Mary Bountree, Glenfarg, Perth PH2 9NL — MB ChB 1995 Dundee. Paediat. SHO Altnagelvin Hosp. L'Derry.

LAMBIE, Anne Templeton (retired) 31 Midmar Gardens, Edinburgh EH10 6DY — MB ChB 1950 Ed.; MB ChB (Hons.) Ed. 1950; FRCP Lond. 1976, M 1954; FRCP Ed. 1965, M 1953. Prev: Sen. Lect. Med. Univ. Edin.

LAMBIE, Lilian 42 Piltdown Close, Hastings TN34 1UU — MB BS 1993 Lond.; MRCGP 1997; DFFP 1997; DCH RCP Lond. 1996. (St. Geos. Hosp.) GP Locum Hastings. Prev: GP/Regist. Hastings VTS.

LAMBIE, Stewart Hamilton 1 Savile Terrace, Edinburgh EH9 3AD — MB ChB 1994 Ed.

LAMBLEY, Julian Charles Gordon Stony Stratford Surgery, Market Square, Stony Stratford, Milton Keynes MK11 1YA Tel: 01908 565555 — MB BS 1973 Lond.; MRCS Eng. LRCP Lond. 1972; MRCGP 1977; DObst RCOG 1976. (St. Bart.)

LAMBOURN, John Overcliffe, Headland Road, Torquay TQ2 6RD — MB BS 1964 Lond.; DM Soton. 1979; MRCS Eng. LRCP Lond. 1964; FRCPsych 1990; MRCPsych 1975; DPM Eng. 1973; DObst RCOG 1966. (Guy's) Cons. Psychiat. (Psychogeriat.) Torbay Hosp. Torquay. Prev: Cons. Psychiat. (Psychogeriat.) Herrison Hosp. Dorchester; Hon. Lect. Soton. Univ. Med. Sch.

LAMBOURN, Robert John Seaton Hirst Health Centre, Norham Road, Ashington NE63 0NG Tel: 01670 813167 Fax: 01670 523889; Windsor House, 24 Front St, Guide Post, Choppington NE62 5LT Tel: 01670 531492 — MB ChB 1983 Bristol; MRCGP 1988; DA (UK) 1990; DRCOG 1989; Cert. Family Plann. JCC 1988; DCCH RCP Ed. 1987. (Bristol) GP Princip.; Trainer in Gen. Pract.

LAMBOURNE, Julie Elizabeth 26 Brookside Avenue, Wollaton, Nottingham NG8 2RD — BM BS 1989 Nottm.; PhD Nottm. 1987, BM BS 1989, BMedSci 1984. Regist. (Gen. Med., Diabetes & Endocrinol.) Nottm. Prev: SHO (Med.) Roy. Devon & Exeter Hosp.

LAMBOURNE, Paul The Wall House Surgery, Yorke Road, Reigate RH2 9HG Tel: 01737 224432 Fax: 01737 244616; 1 Ringley Park Avenue, Reigate RH2 7DW Tel: 01737 240967 — MB BS 1967 Lond.; DObst RCOG 1972. Prev: Ho. Surg. (Obst.) & Ho. Phys. St. Stephens Hosp. Fulham; Ho. Surg. W.m. Hosp.

LAMBOURNE, Pauline Jessica Mental Health Unit, Lister Hospital, Coreys Mill Lane, Stevenage SG1 4AB Tel: 01438 314333; Mole End, The Close, Hinxworth, Baldock SG7 5HS Tel: 01462 743234 — MB ChB 1972 Sheff.; DFFP 1994. (Univ. Sheff.) Staff.Grade. Psych. Lister.Hosps.tevenage. Socs: BMA; Affil. Roy.Coll.Psych. Prev: GP Med. Centre, Oman & Riyadh Armed Forces Hosp., Saudi Arabia.

LAMBOURNE, Vincent Alan 20 Shetland Close, Totton, Southampton SO40 8HY — MB ChB 1992 Bristol.

LAMBRECHTS, Hugo Amos c/o Drive F. J. Colesky, Mid Ulster Hospital, 59 Hospital Road, Magherafelt BT45 5EX — MB ChB 1993 Stellenbosch.

LAMBROS, Theos Alexander (retired) Greenhaven, Wapping, High St., Long Crendon, Aylesbury HP18 9AL Tel: 01844 208526 — MB ChB Manch. 1956. Clin. Asst. (Geriat.) Oldham HA; Assoc. Coll. GP & Manch. Med. Soc. Prev: SHO (Geriat. & Acute Med., & Psychiat.) & Ho. Off. (O & G) Oldham & Dist. Gen. Hosp.

LAMBTON, Mandy Cedars Surgery, 8 Cookham Road, Maidenhead SL6 8AJ Tel: 01628 620458 Fax: 01628 633270 — BM 1988 Soton.; MRCGP 1992; DFFP 1993. Clin. Asst. (Dermat.) Wexham Pk. Hosp. Slough. Prev: Trainee GP Wycombe Gen. Hosp. VTS; SHO (Med., Paediat. & O & G) Wycombe Gen. Hosp.

LAMDEN, Christopher St John Corinthian Surgery, St Paul's Medical Centre, 121 Swindon Road, Cheltenham GL50 4DP Tel: 01242 707777 Fax: 01242 707776; 35 Linden Close, Prestbury, Cheltenham GL52 3DX — MB BS 1980 Lond.; DCH RCP Lond. 1986; MRCGP 1988; DRCOG 1985. GP Cheltenham.

LAMDEN, Kenneth Henry South Lancashire HA, Grove House, Langton Brow, Eccleston, Chorley PR7 5PD Tel: 01257 495174 — MB ChB 1982 Liverp.; MSc (Pub. Health & Epidemiol.) Manch. 1993; FRCS Ed. 1988; MFPHM RCP (UK) 1994; DTM & H Liverp. 1986; Cert. Voc.Train.GP.1996. (Liverp) Cons. Communicable Dis. Control S. Lancs. HA.

LAMERTON, Mr Andrew John Lincoln & County Hospital, Greetwell Road, Lincoln LN2 5QY Tel: 01522 573298 Fax: 01522 573448 Email: andrewlamerton@ulh.nhs.uk; The Manor House, Church Lane, Cherry Willingham, Lincoln LN3 4AB Tel: 01522 751377 Fax: 01522 595536 — MB BS 1970 Lond.; FRCS Eng. 1974; MRCP (UK) 1974; MRCS Eng. LRCP Lond. 1970. (St. Mary's) Cons. Gen. & Vasc. Surg. Lincoln Co. Hosp.,united Lincs Hosps NHS trust; Cons. Gen. & Vasc. Surg. John Conpland Hosp. GainsBoro. Lincs. Socs: Lincoln Med. Soc.; Assn. Surg.; Vasc. Surgic. Soc. GB & Irel. Prev: Sen. Regist. (Cardiovasc. Surg.) St. Mary's Hosp. Lond.; Sen. Regist. (Genitourol.) W. Middlx. Univ. Hosp. Lond.; Research Fell. Irvine Laborat. St. Mary's Hosp. Lond.

LAMERTON, Richard Charles Hospice of The Valleys, Park Gate Business Centre, Morgan St., Tredegar NP22 3ND Tel: 01495 717277 Fax: 01495 724188; Brookfield, Tarrington, Hereford HR1 4HZ Tel: 01432 890341 Fax: 01432 890430 — MRCS Eng.

LRCP Lond. 1968; Cert. Prescribed Equiv. Exp. JCPTGP 1983. (St. Bart.) Med. Dir. Hospice of the Marches Tredegar. Prev: Med. Dir. Macmillan Domiciliary Serv. St. Joseph's Hospice Lond.; Med. Dir. New Age Hospice, Houston, Texas.

LAMERTON, Susan Mary Pencombe Hall, Pencombe, Bromyard HR7 4PA; the Vicarage, Marden, Hereford HR1 3EN Tel: 01432 880256 — MB BS 1981 Lond. Med. Adviser Pencome Hall Rest Home for Elderly. Prev: SHO (Gen. Surg.) Wanganvi Base Hosp. N. Zealand.

LAMEY, Philip John 19 Dalcholin, Holywood BT18 0HR — MB ChB 1982 Glas.; BSc (Hons.) Ed. 1975; DDS Ed. 1983, BDS 1977; FFD RCSI Dub. 1990; FDS RCPS Glas. 1985. Cons. & Sen. Lect. Oral Med. & Path. Glas. Dent. Hosp. & Sch.; Vis. Prof. Baylor Coll. Dent. & Med. Fac. Dallas, Texas. Prev: Lect. Oral Med. & Path. Glas.; Research Asst. Oral Med. & Path. Glas.

LAMKI, Harith Mohamed Nasser Royal Maternity Hospital, Grosvenor Road, Belfast BT12 6BB Tel: 01232 894606 Fax: 01232 235256 Email: harith.lamki@royalhospitals.n-i.nhs.uk; 1 Magheralave Park N., Lisburn BT28 3NL Tel: 01846 663296 — LRCPI & LM, LRSCI & LM 1961; LRCPI & LM, LRCSI & LM 1961; FRCOG 1980, M 1967; FRCPI 1997. Cons. O & G Roy. Matern. Hosp. Belf.

LAMMIE, George Alistair Neuropathology Laboratory, Alexander Donald Building, Western General Hospital, Crewe Road S., Edinburgh EH4 2XU Tel: 0131 537 1975 Fax: 0131 537 1013 Email: al@skull.dcn.ed.ac.uk — MB BChir 1986 Camb.; PhD Lond. 1992; MA Camb. 1986; MRCPath 1994. Sen. Lect. (Path.) Univ. Edin.; Hon. Cons. Neuropath. W.. Gen. Hosp. Edin. Socs: Brit. Atherosclerosis Soc.; Scott. Assn. Neurol. Scis.

LAMMIMAN, David Askey, CB, LVO, QHS, Surg. Rear-Admiral Magdella Cottage, St Michael's Road, St Helen's, Ryde PO33 1JY Tel: 01983 873160; 6 Claridge Court, Munster Road, London SW6 4EY Tel: 020 7731 8303 — MB BS 1957 Lond.; FFA RCS Eng. 1969; DObst RCOG 1962; DA Eng. 1962. (St. Bart.) Cons. Anaesth. Lond. Gyn. & Fertil. Centre. Prev: Med. Dir. Gen. (Naval); Surg. Rear-Admiral Support Med. Servs.; Med. off. RNH Haslar & Plymouth.

LAMMING, Christopher Edward Daniel Newbold Grange Farm, Burrough-on-the-Hill, Melton Mowbray LE14 2QY — BM BS 1991 Nottm.; MRCP 1996; DCH 1996; MRCPCH 1997. (Nottm.) SHO (Paediat. Haemat. & Oncol.) Birm. Childr. Hosp.; Specialist Regist. (Paediat. Oncol.) St. Jas. Univ. NHS Trust Leeds. Prev: SHO Profess. Unit. Med. Birm. Childr. Hosp.

LAMMING, Rachel Elizabeth Mary Rydings Hall Surgery, Church Lane, Brighouse HD6 1AT Tel: 01484 715324 Fax: 01484 400847; 25 Leconfield Garth, Follifoot, Harrogate HG3 1NF — MB ChB 1973 Sheff.; DObst RCOG 1975. Prev: SHO (Radiother.) W.on Pk. Hosp. Sheff.; Ho. Off. (Surg.) N.. Gen. Hosp. Sheff.; Ho. Off. (Med.) Roy. Infirm. Sheff.

LAMOND, Donald Norman Flat 3, Weaver House, 10 Barlow Moor Road, Manchester M20 6TR — MB ChB 1992 Manch.

LAMOND, Ian 192 Newton Road, Birmingham B43 6BX — LRCP LRCS 1946 Ed.; LRCP LRCS Ed. LRFPS Glas. 1946; MRCGP 1953. Prev: Capt. R.A.M.C.

LAMONT, Alan Department of Radiotherapy & Oncology, Southend Hospital, Westcliff on Sea SS0 0RY; 50 Hockley Road, Rayleigh SS6 8EB Email: dr.lamont@hospital.southend.nhs.uk — MB ChB 1979 Dundee; BMSc (Hons. 1st cl.) Dund 1976; MRCP (UK) 1982; FRCR 1987; FRCP Ed. 1998. Cons. (Radiother. & Oncol.) S.end Health Care NHS Trust.

LAMONT, Alison Margaret — MB ChB 1983 Ed.; FRCS Ed. 1988; MRCGP 1990; DRCOG 1990. Prev: Trainee GP W. Linton; SHO Rotat. (Surg.) Bangour Gen. Hosp. Broxburn & W.. Gen. Hosp. Edin.; SHO (O & G) Simpson Memor. Matern. Pavil. Edin.

LAMONT, Allison Margaret Riverside Medical Practice, Ballifeary Lane, Inverness IV3 5PW Tel: 01463 715999 Fax: 01463 718763 — MB ChB 1984 Glas.

LAMONT, Colin Alasdair Robertson (retired) The Old Parsonage, Stoughton, Chichester PO18 9JJ Tel: 0239 263 1269 Fax: 023 9263 1269 — MB ChB Ed. 1958; FRCOG 1979, M 1966. Hon. Clin. Teach. Univ. Soton.; Hon. Cons. Gyn. King Edwd. VII Hosp. Midhurst. Prev: Cons. O & G Portsmouth & SE Hants. Health Dist.

LAMONT, David Alwin West Cumberland Hospital, Hensingham, Whitehaven CA28 8JG — MB BS 1983 Newc. Cons. Psych.

LAMONT, Dennis Anderson (retired) 76 Ambrose Avenue, Colchester CO3 4LN Tel: 01206 549444 Fax: 01206 369910 — MB ChB Ed. 1948; MRCGP 1965; Cert Av Med MoD (Air) & CAA 1976; DObst RCOG 1956. Med. Adviser Complaints Coronor S. Essex HA; Local Treasury Med. Off.; Police Surg. Colchester. Prev: Civil Aviat. Auth. Med. Examr.

***LAMONT, Duncan Charles** 9 Rowan Bank, Scone, Perth PH2 6PU — MB ChB 1997 Aberd.; DRCOG 1999.

LAMONT, Mr Graham Lawrence Department of Paediatric Surgery, Royal Liverpool Childrens NHS Trust, Alder Hey, Liverpool L12 2AP Tel: 0151 228 4811 Email: graham.lamont@rich-tr.nwest.nhs.uk; 60A Graburn Road, Formby, Liverpool L37 3PB — MB ChB 1980 Glas.; DM Nottm. 1993; FRCS (Paediat.) 1994; FRCS Glas. 1984. Cons. Paediat. Surg. Roy. Liverp. Childr. NHS Trust. Prev: Sen. Regist. (Paediat. Surg.) Roy. Hosp. Sick Childr. Edin.

LAMONT, Helen Jean King Street Medical Practice, 144A King Street, Aberdeen AB24 5BD Tel: 01224 644463 Fax: 01224 630231; 27 Cairnaquheen Gardens, Aberdeen AB15 5HJ Tel: 01224 316774 Email: rabbieb@genie.w.uk — MB ChB 1982 Aberd.; DRCOG 1984; MRCGP 1994. (Aberdeen) Princip. in Gen. Pract.; GP audit facilitator GPCT Gramp; Clin. gov fac AICC Gramp. Prev: occ health doc RGTT; Staff grade med off BTS; GP Bolton.

LAMONT, Ian Cook (retired) 11 Queen's Gate, Clarkston, Glasgow G76 7HE Tel: 0141 638 4437 — MB ChB 1951 Glas. Prev: Clin. Asst. (Dermat.) Vict. Infirm. Glas.

LAMONT, Janet Elizabeth Thelma Golding Dr Unit, 92 Bath Road, Hounslow TW3 3EH Tel: 0208 577 9555 Fax: 0208 750 2260; Tel: 020 8894 3982 Fax: 020 8715 3160 — MB BS 1992 Lond.; 1988 BSc Lond.; MRCGP 2001; DRCOG 1996; DFFP 1995. (Char. Cross Hosp., Westm.) Asst. GP Retainer Scheme.

LAMONT, Monica Mary Bristol Breast Unit, Directorate of Surgery, Bristol Royal Infirmary, Bristol BS2 8HW Tel: 0117 928 4560; Poulton Lodge, Hazelwood Road, Sneyd Park, Bristol BS9 1PY — MB ChB 1976 Dundee; DFFP 1993; T(GP) 1991. Clin. Asst. (BrE. Surg.) Bristol Roy. Infirm.; Clin. Asst. Avon BrE. Screening Unit Bristol.

LAMONT, Mr Peter Marshall Directorate of Surgery, Bristol Royal Infirmary, Bristol BS2 8HW Tel: 0117 928 2810; Poulton Lodge, Hazelwood Road, Bristol BS9 1PY — MD 1985 Dundee; MA Oxf. 1989; MB ChB 1976; FRCS Eng. 1986; FRCS Ed. 1981; T(S) 1991. Cons. Surg. Bristol Roy. Infirm.; Hon. Sen. Clin. Lect. (Surg.) Bristol Univ. Socs: Eur. Soc. Vasc. Surg.; Coun. Mem. Vasc. Surg. Soc.; Edr.ial Sec. Surgic. Research Soc. Prev: Clin. Reader (Surg.) Oxf. Univ.; Sen. Regist. (Surg.) W.minster Hosp. Lond.; Price Research Fell. Univ. Louisville USA.

LAMONT, Phillipa Joy Flat 1, 20 Leigh St., London WC1H 9EW — MB BS 1982 Western Australia.

LAMONT, Ronald Francis Canmore, 31 Copperkins Lane, Amersham HP6 5QF Tel: 01494 432056 Fax: 01494 432056 Email: r.camont@ic.ac.uk; Canmore, 31 Copperkins Lane, Amersham HP6 5QF — MB ChB 1977; BSc (Med. Sci.) Ed. 1974; DM Soton. 1989; FRCOG 1996, M 1983. (Ed.) Cons. O & G N.wick Pk. Hosp.; Reader, Imperial Coll. Sch. of Sci., Technol. & Med. Lond. Socs: Blair Bell Res. Soc.; Gyn. Res. Soc.; Brit. Med. Ultrasound Soc. Prev: Hon. Sen. Lect. Inst. Obst. & Gyn. RPMS Hammersmith Hosp. Lond.; Lect. (Human Reproduc. & Obst.) Univ. Soton.; Research Fell. Hammersmith Hosp. Lond.

LAMONT, William Inglis (retired) Findrum, 148 Sinclair St., Helensburgh G84 9AT Tel: 01436 671127 Email: inglisamont@cwcom.net — MB ChB Ed. 1955; FRCP Ed. 1983, M 1967; MRCGP 1963; AFOM 1980; DIH Eng. 1980; DObst RCOG 1960. Prev: Dir. Univ. Health Serv. Soton. Univ.

LAMPARD, Ronald 4 James Gavin Way, Oadby, Leicester LE2 4UE; Hornby Cottage, 1 Lodge Lane, Danby, Whitby YO21 2NX Tel: 01287 660920 — MB ChB 1956 Ed.; MFFP 1994. (Ed.) Surg. (Vasectomy) Family Plann. Assn. Leicester. Socs: Fell. Roy. Med. Soc. Prev: SHO (O & G) City Hosp. Nottm.; SHO (Phys.) Stockton & Thornaby Hosp.; Ho. Phys. W.. Gen. Hosp. Edin.

LAMPARELLI, Mr Michael Joseph 39 Spruce Park, Cumberland Road, Bromley BR2 0EH Email: michael@lamparelli.freeserve.co.uk — BM 1992 Soton.; FRCS Eng. 1996. Specialist Regist. Rotat. (Gen. Surg.) S. Thames (W.). Socs: Fell. Roy. Soc. Med.; Assn.Surg.Train; Affil. Mem. Assn. Coloprol.G B & Irel. Prev: SHO (Gen. Surg.) St. Geo. Hosp. Lond.

LAMPE, Hans 30 Grehound Road, Sutton SM1 4BE — State Exam Med 1984 Munich.

LAMPERT, Irene 38 Clarendon Road, Birmingham B16 9SE — State Exam Med 1986 Munich.

LAMPLUGH, Geoffrey Department of Anaesthesia, Royal Liverpool Hospital, Prescot St., Liverpool L7 8XP Tel: 0151 709 0141 — MB ChB 1971 Liverp.; FFA RCS Eng. 1976. (Liverp.) Cons. Anaesth Roy. Liverp. Univ. Hosp. Socs: BMA & Assn. Anaesth. Prev: Cons. Cardiothoracic Anaesth. BRd.green Hosp. Liverp.; Fell. (Cardiovasc. Anaesth.) Methodist Hosp. Texas Med. Centre, Houston USA; Lect. (Anaesth.) Univ. Liverp.

LAMPLUGH, Marc 2 Hilderthorpe, Nunthorpe, Middlesbrough TS7 0PT — MB ChB 1997 Manch.

LAMPTEY, Christopher 936 Harrow Road, Wembley HA0 2PY — MRCS Eng. LRCP Lond. 1986. Trainee GP Lewisham Hosp. VTS. Prev: Ho. Surg. Whittington Hosp. Lond.; Ho. Phys. Orsett Hosp. Grays.

LAMS, Boris Edward Alexander 5 Pickwick Road, London SE21 7JN; 7a Boxhall Road, Dulwich, London SE21 7JS Tel: 020 7737 1149 Email: borislams@aol.com — MB ChB 1991 Camb.; ChB Camb. 1991. Specialist Regist. Respirat. Med. Socs: MRCP.

LAMS, Edward Julien 3 Fox Hill, London SE19 2UL — MB BS 1996 Lond.

LAMS, Peter Michael 5 Pickwick Road, London SE21 7JN — MB BS 1967 Lond.; FRCR 1975.

LAMUREN, Mr Taiwo Edward 11 Lessar Court, Lessar Avenue, London SW4 9HN — MB BS 1985 Ibadan; FRCS Ed. 1993.

LAN KENG LUN, Kong Fa St Margaret's Hospital, Breast Screening Unit, The Plain, Epping CM2 8QQ Tel: 01253 781126, 01279 827046 — MD 1986 St. Etienne France; FRCR 1992 Royal College of Radiologists; FRCR 1992; DMRD Eng. 1990. (Univ. de St. Etienne, France) Cons. Radiol. St. Margt.'s Hosp. BrE. Screening Unit, P.ss Alexander NHS Trust, Harlow; Quality Assur. Radiologist for E.ern Region NHSBSP (BrE. Screening Program.). Prev: Sen. Regist. Rotat. (Radiol.) Yorks. RHA; Cons. Radiologist Rotherham Gen. Hosp.; Cons. R. Basildon & Thurrock Hosp. Essex.

LAN-PAK-KEE, Lan Yew Kioon 1J Mitchell Road, Cumbernauld, Glasgow G67 1AF — MB ChB 1974 Glas.

LANASPRE, Effie Southampton General Hospital, Tremona Road, Southampton SO16 6YD — BM 1998 Soton.; BM Soton 1998.

LANCASHIRE, Barbara June 4 Nant Clwyd Park, Crosslanes, Marchwiel, Wrexham LL13 1XX — MB BCh 1989 Wales.

LANCASHIRE, Graham Stewart Tonge Moor Health Centre, Thicketford Road, Bolton BL2 2LW Tel: 01204 521094 — MB ChB 1975 Manch.; MRCGP 1984; DRCOG 1977.

LANCASHIRE, Mr Martin John 16 Corbett Avenue, Droitwich Spa, Droitwich WR9 7BE Tel: 01905 773103 — MB BS 1982 Lond.; MD Lond. 1996; FRCS Eng. 1987. (St. Mary's) Cons. Urol. Alexandra Hosp. Redditch. Prev: Regist. (Urol.) S.mead Hosp. Bristol & Glos. Roy. Hosp.; Regist. (Urol.) Manch. Roy. Infirm.

LANCASHIRE, Roger William George, DSC, Surg. Cdr. RN Retd. (retired) 137 Palatine Road, West Didsbury, Manchester M20 3YA Tel: 0161 445 3005 — BM BCh 1936 Oxf.; MA Oxf. 1936; MRCS Eng. LRCP Lond. 1934. Prev: Ho. Surg. Specials Dept. Manch. Roy. Infirm.

LANCASHIRE, Simon Christian Jonathan 2 Vicars Road, Manchester M21 9JA — MB ChB 1991 Manch.

LANCASTER, Christopher John 40 Fox Lane, Leyland, Preston PR25 1HA Tel: 01772 494843 — MB BS 1993 Lond.; BA (Hons) Oxf. Physiol 1990; DRCOG 1997. (St Bartholomews London) GP Regist. The Surg. Shevington Wigan. Socs: BMA; MDU.

LANCASTER, Donna Louise Department of Paediatric Haematology and Oncology, Great Ormond Street Hospital, London WC1N Tel: 020 7829 8831; Flat A, 49 Beresford Road, Highbury, London N5 2HR Tel: 020 7226 2164 Email: donna.lancaster@btopenworld.com — MB ChB 1989 Sheff.; MD 2000; BMedSci Sheff. 1988; MRCP (UK) 1994. Locum Cons. Paediatric Haematologist/Oncologist, Gt. Ormond St. Lond. Socs: MRCPCH; ASPH/O. Prev: Clin. Fell. Paediatric Haemat./Oncol. Hosp. for Sick Childr., Toronto; Specialist Regist. (Paediat. Oncol.) Gt. Ormond St. Hosp. Lond.; Clin. Lect. (Paediat. Oncol.) St. Bart. Hosp. Lond.

LANCASTER, Mr Jeffrey Leslie Deptment of Otolaryngology, Head & Neck Surgery, Arrowe Park Hospital, Arrowe Park Road, Upton, Wirral L49 5PE; 23 Holbrook Close (Stock Meadows Estate), Grt. Sankey, Warrington WA5 3SE — MB ChB 1993 Liverp.; FRCS (Ed.) 1997. (Liverpool) Socs: Fell. Roy. Coll. Surgs. Edin.; BAORL. Prev: SHO Rotat. (ENT) Liverp.

LANCASTER, Mr John Francis 9 Parsonage Road, Long Ashton, Bristol BS41 9LL — MB ChB 1981 Bristol; FRCS Eng. 1985. Research Fell. Dept. Surg. Univ. Bristol.

LANCASTER, John Garth 14 The Gardens, East Carlton, Market Harborough LE16 8YG Tel: 01536 771396 — MB BChir 1958 Camb.; MA Camb. 1958; MRCS Eng. LRCP Lond. 1957; MRCGP 1974; DCH Eng. 1964; DObst RCOG 1962. (Camb. & King's Coll. Hosp.) Prev: GP Corby; Hosp. Pract. (Allergy) Kettering Gen. Hosp.

LANCASTER, Johnathan Mark 13 Woodfield Road, Talbot Green, Pontyclun CF72 8JF — MB BCh 1992 Wales; BSc Wales 1991, MB BCh 1992. SHO (O & G) Addenbrooke's Hosp. Camb. Prev: Ho. Off. (Pharm.) Univ. Hosp. Wales; Ho. Off. (Urol.) Cardiff Roy. Infirm.

LANCASTER, Jonathan 7 Fontwell Drive, Tilehurst, Reading RG30 4QR — MB BCh 1994 Wales.

LANCASTER, Katharine Louise Manor Farm House, Preston Gubbals, Shrewsbury SY4 3AN — MB BS 1997 Lond.

LANCASTER, Michael John 17 Melbourne House, 27-29 Collingham Road, London SW5 0NU — MB BS 1967 Lond.; MRCS Eng. LRCP Lond. 1967; FFA RCS Eng. 1971.

LANCASTER, Paul Simon 9 Shipham Close, Leigh WN7 5DX — MB ChB 1998 Manch.; MB ChB Manch 1998.

LANCASTER, Philip Anthony Holly House, Horse Shoe Hill, Great Hormead, Buntingford SG9 0NL — MB BS 1984 Lond.

LANCASTER, Richard 54 Wimpole Street, London W1M 7DF Tel: 020 7487 3504 Fax: 020 7486 7797; 3 Alexander Street, London W2 5NT Tel: 020 7727 7936 Fax: 020 7792 4460 — MB 1965 Camb.; BChir 1964; PhD Lond. 1972; FRCP Lond. 1979, M 1966. (Middlx.) Cons. Phys. St. Mary's & St. Chas. Hosps. Lond.; Sen. Lect. (Clin. Pharmacol.) St. Mary's Hosp. Med. Sch. Lond. Socs: (pres) Med. Soc. Lond.; Pharmacol. Soc. Prev: Lect. (Clin. Pharmacol.) Middlx. Hosp. Med. Sch. Lond.; Regist. Med. Unit & Ho. Surg. Middlx. Hosp. Lond.

LANCASTER, Tessa Victoria 4 The Gorseway, St. Helens Road, Hayling Island PO11 0DH — MB ChB 1975 Leeds; FRCR 1981. Cons. Radiol. Portsmouth & S.E. Hants. HA.

LANCASTER, Timothy Ross Division of Public Health & Primary Care, Institute of Health Sciences, Old Road, Oxford OX3 7LF Tel: 01865 319125 Fax: 01865 511635 Email: tim.lancaster@dphpc.ox.ac.uk; 5 Walton Crescent, Oxford OX1 2JG — MB BS 1983 Lond.; MSc 1991; BA Oxf. 1977; MRCP (UK) 1986; MRCGP 1992. (Guy's) Princip. in Gen. Pract.; Hon. Sen. Clin. Lect. Oxf. Univ. Prev: Trainee GP Oxf.; Research Fell. Harvard Med. Sch., USA.

LANCASTLE-SMITH, Jonathan 43 Mears Ashby Road, Earls Barton, Northampton NN6 0HQ — BM BS 1985 Nottm.

LANCE, Nicholas Stephen York House Medical Centre, Heathside Road, Woking GU22 7XL; 6 Meadow Rise, Knaphill, Woking GU21 2LJ Tel: 01483 487877 — MB BS 1985 Lond.; DRCOG 1988; DGM 1998. (St. Thos.) Clin. Asst. (Geriat.) Woking Community Hosp.; Clin Asst. St Peter's Hosp., Pk.inson's Dis. Clinic. Prev: Trainee GP Dartford & Gravesham HA; Ho. Phys. St. Peters Chertsey; Ho. Surg. Joyce Green Hosp. Dartford.

LANCEFIELD, Kristin Sarah Strathmore House, The Drive, Brighton Road, Banstead SM7 1DE — MB BS 1993 Lond.; MRCPysch. Specialist Regist.

LANCELEY, Colin Paul Ablett Unit, Glan Clwyd Hospital, Bodelwyddan, Rhyl LL18 5UJ Tel: 01745 585484 Fax: 01745 534405 — MRCS Eng. LRCP Lond. 1977; MRCPsych 1984. Cons. Psychiat. Conwy & Denbighsh. NHS Trust. Prev: Cons. Psychiat. BRd.green Hosp. NHS Trust Liverp.; Sen. Regist. (Psychiat.) St. Thos. Hosp. Lond.; Regist. (Psychiat.) St. Geo. Hosp. Lond.

LANCER, Jack Michael Rotherham District General Hospital, Moorgate Road, Rotherham S60 2UD Tel: 01709 304560 Fax: 01709304496 — MB ChB 1978 Sheff.; FRCS Eng. (Otol.) 1984; MRCS Eng. LRCP Lond. 1978; DLO 1981. Cons. ENT Rotherham Gen. Hosps. Trust; cons Doncaster Roy. infirm and Montague hosp nhs trust. Socs: Fell. Roy. Soc. Med.; N. Eng. Otolaryngol. Soc.; Eur. Acad. Facial Plastic Surg. Prev: Sen. Regist. (ENT) Roy. Hallamsh. & Childr. Hosp. Sheff.; Janet Nash Clin. Fell. (ENT) Univ. Hosp. Zürich,

Switz.; Regist. (ENT) Roy. Hallamsh. Hosp. N.. Gen. & Childr. Hosp. Sheff.

LANCER, Kenneth Leslie Highfield Clinic, Highfield Lane, St Albans AL4 0RJ Tel: 01727 852992 Fax: 01727 853936 Email: kl@lmgmedical.co.uk; Timbers Clinic, Brookshill, Harrow HA3 6RT Tel: 020 8954 3964 Fax: 020 8420 7301 — MB BS 1959 Lond.; MRCS Eng. LRCP Lond. 1959. (King's Coll. Hosp.) Chairm. The Lancer Med. Gp.; JP.; Clin. Asst. (Neurol.) Roy. Free Hosp. Lond.; Examr. Roy. Insur. Gp., Equity & Law Assur. Soc. Ltd., Standard Life Assur. Co. & other Assur. Cos. Socs: Fell. Roy. Soc. Med. (Mem. Sects. Neurol. & Med.); Fell. Med. Soc. Lond.; Assn. Study Obesity. Prev: Ho. Off. (Anaesth. & Cas. Off.) King's Coll. Hosp.; Ho. Phys. (Gen. Med. & Neurol.) Centr. Middlx. Hosp.; Sen. Cas. Off. Roy. Free Hosp.

LANCER, Raymond The Carewell Medical Centre, 74 Kenton Road, Kenton, Harrow Tel: 07970 910 458 Fax: 07092 234 374 Email: gunneray@yahoo.com — MB BS Lond. 1968; DFFP 1993; DObst RCOG 1970. (Lond. Hosp.) Hypnotherapist; Private GP; Medico-Legal Reports Expert. Socs: Brit. Soc. Med. & Dent. Hypn. Prev: SHO (Psychiat.) Warneford Hosp. Oxf.; SHO (Obst.) Roy. Berks. Hosp. Reading; Ho. Phys. & Ho. Surg. Whipps Cross Hosp. Lond.

LAND, Helen Ruth 1 Skottowe Crescent, Great Ayton, Middlesbrough TS9 6DS — MB BS 1986 Newc.; MRCGP 1990. (Newc.) Asst. G.P., Middlesbrough.

LAND, Janet Hopes Fulton Street Surgery, 94 Fulton Street, Glasgow G13 1JE Tel: 0141 959 3391 Fax: 0141 950 2692; 22 Rowallan Gardens, Broomhill, Glasgow G11 7LJ — MB ChB 1978 Glas.; MRCGP 1982; DRCOG 1980.

LAND, John Melville The National Hospital for Neurology & Neurosurgery, Queen Square, London WC1N 3BG Tel: 020 7833 9391 Fax: 020 7833 9391 Email: jland@ion.ucl.ac.uk — BM BCh 1980 Oxf.; PhD (Biochem.) Lond. 1975, BSc (1st cl. Hons. Biochem.) 1971; MBA 1997. (Oxf.) Cons. Chem. Path. Nat. Hosp.,UCLH (nhs) Trust; Sen. Lect. (Neurochem.) Inst. Neurol. Socs: BMA; Biochem. Soc.; Soc. Study of Inborn Errors of Metab. Prev: SHO (Med.) John Radcliffe Hosp. Oxf.; Salters Fell. Univ. Pennsylvania 1975; SHO (Neurol.) Hammersmith Hosp. Lond.

***LAND, Moira-Jane Mackay** 15 Suffolk Road, Edinburgh EH16 5NR Tel: 0131 667 2614 — MB ChB Aberd. 1995.

LAND, Nicholas Mark Flatts Lane Centr, Flatts Lane, Novamby, Middlesbrough TS6 0SX Tel: 01642 283448; 1 Skottowe Crescent, Great Ayton, Middlesbrough TS9 6DS — MB BS 1986 Newc.; MA Camb. 1987; MRCPsych 1990. (Newcastle) Cons. Psychiat. S. Tees Community & Ment. Health Trust Middlesbrough; Cons psychiat and assoc med dir Tees & N. E. York NHS Trust Midd. Prev: Sen. Regist. (Psychiat. of Ment. Handicap) N.gate Hosp. Morpeth.

LAND, Ruth Catherine Society of Brothers, Darvell Community, Robertsbridge TN32 5DR — MB BS 1939 Lond.

LANDAU, David Benzion Dept. of Radiotherapy, St Thomas' Hospital, Lambeth Palace Rd, London SE1 7UH Tel: 020 7928 9292 Ext: 1915 Fax: 020 7928 9968 Email: david.landau@gstt.sthames.nhs.uk — MB BS 1990 Lond.; FRCR Lond. 1997; MRCP Lond. 1993. (CXWMS) Cons. Clin. Oncologist, Guy's and St Thomas' NHS Trust, Lond.; Cons. Clin. Oncologist, Qu. Eliz. Hosp., Woolwich. Prev: Sen. Regist.Roy. Marsden Hosp., Lond.; Sen. Regist. Roy. Surrey Co. Hosp. Guildford; Regist. Char. Cross Hosp. Lond.

LANDAU, Hans Helmuth (retired) 27 Elgood House, St. John's Wood, London NW8 9TG Tel: 020 7722 2001 — LRCP LRCS 1935 Ed.; MD Leipzig 1915; LRCP LRCS Ed. LRFPS Glas. 1935. Prev: Surg. Univ. Clin. For Surg. Charité Hosp. Berlin.

LANDAU, Joyce Estelle (retired) 8 Coniston Court, Stonegrove, Edgware HA8 7TL Tel: 020 8958 2460 — MRCS Eng. LRCP Lond. 1944; MRCGP 1964.

LANDAU, Rosalind Belmont Health Centre, 516 Kenton Lane, Harrow HA3 7LT Tel: 020 8863 0911 Fax: 020 8863 9815; Ye Shiah, 6 Sheraton Close, Elstree, Borehamwood WD6 3PZ — MB BS 1981 Lond.; BSc (Hons.) Lond. 1978; MRCP (UK) 1985; MRCS Eng. LRCP Lond. 1981; DRCOG 1986. (Westm. Med. Sch.)

LANDAU, Sally Celia 22 Donnington Road, Harrow HA3 0NA; 18 Harvist Road, Queens Park, London NW6 9SD Tel: 020 8969 7711 — MB BS 1980 Lond.; MRCP (UK) 1983; DCH RCP Lond. 1983; MRCGP 1986; DRCOG 1986. (Lond. Hosp.) Prev: Regist. (Paediat.) P.ss Alexandra Hosp. Harlow; SHO (Neonat.) St. Geo. Hosp. Tooting; SHO (Paediat.) W.m. Hosp. Lond.

LANDE, Ronald Jeffrey (retired) 99 Woodsford Square, Addison Road, London W14 8DT Tel: 020 7602 4309 — MB ChB 1951 Manch.; DPH Lond. 1954. Prev: Recognised Specialist (Venereol. & Genito-urin.) (BUPA & PPP).

LANDECK, Amir Upper Maisonette, 43 Chalcot Road, Primrose Hill, London NW1 8LS — State Exam Med 1990 Berlin; T(GP) 1996.

LANDEG, Mr Mervyn Russell Westgate House, Davies Avenue, Porthcawl CF36 3NW Tel: 01656 782805 — MB ChB 1956 Birm.; FRCS Glas. 1963; DLO Eng. 1960; DObst RCOG 1958. Prev: Cons. ENT Surg. Mid-Glam. Hosp. Gp.

LANDEN, Justin John 31 Marldon Cross Hill, Marldon, Paignton TQ3 1PB; 2 Harringcourt House, 18 Harrington Lane, Pinhoe, Exeter EX4 8PG — BM 1993 Soton.

LANDER, Mr Anthony David Birmingham Children's Hospital, Steelhouse Lane, Birmingham B4 6NH; 106 Upper St Mary's Road, Bearwood, Birmingham B67 5UN Tel: 01634 56711 Email: a.d.lander@bham.ac.uk — MB BS 1985 Lond.; FRCS (Paediat.); FRCS Ed. 1990; FRCS Eng. 1990; DCH RCP Lond. 1988; PhD 1996. Sen. Lect. Paediat. Surg. Univ. Birm.; Hon cons. Paed. Surg. Brmh child hosp. Prev: SHO (Orthop. & Gen. Surg.) Medway Hosp. Gillingham Kent.; SHO (Paediat. Surg.) Birm. Childr. Hosp.; SHO (Cas.) Kings Coll. Hosp.

LANDER, Beryl Joyce (retired) 1 High Meadow Road, Kings Norton, Birmingham B38 9AP Tel: 0121 458 2579 — MB BS 1951 Lond.; MRCS Eng. LRCP Lond. 1951. Prev: Med. Asst. (Neurosurg.) Midl. Centre for Neurosurg. & Neurol.

LANDER, Deborah Kay Wellesley Road Surgery, 7 Wellesley Road, Chiswick, London W4 4BJ Tel: 020 8995 4396 Fax: 020 8994 4314; 50 Magnolia Road, Strand-on-the-Green, Chiswick, London W4 3RB — MB BS 1989 Lond.; BSc (Hons.) Lond. 1986; MRCGP 1994; DRCOG 1991. (Univ. Coll. Middlx. Hosp. Med. Sch.)

LANDER, Derrick Alan Mortimer Surgery, Victoria Road, Mortimer Common, Reading RG7 1HG Tel: 0118 933 2436 Fax: 0118 933 3801; Stanton, 63 Mortimer Road, Mortimer, Reading RG7 3SL Tel: 0118 933 3084 Fax: 0118 933 1701 Email: derrick@lander100.freeserve.co.uk — MB BS 1972 Lond.; MRCS Eng. LRCP Lond. 1972; MRCGP 1976; DCH Eng. 1975; DObst RCOG 1974. (Roy. Free) Socs: Reading Path. Soc. Prev: Trainee GP Exeter VTS; Ho. Surg. Lister Hosp. Stevenage; Ho. Phys. Roy. Free Hosp. Lond.

LANDER, Joan Neilson 7 Savill Crescent, Wroughton, Swindon SN4 9JG — MB ChB 1968 Glas.; FFA RCS Eng. 1973. (Glas.) Cons. (Anaesth.) Bahrain Defence Force Hosp. Bahrain. Socs: Intractable Pain Soc. & Brit. Med. Acupunc. Soc. Prev: Cons. (Anaesth.) Al Corniche Hosp. Abu Dhabi; Cons. (Anaesth.) Cuckfield Hosp.; Civil Cons. (Anaesth.) P.ss Alex. RAF Hosp. Wroughton.

LANDER, Michael Ian Bryntirion, Seymour Road, Plymouth PL3 5AS Tel: 01752 664710 — MB BChir Camb. 1958; BA Camb. 1953; MRCS Eng. LRCP Lond. 1957; DO Eng. 1968; DCH Eng. 1964; DTM & H Eng. 1961. (Lond. Hosp.) Socs: Fell. Roy. Soc. Trop. Med. & Hyg.; Med. Contact Lens Assn. Prev: Ho. Surg. (Surg. & Gyn.) W. Lond. Hosp.; Med. Off. & Lect. Min. Health N. Nigeria; Asst. Ophth. Surg. W. Eng. Eye Infirm. Exeter.

LANDER, Rosalie Marion Goldsworth Park Health Centre, Denton Way, Woking GU21 3LQ Tel: 01483 767194 Fax: 01483 766042; 7 Oakfields, West Byfleet, Weybridge Tel: 01932 348252 — MB ChB 1962 Ed. (Ed.) Prev: Ho. Phys. W.. Gen. Hosp. Edin.; Ho. Surg. E.. Gen. Hosp. Edin.; Govt. Med. Off. Salisbury, Rhodesia.

LANDER, Stephen John Park Street Surgery, Park St., Bagshot GU19 5 Tel: 01276 76333; 24 Castle Road, Camberley GU15 2DS — MB BS 1976 Lond.; BSc (Biochem.) Lond. 1973, MB BS 1976; MRCGP 1984; DObst 1980; Cert Family Plann. JCC 1981. (St. Thos.) Prev: Ho. Phys. Med. Unit St. Thos. Hosp. Lond.

LANDERS, Mrs Aideen Mary Moorfields Eye Hospital, City Road, London EC1V 2PD; 26 Cambridge Raod, Twickenham TW1 2HL — MB ChB 1987 Bristol; FRCOphth 1993. Specialist Regist. Moorfields Eye Hosp. Socs: BMA. Prev: Regist. (Ophth.) Chelsea & W.m. Hosp.; Regist. Luton & Char. Cross Hosp. Lond.; SHO (Ophth.) Roy. Berks. Hosp. Reading & Dundee.

LANDES, Alain Henri Leon Aristide, 27 Bircholt Road, Liphook GU30 7PQ — MB BS 1973 Lond.; FFA RCS Eng. 1978. (St. Geo.)

Cons. Anaesth. Qu. Mary's Hosp. Roehampton. Prev: Sen. Regist. Atkinson Morley Hosp. Lond.; Sen. Regist. St. Geo. Hosp. Lond.; Regist. Qu. Mary's Hosp. Childr. Carshalton.

LANDES, Caren Jane Little Copse, Bollinway, Hale, Altrincham WA15 0NZ — MB ChB 1997 Birm.

LANDFESTER, Cornelia Molecular Immunogenetics Laboratory, 17th Floor Guy's Tower, Guy's Hospital, St Thomas St., London SE1 9RT — State Exam Med. Freiburg 1990.

LANDHAM, Mr Thevanandham Lal Disablement Services Centre, Windmill Road, Gillingham ME7 5YX Tel: 01634 830000 Fax: 01634 401065; Larkrise, Hearts Delight Road, Tunstall, Sittingbourne ME9 8JA — MB BS 1974 Sri Lanka; FRCS Ed. 1981; LRCP LRCS Ed. LRCP Glas. 1980; FRCP (UK) 1998. Clin. Dir. Rehabil. Directorate Disablem. Servs. Centre Kent; Cons. Rehabil. Med. Kent. Socs: Brit. Soc. Rehabil. Med. Prev: Regist. (Orthop. Surg.) Roy. Sussex Co. Hosp. Brighton; Fell. (Paediat. Orthop.) Mass. Gen. Hosp., USA; Hon. Sen. Regist. (Rehabil. Med.) W. Midl. RHA.

LANDMAN, Rachel Sian 14 Charnwood Grove, West Bridgford, Nottingham NG2 7NT — BM BS 1997 Nottm.; BMedSci Nottm. SHO (Paediat.), Derby Childr.s Hosp. Prev: SHO A+E, Derby Roy. Infirm.; SHO (Gen. Surg.) QMC Nottm.; Jun. Ho. Off. (Gen. Med.) QMC Nottm.

LANDO, John Kerr Motherwell Health Centre, 138-144 Windmill Street, Motherwell ML1 1TB Tel: 01698 263288 Fax: 01698 251267; 14 Doon Street, Motherwell ML1 2BN Tel: 01698 268285 Fax: 01698 268285 — MB ChB 1978 Glas.; AFOM RCP Lond. 1994. Socs: Soc. Occupat. Med.; Brit. Soc. Med. & Dent. Hypn. (Scotl.).

LANDON, Christine Rosemary Spring Grove House, Chapel Hill, Clayton West, Huddersfield HD8 9NH — MB ChB 1981 Leeds; MRCOG 1987; MD 1996; FROCG 1999. Cons. & Sen. Lect. (Gyn.) Gen Infirm. Leeds. Socs: Internat. Continence Soc.; Menopause Soc.; adol Gyn.

LANDON, Professor David Neil (retired) Institute of Neurology, Queen Square, London WC1N 3BG — MB BS 1960 Lond.; BSc (Hons. Anat.) Lond. 1957; MRCS Eng. LRCP Lond. 1959. Prev: Prof. Neurocytol. Inst. Neurol. Lond.

LANDON, Heather Mary Tower House Surgery, 169 West Wycombe Road, High Wycombe HP12 3AF Tel: 01494 529646; 55 St Leonards Road, Amersham HP6 6DS Tel: 01494 721200 — MB BS Durh. 1963; DObst RCOG 1965. (Durham) GP.

LANDON, John 535 Willoughby House, Barbican, London EC2Y 8BN — MD Lond. 1965, MB BS 1955; FRCP Lond. 1977, M 1971; MRCS Eng. LRCP Lond. 1955. (St. Mary's) Emerit. Prof. Chem. Path. St. Bart. Hosp. Lond.

LANDON, Keith Isle of Wight Health Care NHS Trust, St. Mary's Hospital, Newport PO30 5TA; Bowcombe Lodge, Plaish Lane, Carisbrooke, Newport PO30 3HU Tel: 01983 524329 — MB BS 1967 Lond.; FRCA 1991; FANZCA 1992. (Guy's) Cons. Anaesth. St Mary's Hosp. Isle of Wight Health Care NHS Trust.

LANDON, Richard Antony Kings House, Kings Avenue, Rhyl LL18 1LT Tel: 01745 344189 Fax: 01745 351150 — MB ChB 1976 Manch.

LANDOR, Elise Catherine L'Auge, Rue Des Raisies, St Martin, Jersey JE3 6AS — MB ChB 1991 Bristol. SHO (Paediat.) Conquest Hosp. Hastings. Prev: SHO (O & G) All St.s Hosp. Chatham; SHO (A & E) Frenchay Hosp. Bristol.

LANDRAY, Martin Jonathan Department of Medicine, University of Birmingham, Queen Elizabeth Hospital, Birmingham B15 2TH Email: m.j.landray@bham.ac.uk — MB ChB 1992 Birm.; MRCP (UK) 1995. (Univ. Birm.) Lect. (Clin. Pharmacol.) Univ. Birm. Prev: Regist. (Gen. Med.) Horton Gen. Hosp. Banbury; SHO (Gen. Med.) Glos. Roy. Hosp.

LANDRAY, Robert Grange Cottage, High St., Bampton OX18 2JW Tel: 01993 850223 Fax: 01993 852735; Synexus, Clinical Trials Centre, 551:11 Harwell, Didcot OX11 0RA Tel: 01235 434747 — MB ChB Birm. 1961; D.Occ.Med. RCP Lond. 1995. (Birm.) Indep. Occupat. Phys. Occupat. Health Servs. Oxf.; Occupat. Phys. Rutherford Appleton Laborat. Oxf. Socs: Soc. Occupat. Med. Prev: Med. Analyst Benefits Agency Lond.; GP Oxf.; Med. Off. Corporate Health Slough.

LANDSBOROUGH, David (retired) 64 Cordrey Gardens, Coulsdon CR5 2SQ Tel: 020 8668 1396 Fax: 020 8736 9831 — MB BS 1937 Lond.; MD Lond. 1939; FRCP Lond. 1975, M 1947; MRCS Eng. LRCP Lond. 1937. Prev: Supt. & Neurol. Christian Hosp. Changhua, Taiwan.

LANDSMEER, Ronald Ernst 2 Beech Cottage, Church St., Stoke by Naylands, Colchester CO6 4QH — Artsexamen 1982 Amsterdam.

LANDY, Paul Barrie South Park Medical Practice, South Park, Sevenoaks TN13 1ED Tel: 01732 744200 Fax: 01732 744206; The Walled Gdn., 118 Kippington Road, Sevenoaks TN13 2LN — MB BS 1978 Lond.; MRCS Eng. LRCP Lond. 1977; D.Occ.Med. 1996. (St. Barth.)

LANDY, Sara Jane Springmount, 114 Belfast Road, Magheralin, Craigavon BT67 0RP Tel: 01762 329333 Fax: 01762 329333 Email: springmnt@aol.com — MB BS 1985 Lond.; MRCP (UK) 1990. (St. Bart.) Assoc. Specialist (Dermatol.) Craigavon Area Hosp. Gp. Trust. Socs: Roy. Coll. Phys.

LANE, Alan Geoffrey Penylan Surgery, 74 Penylan Road, Cardiff CF23 5SY Tel: 029 2049 8181 Fax: 029 2049 1507 — MB BCh 1976 Wales; MRCGP 1980; DRCOG 1979; DCH Eng. 1978.

LANE, Andrew Dominic Dicconson Terrace Surgery, Dicconson Terrace, Wigan WN1 2AF Tel: 01942 239525 Fax: 01942 826552; 213 Wigan Road, Standish, Wigan WN6 0AE — MRCS Eng. LRCP Lond. 1980.

LANE, Andrew Stuart 42 Helmsley Road, Newcastle upon Tyne NE2 1DL — MB BS 1997 Newc.

LANE, Anthony John (retired) 4 Queens Road, Wilmslow SK9 5HS Tel: 01625 523889 Email: anthonylane@lineone.net — MD (Hon. Causa) Manch. 1986; MA, MB BChir Camb. 1949; FRCP Ed. 1972, M 1963; FRCP Lond. 1973, M 1963; FFPHM 1974. Prev: Regional Med. Off. N. W.. RHA.

LANE, Brian Keith (retired) Penfold, Icen Lane, Shipton Gorge, Bridport DT6 4PP Tel: 01308 897241 — MB BS 1955 Lond.; DObst RCOG 1959. Prev: Ho. Surg. Paddington Green Childr. Hosp. & Sussex Matern. Hosp.

LANE, Carol Myhill University Hospital of Wales, Cardiff CF4 4XW Tel: 029 2074 7747 Fax: 029 2074 2783 Email: nicolajones@uhw.tr.wales.nhs.uk; Plasnewydd, Bonvilston, Cardiff CF5 6TQ Tel: 01446 781408 Fax: 01222 742954 — BM 1978 Soton.; DM Soton. 1991; FRCS Eng. 1983; FRCP (UK) 1999; FRCOphth 1988. (Univ. Soton.) Cons. Ophth. Univ. Hosp. of Wales Cardiff. Socs: Fell. Roy. Soc. Med. (Mem. Sect. Ophth.); Eur. Soc. Oculoplastic & Reconstruc. Surg.; Sec. S. W.. Ophth. Soc. Prev: Lect. & MRC Train. Fell.sh. Inst. Ophth. Lond.; SHO (Med.) Radcliffe Infirm. Oxf.; Resid. Surg. Off. Moorfields Eye Hosp.

LANE, Charles James 44 Rosefield Avenue, Wirral CH63 5JT — MB ChB 1994 Liverp.

LANE, Deborah Marianne Forest Health Care, The Health Centre, Dockham Road, Cinderford GL14 2AN Tel: 01594 598030 — MB 1987 Camb.; BChir 1986.

LANE, Donald John Osler Chest Unit, Churchill Hospital, Headington, Oxford OX3 7LJ Tel: 01865 225252 Fax: 01865 225221 — BM BCh 1960 Oxf.; MA Oxf. 1960, DM 1970; FRCP Lond. 1975, M 1964. (St. Bart.) Cons. Chest Phys. Oxf. Radcliffe Hosp. NHS Trust Oxf.; Vice-Pres. Nat. Asthma Campaign. Socs: Assn. Phys.; Brit. Thorac. Soc. Prev: Lect. Nuffield Depts. Med. & Anaesth. Radcliffe Infirm. Oxf.

LANE, Geoffrey St James's University Hospital, Beckett St., Leeds LS9 7TF Tel: 0113 243 3144 — MB BS 1977 Lond.; MD Lond. 1989; MRCOG 1984. Cons. Gyn. & Gyn. Oncol. St. Jas. Univ. Hosp. Leeds. Socs: Brit. Gyn. cancer soc; Internat. Gynaecol. Cancer Surg.; Brit Soc for coloscopy and cervical Path. Prev: Sen. Regist. Kings Coll. Hosp. Lond.; Vis. Prof. Gyn. Oncol. Univ. St. Florida, Tampa.

LANE, Mr Gerard Francis 16 Cardigan Avenue, Westcliff on Sea SS0 0SF — MB BCh BAO 1985 Dub.; FRCS Ed. 1994; MRCGP 1991; T(GP) 1991.

LANE, Hilary Lorraine Northbrook, 18 Gilbert Road, Swanage BH19 1DY — MB ChB 1964 Birm. (Birm.) Prev: Ho. Surg. & Ho. Phys. Birm. Gen. Hosp.

LANE, Mr Ian Francis University Hospital of Wales, Cardiff CF4 4XW Tel: 029 2074 3356 Fax: 029 2074 2954 Email: ian.lane@cardiffandvalewales.nhs.uk; Plasnewydd, Bonvilston, Cardiff CF5 6TQ Tel: 01446 781408 Fax: 01446 781970 Email: user@laneqq.fsbusiness.co.uk — BM BCh 1976 Oxf.; MA Oxf. 1979, BA 1973, MCh 1988, DM 1987; FRCS Eng. 1981; FRCS Ed. 1981; MRCS Eng. LRCP Lond. 1976. (St. Thos.) . Med. Dir. . &

Cons. Vasc. Surg. Univ. Hosp. Wales, Cardiff; Mem. Ct. Examr. RCS Eng. Socs: Surgic. Research Soc.; Roy. Soc. Med. Sec venus forum); Vasc. Surgic. Soc. GB & Irel. Prev: Lect. (Surg.) Char. Cross & W.m. Med. Sch. Lond.; Resid. Surg. Off. Brompton Hosp. Lond.; Ho. Surg. St. Thos. Hosp. Lond.

LANE, James Richard THe Department of Anaesthesia, The General Hospital, St Helier, Jersey JE2 9BB Tel: 01534 59000; Millfield, La Grande Route De La Cote, Samares, St. Clement, Jersey JE2 5SD Tel: 01534 855929 — MB BS Lond. 1968; MRCS Eng. LRCP Lond. 1968; FFA RCS Eng. 1972. (Univ. Coll. & Univ. Coll. Hosp.) Cons. Anaesth. Gen. Hosp. Jersey. Socs: BMA; Assn. Anaesths. Prev: Cons. Anaesth. St. Jas. Univ. Hosp. Leeds; Cons. Cardiothoracic Anaesth. Killingbeck Hosp. Leeds; Lect. (Anaesth.) Univ. Leeds.

LANE, Jason Warwick James 13 Huntington Green, Ashford Carbonel, Ludlow SY8 4DN — MB BS 1989 Newc.

LANE, John William (retired) The Surgery, 209 Sheffield Road, Killamarsh, Sheffield S21 1DX Tel: 0114 251 0000 — MB ChB 1977 Leeds; MRCGP Lond. 1981.

LANE, Jonathan Department of Obstetrics & Gynaecology, Royal Shrewsbury Hospital, Mytton Oak Road, Shrewsbury SY3 8XQ Tel: 01743 261429; Shirley Goss, 11 Radbrook Road, Shrewsbury SY3 9BB Tel: 01743 366754 Fax: 01743 247575 Email: jonlane@aol.com — MB BS 1964 Lond.; MRCS Eng. LRCP Lond. 1964; FRCOG 1988, M 1973; DObst RCOG 1966. (Lond. Hosp.) Cons. O & G Shropsh. HA; Hon. Sen. Clin. Lect. (Obst. & Gyn.) Univ. Birm. 1995-2000. Socs: BMA & Brit. Soc. Colposcopy & Cervical Path. Prev: Sen. Lect. (O & G) Univ. Birm.; Hon. Cons. (O & G) Birm. Centr. Health Dist. (T); Squadron Ldr. RAF Med. Br., Specialist O & G.

LANE, Marie-Geneviève Marguerite Juliette P 3 Hollis Wood Drive, Wrecclesham, Farnham GU10 4JT Tel: 01252 725298 Fax: 01252 725298 — MD 1955 CM McGill Univ. Canada; BA McGill 1951; LMCC 1956; MRCPCH 1996; MFFP 1994; Cert. FPA 1974. (McGill) Sessional Staff Grade (Child Health) Bournewood Community Ment. Health NHS TrustClin. Med. Off. (Family Plann.) Loddon Community NHS Trust W. Surrey HA; Med. Adviser Boro. Housing Dept.; JP Surrey; Dir. CME, Regist. & Hon. Sec. Fac. Community Health. Socs: BMA (Reg. Rep. Communiy Health Doctors Subcomm.); RIPHH/SPH; MDU. Prev: Clin. Asst. (Med.) Montreal Gen. Hosp., Canada; Research Asst. Ayerst, McKenna & Harrison, St. Laurent, Canada; Jun. Intern Qu. Eliz. Hosp. Montreal, Canada.

LANE, Michael Brookes Daisy Cottage, Ravenshall, Betley, Crewe CW3 9BH — MB ChB Glas. 1963; LMCC 1970. (Glas.)

LANE, Michael Ronald 29 Hawthorn Crescent, Gilesgate Moor, Durham DH1 1ED — MB BS 1989 Lond.; MRCGP 1994; DRCOG 1994; DFFP 1994.

LANE, Michael William Wellington Health Centre, Chapel Lane, Wellington, Telford TF1 1PZ Tel: 01952 242304; 5 Pendil Close, Wellington, Telford TF1 2PQ Tel: 01952 252050 — MB BS 1973 Lond. (Univ. Coll. Hosp.)

LANE, Patrick Newry Health Centre, Newry BT35 8TR Tel: 01693 64840; 1 Fullerton Road, Newry BT34 2BB Tel: 028302 64840 — LAH Dub. 1960. (RCSI) Prev: Vis. Obst. Woodville Matern. Home Birm.; Ho. Off. (Surg., Med. & Obst.) Daisy Hill Hosp. Newry.

LANE, Patrick William Frederick The Health Centre, Midland St., Long Eaton, Nottingham NG10 1NY Tel: 0115 973 2157 Fax: 0115 946 5420; 3 Briar Gate, Long Eaton, Nottingham NG10 4BN — MB ChB 1970 Birm.; FRCGP 1991, M 1975; DObst RCOG 1972. Assoc. Adviser (Gen. Pract.) Univ. Nottm.; Trainer GP Trent RHA. Socs: Nottm. MC Soc. Prev: Course Organiser (Jt.) Nottm. VTS; SHO (O & G) Perth Roy. Infirm; Ho. Surg. & Ho. Phys. United Birm. Hosps.

LANE, Peter Francis Ashville Medical Centre, 430 Doncaster Road, Stairfoot, Barnsley S70 3EX; 26 Woodland Drive, Wakefield WF2 6DD — MB ChB 1983 Birm.

LANE, Peter John c/o Anaesthetics Department, Taunton & Somerset Hospital, Musgrove Park, Taunton TA1 5DA — MB BS 1983 New South Wales.

LANE, Peter John Lockwood Birmingham University Medical School, Vincent Drive, Birmingham B15 2TT Tel: 0121 414 4078 Email: p.j.l.lane@bham.ac.uk; 54 Knightlaw Road, Harborne, Birmingham B17 8QB Tel: 0121 429 1109 — PhD Birm. 1987; MB ChB Ed. 1980; MRCP (UK) 1983; MRCPath. 1987; FRCPath 1997. Sen. Clin. Lect. Hon Cons. Immunol.

LANE, Peter Kennedy c/o North Hampshire Hospital Trust, Aldermaston Road, Basingstoke RG24 9NA — MB BS 1989 Tasmania.

LANE, Philip John Logan and Blands District General Hospital, Glengallon Road, Oban PA34 4HH Tel: 01631 567500 Fax: 01631 567510; Tel: 01680 814206 — MB ChB Liverp. 1967; DMRD Liverp. 1970. p/t Cons. Radiol. Lorn & Is.s S.G.N. Oban Argyll. Socs: Bolton Med. Soc.; BIR; Scott. Radiological Soc. Prev: Cons. Radiol. Bolton Roy. Infirm. & Bolton Gen. Hosp.; Sen. Regist. (Radiol.) Merseyside AHA.

LANE, Phillip Edward BUPA Wellness, Trafalgar House, 29 Park Place, Leeds LS1 2PT Tel: 0113 381 5400; Oakwood, 29 Farnley Road, Menston, Ilkley LS29 6JW — MB ChB 1987 Ed.; MRCGP 1992; DCH RCP Lond. 1989. Regional Phys. i/c, BUPA Wellness, Leeds. Socs: Roy. Med. Soc. of Edin. (Life Mem.). Prev: Trainee GP/SHO Rotat. Huddersfield Roy. Infirm.

LANE, Rebecca Elizabeth Oak Cottage, 1 Middlegreen Road, Slough SL3 7BL — MB BS 1997 Lond.

LANE, Richard Spencer Bayer Corporation Biological Products Division, Loxleys, Chesham Road, Wiggington, Tring HP23 6HX — MD 1974 Lond.; MB BS 1959; MB BS 1959; MRCP (UK) 1980; FRCPath 1986, M 1974. (Westm.) Cons. & Adviser Biological Products Bayer Corpn. Pharmaceuticcal Div. Wiggington, Herts. Socs: Roy. Soc. of Med. Internat. Soc. of Blood Transfus. Prev: Dir. Blood Products Laborat. Elstree, Herts.; Cons. Haemat. NE Thames Regional Transfus. Centre Brentwood; Lect. (Haemat.) St. Geo. Hosp. Med. Sch. Lond.

LANE, Mr Robert Hugh Stanley Royal Hampshire County Hospital, Romsey Road, Winchester SO22 5DG Tel: 01962 863535; Temple Usk, Colden Common, Winchester SO21 1TB Tel: 01962 712383 Fax: 01962 714614 — MB BS 1967 Lond.; MS Lond. 1980; FRCS Eng. 1971; MRCS Eng. LRCP Lond. 1967. (Guy's) Cons. Gen. Colorectal Surg. Winchester & E.leigh Healthcare NHS Trust. Socs: Fell. Roy. Soc. Med.; Fell. Assn. Surgs.; Assn. Coloproctol. Prev: Lect. (Surg.) Univ. Soton.; Research Fell. St. Mark's Hosp. Lond.; Resid. Surg. Off. Pembury Hosp.

LANE, Russell John Morley West London Neurosciences Centre, Charing Cross Hospital, Fulham Palace Road, London W6 8RF Tel: 020 8846 1194 Fax: 020 8383 0015 Email: r.lane@ic.ac.uk; 4 The Bowers, Wokingham RG40 3JX Email: russwindsor@hotmail.com — MB BS 1973 Newc.; MB BS (Hons.) Newc. 1973; BSc (Hons.) Newc. 1970, MD 1984; FRCP Lond. 1992; MRCP (UK) 1975. (Newc.) Cons. Neurol. W. Lond. Neurosci. Centre Char. Cross Hosp. & Ashford & St.Peters NHS Trust; Hon. Sen. Lect. Neuromuscular Dept. Div. Clin. Neurosci. & Psychol. Med. Imperial Coll. Sch. Med. Socs: Fell. Roy. Soc. Med. Prev: Sen. Resid. (Neurol.) Duke Univ. Med. Centre Durh., NC; Ho. Phys. & Ho. Surg. Roy. Vict. Infirm. Newc.

LANE, Sally Ann Department of Cytology, Britannia House, Britannia Road, Morley, Leeds LS27 0BT — MB ChB 1984 Sheff.; BMedSci. Sheff. 1981. Cons. Histopath/Cytopath Dept. of Cytol. Morley & Leeds Gen. Infirm. Prev: Cons. Histopath. Roy. Halifax Infirm.

LANE, Sandra 6 Heffer Close, Stapleford, Cambridge CB2 5EB Tel: 01223 843672 — MB BS 1972 Newc. Staff Grade Practitioner Community Child Health Lifespan Healthcare Trust Camb.; Clin. Asst. Posts (Sessional) in Neonat. Paediat.; Clin. Asst. Posts (Sessional) in Paediat. Orthop. Socs: RCPCH.

LANE, Sheila Mary 44 Long Street, Cerne Abbas, Dorchester DT2 7JG — MB BS 1990 Lond.

LANE, Stuart MacDonald Brentford Group Practice, Boston Manor Road, Brentford TW8 8DS Tel: 020 8321 3844 Fax: 020 8321 3862 — MB BS 1978 Lond.; DCH RCP Lond. 1981; MRCGP 1985. (St. Mary's Hospital, Lond.)

LANE, Suzanne Elizabeth Dept. of Rheumatology, Norfolk & Norwich Hospital, Brunswick Road, Norwich NR1 3SR Fax: 01603 287004 Email: suzannelane@norrheum.demon.co.uk — MB ChB 1994 Birm.; MRCP 1997. (Birm.) Specialist Regisrar Rheum. Norf. & Norwich Hosp., Norwich; ARC Clin. Research Fell. Prev: Research Fell. Rheum. Norf. & Norwich Hosp., Norwich.

LANE, Mr Timothy Mark 10 Sandy Lane, Leighton Buzzard LU7 3BE — MB BS 1992 Lond.; BSc (Hons.) Anat. Lond. 1989; FRCS Eng. 1996; FRCS Ed. 1996. (Middlx. Hosp.) Specialist Regist.

(Gen. Surg.) Maidstone Hosp. Kent. Socs: ASIT. Prev: Specialist Regist. (Gen. Surg.) Kent & Sussex Hosp.; SHO Surg. Rotat. Guy's & St. Thos. Hosp. Lond.

LANE, Valerie Mary 41 Lockhart Road, Cobham KT11 2AX — BM 1979 Soton.

LANE, Vivien Jane Margaret, Squadron Ldr. RAF Med. Br. 7 Cherry Tree Drive, Nether Edge, Sheffield S11 9AE Tel: 0114 255 1932 — MB ChB 1981 Sheff.; Dip. Sports Med. (Merit) 1988; Cert. Prescribed Equiv. Exp. JCPTGP 1987; Cert. Av Med. 1983; Cert. FPA 1982; Cert. NFP Birm. 1979. (Sheffield) Research into Desert Storm Dis. New Orleans, Louisiana, USA; Sports Med. Adviser to Athletics & Swimming Teams BAGA, ESAA, BSAD; BAF, ASA, AAA & WAAA Technical Official; Smith & Nephew Foundat. Schol. Socs: Brit. Assn. Sport & Med.; Fell. Roy. Soc. Med. Prev: Med. Dir. Europ. Basketball Qualifying Tournament Birm. & World Netball Championships Birm. '95; Princip. Sen. Med. Off. Civil Serv. Commiss. Apptd. to MoD; Med. Off. to NoE Athletics Assn. - 2001.

LANE-O'KELLY, Mr Aeneas 4 Jenneth Court, Mauldeth Road, Heaton Mersey, Stockport SK4 3NB — MB BCh BAO 1982 NUI; MSc (Orth.) Lond. 1994; FRCS Ed. 1990; FRCSI 1989; LRCPI & LM, LRCSI & LM 1982; FRCS (Orth.) 1997. Specialist Regist. Wrightington Hosp. Prev: Sen. Regist. (Orthop.) S. Manch. Univ. Hosp. NHS Trust; Specialist Regist. Hope Hosp. Manch.; Specialist Regist. Manch. Gen. Hosp.

LANEY, Donald Roland (retired) Glenroyd, Strawberry Hill, Lympstone, Exmouth EX8 5JZ Tel: 01395 265491 — BM BCh 1956 Oxf.; DObst RCOG 1959. Prev: Asst. Ho. Surg. & Ho. Phys. Guy's Hosp.

LANFEAR, Paul Christopher 5 Gleneagles Road, Leeds LS17 7TA Tel: 0113 269 0842 — MB ChB 1975 Sheff.; BSc Sheff. 1970; MRCGP 1980. Med. Adviser Benefits Agency Leeds.

LANG, Andrew Christopher Station Road Surgery, 69 Station Road, Sidcup DA15 7DS Tel: 020 8309 0201 Fax: 020 8309 9040 — MB BS 1982 Lond.

LANG, Ann Elizabeth Douglas Surgery, 69 Ayr Road, Douglas ML11 0PX — MB ChB 1993 Glas.; DRCOG 1996; MRCGP 1998. (Glasgow) GP Princip. Douglas Surg., Lanark.

LANG, Christopher Charles Edward 6 Jordan Lane, Edinburgh EH10 4RB — MB ChB 1994 Ed.

LANG, D M Silverdale Medical Centre, Mount Avenue, Heswall, Wirral CH60 4RH Tel: 0151 342 6128 Fax: 0151 342 2435.

LANG, Daniel Vincent Anthony Royal Cornwall Hospitals, pendragow House, Gloweth, Truro TR1 3LS Tel: 01872 254552 — MB BCh BAO 1977 Dub.; MSc (Audiol Med.) Manch. 1993; MRCGP 1985; DRCOG 1983; DLO Eng. 1982. Assoc. Specialist (Community Child Health) Roy. Cornw. Hosps. Trust. Socs: Coll. Paediat. Child Health; Brit. Soc. Audiol. (Train. ctte); Brit. Assn. Community Drs in Audiol. Prev: Clin. Med. Off. Camberwell HA; Trainee GP Crawley HA VTS; SHO (ENT) Brighton HA.

LANG, Derek Michael 23 Grove Lane, Cheadle Hulme, Cheadle SK8 7LZ — MB ChB 1982 Manch.

LANG, Miss Dorothy Ann Wessex Neurological Centre, Southampton University Hospitals NHS Trust, Tremona Road, Southampton SO16 6YD Tel: 02380 777222 Fax: 02380 794148 — MB ChB 1980 Glas.; FRCS Eng. 1995; FRCS Glas. 1984. Cons. Neurosurg. Wessex Neurol. Centre Soton. Univ. Hosps. Socs: Brit. Neurol. Surg. Soc.; Eur. Soc. Paediat. Neurosurg.; Brit. Skull Base Soc.

LANG, Eva-Maria The Old Place, 52 High St., Bedmond, Abbots Langley WD5 0RH Tel: 01923 261016; Kitteneshalde 112, D-7312 Kirchheim/Teck, Germany Tel: 07021/6539 — State Exam Med 1987 Frankfurt; MD1991; FRCA 1995; DEAA 1996. Cons. Anaesth. Luton & Dunstable Hosp. Luton.

LANG, Fiona Helen Royal Edinburgh Hospital, Morningside, Edinburgh EH10 5HF Tel: 0131 537 6249 Fax: 0131 537 6117; Carrington House, 27 South Oswald Road, Edinburgh EH9 2HH — MB ChB 1987 Glas.; MSc Univ. Ed. 1992; MRCPsych 1991. Cons. Edin. Healthcare Trust. Prev: Sen. Regist. Edin. Healthcare Trust; MRC Fell. Roy. Edin. Hosp.

LANG, Gordon Drew Aberdeen Royal Infirmary, Foresterhill, Aberdeen AB25 2ZN Tel: 01224 681818 Fax: 01224 840706; Laverockbank, 18 Forost Road, Aberdeen AB15 4BS Tel: 01224 311846 — MB ChB 1975 Glas.; MRCOG 1981; FRCOG 1994. Cons. O & G Aberd. Matern. Hosp. Socs: BMA; BMUS; Blair Bell Res. Soc.

LANG, Graham Stanley 'Littleways', 14 Sandelswood End, Beaconsfield HP9 2NW — MB BS Lond. 1970; MRCP (U.K.) 1974; MRCS Eng. LRCP Lond. 1970; FRCP 1998. (UCH London) Hosp. Pract. Wycombe Gen. Hosp. Socs: Chiltern Med. Soc. High Wycombe (Ex Sec.).

LANG, Helen Mary 26 Spylaw Bank Road, Colinton, Edinburgh EH13 0JW Tel: 0131 441 2659 — MB ChB 1972 Glas. (Glas.) GP Edin. Prev: Regist. (Med.) Grey's Hosp. Pietermaritzburg, S. Africa; SHO (Paediat.) Groot Schuur Hosp. Cape Town, S. Africa.

LANG, Iain James Hill Lane Surgery, 162 Hill Lane, Southampton SO15 5DD Tel: 023 8022 3086 Fax: 023 8023 5487; 38 Glen Eyre Drive, Bassett, Southampton SO16 3NR Tel: 02380 769528 — MB 1978 Camb.; BChir 1977; MRCGP 1982. Prev: GP Trainee W. Herts. VTS; Med. Ho. Off. Chase Farm Enfield; Surgic. Ho. Off. St. Geo. Hosp. Lond.

LANG, Isla Mary Department of Radiology, Sheffield Children's Hospital NHS Trust, Western Bank, Sheffield S10 2TH Tel: 0114 271700 Email: isla.lang@sheffch-tr.trent.nhs.uk — MB ChB 1984 Aberd.; MRCP (UK) 1988; FRCR 1993. (Aberd.) Cons. Radiol. (Paediat.) Sheff. Childr. Hosp. NHS Trust. Socs: BMA; Roy. Coll. Radiologists; ESPR. Prev: Cons. (Radiol.) S. Manch. Univ. NHS Trust; Clin. Fell. (Radiol.) Hosp. Sick Childr. Toronto, Canada; Sen. Regist. (Diagn. Radiol.) NW RHA.

LANG, Joanna Elizabeth The Surgery, Parkwood Drive, Warners End, Hemel Hempstead HP1 2LD Tel: 01442 250117 Fax: 01442 256185; 31 Oakwood, Berkhamsted HP4 3NQ Tel: 01442 873791 — MB ChB 1980 Aberd.; MRCGP 1984; DRCOG 1985. (Aberdeen) Prev: Trainee GP Hemel Hempstead Gen. Hosp. VTS.

LANG, Mr John Anderson Spylaw Bank Road Surgery, 26 Spylaw Bank Road, Edinburgh EH13 0JW — MB ChB 1972 Glas.; FRCS Glas. 1979. (Glas.) Princip. GP Edin. Prev: Regist. Rotat. Train. Scheme Glas. Roy. Infirm.; Regist. (Gen. Surg.) Law Hosp. Carluke.

LANG, John Richard (retired) 76 New Forest Drive, Brockenhurst SO42 7QW Tel: 01590 622740 Fax: 01590 622740 — MB BChir Camb. 1958; MRCS Eng. LRCP Lond. 1957; DTM & H Eng. 1963; DObst RCOG 1962; Mem. Inst. Psychosexual Med. 1984. Prev: Med. Supt. Vom Christian Hosp., Nigeria.

LANG, Joyce Alison Pathology Department, Crosshouse Hospital, Kilmarnock KA2 0BE Tel: 01563 577432 Email: joyce.lang@aaaht.scot.nhs.uk — MB ChB 1979 Glas.; MRCPath 1986.

LANG, Moira Rebecca McLauchlan (retired) 86 Monks Road, Exeter EX4 7BE Tel: 01392 664921 Fax: 01392 664921 — MB ChB 1960 Glas.; MFFP 1993. Family Plann.: Instruc. Doctor. Prev: SCMO Comm. Health, Exeter HA.

LANG, Philip William 9 Carlisle Road, Southport PR8 4DJ Tel: 01704 67339 — LRCP LRCS 1951 Ed.; LRCP LRCS Ed. LRFPS Glas. 1951; MFCM 1974; DPH Liverp. 1966. (Ed.) Socs: Fell. Roy. Inst. Pub. Health & Hyg.. Prev: Dist. Med. Adviser Chorley & S. Ribble HA.; Dist. Med. Off. S.port & Formby HA; MOH & Princip. Sch. Med. Off. S.port Co. Boro.

LANG, Stephen Department of Pathology, Ninewells Hospital & Medical School, Dundee DD1 9SY — MB ChB 1981 Glas.; MRCPath 1989. Cons. Histopath. Ninewells Hosp. Dundee; Hon. Sen. Lect. (Histopath.) Univ. Dundee. Socs: Paediat. Path. Soc.; Path. Soc. Prev: Lect. & Hon. Sen. Regist. Rotat. (Histopath) Hosp for Sick Childr. & St. Bart. Hosp. Lond.; Specialist (Path.) RAF IPTM Halton; Ho. Surg. Vict. Infirm. Glas.

LANG, Stuart Cameron 17 Carolside Avenue, Clarkston, Glasgow G76 7AA — MB ChB 1994 Glas.

LANG, William Flat 1/100, 68 Langside Drive, Glasgow G43 2ST Tel: 0141 637 1207; 10 Prospecthill Road, Glasgow G42 9LE Tel: 0141 632 0203 — MB ChB 1950 Glas.; DObst RCOG 1955. (Glas.)

LANG, Mr William (retired) Glasgow Nuffield Hospital, Beaconsfield Road, Glasgow G12 0PJ Tel: 0141 334 9441 — MB ChB Glas. 1955; FRCS Glas. 1984; FRCS Ed. 1968; DObst RCOG 1959. Prev: Cons. Otolaryngol. Glas. Nuffield Hosp.

LANG-SADLER, Elizabeth Canterbury Road Surgery, 186 Canterbury Road, Davyhulme, Manchester M41 0GR Tel: 0161 748 5559 Fax: 0161 747 1997 — MB ChB 1976 Manch.; BSc St. And. 1973; DRCOG 1978; DCH Eng. 1980.

LANG-STEVENSON, Mr Andrew Innes Havering Hospitals Knee Unit, Oldchurch Hospital, Waterloo Road, Romford RM7 0BE Tel: 01708 708095 Fax: 01277 234123 Email: knee2do@aol.com; Ashcourt, Mill Hill, Shenfield, Brentwood CM15 8EU Tel: 01277 263499 Fax: 01277 234123 — MB ChB 1974 Dundee; BSc (Med. Sci.) St. And. 1971; FRCS Eng. 1979; FRCS Ed. 1979. (Univ. Dundee) Cons. Orthop. Surg. Havering Trust Knee Serv. Romford. Socs: Internat. Arthroscopy Assn.; Eur. Soc. Knee Surg.; Brit. Assn. Knee Surg. Prev: Sen. Regist. (Orthop.) Sheff. HA; Regist. (Orthop.) Roy. Hallmsh. Hosp. Sheff.; Clin. Research Fell. Orthop. & Arthritic Hosp. Toronto, Canada.

LANGA FERREIRA, Bienvenido Arturo 8/2 Drumsheugh Gardens, Edinburgh EH3 7QJ — DMed Nat. U Santo Domingo Republic 1985.

LANGAN, Brenda Catherine 32 Eastbury Avenue, Rochford SS4 1SF — MB ChB 1973 Birm.

LANGAN, Charles E Baillieston Health Centre, 20 Muirside Road, Baillieston, Glasgow G69 7AD Tel: 0141 531 8050 Fax: 0141 531 8067 — MB ChB 1974 Glasgow; MB ChB 1974 Glasgow.

LANGAN, Heather Anne Dalreoch, Inverroy, Roy Bridge PH31 4AQ — MB ChB 1995 Aberd.

LANGAN, John J Baillieston Health Centre, 20 Muirside Road, Baillieston, Glasgow G69 7AD Tel: 0141 531 8050 Fax: 0141 531 8067 — MB ChB 1976 Glasgow; MB ChB 1976 Glasgow.

LANGAN, Stephen Avondale Surgery, 5 Avondale Road, Chesterfield S40 4TF Tel: 01246 232946 Fax: 01246 556246 — MB ChB 1975 Sheff.; MRCGP 1979.

LANGDALE-BROWN, Barbara Department of Pathology, Royal Hospital for Sick Children, Edinburgh Tel: 0131 667 1991 Fax: 0131 662 4864 — MB ChB 1983 Manch.; BSc St. And. 1980; MRCPath 1990. Sen. Regist. (Paediat. Path.) Roy. Hosp. Sick Childr. Edin.; Hon. Clin. Tutor Univ. Edin. Prev: Lect. (Path.) Univ. Edin.; Regist. (Histopath.) Walton Hosp. Liverp.

LANGDALE-BROWN, Moira Elizabeth The Surgery, High Street, Barley, Royston SG8 8HY Tel: 01763 848244 Fax: 01763 848677; 26 Shrubbery Grove, Royston SG8 9LJ Tel: 01763 248826 — MB ChB 1987 Manch.; MB ChB (Hons.) Manch. 1987; BSc (Med. Sci.) St. And. 1984; MRCGP 1991; Cert. Family Plann. JCC 1990; DRCOG 1990. Prev: Trainee GP Borders Gen. Hosp. & Peebles VTS.

LANGDON, Christopher Guy The Holyport Surgery, Stroud Farm Road, Holyport, Maidenhead SL6 2LP Tel: 01628 24469 Fax: 01628 778869; Bray Rise, 57 Windsor Road, Bray, Maidenhead SL6 2DN Tel: 01628 672421 — MB BS 1975 Lond.; BSc Lond. 1972; MRCS Eng. LRCP Lond. 1975; MRCGP 1979; DRCOG 1978. (Guy's) Prev: Trainee GP Whitstable & Canterbury VTS; Ho. Off. (Surg.) Guy's Hosp. Lond.; Ho. Off. (Med.) Greenwich Dist. Hosp.

LANGDON, Miss Ilana Jayne Bristol Royal Infirmary, Marlborough St., Bristol BS2 8HW Tel: 0117 923 0000 — MB ChB 1990 Leic.; FRCS Eng. 1994. Specialist Regist. Orthop. Surg. Bristol Rotat. Socs: Brit. Orthopaedic Assn.; Brit. Orthopaedic Trainees Assn.; Brit. Soc. for Surg. of the Hand. Prev: Specialist Regist. hand Surg., Manch.; SHO Rotat. (Surg.) Bristol Roy. Infirm.; SHO (A & E) & Demonst. (Anat.) Bristol Roy. Infirm. & Univ. Bristol.

LANGDON, Jennifer Ann The Holyport Surgery, Stroud Farm Road, Holyport, Maidenhead SL6 2LP Tel: 01628 24469 Fax: 01628 778869; 57 Windsor Road, Bray, Maidenhead SL6 2DN — MB BS 1975 Lond.; BSc Lond. 1972; MRCS Eng. LRCP Lond. 1975. (Guy's) Prev: Trainee GP Whitstable & Canterbury VTS; Ho. Surg. Guy's Hosp. Lond.; Ho. Phys. Greenwich Dist. Hosp.

LANGDON, Jennifer Anne 7 Cowper Road, Harpenden AL5 5NF — MB BS 1996 Lond.

LANGDON, Professor John Dudley Department Oral & Maxillofacial Surgery, Kings Dental Institute, Caldecot Road, London SE5 9RW Tel: 020 7346 3474 Fax: 020 7346 3754 Email: john.langon@kcl.ac.uk; 14 North Hill, London N6 4QA Tel: 020 8340 5169 Fax: 020 8340 5169 — MB BS 1973 Lond.; MDS Lond. 1991, BDS 1964; LDS RCS Eng. 1964; FRCS Ed. 1985; FDS RCS Eng. 1971; F Med Sci 1998. (Lond. Hosp.) Prof. & Head of Dept. Oral & Maxillofacial Surg. King's Coll. Sch. Med. & Dent.; Cons. Maxillofacial Surg. St. Geo. Hosp., Epsom Gen. Hosp. and; Roy. Surrey Co. Hosp. Socs: (Hon. Treas.) Brit. Assn. Oral & Maxillofacial Surgs.; Fell. Roy. Soc. Med. (Pres. Sect. Odontol.); Fell. (Pres.) Brit. Assn. of Head and Neck Oncol. Prev: Sen. Lect. & Cons. Oral & Maxillofacial Surg. King's Coll. Hosp. Med. Sch. Lond.; Cons. Oral & Maxillofacial Surg. Qu. Mary's Hosp. Roehampton & Ashford Hosp. Middlx.; Sen. Regist. (Maxillofacial Surg.) Lond. Hosp. & King's Coll.

LANGDON, Laurence (retired) Beedle Cottage, Mount Pleasant, Lymington SO41 8LS Tel: 01590 672159 — MB BS Lond. 1953; FFA RCS Eng. 1956; DA Eng. 1955. Prev: Cons. Anaesth. Soton. & SW Hants. Health Dist.

LANGDON, Michelle Linda Brunswick Medical Centre, 53 Brunswick Centre, London WC1N 1BP Tel: 020 7837 3811 Fax: 020 7833 8408 — MB BS 1978 Lond. (St. Mary's) Socs: Parliamentary Gp. Alternative & Complementary Med.; Assoc. Fac. Homeopathy.

LANGDON, Nicola West Two Health Centre, 33-35 Praed Street, London W2 1NR Tel: 020 7262 1307 Fax: 020 7402 3013 — MB BS 1981 Lond.; MRCP (UK) 1985. Prev: SHO St. Mary's Hosp. Lond.; SHO Whittington Hosp. Lond.; Research Regist. King's Coll. Hosp. Lond.

LANGDON, Thomas Cecil (retired) Peverells, Tye Green, Glemsford, Sudbury CO10 7RH Tel: 01787 280320 — MB BChir 1949 Camb.; BA Camb. 1937, MA, MB BChir 1949; MRCS Eng. LRCP Lond. 1942. Prev: Regist. (Med.) W. Middlx. Co. Hosp.

LANGDOWN, Andrew John 10 Statfold Lane, Fradley, Lichfield WS13 8NY — MB ChB 1993 Birm.

LANGE, Bernd Cripps PGMC, Northampton General Hospital, Cliftonville, Northampton NN1 5BD — State Exam Med 1992 Berlin.

LANGE, Kezia Jane De Haviland Flat 7, Beaconsfield, Red Lion St., London WC1R 4PA — MB BCh 1993 Witwatersrand.

LANGE, Leo Stanley 17 Harley Street, London W1N 1DA Tel: 020 7631 0770 — MD 1967 Cape Town; MB ChB 1953; FRCP Lond. 1976, M 1959. (Cape Town) Socs: Fell. Roy. Soc. Med.; Assn. Brit. Neurols. Prev: Cons. Neurol. Char. Cross Hosp. Lond., Mt. Vernon Hosp. N.wood & Harefield Hosp.; Sen. Regist. (Neurol.) St. Mary's Hosp. Lond.; Res. Med. Off. Nat. Hosp. Qu. Sq. Lond.

LANGE, Mr Meyer John (retired) 34 Sunnyfield, Mill Hill, London NW7 4RG Tel: 020 8959 4965 — MRCS Eng. LRCP Lond. 1935; FRCS Ed. 1947; FRCS Eng. (ad eund.) 1965. Prev: Res. Surg. Off. Jersey Gen. Hosp.

LANGE, Peter James 7 Buxley Farm Steading, Ormiston, Tranent EH33 2NG Tel: 01875 612017; Roodlands Hospital, Hospital Road, Haddington EH41 3PF Tel: 0131 536 8300 Fax: 0131 536 8415 — MB ChB 1980 Ed.; MRCGP 1984; DGM RCP Lond. 1987. (Edinburgh) Assoc. Specialist (Geriat. Med.) Roodlands Hosp. Haddington.

LANGENDIJK, Joannes Wilibrordus Gerardus 59 Headlands, Kettering NN15 7EU — Artsexamen 1992 Amsterdam. (Univ. Amsterdam)

LANGFIELD, Judith Ann Haynes Lane surgery, 11 Haynes Lane, Bristol BS16 5JE Tel: 0117 957 1412 Fax: 0117 970 2775; 18 Glenside Close, Frenchay, Bristol BS16 2QY Tel: 0117 965 2265 Fax: 0117 965 2265 — MB BS Lond. 1969; FRCGP 1987, M 1975; DCH Eng. 1972; DObst RCOG 1972. (St. Mary's) Socs: BMA Counc.; (Counc.) BMA; Small Pract.s Assn. Prev: Trainee GP Portsmouth VTS; SHO (Paediat.) Roy. Berks. Hosp. Reading; Ho. Surg. Bedford Gen. Hosp.

LANGFORD, David Charles Stanhope Health Centre, Dales Street, Stanhope, Bishop Auckland DL13 2XD Tel: 01388 528555 Fax: 01388 526122 — MB BS 1965 Durh.

LANGFORD, David Paul, Lt.-Col. RAMC 7 The Glade, Ashley Heath, Ringwood BH24 2HR — MB BS 1980 Lond.; MRCGP 1988. (St. Mary's Hosp. Lond.) Sen. Med. Off. SHAPE. Prev: Regt.. Clin. Dir. Osnabruck; Regional Med. Off. 1RGJ Dhekelia, Cyprus; Sen. Med. Off. Dortmund.

LANGFORD, David Thorne 253 Tubbenden Lane S., Farnborough Village, Orpington BR6 7DW — MB BS 1970 Lond.; MRCS Eng. LRCP Lond. 1970; MRCGP 1976. (Guy's Hosp. Lond.) Socs: Fell. Fac. Pharm. Med.; Fell. St. John's Dermat. Soc. St. John's Hosp. Dis. Skin. Lond. Prev: Med. Dir. Europe Wellcome Foundat. Beckenham; Hon. Clin. Asst. (Dermat.) Gt. Ormond St. & Guy's Hosps. Lond.; Ho. Phys. (Gen. Med. & Paediat.) & Ho. Surg. P.ss Margt. Hosp. Swindon.

LANGFORD, Edward John Bromley Hospital, Cromwell Avenue, Bromley BR2 9AJ Tel: 020 8289 7160 — MB BS 1987 Lond.; MA Camb. 1988; MD Lond. 1996; MRCP (UK) 1990. (Cambridge University/Kings College London) Cons. (Cardiol./Gen. Med.)

Bromley Hosp.; Hon. Cons. (Cardiol.) KCH Lond. Prev: Specialist Regist. (Cardiol. & Med.) Bromley Hosp. Bromley; MRC Train. Fell. Acad. Dept. Med. King's Coll. Hosp. Lond.

LANGFORD, Katherine Sarah Department of Obstetrics & Gynaecology, St Thomas' Hospital, Lambeth Palace Road, London SE1 7EH — MB BChir 1990 Camb.; MA Camb. 1990, MB BChir 1990; MD Camb. 1997. Sen. Regist. (O & G) St. Thos. Hosp. Lond. Socs: Brit. Matern. & Fetal Med. Soc.

LANGFORD, Katrina Joanne 51 Chepstow Road, Leicester LE2 1PB — MB ChB 1997 Leic.

LANGFORD, Nigel James University of Birmingham, University Department of Therapeutics & Pharmological, Queen Elizabeth Hospital, Birmingham B15 2TT Email: n.j.langford@bham.ac.uk — MB ChB 1995 Leicester; MRCP; MRCPharms; BSc 1989 (Hons). Specialist Regist., Therap., Qu. Eliz. Hosp. & Gen. Med.

LANGFORD, Rachel Mary Elizabeth Shaw House, 11 Shaw Lane, Headingley, Leeds LS6 4DH Tel: 0113 278 4914 Fax: 0113 274 5822 — MB BS 1980 Lond.; MRCS Eng. LRCP Lond. 1980. (St. Bart.) Gen. Med. Practitioner; Med. Adviser Leeds Metrop. Univ. Socs: Soc. Occupat. Med.; Roy. Soc. Med.; BMA. Prev: Ho. Surg. St. Bart. Hosp. Lond.

LANGFORD, Richard Julian 162 Northfield Road, Kings Norton, Birmingham B30 1DX — MB ChB 1992 Birm.; BDS Birm. 1982; FDS RCS Ed. 1987.

LANGFORD, Richard Mark Anaesthetics Department, St. Bartholomew's Hospital, Smithfield, London EC1A 7BE Tel: 020 7601 7526 Fax: 020 7601 7528; 28 Beech Drive, East Finchley, London N2 9NY Tel: 020 8444 7721 — MB BS 1979 Lond.; MRCS Eng. LRCP Lond. 1979; FCAnaesth. 1988. (Middlx.) Cons. Anaesth. & Sen. Lect. St. Bart. Hosp. & Med. Coll. Lond. Prev: Sen. Regist. (Anaesth.) Univ. Coll. Hosp. Lond.

LANGFORD, Roger Alan Great Green House, Great Green, Cockfield, Bury St Edmunds IP30 0HQ — BM BS 1997 Nottm.

LANGHAM, Bridget Teresa Moonrakers, Tithebarn Lane, Sutton-on-the-Hill, Derby DE6 5JH — MB ChB 1984 Leic.; FCAnaesth 1991; DA (UK) 1986.

LANGHAM, Mark Ian Nethertown Surgery, Elliot Street, Dunfermline KY11 4TF Tel: 01383 623516 Fax: 01383 624254 — MB ChB 1989 Ed.

LANGHAM, Peter John Byrne, Langham, Apps, Finnie and McIlhinney, 186 Neasham Road, Darlington DL1 4YL Tel: 01325 461128 Fax: 01325 469123 — MB BS 1978 Lond.; MA Camb. 1979.

LANGHAM-BROWN, John James Department of Radiology, Queen Alexandra Hospital, Portsmouth PO6 3LY Tel: 023 92 286000; 19 Pine Walk, Sarisbury Green, Southampton SO31 7DN Tel: 01489 577449 — BM BCh 1978 Oxf.; MA Oxf. 1979, BM BCh 1978; FRCS Eng. 1983; FRCR 1987. (Oxford) Cons. Radiol. Qu. Alexandra's Hosp. Portsmouth. Socs: Brit soc Gastroenterol.; Brit soc of Interven.al radiol; brit inst of radio. Prev: Sen. Regist. (Radiol.) Soton. Gen. Hosp.

LANGHAM-HOBART, Jean Mair (retired) Garden Flat, 69 Willingdon Road, Eastbourne BN21 1TR Tel: 01323 729987 — MB ChB 1941 Leeds. Prev: Clin. Med. Off. N.d. AHA & Newc. & Tyne AHA.

LANGHORNE, Peter 11 Firbank Avenue, Torrance, Glasgow G64 4EJ Tel: 01360 620408 — MB ChB 1986 Aberd.; PhD Aberd. 1984, MB ChB 1986; BSc 1978; MRCP (UK) 1989. Regist. Med. Gtr. Glas. HB.

LANGKAMER, Mr Victor George Orthopaedic Department, Weston General Hospital, Weston Super Mare BS23 4TQ — MB BS 1979 Lond.; MD Bristol 1995; FRCS Eng. 1984. Cons. Orthop. Surg. W.on Gen. Hosp. Avon. Prev: Sen. Regist. Bristol Roy. Infirm.

LANGLANDS, Jean Heron Mann (retired) 39 Lisburn Road, Hillsborough BT26 6HW Tel: 02892 682560 — MB ChB 1954 St. And.MB ChB 1954; 1964 MD St. And. 1964,; 1971 FRCP Ed. 1971; 1959 MRcp Ed 1959. Cons. Phys. Respirat. Investig. Centre Belf. City Hosp. & Lagan Valley Hosp. Lisburn. Prev: Sen. Tutor. (Therap. & Pharmacol.) Qu. Univ. Belf.

LANGLANDS, Jennifer Margaret 18 Ethie Terrace, Arbroath DD11 4AB — MB ChB 1996 Glas.

LANGLANDS, Ross William Duff Newton Port Surgery, Newton Port, Haddington EH41 3NF Tel: 01620 825497 Fax: 01620 824622; Tel: 01620 825575 Fax: 01620 824622 Email: rwdlz@compuserve.com — MB ChB 1973 Ed.; 1973 BSc; MRCGP 1977; Dip. Pract. Dermat. Wales 1992; Dip. Sports Med. Scotl. 1991; BA 1999. (Edin) Socs: Brit. Assn. Sports. Med. Prev: SHO (A & E) W.. Gen. Hosp. Edin.; Ho. Off. (Gen. Surg.) Roy. Infirm. Edin.; Ho. Off. (Gen. Med.) Roy. N.. Infirm. Inverness.

LANGLEY, Alison Mary 67 Fox Hollies Road, Sutton Coldfield B76 2RN — MB ChB 1969 St. And.

LANGLEY, Antony Gordon Scott (retired) 10 Berrow Court, Garden's Walk, Upton upon Severn, Worcester WR8 0JP — MB ChB 1960 Bristol; DObst RCOG 1962. Prev: GP Cheltenham.

LANGLEY, Christopher Norman Maxim Basement Flat, 152 Tachbrook St., London SW1V 2NE Tel: 020 7630 9300 — MB BS 1992 Lond.; MRCP 1997; DRCOG 1996. (St. Thos. & Guys Hosps.) Prev: GP Regist.

LANGLEY, David Charles St Lukes Medical Centre, 17 New Road, Brixham TQ5 8NA Tel: 01803 852731 Fax: 01803 852637; Dormers, Dashpers, Brixham TQ5 9LJ Tel: 01803 853671 — MB BS 1962 Lond.; MRCS Eng. LRCP Lond. 1962; MRCGP 1968; DObst RCOG 1964. (Lond. Hosp.) Prev: SHO (Gyn. & Obst. & Surg.), Ho. Phys. & Ho. Surg. Redhill Gen. Hosp.

LANGLEY, David Raymond (retired) Duggans Land, Wiston, Haverfordwest SA62 4PX — MB BCh 1957 Wales; BSc Wales 1953, MB BCh 1957; FFA RCS Eng. 1962. Prev: Cons. Anaesth. & Pain Relief Dyfed & Pembrokesh. HA's.

LANGLEY, Mr Douglas Arthur (retired) 84 Newberries Avenue, Radlett WD7 7EP — MRCS Eng. LRCP Lond. 1942; FRCS Eng. 1949; DOMS Eng. 1947. Prev: Cons. Ophth. Surg. Roy. N.. Hosp. Lond. & Whittington Hosp. Lond.

LANGLEY, Gordon Edward (retired) Hanningfields, Warborough Hill, Kenton, Exeter EX6 8LR Tel: 01626 890433 Fax: 01626 890433 — MB BS Durh. 1949; FRCP Ed. 1974, M 1963; FRCPsych 1979, M 1971; DPM Eng. 1958. Med. Mem. Ment. Health Review Tribunals; Hon. Research Fell. (Med. Hist.) Univ. of Exeter. Prev: Ment. Health Act Commr.

LANGLEY, Henrietta Kate Kings Farm, Harpenden, Henley-on-Thames RG9 4JG Tel: 01491 628560 — MB BS 1994 Lond.; BSc Lond. 1993. (St Bartholomew's Hospital) p/t Staff Grade (Psychiat.). Socs: Roy. Coll. Psychiat.

LANGLEY, John Frederick Anson 46 Harley Street, London W1N 1AD Tel: 0956 340201 Fax: 020 8866 3907; 72 Woodlands, Harrow HA2 6EW Tel: 020 8933 1579 Fax: 020 8866 3907 — MB BS Lond. 1966; MB BS Lond. 1966; AFOM RCP Lond. 1981; AFOM RCP Lond. 1981. (St. Bart.) Indep. Pract. (Occupat. Med.) Harrow, Middlx. Prev: Sen. Med. Off. & Med. Off. Lond. Transport; GP Harrow.

LANGLEY, Kirk Joseph Christopher 14 Levana Close, London SW19 6HP; 64 Blakeway Drive, Lincoln Green, Harare, Zimbabwe — MB ChB 1988 Zimbabwe; MRCP (UK) 1994. SHO Rotat. (Anaesth.) N. Trent.

LANGLEY, Paul Roger Meddygfa Surgery, Meddygfa Rhydbach, Botwnnog, Pwllheli LL53 8RE Tel: 01758 730266 Fax: 01758 730307 — MB ChB 1972 Leeds.

LANGLEY, Mrs Penelope Susan St Lukes Medical Centre, 17 New Road, Brixham TQ5 8NA Tel: 01803 852731 Fax: 01803 852637; Dormers, Dashpers, Brixham TQ5 9LJ Tel: 01803 853671 — MB BS 1962 Lond.; MRCS Eng. LRCP Lond. 1962. (St. Bart.) Prev: Ho. Surg. & Ho. Phys. Redhill Gen. Hosp.

LANGLEY, Robert Carl Salop House Surgery, Salop House, Chapel Street, Tregaron SY23 6HA Tel: 01974 298218 Fax: 01974 298207; Glan-yr-Afon-Ddu, Blaencaron, Ceredigion, Tregaron SY25 6NG Tel: 01974 298183 — MB BS 1985 Lond.; MRCGP 1991; DRCOG 1989; DCH RCP Lond. 1989; Cert. Family Plann. JCC 1990. Prev: Trainee GP Milton Keynes VTS.

LANGLEY, Ruth Elizabeth Holmefield Farmhouse, Meetinghouse Lane, South Leverton, Retford DN22 0BS — MB BS 1985 Lond.; MRCP (UK) 1989.

LANGLEY, Mr Stephen Edmund Maxim Royal Surrey County Hospital, Egerton Road, Guildford GU2 7XX Tel: 01483 464046 Fax: 01483555848 — MB BS 1988 Lond.; MB BS (Hons.) Lond. 1988; MS Lond. 1994; FRCS Eng. 1993; FRCS (Urol.) 1996. (St. Bartholomew's Medical School London) Cons. Urol. Surg. Roy. Co. Surrey Hosp., Guildford & Frimley Pk. Hosp. Frimley. Socs: Fell. Roy. Soc. of Med.; Brit. Assn. of Urol. Surgs. Prev: Sen. Regist. (Urol.)

Bristol Urol. Inst. S.mead; Hon. Research Fell. St. Thos. Hosp. Lond.; Ho. Off. (Med.) Wexham Pk. Hosp. Slough.

LANGLEY, Stephen Henry 4 Manor Court, Sole St., Gravesend DA13 9BU; 4 Manor Court, Manor Road, Sole St., Gravesend DA13 9BU Tel: 01474 814586 — MB BS 1978 Lond.

LANGLEY, Stephen John North West Lung Research Centre, Wythenshawe Hospital, Southmoor Road, Manchester M23 9LT Tel: 0161 291 2212 Fax: 0161 291 2243 Email: s.langley@zen.co.uk; 32 Barcheston Road, Cheadle SK8 1LL — MB ChB 1983 Manch.; Dip. Pharm. Med. RCP (UK) 1991; Faculty of Pharmaceut Med 1999. (Manch.) Dir. of (Regulatory Drug Developm.), Wythenshawe Hosp. Manch. Socs: Brit. Thorac. Soc. Prev: Dir. of Clin. Trials (Chest Med.) Wythenshawe Hosp. Manch.; Pharmaceut. Phys. Medeval Ltd. Manch.

LANGLOIS, Neil Edward Iain Department of forensic Medicine, ICPMR, Westmead Hospital PO Box 533,, Wentworthville NSW, Australia Tel: 00612 9845 7592 Fax: 00612 9891 4992 — MB BChir 1989 Camb.; MA Camb. 1990, BA 1986; MRCPath 1997; FRCPA 1999; DMJ (Path) 1999; MD Aberd 1999. Staff.special.Dept.Forens..Med.W.mead.Hosp. Socs: BMA; Path. Soc.; BAFM. Prev: Hon. Regist. & Lect. (Path.) Univ. Aberd.; SHO (Accid. & Emerg.) Qu. Eliz. Hosp. King's Lynn; SHO (Neurol. & Neurosurg.) Wessex Neurol. Centre Soton.

LANGMAACK, Claus Hinrich University of Wales College of Medicine, Division of Psychological Medicine, Ysbyty Gwynedd, Bangor LL57 2PW — MD 1990 Copenhagen; Cand. Med. Copenhagen 1990. SHO (Psychiat.) E.bourne Dist. Gen. Hosp.; SHO (Psychiat.) St. Mary's Hosp. Newport. Prev: SHO Inst. Human Genetics Essen Univ. Hosp. Germany; SHO (Clin. Genetics.) E. Hosp. Gothenburg, Sweden.

LANGMAID, John Rendle (retired) Wilverley, 1 Dorrita Close, Southsea PO4 0NY Tel: 023 9273 2406 — MB 1959 Camb.; MB BChir Camb. 1959; BA Camb. 1955; MRCGP 1968. Prev: Ho. Phys. Middlx. Hosp.

LANGMAN, David Andrew Hansell Weelingham Farm, Great Fransham, East Dereham, Dereham NR19 2JF Tel: 0136 287286 — MB BS 1960 Lond.; MRCS Eng. LRCP Lond. 1960; DA Eng. 1971; DObst RCOG 1963. (Guy's) Prev: Ho. Off. Canad. Red Cross Memor. Hosp. Taplow, St. Albans City Hosp.; & Bushey Matern. Hosp.

LANGMAN, Professor Michael John Stratton (retired) Dept. Of Medicine, Queen Elizabeth Hospital, Edgbaston, Birmingham B15 2TH Tel: 0121 627 2380 Fax: 0121 627 2384 — F Med. Sci 1998; BSc Lond. 1956, MD 1965, MB BS (Hons.) 1959; FRCP Lond. 1973, M 1960; MRCS Eng. LRCP Lond. 1958; FFPM. Hon. Prof. Med. Birm. Univ. Med. Sch.; Chairm. Warwicks Ambul. NHS Trust; Chairm. Jt. Comm. on Vaccination & Immunization of Uk; Mem. Comm. on Safety of Med.s of the UK. Prev: Prof. Therap. Univ. Nottm. Med. Sch.

LANGMEAD, Frederica Louise 10 Charity Farm Chase, Billericay CM12 9LF — MB BS 1992 Lond.; BSc (Hons.) Lond. 1989; MRCP (UK) 1995. (Lond. Hosp.) Specialist Regist. (Gastroenterol. & Gen. Med.) The Roy. Hosps. Socs: Brit. Soc. Gastroenterol. Prev: Specialist Regist. (Gastroenterol. & Gen. Med.) Homerton Hosp.; Specialist Regist. S.end Hosp.

LANGMUIR, Marjorie Mary Druieside Cottage, Aviemore PH22 1QH Tel: 01479 810706 — MB ChB 1958 Glas.; DObst RCOG 1960.

LANGMUIR, Robert MacGillivray (retired) 20 Academy Street, Elgin IV30 1LP — MB ChB Glas. 1951; MRCPsych 1986; DPM Eng. 1977. Prev: Cons. Psychiat. Garlands Hosp. Carlisle.

LANGRAN, Michael Aviemore Medical Centre, Aviemore PH22 1SY Tel: 01479 810258 Fax: 01479 810067; Sunnybrae Lodge, Grampian Road, Aviemore PH22 1PZ Tel: 01479 811218 Email: mike@aviemore.globalnet.co.uk — BM 1991 Soton.; BSc Soton. 1990; MRCGP 1995; DRCOG 1993. (Soton) GP Aviemore Med. Pract. Socs: BMA; Highland Med. Soc.; Inducement Practs. Assn. Prev: Sen. Med. Off. (Emerg.) Albury Base Hosp. Albury, NSW, Austral.; Trainee GP Inverness Highland & Is.s VTS.

LANGRICK, Anthony Francis Langrick, Bournbrook Medical Practice, 480 Bristol Road, Selly Oak, Birmingham B29 6BD Tel: 0121 472 0129 — MB ChB 1972 Sheff. Univ. Med. Off. Birm. Univ.

LANGRICK, Helen Elizabeth 42 Lowerfield Road, Chester CH4 7QF — MB ChB 1995 Leeds.

LANGRIDGE, Pauline Kingston & Richmond Health Authority, 22 Hollyfield Road, Surbiton KT5 9AL Tel: 081 339 8119 Fax: 081 339 8100 Email: pauline@langridge@rapidial.co.uk; Highlands, 110 Whyteleafe Hill, Whyteleafe CR3 0AE — MB ChB 1985 Sheff.; BMedSci Sheff. 1984; MFPHM RCP (UK) 1993. (Sheff) Cons. Pub. Health Med. Kingston & Richmond HA. Prev: Sen. Regist. (Pub. Health) St. Geo. Hosp. Med. Sch. Thames RHA; Regist. (Pub. Health) SW Thames; Trainee GP Otford Kent.

LANGRIDGE, Susan Jane Woodside Health Centre, Barr Street, Glasgow G20 7LR Tel: 0141 531 9585 Fax: 0141 531 9339 — MB ChB 1983 Ed.; MRCGP 1987.

LANGRIDGE-SMITH, Jane Elizabeth Dean Terrace Centre, 18 Dean Terrace, Edinburgh EH4 1NL Tel: 0131 332 7941/7705 Fax: 0131 332 2931; 34A Dundas Street, Edinburgh EH3 6JN Tel: 0131 557 0186 — MB ChB 1978 Bristol; BSc (1st cl. Hons.) Anat. Bristol 1975; MFFP 1993. (Bristol) SCMO (Family Plann. & Psychosexual Med.) Lothian Primary Care NHS Trust, Edin. Socs: Brit. Assn. Sexual & Marital Ther.; Scott. Family Plann. Med. Soc. Prev: Research Fell. Roy. Soc. Univ. Edin.; Postdoctoral Research Fell. Univ. Chicago & Univ. Texas, Houston.

LANGRISH, Christopher James 22 Wallace Close, Tunbridge Wells TN2 5HW — MB BS 1994 Lond.

LANGSDALE, Graham Anthony (retired) 21 Carbery Avenue, Southbourne, Bournemouth BH6 3LL Tel: 01202 427264 Email: grahamal@dialstart.net — MB ChB 1958 Sheff.; MRCGP 1976. Prev: Police Surg. Bournemouth.

LANGSFORD, Heather Lucy Denham Farm, Bere Alston, Yelverton PL20 7EF — MB BS 1983 Lond.

LANGSFORD, Marian Joan Highlands Health Centre, Fore Street, Ivybridge PL21 9AE; South Highlands, Blachford Road, Ivybridge PL21 0AD Tel: 01752 893431 — MB BS 1976 Lond.; DCH Eng. 1979. (Royal Free) GP Job Share.

LANGSLEY, Nathan 5B Mary's Place, Edinburgh EH4 1JH; Flat 1 Constitution Court, 66 Constitution Street, Leith, Edinburgh EH6 6RR — BM BS 1995 Nottm.; MPhil; MRCPsych. The Roy. Edin. Hosp.

LANGSTAFF, Rodney James The Surgery, Nevells Road, Letchworth SG6 4TS Tel: 01462 683051 Fax: 01462 485650; 14 Waters End, Stotfold, Hitchin SG5 4QA Email: rodlangstaff@iname.com — MB BS Lond. 1969; MRCGP 1978; DObst RCOG 1972; DCH Eng. 1971. (St. Mary's) Prev: SHO (Paediat.) Windsor Gp. Hosps.; Ho. Surg. King Edwd. Memor. Hosp. Ealing; Ho. Phys. Edgware Gen. Hosp.

LANGSTAFF, Mr Ronald Joseph, Wing Cdr. RAF Med. Br. Retd. The Long Barn, Chesterton, Bicester OX26 1UD — BM BCh 1980 Oxf.; MA Oxf. 1989, BA 1977; FRCS Ed. 1985. Cons. Orthop. Surg. Hillingdon Hosp. Prev: Cons. Orthop. Surg. RAF Hosp. Wroughton Swindon & P.ss Marys RAF Hosp. Halton Aylesbury.; Hon. Sen. Regist. (Orthop.) Trent RHA.; Wing Cdr. RAF Med. Serv.

LANGSTON, Andrew 5 Osprey Close, Rhyddings, Neath SA10 7EP — MB BCh 1995 Wales.

LANGSTON, Crispin James Curlew Syke, Boltshope Park, Hunstanworth, Consett DH8 9UY — MB ChB 1988 Leic.

LANGSTON, Lee 5 Osprey Close, Leiros Park, Rhyddings, Neath SA10 7EP — MB BCh 1998 Wales.

LANGTON, Francis Andrew Monks Park Surgery, 24 Monks Park Avenue, Horfield, Bristol BS7 0UE Tel: 0117 969 3106 Fax: 0117 931 1546; Stratton Lodge, Becket's Lane, Nailsea, Bristol BS48 4LT Email: alangton@bigfoot.com — MB BS 1984 Lond.; Dip. Sports Med. 1995. (Guy's Hospital London) Doctor Bristol Rovers FC. Socs: (Chairm. SW Region) Brit. Assn. Sport & Med. Prev: Club Doctor Bath City FC; Trainee GP Greenwich VTS.

LANGTON, Gertrude Margaret The Hatherton Centre, City Challenge Building, Hatherton Road, Walsall WS1 3QD Tel: 01922 775048; Ganton, Roman Road, Sutton Coldfield B74 3AB Tel: 0121 353 8794 Fax: 0121 353 8794 — MB BS 1963 Lond.; MRCS Eng. LRCP Lond. 1963. (Roy. Free) SCMO Walsall HA. Socs: BMA & Fac. Family Plann. & Reproduc. Healthcare, RCOG. Prev: Clin. Med. Off. Walsall AHA; Sch. Med. Off. Birm.; Ho. Phys. (Paediat.) & Ho. Surg. Walsall Manor Hosp.

LANGTON, Jeremy Adam Department of Anaesthesia, Derriford Hospital, Plymouth — MB BS 1981 Lond.; MD Leic. 1994; FFA RCS Eng. 1988; DA Eng. 1985. (Guy's) Cons. Anaesth. Derriford Hosp. Plymouth. Prev: Sen. Lect. & Hon. Cons. Leicester Roy. Infirm.

LANGTON, John David — MB ChB 1983 Liverp.; MRCPsych 1988. Cons. Psychiat. Shrops. Community & Ment. Health Serv. NHS Trust. Socs: Roy. Coll. Psychiat. Prev: Sen. Regist. (Psychiat. Learning Disabil.) W. Midl. RHA; Regist. (Psychiat.) Glenside Hosp. Bristol.

LANGTON, Julie 2 Ravensdale Road, Heaton, Bolton BL1 5DN Tel: 01204 844867 — MB ChB 1982 Dundee; MRCOG 1987; T(OG) 1991. (Univ. Dundee) Cons. O & G Whiston Hosp. Prev: Sen. Regist. (O & G) Gtr. Glas. HB; Regist. (O & G) & Research SHO (Gyn. Oncol.) Ninewells Hosp. Dundee; SHO (O & G) Ninewells Hosp. Dundee.

LANGTON, Margaret Sutherland Battersby 14 Coltbridge Terrace, Edinburgh EH12 6AE Tel: 0131 337 5746 — MB ChB 1940 Ed.; FFCM 1982, M 1974; DPH Ed. 1942; DCH Eng. 1950. (Univ. Ed.)

LANGTON, Michael John 286 Southway Drive, Plymouth PL6 6QW — MB BS 1992 Lond.; BSc (Human Biol.) Lond. 1986, MB BS 1992. (King's Coll.)

LANGTON, Mr Stephen Geoffrey Department of Oral & Maxillofacial Surgery, Burnley General Hospital, Burnley BB10 2PQ Tel: 01282 474155; 2 Ravensdale Road, Bolton BL1 5DN Email: langts@midthird.demon.co.uk — MB ChB 1988 Dundee; BDS Dundee 1981; FRCS Ed. 1991; FDS RCPS Glas. 1985; FDSRCS Eng. 1999. Cons. Oral & Maxillofacual Surg. Burnley, Bury, Blackburn & Bolton Hosps. Prev: Lect. & Hon. Sen. Regist. (Oral & Maxillofacial Surg.) Manch. Roy. Infirm.; Regist. (Oral & Maxillofacial Surg.) Roy. Infirm. Edin.

LANGTON HEWER, Simon Christopher Department of Respiratory Medicine, Bristol Royal Hospital for Children, Upper Maudlin Street, Bristol BS2 8BJ Tel: 0117 342 8258 Fax: 0117 342 8494 Email: simon.langtonhewer@bristol.ac.uk — MB ChB 1987 Birm.; MRCP(UK) 1991; FRCPCH 1998; MD 1998. (Birm.) Cons. Respirat. Paediat. Bristol Roy. Hosp. for Sick Childr.. Socs: BMA; Brit. Paediat. Respirat. Soc.; Eur. Respirat. Soc. Prev: Sen. Regist. (Paediat.) Derriford Hosp. Plymouth; Paediat. (Intens. Care Unit) Gt. Ormond St. Hosp. Childr. Lond.; King's Lect. Roy. Alexandra Hosp. Sick Childr. Brighton.

LANGTRY, Anna Beatrice Addington Road Surgery, 33 Addington Road, West Wickham BR4 9BW; 10 Irene Road, Orpington BR6 0HA Tel: 01689 833972 — MB BS 1988 Lond.; DCH RCP Lond. 1992. (King's Coll. Lond.) GP.

LANGTRY, James Anthony Albert Sunderland Royal Hospital, Sunderland SR4 7TP Tel: 0191 565 6256 Fax: 0191 569 9201; 3 Westfield, Gosforth, Newcastle upon Tyne NE3 4YE Tel: 0191 246 2801 Fax: 0191 246 2801 — MB BS 1981 Lond.; MRCS Eng. LRCP Lond. 1980; FRCP (UK) 1997, MRCP (UK) 1985. (Char. Cross) Cons. Dermat. Sunderland & S. Tyneside; Fell.sh. (Micrographic Surg. & Cutaneous Oncol.) Vancouver Gen. Hosp. Prev: Sen. Regist. (Dermat.) Gen. Hosp. Birm. & Birm. Childr. Hosp.; Regist. (Dermat.) Dryburn Hosp. Dur.; SHO (Dermat.) W.m. Hosp. Lond.

LANGWORTHY, Geoffrey Watson 10 Bartington Hall Park, Acton Bridge, Northwich CW8 4QU — MRCS Eng. LRCP Lond. 1964. (Liverp.)

LANGWORTHY, Jonathan Norton Deane Northdown Surgery, St Anthony's Way, Cliftonville, Margate CT9 2TR Tel: 01843 296413 Fax: 01843 231231; 9 Alkham Close, Cliftonville, Margate CT9 3JP Tel: 01843 297310 — MB ChB 1982 Manch.; DRCOG 1986.

LANHAM, John Gregory 25 Bishops Road, Highgate, London N6 4HP — MB BCh 1975 Witwatersrand; FRCP Lond. 1994; MRCP (UK) 1978. (Witwatersrand) Cons. Phys. & Rheum. Whipps Cross Hosp. Prev: Sen. Regist. (Med.) St. Bart. Hosp. Lond.

LANHAM, Jonathan Richard Charles The Surgery, 1 Goodrest Croft, Yardley Wood, Birmingham B14 4JL Tel: 0121 474 2059 — MB ChB 1985 Birm.; MRCGP 1990.

LANHAM, Peter Robert White Meadow View, Gaunts Common, Wimborne BH21 4JN Tel: 01258 840512 — MB BS Lond. 1970; FFA RCS Eng. 1976; DA Eng. 1974. (Lond Hosp.) Cons. Anaesth. E. Dorset Health Dist. Prev: Sen. Regist. (Anaesth.) Middlx. Hosp. Lond. & Lond. Chest Hosp.

LANIADO, Mr Marc Elie Department of Urology, Royal Free Hospital, London NW3 2QG Tel: 020 7794 0500 Email: marclaniado@msn.com; 38A Hurlingham Court, Ranelagh Gardens, Fulham, London SW6 3UW Fax: 020 7384 9504 Email: marclaniado@msn.com — MB BS 1989 Lond.; MD London 2001; FRCS (Urol.) 2000; BSc (Hons.) Physiol. Lond. 1986; FRCS Eng. 1993. (Guy's Campus & UMDS) Specialist Regist. Rotat. (Urol.) Char. Cross Hosp. Lond.; Research Regist. (Surg.) Hammersmith Hosp. Lond. Socs: Fell. Roy. Soc. Med.; Eur. Assn. Urol.; BAUS. Prev: Specialist Regist. Rotat. (Urol.) Wexham; Specialist Regist. Rotat. (Urol.) Ashford Middlx.; Research Regist. (Surg.) Hammersmith Hosp. Lond.

LANIGAN, Colm James Marinus Department of Anaesthetics, Lewisham Hospital, Lewisham High St., Lewisham, London SE13 6LH Tel: 020 8333 3000 Fax: 020 8333 3333 — MB BCh BAO 1979 NUI; MD NUI 1988; MRCPI 1983; FRCA 1990; DA (UK) 1988; DCH Dub. 1982. Cons. Anaesth. Univ. Hosp. Lewisham, Lond. Socs: Pain Soc.; Brit. Assn. of Day Surg. Prev: Sen. Regist. (Anaesth.) St. Thos. Hosp. Lond.; Regist. (Anaesth.) Lond. Hosp.; Research Fell. Chest Unit King's Coll. Hosp. Lond.

LANIGAN, Mr Dermot Joseph Department of Urology, Stobhill NHS Trust, Balornock Road, Glasgow G21 3UW Tel: 0141 558 0111 — MB BCh BAO 1984 NUI; MCh NUI 1991; FRCS (Urol.) 1994; FRCSI 1988. Cons. Urol. Stobhill Hosp. Glas. Socs: BMA; Soc. Minimally Invasive Ther.; Roy. Acad. Med. Irel. Prev: Sen. Regist. (Urol.) W.. Infirm. Glas.

LANIGAN, Mrs Lumina Perpetua Fidelis Bromley Hospital NHS Trust, West Kent Eye Centre, Farnborough Hospital, Farnborough, Orpington BR6 2ND Tel: 01689 814400 Fax: 01689 814410 — MB BCh BAO 1981 NUI; MD NUI 1989; FRCS Ed. 1986; FRCOphth 1989; DO Dub. 1984; DCH Dub. 1983. (Univ. Coll. Galway Irel.) Cons. Ophth. Bromley Hosps. Trust & Qu. Mary's Hosp. NHS Trust. Prev: Sen. Regist. (Ophth.) Moorfields Eye Hosp. Lond.; Smith & Nephew Fell. Roy. Coll. Surg. Eng.

LANIGAN, Sean William Birmingham Skin Centre, City Hospital NHS Trust, Dudley Road, Birmingham B18 7QH Tel: 0121 507 6643 Fax: 0121 507 6649 Email: joanne.green@cityhosp.wmids.nhs.uk — MB BCh 1978 Wales; MD Wales 1992; FRCP Lond. 1994; MRCP (UK) 1982; DCH Lond. 1981. (Welsh National School of Medicine) Cons. Dermatol. City Hosp. NHS Trust, Birm.; Cons. Dermatol. P. Chas. Hosp. Merthyr Mid Glam. & Aberdare Gen. Hosp. Socs: Exec. Comm. Mem. Brit. Med. Laser Assoc.; Brit. Assn. Dermatol., Exec. Comm.; Brit. Soc. Of Dermatological Surg. Prev: Lect. (Med. Dermat.) & Hon. Sen. Regist. Univ. of Leeds; Research Fell. Psoriasis Research Inst. Stanford Calif., USA; Cons. Dermatol. P.ss of Wales Hosp. Bro Morgannwg NHS Trust, Bridgend.

LANKESTER, Katharine Jane Wash House, Casewick, Stamford PE9 4RX — BM BCh 1994 Oxf.; MRCP (UK) 1997. (Oxford) Specialist Regist. (Clin. Oncol.) Middlx. Hosp. Lond.

LANKESTER, Peter Felix Ray (retired) Homefield, Station Road, Hillington, King's Lynn PE31 6DE Tel: 01485 600377 — MRCS Eng. LRCP Lond. 1949; DObst RCOG 1952. Prev: Med. Off. Brit. Red Cross Norf.

LANKESTER, Thomas Edwin (Ted) InterHealth, 157 Waterloo Road, London SE1 8US Tel: 020 7902 9000 Fax: 020 7928 0927 Email: tedl@interhealth.org.uk; Shepherd's Rock, Boars Head, Crowborough TN6 3HE Tel: 01892 661421 Fax: 01892 669249 — MB BChir 1972 Camb.; MB BChir Camb. 1971; MA Camb. 1972; MRCGP 1977. (Camb. & St. Thos.) Dir. Sen. Phys. InterHealth Internat. Health Centre Lond.; Med. Adivsor Tearfund, Ch. mission Soc., Interserve.TravelhealthAdvisers Brit. Red Cross, Cadfod; Non exec Dir. People in aid trustee Taj trust. Socs: Fell. Roy. Soc. Trop. Med. & Hyg.; Internat. Soc. Travel Med.(Mem.); Christian Med. Fell.ship - Mem. overseas Serv. c'tee. Prev: Founder Dir. SHARE Community Health Progr., N. India; GP Twickenham; Ho. Surg. & Ho. Phys. Mildmay Mission Hosp. Lond.

LANKSHEAR, William Mark 24A Filey Street, Broomhall, Sheffield S10 2FG — MB ChB 1993 Sheff.

LANMAN, Ian Richard The Child & Family Consultation Service, 146 Broomfield Road, Chelmsford CM1 1RN — MB ChB 1968 Bristol; BSc Bristol 1965; MRCPsych 1972; DPM Eng. 1972. Cons. Child & Adolesc. Psychiat. Chelmsford. Socs: Assoc. Mem. Brit. Psychoanal. Soc. Prev: Cons. Child & Family Psychiat. W. Herts. Community NHS Trust; Sen. Regist. (Psychother.) Cassel Hosp. Richmond; Sen. Regist. (Child & Family Psychiat.) Bristol Childr. Hosp. & Child & Family Guid. Serv.

LANNAS, Paula Anastasia The London Medicolegal Centre, 40 Stockwell St., London SE10 8EY Tel: 020 8853 2100 Fax: 020 8858 3832 — MB ChB 1974 Birm.; MRCPath (Histopath.) 1989; DMJ

1981. Home Off. Path. Prev: Lect. (Forens. Med.) Lond. Hosp. Med. Coll.

LANNES, Beatrice Department of Experimental Psychology, University of Cambridge, Downing St., Cambridge CB2 3EB — MD 1990 Strasbourg.

LANNIGAN, Alan McInnes Accident & Emergency Department, Crosshouse Hospital, Kilmarnock KA2 0BE Tel: 01563 521133 Fax: 01563 572009 Email: alan.lannigan@aaaht.scot.nhs.uk — MB ChB 1982 Glas.; FRCPS Glas. 1991. Cons. A & E Med. CrossHo. Hosp. Kilmarnock.

LANNIGAN, Alison Kerr 9 Smithview, Wishaw ML2 0PY — MB ChB 1989 Glas.; FRCS Glas. 1994.

LANNIGAN, Arthur Michael The Gables, Church Close, Meir Heath, Stoke-on-Trent ST3 7LQ — MB BCh BAO 1969 Belf.

LANNIGAN, Brian George The Orchard, Village Road, Bromborough, Wirral CH62 7EU Tel: 0151 334 2084; Low Eaves, North Close, Bromborough, Wirral CH62 2BU Tel: 0151 334 5417 — MB ChB 1973 Sheff.; MRCP (UK) 1979. (Sheff.) Socs: Birkenhead Med. Soc. Prev: Regist. (Gen. Med.) Mersey Region Hosps.; Research Fell. (Med.) Univ. Liverp.

LANNIGAN, Mr Francis Joseph 22 Meadow Way, Leeds LS17 7QZ — MB ChB 1981 Leeds; FRCS Eng. 1989; FRCS Ed. 1987.

LANNON, Martin Gabriel Friarwood Surgery, Carleton Glen, Pontefract WF8 1SU Tel: 01977 703235 Fax: 01977 600527 — MB BCh BAO 1987 NUI. Prev: Trainee GP Hull HA VTS; Ho. Off. (Gen. Med. & Gen. Surg.) Pontefract Gen. Infirm.

LANNON, Paul Gerard Cleveland House, 16 Spital Terrace, Gainsborough DN21 2HF Tel: 01427 613158 Fax: 01427 616644 — MB BCh BAO 1989 NUI.

LANSBURY, Alastair John 17 North Park Avenue, Leeds LS8 1EJ — MB ChB 1991 Leeds; MRCP (UK) 1994.

LANSBURY, Alison Louise — MB ChB 1991 Leeds; FRCA 2000; MRCGP 1995; DRCOG 1993. Specialist Regist. Leeds United Teachg. Hosp. Prev: Harrogate VTS Scheme.

LANSBURY, Emma Suzanne 9 Orchard Street, West Didsbury, Manchester M20 2LP — MB ChB 1998 Manch.; MB ChB Manch 1998.

LANSBURY, John 8 Depleach Road, Cheadle SK8 1DZ — MB ChB 1965 Liverp.

LANSBURY, Louise Elizabeth 19 Portland Close, Mickleover, Derby DE3 5BR; Clinical Microbiology and Public Health Laboratory, Level 6, Addenbrooke's Hospital, Hills Road, Cambridge CB2 2QW Tel: 01223 257036 — MB BS 1990 Lond.; MSc Manch. 1996; DRCPath 1996. Specialist Regist. (Med. Microbiol.) PHLS Addenbrooke's Hosp. Camb.

LANSBURY, Patricia 8 Depleach Road, Cheadle SK8 1DZ Tel: 0161 428 2035 — MB ChB 1965 Liverp. p/t Clin. Asst., Dept. of Old Age Psychiat., Manch. Ment. Health Partnership. Prev: GP, Manch.

LANSDALL-WELFARE, Richard William 27 Beverley Grove, North Hykeham, Lincoln LN6 8JJ — MB ChB 1980 Sheff.

LANSDELL, Rowland (retired) Aureol House, Pendle Street E., Sabden, Clitheroe BB7 9EQ Tel: 01282 771203 — MB ChB Manch. 1958. Med. Adviser to Indep. Tribunal Serv. Prev: Med. Advisor to FHS Appeal Unit.

LANSDOWN, Mr Mark Reginald John, Air Commodore RAF Dent. Br. St James's University Hospital, Beckett St., Leeds LS9 7TF Tel: 0113 243 3144 Email: mark.lansdown@leedsth.nhs.uk — MB BCh 1981 Wales; BSc (Hons.) Wales 1978, MCh 1992; FRCS Eng. 1985. Cons. Gen. Surg. St. Jas. Univ. Hosp. Leeds; Hon. Sen. Clin. Lect. Univ. Leeds. Socs: Brit. Assn. Surgic. Oncol.; Assn. Endoscopic Surgs.; Brit. Assn. Endocrin. Surg. Prev: Sen. Regist. (Gen. Surg.) Yorks. RHA; Lect. & Regist. (Surg.) Leeds Infirm.

LANSDOWN, Peter Francis Poole (retired) 14 Foxley Lane, Purley CR8 3ED Tel: 020 8668 0004 — MB BS 1951 Lond.; MRCS Eng. LRCP Lond. 1951; DObst RCOG 1956. Prev: Ho. Phys., Resid. Obst. & Resid. Med. Off. (Nuffield Ho.) Guy's Hosp. Lond.

LANSDOWN, Simon Robert Poole Grosvenor Road Surgery, 17 Grosvenor Road, Paignton TQ4 5AZ Tel: 01803 559308 Fax: 01803_ 526702 — MRCS Eng. LRCP Lond. 1974; MRCGP 1990; DGO Papua New Guinea 1981.

LANSDOWNE, John Digby J D Lansdowne and Partners, Helston Medical Centre, Trelawney Road, Helston TR13 8AU Tel: 01326 572637 Fax: 01326 565525; 8 Nansloe Close, Helston TR13 8BP Tel: 01326 562356 — MRCS Eng. LRCP Lond. 1966. (Guy's) Prev: Res. Anaesth. Roy. Cornw. Hosp. Truro; Ho. Surg. N. Middlx. Hosp. Lond.; Ho. Phys. Roy. Cornw. Hosp. Truro.

LANSLEY, Charles Vincent c/o Department of Oral & Facial Surgery, Royal Cornwall Hospital (City), Infimary Hill, Truro TR1 2HZ — MB ChB 1980 Bristol; BDS Bristol 1973; FDS RCPS Glas. 1983; FFD RCSI 1983. Sen. Regist. (Oral & Maxillofacial Surg.) Leeds Gen. Infirm. Prev: Regist. (Oral & Maxillofacial Surg.) Canniesburn Hosp. Glas.

LANSLEY, Marilyn Jane 7 Queens Close, Ascot SL5 8PE — MB BS 1985 Lond.

LANSLEY, Peter Howard, Lt.-Col. RAMC Garrison Medical Centre, Duchess of Kent Barracks, Maida Road, Aldershot GU11 2DW Tel: 01252 340772 Fax: 01252 340435 Email: plaster@pobox.com — MB ChB 1971 Sheff.; MRCGP 1983; DRCOG 1983; MFFP 1996. (Sheff.) Unit Med. Off. Socs: Fell. Roy. Soc. Med. Prev: Sen. Med. Off. Belf. Barracks; Med. Off. Brit. Milit. Hosp. Munster; Sen. Med. Off. Osnabruck.

LANT, Professor Ariel Francis Department of Therapeutics, Chelsea & Westminster Hospital, Fulham Road, London SW10 9NH Tel: 020 8746 8144 Fax: 020 8746 8887; 82 Century Court, Grove End Road, London NW8 9LD — MB ChB 1958 Sheff.; MB ChB (Hons.) Sheff. 1961; PhD Leicester 1969; BSc (1st cl. Hons.) Sheff; FRCP Lond. 1976, M 1966; FRCP Ed. 1973, M 1964; MRCS Eng. LRCP Lond. 1963; FFPM RCP (UK) 1995. (Sheff.) Prof. of Clin. Pharmacol. & Therap. Char. Cross & W.m. Med. Sch. Lond.; Cons. Phys. Chelsea & W.m. Hosp. Lond. Socs: Med. Res. Soc.; Brit. Pharm. Soc.; Fell. Amer. Coll. Clin. Pharmacol. Prev: MRC Clin. Research Fell.; Lect. (Pharmacol. & Therap.) Univ. Sheff.; Winston Ch.ill Memor. Foundat. Fell. 1993.

LANTIN, Harold (retired) 28 The Priory, Priory Park, London SE3 9XA Tel: 020 8852 6947 — MB BCh BAO 1942 Belf.; DPM Eng. 1948. Prev: Hosp. Pract. (Psychiat.) Greenwich Dist. Hosp. & Lewisham Hosp.

LANTOS, Hugh William George 40 Masefield Road, The Scotlands, Wolverhampton WV10 8RZ Tel: 01902 731907 Fax: 01902 727117 — MB BCh BAO 1973 Dub.; MICGP 1986.

LANTOS, Professor Peter Laszlo Department Neuropathology, Institute of Psychiatry, De Crespigny Park, Denmark Hill, London SE5 8AF Tel: 020 7703 8403 Fax: 020 7708 3895 Email: iopnpath@iop.bpmf.ac.uk — MD 1964 Szeged; PhD Lond. 1973, DSc 1992; FRCPath 1987, M 1975. (Med. Univ. Szeged, Hungary) Prof. Neuropath. Univ. Lond.; Hon. Cons. Neuropath. Bethlem Roy. & Maudsley, King's Coll. & St. Thos. Hosps. Lond. Socs: (Pres.) Brit. Neuropath Soc.; Path. Soc.; Amer. Assn. Neuropath. Prev: Acad. Co-ordinator Neurosci. Centre King's Coll. Hosp.; Sen. Lect. (Neuropath.) Middlx. Hosp. Med. Sch. Lond.; Hon. Cons. Neuropath. Middlx. Hosp. Lond.

LANYON, Peter Charles 30 St Leonards Drive, Nottingham NG8 2BB — MB ChB 1986 Birm.; MRCP (UK) 1991; MRCGP 1990; DRCOG 1989; DM Nott 1999. Cons. Rhem. Qu.'s Med. Centre Nottm. Prev: Sen. Regist. (Rheum.) City Hosp. Nottm.; Regist. (Med.) Walsgrave Hosp. Coventry; Trainee GP E. Birm. Hosp. VTS.

LANZ, Jack Paul (retired) Polesworth & Dordon Group Practice, The Surgery, 162 Long St., Dordon, Tamworth B78 1QA Tel: 01827 892893 Fax: 01827 331420 — MB ChB 1958 Glas. Prev: Ho. Surg. & Ho. Phys. Falkirk Roy. Infirm.

LANZON-MILLER, Sandro Milton Keynes General Hospital, Standing Way, Eaglestone, Milton Keynes MK6 5 — MB BCh 1980 Wales; MD Wales 1988; MRCP (UK) 1984. Cons. Milton Keynes Gen. Hosp. Prev: Sen. Regist. Middlx. Hosp. Lond.; Sen. Regist. Univ. Coll. Hosp. Lond.; Sen. Regist. (Med.) Whittington Hosp. Lond.

LAOPODIS, Vasilios The Glenfield Hospital, Department of Thoracic Surgery, Groby Road, Leicester LE3 9QP — Ptychio Iatrikes 1975 Thessalonika.

LAPASSET, Michel Marie Ferdinand 8 Elizabeth Place, St Helier, Jersey JE2 3PN Tel: 01534 874095 — MD 1957 Nancy. (Univ. Nancy) Socs: Brit. Med. Acupunct. Soc.

LAPHAM, Gary Peter, Capt. RAMC Retd. Boehringer Ingelheim, Ellesfield Avenue, Bracknell RG12 8YS Tel: 01344 741488 — MB BCh 1984 Wales; BSc (Hons.) Pharmacol. Wales 1979; MRCP (UK) 1989. Dir. of Med. Operat. Gp. III Pharmaceut. Med. Boehringer Ingelheim Berks. Prev: Regist. (Geriat.) St. Woolos Newport Gwent.

LAPKA, Boguslaw Adam Greencroft Medical Centre (South), Greencroft Wynd, Annan DG12 6GS Tel: 01461 202244 Fax: 01461 205401 — MB ChB 1972 Ed.; DCH Eng. 1976.

LAPPER, John, OStJ, Maj.-Gen. late RAMC (retired) The Chimes, 4 Manor Fields, Alrewas, Burton-on-Trent DE13 7DA Tel: 01283 791628 — MB ChB 1946 Birm.; FFPHM 1980, M 1973; DLO Eng. 1952. Cons. Internat. Hosp. Gp. Prev: Med. Dir. Internat. Hosps. Gp.

LAPPIN, Julia Margaret 6 Downshire Park, Hillsborough BT26 6HB — MB ChB 1997 Ed.

LAPPIN, Kieran Joseph 43 North Circular Road, Lurgan, Craigavon BT67 9LG — MB BCh BAO 1993 Belf.

LAPPIN, Simon Jeremy Top Right Flat, 227 Wilton St., Glasgow G20 6DE — MB ChB 1998 Glas.; MB ChB Glas 1998.

LAPRAIK, Mary Ringrose 24 Corstophine Hill Gardens, Edinburgh EH12 6LA — MB ChB 1984 Aberd.

LAPSIA, Jasmine Bracon Dale House, 141 Buxton Road, Heaviley, Stockport SK2 6EQ — MB ChB 1991 Leeds; DFFP 1995; MRCGP 1996; DRCOG 1996.

LAPSIA, Kishore Chapsi — MB BS 1966 Nagpur; FRCR 1977; DMRD Eng. 1968; DMRE Bombay 1967. (Med. Coll. Nagpur) Cons. (Radiol.) Tameside Gen. Hosp. Aston.

LAPSIA, Snehal Kishore 58 Boddens Hill Road, Heaton Mersey, Stockport SK4 2DG Tel: 0797 437 3856 — MB ChB 1998 Manch.; MB ChB Manch 1998. PRHO.

LAPSLEY, David Henry Michael 66 Balham Park Road, London SW12 8DU Tel: 020 8954 2300 — MB BCh BAO 1981 Belf.; MB BCh Belf. 1981. Lect. Osteoarticular Path. Roy. Nat. Orthop. Hosp. Prev: Lect. Histopath. United Med. & Dent. Schs. of Guy's & St. Thos. Hosps.

LAPSLEY, Marta 66 Balham Park Road, London SW12 8DU — MB BCh BAO 1983 Belf.; MB BCh Belf. 1983.

LAPSLEY, Patricia Mary Southport Primecare, 170 Lord St., Southport PR9 0QA Tel: 01704 544097 Fax: 01704 501032 — MB ChB 1976 Liverp.; BSc (1st cl. Hons.) Leeds 1968.

LAPSLEY, Sandra Aylward 61A Newton Street, Greenock PA16 8SE Tel: 01475 27924 — MB ChB 1966 Glas. Sen. Med. Off. (Community Health) Inverclyde Health Dist.

LAPWOOD, Suzanne Gwendolen Marcham Road Family Health Centre, Abingdon OX14 1BT Tel: 01235 522602; The Vicarage, 24 Church St, Marcham, Abingdon OX13 6NP Tel: 01865 391973 Fax: 01865 391973 Email: susielapwood@bigfoot.com — BM BCh 1982 Oxf.; MA Camb. 1983; MRCGP 1986; DRCOG 1985. (Oxf. And Camb.) GP (Doctors' Retainer Scheme); Dep. Med. Dir., Helen Ho. childr.'s Hospice Oxf. Prev: GP High Wycombe, Castle Hedingham & Ipswich.

LAPWORTH, Caroline 478 Kirkstall Road, Burley Wood, Leeds LS4 2QD — MB ChB 1996 Leeds.

LAQUEUR, Sylvia Ruth Hampstead Group Practice, 75 Fleet Road, London NW3 2QU Tel: 020 7435 4000 Fax: 020 7435 9000 — MB BS 1972 Lond.; MRCS Eng. LRCP Lond. 1972; MRCGP 1977. (Roy. Free) Prev: Ho. Phys. St. Ann's Hosp. Tottenham; Ho. Surg. Roy. Free Hosp. Lond.

LARAH, Deborah Gail Higher Broughton Health Centre, Bevendon Square, Salford M7 4TP Tel: 0161 792 2142 — MB ChB 1980 Manch.

LARAMAN, Catherine Rhoslan Surgery, 4 Pwllycrochan Avenue, Colwyn Bay LL29 7DA Tel: 01492 532125 Fax: 01492 530662 — MB BS 1995 London; MB BS 1995 London.

LARARD, David Geoffrey Moreton Lodge, 9 Eastnor Grove, Leamington Spa CV31 1LD Tel: 01926 422732 — MB ChB 1955 Birm.; FFA RCS Eng. 1960. (Birm.) p/t Indep. Cons. Anaesth. Leamington Spa. Prev: Cons. Anaesth. Warwick Hosp. NHS Trust.

LARBALESTIER, Nicholas Peter 102 Harley Street, London W1N 1AF — MB ChB 1989 Liverp.; MRCP (UK) 1994. Specialist Regist. St Thomas' Hosp. Lond.

LARBI, Emmanuel Douglas 16 Bridge Avenue, London W7 3DJ — MB BCh 1997 Wales.

LARCHER, Victor Frederick Queen Elizabeth Childrens Services at the Royal Lond Hospital, Whitechapel, London E11 BB Tel: 020 7377 7000 Ext: 3986; 51 St. John's Park, Blackheath, London SE3 7JW — MB 1970 Camb.; FRCPCH 1997; MA (Med. Ethics & Law) Lond. 1990; BA Camb. 1966, MB 1970, BChir 1969; FRCP Lond. 1986; MRCP (UK) 1972. (Camb.) Cons. Paediat. Qu. Eliz Childr.s Serv.s; Hon sen. Lec Qu. Mary W.field coll univ lond; Hon. Cons. Paed Gt. Ormond St Hosp for Child NHS Trust, City & Hackney comm trust. Prev: Lect. in Child Health Univ. Lond., King's Coll. Hosp. Med. Sch. Lond.; Med. Regist. Med. Profess. Unit Hosp. Sick Childr. Gt. Ormond St.; Lond.; Alwynne Burser Dept. Experim. Path. St. Bart. Hosp. Lond.

LARCHET, Paul Kenneth 3 Yarley Close, Tonbridge TN9 1QA Tel: 01732 355786; Worthing Hospital, Pk Avenue, Worthing BN11 2DH Tel: 01903 205111 — MB BS 1996 Lond.; BSc (Hons.) Lond. 1993. (Charing Cross and Westminster) SHO (Med.).

LARCOMBE, Celia Silver Birches, Blackpond Lane, Farnham Royal, Slough SL2 3EG — MB ChB 1997 Manch. (Manchester)

LARCOMBE, James Hugh Harbinson House Surgery, Front Street, Sedgefield TS21 3BN Tel: 01740 620300 Fax: 01740 622075; Tel: 01740 620717 — MB ChB 1982 Bristol; FRCGP 1997, M 1987; DRCOG 1986; Dip. Adv. Gen. Pract. 1997. (Bristol) GP Princip. Sedgefield, Durh.; NHSE N.ern & Yorks. Regional Research Fell./ Research Fell.Univ. of Durh.; Sec., Co.Durh. & Darlington Local Research EMD'Cs Comm.; RCGP Examr. Prev: Clin. Asst (Geriat) Sedgefield Community Hosp. GP Trainer.

LARCOMBE, Peter John Flat 1, 21 Chesham Place, Brighton BN2 1FB — MB BS 1993 Lond. SHO (Anaesth.) Roy. Sussex Co. Hosp. Brighton.

LARGE, Alan Hugh Dermot (retired) 1 Barnton Park, Edinburgh EH4 6JF Tel: 0131 336 3370 — MB ChB 1943 Ed.; FRCGP 1979 M 1953. Prev: Capt. RAMC.

LARGE, Constance Murison Barnsley (retired) Barclays Bank plc, PO Box 107, 4 Water St., Liverpool L69 2DU — MB BS 1939 Lond.; MRCS Eng. LRCP Lond. 1937.

LARGE, Mr David Franklin Ayr Hospital, Dalmellington Road, Ayr KA6 6DX Tel: 01292 610558 Email: david_large@aaaht.scot.nhs.uk; 22 Rigwoodie Place, Alloway, Ayr KA7 4PR Email: d.f.large@btinternet.com — MB ChB 1978 Ed.; FRCS (Orth.) 1991; FRCS Ed. 1982. Cons. Orthop. Surg. Ayr Hosp. Prev: Sen. Regist. (Orthop. Surg.) Aberd. Roy. Infirm.

LARGE, David Martin 15 Goose Garth, Wetheral, Carlisle CA4 8JR — MB ChB 1972 Manch.; MD Manch. 1979, BDS (Hons.) 1967; FRCP Lond. 1990; FRCP Ed. 1987; MRCP (UK) 1976. Cons. Phys. Cumbld. Infirm. Carlisle. Socs: Brit. Diabetic Assn. Prev: Sen. Regist. (Med.) Manch. Roy. Infirm.; MRC Research Fell. Hope Hosp. Salford; Lect. (Med.) Univ. Manch.

LARGE, Gareth Adrian 27 Trent Boulevard, Ladybay, West Bridgford, Nottingham NG2 5BB — MB BCh 1993 Wales; MRCP (UK) 1997. Specialist Regist. (Cardiol.) Nottm. City Hosp.

LARGE, Joanne 8 The Incline, Lilleshall, Newport TF10 9AP — MB ChB 1984 Birm.

LARGE, Stephen Helliwell Horse Fair Surgery, 12 Horse Fair, Banbury OX16 0AJ Tel: 01295 259484 Fax: 01295 279293; 17 Silver Street, Chacombe, Banbury OX17 2JR Tel: 01295 711155 — BM BCh 1974 Oxf.; MRCP (UK) 1977. GP Banbury. Prev: Med. Regist. Radcliffe Infirm. Oxf.; SHO Med. (Rotating) Centr. Middlx. Hosp.; SHO (Neurol.) St. Thos. Hosp. Lond.

LARGE, Mr Stephen Ralph c/o Papworth Hospital, Papworth Everard, Cambridge CB3 8RE Tel: 01480 830541 Fax: 01480 364334 Email: stephenrlarge@hotmail.com — MB BS 1976 Lond.; 2000 FETSC; BSc (Hons. Anat. & Physics) Lond. 1973, MS 1989; FRCS Eng. 1980; MRCS Eng. LRCP Lond. 1976; MRCP (UK) 1980; FRCP 1998; MS 1989; MA 1998; MBA 2000. (Guy's) Cons. Cardiothoracic Surg. Papworth Hosp. Camb.; Vice-Dean (Med. Educat.) Papworth Camb.; Assn. Lect. Univ. Camb. Socs: Brit. Cardiac Soc.; Brit. Soc. Heart Failure; ISHLT. Prev: Surgic. Train. Rotatation St. Bart. Hosp.

LARGENT, Tracey Masonic House Surgery, 26 High Street, Buckingham MK18 1NU Tel: 01280 816450 Fax: 01280 823885 — MB BS 1993 Lond.; MRCGP 1997; DFFP 1997; DRCOG 1997.

LARGEY, Patrick Mason 24 Meadow Way, Kinoulton, Nottingham NG12 3RE — MB BS 1965 Lond.; MFPM RCP (UK) 1989. (Char. Cross) Med. Manager Boots Healthcare Internat. Nottm. Prev: Med. Affairs Manager SmithKline Beecham Consumer Brands Weybridge; GP Newbury; Flight Lt. RAF Med. Br.

LARI, Mr Jalal (retired) 161 Plymouth Road, Penarth CF64 5DG Tel: 02920 708968 — MB ChB 1959 Sheff.; FRCS Eng. 1967.

Cons. Paediat. Surg. Univ. Hosp. Wales Cardiff. Prev: Sen. Regist. (Paediat. Surg.) Childr. Hosp. Sheff.

***LARI, Jonathan** 161 Plymouth Road, Penarth CF64 5DG Tel: 01222 708968 — MB BCh 1994 Wales.

LARK, Kathy Anne 19 Valley Place, Glenbuck Road, Surbiton KT6 6DL — MB BS 1991 Newc.; MRCGP 1996. GP. Prev: GP Career Start Durh.

LARKIN, Bernadette Ann 96 Harboro Road, Sale M33 6GF — MB ChB 1983 Leic.; MRCPsych 1988.

LARKIN, Catherine Joanne 3 Bann Lane, Glenavy, Crumlin BT29 4HP — MB ChB BAO 1991 Belf.

LARKIN, Mr Daniel Francis Moorfields Eye Hospital, City Road, London EC1V 2PD Tel: 020 7566 2045 Fax: 020 7566 2972; 62 wimpole Street, London W1G 8AT Tel: 0207935 5900 Fax: 020 7224 5900 — MB BCh BAO 1982 Dub.; MD Bristol 1992; FRCS Glas. 1986; MRCPI 1984; FCOphth 1988; DO RCSI 1986. (Trinity Coll. Dub.) Cons. Ophth. Sug. Moorfields Eye Hosp. Lond. Socs: Transpl. Soc.; Brit. Transpl. Soc. Prev: Sen. Regist. Moorfields Eye Hosp. Lond.; Lect. (Ophth.) Univ. Bristol.

LARKIN, Mr Edward Brendan Royal Wolverhampton Hospitals NHS Trust, New Cross Hospital, Wolverhampton WV1O 0QP Tel: 01902 307999/01902 644901; Email: edlark@lwcdial.net — MB BChir 1986 Camb.; BChD Leeds 1980; FRCS Eng. 1993; FRCS Ed. 1993; FDS RCS Eng. 1990, LDS 1980; DRCOG 1991. (Camb.) Cons. Maxillofacial & Oral Surg. Roy. Wolverhampton Hosps. NHS Trust. Socs: BMA; Fell. Roy. Soc. Med.; Fell. Brit. Assn. Oral & Maxillofacial Surg. Prev: Sen. Regist. Maxilliofacial & Oral Surg. N. Wales; Regist maxillofacial & oral surg canniesburn hosp Glas..; SHO (Surg.) Roy. Hants Co. Hosp. Winchester.

LARKIN, Edward Henry (retired) c/o National Westminster Bank, Harley St., London W1 — MB BS 1930 Sydney; MRCP Lond. 1946; DPM Eng. 1937; FRCPsych 1971. Prev: Cons. Psychiat. W. End Hosp. Neurol.

LARKIN, Elizabeth 2 Ladybower Avenue, Linthwaite, Huddersfield HD4 5XA — MB ChB 1982 Bristol.

LARKIN, Emmet Phelim Arnold Lodge, Regional Secure Unit, Cordelia Close, Leicester LE5 0LE Tel: 0116 225 6083 Fax: 01162256128 Email: larkin9948@aol.com — MB BCh BAO 1973 NUI; MRCPsych 1982. (Univ. Coll. Dub.) Cons. Forens. Psychiat. & Clin. Dir., E. Midl. Centre For Forens. Ment. Health Leicester. Socs: BMA; AUTP. Prev: Cons. Forens. Psychiat. Rampton Hosp. Retford; Sen. Regist. (Psychiat.) Trent RHA (T); Regist. Rotat. (Psychiat.) Notts. AHA (T).

LARKIN, Genevieve Brigid Rosario 3A Cecil Mansions, London SW17 7QN — MB BCh BAO 1981 NUI; MRCPI 1984.

LARKIN, Hugh 88 Pannal Ash Road, Harrogate HG2 9AB — MB ChB 1974 Glas.; MRCP (UK) 1977. Cons. Phys. Harrogate Dist. Hosp. Prev: Sen. Regist. Roy. Infirm Glas.

LARKIN, James Michael George Garfield House, Port Isaac PL29 3SG — BM BCh 1996 Oxf.

LARKIN, Jayne Alexandra Margaret 28 Ballyhay Road, Donaghadee BT21 0LU — MB BCh BAO 1992 Belf.

LARKIN, Joanna Mary Russell House Surgery, Baker's Way, Codsall, Wolverhampton WV8 1HD Tel: 01902 842488 Email: jolarkin@doctors.net.uk — BM 1989; DCH 1991 Glasgow; MRCGP 1992 Edinburgh; DFFP 1995; DRCOG 1991 Manchester. (Southampton)

LARKIN, John Gerarde Victoria Infirmary, Langside Road, Glasgow G42 9T Tel: 0141 201 6000; 51 Newlands Road, Glasgow G43 2JH Tel: 0141 632 3998 — MB ChB 1978 Glas.; MD Glas. 1991; FRCP Glas. 1994; MRCP (UK) 1981. Cons. Phys. & Rheum. Vict. Infirm. Glas.; Hon. Sen. Clin. Lect. Univ. Glas.

LARKIN, Malachy Peter Old Mill Surgery, 100 Old Mill Road, Uddingston, Glasgow G71 7JB Tel: 01698 817219 — MB ChB 1984 Glas.

LARKIN, Mary Patricia Dundalk Street Surgery, 53 Dundalk Street, Newtownhamilton, Newry BT35 0PB Tel: 028 3087 8204 Fax: 028 3087 8196 — MB BCh BAO 1989 Belf.; MRCGP 1994.

LARKIN, Peter Stephen Upton Group Practice, 32 Ford Road, Wirral CH49 0TF Tel: 0151 677 0486 Fax: 0151 604 0635; Virginia, 28 Mount Road, Upton, Wirral CH49 6JB Tel: 0151 677 1471 — MB ChB 1982 Liverp.; MRCGP 1987; DRCOG 1984. Prev: Trainee GP S. Sefton HA VTS; Ho. Off. St. Helens Hosp.

LARKIN, Sarah Catherine 41 Trinity Avenue, Bush Hill Park, Enfield EN1 1HT — MB BS 1998 Lond.; MB BS Lond 1998.

LARKIN, Valerie Jean 44 Shalmsford Street, Chartham, Canterbury CT4 7RL Tel: 01227 738640 — MB ChB 1972 Leeds.

LARKWORTHY, Andrew John The Surgery, 166 New Road, Croxley Green, Rickmansworth WD3 3HD Tel: 01923 778277 — MB BS 1984 Lond.; BSc Lond. 1981; MRCGP 1991; DCH RCP Lond. 1988; DRCOG 1987. (Char. Cross) GP Trainer Herts.; PCT Exec. Comm. Mem., Watford and Three Rivers PCT.

LARKWORTHY, Jean Barbara (retired) 218 Pampisford Road, South Croydon CR2 6DB — MB BS 1953 Lond.; DPH Lond. 1960; DCH Eng. 1957. Prev: SCMO Croydon HA.

LARMER, Simon David Portchester Health Centre, West Street, Portchester, Fareham PO16 9TU; 48 Castle Street, Portchester, Fareham PO16 9PU Tel: 01705 365483 Fax: 01705 365483 — MB BS 1986 Lond.; MRCGP 1992; DRCOG 1991; DCH RCP Lond. 1990. (St. Mary's Hosp. Med. Sch. Lond.) Socs: MRCGP. Prev: Trainee GP Drayton; SHO (O & G) St. Mary's Hosp. Portsmouth; SHO (Paediat.) Roy. Berks. Hosp.

LARMOUR, Pauline Anne Blair Unit, Royal Cornhill Hospital, Aberdeen AB25 2ZH Tel: 01224 403044 Fax: 01224840974; 24 Kingshill Road, Aberdeen AB15 5JY Tel: 01224 318505 Email: plarmour@hotmail.com — MB ChB 1989 Dundee; BMSc Med. Psychol. Dund 1986; MRCPsych 1993. (Dundee) Cons. (Forens. Psychiat.),Roy. Cornhill Hosp., Aberd.. Prev: Sen. Regist. (Forens. Psychiat.) Murray Roy. Hosp. Perth; Regist. (Psychiat.) Liff Hosp. Dundee & Hairmyres Hosp. Glas.; SHO (Psychiat.) Roy. Dundee Liff Hosp.

LARMOUR, Peter Francis Holly Cottage, Platts Lane, Tarvin, Chester CH3 8HR Email: peterlarmour@tarvin6.freeserve.co.uk — MB ChB 1980 Dundee. (Ninewells, Dundee) Socs: Nat. Assn. Non-Princip.

LARNER, Andrew Jonathan National Hospital for Neurology & Neurosurgery, London WC1N 3BG Tel: 020 7837 3611 Fax: 020 7829 8720; 15 Osprey Close, Hartford, Huntingdon PE29 1UX — BM BCh 1987 Oxf.; MA Camb. 1995, MD 1996; MRCP (UK) 1990; DHMSA 1995.

LARNER, Timothy Ronald George 70 Waldegrave Road, Brighton BN1 6GE — MB BS 1991 Lond.

LARSEN, Carole Jane 3 Beckfoot Mill, Beckfoot Lane, Bingley BD16 1AR — MB ChB 1986 Leeds; MRCGP 1990; DRCOG 1991.

LARSEN, Christoph Heinrich Flat 17, 11 Endsleigh Gardens, London WC1H 0EH — State Exam Med 1991 Bonn.

LARSEN, David Paul Frederick 42 Bell Street, Maidenhead SL6 1BR — MB BS 1991 Lond.

LARSEN, Finn Ipsen International, 14 Kensington Square, London W8 5HH Tel: 020 7938 1957 Fax: 020 7938 2976; Kensington Centre, 66 Hammersmith Road, London W14 8UD — MD 1973 Odense.

LARSEN, Jane Elizabeth Loughborough University Medical Centre, Loughborough University of Technology, Loughborough LE11 3TU Tel: 01509 222061; Loughborough University Medical Centre, Loughborough LE11 3TU Tel: 01509 222061 — MB ChB 1988 Manch.; BSc (Med. Sci.) St. And. 1985; MRCGP 1996. Prev: Trainee GP/SHO Chesterfield & N. Derbysh. Roy. Hosp. NHS Trust; SHO (Anaesth.) Derby Roy. Infirm.

LARSEN, Joerg University of Manchester, Department of Medicine, Hope Hospital, Clinical Sciences Building, Eccles Old Road, Salford M6 8HD Tel: 0161 789 7373 Fax: 0161 787 4031; Flat 12, Grosvenor Court, 75 Ashton Lane, Sale M33 5SE — State Exam Med 1992 Kiel; MD Kiel 1992. SHO (Gen. Med.) Hope Hosp. Salford. Prev: SHO (Ment. & Transpl. Med.) Oxf. Regional Renal Unit.

LARSEN, Thomas Andrew Yew Tree Surgery, Yew Tree House, North End Road, Yapton, Arundel BN18 0DU Tel: 01243 551321 Fax: 01243 555101; Lyndhurst, Eastergate Lane, Eastergate, Chichester PO20 6SJ Tel: 01243 543187 — MB BS 1976 Lond.; DA (UK) 1980; DRCOG 1980. (Univ. Coll. Hosp.)

LARSON, Alex George 19 Drift Road, Wallington, Fareham PO16 8SZ Tel: 01329 234758 — MB BS 1952 Durh.; FFA RCS Eng. 1964; DA Eng. 1958. (Newc.) Cons. Anaesth. Portsmouth Hosp. Gp.; Hon. Clin. Teach. Anaesth. Univ. Soton. Socs: Intractable Pain Soc.; Assn. Anaesths. Gt. Brit. & Irel. Prev: Sen. Regist. (Anaesth.)

Qu. Vict. Hosp. E. Grinstead; Fell. Dept. Anaesth. Univ. Penna. Philadelphia; Asst. Med. Off. Cook Is.s.

LARSSON, Eva Magdalena 155A Old Bath Road, Cheltenham GL53 7DN — MB BS 1998 Lond.; MB BS Lond 1998.

LARSSON, Stephan Nikolas 2 Pinfold Cottages, Ribchester, Preston PR3 — MB ChB 1978 Birm.; MRCP (UK) 1982; FRCR 1986. Research Fell. Clin. Trials Unit Qu. Eliz. Hosp. Edgbaston. Prev: Regist. (Med.) N.ampton Gen. Hosp.; Regist. (Radiother. & Oncol.) Christie Hosp. & Holt Radium Inst. Manch.

LARTEY, Ebenezer Hughes c/o Belvidere Hospital, London Road, Glasgow G31 4PG Tel: 0141 554 1855 ext. 391; 6 Harris Close, Newton Mearns, Glasgow G77 6TU — MB ChB 1976 Ghana; FFA RCSI 1985.

LARTEY, Jonathan Paul Akueteh 35 Millfield Close, Chichester PO19 4UR — BM 1998 Soton.; BM Soton 1998.

LARVIN, Mr Michael Leeds Institute of Minimally Invasive Therapy, Wellcome Wing, The General Infirmary, Leeds LS1 3EX Tel: 0113 392 2992 Fax: 0113 392 6305 Email: mikelarvin@limit.ac.uk — MB BS 1981 Lond.; MD Leeds 1994; FRCS 1987; MRCS Eng. LRCP Lond. 1981. (Guy's) Cons. Surg. & Sen. Clin. Lect. Leeds Teachg. Hosps. Trust. Socs: Pancreatic Soc. (Com. Mem Pres elect); Brit. Soc. Gastroenterol. (Counc. Pancreatic Sect.); Eur. Assn. Endoscopic Surgs. Prev: Cons. Surg. Lewisham Hosp. NHS Trust & Hon. Sen. Lect. UMDS Univ. Lond.; Research Fell. & Lect. Univ. Leeds; Regist. & Ho. Surg. Guy's Hosp. Lond.

LASA GALLEGO, Miguel Alfonso 110 Glendale Park, Newtownbreda, Belfast BT8 6HS — LMS 1990 Salamanca.

LASA GEORGAS, Adriana Edurne 22 Campden Hill Gardens, London W8 7AZ — LMS 1990 U Complutense, Madrid.

LASCELLES, Brian Desmond (retired) The Old Stable, Manor Farm, Cattistock, Dorchester DT2 0JJ Tel: 01300 320789 — MB BS Lond. 1952. Prev: Clin. Asst. Diabetic Clinic St Bart.

LASCELLES, Clarence Felix (retired) 30 White Rocks Grove, Mill Lane, Whitburn, Sunderland SR6 7LL Tel: 0191 529 4647 — MB ChB 1944 Aberd.; FRCPsych 1974, M 1971; DPM Durham. 1954. Prev: Cons. Psychiat. Cherry Knowle Hosp. Sunderland.

LASCELLES, Felice Clare 86 Naunton Crescent, Cheltenham GL53 7BE — MB ChB 1991 Bristol.

LASCELLES, Karine Pascale Flat 7 Wilberforce House, 15-17 Clapham Common N., London SW4 0RG — MB ChB 1993 Bristol.

LASCELLES, Peter Terence (retired) Flat 26, Gate Hill Court, 166 Notting Hill Gate, London W11 3QT Tel: 020 7727 9461 — MB BS 1953 Lond.; MD Lond. 1965; FRCPath 1977, M 1965. Prev: Cons. Chem. Path. Nat. Hosp. Qu. Sq. Lond.

LASCELLES, Raymond George 16 St John Street, Manchester M3 4EA — MD Aberd. 1964, MB ChB (Hnrs.) 1955; FRCP Lond. 1974, M 1961; DPM Eng. 1961. Sen. Cons. Neurophysiol. Manch. Roy. Infirm. Socs: Fell. Roy. Soc. Med.; BMA. Prev: Chief Asst. (Neurol.) Guy's Hosp. Lond.; Resid. Med. Off. Nat. Hosp. Qu. Sq.; Regist. (Neurol. & Psychol. Med.) St. Thos. Hosp. Lond.

LASEINDE, Olufunto Oluwatoyin 53 Waterside Drive, Chichester PO19 2PJ — MB BS 1982 Ibadan; MRCOG 1992.

LASHEN, Hany Abdel Maksoud Ali 9 Riverside Crescent, Hall Green, Birmingham B28 0QZ Tel: 0121 474 4630 — MB BCh 1981 Ains Shams; MRCOG 1991.

LASHFORD, Anne Marie Rowden Surgery, Rowden Hill, Chippenham SN15 2SB Tel: 01249 444343 Fax: 01249 446797; Whitley House, Whitley, Melksham SN12 8QG Tel: 01225 703435 Email: amlashford@aol.com — MB ChB 1972 (Hons.) Bristol; BSc (Hons. Biochem.) Bristol 1972; MRCGP 1980; DRCOG 1979; Cert. JCC Lond. 1979; DCH Eng. 1978. (Bristol) Gen. Practitioner, Rowen Surg., Chippenham; Vice Chairm. Wilts. GMC. Socs: UK Advisory Fac. Adv. Life Support in Obstet. Prev: Clin. Asst. (Obst.) Bristol Matern. Hosp.; Research Asst. (Child Health) Univeristy Bristol.; Dep. Police Surg. Wilts. Police Auth.

LASHFORD, Linda Suzanne 11 Wolseley Place, Manchester M20 3LR — BM BS 1979 Nottm.

LASK, Professor Bryan Dean St Georges Hospital Medical School, London SE17 0RE Tel: 020 8682 6683 Fax: 020 8682 6724 Email: b.lask@sghms.ac.uk; Tel: 0208 299 2178 Fax: 0208 299 2178 — MPhil Lond. 1973, MB BS 1966; MRCS Eng. LRCP Lond. 1966; FRCPCH 1997; FRCPsych 1988, M 1973. (St. Bart.) Cons. St. Geo. Hosp. Med. Sch.; Hon. Cons. Gt. Ormond St. Hosp. Lond.; Med. Adviser Huntercombe Manor Hosp. Berks. Socs: Fell. Inst. Coll. Psychosomatic Med.; Acad. of eating disorders; Eating disorders research soc. Prev: Cons. Gt. Ormond St Hosp. Lond.; Regist. Maudsley Hosp. Lond. & Roy. Free Hosp. Lond.; Vis. Prof. Univ. Brit. Columbia.

LASK, Jack Philip, Capt. RAMC Retd. (retired) 19 Knole Wood, Devenish Road, Sunningdale, Ascot SL5 9QR Tel: 01344 622132 — MB ChB Leeds 1940. Prev: Capt. RAMC 1940-46.

LASKIEWICZ, Bozena Maria 24 Brunswick Gardens, London W5 1AP — MB BCh BAO 1968 NUI; FRCS Eng. 1976; DLO Eng. 1972. ENT Surg. Epsom Dist. Hosp. & Qu. Mary's Hosp. Childr. Carshalton. Socs: BMA; Roy. Soc. Med.; Brit. Assn. Paediat. Otol. Prev: Sen. Regist. King's Coll. Hosp. Lond.; Sen. Regist. & Regist. Roy. Nat. Throat, Nose & Ear Hosp. Lond.

LASLETT, Robert McKenzie (retired) Clampers, High Road, Cookham, Maidenhead SL6 9JF Tel: 01628 521362 — MB ChB 1943 Manch.; MRCS Eng. LRCP Lond. 1945; MFCM 1974; DPH Eng. 1960. Prev: MOH Maidenhead Boro. & Cookham RD.

LASMAN, Francesca Camilla Anna Alconbury and Brampton Surgeries, The Surgery, School Lane, Alconbury, Huntingdon PE28 4EQ Tel: 01480 890281 Fax: 01480 891787; 74 Owl End, Great Stukeley, Huntingdon PE28 4AQ — MB BS 1983 Lond.; MA Camb. 1983; MRCGP 1988; DCH RCP Lond. 1986; DRCOG 1985. Prev: Trainee GP Huntingdon VTS; SHO (Paediat., Accid & Emerg., Ophth., ENT, & O & G) Hinchingbrooke Hosp. Huntingdon.

LASOYE, Tunji Abdullah 11 Britton Close, London SE6 1AP Tel: 020 8488 2110 Fax: 020 8488 2110 Email: tlasoy@aol.com — MB ChB 1989 Obafemi Awolowo Univ. Nigeria; FRCS 1997. Specialist Regist. (A&E), Univ. Hosp. Lewisham. Socs: BMA; BAEM; FAEM. Prev: Specialist Regist. (A & E), Conquest Hosp., St Leonards on Sea; SHO (Gen. Surg.) Medway Hosp. Gillingham; SHO (Orthop.) Medway Hosp. Gillingham.

LASRADO, Maya Frances 7 Taylor Road, Wallington SM6 0AY — MB BS 1991 Lond.

LASSEN, Brigadier Edric Henry Peter, CBE, DSO, Brigadier late RAMC Retd. (retired) — MRCS Eng. LRCP Lond. 1933; MRCGP 1961.

LASSERSON, Elias Michael 34 Carver Road, Herne Hill, London SE24 9LT Tel: 020 7274 6821 Fax: 020 7737 5015 — MB BS Lond. 1969; BDS Lond. 1958; MRCS Eng. LRCP Lond. 1969; MRCGP 1978; FDS RCS Eng. 1965; FRCGP 1999. (Guy's & Char. Cross) p/t Sen.Vis. Med. Off. Nightingdale Home, Lond. Socs: BMA; Treas. S. Lond. Fac. RCGP; Fell. RSM. Prev: Clin. Asst. (Gen. Surg.) Croydon Gen. Hosp.; SHO (Paediat. & O & G) St. Mary's Gen. Hosp. Portsmouth; Ho. Phys. & Ho. Surg. Wycombe Gen. Hosp.

LASSERSON, John Anthony The Surgery, 1 Church Road, Mitcham CR4 3YU Tel: 020 8648 2579 Fax: 020 8640 4013; 141 Banstead Road S., Sutton SM2 5LL Tel: 020 8643 2121 — MB BS 1970 Lond.; MRCS Eng. LRCP Lond. 1970; MRCGP 1981. (St. Geo.) Hosp. Pract. (Respirat. Med.) St. Helier Hosp. Carshalton. Socs: BMA. Prev: SHO (Path.) St. Geo. Hosp. Lond.; Ho. Surg. Warneford Gen. Hosp. Leamington Spa; Ho. Phys. Croydon Gen. Hosp.

LASSETTER, Joan (retired) Badgers Cottage, Folly Farm Lane, Ringwood BH24 2NN Tel: 0142 542695 — MB ChB 1932 Ed.; DR 1936. Prev: Res. Med. Off. BeechMt. Annexe & Radium Regist. Roy. Infirm. Edin.

LASSEY, Anyetei Tonyeli 106 Kildale House, Marton Road, Middlesbrough TS4 3TG Tel: 01642 850850 — MB ChB 1978 Ghana; MRCOG 1989.

LAST, Andrew Timothy John Wessex Radiotherapy Centre, Royal South Hants Hosp, Brintons Terrace, Southampton S014 OYG; 62 Shaftsbury Ave, Highfield, Southampton SO17 1SD — BM BCh 1989 Oxf.; MA, DPhil Oxf. 1988; MRCP (UK) 1992; FRCR 1997. Cons (oncol) S.ampton Univ. Hosps. Prev: Regist. (Clin. Oncol.) Roy. Marsden Hosp. Lond.; Regist. (Clin. Oncol.) St Luiles, Guildford; Regist. (Gen. Med.) Salisbury Gen. Infirm.

LAST, Howard Arthur Oakley Terrace Surgery, 12 Oakley Terrace, Leeds LS11 5HT Tel: 0113 272 0900 Fax: 0113 270 7300 — MB BCh 1977 Wales; DCH RCP Lond. 1980; DRCOG 1979. Princip. GP Leeds. Prev: Clin. Asst. (Paediat. Nephrol.) & SHO (Obst.) St. Jas. Univ. Hosp. Leeds; SHO (Paediat.) Harrogate Gen. Hosp.

LAST, Kim Department of Medical Oncology, St Georges Hospital, Blackshaw Road, Tooting, London SW17 0QT Tel: 020 8672 1255 — MB BS 1992 Lond.; MRCP (UK) 1995. (King's Coll. Lond.)

Specialist Regist. Med. Oncol. Dep. Med. Oncol. St. Geos. Hosp. Tooting, Lond.

LAST, Patricia Alma (retired) 26 Handside Lane, Welwyn Garden City AL8 6SF Tel: 01707 371462 Email: palast@handisidewgc.freeserve.co.uk — MB BS Lond. 1958; FRCS Glas. 1964; MRCS Eng. LRCP Lond. 1958; FRCOG 1982, M 1962, DObst. 1959. Prev: Dir. Wom. Unit BUPA Med. Centres Lond.

LAST, Rex Desmond 11 Housman Road, Street BA16 0SD Tel: 01458 442689 Fax: 01458 448010 Email: rexlast@freenet.co.uk — BM BCh 1956 Oxf.; MA Oxf. 1956, BA 1953; FRCGP 1985, M 1965; DRCOG 1958. (Oxf. & Univ. Coll. Hosp.) p/t Med.ly Qualified Panel Mem., The Appeals Serv. Socs: Bristol M-C Soc.; Bath Clin. Soc. Prev: GP St., Som.

LAST, Sarah Elizabeth Mary School House, Buckland, Faringdon SN7 8RB — MB ChB 1997 Leeds.

LAST, Zoe Anne 35 Burkitt Road, Woodbridge IP12 4JJ — BM BS 1990 Nottm.; BMedSci Nottm. 1988. Prev: SHO (Paediat.) Ipswich Hosp.; Cas Off. Geo. Town Hosp. Grand Cayman, BWI; SHO (O & G) Shotley Bridge Hosp. Co. Durh.

LASZLO, Gabriel Liffield House Medical Centre, Clifton Down, Bristol BS8 3LS Tel: 0117 973 1323 Fax: 0117 973 3303; 5 Pembroke Vale, Clifton, Bristol BS8 3DN — MB BChir 1960 Camb.; MRCP 1964 Lond.; MD 1972 Camb.; FRCP 1979 Lond. (Camb. & St. Mary's) Socs: Brit. Thorac. Soc.; Assn. Phys.; Amer. Thoracic Soc. Prev: Cons. Phys. Bristol Roy. Infirm.; Sen. Lect. (Med.) Middlx. Hosp. Lond.; Regist. (Med.) Hammersmith Hosp. Lond.

LASZLO, Tibor Jan Samlesbury Hall Cottage, Preston New Road, Samlesbury, Preston PR5 0UP — MD 1925 Prague; DPH 1927. (Prague) Prev: Cons. (Geriat.) Walsall AHA; Sen. Hosp. Med. Off. Summerfield Hosp. Birm.; Maj. RAMC, Surg. Specialist.

LATA, Aloka Wollaton Vale Health Centre, Wollaton Vale, Nottingham NG8 2GR Tel: 0115 928 1842 Fax: 0115 928 0590.

LATA, Hame Woodhill Cottage, Barry, Carnoustie DD7 7SB — MB ChB 1991 Dundee; MRCGP 1995; DRCOG 1994. SHO (Paediat.) Nobles Hosp. I. of Man.

LATA, Pravin Shah Hanford Health Clinic, New Inn Lane, Hanford, Stoke-on-Trent ST4 8EX Tel: 01782 642992 Fax: 01782 869489 — MB BS 1969 Gujarat; MB BS 1969 Gujarat.

LATCHAM, Frances Papworth Manor, Papworth St Agnes, Cambridge — MB ChB 1977 Birm.; MRCP (UK) 1982.

LATCHAM, Peter Raymond (retired) 35 Westgate, Chichester PO19 3EZ Tel: 01243 781724 — MB BS Lond. 1940; MRCS Eng. LRCP Lond. 1940. Prev: Sen. Ho. Phys. St. Bart. Hosp.

LATCHAM, Richard Waring Papworth Manor, Papworth St Agnes, Cambridge — MD 1985 Birm.; MB ChB 1974; MRCPsych 1979; FRCPsych 1997. Cons. Psychiat. Hinchingbrooke Hosp. Cambs. & Fulbourn Hosp. Camb. Prev: Research Scientist MRC Unit for Epidemiologic. Studies in Psychiat.; Univ. Edin.

LATCHEM, Richard William Church End Medical Centre, Church End, Old Leake, Boston PE22 9LE Tel: 01205 870666 Fax: 01205 870971; 61 Holmes Road, Stickney, Boston PE22 8AZ — BM BS 1989 Nottm.; BMedSci Nottm. 1987; MRCGP 1993; T(GP) 1993; DRCOG 1993; DFFP 1993.

LATCHFORD, Neil Christopher Western Elms Surgery, 317 Oxford Road, Reading RG30 1AT Tel: 0118 959 0257 Fax: 0118 959 7950 — MB BS 1968 Lond.; AFOM RCP Lond. 1983; DA Eng. 1972. (St. Bart.)

LATCHMAN, Marian Zelma The Regent's Park Practice, Cumberland Market, London NW1 3RH — MB BS 1974 Lond. Prev: Clin. Med. Off. (Child Health) Gt. Yarmouth & Waveney Health Dist.; Regist. (Peadiat.) Heath Rd. Hosp. Ipswich; Ho. Off. Surgic Unit Middlx. Hosp. Lond.

LATCHMAN, Peter 10 Shaftesbury Court, Ludlow Road, Maidenhead SL6 2RS — MB ChB 1990 Leic.

LATH, Sadaf 4 Alexandra Road, London E10 5QQ — MB BS 1998 Lond.; MB BS Lond 1998.

LATHAM, Andrew The Medical Centre, 11 & 13 Beards Road, Fremington, Bideford EX31 2PG Tel: 01271 76655 Fax: 01271 321006 Email: andrew.latam@gp_l83067; Tel: 01237 471107 — MB BS 1970 Lond.; MRCP (UK) 1972; Dip. Sports Med. Scotl. 1992; DMJ Soc. Apoth. Lond. 1989; LLM Wales 1997. (St. Mary's) Div. Police Surg. Devon & Cornw. Socs: Roy. Soc. Med.; Assn. Police Surg.; Brit. Assn. of Sport Med.

LATHAM, Ashley Martin Five Points, Theescombe Hill, Amberley, Stroud GL5 5AQ — MB BS 1990 Lond.

LATHAM, Barbara Vivien Department Anaesthetics Hinchingbrooke Hospital, Huntingdon PE29 6NT Tel: 01480 416416 — MB BS Lond. 1966; MRCS Eng. LRCP Lond. 1966; FRCA. 1970; DA Eng. 1968. (Roy. Free) p/t Cons. Anaesth. & Chronic Pain Managem. Hinchingbrooke Health Care Trust Huntingdon Cambs. Socs: Assn. Anaesth.; Pain Soc.; BMA. Prev: Sen. Regist. (Anaesth.) Roy. Devon & Exeter Hosp. & Addenbrooke's Hosp. Camb.; Regist. (Anaesth.) St. Geo. Hosp. Lond.

LATHAM, Brian Alec (retired) 46 Shirley Drive, Hove BN3 6UF Tel: 01273 505769 — MB BChir Camb. 1957; FRCP Lond. 1977, M 1961; FRACP 1973, M 1965. Prev: Cons. Rheumatologist Brighton Health Auth.

LATHAM, Catherine Anne Dore Road Surgery, 137 Dore Road, Sheffield S17 3NF; 456 Abbey Lane, Sheffield S7 2QY Tel: 0114 235 1365 — MB BS 1982 Lond.; MB BS London 1982; MRCGP 1987; DRCOG 1987; DA (UK) 1985. GP Retainer Trent Scheme. Prev: GP Aylesbury Retainer Scheme.

LATHAM, David Sutton Health Clinic, 1 Station Approach, Belmont, Sutton SM2 6DD Tel: 020 8661 1166 Fax: 020 8661 1166; Tresanton, 7 Gledhow Wood, Tadworth KT20 6JQ Tel: 01737 830562 Fax: 01737 830562 — MB BS 1964 Lond.; MRCS Eng. LRCP Lond. 1964. (St. Bart.) Occupat. Health Phys. Sutton Health Clinic Surrey. Socs: BMA; Soc. Occupat. Med. Prev: GP Sutton; Hosp. Pract. (Chest Phys.) Croydon HA; Med. Off. Qacha's Nek Hosp. Lesotho.

LATHAM, Dorothy Mary (retired) 33 St James Court, The Strand, Bromsgrove B61 8AB Tel: 01527 832523 — MB ChB Birm. 1935; DA Eng. 1939.

LATHAM, Frederick, OBE (retired) Riverdown, Letch Lane, Bourton-on-the-Water, Cheltenham GL54 2DG Tel: 01451 822232 Email: fbl@freeuk.com — MB ChB Manch. 1944; DSc Manch. 1959, BSc 1941, MD 1949; DMRD Eng. 1975. Prev: Specialist Radiol. Gen. Hosp. Bandar Seri Begawan, Brunei.

LATHAM, Ian Anthony Downside, Ermleet Road, Bristol BS6 7EZ — MB BS 1990 Lond.

LATHAM, Jennifer Anne Guy's & St. Thomas' Hospital Trust, St. Thomas' Hospital, Lambeth Palace Road SE11 4TH; 63 Summersbury Drive, Shalford, Guildford GU4 8JG — MB BS 1991 Lond.; MB BS (Hons.) Lond. 1991; BSc (Hons.) Lond. 1988; MRCP (UK) 1994; FRCR 1997. (St Mary's Hosp. Lond.) p/t Regist. (Radiol.) St. Thos. Hosp. & Guy's Hosp. Lond. Prev: SHO (Med.) N.wick Pk. Hosp. Harrow.

LATHAM, Mr Jeremy Martin Wessex Nuffield Hospital, Winchester Road, Chandlers Ford, Eastleigh SO53 2DW Tel: 02380 258443 Fax: 02380 258446 — BM BCh 1984 Oxf.; FRCS (Orth.) 1996; FRCS Eng. 1989; FRCS Ed. 1989; MCH Oxf. 1999. (Oxf.) Cons. Orthop. Surg. Soton. Gen. Hosp. Socs: Fell.of Brit. Orthopaedic Assoc.; Brit. Hip Soc. Prev: Sen. Regist. (Orthop.) W. Midl.

LATHAM, Joan Euroclydon, Beckenham Place Park, Beckenham BR3 5BN Tel: 020 8658 3650 — MB BS 1947 Lond. (Univ. Coll. Hosp.)

LATHAM, John Bannerman Turret House, 89 Yarmouth Road, Blofield, Norwich NR13 4LQ Tel: 01603 713977 — MB ChB Cape Town 1966, MMed (Radiodiag.) 1975; FRCR 1977; DMRD Eng. 1975. (Cape Town) Cons. Diag. Radiol. Norf. & Norwich Hosp. Prev: Sen. Regist. Radcliffe Infirm. Oxf.; Regist. Groote Schuur Hosp. Cape Town.

LATHAM, John Walkden 8 Jersey Lane, St Albans AL4 9AE Tel: 01727 852155 — MB BS 1959 Lond.; MRCS Eng. LRCP Lond. 1959; DObst RCOG 1961. (Middlx.) Police Surg. St. Albans. Socs: Assn. Police Surg. Prev: GP St. Albans; Ho. Phys. Mt. Vernon Hosp. N.wood; Ho. Surg. St. Albans City Hosp.

LATHAM, Martin John Birchwood Medical Practice, Jasmin Road, Lincoln LN6 0QQ Tel: 01522 501111 Fax: 01522 682793; Tel: 01522 682358 — MB ChB 1977 Ed.; FRCGP 1992, M 1981; DRCOG 1980. (Edinburgh) GP Princip.; GP Trainer Lincs. VTS; Clin. Governance Ldr., Lincs. PCT. Prev: Course Organiser Lincoln VTS.; Audit Ambassador Lincs. MAAG.

LATHAM, Philip James The Old Greyhound, Tathall End, Hanslope, Milton Keynes MK19 7NF — MB ChB 1972 Dundee; FRCP Lond. 1993; DObst RCOG 1974. Cons. Paediat. Milton Keynes

Gen. NHS Trust. Prev: Sen. Regist. (Paediat.) Char. Cross Hosp. Lond.; Regist (Paediat.) Roy. Hosp. Sick Childr. Edin.

LATHAM, Rosemary Anne Cedar House Surgery, 269A Nine Mile Ride, Finchampstead, Wokingham RG40 3NS Tel: 0118 932 8966 Fax: 0118 973 4710 — MB ChB 1975 Liverp.; MRCGP 1980; DRCOG 1978. (Liverp.)

LATHAM, Susan Gillian 11 Archfield Road, Bristol BS6 6BD Tel: 0117 924 1588 — MB ChB 1988 Bristol. GP Regist. Bristol. Prev: SHO (O & G) Roy. Gwent Hosp. Newport; SHO (Psychiat.) Coney Hill Hosp. Gloucester; SHO (ENT) Bath Roy. United Hosp.

LATHAM, Timothy Brian 86 Great Stone Road, Birmingham B31 2LS — MB ChB 1993 Birm.

LATHAM, Tom 18 Warrender Park Road, Marchmont, Edinburgh EH9 1JG Email: tlatham@dircon.co.uk — MB ChB 1995 Ed.; MRCP 1998. SpR Haemat., SE Scotl. Rotat. Socs: Brit. Soc. of Haemat. Prev: SHO Qu. Margt. Hosp. Dunfermline; SHO Edin. Roy. Infirm.; SHO III, Haemat. W.. Infirm. Glas.

LATHBRIDGE, Alfred Brad Department of Obstetrics and Gynaecology, Singleton Hospital, Swansea SA2 8QA Tel: 01792 280103 — MB ChB 1982 Ghana; MB ChB U Ghana 1982; MRCOG 1992.

LATHBURY, William Clements (retired) 88 Beamhill Road, Burton-on-Trent DE13 0AD Tel: 01283 67679 — MB ChB 1947 Birm.; MRCS Eng. LRCP Lond. 1947. Prev: Ho. Surg. Sussex Matern. Hosp. Brighton.

LATHE, Grant Henry (retired) 12A The Avenue, Leeds LS8 1EH Tel: 0113 266 1507 — MD CM 1938 McGill Univ. Canada; PhD; MD CM McGill 1938; LMS Newfld. 1950; FCPath 1965. Prev: Prof. Chem. Path. Univ. Leeds.

LATHIA, Indira Health Centre, 35 Church St., Wath-upon-Dearn, Mexborough S64 0HG Tel: 01709 3233; 14 Pinfold Close, Swinton, Mexborough S64 8JE Tel: 01709 585865 — MB BS 1965 Calcutta; DGO Calcutta 1967. (Nat. Med. Coll. Calcutta)

LATIEF, Khalid Hussain 14 Braefell Close, West Bridgford, Nottingham NG2 6SS — MB ChB 1986 Dundee; BMSc (Hons.) 1983; MRCP (UK) 1989; FRCR 1993. Cons. Radiol. Nottm. City Hosp. Prev: Cons. (Radiol.) N.ern Gen. Hosp.; Fell. (Radiol.) Univ. Maryland Baltimore; Regist. (Radiol.) QMC Nottm.

LATIEF, Talaat Nagy 68 Arthur Road, Edgbaston, Birmingham B15 2UW — MD (Radiother.) Cairo 1970, MB BCh 1963; FRCR 1976; FFR RCSI 1976; Dip. Med. Cairo 1971; Dip. Surg. Cairo 1970; DMRT Cairo 1966. (Kasr El-Aini) Cons. Radiother. & Oncol. Qu. Eliz. Hosp. Birm.; Hon. Sen. Lect. Med. Sch. Univ. Birm. Prev: Sen. Regist. (Radiother. & Oncol.) Roy. Marsden Hosp. Lond.

LATIF, Abbas Hassan Abdul Pontypridd & Rhondda NHS Trust, Royal Glamorgan Hospital, Childrens Centre, Ynysmaerdy, Llantrisant, Pontyclun CF72 8XR Tel: 01443 443602 Fax: 01443 443658 — MB ChB Baghdad 1970; MRCPI 1988; DCH RCP Lond. 1984; FRCPCH 1997. (College of Medicine University of Baghdad) Cons. Paediat. (Community Child Health). Socs: Welsh Paediat. Soc.; Fell. Roy. Coll. of Paediat. and Child Health; BACCH. Prev: SCMO (Child Health) Mid. Glam. HA; Clin. Med. Off. Oqwr Health Unit; Regist. (Paediat. & Neonat. Med.) E. Glam. Gen. Hosp.

LATIF, Mr Abdul Basildon Hospital, Nether Mayne, Basildon SS16 5NL Tel: 01277 225786; Grangemount, Roundwood Avenue, Hutton, Brentwood CM13 2ND Tel: 01277 225786 Fax: 01277 263691 — MB BS 1968 Peshawar; MB BS Peshawar Pakistan 1968; FRCS Ed. 1981. Cons. ENT Head & Neck Surg. Basildon & Thurrock Hosp. Trust.

LATIF, Ali Hussain Abdul Ameer 18 Long Oaks Avenue, Uplands, Swansea SA2 0LE — LRCP 1978 Ed.; MRCP (UK) 1981; MRCPI 1979; LRCP Ed. LRCS Ed. LRCPS Glas. 1978.

LATIF, Arif Bhatti 33 Brompton Avenue, Bradford BD4 7LP — MB BS 1996 Lond.

LATIF, Fozia Coed-y-Cra Mill, Bryn-y-Carreg Lane, Flint Mountain, Flint CH6 5QU — MB ChB 1989 Liverp.; DTM & H Liverp. 1991.

LATIF, Mohamed Magdi Abdel 59 Spring Hill, Worle, Weston Super Mare BS22 9BA — MB BCh 1970 Ain-Shams; DA (UK) 1978.

LATIF, Mohammed Abdul 22 College Drive, Ruislip HA4 8SB Tel: 01895 632617 — MB BS 1966 Dacca; MRCP (UK) 1976; MRCS Eng. LRCP Lond. 1976. (Dacca Med. Coll.)

LATIF, Mohammed Hamid The Burnham Surgery, Foundry Lane, Burnham-on-Crouch CM0 8SJ Tel: 01621 782054 Fax: 01621 785592 — MB BS 1967 Karachi; DCH Eng. 1973; DTM & H Eng. 1968. Prev: Regist. (Paediat.) Wexham Pk. Hosp. Slough; SHO (Paediat.) W. Middlx. Hosp. Isleworth.

LATIF, Mufti Khalid 174 Bishopsteignton, Thorpe Bay, Southend-on-Sea SS3 8BQ — MB BS 1980 Karachi.

LATIF, Sheik A The Surgery, 119 Alum Rock Road, Saltley, Birmingham B8 1ND Tel: 0121 327 0735 — MB BS 1964 Punjab; MB BS 1964 Punjab.

LATIF, Sylvia Allerton House, 3 Windsor Road, Town Moor, Doncaster DN2 5BN Tel: 01302 360280 — MB BS 1958 Punjab; MRCPsych 1978; DPM Eng. 1976.

LATIF, Zulaidi Brunei Hall, 35-43 Norfolk Square, London W2 1RX — MB ChB 1992 Manch.

LATIF-PURI, Amjad Abdul (Surgery), 203 Emsleigh Drive, Leigh-on-Sea SS9 4JH Tel: 01702 712666 — MB BS 1962 Punjab.

LATIFF, Mr Ahmed Riverside Medical Centrye, Victoria Road, Walton-Le-Dale, Preston PR5 4AY Tel: 01772 556703 Fax: 01772 880861 — MB BS 1967 Madras; FRCS Ed. 1974. Prev: Regist. (Urol.) Preston Roy. Infirm.; Surgic. Regist. (Gen. Surg. & Paediat. Surg.) Bolton Gen. Hosp.; SHO (Gen. Surg.) N. Manch. Gen. Hosp.

LATIFI, Qamar Alhaq 82 Homefield Park, Sutton SM1 2DY Tel: 020 8642 6438 — MB BS 1956 Karachi; FRCA 1961. (Dow Med. Coll. Karachi)

LATIFI, Samir Qamar 82 Homefield Park, Sutton SM1 2DY — MB BS 1990 Lond. (Guy's) Socs: Amer. Bd. Paediat.

LATIMER, Bryan Harcourt (retired) 5 Lodge Close, Middle Hill, Englefield Green, Egham TW20 0JF Tel: 01784 437025 — MB BS 1959 Lond.; MRCS Eng. LRCP Lond. 1959; DObst RCOG 1961. Prev: GP Ashford.

LATIMER, James Gordon (retired) Glengarth, Doncaster Gate, Rotherham S65 1D Tel: 01709 365522 — MRCS Eng. LRCP Lond. 1945. Prev: Dent. Anaesth. (Out-Pats.) Rotherham Gp. Hosps.

LATIMER, Joanne 95 Stan Hope Road S., Darlington DL3 7SF Tel: 01325 353144 — MB BS 1985 Newc.; FRCS Ed. 1990; FRCR 1995. (Newcastle upon Tyne) Cons. (Radiol.) N. Tees Gen. Hosp. Stockton on Tees. Socs: FRCR.

LATIMER, Mark David 103 Norwich Street, Cambridge CB2 1ND Tel: 01223 328478 Email: m.latimer@talk21.com — BChir 1997 Camb.; MEng Oxford 1993. (Pre-clinical-Oxford / clinical Cambridge) SHO (Basic Surgic. Train. Rotat.), Camb. Socs: RCS Affil. Mem.; Christian Med. Fell.ship full Mem. Prev: SHO (Trauma & Orthopedics), Soton.; Ho. Off. (Gen. Surg.), Camb.; Ho. Off. (Gen. Med.) Hinchingbrooke.

LATIMER, Paul Raymond 74 Holbrook Road, Cambridge CB1 7ST — MB BChir 1993 Camb.; MA Camb. 1994, MB BChir 1993. SHO (A & E) Addenbrooke's NHS Trust Camb.

LATIMER, Raymond Douglas 15 Braggs Lane, Hemingford Grey, Huntingdon PE28 9BW — MB BS 1965 Lond.; MA Camb. 1977; MRCS Eng. LRCP Lond. 1965; FFA RCS Eng. 1971. (Middlx.) Cons. Anaesth. Papworth Hosp. Camb.; Assoc. Lect. Univ. Camb; Edr. Cardiothoracic Anaesthia. Socs: Founder Mem. Assn. Cardiothoracic Anaesths.; Sec. Europ. Assn. Cardithoracic Anaesths. Prev: Sen. Regist. (Anaesth.) Ahmadu Bello Univ., Nigeria; Regist. (Anaesth.) & Ho. Surg. Middlx. Hosp. Lond.

LATIMER, Rowan Kaye Church Street Medical Centre, 11B Church Street, Eastwood, Nottingham NG16 3BP Tel: 01773 712065 Fax: 01773 534295 — MB ChB 1977 Bristol.

LATIMER, Susan Hendford Lodge Medical Centre, 74 Hendford, Yeovil BA20 1UJ Tel: 01935 470200 Fax: 01935 470202; 15 Lower Odcombe, Yeovil BA22 8TX — MB BS 1985 Newc.; MRCGP 1990; Cert. Family Plann. JCC 1990; DGM RCP Lond. 1987. Prev: Trainee GP Bideford.

LATIMER-SAYER, Mr Edward Gilbert Highgate Private Hospital, 15-17 View Road, Highgate, London N6 4DJ Tel: 020 8341 4182 Fax: 020 8342 8347; Woodlands, Sway Road, Brockenhurst SO42 7SG Tel: 01590 623226 Fax: 01590 622526 Email: edward@el-s.demon.co.uk — MB BS 1971 Lond.; BSc (Anat.) Lond. 1968; FRCS Eng. 1978; MRCS Eng. LRCP Lond. 1971. (Guy's) Indep. Cosmetic Surg. Highgate Hosp. Lond. Socs: Brit. Assn. Cosmetic Surg.; (Vice-Pres.) Europ. ConFederat. of Aesthetic Surgic. Socs. Prev: Cons. Surg. Sister Rose Private Clinic; Regist. (Surg.) Guy's Hosp. Lond. & King's Coll. Hosp. Lond.

LATORIA, Jagdish Kumar Auchinleck Health Centre, Main Street, Auchinleck, Cumnock KA18 2AY Tel: 01290 424713 Fax: 01290 426192 — MB BS 1973 Jiwaji.

LATORIA, Rekha 3 Lorimer Crescent, Holmhead, Cumnock KA18 1AJ — MB BS 1976 Jiwaji, India.

LATOY, Jennifer Jane Beccles Health Centre, St. Mary's Road, Beccles NR34 9NQ Tel: 01502 712662 — MB ChB 1987 Liverp.; MRCGP 1995; DRCOG 1991; DCH RCP Lond. 1990.

LATT, Maung Maung 38 Oxford Road, St Annes-on-Sea, Lytham St Annes FY8 2DZ — MB BS 1982 Med. Inst. (III) Mandalay; MRCP (UK) 1995; DMR 1997. (Instit.Med.Rome) Staff Phys. Elderly Rehabil. Med. Socs: BMA; BSRM.

LATTA, David Windsor Doctors Surgery, Main Street, Bowmore PA43 7JH Tel: 01496 81273 Fax: 01496 81607 — MB ChB 1973 Glas.

LATTEN, Andrew Holt Medical Practice, High Street, Holt NR25 6BH Tel: 01263 712461 Fax: 01263 713211 — MB ChB 1974 Liverp.

LATTER, Michael Joseph The Lavenders, Pearcroft Road, Stonehouse GL10 2JY — MB BS 1986 Lond.

LATTEY, Nicholas John The Surgery, Ewyas Harold, Hereford HR2 0EU Tel: 01981 240320 Fax: 01981 241023; Oriel House, Peterchurch, Hereford HR2 0SQ Tel: 01981 550542 — MB ChB 1982 Birm.; MRCP (UK) 1986; MRCGP 1986; DRCOG 1986; DCH RCP Lond. 1985. Prev: GP Trainee Dudley HA VTS.; Ho. Surg. Horton Gen. Hosp. Banbury; Ho. Phys. Cheltenham Gen. Hosp.

LATTHE, Madhavi Mohan The Surgery, 36 Bucklands End Lane, Castle Bromwich, Birmingham B34 6BP Tel: 0121 747 2160 Fax: 0121 747 3425; 10 Rectory Lane, Castle Bromwich, Birmingham B36 9DH Tel: 0121 747 8173 — MB BS 1964 Poona.

LATTHE, Manish Mohan 10 Rectory Lane, Birmingham B36 9DH — MB BS 1994 Lond.

LATTHE, Mr Mohan Annasahed The Surgery, 87 Kempson Road, Birmingham B36 8LR Tel: 0121 747 3586 — MB BS 1963 Karnatak; FRCS Ed. 1971.

LATTHE, Ravi Baburao Lichfield Road Surgery, 77 Lichfield Road, Walsall Wood, Walsall WS9 9NP Tel: 01543 361452 Fax: 01543 454587 — MB BS 1970 Mysore.

LATTIMER, Mr Christopher Richard Dept of surgery Queen Elizabeth, Queen Mother Hospital, St Peter's Road, Margate CT9 4AN Tel: 01843 225544 Ext: 62329; Foxglove House, 5, Dilnot Lane, Acol, Nr. Birchington, Birchington CT7 0HW Tel: 01843 847348 — MB BS 1986 Lond.; FRCS Eng. 1990; MS Eng 2000. (St George's Hospital) Cons. Gen. & Vasc. Surg. Qu. Eliz., Qu. Mother Hosp. Margate Kent. Socs: Cheselden Club, St Thomas' Hosp. Lond. Prev: Vis. Fell (Vasc. Surg) Montefiore Med Cent New York USA; Sen. Regist (Gen. & Vasc.) King's Coll. Hosp. Lond.; Sen. Regist. (Gen. & Vasc. Surg.) Perth, W. Australia.

LATTIMORE, Colin Reginald Caxton Court, Caxton, Cambridge CB3 8PG Tel: 01954 719310 — MB BS 1959 Lond.; FFCMI 1988, M 1978; MFPHM RCP (UK) 1991; DA Eng. 1961. (Univ. Coll. Hosp.) Dep. Coroner Huntingdon; JP. Socs: (Ex-Pres.) Camb. Med. Soc. Prev: Dir. Pub. Health Huntingdon HA; Specialist in Community Med. (Serv. Plann.) E. Anglian RHA; Asst. Anaesth. Dumfries & Galloway Roy. Infirm.

LATTO, Mr Conrad (retired) Crossways, 8 The Mount, Caversham, Reading RG4 7RX Tel: 01734 471526 — MB ChB St. And. 1937; FRCS Eng. 1977; FRCS Ed. 1940. Indep. GP Caversham, Reading. Prev: Cons. Surg. Roy. Berks. Hosp. Reading.

LATTO, David Michael B The Surgery, Poynton Road, Shawbury, Shrewsbury SY4 4JS Tel: 01939 250237 Fax: 01939 250093; The Mill House, Stanton upon Hine Heath, Shrewsbury SY4 4LR Tel: 01939 250758 Fax: 01939 250804 Email: david@lattomhs.demon.co.uk — MRCS Eng. LRCP Lond. 1966; DObst RCOG 1969; LLCO 1969. (Lond.) Socs: (Hon.-Sec.) N. Shrops. Med. & Dining Soc.

LATTO, Ian Peter 20 Lochaber Street, Roath Park, Cardiff CF24 3LS Tel: 029 2049 1013 — MB BS Lond. 1964; MRCS Eng. LRCP Lond. 1964; FFA RCS Eng. 1970; DA Eng. 1968. (St. Mary's) Cons. Anaesth. Univ. Hosp. Wales Cardiff. Socs: Anaesth. Research Soc. & Soc. Obst. Anaesths. Prev: Research Fell. Cardiff Roy. Infirm.; Sen. Regist. Univ. Hosp. Wales Cardiff; Teachg. Assoc. Univ. Miami, U.S.A.

LATTO, John Bertram (retired) 8 Dalkeith Road, Branksome Park, Poole BH13 6LQ Tel: 01202 760798 — MRCS Eng. LRCP Lond. 1941; DMR Lond 1948.

LATTO, Mary Gwyneth (retired) 8 Dalkeith Road, Branksome Park, Poole BH13 6LQ Tel: 01202 760798 — MB BCh 1940 Wales; BSc, MB BCh Wales 1940; DMR Lond 1947.

LATTO, Mr Robert James The Red House, Raithby, Spilsby PE23 4DT — MB BS 1975 Lond.; FRCS Eng. 1981; FRCS Ed. 1989.

LAU, Alfred Wing Kuen 10 Strangways Terrace, London W14 8NE Tel: 020 7603 6558 Fax: 020 7603 6360 — MB BChir Camb. 1965; MRCP (UK) 1971; DDerm. 1972. Socs: BMA.

LAU, Annie Yin-Har Redbridge Child & Family Consultation Centre, Loxford Lane, Ilford IG1 2PL Tel: 020 8478 7211 Fax: 020 8478 3101 — MD 1968 Sask.; FRCP 1973 Canada; Dip. Psychiat. 1973 Ottawa; MRCPsych 1997. (Saskaton, Saskatchewan Canada) Cons. Psychiat. Redbridge Child Guid. Clinic & King Geo. Hosp. Ilford; Clin. Dir. (Child & Adolesc. Servs. Ment. Health) Redbridge Health Care Trust.; N. E. Lond. Ment. Health NHS Trust. Socs: MRCPsych.; Ilford Med. Soc.; Canad. Psychiat. Assn. Prev: Cons. Psychiat. Social Servs. Dept. Lond. Boro. Waltham Forest.

LAU, Chui Sing Flat F, Loanhead Place, Loanhead Court, Aberdeen AB25 2TT Tel: 01224 641143; 12A Jalan Ria, Sibu, Sarawak 96000, Malaysia Tel: 084 332571 Fax: 084 315411 Email: singlau@netscape.net — MB ChB 1994 Aberd.; FRCA Lond. 1998. (Univ. Aberd.) Specialist Regist. (Anaesth.) Aberd. Roy. Infirm. Socs: BMA; MRCAnaesth.; MDU. Prev: SHO II (Anaesth.) Aberd. Roy. Infirm.

LAU, David Pang-Cheng Department of ENT Surgery, West Middlessex University Hosptial, Twickenham Road, Isleworth TW7 6AF — BM BS 1989 Nottm.

LAU, Dawn Fayyin c/o G A Luff, 1a Cleeve Hill Ext, Downend, Bristol BS16 6ER — MB ChB 1998 Bristol.

LAU, Ernest Wai Yin Department of Cardiology, Queen Elizabeth Hospital, Queen Elizabeth Medical Centre, Edgbaston, Birmingham Tel: 0121 472 1311; 114 Arlington Drive, Marston, Oxford OX3 0SL — BM BCh 1992 Oxf.; MRCP (UK) 1995. (Oxf.) Clin. Research Fell. (Cardiol.) Qu. Eliz. Hosp. Edgbaston. Socs: BMA; BPEG. Prev: Research Regist. Clin. Trials Serv. Unit Harkness Bldg. Radcliffe Infirm. Oxf.; SHO (Gen. Med.) Nottm. City Hosp.

LAU, Jeshen Hui Giek Block 9, Southampton General Hospital, Tremona Road, Southampton SO16 6YD — BM 1998 Soton.; BM Soton 1998.

LAU, Lewis Kah Sin Mortimer Market Centre, Off Capper St., London WC1E 6AU Tel: 020 7380 9707; 383C Old Ford Road, London E3 2LU Tel: 020 8981 2699 — MB BCh 1988 Wales; DFFP 1998. Staff Grade (Genito-Urin.), Camden & Islington Comm. Health NHS Trust.

LAU, Mr Luk Louis 88 Greystown Avenue, Belfast BT9 6UL — MB BCh BAO 1990 Belf.; FRCS Ed. 1994. Regist. (Surg.) Antrim Hosp. Prev: SHO (Surg.) Daisy Hill Hosp. Newry.

LAU, Maurice Wai-Ming 37 Brindlehurst Drive, Tyldesley, Manchester M29 7NG — MB ChB 1988 Manch.

LAU, Patrick Hon-Hing Coldershaw Road Surgery, 55 Coldershaw Road, London W13 9EA Tel: 020 8840 1757 Fax: 020 8840 2088 Email: patrick.lau@gp-e85671.nhs.uk — MRCS Eng. LRCP Lond. 1976; BSc (Hons.) (Pharmacol.) Lond. 1973, MB BS 1976; DRCOG 1980. (Westm.)

LAU, Pui Fong 21 Queensborough Gardens, Glasgow G12 9PP — MB BS 1992 Sydney.

LAU, Richard Kok Wah Department of Genito-urinary Medicine, St George's Hospital, Tooting, London SW17 0QT — MB BS 1983 Lond.; BSc (Hons.) Lond. 1980, MD 1994; FRCP 2000 UK. (Guy's) Cons. Genitourin. Med. St. Geo. Hosp. Lond. Socs: Med. Soc. Study VD; Assn. Genitourin. Med. Prev: Sen. Regist. (Genitourin. Med.) St. Geo. Hosp. Lond.; Clin. Research Fell. (AIDS) Ludwig Inst. for Cancer Research St. Mary's Hosp. Med. Sch. Lond.; Wellcome Clin. Research Fell. St. Mary's Hosp. Lond.

LAU, Sin Chong 46 Westcliffe Drive, Blackpool FY3 7HG Email: sinchonglau@hotmail.com — MB ChB 1997 Manch.

LAU, Thomas Fook Wing Lliswerry Medical Centre, Fallowfield Drive, Lliswerry, Newport NP19 4TD Tel: 01633 277333 Fax: 01633 290931 — MB BCh 1979 Wales; MRCOG 1985.

LAU, Wai Leung Michael The Health Centre, 20 Cleveland Square, Middlesbrough TS1 2NX Tel: 01642 242746 Fax: 01642 220766 — MB ChB 1988 Dundee.

LAU, Yen Ning Apartment 34, Bombay House, 59 Whitworth St., Manchester M1 3AB — MB ChB 1998 Manch.; MB ChB Manch 1998.

LAU, Yu Sin 31 Kingfisher Wharf, Castle Marina, Nottingham NG7 1GA — BM BS 1993 Nottm.; BM BS Nottm 1993.

LAU, Yuen Kai Department Public Health, Kensington & Chelsea & Westminster HA, 50 Eastbourne Terrace, London W2 6LX Tel: 020 7725 3232 Fax: 020 7725 3259 — MB BS 1971 Singapore; MSc Ed. 1977; FFPHM RCP (UK) 1992; MFCM 1980; DIH Dund 1975; DTM & H Liverp. 1974. (Singapore) Cons. Communicable Dis. Control Kensington & Chelsea & W.m. HA.

LAU LAI LIN, Lilian 65 Chandos Avenue, Southgate, London N14 7ES — MB BS 1976 Hong Kong; FFA RCS 1984.

LAU YEE-LAM, Eileen Flat 9, Grassendale Court, Grassendale Road, Garston, Liverpool L19 0NJ — MB ChB 1982 Liverp.

LAUBE, Simone Dermatology Department, Amersham Hospital, Whielden St., Amersham HP7 0JD Tel: 01494 434411 — State Exam Med 1992 Leipzig; MRCP 1998.

LAUBLE, Saadet 40 Newfields, Welwyn Garden City AL8 6YT — State Exam Med 1993 Ulm.

LAUCHLAN, Michael Oak Lodge, Oak Road, Harold Wood, Romford RM3 — MB BS 1949 Lond.; MRCS Eng. LRCP Lond. 1949; DA Eng. 1954. (Lond. Hosp.) Prev: Anaesth. Regist. Whipps Cross Hosp.; Ho. Surg. Poplar Hosp.

LAUCKNER, David Ian Wansbeck General Hospital, Woodhorn Lane, Ashington NE63 9JJ Tel: 01670 521212 Fax: 01670 529778 Email: david @roentgen.demon.co.uk; 1 The Dye House, Guyzance Bridge, Acklington, Morpeth NE65 9AB — MB BS 1972 Newc.; FRCR 1981; DMRD Eng. 1979. Cons. Radiol. Wansbeck Gen. Hosp. Ashington N.d.

LAUCKNER, Helena Carmichael McIntosh (retired) Conamore, Whickham Park, Whickham, Newcastle upon Tyne NE16 4EH Tel: 0191 488 7037 — MB ChB Ed. 1941; DPH Newc. 1966. Prev: Clin. Med. Off. Gateshead HA.

LAUCKNER, Morag Elizabeth 41 Sneyd Avenue, Westlands, Newcastle ST5 2PZ Tel: 01782 619340 — BM BCh 1972 Oxf.; BA Oxf. 1969; FFA RCS Eng. 1978; T(Anaes.) 1991; DObst RCOG 1975. Cons. Anaesth. City Gen. Hosp. Stoke-on-Trent. Prev: Cons. Stafford Dist. Gen. Hosp.; Sen. Regist. (Anaesth.) Middlx. Hosp. Lond.; Regist. (Anaesth.) Hosp. Sick Childr. Gt. Ormond St. & Univ. Coll. Hosp. Lond.

LAUDE, Augustinus Accident and Emergency Department, Glasgow Royal Infirmary, 84 Castle Street, Glasgow G4 0SF — MB ChB Ed. 1996.

LAUDER, Allan David Tel: 020 8997 4215 Fax: 020 8991 9574; 39 Corfton Road, Ealing, London W5 2HR — MB ChB 1974 Glas.; LLB Glas. 1968, MA 1965; Cert JCC Lond. 1980. Princip. Gen. Practitioner; Forens. Med. Examr. Socs: Fell. Roy. Soc. Med. Prev: Managing Dir. Kabivitrum Ltd.

LAUDER, Gillian Ross 26 Parrys Lane, Stoke Bishop, Bristol BS9 1AA Tel: 0117 928 5203 Fax: 0117 928 5209 Email: 113163.2270@compuserve.com — MB BCh 1985 Wales; FRCA. 1991. Sen. Regist. Rotat. (Anaesth.) Univ. Bristol Hosp. Trusts. Socs: BMA & Assn. Anaesth. Prev: Regist. Rotat. (Anaesth.) Wessex RHA; SHO (Anaesth.) Oxf. & S. W.. RHAs.

LAUDER, Ian Paddock House, Illston-on-the-Hill, Leicester LE7 9EG — MB BS 1969 Newc.; MRCPath 1975. (Newc.) Prof. Path. Univ. Leicester. Prev: Sen. Lect. (Path.) Univ. Leeds; Lect. & Demonst. in Path. Univ. Newc.; Ho. Phys. & Ho. Surg. Roy. Infirm. Newc.

LAUDER, Jean Christine X-Ray Department, Victoria Infirmary, Langside Road, Glasgow G42 9TY Tel: 0141 201 5550 Fax: 0141 201 5497 — MB ChB 1981 Glas.; T(R) (CR) 1991; FRCR 1990. Cons. Radiol. Vict. Infirm. Glas.

LAUDER, Mary Margaret The Surgery, 10 Crofton Road, Ealing, London W5 2HS Tel: 020 8997 4215; 39 Corfton Road, Ealing, London W5 2HR Tel: 020 8998 7072 — MB BCh BAO 1969 Belf.; DObst RCOG 1973; DCH RCPS Glas. 1971. (Belf.) Prev: SHO (Paediat.) Ulster Hosp. Dundonald; SHO (Obst.) Belf. City Hosp.; Clin. Med. Off. (Child Health) Argyll & Clyde Health Bd.

LAUE, B Bradgate Surgery, Ardenton Walk, Brentry, Bristol BS10 6SP Tel: 0117 959 1920 Fax: 0117 983 9332 — DRCOG; FP Cert.; MRCGP; State Exam Med 1978 Hanover.

LAUFER, Neil Elliot 15 Leys Gardens, Cockfosters, Barnet EN4 9NA — MB BChir 1989 Camb.

LAUFFER, Mr Gideon Louis 14 Danescroft Avenue, London NW4 2NE Tel: 020 8202 6434 Fax: 020 8455 6161 — MB BS 1985 Lond.; BSc (Hons.) Lond. 1982, MB BS 1985; FRCS Eng. 1990; FRCS Gen.Surg 1998. (Roy.Lond.Hosp) Cons. Gen. Surg. King. Geo. Hosp. Goodmayes Essex. Socs: Assoc.U.G.S.surg; Assoc.Surg.Gb & Irel.; Brit.Assoc.Surg.Oncol. Prev: Sen.Reg.Gen.Surg.Wolverhampton.Roy.Infirm; Sen.Reg.GenSurg.Walsgrave.Hosp.; Sen.Reg.Gen.Surg.Q.E.Hosp.Birm.

LAUGHARNE, David Malcolm (retired) Holly Bank, 584 Chester Road, Sandiway, Northwich CW8 2DX Tel: 01606 888151 — BM BCh 1961 Oxf.; LMSSA Lond. 1961. Prev: Regist. (Thoracic Surg.) Ch.ill Hosp. Oxf.

LAUGHARNE, Jonathan David Ewart 541 Manchester Road, Sheffield S10 5PL — MB BS 1988 Lond. Regist. (Psychiat.) Middlewood Hosp. Sheff.

LAUGHARNE, Richard Alun St. Georges Hospital Medical School, Cranmer Terrace, London SW17 0RE Tel: 020 8725 5547 Email: richard.langharne@virgin.net — BM BS 1988 Nottm.; MRCPsych 1993. (Nottm.) Cons. (Psychiat.) Springfield Univ. Hosp. & St. Geo.'s Hosp. Med. Sch. Prev: Sen. Regist. (Psychiat.) St. Geo.'s Hosp. Med. Sch.; Clin. Train. Fell. Lond. Hosp. Med. Sch.; Regist. (Psychiat.) Claybury Hosp. Woodford Bridge Essex.

LAUGHEY, William Fenwick Haxby and Wigginton Health Centre, The Village, Wigginton, York YO3 3PL — MB ChB 1989 Sheff.; MRCGP 1994.

LAUGHLAND, Mr Andrew William (retired) 27 Sutherland Avenue, Glasgow G41 4HG Tel: 0141 427 1704 — LRCP LRCS Ed. LRFPS Glas. 1950; FRFPS Glas. 1962; FRCS Ed. 1962; FRCOG 1977, M 1956. Prev: Cons. O & G Roy. Matern. Hosp. Glas. & Vict. Infirm. Glas.

LAUGHLAND, Anne Packe 27 Sutherland Avenue, Glasgow G41 4HG — MB ChB 1957 Glas. (Glas.) Socs: Fell. Roy. Soc. Med.

LAUGHLIN, Alan James 5 The Crescent, New Mills, High Peak SK22 3DB — MB ChB 1989 Manch.; BA Camb. 1986. SHO Stepping Hill Hosp. Stockport VTS.

LAUGHLIN, John (retired) 12 High Street, Chilgrove, Chichester PO18 9HX — MA Camb. 1943, BA 1935, MB BChir 1938; MRCS Eng. LRCP Lond. 1938; AFOM RCP Lond. 1983. JP. W. Sussex. Prev: Ho. Phys. Middlx. Hosp.

LAUGHTON, Mr John Mainwaring High Meadows, 47 Townscliffe Lane, Mellor, Stockport SK6 5AP Tel: 0161 449 9741 — MB BS Lond. 1964; FRCS Eng. 1970; MRCS Eng. LRCP Lond. 1964. (Lond. Hosp.) Cons. Traum. & Orthop. Surg. Stockport AHA.

LAUKENS, Anne Elisabeth Pauline Woodbridge Road Surgery, 165-167 Woodbridge Road, Ipswich IP4 2PE Tel: 01473 256251; 150 Woodbridge Road, Ipswich IP4 2NS Tel: 01473 257877 — MD 1977 Louvain.

LAUNDY, Nicholas Paul December Cottage, 86 Commonside, Lytham St Annes FY8 4DJ Email: nick@doctor4u.com — MB ChB 1997 Liverp. (Univ.Liverp) Basic Surg. Trainee. Merseyside Rotat.

LAUNDY, Trevor John Eastlea, Peterborough District Hospitals Trust, Thorpe Road, Peterborough PE3 6DA Tel: 01733 875785 Fax: 01733 874939; Foxgloves, 310 Thorpe Road, Longthorpe, Peterborough PE3 6LX Tel: 01733 261184 Fax: 01733 266856 Email: laundytgngs@cwcom.net — MB BS 1972 Newc.; BSc (Hons.) Physiol. Newc. 1969; FRCP Lond. 1993; MRCP (UK) 1979; DAvMed FOM RCP Lond. 1989. (Newcastle) Cons. Phys. PeterBoro. Dis. Hosp. Trust; Cons Adviser in Med. (Roy. Airforce). Socs: Renal Assn. & Brit. Soc. Gastroenterol.

LAUNER, John Martin Nicholas Fax: 020 805 9028; 85 Sutton Road, London N10 1HH Tel: 020 8883 0476 — MB BS 1978 Lond.; MA (Family Ther.) Lond. 1994; MA Camb. 1975, BA (English) 1971; MRCGP 1983; DRCOG 1982. (Middlx.) Cons. Gen. Pract. & Primary Care Tavistock Clinic Lond. Prev: Trainee GP Highgate Gp. Pract.; SHO N.wick Pk. Hosp. Harrow; Ho. Phys. & Ho. Surg. St. Albans City Hosp.

LAUNER, Michael Andrew Lamont Clinic, Burnley Health Care NHS Trust, Casterton Avenue, Burnley BB10 2PQ Tel: 01282 474736 Fax: 01282 474736 Email: mikelauner@yahoo.co.uk — MRCS Eng. LRCP Lond. 1970; BA Open 1982; MRCPsych 1975; DPM Leeds 1974; MA 1999 Liverp. John Moores. (Leeds) Cons. Psychiat. & Clin. Dir. Ment. Health Burnley Gen. Hosp.; Nat. Commiss. Sick Doctors; Cons. Sane & NSF. Socs: Fell. Roy. Sch. Med.; FRSA. Prev: Sen. Regist. Claybury Hosp. Woodford Green;

Sen. Regist. BRd.moor Hosp. Berks.; Regist. (Psychiat.) Gen. Infirm. Leeds.

LAURANCE, Jane Amanda 2 Briant Close, Taunton TA1 4NX — MB ChB 1993 Bristol.

LAURENCE, Adrian Dominic John 2 Lyndhurst Terrace, London NW3 5QA Tel: 020 7435 6682 Fax: 020 7935 7817 Email: adjl@demon.co.uk — MB BS 1993 Lond.; BSc 1991; MRCP 1997. (Guys.Hosp) Specialist Regist. UCL Hosp. Socs: ICRF; Fell.RSM. Prev: SHO neurol.Guys.Hosp.

LAURENCE, Alastair Robert (retired) 34A Primrose Bank Road, Edinburgh EH5 3JF Tel: 0131 552 3346 — MB ChB 1942 Ed.; FRCGP 1978.

LAURENCE, Antony Stephen Brook Vale, Nooklands, Fulwood, Preston PR2 8XN — MD 1988 Sheff.; MD (Sheff.) 1988; MB Camb. 1976, BChir 1975; FFA RCS Eng. 1980. (Camb. & Westm.) Cons. Anaesth. Roy. Preston Hosp. Socs: Anaesth. Research Soc.; Assn. Anaesth. Prev: Lect. Anaesth. Univ. Sheff.; Regist. (Anaesth.) Univ. Hosp. Wales Cardiff.

LAURENCE, Bruce Elliott 35A West End Avenue, Pinner HA5 1BH — MB BS 1986 Lond.

LAURENCE, David Tarrant Fairlands Medical Centre, Fairlands Avenue, Worplesdon, Guildford GU3 3NA Tel: 01483 594250 Fax: 01483 598767 — LRCPI & LM, LRSCI & LM 1975; LRCPI & LM, LRCSI & LM 1975; MFFP 1993; MICGP 1985. (Royal College Surgeons in Eire) Socs: Brit. Menopause Soc.; Surrey Med. & Benevolent Soc. Prev: SHO (Obst.) Rotunda Hosp. Dub.; SHO (Obst.) Qu. Charlotte's Matern. Hosp. Lond.; RMO Chelsea Hosp. for Wom. Lond.

LAURENCE, Professor Desmond Roger 37 Denning Road, London NW3 1ST Tel: 020 7794 3612 — MB BS 1945 Lond.; MD Lond. 1949; FRCP Lond. 1965, M 1946. (St. Thos.) Emerit. Prof. Pharmacol. & Therap. Sch. Med. Univ. Coll. Lond. Prev: Sen. Lect. (Therap.) St. Thos. Hosp. Med. Sch.; Maj. RNZAMC; Ho. Phys. Nat. Hosp. Nerv. Dis. Qu. Sq.

LAURENCE, Professor Kurt Michael Springside, Pen-y-Turnpike, Dinas Powys CF64 4HG Tel: 01222 513248 Fax: 01222 513248 — MB ChB 1950 Liverp.; DSc Wales 1976; MA Camb. 1954, BA 1947; FRCP Ed. 1980, M 1975; FRCPCH 1996; FRCPath 1971, M 1963. (Camb. & Liverp.) Emerit. Prof. Univ. Wales Coll. Med. & Hon. Cons. Paediat. Path. & Clin. Geneticist Univ. Hosp. Wales Cardiff; Jt. Head Regional Inst. Med. Genetics of Wales & Head of Regional Cytogenetics Serv Wales. Socs: (Pres.) Clin. Genetics Soc. (Ex-Sec.); (Pres.) Soc. Research Hydrocephalus & Spina Bifida (Ex-Sec.); Path. Soc. Prev: Prof. Paediat. Research Inst. Med. Genetics Univ. Wales Coll. Med. Cardiff; Research Fell. (Hydrocephalus & Spina Bifida) Hosp. Sick. Childr. Gt. Ormond St. Lond.; Regist. (Path.) Portsmouth & I. of Wight Area Path. Serv.

LAURENCE, Mr Michael 106 Harley Street, London W1G 7JE Tel: 020 7486 3131 Fax: 020 7935 7817 Email: mlaurenc@netcomuk.co.uk; 2 Lyndhurst Terrace, Hampstead, London NW3 5QA Tel: 020 7435 6682 — MB BS Lond. 1953; FRCS Eng. 1960. (St. Mary's) Cons. Orthop. Surg. Guy's & St. Thomas' Hosp. Socs: Fell. (Pres. Orthop. Sect. 1993/1994 Pres. Sports Med. Soc.. 1999/2000) RSM.; Fell. (Charim. Bd. Affil. Specialist Socs.) Brit. Orthopaedic Assn.; Huntarian Soc. Fell. Pres.-Elect 2001. Prev: Cons. Orthop. Surg. Hammersmith Hosp.; Sen. Regist. (Orthop.) St. Mary's Hosp. Lond.; Sen. Lect. Inst. Orthop. Lond.

LAURENCE, Michael Desmond Bacon Road Medical Centre, 16 Bacon Road, Norwich NR2 3QX Tel: 01603 503917 Fax: 01603 458793; 21 TheAve.s, Norwich NR2 3PH — MB BChir 1978 Camb.; BSc Lond. 1976; MRCGP 1995. GP Norwich.; Hon. Sen. Lect. Sch. of Health Univ. E. Anglia.

LAURENCE, Nicola Jane Iran 2 Lyndhurst Terrace, London NW3 5QA Tel: 020 7435 6682 — MB BS 1994 Lond.; BSc (Hons) 1991; FRCS Eng. 1998. (St Mary's Hospital Imperial College London) SHO Rotat. St Mary's Hosp. Lond.

LAURENCE, Robert Quentin Frome Valley Medical Centre, 2 Court Road, Frampton Cotterell, Bristol BS36 2DE Tel: 01454 772153 Fax: 01454 250078 — MB ChB 1986 Bristol; DRCOG 1989; MRCGP 1990.

LAURENCE, Virginia Marie Poole Hospital, Longfleet Road, Poole BH15 2JB — MB BS 1982 Lond.; MRCP (UK) 1986; FRCR 1992. Cons. Clin. Oncol. Poole Hosp. Prev: Clin. Lect. (Clin. Oncol.) Univ. Camb.

LAURENCE, Mr Walter Nick The Hove Nuffield Hospital, 55 New Church Road, Hove BN3 4BG Tel: 01273 779471 Fax: 01273 220919; 41 Hove Park Way, Hove BN3 6PW Tel: 01273 502014 Fax: 0127 504551 Email: nicklaurance@bt.internet.com — LRCPI & LM, LRCSI & LM 1940; FRCS Eng. 1952; FRCS Ed. 1945. (RCSI) Hon. Orthop. Surg. Brighton Health Dist. Socs: Fell. Roy. Soc. Med.; Fell. BOA. Prev: Wing-Cdr. Orthop. Specialist RAFVR; Resid. Surg. Off. Robt. Jones & Agnes Hunt Orthop. Hosp.; Regist. (Orthop.) Norf. & Norwich Hosp.

LAURENS, Christine Sunnyside the Square, Ugborough, Ivybridge PL21 0NT — Artsexamen 1990 Free U Amsterdam; Artsexamen Free Univ Amsterdam 1990; MRCGP DRCOG. GP Retainer.

LAURENSON, Ian Fraser Fife Area Laboratory, Hayfield Road, Kirkcaldy KY2 5AG — MB ChB 1986 Ed.; MSc Lond. 1993; MA Camb. 1987, BA 1983; MRCP (UK) 1989; MRCPath 1996; MD Ed. 1998. Cons. Microbiologist Fife Area Laborat.; Hon. Clin. Sen. Lect. Univ. Edin. Prev: Clin. Lect. (Med. Microbiol.) Univ. Edin. Med. Sch.; Regist. (Microbiol. & Infec. Dis.) Roy. Lond. Hosp.; Clin. Teach. Port Moresby Hosp. Papua New Guinea.

LAURENSON, John Anthony Department of Anaesthesia, Wansbeck General Hospital, Woodhorn Lane, Ashington NE63 9JJ Tel: 01670 521212 Fax: 01670 529827 — MB ChB 1987 Ed.; MRCP (UK) 1990; FRCA 1993. Cons. Anaesth. Wansbeck Gen. Hosp. Socs: Collegiate Mem. RCP Edin.; Intens. Care Soc.; N. Eng. Soc. Anaesth. Prev: Sen. Regist. (Anaesth.) Edin. Roy. Infirm.; Clin. Fell. (Intens. Care) W.. Gen. Hosp. Edin.; Regist. & SHO (Anaesth.) Glas. Roy. Infirm.

LAURENT, Richard Jacques The Surgery, Yeoman Lane, Bearsted, Maidstone ME14 4DS Tel: 01622 737326/738344 Fax: 01622 730745; 178 Ashford Road, Bearsted, Maidstone ME14 4NB Tel: 01622 735409 — MB BS 1983 Lond.; MRCGP 1989; DCH RCP Lond. 1986. (St. Bartholomews) Prev: Trainee GP Redhill VTS.

LAURENT, Stephen Charles Department of Anaesthesia, Leicester Royal Infirmary, Infirmary Square, Leicester LE1 5WW; 34 The Wranglands, Fleckney, Leicester LE8 8TW — MB BS 1983 Lond.; FCAnaesth. 1990. (St. Bart.) Sen. Regist. (Anaesth.) Leic. Roy. Infirm. Prev: Regist. (Anaesth.) Bristol Roy. Infirm.; SHO K. Edwd. VII Hosp. Midhurst Sussex; Ho. Phys. St. Bart. Hosp. Lond.

LAURENT, Susan Janeen Barnet General Hospital, Wellhouse Lane, Barnet EN5 3DJ Tel: 020 8216 4000; 24 Bisham Gardens, London N6 6DD Tel: 020 8348 4730 — MB BS 1982 Lond.; MRCP (UK) 1985. (Univ. Coll. Hosp.) Cons. Paediat. & Neonatol. Barnet Gen. Hosp.; Hon. Sen. Lect. UCH Lond. Socs: BMA; Fell. RCPCH; MRCP. Prev: Research Assoc. (Paediat. Endocrinol.) Univ. Chicago, USA; Sen. Regist. (Paediat.) N.wick Pk. & St. Mary's Hosp. Paddington; Regist. (Paediat.) Edgware Gen. & Middlx. Hosps.

LAURIE, Alan Neilson Dumbarton Road Surgery, 1264 Dumbarton Road, Glasgow G14 9PS Tel: 0141 959 6311 Fax: 0141 954 9759; 2 Hughenden Gardens, Hyndland, Glasgow G12 9XW — MB ChB 1981 Dundee; DRCOG 1984. GP Glas. Prev: GP Rotat. Dumfries & Galloway; SHO & Regist. (Anaesth.) Dumfries & Galloway Roy. Infirm.; GP Anaesth. Legrow Health Centre Port Aux Basques Newfld..

LAURIE, Alexander (retired) Ford Cottage, Ford, Pathhead EH37 5RE Tel: 01875 320322 — MB ChB 1937 Glas.; MD Glas. 1961; FRCP Glas. 1974, M 1968; DPH Glas. 1950. Prev: SCM Lothian Health Bd.

LAURIE, Andrew Stuart 4 Grasmere Avenue, London W3 6JU — MSc (Distinc.) Lond. 1985, BSc (Ist. cl. Hons.) 1978, MB BS 1981; MRCP (UK) 1985; MRCPath 1989. (Westm. Hosp. Med. Sch.) Leukaemia Research Fund Fell. Harvard Med. Sch. Boston, USA. Prev: Hon. Sen. Lect. (Haemat.) St. Geos. Hosp. Med. Sch. Lond.; Regist. (Haemat.) N.wick Pk. Harrow.

LAURIE, Gordon Alexander 48 Gartcows Road, Falkirk FK1 5QT — MB ChB 1998 Glas.; MB ChB Glas 1998.

LAURIE, Hugh Campbell Glencoe, Barr's Brae, Kilmacolm PA13 4DE — MB ChB Glas. 1961; DObst RCOG 1963. (Glas.) Med. Adviser SEMA Med. Servs. Glas. Socs: BMA. Prev: Gen. Med. Practitioner Port Glas. Health Centre; Research Regist. (Childh. Leukaemia) Roy. Hosp. Sick. Childr. Glas.; Regist. (Med.) Stobhill Gen. Hosp. Glas.

LAURIE, Marie 152 Craigpark, Dennistown, Glasgow G31 2HE — MB ChB 1983 Glas.

LAURIE, Pamela Scott Department of Anaesthesia, The Horton Hospital, Oxford Road, Banbury OX16 9AL Tel: 01295 229067 Fax: 01295 229067 — MB ChB 1971 Ed.; BSc Ed. 1969,; FRCA. 1976; DA Eng. 1974; DObst RCOG 1973. (Edinburgh) Cons. Anaesth. Horton (Oxf. Radcliffe Hosps. Trust) Hosp. Banbury. Socs: Assn. Anaesth., Obst. Anaesth. Assn., Brit. Assn. of Day Surg. Prev: Sen. Regist. Nuffield Dept. Anaesth. Radcliffe Infirm. Oxf. & St. Geo.'s Hosp. Lond.; Regist. Rotat. (Anaesth.) St. Geo.'s Hosp. Lond.

***LAURIE, Stuart John** 2 Sterling Close, Colchester CO3 5DP — MB ChB 1998 Leic.; MB ChB Leic 1998.

LAURIE, William George Ranald Mundell (retired) 10 Vicar Street, Wymondham NR18 0PL Tel: 01953 605168 — MB BChir 1954 Camb.; MRCS Eng. LRCP Lond. 1954; DObst RCOG 1956. Prev: Ho. Phys. Med. Unit & Ho. Surg. O & G Unit Lond. Hosp.

LAURIE SMITH, Norman (retired) Sunnycroft, Hacketts Lane, Eckington, Pershore WR10 3DG Tel: 01386 750319 — MB ChB 1948 Ed.; FFA RCS Eng. 1956; DA Eng. 1954. Prev: Cons. Anaesth. Ayrsh. & Arran HB & Dartford & Gravesham HA.

LAUTCH, Peter Mark Tel: 01622 752345 Fax: 01622 758133 — MB BS 1988 Lond.; MA Cantab 1987; BA Camb. 1984; MRCGP 1993. Prev: SHO (Obst.) St. Peters Hosp. Chertsey; SHO (Gen. Med.) Kent & Sussex T. Wells; SHO (Gen. Med.) St. Albans City Hosp.

LAUWERS, Angela Josephine 20 Grosvenor Avenue, Hayes UB4 8NL Tel: 020 8845 7100; 56 Brunswick Road, Ealing, London W5 1AF — MB BS 1984 Lond.; DRCOG 1988.

LAVALETTE, David Paul 9 Park Lane, Barnstaple EX32 9AL — MB BS 1993 Lond.

LAVALLEE, Peter John Queen Elizabeth Hospital, Gayton Road, King's Lynn PE30 4ET; The Firs, 4 Ryalla Drift, South Wooton, King's Lynn PE30 3NE Email: plaval1973@aol.com — MB BS 1997 Lond. (Royal Free Hosp. School of Medicine)

LAVANCHY, Oscar Rolando JOSHU, Hampshire Constabulary, Hampshire Fire & Rescue Service, Steele Close, Eastleigh SO53 3AA Tel: 01703 642264 Fax: 01703 620073; 124 Highfield Lane, Southampton SO17 1NP Tel: 01703 582384 Email: lavanchy@doctororg.uk — Medico Cirujano Chile 1973; FFOM RCP Lond. 1992, MFOM 1983; DIH Eng. 1982. Occupat. Health Phys. Hants. Constab. Hants. Fire & Rescue Serv. Socs: Soc. Occupat. Med. Prev: Occupat. Health Phys. BMI Lond.; Health Manager Brit. Gas Serv. Staines; Regional Med. Adviser Brit. Gas Soton.

LAVELL, Tracey Anita — MB BS 1992 Lond.; BSc Lond. 1989; MRCGP 1996; DCH RCP Lond. 1995; DFFP 1995; DGM RCP Lond. 1994; DRCOG 1996. (Lond.) GP Princip. Buckingham.

LAVELLE, Anthony Bannerman Dean Lane Family Practice, 1 Dean Lane, Bedminster, Bristol BS3 1DE Tel: 0117 966 3149 Fax: 0117 953 0699 — MB ChB 1958 Birm.; DObst RCOG 1960. (Birm.) Prev: Ho. Surg. & Obst. Ho. Surg. Qu. Eliz. Hosp. Birm.; Ho. Phys. City Gen. Hosp. Stoke-on-Trent.

LAVELLE, Audrey Evelyn (retired) 67 Myrtlesfield Park, Belfast BT9 — MB BCh BAO 1928 Belf. Prev: Chest Phys. N. Irel. Hosps. Auth.

LAVELLE, Catherine Department of Psychological Medicine, Great Ormond Street Hospital for Children, Great Ormond St., London WC1N 3JH Tel: 020 7405 9200; 20 Ashby Street, London EC1V 0ED Tel: 020 7490 8522 — MB ChB 1990 Birm.; MRCPsych 1995. Sen. Regist. Rotat. (Child & Adolesc. Psychiat.) Gt. Ormond St. Hosp. Prev: Career Regist. Rotat. (Psychiat.) S. Glas. Train. Scheme.

LAVELLE, Ena Theresa 58 Townshend Court, Townshend Road, London NW8 6LB — MB BCh BAO 1987 NUI; LRCPSI 1987.

LAVELLE, Fidelma Margaret Mary Keppoch, 26 West Road, Haddington EH41 3RE — MB BCh BAO 1986 NUI; MRCGP 1990; T(GP) 1991.

LAVELLE, Hannah 2 Brookhill Drive, Wollaton, Nottingham NG8 2PS — MB BCh BAO 1943 NUI.

LAVELLE, Janet Margaret Department of Radiology, Lancaster Royal Infirmary, Ashton Road, Lancaster LA1 4RP — MB ChB 1981 Manch.; FRCR 1987. Cons. Radiol. Lancaster Roy. Infirm. Prev: Sen. Regist. (Radiol.) Leicester & Nottm. Hosps.

LAVELLE, Mr Jonathon Richard Chelsea & Westminster Hospital, 369 Fulham Road, London SW10 9NH Tel: 020 8746 8003; 2 Bamborough Gardens, London W12 8QN — MB BS 1985 Lond.; FRCS (Orth.) 1995; FRCS Lond. 1990. (Char. Cross & Westm. Med. Sch.) Cons. Orthop. Surg. Chelsea & W.m. Hosp. Lond. Prev: Sen. Regist. Roy. Nat. Orthop. Hosp. Stanmore.

LAVELLE, Katharine Gunilla The Orchard Surgery, Commercial Road, Dereham NR19 1AE Tel: 01362 692916 Fax: 01362 698347; 11 Greenfields Road, Dereham NR20 3TE Tel: 01362 691898 — MB BS 1984 Lond. Prev: Trainee GP Norwich VTS.

LAVELLE, Mr Michael Anthony The Princess Royal Hospital, Lewes Road, Haywards Heath RH16 4EX Tel: 01444 441881; Awbrook Old Farm, Ham Lane, Scaynes Hill, Haywards Heath RH17 7PR Tel: 01444 831475 — BM BCh 1971 Oxf.; FRCS Eng. 1977. p/t Cons. Surg. P.ss Roy. Hosp. Haywards Heath Gen. Colorectal Surg. Socs: Brit. Assn. ColoProctol. Prev: Sen. Regist. (Surg.) Guy's Hosp. Lond.; Regist. (Surg.) Pembury Hosp.; SHO (Accid. & Orthop.) Roy. Surrey Co. Hosp. Guildford.

LAVELLE, Michael Ian 12 Beech Court, Ponteland, Newcastle upon Tyne NE20 9NE Tel: 01661 825392 — MB ChB 1957 Sheff.; FFR 1971; DMRD Eng. 1968. Emerit. Cons. Radiol. Roy. Vict. Infirm. Newc. Socs: Fell. Roy. Soc. Med.; Brit. Soc. Gastroenterol. Prev: Cons. Radiol. & Sen. Regist. (Radiol.) Roy. Vict. Infirm. Newc.; Regist. (Med.) S.mead Hosp. Bristol.

LAVELLE, Michael James 270 Wetherby Road, Leeds LS17 8NE — MB ChB 1985 Manch.

LAVELLE, Peter John Ryle Health Centre, Southchurch Drive, Clifton, Nottingham NG11 8EW Tel: 0115 921 2970 — MB ChB 1971 Liverp.; MRCS Eng. LRCP Lond. 1971; FFA RCS 1981; DTM & H Liverp. 1976; DObst RCOG 1975.

LAVELLE, Peter Henry The Health Centre, Byland Road, Skelton-in-Cleveland, Saltburn-by-the-Sea TS12 2NN Tel: 01287 650430 Fax: 01287 651268; 21 Tidkin Lane, Hutton Lowcross, Guisborough TS14 8BX — MB BS 1985 Lond.; BSc (Hons.) Pharmacol. with Basic Med. Sc. 1982; MRCGP 1989; DTM & H Liverp. 1990; DRCOG 1989.

LAVELLE, Richard Charles William 1 Parkway Close, Welwyn Garden City AL8 6HJ — MB ChB 1991 Birm.; ChB Birm. 1991; MRCGP 1995; DRCOG 1994.

LAVELLE, Richard Henry (retired) 138 Stenson Road, Derby DE23 1JH Tel: 01332 760818 Email: lavellerh@supanet.com — MB BChir 1957 Camb.; MRCS Eng. LRCP Lond. 1955. Prev: GP Derby.

LAVELLE, Mr Richard John (retired) Princess Grace Hospital, Nottingham Place, London W1N 3FD Tel: 020 7908 2149, 01344 886849 Email: richard@windserforest.fsnet.co.uk — MB BS 1962 Lond.; FRCS Eng. 1967; MRCS Eng. LRCP Lond. 1961. Ex-Cons. ENT Surg. St. Bart. Hosp., Roy. Masonic Hosp. & King Edwd. VII Hosp. for Off's Lond. Prev: Cons. ENT Surg. St. Bart Hosp. Lond.

LAVELLE, Susan Elizabeth 33 Okus Road, Swindon SN1 4LE — MB ChB 1998 Leeds.

LAVELLE, Terence (retired) John Ryle Health Centre, Clifton Estate, Nottingham NG11 8EW Tel: 0115 929 3343 — LRCPI & LM, LRSCI & LM 1948; LRCPI & LM, LRCSI & LM 1948. Prev: Ho. Surg. (Gyn.) & Cas. Off. Mansfield Gen. Hosp.

LAVELLE-JONES, Mr Michael 68 Bay Road, Wormit, Newport-on-Tay DD6 8LZ — MD 1988 Liverp.; MD (Distinc.) Liverp. 1988; MB ChB Liverp. 1977; FRCS Ed. 1981; FRCS Eng. 1981. Cons. Surg. & Hon. Sen. Lect. Ninewells Hosp. & Med. Sch. Dundee. Prev: Research Fell. Univ. Calif. San Diego, USA.

LAVEN, Lloyd Edmund Dodgson 5 North Hill Way, Burton Road, Bridport DT6 4JX Tel: 01308 56750 — MB BS 1973 Lond.

LAVENDER, Aidan William 155 Crimicar Lane, Sheffield S10 4FD — MB ChB 1990 Sheff.

LAVENDER, Alison Jane Felpham and Middle Health Centre, 109 Flansham Park, Felpham, Bognor Regis PO22 3DH Tel: 01243 783369; Tel: 01243 783369 — MB BS 1992 Lond.; DRCOG 1995. (UMDS) p/t Gen. Pract. Retainer Felpham and Middleton Health Centre, Bognor Regis.

LAVENDER, Mr Andrew 31 North Road, Royston, Barnsley S71 4DE — MB BS 1989 Lond.; FRCSI 1994. Clin. Research Fell. (Orthop.) Roy. Preston Hosp.

LAVENDER, Charles Pinkard 8 Stanbury Close, Bosham, Chichester PO18 8NS — MB BS 1992 Lond.

LAVENDER, Hilary Anne Falmouth Road Surgery, 78 Falmouth Road, London SE1 4JW Tel: 020 7407 4101 Fax: 020 7357 6170 Email: hilary.laveuder@btinternet.com — FRCGP 2000; MB ChB Birm. 1969; MRCGP 1992; DCH RCP Lond. 1972; DObst RCOG

1971; MFFP 1997. (Birmingham) p/t Princip. in Gen. Pract. Prev: Hon. Research Fell (Gen. Pract.) United Med. & Dent. Schs. Lond.; Postgrad. Tutor in Gen. Pract. Guy's Kings & St. Thomas Sch. of Med.; N. Soutwark Primary Care Gp. Bd. Mem., Ment. Health, Leeds.

LAVENDER, Professor John Peter c/o Midland Bank, Walsall Road, Darlaston, Wednesbury WS10 9JP; Rose Cottage, Hill Grove, Lurgashall, Petworth GU28 9EW Tel: 01428 707647 — MB ChB 1950 Birm.; FRCP Ed. 1971; MRCP Lond. 1957; FRCR 1963; DMRD Eng. 1960. (Birm.) Emerit. Prof. Diag. Radiol. Roy. Postgrad. Med. Sch. Lond. Prev: Cons. Radiol. Hammersmith Hosp. Lond.; Radiol. Beth Israel Hosp. Boston, USA; Sen. Regist. Univ. Coll. Hosp. Lond.

LAVENDER, Michael Charles eBeckbank Cottage, Wythop, Cockermouth CA13 5YP — MB BS 1978 Lond.; MRCS Eng. LRCP Lond. 1978.

LAVER, Stephen Richard 39 Cumberland Avenue, Grimsby DN32 0BT — MB ChB 1992 Leeds. SHO (Anaesth.) W. Glam. VTS.

LAVERICK, Mr Michael David Musgrave Park Hospital, Stockmans Lane, Belfast BT9 7JB Tel: 01232 669501; 82 Knockcairn Road, Dundrod, Crumlin BT29 4UE — MB BCh BAO 1983 Belf.; FRCS (Orth.) 1994; FRCS Ed. 1987. Cons. Orthop. Surg. Musgrave Pk. Hosp. & Roy. Belf. Hosp. Sick Childr.

LAVERICK, Sean 29F Queens Av, London N10 3PE — MB BS 1997 Lond.

LAVERS, Kenneth Wilcox (retired) 45 Wellington Road, Hatch End, Pinner HA5 4NF — MB BS 1944 Queensland, Austral.; MB BS Queensland Austral., 1944; DCH Eng. 1951, DMRD 1960. Prev: Cons. Radiol. Enfield Dist. Hosp.

LAVERSUCH, Catherine Jane Department of Rheumatology and General Medicine, Taunton & Somerset Hospital, Musgrave Park, Taunton TA1 5DA Tel: 01823 342132 Fax: 01823 344542 — MB BS 1983 Lond.; MRCP (UK) 1989. Cons. Rheum. And Gen. Med.Taunton & Som..Hosps. Prev: Cons.Phys.Rheum.Homerton & Roy.Lond.hosps; Sen. Regist. Rotat. (Med. & Rheum.) Qu. Mary's Hosp., Char. Cross Hosp. & St. Mary's Hosp. Paddington; Clin. Research Fell. (Immunol.) & Regist. (Med.) St. Geo. Hosp. Med. Sch. Lond.

LAVERTY, Ssusan Elizabeth 2nd Floor Flat, 17 Burlington Road, Bristol BS6 6TJ — MB ChB Bristol 1995.

LAVERTY, Theresa Anne Cambridge House, 3 Cambridge Place, Widcombe, Bath BA2 6AB — MB BCh 1976 Wales; DCH Eng. 1980; MRCGP 1986; DRCOG 1986.

LAVERY, Anneliese Gisela Ballyowen Health Centre, 179 Andersonstown Road, Belfast BT11 9EA Tel: 028 9061 0611 Fax: 028 9043 1323 — MB BCh BAO 1966 Belf.; MICGP 1987. (Bonn & Qu. Univ. Belf.) Socs: Fell. Ulster Med. Soc.; BMA. Prev: Ho. Off. Mater Infirm. Hosp. Belf.

LAVERY, Bernadette Anne Department of Clinical Oncology, Churchill Hospital, Old Road, Oxford OX3 7RJ Tel: 01865 741841 Ext: 25652 — BM BCh 1982 Oxf.; MBA 1999 (Health Exec.) Keele; BSc Glas. 1979; MRCP (UK) 1985; FRCR 1990. Cons. Clin. Oncol. Ch.ill Hosp. Oxf.; Clin. Dir. Dept. of Clin. Oncol., Ch.ill Hosp. Oxf.

LAVERY, Hilary Anne Seahill House, 46 Craigdarragh Road, Helens Bay, Bangor BT19 1UB — MB BCh BAO Belf. 1975; MD Belf. 1980; FRCP Ed. 1996; MRCP (UK) 1978.

LAVERY, James Tees Seahill House, 46 Craigdarragh Road, Helens Bay, Bangor BT19 1UB — MB BCh BAO 1975 Belf.; DRCOG 1977.

LAVERY, Mr Kenneth McCallum Maxillofacial Unit, Queen Victoria Hospital, Holtye Road, East Grinstead RH19 3DZ Tel: 01342 410210 Ext: 313 Fax: 01342 328339; 17 Orhard Rise, Groombridge, Tunbridge Wells TN3 9RY — MB ChB 1979 Dundee; BDS 1973 Dund.; FRCS Eng. 1984; FDS RCS Eng. 1977. Cons. (Maxillo-facial Surg.) Qu. Vict. Hosp. E. Grinstead; Lect. RCS. Prev: Chairm. Soc. Of Oral & Maxillofacial Surg.

LAVERY, Philip Edward 37 Glengoland Gardens, Dunmurry, Belfast BT17 0JE Tel: 01232 621505 — MB BCh BAO 1992 Belf.

LAVERY, Mr Stuart Antony IVF Unit, Hammersmith Hospital, Du Cane Road, London W12 0NN Tel: 020 8383 8160 Fax: 020 8383 8534 Email: cmail.slavery@rpms.ac.uk; Cottesmore, Westhall Hill, Fulbrook, Burford OX18 4BJ Tel: 01993 823211 — MB BCh 1989 Witwatersrand; MRCOG 1996. (Witwatersrand) Sen. Coordinator IVF Unit Hammersmith Hosp. Lond. Socs: BMA; Brit. Fertil. Soc. Prev: Regist. (O & G) John Radcliffe Hosp. Oxf.; SHO (O & G) Qu. Charlotte's & Guy's Hosps. Lond.; SHO (A & E & Neonatol.) Addenbrooke's Hosp. Camb.

LAVIES, Nicholas George Department of Anaesthesia, Worthing Hospital, Worthing Tel: 01903 205111 Fax: 01903 285151; Lelant House, 11 The Quadrangle, Findon, Worthing BN14 0RB Tel: 01903 873693 Email: 100545.1207@compuserve.com — MB ChB 1976 Bristol; BSc Bristol 1973; FFA RCS Lond. 1982; DA Eng. 1979. Cons. Anaesth. Worthing & S.lands Hosps. Prev: Sen. Regist. (Anaesth.) Leicester Roy. Infirm.; Regist. (Anaesth.) St. Bart. Hosp. Lond.

LAVIN, Edward Patrick Gloucester Road Medical Centre, Tramway House, 1A Church Road, Horfield, Bristol BS7 8SA Tel: 0117 949 7774 Fax: 0117 949 7730; 14 Downs Park E., Westbury Park, Bristol BS6 7QD Tel: 0117 962 2484 — BM 1978 Soton.; BSc Manch. 1965; MSc Lond. 1968; DIC 1968; DRCOG 1981; Doctorat d'Univ. Paris 1972. Police Surg. Avon & Som. Constab; Med. Off. Football Assn. of Wales. Prev: Clin. Asst. (Anaesth.) Frenchay Hosp. Bristol.

LAVIN, Irene Short Street Surgery, Brownhills, Walsall; 191 Erdington Hall Road, Erdington, Birmingham B24 8JB — MB ChB 1977 Liverp.

LAVIN, Jacqueline Maria 3 Edinburgh Close, Sale M33 4EZ Tel: 0161 905 1400 — MB ChB 1987 Manch.; MRCOG 1993.

LAVIN, James Bernard Avenue Road Surgery, 28A Avenue Road, Malvern WR14 3BG Tel: 01684 561333 Fax: 01684 893664; Priestfields Barn, Blackmore Road, Hanley Castle, Worcester WR8 0AH Tel: 01684 310719 — MB ChB 1989 Birm.; MRCGP 1995; DCH RCP Lond. 1993; DGM RCP Lond. 1991. (Birmingham)

LAVIN, Mr Michael John Manchester Royal Eye Hospital, Oxford Road, Manchester M13 9WH Tel: 0161 276 5560 Fax: 0161 273 6354 Email: lavin@compuserve.com; Fernleigh Consultanting Centre, 77 Alderley Road, Wilmslow SK9 1PA Tel: 01625 536507 Fax: 01625 536507 — MB BCh 1979 Witwatersrand; FRCS Glas. 1985; FRCOphth 1989. Cons. Ophth. Manch. Roy. Eye Hosp.; Cons. Ophth. Stretford Memor. Hosp. Trafford. Socs: Fell. Roy. Soc. Med.; Assn. Research Vision & Ophth.; BMA. Prev: Lect. Inst. Ophth. Lond.; Regist. & Sen. Regist. Moorfields Eye Hosp. Lond.

LAVIN, Patrick Joseph 467 Chester Road, Hartford, Northwich CW8 2AG — MB BCh BAO 1966 NUI. Socs: Brit. Soc. Med. & Dent. Hypn.

LAVIN, Richard John Pembroke House, 32 Albert Road, Cleethorpes DN35 8LU Tel: 01472 691033 Fax: 01472 291516; Greystones, 281 Station Road, New Waltham, Grimsby DN36 4QJ — MB BChir Camb. 1962; MRCS Eng. LRCP Lond. 1962; DObst RCOG 1964. (Lond. Hosp.)

LAVIN, Stephanie Julia Priestfields Barn, Priestfields, Hanley Castle, Worcester WR8 0AH — MB ChB 1990 Birm.; MRCGP 1995; DCH RCP Lond. 1994.

LAVIN, Mr Thomas Anthony Ashington Hospital, West View, Ashington NE63 0SA Tel: 01670 521212; Tel: 01670 774335 — MB ChB 1972 Bristol; MBA Northumbria 1994; MFFP 1993; FRCOG 1990, M 1978. Cons. O & G Ashington Hosp. Prev: Lect. (O & G) Univ. Leeds; Hon. Sen. Regist. Leeds AHA (T).

LAVIS, Lucy Sarah 20 Cowley Mill Road, Uxbridge UB8 2QB — MB BS 1993 Lond.

LAVIS, Mr Mark Stephen Accident & Emergency Department, Nevill Hall Hospital, Brecon Road, Abergavenny NP7 7EG Tel: 01873 852091 Fax: 01873 859168 — MB BCh 1986 Wales; BSc (Hons.) Wales 1981; FRCS Ed. (A&E) 1996; MRCGP 1990; DCH RCP Lond. 1989. Cons. A & E Med. Nevill Hall Hosp. Abergavenny.

LAVIS, Robert Andrew 82 Westward Road, Caincross, Stroud GL5 4JA Tel: 01453 764117 Fax: 01453 764117; Flat 3, 1 Milford Road, Harborne, Birmingham B17 9RL Tel: 0121 428 2516 Fax: 0121 428 2516 Email: roblavis@msn.com — MB ChB 1996 Birm.; MB ChB Hons. Birmingham 1996; MBChB Hons. Birmingham 1993. SHO (Surgic.) Rotat. Birm. Heartlands Hosp. Prev: SHO (A & E) City Hosp. Birm.; Ho. Off. (Med.) Univ. Hosp.; Ho. Off. (Surg.) City Hosp.

LAVRIC, Jan (retired) Central Surgery, Thurnscoe, Rotherham Tel: 01709 893108 — MD 1941 Zagreb.

LAVRIC, Joseph Marjan Beechwood Surgery, 371 Chepstow Road, Newport NP19 8HL Tel: 01633 277771 Fax: 01633 290631; 3 Shepherd Drive, Langstone, Newport NP18 2LB — MB BCh 1982 Wales; MRCGP 1986; DA (UK) 1990; DRCOG 1989; Cert Family Plann. JCC 1985.

LAVY, Mr Christopher Brian Dyce Malawi Against Polio, P. O. Box 256, Blantyre, Malawi Tel: 00 265 634295 Fax: 00 265 632928 Email: lavy@malawi.net; 35 Chisenhale Road, London E3 5QY Tel: 020 8981 2485 — MB BS 1982 Lond.; BSc Lond. 1979; MCh (Orth.) Liverp. 1991; FRCS Eng. 1988; FRCS Ed. 1986; ECFMG Cert. 1985. (St. Bart.) Surg. to Malawi Against Polio (registered charity) Blantyre Malawi; Assoc. Prof. Malawi Coll. Med. Socs: Christ. Med. Fell.sh.; World Orthop. Concern.; Roy. Soc. Med. Prev: Const. Orthop. Surg. UCL Hosps.; Regist. Roy. United. Hosp. Bath; Demonst. (Human Anat.) Oxf. Univ.

LAVY, Mr Gordon Alexander Dyce (retired) Copsley, 4 Hastings Road, Pembury, Tunbridge Wells TN2 4PD Tel: 01892 824843 — MB BChir 1949 Camb.; MA, MChir Camb. 1968; FRCS Eng. 1957. Prev: Cons. Surg. Tunbridge Wells HA.

LAVY, Mr Jeremy Andrew 107 Harley Street, Alexandra Park, London W1G 6AL Tel: 020 7486 7431 Fax: 020 7935 5087 — MB BS 1988 Lond.; FRCS Eng. 1993; FRCS (ENT) Eng. 1995; FRCS (Orl) 1998. (St. Bartholemews) Cons. (ENT) Roy. Nat. Throat, Nose & Ear Hosp. Lond. Socs: Christ. Med. Fell.sh.; Roy. Soc. Med. (Otol & Laryngol); Brit. Assn. Otol. Head & Neck Surg. Prev: Fell. (Skull Base Surg.) St. Vincent's Hosp. Sydney Australia; Regist. N. Thames Train. Scheme.

LAW, Alastair (retired) 71 Westport Avenue, Mayals, Swansea SA3 5EF Tel: 01792 535184 Email: alastair.law@ntlworld.com — MB ChB Glas. 1951; FRCGP 1987, M 1962.

LAW, Alistair Geekie Robertson (retired) 21 Thomson Street, Dundee DD1 4LF Tel: 01382 669259 — MB ChB 1947 St. And. JP.

LAW, Allison Theresa Riversdale Surgery, 59 Bridge St., Belper, Derby DE56 1AY Tel: 01332 822386; 180 Alfreton Road, Little Eaton, Derby DE21 5AB — MB ChB 1985 Glas.; MRCGP 1989; DRCOG 1988; DCH RCPS Glas. 1988.

LAW, Amanda Lun Chu Summerfield House, The Paddocks, Barnoldby-le-Beck, Grimsby DN37 0BF — MB ChB 1998 Manch.; MB ChB Manch 1998.

LAW, Anita Kathryn Balham Park Surgery, 92 Balham Park Road, London SW12 8EA Tel: 020 8767 8828 Fax: 020 8682 1736 — MB BS 1986 Lond.; MRCGP 1992; DRCOG 1989; Cert. Family Plann. JCC 1989. Clin. Asst. GV Med. St. Geo. Hosp. Tooting. Prev: Trainee GP Lond.; SHO (Rheum.) Qu. Eliz. Milit. Hosp. Woolwich; SHO (Genitourin. Med.) St. Geo.'s Hosp. Tooting.

LAW, Mrs Barbara (retired) High Trees, Ramsay Wood, Gatehouse-of-Fleet, Castle Douglas DG7 2HJ Tel: 01557 814489 Fax: 01557 814489 — MB BS 1944 Lond.; MRCS Eng. LRCP Lond. 1944; DPH Eng. 1948. Prev: Med. Asst. Univ. Coll. Hosp. Lond. & Whittington Hosp. Lond.

LAW, Caroline Jane Laburnam Cottage, Brook Hill, Norley Wood, Lymington SO41 5RQ — MB BS 1989 Lond.

LAW, Catherine Elizabeth Huddersfield Road Surgery, 6 Huddersfield Road, Barnsley S70 2LT Tel: 01226 287589 Fax: 01226 731245; 25 Bradford Road, St Johns, Wakefield WF1 2RF Tel: 01924 201133 — MB ChB 1980 Liverp. Socs: BMA. Prev: SHO (Anaesth., Paediat. & Obst.) Wakefield HA.

LAW, Catherine Mary, OBE MRC Environmental Epidemiology Unit, Southampton General Hospital, Southampton SO16 6YD Tel: 02380 777624 Fax: 02380 704021 Email: claw@mrc.soton.ac.uk; Wellbrook, Dores Lane, Braishfield, Romsey SO51 0QJ Tel: 01794 368406 — MB BS 1989 Lond.; FFPHM 2001; MB BS Lond. 1979; MD Lond. 1989; FRCP Lond. 1996; MRCP (UK) 1981; MFPHM RCP (UK) 1991; FRCPCH 1997. Sen. Lect. Fell. MRC Environm. Epidemiol. Univ. Soton; Hon. Cons. Pub. Health Soton. Univ. Hosps. Trust. Prev: Fell. Johns Hopkins Univ. Sch. Hyg. & Pub. Health Baltimore, USA; Lect. Inst. Child Health Lond.

LAW, David Gordon 39 Church Lane, Nuneaton CV10 0EX — MB BS 1957 Lond.; MRCS Eng. LRCP Lond. 1956. (St. Mary's)

LAW, David Julian Croft Hall Medical Practice, 19 Croft Road, Torquay TQ2 5UA Tel: 01803 298441 Fax: 01803 296104 — BM BS 1984 Nottm.

LAW, David Malcolm (retired) 1 West Park, Redruth TR15 3AJ Tel: 01209 314505 Fax: 01209 314505 — MB BS Lond. 1962. Prev: Chief Med. Off. Gulf Petrochem. Indus. Corp., Bahrain.

LAW, Donald Patrick Fletcher Dr Law and Partners, 1 Vicarage Road, Kings Heath, Birmingham B14 7QA Tel: 0121 444 2005 Fax: 0121 441 4331 — MB ChB 1980 Birm. GP Princip.; Clin. Asst., Lasercare Clinics, Birm.; Prescribing Lead & Bd. Mem. S. E. Bingham PCG Birm. Socs: GP Writers Assn.; Assn. BRd.casting Doctors. Prev: Ho. Off. Birm. Centre for Orthop. Oncol.; Ho. Off. (Radiol.) Qu.. Eliz. Hosp. Birm.

LAW, Elizabeth Anna (retired) 94 Duff Street, Macduff AB44 1PR Tel: 01261 832887 — MB ChB 1958 Aberd.; BSc Aberd. 1947. Prev: Cons. Ment. Defic. Ladysbridge Hosp.

LAW, Evelyn Marie Josephine The Surgery, Penshurst, Tonbridge TN12 8LP; The Small Barn, Nunnery Lane, Penshurst, Tonbridge TN11 8HA Tel: 01892 870401 — MB BS Lond. 1960. (King's Coll. Hosp.)

LAW, Fergus Daniel Bath Royal United Hospital, Combe Park, Bath BA1 3NG Tel: 01225 28331 — MB ChB 1985 Bristol; BSc Bristol 1982, MB ChB 1985. SHO (Psychiat.) Bath & Wessex HA GP VTS.

LAW, Helen Harrogate District Hospital, Lancaster Park Road, Harrogate HG2 7SX Tel: 01423 885959; Email: helen.law@virgin.net — MB ChB 1989 Liverp.; 2000 FFAEM; MRCP (UK) 1993. Cons. (A&E), Harrogate Health care NHS Trust, N.Yorks. Prev: Specialist Regist. (A&E) Yorks.

LAW, Helen Margaret Hill Crescent, Main St., Tatenhill, Burton-on-Trent DE13 9SD — MB ChB 1992 Leic.

LAW, James Brian The Health Centre, Bury New Road, Whitefield, Manchester M45 8GH Tel: 0161 766 8221 — MB ChB 1951 Manch. Prev: Ho. Surg. Manch. Roy. Infirm.

LAW, Jennifer Esmee Mawbey Brough Health Centre, 39 Wilcox Close, London SW8 2UD Tel: 020 7622 3827 Fax: 020 7498 1069 — MB BS 1981 Lond.; MRCGP 1986; DRCOG 1986; Cert. Family Plann. JCC 1985. Prev: Trainee GP Lond. VTS; SHO (O & G) St. Thos. Hosp. Lond.; SHO (Renal Unit) St. Helier Hosp. Carshalton.

***LAW, Jennifer Kirsteen** 12 Clifford Road, Stirling FK8 2AQ — MB ChB 1997 Ed.

LAW, Joanne Claire 24 The Glebe, Lavendon, Olney MK46 4HY — MB ChB 1995 Bristol.

LAW, Julian Christopher Castle Place Surgery, 9 Park Hill, Tiverton EX16 6RR Tel: 01884 252333 Fax: 01884 252152; Cowley Lodge, Blundells Road, Tiverton EX16 4DJ — BM 1984 Soton.; MRCGP 1993; MRCOG 1989. GP; Hosp. Pract. Obst. & Gyn. Tiverton & Dist. Hosp. Socs: Brit. Soc. for Colposcopy and Cervical Path. Prev: GP Princip. Bridport; Trainee GP Ivybridge Devon; Regist. Rotat. (O & G) Centr. & S. Birm.

LAW, Miss Kathleen Patricia ENT Department, Tyrone County Hospital, Omagh BT79 0AP Tel: 028 8224 5211 Fax: 028 8224 7283; 41 Ballinamullan Road, Omagh BT79 0PZ Tel: 01662 243453 — MB BCh BAO Belf. 1968; FRCSI 1974. (Qu. Belfast) Cons. Surg. (ENT) Tyrone Co. Hosp. Omagh & Erne Hosp. Enniskillen. Prev: Sen. Regist. (ENT Surg.) Altnagelvin Hosp. Lond.derry; Regist. (ENT) Roy. Vict. & Belf. City Hosp.; SHO (ENT Surg.) Liverp. ENT Infirm.

LAW, Kathryn Virginia Aldershot Health Centre, Wellington Avenue, Aldershot GU11 1PA Tel: 01252 324577 Fax: 01252 324861; 1 Chatsworth Grove, Farnham GU9 0DJ Tel: 01252 717242 Email: katie@utu-mno.demon.co.uk — BM 1984 Soton.; BM Soton. l984; MRCGP. 1994. (Soton.)

LAW, Lamont Alexander Walnut Cottage, Ebbs Lane, East Hanney, Wantage OX12 0HL — MB ChB 1978 Dundee.

LAW, Marion May Taylor (retired) 21 Thomson Street, Dundee DD1 4LF Tel: 01382 669259 — MB ChB 1952 St. And.; BA (Hons.) Open 1994.

LAW, Michael James Anthony Vennel Street Health Centre, 50 Vennel Street, Dalry KA24 4AG Tel: 01294 832523 Fax: 01294 835771; 16 Parkhill Drive, Dalry KA24 5DA Tel: 01294 833857 — MB ChB 1971 Glas.; MRCGP 1977; DObst RCOG 1973. Prev: Squadron Ldr. RAF Med. Br.; Med. Off. UKSU SHAPE Belgium; Ho. Surg. Stobhill Gen. Hosp. Glas.

LAW, Mr Nicholas Warwick Dancers Hill Farmhouse, Dancers Lane, Barnet EN5 4RX — MB BS 1978 Lond.; BSc Lond. 1975, MS 1988; FRCS Eng. 1983. (St. Bart. Med. Coll.) Cons. Gen. & Vasc. Surg. Chase Farm Hosp. Enfield. Prev: Sen. Regist. (Vasc. Surg.) Char. Cross Hosp.; Sen. Regist. Roy. Bournemouth Hosp.; Regist. Profess. Surg. Unit. W.m. Hosp.

LAW, Nicki 12 Woodland Park Road, Headingley, Leeds LS6 2AZ Tel: 0113 275 5417 — MB ChB 1996 Leeds; DRCOG 2000; MA 2001; BA Oxf. 1993. (Leeds) Prev: GP Trainee, Bradford W. Yorks.

LAW, Patricia Kristeen The Surgery, 28 Claremont Road, Surbiton KT6 4RF Tel: 020 8399 2280 Fax: 020 8390 0371 — MB BS 1978

Lond.; MRCGP 1982; DCH RCP Lond. 1982; DRCOG 1981. (St. Bart.)

LAW, Penelope Anne Department Obstetrics & Gynaecology, St. Mary's Hospital, Praed St., London W2; Flat 4, 31-32 Ford Square, London E1 2HS Tel: 020 7377 2803 Email: p.a.law@ic.ac.uk — MB BS 1993 Lond.; BA (Hons.) Lond. 1983. (Lond.) Research Fell. (O & G) Imperial Coll. St. Mary's Hosp. Lond. Prev: SHO (O & G) Hammersmith Hosp. Lond.

LAW, Penelope Jane Dumfries & Galloway Royal Infirmary, Bankend Road, Dumfries DG1 4AP; Park View, Kirkpatrick Bridge, Thornhill DG3 5JL Tel: 01848 331227 — MB BS 1980 Lond.; BSc Lond. 1977, MB BS 1980; FRCS Glas. 1985; FRCR 1991; T(R)(CR) 1992. Cons. Diag. Radiol. Dumfries. & Galloway Roy. Infirm. Prev: Sen. Regist. (Diag. Radiol.) St. Bart. Hosp. Lond.; Research Fell. (Radiol.) St. Marks Hosp. Lond.; Jun. Regist. (Surg.) St. Bart. Hosp. Lond.

LAW, Peter John Clark Avenue Surgery, Clark Avenue, Pontnewydd, Cwmbran NP44 1RY Tel: 01633 482733 Fax: 01633 867758; Ty Nant, Chapel Lane, Croesyceillog, Cwmbran NP44 2PN Tel: 01633 32201 — MRCS Eng. LRCP Lond. 1966; MB Camb. 1967, BChir 1966. (Westm.) Socs: Chairm. Cwmbran Med. Soc. Prev: Res. Obst. Asst. & Cas. Off. W.m. Hosp.; Ho. Surg. Gordon Hosp.

LAW, Rhoda Rebecca (retired) 1 Beechworth Close, London NW3 7UT Tel: 020 7435 3675 — MB BChir 1951 Camb.; BA, MB BChir Camb. 1951.

LAW, Richard Graham (retired) High Trees, Ramsay Wood, Gatehouse-of-Fleet, Castle Douglas DG7 2HJ Tel: 01557 814489 Fax: 01557 814489 — MB BChir 1947 Camb.; MD Camb. 1952, MA, MB BChir 1947; MRCS Eng. LRCP Lond. 1943; FRCOG 1961, M 1949. Prev: Cons. (Ultrasound) Whittington Hosp. Lond.

LAW, Robert Charles 90 West Broadway, Bristol BS9 4SS — MB ChB 1989 Cape Town.

LAW, Robert Gibb Falkirk Royal Infirmary, Major's Loan, Falkirk FK1 5QE Tel: 0115 931 4424 — MB ChB 1971 Glas.; FFA RCS Eng. 1976. Cons. Anaesth. Falkirk & Dist. Roy. Infirm.

LAW, Ronald (retired) 1 Beechworth Close, London NW3 7UT Tel: 020 7435 3675 — MB BS 1950 Lond.; FRCGP 1977, M 1960. Prev: Nuffield Trav. Fell. Gen. Pract.

LAW, Sara 33 Quarry High Street, Headington Quarry, Oxford OX3 8JU Tel: 01865 741108 — MB ChB 1992 Leeds; BSc (Hons.) Leeds 1989. SHO (Anaesth.), Roy. Berks. Hosp., Reading. Prev: SHO (ENT) Birm. Childr.'s Hosp.; SHO (ENT) Radcliffe Infirm. Oxf.; SHO (Surg.) John Radcliffe Hosp. Oxf.

LAW, Stephen David Hill Crest, Main St., Tatenhill, Burton-on-Trent DE13 9SD — MB ChB 1992 Leic.

LAW, Susan Anne Taylor, Wing Cdr. RAF Med. Br. (retired) Meadow Croft Surgery, Jackson Road, Aylesbury HP19 3EX Email: susan.law@shearer-law.co.uk — MB ChB 1978 Dundee; 1991 BA Open Univ. 1991; 1994 MSc (Gen. Pract.) Lond. 1994; 1983 MRCGP 1983; 1988 DAvMed. 1988; 1982 DA (UK) 1982; 1998 DFFP (UK) 1998; 1999 FRCGP 1999. p/t Princip. Gen. Practl. Meadowcroft Surg. Ayles bury,; Assoc. Tutor OU 2000; GP Educat.alist, Vale of Aylesbury; Princip. Meadowcroft Surg. Prev: Assoc. Adviser (GP) RAF Halton.

LAW, Victoria Anne 22 Muir Road, Ramsgate CT11 8AX — MB ChB 1995 Sheff.

LAW CHIN YUNG, Grace Lynny 10 Spinney Close, Ormskirk L39 4ST — BM BS 1994 Nottm. SHO (Med.) Qu. Med. Centre Nottm.

LAW CHIN YUNG, Yit Foong (retired) 10 Spinney Close, Aughton, Ormskirk L39 4ST — MB BS 1965 Patna; FFA RCS Eng. 1976. Prev: Cons. Anaesth. Wrightinton Hosp. NHS Trust.

LAWAL, Adegboyega Hakeem 21 Warlock Road, London W9 3LP — MB BS 1987 Ibadan; MRCOG 1994.

LAWAL, Olalekan 49 Goring Road, New Southgate, London N11 2BT — MB BS 1977 Ibadan; MFFP 1993; MRCOG 1991.

LAWDEN, Mark Charles Neurology Department, Leicester Royal Infirmary, Leicester LE1 5WW Tel: 0116 258 6192 Fax: 0116 256 9192; 7 Old Charity Farm, Stoughton, Leicester LE2 2EX Tel: 0116 271 8884 Email: lawden01@globalnet.co.uk — BM BCh 1985 Oxf.; PhD Camb. 1983, MA 1982; MRCP (UK) 1988; FRCP (UK) 1999. (Oxford) Cons. Neurol. Leicester Roy. Infirm. Socs: Fell. Roy. Soc. Med. Prev: Sen. Regist. (Neurol.) Roy. Hallamsh. Hosp. Sheff.; Hon. Regist. (Neurol.) Dept. Acad. Neurosci. Char. Cross Hosp. Lond.; Regist. (Neurol.) Newc. Gen. Hosp. & Middlesbrough Gen. Hosp.

LAWES, Daniel Alfred 4 Eveline Court, Connaught Gardens, London N10 3LA — MB BS 1993 Lond.; FRCS 1997.

LAWES, Dorothea Eleanor Phyllida 2 Roseneath Close, Orpington BR6 7SR Tel: 01689 856986 Fax: 01689 856986 — MB BCh BAO 1970 Belf.; MFFP 1993; Cert. JCC Lond. 1977; DObst RCOG 1972; DCH Dub. 1972. (Belf.) Med. Off. Ravensbourne NHS Trust. Socs: Assoc. Mem. Inst. Psycho-Sexual Med. & BMA. Prev: Regist. (Med.) Rockhampton Base Hosp., Austral.

LAWES, Eric George Shackleton Department of Anaesthetics, Southampton General Hospital, Tremona Road, Southampton SO16 6YD Tel: 02380 796135 Fax: 01794 513562; 5 Deansfield, Winchester Hill, Romsey SO51 7NE Tel: 01794 501937 Fax: 01794 513562 — MB BS 1976 Lond.; FFA RCS Eng. 1981. Cons. Anaesth. Soton. Univ. Hosps. Socs: Assn. Anaesth. & BMA. Prev: Sen. Regist. Rotat. (Anaesth.) Bristol; Regist. (Anaesth.) Roy. Free Hosp. Lond.; SHO (Anaesth. & ITU) Middlx. Hosp. Lond.

LAWES, Matthew James 1 Pinefield, Eastfield Terrace, Bristol BS9 4BW — MB ChB 1996 Birm.; ChB Birm. 1996; BSc (Hons.) Birm. 1993. SHO (A & E) P.ss Marg. Hosp. Swindon.

LAWES, Michael Robert Rusthall Medical Centre, Nellington Road, Rusthall, Tunbridge Wells TN4 8UW Tel: 01892 515142 Fax: 01892 532256; 11 Hungershall Park, Tunbridge Wells TN4 8NE — MB BS 1978 Lond.; MA Camb. 1978; MRCGP 1983; DRCOG 1982. Chairm. W. Kent FACE (Focus on Audit & Clin. Effectiveness). Prev: Clin. Asst. (Psychogeriat.) Pembury Hosp.; Trainee Gen. Pract. Tunbridge Wells VTS; Cas. Off. & Ho. Phys. Whipp's Cross Hosp. Lond.

LAWES, Richard John Flat 1, Montpelier Court, Montpelier Road, London W5 2QN — MB ChB 1985 Ed.; BSc Ed. 1987, MB ChB 1985; BA (Hons.) Oxf. 1992. Regist. Rotat. (Psychiat.) Oxf. Prev: Regist. Profess. Unit Roy. Edin. Hosp.; Ho. Off. (Surg. Neurol.) W.. Gen. Hosp. Edin.; Ho. Off. (Gen. Med.) Leith Hosp. Edin.

LAWFIELD, Conrad Hilary Brian (retired) 29 The Avenues, Norwich NR2 3PH Tel: 01603 453967 — MRCS Eng. LRCP Lond. 1946; MA Camb. 1945.

LAWFIELD, Matthew Francis Martin Christmas Maltings Surgery, Camps Road, Haverhill CB9 8HF Tel: 01440 702010 Fax: 01440 714761 — MRCS Eng. LRCP Lond. 1975; MB Camb. 1976, BChir 1975. Prev: Ho. Surg. St. Margt. Hosp. Epping; Ho. Phys. Ipswich Hosp.

LAWFORD, Charles Valentine Piers Chest Clinic, Coventry & Warwickshire Hospital, Stoney Stanton Road, Coventry CV1 4FH Tel: 024 76 224055 Fax: 024 76 221655; 440 Westwood Heath Road, Coventry CV4 8AA Tel: 024 76 470609 — MB BS 1978 Lond.; FRCP Lond. 1992; MRCP (UK) 1973; MRCS Eng. LRCP Lond. 1971. (Lond. Hosp.) Cons. Phys. (Thoracic & Gen. Med.) Coventry Gp. Hosps. Socs: Brit. Thorac. Soc.; Midl. Thoracic Soc. Prev: Sen. Regist. (Thoracic Med.) Aberd. Roy. Infirm.; Lect. (Med.) Univ. Aberd.; Regist. (Med.) N.wick Pk. Hosp. Harrow.

LAWLER, Antoinette Mary 1 Shrewsbury Park, Belfast BT9 6PN — MB BCh BAO 1963 NUI; DCH NUI 1965. Clin. Med. Off. E. Health Bd. Belf. Prev: Regist. (Paediat.) Childr. Hosp. Dub.; Asst. MOH (Child Welf.) Edin. Corp.; Ho. Off. Nat. Matern. Hosp. Dub.

LAWLER, Caroline Elizabeth Mill Street Surgery, Mill Street, North Petherton, Bridgwater TA6 6LX Tel: 01278 662223 Fax: 01278 663727 — BM 1983 Soton.; DRCOG 1987. Clin. Asst. (Genitourin. Med.) MusGr. Pk. Hosp. Taunton. Prev: Med. Off. Kaeo, NZ; Trainee GP Taunton VTS; GP Taunton.

LAWLER, Josephine Sallie Wellington House Surgery, Henrietta Street, Batley WF17 5DN Tel: 01924 470333 Fax: 01924 420981 Email: sallie.lawler@gp-b85015.nhs.uk; Gardeners House, Briestfield Road, Briestfield, Dewsbury WF12 0NX Tel: 01924 848362 — MB ChB 1977 Dundee; MRCGP 1981. (Dundee) Prev: Princip. GP Birstall W. Yorks.

LAWLER, Lynda May (retired) 8 Elmwood Grove, Stockton-on-Tees TS19 0RB Tel: 01642 677490 — MB ChB Manch. 1960; MFFP 1993. Community Med. Off. (Family Plann.) N. Tees NHS Trust & S. Tees Community Health Trust.

LAWLER, Paul Gerard Patrick Trispens, 10 Cambridge Road, Linthorpe, Middlesbrough TS5 5NQ Tel: 01642 289215 Fax: 01642 289216; Intensive Care Unit, South Cleveland Hospital, Marton Road, Middlesbrough TS4 3BW Tel: 01642 854643 Fax: 01642

274655 — BM BCh Oxf. 1969; MA Oxf. 1969; FRCP Lond. 1987; FRCA 1992; FFA RCS 1975. Cons. Anaesth. & Intens. Care S. Cleveland Hosp. Middlesbrough; Examrs. Diploma Intens. Care Med. 1998-; Chairm. Intercoll. BD. Train. Intens. Care.med 1999. Socs: Intens. Care Soc.; Counc. Roy. Coll. Anaesth.; Roy. Soc. Med. Prev: Regist. (Anaesth.) Bristol Roy. Infirm.; SHO Rotat. (Med.) Soton. Gen. Hosp.; Scientif. Off. Div. Anaesth. Clin. Research Centre Harrow.

LAWLER, William Pine House, 21 Alkrington Green, Alkrington, Middleton, Manchester M24 1ED Tel: 0161 654 8149 Fax: 0161 653 5774 — MD 1980 Manch.; MB ChB 1971; FRCPath 1993, M 1981. Indep. Cons. Forens. Path. Manch.; Home Office Path. Prev: Sen. Lect. & Hons. Cons. Path. Manch. Roy. Infirm.; Ho. Phys. & Ho. Surg. Manch. Roy. Infirm.

LAWLESS, John MacDaragh The Poplars, Church Lane, Saltfleetby, Louth LN11 7TU Tel: 01507 338094 — MB BS 1975 Lond.; MRCS Eng. LRCP Lond. 1975; AFOM RCP Lond. 1987. (Westm.) Prev: Regional Med. Off. Brit. Telecom (Lond.); SCMO (Occupat. Health) Wandsworth HA.

LAWLESS, Peter Dudley Street Surgery, 11 Dudley Street, Grimsby DN31 2AW Tel: 01472 353303/4; 18 Seacroft Road, Cleethorpes DN35 0AZ Tel: 01472 691912 — MB ChB 1968 Leeds; DObst RCOG 1970. Prev: Ho. Phys. & Ho. Surg. Otley Gen. Hosp.; Ho. Surg. (Obst.) City Hosp. Chester.

LAWLEY, Bernard John Parkside, Vicarage Lane, Redbourne, Gainsborough DN21 4QW Tel: 01652 648226 — MB ChB 1951 Birm. Prev: Squadron Ldr. RAF Med. Br.

LAWLEY, David Ian Hull and East Riding Community health trust, c/o Malster Lodge, Hauxwell Grove, Middlesex Road, Hull HU8 0RB — MB ChB 1985 Leeds; MB ChB Leeds 1988; BSc (Hons.) Med. Microbiol. Leeds 1985; MMedSc Leeds 1993; MRCPsych 1993. Cons. In old age Psychiat., Hull. Prev: Sen. Regist. (Gen. Adult Psychiat.) Bootham Pk. York; Sen. Regist. (Old Age Psychiat.) De La Pole Hosp. Hull; Sen. Regist. (Gen. Adult Psychiat.) St. Jas. Hosp. Leeds.

LAWLEY, Guy Charles The Sands End Health Clinic, 170 Wandsworth Bridge Road, London SW6 2UQ Tel: 020 7371 8472 Fax: 020 7371 8473 — BM BCh 1984 Oxf.; MA Oxf. 1985.

LAWLEY, Julia Louise Northbrook Health Centre, 93 Northbrook Road, Shirley, Solihull B90 3LX Tel: 0121 744 1872 Fax: 0121 733 6892 — MB ChB 1991 Birm.; T(GP) 1995.

LAWLEY, Margery Anne The Old Toll Cottage, Kalemouth, Kelso TD5 8LE Tel: 01835 850241 — MB ChB 1950 Ed.; MD Ed. 1955. (Ed.) Prev: Research Assoc. Univ. Malaya; Ho. Surg. (Obst.)13 & Ho. Phys. Dudley Rd. Hosp. Birm.

LAWLEY, Ruth 1 Mulcaster Place, Croglin, Carlisle CA4 9RX — MB ChB 1979 Manch.

LAWLOR, Deborah Anne Dept. of Social Medicine, University of Bristol, Carynge Hall, Whiteladies Road, Bristol BS8 2PR Tel: 0117 928 7267 Fax: 0117 928 7292 Email: d.a.lawlor@bristol.ac.uk; 19 Hatherley Road, Bishopston, Bristol BS7 8QA Tel: 0117 924 5067 — MB ChB 1986 Bristol; MRCGP 1993; Cert. Family Plann. JCC 1989; MPH (Distinct.) Leeds 1997; MFPHM Pt I 1997; MFPHM 1999. Lect. in Epidemiol. & Pub. Health Med., Dept Social Med. Bristol Uni. Socs: BMA. Prev: Regist. (Pub. Health) Nuffield; Princip. GP Bradford; Paediat. Doctor Hosp. Provin. Chimoio, Chimoio, Mozambique.

LAWLOR, Ellen Frances Dermatology Unit, St Andrews Hospital, Devons Road, Bow, London E3 3NT Tel: 020 7363 8004 Fax: 020 7363 8352; 24 Cameret Court, Lorne Gardens, London W11 4XX Tel: 020 7610 4711 — MB BCh BAO 1972 NUI; MD NUI 1991; FRCPI 1994, 1978; DCH NUI 1974; DObst RCOG 1975. Cons. Dermat. Newham Health Care; Hon. Sen. Lect. (Dermat.) United Med. & Dent. Schs. of Guys & St. Thos.

LAWLOR, Katherine Mary 26 Mitchley Hill, Sanderstead, South Croydon CR2 9HA — MB ChB 1996 Ed.

LAWLOR, Michael Gerard 28 Oakleigh Avenue, Whetstone, London N20 9JH Tel: 020 8445 7691 — MB BCh BAO 1973 Dub.; BDS Dub. 1966; FDS RCS Eng. 1976; FFD RCSI 1978.

LAWLOR, Terence 12 Stanton Road, Wimbledon, London SW20 8RL — MB BS 1963 Lond.; MRCS Eng. LRCP Lond. 1963; DPM RCPSI 1969; DPM Eng. 1970; MRCPsych 1972. (Middlx.) Prev: Cons. Psychiat. Normansfield Hosp. Teddington; Regist. Long Gr. Hosp. Epsom.

LAWMAN, Sarah Helen Alexandra The Old Vicarage, 10 Church St., Rickmansworth WD3 1BS — MB BS 1993 Lond.

LAWN, Elfred Noel Fulford Way Surgery, Fulford Way, Woodbury, Exeter EX5 1NZ Tel: 01395 232509 Fax: 01395 232065; Nutts Farm, Woodbury Salterton, Exeter EX5 1PG Tel: 01395 232391 — MB BS 1981 Lond.; MRCGP 1987. (Westm.) Prev: SHO (O & G) St. Richards Hosp. Chichester; SHO (Geriat.) Soton. Gen. Hosp.; Trainee GP RN Hops. Haslar.

LAWN, Elizabeth Mary Langley Health Centre, Common Road, Langley, Slough SL3 8LE Tel: 01753 544288 Fax: 01753 592415; Fairwinds, Kingswood Rise, Englefield Green, Egham TW20 0NG Tel: 01784 432609 Fax: 01784 432609 — MB ChB 1980 Manch.; MRCGP 1984; DCCH RCP Ed. 1986.

LAWN, Jennifer Anne Toft Road Surgery, Toft Road, Knutsford WA16 9DX Tel: 01565 632681; Grange Farm, Knolls Green Village, Knutsford WA16 7BN — MB ChB Manch. 1983; MRCGP 1987.

LAWN, John Peter Jeremy Outwood Park Medical Centre, Potoviene Lane, Wakefield WF1 2PE Tel: 01924 822626 — MB BS 1973 Lond.; MRCS Eng. LRCP Lond. 1972; MRCGP 1978; Dip. Sports Med. Lond 1991; Dip. Med. Acupunc. 1995. (St. Bart.) Exec. Mem. Wakefield PCT. Socs: Brit. Inst. Muscular Skeletal Med.; Brit. Med. Acupunct. Soc.; Brit. Assn. Sport & Med. Prev: Sen. Med. Off. RAF Linton on Ouse; SHO (O & G) RAF Hosp. Wegberg; Unit Med. Off. RAF Rheindahlen.

LAWRANCE, Catherine Ann 9 Grove Road, Emmer Green, Reading RG4 8LJ — MB ChB 1987 Leeds; DCH RCP Lond. 1990; DRCOG 1993. GP, Reading.

LAWRANCE, Jeremy Andrew Department of Radiology, Christie Hospital NHS Trust, Wilmslow Road, Withington, Manchester M20 4BX Tel: 0161 446 3324; Belmont Road, Hale, Altrincham WA15 9PT Tel: 0161 928 0057 Email: j.lawrance@which.net — MB ChB 1985 Cape Town; MRCP (UK) 1988; FRCR 1992. Cons. Radiol. Christie Hosp. Manch. Prev: Sen. Regist. (Radiol.) John Radcliffe Hosp. Oxf.; Fell. Abdom. Imaging Duke Univ. Med. Center Durh., NC USA.

LAWRANCE, Mr Richard Jeremy Royal Bournemouth Hospital, Castle Lane E., Bournemouth BH7 7DW Tel: 01202 303626; 60 Strouden Avenue, Bournemouth BH8 9HX Tel: 01202 526526 — MB BS 1981 Lond.; MS Soton. 1993; FRCS Eng. 1986; FRCS Ed. 1986. (Westm.) Cons. Surg. (Gen. & Colorectal Surg.) Roy. Bournemouth Hosp. Socs: Assn. Coloproctol. Prev: Sen. Regist. (Gen. Surg.) Wessex; Regist. Roy. United Hosp. Bath; Ho. Surg. W.m. Hosp. Lond.

LAWRENCE, Adam Gay 19 Claylands Road, London SW8 1NX Tel: 020 7564 3160 — MB Camb. 1962, BChir 1961. (St. Thos.) Cons. Genitourin. Med. Riverside HA. Prev: Sen. Regist. (Venereol.) & Sen. Med. Cas. Off. St. Thos. Hosp.; Med. Regist. Lister Hosp. Hitchin.

LAWRENCE, Angela Doris Mary The Surgery, 32 Foden St., Stoke, Stoke-on-Trent ST4 4BX Tel: 01782 411884; 190 Trent Valley Road, Penkhull, Stoke-on-Trent ST4 5HL Tel: 01782 415728 — MB ChB 1985 Birm.; T(GP) 1990. (Birmingham) GP Retainer Scheme. Socs: BMA.

LAWRENCE, Angela Jane St. Neots Sx, 47 Wolseley Road, Milehouse, Plymouth PL2 3BJ Tel: 01752 561305 — MB ChB 1991 Leic.; MRCGP 1996; DRCOG 1995. (Leic) p/t GP Partner. Prev: GP/Regist. St. Neots Surg. Plymouth.

LAWRENCE, Anne Picton Road Surgery, 194 Picton Road, Liverpool L15 4LL Tel: 0151 733 1347 — MB ChB 1970 Liverp.

LAWRENCE, Anthony James The Medical Centre, High Street, Lindfield, Haywards Heath RH16 2HX Tel: 01444 457666; 2 Keymer End, Ashenground Road, Haywards Heath RH16 4PX — MB BS 1988 Lond.; MRCGP 1994; DRCOG 1991. Prev: Trainee GP Cuckfield Hosp. Haywards Heath.

LAWRENCE, Arthur Charles Kendon (retired) Lawrence Books, Newark Antiques Centre, Lombard St., Newark NG24 1XR Tel: 01636 605865 Fax: 01636 703881 Email: lawrence.newark@diamond.co.uk — MB BS Lond. 1950; MD Lond. 1959; MRCS Eng. LRCP Lond. 1950; FRCPath 1975, M 1963. Prev: Cons. Haematol. N.. Gen. Hosp. Sheff.

LAWRENCE, Benjamin Harry (retired) 1 West Farm Court, 12 Gatcombe Way, Barnet EN4 9TT Tel: 020 8449 6783 — MB BS 1948 Lond.; MRCS Eng. LRCP Lond. 1948. Prev: Ho. Surg. (Thoracic Surg.) Unit Lond. Hosp.

LAWRENCE, Bridget Elaine Tel: 01952 586691; The Woodlands, Sheinton, Cressage, Shrewsbury SY5 6DN Tel: 01952 510545 — MB ChB 1963 St. And.

LAWRENCE, Christopher Friends Provident St. Mary's Stadium, Britannia Road, Southampton SO14 5FP Tel: 02380 868576; 14 Henstead Road, Polygon, Southampton SO15 2DD Tel: 02380 574291 — MB BChir 1968 Camb.; MA Camb. 1968; MRCS Eng. LRCP Lond. 1967; MRCGP 1978; DCH Eng. 1970. (St. Mary's) p/t Med. Off. & Team Phys. Soton. Football Club. Prev: GP Soton.; SHO (Paediat.) Pembury Hosp. Tunbridge Wells; Ho. Phys. St. Mary's Hosp. Lond.

LAWRENCE, Christopher John Wellcome Institute for History of Medicine, 183 Euston Road, London NW1 2BE Tel: 020 7611 8559 Fax: 020 7611 8562 — MB ChB 1970 Birm.; PhD (Hist. Med.) Lond. 1984, MSc (Hist. Sc.) 1974. Reader Hist. Med. Wellcome Inst. Prev: Trainee GP Lerwick Hosp.; Ho. Phys. Co. Hosp. Hereford; Ho. Surg. Gilbert Bain Hosp. Lerwick.

LAWRENCE, Clifford Maitland Skin Department, Royal Victoria Infirmary, Newcastle upon Tyne NE1 4LP Tel: 0191 282 4548 Fax: 0191 227 5058 — MD 1988 Sheff.; FRCP Lond. 1993; MRCP (UK) 1978. (Sheffield) Cons. Dermat. Univ. Hosps. Newc. Socs: Chairm. Brit. Soc. Dermat. Surg.; Brit.Assn. Dermat. Exec. Comm. Prev: Cons. Dermat. N. Staffs. Hosp. Centre Stoke-on-Trent; Sen. Regist. Roy. Vict. Infirm. Newc.; Regist. N. Staffs. Hosp. Centre Stoke-on-Trent.

LAWRENCE, Colin John 15 Mons Avenue, Billericay CM11 2HG — MB BS 1993 Lond.

LAWRENCE, David 11 Coppice Way, South Woodford, London E18 2DU — MB BS 1944 Lond.; MD (Trop. Med.) Lond. 1949; MRCS Eng. LRCP Lond. 1944; DTM & H Eng. 1949. (Lond. Hosp.) Prev: Capt. RAMC; Sen. Regist. (Med.) Hosp. Trop. Dis. Lond.

LAWRENCE, Mr David Conyers Green Farm, Great Barton, Bury St Edmunds IP31 2RZ — MRCS Eng. LRCP Lond. 1968; MS Lond. 1982, MB BS 1968; FRCS Eng. 1972. (King's Coll. Hosp.) Prev: Sen. Regist. (Surg.) King's Coll. Hosp. Lond.; Surg. Regist. St. Jas. Hosp. Balham; Kendall Research Fell. King's Coll. Hosp. Lond.

LAWRENCE, David (retired) 6 Spring Place, Windermere Avenue, London N3 3QB Tel: 020 8349 0369 — MB BS 1943 Lond.; MD Lond. 1947; MRCP Lond. 1949; MRCS Eng. LRCP Lond. 1939. Prev: Resid. Phys. St. Giles Hosp. Lond.

LAWRENCE, David Anthony Swindells 5 Vache Mews, Vache Lane, Chalfont St Giles HP8 4UT Tel: 01494 580540 Email: dasl@excite.co.uk — MB BS Lond. 1970; MRCS Eng. LRCP Lond. 1970; FRCPath 1989, M 1977. (St. Bart.) Cons. Histopath. Luton & Dunstable Hosp. Prev: Lect. (Path.) Roy. Free Hosp. Lond.; SHO (Path.) St. Bart. Hosp. Lond.

LAWRENCE, David John Lowfield Medical Centre, 65-67 Lowfield Street, Dartford DA1 1HP Tel: 01322 224550; 68 Plantation Road, Hextable, Swanley BR8 7SB Tel: 01322 663631 Fax: 01322 228572 — MB BS 1978 Lond.; DFFP Lond. 1996; DCH RCP Lond. 1983; DRCOG 1982; DA Lond. 1980. (St. Thos.) Clin. Asst. Physical Disabil.; Chairm. Livingstone Hosp. Med. Comm.; Bd. Mem. PCG; Comm. Mem. Ment. Health. Socs: Fell.Roy. Soc. Med. Prev: Doctor i/c Kivunge Hosp. Zanzibar, Tanzania VSO; SHO (Paediat.) St. Thomas Hosp. Lond.; Regist. (Anaesthics) Warwick Hosp.

LAWRENCE, David Kenneth Albany House Medical Centre, 3 Queen Street, Wellingborough NN8 4RW Tel: 01933 222309 Fax: 01933 229236; 204 Northampton Road, Wellingborough NN8 3PW Tel: 01933 228759 — MB BChir 1971 Camb.; FRCGP 1996, M 1975; DObst RCOG 1973. (Oxf.) GP Course Organiser Kettering VTS. Socs: Soc. for Med. Decision Making; Assoc. Mem. Brit. Inst. Musc.-Skel. Med. Prev: Trainee GP Swindon VTS; Regist. (Med.) Kingstown Gen. Hosp. St. Vincent, W. Indies.

LAWRENCE, David Seaton 16 Caldy Chase Drive, Caldy, Wirral CH48 2LD Tel: 0151 625 2484 — MB BS 1968 Newc.; FRCP Lond. 1987; MRCP (UK) 1972. Cons. Phys. Arrowe Pk. Hosp. Wirral.

LAWRENCE, Deryk Anthony (retired) 2 Wayville Road, Dartford DA1 1RL Tel: 01322 224734 — MB BS 1950 Lond.; FRCGP 1974. Locum GP. Prev: Surg. Lt. RNVR.

LAWRENCE, Desmond Ronald Pear Tree Surgery, 28 Meadow Close, Kingsbury, Tamworth B78 2NR Tel: 01827 872755 Fax: 01827 874700; The Elms, Old Kingsbury Road, Marston, Sutton Coldfield B76 0DP Tel: 01675 470316 — MB ChB 1975 Birm.; MRCGP 1980; DCH Eng. 1979; DRCOG 1978. (Birm.) Clin. Governance Off. Rural N. Warks PCG. Prev: Trainee GP Hereford VTS.

LAWRENCE, Diana Frances (retired) 20 South Road, Cupar KY15 5JF Tel: 01334 652103 — MB ChB 1967 St. And.; Dip FPA 1976. Prev: Sen. Partner, Glamis Med. Pract. Glenrothes.

LAWRENCE, E R Arulraja and Partners, 161 Wandle Road, Morden SM4 Tel: 020 8648 1877 Fax: 020 8648 4737; Tel: 0208 642 5584 — MB BS 1957 Ceylon; MB BS 1957 Ceylon.

LAWRENCE, Edward Peter (retired) 14 Portland Road, Oxford OX2 7EY Tel: 01865 52854 — MB BChir 1954 Camb.; MA Oxf. 1976; MA, MB BChir Camb. 1954; FFCM 1978, M 1974; DTM & H Eng. 1959, DPH 1963. Prev: MoH Guernsey.

LAWRENCE, Elizabeth Treflan Surgery, Treflan, Lower Cardiff Road, Pwllheli LL53 5NF Tel: 01758 701457 Fax: 01758 701209; Ynys Fawr, Y Ffor, Pwllheli LL53 6RW — MB ChB 1992 Dundee; MRCGP 1996; DCH RCP Lond. 1995; DRCOG 1995; DFFP 1995. GP Princip. Pwllheli. Prev: Trainee GP Stoke VTS.

LAWRENCE, Elizabeth Frances The Surgery, The Furlongs, Alfriston, Polegate BN26 5XT Tel: 01323 870244; Old Tiles, Hellingly, Hailsham BN27 4HA — MB BS 1977 Lond.; MRCS Eng. LRCP Lond. 1977; DFFP 1996; DRCOG 1980. (Guy's) p/t Clin. Med. Off. (Family Plann.) E.bourne & Co. Healthcare Trust. Prev: Ho. Surg. Brighton Gen. Hosp.; Ho. Phys. Worthing Hosp.

LAWRENCE, Enas Sara 45 Haldon Road, Westhill, London SW18 1QF — MB BS 1991 Lond.; MRCP (UK) Lond.; BSc Lond.

LAWRENCE, Frances Barbara 2 Sinns Cottage, North Country, Redpath TN16 4BU — MB ChB 1973 Manch.; DCH Eng. 1975.

LAWRENCE, Gary David 67 Pereira Road, Birmingham B17 9JA — MB ChB 1983 Sheff.

LAWRENCE, Ian George Department of Diabetes & Endocrinology, The Leicester Royal Infirmry NHS Trust, Infirmary Square, Leicester LE1 5WW Tel: 0116 258 5402 Fax: 0116 258 5344; 36 Wright Lane, Grange Farm, Oadby, Leicester LE2 4TU Tel: 0116 271 0075 — MB ChB 1987 Leeds; MRCP (UK) 1990. Cons. (Diabetes & Endocrinol.) Leicester Roy. Inf. Socs: Brit. Diabetic Assn.; Eur. Assn. Study Diabetes; Eur. Dialysis & Transpl. Assn. Prev: Sen. Regist. (Gen. Med., Diabetes & Endocrinol.) Leicester Roy. Infirm.; Research Fell. (Med. & Therap.) Univ. Leicester; Regist. (Gen. Med. & Nephrol.) Leicester Gen. Hosp.

LAWRENCE, Ian Howard (retired) Willow Cottage, Lendales Lane, Pickering YO18 8EE Tel: 01751 477276 — MB ChB 1950 Ed.; MRCP Lond. 1955; DMRD Eng. 1958. Prev: Cons. Radiol. E. Birm. Hosp.

LAWRENCE, Ian James Treflan Surgery, Treflan, Lower Cardiff Road, Pwllheli LL53 5NF Tel: 01758 701457 Fax: 01758 701209 — MB ChB 1992 Dundee; MRCGP 1996; DRCOG 1995; DCH RCP Lond. 1995; DFFD 1996. GP Princip. Pwllheli. Prev: Trainee GP Derby VTS.

LAWRENCE, Ian Sinclair Alma Road Surgery, 68 Alma Road, Portswood, Southampton SO14 6UX Tel: 023 8067 2666 Fax: 023 8055 0972 — MB ChB 1972 Sheff.

LAWRENCE, Ian William The Woodlands, Sheinton, Cressage, Shrewsbury SY5 6DN Tel: 01952 510545 — MB ChB 1963 St. And.; CIH Dund 1974.

LAWRENCE, Jacob Jeremy 24 Warfield Road, Bracknell RG42 2JY — MB BS 1985 Lond.

LAWRENCE, James (retired) Dunbeg, Aberlour AB38 9NT Tel: 01340 871297 — MB ChB 1953 Aberd.

LAWRENCE, James Mark 10 Matthew Gate, Hitchin SG4 9EQ — MB BS 1992 Lond.

LAWRENCE, James Ronald Moncreiffe, Islesteps, Dumfries DG2 8ES — MB ChB 1970 Glas.; BSc (Hons.) Glas. 1966, MD 1978, MB ChB (Hons.) 1970; FRCP Glas. 1984; MRCP (U.K.) 1973; DObst RCOG 1972. (Glas.) Cons. Phys. Dumfries & Galloway Roy. Infirm.; Mem. Med. & Scientif. Sect. Brit. Diabetic Assn. Socs: Scott. Soc. Phys. Prev: Clin. Pharmacol. Hoechst (UK) Ltd. Milton Keynes; Regist. & Sen. Regist. (Gen. Med. & Clin. Pharmacol.) Stobhill Gen.; Hosp. Glas.

LAWRENCE, Jennifer Hazel 20 Gunnell Close, Kettering NN15 7DJ; 13 Olympic Way, Kettering NN15 6FZ Tel: 01536 522761 — MB ChB 1997 Sheff.

LAWRENCE, Joanne Sarah 11 Upton Way, Broadstone BH18 9LT Tel: 01202 693261; Department of Obstetrics and Gynaecology, Princess Anne Wing, Royal United Hospital, Coombe Park, Bath

BA1 2RF Tel: 01225 310106 — MB BS 1994 Lond. (UCL) SHO (O & G) Roy. United Hosp. Prev: SHO (O & G) United Hosp. Bath.

LAWRENCE, John David The Surgery, 1 Kew Gardens Road, Richmond TW9 3HL Tel: 020 8940 1048 Fax: 020 8332 7644 — MB BS 1980 Lond.; MRCP (UK) 1984. (Char. Cross) Prev: Regist. (Cardiol.) Char. Cross Hosp. Lond.; Regist. (Med.) Whittington Hosp. Lond.; Regist. (Med.) Ashford Hosp. Middlx.

LAWRENCE, Josephine Charmain 34 Hengrove Road, Knowle, Bristol BS4 2PS — MB BS 1983 Lond.

LAWRENCE, Judith Farrar (retired) 14 Portland Road, Oxford OX2 7EY Tel: 01865 552854 — MB BS 1955 Lond.; MRCS Eng. LRCP Lond. 1955. Prev: SCMO Oxf. HA.

LAWRENCE, Kathryn Mary Wingfield, Brookside Road, Brockenhurst SO42 7SS — MB BS 1998 Lond.; MB BS Lond 1998.

LAWRENCE, Leanne Kate Honeysuckle Cottage, Newark Road, Wellow, Newark NG22 0EA — MB BCh 1991 Wales.

LAWRENCE, Loraine Marie Weybridge Health Centre, Church Street, Weybridge KT13 8DW Tel: 01932 856633; High Limes, 4 Fiona Close, Bookham, Leatherhead KT23 3JU Tel: 01372 458314 Fax: 01372 458314 — MB BS 1978 Lond.; MSc Audiol. Med. Manch. 1990; Dip. Family Plann. Manch. 1983. (St, George's London) Gen. Practitioner, Princip., Weybridge HC, Weybridge, Surrey; Forens. Med. Examr. (Police Surg.), W. Surrey Police. Socs: Foundat. Mem. Fac. Comm. Child Health; Brit. Soc. Audiol.; Assn. BrE. Clinicians. Prev: BrE. Phys. Roy. Surrey Co. Hosp. Guildford; GP Partner, Oldham, Lancs.; SCMO, Thameside and Glossop AHA.

LAWRENCE, Malcolm The Willows, Kimbridge Corner, Kimbridge, Romsey SO51 0LE Tel: 01794 367702 — MB ChB 1974 Birm. Staff Orthop. Doctor Roy. Hants. Co. Hosp.; Med. Adviser, Occupat. Health & Employee Safety Dept., RHCH Winchester. Prev: Clin. Asst. (Accid. & Orthop.) Roy. Hants. Co. Hosp.; Regist. (Orthop.) Weymouth & Dist. Hosp.; SHO (Anaesth. & Orthop.) Roy. Hants. Co. Hosp.

LAWRENCE, Margaret Anne Nuffield Health Centre, Welch Way, Witney OX28 6JQ Tel: 01993 703641 Fax: 01993 773899 — MB BS 1982 Lond.; MRCGP 1986; DRCOG 1986; DCH RCP Lond. 1985. (Guy's Hospital Medical School) Prev: Trainee GP. Bath VTS.

LAWRENCE, Margaret Rachel Anne (retired) 98 Stafford Road, Bloxwich, Walsall WS3 3PA Tel: 01922 476670 — MB ChB Sheff. 1954; DObst RCOG 1957. Prev: Sessional Med. Off. Walsall HA.

LAWRENCE, Mark Mill Street Health Centre, Mill Street, Crewe CW2 7AQ Tel: 01270 212725 Fax: 01270 216323 — MB BCh BAO 1982 Belf.; MRCGP 1990; DRCOG 1989; DA (UK) 1988; 1993 Dip. Palliative Care Cardiff. (Queens Uni. Belf.) Socs: BMA Hon. Sec. Crewe and Nantwich.

LAWRENCE, Mr Martin Roy North Tyneside General Hospital, Rake Lane, North Shields NE29 8NH — BM BS 1982 Nottm.; BM BS Nottm 1982; BMedSci (Hons.) Nottingham 1980; MRCOG 1990. (Nottm.) Cons. O & G N. Tyneside Gen. Hosp. N. Shields. Prev: Sen. Regist. (O & G) Roy. Victory Infirm. Newc.; Regist.(O & G) Qu. Med. Centre Nottm.

LAWRENCE, Mary Patricia 172 Yardley Wood Road, Moseley, Birmingham B13 9JE — MB BCh BAO 1961 Belf.; DPM Eng. 1966.

LAWRENCE, Mary Susan 33 Talbot Street, Cardiff CF11 9BW — MB BCh 1990 Wales; MSc 1997; MRCPSych 1995. Staff Grade Psychiat. Sully Hosp. Cardiff.

LAWRENCE, Monty Harold (retired) 21 Glan Ysgethin, Talybont LL43 2BB — MB ChB Ed. 1948; DObst RCOG 1959; DA Eng. 1956. Prev: Clin. Asst. (Anaesth.) Birm. Accid. Hosp.

LAWRENCE, Morris Robert 10 Heol Gerrig, Treboeth, Swansea SA5 9BP Tel: 01792 417514 Email: bob.lawrence@ntlworld.com; 10 Heol Gerrig, Treboeth, Swansea SA5 9BP Tel: 01792 417514 Email: bob.lawrence@ntlworld.com — MRCS Eng. LRCP Lond. 1974.

LAWRENCE, Neville Harley (retired) 18 Nunwick Way, Haydon Grange, Newcastle upon Tyne NE7 7GB — MB BS Durh. 1955.

LAWRENCE, Nicholas Wilson Northfield Medical Centre, Villers Court, Blaby, Leicester LE8 4NS; Ashford House, Gables Court, Main St., Frolesworth, Lutterworth LE17 5EG — BM BS 1984 Nottm.; BMedSci Nottm. 1982; MRCGP 1988; DRCOG 1988. (Nottm.)

LAWRENCE, Nicola Jane Hogarth 57 Woodland Road, Northfield, Birmingham B31 2HZ Tel: 0121 475 1065 Fax: 0121 475 6179 — MB ChB 1989 Birm.; MRCGP 1993. (Birm.)

LAWRENCE, Norman (retired) 40 Bickerton Road, Headington, Oxford OX3 7LS Tel: 01865 761377 — MRCS Eng. LRCP Lond. 1948; MRCGP 1975. Prev: Ho. Phys. St. Stephen's Hosp. Lond.

LAWRENCE, Patrick Anthony, TD The Mill House, 30 Mill Lane, Iffley, Oxford OX4 4EJ Tel: 01865 776761 Fax: 01865 776761 — MB BS 1959 Lond.; BSc Lond. 1955; MRCS Eng. LRCP Lond. 1959; AFOM RCP Lond. 1985; DIH Eng. 1985; DObst RCOG 1961. (Univ. Coll. Hosp.) Occupat. Phys. RGIT Culham Oxon; GP Oxf. Socs: Fell. Roy. Soc. Med.; BMA; Oxf. Med. Soc. Prev: Ho. Surg. (O & G) St. Mary's Hosp. Portsmouth; Ho. Phys. (Gen. & Paediat.) Roy. Portsmouth Hosp.

***LAWRENCE, Paulette Louise** 28 Harts Grove, Woodford Green IG8 0BN — MB BS 1996 Lond.

LAWRENCE, Philip Kim Milehouse Road Surgery, 21 Milehouse Road, Milehouse, Plymouth PL3 4AD Tel: 01752 562341 Fax: 01752 606401; Branch Surgery - Efford Surgery, 65 Teign Road, Efford, Plymouth PL3 6PH Tel: 01752 207930 — MB BCh BAO 1973 Dub.; BA Dub. 1973; DRCOG 1981.

LAWRENCE, Philip Wingate 7 The Woodlands, Lowestoft NR32 5EZ Tel: 01502 731640 — MB BS 1972 Lond.; MRCS Eng. LRCP Lond. 1972; FRCR 1984; Cert. Av Med. MoD (Air) & CAA 1986; DMRD Eng. 1983. (Lond. Hosp.) Cons. Radiol. Jas. Paget Hosp. Gorleston. Gt. Yarmouth; Authorised Med. Examr. Civil Aviat. Auth. Prev: Regist. & Sen. Regist. (Diag. Radiol.) Nottm. City & Univ. Hosps.; SHO (Obst.) Norf. & Norwich Hosp.; SHO (Med.) Bedford Gen. Hosp.

LAWRENCE, Ralph Augustus Arthur Rustom, OBE, SBStJ Rosemead, 6 Greenhill Lane, Leabrooks, Alfreton DE55 1LU Tel: 01773 608246 Email: dr@bronral.force9.co.uk — MB ChB 1945 Cape Town; MRCGP 1971; DMJ Soc. Apoth. Lond. 1970. (Cape Town) Forens. Phys.; Special Lect. (Forens. Pathologist) Univ. Nottm. 1995. Socs: Fell.Brit. Med. Assoc.; Fell.Roy. Soc. Med.; Expert Witness Inst. Prev: Sen. Princip. Forens. Phys. Derbysh. Constab.; Regist. (Cas.) Derbysh. Roy. Infirm.; Sen. Resid. Med. Off. Som. Hosp. Cape Town.

LAWRENCE, Richard James 55 Penshurst Gardens, Edgware HA8 9TT — MB BS 1997 Lond.; BA Camb. 1994; MA Camb. 1998. (UCH Middx) Resid..Internal. Med.

LAWRENCE, Richard Stephen 5 The Verralls, Maybury Hill, Woking GU22 8AX Tel: 01483 770257 — MB BS 1972 Lond.

LAWRENCE, Richard William Whitwick Road Surgery, Whitwick Road, Coalville LE67 3FA Tel: 01530 836507; Homecroft, South Lane, Bardon Hill, Leicester LE67 1TG Tel: 01530 833460 — MB ChB 1981 Leic.; DCH RCP Lond. 1985; DRCOG 1984. Prev: Trainee GP Mansfield VTS.

LAWRENCE, Robert Michael South ECMHT, 50 Pampisford Road, Purley CR8 2NE Tel: 020 8401 3525 — DMS Rome 1980; MRCPsych 1990. Cons. Neuropsychiat. & Psychogeriat. Warlingham Pk. Hosp. Surrey. Socs: Brit. Neuropsychiat. Assn. Prev: Clin. Research Fell. (Neuropsychiat.) Nat. Hosp. Neurol. & Neurosurg. Lond.

LAWRENCE, Robert Paul 406A Chester Road, Kingshurst, Bromwich, Birmingham B36 0LF — MB ChB 1998 Manch.; MB ChB Manch 1998.

LAWRENCE, Robin Edward 96 Harley Street, London W1N 1AF Tel: 020 7486 0506 Fax: 020 7487 4146 Email: robn@wild1-2.demon.co.uk — MB ChB 1980 Birm.; MRCP (UK) 1983; MRCPsych 1986. (Birm.) Indep. Cons. Psychiat. Lond. Socs: Indep. Doctors Forum; Fell. Roy. Soc. Med. Prev: Cons. Psychiat. St. Thos. Hosp. Lond.; Sen. Regist. Lond. Hosp. & Maudsley Hosp. Lond.; Sheldon Research Fell. Birm. Univ.

LAWRENCE, Robin Evelyn 6 Cuckoo Hill Drive, Pinner HA5 3PF Tel: 020 8866 9641 — MB ChB 1942 Leeds; DMRD Eng. 1948. (Leeds) Socs: Brit. Inst. Radiol. & Fac. Radiol. Prev: Hon. Cons. Radiol. St. Mary's Hosp. Lond. W2; Sen. Asst. Radiol. Gen. Infirm. Leeds.; T/Maj. RAMC.

LAWRENCE, Mr Roy Nicol Department of Surgery, Princess Margaret Hospital, Okus Road, Swindon SN1 4JU Tel: 01793 426631 Fax: 01793 426949 — MB ChB 1983 Glas.; FRCS Glas. 1987. (Univ. Glas. Med. Sch.) Cons. Gen. & Vasc. Surg. P.ss Margt. Hosp. Swindon. Socs: BMA; Vasc. Surg. Soc. GB & Irel.; FRSM. Prev: Sen. Regist. (Gen. Surg.) S. & W. RHA; Clin. Lect. (Vasc. Surg.) Univ. Coll. & Middlx. Hosps. Sch. Med. Lond.; Regist. Rotat. (Surg.) W. Scotl. Train. Scheme.

LAWRENCE, Sandra Kay 15 Moss Close, East Bridgford, Nottingham NG13 8LG Tel: 01949 20619; Alderley House 4/11, Valley Drive, Chester CH2 1BP Tel: 01244 365848 — MB ChB 1995 Manch. (Manchester University) SHO (A & E) Countess of Chester Hosp. Chester; SHO A & E Hope Hosps. Alford. Prev: SHO.Gen.Me.Countess.Chester.Hosp.

***LAWRENCE, Sarah Vivien** 13 Lockwood Court, Woodfield Road, Northgate, Crawley RH10 8XR — MB BS 1998 Lond.; MB BS Lond 1998.

LAWRENCE, Stephen Martin 7 Montagu Place, Oakwood, Leeds LS8 2RQ — MB ChB 1987 Leeds.

LAWRENCE, Susan Jane 81 Merloy Lane, Merley, Wimborne BH21 3BB Tel: 01202 841288 Email: rutdoc@msn.com; 17 Brunstead Road, Branksome, Poole BH12 1EJ Tel: 01202 268958 — BM 1988 Soton. GP The Harvey Pract. Merley Wimborne Dorset. Prev: SHO (Paediat.) Dorset Health Trust Poole.

LAWRENCE, Susanna Lucy St Martins Practice, 319 Chapeltown Road, Leeds LS7 3JT Tel: 0113 262 1013 Fax: 0113 237 4747 — MB ChB 1982 Leeds; DRCOG 1986. (Leeds) GP Princip. Leeds; Non-Exec. Dir. Leeds HA; Non-Exec. Dir. N.I.C.E.

LAWRENCE, Thomas Michael 3 Merchants Road, Clifton, Bristol BS8 4EP — MB ChB 1998 Bristol.

LAWRENCE, Victor James East House, Kelbarrow, Grasmere, Ambleside LA22 9PX — MB BS 1993 Lond.

LAWRENCE, Ward Hadyn Springfield Hospital, 61 Glenburnie Rd, Tooting, London SW17 7DJ — MB BS 1990 Lond.

LAWRENCE, William Joseph, Col. late RAMC Retd. (retired) 10 Shere Avenue, Cheam, Sutton SM2 7JU Tel: 020 8393 4212 — MRCS Eng, LRCP Lond. 1953; MFOM RCP Lond. 1981; MFCM 1972; DPH (Distinc.) Lond. 1963; DIH Soc. Apoth. Lond. 1963; DTM & H Eng. 1962. Prev: Prof. Army Health RAM Coll. Lond.

LAWRENCE, Mr William Tudor Eastbourne District Gen. Hospital, Kings Drive, Eastbourne BN21 2UD Tel: 01323 417400; Old Tiles, Hellingly, Hailsham BN27 4HA — MB ChB 1976 Manch.; BSc St. And. 1973; FRCS Eng. 1980. (St. And. & Manch.) Cons. Urol. E.bourne Dist. Gen. Hosp. Socs: Hon. Sec., Urol. Sect., Roy. Soc. of Med. Prev: Sen. Regist. (Urol.) Nottm. City Hosp.; Clin. Research Asst. Spinal Injuries Dept. Lodge Moor Hosp. Sheff.; Urol. Regist. Norf. & Norwich Hosp.

LAWRENCE-JONES, Sir Christopher, Bt (retired) — MB BChir 1964 Camb.; MA Camb. 1964; FRCP Lond. 1991; FFOM RCP Lond. 1987, MFOM 1978; DIH Eng. 1968. Prev: Gp. chief med off. Imperial chem industries hlc.

LAWRENSON, Annali Louise 22 Randalls Road, Leatherhead KT22 7TQ — MB BCh 1985 Wales. SHO (Gen. Surg.) & Clin. Asst. (A & E) Epsom Dist. Hosp. Prev: Clin. Asst. (A & E) Qu. Marys Hosp. for Childr. Carshalton; SHO (Gyn.) Dorking Gen. Hosp.; SHO (Geriat.) Dorking Gen. Hosp.

LAWRENSON, Caroline Jane (Surgery), 15 Winters Lane, Long Bennington, Newark NG23 5DW Tel: 01400 281220 Fax: 01400 282551; Charlton Farm, Staunton-in-the-Vale, Orston, Nottingham NG13 9PE Tel: 01400 281604 Fax: 01400 281775 — MB ChB 1971 Sheff.; DFFP 1997; DCH Eng. 1975. (Sheff.) Prev: Regist. (Paediat.) St. Geo. Hosp. Lincoln; SHO (Paediat.) N.. Gen. Hosp. Sheff.; Jun. Resid. Hosp. Sick Childr. Toronto, Canada.

LAWRENSON, Francis Joseph 41 Sutherland Avenue, Roundhay, Leeds LS8 1BY — MB ChB 1978 Bristol; MRCS Eng. LRCP Lond. 1978.

LAWRENSON, Geoffrey William, Lt.-Col. RAMC 39 Peldon Road, Abberton, Colchester CO5 7PB — MB ChB 1977 Leeds; FRCGP 2000; DFFP 1993; MSc Lond. 1994; MRCGP 1986; DRCOG 1982. Civil. Med. Practitioner (CMP); GP Trainer Colchester. Prev: SHO (A & E) Leeds Gen. Infirm.

LAWRENSON, Professor Ross Alexander Postgraduate Medical School, Stirling House, Surrey Research Park, Guildford GU2 7RF Tel: 01483 302239 Fax: 01483 300359 Email: r.lawrenson@surrey.ac.uk; 21 Clandon Road, Guildford GU1 2DR — MB BS 1977 Lond.; MD (Lond.) 1997; MRCGP 1982; FAFPHM 1994; DRCOG 1981; MFPHM 2000. (Roy. Free Hosp. Lond.) Dean Of Med. Head of PostGrad. Med. Sch. Univ. Surrey; Pub. Health Cons. E. Surrey HA. Socs: Mem. Roy. Coll. Gen. Pract.; Of the Fac. of Pub. Health Med. Prev: Sen. Lect. Char. Cross & W.minster Med. Sch.; Med. Off. of Health & Chief Med. Off. Health Waikato, Hamilton, NZ; Med. Superintendent & Community Health Serv. Waikato Area HB.

LAWRENZ, Karin Department of Surgery, Royal Liverpool University Hospital, Prescott St., Liverpool L7 8XP — State Exam Med 1983 Munster; FRCS Eng. 1993.

LAWREY, Kenneth David Edmund (retired) West Rising, Fremington Road, Seaton EX12 2HX Tel: 01297 21338 — MB BS 1959 Lond.; MRCS Eng. LRCP Lond. 1959. Prev: SHO Bideford & Dist. Hosp.

LAWRIE, Andrew William Cherry Knowle Hospital, Ryhope, Sunderland SR2 0NB Tel: 0191 569 9592 Fax: 0191 569 9513 — MB ChB 1987 Liverp.; MRCPsych 1992. (Liverp.) Cons. Psych.Adult.Gen.Cherry knowle Hosps. Sunderland.

LAWRIE, Brian William 48 North Rise, Llanishen, Cardiff CF14 0RN — MB ChB 1963 Bristol; FRCR 1969; DMRD Eng. 1967. (Bristol) Cons. Radiol. Univ. Hosp. Wales Hosp. Gp. Prev: Sen. Regist. Radiol. Cardiff Roy. Infirm.; Vis. Instruc. Stanford Univ. Med. Center, U.S.A.

LAWRIE, Bruce Richard (retired) 8 Hall Close, Whissendene, Oakham LE15 7HN Tel: 01664 474400 Email: lawbru@aol.com — MB BS Lond. 1963; MRCP Lond. 1966; MRCGP 1974; FFPM RCP (UK) 1990; Dip. Pharm. Med. RCP (UK) 1976. Prev: Med. Dir. & Admin. Med. Products Du Pont (UK) Ltd.

LAWRIE, David Errollsfield, Prospect Terrace, Cruden Bay, Peterhead AB42 0HP — MB ChB 1997 Aberd.

LAWRIE, Duncan Macgregor Muncross, 5 Hepburn Gardens, St Andrews KY16 9DE Tel: 01334 73833 — MB ChB 1961 Ed.; FRCP Ed. 1978, M 1965; MRCP Lond. 1966. (Ed.) Cons. Phys. Vict. Hosp. Kirkcaldy. Prev: Cons. Phys. St. Helens & Roy. E. Sussex Hosps. Hastings; Lect. Univ. Dept. Med. Edin.

LAWRIE, Mr Gerald Murray Health Care International, Beardmore St., Clydebank G81 4HX — MB BS 1969 Sydney; FRCS Ed. 1973.

LAWRIE, Henrietta Sophia Lefanu Seymour 13 North Villas, London NW1 9BJ — MB BS 1994 Lond.; MA Oxf. 1995. SHO (O & G) Hemel Hempstead Gen. Hosp.

LAWRIE, Iain 24 Hazel Street, Leicester LE2 7JN — MB ChB 1997 Leic.

LAWRIE, James Alexander, MBE Royal Docks Medical Centre, 21 East Ham, Manor Way, Beckton, London E6 5NA Tel: 020 7511 4466 Fax: 020 7511 1492; Tel: 020 7515 6087 Fax: 020 7510 2290 Email: cgannon@pro-net.co.uk — MB BS 1983 Lond.; MA Oxf. 1986, BA 1980; FRCGP 1994, M 1987. (St. Batholomew's Hospital) GP Roy. Docks Pract. Lond.; Lect. Dept. of Gen. Pract. Qu. Mary & W.field Coll. Prev: SHO (Paediat.) Pembury Hosp. Tunbridge Wells VTS.

LAWRIE, Jean Dorothy (retired) 132 Newton Street, Greenock PA16 8SJ Tel: 01475 720191 — MB BS 1945 Durham. Prev: Med. Off. Inverclyde Health Dist.

LAWRIE, Jean Eileen, CBE (retired) Little Mote, Eynsford, Dartford DA4 0AA Tel: 01322 862197 — MB BS Lond. 1938. Prev: Gen. Phys. Roy. Families Brunei.

LAWRIE, Jennifer Garth Barns Street Surgery, 3 Barns Street, Ayr KA7 1XB; Tel: 01292 313961 — MB ChB 1986 Glas.; DRCOG 1989. Prev: Med. Off. Stud. Health Univ. Aberd.

LAWRIE, John Alexander (retired) 2 Maviscroft, Forfar DD8 1HF Tel: 01307 468500 — MB ChB 1953 St. And. Prev: Ho. Surg. & Ho. Phys. Bridge of Earn Hosp.

LAWRIE, Mr Reginald Seymour (retired) Little Mote, Eynsford, Dartford DA4 0AA Tel: 01322 862197 — MB BS 1939 Lond.; MD Lond. 1941, MS 1951, MB BS (Univ. Medal, Hnrs; Path. & Med.) 1939; FRCP Lond. 1973, M 1940; FRCS Eng. 1942; MRCS Eng. LRCP Lond. 1939. Hon. Vis. Surg. Johns Hopkins Hosp. Baltimore, USA. Prev: Surg. Guy's Hosp. Lond. & Sydenham Childr. Hosp.

LAWRIE, Robert Frazer Peterhead Group Practice, The Health Centre, Peterhead AB42 2XA Tel: 01774 474841 Fax: 01774 474848; Errollsfield, Cruden Way, Peterhead AB42 0HP — MB ChB 1968 St. And.

LAWRIE, Sheila Mary Woodside Health Centre, Barr Street, Glasgow G20 7LR Tel: 0141 531 9560 Fax: 0141 531 9572; 45 Mange Road, Bearsden, Glasgow G61 3PN Tel: 0141 954 2529 — MB ChB 1982 Aberd.; DRCOG 1986.

LAWRIE, Stephen Macgregor Royal Edinburgh Hospital, Morningside Terrace, Edinburgh EH10 5HF Tel: 0131 537 6671 Fax:

0131 447 6860 Email: s.lawrie@ed.ac.uk — MB ChB 1986 Aberd.; MPhil Univ. Ed. 1993; MD (Hons.) Ed. 1997; MRCPsych 1990. Sen. Clin. Res. Fell. & Hon Cons. (Psychiat.) Edin. Univ. Roy. Edin. Hosp. Socs: BMA & Med. & Dent. Defence Union Scotl. Prev: Lect. & Hon. Sen. Regist. (Psychiat.) Edin. Univ. Roy. Edin. Hosp.; Research Regist., Regist. & SHO (Psychiat.) Roy. Edin. Hosp.

LAWRIE, Steven Charles 17 Harling Drive, Troon KA10 6NF Tel: 01292 313961 — MB ChB 1981 Glas.; FFARCS Eng. 1986. Cons. Anaesth. N. Ayrsh. Hosps. Trust. Prev: Cons. Anaesth. Aberd. Roy. Infirm.; Sen. Regist. (Anaesth.) Stobhill Hosp. Glas.

LAWRIE, Professor Thomas Davidson Veitch Flat 2c/19 Woodend, Milverton Road, Glasgow G46 7JN Tel: 0141 616 3060; Flat 2c/19 Woodend, Milverton Road, Glasgow G46 7JN Tel: 0141 616306 — MD 1952 Glas.; BSc Glas. 1940, MD 1952, MB ChB 1943; FRCP Ed. 1964, M 1961; FRCP Glas. 1964. M 1962. (Univ. Glas.) Emerit. Prof. Med. Cardiol. Univ. Glas.; Cons. Cardiol. Roy. Infirm. Glas. Socs: Brit. Cardiac. Soc. & Assn. Phys. Prev: Prof. Med. Cardiol. Univ. Glas.; Cons. Phys. Roy. Infirm. Glas.; Cons. W.ern Infirm. Glas.

LAWS, Catharine Jane 47 Lulworth House, Dorset Road, London SW8 1DR — MB BS 1982 Lond.

LAWS, Mr David Eamonn 316 Mumbles Road, Westcross, Swansea SA3 5AA — MB BCh 1984 Wales; FRCS Eng. 1989; FCOphth 1989; DO RCS Eng. 1988. Cons. Ophth. Singleton Hosp. Swansea. Prev: Sen. Regist. (Ophth.) Roy. Liverp. Univ. Hosp.; Regist. (Ophth.) Birm. & Midl. Eye Hosp.; SHO (Plastic Surg.) City Hosp. Nottm.

LAWS, David Patrick 227 Addycombe Terrace, Newcastle upon Tyne NE6 5TY — MB BS 1992 Newc.

LAWS, Douglas Herrington Medical Centre, Philadelphia Lane, Houghton-le-Spring DH4 4LE Tel: 0191 584 2632 Fax: 0191 584 3786; 4 Silksworth Road, East Herrington, Sunderland SR3 3PW Tel: 0191 528 2305 — MB BS 1963 Durh. Hosp. Pract. (Rheum.) Sunderland AHA.

LAWS, Mr Iain McOlvin, TD 53 Wimpole Street, London W1M 7DF Tel: 020 7935 8239 Fax: 020 8449 4591 Email: ian@greege.demon.co.uk; Fax: 020 8449 4591 — MB ChB 1969 Aberd.; BDS St. And. 1961; FDS RCS Eng. 1964. Emerit. Roy. Free Hosp. Lond. Socs: Fell. Brit. Assn. Oral & Maxillofacial Surg.; BMA. Prev: Lect. King's Coll. Hosp. Lond.; Regist. Mt. Vernon Hosp. N.wood; SHO Nottm. Gen. Hosp.

LAWS, John Oswald (retired) Appartment, Middleton Hall, Middleton-St-George, Darlington DL2 1HA Tel: 01352 333577 Email: jolstoct@aol.com — MB BChir Camb. 1943; PhD Lond. 1952; MA Camb. 1943; MRCP Lond. 1948; FRCPath 1968; FIBiol 1968. Prev: Superintending Insp. under Cruelty to Animals Act, Shrewsbury.

LAWS, Margaret Ross (retired) Beddell House, Sherburn Hospital, Sherburn, Durham — MB ChB 1939 Aberd.; MA Aberd. 1934. Prev: GP Durh.

LAWS, Mark George Danes Dyke Surgery, 463A Scalby Road, Newby, Scarborough YO12 6UB Tel: 01723 375343 Fax: 01723 501582; The Cedars, 1 Dale Rise, Burniston, Scarborough YO13 0EG — MB BS 1989 Newc.; MRCGP 1994; DFFP 1994; T(GP) 1994.

LAWS, Mr Peter Edward 805 Yardley Wood Road, Billesley, Birmingham B13 0PT Tel: 0121 604 0554 — MB ChB 1989 Sheff.; FRCSI 1996. (Sheff.) Specialist Regist. (Gen. Surg.) Qu. Eliz. Hosp. Edgbaston.

LAWSON, Adam John 12 Branksome Gr, Stockton-on-Tees TS18 5DD — BM BS 1997 Nottm.

LAWSON, Alexander Adamson Hutt (retired) 12 The Heathery, Dunfermline KY11 8TS Tel: 01383 622742 Email: doclawson@supanet.com — MB ChB Ed. 1961; MD Ed. 1968; FRCP Ed. 1972, M 1964. Vice Chairm. & Med. Adviser to Barbara Stewart Scott. Laser Centre for Cancer Trust Dunfermline & Dundee; Med. Mem. War Pens. Appeal Tribunal Scotl. Edin. Prev: Cons. Phys. Acute Med. Unit Qu. Margt. Hosp. NHS Trust.

LAWSON, Alison Anne Argyle Street Surgery, 1119 Argyle Street, Glasgow G3 8ND Tel: 0141 248 3698 Fax: 0141 221 5144; 75 Queen Margaret Drive, Glasgow G20 8PA — MB ChB 1979 Glas.; MRCP (UK) 1982; MRCGP 1989.

LAWSON, Andrew Douglas Magill Department of Anaesthesia Intensive Care & Pain Management, Chelsea & Westminster Hospital, 369 Fulham Road, London SW10 9NH Tel: 020 8746 8026 Fax: 020 8746 8801 Email: a.lawson@ic.ac.uk — MB BS 1982 Lond.; FANZCA 1992; FFARACS 1990; FFA RCSI 1988; DA (UK) 1985; FRCA 1999. (Guy's) Cons. Anaesth. Lead Clinician- Pain Managem. Chelsea & W.minster Hosp. Lond.; Hon Sen Lec ICSM. Prev: Cons. Anaesth.Roy. N. Shore Hosp. Sydney, Australia; Sen. Regist. (Anaesth.) Duchess Kent Childr.s Hosp. Sandy Bay, Hong Kong; Regist.(Anaesth.) Frenchay Hosp. Bristol.

LAWSON, Anna Hoppers Barn, Datchworth Green, Knebworth SG3 6RS Tel: 01438 811304 — MB BS 1973 Lond.; MRCP (UK) 1976; DRCOG 1977. (St. Thos.) Consg. Phys. BUPA Lond. & Harpenden; Clin. Med. Off. ConFederat. Life; GP Stevenage. Prev: Specialist Gen. Phys. Riyadh Milit. Hosp.; GP Hertford; Asst. Med. Dir. Stud. Health Serv. Univ. Hertford.

LAWSON, Anne 6 Creek End, Emsworth PO10 7EX Tel: 01243 377519; 6 Creek End, Emsworth PO10 7EX Tel: 01243 377519 — MB BS 1987 Lond.; MRCGP 1992; DRCOG 1991; DCH RCP Lond. 1991.

LAWSON, Mrs Anne Department of Paediatric Surgery, Royal Victoria Infirmary, Queen Victoria St., Newcastle upon Tyne NE1 4LP Tel: 0191 232 5131; 21 Meadowfield Drive, Cleadon Village, Sunderland SR6 7QW Tel: 0191 536 7991 — MB ChB 1982 Manch.; FRCS Ed. 1988; FRCS Eng. 1988; FRCS (paed) 1996. (Manch.) Cons(Paediat. Surg.) Roy. Vict. Infirm. Newc. U. Tyne. Socs: Mem. Brit. Assn. Paediat. Surgs. Prev: Regist. (Paediat. Surg.) Birm. Childr. Hosp.; Regist. (Gen. Surg.) Burton Gen. Hosp.; Regist. Rotat. (Surg.) Newc.

LAWSON, Miss Anne Honeyman Harrogate District Hospital, Lancaster Park Road, Harrogate HG2 7SX Tel: 01423 553564 Email: anne.lawson@hhc-tr.northy.nhs.uk; 6 Crimple Cottages, Crimple Lane, Follifoot, Harrogate HG3 1DG Tel: 01423 885085 Email: ahlawson@uk_consultants.co.uk — MB ChB 1974 Dundee; BSc (Med. Sci.) St. And. 1971; ChM Dund 1983, MB ChB 1974; FRCS Ed. 1979. Cons. Urol. Harrogate Dist. Hosp. Socs: BAUS. Prev: Cons. (Gen. Surg. & Urol.); Sen. Regist. (Gen. Surg. & Urol.) Ninewells Hosp. & Roy. Infirm. Dundee; Regist. (Urol.) Dundee Roy. Infirm.

LAWSON, Barbara (retired) 27 Brookside, Rearsby, Leicester LE7 4YB Tel: 01664 424288 — MB BChir 1948 Lond.; MB BChir Camb. 1948; MA Camb. 1948; MRCS Eng. LRCP Lond. 1947; DObst RCOG 1949. Prev: Asst. Path. Gen. Hosp. & Childr. Hosp. Nottm.

LAWSON, Caroline Susan 2 Ross Place, Edinburgh EH9 3BT Tel: 0131 668 3458 — MB ChB 1988 Ed. GP Edin. Retainer Scheme.

LAWSON, Catherine Ann 59 Denmark Avenue, Woodley, Reading RG5 4RS — MB ChB Ed. 1996. (Edinburgh) Neurol. SHO St Jas. Univ. Hosp.

LAWSON, Catherine Margaret 13 Liberty Mews, Malwood Road, London SE12 8EE Tel: 020 8675 7600; 8 Harboro Road, Sale M33 5AB Tel: 0161 973 3295 — MB BS 1993 Lond.; BSc (Human Genetics & Basic Med. Scis.) Lond. 1991. Prev: SHO (Paediat. Rotat.) Kingston Hosp. & Guy's Hosp.; SHO (Paediat.) Greenwich Dist. Hosp.; SHO (Neurol. & Rheum.) Roy. Surrey Co. Hosp. Guildford.

LAWSON, Catherine Rachel 71 Argyle Street, Cambridge CB1 3LS — MB BChir 1992 Camb.

LAWSON, Catriona 46 Millside Terrace, Peterculter AB14 0WD — MB ChB 1998 Aberd.; MB ChB Aberd 1998.

LAWSON, Catriona Alexander 10 Erichtbank Drive, Kirn, Dunoon PA23 8HB — MB ChB 1992 Glas.

LAWSON, Charles Nicholas 36 Pembroke Drive, Ponteland, Newcastle upon Tyne NE20 9HS — MB BS 1985 Newc.

LAWSON, Charles William The White House, Hastingleigh, Ashford TN25 5HU — MB BS 1979 Lond.; MRCPath 1985. Cons. (Histopath.) William Harvey Hosp. Ashford. Socs: Roy. Coll. Path. Prev: Sen. Regist. (Histopath.) John Radcliffe Hosp. Oxf.

LAWSON, Christopher John Noel Chartered Bank Chambers, 4 Ampang Road, Kuala Lumpur 50450, Malaysia Tel: 3 238 2967 Fax: 3 232 4038; 34 Park Lane E., Reigate RH2 8HN — MB BS 1959 Durh.; DObst RCOG 1960. (Durh.) Socs: BMA & Malayan Med. Assn. Prev: Ho. Phys. Roy. Vict. Infirm. Newc.; Capt. RAMC; Med. Off. Federat. of Malaysia.

LAWSON, Christopher William Thelongley Centre, Norwood Grange Drive, Sheffield S5 7AT Tel: 0114 226 1635 Fax: 0114 226

1695 — MB BS 1981 Lond.; BA Oxf. 1977; MRCGP 1985; MRCPsych 1987. Cons. Adult Psychiat. (Community Health) Sheff.

LAWSON, Clive Stewart Kent and Sussex Hospital, Tunbridge Wells TN2 8AT Tel: 01892 526111; Leafwood House, Bells Yew Green, Tunbridge Wells TN3 9BD Email: clivelawson@compuserve.com — MB BS 1984 Lond.; FRCP 1999; MD Lond. 1994; MA Camb. 1987. Cons. Cardiol. Kent & Sussex Hosp. Tunbridge Wells. Socs: Brit. Cardiac Soc.; Brit. Cardiac Interven. Soc. Prev: Sen. Regist. (Cardiac) Soton. Gen. Hosp.; Regist. (Cardiac) Lond. Chest Hosp. & St. Thos. Hosp. Lond.

LAWSON, David Douglas Alexander Pittarrow, Perth Road, Abernethy, Perth PH2 9LW — BM BCh 1990 Oxf.

LAWSON, David Graham Broadhead Geriatric Office, Harrogate District Hospital, 8 Lancaster Park Road, Harrogate HG2 7SW; 9 Christ Church Oval, Harrogate HG1 5AJ — BM BS 1993 Nottm.; DRCOG 1995; DFFP 1995; DCH 1998. (Nottingham)

LAWSON, Professor David Hamilton, CBE Glasgow Royal Infirmary, Castle Street, Glasgow G4 0SF; 25 Kirkland Avenue, Blanefield, Glasgow G63 9BY — FRCP 2001 London; DSc 2001 Smithclyde; FFPHM 2001; MB ChB Glas. 1962; MD Glas. 1973; FRCP Glas. 1986, M 1984; FRCP Ed. 1975, M 1966; FFPM RCP (UK) 1989; DSc 2000 Herts. Cons. Phys. Roy. Infirm. Glas. & Hon. Prof. Med. & Therap. Univ. Glas.; Vis. Prof. Sch. Pharmaceut. Sc. Univ. Strathclyde; Chairm. Meds. Commiss. Med. Control Agency; Hon prof medic & theraputic uni Glas; Chrm. Scien & eth adv grp gen pra. Res.database DOH lond; Chm Scott. Medicus Consortium. Socs: Roy. M-C Soc. Glas.; Fell. Amer. Coll. Clin. Pharmacol. Prev: Chairm. Comm. Rev. Med. DHSS Lond.; Research Assoc. (Med.) Boston Univ., USA; Mem. Comm. Safety Med. DHSS Lond.

LAWSON, David Neale (retired) 3A Somerset Street, Kingsdown, Bristol BS2 8NB Tel: 0117 924 0503 — MB BChir Camb. 1947; BA Camb. 1939, MD 1950; FRCP Lond. 1970, M 1947; MRCS Eng. LRCP Lond. 1942; FRCPCH 1997. Mem. Exec. Cystic Fibrosis Trust, Lond. Prev: Cons. Paediat. & Med. Admin. Qu. Mary's Hosp. Childr. Carshalton.

LAWSON, Euan Malcolm 94 Harlands Road, Haywards Heath RH16 1NA — MB ChB 1997 Aberd.

LAWSON, Frances Sonia (retired) 1 Lincoln Green, Brunton Park, Gosforth, Newcastle upon Tyne NE3 5PB — MB BS 1940 Durh. Prev: Assoc. Specialist St. Nicholas Hosp. Gosforth.

LAWSON, Geoffrey Richard Sunderland Royal Hospital, Kayll Road, Sunderland SR4 7TP Tel: 0191 565 6256 Fax: 0191 569 9219 Email: geoff.lawson@chs.nothy.uk; 21 Meadowfield Drive, Cleadon Village, Sunderland SR6 7QW Tel: 0191 536 7991 Email: g.r.lawson@ncl.ac.uk — MB ChB 1977 Dundee; FRCP 1995; MRCP (UK) 1982; FRCPCH 1997; DTM & H RCP Lond. 1989. Cons. Paediat. Sunderland Roy. Hosp. Socs: Paediat. Research Soc. Prev: Sen. Regist. Rotat. (Paediat.) Dudley Rd. & E. Birm. Hosps.; Regist. Rotat. (Paediat.) Newc.

LAWSON, George Trevor Nevin Shimna, 11 Larch Hill Avenue, Craigavad, Holywood BT18 0JW Tel: 0123 176453 — MB BCh BAO 1946 Belf.; BA Dub. 1944; DPH 1949; FFCM 1983, M 1974. (Belf.) Sen. Med. Off. Dept. Health & Social Servs. N. Irel. Socs: BMA. Prev: Gp. Med. Supt. S. Belf. Hosp. Gp.; Asst. MOH Co. Down; Ho. Off. Belf. City Hosp.

LAWSON, Mr Graham Mark Princess Margaret Rose Orthopaedic Hospital, Frogston Road W., Edinburgh EH10 7ED; 97 Caiyside, Caerketton, Edinburgh EH10 7HR — MB ChB 1986 Ed.; FRCS (Orth.) 1996; FRCS Ed. 1991. (Ed.) Cons. (Orthop. Surg.) Edin. Socs: BMA; Brit. Orthop. Assn.; BASM. Prev: Sen. Regist. (Orthop. Surg.) Glas.; Regist. (Orthop.) Lothian HB; Clin. Research Fell. (Anat.) Univ. Edin.

LAWSON, Ian James Rolls Royce plc, PO Box 31, Derby DE24 8BJ; Mile-Ash House, 185 Duffield Road, Darley Abbey, Derby DE22 1JB — MB BS 1979 Newc.; MFOM RCP Lond. 1991; DRCOG 1982; FFOM 1998 London. Chief Med. Off. Rolls Royce plc; Med. Ref. Panel Advising DTI on H AVS (hand and arm vibration syndrome); Bd. of Trustees ADDACTION, Lond. Socs: Soc. Occupat. Med.; Brit Occupat Hyg. soc; Mem. Instit Occupat Safety & Health. Prev: Regional Specialty Adviser in Occupat.al Med. Trent 1998-2001; Chairm. Specialty Educat. Comm., Trent Occupat.al Med. 1998-2001; Brit stand inst panel GME.

LAWSON, James Glen (retired) 31 Llandennis Avenue, Cyncoed, Cardiff CF23 6JE Tel: 02920751638 — MD (Commend.) St. And. 1956, MB ChB (Distinc.); FRCOG 1962, M 1949. Prev: Cons. O & G Univ. Hosp. of Wales.

LAWSON, James Hastings Newlands, 7 Newton Park, Hove Edge, Brighouse HD6 2LW — MB ChB 1943 Ed. (Ed.) Prev: Ho. Surg. St. Luke's Hosp. Bradford & Roy. Infirm. Bradford; Capt. RAMC.

LAWSON, Janet Mary Nevill Hall Hospital, Abergavenny NP7 7EG Tel: 01873 852091; 2 Hilltop Rise, Bookham, Leatherhead KT23 4DB Tel: 01372 454101 — MB BCh 1992 Wales; DRCOG 1994; DCH RCP Lond. 1994.

LAWSON, Mr Jeremy Oliver Neil 7 Canonbury Square, London N1 2AU Tel: 020 7354 5622 Fax: 020 7354 5622 Email: jjeramy.lawson@ucl.ac.uk — MB BS 1953 Lond.; FRCS Eng. 1961; FRCPCH 1996. (St. Mary's) Emerit. Cons. Paediat. Surg. & Paediat. Urol. St. Thos. Hosp. Lond., Chelsea & W.m. Hosp. Lond. & Qu. Mary's Hosp. Roehampton. Socs: Fell. Roy. Soc. Med.; Fell. Roy. Coll. Paediat.; Med. Soc. Lond. Prev: Resid. Asst. Surg. Hosp. Sick Childr. Gt. Ormond St.; Regist. (Surg.) St. Mary's Hosp. Lond.; Resid. Surg. Off. Brompton Hosp. Lond.

LAWSON, Joanna Elizabeth 36 Pembroke Drive, Ponteland, Newcastle upon Tyne NE20 9HS; 4 Fairney Col., Ponteland, Newcastle upon Tyne NE20 9ED — MB BS 1984 Lond.; MRCGP 1989; DRCOG 1989. GP Seaton Delaval.

LAWSON, Joanna Mary Murray Royal Free Hospital, Pond St., London NW3 2QG; Pitkins, 6 Pk Avenue, Harpenden AL5 2EA — MB ChB 1982 Dundee; FRCOphth. 1989; FRCS Ed. 1987. Cons. Ophth. Surg. Roy. Free Hosp. Lond. Socs: Roy. Soc. Med. (Vice-Pres. Ophth. Sec.). Prev: Sen. Regist. (Ophth.) Moorfields Eye Hosp. NHS Trust Lond.; Fell. Paediactric Ophth., Gt. Ormond St Hosp for child.

LAWSON, Johan White Kirklea, Gellfield Lane, Uppermill, Oldham OL3 6LJ — MB ChB 1964 Glas.

LAWSON, John Sargan (retired) Greystones, Outwood Lane, Horsforth, Leeds LS18 4HP Tel: 0113 258 5388 — MB ChB 1954 Leeds; DObst RCOG 1958.

LAWSON, John Trevor Department of Radiology, Belfast City Hospital, Lisburn Road, Belfast BT9 7AB Tel: 0289032 9241 Fax: 028 926 3790; 2 Kathleen Drive, Helens Bay, Bangor BT19 1NE — MB BCh BAO 1978 Belf.; MRCP (UK) 1982; FRCR 1984; DMRD Eng. 1983. Cons. Radiol. Belf. City Hosp.

LAWSON, June Patricia Community Health Office, Peel House, Kingston Lane, Uxbridge UB8 3PL Tel: 01895 58191 — MB ChB 1952 Bristol; DObst RCOG 1954. Res. Fell. Inst. O & G Qu. Charlottes & Hammersmith Hosp. Lond.; Hon. Res. Asst. Inst. Populat. Studies Univ. Exeter; Sen. Med. Off. Slough Woms. Health Clinics & Hillingdon AHA. Socs: S.W. Eng. Obst. & Gyn. Soc. Prev: Clin. Adviser Syntex Pharmaceut.; Sen. Res. Off. Childr. Hosp. Bristol; Asst. MOH Berks. CC.

LAWSON, Karen Huntercombe Manor Hospital, Huntercombe Lane S., Taplow, Maidenhead SL6 0PQ Tel: 01628 667881 Fax: 01628 666989 — MB ChB 1988 Birm. Assoc. Specialist Huntercombe Manor Hosp. Maidenhead.

LAWSON, Kirsten Margaret 94 Harlands Road, Haywards Heath RH16 1NA — MB ChB 1997 Dundee.

LAWSON, Mr Lincoln James (retired) Meadowside, Harrowby Drive, Westlands, Newcastle ST5 3JE Tel: 01782 619543 — MB ChB 1954 Birm.; BSc (Hons.) Birm. 1951; FRCS Eng. 1960; MRCS Eng. LRCP Lond. 1954. Cons. Surg. N. Staffs. Roy. Infirm. Prev: Lect. Surg. Univ. Birm.

LAWSON, Louise Linda, Surg. Lt. RN 32 Argyle Place, London W6 0RQ — MB BS 1993 Lond. RN Med. Off.

LAWSON, Michael Horton Park Surgery, The Horton Park Centre, 99 Horton Park Avenue BD7 3EG Tel: 01274 504949 — MB ChB 1981 Leeds; MRCGP 1986; DRCOG 1984. (Leeds)

LAWSON, Nicola Jane 1 Alyth Gardens, Golders Green, London NW11 7EN — MB BS 1996 Lond.; BA Cantab 1993 Roy Free (Clin) Camb. GP VTS, N. Middlx., Lond. Prev: SHO, A+E, Hemel Hempstead Dist. Gen. Hosp., Hemel Hempstead PRHO, Med., Roy. Free Hosp., L:ondon.

LAWSON, Paul MacNaughton Easter Hill, Bankend Road, Bridge of Weir PA11 3EU — MB ChB 1976 Glas.; MRCP (UK) 1978.

LAWSON, Peter Charles (retired) Kenridge Cottage, Shelford Hill, Shelford, Nottingham NG12 1ED Tel: 0115 933 6155 — MB ChB 1956 Liverp.; BSc (Anat., Hons.) Liverp. 1953; MRCGP 1965; FSOM 1984. Med. Assessor. Civil Aviat. Auth.; Med. Examr. RAF; JP. Prev: Ho. Phys. Clatterbridge Hosp.

LAWSON, Peter Richard 18 The Green, Calne SN11 8DQ Tel: 01249 813638 — MRCS Eng. LRCP Lond. 1965; DA Eng. 1971; Dip. Obst Auckland 1969. (St. Mary's) Socs: Clin. Soc. Bath. Prev: GP Calne; Regist. (Anaesth.) Roy. Hants. Co. Hosp. Winchester; Med. Off. (Anaesth.) Qu. Mary Hosp. Hong Kong.

LAWSON, Peter Robert The Market Surgery, 26 Norwich Road, Aylsham, Norwich NR11 6BW Tel: 01263 733331 Fax: 01263 735829 — BM 1985 Soton.; MRCGP 1990; Cert. Family Plann. JCC 1989; DRCOG 1988. Med. Director NENDOC GP Co-op. Prev: Trainee GP Debenham, Suff.; SHO (O & G, Paediat. & A & E) Heath Rd. Hosp. Ipswich.

LAWSON, Phillippa Jane 25 Falconers Field, Harpenden AL5 3EU — BM BS 1998 Nottm.; BM BS Nottm 1998.

LAWSON, Richard George Priory Surgery, 26 High Street, Holywood BT18 9AD Tel: 028 9042 6991 Fax: 028 9042 3643; 228 Bangor Road, Holywood BT18 0JH — MB BCh BAO 1980 Belf.; MRCGP 1984; DRCOG 1983.

LAWSON, Richard Hugh Davies and Lawson, Station Road, Congresbury, Bristol BS49 5DX Tel: 01934 832158 Fax: 01934 834165 — MB BS 1969 Lond.; MRCPsych 1977. (Westm.) Socs: Brit. Soc. Allergy, Environm. & Nutrit. Med. Prev: Regist. (Psychiat.) Barrow Hosp. Barrow Gurney; SHO (Psychiat.) St. Mary Abbot's Hosp. Lond.; Clin. Asst. (Psychiat.) Barrow Hosp. Barrow Gurney.

LAWSON, Richard Ingham Fulham Road Surgery, 630 Fulham Road, London SW6 5RS Tel: 020 7736 4344 Fax: 020 7736 4985; 128 Brompton Park Crescent, Seagrave Road, London SW6 1SP Tel: 020 7385 6195 — MB BS 1983 Lond.; DRCOG 1987; DCH RCP Lond. 1986. (St. Thos.) Socs: Roy. Soc. Med.; Med. Soc. Lond. Prev: SHO (Paediat.) W.m. Hosp., Qu. Marys & St. Stephens Hosps. Lond.; SHO (Orthop. & A & E) Soton. Gen. Hosp.; SHO (O & G) Bedford Gen. Hosp.

LAWSON, Richard Montagu Temple Lodge, 3 Cravengate, Richmond DL10 4RE Tel: 01748 822526 Fax: 01748 822526 — MB BChir 1973 Camb.; MA Camb. 1974; DObst RCOG 1975. (Westm.) Homoeop. Phys. Richmond. Prev: Princip. GP Mid. Devon; Med. Off. Gan, Maldive Isles; SHO (O & G) Odstock Hosp. Salisbury.

LAWSON, Richard Pike, MC (retired) Elm Grove, Calne SN11 0JD Tel: 01249 817461 — MB BS 1939 Lond.; MRCS Eng. LRCP Lond. 1938. Prev: GP Calne.

LAWSON, Mr Robert Alexander Murdoch (retired) The Hollies, 8 Harboro Road, Sale M33 5AB Tel: 0161 973 3295 — 1961 MB ChB Ed. 1961; 1971 FRCS Eng. 1971; 1966 FRCS Ed. 1966. Cons. Cardio-Thoracic Surg. Roy. Manch. Childr.s Hosp. Prev: Sen. Regist. Nat. Heart, Brompton & Lond. Chest Hosps. Lond.

LAWSON, Robert Christopher (retired) Highfield, Wigan Road, Leyland, Preston PR5 6A Tel: 01772 422055 — MB 1954 Camb.; BChir 1953; DObst RCOG 1958.

LAWSON, Robert James The Surgery, Newton Port, Haddington EH41 3NF Tel: 01620 825497 Fax: 01620 824622; 23 Dunpowder Road, East Linton EH40 3BW Fax: 01620 861111 Email: roblawson@compuserve.com — MB ChB 1975 Dundee; BSc (Med. Sci.) St. And. 1972; DFFP 1994. Trainer (Gen. Pract.) E. Lothian; Local Med. Off. Civil Serv. Med. Advis. Serv.; Convenor E. Lothian Cardiac Rehabil. Gp.

LAWSON, Roderick Allan Respiratory Unit, Royal Infirmary of Edinburgh, Lauriston Place, Edinburgh EH3 9 Tel: 0131 536 1000 Email: rod.lawson@ed.ac.uk — MB BS 1985 Lond.; MB BS (Hons. Med.) Lond. 1985; MA (1st cl. Hons.) Oxf. 1982; MRCP (UK) 1988. Research Fell. Respirat. Unit City Hosp. Edin. Socs: Brit. Thorac. Soc. Prev: Regist. (Thoracic. & Gen. Med.) King's Coll. Hosp. Lond.; SHO (Renal Transpl. Med.) Guy's Hosp. Lond.; SHO (Chest Med.) Brook Hosp. Lond.

LAWSON, Rosalind Anne 35 Turnberry Road, Glasgow G11 5AL Email: roslawson@compuserve.com — MB ChB 1985 Ed.; FRCA 1990. Cons. Paediat. Anaesth. Roy. Hosp. Sick Childr. Glas. Socs: Assn. Anaesth.; BMA. Prev: Sen. Regist. (Anaesth.) W.. Infirm. Glas.

LAWSON, Ruth Latimer (retired) 6 Manor Close, Dewlish, Dorchester DT2 7SB Tel: 01258 837435 — MB ChB 1949 Birm.; MRCGP 1956.

LAWSON, Sarah Elizabeth 11 Somery Road, Birmingham B29 5RY — MB ChB 1990 Birm.; BSc Birm. 1987; MRCP (UK) 1993; MRCPath 1995. Regist. (Haemat.) W. Midl. RHA. Socs: Brit. Soc. Haematol. Prev: SHO (Med. & Haemat.) S. Birm. HA.

LAWSON, Sheila Rosemary Family Planning Centre, 18 Dean Terrace, Edinburgh EH4 1NL Tel: 0131 332 7941 Fax: 0131 332 2931; 1 Essex Road, Edinburgh EH4 6LF — MB ChB 1972 Ed.; FRCOG 1990, M 1978; DCH RCPS Glas. 1974. Cons. Reproduc. Health Care Lothian Primary Care Trust.

LAWSON, Spencer Samuel (retired) 12A Chelwood House, Gloucester Square, London W2 2SY — MRCS Eng. LRCP Lond. 1943. Prev: Res. Surg. Off. Mansfield Gen. Hosp.

LAWSON, Stuart James Wellington House Surgery, Henrietta Street, Batley WF17 5DN; 1 Green Lane, Netherton, Wakefield WF4 4JD — MB ChB 1983 Ed.; MRCGP 1987; DRCOG 1986. Police Surg. W. Yorks. Police. Socs: Assn. Police Surg.

LAWSON, Susan Anne Algitha Lodge Surgery, 4 Algitha Road, Skegness PE25 2AQ Tel: 01754 766766 Fax: 01754 760632 — MB BS 1986 Lond.

LAWSON, Sylvia Elizabeth 189 Great North Way, Hendon, London NW4 1PP — MB BS Lond. 1964; DObst RCOG 1966; DCH Eng. 1967.

LAWSON, Tanya Katherine Susan Riverside Surgery, 48 Worthing Road, Horsham RH12 1UD Tel: 01403 262700 Fax: 01403 275158; 9 Eversfield, Southwater, Horsham RH13 7GF Tel: 01403 734694 Email: tanyalawson@compuserve.com — MB BS 1981 Lond.; MRCGP 1985; DCH RCP Lond. 1986; DRCOG 1983. (Middlesex Hospital)

LAWSON, Thomas Muir Tyn-y-Celyn, Llanelltyd, Dolgellau LL40 2TA — MB BCh 1991 Wales.

LAWSON, Thomas Ritchie (retired) Burton Garth, Main St., Knapton, York YO26 6QG Tel: 01904 795489 — MB BS 1960 Lond.; MRCS Eng. LRCP Lond. 1960; DMRD Eng. 1969. Prev: Cons. Radiol. York Health Dist.

LAWSON, Timothy Digby, Capt. RAMC 2 Ranmore Road, Cheam, Sutton SM2 7LT Tel: 020 8394 2489 — MB ChB 1966 St. And.; MRCGP 1974; Cert FPA 1973 (IUD 1975); Cert JCC Lond. 1977. (St. And.) GP.

LAWSON, Wendy Louise Downswood Cottage, Westpark Road, Newchapel, Lingfield RH7 6HT — MB BS 1998 Newc.; MB BS Newc 1998.

LAWSON, William Kennedy (retired) 75 Westover Road, Padgate, Warrington WA1 3JR Tel: 01925 810396 — MB ChB 1952 Glas.; MRCPsych 1971. Prev: Vis. Psychiat. HM Remand Centre Risley & HM Prison Styal.

LAWSON, Mr William Ronald Kirklea, Gellfield Lane, Uppermill, Oldham OL3 6LJ — MB ChB 1962 Glas.; PhD Glas. 1969, MB ChB 1962; FRCS Glas. 1970. Cons. Surg. Roy. Oldham Hosp. Prev: Sen. Regist. (Surg.) Glas. Roy. Infirm.; Asst. Lect. in Physiol. Glas. Univ.

LAWSON, William Thomas Walker (retired) 2 The Laurels, 1 Homefield Road, Bromley BR1 3LA Tel: 020 8290 1541 — MB ChB Liverp. 1944; DIH Eng. 1948. Prev: Chief Med. Off. Occupat. Health Serv. Wellcome Gp.

LAWSON BAKER, Colin James Oral Hygiene Centre, 1 Devonshire Place, London W1A 1PA Tel: 020 7935 9905 Fax: 020 7486 0070 — MRCS Eng. LRCP Lond. 1974; LDS RCS Eng. 1980.

LAWSON-BAKER, Neil Anthony 31 Wilton Place, London SW1 Tel: 020 7235 3824 Fax: 020 7259 5386 — MB BS 1969 Lond.; BDS Lond. 1964; LDS RCS Eng. 1964. (St. Geo. & Guy's) Socs: Brit. Assn. Oral Surgs. Prev: Regist. (Dent.) St. Geo. Hosp. Lond.; Ho. Surg. (ENT) & Ho. Phys. (Radiother.) Char. Cross Hosp.

LAWSON-MATTHEW, John 46 Kettering Road, Rothwell, Kettering NN14 6AF Tel: 01536 710602 — MB BS 1950 Lond.; MRCS Eng. LRCP Lond. 1950.

LAWSON-MATTHEW, Peter James Northern General Hospital, Herries Road, Sheffield S5 7AU Tel: 0114 243 4343 Fax: 0114 271 5981 Email: peter.lawson@sth.nhs.uk; 355 Fulwood Road, Sheffield S10 3BQ — MB ChB 1986 Sheff.; PhD Sheff. 1986; MRCP (UK) 1989; FRCP 1998. Cons. Phys. & Geriat. N. Gen. Hosp. Sheff. Socs: Brit. Geriat. Soc. Prev: Sen. Regist. (Gen. & Geriat. Med.) Nether Edge & Roy. Hallamsh. Hosps. Sheff.; Regist. (Gen. Med.) Chesterfield & N. Derbysh. Roy. Hosp.

LAWTHER, Iain William Victoria Road Health Centre, Victoria Road, Washington NE37 2PU Tel: 0191 416 2578 Fax: 0191 415 7382 — MB BS 1990 Newc.; MRCGP 1994. (Newc.) Princip. GP Vict. Rd. Health Centre, Washington. Socs: BMA; Med. Protec. Soc. Prev: GP Durh.

LAWTHER, Kathleen May 13 The Ridge, Purley CR8 3PF — MB BS 1942 Durh. (Newc.) Prev: Med. Regist. Arthur Stanley Inst. Rheum. Dis. Middlx. Hosp.; Orthop. Ho. Surg. Roy Vict. Infirm. Newc. on Tyne.

LAWTHER, Patrick Joseph, CBE 13 The Ridge, Purley CR8 3PF Tel: 020 8660 6398 — MB BS 1950 Lond.; DSc Lond. 1971, MB BS 1950; FRCP Lond. 1963, M 1954; FFOM (Distinc.) RCP Lond. 1983. (St. Bart.) Emerit. Prof. Environm. & Preven. Med. St. Bart. & Lond. Hosp. Med. Colls. Socs: Assn. of Phys.s of Gt. Britain; Roy. Naval Med. Soc. Prev: Head MRC Toxicol. Unit Clin. Sect.; Director MRC Air Pollution Unit; Assoc. Chief Asst. & Ho. Phys. Med. Profess. Unit, St. Bart. Hosp.

LAWTHER, Mr Roger Edward 77 Riverdale, Annahilt, Hillsborough BT26 6DH — MB BCh BAO 1995 Belf.; MRCS (Eng.) 1998.

LAWTHOM, Charlotte 89 Aberrhondda Road, Porth CF39 0AU — BChir 1995 Camb.

LAWTON, Angela Jayne 52 Watkin Road, Hedge End, Southampton SO30 2TD — MB ChB 1993 Ed. (Edin) Specialist Regist. Med. Oncol. Wessex. Med. Oncol. Unit Roy. S.Hants. Hosps. Oton.

LAWTON, Brian Mengage Street Surgery, 100 Mengage Street, Helston TR13 8RF; Praze Cottage, St. Elvan, Helston TR13 0RF — MRCS Eng. LRCP Lond. 1973.

LAWTON, Claire Alison Fulbourn Hospital, Cambridge CB1 5EF Tel: 01223 218890 Fax: 01223 218992 Email: claire.lawton@dialpipex.com; St Osyth's, 18 High St, Fulbourn, Cambridge CB1 5DH Tel: 01223 881982 — MB BS 1980 Lond.; MRCPsych 1984; FRCPsych 1996. Cons. Psychiat. Addenbrooke's NHS Trust Camb.; Assoc. Lect. Univ. Camb; Assoc. Postgrad. Dean. Prev: Cons. Psychiat. Roy. Lond. Hosp.; Sen. Regist. (Psychol. Med.) St. Bart. Hosp. Lond.; Regist. (Psychiat.) N.wick Pk. Hosp.

LAWTON, David James The Surgery, 24 Albert Road, Bexhill-on-Sea TN40 1DG Tel: 01424 730456/734430 Fax: 01424 225615; 70 Cowdray Park Road, Little Common, Bexhill-on-Sea TN39 4ND — BSc Lond. 1977, MB BS 1980; MRCGP 1984; DRCOG 1984; DCH RCP Lond. 1983.

LAWTON, Frank Grange Department Obstetrics & Gynaecology, Kings College Hospital, Denmark Hill, London SE5 8RX — MD 1987 Manch.; MB ChB 1977; MRCOG 1982; FRCOG 1995. (Univ. Manch.) Cons. Gyn. Oncol. King's Coll. Hosp. Lond.; Cons. Gyn. Cancer Surg. Lewisham Univ. Hosp. Lond. & Medway Hosp. NHS Trust Gillingham Kent; Hon. Cons. Gyn. Cancer Surg. Guys & St Thos. NHS Trust. Socs: Internat. Gyn. Cancer Soc.; Brit. Gyn. Cancer Soc.; Brit. Soc. Colposc. & Cervic. Pathol. Prev: Vis. Fell. Gynaecoloigcal Oncol. Sydney, Australia; Lect. (O & G) Univ. of Birm.; Cancer Research Campaign Fell. (Gyn.) Univ. of Birm.

LAWTON, Geoffrey The Ridge, 31 Aldenham Avenue, Radlett WD7 8HZ Tel: 01923 855813 — MB BS 1964 Lond.; MRCP Lond. 1967; MRCS Eng. LRCP Lond. 1964; FFR 1971; DMRD Eng. 1969. (Univ. Coll. Hosp.) Indep. Cons. The Harley St. Clinic. Lond. W1; Ex. Cons. Radiol. Whittington Hosp. Lond.

LAWTON, Graham Stephen 44 Gipsy Lane, Warminster BA12 9LR — MB BS 1998 Lond.; MB BS Lond 1998.

LAWTON, Helen Lynne Park Road Health Centre, Park Road, Radyr, Cardiff CF15 8DF Tel: 029 2084 2767 Fax: 029 2084 2507; 98 Ryder Street, Cardiff CF11 9BU — MB BS 1988 Lond.; MRCGP 1992; DRCOG 1991; DCH RCP Lond. 1990.

LAWTON, Mr John Oldroyd 19 Park View Crescent, Leeds LS8 2ES — MB BChir 1977 Camb.; MA, MB Camb. 1977, BChir 1976; FRCS (Eng.) 1981. Cons. Orthop. Surg. Gen. Infirm. Leeds; Clin. Lect. Univ. Leeds. Socs: Brit. Orthop. Research Soc.; Brit. Orthop. Assn. Prev: Sen. Regist. (Orthop.) Leeds & Bradford Hosps.; Tutor & Hon. Sen. Regist. Univ. Dept. Orthop. Surg. St. Jas. Hosp. Leeds; Regist. (Surg.) St. Jas. Hosp. Leeds.

LAWTON, Kenneth Great Western Road Medical Group, 327 Great Western Road, Aberdeen AB10 6LT Tel: 01224 571318 Fax: 01224 573865; 20 Belvidere Street, Rosemount, Aberdeen AB25 2QS Email: kslawton@classic.msn.com — MB ChB 1981 Aberd.; MRCGP 1986; FRCGP 1994. (Aberdeen) Assoc. Regional Adviser; Clin. Sen. Lect. (Gen. Pract.) Aberd. Univ.

LAWTON, Mark Edward Brandon Road Surgery, 108 Brandon Road, Binley, Coventry CV3 2JF Tel: 024 7645 3634 Fax: 024 7663 6886 — MB ChB 1988 Birm.; ChB Birm. 1988; T(GP) 1992. Prev: Trainee GP/SHO (Paediat.) Coventry HA.

LAWTON, Neil Robert 12 Springburn Park, Lisburn BT27 5QZ — MB BS 1994 Lond.

LAWTON, Nicholas Frederick Wessex Neurological Centre, Southampton General Hospital, Tremona Road, Southampton SO16 6YD Tel: 02380 777222 Fax: 02380 783839; 15 Edgar Road, Winchester SO23 9TW Tel: 01962 867271 — MD 1974 Lond.; MB BS 1967; FRCP (UK) 1982, M 1969. (Middlx.) Cons. Neurol. Wessex Neurol. Centre Soton. Gen. Hosp.; Hon. Sen. Lect. Univ. Soton. Socs: Assn. Brit. Neurols. & Med. Research Soc. Prev: Middlx. Hosp. Med. Sch. Lond.; Lect. Inst. Neurol. Nat. Hosp. Nerv. Dis. Qu. Sq. Lond.

LAWTON, Nora Millicent (retired) Redcote, 55 Mersey Road, Heaton Mersey, Stockport SK4 3DJ Tel: 0161 432 4534 — MB ChB Liverp. 1956; DObst RCOG 1958; DCH Eng. 1959. Prev: GP Stockport.

LAWTON, Patricia Ann Centre for Cancer Treatment, Mount Vernon Hospital, Northwood HA6 2RN — MB BS 1983 Lond.; PhD Lond. 1995; MA Camb. 1983; MRCP (UK) 1986; FRCR 1989. (Middlx.) Cons. Clin. Oncolology Mt. Vernon Centre for Cancer Treatm. Socs: Fell.Roy. Coll. of Radiologists; Eur. Soc. Therap. Radiat. Oncol.; Roy. Coll. Phys.s. Prev: CRC Clin. research fell. Mt. Vernon Hosp. N.wood Middlx.; Regist.(Radiother. & Oncol.) Middlsex Hosp. Lond., Mt. Vernon Hosp. N.wood Middlsex; SHO (Radiother.) Hammersmith Hosp. Lond.

LAWTON, Raymond Joseph (retired) Redcote, 55 Mersey Road, Heaton Mersey, Stockport SK4 3DJ Tel: 0161 432 4534 — MB ChB 1958 Manch.; DA Eng. 1965. Prev: Cons. Anaesth. Clin. Measurem. & Assoc. Specialist (Anaesth.) Univ. Hosp. S. Manch.

LAWTON, Sarah Louise Kirkstall Lane Medical Centre, 216 Kirkstall Lane, Leeds LS6 3DS Tel: 0113 295 3666 Fax: 0113 295 3650 Email: sarah.lawton@gp.686109.nhs.uk; 19 Park View Crescent, Leeds LS8 2ES Tel: 01132 665309 — MB BChir 1976 Camb.; MA Camb. 1977; DRCOG 1978; Cert Family Plann 1978. (Camb.) GP Trainer; Clin. Asst. (Obst.) Leeds Gen. Infirm. Prev: Clin. Asst. (Gyn.) St. Jas. Univ. Hosp. Leeds.

LAWTON, Vanessa 37 Blackburn Gardens, Palatine Road, Manchester M20 3YH Tel: 0161 276 6309 Fax: 0161 276 6134 Email: vaneesa.lawton@man.ac.uk — MB ChB 1990 Manch.; MRCGP 1994; MRCOG 1998. Clin. Research. Fell. Urolgyn. Univ. Manch. Div. Obst. Gyn. St Marys. Hosp. Prev: Specialist Regist. Obst. Gyn. N-W. Region Manch Deanery.

LAXMINARASIMHAIAH, Tumkur Hanumanthaiah 67 Mile End Lane, Mile End, Stockport SK2 6BP; 505 Buxton Road, Great Moor, Stockport SK2 7HJ — MB BS 1955 Mysore; DO Eng. 1963. (Mysore) Assoc. Specialist (Ophth.) Stepping Hill Hosp. Stockport. Socs: Fell. Manch. Med. Soc.; Roy. Ophth. Soc. UK. Prev: Regist. (Ophth.) Chelmsford & Essex Gp. Hosps., Nottm. Eye & OldCh. Hosp. Romford.

LAXTON, Anthony George Patrick Morfa Farm, Llanstephan Road, Johnstown, Carmarthen SA31 3LY — MB BS 1978 Lond.; BA Oxf. 1975; FFA RCS Eng. 1986. Cons. Anaesth. W. Wales Gen. Hosp. Carmarthen. Prev: Sen. Regist. (Anaesth.) St. Geo. Hosp. Lond.; Regist. (Anaesth.) St. Geo. Hosp. Lond.; SHO (Anaesth.) St. Richard's Hosp. Chichester & Roy. Berks. Hosp. Reading.

LAXTON, Arthur Henry (retired) 9 Elfin Court, 29 Westwood Road, Highfield, Southampton SO17 1DY Tel: 023 8055 4660 — MB ChB Bristol 1949; MRCS Eng. LRCP Lond. 1948; DTM & H Eng. 1952; MLCOM 1980. Osteopath. Phys. Hants. Prev: Med. Off. i/c CMS Hosp. Lui, Sudan.

LAXTON, Caroline Jane (retired) Morfa Farm, Llanstephan Road, Johnstown, Carmarthen SA31 3LY — MB BS 1981 Lond.; MRCGP 1986; DRCOG 1983.

LAXTON, Christina Helen Department of Anaesthesia, Frenchay Hospital, Frenchay Park Road, Bristol BS16 1LE Tel: 0117 970 1212; 34 Great Brockeridge, Westbury on Trym, Bristol BS9 3TZ Tel: 0117 962 2677 — MB ChB 1989 Bristol; FRCA 1995. Regist. Rotat. (Anaesth.) Yeovil & Bristol.; Specialist Regist. (SW N.. Rotat.) Flexible Trainee.

LAXTON, Claire Jeanette Salma Churchfields Surgery, Recreation Road, Bromsgrove B61 8DT Tel: 01527 872163 — MB ChB 1989 Birm.; MRCGP 1993; DFFP 1993; DRCOG 1992. (Birm.)

LAXTON, Clare Elizabeth 34 Gundreda Road, Lewes BN7 1PX Tel: 01273 472333 — MB ChB 1981 Bristol; MFPHM RCP (UK) 1994; MRCGP 1986; DRCOG 1984.

LAXTON, Pearl Désirée 12 Selsey Avenue, Southsea PO4 9QL Tel: 01705 734609 — MB ChB 1952 Bristol; Cert. JCC Lond. 1975. Med. Off. (Community Health) Portsmouth & SE Hants. Health Dist.

LAY, Cathryn Jane Amherst Medical Practice, 21 St. Botolphs Road, Sevenoaks TN13 3AQ Tel: 01732 459255 Fax: 01732 450751; Godden House, Godden Green, Sevenoaks TN15 0HP Tel: 01732 764077 Fax: 01732 764088 Email: katelay@excite.co.uk — BM BCh 1985 Oxf.; MA Oxf. 1985; MRCGP 1989; DRCOG 1988. (Oxf.) p/t GP, Amherst M.P. Sevenoaks, Kent; Course Organiser (since'99) Tunbridge Wells Vocational Train. Scheme for GP; Examr. (since '99) Roy. Coll. of GP's. Socs: Roy. Coll. GPs; Med. Off. Sch. Assn.; Christ. Med. Fell.sh. Prev: Clin. Assitant (Gen. Med.) Sevenoaks Hosp.; GP Princip. Witney Oxon.; Trainee GP E. Dorset VTS.

LAY, Edward Thomas Moorfield, Praze, Camborne TR14 0LG — MB BS 1946 Lond.

LAYBOURN, Joseph Keith Newsam Centre, Seacroft Hospital, York Road, Leeds LS14 6UH Tel: 0113 264 8164 Fax: 0113 280 3368 — MB ChB 1978 Leeds; MRCPsych 1982. Cons. Psychiat. for Elderly Leeds.; Hon. Sen. Clin. Lect. Univ. Leeds.

LAYBOURN, Michelle Louise Sundridge, Grimms Hill, Great Missenden HP16 9BG — MB ChB 1998 Manch.; MB ChB Manch 1998.

LAYBOURN, Susan Mary The Medical Centre, 143 Rookwood Avenue, Leeds LS9 0NL Tel: 0113 249 3011 Fax: 0113 240 1958; 143 Rookwood Avenue, Leeds LS9 0NL Tel: 0113 249 3011 — MB ChB 1978 Leeds; MRCGP 1982. GP Leeds. Prev: Trainee GP Bradford VTS.

LAYBOURNE, Bridget Jane 39 Sandhill Lane, Aiskew, Bedale DL8 1UT — MB BCh 1996 Witwatersrand.

LAYCOCK, Anthony Nigel South View, Heath Lane, Croft, Warrington WA3 7DN — MB ChB 1993 Manch.

LAYCOCK, Catherine Louise 27 Periwood Avenue, Millhouses, Sheffield S8 0HY Tel: 014 274 6274 — MB ChB 1994 Sheff.; DRCOG 1997; MRCGP 1998. (Sheff.)

LAYCOCK, Elaine Vera King Edward's Medical Centre, 19 King Edward's Road, Ruislip HA4 7AG Tel: 01895 632021; 10 Bishops Avenue, Northwood HA6 3DG Tel: 01923 823624 — MB BS 1956 Lond.; DCH Eng. 1959. (Univ. Coll. Hosp.) Hosp. Pract. Continuing Care Unit Michael Sobell Hse. Mt. Vernon Hosp. Prev: Med. Off. Fulham & Seacroft Hosps.

LAYCOCK, Geoffrey John Anthony Department of Anaesthetics, North Devon District Hospital, Barnstaple EX31 4JB Tel: 01271 322718 Fax: 01271 322371 — BM 1978 Soton.; FFA RCS Eng. 1987; DA Eng. 1984; DRCOG Lond. 1982; DCH Lond. 1981. (Southampton) Cons. Anaesth. N. Devon Dist. Hosp. Barnstaple. Socs: SW Soc. Paed. Anaesth.; S.Devon Intens. Therap.; Christ. Med. Fell.sh. Prev: Cons. Staff Specialist Anaesth. Roy. Hobart Teach. Hosp. Tasmania, Austral.; Sen. Regist. (Anaesth.) Roy. Infirm. Glas.; Clin. Instruc. & Staff Specialist (Anaesth.) Univ. Michigan, USA.

LAYCOCK, James Robert David Oakdene, 16 Brookvale Road, Highfield, Southampton SO17 1QP — BM BCh 1976 Oxf.; MSc Bristol 1985; BA Oxf. 1973, BM BCh 1976; FFA RCS Eng. 1983. Cons. Anaesth. Soton Gen. Hosp.

LAYCOCK, Robert Jonathan 30 Coles Lane, Sutton Coldfield B72 1NE — MB ChB 1990 Birm.; ChB Birm. 1990.

LAYFIELD, David John Walnut Tree Cottage, Radley Road, Halam, Southwell NG25 — MB ChB 1972 Dundee; FFA RCS Eng. 1980. Cons. Anaesth. Nottm. Teach. Hosps.

LAYFIELD, James Nicholas Pear Tree Cottage, Fold Hill, Friskney, Boston PE22 8RG — MB BS 1980 Lond.

LAYLAND, William Ralph 13 Jeffrey's Place, Jeffrey's St., Camden Town, London NW1 9PP Tel: 020 7267 8479 — MB ChB 1956 Sheff.; MD Sheff. 1964; MRCPsych 1972; DPM Eng. 1964. (Sheff.) Socs: Brit. Psychoanal. Soc. Prev: Cons. Psychother. Napsbury Hosp.; Clin. Asst. Adolesc. Unit St. Luke's-Woodside Hosp. Lond.; Sen. Regist. (Psychiat.) Napsbury, Qu. Charlotte's & Chelsea Hosps.

LAYLEE, Alexander McDonald (retired) Overlond, Old Roman Road, Osmington, Weymouth DT3 6ER Tel: 01305 832911 — MB ChB 1952 Liverp.; MFOM RCP Lond. 1979. Clin. Asst. W. Dorset Health Dist. Prev: Sen. Med. Off. Atomic Energy Research Estab. Winfrith.

LAYMAN, Paul Robert Brackendene, 10 Copse Road, Verwood BH31 6HB Tel: 01202 824109 Fax: 01202 820739 — MB ChB Ed. 1969; FFA RCS Eng. 1977. Holistic Med. Cons. Brackendene Clinic, Verwood. Prev: Cons. Anaesth. Derby HA.; Sen. Regist. Rotat. Oxf. HA.

LAYNG, Johanna Elizabeth The Surgery, 18 New Wokingham Road, Crowthorne RG45 6JL Tel: 01344 773418 Fax: 01344 762753; 3 Nightingale Place, High Road, Cookham Rise, Maidenhead SL6 9HY Tel: 01628 533015 Email: layng@btinternet.com — MB BS 1993 Lond.; BSc (Hons.) Psychol. Lond. 1990; DRCOG 1996; DGM RCP Lond. 1995; T (GP) 1997; MRCGP 1997. (Univ. Coll. Lond.) GP Princip. Prev: Regist. Lond. Acad. Train. Scheme Chelsea & W.m. Hosp. Lond.; GP/Regist. Amersham & Wycombe Hosps. Bucks VTS; Ho. Off. (Med.) Whittington Hosp. Lond.

LAYTON, Alison Margaret Department of Dermatology, Harrogate District Hospital, Lancaster Park Road, Harrogate HG2 7SX Tel: 01423 885959 Fax: 01423 888054 — MB ChB 1981 Sheff.; MRCP (UK) 1987; FRCP (UK) 1999. Cons. Dermat. Harrogate Dist. Hosp.; Hon. Cons. Dermatol. Leeds Unit. Teach. Hosp. Prev: Tutor & Sen. Regist. (Dermat.) Leeds Gen. Infirm.; Regist. (Gen. Med.) Yorks. RHA; Regist. (Dermat.) Leeds Gen. Infirm.

LAYTON, Clive Allan 50 Wimpole Street, London W1M 7DG Tel: 020 7486 8962 Fax: 020 7486 7918 Email: layton@softlay-software.demon.co.uk — MB BS Lond. 1967; FRCP Lond. 1991; MRCP (UK) 1969. (St. Geo.) Cons. Cardiol. Lond. Chest & S.end Hosps.; Hon. Sen. Lect. Lond. Hosp. Med. Coll. Univ. Lond. Socs: Brit. Cardiac Soc. Prev: Sen. Regist. (Cardiol.) Lond. Hosp.

LAYTON, David Mark Department of Haematological Medicine, King's College Hospital, London SE5 9RS Tel: 020 7346 3242 Fax: 020 7346 3514 Email: mlayton@hgmp.mrc.ac.uk — MB BS 1978 Lond.; FRCP Lond. 1995; MRCP (UK) 1985; FRCPCH 1997. Sen. Lect. & Hon. Cons. Haemat. King's Coll. Sch. Med. & Dent. Lond.

LAYTON, Mark Anthony (retired) Pfizer Global Research & Development, Sandwich Laboratories, Pfizer Ltd, Sandwich CT13 9NJ Tel: 01304 641001 Email: mark_layton@sandwich.pfizer.com — BM BS 1989 Nottm.; BMedSci Nottm. 1987; MRCP (UK) 1992. Prev: Regist. (Gen. Med. & Rheum.) N.. W.. RHA.

LAYTON, Mr Stephen Andrew Department of Oral & Maxillofacial Surgery, County Hospital, Lincoln LN2 5QY Tel: 01522 573497 Fax: 01522 573496 Email: stephen.layton@ush.nhs.org; High Close, Thimbleby, Horncastle LN9 5RB Tel: 01507 524321 Email: layton@thimlleby.org.uk — MB BS Lond. 1988; BDS Lond. 1977; MRCS Eng. LRCP Lond. 1988; FDS RCS Eng. 1982; FRCS Ed. 1991; LDS RCS Eng. 1978. Cons. Oral & Maxillofacial Surg.united Linc hosp. Socs: Fell. Brit. Assn. Oral & Maxillofacial Surg.; BMA; Founding Mem. Expert Witness Inst. Prev: Sen. Regist. Rotat. (Oral & Maxillofacial Surg.) W. Midl. Train. Scheme; Regist. (Oral & Maxillofacial Surg.) Middlesbrough Gen. Hosp.

LAYZELL, Jane Christine Macdonald UWCM Centre for Applied Public Health Medicine, Temple of Peace & Health, Cardiff CF10 3NW — MB BCh 1984 Wales; MSc Lond. 1994; MRCGP 1989. Lect. (Pub. Health Med.) Cardiff.

LAYZELL, Jonathan Mark Rosebank Surgery, 153B Stroud Road, Gloucester GL1 5JQ Tel: 01452 522767; Laburnum House, Hinders Lane, Gloucester GL19 3EZ — BM BS 1990 Nottm.; MRCGP 1995; DFFP 1994; DRCOG 1994; DGM RCP Lond. 1993. (Nottingham)

LAYZELL, Sarah 27 Woodlands Road, Hockley SS5 4PL — BM 1991 Soton.

LAYZELL, Mr Trevor Cleveland Nuffield Hospital, Junction Road, Norton, Stockton-on-Tees TS20 1QB Tel: 01642 360100; Watersedge, 22 Low Green, Gainford, Darlington DL2 3DS Tel: 01325 730305 — MB BS 1972 Newc.; FRCS Eng. 1977. Cons. Gen. & Vasc. Surg. Bishop Auckland Gen. Hosp.; Arris & Gale Lect. RCS. Socs: Fell. Assn. Surgs.; Vasc. Surg. Soc. GB & Irel. Prev: Sen. Regist. (Surg.) Roy. Vict. Infirm. Newc. & Cumbld. Infirm. Carlisle; Demonst. (Anat.) Univ. Newc.; Sen. Research Assoc. (Surg.) Univ. Newc.

LAZANAKIS, Michail Stylianos 117 Belsize Road, West Hampstead, London NW6 4AD — Ptychio Iatrikes 1989 Patras.

LAZAR, Lazar Kako 8 Peacock Close, Abbeymead, Gloucester GL4 5EE — MB ChB 1967 Baghdad; DA Eng. 1980.

LAZAR, Stephen Charles Deben Road Surgery, 2 Deben Road, Ipswich IP1 5EN Tel: 01473 741152 Fax: 01473 743237 — MB BS 1974 Lond.; BSc (Hons.) Lond. 1971, MB BS 1974; MRCGP 1979; FRCGP 1996; MSc (Med. Educat.) Cardiff 1997. GP Princip.; Assoc. Regist. Dir. (Gen. Med.) Anglia Deanery; Med. Off. Ipswich Town Football Club.

LAZAR, Theresa c/o National Westminster Bank, 1 Watford Road, Birmingham B30 1JB — MB ChB 1943 Birm.; MB ChB (1st Cl. Hnrs.) Birm. 1943; MRCP (UK) 1948. (Birm.) Hon. Clin. Asst. (Psychiat.) Hollymoor Hosp. Birm. Socs: BMA. Prev: Assoc. Specialist in Psychiat. Hollymoor Hosp. Birm.; Med. Regist. Qu. Eliz. Hosp. Birm.; Capt. RAMC.

LAZARI, Maria Amvrosios 24 Draycott Place, London SW3 2SB — MB BS 1997 Lond.

LAZARO, Neil Grahame Thomas — MB BS 1992 Lond.; BSc (Hons.) Lond. 1989; MRCGP 1997; DRCOG 1995; DFFP 1995; DTM & H Liverp. Sch Trop. Med. 1997; Dip. GU Med Lond. 1998. (Roy. Free Hosp. Sch. Med.) GP Regist. York; GP Locum Manch. Prev: SHO (ENT) ScarBoro. Hosp.

LAZARO PERLADO, Fernando 9 Sherwood Court, High Road, Leavesden, Watford WD25 7PA — LMS 1991 Navarre.

LAZAROV, Dushica 42 Argyle Road, West Ealing, London W13 8AA — Lekar Novi Sad 1967; MSc (Occupat. Med.) Univ. Lond. 1981; MFOM RCP Lond. 1982; DIH Lond. 1981.

LAZAROWICZ, Henry Peter 103 Queens Road, Hodthorpe, Worksop S80 4UP — BM BS 1994 Nottm.

LAZARUS, David Henry Y Feddycfa, Canolfan Iechyd, Bala LL23 7BA Tel: 01678 520308 — MB BCh 1983 Wales; MRCGP Lond. 1988; Cert. Family Plann. 1988.

LAZARUS, Geraldine Fiona 9 St Andrews Road, Wenvoe, Cardiff CF5 6AF — MB ChB 1990 Sheff.; MRCGP 1994; DGM RCP Lond. 1994.

LAZARUS, Hilary Ira Southgates Medical Centre, 41 Goodwins Road, King's Lynn PE30 5QX Tel: 01553 692333 Fax: 01553 692555; Ling Cottage, 28 Little Carr Road, North Wootton, King's Lynn PE30 3RQ — MB ChB 1981 Leic.; MRCGP 1985; DRCOG 1985. (Univ. Leicester) Course Organiser Kings Lynn VTS. Prev: Trainee GP P'boro. VTS; SHO (Psychiat.) Leics. HA.

LAZARUS, Professor John Henry Department of Medicine, University of Wales College of Medicine, University Hospital of Wales, Heath Park, Cardiff CF14 4XN Tel: 029 2071 6900 Fax: 029 2071 2045 Email: lazarus@cf.ac.uk; 4 Cyncoed Avenue, Cardiff CF23 6SU Tel: 02920 755428 — MB ChB 1966 Glas.; MB BChir Camb. 1967; MA Camb. 1966, BA 1963, MD 1974; FRCP Lond. 1983; FRCP Glas. 1979; MRCP (UK) 1970; FRCP Edin 2000. (Camb. & Glas.) Hon. Cons. Phys. & Prof. Clin. Endocrinol. Univ. Wales Coll. Med. Cardiff. Socs: Eur. Thyroid Assn.; (Sec. Treas.) Europ. Thyroid Assn.; (Treas.) Assn. Study Med. Educat. Prev: Lect. (Med.) Welsh Nat. Sch. Med. Cardiff; Vis. Asst. Prof. Med. Columbia Univ. Coll. Phys. & Surg. New York, USA; Phys. to WhitCh. Hosp, Cardiff.

LAZARUS, Karen Claudia Epsom & St Helier NHS Trust, Wrythe Lane, Carshalton SM5 1AA Tel: 020 8296 2444 Fax: 020 8296 2951; 12 Moore Way, Sutton SM2 5BZ Tel: 020 8643 2259 Fax: 020 8401 0163 Email: claudia@lazarus.freeserve.co.uk — State Exam Med 1987 Berlin; MD Gottingen 1990; DA (UK) 1994; FRCA 1996. (Freie Univ. Berlin) Locum Assoc. Specialist Anaesth. Epsom & St Helier NHS Trust. Prev: Specialist Regist. (Anaesth.) St. Geo.s Healthcare NHS Trust Lond.; Specialist Regist. (Anaesth.) RTR NHS Trust, Roehampton, St. Helier NHS Trust, Carshalton Mayday Univ Hosp., Croydon; Specialist Regist. (Anaesth.) the St. Helier NHS Trust Carshalton.

LAZARUS, Mr Malcolm Campbeltown Health Centre, Stewart Road, Campbeltown PA28 6AT Tel: 01586 552105 Fax: 01586 554997; Marieville, Bellfield Lane, Campbeltown PA28 6EN — MB ChB 1983 Glas.; FRCS Glas. 1988; DRCOG 1991.

LAZARUS, Norman Ronald Langrick, Butlerd Dene Road, Woldingham, Caterham CR3 7HX Tel: 01883 653347 Fax: 01883 653347 — MB BCh 1959 Witwatersrand; PhD State Univ. NY 1968; BSc Witwatersrand 1955; FRCPath 1991, M 1981. (Witwatersrand) Indep. Cons. Toxicol. Catarham; Asst. Lect. Open Univ.

LAZARUS, Paul Anthony Kingsway Medical Centre, 23 Kingsway, Narborough Road South, Leicester LE3 2JN Tel: 0116 289 5081 Fax: 0116 263 0145; Hilltop, Main St, Peckleton, Leicester LE9 7RE — MB BS 1979 Lond.; MRCGP 1984. Lect. (Gen. Pract.) Univ. Leicester.

LAZARUS, Robert Justin 12 Moore Way, Sutton SM2 5BZ Tel: 020 8643 2259 Email: robert@lazarus.freeseve.co.uk — MB ChB 1989 Manch.; DA (UK) 1992; MRCP (UK) 1993; FRCA 1994. (Victoria Univ. Manch.) Medico-Legal advis. Med. Protect.Soc. Ltd. Lond. Prev: Sen. Regist. (Anaesth.) the St. Helier NHS Trust Carsholt; Sen. Regist. (Anaesth.) St. Geo.'s Healthcare NHS Trust Lond.; Sen. Regist. (Anaesth.) E. Surrey Hosp. Redhill.

LAZARUS, Seymour 37 Viewfield Close, Harrow HA3 0PR Tel: 020 8908 6538; 5 Hargood Close, Harrow HA3 0TY Tel: 020 8206 1880 — MB BS 1957 Lond.; DObst RCOG 1962. (Middlx.) Asst. Gen.Pract. Prev: Ho. Surg. (O & G) & Ho. Phys. Chase Farm Hosp. Enfield; Ho. Surg. Chelmsford & Essex Hosp.

LAZDA, Edgar Janis Department of Histopathology, University of Wales, College of Medicine, Heath Park, Cardiff CF14 4XN Tel: 029 2074 2706 Fax: 029 2074 8490 Email: lazdaej@cf.ac.uk; The Old Vicarage, Llancarfan, Barry CF62 3AJ Tel: 01446 751175 Fax: 01446 751175 Email: ed.lazda@doctors.org.uk — MB BS 1979 Lond.; MA Camb. 1980; MRCPath 1997; MRCGP 1983. (Lond. Hosp.) Sen. Lect. (Paediat. Path.) Univ. Wales Coll. Med. Cardiff. Prev: Sen. Regist. Perinatal Path. Hammersmith Hosp.; Sen. Regist. Histopath. UCL Med. Sch.; GP Stamford.

LAZELL, Graham James Billericay Health Centre, Stock Road, Billericay CM12 0BJ Tel: 01277 658071 Fax: 01277 631892; 128 Mountnessing Road, Billericay CM12 9HA Tel: 01277 653670 — MB BS 1980 Lond.; MRCGP 1984; Dip. Sports Med. Lond 1995; DRCOG 1984; DCH RCP Lond. 1984. (Middlx. Hosp.)

LAZEM, Fawzi Jabbar Royal Brompton, Harefield NHS Trust, Harefield Hospital, Harefield UB9 6JH Tel: 01895 823737 Fax: 01895 828896; 48 Ribchester Avenue, Greenford UB6 8TG Tel: 0208 997 6329 Email: flazem@hotmail.com — MB ChB 1971 Bagdad Med. Col.; MD 1999 Imperial Col.; 1983 DCM Lond; 1983 D.Th.M. Lond. Uni. Staff Grade in Transpl. Med. & Cardiol. Socs: MRSM; Transpl. Soc. Prev: Research Fell. to Prof. Sir Magdi Yacuto, Dept. Of Cardiothoracic Surg. at Harefield Hosp.

LAZENBY, Rachel Mary 75 Station Road, Upper Poppleton, York YO26 6PZ — MB ChB 1990 Sheff.

LAZIM, Mr Taha Roudan 51 Domonic Drive, New Eltham, Eltham, London SE9 3LN — MB BCh 1973 Cairo; MPhil Strathclyde 1991; FRCS Ed. 1984. Prev: Assoc. Prof. Gen. Surg. USM Malaysia; Research Studies Biomed. Engin. Strathclyde Univ.; Regist. Burton-on-Trent.

LAZNER, Michaela Ruth 6 Mackenzie Crescent, Sheffield S10 2BU — MB ChB 1998 Leeds.

LAZNOWSKI, Alain 68 North End Road, London NW11 7SY Tel: 020 8209 0506 — MD 1984 Brussels.

LAZZERINI, Vivienne Rosalind Tudor Surgery, 139 Bushey Mill Lane, Watford WD24 7PH Tel: 01923 223724 Fax: 01923 237327 — BM BS 1979 Nottm.; MRCGP 1984; DRCOG 1983; DCH RCP Lond. 1982.

LE BALL, Karen Mary Queen Elizabeth Hospital, Stadium Road, Woolwich, London SE18 4QH Tel: 0208 836 4014 Fax: 0208 836 4013; 23 Ashmead Road, London SE8 4DY — MB BS 1985 Lond.; MA Lond.; FRCP Lond. 1999. (University College London) Cons. Elderly Care Med. Greenwich Healthcare Lond.Cons. Adult Med., Qu. Eliz. Hosp. NHS Trust, Woolwich, Lond. Socs: Brit. Geriat. Soc. Chairm. SIG Med Ethics.

LE BAS, Penelope Sue Ville Bagot, Leoville, St Ouen, Jersey JE3 2DF — BM 1994 Soton.

LE BESQUE, Simon Edward Morey West End Surgery, Moorgreen Road, West End, Southampton SO30 3PY Tel: 023 8047 2126/8039 9200 Fax: 023 8039 9201 — BM 1982 Soton.; Dip. IMC RCS Ed.1992; DA (UK) 1986. Mem. BASICS.

LE BRUN, Mr Henry Ieuan (retired) Ambleside, Firle Road, Seaford BN25 2HU Tel: 01323 897989 — MB ChB 1942 Sheff.; FRCS Eng. 1952; FRCS Ed. 1948. Prev: Cons. Surg. Lewisham & N. S.wark HA.

LE COCQ, Heather Dawn Flora May, West Hill, St Helier, Jersey JE2 3HB — MB BS 1998 Lond.; MB BS Lond 1998. (PRHO Gen.

Surg.), P.ss Alexandra Hosp. Harlow. Prev: (PRHO GEN.Med.) Roy. Lond. Hosp. Whitecapel.

LE CORNU, Julie Le Vignoble, La Rue de la Presse, St Peter, Jersey JE3 7FE — MB BS 1988 Lond. Prev: Ho. Off. (Med.) Jesey; Ho. Off. (Surg.) E. Surrey Hosp.

***LE CORNU, Karen Dianne** Devon Villa, St Martin, Jersey JE3 6UF — LMSSA 1991 Lond.

LE COUILLIARD, Francis James (retired) Woodcote, Headley Road, Hindhead GU26 6TN Tel: 01428 605152 — MB BS 1958 Lond.

LE COUTEUR, Professor Ann Simone Fleming Nuffield Unit, Burdon Terrace, Jesmond, Newcastle upon Tyne NE2 3AE Tel: 0191 219 6423 Fax: 0191 219 6434 Email: a.s.le-couteur@ncl.ac.uk — MB BS 1977 Lond.; BSc Lond. 1974; MRCPsych 1982; FRCPsych 1997; FRCGPCH 1998. Prof. Child & Adolesc. Psychiat. Univ. Newc.; Hon. Cons. Child & Adolesc. Psychiat. Newc. City Health Trust. Prev: Cons. Child & Adolesc. Psychiat. Enfield Child Guid. Serv. Lond.; Hon. Sen. Lect. (Child & Adolesc. Psychiat.) Inst. Psychiat. & Roy. Free Hosp. Med. Sch. Lond.; Lect. Inst. Psychiat. & Hon. Cons. Child & Adolesc. Psychiat. Maudsley Hosp. Lond.

LE COYTE, Tina Susan Jacqueline 7 Cleeve Lawn, Swindon SN3 1LE — BM 1989 Soton.; MRCGP 1994; T(GP) 1995; DFFP 1993; DRCOG 1992. Socs: BMA; MDU. Prev: Trainee GP W.. Coll. Bristol; SHO (Paediat.) S.mead Hosp. Bristol; SHO (Psychiat.) Barrow Hosp. Bristol.

LE DIEU, Helen Rifca Tinnerdy, Parracombe, Barnstaple EX31 4RL — MB BS 1998 Lond.; MB BS Lond 1998.

LE DOUX, Colette Denise Gina (retired) Lady Dorothy's Cottage, Enville, Stourbridge DY7 5HJ Tel: 01384 872139 — MRCS Eng. LRCP Lond. 1939; DObst RCOG 1949.

LE DUNE, Marthe Anna Rosetta, 87 Overstone Road, Harpenden AL5 5PL Tel: 01582 64600 — MB BS 1960 Durh.; MB BS (Hons.) Durh. 1960; MRCP Lond. 1965; DPH (Prize) Lond. 1963; DCH Eng. 1963. (Durh.) Hutchinson Prize Univ. Glas. 1969. Socs: BMA & Med. Wom. Federat. Prev: Paediat. Regist. & Ho. Surg. & Ho. Phys. Roy. Vict. Infirm. Newc.; Ho. Phys. (Paediat.) Univ. Coll. Hosp. Ibadan, Nigeria.

LE FANU, James Richard Mawbey Brough Health Centre, 39 Wilcox Close, London SW8 2UD Tel: 0207 411 5720; 24 Grafton Square, London SW4 0DB Tel: 020 7978 2093 Fax: 020 7978 2093 — MB 1975 Camb.; BChir 1974; MRCP (UK) 1978. Med. Columnist Sunday & Daily Telegraph.

LE FEVRE, Eric John William Glaxosmithkline, Stockleypark West, Uxbridge UB11 1BT Tel: 020 8990 2453 Fax: 020 8990 2937 Email: eyl@gsk.com; 1 Knoll Rise, Orpington BR6 0EH Tel: 01689 826514 Fax: 01689 826514 — MB BChir 1978 Camb.; JCPTGP Cert 1984; BA 1975; MA 1979 Camb. (Cambridge) Head of Med. Affairs - Vaccines UK Med. Affairs Glaxosmithkline; Lakeside Health Centre Thamesmead SE2 9UQ; Hon. Research Fell.; Acad. Dept. of Travel Med.; Royral Free Hosp.; UCL Lond.; Gen. Practitioner. Prev: GP Princip. Triangel Surg. Lewisham; Med. Director: Thomas Cook Travel Clinic Lond.; GP Princip. Orpington Kent.

LE FEVRE, Peter David 121(1F) Hamilton Place, Aberdeen AB15 5BD — BM BS 1987 Nottm.

LE FUR, Roger Mount Vernon Hospital, Rickmansworth Road, Northwood HA6 2RN Tel: 01923 844270 Fax: 01923 835803; 54 Kempton Avenue, Northolt UB5 4HG — MD 1979 Strasbourg. Specialist (Gen. Surg.) Ordre Des Medecins France 1985.

LE GASSICKE, John (retired) 27 King's Avenue, Morpeth NE61 1HX Tel: 01670 512535 — MB BS Lond. 1953; FRCP Ed. 1975, M 1963; FRCPsych 1975, M 1970. Examg. Med. Practitioner War Pens. Agency. Prev: Vis. (Psychiat.) HMP Acklington.

LE GEYT, John David Le Geyt, Erith Health Centre, Queen Street, Erith DA8 1TT Tel: 01322 332838 Fax: 01322 351559; Foxgloves, Plan Pudding Lane, Dargate, Faversham ME13 9EY Tel: 01227 752509 Email: legeyt.msn.com — MB 1981 Camb.; BChir 1980. GP.

LE GRESLEY, John Stanley Windsor Crescent Surgery, 6 Windsor Crescent, Val Plaisant, St Helier, Jersey JE2 4TB Tel: 01534 32341 Fax: 01534 870635 — MB ChB 1964 Glas.; MB ChB (Commend.) Glas. 1964; DObst RCOG 1967; DCH RCPS Glas. 1966. (Glas.) Prev: SHO (Med.) S.. Gen. Hosp. Glas.; Ho. Off. (Paediat. & O & G) Stobhill Hosp. Glas.; Ho. Off. (Surg.) Glas. Roy. Infirm.

LE JEUNE, Helen Jane Swan Lodge, Priory Gdns, St Olaves, Great Yarmouth NR31 9TB — MB ChB 1997 Birm.

LE MAISTRE, Stephen 14 Longbridge Road, Lichfield WS14 9EL — MB BS 1998 Lond.; MB BS Lond 1998.

LE MAITRE, John Paul 9/7 St Leonards Lane, Edinburgh EH8 9SD — MB ChB 1997 Ed.; BSc 1994. (Edin)

LE-MAR, Ceri Ann Elwick Bank Surgery, Elwick Bank, Shapinsay, Orkney KW17 2EA Tel: 01856 711284 Fax: 01856 711348; Sandgarth, Shapinsay, Orkney KW17 2EA Tel: 01856 711306 Email: ceri@martinl.force9.co.uk — MB ChB 1986 Liverp. Assoc. GP Shapinsay, Orkney. Socs: BMA. Prev: SHO (O & G) S. Cleveland Hosp. Middlesbrough; Cas. Off. BRd.green Hosp. Liverp.; SHO (Paediat.) Alder Hey Hosp. Liverp.

LE MASURIER, Marisa Daniele St James' Hospital, Locksway Road, Portsmouth PO4 8LD Tel: 023 92 822 444 Fax: 023 92 894 430; 45 Mint Road, Liss GU33 7DQ — BM BCh 1997 Oxf.; BA Oxf. 1994; MA Religious Sci. Faculte Libre de Thedoge Reformee Aix-en-provance France 1999. (Oxf.) SHO (Psychiat.) Portsmouth. Prev: Ho. Off. (Surg.) Roy. Shrewsbury Hosp.; Ho. Off. (Med.) Hereford Co. Hosp.

LE MASURIER, Richard Robert Stocks Hill House, Hall Lane, Thornham, Hunstanton PE36 6NB Tel: 01485 512594; Stocks Hill House, Hall Lane, Thornham, Hunstanton PE36 6NB Tel: 01485 512594 — MB ChB 1966 Sheff.; DCH Eng. 1969; DObst RCOG 1969. (Univ. Of Sheff.) Free-Lance Gen. Practitioner; Assoc. GP, Isle of Wight, Argyllshire.

LE POIDEVIN, David Upper Garden Villa, Royal Cornhill Hospital, Aberdeen AB25 2ZJ Tel: 01224 663131 Fax: 01224 840691; Willow Wood, 626 King St, Aberdeen AB24 1SN — MB ChB St. And. 1963; MRCPsych 1971; DPM Ed. & Glas. 1966. (St. And.) Cons. Psychiat. & Psychother. Roy. Cornhill & Assoc. Hosps. Gp.; Hon. Clin. Sen. Lect. Univ. Aberd. Prev: Lect. (Psychiat.) Univ. Dundee.

LE QUESNE, Professor Leslie Philip, CBE (retired) Flat 1, 10 Strathray Gardens, London NW3 4NY Tel: 020 7794 9811 Fax: 020 7722 1184 — BM BCh Oxf. 1943; MA Oxf. 1942, MCh 1964, DM 1955; FRCS Eng. 1947; Hon. FACS 1982; Hon. FRACS 1975. Prev: Prof. Surg. Univ. Lond. & Middlx. Hosp. Med. Sch. Lond.

LE ROUX, Andries Abraham Flat 31, Ivy Lane, Headington, Oxford OX3 9DT — MB ChB 1992 Stellenbosch.

LE ROUX, Anne Elizabeth 27 Round Close Road, Adderbury, Banbury OX17 3EP Tel: 01295 812316 — MB ChB 1948 Cape Town; BSc Cape Town 1943. (Cape Town) Prev: Cons. Histopath. Horton Gen. Hosp. Banbury.

LE ROUX, Pieter Hein 105A Kilburn Park Road, London NW6 5LB — MB BS 1998 Lond.; MB BS Lond 1998.

LE SUEUR, Reginald Henry Wadsworth (retired) La Petella, Rue Des Vignes, St. Peter, Jersey JE3 7BE Email: docrema@hotmail.com — MB BS 1965 Lond.; MRCS Eng. LRCP Lond. 1965; DObst RCOG 1968. Designated Med. Off. to local Social Security Dept. Prev: GP St. Helier, Jersey.

LE TOCQ, Martin Charles Lainé Priory Medical Centre Partnership, Cape Road, Warwick CV34 4UN Tel: 01926 494911 Fax: 01926 402394; 3 Hatton Green, Warwick CV35 7LA Tel: 01926 484329 — MB BS 1970 Lond.; MRCS Eng. LRCP Lond. 1970; DCH Eng. 1974; DObst RCOG 1973. (Westm.)

LE VANN, Anthony Martin The Scott Practice, 1 Greenfield Lane, Balby, Doncaster DN4 0TG Tel: 01302 850546 Fax: 01302 855338; 42 Riverhead, Sprotbrough, Doncaster DN5 7QR Tel: 01302 851250 — MB ChB 1968 Liverp. (Liverp.)

LE VAY, John Hilary Suffolk Oncology Centre, Department of Clinical Oncology, Ipswich Hospital, Heath Road, Ipswich IP4 5PD Tel: 01473 704911 Fax: 01473 704916 Email: john.levay@ipsh-tr.anglox.nhs.uk — MB BS 1979 Lond.; MRCS Eng. LRCP Lond. 1979; FRCP ((UK) 1984; FRCR 1988. (Westm. & King's Coll. Lond.) Cons. Clin. Oncol. Ipswich Hosp.; Clin. Dir. Oncol. Servs. Chair Cancer Developm. Gp. Ipswich Hosp. Socs: Brit. Oncol. Assn. Prev: Clin. Fell. P.ss Margt. Hosp. Toronto, Canada.

LEA, Deborah Chamberlain Johnson Birmingham & Midland Eye Centre, City Hospital NHS Trust, Dudley Road, Birmingham B18 7QH; 49A Market Square, Witney OX28 6AG Tel: 01993 702134 — BM BCh 1973 Oxf.; MSc Oxf. 1983; BSc Aston 1981. Clin. Asst. Birm. & Midl. Eye Centre.

LEA, Gillian Trailfinders Travel Clinic, 194 Kensington High St., London W8 7RG Tel: 020 7938 3999; 71 Abbotsbury Road, Holland Park, London W14 8EL — MB BS Lond. 1969. (Westm.) Cons. Adviser (Travel Med.) Trailfinders Travel Clinic Lond.; Cons. Travel Med. Sect. Communicable Dis. Surveillance Centre PHLS Lond. Socs: Fell. Roy. Soc. Trop. Med. & Hyg.; Internat. Soc. Travel Med. Prev: Sen. Med. Off. Brit. Airways.

LEA, Josephine Ray Wittenham Hill, Little Wittenham, Abingdon OX14 4QZ — MB ChB 1971 Bristol; MSc (Med. Immunol.) Lond. 1990. Staff Grade Phys. Blood Transfus. N.B.S. Centre Soton.

LEA, Katharine Susan 38 Blandfield Lane, London SW12 8BG — MB BS 1987 Lond.

LEA, Martin Arthur Simcox (retired) Tedstone, 11 Bound Lane, Hayling Island PO11 9HU Tel: 023 789443 — MB BS Lond. 1949; BDS Ed. 1961. Prev: Capt. RAMC.

LEA, Michael Hardman The Montague Health Centre, Oakenhurst Road, Blackburn BB2 1PP Tel: 01254 63631; Calf House Farm, Abbott Brow, Mellor, Blackburn BB2 7HU Tel: 01254 812354 Fax: 01254 813209 — MB ChB 1954 Ed.; FRCGP 1978, M 1965. Socs: BMA & Soc. Occupat. Med. Prev: Ho. Surg. Falkirk & Dist. Roy. Infirm.; Ho. Phys. Edin. City Hosp. Infec. Dis.; Flight Lt. RAF Med. Br.

LEA, Peter Alexander William Anchor Lodge, Le Bourg, St Clement, Jersey JE2 6FY Tel: 01534 52851 — MB BS 1946 Lond.; FRCR 1975; FFR 1955; DMRD Eng. 1952. (Guy's) Hon. Cons. Radiol. Jersey Gp. Hosp. Prev: Sen. Regist. X-Ray Diag. Dept. Char. Cross Hosp.; Squadron Ldr. RAF Med. Br.; Ho. Surg. Lister Hosp. Hitchin.

LEA, Peter Martin Woodlands Surgery, 24 Woodlands, Meeting House Lane, Balsall Common, Coventry CV7 7FX Tel: 01676 532587 Fax: 01676 535154; Holly Lane Farm, Holly Farm, Balsall Common, Coventry CV7 7EA Tel: 01676 532577 — MB ChB 1962 Birm.; DObst RCOG 1964. (Birm.) Clin. Asst. (Surg.) Walsgrave Hosp. Coventry & Clin. Asst. (ENT) Selly Oak Hosp. Birm.; Clin. Asst. (Obst & Gyn.) Walsgrave Hosp. Coventry; Med. Off. Family Plann. Socs: BMA; Assoc. RCGP. Prev: Ho. Off. (Surg. & Med.) Qu. Eliz. Hosp. Birm.; SHO (Obst.) Profess. Obst. Unit Qu. Eliz. Hosp. Birm.; Lect. Dept. Anat. Univ. Birm. Med. Sch.

LEA, Richard Arnold Charles 67 Lacey Green, Wilmslow SK9 4BG Tel: 01625 540915 — MB ChB 1992 Leeds; MRCP 1997. Regist. Gastroenterol. N. W. Socs: Roy. Coll. Phys.

LEA, Ronald Arthur The Park Medical Centre, 691 Coventry Road, Small Heath, Birmingham B10 0JL Tel: 0121 773 4931 Fax: 0121 753 2210 — MB ChB 1957 Birm.; DA Eng. 1960; DObst RCOG 1958. (Birm.) Prev: SHO (Anaesth.) Dudley Rd. Hosp. Birm.; Ho. Surg. (Obst.) & Ho. Phys. City Gen. Hosp. Stoke-on-Trent.

LEA, Simon 42 Barton Road, Urmston, Manchester M41 7WA — MB ChB 1993 Manch.

LEA-COX, Caroline Margaret Chrisp Street Health Centre, 100 Chrisp St., London E14 6PG — BSc Lond. 1981, MB BS (Distinc.) 1984; MRCGP 1988; DCH RCP Lond. 1987. Prev: Ho. Off. W.m. Hosp.; SHO Lond. Hosp.

LEA-WILSON, Gertrude Morwenna 49 The Gables, Haddenham, Aylesbury HP17 8AD Tel: 01844 291418 — BM BCh 1952 Oxf. Prev: Ho. Phys. (Paediat.) Univ. Coll Hosp. Lond.; Ho. Surg. (O & G) Univ. Coll. Hosp. Lond.

LEABACK, Richard Deveson 5 Links Drive, Radlett WD7 8BD — MB BS 1996 Lond.

LEABEATER, Bruce Ferguson Barnsley District General Hospital, Gawber Road, Barnsley S75 — MB BS 1970 New South Wales; MRCOG 1975. (NSW) Cons. (O & G) Barnsley Dist. Gen. Hosp.

LEACH, Amanda Swallow Court, Wheatley Road, Forest Hill, Oxford OX33 1EH — BM 1986 Soton.; MRCP (UK) 1992.

LEACH, Amanda Louise Mary Westaway, West St., Bampton, Tiverton EX16 9NJ — MB BS 1991 Lond.

LEACH, Andrew Bryan Conquest Hospital, The Ridge, St Leonards-on-Sea TN37 7RD Tel: 01424 755255; Kildare, Woodbury Road, Hawkhurst, Cranbrook TN18 4BY Tel: 01580 752071 Email: tricornleaches@compuserve.com — MB ChB 1973 Aberd.; FFA RCS Eng. 1978; DA Eng. 1975. (Aberd.) Cons. Anaesth. Conquest Hosp. Hastings. Socs: Intens. Care Soc.; Assn. Anaesth. Prev: Sen. Regist. (Anaesth.) Soton. & Portsmouth Gp. Hosps.; Regist. (Anaesth.) Poole Gen. Hosp.

LEACH, Andrew Jonathan Flat 6 The Old Silk Mill, Maythorne, Southwell NG25 0RS Tel: 01636 815298 — MB ChB 1983 Sheff.; MSc (Med.) Lond. 1992; MRCGP 1987; DFFP 1994; DRCOG 1990.

LEACH, Andrew Ronald The Loxwood Surgery, Farm Close, Loxwood, Billingshurst RH14 0SU Tel: 01403 752246 Fax: 01403 752916 — MRCS Eng. LRCP Lond. 1975. (Roy. Free) Prev: Ho. Surg. Roy. Free Hosp. Lond.; Ho. Phys. Stoke Mandeville Hosp.

LEACH, Anthony Michael Woodside House, 261 Low Lane, Horsforth, Leeds LS18 5TW Tel: 0113 283 4200; 128 Skipton Road, Ilkley LS29 9BQ Tel: 01943 608514 — MB ChB 1962 Ed.; FFOM RCP Lond. 1993. (Ed.) Dir. Med. Servs. Health & Safety Exec. Prev: Sen. Med. Adviser Brit. Shipbuilders T.E.S. Ltd., Brit. Steel & BOC Ltd.

LEACH, Brian Montague The Surgery, Queens Square, Attleborough NR17 2AF Tel: 01953 453166 Fax: 01953 454858 Email: brian.leach@gp-d82034.nhs.uk; White Lodge, Cullings Hill, Postwick, Norwich NR13 5HE Tel: 01603 436913 — MB BS Lond. 1972; MRCGP 1977. (King's Coll. Hosp.) Prev: Ho. Phys. St. Giles' Hosp. Lond.; Cas. Off. King's Coll. Hosp. Lond.; Maj. RAMC.

LEACH, Catherine Louise Catherine Cottage Surgery, 21 Catharine Place, Bath BA1 2PS Tel: 01225 421034 Fax: 01225 422756 — MB BS 1983 Lond.; MRCGP 1987; DRCOG 1986. GP Bath.

LEACH, Christopher Guy Dubai London Clinic, Jumeirah, Al Wasl Road, PO Box 12119, Dubai, United Arab Emirates Tel: 00 966 971 4446663 Fax: 00 966 971 4446191; Swifts House, Hambledon Close, South Cerney, Cirencester GL7 6JA Tel: 01285 861838 — MB BS 1966 Lond.; MRCS Eng. LRCP Lond. 1964; FRCOG 1987, M 1987; Foundat. FRACOG 1979; MRCOG 1971; DObst RCOG 1967; FAGO 1976; AKC 1966. (King's Coll. Hosp. Lond.) Cons. Obst. & Gyn. Dubai Lond. Clinic Dubai, UAE; Vis. Cons. & Cons. Obst. & Gyn. Staff Mem. Amer. Hosp. Dubai. Socs: BMA. Prev: Cons. Obst. & Gyn. Al Corniche Hosp. Abu Dhabi; Resid. Obst. Guy's Hosp. Lond.; Resid. Med. Off. Qu. Charlotte's Matern. Hosp. Lond.

LEACH, Iain Hamilton Department of Histopathology, Queens Medical Centre, University Hospital, Nottingham NG7 2UH Tel: 0115 970 4852 — MB ChB 1981 Ed.; DM Nottm. 1994; MRCPath 1995. Cons. Histopath.

LEACH, Jack Morrison Drugs North West, Mental Health Services of Salford, Kenyon House, Prestwich Hospital, Bury New Road, Manchester M25 3BL Tel: 0161 772 3538 Fax: 0161 772 3595; 3 Calva Close, Burnley BB12 8XA Email: jackl@doctors.org.uk — MB ChB 1980 Manch.; MBA 1999; Dip in Addiction Studies 1999 Leeds; MSc (Pub. Health & Epidemiol.) Manch. 1994; MFPHM RCP (UK) 1993; MRCGP 1986; DRCOG 1986; DTM & H Liverp. 1982; Dip (Sub Missue) 1999. (Manchester) Cons. in drug dependence (Pub. Health), Drugs N. W., Ment. Health Servs. of Salford, Manch.. Socs: Soc Study Addic.s, Manch. Med. Soc.; Brit. Assn. of Med. Acupunct.s. Prev: Cons. in Pub. Health, Calderdale and Kirklees HA.; Sen. Regist. (Pub. Health Med.) N. W.. RHA; Regist. (Community Med.) Preston HA.

LEACH, Jane Margaret Davis and Partners, 274 Manchester Road, Warrington WA1 4PS Tel: 01925 631132 Fax: 01925 630079; Birchtree Cottage, Red Lane, Appleton, Warrington WA4 5AD Tel: 01925 67301 — MB ChB 1975 Liverp. Prev: GP Otley; Ho. Surg. Roy. S. Hants. Hosp. Soton; Ho. Phys. P.ss Margt. Hosp. Swindon.

LEACH, Jill Beverley 99 Ember Lane, Esher KT10 8EQ Tel: 020 8398 7158 — MB BS 1974 Lond.; MSc Lond. 1978, MB BS 1974; MRCPath 1982. (St. Geo.) Cons. (Med. Microbiol.) Kingston Hosp. Kingston-upon-Thames. Prev: Sen. Regist. (Med. Microbiol.) King's Coll. Hosp. Lond.; Regist. (Path.) King's Coll. Hosp. Lond.; Ho. Surg. & Ho. Phys. Bromley Hosp.

LEACH, John Christopher David Flat 2, 63 Kew Green, Richmond TW9 3AH — BM BCh 1998 Oxf.; BM BCh Oxf 1998.

LEACH, John Norman Mental Health Administration, Clacton & District Hospital, Clacton-on-Sea CO15 1LH — MB ChB 1987 Bristol; PhD Lond. 1978, BSc 1970; MRCPsych 1991. Comm Psychiat. N. E. Essex Ment. health trust Clacton on Sea. Prev: Hon sec Regist. (psych of old age Bethlem Roy & Maudsley Hosp lond); Research worker inst psychiat lond; Regist. Bethlem Roy. & Maudsley Hosps. Lond.

LEACH, John Paul Walten Centre for Neurology, Lower Lane, Fazakerley, Liverpool L9 7LS Tel: 0151 525 3611 Email:

j.leach@liv.ac.uk; 10 Southpost Road, Formby, Liverpool L37 7EW Tel: 01704 874711 Email: spleach246@aol.com — MB ChB 1986 Glas.; MRCP (UK) 1989; MD (Glasgow) 1997. Specialist Regist. (Neurol.) Walton Hosp. Liverp. Prev: Research Fell. (Epilepsy) W.. Infirm. Glas.

LEACH, John Robert 11 Queenswood Road, Woking GU21 1XJ — MB BCh 1994 Wales.

LEACH, Julia Mary Newmarket Road Surgery, 7 Newmarket Road, Norwich NR2 2HL Tel: 01603 621006 — MB ChB 1971 Bristol; DObst RCOG. (Bristol) GP Norwich.

LEACH, Katharine Jane Clifton Road Surgery, 95 Clifton Road, Rugby CV21 3QQ Tel: 01788 578800/568810 Fax: 01788 541063; 29 Church Street, Crick, Northampton NN6 7TP Fax: 01788 822802 — MB ChB 1981 Manch.; MRCGP 1989; DCH 1988; DCCH Warwick 1987. Princip. in Gen. Pract., Rugby; Clin. Assist. Rugby Community Drug Team; Clin. Asst. Rugby Teenage Family Plann. Clinic. Prev: SCMO W. Birm. HA.

LEACH, Michael Andrew Dr Moss and Partners, 28-38 Kings Road, Harrogate HG1 5JP Tel: 01423 560261 Fax: 01423 501099 — MB BS 1985 Lond.; MA Camb. 1982; MRCGP 1991; DRCOG 1989; DCH RCP Lond. 1988.

LEACH, Michael Timothy John 1 Grange Farm Drive, Worrall, Sheffield S35 0BD — MB ChB 1989 Sheff.; MRCP (UK) 1992; MRCPath 1998.

LEACH, Molly Christine The New Surgery, Adwick Road, Mexborough S64 0DB Tel: 01709 511800 Fax: 01709 512433; 70 Somersby Avenue, Sprotbrough, Doncaster DN5 8HB — MB ChB Leeds 1970. (Doncaster) Gen. Practitioner. Prev: Med. Off. Nat. Blood Transf. Serv. Trent RHA.

LEACH, Nicholas Terence Market Harborough Medical Centre, 67 Coventry Road, Market Harborough LE16 9BX Tel: 01858 464242 Fax: 01858 462929 — MB BS 1969 Lond.; MRCS Eng. LRCP Lond. 1969; MRCGP 1975; DCH Eng. 1972; DObst RCOG 1971; Cert JCC Lond. 1976; FRCGP 1999. (St. Mary's)

LEACH, Peter Michael Great Bansons, Bansons Lane, Ongar CM5 9AR Tel: 01277 363028 Fax: 01277 365264 — MB BS 1968 Lond.; BA Camb. 1961; MRCS Eng. LRCP Lond. 1968; FRCGP 1983, M 1977; DObst RCOG 1971. (Roy. Free) Prev: Ho. Surg. Willesden Gen. Hosp.; SHO & Ho. Phys. P.ss Alexandra Hosp.

LEACH, Richard Mark St. Thomas Hospital, Lambeth Palace Road, London SE1 7EH Tel: 020 7928 9292 Fax: 020 7922 8240; 39 Longton Avenue, Sydenham, London SE26 6RE — MB ChB 1982 Manch.; MB ChB (Hons.) 1982; MD Manch. 1992; MRCP (UK) 1985; FRCP (UK) 1999. Cons. Phys.(Intens. Care & Respirat. Med.) St. Thos. Hosp. Lond.; Hon. Sen. Lect.; Med. Research Counc. Trav. Fell.sh. Johns Hopkins Hosp. Baltimore, USA 1992-93. Prev: Sen. Regist. & Lect. United Med. & Dent. Sch. St. Thos. Hosp. Lond.; SHO Nat. Hosp. for Nerv. Dis. Qu. Sq. Lond.; SHO Lond. Chest Hosp.

LEACH, Richard Maurice Cameron Northlands Surgery, North Street, Calne SN11 0HH Tel: 01249 812091 Fax: 01249 815343 — BM BCh 1985 Oxf.

LEACH, Robert Andrew Oakmeadow Surgery, 87 Tatlow Road, Glenfield, Leicester LE3 8NF Tel: 0116 287 7911 — MB ChB 1981 Leeds. GP.

LEACH, Mr Robin Dudley Oak Cottage, Common Lane, Claygate, Esher KT10 0HY Tel: 013724 63933 Fax: 013724 70650 Email: n7rdl@aol.com — MB BS 1971 Lond.; MS Lond. 1982; FRCS Eng. 1976. (St. Thos.) Cons. Gen. Surg. Kingston Hosp.; Arris & Gale Lect. Socs: Roy. Soc. Med. (Pres. Clin. Sect.); Internat. Soc. Cape Horners & Master Mariners; BASO. Prev: Sen. Regist. (Gen. Surg.) W.m. Hosp. Lond.; Lect. Surgic. Unit. & Regist. (Gen. Surg.) St. Thos. Hosp. Lond.

LEACH, Rosemarie Slade Barton, Payhembury, Honiton EX14 3HR — BM BS 1997 Nottm.

LEACH, Sally Louise 123 Otley Road, Harrogate HG2 0AG — MB BS 1985 Lond.; MA Camb. 1986; DRCOG 1989.

LEACH, Simon 5 Vicarage Lane, Scothern, Lincoln LN2 2UB — MB ChB 1978 Dundee; MRCP (UK) 1981. Cons. Phys. i/c Elderly Trent RHA.

LEACH, Timothy David Wessex Renal & Transplant Unit, St. Mary's Hospital, Portsmouth PO3 6AD — BM 1991 Soton.; MRCP (UK) 1994. Specialist Regist. (Nephrol. & Gen. (Internal) Med.) St. Mary's Hosp. Portsmouth.

LEACH, Tracey Ann The Alexandra Hospital, Woodrow Drive, Redditch B98 7UB Tel: 01527 503030 — MB ChB 1990 Birm.; FRCA 1996. Cons. Anaesth. Alexandra Hosp. Worcs. Acute Hosps. NHS Trust. Socs: Intens. Care Soc.; Assn. of Anaesth.s; W. Midl.s Intens. Care Gp.

LEACH, Vincent Lake Head Cottage, Wellow Lane, Rufford, Newark NG22 9DG Tel: 01623 824341 Fax: 01623 824341 Email: leach_lakehead@compuserve.com — MB ChB 1954 Liverp.; MA Wales 1995; DObst RCOG 1956. Adjudicating Med. Practitioner Nestor Healthcare; Vice-Pres. & Chairm. Educat. Comm. Socs: Assn. Med. Secretaries Practioners Admin.s & Receptionists.

LEADBEATER, Christine Mary Swanpool Medical Centre, St. Mark's Road, Tipton DY4 0UB Tel: 0121 557 2581 Fax: 0121 520 9475; 21 New College Close, Walsall WS1 3TF Tel: 01922 624657 Email: leadbeater@vezelay.demon.co.uk — MB ChB 1972 Leeds; MB ChB (Hons.) Leeds 1972; BSc (Hons.) Leeds 1969; DObst RCOG 1975. (Univ. Leeds) Prev: Ho. Off. (Paediat.) Leeds Gen. Infirm.; Ho. Off. (Surg.) Walsgrave Hosp. Coventry; Ho. Off. (Med.) Wharfedale Gen. Hosp. Otley.

LEADBEATER, Mark Jonathan Department of Anaesthetics, Norfolk & Norwich Hospital, Brunswick Road, Norwich NR1 3SR Tel: 01603 287086 Fax: 01603 287886; The Maltings, South Walsham Road, Panxworth, Norwich NR13 6JG Tel: 01603 270471 — MB BS 1984 Lond.; FRCA 1990. (Westm. Hosp. Med. Sch.) Cons. Anaesth. Norf. & Norwich Hosp. Prev: Sen. Regist. SW Thames RHA; Sen. Regist. Roy. Melbourne Hosp. Vict., Austral.

LEADBEATER, Norman Arthur George Le Chalet, Mont Cambrai, St Lawrence, Jersey JE3 1JN Tel: 01534 725888 Fax: 01534 616912 — MB BS 1954 Lond.; MRCS Eng. LRCP Lond. 1954. (Guy's) p/t Clin. Med. Off. Statco of Jersey Pub. Health N. Helier; Med. Off. Brook Clinic Jersey; Med. Off. States of Jersey Social security; Med. Adviser Jersey Kidney Pat.s Assn. Prev: Capt. RAMC (Path.) Brit. Milit. Hosp. Hanover; Ho. Phys. (Med.) Guy's Hosp. Lond.

LEADBEATTER, Stephen Wales Institute of Forensic Medicine, Institute of Pathology, Royal Infirmary, Cardiff CF2 1SZ Tel: 029 2049 2233; 10 Tyr Winch Road, Old Saint Mellons, Cardiff CF3 5UU Tel: 029 2079 0264 — MB ChB 1980 Bristol; MRCPath 1989; DMJ (Path.) Soc. Apoth. Lond. 1986. Sen. Lect. (Forens. Path.) Univ. Wales Coll. Med.; Home Office Path. Socs: Brit. Assn. Forens. Med. Prev: Sen. Regist. (Forens. Path.) Univ. Hosp. Wales.

LEADBITTER, Henry Hillbank Health Centre, 1A Constitution St., Dundee DD3 6NF Tel: 01382 21976 Fax: 01382 201980; 63 Clepington Road, Dundee DD4 7BQ Tel: 01382 457507 — MB ChB 1966 St. And.; DMJ Soc. Apoth. Lond. 1974. (Dundee) Clin. Asst. Strathmartine Hosp. Dundee. Socs: BMA. Prev: Ho. Phys. Stracathro Hosp.; Ho. Surg. Stirling Roy. Infirm.; SHO King's Cross Hosp. Dundee.

LEADER, Andrew Raymond 273 Shirland Road, London W9 3JW Tel: 020 8969 2099 — MB BCh BAO 1956 NUI; DObst RCOG 1960.

LEADER, Eleanor Clare West Slowley Barn, Luxborough, Watchet TA23 0SY — MB ChB 1953 Liverp. (Liverp.) Clin. Asst. Nat. Blood Transfus. Serv.

LEADER, Geoffrey Leonard The Devonshire Hospital, 29 Devonshire St., London W1G 6PU Tel: 020 7486 7131; 3 Hillcourt Avenue, London N12 8EY Tel: 020 8445 4550 Fax: 020 8446 4504 — MB ChB 1957 Cape Town; FFA RCS Eng. 1964. Indep. Pract. Anaesth. & Chronic Pain Relief. Socs: Intens. Care Soc.; Intractable Pain Soc. Prev: Sen. Cons. St. Hippolytus Hosp. Delft; Sen. Lect. (Anaesth.) Lond. Hosp. Med. Coll.; Sen. Lect. Univ. Erasmus & Sophia Childr. Hosp. Rotterdam, Netherlands.

LEADER, Serena Orden 18 Sherrock Gardens, London NW4 4JJ — MB BS 1992 Lond.

LEADING, Alan Derrick Crofton Health Centre, Slack Lane, Crofton, Wakefield WF4 1HJ Tel: 01924 862612 Fax: 01924 865519; 14 The Balk, Walton, Wakefield WF2 6JU Tel: 01924 250901 — MB BS 1974 Newc.; MB BS Newcastle 1974; DFFP 1978; MRCGP 1983; Dip Advanced GP Newcastle 1998. (Newc. u. Tyne) Socs: Roy. Coll. GPs; Anglo-French Med. Soc.; Nat. Assn. Family Plann. Doctors. Prev: GP Trainer; Course Organiser W. Riding GPEC; Clin. Asst. Diabetes.

LEADLEY, John Martin (retired) Martindale, Tythby Road, Cropwell Butler, Nottingham NG12 3AA Tel: 0115 933 2828 —

MB ChB 1952 Leeds. Prev: Ho. Phys. & Obst. Ho. Off. St. Jas. Hosp. Leeds.

LEAF, Alison Atkinson Neonatal Unit, Southmead Hospital, Bristol BS10 5NB Tel: 0117 950 5050 Fax: 0117 959 5324 — MB ChB 1981 Manch.; BSc St. And. 1978; MD Manch. 1992; MRCP (UK) 1984. Cons. Neonatol. S.mead Hosp. Socs: Roy. coll. Paed & child health; Roy. Soc. Med.; Neonat. Soc. Prev: Cons. Paediat. Glos. Roy. Hosp.; Sen. Regist. (Paediat.) Roy. United Hosp. Bath; Sen. Regist. (Neonat.) Monash Med. Centre Melbourne, Austral.

LEAHY, Adrian Richard HMP Wymott, Ulnes Walton Lane, Leyland, Preston PR5 3LW Tel: 01772 421461 Fax: 01772 624421 Email: adrian@aleahy.freeserve.co.uk — MB BS 1991 Lond. Head of Health Care HMP Wymott.

LEAHY, Alison Jane Department of Genito-Urinary Medicine, Watford General Hospital, Vicarage Road, Watford WD18 0HB Tel: 01923 217918 — MB BS 1982 Lond.; BSc Lond. 1979; MRCGP 1986. Clin. Asst. (Genitourin. Med.) Watford Gen. Hosp. Prev: Clin. Asst. (Genitourin. Med.) Stoke Mandeville Hosp. Aylesbury.

LEAHY, Andrew Charles Child & Family Service, Glebe Centre, Glebe St., Wellington TF1 1JP Tel: 01952 522710 — MB ChB 1979 Manch.; BSc St. And. 1976; MRCPsych 1987; MRCGP 1985. Cons. Child & Adolesc. Psychiat. Shrops. Ment. Health NHS Trust. Prev: Hon. Sen. Lect. Univ. Aberd.

LEAHY, Anthony Charles Brian 115 Fitzjohn Avenue, Barnet EN5 2HR Tel: 020 8449 0742 — MB BCh 1988 Wales; MRCP (UK) 1992. (Univ. Wales Coll. Med.) Specialist Regist. (Gastroenterol.) Basildon Hosp. Prev: Clin. Research Fell. (Gastroenterol.) Roy. Free Hosp. Lond.; Regist. (Med.) Chelsea & W.m. Hosp.

LEAHY, Bernard Christopher Trafford General Hospital, Moorside Road, Manchester M41 5SL Tel: 0161 748 4022 Fax: 0161 746 2793 Email: bernard.leahy@traffdhc-t.nwest.nhs.uk; Tel: 0161 226 0112 Fax: 0161 227 9405 — MB ChB (Hons.) Manch. 1977; FRCP 1997; FRCP Ed. 1994. Cons. Phys. Trafford Healthcare NHS Trust; Hon. Lect. (Med.) Univ. Manch.; Hon. Cons. Phys. Salford Roy. Hosps. Socs: Brit. Thorac. Soc. Prev: Sen. Regist. (Med.) Manch. Roy. Infirm. & Withington Hosp. Manch.; Tutor (Med.) Univ. Manch.

LEAHY, Brendan James Patrick Glen Road, Strabane BT82 8 Tel: 01504 2313 — LRCPI & LM, LRSCI & LM 1951; LRCPI & LM, LRCSI & LM 1951.

LEAHY, Denis Anthony 85a Bensham Road, Gateshead NE8 — LRCPI & LM, LRSCI & LM 1947; LRCPI & LM, LRCSI & LM 1947. (RCSI)

LEAHY, Eileen Patricia 7 Beaufort Place, Grosvenor, Bath BA1 6RP — LRCPI & LM, LRSCI & LM 1950; LRCPI & LM, LRCSI & LM 1950.

LEAHY, Elspeth Sarah (retired) 2 Avenue Road, Brentwood CM14 5EL Tel: 01277 212820 — MB BS 1985 Lond.; DCH RCP Lond. 1990; DRCOG 1988.

LEAHY, Henry Ardroe, Inch, Anmascanl, Newtown — MB BCh BAO 1944 NUI; BA NUI 1938, MB BCh BAO 1944; LM Coombe 1944.

LEAHY, James Desmond 21 Farm Way, Buckhurst Hill IG9 5AH — MB BCh BAO 1951 NUI.

LEAHY, John Francis Xray Department, Sandwell General Hospital, Lyndon, West Bromwich B71 4HJ Tel: 0121 607 3341 Fax: 0121 607 3403; 17 Montague Road, Edgbaston, Birmingham B16 9HR — MB ChB Bristol 1984; BSc Bristol 1981; MRCP (UK) 1988; FRCR 1991. Cons. Radiol. Sandwell Gen. Hosp. Socs: Fell. Roy. Coll. Radiol.; Brit. Soc. Interven. Radiol.; Brit. Inst. Radiol.

LEAHY, Joseph Anthony (retired) 41 Alinora Crescent, Worthing BN12 — MB BCh BAO 1923 NUI. Prev: Out-pat. Phys. & Hon. Anaesth. Bedford Co. Hosp.

LEAHY, Maire Mairead Patricia 2 Greenside Close, Hawkshaw, Bury BL8 4LE Tel: 0120 488 3965 — LRCPI & LM, LRSCI & LM 1951; LRCPI & LM, LRCSI & LM 1951; DA Eng. 1958. (RCSI) Cons. Anaesth. Bury & Rossendale Gp. Hosps. Socs: Fell. Manch. Med. Soc.; Manch. Med-Leg. Soc.

LEAHY, Martin Denis 33 Whitsand Road, Sharston, Manchester M22 4ZA Tel: 0161 945 8420 — MB BS 1996 Lond. (UCL) SHO (Ophth.) Countess of Chester.

LEAHY, Michael (retired) 23 Brincliffe Edge Close, Eccleshall, Sheffield S11 9DG — LRCPI & LM, LRSCI & LM 1957; LRCPI & LM, LRCSI & LM 1957. Prev: GP Sheff.

LEAHY, Michael Gordon Cancer Research Building, Department of Medical Oncology, University of Leeds, St James's Univesity Hospital, Beckett St., Leeds LS9 7TF Tel: 0113 243 3144 Fax: 0113 242 9886 Email: m.g.leahy@leeds.ac.uk; 37 Merchants House, North Street, Leeds — MB BS 1985 Lond.; BSc Lond. 1982; MRCP (UK) 1989; PhD, London. 1998. (St George's Hospital) Sen. Lect. (Med. Oncol.) Univ. of Leeds. Prev: Sen. Regist. (Med. Oncol.) Christie Hosp. Manch.

LEAHY, Michael John 169 Woodward Road, Barking, Romford RM7 4SU; Carass, 63 Blake Hall Road, Wanstead, London E11 2QW — MB BCh BAO 1952 NUI. (Cork) Socs: BMA; MICGP.

LEAHY, Patrick Declan St Andrews In Essex, Clare House, Pound Lane, Benfleet SS12 9JP Tel: 01268 723821; The Old Schoolhouse, Nayland Road, Leavenheath, Colchester CO6 4PH Tel: 01206 263284 Email: declanleahy@doctors.org.uk — MB BCh BAO 1984 NUI; MRCPsych 1989. Cons. Pyschiat & Clin Dir St And.in Essex Clare Ho. Pound La. N. Benfleet; Clin. Dir St And.Gp. of Hosps Billing Rd. N.ampton. Socs: Roy. Coll. Psychiatr.; BMA; Brentwood Med. Soc. Prev: Sen. Regist. St. Bart. Train. Scheme Lond.; Sen. Regist. (Forens. Psychiat.) Hackney Hosp. Lond.; Regist. & SHO (Psychait.) Runwell Hosp. Train. Scheme. Wickford.

LEAHY, Thomas Charles 12 Owen Grove, Henleaze, Bristol BS9 4EF — MB BCh BAO 1948 NUI. Prev: SHMO (Psychiat.) Hortham Brentry Gp. Hosps.; Ho. Phys. Grimsby Gen. Hosp.; Regist. (Psychiat.) Stanley Royd Hosp. Wakefield.

LEAK, Alison Margaret Queen Elizabeth the Queen Mother Hospital, St. Peter's Road, Margate CT9 4AN Tel: 01843 225544 Fax: 01843 220048 Email: alison.leak@thc-tr.sthames.nhs.uk; 6 Seaview Road, Birchington CT7 9LB Tel: 01843 841499 — MB BS 1976 Lond.; BSc (Hons.) Lond. 1973, MD 1991; FRCP Lond. 1995; MRCP (UK) 1980. (St. Thos.) Cons. Rheum.Qu. Eliz. the Qu. Mother Hosp Margate E kent Hosp trust; Dir of med educa E kent Hosp Trust,; Sub Dean GKT Med. sch. Socs: Fell. Roy. Coll. Paediat. & Child Health; Brit. Soc. Rheum.; Treas. Brit. Paed. Rheum. Gp. Prev: Cons. Rheum. Roy. Sea Bathing Hosp. Margate; Sen. Regist. (Rheum.) N.wick Pk. Hosp. Harrow.

LEAKE, Janet Tel: 01279 827222 Fax: 01279 827099; 10 Albion Hill, Loughton IG10 4RA — BM 1982 Soton.; MRCPath 1989; FRCPath 1998. (Southampton) Cons., Cellular Path., St Margt.'s Hosp. Socs: Internat. Acad. Path.; Brit. Soc. Clin. Cytol. Prev: Cons. Histopathol. Basildon Hosp.; Sen. Regist. (Histopath.) Hosp. Sick Childr. Gt. Ormond St.; SHO (Morbid Anat.) Lond. Hosp. Whitechapel.

LEAKE, Robert Antony (retired) 32 Rowan Way, Rottingdean, Brighton BN2 7FP Tel: 01273 303650 — BM BCh Oxf. 1952; MA Oxf. 1956; MRCGP 1965. Prev: Med. Off. Univ. Sussex.

LEAKE, Vivien Frances 3 Poplars Cl, Plumtree, Nottingham NG12 5HL — BM 1997 Soton.

LEAKER, Brian Robert 8 Bellamy Street, London SW12 8BU — MB BCh 1978 Wales; MSc Lond. 1992; MD Melbourne 1987; MRCP (UK) 1981. (Cardiff) Hon. Sen. Lect. Inst. Nephrol. & Urol. Middlx. Hosp. Lond.; Vanguard Medica, Surrey. Prev: Lect. Med. (Nephrol.) Univ. Coll. Hosp. Lond.; Research Regist. (Med.) Sch. Med. Univ. Melbourne, Austral.; Regist. (Med.) Roy. Infirm. Cardiff.

LEALMAN, Geoffrey Terence St Lukes Hospital, Bradford BD5 0NA Tel: 01274 365451 Fax: 01274 365333 — BSc Birm. 1964, MB ChB 1967; FRCP Lond. 1987, M 1971; FRCPCH 1997; DObst RCOG 1969; DCH Eng. 1969. (Birm.) Cons. Paediat. Bradford Hosps. NHS Trust. Prev: Sen. Regist. (Paediat.) Leeds & Bradford HA; Regist. (Paediat.) Roy. Hosp. Sick Childr. Glas.; Med. Off. Ngora Hosp., Uganda.

LEAMAN, Mr Alan Michael The Casualty Department, Princess Royal Hospital, Telford TF1 6TF Tel: 01952 641222 Fax: 01952 243406 — MB BS 1977 Lond.; FRCS Ed. 1983; FFAEM 1993. (Middlesex hosp) Cons. A & E P.ss Roy. Hosp. Telford. Prev: Sen. Regist. (A & E) Roy. Liverp. Hosp.

LEAMAN, Andrew Michael Stanley Mulbarton Surgery, The Common, Mulbarton, Norwich NR14 8JG Tel: 01508 570212 Fax: 01508 570042 — MB BS 1969 Lond.; MRCS Eng. LRCP Lond. 1969; MRCGP 1974; DObst RCOG 1971.

LEAMAN, Christine Anne c/o Shelton Hospital, Bicton Heath, Shrewsbury SY3 8DN; La Beche House, 14 Pitchford, Condover, Shrewsbury SY5 7DP — BM BS 1981 Nottm.; Dip. Gen. Psychiat. Keele 1995; MRCPsych 1999.

LEAN, Anthony Tangye Felpham and Middleton Health Centre, 109 Flansham Park, Felpham, Bognor Regis PO22 6DH Tel: 01243 582384 Fax: 01243 584933 — MB BS 1964 Lond.; DA Eng. 1972. (St. Thos.) Prev: Anaesth. Regist. United Bristol Hosps. & Chichester Hosps.; SHO Univ. Coll. Hosp. Trauma Unit.

LEAN, Bryan William Medical Specialist Group, Alexandra House, Les Frieteaux, St Martin's, Guernsey GY1 3EX Tel: 01481 39917 Fax: 01481 37782; Le Coin du Friquet, Le Friquet, Vale, Guernsey GY3 5SA Email: bryan.lean@virgin.net — MB ChB 1977 Liverp.; FRCP Lond. 1996; MRCP (UK) 1983; FRCPCH 1997; DCH Eng. 1980. Hon. Cons. Paediat. Guernsey. Prev: Paediat. Specialist P.ss Eliz. Hosp Guernsey; Regist. (Neonatol.) St. Mary's Hosp. Manch.; Regist. (Paediat.) Roy. Preston Hosps.

LEAN, Professor Michael Ernest John Department of Human Nutrition, University of Glasgow, Glasgow Royal Infirmary, Glasgow G31 2ER Tel: 0141 211 4686 Fax: 0141 211 4844 Email: mej.lean@clinmed.gla.ac.uk; 6 Regent Park Square, Glasgow G41 2AG Tel: 0141 424 3031 Fax: 0141 424 3031 — MB BChir 1986 Camb.; MB BChir Camb. 1977; MD Camb. 1986, MA (Hons.) 1976; FRCP Glas. 1993; FRCP Ed. 1990; MRCP (UK) 1978. Prof. (Head of Dept.) & Cons. Phys. (Diabetes & Human Nutrit.) Univ. Glas.; Cons. Phys. Glas. Roy. Infirm.; Cons. Nutrit. Gtr. Glas. HB. Socs: Brit. Diabetic Assn.; Nutrit. Soc. Prev: Sen. Regist. (Med. Diabetes & Endocrinol.) Aberd. Roy. Infirm.; Clin. Sc. Off. & Hon. Sen. Regist. (Med.) MRC & Univ. Camb. Dunn Clin. Nutrit. Unit Addenbrooke's Hosp. Camb.; Ho. Surg. (Cardiothoracic Unit) Roy. Infirm. Edin.

LEAN SU-TSENG, Inez Sarah Flat 4, 23 Brunswick Square, Hove BN3 1EJ — MB BS 1990 Lond.

LEANE, Michael Gerard, Surg. Cdr. RN (retired) 72 Old Woolwich Road, Greenwich, London SE10 9NY Tel: 020 8858 8737 — MB BCh BAO 1931 Dub. Prev: Med. Off. H.M. Prison Gartree.

LEANEY, Robert Montague Coltishall Surgery, St John's Road, Rectory Road, Coltishall, Norwich NR12 7HL Tel: 01603 737593 Fax: 01603 737067; 122 Norwich Road, Wroxham, Norwich NR12 8SA Tel: 01603 782462 — MB 1970 Camb.; BChir 1969; DObst RCOG 1973; DCH Eng. 1971. (St. Thos.)

LEANORD, Alistair Thomas 12 Munro Road, Jordan Hill, Glasgow G13 1SF Tel: 0141 357 1301 — MD 1992 Glas.; BSc Glas. 1984, MD 1992, MB ChB 1987; DTM & H RCP Lond. 1993; MRCPath 1996. Cons. Med. (Microbiol.) Law Hosp. NHS Trust Carlake.

LEAPER, Professor David John Professorial Unit of Surgery, Stockton-on-Tees TS19 8PE Tel: 01642 624610 Fax: 01642 624902 Email: fdleaper@email.msn.com — MB ChB 1970 Leeds; MB ChB (Hons.) Leeds 1970; ChM Leeds 1982, MD 1979; FRCS Eng. 1975; FRCS Ed. 1974; FRCS Glas. 1999; FRCS 1988; FACS 1998. Prof. Surg. Univ. Newc. u. Tyne; Hon. Cons. Surg. N. Tees & Hartlepool NHS Trust. Socs: Surgic. Research Soc. (Ex-Comm. Mem.).; (Ex-Pres.) Europ. Wound Managem. Assn.; Pres. Surgic. Infec. Soc. Europ. Prev: Cons. Sen. Lect. Univ. Bristol; Vis. Prof. Surg. Univ. Hong Kong; Sen. Regist. W.m. & King's Coll. Hosps. Lond.

LEAPER, Vincent Alexander Bourne Farm, Bourne Road, Woodlands, Southampton SO40 7GR — BM 1998 Soton.; BM Soton 1998.

LEAR, Brian Lawrence Quarter Jack Surgery, Rodways Corner, Wimborne BH21 1AP Tel: 01202 882112 Fax: 01202 882368 Email: www.doctors@quarterjacksurgery.co.uk; Methuen, 25 Whitecliff Mill St, Blandford Forum DT11 7BQ Fax: 01202 882368 Email: bllear@suponet.com — MB BS 1986 Lond.; MRCGP 1990; Dip. Sports Med. (Scotl.) 1997; Cert. Family Plann. JCC 1990; T (GP) 1990; MRCOG Lond. Part 1. 1988. (Roy. Free Hosp.) Clin. Asst. (Orthop. Med. & Sports Med.) Wimborne Hosp. Dorset; GP Specialist in Orthopaedic Med., Wimborne Hosp. Socs: BASM; BIMM. Prev: Trainee GP Lymington; SHO (Obst.) Acad. Unit Roy. Free Hosp. Lond.; SHO (Paediat.) St. Peter's Hosp. Chertsey.

LEAR, Gary Alan 14 Marston Grove, Sneyd Green, Stoke-on-Trent ST1 6EF — MB ChB 1986 Sheff.

LEAR, John Thomas Department of Dermatology, Bristol Royal Infirmary, Bristol BS2 8HW Tel: 0117 928 2520 — MB ChB 1991 Leic.; MRCP (UK) 1994; MD, Chichester. 1998. (Leicester) Cons. Dermat. Socs: BAD; BSDS. Prev: Regist. (Dermat.) Stoke-on-Trent Hosp.; SHO (Cas.) N.ampton Gen. Hosp.

LEAR, Mr Paul Andrew c/o Southmead Hospital, Monks Park Avenue, Bristol BS10 5NB Tel: 0117 959 5167 Fax: 0117 959 5168 Email: lear-p@southmead.swest.nhs.uk; Woodend Green Farm, Woodend Lane, Cam, Dursley GL11 5HS Tel: 01453 546808 — MB BS 1975 Lond.; MS Lond. 1985; FRCS Eng. 1979; T(S) 1991. Sen. Lect. Bristol Univ.; Cons. Surg. S.mead HA. Socs: Transpl. Soc. Prev: Sen. Lect. St. Bart. Hosp. Lond.; Sen. Regist. Roy. Liverp. Hosp.; Research Fell. Harvard Med. Sch. Boston MA, USA.

LEAR, Roger John Anthony The Surgery, 34 Teme Street, Tenbury Wells WR15 8AA Tel: 01584 810343 Fax: 01584 819734 — MB 1970 Camb.; MA Camb. 1971, MB 1970, BChir 1969; MRCP (U.K.) 1973; DObst RCOG 1971. (Camb. & Lond. Hosp.) Socs: BMA. Prev: Ho. Phys. & Ho. Surg. Lond. Hosp.; Rotating SHO (Med.) Bath Gp. Hosps.; Sen. Regist. (Med.) Qu. Eliz. Hosp. Barbados.

LEARMONT, Mr David (retired) 6 Cliff Way, Frinton-on-Sea CO13 9NL — MB ChB 1954 Birm.; FRCS Eng. 1964; FRCS Ed. 1964; DO Eng. 1960. Cons. Ophth. Surg. Colchester Health Dist. Prev: Sen. Regist. Birm. & Midl. Eye Hosp.

LEARMONT, Mr Jonathan Gordon Women's health directorate, William Harvey Hospital Road, Kennington Road, Willesborough, Ashford TN24 0LE Tel: 01233 616699 Fax: 01233 616745 Email: johnathan.learmont@kch-tr.sthames.nhs.uk; 34 John Newington Close, Kennington, Ashford TN24 9SG Tel: 01725 51197101233 630734 Fax: 01233 630734 Email: jlearmont@hotmail.com — MB BS 1987 Lond.; BSc (1st cl. Hons.) Lond. 1984; MRCOG 1992; Cert. Family Plann. JCC 1991. (St. Barths.Lond) Cons. (Obst. & Gynacology) William Harvey Hosp., Kent. Socs: BSCCP. Prev: Sen. Regist. (O & G) S.ampton Gen Hosp; Research Fell., Hon. Lect. & Hon. Regist. (Obst.) St. Thomas' Hosp. Lond.; SHO (O & G) Qu. Charlotte's & Chelsea Hosp. Lond.

LEARMONTH, Anna Catherine 38 Cluny Gardens, Edinburgh EH10 6BN — MB ChB 1998 Dund.; MB ChB Dund 1998.

LEARMONTH, Mr Duncan John Andrew Royal Orthopaedic Hospital, The Woodlands, Northfield, Birmingham B31 2AP Tel: 0121 685 4210; 65 Eastern Road, Birmingham B29 7JX Tel: 0121 472 1996 Fax: 0121 472 8311 — MB ChB 1982 Birm.; BSc (Hons.) Soton 1978; FRCS Ed 1986. Cons. Orthop. Surg. Roy. Orthop. Hosp. Trust Birm. Socs: Fell.Brit. Orthopaedic Associatoon; Brit. Assn. Surg. Knee; ESSKA. Prev: Sen. Regist. (Orthop.) W. Midl. RHA; Regist. (Orthop.) Leics. HA.

LEARMONTH, Professor Ian Douglas Department of Orthopaedic Surgery, Bristol Royal Infirmary, Marlborough St., Bristol BS2 8HW Tel: 0117 928 2658 Fax: 0117 929 4217; 5 Cotham Road, Cotham, Bristol BS6 6DG Tel: 0117 973 7964 — MB ChB Stellenbosch 1970; FRCS Eng. 1977; FRSC Ed. 1976; FCS(SA) Orth. 1980. (Coll. of Med. of S. Afr.) Prof. & Head (Orthop. Surg.) Univ. Bristol; Vis. Prof. W.. Orthop. Assn. Socs: Brit. Orthop. Assn. Prev: Prof. & Head Dept. Orthop. Surg. Univ. Cape Town, S. Afr.

LEARMONTH, Jessie Clark May The Poplars, Westmuir Road, Kirriemuir DD8 5LH — MB ChB 1957 St. And.; DPH 1963; MFCM 1974. Unit Med. Off. Psychiat/Ment. Handicap. Unit Dundee.

LEARNER, Juliet Margaret 6 Glen Iris Close, Canterbury CT2 8HR — MB BS 1991 Lond.; FRCA 1998.

LEARY, Andrew Christopher Department of Clinical Pharmacology, Ninewells Hospital and Medical School, PO Box 120, Dundee DD1 9SY Tel: 01382 632180 Fax: 01382 644972; Ballinadine, Lismore, County Waterford, Republic of Ireland Tel: 00 353 0158 54346 — MB ChB 1988 Cape Town; BSc (Hons.) Cape Town; MRCPI 1994; Dip. Pract. Derm. Wales 1997; DME RCPI 1993. Clin. Lect. (Clin. Pharmcol.) Ninewells Hosp. & Med. Sch. Dundee'.

LEARY, Bernard Deryck John (retired) Windycroft, Chesterfield Road, Brimington, Chesterfield S43 1AX Tel: 01246 275523 Fax: 01246 275523 Email: bernleary@aol.com — MB BS 1949 Lond.; FFHom 1989; MRCGP 1968; DMHSA 1988; DTM & H Eng. 1959. Prev: Cas. Off. & Ho. Surg. W. Herts. Hosp. Hemel Hemptstead.

LEARY, Elisa Renee 19 The Turnways, Headingley, Leeds LS6 3DT Tel: 0113 275 8850 — MB ChB 1990 Leeds; DA (UK) 1995; FRCA Lond. 1997. (Leeds) Specialist Regist. (Anaesth.) Yorks. Reg. Socs: Roy. Coll. Anaesth.; BMA; Assn. Anaesth. Prev: SHO (Anaesth.) Leeds Gen. Infirm. & Pinderfields Gen. Hosp. Wakefield & Bradford RI; SHO (Anaesth., Neonat. & Cas.) Bradford Roy. Infirm.

LEARY, Jack (retired) Kitt's End, 295 Skircoat Green Road, Halifax HX3 0LQ — MB ChB 1944 Manch.; BSc Manch. 1943, MB ChB

1944; MLCO 1961; MRCGP 1953. Prev: Capt. RAMC, Graded Specialist Phys. & Anaesth.

LEARY, James Anthony Morriston Hospital, Morriston, Swansea SA6 6NL — MB ChB 1988 Cape Town; FRCA 1997 (Lond.); DA (UK) 1996; DCH S. Afr. 1992. Regist. (Anaesth.) Morriston Hosp. Swansea, Cons. Anaesth. Socs: FRCA.

LEARY, Nigel Patrick Department of Anaesthesia, Borders General Hospital, Huntlyburn, Melrose TD6 9BS Tel: 01896 826000 Email: nigel.leary@borders.scot.nhs.uk — MRCS Eng. LRCP Lond. 1979; MA Camb. 1978, MB BChir 1979; FFA RCS Eng. 1984. Cons. Anaesth. Borders Gen. Hosp. Melrose. Socs: Assn. Anaesth. & Anaesth. Research Soc.; Intens. Care Soc.; Scott. Intens. Care Soc. Prev: Sen. Regist. (Anaesth.) Leeds, Bradford & Wakefield Hosps.; Regist. (Anaesth.) Leeds Gen. Infirm.; Regist. (Anaesth.) York Dist. Hosp.

LEARY, Prof Peter Michael Frenchay Hospital, Bristol BS16 1LE Tel: 011 7975 3870 Fax: 011 7975 3909 Email: peter.leary@north-bristol.swest.nhs.uk; Email: mickleary@blueyonder.co.uk — MD 1967 University of Cape Town; DA 1961; DCH 1962; DRCOG 1960; FCP 1968; MB ChB 1958. (University of Cape Town) Cons. Paediatric NeUrol., Frenchay Hosp.; Emerit. Assoc. Prof., Univ. of Cape Town.; Locum Cons., Bristol Childr.'s Hosp. and Univ. Hosp. Cardiff. Socs: Roy. Soc. of Med. (Life Fell.). Prev: Paediatric NeUrol., Red Cross Childr.'s Hosp., Cape Town.

LEARY, Robert Thomas Health Centre, Drumhaw, Lisnaskea, Enniskillen BT92 0JB Tel: 028 6772 2913 — MB BCh BAO 1981 Belf.; MRCGP 1985; DRCOG 1983; FRCGP (Assessment) 1996. (Qu. Univ. Belf.)

LEARY, Roger Mark Capelfield Surgery, Elm Road, Claygate, Esher KT10 0EH Tel: 01372 462501 Fax: 01372 470258 — MB BS 1980 Lond.; MRCGP 1984; MLCOM 1986; DRCOG 1983. (St. Mary's) GP Princip. Socs: Brit. Inst. Musculoskeletal Med.; Inst. Orthop. Med.; Lond. Coll. Osteop. Med. Prev: SHO (Paediat.) Edgware Hosp.; SHO (O & G) St. Thos. Hosp. Lond.; SHO (A & E) St. Mary's Lond.

LEARY, Siobhan Marie 61 Willersley Avenue, Sidcup DA15 9EJ — MB BS 1992 Lond.

LEARY, Timothy Simon 5 Shireoak Road, Withington, Manchester M20 4NY; 61 Stocks Lane15 West Street Gardens, Stamford PE9 2QB Tel: 01780 752241 Email: timkary@tesco.net — BChir 1992 Camb.; FRCA 1997. (Cambridge University) Specialist Regist. Rotat. (Anaesth.) E. Anglian Anaesth. Socs: Fell. Roy. Coll. Anaesth. Prev: SHO (Anaesth.) Addenbrooke's Hosp. Camb.

LEASK, Hugh James Graham 2 Mountain Road, Conwy LL32 8PU — MB ChB 1972 Manch.; DObst RCOG 1974.

LEASK, James Christopher (retired) 10 Sunnybank Road, Inverness IV2 4HE — MB ChB 1941 Aberd.

LEASK, James Thomas Smith Campbeltown Health Centre, Stewart Road, Campbeltown PA28 6AT Tel: 01586 552105 Fax: 01586 554997 — MB ChB 1981 Glas.

LEASK, Kathryn Margaret Booth Hall, Children's Hospital, Charlestown Road, Manchester M28 1LB; Avondale, 50 Altrincham Rd, Wilmslow SK9 5ND — MB ChB 1997 Manch.; BSc (Hons) Manch 1992.

LEASK, Ronald Graham Smith (retired) 9/2 Iddesleigh Avenue, Milngavie, Glasgow G62 8NT Tel: 0141 956 5675 — MB ChB 1958 Glas.; BSc (Hons.) Glas. 1954. Prev: Assoc. Specialist. (Biochem.) Stobhill Gen. Hosp. Glas.

LEASK, Stuart John University Department of Psychiatry, Duncan MacMillan House, Porchester Road, Nottingham NG3 6AA Tel: 0115 969 1300 Fax: 0115 955 5352 Email: stuart.leask@nottingham.ac.uk — MB BChir Camb. 1988; MA Camb. 1989; MRC Psych, 1997. Clin. Lect., Psychiat. & Community Ment. Health, Univ. of Nottm.

LEATHAM, Aubrey Gerald The Heart Hospital, 47 Wimpole St., London W1 Tel: 020 7573 8899 Fax: 020 7573 8898; 27 Sulivan Road, London SW6 3DT Tel: 020 7736 2237 Fax: 01273 514649 — MB BChir 1941 Camb.; MB BChir Camb. 1945; BA (2nd cl. Nat. Sc. Trip.) Camb. 1941; FRCP Lond. 1957, M 1945; MRCS Eng. LRCP Lond. 1944. (St. Thos.) Cons. Phys. St. Geo. Hosp. & Nat. Heart Hosp. Lond.; Cardiol. Edwd. VII Hosp. Lond. Socs: Amer. Heart Assn.; Hon. FACC; Brit. & Foreign Cardiac. Socs. Prev: Dean Inst. Cardiol. Nat. Heart. Hosp.; Med. 1st Asst. & Sherbrook Research Fell. Cardiac Dept. Lond. Hosp.; Ho. Phys. St. Thos. Hosp.

LEATHAM, Edward Winckley The Guildford Nuffield Hospital, Stirling Road, Guildford GU2 7RF Tel: 01483 555918 Fax: 01483 555918 — MB BS 1986 Lond.; BA Camb. 1983; MRCP (UK) 1989; MD Lond. 1996. Cons. (Cardiol.) Roy. Surrey Co. Hosp. & St Thomas & Guys Cardiothoracic Centre Lond. Prev: BHF Jun. Research Fell. & Regist. (Cardiol.) St Geo. Hosp. Lond.; Sen. Regist. (Cardiol.) Lond. Hosp. & Lond. Chest Hosp.

LEATHEM, Anthony John Department of Surgery, 67 Riding House St., London W1P 7LD Tel: 020 7380 9396 Fax: 020 7636 5175 Email: a.leathem@ucl.ac.uk; Fairview, Long Wittenham, Abingdon OX14 4QJ Tel: 01865 407826 Fax: 01865 407065 — MB ChB 1968 Birm.; MD Birm. 1976. Sen. Lect. (Surg.) Univ. Coll. Lond. Med. Sch. Prev: Histopath. Univ. Coll. Lond.; Clin. Scientist Ludwig Inst. & Roy. Marsden Hosp. Lond.; Immunopath. Univ. Paris.

LEATHEM, William Eric 6 Church Lane, Bishopthorpe, York YO23 2QG Tel: 01904 706261 — MB BCh BAO 1948 Belf. (Belf.) Socs: Brit. Acad. Forens. Sci.; Assn. Police Surg. Prev: Res. Med. Off. Belf. City Hosp.

LEATHER, Andrew John Moffat 30 Park Road, Bromley BR1 3HP — MB BS 1984 Lond. Regist. Rotat. (Gen. Surg.) S.end Gen. Hosp. Prev: Research Regist. Imperial Cancer Research Fund; SHO (Gen. Surg.) OldCh. Hosp. Romford; SHO (Hepatobilary Surg.) Hammersmith Hosp. Lond.

LEATHER, Andrew Thomas Ipswich Hospital NHS Trust, Heath Road, Ipswich IP4 5PD Tel: 01473 703 3004 Fax: 01473 703015; 71C Pearson Road, Ipswich IP3 8NL — MB BS Lond. 1985; MRCOG 1993. (King's Coll. Hosp.) Cons. (O&G) Ipswich Hosp. NHS Trust. Prev: Regist. (O & G) Kings Coll. Hosp. Lond.; SHO (O & G & A & E) King's Coll. Hosp. Lond.; Sen. Regist. (O & G) Addenbrooke's Hosp. Camb.

***LEATHER, Carolyn Julie** 139 Grove Lane, Cheadle Hulme, Cheadle SK8 7NG Tel: 0161 439 8962 — MB ChB 1998 Leeds.

LEATHER, Catherine Margaret Leatside, Yelverton PL20 6HY Tel: 01822 852898 — MB ChB Bristol 1954. (Bristol) JP; Sen. Clin. Med. Off. Family Plann. Plymouth DHA. Socs: Inst. Psycho-Sexual Med. Prev: Ho. Surg. & Ho. Phys. Bristol Roy. Infirm.; Obst. Ho. Surg. S.mead Hosp. Bristol.

LEATHER, George Derek (retired) Broomlea East, 649 Chorley New Road, Lostock, Bolton BL6 4AG Tel: 01204 843562 — MB BCh BAO Dub. 1957; MA Dub. 1960, BA 1955. Prev: Ho. Surg. Chester Roy. Infirm.

LEATHER, George St John St Matthew's Medical Centre, Prince Philip House, Malabar Road, Leicester LE1 2NZ Tel: 0116 224 4700 — MB ChB 1984 Leic.

LEATHER, Hugh Moffat Nuffield Hospital, Derriford Road, Plymouth PL6 8BG Tel: 01752 767115; Leatside, Yelverton PL20 6HY Tel: 01822 852898 — MD 1958 Bristol; MB ChB Birm. 1947; FRCP Lond. 1968, M 1951. (Birm.) Examr. MRCP Part 2 RCP Lond. Socs: Renal Assn. & Pres. Plymouth Med. Soc. Prev: Cons. Phys. Plymouth Clin. Area; Counc. RCP Lond.; Sen. Regist. (Med) United Bristol Hosps.

LEATHER, Jacqueline The Caxton Surgery, Oswald Road, Oswestry SY11 1RD Tel: 01691 654646 Fax: 01691 670994; High View, Treflach, Oswestry SY10 9HQ Tel: 01691 652409 — MB ChB 1980 Manch. Prev: Trainee GP Lancaster VTS; SHO (A & E) Roy. Preston. Hosp.; Clin. Med. Off. Lancaster HA.

LEATHER, John Graham (retired) — MB BCh BAO 1954 Dub. Prev: GP Bolton.

LEATHER, Kathryn Elizabeth 80 Lawson Road, Blackpool FY3 9TD — MB ChB 1993 Liverp.

LEATHER, Minna Susanna 134 Holbeck, Bracknell RG12 8XG — MB BS 1994 Lond.; MA Camb. 1995. (Girton Coll. Camb.) SHO (Paediat.) Guy's & St. Thos. Hosp. Lond. Prev: SHO (Paediat.) Pembury Hosp.; Ho. Off. (Surg.) Kent & Sussex Hosp.; Ho. Off. (Med.) Hereford Co. Hosp.

LEATHER, Susan Catherine 30 Park Road, Bromley BR1 3HP — MB BS 1985 Lond. Prev: Clin. Med. Off. (Community Child Health) Dartford & Gravesend.

LEATHERBARROW, Mr Brian Manchester Royal Eye Hospital, Oxford Road, Manchester M13 9WH Tel: 0161 276 1234 Fax: 0161 272 6618; 12A Heyes Lane, Alderley Edge SK9 7JY Tel: 01625 586226 Fax: 01625 586226 Email: bollin@mighty-micro.co.uk — MB ChB 1982 Manch.; MB ChB (Hons.) Manch. 1982; BSc (1st cl. Hons. Pharmacol.) Manch. 1979; FRCS Ed. 1987; FRCOphth 1988;

DO RCS Eng. 1985. (Manch.) Cons. (Ophth. & Oculoplastic Surg.) Manch. Roy. Eye Hosp. Prev: Sen. Regist., Regist. & SHO Manch. Roy. Eye Hosp.; Oculoplastic & Orbital Fell. Univ. Iowa City, USA; Oculoplastic Fell. Moorfields Eye Hosp. Lond.

LEATHERDALE, Brian Anthony Tel: 02380 794391 Fax: 02380 798624 Email: brian.leatherdale@suht.swest.nhs.uk; Hewers Orchard, New Town, Minstead, Lyndhurst SO43 7GD Tel: 02380 812789 — MB BS 1967 Lond.; MD Lond. 1984, BSc (Hons.) 1964; FRCP Lond. 1985; MRCS Eng. LRCP Lond. 1967; DObst RCOG 1969. (Lond. Hosp.) Cons. Phys. Soton. Gen. Hosp., Soton. Socs: Diabetes UK; BMA. Prev: Phys. Dudley Rd. Hosp. Birm.; Sen. Regist. (Med.) King's Coll. Hosp. Lond.; Regist. (Med.) N.wick Pk. Hosp.

LEATHERDALE, Robert Anthony Leatherdale (retired) 125 Pilsdon Drive, Poole BH17 9HT Tel: 01202 604394 — BM BCh 1947 Oxf.; MA Oxf. 1948, BM BCh 1947; FFA RCS Eng. 1954; DA Eng. 1952. Prev: Cons. Anaesth. Bournemouth & E. Dorset Hosp. Gp.

LEATT, Peter Brian The Old Baptist Chapel, Princes Road, Rhuddlan, Rhyl LL18 5PU — MB ChB 1991 Leic.; BSc Liverp. 1984; MSc Toronto 1986.

LEAVER, Alice Anne May St John's House, St Johns Road, Durham DH1 4NU — MB ChB 1998 Bristol.

LEAVER, Anne Teresa Walden-Lea, The Chilterns, Hitchin SG4 9PP — MB BS 1964 Lond.; MRCS Eng. LRCP Lond. 1964. (Roy. Free) Clin. Med. Off. N. Herts. Health Dist.

LEAVER, David Graham (retired) 4 Ridgeway, Epsom KT19 8LB Tel: 01372 729902 Fax: 01372 812155 — MB BChir 1966 Camb.; MD Camb. 1973, MA 1966; FRCP Lond. 1981 M 1968. Prev: Sen. Regist. (Gen. Med.) King's Coll. Hosp. Lond.

LEAVER, David Paul Toberargan Surgery, 27 Toberargan Road, Pitlochry PH16 5HG Tel: 01796 472558 Fax: 01796 473775 — MB ChB 1985 Manch.; BSc St. And. 1982; DRCOG 1989; DCH RCP Lond. 1989.

LEAVER, Diana Conway Community Paediatric Services, Borders General Hospital, Melrose, Melrose TD6 9BP Tel: 01896 754333; Langlee Mains Farm House, Galashiels TD1 2NZ Tel: 01896 752394 — MB ChB 1981 Manch. Staff Grade Community Paediat.

LEAVER, Edith Pauline (retired) 147 Wistaston Green Road, Crewe CW2 8RA Tel: 01270 665341 — MB ChB Liverp. 1962; FRCS Ed. 1968; FRCOG 1981, M 1968. Prev: Cons. Obst & Gyn. Leighton Hosp. Crewe.

LEAVER, Emma Jane 37 Penshurst Road, London E9 7DT — MB BS 1992 Lond.

LEAVER, Jane Margaret (retired) 28 Meynell Crescent, London E9 7AS Tel: 020 8985 2779 — MB BS Lond. 1963; MSc (Community Med.) Lond. 1980; FFPHM 1989, M 1982. Prev: Cons. in Pub. Health Med.

LEAVER, Laurence Bradley Jericho Health Centre, Walton Street, Oxford OX2 6NW Tel: 01865 311234 Fax: 01865 311087; 35 Horwood Close, Headington, Oxford OX3 7RF Tel: 01865 760004 Email: lleaver@jericho10.freeserve.co.uk — BM BCh 1991 Oxf.; MA Camb. 1992, BA 1988; MRCGP 1995; DFFP 1995. GP Princip. Prev: GP/Regist. Leighton Buzzard; Trainee GP/SHO Luton & Dunstable Hosp. VTS; Regist. (Spinal Injuries) Stoke Mandeville Hosp. Aylesbury.

LEAVER, Nigel Mark 23 Cornwall Avenue, Over Hulton, Bolton BL5 1DZ — MB ChB 1984 Birm.

LEAVER, Mr Peter Kenneth (retired) Moorfields Eye Hospital, City Road, London EC1V 2PD Tel: 020 7253 3411 — MB BS 1963 Lond.; FRCS Eng. 1970; MRCS Eng. LRCP Lond. 1963; FRCOphth. 1988; DO Eng. 1968. Cons. Ophth. Moorfields Eye Hosp. Lond. Prev: Cons. Ophth. Hammersmith Hosp. Lond.

LEAVER, Richard John Roxburgh Street Surgery, 10 Roxburgh Street, Galashiels TD1 1PF Tel: 01896 752557 Fax: 01896 755374 — MB ChB 1979 Manch.; MRCP (UK) 1986; MRCGP 1991; DTM & H Liverp. 1981; DCH RCPS Glas. 1981. Lect. (Med.) Univ. Teach. Hosp. Lusaka, Zambia.; Clin. Asst. (Med. for Elderly) Selkirksh.

LEAVER, Sarah 11 Roberts Lane, Chalfont St Peter, Gerrards Cross SL9 0QR — MB BS 1993 Lond.

LEAVER, Susan Ann (retired) Old Riffhams, Danbury, Chelmsford CM3 4AU Tel: 01245 224433 Fax: 0124 5222 6764 — MB 1958 Camb.; BChir 1957. Prev: Cas. Off. Hampstead Gen. Hosp.

***LEAVER, Susannah** 4 Ridgeway, Epsom KT19 8LB Tel: 01372 729902 Fax: 01372 812155 — MB BS 1998 Lond.; MB BS Lond 1998.

LEAVY, Anne Mary 118 Saul Street, Downpatrick BT30 6NJ — MB BCh BAO 1976 Belf.

LEBERMANN, Martha Ella (retired) 4 Redwood Way, Bassett, Southampton SO16 3PU Tel: 01703 69660 — MD 1934 Genoa; MD Wurzburg 1933. Prev: SCMO Soton. & S.W. Hants. Health Dist.

LEBUS, Jennifer Catherine Morris The Surgery, 30 Chartfield Avenue, London SW15 6HG Tel: 020 8788 6442; The Surgery, 30 Chartfield Avenue, London SW15 6HG Tel: 020 8788 6442 Fax: 020 8780 9468 — MB BChir 1976 Camb.; MA Camb. 1976; MRCGP 1985; DFFP 1995; DCH Eng. 1978; DRCOG 1977; Cert JCC Lond. 1977. (Middlx.) GP Princip.; Teachg. Fell. Imperial Coll. Sch. of Med.; Mem. Examg. Panel MRCGP. Socs: BMA (RTR Div.); Roy. Coll. Gen. Pract. (Hon. Sec. S. Thames W. Fac.). Prev: SHO (Paediat.) W. Middlx. Hosp. Isleworth; SHO (A & E) Char. Cross Hosp. Lond.; Ho. Surg. (O & G) Middlx. Hosp. Lond.

LECAMWASAM, Don Ananda Gamini Harold Wood Hospital., Gubbins Lane, Harold Wood, Romford RM3 0BE — MB BS 1972 Sri Lanka. Staff Phys. (c/o Elderly) Harold Wood Hosp. Romford. Prev: Staff Phys. (c/o Elderly) E.bourne.

LECH, Yvonne Mie Haugaard Yamanouchi Pharma Ltd, Yamanouchi House, Pyrford Road, West Byfleet KT14 6RA Tel: 01932 342291 Fax: 01932 353458; 2 Welford Place, London SW19 5AJ Tel: 020 8947 4698 — MD 1981 Copenhagen; MFPM RCP (UK) 1995; Dip. Pharm. Med. RCP (UK) 1994. Med. Dir. Yamanouchi W. Byfleet Surrey.

LECHI, Ai 58 Uphill Drive, Bath BA1 6PA — BM 1990 Soton.

LECHLER, Professor Robert Ian 78 Woodstock Road, Chiswick, London W4 1EQ Email: rlechler@rpms.ac.uk — MB ChB 1975 Manch.; PhD Lond. 1983; FRCP Lond. 1990; MRCP (UK) 1978; FRCPath 1996. Prof. Immunol. & Hon. Cons. Med. Roy. Postgrad. Med. Sch. Hammersmith Hosp. Lond.; Chief Serv. Immunol Hammersmith Hosp. Trust. Socs: (Comm.) Med. Research Soc.; Renal Assn. & Transpl. Soc. Prev: Sen. Regist. & Regist. (Renal Med.) Hammersmith Hosp.

LECI, Michael Keith Churchfields Surgery, Recreation Road, Bromsgrove B61 8DT Tel: 01527 872163 — MB ChB 1977 Birm.; MRCGP 1981.

LECK, Professor Ian Maxwell Pembury, 18 Cadogan Park, Woodstock OX20 1UW Tel: 01993 811528 Fax: 01993 811528 Email: iannleck@supanet.com — MB ChB 1954 Birm.; PhD Birm. 1961, DSc 1983; MSc Manch. 1982; FRCP Lond. 1985; FFPHM RCP (UK) 1972; T(PHM) 1991. (Birm.) Emerit. Prof. Univ. Manch. Socs: Hon. Mem. (Ex-Hon. Sec.) Soc. Social Med.; BMA. Prev: Prof. Epidemiol. Univ. Manch; Lect. (Social Med.) Univ. Birm.; Sen. Lect. (Comm. Med.) Univ. Coll. Hosp. Med. Sch.

LECKERMAN, Arnold Ravendal, 8 Davieland Road, Whitecraigs, Glasgow G46 7LA Tel: 0141 638 9508 — MB ChB 1967 Glas.; DObst RCOG 1969 (Glas.). Socs: BMA.

LECKIE, Alastair Matthew Sighthill Health Centre, 380 Calder Road, Edinburgh EH11 4AU Tel: 0131 453 5335; 2 Traquair Park E., Edinburgh EH12 7AW Tel: 0131 334 3081 — MB ChB 1986 Ed.; AFOM 1997; MRCGP 1991; DRCOG 1990. (Ed.) Occupat. Health Phys. IOM; Edin. Socs: SOM. Prev: GP Princ. Sighthill Health Centre, Edin.

LECKIE, George Brown Wellington Lodge, 53 Sibsey Road, Boston PE21 9QY — MB BChir 1966 Camb.; MA, MB Camb. 1967, BChir 1966; MRCS Eng. LRCP Lond. 1966; FRCOG 1984, M 1972. (Camb. & Lond. Hosp.) Cons. O & G S. Lincs. Health Dist. Prev: Sen. Regist. Nottm. AHA (T); Regist. (O & G) Roy. Free Hosp. Lond.; Ho. Surg. Harold Wood Hosp.

LECKIE, Gordon John Matthews South Queensferry Group Practice, The Health Centre, Rosebery Avenue, South Queensferry EH30 9HA Tel: 0131 331 1396 Fax: 0131 331 5783; The Old Manse, Carriden Brae, Bo'ness EH51 9SL Tel: 0131 331 1396 — MB ChB 1981 Edinburgh; BSc Ed 1978; MRCGP 1985; D. Occ. Med. 1998 Fac Occupat Med RCP. Med. Adviser Hewlett Packard Ltd. S. Qu.sferry; Undergrad. Clin. Tutor (Gen. Pract.) Edin. Univ. Socs: Soc. of Occup. Med.

LECKIE, John Hope (retired) 66 Beech Avenue, Nairn IV12 4SY — MB ChB 1951 St. And.; MA St. And. 1941, MB ChB 1951; DPA Glas. 1967. Prev: Sen. Med. Off. Scott Home & Health Dept.

LECKIE, Margaret Jean The Hammersmith Hopsital, Dept of Rheumatology, Du Cane Road, London W12 0NN Tel: 0208 7403276 Fax: 0208 7433109; 10 Clarion House, Moreton Place, London SW1V 2NN — MB ChB 1993 Bristol; BSc (Hons.) Bristol 1988; MRCP (UK) 1996. Research Fell. (Respirat. Med.) Clin. Studies Unit Roy. Brompton Hosp. Lond. Socs: Med. Defence Union; BMA. Prev: SHO (Gen. Med.) P.ss Margt. Hosp. Swindon; SHO (Renal) Ch.ill Hosp. Oxf.; Ho. Off. (Gen. Surg.) P.ss Margt. Hosp. Swindon & S.mead Hosp. Bristol.

LECKIE, Susan May Clinical Research Centre, The University of Edinburgh, Western General Hospital, Edinburgh EH4 2XU Tel: 0131 332 1205 Fax: 0131 343 6017 Email: s.m.leckie@ed.ac.uk; 2 Traquair Park E., Edinburgh EH12 7AW Tel: 0131 334 3081 — MB ChB 1986 Glas.; MRCGP 1991; DRCOG 1990. Med. Dir., Clin. Reserach Centre. Prev: Clin. Research Phys. Inveresk Clin. Research Edin.; Trainee GP Edin.

LECKY, Bryan Richard Finlay The Walton Centre for Neurology & Neurosurgery, Lower Lane, Liverpool L9 7LJ Tel: 0151 529 5762 Fax: 0151 529 5512 Email: lecky-b@wcnn-tr.nwest.nhs.uk — MB BChir 1973 Camb.; MA Camb. 1973, MD 1983; FRCP (UK) 1991. (Middlx.) Cons. Neurol. Walton Centre Arrowe Pk. Hosp. & Ysbyty Gwynedd; Hon. Clin. Lect. Univ. Liverp. Prev: Sen. Regist. (Neurol.) Nat. Hosp. Nerv. Dis. & Guy's Hosp. Lond.; Regist. (Neurol.) Nat. Hosp. Nerv. Dis. Lond.

LECKY, Fiona Elizabeth Emergency Department, Hope Hospital, Salford M6 8HD Email: flecky@fs1.ho.man.ac.uk — MB ChB 1988 Manch.; 2000 FFAEM; MSc (Epidemiol. & Biostatistics) Manch. 1994; FRCS Ed. 1994; DA (UK) 1994. (Manchester) Sen. Lect./ Hon. Cons. in Emerg. Med., Hope hosp. Socs: Med. Protec. Soc.; Brit. Med. Assn.; Med. Research Soc. Prev: Wellcome Research Fell. (Clin. Epidemiol. for Emerg. Med.) Univ. Manch.; Specialist Regist. (Emerg. Med) NW Region.

LECKY, Julia Margaret Flett Moreton Cross Group Practice, Ashton House, Chadwick Street, Moreton, Wirral L46 7US Tel: 0151 678 0993; The Garth, Hinderton Road, Neston, South Wirral CH64 9PF Tel: 0151 336 5176 — MB ChB 1972 St. And.; MRCGP 1980; DCH Eng. 1976; DObst RCOG 1976. Clin. Asst. (Med.) Wirral Trust. Prev: GP City & E. Lond. FPC; Trainee GP Camden & Islington VTS; GP Chesh..

LEDBURY, Jeanette 136 Stenson Road, Derby DE23 7JG — MB ChB 1965 Leeds; Cert. Prescribed Equiv. Exp. JCPTGP 1982. (Leeds) SCMO (Community Health) S. Derbysh.. Prev: Sen. Community Med. Off. Family Plann. Sheff.; Ho. Phys. United Sheff. Hosps.

LEDDY, Charles Edward 44 Cortworth Road, Sheffield S11 9LP Tel: 0114 262 0910 — MB BCh BAO 1942 NUI. (Univ. Coll. Dub.)

LEDDY, Fionnuala 45 Park Road, Belfast BT7 2FX — MB BCh BAO 1983 Dub.; BA Dub. 1981, MB BCh BAO 1983; MRCPsych 1987. Prev: Intern Adelaide Hosp. Dub.

LEDDY, Jillian Mary 40 Longway Avenue, Charlton Kings, Cheltenham GL53 9JJ — MB ChB 1993 Liverp.

LEDDY, Kevin 44 Fitzjohn's Avenue, Hampstead, London NW3 5LX Tel: 020 7435 6270; 19 Southwood Lawn Road, Highgate, London N6 5SD — LRCPI & LM, LRSCI & LM 1951; LRCPI & LM, LRCSI & LM 1951; DPM Eng. 1961. Socs: Assoc. Mem. Brit. Psychoanalyt. Soc.

LEDDY, Phillip Patrick c/o Williams & Glyns Bank, Holts Branch, Kirkland House, Whitehall, London SW1 — MB BCh BAO 1953 NUI.

LEDERMANN, Erich Kurt 121 Harley Street, London W1N 1DH Tel: 020 7935 8774; 13 Ardwick Road, London NW2 2BX Tel: 020 7435 5133 — LRCP LRCS Ed. LRFPS Glas. 1934; MD Berlin 1932; FRCPsych 1986, M 1971; FFHom 1950. Hon. Cons. Homoeop. Phys. Roy. Lond. Homoeop. Hosp. Socs: Fell. Roy. Coll. Psychiat.; BMA. Prev: Hon. Cons. Psychiat. MarlBoro. Hosp. Lond.; Phys. Childr. Homoeop. Disp.; Regist. (Dermat.) Willesden Gen. Hosp.

LEDERMANN, Jonathan Andrew Department Oncology, University College London Hospitals, London W1N 8BT Tel: 020 7679 9430 Fax: 020 7436 2956 Email: j.ledermann@ucl.ac.uk; 17 Langbourne Avenue, London N6 6AJ Tel: 020 8340 4678 Fax: 020 7419 7057 — MB BS 1978 Lond.; BSc Lond. 1975, MD 1990; FRCP Lond. 1994; MRCP (UK) 1980. (Univ. Coll. Hosp.) Reader (Med. Oncol.) Roy. Free & Uni. Coll. Med. Sch. Lond.; Hon. Cons. UCL Hosps., Whittington & Roy. Free Hosps.; Cirector CRL/UCL Cancer Trial Centre UCL. Socs: Brit. Assn. Cancer Research; Eur. Soc. Med. Oncol.; Amer. Soc. Clin. Oncol. Prev: CRC Clin. Research Fell. & Hon. Sen. Regist. (Med. Oncol.) Char. Cross Hosp. Lond.; Clin. Fell. P.ss Margt. Hosp. Toronto Ontario, Canada; Regist. Univ. Coll. Hosp. & Whittington Hosp. Lond.

LEDERMANN, Sarah Elizabeth Renal Unit, Great Ormond St. Hospital NHS Trust, London WC1N 3JH Tel: 020 7405 9200 Fax: 020 7829 8841; 17 Langbourne Avenue, London N6 6AJ Tel: 020 8340 4678 Fax: 020 7419 7057 — MB BS 1977 Lond.; MRCP (UK) 1981. (Univ. Coll. Hosp.) Assoc. Specialist Gt. Ormond St. Hosp. NHS Trust Lond. Socs: Brit. Soc. Paediat. Nephrol.

LEDGER, Clive Howard Keyworth Health Centre, Bunny Lane, Keyworth, Nottingham NG12 5JU Tel: 0115 937 3527 Fax: 0115 937 6781 — MB BS 1978 Lond.; MRCGP 1988. Undergrad. Tutor Nottm.

LEDGER, David Howard Elm Lodge Surgery, 2 Burbage Road, London SE24 9HJ Tel: 020 7733 3073 Fax: 020 7924 0710; 36 Liphook Crescent, Forest Hill, London SE23 3BW — MB BS 1981 Lond.; MRCGP 1986; DRCOG 1986.

LEDGER, Joanne Lesley Elkstone, Hazel Close, Grewelthorpe, Ripon HG4 3BL — BM BS 1997 Nottm. PRHO (Med.) Bradford Roy. Infirm. St. Luke's Hosp. Bradford; PRHO (Surg.) Leeds Gen. Infirm.

LEDGER, John Alexander Curworthy Farm, Inwardleigh, Okehampton EX20 3AZ — MB BS 1994 Lond.

LEDGER, Moira Anne Department of Psychiatry, Royal South Hants Hospital, Graham Road, Southampton SO14 0YG Tel: 02380 634288 — MB ChB 1982 Sheff.; MRCPsych 1987. Cons. (Rehabil. & Community Psychiat.) Soton. Dist. HA. Prev: Sen. Regist. (Psychiat.) Wessex Regional HA; Regist. (Psychiat.) Sheff. Dist. HA.

LEDGER, Peter Kingsmill (retired) Coed Mawr, Llanbedr LL45 2PF Tel: 01341 241522 — MA Camb. 1949, MB BChir 1946. Prev: Staff Phys. Lond. Hosp.

LEDGER, Shirley 36 Liphook Crescent, London SE23 3BW Tel: 020 8699 5463 Fax: 020 8699 5463 — MB BS 1982 Lond. Clin. Asst. S. Lond. Blood Transfus. Serv. Prev: Regist. (Chem. Path.) Leics Roy. Infirm. & St. Helier Hosp. Carshalton.

LEDGER, Stephen James The Dekeyser Group Practice, The Fountain Medical Centre, Little Fountain, Leeds LS27 9EN Tel: 0113 295 1600 Fax: 0113 238 1901; Hippocratic Blades, 8 Albert Grove, Leeds LS6 4DA Tel: 0113 278 1543 — MB ChB 1979 Leeds; MRCGP 1984; DRCOG 1982; Cert. Family Plann. JCC 1985.

LEDGER, Susan 9 St Leonards Lane, Wallingford OX10 0HA — MB BS 1987 Newc.; DCH RCP Lond. 1991; DRCOG 1990. Trainee GP Headington. Prev: SHO (O & G) Luton & Dunstable Hosp.; SHO (Geriat.) Swindon HA; SHO (Paediat.) John Radcliffe Hosp. Oxf.

LEDGER, Professor William Leigh Jessop Hospital for Women, Leavygreave Road, Sheffield S3 7RE Tel: 0114 226 8317 Fax: 0114 275 2153 Email: w.ledger@sheffield.ac.uk; Norfolk Lodge, Kallow Meadows, Sheffield S6 6GH Tel: 0114 230 2895 — BM BCh 1985 Oxf.; MA, DPhil Oxf. 1982, BM BCh 1985; MRCOG 1989. Prof. of O & G Univ. of Sheff. Socs: Brit. Fertil. Soc.; Europ. Soc. for Human ReProduc. and Embryology. Prev: Lect. & Sen. Regist. Roy. Infirm. Edin.; Regist. (O & G) N.. Gen. Hosp. Sheff.; Reader & Cons. John Radcliffe Oxf.

LEDINGHAM, Elaine Mary 22 Hids Copse Road, Cumnor Hill, Oxford OX2 9JJ — MB BS 1960 Lond.; DObst RCOG 1962. Prev: Ho. Phys. & Ho. Surg. Middlx. Hosp.

LEDINGHAM, Professor Iain McAllan University of Dundee, Clinical Skills Centre, Ninewells Hospital & Medical School, Dundee DD1 9SY Tel: 01382 632615 Fax: 01382 633950; Westown, by Errol, Perth PH2 7SU Tel: 01821 670210 Fax: 01821 670210 — MB ChB 1958 Glas.; FRSE 1981; MD (Hons. & Bellahouston Medal) Glas. 1979; FRCP Ed. 1997; FRCP Glas. 1984; FRCS Ed. 1979; MRCP Glas. 1981; FIBiol 1987. (Univ. Glas.) Prof. Med. Educat. & Dir. Healthcare Learning Network Ninewells Hosp. & Med. Sch. Dundee; Hon. Cons. Phys. Dundee Teachg. Hosps. NHS Trust. Socs: Physiol. Soc.; Intens. Care Soc.; Surg. Res. Soc. Prev: Dean Fac. of Med. & Health Sci.s Univ. UAE; Prof. Intens. Care Univ. Glas.

LEDINGHAM, James George 132 Mountcastle Drive S., Edinburgh EH15 3LL Tel: 0131 669 6101 — MB ChB 1953 Aberd.

LEDINGHAM, Joanna Mary Queen Alexandra Hospital, Cosham, Portsmouth PO6 3LY Tel: 02392 286199 — BM BS 1986 Nottm.; 1995 MD Nottm.; 1984 BMedSci, Nottm; 1989 MRCP (UK). (Nottm.) Cons. Rheum. Portsmouth. Prev: Sen. Regist. (Rheum.) Roy.

Lond. Hosp.; Research Fell. (Rheum.) City Hosp. Nottm.; Regist. (Med. & Rheum.) Newc. HA.

LEDINGHAM, Professor John Gerard Garvin (retired) 22 Hid's Copse Road, Cumnor Hill, Oxford OX2 9JJ Tel: 01865 862023 Fax: 01865 862023 — BM BCh 1957 Oxf.; MA (1st Cl. Hons.) Oxf., DM 1966; FRCP Lond. 1971, M 1959. Prev: Dir. Clin. Studies & Clin. Prof. May Reader Med. Univ. Oxf.

LEDINGHAM, Marie-Anne 1/1, 72 Lauderdale Gardens, Glasgow G12 9QW — MB ChB 1992 Glas.; MRCOG 1997. (Glas.) SHO (O & G) S.. Gen. Hosp. Glas.; Specialist Regist. W. Scotl. Rotat. Obst. & Gyn. Prev: SHO (O & G) Stobhill Hosp. Glas.; SHO (A & E & O & G) Roy. Alexandra Hosp.

LEDINGHAM, Richard George Walkley House Medical Centre, 23 Greenhow Street, Sheffield S6 3TN Tel: 0114 234 3716; 39 Hallam Grange Road, Fulwood, Sheffield S10 4BH — MB BS 1979 Lond.

LEDINGHAM, Roderick George Macdonald (retired) Boyndie, 31 Newfield Lane, Dore, Sheffield S17 3DB Tel: 0114 236 1342 — MRCS Eng. LRCP Lond. 1942; MRCGP 1958.

LEDINGHAM, Sarah Lesley — MB BS 1992 (Hons.) Lond.; MRCGP Lond. 1996; DFCOG Lond. 1995.

LEDINGHAM, Simon John Metcalf 11 Montpelier Wk., Knightsbridge, London SW7 1JL — MB BS 1977 Lond. (Lond. Hosp.)

LEDINGHAM, Stephanie Nanette Ecclesfield Group Practice, 96A Mill Road, Ecclesfield, Sheffield S35 9XQ Tel: 0114 246 9151 — MB BS 1980 Lond.; MRCGP 1985; DCH RCP 1983; DRCOG 1983; Cert Family Plann. JCC 1983.

LEDINGHAM, Mr William Murray Woodend Hospital, Eday Road, Aberdeen AB9 6YS Tel: 01224 66313; Todholes Farm House, Drumoak, Banchory AB31 5HL Tel: 01330 811496 — MB ChB 1980 Aberd.; FRCS Ed. 1986. Cons. Orthop. & Trauma Surg. Woodend Hosp. Aberd. Socs: Fell. BOA; M-C Soc. Aberd. Prev: Sen. Regist. (Orthop. & Trauma Surg.) Wessex RHA; Regist. (Orthop.) Grampian HB.

LEDSON, Mrs Helen Burscough Health Centre, Stanley Court, Lord Street, Burscough, Ormskirk L40 4LA Tel: 01704 892708; Martin Hall Farm, New Lane, Burscough, Ormskirk L40 8JA — MB ChB 1966 Liverp.

LEDSON, James Francis Department of Anaesthetics, 12th Floor, Royal Liverpool University Hospital, Prescot Street, Liverpool L7 8XP — MB ChB 1992 Liverp.

LEDSON, Martin James The Cardiothoracic Centre, Thomas Drive, Liverpool L14 3PE Tel: 01224 869794, 0151 228 1616 Fax: 0151 293 2331; Fax: 0151 293 2331 — MB ChB 1992 Liverp.; MD 2000 Liverp.; BSc (Hons.) Liverp. 1989; MRCP (UK) 1995. Cons. In Respirat. & Gen. Med., The Cardiac Centre, Liverp.. Prev: Cons in Respirat. & Gen. Med., The Roy. Liverp. Univ. Hosp. Liverp..

LEDSON, Michael Andrew Abbey Health Centre, East Abbey Street, Arbroath DD11 1EN Tel: 01241 870307 Fax: 01241 431414; Kirklee, Arbirlot, Arbroath DD11 2NX — MB ChB 1972 St. And.; DObst RCOG 1974.

LEDSON, Thomas Arthur, SHO 70 More Road, Orrell, Wigan WN5 8RR Tel: 01942 513764 Email: maisdunc@aol.com; 70 More Road, Orrell, Wigan WN5 8RR Tel: 01942 513764 — MB ChB 1995 Manch. (Manchester) SHO (Med.) Hope Hosp., salford, Manch.

LEDWARD, David John Prospect Medical Practice, 95 Aylsham Road, Norwich NR3 2HU Tel: 01603 488477; 2 West End Avenue, Brundall, Norwich NR13 5RF — MB ChB 1991 Ed.; DRCOG 1995; DCH RCP Lond. 1994; MRCGP 1998. (Ed.) GP Norwich.

LEE, Adam John Hollyoaks Medical Centre, 229 Station Road, Wythall, Birmingham B47 6ET Tel: 01564 823182 Fax: 01564 824127; 22 Swan Street, Alvechurch, Birmingham B48 7RP Tel: 0121 447 7937 — MB ChB 1988 Birm.; ChB 1988 Birm.; DCH RCP 1991 Lond.; MRCGP 1994; MRCGP 1994; DCH RCP Lond. 1991. (Birmingham) GP Princip. Wythall Birm. Prev: SHO (ENT) Wolverhampton Roy. Hosp.; SHO (A & E & O & G) W. Midl. RHA.

LEE, Adrian Elbury, Broadclyst, Exeter EX5 3BH — MB BS 1998 Lond.; MB BS Lond 1998.

LEE, Adrian Vincent Cohen and Partners, West Lodge Surgery, New Street, Farsley, Pudsey LS28 5DL Tel: 0113 257 0295 Fax: 0113 236 2509; West Lodge, New St, Farsley, Pudsey LS28 5DL — MB BCh BAO 1975 Dub.; MA Dub. 1977; MRCGP 1980; D.Occ.Med. RCP Lond. 1995; DObst RCPI 1977; DCH NUI 1976; Dip. Occupat. Med. 1996.

LEE, Agnes Teck Fong Leicester Royal Infirmary, Leicester LE1 5WW Tel: 0116 254 1414 Fax: 0116 258 5631; Block D, Flat D44, L.R.I. Staff Residences, Walnut St, Leicester LE2 7GJ Email: agnestfl@aol.com — MB BCh 1993 Wales; MRCP (UK) 1997. Specialist Regist. (Clin. Radiol.) Leicester Roy. Infirm. Leicester. Socs: MDU; Roy. Coll. Radiol. Prev: SHO (Gen. Med.) Morriston Hosp. Swansea; SHO (Gen. Med.) Neath Gen. Hosp.

LEE, Ah Loi (retired) 34-5 Netherhall Gardens, London NW3 5TP Tel: 020 7794 8090 Fax: 020 7794 8090 — MB BS 1966 Lond.; MRCS Eng. LRCP Lond. 1966; FRCA 1975; FFA RCSI 1974. Prev: Sen. Regist. (Anaesth.) St. Bart. Hosp. Lond.

LEE, Ai Leen 6B Windsor Close, Windsor Park, Belfast BT9 6FG — MB BCh BAO 1995 Belf.

LEE, Alan Baskerville (retired) Orchard Dene, Ripe, Lewes BN8 6AR — MB BS Lond. 1944; MRCGP 1965.

LEE, Alan Kay Teck Flat 83, Regents Court, Sopwith Way, Kingston upon Thames KT2 5AQ — MB ChB 1993 Sheff.

LEE, Alan Stuart Department of Psychiatry, B Floor-South Block, University Hospital, Queens Medical Centre, Nottingham NG7 2UH Tel: 011592409924 Ext: 41046 Email: aslee@compuserve.com — MB BS 1976 Newc.; MA Camb. 1970; MRCPsych 1981; FRCPsych 1998. Cons. Psychiat. Univ. Hosp. Nottm.; Special Sen. Lect. (Psychiat.) Univ. Nottm. Prev: Sen. Regist. Maudsley Hosp. Lond.; Sen. Regist. (Psychol. Med.) Hammersmith Hosp. Lond.; Research Psychiat. Inst. of Psychiat. Lond.

LEE, Mr Alex Chi Hang 24 Plane Tree Avenue, Leeds LS1 8UB Tel: 0113 266 9464 Fax: 0113 266 9564 Email: achlee@rcsed.ac.uk; 34 Begonia Road, 2/F, Yau Yat Chuen, Kowloon, Hong Kong Tel: 00 852 23972557 Fax: 00 852 27893795 — MB ChB 1994 Ed.; FRCS Ed. 1998. (Univ. Ed.) Specialist Regist. In Paed. Surg., St Jas. Univ. Hosp., Leeds. Socs: BMA; Assoc. Mem. Brit. Ass. of Paed. Surg.; Brit. Ass. Paed. Endoscopic Surg. Prev: Clin. Fell. (Paediat. Intens. Care) Roy. Hosp. Sick Childr. Edin.; SHO (Neonat. Med.), Qu. Mother's Hosp. Glas.; SHO (A & E & Plastic Surg.) St. John's Hosp. Livingston.

LEE, Alice Marjorie Annie (retired) Brondeg, Llanelly Church Road, Gilwern, Abergavenny NP7 0EL — MB BCh Wales 1944. Prev: Med. Off. Family Plann. Clinic Manch. AHA.

LEE, Alison Frances Clare High Craigton, Milngavie, Glasgow G62 7HA — MB ChB 1991 Ed.

LEE, Alison Jane 3 Mont Le Grand, Exeter EX1 2PD — BM 1988 Soton.; MRCGP 1993; DRCOG 1994; MRC Pysch pt1 1999. (Soton) SHO (Pysch.) Wonford Ho.. Hosp. Exeter.

LEE, Alistair 126 Craiglea Drive, Edinburgh EH10 5PR — MB ChB 1979 Ed.; FFA RCS Eng. 1985.

LEE, Alyson Mary Oak Tree Health Centre, 2 Lostock Place, Didcot OX11 7XT Tel: 01235 810099 Fax: 01235 815181; 8 Notgrove, nr Cheltenham GL54 3BS Tel: 01451 850012 Fax: 01451 850012 — BM 1984 Soton.; MRCGP 1988. (Soton.) Gen. Med. Practitioner. Socs: BMA. Prev: GP Oxf.; GP Clin. Audit Adviser.

LEE, Amanda Clare Oakley Surgery, Sainfoin Lane, Oakley, Basingstoke RG23 7HZ Tel: 01256 780338; 6 Hurstbourne Priors, Whitchurch RG28 7SE Fax: 01256 893977 — BM 1992 Soton.; DCH 1996; MRCGP 1997. (Southampton) GP Princip.

LEE, Mr Andrew Clayton 17 Athole Gardens, Glasgow G12 9BA Email: aclee@mailexcite.com — MB ChB 1995 Glas.; AFRCS Ed. 1998. SHO (Gen. Surg.) N. Glas. Universtiy Hosps. NHS Trust Glas.

LEE, Andrew George St James Hospital, Locksway Rd, Milton, Portsmouth PO4 8LD — BM 1985 Soton.; MRCPsych 1996; MRCGP 1992; DA (UK) 1988. Specialist Regist. (Psychiat.) Wessex Rotat. Scheme.

LEE, Andrew Hilary Schokman Tel: 0115 969 1169 Ext: 47204 — MB BChir 1985 Camb.; MA Camb. 1986; MRCP (UK) 1988; MRCPath 1998. (Guy's) Cons. (Histopathol.) Nottm. City Hosp. Prev: Lect. (Path.) Univ. Soton. & Hon. Sen. Regist. (Histopath.) Soton. Gen. Hosp.; Clin. Research Fell. (Histopath.) ICRF Clin. Oncol. Unit Guy's Hosp. Lond.

LEE, Andrew John Brackenwood House, Common Road, East Tuddenham, Dereham NR20 3NF — MB ChB 1993 Bristol.

LEE, Mr Andrew Simon Department of Orthopaedics, Treliske Hospital, Truro Tel: 0872 256012 — BM BCh 1986 Oxf.; MA Oxf. 1987; FRCS Eng. 1990; FRCS (Orthop.) Eng. 1995. Cons. Orthop. Surg. Socs: Brit. Orth. Assn.; Brit. Assn. Surg. Knee; BOFFS. Prev: Sen. Regist. Truro/Exeter Rotat.

LEE, Andrew William West Common Lane Medical Centre, West Common Lane, Dorchester Road, Scunthorpe DN17 1YH Tel: 01724 870414 Fax: 01724 280485; 3 Repton Drive, Bottesford, Scunthorpe DN16 3QX Tel: 01724 869521 — MB ChB 1983 Sheff. CME Tutor N. Lincs.

LEE, Anne Maureen Nobles Hospital, Douglas IM1 4GA Tel: 01624 642642; Cranage, Abbeylands, Douglas IM4 5EH Tel: 01624 621672 — MB BCh BAO Dub. 1961; MA Dub. 1993; DCH RCPSI 1991; DObst RCOG 1963; MRCPCH 1993. (T.C. Dub.) Assoc. Specialist (Neonat. Paediat.) Noble's Hosp. Douglas I. of Man. Socs: BMA & I. of Man Med. Soc.; Brit. Paediat. Assn.

LEE, Avril Joy Pathology Department, Western Infirmary, Glasgow Tel: 0141 339 8822; 33 Lovat Avenue, Bearsden, Glasgow G61 3LQ Tel: 0141 942 2468 — MB ChB 1958 St. And. (St. And.) Cytol. W.. Infirm. Glas. Prev: Regist. Virol. W.. Infirm. Glas.; Asst. Lect. in Bact. Qu. Coll. Dundee; Ho. Phys. Paediat. & Ho. Surg. Midw. & Gyn. Dundee Roy. Infirm.

LEE, Beng Kwan 10 Tankerfield Place, Romeland Hill, St Albans AL3 4HH — MB 1960 Camb.; MA Camb. 1961, MB 1960, BChir 1959; FRCP Lond. 1989, M 1967; DCH Eng. 1962. (Camb. & St. Bart.) Cons. (Paediat.) Hemel Hempstead Gen. Hosp. Socs: BMA. Prev: Cons. (Paediat.) NW Durh. Gp. Hosps.; Clin. Specialist (Paediat.) Gen. Hosp., Kuala Lumpur; Regist. (Med.) St. Albans Hosp.

LEE, Benjamin (retired) 8 Priory Lodge, 93 Brown St., Salisbury SP1 2BX — MRCS Eng. LRCP Lond. 1944; MRCGP 1965.

LEE, Bernadette Tsui Mei Sam Beare Unit, Weybridge Hospital, Church St., Weybridge KT13 8DY Tel: 01932 826042 Fax: 01932 826072 Email: bernadette.lee@bcmhs-tr.sthams.nhs.uk — MB BS 1991 Lond.; MRCP (UK) 1995; Dip Palliat Med. 1998. Cons. in Palliat. Med.; Cons. in Palliat. Med., P.ss Alice Hospice, Esher, Surrey.

LEE, Mr Bernard 82 Marlborough Park N., Belfast BT9 6HL Tel: 01232 668527 — MB BCh BAO 1976 Belf.; MB BCh Belf. 1976; FRCS Ed. 1983.

LEE, Bernard Vincent (retired) 13 Portland Road, Bowdon, Altrincham WA14 2PA Tel: 0161 928 7605 Fax: 0161 928 6338 Email: bernardlee2@compuserve.com — MB ChB 1953 Manch.; BA Open 1983; AFOM RCP Lond. 1985; DLO Eng. 1958. Prev: Med. Off. Blood Transfus. Serv. Manch.

LEE, Beverley Jayne 89 Diglis Lane, Worcester WR5 3DQ — MB BS 1996 Lond.

LEE, Boon Chee 23 Newlandrig, Gorebridge EH23 4NS — MB ChB 1987 Glas.; MRCP (UK) 1990. Career Regist. (Gen. Med. & Gastroenterol.) Roy. Infirm. Edin. Prev: SHO (Gen. Med. & Gastroenterol.) Stobhill Gen. Hosp. Glas.; SHO (Gen. Med.) S.. Gen. Hosp. Glas.; SHO (Gen. Med.) Manor Hosp. Walsall.

LEE, Brian Chihung 16 Mossvale Park, Coleraine BT52 2QL — MB BCh BAO 1991 Belf.; MRCP (UK) 1995.

LEE, Bronia Elizabeth 1 Birch Close, Cannington, Bridgwater TA5 2HX — MB BCh 1982 Witwatersrand; MRCGP 1988.

LEE, Carline Anne Eastgate House, Hockering Road, Woking GU22 7HP — MB BChir 1994 Camb.; BA 1991; FRCS Gen.1997; FRCS Oto 1999. (Cambs)

LEE, Carol Bermondsey and Lansdowne Medical Centre, The Surgery, Decima Street, London SE1 4QX Tel: 020 7407 0752 Fax: 020 7378 8209 — MB BS 1983 Lond.; MRCGP 1987; DRCOG 1986. GP Bermondsey & Lansdowne Med. Mission Lond.

LEE, Carole Elizabeth Kinghorn and Partners, Woodhouse Health Centre, Woodhouse Street, Leeds LS6 2SF Tel: 0113 295 3500 Fax: 0113 295 3503 — MB BS 1984 Lond.; DFFP 1996; DRCOG 1988. (St. Bart.) GP. Prev: Princip. GP W.on-Super-Mare; SHO (O & G) Cheltenham; SHO (Med.) Frenchay Hosp. Bristol.

LEE, Caroline Elizabeth 29 Downshire Pa, Hillsborough BT26 6HB — MB BCh 1998 Belf.; MB BCh Belf 1998.

LEE, Cathryn Sara Appletree Cottage, Wheathampstead Road, Wheathampstead, St Albans AL4 8EE — MB ChB 1996 Birm.; ChB Birm. 1996. (Birmingham) SHO (A & E) Edin. Roy. Infirm. Prev: SHO (A & E) MusGr. Pk., Taunton; SHO (Surg.) Selly Oak Hosp.; SHO (Med.) Qu. Eliz. Birm.

LEE, Charles Andrew 26 Crescent Road, Lundin Links, Leven KY8 6AE — MB BS 1991 Lond.

LEE, Cheng Lian 36 Dacre Row, Hyde Park Flats, St John's Road, Sheffield S2 5LF — MB ChB 1981 Sheff.

LEE, Cheong Hung 21 Priory Hill, Wembley HA0 2QF — MB BS 1998 Lond.; MB BS Lond 1998.

LEE, Chi Yeung Radiology Dept, City Hosp NHS Trust, Dudley Road, Birmingham B18 7QH Tel: 0121 507 4725/8 Fax: 0121 523 5041; 7 Lismore Drive, harborne, Birmingham B17 0TP — BChir 1991 Camb.; MRCP (UK) 1993; FRCR (UK) 1997. (Cambridge University) Cons Radio (Diagnostic Radiol.). Socs: BMA; BSSR. Prev: Specialist Regist. (Diag. Radiol.) W. Midl. Hosps.; SHO (Gen. Med.) Pilgrim Hosp. Boston Lincs.; Ho. Off. P'boro. Dist. Hosp.

LEE, Chooi Nien Kingston Hospital, Ockley Station Approach, Galsworthy Road, Kingston upon Thames KT2 7QB Tel: 0208 546 7711 — MB ChB 1991 Leic.; MRCP (UK) 1995. (Univ. Leics.) Cons. Phys. Gen. and Geriat. Med. Socs: Brit. Geriat.s Soc.; Roy. Coll. Phys.s Lond. Prev: Sen.Reg.Gen.Geriat.Med.Kingston Hosp.; Clin. Lect. & Hon. Sen. Regist. (Geriat.) St. Geo. Hosp. Med. Sch. Lond.

LEE, Choy Hoa 64A Occupation Lane, Hackenthorpe, Sheffield S12 4PP — MB ChB 1986 Sheff.

LEE, Professor Christine Ann Haemophilia Centre & Haemostasis Unit, Royal Free Hampstead, NHS Trust, Pond St., Hampstead, London NW3 2QG Tel: 020 7830 2238 Fax: 020 7830 2178 Email: christine.lee@rfh.nthames.nhs.uk — BM BCh Oxf. 1969; BA (1st cl. Hons.) Animal Physiol. Lond. 1966, MD 1989; MA Oxf. 1969; FRCP Lond. 1990; MRCP (UK) 1972; FRCPath 1994, M 1982; DSc (Med.) 1996. Dir. & Cons. Haemat. Haemophilia Centre & Haemostasis Unit Roy Free Hosp. Lond.; Prof. of Haemophilia; Co-Edr. Haemophilia. Socs: Brit. Socs. Haematol. & World Federat. Haemophilia.; Internat. Soc. Thrombosis & Haemostasis; Brit. Assn. Study Liver. Prev: Sen. Lect. (Haemat.) Char. Cross & W.m. Med. Sch.; Lect. Haemophilia & Haemostasis Unit Roy. Free Hosp. Lond.; Sen. Regist. (Haemat.) St. Geo. Hosp. Lond.

LEE, Christopher 17 Douglas Road, Halesowen B62 9HS — MB ChB 1995 Birm. SHO (Thoracic Surg., Vasc. & Gen. Surg.) Birm. Heartlands Hosp. Socs: BMA; MPS.

LEE, Christopher Joseph Park Parade Surgery, 69 Park Parade, Whitley Bay NE26 1DU Tel: 0191 252 3135 Fax: 0191 253 3566 — MB BS 1989 Newc.; MRCGP 1994; DRCOG 1993.

LEE, Christopher Peter, AE MPN Clinic, St. Catherine's House, 2 Kingsway, London WC2B 6WJ Email: chrislee@ukspecialists.com; Nailsea Court, Chelvey Road, Nailsea BS48 4DQ Tel: 01275 464898 — MB ChB 1973 Bristol; DCCH RCP Ed. RCGP & FCM 1983; DPH Lond. 1980; DRCOG 1977; Cert. Av. Med. 1990; BSc 1966; MSc (Tropical Community Health) Lond. 1980; DRCOG 1977; MFFP 1993, MCPS Sask. 1976; DPH (Lond.) 1980; DLSHTM Lond. 1997; DTM & H (Liverp.) 1977; D.Occ.Med. RCP Lond. 1995. (Univ. Bristol) Sen. Med. Adviser and Cons. Occupat.al Phys. Mobil Producing (Nigeria) Lagos, Nigeria; Squadron Ldr. Roy. Auxil. Air Force Aeromed. Evacuation Squadron, RAF Lyneham, Wilts.; Sen. Med. Adviser, Internat. SOS Ltd, Landmark Ho., Hammersmith Bridge Rd., Lond., W6 9DP. Socs: Fell. Roy. Soc. Trop. Med. & Hyg.; Soc. Occupat. Med.; Internat. Assn. Phys. Overseas Servs. Prev: Princip. Med. Adviser Foreign & Commonw. Off. Lond.; Cons. Occupat. Phys. St. Thos. Hosp. Lond.; DMO Turks & Caicos Is.s and Montserrat.

LEE, Mr Christopher Thomas 1 Earl Close, Princes Gate, Friern Barnet, London N11 3PY — MB ChB 1990 Dundee; FRCS Ed. 1995.

LEE, Chuk Wai c/o 5 East Clyde Street, Helensburgh G84 7NY — MB ChB 1995 Manch.

LEE, Conrad Chi-Yan 19 Harben Road, London NW6 4RH — BChir 1994 Camb.

LEE, Constance Gertrude Little Haven, 52 St Helen's Park Road, Hastings TN34 2DN Tel: 01424 422710 — MB ChB 1944 Liverp.; MRCS Eng. LRCP Lond. 1945; DObst RCOG 1946. Sessional Med. Off. E. Sussex AHA. Prev: Regist. Glenroyd Matern. Hosp. Blackpool; Asst. Med. Off. Matern. & Child Welf. Manch.; GP Hastings.

LEE, Daniel Giles 7 Moortown Farm, Wimborne BH21 3AR — BM 1991 Soton.

LEE, Daniel Ramsay Department of Health for Elderly People, Royal Free Hospital, Pont Street, Hampstead, London NW3 2QR Email: danlee1@crth.nthames.nhs.uk — MB BCh 1986 Wales; MD Wales 1997; MRCP (UK) 1991. (Cardiff) Cons. Phys. Health Serv. for Elderly People Roy. Free Hosp. Lond. Prev: Sen. Regist. (Elderly Med.) Whipps Cross Hosp. Lond.; Research Fell. (Health c/o Elderly) King's Coll. Hosp. Lond.

LEE, Mr David Royal Infirmary, Lauriston Place, Edinburgh EH3 9HB Tel: 0131 536 1000; The Stone House, 1 Pentland Road, Colinton, Edinburgh EH13 0JA Tel: 0131 441 4975 — MB ChB 1971 Ed.; BSc Ed. 1968, MB ChB 1971; FRCS Ed. 1976. Cons. Gen. & Endocrine Surg. Roy. Infirm. Edin. Socs: Brit. Assn. Endocrin. Surgs.; Brit. Assn. Surgs.

LEE, David Anthony (retired) 185 Burges Road, Thorpe Bay, Southend-on-Sea SS1 3JP Tel: 01702 292894 — MB BS 1960 Lond.; MRCS Eng. LRCP Lond. 1960; AFOM RCP Lond. 1980; DObst RCOG 1963. Clin. Asst. Dermat. Dept., S.end-on-Sea Gen. Hosp. Prev: SHO (Gyn. & Obst.) S.end Gen. Hosp. & Ilford Matern. & King Geo. Hosp. Ilford.

LEE, David Egbert 16 Moorland Avenue, Barnsley S70 6PQ Tel: 01226 284254 — MB ChB 1960 Sheff.; FFA RCS Eng. 1965; DA Eng. 1964. (Sheff.) Cons. Anaesth. & Dir. Intens. Ther. Unit Barnsley Dist. Gen. Socs: Intens. Care Soc.

LEE, David James 119 Harrow Road, Leicester LE3 0JZ — MB ChB 1997 Leic.

LEE, David John Hollingsworth Queen Mary's Hospital, Frognal Avenue, Sidcup DA14 6LT Tel: 020 8302 2678 — BM 1987 Soton.; FRCA 1994. (Soton.) Cons. (Anaesth.) Qu. Mary's Hosp. Kent. Socs: Assn. Anaesth.; OAA. Prev: SHO (Anaesth.) William Harvey Hosp. WillesBoro.; Ho. Surg. RHCH Winchester; Ho. Phys. Stoke Mandeville Hosp. Bucks.

LEE, David Trevor 6 Bannview Park, Ballymoney BT53 7LL — MB BCh 1998 Belf.; MB BCh Belf 1998.

LEE, Deborah Mary Department of Cytology, Level 4 Clarence wing, St Mary's Hospital, Praed St, London W2 1NY Tel: 02078861293 Fax: 0207 886775; 65 Cavendish House, Wellington Road, St John's Wood, London NW8 — MB BCh 1976 Wales; MRCPath 1988. Cons. Path St Mary's hosp, Lond. Socs: Internat. Acad. Path.; Brit. Soc. Clin. cytol.; Assn. Clin. Path. Prev: Sen. Regist. (Histopath.) S. Gen. Hosp.; Cons Path, Derriford Hosp Plym.

LEE, Derek (retired) Winstanley Medical Centre, Holmes House Avenue, Winstanley, Wigan WN3 6JN Tel: 01942 221100 Fax: 01942 214372 — MB ChB 1974 Sheff.; BSc (Hons.) Salford 1969. Prev: Clin. Asst. (Dermat.) Roy. Albert Edwd. Infirm. Wigan.

LEE, Douglas (retired) 9 Rushley Drive, Hest Bank, Lancaster LA2 6EF Tel: 01524 823289 — MB BCh BAO 1962 Belf.; MD Belf. 1966; FRCPI 1976, M 1969; FRCPath 1980, M 1968. Prev: Dir. Manch. & Lancaster Blood Centres.

LEE, Douglas Eu Tiong Apartment 6B, Windsor Close, Belfast BT9 6FG — MB BCh 1998 Belf.; MB BCh Belf 1998.

LEE, Edmund Soo Guan 149 King George V Drive, Heath, Cardiff CF14 4EN — MB BCh 1989 Wales.

LEE, Edward Fong-Yin Featherstone Family Health Centre, Old Lane, Hilton Lane, Featherstone, Wolverhampton WV10 7BS Tel: 01902 305899 Fax: 01902 735577; 36 Prestwood Road W., Wednesfield, Wolverhampton WV11 1HN Tel: 01902 305899 — MB BS 1979 Sydney; DRCOG 1983; FFP. (Univ. Sydney) Socs: BMA; MIA.

LEE, Edwin Sze-Hung 9 Cannock Grove, Maghull, Liverpool L31 8EL — MB ChB 1987 Ed.

LEE, Elizabeth Charlotte Horfield Health Centre, Lockleaze Road, Horfield, Bristol BS7 9RR Tel: 0117 969 5391; 26 Goldney Road, Clifton, Bristol BS8 4RB Tel: 0117 929 3741 — MB BS 1981 Lond.; MRCGP 1986; DCH RCP Lond. 1985; DRCOG 1983. Prev: Forens. Med. Examr. Avon & Som. Constab.; GP Hackney, Lond.

LEE, Eluned 4 Bryn Gofal, Llangristiolus, Bodorgan LL62 5PR — MB ChB 1966 Liverp.; MFFP 1993. Med. Co-ordinator (Wom. Health & Contracep. Servs.) Gwynedd. Prev: Clin. Med. Off. Gwynedd HA; GP Gwynedd.

LEE, Elzbieta Rhapsody, 15 Downside Road, Guildford GU4 8PH — Lekarz 1972 Bialystok, Poland. Clin. Asssit. (Geriat.) Frimley Pk. Hosp. Camberley. Prev: Regist. (Geriat.) Frimley Pk. Hosp.

LEE, Eng Sing 8 Broad-Dykes View, Kingswells, Aberdeen AB15 8UG — MB ChB 1997 Aberd.

LEE, Ennis Hilary Medicines Control Agency, Market Towers, 1 Nine Elms Lane, London SW8 5NQ Tel: 020 7273 0193 Fax: 020 7273 0675; 56 Stanford Avenue, Brighton BN1 6FD Tel: 01273 552690 — MB BS Lond. 1980; BSc (Human Genetics) Lond. 1976; MRCS Eng. LRCP Lond. 1979; FFPM RCP (UK) 1996, M 1989; Dip. Pharm. Med. RCP (UK) 1986; DRCOG 1984. (Westm.) Manager(Pharmacovigiliance) Assessm. Gp. Socs: Fell. Roy. Soc. Med.; Worshipful Soc. Apoth. Lond.; BMA. Prev: Med. Dir. Schering Health Care Ltd. Burgess Hill; Dep. Med. Dir. Roche Products Ltd. Welwyn Gdn. City; Sen. Med. Adviser SmithKline & French Laborats. Ltd. Welwyn Gdn.

LEE, Erica Jane Compass House Medical Centre, King Street, Brixham TQ5 9TF — MB BChir 1991 Camb.; DRCOG 1994.

LEE, Evelyn Min Victoria General Hospital, Blackpool; The Chalet, 13 Fendon Road, Cambridge CB1 7RU — MB BChir 1990 Camb.; MA Camb. 1990, BA (Path.) 1986; MRCP (UK) 1992. (Camb. Univ.) Regist. (Cardiol.) Vict. Gen. Hosp. Blackpool. Socs: BMA; Brit. Soc. Echocardiogr. Prev: Regist. (Gen. Med. & Cardiol.) Tameside Hosp. Manch.; Hon. Regist. (Cardiol.) Papworth Hosp. Camb.; Regist. (Gen. Med.) W. Suff. Bury St. Edmunds.

LEE, Francis Hoi-To South London & Maudsley Hospital NHS Trust, Maudsley Hospital, Denmark Hill, London SE5 8AZ; 75 Linwood Close, Camberwell, London SE5 8UX — MB ChB 1997 Birm. (Univ. of Birmingham) SHO (Comm. Psychiat.), Maudsley Hosp. Lond.

LEE, Frank Ian (retired) 25 Ansdell Road N., Lytham St Annes FY8 4EZ Tel: 01253 735058 — MB BS Lond. 1957; FRCP Lond. 1975, M 1959; MRCS Eng. LRCP Lond. 1957. Prev: Cons. Phys. Blackpool & Fylde Hosp. Gp.

LEE, Mr Frank Yu Kei Barnet General Hospital, Barnet EN4 3DJ Tel: 020 8216 4795 Fax: 020 8216 4501 Email: 0958981922@one2one.co.uk; 14 Beaumont Court, Sutton Lane, London W4 4LE Tel: 07050 072810 — MB BChir 1992 Camb.; MA Camb. 1993, BA 1989; MB Camb. 1992, B Chir 1991; FRCS (Eng.) 1997. (Cambridge) Specialist Regist. (Urol.) N. Thames Region.

LEE, Professor Frederick David Pathology Department, Glasgow Royal Infirmary, Glasgow Tel: 0141 552 3535; 33 Lovat Avenue, Bearsden, Glasgow G61 3LQ Tel: 0141 942 2468 — MD 1970 Dundee; MB ChB St. And. 1958; FRCP Glas. 1986, M 1984; FRCPath 1976, M 1964. Hon. Prof. Glas. Univ. Socs: Pres. Assn. Clin. Path.; Path. Soc. Prev: Cons. Path. Glas. Roy. Infirm.; Cons. (Haemat.) W.. Infirm. Glas.

LEE, Frederick Kwok Tung 33 Penrhyn Road, Sheffield S11 8UL — MB ChB 1994 Sheff.

LEE, Geoffrey Barry c/o CMEC, St Richards Hospital, Chichester PO19 4SE Tel: 01243 788 1222; 5 Brookside Close, Runcton, Chichester PO20 6PY Tel: 01243 775492 — PhD Lond. 1984; MB BCh Witwatersrand 1970; FRCP (UK) 1985; T(M) 1991. (Witwatersrand) Cons. Phys. & Gastroenterol. St Richard's Hosp. Socs: Brit. Soc. Gastroenterol.; BMA. Prev: Gastroenterol. Univ. Witwatersrand Med. Sch. Johannesburg, S. Afr.; Wellcome Trop. Lect. Wellcome Research Unit, CMC Hosp. Vellore S. India; Wellcome Lect. Clin. Research Centre Harrow.

LEE, Gerald Anthony (retired) 1097 Oxford Road, Tilehurst, Reading RG31 6YE Tel: 0118 942 7942 Email: gl12uk@yahoo.co.uk — LMSSA 1959 Lond. Prev: Ho. Off. Roy. Hants. Co. Hosp. Winchester.

LEE, Gillian c/o Wessex Regional Renal Unit, St. Mary's Hospital, Milton Road, Portsmouth PO3 6AD; 5 Holyrood Close, Waterlooville PO7 8JQ — MB BS 1980 Lond.

LEE, Grant de Jersey 5 The Chestnuts, Kirtlington, Kidlington OX5 3UB Tel: 01869 350150 Fax: 01869 350150 Email: grant.lee@ndu.on.ac.uk; Tel: 01869 350150 Fax: 01869 350150 Email: grant.lee@ndu.on.ac.uk — MB BS 1944 Lond.; MA Oxf. 1956; MD Lond. 1949; FRCP Lond. 1961, M 1948; MRCS Eng. LRCP Lond. 1944. (St. Thos.) Sen Lect. (Emerit.) Clin. Med. Nuffield Dept. Clin. Med. Oxf.; Hon. Cons. Phys. Oxf. Radcliffe Hosp. NHS Trust & Nuffield Dept. Clin. Med. Oxf. Univ. Socs: (Ex-Sec. & Treas.) Assn. Phys. GB & Ire; Brit. & Europ. Socs. Cardiol. Fell; Med. Research Soc. Prev: Cons. Phys. John Radcliffe Hosp. Oxf.; Vis. Cons. Phys. Waikato Hosp. NZ & Roy. Hobart Hosp. Tasmania; Vis.Cons.Phys.Kimberley Hosp.N Cape Prov.SA.

LEE, Guan Seow Wrexham Maelor Hospital, Croesnewydd Road, Wrexham LL13 7TD Tel: 01978 291100; 40 Goulbourne Avenue, Wrexham LL13 9HQ Tel: 01978 356352 — MD 1959 Wuhan; FRCP Lond. 1985; MRCP (UK) 1973; LRCP LRCS Ed. LRCPS Glas. 1969; T(M) 1991. (Wuhan Med. Coll. & St. Mary's) Cons. Phys. Geriat. Med. Clwyd AHA. Prev: Sen. Regist. (Geriat. Med.) S. Glam. AHA (T).

LEE, Hai Shiang 40 Goulbourne Avenue, Wrexham LL13 9HQ; 10 Chesham Road, Wilmslow SK9 6HA Tel: 0161 998 7070 — MB

BCh 1986 Wales; MRCP (UK) 1989; MD 1994. Sen. Regist. (Cardiol.) Wythenshawe Hosp. Manch. Prev: Research Fell. (Cardiol.) Aberd. Roy. Infirm.

LEE, Helen Mary Lister Hospital, Coreys Mill Lane, Stevenage SG1 Tel: 01438 781028 — MB BS 1982 Lond.; MSc Lond. 1991; BSc (Hons.) Birm. 1977; FRCR (UK) 1988; MRCP (UK) 1985. Cons. Radiol. Lister Hosp. Stevenage. Prev: Cons. Radiol. N. Middlx. Hosp.; Sen. Regist. (Radiol.) Hammersmith Postgrad. Centre & Watford Gen. Hosp.; Regist. Centr. Middlx. Hosp.

LEE, Hilary Alison 5 Meteor Close, Woodley, Reading RG5 4NG — MB BS 1990 West Indies.

LEE, Hiong Ying Basildon Hospital, Basildon SS16 5NL Tel: 01268 533911 — MB BS 1967 Lond.; MB BS (Hons.) Lond. 1967; FRCP Lond. 1989; MRCP (UK) 1970; MRCS Eng. LRCP Lond. 1967. (St. Thos.) Cons. Phys. Basildon Hosp. & Orsett Hosp. Gray's. Socs: Brit. Thorac. Soc. Prev: Research Fell. (Thoracic Med.) Manch. Roy. Infirm.; Lect. (Med.) Univ. Singapore & Univ. Manch.

LEE, Howard Dennis (retired) Whitstable Health Centre, Harbour Street, Whitstable CT5 1BZ Tel: 01277 263033 Fax: 01277 771474 — MB ChB 1963 Birm. Prev: Ho. Surg. (O & G) Hallam Hosp. W. Bromwich.

LEE, Hung Kee Pantalen Stockwell Group Practice, 107 Stockwell Road, London SW9 9TJ Tel: 020 7274 3225 Fax: 020 7738 3005; 12 Alleyn Park, Dulwich, London SE21 8AE — MB BS 1978 Lond.; MA Camb. 1975; MRCGP 1988; DRCOG 1979; DCH RCP Lond. 1979. (Univ. Coll. Hosp.)

LEE, Ian Christopher Whickham Health Centre, Rectory Lane, Whickham, Newcastle upon Tyne NE16 4PD Tel: 0191 488 5555 Fax: 0191 496 0424; 7 Springfield Avenue, Eighton Banks, Gateshead NE9 7HL Tel: 0191 487 3648 Fax: 0191 487 3648 Email: ian@cather.demon.co.uk — MB BS 1981 Newc.; MRCGP 1985; DFFP 1993; DRCOG 1984. Socs: BMA. Prev: Trainee GP N.d. VTS.

LEE, Jackie Wai Kwun 8 Hazelwood Road, Hazel Grove, Stockport SK7 4LZ — MB BS 1996 Newc.

LEE, James Alexander William Arnacraig, Armadale, Thurso KW14 7SA Tel: 01641 541212 Fax: 01641 541226 — MB BCh 1978 N U Ireland; L LM RCP Irel L LM RCS Irel 1978. (N U Ireland) GP Thurso, Caithness.

LEE, James Douglas 15 Cannon Grove, Fetcham, Leatherhead KT22 9LG — MB BS 1997 Lond.

LEE, James Francis South Lewisham Health Centre, 50 Conisborough Crescent, London SE6 2SS Tel: 020 8698 8921; 7 Hill Brow, Bickley, Bromley BR1 2PG — MB BCh BAO 1977 NUI; MICGP 1984; MRCGP 1981; DCH Dub. 1982; DRCOG 1979.

LEE, James Hamilton 58 Prospect View, Hartshead, Liversedge WF15 8BD — MB ChB 1976 Dundee; MRCGP 1980.

LEE, James Toong-Soon 14 Comber Road, Dundonald, Belfast BT16 2AB — LMSSA 1965 Lond.

LEE, Janet Elizabeth Wilsden Medical Practice, Health Centre, Townfield, Wilsden, Bradford BD15 0HT Tel: 01535 273227 Fax: 01535 274860; Cragmere, 29 Larkfield Road, Rawdon, Leeds LS19 6EQ — MB ChB 1978 Manch.; MRCGP 1983; DRCOG 1980; Cert. JCC Lond. 1980. Princip. GP Bradford.

LEE, Janet Mary 57 Woodland Road, Northfield, Birmingham B31 2HZ Tel: 0121 475 1065; 134 Oakfield Road, Selly Park, Birmingham B29 7ED Tel: 0121 472 0715 Fax: 0121 472 0715 — MB ChB 1979 Birm.; MRCGP 1984; T(GP) 1993; DRCOG 1981; DCH Eng. 1981. GP Birm. Retainer Scheme; Clin. Asst. (Dermat.) Birm.

LEE, Jason Barry 42 Top Baro Lane, Rossendale BB4 7UF — MB BS 1994 Lond.

LEE, Jennifer Stranraer Health Centre, Edinburgh Road, Stranraer DG9 7HG Tel: 01776 706513; GFL, 4Forth cresent, Riverside, Sterling FK8 ILE Tel: 01776 706375 Email: jbalmer@tinyworld.co.uk — MB BCh BAO 1983 Belf.; DRCOG 1986. Prev: SHO (Gen. Med.) Belf. City Hosp.; SHO (Psychiat.) Purdysburn Hosp. Belf.; SHO (O & G) Jubilee Matern. Hosp. Belf.

LEE, Jeremy Vernon St Michaels Hospice, 25 Upper Maze Hill, St Leonards-on-Sea TN38 0LG Tel: 01424 445177 Fax: 01424 721255; 23 St. Matthews Gardens, St Leonards-on-Sea TN38 0TT — MB BS Lond. 1960. (Middlx.) Med. Dir. St. Michael's Hospice St. Leonards-on-Sea; Hon. Cons. Palliat. Care Conquest Hosp. St. Leonards-on-Sea.

LEE, Jing Jing 7 Wessex Walk, Shoreham-by-Sea BN43 5FZ — MB BS 1983 Lond.

LEE, Joanne Melissa Highcliffe Medical Centre, 248 Lymington Road, Highcliffe, Christchurch BH23 5ET Tel: 01425 272203 Fax: 01425 271086; Roundhay, Chapel Lane, Bransgrove, Christchurch BH23 8BN Tel: 01425 673395 — MB ChB 1984 Bristol; DRCOG 1990.

LEE, Joanne Nicola 17 Tentergate Road, Knaresborough HG5 9BG — MB BS 1997 Newc.

LEE, Jocelyn Cheuk Lam 18 Balgray Road, Newton Mearns, Glasgow G77 6PB Tel: 0141 639 5301 Fax: 0141 639 5301 Email: jcllee@compuserve.com — MB ChB 1992 Dundee. SHO (Anaesth.) S.. Gen. Hosp. Glas.

LEE, Joel (retired) 76 Fernleigh Road, Glasgow G43 2TZ Tel: 0141 637 3021 — MB ChB 1957 Glas. Prev: Ho. Surg. (ENT & Ophth.) Vict. Infirm. Glas.

LEE, John Latchington, 103 Friars Avenue, Shenfield, Brentwood CM15 8HU Tel: 01277 211811 Fax: 01277 211711; 89 Gubbins Lane, Harold Wood, Romford RM3 0DR Tel: 01708 346666 Fax: 01708 381300 — MB BCh 1985 Wales; MRCGP 1990; DRCOG 1989; DA (UK) 1987. (Cardiff) GP Princip. & Trainer. Socs: BMA. Prev: Trainee GP Shrewsbury VTS.

LEE, John Andre Department of Pathology, Rotherham District General Hospital, Moorgate Road, Oakwood, Rotherham S60 2UD — MB BS 1985 Lond.; PhD Lond. 1990, BSc (Hons.) 1982; MRCPath 1994. (University College London) Cons. Path. Rotherham Dist. Gen. Hosp. Prev: Sen. Lect. (Path.) Univ. Dept. Path. Sheff.

LEE, John Anthony Vanbrugh Hill Health Centre, Vanbrugh Hill, Greenwich, London SE10 9HQ Tel: 020 8312 6090 — MB ChB 1956 Manch.; MSc Surrey 1976; FRCGP 1981, M 1976. (Manch.) Med. Off. Morden Coll. Blackheath. Socs: BMA & W. Kent Med. Soc. Prev: Med. Off. 3rd Bn. Coldstread Guards; Ho. Surg. Manch. Roy. Infirm.; Ho. Phys. Hope Hosp. Salford.

LEE, John Arthur (retired) 1 Luggview Close, Overbury Road, Aylestone Hill, Hereford HR1 1JF Tel: 01432 275565 Fax: 01432 275565 — MB BCh 1960 Witwatersrand; MD Witwatersrand 1973; MFPHM 1974; DPH Lond. 1966. Prev: Cons. Pub. Health Med. Kingston & Esher HA & Hereford HA.

LEE, John Douglas Tieve-Tara, Airedale Drive, Castleford WF10 2QT Tel: 01977 552360; 6 Carleton Road, Pontefract WF8 3ND Tel: 01977 791411 — MB ChB 1980 Leeds; DRCOG 1984. Clin. Asst. (Genitourin. Med.) Clayton Hosp. Wakefield. Prev: Trainee GP Grimsby VTS; Ho. Phys. Leeds Gen. Infirm.; Ho. Surg. St. Luke's Hosp. Bradford.

LEE, Mr John Ormrod Noble's Hospital, Douglas IM1 4QA Tel: 01624 642642; Crofton, The Crofts, Castletown IM9 1LW Tel: 01624 825523 Fax: 01624 825523 — MB ChB 1960 Manch; FRCS Eng. 1966; FRCS Ed. 1965; DObst RCOG 1962; DCH Eng. 1962. (Manch.) Cons. Gen. Surg. Urol Noble's I. of Man Hosp. Douglas. Socs: Country Mem. Liverp. Med. Inst.; Assoc of surg of Gt Brit & Ire fell.; Isle of Man Med Soc mem. Prev: Resid. Surg. Off. Salford Roy. Hosp.; Sen. Regist. (Surg.) Mulago Hosp. Kampala, Uganda; Hon. Lect. (Surg.) Makerere Univ. Kampala, Uganda.

LEE, Mr John Patrick 73 Harley Street, London W1N IDE Tel: 020 7935 5801 Fax: 020 7486 3589; 165 Camberwell Grove, London SE5 8JS Fax: 020 7737 6993 Email: smgxlee@ucl.ac.uk — BM BCh 1971 Oxf.; MA Oxf. 1971, BM BCh 1971; FRCP Lond. 1993; FRCS Eng. 1978; FRCOphth 1988; DO RCS Eng. 1975. Cons. Ophth. Surg. Moorfields Eye Hosp. Prev: Lect. (Clin. Ophth.) Inst. Ophth. Lond.; Fell. Pediat. & Neuro-Ophth. Bascom Palmer Eye Inst. Miami, USA 1983.

LEE, Mr John Richard Beaconwood, Beacon Lane, Rednal, Birmingham B45 9XN; Beaconwood, Beacon Lane, Rednal, Birmingham B45 9XN — MB ChB 1965 Birm.; FRCS Eng. 1972; FRCR 1975; FFR 1974; DMRD Eng. 1973. Cons. Radiol. Gen. Hosp. Birm.

LEE, Johnson Hock Tuck 70 Torbay Road, Rayners Lane, Harrow HA2 9QH — MRCS Eng. LRCP Lond. 1979; BSc Lond. 1976, MB BS 1979; DRCOG 1983.

LEE, Josephine Alexandra 50 Peterborough Road, Inner Avenue, Southampton SO14 6HX — BM 1998 Soton.; BM Soton 1998.

LEE, Julia Millfield Medical Centre, 63-83 Hylton Road, Sunderland SR4 7AF Tel: 0191 567 9179 Fax: 0191 514 7452; South Barn, Tunstall Lodge Farm, Tunstall, Sunderland SR3 2BQ — MB BS 1983

Newc.; MRCGP 1988; DRCOG 1987; DA (UK) 1986. Socs: BMA; Family Plann. Assn.

LEE, Juliette Ellen Stanbrook Farm, Staunton, Gloucester GL19 3QR Tel: 01452 840264 — MB BS 1991 Lond. SHO (Anaesth.) Roy. United Hosp. Bath. Prev: SHO (Gen. Med.) Salisbury Dist. Hosp.

LEE, Kah Wai 11 Poolfield Avenue, Newcastle ST5 2NL — MB ChB 1993 Leic.

LEE, Kelvin Sze Yen 24 Lyndhurst Avenue, Newcastle upon Tyne NE2 3LJ — MB BS 1998 Newc.; MB BS Newc 1998.

LEE, Kenneth (retired) 40 High View Park, Cromer NR27 0HQ Tel: 01263 511725 — MB BS Lond. 1949; MRCS Eng. LRCP Lond. 1949; FFOM RCP Lond. 1981, M 1978; DIH Eng. 1965. Prev: Sen. Med. Off. Brit. Steel.

LEE, Kenneth George 26 Westwood Avenue, Timperley, Altrincham WA15 6QF — MB BS 1980 Lond.; MRCS Eng. LRCP Lond. 1980; FFA RCS Eng. 1986; DA Eng. 1982. Cons. Anaesth. Wythenshawe Hosp. Manch. Prev: Regist. W.m. & Brompton Hosp. Lond.; Regist. Nat. Heart Hosp.; Sen. Regist. Manch.

LEE, Kenneth Milroy Blackwoods Medical Centre, 8 Station Road, Muirhead, Glasgow G69 9EE Tel: 0141 779 2228 Fax: 0141 779 3225; 25 Charles Crescent, Lenzie, Glasgow G66 5HH — MB ChB 1987 Glas.; MRCGP 1991; DRCOG 1991. (Glas.)

LEE, Kevin Michael Stewart The Scott Practice, 1 Greenfield Lane, Balby, Doncaster DN4 0TG Tel: 01302 850546 Fax: 01302 855338 — MB BCh 1988 Wales; BSc Hons. Wales 1983; MRCGP 1993; MFFP 1993. (University of Wales) Prev: Trainee GP Doncaster VTS; SHO Rotat. (CardioPulm.) Cardiff; Ho. Off. (Phys. & Surg.) Univ. Hosp. Wales.

LEE, Kim Shang Room C44, Friendship House, 1 St Nicholas Glebe, Rectory Lane, London SW17 9QH — MB BS 1985 Singapore.

LEE, Kim Wah The Elms Medical Practice, Tilley Close, Main Road, Hoo, Rochester ME3 9AE Tel: 01634 250142 Fax: 01634 255029 — MB BS 1977 Singapore. (University of Singapore) Princip. In Gen. Pract.

LEE, Kirsteen 8 Southview Drive, Blanefield, Glasgow G63 9JF Tel: 01360 770600 — MB ChB 1998 Glas.; MB ChB Glas 1998. SHO A&E.Brisbane. Au.

LEE, Kwang Yoong Flat 23, Royal Tower Lodge, 40 Cartwright St., London E1 8LX — MB BS 1997 Sydney.

LEE, Lesley Jennifer Bourne Bank, Hedsor Road, Bourne End SL8 5EE — MB BS Lond. 1974.

LEE, Lian King Department of Haematology, Victoria Hospital, Whinney Heys Road, Blackpool FY3 8NR — MB ChB 1990 Aberd.; MRCP 1995.

LEE, Ling Keim 97 Summerfield Road, Solihull B92 8PZ — MB ChB 1986 Leic.; FRCS Ed. 1992.

LEE, Lleona Chui Ling 9 Victoria Terrace, Harrow HA1 3EW — BChir 1996 Camb.

LEE, Marc Bruno Department of Human Anatomy, University of Oxford, South Parks Road, Oxford OX1 3QX — MB ChB 1992 Leic.; BSc Genetics Leic. 1989, MB ChB 1992. MRC Clin. Train. Research Fell. Univ. of Oxf.; Lect. (Anat.) Trinity & Christ Ch. Colls. Oxf. Prev: Deptm. Lect. Dept. of Human Anat. Univ. Oxf.

LEE, Mr Marcus Hoe Ming 10 Tankerfield Place, Romeland Hill, St Albans AL3 4HH Email: marcuslee68@hotmail.com — MB BS 1993 Lond.; FRCS Dub. 1998. (Char. Cross & Westm.) Specialist Regist. (Orthop.) NE Thames. Socs: Fell. Roy. Soc. Med. Prev: Specialist Regist. (Orthop.) Epsom Gen. Hosp.; SHO (Orthop.) Kingston Hosp.; SHO (Orthop.) Roy. United Hosp. Bath.

LEE, Mark Andrew The Bield, Wester Aldie Farm, Rumbling Bridge, Kinross KY13 0QQ — MB ChB 1992 Ed.

LEE, Mark Andrew 19 St Leonards Road, Deal CT14 9AS — MB ChB 1994 Sheff.

LEE, Mark Colin Woosehill Practice, The Surgery, Emmview Close, Woosehill, Wokingham RG41 3DA Tel: 0118 978 8266 Fax: 0118 979 3661 — MB ChB 1982 Sheff.; DRCOG 1996; 1995 Docc Med. Sen. Partner Woosehill Surg. Wokingham.

LEE, Martin Anthony 12 Downside Road, Headington, Oxford OX3 8HP — BM BCh 1993 Oxf.; MA Oxf. 1994, BM BCh 1993. SHO Rotat. (Med.) Addenbrooke's Camb.

LEE, Martin John Victoria Cross Surgery, 168/9 Victoria Road, Swindon SN1 3BU Tel: 01793 535584 — MB ChB 1970 Birm.; MRCGP 1977; DObst RCOG 1975.

LEE, Mr Martin John Rathbone City Hospital, Dudley Road, Birmingham B18 7Q Tel: 01215074593 Fax: 0121 507 5755 — MB ChB 1974 Birm.; MA, MSc Oxf. 1974; FRCS Eng. 1978. Cons. Surg. City Hosp. NHS Trust Birm.; Hon. Clin. Sen. Lect. Univ. Birm. Socs: Brit. Assn. Surg. Oncol.; Surgic. Research Soc.; Assn. Surg. Prev: Sen. Regist. (Surg.) Birm. HA; Regist. (Surg.) N. Staffs. Roy. Infirm. Stoke-on-Trent; Regist. (Surg.) Birm. HA.

LEE, Martin Stuart SW London and St Georges Mental Health Services NHS Trust, Sutton Hospital, Cotswold Road, Sutton SM2 5NF Tel: 020 8644 4343 Email: mlee@swlstg-tr.nhs.uk — MB BS 1977 Lond.; MRCPsych. 1982. (Lond. Hosp.) Cons. Psychiat. S. W. Lond. & St. Geo.s Ment. Health Servs. NHS Trust; Hon. Sen. Lect. St. Geo. Hosp. Med. Sch.; Dir. of Med. Educat., S. W. Lond. & St. Geo. Ment. Health Serv. NHS Trust. Socs: BMA. Prev: Sen. Regist. (Psychiat.) Guy's Hosp. Lond.; Ho. Phys. Lond. Hosp.; Ho. Surg. Epsom Dist. Hosp.

LEE, Mary Anne 114 Eastern Way, Darras Hall, Ponteland, Newcastle upon Tyne NE20 9RQ Tel: 01661 22781 — MB BS 1969 Lond.; MRCS Eng. LRCP Lond. 1969; MRCGP 1982. (King's Coll. Hosp.) GP Tyneside & N.umberland Family Plann. Centre. Prev: Ho. Phys. (Paediat.) Belgrave Hosp. Childr. Lond.; Ho. Surg. (Gen. Surg.) Mt. Vernon Hosp. N.wood; SHO (Paediat. Surg.) Soton. Childr. Hosp.

LEE, Matthew Cenarth Mill, Pant-y-Dwr, Rhayader LD6 5LP — MB ChB 1993 Glas.

LEE, Matthew Thomas Wilton 28 Leaside Way, Southampton SO16 3DU Email: jdhp@dial.pipex.com — BM 1994 Soton. SHO (Anaesth.) Roy. Hants. Co. Hosp. Winchester. Prev: SHO (Paediat.; SHO (Med.).

LEE, Mervyn Richard Victoria Clinic, 6 Osbert St., London SW1P 2QU Tel: 020 8746 8066 Fax: 020 8746 8989; 32 Canadian Avenue, Catford, London SE6 3AS Tel: 020 8690 5472 Email: mervyn.lee@lineone.net — MB BS 1988 Lond.; DFFP 1994; DRCOG 1993; Dip. GU. Med 1998. (Charing Cross & Westminster) Clin. Asst. (Genitourin. & HIV Med.) Chelsea & W.m. Hosp. Lond.; Clin.Asst.GU.Med.W..Middx.Univ.hosp. Prev: Trainee GP Lond.; SHO (Geriat. Med.) Qu. Mary's Hosp. Sidcup; SHO (O & G) Guy's Hosp. Lond.

LEE, Mr Michael David The Ashtead Hospital, The Warren, Ashtead KT21 2SB Tel: 01372 276161 Fax: 01372 278704; 5 Ruxley Ridge, Claygate, Esher KT10 0HZ Tel: 01372 466153 Fax: 01372 466153 — MB ChB 1960 Manch.; DLO Eng. 1965; FRCS Eng. 1967. (Manch.) Socs: Fell. Roy. Soc. Med. Prev: Cons. ENT Surg. Epsom Health Care NHS Trust & Kingston Hosp. Trust; Sen. Regist. (ENT) United Sheff. Hosps.; Regist. & Sen. Regist. Roy. Nat. Throat, Nose & Ear Hosp. Lond.

LEE, Michael James Curtis Devon Square Surgery, Devon Square Surgery, Newton Abbot TQ12 2HH Tel: 01626 332182 — MB ChB 1980 Birmingham; MB ChB 1980 Birmingham.

LEE, Michael John Tsen Unit 15 The Rooftops, Gee Street, London EC1V 3RD Email: mjtlee@ibm.net — MB BS 1989 Lond.; BSc Lond. 1986; MRCP (UK) 1992; FRCA 1995. Specialist Regist. (Anaesth.) Univ. Coll. Hosp. Lond.

LEE, Mr Michael Lyell Haddon (retired) 32 Beech Cl, Broadstone BH18 9NJ Tel: 01207 691833 — MB BCh 1947 Oxf.; MB BCh Oxon. 1947; FRCS Eng. 1955. Prev: Cons. Orthop. Surg. Bournemouth & E. Dorset Gp. Hosps.

LEE, Michele Anne Geok Hwa 71C Fitzjohns Avenue, London NW3 6PD — MB BCh BAO 1992 NUI; LRCPSI 1992.

LEE, Michelle Whi Ying 9 Cartwright Way, London SW13 8HD — MB BS 1998 Lond.; MB BS Lond 1998.

LEE, Mylene 4 The Galeb, Leen Court, Nottingham NG7 2HX Tel: 0115 979 1240 — BM BS 1992 Nottm. SHO (Med.) King's Mill Hosp. Nottm.

LEE, Nancy Elizabeth The Surgery, 2 Hanway Place, London W1P 9DF Tel: 020 7323 0760 Fax: 020 7580 5063 — MB BS 1959 London. (St. Geo.)

LEE, Mr Nicholas Blaire The Western Eye Hospital, Marylebone Road, London NW1 5YE Tel: 020 7886 3257 Email: nicklee@leemedical.fsnet.co.uk; Tel: 01895 835144 Fax: 01895 835404 — MB BS 1983 Lond.; BSc Lond. 1980; FRCS Eng. 1988;

FRCOphth 1989. (Guy's) Cons. Ophth. W.. Eye Hosp. Lond. & Hillingdon Hosp. Uxbridge. Socs: Fell. Roy. Soc. Med. Prev: Sen. Regist. Rotat. (Ophth.) St. Bart. & Moorfields Eye Hosps. Lond.; Regist. (Ophth.) St. Geo. & Mayday Hosp. Lond.; SHO (Ophth.) St. Geo. Hosp. Lond.

LEE, Nicola Jane Guildford University Student Health, Guildford GU2 7XH; 6A High Gate, West Hill, London N6 6JR — MB BS 1983 Lond.; DFFP 2000; MRCGP 1988; DRCOG 1987. (Univ. Coll. Hosp.) GP Asst. Guildford Univ. Stud. Health. Prev: Retainer Scheme Hillbrow Surg. Liss Hants & Newtown Surg. Liphook Hants; GP Lodge Surg. St. Albans; Ho. Surg. Whittington Hosp. Lond.

LEE, Patricia 32 Leicester Road, East Finchley, London N2 9EA — MB BS 1965 Lond.; FFA RCS Eng. 1969; DA Eng. 1968; DObst RCOG 1967. (Roy. Free) Cons. Anaesth. Roy. N. Hosp. Lond. & Whittington Hosp. Lond. Socs: BMA.

LEE, Mr Patrick Kin-Chung 26 Cults Avenue, Cults, Aberdeen AB15 9RS Email: 100665.541@compuserve.com — MB ChB 1990 Aberd.; FRCS Ed. 1996. Specialist Regist. (Otolaryngol.) Roy. Infirm. Edin. Prev: SHO (ENT) Addenbrooke's Hosp. Camb., P'boro. & Russells Hall Hosp. Dudley.

LEE, Peter (retired) 4 Cranford Avenue, Whitfield, Manchester M45 7SJ Tel: 0161 766 5713 — BSc (Hons. Physiol.) Ed. 1953, MB ChB 1956; FFCM 1974; DPH Manch. 1968. DMO Wigan HA; Tutor (Comm. Med.) Univ. Manch. Prev: Div. Med. Off. & MOH Health Dist. No. 8 Lancs. CC.

LEE, Peter Frederick Spencer Old Hall, 54 Whittingham Lane, Broughton, Preston PR3 5DB — MB BS 1956 Lond.; DA Eng. 1958. Cons. Anaesth. Roy. Preston Hosp.

LEE, Peter Geoffrey (retired) 2 Newcourt Road, Topsham, Exeter EX3 0BT — MB BChir 1968 Camb.; MB BChir Camb. 1969; MA Camb. 1969; MRCGP 1977; DObst RCOG 1972. Prev: Trainee GP Wessex VTS.

LEE, Peter James The Gratton Surgery, Sutton Scotney, Winchester SO21 3LE Tel: 01962 760394 Fax: 01962 761138; Manor Farm House, Micheldever, Winchester SO21 3DA — MB BChir 1973 Camb. (Camb. & St. Geo.)

LEE, Mr Peter William Ray 61 North Bar, Within, Beverley HU17 8DG Tel: 01482 860412 — MD 1977 Ed.; MB ChB 1968; FRCS Eng. 1973; FRCS Ed. 1972. (Ed.) Cons. Gen. Surg. Hull & E. Yorks. HA. Prev: Sen. Surg. Regist. N. Yorks. AHA; Resid. Surg. Off. St. Mark's Hosp. Lond.; Lect. in Surg. Univ. Dept. Surg. Leeds Gen. Infirm.

LEE, Philip Jonathan Metabolic Unit, The National hosp for neurology and neuroscopy, Queen Square, London WC1N 3BG Tel: 020 7829 8778 Fax: 020 7209 2146 Email: philip.le&euclh.org; 42 Foxbourne Road, London SW17 8EW Tel: 020 8672 4400 — BM BS 1986 Nottm.; BM BS (Hons.) Nottm. 1986; BMedSci (Hons.) Nottm. 1984; DM Nottm. 1995; MRCP (UK) 1989; FRCPCH 1998. (Nottm) Cons. (Metab. Med.) Univ. Coll. Hosp. NHS Trust Lond. Socs: (Comm.) Brit. Inherited Metab. Dis. Gp.; Soc. Study of inborn errors of Metab. (Counc. Mem.); Assn. Glycogen storage Dis. (Med. Adviser). Prev: Sen. Regist. (Metab.) Gt. Ormond St. Hosp. Childr. Lond.; Lect. (Child Health) St. Geo. Hosp. Lond.; Research Regist. Inst. Child Health Lond.

LEE, Ping Siang Armley Medical Centre, 16 Church Road, Armley, Leeds LS12 1TZ Tel: 0113 295 3800 Fax: 0113 295 3810; 11 Keswick Grange, E. Keswick, Leeds LS17 9BX Tel: 01937 74665 — MB ChB 1972 St. And.; MRCP (UK) 1976. Clin. Research Fell. (Med. Cardiol.) Leeds Gen. Infirm.

LEE, Rachel Catherine 118 Woodend Road, Frampton Cotterell, Bristol BS36 2LQ; 118 Woodend Road, Frampton Cotterell, Bristol BS36 2LQ — MB ChB 1993 Birm.; MRCP 1997. (Birmingham)

LEE, Remond Mark 48A Cecilia Road, London E8 2ER — MB BS 1986 Lond.

LEE, Richard Alan 86 Hainault Road, Chigwell IG7 5DH Tel: 020 8500 2046 — MB BS 1959 Lond.; MRCS Eng. LRCP Lond. 1959; MRCOphth 1991; DO Eng. 1964. (Lond. Hosp.) Ophth. Med. Pract. Prev: Assoc. Specialist Regional Eye Unit Harold Wood Hosp. Romford; Sen. Regist. (Research) Ophth. Dept. Lond. Hosp.; Lect.(Physiol).Qu.mary & W.field Coll.

LEE, Richard Edward James Department of Radiology, Royal Victoria Infirmary, Newcastle upon Tyne NE1 4LP — MRCS Eng. LRCP Lond. 1970; BSc (Hons.) (Anat.) Lond. 1967, MB BS 1970; FRCR 1975. (Guy's) Cons. Paediat. Radiol. Roy. Vict. Infirm & Assoc. Hosp. Trusts.; Clin. Lect. (Radiol.) Univ. Newc. Prev: Lect. (Radiodiag.) Univ. Bristol; Sen. Regist. (Radiodiag.) Avon AHA (T); Lect. (Radiol.) Univ. W. Indies, Jamaica.

LEE, Mr Richard Eric The Moor House, Wood Lane, Uttoxeter ST14 8JR — MB ChB 1978 Ed.; FRCS Eng. 1982. Regist. (Surg.) Taunton & Som. Hosp. Prev: Tutor in Surg. Univ. Bristol & Hon. Regist. Bristol Roy. Infirm.; Regist. (Surg. Rotat.) Wessex RHA.

LEE, Richard James Church Street Surgery, 17 Church Street, Bridgwater TA6 5AT Tel: 01278 424901 Fax: 01278 437103; Crowlink, Charlynch Lane, Spaxton, Bridgwater TA5 1BJ Tel: 01278 671276 — BM BCh 1973 Oxf.; MRCGP 1980; DA Eng. 1975. (Oxford) Prev: Princip. GP Glenfield, Leicester; Med. Off. Chas. Johnson Memor. Hosp. Nqutu, Kwazulu, S. Afr.; Trainee GP Camb.

LEE, Richard Peter (retired) The Sycamores, Church St., Golcar, Huddersfield HD7 4AH Tel: 01484 654131 — MB ChB Sheff. 1949. Prev: Ho. Phys. Roy. Hosp. Sheff.

LEE, Richard Wing Him Department of Haematology, Royal Devon and Exeter Hospital, Barrack Road, Exeter EX2 5DW Tel: 01392 411611 Ext: 2462 Fax: 01392 402915; Roach Cottage, Clyst Hydon, Cullompton EX15 2NU Tel: 01884 277350 — MB BS 1974 Lond.; BSc (Hons.) Lond. 1971; FRCP Lond. 1994; MRCP (UK) 1977; FRCPath 1995, M 1983. (King's Coll. Hosp.) Cons. Haemat. Roy. Devon & Exeter Hosp. Exeter. Prev: Lect. (Haemat.) St. Geo. Hosp. Lond.

LEE, Robert David Newtown Clinic, 24 - 26 Lyon Street, Southampton SO14 0LX Tel: 02380 900201 Fax: 02380 900215 — MB BS Lond. 1963; MRCS Eng. LRCP Lond. 1963; MRCGP 1974; DObst RCOG 1965. (Guy's) Prev: Past Mem. Soton. & SW Hants. HA; Hants. FHSA 1990-96; Ex Postgrad. Trainer (Gen. Pract.) Soton.

LEE, Mr Robin John c/o ENT Department, Kettering General Hospital, Rothwell Road, Kettering NN16 8UZ Tel: 01536 492274 Fax: 01536 492295 — MB BCh BAO 1978 Dub.; MA, MD Dub. 1990; FRCSI 1984; FRCS 1999. Cons. ENT Surg. Kettering Gen. Hosp. Socs: BMA; BAO - HNS. Prev: Sen. Regist. (Otolaryngol.) Beaumont Hosp. Dub.; Research Fell. (Otolaryngol., Head & Neck Surg.) Univ. Iowa, USA; Sen. Regist. (Otolaryngol.) Federated Dub. Volun. Hosps. & Roy. Vict. Eye & Ear Hosp. Dub.

LEE, Roger Jeffrey Edgar Room 102, Craigavon Area Hospital, 68 Lurgan Road, Portadown, Craigavon BT63 5QQ Tel: 028 3861 2627 Fax: 028 3861 2814 Email: rjelee@aol.com; Darganstown House, 81 Old Kilmore Road, Moira, Craigavon BT67 0NA Tel: 02892 611655 — MB BCh BAO 1977 Belf.; MD Belf. 1985; MRCP Ed. 1981. Cons. Phys. Craigavon Area Hosp.; Clin. Dir. Med. Directorate Craigavon Area Hosp. Gp. Trust. Socs: Fell. RCP; Coun. Mem. Irish Soc. Rheum.; Brit. Soc. Rheum. Prev: Sen. Regist. (Rheum. Dis.) Musgrave Pk. Hosp. Belf.; Research Fell. & Resid. Ho. Off. Roy. Victory Hosp. Belf.

LEE, Roger Nevill Albany Road Surgery, 5 Albany Road, Earlsdon, Coventry CV5 6JQ Tel: 024 7622 8606 Fax: 024 7622 9985 — MB ChB 1976 Birm.; PhC 1956.

LEE, Mr Ronald Koon Liat 59 Oakleigh Avenue, Surbiton KT6 7PY — MB ChB 1993 Glas.; BDS Glas. 1984; FRCS Eng. 1996; FDS RCS Ed. 1989; LDS RCS Eng. 1985. (King's Coll. Hosp. Glas.)

LEE, Rosemary Joyce Armadale Medical Centre, Arnacraig, Armadale, Thurso KW14 7SA Tel: 01641 541212 Fax: 01641 541226; Achnacraig, Armadale, Thurso KW14 7SA — MB ChB 1970 Aberd.; DObst RCOG 1973.

LEE, Rupert Mark 29 Hamilton Street, Hoole, Chester CH2 3JG — MB BS 1990 Lond. Prev: Ho. Off. (Med.) Colchester Hosp.; Ho. Off. (Surg.) Roy. Berks. Hosp. Reading.

LEE, Ruth Margaret 22 Tithe Barn Drive, Bray, Maidenhead SL6 2DG — MB BS 1981 Lond.; BSc (Hons.) Physiol. Lond. 1978; MFHom 1986. (St. Bart.) Sen. Pharmaceut. Med. Adviser Berks. Prev: Indep. Med. Pract. Warks.; Phys. (Homoeop.) Roy. Lond. Homoeop. Hosp.; SHO (Dermat. & Venereol.) St. Bart. Hosp. Lond.

***LEE, Sammy Ken Men** 19 Pennard Way, Chandlers Ford, Eastleigh SO53 4NJ — MB ChB 1998 Birm.

LEE, Sarah Gillian Belmont House, 3-5 Belmont Grove, Leeds LS 2 9NP Tel: 0113 392 2912 Fax: 0113 392 6219 — MB BS 1974 Lond.; MMedSci Leeds 1996; DCH Eng. 1976. Cons. Community Paediat. Leeds.

LEE, Sarah Jane 44 Queens Road, Cheadle Hulme, Cheadle SK8 5LU — MB ChB 1992 Liverp.

LEE, Sarah Lian Choo Lee, 249 Old Kent Road, London SE1 5LU Tel: 020 7237 2492 Fax: 020 7237 1076 — LMSSA 1962 Lond.

LEE, Sarah Ruth 24 Manor Way, London SE3 9EF — MB ChB 1997 Ed. SHO (A&E), Middlx. Univ. Hosp. Prev: SHO (O & G) E.bourne; SHO (Surg.) Grantham & Dist. Hosp.; SHO (Med.) Qu. Mary's Hosp. Sidcup.

LEE, Sharon Elizabeth 19 Prospect Road, Portstewart BT55 7NF — MB ChB 1997 Dundee.

LEE, Shing Wah 8 Widecombe Road, Stoke-on-Trent ST1 6SL — MB ChB 1993 Dundee.

LEE, Sidney 50 Berkeley Court, Baker St., London NW1 5NB Tel: 020 7935 2881 — MRCS Eng. LRCP Lond. 1933. (Westm.) Med. Exam. Brit. Red Cross Soc.; Med. Ref. Refuge & Other Assur. Cos. Prev: Clin. Asst. (Dermat.) Qu. Mary's Hosp. Lond.; Resi. Med. Off. & Ho. Surg. (Radiother.) W.m. Hosp. Annexe.

LEE, Silke Flat 62, Good Hart Place, Limehouse Basin, London E14 8EQ — MB BS 1990 Lond.

LEE, Simon Anthony 2 Close Gardens Court, Condicote, Cheltenham GL54 1ES; 10 Chepstow Avenue, Berkley Beverborne, Worcester WR4 0EF — MB BCh 1998 Wales.

LEE, Simon Dennis 6 Freeman Road, Wickersley, Rotherham S66 2HH — MB BS 1993 Newc.

LEE, Simon James Canniesburn Hospital, SwitchBank Road, Bearsden, Glasgow G61 1QL Tel: 0141 211 4000; 3/2 63 Gardner Street, Partickhill, Glasgow G11 5BZ — MB BS 1991 Lond.; MSc (Sports Medicine) Lond. 1994; FRCS Lond. 1995. (Regist. (Plastic Surg.) Norwhich) Specialist Regist. Plastic Reconsruictiton Surg. Canniesbarn Hosp. Socs: BASM.

LEE, Siong Sik 24 York Road, Hyde SK14 5JH — MB ChB 1987 Manch.

LEE, Siow Ming The University College London Hospitals, Middlesex Hospital, The Meyerstein Institute of Oncology, Mortimer St., London W1T 3AA Tel: 020 7380 9325 Fax: 020 7436 0160 Email: sm.lee@uclh.org; 78 Brooklawn Drive, Didsbury, Manchester M20 3GZ — MB BS 1982 Lond.; MRCP 1985; PhD Manch. 1994. (St Mary's Hosp. Med. Sch.) Cons. Med. Oncol., Univ. Coll. Lond. & Middlx. Hosps. Lond. & Whittington Hosp. Lond.; Hon. Seniot Lect. Univ. Coll. Med. Sch. Socs: Steering Comm. Mem Europ. Bone Marrow Transpl. Working Party; Steering Comm. Mem Lond. Lung Cancer Gp.; Amer. Acad. Cancer Research. Prev: Sen. Regist./Lect. Christie Hosp. Manch. & Univ. of Manch.; CRC Clin. Research Fell. Christie Hosp. Manch. & Univ. of Manch.; Lect./Med. Oncol. Univ. of Malaya Kuala Lumpur Malaysia.

LEE, Siu Wai Michael 15 Cottown of Balgownie, Bridge of Don, Aberdeen AB23 8JQ — MB ChB 1990 Dundee.

LEE, Song Kiat Song Kiat, Flat 40, Maple Lodge, Abbots Walk, London W8 5UN — MB BCh 1995 Wales.

LEE, Stephen Howard Department of Radiology, Manchester Royal Infirmary, Oxford Road, Manchester M13 9WL Tel: 0161 276 4185 Fax: 0161 276 8916; 20 Prestwich Park Road South, Prestwich, Manchester M25 9PE — MB BS 1981 Lond.; MRCS Eng. LRCP Lond. 1980; FRCS Ed. 1985; FRCR 1988. (St George's hosp med Sch) Cons. Radiol. Manch. Roy. Infirm.; Hon. Lect. Univ. Manch. Prev: Sen. Regist. (Radiol.) Middlx. Hosp. Lond.; GI Radiol. Fell. Vancouver Gen. Hosp. Vancouver, Canada.

LEE, Stewart Bernard Jean-Pierre 70 Heybridge Avenue, London SW16 3DX — MB BS 1994 Lond.

LEE, Stuart Peng-Chung 171 Western Road, Billericay CM12 9JD — MB BS 1994 Lond.; MRCP (UK) 1997.

LEE, Susan Joyce Department of Pathology, Birmingham Women's Hospital, Edgbaston, Birmingham B15 2TG Tel: 0121 627 2729 — MB ChB 1982 Leeds; BSc Leeds 1979, MD 1991; FRCPath 1997; MRCPath 1988. Cons. Path. Birm. Wom. Healthcare NHS Trust. Prev: Hon. Cons. Histopath. Centr. Manch. Healthcare Trust; Lect. (Path.) Univ. Manch. & Birm.

LEE, Susan Margaret West Lodge, Farsley, Pudsey LS28 5DL — MB ChB 1985 Sheff.

LEE, Sze Min 18 Rossdale Road, Belfast BT8 6TG Tel: 01232 793198 Email: min@doctors.org.uk — MB BCh BAO 1994 Belf. SHO (Med.) Roy. Vict. Hosp. Belf.

LEE, Szu Hee 13 Harefields, Oxford OX2 8HG — MB 1976 Camb.; PhD (CNAA) 1986; BChir 1975; MRCP (UK) 1979; MRCPath 1986. Research Fell. Nuffield Dept. Clin. Med. John Radcliffe Hosp. Oxf. Prev: Sen. Regist. (Haemat.) Oxf. RHA; Regist. (Haemat.) John Radcliffe Hosp. Oxf.

LEE, Professor Tak Hong Thomas Guy House, 5:th floor, GKT School of Medicine, Department of Respiratory Medicine and Allergy, Guys Hospital, London SE1 9RT Tel: 020 7955 4571 Fax: 020 7403 8640 Email: tak.lee@kcl.ac.uk — MB BChir 1976 Camb.; ScD 1996; MA Camb. 1976, BA 1972, MD 1983; FRCP Lond. 1989; MRCP (UK) 1977; ScD Camb. 1996; FRCPath 1997; MRCPath 1988. (Camb. & Guy's) Prof. Guy's Hosp. Lond. (Nat. Asthma Campaign Prof. of Allergy & Respirat. Med.). Socs: Brit. Soc. Immunol.; Brit. Thorac. Soc.; Pres. Brit. Soc. Allegy Clin. Immunol. Prev: Sen. Lect. & Cons. Guy's Hosp. Lond.; Lect. & Sen. Regist. Guy's Hosp. Lond.; Vis. Sci. Harvard Med. Sch. Boston, USA.

LEE, Tak Shing 45 Rowan House, The Beeches, Cambridge CB4 1FY Tel: 01223 420070 Fax: 01223 420070 — MB ChB 1991 Chinese Univ. Hong Kong; MB ChB Chinese U Hong Kong 1991.

LEE, Teck Leong Sheepcot Medical Centre, 80 Sheepcot Lane, Garston, Watford WD25 0EA Tel: 01923 672451 Fax: 01923 681404 — DRCOG 1988; MBBS 1984. (The London Hospital Medical College) Gen. Practitioner, Sheepcot Med. Centre, Watford; Health Screening Doctor, BUPA Hosp., Harpenden, Herts.

LEE, Thelma 18 Park Drive, Grimsby DN32 0EF Tel: 01472 78478 — MB BS 1953 Durh. (Durh.) Prev: Clin. Asst. Dermat. Grimsby Hosp. Gp.; Staff Med. Off. Grimsby; Ho. Phys. & Ho. Surg. Newc. Gen. Hosp.

LEE, Thomas Gok 144 Manor Avenue, Burscough, Ormskirk L40 7TU Tel: 01704 894369 — MB ChB 1990 Glas.; DRCOG 1998; DFFP 1999; MRCGP 1999. (Glasgow Univ) GP Princip., W.moreland GP Centre, Fazakerley Hosp. Liverp. Socs: Med. Protec. Soc. & BMA. Prev: GP Regist. SandyLa. Surg., Leyland.

LEE, Thomas Joseph Department of Paediatrics, Good Hope Hospital, Rectory Road, Sutton Coldfield B75 7RR Tel: 0121 308 2211; 131 Lichfield Road, Sutton Coldfield B74 2RY Tel: 0121 398 0641 — MB BS 1971 Lond.; MRCP (U.K.) 1974. Cons. Paediat. Good Hope Hosp. Sutton Coldfield.

LEE, Thomas Rousell The Queens Road Medical Practice, The Queens Road, St Peter Port, Guernsey GY1 1RH; Les Salines, Contrée des Courts Fallaizes, St. Martins, Guernsey Tel: 35909 — MB BChir 1968 Camb.; FRCP Lond. 1987; MRCP (UK) 1972; MRCS Eng. LRCP Lond. 1967; DObst RCOG 1969. (Westm.) Specialist Paediat. & GP Guernsey. Socs: Brit. Paediat. Assn. Prev: Hon. Research Fell. Dept. Cancer Studies Univ. Birm.; Ho. Off. (Paediat.) Hosp. Sick. Childr. Gt. Ormond St. Lond.; Regist. (Paediat.) Childr. Hosp. Birm.

LEE, Timothy David Flat 3, 10 West Park, Bristol BS8 2LT — MB ChB 1993 Bristol.

LEE, Timothy William Rayner Holme House, Church Fenton Lane, Ulleskelf, Tadcaster LS24 9DW Tel: 0411 512119 Email: tim@wrlee.freeserve.co.uk — MB ChB 1994 Leeds; BSc (Hons.) Pharmacol. Leeds 1991; MRCP 1997; MRCP CH 1997. (Leeds) Specialist Regist. (Paediat.) Hull Roy. Infirm. Socs: BMA & Med. Defence Union; MSS. Prev: SHO (Paediat.) St. Jas. Univ. Hosp. Leeds.

LEE, Tong (retired) Greystoke, 5 Roman Crescent, Swindon SN1 4HH Tel: 01793 431392 — MB BS 1952 Hong Kong; TDD Wales 1955; DObst RCOG 1966. Prev: Regist. (Med.) Peppard Hosp. Henley-on-Thames.

LEE, Vickie 19 Harben Road, London NW6 4RH — MB BChir 1993 Camb.; MA Camb. 1993, MB BChir 1993. SHO (Neurosurg.) Roy. Free Hosp. Lond.

LEE, Victoria 16 Pisgah House Road, Sheffield S10 5BJ — MB ChB 1992 Sheff.; MRCP (UK) 1996. Specialist Regist. (Paediat.) N. Trent Paediat. Train. Scheme.

LEE, Vincent 27 Holyrood Avenue, Harrow HA2 8UD — MB ChB 1993 Manch.

LEE, Vincent Felix Bassetlaw District General Hospital, Kilton Hill, Worksop S81 0BD — MB ChB 1997 Sheff.

LEE, Wai Peng 11 Milner Road, Morden SM4 6EN — MB BS 1998 Lond.; MB BS Lond 1998.

LEE, Wee Soon Flat 2, 4 Hatherley Grove, London W2 5RB — LRCPI & LM, LRSCI & LM 1953; LRCPI & LM, LRCSI & LM 1953.

LEE, William Edward 40 The Avenue, Crowthorne RG45 6PG — MB ChB 1998 Aberd.; MB ChB Aberd 1998.

LEE, Professor William Rimmer 6 Sussex Avenue, Didsbury, Manchester M20 6AQ Tel: 0161 445 0095 Fax: 0161 445 0095 — MB BS 1945 Lond.; MSc Manch. 1975; MD Lond. 1963; FRCP Lond. 1977, M 1969; FFOM RCP Lond. 1978; DIH Soc. Apoth. Lond. 1957. (Guy's) Emerit. Prof. Occupat. Health Univ. Manch. Socs: Manch. Med. Soc.; NW Thoracic Soc. Prev: Cons. Occupat. Health Manch. Roy. Infirm.; Edr. Brit. Jl. Indust. Med.; Acad. Regist. Fac. Occupat. Med. RCP Lond.

LEE, William Robert High Craigton, Stockiemuir Road, Milngavie, Glasgow G62 7HA Tel: 0141 956 3286 Fax: 0141 955 1411 Email: wrl1v@clinmed.gla.ac.uk — MB ChB Manch. 1957; FRSE 1990; MD Manch. 1963; FRCOphth 1990; FRCPath 1981 M 1968. Hon. Sen. Research Fell. Glas. Univ. Socs: Path. Soc.; Assn. Research in Ophth. Prev: Prof. Path. Glas. Univ.

LEE, Wyndham (retired) 37 Prince Regents Close, Brighton BN2 5JP — Med. Dipl. Warsaw 1935.

LEE, Yee Chiang Royal Liverpool University Hospital, Prescot St., Liverpool L7 8XP Tel: 0151 706 2000; 12 The Stakes, Moreton, Wirral CH46 3SW — MB ChB 1988 Aberd.; MTropMed. Liverp. 1996; DTCD Wales 1995. Socs: Roy. Acad. Med. Irel.; BMA. Prev: Regist. (Respirat. & Gen. Med.) Roy. Liverp. Univ. Hosp. & Arrowe Pk. Hosp. Merseyside RHA; SHO (Gen. Med., Infec. Dis. & Chest Med.) Castle Hill Hosp. Hull; SHO (Renal, Cardiol. & Gen. Med.) Leeds Gen. Infirm. Leeds.

LEE, Yu-Chuan c/o Dr A Griffiths, St John's Institute of Dermatology, St Thomas's Hospital, Lambeth Palace Road, London SE1 7EH — MB BS 1993 Adelaide.

LEE, Zhamac 17 Denewood, Killingworth, Newcastle upon Tyne NE12 7FA — MB BCh BAO 1992 Belf.; MB BCh Belf. 1992.

LEE CHEONG, Lee Fook Lan Furness General Hospital, Department of Anaesthetic, Dalton Lane, Barrow-in-Furness LA14 4LF — MB ChB 1983 Glas. Staff Grade (Anaesth.) Furness Gen. Hosp. Cumbria. Prev: SHO (Anaesth.) Arrowe Pk. Hosp. Upton.

LEE-CHONG, Francois Li Pook Kong 90 Brighton Road, Horley RH6 7JQ — MB BCh BAO 1978 NUI; MB BCh NUI 1978; LRCPI & LM, LRCSI & LM 1978.

LEE CHONG, Lee Pook Fen 468 Kenton Road, Harrow HA3 9DN — MB ChB 1977 Glas.

LEE-ELDRID, Evelyn Monica (retired) 25 Benlease Way, Swanage BH19 2SX Tel: 01929 424124 — MRCS Eng. LRCP Lond. 1939; DPH Eng. 1947.

LEE-ELLIOTT, Catherine Eve Southampton General Hospital, Southampton SO16 6YD — BChir 1992 Camb.; 2000 FRCR; 1996 MRCP.

LEE HAI EAN, Dr 40 Goulbourne Avenue, Wrexham LL13 9HQ — MB BCh 1986 Wales.

LEE HAI LEONG, Dr 5 Wyeverne Road, Cardiff CF24 4BG — MB BCh 1997 Wales.

LEE-JONES, Michael (retired) Elmleigh, Brightwell-cum-Sotwell, Wallingford OX10 0RQ Tel: 01491 835857 Fax: 01491 835857 — MB BS Lond. 1960; MRCP Lond. 1966; FRCGP 1983, M 1974; DObst RCOG 1962. Clin. Director, Hosp. Accreditation Progr., CASPE Research, Lond.. Prev: GP Wallingford.

LEE KAR CHEUK, Leonard Flat 5, 113 Sloane St., London SW1X 9PQ — MB BS 1987 Hong Kong.

LEE KHET LEONG, David 10C Dickens House, St Georges Grove, London SW17 0PZ — MB BS 1993 Lond.

LEE-MASON, Francesca Victoria Anne Saltoun Surgery, 46 Saltoun Place, Fraserburgh AB43 9RY Tel: 01346 514154 Fax: 01346 517680 — MB ChB 1991 Aberd.

LEE PEK WAN, Dr 36 Viceroy Close, Bristol Road, Birmingham B5 7US — MB BS 1988 Malaya.

LEE PEK YUK, Grace c/o Dr Gan, Flat 2, Larch House, 3 Hardwick Lane, Bury St Edmunds IP33 2QZ — MB BS 1991 Lond. Prev: Ho. Off. (Med.) St. Helier Hosp. Carshalton; Ho. Off. (Surg.) P.ss Roy. Hosp. Haywards Heath.

LEE-POTTER, Jeremy Patrick (retired) Icen House, Stoborough, Wareham BH20 5AN Tel: 01929 556307 Fax: 01929 554363 — MB BS 1958 Lond.; MRCS Eng. LRCP Lond. 1958; FRCPath 1979, M 1967; DCP Lond 1965; DTM & H Eng. 1963. Prev: Cons. Haemat. Poole Hosp. NHS Trust.

LEE-WOOLF, Jean Dorothy (retired) Flat 4 Holland House, 42 Newington Green, London N16 9PQ Tel: 020 7249 6251 — MB BS 1940 Lond.; MRCS Eng. LRCP Lond. 1940.

LEECE, John Geoffrey (retired) The Old Forge, Stevens Crouch, Battle TN33 9LR Tel: 01424 773645 — MB BS 1962 Lond.; MSc Lond. 1971; MRCS Eng. LRCP Lond. 1962; FFPHM RCP (UK) 1986, M 1974; DCH Eng. 1968; DPH Liverp. 1967. Cons. Communicable Dis. Control. E. Sussex HA. Prev: Dir. Pub. Health E.bourne HA.

LEECH, Alison Mary Department of Psychiatry, Withington Hospital, Nell Lane, West Didsbury, Manchester M20 2LR; 28 Ladysmith Road, West Didsbury, Manchester M20 6HL — MB ChB 1994 Dundee. Socs: Inceptor Roy. Coll. of Psychiats.

LEECH, David Leslie The Health Centre, Sunningdale Drive, Eaglescliffe, Stockton-on-Tees TS16 9EA Tel: 01642 780113 Fax: 01642 791020 — MB BS 1972 Lond.; MRCGP 1977. Clin. Asst. (Ment. Handicap.) N. Tees HA; Clin. Asst. (Psychiat.) N. Tees Gen. Hosp.

LEECH, Geoffrey 67 Westgate, Hale, Altrincham WA15 9BA — MB ChB 1965 Manch. (Manch.) Prev: Ho. Off. (Surg.) Manch. Roy. Infirm.; Ho. Off. (Med.) Hope Hosp. Salford; SHO (Surg.) Hammersmith Hosp. Lond.

LEECH, Kenneth William (retired) The Maltsters, 14 Court St., Moreton Hampsted, Newton Abbot TQ13 8LG Tel: 01647 440413 — MB BChir 1949 Camb.; MRCS Eng. LRCP Lond. 1944. Prev: Capt. RAMC, Graded Phys.

LEECH, Philip Andrew NHS Executive, Quarry House, Quarry Hill, Leeds LS2 7UE; Maltings Cottage, 75 Seckford St, Woodbridge IP12 4LZ — MRCS Eng. LRCP Lond. 1969; FRCGP 1998; DMJ Soc. Apoth. Lond. 1990. (Sheff.) Princip. Med. Off. (Primary Care) Leeds; Special Lecturesh. (Gen. Pract.) Univ. Nottm. Prev: GP Minehead, Som.

LEECH, Phillip Winfield (retired) Rowswood Cottage, Higher Walton, Warrington WA4 5LN Tel: 01925 262388 — MB ChB 1960 St. And.

LEECH, Ralph Bosdin (retired) Maseno, 5 Avenue Road, Lymington SO41 9GP Tel: 01590 674456 — MB BChir Camb. 1938; MRCS Eng. LRCP Lond. 1935; TDD Wales 1947. Prev: Med. Off. Mengo Hosp. Uganda.

LEECH, Rebecca Sarah Jane 1 Brook Avenue, Stockton Heath, Warrington WA4 2RY — MB ChB 1991 Manch.

LEECH, Richard Charles Maistone hospital, Hermitage Lane, Maidstone ME16 9QQ — MB BS 1990 Lond.; FRCA 1994. (KCSMD) Cons Anaesth Maidstone Hosp, Kent. Prev: Regist. (Anaesth.) Roy. Perth Hosp. W.. Australia; Regist. (Anaesth.) King's Coll. Hosp. Lond.; Regist. (Anaesth.) Kent & Canterbury Hosp.

LEECH, Samuel Geoffrey Boughton Health Centre, Boughton, Chester CH2 3DP Tel: 01244 325421 Fax: 01244 322224 — MB ChB 1955 Manch.; MRCGP 1963; DObst RCOG 1959. Prev: SHO (O & G) Oldham & Dist. Gen. Hosp.; Ho. Phys. Manch. Roy. Infirm.; RAMC.

LEECH, Susan Claire Department of Child health, Kings College Hospital, Denmark hill, London SE5 9RS Tel: 020 7737 4000 — MB BChir 1987 Cambridge; FRCPCH 2001 London; MB BChir Camb. 1987; MA Camb. 1989, BA 1987; MRCP (UK) 1992; DCH RCP Lond. 1992; MSc London 1998. (Cambs) Cons. Paediat. with spacial interest in Allergy Kings Healthcare NHS Trust Lond.; Cons. Paediat., Allergist Allergy Guys Hosp. , Lond. Socs: Brit. Soc. Immunol.; RCPCH; Paediat. Research Soc. Prev: Clin. Lect. Child. Health. KCL. Hosp; Lect. (Paediat.) Oxf. Univ.; Regist. (Paediat.) King's Coll. Hosp. Lond. & All St.s Hosp. Chatham.

LEECH, Suzanne Nadine Department of Dermatology, Royal Victoria Infirmary, Newcastle upon Tyne Tel: 0191 232 5131 Fax: 0191 227 5058; 15 Auburn Gardens, Fenham, Newcastle upon Tyne NE4 9XP Tel: 0191 274 0366 Email: s.n.leech@ncl.ac.uk — MB ChB 1994 Ed.; MRCP 1997. Specialist Regist. (Dermatol.), Roy. Vict. Inf. Newc. U. Tyne. Prev: Locum COE Regist. Sunderland; SHO (Med.) Newc. U. Tyne.

LEEDER, Alison The Medical Centre, 37A Heaton Road, Heaton, Newcastle upon Tyne NE6 1TH Tel: 0191 265 8121 Fax: 0191 276 6085 — MB BS 1976 Newc.; MRCGP 1980; DRCOG 1979.

LEEDER, David Stanley The Topsham Surgery, The White House, Holman Way, Topsham, Exeter EX3 0EN Tel: 01392 874646 Fax: 01392 875261; 10 Towerfield, Topsham, Exeter EX3 0BZ Tel: 01392 877777 — MB BS 1980 Lond.; BA Camb. 1976; MRCGP 1985; Cert. Family Plann. JCC 1985. (Christ's Cambridge and KCH London) GP Princip.; GP Trainer.

LEEDER, Mr Paul Constantine 11 Fairbairn Road, Chesterton, Cambridge CB4 1UG — MB ChB 1989 Sheff.; FRCS Eng. 1994.
LEEDHAM, Aubrey (retired) 29 Claremont Road, Eccleshall, Stafford ST21 6DP Tel: 01785 851154 — MRCS Eng. LRCP Lond. 1962.
LEEDHAM, Gwenda Dorothy Three Firs, Ghyll Road, Crowborough TN6 1SU Tel: 01892 653976 — MB BS 1959 Lond.; MRCOG 1964, DObst 1961; MMSA Lond. 1963. (Char. Cross) Prev: Regist. (O & G) S. Lond. Hosp. Wom.; SHO Brit. Hosp. Mothers & Babies Woolwich; Ho. Surg. Char. Cross Hosp. Lond.
LEEDHAM, Peter William The Mount House, 6 The Mount, Shrewsbury SY3 8PS Tel: 01743 231333 — MB BS 1964 Lond.; MRCS Eng. LRCP Lond. 1964; FRCPath 1982, M 1970; T(Path.) 1991. (King's Coll. Hosp.) Cons. Path. (Histopath.) Roy. Shrewsbury Hosps. NHS Trust. Socs: Path. Soc.; Brit. Div. Internat. Acad. Path.; BMA. Prev: Lect. (Morbid Anat.) Lond. Hosp. Med. Coll.; Lect. (Morbid Anat.) & Demonst. (Path.) King's Coll. Hosp. Med. Sch.
LEEDHAM, Simon 110 Bourne Hill, London N13 4BD — MB BS 1997 Lond.
LEEDHAM, Wendy Glenys Farrow Medical Centre, 177 Otley Road, Bradford BD3 0HX Tel: 01274 637031 — MB ChB 1984 Manch.; MRCGP 1988; DRCOG 1986. p/t GP Bradford.
LEEDS, Anthony Richard King's College London Rm4-228, Franklin-Wilkins Building, 150 Stamford St., London SE1 8WA Tel: 020 7848 4613 Email: anthony.leeds@kcl.ac.uk; 95 Brixham Crescent, Ruislip HA4 8TT Fax: 01895 622692 — MB BS 1971 Lond.; MSc Lond. 1977; C.Biol F.Biol.1999. (Middx.Hosp) Sen. Lect. (Nutrit.) King's Coll. Lond.; Clin. Asst. (Endocrinol.) Centr. Middlx. Hosp. Lond. & Dir., Dietetic Consults Ltd; Chairm. Forum on Food & Health Roy. Soc. Med.; Edr. Dietary Fibre Biography & Reviews; Chairm. Research Ethics Comm. King's Coll. Lond. Socs: Nutrit. Soc. (Mem. Counc.); Eur. Assn. Sci. Eds.; Register of Nutrit.ists. Nutrit.. Soc (Accredit. Comm.). Prev: Research Fell. MRC Gastroenterol. Unit Centr. Middlx. Hosp. Lond.; SHO (Med.) N.wick Pk. Hosp. Harrow; Ho. Surg. Middlx. Hosp. Lond.
LEEDS, John Robert (retired) Moberleys Church Street, Milborne Port, Sherborne DT9 5DJ — MB BS 1956 Lond. Prev: Ho. Surg. & Ho. Phys. King Edwd. VII Hosp. Windsor.
LEEDS, John Samuel 406A Meanwood Road, Leeds LS7 2LP — MB ChB 1998 Leeds.
LEEGOOD, Helen Mary Joyce Graylingwell Hospital, College Lane, Chichester PO19 4PQ Tel: 01243 787970 — MB BS 1982 Lond.; MRCPsych 1987. Cons. Psychiat. Old Age Graylingwell Hosp. Chichester.
LEEK, Catherine Anne Department of Psychiatry, Princess Alexandra Hospital, Hamstel Road, Harlow CM20 1QX Tel: 01279 444455; 29 Sherwood Avenue, St Albans AL4 9QJ Tel: 01727 859970 — MB BCh 1974 Wales; MSc 1999. Assoc. Specialist.
LEEK, Graham Peter 3 Coltsfield, High Lane, Stansted Mountfitchet, Stansted CM24 Tel: 01279 813068 — MB BCh 1974 Wales.
LEEKS, Andrew David South Hylton Surgery, 3-5 Cambria Street, South Hylton, Sunderland SR4 0LT Tel: 0191 534 7386 — MB BS 1988 Newc.
LEELAKUMARI, Mrs Tripuraneni Station Surgery, 8 Golden Hill Lane, Leyland, Preston PR25 3NP Tel: 01772 622808 — MB BS 1973 Andhra; DA RCPSI 1975. Clin. Asst. (Anaesth.) Chorley & S. Ribble HA. Prev: Trainee GP Birm.; SHO (Psychiat.) Rainhill Hosp. Liverp.; SHO (A & E) Walsall Gen. Hosp.
LEEMAN, Andrew John Pendeen Surgery, Kent Avenue, Ross-on-Wye HR9 5AL Tel: 01989 763535 Fax: 01989 768288 — BM BCh 1985 Oxf.; MA Camb. 1986; MRCGP 1989; DRCOG 1988; DCH RCP Lond. 1987. Socs: Heref. Med. Soc. Prev: Trainee GP N. Wilts. VTS.
LEEMING, Charles Anthony 69 Addington Street, Ramsgate CT11 9JQ Tel: 01843 593544 — BM 1985 Soton.; MRCGP 1990.
LEEMING, David John Manor Farm Close Surgery, 8 Manor Farm Close, Drayton, Norwich NR8 6DN Tel: 01603 867532 — MB ChB 1970 Liverp.; DObst RCOG 1972. Prev: SHO Roy. Liverp. Childr. Hosp.; Ho. Off. Roy. S.. Hosp. Liverp. & Liverp. Matern. Hosp.
LEEMING, James Thompson (retired) 9 Mosswood Park, East Didsbury, Manchester M20 5QW — MB ChB Manch. 1951; MD Manch. 1958; FRCP Lond. 1972, M 1957. Prev: Cons. Phys. (Geriat. Med.) Roy. Infirm. Manch. & Withington Hosp. Manch.
LEEMING, John Allan Health Centre, Park Drive, Stenhousemuir, Larbert FK5 3BB Tel: 01324 552200 Fax: 01324 553623 — MB ChB 1981 Glas.; BSc (Hons.) Glas. 1978, MB ChB 1981; DRCOG 1984.
LEEMING, Mr Robert Desmond (retired) c/o Maelor General Hospital, Wrexham LL13 7TD — LRCPI & LM, LRSCI & LM 1957; LRCPI & LM, LRCSI & LM 1957; FRCS Ed. 1972; DLO Eng. 1964. Cons. ENT Surg. Clwyd S. Health Dist.
LEEMING, Roy Alexander (retired) The Watch House, North View, Brixham TQ5 9TT Tel: 01803 856887 — LMSSA 1944 Lond. Prev: Med. Off. Sainsbury's Depot Buntingford.
LEEMING-LATHAM, Laurence Dow Agrosciences, Letcombe Laboratory, Letcombe Regis, Wantage OX12 9JT Tel: 020 7268 8417 Fax: 01235 774764 Email: lauri.latham@marks-and-spencer.com; Alton House, Wallingford St, Wantage OX12 8AU Tel: 020 7224 3189 — MB ChB 1974 Birm.; DAvMed. Eng. 1981; MMed Sc 1990; MFOM RCP Eng. 1991. Health Sci.s Manager, Marks and Spencer, Baker St., Lond. Socs: Sec. SOM Lond. Gp. Prev: Area Med. Adviser, Dow AgroSci.s; Med. Off. Roy. Air Force.
LEEPER, Anthony Brian Michael Stonehall Surgery, Nethergate St., Clare, Sudbury CO10 8NP Tel: 01787 278999 Fax: 01787 278522; Rowans House, Calford Green, Haverhill CB9 7UN Tel: 01440 713222 — MRCS Eng. LRCP Lond. 1984; MA (Hons.) Camb. 1981; Cert. Family Plann. JCC 1989; Cert. Prescribed Equiv. Exp. 1989. (Westm.) Socs: BMA.
LEEPER, Kenneth Charles Billinghay Medical Practice, 39 High Street, Billinghay, Lincoln LN4 4AU Tel: 01526 860490 Fax: 01526 861860; 10 Foster Close, Timberland, Lincoln LN4 3SE Tel: 01526 378711 — MB ChB 1988 Sheff.; MRCGP 1993; DFFP 1993; DRCOG 1991. Prev: SHO Hereford VTS.
LEEPER, Richard Quinn The Health Centre, Aylesbury Road, Wendover, Aylesbury HP22 6LD Tel: 01296 623452 — MB BS Lond. 1968; MRCS Eng. LRCP Lond. 1968; DCH Eng. 1972; DObst RCOG 1970; Cert JCC Lond. 1977. (The London Hospital)
LEEPER, Wendy Jane 33 Newton Road, Kirkintilloch, Glasgow G66 5LS — MB ChB 1987 Glas.; MRCGP 1991; DRCOG 1990; Cert. Family Plann. JCC 1990.
LEES, Alan Marshall Ashby Turn Primary Care Centre, Ashby Link, Scunthorpe DN16 2UT Tel: 01724 842051 Fax: 01724 280346 — MB ChB 1979 Sheff.
LEES, Alan Phillips Tonypandy Health Centre, De Winton Field, Tonypandy CF40 2LE Tel: 01443 432112; Croft Cottage, Beach Road, Colhugh St, Llantwit Major CF61 1RF Tel: 01446 793514 — MRCS Eng. LRCP Lond. 1960; MSc (Occupat. Med.) Lond. 1982; MFOM RCP Lond. 1982, AFOM 1981; DA (UK) 1961; DAvMed FOM RCP Lond. 1970. (Guy's) Prev: Cons. Adviser Occupat. Med. S. Wales Constab.; Sen. Med. Off. Civil Aviat. Auth.; Regist. (Anaesth.) N. Manch. Hosp. Gp.
LEES, Allan Peter St Brycedale Surgery, St. Brycedale Road, Kirkcaldy KY1 1ER Tel: 01592 640800 Fax: 01592 644944; 3 Southerton Gardens, Kirkcaldy KY2 5NG Tel: 01592 260891 Email: leesap99@hotmail.com — MB ChB 1973 Ed.; BSc (Med. Sci.) Ed. 1970, MB ChB 1973; MRCGP 1977. (Edinburgh) GP Princip.; Paediat. Clin. Asst. Prev: SHO (Med). Milesmark Hosp. Fife; SHO (Cas.) Dunfermline & W. Fife Hosp.; GP Melbourn, Austral.
LEES, Professor Andrew John Private Patients Wing, University College Hospital, Grafton Way, London WC1E 6AU Tel: 020 7388 3894 Fax: 020 7380 9816; 75 Fordington Road, London N6 4TH Fax: 020 7829 8748 Email: alees@ion.ucl.ac.uk — MD 1978 Lond.; MB BS 1970; FRCP Lond. 1987; MRCP (UK) 1974. (Royal Lond. Hosp.) Cons. Neurol. Nat. Hosp. Neurol. & Neurosurg. Middlx. Hosp. & Univ. Coll. Hosp. Lond.; Med. Adviser Pk.insons Dis. Soc.; Co-Dir. Pk.insons Dis. Soc. Brain Bank; Edr. in Chief Movement Disorders; Chrm med adv panel of PSP Assoc Europe; Dir Rita Lila W.on Inst of Neurol. stu. Roy. Free Hosp & UCL Med Sch; Appeal Steward Brit. Boxing Bd. Control; Med. Adviser UK Gilles de la Tourette Assn. Socs: Fell. Roy. Soc. Med.; Co. Chairm. Basal Ganglia Club; Pres. Movement Dis. Soc. Europ. Prev: Sen. Regist. Nat. Hosp. Nerv. Dis. & Univ. Coll. Hosp. Lond.; Clin. Asst. L'Hosp. Salpetriare, Paris; Regist. (Neurol.) Univ. Coll. Hosp. Lond. & Middlx. Hosp. Lond.
LEES, Andrew Robert Hanwell Health Centre, 20 Church Road, Hanwell, London W7 1DR Tel: 020 8567 5738 — MB BS 1986 Lond.; MRCGP 1990; DCH RCP Lond. 1990.

LEES, Andrew Wilson (retired) 65 St Germain's, Drymen Road, Bearsden, Glasgow G61 2RS Tel: 0141 942 4628 — MB ChB Glas. 1939; MD Glas. 1949; FRCP Glas. 1964, M 1962; FRCP Ed. 1956, M 1950; FRFPS Glas. 1949; DPH Glas. 1941. Barrister-at-Law Gray's Inn. Prev: Cons. Chest Phys. Ruchill, Stobhill & Duntocher Hosps. & Dumbarton Dist.

LEES, Audrey Ward (retired) The Cottage, Ashcroft Lane, Chesterfield Vill., Lichfield WS14 0EQ Tel: 01543 480848 — MB ChB 1955 Manch.; DObst. RCOG 1958 (Manch.). Prev: GP Shenstone.

LEES, Barbara Eugenia Orchard Medical Practice, Orchard Road, Broughton Astley, Leicester LE9 6RG Tel: 01445 282599 Fax: 01445 286772; 34 Billington Road W., Elmesthorpe, Leicester LE9 7SD Tel: 01455 850745 — MB BS 1980 Lond.; MRCGP 1985.

LEES, Beecher Hadfield (retired) 15 Healds Green, Chadderton, Oldham OL1 2SP Tel: 0161 624 7119 — MRCS Eng. LRCP Lond. 1946. Prev: GP Chadderton, latecart RAMC.

LEES, Bruce Leighton (retired) Hayfield, Bourne Fields, Twyford, Winchester SO21 1NY Tel: 01962 713164 — MB BS 1956 Lond.; DObst RCOG 1961. Prev: GP Winchester.

LEES, Bryan Antony (retired) 168A High Street, Swanage BH19 2PF Tel: 01929 423026 — MB BS Lond. 1955. Prev: Ho. Surg. Middlx. Hosp. Lond.

LEES, Catherine Mairi Wishaw General Hospital, Netherton St, Wishaw WC2 0DB Tel: 01698 366203; Flat 4, 8 Royal Crescent, Glasgow G3 7SL Tel: 0141 332 0250 Email: cathlees@aol.com — MB ChB 1990 Manch.; 1995 MRCPCH; BSc St. And. 1987; MRCPI 1995. (Manchester) Cons. Paediat., Wishaw Gen. Hosp., Netherton St., Wishaw, MC2 0DB. Prev: Regist. (Neonatol.) Liverp. Wom.'s Hosp.; Specialist Regist., Mersty Deanery.

LEES, Christoph Christopher Harris Birthright Centre, King's College Hospital, Denmark Hill, London SE5 8RX; 29 Cressy House, Queen's Ride, London SW13 0HZ Tel: 020 8788 3578 Fax: 020 8788 3578 — MB BS 1990 Lond.; BSc (Clin. Pharmacol.) Lond. 1987; MRCOG 1996. (Guy's Hosp. (UMDS)) Subspecialty Fell. (FetoMatern. Med.) Harris Birthright Centre King's Coll. Hosp. Prev: Lect. (O & G) St. Geo. Hosp. Med. Sch. Lond.; Regist. King's Coll. Hosp. & Qu. Mary's Hosp. Sidcup; Research Fell. King's Coll. Hosp. Lond.

LEES, Colin Torrens Wilson Airdrie Health Centre, Monkscourt Avenue, Airdrie ML6 0JU Tel: 01236 769333; Beinn Na Fadhla, 23 Garden Square Walk, Airdrie ML6 0HY — MB ChB 1973 Glas. (Glas.) EMP Benefit Agy.

LEES, David Albert Tamarix, Beauchamp Lane, Callow End, Worcester WR2 4UG Tel: 01905 830603 Email: daltamarix@aol.com — MB ChB 1963 Birm.; MRCS Eng. LRCP Lond. 1963; DObst RCOG 1966; DA Eng. 1965. (Birm.) p/t GP, Worchester. Prev: Ho. Off. (Surg.) Gen. Hosp. Birm.; Ho. Off. (O & G) Ronkswood Hosp. Worcester; SHO (Anaesth.) United Birm. Hosps.

LEES, David Arthur Russell Crofthill, Daviot West, Inverness IV2 5XL — MB ChB 1971 Glas.; FRCOG 1989, M 1977; DObst 1973. Cons. (O & G) Raigmore Hosp. Inverness; Hon. Clin. Sen. Lect. Univ. Aberd. Socs: Highland Med. Soc. Prev: Sen. Regist. (O & G) Qu. Mothers Hosp. Glas.; Sen. Regist. (O & G) Stobhill Gen. Hosp. Glas.; Regist. (O & G) Robroyston Hosp. Glas.

LEES, David Michael South Street Doctors Surgery, South Street, Cockermouth CA13 9QP Tel: 01900 324123 Fax: 01900 324122; Paddle Beck House, Eaglesfield, Cockermouth CA13 0RX Tel: 01900 824974 Fax: 01900 829463 Email: leesfm@globalnet.co.uk — MB ChB 1973 Leeds; MRCGP 1979. (Leeds) Socs: BMA.

LEES, Denise Anne Kirby and Partners, Charlton Group Medical Practice, Charlton Street, Oakengates, Telford TF2 6DA Tel: 01952 620138 Fax: 01952 615282 — MB ChB 1987 Manch.; MRCGP 1991; DRCOG 1990. Prev: SHO (Paediat.) Sunderland Dist. Gen. Hosp.; SHO (O & G) Qu. Eliz. Hosp. Gateshead; SHO (Psychiat.) Preston Hosp. N. Shields.

LEES, Doris Irene (retired) 3 Woodburn Avenue, Aberdeen AB15 8JQ Tel: 01224 316250 Email: doris.lees@btinternet.com — MB ChB 1948 Aberd.; FRCP Ed. 1994; MRCP Ed. 1954. Prev: Lect. (Med.) Univ. Aberd.

LEES, Edgar John Newtownards Health Centre, Frederick Street, Newtownards BT23 4LS Tel: 028 9181 7239; 5 Westmount Park, Newtownards BT23 4BP Tel: 01247 815995 — MB BCh BAO 1974 Dub.; MRCGP 1979.

LEES, (Elizabeth) Patricia (retired) Flat 7, Compass Court, North Drive, Wallasey CH45 0LZ — MB BCh BAO 1954; MD Belf. 1959,; Dip Audiol 1977 Manchester. Audiol. Phys. Wirral AHA. Prev: John Rankin Research Fell. Liverp. Univ.

LEES, Gary Andrew Armley Medical Centre, 16 Church Road, Armley, Leeds LS12 1TZ Tel: 0113 295 3800 Fax: 0113 295 3810 — MB ChB 1985 Leeds.

LEES, Gordon McArthur (retired) 3 Woodburn Avenue, Aberdeen AB15 8JQ Tel: 01224 316250 — MB ChB 1961 Aberd.; PhD Aberd. 1968, MB ChB 1961. Hon. Reader (Biomed. Sci.) Univ. Aberd. Prev: Vis. Prof. Kurume Univ. Sch. Med., Japan.

LEES, Heidi 29 Hilltop Road, Liverpool L16 7QL — MB ChB 1993 Liverp.

LEES, Jacqueline Susan Newland Medical Practice, Whitburn Rd, Bathgate EH48 2SS Tel: 01506 655155; 26B Dalrymple Crescent, Edinburgh EH9 2NX Tel: 0131 662 1765 — MB ChB 1980 Ed.

LEES, James Alastair Stirling (retired) Lindisfarne, 74 Woodcrest Road, Purley CR8 4JB Tel: 020 8660 9910 — MB BChir 1954 Camb.; MA 1974 Camb.; DObst. RCOG 1960. Prev: Ho. Surg. & Ho. Phys. Med. Unit Lond. Hosp.

LEES, Mr James Thompson Ardowan, Tannoch Drive, Milngavie, Glasgow G62 Tel: 0141 956 1782 — LRCP LRCS 1948 Ed.; LRCP LRCS Ed. LRFPS Glas. 1948; FRFPS Glas. 1959; FRCS Glas. 1962; DLO Eng. 1954. Cons. ENT Surg. Stobhill Hosp. Glas. Socs: Scott. Otol. Soc.

LEES, Jean Callan 33 Newlands Road, Newlands, Glasgow G43 2JG Tel: 0141 632 9530 — MB ChB 1965 Glas.; FFA RCS Eng. 1971; DObst RCOG 1967. Cons. Anaesth. Hairmyres Hosp. E. Kilbride; Hon. Clin. Sen. Lect. (Anaesth.) Univ. Glas.; Speciality adviser in anaesthetics hairmyres hosp. Socs: Glas. & W. Scot. Soc. Anaesth.; Assn. Anaesth. Prev: Sen. Regist. & Regist. (Anaesth.) W.. Infirm. Glas.; Asst. Med. Off. Mlanje Miss. Hosp., Malawi.

LEES, Jennifer Mary Walnut House, Hollycroft Road, Emneth, Wisbech PE14 8AY — MB ChB 1987 Leeds.

LEES, John Francis (retired) St Helier Hospital, Carshalton SM5 1AA — MB BChir 1950 Camb.; FFA RCS Eng. 1963. Cons. Anaesth. St. Helier Hosp. Carshalton.

LEES, John Michael Ashcroft Surgery, 2 Ashcroft Drive, Denham, Uxbridge UB9 5JF Tel: 01895 834868 — MB BS 1975 Lond.

LEES, Kathleen Patricia Kingswear Court, Dartmouth TQ6 0DX Tel: 0180 425366 — MRCS Eng. LRCP Lond. 1941. (Lond. Sch. Med. Wom.)

LEES, Professor Kennedy Richardson University Department Medicine & Therapeutics, Gardiner Institute, Western Infirmary, Glasgow G11 6NT Tel: 0141 211 2780 Fax: 0141 211 2780 Email: kir.lees@clinmed.gla.ac.uk — MB ChB 1980 Glas.; BSc (Hons.) Glas. 1977, MD 1986; FRCP Glas. 1993; MRCP (UK) 1983. (University of Glasgow) Clin. Dir. Acute Stroke Unit Univ. Dept.Med.& Therap. W.ern Infirm. Glas.; Prof. (CerebroVasc. Med.) & Hon. Cons. W.ern Infirm.; Hon. Cons. W. Infirm. Socs: Europ. Stroke Counc. Exec. (Comm.); Assoc. of Phys.s of UK; Brit. Assoc. of Stroke Phys.s (Chairm.Train. & Educat. Comm.).

LEES, Lionel Andrew (retired) 13 Barbara Close, Church Crookham, Fleet GU52 6AX Tel: 01252 625809 — MB BS Lond. 1959; MRCS Eng. LRCP Lond. 1958; FRCOG 1982, M 1969, DObst. 1965. Prev: Sen. Cons. BAOR O & G Brit. Milit. Hosp. Munster.

LEES, Lorna Jean (retired) The Terrace House, Chalkheugh Terrace, Kelso TD5 7DX — MB ChB 1959 Ed.; FRCP Ed. 1979, M 1966. Prev: Clin. Research Phys. Pfizer Ltd.

LEES, Martin 322 Kennington Road, London SE11 4LD — MB BS 1993 Lond.

LEES, Mr Martin McArthur (retired) — MB ChB Aberd. 1958; MD (Commend.) Aberd. 1971; FRCP Ed 1995; FRCS Ed. 1985; FRCOG 1979, M 1966; DObst RCOG 1960. Prev: Research Fell. (O & G) Univ. Edin.

LEES, Mary (retired) Yarnold Lane Farm, Bournheath, Bromsgrove B61 9JG Tel: 01527 873472 — MB BS 1946 Lond.; DCH Eng. 1950. Prev: Med. Asst. Lea Hosp. BromsGr..

LEES, Matthew Peter 69 Marshals Drive, St Albans AL1 4RD — BM BS 1998 Nottm.; BM BS Nottm 1998.

LEES, Melissa Mary Dept. Of Med. Genetics, St. George's Hospital, London SW17 Tel: 0208 725 1971 Fax: 020 7813 8141

Email: mlees@sghms.ac.uk; Grove House, Dulwich Common, London SE21 7EZ Tel: 020 7693 1458 — MB BS 1986 Lond.; MD LOND 1998; FRACP 2000; MSc (Distinc.) Lond. 1995; MRCP (UK) 1991; DCH RCP Lond. 1988. Cons. (Clin. Genetics) St Geo.'s Hosp. Lond. Prev: Regist. (Paediat.) Roy. Childr. Hosp. Brisbane & Roy. Alexander Hosp. for Childr. Sydney, Austral.; SHO (Paediat.) Kingston Hosp. Kingston-upon-Thames.; SpR GOS Hosp.

LEES, Norman (retired) 145 Norwich Road, Wymondham NR18 0SJ Tel: 01953 602229 — MB BS 1947 Lond.; MRCS Eng. LRCP Lond. 1947; MRCGP 1953; DObst RCOG 1950. Prev: Ho. Surg. (Obst.) Edgware Gen. Hosp.

LEES, Norman Watson 33 Newlands Road, Newlands, Glasgow G43 2JG Tel: 0141 632 9530 — MD 1988 Glas.; BA Open 1986; MB ChB 1968; FFA RCS Eng. 1972; DObst RCOG 1970. Cons. Anaesth. Vict. Infirm. Glas. Socs: Assn. Anaesths.; Scott. Soc. Anaesth. Prev: Research Asst. Dept. Surg. W.. Infirm. Glas.; Regist. Dept. Anaesth. W.. Infirm. Glas.

LEES, Paula Frederica 8 Churchill Way, Painswick, Stroud GL6 6RQ — MB BS 1962 Lond.; MRCS Eng. LRCP Lond. 1962; DA Eng. 1965; DObst RCOG 1965. (Roy. Free) Socs: BAMS. Prev: Princip. GP Gloucester; SHO (Anaesth.) Salisbury Gen. Infirm.; SHO (Paediat.) Univ. Coll. Hosp. W. Indies.

LEES, Peter Bernard, Lt.-Col. RAMC Retd. (retired) 70 Mill Lane, Herne Bay CT6 7DP Tel: 01227 364864 — MB ChB 1950 Manch.; MSc Lond. 1963; DMRD Eng. 1964; DTM & H Eng. 1958. Cons. Radiol. Min. Defence. Prev: Cons. Radiol N. W.. RHA.

LEES, Mr Peter Derick Wessex Neurological Centre, Southampton General Hospital, Southampton SO16 6YD Tel: 02380 796445 Fax: 02380 798678 Email: peter.lees@suht.swest.nhs.uk — MB ChB 1975 Manch.; MS Soton. 1990; FRCS Eng. 1981. (Manchester) Med. Dir. Sot. Uni. Hosp. NHS Trust; Hon. Cons. Neurosurg. Wessex Neurol. Centr. Soton. Gen. Hosp.; Civil. Cons. Neurosurg. to RN; Sen. Lect. in Neurosurg. Univ.Soton. Socs: Brit. Assn. Med. Managers; Brit. Soc. Neurol. Surgs. Prev: Lect. (Neurosurg.) Univ. Soton; Regist. (Gen. Surg.) Nottm. HA; Regist. (Neurosurg.) Regional Dept. Neurosurg. & Neurol. Derby.

LEES, Richard Michael 17 Broad Lane, Lymington SO41 3QN — MB BS 1998 Lond.; MB BS Lond 1998.

LEES, Ronald Forbes Barton Highfield, Reidhaven St., Whitehills, Banff AB45 2NJ — MB ChB 1956 Aberd.; MRCGP 1974; DCH RFPS Glas. 1960. Prev: Med. Off. Budu Developm. Scheme Sarawak.

LEES, Shan 8 Greenmount Drive, Burntisland KY3 9JH — MB ChB 1986 Manch.; BSc St. And. 1983; DRCOG 1991. Clin. Med. Off. Fife HB. Prev: SHO (O & G) Rochford Gen. Hosp. Essex; SHO (Psychiat.) Runwell Hosp. Wickford Essex; SHO (A & E) S.end Gen. Hosp.

LEES, Sheila Jane Hayfield, Bournefields, Twyford, Winchester SO21 1NY — MB BS 1960 Lond. (Middlx.)

LEES, Stephen Alexander Morrill Street Health Centre, Holderness Road, Hull HU9 2LJ Tel: 01482 320046; St Anthony's, 8 Baxtergate, Hedon, Hull HU12 8JN — MB BS 1980 Lond.

LEES, Mr Timothy Andrew Department of Vascular Surgery, Freeman Hospital, Freeman Road, High Heaton, Newcastle upon Tyne NE7 7DN Tel: 0191 284 3111 Email: timothy.lees@ncl.uk; Lealholm, 108 Moorside N., Fenham, Newcastle upon Tyne NE4 9DX — MB ChB 1984 Manch.; MD Newc. 1993; FRCS Eng. 1989. (Manch.) Cons. Vasc. Surg. Freeman Hosp. Newc. u. Tyne. Prev: Sen. Regist. (Gen. & Vasc. Surg.) Roy. Hallamsh. Hosp. Sheff.; Research Fell. (Gen. Surg.) Univ. Newc.; Regist. Rotat. (Gen. Surg.) Freeman Hosp. Newc.

LEES, Vincent Thomas (retired) Hill Cot, 80 The Common, Parbold, Wigan WN8 7EA Tel: 01257 462534 — MB ChB 1936 Manch.; DOMS Eng. 1947. Prev: Cons. Ophth. Surg. Wigan AHA.

LEES, Mr William (retired) The Old Vicarage, Woodside, Witton Park, Bishop Auckland DL14 0AB Tel: 01388 3638 — MB ChB 1946 Glas.; FRCS Eng. 1958. Prev: Cons. Surg. Gen. Hosp. Bishop Auckland.

LEES, William, CBE, OStJ (retired) 13 Hall Park Hill, Berkhamsted HP4 2NH Tel: 01442 863010 — MRCS Eng. LRCP Lond. 1947; MB ChB Manch. 1947, DPH 1958; FRCOG 1970, M 1954, DObst 1951; MFCM 1973; MRCGP. Sen. PMO DHSS; Graded Obst. Specialist, Col. RAMC TAVR. Prev: SCM SW Thames RHA.

LEES, William Cooper 1 The Crescent, Earley, Reading RG6 7NW Tel: 0118 966 3542 — MB ChB Birm. 1947. (Birm.) Med. Adviser Europ. Centre for Medium Range Weather Forecast Reading; Med. Legal Adviser Swift Med. Servs. Reading; Med. Examr. for Various Insur. Cos. Reading. Prev: SCMO W. Berks. HA; Med. Off. Colon. Med. Serv. Malaya.

LEES, Professor William Robert Department of Diagnostic Imaging, The Middlesex Hospital, Mortimer St., London W1T 3AA Tel: 020 7436 2447 Fax: 020 70436 2447; 44 Stamford Brook Road, London W6 0XL Tel: 020 8749 6733 Fax: 020 8932 3585 — MB BS 1972 Lond.; FRCR 1981; Hon. FRACR 1993. Cons. Radiol. Middlx. Hosp. Lond. & King Edwd. VII Hosp. for Off.; Prof. Med. Imaging UCL; Mem. Nat. Radiological Protec. Bd. 1998. Socs: Fell. Roy. Soc. Med.; Brit. Inst. Radiol. Prev: Sen. Regist. (Radiol.) Middlx. Hosp. Lond.; Regist. (Radiol. & Clin. Measurem.) Middlx. Hosp. Lond.

LEES, Yvonne Clare 141 Runnymede Road, Ponteland, Newcastle upon Tyne NE20 9HN — MB ChB 1994 Leic.

LEES-MILLAIS, Jane Vanessa Hammond The Old Rectory, Cranfield Road, Moulsoe, Newport Pagnell MK16 0HL — MB BS 1978 Lond. Indep. GP Bucks.

LEESE, Colette Winifred Monk Bretton Health Centre, High Street, Barnsley S71 2EQ — MB BS 1981 Lond.; MRCGP 1985.

LEESE, Elizabeth Jane Room 605A, Skipton House, 80 London Road, London SE1 6LH Tel: 020 7972 1526; Little Acre, Back Lane, Sheering, Bishop's Stortford CM22 7NF Tel: 01279 725164 — MB ChB 1967 Bristol; FRCP Lond. 1992. Sen. Med. Off. Communicable Dis. DoH Lond. Socs: Fell. Roy. Soc. Med.; Brit. Thorac. Soc.; Brit. Soc. Study of Infec. Prev: Cons. Phys. St. Mary's Hosp. Portsmouth; Sen. Regist. St. Geo. Hosp. Lond.; Attend. Phys. Harlem Hosp. Columbia Univ., NY.

LEESE, Graham John Central Surgery, Welfare Road, Thurnscoe, Rotherham S63 0JZ Tel: 01709 890501 Fax: 01709 898595 (Call before faxing); 15 Ewden Way, Pogmoor, Barnsley S75 2JW — MB BS 1982 Lond.; BA Camb. 1978; MRCGP 1986.

LEESE, Graham Peter Wards 1 and 2, Ninewells Hospital, Dundee DD1 9SY Tel: 01382 660111 Fax: 01382 632317 — MD 1995; FRCP 2000; MB ChB 1987; BMSc (Hons) Dund 1984; FRCPE 1997; MRCP (UK) 1990. (Dundee) NHS Cons. (Gen. Med., Diabetes & Endocrinol.); Hon. Sen. Lect. (Med.). Socs: Soc. Endocrinol.; Brirt. Diabetic Assn. Prev: Lect. (Liverp.); Res. Fell. Dept. Physiol. Dundee.

LEESE, Ian Dennis The Health Centre, Dunning Street, Stoke-on-Trent ST6 5BE Tel: 01782 425834 Fax: 01782 577599; 3 Torridon Close, New Park, Trentham, Stoke-on-Trent ST4 8YA Tel: 01782 659209 — MB ChB 1984 Manch.; MRCGP 1988.

LEESE, Janet Village Surgery, Cheswick Green, Solihull B90 4JA Tel: 01564 703311 Fax: 01564 703794; 12 Claverdon Close, Solihull B91 1QP Tel: 0121 705 4839 — MB BS 1984 Lond.; BSc Lond. 1978; MRCGP 1988. (Char. Cross)

LEESE, Philip Graham 21 Lawton Street, Congleton CW12 1RU Tel: 0126 02 10 — MRCS Eng. LRCP Lond. 1945. (Manch.) Vis. Med. Off. W. Heath Hosp. Congleton. Socs: N. Staffs. Med. Soc.; Fell. Manch. Med. Soc.

LEESE, Ruth Andrea Muirhead Health Centre, Muirhead, By Liff, Dundee; The Ghyll, Old Whisky Road, Auchterhouse, Dundee DD3 0RD Tel: 01382 320214 — MB BCh 1987 Wales; BSc (Hons) St. And. 1984; MRCGP 1991. GP Retainer Scheme - Muirhead Nr Dundee; GP Retainer Scheme, Dermat. - Ninwells NHS Teachg. Hosp. Trust.

LEESE, Trevor Royal Lancaster Infirmary, Ashton Road, Lancaster LA1 4RP Tel: 01524 65944 Fax: 01524 583194 Email: trevor.leese@laht.nwest.nhs.uk; Bank House, Ashton Road, Lancaster LA1 5AZ — MB BS 1979 Lond.; BA, MA Camb. 1980; MD Leic. 1988; FRCS Eng. 1983; MRCS Eng. LRCP Lond. 1979. (Camb. & Westm.) Cons. Surg. Roy. Lancs. Infirm. Socs: Brit. Soc. Gastroenterol. (Comm. Mem.) Pancreatic Sect.; Pancratic Soc. GB & Irel. (ex.-Pres. & Comm. mem.); Assn. Upper G.I. Surg. Prev: Regist. & Sen. Regist. Leics. Roy. Infirm.; Ho. Off. & SHO W.minster Hosp. Lond.; Deptm. Demonst. (Anat.) Univ. Camb.

LEESER, Jenny Elizabeth 7 Riversdene, Stokesley, Middlesbrough TS9 5DD — MB BS 1978 Lond.; MRCP (UK) 1982; AFOM RCP Lond. 1986.

LEESLEY, Debbie Anne 63 Warwick Road, Carlisle CA1 1EB; 63 Warwick Road, Carlisle CA1 1EB — MB BS 1996 Newc. GP Regist. Socs: BMA. Prev: A & E SHO; Paediat. SHO.

LEESON, Christopher Paul Maxted 62 Outwoods Road, Loughborough LE11 3LY — BChir 1998 Camb.; BChir Camb 1998; MB Camb 1998; PhD Camb 1998; BSc (Hons) St. And 1993.

LEESON, Joyce Eve (retired) 36 St Mary's Hall Road, Crumpsall, Manchester M8 5DZ — MB ChB Manch. 1954; DPH Manch. 1958. Prev: Dir. (Pub. Health) N. Manch. HA.

LEESON, Karen Elizabeth The Surgery, 5 Enys Road, Eastbourne BN21 2DQ Tel: 01323 410088 Fax: 01323 644638; Beech Lawn, 4 Selwyn Road, Eastbourne BN21 2LE Tel: 01323 411424 — MB BS 1983 Lond.; DRCOG 1989; DCH RCP Lond. 1986.

LEESON, Nicola Ann 309 Cyncoed Road, Cyncoed, Cardiff CF23 6PB — BM BS 1984 Nottm.; MRCGP 1989; DRCOG 1988.

LEESON, Patricia Mary (retired) Thatched Cottage, Lower Road, Mackworth Village, Derby DE22 4NF Tel: 01332 824282 — MB BCh BAO Dub. 1951; BA Dub. 1951; FRCP Lond. 1973, M 1957. Prev: Cons. Phys. Geriat. Trent RHA (Derby).

LEESON, Mr Peter Charles (retired) 15 Shandon Close, Tunbridge Wells TN2 3RE Tel: 01892 22747 — MB BS Lond. 1945; FRCS Eng. 1956; DLO Eng. 1958. Cons. ENT Surg. Tunbridge Wells Hosp. Gp. Prev: Cons. ENT Surg. Salford & W. Manch. Hosp. Gp.

LEESON, Mr Simon Christian Ysbyty Gwynedd, Gwynedd Hospitals NHS Trust, Penrhoscarnedd, Bangor LL57 2PW Tel: 01248 384954 Fax: 01248 384273 Email: simon.leeson@nww-tr.wales.nhs.uk; 84 Albert Drive, Deganwy, Conwy LL31 9RL Tel: 01492 593298 Fax: 01492 593298 Email: linands@deganwya.fsnet.co.uk — MB ChB 1984 Manch.; BSc (Hons.) Physiol. Manch. 1981; FRCS Eng. 1989; MRCOG 1991. Cons. O & G Ysbyty Gwynedd Bangor Gwynedd. Socs: Brit. Soc. for Colposcopy and Cervical Path., Welsh Represen.; Brit. Gyn. Cancer Soc.

LEESON, William Peter James Foyleside Family Practice, Bridge Street Medical Centre, 30 Bridge Street, Londonderry BT48 6LA Tel: 028 7126 7847 Fax: 028 7137 0723 — MB BCh BAO 1981 Belf.; MRCGP 1986; DCH Dub. 1985; DRCOG 1984. Prev: SHO (Paediat.) Belf. City Hosp.; SHO (O & G) Daisy Hill Hosp. Newry; SHO (Med.) Coleraine Hosp.

LEESON-PAYNE, Catherine Elizabeth Scott Oakwood, Muirschearlich, Banavie, Fort William PH33 7PB — MB ChB 1984 Sheff.

LEESON-PAYNE, Charles Geoffrey Belford Hospital, Belford Rd, Fort William PH33 6BS; Oakwood, Muirshearlich, Banavie, Fort William PH33 7PD — MB ChB 1986 Sheff.; BMedSci (Hons.) Sheff. 1985, MB ChB 1986; FRCA 1993. Cons. Anaesth. Belford Hosp. Fort William Highland. Prev: Sen. Regist. (Anaesth.) Nottm. Hosp.; Research Fell. Univ. Dept. Anaesth. Nottm.; SHO (Anaesth.) Sheff. Hosps. Gp.

LEETCH, Robert James Richhill Clinic, 6 Greenview, Maynooth Road, Richhill, Armagh BT61 9PD; 73 Mullanasilla Road, Richill BT61 9LL — MB BCh BAO 1981 Belf.; MRCGP 1985; DRCOG 1985. (Queens Belf.)

LEETE, Richard John Wyndham House Surgery, Fore Street, Silverton, Exeter EX5 4HZ Tel: 01392 860034 Fax: 01392 861165 — MB BS 1967 Lond.; MRCS Eng. LRCP Lond. 1967; MRCGP 1977; DObst RCOG 1972. (Guy's) Princip. GP Silverton; GP Trainer Devon. Prev: Regist. (Med.) I. of Thanet Gp. Hosps.; SHO (Obst.) Exeter & Mid Devon Gp. Hosps.; Ho. Phys. (Paediat.) Guy's Hosp. Lond.

LEFEBVRE, Miss Louise Mireille Llanelli General Hospital, Marble Hall Road, Llanelli SA15 1NL; Trawscoed, The High St, Llanfyllin SY22 5AR — MB BCh 1988 Wales.

LEFEVER, Robert Promis Unit of Primary Care, 2A Pelham St., London SW7 3HU Tel: 020 7584 6511 Fax: 020 7225 1147; The Promis Recovery Centre, Old Court Hse, Pinners Hill, Nonington, Dover CT15 4LL Tel: 01304 841700 Fax: 01304 841917 — MB 1965 Camb.; MA, BChir Camb. 1965. (Univ Cambs Middlesex Hosp) Prev: Surg. & Cardiol. Ho. Off. The Middlx. Hosp.

LEFEVRE, Dianne Campbell Thameside Community Health Trust, Basildon Hospital, Basildon SS16 5NL Tel: 01268 593843 Fax: 01268 593741 Email: dianne@clara.net; 14 Cranwich Road, London N16 5JX Tel: 020 8880 2340 Fax: 020 8880 2340 Email: dianne@clara.net — MB ChB 1966 Cape Town; MRCP (UK) 1971; FRCPsych 1995, M 1979. (Lond.) Cons. Psychother. Thameside Community Health Trust Basildon. Socs: Roy. Soc. Med. Prev: Sen. Regist. & Regist. (Psychiat.) Maudsley & St. Mary's Hosps. Lond.; Regist. St. Anne's Hosp. Lond.; Volun. Work (Med.) Red. Cresc. Soc. Middle E.

LEFEVRE, Karen Elaine Inverurie Health Centre, 1 Constitution Street, Inverurie, Aberdeen Tel: 01467 621345 Email: karen.lefevre@inverurie.grampian.scot.nhs.uk; Hattonfaulds, Fintray AB21 0YD Email: adrian.karen@lineone.net — MB BS 1993 Lond. p/t GP Retainer; Research Fell., Dept. Gen. Pract., Aberd. Socs: Mem. Roy. Coll. Gen. Practitioner.

LEFF, Alexander Paul 38 Twisden Road, London NW5 1DN — MB BS 1993 Lond.; BSc (Hons.) Lond. 1990, MB BS 1993. (UCLMS) Research Fell. (Neurol.) MRCCU Hammersmith Hosp. Lond. Prev: SHO (Neurol.) Nat. Hosp. Neurol. & Neurosurg.; SHO Rotat. (Med.) Roy. Lond. Hosps. Trust.; Ho. Off. (Med. & Gastroenterol.) Univ. Coll. & Middlx. Hosps. Lond.

LEFF, Professor Julian Paul Institute of Psychiatry, De Crespigny Park, London SE5 8AF Tel: 020 7708 3235 Fax: 020 7708 3235; 1 South Hill Park Gardens, London NW3 2TD — MB BS Lond. Lond. 1961; BSc (Anat.) Lond. 1958, MD 1972; MRCP Lond. 1965; MFPHM RCP (UK) 1993; FRCPsych 1979, M 1972; DPM Lond. 1967. (Univ. Coll. Hosp.) MRC Extern. Scientif. Staff Social Psychiat. Sect. Inst. Psychiat. Lond.; Dir. Team for Assessm. Psychiat. Serv. Roy. Free Hosp. Lond.; Hon. Cons. Psychiat. Bethlem Roy. & Maudsley NHS Trust; Prof. Social & Cultural Psychiat. Inst. Psychiat. Lond. Prev: Ho. Phys. Univ. Coll. Hosp. Lond. & Bethnal Green Hosp.; Ho. Surg. Whittington Hosp. Lond.

LEFF, Sonya Valerie (retired) Peacehaven Clinic, 100 Roderick Avenue, Peacehaven BN10 8BN Tel: 01273 580504 Fax: 01273 587002 — MB BS Lond. 1963; FRCPCH 1997; FFPHM RCP (UK) 1996, M 1979; DPH Lond. 1966; DCH Eng. 1965. Cons. Community Paediat. (Child Health) S. Downs NHS Community Trust. Prev: Sen. Med. Off. S. Downs NHS Community Trust.

LEFFORD, Frances Department of Primary Care & Population Sciences, Royal Free/University College Medical School, Rowland Hill Street, London NW3 2PF Tel: 020 7830 2239 Fax: 020 7794 1224; 20 Burghley Road, Kentish Town, London NW5 1UE — MB BS 1957 Lond.; PhD Lond. 1963; DObst RCOG 1959. (Univ. Coll. Hosp.) p/t Hon. Sen. Lect. Univ. Coll. Lond. Roy. Free Campus; Non-Princip. GP, Parliament Hill Surg. Lond. Socs: Assoc., RSM. Prev: Sen. Lect. (Anat.) Univ. Coll. Lond.; Acad. Advisor Project 2000; Ho. Surg. & Ho. Phys. Whittington Hosp. Lond.

LEFLEY, Peter John Palliaon Health Centre, Hylton Road, Sunderland SR4 &XF Tel: 0191 567 4673 Email: peter.lefley@GP-A89007.nhs.uk; Town Foot Barn, Hayton, Brampton CA8 9HR Fax: 01228 670110 Email: xrh75@dial.pipex.com — MB BS 1980 Lond.; MRCGP 1986. (Charing Cross) G. P. Princip. & Trainer.

LEFROY, David Christopher Cardiology, Hammersmith Hospital, Du Cane Road, London W12 0NN Tel: 020 8383 4967 Fax: 020 8740 8373 Email: dlefroy@rpms.ac.uk; 46 Woodfield Crescent, London W5 1PB — MB BChir 1985 Camb.; MA Camb. 1986; MRCP (UK) 1988; FRCP. 1999. (University of Cambridge, St. Thomas's Hospital, London) Sen. Lect. & Hon. Cons. (Cardiol.) Hammersmith Hosp. Lond. Socs: Brit. Cardiac Soc.; BMA. Prev: Sen. Regist. Hammersmith Hosp. Lond.; BHF Internat. Fell. Brigham & Woman's Hosp. Boston; Sen. Regist. St. Mary's Hosp. Lond.

LEFTLEY, Peter (retired) Park House, 9 Palmerston St., Romsey SO51 8GF Tel: 01794 518961 — MB BS Lond. 1958. Prev: Princip. GP Totton, Hants.

LEFTLEY, Philip Andrew Church Hill Surgery, Station Road, Pulham Market, Diss IP21 4TX Tel: 01379 676227 Fax: 01379 608014 Email: philip.leftley@gp-d8046.nhs.uk; 46 The Close, Norwich NR1 4EG Tel: 01603 886172 Fax: 01603 886173 Email: philip.leftley@gp-d8046.nhs.uk — MB ChB 1974 Sheff.; MRCGP 1985; DRCOG 1977. Prev: Med. Off. (c/o Homeless) Leeds FPC.

LEFTWICK, Peter Daniel James 6 The Cottages, Calveley, Tarporley CW6 9JT Tel: 01829 261503 — MB BS 1993 Lond. SHO.Gen. Med. Leighton.Hosp. Crewe.

LEGASSICK, Robert Anthony 147A Wells Road, Bath BA2 3AL — BChir 1996 Camb.

LEGAT, Peter (retired) St John's House, 22 Monmouth St., Bridgwater TA6 5EJ Tel: 01278 422900 — MB ChB Bristol 1941. Prev: Resid. Obst. Off. Roy. United Hosp. Bath.

LEGER, Benedict James 20 Parkfield Road, Topsham, Exeter EX3 0DR — MB ChB 1984 Manch.; BSc Manch. 1981, MB ChB 1984.

LEGG, Catherine Mary Ferryhill Practice, 193 Bon Accord Street, Aberdeen AB11 6UA Tel: 01224 587484 Fax: 01224 574424 — MB ChB 1970 Aberd.; DObst RCOG 1972. Prev: Hosp. Pract. (Palliat. Med.) Roxburghe Hse. Milltimber Aberd.

LEGG, Janina Renata Greenacres, 21 Ashton Grove, East Hill, Otford, Sevenoaks Tel: 0195 922206 — LMSSA 1973 Lond.; Med. Dipl. Warsaw 1963. (Warsaw) GP Swanley.

LEGG, Joanne 27 Grosvenor Avenue, Newcastle upon Tyne NE2 2NN — MB ChB 1993 Manch.

LEGG, Julian Peter 7 Voylart Road, Dunvant, Swansea SA2 7UA Email: julian@london.com — MB BChir 1991 Camb.; MA Camb. 1991; MRCP (UK) 1994. Sen. Regist. in Respirat. Paediat., Soton. Gen. Hosp. Socs: BSACI - Mem. Prev: Regist. (Paediat.) Soton. Gen. Hosp.; Regist. (Paediat.) N. Hants. Hosp. Basingstoke; SHO (Immunol. & Cardiol.) Gt. Ormond St. Hosp. Childr. Lond.

LEGG, Michele Deanna 1 Beech Grove, Ryde PO33 3AN — MB BS 1994 Lond.

LEGG, Mr Nigel Gordon MacDonald The Health Centre, Adelaide St., Norwich NR2 4JL Tel: 01603 625015 Fax: 01603 766820 — MB BChir 1963 Camb.; MA, MB Camb. 1964, BChir 1963; FRCS Ed. 1970; MRCS Eng. LRCP Lond. 1963. (Camb. & Lond. Hosp.) Socs: BMA. Prev: Orthop. Ho. Surg. St. Bart. Hosp. Rochester; Ho. Phys. Chelmsford & Essex Hosp.; Accid. Off. Poplar Hosp.

LEGG, Nigel John Brampton House, Hospital of St John & St Elizabeth, Grove End Road, London NW8 9NH Tel: 020 7286 3370 Fax: 020 7286 6202 Email: nigel-legg@virgin.net; Salisbury House, Bullens Yard, Highgate, London N6 5JT Tel: 020 8347 9137 — MB BS (Hons.) Lond. 1959; FRCP Lond. 1980, M 1964. (St. Mary's) Sen. Lect. (Neurol.) Roy. Postgrad. Med. Sch. Lond.; Hon. Cons. Neurol. Hammersmith Hosp. Lond.; Hon. Sen. Lect. Dept. Clin. Neurol. Nat. Hosp. Nerv. Dis. Lond.; Dir. Soc. for Relief of Widows & Orphans Med. Men. Socs: Brain Res. Assn.; Assn. Brit. Neurol. Prev: Clin. Research Fell. ICRF Lincolns Inn Fields; Res. Med. Off. Nat. Hosp. Nerv. Dis. Qu. Sq.; Research Fell. Virus Dept. Hosp. Sick Childr. Gt. Ormond. St.

LEGG, Owen Campbell The Medical Centre, The Old School, Hadlow, Tonbridge TN11 0ET Tel: 01732 850248; 152 Hadlow Road, Tonbridge TN9 1PB Tel: 01732 359206 — MB BS 1959 Lond.; MRCS Eng. LRCP Lond. 1959; DObst RCOG 1961. (Guy's)

LEGG, Richard James Ferryhill Practice, 193 Bon Accord Street, Aberdeen AB11 6UA Tel: 01224 587484 Fax: 01224 574424 — MB ChB 1993 Aberd.

LEGG, William John Jackson 97 Clifton Drive, Lytham St Annes FY8 1BY Tel: 01253 736689 — MB BCh BAO 1963 Belf.; MRCS Eng. LRCP Lond. 1964. p/t Apptd. Mem. Med. Bd.ing Panel DHSS Norcross. Prev: Ho. Surg. Musgrave Pk. Hosp. Belf. & Belf. City Hosp.; Ho. Phys. Belf. City Hosp.

LEGGAT, Hilary Margaret Department of Haematology, Warrington Hospital, NHS Trust, Warrington WA5 1QG Tel: 01925 635911; 2 Delavor Road, Heswall, Wirral CH60 4RN Tel: 0151 342 9014 Fax: 0151 342 9414 — MB ChB 1981 Manch.; MRCP 1985 UK; MRCPath 1992; MRCP (UK) 1985; MRCPath 1992. Cons. Haematologist Cons. Haematologist N. Chesh. Hosp. NHS Trust. Prev: Sen. Regist. (Haemat.) Mersey RHA.

LEGGAT, Margaret 9 Brampton Avenue, Leicester LE3 6DA — MB ChB 1990 Ed.

LEGGAT, Peter Ogilvie (retired) Volunteer Cottage, Fore St, Looe PL13 2EZ Tel: 01503 263694 Email: peter@leggat.freeserve.co.uk — MB ChB Aberd. 1941; MD Aberd. 1951; FRCP Lond. 1968, M 1948. Prev: Cons. Phys. Freeman Hosp. Newc. u. Tyne.

LEGGATE, Mr James Renwick Stuart Langham House, 9 Langham Road, Bowdon, Altrincham WA14 2HT Tel: 0161 491 1645 — MRCS Eng. LRCP Lond. 1978; BSc (Hons.) Lond. 1975, MB BS 1978; FRCS Eng. 1982. Cons. (Neurosurg.) Hope Hosp. & Roy. Manch. Childr.'s Hosp. Socs: Soc. Brit. Neurol. Surg. & Surg. Research Soc. Prev: Cons. (Neurosurg.) N. Manch. Gen. Hosp.; Sen. Regist. (Neurosurg.) Dept. Clin. Neurosci. W.. Gen. Hosp. Edin.

LEGGATE, Pamela Anne Dumbarton Road Surgery, 1264 Dumbarton Road, Glasgow G14 9PS Tel: 0141 959 6311 Fax: 0141 954 9759; 180 Hyndland Road, Glasgow G12 9ER — MB ChB 1990 Glas.; MRCGP 1994; Dip. Forens. Med. Glas 1996; DFFP 1994; DRCOG 1993. Med. Off. HMP Barlinnie Glas.

LEGGATT, Henry Dudley (retired) Fletchers, 116 Grove Road, Bladon, Woodstock OX20 1RA Tel: 01993 811334 — BM BCh Oxon. 1946. Prev: RAMC.

LEGGATT, Virginia Jane East Barnwell Health Centre, Ditton Lane, Cambridge CB5 8SP Tel: 01223 728900 Fax: 01223 728901 — MB BS 1978 Lond.; MA (Biochem.) Oxf. 1979; MRCGP 1982; DRCOG 1981. (Univ. Coll. Hosp.)

***LEGGE, Amanda Karen** Room 11, Block 2, Royal Bournemouth Hospital, Castle Lane E., Bournemouth BH7 7DW Tel: 01202 704950; 93 West Coker Road, Yeovil BA20 2JQ Tel: 01935 428136 — BM 1997 Soton.

LEGGE, Joseph Smith 76 Fountainhall Road, Aberdeen AB15 4EH Tel: 01224 639590 — MD 1972 Aberd.; MB ChB 1966; FRCP Lond. 1990; FRCP Ed. 1984; MRCP (UK) 1973. Cons. Thoracic Med. S. Grampian (Aberd.) Health Dist.; Hon. Sen. Lect. Dept. Med. Aberd. Univ.

LEGGE, Mhairi Ballantyne Department of Community Child Health, Grampian Healthcare NHS Trust, Community H.Q., Berryden Road, Aberdeen AB25 3HG Tel: 01224 663131 Fax: 01224 840795; The Beeches, Grange, Keith AB55 6SA — MB ChB Aberd. 1966. Clin. Med. Off. Grampian HB Aberd.

LEGGE, Richard Ian Morningside Medical Practice, 2 Morningside Place, Edinburgh EH10 5ER Tel: 0131 452 8406 Fax: 0131 447 3020; 7 Hope Terrace, Edinburgh EH9 2AP Tel: 0131 447 3291 — MB ChB Ed. 1961; MRCGP 1974; DObst RCOG 1965. Med. Off. Fairmile Marie Curie Centre Edin. Socs: Fell. Roy. Med. Soc. Prev: Med. Off. Marie Curie Centre Fairmile Edin.; Ho. & Sen. Ho. Phys. Copthorne Hosp. Shrewsbury; Ho. Phys. (Med. Paediat.) & Ho. Surg. (O & G) W.. Gen. Hosp. Edin.

LEGGE, Susan Ardroe, 14 Garngaber Avenue, Kirkintilloch, Glasgow G66 4LJ — MB ChB 1995 Glas.

LEGGETT, Christopher Denis Dublin Road Surgery, 56 Main Street, Newcastle BT33 0AE Tel: 028 4372 3221 Fax: 028 4372 3162; 53 Burrenreagh Road, Castlewellan BT31 9HH Tel: 013967 71046 — MB BCh BAO 1985 Belf.; MRCGP 1991; DRCOG 1991; DCH Dub. 1989. Socs: Roy. Coll. Gen. Pract. (Educat. Progr. Organiser); Ulster Med. Soc. Prev: Research Fell. (Gen. Pract.) Qu. Univ. Belf.

LEGGETT, Janet Catherine Murray The Surgery, 62 Windsor Drive, Orpington BR6 6HD Tel: 01689 852204 Fax: 01689 857122; 8 Cudham Park Road, Cudham, Sevenoaks TN14 7RE Tel: 01689 850473 — MB BS 1973 Lond.; MRCS Eng. LRCP Lond. 1973; DCH Eng. 1975.

LEGGETT, Mr John Martyn Flint House, Park Homer Road, Colehill, Wimborne BH21 2SP Tel: 01202 882180 — MB BS 1978 Lond.; MRCS Eng. LRCP Lond. 1977; FRCS Eng. (Orl.) 1983. Assoc. Specialist (Otolaryngol.) Poole Hosp. NHS Trust.; Lect. Inst. Sound & Vibration Research Soton. Univ. Prev: Regist. (ENT) Norf. & Norwich Hosp.; SHO Roy. Nat. Throat Nose & Ear Hosp. Lond.; Ho. Surg. & Cas. Off. Warwick Hosp.

LEGGETT, Julian James 50 Ravenhill Park, Belfast BT6 0DG — MB BCh BAO 1996 Belf.

LEGGETT, Paul Francis 26 Ravensdene Park, Belfast BT6 0DA Tel: 01232 641439 — MB BCh BAO 1989 Belf.; BSc (Hons.) Belf. 1986; MRCGP (Dist.) Ed. 1997; DCH Dub. 1996; DRCOG Lond. 1996. Prev: GP Regist. Downpatrick N. I.

LEGGETT, Raymond John Ebenezer 28 Whin Hill Road, Bessacarr, Doncaster DN4 7AF Tel: 01302 535124 — MB BS 1969 Lond.; FRCP 1990; MRCP (UK) 1972; MRCS Eng. LRCP Lond. 1969. (Westm.) Cons. Phys. Doncaster Roy. Infirm. Socs: Brit. Thorac. Soc. Prev: Sen. Regist. (Gen. Med.) & MRC Research Fell. (Med.) Edin. Roy. Infirm.

LEGGETTER, Peter Philip 54 Clarkes Lane, Chilwell, Beeston, Nottingham NG9 5BL — MB BS 1998 Lond.; MB BS Lond 1998.

LEGGOTT, Morven Julia 427 Harborne Road, Birmingham B15 3LB — MB BCh 1993 Wales.

LEGHARI, Jamil Ahmed Khan Leghari, Lodge and Muktar, The GP Centre, 322 Malden Road, North Cheam, Sutton SM3 8EP Tel: 020 8644 0224 — MB BS 1962 Punjab.

LEHANE, Denis Francis (retired) 15 Berwick Road, Blackpool FY4 2PT Tel: 01253 42824 — MB BCh BAO NUI 1945. Prev: Ho. Phys. Vict. Hosp. Accrington.

LEHANE, Frances Mary 213 Rake Lane, Wallasey CH45 5DQ — MB BCh BAO 1970 NUI; FFA RCSI 1973. SHO (Anaesth.) St. Finbarr's Hosp. Cork. Prev: Ho. Off. (Med.) & (Surg.) St. Finbarr's Hosp. Cork.

LEHANE, John Robert Halton House, High St., Charlton-on-Otmoor, Kidlington OX5 2UG Tel: 01865 331514 Email: john.lehane@nda.ox.ac.uk — MB ChB 1969 Liverp.; MRCP (U.K.) 1975; FFA RCS Eng. 1974. Cons. (Anaesth.) Oxon. HA. Socs: Anaesthetic Research Soc.; Assn. Anaesth. Gt. Brit. & Irel. Prev: Mem. Scientif. Staff. MRC Clin. Research Centre Harrow; Hon.Cons. Anaesth. N.wick Pk. Hosp. Harrow; Regist. Nephrol. Sefton Gen. Hosp.

LEHANY, Gordon Patrick 2 Comely Park, North Craigs, Polmont, Rumford, Falkirk FK2 0RU — MB BS 1994 Lond.

LEHEUP, Rachel Francis — MB ChB 1968 Sheff.; MRCPsych 1974; DPM Eng. 1972. Cons. Child Psychiat. Child & Family Ther. Clinic Nottm.; Co-ordinator of Health Action Zone Project for socially excluded young people in St Anne's Notts. Socs: Of the Roy. Coll of Psychiat.s; Of the Assoc of Family Ther.

LEHMAN, Richard Stephen Lehman and Partners, Hightown Surgery, Hightown Gardens, Banbury OX16 9DB Tel: 01295 270722 Fax: 01295 263000 — BM BCh 1976 Oxf.; MRCGP 1992; DRCOG 1977. Prev: Ho. Phys. Wycombe Gen. Hosp.; Ho. Surg. (Urol.) St. Thos. Hosp. Lond.; SHO (O & G) Middlx. Hosp. Lond.

LEHMANN, Anthea Beatrice Homerton Hospital, Homerton Row, London E9 6SR Tel: 020 8919 7022 Fax: 020 8510 7022 — MD 1988 Newc.; MB BS Lond. 1976; MRCP (UK) 1980; FRCP 1998. Cons. Phys. Med. Elderly Homerton Hosp. Lond.; Hon. Sen. Lect. St. Bart. Hosp. Med. Coll. Lond. Prev: Lect. (Health Care for Elderly) Univ. Nottm.

LEHMANN, Eldon David Academic Department of Radiology, St. Bartholomew's Hospital, London EC1A 7BE Email: aida@globalnet.co.uk; Department of Imaging, National Heart & Lung Institute, Royal Brompton Hospital, London SW3 6NP — MB BS 1993 Lond.; BSc (Hons.) Lond. 1990, MB BS 1993. (UMDS Guy's & St. Thom. Hosps.) Specialist Regist. (Radiol.) The Roy. Hosp. NHS Trust. Socs: Roy. Coll. Radiol. Prev: SHO (Med.) Hammersmith Hosp. Lond.; SHO (Neurol.) Nat. Hosp. Lond.; Ho. Off. (Med.) St. Thos. Hosp. Lond.

LEHMANN, Fritz Michael (retired) Cossins House, Downside Road, Downside, Cobham KT11 3LZ Tel: 01932 64265 — MD 1923 Berlin.

LEHMANN, Gerhard Andreas Department of Anaesthetics, South Cleveland Hospital, Marton Road, Middlesbrough TS4 3BW — State Exam Med 1991 Freiburg.

LEHMANN, Nigel John Paul (retired) The Old Cider Mill, Hook Norton, Banbury OX15 5ND Tel: 01608 730267 — MB BChir 1961 Camb.; DObst RCOG 1963. Prev: GP Hook Norton, Oxon.

LEHMANN, Ordan Jacob Moorfield Eye Hospital, City Road, London EC1Y 2PD Tel: 020 7253 3411 — BM BCh 1989 Oxf.; MA Camb. 1986; FRCOphth 1994. Research.Fell.

LEHNER, Karen Grosvenor Bill Doyle Centre, Greatoaks Clinic, Little Oaks, Basildon Tel: 01268 527493 Fax: 01268 532623; 2 Meadow Gate, Stock CM4 9SB Tel: 01277 829733 — MB ChB 1976 Ed.; MSc (Community Paediat.) Lond. 1993, BSc (Genetics) 1974. (Edinburgh) p/t Cons. Community Paediat. S. Essex Ment. health and community care Trust Basildon. Socs: Fell. Roy. Coll. Paediat. & Child Health. Prev: SCMO Essex & Herts. Community Trust.

LEHNER, Paul Joseph Flat 2, 192 Catheral Road, Cardiff CF1 9JE — MB BS 1985 Lond.; BSc (Hons.) Lond. 1982, MB BS 1985; MRCP (UK) 1988. MRC Train. Fell. (Med.) Univ. Wales Coll. Med. Cardiff. Prev: Regist. (Med.) Hammersmith Hosp. Lond.

LEHNER, Professor Thomas Department of Immunolbiology, * *, London Bridge, London SE1 9RT Tel: 020 7955 4048 Fax: 020 7955 8894 Email: thomas.lehner@kcl.ac.uk — MD 1968 Lond.; PhD Hon. Karolinska Inst. 1987; MB BS 1960; BDS 1955; FDS RCS Eng. 1960; FRCPath 1978, M 1966. (Univ. Coli. Hosp.) Prof. Basic & Applied Immunol. UMDS Guy's & St. Thos. Hosps. Lond.; Hon. Cons. Path. Guy's Hosp. Socs: Fell. Roy. Soc. Med. (Ex-Pres. Sect. Clin. Immunol.); Brit. Soc. Immunol. Prev: Nuffield Fell. Dept. Morbid Anat. Postgrad. Med. Sch. Hammersmith Hosp.; Guy's Research Fell. Guy's Hosp. Med. Sch.; Prof. Oral Immunol. Guy's Hosp.

LEHOVSKY, Alison Jane 60 Normandy Avenue, Barnet EN5 2JA — MB BS 1985 Lond.; BSc Lond. 1982, MB BS 1985; MRCGP 1989. Stud. Lond. Sports Med. Dip. Prev: Trainee GP Leeds VTS.

LEHOVSKY, Mr Jan Royal National Orthopaedic Hospital Trust, Stanmore HA7 4LP — MUDr 1985 Prague; MCh (Orth.) Liverp. 1994; FRCSI 1993. Cons. Orthop. & Spinal Surg. Roy. Nat. Orthop. Hosp. Stanmore. Prev: Cons. Trauma & Orthop. (Spinal Surg.) Frimley Pk. Hosp. NHS Trust.

LEIBEL, David Joseph 46 Lordship Road, Stoke Newington, London N16 0QT — BM BCh 1978 Oxf.; MRCPsych 1983. Research Fell. & Hon. Sen. Regist. Acad. Dept. Psychiat. Roy. Free Hosp. Sch. Med. Lond.

LEIBERMAN, Mr David Paul Janefield, Glengowan Road, Bridge of Weir PA11 3PL — MRCS Eng. LRCP Lond. 1966; FRCS Eng. 1972.

LEIBOWITZ, Ruth Helen 11 Campbell Grove, St. Annes, Nottingham NG3 1HA — BM BS 1987 Nottm.

LEICESTER, Gail Manchester Road Medical Centre, 27 Manchester Road, Knutsford WA16 0LZ Tel: 01565 633101 Fax: 01565 750135 — MB BCh 1980 Wales.

LEICESTER, Mr Roger James, OBE St Georges Hospital, Blackshaw Road, London SW17 0QT Tel: 020 8725 3284 Fax: 020 8725 2910; 107 Thetford Road, New Malden KT3 5DS Tel: 020 8336 0053 Fax: 020 8942 4157 — MB BS 1971 Lond.; FRCS Ed. 1976; FRCS Eng. 1976; MRCS Eng. LRCP Lond. 1971. (St. Mary's) Cons. Surg. St. Geo. Hosp. Lond. Socs: Assn. Coloproctol. (Counc. Mem.); Brit. Soc. Gastroenterol. (Counc. Mem.). Prev: Prof. & Cons. Surg. RN Hosp. Haslar.

LEICESTER, Sandra Valley Medical Centre, Johnson Street, Stocksbridge, Sheffield S36 1BX Tel: 0114 288 3841 Fax: 0114 288 7897 — MB ChB 1977 Bristol.

LEIGH, Amanda Jayne 52 Hallfields Road, Warrington WA2 8DN — MB BS 1997 Newc.

LEIGH, Beatrice Ann Churchfields Surgery, Recreation Road, Bromsgrove B61 8DT Tel: 01527 872163 — MB BS 1969 Lond.; MRCS Eng. LRCP Lond. 1969.

LEIGH, Christopher Wychall Lane Surgery, 11 Wychall Lane, Kings Norton, Birmingham B38 8TE Tel: 0121 628 2345 Fax: 0121 628 8282 — MB BS 1971 Lond.; MRCS Eng. LRCP Lond. 1971.

LEIGH, Edward David 170 Haverstock Hill, London NW3 2AT Tel: 020 7722 7242 — MB BS 1991 Lond.

LEIGH, Frederick Winston 172 Whitham Road, Sheffield S10 2SR Tel: 0114 230 3833 — MB ChB 1952 Sheff.; MRCGP 1960. (Sheff.) Prev: Fulbright Fell. Univ. Hosp. Minneapolis; Ho. Phys. Profess. Unit Roy. Hosp. Sheff.; Ho. Phys. Regional Cardiovasc. Unit, City Gen. Hosp. Sheff.

LEIGH, Gerard Baslow Road Surgery, 148-150 Baslow Road, Totley, Sheffield S17 4DR Tel: 0114 236 9957 Fax: 0114 262 0756 — MB ChB 1974 Sheff.

LEIGH, Gillian Ida Red Roof, Church Path, Merton Park, London SW19 3HL Tel: 020 8542 4872 Fax: 020 8544 0036 — MB BChir 1968 Camb.; MB Camb. 1968, BChir 1967; MA Camb. 1968; MRCS Eng. LRCP Lond. 1967. Assoc. Specialist (Dermat.) Kingston Hosp. Socs: Brit. Assn. Dermat.

LEIGH, Harold Albert (retired) 306 Norton Way S., Letchworth SG6 1SY Tel: 01462 684426 — LMSSA 1965 Lond.; MA Oxf. 1965. Prev: Ho. Surg. N. Herts. Hosp. Hitchin.

LEIGH, Mr Henry Ivor 39 Stenbury View, Wroxall, Ventnor PO38 3DD — MB ChB 1950 Bristol; MB ChB (Distinc. Anat. & Pub. Health) Bristol 1950; FRCS Ed. 1959. (Bristol) Socs: BMA. Prev: GP Shanklin I. of Wight; Regist. (Surg.) S. Som. Clin. Area; Regist. (Neurosurg.) S. W.. RHB.

LEIGH, Howard Woodlands Road Surgery, 6 Woodlands Road, Middlesbrough TS1 3BE Tel: 01642 247982 Fax: 01642 241636; Saltergill Cottage, Low Worsall, Yarm TS15 — MB BS 1969 Newc.

LEIGH, Professor Irene May Centre for Cutaneous Research, Barts and the London, Queen Marys school of Medicine & Doctorary, 2 Newark St., London E1 2AT Tel: 020 7295 7170 Fax: 020 7295 7171 Email: I.leigh@cancer.org.uk — MB BS 1971 Lond.; DSC (med) 1999; Imed sci 1999; BSc (1st cl. Hons.) Lond. 1968, MB BS 1971; FRCP (UK) 1987, MRCP 1975. (Lond. Hosp.) Cons. Dermat.Barts & the Lond. NHS; Prof. Dermat. Barts and the Lond., Qu. Marys Sch. of Med. & dent.; Research Dean. Socs: Brit. Assn. Dermat.; Europ. Soc. Dermatol. Res. (ex pres.). Prev: Sen.

Regist. (Dermat.) St. John's Hosp. Dis. Skin & Middlx Hosp. Lond; Sen. Lect. (Dermat.) Lond. Hosp. Med. Coll.

LEIGH, Jane Marie 2 Mickle Hill Farm Cottages, Mickle Hill Road, Blackhall Rocks, Hartlepool TS27 4DF Tel: 01429 272679 — MB BS 1986 Newc.; MRCGP 1996.

LEIGH, Joan Anthea Sonoma, Valley, Holyhead LL65 3EY Tel: 01407 740337 — MB ChB 1944 Manch. (Manch.) Sen. Med. Off. (S.W. Dist.) Herts. AHA. Late.

LEIGH, John 5 Moorland Crescent, Staincross, Barnsley S75 — MB ChB 1982 Birm.

LEIGH, John 61 Long Ashton Road, Long Ashton, Bristol BS41 9HW — MB ChB 1981 Bristol; FFA RCS Lond. 1986. Cons. Anaesth. S.mead Hosp. Bristol.

LEIGH, Jonathan Rupert Oliver Woodland Road Surgery, 20 Woodland Road, St Austell PL25 4QY Tel: 01726 63311 — MB BS 1968 Lond.; MRCS Eng. LRCP Lond. 1968.

LEIGH, Julian Meyer Sample Oak, 25 Orchard Road, Shalford, Guildford GU4 8ER Tel: 01483 561677 — MB BS Lond. 1961; MD Lond. 1974; MRCS Eng. LRCP Lond. 1961; FFA RCS Eng. 1966; DA Eng. 1963. (Lond. Hosp.) Cons. Anaesth. S.W. Surrey Health Dist.; Hon. Reader Dept. Human Biol. Univ. Surrey Guildford. Socs: Counc. Assn. Anaesth.; Fell. Roy. Soc. Med. Prev: Hon. Reader Dept. Human Biol. Univ. Surrey Guildford; Hunt. Prof. RCS Eng. 1972; Mem. Counc. Assn. Anaesth.

LEIGH, Margaret Eileen 2 Park View Road, London W5 2JB Tel: 020 8997 7617 — MB ChB 1939 Liverp. (Liverp.) Prev: Med. Asst. (Contact Lens) Moorfield Eye Hosp. Lond.; Med. Asst. (Ophth.) W.. Ophth. Hosp. Lond. & King Edwd. VII Hosp. Windsor.

LEIGH, Margaret Elizabeth 8 Milford House, 7 Queen Anne St., London W1G 9HN Tel: 020 7636 1398; 2 Park View Road, Ealing, London W5 2JB — MRCS Eng. LRCP Lond. 1970; MCOphth Eng. 1988; DO Eng. 1973. (St. Mary's) Assoc. Specialist Moorfields Eye Hosp. Lond. Socs: BMA & Fell. RSM. Prev: SHO (Ophth.) Univ. Coll. Hosp. Lond.; Ho. Phys. Eliz. G. Anderson Hosp. Lond.; Ho. Surg. King Edwd. VII Memor. Hosp. Ealing.

LEIGH, Maria 306 Norton Way S., Letchworth SG6 1SY Tel: 01462 684426 — MB BS Lond. 1956; MRCS Eng. LRCP Lond. 1956; MRCGP 1965; DPM Eng. 1974; DObst RCOG 1958. (St. Geo.) Socs: Fell. Roy. Soc. Med. Prev: Ho. Surg. Vict. Hosp. Childr. Chelsea; Resid. Asst. (Obst.) & Ho. Surg. (Gyn.) St. Geo. Hosp. Lond.; Psychiat. & Psychother. Lister Hosp. Stevenage.

LEIGH, Martha Frances Margaret Wapping Health Centre, 22 Wapping Lane, London E1W 2RL Tel: 020 7481 9376 — MB BS 1983 Lond.; MRCGP 1987; DCH RCP Lond. 1987; DRCOG 1985. (Guy's) GP Princip.; GP Trainer. Prev: Trainee GP NE Thames HA VTS.

LEIGH, Mary Eleanor Merkle 22 Gurney Drive, London N2 0DG Tel: 020 8455 2099 — LMSSA 1971 Lond.; FFA RCS Eng. 1975. Cons. (Anaesth.) Barnet Gen. Hosp. & Edgware Gen. Hosp.

LEIGH, Mira 40 Waterloo Road, Bedford MK40 3PG Tel: 01234 400462; Bedford Hospital NHS Trust, Cygnet Wing, Kempston Road, Bedford MK42 9DJ Tel: 01234 792255 Fax: 01234 795820 — MB BS 1973 Lond.; MRCP (UK) 1980; DCH Eng. 1975; FRCP 1996; FRCPCH 1996. (Charing Cross Hospital London) Cons. Paediat. Bedford Gen. Hosp. Socs: RCPCH. Prev: Clin. Fell. Roy. Marsden Hosp. Sutton; Lect. Char. Cross Hosp. Lond.

LEIGH, Norman Fleming Geoffrey Street Health Centre, Preston PR1 5NE Tel: 01772 794545 — MB BChir 1958 Camb.; MA Camb. 1982, MB BChir 1958; BA Open 1983; MRCGP 1968. Med. Off. St. Catherines Hospice Preston. Prev: Med. Off. Lancs. Polytechnic.

LEIGH, Paul Stephen 22 Tithe Barn Drive, Bray, Maidenhead SL6 2DG — MB BS 1978 Lond.; MA Camb. 1978. Assoc. Med. Dir. Glaxo Wellcome UK Stockley Pk. Prev: Head Med. Affairs Bayer plc Newbury; Med. Adviser Servier Laborats. Neuilly-sur-Seine France; Chief Resid. Amer. Hosp. Paris.

LEIGH, Professor Peter Nigel Dept of Neurology, Institute of Psychiatry, London SE5 8AF Tel: 020 8682 4405 — MB BS 1979 Lond.; PhD Lond. 1986, BSc (1st Cl. Hons.) 1967; FRCP Lond. 1988; MRCP (UK) 1972. (Lond. Hosp.) Prof. Neurol. Inst. Psychiat. & Guys,Kings,St Thomas.Sch.Med.Lond; Dir. Kings. MND. Care & Research Centre. Socs: Amer. Neurol. Assn. (Corr. Mem.); Amer. Acad. of Neurol.; Assn. of Brit. Nuerologists. Prev: Cons. Neurol. Wessex Neurol. Centre Soton.; Sen. Lect. (Neurol.) & Hon. Cons. Neurol. St. Geo. Hosp. & Atkinson Morley's Hosp. Lond.

LEIGH, Peter Richard Swanage Health Centre, Railway Station Approach, Station Road, Swanage BH19 1HB Tel: 01929 422231 — MB BChir 1977 Camb.; MA Camb. 1978; MRCGP 1984; DA Eng. 1979. (Camb. & Westm.) Clin. Asst. Swanage Cottage Hosp.; GP Tutor, Poole Hosp. NHS Trust. Prev: Clin. Asst. (Anaesth.) Swanage Cottage Hosp.; SHO (Anaesth.) E. Dorset Health Dist.; SHO (O & G) Poole Gen. Hosp.

LEIGH, Peter Richard Wyndham (retired) Rectory Lodge, Upton Scudamore, Warminster BA12 0AH — BM BCh 1936 Oxf.; BM BCh. Oxf. 1936. Prev: Ho. Phys. (Obst.) St. Thos. Hosp.

LEIGH, Philip Jonathan Shifnal Medical Practice, Shrewsbury Road, Shifnal TF11 8AJ Tel: 01952 460414 Fax: 01952 463192; 10 Swallowfield Close, Priorslee, Telford TF2 9TG Tel: 01952 201561 Email: p.j.leigh@btinternet.com — MB ChB 1983 Birm. (Birm.)

LEIGH, Rebecca Jane Dept of Care of Elderly, Sunderland Royal Hospital, Kahill Road, Sunderland SR4 7TP — MB BS 1994 Newc.; MRCP (UK) 1997. Specialist Regist. (Geriats. & Gen. Meds.underland.Roy.Hosp. Prev: SHO (Med.) Newc.

LEIGH, Richard Douglas 49 Shrewbridge Road, Nantwich CW5 7AD — MB ChB 1984 Manch.

LEIGH, Richard John 63 Park Drive, Sprotbrough, Doncaster DN5 7LN — MD 1985 Manch.; MB ChB 1975; MRCP (UK) 1978. Cons. Phys. Montagu Hosp. MexBoro.. Prev: Research Fell. Hope Hosp. (Univ. Manch. Sch. Med.); Sen. Regist. Roy. Hallamshire Hosp. Sheff.

LEIGH, Rita Franco 100 Osmaston Road, Prenton, Birkenhead CH42 8LP — MB BS 1963 Lond.; LMSSA Lond. 1963. (Guy's) Prev: Clin. Asst. (Ophth.) & (Radiother.) Kent & Canterbury Hosp.

LEIGH, Robert Keith Woodlands & Clerklands Surgery, Tilgate Way, Tilgate, Crawley RH10 5BS Tel: 01293 525204 Fax: 01293 514778; Willow Cottage, Charmans Farm, Warnham, Horsham RH12 3PS Tel: 01403 790032 — MB BS 1989 Lond.; DFFP 1993; DCH RCP Lond. 1991.

LEIGH, Russell David Blackhall Community Health Centre, Hesleden Road, Blackhall Colliery TS27 4LQ Tel: 0191 586 4331 Fax: 0191 586 4844; 2 Mickle Hill Farm Cottages, Mickle Hill Road, Blackhall Rocks TS27 4DF Tel: 0191 518 1580 Email: docleigh@globalnet.co.uk — MB BS 1986 Newc.; Dip. Ther. Newc. 1996. Primary Care Med. Adviser, Tees Health Auth., Middlesbrough.

LEIGH, Sydney 1 The Elms, Elmfield Road, Newcastle upon Tyne NE3 4BD Tel: 0191 285 6227 — MB BS 1945 Durh.

LEIGH, Thomas Henry Medical Defence Union, 230 Blackfriars Road, London SE1 8PJ Tel: 020 7202 1500 Fax: 020 7202 1664 Email: leight@the-mdu.com — MB BS 1987 Lond.; MA Oxf. 1990, BA 1984; MRCPsych 1992. (Middlx. Hosp.) Sen. Med. Claims Handler at the MDU. Prev: Sen. Regist. (Psychother.) Tavistock Clinic Lond.; Lect. (Psychol. Med.) St. Mary's Hosp. Med. Sch.; Regist. (Child & Adolesc. Psychiat.) St. Mary's Hosp. Lond.

LEIGH, Timothy Rupert Department of Gastroenterology, Crawley Hospital, West Green Drive, Crawley RH11 7DH Tel: 01293 600300; Adelaide Cottage, Cuckfield Road, Ansty, Haywards Heath RH17 5AL Email: tim@drbeigh.freeserve.co.uk — MB BS 1982 Lond.; MA Oxf. 1983; MD Lond. 1994; MRCP (UK) 1986. (Oxford University & Charing Cross Hospital) Cons. (Gastroenterol.), Crawley & E. Surrey Hosp.Surrey & Sussex NHS Trust. Socs: Brit. Soc. Gastroenterol.; Roy. Coll. Phys.s. Prev: Sen. Regist. (Gastroenterol.) Roy. Sussex Co. Hosp., Brighton; Sen. Regist. Kings Coll. Hosp. Lond.; Sen. Regist, Chelsea & W.minster Hosp. Lond.

LEIGH, Tracey Jane Hightrees, Quarry Road E., Wirral CH61 6XD; 4 Weetwood Road, West Park, Leeds LS16 5LP — MB ChB 1992 Sheff.; MRCP (Paed.) 1997. (Sheffield) GP Regist. Horsforth Leeds.

LEIGH, Vivien Frances University Health Service, 2 Claremont Place, Sheffield S10 2TB Tel: 0114 222 2100 Fax: 0114 276 7223 — MB ChB 1975 Sheff.; DRCOG 1977.

LEIGH, Ya'acov Hawthorns, Woodlands Road, Bushey, Watford WD23 2LS — MB BS 1996 Lond.

LEIGH-COLLYER, Neil Western Road Medical Centre, 99 Western Road, Romford RM1 3LS Tel: 01708 746495 Fax: 01708 737936 — MB BS 1985 Lond.; BSc (Hons.) Lond. 1980. (Char. Cross) Prev: SHO (Hepatobiliary Surg.) Hammersmith Hosp. Lond.; Ho. Surg. OldCh. Hosp. Romford; Ho. Phys. Gen. Hosp. Jersey, CI.

LEIGH-HOWARTH, Mark, Maj. RAMC Friarage Hospital, Northallerton DL6 1JG Tel: 01609 779911 Email:

marklh@compuserve.com; Email: marklh@compuserve.com — MB BS 1985 Lond.; MRCPsych 1993. (St. Geo. Hosp. Med. Sch.) cons. Psychiat. Friarage hosp N.allerton. Prev: Cons Psychiat. Duchess of Kent's psychiatric hosp.

LEIGH-HUNT, Nicholas Jocelyn 1 Lewis Road, Radford Semele, Leamington Spa CV31 1UB — MB BS 1997 Lond.

LEIGH-SMITH, Simon John, Surg. Lt. RN Treelands, Upleadon, Newent GL18 1EJ Tel: 01531 820317 — MB ChB 1990 Liverp.

LEIGHTON, Erik John (retired) Haining Cottage, Brockenhurst Road, Ascot SL5 9HB Tel: 01344 620840 — MRCS Eng. LRCP Lond. 1941; FFA RCS Eng. 1950. Prev: Cons. Anaesth. Heatherwood Hosp. Ascot.

LEIGHTON, Graham Mulberry Lodge, 79 Conifer Crest, Newbury RG14 6RS — MB BS 1974 Lond.; DA RCS Eng. 1982. Prev: Ho. Phys. WillesBoro. Hosp. Ashford; Ho. Surg. W.m. Childr. Hosp. Lond.

LEIGHTON, Jack Leonard Kilmory, West Glen Road, Kilmacolm PA13 4PW — MB ChB 1985 Glas.; BDS Glas. 1977, MB ChB (Commend.) 1985; MRCGP 1989; FDS RCPS Glas. 1981; DRCOG 1988. GP Paisley. Socs: BMA.

LEIGHTON, Katherine Mary Larkfield Child & Family Centre, Larfield Road, Greenock PA16 0XN Tel: 01475 633777 Fax: 01475 632094 — MB ChB 1979 Glas.; MRCPsych 1983; FMGEMS 1986. p/t Cons. Child & Adolesc. Psychiat. Larkfield Child & Family Centre Greenock. Socs: BMA; Assn. Child Psychol. & Psychiat.; Nat. Autistic Soc. Prev: Lect. & Hon. Sen. Regist. Univ. Glas.; Sen. Regist. (Child & Adoles. Psychiat.) Gtr. Glas. HB.

LEIGHTON, Luis Fernando Almeida 22 High Street, Aveley, South Ockendon RM15 4AD Tel: 01708 865640 Fax: 01708 891658 — MRCS Eng. LRCP Lond. 1979; MRCGP (Distinc.) 1991; AFOM 1997; DMRT Eng. 1984; Cert. Family Plann. JCC 1984. (Middlx.) Police Surg. Essex Police Med. Off. Prev: Ho Phys. Middlx. Hosp. Lond.; Ho. Surg. St. Albans.

LEIGHTON, Marion 3 Craghall Dene, Newcastle upon Tyne NE3 1QQ — MB BS 1998 Newc.; MB BS Newc 1998.

LEIGHTON, Michelle Ann 7 Quadrant House, Burrell St., London SE1 0UW — MB BS 1988 West Indies.

LEIGHTON, Monica Hedy Torrington Park Health Centre, 16 Torrington Park, North Finchley, London N12 9SS Tel: 020 8445 7622/4127; Flat 4, Parkside, 126 Torrington Park, North Finchley, London N12 9AL Tel: 020 8361 1443 — MB BS 1982 Lond.; MA Oxf. 1977; MSc Sussex 1974. (Roy. Free) Sen. Lect. (Primary Care & Populat. Sci.) Roy. Free Hosp. Sch. Med. Lond.

LEIGHTON, Robert Ernest (retired) Wick Barton, Stogumber, Taunton TA4 3TU Tel: 01984 656385 — MRCS Eng. LRCP Lond. 1946; DObst RCOG 1948. Prev: GP Nether Stowey, Bridgwater.

LEIGHTON, Mrs Susanna Elizabeth Jane 57 Highbury Hill, London N5 1SU Tel: 020 7359 6725 Fax: 020 7690 6568 Email: abc89@dial.pipex.com — MB BS 1983 Lond.; BSc Lond. 1980; FRCS (Orl.) 1993; FRCS Eng. 1989. (St. Thos.) Cons. Paediat. Otolaryngol. Gt. Ormond St. Hosp. Childr.; Hon. Sen. Lect. Inst. of Child Health Lond. Socs: Fell. Roy. Soc. Med.; Brit. Assn. Paediat. Otol.; Brit. Assn. Otol. Head & Neck Surg. Prev: Vis. Lect. Div. Otorhinolaryng. (Surg.) Chinese Univ. Hong Kong.; Sen. Regist. (Otolaryngol.) Roy. Nat. Throat. Nose & Ear Hosp. Gt. Ormond St. Hosp. for Childr. & St. Geo. Hosp. Lond.Geo.'s Hosp Lond.; Regist. (Otolaryngol.) Radcliffe Infirm. Oxf.

LEIGHTON, Theresa Jane The Health Centre, Melbourn Street, Royston SG8 7BS Tel: 01763 242981 Fax: 01763 249197 — MB BS 1990 Lond.

LEINHARDT, Mr David Julian Harrogate District Hospital, Lancaster Park Road, Harrogate HG2 7SX Tel: 01423 553744 Fax: 01423 553466; 10 Barnwell Crescent, Harrogate HG2 9EY Email: david-leinhardt@msn.com — MB ChB 1982 Manch.; ChM Manch. 1992; FRCS (Gen.) 1995; FRCS Eng. 1988. Cons. Gen. Surg. Harrogate Dist. Hosp. Prev: Sen. Regist. (Surg.) Roy. Oldham Hosp. & Roy. Preston Hosp.; Tutor (Surg.) Univ. Manch. & Hope Hosp. Salford.

LEINSTER, Professor Samuel John The Medical School, University of East Anglia, Norwich NR4 7TJ Tel: 01603 593061 Fax: 0151 706 5667 Email: s.leinster@uea.ac.uk; Vassars, Common Road, East Tuddenham, Dereham NR20 3AH Tel: 01603 880456 Email: sam.leinster@tinyworld.co.uk — MB BCh 1990 Edin.; BSc (Hons.) Ed. 1968, MB ChB 1971; FRCS Ed. 1976; FRCS Eng 1998. (Edinburgh) Inaugural Dean, Sch. of Med., Health Policy and Pract. Sch., Univ E. Anglia. Socs: Brit. Assn. Surg. Oncol.; Eur. Soc. Mastol.; Assn. Study Med. Educat.(Chair). Prev: Prof of surg, univ of Liverp.; Lect. (Surg.) Welsh Nat. Sch. Med. Cardiff; Squadron Ldr., Surg. Specialist RAF.

LEIPER, Alison Dilys Department of Haematology & Oncology, Great Ormond Street Hospital, Great Ormond St., London WC1N 3JH; 51 Galveston Road, Putney, London SW15 2RZ Tel: 020 8874 1003 — MB BS 1973 Lond.; MRCP (UK) 1977; DCH RCP Lond. 1976. (King's Coll. Hosp.) Assoc. Specialist. (Haemat. & Oncol.) Gt. Ormond St. Lond. Prev: SHO (Paediat.) Middlx. Hosp. Lond.; Regist. (Paediat.) Hillingdon Hosp. Uxbridge; Leukaemia Research Fell. (Regist.) Hosp. Sick Childr. Lond.

LEIPER, Christine Anne Stenhouse Medical Centre, Furlong Street, Arnold, Nottingham NG5 7BP Tel: 0115 967 3877 Fax: 0115 967 3838 — BM BS 1987 Nottm.; BMedSci (Biochem.) Nottm. 1985; DCH RCP Lond. 1990; Cert. Family Plann. JCC 1990.

LEIPER, David Burns 17 Abbotshall Road, Cults, Aberdeen AB15 9JX — MB ChB 1997 Glas.

LEIPER, Edwin James Reid (retired) 62 Maze Green Road, Bishop's Stortford CM23 2PL Tel: 01279 654568 — MB ChB 1930 Aberd.; MB ChB (1st cl. Hons.) 1930; MA Aberd. 1925, MD (Hons.) 1937; FRCP Lond. 1969, M 1936. Prev: Cons. Phys. Herts. & Essex Gen. Hosp. Bishop's Stortford.

LEIPER, James Martin Roxburghe House, Royal Victoria Hospital, Jedburgh Road, Dundee DD1 1SP Tel: 01382 423000 Fax: 01382 423157 — MB ChB 1977 Ed.; BSc (Hons.) Med. Sci. Ed. 1974; FRCP Glas. 1992; MRCP (UK) 1980; FRCP Ed. 1998. (Ed.) Cons. Palliat. Med. Roxburghe Hse. Tayside primary care nhs trust; Hon. Sen. Lect. (Med.) Univ. Dundee. Socs: Chair. Scott. Partnership Agency Palliat. and Cancer Care. Prev: Macmillan Lect. Clin. Centre for Med. Educat. Univ. Dundee; Regist. (Med. & Clin. Pharmacol.) Glas. Roy. Infirm.; Research Regist. (Diabetes) Glas. Roy. Infirm.

LEIPER, Margaret Dilys (retired) 62 Maze Green Road, Bishop's Stortford CM23 2PL Tel: 01279 654568 — MB BS 1938 Lond.; MB BS (Hons.) Lond. 1938; MRCS Eng. LRCP Lond. 1939. Prev: Cons. Contracep. & Allied Problems Univ. Lond. Centr. Insts.

LEIPER, Rachel Grace c/o The Green Wood, Stoke Rivers, Barnstaple EX32 7LD — MB ChB 1991 Manch.

LEISHMAN, Alexander Gilmour (retired) 1 Academy Gardens, Gainford, Darlington DL2 3EN Tel: 01325 730586 — MB BChir Camb. 1942; MA Camb. 1942; MRCP Lond. 1948; DTM & H Eng. 1954; FFCM 1979, M 1974. Prev: Specialist (Community Med.) N.. RHA.

LEISHMAN, Frances Evelyn Augustine Craig Ard, Dupplin Terrace, Kinnoull, Perth PH2 7DG Tel: 01738 624626 Fax: 01738 624626 — MB ChB 1950 Ed.; DObst RCOG 1954.

LEISHMAN, Joan (retired) — MB ChB 1957 Aberd.; DA Eng. 1961. Prev: Regist. (Anaesth.) Aberd. Roy. Infirm.

LEITCH, Alexander 54 Hill Grove, Hanleaze, Bristol BS9 4RQ Tel: 0117 962 2247 — MD 1940 Glas.; MB ChB 1934; MRCPsych 1971; DPM Lond. 1938. Hon. Cons. Psychiat. Avon HA. Socs: BMA; Roy. Coll. Psychiat. Prev: Cons. Psychiat. Glenside & Barrow Gp. Hosps.

LEITCH, Andrew James 64 Glenmachan Road, Belmont, Belfast BT4 2NN — MB BCh BAO 1995 Belf.

LEITCH, Craig Ramsay 60 Vale Close, Heaton Mersey, Stockport SK4 3DS; 14 Royal Place Greenwich, London SE10 8QF — MB ChB 1985 Manch.; BSc (Med. Sci.) St. And. 1982; MRCOG 1991. Cons .(O & G) Greenwich. Dist. Hosp. Prev: Ho. Off. (Surg.) W.. Infirm. Glas.; Ho. Off. (Med.) Stepping Hill Hosp. Stockport.

LEITCH, David Gordon The Grove, 67 North St., Winterton, Scunthorpe DN15 9QL Tel: 01724 733516 — MB ChB 1964 Ed.; FRCP Lond. 1989; FRCP Ed. 1986; MRCP (UK) 1970; DCH Eng. 1974. (Ed.) Cons. Med. Scunthorpe Gen. Hosp. Socs: Brit. Soc. Gastroenterol. Prev: Wing Cdr. RAF Cons. Med.; Ho. Phys. & Ho. Surg. Sedgefield Gen. Hosp.

LEITCH, David Neil Freeman Hospital, High Heaton, Newcastle upon Tyne NE7 7DN Tel: 0191 284 3111 Email: d.n.leitch@newcastle.ac.uk — MB ChB 1991 Manch.; MB ChB (Hons.) Manch. 1991; BSc (Hons.) Manch. 1988; MRCP (UK) 1994; Dip Epidemiol. 1997. (Manch.) Specialist Regist. (Respirat. & Gen Med.) Freeman Hosp. Newc. U. Tyne. Socs: Brit. Thorac. Soc.; BMA;

Roy. Coll. Phys. Prev: Regist. (Gen. Med. & Rheum.) S. Cleveland Hosp. & Sunderland Roy. Infirm.

LEITCH, Derek Christie Hospital, Manchester; Flat 4, 29 Burton Road, Manchester M20 3GB Tel: 0161 374 3213 — MB ChB 1994 Ed.; MRCP 1997. Specialist Regist. (Oncol.) Christie Hosp. Manch.

LEITCH, Mr Gilbert Berkley (retired) Whitebarn House, Llantrisant, Usk NP15 1LU Tel: 01291 673419 — MB BCh BAO Dub. 1947; FRCS Ed. 1956; DLO Eng. 1953. Cons. Surg. ENT Newport & E. Mon. Hosp. Gp. Prev: Sen. Regist. Cardiff Roy. Infirm.

LEITCH, Henry Carson Smyth (retired) 8 Bayview Park, Londonderry BT47 6TA Tel: 028 7134 5496 Email: harryleitch@lineone.net — MB BCh BAO Belf. 1955. Prev: GP Lond.derry.

LEITCH, James Alexander (retired) 40 Church Street, Exning, Newmarket CB8 7EH Tel: 01638 577788 — MD Ed. 1963, MB ChB 1944; DCH Eng. 1948; DPH Ed. 1949.

LEITCH, James Burrell Appleby Health Centre, Low Wiend, Appleby-in-Westmorland CA16 6QP — MB ChB 1971 Ed.; MRCGP 1978. (Edinburgh)

LEITCH, Janet Jennifer Anniesland Medical Practice, 778 Crow Road, Glasgow G13 1LU Tel: 0141 954 8860 Fax: 0141 954 0870 — MB ChB 1987 Ed.; MRCGP 1992; DRCOG 1991.

LEITCH, Jean Elizabeth Brawn Durham Road Surgery, 25 Durham Road, Edinburgh EH16 4DT Tel: 0131 669 1153 Fax: 0131 669 3633; 16 Wilton Road, Edinburgh EH16 5NX Tel: 0131 667 5812 — MB ChB 1976 Ed.; Cert. JCPTGP 1987; DCCH RCP Ed. 1986. (Ed.) GP Edin.

***LEITCH, Joanna Mary** 9 Mid Road, Biggar ML12 6AW — MB ChB 1998 Dund.; MB ChB Dund 1998.

LEITCH, Mr John Mallet Northumbria Healthcare NHS Trust, Wansbeck General Hospital, Woodhorn Lane, Ashington NE63 9JJ Tel: 01670 521212 Fax: 01670 529656; 62 Churchburn Drive, Loansdean, Morpeth NE61 2DE — MB ChB 1976 Ed.; FRCS Ed. 1983. (University of Edinburgh) Cons. Orthop. Surg. N.umbria Healthcare NHS Trust. Prev: Cons. Orthop. Surg. Lancaster Acute Hosps. NHS Trust; Sen. Regist. (Orthop.) N. RHA; Clin. Research Fell. Adelaide Childr.s Hosp.

LEITCH, Mr Keir MacKessack, OStJ (retired) Chart House, Milton Road, Bloxham, Banbury OX15 4HD Tel: 01295 720507 — MB ChB 1942 Ed.; FRCS Ed. 1946. Prev: Pres. St. John Ambul. Brig. & Police Surg. Banbury.

LEITCH, Lois Margaret 2 Lodge Road, Caerleon, Newport NP18 1QS Tel: 01633 422169 — MB ChB 1943 Bristol; DCH Eng. 1951. (Bristol)

LEITCH, Mr Matthew David 48 Meadowfield, Stokesley, Middlesbrough TS9 5HH Tel: 01642 710451 — MB BCh BAO 1940 Dub.; BA, MB BCh BAO Dub. 1940; FRCS Ed. 1947. (T.C. Dub.) Socs: Fell. Brit. Orthop. Assn.; BMA. Prev: Cons. Orthop. Surg. N. Tees Gen. Hosp. Middlesbrough Gen. Hosp.; Orthop. & Sen. Ho. Surg. N. Ormesby Hosp.; Dep. Med. Supt. & Surg. Hemlington EMS Hosp.

LEITCH, Rebecca Jane Epsom and St Helier NHS Trust, Sutton Hospital, Cotswold Rd, Sutton SM2 5N; 31C Elgin Crescent, London W11 2JD — MB BS 1984 Lond.; FRCS Glas. 1988; FCOphth 1989; DO RCS Eng. 1988. Cons. Ophth. Specialising in Paediatric Ophth. and Cataract; Hon. Cons. Ophth., Gt. Ormond St. Hosp. for Childr., Lond. Socs: Vice Pres. S.ern Ophthalmolicol Soc.; Mem. RSM. Prev: Fell. Piadt. Ophth. Gt. Ormond St. Hosp.

LEITCH, Robert Gourlay Biggar Health Centre, South Croft Road, Biggar ML12 6BE Tel: 01899 220383 Fax: 01899 221583; Midcroft, Biggar ML12 6AW Tel: 01899 20383 — MB ChB 1972 Ed.; MRCGP 1977; DRCOG 1976.

LEITCH, Mr Stephen George (retired) 9 Oaklands Gardens, Bessacarr, Doncaster DN4 7DX Tel: 01302 535826 — MB ChB Glas. 1949; FRCS Ed. 1958. Prev: Cons. Surg. Doncaster Roy. Infirm.

LEITCH, Stewart Paul 68 Gambier Parry Gardens, Gloucester GL2 9RE — BM BCh 1997 Oxf.

LEITCH, Thomas William (retired) 41 Brigg Road, Broughton, Brigg DN20 0JG — MB BCh BAO 1949 Belf.

LEITH, Duncan Cramlington Medical Group, The Health Centre, Forum Way, Cramlington NE23 6QN Tel: 01670 713911 Fax: 01670 735958 — MB BS 1982 Newc. GP Cramlington, N.d.

LEITH, Iain McWilliam 16 Melton Hill, Melton, Woodbridge IP12 1AY Tel: 01394 380701; 15 Saxon Way, Woodbridge IP12 1LG Tel: 01394 387253 — MB BS 1968 Lond. (Lond. Hosp.) Indep. Orthop. Phys. Woodbridge. Socs: Brit. Med. Acupunct. Soc.

LEITH, James Marshall 54 Avondale Avenue, East Kilbride, Glasgow G74 1NT — LRCP LRCS Ed. LRFPS Glas. 1945.

LEITH, Siobhan Eileen Arrowe Park Hospital, Arrowe Park Road, Upton, Wirral CH49 5PE Tel: 0151 604 7056 Fax: 0151 604 7126; 288 Meols Parade, Meols, Wirral CH47 7AU Tel: 0151 632 0853 Email: siobhan.leith@btinternet.com — MB BCh BAO 1983 NUI; FRCA 1993. (Univ. Coll. Cork) Cons. Anaesth. Wirral Health Trust. Socs: Obst. Anaesth. Assn.; Assn. Anaesth.; Liverp. Soc. Anaesth.

LEKAKIS, Garyfalia Flat 309, Cinnamon Wharf, 24 Shad Thames, London SE1 2YJ — Ptychio Iatrikes 1989 Patras.

LEKH, Sudesh Kumar Surrey Oaklands NHS Trust, Shaws Corner, Blackborough Road, Reigate RH2 7DG Tel: 01737 272307 Fax: 01737 272346 Email: s.lekh@mcmail.com — BM 1982 Soton.; MRCPsych 1990. (Soton. Univ. Med. Sch.) Cons. Psychiat. (Community Psychiat.) E. Surrey Priority Care NHS Trust Redhill. Socs: Roy. Coll. Psychiat.; BMA.

LELIJVELD, Hubert Anthony Benedict Maria Burlington Road Surgery, 14 Burlington Road, Ipswich IP1 2EU Tel: 01473 211661 Fax: 01473 289187 — MB BS 1987 Lond.

***LELLI, Natasha Marina** 9 Stephenson Drive, Windsor SL4 5LG — MB ChB 1997 Bristol.

LELLO, Mr Glenn Edward 5B Ravelston Park, Edinburgh EH4 3DX Tel: 0131 343 3816 — MB ChB 1978 Sheffield; PhD Witwatersrand 1989, BDS 1972; FRCS Ed 1989; MRCS England LRCP London 1978; FDS RCS Ed 1975; BDS 1972. Cons. & Sen. Lect. Edin. City Hosp. Prev: Sen. Lect. & Hon. Cons. Univ. Manch.; Prof. & Head Dept. Maxillofacial Surg. Med. Univ. S. Africa.

LEMAN, Joyce Anne Department of Dermatology, University of Glasgow, Glasgow G11 6NU — MB ChB 1992 Glas. Lect. (Dermat.) Univ. Glas.

LEMAN, Peter Charles Mayo Old Forge House, Boat Lane, Hoveringham, Nottingham NG14 7JP — MB ChB 1993 Birm.

LEMBERG, Martyn William 44 Durham Road, London SW20 0TW — MB ChB 1990 Otago.

LEMBERGER, Mr Reginald John City Hospital, Hucknall Rd, Nottingham Tel: 0115 962 7791, 0115 969 1169; 24 Richmond Drive, Mapperley Park, Nottingham NG3 5EL Tel: 0115 962 1043 Fax: 0115 985 2600 — MB BS 1973 Lond.; FRCS Eng. 1977. (King's Coll. Hosp.) Cons. Urol. Surg. City Hosp. Nottm. Prev: Jun. Ho. Off. (Surg. Unit.) King's Coll Hosp. Lond.

LEMERLE, Muriel Osbourne (retired) Floralies, Langton Road, Tunbridge Wells TN4 8XA Tel: 01892 523942 — MB ChB 1942 Aberd.

LEMMENS, Fiona Marie The Orrell Park Surgery, 46 Moss Lane, Orrell Park, Liverpool L9 8AL Tel: 0151 525 2736 Fax: 0151 524 1037; Aintree Park Group Practice, 46 Moss Lane, Orrell Park, Liverpool L9 8AL Tel: 0151 525 2736 — MB ChB 1992 Aberd.; MRCGP 1997; DRCOG 1995. (Aberd.)

LEMMENS, Gerrit William Petrel House, Child, Adolescent & Family Therapy Service, Broadway Park, Barclay St., Bridgwater TA6 5YA Tel: 01278 446909 Fax: 01278 446782 — MB BS 1981 Lond.; MRCPsych. 1986. Cons. Child Psychiat. Som. Partership NHS Trust. Prev: Cons. Child Psychiat. N. Derbysh. DHA; Sen. Regist. (Child, Adolesc. & Family Psychiat.) Inst. Family Psychiat. Ipswich; Regist. (Psychiat.) Chrichton Roy. Hosp. Dumfries.

LEMMENS, Johannes Antonius Rectory Road Surgery, 41 Rectory Road, Hadleigh, Benfleet SS7 2NA Tel: 01702 558147 — Artsexamen 1987 Nijmegen.

LEMOINE, Louise 33 St Stephens Road, London W13 8HJ — MB BS 1983 Lond.

LEMOINE, Professor Nicholas Robert ICRF Molecular Oncology Unit, RPMS, Hammersmith Hospital, Du Cane Road, London W12 0NN Tel: 020 8383 3975 Fax: 020 8383 3258 — MB BS 1983 Lond.; MB BS (Hons.) Lond. 1983; PhD Wales 1989; BSc (Hons.) Lond. 1980, MD 1992; MRCPath 1992. (St. Bart. Med. Coll. Lond.) Prof. Molecular Path. RPMS Hammersmith Hosp. Lond.; Edit. Bd. Mem. Gene Ther., Internat. Jl. Cancer, Brit. Jl. Cancer, Jl. Path., Gut Virchows Arch. & Tumour Targeting. Socs: (Pres.) Pancreatic Soc.; Brit. Assn. Cancer Research; Path. Soc. Prev: Cons. Clin. Sci.

ICRF Molecular Path. Hammersmith Hosp. Lond.; Lect. (Path.) Univ. Wales Cardiff.

LEMON, Catherine Mount Vernon Hospital, Northwood HA6 2RN; 7 Mynchen End, Knotty Green, Beaconsfield HP9 2AT — BM BCh 1985 Oxf.; MA Camb. 1986; MRCP (UK) 1988; FRCR 1991.

LEMON, Mr John Gerard The Beeches, Mill Lane, Cheadle SK8 2PY Tel: 0161 491 2441; Bollin House, Hollies Lane, Wilmslow SK9 2BW Tel: 01625 536273 — MB BCh BAO 1970 Belf.; BSc Belf. 1967, MB BCh BAO 1970; FRCS Eng. 1975; FRCS Ed. 1974. Cons. Orthop. Surg. Univ. Hosp. S. Manch. Socs: Fell. Brit. Orthop. Assn.; Brit. Assn. Sport & Med.

LEMON, John Henry (retired) The Old Bakehouse, Lopen, South Petherton TA13 5JU Tel: 01460 241934 — MB BS 1957 Lond.; DAvMed Eng. 1972. Prev: Sen. Med. Off. Civil Aviat. Auth.

LEMON, Marius John Churchill Department of Chemical Pathology, Hallamshire Hospital, Glossop Road, Sheffield S10 2JF; 28 Station Road, Knowle, Solihull B93 0HT Tel: 0156 456238 — MB BS 1983 Newc.

LEMON, Phyllis Grace (retired) 16 Brunswick Place, Lymington SO41 9EQ Tel: 01590 679417 — MB BS 1952 Lond.; MRCS Eng. LRCP Lond. 1951. Prev: SHO (Med.) Kent & Canterbury Hosp.

LEMON, Susan Elizabeth Friars Hill, 26 Old Church Lane, Aghalee, Craigavon BT67 0EY Tel: 01846 651468 — MB BCh BAO 1974 Dub.; BA Dub. 1972; MRCGP 1979; DCH RCPSI 1977; DObst RCOG 1976. (TC Dub.) Med. Off. N. Irel. Blood Transfus. Serv. Prev: GP N. Irel.

LEMONSKY, Isaac The Surgery, 34 Ritchie Street, London N1 0DG; 242 East End Road, E. Finchley, London N2 8AX Tel: 020 8883 1038 — MB ChB 1955 Cape Town. (Cape Town)

LEMPERT-BARBER, Mrs Susanne Martina (retired) Morris Feinmann Home, 178 Palatine Road, Manchester M20 2YW Tel: 0161 445 5586 — MB ChB 1941 Manch.; DPH Manch. 1954. Prev: Med. Asst. (Geriat. Med.) Stockport HA.

LEMUT, Herve Suite 323, 2 Old Brompton Road, London SW7 3DQ Tel: 0836 608052 Fax: 020 7581 4445; 36A Wetherby Mansions, Earl's Court Square, London SW5 9DJ Tel: 020 7370 3291 Fax: 020 7370 3291 — MD 1980 Paris. (Paris) Indep. GP Lond. Socs: BMA; W Lond. Med. Soc.

LENCH, Patricia Annette 18 Kings Oak Meadow, Clutton, Bristol BS39 5SU Tel: 01761 453048; 18 Kings Oak Meadow, Clutton, Bristol BS39 5SU Tel: 01761 453048 — MB BS 1970 Lond.; MRCS Eng. LRCP Lond. 1970; MRCGP 1979; DObst RCOG 1976. (Roy. Free) Non Princip., Gen. Pract., Bath; CMO. Brook Young Peoples Clinic, Bristol; EMP Med. Servicies, Sema, Bristol. Prev: GP N.ampton.; Dist. Med. Off., Palmalmal, Papua, New Guinea; CMO. Bath & W., Family Plann./ Bath.

LENCH, Tristan John 12 Church Street, Bishops Lydeard, Taunton TA4 3AT — MB ChB 1995 Bristol.

LENDEN, Gary James Penlee House, 89 Molesworth Road, Stoke, Plymouth PL3 4EL — MB BS 1989 Lond.

LENDEN, Pamela Memone Friary House Surgery, Friary House, 2a Beaumont Road, Plymouth PL4 9BH Tel: 01752 663138 Fax: 01752 675805 — Artsexamen 1993 Amsterdam; DCH RCOP 1995; DRCOG 1998. (Amersterdam)

LENDON, Donna The Barn, The Green, Collingham, Newark NG23 7LQ — MB BS 1990 Sydney.

LENDON, Mehroo Department of Pathology, Stopford Building, University of Manchester, Oxford Road, Manchester M13 9PL — MRCS Eng. LRCP Lond. 1958; PhD Sheff. 1973; FRCPath 1988, M 1976. (Cardiff) Sen. Lect. in Paediat. Path. Univ. Manch. Prev: Sen. Regist. (Morbid Anat.) Dept. Path. Univ. Manch.; Research Fell. in Developm. Path. Univ. Sheff.

LENDRUM, Andrew Bertram Guthrie Kirriemuir Health Centre, Tannage Brae, Kirriemuir DD8 4DL Tel: 01575 573333 Fax: 01575 574230 — MB ChB 1972 Glas.; MRCGP 1976; DObst RCOG 1974. Prev: SHO (Psychiat.) Roy. Dundee Liff Hosp.; Trainee GP Dundee VTS; Med. Off. Aboriginal/Is.er Health Centre Townsville Australia.

LENDRUM, Mr John BUPA Hospital, Russell Road, Whalley Range, Manchester M16 8AJ Tel: 0161 861 0331; Beech House, Eagle Brow, Lymm WA13 0LZ Tel: 0192 575 3385 — MB BChir 1962 Camb.; MA Camb. 1962; FRCS Eng. 1967. (Camb. & Middlx.) Hon. Cons. Plastic Surg. UHSM; Hon. Assoc. Lect. (Plastic Surg.) Univ. Manch. Socs: Brit. Assn. Plastic Surg. Prev: Cons. Plastic Surg. Univ. Hosp. S. Manch., Booth Hall Childr. Manch. & Rochdale Dist. Gp. Hosps.; Sen. Regist. (Plastic & Jaw Surg.) Frenchay Hosp. Bristol; Cas. Off. (Surg.) & Ho. Surg. Middlx. Hosp. Lond.

LENDRUM, Katherine Chesterfield & North Derbyshire Royal Hospital, Calow, Chesterfield S44 5BL Tel: 01246 277271; Email: katherine.lendrum@dial.pipex.com — BM BS 1991 Nottm.; 1999 FFAEM; 2000 DCH; BMedSci Nottm. 1989; MRCP (UK) 1994. (Nottm. Univ.) p/t Cons. in Emerg. Med., Chesterfield & N. Derbysh. Roy. Hosp. Socs: Fell. of Fac. of A&E Med.; Brit. Assn. of Accid. & Emerg. Med. (Mem.). Prev: SHO Rotat. (Gen. Med.) Qu. Med. Centre Nottm.; SHO (Paediat. A & E) Sheff. Childr. Hosp.; SHO Rotat. (Orthop. & A & E) Camb. HA.

LENDRUM, Richard (retired) Freeman Hospital, High Heaton, Newcastle upon Tyne NE7 7DN Tel: 0191 284 3111 — MB BChir 1967 Camb.; FRCP 1982, M 1970. Cons. Phys. Gastroenterol. Freeman Hosp. Trust Newc. Prev: Sen. Regist. (Med.) Birm. Gen. Hosp.

LENDRUM, Robert Donald Currie The Health Centre, St. Katherine's Court, Newburgh, Cupar KY14 6EB Tel: 01337 840462 Fax: 01337 840996; 29 Anderson Street, Newburgh, Cupar KY14 6DH Tel: 01337 840396 Fax: 01337 840396 — MB BCh BAO 1972 NUI; MA Aberdeen 1966; MRCGP 1977. (Univ. Coll. Galway, Eire) Socs: Anglo-French Med. Soc. Prev: Regist. (Psychiat.) Roy. Dundee Liff Hosp.; Trainee GP Perth VTS.

LENDRUM, Sheila Blairerno, Abernethy, Perth PH2 9LW Tel: 01738 850223 — MB ChB St. And. 1969; DA Eng. 1973; DObst RCOG 1971; MFFP. Med. Off. (Family Plann.) Perth & Kinross Health Dist. Socs: Fac. Family Plann.

LENEGHAN, John Edward The Knoll Surgery Partnership, 46 High Street, Frodsham, Warrington WA6 7HF Tel: 01928 733249 Fax: 01928 739367 — MB ChB 1970 Manch.; MRCGP 1975; DObst RCOG 1973. (Manch.)

LENEHAN, Ruth Margaret 5 Cuttlebrook Close, Sunnyhill, Derby DE23 7RE — MB BS 1992 Newc.

LENEY, Barbara Vera Steps Cottage, Staple, Dartington, Totnes TQ9 6HR — MB BChir 1955 Camb.; MRCS Eng. LRCP Lond. 1952; MRCPsych 1978; DObst RCOG 1953; DPM Eng. 1976. (Lond. Hosp.)

LENEY, Peter Marten Oak Street Medical Practice, 1 Oak Street, Norwich NR3 3DL Tel: 01603 613431 Fax: 01603 767209 — MB 1963 Camb.; MRCS Eng. LRCP Lond. 1962; DObst RCOG 1964. Hosp. Pract. Dept. Dermat. Norf. & Norwich Hosp.

LENFESTEY, Pauline Mary 9 Dale View Close, Barnston, Wirral CH61 1DU Tel: 0151 648 5545 — MB BS 1984 Lond.; MRCOphth 1994. Clin. Asst. (Ophth.) St. Pauls Eye Hosp. & Alderhey Childr. Hosps.

LENFESTY, James Peter Albert Street Health Centre, Albert Street, Belfast BT12 4JR Tel: 028 9032 0777 — MB BCh BAO 1978 Belf.; MRCP (UK) 1981; MRCGP 1983; DRCOG 1985; DCH RCS Dub. 1980.

LENG, Christopher Paul 49 Woodfield Crescent, London W1 1PB — MB BS 1988 Lond.

LENG, Gillian Catherine Nice, 11 Strand WC2N 5HR — MB ChB 1987 Leeds; MD Leeds 1994. Guidelines Progr. Director; Hon. Cons.; Hon. Sen. Lect. Socs: Soc. Social Med.; BMA; Roy. Soc. of Med. Prev: Specialist Regist. (Pub. Health) W. of Scotl.; Clin. Research Fell. Wolfson Unit for Preven. of Peripheral Vasc. Dis.; Trainee GP Bathgate.

LENG, Graham Hospice of the Good Shepherd, Gordon Lane, Backford, Chester CH2 4DG Tel: 01244 851091 Fax: 01244 851108 Email: grahamleng@bigfoot.com; 2 Snabwood Close, Little Neston, South Wirral CH64 0UP — MB ChB 1982 Bristol; BSc Bristol 1979, MB ChB 1982; MRCGP 1986; Dip. Palliat. Med. Wales 1995; DRCOG 1985. Med. Off. Hospice of Good Shepherd Chester. Socs: BMA; BMAS. Prev: GP Willaston S. Wirral.

LENG, John Duncan (retired) Tudor Cottage, Abbots Morton, Worcester WR7 4NA — MB ChB 1955 Birm.

LENG, John Edward Doctors Surgery, 18 Union Street, Kirkintilloch, Glasgow G66 1DJ Tel: 0141 776 1238 Fax: 0141 775 2786 — MB ChB Aberd. 1958; MRCGP 1978; DObst RCOG 1960. Socs: Christian Med. Fell.sh.

LENG, Malcolm David Beverley Road Surgery, 840 Beverley Road, Hull HU6 7HP Tel: 01482 853270; 17 Riverview Gardens, Hull HU7 6DZ Tel: 0482 825468 — MB ChB 1972 Manch.

LENG, Mhoira Edith Fay Roxburghe House, Milltimber AB13 0HR Tel: 01224 681818 Fax: 01224 403004; 39 Mile End Avenue, Aberdeen AB15 5PT — MB ChB 1987 Aberd.; MRCP (UK) 1990. (Aberd.) Cons., Hon. Sen. Lect. & Med. Dir. (Palliat. Med.) Aberd. Roy. Hosps. NHS Trust. Socs: Grampian Rep. Christian Med. Fell.ship; RSM; Roy. Coll. Phys. Prev: Vis. Regist. (Palliat. Care Serv.) Centr. Sydney, Austral.; Sen. Regist. (Palliat. Med.) Countess Mt.batten Hse. Soton.; Regist. (Med.) Ipswich Hosp.

LENGUA QUIJANDRIA, Cesar Augusto Reaside Clinic, Bristol Road S., Rubery, Birmingham B45 9BE Tel: 0121 453 6161; 110 Poplar Road, Smethwick, Smethwick B66 4AP — MB BCh 1987 Wales; MRCPsych 1993. Sen. Regist. (Adolesc. Forens. Psychiat.) Reaside Clinic Birm. Socs: BMA; ACPP.

LENNANE, Simon Benedict Xavier The Lodge, Letheringsett, Holt NR25 7JB — BM 1993 Soton.

LENNARD, Anne Lesley Department of Haematology, Royal Victoria Infirmary, Queen Victoria Road, Newcastle upon Tyne NE1 4LP Tel: 0191 282 4743 Fax: 0191 201 0154 Email: a.l.lennard@ncl.ac.uk; 65 Runnymede Road, Darras Hall, Ponteland, Newcastle upon Tyne NE20 9HJ Tel: 01661 824841 — MB BS 1978 Newc.; MRCP (UK) 1981; FRCPath 1987. p/t Sen. Lect. Univ. Newc. u. Tyne. Socs: Brit. Soc. Haematol.; Europ. bone marrow Transpl. soc. Prev: Sen. Regist. (Haemat.) Roy. Vict. Infirm. Newc.

LENNARD, Mrs Joan Kathleen (retired) 15 Church Road, Sneyd Park, Bristol BS9 1QL Tel: 0117 968 4830 Email: joankl@aol.com — MB ChB 1949 Bristol; FRCGP 1978, M 1960. Prev: Tutor (Radiother.) Univ. Bristol.

LENNARD, Nicola Sue 6 St Alban's Close, Oakham LE15 6EW — MB ChB 1991 Leic.

LENNARD, Rosemary Fiennes Marie Curie Centre, Maudsley Street, Bradford BD3 9LH; 7 Greenhead Drive, Keighley BD20 6EZ — MB ChB 1976 Sheff.; PhD Open Univ. 1984; MRCP (UK) 1988; FRCP 1998. (Sheffield) Cons. Palliat. Med. Bradford Hosp.s NHS Trust. Socs: Assn. Palliat. Med. Prev: Cons. Palliat. Med. Manorlands Hospice Bradford HA.; Macmillan Sen. Lect. Lond. Hosp. Med. Coll.

LENNARD, Russell Hubert 200 Turnpike Link, Croydon CR0 5NZ Tel: 020 8680 2140 Fax: 020 8401 3092 — MB BS 1981 West Indies; MSc (Family Med.) West Indies 1985; DM (Family Med.) West Indies 1988. Staff Grade (A & E) Mayday Univ. Hosp. Croydon Surrey.

LENNARD, Mr Thomas William Jay 65 Runnymede Road, Darras Hall, Ponteland, Newcastle upon Tyne NE20 9HJ Tel: 01661 824841 — MB BS 1977 Newc.; MB BS (2nd cl. Hons.) Newc. 1977; MD Newc. 1986; FRCS Ed. 1994; FRCS Eng. 1981; MRCS Eng. LRCP Lond. 1977. Cons. Surg. & Reader (Surg.) Roy. Vict. Infirm. Newc. Prev: Sen. Lect. & Lect. (Surg.) Univ. Newc.; Regist. & SHO (Surg.) Roy. Vict. Infirm. Newc.

LENNARD-JONES, Andrew Michael Creffield Road Surgery, 19 Creffield Road, Colchester CO3 3HZ Tel: 01206 570371 Fax: 01206 369908 — BM BS 1984 Nottm.; MRCGP 1988; FRCGP 1998. (Nottm.) Socs: Colchester Med. Soc.

LENNARD-JONES, Professor John Edward 72 Cumberland Street, Woodbridge IP12 4AD Tel: 01394 387717 Fax: 01394 387742 — MB BChir Camb. 1953; MA Camb. 1951, BA 1947, MD 1965; FRCS Eng. 1992; FRCP Lond. 1968, M 1956. (Univ. Coll. Hosp.) Emerit. Prof. Gastroenterol Roy. Lond. Hosp. Med. Coll; Emerit. Cons Gastrogenterologist St Mary's Hosp. Socs: Hon. Fell. Roy. Soc. Med.; Hon. Mem. (Ex-Pres.) Brit. Soc. Gastroenterol.; Brit. Paren. & Enteral Nutrit. Prev: Cons. Gastroenterol. St. Marks Hosp.; Vis. Prof. Montreal 1970, Melbourne 1981, Cleveland Clinic 1983, McMaster Univ. 1985, Univ. Iowa 1987; Cons. Phys. Univ. Coll. Hosp.

LENNEY, Warren Department of Academic Paediatrics, City General Hospital, Newcastle Road, Stoke-on-Trent ST4 6QG Tel: 01782 552572 Fax: 01782 713946; Astbury House, 46 Main Road, Wybunbury, Nantwich CW5 7LY Tel: 01270 841366 Fax: 01270 841364 — MB ChB 1970 St. And.; MD Dundee 1979; FRCP Lond. 1988; MRCP (UK) 1976; FRCPCH 1997; DCH Eng. 1972. (St. Andrews) Cons. Paediat. Respirat. Dis. (Child Health) Stoke City Gen. Hosp.; Hon. Sen. Clin. Lect. Keele Univ. Socs: (Ex-Convenor) Brit. Paediat. Respirat. Soc.; Eur. Respirat. Soc.; Amer. Thoracic Soc. Prev: Assoc. Med. Dir. Allen & Hanburys Ltd. Uxbridge; Cons. Paediat. Roy. Alexandra Childr. Hosp. Brighton; Research Fell. (Paediat.) Child Health Nottm. Univ.

LENNIE, Joanne Elizabeth The Old Barn, Newtown Lane, Romsley, Halesowen B62 0EJ — MB ChB 1987 Birm. Trainee GP Worcs.

LENNIE, May Elizabeth Park Medical Practice, 119 Park Road, Timperley, Altrincham WA15 6QQ; 7 Heald Road, Bowdon, Altrincham WA14 2JE — MB ChB 1980 Dundee; MRCGP 1984; DRCOG 1982. p/t GP.

LENNON, Ann Josephine Blackthorn Surgery, 73 Station Road, Netley Abbey, Southampton SO31 5AE Tel: 023 8045 3110 Fax: 023 8045 2747 — MB BCh BAO 1980 NUI.

LENNON, Barbara Brynhild (retired) 3 Brouncker House, Canons Court, Church St, Melksham SN12 6UR Tel: 01225 700291 — MB ChB Birm. 1936. Prev: Flight Lt. RAF Med. Br. 1942-1944.

LENNON, Charles Patrick Brian Munro Medical Centre, West Elloe Avenue, Spalding PE11 2BY Tel: 01775 725530 Fax: 01775 766168 — MB ChB 1983; MRCGP, DGM, DRCOG; Dip. Occ. Med. 1999. (Sheffield) Partner, Munro Med. Centre; Clin. Asst. in c/o the Elderly.

LENNON, Colin Hugh Giffords Surgery, 28 Lowbourne, Melksham SN12 7EA Tel: 01225 703370 — MB BS 1975 Western Australia; FRCA 1979; DA Eng. 1977. (W. Australia)

LENNON, Emer Mary Stranraer Health Centre, Edinburgh Road, Stranraer DG9 7HG; Stables End, Leswalt, Stranraer DG9 0LJ — MB BCh BAO 1990 Belf.; MRCGP 1996; DCH RCPS Glas. 1994. (Qu. Univ. Belf.)

LENNON, Francis Patrick Inverclyde, Hartington Road, St Helens WA10 6AF; Helm Crag Cottage, Easedale Road, Grasmere, Ambleside LA22 9QN — MB ChB 1947 Liverp. (Liverp.) Assoc. Mem. Racecourse Med. Off. Assn. GB. Prev: Sen. Ho. Phys. Co. Hosp. Kendal; Obst. Ho. Surg. Walton Hosp. Liverp.; Capt. RAMC.

LENNON, Mr Gerald Martin Anthony 2 Darleen Park, Londonderry BT48 8DT — MB BCh BAO 1984 Dub.; FRCSI 1988.

LENNON, Geraldine Mary — MB ChB 1991 Leeds; MRCP (UK) 1996. p/t Flexible Specialist Regist. (Paediat.) Nottm. City Hosp., Nottm. Prev: Flexible Specialist Regist. (Paediat.) St. Lukes Hosp. Bradford.

LENNON, Kieran James 11 Hillcrest Road, Crosby, Liverpool L23 9XS — MB ChB 1989 Leeds.

LENNON, Kirsty Helen 130 Brownlow Drive, Nottingham NG5 5DB — MB ChB 1993 Glas.

LENNON, Margaret Mary Cliff Road Health Centre, 4 Cliff Road, Welton, Lincoln LN2 3JH Tel: 01673 860203 Fax: 01673 862888 — MB BCh BAO 1980 NUI.

LENNON, Robert Iain Ballochbuie, Dulnain Bridge, Grantown-on-Spey PH26 3PA — BM 1995 Soton.

LENNON, Samuel Paul 92 Mourne Road, Lurgan, Craigavon BT66 8JB — MB BCh BAO 1982 Belf.; MB BCh Belf. 1982.

LENNON, Sean Patrick Department of Psychiatry, Withington Hospital, Manchester M20 2LR Tel: 0161 445 8111 Fax: 0161 448 1348; 239 Bramhall Lane S., Bramhall, Stockport SK7 3ER — BM 1978 Soton.; MSc Manch. 1988; MRCPsych 1985. Cons. Old Age Psychiat. Withington Hosp. Manch.; Hon. Lect. Manch. Univ.

LENNOX, Alasdair Murray Cromer Group Practice, 48 Overstrand Road, Cromer NR27 0AJ Tel: 01263 513148; Puldoran, Arbor Road, Cromer NR27 9DW Tel: 01263 512538 Email: alasdair.lennox@dial.pipex.com — MB BS 1987 Lond. Clin. Asst. Med. Elderly Berjamin Ct. Rehabil. Unit Cromer.

LENNOX, Alison Ann Tel: 01252 344868 Fax: 01252 342596; Tara, Southview Road, Headley Down, Bordon GU35 8HX Tel: 01428 712661 Fax: 01428 717004 — MB BS 1984 Lond. Prev: Clin. Asst. Highland Hospice Inverness.

LENNOX, Angela Isabela Agnes, MBE St Matthew's Medical Centre, Prince Philip House, Malabar Road, Leicester LE1 2NZ Tel: 0116 224 4700; 19 Powys Avenue, Oadby, Leicester LE2 2DQ — MB BS 1977 Lond.; MRCP (UK) 1980. GP; Dir. Centre Stud. Community Health Care Leics. Univ.

LENNOX, Arthur Scott Woodside Medical Group A, 80 Western Road, Woodside, Aberdeen AB24 4SU Tel: 01224 492631 Fax: 01224 276173 — MB ChB 1986 Dundee.

LENNOX, Barbara Jane 13 Egerton Road N., Chorlton, Manchester M21 0SE Tel: 0161 881 8043 — MB ChB 1979 Manch.; BSc (Med. Sci.) St. And. 1976.

LENNOX, Belinda Rosalind Chestnut Farmhouse, Main St., Farndon, Newark NG24 3SA — BM BS 1993 Nottm. Psychiat. Rotat. Train. Scheme Oxf.

LENNOX, Brian Lennox and Partners, 9 Alloway Place, Ayr KA7 2AA Tel: 01292 611835 Fax: 01292 284982 Email: brianlennox@hotamil.com; 16 Rosebank Crescent, Ayr KA7 2SS Tel: 01292 610471 — MB ChB 1977 Glas.; MRCGP 1981; DRCOG 1980; DA Eng. 1980. Gen. Practitioner; Assoc. Adviser, CPD; W. of Scotl. Deanery. Socs: BMA. Prev: SHO (Obst.) Qu. Mother's Hosp. Glas.; SHO (Anaesth.) W.. Infirm. Glas.; Trainee GP Dumfries.

LENNOX, Catherine McQueen Erskine Hartlepool General Hospital, Hartlepool TS24 9AH Tel: 01429 266654; The Maples, Bank Top, Seaton, Seaham SR7 0NE Tel: 0191 581 8755 — MB ChB 1971 Dundee; FRCS Ed. 1977; FRCS (Orthop.) Ed. 1986; DObst RCOG 1973. Cons. Orthop. Surg. Hartlepool Gen. Hosp. Socs: Fell. BOA; BMA. Prev: Sen. Regist. (Orthop.) Newc. RHA.

LENNOX, Charles Kenneth Brynmor (retired) The Court, 4 Mount PLeasant, Barry CF63 2HE Tel: 01446 733792 — MB BCh 1937 Wales; BSc, MB BCh Wales 1937; MRCGP 1956.

LENNOX, Christopher Elligott Wisham General Hospital, Wishaw ML2 0DP Tel: 01698 361100 Fax: 01698 376671 Email: christopher.lennox@laht.scot.nhs.uk; 18 Douglas Avenue, Ruthergien, Glasgow G73 4RA Tel: 0141 634 4383 — MB ChB 1972 Glas.; FRCOG 1996; MRCOG 1983; DTM & H Liverp. 1976; DObst. RCOG 1976. Cons. O & G Law Hosp. Carluke. Socs: Brit. Soc. Colposc. & Cervic. Pathol.; Glas. Obst. & Gyn. Soc. Prev: Cons. O & G William Smellie Memor. Matern. Hosp. Lanark.; Sen. Regist. (O & G) Ninewells Hosp. Dundee; Med. Supt. Enga Provincal Hosp. Papua New Guinea.

LENNOX, Craig Alexander Topright, 25 Strathblane Road, Milngavie, Glasgow G62 8DL — MB ChB 1989 Glas.

LENNOX, Graham Gordon Department of Neurology, Addenbrooke's Hospital, Cambridge Tel: 01223 216760 Fax: 01223 336941 — BM BCh 1984 Oxf.; BA Oxf. 1981; FRCP Ed. 1995; MRCP (UK) 1987; FRCP 1997. Cons. Neurol. Addenbrookes Hosp. Camb.; Assoc. Clin. Dean Univ. of Camb. Clin. Sch. Socs: Assn. Brit. Neurol.; Brit. Neuropathol. Soc.; Brit. Neuropsych. Assn. Prev: Regist. Nat. Hosp. Neurol. & Neurosurg. Lond.

LENNOX, Hilary Rachel Gordon Sample Oak, 25 Orchard Road, Shalford, Guildford GU4 8ER Tel: 01483 61677 — MB BS 1958 Lond.; MRCS Eng. LRCP Lond. 1958; DCH Eng. 1961. (Roy. Free) Sen. Med. Off. (Pub. Health Med.) SW Surrey HA. Prev: Sen. Med. Off. Lond. Boro. Croydon.

LENNOX, Mr Iain Andrew Craig Basildon & Thurrock General Hospitals, Basildon Hospital, Nether Mayne, Basildon SS16 5NL Tel: 01268 533911 Fax: 01268 593757; 12 The Paddock, Stock, Ingatestone CM4 9BG Tel: 01268 840963 — MB BS 1983 Lond.; MD Aberd. 1996; FRCS (Orth.) 1995; FRCS Ed. 1988; Dip. Bioeng. Strathclyde 1995. Cons. (Orthop. Surg.) Basildon & Thurrock Gen. Hosps. Socs: Brit. Orthop. Assn.; Roy. Soc. Med.; BOSTA. Prev: Sen. Regist. Glas.; Career Regist. Aberd.; Regist. Roy. Lond. Hosp.

LENNOX, Iain MacIntyre Mansionhouse Unit, Victoria Infirmary, South Glasgow University NHS Trust, Glasgow G41 3DX Tel: 0141 201 6129 Fax: 0141 201 6159 Email: ilennox@gvic.scot.nhs.uk; 29 Langtree Avenue, Whitecraigs, Glasgow G46 7LJ Tel: 0141 577 6246 Fax: 0141 201 6159 — MB ChB 1972 Glas.; FRCP Glas. 1986; MRCP (UK) 1976; DObst RCOG 1974; FRCP Ed 1998. Cons. Geriat. Med. Vict. Infirm. Glas. Socs: Brit. Geriat. Soc.; Glas. S.. Med. Soc.; Scott Soc. Phys.

LENNOX, Ian Bruce Lorn Medical Centre, Soroba Road, Oban PA34 4HE Tel: 01631 563175 Fax: 01631 562708 — MB ChB 1981 Ed.; MRCGP (Distinc.) 1986; DRCOG 1985. Prev: Assn. Adviser (Gen. Pract.); Hon. Lect. Univ. Glas.; Lead Audit Facilitator Argyll & Clyde H.B.

LENNOX, Ian Gordon (retired) Skerryvaig, 79 Five Heads Road, Catherington, Horndean, Waterlooville PO8 9NZ Tel: 02392 571584 Email: iglennox@btinternet.com — MB ChB 1954 Ed.; FRCGP 1979, M 1969; MRCPsych 1976; DObst RCOG 1959; DPM Eng. 1976. Prev: GP Didcot.

LENNOX, James David Skegoneill Health Centre, 195 Skegoneill Avenue, Belfast BT15 3LL Tel: 028 9077 2471 Fax: 028 9077 2449; Cherrytree Lodge, 5 Cherry Valley, Belfast BT5 6PH Tel: 01232 799481 — MB ChB 1978 Manch.; BSc Med. Sc. St. And. 1975; DRCOG 1980.

LENNOX, James Stuart Hamilton Chapel Row Surgery, The Avenue, Bucklebury, Reading RG7 6NS Tel: 01189 713252 — MB BS 1991 Lond.; MRCGP; DCCH; DRCOG. (Lond.Hosp) Sch. Dr.Elstree.Sch.Woolhampton.

LENNOX, Mr John Mervyn 2 Ashmore Terrace, Sunderland SR2 7DE Tel: 0191 514 0666; The Maples, Bank Top, Seaton, Seaham SR7 0NG Tel: 0191 581 8755 — MB BS 1966 Newc.; BSc (Anat.) Durham. 1963; MS (Commend.) Newc. 1976; FRCS Eng. 1971. Cons. Surg. Gen. Hosp. Sunderland. Socs: BMA; AESGBI & ASGBI. Prev: Cons. Surg. Gen. Hosp. Sunderland.

LENNOX, Mr Malcolm Stephen 3 Blakesware Manor, Wareside, Ware SG12 7RD Tel: 01920 462718 Fax: 01920 462026 Email: lennox@doctors.org.uk — MB 1975 Camb.; BChir 1974; FRCS Eng. 1979. Cons. Surg. Qu. Eliz. II Hosp. Welwyn Gdn. City. Socs: Assoc. Mem. BAUS.; Assoc mem of Brit ass of Paed surg; Assn. Surg. GB & Ire. Prev: Sen. Regist. (Surg.) W.m. Hosp. Lond.; Regist. (Surg.) St. Stephens Hosp. Lond.; Ho. Surg. Middx. Hosp.

LENNOX, Mary Elizabeth (retired) Medwin, 61 High Cross Avenue, Melrose TD6 9SX Tel: 0189 682 2923 — MB BS Lond. 1946. Prev: Cytol. Roy. Alexandra Infirm. Paisley.

LENNOX, Penelope Ann Anatomy Department, Guy's Hospital, St Thomas St., London SE1 9RT; 15 Lynton Road, London NW6 6BD — BM BCh 1989 Oxf.; BA (Hons.) Oxf. 1986, BM BCh 1989. Demonst. (Anat.) UMDS, St. Thos. & Guy's Hosp. Lond. Prev: SHO (ENT) Addenbrooke's Hosp. Camb.; SHO (Cas.) St. Thos. Hosp. Lond.; Ho. Phys. John Radcliffe Hosp. Oxf.

LENNOX, Roderick Alistair 50 Moor End Road, Mellor, Stockport SK6 5PS Email: roddylennox@yahoo.co.uk — MB ChB 1994 Manch.; BSc St. And. 1991; DFFP 1996. (Manch. & St. And.) GP Princip., Woodley Health Centre, Stockport; Occupat.al Phys., Eart Cherlurie NHS Trust & Indust. Health Care. Socs: Med. Defence Union; Soc. of Occupat.al Med.

LENNOX, Steven David 2 The Glade, West Cross, Swansea SA3 5JL — MB BCh 1985 Wales.

LENNOX, Mr Stuart Craig Ash Farm, Station Road, Little Hadham, Ware SG11 2DE — MB BS 1956 Lond.; FRCS Eng. 1963; MRCS Eng. LRCP Lond. 1956. (Lond. Hosp.) Surg. Brompton Hosp. Lond.; Sen. Lect. Cardio-Thoracic Inst. Socs: Fell. Amer. Coll. Chest Phys.; Soc. Thoracic Surgs.; Amer. Assn. Thoracic Surgs. Prev: Sen. Regist. Hosp. Dis. of Chest Lond.; Sen. Regist. Dept. Thoracic Surg. Lond. Hosp.; Evarts Graham Trav. Fell. Amer. Assn. Thoracic Surgs. 1964-5.

LENNOX, Susan Elizabeth Old Irvine Road Surgery, 4-6 Old Irvine Road, Kilmarnock KA1 2BD Tel: 01563 22413; 13 Killoch Place, Girdle Toll, Irvine KA11 1AZ — MB ChB 1982 Glas.; MFFP 1995. (Glas.) GP Kilmarnock; Police Surg. Strathclyde Police. Socs: BMA; Assn. Police Surg. Prev: GP Saltcoats; Clin. Med. Off. (Community Med.) Ayrsh. Centr. Hosp.

LENNOX, Vivienne Catherine Puldoran, Arbor Road, Cromer NR27 9DW — MB ChB 1987 Sheff.

LENNOX, Mr William Murdoch 10 Hatherley Court Road, Cheltenham GL51 3AQ — MB BS 1954 Lond.; FRCS Eng. 1961; FRCS Ed. 1961; MRCS Eng. LRCP Lond. 1954.

LENO, Emma Marietta 53 Windsor Drive, Market Drayton TF9 1RL — BM 1990 Soton.

LENO, Sarah Maria York House Medical Centre, Heathside Road, Woking GU22 7XL Tel: 01483 761100 Fax: 01483 751185 — MB ChB 1985 Leic.; DRCOG 1990. Trainee GP Melton Mowbray. Prev: SHO (O & G) W. Middlx. Hosp. Lond.; SHO Rotat. (Med.) Leic. Hosps.; SHO (Neurol.) St. Jas. Univ. Hosp. Leeds.

LENOIR, Robert Jean Department of Anaesthetics, Royal Hospital Haslar, Gosport PO12 2AA — MB BChir 1972 Camb.; BA Camb. 1967; FFA RCS Lond. 1983; DRCOG 1975.

LENOX-SMITH, Alan James 154 Murray Road, London W5 4DA Tel: 020 8560 2562 Email: alan@lenox-smith.com — MB BS 1982 Lond.; FFPM RCP (UK) 2000; MRCP (UK) 1987; MFPM RCP (UK) 1992; DPM Eng. 1990. Sen. Med. Advis. Wyeth. Socs: Fell. Hunt. Soc. Prev: Pharmaceut. Phys. Hoechst (UK) Hounslow; Regist. (Gen. Med.) P.ss Alexandra Hosp. Harlow; Regist. (Chest Med.) Lond. Hosp. Whitechapel.

LENOX-SMITH, Ian (retired) North Lodge, 17 Codicote Road, Welwyn AL6 9NF Tel: 01438 714001 — MRCS Eng. LRCP 1952 MB BChir Camb. 1953; MA Camb. 1951; MRCS Eng. LRCP Lond. 1952; Dip. Pharm. Med. RCP (UK) 1976; FFPM RCP (UK) 1990. Prev: Clin. Research Phys. Roche Products Ltd.

LENTEN, Peter Michael (retired) 25 Quaker Road, Sileby, Leicester Tel: 01509 814003 — MB ChB 1958 Manch.; DObst RCOG 1960. Prev: GP Leicester.

LENTHALL, Jeanette 23 McIntyre Road, Stocksbridge, Sheffield S36 1DG Tel: 0114 288 5748 — MB ChB 1994 Sheff.; DRCOG 1998. GP Reg. York; SHO (Elderly Med.) Derriford Hosp. Plymouth. Prev: SHO (Palliat. Med.) St Lukes Hospice Plymouth; SHO (A & E & ENT) Rotherham Dist. Gen. Hosp.; Ho. Off. (Gen. Med. & Gen. Surg.) Roy. Hallamsh. Hosp. Sheff.

LENTIN, Mr Michael Newlands Medical Centre, Chorley New Road, Bolton BL1 5BP Tel: 01204 840342; 261 Stand Lane, Radcliffe, Manchester M26 1JA — MB BCh BAO 1937 NUI; FRCS Ed. 1945. (Cork) Socs: Fell. Internat. Coll. Angiol. 1962; Fell. Manch. Med. Soc.; Bolton Med. Soc. Prev: Vis. Surg. Bolton Roy. Infirm., Bolton Dist. Gen. Hosp. & Hulton Hosp. Bolton.; Res. Med. Off. Manch. Vict. Memor. Jewish Hosp.; SHO (Surg.) Oldham Roy. Infirm.

LENTON, Catherine Elizabeth 81 Pointout Road, Bassett, Southampton SO16 7DL — BM 1995 Soton.

LENTON, Christine Joyce Tel: 01600 713811 Fax: 01600 772652; Old Grove Cottage, Llangrove, Ross-on-Wye HR9 6HA Tel: 01989 770451 Email: christine.lenton@virgin.net — MB BS 1971 Lond.; BSc Lond. 1968; MRCGP 1984. (Middlx.) Princip. GP Monmouth. Prev: Ho. Surg. & Ho. Phys. Cheltenham Gen. Hosp.; SHO (Paediat.) Roy. Berks. Hosp. Reading.

LENTON, Christopher David Ashfield Surgery, 8 Walmley Road, Sutton Coldfield B76 1QN Tel: 0121 351 7955 Fax: 0121 313 2509; 25 Arun Way, Walmley, Sutton Coldfield B76 2BQ — MB ChB 1988 Birm. (Birm.)

LENTON, Elizabeth Beatrice Crawley Hospital, West Green Drive, Crawley RH11 7DH Tel: 01293 600300 Fax: 01293 600341; Stakerleys, Nyetimber Copse, West Chiltington, Pulborough RH20 2NE Tel: 01798 812880 — MB ChB 1965 St. And. Clin. Asst. (Dermat.) Crawley & Horsham. Prev: GP Balcombe & Hancross W. Sussex; RAF Med. Off.; Med. Off. Family Plann. Assn.

LENTON, Richard James 47 Carseview, Bannockburn, Stirling FK7 8LH Tel: 01786 815631 — MB ChB 1974 Ed.; BSc (Hons.) Ed. 1971; FRCP Glas. 1995; FRCP Ed. 1987; MRCP (UK) 1977. Cons. Phys. (Geriat. Med.) Falkirk & Dist. Roy. Infirm.

LENTON, Simon William 29 Maple Grove, Bath BA2 3AF — MB ChB 1977 Aberd.; MRCP (UK) 1984.

LENYGON, Angela Clare 3 Adeline Gardens, Gosforth, Newcastle upon Tyne NE3 4JQ — MB BS 1968 Newc. (Newc.) Clin. Asst. Univ. Health Serv. Univ. Newc.

LENZ, Richard John Chy-an-Guel, Perrancombe, Perranporth TR6 0JA Tel: 0187 257 2524 Fax: 0187 257 2524 — MB BS 1967 Lond.; MRCS Eng. LRCP Lond. 1967; FFA RCS Eng. 1971. (King's Coll. Hosp.) Cons. Anaesth. Roy. Cornw. Hosps. Trust Truro. Prev: Sen. Regist. (Anaesth.) United Bristol Hosps.

LEON, Colin Maurice, MBE Felling Health Centre, Stephenson Terrace, Felling, Gateshead NE10 9QG Tel: 0191 692316 — MB BS 1953 Durh.; FRCGP 1981 M 1974. Assoc. Adviser in Gen. Pract. Newc. Univ.; Mem. Gateshead Med. Advis. Comm. & Gateshead Local Med. Comm. Socs: FRCGP (Ex-Chairm. N. Fac.) & Mem. Educat.Div. Prev: Organiser (Gen. Pract.) N.ld. VTS; RCGP Coll. Tutor Qu. Eliz. Hosp. Gateshead; Hosp. Pract. Qu. Eliz. Hosp. Gateshead.

LEON, David (retired) 21 Millfield Grove, Tynemouth, North Shields NE30 2PZ — MB BS 1940 Durh.; MRCGP 1959. Chairm. Indust. Injuries & War Pens. Med. Bds. Prev: Regist. (Surg.) & Ho. Surg. Roy. Infirm. Sunderland.

LEON, Emma Andree 21 Willow Park, Willow Bank, Fallowfield, Manchester M14 6XT — MB BS 1988 Lond.

LEON VILLAPALOS, Jorge 66 Orchard Lisle House, Talbot Yard, Borough High St., London SE1 1XY — LMS 1990 U Complutense Madrid.

LEONARD, Mr Alan Gerald Ulster Independent Clinic, Stranmillis Road, Belfast BT9 5JH Tel: 028 9066 1212; 28 Knockdene Park S., Belfast BT5 7AB Tel: 028 9065 3162 — MB BCh BAO 1967 Belf.; FRCS Ed. 1972; FRCS (Eng) 1999. Cons. Plastic Surg. N. Irel. Plastic & Maxillofacial Serv. Socs: Brit. Assn. Plastic Surg.

LEONARD, Andrew John Princess Margaret Hospital, Okus Road, Swindon SN1 4JU Tel: 01793 536231 Fax: 01793 426035; Foxhill, The Old Rope Walk, Tetbury GL8 8XQ Tel: 01666 505851 Email: andrew.leonard@virgin.net — MB BChir 1992 Camb.; MB BChir Camb. 1991; MRCP (UK) 1994. (Camb. /UCL) Cons. (Respir. & Gen. Med.) P.ss Margt. Hosp. Swindon. Socs: Comm. Mem. Brit. Thoracic Soc. Prev: Sen. Regist. (Respir. Med.) Newc.

LEONARD, Colin John Tel: 020 8567 0447 Fax: 020 8567 0984; Tel: 020 8560 6910 — MPhil. (Brunel) 1997; MB ChB Birm. 1961; FRCGP 1981, M 1975; DObst RCOG 1963; DCH Eng. 1965. (Birm.) Hon. Sen. Lect. Gen. Pract., Imperial Coll. Sch. of Med. Socs: BMA; RCGP. Prev: Ho. Surg. (Obst.) Birm. Matern. Hosp.; Ho. Phys. (Paediat.) E. Birm. Gen. Hosp.; Clin. Asst. (Psychiat.) Cotshill Hosp. Chipping Norton.

LEONARD, David 20 Blackmoor Drive, West Derby, Liverpool L12 8RA — BM 1981 Soton.

LEONARD, Deirdre Ann 10 Coombe Road, Crookes, Sheffield S10 1FF — MB ChB 1989 Liverp.; MRCGP 1994; DRCOG 1992. GP Clin. Asst. (Genitourin. Med.) Sheff.

LEONARD, Edith Marjorie (retired) Orchard House, Hopesay, Craven Arms SY7 8HD Tel: 01588 660386 — MB ChB 1961 Bristol. Prev: GP Gatley Stockport.

LEONARD, Elizabeth Jane Comber Health Centre, 5 Newtownards Road, Comber, Newtownards BT23 5BA Tel: 028 9187 8391; 28 Knockdene Park S., Belfast BT5 7AB Tel: 01232 653162 — MB BCh BAO 1976 Belf.; DRCOG 1978.

LEONARD, Elizabeth Mary Southampton and South West Hampshire Health Authority, Oakley Road, Southampton SO16 4GX Tel: 02380 725505 Fax: 02380 725557 — MB BS 1983 Lond. SCMO Communicable Dis. Control Soton.

LEONARD, Halcyon Sheila Deriba 36 Norbiton Avenue, Kingston upon Thames KT1 3QR Tel: 020 8546 8884 — MB BChir Camb. 1969; DObst. RCOG 1971. (Middlx.) Med. Dir. Macmillan Continuing Care Team Kingston & Dist. Community NHS Trust.

LEONARD, Helen Claire 4 West Acres, Dinnington, Newcastle upon Tyne NE13 7LZ Tel: 01661 825971 — MB BS 1993 Newc.; BMedSc Newc. 1990; MRCP (UK) 1996. Regist. Rotat. (Paediat.) N. Deanery.

LEONARD, Ian James Beechurst Unit, Chorley and South Ribble District General Hospital, Preston Road, Chorley PR7 1PP Tel: 01257 245158 — MB BS 1983 Lond.; MSc Manch. 1990; BSc Lond. 1980, MB BS 1983; MRCPsych 1988; DGM RCP Lond. 1991. Cons. Psychiat. for Elderly Chorley & S. Ribble NHS Trust. Prev: Sen. Regist. (Psychiat.) Univ. Hosp. S. Manch.; Research Regist. David Lewis Centre Epilepsy Warford Chesh.

LEONARD, Professor James Vivian Institute of Child Health, 30 Guildford St., London WC1N 1EH Tel: 020 7242 9789 Fax: 020 7404 6191 Email: j.leonard@ich.ucl.ac.uk; 36 Norbiton Avenue, Kingston upon Thames KT1 3QR Tel: 020 8546 8884 — MB BChir Camb. 1970; PhD Lond. 1979; FRCP Lond. 1983; MRCP (UK) 1971. Prof. Paediat. Metab. Dis. Inst. Child Health Lond.; Hon. Cons. Phys. Hosp. for Sick Childr. Lond. Prev: Reader & Sen. Lect. (Child Health) Inst. Child Health Lond.

LEONARD, John Cyril (retired) Orchard House, Hopesay, Craven Arms SY7 8HD Tel: 01588 660386 — MRCS Eng. LRCP Lond. 1950; MD Lond. 1952, MB BS 1950; FRCP Lond. 1971, M 1953. Prev: Cons. Phys. Univ. Hosp. S. Manch.

LEONARD, John Dalton 254 Thornhill Road, Falkirk FK2 7AZ Tel: 01324 622826 Fax: 01324 633447; 6 Drossie Road, Falkirk FK1 5LU Tel: 01324 624428 — MB ChB 1977 Glas.; MRCGP 1981; DRCOG 1980; DCH RCPS Glas. 1979. GP Princip. Falkirk; Med. Adviser Scott. RHL Preservation Soc. Bo'wess. Socs: BMA; RMCGP. Prev: Clin. Asst. (Cas. & Orthop.) Kettering Gen. Hosp.; SHO Kettering Gen. Hosp. VTS; Ho. Off. (Med.) & Ho. Off. (Surg.) Dumfries & Galloway Roy. Infirm.

LEONARD, John Francis 8 Regent Street, Paisley PA1 3TG — MB ChB 1980 Dundee.

LEONARD, Jonathan Nicholas 28 Harmont House, 20 Harley Street, London W1N 1AL Tel: 0207 580 7914 Fax: 0207 580 9814 — MD 1983 Lond.; BSc 1971, MB BS 1975; FRCP Lond. 1993; MRCP (UK) 1977. (Univ. Coll. Hosp.) p/t Cons. Dermat. St. Mary's

Hosp. Prev: Cons. Dermat. N. & Mid Staffs HAs; Sen. Regist. (Dermat.) St. Mary's Hosp. Lond.; Regist. (Dermat.) Oxf. HA.

LEONARD, Karen Anne 34 Cash Feus, Strathmiglo, Cupar KY14 7QT — MB ChB 1995 Manch.

LEONARD, Margaret Linda Tweddle Cytology Laboratory, Group Laboratory, Stirling Royal Infirmary, Stirling FK8 2AU Tel: 01786 434000; 6 Drossie Road, Falkirk FK1 5LU Tel: 01324 624428 — MB ChB 1977 Glas. Clin. Asst. (Cytol.) Stirling Roy. Infirm. Prev: Community Med. Off. (Cytol.) Stirling Roy. Infirm.; Clin. Med. Off. N.ants. HA; Ho. Off. (Surg.) & Ho. Off. (Med.) Dumfries & Galloway Roy. Infirm.

LEONARD, Michael 56 Eldon Street, Glasgow G3 6NJ — MB ChB 1995 Glas.

LEONARD, Mr Michael Anthony Cardwell (retired) 13 Cecil Court, Ponteland, Newcastle upon Tyne NE20 9EE — MB BCh Wales 1962; FRCS Eng. 1970; FRCS Ed. 1970. Prev: Cons. Orthop. Surg. Newc. AHA (T).

LEONARD, Michael Joseph Stafford Place Surgery, 4 Stafford Place, Weston Super Mare BS23 2QZ Tel: 01934 415212 Fax: 01934 612463 — MB ChB 1978 Bristol; MRCGP 1983; DRCOG 1981.

LEONARD, Morris James Kilmarnock Road Surgery, 123 Kilmarnock Road, Glasgow G41 3YT Tel: 0141 649 6231 Fax: 0141 632 2012 — MB ChB 1982 Glas.; MRCGP 1986.

LEONARD, Niall 4 Malone Meadows, Belfast BT9 5BG — MB BCh 1998 Belf.; MB BCh Belf 1998.

LEONARD, Niall Joseph Roe Lane Surgery, 172 Roe Lane, Southport PR9 7PN Tel: 01704 228439 Fax: 01704 506878 — MB ChB 1985 Liverp.; MRCP (UK) 1988; MRCGP 1992; Dip. Obs. (Otago) 1990. (Liverpool)

LEONARD, Niamh Department of Histopathology, Royal Victoria Infirmary, Newcastle upon Tyne NE1 4LP Email: niamh.leonard@ncl.ac.uk — MB BCh BAO 1991 Dub.; MRCPath 1997. Sen. Lect. & Hon. Cons.

LEONARD, Paul Antony Accident & Emergency Department, Royal Infirmary of Edinburgh, Lauriston Place, Edinburgh EH3 9PY — MB ChB 1994 Ed.; MRCP 1998. Specialist Regist. (A & E.) Roy. Infirm. Edin.

LEONARD, Pauline Catherine The North Middlesex University Hospital, String Way, London Tel: 0208 887 2434 Fax: 0208 887 4048 Email: pauline-leonard@excite.co.uk; 39 Pages Hill, Muswell Hill, London N10 1EH Tel: 0208 444 3326 Fax: 0208 365 3524 — MB BS 1992 Lond.; 1984 RGN; MRCP (UK) 1995. (St George's Hosp. Medical School) Main Specialist Regist. (Med. Oncol.), Univ. Coll. Hosp. Trust. Socs: Assoc. Cancer Phys.s; Roy. Soc. Med.; BNA. Prev: Specialist Regist. (Oncol.) Whittington/Middx; Specialist Regist. (Oncol.) Roy. Free; Specialist Regist. (Oncol.) Middx.

LEONARD, Richard Creighton Orchard House, Hopesay, Craven Arms SY7 8HD — MB BChir 1989 Camb.; MRCP (UK) 1992; FRCA 1995.

LEONARD, Robert Charles Frederick Department of Clinical Oncology, Western General Hospital, Crewe Road, Edinburgh EH4 2XU Tel: 0131 537 2195 Fax: 0131 537 1014; 129 Craigleith Road, Edinburgh EH4 2EH Tel: 0131 332 2033 Email: rcfl@dial.pipex.com — MB BS 1971 Lond.; MD Lond. 1980, BSc (Hons.) 1968; FRCP Ed. 1993; FRCP Ed. 1985; MRCP (UK) 1974. (Char. Cross) Cons. Med. Oncol. & Hon. Sen. Lect. Univ. Edin.; Cons. Phys. W.. Gen. Hosp. Trust. Socs: Brit. Assn. Cancer Research; Amer. Soc. Clin. Oncol. Prev: Sen. Lect. Univ. Edin.; Sen. Regist. & Lect. (Med.) Newc. AHA; Research Fell. DFCI/Harvard Med. Sch.

LEONARD, Rosemary Anne Paxton Green Health Centre, 1 Alleyn Park, London SE21 8AU Tel: 020 8670 6878 Fax: 020 8766 7057 — MB BChir 1981 Camb.; MA Camb. 1981; MRCGP 1987; DRCOG 1986. Med. Jl.ist BBC Television. Prev: Regist. (O & G) Univ. Coll. Hosp. Lond.

LEONARD, Sarah Jane Colesden Lodge Farm, Colesden, Roxton, Bedford MK44 3DA — MB BS 1993 Lond.

LEONARD, Mr Timothy John Keene 149 Harley Street, London W1G 6BN — MB BS 1973 Lond.; FRCS Ed. 1981; MRCP (U.K.) 1976; FCOphth. 1988. (Westm.) Cons. Ophth. Surg. Char. Cross Hosp. Lond.; Regional Adviser NW Thames RHA; Counc. Mem. (Ophth. Sect.) Roy. Soc. Med Lond. Prev: Sen. Regist. Moorfields Eye Hosp. Lond.; Sen. Regist. St. Thos. Hosp. Lond.

LEONARDI, Giovanni Sebastiano Environmental Epidemiology Unit, London School of Hygiene & Tropical Medicine, 1 Keppel St., London WC1E 7HT Tel: 020 7927 2449 Fax: 020 7580 4524 Email: g.leonardi@lshtm.ac.uk; 22 Ellesmere Road, London E3 5QX Tel: 020 8980 7883 — MSc Environm. Epidemiol. & Policy Univ. Lond. 1994; State Exam Bologna 1986. Clin. Research Fell. (Environm. Epidemiol.) Lond. Sch. Hyg. & Trop. Med. Lond.; Specialist Regist. (Pub. Health Med.) S Essex HA. Socs: Roy. Soc. Med. & Soc. Risk Anal.; Intern. Soc. for Environm. Epidemiol. Prev: SHO (Med. for Elderly) Orsett Hosp. Essex; SHO (A & E) Ealing Hosp. S.all; Ho. Phys. King Geo. Hosp. Ilford.

LEONE GANADO, Anthony 12 Carpenter Road, Edgbaston, Birmingham B15 2JW Tel: 0121 455 7445 Fax: 0121 455 7445 Email: anthony.ganado@intlworld.com — MD 1971 Malta; FRACS 1976; FRACS Eng. 1976; FRCS Ire 1976. (Malta) Cons. (Anaesth.) Birm.Heartlands.Hosp.

LEONG, King Sun Whiston Hosp., Warrington Road, Little Neston, Prescot L35 5DR Tel: 0151 426 1600 — BM BS 1991 Nottm.; MRCP (UK) 1995. (Nottingham University) Cons. (Diabetes, Endocrinol and Gen. Med.) Whiston Hosp. Socs: Diabetes UK; Brit. Endocrine Soc. Prev: SHO (Dermat.) Hope Hosp. Salford; SHO (Gen. Med.) Wythenshawe Hosp. Manch.; Clin. Lect., Univ. Hosp. Aintree.

LEONG, May Ying Flat 2, 20 Perth Road, Dundee DD1 4LN — MB ChB 1998 Aberd.; MB ChB Aberd 1998.

LEONG, Yeo Hong 49 Trenchard Avenue, Beaconside, Stafford ST16 3RD — MB BCh BAO 1993 Belf.

LEONG MOOK SENG, Claude C. K. 10 Heythrop Drive, Ickenham, Uxbridge UB10 8DT — MB ChB 1981 Leeds; MSc Pub. Health Med. Lond. 1991; MFPHM RCP (UK) 1993; T(PHM) 1995. Cons. Communicable Dis. & Pub. Health Med. Middlx. Socs: Fac. Pub. Health Med. Prev: Sen. Regist. (Pub. Health Med.) NW Thames RHA; Regist. (Anaesth.) N.wick Pk. Hosp. Harrow.

LEONHARDT, Johann Heinrich Christian 165 Wakering Road, Shoeburyness, Southend-on-Sea SS3 9TN — MB ChB 1995 Pretoria.

LEONTIADES, George Michael 48 Great Bushey Drive, Totteridge, London N20 8QL Tel: 020 8446 3680 — Ptychio Iatrikes 1978 Athens; MRCOG 1989.

LEONTSINIS, Mr Timothy George Freeman Hospital, Freeman Road, High Heaton, Newcastle upon Tyne NE7 7DN — MB BCh 1978 Witwatersrand; FRCS RCPS Glas. 1985.

LEOPARD, Mr Peter James (retired) Stone House, Basnetts Wood, endon, Stoke-on-Trent ST9 9DQ Tel: 01782 504095 Fax: 01782 504689 Email: peter@leop38.freeserve.co.uk — FRCS (Eng.) 2000; MB BS Lond. 1967; FRCS Ed. 1987; MRCS Eng. LRCP Lond. 1967; BDS Lond. 1961; FDS RCS Eng. 1966. Mem. Fac. Bd. RCS Eng; Chairm. RCS Eng. Manpower Comm.; Mem. Speciality Workforce Ad. Grp.; Mem. (Chairm.) Manpower Advis. Panel, Fac. Dent. Surg. RCS; Mem. (Counc.) RCS Eng.; Mem. (Pres.) Europ. Bd. Oral & Maxillofacial Surgs.; Chairm. W. Midl.s Local Med. Workforce Adv. Gp. Prev: Mem. Exam. Bd. Oral & Maxillofacial Surg. FRCS Intercollegiate Examn.

LEOPOLD, Christina Anne Alexandra Surgery, 2 Wellington Avenue, Aldershot GU11 1SD Tel: 01252 332210 Fax: 01252 312490; High Place, 11 Monkshanger, Farnham GU9 8BU Tel: 01252 714769 — MB BCh 1980 Wales; DRCOG 1983.

LEOPOLD, John David Morriston Hospital, Swansea SA6 6NL Tel: 01792 703614; Swn-y-Mor, Plunch Lane, Mumbles, Swansea SA3 4JY — MB BCh 1974 Wales; MRCP Lond. 1976; FRCP 2000 London. Cons. Phys. Morriston Hosp. Swansea. Socs: Brit. Thoracic Soc.

LEOPOLD, John Gascoyne Glanbrydan Park, Manordeilo, Llandeilo SA19 7AY — MB BCh 1947 Wales; MRCPath 1963.

LEOPOLD, Mr Peter William Frimley Park Hospital, Portsmouth Road, Frimley, Camberley GU16 7UJ Tel: 01276 604604 Fax: 01276 604106; High Place, 11 Monkshanger, Farnham GU9 8BU Tel: 01252 714769 — MB BCh 1979 Wales; MCh Wales 1989, MB BCh 1979; FRCS Ed. 1983; FRCS Eng. 1999; FRCS Eng. 1999. Cons. Vasc. Surg. Frimley Pk. Hosp. Surrey.

LEPSKI, Guy Richard 14 Hocroft Avenue, London NW2 2EH Tel: 020 7435 4028; Clover Cottage, Station Road, Great Longstone, Bakewell DE45 1TS Tel: 01629 640609 Email: lepski@clara.co.uk — MB BS 1992 Lond.; BSc Lond. 1989, MB BS 1992. (St Georges

Hosp) Specialist Regist. Anaesth. Sheff. Rotat. Socs: Assn. Anaesth.GB & Irel.

LERIS, Anne Clare Adela Lister Hospital, Coreys Mill Lane, Stevenage SG1 4AB — MB BS 1994 Lond.; FRCS Eng. 1998.

LERMAN, Anthony Joseph Norfolk & Norwich Hospital, Brunswick Road, Norwich NR1 3SR — MB BChir 1998 Camb.; MB BChir Camb 1998.

LERMITTE, Jeremy Gordon Cheleby 35 Church Walk, Worthing BN11 2LT — BM 1994 Soton.

LEROY, Allan Edwin Dr A Willis and Partners, King Edward Road Surgery, Christchurch Medical Centre, King Edward Road, Northampton NN1 5LY Tel: 01604 633466 Fax: 01604 603227; 49 Billing Road, Northampton NN1 5DB Tel: 01604 622875 — BM BCh 1974 Oxf.; MA Oxf. 1974. (Oxf. & Westm.) Socs: Brit. Med. Acupunct. Soc.; BMA.

LERVY, Bruce Sway Road Surgery, 65 Sway Road, Morriston, Swansea SA6 6JA Tel: 01792 773150 / 771392 Fax: 01792 790880; The Nook, 217 Clasemont Road, Morriston, Swansea SA6 6BT Tel: 01792 771131 — MB BCh 1964 Wales; FRCGP 1980, M 1972. (Wales) Sen. Lect. (Gen. Pract.) Sch. Postgrad. Studies Med. & Health Care Morriston Hosp. Swansea; Med. Off. Brit. Red Cross Soc. (SW Wales Br.). Prev: Regist. (Med.) Morriston Hosp.; SHO (Obst.) Mt. Pleasant Hosp. Swansea.

LESCHEN, Arnold Desmond 3 Beaucroft Lane, Wimborne BH21 2PF — MRCS Eng. LRCP Lond. 1950. (Lond. Hosp.)

LESCHEN, Maureen Elizabeth (retired) 282 Ralph Road, Shirley, Solihull B90 3LF Tel: 0121 744 3124 — MB BCh BAO Belf. 1950. Prev: Ho. Phys. & Ho. Surg. Masserine Hosp. Antrim & Greenbank Hosp.

LESCHZINER, Guy Doron Apt 8, 88A Great Bridgewater St., Manchester M1 5JW — MB BS 1998 Lond.; MB BS Lond 1998.

LESLEY, Barbara Allison Dr J M Beck and Partners, 21 Beaufort Road, Southbourne, Bournemouth BH6 5AJ Tel: 01202 433081 Fax: 01202 430527 — BM 1981 Soton.

LESLEY, Christine Ann Thorpe Wood Surgery, 140 Woodside Road, Norwich NR7 9QL Tel: 01603 701477 Fax: 01603 701512 — MB ChB 1981 Liverp.; MRCGP 1986; DRCOG 1983.

LESLEY, Sarah Winnifred The Surgery, 111 Pembroke Road, Clifton, Bristol BS8 3EU Tel: 0117 973 3790 — MB ChB 1985 Birm.; MRCGP 1990; T(GP) 1991; DRCOG 1990.

LESLIE, Agnes Durham House, 5 Pear Tree Drive, Great Barr, Birmingham B43 6HR Tel: 0121 358 3901 — MB BS 1954 Madras; FFA RCS Eng. 1962; DA Eng. 1959. (Christian Med. Coll. Vellore) Cons. Anaesth. W. Midl. RHA. Socs: Assn. Anaesths.; Assn. Anaesth.; Obst. Anaesth. Assn. Prev: Cons. Anaesth. NW RHA; Sen. Regist. (Anaesth.) United Manch. Hosps. & Manch. RHB; Regist. (Anaesth.) United Bristol Hosps. & S.mead Hosp. Bristol.

LESLIE, Amy 8 Mayburn Walk, Loanhead EH20 9HG — MB ChB 1995 Dundee.

LESLIE, Anna 52 Bedford Avenue, Barnet EN5 2ER — BM 1988 Soton.; MRCP (UK) 1991; FRCR (UK) 1996. Regist. (Radiol.) Bristol Roy. Infirm.

LESLIE, Carolyn Ann 6 Crown Terrace, Dowanhill, Glasgow G12 9HA — MB ChB 1987 Glas.; BSc (Hons.) Glas. 1984, MB ChB 1987; MRCP (UK) 1990.

LESLIE, Carolyn Jean 13 Greenside Avenue, Prestwick KA9 2HB — MB ChB 1993 Glas.

LESLIE, David William Lindsay and Partners, 1413 Pollokshaws Road, Glasgow G41 3RG Tel: 0141 632 9141 Fax: 0141 636 1288; 351 Albert Drive, Pollokshields, Glasgow G41 5PH — MB ChB 1984 Glas.; MRCGP 1988; DRCOG 1987.

LESLIE, Douglas Reginald Sturrock (retired) 9 Mosse Way, Oadby, Leicester LE2 4HL Tel: 0116 271 5258 — MB ChB 1950 Glas.; DPM Eng. 1973; DIH Eng. 1964; DPH Ed. 1963. Prev: Cons. Psychiat. (Ment. Handicap) Glenfrith Hosp. Leicester.

LESLIE, Fiona Caroline — MB ChB 1991 Manch.; BSc (Med. Sci.) St. And. 1988; MRCP (UK) 1994. Wellcome Trust Tring Fell.sh., Univ. of Manch. Prev: SpR Rotat. (Gastroenterol.) Hope Hosp. Manch. Roy. Infirm.; Regist. (Gastroenterol.) N. Manch. Gen. Hosp.; SHO (Med.) Christie Hosp.

LESLIE, Flavia Mary Fair Mile Hospital, Wallingford OX10 9HH Tel: 01491 651281 — MB ChB 1977 Birm.; BA (Hons.) Wales 1970; MRCPsych 1986; MRCGP 1983; DRCOG 1981; Cert Family Plann. 1981. Cons. Psychiat. Fair Mile Hosp. Wallingford. Prev: Sen. Regist. (Psychiat.) Roy. Lond. Hosp.; Sen. Regist. (Psychiat.) Runwell Hosp.; Regist. (Psychiat.) Char. Cross Hosp. Lond.

***LESLIE, Gilliam Jones** 18 Foulpapple Road, Newmilns KA16 9LB Tel: 01560 320015 — MB ChB 1996 Glas.

LESLIE, Gordon Alan MacGregor Langlee, 217 Balgillo Road, Broughty Ferry, Dundee DD5 3QX Tel: 01382 76449 — MB ChB 1975 Dundee; BMSc (Hons.) Dund 1972, MB ChB 1975; DRCOG 1978; Cert JCC Lond. 1978.

LESLIE, Gordon James Booth, TD (retired) 17 The Courtyard, Inchmarlo, Banchory AB31 4AZ Tel: 01330 820108 Fax: 01330 820108 — MB ChB 1955 Aberd.; DO Eng. 1961. Prev: Assoc. Specialist (Ophth.) Glas. Roy. Infirm.

LESLIE, Hamish Carnoustie Medical Group, The Health Centre, Dundee Street, Carnoustie DD7 7RB Tel: 01241 859888 Fax: 01241 852080 — MB ChB 1968 Glas.

LESLIE, Harry Colquhoun (retired) 48 George Reith Avenue, Kelvinside, Glasgow G12 0AN Tel: 0141 334 4300/0880 — MB ChB 1953 Glas.; DObst RCOG 1955. Prev: GP Glas..

LESLIE, Herbert Azariah (retired) 28 Lowfield Road, Cale Green, Stockport SK2 6RN Tel: 0161 429 8584 — MB BS Madras 1952; MRCGP 1975.

LESLIE, Mr Ian James Department Orthopaedic & Trauma Surgery, Bristol Royal Infirmary, Bristol BS2 8HW Tel: 0117 283899 Fax: 0117 928200; (cons. rooms), 2 Clifton Park, Clifton, Bristol BS8 3BS Tel: 0117 906 4208 Fax: 0117 973 0887 — MB BS Queensland 1968; MChOrth Liverp. 1979; FRCS (Eng.) 1995; FRCS Ed. 1974. Cons. Orthop. & Traum. Surg. Bristol Roy. Infirm. & Avon Orthop. Centre; Clin. Sen. Lect. Univ. Bristol. Socs: Brit. Orthop. Research Soc.; (Hon. Sec.) BOA; Brit. Soc. Surg. Hand. Prev: Cons. Sen. Lect. Univ. Liverp.; Sen. Regist. Nuffield Orthop. Centre & Radcliffe Infirm. Oxf.; Squadron Ldr. RAAF Med. Off. Vietnam.

LESLIE, James Robert (retired) Orchard End, 8 Dixon Wood Close, Lindale, Grange-over-Sands LA11 6LN Tel: 015395 33612 — MRCS Eng. LRCP Lond. 1946.

LESLIE, Janice Roy Simpson Langlee, 217 Balgillo Road, Broughty Ferry, Dundee DD5 3QX Email: janl@dth.scot.nhs.uk — MB ChB 1977 Dundee; DRCOG 1979; Cert JCC Lond. 1979. Staff Grade (Obst. Ultrasound) Ninewells Hosp. Dundee. Prev: Regist. (Obst. Ultrasound) Ninewells Hosp. Dundee.

LESLIE, Karin Flat 2/L, 51 Cresswell St., Hillhead, Glasgow G12 8AE — MB ChB 1998 Glas.; MB ChB Glas 1998.

LESLIE, Kieron Seymour 113 Hassett Road, London E9 5SL — MB BS 1996 Lond.

LESLIE, Margaret Anne Mintlaw Group Practice, Newlands Road, Mintlaw, Peterhead AB42 5GP Tel: 01771 623522 Fax: 01771 624349; 35 James Mitchell Place, Mintlaw, Peterhead AB42 5ES Tel: 01771 623616 — MB ChB 1989 Dundee; MRCGP 1993.

LESLIE, Marion Elizabeth 72 Ormonde Drive, Netherlee, Glasgow G44 3RG — MB ChB 1985 Glas.; MRCGP 1989; DRCOG 1988. GP Retainer Scheme Glas. Socs: BMA. Prev: SHO (Obst.) Glas. Roy. Matern. Hosp.; Trainee GP Glas.; SHO (Dermat.) Glas. Vict. Infirm.

LESLIE, Martin David Department of Clinical Oncology, St Thomas' Hospital, Lambeth Palace Road, London SE1 7EH Tel: 020 7928 9292 Ext: 6861 Fax: 020 7928 9968 — MB BS 1991 Lond.; BSc (Hons.) Lond. 1978, MD 1991; MRCP (UK) 1984; FRCR 1988. (University College London) Cons. Clin. Oncol. Guy's & St. Thomas' Cancer Centre Lond.; Cons. to King Edwd VII Hosp. For Offs., Lond. Prev: Sennior Regist. Char. Cross Hosp. Lond. & Mt. Vernon Hosp. Middlx.; Research Fell. Mt. Vernon Hosp. N.wood Middlx.; Jun. Lect. Roy. Marsden Hosp. Lond.

LESLIE, Mary (retired) Ottways, 26 Ottways Lane, Ashtead KT21 2NZ Tel: 01372 274191 — MD 1947 Leeds; MB ChB 1942. Prev: Sessional Med. Off. Community Health Serv. & Child Welf. St. Thos.

LESLIE, Nayanahari Apsara Panchali Leicester General Hospital, Gwendolen Road, Leicester LE5 4NZ Tel: 0116 249 0490 Email: nayles@hotmail.com — MB ChB 1990 Leic.; FRCA 1997. (Leicester) Specialist Regist. (Anaesth.).

LESLIE, Pamela Christine 18 St Ronan's Terrace, Edinburgh EH10 5PG Tel: 0131 447 3883; Sighthill Health Centre, 380 Calder Road, Edinburgh EH11 4AU Tel: 0131 537 7060 — MB ChB 1989 Ed.; MRCGP 1994; DRCOG 1992.

LESLIE, Peter John Alfred Medical Department, Borders General Hospital, Melrose TD6 9BS Tel: 01896 826000 Email:

peter.leslie@borders.scot.nhs.uk; Southbank, Bowden, Melrose TD6 0ST Tel: 01835 822752 — MB ChB 1980 Ed.; BSc (Hons.) Ed. 1977, MD 1988; FRCP Ed. 1995. Cons. Phys. Borders HB; Postgrad. Tutor Borders Gen. Hosp. Prev: Sen. Regist. Roy. Infirm. Edin.; Research Fell. Univ. Newc. u. Tyne; Research Fell. & Regist. Ninewells Hosp. Dundee.

LESLIE, Phyllis Davidson (retired) 40 Bloomfield Place, Aberdeen AB10 6AG Tel: 01224 592364 — MB ChB 1937 Aberd. Prev: GP Moreton Wirral.

LESLIE, Professor Richard David Graham 24 Bramerton Street, London SW3 5LA — MB BS 1972 Lond.; MD Lond. 1980; FRCP Lond. 1989; MRCS Eng. LRCP Lond. 1972; MRCP (UK) 1974. (Westm.) Prof. Diabetes & Autoimmunity & Cons. Phys. St Bartholomews Hosp. & Coll. Lond.; Dir. Immune Sect. Mendel Inst. Rome, Italy; Vis. Prof. Med. Univ. Roma Italy. Socs: Fell. Roy. Soc. Med.; Assn. Phys. Prev: Wellcome Trust Sen. Fell. & Cons. Phys. King's Coll. & W.m. Hosp. Lond.; Sen. Regist. (Med.) Roy. Vict. Infirm. Newc.; MRC Fell. Endocrine Unit Univ. Chicago, USA.

LESLIE, Rosemary Frances (retired) 12 Wheal Golden Drive, Holywell Bay, Newquay TR8 5PE — MRCS Eng. LRCP Lond. 1956; BSc Lond. 1948, MB BS 1956; MRCGP 1973.

LESLIE, Shirley Anne (retired) 13 Windsor Grove, Cheadle Hulme, Cheadle SK8 6HZ — MB ChB 1956 Liverp.; MD Liverp. 1971,; FRCPsych 1979, M 1971; DObst RCOG 1958; DCH Eng. 1959, DPM 1963. Hon. Cons. Child Psychiat. Booth Hall Childr. Hosp. Manch.

***LESLIE, Stephen James** The Old Manse, Avoch IV9 8RW; 3F1 239 Dalkeith Road, Edinburgh EH16 5JS Tel: 0131 667 8143 Email: s.j.leslie@ed.ac.uk — MB ChB 1994 Ed.; BSc (Med. Sci.) Hons. Biochem. Ed. 1994; MRCP Ed. 1997.

LESLIE, Stephen Mansfield The Arwystili Medical Practice, Mount Lane, Llanidloes SY18 6EZ Tel: 01686 412228 / 412322 Fax: 01686 413536 — MB ChB 1979 Ed.; MRCP (UK) 1982; MRCGP 1984. Princip. GP Llanidloes. Prev: Regist. (Paediat.) Ninewells Hosp. Dundee.

LESLIE, Tabassam Anika Department of Dermatology, University College & Middlesex Hospitals, Mortimer St., London W1T 3AA Tel: 020 7636 8333 — MB BS 1987 Lond.; MB BS (Hons.) Lond. 1987; BSc (1st cl. Hons.) Lond. 1984; MRCP (UK) 1990. Sen. Regist. (Dermat.) Middlx. & Univ. Coll. Hosp. Lond. Socs: Fell. Roy. Soc. Med.; Brit. Assn. Dermat. Prev: Sir Jules Thorn Research Fell. Middlx. Hosp. Lond.; Regist & SHO (Dermat.) Middlx. Hosp. Lond.; Regist. (Med.) Edgware & Barnet Hosps.

LESNA, Milena Tarrants, Grange Road, Stoborough, Wareham BH20 5AJ; Department of Pathology, Royal Bournemouth Hospital, Castle Lane E., Bournemouth BH7 7DW Tel: 01202 704840 — MD Palacky 1963; LMSSA Lond. 1973; FRCPath 1988, M 1974. (Palacky Univ. Olomouc) Cons. Histopath. Roy. Bournemouth & ChristCh. Hosps. NHS Trust. Socs: Path. Soc. Gt. Brit. & Internat. Acad. Path.; BSG; IAP. Prev: Regist. (Path.) N.. Gen. Hosp. Sheff.; Lect. (Path.) Newc. Med. Sch.; Cons. Histopath. Newc. Gen. Hosp.

LESNIK OBERSTEIN, Sarit Yael Department of Ophthalmology, Greenwich District Hospital, Vanbrugh Hill, London SE10 9HE — Artsexamen 1992 Leiden.

LESNY, Jan Tarrants, Stoborough, Wareham BH20 5AJ — MUDr Palacky, Czechoslovakia 1967; DMRD Eng. 1973. (Palacky Univ. Olomouc) Cons. Radiol. Dorset Co. Hosp. Dorchester. Socs: Brit. Med. Ultrasonic Soc. Prev: Cons. Radiol. Preston Hosp. N. Shields.

LESSAN, Nader Gholi 7 Doggett Road, Cambridge CB1 9LF — MB BS 1989 Newc.; MRCP (UK) 1994. Regist. (Endocrinol. & Diabetes) N. Manch. Gen. Hosp. Prev: Regist. (Geriat. Med.) Burnley Gen. Hosp.; SHO (Geriat. Med.) St. Woolos Hosp. Newport Gwent; SHO (Gen. Med.) Chase Farm Hosp. Lond.

LESSELL, Colin Brian The Chestnuts, 122 High St., Kempston, Bedford MK42 7BN Tel: 01234 851775 Fax: 01234 856572 — MB BS 1970 Lond.; BDS Lond. 1967; DDFHom 1995; MRCS Eng. LRCP Lond. 1970. (St. Bart.) Homoeop. & Osteopath. Phys. Bedford. Socs: Fell. Brit. Homoeop. Dent. Assn.; Licensed Assoc. Mem. Fac. Homoeop.; Hon. Fell. UK Homoeop. Med. Assn. Prev: Lect. Brit. Homoeop. Assn.; Lect. Fac. Homeop.; Clin. Tutor Fac. Homoeop. 1993-96.

LESSELLS, Alastair Moyes 40 Ormidale Terrace, Murrayfield, Edinburgh EH12 6EF Tel: 0131 337 1144 — MB ChB 1971 Aberd.; FRCP (Hon.) Ed. 1993; FRCPath. 1989, M 1977. Cons. Histopath. W.. Gen. Hosp. Edin. Prev: Lect./Hon. Cons. (Path.) Withington Hosp. Manch.; Lect. (Path.) Aberd. Univ.; Ho. Off. (Surg.) Aberd. Roy. Infirm.

LESSELLS, Kathleen Margaret 40 Ormidale Terrace, Edinburgh EH12 6EF — MB ChB 1971 Aberd. GP Broxburn.

LESSELS, Fiona Alison 11 Skippon Terrace, Thorner, Leeds LS14 3HA — MB BS 1992 Lond.

LESSELS, Susan Elizabeth 100 Hamilton Place, Aberdeen AB15 5BB — MB ChB 1973 Ed. Haemat. Grampian HB.

LESSEPS, Mr Andreas Godden House, Blackhall Lane, Sevenoaks TN15 0HP — MB BS 1973 Lond.; FRCS Eng. 1979; MRCOG 1980. (St. Geo.) Cons. O & G Dartford & Gravesham NHS Trust. Prev: Sen. Regist. St. Thos. Hosp. Lond.; Regist. & Lect. St. Thos. Hosp. Lond.

LESSER, Guy Fenton The Glemsford Surgery, Lion Road, Glemsford, Sudbury CO10 7RF Tel: 01787 280484 Fax: 01787 281711 — MB BS 1984 Lond.; MA Camb. 1985; DCH RCP Lond. 1988; DRCOG 1988. (Guy's) GP Princip. Glemsford. Prev: Ho. Phys. Guy's Hosp. Lond.; Ho. Surg. Lewisham Hosp. Lond.; Trainee GP Thanet Dist. Gen. Hosp. VTS.

LESSER, Jeffrey Joseph The Mavernes, 4 Hill Crescent, Totteridge, London N20 8HD Tel: 020 8445 8280 — MB BS 1950 Lond.; BDS 1960; LDS RCS Eng. 1960. (Middx. & Roy. Dent. Hosp.) Socs: BDA. Prev: Ship Surg. New Austral. & Hilary.; Sen. Dent. Off. SW Herts.; Clin. Ast. ENT.

LESSER, Piers Julian Anthony Department Anaesthetics, The Calderoale Royal Hospital, Salterhebble, Halifax HX3 0PW Tel: 01422 224077; Upper Popplewells, Warley, Halifax HX2 7SW Tel: 01422 886029 — MB ChB 1978 Bristol; FFA RCS Eng. 1983. Cons. Anaesth. Calderoale & Kirklees NHS Trust. Socs: Pain Soc.; Soc. for Computing and Technol. in Anaesth.

LESSER, Mr Tristram Hugh John Department of ENT Surgery, Division of Otolaryngology & Head & Neck Surgery, University Hospital Aintree, Liverpool L9 7AL Tel: 0151 529 5262 Fax: 0151 529 4033; Department of Otolaryngology, Head & Neck Surgery, Southport General Infirmary, Scarisbrick New Road, Southport PR8 6PH Tel: 01704 547471 Fax: 01704 543579 — MB BS 1979 Lond.; MB BS London 1979; MS London 1993; FRCS Ed 1984. Cons. OtorhinoLaryngol. & NeurOtol. Aintree Hosp.; Clin. Lect. Univ. Liverp. Prev: Pres. Young Cons. Otolaryngol. Head & Neck Surg.

LESSEY, Kevin James Patrick 4 Disbrowe Road, London W6 8QF — MB BS 1988 Lond.

LESSHAFFT, Carsten Stephan Good Hope Hospital, Rectory Road, Sutton Coldfield B75 7RR Tel: 0121 378 2211; Flat 16, Coppice Oak, Coppice Road, Birmingham B13 9DP Tel: 0121 449 7892 — State Exam Med 1992 Mainz. Trainee GP/SHO (Gen. Pract.) Birm. Prev: SHO (Gen. Surg., Trauma & Orthop.) City Hosp. Birm.; Ho. Off. (A & E, Urol. & Gen. Surg.) Roy. Preston Hosp.; Ho. Off. (Med.) S. Warks. Hosp. Warwick.

LESSING, Daniela Nora 3 Alma Terrace, Allen St., London W8 6QY Tel: 020 7937 1408; Thelma Golding Centre, 92 Bath Road, Hounslow TW3 3EL Tel: 020 8321 2427 Fax: 020 8321 2467 Email: daniela.lessing@hscmh-tr.nthames.nhs.uk — MB ChB Sheff. 1969; MSc Lond. 1990; FRCP Lond. 1996; DCH Eng. 1972; DObst. RCOG 1971; FRCPCH 1997. (Sheffield University) Cons. Paediat. (Community Child Health) Hounslow & Spelthorne Community & Ment. Health NHS Trust. Prev: Cons. Paediat. E. Berks.; SCMO Paddington & N. Kensington HA; Sen. Regist. & Lect. (Paediat.) Char Cross Hosp. Lond.

LESSING, Maarten Petrus Albertus 60 Kennett Road, Oxford OX3 7BJ — MB ChB 1978 Pretoria; MRCPI 1989.

LESSOF, Leila (retired) — MB BS 1956 lond; FRCP 2000; MRCS Eng. LRCP Lond. 1956; FFPHM 1987, M 1982; DMRD Eng. 1960. Prev: Dir. Pub. Health Kensington, Chelsea & W.m. Commiss.ing Auth.

LESSOF, Professor Maurice Hart 8 John Spencer Square, London N1 2LZ Tel: 020 7226 0919 Fax: 020 7354 8913 Email: lesso@globalnet.co.uk — MB BChir Camb. 1947; MA Camb. 1948, MD 1956; FRCP Lond. 1969, M 1949. (Camb. & Guy's) Emerit. Prof. Med. United Med. & Dent. Sch. of Guy's & St. Thos. Hosps. Lond. Prev: Chairm. Roy. Hosps. Trust; Chairm. Lewisham Hosp. NHS Trust; Vice-Pres. & Sen. Censor RCP Lond.

LESTER, Alexander Allan 8 Maderia Walk, Falmouth TR11 4EJ — LRCP LRCS 1962 Ed.; LRCP LRCS Ed. LRFPS Glas. 1962; LAH Dub. 1962; FICS 1991; MPSI 1962. Socs: Fell. Roy. Soc. Med.; Cas. Surg. Assn. Prev: Cons. A & E Lewisham Hosp.; Retd. Acting Dir. of

Accid. Servs. Herts. HA; Asst. Lect. (Anat. & Embryol.) Univ. Coll. Lond.

LESTER, Eva North Middlesex Hospital, London N18 1QX Tel: 020 8887 2478; 1 Meadway, London NW11 7JY Tel: 020 8458 4595 — MB BS 1960 Lond.; MRCS Eng. LRCP Lond. 1960; FRCPath 1984, M 1972. (Roy. Free) Cons. Chem. Path. N. Middlx. Hosp. Lond.; Phys. Diabetic Clinic N. Middlx. Hosp. Lond. Prev: Sen. Regist. (Chem. Path.) Roy. Free Hosp.; Regist. (Chem. Path.) Postgrad. Med. Sch. Lond.; Research Asst. (Path.) Roy. Free Hosp. Lond.

LESTER, Helen Elizabeth Lee Bank Group Practice, Colston Health Centre, 10 Bath Row, Lee Bank, Birmingham B15 1LZ Tel: 0121 622 4846 Fax: 0121 622 7105; 272 Penns Lane, Sutton Coldfield B76 1LQ — MB BCh 1985 Wales; MRCGP 1989; DCH RCP Lond. 1988; DRCOG 1988.

LESTER, Huw David Edward Ashfield Surgery, 8 Walmley Road, Sutton Coldfield B76 1QN Tel: 0121 351 7955 Fax: 0121 313 2509 — MB BCh 1985 Wales; DRCOG 1988. Trainee GP Cardiff VTS.

LESTER, James Edward 41 Falmouth Road, Truro TR1 2BL — MB ChB 1998 Leeds.

LESTER, Jason Francis 81 Wellesley Road, Ilford IG1 4LJ Tel: 020 8518 1487 — MB BS 1993 Lond.; MRCP Lond. 1997. Specialist Regist. (Oncol.) Velindre Hosp. Cardiff.

LESTER, John Phillips (retired) 24 Belvidere Road, Walsall WS1 3AU Tel: 01922 625862 — MB BChir 1950 Camb.; MRCS Eng. LRCP Lond. 1950; FRCGP 1978, M 1960.

LESTER, John Ritchie (retired) 2 St Georges Close, St. Georges Avenue, Weybridge KT13 0DS Tel: 01932 53115 — MB ChB 1944 Ed.; MA Oxf. 1945. Clin. Asst. (Clin. Ecol.) Basingstoke Dist. Hosp. Prev: Dean Lond. Coll. Osteop. Clin. Asst. Roy. Free Hosp. Lond.

LESTER, John Stephen 131 Bournbrook Road, Birmingham B29 7BY Tel: 0121 472 0295 — MB ChB 1965 Birm.; DObst RCOG 1967. Socs: BMA. Prev: Clin. Asst. (A & E) Leighton Hosp. Crewe; Ho. Phys. E. Birm. Hosp.; Ho. Surg. A & E Dept. Gen. Hosp. Birm.

LESTER, Julie Anne 2 Parr Grove, Pimperne, Blandford Forum DT11 8XE — MB BS 1988 Lond.; MRCGP 1993. Prev: Trainee GP Benson, Oxon.

LESTER, Marc Timothy 37 Cavendish Road, London NW6 7XR — MB BS 1992 Lond.

LESTER, Marcus John The Hollies GP Surgery, 41 Rectory Road, Hadleigh, Benfleet SS7 2NA Tel: 01702 558147 Fax: 01702 558863 — MB BS 1979 Lond.; MRCS Eng. LRCP Lond. 1979; Cert. Family Plann. JCC 1983; DRCOG 1982. (Char. Cross) GP Princip.; Founder Mem. S.end Dist. Formulary Comm.; Founder Mem. Castle Point PCG; PCG Tutor. Socs: Brit. Hyperlipid. Assn.; Coronary Strategy Gp.; Fell. of Roy. Soc. of Med. Prev: SHO (Med.) Rochford Gen. Hosp.; SHO (Paediat.) S.end Gen. Hosp.; Ho. Off (Neurol. Psychiat.) Char. Cross Hosp. Lond.

LESTER, Marjorie Helen Vacquoy, Rousay, Orkney KW17 2PS Tel: 0185 682262 — MRCS Eng. LRCP Lond. 1928. (Roy. Free) Socs: Life Mem. BMA. Prev: Regist. St. John's Hosp. Dis. of Skin Lond.; Gyn. VD Dept. Guy's Hosp. & Roy. Free Hosp.

LESTER, Penelope Kim 188 Swingate Lane, London SE18 2JB — MB ChB 1993 Leic.; DCH 1996; DCOG 1997; DFFP 1997; MRCGP 1998.

LESTER, Robert Boyd The Surgery, Bellyeoman Road, Dunfermline KY12 0AE Tel: 01383 721266 Fax: 01383 625068; 9 Glamis Place, Dalgety Bay, Dunfermline KY11 9UA — MB ChB 1979 Manch.; BSc St. And. 1976; MRCGP 1984; DRCOG 1985.

LESTER, Miss Ruth Louise Birmingham childrens hosp, Steelhouse Lane, Birmingham B4 6NH Tel: 0121 333 8136 Fax: 0121 333 3399; 64 Wellington Road, Edgbaston, Birmingham B15 2ET Tel: 0121 440 4937 Fax: 0121 440 7708 Email: ruth@ruthlester.co.uk — MB ChB 1973 Sheff.; FRCS Eng. 1979; DCH Eng. 1975. Cons plas surg Birm Childr.s hosp. Socs: BAPS & BSSH.; BAAPS. Prev: Cons. plastic surg, Sandwell Gen Hosp; Sen. Regist. (Plastic Surg.) Wexham Pk. Hosp. Slough; Regist. (Plastic Surg.) Stoke Mandeville Hosp. Aylesbury.

LESTER, Shane Elliot 40 Trajan Walk, Heddon-on-the-Wall, Newcastle upon Tyne NE15 0BJ — MB ChB 1997 Manch.

LESTER, Thomas David The Surgery, Church Walk, Eastwood, Nottingham NG16 3BH Tel: 01773 712951 Fax: 01773 534160 — MB ChB 1972 Dundee. Prev: Trainee Gen. Pract. Nottm. VTS; SHO (Anaesth.) Leicester Gp. Hosps.; Ho. Off. Bradford Roy. Infirm.

LESTER, William Arthur 49 Franklin Road, Birmingham B30 2HJ — MB ChB 1993 Birm.

LESTER-SMITH, David 34 Surrey Avenue, High Compton, Shaw, Oldham OL2 7DP — BM BS 1989 Nottm.

LESTNER, Richard Anthony Lingwell Croft Surgery, Ring Road, Middleton, Leeds LS10 3LT Tel: 0113 270 4848 Fax: 0113 272 0030 — MB ChB 1983 Leeds; BSc (Hons. Biochem.) Leeds 1980; MRCGP 1987; DRCOG 1985; D.Occ.Med. RCP Lond. 1995. Socs: Soc. Occupat. Med.

LESZCZYNSKI, Janusz 10 Rock Edge, Headington, Oxford OX3 8NE — MB BCh BAO 1953 NUI.

LETCHER, Alison Michelle Garden Flat, Tree Tops, Corston, Bath BA2 9EX — MB BS 1993 Lond.

LETCHER, Richard George Michael District Histopathology Laboratory, St. Margaret's Hospital, Epping CM16 6TN Tel: 01279 444455 — MB BS 1959 Lond.; FRCPath 1980, M 1968; DCH Eng. 1962. (Middlx.) Cons. Path. P.ss Alexandra Hosp. Trust Harlow. Socs: Fell. Roy. Soc. Med.; Assn. Clin. Path. Prev: Asst. Path. Bland Sutton Inst. Path. Middlx. Hosp. Med. Sch. Lond.; Sen. Regist. W. Middlx. Hosp.; SHO (Path.) Lambeth Hosp.

LETCHUMANAN, V Stretton Medical Centre, 5 Hatton Lane, Stretton, Warrington WA4 4NE Tel: 01925 730412 Fax: 01925 730960 — MB BS 1975 Madurai; MB BS 1975 Madurai; LMSSA 1977 London.

LETHAM, Bruce Baird Eastfield House, 6 St. Johns Road, Newbury RG14 7LW Tel: 01635 41495 Fax: 01635 522751; Westerly, Woodridge, Newbury RG14 6NP Tel: 01635 44568 Email: letham@dctors.org.uk — MB ChB 1979 Bristol; DGM 2001; 1982 FP Cert; MRCGP 1983; DCH RCP Lond. 1983; DRCOG 1981. Gen. Practitioner; Clin. Asst. in Elderly Care.

LETHBRIDGE, John Richard Conquest Hospital, The Ridge, St Leonards-on-Sea TN37 7RD — MB BS 1974 Lond.; FFA RCS Eng. 1983; DCH Eng. 1978; DObst RCOG 1976. (Char. Cross) Cons. in Anaesth. & Pain Managem. Hastings & Rother NHS Trust. Prev: Sen. Regist. Rotat. Guy's Hosp. Lond., Roy. Sussex Co. Hosp. Brighton & Qu. Vict. Hosp. E. Grinsted.; Regist. Rotat. (Anaesth.) Guy's Hosp. Lond.; Regist. (Anaesth.) Poole Gen. Hosp.

LETHBRIDGE, Julie Glyncasnod Farm, Felindre, Swansea SA5 7PU Tel: 01269 592145 — MB BCh 1980 Wales; MRCGP 1987; DRCOG 1983. Prev: GP Maghull; SHO (Cas.) Walton Hosp. Liverp.; SHO (Paediat.) Alder Hey Childr. Hosp. Liverp.

LETHBRIDGE, Keith George Priory Avenue Surgery, 24-26 Priory Avenue, High Wycombe HP13 6SH Tel: 01494 448132 Fax: 01494 686407; 50 Fennels Way, Flackwell Heath, High Wycombe HP10 9BY — MB BS 1980 Lond. (St. Mary's)

LETHBRIDGE, William James 125 Hesperus Crescent, London E14 3AB — MB BS 1987 Lond.; MRCGP 1994.

LETHEM, David George (retired) 59 Osbaldwick Vill., York Tel: 01904 410847 — MB BChir 1953 Camb.; DObst RCOG 1957.

LETHEM, John Allan University Health Centre, University of York, Heslington, York YO10 5DD Tel: 01904 433290 Fax: 01904 433291; 3 New Walk Terrace, Fishergate, York YO10 4BG Tel: 01904 646861 Email: lethem@compuserve.co.uk — MB ChB 1983 Bristol; MRCGP 1987; DRCOG 1987. (Bristol) Socs: BMA; York Med. Soc. (Hon. Treas.); Brit. Assn. Health Servs. in Higher Ed. (Hon. Treas.).

LETHEM, John Ellis (retired) 7 Low Bank, Embsay, Skipton BD23 6SQ — MB ChB 1953 Leeds; DA Eng. 1960.

LETHEM, Kathleen Rosemary East Glade Centre, 1 East Glade Crescent, Sheffield S12 4QN Tel: 0114 271 6480 Fax: 0114 271 6450 Email: letham@doctors.org.uk; 21 Stumperlowe crescent Road, Sheffield S10 3PQ Tel: 0114 230 5537 Fax: 0114 230 6255 Email: letham@doctors.org.uk — MB BChir 1983 Camb.; PhD Camb. 1979, MA 1976; MRCPsych 1987. (Cambridge) Cons. Psychiat. (Acute Gen. Adult Psychiat.) Sheff. Community Health Servs. NHS Trust. Socs: Roy. Soc. Med. (Hon. Tres.1999 Counc. Psychiat. Sect.). Prev: Sen. Regist. (Psychiat.) Camden & Islington Community Health Servs. NHS Trust; Regist. (Psychiat.) Hackney & St. Bart. Hosps. Lond.; Regist. & SHO (Psychiat.) Barrow Hosp. Bristol.

LETHER, Valerie Anne 5 Pembroke Road, Dronfield, Dronfield S18 1WH — MB ChB 1978 Manch.; MRCOG 1987. Regist. (O & G) Jessop Hosp. Sheff.

LETHEREN, Martin John Robert 47 Ridgeway, Penwortham, Preston PR1 9XW — MB ChB 1989 Manch. SHO (Anaesth.) Blackpool Vict. Hosp.

LETLEY, Eric (retired) 3 Barnfield Wood Road, Beckenham BR3 6SR Tel: 020 8650 8957 — MRCS Eng. LRCP Lond. 1962; BSc Lond. 1957, PhD 1960, MB BS 1962; MRCP (U.K.) 1975; FFPM RCP Lond. 1989. Asst. Dir. Div. Med. Sci. Wellcome Research Laborat. Beckenham; Hon. Clin. Asst. (Med.) St. Geo. Hosp. Lond. Prev: Lect. (Pharmacol.) Sch. Med. Leeds.

LETSKY, Elizabeth Alin Queen Charlotte's Chelsea Hospital for Women, Goldhawk Road, London W6 0XG Tel: 020 8383 3098 Fax: 020 8353 3511 Email: e.letsky@rpms.ac.uk; 3 Wellington Terrace, Harrow HA1 3EP Tel: 020 8864 6589 Fax: 020 8864 6589 — MB BS 1960 Durh.; FRCPath 1982, M 1970; FRCPCH 1995; FRCOG (ad eundem) 1995. (Newc.) Cons. Haemat. Qu. Charlotte's Hosp. Wom. Lond.; Hon. Sen. Lect. (Haemat.) Imperial Coll. Lond. Socs: Brit. Soc. Haematol.; Brit. Paediat. Assn.; Assn. Clin. Path. Prev: Lect. (Haemat.) Inst. Child Health Lond.; Resid. (Haemat.) Univ. Calif. Med. Centre, San Francisco; Regist. (Haemat.) Roy. Postgrad. Sch. Med. Lond.

LETT, Kim Son 7 Villiers Road, Isleworth TW7 4HW — MB BS 1997 Lond. SHO Ophth. Countess Chester Hosp. Socs: Med. Defence. Union; BMA.

LETTIN, Mr Alan William Frederick (retired) Moat Farm, Cretingham, Woodbridge IP13 7AZ — MB BS 1956 Lond.; BSc Lond. 1952, MS 1967; FRCS Eng. 1960; MRCS Eng. LRCP Lond. 1955. Hon. Cons. Orthop. Surg. Middlx. & Univ. Coll. Hosps., Roy. Nat. Orthop. Hosp. & Inst Orthop Lond; Hon. Cons. St. Lukes Hosp. for the Clergy; Mem. Gen. Osteop. Counc. Prev: Mem. Counc. R.C.S. & Vice Pres.

LETTINGTON, William Charles Campshill Surgery, 33 Campshill Road, London SE13 6QU Tel: 020 8852 1384 — MB BS 1963 Lond.; MPhil Lond. 1974; Dip. Ther. Wales 1996; Dip. Pract. Dermat. Wales 1995; Dip. Forens. Med. Glas. 1993; Dip. FMSA Forens Med Soc. of Apoth Glas. 1998; DPH Eng. 1972. (St. Bart.) GP Lond.; Forens. Med. Examr. Metrop. Police; Dip. Addic. Behaviour St. Geo. Hosp. Med. Sch. Socs: Fell. Roy. Soc. Med. (Clin. Forens. Med. & Respirat. Sect.); Amer. Acad. Family Phys.s; Fell. Roy. Inst. Pub. Health & Hyg. Prev: Med. Off. Drugs & AIDS Counselling & Advisor Serv. St. Geo. Hosp. Lond.; Asst. Port Med. Off. Port of Lond. HA.

LETTON, Debra Jane Hollywood Farmhouse, Crow Lane, Tendring, Clacton-on-Sea CO16 9AP — BM 1983 Soton.

LETTON, Philip Henry Jodrell Hollywood Farmhouse, Crow Lane, Tendring, Clacton-on-Sea CO16 9AP — BM 1983 Soton.; MRCGP 1989.

LETTS, Anne 11 Malthouse Court, The Lindens, Towcester NN12 6UY Tel: 01327 359215 — MB BCh 1945 Wales; BSc Wales 1945; MB BS Lond. 1949; DPH Wales 1956; DCH Eng. 1950. (Cardiff) Prev: Deptm. Med. Off. Lond. Boro. Croydon; Med. Off. MoH & Educat.; Regist. (Med.) Neath Gen. Hosp.

LETTS, Karen Louise 20 Kingsland Close, Stone ST15 8FF — MB ChB 1991 Leeds. SHO Rotat. (Surg.) N. Staffs. Hosp. NHS Trust Stoke-on-Trent. Socs: BMA.

LETTY, Lillian Joan (retired) 22 Aldersyde Court, Dringhouses, York YO24 1QN Tel: 01904 707384 — MB BS Lond. 1947; MRCS Eng. LRCP Lond. 1947; DObst RCOG 1949; DCH Eng. 1950; MRCGP 1962. Prev: GP. York FPC.

LEUCHARS, Katy Louise 2 Boverton Park, Boverton, Llantwit Major CF61 1UE — MB ChB 1998 Ed.; MB ChB Ed 1998. (Edinburgh) Ho. Off. (Med.). Prev: Ho. Off. (Surg.), Edin.

LEUNG, Andrew Sik Keung Rochester House, 27 Victoria Road, Swindon SN1 3AW; 22 Clayhill Copse, Peatmoor, Swindon SN5 5AL — MB BS 1987 Lond.; Dip. GU. Med 1998; DFP 1996. Clin. Asst. GU Med. Bristol Roy. Infirm. Prev: SHO (Microbiol.) Wycombe Gen. Hosp.; Ho. Phys. (Radiother.) Mt. Vernon Hosp.; Ho. Surg. Sutton Hosp.

LEUNG, Anthony Ting Chu 19 Wardour Street, London W1 — MB ChB 1966 Glas. (Glas.)

LEUNG, Anthony Warren Treetops, Aldenham Grove, Radlett WD7 7BN — BM BS 1985 Nottm. (Nottm.) Assoc. Med. Dir. BUPA.

LEUNG, Anthony Yin-Tuen Robinson, Ashton, Leung, Solari and Thompson, James Preston Health Centre, 61 Holland Road, Sutton Coldfield B72 1RL Tel: 0121 355 5150 — MB ChB 1991 Birm.; ChB Birm. 1991. (Birmingham University)

LEUNG, Chi Bon c/o Drive John Feehally Department of Nephrology, Leicester General Hospital, Gwendolen Road, Leicester LE5 4PW — MB ChB 1986 Chinese Univ. Hong Kong; MB ChB Chinese U. Hong Kong 1986.

LEUNG, Mr Chi Hang Bertrand Upper Charmouth, 11A Townley Road, Dulwich, London SE22 8SR — MB BS 1988 Lond.; FRCS Ed. 1994. SHO (Gen. Surg.) Roy. Marsden Hosp. Lond. Prev: SHO (Urol. & Renal Transpl.) Hammersmith Hosp. Lond.; SHO (Cardiothoracic) Roy. Brompton Nat. Heart & Lung Hosp.; SHO (Gen. Surg.) Joyce Grn. Hosp. Dartford.

LEUNG, Clarence Hin Shuen 9/5 Sienna Gardens, Edinburgh EH9 1PQ — MB ChB 1994 Ed.

LEUNG, Derek Ping Yuen Block 4, Staff Residence, Peterborough District Hospital, Thorpe Road, Peterborough PE3 6DA; 28 Warwick Mansions, Cromwell Crescent, London SW5 9QR Tel: 020 7835 1445 — MB BChir 1993 Camb.; MA Camb. 1993; BA Camb. 1989. (Camb.) Socs: MDU; BMA; Med. Protec. Soc. Prev: SHO (Gen. Med.) Qu. Eliz. Hosp. Gateshead; SHO (A & E) N. Middlx. Hosp. NHS Trust Lond.; SHO (Med. & Care Elderly) P'boro. Dist. Hosp. NHS Trust.

LEUNG, Edward Wai-Yin 117 Terregles Crescent, Pollokshields, Glasgow G41 4BT — MB ChB 1994 Glas.

LEUNG, Gilberto Ka Kit Flat 6, 30 Compayne Gardens, London NW6 3DN; 21 Moorsom Road, Jardine's Lookout, Hong Kong — MB BS 1992 Lond.

LEUNG, Harry Kam Hay Mount Pleasant, Truggist Lane, Berkswell, Coventry CV7 7BW; Bosworth Medical Centre, 16 Crabtree Drive, Birmingham B37 5BU — MB ChB 1966 Birm.; DA Eng. 1969. (Birm.) Prev: Ho. Off. Childr. Hosp. Birm.; SHO (O & G) Marston Green Matern. Hosp. Birm.; SHO (Cas.) E. Birm. Hosp.

LEUNG, Henry Ho-Ying 542 Kenilworth Road, Balsall Common, Coventry CV7 7DQ — MB ChB 1965 Birm. (Birm.)

LEUNG, Hing Yip 46 Kimberley Road, Penylan, Cardiff CF23 5DL — MB ChB 1986 Aberd.

LEUNG, Mr Ho Hoi Lea Road Medical Practice, 35 Lea Road, Wolverhampton WV3 0LS Tel: 01502 423064 Fax: 01502 657800; 6 Claremont Road, Wolverhampton WV3 0EA Tel: 01902 650277 Email: hohoileung@yahoo.co.uk — MBBS 1978; MRCGP 1985; MMed Sc 2001. (Hong Kong Univ.) Partner GP, Lea Rd. Med. Pract., Wolverhampton.

LEUNG, Joanna Oi Shan 4 Staring Close, Middleleaze, Swindon SN5 5TH Tel: 01793 881131 — MB BS 1994 Lond.; MRCP 1997. Med. Off. Dept. Health, Hong Kong. Prev: Ho. Off. (Surg.) W. Middlx. Univ. Hosp.; Ho. Off. (Med.) Watford Gen. Hosp.; SHO (Med. P.ss Margt. Hosp. Swindon.

LEUNG, Pui Man Wharfedale General Hospital, Otley LS21 2LY Tel: 01943 465522; 2 Cawood Road, Wistow, Selby YO8 3XB Tel: 01757 268559 — MB ChB 1989 Aberd.; MRCP (UK) 1993. (Univ. Aberd.) Regist. Rotat. (Diabetes & Endocrinol.) W. Yorks. Socs: Collegiate Mem. RCP Lond.; Soc. Endocrinol.; Profess. Mem. BDA. Prev: Clin. Research Fell. (Med.) Univ. Manch. Bone Dis. Research Centre & Manch. Roy. Infirm.; Regist. (Diabetes & Endocrinol.) Freeman Hosp. Newc. u. Tyne.

LEUNG, Rebecca Shirley 28 Lysias Road, London SW12 8BP — MB BS 1997 Lond.; BSc (Hons), Lond, 1994. (Royal Free Hospital School Of Medicene)

LEUNG, Roland Ching-Yu 24/15 East Parkside, Edinburgh EH16 5XN — MB ChB 1997 Ed.

LEUNG, Susanna Oi May 136A Front Street, Chester-le-Street DH3 3AY; 33 Woodlands, Darras Hall, Ponteland, Newcastle upon Tyne NE20 9EU — MB BS 1985 Lond. Staff Grade (Genitourin. Med.) Sunderland Dist. Gen. Hosp.

LEUNG, Tat Yan David Gravesend & North Kent Hospital, Gravesend DA11 — MB BS 1975 Lond.; MRCP (UK) 1979; MRCS Eng. LRCP Lond. 1975; DRCOG 1977. (Guy's)

LEUNG, Vitus Kun Yu 4 Wroxall Close, Brierley Hill DY5 3TT — BM BS 1984 Nottm.

LEUNG, Wing Chuen Daniel 18 Hambledon Place, Dulwich, London SE21 7EY — MB BS 1984 Lond.; BSc (Path.) Lond. 1981, MB BS 1984; DA (UK) 1988. Regist. (Anaesth.) Mayday Hosp. Lond.

***LEUNG, Yee Ling** 25 Woodbridge Av, Leatherhead KT22 7QL; 11 Knightwick Crescent, Erdington, Birmingham B23 7DA — MB ChB 1997 Leic.; BSc Univ. Coll. N. Wales 1992.

LEUNG, Yim-Lung 19 Glasgow Road, Plaistow, London E13 9HW Tel: 020 8552 6678 — MB ChB 1988 Chinese Univ. Hong Kong.

LEUTY, George Michael Victoria Health Centre, Glasshouse Street, Nottingham NG1 3LW Tel: 0115 948 3030 Fax: 0115 911 1074 — MB ChB 1981 Leeds; BSc Leeds 1978, MB ChB 1981; MRCGP 1985. (Leeds)

LEVACK, Mr Brian 2 Royston Court, Royston Gardens, Redbridge, Ilford IG1 3SU — MB BS 1974 Newc.; FRCS Eng. 1978.

LEVACK, Fiona Caroline Portslade Health Centre, Church Road, Portslade, Brighton BN41 1LX Tel: 01273 422525/418445 Fax: 01273 413510; 18 Richmond Terrace, Brighton BN2 2SA Tel: 01273 606358 — BM BS 1980 Nottm.; BMedSci Nottm. 1978, BM BS 1980; DRCOG 1984. Socs: E. Sussex LMC; Area Child Protec. Comm.

LEVACK, Iain David, TD Department of Anaesthetics, Ninewells Hospital and Medical School, Dundee DD1 9SY Tel: 01382 632175 Fax: 01382 644914; Little Court, 69 Dundee Road, Dundee DD5 1NA — MB ChB 1975 Aberd.; MD Aberd. 1980; FFA RCS Eng. 1981. (Aberd. University) Cons. Anaesth. Ninewells Hosp. Med Sch.; Indep. Mem. MoD Scientif. Advis. Counc. Prev: Cons. Anaesth.W.ern Gen Hosp Edin; cons Anaesth Aberd Roy Infir; Lect Anaesth Univ. Edin.

LEVACK, Pamela Aileen Department of Clinical Oncology, University of Edinburgh, Western General Hospital, Edinburgh EH4 2XU Tel: 0131 332 2525 Fax: 0131 332 8494; Little Court, 69 Dundee Road, Dundee DD5 1NA Tel: 0131 552 1950 Fax: 0131 552 1950 — MB ChB 1976 Aberd.; MSc (Clin. Oncol.) Ed. 1995; BMedBiol (Hons.) Aberd. 1973; MRCP (UK) 1978; MRCGP 1983; FRCP Edin 1999. (Aberdeen University) Cons. Palliat. Med. Roxburghe, Dundee & Vinewells Hosp., Palliat. Care Team, Dundee; Lead clinician hosp pall care team Ninewells hosp & med sch. Socs: Assn. Palliat. Med; (Sec.) E. Scotl. Assoc. Palliat. Med.; APM Ethics Comm. Prev: Sen. Regist. (Palliat. Med.) Edin.; Lect. (Med. Oncol.) W.ern Gen. Hosp. Edin.; Research Fell. (Clin. Surg.) Univ. Edin.

LEVAK, Vojtech 114 Knightwood Crescent, New Malden KT3 5JW — MUDr 1961 Komensky Univ. Czechoslovakia; DA Eng. 1978. Assoc. Specialist (Anaesth.) St. Helier Trust.

LEVAN, David Beckfields Medical Centre, Beckfields Avenue, Ingleby Barwick, Stockton-on-Tees TS17 0QA Tel: 01642 765789 Fax: 01642 750872; Rosegarth, 513 Yarm Road, Eaglescliffe, Stockton-on-Tees TS16 9BG — MB ChB 1975 Bristol; MRCP (UK) 1979; MRCGP 1982; DRCOG 1981.

LEVAN, Susan Margaret Rosegarth, 513 Yarm Road, Eaglescliffe, Stockton-on-Tees TS16 9BG — MB BS 1974 Lond.; MRCS Eng. LRCP Lond. 1974.

LEVANTINE, Ashley Vincent Kingfisher, West Walberton Lane, Walberton, Arundel BN18 0QS Tel: 01243 543252 — MB BS 1966 Lond.; FRCP Lond. 1986; MRCP (UK) 1970; MRCS Eng. LRCP Lond. 1966. (Lond. Hosp.) Cons. Dermat. Chichester & Worthing Health Dists. Socs: Fell. Roy. Soc. Med. (Mem. Sect. Dermat.); BMA. Prev: Sen. Regist. (Dermat.) Middlx. Hosp. Lond.; Med. Regist. Whipps Cross Hosp.; Ho. Surg. Dept. Thoracic Surg. Lond. Hosp.

LEVEAUX, Vivian Michael, CStJ Beech Mount, 7 Farley Road, Derby DE23 6BY Tel: 01332 343827 — MB BS Lond. 1945; MA Nottm. 1987; MD Lond. 1948; FRCP Lond. 1969, M 1948; MRCS Eng. LRCP Lond. 1945. (Westm.) DL; JP; Emerit. Phys. Derbysh. Roy. Infirm. Prev: Sen. Regist. (Med.) W.m. Hosp.; Ho. Phys. Brompton Hosp. & Hosp. Sick Childr. Gt. Ormond St.

LEVECKIS, Mr John The Old Rectory, Church Lane N., Old Whittington, Chesterfield S41 9QY — MB ChB 1982 Manch.; BSc St. And. 1979; FRCS (Urol.) 1994; FRCS Eng. 1988. (St. And. & Manch.) Cons. Urol., Doncaster Roy. Infirm. NHS Trust. Socs: Trent Urol. Gp.; Brit. Assn. Urol. Surg.; Eur. Urol. Assn. Prev: Sen. Regist. (Urol. Surg.) Roy. Hallamsh. Hosp. Sheff.; Research Fell. (Surg.) Univ. Sheff.

LEVELL, Geoffrey Alexander (retired) De Cronjer, Fearnan, Aberfeldy PH15 2PG Tel: 01887 830477 — MRCS Eng. LRCP Lond. 1950; MFCM 1974; DPH Manch. 1956. Prev: Dist. Community Phys. Burnley Health Dist.

LEVELL, Nicholas Julian Norfolk and Norwich University Hospital NHS Trust, Norwich NR4 7UY Tel: 01603 288225 Fax: 01603 288601 Email: nicklevell@norfolk-norwich.thenks.com; Email: nicklevell@hotmail.com — MB ChB 1985 Manch.; MD Manch. 1994; MRCP (UK) 1989; FRCP 2000. (Manch.) Cons. Dermat. Norf. & Norwich Univ. Hosp. NHS Trust; Hon. Sen. Lect. Univ. of E. Anglia. Socs: Brit. Assn. Dermat. E. Rep. Nat. Exec. Comm.; Brit. Soc. Investig. Dermat.; Brit. Soc. Dermat. Surg. Prev: Sen. Regist. (Acting Cons.) Middlx. Hosp. Lond.; Regist. (Dermat.) Roy. Vict. Infirm. Newc. u. Tyne; Regist. (Gen. Med.) Wythenshawe Hosp. Manch.

LEVEN, Catherine Findlay 4 Mayberry Crescent, Glasgow G32 0EN — MB ChB 1992 Aberd.

LEVEN-MELZER, Mrs Hilde 14 Woodthorpe Lodge, The Cedars, Sherwood, Nottingham NG5 3FN — LRCP 1935 Ed.; LRCP, LRCS Ed., LRFPS Glas. 1935.

LEVENE, Eric Alexander 123 Crownfield Road, London E15 Tel: 020 8534 4180 — MB ChB 1954 Birm.

LEVENE, Louis Steven The East Leicester Medical Practice, 131 Uppingham Road, Leicester LE5 4BP Tel: 0116 276 7145 Fax: 0116 246 1637 — MB 1979 Camb.; BChir 1978; MRCGP 1985.

LEVENE, Malcolm Irvin Department Child Health and Paediatrics, Clarendon Wing, The General Infirmary, Leeds Tel: 0113 292 3905 Fax: 0113 292 3902; Monkswood, 45 Vespered, Leeds LS5 3QT Tel: 0113 275 5337 — MRCS Eng. LRCP Lond. 1974; MD Lond. 1982, MB BS 1974; FRCP Lond. 1988; MRCP (UK) 1978. (Guy's) Prof. Child Health. Univ. Leeds. Socs: Fell. Roy. Soc. Med.; Neonat. Soc. Prev: Reader (Child Health) Univ. Leicester Med. Sch.; Research Lect. & Hon. Sen. Regist. Roy. Postgrad. Med. Sch. & Hammersmith Hosp. Lond.; Regist. (Paediat.) Char. Cross Hosp. Lond.

LEVENE, Maurice Mordecai (retired) 14 Hill Brow, Hove BN3 6QF Tel: 01273 552038 — MRCS Eng. LRCP Lond. 1951; LDS RCS Eng. 1943.

LEVENE, Max Moses 46 Cranley Gardens, London SW7 3DE Tel: 020 7373 5960 — MRCS Eng. LRCP Lond. 1944; FRCPath 1972, M 1963; DPath Eng. 1955. (Lond. Hosp.) Cons. Path. Regional Cell Path. & Cytogen. Serv. Wandle Valley Hosp. Mitcham. Socs: Path. Soc. Gt. Brit. & Irel. & Assn. Clin. Pathol. Prev: Asst. Pathol. Christie Hosp. Manch.; Chief of Path. Pondville Hosp. Walpole, Mass.; Instruc. Dept. Path. Harvard Univ. Boston, Mass.

LEVENE, Rachel The Surgery, 66 Long Lane, London EC1A 9EJ Tel: 020 7600 9740, 020 7606 0071 — MB BS 1987 Newc.; DCH RCP Lond. 1993; DRCOG 1993. (University of Newcastle-Upon-Tyne) Princip. in Gen. Pract. Socs: BMA; Balint Soc. Prev: Partner Gillian Ho. Surg. Newc. VTS.

LEVENE, Sara International Clinical Trials, 99 New Cavendish St., London W1W 6XH Tel: 020 7436 8080 Fax: 020 7436 9897 Email: slevene@icttrials.com; 4 Manor Hall Avenue, London NW4 1NX Tel: 020 8203 0504 Fax: 020 8203 0504 Email: s.levene@dial.pipex.com — MB BChir 1979 Camb.; MB BChir Camb.1979; BA Camb. 1977; MA Camb. 1979; MRCP (UK) 1983; FRCPCH 1987. (Camb.) Clin. Research Phys., Internat. Clin. Trials Lond.; Med. Assessor, Indep. Tribunal Serv.; Med. Tribunal Mem. Indep. Tribunal Serv. Socs: Fell. RSM; Lond. Jewish Med. Soc.; BMA. Prev: Med. Cons., Child Accid. Preven. Trust.

LEVENSON, Samuel Limefield Medical Centre, 8 Limefield Road, Salford M7 0LZ Tel: 0161 721 4845 Fax: 0161 720 6494 — MB BCh BAO 1984 NUI; LRCPI & LM, LRCSI & LM 1984.

LEVENSON, Saul (retired) 3A Kingston Close, Salford M7 4JS Tel: 0161 792 4532 — MB ChB 1955 Glas.; MICGP 1986.

LEVENTHALL, Phyllis Anne 250 Langworthy Road, Salford M6 5WW Tel: 0161 736 7422 Fax: 0161 736 4816 — MB ChB 1964 Leeds. GP Salford.

LEVENTHORPE, John Robert Bryan School Lane Surgery, School Lane, Thetford IP24 2AG Tel: 01842 753115 — MB 1987 Camb.; BChir 1986; BSc Hons. (Med. Biol.) St. And. 1983; T(GP) 1992; Cert. Family Plann. JCC 1990. SHO (Rheum. & Rehabil.) St. Michael's Aylsham. Prev: SHO (ENT) Norf. & Norwich Hosp.

LEVENTIS, John Flat 4/7, 109 Bell St., Glasgow G4 0TQ — MB ChB 1990 Glas.

LEVER, Professor Andrew Michael Lindsay Department of Medicine, Level 5, Addenbrooke's Hospital, Hills Road, Cambridge CB2 2QQ Tel: 01223 336844 Fax: 01223 336846 — MB BCh 1978 Wales; MD 2001 Canta.; F. Med. Sa. 2000; BSc (Hons.) (Med. Biochem.) Wales 1975, MD 1987; FRCP Ed. 1993 FRCP 1993; MRCP (UK) 1981; MRCPath 1993; FRCPath 1998; MA(Cantab)

1998. Hon. Cons. Phys.Prof in Infec. Dis.s Univ. of Camb. Socs: Assn. Phys.; Brit. Infect. Soc.; Amer. Soc. MicroBiol. Prev: Sen. Lect. & Hon. Cons. Infec. Dis.s St. Geo.s Hosp. Lond.; Hon. Cons. Phys. Univ. Lect. Med. Univ. Camb.; Hon Cons phys reader, univ Camb.

LEVER, Professor Anthony Fairclough 7 Sydenham Road, Glasgow G12 9NT Tel: 0141 339 0076 — MB BS 1955 Lond.; FRSE 1974; BSc Lond. 1952; FRCP Glas. 1984; FRCP Lond. 1969, M 1958; MRCS Eng. LRCP Lond. 1955. (St. Mary's) Hon. Prof. Univ. Glas. & Dir. MRC Blood Pressure Unit W.. Infirm. Glas. Socs: (Ex-Pres.) Brit. Hypentens. Soc.; (Ex-Vice Pres.) Internat. Soc. Hypertens. Prev: Sen. Research Fell. Univ. Glas.; Lect. Mary's Hosp. Lond.; Resid. Med. Off. Nat. Heart Hosp. Lond.

LEVER, Claire Gabrielle 38 Oakleigh Park S., London N20 9JN — MB BS 1990 Lond.

LEVER, Eric Gilbert Wellington Hospital, Wellington Place, London NW8 9LE Tel: 0207 586 3213 Fax: 0208 371 8396 — MB 1976 Camb.; MA Camb. 1978, BChir 1975; B. Soc Sc. Birm. 1968; MRCP (UK) 1978. (Univ. Coll. Hosp.) Cons. Phys. & Endocrinol. Socs: Soc. for Endocrinol. Prev: Sen. Regist. (Med.) King's Coll. Hosp. Lond.; Research Fell. (Endocrinol. & Diabetes) Univ. Chicago.

LEVER, Professor Jeffrey Darcy Troed y Rhiw Farm, Ystrad Mynach, Hengoed CF82 7EW Tel: 01443 812175 — MB BChir 1946 Camb.; ScD Camb. 1974, MD 1954. (Camb. & St. Thos.) Prof. Anat. Univ. Wales; Emerit. Prof. Univ. Wales. Socs: (Ex-Pres.) Anat. Soc.; Brit. Assn. Clin. Anat. Prev: Dep. Princip. Univ. Coll. Cardiff; Fell. Trinity Coll. Camb.; Lect. (Anat.) Univ. Camb.

LEVER, Joanna Caerwigau Mill, Pendoylan, Cowbridge CF71 7UJ — MB BS 1982 Lond.; DA (UK) 1985; DRCOG 1988. Med. Advisor DVLA. Prev: Princip. in Gen. Pract.

LEVER, Laurence Russell Department of Dermatology, Northwick Park Hospital, Harrow HA1 3UJ Tel: 020 8869 2988 Fax: 020 8869 2939 — MB BS 1980 Lond.; MRCP (UK) 1983. (Middlx.) Cons. Dermat. N.wick Pk. Hosp. Harrow Middlx. Prev: Sen. Regist. (Dermat.) Roy. Vict. Infirm. Newc. u Tyne; Lect. (Dermat.) Univ. Wales Coll. Med. Cardiff; SHO (Med.) N.wick Pk. Hosp. Harrow.

LEVER, Michael James 2 Belgrave Crescent Lane, Edinburgh EH4 3AG — MB ChB 1993 Glas.

LEVER, Rosemary Susan 7 Sydenham Road, Glasgow G12 9NT Tel: 0141 339 0076 — MRCS Eng. LRCP Lond. 1965; MD Lond. 1974, MB BS 1965; FRCP Glas. 1993; MRCP Glas. 1991; MRCP Lond. 1968; MRCGP 1980. (St. Mary's) Cons. Dermat. W.. Infirm. & Roy. Hosp. Sick Childr. Glas. Prev: Sen. Regist. (Dermat.) W.. Infirm. Glas.; Lect. (Med.) W.. Infirm. Glas.; Ho. Phys. Hammersmith Hosp.

LEVERE, Kenneth Howard — MB BS 1972 Lond.; Dip Occ Med 1995; MRCGP 1987; DCH Eng. 1978.

LEVERMENT, Irene Margaret Gregory 118 Station Road, Cropston, Leicester LE7 7HE — MB ChB 1968 Bristol; AFOM RCP Lond. 1995; DObst RCOG 1970. (Bristol) Clin. Asst. (Occupat. Health) Leicester HA.

LEVERMENT, Mr Joseph Neville 118 Station Road, Cropston, Leicester LE7 7HE — MB ChB 1963 Cape Town; FRCS Eng. 1970. Cons. (Cardiothoracic Surg.)Univs Hsps Leics NHS trust,Glenfield Hosp.

LEVERTON, Teresa Jane Northwick Park Hospital, Watford Road, Harrow HA1 3UJ Tel: 0280 869 2639 Fax: 0208 426 6359 — MB BS 1980 Lond.; BSc Lond. 1976, MB BS 1980; MRCPsych 1985. Hon Clin. Sen. lec Imperial coll sch of med; Cons. Child & Adolesc. Psychiat. N.wick Pk. Hosp. Prev: Sen. Regist. (Child Psychiat.) Hosp. for Sick Childr. Lond.

LEVERTON, William Edmund Joseph Bere Alston Medical Practice, Bere Alston, Yelverton PL20 7EJ Tel: 01822 840269 Fax: 01822 841104 Email: beremedics@aol.com — MB BS Lond. 1970; BSc (Physiol.) Lond. 1967; FRCGP 1995; MRCGP 1975. (St. Bart.) p/t Assoc. Director, GP Educat. (Cornw.), S. W.. Deanery. Prev: Trainee GP Mid-Sussex VTS; Ho. Off. (Med.) St. Bart. Hosp. Lond.

LEVESON, Clive Martin 17 St John Street, Manchester M3 4DR Tel: 0161 907 2105 Fax: 0161 907 2108; 88 Rodney Street, Liverpool L1 9AR Tel: 0151 709 7066 Fax: 0151 709 7279 — MRCS Eng. LRCP Lond. 1975. Specialist in Medico Legal work for noncatartrophic injuries. Prev: GP Manch.

LEVESON, Mr Stephen Howard York District Hospital, Wiggington Road, York YO31 8ZZ Tel: 01904 631313 Email: sleveson@doctors.org.uk; 9 Shilton Garth Close, Earswick, York YO32 9SQ Tel: 01904 764344 Fax: 01904 761420 Email: sleveson@ldoctors.org.uk — MD 1978 Manch.; MB ChB 1970; FRCS Eng. 1974. (Manch.) Cons. (Gen. Surg.) York Dist. Hosp.; Mem. Edit. Bd. of Brit. Jl. Surg.; Prof. Surg. St. Geo. Univ. Med. Sch. Grenada; Counc mem assoc coloProctol., GB & Ire. Socs: Surgic. Research Soc. & Brit. Oncol. Assn.; Assoc coloproctol; Assoc Surg.s. Prev: Sen. Lect. & Hon. Cons. Surg. St. Jas. Hosp. Leeds; Research Assoc. (Surg. Oncol.) Roswell Pk. Memor. Inst. Buffalo, USA.

LEVETT, Denny Zelda Hope The Flat, 42 Edbury St, London SW1W 0LZ Tel: 020 7823 6197 Email: dennylevett@hotmail.com — BM BCh 1996 Oxf.; MRCP 1999. SHO (ICU) The Middlx. Hosp.

LEVETT, Mr Ian James Silvanus 12 Strathmore Avenue, Hull HU6 7HJ — BM 1986 Soton.; FRCS Lond. 1996. SHO (A & E) Hull Roy. Infirm. Socs: Christian Med. Fell.sh. Prev: Med. Off. for Aid Agency Worldwide Servs. RePub.an Hosp., Saada, RePub. of Yemen.

LEVETT, John Sidney (retired) 504 Bromsgrove Road, Hunnington, Halesowen B62 0JJ Tel: 0121 550 1302 — MB ChB 1958 Birm.

LEVEY, Cecil (retired) 11 Newman Court, Rotherham S60 3JA Tel: 01709 378190 — MRCS Eng. LRCP Lond. 1937.

LEVI, Judy (Julia Miriam) (retired) 103 Swains Lane, Highgate, London N6 6PJ Tel: 020 8340 9933 Fax: 020 8348 7676 — MB BS 1954 Lond.; DPH Eng. 1961. Participant WHO Regional Office for Europe 1987. Prev: Med. Off. Lond. Boro. Camden & W.m.

LEVI, Mr Moiz (retired) Monita, 44 Gibwood Road, Northenden, Manchester M22 4BS Tel: 0161 998 2010 — MD 1951 Istanbul; MS 1957; LAH Dub. 1960. Prev: Sen. Ho. Off. Roy. Infirm. Leicester.

LEVI, Nicholas Alfred The Surgery, 991 Bristol Road South, Northfield, Birmingham B31 2QT Tel: 0121 476 9191; Fox Gloves, Stretton Drive, Barnt Green, Birmingham B45 8XJ Tel: 0121 445 5336 — MB 1971 Camb.; BChir 1970; MRCP (UK) 1974.

LEVI, Sassoon The Gatehouse, Fulmer Chase, Stoke Common Road, Fulmer, Slough SL3 6HB — MB BS 1984 Lond.; BSc Lond 1981, MD 1990; MRCP (UK) 1987. Cons. Gastroenterol. & Gen. Phys. Wexham Pk. Hosp. Slough; Sen. Lect. (Med.) Roy. Postgrad. Med. Sch. Lond. Prev: Sen. Regist. & Regist. (Gastroenterol.) Hammersmith Hosp. Lond.; Cancer Research Campaign Fell. Inst. Cancer Research Lond.

LEVI, Susan Ruth 27 Lower Vicarage Road, Kennington, Ashford TN24 9AT — MB BChir 1989 Camb.; MA Camb. 1990; MRCP (UK) 1993; MRCGP 1997; DRCOG 1996; DTM & H RCP Lond. 1995. SpR, Pub. Health S.E. Thames Rotat.

LEVICK, Beti Roberta Avalon, Hill Lane, Hathersage, Hope Valley S32 1AY Tel: 01433 50445 — MB BCh Wales 1957. (Cardiff)

LEVICK, Jonathan Frank Queens Road Surgery, 10B Queens Road, Blackhill, Consett DH8 0BN Tel: 01207 502071 Fax: 01207 583717 — MB BS 1986 Newc.; MRCGP 1991.

LEVICK, Mark Philip Department of Medicine, University of Cambridge, Addenbrooke's Hospital, L5, Box 157, Cambridge CB2 2QQ Tel: 01223 336143 Fax: 01223 336846; 28 George Nuttall Close, Cambridge CB4 1YE Tel: 01223 510921 — BMedSc 1989 Newc. NSW; BMedSc Newc. NSW 1987; MB 1989; PhD 1998; DpD 1999. (Univ. Newc. NSW) Med.Assessor. Med. Control.Agency; Clin.Asst.Derm.W. Suff..Hosp.NHS.Trust. Socs: Fell.Aus.Coll.Remote.Rural.med; Fell.Roy.Coll.Path.Au. Prev: Commonw. Schol. Molecular Parasitol. Univ. Camb.; Regist. (Clin. Microbiol.) P. Wales Hosp. Sydney; Resid. Med. Off. Roy. N. Shore Hosp. Sydney.

LEVICK, Mr Paul Lee Priory Hospital, Priory Road, Birmingham B5 7UG Tel: 0121 440 2323 — MB BS 1972 Lond.; FRCS Eng. 1980; FRCS Ed. 1980. Cons. Plastic Surg. Priory Hosp. Birm.

LEVICK, Susan River View, Vindomara Villas, Ebchester, Consett DH8 0PW — MB BS 1986 Newc.; MRCGP 1992. Durh. GP Career Start Scheme. Prev: SHO (Anaesth.) Shotley Bridge Gen. Hosp.

LEVIE, Brian Brewis Park Surgery, 2 Park Road North, Middlesbrough TS1 3LF Tel: 01642 247008 Fax: 01642 245748; 3 Southview, Hutton Rudby, Yarm TS15 0HE Tel: 01642 700893 — MB ChB 1962 Ed.; DObst RCOG 1964.

LEVIN, Arthur The Wellington Hospital, Wellington Place, London NW8 9LE Tel: 020 7586 5959; Flat 2, 63 Hamilton Terrace, London NW8 9QX Tel: 020 7289 4885 Fax: 020 7266 3684 — MRCS Eng. LRCP Lond. 1939; MA Camb. 1939; MRCGP 1953. (St. Bart.) Med. Adviser to Chief Exec. King's Coll. Hosp. & Camberwell HA; Hon. Cons. Phys. Lond. Assn. For Blind. Socs: Fell. Roy. Soc. Med.; Fell. Med. Soc. Lond.; Chairm. Wellington Foundat. & Soc. Prev: Chief

Med. Off. Brit. & Commonw. Holdings; Med. Dir. Wellington Hosp. Lond.; Maj. RAMC Med. Specialist.

LEVIN, Arthur George 13 Queens Gate Place, London SW7 5NX — MB ChB Glas. 1960.

LEVIN, Colin Andrew The Health Centre, 103 Brown Street, Broughty Ferry, Dundee DD5 1EP Tel: 01382 731331 Fax: 01382 737966; 110 Terregles Avenue, Pollockshields, Glasgow G41 4LJ Tel: 0141 423 0343 — MB ChB 1990 Ed.; MRCGP 1994; DRCOG 1992. SHO (A & E) Dundee Roy. Infirm. Prev: Trainee GP Dumfries & Galloway HB VTS; Ho. Off. (Med.) Dumfries Roy. Infirm.; Ho. Off. (Surg.) W.. Gen. Hosp. Edin.

LEVIN, Gerald Eliot 31 Church Crescent, London N3 1BE — MB BS 1965 Lond.; MSc (Biochem.) Lond. 1968, MB BS 1965; MRCPath 1973. (Lond. Hosp.) Sen. Lect. Chem. Path. St. Geo. Hosp. Lond. Prev: Lect. in Chem. Path. Roy. Free Hosp. Lond.

LEVIN, Jeremy Max 4 Cardigan Mansions, 19 Richmond Hill, Richmond TW10 6RD — MB BChir 1981 Camb.; DPhil Oxf. 1978. SHO (Clin. Med.) Hôpital Cantona Univ. de Geneve. Prev: Ho. Off. Addenbrookes & N. Middlx. Hosps.; SHO Roy. Postgrad. Hosp. Hammersmith Lond.

LEVIN, Joseph 12 Gertrude Street, Chelsea, London SW10 0JN — MB BCh 1956 Witwatersrand; MA Camb. 1939; LLB S. Afr. 1940; MRCP Ed. 1960. (Witwatersrand) Adj. Prof. & Vis. Phys. Rockefeller Univ. New. York USA. Prev: Asst. Dir. Clin. Research Center Montefiore Hosp. New York USA; Research Fell. Worcester Foundat. for Experim. Biol. Shrewsbury, USA; Clin. Asst. in Endocrin. Guy's Hosp.

***LEVIN, Phillip David** 23 Church Vale, London N2 9PB — BChir 1987 Camb.

LEVIN, Richard Lewis 110 Terregles Avenue, Glasgow G41 4LJ — MB ChB 1994 Dundee; MSc Glas. 1989; BSc (Hons.) Strathclyde 1987.

LEVIN, Ronald Irwin 4 West Dene, Wigton Lane, Leeds LS17 8QT Tel: 0113 268 7342; 4 West Dene, Wigton Lane, Leeds LS17 8QT — MB ChB 1952 Leeds. (Leeds) Med. Ref. Dept. of Social Security. Socs: BMA. Prev: Capt. RAMC; Ho. Surg. (Obst.) Gen. Hosp. Newc.; Ho. Phys. Gen. Hosp. Wakefield.

LEVINE, Adrian Jeremy Flat 2C, 7 Grosvenor Road, Newcastle ST5 1LW — MB BS 1987 Lond.

LEVINE, Daniel Simon 370 Alwoodley Lane, Leeds LS17 7DN — MB ChB 1997 Birm.

LEVINE, David Francis West Cornwall Hospital, Penzance TR18 2PF Tel: 01736 364352 — MD 1984 Bristol; MB ChB 1972; MRCP (UK) 1974; FRCP Lond. 1992. Cons. (Phys.) W. Cornw. Prev: Lect. (Med.) Lond. Hosp. Med. Coll.

LEVINE, Dorien 51 South Grove House, Highgate South Grove, London N6 6LR — LRCP LRCS 1934 Ed.; LRCP LRCS Ed. LRFPS Glas. 1934; LDS RFPS Glas. 1928.

LEVINE, Edward Laurence Cheshire Hospital., Wilmslow Road, Manchester M20 4BX Tel: 0161 446 3360 Fax: 0161 446 3419 — MB BS 1986 Lond.; MA Camb. 1987; MRCP (UK) 1989; FRCR 1993; MD Camb 2000. Cons. Clin. Oncol. Christie Hosp. Manch. Socs: Eur. Soc. Radiat. Oncol.; Brit. Oncol. Assn.; Amer. Soc. Clin. Oncol. Prev: Clin. Research Fell. & Sen. Regist. (Clin. Oncol.) Christie Hosp. & Paterson Inst. Manch.; Regist. & SHO Rotat. (Gen. Med.) Lond. Hosp.; Ho. Off. (Gen. Surg. & Gen. Med.) W.m. Hosp.

LEVINE, Geoffrey The Laurels Surgery, 20 Newmarket Road, Cambridge CB5 8DT Tel: 01223 350513 Fax: 01223 300445 — MB BChir 1977 Camb.; MA, MB Camb. 1978, BChir 1977; MRCP (UK) 1981; DRCOG 1983. GP Camb.; Hosp. Pract. (Diabetes) Addenbrookes Hosp. Camb.

LEVINE, Harris Rock House, 233 Wigan Road, Ashton-in-Makerfield, Wigan WN4 9SR Tel: 01942 727107 — MB ChB 1939 Leeds. (Leeds)

LEVINE, John Harris Anthony Tel: 01942 727107 Fax: 01942 200911 — MB ChB 1974 Manch.

LEVINE, Sir Montague Bernard (retired) Gainsborough House, 120 Ferndene Road, London SE24 0AA Tel: 020 7274 9196 — FRCPI 2000; Hon DSc Lond. 1996; MRCPI 1960; LRCPI & LM, LRCSI & LM 1955; FRCGP 1988, M 1965; DMJ Soc. Apoth. Lond. 1974. Hon. Lect. (Coroners Law) St. Thos. Hosp. Lond. (Retd. 1997); Hon. Lect. (Coroners Law) KCH Lond. (Retd. 1997). Prev: HM Coroner Lond. S.E. (Inner Dist.).

LEVINE, Lady Rose Gainsborough House, 120 Ferndene Road, London SE24 0AA Tel: 020 7274 9196 — MB BS Lond., 1956; MRCS Eng. LRCP Lond. 1956; MRCGP 1965. Socs: Hunt. Soc. Prev: Hon. Clin. Tutor St. Thos. Hosp. Lond.

LEVINE, Sharon 79 Wood Vale, London N10 3DL — MB BS 1976 Lond.; DRCOG 1979.

LEVINE, Tanya Sophia Department of Cellular Pathology, Nothwick Park Hospital, Watford Way, Harrow — MB BS 1989 Lond.; MA Oxf. 1989; MRCPath 1996; Dip. RCPath (Cytopath.) 1995. Cons. N.wick Pk. Hosp. Prev: Sen. Regist. (Histopath.) St. Mary's Hosp. Lond.; Regist. (Histopath.) N.wich Pk. Hosp.; SHO (Histopath.) Univ. Coll. Hosp. Lond.

LEVINE, Warren Hugh Charles c/o 147 St Walburgas Road, Blackpool FY3 7EY — MB ChB 1989 Liverp.; MRCPsych 1996. Sen. Regist. Child & Adolesc. Psychiat. Mersey.

LEVINSKY, Professor Roland Jacob Institute of Child Health, 30 Guilford St., London WC1N 1EH Tel: 020 7242 9789 Fax: 020 7242 8437; 42 Dukes Avenue, London N10 2PU Tel: 020 8883 4372 — MB BS 1968 Lond.; MD Lond. 1980; BSc (Special, Anat.) Lond. 1965, MB BS 1968; FRCP 1982, M 1972; MRCS Eng. LRCP Lond. 1968. (Univ. Coll. Hosp.) Hugh Greenwood Prof. Immunol.; Dean Inst. of Child Health Lond.; Hon. Cons. (Paediat.) Gt. Ormond St. Hosp. Childr. NHS Trust. Socs: Brit. Soc. Immunol. & B.P.A. Prev: Reader Paediat. Immunol.; Sen. Lect. Immunol. Inst. Child Health Lond.; Hon. Sen. Regist. (Paediat.) Gt. Ormond. St. Hosp. Child. NHS Trust.

LEVINSON, Alice Mary Rebecca Cassel Hospital, 1 Ham Common, Richmond TW10 7JF Tel: 020 8940 8181 — MB BS 1987 Lond.; MRCPsych 1992. (University college hosp & Middlesex hosp) Sen. Regist. Rotat. (Psychother.) Cassel Hosp. Lond.; local cons psychotherapist Epping Fores Psy dept. Loughton Essex.

LEVINSON, Charles Mark 43 Hans Place, Knightsbridge, London SW1X 0JZ Tel: 020 7584 1642 Fax: 020 7589 5862; 43 Hans Place, Knightsbridge, London SW1X 0JZ Tel: 020 7584 1642 Fax: 020 7589 5862 — MB BS 1986 Lond.; MA Oxf. 1983. (Oxf. & Westm.) Chairm. Doctorall Ltd. Socs: Yeoman Soc. of Apoth.; Chelsea Clin. Soc. Prev: SHO Rotat. (Med.) St. Geo.s Hosp. Lond.; SHO Rotat. (Radiother.) W.minster Hosp. Lond.; Honory Phys. (Neurol. & Gen. Med.) Roy. Surrey Co. Hosp.

LEVINSON, Gordon Alfred (retired) 5 Pembroke Villas, The Green, Richmond TW9 1QF Tel: 020 8940 0886 — MB BS 1942 Melbourne; FRCPsych 1978, M 1971; DPM Eng. 1952. Prev: Cons. Child Psychiat. W. Middlx. Hosp.

LEVINSON, Mrs Mary Curtis 5 Pembroke Villas, The Green, Richmond TW9 1QF — MB BS Melbourne 1945. (Melb.) Prev: Clin. Asst. Qu. Eliz. Hosp. Hackney & P.ss Louise Kens. Hosp.; Community Med. Off. Ealing.

LEVINSON, Norman (retired) Flat 17, Westgate Court, 27 The Avenue, Beckenham BR3 5DW Tel: 020 8650 0142 — MB ChB St. And. 1948; MD St. And. 1954. Prev: Hosp. Pract. (ENT) Mayday Hosp. Thornton Heath.

LEVIS, Richard Desmond (retired) 15 Fraydene, Prinsted, Emsworth PO10 8HU Tel: 01243 371216 — MA, MB BCh BAO Dub. 1944; FRCA Eng 1954; DA Eng. 1949. Prev: Cons. Anaesth. Centr. Middlx. Hosp.

LEVISON, Andrew Victor 27 Weston Road, London W4 5NL Tel: 020 8742 2356 Email: andrewflyboy1@aol.com — MB BS 1986 Lond.; FRCA 1992. Locum Cons. Anaesth., Wrexham Pk. Hosp. Slough, Berks. Socs: Assn. Anaesth. Prev: Sen. Regist. St. Thos. Hosp. Lond.; Regist. (Anaesth.) Char. Cross Hosp., Roy. Brompton Chest & Heart Hosp. & Gt. Ormond St. Hosp. Lond.

LEVISON, Professor David Annan Department of Molecular & Cellular Pathology, Ninewells Hospital & Medical School, Dundee DD1 9SY Tel: 01382 632668; 8 Glamis Drive, Dundee DD2 1QL Tel: 01382 668150 — MB ChB 1968 St. And.; MD Lond. 1988; FRCPath 1987, M 1975. Dean Fac. Med. Dent. & Nurs. Univ. Dundee; Hon. Cons. Path. Ninewells Hosp. Dundee; Prof. Path. Univ. Dundee. Socs: (Treas.) Path. Soc. GB & Irel.; Brit. Soc. Gastroenterol.; Assn. Clin. Pathols. Prev: Prof. Clin. Histopath. UMDS Guy's & St. Thos. Hosps. Lond.; Hon. Cons. & Sen. Lect. St. Bart. Hosp. Lond.

LEVISON, John Leon 8 Glamis Drive, Dundee DD2 1QL — MB ChB 1992 Sheff.

LEVISON, Scott Edward Huntly 8 Glamis Dr, Dundee DD2 1QL — MB ChB 1997 Manch.

LEVISON, Wendy Barbara Leavesden Road Surgery, 141A Leavesden Road, Watford WD2 5EP Tel: 01923 225128; 6 Arretine Close, St Albans AL3 4JL Tel: 01727 843142 — MB BS 1981 Lond.; MFFP 1995; MRCGP 1985.

LEVITT, Anne Marie Holdenhurst Road Surgery, 199 Holdenhurst Road, Bournemouth BH8 8DF Tel: 01202 558337 — MB BS 1979 Lond.; BSc Lond. 1976; MRCGP 1983; DRCOG 1984. (Univ. Coll. Hosp.) GP Partner Bournemouth; Assoc. Specialist (Child & Adolesc. Psychiat.) E. Dorset HA. Prev: Regist. (Child & Adolesc. Psychiat.) E. Dorset HA.; Clin. Asst. (Haemat.) Poole Gen. Hosp.

LEVITT, Charles Samuel Alexander Wheatley (retired) Tigh-Na-Leigh, 59 Springfield Avenue, Aberdeen AB15 8JJ Tel: 01224 321511 — MB ChB 1961 Aberd. Prev: Ho. Phys. City Hosp. Aberd.

LEVITT, Charlotte 4A Canford Road, London SW11 6NZ — MB BS 1996 Lond. SHO (Med.) Maidstone. Prev: SHO (A & E) Lewisham.

LEVITT, Gillian Ann Hospital for Children, Great Ormond St., London WC1N 3BH Tel: 020 7405 9200 Fax: 020 7813 8588; Hebberdens, Lower Bordean, Petersfield GU32 1ES Tel: 01730 269172 — MB BS 1972 Lond.; BSc (Hons.) Lond. 1969; MRCP (UK) 1979; MRCS Eng. LRCP Lond. 1972; DCH Eng. 1976. (St. Bart.) Cons. (Haemat. & Oncol.) Hosp. Sick Childr. Lond.; Hon. Cons., Middlx. Hosp., Lond. Socs: Brit. Paediat. Assn.; Chairperson - late effects grp.; Wilsons' Tumour Grp. Prev: Hon. Sen. Regist. Hosp. for Sick Childr. Lond.; Sen. Regist. St. Mary's Hosp. Portsmouth; Research Regist. (Paediat.) Qu. Charlotte's Hosp. Lond.

LEVITT, Martin John 23 Western Road, Chandler's Ford, Eastleigh SO53 5DG Tel: 01703 265043 — MB ChB 1983 Manch.; FCAnaesth 1989. Cons. Anaesth. City Hosp. Nottm.; Clin. Dir. (IC) City Hosp. Nottm. Prev: Sen. Regist. (Anaesth.) Freeman Hosp. Newc.; Fell. Intens. Care Academiscm Ziekenhuis Groningen, Netherlands; Regist. (Anaesth.) Qu. Med. Centre Nottm. & Derby Roy. Infirm.

LEVITT, Nicola Clare 1 Piper Street, Headington, Oxford OX3 7AR — BM BCh 1993 Oxf.

LEVITT, Richard Julian Longfleet Road Surgery, 4 Longfleet Road, Poole BH15 2HT Tel: 01202 676111; The White House, Canford Cliffs Road, Canford Cliffs, Poole — MB ChB 1978 Bristol; MRCGP 1983; DCH RCP Lond. 1982; DRCOG 1982; DA Eng. 1981. Prev: SHO (Anaesth.) Roy. Devon & Exeter Hosp.; GP Trainee Plymouth Vocational Train. Scheme.

LEVSTEIN, Carol Penicuik Health Centre, 37 Imrie Place, Penicuik EH26 8LF Tel: 01968 672612 Fax: 01968 671543 — MB ChB 1981 Ed.; MRCGP 1985; DCCH RCPS Ed. 1986.

LEVY, Andrew Department of Medicine, Bristol Royal Infirmary, Marlborough St., Bristol BS2 8HW Tel: 0117 928 3326 Fax: 0117 928 3315 Email: a.levy@bris.ac.uk; 8 Bell Barn Road, Stoke Bishop, Bristol BS9 2DA Tel: 0117 968 7648 Fax: 0117 968 7648 — BM BS 1981 Nottm.; PhD Lond. 1990; BMedSci (Hons.) Nottm. 1979, BM BS 1981; MRCP (UK) 1984; FRCP (UK) 1997. Cons. Reader (Med.) Bristol Roy. Infirm. Socs: Fell. Soc. Neurosci. (USA); Endocrine Soc. USA; Assn. Phys. Prev: Lect. (Med. Endocrinol.) Char. Cross & W.m. Med. Sch. Lond.; Fell. Lab of Cell Biol. Nat. Inst. Ment. Health Bethesda, USA; Hon. Regist. (Med.) W.m. Hosp. Lond.

LEVY, Anita Jane 18 St Peters Road, Canvey Island SS8 9NQ Tel: 01268 684618; 264 Clarendon Parkes, Leicester LE2 3AG Tel: 0116 244 8945, 0116 244 8975 — MB ChB 1994 Leic.; MRCGP 2000; DRCOG 1999; DFFP 1999. (Leic.) PMS Princip. in GP, Lakeside Surg., Cottingham Rd., Corby; Med. Off. in Family Plann., St. Peters Health Centre, Leicester. Prev: SHO (O & G) Leicester Gen. Hosp.; SHO (Paediat.) Leicester Roy. Informary; SHO (Gen. Med.) Leicester Gen. Hosp.

LEVY, Anthony Henry 78 Adlington Road, Wilmslow SK9 2BS Tel: 01625 526021 — MB ChB 1956 Manch. Med. Advisor Nuffield Hosps. Socs: Fell. Manch. Med. Soc. Prev: Dir. BUPA Health Serv. Ltd. Lond.

LEVY, Anthony Lionel The Surgery, 62 Cranwich Road, London N16 5JF Tel: 020 8802 2002 Fax: 020 8880 2112 — MB ChB 1985 Liverp.

LEVY, Mr Anthony Michael 151 Kenilworth Road, Ainsdale, Southport PR8 2QY — MB ChB 1977 Liverp.; FRCS Ed. 1983. Med. Pract. (Ophth.) S.port.

LEVY, Basil Holly House, Moor Lane, Cleadon, Sunderland SR6 — MD 1960 Malaya; MB BS Durh. 1936. Cons. Venereol. Sunderland & S. Shields Hosp. Gps. Prev: Col. Late RAMC Adviser in Venereol. War Office.

LEVY, Bertram Bridgeton Health Centre, 201 Abercromby St., Glasgow G40 2DA Tel: 0141 554 1866 — LRCP LRCS 1940 Ed.; LRCP LRCS Ed. LRFPS Glas. 1940; MRCGP 1954. (Glas.) Prev: Sen. Ho. Surg. Roy. Albert Edwd. Infirm. Wigan; Capt. RAMC; Ho. Phys. Newc. Gen. Hosp.

LEVY, Christopher Augustus 2 The Chase, London SW16 3AD — MB BS 1998 Lond.; MB BS Lond 1998.

LEVY, David Maxwell 2 Longlands Drive, West Bridgford, Nottingham NG2 6SR Email: david.levy@mail.qmcuh-tr.trent.nhs.uk — MB ChB 1986 Ed.; FRCA 1992; FFA RCSI 1992. Cons. Anaesth. Univ. Hosp. Qu. Med. Centre Nottm.

LEVY, David Michael Flat 2, 21 Cavendish Road, London NW6 7XT Tel: 020 8459 7090 — MB BS 1979 Lond.; MD Lond. 1993; MRCP (UK) 1982. Cons. Phys. (Diabetes, Endocrinol. & Gen. Med.) Whipps Cross Hosp. Lond.

LEVY, David Paul Weston Park Hospital, Whitham Road, Sheffield S10 2SJ Tel: 0114 226 5000 Fax: 0114 226 5555 — MB BS 1984 Lond.; FRCP 2001; BSc Lond. 1981; MRCP (UK) 1988; FRCR 1994. Cons. Oncol. W.on Pk. Hosp. Sheff. Prev: Cons. Oncol. N.ants. Centre of Oncol.; Sen. Regist. Cookridge Hosp. Leeds; Regist. (Clin. Oncol.) Ch.ill Hosp. Oxf.

LEVY, David Philip 1 Rochford Close, Whitefield, Manchester M45 7QR Tel: 0161 766 4967 Email: david@levyfamily100.freeserve.co.uk — MB ChB 1992 Manch.; MRCP 1996. (Manch) SHO (Paediat.) Hosp. Salford. Specialist Regist. Paediat. Booth hall Childr.s hosp. Manch. Prev: Specialist Regist. Paediat.RMCH.Manch; Specialist Regist. Paediat. Qu.s Pk. Hosp. Blackburn; Specialist Regist. Paediat.Salford.Community.

LEVY, David Wilfried (retired) 3 Brownsville Road, Heaton Moor, Stockport SK4 4PE Tel: 0161 432 2042 — MB ChB 1950 Cape Town; FRCP Lond. 1984, M 1955. Prev: Sen. Lect. (Geriat.) Manch. Univ.

LEVY, Eric 241 Queens Drive, Liverpool L15 6YE — MB ChB 1946 Manch.

LEVY, Fred (retired) 12 Eldred Road, Liverpool L16 8PB Tel: 0151 722 1470 — MB BS Durh. 1947.

LEVY, Harold Sydney 6 Lawton Road, Rainhill, Prescot L35 0PP Tel: 0151 426 2411 — MB ChB Liverp. 1946. (Liverp.)

LEVY, Isidore Aaron 19 Mar Drive, Mosshead, Bearsden, Glasgow G61 3LY — MB ChB 1952 Glas.; DA Eng. 1955.

LEVY, Mr Ivor Saul 75 Harley Street, London W1N 1DE Tel: 020 7486 1138 Fax: 071 224 6214 — BM BCh 1965 Oxf.; FRCS Eng. 1973. (Lond. Hosp.) Vis. Prof. Cleveland Clinic 1984; Cons. Ophth. Surg. Lond. Hosp.; Cons. Surg. Moorfields Eye Hosp. Lond.; Cons. Ophth. Hosps. for Sick Childr. Lond. Prev: Ho. Phys. Med. Unit & Ho. Surg. Ophth. Dept. Lond. Hosp.; Resid. Med. Off. Moorfields Eye Hosp. Lond.

LEVY, Mr Jack (retired) 5 Buchanan Drive, Newton Mearns, Glasgow G77 6HT Tel: 0141 639 3966 — MB ChB 1946 Glas.; FRCS Ed. 1956; DOMS Eng. 1949. Cons. Ophth. Glas. Eye Infirm. Prev: SHMO Eye Dept. Edin. Roy. Infirm.

LEVY, Jeremy Bernard Renal Unit, Charing Cross and Hammersmith Hospitals, Fulham Palace Road, London W6 Tel: 020 8846 1680 Email: jlevy@hhnt.org — MB BChir 1988 Camb.; MA Camb. 1989; MRCP (UK) 1991; PhD 1999. Cons Hammersmith hosp Lond Renal Unit. Socs: Renal Assn.; Europ. Renal Assn. Prev: Lect Hammersmith Hosp Lond; Regst Ch.ill john Radcliffe hosp Oxf.

LEVY, Jonathan Gordon House, Station Road, Mill Hill, London NW7 2HZ Tel: 020 8906 2767 Fax: 020 8906 0261 Email: jlevy@advisa.co.uk — MB BS 1975 Lond.; MRCS Eng. LRCP Lond. 1975. Med. Dir. Advisa Medica Lond.; GP Clin. Asst. Mill Hill Lond. Socs: Fell. Roy. Soc. Med.; N. Brit. Pain Assn. Prev: Med. Adviser Kabivitrum Ltd. Uxbridge Middlx.; Dir. Med. Servs. Napp Laborats. Ltd. Camb.; Hon. Clin. Asst. (Obst.) & SHO (A & E) Roy. Free Hosp. Lond.

LEVY, Jonathan Cummings The Radcliffe Infirmary NHS Trust, Woodstock Road, Oxford OX2 6HE Tel: 01865 224767 Fax: 01865 723884 Email: jonathon.ley@drl.ox.ac.uk; 16 Portland Road, Oxford OX2 7EY Tel: 01865 515576 — MB BS 1981 Lond.; BSc (Hons.) Lond. 1978, MB BS (Hons.) 1981, MD 1991; BA Oxf. 1971; FRCP

1998. (St. Bart.) Cons. (Diabetes) Radcliffe Infirm. NHS Trust Oxf. Socs: Brit. Diabetic Assn. Med. & Scientif. Sect.; Eur. Assn. Study Diabetes. Prev: Sen. Regist. (Med.) Radcliffe Infirm. Oxf.

LEVY, Lesley Joan 3 Hirds Yard, Skipton BD23 2AF Tel: 01756 701550 — MD 1988 Leeds; BSc Leeds 1981, MD 1988, MB ChB 1983; MRCP (UK) 1989. Regist. (Gen. Med.) St. Jas. Univ. Hosp.; Staff Doctor Gastroenterol. & Haemat. Airedale Gen. Hosp. Prev: Research Asst. (Med.) St. Jas. Univ. Hosp. Leeds; Ho. Phys. Profess. Med. Unit St. Jas. Univ. Hosp. Leeds.

LEVY, Lesley Patricia Fulshaw Gate, Alderley Road, Wilmslow SK9 1QA — MB ChB 1976 Birm.

LEVY, Mark Lionel 233 Speke Road, Woolton, Liverpool L25 0LA Tel: 0151 486 1736 Fax: 0151 486 1736 — MRCS Eng. LRCP Lond. 1944. (Liverp.) Prev: Asst. Med. Off. Walton Hosp. Liverp.; Div.al Med. Off. DHSS.

LEVY, Mark Lionel Kenton Bridge Medical Centre, 115-175 Kenton Road, Kenton, Harrow HA3 0XY Tel: 020 8907 6989 — MB ChB 1974 Pretoria; FRCGP 1992, M 1981. (Pretoria) Hon. Research Fell. Nat. Heart & Lung Inst.; Edr. Asthma in Pract. (Jl. GP's in Asthma Gp.); Med. Advis. Nat. Asthma & Respirat. Train. Centre Warwick. Socs: Brit. Thorac. Soc.; Amer. Thoracic Soc.; Eur. Respirat. Soc. Prev: Chairm. GPs in Astham Gp.

LEVY, Max Latchford Medical Centre, 5 Thelwall Lane, Latchford, Warrington WA4 1LJ Tel: 01925 637508 Fax: 01925 654384; 29 Farnham Close, Appleton, Warrington WA4 3BG — MB ChB 1985 Liverp.; DRCOG 1990. Bd. Mem. Warrington N. W. & Centr. PCG.

LEVY, Melanie Leona 237 Woolton Road, Childwall, Liverpool L16 8NA — MB BS 1993 Lond.

LEVY, Miles Jonathan 34A Kylemore Road, London NW6 2PT — MB BS 1994 Lond.

LEVY, Miriam 241 Queens Drive, Liverpool L15 6YE — MCRS Eng. LRCP 1948 Lond.; MMRCS Eng. LRCP Lond. 1948. (Liverp.) Socs: BMA. Prev: Res. Asst. Med. Off. Walton Hosp. Liverp.

LEVY, Nicholas Andrew Flat 1, 19 Crescent E., Barnet EN4 0EY — MB BS 1993 Lond.

LEVY, Ralph Bennet Ethelbert Gardens Surgery, 63-65 Ethelbert Gardens, Ilford IG2 6UW Tel: 020 8550 3740 Fax: 020 8550 4300 — MB ChB 1958 Ed.; DObst RCOG 1960. (Ed.) Prev: SHO Bearsted Matern. Hosp.; Ho. Off. (Surg. & Gyn.) Hertford Co. Hosp.; Ho. Phys. Connaught Hosp. Lond.

LEVY, Professor Raymond Flat 52, Westminster Palace Gardens, Artillery Row, London SW1P 1RR Tel: 020 7222 1776 — PhD Ed. 1962, MB ChB 1957; FRCP Ed. 1973, M 1961; FRCPsych 1973; DPM Lond. 1964. Emerit. Prof. Psychiat. of Old Age Inst. Psychiat.; Prof. Psychiat. of Old Age Inst. Psychiat. Socs: Fell.Roy. Soc. of Med.; Fell. Roy. Soc. Med.; BMA. Prev: Cons. Psychiat. Roy. Bethlem & Maudsley Hosps.; Regist. Maudsley Hosp. Lond.; Sen. Regist. Maudsley Hosp. Lond.

LEVY, Richard David Wythenshawe Hospital, Manchester M23 9LT — MD 1987 Lond.; MB BS 1978; FRCP 1998; FACC; FESC. Cons. Cardiol. Regional Cardiothoracic Centre Wythenshawe Hosp. Manch. Socs: Brit. Cardiac Soc.; Brit. Cardiac Interven. Soc.; Fell. Amer. Coll. Cardiol. Prev: Sen. Regist. (Cardiol.) Regional Cardiothoracic Centre Wythenshawe Hosp. Manch.; Aylwen Bursary & Cattlin Schol.sh. St. Bart. Hosp. 1987; Research Fell. & Hon. Regist. Nat. Heart Hosp. Lond.

LEVY, Robert Daniel Drymen Road Surgery, 160 Drymen Road, Bearsden, Glasgow G61 3RD Tel: 0141 942 6644 — MB ChB 1981 Glas.; MRCGP 1987; DA (UK) 1986; DRCOG 1984.

LEVY, Robert Glenn 27 Ringley Drive, Whitefield, Manchester M45 7LX — MB ChB 1987 Manch.

LEVY, Ronald (retired) c/o Clydra, 1 Sandhill Mount, Leeds LS17 8EG — MB ChB Leeds 1942; DMRD Eng. 1948. Prev: Cons. & Sen. Regist. (Radiol.) Roy. Infirm. Sunderland.

LEVY, Sarah Jane St Thomas's Hospital, Lambeth Place Road, London SE1 7EH Tel: 020 7928 9292; 89 Deanfield Road, Henley-on-Thames RG9 1UU — MB BS 1996 Newc. (Newcastel on Tyne) SHO Cardiol. St Thomas's Hosp. Lond.

LEVY, Mr Simon Gabriel Central Middlesex Hospital, Acton Lane, London NW10 7NS — MB BS 1983 Lond.; MD Univ. Lond. 1995; FRCS Ed. 1990; MRCP (UK) 1987; FRCOphth 1991; DO RCS Eng. 1989. Cons. Ophth. N. W. Lond. Hosps. NHS Trust. Socs: UK Soc. Cataract & Refractive Surgs. Prev: Refractive Fell. Gimbel Eye Center; Cornea Fell. Moorfields Eye Hosp.; Sen. Regist. Bristol Eye Hosp.

LEVY, Stephen Franklin Beech House Group Practice, Beech House, Beech Avenue Hazel Grove, Stockport SK7 4QR Tel: 0161 483 6222 Fax: 0161 419 9244 — MB ChB 1975 Manch.; MB ChB Manchester 1975. Socs: LMC. Prev: SHO (A & E) Ancoats Hosp. Manch.; SHO (O & G) Univ. S. Manch.; SHO (Paediat.) Duchess of York Hosp. Manch.

LEVY, Sydney Basil, VRD Thankerton House, Woolton Hill Road, Woolton, Liverpool — MRCS Eng. LRCP Lond. 1933. (Liverp.) Surg. Cdr. RNVR. Prev: Ho. Surg. Ear, Nose & Throat & Specials Depts. & Res. Anaesth. Roy.; S.. Hosp. Liverp.

LEVY, Terry Marc 8 Ash Grove, Basing, Basingstoke RG24 7JT — MB ChB 1990 Bristol.

LEVY, Tessa Louise 1 Dale Road, Leigh-on-Sea SS9 2RQ — MB BS 1998 Lond.; MB BS Lond 1998.

LEVY, Werner (retired) 94 Marlborough Mansions, Cannon Hill, London NW6 1JT Tel: 020 7431 0215 — LRCP LRCS Ed. LRFPS Glas. 1943. Prev: Capt. RAMC & RNZAMC.

LEVYCKY, Helen Margaret Eastham Group Practice, Treetops P.H.C.C., Bridle Road, Bromborough, Wirral CH62 6EE Tel: 0151 327 1391 — MB ChB 1982 Liverp.; BDS Liverp 1974; MRCGP 1988; DRCOG 1986; FRCGP 1996. (Liverpool) Course Organiser Chester VTS; Clin. Asst. (Surg.) BrE. Clinic Clatterbridge Hosp. Socs: RCGP; Brit. Menopause Soc.

LEW-GOR, Simione Tomasi Warren 23 Mulready House, Millbank Est., Marsham Street, Pimlico, London SW1P 4JL Tel: 020 7828 2285 — MB ChB 1994 Sheff.

LEWANDOWSKA, Anna 9 Cotts Close, Westcott Crescent, London W7 1PS Tel: 020 8575 9180 Email: anialew@btinternet.com — MD 1985; MD (Warsaw) 1985; LRCP LRCS Ed. LRCPS Glas. 1996. (Med. Acad. Warsaw; University College London Medical School) Forens. Med. Examr., Metrop. Police; Clin. Asst., Centr. Middx. Hosp. Socs: BMA; Polish Med. Assn.; Assn. Police Surg.

LEWANSKI, Conrad Richard 269 Boston Road, London W7 2AT — MB BS 1990 Lond.; BSc (Hons.) Lond. 1987; MRCP (UK) 1993. (Middlx. Hosp. Med. Sch.)

LEWARS, Mark Dalziel Southend General Hospital, Prittlewell Chase, Westcliff on Sea SS0 0RY Tel: 01702 435555 Fax: 01702 341048; Priory Farm Cottages, 18-22 Sportsmans Lane, Nounsley, Chelmsford CM3 2NW Tel: 01245 381981 — MB BS 1976 Lond.; FRCS Eng. 1982; FRCR 1986; DMRD RCR 1984. (Char. Cross) Cons. Radiol. S.end HA; Clin. Dir. BrE. Screening S. Essex. Prev: Sen. Regist. (Radiodiag.) St. Bart., Hosp. Sick Childr. Gt. Ormond St., Hackney & Homerton Hosps. Lond.; Regist. (Radiodiag.) St. Bart. Hosp. Lond.; Regist. (Gen. Surg. & Urol.) Roy. E. Sussex Hosp. Hastings.

LEWENDON, Gill Soth and West Devon Health Authority, The Lescaze Offices, Dartington, Totnes TQ9 6JE Tel: 01803 861850 Fax: 01803 861853 Email: gill. lewendon@sw-devon-ha.swest.nhs.uk — MB BS 1976 Lond.; BA (Psychol.) Open 1990; MRCS Eng. LRCP Lond. 1976; DCH RCP Lond. 1986; MSc Univ.London 1996. (Char. Cross) SCMO Pub. Health. Socs: BMA.

LEWER ALLEN, Mr Cyril Martin Sherwood, Queens Road, Oswestry SY11 2JB Tel: 01691 655734 — MB BCh 1968 Witwatersrand; FRCS Ed. 1976.

LEWI, Mr Henry Jacob Emil Marchfield, Galleywood Road, Chelmsford CM2 8BT Tel: 01245 264547 — MB BCh 1974 Wales; BSc (Hons.) Wales 1971; FRCS Ed. 1979. (Welsh Nat. Sch. Med.) Cons. Urol. Surg. Broomfield & Chelmsford & Essex Hosps. Chelmsford. Socs: Fell. Europ. Assn. Urol.; Brit. Assn. Urol. Surg. Prev: Sen. Regist. (Urol.) Glas. Teach. Hosp.; Lect. (Surg.) Glas. Roy. Infirm.; Wellcome Fell. (Surg.) Clin. Surg. Roy. Infirm. Edin.

LEWIN, Cherry Anne 42/2F2 Dalkeith Road, Edinburgh EH16 5BS — MB ChB 1997 Ed.

LEWIN, Colette 13 East Street, Johnshaven, Montrose DD10 0ET — MB ChB 1977 Liverp.; MRCP (UK) 1981; MRCPsych 1985.

LEWIN, Ian Geoffrey North Devon District Hosp, Raleigh Park, Barnstaple EX31 4JB Tel: 01271322417 Email: ian.lewin@ndevon.swest.nhs.uk — BSc (Hons.) Lond. 1968, MD 1983, MB BS 1971; FRCP Lond. 1991; FRCP Ed. 1988; MRCP (UK) 1974. Cons. Phys. N. Devon Dist. Hosp. Barnstaple. Socs: Brit. Diabetic Assn. & Soc. Endocrinol. Prev: MRC Research Fell. Middlx. Hosp. Lond.; Sen. Regist. Bristol Roy. Infirm.

LEWIN, Jacqueline Susan Davenal House Surgery, 28 Birmingham Road, Bromsgrove B61 0DD Tel: 01527 872008; Esher, Worcester Rd, Wychbald WR9 0DF Tel: 01527 861023 — MB ChB 1977 Birm.; Certificate of Equivalent Training in G.P.; MFFP. (Birm.) GP Princip. BromsGr.; Clin. Med. Off. (Family Plann.) S. Birm. HA. Socs: BMA; W Midl. Menopause Soc. Prev: Asst. GP St. John's Surg. BromsGr.; Trust Anaesth. WalsGr. Trust Coventry; Asst. GP Solihull.

LEWIN, Jeremy Hart 21 Red Road, Borehamwood WD6 4SR — MB ChB 1992 Birm.

LEWIN, John Philip Over Wyre Medical Centre, Pilling Lane, Preesall, Poulton-le-Fylde FY6 0EX Tel: 01253 810722 Fax: 01253 812039; The Gables, Rosslyn Avenue, Preesall, Poulton-le-Fylde FY6 0HE Tel: 01253 812827 — MB ChB 1970 Manch. (Manch.) Prev: SHO (O & G) Sharoe Green Hosp. Preston; SHO (Cas.), Ho. Surg. & Ho. Phys. Vict. Hosp. Blackpool.

LEWIN, Jonathan Mark Pine, 60 Fairmile Lane, Cobham KT11 2DE — MB BS 1996 Lond.

LEWIN, Kathleen Hood's Place, The Street, Kingston, Canterbury CT4 6JQ Tel: 01227 830116 — MB ChB 1964 Manch.; FFA RCS Eng. 1968; DA Eng. 1966. (Manch.) Cons. Anaesth. Canterbury & Thanet Health Dist. Prev: Cons. Anaesth. Burnley Health Dist.; Cons. Anaesth. Univ. Hosp. W.. Indies & Lect. Fac. Med. Univ. W.. Indies, Kingston Jamaica; Sen. Regist. (Anaesth.) Hammersmith Hosp. & Tutor Roy. Postgrad. Med. Sch.

LEWIN, Richard Anthony (retired) 174 South Street, Bishop's Stortford CM23 3HZ Tel: 01279 654808 — MB BChir 1960 Camb.; MRCS Eng. LRCP Lond. 1961; DObst RCOG 1963. Clin. Asst. Paediat. P.ss Alexandra Hosp. NHS Trust. Prev: Resid. Paediat. Louisville, USA.

LEWIN, Silvia Celeste (retired) 7 Green Farm End, Kineton, Warwick CV35 0LD Tel: 01926 640451 — MB BS 1941 Lond.; MRCS Eng. LRCP Lond. 1941; MRCOG 1949. Prev: Obst. Mid-Glam. AHA.

LEWIN, Simon Arnold 3A Golders Green Road, London NW11 8DY — MB ChB 1991 Cape Town.

LEWINDON, Nicole Highfield, Acton Lane, Acton Bridge, Northwich CW8 3QE — MB BS 1985 Lond.

LEWINDON, Peter James Highfield, Acton Lane, Acton Bridge, Northwich CW8 3QE — MB BS 1982 Lond.; MRCP (UK) 1986. Regist. (Paediat.) Roy. Childr. Hosp. Melbourne, Australia.

LEWINGTON, Andrew James Peter Leicester General Hospital, Gwendolen Road, Leicester LE5 4PW — MB BS 1991 Lond.; BSc 1988 (Hons.) Lond.; BSc Lond. 1988; MRCP (UK) 1994. Lect. in Nephrol.

LEWINGTON, Valerie Jane 16 Bossington Close, Rownhams, Southampton SO16 8DW Tel: 02380 733203 — BM 1981 Soton.; MSc Soton. 1988; MRCP (UK) 1984. Sen. Regist. Nuclear Med. Soton. Gen. Hosp. Prev: SHO Rotat. (Med.) Soton. Dist. Hosps.; Regist. Rotat. (Med.) Sheff. Dist. Hosps.

LEWINGTON, Wendy Ellen (retired) 7 Bramcote Road, London SW15 6UG Tel: 020 8788 8010 — MB BS 1946 Lond.; FRCS Eng. 1950; FRCOG 1971, M 1955. Prev: Cons. Obstetr. & Gynaecol. S.Lond. Hosp.

LEWINS, Ian Geoffrey 28 Sewall Road, Lincoln LN2 5RY — BM BS 1998 Nottm.; BM BS Nottm 1998.

LEWINS, Peter Guy Gallions Reach Health Centre, Bentham Road, Thamesmead, London SE28 8BE Tel: 020 8311 1010 — MB BChir 1984 Camb.; MA Camb. 1985. (Camb. & Guy's)

LEWINSKA, Halina Zofia (retired) 4 Argyle Road, Southport PR9 9LH Tel: 01704 532232 — MB ChB 1949 Liverp.; MRCGP 1962. Prev: GP S.port.

LEWIS, Mr Adam Anthony Murless Private Mail Box,, Dept. of Surgery, The Royal Free hospital, London NW3 2QG Tel: 020 7431 7264 Fax: 020 7431 9485; High Lodge, 23 Loom Lane, Radlett WD7 8AA Tel: 01932 856895 — MB BS Lond. 1963; FRCS Eng. 1969; FRCS Ed. 1968; MRCS Eng. LRCP Lond. 1963. (St. Bart.) Cons. Surg. Roy. Free Hosp. Lond.; Surg. St. John & Eliz. Hosp. & King Edwd. VII Hosp. Lond.; Surg. to H.M The Qu. Prev: Sen. Regist. (Surg.) Roy. Free Hosp. Lond.; Post-Doctoral Fell. Stanford Univ., USA.

LEWIS, Adrian Mark Gordon 24 Hampton Park Road, Hereford HR1 1TQ — MRCS Eng. LRCP Lond. 1976.

LEWIS, Adrian Sidney 3 Heol Bryn Glas, Meadow Farm, Llantwit Fardre, Pontypridd CF38 2DJ Tel: 01443 206576 Fax: 01443 206 631 Email: asl@totalise.co.uk — MB ChB 1994 Bristol; Bpharm 1979 (Hons) Wales; DRCOG 1998; DFFP 1998; MRCGP 2001. (Bristol) GP Non-Princip. Prev: SHO (O & G) E. Glam. Hosp.; GP Regist., AshGr. Surg., Pontypridd; SHO (VTS) O & G, E. Glam. Hosp.

LEWIS, Alan Auckland Medical Group, 54 Cockton Hill Road, Bishop Auckland DL14 6BB Tel: 01388 602728; New Moors Farm, Evenwood Gate, Bishop Auckland DL14 9NN Tel: 01388 833542 Fax: 01388 833542 — MB BS 1956 Durh.; MRCGP 1964; Cert. Family Plann. JCC 1975. Indep.Appeals Serv.

LEWIS, Alan Fenton 10 The Paddocks, Weybridge KT13 9RJ Tel: 01932 223115 Fax: 01932 223115 — MSc (Statistics) Lond. 1970, PhD (Physiol.) 1961; BSc Wales 1951, MB BCh 1954. Sen. Med. Off. Dept. Health & Social Security. Socs: Fell. Roy. Statist. Soc.; Physiol. Soc. Prev: Sen. Lect. in Med. Statistics & Sen. Lect. in Physiol. Char. Cross; Hosp. Med. Sch. Lond.; Lect. in Physiol. Univ. Lond. at King's Coll.

LEWIS, Alan Harkness 5 Rock Park, Rock Ferry, Birkenhead CH42 1PJ Tel: 0151 645 3595 — MB ChB 1959 Liverp.; MB ChB Liverp. 1959.; MRCS Eng. LRCP Lond. 1959. Med. Asst. in Orthop. Clatterbridge Gen. Hosp. Bebington.

LEWIS, Alan Mervyn Whitwick Health Centre, North Street, Whitwick, Coalville LE67 4EB Tel: 01530 839629 — MB ChB 1982 Leic.; MRCGP 1986.

LEWIS, Alastair 15 McCrea's Brae, Whitehead, Carrickfergus BT38 9NZ — MB BCh BAO 1995 Belf.

LEWIS, Aled Gethin 29 Millbrook Close, Dinas Powys CF64 4DD — MB BS 1997 Lond.

LEWIS, Alexander John Mental Health Unit, Northwick Park HospitaL, Watford Road, Harrow HA1 3UJ Email: alex.lewis@kcl.ac.uk — MB BS 1986 Lond.; BSc (Hons.) Lond. 1983; MRCPsych 1995. Cons. Psychiat., N.wick Pk. Hosp.; Hon.Sen.Clin.Research.Fell.Guy's Kings. St Thomas. Sch. Med. Prev: Clin. Lect. King's Coll. Sch. Med. Lond.; Hon.Cons.Psych. Maudsley. Hosp; sen. Clin. Research. Fell. Guys, Kings. St Thomas. Sch. Med.

LEWIS, Alexandra Helen O'Neill L/G/F 256 Blackness Road, Dundee DD2 1RS — MB ChB 1994 Dundee.

LEWIS, Alison Kathryn 72 Lambton Road, London SW20 0LP — MB ChB 1989 Birm.; MRCP (UK) 1993.

LEWIS, Alison Margaret c/o Beatson Oncology Centre, Western Infirmary, Glasgow G11 6NT — MB ChB 1992 Dundee. SHO (A & E) Perth Roy. Infirm. Prev: SHO (Med.) King's Cross Hosp. Dundee; SHO (Surg.) Perth Roy. Infirm.

LEWIS, Alun David West End Surgery, Edward Road, Northolt UB5 6QN Tel: 020 8845 6363 Fax: 020 8841 8837; 29 Bradley Gardens, Ealing, London W13 8HE Tel: profess. 0181 845 6363 — MB 1981 Camb.; MA Camb. 1981, MB 1981, BChir 1980; DRCOG 1983. (St. Mary's) Co. Med. Adviser Quakers Ltd. S.all; Co. Med. Adviser Friskies Sothall; Co. Med. Adviser UKCAN. Prev: SHO (A & E) Roy. Berks. Hosp. Reading; SHO (Psychiat.) W.m. Hosp. Lond.; SHO (O & G) Hillingdon Hosp.

LEWIS, Amanda Mary 9 Winchester Avenue, Chatham ME5 9AR — MB ChB 1998 Manch.; MB ChB Manch 1998.

LEWIS, Andrew David 92 Newtown Road, Worcester WR5 1JL — MB ChB 1987 Leic.; BSc (Med. Sci.) Leic. 1984, MB ChB 1987; DFFP 1993.

LEWIS, Angela Gratton Surgery, Sutton Scotney, Winchester SO21 3LE — MB BS 1981 Lond.; DA Eng. 1983.

LEWIS, Angus Donald Balquhidder, Ashprington, Totnes TQ9 7EB — MB BS 1994 Lond.

LEWIS, Ann Eileen 25 Cranmore Park, Belfast BT9 6JF — MB BCh BAO 1977 Belf. Hon. SHO (A & E) Belf. City Hosp.; Locum Med. Off., Family Plann. Socs: MDU. Prev: SHO Belf. Monica Project.

LEWIS, Ann Margaret 3 Thweng Way, Hutton Lowcross, Guisborough TS14 8BW — MB BS 1961 Durh.; FRCP Lond. 1992; MRCP (UK) 1972; DCH Eng. 1967. Hon. Cons. Palliat. Care at Teesside Hosp. Socs: Roy. Coll. Phys.s Lond. Retd. Mem. Prev: Cons. Phys. Geriat. Med. S. Tees Acute Hosp. Trust.

LEWIS, Ann Marles Public Health Laboratory, Singleton Hospital, Sketty Lane, Sketty, Swansea SA2 8QA Tel: 01792 205666 Fax: 01792 202320 — MBBS 1980; MSc 1986 Lond.; MRCS Eng. LRCP Lond. 1980; FRCPath 1997, M 1986. (Char. Cross) Cons. Med. Microbiol. Swansea Pub. Health Laborat. Prev: Cons. Med.

Microbiol. Roy. Sussex Co. Hosp. Brighton; Sen. Regist. (Med. Microbiol.) St. Bart. & Whipps Cross Hosps. Lond.

LEWIS, Anne Louise Waunlluest, Llanfynydd, Carmarthen SA32 7DB — MB BCh 1979 Wales.

LEWIS, Anne Margaret Knightwick, Worcester WR6 5PH — MB BS 1973 Lond.; DCH Eng. 1975; DObst RCOG 1976. (King's Coll. Hosp.) p/t GP Kt.wick Surg. Worcester. Prev: SHO A & E Dept. Roy. Hants. Co. Hosp. Winchester; SHO (Paediat.) Sydenham Childr. Hosp.; SHO (O & G) Mayday Hosp. Croydon.

LEWIS, Anthea Sara — MB BS 1983 Lond.; DFFP 1993; DRCOG 1988; DCH RCP Lond. 1986. Non Princip. GP; Clin. Asst. Rheum., Broomfield Hosp., Chelmsford. Socs: NANP.

LEWIS, Anthony Arthur Gough Links Pinewood Nursing Home, Victoria Place, Budleigh Salterton EX9 6JP — BA Lond. 1980, BSc 1935, MD 1942, MB BS 1940; FRCP Lond. 1960, M 1941; MRCS Eng. LRCP Lond. 1940. (Middlx.) Emerit. Geriat. Trent RHA. Socs: Assn. Phys. Prev: Cons. Phys. Forest Hosp. Gp.; Regional Postgrad. Dean SE Metrop. Region Brit. Postgrad. Med. Federat.

LEWIS, Anthony Charles Wilson (retired) 7 Y Parc, Groesfaen, Pontyclun CF72 8NP Tel: 01222 890573 — MRCS Eng. LRCP Lond. 1957; MB Camb. 1958, BChir 1957; FRCOG 1978, M 1965, DObst 1962. Cons. (O & G) P.ss of Wales Hosp. Bridgend. Prev: Sen. Regist. (O & G) United Oxf. Hosps.

LEWIS, Anthony Rowland 25 Six Bells Estate, Heolgerrig, Merthyr Tydfil CF48 1TU — MB BCh 1998 Wales.

LEWIS, Antony Peter Imperial Surgery, 49 Imperial Road, Exmouth EX8 1DQ Tel: 01395 224555 Fax: 01395 279282; The Old Vicarage, 26 West Hill, Budleigh Salterton EX9 6BU Tel: 01395 444001 Fax: 01395 444001 Email: alewisc@cix.co.uk — MB BChir 1970 Camb.; BSc (Hons.) Open 1993; MA Camb. 1973; FRCGP 1989, M 1976; DObst RCOG 1973; DCH Eng. 1972. (St. Thos.) Regional Adviser (Gen. Pract.) Devon & Cornw.; Sen. Lect. (Gen. Pract.) Univ. Exeter. Socs: Assn. Child Psychol. & Psychiat. Prev: Trainee GP Wessex VTS; Ho. Surg. Kent & Canterbury Hosp.; Ho. Phys. Roy. Waterloo Hosp. Lond.

LEWIS, Armorel Joan Lichfield, College Crescent, Caerleon, Newport NP18 3NS Tel: 01633 341 — MRCS Eng. LRCP Lond. 1937. (Cardiff) Socs: BMA. Prev: Asst. MOH Mon. CC; Dep. Med. Supt. Co. Hosp. Panteg.

LEWIS, Barbara Susan Carisbrooke House Surgery, 1A Pope Road, Bromley BR2 9SS Tel: 020 8460 4611; Nash Cottage, Nash Lane, Keston BR2 6AP — MB BS 1976 Lond.; DRCOG 1978; Dip. Med. Jurisprudence 1997. (Kings Coll.) Princip. Gen. Pract.; Forens. Med. Examr. Metrop. Police.

LEWIS, Professor Barry London Diabetes and Lipid Centre, 14 Wimpole St., London W1G 9SX Tel: 020 7636 9901 Fax: 020 7636 9902 — MB ChB 1952 Cape Town; PhD Cape Town 1956, MD 1958; FRCP Lond. 1975, M 1964; MRCP Ed. 1960; FRCPath 1980, M 1968. Cons. Phys. & Emerit. Prof. Univ. Lond. Socs: (Ex-Chairm.) Internat. Task Force on Prevent. of Coronary Heart Dis.; Internat. Soc. & Federat. Cardiol. (Ex-Chairm. Counc. on Arteriosclerosis); Eur. Atherosclerosis Soc. Prev: Prof. Chem. Path. Metab. Disorders, Hon. Cons. Med. & Dir. Lipid Clinic St. Thos. Hosp. Lond.; Sen. Lect. (Chem. Path.) Roy. Postgrad. Med. Sch. & Hon. Cons. Phys. Hammersmith Hosp. Lond.

LEWIS, Barry Castleton Health Centre, 2 Elizabeth Street, Castleton, Rochdale OL11 3HY Tel: 01706 658905 Fax: 01706 343990 — MB ChB 1976 Manch.; MRCGP 1981; DRCOG 1978. Assoc. Dir. (GP Educat.) Dept. Post Grad. Med. M/C Univ. Manch.

LEWIS, Mr Barry Victor (retired) 1st Floor Office, Silverwood, Southview Road, Pinner HA5 3YA Tel: 020 8429 2487 Fax: 020 8429 4017 Email: trl456@aol.com or gynae@bvlewis-demon.co.uk — MB ChB 1959 Liverp.; MD Liverp. 1969; FRCS Ed. 1964; FRCOG 1977, M 1964. Prev: Sen. Cons. O & G Watford Gen. Hosp.

LEWIS, Barry Winston 17 Wimpole Street, London W1G 8GB Tel: 020 7486 0044 Fax: 020 7323 9126; Bungeons Farm, Barking, Ipswich IP6 8HN Tel: 01449 721992 — MB BS 1964 Lond.; MRCP 1969 UK; FRCPCH 1997; DCH Eng. 1967. (Univ. Coll. Hosp.) Cons. Paediat. Portland Hosp. Lond. Socs: Brit. Paediat. Assn.; Fell. Roy. Soc. Med. Prev: Cons. Paediat. Whipps Cross Hosp. Lond.; Sen. Med. Regist. Qu. Eliz. Hosp. Lond.; Sen. Regist. Childr. Dept. Lond. Hosp.

LEWIS, Beatrice Broxburn Health Centre, Holmes Road, Broxburn EH52 5JZ Tel: 01506 852008; 5 Well Park, Ecclesmachan, Broxburn EH52 6NU — MB ChB Ed. 1955; DA Eng. 1973.

LEWIS, Beatrice 279B Eastern Road, Brighton BN2 5TA Tel: 01273 688674 — MRCS Eng. LRCP Lond. 1933; MD Lond. 1936, MB BS 1933. (Univ. Coll. Hosp., Paris, Strasbourg, Vienna) Emerit. Cons. Dermat. Guy's Hosp. Lond. Socs: Fell. Roy. Soc. Med. (Mem. Sect. Dermat.); BMA. Prev: Cons. Dermat. New Cross Gen. Hosp. Lond.; St. Leonard's Hosp. Lond. & Roy. Sussex Co. Hosp. Brighton.

LEWIS, Bernard Patrick Lings and Partners, Shotfield Health Centre, Shotfield, Wallington SM6 0HY Tel: 020 8647 0031 Fax: 020 8773 1801; 32 Copse Hill, Purley CR8 4LH Tel: 020 8668 3321 — MB BS 1986 Lond.; DRCOG 1991.

LEWIS, Bernard Russell, TD (retired) 69 Llwyn-y-Bryn, Bonllwyn, Ammanford SA18 2ES — MB BCh 1957 Wales; BSc, MB BCh Wales 1957; DObst RCOG 1967. Lt. Col. RAMC (V). Prev: Civil. Med. Pract. BAOR.

LEWIS, Beth Marles Sunnybank Cottage, Brynteg, Llantrisant, Pontyclun CF7 8LR — MB BS 1984 Lond. SHO (O & G) Morriston & Singleton Hosps. Swansea. Prev: Ho. Surg. Singleton Hosp. Swansea; SHO (Psychiat.) Cefn Coed Hosp. Swansea; SHO (Cas.) Morriston Hosp. Swansea.

LEWIS, Bethan 50 Carlisle Avenue, St Albans AL3 5LX — MB BS 1987 Lond.

LEWIS, Brian Sydney and Partners, St Mary's Medical Centre, Rock St, Oldham OL1 3UL Tel: 0161 620 6667 Fax: 0161 626 2499; 10 Lancaster Terrace, Norden, Rochdale OL11 5TU — MB ChB 1986 Manch.; MRCGP 1990; DRCOG 1989; DCH RCP Lond. 1988.

LEWIS, Candida Claire 39 Upper Lewes Road, Brighton BN2 3FH — MB BS 1994 Lond.

LEWIS, Caroline Jane Berwick Court, Berwick, Polegate BN26 5QS — MB ChB 1986 Manch.; MRCGP 1993; DCH RCP Lond. 1989. Prev: SHO (Paediat.) St. Mary's Hosp. Manch.

LEWIS, Catherine Rivergreen Medical Centre, 106 Southchurch Drive, Clifton, Nottingham NG11 8AD.

LEWIS, Catherine Anne St Margarets Surgery, 8 St. Margarets Road, Solihull B92 7JS Tel: 0121 706 0307 Fax: 0121 765 0161; 25A Hampton Lane, Solihull B91 2QE — MB ChB 1987 Birm.; DRCOG 1990. (Birmingham)

LEWIS, Catherine Jayne Flat 12, The Gables, 85 Manor Dr, Wembley HA9 8DJ — MB BS 1997 Lond.

LEWIS, Celia Kay Stanwlx Medical Practice, 77-81 Scotland Road, Carlisle CA3 9HL Tel: 01228 525768 Fax: 01228 592965; 16 Ryehill Park, Smithfield, Carlisle CA6 6BH Email: clewis7642@aol.com — MB ChB 1975 Birm.; MRCGP 1979; DRCOG 1978. (Birm.)

LEWIS, Charles Edward Steep Farm Lodge, Steep, Petersfield GU32 2DB — MB ChB 1989 Birm.

LEWIS, Charles Howat Sunnyside Doctors Surgery, 150 Fratton Road, Portsmouth PO1 5DH Tel: 023 9282 4725 Fax: 023 9286 1014 — MB BS 1977 Lond.; MRCGP 1982; DCH RCP Lond. 1981; DRCOG 1980. (St. Bart.) Co-Founder Portsmouth Community Micro-Suction Serv.; Co-Founder Portsmouth Primary Care Research Gp.; Chairm. of the Exec. Comm., Portsmouth City PCT Med. Examr. for Benejitn Agency. Prev: Trainee GP Portsmouth VTS; Ho. Phys. St. Mary's Hosp. Portsmouth; Ho. Surg. N.ampton Gen. Hosp.

LEWIS, Charles John Roderick (retired) North Ridge Medical Practice, North Ridge, Rye Road, Hawkhurst, Cranbrook TN18 4EX Tel: 01580 753935 Fax: 01580 754452 — MB BS 1964 Lond.; MRCS Eng. LRCP Lond. 1964. GP. Prev: Ho. Surg. Roy. Sussex Co. Hosp. Brighton.

LEWIS, Charlotte Mary Parker 7 Hull Bridge Road, Beverley HU17 9HY — MB BCh 1991 Wales.

LEWIS, Christine Avenue Medical Centre, Wentworth Avenue, Slough SL2 2DG Tel: 01753 524549 Fax: 01753 552537; Greenlanes, 7 Green Lane, Burnham, Slough SL1 8DR Tel: 01628 660167 — MB BCh 1981 Wales; MB BCh Wales 1978 DRCOG 1981; MRCGP 1982.

LEWIS, Christine Mary (retired) Old Pound House, Weston-Gordano, Portishead, Bristol BS20 8PZ — MB ChB Bristol 1965.

LEWIS, Christopher Westcotes House, Westcotes Drive, Leicester LE3 0QE Tel: 0116 225 2900 Fax: 0116 225 2899; 10 Asquith Boulevard, Knighton, Leicester LE2 6FA Tel: 0116 288 1174 — MB ChB 1974 Dundee; BSc (Med. Sci.) St. And. 1971; MRCPsych 1979.

(St Andrews and Dundee) Cons. Child & Adolesc. Psychiat. Leics. Ment. Health Serv. NHS Trust; Clin. Dir. Leics. Child & Family Psychiatric Serv. Prev: Sen. Regist. Childr. & Young Persons Psychiat. Serv. Tayside Health Bd.; Regist. Psychiat. Serv. Dundee Health Dist.

LEWIS, Christopher John 19 Pembroke Dr, Wellington, Telford TF1 3PT — MB ChB 1997 Manch.

LEWIS, Christopher Keith 7 The Murreys, Ashtead KT21 2LU — MB BCh 1996 Wales.

LEWIS, Christopher Paul Malcolm 166 Kings Road, Westcliff on Sea SS0 8PP Tel: 01702 712863 — MA Camb. 1985; MB Camb. 1983, BChir 1982; MRCGP 1986; DRCOG 1984; DCH RCP Lond. 1985. Non-Exec. Dir. S.end DHA; Chairm. S.end GP Advis. Comm.

LEWIS, Christopher Rimington 33 Dover Road, Southport PR8 4TB — MB ChB 1986 Manch.

LEWIS, Mr Christopher Terence Derriford Hospital, South West Cardiothoracic Centre, Plymouth PL6 8DH Tel: 01752 763833 Fax: 01752 763830; Lifton Park, Lifton PL16 0DE Tel: 01566 784659 — MB BS Lond. 1968; FRCS Eng. 1973; MRCS Eng. LRCP Lond. 1968; Accredit. Cardiothoracic Surg. 1978. (Westm.) Cons. Cardiothoracic Surg. S. W. Cardiothoracic Centre Derriford Hosp. Devon; Civil Cons. Cardiothoracic Surg. RN; Med. Director, Plymouth Hosps. NHS Trust. Socs: Soc. Cardio Thoracic Surgs. & Brit. Cardiac Soc.; Chelsea Clin. Soc.; Cardiac Surgic. Research Club. Prev: Sen. Regist. (Cardiothoracic Surg.) Lond. Hosp., Brompton Hosp. & Lond. Chest Hosp.; Sen. Cardiothoracic Surg. St Bart Hosp.

LEWIS, Claire Gillian Eunice 14A Avondale Gardens, Grangetown, Cardiff CF11 7DY — MB BCh 1991 Wales.

LEWIS, Clive Jonathan 40 Queens Road, Waterlooville PO7 7SB — MB BChir 1994 Camb.

LEWIS, Colin Andrew The Cromwell Hospital, Cromwell Road, London SW5 0TU Tel: 020 7460 2000 Fax: 020 7460 5555; Honeygrove, 4 Compton Heights, Guildford GU3 1DA Tel: 01483 569637 Fax: 01483 569637 Email: drcalewis@aol.com — MB BChir 1975 Camb.; Diploma Med. Acupunc. 1995; MA Camb. 1975; MRCP (UK) 1976; AFOM RCP Lond. 1989; MRCGP 1979. (Camb. & St. Bart.) Occupat. Health Phys. Roy. Coll. Art Lond. Socs: Brit. Diabetic Assn. (Mem. Med. & Scientif. Sect.); Soc. Occupat. Med.; Brit. Med. Acupunc. Soc. (Counc. Mem. and Lect.). Prev: Regist. (Med.) St. Thos. Hosp. Lond.; Ho. Phys. St. Bart. Hosp. Lond.

LEWIS, Colin David Gwynne (retired) 8 Pen Y Morfa, Penclawdd, Swansea SA4 3RF — MB ChB 1958 St. And. Prev: Ho. Surg. Bridge of Earn Hosp.

LEWIS, Corinne Julia 26 Clifton Park Road, Stockport SK2 6LA — MB ChB 1994 Leeds; BSc (Hons) Leeds 1991. SHO (Psychiat.) Hull & Holderness NHS Trust.

LEWIS, Cynthia Sheelagh 1 Church View, Bassaleg, Newport NP10 8ND Email: cjjal.basil@virgin.net — MB BCh BAO 1972 Belf.; MFFP 1993. Staff Grade (Community Child Health) Gwent.

LEWIS, Cyril Ames Shoo Devil Farm House, Ilkestshall St Margaret, Bungay NR35 1QU Tel: 0198 681303 — MRCS Eng. LRCP Lond. 1933; BA Camb. 1930. (Camb. & King's Coll. Hosp.) Prev: Med. Off. Sudan Med. Serv.; Med. Off. King's Coll. & Acton Hosps.

LEWIS, Darren Michael 26 Terry Street, Nelson BB9 8JD — BM BS 1998 Nottm.; BM BS Nottm 1998.

LEWIS, David (retired) — MB BS 1965 Lond.; MRCS Eng. LRCP Lond. 1965; Dip. Bact. Manch. Univ. 1980; MRCPath 1983; FRCPath 1995. Prev: Ho. Off. (O & G) Preston Roy. Infirm.

LEWIS, David Adam Alexander 15 Fraser Close, London E6 5TB — MB BS 1991 Lond.

LEWIS, David Christopher Westbury Medical Centre, Westbury, Shrewsbury SY5 9QX; Breidden, Upper House Farm Drive, Alberbury, Shrewsbury SY5 9AG — MRCS Eng. LRCP Lond. 1977; DA Eng. 1981. (Liverp.) GP W.bury. Prev: SHO (Anaesth.) Staffs. Gen. Infirm. & N. Staffs. Hosp. Centre; SHO (Gen. Pract. Rotat.) Stafford Dist. Gen. Hosp. & St. Geo. Hosp.; Stafford.

LEWIS, Mr David Christopher South Warwickshire NHS Trust, Warwick Hospital, Lakin Road, Warwick CV34 5BW Tel: 01926 495321 Fax: 01926 403715; New Farm, Kineton, Warwick CV35 0EE — MB BCh 1984 Wales; MChir Wales 1993, MB BCh l984; FRCS (Urol) 1994; FRCS Ed. 1988. Cons. Urol. S. Warks. NHS Trust.

LEWIS, David Edward 118 Periton Lane, Minehead TA24 8DY — MB BS 1993 Lond. SHO (Paediat.) E. Glam. Hosp. Ch. Village.

LEWIS, David Geoffrey 3 Shirley Road, Stoneygate, Leicester LE2 3LL Tel: 0116 270 5889 — MB BChir 1964 Camb.; MA Camb. 1967, BA 1960, MD 1976, MB 1964, BChir 1963; MRCS Eng. LRCP Lond. 1963; FFA RCS Eng. 1967. (Lond. Hosp.) Cons. Anaesth. Cardiothoracic Centre Groby Rd. Hosp. Leicester. Socs: Anaesth. Research. Soc. Prev: Sen. Research Off. Dept. Anaesth. Univ. Newc.; SHO Anaesth. Roy. Liverp. Infirm.; Ho. Phys. & Ho. Surg. Lond. Hosp.

LEWIS, David Howard 84 Plasturton Avenue, Pontcanna, Cardiff CF11 9HJ Tel: 029 2034 5756 Email: dailewis8@aol.com — MB BS 1988 Lond.; MRCGP 1995. (St. Bart.)

LEWIS, David Keith 108 Blantyre Road, Liverpool L15 3HT Tel: 0151 733 2461 — MB ChB 1990 Liverp.; MRCGP 1994; DTM & H Liverp. 1994; DRCOG 1992; Dip. Clin. Hyp. (Sheff.) 1997. Assoc. Pract. NW RHA (Primary Care Initiative) Liverp.

LEWIS, David Leon (retired) 108 Streetly Lane, Four Oaks, Sutton Coldfield B74 4TB Tel: 0121 353 3017 — LMSSA 1952 Lond.; MFCM 1974; DPH Liverp. 1956; DIH St. And. 1965. Prev: Asst. Dir. Med. Servs. Mobil Saudi Arabia Inc.

LEWIS, Mr David Lincoln, MC The Old Forge, Longnor, Shrewsbury SY5 7QF — MRCS Eng. LRCP Lond. 1931; MA Camb. 1935, MChir 1934, BChir 1935; FRCS Eng. 1933. (Camb. & St. Geo.) Sen. Fell. Assn. Surgs. Prev: Cons. Surg. Roy. Salop Infirm.; Sen. Surg. Asst. Brit. Postgrad. Med. Sch.; Res. ENT Surg. St. Geo. Hosp.

LEWIS, David Maurice (retired) Allt Fadog, Capel Madog, Aberystwyth SY23 3JA — MB 1964 Camb; BA, Camb. 1964, BChir 1963; MRCP Lond. 1969; MRCS Eng. LRCP Lond. 1963; FRCP; FRCPCH. Wellcome Assoc. Roy. Soc. Med. Prev: Cons. Paediat. Bronglais Hosp. Aberystwyth.

LEWIS, Mr David Morris Tudor Surgery, 139 Bushey Mill Lane, Watford WD2 4PD Tel: 01923 223724 Fax: 01923 237327 — MB BS 1987 Monash; FRCS Ed. 1993; DFFP 1999. (Monash Univ.Au) GP. Socs: Fell. Roy. Soc. Med. (Mem. Sect. GP Counc.); Assoc. Mem. Roy. Coll. Gen. Practs. & GP Regist. Observer to Counc.; MRCGP Hosp. Recon. Comm. Prev: Career Regist. Oxf. RHA; Gp Reg.Windosr.VTS.

LEWIS, David Morrison 22 Barcheston Road, Cheadle SK8 1LL Tel: 0161 428 2963 Email: david.lewis@dial.pipex.com — MB ChB 1986 Leeds; MRCP (UK) 1991. Sen. Regist. (Renal & Gen. Med.) Univ. Hosp. of S. Manch. Prev: Research Fell. (Renal) Roy. Devon & Exeter Hosp.; Regist. (Renal Med.) St. Jas. Univ. Hosp. Leeds.

LEWIS, Mr David Richard 2 Queens Parade, Bristol BS1 5XJ — MB ChB 1991 Bristol; FRCS Eng. 1996. (Bristol) Specialist Regist. (Gen. Surg.) S. W. Deanery. Socs: Assn. Surg.; Vasc. Surg. Soc.; Surg. Research Soc.

LEWIS, David Roland (retired) 6 Gorse Ridge Drive, Baslow, Bakewell DE45 1SL Tel: 01246 583393 — MB BCh 1945 Wales; BSc Wales 1945; TDD 1949. Prev: Cons. Chest Phys. N. Derbysh. Area.

LEWIS, Mr David Ross Hinds (retired) Cedardale, 18 Eastfield, West Hill, Ottery St Mary EX11 1XN Tel: 01404 812251 — MB ChB 1958 Glas.; BSc Sheff. 1952; FRCS Ed. 1969; FRCP Glas. 1981 M 1964; FRCOphth 1988. Examr. Final FBOA. Prev: Cons. Ophth. Bromley Gp. Hosps. & Sub Regional Eye Unit Qu. Mary Hosp. Sidcup.

LEWIS, David Samuel 26 Copthall Drive, London NW7 2NB — MB BS 1972 Lond.; MRCP (U.K.) 1975; MRCPath. 1981; MRCS Eng. LRCP Lond. 1972; FRCP 1992 UK; FRCP 1998; FRCPath 1992. Cons. (Haemat.) OldCh. Hosp. Lond.

LEWIS, Deborah Jocelyn Ground Floor Flat, 105 Holland Road, London W14 8HS — MB BS 1977 Melbourne; FRACP 1987.

LEWIS, Deirdre Alexandra CDSC SouthWest Public Health Laboratory, Gloucestershire Royal Hospital, Great Western Road, Gloucester GL1 3NN Tel: 01452 413080 Fax: 01452 412946 Email: dlewis@phls.org.uk; 4 Parkfield Road, Pucklechurch, Bristol BS16 9PN — MB ChB 1974 Manch.; FRCPath 1993, M 1981; Dip. Bact. Manch. 1979; MPH Birm. 1997; MFPHM 2000. (Manchester) Cons epidemiologist CDSC S. W. Gloucester. Socs: Brit. Soc. Antimicrob. Chem. & Hosp. Infec. Soc. Prev: Cons. Communicable Dis. Control Devizes Wilts.; Cons. Microbiol. Bath HA; Sen. Regist. (Med. Microbiol.) Bristol Roy. Infirm. & S.mead Hosp. Bristol.

LEWIS, Della Katrina 31 Heol Pant Y Celyn, Cardiff CF14 7BX — MB BCh 1987 Wales.

LEWIS, Derek 2 Trevallen Avenue, Cimla, Neath SA11 3UR Tel: 01639 4645 — MB ChB 1960 Ed. (Ed.) Socs: BMA. Prev: GP Neath; Ho. Surg. & Ho. Phys. Stracathro Hosp. Brechin; Ho. Off. Obst. Birch Hill Hosp. Rochdale.

LEWIS, Dewi Morgan (retired) 36 Aubrey Avenue, Cardiff CF5 1AQ — MB BS Lond. 1951; MRCS Eng. LRCP Lond. 1949; FRCPsych 1987, M 1973; DA Eng. 1954, DPM 1961; DIH Soc. Apoth. Lond. 1957. Prev: Cons. Psychiat. St. Bernard's Hosp. S.all, Mt. Vernon & Harefield Hosps.

LEWIS, Dylan Forest Gate House, Ashley Heath, Ringwood BH24 2EU — MB ChB 1998 Manch.; MB ChB Manch 1998.

LEWIS, Edward Claude 105 Station Road, Redhill RH1 1DW Tel: 01737 766961 — MB BS 1950 Lond.; DObst RCOG 1952. (Guy's) Socs: Assur. Med. Soc. Prev: Chief Med. Off. Crusader Insur. Co.; Resid. Obst. Lewisham Hosp. Lond. & Pembury Hosp.; Ho. Phys. Lewisham Hosp. Lond.

LEWIS, Elaine Joy Child Development Centre, Addenbrooke's Hospital, Hills Road, Cambridge CB2 2QQ Tel: 01223 216662 Fax: 01223 242171 — MB ChB 1980 Manch.; FRCPCH 1997; MRCP (UK) l984. Cons. Paediat. (Community Child Health) Camb. Socs: FRCPCH; BPNA; Brit. Assn. Community Child Health. Prev: Sen. Regist. Rotat. (Community Paediat.) Ipswich & Camb.

LEWIS, Elizabeth Anne 30 Lowther Road, Barnes, London SW13 9ND — MB BChir 1962 Camb.

LEWIS, Elkan Flat 30, High Sheldon, Sheldon Avenue, London N6 4NJ Tel: 020 8340 2693; Flat 30, High Sheldon, Sheldon Avenue, London N6 4NJ Tel: 020 8340 2693 Fax: 020 8340 2693 — MB ChB 1955 Liverp.; FRCGP 1981, M 1974; DObst RCOG 1959. (Liverp.) Clin. Asst. (Psychiat.) Newham Gen. Hosp. Lond.; Hon. Med. Adviser to Philharmonia Orchestra Lond. Socs: Fell. Roy. Soc. Med.; Fell. Brit. Soc. Med. & Dent. Hypn. (Ex-Pres. Metrop. Br.); Brit. Assn. for Performing Arts Med. Prev: Ho. Surg. Liverp. Roy. Infirm.; Ho. Phys. Whiston Hosp. Prescot; Ho. Surg. (Obst.) BRd.green Hosp. Liverp.

LEWIS, Elsie May (retired) 17 Mount Agar Road, Carnon Downs, Truro TR3 6HR Tel: 01872 862604 — MD Lond. 1942, MB BS 1939; FRCOG 1959, M 1944. Prev: Cons. Obstetr. & Gynaecol. E. Fife.

LEWIS, Elvet Henry Friesland, Tower Hill, Fishguard SA65 9LA Tel: 01348 873831 — MRCS Eng. LRCP Lond. 1943.

LEWIS, Emanuel 14 Fitzjohns Avenue, London NW3 5NA Tel: 020 7435 4184; 4 Gleneagles, Gordon Avenue, Stanmore HA7 3QG Tel: 020 8954 4994 — MB BS Lond. 1952; MRCP Lond. 1958; FRCPsych 1974, M 1972; DPM Eng. 1961. (Univ. Coll. Hosp.) Socs: Assoc. Mem. Inst. Psychoanal. Prev: Cons. Psychother. Tavistock Clinic Lond.; Cons. Child Psychiat. Char. Cross Hosp. Gp.; Dir. Psychiat. Counselling Serv. Univ. Lond. Inst. Educat.

LEWIS, Eng Siew 3 Dower Park, Windsor SL4 4BQ — MB BS 1970 Adelaide. Clin. Asst. (Rheum.) Windsor, Maidenhead & E. Ascot. Socs: Windsor Med. Soc.; BMA.

LEWIS, Eugene Richard 1A Mount Crescent, Warley, Brentwood CM14 5DB; 6 Wyllen Close, London E1 4HQ Tel: 020 7790 4952 — MB BS 1997 Lond. (St Barts & Royal London) SHO (Endocrinol.), Lond. Prev: SHO (c/o Elderly), Lond.; Ho. Off. (Surg.), Chelmsford; Ho. Off. (Med.) Bury St Edmunds.

LEWIS, Ewart David Locking Hill Surgery, Locking Hill, Stroud GL5 1UY Tel: 01453 764222 Fax: 01453 756278 — MB BS 1982 Lond.

LEWIS, Fiona Jane The Medical Centre, 15 Cawley Road, Chichester PO19 1XT Tel: 01243 786666/781833 Fax: 01243 530042 — MB BS 1980 Lond.; MRCGP 1984; DRCOG 1983. Prev: GP Crawley.

LEWIS, Fiona Mary Worcester Royal Infirmary, Castle Street Branch, Castle St., Worcester WR1 3AS Tel: 01905 763333 Fax: 01905 760237 Email: fiona.lewis@worcsacute.wmids.nhs.uk — MB BCh 1987 Wales; MD 2001 Wales; FRCP 2001 London; MRCP (UK) 1991. Cons. Dermat. Worcester Roy. Infirm. Prev: Sen. Regist. (Dermat.) Roy. Hallamsh. Hosp. Sheff.

LEWIS, Frank William Morley House, 7 Ravenswing Avenue, Blackburn BB2 6DX — MB ChB 1958 Bristol; DMRD Eng. 1966.

LEWIS, Gareth Bishops Medical Centre, Bishops Road, Whitchurch, Cardiff CF14 1LT Tel: 02920 522455/2355 Fax: 02920 522686; White Willows Cottage, Hendre Farm, Lisvane, Cardiff CF14 9UD Tel: 02920 747377 — MB BS 1982 Lond.; BSc Lond. 1979; MRCGP 1987. (Guy's Hosp.) Prev: Trainee GP Cardiff VTS; SHO (Med.) Bevendean Hosp. Brighton; SHO (O & G & Med. Oncol.) Roy. Sussex Co. Hosp. Brighton.

LEWIS, Gareth Huw Lister House Surgery, The Common, Hatfield AL10 0NL Tel: 01707 268822 Fax: 01707 263990 — MB BS 1981 Lond.; T (GP) 1991; MRCGP 1986.

LEWIS, Gareth Richard Rankin Ty Celyn, Berthen Rd, Lixwm, Holywell CH8 8LT — MB ChB 1997 Leic.

LEWIS, Gaynor Elizabeth The Health Centre, Rodney Road, Walton-on-Thames KT12 3LB Tel: 01932 228999 Fax: 01932 225586 — MB BChir 1978 Camb.

LEWIS, Geoffrey David The Barn Surgery, Newbury, Gillingham SP8 4XS Tel: 01747 824201 Fax: 01747 825098; Hiscocks Farm, Moorside, Marnhull, Sturminster Newton DT10 1HF Tel: 01258 821400 — MB BS 1981 Lond.; MRCGP 1987. (Middlx.) Princip. Gen. Pract. Gillingham Dorset.

LEWIS, Geoffrey Francis (retired) Dove Cottage, Askham, Penrith CA10 2PG — MB BS 1955 Durh.; DObst RCOG 1961. Prev: Ho. Surg. (Orthop.) Roy. Vict. Infirm. Newc.

LEWIS, George Michael (retired) Steep Farm Lodge, Steep, Petersfield GU32 2DB Tel: 01730 263065 — MB ChB 1954 Leeds; FRCP Lond. 1980; FRCP Ed. 1970, M 1959; T(M) (Paed) 1991; DCH Eng. 1957. Prev: Cons. Paediat. Portsmouth Hosp. Gp.

LEWIS, Gerald Desmond 1262 Dumbarton Road, Glasgow G14 9PR Tel: 0141 959 5500; 29 West Chapelton Crescent, Bearsden, Glasgow G61 2DE Tel: 0141 959 5500 — MB ChB 1961 Glas.; MFFP 1993; MRCOG 1967. (Glas.) Med. Off. Leyland DAF (Albion Plant); Sessional Med. Off. Blood Transfus. Serv. Socs: BMA; Fam. Plann. Assn. Prev: BMA Research Fell. & Resid. Regist. Roy. Matern. Hosp. Glas.; Ho. Off. Qu. Mother's Hosp. Glas.

LEWIS, Gilbert Aguilar Department of Social Anthropology, Free School Lane, Cambridge CB2 3RF — BM BCh 1962 Oxf.; MRCP Lond. 1965.

LEWIS, Gillian Anne 69 Meriden Road, Hampton in Arden, Solihull B92 0BS Tel: 01675 443517 Email: mjsgal@msn.com — MB ChB 1975 Birm.; FFA RCS Eng. 1982. Cons. Anaesth. Heartlands Hosp. NHS Trust Birm. Prev: Cons. Anasth. City Hosp. NHS trust Birm.; Dir. (Intens. Care) W. Birm. HA; Sen. Regist. Midl. Anaesth. Train. Scheme Centr. Birm.

LEWIS, Gillian Mary Victoria Surgery, Victoria Street, Bury St Edmunds IP33 3BB Tel: 01284 725550; Tel: 01284 752491 — MB BS 1978 Lond.; MRCGP 2001; DFFP. p/t Clin. Asistant Vict. Surg. Vict. St. Bury St. Edmunds; Sen. Clin. Med. Off., Community Day Team, Ipswich.

LEWIS, Gillian Mary Grange Road Surgery, Grange Road, Bishopsworth, Bristol BS13 8LD Tel: 0117 964 4343 Fax: 0117 935 8422 — MB ChB 1981 Manch.; DRCOG 1987; DCH RCP Lond. 1983. (St Andrews and Manchester)

LEWIS, Professor Glyn Hywel University of Wales College of Medicine, Monmouth House, Heath Park, Cardiff CF14 4XN — MB BS 1982 Lond.; PhD Lond. 1991; MSc Epidemiol. Lond. 1989; MSc Oxf. 1980, BA 1978; FRCPsych 1998. Prof. Community & Epidemiol. Psychiat. Univ. Wales Coll. of Med. Cardiff. Prev: Sen. Lect. Inst. Psychiat. & Lond. Sch. Hyg. & Trop. Med.

LEWIS, Gordon Howard Furnace House Surgery, St. Andrews Road, Carmarthen SA31 1EX Tel: 01267 236616 Fax: 01267 222673; Y Wern, Capel Dewi, Carmarthen SA32 8AY Tel: 01267 290084 Email: gordon@lewisgh.demon.co.uk — MB BCh 1978 Wales; MRCGP 1990; DRCOG 1980. (Welsh Nat. Sch. Med.) Course Organiser Carmarthen VTS.

LEWIS, Graham John Hampton Medical Centre, Lansdowne, 49a Priory Road, Hampton TW12 2PB Tel: 020 8979 5150 Fax: 020 8941 9068 — MB ChB 1978 Leeds; MBA Open 1993; MRCGP 1982; DFFP 1993; DRCOG 1980.

LEWIS, Graham John Wordsley Hospital, Stream Road, Stourbridge DY8 5QX; Starts Green Farm, Compton, Kinver, Stourbridge DY7 5NG — MB ChB 1973 Manch.; MRCOG 1978; T(OG) 1991; DObst 1976; FRCOG 1992. (Manch.) Cons. (O & G) Wordlsey Hosp. Stourbridge.

LEWIS, Gwen Eirian Coach and Horses Surgery, The Car Park, St. Clears, Carmarthen SA33 4AA Tel: 01994 230379 Fax: 01994 231449; 4 Llysfelin, Bancyfelin, Carmarthen SA33 5ND Tel: 01267 211420 — MB BCh 1986 Wales; MRCGP 1992.

LEWIS, Gwen Marles Runnymede Medical Practice, Newton Court Medical Centre, Burfield Road, Old Windsor, Windsor SL4 2QF Tel: 01753 863642 Fax: 01753 832180 — MB BS 1980 Lond.; MFFP 1995; DRCOG 1985. (Char. Cross)

LEWIS, Gwyneth Helen Department of Health, Wellington House, 133-155 Waterloo Road, London SE1 8UG Tel: 020 7972 4344 Fax: 020 7972 4348; 27 Ellington Street, London N7 8PN — MB BS 1975 Lond.; FRCOG 2001 UK; FFPHM 2000 FFPHM RCP; MSc Community Med. Lond. 1989; MFPHM RCP (UK) 1995; MRCGP 1981. (Univ. Coll. Hosp.) Princip. Med. Off. DHSS Lond. (Health Servs. Directorate). Prev: GP Sussex; Intern Memor. Univ. St. Johns Newfld.; Cas. Off. Addenbrooke's Hosp. Camb.

LEWIS, Gwynne Vaughan Flat 3, 5 The Paddocks, Martlesham Heath, Ipswich IP5 3UH — MRCS Eng. LRCP Lond. 1957; LMSSA Lond. 1956; DPH Manch. 1970. (Middlx.) Prev: Cas. Off. Ipswich & E. Suff. Gen. Hosp.

LEWIS, Harold Brodie Mather (retired) Hillhead Cottage, Bieldside, Aberdeen AB15 9EL Tel: 01224 868265 — MRCS Eng. LRCP Lond. 1942; FRCPA 1971, M 1962; FRCPath 1971, M (Founder) 1963. Prev: Dir. Aberd. & NE Scotl. Blood Transfus. Serv.

LEWIS, Harold Neville 64 The Fairway, Alwoodley, Leeds LS17 7PD Tel: 0113 268 5518 — MB ChB 1949 Leeds. (Leeds) Prev: Asst. Res. Med. Off. Wakefield Gen. Hosp.

LEWIS, Mr Harry Gordon 11 Pembridge Court, Belmont Road, Belfast BT4 2RW Tel: 02890 471298 Email: harryglewis@hotmail.com — MB BCh BAO 1989 Belf.; 2001 FRCS Plast; MD 1997; FRCSI 1993; FRCS Ed. 1993. (Queens Belf.) Specialist Regist. Plastic Surg. Ulster Hosp. Dundonald Belf.

LEWIS, Helen 22 Tredegar Terrace, Crosskeys, Newport NP11 7PR — MB BCh 1992 Wales.

LEWIS, Helen Jane Woodland veiw, 102 Greenleach Lane, Worsley, Salford M28 2TU Tel: 0161 793 6232 Email: drhelen-j-lewis@hotmail.com; Mem. Bd. Sc. & Educat. (BMA)., 102 Greenleach Lane, Worsley, Salford M28 2TU Tel: 0161 793 6232 — MB ChB 1993 Manch.; MRCP(UK) Lond. 1998. Specialist Regist. (Pub. Health), Salford & Trafford Health Auth. Socs: BMA; MRCP (Ed.).

LEWIS, Helen Jennifer Thornbury Health Centre, Eastland Road, Thornbury, Bristol BS35 1DP Tel: 01454 412167 Fax: 01454 419522 — MB BS 1983 Lond.; MRCGP 1988.

LEWIS, Helen Margaret Department of Dermatology, Selly Oak Hospital, Raddlebarn Road, Birmingham B29 6JD Tel: 0121 627 1627 Fax: 0121 627 8765 Email: julialawton@university-b.wmids.nhs.uk; 65 Blenheim Road, Moseley, Birmingham B13 9TZ Tel: 0121 449 5180 — MB BS 1983 Lond.; MSc Birm. 1989; MD Lond. 1990; MRCP (UK) 1986; FRCP (UK) 1999. (St. Barts Hosp. Med. Sch.) Cons. Dermat. Univ. Hosp. Birm. NHS Trust; Hon. Sen. Clin. Lect. (Med.) Birm. Univ. Prev: Sen. Regist. (Dermat.) Gen. Hosp. Birm.; Regist. (Dermat.) St. Mary's Hosp. Lond.; Lect. (Med. Pharmacol.) Birm. Med. Sch.

LEWIS, Helen Margaret Trafford General Hospital, Moorside Road, Urmston, Manchester M41 5SL Tel: 0161 748 4022 Fax: 0161 746 2381; Sevenoaks, Pk Road, Bowdon, Altrincham WA14 3JF Tel: 0161 941 3887 Email: hmlewis@doctors.org.uk — BM BCh 1971 Oxf.; DM Oxf. 1981; FRCP Lond. 1991; MRCP (UK) 1975; DCH RCP Lond. 1974; DObst RCOG 1973; FRCPCH 1997. Cons. Paediat. Trafford Gen. Hosp. Manch. Socs: Fell. Roy. Coll. of Phys.s; Fell. RSM; Fell.RCPCH. Prev: Sen. Regist. (Paediat.) N.wick Pk. Hosp. Harrow & Roy. Manch. Childr. Hosp.

LEWIS, Hilary 65 Cosmeston Street, Cardiff CF24 4LQ — MB BCh 1989 Wales.

LEWIS, Howard Anthony The Daigles, Loves Green, Highwood, Chelmsford CM1 3Q Tel: Cummins, Brook & Lewis; Dickens Place, Chelmsford CM1 4U — MB ChB 1983 Manch.

LEWIS, Hywel Bernard St Thomas Surgery, Ysyol Street, St. Thomas, Swansea SA1 8LH Tel: 01792 653992; West Cross Medical Centre, 82 West Cross Lane, Swansea SA3 5NG Tel: 01792 404157 — MB BCh Wales 1957. (Cardiff) I.T.S. Med. Mem. Prev: Off. Benefits Agency & Med. Bd.ing for Benefits Agency.; SHO (Matern. & Gyn.) Morriston Hosp. Swansea; Ho. Phys. & Ho. Surg. Swansea Hosp.

LEWIS, Ian Batheaston Medical Centre, Batheaston Medical Centre, Coalpit Road, Batheaston, Bath BA1 7NP Tel: 01225 858686 Fax: 01225 852521; Swans, Ashley Road, Bathford, Bath BA1 7TT Tel: 01225 859818 — MB BS 1957 Lond.; MRCS Eng. LRCP Lond. 1957. (Guy's) Prev: Ho. Surg. Roy. Vict. Hosp. Dover; Ho. Phys. Buckland Hosp. Dover.

LEWIS, Ian Adrian Scott Road Medical Centre, Scott Road, Selby YO8 4BL Tel: 01757 700231 Fax: 01757 213647; 20 Leeds Road, Selby YO8 4HX — MB BS 1972 Lond.; MRCP (UK) 1976; MRCS Eng. LRCP Lond. 1972; MRCGP 1981.

LEWIS, Ian Howard Shackleton Department of Anaesthetics, Southampton General Hospital, Tremona Road, Southampton SO16 6YD; 97 Highfield Lane, Southampton SO17 1NN — MB BS 1979 Lond.; MRCS Eng. LRCP Lond. 1979; MRCP (UK) 1984; FFA RCS Eng. 1987; DA (UK) 1985. Asst. Prof. Univ. Michigan USA. Prev: Sen. Regist. (Anaesth.) Soton. Gen. Hosp.; Instruc. Univ. Michigan, USA.

LEWIS, Ian John Department of Paediatric Oncology, St James's University Hospital, Beckett St., Leeds LS9 7TF Tel: 0113 206 4985 Fax: 0113 247 0248 Email: paedhaemonc@compuserve.com; 62 Blackmoor Court, Alwoodley, Leeds LS17 7RT — MB ChB 1974 Bristol; FRCP Lond. 1994; MRCP (UK) 1978; FRCPCH 1997. Cons. Paediat. Oncol. St. Jas. Univ. Hosp. Leeds; Hon. Sen. Lect. Univ. Leeds. Socs: UK Childr. Cancer Study Gp.; Brit. Paediat. Assn. Prev: Sen. Regist. (Paediat.) Alder Hey Childr. Hosp. Liverp.

LEWIS, Ivor Gwyn Department of Paediatrics, Crawley Hospital, West Green Drive, Crawley RH11 7DH Tel: 01293 600369 — MB BCh 1973 Wales; MRCP (UK) 1979. Cons. Paediat.Surrey & Sussex Healthcare NHS Trust. Socs: Austral. Coll. Paediat. Prev: Cons. Neonat. Paediatrist Childr.'s Hosp. & Qu. Vict. Adelaide, Australia.

LEWIS, Ivor Howells (retired) 8 Wheatlands Road E., Harrogate HG2 8PX — MB ChB 1949 Aberd.; MFCM 1974; DPH Leeds 1955. Prev: Med. Off. Health Edson Health Unit, Alberta, Canada.

LEWIS, Jacqueline Saw Kooi Royal Maisden Hospital, Fulham Road, London — MB BCh BAO 1986 Dub.; FRCS 1999 (Plast.); FRCPS Glas. 1992. (Trinity College Dublin) Hon. Clin. Fell., Roy. Maisden Hosp. Lond. Socs: Brit. Assoc. Plastic Surg.s. Prev: Reseach Fell. Institut Currie, Paris; SpR (Plastic Surg.) Mt. Vernon Hosp. N.wood; SpR (Plastic Surg.) Qu. Vict. Hosp. E. Grinstead.

LEWIS, James Alexander The White House, Treborth Road, Bangor LL57 2RJ — MB BCh 1998 Wales.

LEWIS, James Christopher 117 Earlham Road, Norwich NR2 3RF Email: jc.lewis@virgin.net — MB BS 1991 Lond.; MSc Orth.Eng.University of Wales 1998. (Guys) Specialist Regist. Orthop. & Trauma. Socs: Affil. Mem. Brit. Orthopaedic Assocation; Brit. HIP Soc.

LEWIS, James Edward (retired) Beaupre, St John, Jersey JE3 4FN — BM BCh 1933 Oxf.

LEWIS, Mr James Laurence Department of Urology, Kent and Sussex Hospital, Mount Ephraim, Tunbridge Wells TN4 8AT Tel: 01892 549104 Fax: 01892 549103; Westwood Manor, Castle Walk, Wadhurst TN5 6DB Tel: 01892 784075 Fax: 01892 784075 Email: jim_l_l@email.msn.com — MB BS 1972 Lond.; MS Lond. 1986, MB BS 1972; FRCS Eng. 1976; MRCP (UK) 1974. (Guy's) Cons. (Urol.) Kent & Sussex Weald NHS Trust; Med. Dir. Kent & Sussex Weald NHS Trust. Socs: Brit. Assn. Urol. Surgs. & Soc. for Minimally Invasive Ther..; Corres. Mem. Amer. Urological Assn.; Internat. Continence Soc. Prev: Sen. Regist. Guy's Hosp. Lond.; Research Fell. Harvard Med. Sch. Boston, USA; SHO St. Jas. Hosp. Lond.

LEWIS, James Stewart Gillespie 15B Union Street, Bridge of Allan, Stirling FK9 4NS — MB ChB 1993 Glas. (Glas.)

LEWIS, Jason, Capt. RAMC Anaesthetic Department, Frimley Park Hospital, Portsmouth Road, Camberley GU16 7UJ Tel: 01276 604604 Ext: 4161; 17 Katrine Road, Stourport-on-Severn DY13 8QB Tel: 01299 877001 — BM BS 1994 Nottm. (Univ. of Nottingham) SHO (Anaesth.) Frimley Pk. Hosp., Camberley.

LEWIS, Jeffrey Wayne Market Street Practice, Ton-y-Felin Surgery, Bedwas Road, Caerphilly CF83 1PD Tel: 029 2088 7831 Fax: 029 2086 9037 — MB BCh 1977 Wales. GP Caerphilly. Prev: GP Trainee Newport VTS; Ho. Phys. (Geriat.) W. Wales Gen. Hosp. Glangwili.

LEWIS, Jerome Gerald 18 Dearne Close, Stanmore HA7 3AT Tel: 020 8954 4208 — MD Lond. 1960, MB BS 1951; FRCP Lond. 1973, M 1955; MRCS Eng. LRCP Lond. 1951. (Lond. Hosp.) Socs: Fell. Roy. Soc. Med. & Med. Soc. Lond. Prev: Cons. Phys. Edgware

Gen. & Napsbury Hosps.; Sen. Med. Regist. Char. Cross Hosp.; Med. Regist. Roy. Free Hosp. & Brompton Hosp.

LEWIS, Joanne 40 Deneside Court, Selborne Gardens, Jesmond, Newcastle upon Tyne NE2 1JW — MB BS 1989 Newc.

LEWIS, Joanne Elizabeth Soldridge House, Medstead, Alton GU34 5JF; 6 Norland Road, Southsea PO4 0ED — MB BS 1990 Lond.; MRCGP 1994; DRCOG 1992. SHO (Paediat.) Hants. Prev: Trainee GP/SHO (Community Paediat.) Portsmouth VTS.

LEWIS, John Antony Rees Seaward, 6 Cwm-Halen, New Quay SA45 9SF — MB BCh 1986 Wales.

LEWIS, John Aylmer (retired) Riverside Cottage, Lower Washford, Watchet TA23 0PA Tel: 01984 640494 — MRCS Eng. LRCP Lond. 1952.

LEWIS, John David 1 Oldham Road, Uppermill, Saddleworth, Oldham OL3 6HY — MB ChB 1971 St. And. Assoc. Specialist A & E Rochdale Infirm. Prev: Regist. (A & E) Rochdale Infirm.; Regist. (A & E) N. Manch. Gen. Teachg. Hosp.

LEWIS, John David Gerafon Surgery, Benllech, Tyn-y-Gongl LL74 8TF Tel: 01248 852122 Fax: 01248 853698; Tal Y Bont, Llangefni LL77 Tel: 01248 722105 Fax: 01248 750552 — MB BS 1973 Lond.; MRCS Eng. LRCP Lond. 1973. Socs: Brit. Med. Acupunc. Soc.

LEWIS, John Eurig Tegfan Day Hospital, Whitchurch Hospital, Cardiff CF14 7XB Tel: 029 2033 6592 — MB BS 1981 Lond.; BSc Lond. 1978; MRCPsych 1990; Cert. Psychopharm 1999. (Univ. Lond.) Cons. Psychiat. WhitCh. Hosp. Cardiff.

LEWIS, John Howell Iona, Aberkenfig, Bridgend Tel: 01656 721579 — MRCS Eng. LRCP Lond. 1951. (Lond. Hosp) Clin. Asst. Skin Dept. Bridgend Gen. Hosp.; Clin. Asst. (c/o Subn. Pat.s) Cefn Hirgoed Hosp. Bridgend. Socs: BMA; Ogwr Med. Soc. Prev: Cas. Off. LLa.lly Hosp.; Res. Med. Off. Newbury Dist. Hosp.; Regist. (Surg.) Stepping Hill Hosp. Stockport.

LEWIS, John Kenneth (retired) Wentwood, Llanfair Kilgeddin, Abergavenny NP7 9YE Tel: 01873 880573 — MB ChB 1940 Bristol; FFA RCS Eng. 1954; DA Eng. 1947. Prev: Cons. Anaesth. W. Cornw. Clin. Area & St. Michael's Hosp. Hayle.

LEWIS, John Lester Grasmere Street Health Centre, Grasmere Street, Leigh WN7 1XB Tel: 01942 672835 Fax: 01942 680883 — MB BCh BAO 1979 NUI; LRCPI & LM, LRCSI & LM 1979.

LEWIS, John Malcolm The Bijou, Church St., Settle BD24 9JG Tel: 01729 822611 — BM BCh 1970 Oxf.; MA; DCH Eng. 1973; DObst RCOG 1972. Prev: SHO Airedale Gen. Hosp. Steeton.

LEWIS, John Marles (retired) Eirianfa, 10 Kingston Road, Sketty, Swansea SA2 0ST — MB BCh 1946 Wales; BSc (Distinc. Anat., Alfred Hughes Gold Medal) 1943; FFA RCS Eng. 1953; DA Eng. 1951. Cons. Anaesth. W. Glam. HA. Prev: Anaesth. Regist. Morriston Hosp. Swansea.

LEWIS, John Martin Donald Flat 4/15 Dalhouse Court, 42 West Graham St., Glasgow G4 9LH — MB ChB 1997 Glas.

LEWIS, John Peter David Church View Surgery, 5 Market Hill, Hedon, Hull HU12 8JE Tel: 01482 899348; Ganymede, 25 Ebor Manor, Keyingham, Hull HU12 9SN Tel: 01964 622725 — MB ChB 1982 Birm.

LEWIS, John Roland (retired) Woodcroft, 2 Partridge Road, The Burntwood, Loggerheads, Market Drayton TF9 2QX — MB BCh 1955 Wales; FFA RCS Eng. 1965; DA Eng. 1961. Prev: Cons. Anaesth. N. Staffs. Roy. Infirm.

LEWIS, John Scott (retired) Cilrhedyn, 22 St Margarets Drive, Llanelli SA15 4EW — MB BChir Camb. 1952; MA Camb. 1952; DObst RCOG 1962. Prev: Med. Adviser Benefits Agency.

LEWIS, John Vyvyan Vaughan (retired) 33 Seymour Road, Stratford-upon-Avon CV37 9EP Tel: 01789 296444 — MB BS 1954 Lond.; MRCGP 1965; DCH Eng. 1962; DObst RCOG 1959. Prev: EMO Artific. Limb & Appliance Centre Birm.

LEWIS, John Warburton (retired) Mundens, Horsley Road, Nailsworth, Stroud GL6 0JR Tel: 01453 832918 — MB BS Lond. 1946; DObst RCOG 1950. Prev: Cas. Surg. Off. & Ho. Surg. Middlx. Hosp.

LEWIS, Jon Walford (retired) Willow Wood, Green Lane, Stutton, Tadcaster LS24 9BW Tel: 01937 832669 — MB ChB 1957 Leeds; DObst RCOG 1958. Prev: GP Tadcaster.

LEWIS, Jonathan Michael Caterham Valley Medical Practice, Eothen House, Eothen Close, Caterham CR3 6JU Tel: 01883 347811 Fax: 01883 342929 — MB ChB 1984 Bristol; MRCGP 1995. Local Organiser for Med. Stud. (Gen. Pract.) St. Geo. Hosp. Med. Sch.; Mem. E. Surrey PCG. Socs: Chairm. Caterham Med. Soc. Prev: Trainee GP E. Surrey VTS.

LEWIS, Mr Joseph 'Langen Hoe', Bryntirion Drive, Prestatyn LL19 9NT — MB ChB 1960 Ed.; FRCS Ed. 1968. (Ed.) Cons. Orthop. Surg. Clwyd AHA. Socs: Brit. Orthop. Assn. Prev: Sen. Regist. (Trauma & Orthop.) Univ. Hosp. of Wales Cardiff; SHO (Orthop.) Whittington Hosp. Lond.; Regist. (Orthop.) Robt. Jones & Agnes Hunt Orthop. Hosp. OsW.ry.

LEWIS, Joseph Nathan (retired) 570 Antrim Road, Belfast BT15 5GL Tel: 02890779494 Email: joediy@aol.com — MB BCh BAO 1947 Belf.; FRCGP 1975, M 1954.

LEWIS, Joseph Walter (retired) 9 Saxon Place, Lower Buckland Road, Lymington SO41 9EZ Tel: 01590 670002 — MB BS 1945 Lond.; FRCA 1992; FFA RCS Eng. 1954; DA Eng. 1949. Prev: Cons. Anaesth. Harefield Hosp., Mt. Vernon Hosp. N.wood & Ealing Hosp.

LEWIS, Judith Mary Westway Surgery, 1 Wilson Road, Ely, Cardiff CF5 4LJ Tel: 029 2059 2351 Fax: 029 2059 9956 — MB BS 1984 Lond. (Lond. Hosp. Med. Coll.)

LEWIS, Julia Claire Gwent Community NHS Trust, St Cadocs Hospital, Lodge Road, Caerleon, Newport NP18 3XQ Tel: 01633 436700; 104 Alexandra Road, Six Bells, Abertillery NP13 2LH Tel: 01495 321250 — MB BS 1992 Lond.; BSc (Hons.) Lond. 1989; MRCGP 1996; DRCOG 1994. SHO Rotat. (Psychiat.) Gwent Train. Scheme.

LEWIS, Jyotsna The Surgery, 17B Warmdene Road, Brighton BN1 8NL Tel: 01273 508811 Fax: 01273 559860 — MB BS 1989 Lond.

LEWIS, Katherine Emma Tyllwyd, Dinas Cross, Newport SA42 0SJ — MB BS 1991 Lond.

LEWIS, Kathryn Anne CAE Colley, Mochdre, Newtown SY16 4JN — BM BS 1981 Nottm.; BMedSci. (Nottm.) 1979. Sen. Community Paediat. Prev: Sen. Regist. (Pub. Health Med.).

LEWIS, Miss Kathryn Elizabeth 26 John Batchelor Way, Penarth Haven, Penarth CF64 1SD — MB BCh 1988 Wales; FRCA 1994. Cons. (Anaesth.), P.ss of Wales Hosp., Bridgend.

LEWIS, Keith Madoc McConachie St. Thomas Group Practice, Ysyol St., St Thomas, Swansea Tel: 01792 404157; West Cross Medical Centre, West Cross Lane, est cross, Swansea SA3 5NN Tel: 01792 404157 — MRCS Eng. LRCP Lond. 1952. (Middlx.) Prev: Ho. Phys. Tindal Gen. Hosp. Aylesbury; Med. Regist. Swansea Gen. Hosp.; Capt. RAMC.

LEWIS, Kendall Graeme (retired) 50B Kew Green, Kew, Richmond TW9 3BB Tel: 020 8940 7991 Email: glewis8941@aol.com — MB ChB 1956 New Zealand. Prev: GP Hounslow.

LEWIS, Kenneth Harold 5 Neville Court, Grove End Road, London NW8 9DD Tel: 020 7286 1577 Fax: 020 7266 0181 Email: kenneth.lewis1@virgin.net — BM BCh Oxf. 1952; MA Oxf. 1952. (Oxf. & St. Mary's) Med. Ref. Zool. Soc. Lond.; Phys. Brit. Performing Arts Med. Trust; Med. Adviser Lond. Symphony Orchestra & Carlton TV; Hon. Cons. Phys. Roy. Soc. of Musicians; Surg. Lt. RNR. Socs: Fell. Roy. Soc. Med.; (Ex-Pres.) Hampstead Med. Soc.; Chelsea Clin. Soc. Prev: Ho. Surg. St. Mary's Hosp. Lond.; Cas. Off. Willesden Gen. Hosp.; Resid. Med. Off. King Edwd. VII Hosp. Offs. Lond.

LEWIS, Kevin Russell 38 Hillside Road, Norton, Stockton-on-Tees TS20 1JG Tel: 01642 558336 — MB ChB 1987 Aberd.

LEWIS, Kim Melanie 21 Siward Road, Bromley BR2 9JY — MB ChB 1993 Cape Town.

LEWIS, Leslie 97 Spencefield Lane, Leicester LE5 6HH Tel: 0116 241 3646 — MB ChB Birm. 1955; FRCGP 1982, M 1970; DObst RCOG 1960. (Birm.) Indust. Med. Off.; Examg. Off. HM Forces Recruiting. Socs: (Ex-Pres.) Leic. Med. Soc.; BMA (Ex-Pres. Leics. & Rutland Div.); (Ex-Pres.) Leics. Med.-Leg.l Soc. Prev: GP Leicester; Ho. Off. Qu. Eliz. Hosp. & Sorrento Matern. Hosp. Birm.; Police Surg.

LEWIS, Leslie Samuel Newport Surgery, Long Street, Newport SA42 0TJ Tel: 01239 820397 Fax: 01239 820056 — MB ChB 1972 Manch.; MRCP (UK) 1978. CME Tutor (Gen. Pract.) Pembroksh. Prev: GP Pembrokesh.

LEWIS, Lindsay Margaret Flat 3, 14 Station Road, Lower Weston, Bath BA1 3DY — BM BS 1994 Nottm.

LEWIS, Lionel David 39 Westview Lane, Lebanon NH 03766, USA; 39 Woodfield Road, Rudgwick, Horsham RH12 3EP Tel:

01403 822091 Fax: 01403 822091 — MD 1988 Wales; MB BCh Camb. 1979; MB BCh Wales 1977; MRCP (UK) 1980; FMGEMS 1989. Cons. Phys. Lewisham & Cons. Clin. Pharmacol. Guy's Drug Research Unit. Prev: Sen. Regist. (Gen. & Thoracic Med.) Guy's & Lewisham Hosps. Lond.

LEWIS, Mr Lowell Lyttleton Department of Surgery, Faculty of Medical Sciences, University of West Indies, Queen Elizabeth Hospital, Bridgetown, Barbados Tel: 00 246 436 6450; c/o Mr S. Lynch, 20 Adelaide Terrace, Brentwood Tel: 020 8568 7142 Fax: 00 246 429 6738 — MB ChB 1976 Sheff.; FRCS Ed. 1982; DPH 1984. Lect. and Hon. Cons. in Surg. Sch. of Clin. Med. and Research Univ. of the W. Indies Qu. Eliz. Hosp. Barbados. Socs: Med. Practitioner Soc.; Roy. Soc. of Trop. Med.; Vice-Pres. Caribbean Assn. of Nephrol. and Urol. Prev: Vis. Regist. (Transpl. Surg.) Portsmouth; Director Health Servs. & Surg. Specialist Montserrat, W. Indies; Regist. (Gen. Surg.) Roy. Hallamsh. Hosp. Sheff. & Bury Gen. Hosp. Lancs.

LEWIS, Lynn Teresa 26 Cleveland Close, Ormesby, Middlesbrough TS7 9BX — MB BS 1981 Newc.

LEWIS, Malcolm Kingsway Surgery, 37 The Kingsway, Swansea SA1 5LF Tel: 01792 650716 Fax: 01792 456902; 90 Newton Road, Mamble, Swansea SA3 4SL Tel: 01792 360440 Email: malcom.lewis@btinternet.com — MB BS 1983 Lond.; 1998 LLM; MRCGP 1987; DRCOG 1987. (Univ. Coll. Hosp. Med. Sch.) p/t GP Swansea; Dep. Director PostGrad. Gen. Pract., Educat. Prev: Clin. Asst. Med.; Course Organiser Swansea Bay BTS.

LEWIS, Malcolm Adrian 18 Hereford Drive, Prestwich, Manchester M25 0AG — MB ChB 1979 Manch.; MRCP (UK) 1983.

LEWIS, Malcolm John (retired) 23 Longdale Lane, Ravenshead, Nottingham NG15 9AB Tel: 01623 792346 — MB ChB Bristol 1957; MD Bristol 1970. Prev: Sen. Lect. Univ. Nottm. Med. Sch.

LEWIS, Professor Malcolm John Department of Pharmacology & Therapeutics, University of Wales College of Medicine, Heath Park, Cardiff CF14 4XN Tel: 029 2074 2066 Fax: 029 2074 7484; 62 Parc-y-Coed, Creigiau, Cardiff CF15 9LZ Tel: 029 2089 0107 Fax: 01222 747484 — FESC 2000; MB BCh Wales 1970; DSc Wales 1991, PhD 1976. Prof. Cardiovasc. Pharmacol. Univ. Wales Coll. Med. Cardiff. Socs: Brit. Pharm. Soc.; Brit. Cardiac Soc. Prev: Reader (Clin. Pharmacol.) Univ. of Wales Coll. Med. Cardiff; Sen. Lect. (Clin. Pharmacol.) Univ. of Wales Coll. Med. Cardiff; Lect. (Clin. Pharmacol.) Welsh Nat. Sch. Med. Cardiff.

LEWIS, Margaret Yardley Green Medical Centre, 75 Yardley Green Road, Bordesley Green, Birmingham B9 5PU Tel: 0121 773 3737 — MB ChB Birm. 1974; MRCGP 1979.

LEWIS, Margaret Anne Gwyddelig Farm, Staindrop Road, West Auckland, Bishop Auckland DL14 9JX Tel: 01388 832228 — MB BS 1958 Durh.; MRCPsych 1971; DPM Eng. 1963. Cons. (Adolesc. Psychiat.) St. Lukes Hosp. Middlesbrough. Socs: Assn. Psychiat. Study Adolesc.

LEWIS, Margaret Sian Haematology Department, Singleton Hospital, Sketty, Swansea SA2 8QA Tel: 01792 205666; Wansbeck, Dyffryn Road, Ammanford SA18 3TA — MB BCh 1986 Wales; MRCP (UK) 1989; MRCPath UK 1997. Cons. Haemat. Singleton Hosp. Sketty Swansea. Prev: Clin. Research Fell. Leukaemia Research Fund John Radcliffe Hosp. Oxf.; Regist. (Haemat.) John Radcliffe Hosp. Oxf.; SHO Rotat. (Med. & Haemat.) Univ. Hosp. Wales.

LEWIS, Margo 6 Michael Drive, Birmingham B15 2EL — MB BCh 1970 Wales; FRCA 1978; DA (UK) 1974; DRCOG 1972.

LEWIS, Marian 30 Heol Isaf, Radyr, Cardiff CF15 8AL — MB BS 1986 Lond.

LEWIS, Mark 131 Cranbourne Park, Hedge End, Southampton SO30 0NZ — MB 1987 Camb.; BChir 1986.

LEWIS, Mark Brian 68 Savile Road, Methley, Leeds LS26 9HW — MB BS 1993 Newc.; MRCP (UK). (Newcastle) Specialist Regist. (Neurol.) Pinderfields Wakefield.

LEWIS, Mark Thomas 589 Clarkston Road, Muirend, Glasgow G44 3QD — MB ChB 1989 Glas.

LEWIS, Mark William De-La-Haye 7A Rounds Hill, Kenilworth CV8 1DW — MB ChB 1991 Bristol.

LEWIS, Martin Leonard Haematology Department, Kidderminsterl Hospital, Bewdley Road, Kidderminster DY11 6RJ Tel: 01562 513087 Fax: 01562 513006 Email: martin.lewis@worcsacute.wmids.nhs.uk — MB BS 1964 Lond.; MRCS Eng. LRCP Lond. 1964; MRCPath 1970. (King's Coll. Hosp.) Cons. Haemat. Kidderminster Health Dist. Socs: Brit. Soc. Haematol. Prev: Instruc. in Med. Washington Univ. St. Louis, USA; Sen. Lect., Cons. in Haemat. & Demonst. Path. King's Coll. Hosp. Med. Sch. Lond.

LEWIS, Martin Norman Thornhill Park Road Surgery, 90 Thornhill Park Road, Thornhill, Southampton SO18 5TR Tel: 023 8047 4207 Fax: 023 8047 0004; 88 Billington Gardens, Grange Park, Hedge End, Southampton SO30 2RT — BM 1982 Soton.; Cert. Family Plann. JCC 1986. Assoc. Specialist (ENT) Soton. Community Health Servs. NHS Trust Soton. Prev: Regist. (Rheum. & Rehabil.) & SHO (ENT) Salisbury HA; SHO (Spinal Injuries) Oddstock Hosp. Salisbury.

LEWIS, Marvin Raymond Higher Blackley Medical Centre, 156 Victoria Avenue, Manchester M9 0FN Tel: 0161 740 2106/6926 Fax: 0161 720 6384 — MB ChB 1974 Manch.; DRCOG 1977. (Manch.) Clin. Asst. (Med.) Bury Gen. Hosp. Socs: Manch. Med. Soc.

LEWIS, Mary 4 Parklands Drive, Askam-in-Furness LA16 7JP — MB BCh BAO 1975 NUI.

LEWIS, Mary Lou 10 The Highfields, Wightwick, Wolverhampton WV6 8DW — MB ChB 1961 Birm.; DO Eng. 1965.

LEWIS, Matthew Elfed 10 Lakeside Drive, Lakeside, Cardiff CF23 6DD — MB BCh 1985 Wales.

LEWIS, Matthew Frank Church Street Surgery, 77 Church Street, Tewkesbury GL20 5RY Tel: 01684 292343 Fax: 01684 274305 — MB BS 1965 Lond.; MRCS Eng. LRCP Lond. 1965; MRCGP 1980; DObst RCOG 1967. (Guys) Med. Off. Tewkesbury Hosp.

LEWIS, Matthew James Valentine 8 Swann Grove, Cheadle Hulme, Cheadle SK8 7HW — MB ChB 1991 Manch.; BSc (Hons.) Manch. 1988.

LEWIS, Max 21 The School Close, Westgate-on-Sea CT8 8QS Tel: 01843 35269 — MRCS Eng. LRCP Lond. 1943. (W. Lond.)

LEWIS, Maxine Anne High Royds Hospital, Menston, Ilkley LS29 6AQ — MB BCh 1989 Wales; MMEDSc 1995; MRCPsych 1994. Cons. in Old Age Psychiat., High Royos Hosp., Leeds. Socs: Roy. Coll. of Psychiat. Prev: Regist. (Psychiat.) Leeds.; Regist. (Psychiat.) High Royds Hosp. Leeds.

LEWIS, Melanie Cotgrave Health Centre, Candleby Lane, Cotgrave, Nottingham NG12 3JG Tel: 0115 989 2398 Fax: 0115 989 2249 — MB BCh 1987 Wales; MRCGP 1991. Prev: Trainee GP Nottm. VTS.

LEWIS, Michael Hillfield Health Centre, 1 Howard St., Coventry CV1 4GE — MB ChB 1958 Birm. (Birm.) GP Med. Off. (Occupat. Health) Coventry Gp. Hosps. Socs: BMA.

LEWIS, Michael Alan 76 Antrim Road, Belfast BT15 4EP — MB BCh BAO 1959 Dub.; FFA RCSI 1969.

LEWIS, Michael Alun Hughes (retired) Portland House, 20 Abbey End, Kenilworth CV8 1LS Tel: 01926 859831 — MB BCh Wales 1957; FFA RCS Eng. 1964. Prev: Cons. Anaesth. Coventry Hosp. Gp.

LEWIS, Michael Andrew Briar Barn, Hunter Rise, Beckermet CA21 2YP — MB ChB 1987 Manch.

LEWIS, Mr Michael Edward 104 Ravenhurst Road, Birmingham B17 9HP Email: m.e.lewis@bham.ac.uk — MB ChB 1992 Bristol; FRCS 1996. Regist. (Cardiac Surg.) Qu. Eliz. Hosp. Birm.

LEWIS, Michael Hamilton Manor Farm House, Lower Lane, Kinsham, Tewkesbury GL20 8HT — MB BS 1997 Lond.

LEWIS, Mr Michael Howard 2 Bettws-y-coed Road, Cyncoed, Cardiff CF23 6PL — MD 1982 Wales; MB BCh 1972; FRCS Eng. 1977. Cons. Gen. Surg. E. Glam. Gen. Hosp. Prev: Sen. Regist. Roy. Postgrad. Med. Sch. Hammersmith Hosp. Lond.; Res. Assoc. & Instruc. Dept. Surg. Univ. Chicago Illinois.

LEWIS, Michael John (retired) 1 Buckingham Road W., Heaton Moor, Stockport SK4 4AZ Email: mamlew@ntlworld.com — MB ChB Manch. 1967; MD Manch. 1983; FRCP Lond. 1995; MRCP (UK) 1970; FRCPath 1987, M 1975. Cons. Haemat. N. Manch. Gen. Hosp. Prev: Sen. Regist. (Haemat.) Childr. Hosp. Birm. & Gen. Hosp. Birm.

LEWIS, Michael Reginald Salop Road Medical Centre, Salop Road, Welshpool SY21 7ER Tel: 01938 553118 Fax: 01938 553071 — MB BS 1983 Lond.; BSc (Hons.) Lond. 1980; MRCGP 1990; MRCOphth 1988; DO RCPSI 1987; DRCOG 1985; DFFP 1984. (Univ. Coll. Hosp.) Clin. Asst. (Geriat.) Vict. Memor. Hosp. Welshpool. Socs: Primary Care Spec. Gp. of Brit. Computer Soc.;

Powys MAAG; BASICS. Prev: Trainee GP BasCh. Shrops. VTS; Lect. (Gen. Pract.) Univ. Manch.; Clin. Asst. Manch. Eye Hosp.

LEWIS, Michael Stuart Houlgate Way Surgery, Houlgate Way, Axbridge BS26 2BJ Tel: 01934 732464 Fax: 01934 733488; The Lawn, Compton Bishop, Axbridge BS26 2EU Tel: 01934 732335 — MB BS 1970 Lond.; MRCS Eng. LRCP Lond. 1970; MRCGP 1977. (St. Mary's) Postgrad. Clin. Tutor W.on Gen. Hosp.; Med. Off. Nuclear Electric. Prev: Clin. Asst. (Geriat.) St. John's Hosp. Axbridge; Ho. Surg. & Ho. Phys. King Edwd. VII Hosp. Windsor.

LEWIS, Morgan Guy Howat (retired) 59 Brackley Road, Towcester NN12 6DH Tel: 01327 351360 — MB BChir 1948 Camb.; BA Camb. 1944; DObst RCOG 1949. Sen. Med. Off. Towcester Racecourse. Prev: Resid. Med. Off. Qu. Charlotte's Matern. Hosp. Lond.

LEWIS, Muriel Jennifer c/o Ward 13, Victoria Hospital, Hayfield Road, Kirkcaldy KY2 5AH; 4/6 Carrubbers Close, 135 High St, Royal Mile, Edinburgh EH1 1SJ — MB ChB 1989 Ed.; MRCP (UK) 1995. (Ed.) Staff Grade (Gen. Med.) Vict. Hosp. Kirkcaldy.

LEWIS, Myles Jonathan 3 Dower Park, Windsor SL4 4BQ — BM BCh 1998 Oxf.; BM BCh Oxf 1998.

LEWIS, Naomi Ursula 19 Temple Sheen, London SW14 7RP Tel: 020 8876 7142 — MB BS 1959 Lond. (Univ. Coll. Hosp.) Clin. Med. Off. Prev: Sen. Ho. Off. Manch. Roy. Infirm.; Ho. Phys. Brompton Hosp.; Ho. Surg. Univ. Coll. Hosp. Lond.

LEWIS, Neville McLaren Livingston Fore Street Surgery, 26 Fore Street, Totnes TQ9 5DX Tel: 01803 862671; Balquhidder, Bow Bridge, Ashprington, Totnes TQ9 7EB Tel: 01807 32346 — MB BS 1963 Lond.; MRCS Eng. LRCP Lond. 1963; DObst RCOG 1966. (St. Mary's) Hosp. Pract. (Venereol.) Torbay Hosp. Torquay. Socs: Torquay & Dist. Med. Soc. Prev: Ho. Off. (Orthop.) & Cas. Surg. St. Mary's Hosp. Lond.; Ho. Off. (Gen. Med. & Obst.) Edgware Gen. Hosp.

LEWIS, Nicholas James Trident Medical Services, Building F7.1, AWE, Aldermaston, Reading RG7 4PR Tel: 01189 826868 Fax: 01189 815320 Email: tridentmed@msn.com — MB BS 1978 Lond.; MBA Open 1994; MRCP (UK) 1983; MRCS Eng. LRCP Lond. 1978; FFOM RCP Lond. 1994, MFOM 1988, AFOM 1986; MRCGP 1983; DRCOG 1981. (Char. Cross) Company Sec. Trident Med. Servs. Prev: Dep. Chief Med. Off. Brit. Rail; Princip. Med. Off. Civil Serv.; Occupat. Phys. Lond. Regional Transport.

***LEWIS, Nicola Louise** 8 Beaufort Crescent, Stoke Gifford, Bristol BS34 8QX — BM BS 1994 Nottm.; BMedSci (Hons.) 1992.

LEWIS, Nigel Lea Burnham Health Centre, Minniecroft Road, Burnham, Slough SL1 7DE Tel: 01628 605333 Fax: 01628 663743; Byways, Brantridge Lane, Bourne End SL8 5BY Tel: 01628 521207 — MB BS 1975 Lond.; MRCS Eng. LRCP Lond. 1975; Dip. Sports Med. 1996. (St. Mary's) Prev: Ho. Phys. St. Mary's Hosp. Lond.; Ho. Surg. & Ho. Off. (Obst.) Canad. Red. Cross Hosp. Taplow.

LEWIS, Norman Rollinson, Wing Cdr. RAF Med. Br. Retd. Misterley, Epsom Road, Leatherhead KT22 8ST — MB BChir Camb. 1952; MA Camb. 1952; MRCP (UK) 1970; MRCS Eng. LRCP Lond. 1951; DPhysMed. Eng. 1956. (Westm.) Prev: Cas. Off. W.m. Hosp.

LEWIS, Pamela Ann 51 Skelton Close, Luton LU3 4HF — MB BS 1991 Lond. SHO (Med. for Elderly) Whipps Cross Hosp. Lond. Prev: Ho. Off. (Oncol.) St. Bart. Hosp. Lond.; Ho. Off. (Gen. Med. & Surg.) Homerton Hosp. Lond.

LEWIS, Paul Edwin Gatehampton, Berwick, Polegate BN26 6SZ — MB BS 1974 Lond.; MRCS Eng. LRCP Lond. 1974; DA Eng. 1977. (Guy's)

***LEWIS, Paul John,** Lt. RAMC 110 Brambletye Park Road, Redhill RH1 6EJ Tel: 01737 277626 — MB BS 1997 Lond.; BSc (Hons.) 1994.

LEWIS, Paul Lothian Stockett Lane Surgery, 3 Stockett Lane, Coxheath, Maidstone ME17 4PS Tel: 01622 745585 Fax: 01622 741987 Email: gp-g82024.nhs.uk; Wierton Cottage, Wierton Hill, Boughton Monchelsea, Maidstone ME17 4JT Tel: 01622 741647 Email: plll@kentnet-online.co.uk — MB BS 1969 Lond.; MA Camb. 1965; FRCP 1998; MRCP (U.K.) 1972; FRCGP 1989, M 1976; MRCPsych 1974; Cert JCC Lond. 1977. (St. Thos.) Prev: Regist. Maudsley & Bethlem Roy. Hosp. Lond.

LEWIS, Paul Martin Caldicot Medical Group, Gray Hill Surgery, Woodstock Way, Caldicot, Newport NP26 4DB Tel: 01291 420602 Email: pplewcoba@aol.com; Cobbler's Pitch, Highmoor Hill, Caerwent, Chepstow NP26 5PF Tel: 01291 420602 Fax: 01291 426853 — MB ChB 1968 Bristol; DA Eng. 1973; DObst RCOG 1970. (Bristol) Prev: SHO (Anaesth. & O & G), Ho. Phys. & Ho. Surg. S.mead Hosp. Bristol.

LEWIS, Mr Paul Morcombe (retired) Oxford Fertility Unit, Level 4, Women's Centre, John Radcliffe Hospital, Headley Way, Oxford OX3 9DU Tel: 01865 221900 Fax: 01865 222031 Email: paul.lewis@obs-gyn.ox.ac.uk — MB BS 1963 Lond. 1963; 1968 FRCS Eng. 1968; 1971 FRCOG 1987, M 1971; 1965 DObst RCOG 1965. Prev: Dep. Med. Dir. Bourn Hall Clinic Camb.

LEWIS, Mr Peter 5 Glencarnock Close, Torquay TQ1 4DQ — MB BCh 1979 Wales. Cons. (Gen. Surg.), Torbay Hosp., Torbay.

LEWIS, Peter Mid Cheshire Hospitals (NHS) Trust, Leighton Hospital, Middlewich Road, Crewe CW1 4QJ; Dorfold Cottage, Swanley Lane, Acton, Nantwich CW5 8LP — MB BS 1974 Lond.; FFA RCS Eng. 1985. Cons. Anaesth. Mid. Chesh. Hosps. NHS Trust.

LEWIS, Peter David Manston Surgery, 72-76 Austhorpe Road, Leeds LS15 8DZ Tel: 0113 264 5455 Fax: 0113 232 6181 — MB ChB 1986 Leeds; MRCGP 1991.

LEWIS, Peter John British Biotech plc, Oxford OX4 6LY; Westview Cottage, Fernham Road, Uffington, Swindon SN7 7RD Tel: 01367 820743 Fax: 01367 820316 — MB BChir 1969 Camb.; PhD Lond. 1974; MD Camb. 1976, MA 1968; FRCP Lond. 1982; MRCP (UK) 1971. Pharm. Cons. Prev: Vice Pres. Marion Merrell Dow Kansas City, USA; Sen. Lect. (Clin. Pharm.) Roy. Postgrad. Med. Sch. & Inst. O & G Qu. Charlottes Hosp. Lond.; Dir. Research & Developm. Brit. Biotech. plc Oxf.

LEWIS, Peter John Sydney Natural Medical Centre, 15 South Steyne, Manly, Sydney NSW 2095, Australia Tel: 0061 2 99777888 Fax: 0061 2 99773436; 1 Carclew Terrace, Devoran, Truro TR3 6PN Tel: 01872 862341 — BM BS 1981 Nottm.; BMedSci. Nottm. 1979; FAMAS 1991; FACNEM 1996; MRCGP 1985; Dip. Med.Acupunc. 1997; DRCOG 1985. (Nott.) Phys. Private Pract. Integrative Med. Sydney Natural Med. Centre Sydney, Australia. Socs: Brit. Med. Acupunct. Soc. Prev: Indep. Complementary Phys. Centre for Study Complementary Med. Soton. & Lond.; Cons. Nutrit. & Environm. Med. Roy. Lond. Homoeop. Hosp.; Med. Off. Roy. Flying Doctor Serv., W. Austral.

LEWIS, Peter Roydon William Redlands Surgery, Redlands Road, Penarth CF64 3WX Tel: 029 2070 5013 Fax: 029 2071 2599 — MB BCh 1979 Wales; MRCGP 1989.

LEWIS, Peter Scott Barton House, Barton Road, Headington, Oxford OX3 9JE Tel: 01865 767309 Fax: 01865 437247 Email: peter.s.lewis@btinternet.com — MA, MB BChir Camb. 1959; LMCC 1966; MRCPsych 1972; FRCPsych 1997; MRCGP 1966; DPM Eng. 1968; DA Eng. 1964; MInst. GA 1975; B A Canta 1956. (King's Coll. Hosp.) Socs: Camb. Univ. Med. Soc. & Fac. Anaesths. RCS.; Fell. Roy. Soc. Med. Prev: Dir. Ther. & Clin. Dir. HMP Grendon Underwood 1994-1997; Cons. Psychother. BRd.moor Hosp. 1974-1994; Pheving Cons. Sen. Regist. Warneford Hosp. Oxf. 1969-1973.

LEWIS, Petra Jane Guy's & St Thomas' Clinical PET Centre, St Thomas' Hospital, Lambeth Palace Road, London SE1 7EH Tel: 020 7922 8106 Fax: 020 7620 0790; 39 Woodfield Road, Rudswick, Horsham RH12 3EP Tel: 01403 822091 Fax: 01403 822091 — MB BS 1987 Lond. Lect. (Pet/Nuclear Med.) United Med. & Dent. Sch. Guy's & St. Thos. Hosp. Prev: SHO Rotat. (Med.) Guy's Hosp. Lond.; Clin. Fell. (Nuclear Med.) John Hopkins Med. Inst. Balimore, USA.

LEWIS, Philip David Rhys Maudsley Hospital, Denmark Hill, Camberwell, London SE5 Tel: 020 7703 6333 — MB BCh 1986 Wales; MRCPsych 1990. Specialist Regist. (Psychiat.).

LEWIS, Philip Stephen Eglwysbach Surgery, Berw Road, Pontypridd CF37 2AA Tel: 01443 406811 — MB BCh 1975 Wales; MRCGP 1982.

LEWIS, Philip Stuart Stepping Hill Hospital, Poplar Grove, Stockport SK2 7JE Tel: 0161 419 5478 Fax: 0161 419 5478; Ryley Mount, 432 Buxton Road, Stockport SK2 7JQ Tel: 0161 483 9333 Fax: 0161 419 9913 — MB BS 1971 Lond.; BSc (Hons.) Lond. 1968, MB BS 1971; FRCP Lond. 1992; MRCP (UK) 1974. (St. Thos.) Cons. Phys. Cardiol., Hypertens. & Intens. Care Stepping Hill Hosp. Stockport & Alexandra Hosp. Cheadle. Socs: Brit. Cardiac Soc.; Brit. Hypertens. Soc. Prev: Lect. (Med.) Centr. Middlx. Hosp. Lond.; Sen. Regist. (Med.) St. Mary's Hosp. Lond.; Ho. Phys. St. Thos. Hosp. Lond.

LEWIS, Rachel Margaret 104 Greenway Close, Friern Barnet, London N11 3NT — MB BS 1996 Lond.

LEWIS, Ralph Israel Sindell (retired) 16 Montagu Court, Newcastle upon Tyne NE3 4JL Tel: 0161 285 8882 — MB ChB 1938 Ed.; DPH 1946. Prev: GP Newc.

LEWIS, Raymond Neville (retired) 445 Clifton Drive N., St. Annes, Lytham St Annes FY8 2PW — MB ChB 1954 Leeds; FFA RCS Eng. 1960; DA Eng. 1958. Prev: Cons. Anaesth. & Pain Managem. Blackpool & Fylde Gp. Hosps.

LEWIS, Rebecca Jane 82C The Chase, London SW4 0NG — MB BS 1991 Lond.

LEWIS, Rena 10 Llewellyn Ave, Neath SA10 7AL — MB BCh 1958 Wales; MRCP Lond. 1966; DObst RCOG 1966. (Cardiff) Assoc. Specialist in Gen. Med. Neath Gen. Hosp. Prev: Regist. St. John's Hosp. Dis. of Skin Lond.; Med. Regist. St. Albans City Hosp.

LEWIS, Rhiannon Megan 3 Rosebank, Rednock Drive, Dursley GL11 4BX — BM 1995 Soton.

LEWIS, Rhidian Hywel Castle Surgery, 1 Prince of Wales Drive, Neath SA11 3EW Tel: 01639 641444 Fax: 01639 636288; 2 Pentwyn, Dyffryn Road, Brynioch, Neath SA10 7AQ Tel: 01792 813492 Email: rhidanddilewis@yahoo.com — MB BCh 1971 Wales; MRCGP 1975. (Welsh Nat. Sch. of Med., Cardiff) Gen. Practitioner, Drs Lewis, Sheehan, Morgan, Nathan and Lilley, Neath; Team Doctor (Hon.), Wales Under-21 Rugby Team. Socs: BASEM (Treas. Wales Region).

LEWIS, Richard Alan Lapal Medical Practice, 95 Goodrest Avenue, Halesowen B62 0HP Tel: 0121 422 2345 Fax: 0121 423 3099; 17 Fitzroy Avenue, Harborne, Birmingham B17 8RL — MB ChB 1984 Birm.

LEWIS, Richard Alexander Worcester Royal Hospital, Charles Hastings Way, Worcester WR5 1 DD Email: richard.lewis@worcsacute.winds.nhs.uk; Tel: 01886 884552 Fax: 01886 884552 Email: RichardAlewis@compuserve.com — MB BS 1974 Lond.; DM Soton 1985; BSc (Hons. Physiol.) Lond. 1971; FRCP Lond. 1992; MRCP (UK) 1977; MRCS Eng. LRCP Lond. 1974. (St. Thos.) Cons. Gen. Internal Med. (Respirat. Med.) Worcester Roy. Infirm. NHS Trust; Vice Chairm. Counc. Governors St.Richards Hosps Worcester. Socs: Brit. Thoracic. Soc.; Eur. Respirat.. Soc.; Christian Med. Fell.ship. Prev: Sen. Regist. (Gen. & Thoracic Med.) Portsmouth & Soton. Hosps. Wessex RHA; Regist. Rotat. (Med.) St. Richard's Hosp. Chichester & St. Thos. Hosp. Lond; SHO Rotat. Soton. Dist. Hosps.

LEWIS, Richard Jack William Pooh Corner, Wanborough Lane, Cranleigh GU6 7DT — MB BS 1988 Lond.

LEWIS, Richard James 14 Merkland Road, Aberdeen AB24 3HR Tel: 01224 631308 Email: rich.j.lew@btinternet.com — MB ChB 1997 Aberd.; BSc Med Sci 1995.

LEWIS, Richard John Penry, SBStJ Woodlands Surgery, Woodlands Terrace, Caerau, Maesteg CF34 0SR Tel: 01656 734203 Fax: 01656 734311 Email: rjplewis@epulse.net; Llwydarth House, Llwydarth Road, Maesteg CF34 9EU Tel: 01656 730194 Fax: 01656 730194 — MB ChB 1983 Leeds; MRCGP 1987; Dip. IMC RCS Ed. 1994. (Leeds) Med. Dir. Welsh Ambul. Servs. NHS Trust.; Med. Adviser St. John Ambul. Wales; Co. Surg. Bridgend Co. Boro., St John Ambul. Socs: Roy. Coll. Gen. Pract.; Bridgend Local Health Gp.; Founder Mem. of Fac. of Pre-Hosp. Care, Roy. Coll. of Surg.s of Edin. Prev: Med. Dir. M. Glam. FHSA.

LEWIS, Richard Martin Logan Maindiff Court Hospital, Abergavenny NP7 8NF Tel: 01873 735500 — MB BChir 1980 Camb.; MA 1981 Camb.; MRCPsych 1984. Cons. Psychiat. of Old Age Maindiff Ct. Hosp. Abergavenny. Prev: Sen. Regist. (Psychiat.) Yorks. HA; Hon. Tutor Univ. Leeds; SHO & Regist. Coney Hill Hosp. Gloucester.

LEWIS, Richard Vaughan The Bungalow, Grove Lane, Badsworth, Pontefract WF9 1AN — MB ChB 1978 Leeds; BSc (Hons.) (Pharmacol.) Leeds 1975, MD 1987, MB ChB (Hons; Distinc. Surg. 1978; MRCP (UK) 1981. Cons. Gen. Med. & Cardiol. Pontefract Gen. Infirm. Prev: Regist. (Med.) Airedale Hosp. Yorks.; Lect. (Med.) Univ. Dundee; Regist. (Med.) Auckland, NZ.

LEWIS, Robert Bowman (retired) 25 Empingham Road, Stamford PE9 2RJ — MA Oxf. 1969; MB BS Lond. 1969; FFA RCS Eng. 1975; DObst RCOG 1971. Prev: Cons. (Anaesth.) PeterBoro. Health Dist.

LEWIS, Robert Charles David Oakley Park, Oakley, Diss IP21 4AU — MB BS 1997 Lond.

LEWIS, Robert John c/o Longridge, Aish Road, Stoke Gabriel, Totnes TQ9 6PX — BSc Lond. 1976, MB BS 1979; MRCGP 1985; DCH RCP Lond. 1984; DRCOG 1982. (Lond. Hosp.) GP Melbourne, Australia. Prev: Regist. St. Peters Hospice Bristol; GP Trainee Exeter VTS; Ho. Phys. Lond. Hosp.

LEWIS, Robert John Wessex Regional Renal Unit, St Mary's Hospital, Milton Road, Portsmouth PO3 6AD Tel: 023 92 286000 Fax: 023 92 866108; 134 High Street, Portsmouth PO1 2HW Tel: 023 92 826270 — MB BS 1984 Lond.; FRCP 2001; MD Lond. 1996; MRCP (UK) 1987. (Westm.) Cons. Nephrol. Wessex Regional Renal Unit Portsmouth. Prev: Sen. Regist. (Nephrol.) Wessex Regional Renal Unit Portsmouth; Regist. (Nephrol.) Guy's Hosp. Lond., Roy. Sussex Co. Hosp. Brighton & King's Coll. Hosp. Lond.

LEWIS, Robert Stephen Larksfield Surgery, Aslesey Rd, Stotfield, Hitchin SG5 4HB Tel: 01462 732200 — MB BS 1988 Lond.; MRCGP 1992; DFFP 1993; Dip Occ Med 1998. GP Princip.

LEWIS, Robert Wynne 30 Victoria Road, Ponthenri, Llanelli SA15 5PU — MB BCh 1980 Wales.

LEWIS, Roderic Owen The Surgery, 36 Pagoda Avenue, Richmond TW9 2HG Tel: 020 8948 4217 Fax: 020 8332 7639 — MB BS 1990 Lond.; MB BS London 1990; MRCGP 1996. (Charing Cross and Westminster) GP Princip.

LEWIS, Mr Roger Eugene The Cottage, Woodbridge Road, Grundisburgh, Woodbridge IP13 6UD — MB ChB 1970 Sheff.; FRCS Ed. (Ophth.) 1976; DO Eng. 1974. Cons. Ophth. Surg. Ipswich Hosp.

LEWIS, Roger Russell Guy's Hospital, Thomas Guy House (Ground Floor), London SE1 9RT Tel: 020 7955 5000 ext 3666 Fax: 020 7955 4465; Normanton, 99 Longton Avenue, London SE26 6RF Tel: 020 8699 7851 — MB BS 1968 Lond.; MD Lond. 1981; FRCP Lond. 1989; MRCP (UK) 1972. (Westm. Hosp. Med. Sch.) Cons. Phys. (Geriats. Gen. & Stroke Med.) Guy's & St. Thomas' Hosp. Lond.; Hon. Sen. Lect. Socs: Roy. Soc. Med.; Brit. Geriat. Soc.

LEWIS, Rohan Francis Miles Microbiology Department, Victoria Infirmary, Glasgow G42 9TY Tel: 0141 201 5602 — MB BChir 1978 Camb.; MA, MB BChir Camb. 1978; MSc Med. Microbiol. Lond. 1985; MRCPath 1986; FRCPath 1996. Cons. Microbiol. Vict. Infirm. Glas. Prev: Sen. Regist. (Med. Microbiol.) Chichester & Worthing Hosps.; Sen. Regist. (Med. Microbiol.) St. Geo. Hosp. Lond.

LEWIS, Mr Roland Swaine (retired) 88 Maida Vale, London W9 1PR Tel: 020 7624 6253 — MRCS Eng. LRCP Lond. 1932; BA (Nat. Sc. Trip.) Camb. 1929, MA, MB BChir 1945; FRCS Eng. 1934. Prev: Sen. Surg. (ENT) King's Coll. Hosp. & Mt. Vernon Hosp.

LEWIS, Rollo James War Memorial Health Centre, Beaufort Street, Crickhowell NP8 1AZ Tel: 01873 810255 Fax: 01873 811949; Ty Ffawyddog, Llangattock, Crickhowell NP8 1PY — MB BS 1972 Lond.; MRCP (UK) 1979; MRCGP 1991. (Char. Cross) Prev: Lect. (Haemat.) W.m. Med. Sch. Lond. & Char. Cross Hosp. Lond.; Regist. (Gen. Med.) Nevill Hall Hosp. Abergavenny.

LEWIS, Mr Ronald Hugh (retired) Haroldston Lodge, Broad Haven, Haverfordwest SA62 3JP Tel: 01437 781236 — MB BCh 1948 Wales; BSc Wales 1945, MB BCh 1948; FRCS Eng. 1958. Prev: Cons. Gen. Surg. Withybush Gen. Hosp. HaverfordW.

LEWIS, Rosalyn Anne Greenford Road Medical Centre, 591 Greenford Road, Greenford UB6 8QH Tel: 020 8578 1764 Fax: 020 8578 8347; 2 The Greenway, Rayners Lane, Pinner HA5 5DR — MB ChB 1984 Manch.; MRCGP 1989.

LEWIS, Sally Jane 32 Dovercourt Road, London SE22 8ST — MB BS 1993 Lond.; MB BS (Hons.) Lond. 1993; BSc (Hons.) Lond. 1990; MRCP (UK) 1996. (St. Geo. Hosp. Med. Sch. Lond.) p/t Specialist Regist. (Diagnostic Radiol.) S. Thames (W.).

LEWIS, Sally Margaret 10 Lakeside Drive, Lakeside, Cardiff CF23 6DD — MB BCh 1982 Wales.

LEWIS, Sarah Ann 129 Clarence Avenue, New Malden KT3 3TY — MB BS 1990 Lond.

LEWIS, Sheila Rosemary (retired) 40 Twyford Avenue, Fortis Green, London N2 9NL Tel: 020 8883 5236 — PhD Lond. 1969, MB BS 1956; FRCP Lond. 1978, M 1964; DCH Eng. 1959. Prev: Cons. Paediat. N. Middlx. Hosp. Lond.

LEWIS, Shirley Ada (retired) 23 Longdale Lane, Ravenshead, Nottingham NG15 9AB — MB ChB 1955 Bristol; DPH Bristol 1961; DObst RCOG 1957. Prev: Cons. Community Paediat. Nottm. HA.

LEWIS, (Shirley) Mitchell (retired) Department of Haematology, Hammersmith Hospital, Faculty of Medicine Imperial College, London W12 0NN Tel: 020 8383 3961 Fax: 020 8742 9335 Email: smlenl@intonet.co.uk — MB ChB Cape Town 1949; MD Cape Town 1958, BSc 1949; FRCPath 1973, M 1963; DCP Lond 1954. Emerit. Reader Haemat. & Sen. Research Fell. Imperial Coll. Sch. Med. Lond.; WHO Expert Advis. Panel Health Laborat. Servs.; Dir. WHO Collaborating Centre for Diagn. Haemat. Prev: Cons. Haemat. Hammersmith Hosp.

LEWIS, Professor Shôn William University of Manchester, School of Psychiatry & Behavioural Sciences, Withington Hospital, West Didsbury, Manchester M20 2LR Email: shon.lewis@man.ac.uk — MB BS 1979 Lond.; FRCPsych 1996; MD Lond. 1993; MPhil Lond. 1986, BSc (1st cl. Hons.) 1976; MRCS Eng. LRCP Lond. 1979; MRCPsych 1984. (Guy's) Prof. of Adult Psychiat., Univ. of Manch.; Head, Sch. Of Psychiat. & Behavoural Sci., Univ. of Manch. Prev: Lect. & Sen. Lect. Inst. Psychiat. Lond.; Regist. (Psychiat.) Maudsley Hosp. Lond.; Sen. Lect. & Cons. Psychiat. Char. Cross & W.m. Med. Sch. Lond.

LEWIS, Sian Elspeth St. John's Health Centre, Hermitage Road, St. John's, Woking GU21 1TD Tel: 01483 723451 — MB ChB 1982 Bristol; MRCGP 1986; DCH RCP Lond. 1987; DRCOG 1985.

LEWIS, Sidney (retired) 7 Combemartin Road, Southfields, London SW18 5PP Tel: 020 8788 2292 — MB BS 1946 Lond. Med. Off. Red Cross Wimbledon. Prev: Metrop. Police Surg.

LEWIS, Simon James The Croft, Maddocks Hill, Norley, Warrington WA6 8JX Email: sjlewis@doctors.org.uk — MB BS 1998 Lond.; MB BS Lond 1998; BSc (Hons) Tumor Biology Lond '95. (University college London) SHO (A&E) QEQM Hosp., Margate.

LEWIS, Simon John Geoffrey 1 School Terrace, Monkton, Pembroke SA71 4LH — MB BCh 1995 Wales.

LEWIS, Simon Nicholas Simmons House, St Lukes Hospital, Woodside Avenue, London N10 3HU — MB BS 1991 Lond.; BSc Univ. Lond. 1985; MRCPsych 1996. Cons. Child and Adolescant Psychiat., Simmons Ho. Adolesc. unit, & UCLH; Hon. Sen. Lect. in Child & Adolesc. Psychiat. UCL.

LEWIS, Sophia Elizabeth Hilltop, 76 Manchester Road, Wilmslow SK9 2JY — MB ChB 1995 Manch. SHO (O & G) Glas. Roy. Infirm. NHS Trust. Socs: BMA; Med. Protec. Soc.

LEWIS, Stephen Glyn 43 Asher Reeds, Langton Green, Tunbridge Wells TN3 0AN — MB BS 1993 Lond.

LEWIS, Stephen Ian Clarence Medical Centre, Vansittart Road, Windsor SL4 5AS Tel: 01753 865773 Fax: 01753 833694; 3 Dower Park, Windsor SL4 4BQ Tel: 01753 868053 — MB ChB 1967 Birm.; MRCS Eng. LRCP Lond. 1967. (Birm.) Hosp. Pract. (Gastroenterol. & Gen. Med.) Wexham Pk. Hosp. Slough. Socs: Windsor & Dist. Med. Soc.; Brit. Soc. Gastroenterol.; Soc. Occupat. Med. Prev: Regist (Gen. Med.) Roy. Infirm. & Gen. Hosp. Leicester.

LEWIS, Stephen John 8 Downsway, Salisbury SP1 3QW — MB ChB 1987 Bristol.

LEWIS, Stuart Gilbert Clark and Partners, 20 Aitken Street, Largs KA30 8AU Tel: 01475 674545 Fax: 01475 689645 — MB ChB 1988 Glas.; MRCGP 1993; DRCOG 1993.

LEWIS, Susan Elizabeth Village Surgery, 2 Churchside, New Longton, Preston PR4 4LU Tel: 01772 613804 Fax: 01772 617812 — MB ChB 1977 Manch.; DRCOG 1979.

LEWIS, Susan Jane University Hospital Lewisham, Cardiology Department, Lewisham Hospital, Lewisham High St., London SE13 6LH Tel: 020 8333 3000; 70 Streathbourne Road, Tooting, London SW17 8QY Tel: 020 8767 4961 — BM BS 1980 Nottm.; DM Nottm. 1988, BMedSci 1978; MRCP (UK) 1983; FRCP 1998. p/t Cons. Cardiol. Lewisham Hosp. Lond.; Hon. Cons. & Sen. Lect. Guy's & Thos. NHS Trust. Socs: Brit. Cardiac Soc. Prev: Sen. Regist. (Cardiol.) Guy's Hosp. Lond.; Regist. (Cardiol.) Lond. Chest Hosp.; Brit. Heart Foundat. Jun. Research Fell. Roy. Sussex Co. Hosp. Brighton.

LEWIS, Suzanne Emma Birch Terrace Surgery, 25A Birch Terrace, Hanley, Stoke-on-Trent ST1 3JN Tel: 01782 212436; 8 Glaisher Drive, Meir Park, Blythe Bridge, Stoke-on-Trent ST3 7RF Tel: 01782 393812 — BM 1988 Soton. Prev: Trainee GP Wolverhampton.

LEWIS, Teresa Lindsay Carregwen Surgery, Church Road, Blaenavon NP4 9AF Tel: 01495 790264 Fax: 01495 790334 — MB BCh 1989 Wales; MRCGP 1994; DCH RCP Lond. 1992. (UWCM)

LEWIS, Thomas David (retired) 34 Callington Road, Saltash PL12 6DY Tel: 01752 843251 Email: lewistd@btinternet.com — MB BS Lond. 1950; DPH Bristol 1956. Prev: GP Saltash.

LEWIS, Thomas Dickens Crofts 5 Downs View Close, Aberthin, Cowbridge CF71 7HG — MRCS Eng. LRCP Lond. 1940. (Cardiff) Prev: Ho. Phys. City Lodge Hosp. Cardiff.

LEWIS, Mr Thomas Loftus Townshend, CBE 13 Copse Hill, London SW20 0NB Tel: 020 8946 5089 — MB BChir Camb. 1942; FRCS Eng. 1946; MRCS Eng. LRCP Lond. 1946; FRCOG 1961, M 1948. (Camb. & Guy's) Emerit. Cons. O & G Guy's Hosp., Qu. Charlotte's Hosp. & Chelsea Hosp. for Wom. Lond. Prev: Civil. Cons. to Army; Dir. Dept. Obst. Guy's Hosp. Lond.; Cons. Gyn. St. Olave's Hosp.

LEWIS, Timothy Field House Dolgran, Pencader SA39 9BY — MB BCh 1970 Wales; FRCP 1991; MRCP (UK) 1974. Sen. Cons. Phys. W. Wales Gen. Hosp. Carmarthen.

LEWIS, Timothy Tristan The Retreat, Redhill Lane, Elberton, Olveston, Bristol BS35 4AJ — MB ChB 1975 Birm.; FRCR 1985; DMRD Eng. 1982. Cons. Neuroradiol. Frenchay Hosp. Bristol. Socs: Brit. Inst. Radiol.; Assoc. Mem. Brit. Soc. Neuroradiol. Prev: Sen. Regist. (Neuroradiol.) Nat. Hosp. Qu. Sq. Lond.; Hon. Sen. Regist. (Neuroradiol.) Moorfields Eye Hosp. Lond.; Sen. Regist. (Radiol.) N. Staffs. Hosp. Centre Stoke on Trent.

LEWIS, Valerie Judith Shelton Hospital, Bicton Health, Shrewsbury — MB BS 1984 Lond.; Diploma in Psychiatric Medicine 2000 Stoke (Keele University); BSc Lond. 1980; DRCOG 1988; Cert. Family Plann. JCC 1986. (Univ. Coll. Hosp.) Staff Grade Psychiat. Shrewsbury; Disabil. Analyst, Shrewsbury. Socs: BMA.

LEWIS, Vanessa Anchor Cottage, Middle Road, Lytchett Matravers, Poole BH16 6HJ Tel: 01202 622353 — BM 1988 Soton.; MRCGP 1996. (Univ. Soton.) Locum GP.

LEWIS, Vaughan Edward 14 Melrose Place, Bristol BS8 2NG — BM BCh 1993 Oxf.

LEWIS, Wayne Carregwen Surgery, Church Road, Blaenavon NP4 9AF Tel: 01495 790264 Fax: 01495 790334 — MB BCh 1990 Wales; MRCGP 1995; DRCOG 1993.

LEWIS, William Edward (retired) Y Berllan, Ruthin Road, Mold CH7 1QH — MB ChB Liverp. 1951; MRCGP 1961; DObst RCOG 1954. Dir. St David's Hospice Llandudno.

LEWIS, William Gwyn Wallcrouch Farm, Wallcrouch, Wadhurst TN5 7JH Tel: 01580 200387 — MB BS 1956 Lond.; MRCS Eng. LRCP Lond. 1952; DPH Eng. 1959; DObst RCOG 1954. (Guy's) Prev: Ho. Surg. Roy. E. Sussex Hosp. Hastings; Ho. Phys. Kent & Sussex Hosp. Tunbridge Wells; Ho. Surg. (Obst.) King Edwd. VII Hosp. Windsor.

LEWIS, William John (retired) Whiteways, 14 Dan Y Graig Avenue, Newton, Porthcawl CF36 5AA Tel: 01656 713418 — MRCS Eng. LRCP Lond. 1943; FFA RCS Eng. 1954; DA Eng. 1948. Cons. Anaesth. Bromorgannwg Hosp. Gp. Prev: Surg. Lt. R.N.V.R.

LEWIS, William Kevin 26 Cleveland Close, Ormesby, Middlesbrough TS7 9BX — MB BS 1973 Newc.; MRCPsych. 1980. Cons. (Psychiat.) St. Luke's Hosp. Middlesbrough.

LEWIS, Mr Wyn Griffith Department of Surgery, Royal Gwent Hospital, Cardiff Road, Newport NP20 2UB Tel: 01633 234234 Fax: 01633 238559 Email: wyn.lewis@gwent.wales.nhs.uk — MB BCh 1984 Wales; MD Wales 1995; FRCS Eng. 1989; FRCS Ed. 1989; MRCS Eng. LRCP Lond. 1983. (Univ. Wales Coll. Med.) Cons. Gen. Surg. Glan Hafren NHS Trust Newport. Socs: Assn. Upper G.I. Surg.; Surg. Res. Soc. Prev: Lect. (Surg.) Leeds Gen. Infirm.; Regist. (Gen. Surg.) Yorks. RHA; Research Fell. (Surg.) Leeds Gen. Infirm.

LEWIS, Yvette Karen 3 Sherriff House, The Broadway, Farnham Common, Slough SL2 3QH — MB ChB 1993 Sheff.

LEWIS-BARNED, Caroline Amanda The Rectory Farmhouse, Church Hanborough, Oxford OX29 8AB — MB BS 1982 Lond.

LEWIS-BARNED, Nicholas John Diabetes Resource Centre, North Tyneside General Hospital, Rake Law, North Shields WE29 8NH Tel: 0191 293708 Fax: 01452 394755 Email: nick.lewis-barned@northumbria-healthcare.nhs.uk — MB BS 1982 Lond.; MRCP (UK) 1986; FRACP 1990; FRCP Glas. 1996; FRCP 2000. (Westm.) Sen. Lec in diabetes,N Tyneside Hosp. N Shields; Hon cons endocrinologist, N Tyneside hosp. Socs: Brit. Diabetic Assn.; (Chairm.) NZ Soc. Study Diabetes; Brit. Endocrine Soc. Prev: Cons physc & endocrinologist, Gloucs Roy. Hosp; Sen. Lect. (Med.,

Endocrinol. & Diabetes) Univ. Otago Med. Sch.; Lect. (Med.) Univ. Otago Med. Sch.

LEWIS-JONES, Catherine Mary 6 Salisbury Road, Cressington Park, Liverpool L19 0PJ Tel: 0151 427 3611 — MB ChB 1981 Liverp.; MRCP (UK) 1986; Dip. Palliat. Med. Wales 1994. Cons. Palliat. Med. Liverp. Prev: Regist. (Med.) Liverp. HA.

LEWIS-JONES, David Iwan Reproductive Medicine Unit, Liverpool Women's Hospital, Crown St., Liverpool L8 7SS; 10 Stanlowe View, Grassendale, Liverpool L19 0PX Tel: 0151 494 2099 — MB ChB 1972 Liverp.; MD Liverp. 1983. Sen. Lect. (Obst. & Gyn) Univ. Liverp.; Acad. Sub-Dean Fac. Med. Univ. Liverp; Hon. Cons. Androl. Asst. Conception Unit Liverp. Wom. Hosp. Socs: Soc. Study Fertil. & Brit. Fertil. Soc.; Chairm. of the Brit Andrology Soc.; Europ. Soc. Of human ReProduc. and Embroylology. Prev: Sen. Lect. (Human Anat. & Cell Biol.) Univ. Liverp.; GP Liverp.

LEWIS-JONES, Hilary Jane Elounda, Clos De La Grande Marche, Kings Road, St Peter Port, Guernsey GY1 1Q — MB BS 1973 Lond.; MRCS Eng. LRCP Lond. 1973.

LEWIS-JONES, Huw Gwynedd University Hospital Aintree, Radiology Directorate, London Lane, Liverpool L9 7AL Tel: 0151 529 2880 Fax: 0151 529 3813 Email: huw.lewis-jones@aht.nwest.nhs.uk; 6 Sailsbury Road, Cressington Park, Liverpool L19 0PJ Tel: 0151 427 3611 — MB ChB 1981 Liverp.; MRCP (UK) 1984; FRCR 1987; DMRD 1986; DMRD 1986. Cons. Radiol. Univ. Hosp Aintree Liverp. Prev: Sen. Regist. (Radiol.) Liverp. HA.

LEWIS ROBERTS, Gareth, OStJ Forest Glades Medical Centre, Bromsgrove Street, Kidderminster DY10 1PH Tel: 01562 822509 Fax: 01562 827046; Melford House, 50 Hillgrove Crescent, Kidderminster DY10 3AR Tel: 01562 822445 — MB ChB 1969 Liverp.; Cert. JCC Lond. 1978. Clin. Asst. (ENT) Kidderminster Gen. Hosp. Socs: BMA; Assoc. Mem. RCGP; Kidderminster Med. Soc. Prev: GP Heswall; Trainee GP Chester; SHO Clatterbidge Hosp., Chester Roy. Infirm. & United Liverp. Teach. Hosps.

LEWIS-RUSSELL, Jonathan Mark, Flight Lt. RAF Med. Br. 25 Moortown Avenue, Portsmouth PO6 1EP — MB BCh 1993 Wales. Hon. SHO Burns & Plastic Surg. Dept. Stoke Mandaville Hosp. Prev: Med. Off. (Gen. Pract.) RAF Wittering P'boro.; SHO MDHU P'boro.

LEWITH, George Thomas 51 Bedford Place, Southampton SO15 2DG Tel: 02380 334752 Fax: 02380 231835; Sway Wood House, Mead End Road, Sway, Lymington SO41 6EE Tel: 01590 682129 — MB BChir 1974 Camb.; BA (Biochem.) Camb. 1971, MA 1974; DM Soton. 1994; MRCP (UK) 1977; MRCGP 1980; FRCP 1999. (Camb. & Westm.) Dir. Centre for the Study of Complementary Med. Soton.; Hon. Sen. Research Fell. (Med.) Soton. Univ.; Cons. Phys. (Complementary Med.) CCSF. Prev: Lect. (Primary Med. Care) Univ. Soton.; SHO Rotat. (Med.) Whittington Hosp. Lond. & (Obst.) Univ. Coll. Hosp. Lond.; Ho. Phys. (Med.) & Ho. Surg. (Cardiothoracic) W.m. Hosp. Lond.

LEWKONIA, Raymond Maurice 3 Grosvenor Court, Queens Drive, Liverpool L15 6YA — MB ChB 1966 Liverp.; FRCP Canada 1976; MRCP (U.K.) 1970; FACP 1983; DCH Eng. 1968. Prev: Sen. Regist. & Clin. Tutor Dept. Med. Hammersmith Hosp. Lond.; Research Fell. Dept. Therapeut. Univ. Edin.; Med. Regist. Liverp. Roy. Infirm.

LEWKOWICZ, Nicholas Maciej Tel: 01329 842226 — BM 1981 Soton. Princip. in Gen. Pract. Socs: Fareham Med. Soc.; Brit. Assn. of Sport and Exercise Med. Prev: Trainee GP Cheltenham & Solihull VTS.

LEWSEY, David Martyn (retired) The Surgery, Romney House Surgery, Long St., Tetbury GL8 8AA Tel: 01666 502303 Fax: 01666 504549 — MB BS 1962 Lond.; MRCS Eng. LRCP Lond. 1962; DObst RCOG 1966. Prev: Asst. Ho. Phys. & Ho. Surg. Guy's Hosp. Lond.

LEWTAS, David Allen Meldon, 39 Lyn Grove, Kingskerswell, Newton Abbot TQ12 5AR Tel: 01803 872010 — MB ChB St. And. 1946. (St. And.) SCMO & Hearing Assessm. Med. Off. Torbay Health. Prev: Cas. Off., Ho. Surg. (ENT) & (O & G) Roy. Devon & Exeter Hosp.; Sen. Surg. Brit. India Steam Navigation Co. Ltd.

LEWTHWAITE, Charles Julian, OStJ, Brigadier late RAMC Retd. (retired) Manor Cottage, Much Hadham SG10 6DA Tel: 01279 843826 — BM BCh Oxf. 1957; FFOM RCP Lond. 1987, MFOM 1981; FFCM 1982; DIH Eng. 1969; DPH Lond. 1968; DTM & H RCP Lond. 1963; BM BCh 1957 Oxford. Prev: Dir. Health Defence Med. Servs. Directorate.

LEWTHWAITE, Paul White 13 Maple Court, Brandon, Durham DH7 8PA — MB ChB 1987 Aberd.; MRCP Ed. 1994.

LEWTHWAITE, Penelope Nottingham City Hospital, Hucknall Road, Nottingham NG5 1PB Tel: 0115 969 1169; c/o Clophill Road, Maulden, Bedford MK45 2AA Tel: 01525 403139 — MB BS 1994 Lond.; BSc Lond. 1991. (King's Coll. Sch. Med. & Dent.) SHO Med. Rotat. Nottm. City Hosp. NHS Trust. Prev: SHO (A & E) Lewisham NHS Trust; Med. Off. Manguzi Hosp., Kwangwanase, S. Afr.; Ho. Off. (Surg.) King's Coll. Hosp. Lond.

LEWTHWAITE, Ruth 49/51 Prospect Road, Lakeside, Redditch B98 8NH — MB ChB 1958 Birm.; DA Eng. 1963.

***LEWTHWAITE, Simon Christopher** 3 Small Lane, Eccleshall, Stafford ST21 6AD — MB ChB 1994 Birm.; ChB Birm. 1994.

LEY, Barbara Elaine 7A Cotham Park, Cotham, Bristol BS6 6BZ — MB ChB 1987 Bristol; MRCP (UK) 1992.

LEY, Mr Christopher Charles The Riverside Practice, Marylebone Road, March PE15 8BG Tel: 01354 652611 Fax: 01354 650926 — MB BChir 1980 Camb.; FRCS Ed. 1987; DFFP 1994. Clin. Asst. (Orthop.) Doddington Co. Hosp. Prev: Trainee GP Cambs. FHSA; Regist. Rotat. (Orthop.) P'boro HA.

LEY, Roderick John Stamford Resource Centre, St George's Avenue, Ryhall Road, Stamford PE9 1UN; 6 Queens Walk, Stamford PE9 2QE — BM BS 1990 Nottm.; T(GP) 1995; MRCGP 1994; MRCPsych 1999. (Univ. of Nottingham)

LEYBURN, Peter (retired) Orchard Close, Main St., Alne, York YO61 1RT Tel: 01347 838323 — MB BS Durh. 1956; BSc (Physiol. 1st cl. Hons.) Durh. 1953; FRCP Ed. 1971, M 1959; FRCPsych 1975, M 1971; DPM Eng. 1961. Prev: Cons. Psychiat. Newc. HA (T).

LEYDEN, Hannah Elizabeth Box Surgery, London Road, Box, Corsham SN13 8NA Tel: 01225 742361; 140 Bath Road, Atworth, Melksham SN12 8JU — BA (Hons. Physiol.) Oxf. 1980, BM BCh 1983; MRCGP 1987; DRCOG 1986; DCH RCP Lond. 1985; Dip Occ. Med. 1997. (Oxford)

LEYDEN, Patrick Vincent Weavers Medical Centre, 50 School Lane, Kettering NN16 0DH — MB BCh BAO 1987 NUI; T(GP) 1992; Cert. Family Plann. RCPI 1991; DObst. RCPI 1991; DCH NUI 1989. Socs: BMA & Med. Defence Union. Prev: Trainee GP Leics.

LEYDEN, Paul Edward Francis 45 Bush Road, Antrim BT41 2RL — MB BCh BAO 1981 Belf.; FFA RCSI 1985. Cons. Anaesth. Antrim Area Hosp.

LEYDEN, Thomas Michael Tel: 01327 877770 Fax: 01327 310267 — MB BS 1988 Lond.; D OccMed 2000; MRCGP 1992; DRCOG 1992. (Char. Cross & Westm. Med. Sch.) Socs: Soc. of Occup. Med. Prev: Med. PHO Townsville Gen. Hosp. N. Qu.sland; Trainee GP N.ampton VTS.

LEYDON, Karen Mary (Spivey) Northampton General Hospital, Cliftonville, Northampton NN1 5BD Tel: 01604 634700 — BM BCh 1989 Oxf.; BA 1986 Physiological Sciences; FRCA 1995. (Oxford) p/t Cons. Anaesth. N.ampton Gen. Hosp. Prev: Specialist Regist. (Anaesth.) Oxf. Rotat.

LEYLAND, Barbara Appletree Medical Practice, 47a Town Street, Duffield, Belper DE56 4GG Tel: 01332 841219; The Gables, Town Street, Duffield, Belper DE56 4EH Tel: 01332 840707 — BM BCh 1973 Oxf.

LEYLAND, Frederick Clive c/o Wordsley Hospital, Wordsley, Stourbridge DY8 5QX Tel: 01384 456111 Ext: 3438; 11A Red Hill Close, Stourbridge DY8 1NF — MB BChir 1961 Camb.; MB Camb. 1961, BChir 1960; FRCP Lond. 1984; MRCP (UK) 1972; DCH Eng. 1962; FRCPCH 1998. (Univ. Coll. Hosp.) Cons. Paediat. Dudley HA. Prev: Research Fell. Inst. Child Health Lond.; Med. Regist. St. Margt.'s Hosp. Epping; Ho. Phys. & Ho. Surg. Univ. Coll. Hosp.

LEYLAND, Gillian Ruth The Surgery, Station Road, Claverdon, Warwick CV35 8PH Tel: 01926 842205 Fax: 01926 843467; Porlock, Church Road, Claverdon, Warwick CV35 8PB Tel: 01926 842116 — MB ChB 1966 Liverp. Socs: BMA. Prev: Ho. Phys. & Ho. Surg. Roy. S.. Hosp. Liverp.; SHO (Anaesth.) Roy. S.. Hosp. Liverp. & (Path.) David Lewis N.. Hosp. Liverp.

LEYLAND, Helen Elizabeth Bodmin Road Health Centre, Bodmin Road, Ashton on Mersey, Sale M33 5JH Tel: 0161 962 4625 Fax: 0161 905 3317; 50 Willow Tree Road, Altrincham WA14 2EG — MB BS 1990 Lond.; BA Oxf. 1987; MRCGP 1994. (St. Mary's Hosp. Imperial Coll. Lond.)

LEYLAND, Kathleen Grace (retired) The Southbank Child Centre, 207 Old Ruthergen Rd, Glasgow G5 0RA Tel: 0141 201 0908 Fax: 0141 201 0939 — MB BCh BAO 1980 Belf.; MRCP (UK) 1990; DCH RCP Lond. 1988. Prev: Sen. Regist. (Paediat. & Community Child Health) Soton. Gen. Hosp.

LEYLAND, Martin Daniel 6 The Closes, Haddenham, Aylesbury HP17 8JN — MB ChB 1992 Manch.; FRCOphth 1996. Specialist Regist. Ophth. W.. Eye Hosp. Lond.

LEYLAND, Mary Catherine Rutherford Medical Centre, 1 Rutherford Road, Mossley Hill, Liverpool L18 0HL Tel: 0151 722 1803 Fax: 0151 738 0083 — MB ChB 1980 Liverp.

LEYLAND, Mary Felicia Felin-y-Foel, Brynsiencyn, Anglesey, Llanfairpwllgwyngyll LL61 6TQ Tel: 01248 430329 — MB ChB Liverp. 1948. (Liverp.) Socs: Liverp. Soc. Anaesth.& Assn. Dent. Anaesths.

LEYLAND, Michael Joseph Porlock, Church Road, Claverdon, Warwick CV35 8PB — MRCS Eng. LRCP Lond. 1967; MSc Manch. 1974; BDS Liverp. 1961; FRCP Lond. 1982; MRCP (UK) 1971; LDS RCS Eng. 1961. Cons. Phys. E. Birm. Hosp. Prev: Lect. (Clin. Haemat.) Univ. Manch.; Cons. Clin. Haemat. Liverp. AHA (T); Lect. (Clin. Haemat.) Univ. Liverp.

LEYSHON, Mr Anthony Darent Valley Hospital, Darent Wood Road, Dartford DA2 8DA Tel: 01322 428100 Fax: 01732 822380; Tel: 01732 824145 Fax: 01732 822380 Email: kneeman@ukgateway.net — MB BS Lond. 1968; FRCS Eng. 1973; MRCS Eng. LRCP Lond. 1968. (Guy's) Cons. Orthop. Surg. Dartford & Gravesham HA. Socs: Brit. Assn. for Surg. of Knee. Prev: Sen. Surg. Off. Roy. Nat. Orthop. Hosp. Stanmore; Clin. Lect. Inst. Orthop. Roy. Nat. Orthop. Hosp. Lond.

LEYSHON, Marian Wynne (retired) 121 Hempstead Road, Watford WD17 3HF Tel: 01923 229750 — MB BCh 1952 Wales; 1949 BSc Wales 1949; 1983 FRCPsych 1983, M 1971; 1968 DPM Eng. 1968. Prev: Med. Asst. Napsbury Hosp.

LEYSHON, Rhiannon 11 Ripley Road, Stockton-on-Tees TS20 1NX — MB BS 1991 Newc.

LEYSHON, Mr Robert Lloyd St. David's House, 1 Uplands Terrace, Swansea SA2 0GU Tel: 01792 472922 Fax: 01792 466803; 19 Westport Avenue, Mayals, Swansea SA3 5EA Tel: 01792 403003 — MB BS 1972 Lond.; BSc (Hons. Physiol.) Lond. 1969; FRCS Eng. 1977; MRCS Eng. LRCP Lond. 1972. (St. Mary's) Cons. Orthop. Morriston Hosp. Swansea. Socs: Brit. Orthop. Assn.; Brit. Orthop. Sports Trauma Assn.; Eur. Rheum. Arthrit. Surg. Soc. Prev: Sen. Lect. & Hon. Cons. Orthop. Welsh Nat. Sch. Med.; Sen. Regist. (Orthop.) Cardiff Roy. Infirm.; Ho. Surg. St. Mary's Hosp. Lond.

LEYSHON, Viner Nicholl (retired) Farnhill, 15 Montpelier, Quarndon, Derby DE22 5JW Tel: 01332 559389 — MB BS 1936 Lond.; MD Lond. 1939; MRCS Eng. LRCP Lond. 1936; FFCM 1974; DPH Lond. 1939. Mem. Middle Temple. Prev: MOH & Sch. Med. Off. Co. Boro. Derby.

LEYTON, Eli Grove Road Surgery, 3 Grove Road, Solihull B91 2AG Tel: 0121 705 1105 Fax: 0121 711 4098 — MB ChB 1975 Leeds; DA Eng. 1978; DCH Eng. 1978; DRCOG 1977. Home Office Crematorium Ref.

LEYTON, Hilary Ruth North West Thames RHA, 40 Eastbourne Terrace, London W2 3QR — MB BS 1980 Lond.; MSc Lond. 1987, BSc 1974; MFPHM 1993; DRCOG 1983. (Univ. Coll. Hosp.) Sen. Regist. (Pub. Health Med.) NW Thames RHA. Prev: Sen. Regist. & Lect. (Community Med.) NE Thames RHA Univ. Coll. Lond.; Trainee GP Oxf. FPC.

LEYVA-LEON, Francisco De Asis Dept of Cardiology, Good Hope Hospital, Rectory Rd, Sutton Coldfield B75 7RR — MB ChB 1987 Manch.; MD Manch.; BSc (Hons) Manch.; MRCP 1990 (UK). (Manchester) Cons. Cardiol. Little Asion Hosp. Sutton Coldfield. Socs: Brit. Caricec Soc.

LEZAMA, Margaret Joyce (retired) 177 Menlove Avenue, Liverpool L18 3JE Tel: 0151 428 2898 — MB ChB 1944 Liverp.; DCH Eng. 1946.

LHOPITALLIER, Odile Marie Cromwell Hospital, 162-174 Cromwell Road, London SW5 0TU — MD 1976 Marseilles.

LHOTSKY, Jaromir Cobbler, Harwich Road, Wix, Manningtree CO11 2SA — Lakarexamen 1975 Uppsala.

LI, Adrian Ho-Yin 69 Osborne Drive, Belfast BT9 6LJ — MB BCh BAO 1987 Belf.; FFA RCSI 1992.

LI, Mr Alan Gee Kwong Department of Surgery, Level 8, Clinical Sciences Building, St James's University Hospital, Leeds LS9 7TF Tel: 0113 243 3144; The Coach House, 52 Newconner Lane, Chapel Allerton, Leeds LS7 3NX Tel: 0113 262 0473 — MB ChB 1990 Bristol; FRCS Eng. 1994; FRCS Ed. 1994. (Univ. Bristol) Tutor & Hon. Regist. (Gen. Surg.) St. Jas. Univ. Hosp. Leeds; MRC/RCS Clin.Train. Fell. Univ. Leeds. Prev: SHO St Jas Univ. Hosp. Leeds.

LI, Albert Martin 55 Queen of Denmark Court, Greenland Passage, Findland St., London SE16 7TB — MB BCh 1993 Wales.

LI, Andrew Sau Lai The Imar Institute, 100 Harley St., London W1N 1AF Tel: 020 7487 5077 Fax: 020 7487 5066 — MB BS 1988 Lond.; Dip. Amer. Bd. Internal Med. 1996. (St. Mary's Hosp. Med. Sch. Univ. Lond.) Dir. The Imar Inst. Lond. Socs: BMA; Med. Protec. Soc. Prev: Regist. (Respirat. & Gen. Med.) Guy's Hosp. Lond.; SHO Rotat. (Med.) Barking & OldCh. Hosps.

LI, Charles Kwok-Chong 13 Sovereign Close, Ealing, London W5 1DE Email: ckl1@mcmail.com; Department of Rheumatology, Whipps Cross Hospital, Leytonstone, London E11 1NR — MB BS 1994 Lond.; MA Cantab. 1995; MRCP (UK) 1997. (St. Mary's London) Specialist Regist. Rotat. (Rheum. & Gen. Med.) N. Thames. Prev: SHO (Med.) MusGr. Pk. Hosp. Taunton.

LI, Chung Yeung Andy 5 Kingswood, Maes y Coed, Pontypridd CF38 1RL — MB BS 1993 Lond.

LI, David Windsor House, 40 Upper Parliament St., Liverpool L8 7LF Tel: 0151 250 5300 — MB ChB 1984 Birm.; MRCPsych 1989; Dip. Psychother. Liverp. 1993. Cons. Psychiat. (Community Psychiat.) Windsor Hse. Liverp. Prev: Sen. Regist. (Psychiat.) Mersey RHA.

LI, Jeanette 8 Rose Garden Close, Edgware HA8 7RF — MRCS Eng. LRCP Lond. 1961; DMRD Eng. 1967. (St. Mary's) Prev: Cons. Radiol. Enfield Dist. Hosp. (Chase Wing); Sen. Regist. (Radiol.) Char. Cross Gp. Hosps.; Regist. (Diag. Radiol.) Hammersmith Hosp. Lond.

LI, Ka Che Elderly Care Directorate, Dept of Health Care of Older People, William Harvery Hopsital, Ashford — MB BS 1990 Lond.; MRCP Lond. 1995. (Royal Free Hospital School of Medicine) Cons. Phys. in Elderly Med. and Gen. Internal Med. Socs: BMA; MPS; BGS.

LI, Kai-Wang Kenneth 2/L, 25 Queensborough Gardens, Hyndland, Glasgow G12 9QP — MB ChB 1995 Glas.

LI, Kenric 8 Shawfields Street, London SW3 4BD — MB BS 1985 Lond.

LI, May Lin Tan-y-Bryn, 9 Afan Valley Road, Cimla, Neath SA11 3SS — MB BCh 1995 Wales.

LI, Mei Na Hornbeams Flat 8, Room 4, Queen Elizabeth Hospital, Gayton Road, King's Lynn PE30 4ET — MB ChB 1997 Glas.

LI, Pui-Ling 28 Rhondda Grove, London E3 5AP Tel: 020 8981 6996 — MB BS 1986 Lond.; FFPHM 2001 UK; MFPHM RCP (UK) 1994; MRCGP 1991. Cons. Pub. Health Med. Lond., Head of Corporate Developm., Dept. of Health. Socs: Chairm. Chinese Nat. Healthy Living Centre.

LI, Mr Raymond Shui Ki Mdina, Mount Avenue, Hutton, Brentwood CM13 2PB Tel: 01277 9972224371 — MB BCh BAO 1984 NUI; FRCS Eng. 1989; FRCS Ed. 1989.

LI, Simon Tse Bong 22 Eaton Close, Bristol BS16 3XL — MB ChB 1995 Manch.

LI, Syn Kay Flat 7, 121 Haverstock Hill, London NW3 4RS — MB BS 1986 Lond.

LI, Wai-Yee 35 Oakhill Court, Edge Hill, Wimbledon, London SW19 4NR Tel: 020 8946 3648 — MB ChB 1996 Birm.; ChB Birm. 1996; BSc (Path.) Birm. 1994. (Birm.) SHO (Gen. Surg.) St. Helier Hosp. Carshalton; I/c Surg. Trainee Rotat. Roy. Marsden Hosp. Sutton & St. Helier's Hosp. Carshalton.

LI, Wai-Yung 27 Upper Teddington Road, Kingston upon Thames KT1 4DL — MB BS 1993 Lond.; MRCP (UK) 1996. (St. Geos. Hosp. Med. Sch.) Specialist Regist. (Radiol.) St.Geos. Hosp. Tooting. Prev: SHO (Transpl. Med.) Harefield Hosp.; SHO (Geriat.) Hither Green Hosp. Lond.; SHO (Med.) Lewisham Hosp.

LI, Wendy Chi Wain Reigate, 4 Duffryn Road, Cardiff CF23 6NP Tel: 029 2075 2677 — MB BCh 1989 Wales; DCH Lond. 1994. (UWCM) Staff Grade (Community Paediat.) Cardiff.

LI KAM WA, Tin Chien Chest Clinic, Blackpool Victoria Hospital, Whinney Heys Road, Blackpool FY3 8NR — MB ChB 1983 Dundee; PhD Ed. 1996; MD Dundee 1992; MRCP (UK) 1986; T(M) 1992. Cons. Phys. Blackpool Vict. Hosp. NHS Trust. Prev: Sen. Regist.

(Med.) Leeds Gen. Infirm.; Lect. (Med.) Roy. Infirm. Univ. Edin.; Clin. Research Fell. St. Bart. Hosp. Lond.

LI SAW HEE, Foo Leong 48 Gosberton Road, Balham, London SW12 8LF — MB BS 1989 Lond.

LI TING WAI, Let Seng 122G Blackstock Road, London N4 2DR — MB BS 1988 Lond.

LI WAN PO, George Li Tin Niam Newland Health Centre, 34 Newland, Lincoln LN1 1XP Tel: 01522 543943 Fax: 01522 538088; 19 Massey Road, Lincoln LN2 4BN Tel: 01522 510827 Fax: 01522 512783 — MB ChB 1979 Dundee.

LI YIM, Doris Fee Moy 18 Woodlands Drive, Glasgow G4 9EH — MB ChB 1994 Glas.

LIAKOS, George Minas 68 Kingsway, Chandlers Ford, Eastleigh SO53 1FJ Tel: 01703 612852 — Ptychio Iatrikes 1972 Thessaloniki; DO Eng. 1976. (Aristotelion Univ. Salonika) Ophth. Med. Pract. Hants. AHA. Prev: SHO (Ophth.) Epsom Dist. Hosp.; SHO (Ophth.) Sutton Gen. Hosp.; Regist. Corneo-Plastic Unit Qu. Eliz. Hosp. E. Grinstead.

LIAN, Chee Seong 41 Belmont Gardens, Ashgrove Road, Aberdeen AB25 3GA — MB ChB 1995 Aberd.

LIAN, Tsui Yee 143 Woodhouse Hall, 18 Clarendon Road, Leeds LS2 9NN; 3 Jalan Bintang, Off Jalan Kg. Simee, Ipoh, Perak 31400, Malaysia Fax: 0060 5 548 0881 — MB BS 1989 Adelaide; MRCP (UK) 1995. Specialist Regist. (Rheumatol.) Bradford Hosps. NHS Trust. Socs: Malaysian Soc. Rheumatol.; BMA. Prev: Lect. (Rheumatol.) Univ. of Leeds; Clin. Specialist, Min. of Health, Malaysia.

LIANG, Jun 3 Milnpark Gardens, Kinning Park, Glasgow G41 1DN — MB ChB 1988 Glas.

LIANG, Yi Fan paediatric Dept, Northampton General Hospital, Billing Road, Northampton NN1 5BD Tel: 01604 634700 — BM BCh 1997 Oxf.; MA. (Oxf) SHO Paediat. N.ampton. Gen. Hosp.

LIANG LUNG CHONG, Marie Elizabeth Katia 231 Chester Road, Sunderland SR4 7RA — MB BS 1994 Newc.

LIAO, Shirley The Fertility Centre, Holly House Hospital, High Road, Buckhurst Hill IG9 5HX Tel: 020 8505 3315 Fax: 020 8504 7688; 14 Ossulton Way, London N2 0DS Tel: 020 8201 8819 Fax: 020 8455 4973 — MB BS 1980 Bangalore. (St. Johns Med. Coll., Bangalore) Assoc. Specialist (Fertil. & IVF) Holly Hse. Hosp. Buckhurst Hill. Socs: Eur. Soc. Human Reproduc. & Embryol.; Brit. Fertil. Soc. Prev: Regist. (O & G) Lewisham Hosp. Lond. & Hope Hosp. Manch.; SHO (Urol.) Freeman Hosp. Newc.

LIAS, Malcolm The Surgery, The Meads, Kington HR5 3DQ Tel: 01544 230302 Fax: 01544 230824; Strathmore, Lyonshall, Kington HR5 3HS Tel: 015448 244 — MB ChB 1968 Birm. Prev: SHO (Paediat.) Hereford Co. Hosp.

LIASIDES, Euthyvoulos Chr c/o Derbyshire Royal Infirmary, London Road, Derby DE1 2QY — Ptychio Iatrikes 1973 Athens.

LIAU, Fah Onn 2 Hillview Avenue, Nottingham NG3 5GA — MB BCh 1982 Wales; MRCGP 1990; DPD Cardiff 1997.

LIAW, Voon Ping Langdale Hall, Upper Park Road, Manchester M14 5RJ — MB ChB 1998 Manch.; MB ChB Manch 1998.

LIBAN, Janusz Bernard Department of Anaesthesia, St. Georges's Hospital, Blackshaw Road, London SW17 9QT Tel: 020 8672 1255 Fax: 020 8725 3135; 76 Bathgate Road, London SW19 5PH Tel: 020 8946 8393 Email: liban@mailbox.co.uk — Lekarz 1972 Gdansk; Lekarz (Med. Acad.) Gdansk 1972; FFA RCS Eng. 1981; DA Eng. 1977. Cons. (Anaesth.) St. Geo. Hosp. Lond. Socs: Roy. Soc. Med.; MRCAnaesth.; Assn. Anaesths. Prev: Sen. Regist. (Anaesth.) W.m. & St. Geo. Hosps. Lond.; Asst. Prof. UCLA Sch. Med. Los Angeles.

LIBBERT, Debra Helen Prestwich Health Centre, Fairfax Road, Prestwich, Manchester M25 1BT Tel: 0161 773 2483 Fax: 0161 773 9218; Trefusk, 40 Hilton Lane, Prestwich, Manchester M25 9QY — MB ChB 1986 Manch.; DRCOG 1989.

LIBBERT, Sydney David (retired) 59 Hilton Lane, Prestwich, Manchester M25 9SA Tel: 0161 773 3098 — MRCS Eng. LRCP Lond. 1952.

LIBBY, Gerald William 17 Harley Street, London W1N 1DA Tel: 020 7636 7916 Fax: 020 7637 2373 Email: gwliby@globalnet.co.uk; 48 Morpeth Mansions, Morpeth Terr, London SW1P 1ET Tel: 020 7828 0923 — MRCS Eng. LRCP Lond. 1967; FRCPsych 1996, M 1972; DPM Eng. 1972. (St. Bart.) Cons. Psychiat. (Gastroenterol.) & Hon. Sen. Lect. (Gastroenterol. & Psychol. Med.) St. Bart. Hosp. & Roy. Lond. Sch. Med. & Dent.; Cons.P.ss Grace Hosp.Lond; Vis. Cons. Priory Hosp. Lond.; Prof. Anat. Roy. Acad. Arts. Socs: Fell. Roy. Soc. Med.; Soc. Psychosomatic Research; Brit. Soc. Gastroenterol. Prev: Chief Asst. (Psychol. Med.) St. Bart. Hosp. Lond.; Regist. (Psychiat.) Char. Cross Hosp. Lond.

LIBERMAN, Deborah 71 Cuckoo Hill Road, Pinner HA5 1AU Tel: 020 8866 8398 — BM BS 1994 Nottm.; BMedSci Nottm. 1992. (Univ. Nottm.)

LIBERMAN, Myrna Wood Lane Medical Centre, 2A Wood Lane, Ruislip HA4 6ER Tel: 01895 632677 Fax: 01895 634020; 71 Cuckoo Hill Road, Pinner HA5 1AU Tel: 020 8866 8398 — MA, MB BChir Camb. 1968; MRCGP 1987; DRCOG 1984; DCH RCP Lond. 1985.

LIBMAN, Isaac 26 Greenstead Avenue, Manchester M8 0NR Tel: 0161 740 5992 — MRCS Eng. LRCP Lond. 1937. (Liverp.) Prev: Ho. Off. Boundary Pk. Hosp. Oldham & Walton Hosp. Liverp.

LIBMAN, Maurice 17 Menlove Mansions, Menlove Gardens W., Liverpool L18 2HY Tel: 0151 722 4976 — MB ChB 1937 Liverp. (Liverp.) Prev: Res. Med. Off. Hope Hosp. Salford & Oldham Gen. Hosp.; Blood Transfus. Off. Manch. Region EMS.

LIBRI, Vincenzo Department of Pharmacology, The School of Pharmacy, University of London, 29/39 Brunswick Square, London WC1N 1AX Tel: 020 7753 5907 Fax: 020 7753 5902 Email: vlibri@cua.ulsop.ac.uk; 60 Allendale Close, London SE5 8SG Tel: 020 7703 8133 — State Exam 1985 Reggio Calabria; MD Reggio Calabria 1985; CCST Naples 1988. Lect. (Clin. Pharmacol.) Dept. Pharmacol. Univ. Rome; MRC Grant Holder & Mem. Acad. Staff Dept. Pharmacol. Sch. Pharmacy Univ. Lond.; Hon. Research Fell. Dept. Pharmacol. Med. Sch. Univ. Birm.; Specialist Train. (Clin. Pharmacol. & Toxicol.) Univ. Naples 1988; Hon. Clin. Asst. (Health Care Elderly) King's Coll. Sch. Med. & Dent. Lond. Socs: Brit. Pharm. Soc.; Italian Pharmacol. Soc.; Italian Neurosci. Soc. Prev: Wellcome Trust Grant Holder; Med. Off. Italian Air Force; Regist. (Clin. Pharmacol. & Toxicol.) Dept. Clin. Pharmacol. Univ. Naples, Italy.

LICENCE, Kirsty Ann Maria Directorate of Public Health & Health Policy, Oxfordshire Health Authority, Richards Building, Old Road, Headington OX3 7LG Email: kirsty.licence@oxon-ha.anglox.nhs.uk — MB BS 1990 Lond.; MSc 1999 Aberdeen; BA Oxf. 1987; MRCGP 1995; DRCOG 1994. p/t Specialist Regist. (Pub. Health Med.) Oxon. Health Auth., Headington.

LICHTAROWICZ, Ewa Jadwiga 14 Field Lane, Beeston, Nottingham NG9 5FJ — MB BS 1990 Lond.

LICHTENSTEIGER, Lindsay 1 Meads Cottage, Slindon, Arundel BN18 0QX — MB ChB 1953 Glas.

LICHTENSTEIN, Hans Eugen (retired) Llwynbongam, Cefnllys Lane, Llandrindod Wells LD1 5PD — MB BChir 1952 Camb.; MRCS Eng. LRCP Lond. 1952; DObst RCOG 1959. Prev: Cas. Off. Llandrindod Wells Hosp.

LICHY, Roger James Truro Natural Health Centre, 5 Station Road, Truro TR1 3EX Tel: 01872 40321 — MB ChB 1971 Bristol; MSc (Med. Anthropol.) Lond. 1997; MFHom 1983; DObst RCOG 1976; DCH Eng. 1974. (Univ. Bristol) Med. Dir. Truro Natural Health Centre; Mem. Fac. Homeop. Roy. Homeop. Hosp. Lond. Socs: Assoc. Mem. Soc. Homeop.

LIDDELL, Alan Ross 10 Turnberry Wynd, Bothwell, Glasgow G71 8EE Tel: 0141 853475 — MB ChB 1978 Glas.

LIDDELL, Allan Smith (retired) Larchwood, Riverdale, Wolsingham, Bishop Auckland Tel: 01388 526003 — MB ChB 1949 St. And.; DObst RCOG 1953. Prev: Ho. Surg. Dunfermline & W. Fife Hosp.

LIDDELL, Anne Marie Tramways Medical Centre, 54 Holme Lane, Sheffield S6 4JQ Tel: 0114 234 3418 Fax: 0114 285 5958 — MB ChB 1973 Sheff.; BSc Sheff. 1968, MB ChB 1973; MRCGP 1977; DObst RCOG 1975.

LIDDELL, Charles Richard Wilson Cults Medical Group, Cults Medical Centre, South Avenue, Cults, Aberdeen AB15 9LQ Tel: 01224 867740 Fax: 01224 861392 — MB ChB 1969 Aberd.; MRCGP 1975. (Aberd.) Prev: Ho. Phys. & Ho. Surg. Aberd. Roy. Infirm.

LIDDELL, Elsie Jean 6 Cairn Road, Bieldside, Aberdeen AB15 9AL — MB ChB 1937 Aberd.

LIDDELL, Hazel Woollven Cowley Cottage, Mytten Close, Cuckfield, Haywards Heath Tel: 01444 454435 — MB BS 1945

Lond.; DPM 1951. (King's Coll. Hosp.) Prev: Cons. Psychiat. Runwell Hosp. Wickford; Regist. (Psychiat.) St. Geo. Hosp. Lond.; Sen. Regist. (Psychiat.) Addenbrooke's Hosp. Camb.

LIDDELL, James Bassetts, Ansty, Haywards Heath RH17 5AJ Tel: 01444 454269 Email: bassetts@pavilion.co.uk — MD 1962 Camb.; MB BChir 1952; FRCPath 1976, M 1962. (Camb. & Guy's) Emerit. Cons. Chem. Pathol. Guy's Hosp. Lond. Prev: Cons. Chem. Pathol. Guy's Hosp. Lond.; Cons. Chem. Pathol. United Sheff. Hosps.; Sen. Regist. Nuffield Dept. Clin. Biochem. Radcliffe Infirm. Oxf.

LIDDELL, John Kenneth Crawford (retired) Linstead House Rest Home, 17 Ambleside Drive, Southend-on-Sea SS1 2UT — MB ChB 1920 Ed.; DPM Eng. 1932. Prev: Sen. Asst. Med. Off. Barnwood Ho., Gloucester.

LIDDELL, Keith Roman Villa, 3 Summerdown Close, Eastbourne BN20 8DW Tel: 01323 639058 Fax: 01323 639058 — MB ChB 1967; MD Leeds 1980; FRCP Lond. 1990; MRCP (UK) 1973. (Leeds) Cons. Dermat. E.bourne & Hastings Health Dists. Socs: Fell. Roy. Soc. Med.; BMA (Ex Local Pres.); Mem. Brit. Assn. Dermatol. Prev: Sen. Regist. (Dermat.) Soton. Univ. Hosp. Gp.; Regist. (Gen. Med.) Leeds Gen. Infirm.; Regist. Leeds Dermat. Dept.

LIDDELL, Malcolm Brandon 21 Cardiff Road, Dinas Powys CF64 4DH — MB BS 1980 Lond.; PhD Wales 1991; BSc Lond. 1977; MRCPsych 1992. (King's Coll. Hosp.) Sen. Regist. Rotat. S. Wales Train. Scheme. Prev: Research Fell. (Haemat. & Psychol. Med.) Univ. Wales Coll. med.

LIDDELL, Margaret Livingstone (retired) 71 Caroline Terrace, Edinburgh EH12 8QX Tel: 0131 334 5094 — MB ChB 1951 Ed. Prev: GP W. Lothian.

LIDDELL, Robert William Health Centre, Balmellie Road, Turriff AB53 4DQ Tel: 01888 562323 Fax: 01888 568682; Meadowbank, Turriff AB53 4NA Tel: 01888 562117 Fax: 01888 568682 — MB ChB 1979 Glas.; MRCGP 1983; DRCOG 1981. (Glas.) Chairm. Grampian LMC; Chairm. Banff & Buchan Local Co-op. Socs: (Ex-Chairm.) Scott. Assn. of GP Community Hosps.

LIDDER, Paul Gerard 145 Woolmore Road, Erdington, Birmingham B23 7ED — MB ChB 1998 Manch.; MB ChB Manch 1998.

LIDDIARD, George Stratton Adam Practice, Upton Health Centre, Blandford Road North, Poole BH16 5PW Email: liddiards@doctors.net — MBBS; LRCP; MRCS; DRCOG; MRCGP. (Westminster) GP Poole, Dorset; Clin. Assisitant Cardiol., Roy. Bornemouth Hosp.

LIDDICOAT, Amanda Jane Radiology Department, Leicester Royal Infirmary, Leicester LE1 5WW — MB BCh 1985 Wales; MRCP (UK) 1988; FRCR 1992. Cons. Radiol. Leicester Roy. Infirm.

LIDDINGTON, Mr Mark Ian 79 Cookridge Lane, Leeds LS16 7NE Tel: 0113 230 1800 Email: liddington@aol.com — MB BS 1985 Lond.; FRCS Eng. 1990. Regist. (Plastic Surg.) St. Jas. Univ. Hosp. Leeds. Socs: Brit. Assn. Plastic Surg.; Brit. Transpl. Soc.; Brit. Burns Assn. Prev: Hanson Surg. Research Fell. Nuffield Dept. Surg. John Radcliffe Hosp. Univ. Oxf.

LIDDLE, Alexander Brian Gant Medical Centre, The Grove, Rowlands Gill NE39 1PW Tel: 01207 542136 Fax: 01207 543340 — MB ChB 1979 Dundee. GP Rowlands Gill, Tyne & Wear.

LIDDLE, Amanda Louise Wideopen Medical Centre, Great North Road, Newcastle upon Tyne NE13 6LN Tel: 0191 236 2115; West Meadow House, Heddon Birks, Birks Road, Heddon-on-the-Wall, Newcastle upon Tyne NE15 0HF — MB BChir 1985 Camb.; BSc (Hons.) Lond. 1983; MRCGP 1990; DRCOG 1988.

LIDDLE, Andrew Clive 51 Marine Parade, Gorleston, Great Yarmouth NR31 6EY Tel: 01493 662836 — MB BS 1979 Lond.; MRCP (UK) 1984. Pharmaceut. Phys.; Med. Adviser. Socs: MRAPM Lond. 1997.

LIDDLE, Barbara Jane Northern General Hospital, Herries Road, Sheffield S5 7AU Tel: 01742 434343 — MB BS 1982 Lond.; MRCP (UK) 1986; FRCP 1999. Cons. Phys. (Elderly) N. Gen. Hosp. Sheff. Prev: Sen. Regist. Rotat. St. Geo. Hosp. Lond.

LIDDLE, Donald Richard Plas Iorwerth, Nefyn, Pwllheli Tel: 01758 720339 — MB ChB 1957 Leeds. (Leeds) Prev: Sen. Ho. Off. (Paediat.) & Ho. Phys. & Ho. Surg. City Hosp. York; Ho. Surg. (O & G) Matern. Hosp. York.

LIDDLE, Elizabeth Jean (retired) 8 Abernethy Place, Newton Mearns, Glasgow G77 5UD Tel: 0141 639 4166 — MB ChB 1963 Glas. Prev: Sessional Med. Off. (Community Child Health) Lanarksh. HB.

LIDDLE, George Clive Central Surgery, Sussex Road, Gorleston, Great Yarmouth NR31 6QB Tel: 01493 600011 Fax: 01493 656253; 51 Marine Parade, Gorleston-on-Sea, Great Yarmouth NR31 6EY Tel: 01493 661737 — MB ChB 1957 Sheff.; MRCS Eng. LRCP Lond. 1957. (Sheff.)

LIDDLE, John Pollok (retired) Brookside Cottage, Arrad Foot, Ulverston LA12 7SL Tel: 01229 861766 — MB ChB Ed. 1963; DObst RCOG 1966. Clin. Asst. (ENT) Furness Gen. Hosp. Barrow-in-Furness; Med. Examr. Benefits Agency Med. Servs. Prev: SHO (Radiother.) W.. Gen. Hosp. Edin.

LIDDLE, Michael Walter David Department of Anaesthetics, Stepping Hill Hospital, Poplar Grove, Stockport SK2 7JE; Birch Corner, Murfield Close, Liverpool L12 9LY — MB ChB 1981 Sheff.; BSc (Hons.) 1979, MB ChB Sheff. 1981; FCAnaesth 1989.

LIDDLE, Robert David Sinclair Modyrvalel Health Centre, Toll Street, Motherwell ML1 2PJ Tel: 01698 265566; 30 Cameron Street, Motherwell ML1 3AH Tel: 01698 269802 — MB ChB 1978 Glas. Partner W. Gen. Pract. Modyrvale Med. Centre Motherwell; Med. Off. Motherwell Football Club.

LIDDLE, Ruth Eleanor Springwell Medical Centre, 37 Ardmillan Terrace, Edinburgh EH11 2JL Fax: 0131 537 7505 Email: ruth.liddle@gp71006.lothian-hb.scot.nhs.uk; 17 Burnside Park, Balerno EH14 7LY Tel: 0131 449 5875 Fax: 0131 538 5181 Email: ruth.liddle@blueyonder.co.uk — MB ChB 1978 Ed.; MBA 1999; MRCGP 1982; DCCH RCP Ed. 1986. Princip. in Gen. Pract., Springwell Med. Centre; Regional Quality Inibitors Adviser, RCGP SE Scotl.

LIDGEY, David Arthur Reginald 196B Barnett Wood Lane, Ashtead KT21 2LW — MB ChB 1986 Leic.; BSc (Hons.) (Biochem. & Physiol.) Lond. 1981; Dip. Obst. Otago 1991. Trainee GP Bookham Surrey VTS. Prev: Regist. (Paediat.) Waikato Hosp. Hamilton, NZ.

LIDGEY, Shona Isabella 27 Freethorpe Close, London SE19 3LX — MB BS 1989 Lond.; MRCGP 1993.

LIDHAR, Jaswant Kaur The Health Centre, 130 Upper Commercial Street, Batley WF17 5ED Tel: 01924 474070 Fax: 01924 474070 — MB BS 1965 Punjab; MB BS Punjab (India) 1965; DObst RCOG 1970. (Med. Coll. Amritsar) GP Batley. Prev: Deptm. Med. Off. Health Dept. Dewsbury Co. Boro.; Resid. (Obst.) Shotley Bridge Gen. Hosp.; Res. SHO (Obst.) Staincliffe Hosp. Dewsbury.

LIDHAR, Kundan Singh The Health Centre, 130 Upper Commercial Street, Batley WF17 5ED Tel: 01924 474070 Fax: 01924 474070; Heaton House, Batley WF17 0AT Tel: 01924 477287 — MB BS 1966 Punjab; MB BS Punjabi 1966; DO Eng. 1971. (Med. Coll. Patiala) GP Batley.

LIDHER, Jaswant Flat 2, Heather Court, 48 Russell Road, Moseley, Birmingham B13 8RF Tel: 0121 449 0117 — MB ChB 1992 Leeds. Regist. (Psychiat.) All Birm. Rotat. Scheme.

LIDSTONE, Pamela Anne Pear Tree Cottage, Church Lane, Woodford, Bramhall, Stockport SK7 1PQ Tel: 0161 439 5755 — MB BS 1954 Lond. (King's Coll. Hosp.)

LIDSTONE, Miss Victoria Louise Oakfields Cottage, 30 Broyle Road, Chichester PO19 4BA — BM 1994 Soton. SHO (Med.) St. Richard Chichester. Prev: SHO Haemat. & Palliat. Care, Poole Gen. Hosp.; Ho. Phys. Poole Gen. Hosp.; Ho. Surg. Roy. S. Hants. Hosp. Soton.

LIE, Sonny Eduardo 12C Victoria Drive E., Salisbury District Hospital, Salisbury SP2 8BJ — Artsexamen 1989 Groningen.

LIEBER, Daniel Eugene (retired) The Surgery, Glapthorne Road, Oundle, Peterborough PE8 4JA — MB BS 1961 Lond.; MRCS Eng. LRCP Lond. 1961; DObst RCOG 1964; DA Eng. 1965. Prev: SHO (Anaesth.) St. Bart. Hosp. Lond.

LIEBER, Elinor 2 Benson Place, Oxford OX2 6QH Tel: 01865 514662 — MB ChB Sheff. 1947; DPH Lond. 1963. (Sheffield) Research Assoc. (Med. Hist.) Centre for Hebrew Studies Univ. of Oxf. Socs: (Edit. Bd.) Soc. Ancient Med.

LIEBERMAN, Brian Abraham St. Mary's Hospital, Whitworth Park, Manchester M13 0JH Tel: 0161 224 9633; Thorn Cottage, 25 Eastdown Road, Bowden, Altrincham WA14 2LG — MB BCh Witwatersrand 1965; FRCOG 1984, M 1971. (Witwatersrand) Cons. (Gyn. & Obst.) St. Mary's Hosp. Manch.; Mem. Human Fertilisation & Embryology Auth.

LIEBERMAN, Gidon 3A Arlington Road, Camden, London NW1 7ER Tel: 020 7380 0372 — MB ChB 1993 Manch.; BSc St. And. 1991. SHO (Obst.) Univ. Coll. Hosp. Lond. Prev: SHO (Cas.) Char. Cross Hosp. Lond.; Ho. Off. (Med.) Isle of Man; Ho. Off. (Surg.) Manch. Roy. Infirm.

LIEBERMAN, Ilan 24 Westgate, Hale, Altrincham WA15 9AZ Email: meddirectory@ouraddress.net — MB BS 1990 Lond.; FRAC.

LIEBERMAN, Stuart The Priory Woking, Chobham Road, Knaphill, Woking GU21 2QF Tel: 01483 489211 Fax: 01483 797053 — MD 1966 Miami, USA; MD Miami 1966; FRCPsych 1983, M 1974; Lic. Nova Scotia Med. Bd. 1972; LMCC 1970; Dip. Nat. Bd. Med. Examr. USA 1969. (Univ. Miami) Cons. Psychiat. Proiry Hosp. Woking, Knaphill, Woking, Surrey. Socs: Brit. Assn. PsychoPharmacol.; Inst. of Family Ther.; Assn. Family Ther. Prev: Cons. Psychother. Heathlands Ment. Health Unit; Sen. Lect. (Ment. Health Scis.) St. Geo. Hosp. Med. Sch. Lond.

LIEBERT, Isabel Joanna St Catherine's Surgery, St Pauls Medical Centre, 121 Swindon Road, Cheltenham GL50 4DP Tel: 01242 580668 Fax: 01242 707699; Bogmarsh Cottage, Holme Lacy, Hereford HR2 6PH Tel: 01432 870427 — MB ChB Manch. 1969; DObst RCOG 1973. Prev: SHO (O & G) St. Mary's Hosp. Manch.

LIEBESCHUETZ, Helen Marian 45 Tyrone Road, Thorpe Bay, Southend-on-Sea SS1 3HE Tel: 01702 587895 — MB BCh 1955 Wales; DObst RCOG 1958.

LIEBESCHUETZ, Susan Barbara 155 High Street, Northwood HA6 1ED — MB ChB 1988 Leeds; MRCP (UK) 1991; DCH RCP Lond. 1994. Regist. (Paediat.) Gt. Ormond St. Hosp. Lond..

LIEBLING, Angela Joan 6 Cherry Hill Avenue, Barnt Green, Birmingham B45 8LA Tel: 0121 445 3939 — MB ChB 1962 Birm. (Birm.) p/t Psychoanalyt. Psychotherapist Private Birm. Socs: W. Midl. Inst. Psychotherap.; UKCP. Prev: Clin. Asst. (Dermat.) Birm. Selly Oak Hosp.; Princip. GP Erdington & Aston Univ.

LIEBLING, Leonard Irving The Woodbourne Priory Hospital, 21 Woodbourne Road, Edgbaston, Birmingham B17 8BY Tel: 0121 434 4343 Fax: 0121 434 3270 — MB ChB 1962 Birm.; FRCPsych 1982, M 1971; DPM Eng. 1966. (Birm.) Cons. Psychiat. Woodbourne Priory Hosp. Birm. Socs: Pres. Birm. Medico-legal Soc. Prev: Cons. Psychiat. Highcroft Hosp. Birm.; Sen. Regist. (Psychiat.) United Sheff. Hosps. & Sheff. RHB; Regist. (Psychiat.) United Birm. Hosps.

LIEBLING, Peter Otto (retired) Ashwell Cottage, 18 Chine Walk, West Parley, Ferndown BH22 8PU Tel: 01202 573761 — MRCS Eng. LRCP Lond. 1958; MB Camb. 1959, BChir 1958; FRCGP 1987, M 1977. Hon. Dermat. Roy. Bournemouth. & ChristCh. Hosp. Prev: Clin. Asst. (Med.) Roy. Vict. Hosp. Bournem.

LIEBLING, Rachel Elizabeth 3 Church Road, Horspath, Oxford OX33 1RU — MB ChB 1995 Sheff.

LIEBMANN, Rachael Dorothy Maidstone and Tunbridge Wells NHS Trust, Penbury hosp, Tunbridge Wells TN2 4QJ Tel: 01892 823535 Ext: 3765 Fax: 01892 516697 — MB BCh BAO 1991 Belf.; BSc (Hons.) Belf. 1989; DRCPath 1996; MRCPath 1998. Cons. Histopathelogist, Maidstone and Tunbridge Wells NHS Trust, Pembury Hosp.,Tunbridge Wells. Socs: BMA; IAP; Path. Soc. Prev: Lect./Hon. Sen. Regist. ICRF/Medley Atkins BrE. Path Lab Guy's Hosp. Lond.; Sen. Regist. St. Geos. Hosp. Med. Sch. Lond.; Sen. Regist. St. Helier Hosp. Carshalton.

LIEGEOIS, Henri McDonald (Surgery), 8 St Margarets Road, Solihull B92 7JS Tel: 0121 706 1515 Fax: 0121 765 0161 — MB ChB 1955 Birm.; MRCGP 1977; DObst RCOG 1960.

LIEM, Djien Bing 24 Manor Lane, Rochester ME1 3JN — Artsexamen 1994 Amsterdam.

LIEN, Mr Wing Ming (retired) Little Heath, 10 Halloughton Road, Sutton Coldfield B74 2QQ Tel: 0121 355 3094 — MB ChB 1961 Birm.; FRCS Eng. 1966. Prev: Cons. Surg. Good Hope Dist. Hosp. Sutton Coldfield.

LIEN YEE WUN, Virginia 69 Copse Lane, Marston, Oxford OX3 0AU — MB BS 1985 Singapore.

LIESCHING, Rowena Antoinette Westcroft Health Centre, 16 Wimborne Crescent, Westcroft, Milton Keynes MK4 4DX Tel: 01908 520545 Fax: 01908 520975 — MB ChB 1972 Ed.; MRCP (UK) 1975; MRCGP 1986; DRCOG 1985; DCH 1986; DFFP 1998. (Edinburgh) Sen. Partner.

LIESNER, Raina Joan Great Ormond Street Hospital for Children, Great Ormond St., London WC1N 3JH Tel: 020 7829 8831 Fax: 020 7813 8410; 10 Dalmore Road, London SE21 8HB — MB BChir 1984 Camb.; MB BChi Camb. 1984; MA Camb. 1984; MRCP (UK) 1986; MRCPath 1995, D 1993; MD 1999 (Univ. of London). (Westminster Hospital, London) Cons. Paediat. Haemat. Gt. Ormond St. Hosp. for Childr. Lond. Socs: Brit. Soc. Haematol.; Internat. Soc. Thrombosis & Haemostasis. Prev: Lect. (Paediat. Haem.), Gt. Ormond St. Lond.; Regist. Rotat. (Haemat.) Centr. Middlx. & St. Mary's Hosp. Lond.; Regist. & SHO (Paediat.) Hosp. for Sick Childr. Gt. Ormond St. Lond.

LIEW, Boon Seng Flat 2/R, 22 Polwarth St., Hyndland, Glasgow G12 9TY; 38 Jalan Hujan Emas 5, Kuala Lumpur 58200, Malaysia — MB ChB 1992 Aberd.; MRCP (UK) 1995. SHO III (Renal Med.) Glas. Roy. Infirm. Prev: SHO (Gen. Med.) Withington Hosp. & Gateshead Hosps. NHS Trust.

LIEW, Choon Fong 6B Peak Hill Gardens, London SE26 4LE — MB BS 1994 Lond.

***LIEW, Colin** 34 Greville Drive, Edgbaston, Birmingham B15 2UU — MB ChB 1998 Birm.

LIEW, Elaine Chiew Lin 29 Elizabeth Newcomen House, 38 Newcomen St., London SE1 1YZ — BMed 1991 Newc., New South Wales; B Med Newc, NSW 1991.

LIEW, Leonard Chee Wai 34 Greville Drive, Egbaston, Birmingham B15 2UU Tel: 0121 440 2372 — BM BS 1993 Nottm.; BMedSci (Hons.) Nottm. 1991. SHO (ENT) New Cross Hosp. Wolverhampton. Prev: SHO (Neurosurg.) Qu. Eliz. Hosp. Birm.; SHO (ENT) Birm. Heartlands Hosp.; SHO (Orthop.) N. Staffs. Hosp. Stoke-on-Trent.

LIEW, Lewis Choon How 6B Peak Hill Gardens, London SE26 4LE — MB ChB 1992 Sheff.

LIEW, Reginald Kay Choon The Pines 79 Kingston Hill, Kingston upon Thames KT2 7PX Tel: 020 8546 0086 — MB BS 1997 Lond.; BA Camb. 1994. (Guy's & St. Thos. Lond.) SHO (Med.) Broomfield Hosp. Chelmsford. Prev: SHO (Haematol.) S.end Hosp.; Ho. Surg. Greenwich Hosp.; Ho. Phys. Guy's Hosp.

LIEW, Shiao-Hui 68 Colemans Avenue, Westcliff on Sea SS0 0NX — MB BS 1998 Lond.; MB BS Lond 1998.

LIEW, Mr Wee Liik Flat 17, Bridge Wharf, 230 Old Ford Road, London E2 9PR — MB BCh BAO 1991 Belf.; FRCS Ed. 1996; FRCSI 1995. Regist. (Cardiothoracic Surg.) Lond. Chest Hosp. Prev: Lect. & Demonst. (Anat.) Manch. Univ.; SHO Rotat. (A & E, Gen. Surg., Cardiothoracic Surg., Orthop. & Trauma) Manch. Roy. Infirm.

LIEW, Weng Kwan 93A Castle Court, Castle Hill Hospital, Castle Road, Cottingham HU16 5JQ — MB ChB 1994 Leeds.

LIGGETT, William George, KStJ (retired) Wellington Road, Muxton, Telford TF2 8NN Tel: 01952 604207 — MB BCh BAO 1947 Belf. Prev: med off GKN Telford Occupat.al health.

LIGGINS, Andrew Jon Cambridgeshire Health Authorityy, Kingfisher House, Kingfisher Way, Hichinbrooke Business Park, Huntingdon PE29 6FH Tel: 01480 398500 Fax: 01480 398501 — BM 1981 Soton.; MFPHM RCP (UK) 1993; MPH Leeds 1991; MRCGP 1987; DCH RCP Lond. 1987. Cons. Pub. Health Med.Camb Health Auth.

LIGGINS, Mr Steven John Amberley House, Down Road, Tavistock PL19 9AG Tel: 01752 763764 Fax: 01822 613039 Email: stevenliggins@btinternet.com — MB BCh 1992 Wales; BSc (Hons.) Brunel 1979; BDS Liverp. 1983; FRCS Glas. 1996; FDS RCS Ed. 1988; FRCS 1998. Cons. (Maxillofacial Surg.). Socs: Fell. Brit. Assn. Oral & Maxillofacial Surg.; Fell. Internat. Assn. Maxillofacial Surgs.; The Craniofacial Soc. GB. Prev: Sen. Regist. Canniesburn Hosp. Glas..

LIGHT, Anton Michael Department of Histopathology, Good Hope Hospital, Rectory Road, Sutton Coldfield B75 7RR — MRCS Eng. LRCP Lond. 1972; BSc (Hons.) Lond. 1969, MB BS 1972; FRCPath 1990. (Guy's) Cons. Histopath. Good Hope Hosp. NHS Trust Sutton Coldfield. Prev: Sen. Regist. (Histopath.) Birm. AHA (T); Regist. (Histopath.) Worcester Roy. Infirm.; SHO (Path.) Greenwich & Bexley AHA.

LIGHT, Christine Jane 63B Robislaw Dew South, Aberdeen AB15 4BA Tel: 01224 321576 — MB ChB 1979 Aberd.

LIGHT, Douglas Charles, Group Capt. RAF Med. Br. Retd. Kullen, 16 St Peters Road, Seaford BN25 2HS — LMSSA 1937 Lond.; MRCS Eng. LRCP Lond. 1939; DMRD Eng. 1950. (Guy's) Socs: Fac. Radiol. & Brit. Inst. Radiol. Prev: Radiol. RAF Hosps. Wroughton, Akrotiri & Cosford.

LIGHT, Felicity Wendy Cuckoo Lane Surgery, 14 Cuckoo Lane, Hanwell, London W7 3EY Tel: 020 8567 4315 — MB BS 1973 Lond.; MRCP (U.K.) 1975; MRCS Eng. LRCP Lond. 1973; MRCGP 1981. (Westm.) Prev: SHO (Paediat.) King's Coll. Hosp. Lond.; SHO (Paediat.) Guy's Hosp. Lond.; Ho. Surg. W.m. Hosp. Lond.

LIGHT, James Keith Geoffrey Health Care International (Scotland) Ltd., Beardmore St., Clydebank G81 4HX — MB BCh 1963 Witwatersrand.

LIGHT, Loretta School House, School Lane, Gentleshaw, Rugeley WS15 4LX — MB BS 1971 Lond.; MRCS Eng. LRCP Lond. 1971; Dip. Community Paediat. Warwick 1982; FRCPCH RCPch; FRCPCH. (Guy's) Cons. Community Paediat. S. Staffs. Healthcare NHS Trust. Socs: Soc. Pub. Health (Founder Mem. Fac. Community Health); BMA; BACCH. Prev: SCMO SE Staffs. Health Dist.; Clin. Med. Off. N. Birm. DHA & Worcester Health Dist.

LIGHT, Roger John 57 Franklin Road, Birmingham B30 2HJ — MB ChB 1993 Birm.

LIGHTBODY, Calvin John 2 Glendale Avenue, Bangor BT20 4UG — MB BCh 1998 Belf.; MB BCh Belf 1998.

LIGHTBODY, Thomas Derek (retired) 6 Glen Brae, Bridge of Weir PA11 3BH — MB ChB 1952 Glas.; MB ChB Glas. (Commend.) 1952; FRCP Glas. 1980; MRCP Glas. 1962; FRFPS Glas. 1962; FRCR 1975; FFR 1966; DMRD Eng. 1963. Prev: Cons. Radiol. Glas. Roy. Infirm.

LIGHTEN, Anthony David Institute of Obstetrics & Gynaecology, Royal Postgraduate Medical School, Hammersmith Hospital, Du Cane Road, London W12 0NN Tel: 020 8383 2380 Email: alighten@rpms.ac.uk; 1 Westminster Terrace, Chester CH4 7LF Tel: 01244 679950 — MB BChir 1992 Camb.; BSc Lond. 1989. Research Fell. Inst. O & G Roy. Postgrad. Med. Sch. Hammersmith Hosp. Lond.; Hon. Regist. Hammersmith Hosp. Lond. Prev: SHO (O & G) Hammersmith Hosp. Lond.; SHO (O & G) Rotunda Hosp., Dub.; Ho. Off. (Surg.) Addenbrooke's Hosp. Camb.

LIGHTFOOT, Andrew Main Street Surgery, 45 Main Street, Willerby, Hull HU10 6BP Tel: 01482 652652 — MB ChB 1977 Sheff.; MRCGP 1981.

LIGHTFOOT, Diana Margaret Duke Medical Centre, 28 Talbot Road, Sheffield S2 2TD Tel: 0114 272 0689 Fax: 0114 275 1916; 46 Acorn Drive, Stannington, Sheffield S6 6ER — MB ChB 1977 Liverp.; BSc Lond. 1972; MRCGP 1981.

LIGHTFOOT, Irene Joyce (retired) Orrell Lane Surgery, 47 Orrell Lane, Liverpool L9 8BX — MB ChB 1974 Bristol.

LIGHTFOOT, Nigel Francis Public Health Laboratory Service North, Directorate Office, 17-21 Dean St., Newcastle upon Tyne NE1 1PQ Tel: 0191 261 2577 Fax: 0191 261 2578 Email: grpnligh@newphls.demon.co.uk — MSc (Med. Microbiol.) Lond. 1976, MB BS 1968; MRCS Eng. LRCP Lond. 1968; MRCPath 1979. (St. Mary's) Cons. (Microbiol.) Dir. Pub. Health Laborat. Newc. upon Tyne. Prev: Cons. (Microbiol.) Dir. Pub. Health Laborat. Taunton & Som. Hosp.

LIGHTFOOT, Philippa Jane Well Street Medical Centre, Well Street, Biddulph, Stoke-on-Trent ST8 6HD Tel: 01782 513939 Fax: 01782 523085; St. Cloud, 10 Congleton Edge Road, Mossley, Congleton CW12 3JJ — MB ChB 1986 Sheff.; MRCGP 1990.

LIGHTFOOT, Robert James London Road Surgery, 46-48 London Road, Carlisle CA1 2EL Tel: 01228 27559 Fax: 01228 594434; 52 Newfield Drive, Carlisle CA3 0AF — MB ChB 1981 Sheff.; MRCGP 1985.

LIGHTFOOT, Stephen Roger Tel: 01937 573848 Fax: 01937 574754 — MB BS 1976 Newc.; MRCGP 1980.

LIGHTLEY, Dennis Albert (retired) 25 Rockwood Road, Calverley, Pudsey LS28 5AB — MRCS Eng. LRCP Lond. 1954. Prev: Sen. Ho. Off. (O & G) St. Mary's Hosp. Kettering.

LIGHTMAN, David Julian (retired) Newbury Cottage, 135 Hadham Road, Bishop's Stortford CM23 2QD — MB BS 1960 Lond.; MRCS Eng. LRCP Lond. 1960; FFA RCS Eng. 1964; DA Eng. 1963. Cons. Anaesth. P.ss Alexandra Hosp. NHS Trust. Prev: Sen. Regist. (Anaesth.) Hosp. Sick Childr. & Univ. Coll. Hosp. Lond.

LIGHTMAN, Professor Stafford Louis Department of Medicine, Bristol Royal Infirmary, Marlborough St., Bristol BS2 8HW Tel: 0117 928 2871 Fax: 0117 928 2212 Email: stafford.lightman@bristol.ac.uk — MB BChir 1972 Camb.; PhD Camb. 1984, MA 1973, MB BChir 1972; FRCP Lond. 1987, MA 1974. (Cambridge) Prof. & Head of Med. Univ. Bristol.; Cons. Neuroendocrinol. Nat. Hosp. Qu. Sq. Lond. Socs: Founder Fell. The Acad. Med. Sc. Prev: Prof. Clin. Neuroendocrinol. & Cons. Phys. Endocrinol. Char. Cross & W.m. Med. Sch. Lond.; Reader (Med.) Char. Cross & W.m. Med. Sch.; Sen. Lect. & Lect. (Med.) St. Mary's Hosp. Lond.

LIGHTMAN, Susan Louise Moorfields Eye Hospital, City Road, London EC1V 9PD Tel: 020 7556 3411 Fax: 020 7251 9350 Email: s.lightman@ucl.ac.uk; 27 Westbury Road, Woodside Park, London N12 7NY Tel: 020 8343 8821 Fax: 020 8446 4854 — MB BS 1975 Lond.; PhD Lond. 1987; FRCP Lond. 1992; MRCP (UK) 1978; FRCOphth 1988; DO RCS Eng. 1981. Prof. Clin. Ophth. & Cons. Ophth. Moorfields Eye Hosp. Lond. Prev: Duke-Elder Prof. & Cons. Moorfields Eye Hosp.; Sen. Lect. & Hon. Cons. Moorfields Eye Hosp. Lond.; MRC Trav. Fell. Nat. Eye Inst. Nat. Inst. Health Bethesda, MD, USA.

LIGHTON, Lorraine Lesley West Pennine HA, Westhulme Avenue, Oldham OL1 2PU Tel: 0161 622 6602 Fax: 0161 622 6622 — MB ChB 1979 Manch.; MSc Manch. 1989, MB ChB 1979; MFPHM 1990; FFPHM 2000. Cons. Communicable Dis. Control W. Pennine HA.

LIGHTOWLER, Brian Kenneth Wright Dean Lane Medical Centre, 95 Dean Lane, Hazel Grove, Stockport SK7 6EJ Tel: 01625 874664 Fax: 01625 858136; 29 Broadway, Bramhall, Stockport SK7 3BT Tel: 0161 440 8959 — MB ChB 1974 Manch.; MRCGP 1980; AFOM RCP Lond. 1987; DGM RCP Lond. 1988; DMJ Soc. Apoth. Lond. 1983; DCH Eng. 1979; LLM Cardiff 1996. (Manch.) GP Stockport; Occupat. Phys. Adidas & Various Other Companies; Police Surg. GMP; Div. Surg. St. John's Ambul.; Sect. 12 Approved Psychiat. Socs: BMA (Div. Chairm.); (Asst. Sec.) Police Surgs. Assn.

LIGHTOWLER, Caroline 83 Mill Road, Stock, Ingatestone CM4 9LR — MB BS 1988 Lond.; BSc (Physiol.) Lond. 1985; MRCP Lond. 1992. Regist. Rotat. (ITU Med. Obst. & Gen. Med.) Whipps Cross Hosp. & Regist. (Renal) St. Bart. Hosp. Lond. Prev: SHO (Cardiol.) Lond. Chest Hosp.; SHO Rotat. (Gen. Med.) The Lond. Hosp.; SHO Renal Unit Guy's Hosp. Lond.

LIGHTOWLER, Mr Charles David Richard Quarry House Farm, West Tanfield, Ripon HG4 5JG — MB BS 1961 Lond.; FRCS Eng. 1966; MRCS Eng. LRCP Lond. 1961. (Lond. Hosp.) Hon. Cons. Surg. Black Notley Hosp. Braintree. Socs: Fell. BOA; Life Fell. Roy. Soc. Med. (Past Pres.). Prev: Cons. Orthop. Surg. & Clin. Dir. (Trauma & Orthop.) Basildon & Thurrock Gen. Hosps. NHS Trust; Lect. (Surg.), Regist. (Neurosurg.) & Sen. Regist. (Orthop.) Lond. Hosp.

LIGHTOWLER, Eileen (retired) 83 Mill Road, Stock, Ingatestone CM4 9LR Tel: 01277 840575 — MB BS 1961 Lond.; MRCS Eng. LRCP Lond. 1961; DObst RCOG 1963. GP Billericay. Prev: SHO (Obst. & Paediat.) Orsett Hosp.

LIGHTOWLER, Josephine Victoria Jane 83 Mill Road, Stock, Ingatestone CM4 9LR — MB BS 1994 Lond. (The London Hospital Medical College)

LIGHTOWLERS, Sara Karen St. Andrew's Hospital, Devas St., London E3 3NT — MBBS 1988; MBBS; BSc 1985 Lond.; MRCP Lond. 1993; DCH RCP Lond. 1990; MSC City University 1997. (University College & Middx. Hospitals School of Medicine) Cons. Gen. & Geriat. Med. Newham Healthcare Lond.

LIGHTSTONE, Bertram Lionel 16 Sycamore Close, Knighton Rise, Oadby, Leicester LE2 2RN Tel: 0116 270 0810 — MB BS 1967 Lond.; MRCS Eng. LRCP Lond. 1967; DObst RCOG 1970. (Middlx.) Prev: Ho. Surg. St. And. Hosp. Billericay; Ho. Phys. Leicester Gen. Hosp.; SHO (Obst.) St. And. Hosp. Billericay.

LIGHTSTONE, Elizabeth Beatrice Renal Section, Division of Medicine, ICSM & Hammersmith Hospital, Du Cane Road, London W12 0NN Tel: 020 8383 3152 Fax: 020 8383 2062 Email: llightst@rpms.ac.uk; Seaview, 5 Dalkeith Grove, Stanmore HA7 4SQ Tel: 020 8958 9073 — MB BS 1983 Camb.; MB BS (Hons.) Lond. 1983; PhD Lond. 1993; MA Camb. 1984; MRCP (UK) 1986; FRCP 1999. Sen. Lect. & Hons. Cons. (Renal & Gen. Med.) ICSM Lond. Socs: Renal Assn.; Brit. Soc. Immunol.; (Ex-Sec.) Med. Research Soc. Prev: MRC Clinician Scientist Fell. (Immunol. & Renal.) RPMS & Hammersmith Hosp. Lond.; MRC Train. Fell. ICRF Tumour Immunol Unit Univ. Coll. Lond.; Regist. Rotat. Ealing Hosp., Roy. Postgrad. Med. Sch. & Hammersmith Hosp. Lond.

LIGHTSTONE, Hyman Leon (retired) Flat 28, Young Court, London NW6 7YX — M.R.C.S. Eng., L.R.C.P. Lond. 1931. Prev: Cas. Off. Qu.'s Hosp. Hackney.

LIGHTSTONE, Rachel Jane 16 Sycamore Close, Leicester LE2 2RN — MB BCh 1994 Wales.

LIGHTWOOD, Andrea Mary Hopps House, Hookwood, Horley RH6 0HU Tel: 01293 782530 — MB BS 1967 Lond.; FRCPath 1991, M 1979. (St. Thos.) Clin. Asst. (Haemat.) E. Surrey HA. Prev: Sen. Regist. (Haemat.) Oxf. RHA; Assoc. Haemat. Univ. Calif., San Francisco; Lect. (Path.) St. Thos. Hosp. Med. Sch.

LIGHTWOOD, Mr Robin Giles Hopps House, Hookwood, Horley RH6 0HU Tel: 01293 782530 Email: rlightwood@aol.com — BM BCh BM BCh Oxf. 1967; MA, MCh Oxf. 1982, BA 1967; FRCS Eng. 1973. (St Thos.) Cons. Surg. E. Surrey Hosp. Socs: Assn. of Surg.s; Assn. Endoscopic Surgs.; Assn. Upper G.I. Surg. Prev: Sen. Regist. (Surg.) St. Mary's Hosp. Lond.; Regist. (Surg.) Norwich HA; Research Fell. Univ. Calif. Med. Sch. San Francisco, USA.

LIKEMAN, Marcus John 46 White Lodge Close, Sutton SM2 5TQ Tel: 020 8661 9439 — MB BS 1993 Lond.; MRCP 1996; FRCR Pt1 1997; FRCR Pt 2a 1999; BSc 1987.

LILEY, Andrew Birmingham Childrens Hospital, Steelhouse Lane, Birmingham B4 6NH Tel: 0121 333 9627 Email: andy.liley@birmchildrens.wmids.nhs.uk — MB ChB 1986 Leeds; MB ChB Leeds. 1986. Cons. Peadiat. Anaeseth.Birm.Childr.s.Hosp.

LILEY, Helen Tracey 30 Manor Road, Solihull B91 2BL — MB ChB 1987 Leeds. SHO O & G. Solihull. Prev: SHO.Psych.Solihull.hosp.

LILFORD, Professor Richard James 1 Ampton Road, Edgbaston, Birmingham B15 2UP; Health Services Research, Institute of Public Health & Epidemiology, Medical School, University of Birmingham, Birmingham B15 2TT Tel: 0121 414 7365 — MB BCh 1973 Witwatersrand; MRCP (UK) 1981; MFPHM RCP (UK) 1995; MRCOG 1979; FRCOG 1996; FRCP 1997. (Witwatersrand) Nat. Clin. Trials Advisor NHS Exec.; Regional Dir. R & D, NHS Exec. W. Midl.s; Prof. Health Serv. Research Univ. Birm. Prev: Prof. (O & G) Leeds.

LILFORD, Victoria Alice Park Road Medical Centre, Park Road, Bradford BD5 0SG Tel: 01274 725959; 29 Shire Oak Road, Headingley, Leeds LS6 2DD — MB BS 1980 Lond.

LILJENDAHL, Sarah 154A Dobcroft Road, Sheffield S11 9LH — MB ChB 1976 Sheff. Med. Asst. (Genitourin. Med.) Chesterfield Roy. Hosp.; GPCA (GUM) Barnsley Dist. Gen. Hosp.

LILLEY, Alison Jean Castle Surgery, 1 Prince of Wales Drive, Neath SA11 3EW Tel: 01639 641444 Fax: 01639 636288; 3 Heol Davies Andrews, Tonna, Neath SA11 3EU — MB BCh 1987 Wales; MRCGP 1992.

LILLEY, Carolyn Sian 9 Elm Close, Amersham HP6 5DD — MB BCh 1992 Wales.

LILLEY, Christopher David 3F1, 59 Harrison Road, Edinburgh EH11 1EQ — MB ChB 1992 Manch.

LILLEY, Christopher William 3 Willow Drive, Colehill, Wimborne BH21 2RA — MB BS 1992 Lond.

LILLEY, Isobel Norah The Mount, Ardentinny, Dunoon PA23 8TR — MB ChB 1964 St. And. (St. And.)

LILLEY, Jacqueline The Jay's, Creek Road, March PE15 8SD — MB BS 1998 Lond.; MB BS Lond 1998.

LILLEY, Jane College Medical Centre, Christ Church College, North Holmes Road, Canterbury CT1 1QU Tel: 01227 767700 — MB BS 1986 Lond.; MRCGP 1991; T(GP) 1991; DCH RCP Lond. 1989.

LILLEY, Jean-Pierre 97 Harborne Road, Edgbaston, Birmingham B15 3HG — MB ChB 1977 Birm.; FFA RCS Eng. 1982.

LILLEY, John Arthur The Surgery, 46 Stewkley Road, Wing, Leighton Buzzard LU7 0NE Tel: 01296 688949 Fax: 01296 688575; 9 Redwood Drive, Wing, Leighton Buzzard LU7 0TA Tel: 01296 688451 — MB BS 1978 Newc.; MRCGP 1982; DRCOG 1981.

LILLEY, Julia Anne 15 Lymington Court, Parkwood Est., Maidstone ME15 9PQ — MB BS 1984 Lond.

LILLEY, Michael Edward 60 Greengage Rise, Melbourne, Royston SG8 6DS — MB BS 1976 Lond.; BSc (Pharmacol.) Lond. 1973, MB BS 1976; DRCOG 1979.

LILLEY, Richard James Herrington Medical Centre, Philadelphia Lane, Houghton-le-Spring DH4 4LE Tel: 0191 584 2632 Fax: 0191 584 3786 — MB ChB 1982 Manch.

LILLEYMAN, Professor John Stuart Department of Paediatric Haematology/ Oncology, Royal London Hospital, Whitechapel, London E1 Tel: 020 7377 7000 Ext: 3935 Fax: 020 7377 7796 Email: j.s.lilleyman@qmul.ac.uk; Tel: 01284 708697 Email: johnlilleyman@supanet.com — FRCP Lond. 1986; MRCP (UK) 1973; FRCPath 1986, M 1974; 2000 FRCP E; DSc 1996 London; FRCPCH 1997. (St. Bart.) Prof. of Paediatric Oncol., Barts & The Lond. Med. Sch.; Hon. Cons. Paediatric Haemat. and Oncol., Barts & The Lond. NHS Trust. Socs: Brit. Soc. Haematol.; Assn. of Clin. Pathologists (Pres. 1998/9); Roy. Coll. of Pathdosists (Pres. 1999-2002). Prev: Cons. Haemat. Sheff. HA Childr. Hosp.; Prof. Paediat. Haemat. Univ. Sheff.; Sen. Regist. (Haemat.) Sheff. AHA (T).

LILLICRAP, David Anthony (retired) 29 Princes Gardens, Cliftonville, Margate CT9 3AR Tel: 01843 292335 — BM BCh 1956 Oxf.; FRCP Lond. 1974, M 1959; T(M) 1991. Prev: Cons. Phys. I. of Thanet Hosp.

LILLICRAP, John Sanford Wee Cott, Bullen St., Thorverton, Exeter EX5 5NG — MB BS 1940 Lond.; MRCS Eng. LRCP Lond. 1939. (St. Bart.) Prev: Sen. Med. Off. Camden & Islington AHA; Occupat. Health Med. Off. Roy. N.. Hosp. Lond.; Sch. Med. Off. City Birm.

LILLICRAP, Mark Stephen Rheumatology Research, Box 194, Addenbrooke's Hospital, Hills Road, Cambridge CB4 3UR Tel: 01223 217459 Email: msl29@medsohl.cam.ac.uk; 6A Barton Road, Haslingfield, Cambridge CB3 7LL Tel: 01223 871057 — BM BCh 1992 Oxf.; BA Camb. 1989; MRCP (UK) 1996. (Camb. & Oxf. Univ.) Clin. Fell. Addenbrookes Hosp. Camb. Prev: SHO (Gen. Med.) Nottm. City Hosp.

LILLICRAP, Stephen Hunter Cornwall Gardens Surgery, 77 Cornwall Gardens, Cliftonville, Margate CT9 2JF Tel: 01843 291833 Fax: 01843 293126; 16 Upchurch Walk, Margate CT9 3NT — MB BS 1981 Newc.; MRCGP 1985; DRCOG 1984. Prev: Trainee GP Doncaster VTS; Ho. Phys. Roy. Vict. Infirm. Newc.

LILLIE, Ruth (retired) Lakeshill, Yewtree Lane, Bewdley DY12 2PJ Tel: 01299 403222 — MB ChB 1938 Birm.

LILLINGTON, Alan William, Deputy Lt. (retired) Flat 6, Whitburn Hall, Whitburn, Sunderland SR6 7JQ Tel: 0191 529 4562 Fax: 0191 529 4562 — MB BS 1956 Durh.; MD Newc. 1979; FRCP Ed. 1978, M 1963. Prev: Cons. Paediat. Sunderland AHA.

LILLIOTT, Mairead Mary 65 Stroudwater Park, St. George's Avenue, Weybridge KT13 0DT Tel: 01932 842141 — MB BS 1947 Lond.; MFCM RCP (UK) 1974; DObst RCOG 1949; DPH Lond. 1957. (Roy. Free) Clin. Med. Off. (Community) Hounslow & Spelthorne HA. Socs: BMA. Prev: Dep. MOH Staines & Sunbury UDs; Dep. Div. Med. Off. & Deptm. Med. Off. N.. Div. Surrey CC; Asst. Med. Off. (N.W. Div.) Surrey CC.

LILLO TORREGROSA, Juan Jose 7 Dickens Close, Galley Common, Nuneaton CV10 9SQ — LMS 1985 Alicante.

LILLY, John Bridge (retired) 22 Magdalene Fields, Warkworth, Morpeth NE65 0UF Tel: 01665 711375 — MB BS 1951 Durh. Prev: GP Morpeth.

LILLY, Richard Graham (retired) 2 Phillips Way, Long Buckby, Northampton NN6 7SF Tel: 01327 843145 — MB BS 1941 Durh. Prev: Ho. Phys. Gen. Hosp. & Hosp. Sick Childr. Newc. u. Tyne.

LILLY, Richard John The Surgery, Bridge End, Chester-le-Street DH3 3SL Tel: 0191 388 2038; 142 Gilesgate, Durham DH1 1QQ Tel: 0191 384 6076 — MB BS 1978 Newc.; MRCGP 1983; DCH RCP Lond. 1984; DRCOG 1981.

LILLYWHITE, Alan Richard Llanarth Ct Hosp, Llanarth Ct, Raglan NP15 2XD Tel: 01873 840555 Fax: 01873 840591 — MB BS 1983 Lond.; BSc (Hons.) Lond. 1980. Cons Forens. Psychiat. Llannath Ct Hosp Llanarth Raglan; Cons psychia priory Hill Hosp Bristol. Socs: MRCPsych. Prev: Cons. Forens. Psychiat. Blackberry Hill Hosp. Bristol.

LILLYWHITE, Allan Victor 31 Hainault Road, Chigwell IG7 5DQ Tel: 020 8500 2853 — MB BCh 1944 Wales; MRCS Eng. LRCP Lond. 1944.

LILLYWHITE, Eluned Kathleen 31 Hainault Road, Chigwell IG7 5DQ Tel: 020 8500 2853 — MB BCh 1948 Wales. (Cardiff)

LILLYWHITE, Louis Patrick, MBE, Brigadier Room 9386 Ministry of Defence, Main Building, Whitehall, London SW1A 2HB Tel: 020 7807 8774 Fax: 020 7807 8834 Email: dmedperspoltry@surgeongeneral.co.uk; 38 Inglewood Grove, Streetly, Sutton Coldfield B74 3LW Tel: 020 8950 9244 Fax: 08701 617617 Email: louis@lillywhi.demon.co.uk — MB BCh 1971 Wales; MSc Occupat. Med. Lond. 1989; MFOM RCP Lond. 1990, AFOM 1989. (Univ. Wales) Dir. Med. Personnel Train.& Clin. Policy. Socs: Fell.Med. Soc. Lond.; Soc. Occup. Med.; Fell.Roy.Coll.Med. Prev: Dept. Asst. Chief of Staff HQ Land Command Salisbury; Cdr. Med.

1st Armoured Divisiom Germany & Gulf; Commanding Off. 23 Parachute Field Ambul. Aldershot.

LIM, Adrian Kuok Pheng 23 Heron Wharf, Castle Marina, Nottingham NG7 1GF — BM BS 1995 Nottm.

LIM, Aik Guan Department of Medicine, Dorking Road, Epsom KT18 7EG Tel: 01372 735129 Email: guan@ormomd. demon.co.uk — MB ChB 1987 Bristol; MD Bristol 1996; MRCP (UK) 1990. (Bristol) Cons.(Phys. & Gastroenterolist), Epsom Gen. Hosp., Epsom, Surrey, KT18 7EG; Sen. Research Fell. St. Geo. Hosp. Med. Sch. Lond. Socs: BMA; Brit. Soc. of Gastroenterol.; America Gastroenterol. Assoc. Prev: Research Fell. St. Geo. Hosp. Med. Sch. Lond.; Sen. Regist. (Gastroenterol.) Roy. Lond. Hosp.; Regist. Rotat. (Med.) St. Geo. Hosp. Lond.

LIM, Andrew Boon Huat 1 Beaumont House, Lansdown Road, Lansdown, Bath BA1 5RD — MB BS 1985 Lond.

LIM, Boon Khaw c/o Mei Yen Furey, 2 Kensington Place, Bristol BS8 3AH — MB ChB 1998 Bristol.

LIM, Chea Siang Princess Alexandra Eye Pavilion, Royal Infirmary Edinburgh, Chalmers St., Edinburgh EH3 9HA Tel: 0131 536 1000 — BM BCh 1986 Oxf.; BA Camb. 1983; FRCS Ed. 1992; FRCOphth 1992. Specialist Regist. (Ophth.). Prev: Wellcome Vision Research Fell. Univ. Aberd.; Regist. P.ss Alexandra Eye Pavil. Edin.; SHO (Ophth.) Sunderland Eye Infirm. & Train. Rotat. Croydon & Sutton Eye Units.

LIM, Chee Chian Balmoral Court, Flat 22, 20 Queens Terrace, London NW8 6DW — MB BS 1986 Singapore; MRCP (UK) 1991.

LIM, Chee Hooi 21 Disbrowe Road, London W6 8QG Email: limchehe@hotmail.com; 5 Tingkat, Laksamana 4, Taman Teluk Molek, Butterworth 13050, Malaysia — MB ChB 1993 Leeds; MRCP (UK) 1997. Specialist Regist. (Gastroenterol.).

LIM, Chin Fou c/o Mark Burns, 24 Barrington Drive, Glasgow G4 9DT — MB ChB 1987 Glas.

LIM, Chin Joo 9 Newmount, Lyndhurst Terrace, Hampstead, London NW3 5QA — MB BChir 1981 Camb.; MA, MB Camb. 1982, BChir 1981. Prev: SHO & Ho. Phys. Middlx. Hosp. Isleworth; Ho. Surg. N. Middlx. Hosp. Lond.

LIM, Christopher Thiam Seong Musgrave & Clarke House, The Royal Victoria Hospital, Belfast BT12 6BA — MB BCh 1998 Belf.; MB BCh Belf 1998.

LIM, Chu Chin 92 Broadway Parade, Belfast BT12 6JY Tel: 01232 330890 — MB BCh BAO 1992 Belf.; DCH NUI 1994.

LIM, Dianne Petre 25 Woodwarde Road, Dulwich, London SE22 8UN — MB BS 1974 Lond.; MRCP (UK) 1976; FRCP 1996. (Guy's) Cons. (Audiol. Med.) Roy. Nat. Throat Nose & Ear Hosp. Lond.

LIM, Emma Jane Voluntary Service Overseas, 317 Putney Bridge Road, London SW15 2PN — BM BS 1993 Nottm.

LIM, Floreen Kim Bee 46 Riversdale, Llandaff, Cardiff CF5 2QL — MB BCh 1994 Wales.

LIM, Frederick Thomas Keng Sim Flat 6, 26 Devonshire Place, London W1E 6JE Tel: 020 7487 3529 Fax: 020 7224 1784 — MB BS 1971 Lond.; MRCP (UK) 1974. (Mem. Indep. Cons. Lond.) Cons. Genito-Urin. Phys. (Private Consultations only). Socs: Med. Soc. Study VD; Indep. Doctors Forum. Prev: Cons. Genitourin. Med. King's Coll. Hosp. Lond.; Sen. Regist. Middlx. Hosp. & Char. Cross Hosp. Lond.

LIM, Hau Han Bristol Heart Institute, Level 7, Bristol Royal Infirmary, Bristol BS2 8HW Email: klhh@selangor.demon.co.uk — MB ChB 1991 Dundee; MSc (Med. Sci.) Glas. 1994; FRCS Ed. 1997.

LIM, Hock Hee Market Street Surgery, 102 Market Street, Newton-le-Willows WA12 9BP Tel: 01925 221457; Caulfield, 102 Market St, Newton-le-Willows WA12 9PB Tel: 01925 221457 — MB ChB 1977 Liverp.; MRCGP 1982.

LIM, Hsieh-Mei Sharon 11 Mowbray Road, London NW6 7QX — MB ChB 1991 Leic.

LIM, Hui Ling 9 Rockbourne Avenue, Liverpool L25 4TQ — MB ChB 1996 Ed.

LIM, Jane Chean Ming 89 Hartland Road, London NW6 6BH — MB BS 1987 Lond.

LIM, Jennifer Anne 26 Haygate Avenue, Brightons, Falkirk FK2 0TL Tel: 01324 716327 — MB ChB 1983 Aberd.; DRCOG 1985. GP Grangemouth. Prev: Trainee GP/SHO Forth Valley Health Bd.; Resid. Ho. Off. (Gen. Med.) Falkirk & Dist. Roy. Infirm.; Resid. Ho. Off. (Surg.) Aberd. Roy. Infirm.

LIM, Jerome Christopher Siong 27 Woodhall Drive, London SE21 7HJ — MB BS 1993 Lond.

LIM, Julia Meh Ying 28 Whiston House, Bingham Court, Richmond Grove, London N1 2DH — MB ChB 1992 Liverp.; DCH Lond. 1997; DRCOG Lond. 1996; DFFP 1996; MRCGP 1998. (Liverp.) GP Clin. Asst. Socs: BMA; Assoc. Mem. RCGP.

LIM, Justin Tek Ken 11 Woodville Court, Woodville Road, Cardiff CF24 4DR; 8 Holly House, Stepping Hill hospital, Popular Grove, Stockport SK2 7JE Tel: 0161 419 5759 — MB BCh 1995 Wales. SHO Rotat. (Surg.) Roy. Gwent Hosp. Newport; SHO Orthop. Stepping Hill. Hosp.

LIM, Karen Mae Yee 66 Ack La W., Cheadle Hume, Cheadle SK8 7ES — MB ChB 1985 Glas.; MRCGP 1992.

LIM, Karene Arete Flat 306, Arlington Buildings, Fairfield Road, London E3 2UB — MB BCh 1995 Wales.

LIM, Kean Lee Department of Rheumatology, Kings Mill Centre, Sherwood Foest Hospitals NHS Trust, Mansfield NG17 4JL Tel: 01623 672377 Fax: 01623 676050; 214 Main Road NG15 9GX Tel: 01623 456545 — MB BS 1986 Lond.; FRCP (London); MRCP (UK) 1990. Davidson Lect. (Med. & Rheum.) Roy. Infirm. Glas. Socs: Brit. Soc. Rheum. Prev: Research Fell. (Clin. Immunol.) Qu. Med. Centre Univ. Hosp. Nottm.; Regist. Rotat. (Med.) Norf. & Norwich Hosps.; SHO Rotat. (Med.) Sunderland Hosps.

LIM, Kelvin Jia Hau 61 Cardoness Road, Sheffield S10 5RT — MB ChB 1993 Sheff.

LIM, Kelvin Kwok Jin The Surgery, Church Walk, Eastwood, Nottingham NG16 3BH Tel: 01773 712951 Fax: 01773 534160 — BM BS 1986 Nottm.

LIM, Kelvin Lye Hock 89 Lonsdale Court, West Jesmond Avenue, Newcastle upon Tyne NE2 3HF — MB BS 1992 Newc.

LIM, Keng Peng 27 Bonnymuir Place, Aberdeen AB15 5NJ — MB ChB 1998 Aberd.; MB ChB Aberd 1998.

LIM, Kenneth Chu-Keong 55 Inglefield Avenue, Cardiff CF14 3PY — MB BCh 1992 Wales.

LIM, Kian Chee Apartment 6 (1st Floor) Archbishops House, Church Road, Woolton, Liverpool L25 5JF — MB ChB 1993 Liverp.

LIM, Kian Soon Flat 13, Damers Court, Damers Road, Dorchester DT1 2JR — BM 1995 Soton.

LIM, Kim Hong 239 Minster Court, Crown, Liverpool L7 3QH — MB ChB 1992 Liverp.

LIM, Kim Tho Christopher 7 Avocet Wharf, Nottingham NG7 1TH — BM BS 1997 Nottm.

LIM, Kong Beng Department of Obstetrics & Gynaecology, Southend Hospital, Prittlewell Chase, Westcliff on Sea SS0 0RY Tel: 01702 435555; Tel: 01702 586179 — MB ChB 1974 Bristol; MRCOG 1981; FRCOG 1994. Cons. O & G S.end HA. Prev: Sen. Regist. Hammersmith Hosp. Lond.

LIM, Lian Sin Bennetts End Surgery, Gatecroft, Hemel Hempstead HP3 9LY Tel: 01442 63511 Fax: 01442 235419 — MB BS 1966 Lond.; MRCP (U.K.) 1970; MRCS Eng. LRCP Lond. 1966. (St. Mary's)

LIM, Linda Blackwater Medical Centre, Princes Road, Maldon CM9 7DS Tel: 01621 854204 Fax: 01621 850246 — MD 1986 Antwerp.

LIM, May-Li No 10, Bron-y-Nant, Croesnewydd Road, Wrexham LL13 7TX — MB BS 1993 Queensland.

LIM, Meh-Noi Moray Health Services, Doctor Grays Hospital, Elgin IV30 1SN — MB ChB 1998 Aberd.; MB ChB Aberd 1998.

LIM, Meng Hooi Goodmayes Hospital, Barley Lane, Ilford IG3 8XJ — BM BCh 1973 Oxf.; MA Oxf. 1968, BM BCh 1973; MRCPsych 1978. (Univ. Coll. Hosp.) Cons. Psychiat. Goodmayes Hosp. Ilford. Socs: BMA. Prev: Sen. Regist. Dept. Acad. Psychiat. Middlx. Hosp. Lond.; Sen. Regist. Maudsley Hosp. Lond.; Regist. Maudsley Hosp. Lond.

LIM, Michael Seng Teik High Bank, Offley Road, Hitchin SG5 2BB — MB BS 1992 Lond.

LIM, Ming Jin — BM BS 1993 Nottm.; BMedSci 1991. Specialist Regist. Paediat S. W. Thames. Socs: MRCP; MRCPCH.

LIM, Ming Sheng Royal Peston Hospital, Postgraduate Centre, Watling Street Road, Fulwood, Preston PR2 8DY — MB ChB 1995 Manch.

LIM, Morton 25 Woodwarde Road, Dulwich, London SE22 8UN — MB BS 1974 Lond.; MD Lond. 1985, BSc; MRCP (UK) 1976; FFA RCS Eng. 1980. (Guy's) Cons. Anaesth. St. Thos. Hosp. Lond.; Examr. Final FRCA.

LIM, Natasha Pei Yee 47 Silverburn Drive, Oakwood, Derby DE21 2JH — BM BS 1994 Nottm.

LIM, Paul Chong-Kui Camelon Medical Practice, 3 Baird Street, Camelon, Falkirk FK1 4PP Tel: 01324 622854 Fax: 01324 633858; Ochilview, Newlands Road, Reddingmuirhead, Falkirk FK2 0DY Tel: 01324 715876 Email: paullim@bigfoot.com — MB ChB 1983 Aberd.; DRCOG 1985; Dip. Med. Acupunc. Clin. Asst. (Learning Disabil.) Roy. Scott. Nat. Hosp. Larbert, Falkirk. Socs: Brit. Med. Acupunct. Soc.; Assoc. Mem. Brit. Homoeop. Soc.; Brit. Assn. Med. & Dent. Hypn. Prev: Ho. Off. (Gen. Med.) Falkirk & Dist. Roy. Infirm.; Ho. Off. (Surg.) Aberd. Roy. Infirm.; GP Rotat. - Falkirk & Dist. Roy. Infirm.

LIM, Mr Paul Vey Hong 33 Stone Leigh Court, Coton Road, Nuneaton CV11 5UQ Tel: 01203 347302; Flat 15, William Court, 49 Clarendon Road, Edgbaston, Birmingham B16 9SD Tel: 0121 455 7568 — MB ChB 1990 Leic.; FRCS Glas. 1995; FRCS (Orl.) Eng. 1995; FRCS (Orl.) Ed. 1995. Lect. (Otolarryagel) Univ. Hosp.Kuala Lumpur, Malaysia; Demonst. (Anat.) Univ. Leicester Med. Sch. Socs: MDU; Midl. Inst. Otol. Prev: Regist. (ENT) Burton Hosp. Burton-on-Trent & Russells Hall Hosp. Dudley.

LIM, Peik Loon Department of Medicine, Institute of Clinical Science, Grosvenor Road, Belfast BT12 6BJ Tel: 01232 240503 Ext: 2557 — MB BCh BAO 1991 Belf.; MRCP (UK) 1994. (Queen's University Belfast) Specialist Regist. (Gastroenterol. & Gen. Internal Med.) Roy. Hosps. Trust Belf. Socs: BMA; Roy. Coll. Phys. Lond. Prev: Regist. (Gen. Med.) Belf. City Hosp.; Regist. (Gen. Mecicine) Altnagelvin Hosp. Lond.derry.

LIM, Philip Seng Choong 38 Kings College Court, 55 Primrose Hill Road, London NW3 3EA — MB BS 1985 Lond.

LIM, Pitt Onn Dept of Cardiology, Wales Heart Research Institute, University of Wales, Heath Park, Cardiff CF14 4XN Tel: 02920 747747 Fax: 02920 743500 Email: limpo@cf.ac.uk; PO Box 11447, 88816 Kota Kinabalu, Sabah, Malaysia Tel: 00 60 88 422848 — MB BS 1990 Newc.; MRCP (UK) 1994; DGM RCP Lond. 1994. Brit. heart Foundat. Clin. Lect. in Cardiol.; I. Socs: Brit. Geriat. Soc.; Roy. Coll. Phys. Lond.; Brit. Echocardiogr. Soc. Prev: SHO Rotat. Withington Hosp. Manch. & Univ. Hosp. S. Manch.; SHO Rotat. (Gen. Med.) E. Surrey HA.; Clin. Lect. & Hon. Sen. Regist. (Cardiovasc. Med. & Clin. Pharmacol.) Ninewe.

LIM, Samson Department of Thoracic Medicine, National Heart & Lung Institute, Dovehouse St., London SW3 6LY Tel: 020 7351 8051; Flat 2, 6 Darlaston Road, London SW19 4LG Tel: 020 8296 8420 Fax: 020 8296 8420 Email: sam.lim@ic.ac.uk — MB BS 1986 Monash; FRACP 1994. Clin. Research Fell. (Thoracic Med.) Nat. Heart & Lung Inst. Lond. Socs: Brit. Thorac. Soc.; Amer. Thoracic Soc.; Thoracic Soc. Austral. & NZ. Prev: Sen. Regist. (Thoracic Med.) Whittington Hosp. Lond.

LIM, Sek Chiew Wrafton House Surgery, Wrafton House, 9-11 Wellfield Road, Hatfield AL10 0BS Tel: 01707 265454 Fax: 01707361286 — MB ChB 1974 Sheff.

LIM, Selina Hui Boon Elderly Care Unit, Southampton General Hospital, Tremona Road, Southampton SO16 67D; Tel: 01243 783369 — MB BS 1990 Lond.; BSc Lond. 1987; MRCP (UK) 1993. Regist. (Elderly Care) Soton. Gen. Hosp.

LIM, Sharon Ming Chu (retired) European Operations Marketing, Eli Lilly & Company, Erl Wood Manor, Sunninghill Road, Windlesham Gu20 6PH Tel: 01276 484123 Email: slim.mba2001@london.edu — MB BS 1989 Lond.; BSc Lond. 1988; BSc 1988 Lond.; MBA 2001 Lond.; MRCP (UK) 1993. Sen. Assoc., New Product Plann., Europ. Operat.s, Eli Lilly & Company, Windlesham, Surrey.

LIM, Si Ching 98 Mornington Road, London E11 3DX — MB ChB 1992 Bristol.

LIM, Soon Chye Attenborough Surgery, Bushey Health Centre, London Road, Bushey, Watford WD23 2NN Tel: 01923 231633; 101 Raglan Gardens, Oxhey, Watford WD19 4LJ Email: scapelblade@man.com — MB BS 1989 Lond.; MRCGP 1995. (St. Mary's Hosp. Med. Sch.) GP Watford. Prev: Trainee GP Watford VTS; SHO Rotat. (Surg.) St. Mary's Hosp. Lond.

LIM, Stephen Wordsley Green Health Centre, Wordsley Green, Wordsley, Stourbridge DY8 5PD Tel: 01384 277591 Fax: 01384 401156; 7 Lower Rudge, Pattingham, Wolverhampton WV6 7EB Tel: 01902 700974 Email: stephen.j.lim@btinternet.co.uk — MB ChB 1977 Birm.; MRCGP 1983; DRCOG 1980.

LIM, Tien Wei Jimmy Gordon 12 Hollybank Court, London Road, Leicester LE2 1ZF — MB ChB 1994 Leic.

LIM, Victor Yen Teak c/o Glasgow Chinese Christian Church, 2 Melrose St., Glasgow G4 9BJ — MB ChB 1993 Glas.

LIM, Vun Roei Rheumatology Department, Leicester Royal Infirmary, Infirmary Square, Leicester LE1 5WW Tel: 0116 254 1414 — MB BCh BAO 1991 Belf.; MRCP. Specialist Regist. Roy. Infirm. Leicester Rheum. Dept. Socs: BMA; RCPI; BASEM.

LIM, Wan Chin 24/16 East Parkside, Edinburgh EH16 5XN — MB ChB 1998 Ed.; MB ChB Ed 1998.

LIM, Wendy Wan Dee 36 Fitzroy Crescent, Chiswick Place, London W4 3EL — BM BS 1993 Nottm.; BMedSci (Hons.) Nottm. 1991; MRCP (UK) 1996. (Univ. Nottm. Med. Sch.) Specialist Regist. (Gen. Med.) St. Helier's Hosp. Surrey. Prev: SHO (Nephrol.) Guy's Hosp. Lond.; SHO (Gen. Med.) Qu. Mary's Hosp. Sidcup; SHO (Cardiol.) Brook's Hosp. Lond.

LIM, Yick Hou 2 Melrose Street, Glasgow G4 9BJ — MB ChB 1994 Glas.

LIM, Yit Yoong 3C Stranmillis Court, Kingsbridge, Belfast BT9 5EU — MB BCh BAO 1997 Belf.

LIM HOE KEE, Joseph Area Antrim Hospital, 45 Bush Road, Antrim BT41 2RL Tel: 02894 424523 Fax: 02894 424294; 59 Shellinghill Road, Cullybackey, Ballymena BT42 1NR Tel: 02825 880301 — MB BCh BAO NUI 1964; FRCP Canada 1971; DCH NUI 1966. (Dub.) Cons. Paediat. Antrim Area Hosp. Socs: BMA & BAPM; Brit. Paediat. Assn. Prev: Chief Paediat. Med. Hat & Dist. Hosp. Alberta, Canada.

LIM SU PING, Regina 5 Barnfield Cl, Cardiff CF23 8LN — MB BCh 1997 Wales.

LIMAGE, Steven John New Health Centre, Third Avenue, Canvey Island SS8 9SU Tel: 01268 683758 Fax: 01268 684057; Windin, The Willows, Benfleet SS7 5RS — MB BS 1985 Lond. Prev: Ho. Off. (Gen. Surg. & ENT) St. Bart. Hosp. Lond.; Ho. Off. (Gen. Med.) S.end Gen. Hosp.

LIMAYE, Parvati 345 Colne Road, Burnley BB10 1TP Tel: 01282 26174 — MB BS 1956 Poona; DCH Eng. 1960. (B.J. Med. Coll.) SCMO (Child Health) Calderdale HA. Prev: Regist. (Paediat.) Burnley Gp. Hosps.

LIMAYE, Shankar Hari 345 Colne Road, Burnley BB10 1TP Tel: 01282 426174 — MB BS 1955 Poona.

LIMAYE, Sunil Viniak Dental Centre, 3 Gower Place, London WC1E 6BN Tel: 020 7387 6306 — MB BS 1988 Lond.; MFFP 1993; DRCOG 1993. Sen. Clin. Med. Off. Margt. Pyke Centre Lond. Prev: Regist. Jas. Wigg Pract. Kentish Town Lond.; Clin. Asst. (Genitourin. Med.) Univ. Coll. Hosp. Lond.; Clin. Med. Off. (Child Health) Bloomsbury HA.

LIMB, Catherine Ann Leigh View Medical Centre, Bradford Road, Tingley, Wakefield WF3 1RQ Tel: 0113 253 7629 Fax: 0113 238 1286; The Oaks, 11 Lidgett Pk Road, Roundhay, Leeds LS8 1EE Tel: 0113 294 5769 — MB BS 1985 Lond.; MB BS Lond. 1985.; BSc Basic Med. Scs & Pharmacol. Lond. 1982; MRCGP 1989. (St. Bart.) Socs: BMA; Med. Protec. Soc.

LIMB, Mr David Leslie Academic Department of Orthopaedic Surgery, St. James University Hospital, Beckett St., Leeds LS9 7TF Tel: 0113 243 3144 Fax: 0113 206 6791 Email: d.limb@leeds.ac.uk; The Oaks, 11 Lidgett Pk Road, Roundhay, Leeds LS8 1EE Tel: 0113 294 5769 — MB BS 1985 Lond.; BSc Lond. 1982; FRCS (Orth.) 1994; FRCS Ed. 1990. (St. Bart. Hosp. Lond.) Sen. Lect. & Hon. Cons. (Orthop. Surg.) St. Jas. Univ. Hosp. Leeds; Sen. Lect. (Orthop. Surg.) Univ. Leeds. Socs: Brit. Shoulder & Elbow Soc.; Brit. Orthop. Assn.; Brit. Trauma Soc. Prev: Sen. Regist. (Orthop.) Leeds; Demonst. (Anat.) Med. Coll. St. Bart. Hosp. Lond.

LIMB, Derek George (retired) General Hospital, Bishop Auckland DL14 6AD Tel: 01388 454000 — MB ChB 1968 Ed.; FRCOG 1985, M 1973. Cons. (O & G) N. RHA.

LIMB, Simon Patrick 39 Graces Road, London SE5 8PF — MB BS 1989 Lond.

LIMBREY, Rachel Mary 68 Chapel Lane, Fowlmere, Royston SG8 7SD Tel: 01763 208742 Fax: 01763 208742 — MB BS 1992

Lond.; MRCP (UK) 1995. (Char. Cross & Westm.) Specialist Regist. (LAT) Respirat. Med. St. Richard's Hosp. Chichester. Prev: SHO (Anaesth.) St. Mary's Hosp. Lond.

***LIMBRICK, Rachel Ann** 6 Meadow Rise, Bewdley DY12 1JP Tel: 01299400704 — MB BS 1998 Lond.; MB BS Lond 1998.

LIMENTANI, Alexander Esmond 38 Fitzroy Avenue, Kingsgate, Broadstairs CT10 3LS — MB BS 1973 Lond.; MRCS Eng. LRCP Lond. 1973; FFCM 1988, M 1981; PhD Kent 1997. Dir. Pub. Health E. Kent HA; Cons. Centre Health Servs. Studies Univ. Kent.

LIMOND, Martin Giles Hereford County Hospital, Union Walk, Hereford HR1 2ER; 21 Chartwell Road, Hereford HR1 2TU — MB BS 1996 Lond.

LIMOUSIN, Patricia Human Movement & Balance Unit, National Hospital for Neurology, Queen Square, London WC1N 3BG — MD 1993 Grenoble; MD Greboble 1993.

LIN, Jean-Pierre New Comen Centre, Guy's Hospital, Guy's & St Thomas' NHS Trust, St Thomas' St., London SE1 9RT Tel: 020 7955 5000 Ext: 3200 Fax: 020 7955 2340 Email: jeanpierrelin@compuserve.com — MB ChB 1983 Ed.; MRCP (UK) 1986; PhD Ed. 1998. (Edinburgh) Cons. (Paediat. Neurol.) Newcomen Centre & Guy's & St. Thomas' Guy Ho. Socs: Brit. Paediat. Neurol. Assn.; Physiol. Soc. Lond. 1999; Europ. Paediatric Neurol. Soc. Prev: Sen. Regist. (Paediat. Neurol.) Gt. Ormond St. Childr.'s Hosp. Lond.; Geo. Guthrie Research Fell. Fac. Med. Edin. Univ.; Regist. (Paediat.) Roy. Hosp. for Sick Childr. & Simpson Memor. Matern. Pavil.

LIN, Kai Wei 55 Bower Road, Sheffield S10 1ER — MB ChB 1997 Sheff.

LIN, Michael Ka Kui 178 Lauderdale Manisons, Lauderdale Road, London W9 1NG Tel: 020 7286 1466 — MB BS 1994 Lond.; BSc (Hons.) Lond. 1991. SHO (A & E) Whipps Cross Hosp. Lond. Prev: SHO (Gen. Med.) Ashford Hosp. Middlx. & St. Geo. Hosp. Lond.; Ho. Off. (Med.) E.boure Dist. Gen. Hosp.

LIN SIN CHO, Gaetan Laval 4 Royal Close, Seven Kings, Ilford IG3 8UJ — MB BCh 1992 Witwatersrand.

LINAKER, Barry David Warrington Hospital NHS Trust, Lovely Lane, Warrington WA5 1QG Tel: 01925 635911 Fax: 01925 662042 — MB BS Lond. 1979; MD Lond. 1983; FRCP Lond. 1989; MRCP (UK) 1974; MRCS Eng. LRCP Lond. 1970; T(M) 1991. (King's Coll. Hosp.) Cons. Phys. (Gen. Med. & Gastroenterol.) Warrington . Hosp NHS Trust.; Cons.Gastroenterol.Halton.Hosp.NHS Trust. Socs: Brit. Soc. Gastroenterol.; Liverp. Med. Inst.; Merseyside & N. Wales Soc. Phys. Prev: Sen. Regist. (Gen. Med.) Walton Hosp. Liverp.; MRC Research Fell. & Hon. Sen. Regist. (Med.) Hope Hosp. Salford; Sen. Regist. (Gastroenterol.) BRd.green Hosp. Liverp.

LINARDOU, Helen Department of Clinical Oncology, Royal Postgraduate Medical School, Hammersmith Hospital, Du Cane Road, London W12 0HS Tel: 020 8383 3973 Fax: 020 8383 3258 Email: h.linardou@icrf.icnet.uk; Flat 2, 97 Goldhurst Terrace, London NW6 3HA — Ptychio Iatrikes 1989 Athens; Ptychio Iatrikes Athens Greece 1989. (Univ. Athens) Clin. Research Fell. & Hon. Regist. (Clin. Oncol.) RPMS Hammersmith Hosp. Lond. Prev: SHO (Clin. Oncol.) Hammersmith Hosp. Lond.; SHO Agii Anargiri Cancer Hosp. Athens, Greece.

LINCH, David Christopher Department Haematology, University College London Medical School, 98 Chenies Mews, London WC1E 6HX Tel: 020 7209 6221 Fax: 020 7209 6222; Chess Place, Loudwater Lane, Rickmansworth WD3 4HG Tel: 01923 777140 — MB 1976 Camb.; BChir 1975; FRCP Lond. 1987; MRCP (UK) 1977; FRCPath 1996; F Med Sci 1998. Prof. Clin. Haemat. Univ. Coll. Lond. Med. Sch.

LINCOLN, David Stuart Larksfield Surgery, Arlesey Road, Stotfold, Hitchin SG5 4HB Tel: 01462 732200 — MB BS 1975 Lond.; DRCOG 1980. (Westm.) Prev: RAF Med. Off.

LINCOLN, Mr John Christopher Rutland (retired) (cons. rooms), 38 Devonshire St., London W1G 6QB Tel: 020 7935 7529 Fax: 0207 937 9692 — LRCPI & LM, LRSCI & LM 1959; LRCPI & LM, LRCSI & LM 1959; FRCS Ed. 1964; FRCS Eng. 1968. Prev: Cons. Cardiothoracic Surg. Brompton Hosp. Lond.

LINCOLN, Karen Anne Fairview, Winston, Darlington DL2 3RH — MB ChB 1989 Manch.; MRCOG 1996. Regist. (O & G) S. Cleveland Hosp. Middlesbrough.

LIND, James (retired) The Firs, 56 Crewe Road, Shavington, Crewe CW2 5DW Tel: 01270 567241 Email: jlind18653@cs.com — MB ChB Glas. 1960; DObst RCOG 1965.

LIND, James Frederick 1 Tolliday Close, Wivenhoe, Colchester CO7 9SL — BM BS 1993 Nottm.

LIND, Margaret Isobel (retired) 8 St Bean Ct, Rosebank, Auchterarder PH3 1QP Tel: 01764 660411 — MB ChB Ed. 1961; DCH RCPS Glas. 1963; DObst RCOG 1963. Prev: SCMO Chesh. Community Healthcare Trust.

LIND, Professor Michael John University of Hull, Hull HU6 7RX; 19 Roseworth Avenue, Gosforth, Newcastle upon Tyne NE3 1NB Tel: 0191 284 7971 Fax: 01482 676873 Email: m.j.lindo@medschool.hull.ac.uk — MB BS 1981 Lond.; BSc (Hons.) Lond. 1978, MD 1990; MRCP (UK) 1984; FRCP 1997. Prof. Of Oncol.Hull Univ.; Hon. Cons. Roy.Hull.Hosp.NHS.Trust & Castle Hill.Trust. Socs: Assn. Cancer Phys.; Eur. Org. Research & Treatm. Cancer Pharmacokinetics & Metab.; Brit. Soc. Gyn. Oncol. Prev: Sen. Lect. & Hon. Cons. Clin. Oncol. Univ. Newc.; Lect. & Hon. Sen. Regist. (Clin. Oncol.) Univ. Newc. u. Tyne; CRC Train. Fell. Christie Hosp. Manch.

LIND, Professor Thomas (retired) 3 Dene Close, Jesmond Park W., Newcastle upon Tyne NE7 7BL Tel: 0191 281 3683 Fax: 0191 281 3683 Email: tl25503@aol.com — MB BS 1958 Durh.; DSc Newc. 1982, PhD 1972; FRCOG 1985, M 1968; FRCPath 1984, M 1980. Prev: Prof. Human Reproduc. Physiol. Univ. Newc.

LINDAHL, Andrea Jane 11 Deacon Close, Winterbourne, Bristol BS36 1DT — BChir 1994 Camb.; MB 1994, MA 1996; MRCP 1998. (University of Cambridge School of Clinical Medicine) SHO (Neurol.) Nat. Hosp. for Neurol. & Neurosurg. Lond. Socs: Med. Protec. Soc. Prev: SHO (Neurol.) Qu.s Med. Centre Nottm.; SHO Rotat. Nottm. City Hosp.

LINDALL, Karen Harewood Crescent Surgery, Harewood Crescent, Bournemouth BH7 7BU Tel: 01202 309500 Fax: 01202 309565 — MB BS 1987 Lond.; MRCP (UK) 1993; DA (UK) 1992.

LINDALL, Steven Penrhyn Surgery, 2A Penrhyn Avenue, Walthamstow, London E17 5DB Tel: 020 8527 2563 Fax: 020 8527 6583; 29 Merrivale, Oakwood, London N14 4TE Tel: 020 8360 8778 Fax: 020 8527 6583 Email: steven@stelin.demon.co.uk — MB BS 1982 Lond.; DFFP 1995; DCH RCP Lond. 1986; Dip. Med. Acupunc. 1997. (St George's London)

LINDECK, Miss Judith Flora Lodgeside Surgery, 22 Lodgeside Avenue, Kingswood, Bristol BS15 1WW Tel: 0117 961 5666 Fax: 0117 947 6854 — MB ChB 1988 Manch.; FRCS Ed. 1992; MRCGP 1995. Clin. Asst. (Gen. Surg.) Frenchay Hosp. Bristol. Prev: SHO Rotat. (Surg.) Frenchay Hosp. Bristol & Manch. Roy. Infirm.

LINDEFORS-HARRIS, Britt-Marie Winchester House, Whitehouse Road, Porchfield, Newport PO30 4LJ Tel: 01983 521345 Fax: 01983 521345 Email: bm@harrisassociates.demon.co.uk — Lakarexamen 1982 Stockholm. (The Karolinska Institute, Stockholm, Sweden) Managem. Consultancy. Socs: BMA; Fell. Swedish Soc. Med.; Swedish Med. Assn.

LINDEN, David Lennox and Partners, 9 Alloway Place, Ayr KA7 2AA Tel: 01292 611835 Fax: 01292 284982 — MB ChB 1982 Ed.

LINDEN, Patrick Gerard Joseph (retired) 21 Balmoral Avenue, Whitehead, Carrickfergus BT38 9QA — MB BCh BAO 1946 Belf.

LINDEN, Ronald James (retired) 12 Heather Vale, Ling Lane, Scarcroft, Leeds LS14 3JE — MB ChB 1951 Leeds; PhD 1958, DSc 1965; FRCP Lond. 1974, M 1969. Prev: Prof. Cardiovasc. Studies Univ. Leeds.

LINDENBAUM, Kathleen Mary The Coach House, Old, Northampton NN6 9RJ — MB ChB 1966 Manch.; DO Eng. 1979. Assoc. Specialist (Ophth.) N.ampton Gen. Hosp. Socs: MRCOphth.; Midl. Ophth. Soc. Prev: Ho. Surg. & Ho. Phys. Manch. Roy. Infirm.

LINDENBAUM, Roderic James Edward The Coach House, Old, Northampton NN6 9RJ — MB BCh 1996 Wales.

LINDER, Anne Marshall Catford Cottages, Huish Champflower, Taunton TA4 2BZ Tel: 01984 24298 — MB ChB 1949 Cape Town.

LINDESAY, Professor James Edward Burnet Psychiatry for the Eloeshy, Leicester General Hospital, Gwendolen Road, Leicester LE5 4PW Tel: 0116 258 8161 Fax: 0116 273 1115 Email: jebl1@le.ac.uk — BM BCh 1979 Oxf.; FRCPsych. 2000; MA Oxf. 1979, DM 1990; MRCPsych 1984. (Oxford University) Head of Dept. Psychiat. Univ. Leicester; Hon. Cons. Psychogeriat. Leics. Ment.

Health Servs. NHS Trust. Prev: Sen. Lect. (Psychogeriat.) United Med. & Dent. Sch. Lond.; Hon. Cons. (Psychogeriat.) Guy's Hosp. Lond.; Project Ldr. Sect. Old Age Psychiat. RDP Lond.

LINDHOLM, Karl-Eric Swedish Medical Centre Ltd., 15 Harley St., London W1N 1DA — Med Lic Uppsala 1960.

LINDLEY, Andrew Michael 74 Sidney Grove, Newcastle upon Tyne NE4 5PE — MB BS 1994 Newc.

LINDLEY, Catherine Brenda The Wall House, Yorke Road, Reigate RH2 9HG Tel: 01737 244325; Fax: 01737 770141 — MB BS 1982 Lond.; MRCGP 1986. (St. Geo.) Med. Off. BOC Crawley Sussex. Socs: Surrey Benevolent Med. Soc. Prev: Trainee GP Ipswich VTS; Asst. N. Holmwood Dorking.

LINDLEY, Derek Charles, SBStJ (retired) 35 Hillside Avenue, Worthing BN14 9QS Tel: 01903 230387 Fax: 01903 204323 Email: dcl@lineone.net — MB BS Lond. 1948; MRCGP 1965. Prev: Ho. Phys. King's Coll. Hosp.

LINDLEY, Joanna Christine Fairfield Centre, Fairfield Lane, Barrow-in-Furness LA11 9AJ Tel: 01229 841303 Fax: 01229 432195; Coach House, School Hill, Lindale, Grange-over-Sands LA11 6LE Tel: 015395 33387 Email: dlindley@dircon.co.uk — MB ChB 1965 Aberd.; DA Eng. 1969. (Aberd.) Community Paediat. Bay Community NHS Trust; Asst. Police Surg. Cumbria Constab. Socs: Fell.Roy. Inst. Pub. Health & Hyg.; Brit. Assn. Comm. Doctors in Audiol.; Roy. Coll. Paediat. & Childr.'s Health. Prev: Sen. Clin. & Med. Off. (Community Health) S. Cumbria HA; Clin. Asst. (Anaesth.) Lancaster Roy. Infirm.; SHO (Geriat. & Gen. Med.) Woodend Hosp. Aberd.

LINDLEY, Keith James Institute of Child Health, 30 Guilford St., London WC1N 1EH Tel: 020 7242 9789 Fax: 020 7404 6181 Email: k.lindley@ich.ucl.ac.uk — MB BS 1982 Lond.; PhD Lond. 1994; BSc (Hons.) Lond. 1979; MRCP (UK) 1987. (St. Geo.) Cons. & Hon. Sen. Lect. (Paediat. Gastroenterol.) Gt. Ormond St. Hosp. NHS Trust Lond.). Socs: Brit. Soc. Gastroenterol.; Physiol. Soc.; Amer. Gastroenterol. Assn. Prev: Wellcome Lect. (Paediat. Gastroenterol.) Inst. Child Health Lond.; Sen. Regist. Gt. Ormond St. Hosp. Childr. Lond.; Regist. (Paediat.) Norf. & Norwich Hosp.

LINDLEY, Peter Lawrence (retired) 26 Palace Road, Llandaff, Cardiff CF5 2AF Tel: 01222 563997 — MB BCh 1964 Wales; BPharm. 1940. Prev: Ho. Phys. & Obst. Ho. Surg. St. David's Hosp. Cardiff.

LINDLEY, Richard Mark 94 Townend Street, Sheffield S10 1NN — MB ChB 1997 Sheff.

LINDLEY, Roger Philip Department of Pathology, Medway Maritime Hospital, Windmill Road, Gillingham ME7 5NY — BM BCh 1978 Oxf.; MRCPath 1985. Cons. Histopath. Medway NHS Trust.

LINDLEY-JONES, Michael Francis Hugh 13 The Glebe, Chislehurst BR7 5PX — MB BS 1993 Lond.; MA Zoology Oxford 1998; FRCS Ed, 1997. Specialist Regist., Ipswich Hosp. Camb. Rotat.

LINDNER, Richard Hunter Attleborough Surgeries (Station Road), Station Road, Attleborough NR17 2AS Tel: 01953 452394 Fax: 01953 453569; Crown Lane Cottage, Old Buckenham, Attleborough NR17 1SD Tel: 01953 860615 — MB BS 1977 Lond.; BA Camb. 1974; DRCOG 1981. (Camb. & Westm.) Prev: GP Trainee Norwich VTS.

LINDO, Denis George 40 Chestnut Avenue, Bedford MK40 4HA — MB BS 1996 Lond.

LINDO, Dwight O'Neil St Joseph 1 Border Road, London SE26 6HB Email: jlindo5052@aol.com — MB BS 1986 Jamaica; MRCPI 1995; MRCPCH 1997. (Univ. of West Indies)

LINDO, Frederick Cecil Lake Cottage, Southbury Lane, Ruscombe, Reading RG10 9XN Tel: 01734 345090 — MB BS 1966 Lond. (St. Bart.) Assoc. RCGP. Prev: Ho. Phys. Brighton Gen. Hosp.; Ho. Surg. W. Harts. Hosp.

LINDO, Jacqueline Andrea 1 Border Road, London SE26 6HB Email: jlindo5052@aol.com — MB BS 1987 W. Indies; MRCP (UK) (Paediat.) 1996; MRCPCH 1997; MSc 1998. (Univ. the West Indies)

LINDON, Elizabeth Frances Dept of Psychiatry, Steppinghill Hospital, Stockport — MB ChB 1989 Manch.; MRCPsych 1997. Specialist Regist. Old Age Psych.

LINDON, Robert Lidstone (retired) Jasmine Cottage, Spring Grove Road, Richmond TW10 6EH Tel: 020 8940 5986 — MRCS Eng. LRCP Lond. 1948; FFCM 1974; DPH Eng. 1952, DCH 1957. Prev: Area Med. Off. Ealing, Hammersmith & Hounslow AHA (T).

LINDON, Rosemary Gaenor Southbroom Surgery, 15 Estcourt Street, Devizes SN10 1LQ Tel: 01380 720909; Butts Farm, North Nennton, Pewsey SN9 6LA — MB ChB 1990 Bristol; MRCGP 1995; DRCOG 1995; DA (UK) 1993. (Bristol) GP Partner S.broom Surg. Prev: Trainee GP Glos.; SHO (O & G) Taunton; SHO (Anaesth.) Bristol.

LINDOP, Andrew Robert Wirksworth Health Centre, St. Johns Street, Wirksworth, Matlock DE4 4DT Tel: 01629 822434; Horizon, 12 New Road, Bolehill, Matlock DE4 4GL — MB ChB 1981 Sheff.; MRCGP 1985; DRCOG Liverp. 1984. Course Organiser Derby VTS.

LINDOP, David Julian The Surgery, 19 High Street, Penistone, Sheffield S36 6BR Tel: 01226 762257 Email: david.lindop@ntlworld.com; Royd Moor Court, Royd Moor Lane, Thurlstone, Sheffield S36 9RY Tel: 01226 767825 Email: davidlindop@ntlworld.com — MB ChB 1981 Sheff.; DPD 2000; MRCGP 1985; DCCH RCGP & FCM 1985.

LINDOP, George Black McMeekin University of Glasgow, Department of Pathology, Western Infirmary, Glasgow G11 6NT Tel: 0141 211 2390 Fax: 0141 337 2494; 8 Fifth Avenue, Glasgow G12 0AT — MB ChB 1969 Glas.; BSc (Hons. Physiol.) Glas. 1967; FRCP Glas. 1994; FRCPath 1987, M 1975. (Glasgow) Reader & Hon. Cons. (Histopath.) W.. Infirm. Glas.; Vis. Prof. Dept. Pharm/Physiol. Univ.Strathclyde. Socs: Internat. Acad. Path.; Path. Soc.; Mem. Assn. Clin. Pathol. Prev: Cons. Path. Ayrsh. & Arran HB.; Lect. (Histopath.) W.. Infirm. Glas.

LINDOP, Michael John Department of Anaesthesia, Addenbrooke's Hospital, Hills Road, Cambridge CB2 2QQ Tel: 01223 217434 Fax: 01223 217223 Email: mikelindop@compuserve.com — MB BChir 1967 Camb.; MA Camb. 1967; MRCS Eng. LRCP Lond. 1966; FRCA 1971; DObst RCOG 1968. (Camb. & Guy's) Cons. Anaesth. Addenbrooke's Hosp. Camb.; Mem. (Pres.) Liver IC Gp. of Europe. Socs: Anaesth. Res. Soc.; Intens. Care Soc. Prev: Research Sen. Regist. W.m. Hosp. Lond.; Instruc. Univ. Washington Seattle, USA.

LINDOP, Professor Patricia Joyce 58 Wildwood Road, London NW11 6UP Tel: 020 8455 5860 Fax: 020 8905 5584 Email: pesdale@cix.compulink.uk — MB BS 1954 Lond.; PhD Lond. 1960, BSc (1st cl. Hons.) 1951; DSc 1974; FRCP Lond. 1977, M 1956; MRCS Eng. LRCP Lond. 1954. (St. Bart.) Emerit. Prof. Radiat. Biol. Univ. Lond.; Mem. Advis. Bd. of Nat. Regist. Radiol. Workers. Socs: Fell. Roy. Soc. Med.; Roy. Coll. Radiol. Prev: Emerit. Fell.sh. Leverhulme Trust 1984-86; Head Dept. Radiobiol. St. Bart. Hosp. Med. Coll.; Mem. Roy. Commiss. of Environm. Pollution.

LINDOP, Richard (retired) 27 Pine Road, Heswall, Wirral CH60 2SP Tel: 0151 342 7939 — MB ChB Birm. 1943; MRCP (UK) 1972; DCH Eng. 1948. Prev: Cons. Paediat. Manor & Gen. Hosps. Walsall.

LINDOW, Stephen William Hull Maternity Hospital, Hedon Road, Hull HU9 5LX; 17 The Triangle, North Ferriby HU14 3AT Tel: 01482 633840 — MB ChB 1978 Sheff.; MRCOG 1985. Hon. Cons. O & G & Sen. Lect. (Perinatol.) Hull Matern. Hosp. Prev: Sen. Specialist (O & G) Univ. Cape Town.

LINDSAY, Alexander Morris Plas, Nantgaredig, Carmarthen SA32 7NY Tel: 01267 290206 — LMSSA 1954 Lond. (Middlx.) Police Surg. Dyfed Powis Constab.; Serving Off. St. John Ambul. Brig.. Prev: Ho. Surg. Pembroke Co. Hosp.; Ho. Off. (O & G) Chase Farm Hosp. Enfield.

LINDSAY, Allan Shanks (retired) 46 Woodland Drive, Old Catton, Norwich NR6 7AY — MB ChB St. And. 1949; DPH St. And. 1958. Prev: SCM Gt. Yarmouth & Waveney DHA.

LINDSAY, Andrew Campbell Bridgeton Health Centre, 201 Abercromby Street, Glasgow G40 2DA Tel: 0141 531 6500 Fax: 0141 531 6505; 17B Bruce Road, Pollokshields, Glasgow G41 5EE — MB ChB 1980 Glas.

LINDSAY, Andrew Owen Meddygfa Emlyn, Lloyds Terrace, Adpar, Newcastle Emlyn SA38 9NS Tel: 01239 710479 Fax: 01239 711683; Llysonnen, Adpar, Newcastle Emlyn SA38 9EL Tel: 01239 711320 — MB ChB 1984 Birm.; MRCGP 1991.

LINDSAY, Anna 43 Ferncroft Avenue, London NW3 7PD — BChir 1995 Camb.

LINDSAY, Anne Aberfoyle Medical Centre, Main Street, Aberfoyle, Stirling FK8 3UX Tel: 01877 382421 Fax: 01877 382718 — MB ChB 1975 Glas.

LINDSAY, David Crawford Cardiac Department, Gloucestershire Royal Hospital, Great Western Road, Gloucester GL1 3NN Tel: 01452 394766 Fax: 01452 394894 Email: david@lindsay@gloucr-tr.swest.nhs.uk; Owls Barn, Leckhampton Hill, Cheltenham GL53 9QH Tel: 01242 570057 Fax: 01242 570079 — BM BCh 1983 Oxf.; MA Camb. 1986, BA 1980, MD 1996; MRCP (UK) 1986; FRCP (UK) 1999. (Trinity Hall Camb. & Univ. Oxf.) Cons. Cardiol. Glos. Roy. Hosp., Cheltenham Gen. Hosp.; Med. Ref. Brit. Subaqua Club; Hon. Cons. Cardiol., John Radcliffe Hosp., Oxf. Prev: Lect. & Hon. Sen. Regist. (Cardiol. & Gen. Med.) W.m. & Char. Cross Hosps. Lond. & Roy. Brompton Nat. Heart & Lung Hosp. Lond.; Research Fell. BHF & Regist. (Cardiol.) Nat. Heart & Brompton Hosps. Lond.; Regist. Rotat. (Med.) & SHO Roy. Vict. Infirm. Newc.

LINDSAY, Elspeth Lillias Stuart 18 Monreith Road, Newlands, Glasgow G43 2NY — MB ChB 1979 Glas.; FRCR 1985. Cons. Radiol. CrossHo. Hosp. Kilmarnock.

LINDSAY, Eric Dawson (retired) Craig-y-Don, Rumsam Road, Barnstaple EX32 9EW — MB BCh BAO 1943 Belf.; MRCGP 1968.

LINDSAY, Fiona Vanessa Royal Hallamshire Hospital, Glossop Road, Sheffield S10 2JF; 30 The Dole, Impington, Cambridge CB4 9LP — MB ChB 1995 Leic.; MB ChB (Hons.) Leic. 1995; MRCP 1998. (Leicester) SHO Med. Rotat. Roy. Hallamshire Hosp. Sheff. Prev: SHO (Renal) Bristol; SHO (A&E) Plymouth.

LINDSAY, Fraser Russell 2 Liberton Road, Kirkcaldy KY2 6LZ Tel: 01592 642473 Email: frl51@x-stream.co.uk — MB ChB 1974 Ed. Anaesth. Staffgrade. Socs: BMA; Anaesth. Assn. Prev: Staff Grade (Anaesth.) W.. Gen. Hosp. Edin.; Anaesth. Neu Ulm & Hammelburg, Germany; GP US Army Neu Ulm, Germany.

LINDSAY, Gavin Holm Cottage, Fintry, Glasgow G63 0XG — MB ChB 1963 Glas.; FRCPath 1986. Cons. (Microbiol.) S.. Gen. Hosp. Glas. Prev: Sen. Regist. (Microbiol.) Glas. Roy. Infirm.; Regist. Stobhill Gen. Hosp. Glas.

LINDSAY, Gordon Forbes, CVO (retired) Creagan, Ruh-na-haven road, Aboyne AB34 5JB Tel: 01339 2271 — MB ChB 1944 Aberd. Prev: Apoth. to HM Ho.hold at Balmoral.

LINDSAY, Harold Samuel Thomas (retired) 6 Beech Crescent, Lisburn BT28 2DY Tel: 02892 601089 — MB BCh BAO 1948 Belf.

LINDSAY, Harry 16 Church Road, Leeds LS12 Tel: 0113 263 8329; South View House, Hobberley Lane, Leeds LS17 8JQ Tel: 0113 273 7282 — MRCS Eng. LRCP Lond. 1952.

LINDSAY, Henry Steven John Dept of Cardiology, Bradford Royal Infirmary, Duckworth Lane, Bradford BD9 6RJ Tel: 01274 364181 Fax: 01274 364741 Email: steven.lindsey@bradfordhopitals.nhs.uk — MB BCh BAO 1987 Belf.; MRCP (UK) 1990; MD (Leeds). 1999. (Qu. Univ. Belf.) Cons. Cardiol. Socs: Brit. Cardiac Soc.; Brit. Cardiovasc. Interven. Soc. Prev: Research Regist. (Cardiovasc. Studies) Univ. Leeds & Leeds Gen. Infirm.; Regist. (Cardiol.) Leeds Gen. Infirm.; Lect. & Hon. Sen. Regist. Univ. Leeds & Leeds Gen. Infirm.

LINDSAY, Iain 18 Trenchard Street, Greenwich, London SE10 9PA Tel: 020 8858 8772 — MRCS Eng. LRCP Lond. 1973; MA Oxf. 1971, BM BCh 1973. (Oxf. & Lond. Hosp.) Lect. (Histopath.) Roy. Free Hosp. Sch. Med. Lond.

LINDSAY, Ian David Hickling House, 6B Station Road, Ely CB7 4BS Tel: 01353 614184 Email: smid.lindsay@ntlworld.com — MB BChir 1974 Camb.; DDAM 2002; MSc Lond. 1989; MA Camb. 1974; MRCGP 1978; AFOM RCP (UK) 1982; DAvMed Eng. 1980; DRCOG 1979; DFPHM 1999. (Camb. & Univ. Coll. Hosp.) Med. Adviser, Schlumberger SEMA. Prev: Dep. Dir. (Med. Operat.s), RAF; Commandant RAF Centr. Med. Estabm.; Ho. Off. (Med. & Surg.) W. Suff. Hosp. Bury St. Edmunds.

LINDSAY, Ian Ross, CBE (retired) 7 Blake Court, Trinity Green, Gosport PO12 1EX Tel: 01705 524442 — MB ChB 1948 St. And.; MSc Lond. 1968; MFOM 1981; DPH Lond. 1957. Prev: Cons. Adviser Radiobiol. RAF.

LINDSAY, James David Ian Evercreech Medical Centre, Prestleigh Road, Evercreech, Shepton Mallet BA4 6JY Tel: 01749 830325 Fax: 01749 830604 — MB BS 1971 Lond.; MRCS Eng. LRCP Lond. 1970; DObst RCOG 1974. (Char. Cross) Prev: Orthop. Ho. Surg. Char. Cross Hosp.; Ho. Phys. Stoke Mandeville Hosp. Aylesbury; Trainee Gen. Pract. Swindon Vocational Train. Scheme.

LINDSAY, James Oliver Department Gastroenterology, ICSM, Hammersmith Campus, Du Cane Road, London W12 0NN Tel: 020 8383 3957 Email: jameslindsay@rpms.ac.uk; 37 Petley Road, London W6 9SU Tel: 020 7381 9834 — BM BCh 1993 Oxf.; MRCP (UK) 1996. (Cambridge/Oxford) Research Regist. (Gastroenterol.) ICSM Hammersmith Hosp.; Hon. Regist. (Gastroenterol.) Hammersmith Hosp. Lond.

LINDSAY, Jane Isabel 14 Starling Way, Brickhill, Bedford MK41 7HW — MB ChB 1990 Ed.; DRCOG Lond.; MRCGP Lond.; BSc (Hons.) Ed. 1988; MRCP (UK) 1993. GP Locum. Prev: GP Regist., James Wigg Pract., Lond.; SHO Paediat., Chase Farm Hosp. Lond.; SHO Ostetrics & Gyn., Whittinciton Hosp. Lond.

LINDSAY, Jean McCrorie Drumchapel Road Surgery, 250 Drumchapel Road, Glasgow G15 6EG Tel: 0141 944 3534 Fax: 0141 944 4534 — MB ChB 1968 Glas.; DObst RCOG 1970. (Glas.)

LINDSAY, Mr Jeffrey Alan Regional Rehabilitation Centre, South Birmingham Community Health Trust, Oak Tree Lane, Selly Oak, Birmingham B29 6JA Tel: 0121 627 1627 Fax: 0121 627 8210; The Paddock, 62 Station Road, Hatton, Warwick CV35 8XJ — MB ChB 1972 Bristol; FRCS Ed. 1983. Cons. Rehabil. Med. Reg. Rehabil. Centre S. Birm. Community Health Trust & Moseley Hall Hosp. Birm. Socs: Brit. Soc. Rehabil. Med.; Amputee Med. Rehabil. Soc. Prev: Regist. (Orthop.) Chesterfield Roy. Hosp.; Regist. (Orthop.) Derbysh. Roy. Infirm. Derby; SHO (Surg.) Torbay Hosp.

LINDSAY, John Copp (retired) Cambridge Lodge, Old Torwood Road, Torquay TQ1 1PN Tel: 01803 295454 Fax: 01803 295454 — MRCS Eng. LRCP Lond. 1950; FRCGP 1979.

LINDSAY, John Edward Station Road Surgery, 2 Station Road, Prestwick KA9 1AQ Tel: 01292 671444 Fax: 01292 678023; Davaar, 13 Ayr Road, Prestwick KA9 1SX Tel: 01292 678185 — MB BCh BAO 1984 NUI; MRCGP 1988; DRCOG 1986. (Dub.) GP Princip. Prestwick; Clinc. Asst. (Haematol.) CrossHo. Hosp. Kilmarnock. Prev: Trainee GP Inverclyde Roy. Hosp. Greenock VTS.

LINDSAY, Judith Anne Oakley and Overton Partnership, Overton Surgery, Station Road, Overton, Basingstoke RG25 3DU Tel: 01256 770212 Fax: 01256 771581; Bertha's Cottage, Hannington, Basingstoke RG26 5TY — MB BS 1988 Lond.; MRCGP 1992. (St. Geo. Hosp. Med. Sch.)

LINDSAY, Karen 27 Broster Avenue, Guardhouse, Keighley BD22 6JE — MB ChB 1996 Manch.

LINDSAY, Kenneth Angus 17 Wynmore Drive, Bramhope, Leeds LS16 9DQ — MB ChB 1984 Dundee; MRCP (UK) 1988; FRCR 1992.

LINDSAY, Kenneth Douglas 15B Gloucester Avenue, London NW1 7AU — MB ChB 1982 Dundee. Staff Grade (Psychiat. & Intens. Care) Pk. Roy. Centre for Ment. Health, Centr. Middlx. Hosp. Lond. Prev: Regist. (Psychiat.) Severalls Hosp. Colchester; SHO (Genital Med.) St. Bart. Hosp. Lond.; SHO (Gen. Med.) Crawley Hosp.

LINDSAY, Kenneth George 33 Cabinhill Park, Belfast BT5 7AN Tel: 01232 658412 — MB BCh BAO 1967 Belf.; FFA RCSI 1971. (Belf.) Cons. Anaesth. Ulster Hosp. Dundonald. Prev: Jun. Ho. Off. Moyle Hosp. Larne; Sen. Regist. (Anaesth.) N. Irel. Hosps. Auth.; Sen. Regist. RiksHosp.et, Oslo, Norway.

LINDSAY, Mr Kenneth William Department Neurosurgery, Inst. of Neurol Sciences, Southern General Hospital, Glasgow G51; 14 Kenmure Road, Whitecraigs, Glasgow G46 6TU — PhD Glas. 1975, MB ChB 1970; FRCS Glas. 1976. Cons. Neurosurg. Inst. Neurol Sci. S.. Gen. Hosp. Glas. Socs: Chairm. of Train. Comm. of Europ. Assn. of NeuroSurgic. Societies; Past Vice-Pres. (Surgic.) Roy. Coll. Phys.s & Surg. Glasg. Prev: Cons. Neurosurg. Roy. Free Hosp. Lond.; Sen. Regist. (Neurosurg.) Inst. Neurol. Sc. Glas.

LINDSAY, Kirsty 5 Marlfield Gardens, Bellshill ML4 1JZ — MB ChB 1990 Dundee.

LINDSAY, Kristeen Ann Easterhouse Health Centre, 9 Auchinlea Road, Glasgow G34 9HQ Tel: 0141 531 8170 Fax: 0141 531 8110 — MB ChB 1988 Glas.; MRCGP 1992.

LINDSAY, Malcolm Kerr Currie Road Health Centre, Currie Road, Galashiels TD1 2UA Tel: 01896 754833 Fax: 01896 751389; Burn House, Mossilee Road, Galashiels TD1 1NF Tel: 01896 753425 — MB ChB (Commend.) Glas. 1970; BSc (Hons.) Glas. 1968; FRCP Ed. 1997; MRCGP 1979. (Glas.) Assoc. Adviser Borders Area; GP Manager Centr. Borders Comm. Hosp. Prev: Regist. (Med.) & SHO (Path.) Glas. Roy. Infirm.

LINDSAY, Martin Mitchell 4 Kildoon Drive, Maybole KA19 8AZ — MB ChB 1993 Glas.

LINDSAY, Martin Stephen Somerset Gardens Family Health, 4 Creighton Road, Tottenham, London N17 8NW Tel: 020 8493 9090 Fax: 020 8493 6000 — MB BS 1981 Lond. (Westm.)

LINDSAY, Mary Katherine Martin The Children's Centre, Stoke Mandeville Hospital, Aylesbury HP21 8AL — MB BCh BAO 1951 Belf.; FRCP Lond. 1993; MRCP (UK) 1989; FRCPsych 1979, M 1971; FRCPCH 1997; DCH Eng. 1956, DPM 1965. (Qu. Univ. Belf.) Hon. Cons. Child Psychiat. Stoke Mandeville Hosp. Aylesbury. Socs: Fell. Roy. Soc. Med. (Past Pres. Paediat. Sect.); Brit. Paediat. Assn.; BMA. Prev: Hon. Child Psychiat. John Radcliffe Hosp. Oxf.; Cons. Child Psychiat. & Med. Dir. Aylesbury Child Guid. Clinic Bucks.; Regist. (Paediat.) Ch.ill Hosp. Oxf.

LINDSAY, Maureen Amanda Armley Medical Centre, 16 Church Road, Armley, Leeds LS12 1TZ Tel: 0113 295 3800 Fax: 0113 295 3810; The Old Stable, 2 Manor Cottage mews, Scarcroft, Leeds LS14 3HN Email: amanda@monthux.demon.co.uk — MB ChB 1992 Leeds; MRCGP 1996; DFFP 1995; DRCOG 1995. (Leeds)

LINDSAY, Miriam Dorothy (retired) 97 Laurel Way, Totteridge, London N20 8HT Tel: 020 8445 7884 Fax: 020 8445 7884 — MB BS 1954 Lond. Prev: Clin. Asst. Friern Barnet Hosp. & Diabetic Dept. Edgware Gen. Hosp.

LINDSAY, Norman John Forrest Lindsay and Partners, 1413 Pollokshaws Road, Glasgow G41 3RG Tel: 0141 632 9141 Fax: 0141 636 0414 — MB ChB 1977 Glas.; DRCOG 1980.

LINDSAY, Olwen Glenys Margaret (retired) 9 Hollybush Road, Cyncoed, Cardiff CF23 6SX Tel: 01222 752965 — MB BCh 1957 Wales. Med. Mem. Disabil. Living Tribunals; Adjudicating Med. Off. Indust. Injuries, Disabled Living & Pens. Bd.

LINDSAY, Patricia Henrietta Well Street Surgery, Well Street, Montgomery SY15 6PF Tel: 01686 668217 Fax: 01686 668599 — MB BCh BAO 1983 Dub.; MRCGP 1990.

LINDSAY, Peter Charles Department of Obstetrics & Gynaecology, Llandough Hospital, Penarth CF64 2XX; 110 Plymouth Road, Penarth CF64 5DN — MB BChir 1982 Camb.; MA Camb. 1982; MRCOG 1989. Cons. O & G Llandough Hosp. Cardiff. Prev: Lect. (O & G) Univ. Hosp. Wales.

LINDSAY, Peter John Robin Lane Medical Centre, Robin Lane, Pudsey LS28 7DE Tel: 0113 295 1444 Fax: 0113 295 1440; 14 Kepstorn Road, West Park, Leeds LS16 5HL Tel: 0113 275 8098 — MB ChB 1976 Leeds; MB ChB (Hons.) Leeds 1976; MRCP (UK) 1980; MRCGP 1981; DRCOG 1980; DCH Eng. 1980. (Leeds) Clin. Asst. (Paediat.) & Course Organiser Leeds.

LINDSAY, Robert Ian Thornly (retired) 238 Dover Road, Folkestone CT19 6NS — MRCS Eng. LRCP Lond. 1946. Prev: Cas. Off. Birkenhead Gen. Hosp.

LINDSAY, Robert Scott 5 Royal Circus, Edinburgh EH3 6TL — MB ChB 1988 Ed.

LINDSAY, Robert Stanley (retired) 94 Inkerman Street, Luton LU1 1JD Tel: 01582 415381 Fax: 01582 484216 — MB BCh BAO 1950 Belf.; DIH 1981; DTPH Lond 1976; DObst RCOG 1953. Prev: SCMO S. Beds. DHA.

LINDSAY, Robert Summers Rowan Glenoonah, Fore Road, Kippen, Stirling FK8 3EW — MB ChB 1975 Glas.; MRCPsych 1980; DRCOG 1979. Cons. Psychiat. Dept. Family Psychiat. Hartfield Clinic Dumbarton & Dept. of Child Adolesc. Psychiat. Paisley; Fell. Family Ther. Brown Univ. Rhode. Is., USA. Prev: Sen. Regist. (Child Psychiat.) Roy. Hosp. Sick Childr. Yorkhill & Crichton Roy. Dumfries; Regist. (Psychiat.) S.. Gen. Hosp. & Leverndale Hosp. Glas.

LINDSAY, Robert Thomas Alexander (retired) Priory Surgery, 26 High Street, Holywood BT18 9AD Tel: 028 9042 6991 Fax: 028 9042 3643 — MB BCh BAO 1962 Dub.

LINDSAY, Russell Gordon Stepping Hill Hospital, Poplar Grove, Stockport SK2 7JE Tel: 0161 483 1010; 7 Heald Road, Bowdon, Altrincham WA14 2JE — MB ChB 1979 Dundee; FFA RCS Eng. 1983. Cons. Anaesth. Stepping Hill Hosp. Stockport. Prev: Sen. Regist. (Anaesth.) N. W.. HA; Regist. (Anaesth.) Ninewells Hosp. Dundee.

LINDSAY, Sally Dora Towers Surgery, 163 Holton Rd, Barry CFE3 4HP Tel: 01446 734131; The Beeches, Allerton Hill, Leeds LS7 3QB Fax: 0113 268 3234 — MB BS 1983 Lond.; MRCGP 1991; DRCOG 1990; DCH RCP Lond. 1989; DA (UK) 1986. p/t GP Retainee Towers Surg., Barry.

LINDSAY, Sandra Mary 76 Lumphinnans Road, Lochgelly KY5 9AR — MB ChB 1989 Dundee.

LINDSAY, Shirley-Anne The School House, Hartlebury, Kidderminster DY11 7YE — MB ChB 1987 Birm.; FRCA 1994; DCH RCP Lond. 1990. (Birm.)

LINDSAY, Simon Forrest (retired) Garden Flat, Westoun, Kennedy Gardens, St Andrews KY16 9DJ Tel: 01334 477271 — MB ChB 1940 St. And.; MRCPsych Lond 1971; DPM Eng. 1950. Prev: Consult. in Child Psychiat. Playfield Ho. Cupar.

LINDSAY, Stephen Douglas St Andrews Medical Centre, 30 Russell Street, Eccles, Manchester M30 0NU Tel: 0161 707 5500 Fax: 0161 787 9159 — MB ChB 1979 Liverp.; DRCOG 1981. Princip. in Gen. Pract. Salford PCT; Med. Ref. to Agecroft Cremato fium Salford.

LINDSAY, Thomas Morton Craig (retired) Hollinwood, Roundhill, Woking GU22 8JB — MB BS 1956 Lond.; DPH 1962; MFCM 1974. Cons. Pub. Health NW Surrey HA. Prev: Cons. Pub. Health NW Surrey HA.

LINDSAY, Yvonne Amherst Medical Practice, 21 St. Botolphs Road, Sevenoaks TN13 3AQ Tel: 01732 459255 — MB BS 1988 Lond.; MRCGP 1993; DCH RCP Lond. 1992. (St. Geo.) Prev: Princip. in Gen. Pract., Keston Ho., 70 Brighton Rd, Purley CR8 2LJ.

LINDSAY-MILLER, Mr Anthony Charles Michael, MBE Tall Trees, Whinney Hill, Cultra, Holywood BT18 0HW Tel: 01232 422277 — MB BCh BAO 1952 Belf.; FRCSI 1984; FRCS Ed. 1963. (Qu. Univ. Belf.) Cons. Ulster Indep. Clinic. Socs: Fell. Roy. Soc. Med.; Fell. Ulster Med. Soc.; Irish Otolaryng. Soc. Prev: Cons. ENT Surg. N. Down & Ulster Hosp. Gps.; Jun. Tutor & SHO Roy. Matern. Hosp. Belf.; Ho. Phys. Lurgan & Portadown Hosp.

LINDSAY-REA, Elizabeth Shirley (retired) Chisbury Cottage, Little Bedwyn, Marlborough SN8 3JA Tel: 01672 870230 — MB BCh BAO Belf. 1949; DCH Eng. 1956. Prev: Clin. Asst. (Geriat. & Rheum.) Day Hosp. Swindon HA & Savernake Hosp. MarlBoro.

LINDSELL, David Roger Mackinnon Radiology Department, John Radcliffe Hospital, Headington, Oxford OX3 9DU Tel: 01865 220817 Fax: 01865 220801; 291 Woodstock Road, Oxford OX2 7NY — MB BS 1973 Lond.; FRCR 1981. (St. Bart.) Cons. & Hon. Sen. Clin. Lect. (Radiol.) John Radcliffe Hosp. Oxf. Prev: Sen. Regist. (Radiol.) St. Geo. Hosp. Lond.; Regist. (Radiol.) Roy. Melbourne Hosp. Melbourne, Austral.

LINDSEY, Benjamin 38 West Street, Tavistock PL19 8JZ — MB BS 1993 Lond.

LINDSEY, Caroline Rachel Weinberg Child & Family Department, The Tavistock Clinic, 120 Belsize Lane, London NW3 5BA Tel: 020 7435 7111 Fax: 020 7431 5882 Email: child&family@taui-port.demon.co.uk; 23 Gresham Gardens, London NW11 8NX Tel: 020 8455 2882 Fax: 020 8455 1214 — MB BS Lond. 1967; MRCS Eng. LRCP Lond. 1967; FRCPsych 1987, M 1972; DPM Eng. 1972; DObst RCOG 1969. (Roy. Free) Cons. Child & Adolesc. Psychiat. Child & Family Dept. Tavistock Clinic Lond.; Hon. Sen. Lect. (Child Psychiat.) Roy. Free Hosp. Sch. Med. Lond. Socs: Inst. Gp. Anal. & Mem. Inst. of Family Ther. Prev: Sen. Regist. Maudsley Hosp. Lond.; Ho. Surg. (Obst.) Roy. Free Hosp. Lond.; SHO (Psychiat.) St. Bart. Hosp. Lond.

LINDSEY, Helen Catherine Ely Bridge Surgery, 23 Mill Road, Ely, Cardiff CF5 4AD Tel: 029 2056 1808 Fax: 029 2057 8871 — MB BS 1987 Lond.

LINDSEY, Mr Leon Aleksander 1 Ridgewood Crescent, South Gosforth, Newcastle upon Tyne NE3 1SQ — MB ChB 1987 Ed.; FRCS Ed. 1992.

LINDSEY, Mark Corporation Road Health Centre, 32 Corporation Road, Grangetown, Cardiff CF11 7XA Tel: 029 2022 6057 Fax: 029 2064 0524 — MB BS 1988 Lond.; MRCGP 1993; DFFP 1993; DCH RCP Lond. 1991. GP Cardiff.

***LINDSEY, Mark William** Broadway, Wolverton Road, Norton Lindsey, Warwick CV35 8JN — BM BS 1995 Nottm.; BMedSci Nottm. 1993.

LINDSEY, Mary Patricia Cornwall healthcare Trust Learning Disability Directorate, West Resource Centre, The Kernow Building, Wilson Way, Redruth TR15 3QE Tel: 01209 219251 Fax: 01872 260081 Email: lindsema@cht.swest.nhs.uk; Email: mpl@doctors.org.uk — MB ChB (Hons.) Bristol 1970; MRCPsych 1976; FRCPsych 1998. Cons. Psychiat. (Learning Disabil.)Cornw. healthcare trust. Socs: Chair Fac. Psychiat. of Learning Disabilities Roy. Coll. of Psychiat. Prev: Sen. Regist. (Psychiat.) BoroCt. Hosp. Reading; Regist. (Psychiat.) & SHO (Psychiat.) Littlemore Hosp. Oxf.

LINDSEY, Sally Kay 6A Kenerne Drive, Barnet EN5 2NN — MB BS 1988 Lond.; MRCGP 1993; DCH RCP Lond. 1992; DRCOG 1991.

LINDUP, Rhona (retired) 219 Seabridge Lane, Newcastle ST5 3LS Tel: 01782 618298 — MB BS 1955 Lond.; MRCS Eng. LRCP Lond. 1955; FRCR 1975; FFR 1968; DMRT Eng. 1966, DCH 1960; DObst RCOG 1960. Prev: Cons. Radiother. N. Staffs Roy. Infirm. Stoke-on-Trent.

LINE, Daphne Harrington (retired) 20 Horseguards Drive, Maidenhead SL6 1XL Tel: 01628 625721 Email: dline@ukgateway.net — MB BS Sydney 1950; FRCP Ed. 1982, M 1963; FRCP Lond. 1990; MRCP Lond. 1964; DCH Eng. 1953. Prev: Regist. Hammersmith Hosp. Lond.

LINEEN, John Philip Pius St James Surgery, 89 Wash Lane, Clacton-on-Sea CO15 1DA Tel: 01255 222121; 7 Cottage Grove, Clacton-on-Sea CO16 8DQ Tel: 01255 427438 — MB BCh BAO 1984 NUI; MRCGP 1989; DObst RCPI 1988; DCH NUI 1987. (University College Cork) GP. Prev: SHO (ENT) Vict. Hosp. Blackpool; SHO (Psychiat.) St. Luke's Hosp. Clonmel Irel.; SHO (O & G) St. Josephs Hosp. Clonmel Irel.

LINEEN, Patricia Maureen 73 Hale Lane, Mill Hill, London NW7 3PX — LRCPI & LM, LRSCI & LM 1971; LRCPI & LM, LRCSI & LM 1971.

LINEHAN, Geraldine Mary 125 Newmarket Road, Cambridge CB5 8HA Tel: 01223 364116; 3 Church End, Rampton, Cambridge CB4 8QA Tel: 01954 250681 Email: pgll333@aol.com — MB BCh BAO 1983 NUI; MRCGP 1987; DObst RCPI 1985; DCH NUI 1985. Asst. (GP Retainer Scheme). Prev: Princip. GP Soton.; Trainee GP Soton.; Regist. (Paediat.) Cork Reg. Hosp.

LINEHAN, Heather Tel: 01582 722148 Fax: 01582 485721 — MB ChB 1983 Sheff. Prev: Trainee GP Scunthorpe Gen. Hosp. VTS.

LINEHAN, Mr Ian Patrick Department of Surgery, Basildon Hospital, Nethermayne, Basildon SS16 5NL Tel: 01268 598277 Fax: 01268 598349 — MB BS 1978 Lond.; MS Lond. 1988; FRCS Eng. 1982. Cons. Gen. & Colorectal Surg. Basildon & Thurrock Gen. Hosp. Trust; Lead Clinician for Cancer Serv.s, S. Essex Cancer Network. Socs: Brit. Soc. Gastroenterol.; Assn. Coloproct.; Brit. Assn. Surg. Oncol. Prev: Sen. Regist. (Gen. Surg.) Bloomsbury Lond.; Regist. (Gen. Surg.) N.ampton Gen. Hosp.; Research Asst. Dept. Surg. Studies Middlx. Hosp. Med. Sch.

LINEHAN, Thomas Patrick (retired) 103 Biddulph Mansions, Elgin Avenue, London W9 1HU Tel: 020 7289 2719 Fax: 020 7289 2719 — MB BCh BAO 1949 NUI; MD NUI 1960; MRCS Eng. LRCP Lond. 1959; FRCGP 1981, M 1960; DPhil Med. Soc. Apoth. Lond. 1984; DCH RCP Eng. 1959; DObst RCOG 1951. Edr. Decisions Newsletter. Prev: Med. Adviser Ex-Servs. Ment. Welf. Soc.

LINES, Jacqueline Claire 6 South Street, Walton, Street BA16 9RY Tel: 01458 445582; 5 Bella View Gardens, Glastonbury BA6 9HQ Email: no1drjcl@aol.com — MB ChB 1984 Manch. Clin. Asst. (A & E) Yeovil Dist. Hosp.; Clin. Asst. (A & E) Bridgwater Hosp.

LINES, John North Brink Practice, 7 North Brink, Wisbech PE13 1JR Tel: 01945 585121 Fax: 01945 476423 — MB ChB 1972 Liverp.; MRCGP 1978. Prev: Ho. Off. Ormskirk Gen. Hosp.; Resid. Psychiat. St. Brendans Hosp. Bermuda.

LINES, Leonard Mortimer (retired) 52 Moorcroft Road, Moseley, Birmingham B13 8LU — MB ChB 1957 Manch.; DA Eng. 1970. Prev: GP Birm.

LINFORD, Dawn Vanessa 46 Queens Road, Jesmond, Newcastle upon Tyne NE2 2PQ — MB BS 1987 Newc.; MRCGP 1991.

LINFORD, Steven 21 Kildare Walk, London E14 7DB — MB BS 1998 Lond.; MB BS Lond 1998.

LINFORD, Susan Margaret Jane Royal Shrewsbury Hospital (Shelton), Bicton Heath, Shrewsbury SY3 8DN — MB ChB 1977 Birm.; MRCPsych 1982. (Birm.) Cons. Psychiat. Shelton Hosp., Shrewsbury.

LINFORTH, Richard Anthony 29 Broadway, Atherton, Manchester M46 9HW — MB ChB 1992 Manch.

LING, Chai Seng Flat 6, 29 Southwood Lawn Road, Highgate, London N6 5SE — MB BS 1988 Lond.; MRCS Eng. LRCP Lond. 1987.

LING, David Andrew Woodcock Road Surgery, 29 Woodcock Road, Norwich NR3 3UA Tel: 01603 425989 Fax: 01603 425989 Email: david.ling@gp-d82096.nhs.uk — MB BS 1986 Lond.; FRACS 2000 (Immediate Med. Care) Ed.; Cert. GAM 1991; DRCOG 1991; Dip. IMC RCS Ed. 1989; DCH RCP Lond. 1989. p/t Hosp. Practitioner (A & E) Norwich Univ. Hosp.Trust; Clin. Assit. (A&E) Norf. & Norwich Hosp.

LING, Desmond Queens Avenue Surgery, 14 Queens Avenue, Dorchester DT1 2EW Tel: 01305 262886 Fax: 01305 250607 — MB BS 1985 Lond.; BA York 1978; MRCGP 1990; DGM RCP Lond. 1989; DCCH RCGP & FCM Lond. 1989. Prev: SHO W. Dorset VTS; Assistenzarzt Univ. Hamburg, Germany; SHO (Endocrinol. & Oncol.) St. Bart. Hosp. Lond.

LING, Elisabeth Anne Westrop Surgery, Newburgh Place, Highworth, Swindon SN6 7DN Tel: 01793 762218 Fax: 01793 766073; The Lodge, Trenchard Road, Stanton Fitzwarren, Swindon SN6 7RZ — MB BS 1986 Lond.; MRCGP 1990; DRCOG 1990; DCH RCP Lond. 1990.

LING, Hee-Liong Flitwick Surgery, The Highlands, Flitwick, Bedford MK45 1DZ Tel: 01525 712171 Fax: 01525 718756 — MB ChB 1973 Manch. (Manch.)

LING, Karen Si Lok 17 Anderson Close, Winchmore Hill, London N21 1TH Tel: 020 8360 3258 Fax: 020 8360 3258 Email: kslling@aol.com — MB BS 1997 Lond. (Royal Free) SHO (c/o Elderly Med.) Chase Farm Hosp. Socs: MPS; Med. Sickness Soc. Prev: SHO (A & E) Chase Farm Hosp.; Ho. Off. (Med.) Barnet Gen. Hosp.; Ho. Off. (Surg.) Lister Hosp.

LING, Kevin Lee Chung The Penthouse, 171 Gloucester Place, London NW1 6DX — MB ChB 1990 Wales. (Wales) Clin. Dir. Medicentre (Private GP Clinics) Lond.

LING, Professor Robin Sydney Mackwood, OBE 2 The Quadrant, Wonford Road, Exeter EX2 4LE Tel: 01392 437070 Fax: 01392 438926; Lod Cottage, The Lane, Dittisham, Dartmouth TQ6 0HB Tel: 01803 722451 — BM BCh 1952 Oxf.; MA Oxf. 1958; FRCS Eng. 1957; Hon. FRCS Ed. 1989. (Oxf. & St. Mary's) Hon. Prof. Bioengin. Sch. Engin. Univ. Exeter; Hon. Cons. Orthop. Surg. P.ss Eliz. Orthop. Hosp. Exeter. Socs: Fell. (Ex-Pres.) BOA; Biol. Engin. Soc.; (Pres. Elect.) Internat. Hip Soc. Prev: Orthop. Surg. P.ss Margt. Rose Hosp. Edin.; Hon. Lect. (Orthop. Surg.) Univ. Edin.; Ho. Surg. Surgic. Unit St. Mary's Hosp. Lond.

LING, Ronald Haw Leun 25 Sandyleaze, Bristol BS9 3PZ — BM BCh 1994 Oxf.

LING, Simon Christopher Royal Hospital For Sick Children, Yorkhill NHS Trust, Glasgow G3 8SJ Tel: 0141 201 0000 — MB ChB 1988 Ed.; MRCP (UK) 1992. Cons. Paediat., RHSC, Gasgow. Prev: Regist. (Paediat.) Roy. Hosp. Sick Childr. Edin.; SHO (Paediat.) Roy. Liverp. Childr. Hosp. Alder Hey & Newc. Gen. Hosp.; Sen. Regist. (Paediat.) Roy. Hosp. Sick Childr. Glas.

LING, Stanley St Helier Hospital, Wrythe Lane, Carshalton SM5 1AA Tel: 020 8644 4343 — MB ChB 1962 Cape Town; FFA RCS Eng. 1970; DA Eng. 1967. (Cape Town) Cons. Anaesth. Sutton & W. Merton Health Dist. Prev: Resid. Anaesth. Toronto W.. Hosp. Canada; Research Regist. Dept. Anaesth. RCS Eng.; Sen. Regist. St. Geo. Hosp. Lond.

LING, Tsui Chin 4 Cotlands Green, Dunmurry, Belfast BT17 0BF Tel: 01232 626279 Fax: 01232 626279 — MB BCh BAO 1992 Belf.; MRCP UK 1997.

LING, Yuin Betty (retired) 56 Monks Avenue, New Barnet, Barnet EN5 1DD Tel: 020 8449 6522 — MB BS 1955 Lond.; MRCS Eng. LRCP Lond. 1955; DObst RCOG 1957; DA Eng. 1958. Prev: Cons. Anaesth. Manor Ho. Hosp. Lond.

LINGAM, Kalaivani 61 Cleveden Drive, Glasgow G12 0NX — MB ChB 1987 Glas.; FRCS Ed. 1992. SHO (Urol.) Glas.

LINGAM, Raghu Partheban 32 Lowton Road, St Annes on Sea, Lytham St Annes FY8 3JG — MB ChB 1996 Ed.

LINGAM, Rajini Nesaveni 17 (2F3), Bellevue Road, Edinburgh EH7 4DL — MB BS 1993 Newc.

LINGAM, Ravi Yagasekaran 9 Cross Morpeth Street, Newcastle upon Tyne NE2 4AT Tel: 0191 261 0373 Email: ravi_lingham@yahoo.com — MB BCh BAO 1990 NUI; LRCPSI 1990; MRCPsych 1996. Specialist Regist. (Psychiat. & Psychother.).

LINGAM, Professor Sam Academic Department Community Child Health, St. Ann's Hospital, Tottenham, London N15 3TH Tel: 020 8442 6331 Fax: 020 8442 6796; Number One, Billy Lows lane, Potters Bar EN6 1UT Tel: 01707 662352 Fax: 01707 661602 — MD 1970 (Hons.) Moscow; FRCPCH 1995; LMSSA London 1976; MD (Hons.) 1970; FRCPS 1991; MRCP (UK) 1976; LRCP LRCS Edinburgh LRCPS Glasgow 1974; DRCOG 1976; DCH RCPS Glas

1974. (People's Friendship University, Moscow) Cons. Community Paediat. & Hon. Sen. Lect. (Community Paediat.) St. Ann's Hosp. Lond.; Cons. Paediat. Spastics Soc. Lond. & Hornsey Centre for Childr. Learning Conductive Educat; Med. Dir. Assn. Preven. Disabils.; Hon. Edr World Paediat. & Child Care; Univ. PostGrad. Clin. Tutor Univ. Lond.; Prof. of Med. Educat. & Clin. Developm. for Europe; Trustee - Autism Lond.; Chairm., Hosp. Doctor's Forum - Overseas Doctor's Assn.; Mem. - Bd. of Med. Educat., Brit. Med. Assn. Socs: Fell.Roy. Soc. of Med.; Internat. Coll. of Pediatrics; Amer. Acad. of Pediatrics. Prev: Cons. Community Paediat. W. Essex HA; Sen. Regist. (Developm. Paediat.) Wolfson Centre Inst. Child Health Lond.

LINGAM, Mr Shanmuganathan Muthu Krishna 24 Churchill Drive, Broomhill, Glasgow G11 7LS Tel: 0141 339 9468 — MB ChB 1986 Glas.; MD Glas. 1994; FRCS Ed. 1991; FRCPS Glas. 1991. Specialist Grade Regist. Glas.

LINGARD, Paul Sheldon Lime Grove Medical Centre, Lime Grove Walk, Matlock DE4 3FD Tel: 01629 583223 — MB ChB 1980 Aberd.; MRCGP 1986; DRCOG 1986.

LINGFORD-HUGHES, Anne Rosemary Institute of Psychiatry, De Crespigny Park, London SE5 8AF Tel: 020 7703 5411 — BM BCh 1991 Oxf.; MRCPsych 1994.

LINGGOOD, Rita Margaret c/o Linda Donaldson, Credentialing Analyst, Health Care International, Beardmore St., Clydebank G81 4DY — MB BS 1965 Lond.; MRCS Eng. LRCP Lond. 1965; FRCR 1975.

LINGS, Heather Ruth Lings and Partners, Shotfield Health Centre, Shotfield, Wallington SM6 0HY Tel: 020 8647 0031 Fax: 020 8773 1801; 92 Banstead Road S., Carshalton Beeches, Sutton SM2 5LH — MB BS 1984 Lond.; DRCOG 1988. Prev: Trainee GP Carshalton VTS.

LINGWOOD, Muriel Matthewson (retired) 29 Lower Green Road, Esher KT10 8HE Tel: 020 8398 1221 — MB BS 1944 Durh.; Cert. Family Plann. JCC 1967; DCH Eng. 1957. Prev: Clin. Med. Off. Kingston & Richmond AHA.

LINHAM, Sarah Jane 62 Dale Road, Shirley, Southampton SO16 6QL — BM 1990 Soton.

LINJAWI, Sultan 60 Rannoch Road, London W6 9SP — MB BS 1996 Lond.

LINK, Christopher Gerald Gordon Zeneca Pharmaceuticals, Mereside, Alderley Park, Macclesfield SK10 4TG Tel: 01625 514797 — MB ChB 1983 Ed.; MBA Warwick 1996; MPhil Ed. 1988; MFPM RCP Lond. 1992; MRCPsych 1988; Dip. Pharm. Med. RCP UK 1991. (Ed.) Drug Team Ldr. Zeneca Pharmaceut. Macclesfield. Prev: Assoc. Dir. SmithKline Beecham.

LINKER, Nicholas John Cardiothoracic Unit, South Cleveland Hospital, Marton Road, Middlesbrough TS4 3BW Tel: 01642 282412 Fax: 01642 854190 Email: nick.linker@freenet.co.uk — MB ChB 1981 Manch.; BSc (Anat) Manch. 1978; MRCP(UK) London 1984; MD (Manch.) 1992. (Manchester) Cons. (Cardiol.) S. Cleveland Hosp., Middlesbrough.; Hon clin lec teeside div univ Newc. Upon Tyne. Socs: Fell Euro soc of Cardiol.; N Amer. Soc. Pacing & Electrophysiol. Prev: Sen. Regist., Cardiol., N. W. Region.; Clin. Research Fell., Geo.'s Hosp. Lond.

LINKIN, Andrew Colin 5 Crundale Close, Ashford TN23 5RP — MB BS 1998 Lond.; MB BS Lond 1998.

LINKLATER, David Ivan McGillivray (retired) Pomona, Cark-in-Cartmel, Grange-over-Sands LA11 7NT Tel: 015395 58284 — MB ChB 1955 Ed.; DObst RCOG 1959. Prev: Ho. Off. (Obst.) City Matern. Hosp. Carlisle.

LINKLATER, Mhari Dounby Surgery, Dounby, Orkney KW17 2HT Tel: 01856 771209 Fax: 01856 771320 — MB ChB 1995 Aberd.; DRCOG 1998. (Aberdeen)

LINKS, Lilian (retired) — MB ChB 1942 Glas. Prev: Res. Phys. St. Jas. Hosp. Lond.

LINKS, Morris (retired) Flat C, 7 Castleton Crescent, Newton Mearns, Glasgow G77 5JX Tel: 0141 639 3448 — LRCP LRCS 1941 Ed.; LRCP LRCS Ed. LRFPS Glas. 1941.

LINLEY-ADAMS, Anne Catherine Heath Cottage Surgery, High Street, Lytchett Matravers, Poole BH16 6DB Tel: 01202 632764; Home Farm House, East Morden, Wareham BH20 7DW — MB BS 1984 Lond.; DRCOG 1988; DCH RCP Lond. 1988; DA (UK) 1987. GP Poole. Prev: SHO (O & G & Anaesth.) Poole; SHO (Paediat.) Luton & Dunstable.

LINLEY-ADAMS, Mark Jonathan Walford Mill Medical Centre, Knobcrook Road, Wimborne BH21 1NL Tel: 01202 886999 Fax: 01202 840049; Home Farm House, East Morden, Wareham BH20 7DW — MB BS 1984 Lond.; MRCP (UK) 1988; DRCOG 1988. Prev: SHO (Med.) Soton Gen. Hosp.

LINLEY-ADAMS, Sophie Louise Whitehill Surgery, Oxford Road, Aylesbury HP19 8EN — MB BS 1986 Lond.; DRCOG 1989. Prev: SHO (Paediat.) Pembury Hosp. Tunbridge Wells; SHO (O & G) E.bourne Dist. Gen. Hosp.; SHO (Geriat.) Univ. Coll. Hosp. Lond.

LINN, Helen Alfred 159 Portsmouth Road, Lee-on-the-Solent PO13 9AD Tel: 01705 550716 — MB BS 1957 Lond.; MRCS Eng. LRCP Lond. 1957. (Lond. Hosp.)

LINN, Peter Kyaw Khine 10 Alandale Close, Worden Park, Leyland, Preston PR25 3DX — MB ChB 1995 Leic.

LINNARD, Carol Anne Alma Partnership, 31 Alma Road, Bournemouth BH9 1BP Tel: 01202 519311 Fax: 01202 548532 — BM Soton. 1979; MRCGP 1983; DCH RCP Lond. 1983; DRCOG 1982. GP.

LINNARD, Gillian Rustlings Road Medical Centre, 105 Rustlings Road, Sheffield S11 7AB Tel: 0114 266 0726 Fax: 0114 267 8394 — MB ChB 1986 Bristol; MRCGP 1990; DRCOG 1990; DFFP 1997. (Bristol) Partner in Gen. Pract. Sheff. Prev: Trainee GP/SHO Plymouth VTS.; Gen. Pract. Newmarket.

LINNELL, Anne Elizabeth Teague Sutton Hospital, The St Helier NHS Trust, Cotswold Road, Sutton SM2 5NF Tel: 020 8644 4343 Fax: 020 8770 3869; 78 Arundel Avenue, East Ewell, Epsom KT17 2RJ — MB BS 1980 Lond.; FRCS Ed. 1986; FRCOphth 1994; DO RCS Eng. 1985. (Lond. Hosp.) Cons. Ophth. Sutton Hosp. St. Helier NHS Trust Surrey. Socs: Glaucoma Soc.; (Counc.) Internat. Glaucoma Assn. Prev: Sen. Regist. (Ophth.) W. Midl. RHA; Research Fell. Acad. Unit. Ophth. Univ. Birm.; Regist. Birm. & Midl. Eye Hosp.

LINNELL, Patricia Elizabeth Chestnut Cottage, Heapham, Gainsborough DN21 5PT — MB BS 1956 Lond.; MRCS Eng. LRCP Lond. 1956. (St. Mary's) Prev: Clin. Asst. (ENT) W. Lindsey Health Trust; Clin. Med. Off. Scunthorpe Community Health Care NHS Trust.; SHO Booth Hall Hosp. Childr. Manch.

LINNELL, Phyllis Mary (retired) 5 Bentsbrook Cottages, Spook Hill, North Holmwood, Bridport RH5 4HL — MB ChB 1925 Birm.; MRCS Eng. LRCP Lond. 1925; DPH Eng. 1930. Prev: Asst. MOH Middlx. CC.

LINNEMANN, Alison Mary 34 Southerton Road, Kirkcaldy KY2 5NB — MB ChB 1975 Dundee; BSc (Med. Sci.) St. And. 1972; DRCOG Ed. 1978; DCH 1998. Staff Grade. Paediat.Fife.healthcare. Socs: SACCH.

LINNEMANN, Margaret Patricia 80 Tettenhall Road, Wolverhampton WV1 4TF Tel: 01902 21005; Osborne House, 122 Wood Road, Codsall, Wolverhampton WV8 1DW Tel: 01902 842077 — MB BCh BAO 1971 Dub.; MRCPI 1977; MRCP (UK) 1978. (TC Dub.)

LINNEMANN, Victor John The Health Centre, Whyteman's Brae, Kirkcaldy KY1 2NA Tel: 01592 642178 Fax: 01592 644782 — MB ChB 1975 Dundee; DCH RCP Lond. 1988; DRCOG 1979.

LINNETT, Dorothy Ann Timbers, Stone Street Road, Ivy Hatch, Sevenoaks TN15 0PQ Tel: 01732 810166 — MB BS (Hons.) Durh. 1964; BSc (1st cl. Hons.) Zool. 1959. (Newc.) Indep. GP Sevenoaks.

LINNETT, Paul Joseph Houghton Health Centre, Church Street, Houghton-le-Spring DH4 4DN Tel: 0191 584 2106 Fax: 0191 584 9493; 192 Priors Grange, Pittington, Durham DH6 1DE Tel: 0191 372 1853 — MB BS 1979 Newc.; MRCGP 1984.

LINNETT, Peter James Johnson Matthey plc, Orchard Road, Royston SG8 5HE Tel: 01763 253020 Fax: 01763 253017; 41 Blackhorse Lane, Hitchin SG4 9EG Tel: 01462 433095 Fax: 01462 442364 — MB BS 1967 Lond.; FFOM 1999 RCP Lond; MRCS Eng. LRCP Lond. 1967; MFOM RCP Lond. 1985; DObst RCOG 1969; DA (Conj.) 1970. (St Thomas' Hospital) Gp. Occupat. Phys. Johnson Matthey plc Royston. Socs: Roy. Soc. of Med.; Soc. of Occupat.al Med.; BMA. Prev: Gp. Occupat. Phys. Cookson Gp. Plc. Lond.; Gp. Occupat. Phys. Johannesburg Consolidated Investm. Ltd.; Sen. Med. Off. BCL Ltd. Botswana.

LINNEY, John Graham 32 Foxley Lane, Purley CR8 3EE Tel: 020 8660 1304 Fax: 020 8660 0721; Tel: 01737 557773 Email: jlinney1@aol.com — MB BS 1978 Lond.; BA Oxf. 1975; DPD 1999; DFFP 2000; MRCGP 1989; DRCOG 1983. (Lond. Hosp.) GP Princip./Trainer; PCG Bd. Mem. and prescribing GP (Croydon S.).

LINNEY, Michael John Birtles Farm, London Road, Woore, Crewe CW3 9SF Fax: 0163 647910 Email: jlinney@user.itconsult.co.uk — MB BS 1991 Lond.; BSc (Hons) Lond. 1982; MSc Surrey 1985; MRCP (UK) 1996. (St. Thos. Hosp.) Specialist Regist. (Respirat. Paediat.) N. Staffs Hosp. Stoke-on-Trent.

LINNEY, Pamela Jayne 12 Sherwood Avenue, Edwinstowe, Mansfield NG21 9NE — MB BS 1991 Lond.; MRCGP 1996. (Univ. Coll. and Middlx. Hosp. Sch. Med.)

LINNEY, Stephen Frederick Accident & Emergency Department, Birmingham Heartlands Hospital, Bordesley Green E., Birmingham B9 5SS Tel: 0121 766 6611; 192A Thornhill Road, Streetly, Sutton Coldfield B74 2EP Tel: 0121 353 9174 — MB ChB 1980 Birm.; DRCOG 1983; Dip. Sports Med. Scotl. 1998. (Birm.) Staff Phys. (A & E & Sports Med.) Birm. Heartlands Hosp. Socs: Brit. Assn. Sport & Med.; Assoc. Fell. Fac. A&E Med.

LINSELL, Miss Jane Charlotte University Hospital, Lewisham, London SE13 6LH Tel: 020 8333 3164 Email: jane.linsell@uhl.nhs.uk — MRCS Eng. LRCP Lond. 1978; MS Lond. 1994, MB BS 1978; FRCS Eng. 1983. (Roy. Free) Cons. Gen. Surg. Lewisham Hosp. Lond. Prev: Sen. Regist. (Gen. Surg.) Greenwich Dist. Hosp. Lond.; Sen. Regist. (Gen. Surg.) Roy. Sussex Co. Hosp. Brighton; Regist. (Gen. Surg.) Guy's Hosp. Lond.

LINSELL, John William Brook Farm, Greenhouse Lane, Painswick, Stroud GL6 6SE Tel: 01452 812936 — MB BS 1977 Lond.; MRCGP 1983; MSc 1999 Univ. Wales; MRCGP 1983; DRCOG 1981. (St. Barts.) Family Therapist, Severn NHS Trust, Glos. Prev: Med. Dir. Severn NHS Trust, Glos.; GP St. Albans.

LINSELL, William Duncan (retired) Willoways, 1 Lamberts Lane, Rushmere St Andrew, Ipswich IP5 1DR — MD Lond. 1949, MB BS 1944; MRCS Eng. LRCP Lond. 1943; FRCPath 1963. Prev: Cons. Path. N.E. & N.W. Thames RHAs, Herts & Essex Hosp. & Hertford.

LINTER, Stephen Peter Kenneth Sir Humphrey Davy Department Anaesthesia, Bristol Royal Infirmary, Bristol BS2 8HW Tel: 0117 928 2163 Fax: 0117 928 2098 Email: stephen.lwter@aubht.swest.nhs.uk — MB BS 1978 Newc.; FFA RCS Eng. 1983; DA Eng. 1982. Cardiac Anaesth. Bristol Roy. Infirm.; Sen. Clin. Lect. (Cardiac Anaesth) Univ. Bristol & Bristol Heart Inst.; Dir. of Anaesth. & critical care UBHT; Cons. Cardiac Anaesth. Bristol Roy. Infirm. Socs: Fell.Roy. Soc. Med. Prev: Cons. (Anaesthist) Harefield Hosp. Middlx.; Sen. Lect. (Anaesth.) Univ. Soton.; Cons. Roy. Melbourne Hosp. Vict., Australia.

LINTIN, David John Salisbury District Hospital, Salisbury SP2 8BJ Tel: 01722 336262; Hart House, Martin, Fordingbridge SP6 3LF Tel: 01725 519237 — MB BS 1973 Lond.; FRCA 1980. Cons. Anaesth. Odstock Hosp. Salisbury. Socs: BMA & Assn. Anaesth. Prev: Sen. Regist. (Anaesth.) St. Thos. Hosp. Lond.; Regist. Hosp. Sick Childr. Gt. Ormond St. Lond.

LINTIN, Simon Nicholas Anaesthetic Department, D. Floor Jubilee Wing, Leeds General Infirmary, Great George St., Leeds LS1 3EX; Black Rock, 101 Breary Lane E., Bramhope, Leeds LS16 9EU — MB BS 1980 Lond.; FFA RCS Lond. 1985. Cons. Anaesth. Leeds Gen. Infirm.

LINTNER, Brenda Raj Medvedu, Higher Sea Lane, Charmouth, Bridport DT6 6BD Tel: 01297 560996 — MB ChB Liverp. 1954; DPM Eng. 1957; BA (Hon.) Open 1989; MD State Univ. New York 1959; FRCP Ed. 1994; MRCP Ed. 1962; MRCP Glas. 1962; MRCS Eng. LRCP Lond. 1954; FRCPsych 1987, M 1971; DPM RCPSI 1957. (Liverp. & Birm.) Cons. Psychiat. Ment. Health Review Tribunals. Socs: Dorchester Med. Soc.; Roy. Coll Psychiat.; Roy. Coll. Phys.s Edin. Prev: Cons. Psychiat. S.end Hosps. Gp.; Sen. Lect. & Lect. (Psychiat.) Univ. Leeds; Supervis. Psychiat. Gracie Sq. Hosp., New York.

LINTNER, Jiri Karel (retired) Ráj Medvedu, Higher Sea Lane, Charmouth, Bridport DT6 6BD Tel: 01297 560996 — MD Beirut 1943; MD Brno 1946. Prev: Clin. Asst. Otorhinolaryng. Clin. Masaryk Univ. Brno.

LINTON, Andrew Finlay Foyleside Family Practice, Bridge Street Medical Centre, 30 Bridge Street, Londonderry BT48 6LA Tel: 028 7126 7847 Fax: 028 7137 0723 — MB BCh 1979 Belfast; MB BCh Belf. 1979. (Belfast) GP Lond.derry.

LINTON, Caroline Ruth 3 Veronica Close, Rogerstone, Newport NP10 9ED Tel: 01633 896099 — MB ChB 1990 Ed. SHO (Psychiat.) St. Cadocs Hosp. Caerleon, Gwent.

LINTON, Carolyn Margaret Dalvennan Avenue Practice, 27 Dalvennan Avenue, Patna, Ayr KA6 7NA Tel: 01292 531367 Fax: 01292 531033 — MB ChB 1977 Glas.

LINTON, Christopher Duncan (retired) Old Fleet Manor, 2 Yew Tree Road, Hayling Island PO11 0QE Tel: 02392 467261 Fax: 02392 467261 — MB ChB Bristol 1949; FFA RCS Eng. 1957; DA Eng. 1953; DObst RCOG 1951. Prev: Cons. Anaesth. Portsmouth Hosp. Gp.

LINTON, Doreen Elizabeth 2 Marquis Way, Bognor Regis PO21 4AT — MB BCh BAO 1950 Belf.; DO RCPSI 1970.

LINTON, Lorraine Susan Kendrick Milestone Surgery, 208 Farnborough Road, Farnborough GU14 7JN Tel: 01252 545078 Fax: 01252 370751 — MB ChB 1975 Birm.; MRCP (UK) 1977. Prev: Regist. (Geriat. Med.) & SHO (Med.) Frimley Pk. Hosp.; SHO (Infec. Dis.) E. Birm. Hosp.

LINTON, Magdalene (retired) 18 Greenside Place, St Andrews KY16 9TH — M.B., Ch.B. Glas. 1934.

LINTON, Robert Anthony Fox The Rayne Institute, St. Thomas' Hospital, London SE1 7EH Tel: 020 7928 9292; 83 Deodar Road, Putney, London SW15 2NU Tel: 020 8874 9694 Email: robert@foxlinton.org — MB BS 1968 Lond.; MD Lond. 1977; MRCS Eng. LRCP Lond. 1968; FRCA Eng. 1972. (St. Thos.) Cons. Anaesth.Guys and St Thomas' Lond. Socs: Physiol. Soc. Prev: Sen. Regist. (Intens. Care) Roy. Perth Hosp., Austral.; SHO (Intens. Care) & Ho. Phys. St. Thos. Hosp. Lond.

LINTON, Sidney (retired) 12 Highlands, 622 Harrogate Road, Alwoodley, Leeds LS17 8WA Tel: 0113 268 8880 — MRCS Eng. LRCP Lond. 1945; 2001 MRCS; FFPM 1989. Med. Cons. Med. Scientif. & Financial Servs. Leeds; Hon. Clin. Asst. Killingbeck Hosp. Leeds; Med dir. Lewis labs ltd; med dir. Lewis labs (app). Prev: Resid. Surg. Off. & Resid. Med. Off. Meanwood Pk. Hosp.

LINTON, Stephen Paul Milestone Surgery, 208 Farnborough Road, Farnborough GU14 7JN Tel: 01252 545078 Fax: 01252 370751 — MRCS Eng. LRCP Lond. 1973; MD Lond. 1980, MB BS 1973; MRCP (UK) 1975. (St. Mary's) Prev: Research Fell. & Hon. Regist. (Med.) Selly Oak Hosp. Birm.; SHO (O & G) Dudley Rd. Hosp. Birm.; SHO (Gen. Med.) Selly Oak Hosp. Birm.

LINTON, Stuart Murray Nevill Hall Hospital, Brecon Rosfq, Abergavenny NP7 7EG; Tel: 01633 431446 — MB ChB 1990 Ed.; BSc (Hons.) Ed. 1987; MRCP (UK) 1993. Socs: BMA; Brit Soc Rheum. Prev: Regist. (Gen. Med. & Rheum.) City Hosp. Birm. & Walsgrave Hosp. Coventry; Sen reg univ hosp Wales Cardiff.

LINTON, Thomas Ernest Colvin (retired) Linden Lea, Ardcumber Road, Cookstown BT80 9AQ Tel: 0164 87 62034 — MB BCh BAO Belf. 1947.

LINTOTT, Patrick Neil Thomas 270 Iffley Road, Oxford OX4 4AA — MB ChB 1991 Birm. SHO (Cas.) Heartlands Hosp. NHS Trust Birm.

LINTS, Anthea Valerie Brook Hill Surgery, 30 Brook Hill, Little Waltham, Chelmsford CM3 3LL Tel: 01245 360253 Fax: 01245 361343; Westbury House, Stortford Road, Great Dunmow, Dunmow CM6 1DJ Tel: 01371 872578 Email: anthealints@compuserve.com — MB ChB 1975 Ed.; BSc Ed. 1972; MRCGP 1979; DRCOG 1978; MCliSci 1987. (Edin.) Course Organiser Chelmsford GPVTS.; Assoc. Dean (Gen. Pract.) N. Thames (E.).

LINZEE-GORDON, Philip Alexander Hood Auchenault, 9 East Abercromby St., Helensburgh G84 7SQ — MB ChB 1988 Manch.

LIONAKI, Anastasia 1 Victoria House, Hinchingbrooke Park, Huntingdon PE18 8NS — Ptychio Iatrikes 1983 Athens.

LIOUMI, Demitra 37 Rydale Road, Nottingham NG5 3GS — Ptychio Iatrikes 1987 Athens.

LIOW, Raymond Yee Luen 43 Rosemont Road, London W3 9LU — MB BS 1991 Lond.

LIP, Professor Gregory Yoke Hong University Department of Medicine, City Hospital, Dudley Road, Birmingham B18 7QH Tel: 0121 554 3801 Fax: 0121 554 4083 — MB ChB 1988 Glas.; MD Glas. 1994; MRCP (UK) 1991; FRCP (Lond, Glasgow, Edinburgh); Dip. Forens. Med. Glas. 1992; FRCP London, Glasgow, Edinburgh. (Univ. Glas.) Cons. Cardiol. & Prof. of Cardiovasc. Med. Univ. Dept. Med. & Cardiol. City Hosp. Birm.; Dir. Haemostasis Thrombosis & Vasc. Biol. Unit, Univ. Dept. of Med. at City Hosp.; Dep Edr. Jl. of human Hypertens. Prev: Sen. Regist. (Cardiol.) W. Midl. RHA; Honoray Lect. (Med.) City Hosp. Birm. Univ. Birm.; Regist. (Cardiol. Med.) Dudley Rd Hosp. Birm.

LIP, Peck Lin 3 Hitches Lane, Edgbaston, Birmingham B15 2LS — MB ChB 1990 Glas.; FRCS Ed. 1995. (Univ. Glas.) Regist. Rotat. (Ophth.) W. Midl.

LIPETZ, Clare 48 Cosmeston Street, Cardiff CF24 4LR — MB BCh 1995 Wales.

LIPITCH, Henry Samuel 96 Umfreville Road, London N4 1SA Tel: 020 8374 0707 Fax: 020 8372 2096; 91 Raleigh Drive, London N20 0UZ Tel: 020 8368 6218 — MB ChB Ed. 1962. Hosp. Pract. (Occupat. Med.) Edgware Gen. Hosp. Socs: Fell. Hunt. Soc. Prev: SHO Barnet Gen. Hosp.

LIPKA, Andrew Wladyslaw Crosshouse Hospital, 5 Simpson St., Kilmarnock Road, Kilmarnock KA2 0BE — MB ChB 1989 Dundee.

LIPKIN, Bron David Grovelands Priory Hospital, The Bourne, Southgate, London N14 6RA — MB BS 1971 Lond.; FRCPsych 1992, M 1976; DPM Eng. 1974. (Univ. Coll. Hosp.) Indep. Cons. Psychiat. Lond. Prev: Sen. Cons. Psychiat. Claybury Hosp. Woodford; Dep. Med. Dir. Gr.lands Priory Hosp. Lond.; Mem. Pt. II Bd. Examrs. RCPsychiat.

LIPKIN, David Philip Royal Free Hospital, Pond St., Hampstead, London NW3 Tel: 020 7830 2851 Fax: 020 7830 2857; The Gables, 1 Brockley Hill, Stanmore HA7 4LS — MB ChB 1978 Leeds; BSc (Hons.) Leeds 1975, MD 1987; FRCP Lond. 1994; MRCP (UK) 1980. Cons. Cardiol. Roy. Free Hosp. Lond.

LIPKIN, Graham William Renal Unit, St. Bartholomew's Hospital, London EC1A 7BE Tel: 020 7601 8787 — MB ChB 1984 Leeds; BSc (Hons.) Leeds 1981, MB ChB 1984; MRCP (UK) 1988. Research Regist. (Renal) St. Bart. Hosp. Lond.

LIPKIN, Neville Emmanuel 1 Rowbottom House, New Mill Stile, Liverpool L25 6JY — MB ChB 1960 Liverp. Med. Off. Blood Transfus. Serv. & Indep. Tribunal Serv. Liverp. Prev: GP Liverp.; Ho. Surg. & Ho. Phys. Leigh Infirm.

LIPMAN, Anne 43 Henry Street, Redhill, Nottingham NG5 8JW — MB BS 1989 Lond.; MRCGP 1994; DRCOG 1994; DFFP 1993; DGM RCP Lond. 1992.

LIPMAN, David Toby Westerhope Medical Group, 377 Stamfordham Road, Westerhope, Newcastle upon Tyne NE5 2LH Tel: 0191 243 7000 Fax: 0191 243 7006; Lovaine, Elmfield Park, Newcastle upon Tyne NE3 4UX — MB BS 1975 Newc. GP Newc. Prev: SHO (Rheum.) Roy. Vict. Infirm. Newc.; Ho. Surg. & Ho. Phys. Cumbld. Infirm. Carlisle.

LIPMAN, Geoffrey Allerton Medical Centre, 6 Montreal Avenue, Leeds LS7 4LF Tel: 0113 295 3460; 50 Sandhill Oval, Leeds LS17 8EA Tel: 0113 268 3891 Email: drlipman@aol.com — MB ChB 1972 Leeds. (Leeds) Gen. Med. Practitioner; Health Screening Pract. Nuffield Hosp. Leeds. Socs: Mem. Of Soc. Of Expert Witnesses.

LIPMAN, Harald Martin 134 Greenhill, Prince Arthur Road, London NW3 5TY Tel: 020 7435 3074 Fax: 020 7435 3074 Email: haraldlipman@compuserve.com — MB BS Lond. 1955; DCH Eng. 1958. (Univ. Coll. Hosp.) Socs: Fell. Roy. Soc. Med.; Roy. Coll. Gen. Pract.; Liveryman Worshipful Soc. Apoth. Prev: Sen. Med. Adviser Foreign & Commonw. Off.; 1st Sec. & Regional Med. Adviser Brit. Embassy Moscow; Cons. Phys. to RePub. of Sudan in Lond.

LIPMAN, Marc Caeroos Isaac Department of Thoracic Medicine, Royal Free Hospital, Pond St., London NW3 2QG Tel: 0207 830 2747 Fax: 0207 830 2747 Email: marc.lipman@rfh.nthames.nhs.uk; Fax: 0207 830 2201 — MB BS 1987 Lond.; FRCP 2001 London; MA Camb. 1988; MRCP (UK) 1990; MD Cambridge 1998. (UC and Middlesex) Cons. & Sen. Lect. (Thoracic/HIV/Gen. Med.) Roy. Free Hosp. Lond.; Assoc. Johns Hopkins Sch. of Pub. Health Baltimore, USA. Socs: Brit. Thorac. Soc.; Brit. HIV Assn. Prev: Harkness Fell. John Hopkins Sch.; Sen. Regist.Roy. Brompton Hosp; MRC Clin. Research Fell. (Immunol. & Thoracic Med.) Roy. Free Hosp.

LIPMAN, Robert Neil 11 Brompton Court, Aran Drive, Stanmore HA7 4NB — MB BS 1980 Lond.

LIPNER, Mr Anthony Emanuel 16 Baker's Hill, London E5 9HL — MB ChB 1974 Ed.; FRCS Eng. 1979.

LIPOWSKY, Renate 37 Cathles Road, London SW12 9LE — State Exam Med 1985 Berlin; MD Heidelberg 1988; MRCP (UK) 1994.

LIPP, Alistair Charles Norfolk Health Authority, St Andrew's Business Park, Thorpe St Andrew, Norwich NR7 0HT Tel: 01603 307000 Ext: 397 Fax: 01603 307104 Email: alistair.lipp@norfolk.nhs.uk; Tas Lodge, 47 Norwich Road, Stoke Holy Cross, Norwich NR14 8AB Tel: 01508 494849 Fax: 01508 494276 Email: alistair@lipp.org.uk — MB BS 1984 Lond.; BSc Lond. 1981; MFPHM RCP (UK) 1996; DFFP 1994; DPH Camb. 1993; Cert. Prescribed Equiv. Exp. JCPTGP 1989; DRCOG 1987; Cert. Family Plann. JCC 1987. (King's Coll. Hosp.) Cons. (Pub. Health Med.) Norwich; Hon Sen Lec Univ of E. Anglia. Socs: BMA; Fac. Pub. Health Med.; Soc. Social Med. Prev: Cons. WHO Healthy Cities Project Copenhagen, Denmark; Research Fell. Liverp. Sch. Trop. Med.; WHO Field Coordinator S. Afghanistan Progr., Quetta, Pakistan.

LIPP, Anna Katherine Norfolk and Norwich University Hospital, Colney Lane, Norwich NR4 7UY Tel: 01603 286286 Email: anna@lipp.org.uk; Tas Lodge, 47 Norwich Road, Stoke Holy Cross, Norwich NR14 8AB Tel: 01508 494849 Fax: 01508 494276 Email: annalipp@doctors.org.uk — MB BS 1984 Lond.; MRCP (UK) 1989; FRCA 1994; DA (UK) 1987. p/t Cons Anaesth. Norf. & Norwich Hosp, Norwich. Socs: World Anaesth. Assn. Anaesth.; BMA; Brit Assoc of day surg. Prev: Regist. (Anaesth.) Addenbrooke's Hosp. Cambs.; Immunisation Progr. Manager Quetta, Pakistan; Regist. (Anaesth.) Harare Centre Hosp., Zimbabwe.

LIPP, Charles Woodville, Annesley Cutting, Annesley, Nottingham NG15 0AJ — LRCP LRCS 1950 Ed.; LRCP LRCS Ed. LRFPS Glas. 1950. (St. Mungo's Coll. & Univ. Glas.) Prev: Capt. RAMC; Maj. RAMC RARO.

LIPP, Donald (retired) South View, Woodall, Harthill, Sheffield S26 7UA Tel: 01909 770718 Fax: 01909 770718 Email: donaldlipp@btinternet.com — MB ChB Aberd. 1959. Prev: GP Sheff.

LIPPETT, Stephanie Clare 10 Carnforth Drive, Greenmount, Bury BL8 4DQ — MB BS 1996 Lond. SHO (A & E) N. Staffs. Roy. Infirm. Stoke on Trent. Prev: SHO (Ear, Nose & Throat) Whiston Hosp. Prescot Merseyside; Ho. Off. (Gen. Med.) New Cross Hosp. Wolverhampton; Ho. Off. (Gen. Surg. & Ear, Nose & Throat) Manor Hosp. Walsall.

LIPPIETT, Peter Vernon Twyford Surgery, Hazeley Road, Twyford, Winchester SO21 1QY Tel: 01962 712202 Fax: 01962 715158; The Vicarage, Church Lane, Twyford, Winchester SO21 1NT Tel: 01962 712208 — MB BS 1973 Lond.; MRCGP 1980; DRCOG 1979. (St. Thos.) Asst. GP Twyford Retainer Scheme. Prev: GP Barnstaple, N. Devon; Regist. (Psychiat.) Roy. Edin. Hosp.; Ho. Surg. St. Thos. Hosp.

LIPPMANN, Marion Elisabeth Manuela Blackpool Victoria Hospital NHS Trust Residences, Whinney Heys Road, Blackpool FY3 8NR — State Exam Med 1993 Munich.

LIPPOLD, Olof Conrad John (retired) 117 Dudley Road, Walton-on-Thames KT12 2JY Tel: 01932 244598 Email: olippo@aol.com — MD 1969 Lond.; MB BS 1946; FRSH 1996. Prev: Vis. Prof. Physiol. Univ. Auckland, NZ.

LIPPOLD, Peter Frederick Brooms Hall, Hucking, Hollingbourne, Maidstone ME17 1QY Tel: 01622 880454; Occupational Health Department, Royal British Legion Industries, Royal British Legion Village, Aylesford ME20 7NL Tel: 01622 795903 Fax: 01622 882195 — MB BS Lond. 1954; Assoc. Fac. Occupat. Med. RCP Lond. 1979; DA Eng. 1963. (Univ. Coll. Hosp.) Occupat. Health Med. Adviser Roy. Brit. Legion Industries Aylesford Kent. Prev: Ho. Off. St. Helier Hosp. Carshalton; Ho. Surg. Univ. Coll. Hosp.

LIPSCOMB, Anthony Pitt Paediatric Department, St. John's Hospital, Wood St., Chelmsford CM2 9BG Tel: 01245 513260 Fax: 01245 353634 Email: lipscombe@rosewarne.fsnet.co.uk; Rosewarne House, Lodge Road, Bicknacre, Chelmsford CM3 4HG Tel: 01245 320174 — MB BS 1971 Lond.; FRCP Lond. 1995; MRCS Eng. LRCP Lond. 1971; DCH Eng. 1977. (St. Bart.) Cons. Paediat. St. John's Hosp. Chelmsford.; Clin. directors Paediat. Prev: Sen. Regist. (Paediat.) Univ. Coll. Hosp. Lond.; Med. Off. Adelaide Is., Antarctica; Ho. Surg. St. Bart. Hosp. Lond.

LIPSCOMB, George Robert Tel: 01204 390173; 2 Winchester Park, Didsbury, Manchester M20 2TN Tel: 0161 434 4591 — MB BS 1986 Lond.; MD Lond. 1996; MRCP (UK) 1990. (St. Bart. Hosp. Med. Sch.) Socs: Brit. Soc. Gastroenterol.

LIPSCOMB, Karen Jane Cardiology Department, Royal Bolton Hospital, Minerva Road, Farnworth, Bolton BL4 0JL Tel: 01204 390390 — MB BS 1988 Lond.; MD 2000; BSc (Hons.) Lond. 1985; MRCP (UK) 1991. (Univ. Lond. & St. Bart.) Cons. Cardiol. & Gen. Phys. Roy. Bolton Hosp. Socs: BMA; Brit. Cardiac Soc.; Manch. Med. Soc. Prev: Research Regist. (Cardiol. & Genetics) Manch. Roy.

Infirm.; Regist. (Gen. Med.) Manch. Roy. Infirm.; SHO Rotat. (Med.) Guy's Hosp. Lond.

LIPSCOMB, Nicholas Charles Rhinefield, 2 Lovett Walk, Orient Dr, Winchester SO22 6NZ — BM BCh 1997 Oxf.

LIPSCOMBE, Susan Lynn Park Crescent New Surgery, 1A Lewes Road, Brighton BN2 3JJ Tel: 01273 603531 Fax: 01273 698863 — MB ChB 1972 Birm.; MRCP (UK) 1974; Cert. Family Plann. JCC 1980. (Birm) GP Princip. Pk. Cresc. New Surg. Brighton; Hosp. Specialist (Cardiol.) Roy. Sussex Co. Hosp. Brighton. Prev: Hon. Sen. Regist. Hosp. Sick Childr. Gt. Ormond St. Lond.; GP Family Health Centre Stepgates Chertsey Surrey.

LIPSEDGE, Maurice Stanley Keats House, Guy's Hospital, 24-26 St Thomas St., London SE1 9RT Tel: 020 7407 7517 Fax: 020 7378 0931 — MB BS 1966 Lond.; MPhil Lond. 1974, MB BS 1966; FRCP Lond. 1982, M 1969; FRCPsych 1981 M 1972; DPM Eng. 1971; FFOM (Hon). (St. Bart.) Cons. Paychiat. S. Lond. & The Mandsley NHS Trust; Sen. Lect. Dept. Psychiat. & Psychol. Guy's, King's & St. Thomas' Med. Sch.; Head Sect. Occupat. Psychiat & Psychol. Guy's, King's & St. Thos. Med. Sch. Socs: Fell. Roy. Soc. Med.; Soc. Psychosomat. Research; Assn. Univ. Teach. Psychiat. Prev: Cons. Psychiat. City & Hackney (St. Bart.) Health Dist. (T); Psychiat. Adviser Alcoholics Recovery Project; Lect. in Psychol. Med. Med. Coll. St. Bart. Hosp. Lond.

***LIPSETT, Isabel Agnes** 207a Kimbolton Road, Bedford MK41 8AA Tel: 01234 353225 — MB BS 1997 Lond.

LIPSHEN, Gabrielle Sharon 2 Moss Bank, Bramhall, Stockport SK7 1HA — MB BCh 1997 Wales.

LIPTON, Mr Jonathan Richard Royal Oldham Hospital, Rochdale Road, Oldham OL1 2JH Tel: 0161 627 8266 Fax: 0161 627 8478; Highfield Hospital, Manchester Road, Rochdale OL11 4LZ Tel: 01706 655121 Fax: 01706 356759 Email: john.lipton@oldham-tr.nwest.nhs — MB ChB 1980 Manch.; FRCS Glas. 1985; DO RCS Eng. 1984; FRCOphth 1988. p/t Cons. Ophth. Surg. Roy. Oldham Hosp. Socs: Oxf. Ophth. Congr.; N. Eng. Ophth. Soc.; Amer. Acad. Ophth. Prev: Sen. Regist. Wolverhampton & Midl. Counties Eye Infirm.; Regist. Manch. Roy. Eye Hosp.; SHO (Ophth.) St. Paul's Eye Hosp. Liverp.

LIPTON, Mark Edward Arrowe Park Hospital, Upton, Wirral CH49 5PE — MB ChB 1982 Manch.; FRCR 1990; DMRD Liverp. 1987. Cons. Radiol. Arrowe Pk. Hosp. Wirral.

LIPTROT, Saram 22 Stuart Road, Windle, St Helens WA10 6HX — MB ChB 1998 Glas.; MB ChB Glas 1998.

LIPWORTH, Leslie (retired) 36 Philips Park Road W., Whitefield, Manchester M45 7GJ Tel: 0161 796 0111 — MB ChB Manch. 1951. Prev: Ho. Phys. Hope Hosp. Salford.

LIRATSOPULOS, Georgios 11 Canmore Close, Bolton BL3 4TN — Ptychio latrikes 1991 Thessalonika.

LISCOMBE, Robert Michael (retired) 54 Brompton Park Crescent, Seagrave Road, London SW6 Tel: 020 7385 8660 — MB BS 1953 Lond.; FFA RCS Eng. 1965; DA Eng. 1961. Prev: O & G Ho. Surg. Roy. Vict. Hosp. Bournemouth.

LISHMAN, Angela Helen Spindlestone, 9 Westoe Village, South Shields NE33 3EB — MB BChir 1973 Camb.; MA, MB Camb. 1973, BChir 1972; FRCP Lond. 1991; FRCP Ed. 1986; MRCP (UK) 1977. Cons. Phys. (Thoracic & Gen. Med.) S. Shields Gen. Hosp. Prev: Sen. Regist. Freeman Hosp. Newc.; Regional Research Fell. Roy. Vict. Infirm. Newc.; Med. Regist. N. Tees Gen. Hosp. Stockton-on-Tees.

LISHMAN, David Conrad Tranmore, Sellerdale Drive, Wyke, Bradford BD12 — MRCS Eng. LRCP Lond. 1956. (Leeds) Prev: Ho. Off. Vict. Hosp. Keighley.

LISHMAN, Edward John 226A Gloucester Terrace, London W2 6HU — MB BS 1970 New South Wales.

LISHMAN, John Derek (retired) Tel: 01354 656841 Fax: 01354 660788 — MRCS Eng. LRCP Lond. 1968. Prev: Clin. Asst. (Cas.) Pontefract Gen. Infirm.

LISHMAN, Stanley Hackworth Alndale, Alnwick Road, Lesbury, Alnwick NE66 3PJ Tel: 01665 30365 — MB BS 1942 Durh. (Durh.) Prev: Ho. Phys. Alnwick Infirm.; Ho. Surg. Roy. Infirm. Sunderland; Capt. RAMC.

LISHMAN, Suzannah Claire 27B Roland Mews, Stepney Green, London E1 3JX — MB BChir 1993 Camb.; MA Camb. 1993, MB BChir Camb. 1993. Regist. (Histopath.) Univ. Coll. Lond. Med. Sch. Prev: SHO (Histopath.) Univ. Coll. Lond. Med. Sch.; Ho. Phys. Newham Gen. Hosp.; Ho. Off. (Surg.) Harold Wood Hosp. Romford.

LISHMAN, Professor William Alwyn 9 Elwill Way, Beckenham BR3 3AB; 9 Elwill Way, Beckenham BR3 3AB — MB ChB (Hons.) Birm. 1956; BSc (Hons.) Birm. 1953, MD 1965; DSc Lond. 1985; FRCP Lond. 1972, M 1958; MRCS Eng. LRCP Lond. 1956; FRCPsych 1972; DPM Lond. 1963. (Birm.) Emerit. Prof. Neuropsychiat. Inst. Psychiat. Lond. Socs: Experim. Psychol. Soc.; (Hon. Life Pres.) Brit. Neuropsychiat. Assn. Prev: Prof. Neuropsychiat. Inst. Psychiat. Lond.; Hon. Cons. Phys. Bethlem Roy. & Maudsley Hosps.; Cons. Phys. Nat. Hosp. Qu. Sq. Lond.

LISK, Christopher Henry Linden Hall Surgery, Station Road, Newport TF10 7EN; Stoneleigh House, Field Aston Lane, Newport TF10 9LE — MB BS 1974 Lond.; MRCS Eng. LRCP Lond. 1974; DRCOG 1981. (St. Geo.) Sen. Partner Gen. Pract. Newport Shrops.; Dep. Police Surg. W. Mercia Constab.; Sen. Med. Off. HMYOI Stoke Heath Market Drayton Shrops. Socs: Assn. Police Surg. Prev: Regist. (Gen. Surg.) Orpington Hosp.; SHO (Urol.) Hammersmith Hosp. Lond.; SHO (Gen. Surg.) St. Geo. Hosp. Lond.

LISKIEWICZ, Mr Witold Józef, Squadron Ldr. RAF Med. Br. Retd. Oak Tree Cottage, Mether Compton, Sherborne DT9 4QA Tel: 01935 816363 Fax: 01935 816363 — MB BS 1975 Lond.; BSc Lond. 1972, MB BS 1975; FRCS Ed. 1992; MRCP (UK) 1983; DCH Eng. 1978; FRCP Ed 1998. (St. Geo.) Socs: Assn. Advancem. of Automotive Med. Prev: Cons. A & E Yeovil Dist. Hosp.

LISLE, Jennifer Robertson Joint Research & Health Advisers, 29 Great Pulteney St., London W1R 3DD Tel: 020 7439 7263 Fax: 020 7434 0839 Email: jrha@lisle.demon.co.uk; 57 The Chase, London SW4 0NP Tel: 020 7720 2588 Fax: 020 7978 2218 — MB BS Lond. 1965; MSc (Social Med.) Lond. 1974; MRCS Eng. LRCP Lond. 1965; MFFP 1993; FFPHM 1997, MFPHM 1989; MFCM 1975; T(PHM) 1989; DObst RCOG 1967. (Univ. Coll. Hosp.) Dir. Jt. Research & Health Advisers; Sen. Vis. Fell. City Univ. Socs: Fell. Roy. Soc. Med.; Soc. Occupat. Med.; Fell. Roy. Inst. Pub. Health & Hyg. Prev: Research Fell. (Clin. Epidemiol. & Social Med.) St. Geo. Hosp. Med. Sch. Lond. & Univ. Coll. Lond.

LISMORE, Jonathan Richard 9 Montroy Close, Henleaze, Bristol BS9 4RS — MB ChB 1974 Birm.; MRCP (UK) 1978.

LISNEY, Fiona Jane 2 Orchard Close, Woolhampton, Reading RG7 5SD — MB ChB 1991 Leic.

LISS, Marion Ruth Weeping Cross Health Centre, Bodmin Avenue, Stafford ST17 0EG Tel: 01785 662505 Fax: 01785 661064; Castle Hill, Newport Road, Stafford ST16 1DD Tel: 01785 258432 Fax: 01785 258432 — MB BS 1958 Lond.; MRCS Eng. LRCP Lond. 1958. (Lond. Hosp.) Med. Off. Stafford Family Plann. Assn. Socs: Mid Staffs. Med. Soc.; Fac. Homoeop. Prev: Sessional Med. Off. Marks & Spencer Stafford & Stoke-on-Trent; Ho. Phys. Stafford Gen. Infirm.

LISSAMORE, Jeremy Roy 18 Fairford Close, Haywards Heath RH16 3EF — MB BS 1977 Lond.; BSc (Hons.) Lond. 1974; MRCPsych 1982; MFPHM 1994. (St. Mary's) Cons. Psych. Care. Principles. Prev: Cons. Psychiat. (Learning Disabilities) Crawley Horsham NHS Trust.; Sen. Med. Off. DoH Lond.

LISSAUER, Thomas Jack Paddington Green Children's Unit, St. Mary's Hospital, Paddington, London W2 1NY Tel: 020 7886 6402 Fax: 020 7886 6249; 92 Hampstead Way, London NW11 7XY Tel: 020 8458 2989 Fax: 020 8381 4744 — MB 1974 Camb.; BChir 1973; FRCP Lond. 1990; MRCP (UK) 1976; FRCPCH 1997. Cons. Paediat. St. Mary's Hosp. Lond.

LISSENDEN, John Philip The Surgery, Red Houses, St Brelade, Jersey JE2 6QA Tel: 01534 45511 Fax: 01534 46475; 12 Cleveland Road, St Helier, Jersey JE2 4PB Tel: 01534 22381 Fax: 01534 22560 — MB BS 1958 Lond.; MRCS Eng. LRCP Lond. 1957; DObst RCOG 1960; LM Rotunda 1960. (Guy's) Prev: Surg. Lt-Cdr. RN; Clin. Clerk Rotunda Hosp. Dub.; Ho. Surg. Guy's Unit, New Cross Gen. Hosp.

LISSETT, Catherine Ann Department of Endocrinology, Christie Hospital, Wilmslow Road, Manchester M20 4BX Email: kate.lissett@christie-tr.nwest.nhs.uk — MB ChB 1993 Sheff.; MRCP; MB ChB 1933 Sheff.

LISSMANN, Martin Robert The Surgery, Mount Avenue, Shenfield, Brentwood CM13 2NL; 230 Priests Lane, Shenfield, Brentwood CM15 8LG Tel: 01277 234064 — MB BS 1978 Lond.

LISTER, Anthony John Old Palace Medical Practice, 148 Old Palace Road, Norwich NR2 4JA Tel: 01603 663363 Fax: 01603 664173 Email: oldpalace@lineone.net; 50 Intwood Road, Norwich

NR4 6AA Tel: 01603 56045 — MB BS 1973 Lond.; MRCS Eng. LRCP Lond. 1976; MRCGP 1986; DRCOG 1978. (Char. Cross) Course Organiser Norwich 1993; Hon. Sen. Lect UEA.

LISTER, Arthur Hugh Department of Anaesthetics, Scarborough General Hospital, Woodlands Drive, Scarborough YO12 6QL — MB BS 1984 Lond.; BSc (Hons) Bristol 1970. (Roy. Free Hosp. Lond.) Assoc. Specialist (Anaesth.) ScarBoro. Gen. Hosp. Socs: BMA; Yorks. Soc. Anaesth. Prev: Regist. (Anaesth.) Hull Roy. Infirm.; SHO (Cas.) Middlesbrough Gen. Hosp.; SHO (Anaesth.) S. Cleveland Hosp. & Leeds Gen. Infirm.

LISTER, Baron Simon 1 Stand Lane, Radcliffe, Manchester M26 1NW Tel: 0161 724 8703 Fax: 0161 795 3930 — MB ChB 1981 Manch.; MRCPsych 1989; DRCOG 1984. Personal injury specialist. Prev: Sen. Regist. (Old Age Psychiat.) Manch. Roy. Infirm.; Clin. Research Fell. (Psychiat.) Univ. Manch. Med. Sch.; GP Manch. VTS.

LISTER, Brendon Anthony Milman Road Health Centre, Milman Road, Reading RG2 0AR Tel: 0118 968 2285 Fax: 0118 975 5033 — MB BS 1979 Lond.

LISTER, Charles Owen (retired) 165 Whitworth Road, Swindon SN25 3BX Tel: 01793 490182 Fax: 01793 490182 Email: owen.lister@doctors.org.uk — MB BS 1958 Lond. Prev: GP Slough.

LISTER, Mr David Monteagle Surgery, Tesimond Drive, Yateley GU46 6FE Tel: 01252 878992 Fax: 01252 860677; Hollywell, Copes Lane, Bramshill, Hook RG27 0RQ — MB BChir Camb. 1963; FRCS Ed. 1977; DTM & H Lond. 1972. (Middlesex Hospital) Socs: BMA.

LISTER, Deborah Susannah 7 Branch Road, St Albans AL3 4ST — MB ChB 1991 Liverp.; MRCGP 1995; DRCOG 1993. GP Retainee.

LISTER, Diane — BM BS 1986 Nottm.; BMedSci Nottm. 1984; FRCR 1993. (Nottingham) Cons. Radiol. Univ. of Leics Hosps. NhS Trust. Socs: RCR; RCR BrE. Gp.; BMA. Prev: Sen. Regist. (Radiol.) Qu.s Med. Centre Nottm.; Regist. (Radiol.) Leicester Roy. Infirm.

LISTER, Doris Anne Abbey Medical Centre, 87-89 Abbey Road, London NW8 0AG Tel: 020 7624 9383 Fax: 020 7328 2147; 58 Kenneth Crescent, London NW2 4PN Tel: 020 8452 7393 Fax: 020 8450 0860 Email: doris@mackonochie.freeserve.co.uk — MB ChB Aberd. 1970; MRCGP 1978; DObst RCOG 1974. (Aberdeen) Princip. GP. Prev: Research Fell. (Therap.) Aberd. Univ.; SHO (Paediat.) Paddington Green Childr. Hosp.; SHO (Obst.) Dundee Roy. Infirm.

LISTER, Dorothy Margaret Health Centre, Oxford Road, Kidlington OX5 1AP Tel: 01865 841941; 9 Gibson Lane, Haddenham, Aylesbury HP17 8AP — MB BS 1981 Lond.; MRCP (UK) 1984; DRCOG 1988. (St. Mary's)

LISTER, Elizabeth Susan Hill Crest, Quinneys Lane, Redditch B98 7WG — MB BS 1983 Newc.; MRCPsych 1987. Cons. Psychiat. Worcs. Community Trust. Prev: Sen. Regist. (Psychiat.) Univ. Hosp. Qu. Med. Centre Nottm.; Regist. & SHO (Psychiat.) Newc. Train. Scheme; Ho. Phys. & Surg. Roy. Vict. Infirm. Newc.

LISTER, Gillian Elizabeth 125 The Street, Old Costessey, Norwich NR8 5DF Tel: 01603 744022 — MB BS 1980 Nottm.; DCH RCP Lond. 1983.

LISTER, Gillian Sandra Sedgwick, 56 Bridland Avenune, Ilkley LS29 6PD — MB BS 1973 Lond.; AKC. (King's Coll. Hosp.) p/t Health Screening Doctor, Nuffield Hosp.s at Harrogate and Leeds. Prev: Asst. GP W.gate Med. Centre Otley.

LISTER, Mr Ian Stuart (retired) 1 Alderwood Close, Caterham CR3 6AT Tel: 01883 347144 — MB BChir 1952 Camb.; MA Camb. 1952; FRCS Eng. 1960. Prev: Civil. Cons. Urol. Qu. Eliz. Milit. Hosp. & Qu. Alexandra Milit. Hosp.

LISTER, Professor James (retired) Kailheugh, Hownam, Kelso TD5 8AL Tel: 01573 440224 — MB ChB Ed. 1945; MD Ed. 1972; FRCS Eng. 1975; FRCS Glas. 1969; FRCS Ed. 1950. Prev: Prof. Paediat. Surg. Univ. Liverp.

LISTER, James Hugh 102 Stroud Road, Gloucester GL1 5JN Tel: 01452 24506 — MB BS 1955 Lond.; Cert Av Med MoD (Air) & CAA; Aviat. Auth. 1980. (Lond. Hosp.) Prev: Capt. RAMC, Regtl. Med. Off. 1st Bn. Duke of Cornw.'s Light; Infantry; Sen. Ho. Off. (O & G) St. Margt.'s Hosp. Epping.

LISTER, Jeremy (retired) Prior's Hatch, Fairwood, Upper Killay, Swansea SA2 7HP Tel: 01792 202838 — MRCS Eng. LRCP Lond. 1951; FRCPsych 1983, M 1971; DPM Eng. 1958; DCH Eng. 1955. Prev: Cons. Psychiat. W. Glam. HA.

LISTER, John (retired) Farm End, 10 Burkes Road, Beaconsfield HP9 1PB Tel: 01494 674393 — MB BChir 1943 Camb.; BA Camb. 1941, MA, MD 1952; FRCP Lond. 1961, M 1947; MRCS Eng. LRCP Lond. 1943; Hon. FACP 1983. Prev: Linacre Fell. Roy. Coll. Phys. Lond.

LISTER, John Brian (retired) Rushmere, New England Lane, Sedlescombe, Battle TN33 0RP Tel: 01424 870372 — MB ChB 1947 Glas.; FFA RCS Eng. 1954; DA Eng. 1952. Prev: Cons. Anaesth. Hastings Health Dist.

LISTER, Joseph (retired) 55 Grange Gardens, Pinner HA5 5QD Tel: 020 8866 1083 — MB BS Lond. 1943; MRCS Eng. LRCP Lond. 1943; DPH Eng. 1947. Prev: Employm. Med. Adviser Health & Safety Exec.

LISTER, Keith Norton (retired) Chapel Knap, Porlock Weir, Minehead TA24 8PA Tel: 01643 862364 — MRCS Eng. LRCP Lond. 1949; MA Camb. 1950, BA 1946. Prev: Ho. Surg. & Ho. Phys. S. Devon & E. Cornw. Hosp. Plymouth.

LISTER, Paul Jonathan Queen Mary's Hospital, Roehampton Clinic, Roehampton Lane, London SW15 5PN — MB BS 1985 Lond.; MA Camb. 1985, BA 1981; MRCP (Lond.) 1990; FRCP Lond. 1998. (King's Coll. Hosp.) Cons. Phys. (Genito-Urin. Med. & HIV/AIDS) Qu. Mary's Hosp. Lond.; Cons. (GUM.) St Geo. Hosp. Lond. Socs: Med. Soc. Study VD; Assn. Genito-Urin. Med.; Brit. HIV Assn. Prev: Sen. Regist. (Genito-Urin. Med.) Univ. Coll. Hosp. Lond.; Regist. (Genito-Urin. Med.) Univ. Coll. Hosp. Lond.

LISTER, Robert Keighley 5 Newhouse Road, Wavertree, Liverpool L15 0HL — MB ChB 1991 Liverp.

LISTER, Russell Frederick Glan Clwyd Hospital, Bodelwyddan, Denbigh LL16 5UJ Tel: 01745 583275 — MB BChir 1973 Camb.; MA Cambridge 1970; MRCPsych 1979. (Camb. & Westm.) Cons. Pychogeriats. Conwy & Denbighsh. NHS Trust. Prev: Cons. PsychoGeriat.s Clwydian Community Care NHS Trust; Cons. Psychogeriatics W. Lambeth HA.

LISTER, Ruth (retired) 52 Whiting Street, Bury St Edmunds IP33 1NP Tel: 01284 753676 — BM BCh Oxf. 1950; MA Oxf. 1951; DObst RCOG 1953. Prev: Princip. GP Bury St Edmunds.

LISTER, Terence Paul Charing Surgery, Charing, Ashford TN27 0HZ Tel: 01233 714141 Fax: 01233 713782; Tutt Hill Farm Cottage, Westwell, Ashford TN26 1AH Tel: 01233 712981 — BM BCh 1974 Oxf.; MRCGP 1978; DRCOG 1977. (Oxford) Prev: Trainee Gen. Pract. Bath Vocational Train. Scheme; Ho. Surg. Kent & Canterbury Hosp.; Ho. Phys. St. Thos. Hosp. Lond.

LISTER, Professor Thomas Andrew Department of Medical Oncology, St. Bartholomew's Hospital, West Smithfield, London EC1A 7BE Tel: 020 7601 7462; 8 Diamond Terrace, Greenwich, London SE10 8QN — MD Camb. 1979, MB 1970, BChir 1969; FRCP Lond. 1982; MRCP (U.K.) 1972; MRCS Eng. LRCP Lond. 1969; FRCPath. Prof. Med. Oncol.; Dir. ICRF Med. Oncol. Unit. Prev: Imp. Cancer Research Fund Research Fell. & Hon. Sen. Regist. Dept.; Med. Oncol. St. Bart. Hosp. Lond.; Jun. Regist. St. Bart. Hosp. Lond.

LISTER CHEESE, Ian Arthur Frederick Fritwell Cottage, Locks Lane, Wantage OX12 9EH Tel: 01235 765217 Fax: 01235 771887 Email: helene@listercheese.freeserve.co.uk; Fritwell Cottage, Locks Lane, Wantage OX12 9EH Tel: 01235765217 Fax: 01235771887 — MB BChir 1968 Camb.; PhD Lond. 1962; MA Camb. 1968; FRCP Lond. 1990; MRCP (UK) 1970; FRCPCH 1997. (Camb. & St. Thos.) Prev: Sen. Civil Servant DoH HQ Lond.; GP Princip. & Trainer Wantage; Regist.Depts.s Regius & Nuffield Prof's Med.Radcliffe Infirm.Oxf.

LISTON, Ashley Miller Lane End Surgery, 2 Manor Walk, Benton, Newcastle upon Tyne NE7 7XX Tel: 0191 266 5246 Fax: 0191 266 6241; Email: thelistons@aol.com — MB BS 1982 Newc.; MRCGP 1986; DRCOG 1985. GP Benton, Newc. on Tyne; GP Tutor. Prev: Clin. Governance Head.

LISTON, Jane Elizabeth 34 Church Road, Low Fell, Gateshead NE9 5RJ — MB ChB 1982 Dundee.

LISTON, Joyce Carol Leeds & Wakefield Breast Screening Service, Seacroft Hospital, York Road, Leeds LS14 6UH Tel: 0113 206 3769 Fax: 0113 206 3796 Email: joyce.liston@leedsth.nhs.uk; 10 Drummond Road, Leeds LS16 5LB — MB BS 1975 Lond.; MRCS Eng. LRCP Lond. 1975; FRCR 1990; DMRD Lond. 1981. Cons. Radiol. Leeds Teach. Hosp.; Dir. of Leeds & Wakefield BrE.

Screening Serv. Prev: Cons. Radiol. Bradford HA; Sen. Regist. (Radiodiag.) Leeds HA.

LISTON, Mary Philomena The Park Surgery, St. Flora's Road, Littlehampton BN17 6BF; Pilgrims, 43 Ilex Way, Goring By Sea, Worthing BN12 4UY — MB BCh BAO 1979 NUI; MRCGP 1985; DObst RCPI 1983; DCH RCPSI 1982. Socs: Fell. RSM; Mem. Of the Worshipful Soc. Of Apothecaries of Lond.

LISTON, Mr Thomas Gerard Department of Urology, Worthing Hospital, Park Avenue, Worthing BN11 2DH Tel: 01903 205111; Pilgrims, 43 Ilex Way, Goring-by-Sea, Worthing BN12 4UY Tel: 01903 507129 — MB BCh BAO 1979 NUI; MCh NUI 1993; FRCS (Urol.) 1993; FRCS Glas. 1983; FRCSI 1983. Cons. Urol. Worthing S.lands Hosp. Worthing. Prev: Sen. Regist. (Urol.) St. Thos. Hosp. Lond.

LISTON, William Alexander 36A Inverleith Place, Edinburgh EH3 5QB Tel: 0131 552 2994 — MB ChB 1966 Ed.; BSc (Hons. Pharmacol.) Ed. 1964, MB ChB 1966; FRCOG 1983, M 1970. Cons. (O & G) Roy. Infirm. Edin. & E. Gen. Hosp. Edin.

LITCHFIELD, Jennifer Ann Poundhill Surgery, 1 Crawley Lane, Crawley RH10 7DX Tel: 01293 549916 Fax: 01293 615382 — BM BS 1987 Nottm.; BMedSci (Hons.) 1985; DRCOG 1991. GP.

LITCHFIELD, Mr John Charles Accident & Emergency Department, Wexham Park Hospital, Wexham St., Slough SL2 4HL Tel: 01753 634011 Fax: 01753 634012 — MB ChB 1976 Birm.; FRCS Ed. 1984. Cons. Accid & Emerg. Wexham Pk. Hosp. Slough & Heatherwood Hosp. Ascot. Prev: Sen. Regist. (A & E) Dudley Rd. Hosp. Birm.; Regist. Accid & Emerg. Dept. Walsall Gen. Hosp.; Regist. Birm. Accid. Hosp.

LITCHFIELD, Madeleine Ann Douglas and Partners, 28 The Spain, Petersfield GU32 3LA Tel: 01730 267722/268585 Fax: 01730 233526; Durford Abbey Lodge, Rogate Road, Petersfield GU31 5AU Tel: 01730 821810 — MB BS 1980 Lond.; MRCGP 1986.

LITCHFIELD, Mark 3 Guest Avenue, Branksome, Poole BH12 1JA — MB BS 1997 Lond.

LITCHFIELD, Paul BT Centre, PP B2n, 81 Newgate Street, London EC1A 7AJ Tel: 020 7356 3030 Fax: 020 7356 6047 Email: paul.litchfield@bt.com; 4 Littleton Close, Kenilworth CV8 2WA Tel: 01926 864844 Email: plitchfield@talk21.com — MB ChB 1977 Manch.; FFOM 1993 RCP London; MSc Lond. 1982; BSc St. And. 1975; MFOM RCP Lond. 1986, AFOM 1984; FRCP 2000 RCP London. Chief Med. Off., BT grp, Lond. Socs: Fac. of Occupat. Med. - Treas.; Soc. of Occup. Med.; Brit. Med. Assn. Prev: Clin. Developm. Director, OM, BMI Health Serv.s, Coventry; Director of Med.Serv.s, OM, Civil Serv. Occupat.al Health Serv., Edin..

LITEWSKI, Jerzy Ignacy (retired) 100 Lavender Hill, London SW11 5RF — MB BCh BAO 1957 NUI.

LITHERLAND, David John 47 Melbourne Grove, Horwich, Bolton BL6 5NB — MB ChB 1985 Manch.

LITHERLAND, Janet Catherine Department of Radiology, Glasgow Royal Infirmary, 84 Castle St., Glasgow G31 2ER — MB ChB 1986 Manch.; BSc St. And. 1983; MRCP (UK) 1989; FRCR 1993. Cons. (Radiol.) Glas. Roy. Infirm. & W. Scotl. BrE. Screening Serv. Glas. Prev: Research Fell. (Diagn. Radiol.) BrE. Screening Train. Unit Nottm. City Hosp.; Sen. Regist. NW RHA; Regist. (Radiol.) NW Region HA.

LITHGOW, Patricia Anne Child Development Centre, North Staffs Hospital Trust, Newcastle Road, Stoke-on-Trent ST4 6QG Tel: 01782 718249 — MB ChB 1977 Manch.; DCH Eng. 1979. (Manchester University) Cons. Community Paediat. N. Staffs. Hosp. Trust. Prev: SCMO (Child Health) N. Staffs. AHA; SHO (Paediat.) City Gen. Hosp. Stoke-on-Trent.

LITHGOW, Robert Somerville Newbyres Medical Group, Gorebridge Health Centre, Gorebridge EH23 4TP Tel: 01875 820405 Fax: 01875 820269 — MB ChB 1969 Ed.; BSc Ed. 1966, MB ChB 1969; DObst RCOG 1971.

LITMAN, Caroline Linsay 10 Chaffers Mead, Ashtead KT21 1NG Tel: 01372 278768 — MB BCh 1992 Wales.

LITSTER, Rachel Yvonne 49 Alderley Drive, Ashdown Manor, Killingworth, Newcastle upon Tyne NE12 6FS Tel: 0191 268 8554 — MB BS 1987 Lond.

LITTLE, Adam Stewart (retired) Gateside Cottage, Duchal Moor, Kilmacolm PA13 4TG Tel: 0150 587 3411 — LRCP LRCS 1944 Ed.; LRCP LRCS Ed. LRFPS Glas. 1944; DObst RCOG 1957. Prev: Resid. Roy. Matern. Hosp. Glas.

LITTLE, Alan Frank Milman (retired) Greystones, Nassington, Peterborough, Stamford PE9 4BE Tel: 01780 782440 — MB BS 1954 Lond.; MRCS Eng. LRCP Lond. 1954; FFA RCS Eng. 1959, DA 1956. Cons. Anaesth. PeterBoro. & Stamford Gp. Hosps. Prev: Regist. (Anaesth.), Jun. Anaesth. & Cas. Off. King's Coll. Hosp.

LITTLE, Andrew David 86 Ford Road, Wirral CH49 0TG — MB ChB 1997 Dundee.

LITTLE, Mr Brian Charles Royal Free Hospital Trust, Pond St., London NW3 2QG Tel: 020 7794 0500 Fax: 020 7830 2208; 24 Anson Road, London N7 0RD Tel: 020 7607 1713 Fax: 020 7607 1713 Email: little.london@virgin.net — MB BChir 1983 Camb.; FRCS Glas. 1987; FCOphth 1988; DO RCS Eng. 1987. (Univ. Camb.) Cons. & Hon. Sen. Lect. (Ophth.) Roy. Free Hosp. Trust Lond.; Volunteer Fac., ORBIS Internat. Socs: Fell. Roy. Soc. Med.; Fell. Med. Soc. Lond.; Fell. Hunt. Soc. Prev: Sen. Regist. Moorfields Eye Hosp. Lond.

LITTLE, Brian Timothy 20 Ardmore Road, Holywood BT18 0PJ — MB BCh BAO 1995 Belf.

LITTLE, Christopher Paul 28 West Oak, The Avenue, Beckenham BR3 5EZ — MB ChB 1993 Bristol.

LITTLE, Clare Laidler Drumhar Health Centre, Perth PH1 5PD Tel: 01738 621726 Fax: 01738 643757; 7 Netherlea, Scone, Perth PH2 6QA Tel: 01738 551506 — MB ChB 1959 Glas.

LITTLE, David James The Avenue Surgery, 14 The Avenue, Warminster BA12 9AA Tel: 01985 224600 Fax: 01985 847059 Email: david.little@gp-j83018; Willow Cottage, 22 Virginia Drive, Warminster BA12 8RW Tel: 01985 214667 Fax: 01985 214667 — MB BS 1978 Lond.; MRCS Eng. LRCP Lond. 1978; MRCGP 1984; DRCOG 1981. (St. Thos.) Partner, Avenue Surg. Partnership, Warmister; Clin. Asst. Warminster Community Hosp. & Minor Injuries Unit. Prev: SHO (O & G) Univ. Hosp. Nottm.; SHO (Endocrinol.) Jessop Hosp. for Wom. Sheff.; Ho. Surg. (Urol.) St. Thos. Hosp. Lond.

LITTLE, Elsa 13 North Parade, Whitley Bay NE26 1NU — MD 1965 Newc.; MB BS Durh. 1952. (Durh.)

LITTLE, Felicity Anne 9 Jordan Lane, Edinburgh EH10 4RB — MB BS 1986 Lond.; BSc (Path.) Lond. 1983; MRCP (UK) 1991; FRCR 1995. Cons. (Clin. Oncol.), W. Gen. Hosp., Edin. Prev: Sen. Regist. (Clin. Oncol.) W.. Gen. Hosp. Edin.; Regist. (Radiother.) St. Bart. Hosp. Lond.; SHO (Radiother.) Char. Cross Hosp. Lond.

LITTLE, George Francis Joseph 115 Clapham Common Northside, London SW4 9SW — MB BCh BAO 1988 Dub.; MB BCh Dub. 1988.

LITTLE, Helen Judith Spring Lodge, 23 Western Road, Poole BH13 7BQ — MB ChB 1989 Bristol.

LITTLE, Helen Kaye 6 Sunnyside, Caeherbert Lane, Rhayader LD6 5ED — MB BS 1967 Lond.; MRCS Eng. LRCP Lond. 1967; FRCR 1975.

LITTLE, Helen Mary, Flight Lt. RAF Med. Br. (retired) New Sheepmarket Surgery, Ryhall Road, Stamford PE9 1YA Tel: 01780 758123 Fax: 01780 758102 — MB ChB 1991 Aberd.; MRCGP 1995; DRCOG 1995; Dip. IMC RCS Ed. 1994; DFFP 1997. GP Sheepmarket Surg. Stamford Lincs. Prev: Unit Med. Off. Regional Med. Centre RAF Marham.

LITTLE, James Alexander (retired) The Red House, Westleaze Close, Charminster, Dorchester DT2 9QA — MRCS Eng. LRCP Lond. 1940; FFA RCS Eng. 1962; DA Eng. 1954. Prev: Cons. Anaesth. W. Dorset Health Dist.

LITTLE, Mr James Timothy ENT Dept, A Block, City General Site, Stoke-on-Trent ST4 6QL Tel: 01782 552074 Fax: 01782 639866; Parklands, Second Ave, Porthill, Newcastle Under Lyme ST5 8NG Tel: 01782 639866 Fax: 01782 639866 Email: timandpip@supranet.com — MB ChB 1965 Sheff.; FRCS Eng. 1972. Cons. ENT Surg. N. Staffs. Hosp. Centre.

LITTLE, Jane Aleksandra 52 Langley Hall Road, Solihull B92 7HE — MB ChB 1990 Birm.; ChB Birm. 1990.

LITTLE, Janet Mary 12-22 Linenhall Street, Belfast BT2 Tel: 01232 321313 — MB BCh BAO 1980 Belf.; MSc Ed. 1984; MFCM 1988; FRCP 1997. Cons. Pub. Health Med. E. HSSB.

LITTLE, John Cumming Gloucester Avenue Surgery, 158 Gloucester Avenue, Chelmsford CM2 9LQ Tel: 01245 353182 Fax: 01245 344479 — MB BS 1971 Lond. Princip. Gen. Pract. Prev:

SHO (Neurol.) OldCh. Hosp. Romford; Ho. Off. A & E Dept. Lond. Hosp.; Ho. Off. (Med.) OldCh. Hosp. Romford.

LITTLE, John David (retired) The Towers, Walworth, Darlington DL2 2LY Tel: 01325 353833 — BM BCh 1942 Oxf.; MA Oxf. 1950, BA 1940; MRCGP 1953. Prev: Ho. Phys. Roy. Berks. Hosp. Reading.

LITTLE, Julian Francis Mellanby, Lt.-Col. RAMC British Military Hospital, Rinteln BFPO 29 Tel: 01609 779911; 2 Cunningham Road, Catterick Garrison DL9 4JG Tel: 01748 832943 — MB BS 1969 Lond.

LITTLE, Mr Keith Accident & Emergency Department, Edinburgh Royal Infirmary, Edinburgh EH3 9YW Tel: 0131 536 4007 Fax: 0131 536 4041; 4 Little France Mills, Old Dalkeith Road, Edinburgh EH16 4SF — MB ChB 1968 Ed.; MD Ed. 1977; FRCP Ed. 1986; FRCS Ed. 1985; MRCP (UK) 1984; FFAEM 1994. (Ed.) Cons. A & E Roy. Infirm. Edin.; Hon. Sen. Lect. Edin. Med. Sch. Socs: Brit. Assn. Accid. & Emerg. Med.; Fac. A & E Med.

LITTLE, Lorna Inglewood, Gallants Lane, East Farleigh, Maidstone ME15 0LG Tel: 01622 45498 — MB ChB 1968 Liverp. Regist. (Anaesth.) W. Kent Hosp. Maidstone.

LITTLE, Margaret Ann Woodstock Medical Centre, 222 Woodstock Road, Belfast BT6 9DL Tel: 028 9045 8103 Fax: 028 9073 9889 — MB BCh BAO 1975 Belf.; 2000 Master of Med. Sci. in Educat. for the Health Care Professions Q.U.B.; FRCGP 1995; MRCGP 1979; FRCG 1995.

LITTLE, Paul Stephen Primary Medical Care, Aldermoor Health Centre, Aldermoor Close, Southampton SO16 5ST; 60 Alma Road, Romsey SO51 8ED — MD 1992 Lond.; MB BS 1984; MRCP (UK) 1989; MRCGP 1992. GP S.ampton; Sen. Lect. Univ. S.ampton.

LITTLE, Richard Mark 51 Attwood Street, Halesowen B63 3UG — MB ChB 1998 Leeds.

LITTLE, Stephen Richard Charles James Lombard House, 12/17 Upper Bridge St., Canterbury CT2 2NF Tel: 01227 787199; Flat Two, 29 Central Parade, Herne Bay CT6 5HX Tel: 01227 371329 Fax: 01227 787199 — BM BCh 1967 Oxf.; MA Oxf. 1967; MRCPsych 1973; DPM Ed. 1972. (Guy's) Prev: Cons. (Adolesc. Psychiat. & List 'D' Schs.) & Sen. Regist. (Child & Adolesc. Psychiat.) Roy. Edin. Hosp.; Cons. (Child & Adolesc. Psychiat.) Medway Health Dist.

LITTLE, Steven William Wilson Street Surgery, 11 Wilson Street, Derby DE1 1PG Tel: 01332 344366 Fax: 01332 348813; 6 Thistledown Close, Darley Abbey, Derby DE22 1JR Tel: 01332 551626 — MB ChB 1980 Sheff.; MRCGP 1985; DRCOG 1984.

LITTLE, Stuart Alistair 92 Dartmouth Avenue, Newcastle ST5 3PA — MB ChB 1992 Birm.

LITTLE, Susan (retired) Greystones, Nassington, Peterborough PE8 6QB Tel: 01780 782440 — MB BS 1956 Lond.; DCH Eng. 1958.

LITTLE, Thomas Maurice Inglewood, Gallants Lane, East Farleigh, Maidstone ME15 0LG Tel: 01622 745498 — MB BCh BAO Belf. 1965; FRCP Lond. 1982, M 1969. Cons. (Paediat.) Medway Maritime Hosp., Gillingham. Prev: Paediat. Regist. Alder Hey Hosp. Liverp.; Sen. Regist. Univ. Hosp. of Wales Cardiff.; Cons. (Paediat.) All St.s Hosp. Chatham.

LITTLE, Thomas Smith (retired) Drumhar Health Centre, North Methven St., Perth PH1 5PD Tel: 01738 21726 Fax: 01738 43757 — MB ChB 1959 Glas.; DObst RCOG 1961. Undergrad. Tutor (Gen. Pract.) Dundee Univ.

LITTLE, Valerie 28 West Oak, The Avenue, Beckenham BR3 5EZ — BSc (Physiol.) Lond. 1955, MB BS (Hons.) 1958; MRCS Eng. LRCP Lond. 1958. (Univ. Coll. Hosp.) Clin. Asst. Univ. Coll. Hosp. Lond.; S.C.M.O. Margt. Pyke Centre Lond.

LITTLE, William Robert 1 Angel Hill, Bury St Edmunds IP33 1LU Tel: 01284 753008 — MB BS 1958 Lond.; DObst RCOG 1966. (St. Mary's) Prev: Res. Med. Off. St. Michael's Hosp. Hayle; Gyn. Ho. Surg. & Obst. Ho. Off. St. Mary's Hosp.; Squadron Ldr. RAF Med. Br.

LITTLE, William Roger (retired) Cranstons, 241 High St., Aldeburgh IP15 5DN Tel: 01278 453429 — MB BS 1950 Lond.; MRCP Lond. 1956; DPM Lond. 1960. Prev: Psychiat. Longview Unit & Child Guid. N.E. Essex & Sch. for Childr. with Special Needs.

LITTLE OF MORTON RIG, James Crawford (retired) Fearnhill, Bankend Road, Dumfries DG1 4TP Tel: 01387 252538 — MB ChB Bristol 1947; MD Bristol 1966; FRCP Ed. 1971, M 1956; FRCPsych 1971; DPM Durham. 1954. Prev: Dir. Clin. Research & Cons. Psychiat. Crichton Roy. Hosp. Dumfries.

LITTLECHILD, Patricia 21/9 East Cross Causeway, Edinburgh EH8 9HE — MB ChB 1989 Ed.; FRCS Ed. 1994.

LITTLEDALE, Edward John Felton House, High St., Old Portsmouth, Portsmouth PO1 Tel: 023 925422 — LMSSA 1932 Lond. (Guy's) Ophth. Clin. Asst. Portsmouth Eye & Ear Hosp. & Roy. W. Sussex Hosp. Prev: Ho. Surg. Roy. Hants. Co. Hosp. Winchester & Kent & Canterbury Hosp.; Surg. Cdr. RN (Ret.).

LITTLEDALE, Richard Montagu (retired) Little Farm, Pluckley, Ashford TN27 0RW — MRCS Eng. LRCP Lond. 1933; DCH Eng. 1948. Prev: GP.

LITTLEJOHN, Alastair Ironside (retired) Braeburn, 7 Marlefield Grove, Tibbermore, Perth PH1 1QG Tel: 01837 583197 — MB ChB 1955 Aberd.

LITTLEJOHN, Clare Imogen Townhead Surgery, Settle BD24 9JA Tel: 01729 822611; Illingworth's Barn, Greenhead Lane, Settle BD24 9HG Tel: 01729 824159 — MB BS 1983 Lond.; MA Camb. 1984; DCH RCP Lond. 1986; DRCOG 1985.

LITTLEJOHN, Doreen Innes (retired) The Old School, Betws Garmon, Caernarfon LL54 7YY Tel: 01286 650010 — MB ChB Ed. 1947. Prev: Clin. Asst. Liverp. Regional Blood Transfus. Serv.

LITTLEJOHN, Ian Hindley The Princess Royal Hospital, Haywards Heath RH16 4EX; Asulea, 63A Wilkham Hill, Hurst Pierpoint, Hassocks BN6 9NR — MB BS 1987 Lond.; FRCA 1992. (Guy's) Cons. Anaesth. P.ss Roy. Hosp. Haywards Health W. Sussex. Prev: Sen. Regist. (Anaesth.) Roy. Free Hosp. & Gt. Ormond St. Lond.; Research Fell. & Regist. (Anaesth.) Roy. Lond. Hosp.

LITTLEJOHN, Mrs Margaret Jane 19 Ferndown Gardens, Cobham KT11 2BH; 19 Ferndown Gardens, Cobham KT11 2BH — MB ChB 1961 Manch. Prev: Ho. Surg. Crumpsall Hosp. Manch.; Ho. Phys. Hope Hosp. Salford.

LITTLEJOHN, Ralph Child and Family Consultation Centre, Coxford Hall, Coxford Lane, Ilford IG1 2PL Tel: 020 8478 7211 Fax: 020 8478 3101 — MB BS 1982 Lond.; MRC Psych. 1992. (Westminster) Cons. in (Child & adolscent Psychiat.) NELMHT.

LITTLEJOHNS, Carl Stephen Llwyn y Groes, Croesnewydd Road, Wrexham LL13 7TD Tel: 01978 291100 — MB ChB 1982 Birm.; MRCPsych 1986. Cons. Psychiat. Deeside N. Wales. Socs: Welsh Psychiat. Soc.; BMA.

LITTLEJOHNS, David Walter Newham General Hospital, Glen Road, Plaistow, London E13 8SL Tel: 020 7363 8002 Fax: 020 7363 8577 Email: david@littlejohns@newhamhealth.nhs.uk; Tel: 020 8989 4746 — MB BS 1964 Lond.; BSc Lond. 1961; FRCP Lond. 1990; MRCP Lond. 1968; MRCS Eng. LRCP Lond. 1964. (Univ. Coll. Hosp.) Cons. Phys. Newham Healthcare; Clin. Audit. Lead. Socs: Brit. Pharm. Soc. Prev: Sen. Lect. (Clin. Pharmacol.) Lond. Hosp. Med. Coll.

LITTLEJOHNS, Judith Helen 110 Clark Street, London E1 3HB — MB BS 1998 Lond.; MB BS Lond 1998.

LITTLEJOHNS, Peter 78 Kenilworth Crt., Lower Rchmond Road, Putney, London SW15 — MB BS 1979 Lond.

LITTLEJOHNS, Peter Alan Bitterne Park Surgery, 28 Cobden Avenue, Bitterne Park, Southampton SO18 1BW Tel: 023 80585 655/6 Fax: 023 8055 5216 — MB BCh 1981 Wales; MRCGP 1992.

LITTLEMORE, Andrew John Grove Lodge Surgery, 72 Queensway, Holland-on-Sea, Clacton-on-Sea CO15 5JU Tel: 01255 815550 — MB ChB 1976 Leeds.

LITTLEPAGE, Beverley Nigel Cyrlas, QHP West Glamorgan Health Authority, 36 Orchard St., Swansea SA1 5AQ Tel: 01792 458066 Fax: 01792 655364; 15 Birchfield, Pontardawe, Swansea SA8 4PF Tel: 01792 862827 — LRCPI & LM, LRSCI & LM 1957; LRCPI & LM LRCSI & LM 1957; MSc (Social Med.) Lond. 1974; MFPHM Distinc. 1993; FFPHMI 1984, M 1979; MRCOG 1968, DObst 1964; LM Rotunda 1963. (RCSI) Hon. Cons. Pub. Health Med. W. GLam. HA; Non.-Exec. Dir. W. Wales Acupunc. Trust; Hon. Sec. Lect. Inst. Health Care Studies, Univ. Coll. Swansea. Socs: Welsh Obst. & Gyn. Soc.; FBIM; NY Acad. of Sci. Prev: Dir. Pub. Health & Specialist Community Phys. W. Glam. HA; Lect. (O & G) Bristol; RMO 1/7 DEO Gurkha Rifles.

LITTLER, Andrew David Sandy Lane Health Centre, Sandy Lane, Skelmersdale WN8 8LA Tel: 01695 723279 Fax: 01695 556143 — MB ChB 1985 Liverp.; DRCOG 1989. Socs: Local Med. Comm. Represen. Prev: Trainee GP Bolton.

LITTLER, Brian Oswald Whipps Cross Hospital, Whipps Cross Road, London E11 1NR Tel: 0208 539 5522 Fax: 0208 535 6660; Pentlowend, High Easter, Chelmsford CM1 4RE Tel: 01245 231626 Fax: 01279 721811 (Secretary) Fax add *51 — MB BS 1974 Lond.; BDS Lond. 1964; FDS RCS Eng. 1969. p/t Cons. Oral Surg. Waltham Forest, W. Essex & Roy. Lond. Hosp.

LITTLER, Christopher Anaestetic Department, Wrexham Maelor Hospital, Croesnewydd Rd, Wrexham LL13 7TD Tel: 01978 725955 Fax: 01978 725932 Email: c.littler@new-tr.wales.nhs.uk; 4 Lilac Drive, Wood Lane Farm, Penyffordd, Chester CH4 0GF — MB ChB 1985 Manch.; FRCA 1992; DA (UK) 1988. (Manchester) Cons. Anaesth. Wrexham Maelor Hosp. Socs: Assn. Anaesth.; Intens. Care Soc.; Vasc. Anaesth. Soc. GB & Irel. Prev: Sen. Regist. (Anaesth.) NW RHA Manch.

LITTLER, Mr John (retired) Abernethy, Vyner Road S., Bidston, Prenton CH43 7PR Tel: 0151 652 4716 — MB ChB 1942 Liverp.; FRCS Eng. 1952; MRCS Eng. LRCP Lond. 1942. Vis. Prof. Tripoli Med. Sch. Libya. Prev: Cons. Surg. Walton Hosp. Liverp.

LITTLER, John Alun Halliday 4 Kingsway, Bebington, Wirral CH63 5NS — MB BChir 1982 Camb.; MRCP (UK) 1985.

LITTLER, Thomas Richard (retired) Rosecroft, 9 Thornton Crescent, Gayton, Heswall, Wirral CH60 3RR — MB ChB 1946 Liverp.; MB ChB Liverp. 1945; MD Liverp. 1950; FRCP Lond. 1973, M 1948; MRCS Eng. LRCP Lond. 1946. Prev: Cons. Phys. Mersey Regional Rheum. Unit Arrowe Pk. Hosp. Wirral.

LITTLER, Professor William Austin Department of Cardiovascular Medicine, Queen Elizabeth Hospital, Birmingham B15 2TH Tel: 0121 472 1311 Fax: 0121 414 1045; 21 Frederick Road, Edgbaston, Birmingham B15 1JN Tel: 0121 454 7934 — MD 1971 Liverp.; MB ChB (Hons.) 1966; FRCP Lond. 1979, M 1969; FESC 1994. (Liverp.) Prof. Clin. Cardiol. Univ.Birm; Cons. Qu. Eliz. Hosp.; Divis. Dir. Univ.Hosp.Birm. Socs: Brit. Cardiac Soc. & Assn. Phys.; Europ. Soc. of Cardiol.; Internat. Soc. of Hypertens. Prev: Wolfson Research Fell. RCP Lond.; Clin. Lect. (Cardiovasc. Med.) Univ. Oxf.; Vis. Prof. Med. Univ. Calif. San Francisco, USA 1981.

LITTLER, William Ian Flat 2, Gemimas Tearooms, The Green, Finchingfield, Braintree CM7 4JZ — MB BS 1994 Lond.

LITTLER, William Watson 5 Midland Road, Royston, Barnsley S71 4QN — MD 1960 Liverp.; MB ChB 1956. (Liverp.)

LITTLESTONE, Wilfred (retired) 51 Lodge Close, Canons Drive, Edgware HA8 7RL Tel: 020 8952 1784 — LMSSA 1947 Lond. Prev: Capt. RAMC.

LITTLETON, Edward Theodore 14 Ashwood Park, Fetcham, Leatherhead KT22 9NT Tel: 01372 451953 Fax: 01372 451953 — MB BS 1996 Lond.; MA (Cantab.) 1997. (Jesus Coll. Camb. & Univ. Coll. Lond. Med. Sch.) SHO (Gen. Med.) Epsom Healthcare NHS Trust Surrey. Prev: Ho. Off. (Med.) Univ. Coll. Lond. Hosp. NHS Trust; Ho. Off. (Surg.) St. Albans & Hemel Hempstead NHS Trust.

LITTLEWOOD, Adrienne Jane Woodgrove Surgery, 2 Doncaster Road, Wath-upon-Dearne, Rotherham S63 7AL Tel: 01709 877649; 23 Bowden Grove, Dodworth, Barnsley S75 3TB Tel: 01226 204281 — MB ChB 1993 Sheff.; DFFP 1997. (Sheffield) GP Partner. Prev: GP Regist. Epworth.

LITTLEWOOD, Mr Arthur Henry Martin 31 Rodney Street, Liverpool L1 9EH — MB BChir 1946 Camb.; BA Camb. 1946; MRCS Eng. LRCP Lond. 1945; FRCS Eng. 1953. (Camb. & Univ. Coll. Hosp.) Emerit. Cons. Plastic Surg. Roy. Liverp. Hosp. Socs: Liverp. Med. Inst. & Brit. Assn. Plastic Surg. Prev: Sen. Regist. Liverp. Regional Hosp. Bd.; Fell. Roswell Pk. Memor. Inst. Buffalo, USA; Ho. Surg. Roy. N.. Hosp. Lond.

LITTLEWOOD, Carl Raymond Brig Royd Surgery, Brig Royd, Ripponden, Sowerby Bridge HX6 4AN Tel: 01422 822209 — MB ChB 1985 Manch.; MRCGP (Distinc.) 1992; D.Occ.Med. RCP Lond. 1995; DCH RCP Lond. 1990. Med. Adviser Halifax plc.

LITTLEWOOD, Claire Services for Older People and Rehabilitation, The Longley Centre, Northern General Hospital, Norwood Grange Drive, Sheffield S5 7JT Tel: 0114 271 6310; 45 Stainton Road, Endcliffe, Sheffield S11 7AX — MB ChB 1990 Ed. Staff Grade (Psychiat. of Old Age), Longley Centre & Grange Day Hosp., Sheff.

LITTLEWOOD, Clare Magdalen 16 Merrilocks Road, Liverpool L23 6UN; St. Helens & Knawsley Hospice, Portico Lane, St Helens WA10 1NW — MB ChB 1980 Liverp.; MA Keele 1997; MRCGP 1985; Dip. Palliat. Med. Wales 1991; DRCOG 1985. Macmillan Cons. (Palliat. Med.) St. Helen's & Knowsley Hospit. Trust.

LITTLEWOOD, David George 6 Merchiston Gardens, Edinburgh EH10 5DD Tel: 0131 346 4001 Email: david.g.littlewood@btinterner.com — MB ChB 1970 Ed.; FRCA 1974. (Ed.) Cons. Anaesth. Roy. Infirm. Edin.

LITTLEWOOD, Elisabeth Maria 59 York Mansions, Prince of Wales Drive, London SW11 4BP — MB BS 1994 Lond.

LITTLEWOOD, Erle Rodney The Health Centre, Rodney Road, Walton-on-Thames KT12 3LB Tel: 01932 228999 Fax: 01932 225586 — MB ChB 1973 Bristol; MD Bristol 1983; MRCP (U.K.) 1976; DRCOG 1982; Ed. Cert. 1983. Socs: BMA. Prev: Temp. Sen. Regist. (Gasroenterol.) Char. Cross Hosp. Lond.; Research Regist. W. Middlx. Hosp. Isleworth & Univ. Coll. Hosp. Lond.; Ho. Phys. (Profess. Unit) Bristol Roy. Infirm.

LITTLEWOOD, James Malcolm, OBE (retired) Cystic Fibrosis Trust, 11 London Road, Bromley BR1 1BY Tel: 020 8464 7211 Fax: 020 8313 0472 — MB ChB Leeds 1956; MD Leeds 1969; FRCP Lond. 1990; FRCP Ed. 1971, M 1962; FRCPCH 1997; DCH Eng. 1960. Hon. Cons. Paediat. St. Jas. Univ. Hosp. Leeds; Chairm. Research & Med. Advis. Comm. Cystic Fibrosis Trust; Hon. Sen. Clin. Lect. (Paediat.) Univ. Leeds. Prev: Sen. Lect. (Paediat. & Child Health) Univ. Leeds.

LITTLEWOOD, Jeffrey Slaithwaite Health Centre, New Street, Slaithwaite, Huddersfield HD7 5AB Tel: 01484 846674 — MB ChB 1983 Leeds.

LITTLEWOOD, Mark John (retired) 41 Regent Road, Gillingham ME7 5JD Tel: 01634 570309 Fax: 01631 570309 Email: xre82@dial.pipex.com — 1954 MB Camb. 1955, BChir 1954; 1980 MFOM RCP Lond. 1980; 1977 DIH Eng. 1977; 1966 DTM & H Eng. 1966; 1982 Accredit. Specialist Occupat. Med. 1982. Prev: Med. Off. Brit. Petroleum.

LITTLEWOOD, Michael Stanley 150A Shay Lane, Walton, Wakefield WF2 6LA — MB BCh BAO 1974 Belf.

LITTLEWOOD, Peter Bruce Harborough Road Surgery, Harborough Road North, Northampton NN2 8LL Tel: 01604 845144 Fax: 01604 820241; 9 Favell Way, Weston Favell, Northampton NN3 3BZ Tel: 01604 401821 — MB ChB 1967 Sheff.; DObst RCOG 1972. Med. Dir. Favell Hse. Young Disabled Unit N.ampton.

LITTLEWOOD, Ralph Noel Cefnmeusydd, Abercrave, Swansea SA9 1TS Tel: 0163 977256 — M.B., Ch.B. Ed. 1939. (Ed.) Prev: Phys. Co. Hosp. Hereford; R.A.M.C.

LITTLEWOOD, Robert Pikes Lane centre, deane Road, Bolton BL3 5HP Tel: 01204 874300 Fax: 01204 874305 Email: robert.littlewood@gp-p82002.nhs.uk — MB ChB 1979 Manch.; MRCGP 1983; DRCOG 1983.

LITTLEWOOD, Professor Roland Martin Psychiatry Department, University College London Medical School, Middlesex Hospital, London W1P 7PN Tel: 020 7380 9478 Fax: 020 7323 1459; Anthropology Department, University College London, Gower St, London WC1E 6BT Tel: 020 7387 7050 Fax: 020 7323 1459 Email: r.littlewood@ucl.ac.uk — MB BS 1973 Lond.; DPhil Oxf. 1987; BSc Lond. 1969; MRCPsych 1978; Dip. Soc. Anthropol. Oxf. 1979; FRCPsych 1999. (St. Bart.) Prof. Psychiat. & Anthropol. Univ. Coll. Lond.; Dir. UCL Med. Anthropol. Centre; Hon. Cons. Psychiat. Camden & Islington Community Health Servs. NHS Trust; Clin. Adviser Nat. Intercultural Ther. Centre. Prev: Pres. Roy. Anthropol. Inst.; Sen. Lect. (Psychiat.) Birm. Univ.; S.S.R.C Research Fell. Inst. Social Anthropol. Univ. Oxf.

LITTLEWOOD, Sheelagh Mary The Park Hospital, Sherwood Lodge Drive, Nottingham NG5 8RX Tel: 0115 967 0670 Fax: 0115 969 2967; 132 Nottingham Road, Ravenshead, Nottingham NG15 9HL — MB ChB 1976 Liverp.; FRCP (UK) 1995. (Liverp.) Cons. Dermat. Kings Mill Centre Sutton in Ashfield. Prev: Sen. Regist. (Dermat.) Qu. Univ. Hosp. Notts.

LITTLEWOOD, Stephen Richard 120 Goldington Avenue, Oakes, Huddersfield HD3 3QD — MB ChB 1980 Manch. Sen. Regist. (Child & Adolesc. Psychiat.) Roy. Manch. Childr. Hosp. Prev: Regist. (Psychiat.) Univ. S. Manch.; SHO (Psychiat.) Univ. S. Manch. Withington; Ho. Surg. Vict. Hosp. Blackpool.

LITTLEWOOD, Timothy James Department Haematology, John Radcliffe Hospital, Oxford OX3 9DU Tel: 01865 220331 Fax: 01865 220331 Email: tim.littlewood%mailgate.jr2@ox.ac.uk — MD Wales 1989; MB BCh Wales 1978; MRCP (UK) 1981; MRCPath 1988. Cons. Haemat. John Radcliffe Hosp. Oxf. Socs: Fell. Roy. Coll. Phys.; Fell. Roy. Coll. Path.

LITTLEY, Malcolm Donald Department of Medicine, Burnley Healthcare NHS Trust, Casterton Avenue, Burnley BB10 2PQ Tel: 01282 474064 — MB ChB 1981 Manch.; MD Manch. 1991; MRCP (UK) 1984. Cons. Phys. (Diabetes & Endocrinol.) Burnley Gen. Hosp. Prev: Sen. Regist. (Med., Diabetes & Endocrinol.) Salford Hosps.; Research Regist. (Endocrinol.) Christie Hosp. & Holt Radium Inst. Manch.; Regist. (Gen. Med.) Llandough Hosp. Penarth.

LITTON, Mr Adrian (retired) 6 Calder Drive, Cambuslang, Glasgow G72 8NE Tel: 0141 641 3466 — MB ChB 1951 Glas.; ChM (Commend.) Glas. 1967, MB ChB (Commend.) 1951; FRCS Glas. 1974; FRCS Eng. 1957; FRCS Ed. 1957. Cons. Surg. S.. Gen. Hosp. Glas. Prev: Surg. Research Fell Harvard Med. Sch. & Asst. Surg. Peter Bent.

LIU, Andrea Cze Yu X-Ray Department, Level C, Southampton General Hospital, Tremona Road, Southampton SO16 6YD Tel: 02380 777222 — MB BS 1992 Lond.; MRCP (UK) 1995. (King's Coll Lond.) Specialist Regist. (Radiol.) Soton. Gen. Hosp. Prev: SHO (Neurol. & Renal Med.) Univ. Hosp. Wales; SHO (Renal & Geriat. Med.) Cardiff Roy. Infirm.; SHO Rotat. (Gen. & Geriat. Med.) Medway HA.

LIU, Mr Christopher Swee Chau Hove Nuffield Hospital, 55 New Church Road, Hove BN3 4BG Tel: 01273 779471 Fax: 01273 220919; 4 Tongdean Road, Hove BN3 6QB Tel: 01273 552305 Fax: 01273 553038 Email: cscliu@aol.com — MB BS 1985 Lond.; BSc (Hons.) Lond. 1982; FRCOphth 1989; DO RCS Eng. 1988; FHKAM 1990. (Char. Cross) Cons. Ophth. Sussex Eye Hosp.Brighton; Hon. Vis. Ophth. Moorfield Eye Hosp.Lond. Socs: Assn. Research in Vision & Ophth.; Med. Contact Lens & Ocular Surface Assn. (Ex-Pres.); (Mem. Counc.) UK & Irel. Soc. of Cataract & Refractive Surgs. Prev: Sen. Regist. (Ophth.) W. Norwich Hosp. & Addenbrooke's Hosp. Camb.; Regist. (Ophth.) Moorfields Eye Hosp. Lond.; Lect. (Anat.) Chinese Univ., Hong. Kong.

LIU, Clarence King Lun 23 Orchard Mead House, 733 Finchley Road, London NW11 8DJ — BM BCh 1992 Oxf.

LIU, David Wing Hoo Department of Anaesthetics, Bedford Hospital, Kempston Road, Bedford MK42 9DJ Tel: 01234 355122 — MB BCh 1982 Wales; FRCA 1988. Cons. Anaesth. Bedford Hosp. Socs: Anaesth. Res. Soc.; Obst. Anaesth. Assn. & Difficult Airway Soc. Prev: Cons. Anaesth. Qu. Med. Centre Nottm.; Sen. Regist. Rotat. Attend. Anesthesiologist Med. Coll. Virginia Richmond, Virginia, USA; Research Fell. Univ. Nottm.

LIU, Edwina Nga-Wing 17 Courthouse Road, London N12 7PH — MB BS 1998 Lond.; MB BS Lond 1998.

LIU, Hern Choon Eugene c/o Department of Anaesthesia, Royal Brompton Hospital, Sydney St., London SW3 6NP — MB ChB 1988 Leic.; FRCA 1995. Regist. (Anaesth.) Roy. Brompton Hosp. Prev: Regist. (Anaesth.) Addenbrooke's Hosp. Camb.

LIU, Hwa Lon Holbrook Surgery, Bartholomew Way, Horsham RH12 5JL Tel: 01403 755900/1 Fax: 01403 755909 Email: enquiries@holbrooksurgery.com — MB BS 1995 Lond.; 2001 PGdipENT; MRCGP 2000; DFFP 1999; BSc Lond. 1991; DRCOG 1997. (United Med. & Dent. Schs. Guy's & St. Thos. Hosp.) Gen. Practitioner, Holbrook Surg., Horsham; GPSI ENT clinic, Horsham. Prev: GP Regist. Newtons Health Centre Haywards Heath; SHO (Psychiat.) P.ss Roy. Hosp. Haywoods Heath; SHO (Med.) P.ss Roy. Hosp. Haywoods Heath.

LIU, Mei Chen (retired) 49 Howard Road, King's Heath, Birmingham B14 7PG Tel: 0121 441 4651 — LMSSA 1958 Lond.; MD Cheeloo Univ. 1940; FRCPsych 1975, M 1971; DPM Eng. 1951. Prev: Cons. Psychiat. Monyhull Hosp. Birm.

LIU, Mun Yee 4 Cricketer's Terrace, Carshalton SM5 2RD — BChir 1994 Camb.

LIU, Rebecca Shook Ning 11 Poynings Way, London N12 7LP — MB BS 1994 Lond.; BSc Lond. 1991. (UMDS Guy's & St. Thos. Hosp. Lond.) SHO (Med. Oncol.) Roy. Marsden Hosp. Sutton.

LIU, Mr Samson Department of Urology, New Surgical Block, City General Hospital, Newcastle Road, Stoke-on-Trent ST4 2QG Tel: 01782 552166 Fax: 01782 553056; The Old Rectory, Haddon Lane, Chapel Chorlton, Newcastle ST5 5JL — MB ChB 1981 Sheff.; FRCS Urol. 1994; FRCS Glas. 1987. (Sheffield) Cons. Urol. Stoke-on-Trent.

LIU, Shi Ming Victoria Hospital, Whinneys Heys Road, Blackpool FY3 8NR — MB BCh BAO 1988 Dub. SHO Rotat. (Med.) Vict. Hosp. Blackpool. Prev: SHO (Geriat. Med.) Whittington Hosp. Manch.; Ho. Off. (Gen. Med. & Cardiol.) Wythenshawe Hosp. Manch.; Ho. Surg. St. Vincent's Hosp. Dub.

LIU, Si Hung 128 Heath Park Road, Romford RM2 5XL — MB ChB 1994 Manch.

LIU TEK-YUNG, David Department of Obstetrics & Gynaecology, City Hospital, Hucknall Road, Nottingham NG5 1PB Tel: 0115 969 1169 Fax: 0115 962 7670 — MB BS 1966 Sydney; MPhil (Bioeng.) Sussex 1976; DM Nottm. 1991; FRACOG 1992; FRCOG 1986, M 1971; MBA 1999. Cons. & Tutor City Hosp. Univ. Nottm.; Founder Mem. Nottm. Trent Univ. BioMech. Study Gp.; Clin dir dept. O + Gcity Hosp Notts. Socs: Blair Bell Res. Soc.; (Counc.) Birm. & Midl. Obst. & Gyn. Soc. Prev: Lect. & Hon. Sen. Regist. Univ. Coll. Hosp. Lond.; Research Fell. (Bioengin.) Univ. Sussex Brighton; Research Regist. (Obst.) Univ. Lond.

LIU YIN, Professor Ahman (John) Department of Haematology, Manchester Royal Infirmary, Manchester M13 9WL Tel: 0161 276 4984 Fax: 0161 276 4814; 64 Broadwalk, Pawnall Park, Wilmslow SK9 5PN — MB ChB 1975 Manch.; BSc (Hons.) Manch. 1972; FRCP Lond. 1991; MRCP (UK) 1978; FRCPath 1995, M 1983. (Manchester Univ.) Cons. Haemat. Centr. Manch. HA; Hon. Prof. Of Haemat., Univ. Of Manch. Socs: Brit. Soc. for Haemat.; Amer. Soc. of Haemat.; Manch. Med. Soc.

LIVER, Michael Robert, SBStJ, Capt. RAMC Retd. (retired) 3 Eaton Court, Duffield, Belper DE56 4FT Tel: 01332 841736 — MRCS Eng. LRCP Lond. 1944; MA Camb. 1944; MRCGP 1956. Prev: GP Belper, Derbysh.

LIVERMORE, Anna Louise 57 Out Risbygate, Bury St Edmunds IP33 3RQ — MB BChir 1994 Camb.

LIVERSEDGE, Neil Harvey 120 Station Road, Nailsea, Bristol BS48 1TB — MB ChB 1988 Liverp.; MRCOG 1994. Clin. Research Fell. (Reproduc. Med.) Bristol Univ. Prev: SHO (O & G) Fazakerley Hosp. Liverp.

LIVERSEDGE, Richard Lorton Flat 1, 43 Wimpole St., London W1G 8AE Tel: 020 7935 7909 — MB BS 1968 Lond.; MRCS Eng. LRCP Lond. 1968; FDS RCS Ed. 1970; FDS RCS Eng. 1971. (Lond. Hosp.) Cons. Oral Surg. Middlx. Hosp. Lond., Edgware Gen. Hosp. & Barnet Gen. Hosp. Socs: Brit. Assn. Oral Surg. Prev: Sen. Regist. (Oral Surg.) Roy. Dent. Hosp. Lond.; Ho. Surg. & Regist. (Oral. Surg.) Lond. Hosp.

LIVERSEDGE, Stephen Nicholas Liversedge and Joyce, Egerton & Dunscar Health Centr, Darwen Road, Bromley Cross, Bolton BL7 9RG Tel: 01204 309525 Fax: 01204 596562; Clough House Farm, Turton, Bolton BL7 0HE Tel: 01204 852717 — MB BS 1975 Lond.; MB BS London 1975; BA Oxf 1972. (University College Hospital Medical School) Chairm. Bolton N. E. PCG.

LIVESEY, Anthony Edward Child,Adolescent & Family Therapy Service, The Marsden St Clinic, Marsden Street, Chesterfield S40 1JY Tel: 01246 552960 Fax: 01246 237837 Email: tlivesey@cafts-chcs.demon.co.uk — MB ChB 1979 Dundee; BMedSci (Hons.) Dundee 1976, MB ChB 1979; MRCPsych 1983; T(Psych) 1991. (Dundee) Cons. (Child & Family Psychiat.) C.H.C.S. (N. Derbysh.) NHS Trust, Chesterfield, Derbysh.

LIVESEY, Mr Brian, CB, Maj.-Gen. late RAMC Retd. 7 Highview, Caterham CR3 6AY — MB ChB 1952 Bristol; FRCS Eng. 1965; DLO Eng. 1958. Prev: Chairm. St. Mary's Hosp. NHS Trust I. of Wight; Commandant & Postgrad. Dean Roy. Army Med. Coll. Lond.; Hon. Surg. to HM the Qu.

LIVESEY, Carole Andrea The Bramblefield Clinic, Grovehurst Road, Kembley, Sittingbourne ME10 2ST Tel: 01795 431266 Fax: 01795 431277; Hospital Farm Oast, Church Hill, Harbledown, Canterbury CT2 9AH Tel: 01227 761180 Fax: 01227 784702 — MB BS 1977 Lond. (Middx.Hosp) Specialist (HRT/Menopause Med.) Bramblefield Clinic Sittingbourne & Bridge Surg. Canterbury; SRN 1970. Prev: Clin. Asst. (Renal Med.) Keycol Hosp.; Community Health Dr. - Maidstone, Canterbury Faversham.

LIVESEY, David St John Avenue Medical Practice, 7 Reney Avenue, Sheffield S8 7FH Tel: 0114 237 7649 — MB BS 1990 Newc.; MRCGP 1996. GP.

LIVESEY, Deborah Jayne 49 Rose Terrace, Horsforth, Leeds LS18 4QA — MB ChB 1991 Leeds.

LIVESEY, Elizabeth Anne MacKeith Centre, Royal Alexandra Hospital, Dyke Road, Brighton BN1 3JN Tel: 01273 28145; The Knowle, Spithurst, Barcombe, Lewes BN8 5EF — MB ChB 1975 Liverp.; FRCP Lond. 1995; MRCP (UK) 1980; MRCGP 1983. Cons.

Community Paediat. Brighton Health Dist. Sussex. Prev: GP Lond.; Sen. Regist. (Paediat.) Char. Cross Hosp. Lond.; Regist. & Research Fell. Middlx. Hosp. Lond.

LIVESEY, Mr Jonathan Peter 47 West End, South Cave, Brough HU15 2EX — MB ChB 1989 Sheff.; BMedSci Sheff. 1988; FRCS Eng. 1994. Specialist Regist. Yorks. Train. Scheme.

LIVESEY, Oonagh Michaela The Surgery, 178 Musters Road, West Bridgford, Nottingham NG2 7AA Tel: 0115 981 4472 Fax: 0115 981 2812 — MB ChB 1965 Leeds.

LIVESEY, Paula Michelle The Maltings Family Practice, 10 Victoria Street, St Albans AL1 3JB Tel: 01727 853296 Fax: 01727 862498; 4 Henrys Grant, Riverside Road, St Albans AL1 1RY — MB ChB 1992 Ed. (Edinburgh)

LIVESEY, Peter Gerard Cossington House Surgery, 51 Cossington Road, Canterbury CT1 3HX Tel: 01227 763377 Fax: 01227 786908; Kiln House, Tile Kiln Hill, Blean, Canterbury CT2 9EE Tel: 01227 471433 Fax: 01227 786908 — MB ChB Leeds 1968; MD Leeds 1978; DObst RCOG 1974. (Leeds) Princip. GP Canterbury; Course Organiser & Trainer (Gen. Pract.) Canterbury; Hon. Clin. Asst. (Nuclear Med.) Kent & Canterbury Hosp.; Mem. (Exec. Comm.) Kent. Inst. Med. & Health Scis. Univ. Kent Canterbury; Med. Off. Kent Coll.; Assessor of GP Consultation Videos for Summative Assessm.; Sen. Lect. in GP Kings Coll. Lond.; Sub Dean & Head of Dept. Of GP in Kent Inst. Med. & Health Sci. Univ. Kent Canterbury; Med. Off. Kent Couty Cricket Club (Hon.). Prev: Regist. (Med.) Leeds Gen. Infirm.; Anglo-German Wellcome Fell.; Assoc. Reg. Adviser (Gen. Pract.) SE Thames HA.

LIVESEY, Roger Michael Tudor Square Medical Practice, 1st Floor, Barclays Bank Chambers, Tudor Square, West Bridgford, Nottingham NG2 6BT Tel: 0115 914 3200 Fax: 0115 914 3201; 32 Firs Road, Edwalton, Nottingham NG12 4BX Tel: 0115 923 2179 — MB ChB 1965 Leeds. Socs: MEDCHI. Prev: Clin. Asst. (Chest Med.) City Hosp. Nottm.

LIVESEY, Sara Janet c/o Eye Department, Torbay Hospital, Lawes Bridge, Torquay TQ2 7AA Tel: 01803 614567 — MB ChB 1980 Leeds; FRCS Ed. 1985; FRCOphth 1989; DO RCS Eng. 1984. (Leeds) Cons. Ophth. Torbay Hosp. Torquay. Socs: (Sec.) Torquay Dist. Med. Soc. Prev: Sen. Regist. (Ophth.) Qu. Med. Centre Nottm.

LIVESEY, Sarah Helen 47 West End, South Cave, Brough HU15 2EX — MB ChB 1988 Sheff.; MRCGP 1993; DRCOG 1991. Prev: Community Med. Off. (Community Paediat. & Paediat. Accid. Emerg.) Sheff.

LIVESEY, Mr Steven Andrew 32 Hartfield Crescent, Wimbledon, London SW19 3SD — MB ChB 1979 Manch.; FRCS Eng. 1984.

LIVESLEY, Professor Brian, KStJ P.O. Box 295, Oxford OX2 9GD; P.O. Box 295, Oxford OX2 9GD — MB ChB 1960 Leeds; MD Lond. 1979; FRCP Lond. 1989; MRCP (UK) 1971; DHMSA 1974. (Leeds) Forens. Phys. Socs: Fell. Roy. Soc. Med.; Fell. Fac. Hist., Philos. Med. & Pharmacy Soc. Apoth. Lond.; BMA. Prev: Prof. c/o Elderly (Geriat.) Imperial Coll. Sch. Med. Lond.; Ho. Phys. Med. Profess. Unit Gen. Infirm. Leeds; Cons. Phys. (Geriat.) King's Coll. Hosp. Lond.

LIVESLEY, Mr Peter James Rose Cottage, Sookholme Lane, Warsop, Mansfield NG19 8LW Tel: 01623 847237 Fax: 01623 847237 — MB BS 1983 Lond.; BSc Lond. 1980; MChOrth Liverp. 1993; FRCS (Orth.) 1993; FRCS Ed. 1987; FRCS Eng. 1987. (Roy. Free) Cons. Orthop. Surg. Kingsmill Centre Mansfield. Socs: Fell. BOA; Brit. Soc. Paediat. Orthop. Surg.; Brit. Trauma Soc. Prev: Regist. (Orthop. Surg.) Qu. Med. Centre Nottm.; Regist. (Surg. & Orthop.) Qu. Eliz. Hosp. Kings Lynn.; Sen. Regist. Roy. Nat. Orthop. Hosp.

LIVESLEY, Valerie Anne The Surgery, 109A Crofton Road, Orpington BR6 8HU Tel: 01689 822266 Fax: 01689 891790; 4 Berger Close, Petts Wood, Orpington BR5 1HR Fax: 01689 896979 — MB BS 1966 Lond.; MRCS Eng. LRCP Lond. 1966; T(GP) 1993; DObst RCOG 1968. (King's Coll. Hosp.) Socs: BMA; Assoc. Mem. Roy. Soc. Med. Prev: Ho. Surg. & Ho. Phys. Dulwich Hosp.; Ho. Surg. (O & G) Withington Hosp. Manch.; Ho. Phys. Birch Hill Hosp. Rochdale.

LIVINGS, Richard Robert Brimington Surgery, Church Street, Brimington, Chesterfield S43 1JG Tel: 01246 273224 Fax: 01246 556616 — MB BChir 1979 Camb.; MRCGP 1985; DRCOG 1984. (St. Bart.) Prev: SHO (Path.) Lewisham Hosp. Lond.; SHO (Radiother.) St. Bart. Hosp. Lond.; Ho. Off. (Med.) Essex Co. Hosp. Colchester.

LIVINGSTON, Clare Joan 31 Southside Road, Inverness IV2 4XA — MB ChB 1988 Ed.; DObst. Otago 1991.

LIVINGSTON, Edward Colin Wyck Cottage, Barrow Point Lane, Pinner HA5 3DJ Tel: 020 8868 1973 — MB BS 1948 Lond. (St. Mary's) JP; Medico-legal Cons. Med. Foundat.; Barrister-at-Law Middle Temple 1960. Socs: Assoc. Fac. Occupat. Med. RCP Lond. Prev: Apptd. Doctor EMAS; Chairm. Social Security Appeal Tribunal Harrow; Flight Lt. RAFVR.

LIVINGSTON, Elizabeth Howat (retired) Highfield Hall, Stafford Road, Uttoxeter ST14 — MB ChB 1925 Glas.

LIVINGSTON, Eric 17 Pier Road, Aultbea, Achnasheen IV22 2JQ Tel: 0144 582221 — MB ChB 1969 Glas.; MRCGP 1974; DObst RCOG 1972. (Glas.)

LIVINGSTON, Eric Dumgoyach, Moor Road, Strathblane, Glasgow G63 9EX — MB ChB 1997 Aberd.

LIVINGSTON, Gillian Avril 7 Branksome Court, 158 East End Road, E. Finchley, London N2 0RX Tel: 020 8444 9116 — MB ChB 1981 Glas.

LIVINGSTON, Graham, Air Vice-Marshal RAF Med. Br. Retd. Chimanimani, Tom's Hill Road, Aldbury, Tring HP23 5SA — MB ChB 1951 Ed.; MFPHM 1989; MFOM Lond. 1981; MFCM (UK) 1974; DPH Ed. 1963; DIH Eng. 1963. (Ed.) Cons. Occupat. Health Physi. Prev: Hon. Surg. to HM The Qu.; Princip. Med. Off. RAF Support Command & RAF, Germany.

LIVINGSTON, Mr Hector Stewart (retired) Kentra, Easterton, Dalcross, Inverness IV2 7JE Tel: 01667 462358 Fax: 01667 462358 — MB ChB 1961 Glas.; FRCS Glas. 1966; MFPHM 1980; DPH Glas. 1974; DObst RCOG 1963. Princip. Med. Off. Manguzi Hosp. S. Africa. Prev: Cons. Pub. Health Med. Highland HB.

LIVINGSTON, Hilary Monica Royal Alexandra Hospital, Department of Geriatric Psychiatry, Paisley — MB ChB 1977 Glas.; MRCPsych 1981. Cons. Psychiat. Roy. Alexandra & Dykebar Hosps. Paisley. Prev: Sen. Regist. Gtr. Glas. Health Bd.

LIVINGSTON, John Alexander (retired) 64 London Road, Stanmore HA7 4NS Tel: 020 8954 3438 — MB BS 1926 Durh.; BHy & DPH Durham. 1937. Prev: Consult. (Infec. Dis.) W. Hendon Hosp. Lond.

LIVINGSTON, John Henry Clarendon Wing, The General Infirmary, Leeds LS2 9NS Tel: 0113 392 6903 Email: jlive@ultn.northy.nhs.uk; 26 Claremont Road, Leeds LS6 4EB — MB ChB 1980 Ed.; MRCP 1983; FRCPCH 1997; FRCP 1992. Cons. Paediat. Neurol. Clarendon Wing Leeds Gen. Infirm. Prev: Sen. Regist. (Paediat.) Roy. Hosp. for Sick Childr. Edin.; Resid. Etranger Hosp. Necker Enfants Malades, Paris.

LIVINGSTON, Justin Patrick Elizabeth Ave Group Practice, 2 Elizabeth Avenue, London N1 3BS Tel: 020 7226 6363; 42 Wilton Square, Islington, London N1 3DW Tel: 020 7359 0070 — MB BS 1966 Queensland; MRCGP 1976. (Lond.) GP Lond. Prev: GP Trainer Lond.

LIVINGSTON, Martin Gerard Department of Psychiatry, Southern General Hospital, 1345 Govan Road, Glasgow G51 4TF Tel: 0141 201 1947 Fax: 0141 201 1947 Email: mgl2w@udcf.gla.ac.uk — MD 1986 Glas.; MD Glasgow 1986, MB ChB 1976; FRCPsych 1994, M 1980. Cons. Psychiat. S.ern Gen. Hosp.; Hon. Clin. Sen. Lect. Socs: Brit. Assn. Psychopharmacol.; CINP; ECNP. Prev: Lect.(Psychol.) Med. Univ. Glas.; Hon. Sen. Regist. Gartnavel Roy. & Gartnavel Gen. Hosp. Glas.; Sen.Lect.Glas. Univ. (Psychol.Med).

LIVINGSTON, Moira Margaret Dept of Older Age Psychology, North Tyneside General Hospital, Ash Court, Rake Lane, North Shields Tel: 0191 293 2749; 9 Woodbine Road, Gosforth, Newcastle upon Tyne NE3 1DD Tel: 0191 284 1401 — MB ChB 1984 Ed.; CME 2000; MRCPsych 1989. p/t Cons. in Older Age Psychiat.; Assoc. Post Grad. Dean, N.. Deanery; Post Grad. Inst. of Med. and Dent., Newc. Univ. Prev: Regist. Rotat. (Psychiat.) Dept. Psychiat. Roy. Vict. Infirm.

LIVINGSTON, Sara Jane Margaret Chimanimani, Toms Hill Road, Aldbury, Tring HP23 5SA Tel: 01442 851527 — MB BS 1996 Lond.; BSc Lond. 1993. (St. Mary's Hospital Medical School) SHO (A & E) Univ. Coll. Hosp. Prev: SHO (Paediat. Orthop.) RNOH Stanmore.

LIVINGSTON, Sheila Catherine 3F2, 4 Bruntsfield Terrace, Edinburgh EH10 4EX — MB ChB 1993 Ed.

LIVINGSTON, Steven Irving 1 Grange Road, Elstree, Borehamwood WD6 3LY; 70 Union Street, Barnet EN5 Tel: 020 8441 9440 — MB ChB 1982 Manch.; BSc St. And. 1979. Prev: Trainee GP Borehamwood VTS; SHO (Geriat. Med.) Roy. Free Hosp. Lond.; SHO (Psychiat.) Napsbury Hosp. & Edgware Gen. Hosp.
LIVINGSTON, Stuart 25 Upper Wish Hill, Willingdon, Eastbourne BN20 9HB — MB BS 1996 Lond.
LIVINGSTON, Vivian Sidney (retired) 5 The Hollows, 6 Ayr Road, Glasgow G46 7JB — MB ChB 1955 Glas.; MRCGP 1962. Mem. Disabil. Appeal Tribunals Benefits Agency. Prev: GP Glas.
LIVINGSTON, William Stanley 4 Old Irvine Road, Kilmarnock KA1 2BD Tel: 01543 22413 — MB ChB 1956 Glas. (Glas.) Socs: BMA. Prev: Jun. Ho. Phys. (Med.) & SHO (Anaesth.) Glas. Roy. Infirm.; Jun. Ho. Surg. W.wood Hosp. Beverley.
LIVINGSTONE, Alexander George Penicuik Health Centre, 37 Imrie Place, Penicuik EH26 8LF Tel: 01968 672612 Fax: 01968 678839; Kincraig, 31 Jackson St, Penicuik EH26 9BJ Tel: 01968 672260 — MB ChB 1959 Ed.; MRCGP 1968; DObst RCOG 1962. Prev: Ho. Surg. (Obst.) W.. Gen. Hosp. Edin.; Ho. Surg. Roy. Infirm. Edin.; Ho. Phys. Deaconess Hosp. Edin.
LIVINGSTONE, Alison Florence 10 Hopedene Court, Belfast BT4 3DP — MB ChB 1989 Ed.; MRCP (UK) 1993. Cons. Community Paediat. Home1st Community & Social Servs. Trust Co. Antrim. Socs: BMA; RCPCH; Ulster Paediat. Soc. Prev: Sen. Regist. (Paediat. Neurol.) Roy. Belf. Hosp. Sick Childr. Belf.
LIVINGSTONE, Angus Muir The Surgery, Park St., Ripon HG4 2BE Tel: 01765 692366; The Barn, Winksley, Ripon HG4 3NR Tel: 01765 658941 — MRCS Eng. LRCP Lond. 1973. (Leeds) Clin. Asst. Ripon Dist. Hosp. Prev: SHO (Obst.) W. Cumbld. Hosp. Hensingham; Regist. (Med.) Waikato Hosp. Hamilton, NZ.
LIVINGSTONE, Anna Eleri Gill Street Health Centre, 11 Gill Street, London E14 8HQ Tel: 020 7515 2211; 61 Chesterton Road, Plaistow, London E13 8BD — MB BS 1978 Lond.; MSc (Epidemiol.) Lond. 1994; MA Oxf. 1977; MRCGP 1983; DCH RCP Lond. 1983; DRCOG 1981. (Lond. Hosp.) Trainer GP Lond.; Mem. THPCT Exel. Socs: Med. Pract. Union. Prev: Trainee GP City & E. Lond. VTS.
LIVINGSTONE, Anthony Vere (retired) Beam Brook, Old Rusper Road, Newdigate, Dorking RH5 5EE Tel: 01293 862604 — MB BS Lond. 1953; FRCP Lond. 1975, M 1956; MRCS Eng. LRCP Lond. 1944. Hon. Cons. Phys. Roy. Free Hosp. Lond. Prev: Cons. Phys. Mid Downs HA.
LIVINGSTONE, Mr Brian Nicholas Royal Infirmary, Wigan Lane, Wigan WN1 2NN Tel: 01942 244000 — MB ChB 1970 Liverp.; FRCS Eng. 1974. Cons. Orthop. Surg. Wigan & Leigh Hosps. Socs: Fell. Brit. Orthop. Assn. Prev: Sen. Regist. (Orthop.) N.W. RHA; Tutor (Orthop.) Univ. Manch.; Regist. St. Geo. Hosp. Lond.
LIVINGSTONE, Callum Department of Clinical Biochemistry, Royal Victoria Infirmary, Newcastle upon Tyne NE2 4BW — MB ChB 1987 Ed.
LIVINGSTONE, Colina Carrie Beam Brook, Old Rusper Road, Newdigate, Verwood Tel: 0192 74 862604 — MB BS 1951 Lond.; BSc Lond. 1942, MB BS 1951. (Roy. Free) Prev: Ho. Phys. & Lect. Pharmacol. Roy. Free Hosp.
LIVINGSTONE, David Adam 33 Norrys Road, Cockfosters, Barnet EN4 9JU Tel: 020 8449 2711 — MB ChB 1987 Manch.
LIVINGSTONE, David Isidor (retired) 14 Ashfield Lodge, Palatine Road, Didsbury, Manchester M20 2UD — MB ChB Glas. 1935; BSc Glas. 1933; MRCGP 1954.
LIVINGSTONE, David Wilson (retired) The Old School, Holehead, The Bailey, Newcastleton TD9 0TR Tel: 01697 748394 — MB ChB 1943 Ed.; MRCGP 1953. Prev: Ship's Surg. Cunard White Star Ltd.
LIVINGSTONE, Doris Seasgur, Moor Road, Strathblane, Glasgow G63 9EU — MB ChB 1965 Glas.
LIVINGSTONE, Douglas Nicol Our Lady of Victory, Brownshill, Stroud GL6 8AS — MB ChB 1963 Glas.; DPM Ed. & Glas. 1967. (Glas.) Dir. Our Lady of Victory Therap. Community Stroud. Prev: Dir. Villa Louis Martin Therap. Community, New Mexico; Regist. (Psychol. Med.) S. Gen. Hosp. Glas.
LIVINGSTONE, Eric David Gorbals Health Centre, 45 Pine Place, Glasgow G5 0BQ Tel: 0141 531 8290 Fax: 0141 531 8208; 98A St Andrew's Drive, Pollock Shields, Glasgow G41 4RX — MB ChB 1971 Glas. (Glasgow) Prev: Regist. (Anaesth.) Vict. Infirm. Glas.
LIVINGSTONE, Francis Donald Macfarlane (retired) 15 Chaff Close, Whiston, Rotherham S60 4JH Tel: 01709 828310 — MB BChir Camb. 1937; BA Camb. 1931; MRCP Lond. 1938; MRCS Eng. LRCP Lond. 1934; DPH Lond. 1939; DCH Eng. 1938. Prev: MOH Mid.-Warks. Combined Dists.
LIVINGSTONE, Harvey William Pollokshaws Doctors Centre, 26 Wellgreen, Glasgow G43 1RR Tel: 0141 649 2836 Fax: 0141 649 5238; 60 Broomfield Avenue, Newton Mearns, Glasgow G77 5JP Tel: 0141 639 6767 — MB ChB 1966 Glas.; DObst RCOG 1968. (Glas.)
LIVINGSTONE, Helen Jayne 3 Ivy Road, Shipley BD18 4JY — MB ChB 1989 Leeds.
LIVINGSTONE, Iain Graham (retired) 1 Normans, Preston Road, Lavenham, Sudbury CO10 9QE Tel: 01787 247454 — MB ChB Glas. 1955. Prev: GP Livingstone Heinink Baird Randhawa - Abaniwo.
LIVINGSTONE, James Alexander Tamaris Cottage, The Street, Frampton on Severn, Gloucester GL2 7DY — MB BS 1988 Lond. Anat. Demonst. St. Geo. Hosp. Lond. Prev: Ho. Surg. Orsett Hosp. Essex; Ho. Phys. Kent & Sussex Hosp. Tunbridge Wells.
LIVINGSTONE, Mr Jeremy Rae Braithwaite (retired) 2 Lennox Street, Edinburgh EH4 1QA Tel: 0131 332 2038 Fax: 0131 624 4850 Email: jlivinsc18@aol.com — MB ChB 1956 Ed.; FRCS Ed. 1964; FRCOG 1977, M 1964; DObst 1960. Cons. Simpson Memor. Matern. Pavil. & Roy. Infirm. Edin. Prev: Chairm. (O & G) King Faisal Specialist Hosp. Riyadh, Saudi Arabia.
LIVINGSTONE, Johan 47 Newton Drive, Greenmount, Bury BL8 4DH — MB ChB 1998 Glas.; MB ChB Glas 1998.
LIVINGSTONE, John Stuart Eltham Park Surgery, 46 Westmount Road, London SE9 1JE Tel: 020 8850 1030 Fax: 020 8859 2036; 8 Vivian Road, Bethnal Green, London E3 5RF Tel: 020 8981 6364 — MB BChir 1979 Camb.; LLB Camb. 1981. Chairm. Greenwich PEC. Socs: Primary Soc. Gastroenterol.; Anglo-French Med. Soc. Prev: Trainee GP Swindon; Ho. Surg. OldCh. Hosp. Romford; Ho. Phys. Bedford Gen. Hosp.
LIVINGSTONE, Joshua Cranbrook, 12 West Braes Crescent, Crail, Anstruther KY10 3SY Tel: 0133 35 559 — MB ChB 1940 Glas.; BSc, MB ChB Glas. 1940. (Univ. Glas.)
LIVINGSTONE, Judith Alexis Queens Walk Surgery, 69 Queens Walk, Ruislip HA4 0NT Tel: 020 8842 2991 Fax: 020 8842 2245 — MB BS 1983 Lond.; MFPM RCP (UK) 1992; MRCGP 1988; DCH RCP Lond 1987; DRCOG 1987; Cert. Family Plann JCC 1987. Chairm. NW Thames Region GP Train. Comm.; GP Partner. Socs: BMA; Brit. APP. Prev: Med. Adviser Allen & Hanburys Ltd. Stockley Pk. Middlx.; Asst. (Gen. Pract.) Ruislip.; Trainee GP Edgware Gen. Hosp.
LIVINGSTONE, Kenneth 2 Ballymore Park, Tandragee, Craigavon BT62 2AX — MB BCh BAO 1974 Belf.
LIVINGSTONE, Michael D Wentloog Road Health Centre, 98 Wentloog Road, Rumney, Cardiff CF33XE Tel: 029 2079 7746 Fax: 029 2079 0231 — MBBCh. (University of Wales College of Medicine)
LIVINGSTONE, Morag Barn Surgery, Christchurch Medical Centre, Purewell Cross Road, Christchurch BH23 3AF Tel: 01202 486456 Fax: 01202 486678; 24 Westlands, West Road, Bransgore, Christchurch BH23 8BY — MB ChB 1984 Glas. Prev: SHO (O & G) Glas. Roy. Matern. Hosp. & Glas. Roy. Infirm.; SHO (Gen. Surg.) Vict. Infirm. Glas.; SHO (Geriat. Med.) Vict. Geriat. Unit Glas.
LIVINGSTONE, Neil Michael Central Surgery, Sussex Road, Gorleston-on-Sea, Great Yarmouth NR31 6QB Tel: 01493 414141 Fax: 01493 656253 — MB BS 1973 Lond.; MRCS Eng. LRCP Lond. 1973; DObst RCOG 1976.
LIVINGSTONE, Patricia Rosemary Park Street, Ripon HG4 2BE; The Barn, Winksley, Ripon HG4 3NR Tel: 01765 658941 — MB ChB 1972 Leeds. (Leeds) GP Partner Ripon. Prev: SHO (Nuclear Med.) Leeds Gen. Infirm.; Regist. (Med.) Waikato Hosp. Hamilton, N.Z.; Vice Chairm. N. Yorks. Heath Auth.
LIVINGSTONE, Mr Peter Deans (retired) 128 Bentinck Drive, Troon KA10 6JB Tel: 01292 311806 — MB ChB 1946 Ed.; FRCS Ed. 1954; FRCS Eng. 1960; FRCS Glas. 1975. Cons. Surg. CrossHo. Hosp.; Hon. Clin. Lect. (Postgrad. Med.) Glas. Univ. Prev: Sen. Regist. (Surg.) United Sheff. Hosps. & Nottm. Gen. Hosp.
LIVINGSTONE, Quentin Gavin Newbury Street Practice, Newbury Street, Wantage OX12 7AY Tel: 01235 763451; Ardgay, 11 Springfield Road, Wantage OX12 8ES Tel: 01235 764521 — MB BS 1967 Lond.; MRCS Eng. LRCP Lond. 1967; MRCGP 1976; DCH

Eng. 1970; DObst RCOG 1969. (St. Thos.) Socs: BMA. Prev: Hosp. Pract. (Paediat. Surg.) John Radcliffe Hosp. Oxf.; Ho. Surg. (Orthop. & Plastic Surg.) St. Thos. Hosp. Lond.; Ho. Phys. Worthing Hosp.

LIVINGSTONE, Russell Ian 3 Ivy Road, Shipley BD18 4JY — MB ChB 1989 Leeds.

LIVINGSTONE, Ruth Keren The Little Practice, 21 St. Mary Street, Stamford PE9 2DH Tel: 01780 763308 Fax: 01780 755878; Cowick Lodge, New Cross Road, Stamford PE9 1AJ Tel: 01780 766862 Email: ruth.livingstone@ukonline.co.uk — BM 1979 Soton.; DRCOG 1982; Dip. Med. Acupunc BMAS 1997.

LIVINGSTONE, Susan Elizabeth 6 Laurel Bank, Castle Douglas DG7 1BP — MB ChB 1987 Dundee.

LIVINGSTONE, William Niel (retired) Banbury Road Surgery, 172 Banbury Road, Oxford OX2 7BT Tel: 01865 515731 Fax: 01865 510711 — BM BCh 1963 Oxf.; MA Oxf. 1963.

LIVSEY, Jacqueline Erica 12 Vale Avenue, Bury BL9 9LW — BM BCh 1991 Oxf.

LIXI, Giovanni 31 The Gardens, Harrow HA1 4HE — State Exam 1988 Rome.

LIYANAGE, Isabella Selvadevi Princess Margaret Hospital, Windsor SL4 3SJ Tel: 01753 743464; Waverley Court, Wentworth Drive, Wentworth, Virginia Water GU25 4NY — MB BS 1965 Ceylon; MRCP (U.K.) 1971; FRCR 1975; FFR 1974; DMRD Eng. 1973. (Ceylon) Cons. Radiol. St. Marks Hosp. Maidenhead, Wexham Pk. Hosp. Slough & P.ss Margt. Hosp. Windsor. Socs: BMA; Fell. RSM. Prev: SHO (Rheum.) Battle Hosp. Reading; Sen. Regist. (Radiol.) N.wick Pk. Hosp. Harrow & Roy. Nat. Orthop. Hosp. Lond.

LIYANAGE, Padmalata Priyadarshini 19 Links Road, Epsom KT17 3PP Tel: 0137 27 29075 — MB BS 1969 Ceylon. (Colombo) Clin. Med. Off. Mid Surrey Health Dist.

LIYANAGE, Sunil Porambe (cons. rooms), The Princess Margaret Hospital, Windsor SL4 3SJ Tel: 01753 743348 Fax: 01753 743439 Email: rheumatology@lineone.net; Waverley Court, Wentworth Drive, Wentworth, Virginia Water GU25 4NY — MB BS 1965 Ceylon; FRCP Lond. 1985; MRCP (UK) 1970; DCH Eng. 1967. (Ceylon) Cons. Rheum. Heatherwood Hosp. Ascot, King Edwd. VII Hosp. Windsor & St. Marks Hosp. Maidenhead. Socs: Brit. Soc. Rheum.; (Ex-Chairm.) Brit. Med. Acupunc. Soc.; Amer. Soc. Bone & Mineral Research. Prev: Sen. Regist. (Rheum.) Lond. Hosp.; Regist. (Rheum.) Reading Area Hosps.; SHO (Med.) St. Ann's Gen. Hosp. Tottenham.

LJUNGGREN, Ake Mats Oskar (retired) Department of Pathology, General Hospital, Hartlepool TS24 9AQ Tel: 01429 66654 — Med Lic 1957 Goteborg; Med. Lic. Goteborg 1957. Cons. (Clin. Microbiol.) Gen. Hosp. Hartlepool.

LLAHI CAMP, Josep Maria Flat B, 1 Cranley Gardens, London N13 4LT — LMS 1988 U Autonoma Barcelona.

LLEDO MACAU, Alberto Lilly Research Centre Ltd., Erl Wood Manor, Sunninghill Road, Windlesham GU20 6PH — LMS 1985 U Complutense Madrid; PhD (Neurosci.) Madrid 1994; BSc (Clin. Neurol.) Univ. Complutense de Madrid 1991. (Univ. Complutense Madrid) Europ. Clin. Research Phys. Lilly Research Centre Windlesham, Surrey; Assoc. Researcher Cajal Inst. Madrid. Prev: Cons. Neurol. Hosp. Universitario, Madrid.

LLEWELLIN, Gwyn States of Jersey Public Health Services, Le Bas Centre, St Saviours Road, St Helier, Jersey JE1 4HR Tel: 01534 789933 Fax: 01534 623720; Pen Y Craig House, Pen Y Craig Avenue, St Helier, Jersey JE2 3GN Tel: 01534 725950 — MB BS 1968 Lond.; MRCS Eng. LRCP Lond. 1965; MRCGP 1973. (Guy's) SCMO (Pub. Health Servs.) Jersey. Socs: Fell. Soc. Pub. Health; Jersey Med. Soc.; BMA. Prev: Ho. Phys. Guy's Hosp.; Ho. Surg. & SHO (Cas.) Lewisham Hosp.; Ho. Surg. (O & G) All St.s Hosp. Chatham.

LLEWELLYN, Carol Grace Queen Elizabeth Hospital, Department of Medicine, Edgbaston, Birmingham B15 2TH Tel: 0121 472 1311 Fax: 0121 627 2384 — MB BCh 1985 Wales; MRCP (UK) 1989; FRCP (uk) 2000; MD Wales 1994. Cons. (Gen. & Respirat. Med.) Qu. Eliz. Hosp. Birm. Socs: Brit. Thorac. Soc.; Eur. Respirat. Soc.; Amer. Thoracic Soc. Prev: Sen. Regist. (Gen. & Respirat. Med.) Qu. Eliz. Hosp. Birm.; Research Regist. Univ. Birm.; Regist. Roy. Gwent Hosp. Newport.

LLEWELLYN, David John Kelso Avenue Health Centre, Kelso Avenue, Thornton-Cleveleys FY5 3LF Tel: 01253 853992 Fax: 01253 822649; Ramperpot Cottage, Underbank Road, Thornton-Cleveleys FY5 5LL Tel: 01253 826527 — MB ChB 1971 Manch.

LLEWELLYN, Mrs Dawn Clarenda Mary (retired) Portobello House, Ogmore-by-Sea, Bridgend CF32 0PA Tel: 01656 880207 — MB BS 1955 Lond.; MRCS Eng. LRCP Lond. 1955. JP. Prev: Sessional Med. Off. Mid Glam. AHA.

LLEWELLYN, Derek John, OBE (retired) Ty Gwyn, Llanmaes, Llantwit Major CF61 2XR Tel: 01446 792664 Fax: 01446 792664 Email: derek@llanmaes.demon.co.uk — MRCS Eng. LRCP Lond. 1956; MEd Wales 1977; FRCGP 1973, M 1966; MFOM RCP Lond. 1983, AFOM 1980; DIH Soc. Apoth. Lond. 1960, DMJ (Clin.) 1965. p/t Clin. Adviser, Bro Taf Primary Care Audit Gp. Cardiff. Prev: Postgrad. Sub-Dean (Gen. Pract.) Univ. Wales Coll. Med.

LLEWELLYN, Hilary Old Parsonage Surgery, Balcombes Hill, Goudhurst, Cranbrook TN17 1AN Tel: 01580 211241 Fax: 01580 211659; Frith Farm House, Bedgebury Forest, Hawkhurst, Cranbrook TN18 5AL Tel: 01580 754153 — MB BCh 1977 Wales.

LLEWELLYN, Huw David Frederick Place Surgery, 11 Frederick Place, Weymouth DT4 8HQ Tel: 01305 774411 Fax: 01305 760417 — MB BS 1982 Lond.; MRCGP 1986; DRCOG 1985. (St. Mary's)

LLEWELLYN, Imogen Elizabeth Corner House, Alhampton, Shepton Mallet BA4 6PY — MB BCh 1994 Wales.

LLEWELLYN, Isabella Victoria 3 Woodside, Longreach, West Horsley, Leatherhead KT24 6NA — MB BS 1985 Lond.

LLEWELLYN, John Owain 9 Troed-Y-Rhiw, Rhiwbina Hill, Cardiff CF14 6UR — MB ChB 1981 Bristol. (Bristol University) Regional Med. Off. FCO New Delhi India.

LLEWELLYN, Lise Jayne 2 Huttles Green, Shepreth, Royston SG8 6PR — MB BCh 1986 Wales; MSc Wales 1993, MB BCh 1986; MRCGP 1990; DRCOG 1990.

LLEWELLYN, Martin Brett Weaverham Surgery, Northwich Road, Weaverham, Northwich CW8 3EU Tel: 01606 853106 Fax: 01606 854980 — MB ChB 1975 Manch.; BSc Manch. 1972; DRCOG 1983. Socs: Brit. Soc. Rheum. Prev: Tutor (Rheum. & Med.) Univ. Manch.; SHO (Med.) Wythenshawe Hosp. Manch. & Leighton Hosp. Crewe; Ho. Off. (Med.) Manch. Roy. Infirm.

LLEWELLYN, Michael Howard New Mount Surgery, Margam Road, Port Talbot SA13 2BN Tel: 01639 884111; Cartref, Saint David's Park, Port Talbot SA13 2PA — MB BCh 1981 Wales; DRCOG 1983.

LLEWELLYN, Michael James Bayer plc, Stoke Poges, Slough SL2 4LY Tel: 01635 566764; 1 Simmons Place, Staines TW18 3HW — MB ChB 1979 Liverp.; MRCP (UK) 1982. EU Cardiovasc. Head, Bayer PLC. Prev: Head of Cardiovasc. Area Bayer plc; Regist. (Cardiol.) BRd.green Hosp. Liverp. & Wythenshawe Hosp. Manch.

LLEWELLYN, Rhian 11 Talyfan Close, Cowbridge CF71 7HT Tel: 0144 634895 — MB BCh 1978 Wales.

LLEWELLYN, Rhiannon St Andrews Surgery, 1 De Winton St., Rhondda, Tonypandy CF40 2QZ Tel: 01443 432243 Fax: 01443 442508; Bronllys, Vicarage Road, Penygraig, Rhondda, Tonypandy CF40 1HR Tel: 01443 432542 — MB BCh Wales 1966; MFFP 1993. (Welsh Nat.)

LLEWELLYN, Richard Edward 26 Ridgebourne Road, Shrewsbury SY3 9AB — MB ChB 1997 Birm.

LLEWELLYN, Mr Thomas David Cheltenham General Hospital, Sandford Road, Cheltenham GL53 7AN Tel: 01242 222222 — MB BCh 1983 Wales; FFAEM 1996; FRCS Ed. 1990. (WNSM) Ons. A & E Cheltenham Gen. Hosp. Prev: Sen. Regist. (A & E) City Hosp. Birm.; Regist. (A & E) Edin. Roy. Infirm.

LLEWELLYN-JONES, Sian Annette 24 Sketty Park Road, Sketty, Swansea SA2 9AS — MB BS 1992 Lond.

LLEWELLYN-MORGAN, Constance Ada Mary (retired) 1 Parc Howard Avenue, Llanelli SA15 3LQ Tel: 01554 772794 — MB BCh Wales 1947; BSc Wales 1944. JP.; Clin. Med. Off. (Community) Dyfed AHA. Prev: Clin. Med. Off. (Community) Dyfed AHA.

LLEWELLYN SMITH, Margaret Larch Corner, Ballinger Road, South Heath, Great Missenden HP16 9QJ — MB BS 1981 Lond.

LLEWELLYN SMITH, Stephen Hubert Orchardside, 237 Tubbenden Lane, Orpington BR6 9NN Tel: 01689 859136 — BM BCh 1938 Oxf.; FRCP Lond. 1965, M 1946. (Oxf. & Guy's) Hon. Cons. Phys. Lewisham & S.wark Health Dist. Prev: Chief Asst. to Phys. Moorfields Eye Hosp. (High Holborn Br.); Ho. Phys. & Med. Regist. Guy's Hosp.; Specialist Med. & Neurol. RAMC 1942-5.

LLEWELYN, Alison Audrey Department of Neurology, University Hospital of Wales, Heath Park, Cardiff CF14 4XN Tel: 029 2074 7747 Email: a.a.@cardiff.ac.uk — MB BCh 1990 Wales; PhD Wales 1985; BSc Soton. 1981. Clin. Research Fell., Dept. of Neurol., Univ. Hosp. of Wales; Clin. Asst. Dept. of Infec. Dis.Univ. Hosp. of Wales. Prev: SHO (Dermat.) Univ. Hosp. Wales Cardiff; SHO (ENT) Bedford Gen. Hosp.; Ho. Off. (Neurol. & Neurosurg.) Univ. Hosp. Wales Cardiff.

LLEWELYN, Andrew Humphrey The Lyme Practice, Pound Road, Lyme Regis DT7 3HX Tel: 012974 5777; Church Acre, Rhode Lane, Uplyme, Lyme Regis DT7 3TX — MB BS 1980 Lond.; BSc, MB BS Lond. 1980.

LLEWELYN, Ann Doreen Gurry Farm, Nantrhibo, Llandeilo SA19 6AJ — MB BCh 1984 Wales.

LLEWELYN, David Evan Huw 73 Court Lane, Dulwich, London SE21 7EF Tel: 020 8693 5334 — MB BCh 1970 Wales; MD Lond. 1988; MRCP (UK) 1972; FRCP Lond. 1992. (Welsh Nat. Sch. Med.) Sen. Lect. Med. & Hon. Cons. Phys. King's Coll. Hosp. Med. Sch. Lond. Socs: Med. Res. Soc. & Soc. Endocrinol. Prev: Ho. Phys. Bridgend Gen. Hosp.; Regist. (Gen. Med. & Endocrinol.) Univ. Hosp. Wales; Lect. Med. & Hon. Sen. Regist. St. Bart. Hosp. Med. Sch. Lond.

LLEWELYN, Janet Margaret Cheshire Community Health Care Trust, Wharton Primary Healthcare Centre, Crook Lane, Wharton, Winsford CW7 3GY Tel: 01606 542536 Fax: 01606 590807; Sandy Mount, 3 Hard Lane, Dentons Green, St Helens WA10 6JP Tel: 01744 601434 Email: janet_ellison@hotmail.com — MB ChB Liverp. 1980. p/t Cons. Community Paediat. Chesh. Community Healthcare Trust. Socs: MRCPCH. Prev: Sen. Clin med. Off. (child health) St. Helen's & Knowsley H A.

LLEWELYN, Joan Veronica (retired) The Mill House, Stour Provost, Gillingham SP8 5DF Tel: 01747 838681 — MB BS 1945 Lond.; MRCS Eng. LRCP Lond. 1945; DCH Eng. 1951. Prev: Med. Off. Kenya Girls' High Sch. Nairobi.

LLEWELYN, John Old Society House, Church St., Waltham Abbey EN9 1DX Tel: 01992 719000 Fax: 01992 788457 — MB ChB 1951 Birm.; MRCS Eng. LRCP Lond. 1951; MRCGP 1966; AFOM RCP Lond. 1979. (Birm.) Med. Adviser Pan Britannica Indust. Waltham Cross; Med. Off. P.E.R.M.E. (MoD). Socs: Assn. Police Surgs.

LLEWELYN, Mr John Department of Maxillofacial & Oral Surgery, Royal Gwent Hospital, Newport NP20 2UB Tel: 01633 238169 Fax: 01633 238373; Beech Lodge, Sophia Walk, Catherdral Road, Cardiff CF11 9LE Tel: 02920 664621 Email: john.llewelyn@tesco.net — MB BS 1986 Lond.; BDS Wales 1975; FRCS Ed. 1990; FDS RCS Eng. 1980. (Roy. Free Hosp. Sch. Med.) Cons. Oral & Maxillofacial Surg. Roy. Gwent Hosp. Newport. Socs: (Ex-Pres.) Univ. Wales Dent. Alumi Assn.; BMA. Prev: Sen. Regist. (Maxillofacial Surg.) City Hosp. Edin.; Regist. (Oral & Maxillofacial Surg.) Univ. Hosp. Wales Cardiff; Regist. (Oral & Maxillofacial Surg.) Welsh Regional Centre for Plastic Burns & Maxillofacial Surg.

LLEWELYN, John Gareth Department of Neurology, Royal Gwent Hospital, Cardiff Road, Newport CF14 4WZ Tel: 01633 234453; 50 South Rise, Llanishen, Cardiff CF14 0RH Tel: 029 2074 7669 Fax: 0290 754100 — MB ChB 1980 Wales; BSc (Hons.) Wales 1977, MD 1991; FRCP (UK) 1997; MRCP (UK) 1983. Cons. Neurol. Univ. Hosp. of Wales Cardiff, Roy. Gwent Hosp. Newport, Nat. Hosp. Neurol. & Neurosurg. Lond. Prev: Cons. Neurol. Roy. Free Hosp. & Nat. Hosp. for Neurol. & Neurosurg. Lond.

LLEWELYN, Martin John 39 Gloucester Mews, Bayswater, London W2 3HE — MB BS 1992 Lond.; BSc (1st cl. Hons.) Phys. Lond. 1989; MRCP (UK) 1995. (Roy. Lond. Hosp.) Regist. (Respirat. & Infec. Dis. Med.) N.wick Pk. Hosp. Harrow.

LLEWELYN, Meirion Bowen Department of Infectious Diseases, University Hospital of Wales, Heath Park, Cardiff CF14 4XN — MB BCh 1985 Wales; PhD Wales 1982, BSc 1979; MRCP (UK) 1988. Cons. Infect. Dis. Roy. Gwent Hosp. Newport, Gwent; Hon. Sen. Lect. Infect. Dis. Univ. Hosp. Wales, Cardiff. Prev: Sen. Regist. (Infect. Dis.) Univ. Hosp. Wales, Cardiff; MRC Fell. Laborat. Molecular Biol. Camb.; Regist. (Infec. Dis.) Addenbrooke's Hosp. Camb.

LLEWELYN, Nia Llynyfran Surgery, Llynyfran Road, Llandysul SA44 4JX Tel: 01559 363306 Fax: 01559 362896; Penlon Goitre, Drefach Felindre, Llandysul SA44 5YD Tel: 01559 370937 — MB BCh 1979 Wales; DA Eng. 1984; DRCOG 1981; Dip. Therap. 1998. (University Hospital Wales Cardiff)

LLEWELYN, Rachel Isolde Hereford County Hospital, Union Walk, Hereford HR1 2ER; 17 White Horse Street, Whitecross, Hereford HR4 0EP — MB ChB 1996 Birm.; ChB Birm. 1996.

LLEWELYN, Mr Robert William Department of Obstetrics & Gynaecology, Singleton Hospital, Swansea SA2 8QA Tel: 01792 205666 Fax: 01792 285874; Gerdinen, Cilibion, Gower, Swansea SA3 1ED Tel: 01792 390504 Email: rob.llewelyn@virgin.net — MB ChB 1987 Birm.; BSc (Hons.) Birm. 1984; MRCOG 1994. Cons. O & G Singleton Hosp. Swansea. Socs: Blair Bell Res. Soc.; Internat. Continence Soc.; Mem. Brit. Soc. Matern. & Fetal Med. Prev: Sen. Regist. Rotat. (O & G) Univ. Wales; Regist. Rotat. (O & G) Merseyside.

LLOPIS MIRO, Rafael UTS Oxford Centre, Wolsey Hall, 66 Banbury Road, Oxford OX2 6PR — LMS 1984 Alicante.

LLOYD, Adrian John 131 Kenton Lane, Newcastle upon Tyne NE3 3QB Tel: 0191 284 3409 Email: ajjalloyd1@compuserve.com — MB BS 1991 Newc.; MRCPsych 1996. Regist. (Learning Disabil. & Child & Adolesc. Psychiat.) Prudhoe Hosp. N.d. & Qu. Eliz. Hosp. Gateshead; Research Assoc. & Hon. Specialist Regist. Psychiat. Newc. Socs: BMA; Med. Protec. Soc.; Fell. Roy. Soc. Med. Prev: Specialist Regist. (Gen. Adult Psychiat.) St Nicholas Hosp. Newc.; Regist. (Old Age Psychiat.) N. Tees Hosp.; Regist. (Adult Psychiat.) St. Geo. Hosp. Morpeth.

LLOYD, Adrian Phillip The Mumbles Medical Practice, 10 West Cross Avenue, Norton, Mumbles, Swansea SA3 5UA Tel: 01792 403010 Fax: 01792 401934 — MB BCh 1977 Wales; MA Camb. 1978.

LLOYD, Alan Thomas Sandy Mount, Slon Lane, Ogmore-by-Sea, Bridgend CF32 0PN Tel: 01656 880533 — MB ChB 1956 Bristol; MRCP Ed. 1964; MRCPsych 1971; DPM Eng. 1960. Cons. Psychiat. Glanrhyd Hosp. Bridgend & Dist. NHS Trust. Prev: Sen. Regist. (Psychiat.) United Leeds Hosps. & Univ. Leeds; Sen. Regist. (Psychiat.) Addenbrooke's Hosp. Camb.

LLOYD, Alison Margaret Sheen Lane Health Centre, 70 Sheen Lane, London SW14 8LP Tel: 020 8876 3901 Fax: 020 8878 9620 — MB BS 1983 Lond.; MRCGP 1990.

LLOYD, Allan Henry Occupational Health, Norfolk & Norwich Hospital, Norwich NR1 3SR Tel: 01603 286286 Fax: 01603 287884 — MB ChB Bristol 1965; 2001 Cert. Of Acquired Rights. RCGP; PhD (Commend.) St. And. 1970, BSc (Hons.) 1968; CBiol 1991; MIBiol 1971; D.Bio.Sci UEA Norwich 1990. (Bristol) GP & Hosp. Pract. (Gen. Med. & Surg.) Drug Trial Investigator & Med. Scientist Norf.; Communicable Dist. Control Doctor Norf. & Norwich Trust Hosp.; Occupat. Health Doctor, Laser Clinician Plastic Surg.; Med. Off. Norf. Fire Brig. H/Q Norwich. Socs: Norf. Med. Soc.; Molecular Biol. Soc.; Norf. & Norwich Univ. Hosp. Trust weekly P/G Meetings. Prev: GP Gt. Yarmouth; Study Dir. Safety of Med. ICI Pharmaceut. Alderley Pk.; Med. Adviser Ciba-Geigy UK Ltd. Macclesfield.

LLOYD, Alwyn Ruth Noelle The Ongar Health Centre, Great Bansons, Bansons Lane, Ongar CM5 9AR; 9 Warwick Place, Pilgrims Hatch, Brentwood CM14 5QB — MB ChB 1979 Liverp.; DRCOG 1981; DFFP 1995.

LLOYD, Ambrose Goring Pyllaucrynion, Cwm Ann, Lampeter SA48 8EX — MRCS Eng. LRCP Lond. 1956.

LLOYD, Andrew 20 South Road, Sully, Penarth CF64 5TG — MB BCh 1978 Wales.

LLOYD, Andrew James The Brambles, Broad Layings, Woolton Hill, Newbury RG20 9TT — MB BS 1994 Lond.

LLOYD, Andrew Leonard 26 Meadow Close, Pengam, Blackwood NP12 3RB — MB ChB 1993 Manch.

LLOYD, Anthony Mills Woodlands, Maindy Croft, Ton-Pentre, Pentre CF41 7ET Tel: 01443 435846 — MB ChB 1963 Bristol. (Bristol) Socs: BMA.

LLOYD, Antony David (retired) Hill Cottage, Stoneleigh Road, Bubbenhall, Coventry CV8 3BT Tel: 024 76 302836 — MB BChir 1964 Camb.; MA Camb. 1964; MRCS Eng. LRCP Lond. 1963; FRCR 1975; FFR 1973; DMRD Eng. 1969. Prev: Sen. Regist. (Radiol.) & SHO (Neurol. & Neurosurg.) Addenbrooke's Hosp. Camb.

LLOYD, Arthur Llewellyn, OBE, KStJ 95 Grange Road, Small Heath, Birmingham B10 9QT Tel: 0121 772 0084 Fax: 0121 772 0084 — MB ChB 1951 Birm.; MRCS Eng. LRCP Lond. 1951. (Birm.) JP.; Local Treasury Med. Off. Socs: Fell. BMA; Vice-Pres. Birm. Med.

Inst.; Chap. Gen. Order of St. John. Prev: Mem. Birm. Regional Hosp. Bd.; Chairm. Birm. Family Pract. Comm.; Cdr. St. John Ambul. W. Midl.

LLOYD, Arthur Rees (Surgery) 842 Newport Road, Rumney, Cardiff CF3 4LH Tel: 029 2079 7751; 37 Llyswen Road, Cyncoed, Cardiff CF23 6NH Tel: 02920 752578 — MB BCh 1958 Wales. (Cardiff) GP Cardiff. Prev: Obst. Ho. Surg. & Ho. Surg. & Ho. Phys. Cardiff Roy. Infirm.; Capt. RAMC.

LLOYD, Barbara Elizabeth Mansell 95 Grange Road, Small Heath, Birmingham B10 9QT Tel: 0121 772 0084 Fax: 0121 772 0084 — MB ChB Birm. 1948. (Birm.)

LLOYD, Benjamin William Royal Free Hospital, Hampstead NHS Trust, London NW3 2QG Tel: 0207 830 2440 Fax: 0207 830 2003 Email: blloyd@rjc.ucl.ac.uk; 6 Woodland Rise, London N10 3UG Tel: 0208 372 1512 Fax: 0208 372 1513 — MB BChir 1974 Camb.; MRCP (UK) 1976; T(M) 1991; MD 1987. Cons. Paediat. Roy. Free Hosp NHS Trust.

LLOYD, Bernita Ann (retired) c/o 7 Kenward Court, Hadlow, Tonbridge TN11 0DX — MB ChB 1982 Bristol; MRCGP 1987; DCCH RCP Ed. 1992. Prev: Clin. Med. Off. Preston HA.

LLOYD, Brendan Walsh Sway Road Surgery, 65 Sway Road, Morriston, Swansea SA6 6JA Tel: 01792 773150 / 771392 Fax: 01792 790880 — MB BCh 1983 Wales.

LLOYD, Carys Rowena Sunnyside, Station Road, Whittington, Oswestry SY11 4BQ Email: lloyd@carys.freeserve.co.uk — MB ChB 1996 Birm.; ChB Birm. 1996; MRCPCH. 1999. (Birmingham) Pediatric SHO, Chelsea & Wstminster.

LLOYD, Catherine The Henry Moore Clinic, 26 Shawthorne Lane, Castleford WF10 4EN; 10 Maypole Mews, Barwick-in-Elmet, Leeds LS15 4PE Tel: 0113 281 1161 — MB BS 1990 Lond.; BSc (Clin. Sci.) Lond. 1989; DRCOG 1994. Prev: Trainee GP/SHO Ealing VTS.; SHO (Genitourin. Med.) Char. Cross Hosp. Lond.; Ho. Off. (Med. & Surg.) Ealing Hosp.

LLOYD, Catherine Margaret Department of Neurology, King's Healthcare NHS Trust, Kings College Hospital, Denmark Hill, London SE5 9RS Tel: 020 7737 4000; 96B Elmbourne Road, Tooting, London SW17 8JH — MB BS 1984 Lond.; MRCP (UK) 1989; MD Lond. 1996. Specialist Regist. Neurol. King's Coll. Hosp. Lond. Prev: Specialist Regist. Neurol. Guy's Hosp. Lond.; Lect. Mulago Hosp. Makerere Univ. Kampal, Uganda; Research Regist. Inst. Psychiat.

LLOYD, Ceri Nigel 2 Holbein Way, Gunton, Lowestoft NR32 4NN — MB BS 1980 Lond.; DRCOG 1983.

LLOYD, Charles Geoffrey The Old School, Shirley, Ashbourne, Derby DE6 3AS Tel: 01335 360466 — MB ChB 1952 Birm.; FFA RCS Eng. 1961; DA Eng. 1956. (Birm.) Emerit. Cons. Anaesth. Derby. Prev: Regist. (Anaesth.) Sefton Gen. Hosp. Liverp.; Regist. (Anaesth.) Alder Hey Childr. Hosp. Liverp.; Sen. Regist. (Anaesth.) United Liverp. Hosps.

LLOYD, Charles John Faulkner Roborough Surgery, 1 Eastcote Close, Plymouth PL6 6PH — MB BS 1986 Lond.; MRCGP 1993.

LLOYD, Christine Elizabeth Northgate Medical Centre, Anchor Meadow Health Centre, Aldridge, Walsall WS9 8AJ Tel: 01922 450900 Fax: 01922 450910; 8 Grosvenor Avenue, Streetly, Sutton Coldfield B74 3PB — BMedSci Nottm. 1984, BM BS 1986; DRCOG 1992; DCH RCP Lond. 1990; MRCGP 1994. Prev: Trainee GP Sutton Coldfield; SHO (O & G) Marston Green Hosp. Birm.; SHO (Community Paediat.) Cottage Hosp. Sutton Coldfield.

LLOYD, Christine Penelope St Andrews Hospital, Billing Road, Northampton NN1 5DG Tel: 01604 616303/616000 Fax: 01604 616306; Sweetacres, The Knoll, Grendon, Northampton NN7 1JG Tel: 01933 663207 Fax: 01933 663207 — MB ChB Sheff. 1967; MRCPsych 1980. (Sheff.) p/t Cons. Psychiat. St. And. Hosp. N.ampton. Prev: Assoc. Specialist (Psychiat.) St. Crispins Hosp. N.ampton; Research Asst. Univ. Sheff.; Ho. Phys. (Gen. Med. & Dermat., Ho. Surg. & Paediat. Surg.) Stoke Mandeville Hosp. Aylesbury.

LLOYD, Christopher 8 Telford Road, Wellington, Telford TF1 2EL Tel: 01952 255563 — MB BS 1997 Lond. (St Georges)

LLOYD, Christopher Cooke 41 Yarmouth Road, Great Sankey, Warrington WA5 3EJ — MB ChB 1997 Liverp.

LLOYD, Christopher Edward Faulkner 48 Thorn Park, Mannamead, Plymouth PL3 4TF — MB BChir 1989 Camb.; MRCGP 1994. Trainee GP Plymouth VTS.

LLOYD, Christopher Robert Westrop Surgery, Newburgh Place, Highworth, Swindon SN6 7DN Tel: 01793 762218 Fax: 01793 766073 — MB BS 1985 Lond.; DRCOG 1990; DGM RCP Lond. 1990; DCH RCP Lond. 1989.

LLOYD, Claire Pepita Princess Street Group Practice, 2 Princess Street, London SE1 6JP Tel: 020 7928 0253 Fax: 020 7261 9804; 29 Champion Grove, London SE5 8BN Tel: 020 7733 0958 — MB BS 1985 Lond.; DGM RCP Lond. 1988; DRCOG 1989; MRCGP 1998.

LLOYD, Clinton Thomas 2A Crabtree Road, Haddenham, Aylesbury HP17 8AT — MB ChB 1990 Cape Town.

LLOYD, David 257 Badger Avenue, Crewe CW1 3LN — BM BS 1989 Nottm.

LLOYD, Professor David Allden Institute of Child Health, Royal Liverpool Childrens Hospital Alder Hey, Eaton Road, Liverpool L12 2AP Tel: 0151 228 4811; 15 Eshe Road N., Liverpool L23 8UE — MChir Camb. 1979, MB BChir 1965; FRCS Eng. 1975; FRCSC 1986; FACS 1988; FCS(SA) 1971. Prof. Paediat. Surg. Univ. Liverp.; Hon. Cons. Paediat. Surg. Roy. Liverp. Childr. Hosp. Alder Hey. Prev: Assoc. Prof. Surg. Univ. Pittsburgh.

LLOYD, David Ayodeji Justin Flat 3, 45 Rectory Road, Oxford OX4 1BU — BM BCh 1998 Oxf.; BM BCh Oxf 1998.

LLOYD, David Beswick (retired) Linden Lea, 19 Manor Park, Bath BA1 3RJ Tel: 01225 422259 — MB BS 1956 Lond.; DObst RCOG 1961. Prev: GP Bath.

LLOYD, David Charles Findlay Department of Radiology, University Hospital of Wales, Heath Park, Cardiff CR4 4XW Tel: 029 2074 7747 Email: dcflloyd@aol.com; 11 Millbrook Road, Dinas Powys CF64 4BZ Tel: 029 2051 2281 — MB BS 1984 Lond.; MRCP (UK) 1987; FRCR 1990. Cons. Diag. Radiol. Univ. Hosp. of Wales HC Trust. Prev: Sen. Regist. (Diag. Radiol.) S. Glam. HA; Lect. (Diag. Radiol.) S. Glam. HA; Regist. (Radiol.) Centr. Manch. HA.

LLOYD, David Huw Owen Cadwgan Surgery, 11 Bodelwyddan Avenue, Old Colwyn, Colwyn Bay LL29 9NP Tel: 01492 515410 Fax: 01492 513270; Maes Yr Onnen, Abergele Road, Llanddulas, Abergele LL22 8EN Tel: 01492 516909 Email: huw.lloyd@dial.pipex.com — MB BChir 1974 Camb.; MB BChir Camb. 1975; MA Camb. 1975; FRCGP 1991, M 1979; DRCOG 1978. (Guy's) Clin. Governance Lead. Conwy LHG; Chairm. RCGP Ment. Healthtask Gp.; Chairm. Jt. Comm. on Palliat. Med. RCP/RCGP. Socs: BMA; Fell. RCGP; Roy. Coll. Gen. Pract. (Chairm. Jt. Welsh GMSC & Welsh Counc.). Prev: Trainee GP Taunton VTS; Ho. Surg. (Orthop.) Guy's Hosp. Lond.; Ho. Phys. Beckenham Hosp. Kent.

LLOYD, David John 128 Desswood Place, Aberdeen AB15 4DQ Tel: 01224 646556 — MB BS 1969 Lond.; FRCPCH 1997; FRCP Ed. 1989; FRCP Lond. 1986; MRCP (UK) 1973. (St. Geo.) Cons. (Perinatal Med.) Aberd. Matern. Hosp. Prev: Sen. Lect. (Child Health) Univ. Aberd. & Hon. Cons. (Paediat.) Aberd. Matern. Hosp. & Roy. Aberd. Childr. Hosp.; Research Fell. (Neonatol.) Dalhousie Univ. Halifax, Canada; Lect. (Child Health) Univ. Aberd. & Hon. Sen. Regist. Roy. Aberd. Childr. Hosp.

LLOYD, David John The Ridgeway Surgery, 71 Imperial Drive, North Harrow, Harrow HA2 7DU Tel: 020 8427 2470; 31 Castlebar Park, Ealing, London W5 1DA Tel: 020 8997 4149 — MB ChB 1977 Bristol; FRCGP 1994, M 1982. GP Tutor N.wick Pk. Hosp.; Chairm. Harrow Harment CP Co-op. Socs: Med. Pract. Union.

LLOYD, David Rees University Health Centre, Fulton House, Singleton Park, Swansea SA2 8PR Tel: 01792 295321 — MB BCh 1980 Wales; MRCGP 1989; Dip. Ther. Wales 1995.

LLOYD, David Robert Esgairgarn, 13 Camborne Drive, Huddersfield HD2 2NF Tel: 01484 452218 — MB BS 1973 Lond.; MB BS (Hons. Med.) Lond. 1973; MRCP (UK) 1976; MRCS Eng. LRCP Lond. 1973; FFA RCS Eng. 1980. (Westm.) Dir. of Anaesth. Huddersfield Roy. Infirm. Prev: Cons. Anaesth. & Dir. of ICU Dewsbury Dist. Hosp.; Cons. Anaesth. Hull; Sen. Regist. (Anaesth.) Soton & Portsmouth Hosps.

LLOYD, Deborah 31 Castlebar Park, Ealing, London W5 1DA Tel: 020 8997 4149 Email: ddlloyd@demon.co.uk — MB ChB 1979 Bristol; MRCGP 1986; DRCOG 1982. Prev: GP Lond.

LLOYD, Deborah Jane 7 Littledown Road, Cheltenham GL53 9LW — MB BS 1998 Lond.; MB BS Lond 1998.

LLOYD, Dinah Kathleen 15 Chiltern Hills Road, Beaconsfield HP9 1PL — MB ChB 1972 Birm.; MRCP (UK) 1979; Dip. Pharm. Med. RCP (UK) 1986.

LLOYD, Edwina Ann Robert Jones and Agnes Hunt Orthopaedic Hospital, Oswestry SY10 7AG Tel: 01691 404000; 12 LLwyn-y-Garth, Llanfyllin SY22 5JZ — MB ChB 1977 Leeds; FFA RCS Eng. 1983; DA Eng. 1980. Cons. Anaesth. Robt. Jones & Agnes Hunt Orthop. Hosp. OsW.ry. Prev: Sen. Regist. (Anaesth.) N. Staffs. Hosps.; Regist. (Anaesth.) N. Staffs. Hosps.; Staff Grade (Anaesth.) P.ss Roy. Hosp. Telford.

LLOYD, Elizabeth Anne 5 Lindale Road, Liverpool L7 0JS — MB ChB 1998 Liverp.; MB ChB Liverp 1998.

LLOYD, Eluned 37 Llyswen Road, Cyncoed, Cardiff CF23 6NH Tel: 029 2075 2578 — MB BCh 1959 Wales. (Cardiff) Sessional Clin. Med. Off. M. Glam. HA. Socs: Fac. Fam. Plann. & Reproduc. Health Care.

LLOYD, Evan Llewelyn Dept of Anaestheticl, Western Gen Hospital, Crewe Road, Edinburgh EH4 2XU Tel: 0131537 1652 Fax: 0131 537 1025; 72 Belagrave Road, Edinburgh EH12 6NQ Tel: 0131 334 5690 — MB ChB 1961 Ed.; FRCP Ed. 1982, M 1966; FFA RCS Eng. 1968. (Edinburgh) Cons. Anaesth. W.. Gen. Hosp. NHS Trust; Med. adviser Scott.disab sport Edin; Med. Adviser Scott hockey assoc. Edin. Socs: (Chairm.) Brit. Assn. Sport & Med.; Hon Press Off. Lothian div.; Mem. Scott Counc. Prev: Regist. (Geriat. & Gen. Med.) Roy. Infirm. Glas.; Staff Anaesth. & Clin. Teach. Toronto Univ. & Gen. Hosp., Canada; Med. Off. Bamdah Mission Hosp. India.

LLOYD, Fiona Elizabeth 8 Burns Road, Sheffield S6 3GJ — MB ChB 1997 Sheff.

LLOYD, Fiona Helene 9 Plewlands Terrace, Edinburgh EH10 5JX — MB ChB 1987 Ed.; MRCOG 1993. Regist. (O & G) Simpson Memor. Matern. Hosp. Edin.

LLOYD, Gareth (retired) 2 Saxfield Drive, Baguley Hall, Manchester M23 1PY Tel: 0161 998 4155 Fax: 0161 945 0565 Email: garethllloyd@compuserve.com — MB ChB 1954 Liverp.; BSc (Hons. Physiol.) Liverp. 1951, MD 1973; FRCGP 1973, M 1968; MRCOG 1961. Prev: Med. Adviser Bury, Lancs. & Salford FPC.

LLOYD, Gareth Aldwyn 13 Hollybush Grove, Porth CF39 9UG — MB BCh 1995 Wales.

LLOYD, Gaynor Lynn core Rehabilitation Team Rose Cottage, 150 Canterbury Road, Westbrook, Margate CT9 5DD Tel: 01843 255430 Fax: 01843 255428; 4 Jubilee Cottages, King St, Fordwich, Canterbury CT2 0BZ Tel: 01227 711441 — MB BS 1973 Lond.; MRCS Eng. LRCP Lond. 1973. (Westm.) Assoc. Specialist (Neurorehabil.) Canterbury & Thanet Community Healthcare Trust; Clin. Dir. Vict. Hse. YDU & Strope Pk. Day Care Centre Canterbury. Socs: Affil. Mem. Soc. Research & Rehabil.; Brit. Soc. Rehabil. Med. Prev: Staff Grade (Geriat. Med.) Thanet Healthcare Trust; GP Brixton.

LLOYD, Geoffrey Gower 148 Harley Street, London W1N 1AH Tel: 020 7935 1207; 4 The Ridgeway, Mill Hill, London NW7 1RS Tel: 020 8346 5090 — MB Bchir 1966 Camb.; MPhil 1973 Lond.; MA 1966 Camb.; MD 1983; FRCP 1988 Lond.; FRCP 1981; MRCP 1969 UK; FRCPsych 1984. (Camb. & Westm.) Cons. Psychiat. Roy. Free Hosp. Lond.; Hon. Sen. Lect. Roy. Free & Univ Coll Med.Sch; Cons Psychiat., Priory Hosp, N. Lond. Socs: Fell. Roy. Soc. Med. (Ex-Pres. Sect. Psychiat.). Prev: Cons. Psychiat. Roy. Infirm. Edin.; Lect. Inst. Psychiat. & King's Coll. Hosp. Med. Sch. Lond.; Sen. Regist. Bethlem Roy. & Maudsley Hosps. Lond.

LLOYD, Geoffrey John 21 Devonshire Place, London W1G 6HZ Tel: 020 7935 8071 Fax: 020 7935 4913; 3 The Drive, Banstead SM7 1DF Tel: 01737 354708 Fax: 01737 210487 Email: medilloyd@pobox.com — MB BS Lond. 1970; BSc (Hons.) Lond. 1967; LLB (Hons.) Lond. 1994; FRCP Lond. 1984; MRCP (UK) 1973. Private Pract. Socs: Fell. Roy. Soc. Med. Prev: Cons. Phys. Awali Hosp. Bahrain; Sen. Lect. & Hon. Cons. Acad. Dept. Med. Roy. Free Hosp. Med. Sch. Lond.; Sen. Med. Off. Kuwait Oil Co. Kuwait.

LLOYD, George Holt (retired) St. Helier, 117 Ilsham Road, Torquay TQ1 2HY Tel: 01803 291847 — MRCS Eng. LRCP Lond. 1944; MRCGP 1961; DObst RCOG 1949. Prev: Flight Lt. RAFVR.

LLOYD, George Kenneth (retired) 26 High Street, Topsham, Exeter EX3 0ED — MB ChB 1934 Ed.

LLOYD, Geraint Elis Bryn Teg, 16 Ty-Gwyn Road, Penylan, Cardiff CF23 5JE — MB BS 1998 Lond.; MB BS Lond 1998.

LLOYD, Geraint Murdoch 100 St Davids Road, Otley LS21 2RQ — MB ChB 1998 Leic.; MB ChB Leic 1998.

LLOYD, Gilbert Leonard 11 Windmill Road, Minchinhampton, Stroud GL6 9DX — MB ChB 1974 Sheff.; MRCPsych 1980. Cons. Psychiat. Pk. Ho. Day Hosp. Stroud. Prev: Cons. Psychiat. Coney Hill Hosp. Gloucester.

LLOYD, Glyn Arthur Simpson (private rooms), 107 Harley St., London W1 Tel: 020 7487 4061; 11 Sheridan Place, London SW13 0LH Tel: 020 8876 6371 — BM BCh 1946 Oxf.; MA, DM Oxf. 1973; FRCOphth 1993; FRCR 1975; FFR 1956; DMRD Eng. 1951. Socs: Fell. Roy. Soc. Med. Prev: Dir. (Radiol.) Roy. Nat. Throat, Nose & Ear Hosp. Lond; Cons. Radiol. Moorfields Eye Hosp. Lond.; Cons. Radiol. Chelsea & Kensington Gp. Hosps.

LLOYD, Guy William Llewelyn 8 Balham New Road, London SW12 9PG — MB BS 1991 Lond.; MRCP UK 1995. Specialist Regist. Guy's & St Thos. Trust.

LLOYD, Mrs Helen 65 Blakedown Road, Halesowen B63 4NG Tel: 0121 501 3194 Fax: 0121 501 3194 Email: hlloyd@blueyonder.co.uk — MB BCh BAO 1958 NUI; MRCPsych 1972; DPM RCPSI 1963. (NUI) Indep. Pract. (Psychoanal. Psychother.) W. Midl.Inst. Of Psychother. Socs: BMA; Qu. Eliz. Postgrad. Med. Soc.; UKCP. Prev: Cons. Child & Adolesc. Psychiat. Dudley Priority Health.

LLOYD, Herbert Jeffrey 4 Sarazen Drive, Troon KA10 6JP Tel: 01292 315126 — MB 1958 Camb.; BChir 1957; FRCP Ed. 1978, M 1966; MRCP Lond. 1966; MRCP Glas. 1966; DIH Eng. 1978. (Lond. Hosp.) Sen. Med. Adviser Shell Internat. Petroleum. Prev: Chief Med. Off. Shell Nigeria; Chief Med. Off. PDO Oman; Specialist Phys. Brunei Shell Petroleum.

LLOYD, Hilary Department of Child Psychiatry, Royal Manchester Children's Hospital, Pendlebury, Manchester M27 4HA Tel: 0161 794 4696; 29 Weylands Grove, Salford M6 7WX — MB ChB 1978 Manch.; MRCPsych 1982. Cons. (Child & Adolesc. Psychiat.) Roy. Manch. Childr. Hosp. Prev: Tutor (Child & Adolesc. Psychiat.) Univ. Manch.; Cons. Child & Adolesc. Psychiat. S. Manch. HA.

LLOYD, Hilary Anketell (Surgery), Roath Hse, 100 Penylan Road, Cardiff CF23 5RH Tel: 02920461100; 24 Hollybush Road, Cyncoed, Cardiff CF23 6TA — MB BCh 1955 Wales; DObst RCOG 1957. MO Univ. Wales Coll. Cardiff; MO Howell's Sch.

LLOYD, Hilda Mary (retired) Winster, 39 Wealstone Lane, Upton, Chester CH2 1HD Tel: 01244 380338 — MRCS Eng. LRCP Lond. 1940. Prev: Clin. Med. Off. Chesh. AHA.

LLOYD, Howell John 2 St Edeyrns Close, Cyncoed, Cardiff CF23 6TH Tel: 029 2075 3367 — MB BS 1965 Lond.; FRCP Lond. 1982, M 1969. (St. Geo.) Cons. Phys. Roy. Gwent Hosp. Newport. Socs: BMA; BDA. Prev: Sen. Regist. (Med.) Univ. Hosp. Wales Cardiff; Ho. Surg. & Ho. Phys. St. Geo. Hosp. Lond.; Ho. Phys. Brompton Hosp. Lond.

LLOYD, Hywel Spencer Penpadarn, Cefnllan, Llanbadarn, Aberystwyth SY23 3AP — MB ChB 1989 Liverp.

LLOYD, Mr Ian Christopher The Royal Eye Hosp, Oxford Road, Manchester M13 9WH Email: chrislloyd@wilmslow1.demon.co.uk; 10 Greenway, Wilmslow SK9 1LU — MB BS 1985 Lond.; FRCS Eng. 1989; FCOphth 1990; DO RCS Eng. 1988. (St. Bart.) Cons. Paediat. Ophth. Manch. Roy. Eye Hosp. Socs: BMA; Manch. Med. Soc.; N. Eng. Ophth. Soc. Prev: Clin. Research Fell. (Ophth.) Hosp. Sick Childr. Gt. Ormond St. Lond.; Clin. Lect. & Regist. (Ophth.) Manch. Roy. Eye Hosp.; Ho. Off. (Surg.) St. Bart. Hosp. Lond.

LLOYD, Ian Guy (retired) Bishopgate Medical Centre, 178 Newgate St., Bishop Auckland DL14 7EJ Tel: 01388 603983 Fax: 01388 607782 — MB BS 1959 Durh. Prev: GP Trainer Durh.

LLOYD, Ieuan Winsey Brynderwen Surgery, Crickhowell Road, St. Mellons, Cardiff CF3 0EF Tel: 029 2079 9921 Fax: 029 2077 7740; Cornhill, 99 Cyncoed Road, Cardiff CF23 6AE — MB BS 1977 Lond.; BSc Lond. 1974, MB BS Lond. 1977; DRCOG 1982. (St. Mary's)

LLOYD, James Alexander White House Farm, Knapton, North Walsham NR28 0RX; Residence 9, Southampton General Hospital, Southampton SO16 6YD Tel: 01723 777222 — MB BS 1996 Lond.; BSc Lond. 1993; DTM & H Liverp. 1997. (Roy. Free Hosp. Lond.) SHO (Gen. Med.) Soton. Gen. Hosp. Soton. Prev: SHO (Cardiol.) Lond. Chest Hosp. Lond.; Ho. Off. (Surg.) Derriford Hosp. Plymouth; Ho. Off. (Med.) King Geo. Hosp. Ilford.

LLOYD, Janet Leighton Hospital, Middlewich Road, Crewe CW1 4QJ — MB BS 1984 Lond.; FRCP 2001 Lond.; MD Lond. 1996; MRCP (UK) 1989; DA (UK) 1987. (Char. Cross) Cons. Phys.Leighton.hosp.Crewe. Prev: Sen. Regist. (Endocrinol.) Christie Hosp. Manch.; Research Regist. Roy. United Hosp. Bath; Sen. Regist. (Diabetes & Endocrinol.) Hope Hosp. Salford.

LLOYD, Janette Patricia The Surgery, 1 Rowner Road, Gosport PO13 9UA Tel: 023 9258 0093 Fax: 023 92 504060; 1 Vicarage Lane, Stubbington, Fareham PO14 2JU — BM 1985 Soton.; BSc (Biochem. & Physiol.) Lond. 1976. Socs: BMA; Roy. Soc. Med. Prev: Trainee GP Cheltenham & Banbury VTS; SHO (Paediat.) Cheltenham.

LLOYD, Jennifer Flat 111, Butlers Wharf, 36 Shad Thames, London SE1 2YE — MB BS 1961 Lond.; MFPHM RCP (UK) 1987. (Lond. Hosp.) Prev: Sen. Med. Off. DoH; Sen. Med. Off. & Med. Off. Welsh Office.

LLOYD, John Benjamin (retired) 7 Ffordd Pantyrhos, Waunfawr, Aberystwyth SY23 3QE Tel: 01970 624142 — MB BS 1958 Lond.; DObst RCOG 1959.

LLOYD, John Crewdson (retired) Candleford, 57 Chipstead Lane, Riverhead, Sevenoaks TN13 2AJ Tel: 01732 452725 — MB BChir 1943 Camb.; BA Camb. 1939; MRCS Eng. LRCP Lond. 1942; MRCGP 1957; DObst RCOG 1967. Prev: Clin. Asst. (Med.) Orpington Hosp.

LLOYD, John Edwin, KStJ (retired) The Little Milton Court, Cot Farm Hill, Llanwern, Newport NP18 2DP Tel: 01633 412863 — MB BCh 1952 Wales. Prev: Sen. GP Gwent.

LLOYD, John Gavin Emergency Dept, Bristol Royal Infirmary, Bristol Tel: 0117 928 2713 Email: gavin.lloyd@ubht.swest.nhs.uk — MB BS 1987 Lond.; FRCS (A&E) Ed. 1993; Dip. Sports Med. Lond 1991; Dip Med. Education Cardiff 1998. Cons Emerg. dept Bristol Roy. Infirm. Prev: Sen Reg (Emerg Med) S.ampton Gen Hosp; Regist. (Emerg. Med.) Roy. Perth Hosp. W. Austral.

LLOYD, John Keith (retired) Little Cumbre, 145 Pennsylvania Road, Exeter EX4 6DZ Tel: 01392 258315 — MB BS 1955 Lond.; MRCGP 1966; DObst RCOG 1960. Med. Off. DSS Trib. Panel. Prev: GP Mt. pleasant Health Centre Exeter 1967-1991.

LLOYD, John Walter, OBE, Squadron Ldr. RAF Med. Br. Retd. The Gate House, Mill St., Eynsham, Oxford OX29 4JU Tel: 01865 881477; Bays Hill, Llandeilo SA19 6BD Tel: 01552 2561 — MRCS Eng. LRCP Lond. 1949; FFA RCS Eng. 1961; DA Eng. 1958. (Lond. Hosp.) Hon. Cons. Pain Relief Unit Ch.ill Hosp. Oxf. Socs: Fell. Roy. Soc. Med.; (Vice-Pres.) Intractable Pain Soc. Gt. Brit. & Irel. Prev: Hon. Cons. Anaesth. Nuffield Dept. Anaesth. Radcliffe Infirm. Oxf.; Ho. Surg. Orthop. & ENT Depts. Lond. Hosp.; Squadron Ldr. RAF Med. Br.

LLOYD, Jonathan Arnold The Health Centre, Bailey Street, Old Basford, Nottingham NG6 0HD Tel: 0115 978 1231 Fax: 0115 979 0419 — MB BCh 1992 Wales.

LLOYD, Jonathan Robert Priory Medical Group, Cornlands Road, Acomb, York YO24 3WX Tel: 01904 781423 Fax: 01904 784886 — MB ChB 1978 Ed.; DCH Lond. 1981.

LLOYD, Jonathon Edward 1 Hammond Road, Hatfield Broad Oak, Bishop's Stortford CM22 7JN — BM BS 1994 Nottm.; BMedSci Nottm. 1992. (Nottm.)

LLOYD, Julia Helen Abbey Medical Practice, Health Centre, Merstow Grove, Evesham WR11 4BS Tel: 01386 761111 Fax: 01386 761111; Elsdon, Station Road, Broadway WR12 7DE — MB ChB 1990 Birm.; DRCOG 1993.

LLOYD, Julian Magnus The Old Dairy, Storrs Lane, Storrs, Stannington, Sheffield S6 6GY — MB ChB Sheff. 1969; MRCGP 1976; DCH Eng. 1972; DObst RCOG 1971. (Sheffield) Med. Off. Twil UK Ltd. Prev: GP Sheff.; SHO Profess. Med. Unit Sheff. Childr. Hosp.; SHO (Obst.) & Ho. Phys. N.. Gen. Hosp. Sheff.

LLOYD, Dame June Kathleen, DBE (Baroness Lloyd of Highbury), 37 Allingham St., Islington, London N1 8NX Tel: 020 7359 4870 — MB ChB 1951 Bristol; MB ChB (Hons.) Bristol 1951; MD Bristol 1966; Hon. DSc 1991; FRCP Ed. 1990; FRCP Lond. 1969, M 1954; FRCGP 1990; DPH Durh. 1958. (Bristol) Emerit. Nuffield Prof. Child Health Inst. Child Health Univ. Lond. Socs: (Ex-Pres.) Brit. Paediat. Assn.; Eur. Soc. Paediat. Research; Ex-Chairm. Advis. Comm. Gene Ther. Prev: Prof. Child Health St. Geo. Hosp. Med. Sch. Univ. Lond.; Hon. Cons. Paediat. St. Geo. Hosp. Lond.; Prof. Paediat. & Reader Child Health Inst. Child Health Univ. Lond.

LLOYD, Keith Robert University of Exeter PGMS, Department of Mental Health, Wonford House, Dryden Road, Exeter EX2 5AF — MB BS 1984 Lond.; MSc Lond. 1986, MB BS 1984; MSc Lond. 1992; MRCPsych 1989.

LLOYD, Kenneth Northampton General Hospital NHS Trust, Cliftonville, Northampton NN1 5BD Tel: 01604 34700; Sweetacres, The Knoll, Grendon, Northampton NN7 1JG Tel: 01933 663207 — MB ChB 1967 Sheff.; FRCR 1975; FFR 1973; DMRT Eng. 1971. (Sheff.) Chief Exec. N.ampton Gen. Hosp. NHS Trust. Prev: Cons. Radiother. & Oncol. & Gen. Manager N.ampton Gen. Hosp.; Sen. Regist. (Radiother.) W.on Pk. Hosp. Sheff.; Ho. Surg. (Paediat. Surg.) & Ho. Phys. (Gen. Med. & Dermat.) Stoke Mandeville Hosp. Aylesbury.

LLOYD, Kenneth Newton (retired) 136 Cathedral Road, Cardiff CF11 9JB Tel: 01222 225640 — MB BS 1938 Lond.; FRCP Lond. 1969, M 1947; MRCS Eng. LRCP Lond. 1938. Prev: Cons. Phys. (Rheum.) Univ. Hosp. Wales Cardiff & Lect. Welsh Coll. Med.

LLOYD, Margaret Elizabeth (retired) Escheatlands Farm, Beckley, Rye TN31 6SB Tel: 01424 882279 — MRCS Eng. LRCP Lond. 1950; MA, BM BCh Oxf. 1951. Prev: SCMO Hastings HA.

LLOYD, Margaret Hazel 4 The Ridgeway, Mill Hill, London NW7 1RS Tel: 020 8346 5090 — MB BS 1966 Lond.; BSc Lond. 1963, MD 1977; FRCP Lond. 1992; MRCS Eng. LRCP Lond. 1966; AFOM RCP Lond. 1987; FRCGP 1993. (St. Mary's) Reader (Gen. Pract.) Roy. Free Hosp. Sch. Med. Lond. Prev: Dep. Head Med. Br. Inst. Occupat. Med. Edin.; Lect. Med. Unit Lond. Hosp.

LLOYD, Margaret Winifred (retired) Little Cumbre, 145 Pennsylvania Road, Exeter EX4 6DZ Tel: 01392 58315 — MB BS 1954 Lond. Prev: Med. Off. Family Plann. Assn. Exeter.

LLOYD, Marianne 83 Brynhyfryd, Ferndale CF43 3AR — MB BS 1982 Lond.

LLOYD, Mark Hatfield Road Surgery, 70 Hatfield Road, Ipswich IP3 9AF Tel: 01473 723373 — MB BS 1984 Lond.; MRCP (UK) 1988. Prev: SHO (O & G) Lond. Hosp. Whitechapel; SHO (Gen. Med.) Qu. Mary's Hosp. Sidcup; SHO (Cardiol.) Brook Hosp. Lond.

LLOYD, Mark Edwin Department of Rheumatology, Frimley Park Hospital, Frimley GU16 5UJ Tel: 01276 604348 Fax: 01276 604743 Email: mark.lloyd@fph-tr.nhs.uk — MB ChB 1986 Manch.; MRCP (UK) 1990. Cons. (Rheumatol.) Frimley Pk. Hosp. Frimley. Socs: Fell. Roy. Soc. Med.; Brit. Soc. Rheum. Prev: Sen. Regist. (Gen. Med. & Rheumatol.) St Thomas' Hosp. Lond.

LLOYD, Mark Sheldon 17 Pampisford Road, Purley CR8 2NG — BM 1997 Soton.

LLOYD, Mary Isabel (retired) 1 St Catwg Walk, Mayals, Swansea SA3 5ED — MB BCh Wales 1951; FRCOG 1977, M 1963, DObst 1953. Prev: Cons. O & G Neath Gen. Hosp.

LLOYD, Mary Judith St Johns Medical Centre, St. Johns Road, Altrincham WA14 2NW; The Downs Cottage, Woodville Road, Altrincham WA14 2AN Tel: 0161 928 4946 — MB BS 1964 Lond.; MRCS Eng. LRCP Lond. 1964. (Roy. Free) GP Altrincham; Hosp. Pract. (Dermat.) Wythenshawe Hosp. Manch.; Hosp. Pract. (Immunol.) Manch. Roy. Infirm. Prev: SHO St. John's Hosp. Dis. of Skin Lond.; Research Regist. (Dermat.) Roy. Free Hosp. Lond.; Sen. Fell. in Med. Univ. Toronto, Canada.

LLOYD, Michael David (retired) Pennycote, Leech Lane, Harden, Bingley BD16 1DF — MB ChB 1959 Leeds; DObst RCOG 1964. Prev: GP Bradford.

LLOYD, Michael Ernest Miller Street Surgery, Miller Street, Off Kings Street, Newcastle ST5 1JD Tel: 01782 711618 Fax: 01782 713940; 42 Sneyd Avenue, The Westlands, Newcastle ST5 2PR Tel: 01782 611926 — MB ChB 1971 Birm.

LLOYD, Michael Norman Hastings 14 The Holdings, Hatfield AL9 5HQ — BChir 1979 Camb.

LLOYD, Michael Thomas — MRCP 1978 UK; DCH 1981; MB BS 1975 London; MB BS 1975 London. (St Thomas's Hospital Medical School) Socs: Collegiate Mem. Roy. Coll. of Phys.s (Lond.); Mem. Primary Care Soc. for Gastroenterol.

LLOYD, Monica Mary 6 Berwick Close, Seaford BN25 2NU Tel: 01323 896296; 6 Berwick Close, Seaford BN25 2NU Tel: 01323 896296 — MB BCh BAO 1954 NUI. Med. Off. DSS E. Sussex. Socs: Assn. Anaesth. Prev: Anaesth. Birm. AHA (T) S. Dist.

LLOYD, Naomi Margaret 20 Marine Terrace, Rosemarkie, Fortrose IV10 8UL — MB ChB 1972 Bristol; DObst RCOG 1974.

LLOYD, Nesta Elizabeth (retired) The Corner House, 57 Four Oaks Road, Four Oaks, Sutton Coldfield B74 2XU Tel: 0121 308 3650 Fax: 0121 323 2046 — MB ChB Ed. 1957; FRCOG 1986, M 1962, DObst 1960. Prev: Assoc. Specialist (O & G) Good Hope Hosp. Sutton Coldfield.

LLOYD, Nichola Claire Joanne 12 Greenways Drive, Sunningdale, Ascot SL5 9QS Tel: 01344 620522 Email: md3082@hotmail.com — MB ChB 1998 Bristol. SHO.Gen. Med.Gloucester.

LLOYD, Owen Walter Middleton Medical Centre, Elmer Road, Middleton-on-Sea, Bognor Regis PO22 7SR Tel: 01243 584154 Fax: 01243 583596; Yew Tree Surgery, North End Road, Yapton, Arundel BN18 0DU Tel: 01243 551321 — MB BS 1958 Lond.; DObst RCOG 1963. (Lond. Hosp.) Police Surg. Prev: Clin. Asst. Roy. Nat. Throat, Nose & Ear Hosp.; SHO (Cas.) Roy. Hants. Co. Hosp. Winchester; Ho. Phys. (Cardiac) Lond. Hosp.

LLOYD, Peggy Christine (retired) Green Acres, South Ridge, Odiham, Basingstoke RG29 1NG Tel: 01252 702334 — MB ChB 1948 Sheff. Prev: Med. Adviser John Lewis Partnership.

LLOYD, Philip Andrew Roach Penylan Road Surgery, 100 Penylan Road, Cardiff CF2 5HY Tel: 029 2046 1100 Fax: 029 2045 1623; 38 Malefant Street, Cathays, Cardiff CF24 4QH Tel: 0122 397943 — MB ChB 1990 Leic.; MRCGP 1994; DFFP 1994; DRCOG 1993. GP S. Glam.

LLOYD, Rachel Catherine University Medical Centre, University College, Swansea SA2 8PR Tel: 01792 295321 — MB BCh 1981 Wales. (Welsh National School of Medicine) p/t Gen. Practitioner; Clin. Asst.; GU Med. Socs: Y Gymdeithas Meddygol; BASHE.

LLOYD, Reginald Stuart The Health Clinic, Weeping Cross, Bodmin Avenue, Stafford ST17 0HE Tel: 01785 662505 Fax: 01785 661064 — MB ChB 1977 Birm.; MRCP (UK) 1980.

LLOYD, Rhiannon Vaughan Willow Tree Family Doctors, 301 Kingsbury Road, London NW9 9PE Tel: 020 8204 6464 Fax: 020 8905 0946; 21 Antrim Mansions, Antrim Road, Belsize Park, London NW3 4XT Tel: 020 7722 0990 Fax: 020 7722 2127 — MB BS 1986 Lond.; MRCGP 1991; Cert. Family Plann. JCC 1991. (Royal Free Hospital School of Medicine) GP Tutor Roy. Free UCL Sch. Med. Socs: NHS Alliance.

LLOYD, Mr Richard Ernest Oral & Maxillofacial Surgery Department, Hope Hospital, Eccles Old Road, Salford M6 8HD Tel: 0161 787 4728 Fax: 0161 787 4329 Email: rlloyd@hope.srht.nwest.nhs.uk; Farthings, Towers Road, Poynton, Stockport SK12 1DD Tel: 01625 879591 Fax: 01628 879591 Email: rlloyd@globalnet.co.uk — MB ChB 1981 Liverp.; BDS Wales 1973; FRCS Ed. 1985; FDS RCS Eng. 1976. Cons. Oral & Maxillofacial Surg. Hope Hosp. Salford, Trafford Gen. Hosp. & Manch. Roy. Infirm.; Cons. Implantology Clinic Manch. Centr. Hosp. Socs: Fell. Brit. Assn. Oral & Maxillofacial Surg.; BMA; BDA. Prev: Sen. Regist. (Maxillofacial Surg.) St. Richards Hosp. Chichester, St. Thos. Hosp. Lond. & Roy. Surrey Hosp. Guildford.

LLOYD, Richard Harold Gordon The Surgery, Roath House, 100 Penylan Road, Cardiff CF23 5RH Tel: 029 2046 1100 Fax: 029 2045 1623; 24 Hollybush Road, Cyncoed, Cardiff CF23 6TA Tel: 029 2075 8818 — MB BS 1956 Lond.; DObst RCOG 1963. (Univ. Coll. Hosp.) Socs: Eur. Undersea Biomed. Soc.

LLOYD, Richard James 10 Bekesbourne Lane, Little Bourne, Canterbury CT3 1UY — MB BS 1996 Lond.

LLOYD, Richard John Storrar Beaumont Street Surgery, 28 Beaumont Street, Oxford OX1 2NT Tel: 01865 311811 Fax: 01865 310327 — MB BS 1974 Lond.; MRCS Eng. LRCP Lond. 1974; MRCGP 1978; DFFP 1995; DCH Eng. 1977; DRCOG 1976. (Char. Cross) Med. Off. Home Office. Prev: Trainee GP Oxf. VTS; SHO (Obst. & Paediat.) Char. Cross Hosp. Lond.

LLOYD, Mr Robert Geoffrey 12 Wellgate, Old Glossop, Glossop SK13 7RS — MB ChB 1971 Birm.; FRCS Eng. 1980.

LLOYD, Sandra Charmian (retired) Apollo Surgery, 619 Kings Rd, Great Barr, Birmingham B44 9HW — MB ChB Birm. 1966.

LLOYD, Sarah Margaret Leeds teaching hospitals NHS trust, St James's Hospital, Beckett Street, Leeds LS9 7TF Tel: 0113 206 5789; 6 North Park Grove, Roundhay, Leeds LS8 1JJ Tel: 0113 2684 178 Fax: 0113 225 9525 Email: lloydmorval@cwcom.net — MB BS 1984 Lond.; FRCA 1990. (St Thomas's) Cons. Anaesth. St. James'. Univ. Hosp. Leeds. Prev: Sen. Regist. (Anaesth.) W.. Infirm. Glas.; Regist. (Anaesth.) Ipswich.

LLOYD, Sian Dwyryd 24 Gelligaer Street, Cardiff CF24 4LA — MB BCh 1995 Wales.

LLOYD, Simon Kingsley Wickham 14 Ornan Road, Belsize Park, London NW3 4PX — MB BS 1996 Lond.; BSc (Hons.) 1993. (Roy. Free Hosp.) SHO (A&E) Barnet Gen. Hosp. Herts. Prev: Jun. Ho. Off. (Surg.) Roy. Free Hosp.

LLOYD, Stephen Murray 13 Bloose Road, Nantyffyllon, Maesteg, Bridgend CF32 9NX — MB BCh 1979 Wales.

LLOYD, Steven 94 Holymoor, Holymoorside, Chesterfield S42 7DX — MB ChB 1994 Sheff.

LLOYD, Stewart Caritas Limited, 17 College Yard, Brigg DN20 8JL Tel: 07885 652097 Fax: 01652 651509 Email: stewart@caritas.co.uk — MB BS 1979 Lond.; MFOM RCP Lond. 1997. (Lon. Hosp. Med. Coll.) Indep. Cons. (Occupat. Med.); Med. director, carital ltd brigg. Socs: ALAMA; BMA, (Mem., O.H Comm.); Soc. Occupat. Med. (Treas., Yorks G.P). Prev: Works Med. Off. Brit. Steel Scunthorpe; Sen. Med. Off. Roy. Fleet Aux.; Regist. (ENT Surg.) Orsett Hosp. Grays.

LLOYD, Mr Stuart Nigel — MB BS 1983 Lond.; MS Lond. 1992; FRCS Eng. 1988; FRCS Glas. 1988. Cons. Urol. St. Jas. Univ. Hosp. Leeds. Socs: Brit. Assn. Urol. Surgs.; Roy. Soc. Med.

LLOYD, Susan Rebecca Leicester General Hospital, Gwendolen Road, Leicester LE5 4PW — MB ChB 1997 Leic.

LLOYD, Thomas David Rees 31 Edward Road, Leicester LE2 1TF — MB ChB 1997 Leic. SHO Rotat. (Surg.) Leicester Roy. Infirm.

LLOYD, Thomas Herbert Lewis 43 Palace Road, Llandaff, Cardiff CF5 2AG Tel: 029 2056 3979 Email: tom@llandaff43.freeserve.co.uk — MB BCh Wales 1957. (Cardiff) Clin. Cons. Mediprobe Ltd.; Med. Examr. Benefits Agency & Various Insur. Companies; Adviser to Dept. of Work & Pens. and War Pens. Agency. Socs: Fell. Assur. Med. Soc. (Ex-Counc. Mem.); Mem. Cardiff Med. Soc. Prev: Med. Policy Manager DSS; GP Mid & S. Glam.; Regist. (Med.) Maelor Gen. Hosp. & Wrexham War Memor. Hosp.

LLOYD, Thomas Holt 17 The Cloisters, Littlehampton BN17 5ST — MB ChB 1979 Bristol. Clin. Med. Off. Community Child.Health.Worthing.Priority.Care.NHS.Trust. Prev: SHO Paediat.Commun.Child.Health.Chichester; SHO.Old.Age.Psych.Rehabil.Basingstoke & N..hants; GP trainee.Portsmouth.

LLOYD, Timothy William Uphill, Tweed Lane, Boldre, Lymington SO41 8NF — MB BS 1993 Lond.; BDS Lond. 1984.

LLOYD, Trevor (retired) The Health Centre, Priest Lane, Pershore WR10 1DR Tel: 01386 554567 — MB ChB 1961 Birm.

LLOYD, Mrs Ursula Elizabeth Portland Hospital for Women & Children, 209 Great Portland St., London W1W 5AH Tel: 020 7935 3732 Fax: 020 7935 3732; 8 Southwick Place, London W2 2TN Tel: 020 7723 8721 Fax: 020 7706 1745 — MB BS Lond. 1967; MRCS Eng. LRCP Lond. 1967; FRCOG 1987, M 1971, DObst 1969. (Middlx.) Cons. O & G Portland Hosp. Lond. Socs: Fell. Roy. Soc. of Med. Prev: Cons. O & G St. Geo. Hosp. Lond.; Sen. Regist. Qu. Mary's Hosp. Roehampton; SHO Qu. Charlotte's Hosp. Lond. & Chelsea Hosp. Wom. Lond.

***LLOYD, Victoria Caroline** Rosen La Vie, North Road, Tattersall Thorpe, Lincoln LN4 4PQ — MB ChB 1998 Birm.

LLOYD, Vincent Arthur (retired) 34 Mackenzie Road, Birmingham B11 4EL — MB ChB 1951 Birm.; MRCS Eng. LRCP Lond. 1948; DPH Eng. 1958. Assoc. MRCGP. Prev: MOH Redditch UD.

LLOYD, William Harry (retired) The Old Pound, Cadbury Camp Lane, Clapton in Gordano, Bristol BS20 7SE Tel: 0117 92788 — MB ChB 1946 Ed.; FRCP Ed. 1971, M 1951. Prev: Cons. Phys. Manor Pk. Hosp. Bristol & Bristol HA(T).

LLOYD, Winifred Audrey (retired) Caprice, High St., Islip, Kidlington OX5 2RX Tel: 01865 377535 Email: wdabirch@netscapeonline.co.uk — LRCP LRCS 1950 Ed.; LRCP LRCS Ed. LRFPS Glas. 1950. Prev: Jun. Hosp. Med. Off. St. Geo. Hosp. Lincoln.

LLOYD-BROADHURST, Annie (retired) 59 King's Road, Windsor SL4 2AD — MRCS Eng. LRCP Lond. 1917.

LLOYD DAVIES, Alan Trevor (retired) Godewirda, 12 St Anns Close, Goodworth Clatford, Andover SP11 7RW Tel: 01264 352983 Fax: 01264 339472 Email: lloyd@btinterner.com — MB BS 1962 Lond.; MRCS Eng. LRCP Lond. 1962; Dip. Musculoskel Med (Soc. Apoth.) 1996; DObst RCOG 1965. Clin. assist.Dept.of Rehabil.

Salisbury Dist. Hosp. Prev: Hosp. Pract. (Geriat.) St John's Unit War Memor. Hosp. Andover.

LLOYD-DAVIES, Mr Edward Roderic Vaughan Greenwith Place, Silver Hill, Perranwell Station, Truro TR3 7LR — MRCS Eng. LRCP Lond. 1973; MS Lond. 1986, MB BS 1973; FRCS Eng. 1978. (St. Bart.) Cons. Surg. Roy. Cornw. Hosps. Trust. Socs: Assn. Coloproctol. & St. Mark's Hosp. Assn. Prev: Resid. Surg. Off. St. Marks Hosp. Lond.; Regist. (Gen. Surg.) Ipswich Hosp.; Cas. Surg. Off. Middlx. Hosp. Lond.

LLOYD-DAVIES, Mr Reginald Wyndham (retired) 35 Wimpole Street, London W1G 8GY Tel: 020 7637 9411 Fax: 020 7636 4596 — MB BS Lond. 1958; MS Lond. 1968; FRCS Eng. 1962; FEBU 1992. Hon. Cons. Urol. Guys & St Thomas' Trust; Cons. Surg. Metrop. Police; Surg. Hosp. for Off. Kings Edwd. VII. Prev: Clin. Dir. (Urol. & Lithotripsy) Guy's & St. Thos. Trust.

LLOYD DAVIES, Sally Katherine Child & Family mental health team, Homeopathic hosp, 41 church Road, Tunbridge Wells TN1 1JU Tel: 01223 746001 Fax: 01223 746002 — MB BS 1988 Lond.; MRCPsych 1993; DCH 1990. (St. Georges) Cons.. Child & Adolesc. Psychiat. Tunbridge Wells.

LLOYD-DAVIES, Susan Vanessa, MBE 4 Adelphi Row, Glooston, Market Harborough LE16 7ST Tel: 01858 545 5531 — MB BS 1987 Lond.; MA Oxf. 1986, BA (Hons.) 1982; MRCGP 1994; Dip. IMC RCS Ed. 1995; DMCC Soc. Apoth. Lond. 1995.

LLOYD-EVANS, Gwerfyl Nerys Tawelan, Siliwen, Bangor LL57 2BH Email: gwerfyl@btinternet.com — MB ChB 1994 Manch.; BSc (Hons.) St. And. 1991. (St. And. & Univ. Manch.) SHO (A & E) Ysbyty Gwynedd Bangor. Prev: SHO (Anaesth.) Ysbyty Gwynedd Bangor; Ho. Off. (Urol., Gen Surg.) Ysbyty Gwynedd Bangor; Ho. Off. (Diabetes, Endocrinol. & Med. for Elderly) Manch. Roy. Infirm.

LLOYD-EVANS, Mary 10 The Yews, Oadby, Leicester LE2 5EF — MRCS Eng. LRCP Lond. 1948; DCH Eng. 1954.

LLOYD-HARRIS, Quentin Lionel Genghis 25 Parkside, London SW1X 7JW — MB ChB 1980 Liverp.

LLOYD-JONES, Mr Don Roundwood, Saxon Hill, Battle TN33 0HN Tel: 01424 772230 — MB BChir 1968 Camb.; MA Camb. 1968; FRCS Eng. 1975; FRCOphth 1989; T(Ophth) 1991; DO Eng. 1971. (Camb. & Univ. Coll. Hosp.) Cons. Ophth. Surg. Conquest Hosp. Hastings. Socs: Fell. Roy. Soc. Med. Prev: Sen. Regist. Kings Coll. & Moorfields Hosp. Lond.; Resid. Surg. Off. Moorfields Eye Hosp. Lond.; Hon. Asst. Glaucoma Unit Moorfields Eye Hosp. Lond.

LLOYD-JONES, Elisabeth Babington 13A Warwick Avenue, London W9 2PS Tel: 020 7286 5371; Kiln Cottage, Cadmore End, High Wycombe HP14 3PS — MB ChB Ed. 1945; FFA RCS Eng. 1955; DA Eng. 1950. (Ed,) Prev: Cons. Anaesth. Hammersmith Hosp. Lond.; Sen. Lect. (Anaesth.) Postgrad. Med. Sch. Lond.; Regist. (Anaesth.) Nuffield Dept. Anaesth. Oxf.

LLOYD-JONES, Mrs Elsa May (retired) 5 Kensington Gardens, Hale, Altrincham WA15 9DP Tel: 0161 980 4932 — MB BS Punjab 1942. Prev: Sessional Med. Off. Family Plann. Clinics.

LLOYD JONES, Fiona Rhianon 78 Newton Road, Mumbles, Swansea SA3 4BE — MB BS 1987 Lond.

LLOYD-JONES, Gaynor Howell Department Health Care Education, 3rd Floor, University Clinical Department, Duncan Building, Liverpool University, Liverpool L69 3BX Tel: 0151 706 5876; 53 Rodney Street, Liverpool L1 9ER — MB ChB 1968 Liverp.; FFA RCS Eng. 1972. (Liverp.) Research Fell. (Health Care Educat.) Liverp. Univ. Socs: BMA. Prev: Cons. Anaesth. Wirral AHA.

LLOYD JONES, John Kenneth Sherwood, 10 Kirkby Road, Ravenshead, Nottingham NG15 9HF — MB BChir 1956 Camb.; MA Camb. 1957, MB BChir 1956; FRCP Lond. 1977, M 1963; DObst RCOG 1958. (Guy's) Cons. Rheum. & Rehabil. Harlow Wood Orthop. Hosp. Mansfield, King's Mill Hosp. Sutton-in-Ashfield; Clin. Teach. Univ. Nottm. Med. Sch.; Post-Doctoral Fell. Rancho Los Amigos Hosp. Calif. Socs: Fell. Roy. Soc. Med. (Ex-Pres. Sect. Rheum. & Rehabil.); E. Midl. Soc. Phys. Prev: Sen. Regist. King's Coll. Hosp. Lond.; Res. Med. Off. Nat. Heart Hosp. Lond.; Ho. Off. Guy's Hosp. Lond.

LLOYD JONES, John Owen (retired) Ringland Health Centre, Newport NP9 8BJ Tel: 01633 277011 Fax: 01633 290703 — MRCS Eng. LRCP Lond. 1957; DPH Bristol 1963; DObst RCOG 1960. Prev: Ho. Phys. & Ho. Surg. United Cardiff Hosps.

LLOYD-JONES, Katrina Jane St. Elsewhere, Nunnery Green, Wickhambrook, Newmarket CB8 8XT — MB ChB 1980 Birm.; MRCGP 1984.

LLOYD-JONES, Michael, OStJ (retired) 10 East Castle Street, Bridgnorth WV16 4AL Tel: 01746 763212 — LRCP LRCS Ed. LRFPS Glas. 1947; FRSH 1981.

LLOYD-JONES, Neil Daniel University Medical Centre, Claremont Road, Newcastle upon Tyne NE2 4AN Tel: 0191 232 2973 Fax: 0191 230 3631 — MB BS 1984 Newc.; MRCGP 1989. Sen. Partner Univ. Med. Centre Newc.u.Tyne.

LLOYD JONES, Peter Marshall (retired) Glyn-Cerrig, 78 Newton Road, Mumbles, Swansea SA3 4BE Tel: 01792 367805 — MB BS 1955 Lond.

LLOYD-JONES, Philip Martin Dr Polkinhorn and Partners, The Surgery, Boyden Close, Nunnery Green, Wickhambrook, Newmarket CB8 8XU Tel: 01440 820140 Fax: 01440 820534 — MB BS 1966 Lond.; MRCP (UK) 1970; MRCS Eng. LRCP Lond. 1966.

LLOYD-JONES, Mr Rees Lloyd (retired) Kiln Cottage, Cadmore End Common, High Wycombe HP14 3PS Tel: 01494 881424 — MB BS 1947 Lond.; FRCS Eng. 1951; FRCOG 1965, M 1953. O & G Surg. Middlx. Hosp. & Univ. Coll. Hosp. Lond.; Surg. Hosp. Wom. Lond.; Examr. Univs. Camb., Lond. & Glas., & RCOG & Conj. Bd. Prev: Hon. Cons. O & G St. And. Hosp. Dollis Hill.

LLOYD-JONES, Sarah Judith 4 Gelligaer Gardens, Cardiff CF24 4LT — MB BCh 1990 Wales. SHO (Anaesth.) Morriston Hosp. Swansea.

LLOYD-JONES, Mr Will Lourdes Hospital, Greenbank Road, Liverpool L18 1HQ Tel: 0151 734 3737 — MB ChB 1963 (Hons) Liverp.; ChM Liverp. 1973; FRCS Ed. 1967; FRCS Eng. 1968. (Liverp.) Cons. Surg. Liverp. AHA (T). Socs: Fell. Assn. Surgs.; Brit. Soc. Gastroenterol. Prev: Sen. Lect. (Surg.) Univ. Liverp.; Lect. (Surg.) Univ. Glas.; Research Fell. Lahey Clinic Foundat. Boston, U.S.A.

LLOYD-MOSTYN, Roger Hugh King's Mill Hospital, Sutton-in-Ashfield NG17 4JL Tel: 01623 22515; 42 Lichfield Lane, Mansfield NG18 4RE Tel: 01623 24398 — MB BS 1965 Lond.; FRCP Lond. 1982, M 1969; MRCS Eng. LRCP Lond. 1965. (Westm.) Cons. Phys. King's Mill Hosp. Sutton-in-Ashfield. Socs: Brit. Diabetic Assn.; Brit. Hyperlipid. Assn. Prev: Sen. Med. Regist. Qu. Eliz. Hosp. Birm.; Med. Regist. King's Coll. Hosp. Lond.; Research Fell. & Hon. Sen. Regist. Kings Coll. Hosp. Lond.

LLOYD-OWEN, Simon James 43B Claremont Square, London N1 9LS Tel: 020 7278 0973 Email: sio1@compuserve.com — MB BChir 1992 Camb.; MA 1992; MRCP 1996. (Cambridge) Specialist Regist. (Rspiratory & Gen. Med.) N. E. Thames Rotat. Curr.ly at Roy. Lond. Hosp. Lond. Socs: Brit. HIV Assn.; Brit. Thorac. Soc. Prev: HIV Regist. Roy. Free Hosp. Lond.; Med. Regist. Whipps Cross Hosp. Lond.

LLOYD PARRY, John Merfyn, OStJ Cardiology Unit, Wexham Park Hospital, Wexham Street, Slough SL2 4HL; Widbrook Cottage, Widbrook Common, Cookham, Maidenhead SL6 9RB Tel: 01628 851199 Fax: 01628 850542 — MB BChir Camb. 1963; MA Camb. 1966; Dip. Sports Med. 1997; DObst RCOG 1965. (St. Bart.) Cons. Adviser (Sports Med.) St. John Ambul. Brig.; Hon. Clin Regist. (Cardiol.) Heatherwood & Wexham Pk. Hosps. Trust; Hon. Med. Adviser Brit. Horse Soc.; Hon. Med. Adviser Pony Club; Hon. Med. Adviser Brit. Equestrian Federat. Socs: (Ex-Chairm.) Med. Equestrian Assn.; Brit. Olympic. Med.; Fell. Roy. Soc. Med. (Pres. Counc. Sect. Sports Med.). Prev: GP Bourne End; Ho. Phys. Qu. Alexandra Hosp. Portsmouth; Ho. Surg. St. Bart. Hosp. Lond.

LLOYD-POWIS, Nicola 16 Rose Crescent, Kingswood, Leicester Forest East, Leicester LE3 3QX Tel: 0116 238 8065 — MB ChB 1994 Leic. GP Regist. Leicester VTS.

LLOYD-ROBERTS, Robert Edmund, TD (retired) Longport House, 8 Longport, Canterbury CT1 1PE Tel: 01227 464175 — MB BS 1951 Lond.; MRCS Eng. LRCP Lond. 1951. Med. Adviser Kent; Chairm. Med. Bds. DHSS; Lt.-Col. RAMC (TAVR).

LLOYD ROE, Claudia Anne The Alpha Practice, 109 York Road, Chingford, London E4 8LF Tel: 020 8524 8422 Fax: 020 8559 3538 — MB BS 1976 Lond.; BSc (Hons.) Lond. 1973; MRCS Eng. LRCP Lond. 1976; MRCGP 1981; DFFP 1994; DCH RCP Lond. 1980. (Guy's) GP Redbridge & Waltham Forest & Essex FHSA; Mem. Christian Healing Min. Team. Socs: Roy. Coll. Gen. Pract.; MWF; Diplomate Fac. Family Plann. Prev: SHO (Dermat.) The Middlx.

Hosp.; SHO (Paediat.) Roy. Free Hosp.; SHO (A & E) Univ. Coll. Hosp. Lond.

LLOYD-SMITH, Alan Richard The Surgery, Ivy Court, Tenterden TN30 6RB Tel: 01580 763666/764022 Fax: 01580 766199; Potmans Heath House, Moons Green, Wittersham, Tenterden TN30 7PU Tel: 01797 270221 — MB ChB 1975 Dundee; MRCGP 1988; DCH Eng. 1977. (Dundee) Course Organiser Ashford VTS; Clin. Asst. (Geriat.) W. View Hosp. Tenterden; Mem. Kent LMC. Socs: BMA; Wield and Marsh Med. Soc. Prev: Clin. Asst. (Geriat.) W. View Hosp. Tenterden.

LLOYD-SMITH, Wilma New Hayesbank Surgery, Cemetery Lane, Kennington, Ashford TN24 9JZ Tel: 01233 624642 Fax: 01233 637304; Portmans Heath, Moons Green, Wittersham, Tenterden TN30 7PU Tel: 01797 270221 Fax: 01797 270638 — MB ChB 1975 Dundee; MRCGP 1993; DRCOG 1977; DFFP 1997. (Dundee) GP Kent; Clin. Asst. (Gen. & Respirat. Med.) E. Kent HA. Prev: Med. Off. Holy Cross Hosp. Transkei, S. Afr.; Med. Off. Roy. Geogr. Soc. Expedit. to Gunong Mulu Nat. Pk., Sarawak; SHO (A & E) Roy. Sussex Co. Hosp. Brighton.

LLOYD-THOMAS, Adrian Richard Great Ormond Street Hospital for Children NHS Trust, London WC1N 3JH Tel: 020 7405 9200 Fax: 020 7829 8866 Email: lloyda@gosh.nhs.uk; 12A South Hill Park Gardens, Hamstead, London NW3 2TG Tel: 020 7431 6133 Fax: 020 7431 0546 Email: al-t@dial.pipex.com — MB BS 1978 Lond.; FFA RCS Eng. 1984. (Lond. Hosp.) p/t Cons. Paediat. Anaesth. & Dir. Acute Pain Servs. & Clinc. Dir. Dept. Anaesth. Gt. Ormond St. Hosp. for Childr. NHS Trust Lond.; Sen. Lect. (Paediat. Anaesth.) Inst. Child Health Lond. Socs: Fell. Roy. Soc. Med.; Assn. Anaesth. Prev: Coll. Tutor Roy. Coll. Anaesth.; Sen. Regist. (Anaesth. & Intens. Care) St. Bart. Hosp. Lond.; Regist. (Paediat. Anaesth. & Intens. Care) Alder Hey Childr. Hosp.

LLOYD-THOMAS, Anne Rosemary Highcliffe Medical Centre, Heila House, 248 Lymington Road, Highcliffe, Christchurch BH23 5ET Tel: 01425 272203 Fax: 01425 271086 — BM BCh 1984 Oxf.; MA (Hons.) Camb. 1981; MRCP (UK) 1987; MRCGP 1992. (Oxf.) p/t Gen. Practitioner, Highcliffe Med. Centre, ChristCh. Prev: Trainee GP Eynsham; Regist. (Med.) Middlx. Hosp. Lond.; SHO Brompton Hosp. Lond.

LLOYD-THOMAS, Hywel Geoffrey Lloyd 52 Fordington Road, Highgate, London N6 4TJ — MB BChir 1948 Camb.; BA Camb. (1st cl. Nat. Sc. Trip.) 1945 MA 1949; MD 1959, MB BChir 1948; FRCP Lond. 1972, M 1952. (Camb. & Lond. Hosp.) Hon. Cons. Phys. Lond. Hosp. Whitechapel. Socs: Brit. Cardiac Soc. Prev: Cons. Phys. St. And. Hosp. Bow; Cons. Phys. Newham Hosp.; Lect. Med. Lond. Hosp. Med. Coll.

LLOYD-THOMAS, Joyce Foulds (retired) 1 Pettits Lane, Romford RM1 4HL — MB BChir 1956 Camb.; MA, MB Camb. 1956, BChir 1955; DObst RCOG 1957. Prev: GP Romford.

LLOYD-THOMAS, Ruth Margery 52 Fordington Road, Highgate, London N6 4TJ Tel: 020 8444 3533 — MB BChir 1948 Camb.; MA 1949, MB BChir Camb. 1948. (Camb. & King's Coll. Hosp.) Socs: Fell. Roy. Soc. Med. Prev: Med. Adviser Nat. Childr. Home; Sen. Med. Off. Civil Serv. Med. Advis. Serv.

LLOYD-WILLIAMS, Christopher Barrie Anthony The Ashgrove Surgery, Morgan Street, Pontypridd CF37 2DR Tel: 01443 404444 Fax: 01443 480917; Stoneleigh, Park Lane, Groesfaen, Pontyclun CF72 8PB Tel: 01222 891200 — MB BCh 1964 Wales; MRCS Eng. LRCP Lond. 1964; FRCGP 1992, M 1972; DFFP 1993. (Cardiff) Examg. Med. Pract. Benefits Agency M. Glam.; Mem. Disabil. Living Allowance Tribunal. Socs: BMA; Rhondda Med. Soc. Prev: Ho. Surg. Cardiff Roy. Infirm.; Ho. Phys. Llandough Hosp. Cardiff; Capt. RAMC, Med. Off. 1st Bn. Scots Guards 1966.

LLOYD-WILLIAMS, David James The Symons Medical Centre, 25 All Saints Avenue, Maidenhead SL6 6EL Tel: 01628 626131 Fax: 01628 410051; Sarum Meads, Newlands Drive, Maidenhead SL6 4LL Tel: 01628 24989 — MB BCh 1952 Wales; DObst RCOG 1954. (Cardiff) Clin. Asst. in Obst. Upton Hosp. Slough; Mem. Berks. Local Med. Comm. & E. Berks. Dist. Med. Comm. Socs: BMA (Ex-Pres. E. Berks. Div.); (Ex-Hon. Sec.) Windsor & Dist. Med. Soc. Prev: Ho. Surg. Morriston Gen. Hosp. Swansea; Ho. Surg. Profess. Dept. O & G Cardiff Roy. Infirm.; Surg. Lt. RNVR.

LLOYD-WILLIAMS, John (retired) 2 Headley Park, Tilley Lane, Headley, Epsom KT18 6EE Tel: 01372 378848 Email: adjon@jlloyd-williams.freeserve.co.uk — MB BS Lond. 1965; MRCS Eng. LRCP Lond. 1966; MRCGP 1974; Cert. Family Plann. JCC 1976. Prev: Clin. Asst. (Med.) Long Gr. Hosp. Epsom & Tolworth Hosp. Surrey.

LLOYD WILLIAMS, Mari Angharad Wern Ddu, Waen, St Asaph LL17 0DY — MB ChB 1991 Leic.; M.Med. Sci. (Med. Ed.) 2001; MRCGP 1995; Dip. Palliat. Med. Wales 1996; MD. 1999. Cons. Sen. Lect. In Palliat. Med. Leicst. Lecture Centre & Hospice. Socs: Assn. Palliat. Med.; (Exec. Comm.) Brit. Psychosocial Oncol. Soc.; Palliat. Care Research Forum (Exec. Comm). Prev: SHO (Palliat. Med.) St. Giles Hospice; SHO (Clin. Oncol.) Leicester Roy. Infirm.; Specialist Regist. Lords Hospice Leicester & Hon. Clin. Research Fell. (Psychiat.) Univ. Leicester.

LLOYDS, Darren Upper Stone House, Rose Hill, Stone in Oxney, Wittersham, Tenterden TN30 7HH — MB BCh 1998 Wales.

LLWYD, Esyllt Mererid Ystrad, Station Rd, Llanrug, Caernarfon LL55 4AG — MB BCh 1997 Wales.

LLYWARCH, Bryan Vyrnwy Powys, Grimpo, West Felton, Oswestry SY11 4HG Tel: 01691 610419 — MB ChB 1954 Birm. Prev: Ho. Surg. (O & G) City Hosp. Chester; Ho. Surg. Llandudno Gen. Hosp.; Ho. Phys. Caernarvon & Anglesey Hosp. Bangor.

LO, Kwok Wai 2 Lytham Way, West Derby, Liverpool L12 9NB Tel: 0151 220 8824 — MB ChB 1982 Liverp.; DA Eng. 1984.

LO, Michael Chi Kit Flat 8, Rosebank Mews, Dundee DD3 6PS — MB ChB 1997 Dundee.

LO, Nangi Michelle Karling 5 Filbert St E., Leicester LE2 7JG — MB ChB 1997 Leic.

LO, Raymond See-Kit Boland House, Guy's Hospital, London SE1 9RT; 565 Park W., Edgeware Road, London W2 2RA — MB BS 1988 Lond.

LO, Soo Kien 63 Ivor Court, Gloucester Place, London NW1 6BN — MB ChB 1993 Sheff.

LO, Stephen Dick Chung 2 Trinity, Leen Court, Leen Gate, Nottingham NG7 2JB — BM BS 1996 Nottm.

LO, Su Kong Liver Unit, King's College Hospital, London SE5 9RS Tel: 020 7737 4000 Fax: (20) 7737 4410; PO Box 559, Tawau, Sabah 91008, Malaysia — MB ChB 1987 Liverp.; DPhil Oxf. 1994; MRCP (UK) 1990. Regist. (Liver) King's Coll. Hosp. Lond. Prev: Regist. (Med.) Medway Hosp. Gillingham; Research Regist. (Gastroenterol.) John Radcliffe Hosp. Oxf.; SHO Rotat. (Med.) Qu. Eliz. & Gen. Hosps. Birm.

LO, Su Neng 21 Richard Street, Cardiff CF24 4DA — MB BCh 1992 Wales.

LO, Su Vui F63 Green Block Residence, Roch House Fairfield General Hospital, Rochdale Old Road, Bury BL9 7TD; 76 Pennington Road, Bolton BL3 3BR — MB ChB 1991 Glas.

LO, Susan Hoi-Shang Flat 7, Derwent Court, Eleanor Close, London SE16 6PS — MB BS 1998 Lond.; MB BS Lond 1998.

LO, Tai Cheung Nelson Department of Medicine, Leicester General Hospital, Gwendolen Road, Leicester LE5 4PW Tel: 0116 258 4048 Fax: 0116 258 8169 — MB BCh BAO 1981 NUI; LLM RCP Irel. LLM RCS Irel. 1981.; MRCP (UK) 1987; MRCPI 1987; FRCP Lond. 1998 (Royal College of Surgeons in Ireland) Cons. Phys. Leicester Gen. Hosp. Socs: Brit. Geriat. Soc.; Brit. Soc. Gastroenterol.; Midl. Gastroenterol. Soc. Prev: Sen. Regist. (Gen. Med., Gastroenterol. & Med. for Elderly) Leicester Gen. Hosp.; Regist. (Gastroenterol.) Edin. Roy. Infirm.

LO, Wendy Wan Ching 42 Westport Avenue, Mayals, Swansea SA3 5EQ Tel: 01792 401947 — MB BCh 1985 Wales; MRCGP 1994. Socs: BMA. Prev: Trainee GP Swansea.; SHO (Psychiat.) Gefn Coed Hosp. Swansea; SHO (O & G) Singleton Hosp. Swansea.

LO, Yuk-Ming Dennis Nuffield Department of Clinical Biochemistry, John Radcliffe Hospital, Oxford OX3 9DU Tel: 01865 220366 Fax: 01865 221778; 32 Osler Road, Headington, Oxford OX3 9BJ Tel: 01865 750007 — BM BCh 1989 Oxf.; DPhil Oxf. 1994; MA Camb. 1990; MRCP (UK) 1995. Univ. Lect. (Clin. Biochem.) Oxf. Socs: Path. Soc. Prev: Wellcome Career Developm. Fell. Univ. Oxf. Nuffield Dept. Clin. Med. John Radcliffe Hosp. Oxf.; Ho. Off. Qu. Eliz. Hosp. Birm.; Ho. Off. John Radcliffe Hosp. Oxf.

LOACH, Alan Bruce 23 Banbury Road, Oxford OX2 6NN Tel: 01865 559157 Fax: 01865 513089; The Threshing Barn, Pound Court, Earls Lane OX15 0TH Tel: 01993 813332 Email: a.loach@hospital-doctor.net — MB BChir 1968 Camb.; MA, BChir 1967; FFA RCS Eng. 1973; DA Eng. 1970. (Guy's) Cons. Nuffield Dept. Anaesth. Oxf. Socs: Assn. Anaesth. & BMA. Prev: Ho. Surg.

Guy's Hosp. Lond.; Surg. Lt. RN; Clin. Lect. Nuffield Dept. Anaesth. Oxf.

LOACH, Richard Simon Dene House, Seaview Lane, Seaview PO34 5DJ — BM 1990 Soton.

LOADER, Andrea Catherine 87 Ethel Street, Bearwood, Smethwick B67 5AJ Tel: 0121 434 5304 — MB ChB 1996 Birm.; ChB Birm. 1996; DRCOG 1998. GP Regist., Birm. Prev: SHO (O & G) Good Hope Hosp. Sutton Coldfield; SHO (Paediat.) Birm. Childr.s Hosp./City Hosp. Birm.

LOADER, Barrington Wayne Department of Anaesthetics, North Devon District Hospital, Barnstaple EX31 4JB — MB ChB 1977 Bristol; FFA RCS Eng. 1985; DA Eng. 1979. Cons. Anaesth. N. Devon Dist. Hosp. Barnstaple. Prev: Cons. Anaesth. Dunedin Hosp., NZ.

LOADER, Joseph Sven 77 Waverley Road, Bristol BS6 6ET — MB ChB 1997 Bristol.

LOADER, Peter John Department of Child & Family Psychiatry, 35 Black Prince Road, London SE11 6JJ Tel: 020 7793 7113 Fax: 020 7793 1810; The Coach House, St Martins Mews, Ongar CM5 9HY — MB BS Lond. 1970; MRCPsych 1976. Sen. Lect. (Child & Family Psychiat.) UMDS Guy's & St. Thos. Hosp. Lond.; Hon. Cons. & Clin. Dir. (Child & Family Psychiat.) W. Lambeth Community Care Trust Lond. Prev: Cons. Child & Adolesc. Psychiat. Hornsey Rise Child Guid. Unit & Whittington Hosp. Lond.; Res. Fell. & Hon. Sen. Regist. (Child Psychiat.) Hosp. Sick Childr. Gt. Ormond St. Lond.

LOADER, Simon Michael 87 Ethel Street, Bearwood, Smethwick B67 5AJ — MB ChB 1996 Birm. (Birmingham) SHO (O & G) Goodhope Hosp. Sutton Coldfield.

LOAN, William Brereton (retired) 71 Richmond Court, Lisburn BT27 4QX — MB BCh BAO 1958 Belf.; MD Belf. 1967; FFA RCSI 1963. Cons. Anaesth. Belf. City Hosp. Prev: Cons. Anaesth. Lagan Valley Hosp. Lisburn.

LOAN, William Charles 26 Greenwood Glen, Purdysburn Road, Belfast BT8 7WE Tel: 01232 491018 — MB BCh BAO 1989 Belf.; MB BCh Belf. 1989; FRCS Ed. 1993. Specialist Regist. (Radiol.). Socs: Fell. Roy. Coll. Surgs. Ed.; Assoc. Mem. Roy. Coll. Radiol.

LOANE, Brendan Joseph 21 Manse Park, Carryduff, Belfast BT8 8RX — MB BCh BAO 1995 Belf.

LOANE, Mr Robert Andrew Ormeau Park Surgery, 281 Ormeau Road, Belfast BT7 3GG Tel: 028 9064 2914 Fax: 028 9064 3993 — MB BCh BAO 1961 Belf.; BSc Belf. 1958, MB BCh BAO 1961; FRCS Ed. 1966. (Belf.) Prev: Sen. Regist. (Surg.) Roy. Vict. Hosp. Belf.; Tutor in Physiol. Qu. Univ. Belf.; Res. Med. Off. Roy. Vict. Hosp. Belf.

LOB-LEVYT, Julian Peter London School of Hygiene & Tropical Medicine, London WC1E 7HT; 3 Linzee Road, London N8 7RG — MB ChB 1980 Bristol; MSc (Distinc.) Lond. 1989; DRCOG 1985. Clin. Research Fell. Lond. Sch. Hyg. & Trop. Med. Lond.

LOBACZ, Raymond Miroslaw Central Surgery, King St., Barton-upon-Humber DN18 5ER; Maltby Cottage, Maltby Lane, Barton-upon-Humber DN18 5PY — BM BS 1975 Nottm. GP Barton-on-Humber.

LOBB, Brian Robert Blackburn Road Medical Centre, Blackburn Road, Birstall, Batley WF17 9PL Tel: 01924 478265 — MB ChB 1988 Leeds; BSc (Hons. Pharmacy) Aston 1982. Prev: SHO (O & G, Paediat. & Gen. Med.) Dewsbury.

LOBB, Catherine Jane The Surgery, 72 Gordon St., Burton-on-Trent DE14 2JA Tel: 01283 563175; 6 Clay Street, Stapenhill, Burton-on-Trent DE15 9BB — MB ChB 1985 Manch.; MRCGP 1993; DRCOG 1992. Prev: SHO (O & G) St. Mary's Hosp. Manch.; SHO (Cas. & Paediat.) Tameside Gen. Hosp. Ashton-u-Lyne.

LOBB, (Dorothy) Meryl (retired) Braeside, Rockbourne, Fordingbridge SP6 3NT — MB BCh 1957 Wales; FRCS Eng. (Ophth.) 1971; FRCS Ed. 1969; FRCOphth 1991; DO Eng. 1961. Prev: Cons. Ophth. Salisbury Health Dist.

LOBB, Mr Michael Owen 14 The Avenue, Bedford MK45 1BP Tel: 01234 712381 — MB ChB 1972 Liverp.; FRCS Ed. 1978; FRCOG 1989, M 1977. Cons. (O & G) Luton & Dunstable Hosp. Prev: Lect. (O & G) Univ. Liverp.; Regist. (Surg.) Liverp. Roy. Infirm.; Regist. (Obst.) Liverp. Matern. Hosp.

LOBB, Patricia Mary Martyn (retired) 2 Yew Tree View, High Lorton, Cockermouth CA13 9UJ Tel: 01900 85654 — MRCS Eng. LRCP Lond. 1948.

LOBBAN, Mairead Seona Macdonald 55 Hawksworth Road, Horsforth, Leeds LS18 4JP — MB ChB 1987 Aberd.; MRCPsych 1992. Sen. Regist. Psychiat. (Child & Adolesc.) N. Yorks.

LOBBAN, William Douglas 16 Middleshade Road, St Andrews KY16 9NA — MB ChB 1951 St. And.

LOBL, Elizabeth Franziska 14 Isokon Flats, Lawn Road, London NW3 2XD — MD 1926 Vienna. Socs: Brit. Soc. Psychoanal. Prev: Med. Off. St. Augustine's Hosp. Chartham & Bethlem Roy. Hosp.; Sen. Regist. Tavistock Clinic.

LOBLEY, Charles Frederick Martyn Gallions Reach Health Centre, Bentham Road, Thamesmead, London SE28 8BE Tel: 020 8333 5001 Fax: 020 8333 5020; Island House, 68 Parkhurst Road, Bexley DA5 1AS Tel: 01322 522270 — MB BS 1981 Lond.; MRCGP 1985; DRCOG 1985. (St. Geos.) Part. Thamesmead Med. Assocs. Prev: Hon. Lect. (Gen. Pract.) UMDS Guy's & St. Thos. Univ. Lond.

LOBNITZ, Olive Balfour 64 Main Road, Fenwick, Kilmarnock KA3 6DU Tel: 01560 600307 — MB ChB 1938 Ed.; DPH Ed. 1941. (Ed.)

LOBO, Agnelo Alison Xavier Croydon Farm, Royston SG8 0EH — MB 1982 Camb.; BSc Camb. 1976, MB 1982, BChir 1981.

LOBO, Allan Joseph Gastroenterology Unit, Royal Hallamshire Hospital, Glossop Road, Sheffield S10 2JF Tel: 0114 271 2353 Fax: 0114 271 2832 — MB BS 1984 Lond.; MD Lond. 1995; FRCP 1998. Cons. Phys. & Gastroenterol. Roy. Hallamsh. Hosp. Sheff. Prev: Sen. Regist. Rotat. (Med. & Gastroenterol.) Bristol & Gloucester Hosps.; Regist. (Med. & Gastroenterol.) Leeds Gen. Infirm.; SHO (Renal Unit) Ch.ill Hosp. Oxf.

LOBO, Benjamin John 3 Churchill Close, Streatley, Luton LU3 3PJ — BM BS 1993 Nottm.

LOBO, Cecil Emile 26 Nightingale Lane, London SW12 8TD Tel: 020 8673 3737 Fax: 020 8265 5406; 100 Lavender Hill, London SW11 5RE Tel: 020 8673 3737 Fax: 0182 207 3302 — MB BS Ceylon 1956. (Univ. Ceylon Med. Coll.)

LOBO, Christopher James 1 Highfield Drive, Eccles, Manchester M30 9PZ — MB BS 1985 Univ. Poona.

LOBO, Mr Frank Xavier Pallion Health Centre, Hylton Road, Sunderland SR4 7XF Tel: 0191 565 8598 Fax: 0191 514 7467; 8 Ashmore Terrace, Sunderland SR2 7DE Tel: 0191 565 6150 — MB BS 1956 Karachi; FRCS Ed. 1965. (Dow Med. Coll. Karachi) Prev: Regist. (Surg.) Scartho Rd. Hosp. Grimsby & Harrogate & Dist. Gen. Hosp.; SHO York Co. & City Hosps.

LOBO, Melvin David 48 Great Woodcote Park, Purley CR8 3QR — MB ChB 1989 Manch.

LOBO, Mr Victor John Eudes Dominic 201a Maidstone Road, Rochester ME1 3ES Tel: 01634 846450 — MB BS Lond. 1959; FRCS Eng. 1969; FRCS Ed. 1964; DObst RCOG 1960. (St. Mary's) Cons. ENT Surg. Medway & Maidstone Gps. Hosps.

LOCAL, Francis Knox Department of Elderly Care, West Cumberland Hospital, Whitehaven CA28 8JG Tel: 01946 693181 Fax: 01946 523520 Email: frank.local@carlh-tr.northy.nhs.uk — MB BS 1973 Newc.; FRCP Lond. 1993; MRCP (UK) 1978. Cons. Geriat. W. Cumbria Health Care NHS Trust. Prev: Sen. Regist. (Gen. & Geriat. Med.) Manch. AHA (T).

LOCH, Alexander Buchanan Bingham Health Centre, Eaton Place, Bingham, Nottingham NG13 8BE; The Firs, Main St, Cropwell Butler, Nottingham NG12 3AB — MB BS 1974 Lond.; MRCGP 1979; DCH RCP Lond. 1977; DObst RCOG 1976.

LOCHAM, Jagdeep 33 Antrim Road, Reading RG5 3NU — MB ChB 1995 Manch.

LOCHEE BAYNE, Eleanor Mary 22 Knowle Road, Weeping Cross, Stafford ST17 0DN Tel: 01785 664980 Email: alocheebay@cyberphile.co.uk — MB BS 1974 Lond.; BSc Lond. 1971; DCH Eng. 1978. (Univ. Coll. Hosp.)

LOCHEE BAYNE, Wykeham Andrew The Surgery, High Street, Cheslyn Hay, Walsall WS6 7AB Tel: 01922 701280; 22 Knowle Road, Weeping Cross, Stafford ST17 0DN Tel: 01785 664980 Email: andrew.locheebayne@ntlworld.com — MB BS 1973 Lond.; DA Eng. 1975. (St. Geo.)

LOCHHEAD, James 47 Adele Street, Motherwell ML1 2QE — MB ChB 1968 Glas.

LOCHHEAD, Mr Jonathan 14 Bainbridge Avenue, Plymouth PL3 5QZ; 65 St. Augustine's Road, Camden, London NW1 9RR Tel: 020 7267 7898 — MB BS 1992 Lond.; FRCOphth 1997.

LOCHRIE, Allan Stewart Old Irvine Road Surgery, 4-6 Old Irvine Road, Kilmarnock KA1 2BD Tel: 01563 22413 — MB ChB 1973 Glas.; MRCGP 1980; DCH RCPS Glas. 1975. Prev: Regist. (Med.) Roy. Alexandra Infirm. Paisley; SHO (Infec. Dis.) Belvidere Hosp. Glas.; Ho. Off. (Med. Paediat.) Roy. Hosp. Sick Childr. Glas.

***LOCK, Anna Louise** Great House, Southerndown, Bridgend CF32 0RW — MB ChB 1996 Birm.

LOCK, Bridget Ann Orpington Hospital, Sevenoaks Road, Orpington BR6 9JU Tel: 01689 815082 — MB BS 1977 Lond.; FRCP Lond. 1994; FRCP (UK) 1994; MRCP 1984. Cons. Phys. Elderly People Bromley Hosp. NHS Trust. Prev: Sen. Regist. (Geriat. Med.) Middlx. Hosp. & N.wick Pk. Hosp.; Regist. (Med.) Kingston Hosp.

LOCK, Darren John Clifton Cottage, Wellington Avenue, Virginia Water GU25 4QY — MB ChB 1988 Liverp.

LOCK, Deborah Jane Twyford Surgery, Hazeley Road, Twyford, Winchester SO21 1QY Tel: 01962 712202 Fax: 01962 715158; The Cobblers Cottage, Queens St, Twyford, Winchester SO21 1QG Tel: 01962 713137 — BM BS 1989 Nottm.; MRCGP 1993; DRCOG 1992; DCH RCP Lond. 1990. (Nottingham University) GP. Prev: Trainee GP Reading VTS.

LOCK, Jane Alison Moore Potterells Medical Centre, Station Road, North Mymms, Hatfield AL9 7SN Tel: 01707 273338 Fax: 01707 263564; Skimpans Farm House, Bulls Lane, North Mymms, Hatfield AL9 7PE Tel: 01707 271503 — MB BS 1971 Lond.; MRCS Eng. LRCP Lond. 1971; DCH Eng. 1973; DObst RCOG 1973. (Westm.) Socs: Nat. Assn. Family Plann. Doctors & Brit. Menopause Soc. Prev: SHO S.end Gen. Hosp.

LOCK, Jonathan David Thomas Jubilee Medical Centre, 52 Croxteth Hall Lane, Croxteth, Liverpool L11 4UG Tel: 0151 546 3956 Fax: 0151 546 3221; 89 Foxhouse Lane, Liverpool L31 6EE — MB ChB 1980 Manch.; BSc (Hons.) (Psychol.) 1977; MRCGP 1984; DRCOG 1984. (Manch.)

LOCK, Karen Jane 33 Dean Close, Woking GU22 8NX — BM BCh 1991 Oxf.

LOCK, Mr Martin William Harvey Hospital, Willesborough, Ashford TN24 0LZ Tel: 01233 633331; Karibu, Nash Hill, Lyminge, Folkestone CT18 8ED Tel: 01303 862195 — MB ChB 1969 Birm.; FRCS Ed. 1979. (Univ. Coll. Rhodesia) Cons. (Orthop.) William Harvey Hosp. Ashford. & Buckland Hosp. Dover. Socs: Fell. BOA; Brit. Scoliosis Soc. Prev: Sen. Regist. (Orthop.) King's Coll. Hosp. Lond.; Regist. (Orthop.) Char. Cross Hosp. Lond. & Roy. Surrey Co. Hosp. Guildford.

LOCK, Martin Peter Anthony Wannell Three Bridges Regional Secure Unit, St Bernard's Wing, Ealing Hospital, Southall UB1 3EU Tel: 020 8354 8200 Fax: 020 8967 5477 — MB BS 1987 Lond.; MRCPsych 1992. Cons. Forens. Psychiat.; Psychiatric Mem. of the parole Bd.

LOCK, Mr Martin Russell Whittington Hospital, Highgate Hill, London N19 5NF Tel: 020 7272 3070 — MB BS 1968 Lond.; MRCS Eng. LRCP Lond. 1968; FRCS Eng. 1972. (Westm.) Cons. Surg. Whittington Hosp. Lond.; Cons. Surg. Whittington Hosp. Lond.; Hon. Sen. Lect. Univ. Coll. Lond. Socs: Fell. Assn. Surgs. Gt. Brit. & Irel.; Mem. RSM. Prev: Fell. (Colon & Rectal Surg.) Cleveland Clin. Cleveland, Ohio, USA; Lect. (Surg.) W.m. Med. Sch. Lond.; Regist. St. Mark's Hosp. Lond.

LOCK, Martin William Ventnor Medical Centre, 3 Albert Street, Ventnor PO38 1EZ Tel: 01983 852787 Fax: 01983 855447 — MB BS 1983 Lond.; MRCGP 1994; DRCOG 1994; DA (UK) 1986. (Lond. Hosp. Med. Coll.)

LOCK, Peter Timothy King's Ride Surgery, Quidenham Road, Kenninghall, Norwich NR16 2EF Tel: 01953 887208 Fax: 01953 887515; The Firs, The Butts, Kenninghall, Norwich NR16 2EQ — BM 1981 Soton.

LOCK, Sara Helen Department of Respiratory Medicine, Whittington Hospital, Highgate Hill, London N19 5NF Tel: 020 7288 5354 — MB BS 1986 Lond.; FRCP 2001; BA Camb. 1983; MRCP (UK) 1989. p/t Cons. Respirat. & Gen. Med. Prev: Flexible Sen. Regist. Rotat. (Respirat. & Gen. Med.) Chelsea & W.m. & Roy. Brompton Hosps. Lond.; Research Fell. NHLI Lond.; Regist. Rotat. Whittington Hosp. Lond.

LOCK, Stephen Penford, CBE (retired) 3 Alde House, Alde House Drive, Aldeburgh IP15 5EE Tel: 01728 452411 Fax: 01728 454228 Email: splock@globalnet.co.uk — MB BChir 1954 Camb.; MA Camb. 1954, MD 1987; MSc Manch. 1985; FRCP Ed. 1989; FRCPI 1987; FRCP Lond. 1974, M 1963; FACP 1989. Research Assoc. Wellcome Inst. Hist. Med. Lond. Prev: Sen. Research Assoc. RCP.

LOCK, Susan 31 Locks Road, Westhall, Halesworth IP19 8RD; Creekside, Quay St, halesworth IP19 8ET Tel: 01986 875021 — MB ChB 1986 Dundee.

LOCKE, Frederick Ingram (retired) 5 Fieldside, East Rainton, Houghton-le-Spring DH5 9RP Tel: 0191 584 0060 — MB BS 1947 Durh.

LOCKE, Imogen 11A Birchington Road, London N8 8HR — MB BS 1994 Lond.

LOCKE, James William Wallacetown Health Centre, 3 Lyon Street, Dundee DD4 6RF Tel: 01382 459519 Fax: 01382 453110 — MB ChB 1977 Dundee; DRCOG 1979.

LOCKE, Penelope Ruth Hillview Medical Centre, 60 Bromsgrove Road, Redditch B97 4RN Tel: 01527 66511; 19 Weatheroak Close, Webheath, Redditch B97 5TF Tel: 01527 457438 — MB BCh 1987 Wales. (Univ. Wales)

LOCKE, Rebecca Mary Dr MacLean and Partners, Monifieth Health Centre, Victoria Street, Monifieth, Dundee DD5 4LX Tel: 01382 534301 Fax: 01382 535959; 1 Grange Lane, Monifieth, Dundee DD5 4NB — MB ChB 1986 Dundee; PhD Dundee 1982; BSc (Hons.) St. And. 1978. Locality Ldr. LHCC Steering Gp. Angus. Socs: Assoc. Mem. RCGP.; BMA.

LOCKE, Stephen Matthew Adcroft Surgery, Prospect Place, Trowbridge BA14 8QA Tel: 01225 755878 Fax: 01225 775445; The Old Police House, 198 Devizes Road, Hilperton, Trowbridge BA14 7QR Tel: 01225 776191 — MB BS 1990 Lond.; MB BS (Hons. Obst. & Gyn.) Lond. 1990; MRCGP 1994; DRCOG 1993. GP; Clin. Asst. Oncol. Prev: Trainee GP/SHO Bath Roy. United Hosp. VTS.

LOCKE, Mr Timothy John 7 Stortholme Mews, Ranmoor, Sheffield S10 3HT — MB ChB 1978 Sheff.; MD Sheff. 1989, MB ChB 1978; FRCS Ed. (Cth.) 1988; FRCS Ed. 1983. Cons. Cardiothoracic Surg. N. Gen. Hosp. Sheff. Prev: Fell. (Cardiac Surg.) Mayo Clinic Rochester, USA.

LOCKE, William John Health Centre, St. Marys Place, Townend, Kirkcudbright DG6 4BJ Tel: 01557 330755 Fax: 01557 330917; Dairy House, Park of Tongland, Kirkcudbright DG6 4NE — MB ChB 1981 Ed.; DRCOG 1986.

LOCKENS, Rosalind The Health Centre, 2 The Tanyard, Cumnock KA18 1BF Tel: 01290 422723 Fax: 01290 425444 — MB BCh BAO 1989 Belf.; DCH RCP Dub. 1993; DRCOG 1992.

LOCKER, Adrian Philip Y Felin, Felindre, Dryslwyn, Carmarthen SA32 8RJ — MB BCh 1980 Wales.

LOCKER, Ian 81 Ferriby Road, Hessle HU13 0HU — MB ChB 1978 Leeds.

LOCKER, Malcolm Montaigne Crescent Surgery, 17 Montaigne Crescent, Glebe Park, Wragby Road, Lincoln LN2 4QN; 10 The Green, Nettleham, Lincoln LN2 2NR — MB ChB 1971 Sheff.; DObst RCOG 1974.

LOCKERBIE, Graham Dempster Clifton Surgery, Victoria Place, 35 Victoria Road, Dartmouth TQ6 9RT Tel: 01803 832212 Fax: 01803 837917 — MB ChB 1980 Dundee; DRCOG 1982.

LOCKET, Sidney (retired) Thatchers Hall, Ranters Lane, Goudhurst, Cranbrook TN17 1HR Tel: 01580 211360 — MB BS Lond. 1946; FRCP Lond. 1972, M 1945; MRCS Eng., LRCP Lond. 1938. Prev: Phys. i/c NE Thames RHA Poisoning Centre.

LOCKETT, Anthony Earl 32 York Street, Newcastle upon Tyne NE4 6ET — MB BS 1986 Newc.

LOCKETT, Christopher John 23 College La, London NW5 1BJ — MB BS 1997 Lond.

LOCKETT, Geoffrey William Edwin, SBStJ (retired) 29 Baginton Road, Coventry CV3 6JX Tel: 02476 414769 — MB ChB Bristol 1960. Prev: GP Moseley Avenue Surg. Coventry W. Midl.s.

LOCKETT, Geraldine Ann 51 Mill Road, Lode, Cambridge CB5 9EN — MB ChB 1973 Liverp.

LOCKETT, Harry Ian The Hay Barn, Pound Farm, Chaxhill, Westbury on Severn, Gloucester GL14 1QP — MB BS Lond. 1952; FFPHM 1989; FFCMI 1979; FFCM 1974; DPH Bristol 1958; DObst RCOG 1957. (St. Bart.) Prev: MOH E. Wilts. United Dists.; Co. Med. Off. Health & Princip. Sch. Med. Off. Notts. CC; Area Med. Off. Notts. AHA (T).

LOCKETT, Melanie Jane 4c, Burlington Gardens, Chiswick, London W4 4LT Tel: 020 8747 8261 — MB BS 1994 Lond.; BSc Lond. 1991; MRCP 1997. (St. Barths. Hosp.) Clin. Research. Fell. Gastroent. ICRF. St Marks Hosp. Harrow. Prev: Specialist Regist. Gastro.Hammersmith.Hosp.; Specialist Regist. Gastorenterol. & Gen. Med. Ealing Hosp. Middlx.; Lat.Sp.Gastr/HIV/Gen.Med.Roy.Free.Hosp.

LOCKETT, Simon Richard Taverham Surgery, Sandy Lane, Taverham, Norwich NR8 6JR Tel: 01603 867481 Fax: 01603 740670; 3 Pitt Barns, 26 The St, Ringland, Norwich NR8 6JG Tel: 01603 860026 Email: slocdoc@aol.com — MB BChir 1977 Camb.; MA, MB Camb. 1977, BChir 1976; MRCGP 1981; DRCOG 1979; FRCGP 1997. (Cambridge)

LOCKEY, Andrew Steven 7 Lidgett Park Mews, Lidgett Park Road, Roundhay, Leeds LS8 1DB — MB ChB 1991 Leeds; DA (UK) 1996; Dip. IMC RCS Ed. 1996; FRCS Ed. 1997. Specialist Regist. (A & E) Yorks.

LOCKEY, Brian Federick 21 Colborne Close, Baiter Park, Poole BH15 1UR — MB BS 1996 Lond. (Univ. Coll. Lond.)

LOCKEY, David John 28 Elms Avenue, London N10 2JP — MB BS 1988 Newc.

LOCKEY, Eunice (retired) 56 Clarence Gate Gardens, Glentworth St., London NW1 6QS Tel: 020 7723 9926 — MB BS Lond. 1950; BSc (Chem.) Lond. 1945, MD 1957; MRCS Eng. LRCP Lond. 1950; FRCPath 1972, M 1963. Prev: Cons. Chem. Path. Lond. Chest Hosp. & Barnet Gen. Hosp.

LOCKEY, Kenneth Nelson Enfield Villa, 68 Station Road, Billingham TS23 1AB Tel: 01642 531901; 4 Hamilton Drive, Whitley Bay NE26 1JG Tel: 0191 252 3069 — MB BS 1954 Durh. (Newc.) Socs: BMA.

LOCKHART, Alan Struan 127A Breck Road, Poulton-le-Fylde FY6 7HJ — MB ChB 1975 Dundee; FFA RCS Eng. 1982.

LOCKHART, Donna Louise Parke Davis & Co ltd, Lambert Court, Chestnut Avenue, Eastleigh SO53 3ZQ Tel: 02380 628277 Fax: 02380 629819 Email: donna.mcvey@wl.com — MB BS 1983 Lond.; BSc Lond. 1980; MBA Open 1995; MRCGP 1989; Dip. Pharm. Med RCP (UK) 1991. (St. Mary's Hosp. Lond.) Med.Dir. Pk.e-Davis & Co. Ltd. Prev: Marketing & Med. Manager Gastroenterol. Lederle Labs.; Dir. Anti-Infec. & Oncol. Research Lederle Laborat.; Trainee GP Twyford.

LOCKHART, Elaine Patricia 14 Bower Street, Glasgow G12 8PT — MB BCh BAO 1988 NUI.

LOCKHART, Gillian Dickson Elmwood Avenue Surgery, 3 Elmwood Avenue, Newton Mearns, Glasgow G77 6EH Tel: 0141 639 2478 Fax: 0141 639 6708 — MB ChB 1991 Glas. (Glas.) GP Elmwood Med. Pract. Glas.

LOCKHART, James Denis Fair (retired) Croome Cottage, Fishery Road, Maidenhead SL6 1UP Tel: 01628 630217 — BA, MB BCh BAO Dub. 1956; DPH Lond. 1963. Prev: Dir. Marion Merrell Dow Research & Developm. Centre Winnersh. Berks.

LOCKHART, Michael Cecil 11 Anniesdale Avenue, Stepps, Glasgow G33 6DR — MB ChB 1989 Dundee.

LOCKHART, Norman Stanley Godden Green Clinic, Godden Green, Sevenoaks TN15 0JR Tel: 01732 763491 Fax: 01732 763160 — MB BCh BAO 1980 Belf.; BSc (Hons.) Belf. 1968; PhD Glas. 1972; MRCPsych 1987. Med Dir Cygnet Clinic Beckton Lond; Hon. Cons. Psychiat. Godden Green Clinic Sevenoaks Kent. Prev: Dir. Ment. Health Servs. N. Kent Heathcare Trust; Sen. Regist. (Psychiat.) Guy's Hosp. & St. Thomas' Hosp. Lond.; Regist. (Psychiat.) W.minster Hosp. W.minster Childr.'s Hosp. & Char. Cross Hosp. Lond.

LOCKHART, Olivia Anne Butts Road Medical Centre, Butts Road, Bakewell DE45 1ED Tel: 01629 812871 Fax: 01629 814958; Beverly, Baslow Road, Bakewell DE45 1AA Tel: 01629 814194 — MB BS 1977 Lond.; DRCOG 1982. (Royal Free) Clin. Asst. (Geriat. Med.) Newholme Hosp. Bakewell.

***LOCKHART, Pauline Marja** 13 Pitreavie Place, Kirkcaldy KY2 6JX Tel: 01592 200586 Email: pmlockhart@doctors.org.uk — MB ChB 1998 Dund.; MB ChB Dund 1998.

LOCKHART, Stephen Paul Wyeth Lederle Vaccines, Huntercombe Lane S., Taplow, Maidenhead SL6 0PH Tel: 01628 413889 Fax: 01628 413891 Email: 100656.45@compuserve.com — BM BCh 1980 Oxf.; MA Camb. 1981, BA 1977; DM Oxf. 1988; MRCP (UK) 1983; MFPM RCP (UK) 1990; Dip. Pharm. Med. RCP (UK) 1988. (Jesus Coll. Camb. & New. Coll. Oxf.) Europ. Dir. Clin. Research Wyeth Lederle Vaccines. Prev: Dir. UK Clin. Developm. Lederle Laborat.; Clin. Research Fell. Radiother. Research Unit Inst. Cancer Research Roy. Marsden Hosp. Sutton; Regist. (Gen. Med. & Nephrol.) St. Mary's Hosp. Lond.

LOCKHAT, Moosaji Dawji Rising Brook Surgery, Merrey Road, Stafford ST17 9LY Tel: 01785 251134 Fax: 01785 222441; 8 Shannon Road, Burton Manor, Stafford ST17 9PX Tel: 01785 53756 — MB BS 1960 Calcutta. (Calcutta) Clin. Asst. (Genitourin. Med.) Staffs. Gen. Infirm.; Police Surg. Boro. Stafford. Socs: Overseas. Doctors. Assn; Muslim Doctors & Dentist Assn; Stafford. Med. Soc. Prev: Ho. Phys. & Ho. Surg. E. Birm. Gen. Hosp.; SHO Med. Lincoln Co. Hosp.; Regist. (Med. & Geriat.) St. John's Hosp. Lond.

LOCKHAT-CLEGG, Farhana Banu Leicester General Hospital, Gwendolen Road, Leicester LE4 Tel: 0116 249 0490; 20 Chatsworth Drive, Whitestone, Nuneaton CV11 6SB Email: salfar@loclegg.freeserve.co.uk — MB ChB 1995 Manch.; DFFP 1997. SHO (O & G), Leicester Gen. Hosp. Prev: SHO (Neonatol.) Leicester Gen. Hosp. & Leicester Roy. Inf.; SHO (O & G) Leicester Roy. Inf.; SHO (Gen. Med.), Leicester Roy. Inf.

LOCKIE, Andrew Cameron Knight, MBE Green Lanes, Alveston, Stratford-upon-Avon CV37 7QD Tel: 01789 268588 Fax: 01789 268588 Email: cameron@lockie.demon.co.uk — MB ChB Ed. 1966; BSc (Hons. Pharmacol.) Ed. 1964; FRCP Ed 1997; MRCP (Lond.); MICGP 1986; FRCGP 1986, M 1971; Cert. Family Plann. JCC 1974; DObst RCOG 1972. (Ed.) Vis. Prof., Coll. of Med. Sultan Qaboos Univ., Muscat, Oman; RCGP Oman Fell.; Pres. Brit. Travel Health Assn.; Extern. Examr. Oman MRCGP (Internat.) Exams. Socs: BMA; Internat. Soc. Travel Med.; Fell. Roy. Geogr. Soc. Lond. Prev: Sen. Partner Rother Ho. Med. Centre, Stratford Upon Avon; Hosp. Pract. (Gyn.) Stratford upon Avon Gen. Hosp.; Convener Modified Essay Quest. Paper of Mem.sh. Exam. RCGP & Mem. Panel Examrs.

LOCKIE, Andrew Hart 4 Waterden Road, Guildford GU1 2AW Tel: 01483 503240 Fax: 01483 531 177 Email: drlockie@drlockie.com; Lark Rise, Franks Field, Peaslake, Guildford GU5 9SS — MB ChB 1972 Aberd.; Dobst RCOG 1976; MFHom 1975; MRCGP 1978; 1976 Cert JCC Lond.

LOCKIE, David The Old Mansion House Surgery, 15 Church St. N., Old Whittington, Chesterfield S41 9QN Tel: 01246 455410 & 454411 — MB ChB 1963 Glas.; MRCOG 1970; Dip. Psychother. Sheff. 1982. (Glas.) Socs: BMA & Brit. Holistic Med. Assn. Prev: Regist. St. Mary's Hosp. Lond. (Harrow Rd. Br.); Regist. Ayrsh. Centr. Hosp. Irvine; SHO Qu. Mother's Hosp. Glas. & W.. Infirm. Glas.

LOCKIE, Jane Flat 4, 8 Warrington Crescent, London W9 1EL; 170 Gwydir Street, Cambridge CB1 2LW — MB ChB 1983 Manch.; FCAnaesth 1990. Cons. Paediat. Anaesth. UCL Hosp.Gt ormond St.hosp. Prev: Regist. (Anaesth.) Alder Hey Hosp. Liverp.; Regist. Rotat. (Anaesth.) W. Midl. HA.; Sen. Regist. Rotat. Univ. Coll. Hosp. Lond.

LOCKIE, Mr John (retired) 99 Eldon Street, Greenock PA16 7RJ Tel: 01475 721699 — MB ChB Glas. 1941; FRFPS Glas. 1949; FRCS Glas. 1962; MFOM RCP Lond. 1979. Prev: Med. Off. S. Scotl. Elec. Bd.

LOCKIE, Paul Teviot Medical Practice, Teviot Road, Hawick TD9 9DT; Scawmill, Wilton Dean, Hawick TD9 7HY — MB ChB 1990 Dundee; MRCGP 1994; DRCOG 1992. (Dundee) Socs: Hawick Med. Soc. (Treas.); GP SubComm. (Vice Pres.); Local Med. Comm. (Vice Pres.). Prev: Assoc. GP I. of Jura & Islay.

LOCKIE, Philip David 4 Castlehill Manor, Belfast BT4 3QH — MB BCh BAO 1991 Belf.

LOCKIE, Shona Mary Campbell Paediatric Department, Guy's Hospital, St Thomas's St., London SE1 Tel: 020 7955 5000; 8 Roseneath Road, London SW11 6AH — MB BS 1991 Lond.; MRCP (UK) 1995.

LOCKIE, William John (retired) 96 Terregles Avenue, Pollokshields, Glasgow G41 4PQ Tel: 0141 423 0929 — MB ChB 1952 Glas.; MRCGP 1960. Prev: Pres. Glas. S.. Med. Soc.

LOCKINGTON, Timothy John The Ipswich Hospital, Health Road, Ipswich Tel: 01473 712233; 147 Westerfield Road, Ipswich IP4 3AA Tel: 01473 213444 — MB 1980 Camb.; MRCP (UK) 1982. (Camb. & Lond. Hosp. Med. Coll.) Cons. (Geriat. & Gen. Med.) Ipswich Hosp. Socs: Brit. Geriat. Soc. Prev: Sen. Regist. (Roy. Lond. Hosp.); Pfizer Research Fell. Char. Cross Hosp.; Regist. Qu. Eliz. Hosp. Birm.

LOCKLEY, Miss Dora Monica (retired) Greenhill Cottage, 10 Ford St., Braughing, Ware SG11 2PW — MB BS 1948 Madras; MRCOG 1964; DGO Madras 1951. Prev: GP Nutbourne & Lockley.

LOCKLEY, Margaret Ruth Public Health Laboratory, Heartlands Hospital, Bordesley Green E., Birmingham Tel: 0121 753 1505 Fax: 0121 772 6229 Email: sccdc@hsrc.org.uk — MB ChB 1978 Birm.; MSc (Immunol.) Birm. 1991, BSc 1975; MRCP (UK) 1984; FRCPath 1997. (Birmingham) Cons. Microbiol. & Communicable Dis. Control PHLS & Solihull HA.

***LOCKLEY, Michelle** 14 South Cottage Gardens, Chorleywood, Rickmansworth WD3 5EH — MB BS 1997 Lond.; BSc Lond. 1994.

LOCKLEY, William John Oliver Street Surgery, 57 Oliver Street, Ampthill, Bedford MK45 2SB Tel: 01525 402641 Fax: 01525 840764; Sandown, 107 Flitwick Road, Ampthill, Bedford MK45 2NT Tel: 01525 404238 Fax: 01525 840764 — MB BChir 1973 Camb.; MA Camb. 1975. (Camb. & Lond. Hosp.) Resource Librarian Assn. of BRd.casting Doctors. Socs: Brit. Computer Soc. (Primary Health Care Sect.). Prev: Trainee GP Colchester VTS.

LOCKSTONE, Derek Reginald (retired) Cherry Garth, Stakesby Vale, Whitby YO21 1JZ Tel: 01947 603966 Fax: 01947 603966 Email: lockstone@chrrygarthwhitby.freeserve.co.uk — MB BS 1962 Lond.; MRCS Eng. LRCP Lond. 1962; LMSSA Lond. 1962; MRCGP 1976; FFA RCSI 1970; Dip. IMC RCS Ed. 1989; DA Eng. 1968; DObst RCOG 1964. GP; Med. Adviser to Childr. in distress. Prev: Regist. (Anaesth.) Plymouth Hosp. Gp.

LOCKTON, John Andrew Department of Experimental Medicine, Astra Charnwood, Bakewell Road, Loughborough LE11 5RH Tel: 01509 644008 Fax: 01509 645586 — MB ChB 1985 Manch.; MD Manch. 1993; MRCP (UK) 1988. Clin. Pharmacol. Astra Charnwood LoughBoro.. Prev: Regist. (Med.) Aberd. Roy. Infirm. & N. Manch. Gen. Hosp.; Research Regist. Leeds Univ.

LOCKWOOD, Alison Jane St Nicholas House, Burton, South Wirral CH64 5SH — MB ChB 1986 Dundee; MRCGP 1993.

LOCKWOOD, Catherine Mary 140 Leahurst Road, London SE13 5NN Tel: 020 8852 3440; Tavistock Clinic, 120 Belsize Lane, London NW3 5BA Tel: 020 7435 7111 — MB BS 1985 Lond.; MRCPsych 1994. (UMDS (Guy's) London) Sen. Regist. (Psychother.) Forest Healthcare Trust & Tavistock Clinic Lond. Prev: Regist. Rotat. (Psychiat.) Guy's & UMDS Hosps. Lond.

LOCKWOOD, Christine Susan Hill Cote, 72 Whirlow Lane, Sheffield S11 9QF — MB ChB 1980 Dundee; MRCGP 1991; DRCOG 1985. (Dundee) Socs: BMA.

LOCKWOOD, Christopher Mark Langton Medical Group, St. Chads Health Centre, Dimbles Lane, Lichfield WS13 7HT Tel: 01543 258983 Fax: 01543 414776 — MB ChB 1966 Manch; MB ChB Manch. 1966; FRCGP 1999; MRCGP 1980 - FRCGP 1999; DA Eng. 1968; DObst RCOG 1968; DTM & H Liverp. 1968. Clin. Asst. (Palliat. Care) St. Giles Hospice Whittington. Prev: Med. Off. Min. of Overseas Developm. (Botswana); SHO (Anaesth.) & Ho. Phys. Hope Hosp. Salford; Ho. Surg. Salford Roy. Hosp.

LOCKWOOD, Claire Alexandra Laindon Health Centre, Basildon SS15 5TR Tel: 01268 546411; 199 Stock Road, Billericay CM12 0SE — MB ChB 1986 Manch.; MRCGP 1994; DCH RCP Lond. 1994; DRCOG 1988; DFFP 1996. GP Princip. Laindon Health Centre Laindon Basildon Essex. Socs: BMA Mem.; Brit. Med. Acupunc. Soc. Prev: GP Retainer Watford; GP Retainer Rickmansworth; GP Retainer Beaconsfield.

LOCKWOOD, Diana Nancy Johanna Hospital for Tropical Diseases, Copper St, London WC1E 6AU Tel: 020 7387 9300 Ext: 5970 — MB ChB 1981 Birm.; BSc (Anat. Sci.) Birm. 1978, MB ChB 1981; MRCP (UK) 1986; MD Birm 1996. Cons. Leprologist Hosp. Trop. Dis. Lond.; Sen. lec Lond. Sch. of Hyg. & Trop. Med. Prev: Sen. Regist. (Infec. Dis. & Trop. Med.) St. Mary's Hosp. Lond.; Wellcome Research Fell. (Clin. Sci.) Lond. Sch. Hyg. & Trop. Med. Lond.; Regist. (Med.) Hammersmith Hosp. Lond.

LOCKWOOD, Eric The Health Centre, Saunder Bank, Burnley BB11 2EN Tel: 01282 831249; Kilburn, 4 Westwood Road, Burnley BB12 0HR Tel: 01282 31585 — MB ChB 1965 Leeds; MD Leeds 1971; MRCGP 1972; Dip. Soc. Med. Ed. 1969. (Leeds) Prev: Lect. (Gen. Pract.) Univ. Edin.

***LOCKWOOD, Frances Joan** Cheyney House, Upton Cheyney, Bitton, Bristol BS30 6NJ Tel: 0117 932 2976 — BM BS 1998 Nottm.; BM BS Nottm 1998; BMedSci Nottm 1996.

LOCKWOOD, Frank Howard (retired) 9 Abbey Fields, Crewe CW2 8HJ Tel: 01270 67854 — MB ChB 1950 Ed.; MB ChB. Ed. 1950.

LOCKWOOD, Geoffrey Gordon Department of Anaesthetics, Hammersmith Hospital, Du Cane Road, London W12 0NN Tel: 020 8743 2030 Fax: 020 8749 9974; 74 Underhill Road, London SE22 0QT — MB BS 1978 Lond.; BSc (Hons) Lond. 1987; FFA RCS Eng. 1983. Sen. Lect. (Anaesth.) Hammersmith Hosp. Lond.

LOCKWOOD, Gillian Mary 51 Chalfont Road, Oxford OX2 6TJ Tel: 01865 52635 — BM BCh 1986 Oxf. Clin. Research Fell. Fell. Oxf. IVF Unit.

LOCKWOOD, Janet Elizabeth PAH NHS Trust, Hamstel Road, Harlow CM20 1QX; The Old House, 31 High St, Cambridge CB2 5HW — MA, BSc Oxf. 1969, BM BCh 1970; MRCP (UK) 1973; FRCR 1977; DMRD Eng. 1976. Cons. Radiol. P.ss Alexandra Hosp. NHS Trust. Prev: Cons. Radiol. Ealing Hosp. Lond. & Ashford Hosp. Middlx.; Sen. Regist. (Radiol.) Hammersmith Hosp. & Ealing Hosp. Lond.

LOCKWOOD, Jeremy Augustus Frederick Stapenhill Surgery, Fyfield Road, Stapenhill, Burton-on-Trent DE15 9QD Tel: 01283 565200 Fax: 01283 500617; 361 Roliston Road, Stapenhill, Burton-on-Trent DE15 9RH — MB ChB 1981 Liverp.

LOCKWOOD, John Ralph (retired) The Old Post House, Tarrington, Hereford HR1 4HZ Tel: 0143279 201 — MB BS 1954 Lond.; DObst RCOG 1959. Prev: GP Oxted.

LOCKWOOD, Marjorie The Health Centre, Central Road, Partington, Manchester M31 4FL Tel: 0161 775 7032 Fax: 0161 777 8003; 12 Sunningdale Drive, Irlam, Manchester M44 6WH Tel: 0161 775 9140 — MB ChB 1981 Liverp.

LOCKWOOD, Michael John Adelaide Medical Centre, 36 Adelaide Road, Andover SP10 1HA Tel: 01264 351144 Fax: 01264 358639 — MB BS 1967 Lond.; MRCS Eng. LRCP Lond. 1967; DA Eng. 1970; DObst RCOG 1970. (Guy's) Mem. Exec. Comm. Nat. VAMP User Gp. Ltd.; Chairm. N. & Mid Hants. LMC; Mem. Scientif. & Ethical Advis. Gp. for The Gen. Pract. Research Database. Socs: BMA; Primary Care Spec. Gp. of Brit. Computer Soc. Prev: Trainee GP Winchester VTS; SHO (Anaesth.) Roy. Hants. Co. Hosp. Winchester; Ho. Surg. Guy's Hosp. Lond.

LOCKWOOD, Penny Fintry Mill Medical Centre, Finavon St., Dundee DD4 9DU; 7 Wemyss Gardens, Balgillo Park, Broughty Ferry, Dundee DD5 3BX — MB ChB 1991 Liverp.; DRCOG 1997; DFFP 1997. (Liverp.)

LOCKWOOD, Susan Elizabeth Cherry Tree Cottage, Wortley, Sheffield S35 7DQ — MB ChB 1985 Leeds. Clin. Asst. (Diabetes) Rotherham Gen. Hosp.

LOCKWOOD, Trevor John Ivry Street Medical Practice, 5 Ivry Street, Ipswich IP1 3QW Tel: 01473 254718 Fax: 01473 287790 — BM 1981 Soton.; MRCGP 1986; Dip. Occ. Med. 1995.

LOCKWOOD, Wilhelmina (retired) Church Row, Llowes, Hereford HR3 5JB Tel: 01497 847664 — MB 1954 Leiden; LRCP LRCS Ed. LRFPS Glas. 1957; DObst RCOG 1962. Prev: GP Kingsland Herefordsh.

LOCKYEAR, Susan Kay The Surgery, 25 St Mary's Road, Tickhill, Doncaster DN11 9NA Tel: 01302 742503; Wooffendon House, Chapel Lane, Scrooby, Doncaster DN10 6AE Tel: 01302 710253 — MB ChB 1988 Sheff.; MRCGP 1992. GP Doncaster. Socs: Med. Protec. Soc. Prev: Trainee GP Doncaster VTS.

LOCKYER, Charles Richard William Arderne Cottage, Utkinton, Tarporley CW6 0JX; 20 heathfields, Downend, Bristol BS16 6HS — MB BS 1993 Lond.; BSc Lond. 1990, MB BS 1993; FRCS 1998. (Lond.hosp) Clin. Research. Fell. Urol. Prev: SHO. Urol. S.mead.hosp; SHO Surg. Rotat. Chelmsford; SHO O & G Ipswich.

LOCKYER, Gavin James Simon The Surgery, High Street, Lowestoft NR32 1JE Tel: 01502 589151 Fax: 01502 566719 — MB BS 1989 Lond.; DRCOG 1993.

LOCKYER, Jane Alison Cluny, Victoria Road, Huntly AB54 8AH — MB ChB 1982 Dundee; MRCPath 1994. Prev: Clin. Asst. (Path.) Raigmore Hosp. Inverness; Lect. & Hon. Sen. Regist. (Path.) Ninewells Hosp. Dundee.

LOCKYER, Jennifer Susan Temple House Surgery, Temple House, Temple Street, Keynsham, Bristol BS31 1EJ Tel: 0117 986 2406 Fax: 0117 986 5695 — MB BS 1986 Lond.; MRCGP 1991; DRCOG 1990; DCH RCP Lond. 1989. (Westm.) GP Princip.

LOCKYER, Mark William Hope Farm Medical Centre, Hope Farm Road, Great Sutton, South Wirral CH66 2WW; Beacon Cottage, Moorland Close, Heswall, Wirral CH60 0EL — MB ChB 1986 Liverp.; MRCGP 1991.

LOCKYER, Martin Stephen Almondsbury Surgery, Sundays Hill, Almondsbury, Bristol BS32 4DS Tel: 01454 613161 Fax: 01454 615745 — MB BS 1977 Lond. (Lond. Hosp.)

LOCKYER, Matthew James Ixworth Surgery, Peddars Close, Ixworth, Bury St Edmunds IP31 2HD Tel: 01359 230252 Fax: 01359 232586; Fairfield House, Mill Gardens, Walsham le Willows, Bury St Edmunds IP31 3BD Tel: 01359 259431 — MB BS 1984 Lond.; BSc (Hons.) Liverp. 1979; MRCGP 1988; DRCOG 1988; DCH RCP Lond. 1987. Clin. Asst. (Diabetic & Gen. Med.) W. Suff. Hosp. Bury St. Edmunds. Prev: Trainee GP Ipswich Hosp. VTS.

LODEN, Arthur Edwin, MBE (retired) 2 Cadogan Court, Barley Lane, Exeter EX4 1TA Tel: 01392 51436 — MB BS 1939 Lond.; MRCS Eng., LRCP Lond. 1937. Prev: Asst. Surg. Regist. Guy's Hosp.

LODER, Robert Edward (retired) Middle Cleave, Northam, Bideford EX39 2RJ Tel: 01237 477959 — MRCS Eng. LRCP Lond. 1943; MA Camb. 1944, MB BChir 1943; FRCA 1992; FFA RCS Eng. 1954; DA Eng. 1947. Prev: Cons. Anaesth. P'boro. Health Dist.

LODGE, Adrian Morris Royal Edinburgh Hospital, Morningside Terrace, Edinburgh EH10 6AW Tel: 01905 352255 — MB ChB 1969 Ed.; BSc (Hons.) Pharmacol. Ed. 1966; MRCPsych 1973; DPM Ed. 1972. (Ed.) Cons. Psychiat. Roy. Edin. Hosp.; Med. Commr., Ment. Welf. Commiss. for Scotl. Prev: Sen. Regist. & Regist. Roy. Edin. Hosp.

LODGE, Alan Blakey (retired) 1B The Avenue, Dallington, Northampton NN5 7AJ Tel: 01604 759621 — MB BS Lond. 1952; FFA RCS Eng. 1960; DA Eng. 1956. Cons. Anaesth. N.ampton Health Dist. Prev: Ho. Surg., Sen. Res. Anaesth. & Sen. Regist. (Anaesth.) St. Bart.

LODGE, Mrs Alwynne (retired) Nags Fold Farm, Pity Me, Durham DH1 5RS Tel: 0191 386 4895 — MB BS 1956 Durh.

LODGE, Briony Clare 24 Cambridge Crescent, Bristol BS9 3QG — MB ChB 1995 Leic.

LODGE, George John Green Lane Hospital, Devizes SN10 5DS Tel: 01380 731200 Fax: 01380 731308 — MB BS 1971 Lond.; BSc (Hons., Biochem.) Lond. 1968; MRCS Eng. LRCP Lond. 1971; MRCPsych 1976; DPM Manch. 1976. (St. Bart.) Cons. Psychiat. Green La. Hosp. Devizes. Prev: Sen. Regist. (Psychiat.) Univ. Hosp. S. Manch.; Ho. Surg. Whipps Cross Hosp.; Ho. Phys. Roy. S. Hants Hosp.

LODGE, Jacqueline Anne Skerries, Ferry Road, Studland, Swanage BH19 3AQ — MB BS 1989 Lond.; MRCGP 1995.

LODGE, James Samuel Harvey (retired) The Keep, Scott Lane, Wetherby LS22 6LH Tel: 01937 582401 — MB BChir 1952 Camb.; DCH Eng. 1954. Prev: Med. Off. H.M. Youth Custody Centre Wetherby.

LODGE, Mr Jeremy Peter Alan 2 Wigton Park Close, Wigton Lane, Leeds LS17 8UH; 2 Wigton Park Close, Wigton Lane, Leeds LS17 8UH — MD 1993 Leeds; MB ChB 1983; FRCS Eng. 1988. Cons., Transpl. Surg., St. James' Leeds.

LODGE, June Winifred Leghari, Lodge and Muktar, The GP Centre, 322 Malden Road, North Cheam, Sutton SM3 8EP Tel: 020 8644 0224 Fax: 020 8288 1012; 25 High Beeches, Banstead SM7 1NB Tel: 01737 353811 — MB BS 1971 Lond.; MRCS Eng. LRCP Lond. 1971; MRCGP 1976; Dip. Dermat. Wales 1990; DObst RCOG 1973; DCH Eng. 1973; DCM Beijing 1999. (Roy. Free Hosp.)

LODGE, Kathleen Vernell (retired) Dale Garth, Queens Drive, Heswall, Wirral CH60 6SH Tel: 0151 342 4378 — MB ChB 1945 Manch.; MD (Commend.) Manch. 1954; FRCPath 1966, M 1964; DObst RCOG 1946. Hon. Cons. Path. Wythenshawe Hosp. Manch. Prev: Cons. Pathol. Wythenshawe, Duchess of York & Baguley Hosps. Manch.

LODGE, Laura Janet Roundstone Surgery, Polebarn Circus, Trowbridge BA14 7EG — MB ChB 1973 Manch.; MRCGP 1978.

LODGE, Lionel Cresswell (retired) 1 Denham Drive, Highcliffe, Christchurch BH23 5AT Tel: 0142 52 72126 — MRCS Eng. LRCP Lond. 1931.

LODGE, Lois Helen, Lt.-Col. RAMC Retd. Moonraker, Tower Hill, Dorking RH4 2BB Tel: 01306 885250 Email: lois.lodge@supanet.com — MB ChB 1976 Liverp.; MSc Lond. 1987; T(PHM) 1991; MFPHM 1990; FFPHM 1998. (Liverpool) Cons. (Pub. Health Med.); Asst. Dep. Coroner Surrey. Prev: Cons. in Pub. Health Med., E. Surrey Health Auth.; Acting Director of Pub. Health, S. E. Region of the NH Exec.; Dep. Director of Pub. Health, S. Thames Regional Office of NH Exec.

LODGE, Mary Catherine 39 Braid Road, Edinburgh EH10 6AW — MB ChB 1998 Ed.; MB ChB Ed 1998.

LODGE, Philip John Ground Floor Flat, 13 Oak Avenue, Crouch End, London N8 8LJ Tel: 020 8348 0295 — MB BS 1989 Lond.; DTM & H Liverp. 1991; MRCGP 1998. (Royal Free) SHO St Josephs.Hospice.Hackney. Prev: GP Regist. Potters Bar Herts.; SHO (Palliat. Med.) Mildmay Mission Hosp. Hackney; SHO (Paediat.) Barnet Hosp.

LODGE, Richard Park Surgery, 60 Ilkeston Road, Heanor DE75 7DX Tel: 01773 531011 Fax: 01773 534440; 179 Heanor Road, Heanor DE75 7QY Tel: 01773 531171 — MB ChB 1976 Sheff.; MRCGP 1980; DRCOG 1979. (Sheffield)

LODGE PATCH, Ian Charles (retired) 152 Harley Street, London W1N 1HH Tel: 020 7935 2477 — MB BS 1946 Lond.; MD Lond. 1949; FRCP Lond. 1978, M 1948; FRCPsych 1974, M 1971; DPM Lond. (Acad.) 1956. Prev: Hon. Cons. Psychiat. Hammersmith & St. Chas. Hosps. Lond.

LODH, M K Central Park Medical Centre, 132-134 Liscard Road, Wallasey CH44 0AB Tel: 0151 638 8833 Fax: 0151 637 0208.

LODHA, Lila Amarsingh Harbour View Surgery, 56 Station Road, Burry Port SA16 0LW Tel: 01554 835555 Fax: 01554 835123 — MB BS 1972; DRCOG 1982 London; MD 1977; DGO 1976. (B.J. Medical College)

LODHI, Khateeb Ahmad Khan 118 Albert Road, Jarrow NE32 5AQ — MB BS 1957 Punjab; MB BS Punjab (Pakistan) 1957.

LODHI, Mr Manzoor Ahmad Khan 35 Dollis Hill Avenue, London NW2 6EU Tel: 020 8452 9656 — MB BS 1958 Karachi; BSc Agra 1947; FRCS Ed. 1969. (Dow Med. Coll. Karachi) Prev: Surg. Regist. Acton Hosp., St. Mary's Hosp. Plaistow & St. And. Hosp.; Dollis Hill.

LODHIA, Bhanuchandra Rugnath Walnut Street Surgery, 110 Walnut Street, Leicester LE2 7LE Tel: 0116 285 5300; 2 Woodborough Road, Evington, Leicester LE5 4LR Tel: 0116 241 6047 — MB BS 1975 Karnatak; LMSSA Lond. 1993; MRCGP 1995; DRCOG 1994; DTM & H 1987; FRSH 1987. GP Walnut St. Med. Centre; Med. GP, Leicester Gen. Hosp.; HMP Gartree, Market HarBoro. Socs: MRCGP; MRCOG; LMSSA Lond. Prev: GP Monrovia, Liberia, W. Afr.

LODWICK, Joscelin Mary 13 Quicksand Lane, Aldridge, Walsall WS9 0BD Tel: 01922 52891 — MB BS 1979 Lond.; MRCGP 1983; DRCOG 1982; Cert. JCC Lond. 1982. Med. Off. W. Midl. Cardiac Rehabil. Unit Walsall. Prev: Trainee GP Humberside VTS; SHO (Cas.) Hull Roy. Infirm.

LODWICK, Lisa Margaret 31 Packwood Close, Chesterton Heights, Leamington Spa CV31 1FL Tel: 01926 313158; 31 Packwood Close, Chesterton Heights, Leamington Spa CV31 1FL Tel: 01926 313158 — BM BCh 1991 Oxf.; BA (Hons.) Physiol. Sci. Oxf. 1988; MRCGP 1996; DFFP 1998. (Oxf.) GP Non-Princip. Leamington Spa. Prev: GP/Regist. Clarendon Lodge Surg. Leamington Spa & Stretton-on-Dunsmore, Warks.; SHO (A & E) Darlington Memor. Hosp.

LODWICK, Rhys 13 Quicksand Lane, Aldridge, Walsall WS9 0BD Tel: 01922 52891 — MSc (Gerontol.) Lond. 1990, MB BS (Hons.) 1979; MRCP (UK) 1986; MRCGP 1983; Cert. JCC Lond. 1982; DCH RCP Lond. 1982; DRCOG 1982. (King's Coll.) Cons. Geriat. & Gen. Med. New Cross Hosp. Wolverhampton. Prev: Regist. (Rheum. & Chest Med.) Dudley Rd. Hosp. Birm.; Regist. (Rheum.) Manor Hosp. Walsall; Lect. (Geriat. Med.) Univ. Birm.

LODWIG, Graham Stuart 25 Neath Road, Maesteg CF34 9PG — MB BCh 1956 Wales. (Cardiff) Prev: Ho. Surg. Surgic. Unit & Dept. Neurosurg. Cardiff Roy. Infirm.; Ho. Phys. E. Glam. Hosp. Pontypridd; RAMC (Nat. Serv.).

LODWIG, Thomas Stephen 73 Dinas Baglan Road, Port Talbot SA12 8DT — MB BS 1986 Lond.

LOEFFLER, Mr Frank Elias 86 Harley Street, London W1N 1AE Tel: 020 7486 2966 Fax: 0171 637 0994; 20 Stanley Crescent, London W11 2NA Tel: 020 7221 1662 Fax: 020 7229 4032 — MB BChir 1956 Camb.; FRCS Eng. 1958; FRCOG 1974, M 1963; MRCS Eng. LRCP Lond. 1955. (Lond. Hosp.) Hons. Cons. O & G St. Mary's Hosp. & Samarit. Hosp. Wom. Lond.; Hon. Cons. Obst. Qu. Charlotte's Matern. Hosp. Lond. Socs: Fell. Roy. Soc. Med. Prev:

Edr. Brit. Jl. O & G; Cons. O & G Centr. Middlx. & Willesden Gen. Hosps.; Sen. Regist. Qu. Charlotte's Hosp. & Chelsea Hosps.

LOEFFLER, Mr Mark David Colchester General Hospital, Turner Road, Colchester CO4 5JL Tel: 01206 853535; The Frith, Colchester Road, Colchester CO7 6DL Tel: 01206 322358 — MB BS 1984 Lond.; FRCS (Orth.) 1994; FRCS Eng. 1989. Cons. Orthop. Surg. Colchester Gen. Hosp. Prev: Sen. Regist. & Regist. (Orthop.) Roy. Lond. Hosp.; SHO Rotat. (Surg.) Whipps Cross Hosp.; SHO. Rotat. (Trauma) Addenbrooke's Hosp.

LOEHRY, Christian Alexander Edward Hugh Royal Bournemouth Hospital, Castle Lane, Bournemouth BH7 7DW Tel: 01202 303626; Lytchett St. Mary, High St, Lytchett Matravers, Poole BH16 6BS — MD 1968 Camb.; MB 1963, BChir 1962; FRCP Lond. 1977, M 1965. (St. Thos.) Cons. Phys. E. Dorset Health Dist. Socs: BMA & Assoc. Phys.

LOEHRY, Juliette Kate 17 Lizban Street, Blackheath, London SE3 8SS — BM 1992 Soton.; MRCP (UK) 1996. Specialist Regist. (Gastroenterol. & Gen. Med.) Newham Gen. Hosp. Lond. Prev: Regist. (Intens. Care) Austral.; SHO Rotat. (Med.) Derriford Hosp. Plymouth.

LOESCHER, Alison Ruth 2 Canterbury Avenue, Fulwood, Sheffield S10 3RT — MB ChB 1994 Sheff.; PhD Birm. 1989. Lect. (Oral Surg.) Sheff. Univ.

LOFFELD, Annette 7 Gilchrist Drive, Edgbaston, Birmingham B15 3NG Tel: 0121 684 1236 — State Exam Med 1993 Bonn; MRCP(UK) 1999. (Dermat.) Specialist Regist. (LAT) Birm. Childr.'s Hosp.

LOFFHAGEN, Richard James 3 Charles Close, Osbaston, Monmouth NP25 3JD — MB BS 1997 Lond.

LOFIEGO, Maria Cristina 2 Albert Road, Fairfield, Stockton-on-Tees TS19 7EW — State Exam 1982 Rome.

LOFT, Duncan Edward Department of Gastroenterology, Walsgrave Hospital, Coventry CV2 2DX Tel: 024 76 602020 Fax: 024 76 622197 — MB ChB 1978 Birm.; MD Birm. 1991; FRCP Lond. 1996; MRCP (UK) 1982; Spec. Accredit. Gen. Med. & Gastroenterol. JCHMT 1991. (Birm.) Cons. Med. & Gastroenterol. Walsgrave Hosp. Coventry; Hon. Sen. Lect. Warwick Univ. Socs: Hon Sec Brit Soc Gastroenterol. Prev: Sen. Regist. (Med. & Gastroenterol.) Centr. Middlx. Hosp. Lond.; Regist. (Gastroenterol. & Gen. Med.) Hope Hosp. Salford; MRC Research Fell. Hope Hosp. Salford. 1984-1987.

LOFTHOUSE, Craig Maxwell Alder Hey Childrens Hospital, Alder Road, Liverpool L12 2AP; 12 Arnesby Avenue, Sale M33 2WJ Tel: 0161 291 1861 Email: craig@lofthouse3.freeserve.co.uk — MB ChB 1990 Manch.; MRCPCH 1996. Socs: BMA.

LOFTHOUSE, Jane Anne Library House Surgery, Avondale Road, Chorley PR7 2AD Tel: 01257 262081 — MB ChB 1979 Manch.; DRCOG 1983 Lond.; DCH RCP 1982 Lond. Prev: Trainee GP Leicester Hosp. VTS; Ho. Surg. Sharoe Green Hosp. Preston; Ho. Phys. Vict. Hosp. Blackpool.

LOFTHOUSE, Robert Amos Hilldyke Cottages, Lanebottom, Todmorden — MB BChir 1991 Camb.

LOFTHOUSE, Mrs Susan Midway Surgery, 93 Watford Road, St Albans AL2 3JX Tel: 01727 832125 Fax: 01727 836384; 52 Leverstock Green Road, Hemel Hempstead HP3 8PR Tel: 01442 246115 — MB ChB 1971 Bristol; MRCGP 1986; DRCOG 1974. Trainer. Prev: Course Organiser NW Herts. VTS.

LOFTING, John Anthony (retired) Edgehill, St. Leonard's Road, Norwich NR1 4JW Tel: 01603 623607 — BM BCh 1956 Oxf.; MA Oxf. 1956; MRCS Eng. LRCP Lond. 1956; DObst RCOG 1958. JP. Prev: Ho. Surg. (O & G) Roy. Infirm. Huddersfield.

LOFTS, Fiona Jane Med. Oncol. Department, St. Geroge's Hospital, Blackshaw Road, London SW17 0QT Tel: 020 8725 2955 Fax: 020 8725 1199 — MB BS 1983 Lond.; PhD Lond. 1993, BSc (Hons.) 1980; FRCP (UK) 1987. (Westm.) Cons./Hon. Sen. Lect. (Med. Oncol.) St. Geo. Hosp. Lond. Socs: Assn. Cancer Phys.; Brit. Cancer Res.; Eur. Med. Oncol. Prev: Sen. Regist. (Med. Oncol.) St. Geo. Hosp. Lond.; ICRF Clin. Research Fell. Molecular Oncol. Gp. Hammersmith Hosp. Lond.

LOFTS, Jane Anne The Surgery, 1 Arlington Road, Eastbourne BN21 1DH; 30 Summerdown Road, Eastbourne BN20 8DR — MB BS 1984 Lond.; MRCGP 1988; DRCOG 1988. GP E.bourne.

LOFTS, Julian Argus 43 Freedom Street, London SW11 5AQ — MB ChB 1982 Otago.

LOFTUS, Anthony 1 Vine Road, Skegness PE25 3DB — LRCPI & LM, LRCSI & LM 1950; MFCM 1974; DPH NUI 1953. Environm. Health N. Lincs. HA. Prev: Med. Off. S. Lincs. HA.

LOFTUS, Christine Elizabeth 61 Clarence Road, King's Heath, Birmingham B13 9UH — MB ChB 1976 Birm.; DRCOG 1978.

LOFTUS, Dorothy Ann 3 Saxonbury Close, Crowborough TN6 1EA Tel: 0189 262746 — MB BS 1965 Lond.; MRCS Eng. LRCP Lond. 1965; DA Eng. 1980; DObst RCOG 1970. (Roy. Free) Regist. (Anaesth.) Kent & Sussex Hosp. Tunbridge Wells. Prev: Clin. Asst. (Cas.) Kent & Sussex Hosp. Tunbridge Wells; Surg. Regist. Wellington Pub. Hosp., N.Z.

LOFTUS, Mr Ian Magnus Department of Surgery, Clinical Sciences Building, Leicester Royal Infirmary, Leicester LE2 7LX Tel: 0116 252 3140 Fax: 0116 252 3179 Email: ianloftus@aol.com; 21 Bankart Avenue, Leicester LE2 2DD — MB ChB 1992 Leic.; BSc Leic. 1990; FRCS Eng. 1996. Lect. in Surg., Leicester Univ. Prev: Research Fell. Vasc. Surg. Leicester Roy. Infirm.

LOFTUS, Jean Eden Brae, Linstock, Carlisle CA6 4PZ — MB BS 1954 Durh.

LOFTUS, John Kevin Mary Paediatric Department, Central Middlesex Hospital, Park Royal, London NW10 7NS Tel: 020 8965 5733 Fax: 020 8453 2096; 23 Wilton Square, London N1 3DL — MB BCh BAO NUI 1980; MRCP (UK) 1986; DCH NUI 1982. Cons. Paediat. & Child Health Centr. Middlx. Hosp. & Pk.side Health NHS Trust Lond. Socs: Fell. Roy. Acad. Med. Irel.; BMA; Fell. Roy. Coll. Paediat. Child Health. Prev: Sen. Regist. (Paediat.) St. Mary's Hosp. Lond.; Research Fell. (Paediat. Rheum.) Clin. Research Centre Harrow.

LOFTUS, Judith Anne 132 Strathmore Avenue, Dundee DD3 6RU — MB BCh BAO 1975 Belf.

LOFTUS, Neil Anthony 6 Rothesay Court, Sale M33 4NL — MB ChB 1985 Manch.

LOFTUS, Rosemary Christine The Surgery, Miller Way, Wainscott, Rochester ME2 4LP Tel: 01634 717450 — MB ChB 1985 Birm.; ChB Birm. 1985; DRCOG 1988. Clin. Asst. Heart of Kent Hospice Maidstone.

LOFTUS, Thomas (retired) Connemara, 1 Dunsdon Road, Woolton, Liverpool L25 6JF Tel: 0151 722 3982 — MB ChB BAO 1944 NUI; MB BCh BAO NUI 1944.

LOGAN, Alan Donald New Close Cottage, 138 Watergate Road, Newport PO30 1YP — MB BS 1969 Lond.; MRCS Eng. LRCP Lond. 1969; DObst RCOG 1971; FFA RCS Eng. 1974. (Char. Cross) Cons. Anaesth. I. of Wight DHA. Socs: BMA & Assn. Anaesth. Gt. Brit. Irel. Prev: Sen. Regist. Anaesth. Portsmouth Gp. & Soton. Gen. Hosp.; Regist. (Anaesth.) Portsmouth & W. Dorset Gp. Hosps.; SHO (Obst.) Char. Cross. Hosp. Lond.

LOGAN, Alastair Rowatt Wishaw Health Centre, Kenilworth Avenue, Wishaw ML2 7BQ Tel: 01698 373341 Fax: 01698 373736; 34 Alexander Gibson Way, Motherwell ML1 3FA Tel: 01698 260635 — MB ChB 1973 Glas. (Glasgow Univ)

LOGAN, Alexander 47 Orchard Street, Motherwell ML1 3JE — MB ChB 1982 Glas.

LOGAN, Alexander 14 Tabors Avenue, Great Baddow, Chelmsford CM2 7ES Tel: 01245 471237 — LRCP LRCS Ed. LRFPS Glas. 1948. (Glas.) Ref. Chelmsford Crematorium. Prev: Ho. Surg. (O & G) St. John's Hosp. Chelmsford; Ho. Phys. Roy. Alexandra Infirm. Paisley; Cas. Off. Chelmsford & Essex Hosp.

LOGAN, Mr Andrew (retired) 13 Merchiston Gardens, Edinburgh EH10 5DD — MB ChB 1929 St. And.; DSc St. And. 1974, MA 1926, MB ChB 1929; FRCS Ed. 1932; FRCP Ed. 1964; FRCS Eng. 1934. Hon. Cons. Thoracic Surg. Roy. Infirm. Edin.

***LOGAN, Andrew Johnson** Ground Floor Flat, 44 Llanishen St., Cardiff CF14 3QD — MB BCh 1997 Wales.

LOGAN, Mr Andrew Malcolm Plastic Surgery Associates, Hill House, BUPA Hospital, Colney, Norwich NR4 7TD Tel: 01603 255505 Fax: 01603 250404 Email: plasticsurgery@enterprise.net — BM BCh 1973 Oxf.; MA Oxf. 1973; FRCS Lond. 1978. (Oxf. Univ.) Cons. Plastic & Reconstruc. Surg., Plastic Surg. Assocs. Norwich. Socs: Brit. Assn. Plastic Surg.; Brit. Soc. Surg. Hand; BAAPS.

LOGAN, Andrew St Clair Redwood House, Woodlands Road, Chester CH4 8LB — MB BChir 1985 Camb.; FCAnaesth. 1990. Regist. (Anaesth.) Manch. Roy. Infirm.

LOGAN, Ashley Johnson Logan, Harper and Munslow, Castlefield Surgery, Castle Way, Stafford ST16 1BS; Castlefields Surgery,

Castleway, Stafford ST16 1BS Tel: 01785 254045 — MB ChB 1970 Manch.; MRCGP 1980. Prev: Ho. Off. Stafford Gen. Infirm.

LOGAN, Bernhard 22 Chiltern House, 16 Hillcrest Road, Ealing, London W5 1HL Tel: 020 8998 1305 Fax: 020 8998 1305 Email: ddrblogan@aol.com — MB BS Lond. 1966; MRCS Eng. LRCP Lond. 1966; FFA RCS Eng. 1974; T(Anaesth.) 1991. Cons. Anaesth. Moorfields Eye Hosp. Lond. Socs: Roy. Coll. Anaesth.; Roy. Soc. Med.

LOGAN, Mr Charles James Hume (retired) 86 Ballydrain Road, Comber, Newtownards BT23 6EA Tel: 01247 872010 — MB BCh BAO 1955 Belf.; MCh (Hons.) Belf. 1966; FRCSI 1978; FRCS Ed. 1960; FRCS Eng. 1960. Cons. Surg. Ulster Hosp. Dundonald. Prev: Fell. (Surg.) Lahey Clinic Boston, USA.

LOGAN, Christine Mary Westwood (retired) 43 Crosspath, Radlett WD7 8HR Tel: 01923 856626 — MB BS 1965 Lond.; FRCPsych 1986, M 1975; DPM Eng. 1972. Cons. Psychiat. & Med. Dir. Harperbury Hosp. Radlett. Prev: Sen. Regist. Leavesden Hosp. Watford.

LOGAN, Christopher John Lawther Asplands Medical Centre, Wood Street, Woburn Sands, Milton Keynes MK17 8QP Tel: 01908 582069 Fax: 01908 281597; Mill Farm, Church End, Eversholt, Milton Keynes MK17 9DU Tel: 01525 280223 — MB BS 1971 Lond.; FRCP (UK), MRCP 1973; MRCS Eng. LRCP Lond. 1971; FRCGP 1992, M 1984; DObst RCOG 1974. (Guy's) Hosp. Pract. (Diabetes) Milton Keynes Hosp. Prev: Course Organiser Milton Keynes VTS.

LOGAN, Derek Robert Dumbarton Health Centre, Station Road, Dumbarton G82 1PW Tel: 01389 602611 Fax: 01389 602621 — MB ChB 1979 Glas.; MRCGP 1984; DRCOG 1981. Prev: Dep. Sen. Med. Off. RAF Lyneham.; GP E. Kilbride.

LOGAN, Mrs Elisabeth Christine Macgregor Department of Haematology, Kings Mill Centre, Sutton-in-Ashfield NG17 4JL; 36 Richmond Drive, Mapperley Park, Nottingham NG3 5EL — MB ChB 1972 Ed.; BSc (Med. Sci) Ed. 1969; FRCP Lond. 1995; MRCP (UK) 1974; FRCPath 1996, M 1984. Cons. Haematoloyg King's Mill Hosp. Sutton-in-Ashfield; Dir. Med. Educat. Socs: Inst. Health Serv. Managem.; Brit. Blood Transfus. Soc.; Brit. Soc. Haemat. Prev: Cons. Haemat. Bassetlaw Dist. Gen. Hosps. Workshop; Sen. Regist. (Haemat.) City Hosp. Nottm.; Lect. (Haemat.) Univ. Edin. Dept. Med. W.ern Gen. Hosp. Edin.

LOGAN, Elspeth Sarah Greystones Surgery, Greystones, Evie, Orkney KW17 2PQ Tel: 01856 751283 Fax: 01856 751452 — MB ChB 1990 Aberd.

LOGAN, Fiona Anne Cranyke Farmhouse, Eastwell Road, Scalford, Melton Mowbray LE14 4SS — MB ChB 1972 Glas.; MRCPsych 1983; DCH RCPS Glas. 1974. (Glas.) Indep. Psychother. Pract. Leics. Prev: Cons. Child & Adolesc. Psychiat. S. Lincs. HA; Sen. Regist. (Child & Adolesc. Psychiat.) W.cotes Hse. Leicester; Fell. (Child Psychiat.) Stanford Univ. Med. Centre, USA.

LOGAN, Garth Lisburn Health Centre, Linenhall St., Lisburn BT28 1LU Tel: 01846 603088; 5 The Lawns, Waringstown, Craigavon BT66 7GD Tel: 01762 882330 Fax: 01762 882189 Email: garthlogan@aol.com — MB BCh BAO 1989 Belf.; MRCGP 1994; DRCOG 1993; DGM RCP Lond. 1991; DCH RCPI 1991. Socs: Ulster Med. Soc.; Soc. Primary Care Rheum.; Irish Soc. Rheum.

LOGAN, George Bernard (retired) 10 Haughview Road, Motherwell ML1 3EA Tel: 01698 264894 — MB ChB 1944 Glas. Prev: Ho. Surg. Law Emerg. Hosp.

LOGAN, Godfrey Stuart Institute Child Health, 30 Guilford St., London WC1N 1EH Tel: 020 7242 9789 — MB ChB 1977 Cape Town; MSc Epidemiol. Lond. 1987; MSc (Econ.) Lond. 1984; MRCP (UK) 1984. Sen. Lect. (Paediat. Epidemiol.) Inst. Child Health Lond.; Hon. Cons. (Paediat.) Gt. Ormond St. Hosp. Lond.

LOGAN, Grant David AON Occupational Health, Foresterhill, Aberdeen AB25 2ZP — MB ChB 1991 Aberd.; FRACGP 1996; MRCGP 1995; DFFP 1995. Specialist Regist.in Occupat.al Med. Socs: Roy. Coll. Gen. Pract.; Fell. Roy. Austral. coll. Gen. Practitioners; Mem. Soc. of Occupat.al Health.

LOGAN, Ian Douglas Cable House, 32 Cable Road, Whitehead, Carrickfergus BT38 9PY Tel: 01960 72142 — MB ChB 1977 Sheff.; BSc (Hons. Chem.) Sheff. 1972; DPhil Ulster 1997. Lect. (BioMed. Sci.s) Univ. of Ulster. Socs: Biochem. Soc.; Irish Radiat. Research Soc. Prev: GP Sheff.

LOGAN, Ian Stewart Medical Services, Five Ways Complex, Frederick Road, Birmingham B15 1ST Tel: 0121 626 3204 Fax: 0121 626 3210; 48 Regent Close, Birmingham B5 7PL Tel: 0121 249 1226 — MB ChB Sheff. 1970; MRCGP 1975. Med. Adviser.

LOGAN, James Hugh Craig Blair Ballyclare Group Practice, Ballyclare Health Centre, George Avenue, Ballyclare BT39 9HL Tel: 028 9332 2575 Fax: 028 9334 9897 — MB BCh BAO 1979 Belf. Socs: Fell. Ulster Med. Soc.

LOGAN, James Michael 126 Moor Road, Shanless, Stewartstown, Dungannon BT71 5QD — MB BCh BAO 1989 Belf.; MRCGP 1994; DMH Belf 1994; DRCOG 1993; DFFP 1993; DCH NUI 1992. Socs: BMA; Brit. Assn. Sport & Med.

LOGAN, James Rowatt (retired) Wishaw Health Centre, Kenilworth Avenue, Wishaw ML2 7BQ Tel: 01698 373341 — MB ChB 1958 Glas. Prev: Ho. Off. Co. Hosp. StoneHo. & Bellshill Matern. Hosp.

LOGAN, Jeremy Joseph 126 Moor Road, Stewartstown, Dungannon BT71 5QD — MB BCh BAO 1997 Belf.

LOGAN, John Irwin 9 Myrtlefield Park, Belfast BT9 6NE Tel: 028 9066 0302 — MB BCh BAO 1972 Belf.; FRCP Lond. 1992; FRCP Ed. 1989; MRCP (UK) 1975. Phys. Belf. City Hosp. & Musgrave Pk. Hosp. Belf. Socs: Fell. Ulster Med. Soc.; Ulster Soc. Internal Med. Prev: Research Fell. & Sen. Regist. Roy. Vict. Hosp. Belf.; Regist. N. Middlx. Hosp. Lond.

LOGAN, John Martyn Department of Public Health Medicine, Forth Valley Health Board, 33 Spittal St., Stirling FK8 1DX Tel: 01786 463031; 4 The Roundel, Auchterarder PH3 1PU Tel: 01764 663620 Email: whistletest@msn.com — MB ChB 1987 Ed.; MRCGP 1992; DRCOG 1992. Sen. Regist. (Pub. Health Med.) Forth Valley HB. Prev: Trainee GP Muirhead; Gen.ist Scott Hosp., Lesotho; Sen. Resid. Med. Off. (O & G) Sunshine Hosp., Melbourne, Australia.

LOGAN, John Stephens (retired) 27 Myrtlefield Park, Belfast BT9 6NF Tel: 02890 666226 — MB BCh BAO 1939 Belf.; MB BCh BAO (2nd cl. Hons.) Belf. 1939; MD Belf. 1946; FRCP Lond. 1966, M 1947. Cons. Phys. Roy. Vict. Hosp. Belf. Prev: Cas. Phys. Roy. Vict. Hosp. Belf.

***LOGAN, Judith Johnson** Department of Histopathology, University hospital of Wales, Heath Park, Cardiff CF14 4XW Tel: 029 2074 7747 — MB BCh 1997 Wales.

LOGAN, Julie Anne 76 Greenlees Road, Cambuslang, Glasgow G72 8DX — MB ChB 1987 Glas.

LOGAN, Karen Lesley Fountain Medical Centre, Little Fountain St., Morley, Leeds LS27 9EN Tel: 0113 295 1600 Fax: 0113 295 1600; 14 Lake Yard, Stanley, Wakefield WF3 4AE Tel: 01924 826797 Fax: 01924 872264 — MB ChB 1985 Leeds; MRCGP 1989; DCH RCP Lond. 1989. (Leeds) Gen. Practitioner, Fountain Med. Centre, Morley, Leeds. Prev: Ho. Off. (Surg. & Med.) Chapel Allerton Hosp. Leeds.

LOGAN, Kathleen Rosemary Lagan Valley Hospital, Lisburn BT28 1JP Tel: 01846 665141 — MB BCh BAO 1970 Belf.; FRCP Lond. 1990; MRCP (UK) 1973. Cons. Phys. (Gen. Internal Med.) Lagan Valley Hosp. Lisburn.

LOGAN, Laurence Charles Faversham Health Centre, Bank Street, Faversham ME13 8QR Tel: 01795 536621/533987/534150; The Cottage, Upper St Anns Road, Faversham ME13 8SY — MB BS 1978 Lond. (St. Thos.)

LOGAN, Margaret Nell Gloucester Public Health Laboratory, Gloucestershire Royal Hospital, Great Western Road, Gloucester GL1 3NN Tel: 01452 305334 Fax: 01452 307213 Email: jwhiting@phls.co.uk — MB ChB Birm. 1973; FRCPath 1997; MRCPath (Microbiol.) 1989. Cons. Microbiol. & Laborat. Dir. Pub. Health Laborat. Gloucester. Socs: Brit. Soc. Study of Infec.; Brit. Soc. Antimicrob. Chemother.; Hosp. Infec. Soc. Prev: Sen. Regist. (Microbiol.) Good Hope Hosp., Russells Hall & Dudley Rd. Hosps.

LOGAN, Marie-Louise 26 Lucerne Parade, Belfast BT9 5FT — MB BCh BAO 1995 Belf.

LOGAN, Mark Andrew James Third Space Medicine, 13 Sherwood Street, London W1F 7BR Tel: 020 7439 7332; 15 Bowbrook, Gathorne St, London E2 0PW Fax: 020 8981 9090 Email: drandrewlogan@aol.com — MB BS 1986 Lond. (Lond. Hosp.) Wellbeing Cons. Third Space Med.; Naturopathic Phys. third space Lond.; Sen. Lect. (Exercise & Health) City Univ. Lond.; Nat. Lect. (Integrated Stress Managem. for Health Care Professionals) APT. Prev: Med. Cons. Health Educat. Soho Athletic Club Lond.;

Med. director, centre for integrative med.lond; Wellness Phys soc. Complementary med Lond.

LOGAN, Martin Charles 3 Guiltreehill, Ayr KA7 4XG — MB ChB 1997 Glas.

LOGAN, Mary Bridget The Health Centre, 2A Forest Road, Edmonton, London N9 8RZ Tel: 020 8804 0121 — MB BS 1980 Lond.; MRCGP 1985.

LOGAN, Michael Robert Department of Anaesthetics, Royal Infirmary of Edinburgh, Lauriston Place, Edinburgh EH3 9YW Tel: 0131 536 3651 Fax: 0131 536 3672 Email: m.logan@ed.ac.uk — MB ChB 1978 Ed.; BSc (Med. Sci.) Ed. 1975, MB ChB 1978; FRCA Eng. 1982. Cons. Anaesth. Roy. Infirm. Edin. Prev: Lect. (Anaesth.) Univ. Edin.

LOGAN, Patricia Jane Alison Mawbey Brough Health Centre, 39 Wilcox Close, London SW8 2UD Tel: 020 7622 3827 Fax: 020 7498 1069 — MA, MB BChir Camb. 1980; MRCGP 1985; DRCOG 1984; DCH RCP Lond. 1983.

LOGAN, Peter James Badgars Brake, Low Road, Church Lench, Evesham WR11 4UH — MB BChir 1993 Camb.

LOGAN, Richard Aicken Princess of Wales Hospital, Coity Road, Bridgend CF31 1RQ Tel: 01656 752827 Fax: 01656 752821 Email: richard.logan@bromor-r.wales.nhs.uk; 79 Park Street, Bridgend CF31 4AZ Tel: 01656 663713 Email: drskin@hotmail.com — MB ChB 1977 Bristol; FRCP Lond. 1995; MRCP (UK) 1980. Cons. Dermat. Bro Morgannwg NHS Trust; Hon. Clin. Tutor (Dermat.) Univ. Wales Coll. Med. Cardiff. Prev: Sen. Regist. & Tutor (Dermat.) St. John's Hosp. for Dis. of Skin Lond.; Regist. (Dermat. & Gen. Med.) Stoke Mandeville Hosp. Aylesbury.

LOGAN, Professor Richard Francis Alastair Department of Public Health & Epidemiology, University of Nottingham, Queens Medical Centre, Nottingham NG7 2UH Tel: 0115 970 9308 Fax: 0115 970 9316 Email: richard.logan@nottingham.ac.uk; 36 Richmond Drive, Mapperley Park, Nottingham NG3 5EL — MB ChB 1970 Ed.; BSc (Med. Sci.) Ed. 1967, MB ChB 1970; MSc (Epidemiol.) Lond. 1981; FRCP Lond. 1992; FRCP Ed. 1987; MRCP (UK) 1973. (Ed.) Prof. Clin. Epidemiol.; Hon. Cons. Phys. Univ. Hosp. Nottm. Socs: Brit. Soc. Gastroenterol.; Internat. Epidemiol. Assn.; Amer. Gastroenterol. Assn. Prev: Reader (Clin. Epidemiol. & Pub. Health) Univ. Nottm.; Wellcome Research Fell. & Hon. Sen. Regist. (Med.) Univ. Nottm.; Sen. Regist. (Med.) Lothian HB.

LOGAN, Robert 37 Maxwell Road, Bangor BT20 3SG Tel: 01247 61931 — MB BCh BAO 1948 Belf.; DPH 1951; FFCM 1978, M 1974. (Belf.) Sen. Med. Off. Dept. Health & Social Servs. N. Irel. Prev: Div. MOH Down Co. Health Comm.; MOH Holywood, Castlereagh, & HillsBoro. Counc.s. Asst. Med. Off.; Nottm. CC.

LOGAN, Robert Alexander Gilford Health Centre, Castleview, Gilford, Craigavon BT63 6JS; 19 Pineview Court, Gilford, Craigavon BT63 6AY Tel: 02838 831225 — MB BCh BAO 1983 Belf.; MRCGP 1987; DRCOG 1986; DCH Dub. 1985.

LOGAN, Robert Francis Leslie 4 High Elms, Hatching Green, Harpenden AL5 2JU Tel: 0158 271 2854 — MD Belf. 1947, MB BCh BAO (Hnrs.) 1940; FRCP Lond. 1971, M 1948; MFOM RCP Lond. 1982; FFCM 1976; DIH Eng. 1948; CPH Manch. 1947. (Queen's Belfast) Prof. Emerit. Organisation of Med. Care Lond. Sch. Hyg.; Med. Adivser Netherlands Antilles; Med. Adviser Lead Battery Co. Socs: Fell. Soc. Social Med.; Internat. Epidemiol. Assn.; Fell. Assoc. Soc. Pub. Health Europe. Prev: Milroy Lect. RCP Lond. 1962; Dir. Med. Care Research Unit & Coordinator Jt. Progr. for Master In Health Admin. Univ. Riyad; Cons. WHO, PAHO NE & NW Thames RHAs & DHSS (N. Irel.).

LOGAN, Robert Frederick Department of Geriatrics, Queen Alexandra Hospital, Cosham, Portsmouth PO6 3LY Tel: 023 92 286958; The Myrtles, Prinsted Lane, Prinsted, Emsworth PO10 8HR — MB ChB 1979 Bristol; FRCP Lond. 1995; MRCP (UK) 1982. Cons. Geriat. Portsmouth & SE Hants. HA.

LOGAN, Robert Malcolm Faithlie Medical Practice, 17 Saltoun Place, Fraserburgh AB43 9RX Tel: 01346 518144 Fax: 01346 510206; Carbyne, 69 King Edward St, Fraserburgh AB43 9PL Tel: 01346 518246 — MB ChB 1960 Aberd.

LOGAN, Robert Phillip Howell Division of Gastroenterology, Queens Medical Centre, Nottingham NG7 2UH Tel: 0115 970 9447 Fax: 0115 942 2232 Email: robert.logan@nottingham.ac.uk — MB BS 1983 Lond.; FRCP (UK) 2001; DM (Nottm.) 1997. Sen. Lect. Hon. Cons. (Gastroenerol.) Qu. Med. Centre, Nottm. & Kings Mill Centre, Mansfield. Socs: Fell. Roy. Soc. Med.; Brit. Soc. Gastroenterol.; Amer. Gastroenterol. Assn. Prev: Wellcome Research Fell, Hon. Sen. Regist. & Lect. (Gastroenterol.) Qu. Med. Centre Nottm.; Research Fell. (Gastroenterol.) Centr. Middlx. Hosp. Lond.; Regist. (Gen. Med. & Gastroenterol.) St. Mary's Hosp. Lond.

LOGAN, Robert Williamson, TD (retired) Department of Biochemistry, Royal Hospital for Sick Children, Queen Mother's Hospital, Yorkhill, Glasgow G3 8SJ Tel: 0141 201 0336 Fax: 0141 201 0834 — MB ChB 1957 Glas.; BSc (Hons. Biochem.) Glas. 1961; FRCP Glas. 1976, M 1973; FRCPath 1978, M 1966. Clin. Dir. Laborat. Servs.; Ethics Comm. Yorkhill NHS Trust Glas.; Gen. Counc. Erskine Hosp. Bishopton; Vice-Pres. St Andrews Ambul. Assoc. Glas. Prev: Cons. Biochem. Dumfries Roy. Infirm.

LOGAN, Rosemary Margaret — MB ChB 1982 Ed.; MRCGP 1986; MRCPsych 1990. (Edinburgh) Cons. Psychiat. Fife Primary Care NHS Trust Dunfermline. Prev: Regist. Bangour Village Hosp.; Regist. Roy. Edin. Hosp.; SHO Bangour Village Hosp.

LOGAN, Samuel Hilary Mervyn The Royal Oldham Hospital, Rochdale Road, Oldham OL1 2JH Tel: 0161 627 8093; The Coach House, 2A Gorsey Lane, Altrincham WA14 4BN — MB BCh BAO Dub. 1958; MA Dub. 1959; FFOM RCP Lond. 1990; MRCGP 1966; DIH Soc. Apoth. Lond. 1967; DObst RCPI 1960; LM Rotunda 1960; FFOM 1999 Dublin. (TC Dub.) Cons. Occupat. Phys. Roy. Oldham Hosp. NHS Trust. Socs: Soc. Occupat. Med. (Ex-Chairm. N.W. Gp.). Prev: Sen. Med. Adviser Shell UK Ltd.; Employm. Med. Advis EMAS; Apptd. Fact. Doctor.

LOGAN, Sheila Mary (retired) Skythorn, 48 Back Road, Dollar FK14 7EA Tel: 01259 742058 — MB ChB 1955 Glas.; DPH Glas. 1960. Med. Examr. Benefits Agency Med. Servs. Clackmannansh. Prev: GP Dollar, Clackmannansh.

LOGAN, Simon William Dept of Anaesthetics and Intensive Care, Heath Park, Cardiff CF14 4XW Tel: 029 2074 3107 — MB ChB 1987 Dundee; FRCA 1993. Cons. Anaesth. Unversity Hosp. of Wales. Prev: Cons. S. Tees NHS Trust.; SR S.hampton/Swindon; Lect., Univ. of Cardiff.

LOGAN, Stuart 9 Northamton Road, Oxford OX1 4TG; 1 Staik Hill, Lanark ML11 7PW — MB ChB 1989 Glas.

LOGAN, Mr Victor St Clair Dudgeon (retired) Skyreholme, Layton Avenue, Rawdon, Leeds LS19 6QQ Tel: 0113 250 2004 Fax: 01132261475 Email: vsdl@aol.com — MB ChB 1956 Liverp.; MB ChB (2nd cl. Hons.) Liverp. 1956; FRCS Eng. 1966; FRCS Ed. 1965; MRCS Eng. LRCP Lond. 1956. Prev: Cons. Surg. Dewsbury Health Dist.

LOGAN, Victoria Katherine 36 Edington Av, Cardiff CF14 3QG — MB BCh 1997 Wales. SHO O & G, St Michael's Hosp., Bristol. Prev: SHO O & G, UHW, Cardiff.

LOGAN, William (retired) Skythorn, Dollar FK14 7EA Tel: 01259 42058 — MB ChB 1955 Glas.; MRCGP 1968. Prev: GP Tillicoultry.

LOGAN, Mr William Caskey (retired) 9 Strandview Drive, Portstewart BT55 7LN Tel: 01232 834073 — MB BCh BAO 1953 Belf.; FRCS Eng. 1963; FRCS Ed. 1962; DO Eng. 1960; DObst RCOG 1956. Cons. Ophth. Surg. E. Area Health & Social Serv. Bd. Prev: Res. Surg. Off. Birm. & Midl. Eye Hosp.

LOGAN, William Frederick Wulstan Ettienne 17 Links Gate, Lytham St Annes FY8 3LF Tel: 01253 721720 — MB ChB 1958 Liverp.; MD Liverp. 1967; FRCP Lond. 1976, M 1962. (Liverp.) Cons. Cardiol. Vict. Hosp. Blackpool. Socs: Brit. Cardiac Soc. Prev: Sen. Regist. (Med.) Univ. Dept. Cardiol. Manch. Roy. Infirm.

LOGAN, William John (retired) The Rowans, 69 Gailes Road, Troon KA10 6TB — MB ChB 1943 Glas.

LOGAN-EDWARDS, Mr Robert (retired) Tump House, Abberley, Worcester WR6 6BP Tel: 01299 896547 — MB BS 1951 Lond.; MSc Camb. 1966; FRCSE Ed. 1963; MRCS Eng. LRCP Lond. 1947; FRCOG 1966, M 1953, DObst 1949. Prev: Cons. O & G Qu. Eliz., Matern. & Wom. Hosp. Birm.

LOGARAJAH, Veena 33 Langtons Wharf, Leeds LS2 7EF — MB ChB 1997 Leeds.

LOGENDRAN, Mr Maharatnam 6 Geralds Close, Lincoln LN2 4AL — MB BS 1983 Colombo; FRCS Ed. 1991; MRCS Eng. LRCP Lond. 1988. (Sri Lanka) Assoc. Specialist (Opth.) Co. Hosp. Lincoln. Prev: Staff Grade (Ophth.) Co. Hosp. Lincoln.

LOGIE, Brian Richard Orchard Medical Centre, 41 Ladywell Road, Motherwell ML1 3JX Tel: 01698 264187 Fax: 01698 267717 — MB ChB 1981 Dundee; MRCGP 1987; DCH RCPS Glas 1983.

LOGIE, Dorothy Elizabeth Borders Health Board, Newstead, Melrose TD6 9DB Tel: 01896 825508 Fax: 01896 823401; Cheviot View, Bowden, Melrose TD6 0ST Tel: 01835 822763 Fax: 01835 822763 Email: delogie@aol.com — MB ChB 1966 Aberd.; FRCGP 1984, M 1973. (Aberd.) Princip. GP Adviser Borders HB. Socs: MEDACT; GP Writers Assn. Prev: GP Earlston, Berwicksh.; Med. Off. MRC Laborats. Fajara, Gambia.

LOGIE, Mr John Robert Cunningham Raigmore Hospital, Inverness IV2 3UJ Tel: 01463 704000 Fax: 01463 711322; The Darroch, Little Cantray, Culloden Moor, Inverness IV2 5EY Tel: 01463 792090 Fax: 01463 798478 Email: john.r.c.logie@lineone.net — MB ChB 1970 Aberd.; PhD Aberd. 1978; FRCS Glas. 1993; FRCS Eng. 1975; FRCS Ed. 1974. (Aberd.) Cons. Gen. Surg. Inverness Hosps.; Hon. Clin. Sen. Lect. Aberd. Univ. Socs: Counc. Mem. Roy. Coll. Surgs. Edin. Prev: Sen. Regist. (Urol.) Aberd. Roy. Infirm.; Lect. & Hon. Sen. Regist. (Surg.) & Research Fell. Surg. Univ. Aberd.

LOGIE, Lindsay Jane Royal Hospital for sick children, Sciennes Road, Edinburgh EH9 Tel: 0131 536 0000; Email: lindsay.logie@btinternet.com — MB ChB 1986 Aberd.; MRCP Ed. 1992. (Aberdeen) p/t Cons. Paediat. Lothian Univ. Hosp. NHS Trust Edin. Socs: Clin. Genetics Soc.; RCPCH; BMA. Prev: Genetics Edin. Univ.; Regist. (Paediat.) Edin.; SHO (Paediat.) Aberd. Roy. Infirm.

LOGIE, Susan Ann Sunnyside Royal Hospital, Hillside, Montrose DD10 9JP; Kitty Knowe, Lamondfauld Road, Hillside, Montrose DD10 9HY — MB ChB 1983 Glas.; BSc (Hons.) Glas. 1981, MB ChB 1983; MRCPsych. 1987. Cons. Psychiat. Sunnyside Roy. Hosp. Montrose. Prev: SHO (Psychiat.) Gartnavel Roy. Hosp. Glas.

LOGSDAIL, Stephen James Milton Keynes Primary Care Trust, Standing Way, Eaglestone, Milton Keynes MK6 5NG Tel: 07908 243143 — MB BS 1977 Lond.; MRCS Eng. LRCP Lond. 1977; MRCP (UK) 1980; MRCPsych. 1982; FRCPsych 1999. (St. Mary's) Cons. Liaison Psychiat. milton Keynes Hosp.; Cons. NeuroPsychiat. Wycombe Hosp. NHS Trust. Prev: Cons. (Neuropsychiat.), Frenchay Hosp. Bristol and Med. Director; Cons. Psychiat. St. John's Hosp. Aylesbury; Sen. Regist. (Psychiat.) Rotat. Bethlem & Maudsley Hosp. Lond.

LOGUE, Charlotte Pamela Portrush Medical Centre, Dunlace Avenue, Portrush BT56 8DW Tel: 028 7082 3767 Fax: 028 7082 3413; 27 Ferndale Park, Portstewart BT55 7JB Tel: 01265 833303 — MB ChB 1973 Ed. Med. Assoc. (Genitourin. Med.) Coleraine Hosp.

LOGUE, Jacqueline Ann Greenhills Health Centre, 20 Greenhills Square, East Kilbride, Glasgow G75 8TT Tel: 01355 236331 Fax: 01355 234977; 21 Woodvale Avenue, Giffnock, Glasgow G46 6RG — MB ChB 1987 Glas.; MRCGP 1993; DRCOG 1990.

LOGUE, John 39 Elms Road, Heaton Moor, Stockport SK4 4PS — MB ChB 1981 Glas.; MRCP (UK) 1986; FRCR 1989. Cons. Clin. Oncol. Christie Hosp. Manch.

LOH, Mr Alexander Barnet Hospital, Wellhouse Lane, Barnet EN5 3DN Tel: 020 8216 5440 Fax: 020 8216 5447; Tel: 020 8449 5581 — MB BS 1982 Lond.; FRCS Glas. 1986; MS 1997. Cons. Surg. Vasc. and Gen. Surg. Barnet Hosp.

LOH, Caron Phaik Lin The Surgery, 66 Long Lane, London EC1A 9EJ; 17 Kelly Street, London NW1 8PG — MB BS 1986 Lond.

LOH, Mr Dale Lincoln c/o Mrs Jean Walker, Department of Surgical Paediatrics, Royal Hospital for Sick Children, 9 Sciennes Road, Edinburgh EH9 1LF — MB ChB 1989 Glas.; FRCS Glas. 1994.

LOH, Laurence Nuffield Department Anaesthetics, The Radcliffe Infirmary NHS Trust, Oxford OX2 6HE Tel: 01865 311188; 39 Barton Road, Headington, Oxford OX3 9JD Tel: 01865 311188 — MB BS 1962 Lond.; MRCS Eng. LRCP Lond. 1962; FFA RCS Eng. 1968. (St. Mary's) Cons. Anaesth. Oxf. Radcliffe NHS Trust. Prev: Cons. Anaesth. Nat. Hosps. Nerv. Dis. Lond.; Sen. Regist. Anaesth. Hammersmith Hosp. Lond.; Regist. Anaesth. St. Mary's Hosp. Lond.

LOH, Liew Cheng 61 Cardoness Road, Sheffield S10 5RT — MB ChB 1993 Sheff.

LOH, Mong Yang Room 8, Block K, Staff Village, Royal Preston Hospital, Sharoe Green Lane, Fulwood, Preston PR2 9HT — MB ChB 1997 Manch.

LOH, Raymond Ser Keat 20 Birkett Way, Chalfont St Giles HP8 4BH — MB BCh BAO 1989 Belf.

LOH, Richard Yeow Meng Barnsley District General Hospital, Pogmoor Road, Barnsley S75 2EP — MB ChB 1993 Leic.

LOH, Mr Yeok Chuan 170 Park Road, Great Sankey, Warrington WA5 3PJ Email: ycloh18@hotmail.com — MB ChB 1987 Liverp.; FRCS Glas. 1992; MCh (Orth)Liverp. 1997; FRCS (Orth.) 1998. Career Specialist Regist. Rotat. (Orthop.) Mersey VTS; Fell.sh. (Hand Surg.) St Jas. Univ. Hosp., Leeds. Socs: Assoc. Brit. Orthop. Assn.; Brit. Orthop. Train. Assn.; BMA. Prev: Fell. (Hand & Upper Limb Surg.) Wrightington Hospial; Regist. (Orthop.) Cheltenham Gen. Hosp.; SHO (Orthop. Surg.) s/i Hand Surg. Macclesfield Dist.

LOHFINK, Andrew Bernard Greenmeadow Surgery, Greenmeadow Way, Cwmbran NP44 3XQ Tel: 01633 864110 Fax: 01633 483761 — MB BCh 1989 Wales.

LOHIA, Shekhar 4 The Briars, Ash, Aldershot GU12 6NX Tel: 01252 662789 Email: sl.a0500386@infotrade.co.uk — MB BS 1976 Ranchi; MRCPI 1995; MRCPCH 1996; DCH RCP Glas. 1989. GP Regist. Socs: MRCPCH. Prev: Staff Paediat. Glan Clwyd Hosp. Rhyl.

LOHN, Matthew Simon Field Fisher Water House, 35 Vine St., London EC3N 2AA Tel: 020 7861 4000 Email: msl@ffwlaw.com — MB BS 1991 Lond.; BSc (Hons.) Lond. 1988.

LOHRKE, Britta c/o 33 Herne Street, Herne Bay CT6 7HL — MB ChB 1987 Stellenbosch.

LOIZOU, Eleni 11 Grosvenor Road, Harborne, Birmingham B17 9AL — MB ChB 1991 Birm.; MRCPsych. 1998.

LOIZOU, Louis Anastasiou Tel: 01924 201688 Fax: 01924 201528; The Pines, 24A Old Lane, Bramhope, Leeds LS16 9AZ Tel: 01924 201688 Fax: 01924 201528 — MB ChB 1973 Birm.; PhD Birm. 1970, BSc (Hons.) 1967; FRCP Lond. 1993; MRCP (UK) 1975. (Birm.) Cons. Neurol. Pinderfields Gen. Hosp. Wakefield; Sen clin lec in Neurol., univ Leeds. Socs: Assn. Brit. Neurols. & N. Eng. Neurol. Soc.; BMA. Prev: Sen. Regist. (Neurol.) Midl. Centre Neurosurg. & Neurol. Smethwick & Qu. Eliz. Hosp. Birm.; Regist. (Gen. Med.) City Gen. Hosp. & N. Staffs. Roy. Infirm.

LOIZOU, Marilyn The Pines, 24A Old Lane, Bramhope, Leeds LS16 9AZ — MB ChB 1970 Birm.; BSc (Hons.) Physiol. Birm. 1967; MRCPsych. 1984. Cons. Psychiat. Yorks. RHA. Prev: Sen. Regist. (Psychiat.) Leeds Train. Scheme; Regist. (Psychiat.) Stanley Royd Hosp. Wakefield; Clin. Asst. (Psychiat.) Birm. Train. Scheme.

LOK, Chiming 59 Hawksworth Road, Horsforth, Leeds LS18 4JP — MB ChB 1993 Leeds.

LOK, She Sing Queen Elizabeth II Hospital, Howlands, Welwyn Garden City AL7 4HQ Tel: 01707 365056 Fax: 01707 365058; 10A Busley Way, Christchurch BH23 2HF Tel: 01202 475032 Email: nwalshaq@eurobell.co.uk — MB ChB 1989 Manch.; MRCP (UK) 1993. Cons., Gen. and Respirat. Med., QE II Hosp. Welyyn Garden City. Prev: Regist. (Gen. & Respirat. Med.) Wycombe Gen. Hosp.

LOKA-SALEH, Mr Ragai Moris Bideford Medical Centre, Abbotsham Road, Bideford EX39 3AF Tel: 01237 476363 Fax: 01237 423351 — MB BCh 1978 Cairo; FRCS Eng. 1986; FRCS Ed. 1986; FRCS Glas. 1986. Prev: Trainee GP Bideford; Regist. (Surg.) Roy. Cornw. Hosp. Truro & N. Devon Dist. Hosp. Barnstaple.

LOKE, Andrew Tien-Hsi c/o Accident & Emergency Department, Manchester Royal Infirmary, Manchester M13 9WL Tel: 0161 276 1234; 21 Crondall Street, Manchester M14 4UB Tel: 0161 226 2242 — MB ChB 1992 Glas. SHO Rotat. (Surg.) Manch. Roy. Infirm. Prev: SHO (A & E & Orthop.) Leighton Hosp. Crewe; SHO (Gen. Med.) Vict. Infirm. Manch.

LOKE, David Kok Teik 20 Melbourn Road, Sheffield S10 1NS — MB ChB 1995 Sheff.

LOKE, Evelyn Soo Ing Community Paediactrics, Wharton Primary Healthcare Centre, Crook Lane, Wharton, Winsford CW1 3GY — MB ChB 1986 Liverp.; MRCP (UK) 1992; DCH RCPS Glas. 1990. p/t Cons. Community Paediat.)Chesh. comm Healthcare Trust.

LOKE, Hong Toh Richard 2 Marlborough Close, Tunbridge Wells TN4 8XZ — MB BS 1980 Lond.; MRCP UK) 1985; FRCP Lond 1998. (St Mary's Lond) Cons. Gastroenterol. & Gen. MedMaidstone & Tunbridge Wells NHS Trust. Socs: Brit. Soc. Study Liver Dis. Prev: Sen. Regist. (Gen. Med. & Gastroenterol.) Univ. Coll. Hosp. Lond., Middlx. & Wh ittington Hosps. Lond.; Research Fell. Char. Cross Hosp. Lond.; Regist. (Med.) W. Dorset Hosp.

LOKE, Mun Yee (Jimmy) Flat B, 12 Acton St., London WC1X 9NG — MB BS 1983 Lond.; LMSSA Lond. 1983; MRCS Eng.

LRCP Lond. 1983; MRCOG 1996; MRCPI 1997. Socs: Fell. Roy. Soc. Med.; BMA.

LOKE, Siu Cheng 267 Clarendon Park Road, Leicester LE2 3AQ — MB ChB 1998 Leic.; MB ChB Leic 1998.

LOKE, Wei Ian 35 Brinsmead Road, Leicester LE2 3WD — MB ChB 1994 Leic.

LOKE, Yoon Kong Department Clinical Pharmacology, Radcliffe Infirmary NHS Trust, Oxford OX2 6HE Tel: 01865 224588 Fax: 01865 791712 Email: yoon.loke@clinpharm.ox.ac.uk — MB BS 1990 Lond.; MRCP 1993. Clin. Lect. Dept. Clin. Pharmacol. Oxf. Univ.; Hon. Specialist Regist. John Radcliffe Hosp. Oxf.

LOKE, Yung Wai Department of Pathology, Tennis Court Road, Cambridge CB2 1QP Tel: 01223 333727 — MB BChir 1960 Camb.; MA Camb. 1961, MD 1964; DTM & H Eng. 1964. (St. Thos.) Fell. & Dir. Studies Med. Sc. King's Coll. Camb.; Reader (Path.) Camb. Socs: Fell. Roy. Soc. Med. Prev: Lect. (Path.) Univ. Camb.

LOKER, Janet Elsie The Surgery, 59 Mansfield Road, Blidworth, Mansfield NG21 0RB Tel: 01623 795461 Fax: 01623 490514; 11 Rowan Avenue, Ravenshead, Nottingham NG15 9GA Tel: 01623 794687 — BM 1979 Soton.; BSc (Hons.) Soton. 1969, PhD 1973, BM 1979. (Soton.) GP Princip. Socs: BMA.

LOKUBALASURIYA, Don Edmund Angelo 58 Water Meadows, Worksop S80 3DF — MB BS 1964 Ceylon.

LOKUGAMAGE, Amali Upilmini 3 Aldridge Avenue, Stanmore HA7 1DB — MB ChB 1990 Manch.

LOKULO-SODIPE, Oluseye Ayodeji 41 Burlington Close, Orpington BR6 8PP — MB BS 1974 Ibadan; MRCOG 1981.

LOLAYEKAR, Divakar Tukaram Medicine for the Elderly Department, Burnley General Hospital, Casterton Avenue, Burnley BB10 2PQ Tel: 01282 25071 — MB BS 1972 Bombay; DTCD Wales 1980; DTM & H Liverp. 1985.

LOLE-HARRIS, Carol Ann Deer Park Medical Centre, 6 Edington Square, Witney OX28 5YT Tel: 01993 700088 — MB ChB 1984 Leeds.

LOLLEY, Jane Royal Cornhill Hospital, Cornhill Road, Aberdeen AB25 2ZH Tel: 01224 663131 — MB BS 1984 Lond.; BSc (Psychol.) Lond. 1979; MRCPsych 1989. Cons. Psychiat. Roy. Cornhill Hosp. Aberd.

LOMAS, Anne Carolyn 16 High Street, Hinderwell, Saltburn-by-the-Sea TS13 5JH — MB BS 1993 Newc.; BA (Hons.) Leeds 1975. Indep. non Princip. GP; Forens. Med. Examr. N. Yorks Police.

LOMAS, Professor David Arthur Department of Medicine, Cambridge Institute for Medical Research, Wellcome Trust/ MRC Building, Cambridge CB2 2XY Tel: 01223 762818 Fax: 01223 336827 Email: dal16@cam.ac.uk; Pembroke House, 10 Church Street, Stapleford, Cambridge CB2 5DS — BM BS 1985 Nottm.; PhD Camb. 1993; BMedSci (Hons.) Nottm. 1983, BM BS (Hons.) 1985; MRCP (UK) 1988; FRCP (Lond) 1997. Prof. of Respirat. Biol. & Hon. Cons. Phys. Univ. Camb. Socs: Brit. Thorac. Soc.; Assoc. of Phys.s. Prev: Lect. (Med.) & Honarary Cons. Phys. Univ. Camb.; MRC Clin. Scientist & MRC Trainng Fell. Univ. Camb.; Regist. (Respirat. Med.) Birm. Gen. Hosp.

LOMAS, David John University Department of Radiology, Box 219, Addenbrooke's Hospital, Cambridge CB2 2QQ Tel: 01223 336890 Fax: 01223 217847; The Windmill, Little Wilbraham, Cambridge CB1 5LG — MB 1983 Camb.; MA Camb. 1983, BA 1979, MB 1983, BChir 1982; MRCP (UK) 1985; FRCR 1989. Univ. Lect. & Hon. Cons. Addenbrooke's Hosp. Camb. Prev: Sen. Regist. & Regist. (Radiol.) Addenbrooke's Hosp. Camb.; Regist. (Med.) P.ss Margt. Hosp. Swindon.

LOMAS, David Michael The Surgery, 12 Sternhall Lane, London SE15 4NT Tel: 020 7639 3553 Fax: 020 7639 0835; 29 Sydenham Hill, London SE26 6SH Tel: 020 8670 5355 Fax: 020 8670 5355 — MB ChB 1954 Sheff. (Sheff.) Med. Off. Ammon, Corbett & Wilkinson Hse. Resid. Homes for Elderly. Socs: W Kent M-C Soc.; BMA. Prev: Cas. Off. & Ho. Surg. Montagu Hosp. MexBoro.; Ho. Phys. Birch Hill Hosp. Rochdale; Med. Off. RAF Med. Br.

LOMAS, Debra Ellen Great Ormond Street Hospital for Sick Children, London WC1 3JH Tel: 020 7405 9200; 1 Aubert Park, London N5 1TL — MB BChir 1984 Camb.; MA Camb. 1981, MB BChir 1984; MRCP (UK) 1987. Assoc. Specialist in (Paediat.) Dermatol.) Gt. Ormond St. Hosp. Lond. Socs: Brit. Soc. Paediat. Dermatol.; Dowling Club.

LOMAS, Joyce Jean Pearl (retired) 25 Midhurst Drive, Goring-by-Sea, Worthing BN12 5BD — MD Lond. 1952, MB BS 1949; MRCP Lond. 1957; MRCS Eng. LRCP Lond. 1947; DPhysMed. Eng. 1959. Prev: Cons. Phys. & Dir. Dept. Rheum. & Rehabil. St. Jas. Hosp. Lond.

LOMAS, Judith Amanda Pembroke House, 10 Church St., Stapleford, Cambridge CB2 5DS — BMedSci (Hons.) Nottm. 1983, BM BS 1985; MRCP (UK) 1989; MRCGP 1992; DRCOG 1990; DCH RCP Lond. 1988.

LOMAS, Paul Andrew 28 Market Street, Denton, Manchester M34 2FH Tel: 0161 336 5720 — MB ChB 1989 Leeds.

LOMAS, Peter Eric Samuel 41 Beaulands Close, Cambridge CB4 1JA Tel: 01223 354851; 8 Lower Street, Thriplow, Royston SG8 7RJ Tel: 01763 208535 — MB ChB Manch. 1946; MRCPsych 1971. Psychother. Pract. Camb. Socs: Founder Mem. Camb. Soc. for Psychother. Prev: Psychiat. i/c Mitcham Child Guid. Clinic; JHMO Cassel Hosp. Richmond; SHO (Neurosurg.) Manch. Roy. Infirm.

LOMAS, Thomas Edward 3 Swiss Cottage, Bollinbrook Road, Macclesfield SK10 3DF Tel: 01625 262250 — LRCPI & LM, LRSCI & LM 1961. (RCS)

LOMAX, David Martin Department of Anaesthesia, St. Mary's Hospital, London W2 1NY — MB BS 1986 Lond.; FRCA 1991. (St. Bart.) Cons. Anaesth. St. Mary's Hosp. Lond. Socs: BMA; Assoc. Mem. Cardiothoracic Anaesth. Prev: Sen. Regist. (Anaesth.) St. Mary's Hosp. Lond.; Sen. Regist. Roy. Perth Hosp. W.. Austral.; Regist. (Anaesth.) Brompton, Middlx. & Univ. Coll. Hosps. Lond.

LOMAX, Grace Petula 53 Waldren Close, Poole BH15 1XR Tel: 01202 666366 Email: gracelomax@virgin.net — MB BCh 1991 Wales. GP Regist. Poole.

LOMAX, Jennifer Anne The Highfield Surgery, Highfield Way, Hazlemere, High Wycombe HP15 7UW Tel: 01494 813396; 16 Beechtree Road, Holmer Green, High Wycombe HP15 6UZ Tel: 01494 712186 Email: jen@lomaxfamily.com — MB ChB 1990 Liverp.; MRCGP 1995; DFFP 1994; DRCOG 1993. GP Retainee. Socs: BMA. Prev: SHO (O & G & Paediat.) Wycombe Gen. Hosp.; SHO (Cas.) Walton Hosp. Merseyside.

***LOMAX, Nicola Jane Clare** 3 Wigwam Close, Poynton, Stockport SK12 1XF — MB BS 1998 Lond.; MB BS Lond 1998.

LOMAX, Philip Miles Springhill Hospice, Broad Lane, Rochdale OL16 4PZ; 1 Alder Road, Eccleston Park, Prescot L34 2SG — MRCS Eng. LRCP Lond. 1984.

LOMAX, Rebecca Jane Long Orchard, Beetham, Milnthorpe LA7 7AL — BM BS 1998 Nottm.; BM BS Nottm 1998.

LOMAX, Roger (retired) Larchfield, 12 Pinewood Close, Lancaster LA2 0AD Tel: 01524 69667 — MB 1960 Camb.; BChir 1959. Prev: GP Lancaster.

LOMAX, Simon Harold Michael The Simpson Health Centre, 70 Gregories Road, Beaconsfield HP9 1PS Tel: 01494 671571 Fax: 01494 680219; 16 Beechtree Road, Holmer Green, High Wycombe HP15 6UZ Tel: 01494 712186 Email: slo@breathemail.net — MB ChB 1991 Liverp.; MB ChB 1991 (Hons.) Liverpool; BSc 1988 (Hons) Liverpool; DRCOG 1994; MRCGP 1995. (Liverpool) GP Princip. Socs: Assoc. Mem. Brit. Med. Acupunc. Soc.; BMA. Prev: SHO (Geriat., O & G & Med.) Wycombe Gen. Hosp.

LOMAX, Steven Roger Kemple View Psych Serv, Longsight Road, Langho, Blackburn BB6 8AD Tel: 01254 248021 Fax: 01254 248023 — MB ChB 1970 Manch.; MSc (Criminol) Wales 1997; MRCPsych 1975; DPM Eng. 1975. Dir. of Med. Sens. Cons. Forens. Psychiat. Socs: Manch. Med. Soc. Prev: Cons. (Psychother.) Castel Hosp. Guernsey.

LOMAX, Wilfred (retired) Dunelm, Martin Lane, Bawtry, Doncaster DN10 6NJ Tel: 01302 710312 — MB ChB Leeds 1934; MD (State Med.) Leeds 1939; DPH Leeds 1936. Prev: Cons. Geriat. Doncaster Hosp. Gp.

LOMAX-SIMPSON, Josephine Mary 17 Malcolm Road, Wimbledon, London SW19 4AS — MB ChB 1948 Aberd.; FRCPsych 1984, M 1971; DPM 1953. Indep. GP Lond. Socs: Gp. Analyt. Soc.; Assn. Child Psychol. & Psychiat.; Assoc. Mem. Inst. Psychoanal. Prev: Cons. Psychother. Chiltern Wing, Sutton Hosp.; Cons. Psychiat. Family Cons. Clinic E. Grinstead; Psychother. S. Lond. Hosp. Wom. & Wimbledon Gen. Hosp.

LOMBARD, David Charles 103 Warworth Drive, Chester-le-Street DH2 1NN — MB ChB 1989 Birm.; ChB Birm. 1989.

LOMBARD, Lily 57 The Cedars, Whickham, Newcastle upon Tyne NE16 5TL — MB BS 1959 Durh.; DPH Newc. 1964; FFPHM 1988, M 1974.

LOMBARD, Martin Gerard Department of Gastroenterology, 52 Link, Royal Liverpool University Hospital, Prescot St., Liverpool L7 8XP Tel: 0151 706 4078 Fax: 0151 706 5802 — MB BCh BAO 1980 NUI; MD NUI 1989; MSc (Biochem.) Lond. 1988; MRCPI 1983; FRCPI 1997; FRCP Lond. 1998. (University College Dublin) Cons. Med. & Hon. Sen. Lect. (Gastroenterol.) Univ. of Liverp. & Roy. Liverp. Univ. Hosp. Socs: Amer. Assn. Study Liver Dis.; RCP Lond. (Reg. Rep. & Specialist Regist. Prog. Director); Brit. Soc. Gastroenterol. (Liver Sect.). Prev: Hon. Cons. Med. & Gastroenterol. Aintree Hosp. Liverp.; Sen. Regist. Inst. Liver Studies King's Coll. Hosp. Lond.; Regist. Mater Miser. Hosp. Dub.

LONCASTER, Juliette Anne 17 Churchwood Road, Manchester M20 6TZ — MB ChB 1990 Manch.; MRCP (UK) 1994; FRCH 1998.

LONDON, Annabel Aulene Mary Holy Land, Threapwood, Malpas SY14 7AL — MB BS 1990 Lond.; MRCGP 1995; DRCOG 1995; DCH RCP Lond. 1993. p/t GP Princip.

LONDON, David Robin Ward 1 Office, General Hospital, Steelhouse Lane, Birmingham B4 6NH Tel: 0121 236 8611; Middleton Cottage, Salwarpe, Droitwich WR9 7NB Tel: 01905 774990 — BM BCh 1957 Oxf.; DM Oxf. 1963, BM BCh 1957; FRCP Lond. 1973, M 1960. (Oxf. & St. Thos.) Hon. Prof. Med. Univ. Birm.; Cons. Phys. Gen. Hosp. Birm. Socs: Comm. Med. Research Soc. & Pres. Endocrinol. Sect. Roy. Soc. Med. Prev: Regist. Profess. Med. Unit, W.m. Hosp. Lond; MRC Trav. Fell.; Sen. Lect. in Chem. Path. & Med. St. Thos. Hosp. Lond.

LONDON, Eileen Margaret (retired) Kirkfield, 8 Meadow View, Wyke, Bradford BD12 9LA Tel: 01274 671722 — MB ChB 1960 Leeds. Clin. Asst. (Research Bone Tumour) St. Jas. Hosp. Leeds; Med. Off. BAMS. Prev: Clin. Asst. (A & E & Orthop.) St. Jas. Hosp. Leeds.

LONDON, Helen Morrison East House, Torryleith, New Machar, Aberdeen AB21 0QE — MB ChB 1976 Ed.; FFA RCS (Dub.) 1981. Staff Grade (Anaesth.) Aberd. Roy. Infirm. Socs: Jun. Mem. Assn. Anaesth. Prev: Regist. (Anaesth.) Bangour Gen. Hosp. Broxburn.

LONDON, Ian James Leighton Hospital, Middlewich Rd, Crewe CW1 4DJ Tel: 01270 612460 Email: londonig@yahoo.com — MB BS 1990 Lond.; MRCP (UK) 1993. Cons. Gastroenterologist. Socs: BSG; RC of P of Lond.

LONDON, Joanna 30 Sycamore Road, Bournville, Birmingham B30 2AD — MB ChB 1987 Leeds.

LONDON, Mr John Alfred (retired) Little Court, Churchstow, Kingsbridge TQ7 3QW Tel: 01548 853249 — MB BS 1955 Lond.; FRCS Ed. 1959; MRCS Eng. LRCP Lond. 1955; DObst RCOG 1960. Prev: SHO (Surg.) S. Devon & E. Cornw. Hosp. Plymouth.

LONDON, John Milton (retired) Milkwood, Hay-on-Wye, Hereford HR3 5PL Tel: 01497 821071 — MB ChB 1951 Birm.; MRCS Eng. LRCP Lond. 1951; MRCGP 1964. Prev: Surg. Lt. RN.

LONDON, Katherine Margaret Dermatology Department, St. Luke's Hospital, Little Horton Road, Bradford BD5 0NA Tel: 01274 365540; 11 Slead Avenue, Brighouse HD6 2JB Tel: 01484 712008 — MB ChB 1987 Sheff.; DRCOG 1992. Staff Dermat. Grade. Prev: Trainee GP Calderdale VTS; Ho. Surg. Roy. Halifax Infirm.; Ho. Phys. Lodge Moor Hosp. Sheff.

LONDON, Mervyn Mill House, Brookfield Hospital, Mill House, Cambridge CB1 3DF — MB ChB 1978 Cape Town; MA (Hons.) Camb. 1994; MRCPsych 1984.

LONDON, Mr Nicholas John Harrogate District Hospital, Dept of Orthopsedics, Lancaster Park Road, Harrogate HG2 7SX Tel: 01423 553750; Apple Garth House, Wood Hall, Linton, Wetherby LS22 4HZ Tel: 01937 585456 Email: nick.london@bigfoot.com — MB BChir 1989 Camb.; MD Camb. 1994, MA 1991; FRCS Eng. 1994; FRCS Tr & Orth.1998. (Cambridge) Cons. in Trauma and Orthopaedic Surg., NHS Harrogate. Socs: Brit. Orthop. Assn.; Brit. Orthop. Sports Trauma Assn. Prev: SHO (Orthop.) Leeds Gen. Infirm.; SHO Rotat. (Surg.) St Jas. Hosp. Leeds; Research Fell. & Hon. SHO (Surg.) Univ. Leeds.

LONDON, Professor Nicholas John Milton The Department of Surgery, Clinical Sciences Building, Leicester Royal Infirmary, Leicester LE2 7LX Tel: 0116 252 3252 Fax: 0116 252 3179 Email: sms16@le.ac.uk; 4 The Spinney, Thurnby, Leicester LE7 9QS Tel: 0116 252 3252 Fax: 0116 252 3179 Email: nicklondon@btinternet.com — MB ChB 1980 Birm.; MD Leic. 1990; FRCS Eng. 1986; MRCP (UK) 1984; FRCP 1999. (Birmingham) Prof. (Surg.) Univ. Leics.; Hon. Cons. (Vasc. & Endocrine Surg.) Leicester Roy. Infirm. Socs: Vasc. Surgic. Soc. of GB & Irel.; Assn. of Surg.s; Europ. Soc. for Vasc. and endoVasc. Surg.

LONDON, Mr Peter Stanford, MBE, CStJ (retired) The Ridings, Singleborough, Milton Keynes MK17 0RF Tel: 01296 712425 — MB BS 1944 Lond.; MB BS (Hons. Surg.) Lond. 1944; FRCS Eng. 1950; MRCS Eng. LRCP Lond. 1944; MFOM RCP Lond. 1980; Hon. FACEM 1983. Hon. Edr. Med. Soc. Lond. Prev: Surg. Birm. Accid. Hosp.

LONDON, Sue Patricia Severn Surgery, 159 Uplands Road, Oadby, Leicester LE2 4NW Tel: 0116 271 9042 — BM 1979 Soton.; MRCGP 1984; DRCOG 1982.

LONE, Iftikhar Ahmed Normanby Road Surgery, 502-508 Normanby Road, Normanby, Middlesbrough TS6 9BZ Tel: 01642 452727/440501 Fax: 01642 466723; 21 Whernside, Marton, Middlesbrough TS7 8PJ Tel: 01642 322768 Fax: 01642 466723 — MB BS 1970 Karachi. (Dow Medical College) p/t Liaison Off. Tees Health Middlesbrough; Governor Univ. Teesside; PCG Clin. Governance Lead. Socs: (Treas.) Pakistani Med. Soc.; BMA.

LONERGAN, Bridget Anne Selkirk Health Centre, Viewfield Lane, Selkirk TD7 4LJ; 4 Spion Kop, Selkirk TD7 4JW Tel: 01750 22287 — MB BCh BAO 1987 NUI.

LONERGAN, Fintan James 51 Ramenck Gardens, Arlesey SG15 6XZ — MB BS 1990 Lond.

LONERGAN, James Gerard 10 Upland Road, Birmingham B29 7JR — LAH Dub. 1962.

LONES, Anthony Richard Warwick Glaxo Wellcome Research and Development, Greenford Road, Greenford UB6 0HE Tel: 020 8966 3448 Fax: 020 8423 2097; 49 Pepys Close, Uxbridge UB10 8NX Tel: 01895 630291 Email: rick@lones.karoo.co.uk — BM 1987 Soton.; MRCGP 1994; DRCOG 1993; Dip. IMC RCS Ed. 1992. (Soton.) Research Phys. Internat. Product Safety & Pharmacovigilance. Prev: Civil. Med. Pract. HMS Warrior N.wood.

LONEY, Mrs Elizabeth Lucille 26 Lammas Road, Watford WD18 0BA — MB BS 1993 Lond.; BSc (Hons.) Lond. 1990; FRCS Eng. 1997. (Univ. Coll. Lond. Med. Sch.) SHO (ENT) Roy. Free Hosp. Hampstead Lond. Prev: SHO (Orthop.) Luton & Dunstable; SHO (A & E & Anat.) Roy. Free Hosp. Lond.; Ho. Off. (Surg.) Whittington Hosp. Lond.

LONG, Aidan George Gabriel (retired) Bridge Cottage, Church Road, Brasted, Westerham TN16 1HZ Tel: 01959 562103 — MB BChir 1940 Camb.; MRCS Eng. LRCP Lond. 1940. Prev: Ho. Surg. Poplar Hosp. Accid. & St. Mary's Hosp. For E. End.

LONG, Andrew Colin Toddington Medical Centre, Luton Road, Toddington, Dunstable LU5 6DE Tel: 01525 872222 Fax: 01525 876711; St. Andrews, Pk Road, Toddington, Dunstable LU5 6AB — MB BS 1980 Lond.; MRCGP 1986.

LONG, Andrew Martin Department of Child Health, Farnborough Hospital, Farnborough Common, Orpington BR6 8ND Tel: 01689 814189 Fax: 01689 814038 Email: andrew.long@bromleyhopitals.nhs.uk; The Wood, 101 Paynesfield Road, Tatsfield, Westerham TN16 2BQ Tel: 01959 541084 Fax: 01959 540671 Email: along@btinternet.com — MB BS 1977 Lond.; FRCP Lond. 1996; MRCP (UK) 1982; FRCPCH 1997; DCH 1981. (St. Mary's) Cons. Paediat. FarnBoro. Hosp. Kent; Dir. Med. Educat. & Clin. Tutor W. Kent PostGrad. Med. Centre FarnBoro. Hosp. Kent. Socs: Roy. Soc. Med.; Hon.sec. Counc. Mem. Nat. Assoc. Clin. Tutors; Asst. Sec. RCPCH. Prev: Sen. Regist. Univ. Hosp. Wales; Research Fell. (Neonat. Med.) Bristol Matern. Hosp.; Lect. Child Health (Neonat. Med.) Univ. Bristol.

LONG, Anthony James Sanderson and Partners, Adan House Surgery, St. Andrews Lane, Spennymoor DL16 6QA Tel: 01388 817777 Fax: 01388 811700; 10 St. Charles Road, Spennymoor DL16 6JY — MB ChB 1979 Glas.; MRCGP 1983.

LONG, Audrey Ann 1A Old Hall Gardens, Rainford, St Helens WA11 8NS — MB ChB 1992 Leic. Research Fell. (O & G) Countess of Chester Hosp. Chester.

LONG, Carl Anthony Elderly Medicine Unit, St Peter's Hospital, Guildford Road, Chertsey KT16 0PZ Tel: 01832 722422; 1 Portmore Quays, Weybridge KT13 8HF — MBBS 1979 Lond.; BSc (Hons.) Lond. 1976; MRCS Eng. LRCP Lond. 1979; MRCP (UK) 1988; MRCGP 1984; DCH RCP Lond. 1985; DRCOG 1983; FRCP (Lond.)

1998. (Char. Cross) Cons. Phys. (Elderly Med.) St. Peter's Hosp. Chertsey. Prev: Sen. Regist. (Gen. Internal & Elderly Med.) Watford Gen. Hosp., Chelsea & W.m. Hosps. Lond.; Research Regist. (Geriat. Med.) Cardiff Roy. Infirm.

LONG, Charles Colin Department of Dermatology, Llandough Hospital, Penlan Road, Penarth CF64 2XX Tel: 029 2071 5501 Fax: 029 2070 1771; 9 Mill Road, Lisvane, Cardiff CF14 0XA Tel: 029 20753 400 — MB BS Lond. 1982; MRCPI 1988. Cons. Dermat. Llandough Hosp. Cardiff & Univ hosp of Wales, Cardiff; Clin. Teach. Uni. Wales Coll. Med. Cardiff; Cons Dermatol. Roy Glam Hosp. Socs: Rhondda Med. Soc.; Brit. Assn. Dermat.; Brit. Soc. Dermat. Surg. Prev: Sen. Regist. & Regist. (Dermat.) Univ. Hosp. Wales Cardiff; Regist. Morriston Hosp. Swansea.

LONG, Chin Wan 5 Asmuns Place, London NW11 7XE Tel: 020 8201 8363 — MB BS 1989 Lond.; FRCS Glas. 1996. (University College London) SHO (Otolaryngol.) Stoke Mandeville Hosp. Aylesbury. Prev: SHO (Orthop.) Chase Farm Hosp. Enfield; SHO (Cas.) Newham Gen. Hosp.; SHO (ENT) Barnet Gen. Hosp.

LONG, Colm Martin Mary Wilton Cottage, 31 The Street, Kennington, Ashford TN24 9HB Tel: 01233 622439 — MB BCh BAO 1990 NUI; DGM RCP Lond. 1992; DCH RCSI 1992.

LONG, Cynthia Hilda 65 Chaucer Avenue, Hayes UB4 0AR — MB BS 1963 Rangoon.

LONG, Dagmar Eva 62 Gledhow Wood Grove, Leeds LS8 1PA — MB BS 1980 Lond.; MRCP (UK) 1984.

LONG, Professor David (retired) Brook Cottage, Stream Lane, Sedlescombe, Battle TN33 0PB Tel: 01424 870425 — MB BS Lond. (Hons. Med., Pharm. & Therap.) 1941; DSc Lond. 1972, MD (Path.) 1947; MRCP Lond. 1971; FRCPath 1971; FIBiol 1970. Dir. Infec. Control Research Dept.; Prof. Univ. Brighton; Vis. Prof. Sch. Molecular Scs. Univ. Sussex; Vis. Prof. Clin. Microbiol. Univ. Surrey; Hon. Cons. Microbiol. E.bourne Health Dist.; Mem. WHO Expert Advis. Panel on Biol. Standardisation. Prev: Cons. Tumour Immunol. Unit, Chester Beatty Research Inst., Roy. Cancer Hosp.

LONG, David Howard Westlands, Caswell Bay, Swansea SA3 3BU — MB ChB 1970 Bristol; FFA RCS Eng. 1976. Cons. Anaesth. Morriston Hosp. Trust Swansea.

LONG, David Robert Kent & Canterbury Hospital, Ethelbert Road, Canterbury CT1 3NG; 16 St. Augustine's Road, Canterbury CT1 1XR — BM 1976 Soton.; MRCP (UK) 1980; FRCPC 1990. Cons. Paediat. Kent & Canterbury Hosp. Prev: Asst. Prof. Paediat. Mem. Univ. of Newfld. St. John's, Canada.

LONG, Elizabeth Doreen 50 Warren Road, Donaghadee BT21 0PD — LRCP LRCS 1940 Ed.; LRCP LRCS Ed. LRFPS Glas. 1940.

LONG, Elizabeth Kirstie Elms Medical Practice, 5 Stewart Road, Harpenden AL5 4QA Tel: 01582 769393 Fax: 01582 461735; 10 Necton Road, Wheathampstead, St Albans AL4 8AU — MB BS 1991 Lond.; MRCGP 1995; DRCOG 1994; DFFP 1994. Socs: Med. Defence Union; BMA; RCGP. Prev: Trainee GP Abbotts Langley; SHO (Paediat., O & G & Geriat.) Lister Hosp. Stevenage; Ho. Surg. (Med.) Roy. Free Hosp. Lond.

LONG, Ervine Dean Pathology Laboratory, Cumberland Infirmary, Carlisle CA2 7HY Tel: 01228 23444 Fax: 01228 592355; Moss Side, Newton Arlosh, Carlisle CA7 5HE Tel: 016974 76326 — BM BCh 1977 Oxf.; MA Oxf. 1978, BM BCh 1977; MRCPath 1983; FRCPath 1995. Cons. Path. Cumbld. Infirm. Carlisle. Socs: Assn. Clin. Path; Soc. Path. Prev: Lect. (Path.) St. Geo. Hosp. Lond.; Asst. Lect. (Path.) St. Thos. Hosp. Lond.; Ho. Phys. Radcliffe Infirm.

LONG, Gillian Department of Radiology, Sheffield Children's Hospital, Western Bank, Sheffield S10 2TH Tel: 0114 271 7166 Fax: 0114 271 7514; 15 Ranmoor Crescent, Ranmoor, Sheffield SI0 3GY Tel: 0114 230 4786 — BM 1985 Soton.; BM Soton 1985; MRCP (UK) 1988; FRCR 1993; DRCOG 1989; DCH RCP Lond. 1988. Cons. Paediat. Radiol. Sheff. Childr. Hosp. Prev: Sen. Regist. (Radiol.) Roy. Hallamsh. Hosp. Sheff.; Regist. (Radiol.) Univ. Hosp. Wales; SHO (Med.) Qu. Alexandra Hosp. Portsmouth.

LONG, Helen Ann Birbeck Medical Group, Penrith Health Centre, Bridge Lane, Penrith CA11 8HW Tel: 01768 245200 Fax: 01768 245295 — MB BS 1986 Lond.; MRCGP 1990; DRCOG 1990; DCH RCP Lond. 1989.

LONG, Helen Ruth Meddygfa Pengorof, Gorof Road, Ystradgynlais, Swansea SA9 1DS Tel: 01639 843221 Fax: 01639 843790 — MB BS 1986 Lond.; DRCOG 1990. Prev: SHO (Anaesth.) Singleton Hosp. Swansea W. Glam. HA.

LONG, James Melbourne Health Care Centre, Penn Lane, Melbourne, Derby DE73 1EF Tel: 01332 862124 Fax: 01332 865154 — MB BCh 1984 Wales; BDS Birm. 1975; MRCGP 1988; DRCOG 1987.

LONG, Jason Ronald Flat 2/R, 7 Naseby Avenue, Glasgow G11 7JQ — MB ChB 1993 Glas.; MRCP (UK) 1998. Specialist Regist. in A & E, Monklands Hosp., Airdrie.

LONG, Joanne Maureen 67 Anglesey Road, Burton-on-Trent DE14 3PF — MB BS 1992 Lond.

LONG, Marcus Henry Penalverne Surgery, Penalverne Drive, Penzance TR18 2RE Tel: 01736 363361 Fax: 01736 332118 — MB BS 1975 Lond.; MRCGP 1980. (St. Thos.) Prev: SHO (Obst.) St. Thos. Hosp. Lond.; Ho. Phys. St. Helier Hosp. Carshalton; Ho. Surg. Gen. Hosp. Jersey.

LONG, Mr Matthew Gerard Gatwick Park Hospital, Povey Cross Road, Horley RH6 0BB Tel: 01293 785511 Email: mglong@compuserve.com — MB BS 1983 Lond.; MRCOG 1989; MD Lond. 1995. (Charing Cross Hospital) Cons. Obst./Gyn. E. Surrey Hosp. Redhill. Socs: Brit. Menopause Soc.; Brit. Soc. Gyn. Endoscopy; Brit. Soc. Colposc. & Cervic. Pathol. Prev: Sen. Regist. Rotat. W. Middlx. Hosp. Char. Cross & W.minster; Regist. Kings Coll. Hosp.; SHO Qu. Charlotte's & Chelsea Hosp. for Wom.

LONG, Michael Andrew Princess Alexandra Hospital, Hamstel Road, Harlow CM20 1QX Tel: 01279 444455 Ext: 2825 — MB BS 1987 Lond.; BSc Lond. 1983; MRCP (UK) 1990; FRCR 1993. (St. Bart. Hosp. Med. Sch.) Cons. Radiol. P.ss Alexandra Hosp. Harlow. Socs: BMA. Prev: Sen. Regist. (Radiol.) Char. Cross Hosp. Lond.; Regist. (Med.) S.end Gen. Hosp.

LONG, Rachel Marian Erne Health Centre, Erne Hospital, Cornagrade Road, Enniskillen BT74 6AY Tel: 028 6632 5638 — MB BCh BAO 1979 NUI; MRCGP 1986; DRCOG 1982.

LONG, Richard Glover City Hospital, Nottingham NG5 1PB Tel: 0115 969 1169 Ext: 46693; The Coach House, Old Hall Drive, Widmerpool, Nottingham NG12 5PZ Tel: 0115 937 2467 — MRCS Eng. LRCP Lond. 1972; MB BS 1972 Lond.; MD 1978 Lond.; FRCP Lond. 1989; MRCP (UK) 1974. (Roy. Free) Cons. Phys. & Gastroenterol. City Hosp. & Univ. Hosp. Nottm.; Clin. Teach. Univ. Nottm. Med. Sch. Socs: Brit. Soc. Gastroenterol. & Assn. Phys.; Am. Gastro. Assn.; biochem soc. Prev: MRC Trav. Research Fell. VAMC Dept. Med. San Francisco, USA; Sen. Regist. (Med.) St. Thos. Hosp. Lond.; Hon. Sen. Regist. (Med.) Hammersmith Hosp. Lond.

LONG, Robert John Keresley Road, 2 Keresley Road, Coventry CV6 2JD Tel: 024 7633 2628 Fax: 024 7633 1326 — MRCS Eng. LRCP Lond. 1976; MB BS Lond. 1976, BDS 1971; LDS RCS Eng. 1971.

LONG, Sarah Mary 86 Rectory Road, Sutton Coldfield B75 7RP Tel: 0121 378 0624 — MB ChB 1979 Birm.

LONG, Simon Geoffrey Chugai Pharma UK, Mulliner House, Flanders Road, Turnham Green, London W4 1NN Tel: 020 8987 5680 Fax: 020 8987 5661 Email: sg.long@chugai_pharm.co.uk; Flint Cottage, Yarm Way, Leatherhead KT22 8RQ Tel: 01372 374967 — MB ChB 1985 Leeds; MRCP (UK) 1988; Dip. Pharm. Med. RCP (UK) 1996. Med. Dir. Chugai Pharma UK. Socs: Brit. Soc. Haematol.; Brit. Assn. Pharmaceut. Phys.; Assoc. Fac. Pharmaceut. Med. Prev: Sheldon Clin. Research Fell.; Regist. (Haemat.) Worcester Roy. Infirm.; SHO (Neurol.) Pinderfields Gen. Hosp. Wakefield.

LONG, Timothy Mark Warwick 4 Beech Cliffe, Coventry Road, Warwick CV34 5HY Tel: 01926 407008; South Warwicks General Hospital Trust, Anaesthetic Department, Lakin Road, Warwick CV34 5BW Tel: 01926 495321 Ext: 4136 Fax: 01926 482613 — BM BS 1980 Nottm.; FRCA 1985. Cons. Anaesth. S. Warwick Gen. Hosps. Trust; Hon. Sen. Lect. (Anaesth.) Univ. of Birm. Med. Sch. Socs: Intens. Care Soc.; Assn. Anaesth.; W Midl. Intens. Care Gp. (Ex-Chairm.).

LONGAN, John Frederick L'Aumone and St. Sampsons Practice, L'Aumone Surgery, Castel, Guernsey GY5 7RU Tel: 01481 256517 Fax: 01481 251190 — MB BS 1979 Lond.; MRCGP 1985. Prev: Trainee GP Aberystwyth; Ho. Surg. N. Devon Dist. Hosp. Barnstaple; Ho. Phys. Prof. Dept. of Med. Char. Cross Hosp. Lond.

LONGAN, Maureen Anne 6 Crag View, Thurgoland, Sheffield S35 7BW — MB BS 1973 Newc.; FFA RCS Eng. 1978.

LONGBOTHAM, Roger Charles The Almitage Surgery, Shropshire Brook Road, Armitage, Rugeley WS15 2UZ Tel: 01543 490444; Ash Ling, Stone Road, Colwich, Stafford ST17 0XQ — MB ChB Sheff. 1968; MRCGP 1975; DObst RCOG 1970. (Sheff.) Socs: BMA; BASICS (Mid Staffs. Br.). Prev: SHO (Obst.) Jessop Hosp. Sheff.

LONGBOTTOM, Mr Donald Nigel Orthopaedic Dept, Queen Alexandra Hospital, Portsmouth — MB BS 1973 Lond.; FRCS Ed. 1982; MRCS Eng. LRCP Lond. 1973.

LONGBOTTOM, Graham Fieldhead Surgery, 65 New Road Side, Horsforth, Leeds LS18 4JY Tel: 0113 295 3410 Fax: 0113 295 3417; 4 Redbeck Cottages, Woodbottom, Horsforth, Leeds LS18 4EQ Tel: 0113 250 3402 — MB ChB 1978 Leeds; DRCOG 1981. (Leeds) GP Horsforth W. Yorks. Prev: Med. Off. Sandoz Products Horsforth W. Yorks.

LONGBOURNE, David (retired) The Old Rectory Cottage, Mere, Warminster BA12 6DS Tel: 01747 860243 — MB BS 1954 Lond.; MRCS Eng. LRCP Lond. 1953; MRCGP 1976; DObst RCOG 1957. Prev: Cas. Off. & Ho. Phys. Childr. Hosp. Birm.

LONGBOURNE, John Richard Fairbrook Medical Centre, 4 Fairway Avenue, Borehamwood WD6 1PR Tel: 020 8953 7666; Palmers Lodge, Allun Lane, Elstree, Borehamwood WD6 3NN Tel: 020 8953 1091 — MRCS Eng. LRCP Lond. 1963; MA, MB BChir Camb. 1965. (Middlx.) Clin. Asst. Barnet Gen. Hosp.; Med. Adviser Centr. Television PLC. Prev: Ho. Phys. & Ho. Surg. St. Albans City Hosp.; Obst. Ho. Off. Edgware Gen. Hosp.

LONGDEN, David John Dalton Square Surgery, 8 Dalton Square, Lancaster LA1 1PP Tel: 01524 842200; Broadheath, 9 Hall Park, Scotforth, Lancaster LA1 4SH — MB ChB 1974 Leeds; MRCGP 1978. Prev: Trainee GP Lancaster VTS; Ho. Off. (Gen. Med.) & Ho. Surg. (Gen. Surg.) Wharfedale Gen. Hosp.

LONGDEN, Douglas Ernest (retired) 2 Brookside, Gillingham SP8 4HR — MA, MB BChr Camb. 1955; MRCS Eng. LRCP Lond. 1954; DPM Eng. 1959.

LONGDEN, Paul Bell, OBE (retired) 30 Kelly Street, London NW1 8PH Tel: 020 7482 2144 — MRCS Eng. LRCP Lond. 1939. Prev: Lt. Col. RAMC.

LONGDON, David Neal Yelverton Surgery, Westella Road, Yelverton PL20 6AS Tel: 01822 852202 Fax: 01822 852260 — MB ChB 1976 Bristol.

LONGFIELD, Ian Vincent (retired) 40 Newlands Avenue, Newcastle upon Tyne NE3 5PX Tel: 0191 236 3591 — MB BChir 1954 Camb.; MRCS Eng. LRCP Lond. 1954; DObst RCOG 1956.

LONGFIELD, Miss Jane Christine 74 Church Road, Woodley, Reading RG5 4QB Tel: 0113 228 8051 — MB BS 1983 Newc.; MD Newc. 1995; MRCOG 1989. Clin. Assit in coloscopy Roy. Berks. Hosp. Socs: Brit. Gynae Cancer Soc; Brit. Soc for coloscopy & cervical Path. Prev: Sen. Regist. (O & G) St Jas. Univ. Hosp. Leeds.; Sen. Regist. (O & G) Leeds Gen. Infirm.; Sen. Regist (O& G) Bradford Roy Infirm.

LONGFIELD, Michael HM Prison Service, Directorate of Health Care, Cleland House, Page St., London SW1P 4LN Tel: 020 7217 6182 Fax: 020 7217 6224 — MB ChB 1978 Manch.; MHM 1996. Dir. (Health Care) Home Off. Prison Serv. Lond. Prev: Princ. Med Off. Home Office Prison Serv. Lond.; Sen. Med. Off. Home Off. Prison Serv. HM Prison Leeds.

LONGFIELD, Shauna Rosamund Waddell Dinnington Group Practice, Medical Centre, New Street, Dinnington, Sheffield S25 2EZ — MB ChB 1991 Bristol; DRCOG 1994; DCH 1995; MRCGP 1996. GP Dinnington. Socs: BMA & Med. Protec. Soc. Prev: GP Regist. Gleadless Sheff.; GP Regist. Tickhill Doncaster.

LONGHORN, Ian Robert Flat 3, 6 Atlantic Road, Weston Super Mare BS23 2DG — MB ChB 1979 Bristol.

LONGHORN, Piers Duncan Station Meadows, Hawes Road, Horton-in-Ribblesdale, Settle BD24 0HT — MB ChB 1992 Manch.

LONGHORN, Ralph Kenrick Station Meadows, Haws Road, Horton in Ribblesdale, Settle BD24 — MB ChB 1991 Leeds.

LONGHURST, Hilary Jane Woodside, East Hanningfield Road, Howe Green, Chelmsford CM2 7TQ Tel: 01245 471367 — MB BS 1984 Lond.; MCPath 1999; PhD Open 1995; BA Camb. 1981; MRCP (UK) 1987. (Univ. Camb. & St. Mary's Hosp. Lond.) Lect. & Hon. Sen. Regist. (Clin. Immunol.) St. Bart. Hosp. Lond. Socs: Brit. HIV Assn.; Europ. Soc. Of Immunodeficiencies; Brit. Soc. Of Immunol. Prev: MRC Train. Fell. Nat. Inst. Med. Research Lond.; Regist. (Med.) Kingston Hosp. Surrey; SHO (Infec. Dis.) Coppetts Wood Hosp. Lond.

LONGHURST, Margaret Jane Stoke Surgery, Belmont Villas, Stoke, Plymouth PL3 4DP Tel: 01752 562569 Fax: 01752 607299; Tideways, Yealm Road, Newton Ferrers, Plymouth PL8 1BL — MB ChB 1975 Sheff.; BSc Lond. 1969.

LONGHURST, Melanie Grace West Berks Priority Care NHS Trust, Fair Mile Hospital, Wallingford OX10 9HH Tel: 01491 651281 Fax: 01491 651128 — MB BS 1976 Lond.; BSc Lond. 1972; MRCS Eng. LRCP Lond. 1975; MRCPsych 1983. (Guy's Hospital) Assoc. Specialist (Psychiat.) Fairmile Hosp. Wallingford.

LONGHURST, Nicholas West Berks Priority Care NHS Trust, Fairmile Hospital, Reading Road, Cholsey, Wallingford OX10 9HH Tel: 01491 651281 — MB BS Lond. 1970; MRCP (U.K.) 1972; MRCS Eng. LRCP Lond. 1970; MRCPsych 1975; FRCP 1997; FRCPsych 1997. (Guy's) Cons. Psychiat. Fairmile Hosp. Prev: Regist. Maudsley Hosp. Lond.; Sen. Regist. (Psychiat.) Guy's Health Dist. (T).

LONGHURST, Sian Elizabeth Bristol Children's Hospital, St. Michael's Hill, Bristol BS2 8BJ Tel: 0117 921 5411 — MB BS 1985 Lond.; BSc Lond. 1982; MRCP Paediat. (UK) 1991; DTM & H RCP Lond. 1992; DRCOG 1988. Regist. (Paediat.) Bristol Childr. Hosp. Socs: Brit. Paediat. Assn. Prev: Med. Off. Micheweni Hosp. Pemba Is., Tanzania.

LONGIN, Milo Jerko 130 Harley Street, London W1 Tel: 020 7935 6558; Mansfield House, 29 Mount Sion, Tunbridge Wells TN1 1TZ — MD 1954 Zagreb; LAH Dub. 1961; FRCOG 1983, M 1970. Cons. (O & G) N. Kent & Gravesend Hosp., W. Hill Hosp. Dartford & Ital. Hosp. Lond.; Hon. Tutor (Obst. & Gyn.) Guy's Hosp. Med. Sch. Lond. Socs: Fell. Roy. Soc. Med. (Mem. Sect. Obst. & Gyn.). Prev: Regist. (O & G) Woolwich & Hillingdon Gps. Hosps. & Pembury; Hosp.; Examr. Centr. Midw. Bd.

LONGLEY, Janice Isobel Hollands and Partners, Bridport Medical Centre, North Allington, Bridport DT6 5DU Tel: 01308 421896 Fax: 01308 421109 — MRCGP 1990; MB BS 1983 London; MB BS 1983 London. (Middlesex Hospital) Gen. Practitioner; Clin. Asst. in Elderly Care.

LONGLEY, Judith Penelope Ash Trees Surgery, Market Street, Carnforth LA5 9JU Tel: 01524 720000 Fax: 01524 720110 Email: hudith.longley@gp-p81029.nwest.nhs.uk — MB BS 1980 Newc.; MA Oxf. 1980, BA 1977; MRCP (UK) 1984; MRCGP 1986; DRCOG 1982; Dip. Pract. Dermat. Wales 1996.

LONGLEY, Juliana Michal Longley and Jolly, The GP Centre, 322 Malden Road, North Cheam, Sutton SM3 8EP Tel: 020 8644 0224; 2 Cavendish Drive, Claygate, Esher KT10 0QE Tel: 01372 810145 — MB BS Lond. 1969; MRCS Eng. LRCP Lond. 1969; DA Eng. 1973; DObst RCOG 1971; Cert. FPA JCC 1971; Dip Acupunc. 1997; Dip Family Plann 1998. (St. Mary's) Socs: Brit. Med. Acupunct. Soc. Prev: GP Soton.; SHO (Anaesth.) Norf. & Norwich Hosp.; SHO Off. (O & G) Univ. Hosp. S. Manch.

LONGLEY, Martin Charles c/o Officers Mess, MBH Rinteln BFPO 31 — MB BS 1991 Lond.

LONGLEY, Michael Andrew 32 Rest Bay Close, Porthcawl CF36 3UN — MB BS 1990 Lond.

LONGLEY, Rupert Hillary Coleford Health Centre, Railway Drive, Coleford GL16 8RH Tel: 01594 832117 — MB BS 1978 London. (London) GP Coleford, Glos.

LONGMAN, Cheryl Amanda The Bower, 12 Prestwick Road, Monkton, Prestwick KA9 2PB — MB ChB 1994 Glas.

LONGMAN, Richard James Rookery Medical Centre, Rookery House, Newmarket CB8 8NW Tel: 01638 665711 Fax: 01638 561280 — MB ChB 1975 Bristol; DCH Eng. 1978; DRCOG 1977.

LONGMAN, Robert John 8 Rosetrees, Warren Road, Guildford GU1 2HS — MB ChB 1992 Bristol.

LONGMATE, Andrew George Stirling Royal infirmary, Livilands, Stirling Tel: 01786 484000 — MB ChB 1990 Ed.; FRCA 1996. (Edinburgh) Cons. Anaesth. Prev: Regist. (Anaesth.) Roy. Infirm. Edin.

LONGMORE, Charmian Helen (retired) Ivy House, Shenstone, Lichfield WS14 0NT Tel: 01543 480251 — MB ChB 1941 Birm.; MRCS Eng. LRCP Lond. 1941; DOMS Eng. 1947. Clin. Asst. Walsall HA (T). Prev: Clin. Asst. Birm. & Midl. Eye Hosp. & Good Hope Dist. Gen. Hosp.

LONGMORE, Professor Donald Bernard, OBE (retired) Brompton MR Enterprises, South Parade, London SW3 6LL Tel: 020 7351 8933 — MB BS 1953 Lond.; FRCS Ed. 1958; MRCS Eng. LRCP Lond. 1953; FRCR 1990; FRCS Lond 1955. Chairm. MR 3000; Dir. Brompton MR Enterprises. Prev: Prof. Magnetic Resonance Med. & Dir. MR Unit Roy. Brompton Nat. Heart & Lung Hosp. Lond.

LONGMORE, Herbert John Alexander (retired) Lynnhurst, Lochmaben, Lockerbie DG11 1NJ Tel: 01387 810536 Email: plaidslongmore@sol.co.uk — MB ChB Aberd. 1954; FRCGP 1984, M 1966; DObst RCOG 1958. Prev: Clin. Asst. (Orthop.) Dumfries Infirm.

LONGMORE, John Murray Barn Surgery, 22 Ferring Street, Ferring, Worthing BN12 5HJ Tel: 01903 242638 Fax: 01903 700574 — BM BCh 1980 Oxf.; MA Oxf. 1981, BM BCh 1980; MRCGP 1984; DRCOG 1984. GP. Socs: Fell. Roy. Soc. Trop. Med. & Hyg. Prev: GP Trainee St. John's Ho., Bridgwater, Som.; SHO Paediat. Musgrave Pk. Hosp. Som.; Ho. Phys. John Radcliffe Hosp. Oxf.

LONGMORE, Timothy Brian Blackburn Road Medical Centre, Blackburn Road, Birstall, Batley WF17 9PL Tel: 01924 478265 — MB ChB 1988 Sheff.; MRCGP 1994. Med. Off. Ment.ly Ill Rehabil. Unit. Mumbauzo, Nigeria.

***LONGRIDGE, Clare Francesca** 2 Kew Gardens, Priorslee, Telford TF2 9SY — MB ChB 1995 Birm.; DRCOG 1997.

LONGRIGG, Mr John Neil Causey House, Causey Hill, Hexham NE46 2DL — MD 1974 Manch.; MB ChB 1967; FRCS Ed. 1971. Cons. Gen. Surg.

LONGSHAW, Catherine Lyn 37 Dransfield Road, Sheffield S10 5RL — MB ChB 1990 Sheff.

LONGSHAW, Mark Stephen 37 Dransfield Road, Sheffield S10 5RL — MB ChB 1990 Sheff.

LONGSON, Damien Department of Psychiatry, Rawnsley Building, Manchester Royal Infirmary, Oxford Road, Manchester M13 9WL Tel: 0161 276 5362 Fax: 0161 276 5444 Email: dlongson@man.ac.uk — MB ChB 1986 Manch.; MSc Manch. 1993; BSc (Hons.) Manch. 1983, MB ChB 1986; MRCPsych 1993; PhD Manch. 1998. (Manch.) Cons. Psychiat. Manch. Roy. Infirm. Prev: Sen. Regist. Manch. Roy. Infirm.; Wellcome Clin. Research Fell. Manch. Roy. Infirm.; SHO Med. Manch. Roy. Infirm.

LONGSON, Donald (retired) 24 Torkington Road, Wilmslow SK9 2AE Tel: 01625 525938 Email: donald@longsonia.freeserve.co.uk — MB ChB 1946 Manch.; MD (Hon. Causa) Manch. 1990; FRCP Lond. 1965, M 1948. Lect. (Clin. Endocrinol.) Univ. Manch.; Sub-Dean Postgrad. Studies; Hon. Phys. Manch. Roy. Infirm. Prev: Phys. Manch. Roy. Infirm.

LONGSON, Joan 24 Torkington Road, Wilmslow SK9 2AE Tel: 01625 525938 — MB ChB 1948 Manch. (Manch.) Clin. Asst. St Mary's Hosp. Manch. Socs: Fell. Manch. Med. Soc. Prev: Sch. Med. Off. Manch. High Sch. for Girls; Ho. Phys. & Res. Clin. Pathol. Roy. Infirm. Manch.; Regist. (Path.) Booth Hall Hosp. Manch.

LONGSON, Peter James 23 Queen Eleanor's Drive, Copt Heath, Knowle, Solihull B93 9LY Tel: 01564 779963 — MB ChB 1976 Sheff.; AFOM RCP Lond. 1993; Cert. Av. Med. 1989. (Sheff.) Occupat. Phys Brit. Gas Trading Med. Adviser. Socs: Soc. Occupat. Med. Prev: Occupat. Phys. Rover Gp. (Land Rover) Solihull & Manch. Airport.

LONGSTAFF, Andrew John The Old Vicarage, Hill, Berkeley GL13 9JX Tel: 01454 260262 — MB BS 1971 Lond.; FRCR 1981; MRCP (UK) 1976; DMRD Eng. 1979. Cons. Radiol. Frenchay Hosp. Bristol. Prev: Sen. Regist. (Radiol.) Roy. Hallamsh. Hosp. Sheff.; Surg. Lt.-Cdr. RN.

LONGSTAFF, John (retired) Brombil, 20 Middlegate Court, Cowbridge CF71 7EF Tel: 01446 772520 — MB ChB 1953 Sheff.; DObst RCOG 1958. Prev: Ho. Surg. Roy. Hosp. Sheff.

LONGSTAFF, Keith 12A Selby Terrace, Maryport CA15 Tel: 01900 815544 Fax: 01900 816626; The Hastings, Crosby, Maryport CA15 6RW — MB ChB 1956 Liverp.; MRCS Eng. LRCP Lond. 1956. (Liverp.)

LONGSTAFF, Margaret Alice (retired) Brombil, 20 Middlegate Court, Cowbridge CF71 7EF Tel: 01446 772520 — MRCS Eng. LRCP Lond. 1953. Prev: Ho. Surg. & Ho. Phys. Bridgend Gen. Hosp.

LONGSTAFF, Sarah Frances Hook and Hartley Wintney Medical Partnership, 1 Chapter Terrace, Hartley Wintney, Hook RG27 8QJ Tel: 01252 842087 Fax: 01252 843145; Gorse Cottage, Up Green, Eversley, Hook RG27 0PB Tel: 01252 872244 — MB BS 1988 Lond.; MRCGP 1993; DRCOG 1992. (St Georges) Princip. GP.

LONGSTAFF, Mr Simon Department of Ophthalmology, Royal Hallamshire Hospital, Sheffield — MB ChB 1981 Dundee; FRCS Ed. 1985. Cons. Ophth. Surg. Roy. Hallamsh. Hosp. Sheff. Prev: Sen. Regist. (Ophth.) Roy. Hallamsh. Hosp. Sheff.

LONGSTAFFE, Brian Charles 3A Civic Way, Ellesmere Port, South Wirral L65 0AF — MB ChB 1960 Liverp.

LONGSTAFFE, Joanna Elizabeth Countisbury Avenue Surgery, 152 Countisbury Avenue, Llanrumney, Cardiff CF3 5YS Tel: 029 2079 2661 Fax: 029 2079 4537; 12 Harrismith Road, Penylan, Cardiff CF23 5DG Tel: 01222 482907 — MB BCh 1988 Wales; MRCGP 1992.

LONGTHORNE, Peter Norman Schering Health Care Ltd, The Brow, Burgess Hill RH15 9NE Tel: 01444 232323 Fax: 01444 246613 Email: plongthorne@schering.co.uk — MB BS Lond. 1969; MRCS Eng. LRCP Lond. 1969; MFPHM 1989; DObst RCOG 1970; FFPM 1998. (Char. Cross) Med. Dir. Schering Health Care Ltd. Socs: Brit. Assn. Pharmaceut. Phys.; Brit. Inst. Radiol.; Fell. Fac. Pharmaceut. Med. Prev: Marketing & Sales Dir., Head of Clin. Research & Med. Adviser Schering Health Care Ltd.; Princip. GP Essex.

LONGTON, Mr Edward Berry (retired) The Croft, Main St., Stainforth, Settle BD24 9PE — MB ChB 1956 Ed.; MChOrth Liverp. 1964; FRCS Ed. 1963; DA Eng. 1959. Prev: Cons. Orthop. Surg. United Leeds Hosps. & Leeds RHB.

LONGTON, Mary Angela Park Place, Woodside, Epping CM16 6LG Tel: 01378 72594 — MB BCh BAO 1948 NUI. (Cork) Prev: Rotating Intern Bon Secours Hosp. Baltimore, U.S.A.; Regist. (Anaesth.) Chelmsford & Essex Hosp. & Bon Secours Hosp. Cork.

LONGTON, Roderick Hunt Park Place, Woodside, Epping CM16 6LG Tel: 01992 572594 — MB BS 1948 Lond.; MRCS Eng. LRCP Lond. 1948. (St. Mary's) Clin. Asst. (Orthop.) Wanstead Hosp. & (Gen. Med.) Harlow Hosp.; Med. Ref. Pruden. & Guardian Assur. Cos. Prev: Ho. Phys. Fulham Hosp. & Atkinson Morley's Hosp. Wimbledon; Regist. (Med.) St. Margt. Hosp. Epping.

LONGWILL, John Alexander Rankin, Col. late RAMC (retired) — MB ChB 1964 Liverp.; MRCGP 1971; DFFP 1993; DObst RCOG 1975; DCH Eng. 1973; DTM & H Eng. 1971. Sen. Med. Off. ATR Bassingbourn. Prev: CO Brit. Milit. Hosp. & Sen. Med. Off. Falkland I.

LONGWILL, Joyce Maud Kingsway Medical Centre, Kingsway, Billingham TS23 2LS Tel: 01642 553738 Fax: 01642 533011; 608 Yarm Road, Eaglescliffe, Stockton-on-Tees TS16 0DQ Tel: 01642 785547 — MB BS 1972 Newc.; MRCGP 1990. (Newcastle upon Tyne) Prev: Trainee GP Cleveland VTS.

***LONGWILL, Sarah** 8 Woodstock Terrace, Poplar, London E14 0AD Tel: 020 7538 5290; 8 Oxford Close, Bassingbourn, Royston SG8 5LL Tel: 01763 245500 — MB BS 1997 Lond.; BSc Lond. 1995.

LONGWORTH, Ann Elizabeth Motown Barn, Ponsonby, Calderbridge, Seascale CA20 1BX; Beech House, Main St, Egremont CA22 2BD Tel: 01946 820203 & 820214 — MB ChB 1983 Leic.

LONGWORTH, David 5A The Avenue, York YO30 6AS — MB ChB 1985 Ed.

LONGWORTH, Janice Lesley Salisbury Road Surgery, 43 Salisbury Road, Plymouth PL4 8QU Tel: 01752 665879; Court Gate House, Harbourneford, South Brent TQ10 9DT Tel: 01364 72772 — BM BS 1984 Nottm.; BMedSci Nottm. 1982; D.Occ.Med. RCP Lond. 1996; DFFP 1994. (Univ. Nottm.) Gen. Practitioner; Occupat.al Phys. Socs: Soc. Occupat. Med. Prev: Estabm. Med. Off. RN Hosp. Plymouth; Trainee GP Truro; Occupat. Phys. Occupat. Health & Safety Centre Univ. of Plymouth.

LONGWORTH, Stephen The East Leicester Medical Practice, 131 Uppingham Road, Leicester LE5 4BP Tel: 0116 276 7145 Fax: 0116 246 1637; 9 Hollies Way, Bushby, Leicester LE7 9RL — MB ChB 1981 Manch.; MRCGP 1985. Princip. GP Leics. FPC.

LONGWORTH-KRAFFT, Catherine Vallance (retired) 44 Stockers Avenue, Winchester SO22 5LB Tel: 01962 68472 — MB BS 1947 Durh.; DMRD Eng. 1955. Prev: Cons. Radiol. St. Mary's Hosp. Portsmouth.

LONGWORTH-KRAFFT, Mr Gerard (retired) 44 Stockers Avenue, Winchester SO22 5LB — MB BS 1943 Lond.; FRCS Eng. 1951;

MRCS Eng. LRCP Lond. 1940. Prev: Med. Off. Dept. Health & Social Security.

LONIE, Diana Susan The Beeches, Roseacre Road, Elswick, Preston PR4 3UD — MB BS 1971 Newc.; FFA RCS Eng. 1979; DA Eng. 1977; DObst RCOG 1975.

LONNON, Janet Anne 11 Larch Grove, Lisvane, Cardiff CF14 0TH Tel: 029 2075 6452 — MB ChB 1960 Ed. (Ed.)

LONSDALE, Jane Kathryn Court View Surgery, 2A Darnley Road, Strood, Rochester ME2 2HA Tel: 01634 290333 Fax: 01634 295131 — MB BS 1987 Lond.; BSc Lond. 1984.

LONSDALE, Margaret Department of Anaesthesia, St. John's Hospital, Livingston EH54 6PP — MB ChB 1982 Dundee; FFA RCS Ed. 1986. Cons. Anaesth. W. Lothian Trust.

LONSDALE, Raymond Neil Department of Histopathology, Norfolk & Norwich NHS Health Care Trust, Brunswick Road, Norwich NR1 3SR Tel: 01603 287613 Fax: 01603 286017; 227 Earlham Road, Norwich NR2 3RQ — MB ChB 1986 Sheff.; BMedSci Sheff. 1985, MB ChB 1986; MRCPath 1992. Cons. Histopath. & Cytopath. Norf. & Norwich NHS Health Care Trust. Prev: Sen. Regist. (Histopath.) Addenbrooke's Hosp. & Norf. & Norwich Hosp.; Regist. (Histopath.) Ipswich Hosp. & Addenbrooke's Hosp. Camb.; SHO (Clin. Path.) & Ho. Surg. Roy. Hallamsh. Hosp. Sheff.

LONSDALE, Richard Evans Radford Health Centre, Ilkeston Road, Nottingham NG1 3GW Tel: 0115 979 2691; 261 Loughborough Road, West Bridgford, Nottingham NG2 7EG Tel: 0115 923 4597 — MB BS 1982 Lond.; MA Camb. 1983; DCH RCP Lond. 1986.

LONSDALE, Mr Robert John Sheffield Vascular Institute, Northern General Hospital, Herres Road, Sheffield S5 7AU Tel: 01142 266991; Tel: 01909 773400 — MB BS 1985 Lond.; BSc (Hons.) Lond. 1982; DM Nottm. 1995; FRCS Eng. 1990; FRCS Ed. 1989. (Univ. Coll. Lond.) Cons. (Vasc. Surg.), Sheff. Socs: Surgic. Research Soc.; Vasc. Surg. Soc. Prev: Lect. (Vasc. Surg.) Univ. Nottm.; Sen. Regist. & Regist. Rotat. Mid Trent; Research Fell. (Vasc.) Univ. Hosp. Nottm.

LONSDALE, Stephen 18B High Market Place, Kirkbymoorside, York YO62 6BQ; Forest View, North St, South Molton EX36 3AW Tel: 01769 573722 Email: steve@slonsdale.freeserve.co.uk — MB BS 1964 Lond.; MRCS Eng. LRCP Lond. 1964; DTM & H Liverp. 1989; DCH Eng. 1966; DObst RCOG 1966. (Univ. Coll. Hosp.)

LONSDALE-ECCLES, Ann Alleyne 121 Warton Terrace, Heaton, Newcastle upon Tyne NE6 5LS — MB BS 1997 Newc.

LOO, Paul Soo Lim Department of Genitourinary Medicine, Kettering General Hospital, Rothwell Road, Kettering NN16 8UZ Tel: 01536 410647 Fax: 01536 419 2223 — MRCS Eng. LRCP Lond. 1978; Dip. Ven. 1980. Cons. Phys. (Genitourin. Med.) Kettering Gen. Hosp. Socs: MSSVD & AGUM. Prev: Regist. (Genitourin. Med.) Univ. Coll. Hosp. Lond.

LOO, Wei Jing Flat 36 Staff Residence, James Paget Hospital, Lowestoft Road, Gorleston, Great Yarmouth NR31 6LA — MB BS 1997 New South Wales.

LOO WING HING, Henry 21 Spencer Walk, London NW3 1QZ — MB BS 1963 Hong Kong.

LOOI, Doris Boe-Eng Mei-Lan, 5 Rosebriars, Esher KT10 9NN Tel: 01372 471281 — MB BS 1962 Lond.; MRCS Eng. LRCP Lond. 1961; DA Eng. 1966. (Roy. Free) Sen. Med. Off. DHSS. Prev: Clin. Asst. (Anaesth.) Char. Cross Hosp. Lond.; Clin. Research Phys. Roche Products Ltd.

LOOKER, David Nicholas Public Health Laboratory, Glan Clwyd Hospital, Bodelwyddan, Rhyl LL18 5UJ Tel: 01745 583737 Fax: 01745 584179 Email: nicklooker@phls.wales.nhs.uk; Celyn, 1 The Circle, Bryn Newydd, Prestatyn LL19 9EU Tel: 01745 886657 — MB BS 1978 Lond.; MSc Lond. 1983; FRCPath 1996, M 1985. Dir./Cons. Microbiol. Pub. Health Laborat. Ysbyty Glan Clwyd, Bodelwyddan. Prev: Asst. Med. Microbiol. Pub. Health Laborat. Luton & Dunstable Hosp.; Regist. (Microbiol.) Coventry & Warwicks. Hosp. Coventry.

LOOKER, Helen Catherine 6 Clifton Dale, Clifton, York YO30 6LJ — MB BS 1991 Lond.

LOOMBA, Bharat Kalyan (retired) 17 Newton Drive, Greenmount, Bury BL8 4DH — MB BS 1953 Panjab; MB BS Panjab (India) 1953. Prev: GP Bury.

LOOMBA, Ram Lal 83 Kingsley Avenue, Hounslow TW3 4AE — MB BCh BAO 1991 NUI; LRCPSI 1991.

LOOMBA, Yogesh Wakefield and Partners, Lever Chambers Centre for Health, 1st Floor, Ashburner Street, Bolton BL1 1SQ Tel: 01204 360030/31 Fax: 01204 360033 — MB BS 1979 Nagpur; MB BS Nagpur India 1979; MRCP (UK) 1989.

LOON, Naomi PO Box 14469, South Kensington, London SW7 2ZJ Tel: 020 7589 3579 Fax: 020 7581 0381 — MB ChB Cape Town 1961; DIH Eng. 1980.

LOOPSTRA, Ellen Marjolein Adelaide Street Surgery, 20 Adelaide Street, Stonehouse, Plymouth PL1 3JF Tel: 01752 667623 Fax: 01752 667623 — Artsexamen 1988 Leiden; T(GP) 1992.

LOOSE, Heidrun Claudia 108 Long Lane, Charlesworth via Hyde, Hyde SK13 5ES — State Exam Med 1987 Gottingen.

LOOSE, Henry William Carrington X-Ray Department, Freeman Hospital, Freeman Road, High Heaton, Newcastle upon Tyne NE7 7DN — MRCS Eng. LRCP Lond. 1965; FRCR 1975; FFR 1973.

LOOSE, James Halyburton Church Street Surgery, 2 Church Street, Sutton, Hull HU7 4TT Tel: 01482 826457 Fax: 01482 824182 — MB ChB 1973 Ed.; BSc Ed. 1970, MB ChB 1973; MRCGP 1978; DObst RCOG 1975. Police Surg. Humberside Police HQ. Prev: Squadron Ldr. RAF Med. Br.; Cas. Off. Roy. Infirm. Edin.; Ho. Phys. Univ. Dept. Therap. Roy. Infirm. Edin.

LOOSEMORE, Michael Paul The Health Centre, Aylesbury Road, Wendover, Aylesbury HP22 6LD Tel: 01296 623452 — MB BS 1985 Lond.

LOOSEMORE, Mr Thomas Mark East Surrey Hospital, Three Arch Road, Redhill RH1 5RH Tel: 01737 768511; Sixways, 31 Court Road, Banstead SM7 2NQ Tel: 01737 359518 — MB BS 1980 Lond.; MS Lond. 1991, BSc 1977, MB BS 1980; FRCS Eng. 1985. Cons. Gen. & Vasc. Surg. E. Surrey Hosp. Redhill & St. Geo. Hosp. Lond. Socs: Vasc. Surg. Soc.

LOOSMORE, Simon John Peter Hodgkinson Centre, Greetwell Road, Lincoln LN2 5UA Tel: 01522 573553 — MB ChB 1980 Leic.; MRCPsych 1984. Cons. (Gen. Adult Psychiat.) Peter Hodgkinson Centre Lincoln.

LOPES, Albert Victor 9 Prince Regent's Court, Prince Regent's Close, Brighton BN2 5JQ Tel: 01273 601314 — MRCS Eng. LRCP Lond. 1917. (St. Bart.) Prev: Retd. Col. IMS.

LOPES, Mr Alberto De Barros Department of Gynaecological Oncology, Queen Elizabeth Hospital, Gateshead NE9 6SX Tel: 0191 482 0000 Fax: 0191 482 5604; The Cottage, Ravensworth Park Estate, Gateshead NE11 0HQ — MB ChB 1980 Liverp.; MRCOG 1986. Cons. Gyn. & Oncol. Qu. Eliz. Hosp. Gateshead.

LOPES, Odete Bairrada 6 High Street, Weston, Towcester NN12 8PU — MB BCh 1992 Witwatersrand. SHO. Psych. Oxf. Rotat.

LOPETEGUI MENDIZABAL, Maria Amaia Tameside General Hospital, Fountain St., Ashton-under-Lyne OL6 9RW; 88 Church Lane, Scunthorpe DN15 7HA — LMS 1990 Basques Provinces.

LOPEZ, Anthony James X-Ray Department, Royal Surrey County & St Luke's Hospital NHS Trust, Egerton Road, Guildford GU2 7XX Tel: 01483 571122 Fax: 01483 464018; Email: antelope@radiologist.co.uk — MB BS 1988 Lond.; BSc (Hons.) Lond. 1985; MRCP (UK) 1991; FRCR 1994. (St. Thos. Hosp.) Cons. Radiol. Roy. Surrey Co. Hosp. Guildford; Hon. Sen. Lect. to the Univ. of Surrey. Socs: BMA; Brit. Soc. Interven. Radiol.; Cardiovasc. & Interven. Radiol. Soc. Europe. Prev: Sen. Regist. (Radiol.) St. Geo. Hosp. Lond.; Regist. (Diag. Radiol.) Hammersmith Hosp. & Roy. Postgrad. Med. Sch. Lond.; SHO (Thoracic Med.) Roy. Brompton & Nat. Heart Hosp. Lond.

LOPEZ, Antony Paediatric Department, Southmead Hospital, Southmead Road, Westbury-on-Trym, Bristol BS10 5NB — BM BS 1986 Nottm.; MRCP (Paediat.) (UK) 1991.

LOPEZ, Berenice Hydein Email: berenice@blueyonder.co.uk — BMedSci; BM BS; DFFP; DRCOG; MRCGP. GP.

LOPEZ, Joseph Francis 15023 Dickens Street, Sherman Oaks CA 91403, USA; 89 Leadale Avenue, London E4 8AX — MB BS 1951 Madras. (Madras Med. Coll.) Med. Dir. CEO Trinity Med. Network Calif., USA; Fell. Amer. Acad. Disabil. Eval. Phys. Ann Arbor Michigan, USA. Socs: Amer. Aero Space Med. Assn.; Roy. Coll. Gen. Practs.; Civil Aviat. Med. Assn. USA. Prev: Med. Director Beyond Rejection Hospice Long Beach, Calif.; Chief Exec. Off. San Louris Med. Centre Los Angeles, Calif., USA.

LOPEZ-BERNAL, Andres Nuffield Department of Obstetrics & Gynaecology, The John Radcliffe, Headington, Oxford OX3 9DU Tel:

01865 221001 Fax: 01865 769141 Email: alb@ermine.ox.ac.uk — LMS 1976 Murcia; DMC Murcia 1986; MA Oxf. 1990, DPhil 1985. Reader (O & G) Oxf.

LOPEZ HIJOS, Carmen Flat 6, 40 Belsize Park, London NW3 4EE — LMS 1985 Barcelona.

LOPEZ-IBOR ALCOCER, Maria Ines 60 Lexham Gardens, Flat 7, London W8 5JA — LMS 1992 U Complutense Madrid.

LOPEZ LAPENA, Nuria Fitzroy College, Northdown House, Margate CT9 3TP — LMS 1994 U Autonoma Barcelona.

LOPEZ LEZA, Pilar 5 Lorne Place, Wells BA5 2XF; 11 Church Street, Titchfield, Fareham PO14 4AG — LMS 1983 Saragossa.

LOPEZ LONGAS, Jose Francisco Weymouth & District Hospital, Melcombe Avenue, Weymouth DT4 7TB — LMS 1992 Saragossa.

LOPEZ MANAS, Jose Manuel 2 Hill Place, Edinburgh EH8 9DS — LMS 1989 Granada.

LOPEZ SANCHEZ, Carolina c/o Christian Trenkel, School of Physics & Space Research, Birmingham University, Birmingham B15 2TT — LMS 1992 Barcelona.

LOPEZ SANCHEZ, Jose Enrique 16 Beech Avenue, Grimsby DN33 2AZ — LMS 1988 Malaga.

LOPIAN, Noemie Heli 1 Park Lane, Salford M7 4HT Tel: 0161 792 8887 — MB ChB 1991 Manch.

LOQUEMAN, Naila 15 Nethergate, Nafferton, Driffield YO25 4LP — MB BS 1994 Lond.; BSc (Hons.) Lond. 1988. (Univ. Coll. Lond.) GP Regist. E. Ridings of Yorks. Socs: Med. Defence Union; BMA. Prev: Ho. Off. (Med.) OldCh. Hosp. Romford; Ho. Off. (Surg.) Broomfield Hosp. Chelmsford.

LORAINE, Clive Donald 58 Elsdon Road, Newcastle upon Tyne NE3 1HY — MB BS 1992 Newc.

LORAINS, John William Pine Ridge, Long Hey Road, Caldy, Wirral CH48 1LY Tel: 0151 625 1454 — MB BS 1971 Lond.; BSc Lond. 1968, MB BS 1971; FRCP (UK) 1990, M 1974. (King's Coll. Hosp.) Cons. Phys. Wirral Hosp. NHS Trust. Prev: Sen. Regist. (Gen. Geriat. Med.) Roy. Devon & Exeter Hosps.; Research Asst. Dept. Chem. Path. Sheff. Univ. Med. Schl.; Regist. Acad. Div. Med. Roy. Hosp. Sheff.

LORCH, Christa Ulrike 21 Richmond Hill Court, Richmond TW10 6BD — State Exam Med 1993 Frankfurt; MD Frankfurt 1994.

LORCH, Diana Mary Buckwood, Fulmer, Slough SL3 6JN Tel: 01753 662606 — MRCS Eng. LRCP Lond. 1947; MA Camb. 1947. (Camb. & Univ. Coll. Hosp.) Prev: Surg, Out-pat. Asst. St. Mary's Hosp. Paddington.

LORD, Barbara Mary Dept. of Anaesthetics, Blackpool Victoria Hospital, Whinney Heys Road, Blackpool FY3 8BD Tel: 01253 303499 Fax: 01253 303510 — MB BCh 1987 Wales; FRCA. (University of Wales college of medicine) Cons. in Anaesth. & chronic pain.

LORD, Bernard 2 Calla Drive, Garstang, Preston PR3 1JN Tel: 01995 601851 — MB ChB 1974 Manch. Med. Off. Med. SS Norcross Blackpool. Socs: Assoc. Mem. MDU. Prev: GP Padiham Lancs.

LORD, Catherine Barbara 19 Woodlands Crescent, Swinton, Mexborough S64 8ER — BM BCh 1998 Oxf.; BM BCh Oxf 1998.

LORD, Christine Frances 207 Myton Road, Warwick CV34 6QD — MB ChB 1957 Birm. (Birm.) Med. Off. Family Plann. Assn. Prev: Ho. Surg. & Ho. Phys. Birm. Gen. Hosp.

LORD, Christopher Biochemistry Department, Cumberland Infirmary, Carlisle CA2 7HY Tel: 01228 814028 Fax: 01228 814831 — MB ChB 1973 Liverp.; MSc Surrey 1978; MRCPath 1981. Cons. Chem. Path. Cumbld. Infirm. Carlisle. Prev: Sen. Regist. (Clin. Biochem.) St. Luke's Hosp. Guildford; Regist. (Path.) Liverp. AHA (T); Regist. (Chem. Path.) Surrey AHA.

LORD, Christopher John 6 Kenilworth Avenue, Romford RM3 9NE — MB ChB 1995 Leeds.

LORD, Christopher Peter Beech Hill Medical Practice, 278 Gidlow Lane, Wigan WN6 7PD Tel: 01942 821899 Fax: 01942 821752; 32 Hurst Mill Lane, Glazebury, Warrington WA3 5NR Tel: 01942 678828 — MB ChB 1985 Leic. (Univ. Leic. Med. Sch.) GP Wigan. Prev: Regist. (Haemat.) Manch. Roy. Infirm.; SHO (O & G) Billinge Hosp. Wigan; Trainee GP Atherton.

LORD, David Thompson Norwood, Skircoat Green Road, Halifax HX3 0LJ Tel: 01422 358733 Fax: 01422 349621 — MB BS 1967 Newc.; DMJ (Clin.) Soc. Apoth. Lond. 1991; DObst RCOG 1972. (Newc.) Socs: Fell.Roy. Soc. Med.; Assn. Police Surg. Prev: Sen. GP Partner.

LORD, Ernest Renny Scott Road Medical Centre, Scott Road, Selby YO8 4BL Tel: 01757 700231 Fax: 01757 213647; Rashgate Cottage, Cawood Common, Selby YO8 3RB Tel: 01757 268361 — MB ChB 1978 Liverp.; MRCGP (Distinc.) 1983; DCH RCP Lond. 1982; DRCOG 1981. (Liverp.)

LORD, Graham Michael 152 Finney Lane, Cheadle SK8 3PU — MB BChir 1991 Camb.; MA Camb. 1992, MB BChir 1991; MRCP (UK) 1993. (Cambridge University) Regist. (Renal Med.) Hammersmith Hosp. Lond.; MRC Clin. Research Fell. (Immunol.) Imperial Coll. Sch. of Med. Hammersmith Hosp. Lond. Prev: SHO Roy. Brompton & Hammersmith Hosps. Lond. & Radcliffe Infirm. Oxf.

***LORD, Hannah Kate** 11 Amberley Gardens, Bedford MK40 3BT Tel: 01234 210447 Email: hannahlord@hotmail.com; 11 Amberley Gardens, Bedford MK40 3BT Tel: 01234 210447 — MB BS 1998 Lond.; BSc Univ Coll Lond 1995; MB BS Lond 1998.

LORD, Mr Ian James Bayonne, Cockfield Hall Lane, Westerfield, Ipswich IP6 9AN Tel: 01473 258210 Fax: 01473 258210 Email: ian.lord@ic24.net — MB BChir 1963 Camb.; MA Camb. 1963; FRCS Eng. 1968; MRCS Eng. LRCP Lond. 1962. (St. Thos.) Socs: Fell. Roy. Soc. Med.; BMA. Prev: Sen. Regist. (ENT) King's Coll. Hosp. Lond.; Research Fell. (Otolaryngol.) Univ. Toronto, Canada.; Cons. ENT Surg. Ipswich Hosp. NSH Trust.

LORD, John Robert The Surgery, Marsh Gardens, Honley, Huddersfield HD9 6AG Tel: 01484 303366 Fax: 01484 303365 — MB ChB 1974 Liverp.; DObst RCOG 1976; Dip. Med. Acupunc. (BMAS) 1997. Tutor (Comm. Med. Educat.) Huddersfield; Mem. MAAG. Socs: Brit. Med. Acupunct. Soc. Prev: Chairm. Kirklees Med. Audit Advis. Gp.

LORD, John Sinclair (retired) Tall Trees, 8 Greenbank Park, Rawtenstall, Rossendale BB4 7SY — MB ChB 1953 Manch.; DObst RCOG 1955. Prev: Ho. Phys. Manch. Roy. Infirm.

LORD, Jonathan Andrew David Fiddlers Field, Westerham TN16 1TX — MB BS 1987 Lond.; FRCA 1995. Cons. Anaesth. Moorfields Eye Hosp. Lond.

LORD, Jonathan Michael Gue Gassel, Church Cove, The Lizard, Helston TR12 7PH — MB ChB 1990 Birm.

LORD, Julie Elizabeth 8 St Timothys Mews, Bromley BR1 3TJ — MB BS 1987 Lond.

LORD, Kathryn Mary 11A Heathfield Park, Grappenhall, Warrington WA4 2LA — MB ChB 1996 Bristol.

LORD, Lesley Rosegarth Surgery, Rothwell Mount, Halifax HX1 2XB Tel: 01422 353450/350420; Norwood, Skircoat Green Road, Halifax HX3 0LJ Tel: 01422 358733 Email: lesley@skircoat.demon.co.uk — MB BS Newc. 1967; DMJ (Clin.) Soc. Apoth. Lond. 1988; DObst RCOG 1969. (Newcastle upon Tyne) Princip. GP; Police Surg.

LORD, Margaret Elizabeth 30 Woodcote Park Road, Epsom KT18 7EX Tel: 01372 727651 — MB ChB 1959 Cape Town. (Cape Town) Clin. Med. Off. Mid. Surrey Health Dist. Prev: SHO Sydenham Childr. Hosp.; Ho. Phys. & Ho. Obstetr. Groote Schuur Hosp. Cape Town.

LORD, Margaret Mary Linda Trefin, Llangeinor, Bridgend CF32 8PF Tel: 01656 870883 — MB BCh 1960 Wales. (Cardiff)

LORD, Mark Gregson Meddygfa'r Llan, Church Surgery, Portland Street, Aberystwyth SY23 2DX Tel: 01970 624855 Fax: 01970 625824; Cefn Llech, New Cross, Aberystwyth SY23 4LY — MB BChir 1982 Camb.; MA Camb. 1983; MRCPath 1989; MRCGP 1995; DFFP 1995. Prev: Sen. Regist. (Histopath.) Childr. Hosp. Sheff.; Regist. (Histopath.) Univ. Birm., Childr. Hosp. Birm. & Warwick Hosp.

LORD, Mr Michael David (retired) 207 Myton Road, Warwick CV34 6QD Tel: 01926 492757 — MB ChB 1948 Birm.; MRCS Eng. LRCP Lond. 1948; FRCS Eng. 1957. Cons. Surg. S. Warw. Hosp. Gp. Prev: Res. Surg. Off. Birm. Childr. Hosp. & Birm. Gen. Hosp.

LORD, Mr Michael Graham 347 Cranbrook Road, Ilford IG1 4UF — MB ChB 1965 Manch.; FRCS Eng. 1970; FRCS Ed. 1970. (Manch.) RSO N. Hosp. Manch. Socs: Fell. Manch. Med. Soc.

LORD, Myra Kidderminster General Hospital, Bewdley Road, Kidderminster DY11 6RJ Tel: 01562 823424 — MB BS 1960 Lond.; MRCS Eng. LRCP Lond. 1960; FFA RCS Eng. 1972; DA Eng. 1962; DObst RCOG 1961.

LORD, Nigel Philip Flat 5 Windlehurst, St. John's Road, Altrincham WA14 2NA Tel: 0161 929 4472 — MB ChB 1991 Sheff.; MRCGP 1995; DFFP 1995; Cert. Prescribed Equiv. Exp. JCPTGP 1995.

LORD, Mr Peter Herent, OBE (retired) (cons. rooms), Holly Tree House, 39 Grove Road, Beaconsfield HP9 1PE Tel: 01494 674488 Fax: 01494 675188 — MB BChir 1949 Camb.; MChir Camb. 1961; FRCS Eng. 1955. Penrose May Teach. RCS Eng.; Hon. Med. Colonic & Rectal Surg. RACS. Prev: Cons. Surg. Wycombe Gen. Hosp. High Wycombe.

LORD, Peter William Royal Infirmary, Ronkswood Branch, Newtown Road, Worcester WR5 1HN — MB BChir 1960 Camb.; MRCS Eng. LRCP Lond. 1959; FFA RCS Eng. 1965; DA Eng. 1962. (Camb. & St. Mary's) Prev: Sen. Regist. Roy. Infirm. Edin.; Regist. St. Mary's Hosp. Lond.

LORD, Robert Christopher Cornwallis 80 Blake Street, Walkley, Sheffield S6 3JR — BChir 1990 Camb.

LORD, Rosemary Helen 152 Finney Lane, Heald Green, Cheadle SK8 3PU — MB ChB 1993 Dundee.

LORD, Rozanne Herent Hirst Cardiff Royal Infirmary, Newport Road, Cardiff CF24 0SZ; Hen Felin, The Mill, Dyffryn, Cardiff CF5 6SU — MB BS 1977 Lond.; FRCS Eng. 1981. Cons. Transpl. Surg. Cardiff Roy. Infirm. Socs: Soc. Med. & Brit. Transpl. Soc. Prev: Cons. Surg. & Sen. Lect. Transpl. Surg. Roy. Lond. Hosp.

***LORD, Stephen Robert** Gask Ridge, Perth PH1 1QS; Gask Ridge, Perth PH1 1QS — MB BS 1998 Lond.; MB BS Lond 1998.

LORD, Stephen Rostron Euxton Medical Centre, St. Marys Gate, Euxton, Chorley PR7 6AH; 91 Lower Bank Road, Fulwood, Preston PR2 8NU Tel: 01772 715457 — MB BS 1976 Lond.

LORD, Stephen William 40 Denewell Avenue, High Heaton, Newcastle upon Tyne NE7 7YB — BM BCh 1991 Oxf.

LORD, Mr Stuart Moffat Gask Ridge, Findo Gask, Perth PH1 1QS Tel: 01738 730311 Fax: 01738 730311 — MB BS 1971 Lond.; BSc (Hons. Anat.) Lond. 1966; FRCS Glas. 1977; MRCS Eng. LRCP Lond. 1969. (St. Thos.) Prev: Dir. Clin. Servs. Perth & Kinross Healthcare NHS Trust; Cons. A & E Roy. Liverp. Hosp.; Sen. Regist. (A & E) Glas. Roy. Infirm.

LORD, Walter John Harcourt (retired) 93 Heathermount Drive, Crowthorne RG45 6HJ Tel: 01344 775684 — MB ChB 1944 Ed.; FRCP Ed. 1971, M 1950; FRCGP 1970. Prev: Pres. Reading Path. Soc.

LORD, William David Pennant End, Start Lane, Whaley Bridge, High Peak SK23 7BR — MB ChB 1973 Liverp.; BSc (Hons.) Liverp. ChB 1973; FFA RCS Eng. 1978. Cons. (Anaesth.) Booth Hall Childr. Hosp. Manch. Prev: Sen. Regist. (Anaesth.) Manch. AHA (T); SHO (Anaesth.) Alder Hey Childr. Hosp. Liverp.; Regist. (Anaesth.) Walton Hosp. [illegible]

LOREGNARD, Alison Elizabeth Fox Barn, Thame Road, Warborough, Wallingford OX10 7DH — MB BS 1996 Lond.

LOREK, Ann Kathryn Community Health South London NHS Trust, Mary Sheridan Centre for Child Health, 5 Dugard Way, Renfrew Road, Kennington, London SE11 4TH Tel: 0207 414 1457 Fax: 0207 414 1371 Email: ann.lorek@chsltr.sthames.nhs.uk — MB BS 1985 Lond.; BA Oxf. 1980; MRCP (UK) 1991. Cons. (Comm. Peadiat.) Comm. Health S. Lond. NHS Trust. Prev: Staff Grade (Comm. Paediat.) Optimum Health Servs. Lewisham, Lond.; Cons. (Paediat.) Lewisham Childr.s Hosp. Lond.

LORENCES RUIZ, Carlos Ignacio 59 Eastgate, Hessle HU13 9LW — LMS 1988 Oviedo.

LORENZ, Eleanor 27 Crookes Road, Sheffield S10 5BA — MB ChB 1990 Sheff.

LORENZ, James Robert Newland Avenue Surgery, 239-243 Newland Avenue, Hull HU5 2EJ Tel: 01482 448456 Fax: 01482 449536; 52 Hambling Drive, Beverley HU17 9GD — MB ChB 1982 Leeds.

LORENZI, Alice Ruth Kimberley, Chollacott Lane, Whitchurch, Tavistock PL19 9DD — BM BCh 1997 Oxf.

LORENZO GALLEGO, Susana Medical School, Department of Public Health Sciences, Teviot Place, Edinburgh University, Edinburgh EH8 9AG Tel: 0131 650 6963; 68/5 Grassmarket, Edinburgh EH1 2JR Tel: 0131 226 2715 — LMS 1987 Santiago de Compostela; MSc (Med. Statistics) Newc. 1991. Research Fell. (Molecular Epidemiol.) Edin. Univ.

LORGE, Margaret Alice 2/9 Craufurdland, Braepark Road, Edinburgh EH4 6DL — MB ChB 1950 Ed. (Univ. Ed.)

LORGE, Robert Eliot Oakley and Overton Partnership, Overton Surgery, Station Road, Overton, Basingstoke RG25 3DU Tel: 01256 770212 Fax: 01256 771581; Canterbury Cottage, Freefolk, Whitchurch RG28 7NJ Tel: 01256 892574 — MB BS 1972 Lond.; MRCP (UK) 1974; FRCGP 1992, M 1985. GP Tutor Basingstoke Dist. Hosp. Socs: Med. Audit Advis. Gp. (Hants. FHSA). Prev: Regist. (Med.) & Ho. Phys. St. Geo. Hosp. Lond.; Sen. Ho. Phys. Roy. Marsden Hosp. Lond.

LORIGAN, Paul Christopher Department of Medical Oncology, Christie Hosp. NHS Trust, Oak Road, Manchester M23 Tel: 0114 226 5000; Tel: 01433 670 371 — MB BCh BAO 1986 Dub.; FRCP 2000; MRCP 1990 UK. (Univ. Of Dublin, Trinity Coll.) Sen. Lect. (Med. Oncol.) Christie Hosp, Manc. Socs: Assn. Cancer Phys.; Amer. Soc. Clin. Oncol.; Eur. Blood & Marrow Transpl. Prev: Sen. Lect. (Med. Oncol.) W.on Pk. Hosp. Sheff.

LORIMER, Professor Andrew Ross (retired) Benvue, 6 Homeston Avenue, Bothwell, Glasgow G71 8PL — MB ChB 1960 Glas.; MD Glas. 1976; FRCP Ed. 1981 M 1964; FRCP Glas. 1972, M 1964; FRCP Lond. 1978, M 1964; F Med Sci 1998. Cons. Cardiol. Roy. Infirm. Glas.; Hon. Prof. Med. Univ. Glas. Prev: Lect. (Med.) Cardiol. Univ. Glas.

LORIMER, Archibald Harkness 212 Grantham Road, Sleaford NG34 7NU — MB ChB 1948 Aberd.; MRCPsych 1971; Dip. Psych. Ed. 1956. (Aberd.) Cons. Psychiat. Rauceby Hosp. Sleaford; Cons. i/c Sheff. Regional Adolesc. Unit. Prev: Psychiat. Bangour Village Hosp. Broxburn; Regist. Prestwich Hosp. Manch.; Sen. Ho. Off. Craig Dunain Hosp. Inverness.

LORIMER, James (retired) Safari Lodge, Droveway, Stelling Minnis, Canterbury CT4 6AJ Tel: 01303 840030 Fax: 01303 840030 Email: lorimer@safarilodge.freeserve.co.uk — MB ChB 1970 Aberd.; MRCGP 1976; DObst RCOG 1973. p/t Private Gen. Practitioner; Company Med. Off.

LORIMER, James Derek The Sycamores, 5 Almoners Barn, Potters Bank, Durham DH1 3TZ — MB ChB 1967 Glas.; FRCOG 1985, M 1971. Cons. O & G Dryburn Hosp. Durh.

LORIMER, Sheryl 2 Hillside Road, Dundee DD2 1QY — MB ChB 1992 Manch.

LORIMER, Stuart Mckenzie Reid 10/7 Grays Loan, Edinburgh EH10 5BS — MB ChB 1993 Aberd.

LORT, David John Gold Street Surgery, Gold Street, Saffron Walden CB10 1EJ Tel: 01799 525325 Fax: 01799 524042; School Street Surgery, Great Chesterford, Saffron Walden CB10 1NN Tel: 01799 530950 Fax: 01799 524042 — MB ChB 1980 Birm.; DRCOG 1983; LLM 2001 Wales, Cardiff; DCH RCP 1983 Lond.; MRCGP 1984; MRCGP 1984; DRCOG 1983; DCH RCP Lond. 1983. Prev: Trainee GP Plymouth VTS.

LORT, Elizabeth Ann Frambury Lane Surgery, Frambury Lane, Newport, Saffron Walden CB11 3PY Tel: 01799 540570 Fax: 01799 542126; The Surgery, Frambury Lane, Newport, Saffron Walden CB11 3PY Tel: 01799 540570 — MB ChB 1980 Birm.; MRCGP 1984. Prev: Trainee GP Plymouth VTS.

LORTAN, Jennifer Elizabeth Nuffield Dept of Clinical Laboratory Sciences level 4A academic block, John Radcliffe Hospital, Oxford OX3 9DU Tel: 01865 220506 Fax: 01865 220524 Email: jennifer.lortan@indels.ox.ac.uk — MB ChB 1976 Natal; MB ChB Univ. Natal S. Afr. 1976; PhD Birm. 1989, MSc 1980; FRCP 1998; FRCPath 1996. Clin. tutor in Laborat. Sci.s, Univ Oxf.; Hon. Cons. Immunol.s Radcliffe hosp trust. Prev: Sen. Lect. & Hon. Cons. Immunol. Char. Cross & W.m. Med. Sch. Lond.; Clin. Lect. & Hon. Sen. Regist. (Immunol.) Univ. Birm. Med. Sch.; Sen lect & Hon cons immunopath & clin Immun Imperial coll sch of med.

LORYMAN, Benjamin Jeffrey Leigh 91 Dudley Road, Tipton DY4 8EB — MB ChB 1996 Birm.

LOSA, Ignatius Ethri 4 Quentin House, Wyvil Road, London SW8 2NA — MB ChB 1984 Ife, Nigeria; MB ChB Ife Nigeria 1984; BSc (Health Sci.) Ife, Nigeria 1980; MRCP (UK) 1994. (Fife) Staff Grade (Paediat.) Leighton Hosp. Crewe. Prev: Staff Grade (Paediat.) Staffs. Gen. Hosp.; Regist. (Paediat.) Wrexham Maelor Hosp.; Regist. (Paediat.) Glan Clwyd Hosp. Bodelwyddan.

LOSEL, Thomas Michael 32 Hill Drive, Whaley Bridge, High Peak SK23 7BH — MB ChB 1993 Sheff.

LOSOWSKY, Professor Monty Seymour Southview, Ling Lane, Scarcroft, Leeds LS14 3HT Tel: 0113 289 2699 Fax: 0113 289 2699 Email: mlsowsky@email.com — MB ChB (Hons.) Leeds 1955; MD Leeds 1961; FRCP Lond. 1969, M 1958. Emerit. Prof. Med. Univ. Leeds; Gov. Leeds Grammar Sch.; Gov.Coeliac Soc.; Chairm. Med. Advis. Counc.Coeiacl Soc.; Gov. & Chairm. Med. Advis. Comm. Brit. Liver Trust. Socs: Brit. Soc. Gastroenterol.; (Governor & Counc. Mem.) Brit. Nutrit. Foundat., Trustee Thackray Med. Museum Leeds; Fell. Roy. Soc. Med. Prev: Vis. Prof. Roy. Postgrad, Med. Sch. & Univ. Bombay & Univ. Qu.sland Australia; Research Fell. (Med.) Harvard Univ., USA; Asst. Externe Hosp. St Antoine Paris.

LOSSEFF, Nicholas Andrew 52 Carlton Mansions, Randolph Avenue, London W9 1NR — MB BS 1988 Lond.; MRCP (UK) 1991. Lect. (Neurol. & Neurorehabil.) Inst. Neurol. Nat. Hosp. Qu. Sq. Lond. Prev: Regist. (Neurol.) St. Thos. Hosp. Lond.; Regist. (Med.) Middlx. Hosp. Lond.

LOSSOCK, Fiona Helen Colinton Surgery, 296B Colinton Road, Edinburgh EH13 0LB Tel: 0131 441 4555 Fax: 0131 441 3963; 126 Muir Wood Road, Currie EH14 5HF Tel: 0131 449 4007 — MB ChB 1972 Ed. G.P. Princip.

LOSTY, Mr Paul Damion Royal Liverpool Children's Hospital, Alder Hey, Liverpool L12 2AP Tel: 0151 228 4811 Fax: 0151 228 2024 Email: paul.losty@rlch-tr.nwest.nhs.uk — MB BCh BAO NUI 1985; FRCSI 1989; FRCS (Paed.) 1996; MD Thesis (NUI) 1996; FRCS (Eng.) ad eundem 1998. (University College Dublin, Ireland) Sen. Lect. Paediatric Surg. Univ. of Liverp.; Hon. Cons. Paediat. Surg. Roy. Liverp. Childr. Hosp. (Alder Hey). Socs: Brit. Assn. Paediat. Surg.; BMA; Surgic. Res. Soc.

LOTAY, Narwinder Singh Carlisle Road Surgery, 23C Carlisle Road, Queens Park, Bedford MK40 4HT Tel: 01234 351661 Fax: 01234 364884; 2 Hailes Close, Bedford MK41 8NR — MB BS 1975 Newc. (Newcastle Upon Tyne) Sen. Partner; Bedford PCT Exec. Bd. Mem.; Caldicot Guardian, Bedford PCT; Med. Centre, 8 Honeysuckle Way, Goldington, Bedford, MK41 0TF, Tel: 01234 213300, Fax: 01234 213345. Prev: Bedford PCG Bd. Mem.

LOTAY, Rajindah Kaur (retired) Moulsham Street Surgery, 104 Moulsham Street, Chelmsford CM2 0JG Tel: 01245 491247 Fax: 01245 265544 — MB BCh 1979 Wales; MRCS England, LRCP London 1979; MSc 1989; PhD 1997. GP Princip.; Surg. to St. John's & Red Cross Radio BRd.caster.

LOTERY, Andrew John 7 Beechgrove Rise, Belfast BT6 0NH — MB BCh BAO 1989 Belf.; FRCOphth 1994; MD, Queen's University, Belfast. 1997. Regist. (Ophth.) Roy. Vict. Hosp. Belf.

LOTERY, Helen Elisabeth 7 Beechgrove Rise, Belfast BT6 0NH Tel: 01232 794794 — MB BCh BAO 1990 Belf.; MRCGP 1994; MRCP (Ireland) 1999. SHO Roy. Gp. of Hosps. Belf. Prev: Med. Pract. (Dermat.) Craigavon Area Hosp. Co. Armagh.

LOTFALLAH, Hany Nassim Barnsley District General Hospital, Gawber Road, Barnsley S75 2EP Tel: 01226 730000; 28 Oaks Wood Drive, Darton, Barnsley S75 5PT Tel: 01226 390448 — MB BCh 1982 Cairo. Socs: MRCOG.

LOTFI, Gamal Bronglais General Hospital, Aberystwyth SY23 1ER — MB BCh 1983 Cairo, Egypt.

LOTHA, Longsobemo Mozhui Oxford Road Medical Centre, 25 Oxford Road, Burnley BB11 3BB Tel: 01282 423603 Fax: 01282 832827 — MB BS 1968 Dibrugarh; MB BS 1968 Dibrugarh.

LOTHE, Karen Jane Upper Gordon Road Surgery, 37 Upper Gordon Road, Camberley GU15 2HJ Tel: 01276 26424 Fax: 91276 63486 — MB ChB 1981 Sheff.; MSc Sports Med. (Univ. Lond.); MRCP (UK) 1985. Course Organiser for Frimley VTS Scheme.

LOTHIAN, Andrew William Russell Shrub End Road Surgery, 122 Shrub End Road, Colchester CO3 4RY Tel: 01206 573605 Fax: 01206 200219; Pantiles, 68 Braiswick, Colchester CO4 5AY Tel: 01206 852097 — MB BS 1976 Lond.; DCH RCP Lond. 1982; DObst 1979. (Middlx.) GP Colchester; Clin. Asst. (Rheum.) Severalls Hosp. Colchester.; Dist. Gen. Hosp. Colchester.

LOTHIAN, Jane Lesley Evelyn 2 Benlaw Grove, Felton, Morpeth NE65 9NG — MB BS 1982 Lond.; LLB (Hons.) Lond. 1992, BSc 1979, MB BS 1982; MRCGP 1988; Dip. Pharm. Med. RCP (UK) 1994; DRCOG 1987.

LOTHIAN, Mr Keith Remington (retired) 1 Chapel Court, Silver Street, Wragby, Market Rasen LN8 5PJ Tel: 01673 857190 — MB ChB 1943 N.Z.; FRCS Eng. 1948. Prev: Cons. Surg. Arrowe Pk. Hosp. Birkenhead.

LOTHIAN, Marjory Trenton Ford Road, Lanchester, Durham DH7 6SN — MB BS 1969 Newc.; FFA RCS Eng. 1975. Cons. Anaesth. Shotley Bridge Gen. Hosp. Consett. Socs: Assn. Anaesths. Prev: Sen. Regist. St. Geo. Hosp. Lond.

LOTHIAN, William (retired) Orchard House, 83 High St., Shoreham Village, Sevenoaks TN14 7TB Tel: 01959 523511 — MB ChB 1946 St. And. Prev: Clin. Asst. (Orthop.) Sevenoaks Hosp.

LOTINGA, John Kenneth (retired) 4 Wandleys Close, Eastergate, Chichester PO20 6SH — MB BS 1941 Durh.; LRCP LRCS Ed. LRFPS Glas. 1941; MRCPsych 1971. Prev: PMO H.M. Prison Wormwood Scrubs.

LOTINGA, Mrs Kathleen Hilda Mary (retired) 4 Wandleys Close, Eastergate, Chichester PO20 6SH — MD 1943 Durh.; MB BS 1939; MRCPsych 1971; DPM Eng. 1961. Prev: Cons. Psychiat. St. And. Hosp. N.ampton.

LOTT, Carolyn Mary Adam House Medical Centre, 85-91 Derby Road, Sandiacre, Nottingham NG10 5HZ Tel: 01602 491194 Fax: 01602 491522; 17 Hampden Grove, Beeston, Nottingham NG9 1FG — MB ChB 1987 Sheff. Prev: Trainee GP/SHO Exeter VTS.

LOTT, David John Farthingleys, 24 Towson Field, East Leake, Loughborough LE12 6RY Tel: 01509 559214 Email: david_lott@supnet.com — MB BS Lond. 1967; Dip. Pharm. Med. RCP Lond. 1983; DObst RCOG 1969. (St. Geo.) Head of Med affairs, Crooks healthcare Notts. Socs: Fell. Fac. Pharm. Med. Prev: Head Pub. Affairs Ciba Pharmaceut. Horsham.

LOTT, Margaret Fiona Weston General Hospital, Grange Road, Clifton, Uphill, Weston Super Mare BS23 4TQ Tel: 01934 636363; The Old Granary, East Breut, Highbridge TA9 4HP — BChD Leeds 1968; MRCPath 1986; FDS RCS Eng. 1972; LDS RCS Eng. 1968. Cons. Histopath. W.on Super Mare Gen. Hosp. Prev: Sen. Regist. (Histopath.) Wexham Pk. Hosp. Slough & Hammersmith Hosp. Lond.

LOTZ, Mr John Cunningham 29 Burton Manor Road, Stafford ST17 9QJ Tel: 01785 252980 — MB BS Sydney 1964; FRCS Eng. 1970. (Sydney) Cons. Gen. Surg. Stafford Dist. Gen. Hosp. Socs: Assn. Endoscopic Surgs.; Assn. Surg.; Brit. Assn. Paediat. Surg. Prev: Sen. Regist. Guy's Hosp. Lond.; Sen. Regist. (Surg.) Roy. Berks. Hosp. Reading; Regist. (Surg.) Hillingdon Hosp.

LOTZOF, Kevin Garth 30A Kemplay Road, London NW3 1SY — MB BCh 1989 Witwatersrand.

LOUCA, Loucas Lefteris 32 Auburn Road, Old Trafford, Manchester M16 9NT — MB ChB 1982 Manch.; MRCGP 1990; DCH RCP Lond. 1991; DRCOG 1988. GP Manch. Prev: Trainee GP Manch.; Gen. Med. Auckland New Zealand; Dermat. Manch. Skin Hosp.

LOUCA, Onsy Adly Bakhit 16 Kinver Drive, H[illegible], Stourbridge DY9 0GZ — MB BCh 1983 Ain Shams; MB BCh Ain Shams Egypt 1983; MRCOG 1991.

LOUCA, Prodromakis 10 Fuller Close, London E2 6DX — MB BS 1998 Lond.; MB BS Lond 1998.

LOUCAS, Kypros Old Dean, London Road, Camberley GU15 — MRCS Eng. LRCP Lond. 1953.

LOUD, Benjamin William 14 Redwing Road, Milborne Port, Sherborne DT9 5DB — MB BS 1998 Lond.; MB BS Lond 1998.

LOUD, Steven Graham 17 Kelly Street, London NW1 8PG Email: steve@loud1.demon.co.uk — MB BS 1984 Lond.; BSc Lond. 1981, MB BS 1984; MRCGP 1991.

LOUDEN, Jonathan David Medical Unit, Walsgrave Hospital, Coventry CV2 2DX Tel: 024 76 602020; 12 Atlas Wynd, Yarm TS15 9AD Tel: 01642 875216 — BM 1991 Soton.; MRCP 1995. Research.Fell.Nephrol.Univ.Newc.; Hon. Specialist Regist. Nephrol .Gen. Intern. Med. Socs: Eur. Renal Assn/Eur. Dialysis Transpl. Assn.; Coll.Mem.Roy.Coll.Phys.Lond.

LOUDEN, Keith Anthony Department of Obstetrics & Gynaecology, Freedom Fields Hospital, Plymouth PL4 7JJ Tel: 01752 668080; 1 Rossett Green Lodge, Harrogate HG2 9LL Tel: 01423 871022 — BM BS 1983 Nottm.; DM Nottm. 1989, BM BS 1983, BMedSci 1981; MRCOG 1990. Sen. Regist. (O & G) Freedom Fields Hosp. Plymouth & S.mead Hosp. Bristol. Socs: Blair Bell Research Soc.; Internat. Soc. Study Hypertens. in Pregn. Prev: Research Regist. Trent RHA; Regist. (O & G) S.mead & Frenchay Hosps. Bristol.

LOUDEN, Sally Frances Alton Health Centre, Anstey Road, Alton GU34 2QX Tel: 01420 84676 Fax: 01420 542975; 13 Christchurch Road, Winchester SO23 9SR Tel: 01962 855893 Email:

LOUTH, Suzana c/o C.J. Louth, Thicket Meadows, Mewlands Drive, Maidenhead SL6 4LL — LMSSA 1996 Lond.

LOVAT, Laurence Bruce National Medical Laser Centre, University College London, Charles Bell House, 67-73 Riding House St., London W1W 7EJ Tel: 020 7679 9060 Email: l.lovat@ucl.ac.uk — MB BS 1987 Lond.; BSc (1st cl. Hons.) Lond. 1984; MRCP (UK) 1991; PhD (Lond.) 1997. (Univ. Coll. Hosp.) Cons. Gastroenterol. UCL Hosp. Lond.; Hon. Sen. Lect. Laser Med. UCL. Lond. Socs: Brit. Soc. of Gastroenterol.; Brit. Med. Laser Assoc.; Brit. Oesophago-Gastric Cancer Gp. Prev: Sen. Lect., Gastroenterol. & Laser Med. UCL Lond. 1999-2001; MRC Research Train. Fell. (Immunol. Med.) Hammersmith Hosp. Lond.; Regist. (Gastroenterol.) Hammersmith Hosp. Lond.

LOVATT, Christopher John Abbey House Surgery, Golding Close, Daventry NN11 5RA Tel: 01327 877770 Fax: 01327 310267 — MB BChir 1990 Camb.; BA Camb. 1988; MRCGP 1995; DFFP 1995; DGM RCP Lond. 1994. Clin. Asst. (Dermat.) Hosp. St. Cross Rugby. Prev: Ho. Phys. Bedford Gen. Hosp.

LOVATT, Gemma Louise Yew Tree Cottage, Main Road, Betley, Crewe CW3 9AD — MB ChB 1994 Manch.; BSc 1991 (Med Sci) St. Andrews. Gen. Practitioner, Crewe, Chesh.; Clin. Asst., S.Chesh. Drugs Serv., Crewe, Chesh.

LOVATT, George Earle (retired) 11 Clarrie Road, Tetbury GL8 8EW Tel: 01666 502662 Email: ge.lovatt@virgin.net — MRCS Eng. LRCP Lond. 1954; BSc (Special) Lond. 1951, MB BS 1955; FRCPC 1972; DObst RCOG 1956; LMCC 1958. Prev: Hon. Cons. Phys. Hackney Hosp.

LOVATT, Heather May Windy Nook Surgery, Cartmel, Grange-over-Sands LA11 6PJ Tel: 015395 36366 Fax: 015395 36766; Braban House, Burneside, Kendal LA8 9AE Tel: 01539 722020 Email: milligan@braban.freeserve.co.uk — MB BS 1985 Lond.; BSc Lond. 1982; MRCGP 1991; DCH RCP Lond. 1991; Dip. Obst. Otago 1988. (Lond. Hosp.) Clin. Asst. (Gyn.) Cumbria.

LOVATT, Wendy Patricia Forum Health Centre, 1A Farren Road, Wyken, Coventry CV2 5EP Tel: 024 7626 6370 Fax: 024 7663 6518; Shilton Farm, Leicester Road, Shilton, Coventry CV7 9HT Tel: 024 76 614456 Email: wlovatt@epulse.net — MB ChB 1972 Dundee; DCH Eng. 1976; DObst RCOG 1974.

LOVE, Alison Mary Lagan Valley Hospital, Hillsborough Road, Lisburn BT28 1JP Tel: 01846 665141 Email: alison.love@dltrust.n-i.nhs.uk; Tel: 01846 621807 — MB BCh BAO 1977 Dub.; MRCOG 1986; DCH Dub. 1980; DO RCPSI 1980. Cons. O & G Lagan Valley Hosp. Lisburn. Socs: Ulster Obst. & Gyn.Soc; Ulster GynaeUrol. Soc.; Brit soc for colposcopy & cervica; Path.

LOVE, Caroline Anne 3 Boltby Road, York YO30 4UW — MB ChB 1998 Liverp.; MB ChB Liverp 1998.

LOVE, Corinne Dawn Balfour Hope Cottage, Loch Road, South Queensferry EH30 9LS — MB ChB 1992 Ed.

LOVE, David Muir Hook and Hartley Wintney Medical Partnership, 1 Chapter Terrace, Hartley Wintney, Hook RG27 8QJ Tel: 01252 842087 Fax: 01252 843145; 16 Goose Green, Hook, Basingstoke RG27 9QY Tel: 01256 764637 — MB BS 1977 Lond.; DRCOG 981. (St Bartholomew's) Prev: Trainee GP Ashford, Kent VTS.

VE, David Robert Haylodge Health Centre, Neidpath Road, les EH45 8JG Tel: 01721 720380 Fax: 01721 723430; Kerfield , Peebles EH45 8BG — MB ChB 1968 Glas.; FRCP Ed. 1995; (UK) 1971; MRCGP 1975. (Glas.)

avid Robert Borders General Hospital NHS Trust, Melrose el: 01896 754333 Email: david.love@borders.scot.nhs.uk; Midlem, Selkirk TD7 4QD Tel: 01835 870233 — MB FRCA 1993; FFA RCSI 1992. (Ed.) Cons. Anaesth. sp. Melrose. Socs: Assn. Anaesth.; Ed. & E. Scot. ott. Soc. Anaesth. Prev: Sen. Regist. (Anaesth.) Regist. & Research Fell. (Anaesth.) Flinders Med.

Pfizer Clinical Research Unit, Kent & thelbert Road, Canterbury CT1 3NG Tel: 227 783164; 35 Lavender Hill, Tonbridge 558 — MB BS 1986 Lond.; PhD Lond. rch Phys. Pfizer Clin. Research Unit iol. Soc.; Harveian Soc.; Brit. Assn. of gist. (Chem. Path.) Whittington Univ. Coll. Hosp. Lond.

LOVE, Elizabeth Mary Manchester Blood Centre, Plymouth Grove, Manchester M13 9LL Tel: 0161 251 4279 Fax: 0161 251 4331 Email: elizabeth.love@nbs.nhs.uk; Heathfield, Bereton Heath Lane, Bereton Heath, Congleton CW12 4SZ — MB ChB 1973 Sheff.; FRCP Lond 1993; MRCP (UK) 1976; FRCPath 1993, M 1981. Cons. Haemat. Manch. Blood Centre, Nat. Blood Auth.; Hon. Cons. Haemat. Manch. Roy. Infirm.; Dep. Dir. N. W.ern Regional Transfus. Serv. Socs: Brit. Soc. Haemat.; Brit. Blood Transfus. Soc.; Amer. Assn. of Blood Banks. Prev: Sen. Regist. (Haemat.) N. W.ern RHA; Regist. (Haemat.) Kingston Gen. Hosp. Hull.

LOVE, Gilbert Peter (retired) Church Barn, Church Lane, Gargrave, Skipton BD23 3PF — MB ChB 1947 Manch.; DObst RCOG 1952.

LOVE, Gillian Mary Halesowen Medical Practice, 14 Birmingham Street, Halesowen B63 3HN Tel: 0121 550 1185 Fax: 0121 585 0699; 93 Leavale Road, Stourbridge DY8 2AY Email: gmlove@stbridge.demon.ac.uk — MB ChB 1991 Birm.; MRCGP 1996. (Birm.)

LOVE, Graham Hamilton Woodside Health Centre, Barr Street, Glasgow G20 7LR Tel: 0141 531 9560 Fax: 0141 531 9572; 14 Gartconnell Drive, Bearsden, Glasgow G61 3BJ — MB ChB 1981 Dundee; MRCGP 1985; DRCOG 1983.

LOVE, Honor Elizabeth Sarah 207 Dunminning Road, Glarryford, Ballymena BT44 9PP — MB BCh BAO 1997 Belf.

LOVE, James Lyons (retired) Sarden Cottage, 81A Glen Road, Maghera BT46 5AP Tel: 01648 42266 — MB BCh BAO Belf. 1938.

***LOVE, Karl Douglas** Dept. of Histopathology & Cytopathology, Norfolk & Norwich Hospital, Brunswick Road, Norwich NR1 3SR — MB BCh 1977 Wales.

LOVE, Lucia Frances Charlotte Coldrum House, Coldrum Lane, Trottiscliffe, West Malling ME19 5EG Tel: 01732 822225 — MB BS 1981 Lond.; BSc Lond. 1976. (U. C. H. London) Clin. Asst. (Genitourin. Med.) W.hill Hosp. Dartford; F.M.E. (Lond.). Socs: Med. Soc. Study VD; Fac. Fam. Plann. & Reproduc. Health Care. Prev: Regist. & SHO (Genitourin. Med.) St. Giles Hosp. Lond.; Clin. Med. Off. Family Plann. Clinic. Sevenoaks Hosp.

LOVE, Malcolm Barr (retired) 9A Blenheim Terrace, London NW8 0EH Tel: 020 7372 0651 Email: brigmer@aol.com — MB ChB Birm. 1955; MRCGP 1968. Prev: Regist. (Med.) Brook Gen. Hosp. Lond. & Gen. Hosp. Birm.

LOVE, Moya Elizabeth Warders Medical Centre, 47 East Street, Tonbridge TN9 1LA Tel: 01732 770088 Fax: 01732 770033; 28 Portman Park, Tonbridge TN9 1LW Tel: 01732 365061 Email: moya@pinelaven.demon.co.uk — MB ChB 1972 Sheff.; MRCGP 1984; DObst Auckland 1980; DFFP 1998. (Sheffield)

LOVE, Peter Stuart St Margarets Surgery, 8 St. Margarets Road, Solihull B92 7JS Tel: 0121 706 0307 Fax: 0121 765 0161 — MB ChB 1992 Sheff.; MRCGP 1997. Princip. GP St. Margat. Med. Pract. Olton Solihull. Prev: GP/Regist. Gr. Surg. Solihull.

LOVE, Peter William Sandringham Practice, Sandringham Road Health Centre, Sandringham Road, Intake, Doncaster DN2 5JH Tel: 01302 321521 Fax: 01302 761792 — MB ChB 1973 Dundee; DFFPM; MRCGP 1977; D.Occ.Med. RCP Lond. 1996; DRCOG 1977. Hosp. Practitioner Rheum., Doncaster & Bassetlaw Hosps. NHS Trust; Company Med. Off. Cooper Lighting & Security Ltd. Doncaster.

LOVE, Professor Seth Department of Neuropathology, Frenchay Hospital, Bristol BS16 1LE Tel: 0117 970 1700 Fax: 0117 975 3760 Email: seth.love@bris.ac.uk — MB BCh 1978 Witwatersrand; PhD Lond. 1984; FRCP Lond. 1996; MRCP (UK) 1980; FRCPath 1995, M 1985. Cons. Neuropath. Frenchay Hosp. Bristol; Prof. Neuropath. Univ. Bristol.

LOVE, Stanley (retired) 1 Cathedral Court, Newport NP20 4EU — MB BCh 1940 Wales; BSc Wales 1937, MB BCh 1940. Clin. Med. Off. Gwent AHA. Prev: Capt. RAMC.

LOVE, Susan Valerie Curzon Avenue Surgery, 74 Curzon Avenue, Ponders End, Enfield EN3 4UE Tel: 020 8364 7846 Fax: 020 8443 0503 — MB BS 1976 Lond. GP/SHO Chase Farm VTS.

LOVE, Wendy Elizabeth 9A Blenheim Terrace, London NW8 0EH — MB BS 1954 Lond.; MRCS Eng. LRCP Lond. 1954; FRCOG 1975, M 1961, DObst 1956. (Roy. Free) O & G Eliz. G. Anderson Hosp. Lond. Prev: Resid. Surg. Off. Birm. Matern. & Wom. Hosps.; Annie McCall Research Fell. Roy. Free Hosp. Lond.

LOVE, William Campbell (retired) 145 Brownside Road, Cambuslang, Glasgow G72 8AH Tel: 0141 1041 1540 — MB ChB 1955 Glas.; FRCP Ed. 1981, M 1963; FRCP Glas. 1970, M 1962; FRFPS Glas. 1959. Hon. Clin. Sen. Lect. Univ. Glas. Prev: Cons. Phys. (Infec. Dis.) Ruchill Hosp.

LOVEDALE, Charles The Medical Centre, 37A Heaton Road, Heaton, Newcastle upon Tyne NE6 1TH Tel: 0191 265 8121 Fax: 0191 276 6085; 70 Reid Park Road, Newcastle upon Tyne NE2 2ES Tel: 0191 281 2524 Email: lovedalec@aol.com — MB BS 1975 Newc.; BMedSc (Hons.) Newc. 1972, MB BS 1975; MRCP (UK) 1978; MRCGP 1982; DRCOG 1979. (Newc.) Hosp. Pract. (Gen. Med.) Newc. Gen. Hosp.; Hops. Pract. (Gen. Med.) Freeman Hosp. Newc.

LOVEDALE, Irayna Lillian Osborne Road Surgery, 200 Osborne Road, Jesmond, Newcastle upon Tyne NE2 3LD Tel: 0191 281 4777 Fax: 0191 281 4309; 70 Reid Park Road, Newcastle upon Tyne NE2 2ES Tel: 0191 281 2524 — MB BS 1975 Newc.; MRCGP 1979; DRCOG 1978. GP Newc.

LOVEDAY, Bertram John No. 7 Gilston Park House, Gilston, High Wych CM20 2SF Tel: 01279 444296; No.7 Gilston Park House, Gilston CM20 2SF Tel: 01279 444296, 0208 850 7796 Fax: 0208 265 1101 — MB BS 1964 Lond.; MRCS Eng. LRCP Lond. 1964; FFR 1971; DMRD Eng. 1969. (Roy. Free) Prev: Cons. Radiol. Roy. Surrey Co. Hosp. Guildford; Cons. Radiol. Camb. Milit. Hosp. Aldershot; Ho. Phys. Willesden Gen. Hosp.

LOVEDAY, David John Plas Ffynnon Medical Centre, Middleton Road, Oswestry SY11 2RB Tel: 01691 655844 Fax: 01691 668030; 5 The Maltings, West Felton, Oswestry SY11 4EL Tel: 01691 610469 — MB BS Lond. 1989; MRCGP 1996. (Roy. Free Hosp.) GP OsW.ry.

LOVEDAY, Eric Julian Department of Radiology, Southmead Hospital, Bristol BS10 5NB Tel: 0117 959 5123 Fax: 0117 959 5122 Email: ejloveday@compuserve.com — MB BS 1984 Lond.; MRCP (UK) 1987; FRCR 1991. Cons. Radiol. S.mead Hosp. Bristol. Prev: Sen. Regist. (Radiol.) St Thomas' Hosp. Lond.; Lect. (Radiol.) Chinese Univ. Hong Kong.

LOVEDAY, J H 3 Windermere Road, Newbold, Chesterfield S41 8DU — MB ChB 1972 Sheffield; MB ChB 1972 Sheffield.

LOVEDAY, Mary Olween 126 Harley Street, London W1N 1AH Tel: 020 7487 4526; Applelands House, Boundstone, Farnham GU10 4TL — MB BS Lond. 1964; MRCS Eng. LRCP Lond. 1964. (Roy. Free) Allergist & Clin. Ecologist Lond. Prev: Clin. Ecol. Lister Hosp. Lond.; Ho. Surg. (Gyn.) Roy. Free Hosp.; Ho. Phys. S. Lond. Hosp. Wom.

***LOVEDAY, Nicola** 16 Harrowdene Gardens, Teddington TW11 0DH — MB ChB 1998 Birm.

LOVEDAY, Nigel Frank James 11 Swallow Close, Barton Seagrave, Kettering NN15 6PJ — MB ChB 1992 Leic.; DRCOG 1995.

LOVEDAY, Robin Harambee, 21 St Lawrence Avenue, Bidborough, Tunbridge Wells TN4 0XA Tel: 01892 533296 — MB BS Lond. 1964; MRCS Eng. LRCP Lond. 1964; FFA RCS Eng. 1967; DObst RCOG 1966. (King's Coll. Hosp.) Cons. Anaesth. Kent & Sussex Weald Trust. Socs: Hosp. Cons. & Special. Assn. (Immediate Past Pres.); Obst. Anaesth. Assn. Prev: Sen. Regist. (Anaesth.) King's Coll. Hosp. & SE Metrop. Neurosurg. & Thoracic Units Woolwich.; Regist. (Anaesth.) & Ho. Off. (O & G) King's Coll. Hosp. Lond.

LOVEDEN, Lorraine May Caen Health Centre, Braunton EX33 1LR Tel: 01271 812005 Fax: 01271 814768; Park Cottage, Higher Pk Road, Braunton EX33 2LG Tel: 01271 817098 — MB ChB 1984 Bristol.

LOVEGROVE, Mr John Ernest Department of Surgery, Dewsbury District Hospital, Healds Road, Dewsbury WF12 4HS — MB BS Lond. 1969; FRCS Eng. 1975; MRCS Eng. LRCP Lond. 1969; T(S) 1991. (St. Bart.) Cons. Surg. (Gen. & Coloproctol.) Dewsbury Dist. Hosp.

LOVEGROVE, Simon Cloudesley 7 Deanwood House, Stockcross, Newbury RG20 8JP — MB BS 1994 Lond. SHO (Oncol.) Middlx. Hosp. Lond. Prev: SHO (Elderly Care) Univ. Coll. Hosp.; SHO (A & E) & Ho. Off. Salisbury Dist. Hosp.

LOVEJOY, James John Rosemary Medical Centre, 2 Rosemary Gardens, Parkstone, Poole BH12 3HF Tel: 01202 741300 — MB BS 1972 Lond.; MRCS Eng. LRCP Lond. 1972; MRCGP 1980. (Westm.) Prev: Med. Off. St. Francis' Hosp. Katete, Zambia.

LOVEL, Joan Patricia (retired) Kiln Park House, Burton Ferry, Milford Haven SA73 1NY Tel: 01646 600301 Fax: 01646 600301 — MB BCh BAO 1945 Belf.; MD Belf. 1951; DCH Eng. 1949. Prev: Asst. Med. Off. Surrey CC.

LOVEL, Keith Willerby 12A Raleigh Court, Stanley Park Road, Wallington SM6 0HH Tel: 020 8669 1931 — BM BCh 1942 Oxf.; MA, BM BCh Oxf. 1942; MRCP Lond. 1950; DIH Eng. 1962; MFOM RCP Lond. 1983. Med. Off. Comm. on Safety of Med. Socs: Fell. Roy. Soc. Med. (Mem. Sect. Paediat., Occupat. Med., Geriat. &; Soc. Occupat. Med. Prev: Regist. (Med.) Postgrad. Med. Sch. Lond.; Sen. Regist. Hosp. Sick Childr. Gt. Ormond St.; Tutor (Child Health) Univ. Oxf.

LOVEL, Professor Timothy William Isherwood (retired) St. Benedicts Hospice, Monkwearmouth Hospital, Newcastle Road, Sunderland SR5 1NB Tel: 0191 569 9199 Fax: 0191 569 9253 Email: tim.lovel@phw-tr.northy.nhs.uk — BM BCh 1961 Oxf.; DSc (Hon.) Sunderland 2001; MA Oxf. 1961; FRCP Lond. 1993; MRCP Lond. 1964; AFOM RCP Lond. 1981. Prev: Med. Dir. Hartlepool Hospice.

LOVELAND, Robin Clive Intensive Care Unit, Wexham Park Hospital, Wexham, Slough SL2 4HL Tel: 01753 633204; 1 Mortlake Road, Kew, Richmond TW9 3JE Tel: 020 8948 5848 Fax: 020 8332 0183 Email: rob_loveland@email.msn.com — MB BS 1980 Lond.; FFA RCS Eng. 1984. Cons. Anaesth. Dir. ITU Wexham Pk. Hosp. Prev: Sen. Regist. Univ. Coll. Hosp. Lond.

LOVELESS, John Alan (retired) 6 Western Esplanade, Broadstairs CT10 1TG Tel: 01843 62102 Fax: 01843 862102 — MRCS Eng. LRCP Lond. 1943; MA Camb.; DCH Eng. 1950. Prev: GP Ramsgate.

LOVELESS, Peter Martin Hillingdon Hospital, Pield Heath Road, Uxbridge UB8 3NN Tel: 01895 238282; Claddagh, Blackpond Lane, Farnham Royal, Slough SL2 3DS — BM 1980 Soton. Assoc. Specialist (Anaesth.) Hillingdon Hosp. Uxbridge.

LOVELESS, Richard Alan Cape Hill Medical Centre, 147 Cape Hill, Smethwick, Warley B66 4SH Tel: 0121 558 0871 Fax: 0121 558 8960; 72 Willow Avenue, Edgbaston, Birmingham B17 8HE Tel: 0121 429 3241 Fax: 0121 558 8960 Email: richard_loveless@becomm.co.uk — MB BS 1982 Lond.; MMedSci Birm. 1996; MRCS Eng. LRCP Lond. 1982; MRCGP 1989; DCH RCP Lond. 1986. (Char. Cross Hosp.) Hon. Lect. (Gen. Pract.) Univ. Birm. 1996. Prev: Dep. Med. Superintend. Nangina Mission Hosp., E. Afr.

LOVELESS, Stephen Robert New House Surgery, 142A South Street, Dorking RH4 2QR Tel: 01306 881313 Fax: 01306 877305 — MB BS 1984 Lond.; BSc (Hons) Aberd. 1978; MRCGP 1988; DRCOG 1987.

LOVELL, Alun Glyndwr Roundway House, Barry Place, Derry Hill, Calne SN11 9NX — MB ChB 1991 Liverp.

LOVELL, Andrew Timothy Department of Anaesthetics, The Middlesex Hospital, Mortimer St., London W1T 3AA Tel: 020 7636 8333 Fax: 020 7580 6423 Email: a.lovell@ucl.ac.uk — MB BS 1988 Lond.; BSc (Hons.) Lond. 1985, MB BS 1988; FRCA 1993; DA (UK) 1991. Research Fell. (Anaesth.) Middlx. Hosp. Lond. Socs: Assn. Anaesth.; BMA; Assoc. Mem. Assn. Cardiothoracic Anaesth. Prev: Regist. (Anaesth.) Univ. Coll. Hosp. & Middlx. Hosp. Lond.; Regist. (Anaesth.) Whipps Cross Hosp. Lond.; SHO (Anaesth.) Univ. Coll. Hosp. & Middlx. Hosp. Lond.

LOVELL, Christopher Roland Department of Dermatology, Ro United Hospital, Bath Tel: 01225 824524 Fax: 01225 824524; Green Farm Cottage, The Green, Farmborough, Bath BA2 0B 01761 470425 — MD 1983 Bristol; MB ChB 1973; FRCP L 1993; MRCP (UK) 1977. Cons. Dermat. Bath Health Dist. Hon. Pres. & Ex-Hon. Sec.) Dowling Club; Brit. Assn. De Sen. Regist. St. John's Hosp. Dis. Skin Lond.; Regist. (Bristol Roy. Infirm.; SHO Nevill Hall Hosp. Abergaven

LOVELL, David 26 Fairfax Road, London NW6 4H 6358 — MB BCh 1957 Wales; PhD Lond. 1964; F 1974; MRCS Eng. LRCP Lond. 1957; MRCPath 19 Histopath. Centr. Middlx. Hosp. Lond. Socs: Fell. Path. Soc. Prev: Research Asst. Med. Unit Univ Sch. Lond.; Lect. (Morbid Anat.) St. Thos. Ho

LOVELL, Helen Mary 6 Sullivan Way, Lich BS 1997 Nottm.

LOVELL, Mr Martyn Edward South M Hospitals Healthcare Trust, Withingt Manchester M20 2LR Tel: 0161 2

Quayside Mews, Lymm WA13 0HZ Email: martynlovell@aol.com — MB ChB 1988 Liverp.; FRCS Eng. 1992; FRCS (Orth.) 1996. Cons. Orhthopaedic Surg., S. Manch. Univ. Hosp. Healthcare Trust. Socs: Brit. Trauma Soc.; Brit. Hip Soc. Prev: Sen. Regist. Rotat. (Orthop.) Manch.; Regist. Rotat. (Orthop.) Liverp.

LOVELL, Matthew John 21 Dryden Court, Renfrew Road, London SE11 4NH — MB BS 1998 Lond.; MB BS Lond 1998.

LOVELL, Peter The Surgery, The Coppice, Herne Lane, Rustington, Littlehampton BN16 3BE Tel: 01903 783178 Fax: 01903 859027; Southerndown, 29 Sea Avenue, Rustington, Littlehampton BN16 2DQ — MB BS 1970 Lond.; DObst RCOG 1972. (St. Mary's)

LOVELL, Philippa Read 11 Fellside, Kenton, Newcastle upon Tyne NE3 4LJ Tel: 0191 285 7175 Email: simon_lewis@tesco.net — MB BS 1984 Lond.; Dip. In Palliative Med. 2000. (St. Batholomews Hospital) p/t Clin. Asst. Marie Curie Centre Newc. Socs: Assn. of Palliat. Med. Prev: Regist. (A & E) N.wick Pk. Hosp. Harrow.

LOVELL, Richard Andrew 22 Huxnor Road, Kingskerswell, Newton Abbot TQ12 5DX — MB BS 1992 Lond.; MRCP 1997. (St Georges.Hosp.Lond) Specialist Regist. Haem.W. Midl.Deanery. Socs: MRCP. Prev: Lat. Specialist Regist. Haem. S.mead. Hosp. Bristol; Lat.Specialist Regist.haem.Bristol.Roy.Infirm; Las.Care.Elderly.Chase Farm Hosp.Enfield.

LOVELL, Robert Anders 29 Sea Avenue, Rustington, Littlehampton BN16 2DQ — MB BS 1998 Lond.; MB BS Lond 1998.

LOVELL, Rosemary Anne c/o Department of General Practice, St. Georges Hospital Medical School, Cranmer Terrace, Tooting, London SW17 0RE — MB BCh 1990 Wales; BA (Hons.) Leic 1983; MRCGP 1995; DCH RCP Lond. 1994; DRCOG 1993. SHO (Paediat., O & G & A & E) Lond.; Community Med. Off. (Child Health) Lambeth Community Trust; Trainee GP Brocklebank Health Centre Lond.; Acad. Asst. (Gen. Pract.) St. Geo. Hosp. Med. Sch. Lond. Prev: SHO (Radiother. & Oncol.) Clatterbridge Regional Centre; Ho. Off. (Surg.) St. Helier Hosp. Carshalton; Ho. Off. (Med.) Llandough Hosp. Penarth.

LOVELL, Sharon Lynne 9 Muskett Heights, Carryduff, Belfast BT8 8SP — MB BCh BAO 1992 Belf.

LOVELOCK, Hilary Ann — MB BS 1979 Lond.; MRCGP 2001; FFA RCS Eng. 1985. (St. Thos.) p/t Gen. Practitioner, Huthwaite Health Centre, Huthwaite, Notts.

LOVELY, Betsy Eirlys (retired) Swn Y Don, 11 St George's Avenue, Dovercourt, Harwich CO12 3RR Tel: 01255 503730 — MB ChB 1949 Liverp. Prev: Med. Off. E. Cos. Br. Family Plann. Assn.

LOVEROCK, Michael Leatside Surgery, Babbage Rd, Totnes TQ9 6PD Tel: 01803 862671 Fax: 01803 860309; Jepthahs, Staverton, Totnes TQ9 6PD Tel: 01803 677 Email: michael.loverock@doctors.net.uk — MB BS 1975 Lond.; MRCS Eng. LRCP Lond. 1975; MRCGP 1980; DRCOG 1980; DCH Eng. 1979. (St. Mary's) Prev: GP Dudley VTS; Ho. Surg. St. Mary's Lond.; Ho. Phys. Edgware Gen. Hosp.

LOVESEY, Edwina Marianne (Surgery) 112 Weoley Park Road, Birmingham B29 5HA Tel: 0121 472 1965; 25 Middle Park Road, Weoley Hill, Birmingham B29 4BE Tel: 0121 476 1901 — MB ChB 1963 Birm. (Birm.) Socs: BMA & Sands Cox Soc. Prev: Med. Off. Birm. Regional Blood Transfus. Serv.; Ho. Surg. Birm. Childr. Hosp.; Ho. Phys. Gen. Hosp. Birm.

LOVESTONE, Simon Harold Institute of Psychiatry, De Crespingy Park, London SE5 8AZ — BM 1986 Soton.; MPhil. Lond. 1994; BSc Sheff. 1982; MRCPsych 1991. Sen. Lect. (Old Age Psychiat.) Inst. Psychiat. Lond.; Hon. Cons. Maudsley Hosp. Prev: Lect. (Old Age Psychiat.) Inst. Psychiat. Lond.; Regist. (Psychiat.) Maudsley Hosp. Lond.

LOVETT, Miss Bryony Ellen 103 Old Church Lane, Stanmore HA7 2RT — MB BChir 1989 Camb.; FRCS Eng. 1992; MChir. 1998. (Cambridge and Royal London Hospital) Specialist Regist. (Surg.), N. E. Thames. Socs: (Region. Rep.) Assn. Surg. in Train.; Comm. Mem. Wom. in Surgic. Train.; Roy. Soc. Med. Prev: Research Regist. (Surg.) Roy. Free Hosp. Lond.

LOVETT, Diane Margaret Latham House Medical Practice, Sage Cross Street, Melton Mowbray LE13 1NX Tel: 01664 854949 Fax: 01664 501825; 108 Burton Road, Melton Mowbray LE13 1DL Tel: 01664 500553 — BM BS 1979 Nottm.; BMedSci. Nottm. 1977, BM BS 1979; MRCGP 1983; DRCOG 1982.

LOVETT, Doon Laura (retired) Glebe Lodge, Thames St., Sonning, Reading RG4 6UR — MB BS 1981 Lond.; MB BS Lond. 1984; BSc (1st cl. Hons. Physiol.) Lond. 1981; DRCOG 1989. Clin. Asst. (Haemat.) Roy. Berks. Hosp. Prev: SHO (Respirat.) St. Richards Chichester.

LOVETT, Eileen Walnut Tree House, 65 High St., Harlton, Cambridge CB3 7ES — MB 1961 Camb.; BChir 1960. (Univ. Coll. Hosp.) SCMO (Community Health) Barnet Healthcare Trust. Socs: BMA. Prev: Research Fell. St. Mark's Hosp. Lond.; Ho. Surg. Hackney Hosp.; Ho. Surg. (Obst.) N. Middlx. Hosp.

LOVETT, Jennifer Josephine Department of Palliative Medicine, Derriford Hospital, Plymouth PL6 8DH Tel: 01752 763996 Fax: 01752 763997 Email: jenny.lovett@phnt.swest.nhs.uk — MB ChB Bristol 1965; FRCR 1981; DObst RCOG 1967; DMRT Eng. 1969. Cons. Palliat. Med. Freedom Fields Hosp. Plymouth. Prev: Med. Dir. St. Margt. Som. Hospice Taunton.

LOVETT, John Michael (retired) The Surgery, 4-6 High Street, kinver, Stourbridge DY7 6HG Tel: 01384 873311 Fax: 01384 877328 — MB ChB 1970 Birm. GP S. Staffs HA. Prev: GP Birm.

LOVETT, John Murchison Ashfield House Surgery, Ashfield House, 1 Ashfield Road, Milngavie, Glasgow G62 6BT Tel: 0141 956 1339 Fax: 0141 956 7098; 13 Nasmyth Avenue, Bearsden, Glasgow G61 4SQ Tel: 0141 943 1990 — MB ChB 1985 Ed.; MRCGP 1989; Dip. Pract. Dermat. Cardiff 1995; Cert. Family Plann. JCC 1989; DRCOG 1989. (Ed.) Socs: BMA. Prev: SHO (Ophth.) Glas. Eye Infirm.; Ho. Off. (Gen. Med.) CrossHo. Hosp. Ayrsh.; Ho. Off. (Surg. Paediat.) Leith Hosp. Edin.

LOVETT, Jonathan Walter Turberville The Chrysalis Centre, Wellington House, Delamere St., Crewe CW1 2LZ Tel: 01270 253841 Fax: 01270 252398; Dorrington Old Hall, Dorrington, Woore, Crewe CW3 9RR Tel: 0163 064 7097 — MB BS 1981 Lond.; MA Oxf. 1981; MRCPsych 1986. Cons. Child (Adolesc. Psychiat.) E. Chesh. NHS Trust; Clin. Lect. Univ. Liverp. Socs: Welsh Psychiat. Soc. Prev: Sen. Regist. (Child Adolesc. Psychiat.) Mersey RHA; Regist. (Psychol. Med.) S. Glam. HA.

LOVETT, Katherine Fiona Castell-y-gionc, Brynberian, Crymych SA41 3UB — MB ChB 1990 Manch.; BSc (Med. Sci.) St. And. 1987; MRCPsych 1995; MSc 1997. (Manch.) Cons. Gen. Adult Psychiat., Plymouth Primary Care Trust. Prev: Sen. Regist. Manch. 1995-99; Specialist Regist. S. W. Peninsular Rotat. 1999-01.

LOVETT, Mrs Lisetta Marianne Lomas Department of Psychiatry, The Foundation NHS Trust, St Georges' Hospital, Corporate St., Stafford ST16 3AG Tel: 01785 257888; Dorrington Old Hall, Dorrington, Woore, Crewe CW3 9RR — MB BS 1982 Lond.; BSc Lond. 1976, MB BS 1982; MRCPsych 1987; DHMSA 1979. (Guys) Cons. Psychiat. St. Geo. Hosp. Staff. Socs: Fell. Fac. Hist. Med. & Soc. Apoth. Prev: Cons. Psychiat. Leighton Hosp. Crewe; Cons. Psychiat. Stafford; Lect. Univ. Liverp.

LOVETT, Margaret Susan Sydenham House Group Practice, Boulevard, Hull HU3 2TA Tel: 01482 326818 Fax: 01482 218267 — MB ChB 1979 Sheff.

LOVETT, Michael Christopher Riverside Medical Practice, Roushill, Shrewsbury SY1 1PQ Tel: 01743 352371 Fax: 01743 340269 — MB ChB 1982 Birm.

LOVETT, Patrick Dawton 2 Upper Cheyne Row, Chelsea, London SW3 5JN Tel: 020 7352 5515 — MB BS 1955 Lond. (St. Thos.) Vis. Phys. St. Luke's Hosp. Chelsea; Phys. Inst. of Dirs. Med. Centre; Hon. Med. Off. Centre for Spastic Childr. Chelsea. Socs: Chelsea Clin. Soc. Prev: Ho. Phys. & SHO St. Thos. Hosp. Lond.

LOVETT, Peter Charles Albert 14 Aldbury Avenue, Wembley HA9 6EY — MB BS 1986 Lond.; MRCGP 1993; DCH RCP Lond. 1990. GP Lond.; GP Tutor UCL Med. Sch.

LOVETT, William Charles Donald, OBE (retired) Summerfield, 10 Heol Isaf, Radyr, Cardiff CF15 8AL Tel: 029 208423546 — MB BCh 1942 Wales; BSc (Hons.), MB BCh (Distinc. Pharmacol.); Pub. Health; Path. & Surg.) Wales 1942; MD Lond. 1947, MB BS 1942; FFCM 1976, M 1972; DPH Eng. 1948, DTM & H 1950. Prev: Princip. Med. Off. Health & Social Work Dept. Welsh Office.

LOVICK, Russell Lesley James 'Ivanhoe', Lillington Avenue, Leamington Spa CV32 5UE Tel: 01926 21202 — MB BS 1953 Lond.; MRCS Eng. LRCP Lond. 1953. (St. Mary's) Prev: Res. Med. Off. Jenny Lind Childr. Hosp. Norwich; Obst. Ho. Surg. City Matern. Hosp. Carlisle.

LOVISETTO, Stefano Giorgio 1 The Terrace, Boston Spa, Wetherby LS23 6AH — MB ChB 1998 Sheff.; MB ChB Sheff 1998.
LOW, Alvin Cheong Siu Health Centre, Saffron Road, Biggleswade SG18 8DJ Tel: 01767 313647 Fax: 01767 312568 Email: alvinlow@doctors.org.uk — MB BS 1990 Lond.; MRCGP 1994; DGM RCP Lond. 1992. (Roy. Free Hosp.) GP; Clin. Asst. Genitourin. Med. Lister Hosp. Stevanage; Med. Adviser 1st Aid Ltd Guernsey. Prev: GP Hitchin, Herts.; Chief Med. Off. Foundat. Health Lond.; Lister Hosp. GP VTS Stevenage Herts.
LOW, Boon Kee Waveney Hospital, Cushendall Road, Ballymena BT43 6HH; 4 Balmoral Park, Finaghy, Belfast BT10 0QD — MB BCh BAO 1991 Belf.
LOW, Charles Bruce Dingleton Hospital, Melrose TD6 9HN Tel: 0189 682 2727 — MB ChB 1976 Ed.; MRCPsych. 1987. Cons. Psychiat. Dingleton Hosp. Melrose. Socs: Roy. Coll. Psychiats. Prev: GP Kelso.
LOW, Mr Christopher David Tullis, Surg. Cdr. RN Department of Ophthalmology, Royal Hospital Haslar, Gosport PO12 2AA Tel: 023 9276 2066, 023 9276 2411 Fax: 023 9076 2210; 152 Barnham Road, Barnham, Bognor Regis PO22 0EH Tel: 01243 552289 — MB ChB Dundee 1985; FRCS Ed. 1992. Cons. Ophth. Surg. Ophth. Portsmouth Hosp.s Trust; Med. Off. (Full Career Commiss.) RN; Cons. Adviser in Ophth. to the Med. Director Gen. (Naval); Vis. Cons. Ophth. Surg. Brit. Forces Cyprus and Gibraltar. Prev: Fell. Corneal Surg. Flinders Med. Centre Adelaide; Sen. Regist. (Ophth.) Soton. Eye Unit; Sen. Regist. & Regist. St. Mary's & W.. Eye Hosps. Lond.
LOW, David Christie Department of Paediatrics, Sandwell Healthcare Trust, West Bromwich, Birmingham B71 4HJ Tel: 0721 607 3471 Email: davidc.low@virgin.net; 34 Reddings Road, Moseley, Birmingham B13 8LN Tel: 0721 449 1324 — MB BChir 1976 Camb.; MA Camb. 1976; FRCP Lond. 1994; MRCP (UK) 1978; FRCPCH 1996. Cons. Paediat. Sandwell Health Care Trust W. Bromwich & Med Dir Integrated Care. Socs: BAMM; Roy. Coll Paediat. & Child Health; BMA. Prev: Sen. Regist. (Paediat.) Dudley Rd. Hosp.; Regist. Birm. Childr. Hosp.; Sen. Regist. & Regist. Ahmadu Bello Univ. Hosp. Zaria, Nigeria.
LOW, Eleanor Margaret Department of Clinical Oncology, St. Mary's Hospital, Portsmouth PO3 6AD Tel: 023 9282 2331; Wentworth, Bassett Wood Road, Southampton SO16 3LS Tel: 01703 786597 — MB ChB Sheff. 1970; FRCOG 1994, M 1975; DMRT Eng. 1980; DObst RCOG 1972. Assoc. Specialist (Clin. Oncol.) St. Mary's Hosp. Portsmouth. Prev: Cons. Radiother. & Oncol. W.on Pk. Hosp. Sheff.; Sen. Regist. (Radiother. & Oncol.) Roy. S. Hants. Hosp. Soton.; SHO (O & G) Jessop. Hosp. Wom. Sheff.
LOW, Enq Joo 53 Shelley Court, Glasgow G12 0XD — MB BS 1988 Malaya.
LOW, Francis MacPherson (retired) Langlands, Square Drive, Haslemere GU27 3LP Tel: 01428 652961 — MB BChir 1954 Camb.; MA, MB BChir Camb. 1954; FRCR 1975; FFR 1964; DMRD Eng. 1961. Prev: Sen. Regist. Dept. Radiol. King's Coll. Hosp. Lond.
LOW, Gavin Weng Yew 64/1 West Mains Road, Edinburgh EH9 3JE — MB ChB 1998 Ed.; MB ChB Ed 1998.
LOW, Gillian Ann (retired) 72 Boston Road, Hanwell, London W7 2ET — MB BS 1983 Lond.; BSc Lond. 1980, MB BS 1983. Prev: Ship's Surg. Sea Managem. Servs. Ltd.
LOW, Gordon Davidson Brampton Medical Practice, 4 Market Place, Brampton CA8 1NL Tel: 016977 2551 Fax: 016977 41944 — MB ChB 1991 Manch.; BSc St. And. 1988; MRCGP 1995.
LOW, Hsiu Ling 25 Abbey Road, Beeston, Nottingham NG9 2QF — BM BS 1997 Nottm.
LOW, Mr Hu Liang Room 4/5 B Block, Newcastle General Hospital, Grainger Park Road, Newcastle upon Tyne NE4 8RQ — MB BCh BAO 1992 Belf.; FRCS Eng. 1996. Regist. (Neurosurg.) Frenchay Hosp. Bristol. Prev: SHO (Neurosurg.) Roy. Lond. Hosp.
LOW, Ian Hewson 118 Foley Road, Claygate, Esher KT10 0NA — MB ChB 1998 Sheff.; MB ChB Sheff 1998.
LOW, James Scott Middleton (retired) Manor House, Wansford, Driffield YO25 8NU Tel: 01377 44310 — MB ChB 1947 St. And.; DPH 1952; MRCGP 1960. Prev: Capt. RAMC, 68th (Lagos) Milit. Hosp.
LOW, Jee Keem 37 Mount Pleasant Road, Brondesbury Park, London NW10 3EG Tel: 020 8459 3682 — MB ChB 1992 Sheff.; FRCS Eng. Ed. 1997. (Sheff.) SHO Peri Fell.sh. Rotat. Newc. Prev: SHO (Cardiothoraic Surg.) Cardiothoracic Centre Liverp.; SHO Rotat. (Gen. Surg.) Hull Roy. Infirm.
LOW, King-Wai 23 Tattershall Drive, Beeston, Nottingham NG9 2GP — BM BS 1997 Nottm.
LOW, Kirsten Morag New Cumnock Surgery, 67 Afton Bridgend, New Cumnock, Cumnock KA18 4BA Tel: 01290 338242 Fax: 01290 332010; 1 Muirfoot Place, New Cumnock, Cumnock KA18 4DU Tel: 01290 338699 — MB ChB 1966 Ed.
LOW, Lynne Soon Li Archway Sexual Health Clinic, Whittington Hospital, Highgate Hill, London N19; Brook Studio, 27A Stamford Brook Road, London W6 0XJ — MB ChB 1987 Aberd.; DA (UK) 1993; Dip. GU Med. Soc. Apoth. Lond. 1996. Clin. Asst. (Genitourin. Med.) Archway Sexual Health Clinic, Whittington Hosp., Lond.; Med. Jl.ist Lond.
LOW, Nesta Mary Heard The Croft Surgery, Barnham Road, Eastergate, Chichester PO20 6RP Tel: 01243 543240 Fax: 01243 544862; West Dene, 152 Barnham Road, Barnham, Bognor Regis PO22 0EH Tel: 01243 552289 — MB ChB 1957 St. And. (St. And.)
LOW, Nicholas James Lowgate Surgery, 19 Lowgate, Gosberton, Spalding PE11 4NL Tel: 01775 840204 Fax: 01775 841108 — MB ChB 1982 Liverp.
LOW, Nicola Minling 17 Park Hill, London SW4 9NS — MB BS 1987 Lond. SHO (Infec. Dis.) Regional Infec. Dis. Unit Fazakerley Hosp. Liverp.
LOW, Mr Robert Andrew Lochhead, SBStJ, TD 9 Chapelton Gardens, Bearsden, Glasgow G61 2DH Tel: 0141 942 9103 Fax: 0141 942 1658 Email: eileen@rall98.freeserve.co.uk — MB ChB 1964 Glas.; FRCOG 1982, M 1969; FRCS Glas. 1982. (Glas.) Con. Gyn. Glas. Nuffield Hosp.; Hon. Clin. Sen. Lect. (Obst. & Gyn.) Univ. Glas.; Con. Gyn. Rosshall Hosp. Glas. Socs: Glas. Obst. & Gyn. Soc.; Ospeys Obst. & Gyn. Soc.; Nines Obst & Gyn Soc. Prev: Cons. O & G Robroyston Hosp. Glas.; Cons. Obst & Gyn. Stobhill Hosp. NHS Trust Glas.; Cons. Obst. Glas. Roy. Matern. Hosp.
LOW, Ronald Watterston Duncan, CD (retired) Occupational Health Unit, Raigmore Hospital, Inverness IV2 3UJ Tel: 01463 234151 ext. 418 — MB ChB 1952 St. And.; DPH Toronto 1969. Prev: Phys. i/c Occupat. Health Unit Raigmore Hosp. Inverness.
LOW, Sheau Wen Wendy 103C Gunterstone Road, London W14 9BT — MB BS 1990 Sydney.
LOW-BEER, Naomi Mira 35 Kenyon Street, London SW6 6JZ Tel: 020 7385 6165 — MB BS 1989 Newc. Clin. Research Fell. Imperial Coll. St. Mary's Lond. Prev: SHO (O & G) Chelsea & W.m. Hosp. Lond.
LOW-BEER, Thomas Stephen (retired) Selly Oak Hospital, Selly Oak, Birmingham B29 6JD Tel: 0121 627 1627 — BM BCh 1960 Oxf.; MA Oxf. 1960; FRCP Lond. 1980, M 1965. Prev: Cons. Phys. & Gastroenterol. Selly Oak Hosp. Birm.
LOWBURY, Edward Joseph Lister, OBE (retired) 79 Vernon Road, Birmingham B16 9SQ — BM BCh 1939 Oxf.; MA Oxf. 1939, DM 1957; FRCS Eng. 1978; FRCP Lond. 1977, M 1972; FRCPath 1963; Hon. LLD Birm. 1980; Hon. DSc Aston 1977. Prev: Founder & Hon. Dir. Hosp. Infec. Research Laborat.
LOWCOCK, Joanne 12 Ravensworth Crescent, Hart Station, Hartlepool TS24 9RJ — MB ChB 1990 Manch.
LOWDELL, Charles Peter Tel: 0208 846 1732 Fax: 0208 846 1603 — MB BS 1978 Lond.; BSc (Hons.) Anat. Lond. 1975; MRCS Eng. LRCP Lond. 1978; MRCP (UK) 1981; FRCR 1988; FRCP 2000. (Char. Cross) Cons. Radiother. & Oncol. Char. Cross & W.m. Hosp.; Hon. Cons. Chelsea & W.m. Hosp., Qu. Mary's Hosp. Roehampton, W Middlx Univ Hosp Lond. Socs: Fell. Roy. Soc. Med.; Brit. Oncol. Assn.; Brit. Inst. Radiol. Prev: Hon. Sen. Regist. (Research) Cookridge Hosp. Leeds; Sen. Regist. (Radiother. & Oncol.) W.m. & Char. Cross Hosp. Med. Sch. Lond.
LOWDEN, Margaret The Riding, Riding Mill NE44 6HW — MB BS 1940 Durh.
LOWDEN, Mr Thomas Geoffrey (retired) The Riding, Riding Mill NE44 6HW Tel: 0143 482333 — BM BCh 1934 Oxf.; BM BCh Oxon. 1934; FRCS Eng. 1938. Prev: Cons. Surg. Sunderland Gp. Hosps.
LOWDON, David Gilchrist Ross Prescott Surgery, Prescott Road, Prescott, Baschurch, Shrewsbury SY4 2DR Tel: 01939 260210 Fax: 01939 260752 — MB ChB 1979 Birm.; MRCGP 1986; DRCOG 1984.

LOWDON, Glenys Mairi Macdonald (retired) 26 Brandling Park, Newcastle upon Tyne NE2 4RR Tel: 0191 281 0836 — MB ChB Ed. 1939; FRCP Ed. 1994; MRCP Ed. 1944; MRCP Lond. 1946; DCH Eng. 1945. Prev: Med. Off. Newc. HA.

LOWDON, Mr Ian Macdonald Ross Princess Margaret Hospital, Okus Road, Swindon SN1 4JU Tel: 01793 426587 Email: imr@lowdon.com — MB ChB 1976 Ed.; MA Camb. 1977; FRCS Ed. 1980; FRCS Lond. 1980. Cons. Orthop. Surg. Swindon & MarlBoro. NHS Trust. Socs: Brit Soc. Surg. of the Hand. Prev: Med. Dir. Swindon & MarlBoro. NHS Trust; Sen. Regist. (Orthop.) Oxf. RHA; Hand Fell. Duke Univ., USA.

LOWDON, Nicola Margaret 5 Pitcullen Crescent, Perth PH2 7HT — MB ChB 1998 Dund.; MB ChB Dund 1998.

LOWE, Alison Louise The Whitlands, Aqueduct Lane, Alvechurch, Birmingham B48 7BP — MB ChB 1986 Bristol.

LOWE, Bryan Alexander (retired) 39 St Michaels Avenue, Bramhall, Stockport SK7 2PW — MRCS Eng. LRCP Lond. 1954; BSc, MB ChB Liverp. 1954; MRCPsych 1971; DPM Eng. 1961. Prev: Cons. Psychiat. Cheadle Roy. Hosp. Chesh.

LOWE, Catherine Helen Redcoll Cottage, Longniddry EH32 0PL Tel: 01875 53184 — MB ChB 1980 Ed.

LOWE, Catherine Sands Redcoll, Longniddry EH32 0PL Tel: 01875 53184 — MB ChB 1946 Ed. (Ed.)

LOWE, Charles Henry Waterloo Surgery, 191 Devonport Road, Stoke, Plymouth PL1 5RN Tel: 01752 563147 Fax: 01752 563304 — MB ChB 1982 Manch.; MRCGP 1986. Prev: GP Plymouth; SHO (O & G) Freedom Fields Hosp. Plymouth; Trainee GP Plymouth VTS.

***LOWE, Christy Louise** 123 Windsor Avenue, Penn, Wolverhampton WV4 4BJ; 12 Willowbank, Finchaeld, Wolverhampton WV3 9HH Tel: 01902 751452 Fax: 01902 751452 — MB BS 1998 Lond.; MB BS Lond 1998.

LOWE, Collette Frances 4 Hampton Dene Road, Tupsley, Hereford HR1 1UX — MB ChB 1990 Liverp.

LOWE, Daphne Cynthia (retired) 10 Lower Ballinderry Road, Upper Ballinderry, Lisburn BT28 2JB Tel: 01846 651298 Fax: 02892 651515 — MB BCh BAO 1961 Belf.; FRCP Ed. 1980, M 1968. Lect. (Geriat. Med.) Qu.'s Univ. Belf. Prev: Cons. Phys. (Geriat. Med.) Belf. City Hosp.

LOWE, David Ashley Flat 1, 19 Shepherds Hill, Highgate, London N6 5QJ — MB BS 1993 Lond.

LOWE, David Charles (Surgery) 525 New Chester Road, Rock Ferry, Birkenhead CH42 2AG Tel: 0151 645 3464 Fax: 0151 643 1676; 70 Osmaston Road, Prenton, Birkenhead CH42 8LL Tel: 0151 608 2750 — MB ChB 1978 Manch.; DRCOG 1981; DA Eng. 1980. Prev: SHO (Med.) & (O & G) & Ho. Off. (Med. & Surg.) Pk. Hosp.; Davyhulme; SHO (Anaesth.) Withington Hosp. Manch.

LOWE, Professor David George Department of Histopathology, St. Bartholomew's & The Royal London School of Medicine & Dentistry, West Smithfield, London EC1A 7BE Tel: 020 7601 8530 Fax: 020 7601 8530 Email: d.g.lowe@mds.qmw.ac.uk; 46 Thurlow Park Road, West Dulwich, London SE21 8HZ Tel: 020 8670 9200 Fax: 020 8670 9200 — MB BS 1975 Lond.; MD Lond. 1988; FRCS Eng. 1994; FRCPath 1994, M 1982; FIBiol 1994. (Middlx.) Prof. (Surgic. Path.) St. Bartholomews & Roy. Lond. Sch. of Med. & Dent. Prev: Lect. & Hon. Sen. Regist. (Histopath.) St. Thos. Hosp. Med. Sch. Lond.

LOWE, Deborah Bryony 135A Soughers Lane, Ashton-in-Makerfield, Wigan WN4 0JT — MB ChB 1997 Liverp.

LOWE, Diana Mary (retired) 23 Torside, Wilnecote, Tamworth B77 4NH Tel: 0121 472 5021 — MB ChB 1970 Sheff.; MRCS Eng. LRCP Lond. 1970; MRCPsych 1977; DObst RCOG 1972.

LOWE, Dorothy Isabel (retired) 228 Cambridge Road, Great Shelford, Cambridge CB2 5JU Tel: 01223 840019 — MB BCh BAO Dub. 1955; BA Dub. 1953; DPM Eng. 1973. Prev: Clin. Asst. (Psychiat. of Old Age) Bexley Hosp. Kent.

LOWE, Eithne Menzies Ground Floor Flat, 2 Tadmor St., London W12 8AH — MB BCh BAO 1987 Belf.; MRCOG 1994. Regist. (O & G) Homerton Hosp. Lond.

LOWE, Elaine Marie Department of Obstetric Ultrasound, Level 7, Ninewells Hospital, Dundee DD1 9SY Tel: 01382 632019 Email: elainel@dth.scot.nhs.uk; 147 Coupar Angus Road, Muirhead, Dundee DD2 5QN Tel: 01382 580438 — MB ChB 1978 Dundee. Staff Grade (Obst. Ultrasound) Ninewells Hosp. Dundee.

LOWE, Professor Gordon Douglas Ogilvie University Department of Medicine, Royal Infirmary, 10 Alexandra Parade, Glasgow G31 2ER Tel: 0141 211 5412 Fax: 0141 552 2953 — MB ChB 1972 (Hons.) St. And.; FFPHM 2001; MD Dundee 1984; FRCP Lond. 1989; FRCP Ed. 1986; FRCP Glas. 1986; MRCP (UK) 1974. Prof. Vasc. Med. Univ. Glas.; Hon. Cons. Phys. Glas. Roy. Infirm.; Hon. Prof. (Bioeng.) Univ. Strathclyde. Socs: Assn. Phys.; (Ex-Pres.) Brit. Soc. Thrombosis & Haemostasis.; Assessor, Roy. Coll. Phys. Ed.

LOWE, Gwendolyn Liliane 18 Palace Avenue, Llandaff, Cardiff CF5 2DW — MB BCh 1990 Wales; MRCGP 1995; DFFP 1995; DRCOG 1994. Specialist Regist. (Pub. Health Med.) Cardiff.

LOWE, Harry Bodey Medical Centre, 363 Wilmslow Road, Fallowfield, Manchester M14 6XU Tel: 0161 248 6644 Fax: 0161 224 4228 — MB ChB 1970 Manch.; MRCP (U.K.) 1974.

LOWE, Professor James Steven School of Clinical Laboratory Science, Nottingham University Medical School, Clifton Boulevard, Nottingham NG7 2UH — BM BS 1978 Nottm.; DM Nottm. 1992, BMedSci 1976; FRCPath 1996, M 1984. Prof. & Hon. Cons. Neuropath. Univ. Hosp. Nottm.; Edr. Neuropathol. & Applied NeuroBiol.; Edr. Bd. Jl. Pathol. Acta Neuropathologica & Brain Pathol. & Internet Med.; Mem. Counc. Roy. Coll. Pathologists. Socs: Path. Soc.; Neuropath. Soc.; Internat. Acad. Path. Prev: Reader (Neuropath) Univ. Hosp. Nottm.; Sen. Lect. (Histopath.) Univ. Hosp. Nottm.

LOWE, Jane Tonge Fold Health Centre, Hilton St., Bolton BL2 6DY — MB ChB 1977 Manch.; DCH Glas. 1979.

LOWE, Janet Christine RM LG 21, Cheyne Child Development Service, Chelsea & Westminster Hospital, London SW10 9NH Tel: 020 8846 1635 Fax: 020 8846 1633; 46 Thurlow Park Road, West Dulwich, London SE21 8HZ Tel: 020 8670 9200 Fax: 020 8670 9200 Email: janet.lowe@doctors.net.uk — MB BS 1975; MSc 1994; DCH RCP 1982; DRCOG 1977; MRCP Ch. (Middlx.) Cons. Community Paediat. (Audiol.) Chelsea & W.m. Healthcare Trust; Cons. Community Paediat. (Audiol.) Hounslow & Spelthorne Community Servs. Prev: Clin. Med. Off. Kensington, Chelsea & W.m. AHA.

LOWE, Jillian 6 Gibsons Road, Heaton Moor, Stockport SK4 4JX Tel: 0161 374 2135 — MB ChB 1993 Manch.; BSc Med. Sci. St And. 1990; DRCOG 1996; MRCGP 1997. GP Stockport. Socs: MRCGP.

LOWE, Joanne 14 Ranelagh Drive, Southport PR8 3EP — MB BS 1994 Newc.

LOWE, John Graham Department of Dermatology, Ninewells Hospital, Dundee DD1 9SY Tel: 01382 633901 Fax: 01382 633916 — MB ChB 1976 Dundee; FRCP Glas. 1995; MRCP (UK) 1983. Cons. Dermat. Ninewells Hosp. Dundee.

LOWE, John Joseph Herbert (retired) 12 Chartcombe, Compton Acres, Canford Cliffs, Poole BH13 7EJ Tel: 01202 701362 — MB BS 1931 Durham; MB BS Durh. 1931; MD Durh. 1935; FRCP Ed. 1972, M 1936; MRCP Lond. 1936; MRCS Eng. LRCP Lond. 1931; DPM Eng. 1941; LLB Lond. 1970. Prev: Cons. Psychiat. St. Crispin Hosp. N.ampton & Kettering Hosps.

LOWE, John Nicholas 40B Allcroft Road, London NW5 4NE; Department of Pyschological Hospital, University College Hospital, 4th Floor, Cecil Flemming Housing, Grafton Way, London WC1E 6AU — MB BChir 1989 Camb.

LOWE, John Robert Health Centre, Candleby Lane, Cotgrave, Nottingham NG12 3JQ Tel: 0115 989 2398; Grove House, 29 Bingham Road, Radcliffe-on-Trent, Nottingham NG12 2FY — MRCS Eng. LRCP Lond. 1971; PhD Lond. 1971, BSc 1965, MB BS 1971; MRCGP 1983. Lect. Anat. Nottm. Univ.; Clin. Asst. Diabetic Clin. Qu.s Med. Centre Nottm.; Trainer Nottm. VTS.

LOWE, Judith Anne Leigh View Medical Centre, Bradford Road, Tingley, Wakefield WF3 1RQ Tel: 0113 253 7629 Fax: 0113 238 1286 — MB ChB 1975 Manch.; MRCGP 1981; DRCOG 1980. Prev: GP Oldham.

LOWE, Kathryn Sara 41 Foxyldiate Lane, Redditch B97 5PB — MB BS 1989 Lond.; MRCPsych 1995. Sen. Regist. (Psychiat.) W. Midl. HA.

LOWE, Mr Ken James Cardiff Eye Unit, University Hospital of Wales, Heath Park, Cardiff CF1 5NH Tel: 029 2074 3904 — MB ChB 1981 Manch.; MD Bristol 1996; FRCS Ed. 1986; FCOphth. 1989; DO RCS Eng. 1984. Cons. Ophth. Univ. Hosp. Wales Cardiff.

LOWE, Kenneth The Surgery, 3 Glasgow Road, Paisley PA1 3QS Tel: 0141 889 2604 Fax: 0141 887 9039 — MB ChB 1982 Glasgow. (Glasgow) GP Paisley, Renfrewsh.

LOWE, Kenneth Gordon, CVO Bay House, 36 Dundee Road, West Ferry, Dundee DD5 1HY Tel: 01382 778787 — MB ChB 1941 St. And.; MD (Hons., Rutherford Gold Medal) St. And. 1950; FRCP Glas. 1967, M 1965; FRCP Lond. 1963, M 1951; FRCP Ed. 1954, M 1951. (Dundee) Emerit. Prof. Med. Univ. Dundee. Socs: Assn. Phys. & Brit. Cardiac Soc. Prev: Cons. Phys. Ninewells Hosp. Dundee; Phys. to H.M. the Qu. in Scotl.; Sen. Lect. (Med.) Univ. St. And.

LOWE, Louise Margaret Westgate Health Centre, Charleston Drive, Dundee DD2 4AD Tel: 01386 668189; Carse View, The Old Orchard, Wester Ballindean, Inchture, Perth PH14 9QS Tel: 01828 686711 — MB ChB 1987 Dundee; MRCGP 1991; DRCOG 1990. (Dundee) Asst. GP Doctors Retainer Scheme Dundee. Prev: Trainee GP Perth VTS.

LOWE, Martin David Department of Cardiology, Papworth Hospital, Papworth Everard, Cambridge CB3 8RE Tel: 01480 830541 Fax: 01480 364355 Email: martin.lowe@papworth-tr.anglox.nhs.uk; Email: mdlowe@talk21.com — MB BS 1990 Lond.; BSc Durham. 1985; MRCP (UK) 1993. Regist. (Cardiol.) Papworth Hosp. Camb.; Research Fell., Univ. of Camb. Socs: RCPhys; BMA; BPEG.

LOWE, Maurice Douglas Clive Surgery, 20 High Street, Clive, Shrewsbury SY4 5PS Tel: 01939 220295; The Old Vicarage, Clive, Shrewsbury SY4 3JP Tel: 01939 220383 — MB ChB 1960 Aberd.; DMJ Soc. Apoth. Lond. 1987. Capt. RAMC RARO; Police Surg. W. Mercia Police. Prev: SHO (Orthop.) Ayr Co. Hosp.; Ho. Off. (Obst.) Ayrsh. Centr. Hosp. Irvine; Ho. Phys. & Ho. Surg. Stracathro Hosp. Brechin.

LOWE, Michael Robin Basildon Hospital, Nethermayne, Basildon SS16 5NL Tel: 01268 593700; West House, Goldsmiths, Langdon Hills, Basildon SS16 6JB Fax: 01268 414355 — MB BS 1972 Lond.; MRCS Eng. LRCP Lond. 1972; LMCC 1974; FRCPsych 1990, M 1976; DObst RCOG 1974. (Middlx.) Cons. Psychiat. Basildon Hosp. Fell. Roy. Soc. Med.

LOWE, Muriel Josephine (retired) 1 Rosehill, Billingshurst RH14 9QN Tel: 01403 782367 — MB BS 1947 Lond.; MRCS Eng. LRCP Lond. 1944; MFCM 1974; DCH Eng. 1946; DPH Lond. 1950. Prev: SCM (Child Health) Humberside AHA.

LOWE, Nicholas Charles The Health Centre, Douglas Drive, Freckleton, Preston PR2 1HL; Holland House, 29-31 Church Road, Lytham St Annes FY8 5LL Tel: 01253 794999 Fax: 01253 795744 Email: 100530.3412@compuserve.com — MB ChB 1982 Liverp.; DFFP 1993; DRCOG 1988; DA Eng. 1984. Clin. Asst. (Cardiol.) Blackpool Vict. Hosp.; Hon. Med. Adviser Lytham Lifeboat Station. Prev: Regist. (Anaesth.) Walton Hosp. Liverp.; SHO (Paediat.) Roy. Liverp. Childr. Hosp.; SHO (O & G) Walton Hosp. Liverp.

LOWE, Nicholas James 5 Southampton Road, Lymington SO41 9GH — BM 1993 Soton.

LOWE, Paul Penrose Coorie Doon, Montford, Montford Bridge, Shrewsbury SY4 1AD — MB ChB 1970 Bristol; BSc Bristol 1967, MB ChB 1970; FRCR 1976. Cons. Radiol. P.ss Roy. Hosp. Telford. Prev: Cons. Radiol. Roy. Shrewsbury Hosp.; Sen. Regist. (Radiol.) Bristol Roy. Infirm.

LOWE, Peter Angus (retired) San Remo, 85 Morley Road, Chaddesden, Derby DE21 4QW Tel: 01332 672123 — LRCP LRCS 1952 Ed.; LRCP LRCS Ed. LRFPS Glas. 1952; DObst RCOG 1954. Prev: SHO Med., Surg. & Obst. Derby City Hosp.

LOWE, Peter Frank Hexham General Hospital, Corbridge Road, Hexham NE46 1QJ Tel: 01434 655655; 13 Cotswold Gardens, High Heaton, Newcastle upon Tyne NE7 7AD — MB BS 1985 Newc.; MBA Newc. 1994. Staff Grade (A & E) Hexham Gen. Hosp.

LOWE, Peter John Tower House Surgery, 169 West Wycombe Road, High Wycombe HP12 3AF Tel: 01494 526840 — BM 1982 Soton.; MRCGP 1989; DRCOG 1988.

LOWE, Philip John Mackenzie Flat 8, Holly Court, 52 Palatine Road, Manchester M20 3JE Tel: 0161 448 1651 — MB ChB 1988 Manch.; BSc (Hons.) Path. Manch. 1986; MRCOG 1994; CCST. Sen. Lect. Obst. and Gyn. Monash Univ. Melbourne Australia; Specialist IVF Clinician Monash IVF Melbourne Australia. Socs: Brit. Fertil. Soc.; Fertil. Soc. Austral. Prev: Sen. Regist. (O & G) Monash Med. Centre Melbourne, Australia & Clin. Fell Monash IVF.; Clin. Research Fell. (O & G) Univ. Hosp. S. Manch. Withington, Manch.; Regist. (O & G) Hope Hosp. Salford.

LOWE, Philippa Louise Apartment 317, The Colonnades, Albert Dock, Liverpool L3 4AB — MB ChB 1998 Liverp.; MB ChB Liverp 1998.

LOWE, Rachel Jane Elgin Medical Centre, 10 Victoria Crescent, Elgin IV30 1RQ Tel: 01343 547512 Fax: 01343 546781 — MB ChB 1990 Glas.; BSc (Hons.) 1987; MRCGP 1994; DRCOG 1995. (Glas.) GP Elgin, Moraysh. Socs: BMA; Diplomatic Fac. Family Plann. RCOG; Scott. Family Plann. Med. Soc.

LOWE, Richard Green Bank Surgery, Manchester Road, Warrington WA1 3RB Tel: 01925 631132 Fax: 01925 624561; 7 Isherwood Close, Warrington WA2 0DJ Tel: 01925 817125 — MB ChB 1977 Manch.

LOWE, Robert 26 Oakleigh Avenue, Wakefield WF2 9DF — MB ChB 1992 Leeds.

LOWE, Roger Alan 10 South Close, Tranmere Park, Guiseley, Leeds LS20 8JD — MB BChir 1979 Camb.; MA, MB Camb. 1979, BChir 1978; MRCP (UK) 1981; FRCR 1985. (Camb.) Cons. Radiol. Bradford Roy. Infirm. Prev: Sen. Regist. & Regist. (Diag. Radiol.) Leeds Gen. Infirm.; SHO (Gen. Med.) Wharfedale Gen. Hosp. Otley.

LOWE, Ronald Fishergate Hill Surgery, 50 Fishergate Hill, Preston PR1 8DN Tel: 01772 254484 Fax: 01772 881835; 21A Main Road, Nether Kellet, Carnforth LA6 1EZ — MB ChB 1985 Manch.; BSc St. And. 1983.

LOWE, Sarah Jane 34 Hyde Lane, Upton-upon-Severn, Worcester WR8 0SE — MB ChB 1996 Leic.

LOWE, Simon John 29 Bingham Road, Radcliffe-on-Trent, Nottingham NG12 2FY — MB BS 1992 Lond.

LOWE, Simon Wyndham De Parys Medical Centre, 23 De Parys Avenue, Bedford MK40 2TX Tel: 01234 350022 Fax: 01234 213402 — MB ChB 1981 Bristol; MRCGP 1985; DRCOG 1983.

LOWE, Stephen Harcourt Patterdale Lodge Medical Centre, Legh Street, Newton-le-Willows WA12 9NA Tel: 01925 227111 Fax: 01925 290605; Rosebank Cottage, 1 Yeald Brow, Lymm WA13 9DA Tel: 01925 754037 Fax: 01925 758108 — MB ChB 1971 Liverp. Prev: Ho. Surg. & Ho. Phys. BRd.green Hosp. Liverp.

LOWE, Stuart Shepherd West Suffolk Hospital, Hardwick Lane, Bury St Edmunds IP33 2QZ Tel: 01284 713000 Fax: 01284 713100 Email: stuart.lowe@wsh-tr.anglox.nhs.uk; 88 Barons Road, Bury St Edmunds IP33 2LY — MB BS 1977 Lond.; MRCS Eng. LRCP Lond. 1977; FFA RCS Eng. 1981. (St. Mary's) Socs: Intens. Care Soc.; Assn. Anaesth. Prev: Sen. Regist. (Anaesth.) Addenbrookes Hosp. Camb.; Regist. (Anaesth.) Char. Cross Hosp. Lond.

LOWE, Susan X Ray Department, Mayday University Hospital, Mayday Road, Croydon CR7 7YE Tel: 020 8401 3054 Fax: 020 8401 3454; 3 Gipsy Road, London SE27 9TD Tel: 020 8761 3380 Email: s.lowe@gipsy.clara.net — BM BCh 1973 Oxf.; MA, BM BCh Oxf. 1973; FRCR Lond. 1980. (King's Coll. Hosp.) Cons. (Diag. Radiol.) Mayday Univ. Hosp. Croydon; Cons. (Diag. Radiol.) St. Geo. Hosp. Tooting. Socs: BMUS; FRCR BrE. Gp.; MWF. Prev: Sen. Regist. (Diag. Radiol.) St. Geo. Hosp. Tooting.

LOWE, Susan Elizabeth 14 Durham Road, Wilpshire, Blackburn BB1 9LR — BM BS 1997 Nottm.

LOWE, Mr Terrence 257 Hasland Road, Chesterfield S41 0AA — MB ChB 1995 Sheff.; FRCS Glas. 1998. Socs: BAOMS.

LOWE, Thomas Bruce Gordon 11 Mansefield Road, Tweedmouth, Berwick upon Tweed TD15 2DX Tel: 01289 307050 — MB BS Durh. 1967; MRCGP 1974. (Kings College Newcastle-upon-Tyne) p/t GP Berwick-upon-Tweed; Hosp. Pract. (Dermat.) Berwick Infirm., Alnwick Infirm.; Chair, N. N.umberland Community Hosp.s Bd. Prev: SHO (Dermat.) Roy. Vict. Infirm. Newc.; Ho. Off. (Paediat. & Gen. Med.) Newc. Gen. Hosp.

LOWE-PONSFORD, Francesca Louise Ravenswood House, Knowle Hospital, Fareham PO17 5NA — MB BChir 1985 Camb.; MRCP (UK) 1988; MRCPSych 1992. (Addenbrooke's Hosp. Camb.)

LOWENSON, Lisa Flora Carole 7 Newhall Avenue, Broughton Park, Salford M7 4JY — MB BS 1975 Lond.; MRCGP 1985; DRCOG 1983; DCH Eng. 1979. (Guy's)

LOWENTHAL, Leslie Mark Downland Practice, East Lane, Chieveley, Newbury RG20 8UY Tel: 01635 248251 Fax: 01635 247261; The Lodge, Curridge Road, Curridge, Newbury RG18 9DL Tel: 01635 202056 — MB BS 1980 Lond.; MRCP (UK) 1983; MRCGP 1988; DRCOG 1988.

LOWER, Mr Adrian Michael Centre of Reproduction Medicine, Barts & The London NHS Trust, 2nd Floor, King George V Wing, St Bartholomew's Hospital, London EC1A 7BE Tel: 020 7601 7175 Fax: 020 7601 7037 Email: adrian@lowe.com; 136 Harley Street, London W1G 7JZ Tel: 020 7486 2440 Fax: 020 7487 4488 Email: adrian@lower.com — BM BS 1983 Nottm.; BMedSc 1981; MRCOG 1990. Cons. Gyn. & Reproductive Med. Bart's and the Lond. NHS Trust Lond.; Med. Dir. Isis Fertil. Care The Oaks Hosp. Colchester. Socs: Fell. Roy. Soc. Med.; BFS; BSGE.

LOWER, Alan Douglas (retired) 5 Beech Rise, Bury St Edmunds IP33 2QE Tel: 01284 764672 — BM BCh Oxf. 1957; MA Oxf. 1957; DObst RCOG 1959. Prev: Ho. Off. (Radiother.) Middlx. Hosp.

LOWER, Barbara Mary Leyfield Surgery, 2 Eckington Road, Staveley, Chesterfield S43 3XZ Tel: 01246 473321 Fax: 01246 477303 — MB ChB 1978 Sheff.; MB ChB Sheffield 1978; DRCOG 1981. (Sheffield)

LOWER, Edmund Stanley Tobermory, 81 Acreman St., Sherborne DT9 3PH Tel: 01426 310493 — MRCS Eng. LRCP Lond. 1944; MRCPsych 1971; DPM Durham. 1958. (Lond. Hosp.) Cons. Psychiat. Sherborne. Socs: Fell. Roy. Soc. Med. Prev: Cons. Psychiat. S. W.. RHA; Psychiat. & Dep. Phys. Supt. Coldharbour Hosp. Sherborne; Asst. Psychiat. Aycliffe Hosp. Darlington.

LOWER, Malcolm John (retired) 10 Coventry Road, Bulkington, Nuneaton CV12 9ND Tel: 01203 313277 — MB ChB 1944 Birm. Prev: Res. Anaesth. Birm. United Hosps.

LOWERSON, Brian Benefits Agency Medical Service, Arden House, Regent Centry, Gosforth, Newcastle upon Tyne NE3 3JN; 5 Serpentine Gardens, Hartlepool TS26 0HQ — MB BS 1963 Durh. Med. Adviser Benefits Agency Med. Servs. Prev: Dir. Contracting & Plann. Hartlepool & N. Tees HAs; Med. Off. Dept. Health & Social Security; Med. Off. (Surg.) RAMC.

LOWERY, Samantha Dee 11 Sapperton Close, Kingswood, Hull HU7 3EA — MB ChB 1997 Liverp.

LOWERY-LEIGH, Gillian 26 Woodlands Park Drive, Axwell Park, Blaydon-on-Tyne NE21 5PQ — MB BS 1985 Newc.

LOWES, Anne Judith Old Farm Surgery, 67 Foxhole Road, Paignton TQ3 3TB Tel: 01803 556403 Fax: 01803 665588 — MB BS 1980 Lond.; MA Camb. 1980; MRCP (UK) 1984; MRCGP 1986. (King's Coll. Hosp.) GP Princip. Prev: GP Birm.; GP Retainer Scheme Birm.; Trainee GP Thamesmead Lond.

LOWES, John Andrew The Public Health Laboratory, Southampton General Hospital, Tremona Road, Southampton SO16 6YD Tel: 02380 796874 Fax: 02380 702530 — MB BS 1974 Lond.; BSc (Hons.) Lond. 1971, MB BS 1974; MRCP (UK) 1977; FRCPath 1994, M 1981. Dir. PHLS Laborat. Soton.; Hon. Cons. Microbiol. Soton. & SW Hants. HA. Prev: Lect. (Med. Microbiol.) St. Bart. Hosp. Lond.

LOWES, John Jordan Gilbert House, 39 Woodfields Lane, Ashtead KT21 2BT Tel: 01372 276385 Fax: 01372 360117; 3 Mickleham Hall, Mickleham, Dorking RH5 6DL Tel: 01372 373106 — MB BChir 1983 Camb.; MRCGP 1990; DRCOG 1990. Hosp. Pract. (Endoscopy) Epsom Hosp. Prev: Regist. W.m. Hosp. Lond.; Regist. Roy. Surrey Hosp. Guildford; SHO St. Bart. Hosp. Lond.

LOWES, John Robert Gastroenterology Unit, Torbay Hospital, Lawes Bridge, Torquay TQ2 7AA Email: john.lowes@virgin.net; The Old House, Compton, Paignton TQ3 1TD Tel: 01803 873929 Email: john.lowes@virgin.net — MD 1993 Camb.; MA Camb. 1980, MB 1981, BChir 1980; FRCP 1998. (Cambridge and King's) Cons. Phys. S. Devon Healthcare Torquay; Hon. Sen. Lect. Plymouth Postgrad. Med. Sch. Socs: Med. Res. Soc. & Brit. Soc. Gastroenterol.; Brit. Assn. Paren. & Ente. Nutrit. Prev: Sen. Regist. (Gen. Med. & Gastroenterol.) W. Midl. RHA; Research Fell. (Gastroenterol.) John Radcliffe Hosp. Oxf.; Regist. (Gastroenterol. & Gen. Med.) Middlx. Hosp. Lond.

LOWES, Marie Elizabeth Maldwyn Post Office, Lon Ganol, Llandegfan, Menai Bridge LL59 5UA — MB ChB 1998 Liverp.; MB ChB Liverp 1998.

LOWES, Suzanne Catherine 2 Loweswood Close, Newcastle upon Tyne NE7 7DD — MB ChB 1998 Sheff.; MB ChB Sheff 1998.

LOWES, Timothy, Capt. RAMC Anaesthetic Department Park Hospital, Portsmouth Road, Frimley, Camberley GU16 7UJ Tel: 01276 604604; 13 Grange Close, Winchester SO23 9RS Tel: 01962 870114 — MB BS 1993 Newc. SHO (Anaesth.) Frimley Pk. Hosp. Socs: BMA. Prev: Regtl. Med. Off. Hants.; SHO (A & E) N. Tees Gen. Hosp.; Ho. Off. (Orthop. & Gen. Surg.) Camb. Milit. Hosp.

LOWETH, Sheila Margaret The Elms Medical Practice, 5 Stewart Road, Harpenden AL5 4QA Tel: 01582 769393 Fax: 01582461735 — MB ChB 1973 Manch.; MRCGP 1978.

LOWICK, Sarah Jane 10 Abbey Gardens, St. John's Wood, London NW8 9AT — MB BCh 1991 Witwatersrand.

LOWINGS, Elizabeth Ann Great Halls, Aylesbeare, Exeter EX5 2BY Tel: 01395 32034 — MB ChB 1972 Bristol; DA Eng. 1977. Asst. Dep. Coroner Exeter & E. Devon Dist. Socs: Fac. Anaesth. & Assn. Anaesth.; Law Soc. Prev: Trainee Solicitor (Med. Litigation) Exeter; Clin. Asst. & SHO (Anaesth.) Roy. Devon & Exeter Hosp. Exeter; Specialist Anaesth. Abu Dhabi Defence Force Milit. Hosp. Abu Dhabi, UAE.

LOWIS, Stephen Paul Department of Oncology, Bristol Royal Hospital for Sick Children, St Michael's Hill, Bristol Tel: 0117 928 5521 Fax: 0117 928 5682 Email: s.p.lowis@bristol.ac.uk — BM BCh 1985 Oxf.; PhD Newc. 1996; BA (Hons.) Oxf. 1982; MRCP (UK) 1989. (Oxf.) Macmillan Cons. (Paediat. & Adolecent Oncol.) Bristol Childr.s' Hosp. Prev: Sen. Regist. (Paediat. Oncol.) Bristol Childr.'s Hosp.; Research Fell. (Child Health) Univ. Newc.

LOWIT, Ian Michael (retired) 72 Burns Road, Aberdeen AB15 4NS Tel: 01224 316805 — MB ChB 1953 Aberd.; FRCP Ed. 1994; MRCP Ed. 1959; FRCPsych 1980, M 1971; DPM Eng. 1957. Prev: Cons. Child Psychiat. Roy. Aberd. Childr. Hosp.

LOWLES, Ian Edward, Squadron Ldr. RAF Med. Br. Retd. Borders General Hosp NHS Trust, Melrose TD6 9BS Tel: 01896826000; Morven, Ormiston Terrace, Melrose TD6 9SW Tel: 01896 822797 Fax: 01896 823077 Email: lowes@compuserve.com — MB ChB 1973 Glas.; FRCOG 1992, M 1980. (Glasgow) Sen. Cons. (O. & G.) Borders Gen. Hosp., Huntlyburn, Melrose; Non-Exec. Mem. NHS Borden.; Chairm. Area Med. Comm.; Chairm. Area Clin. Forum. Socs: Ed. Obst. Soc. Counc. 91-94; E. Anglia Obst. & Gyn. Soc.; BSCCP. Prev: Cons. O & G RAF Med. Br.; Hon. Cons. Addenbrooke's Hosp. Camb.; Hon. Lect. & Sen. Regist. Camb. Univ. Clin. Sch.

LOWLES, Jennifer Margaret Leader Medical Group, 1 Factors Park, Lauder TD2 6QW Tel: 01578 718670 Fax: 01578 718744; Morven, Ormiston Terrace, Melrose TD6 9SW Tel: 01896 822797 — MB ChB 1972 St. And.; DCH Eng. 1975; DObst RCOG 1974. (Univ. St. And.) Prev: SHO (Paediat. Med.) Dundee Roy. Infirm.; SHO (Paediat. Surg.) Roy. Hosp. Sick Childr. Glas.

LOWMAN, Andrea Jane 20 Castle High, Haverfordwest SA61 2SP Tel: 01437 767126 — MB ChB 1995 Sheff. SHO (Gen. Med. & Cardiol.) P.ss of Wales Hosp Bridgend. Prev: SHO (Neurol.) Univ. Hosp. Wales; SHO (Respirat. Med.) Llandough Hosp. Cardiff; Ho. Off. (Gen. Med., Surg. & Orthop.) N.. Gen. Hosp. Sheff.

LOWMAN, Ann Catherine Alresford Surgery, Station Road, Alresford SO24 9JL Tel: 01962 732345 Fax: 01962 736034 — BM 1987 Soton.; DRCOG 1991.

LOWN, Kenneth Robert (retired) 14 The Ridings, Cliftonville, Margate CT9 3EJ — MB BS Lond. 1952; MRCS Eng. LRCP Lond. 1952; MRCGP 1964. Prev: Clin. Asst. (Ophth.) Margate & Canterbury Hosp.

LOWNDES, Katharine Elizabeth Malthouse Farm, Braishfield, Romsey SO51 0PT — MB BS 1996 Lond.

LOWNDES, Sarah Ann Malthouse Farm, Eldon Lane, Braishfield, Romsey SO51 0PT — BM BCh 1998 Oxf.; BM BCh Oxf 1998.

LOWREY, Gillian Elizabeth Hawkbarrow Farm, Gosforth, Seascale CA20 1ER — MB BS 1997 Lond.

LOWREY, Sophie 20 Wallgrave Road, London SW5 0RF — BM BS 1997 Nottm.

LOWREY, Susan Hanham Surgery, 33 Whittucks Road, Hanham, Bristol BS15 3HY Tel: 0117 967 5201 Fax: 0117 947 7749 — BM 1987 Soton.; BA (Hons) Newc. 1980; MRCGP 1992; DGM RCP Lond. 1990.

LOWRIE, Angela 4 Victoria Court, Woodplumpton Lane, Brougton, Preston PR3 5EQ — BM BS 1977 Nottm.; FFA RCS Eng. 1982. Cons. Anaesth. Roy. Preston Hosp.

LOWRIE, Mr Iain Gordon Blackburn Royal Infirmary, Bolton Road, Blackburn BB2 3LR Tel: 01254 263555 — MB ChB 1976 Manch.; FRCS Ed. 1981. Cons. Orthop. Surg. Blackburn, Hyndburn & Ribble Valley HA.

LOWRIE, Michael John Shaun Elms Medical Centre, 31 Hoole Road, Chester CH2 3NH Tel: 01244 351000 — MB ChB 1983 Birm.; MRCGP 1987.

LOWRY, Barbara Elizabeth Choach House, Tween Walls Lane, Mangrove Bay, Sandys, Bermuda; 8 Killaire Avenue, Bangor BT19 1EW — MB BCh BAO 1967 Belf.; Dip. Ven. Soc. Apoth. Lond. 1987. (Belf.) Prev: Fell. (Pediat.) Maine Med. Center, Portland, U.S.A.

LOWRY, Charles Gibson Bellaghy, Magherafelt BT45 8 — MB BCh BAO 1945 Belf. (Qu. Univ. Belf.)

LOWRY, Cheryl Ruth 1 Perry Road, Bangor BT19 6UA — MB BCh BAO 1995 Belf.

LOWRY, Darrell William Craigavon Area Hospital, 68 Lurgan Road, Portadown, Craigavon BT63 5QQ Tel: 028 3861 2307 Email: d.lowry@cahgt.n-i.nhs.uk — MB BCh BAO 1990 Belf.; FFA RCSI 1995. (Belf.) Cons. (Anaesth.) Craigavon Area Hosp. Portadown. Prev: Specialist Regist. (Anaesth.) Roy. Gp. of Hosps. Trust, Belf.; Clin. Research Fell. (Anaesth.) Qu.s Univ., Belf.

LOWRY, David Sterling 5 Ridgeway Park Sth., Portadown, Craigavon BT62 3DQ — MB BCh BAO 1968 Belf.; FRCOG 1989, M 1973, DObst 1970. Cons. (O & G) Craigavon Area Hosp.

LOWRY, Diana Margaret High Street Surgery, 301 High Street, Epping CM16 4DA Tel: 01992 572012 Fax: 01992 572956; 12 Bury Road, Epping CM16 5EU Tel: 01992 560191 — MB BS 1978 Lond.; MRCGP 1982; DRCOG 1981. (Middlx.)

LOWRY, John Ballymena Health Centre, Cushendall Road, Ballymena BT43 6HQ Tel: 028256 42181 — MB BCh BAO 1952 Belf. (Belf.)

LOWRY, Mr John Christopher Royal Bolton Hospital, Minerva Road, Farnworth, Bolton BL4 0JR Tel: 01204 390937 Fax: 01204 390937; The Valley House, 50 Ravenswood, Bolton BL1 5TL Tel: 01204 848815 Fax: 01204 845821 — MB ChB Manch. 1970; BDS Manch. 1963; FRCS Ed. 1985; MRCS Eng. LRCP Lond. 1970; FDS RCS Eng. 1968, LDS 1964; T(S) 1991; FDSRCS(Edin.) 1999 AD HOMINEM. (Manch.) Cons. Maxillofacial & Oral Surg. Bolton, Blackburn, Burnley & Bury HAs; Lect. (Cell & Structural Biol.) Univ. Manch.; Clin. Dir. Gen. Surg; Examr. RCS Eng. & Edin.; Mem. Edit. Bd. Jl. Cranio-Maxillofacial Surg. Socs: Pres Brit. Assn. Oral & Maxillofacial Surg.; Dean Fac. Dent. Surg. RCS/ Eng.; Eur. Assn. Craniofacial Surg. (Sec. Gen. & Mem.Exec. Comm.). Prev: Sen. Regist. (Oral & Maxillofacial Surg.) Manch. HA; Leverhulme Trav. Fell.; SHO (Orthop. & Plastic Surg.) Univ. Hosp. S. Manch.

LOWRY, Mr John Henry Escale, Cahard, Ballynahinch — MB BCh BAO 1954 Belf.; FRCS Ed. 1959. Cons. Orthop. Surg. Roy. Vict. Hosp. Belf. & Musgrave Pk. Hosp. Belf.

LOWRY, John Patrick Stuart Radiology Dept, Belfast City Hospital Tower Block, Lisbon Road, Belfast BT9 7AB Tel: 01232 647952 Email: paddy.lowry@virgin.net; 56 Hampton Park, Belfast BT7 3JP Tel: 02890 647952 — MB BCh BAO 1985 Belf.; FRCR 1992. Cons. Radiol.Belf. city hosp.

LOWRY, Joseph, OBE Eden Crest, Markethill, Armagh — MB BCh BAO 1945 Belf.; FRCPI 1966, M 1955; FCPath 1969, M 1964. (Qu. Univ. Belf.) Cons. Clin. Pathol. Craigavon Area Hosp. Prev: Pathol. Colon. Med. Serv. Kenya; Princip. Regist. Clin. Path. Roy. Vict. Hosp. Belf.

***LOWRY, Karen Jane** 1 Perry Road, Bangor BT19 6UA Tel: 01247 460242 — MB ChB 1997 Dundee.

LOWRY, Katherine Anna 16 Slievemoyne Park, Belfast BT15 5GZ — MB BCh BAO 1997 Belf.

LOWRY, Kenneth Gilmour Regional Intensive Care Unit, Royal Hospitals Trust, Grosvonor Road, Belfast BT12 6BA Tel: 02890 894730 Fax: 02890 236167 — MB ChB 1978 Manch.; FFA RCSI 1982; MMed Sc 1990 Belfast. Cons. in Intens. Care, Roy. Hosp.s Belf. Socs: BMA; Intens. Care Soc. of Irel. Prev: Cons. Anaesth. Altngolvin Hosp. Lond.derry; Sen. Regist. (Anaesth.) Roy. Vict. Hosp. Belf.; Sen. Regist. Craigavon Area Hosp.

LOWRY, Lisa Mary 18/4 Livingstone Place, Edinburgh EH9 1PD — MB ChB 1998 Ed.; MB ChB Ed 1998.

LOWRY, Matthew Teev Cottage, Dunclug, Ballymena Tel: 01266 6184 — MB BCh BAO 1952 Belf.

LOWRY, Michael Frank Department of Paediatrics, Sunderland Royal Hospital, Sunderland SR4 7TP Tel: 0191 565 6256 Fax: 0191 569 9219 Email: m.f.lowry@ncl.ac.uk; 28 Thornhill Terrace, Sunderland SR2 7JL Tel: 0191 565 6006 Fax: 0191 569 9219 — MB ChB 1962 Birm.; FRCP Lond. 1984; MRCP (UK) 1970; FRCPCH 1997; DCH RCPS Dub. 1964. Cons. (Paediat.) Sunderland Dist. Gen. Hosp.; Assoc. Clin. Lect. Univ. Newc. Prev: Sen. Lect. Dept. Child Health Univ. W. Indies Jamaica; Research Fell. Case W.. Reserve.

LOWRY, Patricia Jane Alexandra Hospital, Woodrow Drive, Redditch B98 7UB; Bramble Cottage, Beoley Court, Beoley, Redditch B98 9AL — MD 1984 Birm.; MB ChB 1976; FRCP 1995; MRCP (UK) 1979. Cons. Phys. i/c Cardiol. Redditch Worcs.

LOWRY, Paul Patrick (retired) Springfield Road Surgery, 66-70 Springfield Road, Belfast BT12 7AH Tel: 028 9032 3571 Fax: 028 9020 7707 — MB BCh BAO 1966 Belf.; DObst RCOG 1968.

LOWRY, Raymond James 35 King Edward Road, Tynemouth, North Shields NE30 2RW Tel: 0191 258 6333 — MB ChB 1982 Leic.; BDS Birm. 1972; MFPHM RCP (UK) 1988; DRCOG 1984. Cons. Pub. Health Med. Newc. & N. Tyneside HA; Sen. Lect. (Dent. Pub. Health) Univ. Newc. on Tyne. Socs: BMA; Brit. Dent. Assn. Prev: Sen. Regist. (Community Med.) N.. RHA; Regist. (Community Med.) Leic. HA; SHO (Community Med.) Leic. HA.

LOWRY, Roger Clark Milecross House, Belfast Road, Newtownards BT23 4TR Tel: 028 3284 Email: roger.lowry@btinternet.com — MB BCh BAO 1963 Belf.; FRCP Lond. 1981, M 1968. (Belf.) Cons. Phys. Belf. City Hosp. Socs: BMA & Brit. Thoracic Soc. Prev: Assoc. Prof. Div. Pulm. Med. Univ. Tennessee, USA.

LOWRY, Simon Charles 142 Eastern Way, Darras Hall, Ponteland, Newcastle upon Tyne NE20 9RH — BChir 1995 Camb.

LOWRY, Stella Russell New Sheepmarket Surgery, Ryhall Road, Stamford PE9 1YA; 3 The Paddocks, Carlby, Stamford PE9 4NH — MB ChB 1985 Birm.; BSc Birm. 1982. GP, Stamford. Prev: GP Trainee PeterBoro. VTS; Asst. Sec. BMA; Asst. Edr. BMJ.

LOWRY, Thomas Gilliland (retired) 4 Croft Road, Auchterarder PH3 1EW Tel: 01764 64095 — MB BCh BAO 1945 Belf.

LOWRY, Walter Magilton (retired) 22 Egerton Road, Hartlepool TS26 0BW Tel: 01429 273910 — MB BCh BAO Belf. 1945. Prev: Ho. Surg. & Phys. Roy. Vict. Hosp. Belf.

LOWRY, William Shields Lowry, Bonn and Desai, Cairn Valley Medical Practice, Kirkgate, Dunscore, Dumfries DG2 0UQ Tel: 01387 820266 Fax: 01387 820562 — MB BCh BAO 1986 Belf.; MRCGP 1991; DRCOG 1990; DCH RCPSI 1989.

LOWSON, Keith Ash Trees Surgery, Market Street, Carnforth LA5 9JU Tel: 01524 720000 Fax: 01524 720110 — MB BS 1966 Durh. (Newc.) Prev: Ho. Off. (Child Health) & (Surg.) Roy. Vict. Infirm. Newc.

LOWSON, Tara Amelia 12 Lodge Court, The Nook, Staining, Blackpool FY3 0EH — MB ChB 1993 Manch.

LOWTHER, Clifton Paget (retired) 15 Lennox Street, Edinburgh EH4 1QB Tel: 0131 332 2854 — MB ChB 1946 Glas.; FRCP Glas. 1968; FRCP Ed. 1968, M 1958; FRFPS Glas. 1951. Prev: Cons. Phys. Gen. Med. c/o the Elderly.

LOWTHER, David James 21 Cranmore Avenue, Belfast BT9 6JH — MB BCh BAO 1970 Belf.

LOWTHER, Johanna Jean Herbert Kippax Health Centre, Gibson Lane, Kippax, Leeds LS25 7JN Tel: 0113 287 0870 — MB BS 1989 Newc.; MA Cambridge 1990; MRCGP 1994; DFFP 1993; DA (UK) 1992; 1997 Dip. Health Care Ethics. (MBBS Newcastle) Princip. in Gen. Pract.

LOWTHER, John (retired) Salvation Army IHQ, 101 Queen Victoria St., London EC4P 4EP Tel: 020 7236 5222 Fax: 020 7236 4153 — MB BCh 1958 Wales; MRCPsych 1972; DPM Eng. 1966. Cons. Psychiat. & Med. Off. Salvation Army Internat. HQs. Lond. Prev: Cons. Psychiat. Gwent Area HA.

LOWY, Adam Gulliver Jack 47 Springfield Road, Leicester LE2 3BB — MB ChB 1983 Leic.

LOWY, Professor Clara Endocrine & Diabetic Day Centre, St Thomas Hospital, London SE1 7EH Tel: 020 7928 9292 Fax: 020 7922 8289; 44A Rosemont Road, Acton, London W3 9LY Tel: 020 8992 2404 Email: c.lowy@rcl.ac.uk — MB BS 1958 Lond.; MSc Lond. 1972, MD 1995; FRCP Lond. 1977, M 1961. (Middlx.) Reader UMDS, St. Thos. Campus; Hon. Cons. Phys. St. Thos. Hosp.; Prof. Guy's kings & St Thoma's Sch. of med. Socs: Fell. Roy. Soc. Med.; Brit. Diabetic Assn. (Progr. Ex-Sec. Endocrine Sect., Ex-Hon. Sec. Scientif. Sect.); Assn. Phys. Prev: Regist. Hammersmith Hosp. Lond.; Ho. Phys. Middlx. Hosp. & Brompton Hosp. Lond.

LOWY, Mr Martin (retired) 44A Rosemont Road, London W3 9LY Tel: 020 8992 2404 Fax: 020 8992 3031 — MB BS 1958 Lond.; FRCS Eng. 1963. Prev: Cons. Orthop. Surg. Whittington Hosp. Lond.

LOXDALE, Hector Alasdair Robert (retired) Applegarth, 52 Glynderi, Carmarthen SA31 2EX Tel: 01267 234185 — MRCS Eng. LRCP Lond. 1946; DObst RCOG 1951. Prev: SCM E. Dyfed HA.

LOXDALE, Hilary Kathleen Ross (retired) Applegarth, 52 Glynderi, Carmarthen SA31 2EX Tel: 01267 234185 — BM BCh 1952 Oxf.; BA, BM BCh Oxf. 1952; MRCOphth 1989; DObst RCOG 1955; DO Eng. 1956. Prev: Assoc. Specialist Ophth. Dept. Withybush Hosp. HaverfordW. & W. Wales Gen. Hosp. Carmarthen.

LOXDALE, Mr Patrick Henry Level 11, derriford Hospital, Plymouth PL8 8DH Tel: 01752 763787; Wollaton House, Brixton, Plymouth PL8 2DL — MB BS 1984 Lond.; FRCS Orth 1997; FRCS Eng. 1990. Cons. Orthop. Surg. Derriford Plymouth. Prev: Fost Fell., S.mead Hosp. Bristol; Regist. (Orthop.) Nuffield Orthop. Centre Oxf.

LOXDALE, Susan Jane, Surg. Lt.-Cdr. RN RNH Haslar, Gosport PO12 2AA Fax: 01705 584255; Wollaton House, Brixton, Plymouth PL8 2DL — MB BS 1989 Lond.; DA (UK) 1994. Regist. (Anaesth.) Roy. Naval Hosp. Haslar. Prev: Regist. & SHO (Anaesth.) Roy. Naval Hosp. Haslar; SHO (Anaesth.) Roy. Naval Hosp. Plymouth.

LOXLEY, Christopher Giles William Church Langley Medical Practice, Church Langley CM17 9TG Email: chris.loxtey@doctors.org.uk; The Old Bell, Bell Lane, Nuthampstead, Royston SG8 8ND Tel: 01763 848476 — MB BChir 1982 Camb.; MA Camb. 1982; T(GP) 1991; Cert. Av. Med. 1996. Prev: Civil. Med. Practit. RAF Wyton & Brampton; GP Herts.; Regist. Rotat. (Anaesth.) St. Geo. Hosp. Lond.

LOXTON, Jane Elizabeth Sunnyside Doctors Surgery, 150 Fratton Road, Portsmouth PO1 5DH Tel: 023 9282 4725 Fax: 023 9286 1014 — MB ChB 1980 Manch.

LOXTON, Michael John (retired) Packers Surgery, Christchurch Road, Virginia Water GU25 4RL Tel: 01344 842951 Fax: 01344 845121 — MB BS 1958 Lond.

LOXTON, Paul Maxwell Packers Surgery, Christchurch Road, Virginia Water GU25 4RL — MB BS 1977 Lond.; MRCGP 1986; DCH RCP Lond. 1980.

LOYDEN, Christopher Francis West Wales General Hospital, Carmarthen SA31 2AF Tel: 01267 235151 — MB ChB 1977 Aberd.; FFA RCS Eng. 1984; DA Lond. 1981; DTM & H Liverp. 1979. Cons. Anaesth. W. Wales Gen. Hosp. Carmarthen. Prev: Dir. Anaesth. Chorley & S. Ribble NHS Trust.

LOYN, William George Grenville, ERD, TD, OStJ (retired) Llechwedd, 58 Maeshendre, Wallnfawr, Aberystwyth SY23 3PS Tel: 01970 623090 — MB BS Lond. 1947; FFA RCS Eng. 1954; DA Eng. 1949. Prev: Cons. Anaesth. Bronglais Hosp. Aberystwyth & Whittington Hosp. Lond.

LOYNDS, Peter Allen Loch-na-Beich House, North Connel, Oban PA37 1QX — MB ChB 1959 Ed.

LOYNES, Mr Robert David Stafford General Hospital, Weston Road, Stafford ST16 3SA Tel: 01785 257731 Fax: 01785 230290 Email: robert.loynes@virgin.net; Congreve House, Walton-on-the-Hill, Stafford ST17 0LN Tel: 01785 664300 Fax: 01785 660922 Email: robert.loynes@virgin.net — MB ChB 1966 Liverp.; MChOrth 1974; FRCS Eng. 1972. (Liverp.) Cons. Orthop. Surg. Staffs. Dist. Gen. Hosp. Socs: Fell. Brit. Orthop. Assn.; Brit. Soc. Surg. Hand. Prev: Sen. Regist. (Orthop.) Liverp. AHA (T).

LOYNES, Rosalie Peta Congreve House, Walton-on-the-Hill, Stafford ST17 0LN Tel: 01785 64300 — MB ChB 1967 Liverp.; FRCR 1975; FFR 1974; DMRD Liverp. 1970. (Liverp.) Cons. Radiol. Roy. Hosp. Wolverhampton. Prev: Cons. Radiol. BRd.green Hosp. Liverp.

LOZEWICZ, Stefan 2B Oakhill Avenue, Hampstead, London NW3 7RE — MB BS Lond. 1977; MD Lond. 1983; FRCP Lond. 1996; MRCP (UK) 1979. Cons. Phys. (Gen. & Respirat. Med.) N. Middlx. & St. Bart. Hosps. Lond.

LOZSADI, Dora Alexandra Gloucestershire Royal Hospital, Great Western Road, Gloucester GL1 3NN Tel: 01452 528555 — LMSSA 1997; LMSSA Lond. 1997; DPhil 1994; MD Semmelweis, Hungary. (Univ. of Oxford) SHO (Med. Rotat.), Gloucestershire Roy. Hosp. Socs: BMA.

LU, John Chen Yui Flat 3/1, 60 Ashley St., Glasgow G3 6HW — MB ChB 1995 Dundee.

LU, Vivien Rennie (retired) 39D Sans Souci Park, Malone Road, Belfast BT9 5BZ Tel: 01232 289881 — MB BCh BAO Belf. 1950. Prev: Assoc. Specialist S. Tyrone Hosp. Dungannon in Radiol.

LUA, Suet Hong Bedford Hospital NHS Trust, South Wing, Kempston Road, Bedford MK42 9DJ; St Davids Flat, Lough Rd, London N7 8RH — MB BS 1986 Newc.; DA (UK) 1991; FFARCSI 1996.

LUA, Yu Chai 19 The Crescent, Belfast BT10 0GJ — MB BCh 1998 Belf.; MB BCh Belf 1998.

LUBBEN-DINKELAAR, Maria Magdalena 77 Field Lane, York YO10 5JL Tel: 01904 411284 — Artsexamen 1972 Leiden; MPH Leeds 1990.

LUBEGA, Stephanie Louise 98A Furness Road, London NW10 5UE — MB ChB 1996 Ed.

LUBEL, David Daniel 66 Waxwell Lane, Pinner HA5 3EU Email: lubel@dial.pipex.com — MB BS 1983 Lond.; MRCP (UK) 1986; FRCP Lond. 1998. (Guy's) Cons. Phys. N.wick Pk. Hosp. Lond. Socs: Hon. Sec. Brit. Geriat.s Soc. Prev: Sen. Regist. (Geriat. Med) N.wick Pk. Hosp. Lond.; Regist. (Med.) St. Thos. Hosp. Lond.; SHO (Nephrol.) St. Thos. Hosp. Lond.

LUBEL, John Samuel 595 London Road, Westcliff on Sea SS0 9PQ Email: johnlubel@hotmail.com — MB BS 1996 Lond.; BDS Lond. 1988; FDS RCS 1992. Socs: MPS.

LUBERT, Sidney (retired) 4 Little Rowsham, 94 South Hill Avenue, Harrow-on-the-Hill, Harrow HA1 3NX Tel: 020 8423 7420 — MRCS Eng. LRCP Lond. 1951; FRCOG 1972, M 1959. Examr. Centr. Midw. Bd. & RCOG. Prev: Cons. O & G Bournemouth & E. Dorset Hosp. Gp.

LUBIN, Jonathan Richard Derwent Crescent Surgery, 20 Derwent Crescent, Whetstone, London N20 0QQ Tel: 020 8446 0171 Fax: 020 8446 0073; 26 Windermere Avenue, London N3 3QY Tel: 020 8343 2047 — MB BS 1980 Lond.; MB BS London 1980; MRCP (UK) 1983; MRCGP 1987; Dip Occupat Med 1997. Occupat. Health Adviser Barnet Coll. & Garden Hosp.; Clin. Tutor (Gen. Pract.) Roy. Free Hosp.; Mem. Barnet LMC; Bd. Mem. N. Barnet PCG. Socs: Soc. Occupat. Med.; Primary Care Gastroenterol. Soc. Prev: Regist. (Med.) Dept. Gastroenterol. Char. Cross Hosp Lond. & W. Middlx. Hosp.

LUBMAN, Daniel Ian 12 Primrose Road, Liverpool L18 2HE — MB ChB 1992 Manch.; BSc Physiol. (Hons.) Manch. 1989, MB ChB 1992.

LUBOMIRSKA, Krystyna Maria (retired) Trees, 8 Chestnut Walk, Woodford Green IG8 0TE Tel: 020 8504 4272 — MRCS Eng. LRCP Lond. 1951; FFA RCS Eng. 1962; DA Eng. 1956. Prev: Cons. Anaesth. Newham Health Dist. & St. Clement's Hosp. (Lond. Hosp.).

LUBRANO DI SCORPANIELLO, Ennio Rheumatology & Rehabilitation Research Unit, University of Leeds, 36 Clarendon Road, Leeds LS2 9NZ — State Exam 1989 Naples.

LUCAROTTI, Michele Elizabeth Gloucester Royal Hospital, Great Western Road, Gloucester GL1 3NN; Greenacres, Cheltenham Road, Painswick, Stroud GL6 6SJ — MB ChB 1979 Sheff.; MD Sheff. 1991; FRCS Eng. 1984. Cons. Gen. Surg. Glos. Roy. Hosp. Prev: Sen. Regist. (Gen. Surg.) SW RHA.

LUCAS, Alan 6 St Bernards Road, Oxford OX2 6EH — MB BChir 1972 Camb.; BA (1st cl. Hons.) Camb. 1968, MB 1972, Bchir 1971; MRCP (UK) 1976. (Oxf.) Lect. (Paediat.) Addenbrooke's Hosp. Camb.; Tutor (Med.) Gonville & Caius Coll. Camb. Socs: Paediat. Research Soc. Prev: Regist. (Paediat.) John Radcliffe Hosp. Oxf.; Regist. (Med.) United Camb. Hosps.; SHO (Neonat. Med.) John Radcliffe Hosp. Oxf.

LUCAS, Angela Mary 4 Longthorpe House Mews, South Bretton, Peterborough PE3 9TL Tel: 01733 264694 Fax: 01733 264694 Email: jlucas1958@aol.com — MB BS 1992 Newc. Staff Grade (A & E) PeterBoro. Dist. Hosp.

LUCAS, Arthur John Cockshoot House, Sheepscombe, Stroud GL6 7QT — MB ChB 1962 Birm.; BSc Bristol 1952; PhD Birm. 1957, MB ChB 1962; DObst RCOG 1967. Socs: BromsGr. Med. Soc. Prev: Sen. Research Fell. Dept. O & G Univ. Birm.; Ho. Surg. & Ho. Phys. Qu. Eliz. Hosp. Birm.

LUCAS, Barbara Anne Constance Canon Street Medical Centre, 122 Canon Street, Leicester LE4 6NL Tel: 0116 266 1247 — BM BS 1975 Nottm.; BMedSci Nottm. 1972, BM BS 1975.

LUCAS, Benjamin Brinham Mead House, Community Mental Health Resource Centre, Hayes End Road, Hayes UB4 8EW — MB BS 1987 Lond.; MA Camb. 1988, BA 1984; MRCPsych 1993. (Lond. Hosp. Med. Coll.) Cons. Psychiat. Prev: Clin. Research Fell. NW Lond. Ment. Health Trust.

LUCAS, Caroline Fiona 3 Brendon Drive, Esher KT10 9EQ — BM BCh 1975 Oxf.; BSc Lond. 1972; FRCP 1997; MRCP (UK) 1979; DMRT Eng. 1990; DCH Eng. 1978. (St Mary Hosp. Lond./Oxf.) Cons. Palliat. Med. Bournewood Community Trust & P.ss Alice Hospice Esher. Prev: Med. Off. (Radiotherap. & Oncol.) Roy. Marsden, W.m. Paediat. W.m.

LUCAS, Christina Mary 37 Western Gardens, Ealing, London W5 3RS Tel: 020 8993 9946 Email: christina_lucas@hotmail.com — MB BS 1982 Lond.; MRCGP 1991; MFHOM 1999. (Middlesex Hospital Medical School')

LUCAS, Christopher 1 Parkstone Avenue, Parkstone, Poole BH14 9LW Tel: 01202 738241 — BM 1995 Soton. SHO (Trauma & Orthop.) Treliske Hosp. Treuro Cornw. Prev: Anat. Demonst. Soton. Univ. Soton.

LUCAS, Christopher James (retired) 44 East Stockwell Street, Colchester CO1 1SR Tel: 01206 768211 — MB BS 1949 Lond.; FRCP Lond 1978, M 1953; FRCPsych 1978, M 1971; DPM Eng. 1957. Prev: Cons. Psychother. Portman Clinic Lond.

LUCAS, Christopher Richard 19 Amersham Court, Craneswater Park, Southsea PO4 0NX — MRCS Eng. LRCP Lond. 1962; MA, MB BChir Camb. 1963. (Camb. & Guy's) Med. Dir. Upjohn Scand. Socs: Assn. Med. Advisers Pharmaceut. Indust.; Brit. Assn. Pharmaceutical Phys. Prev: Head Med. Dept. Organon Laborat. U.K.

LUCAS, Cynthia 16 Cressy Road, Hampstead, London NW3 2LY Tel: 020 7267 0195 — MB BS Lond. 1959; MRCS Eng. LRCP Lond. 1959; FRCOG 1984, M 1964. (Roy. Free) Emerit. Cons. Univ. Coll. Lond. Hosps.; Cons. Gyn. Eliz. G. Anderson Hosp. Lond. Socs: Brit. Soc. Colpos. & Cerv. Path.; BMA. Prev: Cons. Gyn. Eliz. G. Anderson Hosp. Lond.; Cons. O & G & Hon. Lect. Univ. Zambia Sch. Med. Lusaka, Zambia; Regist. Mile End Hosp. Lond.

LUCAS, David Roy (retired) Port House, 20 Watling Lane, Dorchester-on-Thames, Wallingford OX10 7JG Tel: 01865 340422 — MB BS Lond. 1944; MD Lond. 1952; FRCPath 1966, M 1963. Prev: Hon. Cons. Ophth. Path. Manch. HA.

LUCAS, Deirdre Joan Nuffield Hearing & Speech Centre, Royal National Throat, Nose & Ear Hospital, Grays Inn Road, London WC1X 8DA Tel: 020 7915 1568 Fax: 020 7915 1666 Email: deirdre.lucas@rfh.nthames.nhs.uk — MB BS 1972 Lond.; MRCP (UK) 1977; FRCP 1998. (St. Bart.) Cons. Audiolog. Med. Roy. Nat. Throat, Nose & Ear Hosp. Lond.; Hon. Sen. Lect. Inst. Laryngol. & Otol. UCL. Prev: Sen. Regist. (Audiol. Med.) Roy. Nat. Throat Nose & Ear. Hosp. Lond.; Sen. Med. Off. N.ampton HA; Clin. Med. Off. (Child Health) Tower Hamlets HA.

LUCAS, Dominique Nuala 14A Dartmouth Park Avenue, London NW5 1JN — MB BS 1991 Lond.

LUCAS, Dorothy Jane 50 Houndean Rise, Lewes BN7 1EH — MB BS 1951 Lond.; MRCS Eng. LRCP Lond. 1951; DA Eng. 1954.

LUCAS, Erica Anne The Dutch Cottage, 125 Totteridge Lane, London N20 8NS Tel: 020 8445 2499 — MB BS 1965 Lond.; MRCS Eng. LRCP Lond. 1965; DO Eng. 1969. (Roy. Free) Clin. Asst. Moorfields Eye Hosp. Lond.

LUCAS, Guy Stuart Department of Haematology, Manchester Royal Infirmary, Oxford Road, Manchester M13 9WL Tel: 0161 276 4813 Fax: 0161 276 4814 Email: guy.lucas@man.ac.uk — MB ChB Birm. 1978; MA Camb. 1976, BA (1st cl. Hons. Maths.) 1972; MD Birm. 1987; FRCP Lond. 1996; MRCP (UK) 1981; MRCPath 1987. (Birm.) Cons. Haemat. Manch. Roy. Infirm.

LUCAS, Helen Mary Lambrook House, Silver St., East Lambrook, South Petherton TA13 5HW — MB BS 1992 Newc.

LUCAS, Jane Sarah Anne Child health G Floor, Southampton General Hospital, Tremona Road, Southampton SO16 6YD Tel: 02380 777222 — BM 1989 Soton.; MRCP 1994; DA.1993. (Soton) Specialist Regist. Resp. Paediat. Soton.

LUCAS, Jasmine Gladys Taunton & Somerset Hospital, Musgrove Park, Taunton TA1 5DA — MB BS 1969 Lond.; MRCS Eng. LRCP Lond. 1969; FFA RACS RCS 1987; FRCA. 1974. Cons. Anaesth. Taunton & Som. Hosp.

LUCAS, John Michael Cambridge Gardens Surgery, 18 Cambridge Gardens, London NW6 5AY Tel: 020 7624 1034 Fax: 020 7328 8193; 118 Harley Street, London W1N 1AG Tel: 020 7935 0365 Fax: 020 7328 8193 — MB BS 1964 Lond. (Lond. Hosp.) Socs: BMA. Prev: Ho. Phys. Lond. Hosp.

LUCAS, Mr Jonathan Delight Guy's and St Thomas' NHS Hospital Trust, Department of Orthopaedics, Guy's Hospital, St Thomas St., London SE1 Tel: 0207 953 5000 Fax: 0207 955 5000 Ext: 6203 — MB BS 1988 Lond.; 1998 FRCS Ortn. & Tr.; FRCS Eng. 1992. Cons.(Orthop. & Spine) Guy's & St. Thos. Hosp. Lond.

LUCAS, Judith Barbara Sherbourne Medicial Centre, 40 Oxford St., Leamington Spa CV32 4RA Tel: 01926 424736 Fax: 01926 470884; 66 Kenilworth Road, Coventry CV4 7AH Tel: 01203 410004 — MB ChB 1980 Leic.; DRCOG 1983. (Leicester)

LUCAS, Kathryn Bank House, 91 Market Place, South Cave, Brough HU15 2AS — MB ChB 1998 Sheff.; MB ChB Sheff 1998.

LUCAS, Leslie Ely Hunters Moon, Far Dene, Kirkburton, Huddersfield HD8 0QZ Tel: 01484 602775 — MB ChB Ed. 1929. (Ed.)

LUCAS, Mr Malcolm George Department of Urology, Morriston Hospital, Swansea SA6 6NL Tel: 01792 703116 Fax: 01792 796438 — MB ChB 1978 Sheff.; ChM Sheff. 1989; FRCS Eng. 1983. Cons. Urol. Morriston Hosp. Swansea. Prev: Sen. Regist. (Urol.) W.. Gen. Hosp. Edin.; Clin. Asst. (Neurourol.) Lodge Moor Hosp. Sheff.; Regist. (Surg.) John Radcliffe Hosp. Oxf.

LUCAS, Marlon Anthony, Wing Cdr. RAF Med. Br. Frimley Park Hospital NHS Trust/MDHU, Department of Anaesthetics, Camberley GU16 5UJ Tel: 01276 604604 Fax: 01276 61453; 31 Theobalds Way, Frimley, Camberley GU16 9RF — MB ChB 1982 Glas.; FRCA 1994; DA (UK) 1986. (Glas.) Cons. Anaesth. Frinmley Pk. Hosp. Surrey. Socs: Assn. Anaesth.; Triserv. Anaesth. Soc. Prev: Sen. Regist. & Hon. Lect. (Anaesth.) St. Mary's Hosp. Lond.; Sen. Specialist (Anaesth.) RAF Hosp. Wroughton.

LUCAS, Norman William Reginald (retired) Troed-yr-Allt, Dolgran Road, Pencader SA39 9BX Tel: 0155 934 384415 — MRCS Eng. LRCP Lond. 1941; LMSSA Lond. 1940.

LUCAS, Philip Andrew Newberry Centre, West Lane Hosp, Acklam Road, Middlesbrough Tel: 01642 352114 — MB ChB 1987 Leeds; MRCPsych 1992; MMedSci (Clin. Psychiat.) 1993. (Leeds) Cons. Adolesc. Psychiat. Newberry centre Middlesbrough,W.La. Hosp. Prev: Sen. Regist. (Child. Psychiat.) Yorks; Regist. (Psychiat.) Leeds; SHO (Psychiat.) Stanley Royd Wakefield.

LUCAS, Philip Anthony Maudsley Hospital, Denmark Hill, London SE5 8AZ — MB BS (Hons.) Lond. 1976; MD Lond. 1988; MRCP (UK) 1979; MRCPsych 1991; T(M) 1991.

LUCAS, Philippa Louise Mary Marysville Surgery, 27 Belle Vue Gardens, Shrewsbury SY3 7JQ Tel: 01743 244000; Berneray Cottage, Ford Heath, Shrewsbury SY5 9GB — MB ChB 1985 Birm.; MRCGP 1991; DCH Otago 1989; DObst Otago 1988; DA (UK) 1987. GP Retainer. Prev: Regist. (Paediat.) S.lands Hosp. Invercargill NZ; SHO (Paediat. & O & G) S.lands Hosp. Invercargill, NZ; SHO (Anaesth.) Roy. Shrewsbury Hosp.

LUCAS, Richard Arthur 28 Heathcote Road, Twickenham TW1 1RX Tel: 020 8891 3773 — MB BS 1967 Lond.; MB BS (Hons.) Lond. 1967; MRCP (U.K.) 1971; MRCS Eng. LRCP Lond. 1967. (St. Mary's) Med. Adviser Lilly Indust. Ltd. Prev: Regist. (Med.) Roy. Free Hosp. Lond.; Ho. Phys. Padd. Gen. Hosp. Lond.; Ho. Surg. Surgic. Unit St. Mary's Hosp. Lond.

LUCAS, Richard Michael Buckley Health Centre, Padeswood Road, Buckley CH7 2JL Tel: 01224 550555 Fax: 01224 545712 — MB BS 1975 Newc.; MRCGP 1979; DCH Eng. 1979; DRCOG 1977.

LUCAS, Richard Neil 63 Ossulton Way, London N2 0JY Tel: 020 8883 7714 Fax: 020 8883 7714 — MB BS Lond. 1967; MPhil (Psychiat.) Lond. 1973, BSc (Hons. Physiol.) 1963; MRCS Eng. LRCP Lond. 1967; FRCPsych 1987, M 1972; DPM Eng. 1971. Cons. Psychiat. St Ann's & N. Middlx. Hosps. Socs: Brit. Psychoanal. Soc. Prev: Sen. Regist. Bethlem Roy. & Maudsley Hosps.; Regist. (Psychol. Med.) Roy. Free Hosp. Lond.; Ho. Phys. Lond. Hosp.

LUCAS, Sebastian Brendan Department of Histopathology, UCL Medical School, University St., London WC1E 6JJ Tel: 020 7380 9770 Fax: 020 7387 3674; 5 Kelross Road, London N5 2QS Tel: 020 7226 7435 — BM BCh 1973 Oxf.; MA, BM BCh Oxf. 1973; FRCP Lond. 1992; MRCP (UK) 1975; FRCPath 1990, M 1978. Sen. Lect. (Histopath.) Univ. Coll. Lond. Med. Sch.

LUCAS, Shelagh Jean 18 Champneys Walk, Newnham, Cambridge CB3 9AW Tel: 01223 464316 — MB ChB 1949 Liverp. (Liverp.)

LUCAS, Sigurd Oliver Everest House Surgery, Everest Way, Hemel Hempstead HP2 4HY Tel: 01442 240422 Fax: 01442 235045; Bourne Cottage, Bourne End, Hemel Hempstead HP1 2RH Tel:

01442 871000 — MRCS Eng. LRCP Lond. 1973; MA Camb. 1966, MB BChir 1973; DCH Eng. 1976. (Univ. Coll. Hosp.)

LUCAS, Susan Ann 20 Ollerbarrow Road, Hale, Altrincham WA15 9PP Tel: 0161 941 1682 — MB ChB 1978 Birm.; MRCGP 1982; DRCOG 1981. (Birm.) Clin. Asst. (c/o Elderly) Manch. Roy. Infirm.

LUCAS, Violet McAndrew (retired) — MB ChB 1955 Aberd.; 1989 MCOphth 1989; 1968 DO Eng. 1968. Prev: Assoc. Specialist (Ophth.) Sutton Gen. Hosp.

LUCAS, Vivian Christopher Garden House Hospice, Gillison Close, Letchworth SG6 1QU Tel: 01462 679540; 4 Woolston Avenue, Letchworth SG6 2ED — MB ChB 1983 Leic.; MRCGP 1990; DRCOG 1989; DA (UK) 1986. Med. Dir. Garden Hse. Hospice Letchworth.; Hon. Cons. (Palliat. Med.) N. Herts. NHS Trust; E+N Herts. NHS Trust. Socs: Assn. Palliat. Med. Prev: Trainee GP Huntingdon VTS.

LUCASSEN, Anneke Margaretha Department of Clinical Genetics, Churchill Hospital, Headington, Oxford OX3 7LJ Tel: 01865 226062 Fax: 01865 226011 Email: anneke.lucassen@ndm.ox.ac.uk; 29 Essex Street, Oxford OX4 3AW Tel: 01865 246138 — MB BS 1986 Newc.; DPhil Oxf. 1994; BMedSci. Newc. 1985; MRCP (UK) 1989. (Newc. u.Tyne) Cons. (Clin. Genetics) (8 sessions). Prev: Clin. Lect. Nuffield Dept. Med. Oxf.; Locum Cons. (Clin. Genetics); Hon. Sen. Regist. (Clin. Genetics) John Radcliffe Hosp. Oxf.

LUCASSEN, Antoinette Elizabeth Aldegonde Oakwood Surgery, Church Street, Mansfield Woodhouse, Mansfield NG19 8BL Tel: 01623 633111 Fax: 01623 423480 — Artsexamen 1987 Nijmegen.

LUCE, Peter John 49 Beauval Road, Dulwich, London SE22 8UG — MB BS 1978 Lond.; MRCP (UK) 1980. Cons. Phys. (Geriat. & Thoracic Med.) Lewisham & N. S.wark HA.

LUCEY, James Vincent Institute of Psychiatry, De Crespigny Park, London SE5 8AF Tel: 020 7701 9044; 109 Monks Orchard Road, Beckenham BR3 3BJ — MB BCh BAO 1983 NUI; LRCPI & LM, LRCSI & LM BAO 1983; MRCPsych 1989; DCH NUI 1986. Lect. & Hon. Sen. Regist. Inst. Psychiat. Lond.; Wellcome Clin. Lect. Socs: Brit. Assn. Psychopharmacol. Prev: Sen. Regist. Bethlem Roy. & Maudsley Hosps.; Research Fell. (Psychiat.) Trinity Coll Dub.; Regist. St. Patricks Hosp. Dub.

LUCEY, John Desmond (retired) 2 Summer Court, 31 Second Avenue, Bridlington YO15 2LW Tel: 01262 672323 — MB BCh BAO NUI 1946; MRCGP 1956; LM Coombe. Prev: GP Bridlington.

LUCEY, Ruth 15 Alnham Court, Dorrington Road, Fawdon, Newcastle upon Tyne NE3 2JT — MB ChB 1991 Otago.

LUCIE, Norman Phillip 19 Borden Road, Glasgow G13 1RB Tel: 0141 959 4529 — MB ChB 1966 Glas.; MRCP (U.K.) 1972; MRCPath 1973. Cons. (Haemat.) W.. Infirm. Glas. Prev: Regist. (Haemat.) W.. Infirm. Glas.

LUCIE-SMITH, Rosalie Evaleen Badger (retired) 66 Manor Green Road, Epsom KT19 8RN Tel: 01372 721555 — MB ChB Glas. 1951.

LUCIRE, Yolande 14 Devonshire Place, London W1N 1PB — MB BS 1964 Sydney.

LUCK, Brenda Mary The Surgery, Sandy Lane, Brewood, Stafford ST19 9ES Tel: 01902 850206 Fax: 01902 851360; Hope Cottage, 38 Sandy Lane, Brewood, Stafford ST19 9ET Tel: 01902 851613 — MB ChB 1975 Leeds; BSc (Hons. Physiol.) Leeds 1972; MRCGP 1979; DCH Eng. 1978; DRCOG 1978. Prev: Trainee GP Hull VTS; Ho. Phys. Kingston Gen. Hosp. Hull; Ho. Surg. Roy. Infirm. Hull.

LUCK, Carole Ann Meadowbank, Heatherwood Hospital, London Road, Ascot SL5 8AA Tel: 01344 877677 Fax: 01344 883936; Winkfield Street, Winkfield, Windsor SL4 4SW Tel: 01344 882762 Fax: 01344 883936 — MB BS Lond. 1967; MRCS Eng. LRCP Lond. 1967; FRCR 1975; FFR 1974; DMRD Eng. 1972. (Roy. Free) Cons. Radiol. Heatherwood & Wexham Pk. Hosps. Trust. Socs: Brit. Inst. Radiol.; Brit of Soc of Pae Radiol.; Found Mem. Internat. Soc. Ultrasound in Obst. & Gyn. Prev: Cons. Radiol. Ashford Hosp. Middlx.; Regist. (Radiol.) N.wick Pk. Hosp. Harrow; Ho. Phys. Med. Unit Roy. Free Hosp. Lond.

LUCK, Derek James (retired) 10 Cumberland Avenue, Grimsby DN32 0BT — MB ChB 1969 Liverp.; MRCP (UK) 1973; FRACGP 1978; DRCOG 1978; DA Eng. 1975; DCH Eng. 1971.

LUCK, Dorothy Joyce (retired) 80 Sheepcot Lane, Watford WD25 0EA Tel: 01923 672451 — MB BCh Wales 1952. Prev: Regist. (Surg.) Roy. Gwent Hosp. Newport.

LUCK, John David 12 Green Lane, Horstead, Norwich NR12 7EL — MB ChB 1995 Leeds.

LUCK, John Franco c/o McDougald, 378 Edinburgh Road, Carntyne, Glasgow G33 2PL — MB ChB 1995 Dundee.

LUCK, Mr Jonathan Royal United Hospital, Combe Park, Bath BA1 3NG Tel: 01225 835555 Fax: 01225 835900 Email: jon.luck@dial.pipex.com — MB ChB 1985 Manch.; FRCS Eng. 1991; FRCOphth 1991. (Univ. Manch.) Cons. & Clin. Dir. Ophth. Bath; Mem. Oxf. Congr. Prev: Sen. Regist. & Regist. Rotat. (Ophth.) Leeds; Demonst. (Anat.) Univ. Liverp. Med. Sch.; Ho. Surg. & Ho. Phys. Hope Hosp. Salford.

LUCK, Mr Richard John Meadowbank, Maidens Green, Winkfield, Windsor SL4 4SW — MB BS 1954 Lond.; FRCS Eng. 1959. (St. Mary's) Cons. Surg. E. Berks. Health Dist. Socs: Fell. Brit. Assn. Urol. Surgs. Prev: Hon. Cons. Surg. & Sen. Lect. (Surg.) St. Mary's Hosp. Lond.

LUCK, Susan Elizabeth Walton Medical Centre, 2-4 Bedford Road, Liverpool L4 5PX Tel: 0151 525 6438 Fax: 0151 530 1748; 6 Swan Delph, Aughton, Ormskirk L39 5QG — MB ChB 1985 Leeds; DRCOG 1989.

LUCK, Suzanne Elizabeth 41 Spital Lane, Brentwood CM14 5PQ Tel: 01277 227595 — MB ChB 1996 Birm.; ChB Birm. 1996. (Birm.) SHO (Paediat.) All St.s Hosp. Magpie Hall Rd. Chatham. Prev: RMO Ryde Hosp. Sydney Australia; Ho. Off. (Surg.) WalsGr. Coventy; Ho. Off. (Med.) Stoke Gen. Hosp.

LUCKAS, John Richard Ainley, OStJ (retired) Ty'n Rhos, Llydan Road, Rhosneigr LL64 5JE Tel: 01407 810650 — MB ChB 1950 Ed.; MRCGP 1962.

LUCKAS, Murray James Machray City Hospital NHS Trust, Dudley Road, Birmingham B18 7QH Tel: 0121 507 5335 Email: m.lucas@30am.co.uk; 10 Newlands Road, Stockton Heath, Warrington WA4 2DS Tel: 0121 449 0476 — MB ChB 1988 Leic.; BSc Sheff. 1983; MRCOG 1993; MD 2000. Cons. Hon. Sen. lec.city hosp Birm. Socs: Brit Matern. fetal med soc.; Brit Fert Soc.

LUCKENS, Christopher John Midanbury Surgery, 1 Woodmill Lane, Midanbury, Southampton SO18 2PA Tel: 023 8055 5407 Fax: 023 8067 1491; Swallowfield, Manor Road, Durley, Southampton SO32 2AF Tel: 01489 860368 — MB ChB 1970 Glas.; DObst RCOG 1974.

LUCKETT, Jonathan Peter Holmwood Corner Surgery, 179 Malden Road, New Malden KT3 6AA Tel: 020 8942 0066 Fax: 020 8336 1377; 43 Alfred Road, Kingston upon Thames KT1 2UA Tel: 020 8546 4242 — MB BS 1981 Lond.; MRCGP 1986; DRCOG 1984. Prev: Trainee GP Char. Cross Hosp. VTS; SHO (A & E) N.wick Pk. Hosp.

LUCKHURST, Stephen Paul 67 Cudham La N., Orpington BR6 6BX — MB ChB 1997 Glas.

LUCKIE, Matthew James 40 The Avenue, West Moors, Ferndown BH22 0LU — MB ChB 1998 Sheff.; MB ChB Sheff 1998.

LUCKING, Martyn Taylor 467 Lytham Road, Blackpool FY4 1JH Tel: 01253 45086; 4 Headroomgate Road, Lytham St Annes FY8 3BD Tel: 01257 725921 — MRCS Eng. LRCP Lond. 1962. (St. Mary's) Assoc. Specialist Spinal Managem. Clinic Vict. Hosp. Blackpool. Prev: Regist. (Physical Med.) Radcliffe Infirm. Oxf.; SHO Vict. Hosp. Blackpool; Ho. Phys. Sir Chas. Gairdner Hosp. W. Austral.

LUCKIT, John Kitti Haematology Department, The North Middlesex Hospital, Sterling Way, London N18 1QX Tel: 020 8887 2584 Fax: 020 8807 9644 — MB BS 1981 Lond.; BSc Lond. 1978; MRCPI 1986; FRCPath 2001. (St. Mary's) Cons. Haemat. The N. Middlx. Hosp. Lond. Socs: Brit. Soc. Haematol.; BMA; Brit. Blood Transfus. Soc. Prev: Sen. Regist. (Haemat.) St. Geo., Roy. Marsden & Mayday Hosps. Lond.; Regist. (Gen. Med.) Epsom Dist. Hosp.; SHO Rotat. (Med.) St. Mary's Hosp. Lond.

LUCKMAN, Kenneth Edward (retired) Wits' End, Dunedin Drive, Birmingham B45 8HZ Email: ken@luckman70freeserve.co.uk — MB ChB Birm. 1958; DObst RCOG 1960. Prev: GP BromsGr., Hereford & Worcs.

LUCKRAFT, Graham George 261 Reservoir Road, Selly Oak, Birmingham B29 6SX — MB ChB 1981 Birm.; DRCOG 1984. SHO

(Paediat.) Selly Oak Hosp. Birm. Prev: Ho. Off. E. Birm. Hosp.; Ho. Surg. Qu. Eliz. Hosp. Birm.

LUCOCQ, John Milton Department of Anatomy & Physiology, University of Dundee, Dundee DD1 4HN — MB BCh 1979 Wales.

LUCRAFT, Helen Hunter Northern Centre for Cancer Treatment, Newcastle General Hospital, Westgate Road, Newcastle upon Tyne NE4 6BE Tel: 0191 219 4246 Fax: 0191 272 4236 Email: helen.lucraft@nuth.northy.nhs.uk — MB ChB 1973 Birm.; FRCP Lond. 1993; MRCP (UK) 1976; FRCR 1979. Cons. Clin. Oncol. Gen. Hosp. Newc.

LUCRAFT, Linda Groby Road Medical Centre, 9 Groby Road, Leicester LE3 9ED Tel: 0116 253 8185; 38 Monsell Drive, Leicester LE2 8PN — MB ChB 1979 Leeds. Prev: Trainee GP Sheff. HA VTS.

LUCY, Betty Cecil (retired) 21 Middleton Avenue, Hove BN3 4PH — MB BS 1941 Lond.; MRCS Eng. LRCP Lond. 1940. Prev: Asst. Phys. EMS.

LUCY, Margaret Helen (retired) 14 Howard Road, Kings Heath, Birmingham B14 7PA Tel: 0121 444 1712 — MB BS 1960 Lond.; DObst RCOG 1964.

LUDER, Hilary Jane The Jubilee Medical Group, Cobblers Hall Surgery, Cobblers Hall, Burn Lane, Newton Aycliffe DL5 4SE Tel: 01325 311300 Fax: 01325 301389; 17 High Green, Newton Aycliffe DL5 4RZ — MB ChB 1986 Manch.; MB ChB Manchester 1986. Socs: Roy. Coll. Gen. Pract. Prev: Trainee GP Moorlands Surg. Darlington.

LUDER, Joseph (retired) 152 Harley Street, London W1N 1HH Tel: 020 7935 3834 — MB BS (Hons. Med.) Lond. 1945; MD Lond. 1950; FRCP Lond. 1973, M 1946; FRCPCH 1996; DCH Eng. 1950; MAE 1995; FRCPCH 1996. Prev: Cons. Paediat. Roy. N.. Hosp. & Whittington Hosp.

LUDERS, Kathryn Siobhan 8 Fairview Drive, Bristol BS6 6PW Tel: 0117 944 5372 — MB BCh BAO 1982 NUI; MRCGP 1986. Trainee GP S. Derbysh. HA.

LUDFORD, Cynthia Nora Dept. of Health, Richmond House, 79 Whitehall, London SW1A 2NL Tel: 020 7972 2524 Fax: 020 7972 2550 Email: cynthia.ludford@doh.gsi.gov.uk; Halcyon House, Old Blandford Road, Salisbury SP2 8DE Tel: 01722 324557 Email: cynthia@ludford.net — MB BS 1970 Lond.; MSc Soton. 1997; MRCS Eng. LRCP Lond. 1969; Cert Family Plann JCC. 1980. (Middlx.) Socs: Salisbury Med. Soc. Prev: Princip. GP Wilton Health Centre; Chairm. Salisbury Dist. Primary Med. Care Community; Clin. Asst. (Path.) Salisbury Health Dist. Hosps.

LUDGATE, Susanne Marion Medical Devices Agency (Dept of Health), Room 1110, Hannibal House, Elephant & Castle, London SE1 6TQ Tel: 020 7972 8123 Fax: 020 7972 8111 Email: susanne.ludgate@doh.gsi.gov.uk; Widmer Pond Cottage, Bank Road, Penn, High Wycombe HP10 8LA Tel: 01494 814436 Fax: 01494815267 — MB ChB 1972 Ed.; BSc Ed. 1969, MB ChB 1972; FRCR 1979; FRACR 1987. (Ed.) Med Dir DoH. Prev: Cons. Radiat. Oncol. W.. Gen. Hosp. Edin. & W.mead Hosp. Sydney, Austral.; Sen. Regist. (Med. Oncol.) W.. Gen. Hosp.

LUDKIN, Stanley, OBE (retired) Beddell House, Sherburn House, Durham DH1 2SE Tel: 0191 372 0030 — MB BS 1941 Durh.; MD Durh. 1957; FFCM RCP (UK) 1972; DPH Bristol 1947. Prev: Co. Med. Off. of Health Durh. CC.

LUDLAM, Ailsa Mary Tel: 023 9221 0200 Fax: 023 9223 0316; 42 Carmarthen Ave, Cosham, Portsmouth PO62 2AQ Tel: 02392 379152 — MB ChB Ed. 1966; DObst RCOG 1969.

LUDLAM, Professor Christopher Armstrong Department of Haematology, Royal Infirmary, Edinburgh EH3 9YW Tel: 0131 536 2122 Fax: 0131 536 2145 Email: christopher.ludlum@ed.ac.uk; 20 Tantallon Place, Edinburgh EH9 1NZ Tel: 0131 667 6232 — MB ChB 1971 Ed.; PhD Ed. 1977, BSc (Biochem.) 1968, MB ChB 1971; FRCP Ed. 1982, M 1973; FRCPath 1989, M 1977. Cons. Haemat. Roy. Infirm. Edin.; Dir. Haemophilia Centre Edin.; Prof. of Haemat. and Coagulation Med. Edin. Socs: MRCPCH 1997. Prev: Lect. (Haemat.) Welsh Nat. Sch. Med. Cardiff; Sen. Regist. (Haemat.) Univ. Hosp. Wales Cardiff; MRC Jun. Research Fell. (Therap.) Univ. Edin.

LUDLAM, Hugo Anthony Public Health & Clinical Microbiology Laboratory, Addenbrooke's Hospital, Cambridge CB2 2QW Tel: 01223 242111 — MB BS 1978 Lond.; MD Lond. 1989; FRCPath 1996, M 1985. Cons. Med. Microbiol. Addenbrooke's Hosp. Camb.; Assoc. Lect. (Path.) Univ. Camb. Prev: Sen. Lect. (Med. Microbiol.) St. Bart. Hosp. Lond.

LUDLAM, Martin (retired) 2 Castleview Gardens, Lochmaben, Lockerbie DG11 1ND Tel: 01387 811728 — MB ChB Ed. 1937; MRCGP 1953. Prev: GP Carlisle.

LUDLAM, Ronald Bowman 13 Trafalgar Street, Carlisle CA2 5XX — MB BS 1965 Newc.; MRCPsych 1976; DPM Eng. 1975.

LUDLOW, Brian Peter, Wing Cdr. RAF Med. Br. Chief Medical Officer, Jaguar Cars Ltd, Browns Lane, Allesley, Coventry CV5 9DR Tel: 01203 202076 Fax: 01203 202441; Timaru, Church Road, Gloucester GL3 2ES Tel: 01452 714055 Fax: 01452 714055 Email: 106016.1220@compuserve.com — MB BS 1978 Lond.; MMedSc Birm. 1990; MRCS Eng. LRCP Lond. 1978; DAvMed FOM RCP Lond. 1986; MFOM RCP Lond. 1992, A 1990. (St. Bartholemews Hospital) Chief Med. Off., Jaguar Cars; Co. Surg. St. John Ambul. Glos.; Cons in OM to. St. John Ambul. Med. Advis. Commitee. Socs: Fell. Roy. Soc. Med.; Soc. Occupat. Med. Prev: Occupat. Physiotherapist (RAF); Command Occapational Phys. HQ Logistics Command & HQ Support Command; RAF Staff Coll.

LUDLOW, Elizabeth Jane Welsh Office, Cathays Park, Cardiff CF10 3NQ; Cross House, Tredodridge, Cowbridge CF71 7UL — MB ChB 1975 Bristol; FFPHM RCP (UK) 1994; MFCM RCP (UK) 1984. p/t Sen. Med. Off. Welsh Off. Cardiff. Prev: Cons. Pub. Health Med. E. Dyfed HA; Med. Off. (Environm. Health) E. Dyfed HA.

LUDLOW, Emma Louise 4 The Locks, Bingley BD16 4BG — MB BS 1994 Newc.

LUDLOW, Joanne Patricia 10 Hilton Grove, Little Hulton, Worsley, Manchester M28 0RY — MB ChB 1987 Leeds.

LUDMAN, Mr Harold (retired) — MB BChir MB BChir Camb. 1958; MA Camb. 1958, BA (1st cl. Nat. Sc. Trip.) 1953; FRCS Eng. 1961; LRPS 1999. Prev: Cons. Neurotol. Surg. Nat. Hosp. Qu. Sq.

LUDMAN, Peter Frederick Queen Elizabeth Hospital, Edgbaston, Birmingham B15 2TH Email: p.f.ludman@bham.ac.uk — MB BChir 1985 Camb.; FESC 1998; FRCP 2001; MA Camb. 1986, MD 1993; MRCP (UK) 1987. (Cambridge University & St. Thomas' Hopsital) Cons. Cardiol. Qu. Eliz. Hosp., Birming.; Sen. Clin. Lecture Dept. of Med. Univ. of Birm. Prev: Sen. Regist. (Cardiol.) Papworth Hosp. Camb.; Research Regist. (Cardiol.) Roy. Brompton Hosp.; Regist. (Cardiol.) Hammersmith Hosp. Lond.

LUDWIG, Zbigniew Jozef 67B Cantelope Road, Bexhill-on-Sea TN40 1PP Tel: 01424 720574 — LRCPI & LM, LRCSI & LM 1951. (RCSI) Police Surg. Hastings, Battle & E.bourne Constab. Socs: Fell. Roy. Soc. Med. (Forens. Dept.). Prev: Ho. Phys. Paddington Gen. Hosp. Lond.

LUECK, Christian Joseph Department of Clinical Neuroscience, Western General Hospital, Crewe Road, Edinburgh EH4 2XU Tel: 0131 537 2452 Fax: 0131 537 1030 — MB BChir 1983 Camb.; PhD Lond. 1991; MA Camb. 1983; FRCP (Ed.) 1996; MRCP (UK) 1985. Cons. Neurol. W.. Gen. Hosp. Edin.

LUEN, Sidney Campbell 16 Cold Knap Way, Barry CF62 6SQ Tel: 01446 739748 — LMSSA 1951 Lond. (Cardiff) Prev: WHO Epidemiol. Malaria Eradicat. Serv. Ethiopia; WHO Epidemiol. Hyderabad, India; Sen. WHO Malariol. Nepal.

LUESLEY, Professor David Michael Birmingham Womens Hospitalt, Hetchley Lane, Edgbaston, Birmingham B15 2T6 Tel: 0121 6236833 Fax: 0121 4497438 Email: d.ivesley@virgin.net; 56 Chantry Road, Moseley, Birmingham B13 8DJ Tel: 0121 449 7438 Email: d.luesley@virgin.net — MB ChB 1975 Birm.; MA Camb. 1975; MD Birm. 1985; FRCOG 1993, M 1980. Prof. (Gyn. Oncol.) Univ. Birm.; Hon. Cons.Gynaecologist, Birm. Wom.s Hosp. and City Hosp. NHS Trust, Dudley Rd. Socs: Brit. Soc. Colposcopy & Cervical Path.; Past Pres. Brit. Soc. for Colposcopy and Cervical Path.; Chair of By-laws Comm., Internat. Gyn. Cancer Soc.

LUFF, Mr Andrew John Wessex Nuffield Hospital, Winchester Road, Chandler's Ford, Eastleigh SO53 2DW Tel: 01703 258411 Fax: 01703 258446; Merritrees, Church Lane, Awbridge, Romsey SO51 0HN — MB BS 1982 Lond.; MA Oxf. 1983; FRCS Ed. (Ophth.) 1990; FRCS Ed. 1987; FRCOphth 1991. Cons. Ophth. Soton. Eye Unit. Prev: Fell. (Vitreoretinal Surg.) Moorfields Eye Hosp. Lond.; Sen. Regist. (Ophth.) Eye Hosp. Soton.

LUFF, Mr David Anthony 57 Albert Drive, Conwy LL31 9RL Tel: 01492 583137; 57 Albert Drive, Conwy LL31 9RL Tel: 01492 583137 — BM BS 1993 Nottm.; FRCS (Eng). 1997 RCS Eng; FRCS (Oto) 1999 RCS Eng. Specialist Regist. ENT Surg., N. W. Rotat.

Prev: SHO ENT Surg. Manch. Roy. infirm.; SHO ENNT Surg. Hope Hosp. Salford; SHO (Neurosurg. & Orthop. Surg.) Hope Hosp. Salford.

LUFF, Robin Hamilton King's Healthcare, Rehabilitation Centre, Bowley Close, London SE19 1SZ Tel: 020 7346 5230 Fax: 020 7346 5234 Email: luff29095@aol.com — MB BS 1976 Lond.; BSc (Biochem.) Bristol 1968; FRCS Eng. 1980; FRCP 1997. (St. Thos.) Cons. Rehabil. Med. King's Healthcare NHS Trust; Clin. Dir. Socs: Fell. Roy. Soc. Med.; BMA & Internat. Soc. Prosth. & Orthotics; Brit. Soc. Rehabil. Med. Prev: Med. Off. & Sen. Med. Off. Disablem. Serv. Auth.; Regist. (Orthop.) Char. Cross & Guildford Hosps.

LUFFINGHAM, George Harold (retired) 20 Atkinson Close, Alverstoke, Gosport PO12 2BZ Tel: 01705 589385 — MB BS Lond. 1946. Prev: Regist. & Ho. Phys. (Outpats.) St. Mary's Hosp. Lond.

LUFFINGHAM, John Noel Kent House Surgery, 36 Station Road, Longfield DA3 7QD Tel: 01474 703550; 26 Park Road, Southborough, Tunbridge Wells TN4 0XN Tel: 01892 534868 — MB BS 1979 Lond.; MRCGP 1995; DRCOG 1983; DCH RCP Lond. 1982. Couse Organiser Dartford & Gravesham VTS. Prev: Trainee GP Canterbury & Thanet HA.

LUFFINGHAM, Raymond Laurence 54 Pearson Park, Hull HU5 2TG Tel: 01482 342842 — MB BS Lond. 1950; MFOM 1980; DIH Soc. Apoth. Lond. 1954; Cert Av Med. MoD (Air) & CAA; Aviat. Auth. 1976. (Guy's) Indep. Cons. Occupat. Med. Hull. Socs: Fell. BMA; (Hon. Librarian) Hull Med. Soc. Prev: Employ. Med. Adv.; Med. Off. BR; Ship's Surg. Qu. of Bermuda.

LUFFMAN, Patrick Seton (retired) Burnham Market, King's Lynn PE31 8DW Tel: 01329 738356 — MRCS Eng. LRCP Lond. 1935. Prev: Med. Off. Wells & Dist. Hosp.

LUFT, George Andrew Nicholas Carlton Street Surgery, Carlton Street, Horninglow, Burton-on-Trent DE13 0TE Tel: 01283 511387 Fax: 01283 517174; Hillcrest, Anslow, Burton-on-Trent DE13 9QE Tel: 01283 814390 — MB BS 1969 Lond.; MRCS Eng. LRCP Lond. 1969. (St. Thos.) Gen. Practiioner, Burton on Trent; Clin. Asst., Dept. of Surg./Oncol., Qu.'s Hosp., Burton on Trent.

LUGG, Margaret Anne 15 Hatchlands Road, Redhill RH1 6AA Tel: 01737 772919 Fax: 01737 772919 Email: margaretlugg@hotmail.com; 15 Hatchlands Road, Redhill RH1 6AA Tel: 01737 772919 Fax: 01737 772919 Email: margaretlugg@hotmail.com — MB BS 1960 Lond.; MRCS Eng. LRCP Lond. 1960. (Lond. Hosp.) Socs: BMA (Hon. Sec. E. Surrey Div.).

LUGONE, Helen Aloyd 141 Michael Cliffe House, Finsbury Est., London EC1R 0LN — MB ChB 1994 Dundee.

LUGTON, Mrs Jessie Helen (retired) Farcroft, 187 Lache Lane, Chester CH4 7LU — MB ChB Ed. 1945.

LUI, Arthur Ling Sing 1 The Mead, London W13 8AZ — MB BS 1976 Lond.; MRCP (UK) 1983; DCH RCPSI 1983; DCH Lond. 1981.

LUI, Gerald Jeet Loh 145 Weymouth Drive, Glasgow G12 0EW — MB ChB 1993 Glas.

LUI, Rupert Yau Han Room 2, Flat 20D, Residential Complex, Inverclyde Royal Hospital, Larkfield Road, Greenock PA16 0XN — MB ChB 1992 Glas.

LUIS, Joao Ladislaus Clyde 81 Prestwood Road W., Wednesfield, Wolverhampton WV11 1HT Tel: 01902 721021; 1Tudor Crescent, Penn, Wolverhampton WV2 4PX — MB ChB 1990 Sheff. Prev: SHO (Paediat.) Birm.

LUIS RUIZ, David Staff House 6, Ayrshire Central Hospital, Kilwinning Road, Irvine KA12 8SS — LMS 1995 La Laguna.

LUITHLE, Eberhard Roland Eduard Cae Clyd, Promenade, Llanfairfechan LL33 0BU — State Exam 1989 Heidelberg.

LUK, Tien Loong 30E Sandilands Drive, Aberdeen AB24 2QA — MB ChB 1995 Aberd.

LUK, Tse Li 5 Cambridge Road, Newport NP19 0BQ — MB BCh 1985 Wales.

LUKA, Albert 161 Cranley Gardens, London N10 3AG Tel: 020 8883 3772 — MRCS Eng. LRCP Lond. 1962.

LUKARIS, Christopher Peter 53 Tewkesbury Street, Cardiff CF24 4QR — MB BCh 1991 Wales.

LUKASZEWICZ, Christopher Mark Fairlands Medical Centre, Fairlands Avenue, Worplesdon, Guildford GU3 3NA Tel: 01483 594250 Fax: 01483 598767; The Glaziers Lane Surgery, Glaziers Lane, Normandy, Guildford GU3 2DD Tel: 01483 594250 Fax: 01483 811880 — MB BS 1984 Lond.; Cert. Prescribed Equiv. Exp. JCPTGP 1990; Cert. Family Plann. JCC 1990; LFHom (Med) 1999, Faculty of Homeopathy. (Char. Cross) Princip. in Gen. Pract., Guildford; Gen. Practitioner, Private GP Serv., The Guildford Nuffield Hosp., Stirling Rd., Guildford, Surrey, GU2 5RF. Tel. 01483 555800; Practitioner in Threadvein ScleroTher., The Leg Care Company Ltd, c/o The Fairlands Med. Centre, Fairlands Avenue, Guildford, Surrey, GU3 3NA. Socs: BMA & Med. Protec. Soc.; Licenced Assoc. Fac. of Homeopathy. Prev: Trainee GP/SHO Guildford Hosps. VTS; SHO (Psychiat.) Frimley Pk. Hosp. Frimley; SHO (A & E) Roy. Surrey Co. Hosp. Guildford.

LUKATS, Sandra 41 Orchard Street, Otley LS21 1JU — MB BS 1992 Lond.

LUKATS, Victoria Elizabeth Joyce Joustings, Jasmore Avenue, Lower Shiplake, Henley-on-Thames RG9 3NU — MB BS 1998 Lond.; MB BS Lond 1998.

LUKE, Arthur Jeremy Balkwill (retired) 69 Sandpit Lane, St Albans AL1 4EY Tel: 01727 866167 Email: ldadluke@aol.com — MB BS 1956 Lond.; DObst RCOG 1961. Prev: Med. Off. St. Albans Sch.

LUKE, Mr Irving Keiva (cons. rooms), 42 Harley St., London W1N 1AB Tel: 020 7580 1354 Fax: 020 7636 5686; 44 Fairfax Road, London NW6 4HA Tel: 020 7722 2576 — MB ChB Liverp. 1961; FRCS Eng. 1969; MRCS Eng. LRCP Lond. 1961; DO Eng. 1965; DCH Eng. 1963; DObst RCOG 1963. (Liverpool University) Sen. Cons. Ophth. Surg. St. Geo. Hosp. Lond. Socs: FCOphth. Prev: Sen. Regist. (Ophth.) Univ. Coll. Hosp. Lond.; Sen. Resid. Off. Moorfields Eye Hosp. (High Holborn Br.) Lond.; SHO St. Paul's Eye Hosp. Liverp.

LUKE, Jeremy Russell The Health Centre, Coachmans Drive, Broadfield, Crawley RH11 9YZ Tel: 01293 531951; 24 The Millbank, Crawley RH11 0JH — MB BS 1985 Lond.; MRCGP 1989; DRCOG 1989.

LUKE, John James 15 Catherine Road, Surbiton KT6 4HA — MB BS 1980 Lond.; BA Oxf.; MRCS Eng. LRCP Lond. 1979.

LUKE, Warren Munro, RD 254 Thornhill Road, Falkirk FK2 7AZ; 11 Learmonth Street, Falkirk FK1 5AG Tel: 01324 635870 — MB ChB 1972 Glas.; MRCGP 1978; DRCOG 1977; DCH RCPS Glas. 1974.

LUKEMAN, Philip Jonathan Woodside, Brooks Drive, Hale Barns, Altrincham WA15 8TP — MB ChB 1978 Ed.

LUKER, Mr Bryan Carsten Hauch 66 Moorgate Road, Rotherham S60 2AU Tel: 01709 363638 — MB BChir 1940 Camb.; MA, MB BChir Camb. 1940; FRCS Eng. 1948. (Camb. & St. Thos.) Emerit. Cons. Surg. Rotherham Dist. Hosp. & Montagu Hosp. MexBoro.. Prev: Res. Surg. Off. Leicester Roy. Infirm.; Ho. Surg. St. Mark's Hosp. For Rectal Dis. Lond. & Bradford Roy.; Infirm.

LUKEY, David Charles Loughton Health Centre, The Drive, Loughton IG10 1HW Tel: 020 8508 4403 Fax: 020 8508 7269; 82 Heathfield Park Drive, Chadwell Heath, Romford RM6 4FJ Tel: 020 8598 1549 — MB ChB 1984 Pretoria. (Univ.pretoria) GP.

LUKIC, Milos The Health Centre, Doctor Lane, Mirfield WF14 8DU Tel: 01924 495721 Fax: 01924 480605 — MB BS 1984 Lond.

LUKKA, Himanshu Ranchhoddas 7 Valley Road, Bramhall, Stockport SK7 2NH Tel: 0161 439 2938 — MB ChB 1978 Manch.; MRCP (UK) 1981. Regist. (Radiother./Oncol.) Christie Hosp. Manch. Prev: SHO (Radiother./Oncol.) Christie Hosp. Manch.; SHO (Gen. Med.) Wythenshawe Hosp. Manch.; SHO (Gen. Med.) Bolton Gen. Hosp.

LUKMAN, Henny Flat 10, 6 Riverview Place, Glasgow G5 8EB — MB ChB 1993 Glas.

LUKMANY, Mohamedali Fazlehusein 407 Lansbury Drive, Hayes UB4 8SA Tel: 020 8845 6260 — MB BS 1966 Indore. (Mahatma Gandhi Memor. Med. Coll.) Res. Anaesth. E. Herts. Health Dist.

LUKSCH, Marina 18 Newstead Way, London SW19 5HS — State Exam Milan 1991.

LUKSENBERG, Susannah Rose Belsize Priory Health Centre, 208 Belsize Road, London NW6 4DX Tel: 020 7625 6181 Fax: 020 7530 2661 — MB BS 1975 Lond.; MRCS Eng. LRCP Lond. 1975; DRCOG 1978. (St. Mary's)

LUKSZA, Andrzej Ryszard Salusbury House, Flan How, Ulverston LA12 7PU — MB ChB 1975 Bristol; FRCP Lond. 1993; MRCP (UK) 1978. Morecambe Bay Hosps. Trust; Med. Director, Morecambe Bay Hosps. Trust.

LULSEGGED, Abbiyyu 49 Friar Road, Brighton BN1 6NH — MB BS 1994 Lond.

LUM, Laurence Claude 54 Windmill Grange, Histon, Cambridge CB4 9JF — MB BS 1939 Adelaide; MA Camb. 1977; FRCP Lond. 1970, M 1948; FRACP 1973, M 1946. (Adelaide) Socs: Founder Mem. Internat. Soc. for Advancem. of Respirat. Psychophysiol.; E. Anglian Thoracic Soc.; Fell. Roy. Soc. Med. (Ex-Vice Pres. & Pres. Sect. Med. & Dent. Hypn.). Prev: Cons. Chest Phys. Papworth Hosp. Camb.; Phys. Supt. Brit. Legion Sanat. Nayland; Med. Supt. & Flying Doctor Alice Springs.

LUM HEE, Wendy 2 Newlay Wood Fold, Horsforth, Leeds LS18 4HJ Tel: 0113 258 7030 Email: wendy.lum_lee@virgin.net — MB ChB Bristol 1992. Specialist Regist. Sheff. Univ. Hosp. Prev: SHO (Anaesth.) Torbay Hosp. Torquay.

LUMB, Andrew Brian Department of Anaesthetics, St James' University Hospital, Beckett Street, Leeds LS9 7TF Email: a.lumb@leeds.ac.uk — MB BS 1985 Lond.; FCAnaesth 1989. Cons. Anaesth. St. Jas. Univ. Hosp. Leeds. Prev: Sen. Regist. Rotat. (Anaesth.) Middlx. Hosp. Lond.; Regist. Rotat. (Anaesth.) Roy. Free Hosp. Lond.; Research Regist. (Anaesth.) N.wick Pk. Hosp.

LUMB, Mr Geoffrey Norman (retired) Kirkstall, 59 Kingsway, Fullands Park, Taunton TA1 3YD Tel: 01823 284802 — MB BS 1948 Lond.; FRCS Eng. 1956; MRCS Eng. LRCP Lond. 1948. Prev: Cons. Urol. Som. Clin. Area.

LUMB, Kathleen Mary (retired) 29 Westborough Drive, Highroad Well, Halifax HX2 7QN — MB ChB Birm. 1953; FFCM 1982, M 1974; DObst RCOG 1955; DCH Eng. 1957; DPH Bristol 1959. Prev: Cons. Pub. Health Med. Bradford.

LUMB, Michael Andrew 19 Hallam Crescent, Nelson BB9 9PD — MB ChB 1991 Dundee.

LUMB, Mr Michael Robert Peterborough District Hospital, Thorpe Road, Peterborough PE3 6DA Tel: 01733 875249 Fax: 01733 875699 — MB BS 1983 Lond.; MA Camb. 1984, BA (Hons.) 1980; MRCOG 1989. (St. Geo.) Cons. O & G P'boro. Hosps. NHS Trust. Socs: E. Anglia Obst. & Gyn. Soc.; Brit. Med. Ultrasound Soc.; Brit. Matern. & Fetal Med. Soc. Prev: Sen. Regist. (O & G) Simpson Memor. Matern. Pavil., Roy. Infirm. Edin. & E. Gen. Hosp. Edin.; Regist. Rotat. (O & G) Rosie Matern. Hosp., Addenbrooke's Hosp. Camb. & Ipswich Hosp.; Regist. Rotat. (Obst.) Paisley Matern. Hosp., (Gyn.) Roy. Alexandra Hosp. Paisley.

LUMB, Peter George The Surgery, 6 Longton Grove Road, Weston Super Mare BS23 1LT Tel: 01934 628 118/ Fax: 01934 645893; 27 Brean Down Avenue, Weston Super Mare BS23 4JQ Tel: 01934 628330 — MB ChB 1975 Bristol; DRCOG 1978; DA Eng. 1977. GP W.on-super-Mare. Prev: Trainee GP Dorchester & Weymouth VTS; SHO (Anaesth.) Frenchay Hosp. Bristol; Ho. Phys. & Ho. Surg. Frenchay Hosp. Bristol.

LUMB, Philip Derek 148 Wendover Road, Manchester M23 9JX — MB ChB 1995 Sheff.; B.Med.Sci. (Path.) 1993. (Sheffield) Prev: Mem. Brit. Assn. Forens. Med.; Mem. Assn. Clin. Pathol.; Mem. BMA.

LUMB, Robert Alan The Surgery, 20 Lee Road, Blackheath, London NW7 1LJ Tel: 020 8852 1235 Fax: 020 8297 2193 — MB BS 1976 Lond.; MRCS Eng. LRCP Lond. 1976; DRCOG 1980; MRCGP 1980.

LUMB, Stephen Andrew Stanhope Health Centre, Dales Street, Stanhope, Bishop Auckland DL13 2XD Tel: 01388 528555 Fax: 01388 526122; Dales Street, Stanhope, Bishop Auckland DL13 2TY Tel: 01388 528555 — MB BS 1980 Newc.; MRCGP 1984; DRCOG 1983. GP Vocational Trainer; Hosp. Practitioner, Horn Hall Hosp., Stanhope, Co. Durh.

LUMB, Susan Elizabeth Haslam Northern Avenue Surgery, 141 Northern Avenue, Sheffield S2 2EJ Fax: 0114 253 1929 — MB ChB 1980 Sheff. Socs: MRCGP.

LUMB, William John Tel: 01748 833904; Yealands House, Eskeleth, Arkengarthdale, Richmond DL11 6RW — MB BS 1992 Lond. (St. Mary's Hospital Medical School) GP; Clin. Governance Lead, Elderley Care, Hambleton & Richmondshire. Prev: SHO (Orthoptics) Bishop Auckland Gen. Hosp.; SHO Rotat. (Gen. Med.) Reading Hosps.; Trainee GP N.allerton VTS.

LUMLEY, Hilary Susan Department of Haematology, Mayday Hospital, London Rd, Thornton Heath CR7 7YE; 1 Shortheath Road, Farnham GU9 8SR Tel: 01372 274561 Email: h.s.lumley@doctors.org.uk — MB BS 1976 Lond.; MRCP (UK) 1979; MRCS Eng. LRCP Lond. 1976; MRCPath 1983; FRCP 1995; FRCPath 1996. (Westminster Medical School) Cons. (Haemat.) Croydon Dist.Mayday Healthcare NHS Trust. Prev: Sen. Regist. (Haemat.) Roy. Marsden Hosp.

LUMLEY, Jean (retired) 32 Gurney Drive, Hampstead Garden Suburb, London N2 0DG — MB BS Lond. 1960; MRCS Eng. LRCP Lond. 1960; FRCA; DA (UK) 1962. Prev: Vice-Pres. Roy. Coll. Anaesth. 1992-1994.

LUMLEY, Mr John Stuart Penton 392 Shakespear Tower, Barbican, London EC2Y 8NJ — MB BS 1960 Lond.; MS Lond. 1981; FRCS Eng. 1966; MRCS Eng. LRCP Lond. 1960. (Univ. Coll. Hosp.) Prof. Vasc. Surg. & Hon. Cons. Surg. St. Bart. Hosp. Lond. Socs: MRC Cerebral Func. Research Gp. (Anat. Dept.) Univ. Coll.; World Pres. Internat. Coll. Surgs.; (Ex-Sec.) Assn. Surgs. Gt. Brit. & Irel. Prev: Res. Surg. Off. Roy. Marsden Hosp. Lond.; Cas. Surg. Off. Univ. Coll. Hosp. Lond.; Asst. Lect. Anat. Dept. Univ. Coll. Lond.

LUMLEY, Kevin Patrick Shortall 8 Kingslawn Close, Howards Lane, Putney, London SW15 6QJ Tel: 020 8789 9905 — BM BCh 1956 Oxf.; FFOM RCP Lond. 1991, MFOM 1978; MFCM 1974; DPH Lond. 1965; DIH Soc. Apoth. Lond. 1964. (Oxf. & St. Mary's)

LUMLEY, Kim The Health Centre, Oakleigh Road North, Whetstone, London N20 0DH Tel: 020 8368 6550; 53 Grovelands Road, London N13 4RJ Tel: 020 8886 2128 — MB BS 1980 Lond.; MRCGP 1986; DRCOG 1985. (St. Mary's)

LUMLEY, Louise Claire The Surgery, 713 Yardley Wood Road, Kings Heath, Birmingham B13 0PT Tel: 0121 444 3597 — MB BS 1989 Newc.

LUMLEY, Matthew Armstrong Department of Haematology, Good Hope Hospital, Rectory Road, Sutton Coldfield B75 7RR Tel: 0121 378 2211 Fax: 0121 311 1800 Email: matthew.lumley@goodhot.wmids.nhs.uk; 9 Driffold, Sutton Coldfield B73 6HE — MB ChB 1985 Leic.; MD (Uni. Of Birm.) 2001; MRCP (UK) 1989; DRCPath 1994; MRCPath 1997. (Leic.) Cons. Haematologist Good Hope Hosp. Sutton coldfield. Socs: Brit. Soc. Haematol.; Assn. Clin. Pathologists. Prev: Sen. Regist. (Haemat.) Qu. Eliz. Hosp. Birm.; Clin. Train. Fell. & Hon. Regist. (Haemat.) Birm. Heartlands Hosp.

LUMLEY, Philip William The Surgery, Forge Close, Hayes, Bromley BR2 7LL Tel: 020 8462 1601; Southbourne, 27 Stone Road, Bromley BR2 9AX Tel: 020 8464 2611 — MRCS Eng. LRCP Lond. 1951; MRCGP 1960; DObst RCOG 1953. (St. Bart.) Socs: BMA. Prev: Ho. Surg. & Sen. Ho. Off. (Obst.) W. Norf. Hosp. Kings Lynn.

LUMLEY, Susan Penelope Blood Transfusion Service, Raigmore Hospital, Inverness Tel: 01463 704212 Fax: 01463 237020 — MB ChB 1982 Ed.; BSc (Hons. Path.) Ed. 1979. (Univ. Ed.) Assoc. Specialist Blood Transfus. Serv. Raigmore Hosp. Inverness. Socs: BMA; Brit. Blood Transfus. Soc.; Brit. Assn. Tissue Banks. Prev: Assoc. Specialist (Transfus. Med.) Roy. Infirm. Edin.

LUMSDEN, Anne Sutherland 57 Belmont Road, Ayr KA7 2PE — MB ChB 1977 Glas.

LUMSDEN, Colin James 20 Hillview Terrace, Cults, Aberdeen AB15 9HJ — MB ChB 1995 Manch.

LUMSDEN, Elizabeth Heather Thompson 4 North Place, Oxford OX3 9HX — MB BS 1983 Lond.; MA Oxf. 1974; MRCGP 1987; DRCOG 1985. Prev: SHO John Radcliffe Hosp. Oxf.

LUMSDEN, Gail Victoria 2 Fixby Park Drive, Huddersfield HD2 2NN — MB BS 1994 Lond.

LUMSDEN, Graeme Robert 19 Ulster Gardens, Edinburgh EH8 7JZ — MB ChB 1997 Glas.

LUMSDEN, Mary Ann Department of Obstetrics & Gynaecology, University of Glasgow, Queen Mothers Hospital, Yorkhill, Glasgow G3 8SH; The Myretoun, Menstrie FK11 7EB Tel: 01259 61453 — MB BS 1977 Lond.; BSc (Hons.) Lond. 1974, MD 1985; MRCOG 1984. Sen. Lect. & Cons. Qu. Mother's Hosp. & W.. Infirm.; Assoc. Dean for Admissions, Fac. of Med., Glas. Univ. Prev: Sen. Regist. (O & G) Roy. Infirm. & W.. Gen. Hosp.; Birthright/Edgar Fell.sh. Univ. Edin. 1985-1987; MRC Train. Fell. (O & G) Univ. Edin.

LUMSDEN, William The Bank House, Dornoch Road, Bonar Bridge, Ardgay IV24 3EB — MB ChB 1951 Ed.; MRCGP 1963.

LUMSDEN, Professor William Hepburn Russell (retired) 16A Merchiston Crescent, Edinburgh EH10 5AX Tel: 0131 229 2702 — MB ChB 1938 Glas.; FRSE; DSc Glas. 1957, BSc 1935, MD 1975; FRCP Ed. 1972, M 1967; DTM & H Liverp. 1939. Prev: Prof. Med. Protozool. Lond. Sch. Hyg. & Trop. Med. Univ. Lond.

LUMSDEN, Winifred Wright Ridgeland, 34 The Mall, Montrose DD10 8SS — MB ChB 1950 Aberd. (Aberd.) Sen. Med. Off. (Community) Tayside Region (Angus) Forfar.

LUNAN, Mr Charles Burnett Royal Maternity Hospital, Rottenrow, Glasgow G4 0NA — MD Glas. 1977, MB ChB 1965; FRCS Glas. 1985; FRCOG 1983, M 1970. Cons. O & G Roy. Matern. Hosp. & Roy. Infirm. Glas. Socs: (Ex-Pres. & Ex-Treas.) Roy. Medico-Chir. Soc. Glas.; (Ex-Sec.) Glas. Obst. & Gyn. Soc.; Vice-Pres. Glas. Obst. & Gyn. Soc. Prev: Lect. (O & G) Univ. Aberd. at Aberd. Matern. Hosp.; Sen. Lect. (O & G) Univ. Nairobi, Kenya.

LUNAN, Helen Russell Springfield Medical Practice, 9 Springfield Road, Bishopbriggs, Glasgow G64 1PJ Tel: 0141 772 4744 Fax: 0141 772 3035; 1 Moncrieff Avenue, Lenzie, Glasgow G66 4NL — MB ChB 1967 Glas.; DObst RCOG 1969. Prev: Med. Off. Stud. Health Serv. Univ. Aberd.

LUND, Andrew Denton Well Street Medical Centre, Well Street, Biddulph, Stoke-on-Trent ST8 6HD Tel: 01782 513939 Fax: 01782 523085 — MB ChB 1971 Manch.

LUND, Carole Elizabeth Windsor House, 40 Upper parliament St., Liverpool L8 7LF Tel: 0151 250 5324 — MB ChB 1982 Liverp.; MMedSci. Leeds 1989; MRCPsych 1986.

LUND, Charles Ames (retired) 92 Errington Road, Darras Hall, Ponteland, Newcastle upon Tyne NE20 9LA Tel: 01661 872018 — MB ChB 1967 Liverp.; FRCPsych 1987, M 1972; DPM Eng. 1970; Dip. Psychother. Aberd. 1975. Cons. Psychotherap. Newc. Ment. Health Trust. Prev: Lect. (Ment. Health) Univ. Aberd.

LUND, Christopher David, CStJ Hall Grove Surgery, 4 Hall Grove, Welwyn Garden City AL7 4PL Tel: 01707 328528 Fax: 01707 373139; 1 Fern Grove, Welwyn Garden City AL8 7ND Tel: 01707 392120 Fax: 01707 392120 Email: chris_lund@compuserve.com — MB BS (Hons.) Lond. 1968; MRCS Eng. LRCP Lond. 1968; MRCGP 1983; DMJ (Clin.) Soc. Apoth Lond. 1976; AKC. (King's Coll. Hosp.) Dep. Surg.-in-Chief St. John Ambul.; Princip. Police Surg. Herts. Constab. Socs: Fell. Roy. Soc. Med.; BMA. Prev: SHO (Cas. & Orthop.) Brook Gen. Hosp. Lond.; Ho. Phys. Renal Unit Dulwich Hosp.; Ho. Surg. King's Coll. Hosp.

LUND, Jennifer Anne The Health Centre, Bramhope, Leeds Tel: 01943 464001; 3 Bridge Street, Otley LS21 1BQ Tel: 01943 464001 — MB BS 1985 Newc.; MRCGP 1990; DRCOG 1990; DFFP 1998. (Newc. u. Tyne) Socs: BMA. Prev: Trainee GP E. Cumbria & Harrogate VTS.

LUND, John Beaumonde, 9 Bell View, Windsor SL4 4ET Tel: 01753 770880 Fax: 01753 854678 — MD 1968 Copenhagen; FACS 1977; FACTM 1975. Base Health Serv. Dir. G.C. PO Box 737 DK-3970 Pituffik, Greenland; Ships Surg. Roy. Caribbean Cruises Ltd. Florida, USA. Socs: Fell. Roy. Soc. Trop. Med. & Hyg.; Danish Doctors Assn.; BMA. Prev: Chief Surg. Al-Fanateer Hosp., Saudi Arabia; Cons. Surg. Brunei Shell Internat., Borneo & Mobil Oil Indonesia, N. Sumatra.

LUND, John Fraser (retired) Brook Villa, The Green, Lanchester, Durham DH7 0LE Tel: 01207 521911 Email: fraserj@primex.co.uk — MB BS 1953 Durh.; MRCGP 1960. Prev: GP Lanchester.

LUND, Jonathan Michael Rothera Base, British Antarctic Survey, Stanley, Falkland Islands Email: rothera@bas.ac.uk; The Laurels, 1A Penzance Road, Kesgrave, Ipswich IP5 1LY — MB ChB 1994 Manch.; MB ChB Manch.; BSc (Hons.) Manch. 1989. Med. Off. Brit. Antarctic Survey. Prev: SHO (Accid. & Emerg.) N. Manch. Gen. Hosp.

LUND, Mr Jonathan Norman 12 Stanhope Street, Stanton-By-Dale, Ilkeston DE7 4QA Email: jonlund@doctors.org.uk — BM BS 1990 Nottm.; BMedSci (Hons.) Nottm. 1988; FRCS Eng. 1994; DM Nottm 1999. (Nottingingham) (Specialist Regist.), Nottm. Prev: Wellcome Research Fell. (Surg.) Qu. Med. Centre Nottm.

LUND, Kathryn Anne Parkhall Surgery, Parkhall Road, Somersham, Huntingdon PE28 3EU Tel: 01487 740888 Fax: 01487 843635; 122 Boxworth End, Swavesey, Cambridge CB4 5RA — MB BS 1981 Lond.; MRCGP 1985; DRCOG 1984. (St. Bartholomews)

LUND, Stewart Thomas 13 Albert Road, Cheadle Hulme, Cheadle SK8 5DB — MB ChB 1991 Manch.

LUND, Professor Valerie Joan Institute of Laryngology and Otology, 330 Gray's Inn Road, London WC1X 8DA Tel: 020 7915 1497 Fax: 020 7833 9480 — MB BS 1977 Lond.; MS Lond. 1987; FRCS Ed. 1993; FRCS Eng. 1982; MRCS Eng. LRCP Lond. 1977. Prof. Rhinol. Inst. Laryngol. & Otol. Lond.; Cons. ENT Roy. Nat. Throat, Nose & Ear Hosp. & Moorfields Hosp. Lond. Socs: (Counc.) Roy. Coll. Surg. Eng.; (Rep. N.E. Thames) BAORL-HNS.

LUND, Mr William Spencer (retired) 23 Banbury Road, Oxford OX2 6NN Tel: 01865 404142 — MB BS 1954 Lond.; MS Lond. 1963; FRCS Eng. 1959. Prev: Cons. ENT Surg. Radcliffe Infirm. Oxf.

LUNDHOLM, Eric Olof (retired) 12 Frogston Terrace, Edinburgh EH10 7AD Tel: 0131 445 2443 — MB ChB 1950 Glas.; BSc Glas. 1937; DPM RCPSI 1953.

LUNDY, Gerard Patrick Pancreas Stewartstown Health Centre, 212 Stewartstown Road, Dunmurry, Belfast BT17 0FB Tel: 028 9060 2931 Fax: 028 9060 5728 — MB BCh BAO 1976 Belf.

LUNDY, Martin Thomas Offerton Health Centre, 10 Offerton Lane, Offerton, Stockport SK2 5AR Tel: 0161 480 0326 — MB BCh BAO 1985 Belf.; DCH RCSPI Lond. 1990; MRCGP 1991; DRCOG 1989.

LUNEY, Gillian Margaret Newtownards Health Centre, Frederick Street, Newtownards BT23 4LS; 14 Belmont Drive, Lisburn BT28 3DB — MB BCh BAO 1984 Belf.; MRCGP 1989; DRCOG 1989; DCH RCSI 1988. Socs: BMA & Christian Meditation Fell.sh.; RCGP.

LUNEY, Stephen Robert 81 Ballymena Road, Doagh, Ballyclare BT39 0RN — MB BCh BAO 1987 Belf.

LUNG, Charles Pak Chiu Watford General Hospital, Vicarage Road, Watford WD18 0HB Tel: 01923 244366 Fax: 01923 217141; 11 Alston Road, Boxmoor, Hemel Hempstead HP1 1QU Tel: 01442 257357 Fax: 01442 393264 — MB BCh BAO 1965 Dub.; MA Dub. 1966; FRCA 1972; DA Eng. 1968. (Univ. Dub.) Cons. Anaesth. Watford Gen. Hosp. Prev: Sen. Regist. (Anaesth.) Univ. Coll. Hosp. Lond. & Nat. Hosp. Nerv. Dis. Qu. Sq. Lond.; SHO (Anaesth.) Middlx. Hosp. Lond.

LUNKEN, Catherine Rosemary 28 Cromwell Avenue, Highgate, London N6 5HL — BM BCh 1973 Oxf.; MRCP (UK) 1979.

LUNN, Alexandrina (retired) 1 Newton Close, Newton Ferrers, Plymouth PL8 1AL Tel: 01752 872864 — MRCS Eng. LRCP Lond. 1943. Sen. Med. Off. Plymouth Health Dist. Prev: Asst. MOH Nairobi City Counc., Kenya.

LUNN, Andrew John Fletcher 148 Burley Lane, Quarndon, Derby DE22 5JR — BM 1998 Soton.; BM Soton 1998.

LUNN, Brian Stephen University of Newcastle upon Tyne, Division of Psychiatry, Leazes Wing, Royal Victoria Infirmary, Newcastle upon Tyne NE1 4LP Tel: 0191 202 4056 Fax: 0191 227 5108 Email: b.s.lunn@ncl.ac.uk — MB ChB 1985 Ed.; MRCPsych 1993. Sen. Lect. & Hon. Cons., Univ. Newc. U. Tyne. Prev: Lect. (Neuropsychiat.) & Hon. Sen. Regis. Univ. Newc.; Regist. (Psychiat.) Train. Scheme Roy. Cornhill Hosp. Aberd.

LUNN, Edward Ian (retired) 4 Sevenoaks Avenue, Heaton Moor, Stockport SK4 4AW Tel: 0161 432 8998 — MB ChB Ed. 1948. Prev: Cons. Anaesth. Tameside DHA.

LUNN, Gilbert Roy (retired) 69 St John's Road, Buxton SK17 6UU Tel: 01298 3938 — MD 1943 Ed.; MB ChB 1933; MRCP Ed. 1937. Prev: Ho. Surg. Edin. Roy. Matern. Hosp.

LUNN, Mr Henry Fletcher (retired) The Meadows, Kempley, Dymock GL18 2BN Tel: 01531 890784 — MRCS Eng. LRCP Lond. 1939; BSc Lond. 1937, MB BS 1939; FRCS Eng. 1946. Prev: Cons. Surg. I. of Arran War Memor. Hosp. Lamlash.

LUNN, Janet Seddon Monkseaton Medical Centre, Cauldwell Avenue, Whitley Bay NE25 9PH Tel: 0191 252 1616; 12 Beaumont Drive, Whitley Bay NE25 9UT Tel: 0191 253 4785 — BSc (Physiol., Hons.) Newc. 1966, MB BS (Hons.) 1971; MRCGP 1975; DObst RCOG 1973.

LUNN, John Arthur Top Farm, Parish Lane, Farnham Common, Slough SL2 3JH Tel: 01753 644597 — MB BS 1953 Lond.; MD Lond. 1967; FFOM RCP Lond. 1982, MFOM 1978; FFCM RCP (UK) 1978, M 1974; DIH Soc. Apoth. Lond. 1962. (St. Mary's) Hon. Research Worker N.wick Pk. Inst. Med. Research Harrow. Socs: Fell. Roy. Soc. Med. Prev: Cons. Occupat. Med. N.wick Pk. Hosp. Harrow; Sen. Lect. (Occupat. Med.) St. Geo. Hosp. Med. Sch. Lond.; Dep. Med. Dir. Slough Indust. Health Serv.

LUNN, John Edward (retired) Woodleigh, Pitchford Lane, Sheffield S10 3PL — MB ChB 1956 Glas.; PhD Sheff. 1967; MD Glas. 1961; DPA 1959; DPH 1958.

LUNN, John Morgan (retired) The Surgery, Silver St., Coningsby, Lincoln LN4 4SG Tel: 01526 342348 Fax: 01526 344658 Email: jluw@doctors.org.uk — MB BChir 1960 Camb.; MA Camb., MB

1960, BChir 1959; DObst RCOG 1962; MRCGP 1968; DFFP 1993. Authorised Med. Examr. Civil Aviat. Auth., Federal Aviat. Auth. & Canad. Aviat. Auth. Prev: SHO (Obst.) Univ. Coll. W. Indies.

LUNN, John Neville, OBE (retired) Nr The Old Nursery, Tidenham, Chepstow NP16 7JL Tel: 01291 622972 Email: jnlunn@bspring.freeserve.co.uk — MD Lond. 1968, MB BS 1956; MRCS Eng. LRCP Lond. 1956; FANZCA 1990; FRCA 1962; DA Eng. 1958. Reader (Anaesth.) Univ. Wales Coll. Med.; Trustee Nat. Confidential Enquiry into Perioperat. Deaths; Hon. Cons. Anaesth. Univ. Hosp. of Wales Cardiff Gp. Hosps. Prev: Sen. Regist & Research Asst. (Anaesth.) Univ. Newc.

LUNN, Marita Katherine Blackpool Victoria Hospital, Whinney Keys Road, Blackpool FY3 8NR Tel: 01253 300000; Blackpool Victoria Hospital, Whinney Keys Road, Blackpool FY3 8NR Tel: 01253 300000 — BM BS 1998 Nottm.; BM BS Nottm 1998. SHO (Psychiat.), Blackpool Vict. Hosp.

LUNN, Michael Peter Thomas 38 The Moat, Charing, Ashford TN27 0JH Tel: 01233 712707 Email: michael.lunn@kcl.ac.uk — MB BS 1993 Camb.; MB BS (Lond.) 1993; BA (Hons.) Camb. 1990; MRCP (UK) 1996. (Emmanuel Coll. (Camb.) & Char. Cross & Westm. Med. Sch.) Research Regist. (Neurol.).

LUNN, Neil (retired) Lower Goodameavy, Roborough, Plymouth PL6 7AP — MB ChB 1954 Sheff. Prev: Ho. Phys. & Orthop Ho. Surg. Roy. Hosp. Sheff.

LUNN, Sybil May (retired) Lower Goodmeavy, Roborough, Plymouth PL6 7AP — MB ChB 1954 Sheff. Prev: ENT & Cas. Off. Sheff. Roy. Infirm.

LUNN, Trevor Monkseaton Medical Centre, Cauldwell Avenue, Whitley Bay NE25 9PH Tel: 0191 252 1616; 12 Beaumont Drive, Whitley Bay NE25 9UT — MB BS 1969 Newc.; BSc (Hons.) (Anat.) Newc. 1966, MB BS 1969; MRCP (U.K.) 1972. Prev: Regist. Profess. Med. Unit Roy. Vict. Infirm. Newc.; Ho. Surg. Profess. Surgic. Unit & Ho. Phys. Profess. Med. Unit Roy.; Vict. Infirm. Newc.

LUNNEY, Dorothy Christine Hilary Cottage Surgery, Keble Lawns, Fairford GL7 4BQ Tel: 01285 712377 Fax: 01285 713084; Beaumoor Barn House, East End, Fairford GL7 4AP Tel: 01285 713395 Fax: 01285 713395 Email: benzie@doctors.org.uk — MB ChB Aberd. 1970; MRCGP 1976; DObst RCOG 1973. (Aberd.)

LUNNEY, Rachel Whitworth Lane End Surgery, 2 Manor Walk, Benton, Newcastle upon Tyne NE7 7XX Tel: 0191 266 5246 Fax: 0191 266 6241; 63 Rosebery Crescent, Jesmond, Newcastle upon Tyne NE2 1EX Tel: 0191 209 1170 — BM BCh 1992 Oxf.; BA (Hons.) Oxf. 1989; DRCOG 1997; MRCGP (Distinc.); DFFP. (Oxford) GP Princip.; GP Tutor in Univ. of Newc.; Dept. of Primary Care. Socs: MDU; BMA. Prev: N.umbria VTS; SHO (Oncol.) N.. Centre for Cancer Treatm. Newc.; SHO (Med.) Freeman Hosp. Newc. u. Tyne.

LUNNISS, Mr Peter James 32 Friars Mead, Isle of Dogs, London E14 3JZ — MB BS 1983 Lond.; BSc Lond. 1980, MS 1994, MB BS 1983; FRCS (Gen.) 1997; FRCS Eng. 1988. Sen. Lect., Acad. Dept. Surg. The Roy Lond. Hosp.; Hon. Cons., Gen. Surg., Homerton Hosp. Prev: Sen. Regist. (Gen. Surg.) The Roy. Lond. Hosp.; Lect. (Gen. Surg.) St. Bart. Hosp. Lond.

LUNNISS, Richard James (retired) 515 Willoughby House, Barbican, London EC2Y 8BN Tel: 020 7628 7505 — MRCS Eng. LRCP Lond. 1950; MA Camb. 1948.

LUNNY, James Joseph The Surgery, Hillson Close, Port Isaac PL29 3TR — MB ChB 1971 Glas.; MRCGP 1976; DObst RCOG 1974.

LUNT, Linsley Grace Breast Screening Unit, Queen Elizabeth Hospital, Gateshead — MB BS 1976 Lond.; MRCP (UK) 1979; FRCR 1987. (St Mary's London) Cons. Radiol. BrE. Screening Unit Qu. Eliz. Hosp. Gateshead. Prev: Sen. Regist. (Radiol.) Newc. Univ. Hosps.

LUNT, Peter William Bristol Hospital For Sick Children, St. Michaels Hill, Bristol BS2 8BJ Tel: 0117 921 5411; 11 Old Sneed Road, Stoke Bishop, Bristol BS9 1ES — MB ChB 1980 Ed.; BA (Nat. Sc.) Camb. 1974; MSc (Human Genetics) Ed. 1975; MRCP (UK) 1985. Cons. Clin. Geneticist Roy. Hosp. Sick Childr. Bristol. Prev: Sen. Regist. (Clin. Genetics) St. Marys Hosp. Manch.; Clin. Research Fell. Neurogenetics Univ. Wales Coll. Med. Cardiff.

LUNT, Reginald Lysons 33 Whiteley Wood Road, Whiteley Woods, Sheffield S11 7FF Tel: 0114 230184 — MB ChB 1942 Manch.; MRCS Eng. LRCP Lond. 1942; FRCOG 1965, M 1949. (Manch.) Cons. O & G N. Gen. Hosp. Sheff.; Clin. Teach. Obst. & Gyn. Univ. Sheff. Socs: Sheff. M-C Soc. & N. Eng. Obst. & Gyn. Soc. Prev: Maj. RAMC; Sen. Regist. (O & G) City Gen. Hosp. Sheff.; Ho. Surg. (O & G) St. Mary's Hosp. Manch.

LUNT, Tracey Jane 41 Dorrington Road, Greaves, Lancaster LA1 4TB; 18 Caithness Road, Rochdale OL11 5PB — MB ChB 1988 Manch.; DRCOG 1991. Trainee GP Lancaster.

LUNTS, Elaine Sarah Bradgate Surgery, Ardenton Walk, Brentry, Bristol BS10 6SP Tel: 0117 959 1920 — MB BS 1989 Lond.; MRCGP London 1999; DTM + H Liverpool 1997; BSc (Hons.) Lond. 1986; MRCP (UK) 1994; DCH RCP Lond. 1991. Retainer, Bradgate Surg., Ardenton Walk Brentry, Bristol. Prev: Regist. (Paediat.) S.mead Hosp. Bristol.

LUONG, Chan Bao 7 Longford House, Brangbourne Road, Bromley BR1 4LW — MB BS 1998 Lond.; MB BS Lond 1998.

LUPA, Henry Tomasz, Flight Lt. RAF Med. Br. S.M.C., RAF Bruggen BFPO 25 — MB ChB 1983 Birm.; BSc Birm. 1980, MB ChB 1983. Unit Med. Off. RAF Bruggen. Prev: Cas. Off. RAF (H) Ely; SHO (Paediat.) Sandwell Dist. Gen. Hosp. W. Bromwich.

LUPIN, Mr Lawrence Cockfosters Medical Centre, Heddon Court Avenue, Cockfosters, Barnet EN4 9NB Tel: 020 8441 7008 Fax: 020 8441 0550 — MB BS 1960 Lond.; FRCS Eng. 1966; MRCS Eng. LRCP Lond. 1960. (Lond. Hosp.) Hosp. Pract. (Surg.) Chase Farm Hosp. Enfield. Prev: Regist. (Surg.) Lond. Hosp. & Whipps Cross Hosp. Lond.

LUPINI, Nicholas John Ty-Elli Group Practice, Ty Elli, Llanelli SA15 3BD Tel: 01554 772678 / 773747 Fax: 01554 774476; 39 Hendre Park, Llangennech, Llanelli SA14 8UP — MB BS 1971 Lond.; BSc Lond. 1968. (Lond. Hosp.) Clin. Asst. (Genitourin. Med.) Singleton Hosp. Swansea.

LUPOLI, Arturo Monkspath Surgery, 27 Farmhouse Way, Monkspath, Shirley, Solihull B90 4EH Tel: 0121 711 1414 Fax: 0121 711 3753; 12 Copt Heath Croft, Knowle, Solihull B93 9LT — MB BS 1987 Lond.

LUPPRIAN, Keith Granville (retired) 33 Cranford Avenue, Exmouth EX8 2QA Tel: 01395 270799 — MB BS Lond. 1949; MRCS Eng. LRCP Lond. 1952; FFA RCS Eng. 1959; DA Eng. 1955. Prev: Sen. Cons. Anaesth. Roy. Devon & Exeter Hosp. Exeter.

LUPTON, David Joseph Gerafon Surgery, Benllech, Tyn-y-Gongl LL74 8TF Tel: 01248 852122 Fax: 01248 853698; Bryn Dyfnan, Talwrn, Llangefni LL77 8JD — MB ChB 1987 Manch.

LUPTON, Mr Eric William 25 Hillington Road, Sale M33 6GQ Tel: 0161 962 1101 — MD 1981 Lond.; MB BS Lond. 1970; FRCS Ed. 1977. (Univ. Coll. Hosp.) Cons. Urol. Univ. Hosp. S. Manch. Socs: Brit. Assn. Urol. Surgs.; Amer. Urol. Assn. Prev: Sen. Regist. (Urol.) Manch. & Salford HAs; Surg. Regist. Leics. HA; Ho. Surg. St. Pancras Hosp. (Univ. Coll. Hosp.) Lond.

LUPTON, Harriet Anne The Surgery, 40 St. Johns Road, Bedminster, Bristol BS3 4JE Tel: 0117 966 5238 Fax: 0117 963 1422 — MB BChir 1977 Camb.; MRCP Lond. 1980; MRCGP 1986. (King's Coll. Hosp.) GP Partner. Prev: GP Runcorn; Clin. Asst. (Psychiat.) S.mead Health Serv. Bristol; Regist. (Gen. & Renal Med.) E. Birm. Hosp.

LUPTON, Kathleen Julia Park Surgery, Park Surgery, Hursley Road, Chandlers Ford, Eastleigh SO53 2ZH Tel: 023 8026 7355 Fax: 023 8026 5394 — BM 1977 Soton.

LUPTON, Margaret Elizabeth Parkview Surgery, 23 Ribblesdale Place, Preston PR1 3NA Tel: 01772 2584474 — MB ChB 1992 Liverp.; DFFP 1995; MRCGP 1998. p/t Princip. G.P.; Family Plann. Clin. Med. Off. Socs: BMA & Med. Protec. Soc.; Diplomate of the Fac. of Familty Plann. & Reproductive Health Care.

LUPTON, Marjorie Frances 229 Queen Victoria Drive, Jordanhill, Glasgow G13 1UU Tel: 0141 959 1480 — MB BCh BAO 1979 Belf. Clin. Med. Off. (Family Plann. & Reproduc. Health) Centre for Family Plann. & Sexual Health Glas. Socs: Fac. Family Plann. & Reproduc. Health.

LUPTON, Mr Martin Geoffrey Francis 118 Asylum Road, London SE15 2LW — MB BS 1988 Lond.; MRCOG 1998. (University College Hospital London)

LUPTON, Penelope Mary Hilda Teixeira 30 Spring Walk, Whitstable CT5 4PP — MB ChB 1993 Dundee.

LUPTON, Susan Charlotte 3 The Stables, Berkswell, Coventry CV7 7BG — MB ChB 1996 Liverp.

LUPTON, Susannah Dawn Norwood Medical Centre, 360 Herries Road, Sheffield S5 7HD Tel: 0114 242 6208; 78 Carsickhill Road,

Sheffield S10 3LX — MB ChB 1994 Sheff.; DFFP 1999; MRCGP 1999; DGM RCP Lond. 1997; DRCOG 1999. GP Princip. Norwood Med. Centre Sheff. Prev: GP Asst. Grimethorpe Surg. Barnsley; GP Regist. Richmond Med. Centre, Sheff.; SMO O&G Rotterham Dist. Gen. Hosp.

LUQMANI, Raashid Ahmed Rheumatology Department, Western General Hospital, Crewe Road S., Edinburgh EH4 2XU Tel: 0131 537 1803 Fax: 0131 537 1051 Email: raashid.luqmani@ed.ac.uk — BM BS 1982 Nottm.; DM Nottm. 1992, BMedSci (Hons.) 1980; FRCP Ed. 1997; MRCP (UK) 1985. (Nottm.) Cons. Rheum. & Sen. Lect. (Rheum.) W.. Gen. Hosp. & Univ. Edin. Prev: Sen. Regist. (Rheum.) & Hon. Lect. Selly Oak Hosp. Birm. & Univ. Birm.

LURIE, Philip Solomon 164 Greendyked Road, Edinburgh — MB ChB 1945 Ed.

LURKINS, Michael David The Hamilton Practice, Keats House, Bush Fair, Harlow CM18 6LY Tel: 01279 692700 Fax: 01279 692719; 105 Godfrey Way, Great Dunmow, Dunmow CM6 2SQ Tel: 01371 872247 — MB BS 1983 Lond.; BSc Lond. 1980. (St. Thos. Hosp.) Princip. Gen. Pract.

LURRING, Elisabeth Margaret (retired) 43A Brackenbury Road, London W6 0BG Tel: 020 8748 9215 — MB BCh BAO 1959 Dub.; BA, MB BCh BAO Dub. 1959; DRCOG 1961.

LUSCOMBE, Angus Henry (retired) Charterhouse, 10 Broad Walk, Wilmslow SK9 5PJ Tel: 01625 524849 Fax: 01625 524849 — MB BS Lond. 1955; MRCGP 1965.

LUSCOMBE, Ann Constance Margaret (retired) Charterhouse, 10 Broad Walk, Wilmslow SK9 5PJ Tel: 01625 524849 Fax: 01625 524849 — MA Oxf. 1955, BM BCh 1954. Prev: Med. Off. Blood Transfus. Serv.

LUSCOMBE, Bronwen Richard (retired) 1 Ashwood, Warlingham CR6 9HT Tel: 01883 624420 — MRCS Eng. LRCP Lond. 1943. Prev: Sen. Med. Off. (Clin.) Merton & Sutton HA.

LUSCOMBE, Francis Edward Mid Tors, Dousland, Yelverton PL20 6PA — MB BS 1980 Lond.; MRCS Eng. LRCP Lond. 1980; FCAnaesth. 1984. (Char. Cross) Cons. Anaesth. with Interest in Pain Relief Derriford Hosp. Plymouth; Surg. Lt.-Cdr. RNR. Socs: Assn. Anaesths. & Pain Soc. Prev: Cons. Anaesth. with interest in Pain Relief Roy. Cornw. Hosp. (Treliske); Sen. Regist. (Anaesth.) Wessex RHA; Regist. (Anaesth.) Bristol & W.on HA.

LUSCOMBE, Hilary Caroline Silver Lane Surgery, 1 Suffolk Court, Yeadon, Leeds LS19 7JN Tel: 0113 250 4953 Fax: 0113 250 9804 — MB BS 1982 Lond.; MRCGP 1986; DRCOG 1987; DA (UK) 1984. (Char. Cross) Socs: BMA.

***LUSCOMBE, Jonathan Charles** Myle House, 4 Mill Place, Lisvane, Cardiff CF14 0TF — MB ChB 1995 Birm.

LUSCOMBE, Mark David Springfield, 6 Main Rd, Grindleford, Sheffield S32 2JN — MB ChB 1997 Sheff.

LUSCOMBE, Nicholas Dominic Richard 4 Caxton Road, Sheffield S10 3DE — MB BChir 1987 Camb.

LUSH, Adrian Montague 14 Burlington Road, Ipswich IP1 2EU Tel: 01473 211661 Fax: 01473 289187 — MRCS Eng. LRCP Lond. 1958; MFCM 1974; DPH Lond. 1962; DObst. RCOG 1961; DCH RCPSI 1960.

LUSH, Brandon Stuart (retired) Hazel Cottage, Lower Hazel, Rudgeway, Bristol BS35 3QP Tel: 01454 412112 — MB BS Lond. 1942; MD Lond. 1949; FRCP Lond. 1964, M 1947; MRCS Eng. LRCP Lond. 1942. Cons. Phys. (Geriat. Med.) Frenchay & Manor Pk. Hosps. Bristol. Prev: Cons. Phys. (Gen. Med.) DHSS Med. Bd.ing Centre.

LUSH, Christopher John Department of Haematology, Raigmore Hospital, Inverness IV2 3UJ Tel: 01463 234151 Fax: 01463 705878 Email: chris.lush@raigmore.scot.nhs.uk; Drynie Lodge, Kilmuir, North Kessock, Inverness IV1 3ZG — MB BS 1978 Lond.; BSc 1976 Lond.; MRCP (UK) 1986; MRCPath 1989. (St. Bartholomens) Cons. Haemat. Raigmore Hosp. Inverness. Socs: FRCPath; MRCP. Prev: Sen. Regist. (Haemat.) Leic. Roy. Infirm.

LUSH, David (retired) 15 Andrew Crescent, Queen's Park, Chester CH4 7BQ Tel: 01244 676940 — MB ChB Bristol 1962; FRCA 1969; DObst RCOG 1965. Prev: Cons. Anaesth. Countess of Chester Hosp.

LUSH, Margaret Alison (retired) Hazel Cottage, Lower Hazel, Rudgeway, Bristol BS35 3QP Tel: 01454 412112 — MRCS Eng. LRCP Lond. 1946. Clin Asst.Barrow Hosp. Bristol; Mem. Med. Bd.ing Panel DHSS; Cons. ENT Surg. Ipswich Hosp. NSH Trust. Prev: Clin. Asst. Belmont Hosp.

LUSH, Patrick St Lawrence Bartongate Surgery, 115 Barton Street, Gloucester GL1 4HR Tel: 01452 422944 Fax: 01452 387871; The New House, 14 Georgian Close, Abbeydale, Gloucester GL4 5DG Tel: 01452 613830 — MRCS Eng. LRCP Lond. 1976; LMSSA Lond. 1975; Dip. Criminol. Lond. 1993. (Brist.) Socs: BMA. Prev: Ho. Phys. Ham Green Hosp. Bristol; Ho. Surg. Sharoe Green Hosp. Fulwood.

LUSH, Richard John Department of Haematology, Bristol Royal Infirmary, Marlborough St., Bristol BS2 8HW — MB ChB 1990 Bristol; MRCP (UK) 1993. Regist. (Haemat.) Roy. United Hosp. NHS Trust. Prev: SHO (Med.) Frenchay Hosp. Bristol.; SHO (Med.) Singleton Hosp. Swansea; Ho. Surg. MusGr. Pk. Hosp. Taunton.

LUSH, Robin (retired) Hayter's Cottage, Trotton, Petersfield GU31 5JR — MA Oxf. 1958, BM BCh 1957; DObst RCOG 1961; DA Eng. 1962. Prev: Obst. Ho. Surg. St. And. Hosp. Billericay.

LUSH, Stephen Graham Corporation Road Health Centre, 32 Corporation Road, Grangetown, Cardiff CF11 7XA Tel: 029 2022 6057 Fax: 029 2064 0524; 28 Charlotte Square, Rhiwbina, Cardiff CF14 6NE — MB BCh 1977 Wales; MRCGP 1982.

LUSK, John Alexander Rogers Ribblesdale Place Surgery, 23 Ribblesdale Place, Preston PR1 3NA Tel: 01772 258474; 13 Manor Avenue, Fulwood, Preston PR2 8DN Tel: 01772 700439 Fax: 01772 884200 — MB ChB 1965 Ed.

LUSMAN, Diane Ailsa Hospital, Dalmellington Road, Ayr KA6 6AB Tel: 01292 610556 — MB ChB 1987 Glas.; MRCPsych 1992. Sen. Regist. (Old Age Psychiat.) Glas. (W. Scotl. Higher Profess. Train. Scheme). Prev: Staff Grade Psychiat. (Old Age Psychiat.) Roy. Alexandra Hosp. Paisley; Regist. (Psychiat.) Dykebar Hosp. Paisley.

LUSTMAN, Alexander James 56 The Drive, Gosforth, Newcastle upon Tyne NE3 4AJ — MB ChB 1994 Manch.

LUSTMAN, Felix 5 Walker Terrace, Gateshead NE8 1HX — MB BS 1960 Durh.; DPH 1964; DObst RCOG 1962.

LUSTY, Timothy David Upper Whitley Farm, Cumnor, Oxford OX2 9QQ — MB BCh 1965 Oxf.

LUSTY, William John 16 Trewirgie Road, Redruth TR15 2SX — MB BS 1996 Newc.

LUSZNAT, Rose-Marie Gudrun St Christopher's Hospital, Fareham PO16 7JD Tel: 01329 316410 Fax: 01329 220670; The Limes, 36 Veryan, Fareham PO14 1NN — State Exam Med 1980 Munster; MRCPsych 1986; Dip. Psychol. Münster 1978. (Westphalia Wilhelms Univ.) Cons. Psychogeriat. Portsmouth Health Care Trust. Prev: Sen. Regist. (Psychiat.) Wessex RHA; Regist. (Psychiat.) Soton. HA; Research Regist. (Psychiat.) Soton. HA.

LUTFY, Awni Michael, OBE Dumfries & Galloway Royal Infirmary, Bankend Road, Dumfries DG1 4AP Tel: 01387 241472 Fax: 01387 241690; 7 Corbelly Hill, Dumfries DG2 7SQ Tel: 01387 254583 — MB ChB 1975 Baghdad; FRCPath 1994,; MRCPath 1983. Cons. Path. Dumfries & Galloway Roy. Infirm. Socs: Assn. Clin. Path.; Internat. Acad. Path. (Brit. Div.).

LUTHER, Arnold Martin (retired) Cedar House, Fowey PL23 1JJ Tel: 01726 3558 — MRCS Eng. LRCP Lond. 1951. Prev: Ho. Surg. ENT & Ophth. Depts. & Cas. Off. W.m. Hosp.

LUTHERT, Professor Philip John Department of Pathology, Institute of Ophthalmology, Bath St., London EC1V 9EL Tel: 020 7608 6800 Fax: 020 7608 6862 — MB BS 1980 Lond.; BSc Lond. 1977; MRCP (UK) 1983; MRCPath 1989. Prof. Path. Inst. Ophth. Lond. Prev: Sen. Lect. (Neuropath.) Inst. Psychiat. Lond.; Research Fell. (Neuropath.) Inst. Psychiat. Lond.; SHO (Cardiol.) St. Geo. Hosp. Lond.

LUTHMAN, Judith Anne Kettering General Hospital, Rothwell Road, Kettering NN16 8UZ Tel: 01536 492000; Grafton Lodge, Upper Harlestone, Northampton NN7 4EH — MB BS 1977 Lond.; BSc Lond. 1977; FFA RCS 1981. Cons. Anaesth. Kettering Gen. Hosp. N.ants. Socs: Assn. Anaesth.; Obst. Anaesth. Assn.; BADS.

LUTHRA, Avnish 3 Eveline Court, Connaught Gardens, London N10 3LA — MB ChB 1993 Ed.

LUTHRA, Devinder Singh Bedford General Hospital, South Wing, Kempston Road, Bedford MK42 9DJ — MB BS 1969 All India Inst. of Med. Sci.

LUTHRA, Mr Pran Nath Roding Lane North Surgery, Roding Lane North, Woodford Bridge, Woodford Green IG8 8NR Tel: 020 8559

0280 Fax: 020 8559 1349; 70 Manor Road, Chigwell IG7 5PG — MB BS 1966 Delhi; FRCS Ed. 1980.

LUTHRA, Rajnish 259 Hoyles Lane, Cottam, Preston PR4 0LD — MB ChB 1992 Liverp.

LUTMAN, Daniel Henry 46 Foxbury Road, Bromley BR1 4DQ — MB BS 1992 Newc.

LUTTER, Paul Stephen White House Surgery, High Street, Moreton-in-Marsh GL56 0AT Tel: 01608 650317 Fax: 01608 650071 — MB ChB 1974 Bristol; BSc (Cellular Path. 1st cl. Hons.) Bristol 1971, MB ChB 1974; DObst 1978; Cert JCC Lond. 1978. Socs: BMA. Prev: SHO (O & G, Med. & Paediat.) Glos. Roy. Hosp.

LUTTER, Peter Fforde, OStJ, Col. late RAMC Retd. (retired) Velindre, Pant-y-Goitre, Llanvair Kilgeddin, Abergavenny NP7 9BB Tel: 01873 840358 Email: hflutter@aol.com — MB BS 1965 Lond.; MRCGP 1975; DObst RCOG 1973. Prev: Brit. Med. Liaison Off. USA & Canada.

LUTTERLOCH, Mr Michael John Longwood House, The Bath Clinic, Bath BA2 7BR Tel: 01225 835555; Roadmenders Cottage, Norton St. Philip, Bath BA2 7LN Tel: 01373 834214 Fax: 01374 834214 — MB BS 1974 Lond.; BDS 1968; FRCS Ed. 1988; FDS RCS Eng. 1976. (King's Coll. Hosp. & St. Geo.) Cons. Oral & Maxillofacial Surg. Roy. United Hosp. Bath; Clin. Lect. (Oral & Maxillofacial Surg.) Bristol Univ. Dent. Sch. Socs: Fell. Brit. Assn. Oral & Maxillofacial Surg.; BMA. Prev: Sen. Regist. (Oral Surg.) Qu. Mary's Hosp. Roehampton, W.m. Hosp. & Univ. Coll. Hosp.

LUTTON, Clifford Cuthbert, OStJ (retired) — MB ChB 1947 Ed.; MRCGP 1964. Prev: Capt. RAMC.

LUTTON, Mary (retired) 2Hullaghadon Lane, Dungannon BT71 6LH Tel: 02887 725392 — MB BCh BAO 1971 Belf.; DObst RCOG 1973; FFA RCSI 1975. Prev: Cons. S. Tyrone Hosp.

LUTTRELL, Steven Richard Rankin Peckwater Centre, 6 Peckwater Street, London NW5 2TX Tel: 0207 530 6400 Fax: 0207 530 6405 Email: steven.luttrell@cichs-tr.nthumes.nhs.uk — MB ChB 1984 Glas.; BSc (Hons.) Glas. 1981; MRCP (UK) 1987. (Glasgow Univ) Cons. Phys. & Geriat. Camden & Islington Comm. Health NHS Trust; Barrister at Law Lincolns Inn 1992. Prev: Sen. Regist. (Geriat. Med.) Univ. Coll. Hosp. Lond.; Sen. Regist. (Geriat. Med) Whittington Hosp., Lond.

LUTY, Jason Spencer 8 Ravenswood Road, Redland, Bristol BS6 6BN — MB ChB 1991 Birm.

LUXEN, Arthur Armand Joseph 12 Elvaston Place, London SW7 5QG — MD 1978 Paris.

LUXON, Professor Linda Maitland National Hospital for Neurology & Neurosurgery, Queen Square, London WC1N 3BG Tel: 020 7837 3611 Ext: 3385 Fax: 020 7813 8107 Email: lindal.luxon@gosh-tr.nthames.nhs.uk; 15 Upper Wimpole Stl, London W1M 7TB Tel: 020 7486 5787 Fax: 020 7486 5470 Email: linda.luxon@coltarts.demon.co.uk — MB BS 1972 Lond.; MB BS (Hons.) Lond. 1972; BSc (Hons.) Lond. 1969; FRCP Lond. 1987, M 1974. (St. Thos.) Prof. Audiol. Med. Inst. Of Child health Univ. Coll. Lond.; Cons. Phys. Neurotol. Nat. Hosp. Neurol. & Neurosurg. Lond.; Hon cons phys Gt. Ormond St Hosp. for Childr. Nhs trust Lond.; Med. Adviser, Roy. Nat. Inst. for deaf Lond. Socs: (Chairm.) Brit. Assn. Audiol. Phys.; Vice-chair. Brit. Soc. Audiol.; Sect. of Otol., Roy. Soc.Med. Prev: Sen. Regist. (Otoneurol.) Nat. Hosp. Nerv. Dis. Lond.; Lect. (Clin. Neurochem.) Inst. Neurol. Nat. Hosp. Nerv. Dis. Lond.; Regist. (Neurol.) Middlx. Hosp. Lond.

LUXTON, Bruce Peter (retired) 6 Ora Close, Croyde, Braunton EX33 1NJ Tel: 01271 890473 Email: bruce@luxtongp.freeserve.co.uk — BM BCh 1955 Oxf.; MA (Physics) Oxf. 1947. Prev: Ho. Surg. Lond. Hosp.

LUXTON, Dimitrius Edward Anthony 86 Gayton Road, King's Lynn PE30 4ER Tel: 01553 774868 — MA, BM BCh Oxf. 1970; FRCP 1989; MRCP (UK) 1975. Cons. Geriat. Lifespan Healthcare NHS Trust Davison Ho., Brookfields Hosp. Mill Rd., Camb. Socs: Brit. Geriat. Soc. & BMA; Alzheimers Dis. Soc. Prev: Resid. Ho. Phys. St. Geo. Hosp. Lincoln; Resid. Ho. Surg. Stoke Mandeville Hosp. Aylesbury; Sen. Regist. (Geriat. Med.) Chesterton Hosp. Camb.

LUXTON, Karen Doreen Battle Hospital, Oxford Road, Reading RG30 1AG Tel: 01734 583666; 31 Underhill, Moulsford, Wallingford OX10 9JH — MB BS 1983 Lond. Staff Cardiol. Battle Hosp. Reading. Prev: Regist. (Gen. Med.) Battle Hosp. Reading & Watford Gen. Hosp.; SHO (Gen. Med.) Harold Wood Hosp. Essex.

LUYT, David Kenneth 3 Welford Court, Knighton, Leicester LE2 6ER — MB BCh 1980 Witwatersrand.

LUYT, Karen Department of Paediatrics, Derriford Hospital, Plymouth PL6 8DH Tel: 01752 777111; 4 Simmons Yard, Harberton, Totnes TQ9 7SQ Tel: 01803 865674 Fax: 01803 865674 Email: geer@compuserve.com — MB ChB 1992 Pretoria; MRCP; MRCPCH. (University of Pretoria) Specialist Regist. Rotat. (Paediat.) Derriford Hosp. Plymouth. Prev: Fell. (Paediat. IC) Bristol Childr.'s Hosp.; SHO Rotat. Bristol.

LUZIETTI, Roberto 227 Ham Drive, Plymouth PL2 3NF — State Exam Modena 1985.

LUZZI, Graziano Adriano Wycombe Hospital, High Wycombe HP11 2TT Tel: 01494 425079 Fax: 01494 425661; Radcliffe Infirmary, Oxford OX2 6HE Tel: 01865224053 Fax: 01865 224378 — BM BCh 1981 Oxf.; MA Camb. 1982, BA 1978; DM Oxf. 1993; MRCP (UK) 1984; FRCP 1998. Cons. Phys. Genitourin. Med. & HIV Wycombe Hosp.; Hon. Cons. Harrison Dept. Radcliffe Infirm. Oxf. Prev: Clin. Lect. & Hon. Sen. Regist. (Med.) John Radcliffe Hosp. Oxf.

LWANDA, John Lloyd Airdrie Health Centre, Monskcourt Avenue, Airdrie ML6 0JU Tel: 01236 768900 Fax: 01236 750456; 4 Gailes Park, Bothwell, Glasgow G71 8TS Tel: 01698 854290 Fax: 01698 854472 Email: 106671.3551@compuserve.com — MB ChB 1976 Glas.; MRCP (UK) 1979; MFFP 1993; DCH RCPSI 1978; MRCP Ed.; MRCP Glas.; FRCP Ed. 1998. (Univ. Glas.) GP Airdrie; Prison Med. Off. Longriggend Remand Unit.; Clin. Tutor Univ. Glas. Dep. Gen. Pract. Socs: FRCP Ed. Prev: Med. Specialist Kamuzu Centr. Hosp. Lilongwe, Malawi; Sen. Lect. Coll. Med. Malawi; Hosp. Pract. Glas. Roy.

LWIN, K Gillmoss Medical Centre, 48 Petherick Road, Liverpool L11 0AG Tel: 0151 546 3867.

LWIN, Michael Kyaw-Kyaw 22 Dudley Road, Liverpool L18 1ET — MB ChB 1997 Liverp.

LWIN, Tun (Surgery), 343 Prince Regent Lane, London E16 3JL Tel: 020 7511 2980 Fax: 020 7474 7816; 18 Hickman Close, West Beckton, London E16 3TA Tel: 020 7476 5973 Fax: 020 7476 5973 — MB BS 1971 Med. Inst. (III) Mandalay; BA (Psychol.) Rangoon Arts & Sc. Univ. 1978. (Inst. Med. Mandalay) Hosp. Pract. (Ophth.) Newham Gen. Hosp. Lond. Socs: St Paul. Prev: Trainee GP Swanley; SHO (Psychiat.) Winterton Hosp. Sedgefield.

LY, Ien Soun Sana Flat 4/R, 5 University Av, Glasgow G12 8NN — MB ChB 1997 Glas.

LY, Mary Helen 46 Ballyalbana Road, Ballyclare BT39 9SP Tel: 01960 323352 — MB BCh BAO 1997 Belf. SHO Paediat. Antrim Area Hosp.

***LY, Thi Phung** 12 Radegund Road, Cambridge CB1 3RL — MCRS Eng. LRCP 1983 Lond.

LYALL, Alan Richards Melrose Bank, Garvock Road, Laurencekirk AB30 1FJ — MB ChB 1951 Aberd.; DRCOG 1957.

LYALL, Elizabeth Grace Hermione 75 Carleton Road, Tufnell Park, London N7 0ET Tel: 020 7700 1355 Email: h.lyall@ic.ac.uk — MB ChB 1983 Ed.; BSc (Hons.) Ed. 1980, MB ChB (Hons.) 1983; MRCP (UK) 1986. Lect. (Paediat. Infec. Dis.) St Mary's Hosp. Lond. Prev: Clin. Research Fell. Dept. Childlife & Health Univ. Edin.; Regist. (Paediat.) Roy. Hosp. for Sick Childr. Edin.

LYALL, Fiona Jane, MBE Melrose Bank, Laurencekirk AB30 1AL — MB ChB 1954 Aberd.; DPH Aberd. 1958. Dep. Lt. Co. of Kincardine.; Dir. Grampian Television plc. Prev: Regist. (Paediat.) Aberd. Matern. Hosp.; Ho. Surg. Raigmore Hosp. Inverness; Ho. Phys. Roy. Aberd. Hosp. Sick Childr.

LYALL, Hamish Glen Arthur House, 70 Netley St., Farnborough GU14 6AT — MB ChB 1998 Dund.; MB ChB Dund 1998.

LYALL, Mr Harry Alexander Bishops Hall, Great Leighs, Chelmsford CM3 1PP Tel: 01376 325653 — MB BChir 1985 Camb.; MA Camb. 1985; FRCS (Orth.) Ed. 1995; FRCS Ed. 1990; FRCS Eng. 1990. (St. Thos. Hosp. Med. Sch.) Cons. Orthop. Surg. Broomfield Hosp. Chelmsford.

LYALL, Helen 32 Dalziel Drive, Pollokshields, Glasgow G41 4HY — MB ChB 1988 Dundee; MD Dundee 1994, BMSc 1985; MRCOG 1995. Sen. Lect./Hon. Cons. O & G, Glas. Roy. Infirm. Prev: Sen. Regist. Rotat. O & G, W. Scotl.; SHO (O & G) Ninewells Hosp. Dundee; Regist. Rotat. (O & G) SE Scotl.

LYALL, Ian McClelland Ashbourne, Claxton, York YO60 7SD Tel: 01904 468209; Strensall, York YO32 5UA Tel: 01904 490532 —

MB ChB 1977 Manch.; BSc St. And. 1974; MRCGP 1982; DRCOG 1983. Socs: York Med. Soc. Prev: Capt. RAMC.

LYALL, Mr James Bowmont Farquharson Queen Margaret Hospital, Dunfermline KY12 0SU Tel: 01383 623623; 10 McLauchlan Rise, Aberdour KY3 0SS Tel: 01383 860579 — MB BS 1993 Lond.; BDS 1974; FRCS Ed. 1997; FDS RCS 1980. (Char. Cross) Cons. Surg. (Oral & Maxillofacial); Hon. Cons. Armed Forces, Scotl. Socs: BAOMFS; Fell. RCS (Eng.); Fell. RCS (Ed.). Prev: Sen. Regist. Oral & Maxillofacial Surg. Char. Cross Hosp. 1987-1989; Sen. Regist. Oral & Maxillofacial Surg. Guildford 1995-1996.

LYALL, James Robert Watt The Old Vicarage, Aldworth, Reading RG8 9SB Email: lyall@bigfoot.com — MSc Manch. 1962, BSc (Hons.) 1960; MD Lond. 1978, MB BS 1969; FRCP Lond. 1986; MRCP (U.K.) 1972. (St. Thos.) Cons. Phys. W. Berks. (Reading) Health Dist. Socs: Med. Research Soc. & Brit. Thoracic Soc. Prev: Lect. in Med. St. Thos. Hosp. Med. Sch. Lond.; Regist. (Med.), & Ho. Phys. Dept. Neurol. & Thoracic Med. St. Thos.; Hosp. Lond.

LYALL, Mr Malcolm George (retired) The Mulligan, 30 Links View, Cruden Bay, Peterhead AB42 0RF Tel: 01779 812449 Fax: 01779 812928 — MA Aberd. 1950, MB ChB 1956; FRCS Ed. 1970; FCOphth 1990; DO Eng. 1958. Prev: Cons. Ophth. Basildon & Thurrock HA.

LYALL, Marc 42 Emerson Avenue, Middlesbrough TS5 7QH — MB BS 1997 Lond.

LYALL, Mr Michael Hodge Ninewells Hospital & Medical School, Dundee Tel: 01382 660111 Fax: 01382 633858 Email: michael.h.lyall@tuht.scot.nhs.uk — MB ChB 1965 St. And.; ChM Dund 1974; FRCS Ed. 1970. (St. And.) Med. Director, Tayside Univ. Hosps. NHS Trust; Hon. Sen. Lect. Univ. Dundee; Cons. Surg., Ninewells Hosp., Dundee. Socs: Brit. Assn. Paediat. Surg.; Moynihan Chir. Club; Assn. Surg. Prev: Lect. (Surg.) Univ. Dundee & Hon. Sen. Regist. Ninewells Hosp. Dundee; SHO S.. Gen. Hosp. Glas.; Demonst. (Anat.) Univ. St. And.

LYALL, Rebecca Ann 29 Redhill Drive, Brighton BN1 5FH — MB BS 1990 Lond.

LYALL, Rosalind Mary Learning Disabilty Service, Lothian Primary Care Trust, 65 Morningside Drive, Edinburgh EH10 5NQ Tel: 0131 446 6819 Ext: 6802 Fax: 0131 446 6803; Melbreck, Romanno Bridge, West Linton EH46 7BZ — MB ChB 1977 Dundee; MPhil Ed. 1987; MRCPsych 1984; T(Psychiat.) 1991; MBA Stirling 1998. (Dundee) Cons. Psychiat. (Learning Disabil.); Clin. Director, Learning Disabil. Serv. Prev: Med. Off. Ment. Welf. Commiss. for Scotl.; Sen. Regist. (Ment. Handicap) Fife HB; Regist. (Psychiat.) Lothian HB.

LYALL, Sewa Singh Foleshill Road Surgery, 949 Foleshill Road, Coventry CV2 5HW Tel: 024 7668 8482/8230 Fax: 024 7663 8273; 21 Poppeyfield Court, Gibbet Hill, Coventry CV7 7HW — MB ChB 1974 Birm. Prev: Trainee Gen. Pract. Kettering Vocational Train. Scheme; SHO (O & G) Kettering Gen. Hosp.

LYBURN, Iain Douglas Depart. Of Radiology, Frenchay Hospital, Bristol BS16 1LE Tel: 0117 975 3966 Email: ilyburn@hotmail.com — MB ChB 1991 Bristol; BSc Bristol 1988; MRCP (UK) 1994; FRCR 1998. Cons. (Clin. Radiol.) Bristol. Prev: Fell. Abdom.. Imaging.Vancouver. Gen. Hosp. Univ. Brit.Columbia Canada; Regist. (Clin. Radiol.) Bristol; SHO (Internal Med.) Univ. Hosp. Nottm.

LYCETT, Christopher Douglas Lycett (retired) 14 Langdale Close, Maidenhead SL6 1SY Tel: 01628 419183 — MB BS Lond. 1940; MD (Hyg.) Lond. 1948; MRCS Eng. LRCP Lond. 1940; FFCM RCP (UK)1974; DIH Eng. 1980; DPH Eng. 1947. Prev: Area Med. Off. Wilts. AHA.

LYCETT, Norman Austin Tir Na Nog, 9 Bryn-y-Paderau, Tywyn LL36 9LA Tel: 01654 710829 — MB ChB 1960 Liverp.

LYDEN, Christopher James (retired) Troodos, Littledean Hill, Cinderford GL14 2TT — MB BS 1964 Lond.; DObst RCOG 1971. Computer Cons. Vamp Health Ltd. Lond.; Fund Holding Train. Cons. Software Systems Adviser. Prev: Squadron Ldr. RAF Med. Br., Sen. Med. Off. RAF Binbrook.

LYDFORD-DAVIS, Helen The Nook, Wigston Road, Oadby, Leicester LE2 5QE — BM BCh 1990 Oxf.; BA (Zool.) Oxf. 1985; MRCP (UK) 1995.

LYDON, Anna Patricia Mary Glebe Farmhouse, Shillingford St George, Exeter EX2 9QN — MB BS 1985 Lond.; MRCP (UK) 1989; FRCR 1993. Sen. Regist. (Clin. Oncol.) Roy. Devon & Exeter Hosp. & Freedom Fields Hosp. Plymouth. Prev: Regist. (Radiother. & Oncol.) Middlx. Hosp. & Mt. Vernon Hosp.

LYDON, Bridget Nuala (retired) Didsbury Medical Centre, 645 Wilmslow Road, Didsbury, Manchester M20 6BA Tel: 0161 445 1957 Fax: 0161 434 9931 — MB BCh BAO 1962 NUI.

LYDON, Christopher 2 Blakesley Court, 26 Blakesley Avenue, Ealing, London W5 2DU Tel: 020 8998 4874 — MB BCh BAO 1951 NUI; MFOM RCP 1980; MFCM 1974; MFOM RCPI 1982; DCH Eng. 1957; DPH Lond. 1958. (Galway) Accredit. Occupat. Health Specialist. Lond. Socs: BMA & Soc. Occupat. Med. Prev: Employm. Med. Adviser EMAS; Dep. MOH Lond. Boro. Hillingdon; SHO Brighton & Lewes Hosp. Gp. & United Liverp. Hosps.

LYDON, Richard John Tutbury Health Centre, Monk Street, Tutbury, Burton-on-Trent DE13 9NA Tel: 01283 812210 Fax: 01283 815810; Raeburn, Boggy Lane, Church Broughton, Derby DE65 5AR Tel: 01283 585470 — MB ChB 1971 Aberd.; BMedBiol (Hons.) Aberd. 1968, MB ChB 1971; MRCGP 1983. Course Organiser Burton-on-Trent VTS.

LYDON, Yvette Helen Findlay Tutbury Health Centre, Monk Street, Tutbury, Burton-on-Trent DE13 9NA Tel: 01283 812210 Fax: 01283 815810; Raeburn Boggy Lane, Church Broughton, Derby DE65 5AR Tel: 01283 585470 — MB ChB 1972 Aberd.

LYE, Professor Michael David William Geriatric Medicine, University Clinical Department, The Duncan Building, Daulby St., Liverpool L69 3GA Tel: 0151 706 4062 Fax: 0151 706 4064 Email: m.lye@liv.ac.uk; Orchard cottage, Oldhall Farm, Puddington, South Wirral CH64 5SG Tel: 0151 353 1121 Email: mq33@air.ac.uk — MB ChB 1965 Leeds; MD Leeds 1980; FRCP Lond. 1985; MRCP (UK) 1970. (Leeds) Prof. Geriat. Med. Univ. Liverp.; Cons. Geriat. Roy. Liverp. Hosp. Socs: (Exec. & Counc.) Brit. Geriat. Soc.; (Exec.) Brit. Soc. Research on Ageing; Internat. Assn. Gerontol. (Treas. Europ. Sect.). Prev: Sen. Lect. (Geriat. Med.) Univ. Manch.; Lect. (Geriat. Med.) Univ. Soton; Sen. Regist. (Med.) United Birm. Hosps.

LYELL, Alan (retired) Craigallion, Skelmorlie PA17 5DT Tel: 01475 520729 — MD 1950 Camb.; MB BChir 1942; FRCP Ed. 1962, M 1951; FRCP Glas. 1967, M 1964. Prev: Cons. i/c Dept. Dermat. Glas. Roy. Infirm.

LYELL, David Alexander The Farley Road Medical Practice, 53 Farley Road, South Croydon CR2 7NG Tel: 020 8651 1222 Fax: 020 8657 9297 Email: d.lyell@ukonline.co.uk — MB BS 1979 Lond.; DRCOG 1981. (St. Mary's)

LYELL, Veronica Rachel 16 Christmas Steps, Bristol BS1 5BS — MB ChB 1995 Bristol.

LYGO, Martin Howard The Wardroom, HMS Neptune, Clyde Submarine Base, Faslane, Helensburgh G84 8HL — MB BS 1985 Lond.; MA Oxf. 1982.

LYLE, Alexis 80 Hamilton Place, Aberdeen AB15 5BA — MB ChB 1984 Aberd.

LYLE, David John Ranken Worth Hall Paddock, Turners Hill Road, Worth, Crawley RH10 4PE Tel: 01293 883962 — MB BS 1972 Lond.; FFA RCS Eng. 1978. (St. Thos.) Cons. Anaesth. Crawley Hosp. & BUPA Gatwick Pk. Hosp. Socs: Fell. Roy. Soc. Med. Prev: Sen. Regist. (Anaesth.) Middlx. Hosp.; Regist. (Anaesth.) St. Thos. Hosp. Lond. & Alder Hey Childr. Hosp.; Liverp.

LYLE, David William Sevenposts Surgery, 326A Prestbury Road, Prestbury, Cheltenham GL52 3DD Tel: 01242 244103; 2 Shaw Green Lane, Prestbury, Cheltenham GL52 3BP — MB BS 1978 Lond.; MRCGP 1982; DRCOG Lond. 1981.

LYLE, David Wreford Ranken (retired) 60 Folders Lane, Burgess Hill RH15 0DX — MA Camb. 1946, MB BChir 1945; MRCS Eng. LRCP Lond. 1944. Prev: Cas. Off. & Ho. Surg. St. Thos. Hosp.

LYLE, Dorothy Lena Neilson 14 Elm Walk, Bearsden, Glasgow G61 3BQ — MB ChB 1951 Glas.; DPM Eng. 1960. Clin. Asst. Gartnavel Roy. Hosp. Glas.

LYLE, Fiona Elizabeth Park Avenue Medical Centre, 9 Park Avenue, Stirling FK8 2QR Tel: 01786 473529 — MB ChB 1989 Glas.; MRCGP 1995. (Glasgow)

LYLE, Henry McWilliam 1 Ivanhoe Road, Thurcroft, Rotherham S66 9EE — MB BCh BAO 1949 Belf.; MB BCh BAO (Hons.) Belf. 1949. (Qu. Univ. Belf.) Prev: Ho. Surg. Roy. Vict. Hosp. Belf.

LYLE, John Hill The Coatham Surgery, 18 Coatham Road, Redcar TS10 1RJ Tel: 01642 483495 Fax: 01642 487520; 3 De Havilland Drive, The Landings, Marske-by-Sea, Redcar TS11 6NB — MB BCh BAO 1981 Belf.; MRCGP 1986. Clin. Asst. (Diabetic Care/Lipids) MiddlesBoro. Gen. Hosp. Prev: Clin. Asst. (ENT) N.. RHA.

LYLE, Nicola Jane 60 Eastmead, Goldsworth Park, Woking GU21 3BP — MB BS 1998 Lond.; MB BS Lond 1998.

LYLE, Peter Thomas Wreford Lyle and Partners, The Surgery, 4 Silverdale Road, Burgess Hill RH15 0EF Tel: 01444 233450 Fax: 01444 230412 — MB BChir 1978 Camb.; MA, MB Camb. 1978, BChir 1977; MRCGP 1989; DRCOG 1980. (Gonville and Cairns College Cambridge and Kings Coll. Hosp.) Trainer GP Burgess Hill.

LYLE, Robert Charles Heard Lower Clapton Health Centre, 36 Lower Clapton Road, London E5 0PQ; 7 Clarence Place, London E5 8HN Tel: 020 8986 5466 — MB BChir 1976 Camb.; BA Camb. 1971. Med. Adviser (Occupat. Health) Lond. Boro. Hackney.

LYLE, Robert William, VRD (retired) Tatchley House, Prestbury, Cheltenham GL52 3DD Tel: 01242 245511 — MB BS 1948 Lond.; DObst RCOG 1952. Prev: Surg. Lt.-Cdr. RNR.

LYLE, Sarah Ann 14 Hardwick Drive, Shrewsbury SY3 8UZ — MB ChB 1978 Liverp.; DRCOG 1980.

LYLE, Thomas 32 Huntingdon Street, St. Neots, Huntingdon PE19 1BQ Tel: 01480 2014 — LRCP LRCS 1941 Ed.; LRCP LRCS Ed. LRFPS Glas. 1941. (Ed.) Prev: Ho. Surg. Roy. S. Hants. & Soton. Hosp.

LYN, Basil Ethan Mount Vernon Centre for Cancer Treatment, Mount Vernon Hospital, Northwood HA6 2RN Tel: 01923 826111 Fax: 01923 844138; 139 Hilliard Road, Northwood HA6 1SL Email: e_lyn@compuserve.com — MB BChir 1982 Camb.; BA (Hons.) Camb. 1979; MRCP (UK) 1986; FRCR 1992. (Univ. Camb.) Cons. Clin. Oncol. Mt. Vernon Hosp. N.wood Middlx. Prev: Hon. Sen. Regist. & Sen. Regist. (Clin. Oncol.) Mt. Vernon Hosp. N.wood; Regist. (Clin. Oncol.) Middlx. & Mt. Vernon Hosps.

LYN, Chong Woon 19 Woodlands Close, Headington, Oxford OX3 7RY Tel: 01865 62144; Shoplot 2 Taman Layang Layang, Jalan Kolam, Kota Kinabalu, Sabah 88100, Malaysia Tel: 00 60 88 238668 Fax: 00 60 88 225278 Email: phillyn@pop.jaring.my — BM BCh 1978 Oxf.; MA Oxf. 1983, BA 1975; MRCP (UK) 1982. (Univ. Oxf.) Cons. Phys. Indep. Pract. & Sabah Med. Centre, Kota Kinabalu, Malaysia. Socs: BMA; Acad. Med. Malaysia; Fell. Coll. Chest Phys. USA. Prev: State Phys. Qu. Eliz. Hosp. Sabah, Malaysia; Cons. Malaria & Drug Resistance WHO; Regist. (Med.) Mt. Vernon Hosp. N.wood.

LYNAGH, John Marsh Street Surgery, 25A Marsh Street, Rothwell, Leeds LS26 0AG Tel: 0113 282 1571 Fax: 0113 282 4720; Marsh Street Surgery, 25A Marsh St, Rothwell, Leeds LS26 0AG Tel: 0113 282 0756 Fax: 0113 282 4720 — MB ChB 1975 Leeds. Clin. Asst. (Orthop.) St. James Univ. Hosp. Leeds.

LYNAM, Alison Mary Amherst Medical Practice, 21 St Botophs Road, Sevenoaks TN13 3AQ Tel: 01732 459255 Fax: 01732 450751; Beech House, 9 Pendennis Road, Sevenoaks TN13 3JS Tel: 01732 458989 — MB BS 1976 Lond.; MRCS Eng. LRCP Lond. 1976. (Westm.) GP Princip. Socs: Non-Princip. Rep. W. Kent LMC. Prev: GP Doctors Retainer Scheme; GP Princip. Sevenoaks; Cas. Off. Kent & Sussex Hosp. Tunbridge Wells.

LYNAS, Alan George Alfred 232 Glenshane Road, Londonderry BT47 3SN Tel: 01504 301033 — MB BCh BAO 1979 Belf.; FFA RCSI 1983. Cons. Anaesth. Altnagelvin Hosp. Lond.derry.

LYNAS, Anne Mary Health Centre, Market Place, Carluke ML8 4AZ Tel: 01555 770635; 10 Skipness Avenue, Carluke ML8 4LT — MB ChB 1976 Manch. Clin. Med. Off. (Comm. Child Health) Carluke Health Centre.

LYNAS, Audrey Helen 149 Hillview Dr, Clarkston, Glasgow G76 7LE — MB ChB 1997 Glas.

LYNAS, Brian Robert The Surgery, 53 Burnbank Road, Hamilton ML3 9AQ Tel: 01698 281407 — MB ChB 1970 Glas.

LYNAS, Gerard John Bridgeton Health Centre, 210 Abercromby Street, Glasgow G40 2DA Tel: 0141 531 6650 Fax: 0141 531 6639 — MB ChB 1992 Glas.

LYNAS, Patricia Margaret 25 Upper Malone Road, Belfast BT9 6TY Tel: 01232 615462 — MB BCh BAO 1969 Belf. Clin. Med. Off. Family Plann. E. Area Health & Social Serv. Bd.

LYNAS, Robert Francis Alistair 24 Windsor Park, Malone Road, Belfast BT9 6FR — MB BCh BAO 1960 Belf.

LYNAS, Timothy Hugh Bangor Health Centre, Newtownards Road, Bangor BT20 4LD Tel: 028 9146 9111 — MB BCh BAO 1975 Belf.

LYNAS, William James 2 Cooldarragh Park N., Belfast BT14 6TL Tel: 01232 716153 — MB BCh BAO Belf. 1953.

LYNCH, Anthony Stephen The College Yard Surgery, Mount St., Westgate, Gloucester GL1 2RE Tel: 01452 412888; The Highnam Surgery, Lassington Lane, Highnam, Gloucester GL2 8DH Tel: 01452 529699 — MB BS 1975 Lond.; MA (Hons.) Camb. 1960; MRCS Eng. LRCP Lond. 1975.

LYNCH, Barry Andrew Prospect Pictures Ltd., Capital Studios, Wandsworth Plain, London SW18 1ET Tel: 020 7636 1234 Fax: 020 7636 1236 — MB ChB 1977 Manch.; BSc St. And. 1975. Managing Dir. Prospect Pictures Ltd. Prev: Ho. Surg. Manch. Roy. Infirm.; Ho. Phys. Univ. Hosp. S. Manch.

LYNCH, Beth Magley 14 Hollin Crescent, Greenfield, Oldham OL3 7LW — MB ChB 1998 Leeds.

LYNCH, Brendan 5 Novar Gardens, Bishopbriggs, Glasgow G64 2ER — MB ChB 1997 Glas.

LYNCH, Brian Dermot Grove House Surgery, Soothill, Batley WF17 5SS Tel: 01924 476363 Fax: 01924 474119; The Gables, Upper Batley Lane, Batley WF17 0AR Tel: 01924 445893 — MB BCh BAO 1986 NUI; LRCPI & LM, LRCSI & LM 1986; DRCOG 1991.

LYNCH, Brian Samuel 30 Agherton Road, Ballylease, Portstewart BT55 7PJ — MB BCh BAO 1978 Belf.; MRCGP 1982; LMCC 1986; DCH Dub. 1981; DRCOG 1980.

LYNCH, Carolyn Mary Little Park Surgery, 281 Hounslow Road, Hanworth, Feltham TW13 5JG Tel: 020 8894 6588 Fax: 020 8894 6668; 75 Manor Lane, Sunbury-on-Thames TW16 6JE Tel: 01932 766110 — MB BCh BAO 1983 NUI; LRCPI & LM, LRCSI & LM 1983; MRCGP 1988; DRCOG 1988. GP Trainer & Course Organiser Post VTS Non Princips. Socs: BMA. Prev: SHO (O & G) Jessop Hosp. for Wom. Sheff.; SHO Rotat. (Med.) St. Laurences & Letterkenny Gen. Hosps.; SHO (Paediat.) Sheff. Childr. Hosp.

LYNCH, Charles Doctors Surgery, Newton Way, Baildon, Shipley BD17 5NH Tel: 01274 582506 Fax: 01274 532426; 33 Belmont Rise, Baildon, Shipley BD17 5AW Tel: 01274 591724 — MB ChB 1960 Glas.

LYNCH, Mr Christopher Balogun Milton Keynes General Hospital NHS Trust, Standing Way, Eaglestone, Milton Keynes MK6 5LD Tel: 01908 660033 Fax: 01908 617449; Linford Court, Church Lane, Little Linford, Milton Keynes MK19 7EB Tel: 01908 617449 Fax: 01908 617449 — MB BS 1974 Lond.; MA Oxf. 1974; FRCS Ed. 1979; MRCS Eng. LRCP Lond. 1973; FRCOG 1991, M 1979; Hon Doctorate OU 1997. (Barts) Cons. O & G Surg. Milton Keynes Gen. Hosp.; Dir. Diag. Colposcopy & Gyn. Laser Surg. Unit; Clin. direc MKnhs O+G; Surg train of spec Regist.s. Socs: Fell. Roy. Soc. Med. Form.; Brit. Acad. Experts (Mem. Counc.); Blair Bell Research Soc.Form. Prev: Clin. Lect. & Sen. Regist. (O & G) St. Bart. Hosp. Lond.; Demonst. (Anat.) St. Bart. Med. Coll. Lond.; Regist. Intens. Care Unit Amer. Hosp., France.

LYNCH, Christopher Graham MacLeod Preston Court, Canterbury Road, Faversham ME13 8LL Tel: 01795 535260 — BM BCh 1968 Oxf.; MA Oxf. 1968; MRCS Eng. LRCP Lond. 1968; FFA RCS Eng. 1973. Cons. Anaesth. Kent & Canterbury Hosp. Socs: BMA & Assn. Anaesth. Prev: Sen. Regist. (Anaesth.) Oxf. United Hosps.

LYNCH, Damien Anthony Francis Blackburn, Royal Infirmary, Bolton Road, Blackburn BB2 3LR Tel: 01254 294546 Fax: 01254 294555; Pale Farm Barn, Moss Lane, Chipping, Preston PR3 2TR Tel: 01995 61138 Email: damien@palefarm.freeserve.co.uk — MB ChB 1984 Manch.; BSc St. And. 1981; MRCP (UK) 1988; MRCGP 1988; MD 1998; FRCP 1999. (Manch.) Cons. Gen. Med. & Gastroenterol. Blackburn Roy. Infirm.; Hon. Clin. Lect. (Med.) Univ. of Manch.; Undergrad. Tutor Blackburn Roy. Infirm. Socs: Fell.Roy. Soc. Med.; Brit. Soc. Gastroenterol. Prev: Sen. Regist. (Gen. Med. & Gastroenterol.) Bradford Roy. Infirm.; Research Regist. Gen. Infirm. Leeds; Regist. (Gen. Med. & Gastroenterol.) Gen. Infirm. Leeds.

LYNCH, Declan Nigel The Surgery, 66-68 Stoke Road, Gosport PO12 1PA Tel: 023 9258 1529 Fax: 023 9250 1417; Starlings, 14 Beechcroft Road, Alverstoke, Gosport PO12 2ER — MB BS 1979 Lond.; MRCGP 1984; DRCOG 1982. Prev: Trainee GP Portsmouth VTS.

LYNCH, Dermot (retired) 19 Wensleydale Road, Hampton TW12 2LP Tel: 020 8979 1155 Fax: 020 8979 1155 Email: dermotlynch@compuserve.com — LRCPI & LM, LRCSI & LM 1953; FRCGP 1983, M 1968; MICGP 1987. Med. Adviser United Airline. Prev: Mem. Ealing, Hammersmith & Hounslow FPC.

LYNCH, Dorothy Jean Lambie Holburn Medical Group, 7 Albyn Place, Aberdeen AB10 1YE Tel: 01224 400800 Fax: 01224 407777; 17 St. Swithin Street, Aberdeen AB10 6XB Tel: 01224 322621 — MB ChB 1981 Glas.; MRCGP 1985; DCH RCPS Glas. 1984; DRCOG 1983.

LYNCH, Emma Elizabeth Flat 16/11, Kempton Court, Durward St., London E1 5BE — MB BS 1996 Lond.

LYNCH, Finbarr Kieran Talarfon, Holyhead Road, Bangor LL57 2EE Tel: 01248 355825 — MB BCh BAO 1975 NUI; MRCGP 1981; MRCPsych 1983. Cons. Child Psychiat. Gwynedd HA.

LYNCH, Gerard Mary 104 Salisbury Avenue, Belfast BT15 5ED — MB BCh BAO 1985 Belf. Cons. Psychiat. Holywell Hosp. Antrim.

LYNCH, Jacqueline Ann — MB BS 1995 Lond.; MRCS 2000 (A & E); DCH, 1998, Roy Coll Med. Prac.; DRCOG, 1998, RCOG; DIMC RCSEd. 2001. (St. Geo. Hosp.) Regist. (A & E) Soton. Gen. Hosp. Prev: Regist. (A & E) Qu. Alexandra, Portsmouth; ITU SHO Qu. Alexandra, Portsmouth.

LYNCH, Mr James Brendan (retired) High Leas, Eccup Lane, Adel, Leeds LS16 8AJ Tel: 0113 267 8404 — MD Liverp. 1957, MB ChB 1944; FRCS Eng. 1950; FRCPath 1969, M 1963. Prev: Dean Postgrad. Med. Educat. Leeds.

LYNCH, Janine Violet Flat 3, 268 Lisburn Road, Belfast BT9 6GF — MB BCh BAO 1987 Belf.

LYNCH, Janis Rutherglen Health Centre, 130 Stonelaw Road, Rutherglen, Glasgow G73 2PQ Tel: 0141 531 6010 Fax: 0141 613 3460; 313a Albert Drive, Pollokshields, Glasgow G41 5RP — MB ChB 1990 Ed.; MRCGP 1994. (Edin.) Socs: BMA.

LYNCH, John Bernard, OBE (retired) Moy House, The Green, Denbigh LL16 5TL Tel: 01745 812444 — MB ChB Manch. 1956; MRCS Eng. LRCP Lond. 1956.

LYNCH, John Peter William Framfield House Surgery, 42 St. Johns Street, Woodbridge IP12 1ED Tel: 01394 382157; The Old Vicarage, Boot St, Great Bealings, Woodbridge IP13 6PB — MB ChB 1991 Bristol; MRCGP 1995.

LYNCH, Louise Ann 9 Ladywood, Leeds LS8 2QF — MB ChB 1987 Leeds.

LYNCH, Lucy Mary (retired) 12 The Willows, Frenchay Manor Park, Bristol BS16 1PR — LM 1946 Dub.; MB BCh BAO NUI 1946, CPH 1950; LM Nat. Matern. Hosp. Dub. 1946. Prev: Asst. Psychiat. Stoke Pk. Hosp. Stapleton.

LYNCH, Margaret Alison Preston Court, Canterbury Road, Faversham ME13 8LL Tel: 01795 535260 — MD 1983 Newc.; MB BS Durh. 1966; MRCP (U.K.) 1972; DCH Eng. 1968. Sen. Lect. (Community Paediat.) Guy's Hosp. Med. Sch. Lond. Prev: Sen. Regist. (Research) Pk. Hosp. Childr. Oxf.

LYNCH, Margaret Mary Parkhead Farm Cottages, Maryculter, Aberdeen AB12 5GL — MB BCh BAO 1988 NUI; MRCPI 1992; DObst RCPI 1995. (Univ. Coll. Dub.) Prev: GP/Regist. Turriff; Regist. (Geriat.) St. Jas. Hosp. Dub.; SHO (Paediat.) Temple St. Hosp. Dub.

LYNCH, Margaret Theresa The Old Manor, Salisbury — LRCPI & LM, LRSCI & LM 1946; LRCPI & LM, LRCSI & LM 1946. Med. Asst. (Psychiat.) Old Manor Hosp. Salisbury. Socs: BMA. Prev: Med. Asst. (Psychiat.) St. Lawrence's Hosp. Bodmin; Med. Off. Woodbridge Psychiat. Hosp. Singapore & Grangegorman Ment.; Hosp. Dub.

LYNCH, Maria Bernadette Central Middlesex University Hospital, Acton Lane, Park Royal, London SW15; 32 Aynhoe Road, Brook Green, West Kensington, London W14 0QD Tel: 020 7603 3208 — MB BS Lond. 1991; MRCP (UK) 1994. Sen. Regist. (A & E) N. W. Thames Rotat. - Chelsea & W.minster, Centr. Middlx. & Char. Cross Hosps. Socs: Brit. Assn. Emerg. Med.; Roy. Soc. Med.; Fac. Emerg. Med. Prev: SHO Rotat. (Med.) St. Bart. NHS Trust; SHO (Neurol.) King Geo. Hosp.; Regist. Rotat. S. W. Thames.

LYNCH, Mark Thomas The Health Centre, Madeira Road, West Byfleet KT14 6DH Tel: 01932 336933 Fax: 01932 355681 — MB BS 1984 Lond.; MRCGP 1988; DRCOG 1987. Prev: GP Woking; Trainee GP St. Peter's Hosp. Chertsey VTS.

LYNCH, Mark Vincent Department of Anaesthetics, Princess Royal Hospital, Lewes Road, Haywards Heath RH16 4EX — MB BS 1975 Lond.; MRCP (UK) 1981; FRCA Eng. 1986. (St. Bart. Lond.) Cons. Anaesth. P.ss Roy. Hosp. & Hurstwood Pk. Neurosci.s Centre, Haywards Heath, W. Sussex. Socs: Neuroanesth. Soc.; Assn. Anaesth. Prev: Cons. Anaesth. Roy. Free Hosp. Lond.; Regist. (Anaesth.) St. Bart. Hosp. Lond.; Sen. Regist. (Anaesth.) Roy. Free Hosp. Lond.

LYNCH, Mr Martin Christopher 44 Knowsley Road, Cressington Park, Liverpool L19 0PG — MD 1992 Liverp.; MChOrth Liverp. 1983, MB ChB 1976; FRCS Eng. 1980. Cons. Orthop. Surg. BRd.green NHS Trust Liverp.; Hon. Sen. Lect. (Orthop. & Accid. Surg.) Univ. Liverp. Socs: Liverp. Med. Inst. (Counc. Mem.); BMA. Prev: Sen. Lect. (Orthop. & Accid. Surg.) Univ. Liverp.

LYNCH, Matthew Robert John 299 Sandbrook Road, Ainsdale, Southport PR8 3RP — MB ChB 1993 Liverp. SHO (Trauma & Orthop.) Chorley Dist. Hosp. Prev: SHO (Gen. Surg.) Walton Gen. Hosp. Runcorn; SHO (Orthop.) Roy. Liverp. Univ. Hosp.; SHO (Gen. Surg.) Warrington Dist. Gen. Hosp.

LYNCH, Maura Paidraigin Grove House Surgery, Soothill, Batley WF17 5SS Tel: 01924 476363 Fax: 01924 474119; The Gables, Upper Batley Lane, Upper Batley, Batley WF17 0AR Tel: 01924 445893 — MB BCh BAO 1984 NUI; LRCPI & LM, LRCSI & LM 1984; DRCOG 1991; DCH NUI 1986.

LYNCH, Michael Derwent Practice, Norton Road, Malton YO17 9RF Tel: 01653 600069 Fax: 01653 698014; 33 Middlecave Road, Malton YO17 7NE — MB ChB 1978 Leeds; DRCOG 1981; DA Lond. 1981.

LYNCH, Michael James Dept Radiology, Charing Cross Hospital, Fulham Palace Road, London W6 — MB BS 1994 Lond.; BSc 1991; MRCP 1998.

LYNCH, Mr Michael John — MB BCh BAO 1982 NUI; FRCS (Urol.) 1994; FRCSI 1986; MCh Dub 1997. Cons. Urol. Kettering Gen. Hosp. Socs: Brit. Assn. Urol. Surgs. Prev: Sen. Regist. (Urol.) Epsom Health Care NHS Trust & Inst. Urol. Nephrol. Lond.; Regist. (Urol.) Bradford Roy. Infirm.; Regist. (Gen. Surg.) Memor. Hosp. Darlington.

LYNCH, Michael Patrick Danecliffe, 8 Whitbarrow Road, Lymm WA13 9AE — MB ChB 1973 Aberd.; MRCP (U.K.) 1975.

LYNCH, Niall Fionan Stepping Hill Hospital, Poplar Grove, Stockport SK2 7JE Tel: 0161 483 1010; 5 Highfield Park, Heatoon Mersey, Stockport SK4 3HD Tel: 0161 442 2102 — MB BCh BAO 1985 NUI; LRCPS & I 1985; FRCR 1993; FFR RCSI 1992; DCH NUI 1988. (RCSI) Cons. Radiol., Stepping Hill Hosp. Stockport. Prev: Sen. Regist. (Radiol.), Manc. Radiol. rotaion; Regist. (Radiol.), The Meath, Adelaide & Nat. Childr.s Hosp. Dub.

LYNCH, Nuala Patricia 43 Shortheath CreStreet, Farnham GU9 8SB — MB BS 1988 Lond.; DRCOG 1991. Ho. Off. St. Geo. Hosp. Lond. Prev: Ho. Off. St. Richards Hosp. Chichester.

LYNCH, Oonagh, OStJ (retired) 19 Wensleydale Road, Hampton TW12 2LP Tel: 020 8979 1155 Fax: 020 8979 1155 Email: dermotlynch@compuserve.com — MB BCh BAO NUI 1955. Med. Advis. United Airlines. Prev: GP Hanworth Middlx.

LYNCH, Patrick Garven (retired) Department of Neuropathology, Royal Preston Hospital, Sharoe Green Lane, Preston PR2 9HT Tel: 01772 710146 Fax: 01772 710181 — BM BCh 1960 Oxf.; BA (Hons.) Oxf. 1956; FRCPath 1978, M 1966; DPath Eng. 1963. Cons. Neuropath. Depts. Neurosurg. & Neurol. Roy. Preston Hosp. Prev: Resid. Clin. Path. St. Mary's Hosp. Lond.

LYNCH, Patrick Norbert Lisnaskea Health Centre, Drumhaw, Lisnaskea, Enniskillen BT92 0JB Tel: 028 6772 1443 Fax: 028 6772 2526; Bally Hullagh, Lisnaskea, Enniskillen BT92 5FG Tel: 01365 722302 Fax: 013650722353 Email: norbertly@aol.com — MB BCh BAO 1979 NUI; MRCGP 1983; DRCOG 1983; DObst RCPI 1983. (University College Dublin) GP Commr.; Dir. A.S.A.D.O.C. Ltd.

LYNCH, Paul Michael Tel: 028 9024 0503 Email: lynch_paul@yahoo.com; Email: lynch_paul@yahoo.com — MB BCh BAO 1995 Belf.; MRCP 1999. (QUB) Clin. Research Fell., United Hosps. Trust.

LYNCH, Pauline Teresa Perth Royal Infirmary, Taymount Terrace, Perth PH1 1NX — MB ChB 1987 Ed.; MRCOG 1993.

LYNCH, Peter, Brigadier late RAMC MDHU, Derriford Hospital, Derriford, Plymouth PL6 8DH Tel: 01752 777111 Ext. 57539 Fax: 01752 763755 Email: peter.lynch@phnt.swest.nhs.uk; 16 Abbey Close, Crapstone, Yelverton PL20 7PX Tel: 01822 859132 Email: plynch1@freeuk.com — MB ChB Glas. 1968; MD Glas. 1984; FRCP Lond. 1989; DObst RCOG 1975. (Glas.) Cons. In Gen. Med., UK Armed Forces MDHU Derriford Hosp. Plymouth. Prev: Comd. Med. HQ1 (UK) Armd. Div.; Comd. Med. HQBF Hong Kong BFPO 1; Med. Dir. Defence Secondary Care Agency Lond.

LYNCH, Mr Peter Francis (retired) 7 Park Avenue, Southport PR9 9LS Tel: 01704 531598 — MB ChB 1953 Liverp.; ChM Liverp.

1961, MB ChB 1953; FRCS Eng. 1958. Prev: Cons. Surg. S.port Dist. Gen. Hosp.

LYNCH, Philip Patrick Health Centre, Park Drive, Stenhousemuir, Larbert FK5 3BB Tel: 01324 552200 Fax: 01324 553623; Beechmount House, Carronvale Road, Larbert FK5 3LG Tel: 01324 554629 — MB ChB 1965 Glas.; DObst RCOG 1967. Clin. Asst. Roy. Scott. Nat. Hosp. Larbert. Socs: Scott. Thoracic Soc. Prev: Med. & Surg. Ho. Off. Glas. Roy. Infirm.; O & G & Paediat. Ho. Off. Stobhill Gen. Hosp. Glas.

LYNCH, Robert (retired) 6 Old Woodwynd Road, Kilwinning KA13 7DL Tel: 01294 52825 — MB ChB 1953 Aberd.

LYNCH, Robert (retired) DSS, North Fylde Central Office, Norcross, Blackpool FY3 3TA Tel: 01253 333757 — MB ChB 1959 Liverp. Prev: Med. Adviser DSS (War Pens. Agency).

LYNCH, Sarah Ann Institute of Human Genetics, International Centre for Life, Central Parkway, Newcastle NE1 3BZ Tel: 0191 241 8740 Fax: 0191 241 8799 — MB BCh BAO 1986 NUI; MD Dub. 1993; MRCPI 1990; LRCPSI 1986; DCH RCSI 1989. (Royal College Surgeons Ireland) Cons. Clin. Genetics N.ern Region Genetics Unit Newc.; Reg.spec advis genetics. Socs: Collegiate Mem. RCP Irel..; Clin. Genetics Soc.; Skeletal Dysplasia Soc. Prev: Sen. Regist. (Genetics) N.ern Region Genetics Unit Newc.; Regist. (Genetics) Leeds HA; Research Asst. (Genetics) Trinity Coll. Dub.

LYNCH, Sean Francis Queen Mary's Hospital, Sidcup DA14 6L2 — MB BCh BAO 1987 Dub.

LYNCH, Sean Patrick Jeremy St Mary's Hospital, Newport PO30 5TG — MB ChB 1982 Manch.; MRCPsych 1986; PhD1999; MBA2000. Cons. Psychiat.,Isle of Wight Healthcare NHS Trust 2000-present; Edr.,Primary Care Psychiat. 2000-. Socs: Brit. Assn. Psychopharmacol.; Roy. Coll. Psychiat. (s/i Gp. Liaison); Roy.Coll.Psychiat (Exec. Comm. s/i Gp. Psychopharmacol.) Prev: Lect. (Psychiat.) & Hon. Sen. Regist. St. Mary's Hosp. Med. Sch. Lond.; Sen.Lect.(Psychiat) Univ.Leeds & Cons. Psychiat. St.Jas. Univ.Hosp.Leeds

LYNCH, Sheila Mary Elizabeth The Surgery, 1 Rowner Road, Gosport PO13 9UA Tel: 023 9258 0093 Fax: 023 92 504060; Starlings, 14 Beechcroft Road, Alverstone, Gosport PO12 2ER — MB ChB 1978 Aberd.

LYNCH, Stephen 1 Eskdale Grove, Knott End on Sea, Blackpool FY3 0DH — MB ChB 1985 Manch.; MRCGP 1989. GP Blackpool.

LYNCH, Stephen John Calsayseat Medical Group, 2 Calsayseat Road, Aberdeen AB25 3UY Tel: 01224 634345 Fax: 01224 620210; 17 St. Swithin Street, Aberdeen AB10 6XB Tel: 01224 322621 Email: sjlynch@msn.com — MB ChB 1983 Aberd.; MRCGP 1987; DCH RCPS Glas. 1986; DRCOG 1985; FRCGP 1998. (Aberd.) Hon. Sec. RCGP N. E. Fac.

LYNCH, Susan Christine Lakeside Surgery, Lakeside Road, Lymm, Warrington WA13 0QE Tel: 01925 755050; 18 All Saints Drive, Thelwall, Warrington WA4 2JQ — MB ChB 1983 Manch.; MRCGP 1987; DRCOG 1986.

LYNCH, Susan Margaret 84 Rogers Lane, Stoke Poges, Slough SL2 4LF Tel: 01753 643445 Fax: 01753 646906 Email: threeways@clara.co.uk; 12 Duffield Lane, Stoke Poges, Slough SL2 4AB Tel: 01753 646582 — MB ChB 1974 Bristol; MRCGP 1978; DRCOG 1977. Prev: Trainee GP High Wycombe & Dist. VTS; Ho. Surg. Croydon Gen. Hosp.; Ho. Phys. Stoke Mandeville Hosp. Aylesbury.

LYNCH, Thomas Dunstan Medical Centre, 284 Bury Road, Bolton BL2 6AY Tel: 01204 531557 Fax: 01204 364407 — MB ChB 1979 Manch.; MRCGP 1983.

LYNCH, Mr Thomas Hugh Department of Urology, Belfast City Hospital, Belfast BT9 7AB Tel: 02890 263916 Fax: 02890 263516 — MB BCh BAO 1984 NUI; MCh NUI 1991, MMSc 1990; FRCS Ed. 1988; FRCS (E)1988; FRCS (Urol.) 1995; FRCS 1988 Irel. (University College Galway, Ireland) Cons. Urol. Belf. City Hosp. Socs: Brit. Assn. Urol. Surg.; Irish Soc. Urol.; Brit. Med. Assn. Prev: Clin. Fell. (Paediat. Urol.) Childr.'s Hosp. Bristol; Sen. Regist. St Vincents Hosp. Dub.; Research Fell., Loyola Univ., Chicago.

LYNCH, Timothy Michael Cranleigh Health Centre, Cranleigh GU6 8AE Tel: 01483 273951; Hunting Barn, New Pk Road, Cranleigh GU6 7HJ Tel: 01483 273951 — MB BS 1969 Lond.; MRCS Eng. LRCP Lond. 1969; MRCGP 1985; DCH Eng. 1971. (Guy's)

LYNCH, Vanessa Jane 9 Pinks Hill, Swanley BR8 8AG — MB BS 1990 Lond.

LYNCH, Mrs Veronica (retired) 48 St Christopher's Road, Sunderland SR3 1NS Tel: 0191 528 5044 — MB BS 1955 Durh. Prev: GP Sunderland.

LYNCH, Victoria Juliet The Old School House, 25 Main St., Prickwillow, Ely CB7 4UN — MB ChB 1998 Leeds. PRHO.Gen. Med.Dewsbury.Dis.Hosp. Prev: PRHO.Gen.Surg.Urol.Huddesfield.Roy.Infirm.

LYNCH, Victoria Mary (Surgery), 15 Brook Green, London W6 7BL Tel: 020 7603 7563; 13 Devonshire Gardens, London W4 3TN Tel: 020 8994 1066 — MB BS 1973 Lond.; DCH Eng. 1975. (Middlx.) Socs: BMA. Prev: Hosp. Pract. (Rheum.) Char. Cross & Chelsea & W.m Hosps. Lond.; SHO (Paediat.) S.lands Hosp. Shoreham-by-Sea & St. Chas. Hosp. Lond.; SHO (Rheum. & Rehabil.) Qu. Mary's Hosp. Roehampton.

LYNCH, William Anthony 5 Brinsley Close, Solihull B91 3FR — MB BCh BAO 1986 NUI; FFA RCSI 1989.

LYNCH, William Martin Gerard (Surgery) 140 Robert Street, Milford Haven SA73 2HS Tel: 01646 690690 Fax: 01646 690690 Email: williamlynch@cluainnambo.demon.co.uk; Cluain na MBO, Lower Priory, Milford Haven SA73 3UA — MB BCh BAO 1986 NUI; MRCGP 1990; Dip. Pract. Dermat. Wales 1993; DObst RCPI 1990; DCH RCPSI 1990; Dip. Occ. Med. RCP Lond. 1995.

LYNCH-BLOSSE, Sir Richard Hely, Bt Lynch-Blosse and Bradley, The Surgery, Watery Lane, Clifton Hampden, Abingdon OX14 3EJ Tel: 01865 407888 Fax: 01865 407946 — MB BS 1979 Lond.; MRCS Eng. LRCP London 1978; MRCGP 1983; DRCOG 1983. (Roy. Free) NHS Princip.; Med. Off. Europ. Sch.; Med. Off. Oxon. ACF (Roy. Green Jackets); Bd. Mem. Vale of White Horse out-of-hours CoOperat. Prev: Short Serv. Commiss. RAMC.

LYNCH-FARMERY, Ellen Mary (Elaine) Berkshire H.A, 55-57 Bath Road, Reading RG30 2BA Tel: 0118 982 2755 Fax: 0118 982 2734 Email: elaine.farmery@berkshire.nhs.uk; 20 Belmont Crescent, Old Town, Swindon SN1 4EY — MB BCh BAO 1971 NUI; FFPHM 2001; MFPHM 1988; MRCOG 1978; FRCOG 1992. (Cork) Cons. Pub. Health Med. Berks. Socs: BMA Collaborator. Prev: Cons. Pub. Health Med Wilts. & Bath HA; Cons. Pub. Health Med Swindon HA; Sen. Regist. (Community Med) Wessex RHA & Swindon HA.

LYNDON, Mr Philip John The Mansion House, Heaton Lodge, Huddersfield HD5 0PW — MB ChB 1970 Leeds; FRCS Eng. 1977; FRCS Ed. 1976; MRCS Eng. LRCP Lond. 1970.

LYNDON, Stuart Occupational Health Department, City of Sunderland, 10 Stockton Road, Sunderland SR1 Tel: 0191 553 2970 Fax: 0191 553 2974; 8 Grenville Court, Darras Hall, Ponteland, Newcastle upon Tyne NE20 9HT Tel: 01661 822502 — MB ChB 1979 Dundee; MRCGP 1984. Phys. (Occupat. Health) City of Sunderland. Socs: Soc. Occupat. Med. Prev: GP Dundee.

LYNDSAY, David Morton 40 Cambridge Street, London SW1V 4QH — LRCPI & LM, LRSCI & LM 1957; LRCPI & LM, LRCSI & LM 1957. (RCSI) Benefits Agency Med. Off. S.. Div. Prev: GP Broughton; Hosp. Pract. (Orthop.) Roy. Hants. Co. Hosp. Winchester.

LYNE, Juliet Anne 6 Cock-A-Dobby, Sandhurst GU47 8LB — MB ChB 1997 Birm.

LYNE, Peter Jespersen (retired) Rinteln, Barrowfield Close, Hove BN3 6TP Tel: 01273 507328 Email: lyne.tinteln@tesco.net — MB BChir Camb. 1952. Prev: Cas. Off. & Ho. Surg. Roy. Sussex Co. Hosp. Brighton.

LYNE, Peter Nigel Dillon Welsh Office, Cathays Park, Cardiff CF10 3NQ; The Old Rectory, Llanmadoc, Swansea SA3 1DE — MB BCh 1980 Wales; BSc (Econ) Wales 1969, MB BCh 1980. Sen. Med. Off. Health Profess. Gp. Welsh Office. Prev: Med. Off. Dept. of Transport DVLA Swansea; Princip. GP Woodhall Spa Lincs.; Trainee GP N. Lincs. VTS.

LYNES, Joanna Sunnyside Cottage, Elm Grove, Hoylake, Wirral CH47 3DL — MB ChB 1994 Ed. SHO (Anaesth.) WIrral Hosp. NHS Trust. Socs: Assoc. Mem. Assoc. Anaesth. GB & Irel.

LYNESS, Anna Louise Stainton Gap, Broughton Beck, Ulverston LA12 7PL — MB BCh BAO 1974 Belf.; FRCOphth 1980; DObst RCOG 1976. Cons. Ophth. Furness Gen. Hosp. Barrow in Furness.

LYNESS, Robert William c/o Department of Histopath, Belfast City Hospital, Belfast BT9 7AD Tel: 01232 329241 — MB BCh BAO 1974 Belf.

LYNN, Anthony Henry 3 Barn Close, Watford Road, Radlett WD7 8LA Tel: 01923 853853 — MRCS Eng. LRCP Lond. 1967; MB BS Lond. 1967, BDS 1961; FRCR 1975; FDS RCPS Glas. 1970; DMRD Eng. 1973. (St. Geo.) Cons. Radiol. Hertford Co. Hosp. & Qu. Eliz. II Hosp. Welwyn Gdn. City. Prev: Cons. Radiol. Chelmsford Health Dist.; Sen. Regist. (Radiodiag.) Lond. Hosp.; Ho. Phys. (Med.) St. Geo. Hosp. Lond.

LYNN, Conrad Reuben (retired) 2 Alleyn Park, Dulwich, London SE21 8AE Tel: 020 8670 8015 — LMSSA 1950 Lond. Prev: Capt. RAMC.

LYNN, Mr John Anthony Department of Surgery, Royal Postgraduate Medical School, Hammersmith Hospital, Du Cane Road, London W12 0HS Tel: 020 8743 2030 Fax: 020 8740 3333 — MB BS 1964 Lond.; MS Lond. 1977, MB BS 1964; FRCS Eng. 1971. (King's Coll. Hosp.) Cons. Endocrine & BrE. Surg. Hammersmith Hosps. Trusts Lond.; Hon. Sen. Lect. Roy. Postgrad. Med. Sch. Lond.; Cons. Surg. Ealing Hosp. Lond.; Recognised Teach. (Surg.) Univ. Lond.; Arris & Gale Lect. RCS Eng. Prev: Lect. (Surg.) W.m. Med. Sch. Lond.; Sen. Regist. W.m. Hosp. Lond.; Surgic. Research Fell. Boston Univ. Med. Centre, USA.

LYNN, Karen Louise Ash Surgery, 1 Ashfield Road, Liverpool L17 0BY Tel: 0151 727 1155 Fax: 0151 726 0018 — BM BS 1990 Nottm.; MRCGP 1994; DCH RCP Lond. 1993.

LYNN, Kenneth Nigel Dumbarton Health Centre, Station Road, Dumbarton G82 1PW Tel: 01389 602655 Fax: 01389 602622; 14 Glenpath, Dumbarton G82 2QL Tel: 01389 764907 — MB ChB 1986 Ed.; MRCGP ED. 1990. (Edinburgh) Gen. Med. Practitioner.

LYNN, Peter Robert Alan (retired) Fargates, 42 Southfield Road, Wetwang, Driffield YO25 9XX Tel: 01377 236559 — MB BCh BAO 1958 Belf. Prev: GP health centre Lisburn Co Antrim N Irel.

LYNN, William Arthur 19 Claydon Road, Horsell, Woking GU21 4XE; Ealing Hospital NHS Trust, Uxbridge Road, Southall UB1 3HW Tel: 020 8354 5446 Fax: 020 8354 5448 Email: william.lynn@beccao.demon.co.uk — MB BS 1983 Lond.; MD Lond. 1994; MRCP (UK) 1986. Cons. Gen. Med. & Infec. Dis. Ealing Hosp. Lond.; Hon. Sen. Lect. Hammersmith Hosp. Lond. Prev: Sen. Regist. (Infec. Dis.) Hammersmith Hosp. Lond.; Research Fell. Boston. Univ., USA; Regist. (Med.) Hammersmith Lond. & Hillingdon Hosp. Uxbridge.

LYON, Alexander (retired) 150 Bawtry Road, Doncaster DN4 7BT Tel: 01302 535350 — MB ChB Aberd. 1951.

LYON, Alexander Richard 35 Sedley Taylor Road, Cambridge CB2 2PN — BM BCh 1998 Oxf.; BM BCh Oxf 1998.

LYON, Alison Lesley Wakefield and Partners, Lever Chambers Centre for Health, 1st Floor, Ashburner Street, Bolton BL1 1SQ Tel: 01204 360030/31 Fax: 01204 360033 — MB ChB 1985 Liverp.; MRCGP 1991. SHO (Gen. Med.) Walton Hosp. Liverp. Prev: SHO (Chest & Geriat. Med.) Fazakerley Hosp. Liverp.; SHO (Neurol.) Walton Hosp. Liverp.

LYON, Andrew James Neonatal Unit, Simpson Memorial Maternity Pavilion, Lauriston Place, Edinburgh EH3 9EF Tel: 0131 536 1000 Fax: 0131 536 4297 Email: andy.lyon@ed.ac.uk; 11 Stennis Gardens, Edinburgh EH17 7QW — MB ChB 1976 Birm.; MA Oxf. 1977; FRCP Ed. 1994; MRCP (UK) 1980; FRCPCH 1997. Cons. Neonat. & Hon. Sen. Lect. (Child Life & Health) Univ. Edin. Prev: Cons. Paediat. Mayday Hosp. Croydon; Cons. Paediat. Camb. Milit. Hosp. Aldershot.

LYON, Andrew Robert Janeville, 4 Main St., New Abbey, Dumfries DG2 8BY — MB ChB 1979 Glas.; MRCGP 1986; DObst. RCOG 1981.

LYON, Anna Katherine 16 Heronsforde, London W13 8JE Tel: 020 8997 6957 — MB ChB 1997 Birm. (Univ. Birm.) Registration Med. H. O. Sandwell Healthcare W. Bromwich; Registration Surg. H.O. Russells Hall Hosps., Dudley; GP VTS, Watford Gen. Hosp. Prev: SHO (A & E) Newham Gen. Hosp. Lond.

LYON, Calum Charles York District Hospital, Wiggigton Rd, York YO31 8HZ; High Rising, Brandsby, York YO61 4RB — MB BChir 1992 Camb.; MA Camb. 1994; MRCP (UK) 1995. (Camb.) Cons. Deramtologist, York Dist. Hosp.; Hon. Cons. Dermatol.; Hon. Clin. Lect., Univ. of Manch., Hope Hosp., Stott La., Salford. Socs: Fell. Roy. Soc. Med.; Brit. Assn. Dermat. Prev: Regist. (Dermat.) NW Region.

LYON, Dorothy Constance (retired) 5 Danefield Avenue, Largs KA30 8RU Tel: 01475 686006 — MB BCh BAO 1948 Dub.; DPH Belf. 1966.

LYON, Dugald (retired) 45 Newark Street, Greenock PA16 7TA Tel: 01475 722170 — MB ChB 1945 Glas.; MRCGP 1956. Prev: GP Greenock.

LYON, Ian Barclay 28 Abington Park Crescent, Northampton NN3 3AD — MB BChir 1953 Camb.; DObst RCOG 1954. (St. Thos.)

LYON, Jacqueline Beverley (retired) 173 Ashley Road, Parkstone, Poole BH14 9DL Tel: 01202 743678 — BM BCh 1954 Oxf.; MA, BM BCh Oxf. 1954. Prev: Ho. Surg. Brighton Gen. Hosp.

LYON, John Alexander Health Centre, 1-13 Milson Road, London W14 0LJ Tel: 020 7603 4131 — MB ChB 1956 Aberd. (Aberd.) Med. Off. Harrison Homes, Mem. W. Lond. M-C Soc. Prev: Ho. Phys. Aberd. City Hosp.; Cas. Off. Aberd. Roy. Infirm.

LYON, John Brinley (retired) 1 North Warren, Leiston Road, Aldeburgh IP15 5QF Tel: 0172 885 2197 — MRCS Eng. LRCP Lond. 1943; MA Camb. 1945, MD 1957, MB BChir 1944; FRCP Lond. 1969, M 1949. Prev: Cons. Dermatol. Ipswich Hosp. Gp.

LYON, John Marechal The Surgery, Taynuilt PA35 1JE Tel: 01866 822684 Fax: 01866 822363; Telowie, Oban PA37 1PH Tel: 01631 710691 Fax: 01631 710767 Email: dr.john.lyon@lineoen.net — MB ChB 1986 Birm.; MB ChB Birmingham 1986; MRCGP 1990; DRCOG 1989; Cert. Family Plann. JCC 1989. (Birmingham) Hon. Med. Adviser Roses Charitable Trust; GP Network Co-ordinator Argyll & Clyde HB; GP Audit Facilitator Argyll & Clyde HB; Clin. Asst. (Dermat.) Argyll & Bute NHS Trust; Med. Adviser Hydro Seafood GSP Ltd. Prev: GP Brisbane, Qu.sland, Roxby Downs & Leigh Creek, Australia.

LYON, John Stuart Hampshire Clinic, Basing Road, Basingstoke RG24 7AL Tel: 01256 57111; Oakwood Cottage, Nately, Scures, Hook RG27 9JR Tel: 01256 762455 Fax: 01256 762455 Email: lyonjc@ukgateway.net — MA Camb. 1966, MB 1958, BChir 1957; FRCP Lond. 1983; MRCP (UK) 1972; FRCPsych 1980, M 1972; DPM Eng. 1966. (Camb. & Westm.) Indep. Cons. Psychiat. Basingstoke; Non. Exec. Dir. (Vice-Chairm.) Loddon Trust. Prev: Cons. Psychiat. N. Hants. Hosp. Gp.; Clin. Hosp. Tutor Univ. Soton.; Med. Dir. Priority Servs. Unit.

LYON, Philip Russell (retired) Camalaig, Dunvegan, Isle of Skye IV55 8WA — MB BS 1954 Lond. Prev: Asst. Ho. Phys., Ho. Surg. & Res. Obstetr. Guy's Hosp.

LYON, Rae Llewelyn 9 Viewlands Road, Perth PH1 1BH Tel: 01738 639798 — MD 1960 Ed.; MB ChB 1945; FRCP Ed. 1965. (Ed.) Hon. Phys. Blackburn & Dist. Hosp. Gp. Socs: Fell. Roy. Med. Soc. Edin. & Manch. Med. Soc. Prev: Asst. Phys. Roy. Infirm. Inverness; Clin. Tutor Roy. Infirm. Edin.; Lect. (Path.) Edin. Univ.

LYON, Susan Catherine Drumchapel Health Centre, 80-90 Kinfauns Drive, Glasgow G15 7TS Tel: 0141 211 6100 Fax: 0141 211 6104; 50 Rowallan Gardens, Broomhill, Glasgow G11 7LJ Tel: 0141 339 0875 — MB ChB 1988 Glas.; MRCGP 1992.

LYON, Terence 27 Edward VII Avenue, Newport NP20 4NG — MB BCh 1967 Wales.

LYON, Walter Carson (retired) Stanley Farm, Quernmore, Lancaster LA1 3JN Tel: 01524 65397 — MRCS Eng. LRCP Lond. 1941. Med. Dir. Inward Ho. Lancaster. Prev: Med. Asst. (Psychiat.) Lancaster Moor Hosp.

LYON, William Malcolm Murray 48 Bonaly Crescent, Colinton, Edinburgh EH13 0PZ Tel: 0131 441 5754 — MB ChB 1943 Ed.; FRCP Ed. 1968, M 1948; DPM Eng. 1955. (Ed.) Socs: Fell. (Ex-Sen. Pres.) Roy. Med. Soc. Edin. Prev: Phys. Supt. Sunnyside Roy. Hosp. Montrose; Dep. Med. Supt. St. Mary's Hosp. Stanmington N.d.; Dep. Phys. Supt. Dundee Roy. Ment. Hosp.

LYON DEAN, Charles William, Lt.-Col. RAMC The Hospital, RMA Sandhurst, Camberley GU15 4PH Tel: 01276 412545; 8 The Terrace, Royal Military Academy Sandhurst, Camberley GU15 4NS Tel: 01276 64500 — MB ChB 1971 Aberd.; FRCGP 1987, M 1976. (Aberd.) Sen. Med. Off. Trainer (Gen. Pract.) Roy. Milit. Acad. Sandhurst. Socs: Roy. Soc. Med. Prev: Brit. Med. Liaison Off., USA & Canada; Sen. Med. Off. & Trainer Catterick Garrison; Sen. Med. Off. & Trainer Münster.

LYON-MARIS, Jonathon James 131 Balfron Tower, St. Leonards Road, London E14 0QT Tel: 020 7515 4359 — MB BS 1989 Lond.; BSc Lond. 1986, MB BS 1989; MRCP (UK) 1993. SHO Rotat. Roy. Lond. Hosp.

LYONS, Alan John, SBStJ The Surgery, 207 Hook Road, Chessington KT9 1EA Tel: 020 8397 6361 Fax: 020 8973 1573; 27 Manor Crescent, Surbiton KT5 8LG Tel: 020 8399 1452 — MB BS 1965 Lond.; MRCS Eng. LRCP Lond. 1965; DMJ Soc. Apoth. Lond. 1982; DObst RCOG 1967. (St. Bart.) Surbiton Hosp. & New Vict. Hosp. Kingston; Sen. Surg. Metrop. Police; Div. Surg. St. John Ambul. Brig. Socs: Fell. Roy. Soc. Med. Prev: SHO (Anaesth.) St. Margt. Hosp. Epping; Ho. Phys. Tel Hashomer Hosp. Israel; Ho. Surg. (Cas.) St. Bart. Hosp. Lond.

LYONS, Alexander George Rydal, 375 High Road, Woodford Green IG8 9QJ Tel: 020 8504 0532 Fax: 020 8559 1503 — MB BS 1971 Lond.

LYONS, Mr Andrew John Department Oral and Maxillofacial Surgery, King's College Hospital, London SE5 9RS Tel: 020 7737 4000 Fax: 020 7346 3445; Townhouse, The Street, Ightham, Sevenoaks TN15 9HH — MB BS 1990 Lond.; 1993 FRCS Eng.; 1989 FDS RCS Eng.; 1978 BSc (Biochem) Lond., BDS; 1996 FRCS (Max-fac.). Cons. King's Coll. Hosp. Lond. Socs: Brit. Assn. Oral & Maxillofacial Surg.; Brit. Assn. Clin. Anat. Prev: Sen. Regist. St. Richards Hosp. Chichester; Sen. Regist. Soton. Gen. Hosp. & Qu. Alexandra Hosp. Portsmouth; Regist. Poole Gen. Hosp.

LYONS, Anne Frances Mary 72 Birchwood Road, Brislington, Bristol BS4 4QN Tel: 0117 977 6223 — MB ChB 1959 Bristol. (Bristol) Socs: BMA. Prev: Ho. Phys. Bristol Roy. Infirm.; Ho. Surg. Frenchay Hosp. Bristol.

LYONS, Anthea Jane 11 Wroxham Close, Brandlesholme, Bury BL8 1EN Tel: 0161 797 0111 Email: jane@irlyons.demon.co.uk; Audiology Department, Fairfield General Hospital, Rochdale Old Road, Bury BL9 7TD Tel: 0161 705 3664 Fax: 0161 705 3671 — MB ChB 1977 Dundee; MSc Audiol. Med. Manch. 1991; DCH RCP Lond. 1985; FRCPCH. Cons. Community Paediat. Audiol. Bury.

LYONS, Arnold Richard, OBE Northern Ireland Radiotherapy Centre, Belvoir Park Hospital, Belfast BT8 Tel: 01232 642942; 67 Roughfort Road, Newtownabbey BT36 4RE Tel: 018494 32308 — MD Belf. 1947, MB BCh BAO 1940; FRCP Lond. 1969, M 1948; FFR RCSI 1962; FRCR 1975; DMRT Ed. 1952. Cons. Radiotherap. N. Irel. Radiother. Centre. Socs: Fell. Ulster Med. Soc.; BMA. Prev: Sen. Regist. Radiother. Dept. Roy. Infirm. Edin.; Med. Sen. Regist. Roy. Vict. Hosp. Belf.; Flight Lt. RAF.

LYONS, Carine Rooks, Coombe Keynes, Wareham BH20 5PP — MB ChB 1988 Manch.; BSc St. And. 1985.

***LYONS, Cheryl Louise** 35 Beverley Parklands, Beverley HU17 0RA Tel: 01482 869334 — MB ChB 1995 Sheff.

LYONS, Christine Anne 7 Maureen Avenue, Manchester M8 5AR — MB ChB 1993 Birm.; MRC Psych, 1999.

LYONS, Colin 12 Cornwallis Crescent, Bristol BS8 4PL — State Exam Med. Berlin 1987.

LYONS, Diana Mary Tel: 0191 223 2501 — MB ChB 1986 Manch.; MSc; MRCPsych 1992; DRCOG 1990. (St. And. & Manch.) p/t Cons. in Gen. Adult Psychiat., Newc./N. Tyneside and N.umberland MH NHS Trust, Newc. upon Tyne. Socs: MRCPsych (1992).

LYONS, Donald 48 Poplar Avenue, Newton Mearns, Glasgow G77 5QZ — MB ChB 1981 Glas.; MRCPsych 1985. Cons. Leverndale Hosp. Glas.

LYONS, Mr Edward (retired) Bron-y-Graig, Llanddulas, Abergele LL22 8EH Tel: 01492 515857 Email: byg@cwcom.net — MB ChB 1944 Leeds; FRCOphth 1989; DOMS Eng. 1946. Prev: Cons. Ophth. Surg. Clwyd HA.

LYONS, Eileen 18 Corsie Drive, Perth PH2 7BU — MB ChB 1983 Dundee; MRCGP 1990; DRCOG 1990; DA (UK) 1986.

LYONS, Emily Laura Philippa 154 Trent Valley Road, Stoke-on-Trent ST4 5HL — MB ChB 1997 Leic.

LYONS, Fionnuala Margaret 145A Harbord Street, London SW6 6PN — MB BCh BAO 1989 NUI.

LYONS, Françoise Marcelle Carlisle House Surgery, 53 Lagland St., Poole BH15 1QD Tel: 01202 678484; Westbrow, 22 Western Avenue, Branksome Park, Poole BH13 7AN — MB BS 1981 Lond.; MRCGP 1989; DRCOG 1986; DFFP 1998. (Univ. Coll. Hosp.) GP Poole Retainer Scheme. Prev: GP Princip. Lond.

LYONS, Gill Jennifer Dunstan Hall, Craster, Alnwick NE66 3TF — MB ChB 1995 Manch.; MA Health Care Ethics Manch. 1988. (Manch.) SHO (Psychiat.) N.d. Ment. Health Trust. Socs: Inceptor Roy. Coll. Psychiat.

LYONS, Gordon Richard 27 Davies Avenue, Leeds LS8 1JZ — MB ChB 1971 Leeds; FFA RCS Eng. 1977. Cons. Anaesth. St. Jas. Hosp. Leeds. Prev: Sen. Regist. (Anaesth.) St. Jas. Hosp. Leeds; Regist. (Anaesth.) Roy. Sussex Co. Hosp. Brighton & Aberd. Roy.; Infirm.

LYONS, Graham Lennox 46 Stewartfield Cr, Broxburn EH52 5ET — MB ChB 1997 Glas.

LYONS, Graham Mark The Surgery, Grove Street, Petworth GU28 0LP Tel: 01798 342248 Fax: 01798 343987 — MB BS 1976 Lond.; DObst 1980. (Westm.)

LYONS, Hugh Alexander 32 Marlborough Park S., Belfast BT9 6HR Tel: 028 663105 Fax: 028 663105; Dunbarton House, Gilford, Craigavon BT63 6HJ Tel: 01762 831344 — MB BCh BAO 1954 Belf.; FRCPI 1972, M 1959; FRCPsych 1977; DPM RCPSI 1957. (Belf.) Cons. Psychiat. Purdysburn Hosp., Ulster Hosp., Alexandra Gdns. & Mater Hosps. Socs: BMA; Roy. Acad. Med. Irel.; Ulster Med. Soc. Prev: Pres. Ulster Medico/Legal Soc.; Chairm. Roy. Coll. Psychiats. Irel.; Sen. Regist. Pudysburn Hosp. Belf.

LYONS, Ita 137 Pencisily Road, Cardiff CF5 1DL — MB BCh BAO 1985 Dub.; MRCPsych 1993.

LYONS, Jeremy David Morrell 77 Upper Malone Road, Belfast BT9 6PW — MB BCh BAO 1989 Belf. Prev: Ho. Off. Roy. Vict. Hosp. Belf.

LYONS, John Maguire 143 Askew Avenue, Hull HU4 6NH Tel: 01482 54251; Kinvara, Beech Hill Road, Swanland, North Ferriby HU14 3QY Tel: 01482 631541 — MB BCh BAO 1960 NUI; LM Nat. Matern. Hosp. Dub. 1960. (Univ. Coll. Dub.) Socs: Hull Med. Soc. & BMA. Prev: SHO St. Columb's Chest Hosp. Lond.derry; Ho. Surg. Nat. Matern. Hosp. Dub.; Ho. Phys. Altnagelvin Hosp. Lond.derry.

LYONS, John Patrick 49 Magpie Drive, Totton, Southampton SO40 8TE — MB BCh BAO 1990 NUI.

LYONS, John Patrick 54 Cockshot Hill, Reigate RH2 8AN Tel: 01737 244104 — MB BS 1978 Lond.; MA Oxf. 1980; FRCP Lond. 1995; MRCP (UK) 1980. (St. Thos.) Cons. Phys. & Cardiol. E. Surrey Hosp. Socs: Brit. Cardiac Soc. Prev: Lect. (Cardiol.) Lond. Chest Hosp.; Regist. (Cardiol.) Lond. Chest Hosp.; Regist. (Gen. Med.) Whipps Cross Hosp. Lond.

LYONS, Jonathan Douglas Wycombe General Hospital, High Wycombe HP11 2TT Tel: 01494 26161 — MB BS 1982 W. Indies.

LYONS, Joseph (retired) 10 Whidborne Avenue, Marine Drive, Torquay TQ1 2PQ Tel: 01803 295511 — MB ChB Leeds 1941, DPH 1948; MRCS Eng. LRCP Lond. 1941; FFPHM 1990; FFCM 1974. Prev: Area Med. Off. Devon AHA.

LYONS, Josephine Deirdre 39A St John's Wood High Street, London NW8 7NJ — MB BCh BAO 1990 NUI.

LYONS, Julianne Catherine Govan Health Centre, 5 Drumoyne Road, Glasgow G51 4BJ Tel: 0141 531 8490 Fax: 0141 531 8487 — MB ChB 1988 Glas.

LYONS, Kathleen Anne Gatenby and Lyons, The Surgery, Parkview, Aberchirder, Huntly AB54 7SW Tel: 01466 700213 Fax: 01466 780580 — MB BCh BAO 1977 Dub.; DObst RCPI 1980; DCH NUI 1979. Prev: Med. Off. St. Eliz. Hosp. Transkei.

LYONS, Kenneth George Blair Renfrew Health Centre, 103 Paisley Road, Renfrew PA4 8LL Tel: 0141 886 3535 Fax: 0141 885 0098; 31 Manse Crescent, Houston, Johnstone PA6 7JN Tel: 0141 886 3535 Fax: 0141 885 0098 — MB ChB 1978 Dundee.

LYONS, Malcolm 16 Derby Road, St. Andrews, Bristol BS7 9AQ Tel: 0117 908 7676 Email: mandala@netgates.co.uk; 16 Derby Road, St. Andrews, Bristol BS7 9AQ Tel: 0117 908 7676 — MB ChB 1979 Bristol; MRCGP 1985. GP Locum.

LYONS, Margaret Scott 53A Kensington Road, Belfast BT5 6NL — MB BCh BAO 1966 Belf.; MFFP 1993; DObst RCOG 1968. (Qu. Univ. Belf.) SCMO (Family Plann.) N. & W. Belf. HSS Trust.

LYONS, Marie Jennifer Flat 1, 39A St Johns Wood High St., London NW8 7NJ — BChir 1995 Camb.

LYONS, Mary Margaret Department of Microbiology, Wycombe General Hospital, Queen Alexandra Road, High Wycombe HP11 2TT Tel: 01494 425246 Fax: 01494 425090; 20 Millers Turn, Chinnor OX39 4JZ — BM BS 1983 Nottm.; MRCP (UK) 1988; MRCPath 1993. Cons. Microbiol. Wycombe Gen. Hosp. Prev: Sen. Regist. (Microbiol.) Oxf.; Regist. (Microbiol.) Leicester; Regist. (Med.) Hull & E. Humberside.

LYONS, Michael Anthony The Surgery, 24 Broadwater Road, Worthing BN14 8AB Tel: 01903 231701 — MB ChB 1969 Liverp.

LYONS, Michael John 5 Underbank Avenue, Charlestown, Hebden Bridge HX7 6PP Tel: 01422 845424 — MB ChB 1984 Liverp.; BSc (Hons.) Biochem. Liverp. 1979, MB ChB 1984; MRCGP 1988; DCH RCP Lond. 1987; DRCOG 1987. (Liverpool) Staff Grade (Paediat.) Burnley Health Care Trust.

LYONS, Nicholas Twyford Wool Surgery, Folly Lane, Wool, Wareham BH20 6DS Tel: 01929 462376; Rooks, Coombe Keynes, Wareham BH20 5PP — MB ChB 1988 Manch.; BSc St. And. 1985; MRCGP 1993; DRCOG 1992.

LYONS, Nigel Stephen Lyons and Partners, Shoreham Health Centre, Pond Road, Shoreham-by-Sea BN43 5US Tel: 01273 440550 Fax: 01273 462109 — MB BS 1976 Lond.; DRCOG 1979. (Westm.)

LYONS, Paul 3 Glenkyle Park, Manse Road, Newtownabbey BT36 6ST — MB ChB 1997 Dundee.

LYONS, Paul Richard c/o Department of Neurology, Royal United Hospital, Combe Park, Bath BA1 3NG Fax: 01225 824578 Email: plyons@globalnet.co.uk — BM BS 1980 Nottm.; MD Newc. 1993; BMedSci Nottm. 1978; FRCP. (Nottingham) Cons. Neurol. Roy. United Hosp. Trust Bath.

LYONS, Rachel Ann 138 Rusthall Avenue, London W4 1BS — MB BS 1989 Lond.; BSc (Hons.) Lond. 1986; MRCOG 1995. Regist. (O & G) Roy. Free Hosp. Lond.

LYONS, Richard Mostyn Chorley Health Centre, Collison Avenue, Chorley PR7 2TH Tel: 01257 265080 Fax: 01257 232285; Ivy Cottage, Bradshaw Lane, Mawdesley, Ormskirk L40 3SE — MB BCh BAO 1978 Belf.

LYONS, Robert David James Tudor Lodge, Birks Drive, Ashley Heath, Market Drayton TF9 4PQ — MB ChB 1970 Birm.

LYONS, Ronan Anthony Iechyd Morganning Health, 41 High St., Swansea SA1 1LT Tel: 01792 458066 Fax: 01792 655364 Email: lyonsra@cardiff.ac.uk — MB BCh BAO 1983 Dub.; MD Dub. 1993; FFPHM RCPI 1996; MPH Dub. 1988; DCH Dub. 1985; FFPHM 1998. (Trinity Coll.) Prof. of Pub. Health Med., Univ. of Wales Coll..; Hon. Cons. (Pub. Health Med.) Swansea; Hon. Cons. (A & E) Swansea. Socs: BMA; Fell. Fac. Pub. Health Med. RCPI; Fell. Fac. Pub. Health Med.

LYONS, Rory Anthony Derwendeg Medical Centre, 19 Heol Llanelli, Trimsaran, Kidwelly SA17 4AG Tel: 01554 810223 — MB BCh 1975 NUI. (NUI) GP Kidwelly, Dyfed.

LYONS, Samuel Morrell, OBE Department of Anaesthetics, Royal Victoria Hospital, Belfast BT12 6BA Tel: 028 9024 0503 Fax: 028 9032 5725; 28 Bristow Park, Belfast BT9 6TH Tel: 028 9066 1529 Fax: 028 9066 0756 Email: morrell.lyons@ukgateway.net — BSc Belf. 1957, MD 1975; MB BCh BAO 1960; FFA RCSI 1971; FRCA 1965. (Belf.) Non-exec. Dir. N. Irel. Blood Transfus. Agency. Socs: BMA; Past-Pres. Assn. Anaesths.; Roy. Soc. Med. Prev: Hon. Cons. (Anaesth.) Roy. Vict. Hosp.Belf.; Cons. Anaesth. Roy. Vict. Hosp. Belf.; Fell. (Anaesth.) Baylor Univ. Coll. Med. Houston, USA.

LYONS, Susan 143 Rookwood Avenue, Leeds LS9 0NL; 27 Davies Avenue, Leeds LS8 1JZ — MB ChB 1971 Leeds; DObst RCOG 1974.

LYONS, Valerie Heather 8 Cavendish Road, Sheffield S11 9BH; 7 The Promenade, Castletown IM9 1BJ — MB BS 1964 Lond.; MRCS Eng. LRCP Lond. 1964; DObst RCOG 1970; DCH Eng. 1968. (Middlx.)

LYONS, Victoria Louise Barbican Health, 2-6 Austin Friars, London EC2N 2HD Tel: 020 7638 4988 Fax: 020 7628 6002; The Cottage, Church Path, Cublington, Leighton Buzzard LU7 0LN Tel: 01296 682704 — BM BS 1991 Nottm.; BMedSci 1991. GP Barbican Health Lond.

LYTH, Mr David Robin Department of Urology, Queen Margaret Hospital, Whitefield Road, Dunfermline KY12 0SU Tel: 01383 623623; 2 Muir Close, Dunfermline KY12 0FB Tel: 01383 626234 Email: dlyth@compuserve.com — MB BS 1972 Lond.; FRCS Eng. 1978; MRCS Eng. LRCP Lond. 1972. (St Bartholomews) Cons. Urol. Qu. Margt. Hosp. Dunfermline. Socs: Brit. Assn. Urol. Surg.; Internat. Continence Soc.; BMA. Prev: Staff Grade Urol. P.ss Margt. Hosp. Swindon; Clin. Research Fell. Colchester Gen. Hosp.; Cons. (Urol.) King Abdul Aziz Hosp. Jeddah, Saudi Arabia.

LYTH, Natalie Allison Friarage Hospital, Department of Paediatrics, Northallerton DL6 1JG; 10 Grenadier Drive, Northallerton DL6 1SB — MB ChB 1987 Liverp.; MRCGP 1992; DCH RCP Lond. 1991; DRCOG 1990. Staff Grade (Paediat.) Friarage Hosp. N.allerton. Socs: Chair.N.allerton.div.BMA. Prev: Trainee GP N.allerton VTS.

LYTHALL, David Ashley Kent & Canterbury Hospital, Ethelbert Road, Canterbury CT1 3NG Tel: 01227 766877; St. Thomas's Hospital, London SE1 7EH Tel: 020 7928 9292 — MB BS 1979 Queensland; MB BS 1979 (1st cl. Hons.) Queensland; MD Queensland 1994; FRACP 1989. Cons. Cardiol. Kent & Canterbury Hosp.; Hon. Cons. Cardiol. St. Thos. Hosp. Lond. Socs: Brit. Soc. Echocardiogr.; Austral. & New Zealand Cardiac Soc. Prev: Brit. Heart Foundat. Fell. Harefield Hosp.; Regist. (Cardiol.) St. Thos. Hosp. Lond.

LYTHGOE, Anne (retired) Tigh-an-Leigh, Shieldaig, Strathcarron IV54 8XN Tel: 01520 755309 Email: lythgoe@post.com — MB ChB 1956 Aberd.; MA Aberd. 1951; DA Eng. 1959. Prev: Asst. Anaesth. Chorley & Dist. Hosp.

LYTHGOE, Mark William 27 Kingsmead Drive, Hunts Cross, Liverpool L25 0NG — MB BS 1984 Lond.

LYTHGOE, Sarah Anne 91 Uplands, Peterborough PE4 5AF; 91 Uplands, Werrington, Peterborough PE4 5AF Tel: 01733 575325 — MB ChB 1985 Dundee; MRCGP 1991; T(GP) 1992; DTM & H RCP Lond. 1991; DGM RCP Lond. 1990.

LYTLE, John Department of Anaesthetics, Derriford Hospital, Plymouth PL6 8DH Tel: 01752 792691 Fax: 01752 763287; Maryknowle, Riverside Road, Newton Ferrers, Plymouth PL8 1AD — MB BS 1967 Lond.; FFA RCS Eng. 1973. (St. Thos.) Cons. Anaesth. Plymouth Hosps. NHS Trust Derriford Hosp. Socs: Soc. Anaesth. of SW Region; Anaesth. Sect. Roy. Soc. Med. (Former Counc.. Mem.). Prev: Sen. Regist. & Ho. Surg. St. Thos. Hosp. Lond.; Ho. Off. Qu. Alexandra Hosp. Portsmouth.

LYTLE, John Desmond Mathews (retired) The Spinney, 44 Heath Ridge Green, Cobham KT11 2QJ Tel: 01372 842478 — MRCS Eng. LRCP Lond. 1944; DObst RCOG 1948. Prev: Jun. Obst. Ho. Phys. St. Thos. Hosp.

LYTTELTON, Matthew Peregrine Anthony 43 High Street, Hallaton, Market Harborough LE16 8UD — MB ChB 1983 Birm.; BA Camb. 1977; MRCP (UK) 1986.

LYTTLE, John Alexander 21 Cadogan Park, Lisburn Road, Belfast BT9 6HG Tel: 01232 661338 — MB BCh BAO Belf. 1957; MD Belf. 1963; FRCP Lond. 1979. (Qu. Univ. Belf.) Hon. Cons. Neurol. Roy. Vict. Hosp. Belf. Socs: Fell. Ulster Med. Soc.

LYTTLE, Mr John Austin Conquest Hospital, St Leonards-on-Sea TN37 7RD Tel: 01424 755255; Rivendell, 103 St. Helen's Pk Road, Hastings TN34 2JW Tel: 01424 715529 — MB BS 1968 Lond.; BSc Lond. 1965, MS 1979; FRCS Eng. 1974. (Lond. Hosp.) Cons. Surg. Hastings HA.; Regional Speciality Adviser in Gen. Surg. S. Thames E. to Roy. Coll. Of Surg. Socs: Assn. Surg.; Assoc. ColoProctol. GBI; Assoc. Upper Gastro-Intestinal Surg.s. Prev: Sen. Regist. (Gen. Surg. & Urol.) Guy's Hosp.; Sen. Regist. St. Mark's Hosp.; Regist. (Gen. Surg.) Lond. Hosp.

LYTTLE, Kathrine Deirdre Louise 21 Cadogan Park, Belfast BT9 6HG — MB BCh 1989 Wales.

LYTTLE, Margaret Eirene Anne Christine 17 St Augustines Avenue, Bickley, Bromley BR2 8AG — MB BCh BAO 1965 Belf.

LYTTLE, Timothy William 2 Hillingdale, Biggin Hill, Westerham TN16 3NS — MB BCh BAO 1994 Belf.

LYTTLETON, Laura Katherine Tel: 020 7690 1172 Fax: 020 8809 0999; Ground Floor Flat, 46 Wilberforce Road, London N4 2SR — MB BS 1983 Lond.; MSc Lond. 1972; BA Oxf. 1971; MRCGP 1987; DRCOG 1987. (Charing Cross & London) GP Partner. Socs: Med. Pract. Union. Prev: Princip. GP Leyton Green; Trainee GP Char. Cross Hosp. & Goodinge Health Centre Lond. VTS.

LYTTON, Mr Alfred Fairleigh Cottage, Highleigh, Chichester PO20 7NR Tel: 01243 641271 — MB BS 1955 Lond.; FRCS Eng. 1964; DO Eng. 1958. (St. Bart.) Cons. Ophth. Chichester & Worthing Health Dists. & W. Sussex CC. Socs: Fell. Coll. Ophth.; Ophth. Soc. U.K. & S. Ophth. Soc. Prev: Sen. Regist. Qu. Vict. Hosp. E. Grinstead & Kent Co. Ophth. Hosp.; Clin. Asst. Moorfields Eye Hosp. Lond.; Res. Surg. Off. Birm. & Midl. Eye Hosp.

LYTTON, Graham Jeffrey Goldsworth Park Health Centre, Denton Way, Woking GU21 3LQ Tel: 01483 767194 Fax: 01483 766042; York House Medical Centre, Heathside Road, Woking GU22 7XL

Tel: 01483 760014 Fax: 01483 766042 — MB ChB 1964 Leeds; DObst RCOG 1966. (Leeds)

LYTTON, Jacqueline Mary Rosemead Surgery, 8A Ray Park Avenue, Maidenhead SL6 8DS Tel: 01628 622023 Fax: 01628 639495; 1 Grove Cottage, Waltham Road, White Waltham, Maidenhead SL6 3SQ Tel: 01628 822456 — MB BS 1988 Lond.; BSc Lond. 1985; MRCGP 1994; DRCOG 1992; DCH RCP Lond. 1991. (St. Mary's Hosp. Med. Sch. Lond.) Clin. Asst. (A & E) Wexham Pk. Hosp. Slough. Prev: Trainee GP Maidenhead & Windsor VTS.

LYTTON, Stephen Timothy Seaside Medical Centre, 18 Sheen Road, Eastbourne BN22 8DR Tel: 01323 725667 Fax: 01323 417169 — MB BS 1986 Lond.; BSc (Hons.) Lond. 1983; MRCGP 1991; DRCOG 1991. (St Georges.Hosp.Lond) GP. Socs: MRCP; DRCOG.